+

D1562281

Important Information About This Directory

How This Directory Was Compiled

Great care has been taken in compiling the information in this directory. Facts were obtained from the D&B database, telephone interviews, and annual reports. Upon request, the page proofs of proposed listings have been submitted to officials of companies for approval or correction.

We have made every effort to ensure that the information is complete, correct, and current. However, because of the human factors and possibilities for error that are inherent in compiling a directory of this size, D&B does not assume liability for the correctness of these listings or for the information upon which they have been based. Errors, after they have been detected, will be corrected in the next edition.

A listing in this directory neither constitutes nor implies in any manner whatsoever, an appraisal by D&B of the products, facilities, financial condition, credit worthiness, or any other factor bearing on the service, performance, or operations of the company listed.

No charge of any kind is made for inclusion in this publication.

Subscription Agreements

To ensure that the information you use is the most current and accurate available, most D&B publications are provided on a lease basis. Most of our subscribers renew their subscriptions each year. During the period of your annual lease, you will automatically receive the next edition of this directory when it is released. This protects you and your research by making sure the publication you use is the most current available.
The information compiled in D&B publications is proprietary. Having compiled the information through various D&B resources, D&B legally owns the information. This is why publications remain the property of D&B at all times.

Our leasing policy is intended to provide you with the most up-to-date information we have available. If you have any questions about this leasing procedure, please call us, at 1.800.526.0651.

Notice Concerning Use For Compilation For Dissemination To Third Parties

Subscribers to D&B publications have, on occasion, used those publications to compile mailing lists, marketing aids, and other types of information compilations, then sell or otherwise provide those materials to third parties. D&B considers such use to be wrongful and illegal. The information contained in these publications is the legal property of The Dun & Bradstreet Corporation. Selling or otherwise providing this information to third parties violates the contractual agreement under which the directory is provided to the subscriber. This is also a violation of the federal copyright laws. D&B does not permit or acquiesce in such uses of its publications. Any subscriber or other person engaging in or facilitating such impermissible use should expect to experience legal and financial consequences.

No waiver or amendment of the agreement is binding unless it is in writing and signed by an authorized official of D&B and the subscriber. Should any subscriber or other person not understand any aspect of this policy, please contact the Legal Department of Dun & Bradstreet, at 103 JFK Parkway, Short Hills, N.J. 07078.

dun & bradstreet

MILLION DOLLAR DIRECTORY

Series

America's Leading Public & Private Companies

2016

ISSN 0742-9649
ISBN 978-1-63053-916-0

2016 Million Dollar Directory

Management

Jonathan Worrall	Publisher
John Pedernales	Executive Managing Director
Fred Jenkins	Vice President Sales
Thomas Wecera	Managing Director Print Products

Editorial Department

Charlot Volny
Wayne Arnold

Customer Service & Billing

Melanie Horvat
580 Kingsley Park Drive
Fort Mill, SC 29715
(704)559-7601
(800)342-5647

To Contact Mergent:

Call us at 800.342.5647
Or visit us at: www.mergentbusinesspress.com

Contents

Overview

Introduction

Thank you for using the *Million Dollar Directory*. As one of the business world's most widely recognized and frequently used reference publications, it has provided information to executives, librarians, students, researchers, sales and marketing managers, and others for more than 35 years. The *Million Dollar Directory* is a primary source of business information and is a valuable source of information on privately held companies.

You will find the *Million Dollar Directory* provides many advantages to its users. It offers extensive coverage of public and private companies, easy cross-referencing, primary and secondary lines of business (up to six for each company), and the names and titles of key decision makers.

In publishing this directory, we seek to provide several specific benefits to you:

- Quality. To provide the highest quality information available, The Dun & Bradstreet Corporation maintains unparalleled information gathering resources. First-hand information is obtained through in-person and telephone interviews by business analysts across the United States.
- Reliability. Appropriate listing criteria ensure that the top 150,000 U.S. companies are profiled using the most current, accurate and comprehensive information available today.
- Coverage. A broad range of industries is presented.
- Ease of use. The information has been designed to be thorough, yet simple to use. Complete company listings are arranged alphabetically by company name. Cross-references enable users to access information geographically and by line of business.

The sections that follow have been provided to help you obtain information from this directory more easily. A quick glance at the various headings should help you find the answers to your questions.
If you have any further questions about either the *Million Dollar Directory* or our other business reference publications, or if you would like to obtain a directory, please call us at 1.800.342.5647.

Criteria For Inclusion

For a company to be selected for the *Million Dollar Directory*, it must meet one of the two inclusion requirements:

1. More than 275 employees total if the company is a headquarters or single location; 900 or more employees at that location if the company is a branch.
2. More than $20,000,000 in sales volume.

You will find subsidiaries and branches in the *Million Dollar Directory* if they meet the listing criteria. However, divisions are not included (for precise definitions of terms such as subsidiary, branch, and division, please see the glossary on page IX).

More than 136,000 of these listings are privately owned businesses — information that can be difficult to obtain from other sources.

If you have any questions about the criteria for the *Million Dollar Directory*, please call 1.800.342.5647.

Directory Contents

To make the *Million Dollar Directory* easier for you to use, it has been published in five volumes. The first three volumes list businesses alphabetically; the fourth and fifth volumes cross-reference businesses geographically and by Standard Industrial Classification (SIC) code. Additional information on all of the sections is presented on pages VI and VII.

Description of Business Listings

Each business description includes many facts about the company. They include:

- Headquarters address and telephone number
- Trade style
- Annual sales volume (where available)
- Total employment size (where available)
- Up to six industry classifications (Standard Industrial Classification [SIC] codes), with the primary industry shown first
- Company officers and directories by name and title (for officers)
- D&B D-U-N-S® Number
- Members of the board of directors
- Founded/ownership date

Plus (where available):

- Banking and accounting relationships
- Indications of import/export business
- Indication of public ownership
- Indication of public family membership
- State of incorporation
- Indication of a parent company listing in the current *Million Dollar Directory*

Types of Businesses

Many different types of businesses are included. They generally include:

- Agriculture, Forestry, and Fishing
- Mining
- Construction
- Manufacturing
- Transportation, Communication & Public Utilities
- Wholesale Trade
- Retail Trade
- Finance, Insurance & Real Estate
- Business Services

A company may be referenced under as many as six SIC codes: the primary industry from which it derives its main source of revenue, and up to five secondary business activities.

Subsidiaries, Branches and Divisions

For your convenience, a brief glossary of reporting relationships, as defined by D&B, has been provided on page VIII. You will find subsidiaries and branches listed in the *Million Dollar Directory* if they meet the listing criteria. Divisions, however, are not included.

Public and Private Companies

In response to customer requests, D&B has begun the process of indicating public ownership of companies listed in the *Million Dollar Directory.* A triangle ▲ before a business name indicates that it is a publicly held company.

A square ■ before a business name denotes that the company is a member of a publicly traded company, but is not the trading location. If a subsidiary trades under its own ticker symbol separately from its parent, a triangle will appear before the name of the subsidiary in the listing.

To help you identify public companies more easily, the triangle and square indicators have been included in both the alphabetical and cross-reference volumes.

How to Use This Directory

To help you use the *Million Dollar Directory* more easily, it is divided into five volumes. The divisions are as follows:

Businesses Alphabetically

D-U-N-S 00-007-6596 IMP/EXP
▲VIAGRAPHICS INC (IL)
VIAGRAPHICS SILK SCREENING
(Suby of WILSON BARTH & DRAPER INC)★
5877 Valley Road, Chicago, IL 60660-1428
Tel (999) 555-1212 *Founded/Ownership* 1982
Sales 15MM^E *Emp* 340^E
Tkr Sym ABP *Exch* AMS
Accts Johnson & Johnson
SIC 7333 7332 Silk screen; Graphic Design.
**Ch Bd:* Victor R Schultz
**Pr:* Patricia M McCoombe
**Ex VP:* Oscar M Stevensen
Sr VP: Oscar M Stevenson
Sr VP Advt: Henry Van Horne
Sr VP Lgl: Edward T Balbouce
VP: Howard Trapp
VP Fin: Merynda H French
VP Mktg: Frederick L Stone
VP Prs: Richard B Torney
VP Sls: Lucy L Daniels
Sec Tr: Gordon S Fletcher
Comp: Smantha D Kruze
Board of Directors: Alice Bell, Louis Bell, Lester P Manthey, Thomas Jones

All sample information is fictitious

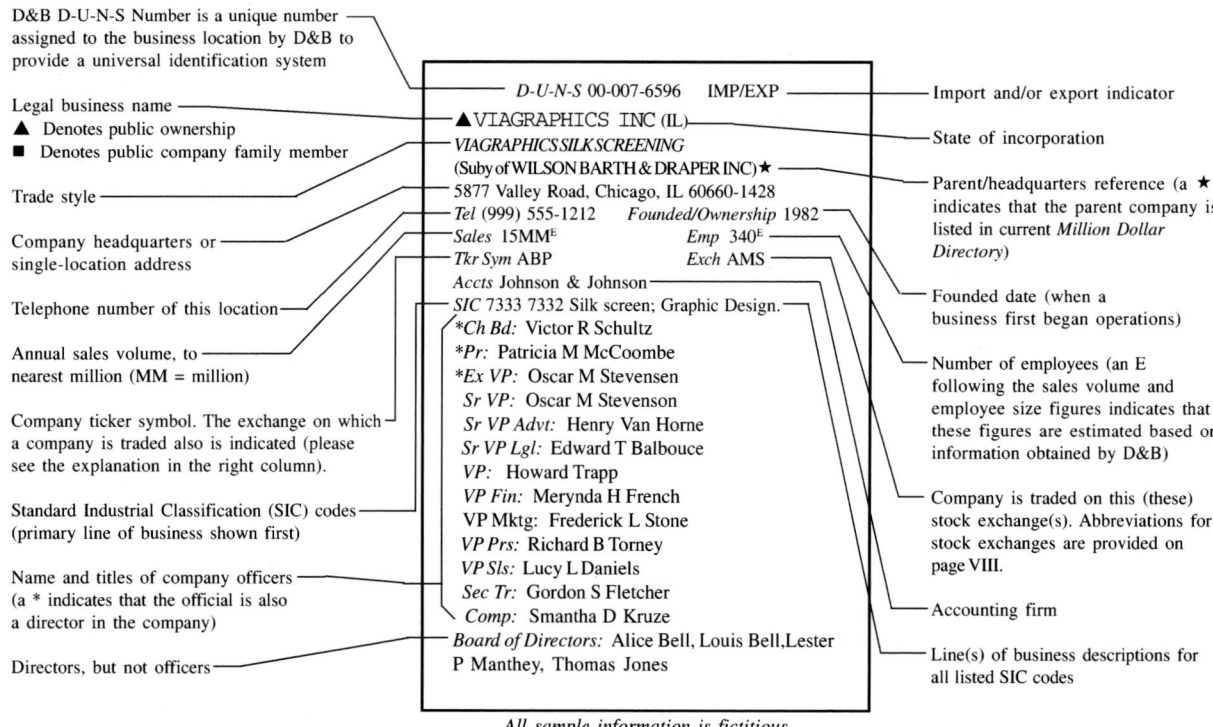

D&B D-U-N-S Number is a unique number assigned to the business location by D&B to provide a universal identification system

Legal business name
▲ Denotes public ownership
■ Denotes public company family member

Trade style

Company headquarters or single-location address

Telephone number of this location

Annual sales volume, to nearest million (MM = million)

Company ticker symbol. The exchange on which a company is traded also is indicated (please see the explanation in the right column).

Standard Industrial Classification (SIC) codes (primary line of business shown first)

Name and titles of company officers (a * indicates that the official is also a director in the company)

Directors, but not officers

Import and/or export indicator

State of incorporation

Parent/headquarters reference (a ★ indicates that the parent company is listed in current *Million Dollar Directory*)

Founded date (when a business first began operations)

Number of employees (an E following the sales volume and employee size figures indicates that these figures are estimated based on information obtained by D&B)

Company is traded on this (these) stock exchange(s). Abbreviations for stock exchanges are provided on page VIII.

Accounting firm

Line(s) of business descriptions for all listed SIC codes

The first three volumes of the *Million Dollar Directory* list companies in alphabetical sequence by business name. Full details on each company are provided in this section. The listing for each company includes the following:

- Address and telephone number (headquarters and single locations only)
- Indication of public ownership, where available
- Indication of public company family membership
- SIC code (up to six; the primary SIC is listed first) and description of the line(s) of business
- Annual sales volume, where available
- Total number of employees, where available
- Names, titles and functions of officers
- Names of directors
- D&B D-U-N-S® Number
- Founded/ownership date

Also, where available

- Import/export indication
- Accounting firm
- State of incorporation
- Company ticker symbol on stock exchange, and/or stock exchange abbreviations
- Indication of parent company in current *Million Dollar Directory*

Public companies are denoted by the stock ticker symbol and/or stock exchange location and by a triangle or a square before the company name. The alphabetic volumes are particularly useful when only the name of a company is known. It enables you to:

- Identify key decision makers
- Assess the buying potential of a company by sales volume and employee size
- Determine whether a company is publicly owned
- Identify primary or secondary markets by SIC code

The fourth and fifth volumes of the *Million Dollar Directory* enable you to cross-reference businesses by geographical area or line of business.

Businesses Geographically

This volume presents a geographic cross-reference. Business names are listed in alphabetical order within states and cities. The company name, address, telephone number, and SIC codes are provided. An indication of companies noted in our file of public ownership is also included, as is a page reference for a company's listing in the alphabetical section.

You can use the information in this volume to:

- Target your sales efforts more effectively
- Identify companies by region, state or city
- Select prime sales areas
- Assess market concentrations and analyze or compare markets by area
- Align sales territories and assign quotas based on the number of prospects in each geographic area
- Compile targeted mailing and telemarketing lists by location and size
- Identify local businesses
- Create telemarketing and prospect lists
- Conduct telemarketing campaigns
- Assess new market potential
- Identify prospective employers by city and within state

ILLINOIS

CHICAGO, IL

p VIAGRAPHICS INC *p* 5307
5877 Valley Road 60660
Tel (999) 555-1212 *SIC* 7333 7332
VILLAGE NURSING HOME
p 5312
2182 South St 60661
Tel (999) 555-1212 *SIC* 2051
VITA-LINK *p* 5319
4932 Lenox Ave 60231
Tel (999) 555-1212 *SIC* 3446

All sample information is fictitious

Businesses By Industry Classification

All businesses listed in the *Million Dollar Directory* are segmented by industry. Business names are listed in geographical order by state, city and then listed alphabetically within each city. Based on the SIC code system (see explanation on page X), this volume lists company information organized by line of business. Primary and secondary SIC codes are covered; therefore, a single company may be listed under as many as six different industry classifications. Individual business descriptions in this section include the company name and address, telephone number, primary SIC code, a page reference for its appearance in the alphabetic section, and an indication of public ownership.

The industry cross-reference can help you develop more effective strategies to:

- Identify prime prospects by line of business
- Precisely define specific industries
- Assess your competition
- Evaluate market potential for new or specific products
- Identify hidden markets by secondary lines of business
- Select suppliers from industry leaders
- Identify companies active in more than one industry
- Compile targeted mailing lists by industry
- Identify new companies in existing markets
- Determine the best geographic area for an industry
- Conduct industry-concentrated telemarketing campaigns

7333 COMM PHOTOGRAPHY, ART & GRAPHIC

p VIAGRAPHICS INC *p* 5307
5877 Valley Road, Chicago, IL 60660
Tel (999) 555-1212 *SIC* 7333 7332
QUIK GRAPH *p* 4211
594 Willow Ave, Chester, NJ 07930
Tel (999) 555-1212 *SIC* 7333 7332
WINSTON OUTDOOR ADVERTISING*p* 4802
3943 McConnell Rd, Williamsport, PA 17770
Tel (999) 555-1212 *SIC* 7333 7312

All sample information is fictitious

Abbreviations and Symbols

Abbreviations

Acctg	Accounting
Admn	Administration
Advt	Advertising
AMS	American Stock Exchange
BSE	Boston Stock Exchange
CEO	Chief Executive Officer
CFO	Chief Financial Officer
Ch Bd	Chairman of the Board
Ch Em	Chairman Emeritus
CHI	Chicago Board of Trade
CIN	Cincinnati Stock Exchange
Clk	Clerk
Co	Company
Coml	Commercial
Commctns	Communications
Comp	Comptroller
Cont	Controller
COO	Chief Operating Officer
Corp	Corporation
Cshr	Cashier
Dev	Development
Dir	Director
Distrn	Distribution
Div	Division
Dt Pr	Data Processing
ECM	Emerging Company Market Place
Engg	Engineering
Ex	Executive
Ex VP	Executive Vice President
Exp	Export
FSB	Federal Savings Bank
Fin	Finance
Fndr	Founder
GC	General Counsel
Genl	General
GM	General Manager
Govt	Government
Imp	Import
Inc	Incorporated
Indus	Industrial
Intl	International
Jr	Junior
Lgl	Legal
LON	London Stock Exchange
Ltd	Limited
M	Thousand
Merchds	Merchandise
Merchdsng	Merchandising
Mfg	Manufacturing
Mgr	Manager
Mgt	Management
Mktg	Marketing
M M	Million
M M M	Billion
M M M M	Trillion
MSE	Midwest Stock Exchange
NA	Not Available or National Association
NAS	NASDAQ Stock Exchange
NMS	NASDAQ National Market System
NYS	New York Stock Exchange Inc
Opers	Operations
Optg	Operating
OTC	Over the Counter
Ownr	Owner
PBS	Philadelphia Stock Exchange
PCS	Pacific Coast Stock Exchange
Pb Rlns	Public Relations
Pers	Personal
Pr	President
Prd	Production
Prin	Principal
Prs	Personnel
Pt	Partner
Pur	Purchasing
Ret	Retail or Retailer
Rlns	Relations
Rsch	Research
Sec	Secretary
SIC	Standard Industrial Classification
Sls	Sales
Sr	Senior
Sr VP	Senior Vice President
Suby	Subsidiary
Tr	Treasurer
Trst	Trustee
Trst Ofcr	Trust Officer
TSE	Toronto Stock Exchange
V Ch Bd	Vice Chairman of the Board
VAN	Vancouver Stock Exchange
VP	Vice President
Whl	Wholesale or Wholesaler

Symbols

▲ Denotes public ownership

■ Denotes member of public family

★ Denotes parent company is in current *Million Dollar Directory*

* Denotes that the officer is also a corporate director

Glossary

Affiliate Company—A company in which another firm holds an interest of less than 50%.

Asset—Property or resources such as money, buildings and equipment.

Associate Company—A company in which another company holds an interest of less than 50% (British equivalent of affiliate company).

Branch—A secondary location of a business which reports to a headquarters. A branch never reports to another branch and always carries the parent name. *Example:* A sales office is a branch location.

Business Organization—Various types of business organizations exist including corporations, partnerships and proprietorships. A corporation may be a public or a private company. Each type may have subsidiaries, divisions, branch locations, headquarters locations, and more.

Corporation—A legal form of business organization consisting of an association of owners called stockholders.

Corporate Structure—The hierarchy of a business establishment (*i.e.,* a parent company may have a division reporting to it, with branch locations reporting to the divisions).

Division—A separate operating unit of a corporation. A division may have its own officers, but it is not incorporated nor does it issue stock. All divisions are also classified as branches. Divisions will often have an additional commonly known business name called a trade style (see Trade Style).

D&B D-U-N-S® Number—A nonindicative number assigned to business establishments by D&B and used as a numeric identifier for business locations (Dun's Universal Numbering System).

Establishment—A term used by the U.S. Bureau of Census for any business location that has one or more employees.

Founded Date—The date when a business first began operations.

Headquarters—A business establishment where the executive offices of the corporation are located. Branch locations report to headquarters. *Example:* Ford Motor Company's headquarters location is in Dearborn, Michigan.

Immediate or Direct Parent—The company to which a subsidiary directly reports.

Liability—All debts and obligations of a business.

Net Worth—A company's total assets minus its total liabilities.

Ownership Date—The ownership date represents the "control date" of the business which is the date that current management assumed ownership, or majority stock ownership, of a business. In many cases, especially smaller businesses, current ownership date and year started are synonymous. However, with the current trend of mergers and acquisitions among larger corporations, the current ownership date represents the year present management assumed control, not necessarily the founding date of the business.

Parent Company—A business that owns more than 50% of another company's stock.

Partnership—A form of business organization in which two or more persons or entities carry on a business as co-owners for profit.

Privately Held Company—A business in which most or all of the company's stock is owned by a few persons and is not available for sale to the general public.

Proprietorship—A form of business organization in which an individual owns the entire enterprise.

Publicly Held Company—A business whose stock is available for sale to the general public at one or more of the stock exchanges.

Public Family Member—Subsidiaries of publicly held companies.

Single Location—A business establishment with no branches reporting to it. A single location may still be a parent and/or a subsidiary.

Standard Industrial Classification (SIC) Code—A hierarchical system of numerically categorizing the type of business activity which is conducted at a business establishment.

State of Incorporation—The state laws under which a company was incorporated. This can have implications in legal, organizational, and tax matters.

Subsidiary—A corporation that is controlled by another corporation through ownership of greater than 50% of its voting stock. The subsidiary may have a different name than the controlling corporation.

Ticker Symbol—The code representing the corporation in the stock exchange on which the corporation is traded.

Trade Style—An additional name used by a business for advertising and/or buying purposes.

Ultimate Parent—The topmost U.S. company within the hierarchy of the entire organization.

Year Founded—The original date a business was started.

Understanding Standard Industrial Classification (SIC) Codes

The Standard Industrial Classification (SIC) code is a simple and effective coding system that is used to gather and classify information on U.S. businesses.

The SIC system divides virtually all economic activity into ten major categories:

Agriculture, Forestry, and Fishing	01-09
Mining	10-14
Construction	15-17
Manufacturing	20-39
Transport, Communications, Utilities	40-49
Wholesale Trade	50-51
Retail Trade	52-59
Finance, Insurance, Real Estate	60-67
Services	70-89
Public Administration	91-97

The SIC system places each line of business within one of these ten divisions and assigns a four-digit code. The first two digits describe the general nature of the activity:

22 Manufacturing–Textile mill products

The third and fourth digits of the SIC code describe the specific activity:

2273 Manufacturing–Tufted carpets, rugs

Under the SIC system, many companies can be categorized under several "lines of business" and therefore are assigned several SIC codes. The line of business which represents the largest percentage of sales is known as the primary SIC, others are referred to as secondary SICs.

Example: An automotive parts wholesaler (SIC 5013) also distributes automobile and truck tires (SIC 5014) and has a small retail trade in auto placement glass (SIC 5331). In this directory, the SIC codes for this firm would be displayed as follows:

SIC 5013, 5014, 5531

Each SIC code is presented according to the percentage of its sales volume. The primary SIC is listed first (largest percentage of sales) and secondary SICs are listed in descending order of their respective sales percentages.

In this example, we know at a glance that this company's main business activity is wholesale auto parts, but it also has other sales in wholesale tires and some volume in retail automotive glass.

A typical display of SIC codes in this directory not only classifies the nature of the enterprise, but shows the relative size and importance of its various business activities as well.

A complete listing of SIC codes and their descriptions is included in this directory. If you wish to know more about SIC codes, please consult the *Standard Industrial Classification Manual SIC 2+2,* published by D&B.

Who Uses SIC Codes?

Sales professionals looking for new sales prospects may use SIC codes in searching among business names and addresses.

Job hunters often use SICs as a fast way to identify appropriate or interesting prospective employers. Advertisers rely upon SIC codes to pinpoint the kind of businesses they want to reach.

Economists studying changes and trends in business and the economy, use SICs to identify and compare industries.

Marketing researchers employ SIC codes in gathering information about potential markets for new products.

Computer-assisted searches in business and research use SIC codes for fast and reliable selections, sorting, and sampling.

Standard Industrial Classification (SIC) Codes – Numerical

01 Agricultural Production — Crops
0111 Wheat
0112 Rice
0115 Corn
0116 Soybeans
0119 Cash Grains
0131 Cotton
0132 Tobacco
0133 Sugarcane & Sugar Beets
0134 Irish Potatoes
0139 Field Crops, Except Cash Grain
0161 Vegetables & Melons
0171 Berry Crops
0172 Grapes
0173 Tree Nuts
0174 Citrus Fruits
0175 Deciduous Tree Fruits
0179 Fruits & Tree Nuts
0181 Ornamental Nursery Products
0182 Food Crops Grown Under Cover
0191 General Farms, Primarily Crop

02 Agricultural Production — Livestock & Animal Specialities
0211 Beef Cattle Feedlots
0212 Beef Cattle Except Feedlots
0213 Hogs
0214 Sheep & Goats
0219 General Livestock
0241 Dairy Farms
0251 Broiler, Fryer & Roaster Chickens
0252 Chicken Eggs
0253 Turkeys & Turkey Eggs
0254 Poultry Hatcheries
0259 Poultry & Eggs
0271 Fur-bearing Animals & Rabbits
0272 Horses & Other Equines
0273 Animal Aquaculture
0279 Animal Specialties
0291 General Farms, Primarily Animals

07 Agricultural Services
0711 Soil Preparation Services
0721 Crop Planting & Protection
0722 Crop Harvesting
0723 Crop Preparation Services For Market
0724 Cotton Ginning
0741 Veterinary Services For Livestock
0742 Veterinary Services, Specialties
0751 Livestock Services, Except Veterinary
0752 Animal Specialty Services
0761 Farm Labor Contractors
0762 Farm Management Services
0781 Landscape Counseling & Planning
0782 Lawn & Garden Services
0783 Ornamental Shrub & Tree Services

08 Forestry
0811 Timber Tracts
0831 Forest Products
0851 Forestry Services

09 Fishing, Hunting & Trapping
0912 Finfish
0913 Shellfish
0919 Miscellaneous Marine Products
0921 Fish Hatcheries & Preserves
0971 Hunting, Trapping,Game Propagation

10 Metal Mining
1011 Iron Ores
1021 Copper Ores
1031 Lead & Zinc Ores
1041 Gold Ores
1044 Silver Ores
1061 Ferroalloy Ores, Except Vanadium
1081 Metal Mining Services
1094 Uranium-Radium-Vanadium Ores
1099 Metal Ores

12 Coal Mining
1221 Bituminous Coal & Lignite-Surface
1222 Bituminous Coal-Underground
1231 Anthracite Mining
1241 Coal Mining Services

13 Oil & Gas Extraction
1311 Crude Petroleum & Natural Gas
1321 Natural Gas Liquids
1381 Drilling Oil & Gas Wells
1382 Oil & Gas Exploration Services
1389 Oil & Gas Field Services

14 Mining & Quarrying of Nonmetallic Minerals, Except Fuels
1411 Dimension Stone
1422 Crushed & Broken Limestone
1423 Crushed & Broken Granite
1429 Crushed & Broken Stone
1442 Construction Sand & Gravel
1446 Industrial Sand
1455 Kaolin & Ball Clay
1459 Clay & Related Minerals
1474 Potash, Soda & Borate Minerals
1475 Phosphate Rock
1479 Chemical & Fertilizer Mining
1481 Nonmetallic Mineral Services
1499 Miscellaneous Nonmetallic Minerals

15 Building Construction — General Contractors & Operative Builders
1521 Single-family Housing Construction
1522 Residential Construction
1531 Operative Builders
1541 Industrial Buildings & Warehouses
1542 Nonresidential Construction

16 Heavy Construction Other Than Building Construction — Contractors
1611 Highway & Street Construction
1622 Bridge, Tunnel & Elevated Highway
1623 Water, Sewer & Utility Lines
1629 Heavy Construction

17 Construction — Special Trade Contractors
1711 Plumbing, Heating, Air-conditioning Contractors
1721 Painting & Paper Hanging
1731 Electrical Work
1741 Masonry & Other Stonework
1742 Plastering, Drywall & Insulation
1743 Terrazzo, Tile, Marble, Mosaic Work
1751 Carpentry Work
1752 Floor Laying & Floor Work
1761 Roofing, Siding & Sheet Metal Work
1771 Concrete Work
1781 Water Well Drilling
1791 Structural Steel Erection
1793 Glass & Glazing Work
1794 Excavation Work
1795 Wrecking & Demolition Work
1796 Installing Building Equipment
1799 Special Trade Contractors

20 Food & Kindred Products
2011 Meat Packing Plants
2013 Sausages & Other Prepared Meats
2015 Poultry Slaughtering & Processing
2021 Creamery Butter
2022 Cheese, Natural & Processed
2023 Dry, Condensed, Evaporated Dairy Products
2024 Ice Cream & Frozen Desserts
2026 Fluid Milk
2032 Canned Specialties
2033 Canned Fruits & Specialties
2034 Dehydrated Fruits, Vegetables, Soups
2035 Pickles, Sauces & Salad Dressings
2037 Frozen Fruits & Vegetables
2038 Frozen Specialties
2041 Flour & Other Grain Mill Products
2043 Cereal Breakfast Foods
2044 Rice Milling
2045 Prepared Flour Mixes & Doughs
2046 Wet Corn Milling
2047 Dog & Cat Food
2048 Prepared Feeds
2051 Bread, Cake & Related Products
2052 Cookies & Crackers
2053 Frozen Bakery Products, Except Bread
2061 Raw Cane Sugar
2062 Cane Sugar Refining
2063 Beet Sugar
2064 Candy & Other Confectionery Products
2066 Chocolate & Cocoa Products
2067 Chewing Gum
2068 Salted & Roasted Nuts & Seeds
2074 Cottonseed Oil Mills
2075 Soybean Oil Mills
2076 Vegetable Oil Mills
2077 Animal & Marine Fats & Oils
2079 Edible Fats & Oils
2082 Malt Beverages
2083 Malt
2084 Wines, Brandy & Brandy Spirits
2085 Distilled & Blended Liquors
2086 Bottled & Canned Soft Drinks
2087 Flavoring Extracts & Syrups
2091 Canned & Cured Fish & Seafoods
2092 Fresh or Frozen Packaged Fish
2095 Roasted Coffee
2096 Potato Chips & Similar Snacks
2097 Manufactured Ice
2098 Macaroni & Spaghetti
2099 Food Preparations

21 Tobacco Products
2111 Cigarettes
2121 Cigars
2131 Chewing & Smoking Tobacco
2141 Tobacco Stemming & Redrying

22 Textile Mill Products
2211 Broadwoven Fabric Mills, Cotton
2221 Broadwoven Fabric Mills, Manmade
2231 Broadwoven Fabric Mills, Wool
2241 Narrow Fabric Mills
2251 Women's Hosiery, Except Socks
2252 Hosiery
2253 Knit Outerwear Mills
2254 Knit Underwear Mills
2257 Weft Knit Fabric Mills
2258 Lace & Warp Knit Fabric Mills
2259 Knitting Mills
2261 Finishing Plants, Cotton
2262 Finishing Plants, Manmade Fiber & Silk Fabrics
2269 Finishing Plants
2273 Carpets & Rugs
2281 Yarn Spinning Mills
2282 Throwing & Winding Mills
2284 Thread Mills
2295 Coated Fabrics, Not Rubberized
2296 Tire Cord & Fabrics
2297 Nonwoven Fabrics
2298 Cordage & Twine
2299 Textile Goods

23 Apparel & Other Finished Products Made from Fabrics & Similar Materials
2311 Men's & Boys' Suits & Coats
2321 Men's & Boys' Furnishings
2322 Men's & Boys' Underwear & Nightwear
2323 Men's & Boys' Neckwear
2325 Men's & Boys' Trousers & Slacks
2326 Men's & Boys' Work Clothing
2329 Men's & Boys' Clothing
2331 Women's & Misses' Blouses & Shirts
2335 Women's, Juniors' & Misses' Dresses
2337 Women's & Misses' Suits & Coats
2339 Women's & Misses' Outerwear
2341 Women's & Children's Underwear
2342 Bras, Girdles & Allied Garments
2353 Hats, Caps & Millinery
2361 Girls' & Children's Dresses, Blouses & Shirts
2369 Girls' & Children's Outerwear
2371 Fur Goods
2381 Fabric Dress & Work Gloves
2384 Robes & Dressing Gowns
2385 Waterproof Outerwear
2386 Leather & Sheep-lined Clothing
2387 Apparel Belts
2389 Apparel & Accessories
2391 Curtains & Draperies
2392 Household Furnishings
2393 Textile Bags
2394 Canvas & Related Products
2395 Pleating & Stitching
2396 Automotive & Apparel Trimmings
2397 Schiffli Machine Embroideries
2399 Fabricated Textile Products

24 Lumber & Wood Products, Except Furniture
2411 Logging
2421 Sawmills & Planing Mills, General
2426 Hardwood Dimension & Flooring Mills
2429 Special Product Sawmills
2431 Millwork
2434 Wood Kitchen Cabinets
2435 Hardwood Veneer & Plywood
2436 Softwood Veneer & Plywood
2439 Structural Wood Members
2441 Nailed Wood Boxes & Shook
2448 Wood Pallets & Skids
2449 Wood Containers
2451 Mobile Homes
2452 Prefabricated Wood Buildings
2491 Wood Preserving
2493 Reconstituted Wood Products
2499 Wood Products

25 Furniture & Fixtures
2511 Wood Household Furniture
2512 Upholstered Household Furniture

STANDARD INDUSTRIAL CLASSIFICATION (SIC) CODES – NUMERICAL

2514 Metal Household Furniture
2515 Mattresses & Bedsprings
2517 Wood Television & Radio Cabinets
2519 Household Furniture
2521 Wood Office Furniture
2522 Office Furniture, Except Wood
2531 Public Building & Related Furniture
2541 Wood Partitions & Fixtures
2542 Partitions & Fixtures, Except Wood
2591 Drapery Hardware & Blinds & Shades
2599 Furniture & Fixtures

26 Paper & Allied Products

2611 Pulp Mills
2621 Paper Mills
2631 Paperboard Mills
2652 Setup Paperboard Boxes
2653 Corrugated & Solid Fiber Boxes
2655 Fiber Cans, Drums & Similar Products
2656 Sanitary Food Containers
2657 Folding Paperboard Boxes
2671 Packaging Paper & Plastics Film, Coated & Laminated
2672 Coated & Laminated Paper
2673 Bags: Plastic, Laminated & Coated
2674 Bags: Uncoated Paper & Multiwall
2675 Die-cut Paper & Board
2676 Sanitary Paper Products
2677 Envelopes
2678 Stationery Products
2679 Converted Paper Products

27 Printing, Publishing & Allied Industries

2711 Newspapers
2721 Periodicals
2731 Book Publishing
2732 Book Printing
2741 Miscellaneous Publishing
2752 Commercial Printing, Lithographic
2754 Commercial Printing, Gravure
2759 Commercial Printing
2761 Manifold Business Forms
2771 Greeting Cards
2782 Blankbooks & Looseleaf Binders
2789 Bookbinding & Related Work
2791 Typesetting
2796 Platemaking Services

28 Chemicals & Allied Products

2812 Alkalies & Chlorine
2813 Industrial Gases
2816 Inorganic Pigments
2819 Industrial Inorganic Chemicals
2821 Plastics Materials & Resins
2822 Synthetic Rubber
2823 Cellulosic Manmade Fibers
2824 Organic Fibers, Noncellulosic
2833 Medicinals & Botanicals
2834 Pharmaceutical Preparations
2835 In Vitro & In Vivo Diagnostic Substances
2836 Biological Products, Except Diagnostic
2841 Soap & Other Detergents
2842 Specialty Cleaning, Polishes & Sanitation Goods
2843 Surface Active Agents
2844 Toilet Preparations
2851 Paints & Allied Products
2861 Gum & Wood Chemicals
2865 Cyclic Crudes & Intermediates
2869 Industrial Organic Chemicals
2873 Nitrogenous Fertilizers
2874 Phosphatic Fertilizers
2875 Fertilizers, Mixing Only
2879 Agricultural Chemicals
2891 Adhesives & Sealants
2892 Explosives
2893 Printing Ink
2895 Carbon Black
2899 Chemical Preparations

29 Petroleum Refining & Related Industries

2911 Petroleum Refining
2951 Asphalt Paving Mixtures & Blocks
2952 Asphalt Felts & Coatings
2992 Lubricating Oils & Greases
2999 Petroleum & Coal Products

30 Rubber & Miscellaneous Plastic Products

3011 Tires & Inner Tubes
3021 Rubber & Plastic Footwear
3052 Rubber & Plastics Hose & Beltings
3053 Gaskets, Packing & Sealing Devices
3061 Mechanical Rubber Goods
3069 Fabricated Rubber Products
3081 Unsupported Plastics Film & Sheet
3082 Unsupported Plastics Profile Shapes
3083 Laminated Plastics Plate & Sheet
3084 Plastics Pipe
3085 Plastics Bottles
3086 Plastics Foam Products
3087 Custom Compound Purchased Resins
3088 Plastics Plumbing Fixtures
3089 Plastics Products

31 Leather & Leather Products

3111 Leather Tanning & Finishing
3131 Footwear Cut Stock
3142 House Slippers
3143 Men's Footwear, Except Athletic
3144 Women's Footwear, Except Athletic
3149 Footwear, Except Rubber
3151 Leather Gloves & Mittens
3161 Luggage
3171 Women's Handbags & Purses
3172 Personal Leather Goods
3199 Leather Goods

32 Stone, Clay, Glass & Concrete Products

3211 Flat Glass
3221 Glass Containers
3229 Pressed & Blown Glass
3231 Products of Purchased Glass
3241 Cement, Hydraulic
3251 Brick & Structural Clay Tile
3253 Ceramic Wall & Floor Tile
3255 Clay Refractories
3259 Structural Clay Products
3261 Vitreous Plumbing Fixtures
3262 Vitreous China Table & Kitchenware
3263 Semivitreous Table & Kitchenware
3264 Porcelain Electrical Supplies
3269 Pottery Products
3271 Concrete Block & Brick
3272 Concrete Products
3273 Ready-mixed Concrete
3274 Lime
3275 Gypsum Products
3281 Cut Stone & Stone Products
3291 Abrasive Products
3292 Asbestos Products
3295 Minerals, Ground or Treated
3296 Mineral Wool
3297 Nonclay Refractories
3299 Nonmetallic Mineral Products

33 Primary Metal Industries

3312 Blast Furnaces & Steel Mills
3313 Electrometallurgical Products
3315 Steel Wire & Related Products
3316 Cold Finishing of Steel Shapes
3317 Steel Pipe & Tubes
3321 Gray & Ductile Iron Foundries
3322 Malleable Iron Foundries
3324 Steel Investment Foundries
3325 Steel Foundries
3331 Primary Copper
3334 Primary Aluminum
3339 Primary Nonferrous Metals
3341 Secondary Nonferrous Metals
3351 Copper Rolling & Drawing
3353 Aluminum Sheet, Plate & Foil
3354 Aluminum Extruded Products
3355 Aluminum Rolling & Drawing
3356 Nonferrous Rolling & Drawing
3357 Nonferrous Wiredrawing & Insulating
3363 Aluminum Die-castings
3364 Nonferrous Die-castings Except Aluminum
3365 Aluminum Foundries
3366 Copper Foundries
3369 Nonferrous Foundries
3398 Metal Heat Treating
3399 Primary Metal Products

34 Fabricated Metal Products, Except Machinery & Transportation Equipment

3411 Metal Cans
3412 Metal Barrels, Drums & Pails
3421 Cutlery
3423 Hand & Edge Tools
3425 Saw Blades & Handsaws
3429 Manufactured Hardware (General)
3431 Metal Sanitary Ware
3432 Plumbing Fixture Fittings & Trim
3433 Heating Equipment, Except Electric
3441 Fabricated Structural Metal
3442 Metal Doors, Sash & Trim
3443 Fabricated Plate Work (Boiler Shop)
3444 Sheet Metalwork
3446 Architectural Metalwork
3448 Prefabricated Metal Buildings
3449 Miscellaneous Metalwork
3451 Screw Machine Products
3452 Bolts, Nuts, Rivets & Washers
3462 Iron & Steel Forgings
3463 Nonferrous Forgings
3465 Automotive Stampings
3466 Crowns & Closures
3469 Metal Stampings
3471 Plating & Polishing
3479 Metal Coating & Allied Service
3482 Small Arms Ammunition
3483 Ammunition, Except For Small Arms
3484 Small Arms
3489 Ordnance & Accessories
3491 Industrial Valves
3492 Fluid Power Valves & Hose Fittings
3493 Steel Springs, Except Wire
3494 Valves & Pipe Fittings
3495 Wire Springs
3496 Miscellaneous Fabricated Wire Products
3497 Metal Foil & Leaf
3498 Fabricated Pipe & Fittings
3499 Fabricated Metal Products

35 Industrial & Commercial Machinery & Computer Equipment

3511 Turbines & Turbine Generator Sets
3519 Internal Combustion Engines
3523 Farm Machinery & Equipment
3524 Lawn & Garden Equipment
3531 Construction Machinery
3532 Mining Machinery
3533 Oil & Gas Field Machinery
3534 Elevators & Moving Stairways
3535 Conveyors & Conveying Equipment
3536 Hoists, Cranes & Monorails
3537 Industrial Trucks & Tractors
3541 Machine Tools, Metal Cutting Type
3542 Machine Tools, Metal Forming Type
3543 Industrial Patterns
3544 Special Dies, Tools, Jigs & Fixtures
3545 Machine Tool Accessories
3546 Power-driven Handtools
3547 Rolling Mill Machinery
3548 Welding Apparatus
3549 Metalworking Machinery
3552 Textile Machinery
3553 Woodworking Machinery
3554 Paper Industries Machinery
3555 Printing Trade Machinery
3556 Food Products Machinery
3559 Special Industry Machinery
3561 Pumps & Pumping Equipment
3562 Ball & Roller Bearings
3563 Air & Gas Compressors
3564 Blowers & Fans
3565 Packaging Machinery
3566 Speed Changers, Drives & Gears
3567 Industrial Furnaces & Ovens
3568 Power Transmission Equipment
3569 General Industrial Machinery
3571 Electronic Computers
3572 Computer Storage Devices
3575 Computer Terminals
3577 Computer Peripheral Equipment
3578 Calculating & Accounting Equipment
3579 Office Machines
3581 Automatic Vending Machines
3582 Commercial Laundry Equipment
3585 Refrigeration & Heating Equipment
3586 Measuring & Dispensing Pumps
3589 Service Industry Machinery
3592 Carburetors, Pistons, Rings, Valves
3593 Fluid Power Cylinders & Actuators
3594 Fluid Power Pumps & Motors
3596 Scales & Balances, Except Laboratory
3599 Industrial Machinery

36 Electronic & Other Electrical Equipment & Components Except Computer Equipment

3612 Transformers, Except Electric
3613 Switchgear & Switchboard Apparatus
3621 Motors & Generators
3624 Carbon & Graphite Products
3625 Relays & Industrial Controls
3629 Electrical Industrial Apparatus
3631 Household Cooking Equipment
3632 Household Refrigerators & Freezers
3633 Household Laundry Equipment
3634 Electric Housewares & Fans
3635 Household Vacuum Cleaners
3639 Household Appliances
3641 Electric Lamps
3643 Current-carrying Wiring Devices
3644 Noncurrent-carrying Wiring Devices
3645 Residential Lighting Fixtures
3646 Commercial Indusl & Institutional Electric Lighting Fixtures
3647 Vehicular Lighting Equipment
3648 Lighting Equipment
3651 Household Audio & Video Equipment
3652 Pre-recorded Records & Tapes
3661 Telephone & Telegraph Apparatus
3663 Radio & TV Communications Equipment
3669 Communications Equipment
3671 Electron Tubes
3672 Printed Circuit Boards
3674 Semiconductors & Related Devices
3675 Electronic Capacitors
3676 Electronic Resistors
3677 Electronic Coils, Transformers & Other Inductors
3678 Electronic Connectors
3679 Electronic Components
3691 Storage Batteries
3692 Primary Batteries, Dry & Wet
3694 Engine Electrical Equipment
3695 Magnetic & Optical Recording Media
3699 Electrical Equipment & Supplies

37 Transportation Equipment

3711 Motor Vehicles & Car Bodies
3713 Truck & Bus Bodies
3714 Motor Vehicle Parts & Accessories
3715 Truck Trailers
3716 Motor Homes
3721 Aircraft
3724 Aircraft Engines & Engine Parts
3728 Aircraft Parts & Equipment
3731 Shipbuilding & Repairing
3732 Boat Building & Repairing
3743 Railroad Equipment
3751 Motorcycles, Bicycles & Parts
3761 Guided Missiles & Space Vehicles
3764 Guided Missile & Space Vehicle Propulsion Unit Parts
3769 Guided Missile & Space Vehicle Parts & Auxiliary Equipment
3792 Travel Trailers & Campers
3795 Tanks & Tank Components
3799 Transportation Equipment

38 Measuring, Analyzing & Controlling Instruments; Photographic, Medical & Optical Goods; Watches & Clocks

3812 Search & Navigation Equipment
3821 Laboratory Apparatus & Furniture
3822 Auto Controls Regulating Residential & Commercial Environment & Appliances
3823 Industrial Instruments Measurement Display/ Control Process Variable
3824 Fluid Meters & Counting Devices
3825 Instruments To Measure Electricity
3826 Analytical Instruments
3827 Optical Instruments & Lenses
3829 Measuring & Controlling Devices
3841 Surgical & Medical Instruments
3842 Surgical Appliances & Supplies
3843 Dental Equipment & Supplies
3844 X-ray Apparatus & Tubes
3845 Electromedical Equipment
3851 Ophthalmic Goods
3861 Photographic Equipment & Supplies
3873 Watches, Clocks, Watchcases & Parts

39 Miscellaneous Manufacturing Industries

3911 Jewelry, Precious Metal
3914 Silverware & Plated Ware
3915 Jewelers' Materials & Lapidary Work
3931 Musical Instruments
3942 Dolls & Stuffed Toys
3944 Games, Toys & Children's Vehicles
3949 Sporting & Athletic Goods
3951 Pens & Mechanical Pencils
3952 Lead Pencils & Art Goods
3953 Marking Devices
3955 Carbon Paper & Inked Ribbons
3961 Costume Jewelry
3965 Fasteners, Buttons, Needles & Pins
3991 Brooms & Brushes
3993 Signs & Advertising Specialties
3995 Burial Caskets
3996 Hard Surface Floor Coverings
3999 Manufacturing Industries

40 Railroad Transportation

4011 Railroads, Line-haul Operating
4013 Switching & Terminal Services

41 Local & Suburban Transit & Interurban Highway Passenger Transportation

4111 Local & Suburban Transit
4119 Local Passenger Transportation
4121 Taxicabs
4131 Intercity & Rural Bus Transportation
4141 Local Bus Charter Service
4142 Bus Charter Service, Except Local
4151 School Buses
4173 Bus Terminal & Service Facilities

42 Motor Freight Transportation & Warehousing

4212 Local Trucking, Without Storage
4213 Trucking, Except Local
4214 Local Trucking With Storage
4215 Courier Services, Except By Air
4221 Farm Product Warehousing & Storage
4222 Refrigerated Warehousing & Storage
4225 General Warehousing & Storage
4226 Special Warehousing & Storage
4231 Trucking Terminal Facilities

43 United States Postal Service

4311 U.S. Postal Service

44 Water Transportation

4412 Deep Sea Foreign Transportation of Freight
4424 Deep Sea Domestic Transportation of Freight
4432 Freight Transportation on The Great Lakes
4449 Water Transportation of Freight
4481 Deep Sea Passenger Transportation, Except Ferry
4482 Ferries
4489 Water Passenger Transportation
4491 Marine Cargo Handling
4492 Towing & Tugboat Service
4493 Marinas
4499 Water Transportation Services

45 Transportation by Air

4512 Air Transportation, Scheduled
4513 Air Courier Services
4522 Air Transportation, Nonscheduled
4581 Airports, Flying Fields & Services

46 Pipelines, Except Natural Gas

4612 Crude Petroleum Pipelines
4613 Refined Petroleum Pipelines
4619 Pipelines

47 Transportation Services

4724 Travel Agencies
4725 Tour Operators
4729 Passenger Transportation Arrangement
4731 Freight Transportation Arrangement
4741 Rental of Railroad Cars
4783 Packing & Crating
4785 Inspection & Fixed Facilities
4789 Transportation Services

48 Communications

4812 Radio Telephone Communication
4813 Telephone Communication, Except Radio
4822 Telegraph & Other Communications
4832 Radio Broadcasting Stations
4833 Television Broadcasting Stations
4841 Cable & Other Pay Television Services
4899 Communication Services

49 Electric, Gas & Sanitary Services

4911 Electric Services
4922 Natural Gas Transmission
4923 Gas Transmission & Distribution
4924 Natural Gas Distribution
4925 Gas Production and/or Distribution
4931 Electric & Other Services Combined
4932 Gas & Other Services Combined
4939 Combination Utilities
4941 Water Supply
4952 Sewerage Systems
4953 Refuse Systems
4959 Sanitary Services
4961 Steam & Air-conditioning Supply
4971 Irrigation Systems

50 Wholesale Trade — Durable Goods

5012 Automobiles & Other Motor Vehicles
5013 Motor Vehicle Supplies & New Parts
5014 Tires & Tubes
5015 Motor Vehicle Parts, Used
5021 Furniture
5023 Home Furnishings
5031 Lumber, Plywood & Millwork
5032 Brick, Stone & Related Material
5033 Roofing, Siding & Insulation
5039 Construction Materials
5043 Photographic Equipment & Supplies
5044 Office Equipment
5045 Computers, Peripherals & Software
5046 Commercial Equipment
5047 Medical & Hospital Equipment
5048 Ophthalmic Goods
5049 Professional Equipment
5051 Metals Service Centers & Offices
5052 Coal & Other Minerals & Ores
5063 Electrical Apparatus & Equipment
5064 Electrical Appliances, Television & Radio
5065 Electronic Parts & Equipment
5072 Hardware
5074 Plumbing & Hydronic Heating Supplies
5075 Warm Air Heating & Air Conditioning
5078 Refrigeration Equipment & Supplies
5082 Construction & Mining Machinery
5083 Farm & Garden Machinery
5084 Industrial Machinery & Equipment
5085 Industrial Supplies
5087 Service Establishment Equipment
5088 Transportation Equipment & Supplies
5091 Sporting & Recreation Goods
5092 Toys & Hobby Goods & Supplies
5093 Scrap & Waste Materials
5094 Jewelry & Precious Stones
5099 Durable Goods

51 Wholesale Trade — Nondurable Goods

5111 Printing & Writing Paper
5112 Stationery & Office Supplies
5113 Industrial & Personal Service Paper
5122 Drugs, Proprietaries & Sundries
5131 Piece Goods & Notions
5136 Men's & Boys' Clothing
5137 Women's & Children's Clothing
5139 Footwear
5141 Groceries, General Line
5142 Packaged Frozen Goods
5143 Dairy Products, Except Dried or Canned
5144 Poultry & Poultry Products
5145 Confectionery
5146 Fish & Seafoods
5147 Meats & Meat Products
5148 Fresh Fruits & Vegetables
5149 Groceries & Related Products
5153 Grain & Field Beans

5154 Livestock
5159 Farm-Product Raw Materials
5162 Plastics Materials & Basic Shapes
5169 Chemicals & Allied Products
5171 Petroleum Bulk Stations & Terminals
5172 Petroleum Products
5181 Beer & Ale
5182 Wine & Distilled Beverages
5191 Farm Supplies
5192 Books, Periodicals & Newspapers
5193 Flowers & Florist Supplies
5194 Tobacco & Tobacco Products
5198 Paints, Varnishes & Supplies
5199 Nondurable Goods

52 Building Materials, Hardware, Garden Supply & Mobile Home Dealers

5211 Lumber & Other Building Materials
5231 Paint, Glass & Wallpaper
5251 Hardware
5261 Nurseries & Garden Centers
5271 Mobile Homes

53 General Merchandise Stores

5311 Department Stores
5331 Variety Stores
5399 Miscellaneous General Merchandise

54 Food Stores

5411 Grocery Stores
5421 Meat & Fish Markets
5431 Fruit & Vegetable Markets
5441 Candy, Nut & Confectionery Stores
5451 Dairy Products Stores
5461 Bakeries
5499 Miscellaneous Food Stores

55 Automotive Dealers & Gasoline Service Stations

5511 New & Used Car Dealers
5521 Used Car Dealers
5531 Automotive & Home Supply Stores
5541 Gasoline Service Stations
5551 Boat Dealers
5561 Recreational Vehicle Dealers
5571 Motorcycle Dealers
5599 Automotive Dealers

56 Apparel & Accessory Stores

5611 Men's & Boys' Clothing Stores
5621 Women's Clothing Stores
5632 Women's Accessory & Specialty Stores
5641 Children's & Infants' Wear Stores
5651 Family Clothing Stores
5661 Shoe Stores
5699 Miscellaneous Apparel & Accessories

57 Home Furniture, Furnishings & Equipment Stores

5712 Furniture Stores
5713 Floor Covering Stores
5714 Drapery & Upholstery Stores
5719 Miscellaneous Home Furnishings
5722 Household Appliance Stores
5731 Radio, Television & Electronic Stores
5734 Computer & Software Stores
5735 Record & Prerecorded Tape Stores
5736 Musical Instrument Stores

58 Eating & Drinking Places

5812 Eating Places
5813 Drinking Places

59 Miscellaneous Retail

5912 Drug Stores & Proprietary Stores
5921 Liquor Stores
5932 Used Merchandise Stores
5941 Sporting Goods & Bicycle Shops
5942 Book Stores
5943 Stationery Stores
5944 Jewelry Stores
5945 Hobby, Toy & Game Shops
5946 Camera & Photographic Supply Stores
5947 Gift, Novelty & Souvenir Shops
5948 Luggage & Leather Goods Stores
5949 Sewing, Needlework & Piece Goods
5961 Catalog & Mail-Order Houses
5962 Merchandising Machine Operators
5963 Direct Selling Establishments
5983 Fuel Oil Dealers
5984 Liquefied Petroleum Gas Dealers
5989 Fuel Dealers
5992 Florists
5993 Tobacco Stores & Stands
5994 News Dealers & Newsstands
5995 Optical Goods Stores
5999 Miscellaneous Retail Stores

60 Depository Institutions

6011 Federal Reserve Banks
6019 Central Reserve Depository
6021 National Commercial Banks
6022 State Commercial Banks
6029 Commercial Banks
6035 Savings Institutions, Federally Chartered
6036 Savings Institutions, Not Federally Chartered
6061 Federal Credit Unions
6062 State Credit Unions
6081 Branches & Agencies Of Foreign Banks
6082 Foreign Trade & International Banking Institutions
6091 Nondeposit Trust Facilities
6099 Functions Related To Deposit Banking

61 Nondepository Credit Institutions

6111 Federal & Federally Sponsored Credit Agencies
6141 Personal Credit Institutions
6153 Short-Term Business Credit
6159 Miscellaneous Business Credit
6162 Mortgage Bankers & Correspondents
6163 Loan Brokers

62 Security & Commodity Brokers, Dealers, Exchanges & Services

6211 Security Brokers & Dealers
6221 Commodity Contracts Brokers, Dealers
6231 Security & Commodity Exchanges
6282 Investment Advice
6289 Security & Commodity Service

63 Insurance Carriers

6311 Life Insurance
6321 Accident & Health Insurance
6324 Hospital & Medical Service Plans
6331 Fire, Marine & Casualty Insurance
6351 Surety Insurance
6361 Title Insurance
6371 Pension, Health & Welfare Funds
6399 Insurance Carriers

64 Insurance Agents, Brokers & Service

6411 Insurance Agents, Brokers & Service

65 Real Estate

6512 Nonresidential Building Operators
6513 Apartment Building Operators
6514 Dwelling Operators, Except Apartments
6515 Mobile Home Site Operators
6517 Railroad Property Lessors
6519 Real Property Lessors
6531 Real Estate Agents & Managers
6541 Title Abstract Offices
6552 Subdividers & Developers
6553 Cemetery Subdividers & Developers

67 Holding & Other Investment Offices

6712 Bank Holding Companies
6719 Holding Companies
6722 Management Investment, Open-end
6726 Investment Offices
6732 Trusts: Educational, Religious, Etc.
6733 Trusts
6792 Oil Royalty Traders
6794 Patent Owners & Lessors
6798 Real Estate Investment Trusts
6799 Investors

70 Hotels, Rooming Houses, Camps & Other Lodging Places

7011 Hotels & Motels
7021 Rooming & Boarding Houses
7032 Sporting & Recreational Camps
7033 Trailer Parks & Campsites
7041 Membership-basis Organization Hotels

72 Personal Services

7211 Power Laundries, Family & Commercial
7212 Garment Pressing & Cleaners' Agents
7213 Linen Supply
7215 Coin-operated Laundries & Cleaning
7216 Drycleaning Plants, Except Rugs
7217 Carpet & Upholstery Cleaning
7218 Industrial Launderers
7219 Laundry & Garment Services
7221 Photographic Studios, Portrait
7231 Beauty Shops
7241 Barber Shops
7251 Shoe Repair & Shoeshine Parlors
7261 Funeral Service & Crematories
7291 Tax Return Preparation Services
7299 Miscellaneous Personal Service

73 Business Services

7311 Advertising Agencies
7312 Outdoor Advertising Services
7313 Radio, Television, Publisher Representatives
7319 Advertising
7322 Adjustment & Collection Services
7323 Credit Reporting Services
7331 Direct Mail Advertising Services
7334 Photocopying & Duplicating Services
7335 Commercial Photography
7336 Commercial Art & Graphic Design
7338 Secretarial & Court Reporting
7342 Disinfecting & Pest Control Services
7349 Building Maintenance Services
7352 Medical Equipment Rental
7353 Heavy Construction Equipment Rental
7359 Equipment Rental & Leasing
7361 Employment Agencies
7363 Help Supply Services
7371 Custom Computer Programming Services
7372 Prepackaged Software
7373 Computer Integrated Systems Design
7374 Data Processing & Preparation
7375 Information Retrieval Services
7376 Computer Facilities Management
7377 Computer Rental & Leasing
7378 Computer Maintenance & Repair
7379 Computer Related Services
7381 Detective & Armored Car Services
7382 Security Systems Services
7383 News Syndicates
7384 Photofinish Laboratories
7389 Business Services

75 Automotive Repair, Services & Parking

7513 Truck Rental & Leasing, No Drivers
7514 Passenger Car Rental
7515 Passenger Car Leasing
7519 Utility Trailer Rental
7521 Automobile Parking
7532 Top & Body Repair & Paint Shops
7533 Auto Exhaust System Repair Shops
7534 Tire Retreading & Repair Shops
7536 Automotive Glass Replacement Shops
7537 Automotive Transmission Repair Shops
7538 General Automotive Repair Shops
7539 Automotive Repair Shops
7542 Carwashes
7549 Automotive Services

76 Miscellaneous Repair Services

7622 Radio & Television Repair
7623 Refrigeration Service & Repair
7629 Electrical Repair Shops
7631 Watch, Clock & Jewelry Repair
7641 Reupholstery & Furniture Repair
7692 Welding Repair
7694 Armature Rewinding Shops
7699 Repair Services

78 Motion Pictures

7812 Motion Picture & Video Production
7819 Services Allied To Motion Pictures
7822 Motion Picture & Tape Distribution
7829 Motion Picture Distribution Services
7832 Motion Picture Theaters, Except Drive-In
7833 Drive-In Motion Picture Theaters
7841 Video Tape Rental

79 Amusement & Recreation Services

7911 Dance Studios, Schools & Halls
7922 Theatrical Producers & Services
7929 Entertainers & Entertainment Groups
7933 Bowling Centers
7941 Sports Clubs, Managers & Promoters
7948 Racing, Including Track Operation
7991 Physical Fitness Facilities
7992 Public Golf Courses
7993 Coin-operated Amusement Devices
7996 Amusement Parks
7997 Membership Sports & Recreation Clubs
7999 Amusement & Recreation

80 Health Services

8011 Offices & Clinics of Medical Doctors
8021 Offices & Clinics of Dentists
8031 Offices & Clinics of Osteopathic Physicians
8041 Offices & Clinics of Chiropractors
8042 Offices & Clinics of Optometrists
8043 Offices & Clinics of Podiatrists
8049 Offices of Health Practitioners
8051 Skilled Nursing Care Facilities
8052 Intermediate Care Facilities
8059 Nursing & Personal Care
8062 General Medical & Surgical Hospitals
8063 Psychiatric Hospitals
8069 Specialty Hospitals, Except Psychiatric
8071 Medical Laboratories
8072 Dental Laboratories
8082 Home Health Care Services
8092 Kidney Dialysis Centers
8093 Specialty Outpatient Clinics
8099 Health & Allied Services

81 Legal Services

8111 Legal Services

82 Educational Services

8211 Elementary & Secondary Schools
8221 Colleges Universities & Professional Schools
8222 Junior Colleges & Technical Institutes
8231 Libraries
8243 Data Processing Schools
8244 Business & Secretarial Schools
8249 Vocational Schools
8299 Schools & Educational Services

83 Social Services

8322 Individual & Family Services
8331 Job Training & Vocational Rehabilitation Services
8351 Child Day Care Services
8361 Residential Care
8399 Social Services

84 Museums, Art Galleries & Botanical & Zoological Gardens

8412 Museums & Art Galleries
8422 Arboreta & Botanical r Zoological Gardens

86 Membership Organizations

8611 Business Associations
8621 Professional Membership Organizations
8631 Labor Unions & Similar Labor Organizations
8641 Civic Social & Fraternal Associations
8651 Political Organizations
8661 Religious Organizations
8699 Membership Organizations

87 Engineering, Accounting, Research, Management & Related Services

8711 Engineering Services
8712 Architectural Services
8713 Surveying Services
8721 Accounting, Auditing & Bookkeeping
8731 Commercial Physical Research
8732 Commercial Nonphysical Research
8733 Noncommercial Research Organizations
8734 Testing Laboratories
8741 Management Services
8742 Management Consulting Services
8743 Public Relations Services
8744 Facilities Support Services
8748 Business Consulting

88 Private Households

8811 Private Households

89 Services, Not Elsewhere Classified

8999 Services

91 Executive, Legislative & General Government, Except Finance

9111 Executive Offices
9121 Legislative Bodies
9131 Executive & Legislative Combined
9199 General Government

92 Justice, Public Order & Safety

9211 Courts
9221 Police Protection
9222 Legal Counsel & Prosecution
9223 Correctional Institutions
9224 Fire Protection
9229 Public Order & Safety

93 Public Finance, Taxation & Monetary Policy

9311 Finance, Taxation & Monetary Policy

94 Administration of Human Resource Programs

9411 Administration of Educational Programs
9431 Administration of Public Health Programs
9441 Administration of Social & Manpower Programs
9451 Administration of Veterans' Affairs

95 Administration of Environmental Quality & Housing Programs

9511 Air, Water & Solid Waste Management
9512 Land, Mineral & Wildlife Conservation
9531 Housing Programs
9532 Urban & Community Development

96 Administration of Economic Programs

9611 Administration of General Economic Programs
9621 Regulation, Administration of Transportation
9631 Regulation, Administration of Utilities
9641 Regulation of Agricultural Marketing
9651 Regulation, Miscellaneous Commercial Sectors
9661 Space Research & Technology

97 National Security & International Affairs

9711 National Security
9721 International Affairs

99 Nonclassifiable Establishments

9999 Nonclassifiable Establishments

A

3291 Abrasive Products
6321 Accident & Health Insurance
8721 Accounting, Auditing & Bookkeeping
2891 Adhesives & Sealants
7322 Adjustment & Collection Services
9411 Administration Of Educational Programs
9611 Administration Of General Economic Programs
9431 Administration Of Public Health Programs
9441 Administration Of Social & Manpower Programs
9451 Administration Of Veterans' Affairs
7319 Advertising
7311 Advertising Agencies
2879 Agricultural Chemicals
3563 Air & Gas Compressors
4513 Air Courier Services
4522 Air Transportation, Nonscheduled
4512 Air Transportation, Scheduled
9511 Air, Water & Solid Waste Management
3721 Aircraft
3724 Aircraft Engines & Engine Parts
3728 Aircraft Parts & Equipment
4581 Airports, Flying Fields & Services
2812 Alkalies & Chlorine
3363 Aluminum Die-castings
3354 Aluminum Extruded Products
3365 Aluminum Foundries
3355 Aluminum Rolling & Drawing
3353 Aluminum Sheet, Plate & Foil
3483 Ammunition, Except For Small Arms
7999 Amusement & Recreation
7996 Amusement Parks
3826 Analytical Instruments
2077 Animal & Marine Fats & Oils
0273 Animal Aquaculture
0279 Animal Specialties
0752 Animal Specialty Services
1231 Anthracite Mining
6513 Apartment Building Operators
2389 Apparel & Accessories
2387 Apparel Belts
8422 Arboreta & Botanical Or Zoological Gardens
3446 Architectural Metalwork
8712 Architectural Services
7694 Armature Rewinding Shops
3292 Asbestos Products
2952 Asphalt Felts & Coatings
2951 Asphalt Paving Mixtures & Blocks
3822 Auto Controls Regulating Residntl & Coml Environmt & Applncs
7533 Auto Exhaust System Repair Shops
3581 Automatic Vending Machines
7521 Automobile Parking
5012 Automobiles & Other Motor Vehicles
2396 Automotive & Apparel Trimmings
5531 Automotive & Home Supply Stores
5599 Automotive Dealers
7536 Automotive Glass Replacement Shops
7539 Automotive Repair Shops
7549 Automotive Services
3465 Automotive Stampings
7537 Automotive Transmission Repair Shops

B

2673 Bags: Plastic, Laminated & Coated
2674 Bags: Uncoated Paper & Multiwall
5461 Bakeries
3562 Ball & Roller Bearings
6712 Bank Holding Companies
7241 Barber Shops
7231 Beauty Shops
0212 Beef Cattle Except Feedlots
0211 Beef Cattle Feedlots
5181 Beer & Ale
2063 Beet Sugar
0171 Berry Crops
2836 Biological Products, Except Diagnostic
1221 Bituminous Coal & Lignite-surface
1222 Bituminous Coal-underground
2782 Blankbooks & Looseleaf Binders
3312 Blast Furnaces & Steel Mills
3564 Blowers & Fans
3732 Boat Building & Repairing
5551 Boat Dealers
3452 Bolts, Nuts, Rivets & Washers
2732 Book Printing
2731 Book Publishing
5942 Book Stores
2789 Bookbinding & Related Work
5192 Books, Periodicals & Newspapers
2086 Bottled & Canned Soft Drinks
7933 Bowling Centers
6081 Branches & Agencies Of Foreign Banks
2342 Bras, Girdles & Allied Garments
2051 Bread, Cake & Related Products
3251 Brick & Structural Clay Tile
5032 Brick, Stone & Related Material
1622 Bridge, Tunnel & Elevated Highway
2211 Broadwoven Fabric Mills, Cotton
2221 Broadwoven Fabric Mills, Manmade
2231 Broadwoven Fabric Mills, Wool
0251 Broiler, Fryer & Roaster Chickens
3991 Brooms & Brushes
7349 Building Maintenance Services
3995 Burial Caskets
4142 Bus Charter Service, Except Local
4173 Bus Terminal & Service Facilities
8244 Business & Secretarial Schools
8611 Business Associations
8748 Business Consulting
7389 Business Services

C

4841 Cable & Other Pay Television Services
3578 Calculating & Accounting Equipment
5946 Camera & Photographic Supply Stores
2064 Candy & Other Confectionery Products
5441 Candy, Nut & Confectionery Stores
2062 Cane Sugar Refining
2091 Canned & Cured Fish & Seafoods
2033 Canned Fruits & Specialties
2032 Canned Specialties
2394 Canvas & Related Products
3624 Carbon & Graphite Products
2895 Carbon Black
3955 Carbon Paper & Inked Ribbons
3592 Carburetors, Pistons, Rings, Valves
1751 Carpentry Work
7217 Carpet & Upholstery Cleaning
2273 Carpets & Rugs
7542 Carwashes
0119 Cash Grains
5961 Catalog & Mail-order Houses
2823 Cellulosic Manmade Fibers
3241 Cement, Hydraulic
6553 Cemetery Subdividers & Developers
6019 Central Reserve Depository
3253 Ceramic Wall & Floor Tile
2043 Cereal Breakfast Foods
2022 Cheese, Natural & Processed
1479 Chemical & Fertilizer Mining
2899 Chemical Preparations
5169 Chemicals & Allied Products
2131 Chewing & Smoking Tobacco
2067 Chewing Gum
0252 Chicken Eggs
8351 Child Day Care Services
5641 Children's & Infants' Wear Stores
2066 Chocolate & Cocoa Products
2111 Cigarettes
2121 Cigars
0174 Citrus Fruits
8641 Civic Social & Fraternal Associations
1459 Clay & Related Minerals
3255 Clay Refractories
5052 Coal & Other Minerals & Ores
1241 Coal Mining Services
2672 Coated & Laminated Paper
2295 Coated Fabrics, Not Rubberized
7993 Coin-operated Amusement Devices
7215 Coin-operated Laundries & Cleaning
3316 Cold Finishing Of Steel Shapes
8221 Colleges Universities & Professional Schools
4939 Combination Utilities
7336 Commercial Art & Graphic Design
6029 Commercial Banks
5046 Commercial Equipment
3646 Commercial Indusl & Institutional Electric Lighting Fixtures
3582 Commercial Laundry Equipment
8732 Commercial Nonphysical Research
7335 Commercial Photography
8731 Commercial Physical Research
2759 Commercial Printing
2754 Commercial Printing, Gravure
2752 Commercial Printing, Lithographic
6221 Commodity Contracts Brokers, Dealers
4899 Communication Services
3669 Communications Equipment
5734 Computer & Software Stores
7376 Computer Facilities Management
7373 Computer Integrated Systems Design
7378 Computer Maintenance & Repair
3577 Computer Peripheral Equipment
7379 Computer Related Services
7377 Computer Rental & Leasing
3572 Computer Storage Devices
3575 Computer Terminals
5045 Computers, Peripherals & Software
3271 Concrete Block & Brick
3272 Concrete Products
1771 Concrete Work
5145 Confectionery
5082 Construction & Mining Machinery
3531 Construction Machinery
5039 Construction Materials
1442 Construction Sand & Gravel
2679 Converted Paper Products
3535 Conveyors & Conveying Equipment
2052 Cookies & Crackers
3366 Copper Foundries
1021 Copper Ores
3351 Copper Rolling & Drawing
2298 Cordage & Twine
0115 Corn
9223 Correctional Institutions
2653 Corrugated & Solid Fiber Boxes
3961 Costume Jewelry
0131 Cotton
0724 Cotton Ginning
2074 Cottonseed Oil Mills
4215 Courier Services, Except By Air
9211 Courts
2021 Creamery Butter
7323 Credit Reporting Services
0722 Crop Harvesting
0721 Crop Planting & Protection
0723 Crop Preparation Services For Market
3466 Crowns & Closures
1311 Crude Petroleum & Natural Gas
4612 Crude Petroleum Pipelines
1423 Crushed & Broken Granite
1422 Crushed & Broken Limestone
1429 Crushed & Broken Stone
3643 Current-carrying Wiring Devices
2391 Curtains & Draperies
3087 Custom Compound Purchased Resins
7371 Custom Computer Programming Services
3281 Cut Stone & Stone Products
3421 Cutlery
2865 Cyclic Crudes & Intermediates

D

0241 Dairy Farms
5451 Dairy Products Stores
5143 Dairy Products, Except Dried Or Canned
7911 Dance Studios, Schools & Halls
7374 Data Processing & Preparation
8243 Data Processing Schools
0175 Deciduous Tree Fruits
4424 Deep Sea Domestic Transportation Of Freight
4412 Deep Sea Foreign Transportation Of Freight
4481 Deep Sea Passenger Transportation, Except Ferry
2034 Dehydrated Fruits, Vegetables, Soups
3843 Dental Equipment & Supplies
8072 Dental Laboratories
5311 Department Stores
7381 Detective & Armored Car Services
2675 Die-cut Paper & Board
1411 Dimension Stone
7331 Direct Mail Advertising Services
5963 Direct Selling Establishments
7342 Disinfecting & Pest Control Services
2085 Distilled & Blended Liquors
2047 Dog & Cat Food
3942 Dolls & Stuffed Toys
5714 Drapery & Upholstery Stores
2591 Drapery Hardware & Blinds & Shades
1381 Drilling Oil & Gas Wells
5813 Drinking Places
7833 Drive-in Motion Picture Theaters
5912 Drug Stores & Proprietary Stores
5122 Drugs, Proprietaries & Sundries
2023 Dry, Condensed, Evaporated Dairy Products
7216 Drycleaning Plants, Except Rugs
5099 Durable Goods

6514	Dwelling Operators, Except Apartments

E

5812	Eating Places
2079	Edible Fats & Oils
4931	Electric & Other Services Combined
3634	Electric Housewares & Fans
3641	Electric Lamps
4911	Electric Services
5063	Electrical Apparatus & Equipment
5064	Electrical Appliances, Television & Radio
3699	Electrical Equipment & Supplies
3629	Electrical Industrial Apparatus
7629	Electrical Repair Shops
1731	Electrical Work
3845	Electromedical Equipment
3313	Electrometallurgical Products
3671	Electron Tubes
3675	Electronic Capacitors
3677	Electronic Coils, Transformers & Other Inductors
3676	Electronic Resistors
8211	Elementary & Secondary Schools
3534	Elevators & Moving Stairways
7361	Employment Agencies
3694	Engine Electrical Equipment
8711	Engineering Services
7929	Entertainers & Entertainment Groups
2677	Envelopes
7359	Equipment Rental & Leasing
1794	Excavation Work
9131	Executive & Legislative Combined
9111	Executive Offices
2892	Explosives
3679	Electronic Components
3571	Electronic Computers
3678	Electronic Connectors
5065	Electronic Parts & Equipment

F

2381	Fabric Dress & Work Gloves
3499	Fabricated Metal Products
3498	Fabricated Pipe & Fittings
3443	Fabricated Plate Work (Boiler Shop)
3069	Fabricated Rubber Products
3441	Fabricated Structural Metal
2399	Fabricated Textile Products
8744	Facilities Support Services
5651	Family Clothing Stores
5083	Farm & Garden Machinery
0761	Farm Labor Contractors
3523	Farm Machinery & Equipment
0762	Farm Management Services
4221	Farm Product Warehousing & Storage
5191	Farm Supplies
5159	Farm-product Raw Materials
3965	Fasteners, Buttons, Needles & Pins
6111	Federal & Federally Sponsored Credit Agencies
6061	Federal Credit Unions
6011	Federal Reserve Banks
4482	Ferries
1061	Ferroalloy Ores, Except Vanadium
2875	Fertilizers, Mixing Only
2655	Fiber Cans, Drums & Similar Products
0139	Field Crops, Except Cash Grain
9311	Finance, Taxation & Monetary Policy
0912	Finfish
2269	Finishing Plants
2261	Finishing Plants, Cotton
2262	Finishing Plants, Manmade Fiber & Silk Fabrics
9224	Fire Protection
6331	Fire, Marine & Casualty Insurance
5146	Fish & Seafoods
0921	Fish Hatcheries & Preserves
3211	Flat Glass
2087	Flavoring Extracts & Syrups
5713	Floor Covering Stores
1752	Floor Laying & Floor Work
5992	Florists
2041	Flour & Other Grain Mill Products
5193	Flowers & Florists' Supplies
3824	Fluid Meters & Counting Devices
2026	Fluid Milk
3593	Fluid Power Cylinders & Actuators
3594	Fluid Power Pumps & Motors
3492	Fluid Power Valves & Hose Fittings
2657	Folding Paperboard Boxes
0182	Food Crops Grown UnderCover
2099	Food Preparations
3556	Food Products Machinery
5139	Footwear
3131	Footwear Cut Stock
3149	Footwear, Except Rubber
6082	Foreign Trade & International Banking Institutions
0831	Forest Products
0851	Forestry Services
4731	Freight Transportation Arrangement
4432	Freight Transportation On The Great Lakes
5148	Fresh Fruits & Vegetables
2092	Fresh Or Frozen Packaged Fish
2053	Frozen Bakery Products, Except Bread
2037	Frozen Fruits & Vegetables
2038	Frozen Specialties
5431	Fruit & Vegetable Markets
0179	Fruits & Tree Nuts
5989	Fuel Dealers
5983	Fuel Oil Dealers
6099	Functions Related To Deposit Banking
7261	Funeral Service & Crematories
2371	Fur Goods
0271	Fur-bearing Animals & Rabbits
5021	Furniture
2599	Furniture & Fixtures
5712	Furniture Stores

G

3944	Games, Toys & Children's Vehicles
7212	Garment Pressing & Cleaners' Agents
4932	Gas & Other Services Combined
4925	Gas Production And/or Distribution
4923	Gas Transmission & Distribution
3053	Gaskets, Packing & Sealing Devices
5541	Gasoline Service Stations
7538	General Automotive Repair Shops
0291	General Farms, Primarily Animals
0191	General Farms, Primarily Crop
9199	General Government
3569	General Industrial Machinery
0219	General Livestock
8062	General Medical & Surgical Hospitals
4225	General Warehousing & Storage
5947	Gift, Novelty & Souvenir Shop
2361	Girls' & Children's Dresses, Blouses & Shirts
2369	Girls' & Children's Outerwear
1793	Glass & Glazing Work
3221	Glass Containers
1041	Gold Ores
5153	Grain & Field Beans
0172	Grapes
3321	Gray & Ductile Iron Foundries
2771	Greeting Cards
5149	Groceries & Related Products
5141	Groceries, General Line
5411	Grocery Stores
3769	Guided Missile & Space Vehicle Parts & Auxiliary Equipment
3764	Guided Missile & Space Vehicle Propulsion Unit Parts
3761	Guided Missiles & Space Vehicles
2861	Gum & Wood Chemicals
3275	Gypsum Products

H

3423	Hand & Edge Tools
3996	Hard Surface Floor Coverings
5072	Hardware
5251	Hardware
2426	Hardwood Dimension & Flooring Mills
2435	Hardwood Veneer & Plywood
2353	Hats, Caps & Millinery
8099	Health & Allied Services
3433	Heating Equipment, Except Electric
1629	Heavy Construction
7353	Heavy Construction Equipment Rental
7363	Help Supply Services
1611	Highway & Street Construction
5945	Hobby, Toy & Game Shops
0213	Hogs
3536	Hoists, Cranes & Monorails
6719	Holding Companies
5023	Home Furnishings
8082	Home Health Care Services
0272	Horses & Other Equines
2252	Hosiery
6324	Hospital & Medical Service Plans
7011	Hotels & Motels
3142	House Slippers
5722	Household Appliance Stores
3639	Household Appliances
3651	Household Audio & Video Equipment
3631	Household Cooking Equipment
2392	Household Furnishings
2519	Household Furniture
3633	Household Laundry Equipment
3632	Household Refrigerators & Freezers
3635	Household Vacuum Cleaners
9531	Housing Programs
0971	Hunting, Trapping, Game Propagation

I

2024	Ice Cream & Frozen Desserts
2835	In Vitro & In Vivo Diagnostic Substances
8322	Individual & Family Services
5113	Industrial & Personal Service Paper
1541	Industrial Buildings & Warehouses
3567	Industrial Furnaces & Ovens
2813	Industrial Gases
2819	Industrial Inorganic Chemicals
3823	Industrial Instrmnts Msrmnt Display/control Process Variable
7218	Industrial Launderers
3599	Industrial Machinery
5084	Industrial Machinery & Equipment
2869	Industrial Organic Chemicals
3543	Industrial Patterns
1446	Industrial Sand
5085	Industrial Supplies
3537	Industrial Trucks & Tractors
3491	Industrial Valves
7375	Information Retrieval Services
2816	Inorganic Pigments
4785	Inspection & Fixed Facilities
1796	Installing Building Equipment
3825	Instruments To Measure Electricity
6411	Insurance Agents, Brokers Service
6399	Insurance Carriers
4131	Intercity & Rural Bus Transportation
8052	Intermediate Care Facilities
3519	Internal Combustion Engines
9721	International Affairs
6282	Investment Advice
6726	Investment Offices
6799	Investors
0134	Irish Potatoes
3462	Iron & Steel Forgings
1011	Iron Ores
4971	Irrigation Systems

J

3915	Jewelers' Materials & Lapidary Work
5094	Jewelry & Precious Stones
5944	Jewelry Stores
3911	Jewelry, Precious Metal
8331	Job Training & Vocational Rehabilitation Services
8222	Junior Colleges & Technical Institutes

K

1455	Kaolin & Ball Clay
8092	Kidney Dialysis Centers
2253	Knit Outerwear Mills
2254	Knit Underwear Mills
2259	Knitting Mills

L

8631	Labor Unions & Similar Labor Organizations
3821	Laboratory Apparatus & Furniture
2258	Lace & Warp Knit Fabric Mills
3083	Laminated Plastics Plate & Sheet
9512	Land, Mineral & Wildlife Conservation
0781	Landscape Counseling & Planning
7219	Laundry & Garment Services
3524	Lawn & Garden Equipment
0782	Lawn & Garden Services
1031	Lead & Zinc Ores
3952	Lead Pencils & Art Goods
2386	Leather & Sheep-lined Clothing
3151	Leather Gloves & Mittens
3199	Leather Goods
3111	Leather Tanning & Finishing
9222	Legal Counsel & Prosecution
8111	Legal Services
9121	Legislative Bodies
8231	Libraries
6311	Life Insurance
3648	Lighting Equipment
3274	Lime
7213	Linen Supply
5984	Liquefied Petroleum Gas Dealers
5921	Liquor Stores
5154	Livestock
0751	Livestock Services, Except Veterinary
6163	Loan Brokers
4111	Local & Suburban Transit
4141	Local Bus Charter Service
4119	Local Passenger Transportation
4214	Local Trucking With Storage
4212	Local Trucking, Without Storage
2411	Logging

2992 Lubricating Oils & Greases
3161 Luggage
5948 Luggage & Leather Goods Stores
5211 Lumber & Other Building Materials
5031 Lumber, Plywood & Millwork

M

2098 Macaroni & Spaghetti
3545 Machine Tool Accessories
3541 Machine Tools, Metal Cutting Type
3542 Machine Tools, Metal Forming Type
3695 Magnetic & Optical Recording Media
3322 Malleable Iron Foundries
2083 Malt
2082 Malt Beverages
8742 Management Consulting Services
6722 Management Investment, Open-end
8741 Management Services
2761 Manifold Business Forms
3429 Manufactured Hardware (General)
2097 Manufactured Ice
3999 Manufacturing Industries
4493 Marinas
4491 Marine Cargo Handling
3953 Marking Devices
1741 Masonry & Other Stonework
2515 Mattresses & Bedsprings
3829 Measuring & Controlling Devices
3586 Measuring & Dispensing Pumps
5421 Meat & Fish Markets
2011 Meat Packing Plants
5147 Meats & Meat Products
3061 Mechanical Rubber Goods
5047 Medical & Hospital Equipment
7352 Medical Equipment Rental
8071 Medical Laboratories
2833 Medicinals & Botanicals
8699 Membership Organizations
7997 Membership Sports & Recreation Clubs
7041 Membership-basis Organization Hotels
2329 Men's & Boys' Clothing
5136 Men's & Boys' Clothing
5611 Men's & Boys' Clothing Stores
2321 Men's & Boys' Furnishings
2323 Men's & Boys' Neckwear
2311 Men's & Boys' Suits & Coats
2325 Men's & Boys' Trousers & Slacks
2322 Men's & Boys' Underwear Nightwear
2326 Men's & Boys' Work Clothing
3143 Men's Footwear, Except Athletic
5962 Merchandising Machine Operators
3412 Metal Barrels, Drums & Pails
3411 Metal Cans
3479 Metal Coating & Allied Service
3442 Metal Doors, Sash & Trim
3497 Metal Foil & Leaf
3398 Metal Heat Treating
2514 Metal Household Furniture
1081 Metal Mining Services
1099 Metal Ores
3431 Metal Sanitary Ware
3469 Metal Stampings
5051 Metals Service Centers & Offices
3549 Metalworking Machinery
2431 Millwork
3296 Mineral Wool
3295 Minerals, Ground Or Treated
3532 Mining Machinery
5699 Miscellaneous Apparel & Accessories
6159 Miscellaneous Business Credit
3496 Miscellaneous Fabricated Wire Products
5499 Miscellaneous Food Stores
5399 Miscellaneous General Merchandise
5719 Miscellaneous Home Furnishings
0919 Miscellaneous Marine Products
3449 Miscellaneous Metalwork
1499 Miscellaneous Nonmetallic Minerals
7299 Miscellaneous Personal Service
2741 Miscellaneous Publishing
5999 Miscellaneous Retail Stores
6515 Mobile Home Site Operators
2451 Mobile Homes
5271 Mobile Homes
6162 Mortgage Bankers & Correspondents
7822 Motion Picture & Tape Distribution
7812 Motion Picture & Video Production
7829 Motion Picture Distribution Services
7832 Motion Picture Theaters, Except Drive-in
3716 Motor Homes
3714 Motor Vehicle Parts & Accessories
5015 Motor Vehicle Parts, Used
5013 Motor Vehicle Supplies & New Parts
3711 Motor Vehicles & Car Bodies
5571 Motorcycle Dealers
3751 Motorcycles, Bicycles & Parts
3621 Motors & Generators
8412 Museums & Art Galleries
5736 Musical Instrument Stores
3931 Musical Instruments

N

2441 Nailed Wood Boxes & Shook
2241 Narrow Fabric Mills
6021 National Commercial Banks
9711 National Security
4924 Natural Gas Distribution
1321 Natural Gas Liquids
4922 Natural Gas Transmission
5511 New & Used Car Dealers
5994 News Dealers & Newsstands
7383 News Syndicates
2711 Newspapers
2873 Nitrogenous Fertilizers
9999 Nonclassifiable Establishments
3297 Nonclay Refractories
8733 Noncommercial Research Organizations
3644 Noncurrent-carrying Wiring Devices
6091 Nondeposit Trust Facilities
5199 Nondurable Goods
3364 Nonferrous Die-castings Except Aluminum
3463 Nonferrous Forgings
3369 Nonferrous Foundries
3356 Nonferrous Drawing
3357 Nonferrous Wiredrawing & Insulating
3299 Nonmetallic Mineral Products
1481 Nonmetallic Mineral Services
6512 Nonresidential Building Operators
1542 Nonresidential Construction
2297 Nonwoven Fabrics
5261 Nurseries & Garden Centers
8059 Nursing & Personal Care

O

5044 Office Equipment
2522 Office Furniture, Except Wood
3579 Office Machines
8041 Offices & Clinics Of Chiropractors
8021 Offices & Clinics Of Dentists
8011 Offices & Clinics Of Medical Doctors
8042 Offices & Clinics Of Optometrists
8031 Offices & Clinics Of Osteopathic Physicians
8043 Offices & Clinics Of Podiatrists
8049 Offices Of Health Practitioners
1382 Oil & Gas Exploration Services
3533 Oil & Gas Field Machinery
1389 Oil & Gas Field Services
6792 Oil Royalty Traders
1531 Operative Builders
3851 Ophthalmic Goods
5048 Ophthalmic Goods
5995 Optical Goods Stores
3827 Optical Instruments & Lenses
3489 Ordnance & Accessories
2824 Organic Fibers, Noncellulosic
0181 Ornamental Nursery Products
0783 Ornamental Shrub & Tree Services
7312 Outdoor Advertising Services

P

5142 Packaged Frozen Goods
3565 Packaging Machinery
2671 Packaging Paper & Plastics Film, Coated & Laminated
4783 Packing & Crating
5231 Paint, Glass & Wallpaper
1721 Painting & Paper Hanging
2851 Paints & Allied Products
5198 Paints, Varnishes & Supplies
3554 Paper Industries Machinery
2621 Paper Mills
2631 Paperboard Mills
2542 Partitions & Fixtures, Except Wood
7515 Passenger Car Leasing
7514 Passenger Car Rental
4729 Passenger Transportation Arrangement
6794 Patent Owners & Lessors
3951 Pens & Mechanical Pencils
6371 Pension, Health & Welfare Funds
2721 Periodicals
6141 Personal Credit Institutions
3172 Personal Leather Goods
2999 Petroleum & Coal Products
5171 Petroleum Bulk Stations & Terminals
5172 Petroleum Products
2911 Petroleum Refining
2834 Pharmaceutical Preparations
1475 Phosphate Rock
2874 Phosphatic Fertilizers
7334 Photocopying & Duplicating Services
7384 Photofinish Laboratories
3861 Photographic Equipment & Supplies
5043 Photographic Equipment & Supplies
7221 Photographic Studios, Portrait
7991 Physical Fitness Facilities
2035 Pickles, Sauces & Salad Dressings
5131 Piece Goods & Notions
4619 Pipelines
1742 Plastering, Drywall & Insulation
3085 Plastics Bottles
3086 Plastics Foam Products
5162 Plastics Materials & Basic Shapes
2821 Plastics Materials & Resins
3084 Plastics Pipe
3088 Plastics Plumbing Fixtures
3089 Plastics Products
2796 Platemaking Services
3471 Plating & Polishing
2395 Pleating & Stitching
5074 Plumbing & Hydronic Heating Supplies
3432 Plumbing Fixture Fittings & Trim
1711 Plumbing, Heating, Air-conditioning Contractors
9221 Police Protection
8651 Political Organizations
3264 Porcelain Electrical Supplies
1474 Potash, Soda & Borate Minerals
2096 Potato Chips & Similar Snacks
3269 Pottery Products
0259 Poultry & Eggs
5144 Poultry & Poultry Products
0254 Poultry Hatcheries
2015 Poultry Slaughtering & Processing
7211 Power Laundries, Family & Commercial
3568 Power Transmission Equipment
3546 Power-driven Handtools
3652 Pre-recorded Records & Tapes
3448 Prefabricated Metal Buildings
2452 Prefabricated Wood Buildings
7372 Prepackaged Software
2048 Prepared Feeds
2045 Prepared Flour Mixes & Doughs
3229 Pressed & Blown Glass
3334 Primary Aluminum
3692 Primary Batteries, Dry & Wet
3331 Primary Copper
3399 Primary Metal Products
3339 Primary Nonferrous Metals
3672 Printed Circuit Boards
5111 Printing & Writing Paper
2893 Printing Ink
3555 Printing Trades Machinery
8811 Private Households
3231 Products Of Purchased Glass
5049 Professional Equipment
8621 Professional Membership Organizations
8063 Psychiatric Hospitals
2531 Public Building & Related Furniture
7992 Public Golf Courses
9229 Public Order & Safety
8743 Public Relations Services
2611 Pulp Mills
3561 Pumps & Pumping Equipment

R

7948 Racing, Including Track Operation
3663 Radio & TV Communications Equipment
7622 Radio & Television Repair
4832 Radio Broadcasting Stations
4812 Radio Telephone Communication
5731 Radio, Television & Electronic Stores
7313 Radio, Television, Publisher Representatives
3743 Railroad Equipment
6517 Railroad Property Lessors
4011 Railroads, Line-haul Operating
2061 Raw Cane Sugar

STANDARD INDUSTRIAL CLASSIFICATION (SIC) CODES – ALPHABETICAL

3273 Ready-mixed Concrete
6531 Real Estate Agents & Managers
6798 Real Estate Investment Trusts
6519 Real Property Lessors
2493 Reconstituted Wood Products
5735 Record & Prerecorded Tape Stores
5561 Recreational Vehicle Dealers
4613 Refined Petroleum Pipelines
4222 Refrigerated Warehousing & Storage
3585 Refrigeration & Heating Equipment
5078 Refrigeration Equipment & Supplies
7623 Refrigeration Service & Repair
4953 Refuse Systems
9641 Regulation Of Agricultural Marketing
9621 Regulation, Administration Of Transportation
9631 Regulation, Administration Of Utilities
9651 Regulation, Miscellaneous Commercial Sectors
3625 Relays & Industrial Controls
8661 Religious Organizations
4741 Rental Of Railroad Cars
7699 Repair Services
8361 Residential Care
1522 Residential Construction
3645 Residential Lighting Fixtures
7641 Reupholstery & Furniture Repair
0112 Rice
2044 Rice Milling
2095 Roasted Coffee
2384 Robes & Dressing Gowns
3547 Rolling Mill Machinery
5033 Roofing, Siding & Insulation
1761 Roofing, Siding & Sheet Metal Work
7021 Rooming & Boarding Houses
3021 Rubber & Plastics Footwear
3052 Rubber & Plastics Hose & Beltings

S

2068 Salted & Roasted Nuts & Seeds
2656 Sanitary Food Containers
2676 Sanitary Paper Products
4959 Sanitary Services
2013 Sausages & Other Prepared Meats
6035 Savings Institutions, Federally Chartered
6036 Savings Institutions, Not Federally Chartered
3425 Saw Blades & Handsaws
2421 Sawmills & Planing Mills, General
3596 Scales & Balances, Except Laboratory
2397 Schiffli Machine Embroideries
4151 School Buses
8299 Schools & Educational Service
5093 Scrap & Waste Materials
3451 Screw Machine Products
3812 Search & Navigation Equipment
3341 Secondary Nonferrous Metals
7338 Secretarial & Court Reporting
6231 Security & Commodity Exchanges
6289 Security & Commodity Service
6211 Security Brokers & Dealers
7382 Security Systems Services
3674 Semiconductors & Related Devices
3263 Semivitreous Table & Kitchenware
5087 Service Establishment Equipment
3589 Service Industry Machinery
8999 Services
7819 Services Allied To Motion Pictures
2652 Setup Paperboard Boxes
4952 Sewerage Systems
5949 Sewing, Needlework & Piece Goods
0214 Sheep & Goats
3444 Sheet Metalwork
0913 Shellfish
3731 Shipbuilding & Repairing
7251 Shoe Repair & Shoeshine Parlors
5661 Shoe Stores
6153 Short-term Business Credit
3993 Signs & Advertising Specialties
1044 Silver Ores
3914 Silverware & Plated Ware
1521 Single-family Housing Construction
8051 Skilled Nursing Care Facilities
3484 Small Arms
3482 Small Arms Ammunition
2841 Soap & Other Detergents
8399 Social Services
2436 Softwood Veneer & Plywood
0711 Soil Preparation Services
2075 Soybean Oil Mills
0116 Soybeans
9661 Space Research & Technology
3259 Structural Clay Products
1791 Structural Steel Erection
2439 Structural Wood Members
6552 Subdividers & Developers
0133 Sugarcane & Sugar Beets
6351 Surety Insurance
2843 Surface Active Agents
3841 Surgical & Medical Instruments
3842 Surgical Appliances & Supplies
8713 Surveying Services
3613 Switchgear & Switchboard Apparatus
4013 Switching & Terminal Services
2822 Synthetic Rubber
5941 Sporting Goods & Bicycle Shops
7941 Sports Clubs, Managers & Promoters
6022 State Commercial Banks
6062 State Credit Unions
5112 Stationery & Office Supplies
2678 Stationery Products
5943 Stationery Stores
4961 Steam & Air-conditioning Supply
3325 Steel Foundries
3324 Steel Investment Foundries
3317 Steel Pipe & Tubes
3493 Steel Springs, Except Wire
3315 Steel Wire & Related Products
3691 Storage Batteries
3544 Special Dies, Tools, Jigs & Fixtures
3559 Special Industry Machinery
2429 Special Product Sawmills
1799 Special Trade Contractors
4226 Special Warehousing & Storage
2842 Specialty Cleaning, Polishes & Sanitation Goods
8069 Specialty Hospitals, Except Psychiatric
8093 Specialty Outpatient Clinics
3566 Speed Changers, Drives & Gears
3949 Sporting & Athletic Goods
5091 Sporting & Recreation Goods
7032 Sporting & Recreational Camps

T

3795 Tanks & Tank Components
7291 Tax Return Preparation Services
4121 Taxicabs
4822 Telegraph & Other Communications
3661 Telephone & Telegraph Apparatus
4813 Telephone Communication, Except Radio
4833 Television Broadcasting Stations
1743 Terrazzo, Tile, Marble, Mosaic Work
8734 Testing Laboratories
2393 Textile Bags
2299 Textile Goods
3552 Textile Machinery
7922 Theatrical Producers & Services
2284 Thread Mills
2282 Throwing & Winding Mills
0811 Timber Tracts
2296 Tire Cord & Fabrics
7534 Tire Retreading & Repair Shops
3011 Tires & Inner Tubes
5014 Tires & Tubes
6541 Title Abstract Offices
6361 Title Insurance
0132 Tobacco
5194 Tobacco & Tobacco Products
2141 Tobacco Stemming & Redrying
5993 Tobacco Stores & Stands
2844 Toilet Preparations
7532 Top & Body Repair & Paint Shops
4725 Tour Operators
4492 Towing & Tugboat Service
5092 Toys & Hobby Goods & Supplies
7033 Trailer Parks & Campsites
3612 Transformers, Except Electric
3799 Transportation Equipment
5088 Transportation Equipment & Supplies
4789 Transportation Services
4724 Travel Agencies
3792 Travel Trailers & Campers
0173 Tree Nuts
3713 Truck & Bus Bodies
7513 Truck Rental & Leasing, No Drivers
3715 Truck Trailers
4231 Trucking Terminal Facilities
4213 Trucking, Except Local
6733 Trusts
6732 Trusts: Educational, Religious, Etc.
3511 Turbines & Turbine Generator Sets
0253 Turkeys & Turkey Eggs
2791 Typesetting

U

4311 U.S. Postal Service
3081 Unsupported Plastics Film & Sheet
3082 Unsupported Plastics Profile Shapes
2512 Upholstered Household Furniture
1094 Uranium-radium-vanadium Ores
9532 Urban & Community Development
5521 Used Car Dealers
5932 Used Merchandise Stores
7519 Utility Trailer Rental

V

3494 Valves & Pipe Fittings
5331 Variety Stores
2076 Vegetable Oil Mills
0161 Vegetables & Melons
3647 Vehicular Lighting Equipment
0741 Veterinary Services For Livestock
0742 Veterinary Services, Specialties
7841 Video Tape Rental
3262 Vitreous China Table & Kitchenware
3261 Vitreous Plumbing Fixtures
8249 Vocational Schools

W

5075 Warm Air Heating & Air Conditioning
7631 Watch, Clock & Jewelry Repair
3873 Watches, Clocks, Watchcases & Parts
4489 Water Passenger Transportation
4941 Water Supply
4449 Water Transportation Of Freight
4499 Water Transportation Services
1781 Water Well Drilling
1623 Water, Sewer & Utility Lines
2385 Waterproof Outerwear
2257 Weft Knit Fabric Mills
3548 Welding Apparatus
7692 Welding Repair
2046 Wet Corn Milling
0111 Wheat
5182 Wine & Distilled Beverages
2084 Wines, Brandy & Brandy Spirits
3495 Wire Springs
5137 Women's & Children's Clothing
2341 Women's & Children's Underwear
2331 Women's & Misses' Blouses & Shirts
2339 Women's & Misses' Outerwear
2337 Women's & Misses' Suits & Coats
5632 Women's Accessory & Specialty Stores
5621 Women's Clothing Stores
3144 Women's Footwear, Except Athletic
3171 Women's Handbags & Purses
2251 Women's Hosiery, Except Socks
2335 Women's, Juniors' & Misses' Dresses
2449 Wood Containers
2511 Wood Household Furniture
2434 Wood Kitchen Cabinets
2521 Wood Office Furniture
2448 Wood Pallets & Skids
2541 Wood Partitions & Fixtures
2491 Wood Preserving
2499 Wood Products
2517 Wood Television & Radio Cabinets
3553 Woodworking Machinery
1795 Wrecking & Demolition Work

X

3844 X-ray Apparatus & Tubes

Y

2281 Yarn Spinning Mills

G

G & B ENERGY
See G & B OIL CO INC

D-U-N-S 02-453-7417
G & B OIL CO INC (NC)
G & B ENERGY
667 N Bridge St, Elkin, NC 28621-3004
Tel (336) 835-3607 *Founded/Ownrshp* 1930, 1962
Sales 26.9MM^E *EMP* 110
SIC 5461 5172 Doughnuts; Gases, liquefied petroleum (propane)
Pr: Jeff Eidson
**CFO:* Kelly Douglas
**Treas:* Fred Eidson
**VP:* Rick Caudle
Brnch Mgr: Jason Culler
Dist Mgr: Gary Hollifield
Mktg Mgr: Gray Burchette
Sls Mgr: Becky Hollifield
Sls Mgr: Woody Johnson
Sls Mgr: Paul Stout

D-U-N-S 09-943-7659 IMP
G & B SPECAILTIES INC
535 W 3rd St, Berwick, PA 18603-2937
Tel (570) 752-5901 *Founded/Ownrshp* 1979
Sales 41.4MM^E *EMP* 165
SIC 3599 3462 Machine & other job shop work; Railroad, construction & mining forgings; Machine & other job shop work; Railroad, construction & mining forgings
Pr: John Mensinger
**VP:* Ralph Pollock

D-U-N-S 06-887-6192
G & B WHOLESALE FOODS INC
540 W 15th St, Long Beach, CA 90813-1506
Tel (562) 436-6155 *Founded/Ownrshp* 1980
Sales 24.7MM^E *EMP* 30
SIC 5142 5149 Packaged frozen goods; Dried or canned foods
Pr: George Pappas
**CEO:* Bill Paxos
**Sec:* Tim Pappas

D-U-N-S 82-998-3766 IMP/EXP
G & C AUTOMOTIVE DISTRIBUTORS INC
WORLD TRADING
12999 Executive Dr, Sugar Land, TX 77478-4505
Tel (281) 565-5457 *Founded/Ownrshp* 1988
Sales 21.7MM *EMP* 90^E
SIC 5013 Automotive supplies & parts; Automotive supplies & parts
Pr: Gerald Fleishman
**Treas:* Clive Fleishman
**VP:* David Fleishman
Brnch Mgr: Russel Morris

D-U-N-S 00-184-8266
G & C EQUIPMENT CORP (CA)
1875 W Redondo Beach Blvd # 102, Gardena, CA 90247-3627
Tel (310) 515-6715 *Founded/Ownrshp* 1981
Sales 56.5MM^E *EMP* 17
SIC 5082 7353 Construction & mining machinery; Heavy construction equipment rental
Pr: Gene Hale
COO: Bill Dufour
Sec: Cecilia L Hale
Exec: Eddie Piotrowski

D-U-N-S 07-085-0607
G & C FOOD DISTRIBUTORS & BROKERS INC (NY)
PARK ST REFRIGERATED SERVICES
3407 Walters Rd, Syracuse, NY 13209-9725
Tel (315) 422-3191 *Founded/Ownrshp* 1976, 1988
Sales 196.5MM^E *EMP* 100
SIC 5147 5146 4222 Meats & meat products; Meats, fresh; Fish, fresh; Fish, frozen, unpackaged; Refrigerated warehousing & storage; Meats & meat products; Meats, fresh; Fish, fresh; Fish, frozen, unpackaged; Refrigerated warehousing & storage
Ch Bd: Dwight M Palmer
Recvr: Lyndell Graves
**Pr:* David Lepge
Exec: James Emm
Sfty Mgr: Joe Perrone
Sales Exec: Richard Chapman
VP Sls: Steven Levine

D-U-N-S 09-869-1632
G & C MARKETING CO
J & J SALES
1127 S Marsh Wind Way, Ponte Vedra Beach, FL 32082-6508
Tel (904) 217-7127 *Founded/Ownrshp* 1994
Sales 80.0MM *EMP* 3
SIC 5141 Food brokers; Food brokers
Pr: James Cianci
**Ex VP:* Hector Garcia
**VP:* Joan Cianci

D-U-N-S 07-351-0588
G & C SUPPLY CO INC
1105 State Route 77, Atwood, TN 38220-2229
Tel (731) 662-7193 *Founded/Ownrshp* 1974
Sales 26.4MM *EMP* 68
Accts Hall Cpa Firm Jackson Tennes
SIC 5074 5084 5099 3993 Plumbing & hydronic heating supplies; Pipes & fittings, plastic; Plumbers' brass goods & fittings; Meters, consumption registering; Safety equipment & supplies; Signs & advertising specialties; Plumbing & hydronic heating supplies; Pipes & fittings, plastic; Plumbers' brass goods & fittings; Meters, consumption registering; Safety equipment & supplies; Signs & advertising specialties
Pr: James R Halford Jr
**Sec:* Gina Burton
Off Mgr: Stevhen Foster
Sfty Dirs: Eric Howell
Sfty Dirs: Clint McAdams
Sales Asso: Nick Bryant
Sales Asso: Thomas Shaw
Board of Directors: Stephen Foster, Gregory McClain

G & D INTEGRATED
See G&D INTEGRATED TRANSPORTATION INC

D-U-N-S 11-224-6256
G & E FLORIDA CONTRACTORS INC
5555 Ravenswood Rd Ste 4, Fort Lauderdale, FL 33312-6654
Tel (954) 961-0078 *Founded/Ownrshp* 2002
Sales 20.1MM^E *EMP* 200
SIC 1522 Residential construction; Residential construction
Pr: Enquere Hersman

G & F GRAPHIC SERVICES
See INSERTS EAST INC

D-U-N-S 00-113-6787 IMP
G & F INDUSTRIES INC (MA)
709 Main St, Sturbridge, MA 01566
Tel (508) 347-9132 *Founded/Ownrshp* 1962
Sales 34.5MM^E *EMP* 140
SIC 3089 3544 3469 Injection molding of plastics; Special dies & tools; Metal stampings; Injection molding of plastics; Special dies & tools; Metal stampings
Pr: John G Argitis
**Pr:* John J Argitis
CFO: Gary Degroat
**VP:* Dennis A Astrella
VP: Charlie Feeley

D-U-N-S 08-085-0159 IMP
G & G BEVERAGE DISTRIBUTORS INC
G & G RECYCLING CENTER
207 Church St, Wallingford, CT 06492-6202
Tel (203) 949-6220 *Founded/Ownrshp* 1980
Sales 21.3MM^E *EMP* 62
SIC 5181 5149 4953 2086 Beer & other fermented malt liquors; Soft drinks; Water, distilled; Recycling, waste materials; Bottled & canned soft drinks
Pr: Mark Gingras
**Sec:* Chris Gingras
Sales Exec: Tom Larosa

G & G CONSTRUCTION CO
See GINO/GIUSEPPE INC

D-U-N-S 02-165-7424 IMP
G & G DISTRIBUTION INC
RYAN'S PET SUPPLIES
1805 E Mcdowell Rd, Phoenix, AZ 85006-3052
Tel (602) 255-0900 *Founded/Ownrshp* 1988
Sales 23.1MM^E *EMP* 60
SIC 5199 5999 Pet supplies; Pet supplies
Pr: David Goldfarb
**VP:* Warren Goldfarb

D-U-N-S 06-525-1183
G & G ELECTRIC AND PLUMBING DISTRIBUTORS INC
GROVER PAY & PACK ELC & PLBG
1900 Ne 78th St Ste 101, Vancouver, WA 98665-7976
Tel (360) 574-3134 *Founded/Ownrshp* 1954
Sales 20.8MM^E *EMP* 95
SIC 5999 5211 5251 Plumbing & heating supplies; Electrical construction materials; Hardware
Pr: David Blaydon
**CFO:* Vicki S Siemer

D-U-N-S 01-202-7231
G & G ELECTRIC SUPPLY CO INC
137 W 24th St, New York, NY 10011-1901
Tel (212) 243-0051 *Founded/Ownrshp* 1914
Sales 33.5MM^E *EMP* 40
Accts Virtus Group Llc Princeton N
SIC 5063 Electrical supplies
Ch Bd: Laurence Heimrath
**Pr:* Joseph Fusco

D-U-N-S 00-726-0698 IMP
G & G MANUFACTURING CO
G&G MANUFACTURING COMPANY
4432 Mckinley St, Omaha, NE 68112-1645
Tel (402) 453-9595 *Founded/Ownrshp* 1986
Sales 21.6MM^E *EMP* 120
SIC 3545 Machine tool accessories; Machine tool accessories
Pr: Travis M Smith
CFO: Linda Thier
**Sec:* Cynthia Smith
**Ex VP:* Leland Graske
**Sr VP:* Bill Yeomans
**VP:* Rod Van Slyke
**VP:* Don Watson
Exec: Lowell Eipperle
**Prin:* Roxann J Tucker
Mktg Dir: John Donahue
Mktg Mgr: Michelle McKee

D-U-N-S 94-423-1695
G & G MARINE INC
G & G SHIPPING
1300 Eller Dr, Fort Lauderdale, FL 33316-4216
Tel (954) 920-9292 *Founded/Ownrshp* 1981
Sales 30.1MM^E *EMP* 100
SIC 4731 Freight transportation arrangement; Freight transportation arrangement
Pr: Steven R Ganoe
**Pr:* Mike J Grandonico
COO: Jim Hampel
COO: Richard Teubner
CFO: Nathan Kantrowitz
Ofcr: John Plasencia
Exec: Pauleria Hill
IT Man: Lisa Martin
Opers Mgr: Kent Dunston
Snr Mgr: Michael Magus

D-U-N-S 08-153-0990
G & G OIL CO OF INDIANA INC
220 E Centennial Ave, Muncie, IN 47303-2902
Tel (765) 288-7795 *Founded/Ownrshp* 1956, 1982
Sales 80.0MM *EMP* 50
SIC 5172 Gasoline; Gasoline
Pr: Hoyt Neal
**VP:* Dale Flannery
Dir IT: Liane Harrold
IT Man: Bruce Campbell
Opers Mgr: Ryan Flannery
Mktg Dir: Shane Neal
Sls Mgr: Scott Arrington

G & G RECYCLING CENTER
See G & G BEVERAGE DISTRIBUTORS INC

D-U-N-S 11-104-4645
G & G RISK MANAGEMENT CONSULTANTS INC
9980 Indiana Ave Ste 10, Riverside, CA 92503-5466
Tel (877) 775-7723 *Founded/Ownrshp* 2004
Sales 21.0MM *EMP* 42
SIC 8742 1623 Management consulting services; Underground utilities contractor; Management consulting services; Underground utilities contractor
Pr: Edwin Garcia
**CFO:* Julia Garcia
**VP:* Raymond Flores
Sfty Mgr: Jay Youngkamp

G & G SHIPPING
See G & G MARINE INC

D-U-N-S 06-214-7871
G & G STEAM SERVICE INC
GALMOR'S
120 W 12th St, Elk City, OK 73644-6745
Tel (580) 225-4254 *Founded/Ownrshp* 1975
Sales 205.3MM^E *EMP* 185
SIC 1389 Servicing oil & gas wells; Excavating slush pits & cellars; Servicing oil & gas wells; Excavating slush pits & cellars
Pr: Steve Galmor
**CFO:* Jeff Klick

D-U-N-S 07-898-2568
G & G STEEL INC (AL)
(*Suby of* GENERAL SOUTHERN INDUSTRIES INC) ★
15825 Hwy 243 Indus Park, Russellville, AL 35653
Tel (256) 332-6652 *Founded/Ownrshp* 1975, 1985
Sales 55.6MM *EMP* 194
Accts Boohaker Schillaci & Co Birm
SIC 3444 3441 Sheet metalwork; Fabricated structural metal; Sheet metalwork; Fabricated structural metal
Pr: Danny Gist
**Sec:* Patricia Gist
**VP:* Bret Gist

G & G SUPER MARKET
See GAGMARS INC

G & G SYSTEMS
See LA NEVADA INC

D-U-N-S 07-973-0700
G & G TRUCKING
30305 Bradham Dr, Visalia, CA 93291-9455
Tel (559) 627-0772 *Founded/Ownrshp* 2015
Sales 28.7MM^E *EMP* 15^E
SIC 4789 Cargo loading & unloading services
Pr: Michael Glynn

G & H CONSTRUCTION
See HIGDON CONSTRUCTION INC

D-U-N-S 00-806-5641
G & H DIVERSIFIED MFG LP (TX)
11660 Brittmoore Park Dr, Houston, TX 77041-6917
Tel (713) 856-1600 *Founded/Ownrshp* 1958, 1983
Sales 42.1MM^E *EMP* 85
SIC 3544 3441 3469 Special dies & tools; Die sets for metal stamping (presses); Fabricated structural metal; Metal stampings
Pr: Edward Kash
Pt: Janan Kash
Ex VP: Bobby McIntire
Mtls Mgr: Tam Ngo

D-U-N-S 04-449-9598 IMP
G & H SEED CO INC
1110 W Mill St, Crowley, LA 70526-5413
Tel (337) 783-7762 *Founded/Ownrshp* 1968
Sales 27.7MM^E *EMP* 121
Accts Dugas Soileau And Breaux Llc
SIC 5999 5191 0723 Feed & farm supply; Farm supplies; Seeds & bulbs; Animal feeds; Fertilizers & agricultural chemicals; Seed cleaning
Pr: Raymond Hensgens
**Pr:* Barry Knight
**Sec:* Lamar Taylor
**VP:* Tony Bond
**VP:* Michael K Hensgens

D-U-N-S 04-112-6509
G & H TOWING CO
200 Pennzoil Rd, Galveston, TX 77554-2802
Tel (281) 474-9538 *Founded/Ownrshp* 1934
Sales 38.3MM^E *EMP* 124
SIC 4492 Marine towing services; Tugboat service; Marine towing services; Tugboat service
Pr: S N Huffman
Pr: Mike Nigro
**Treas:* N K Jackson
**VP:* S J Huttman
**VP:* JM Nigro
VP: Robert Young

D-U-N-S 06-055-6958
G & J AUTOMOTIVE INC
ALLSTAR DODGE CHRYSLER JEEP
11503 St Charles Rock Rd, Bridgeton, MO 63044-2726
Tel (314) 291-2050 *Founded/Ownrshp* 1979
Sales 26.3MM^E *EMP* 60
SIC 5511 Automobiles, new & used; Automobiles, new & used
Pr: Vince Capatosta
**VP:* Tim Pusateri
Genl Mgr: Justin Atkin
Store Mgr: Rich Hampton
Sls Mgr: Scott Hamilton

D-U-N-S 15-554-2962
G & J BROOKS ENTERPRISES INC
SANTA FE SUPERMART
608 Adams St Ne, Albuquerque, NM 87110-6222
Tel (505) 268-4123 *Founded/Ownrshp* 1984
Sales 27.9MM^E *EMP* 200
SIC 5411 Supermarkets, independent; Supermarkets, independent
Pr: John Brooks

D-U-N-S 16-910-6739
G & J INC
SATURN
421 Tunxis Hill Rd, Fairfield, CT 06825-4454
Tel (203) 384-0006 *Founded/Ownrshp* 1984
Sales 39.4MM^E *EMP* 150
SIC 5511 Automobiles, new & used; Automobiles, new & used
Pr: Geza Scap
**VP:* Julie Scap

D-U-N-S 03-435-1825
G & J LAND AND MARINE FOOD DISTRIBUTORS INC (LA)
506 Front St, Morgan City, LA 70380-3708
Tel (985) 385-2620 *Founded/Ownrshp* 1964
Sales 51.5MM^E *EMP* 103
SIC 5141 Groceries, general line; Groceries, general line
Pr: Mike Lind
**VP:* Erik Lind

D-U-N-S 04-888-7046
G & J PEPSI-COLA BOTTLERS INC
9435 Waterstone Blvd # 390, Cincinnati, OH 45249-8227
Tel (513) 785-6060 *Founded/Ownrshp* 1968
Sales 500.9MM^E *EMP* 1,612
SIC 2086 Soft drinks: packaged in cans, bottles, etc.; Soft drinks: packaged in cans, bottles, etc.
COO: Daniel D Sweeney
V Ch: Thomas R Gross
**Pr:* Sydnor I Davis
**COO:* Tim Hardid
**Ch:* Stanley Kaplan
**V Ch Bd:* Thomas D Heekin
VP: Rick Kaplen
**Prin:* George G Grubb
MIS Mgr: Con Colovos
Dir Opers: Mel Sutton
Mktg Mgr: Wanda Austin-Wingood

D-U-N-S 18-289-6423
G & L AUTO SALES INC
28990 Groesbeck Hwy, Roseville, MI 48066-2337
Tel (586) 773-8100 *Founded/Ownrshp* 1984
Sales 48.0MM *EMP* 15
Accts Rosemary Grand Master Tax Ser
SIC 5521 Automobiles, used cars only; Pickups & vans, used; Automobiles, used cars only; Pickups & vans, used
Pr: Gary Ring
**VP:* Larry Ring
Genl Mgr: Dan Hughes

D-U-N-S 01-283-4487
G & L DAVIS MEAT CO INC
GIANELLI SAUSAGE
111 Gateway Park Dr, North Syracuse, NY 13212
Tel (315) 471-9164 *Founded/Ownrshp* 1946
Sales 23.6MM^E *EMP* 68
SIC 5147 2011 Meats & meat products; Sausages from meat slaughtered on site; Meats & meat products; Sausages from meat slaughtered on site
Pr: I Stephen Davis
CFO: Jennifer Swindon
Sls Mgr: Jim Judge

G & L DISTRIBUTORS
See STEW LEONARDS HOLDINGS LLC

G & L DISTRIBUTORS
See STEW LEONARDS-DANBURY LLC

D-U-N-S 06-439-4067 IMP
G & L MANUFACTURING INC
1975 Fisk Rd, Cookeville, TN 38506-5009
Tel (931) 303-0678 *Founded/Ownrshp* 2005
Sales 74.7MM^E *EMP* 110
SIC 3317 Tubing, mechanical or hypodermic sizes: cold drawn stainless; Tubing, mechanical or hypodermic sizes: cold drawn stainless
Pr: Phillip E Jones
**VP:* Robert Adams
Sales Asso: Paulina Herrmann

D-U-N-S 02-548-6556 IMP
G & M DISTRIBUTORS INC
200 N Linwood Rd, Galesburg, IL 61401-3278
Tel (309) 342-6185 *Founded/Ownrshp* 1946
Sales 32.0MM^E *EMP* 75^E
Accts William R Pillman Peoria Il
SIC 5181 5149 5182 Beer & other fermented malt liquors; Soft drinks; Liquor; Wine; Beer & other fermented malt liquors; Soft drinks; Liquor; Wine
Pr: Adam Vitale
**Treas:* Mike Heckenkamp
**Treas:* Gordon Henderson
Off Mgr: Becca Knaack
Sls Mgr: Brent Bennett

D-U-N-S 00-523-5098
G & M ELECTRICAL CONTRACTORS CO (IL)
(*Suby of* GOAL INC) ★
1746 N Richmond St, Chicago, IL 60647-5124
Tel (773) 278-8200 *Founded/Ownrshp* 1945
Sales 21.4MM^E *EMP* 120^E
Accts Altschuler Melvoin & Glasser L
SIC 1731 General electrical contractor; General electrical contractor
Ch Bd: Domenic Rivi
**Pr:* Thomas Rivi
**CFO:* Daniel Gooze
VP: David Garcia
VP: Dave Russell
Sfty Dirs: Bill Klier
Snr Mgr: Tom Safko

D-U-N-S 05-000-5214
G & M OIL CO INC
76 Old 25 E, Barbourville, KY 40906-7282
Tel (606) 546-3909 Founded/Ownrshp 1962
Sales 32.7MM^E EMP 100
SIC 5171 5411 5541 Petroleum bulk stations; Convenience stores, independent; Filling stations, gasoline; Petroleum bulk stations; Convenience stores, independent; Filling stations, gasoline
Pr: Jerry Garland

D-U-N-S 06-258-0410
G & M OIL CO INC
16868 A Ln, Huntington Beach, CA 92647-4831
Tel (714) 375-4700 Founded/Ownrshp 1971
Sales 224.2MM^E EMP 525
SIC 5541

D-U-N-S 78-707-8174
G & M OIL CO LLC
CHEVRON
(Suby of G & M OIL CO INC) ★
16868 A Ln, Huntington Beach, CA 92647-4831
Tel (714) 375-4700 Founded/Ownrshp 2006
Sales 64.6MM^E EMP 404^E
SIC 5541 Filling stations, gasoline
Pr: George Pearson

D-U-N-S 02-457-5318 IMP
G & M SALES OF EASTERN NORTH CAROLINA INC (NC)
103 Industry Ct, Goldsboro, NC 27530-9124
Tel (919) 734-1062 Founded/Ownrshp 1959
Sales 27.8MM^E EMP 42
SIC 5083 5999 Poultry equipment; Farm machinery
Pr: Sandra J Murphy
*Sec: Beverly Bragg

D-U-N-S 00-805-2321
G & P FINANCIAL INC
336 W College Ave, Santa Rosa, CA 95401-5022
Tel (707) 584-9000 Founded/Ownrshp 1997
Sales 36.6MM EMP 25
Accts Ernst & Young Llp
SIC 6719 Investment holding companies, except banks; Investment holding companies, except banks
Pr: Paul E Pennington
CFO: Randy German

D-U-N-S 00-952-2041
G & R FOODS INC
MCDONALD'S
225 E Robins St, Conway, AR 72032-7161
Tel (501) 327-2262 Founded/Ownrshp 1986
Sales 14.7MM^E EMP 550
SIC 5812 Fast-food restaurant, chain; Fast-food restaurant, chain
Pr: Chandler Johnson
*VP: Gigi Perry

D-U-N-S 88-477-9836 IMP
G & R FOODS INC
321 Wengel Dr, Reedsburg, WI 53959-9108
Tel (608) 524-3776 Founded/Ownrshp 1995
Sales 20.3MM^E EMP 9^E
SIC 5143 Dairy products, except dried or canned
Ch: Jarold Glick
*Pr: Michael Glick
CFO: Beverly Rohde
*Sec: Carol Glick

D-U-N-S 00-544-1083
G & R GAS SERVICE INC (VA)
111 Branch Rd, Pounding Mill, VA 24637-4501
Tel (276) 963-3865 Founded/Ownrshp 1992
Sales 27.5MM^E EMP 86
SIC 5541 Gasoline service stations
Pr: Bostic John Gregory

D-U-N-S 19-512-0324
G & R MINERAL SERVICES INC
2355 Alton Rd, Irondale, AL 35210-3701
Tel (205) 956-7300 Founded/Ownrshp 1988
Sales 54.5MM^E EMP 1,500
SIC 7349 7699 Building maintenance services; Industrial equipment services; Building maintenance services; Industrial equipment services
Pr: Bobby B Rushen
Off Mgr: Beverly Bailey
Off Mgr: Beverly Washburn

G & S
See GONZALEZ & SONS EQUIPMENT INC

D-U-N-S 00-420-6512 IMP/EXP
G & S METAL PRODUCTS CO INC
3330 E 79th St, Cleveland, OH 44127-1831
Tel (216) 441-0700 Founded/Ownrshp 1949
Sales 39.6MM^E EMP 300
SIC 3411 5023 5072 3556 3469 3421

D-U-N-S 01-137-0525 IMP/EXP
G & S MOTOR EQUIPMENT CO INC
G & S TECHNOLOGIES
1800 Harrison Ave, Kearny, NJ 07032
Tel (201) 998-9244 Founded/Ownrshp 1963
Sales 34.4MM^E EMP 100
SIC 4953 5063 Hazardous waste collection & disposal; Transformers & transmission equipment; Hazardous waste collection & disposal; Transformers & transmission equipment
Pr: Gabor Newmark
*Sec: Zoltan Lefkovits
*VP: Jeffery Lefkovits
*VP: George Newmark

D-U-N-S 84-712-7545
G & S STAFFING SERVICES INC
305 7th St Sw Ste 4, Willmar, MN 56201-2789
Tel (320) 235-3949 Founded/Ownrshp 1991
Sales 1.5MM EMP 600
SIC 7389 Telemarketing services; Telemarketing services
Pr: Sandra K Nielsen

G & S TECHNOLOGIES
See G & S MOTOR EQUIPMENT CO INC

D-U-N-S 01-708-3080 IMP
G & T INDUSTRIES INC
1001 76th St Sw, Byron Center, MI 49315-7956
Tel (616) 452-8611 Founded/Ownrshp 1954
Sales 43.4MM^E EMP 170
SIC 3086 5072 Insulation or cushioning material, foamed plastic; Packaging & shipping materials, foamed plastic; Hardware; Insulation or cushioning material, foamed plastic; Packaging & shipping materials, foamed plastic; Hardware
Pr: Roland Grit
*CFO: Darryl Kragt
CFO: Terry Mead
*Ex VP: Kevin Kolesar
VP: Jeff Butler
Genl Mgr: David Boggiano
Genl Mgr: John Bosch
Genl Mgr: Amanda Kronemeyer
Off Mgr: Lisa Kerkstra
QA Dir: Jo Bullers
VP Mfg: Jay Loprest

D-U-N-S 83-624-0390
G & T SERVICES INC
VINTAGE WINDOWS & GIFTS
4117 255th St E, Spanaway, WA 98387-4331
Tel (253) 847-6750 Founded/Ownrshp 1984
Sales 25.0MM EMP 20
SIC 5211 Door & window products; Door & window products
Pr: Gaynor Lorentzen
*Pr: Threesa Lorentzen

D-U-N-S 00-507-6625 IMP/EXP
G & W ELECTRIC CO
305 W Crossroads Pkwy, Bolingbrook, IL 60440-4938
Tel (708) 388-5010 Founded/Ownrshp 1905
Sales 93.1MM^E EMP 550
SIC 3613 3643

D-U-N-S 05-300-8280 IMP
G & W EQUIPMENT INC (NC)
600 Lawton Rd, Charlotte, NC 28216-3437
Tel (704) 394-6316 Founded/Ownrshp 1963
Sales 48.8MM^E EMP 117
SIC 5084 Materials handling machinery; Materials handling machinery
CEO: Michael G Sabbagh
*Pr: Michael R Sabbagh
*Treas: Lyndon Kennedy
*VP: John Sabbagh
Exec: Brenda Fink
IT Man: Patrick Bowman
IT Man: Fannye McGee
Netwrk Mgr: Beth Wilkinson
Opers Mgr: Greg Short
Opers Mgr: Garry Wallace
Sls Mgr: Steven Burton

D-U-N-S 00-127-1188 IMP
G & W LABORATORIES INC
111 Coolidge St, South Plainfield, NJ 07080-3801
Tel (908) 753-2000 Founded/Ownrshp 1918
Sales 224.4MM^E EMP 900
SIC 2834 Suppositories; Ointments; Suppositories; Ointments
CEO: Ronald Greenblatt
*Pr: Kurt Orlofski
Pr: Michael Pavlak
CFO: Glenn Vranlak
VP: Don Bauch
VP: James Coy
VP: Michael Cutrera
VP: Kevin Fennell
*VP: Aaron Greenblatt
VP: Stephen Greene
VP: Joseph Greer
VP: Edward Hazell
VP: Scott Lamb
Exec: Gigi Gebremeskel

D-U-N-S 79-077-5675 IMP
G & W PRODUCTS LLC
8675 Seward Rd, Fairfield, OH 45011-9716
Tel (513) 860-4050 Founded/Ownrshp 2006
Sales 41.1MM^E EMP 125
SIC 2541 3441 3469 Cabinets, lockers & shelving; Fabricated structural metal; Metal stampings; Cabinets, lockers & shelving; Fabricated structural metal; Metal stampings
CEO: Gary Johns
Pr: Wayde Hunker
CFO: Michael R Janson
VP: Douglas Henderson
VP: Randy Sagraves
Dir IT: Larry Wells
IT Man: Matt Deters
IT Man: Jeff Karen
VP Mfg: Eric Davis
QC Dir: Guerdon Gootee
Mtls Mgr: Joey Seymour

G 4 S
See G4S SECURE SOLUTIONS (USA) INC

G 4 S
See G4S SECURE INTEGRATION LLC

G. A. & F. C. WAGMAN, INC.
See WAGMAN HEAVY CIVIL INC

G A A
See GREENSBORO AUTO AUCTION INC

D-U-N-S 62-380-5108
G A B EMPACADORA INC
9330 San Mateo Dr, Laredo, TX 78045-8728
Tel (956) 727-0100 Founded/Ownrshp 1990
Sales 68.9MM EMP 12
SIC 5142 5148 Vegetables, frozen; Vegetables, fresh; Vegetables, frozen; Vegetables, fresh
Pr: Javier Usabiaga A
*Treas: Ilsalinda P Barreda
*VP: Jaime Usabiaga G

D-U-N-S 01-287-6413
G A BOVE & SONS INC
BOVE FUELS
76 Railroad St, Mechanicville, NY 12118-1518
Tel (518) 664-5111 Founded/Ownrshp 1971
Sales 21.0MM^E EMP 55
SIC 5983 5984 Fuel oil dealers; Liquefied petroleum gas dealers
CEO: Frank A Bove
CFO: John Bove
Genl Mgr: Larry Taplin
IT Man: Victor Dorato
Trfc Dir: Zach Taber
Mktg Dir: Alexa Dalberto

D-U-N-S 00-223-2338 IMP
G A BRAUN INC
79 General Irwin Blvd, North Syracuse, NY 13212-5279
Tel (315) 452-7870 Founded/Ownrshp 1946
Sales 25.8MM^E EMP 150
SIC 3582 5087 Washing machines, laundry: commercial, incl. coin-operated; Laundry equipment & supplies; Washing machines, laundry: commercial, incl. coin-operated; Laundry equipment & supplies
Ch Bd: JB Werner
*Pr: Joe Gudenburr
*COO: Joseph B Gudenburr IV
CFO: Joel Graham
*CFO: Dennis Lewis
*VP: David Clark
VP: Daniel Hertig
VP: Todd Pfeiffer
Genl Mgr: David Welsh
IT Man: Clifton Cliff
Netwrk Eng: Art Leclair

G A F
See LL BUILDING PRODUCTS INC

G A F
See G-I HOLDINGS INC

D-U-N-S 01-243-2738 IMP
G A F SEELIG INC
5905 52nd Ave, Woodside, NY 11377-7480
Tel (718) 899-5000 Founded/Ownrshp 1871
Sales 24.8MM^E EMP 105
SIC 5143

D-U-N-S 04-566-6443
G A FLEET ASSOCIATES INC
GAFLEET
55 Calvert St Ste 1, Harrison, NY 10528-3241
Tel (914) 835-4000 Founded/Ownrshp 1960
Sales 46.6MM^E EMP 26
SIC 5084 5074 7699 7359 Pumps & pumping equipment; Plumbing fittings & supplies; Heating equipment (hydronic); Pumps & pumping equipment repair; Equipment rental & leasing
Ch Bd: Jules Leibman
*Pr: David Shepard
*CEO: Raymond Giorgio
COO: Craig Frey
VP: Eva Barlow
VP: Ed Kipp
VP: Peter Pastore
Exec: Julia French
Sfty Mgr: Ray Giogio
VP Sls: John D'Iorio
Sales Asso: Katherine Tracey

D-U-N-S 02-517-7684
G A JOHNSON & SON
828 Foster St, Evanston, IL 60201-3297
Tel (847) 869-5905 Founded/Ownrshp 1874
Sales 42.0MM^E EMP 40
SIC 1542 1541

D-U-N-S 13-965-1384 IMP/EXP
G A M INC
(Suby of MOVIE GALLERY INC) ★
900 W Main St, Dothan, AL 36301-1410
Tel (334) 677-2108 Founded/Ownrshp 1994
Sales 230.1MM^E EMP 19,500
SIC 7841 5735 Video tape rental; Video tapes, prerecorded
Pr: Joe T Malugen
*CFO: Thomas Johnson
*VP: Harrison Parrish
*VP: Jeff Stubbs

D-U-N-S 00-544-8428
G A MAVON & CO (IL)
10 W Chicago Ave, Hinsdale, IL 60521-3499
Tel (630) 655-2410 Founded/Ownrshp 1916
Sales NA EMP 45
SIC 6331 6311 Fire, marine & casualty insurance; Life insurance
Ch Bd: Philip G Mavon Jr
*Treas: James H Davis
VP: James Skelton

D-U-N-S 62-061-5880 EXP
G A P ROOFING INC
4444 Hunt St, Pryor, OK 74361-4510
Tel (918) 825-5200 Founded/Ownrshp 1990
Sales 21.2MM^E EMP 85^E
SIC 2952 Roofing felts, cements or coatings
Pr: Glen Passmore Jr
*Sec: George Beard Jr
*VP: Mary Passmore

G A R P
See GLOBAL ASSOCIATION OF RISK PROFESSIONALS INC

D-U-N-S 10-311-7362
■ **G AND A SNACK DISTRIBUTING INC**
(Suby of S-L SNACKS REAL ESTATE INC) ★
8521 Loch Lomond Dr, Pico Rivera, CA 90660-2509
Tel (562) 568-1400 Founded/Ownrshp 2005
Sales 24.9MM^E EMP 1^E
SIC 5145 Snack foods
Pr: Carl E Lee Jr

G AND S FOODS
See GOLDBERG AND SOLOVY FOODS INC

D-U-N-S 00-630-2608
G AND S FOUNDRY AND MANUFACTURING CO (IL)
210 Kaskaskia Dr, Red Bud, IL 62278-1386
Tel (618) 282-4114 Founded/Ownrshp 1946
Sales 20.6MM^E EMP 75
SIC 3363 3364 3366 3365 3322 3321 Aluminum die-castings; Brass & bronze die-castings; Copper foundries; Aluminum foundries; Malleable iron foundries; Gray & ductile iron foundries
Pr: Charles Wasem
*Sec: Christine Wasem
*VP: Kate Wasem
IT Man: Robert Walls

D-U-N-S 05-360-6307 IMP
■ **G AY LORD INDUSTRIES INC**
(Suby of ILLINOIS TOOL WORKS INC) ★
10900 Sw Avery St, Tualatin, OR 97062-8578
Tel (503) 691-2010 Founded/Ownrshp 1999
Sales 30.6MM^E EMP 85
SIC 3564 Ventilating fans: industrial or commercial; Ventilating fans: industrial or commercial
Pr: Kevin Gaylord
*Genl Mgr: Aaron Zell
IT Man: Scott Longton
Prd Mgr: Brian O'Keefe
Natl Sales: Keven Hass
Manager: John Anderson
Manager: Rob Carmichael
Manager: Daniela Salagean
Manager: Ralph Stark
Sls Mgr: Terry Shearer

D-U-N-S 00-982-4376
G B "BOOTS" SMITH CORP
2501 Airport Dr, Laurel, MS 39440-4719
Tel (601) 649-1220 Founded/Ownrshp 1954
Sales NA EMP 300
SIC 1623

G B C
See GENERAL BINDING CORP

D-U-N-S 82-777-9505
G B C HOLDINGS INC
GUARANTEED BANKING CALIFORNIA
5670 Wilshire Blvd # 1780, Los Angeles, CA 90036-5605
Tel (310) 826-4228 Founded/Ownrshp 1991
Sales NA EMP 65
SIC 6022 State trust companies accepting deposits, commercial
Pr: Dennis Lam
CFO: Jessica Lee
Ex VP: David Eagleson
VP: Jeffery King
VP: Ben Lee
VP: Virginia Reid
VP: Bonny Wijoyo
Brnch Mgr: Emma Lutskevich
VP Opers: Dan Forgey

G B COOLEY SERVICES
See COOLEY GB HOSPITAL FOR RETARDED CITIZENS

D-U-N-S 87-691-2684
G B GROUP INC
8921 Murray Ave, Gilroy, CA 95020-3633
Tel (408) 848-8118 Founded/Ownrshp 1992
Sales 56.6MM^E EMP 174
SIC 1522 1542 Hotel/motel & multi-family home renovation & remodeling; Condominium construction; Nonresidential construction; Hotel/motel & multi-family home renovation & remodeling; Condominium construction; Nonresidential construction
CEO: Gregory D Brown
*Pr: Mark Greening
*CFO: Jeffery Dame
*Sec: Regan L Brown
*Ex VP: Pat Falconio
*VP: Alec Peterson
*VP: Toni Rodriguez

D-U-N-S 16-184-3271 IMP/EXP
G B INTERNATIONAL TRADING CO LTD
408 Airport Rd, Endicott, NY 13760-4494
Tel (607) 785-0938 Founded/Ownrshp 1986
Sales 42.4MM^E EMP 250
SIC 3629 5065 5999 Power conversion units, a.c. to d.c.: static-electric; Electronic parts & equipment; Electronic parts & equipment; Power conversion units, a.c. to d.c.: static-electric; Electronic parts & equipment; Electronic parts & equipment
Pr: August Garufy

G B MANCHESTER
See PRAIRIE ELECTRIC INC

G B N
See PREMIER IMAGE CORP

G B U
See GBU FINANCIAL LIFE

D-U-N-S 96-781-0776
G BRADFORD CO INC
(Suby of BRADFORD HOLDING CO INC) ★
4646 Corona Dr Ste 100, Corpus Christi, TX 78411-4383
Tel (361) 852-6392 Founded/Ownrshp 1993
Sales 46.4MM^E EMP 3,400
SIC 7363 Employee leasing service; Employee leasing service
CFO: Rick Delano

G C C
See GCC RIO GRANDE INC

G C C
See GREEN CONTRACTING CO INC

G C C
See GENERAL CAULKING & COATINGS CO INC

G C C
See GREENFIELD COMMUNITY COLLEGE

D-U-N-S 00-223-8863
G C HANFORD MANUFACTURING CO (NY)
HANFORD PHARMACEUTICALS
304 Oneida St, Syracuse, NY 13202-3433
Tel (315) 476-7418 Founded/Ownrshp 1846, 2004
Sales 52.7MM^E EMP 300^E

SIC 2834 2833 5122 Penicillin preparations; Antibiotics; Pharmaceuticals; Penicillin preparations; Antibiotics; Pharmaceuticals
Prin: George R Hanford
CFO: Trish Dalfo
VP: Greg Cross
VP: Bill Flaherty
VP: Bill Krichbaum
Dir Lab: Amy Stanistreet
**Prin:* Joseph J Heath
**Prin:* Peter Ward
MIS Dir: Jake Lazore
QA Dir: Jane Ortiz
VP Mfg: Nicholas Walp

G C I
See GREEN COUNTRY INTERIORS INC

G C I
See COLLABERA INC

D-U-N-S 13-250-3371
■ G C I HOLDINGS INC
(*Suby of* GENERAL COMMUNICATION INC) ★
2550 Denali St Ste 1000, Anchorage, AK 99503-2751
Tel (907) 265-5600 *Founded/Ownrshp* 1997
Sales NA *EMP* 1,150
SIC 6719 Public utility holding companies; Public utility holding companies
Pr: Ron Duncan
**CFO:* John Lowber
**Treas:* Fred Walker

D-U-N-S 15-763-7570
G C MICRO CORP
3910 Cypress Dr, Petaluma, CA 94954-5694
Tel (707) 789-0600 *Founded/Ownrshp* 1986
Sales 61.1MM[E] *EMP* 30
SIC 5045 Computers, peripherals & software
Pr: Belinda Guadarrama
IT Man: Wilfred Leung
Sales Exec: Eric Muran
Sls Mgr: Ray Engan
Sales Asso: Eleni Katsaros
Sales Asso: Michael Kerby

G C P
See GARVIN CONSTRUCTION PRODUCTS INC

D-U-N-S 87-836-5550
G C PARTNERS INC
GOLDEN CORRAL
3816 Forrestgate Dr, Winston Salem, NC 27103-2929
Tel (336) 767-1600 *Founded/Ownrshp* 1993
Sales 37.0MM *EMP* 700
SIC 5812 Restaurant, family: chain; Restaurant, family: chain
Ch Bd: Nathan Leder
**Pr:* Dave Gronewoller
**CFO:* Tim Weavil

G C S
See GLOBAL COMMUNICATION SEMICONDUCTORS LLC

G C S
See GUILFORD COUNTY SCHOOL SYSTEM

G C S
See GONZALEZ CONTRACT SERVICES INC

D-U-N-S 06-137-4864
G CEFALU & BRO INC (MD)
8005 Rappahanock Ave, Jessup, MD 20794-9438
Tel (410) 799-2910 *Founded/Ownrshp* 1904, 1972
Sales 92.4MM[E] *EMP* 113
SIC 5148 Fruits, fresh; Fruits, fresh
Pr: John Cefalu
**CEO:* Michael Davies
**VP:* Salvatore Cefalu

G D
See GENERAL DISTRIBUTING CO

G D B
See GUIDE DOGS FOR BLIND INC

D-U-N-S 61-345-6110
G D BARRI & ASSOCIATES INC
6860 W Peoria Ave, Peoria, AZ 85345-6000
Tel (623) 773-0410 *Founded/Ownrshp* 1990
Sales 41.9MM *EMP* 250
SIC 7363 Engineering help service; Engineering help service
Pr: Georgia D Barri
**COO:* Rick W Duff
**CFO:* Alexandria Dorsey

G D C
See GDC INC

D-U-N-S 78-815-0050
G D C INTERNATIONAL INC
GERARD DANIEL WORLDWIDE
34 Barnhart Dr, Hanover, PA 17331-9586
Tel (717) 633-0189 *Founded/Ownrshp* 1987
Sales 55.0MM *EMP* 280
SIC 6719 Personal holding companies, except banks; Personal holding companies, except banks
Pr: Gary Shultis
**VP:* Steven Pfeffer

G D I
See GENERAL DISTRIBUTORS INC

D-U-N-S 78-387-7616
G D LEASING CO
G D LEASING OF INDIANA, INC
(*Suby of* FALCON TRANSPORT CO) ★
2399 E 15th Ave, Gary, IN 46402-3008
Tel (219) 881-0215 *Founded/Ownrshp* 1989
Sales 19.1MM[E] *EMP* 800
SIC 8741 8721 Personnel management; Accounting, auditing & bookkeeping; Personnel management; Accounting, auditing & bookkeeping
Pr: Tom Walsh

G D LEASING OF INDIANA, INC
See G D LEASING CO

D-U-N-S 15-668-7550
G D M ELECTRONIC ASSEMBLY INC
GDM ELECTRONIC & MEDICAL
2070 Ringwood Ave, San Jose, CA 95131-1745
Tel (408) 945-4100 *Founded/Ownrshp* 1983
Sales 23.1MM[E] *EMP* 77
SIC 3643 3565 Current-carrying wiring devices; Packaging machinery
Pt: Grant Murphy
**Pt:* Susie Perches
QC Dir: Russ Stuart

D-U-N-S 15-541-3313
G D S FOODS INC
148 County Rd 565, Sussex, NJ 07461-2633
Tel (973) 875-1008 *Founded/Ownrshp* 1985
Sales 24.3MM[E] *EMP* 40
SIC 5141 5142 Groceries, general line; Packaged frozen goods
CEO: Sal Riggio
**Sec:* Dawn Licata Johnson

D-U-N-S 15-117-0800
G DAVIS ROBERT & ASSOCIATES INC
TRANE OREGON
7257 Sw Kable Ln Ste 300, Portland, OR 97224-7181
Tel (503) 620-8031 *Founded/Ownrshp* 1982
Sales 50.0MM[E] *EMP* 85[E]
SIC 5075 7623 1731 7699 Warm air heating & air conditioning; Air conditioning repair; Electronic controls installation; Boiler & heating repair services; Warm air heating & air conditioning; Air conditioning repair; Electronic controls installation; Boiler & heating repair services
Pr: Robert G Davis
**CFO:* Tammy Nelson
VP: Thomas Mathen
Snr Mgr: Kacie Jederberg
Snr Mgr: Lisa Mattingly

G E APPLIANCES
See GE CONSUMER CORP

G E C
See GLOUCESTER ENGINEERING CO INC

G E C A C
See GREATER ERIE COMMUNITY ACTION COMMITTEE

D-U-N-S 18-002-1321 IMP
G E C O M CORP
(*Suby of* MITSUI MINING & SMELTING CO.,LTD.)
1025 Barachel Ln, Greensburg, IN 47240-1269
Tel (812) 663-2270 *Founded/Ownrshp* 1987
Sales 290.2MM[E] *EMP* 1,100
SIC 3714 Motor vehicle body components & frame; Motor vehicle body components & frame
Pr: Makoto Sakamoto
**Treas:* Hidekazu Urushibara
VP: Brian Burke
**VP:* Hiromasa Iwaya
VP: Steve Steele
**Prin:* Toru Shibata
Cmptr Lab: Kevin Foster
IT Man: Jeff Wright
Ql Cn Mgr: Lanna Bush
Ql Cn Mgr: Terry Glover
Ql Cn Mgr: Christine Pearson

D-U-N-S 13-161-5176
■ G E COMMERCIAL FINANCE REAL ESTATE
(*Suby of* SECURITY CAPITAL GROUP INC) ★
292 Long Ridge Rd, Stamford, CT 06902-1627
Tel (203) 373-2211 *Founded/Ownrshp* 1990
Sales 98.4MM[E] *EMP* 687[E]
SIC 6798 Real estate investment trusts; Real estate investment trusts
Pr: Michael Pralle
Sr VP: Stephen Pierson

D-U-N-S 08-900-0731
G E FOODLAND INC
ELRODS COST PLUS
1105 E Belt Line Rd, Carrollton, TX 75006-6213
Tel (972) 245-0470 *Founded/Ownrshp* 1977
Sales 1.3MM *EMP* 450
SIC 5411

D-U-N-S 00-324-7467
G E FRISCO CO INC (MD)
2 Crain Hwy, Upper Marlboro, MD 20774-8805
Tel (301) 249-5100 *Founded/Ownrshp* 1957
Sales 37.2MM[E] *EMP* 30
SIC 5031 Lumber: rough, dressed & finished
Pr: Prem Agarwal
**Treas:* Leena Agarwal
**VP:* Libby Mendiratta
Genl Mgr: Charles Turlington
Off Mgr: Amy Nagle
Off Mgr: Jenny Williams

G E GENERATORS
See GE GENERATORS (PENSACOLA) LLC

G E H A
See GOVERNMENT EMPLOYEES HEALTH ASSOCIATION INC

D-U-N-S 18-695-7072
■ G E INSPECTION TECHNOLOGIES LP
(*Suby of* GE SENSING & INSPECTION TECHNOLOGIES GMBH)
721 Visions Dr, Skaneateles, NY 13152-6475
Tel (315) 554-2000 *Founded/Ownrshp* 2005
Sales 32.4MM[E] *EMP* 300
SIC 7359 8734 3829 3651 Equipment rental & leasing; Testing laboratories; Physical property testing equipment; Household audio & video equipment; Equipment rental & leasing; Testing laboratories; Physical property testing equipment; Household audio & video equipment
Pt: Jeff Anderson
**Pt:* John Feeney
**Pt:* Jeff Ingram
**Pt:* Jessica Wenzell
Sls Mgr: Jim Graham

D-U-N-S 03-192-6652
G E JOHNSON CONSTRUCTION CO INC
25 N Cascade Ave Ste 400, Colorado Springs, CO 80903-1647
Tel (719) 473-5321 *Founded/Ownrshp* 1967
Sales 416.8MM *EMP* 300
Accts Martin Vejvoda And Associates
SIC 1542 Commercial & office building, new construction; Commercial & office building, new construction
Pr: James Johnson
**Ex VP:* Dave Ivis
VP: Justin Cooper
**VP:* Mike Harms
**VP:* Dan Starr
Exec: Kim Neuhaus
Trfc Dir: Doug Ellis
Mtls Mgr: Mario Elliott
Sfty Mgr: Al Miller
Mktg Mgr: Lori Black
Snr PM: Jeff AP

G E L
See GEL GROUP INC

G E M
See GEM MECHANICAL SERVICES INC

D-U-N-S 01-666-2298
G E MARSHALL INC
1351 Joliet Rd, Valparaiso, IN 46385-5474
Tel (219) 462-3415 *Founded/Ownrshp* 1954
Sales 32.6MM *EMP* 50
Accts Somerset Cpas Pc Indianapol
SIC 1794 1795 Excavation work; Wrecking & demolition work
Pr: Frank Marshall
**Treas:* Clint Marshall
Treas: Clinton Marshall
**VP:* Roger Marshall

D-U-N-S 00-513-8367 IMP
G E MATHIS CO
6100 S Oak Park Ave, Chicago, IL 60638-4014
Tel (773) 586-3800 *Founded/Ownrshp* 1954
Sales 38.2MM[E] *EMP* 96
SIC 3443 Fabricated plate work (boiler shop); Fabricated plate work (boiler shop)
Pr: Lael Mathis
**VP:* Craig Mathis
Dir IT: Jeff Gahn
Plnt Mgr: James Wright
Sales Exec: Bill Mathis
Sls Mgr: William Mathis

D-U-N-S 60-752-7397
G E N P R O INC
201 State Rt 17 Ste 902, Rutherford, NJ 07070-2598
Tel (201) 729-9400 *Founded/Ownrshp* 1989
Sales 26.3MM[E] *EMP* 65
SIC 4731 Truck transportation brokers
Pr: Robert Goldstein
VP: Jeff Garison
CIO: William McCrea
Dir IT: Bill McCrea
IT Man: ARI Weinstock
Opers Mgr: Dru Hopper
Sls Dir: Danny Delgado

G E O
See GEO CORRECTIONS HOLDINGS INC

G E REINSURANCE
See FIRST EXCESS AND REINSURANCE CORP

D-U-N-S 01-023-8574
G E REINSURANCE CORP (IL)
GE
(*Suby of* SWISS RE AMERICA HOLDING CORP) ★
540 W Northwest Hwy, Barrington, IL 60010-3051
Tel (847) 277-5300 *Founded/Ownrshp* 1969, 2008
Sales NA *EMP* 120
SIC 6321 Reinsurance carriers, accident & health
Pr: James R Miller
**CFO:* William E Flaherty
**Treas:* William S Papastefan
**Ex VP:* Rex O Skidmore
**Sr VP:* Bill Faltas
Sr VP: Michael Jackman
**Sr VP:* Frank J Kehrwald
**Sr VP:* Larry P Spoolstra
Genl Mgr: Tony Sikorski
Snr Sftwr: Naveed Rabbani
Sftwr Eng: Dorothy Forbes
Board of Directors: John M Connelly, Robert J Dellinger, William E Flaherty, Joseph W Levin, James R Miller, Thomas M Powers, Rex O Skidmore, Larry P Spoolstra, Hoyt H Wood Jr

G E S C
See GUADALUPE ECONOMIC SERVICES CORP

G E S GLOBAL EXPERIENCE
See GLOBAL EXPERIENCE SPECIALISTS INC

D-U-N-S 17-756-7120 IMP/EXP
G E T ENTERPRISES LLC
G.E.T. ENTERPRISES
1515 W Sam Houston Pkwy N, Houston, TX 77043-3112
Tel (713) 467-9394 *Founded/Ownrshp* 2011
Sales 20.2MM[E] *EMP* 50
SIC 5023 Kitchenware
CEO: Heidi Modaro
**Pr:* Man Tang Glen Hou
**CFO:* James L Dunn Jr
CFO: Ed Long
**VP:* Eve Tsai
Sls Dir: Matthew Streng
Sls Mgr: Janelle Tassone
Snr Mgr: Jim Westerman

D-U-N-S 04-856-9966
G E TIGNALL & CO INC
14 Mccann Ave, Cockeysville, MD 21030-2102
Tel (410) 666-3000 *Founded/Ownrshp* 1969
Sales 28.1MM *EMP* 80
Accts Grandizio Wilkins Little & M
SIC 1711 Mechanical contractor; Mechanical contractor

Pr: Joseph Logue III

D-U-N-S 08-137-7798
G E WALKER INC
4420 E Adamo Dr Ste 206, Tampa, FL 33605-5943
Tel (813) 623-2481 *Founded/Ownrshp* 1976
Sales 47.1MM[E] *EMP* 140
SIC 5047 7699 X-ray machines & tubes; X-ray equipment repair; X-ray machines & tubes; X-ray equipment repair
Pr: George E Walker
**Sec:* Rita Walker
**VP:* Amber Trombley
Plng Mgr: Joshua Anderson
IT Man: Brian Harrell
VP Sls: Joe Lamotta
Sls Mgr: Tom Johanningmeier

D-U-N-S 02-434-6421
G F BUCHE CO INC (SD)
BUCHE FOODS
102 S Main Ave, Wagner, SD 57380-2000
Tel (605) 384-5411 *Founded/Ownrshp* 1905, 1914
Sales 28.9MM[E] *EMP* 200
SIC 5411 5331 Grocery stores, independent; Variety stores; Grocery stores, independent; Variety stores
Pr: R F Buche III

G F C
See GOMEZ FLOOR COVERING INC

G F I
See GFI MANAGEMENT SERVICES INC

G F P
See GREENWOOD FABRICATING & PLATING LLC

D-U-N-S 00-877-8185 IMP/EXP
G F VAUGHAN TOBACCO CO INC
1247 Versailles Rd, Lexington, KY 40508-3117
Tel (859) 252-1733 *Founded/Ownrshp* 1986
Sales 20.3MM[E] *EMP* 60[E]
SIC 5159 4221 Tobacco, leaf; Tobacco warehousing & storage
CEO: Derek Vaughan
**Pr:* Conrad Whitaker
**Sec:* Greg Kever

D-U-N-S 17-736-5210
G FISHER CONSTRUCTION CO
GF
31313 Northwestern Hwy, Farmington Hills, MI 48334-2559
Tel (248) 855-3500 *Founded/Ownrshp* 1987
Sales 29.7MM[E] *EMP* 75
SIC 1542 1521 Commercial & office building, new construction; Commercial & office buildings, renovation & repair; General remodeling, single-family houses
Pr: Glen Fisher
**VP:* Eric Fisher
VP: Michael Yurgalite

D-U-N-S 18-620-4251 IMP/EXP
G G MARCK & ASSOCIATES INC
300 Phillips Ave, Toledo, OH 43612-1470
Tel (419) 478-0900 *Founded/Ownrshp* 1986
Sales 30.0MM *EMP* 45[E]
SIC 5023 Kitchenware
Pr: Gary Marck
**CFO:* Christopher Miller
Natl Sales: Nick Arnold
Natl Sales: Joe Marck

G G S
See GGS INFORMATION SERVICES INC

D-U-N-S 00-300-7192 IMP
G G SCHMITT & SONS INC
2821 Old Tree Dr, Lancaster, PA 17603-7301
Tel (717) 394-3701 *Founded/Ownrshp* 1951
Sales 23.1MM[E] *EMP* 135
SIC 3429 3743 Marine hardware; Railroad equipment; Marine hardware; Railroad equipment
Pr: Ronald Schmitt
**VP:* Gervase A Schmitt
Ql Cn Mgr: Mark Early

D-U-N-S 00-641-1623
G G T INC (MI)
GROTENHUIS
588 3 Mile Rd Nw Ste 101, Grand Rapids, MI 49544-8221
Tel (616) 647-4692 *Founded/Ownrshp* 1958
Sales NA *EMP* 48
SIC 6411 Insurance agents & brokers
Pr: Don Vroon

G H BERLIN OIL CO, THE
See BOOTH WALTZ ENTERPRISES INC

G H G
See GREY HEALTHCARE GROUP INC

G H S
See GREENVILLE HEALTH SYSTEM

D-U-N-S 16-491-6913 IMP/EXP
G HOLDINGS INC
1 Campus Dr, Parsippany, NJ 07054-4404
Tel (973) 628-3000 *Founded/Ownrshp* 2001
Sales 2.0MMM[E] *EMP* 4,300
SIC 2869 2843 3295 Solvents, organic; Surface active agents; Roofing granules; Solvents, organic; Surface active agents; Roofing granules
CEO: Robert B Tafaro
Sales Exec: Chris Duncan

D-U-N-S 10-573-1301 IMP
G HOUSEN AND CO INC
DUWITT BEVERAGE
(*Suby of* CLARKE DISTRIBUTORS INC) ★
1568 Putney Rd, Brattleboro, VT 05301-5103
Tel (802) 257-1151 *Founded/Ownrshp* 1983
Sales 57.5MM[E] *EMP* 63
SIC 5149 Soft drinks
CEO: Jeffrey Clarke
VP: Justin Anderson
Genl Mgr: Debbie Fisher
Genl Mgr: Ananda Fleuriel

D-U-N-S 87-296-9712
G I A A INC
A.G.I.A.
1155 Eugenia Pl, Carpinteria, CA 93013-2062
Tel (805) 566-9191 *Founded/Ownrshp* 1965
Sales NA *EMP* 300E
SIC 6411 Medical insurance claim processing, contract or fee basis; Medical insurance claim processing, contract or fee basis
Pr: John Wigle
**CFO:* Andrew Dowen
**VP:* Julie Capritto
**VP:* David McCarty
**VP:* Susan Roe
**VP:* Daglin Von Ruden

G I C
See GLOBAL INDUSTRIAL COMPONENTS INC

G I D
See WINDSOR INVESTMENT CO INC

D-U-N-S 02-772-4293 IMP
G I JOES INC
JOE'S SPORTS, OUTDOOR & MORE
(*Suby of* GRYPHON INVESTORS INC) ★
9805 Sw Boeckman Rd, Wilsonville, OR 97070-9282
Tel (503) 682-2242 *Founded/Ownrshp* 2007
Sales 105.1MME *EMP* 1,350
Accts Pricewaterhousecoopers Llp Po
SIC 5941 5699 5531 5999 Sporting goods & bicycle shops; Camping & backpacking equipment; Sports apparel; Automotive accessories; Electronic parts & equipment; Sporting goods & bicycle shops; Camping & backpacking equipment; Sports apparel; Automotive accessories; Electronic parts & equipment
Pr: Hal Smith
CFO: Phil Pepin
VP: Ron Menconi
CIO: Matt Miehers

G I L T
See GILT GROUPE HOLDINGS INC

G I R
See GLOBAL INVESTMENT RECOVERY INC

G I V
See GENERAL INJECTABLES & VACCINES INC

D-U-N-S 07-824-5503 IMP
G J CHEMICAL CO (INC)
40 Veronica Ave, Somerset, NJ 08873-3417
Tel (973) 589-1450 *Founded/Ownrshp* 1974
Sales 20.8MME *EMP* 44
SIC 5169 2819 Industrial chemicals; Industrial inorganic chemicals; Chemicals, reagent grade: refined from technical grade
Pr: Diane Colonna
IT Man: Nicolas Colonna
Sales Exec: Fiore Masci

D-U-N-S 06-709-9481 IMP
G J OLIVER INC
50 Industrial Rd, Phillipsburg, NJ 08865-4083
Tel (908) 454-9743 *Founded/Ownrshp* 1973
Sales 42.8MME *EMP* 80
SIC 3441 3443 Fabricated structural metal; Vessels, process or storage (from boiler shops): metal plate
CEO: Theresa P Oliver
**Pr:* John G Oliver
**VP:* Charles A Parker
Plnt Mgr: Dave Layman
Sls Mgr: Mark Dougherty

D-U-N-S 09-258-4895
G K C THEATRES INC
755 Apple Orchard Rd, Springfield, IL 62703-5914
Tel (217) 528-4981 *Founded/Ownrshp* 2007
Sales 7.3MME *EMP* 450
SIC 7832 Motion picture theaters, except drive-in; Motion picture theaters, except drive-in
Ch Bd: George G Kerasotes
**Pr:* Beth Kerasotes
CFO: Jeff Cole
**VP:* Marge Kerasotes
VP: Krystal Lareese

D-U-N-S 09-330-0788
G K CONSTRUCTION INC
1169 Lane 11 1/2, Lovell, WY 82431
Tel (307) 548-6155 *Founded/Ownrshp* 1978
Sales 25.0MME *EMP* 135
SIC 1459 4212 4213 Bentonite mining; Local trucking, without storage; Contract haulers; Bentonite mining; Local trucking, without storage; Contract haulers
Pr: Richard Grandalen
**Treas:* Lori Grandalen

D-U-N-S 18-884-1795 IMP
G K ENTERPRISES INC
26000 S Whiting Way Ste 2, Monee, IL 60449-8162
Tel (708) 587-2150 *Founded/Ownrshp* 1988
Sales 91.3MME *EMP* 320
SIC 3743 3443 3559 3556 3536 Railroad equipment; Fabricated plate work (boiler shop); Cupolas, metal plate; Towers (bubble, cooling, fractionating, etc.): metal plate; Ladles, metal plate; Chemical machinery & equipment; Food products machinery; Hoists, cranes & monorails; Cranes, overhead traveling; Hoists; Railroad equipment; Fabricated plate work (boiler shop); Cupolas, metal plate; Towers (bubble, cooling, fractionating, etc.): metal plate; Ladles, metal plate; Chemical machinery & equipment; Food products machinery; Hoists, cranes & monorails; Cranes, overhead traveling; Hoists
Pr: Kenneth Hoving
**Pr:* Jeffrey Kahn
**Treas:* Marilyn Platter
VP Sls: Greg Ciecierski

D-U-N-S 93-160-5950
G K N AEROSPACE AEROSTRUCTURES INC
(*Suby of* GKN AMERICA CORP) ★
1000 New Horizons Blvd, Amityville, NY 11701-1138
Tel (630) 719-7204 *Founded/Ownrshp* 2006
Sales 23.1MME *EMP* 700
SIC 8734 6719 Industrial sterilization service; Personal holding companies, except banks; Industrial sterilization service; Personal holding companies, except banks
Ch Bd: Roger Pollazzi
**Pr:* Ray Benvenuti

D-U-N-S 00-355-7969 IMP
G K N AEROSPACE NORTH AMERICA INC (DE)
(*Suby of* GKN PLC)
142 Js Mcdonnell Blvd, Saint Louis, MO 63135
Tel (314) 264-3000 *Founded/Ownrshp* 2000
Sales 287.4MME *EMP* 1,325
SIC 3812 3728 Search & navigation equipment; Aircraft parts & equipment; Search & navigation equipment; Aircraft parts & equipment
CEO: Paul J Gutierrez
CFO: Peter Spears
**Treas:* Hugo Perez
VP: Bob Francis
VP: Jim Gibson
VP: Gary Kahrau
VP: Paul Westman

D-U-N-S 00-138-1649 EXP
■ **G K TECHNOLOGIES INC** (NJ)
GENERAL CABLE
(*Suby of* GENERAL CABLE CORP) ★
4 Tesseneer Dr, Highland Heights, KY 41076-9167
Tel (859) 572-8000 *Founded/Ownrshp* 1902, 1999
Sales 261.3MME *EMP* 4,200
SIC 3357 3315 Building wire & cable, nonferrous; Aluminum wire & cable; Coaxial cable, nonferrous; Communication wire; Wire, steel: insulated or armored; Building wire & cable, nonferrous; Aluminum wire & cable; Coaxial cable, nonferrous; Communication wire; Wire, steel: insulated or armored
CEO: Gregory B Kenny
VP: Robert Jamieson

G K V
See CWI SPECIALTY FOODS LLC

D-U-N-S 96-384-5875
G KATEN & PARTNERS LIMITED LIABILITY CO
MY EXPRESS FREIGHT
9903 Santa Monica Blvd, Beverly Hills, CA 90212-1671
Tel (424) 354-3241 *Founded/Ownrshp* 2010
Sales 44.6MME *EMP* 550
SIC 4731 Freight transportation arrangement; Freight forwarding; Freight consolidation; Freight rate information service; Freight transportation arrangement; Freight forwarding; Freight consolidation; Freight rate information service

D-U-N-S 09-738-7914
G L & V CELLECO INC
(*Suby of* 9189-6175 QUEBEC INC)
1000 Laval Blvd, Lawrenceville, GA 30043-5913
Tel (770) 963-2100 *Founded/Ownrshp* 1998
Sales 36.0MM *EMP* 39
SIC 5084 Pulp (wood) manufacturing machinery; Paper manufacturing machinery; Pulp (wood) manufacturing machinery; Paper manufacturing machinery
Pr: Richard Verreault
**CFO:* Nicholas Babyak

D-U-N-S 15-155-4883 IMP
G L & V USA INC
G L V
(*Suby of* 9189-6175 QUEBEC INC)
175 Crystal St, Lenox, MA 01240
Tel (413) 637-2424 *Founded/Ownrshp* 1975
Sales 84.3MME *EMP* 330
SIC 3554 Paper industries machinery; Paper industries machinery
Pr: Richard Verreault
**Ch:* Laurent Verreault
**VP:* Marc Barbeau
**VP:* Bill Mahoney
**VP:* Valere Morissette
**Site Mgr:* J Michael Mc Kenney

G L C A C
See GREATER LAWRENCE COMMUNITY ACTION COUNCIL INC

D-U-N-S 15-275-7639
G L HOMES OF FLORIDA CORP
1600 Sawgrs Corp Pkwy # 400, Sunrise, FL 33323-2890
Tel (954) 753-1730 *Founded/Ownrshp* 1985
Sales 178.8MME *EMP* 450
SIC 1521 New construction, single-family houses; New construction, single-family houses
Pr: Itzhak Ezratti
VP: George M Atkinson Jr
VP: Paul Corbin
**VP:* Alan J Fant
**VP:* N Maria Menendez
**VP:* Richard M Norwalk
Sales Asso: Deborah Smith

G L I
See GAMING LABORATORIES INTERNATIONAL INC

D-U-N-S 09-346-1382 IMP/EXP
G L MEZZETTA INC
105 Mezzetta Ct, American Canyon, CA 94503-9604
Tel (707) 648-1050 *Founded/Ownrshp* 1935
Sales 24.9MME *EMP* 80
SIC 5812 2033 Eating places; Pizza sauce: packaged in cans, jars, etc.; Spaghetti & other pasta sauce: packaged in cans, jars, etc.
Pr: Jeffery Mezzetta
CFO: David Wong
Natl Sales: Tabitha Jones
Sls Dir: Rose Schmidt
Sls Mgr: Tom Rickard
Sls Mgr: Dru Walker

D-U-N-S 05-371-3566
G L N INC
NICHOLS SUPER THRIFT
207 S Broadway St, Checotah, OK 74426-3807
Tel (918) 473-2369 *Founded/Ownrshp* 1971
Sales 76.8MME *EMP* 700
SIC 5411 Grocery stores, independent; Grocery stores, independent
Pr: Gary L Nichols
**Sec:* Nora K Nichols

D-U-N-S 01-904-3389
G L N OF CHECOTAH INC
NICHOLS DOLLAR SAVER
(*Suby of* G L N INC) ★
207 S Broadway St, Checotah, OK 74426-3807
Tel (918) 473-2369 *Founded/Ownrshp* 1969
Sales 65.7MM *EMP* 220
SIC 5411 5912 Grocery stores, independent; Drug stores & proprietary stores; Grocery stores, independent; Drug stores & proprietary stores
Pr: Gary L Nichols
**Sec:* Nora Kay Nichols

G L ROLLER DIVISION
See W OLIVER TRIPP CO

D-U-N-S 00-291-8621
G L SAYRE INC (PA)
1231 W Ridge Pike, Conshohocken, PA 19428-1089
Tel (610) 277-2000 *Founded/Ownrshp* 1934
Sales 38.0MM *EMP* 44
Accts Lawrence F Tornetta Ltd Ply
SIC 5511 5012 Trucks, tractors & trailers: new & used; Trucks, commercial; Trucks, tractors & trailers: new & used; Trucks, commercial
Pr: James R Sayre Jr
**Pr:* James L Sayre Sr
**Sec:* Florence Sayre
Genl Mgr: Dan Horvath
Dir IT: Jason Conlan
Mktg Dir: Mark Miller
Mktg Dir: Mark Schmidt

D-U-N-S 82-920-0968 IMP
G L SEAMAN & CO
4201 International Pkwy, Carrollton, TX 75007-1911
Tel (214) 764-6400 *Founded/Ownrshp* 2008
Sales 87.7MME *EMP* 100
SIC 5021 Furniture; Furniture
Pr: Rebecca Lutz
**CFO:* Ken Hartley
**Off Mgr:* Carolyn Roberts
**VP Sls:* Mary Edwards

G L V
See G L & V USA INC

D-U-N-S 00-347-0408
G L WILSON BUILDING CO (NC)
190 Wilson Park Rd, Statesville, NC 28625-8506
Tel (704) 872-2411 *Founded/Ownrshp* 1945
Sales 41.0MME *EMP* 95
SIC 1541 1542 Industrial buildings, new construction; Commercial & office building, new construction; Industrial buildings, new construction; Commercial & office building, new construction
Pr: Thomas L Wilson
**Pr:* James D Wilson
**Treas:* Kevin Combs
**Treas:* Meredith M Nicholson
**VP:* Julia L Wilson
**VP:* Thomas L Wilson Jr
CIO: Kim Austin
Sfty Mgr: Danny Millsapf

G L Y
See GLY CONSTRUCTION INC

D-U-N-S 09-942-1307
G LOPES CONSTRUCTION INC
490 Winthrop St, Taunton, MA 02780-2185
Tel (508) 824-4834 *Founded/Ownrshp* 1964
Sales 75.8MME *EMP* 200
SIC 1794 4212 4214 1542 Excavation & grading, building construction; Local trucking, without storage; Local trucking with storage; Nonresidential construction; Excavation & grading, building construction; Local trucking, without storage; Local trucking with storage; Nonresidential construction
Pr: Gilbert Lopes Jr
**Treas:* Deborah Dutra
VP: John Horton
**VP:* Gary Lopes
**VP:* Joseph Tutsch Jr
**Prin:* Gilbert Lopes Sr
Mtls Mgr: Mark Nadeau
Sfty Mgr: Glen Regan
Sls&Mrk Ex: Diane Perry
Sls Mgr: Steven Goldstein

G M A
See GROCERY MANUFACTURERS ASSOCIATION

G M A C INSURANCE CENTER
See PASCO INC

D-U-N-S 62-260-6473
G M B AUTOMOTIVE LLC
ACURA
6549 Whittlesey Blvd, Columbus, GA 31909-7250
Tel (706) 596-2888 *Founded/Ownrshp* 2003
Sales 31.0MM *EMP* 67
SIC 5511 5531 5521 General automotive repair shops; Automobiles, new & used; Automotive parts; Automobiles, used cars only; Automobiles, new & used; Automotive parts; Automobiles, used cars only
Sales Exec: Kevin Loncher

G M C
See GLOBAL MINERALS CORP

G M F
See GMF INDUSTRIES INC

D-U-N-S 60-452-1760
G M H COMMUNITIES LP
10 Campus Blvd, Newtown Square, PA 19073-3200
Tel (610) 355-8000 *Founded/Ownrshp* 2004
Sales 38.2MME *EMP* 1,574E
SIC 6531 Real estate leasing & rentals; Real estate leasing & rentals
VP: Joseph Macchione
Genl Couns: John Ferer

G M I
See GUARD MANAGEMENT INC

G M I
See GLOBAL MEDICAL IMAGING LLC

G M I
See GREATER METROPLEX INTERIORS INC

G M L
See INNOVIZE INC

G M MCCROSSIN CONSTRUCTORS
See G M MCCROSSIN INC

D-U-N-S 01-385-5655
G M MCCROSSIN INC
G M MCCROSSIN CONSTRUCTORS
2780 Benner Pike, Bellefonte, PA 16823-8429
Tel (814) 355-4848 *Founded/Ownrshp* 1993
Sales 44.9MME *EMP* 100
SIC 1542 1541

G M R
See GULF MARINE REPAIR CORP

D-U-N-S 07-785-2242
G M R AERIAL SURVEYS INC
PHOTO SCIENCE
(*Suby of* A M E) ★
523 Wellington Way # 375, Lexington, KY 40503-1394
Tel (859) 277-8700 *Founded/Ownrshp* 2013
Sales 29.6MME *EMP* 175
SIC 8713

G M S
See GYPSUM MANAGEMENT AND SUPPLY INC

G M S
See GENERAL MICRO SYSTEMS INC

D-U-N-S 15-693-1347 IMP
G M T CORP
GMT
Carre 175km 27 2 Hc 34 Bo, Caguas, PR 00725
Tel (787) 783-1988 *Founded/Ownrshp* 1989
Sales 94.5MM *EMP* 160
Accts Marques-Guillermety Cpa Ps
SIC 5147 Meats & meat products; Meats & meat products
Pr: Sam Ramos Cordova
**Sec:* Miriam Montes
**VP:* Sammy Ramos Montes

G M Z
See CL ZIMMERMAN CO OF DELAWARE INC

G MORONI COMP
See SMART MANAGEMENT & COMPANIES

G N D
See GOLD N DIAMONDS INC

G N NETCOM UNEX
See GN NETCOM INC

D-U-N-S 00-232-6650 IMP/EXP
G O CARLSON INC
ELECTRALLOY
175 Main St, Oil City, PA 16301-1038
Tel (814) 678-4100 *Founded/Ownrshp* 1936
Sales 38.4MME *EMP* 220
SIC 3356

G O P
See GENERAL OFFICE PRODUCTS CO

G O S
See GREENVILLE OFFICE SUPPLY CO INC

G P
See GLOBAL PACKAGING INC

G P
See GEORGIA-PACIFIC BREWTON LLC

D-U-N-S 18-341-1354 IMP
G P & W INC
CENTER OIL COMPANY
600 Mason Ridge Center Dr # 2, Saint Louis, MO 63141-8571
Tel (314) 682-3500 *Founded/Ownrshp* 1986
Sales 221.8MME *EMP* 52
SIC 5172 Petroleum brokers; Petroleum brokers
Pr: Ralph Casazzone
**Treas:* Jerry Jost
**Treas:* Richard Powers

D-U-N-S 02-267-0850 IMP
■ **G P HOLDING INC**
SIX FLAGS
(*Suby of* SIX FLAGS ENTERTAINMENT CORP) ★
924 E Avenue J, Grand Prairie, TX 75050-2622
Tel (972) 595-5000 *Founded/Ownrshp* 1998
Sales 22.2MME *EMP* 120E
SIC 7996 Theme park, amusement
CEO: Jim Reid-Anderson
**CFO:* John M Duffey
Treas: Mark Kupferman
**Sr VP:* Michael S Israel
VP: Jeff Portugal
Comm Man: Katy Enrique
Area Supr: Miguel Espina
Genl Mgr: Cha Williams
IT Man: Scott Ahnberg
IT Man: Stephen Wright
Opers Mgr: Megan Fulbright

G P I
See GREENMAN-PEDERSEN INC

G P I
See GREAT PLAINS INDUSTRIES INC

D-U-N-S 08-921-3268
G P JOHNSTON INC
JOHNSTON CMMNCTIONS VOICE DATA
322 Belleville Tpke, North Arlington, NJ 07031-6411
Tel (201) 991-7400 *Founded/Ownrshp* 1977
Sales 84.2MM^E *EMP* 105
SIC 5065 Telephone equipment; Telephone equipment
Pr: Philip G Johnston
**Sr VP:* Joe Martino
**VP:* Mike Fleming

G P RESOURCES
See GENERAL PETROLEUM CORP

D-U-N-S 09-768-9996
G P ROADWAY SOLUTIONS INC
PETERSON SIGN COMPANY
660 Mapunapuna St, Honolulu, HI 96819-2031
Tel (808) 521-6785 *Founded/Ownrshp* 1978
Sales 32.8MM^E *EMP* 150^E
SIC 1799 1611 5084 7359 Sign installation & maintenance; Guardrail construction, highways; Safety equipment; Work zone traffic equipment (flags, cones, barrels, etc.); Sign installation & maintenance; Guardrail construction, highways; Safety equipment; Work zone traffic equipment (flags, cones, barrels, etc.)
Pr: William Paik
**Sec:* Maggie Hamamoto
VP: William Kapololu
VP: Rusty Niau
VP: Bill Paik
Exec: Chito Batoon
Dept Mgr: Kenneth Young
Genl Mgr: Ben Bauer
Genl Mgr: Cindy Saiki
Plnt Mgr: Bob Peterson
Sls Mgr: Jeffrey Hung

G P S
See GENERAL PRODUCTION SERVICE OF CALIFORNIA INC

G P S
See GLOBAL POWER SUPPLY LLC

D-U-N-S 02-044-4241
G P SECURITY INC
PLATINUM GROUP SECURITY
212 N Federal Hwy, Deerfield Beach, FL 33441-3612
Tel (954) 571-9080 *Founded/Ownrshp* 1999
Sales 13.7MM^E *EMP* 525^E
SIC 7381 Security guard service; Security guard service
Pr: Kevin M Vanmiddlesworth
Pr: Jorge Rosero
Ex VP: Goran Milich
Sr VP: Rony Joseph
Dir Bus: Bryan Orr
Dir Sec: Nicholas Nembhard
Opers Mgr: Robert Blandford

D-U-N-S 09-657-8745 IMP/EXP
G PROULX INC
3275 Sw 42nd St, Fort Lauderdale, FL 33312-6812
Tel (954) 327-3465 *Founded/Ownrshp* 1980
Sales 60.0MM^E *EMP* 54
SIC 5032 Drywall materials
Pr: Jocelyn Vinet
**VP:* Yves Surprenant
Sales Asso: Jorge Alvarez
Sales Asso: Luis Cabassa
Sales Asso: Scott McDonald
Sales Asso: Carla Mendoza
Sales Asso: Larry Short

D-U-N-S 03-145-0024
G R A Z A K CORP
SWISHER HTG & AIR-CONDITIONING
21639 N 14th Ave, Phoenix, AZ 85027-2805
Tel (623) 535-5905 *Founded/Ownrshp* 2001
Sales 36.5MM^E *EMP* 120
SIC 1542 Commercial & office building contractors; Commercial & office building contractors
Pr: Garry L Beer

D-U-N-S 06-397-4430 IMP
G R B INC
TRIANGLE LABEL
6392 Gano Rd, West Chester, OH 45069-4869
Tel (513) 755-7100 *Founded/Ownrshp* 1973
Sales 97.9MM^E *EMP* 102
SIC 5113 Shipping supplies; Shipping supplies
Pr: Roger Neiheisel
**VP:* Allen Backscheider

G R C
See GENERAL RIBBON CORP

G R C
See GENERAL REVENUE CORP

D-U-N-S 06-959-0727
G R NOTO ELECTRICAL CONSTRUCTION INC
2 Skyline Dr E, S Abingtn Twp, PA 18411-9097
Tel (570) 585-8016 *Founded/Ownrshp* 1969
Sales 42.9MM^E *EMP* 200
SIC 1731 General electrical contractor; General electrical contractor
Pr: Armond S Palazzari
**Pr:* Gabriel J Noto
**VP:* Gerard Nichols

D-U-N-S 00-302-7877
G R SPONAUGLE & SONS INC (PA)
4391 Chambers Hill Rd, Harrisburg, PA 17111-2402
Tel (717) 564-1515 *Founded/Ownrshp* 1986
Sales 18.7M *EMP* 350
SIC 1711 1731 7623 4899 Plumbing contractors; Warm air heating & air conditioning contractor; General electrical contractor; Refrigeration service & repair; Data communication services; Plumbing contractors; Warm air heating & air conditioning contractor; General electrical contractor; Refrigeration service & repair; Data communication services
Pr: Glen R Sponaugle
**Treas:* Roseann Lavia
**VP:* Mike Desanto
**VP:* Christopher Haynes
VP: Duane Snell
IT Man: Tammy Smith

D-U-N-S 14-519-8474
G R SPONAUGLE SERVICE CO LLC
4391 Chambers Hill Rd, Harrisburg, PA 17111-2402
Tel (717) 346-3030 *Founded/Ownrshp* 1956
Sales 21.3MM^E *EMP* 44
SIC 4911 Electric services
Pr: Glen Sponaugle
Prin: Christopher Haynes
Prin: Kirk Sponaugle

D-U-N-S 07-121-2708
G ROBERT BILGER INC
STEVE MOYER SUBARU
201 S Centre Ave, Leesport, PA 19533-8842
Tel (610) 916-7000 *Founded/Ownrshp* 1999
Sales 61.1MM *EMP* 56
SIC 5511 Automobiles, new & used; Automobiles, new & used
Pr: Stephen M Moyer Sr
**Treas:* Eric A Moyer
**VP:* Stephen Moyer Jr
Off Mgr: Connie Clemens

D-U-N-S 04-149-4402 EXP
G ROE WM & SONS INC
NOBLE WORLDWIDE FLA CITRUS SLS
500 Avenue R Sw, Winter Haven, FL 33880-3871
Tel (863) 294-3577 *Founded/Ownrshp* 1959
Sales 101.2MM^E *EMP* 500
SIC 2033 Fruit juices: fresh; Fruit juices: fresh
Pr: Quentin J Roe
**CFO:* April Porter
**VP:* William G Roe II
**Prin:* Allison Lee
Mktg Dir: Darrell Genthner

G S
See GIPSON STEEL INC

D-U-N-S 13-122-5302
G S & L ENTERPRISES INC
408 Highway 49 S, Jackson, MS 39218-8403
Tel (601) 939-1000 *Founded/Ownrshp* 1983
Sales 208.1MM^E *EMP* 475
SIC 5012 5082 Trucks, commercial; General construction machinery & equipment; Trucks, commercial; General construction machinery & equipment
Pr: Gerald S Swanson
**Ch Bd:* Sherry Stribling Greener
**Ex VP:* John Lyle

G S A
See GENERAL SERVICES ADMINISTRATION US

D-U-N-S 60-597-8977
G S A PBS NJ SERVICE CENTER
PROPERTY MANAGEMENT DIVISION
970 Broad St Ste 939a, Newark, NJ 07102-2500
Tel (973) 645-2413 *Founded/Ownrshp* 2005
Sales 15.9MM^E *EMP* 800
SIC 8741 Management services; Management services

G S C BALL
See GROCERS SPECIALTY CO

G S F
See GSF USA INC

G S I
See GEO-SYNTHETICS LLC

G S I
See GO-STAFF INC

G S I
See GOURMET SERVICES INC

G S I
See GOVERNMENT SUPPORT SERVICES INC

G S I
See GULF STATES INC

G S I
See GRAPHIC SPECIALTIES INC

G S K
See GLAXOSMITHKLINE LLC

D-U-N-S 55-691-4711 EXP
G S L CORP
GREAT SALT LAKE MINERALS
765 N 10500 W, Ogden, UT 84404-9761
Tel (801) 731-3100 *Founded/Ownrshp* 1973
Sales 98.2MM^E *EMP* 250
SIC 2819 2899 3339 Potasssium nitrate & sulfate; Salt; Magnesium refining (primary); Potasssium nitrate & sulfate; Salt; Magnesium refining (primary)
Pr: Angelo C Brisimitzakis
COO: Ron Bryan
**Treas:* James D Standen
**VP:* Bob E Carter
Sfty Mgr: Craig Smith
Plnt Mgr: Eric Beaumont
Plnt Mgr: Dean Wehr

D-U-N-S 03-799-1684
G S LONG CO INC
2517 Old Town Rd, Union Gap, WA 98903-1657
Tel (509) 575-8382 *Founded/Ownrshp* 1980
Sales 83.4MM *EMP* 100
SIC 5191

G S M
See GLOBAL SCRAP MANAGEMENT INC

G S N
See GAME SHOW NETWORK LLC

G S PARSONS CO.
See PARSONS AIRGAS INC

D-U-N-S 00-107-8757 IMP
G S PRECISION INC (VT)
101 John Seitz Dr, Brattleboro, VT 05301-3642
Tel (802) 257-5200 *Founded/Ownrshp* 1958
Sales 112.2MM^E *EMP* 410
Accts Gallagher Flynn & Co Llc Bu
SIC 3728 Aircraft assemblies, subassemblies & parts; Guided missile & space vehicle parts & auxiliary equipment; Dental equipment & supplies; Switchgear & switchboard apparatus; Motor vehicle parts & accessories; Aircraft assemblies, subassemblies & parts
Pr: Norman A Schneeberger
**CFO:* John Hanley
Mfg Mgr: Mark Gouger
Ql Cn Mgr: John Lynde
Pgrm Dir: John Perreault
Board of Directors: Norman Schneeberger

G S S
See GOVERNMENT SCIENTIFIC SOURCE INC

G S S
See GLOBAL STEERING SYSTEMS LLC

G S T
See GOLDEN STAR TECHNOLOGY INC

D-U-N-S 18-527-7159 IMP
G S WIRING SYSTEMS INC
(*Suby of* G.S.ELECTECH,INC.)
1801 Production Dr, Findlay, OH 45840-5446
Tel (419) 423-7111 *Founded/Ownrshp* 1987
Sales 141.5MM^E *EMP* 412
SIC 3714 5013 Automotive wiring harness sets; Motor vehicle supplies & new parts; Automotive wiring harness sets; Motor vehicle supplies & new parts
Pr: George Suzuki
**Pr:* Shinichi Inagaki
**Treas:* Yukinobu Ukai
Sls Mgr: Masami Kunimi

D-U-N-S 02-423-9139
G ST REMNANT SHOP LTD
G STREET REMNANT SHOP LTD
5520 Randolph Rd, Rockville, MD 20852-2629
Tel (301) 231-8982 *Founded/Ownrshp* 1955
Sales 43.7MM^E *EMP* 525
SIC 5949 5712 5722 Fabric stores piece goods; Sewing supplies; Customized furniture & cabinets; Sewing machines; Fabric stores piece goods; Sewing supplies; Customized furniture & cabinets; Sewing machines
Pr: Joel Greenzaid
**COO:* Michael Greenzaid
**Ch:* Judah Greenzaid

G STREET REMNANT SHOP LTD
See G ST REMNANT SHOP LTD

G T A
See GEORGIA TECHNOLOGY AUTHORITY

G T C
See GEORGIA TRANSMISSION CORP

D-U-N-S 14-713-1627
G T DISTRIBUTORS INC
2545 Brockton Dr Ste 100, Austin, TX 78758-4411
Tel (512) 451-8298 *Founded/Ownrshp* 1984
Sales 44.9MM^E *EMP* 100^E
SIC 5049 Law enforcement equipment & supplies
Pr: William J Orr Jr
**VP:* Tim Brown
VP: Lori Stansell
Genl Mgr: Peter Hernandez
Sls&Mrk Ex: Chyrlynne Crockett
Sls&Mrk Ex: Preston Whelan
Sls Mgr: Russell Faulkner
Sls Mgr: Brad Fisher
Sls Mgr: Clint Welch
Sales Asso: Chris Skelton

D-U-N-S 06-025-3069
G T E FEDERAL CREDIT UNION
711 S Dale Mabry Hwy Frnt, Tampa, FL 33609-4400
Tel (813) 871-2690 *Founded/Ownrshp* 1930, 1935
Sales NA *EMP* 300
SIC 6061 Federal credit unions; Federal credit unions
Ch Bd: Frances James
**Pr:* Wendell Sebastian
**CEO:* Joseph Brancusi
CFO: Brad Baker
**Sec:* Charlie Beauchamp
**V Ch Bd:* Rick Hagan
**V Ch Bd:* Thomas V Quayle
Ofcr: Zach Davis
Ofcr: Samantha Gifford
Ofcr: Jesse Husted
Ofcr: Jorge Polanco
**Ex VP:* Brian K Crawford
Ex VP: EC Williams
Sr VP: Chad Burney
Sr VP: Scott Dethomas
Sr VP: Linda Moore-Jason
VP: Max Coberly
VP: Shamus McConomy
VP: Bryon Nabors
VP: Tina Narron
VP: Kenny Rywant

D-U-N-S 04-217-9606
G T MICHELLI CO INC
130 Brookhollow, Harahan, LA 70123
Tel (504) 733-9822 *Founded/Ownrshp* 1980
Sales 37.6MM^E *EMP* 62
SIC 5046 Scales, except laboratory
Pr: Gasper T Michelli Jr
**Pr:* Joel McMullen
**Treas:* Ronald J Michelli
**VP:* David Barnett
Rgnl Mgr: Mark Vicknair
Brnch Mgr: Jeff Chapman

G T P
See GLOBAL TOWER LLC

D-U-N-S 00-747-4646 IMP
G T SALES & MANUFACTURING INC
HEWITT USA
2202 S West St, Wichita, KS 67213-1114
Tel (316) 943-2171 *Founded/Ownrshp* 1946
Sales 97.1MM^E *EMP* 177
SIC 5085 3053 3052 Industrial supplies; Rubber goods, mechanical; Hose, belting & packing; Industrial fittings; Gaskets, all materials; Hose, pneumatic: rubber or rubberized fabric; Industrial supplies; Rubber goods, mechanical; Hose, belting & packing; Industrial fittings; Gaskets, all materials; Hose, pneumatic: rubber or rubberized fabric
CEO: N M Onofrio Jr
VP: Rick Mullen
Dept Mgr: Gary Best
Off Mgr: Julie Ahlquist
Dir IT: Steve Hannah
Dir IT: Nick Onofrio

D-U-N-S 80-809-5988
G V C HOLDINGS INC
1215 Main St, Port Neches, TX 77651-3038
Tel (409) 722-8321 *Founded/Ownrshp* 1992
Sales 25.7MM^E *EMP* 450
SIC 2822 2895 3069 Chlorinated rubbers, synthetic; Cyclo rubbers, synthetic; Isoprene rubber, synthetic; Carbon black; Latex, foamed; Chlorinated rubbers, synthetic; Cyclo rubbers, synthetic; Isoprene rubber, synthetic; Carbon black; Latex, foamed
Pr: Mahendra Parekh

G V S
See GENERAL VISION SERVICES LLC

G W
See GOLDEN WEST PAPER CONVERTING CORP

G W A
See GREG WELTEROTH HOLDING INC

D-U-N-S 93-189-7607
G W AUTOMOTIVE INC
BILL GATTON HONDA
2130 Volunteer Pkwy, Bristol, TN 37620-6709
Tel (423) 968-5111 *Founded/Ownrshp* 1993
Sales 38.9MM^E *EMP* 100
SIC 5511 7513 Automobiles, new & used; Truck rental & leasing, no drivers; Automobiles, new & used; Truck rental & leasing, no drivers
Pr: Carroll M Gatton
Sls Mgr: Jason Vance
Sls Mgr: Denny Wagers
Sales Asso: Matt Blevins
Sales Asso: Bill Caffey
Sales Asso: Scott Fields
Sales Asso: Jeff Huffman
Sales Asso: Don Minga
Sales Asso: Karl Mock
Sales Asso: Chip Thomas
Sales Asso: Bill White

D-U-N-S 00-798-5096
G W BERKHEIMER CO INC
JOHNSON CONTROLS
6000 Southport Rd, Portage, IN 46368-6405
Tel (219) 764-5200 *Founded/Ownrshp* 1919, 1961
Sales 87.4MM^E *EMP* 300
SIC 5075 5078

G W C
See GWC WARRANTY CORP

D-U-N-S 02-960-5425
G W D MANAGEMENT CORP
MCDONALD'S
321 Fraser Dr, Hinesville, GA 31313-3712
Tel (912) 876-9301 *Founded/Ownrshp* 1977
Sales 11.5MM^E *EMP* 355
SIC 5812 Fast-food restaurant, chain; Fast-food restaurant, chain
Pr: Gary Dodd

D-U-N-S 03-117-6456
G W FOODS INC
HUDSON'S SUPERMARKET
2041 Railroad Ave, Willow Springs, MO 65793-9412
Tel (417) 469-4000 *Founded/Ownrshp* 1981
Sales 117.4MM^E *EMP* 730
SIC 5411 Grocery stores, independent; Grocery stores, independent
Pr: Dan R Williams
**Sec:* Samuel H Grisham
**VP:* R Bruce Grisham

D-U-N-S 07-352-0603
G W PALMER & CO INC
1080 W Rex Rd, Memphis, TN 38119-3820
Tel (901) 761-7900 *Founded/Ownrshp* 1981
Sales 52.3MM *EMP* 22
Accts Lewis Allen Jones Cpa Memphis
SIC 5148 Fruits, fresh; Vegetables, fresh; Fruits, fresh; Vegetables, fresh
Pr: Alston J Palmer
**Treas:* W Parks Dixon Jr
**VP:* Parks Dixon
Off Mgr: John Allen
Off Mgr: Jim Corbin
Off Mgr: Marie Tallant

D-U-N-S 86-105-6349
G W PEOPLES CONTRACTING CO INC
2011 Crystal Dr Ste 400, Arlington, VA 22202-3709
Tel (202) 488-7185 *Founded/Ownrshp* 1952
Sales 37.0MM^E *EMP* 130
SIC 1629 Railroad & railway roadbed construction; Railroad & railway roadbed construction
CEO: Melvin E Clark
**Pr:* Renee Y Banks
**CFO:* Alan Brown
Corp Couns: Edward Parker

D-U-N-S 10-887-1096 IMP
G W PLASTICS INC
239 Pleasant St, Bethel, VT 05032-9762
Tel (802) 234-9941 *Founded/Ownrshp* 1983
Sales 181.4MM^E *EMP* 450
SIC 3089 3544 Injection molding of plastics; Industrial molds; Injection molding of plastics; Industrial molds
Pr: Brenan Riehl
Pr: Tim Holmes
**CFO:* Thomas Johansen
VP: Larry Bell
Genl Mgr: James Ford

Dir IT: John Lemmon
Dir IT: Cathy Tempesta
VP Opers: Art Bennert
Plnt Mgr: Scott Rosen
Ql Cn Mgr: Jorge Altamirano
Ql Cn Mgr: Robert Halaquist

G W S
See GLOBAL WORKPLACE SOLUTIONS LLC

D-U-N-S 08-220-8083
G W SURFACES
SHOWERSHAPES
2432 Palma Dr, Ventura, CA 93003-5732
Tel (805) 642-5004 *Founded/Ownrshp* 1976
Sales 20.5MM^E *EMP* 170
SIC 3281 Cut stone & stone products; Cut stone & stone products
Pr: James A Garver
**Sec:* Georgann Garver
**VP:* Tidus Gutierrez
Plnt Mgr: Ron Fidley
S&M/VP: Bill Gooch

D-U-N-S 00-696-6451 IMP
G W VAN KEPPEL CO (MO)
VAN KEPPEL LIFTRUCK
1801 N 9th St, Kansas City, KS 66101-2023
Tel (913) 281-4800 *Founded/Ownrshp* 1926
Sales 139.1MM^E *EMP* 200
SIC 5082 7699 5084 7359 General construction machinery & equipment; Construction equipment repair; Lift trucks & parts; Equipment rental & leasing; General construction machinery & equipment; Construction equipment repair; Lift trucks & parts; Equipment rental & leasing
Pr: William S Walker
**Ex VP:* Kevin L Kientz
**VP:* Brian Loderhose
Brnch Mgr: Brady Romine
Genl Mgr: Glenn Henry
Genl Mgr: David Miguel
Genl Mgr: Stan Yates
IT Man: Jeff Duft
Mtls Mgr: Dave Griffin
Sfty Mgr: Mel Williams
Opers Mgr: Dennis Hagerman

D-U-N-S 10-308-9558
G W WYATT CONTRACTING LLC
803 E Broadway Blvd, Jefferson City, TN 37760-4928
Tel (865) 475-1222 *Founded/Ownrshp* 2001
Sales 25.9MM^E *EMP* 80
SIC 1521 New construction, single-family houses
**CFO:* Mark Williamson

D-U-N-S 01-794-9264
G Z K INC (OH)
ARBY'S
660 Fame Rd, Dayton, OH 45449-2356
Tel (937) 461-7500 *Founded/Ownrshp* 1960, 1989
Sales 43.6MM^E *EMP* 1,000^E
SIC 5812 Fast-food restaurant, chain; Fast-food restaurant, chain
CEO: Neal Kaufman
**CFO:* Steven R Stanforth
VP: Steve Judge
**VP:* John McKeon

D-U-N-S 79-924-9339
G&A OUTSOURCING INC
G&A PARTNERS
4801 Woodway Dr Ste 210w, Houston, TX 77056-1888
Tel (713) 784-1181 *Founded/Ownrshp* 1995
Sales 33.4MM^E *EMP* 147
SIC 8721 8742 Payroll accounting service; Human resource consulting services; Payroll accounting service; Human resource consulting services
CEO: Antonio R Grijalva
**Pr:* John W Allen
CFO: Bill Bishop
**VP:* John G Allen
**VP:* Aaron Call
**VP:* Anthony R Grijalva Jr
CTO: Scott Young
IT Man: Luis Moyano
VP Sls: Robert Colmenares
Manager: Christopher Reed
Sls Mgr: Rob Halvorsen

G&A PARTNERS
See G&A OUTSOURCING INC

D-U-N-S 01-090-0405
G&B PACKING CO INC
8 Hook Rd, Bayonne, NJ 07002-5007
Tel (201) 339-1531 *Founded/Ownrshp* 1975
Sales 21.5MM^E *EMP* 65
SIC 4783 4731 Packing goods for shipping; Crating goods for shipping; Freight transportation arrangement
Pr: Stanley Grossman
**VP:* Lawrence Grossman

D-U-N-S 01-842-1227
■ **G&B SOLUTIONS INC**
(*Suby of* VSE INTERNATIONAL CORP) ★
1861 Wiehle Ave Ste 200, Reston, VA 20190-5254
Tel (703) 883-1140 *Founded/Ownrshp* 2001, 2008
Sales 17.7MM^E *EMP* 400^E
SIC 7379 8742 ; Business consultant; ; Business consultant
Pr: John Harris
Treas: Richard Hannah
VP: Matt Ater
Prgrm Mgr: Asma Idriss
Snr Ntwrk: Christopher Archer
IT Man: Robert Pegues
Netwrk Eng: Timothy Gollner
Opers Mgr: Joe Barnard

G&D AMERICA
See GIESECKE & DEVRIENT AMERICA INC

D-U-N-S 60-279-1048
G&D INTEGRATED DISTRIBUTION INC
CDO DISTRIBUTION
50 Commerce Dr, Morton, IL 61550-9196
Tel (800) 451-6680 *Founded/Ownrshp* 1988
Sales 32.5MM^E *EMP* 447
SIC 4225 General warehousing; General warehousing
Pr: Patrick Roesler
**Treas:* Chris B Sanders
**VP:* Jeff Cohen
**VP:* Mark London
Board of Directors: Margaret L O'neill

D-U-N-S 16-493-0849 IMP
G&D INTEGRATED MANUFACTURING LOGISTICS INC
50 Commerce Dr, Morton, IL 61550-9196
Tel (309) 284-6700 *Founded/Ownrshp* 1996
Sales 50.5MM^E *EMP* 486
SIC 3531 Construction machinery; Construction machinery
Pr: P Joseph O'Neill
COO: Frank McCloud
**CFO:* Patrick Roesler
**Treas:* Chris B Sanders
**VP:* Charles T Purcell
Board of Directors: Maureen A Fulton, Nora J O'neill

D-U-N-S 12-257-6374
G&D INTEGRATED TRANSPORTATION INC
G & D INTEGRATED
50 Commerce Dr, Morton, IL 61550-9196
Tel (309) 284-6700 *Founded/Ownrshp* 1984
Sales 150.9MM^E *EMP* 590
SIC 4213 Trucking, except local; Trucking, except local
CEO: P Joseph Oneill
**Pr:* Patrick Roesler
COO: Frank McCloud
CFO: Becki Salmon
Ofcr: Tim Pierantoni
VP: Jeff Cohen
Dir Risk M: Ron Murray
Dir Bus: Dale Timmons
Genl Mgr: Cort Mills
Software D: Billy Beach
Mtls Mgr: Dave Hasty

G&G MANUFACTURING COMPANY
See G & G MANUFACTURING CO

D-U-N-S 62-282-4654 IMP/EXP
G&G OUTFITTERS INC
4901 Forbes Blvd Ste 100, Lanham, MD 20706-4414
Tel (301) 731-2099 *Founded/Ownrshp* 1989
Sales 21.3MM^E *EMP* 150^E
SIC 2759 2395 2396

D-U-N-S 02-292-7230
▲ **G&K SERVICES INC**
5995 Opus Pkwy Ste 500, Minnetonka, MN 55343-9078
Tel (952) 912-5500 *Founded/Ownrshp* 1902
Sales 937.6MM *EMP* 8,000
Accts Kpmg Llp Minneapolis Minnes
Tkr Sym GK *Exch* NGS
SIC 7218 7213 7219 Industrial uniform supply; Laundered mat & rug supply; Treated equipment supply: mats, rugs, mops, cloths, etc.; Work clothing supply; Apron supply; Towel supply; Uniform supply; Garment making, alteration & repair; Industrial uniform supply; Laundered mat & rug supply; Treated equipment supply: mats, rugs, mops, cloths, etc.; Work clothing supply; Apron supply; Towel supply; Uniform supply; Garment making, alteration & repair
Ch Bd: Douglas A Milroy
Pr: Kevin Fancey
Pr: David Miller
CFO: Tracy C Jokinen
CFO: Tracy Jokinen
Ch: Robert G Wood
Sr VP: Jacqueline Tschida Punch
VP: Sally Bredehoft
VP: Jeffrey L Cotter
Exec: Kim Bodine
Prgrm Mgr: Michael Marker
Board of Directors: John S Bronson, Lynn Crump-Caine, Wayne M Fortun, Thomas R Greco, Ernest J Mrozek, M Lenny Pippin, Alice M Richter, Lee J Schram

D-U-N-S 07-936-2214
■ **G&L INTERMEDIATE HOLDINGS INC**
(*Suby of* EXAMWORKS INC) ★
101 Riverfront Blvd # 100, Bradenton, FL 34205-8812
Tel (941) 798-2098 *Founded/Ownrshp* 2014
Sales 26.4MM^E *EMP* 230^E
SIC 6719 Investment holding companies, except banks; Investment holding companies, except banks
CEO: Deborah Pfeiffle

D-U-N-S 09-746-2824 IMP
G&L REALTY CORP LLC
439 N Bedford Dr, Beverly Hills, CA 90210-4302
Tel (310) 273-9930 *Founded/Ownrshp* 1976
Sales 220.3MM^E *EMP* 1,010
SIC 6552 Subdividers & developers; Subdividers & developers
Ch Bd: Daniel M Gottlieb
**Ch Bd:* Steven D Leibowitz
VP: Andrew Lebowitz
VP: George Nagler
**VP:* Paul Schneider

D-U-N-S 00-379-3056
G&P TRUCKING CO INC (SC)
126 Access Rd, Gaston, SC 29053-9501
Tel (803) 791-5500 *Founded/Ownrshp* 1986
Sales 158.7MM^E *EMP* 700
Accts Grant Thornton Llp Columbia
SIC 4213 Contract haulers; Contract haulers
Pr: G Clifton Parker
**Treas:* Richard Whitmire
**Sr VP:* Billy Lynch
**Sr VP:* Steve McCourt
**Sr VP:* Richard Strobel
Exec: Tom Reed

D-U-N-S 96-839-5033 IMP
G&S IMPORT-EXPORT INC
8475 Canoga Ave, Canoga Park, CA 91304-2607
Tel (818) 601-1561 *Founded/Ownrshp* 2003
Sales 28.0MM *EMP* 12
SIC 5065 Electronic parts; Electronic parts
Pr: Gunasena De Silva
VP: Mike Khanna

G&S METALS
See SRT INVESTMENTS LLC

G&T CONVEYOR COMPANY
See FIVE STAR AIRPORT ALLIANCE INC

D-U-N-S 07-941-9931
G&W NC LABORATORIES LLC
1877 Kawai Rd, Lincolnton, NC 28092-5905
Tel (908) 753-2000 *Founded/Ownrshp* 2014
Sales 45.4MM^E *EMP* 150
SIC 2834 Pharmaceutical preparations; Pharmaceutical preparations

D-U-N-S 07-976-3718
G&W PA LABORATORIES LLC
(*Suby of* G & W LABORATORIES INC) ★
650 Cathill Rd, Sellersville, PA 18960-1512
Tel (908) 753-2000 *Founded/Ownrshp* 2014
Sales 50.0MM *EMP* 250
SIC 2834 Pharmaceutical preparations

D-U-N-S 05-024-9481
G-A-P SUPPLY CORP
JOHNSON CONTROLS
16650 Sw 72nd Ave Ste 120, Tigard, OR 97224-7775
Tel (503) 597-7200 *Founded/Ownrshp* 1981
Sales 40.5MM^E *EMP* 125
SIC 5075 Warm air heating & air conditioning; Ventilating equipment & supplies; Air conditioning equipment, except room units; Warm air heating & air conditioning; Ventilating equipment & supplies; Air conditioning equipment, except room units
Pr: Gregory Popma
CFO: Jay Jaffe
**CFO:* Julie Schultz
**VP:* Ray Kernagis
**VP:* Steve Porter
**VP:* Andrew Verey
Brnch Mgr: Eric Dimmick
VP Mktg: Mike Martinson
Sls Mgr: Rick Birket
Sls Mgr: Joel Hopkins
Sls Mgr: David Petrarca

D-U-N-S 78-760-0469 EXP
G-COR AUTOMOTIVE CORP
2100 Refugee Rd, Columbus, OH 43207-2841
Tel (614) 443-6735 *Founded/Ownrshp* 1991
Sales 27.5MM^E *EMP* 75
SIC 5013 5015 5093 Automotive supplies & parts; Automotive parts & supplies, used; Metal scrap & waste materials
Pr: Stanley Greenblott
**VP:* Kenny Greenblott
**Prin:* Donald L Feinstein

D-U-N-S 04-059-1166
G-F FOUR INVESTMENTS INC
GODFATHER'S PIZZA
1512 S Marshall St, Boone, IA 50036-5311
Tel (515) 432-1200 *Founded/Ownrshp* 1980
Sales 6.3MM^E *EMP* 300
SIC 5812 Pizzeria, chain; Pizzeria, chain
Pr: Dennis Gano
**Treas:* Jack Gano
**VP:* Roger Frisbie

D-U-N-S 61-681-3853 IMP/EXP
G-I HOLDINGS INC
G A F
(*Suby of* G HOLDINGS INC) ★
1361 Alps Rd, Wayne, NJ 07470-3700
Tel (973) 628-3000 *Founded/Ownrshp* 2001
Sales 1.1MMM^E *EMP* 4,300
SIC 2869 2843 3295 Solvents, organic; Surface active agents; Roofing granules; Solvents, organic; Surface active agents; Roofing granules
CEO: Robert B Tafaro
**Pr:* Peter Ganz
**Pr:* Susan Yoss
COO: Richard A Nowak
CFO: John F Rebele
Ex VP: Frank Jalili
Ex VP: James Schnepper
**Ex VP:* John M Sergey
Sr VP: Tom Anderson
Sr VP: Dave Harrison
VP: Randy Bargfrede
VP: Brian Kimber

D-U-N-S 60-621-3023 IMP
▲ **G-III APPAREL GROUP LTD**
512 7th Ave Fl 40, New York, NY 10018-4701
Tel (212) 403-0500 *Founded/Ownrshp* 1974
Sales 2.1MMM *EMP* 6,641^E
Accts Ernst & Young Llp New York
Tkr Sym GIII *Exch* NGS
SIC 2337 2339 2311 2329 2386 5136 Women's & misses' suits & coats; Women's & misses' outerwear; Men's & boys' suits & coats; Coats, overcoats & vests; Jackets (suede, leatherette, etc.), sport: men's & boys'; Garments, leather; Coats & jackets, leather & sheep-lined; Pants, leather; Men's & boys' clothing; Women's & misses' suits & coats; Women's & misses' outerwear; Men's & boys' suits & coats; Coats, overcoats & vests; Jackets (suede, leatherette, etc.), sport: men's & boys'; Garments, leather; Coats & jackets, leather & sheep-lined; Pants, leather; Men's & boys' clothing
Ch Bd: Morris Goldfarb
Pr: David Winn
COO: Wayne S Miller
CFO: Neal S Nackman
**V Ch Bd:* Sammy Aaron
VP: Michael Laskau III
Dir IT: Sam Deutscher
Board of Directors: Thomas J Brosig, Alan Feller, Jeffrey Goldfarb, Jeanette Nostra, Laura Pomerantz, Allen Sirkin, Willem Van Bokhorst, Cheryl Vitali, Richard White

D-U-N-S 06-822-5002 IMP
■ **G-III LEATHER FASHIONS INC** (NY)
J L COLEBROOK DIVISION
(*Suby of* G-III APPAREL GROUP LTD) ★
512 Fashion Ave Fl 35, New York, NY 10018-0832
Tel (212) 403-0500 *Founded/Ownrshp* 1974
Sales 233.9MM^E *EMP* 1,300
SIC 5199 Leather, leather goods & furs; Leather, leather goods & furs
Ch Bd: Morris Goldfarb
**Pr:* Janet Nostra-Katz
**COO:* Wayne S Miller
**CFO:* Neal S Nackman
VP: Erez Levy
CTO: Max Norman
MIS Mgr: Gary Seagobind

G-M GRAPHICS
See G-M WOODS PRODUCTS INC

D-U-N-S 18-351-1104 IMP
G-M WOODS PRODUCTS INC
G-M GRAPHICS
531 Clay St, Newaygo, MI 49337-8521
Tel (231) 652-2201 *Founded/Ownrshp* 1987
Sales 40.0MM *EMP* 80^E
SIC 2431 5199 Windows & window parts & trim, wood; Art goods & supplies
Pr: Mark Micho
VP: Kevin Karrip
**VP:* J Kevin Kirrip
CIO: Mary Bulson
Sfty Mgr: Dan Robeck

G-TECH PROFESSIONAL STAFFING
See GTECH SERVICES INC

G/I/S
See GEOGRAPHIC INFORMATION SERVICES INC

G/M BUSINESS INTERIORS
See GOFORTH & MARTI

G/O DIGITAL MARKETING SERVICES
See VIKRAM SHARMA

D-U-N-S 12-375-1976
G2 DIRECT AND DIGITAL
(*Suby of* GREY ADVERTISING) ★
777 3rd Ave Ste 37, New York, NY 10017-1401
Tel (212) 537-3700 *Founded/Ownrshp* 1979
Sales 20.0MM^E *EMP* 375
SIC 7331 7311 Direct mail advertising services; Advertising agencies; Direct mail advertising services; Advertising agencies
CEO: Lawrence Kimmel
**Pr:* Wendy Lurrie
Ex VP: Richard Shuback
VP: Mike Dennelly
Creative D: Jeremy Feldman
Dir IT: Matt Choplick
Info Man: Timmy Hegarty
Art Dir: Maria Samodra

D-U-N-S 15-955-3713
G2 INVESTMENT GROUP LLC
142 W 57th St Fl 12, New York, NY 10019-3313
Tel (212) 887-1150 *Founded/Ownrshp* 2008
Sales 25.4MM^E *EMP* 100^E
SIC 6799 Investors
Ch: Todd Morley
**Pt:* David L Conrod
Mng Pt: Norris Lam
**CEO:* Maria Boyazny
VP: Karen Hui
Exec: Gygmy Gonnot
Mng Dir: John Murphy
Mng Dir: John Pitts
Mng Dir: Peter Rockefeller

D-U-N-S 79-253-4328
G2 SECURE STAFF LLC
400 Las Colinas Blvd E # 750, Irving, TX 75039-5593
Tel (972) 915-6979 *Founded/Ownrshp* 2005
Sales NA *EMP* 3,500
SIC 6411 4789 4729 Patrol services, insurance; Cargo loading & unloading services; Transportation ticket offices; Patrol services, insurance; Cargo loading & unloading services; Transportation ticket offices
Pr: Dan Norman
**Pr:* Tom Del Valle
**COO:* John Graham
**CFO:* Linda Hill
**VP:* Tim Reddell
Rgnl Mgr: Eddie Harris
Genl Mgr: Peter Adams-Wash
Genl Mgr: Adriana Briones
Genl Mgr: Lisa Ekstrand
Genl Mgr: Kent Opdahl
Genl Mgr: Salim Rashad

D-U-N-S 94-806-4365
G2 SOFTWARE SYSTEMS INC
4025 Hancock St Ste 105, San Diego, CA 92110-5168
Tel (619) 222-8025 *Founded/Ownrshp* 1898
Sales 38.0MM *EMP* 140
SIC 8711 Engineering services
CEO: Georgia D Griffiths
CFO: Bill Long
CFO: William Long
Prgrm Mgr: Charlie Hopkins
Genl Mgr: Peter Keyes
Snr Sftwr: Dennis Ahern
Snr Sftwr: Mark Bertone
Snr Sftwr: Karen Knauth
Snr Sftwr: Robert Law
IT Man: Robert Nickel
Sftwr Eng: David Borjas

G2 SPORTS THERAPY
See DRAYER PHYSICAL THERAPY INSTITUTE LLC

D-U-N-S 15-324-0416
G2 WORLDWIDE INC
(*Suby of* WPP GROUP USA INC) ★
200 5th Ave, New York, NY 10010-3302
Tel (212) 537-3700 *Founded/Ownrshp* 2005
Sales 22.5MM^E *EMP* 204
SIC 7311 Advertising agencies
CEO: Harvey Kipnis
**Pr:* Joe Celia

Ofcr: David Baker
VP: Michael Asaro
VP: Andy Bohjalian
VP: Lindsey Christensen
VP: Karla Fleming
VP: Steven Frank
VP: Ernesto James
VP: Bennett McCarroll
VP: Denise O'Bleness
VP: Paul Safsel
**VP:* Mathew Schetlick
VP: Barry Silverman
Creative D: Mark Chew
Creative D: Yasuhito Imai
Creative D: Mimia Johnson
Creative D: Jordan Korfine
Creative D: Daniela Masiello
Creative D: Andrew Prahin
Creative D: Brian Riemer

D-U-N-S 00-943-7799
G3 ENTERPRISES INC
502 E Whitmore Ave, Modesto, CA 95358-9411
Tel (209) 341-7515 *Founded/Ownrshp* 1961
Sales 109.5MM^E *EMP* 400
SIC 4731 Transportation agents & brokers; Transportation agents & brokers
CEO: Robert Lubeck
COO: Tom Cook
CFO: Michael Ellis
VP: Steven Anderson
VP: John Kalal
VP: Kristi Marsella
Exec: John Cunningham
QA Dir: David Weiss
Tech Mgr: Gordon Thomsen
Opers Mgr: Mike Riley
Ql Cn Mgr: Wesley Ayala

D-U-N-S 02-753-5215
G3 TECHNOLOGIES INC
10280 Old Columbia Rd, Columbia, MD 21046-1796
Tel (443) 692-5858 *Founded/Ownrshp* 2001
Sales 20.9MM^E *EMP* 60
SIC 8711 Engineering services
Pr: Gregory Rowe
IT Man: Cary Converse
IT Man: Eric Lee
Tech Mgr: Chinmay Shah
Sftwr Eng: Jeff Barbieri
Sftwr Eng: Aaron Lewis
Sftwr Eng: Tom Rogan

G4S
See RONCO CONSULTING CORP

G4S AMERICAS
See G4S TECHNOLOGY HOLDINGS (USA) INC

D-U-N-S 62-177-1229
G4S COMPLIANCE & INVESTIGATIONS INC
(*Suby of* G4S HOLDING ONE INC) ★
910 Paverstone Dr, Raleigh, NC 27615-4701
Tel (800) 927-0456 *Founded/Ownrshp* 2008
Sales NA *EMP* 450
SIC 6411 Inspection & investigation services, insurance; Inspection & investigation services, insurance
CEO: Michael J Malone
Pr: Carl Demarais
**Sec:* Brent Faggart
VP: Russ Buchanan
**VP:* Jodi A Darrohn
**VP:* Carl H Demarais
IT Man: Dave Sheldon
IT Man: Angela Weatherford

D-U-N-S 11-104-1401
G4S HOLDING ONE INC
(*Suby of* G4S US HOLDINGS LIMITED)
1395 University Blvd, Jupiter, FL 33458-5289
Tel (561) 622-5656 *Founded/Ownrshp* 2002
Sales 2.1MMM^E *EMP* 68,000^E
SIC 7381 7382 8744 8748 8742 Security guard service; Burglar alarm maintenance & monitoring; Facilities support services; Business consulting; Training & development consultant; Security guard service; Private investigator; Burglar alarm maintenance & monitoring; Facilities support services; Base maintenance (providing personnel on continuing basis); Correctional facility; Jails, privately operated; Business consulting; Training & development consultant
Pr: John Kenning
CFO: Susanne Jorgensen
Treas: Ian A Green
Sec: John Sumner
VP: Soren Lundsberg-Niels

D-U-N-S 11-829-4722
G4S SECURE INTEGRATION LLC
G 4 S
(*Suby of* G4S AMERICAS) ★
1299 Farnam St Ste 1300, Omaha, NE 68102-1892
Tel (402) 233-7700 *Founded/Ownrshp* 2010
Sales 218.8MM^E *EMP* 425
SIC 1623 7382 Water, sewer & utility lines; Security systems services; Water, sewer & utility lines; Security systems services
CEO: Robert E Sommerfeld
CFO: Joseph Schwaderer
VP: Louie Enriquez
VP: Ramiro Hernandez
VP: Ajay Koul
Dir IT: Larry Beasley
IT Man: Erika Kirchmann
IT Man: Cindy Lembke
IT Man: Teri Shindo
Opers Mgr: Charles Boyd
Counsel: Bill Latka

D-U-N-S 77-992-5478
G4S SECURE SOLUTIONS (PUERTO RICO) INC
(*Suby of* G4S SECURE SOLUTIONS INTERNATIONAL INC) ★
Road 1 Km 34 4 St Ro, Caguas, PR 00725
Tel (787) 641-3300 *Founded/Ownrshp* 1957
Sales 12.6MM^E *EMP* 500
Accts Roberto Afanador Cpa In Guayn
SIC 7381 1731 Detective & armored car services; Electrical work; Detective & armored car services; Electrical work
Pr: Drew Levine
**Sr VP:* Jeff Morrow
Genl Mgr: Louis Pagan

D-U-N-S 00-190-3723
G4S SECURE SOLUTIONS (USA) INC (FL)
G 4 S
(*Suby of* G4S HOLDING ONE INC) ★
1395 University Blvd, Jupiter, FL 33458-5289
Tel (561) 622-5656 *Founded/Ownrshp* 1954, 2002
Sales 1.7MMM^E *EMP* 38,425
SIC 7381 8744 8748 8742 Security guard service; Private investigator; Facilities support services; Base maintenance (providing personnel on continuing basis); Correctional facility; Jails, privately operated; Business consulting; Training & development consultant; Security guard service; Private investigator; Facilities support services; Base maintenance (providing personnel on continuing basis); Correctional facility; Jails, privately operated; Business consulting; Training & development consultant
CEO: Grahame Gibson
Pr: Shauna Espericueta
COO: Alan Bernstein
**COO:* Jeff Morrow
**CFO:* Susanne Jorgensen
CFO: Tim McCormick
CFO: Eric Ospina
**Treas:* Jeff Cappelletti
Ofcr: Matthew Watts
Ex VP: D Buchanan
Sr VP: Robert Burns
Sr VP: Donald Keens
VP: John D'Agata
**VP:* Ian A Green
**VP:* Drew Levine
**VP:* Julie T Payne
VP: Mark Tsuji
Exec: Wayne Beck
Exec: Tracey Castillo
Exec: Chris Dittmer
Exec: Jenni Myles
Board of Directors: Brian McCabe

D-U-N-S 18-823-6160
G4S SECURE SOLUTIONS INTERNATIONAL INC
(*Suby of* G4S HOLDING ONE INC) ★
1395 University Blvd, Jupiter, FL 33458-5289
Tel (561) 622-5656 *Founded/Ownrshp* 1979
Sales 47.1MM^E *EMP* 2,184
SIC 7382 7381 Burglar alarm maintenance & monitoring; Security guard service; Burglar alarm maintenance & monitoring; Security guard service
CEO: Grahame Gibson
**COO:* Jeff Morrow
**CFO:* Susanne Jrgensen
**Sr VP:* Julie Payne
**Sr VP:* Marc Shapiro
Dir IT: Rich Villa

D-U-N-S 96-399-8906
G4S TECHNOLOGY HOLDINGS (USA) INC
G4S AMERICAS
(*Suby of* G4S HOLDING ONE INC) ★
1395 University Blvd, Jupiter, FL 33458-5289
Tel (561) 622-5656 *Founded/Ownrshp* 2008
Sales 252.2MM^E *EMP* 478^E
SIC 7381 Security guard service
CEO: Grahame Gibson
Pr: Michael Janney
**COO:* Jeff Morrow
**CFO:* Susanne Jorgensen
**Sr VP:* Julie Payne
**Sr VP:* Marc Shapiro
Dir IT: Rich Villa

D-U-N-S 95-916-3064
G4S YOUTH SERVICES LLC
HASTINGS YOUTH ACADEMY
(*Suby of* G4S PLC)
6302 Benjamin Rd Ste 400, Tampa, FL 33634-5116
Tel (813) 514-6275 *Founded/Ownrshp* 1997
Sales 53.9MM^E *EMP* 1,600
SIC 8322 Youth center; Youth center
Pr: Jim Hill
CFO: Peter Loughlin
IT Man: Dan Aderhood
VP Mktg: Chuck Kehoe

D-U-N-S 07-864-9057
G6 HOSPITALITY LLC
4001 International Pkwy, Carrollton, TX 75007-1914
Tel (972) 360-9000 *Founded/Ownrshp* 1986
Sales NA *EMP* 2,015^E
SIC 8741 Business management

D-U-N-S 19-466-9610
G6 HOSPITALITY LLC
MOTEL 6
4001 International Pkwy, Carrollton, TX 75007-1914
Tel (972) 360-9000 *Founded/Ownrshp* 1985
Sales 332.0MM^E *EMP* 4,016^E
SIC 7011 Hotels & motels; Hotels & motels
CEO: Olivier Poirot
**Pr:* Jim Amorosia
**COO:* Mike Brower
**CFO:* Didier Bosc
Treas: Stephen Manthey
**Treas:* Gregg Toon
Ex VP: Patrick Ollivier
Ex VP: Jeff Palmer
**Ex VP:* Alan Rabinowitz
**VP:* John Valletta
Exec: Jacques Aferiat
Exec: Hughes Jaquier
Comm Man: David Bates

GA COMMUNICATION GROUP
See GOBLE & ASSOCIATES INC

D-U-N-S 96-054-3858
GA COMMUNICATIONS INC
GRAPHICS ATLANTA
2196 W Park Ct, Stone Mountain, GA 30087-3528
Tel (770) 498-4091 *Founded/Ownrshp* 1995
Sales 31.2MM^E *EMP* 430
Accts Frazier & Deeter Llc Atlanta
SIC 7311 Advertising agencies; Advertising agencies
CEO: Richard Davis
**Pr:* Chad Sumner
**CFO:* Greg Latham
**VP:* Ken Bash
VP: Martin Disher
**VP:* Amy Reach
Creative D: Koko Tadros
Genl Mgr: Mark Tarpley
Tech Mgr: Kim Eichenlaub
VP Sls: Jeff Davis
Mktg Dir: Gina Pinchotti

D-U-N-S 06-860-4479
GA CRANDALL & CO INC
6851 167th St, Tinley Park, IL 60477-2501
Tel (708) 633-8100 *Founded/Ownrshp* 1965
Sales NA *EMP* 32^E
SIC 6411 Insurance agents & brokers; Property & casualty insurance agent; Insurance agents & brokers; Property & casualty insurance agent
Pr: Gerald A Crandall
**Treas:* Gerald S Crandall
**VP:* David A Crandall

D-U-N-S 07-321-5956
GA FOOD SERVICES OF PINELLAS COUNTY INC
G.A.FOOD SERVICE
12200 32nd Ct N, Saint Petersburg, FL 33716-1803
Tel (727) 573-2211 *Founded/Ownrshp* 1973
Sales 142.0MM^E *EMP* 400
Accts Ernst & Young
SIC 2038 5812 Frozen specialties; Contract food services; Frozen specialties; Contract food services
Pr: Glenn Davenport
**COO:* John D Hale
**CFO:* Kenneth A Lobianco
**VP:* David P Karpan
Exec: Annette Henry
Dir IT: John Forman
Dir IT: Andrew Gronek
Prd Mgr: Lou Hurd
VP Mktg: Bill Basto

D-U-N-S 07-621-8270 IMP
GA GERTMENIAN AND SONS LLC
300 W Avenue 33, Los Angeles, CA 90031-3503
Tel (213) 250-7777 *Founded/Ownrshp* 1980
Sales 26.4MM^E *EMP* 80^E
SIC 5023

D-U-N-S 07-216-1532 IMP
■ **GA INDUSTRIES LLC**
(*Suby of* REXNORD LLC) ★
9025 Marshall Rd, Cranberry Township, PA 16066-3696
Tel (724) 776-1020 *Founded/Ownrshp* 2008
Sales 38.0MM^E *EMP* 375
SIC 3441 3494 3491 3492

D-U-N-S 79-696-5049
GA NET SOL PARENT LLC
(*Suby of* GENERAL ATLANTIC CORP) ★
13861 Sunrise Valley Dr # 300, Herndon, VA 20171-6124
Tel (703) 668-4600 *Founded/Ownrshp* 2007
Sales 39.6MM^E *EMP* 900
SIC 4813 ;

GA STATE PATROL
See GEORGIA DEPARTMENT OF PUBLIC SAFETY

D-U-N-S 08-545-3806 IMP
GA TELESIS LLC
1850 Nw 49th St, Fort Lauderdale, FL 33309-3004
Tel (954) 676-3111 *Founded/Ownrshp* 2002
Sales 221.5MM^E *EMP* 400
Accts Grant Thornton Fort Lauderdal
SIC 5088 3724 Aircraft & parts; Aircraft engines & engine parts; Aircraft & parts; Aircraft engines & engine parts
Pr: Abdol Moabery
Pr: Jason Reed
**CFO:* Alvin Khoo
**CFO:* Jack Portlock
**Ex VP:* Andrew Toutt
VP: Gokhan Aydogan
VP: Nona Caroll
VP: David Ellis
**VP:* Kevin Geissler
VP: Gordon Humphreys
VP: Paul Lochab
VP: Robert Loesch
VP: Rebecca Longo
VP: Irvin Lucas
VP: Hooman Rezaei

D-U-N-S 17-524-8681 IMP
GA WEST & CO INC
12526 Celeste Rd, Chunchula, AL 36521-3578
Tel (251) 679-1965 *Founded/Ownrshp* 1987
Sales 135.3MM *EMP* 1,000
Accts The Anthony Financial Group In
SIC 1541 Industrial buildings, new construction; Industrial buildings, new construction
Pr: Gary A West
**CFO:* J Randall Bevis
**Treas:* David Phillips
**Ex VP:* George Busby
**VP:* John Harris
**VP:* Sam Jackson
**VP:* Terry Swayne
Exec: Fred Bates
Area Mgr: Butch Baggett
Area Mgr: Roger Brown
Area Mgr: Marty Friddle

GA-ASI
See GENERAL ATOMICS AERONAUTICAL SYSTEMS INC

D-U-N-S 11-103-1287 IMP
GAAG LLC
GLOBAL SECURITY GLAZING
(*Suby of* CONSOLIDATED GLASS HOLDINGS INC) ★
616 Selfield Rd, Selma, AL 36703-8702
Tel (334) 875-1900 *Founded/Ownrshp* 2012
Sales 33.3MM^E *EMP* 100
SIC 3211 Laminated glass; Strengthened or reinforced glass
Sls Mgr: Erin Bellis

D-U-N-S 08-464-2990
GABELLI & CO INC
(*Suby of* GABELLI GROUP CAP PARTNERS INC) ★
1 Corporate Ctr, Rye, NY 10580-1485
Tel (914) 921-3700 *Founded/Ownrshp* 1986
Sales 252.0MM *EMP* 30
SIC 6211 6282 Brokers, security; Dealers, security; Investment advice; Brokers, security; Dealers, security; Investment advice
Ch Bd: Daniel M Miller
CFO: John Givissis

GABELLI FUNDS
See GABELLI GROUP CAPITAL PARTNERS INC

GABELLI GROUP CAP PARTNERS INC
See GABELLI SECURITIES INC

D-U-N-S 03-306-7497
GABELLI GROUP CAPITAL PARTNERS INC
GABELLI FUNDS
555 Theodore Fremd Ave C300, Rye, NY 10580-1455
Tel (914) 921-3700 *Founded/Ownrshp* 1981
Sales 264.6MM^E *EMP* 359
SIC 6211 6282 Brokers, security; Dealers, security; Investment advisory service; Brokers, security; Dealers, security; Investment advisory service
Ch Bd: Mario J Gabelli
**Pr:* Marc Gabelli
Sr VP: Darryl S Grayson
**VP:* Raffaele Pisacane

D-U-N-S 60-264-1789
GABELLI SECURITIES INC
GABELLI GROUP CAP PARTNERS INC
(*Suby of* GABELLI FUNDS) ★
1 Corporate Ctr 401, Rye, NY 10580-1485
Tel (914) 921-3700 *Founded/Ownrshp* 1986
Sales 252.0MM^E *EMP* 250
SIC 6211 Brokers, security; Dealers, security; Brokers, security; Dealers, security
Pr: Mario Gabelli
**V Ch Bd:* Salvatore F Sodano
Genl Couns: David L Fitzgerald

D-U-N-S 12-221-1501
GABELLI UTILITY TRUST INC
1 Corporate Ctr, Rye, NY 10580-1485
Tel (914) 921-5070 *Founded/Ownrshp* 1986
Sales 21.1MM *EMP* 100
SIC 6726 Management investment funds, closed-end; Management investment funds, closed-end
Pr: Bruce Alpert
VP: Chrisotpher Mantel
VP: David Schachter
Board of Directors: P R Ades, T E Bratter, William Callaghan, T F Christiana, J Lee Conn, Kuni Nakamura, K O Pohl, A R Pustorino, S J Zizza

GABE'S
See GABRIEL BROTHERS INC

D-U-N-S 07-960-7215
GABLES ENERGY PARTNERS LLC
75 Valencia Ave Ste 600, Coral Gables, FL 33134-6132
Tel (305) 851-8450 *Founded/Ownrshp* 2014
Sales 23.4MM^E *EMP* 200^E
SIC 6719 1221 1389 2819 5084 Investment holding companies, except banks; Bituminous coal & lignite loading & preparation; Oil field services; Bleaching powder, lime bleaching compounds; Industrial machinery & equipment; Investment holding companies, except banks; Bituminous coal & lignite loading & preparation; Oil field services; Bleaching powder, lime bleaching compounds; Industrial machinery & equipment
CEO: David Schwedel

D-U-N-S 00-411-8386
GABLES ENGINEERING INC
247 Greco Ave, Coral Gables, FL 33146-1881
Tel (305) 774-4400 *Founded/Ownrshp* 1947
Sales 84.4MM^E *EMP* 277
SIC 3679 Electronic circuits; Electronic circuits
Pr: Victor E Clarke
Treas: Gary A Galimidi
VP: Charles E Rogers Jr
Exec: Richard Finale
Dir Bus: Charlie Bibb
Genl Mgr: Maritza Pedron
Genl Mgr: Rene Ramos
Genl Mgr: Raul Sanchez
MIS Dir: Jim Dyches
Dir IT: Maria Miranda
Dir IT: Mike Perrin

D-U-N-S 96-880-6554
GABLES REALTY LIMITED PARTNERSHIP
(*Suby of* GABLES RESIDENTIAL TRUST) ★
225 Ne Mizner Blvd # 400, Boca Raton, FL 33432-4078
Tel (561) 997-9700 *Founded/Ownrshp* 1994
Sales 82.7MM^E *EMP* 1,400
SIC 6798 Real estate investment trusts; Real estate investment trusts
Ch Bd: Chris Wheeler
CFO: Don Stewart

D-U-N-S 80-362-7355
GABLES RESIDENTIAL SERVICES INC
(*Suby of* LION GABLES REALTY LIMITED PARTNERSHIP) ★
3399 Peachtree Rd Ne # 600, Atlanta, GA 30326-2832
Tel (404) 923-5500 *Founded/Ownrshp* 1994
Sales 100.2MM^E *EMP* 1,200
SIC 6531 Real estate managers; Real estate managers
CEO: Susan M Ansel

CFO: Dawn H Severt
VP: Edward Fish
VP: Robert Lamb
VP: Sang Park
VP: Chris Smurda
VP: Mark Vernon
Rgnl Mgr: Stephanie Barbabosa
Rgnl Mgr: Alyson Beall
Rgnl Mgr: Mary Brennan
Rgnl Mgr: Joe Markonic

D-U-N-S 86-727-2726
GABLES RESIDENTIAL TRUST
(*Suby of* TORCHLIGHT DEBT OPPORTUNITY) ★
225 Ne Mizner Blvd # 400, Boca Raton, FL 33432-4078
Tel (561) 997-9700 *Founded/Ownrshp* 2005
Sales 82.7MM^E *EMP* 50^E
SIC 6531 6513 6552 6798 Real estate agents & managers; Apartment building operators; Subdividers & developers; Real estate investment trusts; Real estate agents & managers; Apartment building operators; Subdividers & developers; Real estate investment trusts
Pr: Susan Ansel
**Ch Bd:* Chris Wheeler
**Pr:* David Fitch
Pr: Michael J Ging
**CFO:* Marvin R Banks Jr
**CFO:* Dawn Severt
**Ex VP:* Benjamin Pisklak
Sr VP: Catherine K Cabell
**Sr VP:* Michael M Hefley
VP: Albert Palombo
VP: David L Skelton
VP: Donna Summers
VP: Maria Xirau
Board of Directors: Marcus E Bromley, John W McIntyre, James Motta

D-U-N-S 01-610-6882 IMP
GABRIEL BROTHERS INC
GABE'S
(*Suby of* AMCP RETAIL ACQUISITION CORP) ★
55 Scott Ave, Morgantown, WV 26508-8853
Tel (304) 292-6965 *Founded/Ownrshp* 1961, 2012
Sales 630.3MM^E *EMP* 3,500
SIC 5651 Family clothing stores; Family clothing stores
Pr: Ken Seipel
**Treas:* Ronald Gabriel
**Treas:* James Kline
**VP:* George Bellino
VP: Jeff Bruce
VP: Kal Gibron
VP: Mickey Kimball
VP: Shari Rudolph
IT Man: Steve Morris

D-U-N-S 03-177-0972
■ **GABRIEL COMMUNICATIONS FINANCE CO**
(*Suby of* NEWSOUTH COMMUNICATIONS) ★
2 N Main St Ste 300, Greenville, SC 29601-4875
Tel (864) 672-5000 *Founded/Ownrshp* 1999
Sales 254.7MM^E *EMP* 1,800^E
SIC 4813 Telephone communication, except radio; Telephone communication, except radio
CEO: James Akerhielm
Exec: Jim Pennington

D-U-N-S 00-833-1910
GABRIEL CONTAINER CO (CA)
RECYCLED PAPER PRODUCTS
8844 Millergrove Dr, Santa Fe Springs, CA 90670-2013
Tel (562) 699-1051 *Founded/Ownrshp* 1935
Sales 37.0MM^E *EMP* 200
SIC 2653 2621 Boxes, corrugated: made from purchased materials; Paper mills; Boxes, corrugated: made from purchased materials; Paper mills
Pr: Ronald H Gabriel

D-U-N-S 96-103-4691 IMP
GABRIEL HOLDINGS LLC
GABRIEL'S LIQUOR
10903 Industry Dr, San Antonio, TX 78217
Tel (210) 646-9992 *Founded/Ownrshp* 1995
Sales 36.4MM^E *EMP* 165
SIC 5921 5181 5182 Liquor stores; Beer & ale; Wine & distilled beverages
Dir IT: Bill Geraths

D-U-N-S 84-473-2839
GABRIEL PROPERTIES LLC
1302 Joe Yenni Blvd, Kenner, LA 70065-4886
Tel (504) 466-9788 *Founded/Ownrshp* 1998
Sales 30.0MM *EMP* 15
SIC 6552 8741 Land subdividers & developers, commercial; Land subdividers & developers, residential; Construction management; Land subdividers & developers, commercial; Land subdividers & developers, residential; Construction management
Prin: Marie Krantz

GABRIEL RIDE CONTROL
See RIDE CONTROL LLC

D-U-N-S 10-112-7959
GABRIELLI TRUCK SALES LTD
FORD
15320 S Conduit Ave, Jamaica, NY 11434-4221
Tel (718) 977-7348 *Founded/Ownrshp* 1991
Sales 92.3MM^E *EMP* 155
SIC 5511 5531 7538 Trucks, tractors & trailers: new & used; Truck equipment & parts; General truck repair; Trucks, tractors & trailers: new & used; Truck equipment & parts; General truck repair
Pr: Armando Gabrielli
**VP:* Amedeo Gabrielli
Sls Mgr: Osmond Diaz
Sls Mgr: J Loiacono
Sls Mgr: Richard Pesto

GABRIEL'S LIQUOR
See GABRIEL HOLDINGS LLC

D-U-N-S 86-101-0742
GAC CHEMICAL CORP
34 Kidder Point Rd, Searsport, ME 04974-3111
Tel (207) 548-2525 *Founded/Ownrshp* 1994
Sales 20.3MM^E *EMP* 60
SIC 2819 2873 5169 5084 Aluminum sulfate; Ammonium nitrate, ammonium sulfate; Chemicals & allied products; Chemical process equipment
Ch Bd: James A Poure
**Pr:* David Colter
**VP:* Barbara Haase
S&M/VP: John Wolanski
Board of Directors: E Bergsmark, Paul Hood, Frank Horton, Alan Kimbell, J M Murphey, W L Tatay

D-U-N-S 00-581-9438
GAC CONTRACTORS INC (FL)
4116 N Highway 231, Panama City, FL 32404-9235
Tel (850) 785-4675 *Founded/Ownrshp* 1958
Sales 88.1MM^E *EMP* 365
SIC 1611 1629 Highway & street maintenance; Land preparation construction; Highway & street maintenance; Land preparation construction
Ch Bd: L Charles Hilton Jr
**Pr:* Richard M Dodd
**VP:* Carol S Atkinson
**VP:* Derwin White
IT Man: Shane Cook
IT Man: Andrew Rowell

D-U-N-S 05-054-1309
GAC INC
1845 W 1st St Ste 108, Tempe, AZ 85281-7253
Tel (480) 759-4588 *Founded/Ownrshp* 1977
Sales 27.7MM^E *EMP* 200
SIC 3585 1711 Heat pumps, electric; Air conditioning units, complete: domestic or industrial; Heating & air conditioning combination units; Mechanical contractor; Heat pumps, electric; Air conditioning units, complete: domestic or industrial; Heating & air conditioning combination units; Mechanical contractor
Ch Bd: David H Murdock
VP: Patricia Cippon
Prin: Daniel Burke
Genl Mgr: Brad Morari
Genl Mgr: Doug Wilcock
VP Sls: John Ryan

D-U-N-S 04-920-7038 IMP
■ **GAC INTERNATIONAL LLC**
(*Suby of* DENTSPLY INTERNATIONAL INC) ★
1 Ca Plz Ste 100, Islandia, NY 11749-5303
Tel (631) 419-1500 *Founded/Ownrshp* 2002
Sales 30.3MM^E *EMP* 170
SIC 5047 Dental equipment & supplies; Dental equipment & supplies
Prin: Ed Marill
Sls Dir: David Painter
Sales Asso: Michael Leger

GAC NORTH AMERICA
See GAC SHIPPING (USA) INC

D-U-N-S 12-237-2654
GAC SHIPPING (USA) INC
GAC NORTH AMERICA
(*Suby of* GAC LOGISTICS PARK)
1 International Plz # 250, Philadelphia, PA 19113-1510
Tel (484) 953-3310 *Founded/Ownrshp* 2001
Sales 22.7MM^E *EMP* 67
SIC 4731 Agents, shipping
Pr: Walter J Bandos
**Treas:* Darren Martin
**VP:* Lars Heisselberg
**Mng Dir:* Walter Bandos

D-U-N-S 19-411-7255
GACHINA LANDSCAPE MANAGEMENT INC
1130 Obrien Dr, Menlo Park, CA 94025-1411
Tel (650) 853-0400 *Founded/Ownrshp* 1988
Sales 32.8MM^E *EMP* 269
SIC 0782 Landscape contractors; Landscape contractors
CEO: John P Gachina
Dir Bus: Stacie Callaghan
Dir Bus: Stacie Sadler
Brnch Mgr: William Cruz
CTO: Jennifer Nix
IT Man: Denise Ritch
Snr PM: Lauren Galanes

D-U-N-S 00-924-1027 IMP/EXP
GACO WESTERN LLC
200 W Mercer St Ste 202, Seattle, WA 98119-3958
Tel (206) 575-0450 *Founded/Ownrshp* 2006
Sales 29.9MM^E *EMP* 170
SIC 2822 2821 2891 2851 Synthetic rubber; Neoprene, chloroprene; Polyethylene, chlorosulfonated (hypalon); Polyurethane resins; Adhesives & sealants; Paints & allied products
CEO: Peter A Davis
CFO: Eric Peterson
VP: Dan Nelson
VP: Charles Skalski
VP: Chuck Skalski Jr
VP: Eric Zimmerman
Rgnl Mgr: Jason Kron
Area Mgr: Greg Abernathy
Area Mgr: Bill Bradley
Area Mgr: Kynny Carlson
Area Mgr: Trent Denny

GACSC
See GRAPHIC ARTS CENTER INC

D-U-N-S 01-654-1179
GADDIS BILL CHRYSLER PLYMOUTH DODGE INC
1717 N Wheeling Ave, Muncie, IN 47303-1667
Tel (765) 289-2361 *Founded/Ownrshp* 1977
Sales 35.0MM *EMP* 42
SIC 5511 Automobiles, new & used; Automobiles, new & used
Pr: Bill Gaddis
**Genl Mgr:* Steve Gaddis

D-U-N-S 05-692-4202
GADDIS CAPITAL CORP
221 W Oakland Park Blvd, Wilton Manors, FL 33311-1757
Tel (954) 565-8900 *Founded/Ownrshp* 1985
Sales NA *EMP* 300
SIC 6159 Equipment & vehicle finance leasing companies; Equipment & vehicle finance leasing companies
Pr: Jesse Gaddis

D-U-N-S 92-928-3117
GADDIS PARTNERS LTD
T 3
1801 N Lamar Blvd, Austin, TX 78701-1051
Tel (512) 499-8811 *Founded/Ownrshp* 1989
Sales 20.6MM^E *EMP* 160
SIC 7311 8743 8742 Advertising agencies; Public relations & publicity; Marketing consulting services; Advertising agencies; Public relations & publicity; Marketing consulting services
Pt: Gay Gaddis
COO: Keith Johnston
Sr VP: Greg Pomaro
VP: Ben Gaddis
VP: Kirk Sdrummond
Creative D: Ashley Lapin
Creative D: Jamieson Mackie
Mng Dir: Tamara Weinman
Snr Sftwr: Mike Ross
CIO: Russell Harris
Mktg Dir: Jill Prentice

D-U-N-S 80-918-6174 IMP
GADGE USA INC
3000 Marcus Ave Ste 3e3, New Hyde Park, NY 11042-1007
Tel (516) 437-6340 *Founded/Ownrshp* 1993
Sales 63.1MM^E *EMP* 50
SIC 5113 Corrugated & solid fiber boxes
Ch: Mel Weiser
**Pr:* Glenn Weiser
CFO: Frank Rizzo
CFO: Dean Zambelli
VP: Dennis Wilson
IT Man: Giovanni Gregori
Sales Exec: Jeffery Greenstein
VP Sls: Stanley Caputo
Manager: Chris Neal

GADSDEN BUDWEISER
See BIRMINGHAM BUDWEISER DISTRIBUTING CO INC

D-U-N-S 18-641-4025
GADSDEN CITY BOARD OF EDUCATION
1026 Chestnut St, Gadsden, AL 35901-3918
Tel (256) 543-3512 *Founded/Ownrshp* 1889
Sales 43.3MM^E *EMP* 694
SIC 8211 Public combined elementary & secondary school; Public combined elementary & secondary school

D-U-N-S 07-979-8884
GADSDEN CITY SCHOOLS
1026 Chestnut St, Gadsden, AL 35901-3918
Tel (256) 549-2903 *Founded/Ownrshp* 2015
Sales 15.5MM^E *EMP* 446^E
SIC 8211 Public elementary & secondary schools
Pr Dir: Don Campbell
Teacher Pr: David Asbury

D-U-N-S 03-160-6239 IMP
GADSDEN COFFEE CO INC
MAX PACKAGING
109 6th Ave Nw, Attalla, AL 35954-2016
Tel (256) 538-2233 *Founded/Ownrshp* 1949
Sales 41.1MM^E *EMP* 250
Accts Ronnie L Mcclure Cpa
SIC 3089 Plastic kitchenware, tableware & houseware; Plastic kitchenware, tableware & houseware
Pr: Jerry Randick
**Owner:* David Mc Farland
**Treas:* Gary Mc Farland
Plnt Mgr: Frank James
S&M/VP: David M Farland
Snr Mgr: Dennis Ashley

D-U-N-S 06-023-7690
GADSDEN COUNTY BOARD OF COMMISSIONERS
9b E Jefferson St, Quincy, FL 32351-2405
Tel (850) 875-8601 *Founded/Ownrshp* 1824
Sales NA *EMP* 440
SIC 9111 Executive offices; ; Executive offices;
**Prin:* Robert Presnell
Board of Directors: Ed Dickson, Carolyn Robinson, Dr Sterling Watson

D-U-N-S 15-281-1279
GADSDEN COUNTY BOARD OF EDUCATION
35 Martn Luter Kng Jr Blv, Quincy, FL 32351-4411
Tel (850) 627-9651 *Founded/Ownrshp* 1885
Sales 40.0MM *EMP* 980
SIC 8211 Public elementary & secondary schools; School board
Ch Bd: Audrey Lewis
Brnch Mgr: Mahala Walker
Schl Brd P: Isaac Simmons
Teacher Pr: Erica Starling

D-U-N-S 07-979-9066
GADSDEN COUNTY SCHOOLS
35 Martin Luther King, Quincy, FL 32351-4411
Tel (850) 627-9651 *Founded/Ownrshp* 2015
Sales 8.5MM^E *EMP* 1,165^E
SIC 8211 Public elementary & secondary schools

D-U-N-S 10-000-1452
GADSDEN ELEMENTARY SCHOOL DISTRICT 32
1453 N Main St Ste F, San Luis, AZ 85349
Tel (928) 627-6540 *Founded/Ownrshp* 1933
Sales 35.9MM^E *EMP* 718
Accts Heinfeld Meech & Co PcT
SIC 8211 Public elementary & secondary schools; Public elementary & secondary schools
Pr: Ray Aguilera
**CFO:* Bob Bernhard
IT Man: Rocio Godoy
HC Dir: Rosie Figueroa

D-U-N-S 08-766-7267
GADSDEN INDEPENDENT SCHOOL DISTRICT
4950 Mcnutt Rd, Sunland Park, NM 88063
Tel (575) 882-6200 *Founded/Ownrshp* 1949
Sales 90.7MM^E *EMP* 2,000
Accts Griego Professional Services
SIC 8211 Public elementary & secondary schools; Public elementary & secondary schools
Pr: Jennifer Viramontes
**Pr:* Daniel Castillo
**Prin:* Craig Ford
**Prin:* Maria Saenz
IT Man: Ivan Strnad
HC Dir: Judy Creegan

D-U-N-S 15-359-3074
■ **GADSDEN REGIONAL MEDICAL CENTER LLC**
CHS
(*Suby of* COMMUNITY HEALTH SYSTEMS INC) ★
1007 Goodyear Ave, Gadsden, AL 35903-1195
Tel (256) 494-4000 *Founded/Ownrshp* 2001
Sales 243.8MM *EMP* 1,300
SIC 8062 8082 8011 7352 General medical & surgical hospitals; Home health care services; General & family practice, physician/surgeon; Medical equipment rental; General medical & surgical hospitals; Home health care services; General & family practice, physician/surgeon; Medical equipment rental
CEO: Stephen Pennington
COO: Bill Keith
**CFO:* Michael Cotton
CFO: Kandi Garmany
Ofcr: Angela Tillis
Dir Rx: Wayne Cornutt
Dir Sec: Mark Harper
Nurse Mgr: Oakley Patterson
Mktg Dir: Leslie Harp
Psych: Shane McCurry
Doctor: Randy Holmes

D-U-N-S 07-210-3138
GADSDEN STATE COMMUNITY COLLEGE
WALLACE DRIVE CAMPUS
(*Suby of* ALABAMA COMMUNITY COLLEGE SYSTEM) ★
1001 George Wallace Dr, Gadsden, AL 35903-2269
Tel (256) 549-8200 *Founded/Ownrshp* 1965
Sales 14.8MM^E *EMP* 574
SIC 8222 9199

D-U-N-S 15-518-3221
GAETA CONSOLIDATED LTD
NOURIA ENERGY
14 Newbury St, Peabody, MA 01960-3805
Tel (978) 535-4762 *Founded/Ownrshp* 1974
Sales 21.6MM^E *EMP* 30
SIC 5541 7538 7549 Filling stations, gasoline; General automotive repair shops; Towing service, automotive
Pr: Matthew Gaeta

D-U-N-S 07-932-7581
GAETA RECYCLING CO INC
278 W Railway Ave, Paterson, NJ 07503
Tel (973) 278-0145 *Founded/Ownrshp* 1951
Sales 33.3MM^E *EMP* 96
SIC 4953 Refuse collection & disposal services; Refuse collection & disposal services
Pr: Anthony R Gaeta Jr
Off Mgr: Mariusz Gruca

D-U-N-S 10-665-1540 IMP/EXP
GAF CORP
GAF MATERIALS
(*Suby of* BMCA) ★
1 Campus Dr, Parsippany, NJ 07054-4404
Tel (973) 628-3000 *Founded/Ownrshp* 1998
Sales 232.6MM^E *EMP* 525^E
SIC 3444 3634 Ducts, sheet metal; Fans, exhaust & ventilating, electric: household; Ducts, sheet metal; Fans, exhaust & ventilating, electric: household
CEO: Bob Tafaro
**Ex VP:* Jim Schnepper
**Sr VP:* Mike Kiik
**Sr VP:* Tim Machelski
VP: Denby Snell
VP: Todd Tarchalski
QA Dir: Lori Charpentier
QA Dir: Kiran Mayi
IT Man: Daniel Doyle
Tech Mgr: Brandon Burton
Tech Mgr: Rick Weiman

D-U-N-S 04-907-8155 IMP
GAF ELK MATERIALS CORP
1361 Alps Rd, Wayne, NJ 07470-3700
Tel (973) 628-4083 *Founded/Ownrshp* 2010
Sales 69.3MM^E *EMP* 148^E
SIC 3271 3272 3444 Roof ballast block, concrete; Roofing tile & slabs, concrete; Metal roofing & roof drainage equipment; Roof deck, sheet metal
CEO: Robert B Tafaro
Sls Mgr: Rich Nelson

D-U-N-S 06-095-0297
GAF HOLDINGS INC (CA)
1300 E Mineral King Ave, Visalia, CA 93292-6913
Tel (559) 734-3333 *Founded/Ownrshp* 1999
Sales NA *EMP* 300
SIC 6719 Personal holding companies, except banks; Personal holding companies, except banks
Pr: Don Groppetti

GAF MATERIALS
See ELKCORP

GAF MATERIALS
See GAF CORP

D-U-N-S 61-156-5508
GAFCON INC
5960 Cornerstone Ct W # 100, San Diego, CA 92121-3780
Tel (619) 231-6100 Founded/Ownrshp 1987
Sales 29.3MM^E EMP 120
SIC 8741 8111 Construction management; Legal services
CEO: Yehudi Gaffen
*Pr: Pam Gaffen
*Pr: Paul Najar
*COO: Robin Duveen
CFO: James Baum
*CFO: Jon Rodriguez
Prgrm Mgr: Tim Meehan
Prgrm Mgr: Ronald Takaki
CTO: Doug Eveland
VP Mktg: John Turner
Mktg Dir: Michael Bruce

D-U-N-S 06-932-9464
GAFFNEY BOARD OF PUBLIC WORKS
210 E Frederick St, Gaffney, SC 29340-2426
Tel (864) 488-8800 Founded/Ownrshp 1907
Sales 33.4MM EMP 92
Accts Mcabee Schwartz Halliday & C
SIC 4941 4952 4911 Water supply; Sewerage systems; Electric services; Water supply; Sewerage systems; Electric services
Genl Mgr: Donny L Hardin
Dir Lab: Bobby Jones
Site Mgr: Adam Ruppe

GAFFNEY PLUMBING & HEATING SUP
See CLEMENT J GAFFNEY WATER METER REPAIRS INC

D-U-N-S 00-187-0138 IMP/EXP
GAFFNEY-KROESE ELECTRICAL SUPPLY CORP (NY)
50 Randolph Rd, Somerset, NJ 08873-1240
Tel (732) 885-9000 Founded/Ownrshp 1931, 1946
Sales 343.4MM^E EMP 275
SIC 5063 5082 Electrical supplies; Oil field equipment; Industrial machinery & equipment; Electrical supplies; Oil field equipment
Ch Bd: Christopher C Kroese
COO: Robert Jouas
*VP: John S Kroese III
Mktg Dir: Joseph Delgiorno

D-U-N-S 07-967-0008
GAFFNEY-KROESE SUPPLY CORP
GK
50 Randolph Rd, Somerset, NJ 08873-1240
Tel (732) 885-9000 Founded/Ownrshp 2014
Sales 20.3MM^E EMP 98^E
SIC 3699 Electrical equipment & supplies
Pr: Christopher Kroese
Prin: John S Kroese

D-U-N-S 04-595-4625
GAFFOGLIO FMLY METALCRAFTERS INC
CAMERA READY CARS
11161 Slater Ave, Fountain Valley, CA 92708-4921
Tel (714) 481-0790 Founded/Ownrshp 1979
Sales 20.5MM^E EMP 109^E
SIC 3231 3711 3365 Mirrors, truck & automobile: made from purchased glass; Automobile assembly, including specialty automobiles; Aerospace castings, aluminum; Mirrors, truck & automobile: made from purchased glass; Automobile assembly, including specialty automobiles; Aerospace castings, aluminum
CEO: George Gaffoglio
*Pr: Ruben Gaffoglio
*COO: Mike Alexander
VP: Marcelo Gaffoglio

D-U-N-S 07-971-0953
GAFFTECH LLC
1307 W Valley Hwy N, Auburn, WA 98001-4110
Tel (844) 423-3486 Founded/Ownrshp 2013
Sales 60.0MM EMP 7
SIC 2241 Slide fastener tapes

GAFLEET
See G A FLEET ASSOCIATES INC

G.A.FOOD SERVICE
See GA FOOD SERVICES OF PINELLAS COUNTY INC

D-U-N-S 10-242-1757 IMP
GAFP INC
AMERISTAR FENCE PRODUCTS
(Suby of ASSA ABLOY INC) ★
1555 N Mingo Rd, Tulsa, OK 74116-1506
Tel (918) 835-0898 Founded/Ownrshp 2013
Sales 228.8MM^E EMP 650
SIC 3315 Fences or posts, ornamental iron or steel; Fence gates posts & fittings: steel
Pr: Johan Molin
VP: Keith Armour
VP: Scott Galbraith
VP: Bridgett Hood
VP: Steve Steele
Ex Dir: Ken White
Brnch Mgr: Robert Dobson
Brnch Mgr: Christopher Sweet
Dir IT: Steve Overacker
Sys Mgr: Chris Irwin
Sfty Mgr: Galen Sawyer

D-U-N-S 19-648-2942
GAFVT MOTORS INC
GWINNETT PLACE FORD
3230 Satellite Blvd, Duluth, GA 30096-4641
Tel (404) 418-6877 Founded/Ownrshp 1999
Sales 70.0MM^E EMP 200^E
SIC 5511 Automobiles, new & used; Automobiles, new & used
CEO: Larry Van Tuyl
*CFO: Allan M Cady
Exec: Brian McFarland
MIS Dir: Alan Bishop
Sls Dir: Casey Coffey
Sls Mgr: Stacy Kelley

D-U-N-S 00-725-7108
GAGE BROS CONCRETE PRODUCTS INC
4301 W 12th St, Sioux Falls, SD 57106-0303
Tel (605) 336-1180 Founded/Ownrshp 1946
Sales 34.5MM^E EMP 240^E
SIC 3272 Panels & sections, prefabricated concrete; Panels & sections, prefabricated concrete
Ch: Fredrick Gage
*Pr: Tom Kelley
*CFO: David Honner
*VP: Joe Bunkers
*VP: Chuck Smith
Sfty Mgr: Bret Doyle
Plnt Mgr: Jim Miller
Ql Cn Mgr: Don Hall
Trfc Mgr: Karla Westendorf
Mktg Mgr: Stephanie Pendrys
Sls Mgr: Eric Kurtz

D-U-N-S 08-212-9776
GAGES FERTILIZER & GRAIN INC
105 S High St, Stanberry, MO 64489-1823
Tel (660) 783-2167 Founded/Ownrshp 1982
Sales 35.1MM^E EMP 64
SIC 5191 5153

D-U-N-S 02-942-9313
GAGMARS INC
G & G SUPER MARKET
1211 W College Ave, Santa Rosa, CA 95401-5044
Tel (707) 546-3071 Founded/Ownrshp 1963
Sales 40.1MM^E EMP 300
SIC 5411 Supermarkets, independent; Supermarkets, independent
CEO: Teejay Lowe
Pr: Robert Gong
VP: Betty Gong
VP: Dick Gong
VP: Lee Gong
Dir IT: Jack Gong

D-U-N-S 02-326-7198
GAGNON INC
2315 Hampden Ave, Saint Paul, MN 55114-1204
Tel (715) 386-3096 Founded/Ownrshp 1948
Sales 34.5MM^E EMP 200
SIC 1711 Boiler maintenance contractor; Boiler setting contractor; Heating systems repair & maintenance; Boiler maintenance contractor; Boiler setting contractor; Heating systems repair & maintenance
CEO: Ronald Gagnon
*VP: Gary Jaje
Area Mgr: Terry Harm
Off Mgr: Judy Larson
Sfty Dirs: Bruce Mueller

D-U-N-S 08-429-6839 IMP
■ **GAGS AND GAMES INC**
MAN STORE, THE
(Suby of PARTY CITY HOLDINGS INC) ★
35901 Veronica St, Livonia, MI 48150-1207
Tel (734) 591-1717 Founded/Ownrshp 2007
Sales 48.4MM^E EMP 300
Accts Mary Frances Mcginity By Fax O
SIC 2389 5947 Costumes; Party favors; Costumes; Party favors
Co-Pr: John Mc Intire
*Co-Pr: Christopher Bearss

D-U-N-S 15-274-1633
GAHANNA-JEFFERSON PUBLIC SCHOOL DISTRICT
160 S Hamilton Rd, Gahanna, OH 43230-2919
Tel (614) 471-7065 Founded/Ownrshp 1927
Sales 54.9MM^E EMP 800
Accts Kennedy Cottrell Richards Llc
SIC 8211 Public elementary & secondary schools; Public elementary & secondary schools
COO: Dan Rotella
*Treas: Julio Valladares
*Ex Dir: Math Cygnor

GAHS
See GREAT AMERICAN HOME STORE INC

D-U-N-S 09-274-8474 IMP
GAHVEJIAN ENTERPRISES INC
MID VALLEY PACKAGING & SUP CO
2004 S Temperance Ave, Fowler, CA 93625-9759
Tel (559) 834-5956 Founded/Ownrshp 1980
Sales 53.3MM^E EMP 50
SIC 5113 Bags, paper & disposable plastic; Boxes, paperboard & disposable plastic; Folding paperboard boxes
Pr: Carrie L Gahvejian
*Pr: John Gahvejian
*Sec: Lorrie Gahvejian
*Prin: Erik Creede

D-U-N-S 04-721-1677
GAI CONSULTANTS INC (PA)
385 E Waterfront Dr Fl 1, Homestead, PA 15120-5070
Tel (412) 476-2000 Founded/Ownrshp 1958, 2003
Sales 226.9MM^E EMP 800
Accts Markovitz Dugan & Associates
SIC 8711 Consulting engineer; Consulting engineer
Pr: Gary M Dejidas
*CFO: Karl S Palvisak
*Ex VP: Lawrence R Dodds
Ex VP: Sarah Miloski
Ex VP: Aaron Speaks
*Sr VP: J M Sievers
VP: John Edwards
*VP: Diane B Landers
*VP: Anthony F Morrocco
Tech Mgr: Judson Fohr
Tech Mgr: Kenneth Jones

D-U-N-S 00-232-4473 IMP/EXP
■ **GAI-TRONICS CORP**
(Suby of HUBBELL INC) ★
400 E Wyomissing Ave, Mohnton, PA 19540-1503
Tel (610) 777-1374 Founded/Ownrshp 1981, 2000
Sales 60.9MM^E EMP 375
SIC 3661 3663 Telephones & telephone apparatus; Radio & TV communications equipment; Telephones & telephone apparatus; Radio & TV communications equipment

Pr: Steven Noecker
*Treas: Jam H Biggart
Sr VP: Michelle Kuplic
*VP: Wayne A Cable
VP: Bret Hatt
*VP: James A Jurczyk
VP: John Marranucci
VP: Joseph J Radomski
Snr Sftwr: Michael Hottenstein
Snr Sftwr: Rick Monyer
VP Mfg: Brad Snyder

D-U-N-S 16-620-3435
GAIA ENTERPRISES INC
SAFE PAW
103 Roy Ln, Huntingdon Valley, PA 19006-3119
Tel (800) 783-7841 Founded/Ownrshp 2013
Sales 21.0MM EMP 10
SIC 2097 Manufactured ice; Manufactured ice
CEO: Steven Greenwald

D-U-N-S 96-322-9849
GAIA FUND
235 Montgomery St # 1011, San Francisco, CA 94104-3003
Tel (415) 391-6943 Founded/Ownrshp 2010
Sales 34.9MM EMP 2
SIC 8699 Charitable organization
Prin: Mark Schlesinger

GAIA PARK VIEW
See GAIA REAL ESTATE INVESTMENT LLC

D-U-N-S 00-988-6696
GAIA REAL ESTATE INVESTMENT LLC
GAIA PARK VIEW
152 W 57th St Ste 902, New York, NY 10019-3596
Tel (212) 563-2726 Founded/Ownrshp 2009
Sales 21.9MM^E EMP 25^E
SIC 6531 Real estate agents & managers
Mng Pt: Amir Yerushalmi
Mng Pt: Danny Fishman
Mng Pt: Ken Woolley
CFO: Manan Shukla
Mng Dir: Laurance Kaufman
Off Mgr: Alison Maguire

D-U-N-S 12-140-0063
▲ **GAIAM INC**
833 W South Boulder Rd G, Louisville, CO 80027-2401
Tel (303) 222-3600 Founded/Ownrshp 1988
Sales 166.6MM EMP 261
Accts Eks&H Lllp Denver Colorado
Tkr Sym GAIA Exch NGM
SIC 7299 7812 7999 Personal appearance services; Training motion picture production; Video production; Yoga instruction; Personal appearance services; Training motion picture production; Video production; Yoga instruction
CEO: Lynn Powers
*Ch Bd: Jirka Rysavy
CFO: Stephen J Thomas
Chf Mktg O: Cynthia Rhea
Sr VP: Patricia Karpas
Sr VP: Suzette Schafer
VP: Elena Cortes
VP: Dustin Howard
VP: John Jackson
VP: Reinhold Reiter
Mng Dir: John Mills

D-U-N-S 04-992-8385
GAIDOS OF GALVESTON INC (TX)
GAIDO'S SEAFOOD RESTAURANT
3828 Seawall Blvd, Galveston, TX 77550-8848
Tel (409) 762-9625 Founded/Ownrshp 1911
Sales 13.7MM^E EMP 350
SIC 5812 7011 Seafood restaurants; Motels; Seafood restaurants; Motels
Pr: John Paul Gaido
VP: Gaido M J III
*Prin: Michael J Gaido Jr
Counsel: Peter Gaido

GAIDO'S SEAFOOD RESTAURANT
See GAIDOS OF GALVESTON INC

D-U-N-S 03-446-0352 IMP
GAIENNIE LUMBER CO LLC
619 W Grolee St, Opelousas, LA 70570-4223
Tel (337) 948-3066 Founded/Ownrshp 2006
Sales 26.2MM^E EMP 45
SIC 5031 Lumber: rough, dressed & finished
Sales Asso: Richard Gaiennie
VP: George C Gaiennie Jr
VP: George Gaiennie

GAILE PACIFIC
See GALE PACIFIC USA INC

D-U-N-S 14-220-6015
■ **GAIN CAPITAL GROUP LLC**
(Suby of GAIN CAPITAL HOLDINGS INC) ★
135 Us Highway 202 206 # 11, Bedminster, NJ 07921-2608
Tel (908) 731-0700 Founded/Ownrshp 2006
Sales NA EMP 333
SIC 6099 Foreign currency exchange; Foreign currency exchange
Pr: Glenn Stevens
COO: Jeff Scott
CFO: Henry C Lyons
Bd of Dir: Mark Galant
VP: Thomas Baxter
VP: Samantha Roady
Prgrm Mgr: Jill Augustine
Snr Sftwr: Dimitar Entchev
Software D: Karthika Inugala
Sls Dir: Ric Conradt
Sls Mgr: Mario Soto

D-U-N-S 83-168-2146
▲ **GAIN CAPITAL HOLDINGS INC**
135 Route 202 206, Bedminster, NJ 07921
Tel (908) 731-0700 Founded/Ownrshp 1999
Sales 370.1MM EMP 479^E
Tkr Sym GCAP Exch NYS
SIC 6211 6221 Security brokers & dealers; Commodity contracts brokers, dealers; Security brokers & dealers; Commodity contracts brokers, dealers

Pr: Glenn H Stevens
*Ch Bd: Peter Quick
COO: Jeffrey A Scott
CFO: Nigel Rose
Ofcr: Samantha Roady
Ex VP: Diego A Rotsztain
Sr VP: Dina Grochowski
VP: Joseph Gelsomino
VP: Keith Ginder
VP: Daniel Gladding
VP: Nayan Patel
VP: Rob Perez
VP: Evangelos Tzoulafis
Exec: Kemi Ajetunmobi
Board of Directors: Thomas A Bevilacqua, Christopher W Calhoun, Joseph Schenk, Christopher S Sugden

D-U-N-S 80-853-5236
GAIN INTERNATIONAL
NEW LIFE PUBLICATIONS
(Suby of CAMPUS CRUSADE FOR CHRIST INC) ★
2001 W Plano Pkwy # 2200, Plano, TX 75075-8611
Tel (972) 234-0800 Founded/Ownrshp 2003
Sales 27.3MM EMP 37
Accts Capin Crouse Llp Grapevine T
SIC 8322 Individual & family services; Individual & family services
IT Man: Keith Anderson

D-U-N-S 00-282-8218
GAINES AND CO INC
112 Westminster Pike, Reisterstown, MD 21136-1027
Tel (410) 833-9833 Founded/Ownrshp 1954
Sales 52.3MM^E EMP 119
SIC 1623 Water & sewer line construction; Sewer line construction; Water main construction; Water & sewer line construction; Sewer line construction; Water main construction
Pr: William Lee Gaines Jr
*VP: L Myrton Gaines
*VP: George Grammer

D-U-N-S 00-352-2117
GAINES MOTOR LINES INC
2349 13th Ave Sw, Hickory, NC 28602-4740
Tel (828) 322-2000 Founded/Ownrshp 1940
Sales 27.8MM^E EMP 190
SIC 4213 4731 Contract haulers; Freight transportation arrangement; Contract haulers; Freight transportation arrangement
CEO: Forest M Gaines
*Pr: Dennis Gaines
*Ex VP: Tim Gaines

D-U-N-S 07-592-6923
GAINESVILLE CITY OF (INC)
300 Henry Ward Way Se, Gainesville, GA 30501-3753
Tel (770) 535-6865 Founded/Ownrshp 1821
Sales NA EMP 640
Accts Rushton & Company
SIC 9111 City & town managers' offices; ; City & town managers' offices;
Ofcr: Louis Acevedo
Ofcr: Miguel Bekkevold
Ofcr: Mary Davis
Ofcr: James Franklin
Ofcr: William Gough
Ofcr: Jaron Griffin
Ofcr: Thomas Harrison
Ofcr: Norwood Hope
Ofcr: Deforrest Houston
Ofcr: Michael Kay
Ofcr: Brett Kikendall
Ofcr: John Mazzuca
Ofcr: Ryan McCazzio
Ofcr: Lisa Orengo
Ofcr: Wilfredo Perez
Ofcr: Ronnie Pirtle
Ofcr: Matthew Quinn
Ofcr: Jason Rarey
Ofcr: Justine South
Ofcr: Jacob Sowards
Ofcr: Douglas Williams

D-U-N-S 18-127-0646
GAINESVILLE CITY SCHOOL SYSTEM
508 Oak St Ste 2, Gainesville, GA 30501-3576
Tel (770) 536-5275 Founded/Ownrshp 1892
Sales 34.5MM^E EMP 550
Accts Russell W Hinton Cpa Cgfm
SIC 8211 Public elementary & secondary schools; Public elementary & secondary schools
*Ch: David Syfan

D-U-N-S 10-183-1923
GAINESVILLE COUNCIL ON AGING INC
GAINESVILLE HEALTHCARE CENTER
1311 Sw 16th St, Gainesville, FL 32608-1128
Tel (352) 376-8821 Founded/Ownrshp 2004
Sales 34.1MM^E EMP 350
Accts Carr Riggs & Ingram Llc Gaine
SIC 8051 Skilled nursing care facilities; Skilled nursing care facilities
CEO: Maxcine Darville
*CFO: Jim Ecklof
*Ch: Andrew Turner
Exec: Darlene Graves
Off Mgr: Angela Lopez

D-U-N-S 09-783-0624
GAINESVILLE HEALTH AND FITNESS CENTER INC
4820 W Newberry Rd, Gainesville, FL 32607-2249
Tel (352) 377-4955 Founded/Ownrshp 1978
Sales 17.8MM^E EMP 450
SIC 7991 Physical fitness clubs with training equipment; Exercise facilities; Physical fitness clubs with training equipment; Exercise facilities
Pr: Joseph D Cirulli
CFO: Mike Klien
DP Exec: Mike Kline
Dir IT: Tammy Pritchard
Opers Mgr: Debbie Lee

GAINESVILLE HEALTHCARE CENTER
See GAINESVILLE COUNCIL ON AGING INC

D-U-N-S 07-486-4216
GAINESVILLE HOSPITAL DISTRICT
NORTH TEXAS MEDICAL CENTER
1900 Hospital Blvd, Gainesville, TX 76240-2002
Tel (940) 665-1751 *Founded/Ownrshp* 1962
Sales 27.1MM *EMP* 300
Accts Durbin & Company Llp Lubbock
SIC 8062 General medical & surgical hospitals; General medical & surgical hospitals
CEO: Randy Bacus
COO: Lucy Krahl
CFO: Kelly Hayes
Bd of Dir: Roane McLaughlin
Dir Lab: Margaret Casey
Dir Rad: James Hennigan
Dir Rad: Debbie Smart
Dir Rx: Danny Reeves
CIO: Beth Comer
Dir IT: Edison Sincalair
Dir IT: Eddie Sinclair

D-U-N-S 07-838-1852
GAINESVILLE INDEPENDENT SCHOOL DISTRICT
800 S Morris St, Gainesville, TX 76240-5412
Tel (940) 665-0255 *Founded/Ownrshp* 1948
Sales 27.3MM *EMP* 425
Accts Schalk & Smith Pc Gainesville
SIC 8211 Public elementary school; Public junior high school; Public senior high school; Public elementary school; Public junior high school; Public senior high school
**Pr:* Charley Henderson
Bd of Dir: Robin Atteberry
Bd of Dir: Danny Baggett
Bd of Dir: Jason Fielder
**VP:* Zach Nichols
Teacher Pr: Paula Moore

D-U-N-S 60-991-3926
GAINESVILLE MECHANICAL INC
2519 Monroe Dr, Gainesville, GA 30507-7349
Tel (770) 532-9130 *Founded/Ownrshp* 1989
Sales 22.6MM^E *EMP* 60
SIC 1711 Warm air heating & air conditioning contractor
Pr: Rusty B Gravitt
VP Opers: Glenn Criner
VP Opers: Dennis Fuller

D-U-N-S 03-232-1952
GAINESVILLE MOTORS INC
GAINESVLLE CHRYSLER DODGE JEEP
3000 N Main St, Gainesville, FL 32609-3001
Tel (352) 372-4343 *Founded/Ownrshp* 1980
Sales 26.5MM^E *EMP* 64
SIC 5511 Automobiles, new & used; Pickups, new & used; Automobiles, new & used; Pickups, new & used
Pr: Arthur Sullivan
**Sec:* Wanda Bostic
Sls Mgr: Rod Demurias

GAINESVILLE NISSAN
See TT OF ALACHUA INC

GAINESVILLE REGIONAL UTILITIES
See CITY OF GAINESVILLE

D-U-N-S 08-263-5004
GAINESVILLE REGIONAL UTILITIES (INC)
GRU
301 Se 4th Ave, Gainesville, FL 32601-6857
Tel (352) 334-3400 *Founded/Ownrshp* 1912
Sales 622.0MM^E *EMP* 750
Accts Earnst & Young Llp Orlando F
SIC 4939 4941 4924 4911 Combination utilities; Water supply; Natural gas distribution; ; Combination utilities; Water supply; Natural gas distribution;
**CFO:* Jennifer L Hunt
**CFO:* David M Richardson
VP: Patricia Kafle
VP: John Spencer
VP: Lewis Walton
Exec: Sara Smith
Genl Mgr: Robert Hunzinger
Genl Mgr: John Stanton
Genl Mgr: Kathy E Viehe
Off Mgr: Marsha Anderson
CIO: Ronald Key

D-U-N-S 08-965-6532
GAINESVILLE SUN PUBLISHING CO
(*Suby of* HALIFAX MEDIA HOLDINGS LLC) ★
2700 Sw 13th St, Gainesville, FL 32608-2015
Tel (352) 378-1411 *Founded/Ownrshp* 2012
Sales 20.8MM^E *EMP* 293
SIC 2711 Newspapers, publishing & printing; Newspapers, publishing & printing

GAINESVLLE CHRYSLER DODGE JEEP
See GAINESVILLE MOTORS INC

D-U-N-S 06-536-9258
GAINEY MACHINE & FABRICATOR LLC
961 Patrick Hwy, Hartsville, SC 29550-3186
Tel (843) 332-0781 *Founded/Ownrshp* 1982
Sales 45.0MM *EMP* 9
SIC 3599 3743 3451 Machine shop, jobbing & repair; Railroad equipment; Screw machine products; Machine shop, jobbing & repair; Railroad equipment; Screw machine products

GAINSBROUGH SPECIALIST BATHING
See PREMIER BATHS INC

GAINSCO AUTO INSURANCE
See GAINSCO INC

D-U-N-S 03-790-2590
▲ GAINSCO INC
GAINSCO AUTO INSURANCE
3333 Lee Pkwy Ste 1200, Dallas, TX 75219-5134
Tel (972) 629-4301 *Founded/Ownrshp* 1978
Sales NA *EMP* 395^E
Tkr Sym GANS *Exch* OTO
SIC 6331 Fire, marine & casualty insurance & carriers; Property damage insurance; Fire, marine & casualty insurance & carriers; Property damage insurance
V Ch Bd: James R Reis
**Ch Bd:* Robert W Stallings
Pr: Glenn Anderson
Pr: McRae B Johnston
COO: Andre Zuniga
CFO: Daniel Coots
Sr VP: Richard M Buxton
Sr VP: Wade Chance
Sr VP: Stephen L Porcelli
Sr VP: Carolyn E Ray
VP: Don Baker
VP: Greg Castleman
VP: Danny Earnest
Exec: Tracy Davis
Board of Directors: Robert J Boulware, John C Goff, Joel C Puckett, Sam Rosen, Harden H Wiedemann, John H Williams

D-U-N-S 88-479-8377
GAINSPAN CORP
3590 N 1st St Ste 300, San Jose, CA 95134-1812
Tel (408) 627-6500 *Founded/Ownrshp* 2006
Sales 33.2MM^E *EMP* 100
SIC 3674 Semiconductors & related devices; Semiconductors & related devices
CEO: Gregory Alan Winner
Pr: Thai Nguyen
Pr: Nguyen Thai
**Pr:* Greg Winner
**CFO:* Dennis Wittman
VP: David Casey
VP: Pankaj Vyas
Off Mgr: Michele Yano
QA Dir: Teley Yu
Tech Mgr: Qiang Lin
Web Dev: Ian Swan
Board of Directors: Ravi Subramanian

GAITHERSBURG EQUIPMENT COMPANY
See GAITHERSBURG FARMERS SUPPLY INC

D-U-N-S 02-259-5490 IMP/EXP
GAITHERSBURG FARMERS SUPPLY INC
GAITHERSBURG EQUIPMENT COMPANY
700 E Diamond Ave, Gaithersburg, MD 20877-3065
Tel (301) 670-9300 *Founded/Ownrshp* 1945
Sales 49.0MM *EMP* 75^E
Accts Burdette Smith & Bish Llc Fai
SIC 5999 Farm tractors; Farm tractors
Pr: David E Rippeon
**Treas:* Betsy Jeanne Rippeon
**VP:* James W Jacobs Jr
Sls Mgr: Bill Lind
Sls Mgr: Jonathan Rippeon
Sales Asso: Bill Lindner

D-U-N-S 15-720-2953
GAJESKE INC
6200 N Houston Rosslyn Rd, Houston, TX 77091-3410
Tel (713) 688-2728 *Founded/Ownrshp* 1986
Sales 29.8MM^E *EMP* 70
SIC 5074

D-U-N-S 00-201-7531 IMP/EXP
GAL MANUFACTURING CORP
50 E 153rd St, Bronx, NY 10451-2104
Tel (718) 292-9000 *Founded/Ownrshp* 1927
Sales 52.5MM^E *EMP* 330^E
SIC 3534

D-U-N-S 06-724-7072
GAL-TEX HOTEL CORP
1859 HISTORIC HOTELS
2322 Mac Davis Ln, Lubbock, TX 79401-2219
Tel (888) 776-7001 *Founded/Ownrshp* 1940
Sales 79.0MM *EMP* 1,953
SIC 7011 8741

GALA FRUIT
See TROPICAL FRUIT TRADING INC

D-U-N-S 00-311-7470 IMP/EXP
GALA INDUSTRIES INC (VA)
181 Pauley St, Eagle Rock, VA 24085-3602
Tel (540) 884-2589 *Founded/Ownrshp* 1959
Sales 44.1MM^E *EMP* 240
SIC 3559

GALACTIC COMMUNICATIONS
See VERGE MOBILE LLC

D-U-N-S 07-973-0360
GALACTIC PERFORMANCE SOLUTIONS LLC
1903 Stadium Oaks Ct, Arlington, TX 76011-7801
Tel (817) 275-8611 *Founded/Ownrshp* 2013
Sales 30.0MM *EMP* 42
SIC 8742 Incentive or award program consultant
Pr: Daniel Mohorc
COO: Gary Cornwell
CFO: William Faist

D-U-N-S 00-963-9436
GALARDI GROUP INC
7700 Irvine Center Dr # 550, Irvine, CA 92618-3036
Tel (949) 892-2699 *Founded/Ownrshp* 1961
Sales 31.4MM^E *EMP* 50
SIC 6794 Franchises, selling or licensing
CEO: Cindy Culpepper
**Pr:* Dennis Tase
**CFO:* William Wagstaff

D-U-N-S 96-898-1795
GALASSO MATERIALS LLC
60 S Main St, East Granby, CT 06026-9550
Tel (860) 527-1825 *Founded/Ownrshp* 1997
Sales 35.2MM^E *EMP* 160
SIC 1499 1429 1442 Asphalt mining & bituminous stone quarrying; Grits mining (crushed stone); Construction sand & gravel; Asphalt mining & bituminous stone quarrying; Grits mining (crushed stone); Construction sand & gravel
IT Man: Collin McAvoy
Mtls Mgr: J Elorita
Sls&Mrk Ex: Mike Mogensen
Sls Mgr: Michael Mogensen

GALASSO TRUCKING & RIGGING
See GALASSO TRUCKING INC

D-U-N-S 00-887-3622
GALASSO TRUCKING INC (NY)
GALASSO TRUCKING & RIGGING
2 Galasso Pl, Maspeth, NY 11378-2010
Tel (718) 456-1800 *Founded/Ownrshp* 1947
Sales 25.5MM^E *EMP* 100
SIC 4212 Local trucking, without storage
Ch Bd: Frank Galasso
Pr: Robert Henrichs
Opers Supe: Lou Galasso
VP Sls: Richard Kaye
Snr Mgr: Brent Graham

D-U-N-S 04-434-7771
GALASSOS BAKERY
10820 San Sevaine Way, Mira Loma, CA 91752-1116
Tel (951) 360-1211 *Founded/Ownrshp* 1923
Sales 119.4MM^E *EMP* 300
SIC 2051 Bakery: wholesale or wholesale/retail combined; Bakery: wholesale or wholesale/retail combined
Pr: Jeannette Galasso
CFO: Ken Hutchinson
**Treas:* Mark Bailey
**VP:* Rick Vargas
IT Man: Ashish Dhawan
Ql Cn Mgr: Paul Chelala
Sls Mgr: Sean Belger
Snr Mgr: George Madrigal

D-U-N-S 96-275-1967
GALATA CHEMICALS HOLDING CO LLC
464 Heritage Rd Ste 1, Southbury, CT 06488-3863
Tel (203) 236-9000 *Founded/Ownrshp* 2010
Sales 200.0MM *EMP* 120
SIC 5169 6719 Industrial chemicals; Personal holding companies, except banks; Industrial chemicals; Personal holding companies, except banks
Pr: Steven McKeown
**CEO:* Erick Wisnefsky
**CFO:* Joseph Falsbury
**Treas:* Matthew Yopchick

D-U-N-S 96-275-3716 IMP
GALATA CHEMICALS LLC
(*Suby of* ARTEK SURFIN CHEMICALS LIMITED)
464 Heritage Rd Ste A1, Southbury, CT 06488-3863
Tel (203) 236-9000 *Founded/Ownrshp* 2014
Sales 149.8MM^E *EMP* 100
SIC 5169 Organic chemicals, synthetic; Organic chemicals, synthetic
CEO: Luc De Temmerma
**Pr:* Steven McKeown
**CFO:* Joseph Falsbury
CFO: Joe Salsbury
Treas: Matthew Yopchick

D-U-N-S 08-193-9167
GALATI YACHT SALES LLC
900 S Bay Blvd, Anna Maria, FL 34216
Tel (941) 778-0755 *Founded/Ownrshp* 1976
Sales 75.6MM^E *EMP* 175
SIC 5551 4493 Boat dealers; Marine supplies & equipment; Marinas; Boat dealers; Marine supplies & equipment; Marinas
CFO: Mike Eissert
Dir IT: Chris Burkett
Mktg Dir: Randy Bright
Sales Asso: Chris Carrere
Sales Asso: Steve Gilliam
Sales Asso: Lee Hutton
Sales Asso: Alex Matheson
Sales Asso: Bill McCormick

D-U-N-S 02-659-4077
GALATIAN INC
FOODLAND SUPER MARKET
10420 Eastex Fwy, Houston, TX 77093-4904
Tel (713) 697-2904 *Founded/Ownrshp* 1967
Sales 26.0MM *EMP* 250
SIC 5411 5651 Grocery stores, independent; Family clothing stores; Grocery stores, independent; Family clothing stores
Pr: Richard H Galatian
**Sec:* Barbara Galatian
**VP:* Hugh Taylor

D-U-N-S 96-174-1498
GALAXESOLUTIONS INC
2 Executive Dr Ste 430, Somerset, NJ 08873-4003
Tel (732) 868-0400 *Founded/Ownrshp* 2002
Sales 67.6MM^E *EMP* 300^E
SIC 7379 Computer related consulting services; Computer related consulting services
CEO: Timothy M Bryan
**Pr:* Sandipan Gangopadhyay
**CFO:* Steve Weiss
**Ex VP:* Dheeraj Misra
Sr VP: George Ringel
**VP:* Tore Carlson
**VP:* Jim Dietrich
VP: Brett Kerbel
VP: Suresh Pande
QA Dir: Shiv Mallela
Dir IT: Venkata Nanduri

D-U-N-S 15-526-6372 IMP
GALAXIE CORP
5170 Galaxie Dr, Jackson, MS 39206-4308
Tel (601) 366-8413 *Founded/Ownrshp* 1990
Sales 35.7MM^E *EMP* 424
SIC 2911 6141 Asphalt or asphaltic materials, made in refineries; Oils, fuel; Jet fuels; Naphtha; Licensed loan companies, small; Asphalt or asphaltic materials, made in refineries; Oils, fuel; Jet fuels; Naphtha; Licensed loan companies, small
Pr: Matthew L Holleman III
**Treas:* Dan M Swain Jr

D-U-N-S 15-764-9497
GALAXY ASSOCIATES INC
(*Suby of* DUBOIS CHEMICALS INC) ★
3630 E Kemper Rd, Cincinnati, OH 45241-2011
Tel (513) 731-6350 *Founded/Ownrshp* 2012
Sales 28.8MM^E *EMP* 103
SIC 5169 Industrial chemicals; Industrial chemicals
Pr: William D Oeters
**CFO:* Philip P Dober
**CFO:* Shawn Garver
VP: Edward Rieskamp
VP Sls: Timothy Scarbrough
VP Sls: Scarbrough Timothy
Snr Mgr: Shawn McCall

D-U-N-S 61-484-2680 IMP
GALAXY BALLOONS INC
11750 Berea Rd Ste 3, Cleveland, OH 44111-1603
Tel (216) 476-3360 *Founded/Ownrshp* 1990
Sales 21.9MM^E *EMP* 130
SIC 2752 7336 5092 5199 3993 3949 Commercial printing, offset; Silk screen design; Balloons, novelty; Advertising specialties; Signs & advertising specialties; Sporting & athletic goods; Commercial printing, offset; Silk screen design; Balloons, novelty; Advertising specialties; Signs & advertising specialties; Sporting & athletic goods
Pr: Terry Brizz
Genl Mgr: Nellie Elwell
Sls&Mrk Ex: Jason Broadbent
Mktg Mgr: Chelsea Morris

D-U-N-S 16-732-8095 IMP
GALAXY DESSERTS
(*Suby of* BRIOCHE PASQUIER CERQUEUX)
1100 Marina Way S Ste D, Richmond, CA 94804-3727
Tel (510) 439-3160 *Founded/Ownrshp* 2012
Sales 42.0MM^E *EMP* 160
SIC 2053 Frozen bakery products, except bread; Frozen bakery products, except bread
CEO: Paul Levitan
**VP:* Jean-Yves Charon
IT Man: John Mitchell
Sales Exec: Laure Chatard
Sls Dir: Lisa Weaver
Sls Mgr: Jonathan Kenyon

GALAXY FANS & HEATERS
See LASKO PRODUCTS INC

D-U-N-S 08-396-5152 IMP/EXP
GALAXY NUTRITIONAL FOODS INC (DE)
66 Whitecap Dr, North Kingstown, RI 02852-7445
Tel (401) 667-5000 *Founded/Ownrshp* 1972, 2009
Sales 23.0MM^E *EMP* 21
Accts Khan Litwin Renza & Co Ltd
SIC 2022 Cheese, natural & processed; Cheese, natural & processed
CEO: Brian O'Farrell
Ch Bd: Rick Antonelli
VP: Jerry Scwartz
VP: Whitney Velasco-Azmar
Sls Dir: Sabrina Mak
Sls Mgr: Kim Ferentinos
Sls Mgr: Perry Heiner
Sls Mgr: Brian Keever

D-U-N-S 88-405-6631
GALAXY NYACK INC
ROCKLAND TOYOTA
618 Route 303, Blauvelt, NY 10913-1170
Tel (845) 358-2220 *Founded/Ownrshp* 1999
Sales 22.9MM^E *EMP* 53
SIC 5511 Automobiles, new & used; Automobiles, new & used
Ch Bd: Neale Kuperman
**CEO:* Anthony March
Sls Dir: Frank Caputo
Sls Mgr: Reggie Pierre
Sls Mgr: Jonu Sam
Sales Asso: Ana Collado
Sales Asso: Fitz Crooks
Sales Asso: Alberto Guzman
Sales Asso: Earl Hernandez
Sales Asso: Jeff Leon
Sales Asso: Francisco Marquez

D-U-N-S 95-905-0675 EXP
GALAXY RECYCLING INC
3 New York Ave, Jersey City, NJ 07307-1340
Tel (201) 420-4321 *Founded/Ownrshp* 1996
Sales 39.8MM^E *EMP* 185
SIC 4953 Recycling, waste materials; Recycling, waste materials
Pr: Gary Giordano

D-U-N-S 13-072-0824 IMP
GALAXY TECHNOLOGIES INC
1111 Industrial Blvd, Winfield, KS 67156-9133
Tel (620) 221-6262 *Founded/Ownrshp* 1985
Sales 30.0MM *EMP* 200
SIC 3549 Wiredrawing & fabricating machinery & equipment, ex. die; Wiredrawing & fabricating machinery & equipment, ex. die
Pr: John Boyington Jr
**Ch Bd:* Jim Schuster
Sr VP: Paul Maples
VP: David Nissen
VP: Gary Samms
Prgrm Mgr: Michael Cave
Prgrm Mgr: Tim Hoover
Prgrm Mgr: April Morris
IT Man: Jerry Bolack
IT Man: Jamie Seahorn
Plnt Mgr: Mike Kelly

D-U-N-S 05-220-1209
GALAXY TOYOTA (NJ)
BOB CIASULLI II
750 State Route 36, Eatontown, NJ 07724-2522
Tel (732) 544-1000 *Founded/Ownrshp* 1970
Sales 22.8MM^E *EMP* 70
SIC 5511 7538 5521 Automobiles, new & used; General automotive repair shops; Used car dealers; Automobiles, new & used; General automotive repair shops; Used car dealers
Pr: Robert Ciasulli Jr
Genl Mgr: Patti Schneider
Sls Mgr: Michael Defilippis
Sls Mgr: Dave Mitchell
Sales Asso: Adam Iorlano
Sales Asso: Stephen Kokenge

D-U-N-S 00-517-5237 IMP
GALBREATH LLC (IN)
(*Suby of* WASTEQUIP LLC) ★
480 E 150 S, Winamac, IN 46996-7768
Tel (574) 946-6631 *Founded/Ownrshp* 1947

Sales 38.7MM^E *EMP* 200^E
SIC 3443 3523 Industrial vessels, tanks & containers; Planting, haying, harvesting & processing machinery; Industrial vessels, tanks & containers; Planting, haying, harvesting & processing machinery
VP: Keven Crawford
VP: Richard Garcia
Genl Mgr: Warren Cole

GALCO BUILDING PRODUCTS
See SPENARD BUILDERS SUPPLY LLC

D-U-N-S 01-086-9477 EXP
GALCO INDUSTRIAL ELECTRONICS INC
(*Suby of* GII HOLDING III CORP)
26010 Pinehurst Dr, Madison Heights, MI 48071-4189
Tel (248) 542-9090 *Founded/Ownrshp* 2014
Sales 107.1MM^E *EMP* 122^E
SIC 5065 Electronic parts; Electronic parts
Pr: Michael Conwell
CFO: Karen Mandarino
IT Man: David Gardner
IT Man: Yoom Nguyen
Sales Exec: Mark Higdon
Sales Exec: Steve Misiakowski
Sls Dir: Peter Maurer
Sales Asso: Carolyn Morrison

D-U-N-S 04-735-0186 IMP/EXP
GALDERMA LABORATORIES LP
(*Suby of* GALDERMA PHARMA S.A.)
14501 North Fwy, Fort Worth, TX 76177-3304
Tel (817) 961-5000 *Founded/Ownrshp* 1981
Sales 147.5MM^E *EMP* 499
SIC 2834 Dermatologicals; Dermatologicals
Pr: Todd Zavodnick
CFO: Mark Ponce
Sr VP: Phil Brown
Sr VP: Philip Brown
Sr VP: Ken Ferrell
VP: Quintin Cassady
VP: Brian Foard
VP: Miles Harrison
VP: Kelly Huang
VP: Safia Rizvi
VP: Carol Stuckley
Exec: Donna Brunson
Exec: Kathy Gray
Assoc Dir: Bill Little
Dir: Melissa Oneal

D-U-N-S 06-515-1979
GALE ASSOCIATES INC
163 Libbey Indstrl Pkwy, Weymouth, MA 02189-3136
Tel (781) 335-6465 *Founded/Ownrshp* 1964
Sales 20.1MM^E *EMP* 124
SIC 8711 8713 8712 8748 Engineering services; Surveying services; Architectural services; Environmental consultant; Engineering services; Surveying services; Architectural services; Environmental consultant
Pr: Jon F Lindberg
**Treas:* Edward J Madden
IT Man: Chris Foley

D-U-N-S 04-404-3958 IMP
GALE BANKS ENGINEERING (CA)
BANKS POWER PRODUCTS
546 S Duggan Ave, Azusa, CA 91702-5136
Tel (626) 969-9600 *Founded/Ownrshp* 1970
Sales 73.6MM^E *EMP* 195
SIC 3519 3714 Parts & accessories, internal combustion engines; Motor vehicle parts & accessories; Parts & accessories, internal combustion engines; Motor vehicle parts & accessories
Pr: Gale C Banks III
**VP:* Vicki L Banks

GALE FORCE HOLDINGS
See GALE FORCE SPORTS AND ENTERTAINMENT LLC

D-U-N-S 12-701-4558
GALE FORCE SPORTS AND ENTERTAINMENT LLC
GALE FORCE HOLDINGS
1400 Edwards Mill Rd, Raleigh, NC 27607-3624
Tel (919) 861-2300 *Founded/Ownrshp* 1998
Sales 35.6MM^E *EMP* 400
SIC 8741 7941 Management services; Stadium event operator services; Management services; Stadium event operator services
IT Man: Patty Hilliard

D-U-N-S 87-924-8201 IMP/EXP
GALE GROUP INC
27500 Drake Rd, Farmington Hills, MI 48331-3535
Tel (248) 699-4253 *Founded/Ownrshp* 2007
Sales NA *EMP* 1,232
SIC 7375 On-line data base information retrieval

D-U-N-S 87-842-3839 IMP
GALE PACIFIC USA INC
GAILE PACIFIC
285 W Central Pkwy # 1704, Altamonte Springs, FL 32714-2533
Tel (407) 774-1322 *Founded/Ownrshp* 1994
Sales 23.1MM^E *EMP* 55
SIC 5039 Prefabricated buildings; Prefabricated buildings
CEO: Peter McDonald
**Pr:* Martin Denney
**Pr:* Donna Galante
**CEO:* Nick Pichard
**VP:* James Douglas White
IT Man: Karen Natale
Mktg Mgr: Patrick Lane

D-U-N-S 00-188-4899
GALEANA CHRYSLER JEEP INC
14375 S Tamiami Trl, Fort Myers, FL 33912-1943
Tel (239) 481-2600 *Founded/Ownrshp* 1981
Sales 43.0MM^E *EMP* 125^E
SIC 5511 5521 Automobiles, new & used; Used car dealers; Automobiles, new & used; Used car dealers
Pr: Carl Galeana
**VP:* Frank Galeana
Genl Mgr: Leon Mudry
IT Man: Donald Griffen

D-U-N-S 03-740-2906
GALEANA CHRYSLER JEEP INC
GALEANA KIA
(*Suby of* GALEANAS DODGE) ★
180 Greystone Blvd, Columbia, SC 29210-8003
Tel (803) 779-7300 *Founded/Ownrshp* 1988
Sales 51.4MM^E *EMP* 99
SIC 5511 Automobiles, new & used; Automobiles, new & used
Pr: Carl Galeana
**VP:* Frank Galeana Jr
VP Mktg: John Karaniuk
Sls Mgr: John Reit

GALEANA KIA
See GALEANA CHRYSLER JEEP INC

GALEANA'S DODGE
See VAN DYKE DODGE INC

GALEN COLLEGE
See GALEN HEALTH INSTITUTES INC

D-U-N-S 00-890-3122
GALEN E WILSON PETROLEUM CO (MI)
3057 Davenport Ave, Saginaw, MI 48602-3652
Tel (989) 793-2181 *Founded/Ownrshp* 1947
Sales 54.1MM^E *EMP* 220
SIC 5541 5172 Filling stations, gasoline; Gasoline; Fuel oil; Filling stations, gasoline; Gasoline; Fuel oil
Pr: Tim Corrigan

D-U-N-S 87-712-2994
GALEN HEALTH INSTITUTES INC
GALEN COLLEGE
1031 Zorn Ave Ste 400, Louisville, KY 40207-1064
Tel (502) 410-6200 *Founded/Ownrshp* 2004
Sales 17.9MM^E *EMP* 500
SIC 8249 Practical nursing school; Practical nursing school
Pr: Mark A Vogt
Ofcr: Steve Wilson
VP: Audria Denker
**VP:* Steve Diamond
**VP:* Tom Dwyer
**VP:* Steve Hyndman
**VP:* Joseph R Peters
**VP:* David Ray
CTO: Tonya Belknap
Dir IT: Duane Hellums
Netwrk Mgr: Michael Lyster

D-U-N-S 07-663-0060
GALEN HOSPITAL ALASKA INC
ALASKA REGIONAL HOSPITAL
2801 Debarr Rd, Anchorage, AK 99508-2932
Tel (907) 276-1131 *Founded/Ownrshp* 1995
Sales NA *EMP* 800
SIC 8062 General medical & surgical hospitals; General medical & surgical hospitals
CEO: Julie Taylor
Chf Rad: Lawrence Wood
**Pr:* Samuel N Hazen
**Pr:* Ernie Meier
**CEO:* Annie Holt
**COO:* Rick Davis
COO: Vic Rosenbaum
**COO:* Victor Rosenbaum
**CFO:* Lynn Kennington
CFO: Paul Morris
Chf Mktg O: William Compton
Exec: Marilyn Cooper
Exec: Elaine Mello
Dir Risk M: Rosemary Craig
Dir Lab: Karen Lakey

D-U-N-S 01-038-3909
■ **GALEN OF FLORIDA INC**
ST. PETERSBURG GENERAL HOSP
(*Suby of* HCA INC) ★
6500 38th Ave N, Saint Petersburg, FL 33710-1629
Tel (727) 341-4055 *Founded/Ownrshp* 1967
Sales 95.5MM *EMP* 600
SIC 8062 General medical & surgical hospitals; General medical & surgical hospitals
CEO: Robert B Conroy Jr
**COO:* Jack Bovender
**CFO:* Shawn Gregory
**CFO:* Stephanie McNulty
Trst: Wayne Garcia
**VP:* Ronald L Grubbs
Dir Rad: Joyce Hopkins
Opers Mgr: Valerie Jaeger
Doctor: Robert Abady
Doctor: Abraham I Awwad
Doctor: Romeo Acosta

D-U-N-S 55-689-6306
GALEN PARTNERS LLC
GALEN PARTNERS LTD I
680 Washington Blvd Fl 11, Stamford, CT 06901-3727
Tel (203) 978-0326 *Founded/Ownrshp* 1990
Sales 34.9MM^E *EMP* 186
SIC 6722 Management investment, open-end; Management investment, open-end
**Pt:* Toby Wesson
**Pt:* L John Wilkerson
CFO: Stacey Bauer
CFO: Srini Conjeevaram
**Ex VP:* William Grant
VP: Paula Semelmacher

GALEN PARTNERS LTD I
See GALEN PARTNERS LLC

D-U-N-S 15-090-8994
GALENA ASSOCIATES LLC
VALVOLINE INSTANT OIL CHANGE
25 Main St Fl 4, Hartford, CT 06106-1896
Tel (860) 244-9310 *Founded/Ownrshp* 1996
Sales 20.1MM^E *EMP* 320
SIC 7549 Automotive maintenance services; Automotive maintenance services

GALENA MINE
See US SILVER - IDAHO INC

GALENA MINE DIVISION
See CALLAHAN MINING CORP

D-U-N-S 09-934-8088
■ **GALENCARE INC**
COLUMBIA HCA
(*Suby of* HCA INC) ★
119 Oakfield Dr, Brandon, FL 33511-5779
Tel (813) 681-5551 *Founded/Ownrshp* 1993
Sales 358.4MM *EMP* 1,300
SIC 8062 General medical & surgical hospitals; General medical & surgical hospitals
Pr: Samuel N Hazen
**CEO:* Bland Eng
**COO:* Janice Balzano
COO: Hal Muetzel
**CFO:* Michael Terrell
**Sec:* David G Anderson
**Sr VP:* Robert T Waterman
**VP:* David Park
**VP:* Donald W Stinnett
Dir Risk M: Misty Milling
Dir Lab: Keith Pautler
Dir Rad: Gary Litvin

GALERIE AU CHOCOLAT
See ROSS ACQUISITION CO

D-U-N-S 03-182-4600
GALESBURG CO-OPERATIVE ELEVATOR CO
105 Dakota Ave W, Galesburg, ND 58035
Tel (701) 488-2216 *Founded/Ownrshp* 1917
Sales 37.5MM *EMP* 12
Accts Erickson And Associates Ltd
SIC 5153 5191 Grain elevators; Chemicals, agricultural; Grain elevators; Chemicals, agricultural
Pr: Tom Boeka
**Sec:* Rick Halvorson
**VP:* Maynard Satrom

GALESBURG COTTAGE HOSPITAL
See GALESBURG HOSPITAL CORP

D-U-N-S 04-913-0859
■ **GALESBURG HOSPITAL CORP**
GALESBURG COTTAGE HOSPITAL
(*Suby of* COMMUNITY HEALTH SYSTEMS INC) ★
695 N Kellogg St, Galesburg, IL 61401-2807
Tel (309) 343-8131 *Founded/Ownrshp* 2004
Sales 949.9M *EMP* 820
SIC 8062 General medical & surgical hospitals; General medical & surgical hospitals
Pr: Kenneth Hutchenrider
**Pr:* Martin G Schweinhart
**CFO:* Michael Johnson
**CFO:* Earl Tamar
Dir Lab: John Belleville
Dir Rad: Patrick Engelhaupt
Dir Sec: Blain Piersee
Dir IT: Grant Morris
Mtls Mgr: John Anderson
Pharmcst: Brad Buchen
Snr Mgr: Roni Benson

D-U-N-S 02-548-6721
GALESBURG ORDER BUYERS INC
GRAINSTORE ELEVATORS
538 Louisville Rd, Galesburg, IL 61401-5865
Tel (309) 342-2112 *Founded/Ownrshp* 1985
Sales 30.0MM *EMP* 23
SIC 5153 5191 Grains; Feed; Grains; Feed
Ch Bd: Martin Anderson
**Sec:* Lisa Nelson
**VP:* Randall Anderson

GALESI GROUP
See ROTTERDAM VENTURES INC

D-U-N-S 18-793-9343
GALETTO REALTY CO LP
317 W Elmer Rd, Vineland, NJ 08360-6311
Tel (856) 692-8098 *Founded/Ownrshp* 1980
Sales 35.9MM *EMP* 30
Accts Schad & Schad Vineland Nj
SIC 6512 1611 Nonresidential building operators; General contractor, highway & street construction; Nonresidential building operators; General contractor, highway & street construction
Pr: Peter Galetto Jr
**Sec:* F Mark D'Onofrio
**Ex VP:* Russell Kadlac
**Ex VP:* Albert Rochetti
Snr PM: Rob Yood

D-U-N-S 36-180-2593 IMP/EXP
GALEY & LORD INDUSTRIES LLC
(*Suby of* GALEY & LORD LLC) ★
670 N Main St, Society Hill, SC 29593-8502
Tel (843) 378-4511 *Founded/Ownrshp* 2004
Sales 28.0MM^E *EMP* 175^E
SIC 2211 Broadwoven fabric mills, cotton
CEO: Kevin Nisbet
**CFO:* Kaustubh Desphande

D-U-N-S 17-471-6394 IMP/EXP
GALEY & LORD LLC
(*Suby of* PATRIARCH PARTNERS LLC) ★
670 N Main St, Society Hill, SC 29593-8502
Tel (843) 378-4511 *Founded/Ownrshp* 2003
Sales 292.9MM^E *EMP* 1,275
SIC 2211 2221 2325 2339 Broadwoven fabric mills, cotton; Broadwoven fabric mills, manmade; Polyester broadwoven fabrics; Men's & boys' dress slacks & shorts; Shorts (outerwear): women's, misses' & juniors'; Broadwoven fabric mills, cotton; Denims; Broadwoven fabric mills, manmade; Polyester broadwoven fabrics; Men's & boys' dress slacks & shorts; Shorts (outerwear): women's, misses' & juniors'
CEO: John Heldrich
IT Man: Charles Puett
Ql Cn Mgr: Kaye Hutchinson

D-U-N-S 78-741-1552
GALFAB ACQUISITION LLC
(*Suby of* WASTEBUILT ENVIRONMENTAL SOLUTIONS LLC) ★
612 W 11th St, Winamac, IN 46996-1211
Tel (574) 946-7767 *Founded/Ownrshp* 2013
Sales 22.9MM^E *EMP* 60
SIC 3537 3443 3536 3531 Industrial trucks & tractors; Dumpsters, garbage; Hoists, cranes & monorails; Construction machinery
CEO: Greg Podell
**VP:* Jerry Samson
Sls Mgr: Jeff Hadley

D-U-N-S 80-909-0756
GALI SERVICE INDUSTRIES INC
12312 Wilkins Ave Ste 100, Rockville, MD 20852-1815
Tel (301) 986-8890 *Founded/Ownrshp* 1989
Sales 45.8MM^E *EMP* 1,350
SIC 7349 Cleaning service, industrial or commercial; Cleaning service, industrial or commercial
CEO: Francisco Gali
**Pr:* Leroy Dock
**CFO:* Mark Terenzi

D-U-N-S 80-952-9469
GALIL MEDICAL INC
(*Suby of* GALIL MEDICAL LTD)
4364 Round Lake Rd W, Arden Hills, MN 55112-3923
Tel (651) 287-5000 *Founded/Ownrshp* 2005
Sales 25.0MM^E *EMP* 94
SIC 3841 Surgical & medical instruments
Pr: Martin J Emerson
**CFO:* Elissa Lindsoe
**VP:* Bill Jacqmein
VP: Trevor Minnie
**VP:* Roy Richard
**VP:* Andy Swanson
IT Man: Ken Downie
Ql Cn Mgr: Huong Tran
Sls Mgr: Devaul Lanier

D-U-N-S 09-449-3459
GALION CITY SCHOOL DISTRICT
470 Portland Way N, Galion, OH 44833-1115
Tel (419) 468-3432 *Founded/Ownrshp* 1900
Sales 27.0MM^E *EMP* 470
SIC 8211 9411 Public elementary & secondary schools; School board; Administration of educational programs; Public elementary & secondary schools; School board; Administration of educational programs
**Treas:* Julie Henke
Treas: Charlene Parkinson

D-U-N-S 07-454-7175
GALION COMMUNITY HOSPITAL
269 Portland Way S, Galion, OH 44833-2399
Tel (419) 468-4841 *Founded/Ownrshp* 1954
Sales 127.7MM *EMP* 465
Accts Plante & Moran Pllc Columbus
SIC 8062 8051 General medical & surgical hospitals; Skilled nursing care facilities; General medical & surgical hospitals; Skilled nursing care facilities
Pr: Lamar Wyse
COO: Andrew Daniels
**CFO:* Robert Melaragno
VP: Eric Draime
Dir Inf Cn: Joyce Weaver
Off Mgr: Rhonda Ridenouer
Obsttrcn: Eric Hoff

D-U-N-S 87-926-8423
GALION LLC
515 N East St, Galion, OH 44833-2142
Tel (419) 468-5214 *Founded/Ownrshp* 2003
Sales 51.0MM^E *EMP* 105
SIC 3482 3444 Small arms ammunition; Sheet metalwork
CEO: Richard Voorde

D-U-N-S 02-936-3876
GALLADE CHEMICAL INC
1230 E Saint Gertrude Pl, Santa Ana, CA 92707-3094
Tel (714) 546-9901 *Founded/Ownrshp* 1964
Sales 32.6MM^E *EMP* 70
SIC 5169

GALLAGER BASSETT SERVICES
See RISK PLACEMENT SERVICES INC

D-U-N-S 09-552-8923
GALLAGER BUICK G M C INC
325 Columbus Blvd, New Britain, CT 06051-3102
Tel (860) 229-4881 *Founded/Ownrshp* 1978
Sales 21.2MM^E *EMP* 47
SIC 5511 7532 7538 5521 Automobiles, new & used; Pickups, new & used; Exterior repair services; General automotive repair shops; Used car dealers; Automobiles, new & used; Pickups, new & used; Exterior repair services; General automotive repair shops; Used car dealers
Pr: James T Gallagher III
Store Mgr: Paul Marshall
Sls Mgr: Brian Begin
Sls Mgr: Mackey Harris
Sales Asso: Fred Strasser

GALLAGHER & ASSOCIATES
See RJF AGENCIES INC

GALLAGHER & BURK
See OLIVER DE SILVA INC

D-U-N-S 80-398-6343
GALLAGHER AND KENNEDY PA
2575 E Camelback Rd # 810, Phoenix, AZ 85016-9279
Tel (602) 530-8000 *Founded/Ownrshp* 2007
Sales 20.5MM^E *EMP* 200
SIC 8111 Legal services; Legal services
Prin: Kevin Omalley

GALLAGHER BASSETT INSUR SVCS
See GALLAGHER BASSETT SERVICES INC

D-U-N-S 14-752-5224
■ **GALLAGHER BASSETT SERVICES INC**
GALLAGHER BASSETT INSUR SVCS
(*Suby of* ARTHUR J GALLAGHER & CO) ★
2 Pierce Pl Ste 100, Itasca, IL 60143-1277
Tel (630) 773-3800 *Founded/Ownrshp* 1985
Sales NA *EMP* 3,400
SIC 6411 8741 Insurance agents & brokers; Business management; Insurance agents & brokers; Business management
Pr: Scott R Hudson

Pr: Jeanne Fryman
**Treas:* Jack Lazzaro
Treas: Mark Strauch
Sr Cor Off: Jon Wawrzyniak
**Chf Mktg O:* Dave Gordon
Ofcr: Gary R Fansler
Ex VP: Joe Tixier
Sr VP: Gary Anderberg
Sr VP: Michael Bell
Sr VP: Carrie Cannataro
Sr VP: David Kocourek
Sr VP: Ajay Sinha
Sr VP: Srivatsan Sridharan
Sr VP: Steve Stegall
VP: Thomas Barnes
VP: James Braniff
VP: Michael Creighton
VP: Arthur Gallagher
**VP:* J Patrick Gallagher Jr
VP: Rex W Martin

D-U-N-S 00-134-9914
■ GALLAGHER BENEFIT SERVICES INC
(*Suby of* ARTHUR J GALLAGHER & CO) ★
2 Tw Pierce Pl, Itasca, IL 60143
Tel (630) 773-3800 *Founded/Ownrshp* 1999
Sales NA *EMP* 146
SIC 6411 Insurance agents, brokers & service
Pr: James Durkin
Pr: John Callahan
Pr: Sandie Hord
Pr: Dale Zimmerman
VP: David M Ziegler

D-U-N-S 03-492-3672
GALLAGHER FORD-LINCOLN INC
650 30th St, Elko, NV 89801-4613
Tel (775) 738-3147 *Founded/Ownrshp* 1946
Sales 20.2MM^E^ *EMP* 44
SIC 5511 5531 7538 Automobiles, new & used; Automotive parts; General automotive repair shops
Pr: Mike Gallagher
**Treas:* Tana M Gallagher

D-U-N-S 60-653-2737
■ GALLAGHER HEALTHCARE INSURANCE SERVICES INC
(*Suby of* ARTHUR J GALLAGHER & CO) ★
9821 Katy Fwy Ste 700, Houston, TX 77024-1230
Tel (713) 461-4000 *Founded/Ownrshp* 2001
Sales NA *EMP* 196
SIC 6411 6321 6311 Insurance agents, brokers & service; Accident & health insurance; Life insurance; Insurance agents, brokers & service; Accident & health insurance; Life insurance
Pr: William F Galtney Jr

D-U-N-S 08-483-0751 IMP
GALLAGHER NORTH AMERICA INC
GALLAGHER POWER FENCE
(*Suby of* GALLAGHER GROUP LIMITED)
5005 Nw 41st St, Riverside, MO 64150-7801
Tel (816) 421-2005 *Founded/Ownrshp* 1977
Sales 32.8MM^E^ *EMP* 58
SIC 5039 Wire fence, gates & accessories
Pr: Steven Hoffman
**VP:* Dan Geller
IT Man: Don Steele
Sales Exec: Greg Morrissey
Sales Exec: Don Steale
Sls Mgr: Paul Gordon
Board of Directors: Gallagher North America

GALLAGHER POWER FENCE
See GALLAGHER NORTH AMERICA INC

GALLAGHER PREMIER
See ARTHUR J GALLAGHER RISK MANAGEMENT SERVICES INC

D-U-N-S 00-534-8362 IMP
GALLAGHER-KAISER CORP
777 Chicago Rd Ste 1, Troy, MI 48083-4234
Tel (313) 368-3100 *Founded/Ownrshp* 1952
Sales 69.8MM^E^ *EMP* 150
SIC 3444 1761 3567 3564 Booths, spray: prefabricated sheet metal; Sewing machines & hat & zipper making machinery; Sheet metalwork; Paint baking & drying ovens; Air purification equipment; Dust or fume collecting equipment, industrial; Booths, spray: prefabricated sheet metal; Sheet metalwork; Paint baking & drying ovens; Air purification equipment; Dust or fume collecting equipment, industrial
CEO: Robert S Kaiser
**COO:* Tracy E Roberts
CFO: Mary Hurbert
**CFO:* Kenneth M Krause
CFO: Philip M Rice
VP: Daniel Butkus

D-U-N-S 04-153-3001
GALLAHAN OIL CO INC
2964 W 100 N, Peru, IN 46970-7587
Tel (765) 472-1963 *Founded/Ownrshp* 1946
Sales 29.0MM^E^ *EMP* 115
SIC 5541 5411 5172 Filling stations, gasoline; Convenience stores, independent; Diesel fuel; Gasoline; Fuel oil; Lubricating oils & greases; Filling stations, gasoline; Convenience stores, independent; Diesel fuel; Gasoline; Fuel oil; Lubricating oils & greases
Pr: Ronald D Gallahan
**Treas:* Mary Gallahan
**VP:* Kevin Gallahan

D-U-N-S 10-340-4752
GALLAHER CONSTRUCTION INC
220 Concourse Blvd, Santa Rosa, CA 95403-8210
Tel (707) 535-3200 *Founded/Ownrshp* 1979
Sales 30.0MM *EMP* 50
SIC 1521 6552 New construction, single-family houses; Land subdividers & developers, residential; Land subdividers & developers, commercial; New construction, single-family houses; Land subdividers & developers, residential; Land subdividers & developers, commercial
Pr: William P Gallaher
CFO: Joe Lin

D-U-N-S 00-609-1391
GALLAND HENNING NOPAK INC (WI)
GHN
10179 S 57th St, Franklin, WI 53132-8617
Tel (414) 645-6000 *Founded/Ownrshp* 1889
Sales 23.0MM^E^ *EMP* 75
SIC 3542 3593 3492 Presses: hydraulic & pneumatic, mechanical & manual; Shearing machines, power; Fluid power cylinders, hydraulic or pneumatic; Fluid power valves & hose fittings
Pr: Brian Sternberg
VP: Chris Wolf
VP Opers: Dan Ryan
Prd Mgr: Bob Weil
Manager: Phil Krueger

D-U-N-S 01-202-9245 IMP
GALLANT & WEIN CORP
1120 43rd Rd, Long Island City, NY 11101-6826
Tel (718) 784-5210 *Founded/Ownrshp* 1993
Sales 39.1MM^E^ *EMP* 40
SIC 5063 Wire & cable
Pr: Stuart Gruman
**Sec:* Harold Rosenberg
**VP:* Lori Rosenberg
IT Man: James Wagner
Opers Mgr: Andy Skowronski

GALLANT BELK
See GALLANT-BELK CO (INC)

D-U-N-S 00-894-0660
GALLANT-BELK CO (INC)
GALLANT BELK
3101 N Main St Ste C, Anderson, SC 29621-2766
Tel (864) 225-2511 *Founded/Ownrshp* 1919
Sales 62.0M^E^ *EMP* 300
SIC 5311 Department stores, non-discount
Ch Bd: John M Belk
Board of Directors: Henderson Belk, Irwin Belk, David Belk Gallant, Sarah B Gambrell, Leroy Robinson

D-U-N-S 96-427-0644
GALLATIN COUNTY REST HOME
1221 Durston Rd, Bozeman, MT 59715-2725
Tel (406) 582-3300 *Founded/Ownrshp* 2010
Sales 406.4MM *EMP* 15^E^
SIC 8051 Skilled nursing care facilities; Skilled nursing care facilities
Prin: Vickie West

D-U-N-S 19-322-4649
GALLATIN COUNTY SCHOOL DISTRICT
75 Boardwalk, Warsaw, KY 41095-9375
Tel (859) 567-1820 *Founded/Ownrshp* 1970
Sales 10.2MM^E^ *EMP* 300
SIC 8211 9111 Public elementary & secondary schools; County supervisors' & executives' offices; Public elementary & secondary schools; County supervisors' & executives' offices
MIS Dir: Michelle Lawrence

D-U-N-S 18-231-1621
GALLATIN COUNTY SCHOOL DISTRICT 44
BELGRADE SCHOOLS
312 N Weaver St, Belgrade, MT 59714-3732
Tel (406) 388-6951 *Founded/Ownrshp* 1930
Sales 23.7MM^E^ *EMP* 415
SIC 8211 Public senior high school; Public elementary school; Public senior high school; Public elementary school
**Prin:* Candy Lubansky
Schl Brd P: Lance Voegele

D-U-N-S 04-764-3825
■ GALLATIN RIVER COMMUNICATIONS LLC
CENTURYLINK
(*Suby of* QWEST CORP) ★
200 Enterprise Dr, Pekin, IL 61554-9310
Tel (309) 477-0380 *Founded/Ownrshp* 1998
Sales 31.8MM^E^ *EMP* 175
SIC 4813 Local & long distance telephone communications; Local & long distance telephone communications
CEO: J Stephen Vanderwoude
**Pr:* Fred Mari
**CFO:* Paul H Sunu
Treas: Rick Whitener

GALLAUDET CMNTY INTERPRETING
See GALLAUDET UNIVERSITY

D-U-N-S 00-325-9439 IMP
GALLAUDET UNIVERSITY
GALLAUDET CMNTY INTERPRETING
800 Florida Ave Ne, Washington, DC 20002-3600
Tel (202) 651-5000 *Founded/Ownrshp* 1857
Sales 183.5MM *EMP* 1,200
Accts Grant Thornton Llp New York
SIC 8221 University; University
Pr: Dr T Alan Hurwitz
COO: Stephanie Walden
CFO: Ivey Wallace
Treas: Sarah McMillen
**VP:* Paul Kelly
Exec: Barbara Kelley
Exec: Thomas Martin
Ex Dir: Jean Cibuzar
Off Admin: Matthew Gilbert
CTO: Louis Schwarz
IT Man: Suzy McKenzie
Board of Directors: Gary Aller Nicole Sutliffe

D-U-N-S 09-828-4821 IMP
GALLEGOS MASONRY INC
100 Yacht Club Dr, Wolcott, CO 81655
Tel (970) 926-3737 *Founded/Ownrshp* 1977
Sales 65.8MM^E^ *EMP* 450
SIC 1741 Masonry & other stonework; Masonry & other stonework
CEO: Gery Gallegos
**Pr:* Robert Gallegos
**CEO:* Gary Woodworth
VP: Seth Cole
VP: Kevin Hughey
VP: Randall Olin
Dir IT: Marvin Franklin

IT Man: Richard Hughes
Sfty Dirs: Mike Haller
Mktg Mgr: Courtney Armitage
Sls Mgr: Gary Herr

D-U-N-S 15-364-2020
GALLEGOS SANITATION INC
1941 Heath Pkwy Ste 2, Fort Collins, CO 80524-4792
Tel (970) 484-5556 *Founded/Ownrshp* 1983
Sales 34.6MM^E^ *EMP* 95
SIC 4953 7359 4212 Rubbish collection & disposal; Portable toilet rental; Local trucking, without storage
Pr: Arthur J Gallegos
**Sec:* Rudy Gallegos
**VP:* Gerald E Gallegos
VP: Katie Rodriguez
IT Man: Mark Glorioso
Sfty Mgr: Jeremy Gallegos
Sls Mgr: Levi Gallegos

D-U-N-S 00-796-5346 IMP
GALLEHER CORP (DE)
9303 Greenleaf Ave, Santa Fe Springs, CA 90670-3029
Tel (562) 944-8885 *Founded/Ownrshp* 1937, 2010
Sales 105.4MM^E^ *EMP* 150
SIC 5023 Wood flooring; Wood flooring
CEO: Jeff Hamar
Pr: Derek Hui
CFO: Raymond Iodice
**Sr VP:* Rick Coates
**Sr VP:* Todd Hamar
**VP:* Ray Iodice
VP: Patty Prieto
Dir Bus: Chris Breslin
Dir IT: Rene Peregrina
Mktg Mgr: Genny Rivas
Sales Asso: Ron Cutler

GALLERIA BATH SHOWPLACE
See CASTLE SUPPLY CO INC

D-U-N-S 16-892-0234 IMP
GALLERIA FURNITURE INC
3700 W I 40 Service Rd, Oklahoma City, OK 73108-1044
Tel (405) 942-9222 *Founded/Ownrshp* 2004
Sales 24.0MM^E^ *EMP* 80
SIC 5712 Furniture stores
Pr: Gary D Owens
**Sec:* Terri Owens

D-U-N-S 08-149-4031
GALLERIA LTD
5075 Westheimer Rd # 875, Houston, TX 77056-5643
Tel (713) 621-1907 *Founded/Ownrshp* 1976
Sales 23.5MM^E^ *EMP* 900
SIC 6512 6531 Commercial & industrial building operation; Real estate agents & managers; Commercial & industrial building operation; Real estate agents & managers
Genl Pt: Gerald D Hines
Ltd Pt: Chase Manhattan Bank As Truste
Treas: Savador Puente
VP: Gary Firoz
VP: Francisco Llano

D-U-N-S 03-876-5538 IMP
GALLERIA MARKET LP (CA)
HK MARKET
3250 W Olympic Blvd # 100, Los Angeles, CA 90006-2370
Tel (323) 732-2480 *Founded/Ownrshp* 2000
Sales 24.9MM^E^ *EMP* 160
SIC 5411 Grocery stores, independent; Grocery stores, independent
Genl Pt: Young Jun Kim
Pt: Ik Whan OH
Store Mgr: Sally Park
Telecom Ex: P J Kim
Dir IT: Jun Sohn

GALLERIE II
See C & F ENTERPRISES INC

D-U-N-S 01-955-1050
GALLERY AUTOMOTIVE GROUP LLC
SUZUKI GALLERY
(*Suby of* MARUBENI AUTO & CONSTRUCTION MACHINERY (AMERICA) INC) ★
918 Providence Hwy, Norwood, MA 02062
Tel (877) 201-8871 *Founded/Ownrshp* 2003
Sales 91.3MM^E^ *EMP* 202
SIC 5511 5012 7538 Automobiles, new & used; Automobiles; General automotive repair shops; Automobiles, new & used; Automobiles; General automotive repair shops
Sls Mgr: Frank McLaughlin
Sls Mgr: Kevin Misanko

GALLERY COLLECTION
See PRUDENT PUBLISHING CO INC

GALLERY CUSTOM HOMES
See FIRSTTEXAS HOMES INC

GALLERY FURNITURE
See GALLERY MODEL HOMES INC

D-U-N-S 02-984-1350 IMP/EXP
GALLERY MODEL HOMES INC
GALLERY FURNITURE
6006 North Fwy, Houston, TX 77076-4029
Tel (713) 692-1111 *Founded/Ownrshp* 1981
Sales 71.8MM^E^ *EMP* 400
SIC 5712 Furniture stores; Furniture stores
Pr: James McIngvale
**VP:* Linda L McIngvale
**CIO:* Walter Dunnigan
Sls Mgr: Greg Hopf
Sls Mgr: Steve Salazar

GALLERY OF LIGHTING, THE
See HOLDER ELECTRIC SUPPLY INC

GALLES CHEVROLET
See GALLES MOTOR CO

D-U-N-S 00-697-5320
GALLES MOTOR CO (NM)
GALLES CHEVROLET
1601 Lomas Blvd Ne, Albuquerque, NM 87102-2710
Tel (505) 766-6804 *Founded/Ownrshp* 1908, 1933
Sales 64.4MM^E^ *EMP* 150
SIC 5511 7514 7515 6141 Automobiles, new & used; Pickups, new & used; Vans, new & used; Rent-a-car service; Passenger car leasing; Automobile loans, including insurance; Automobiles, new & used; Pickups, new & used; Vans, new & used; Rent-a-car service; Passenger car leasing; Automobile loans, including insurance
Ch Bd: H L Galles Jr
**Pr:* F R Galles
**Pr:* Rick Galles
**VP:* Jamie Galles
**Genl Mgr:* Joe Ruth

D-U-N-S 00-587-0928
GALLES OLDSMOBILE-CADILLAC CO
GALLES PERFORMANCE PARTS
(*Suby of* GALLES CHEVROLET) ★
1601 Lomas Blvd Ne, Albuquerque, NM 87102-2710
Tel (505) 766-6800 *Founded/Ownrshp* 1908
Sales 33.6MM^E^ *EMP* 190
SIC 5511 7538 7532 5521 Automobiles, new & used; Pickups, new & used; Vans, new & used; General automotive repair shops; Top & body repair & paint shops; Used car dealers; Automobiles, new & used; Pickups, new & used; Vans, new & used; General automotive repair shops; Top & body repair & paint shops; Used car dealers
Pr: F R Galles
COO: Matt Thomas
VP: Michelle Aragetti
Sales Exec: Will Gustafuson
Sales Exec: Bob Pond

GALLES PERFORMANCE PARTS
See GALLES OLDSMOBILE-CADILLAC CO

D-U-N-S 02-933-5809
GALLI PRODUCE CO
1650 Old Bayshore Hwy, San Jose, CA 95112-4304
Tel (408) 436-6100 *Founded/Ownrshp* 1966
Sales 20.3MM^E^ *EMP* 60
SIC 5148 5142 Fruits, fresh; Vegetables, fresh; Fruits, frozen; Vegetables, frozen; Fruits, fresh; Vegetables, fresh; Fruits, frozen; Vegetables, frozen
Pr: Gerald Pieracci
**Sec:* Kristin Killin
**VP:* Jeff Pieracci
**VP:* Dennis Tinucci
**VP:* Joseph Vanni

GALLIA COUNTY COMMISSIONERS
See COUNTY OF GALLIA

D-U-N-S 08-131-9212
GALLIA-JACKSON-VINTON JOINT VOCATIONAL SCHOOL
BUCKEYE HILLS CAREER CENTER
351 Buckeye Hills Rd, Rio Grande, OH 45674
Tel (740) 245-5334 *Founded/Ownrshp* 1973
Sales 8.8MM *EMP* 290^E^
SIC 8211 Public elementary & secondary schools; Public vocational/technical school; Public elementary & secondary schools; Public vocational/technical school
Treas: Donaline Smith
**Treas:* Donalyn Smith

D-U-N-S 06-263-8986
GALLIANO MARINE SERVICE LLC
16201 E Main St, Galliano, LA 70354
Tel (985) 632-7144 *Founded/Ownrshp* 1968
Sales 56.9MM^E^ *EMP* 700
SIC 8741 Management services; Management services
Sec: Ted Smith

D-U-N-S 00-893-6379
GALLIKER DAIRY CO
GALLIKER'S QUALITY CHEKD
143 Donald Ln, Johnstown, PA 15904-2829
Tel (814) 266-8702 *Founded/Ownrshp* 1914
Sales 101.9MM^E^ *EMP* 365
SIC 2026 2086 2024 Buttermilk, cultured; Eggnog, fresh: non-alcoholic; Milk drinks, flavored; Tea, iced: packaged in cans, bottles, etc.; Ice cream & ice milk; Buttermilk, cultured; Eggnog, fresh: non-alcoholic; Milk drinks, flavored; Tea, iced: packaged in cans, bottles, etc.; Ice cream & ice milk
Ch: Louis G Galliker
**Pr:* Charles Price
CFO: Evan Fineman
**Treas:* Douglas B Roberts
VP: Hans Iten
VP: William Livingston
VP: George Pisula
**VP:* Charles D Price
Exec: Wendy Schultz
Dir IT: Wendy Shultz
IT Man: Jim Miller

GALLIKER'S QUALITY CHEKD
See GALLIKER DAIRY CO

D-U-N-S 08-280-1986
GALLINA LLP
925 Highland Pointe Dr # 450, Roseville, CA 95678-5423
Tel (916) 784-7800 *Founded/Ownrshp* 1972
Sales 3.5MM *EMP* 300
Accts Gallina Llp Rancho Cordova C
SIC 8721 Certified public accountant
Mng Pt: Larry Taylor
Pt: Jack Bosley
Pt: William Clark
Pt: Bob Fox
Pt: Robert Fox
Pt: Robert Harrison
Pt: Lisa Hubbart
Pt: Donald Pfluger
Pt: Patrick Piacentini
Pt: Steve Schultz
Pt: Lawrence Taylor

Pt: Edward Traille
CFO: Mary Bradley
Treas: Peggy Simmet

D-U-N-S 07-942-0626
GALLIPOLIS CITY SCHOOL DIST
61 State St, Gallipolis, OH 45631-1185
Tel (740) 446-3211 *Founded/Ownrshp* 1964
Sales 24.3MM^E *EMP* 485
SIC 8211 Elementary & secondary schools; School board; Elementary & secondary schools; School board
Pr: Lynn Angel-Queen
**Treas:* Ellen Marple
Schl Brd P: Robert Cornwall
Schl Brd P: Dann Greene

D-U-N-S 19-557-1419
GALLO CATTLE CO A LIMITED PARTNERSHIP
JOSEPH FARMS CHEESE
10561 State Highway 140, Atwater, CA 95301-9309
Tel (209) 394-7984 *Founded/Ownrshp* 1941
Sales 57.6MM^E *EMP* 500
SIC 0241 2022 Dairy farms; Cheese, natural & processed; Dairy farms; Cheese, natural & processed
CEO: Michael Gallo
Pt: Micah Gallo
Pt: Tiffanie Gallo
Pt: Linda Jelacich
CFO: Marv Bennett
VP: Asadero Cheddar
VP: Tom Nagle
Genl Mgr: Carl Morris

GALLO CLOTHING
See ALKO DISTRIBUTORS INC

D-U-N-S 00-420-3154 IMP/EXP
GALLO DISPLAYS INC
4922 E 49th St, Cleveland, OH 44125-1016
Tel (216) 431-9500 *Founded/Ownrshp* 1928
Sales 33.3MM^E *EMP* 207^E
SIC 2542 3993 Partitions & fixtures, except wood; Signs & advertising specialties; Partitions & fixtures, except wood; Signs & advertising specialties
Pr: Don Lockwood
CFO: Sandy Bellamy
**CFO:* Phil Ridolfi
Exec: Chrissy Adamescu
Dir Soc: Don Szabo
Rgnl Mgr: Kelly Palivec
Sls Mgr: Mike Keefe

D-U-N-S 96-660-1374
GALLO EMPLOYEE BENEFIT TRUST
P.O. Box 1130 (95353-1130)
Tel (209) 341-3024 *Founded/Ownrshp* 2011
Sales NA *EMP* 2^E
SIC 6411 Insurance agents, brokers & service; Insurance agents, brokers & service

D-U-N-S 00-910-7749 IMP
GALLO GLASS CO
(*Suby of* E & J GALLO WINERY) ★
605 S Santa Cruz Ave, Modesto, CA 95354-4299
Tel (209) 341-3710 *Founded/Ownrshp* 1957
Sales 206.0MM^E *EMP* 1,205
SIC 3221 Glass containers; Glass containers
Pr: Robert J Gallo
IT Man: Craig Beck
Opers Mgr: Dean McMeechan
VP Mktg: Jere Johnson
Snr Mgr: Joshua Self

D-U-N-S 11-898-0879
GALLO GROUP LLC
3850 N Causeway Blvd # 1300, Metairie, LA 70002-8158
Tel (504) 944-6736 *Founded/Ownrshp* 1983
Sales 67.3MM^E *EMP* 400
Accts Laporte Apac Metairie La
SIC 1711 1542 Mechanical contractor; Commercial & office building, new construction; Commercial & office buildings, renovation & repair; Mechanical contractor; Commercial & office building, new construction; Commercial & office buildings, renovation & repair

D-U-N-S 03-439-6069
GALLO MECHANICAL LLC
(*Suby of* GALLO GROUP LLC) ★
3850 N Causeway Blvd # 1300, Metairie, LA 70002-8158
Tel (504) 944-6736 *Founded/Ownrshp* 1945
Sales 66.1MM^E *EMP* 150
SIC 1711 Mechanical contractor; Mechanical contractor
CFO: Gene Phauff

D-U-N-S 15-275-9387
GALLO SALES CO INC
(*Suby of* GALLO GLASS CO) ★
30825 Wiegman Rd, Hayward, CA 94544-7893
Tel (510) 476-5000 *Founded/Ownrshp* 1952
Sales 42.1MM^E *EMP* 255
SIC 5182 Beauty shops; Wine
Pr: Joseph E Gallo
VP: Herbert Smith
Dist Mgr: Alexander Bassi
Dist Mgr: Stewart Fine
Dist Mgr: Miriam Hawk
Sales Exec: Mike Sellitti
Sls Mgr: Matthew Ippolito

D-U-N-S 00-253-4451 IMP
GALLO WINE SALES OF NJ INC (NJ)
520 Division St, Elizabeth, NJ 07201-2099
Tel (908) 558-0711 *Founded/Ownrshp* 1947, 1987
Sales 58.2MM^E *EMP* 200
SIC 5182 Wine; Wine
Pr: John Pepe
**Pr:* Joseph Tubertini
**VP:* Nencho Kolev
**VP:* J Waldron
IT Man: Vickie Croad
Sfty Mgr: Drew Murtha

Sls Mgr: Tom Contessa
Sls Mgr: Eddy Rivera

D-U-N-S 16-907-8151
GALLOPING HILL SURGICAL CORP
ALLCARE MEDICAL
(*Suby of* ALLCARE MEDICAL) ★
4470 Bordentown, Sayreville, NJ 08872
Tel (732) 251-8000 *Founded/Ownrshp* 2012
Sales 33.7MM^E *EMP* 130^E
SIC 5999 Medical apparatus & supplies; Medical apparatus & supplies
Pr: Richard Lerner

D-U-N-S 00-612-0513 IMP
GALLOWAY CO
CLASSIC MIX PARTNERS
601 S Commercial St, Neenah, WI 54956-3392
Tel (920) 722-8903 *Founded/Ownrshp* 1938
Sales 40.1MM^E *EMP* 75
SIC 2023 2026 Condensed milk; Ice cream mix, unfrozen: liquid or dry; Milk processing (pasteurizing, homogenizing, bottling); Condensed milk; Ice cream mix, unfrozen: liquid or dry; Milk processing (pasteurizing, homogenizing, bottling)
CEO: Tim Galloway
**Ch Bd:* John R Galloway
**Pr:* Doug Dieterich
Pr: Edwin Galloway
**CFO:* Greg Pollesch
**Treas:* Tod Galloway
VP: Jim Bastian
**VP:* Theodore P Galloway

D-U-N-S 11-905-9124
GALLOWAY GROUP INC
5840 Youngquist Rd Ste 1, Fort Myers, FL 33912-2271
Tel (239) 481-7448 *Founded/Ownrshp* 2002
Sales 22.0MM^E *EMP* 25
SIC 7374 Data processing service; Data processing service
Pr: David O Galloway
**VP:* Robert D Galloway
VP Sls: Bob Galloway

D-U-N-S 60-769-7232
GALLOWAY JOHNSON TOMPKINS BURR & SMITH A PROFESSIONAL LAW CORP
A. RAY LIGHTELL, JR
701 Poydras St Fl 40, New Orleans, LA 70139-6001
Tel (504) 525-6802 *Founded/Ownrshp* 1987
Sales 32.3MM^E *EMP* 200
SIC 8111 General practice law office; General practice law office
Pr: John E Galloway
**Treas:* Timothy F Burr
Mng Dir: Larry Canada
Mng Dir: Michael Ecuyer
Mng Dir: James She
Dir IT: Ray Lightell

D-U-N-S 08-659-8807
GALLOWAY RIDGE INC
3000 Galloway Rdg, Pittsboro, NC 27312-8639
Tel (919) 542-7242 *Founded/Ownrshp* 1999
Sales 22.7MM *EMP* 260
Accts Dixon Hughes Goodman Llp Rale
SIC 8361 Residential care; Residential care
Prin: Jason R Cronk
**Pr:* Sylvanus Nye
VP: Bill Nye
Exec: Beatrice Runyan
**Ex Dir:* Jason Cronk
CTO: Catherine Hartwell
Nrsg Dir: Anita Scott-Spake

D-U-N-S 96-265-6893
GALLOWAY TOWNSHIP MIDDLE SCHOOL
100 S Reeds Rd, Galloway, NJ 08205-3423
Tel (609) 748-1250 *Founded/Ownrshp* 2014
Sales 11.7M *EMP* 370^E
SIC 8211 Public junior high school
Prin: Annette Giaquinto

D-U-N-S 13-523-5505
GALLOWAY TWP SCHOOL DISTRICT
101 S Reeds Rd, Galloway, NJ 08205-3422
Tel (609) 748-1250 *Founded/Ownrshp* 1829
Sales 22.8MM^E *EMP* 425
SIC 8211 8741 Public elementary & secondary schools; Management services; Public elementary & secondary schools; Management services

D-U-N-S 04-259-8482 IMP
GALLS LLC
QUARTER MASTER
1340 Russell Cave Rd, Lexington, KY 40505-3114
Tel (859) 266-7227 *Founded/Ownrshp* 2011
Sales 162.4MM^E *EMP* 600^E
SIC 5961 5399 2395 Catalog sales; Mail order house; Catalog showrooms; Pleating & stitching; Catalog sales; Mail order house; Catalog showrooms; Pleating & stitching
CEO: Michael Wessner
**CFO:* Michael Andrews
Top Exec: Eric Helton
**VP:* Rusty Cook
VP: Griggs Eldon
VP: Alex Marino
VP: Abe Rabiner
Prgrm Mgr: Bill Erwin
Store Mgr: Mike Agustin
Store Mgr: Lori Moth
Store Mgr: Virginia Puailoa

D-U-N-S 07-375-0192
GALLUP INC
GALLUP ORGANIZATION
901 F St Nw Ste 400, Washington, DC 20004-1419
Tel (202) 715-3030 *Founded/Ownrshp* 1998
Sales 249.1MM *EMP* 2,000
Accts Kpmg Omaha Ne
SIC 8742 Management consulting services; Management consulting services
Ch: Jim Clifton
Mng Pt: Randy Beck
V Ch: Gale D Muller
V Ch: Gale Muller
**V Ch:* Connie Rath
**COO:* Jane Miller
**CFO:* James R Krieger
**Treas:* Emily Nielsen
Sr VP: Annette Templeton
Exec: Jeff Bollettino
Exec: Steve D O'Brien

GALLUP ORGANIZATION
See GALLUP INC

D-U-N-S 06-941-2153
GALLUP-MC KINLEY COUNTY PUBLIC SCHOOL DISTRICT 1 (INC) (TX)
700 Boardman Dr, Gallup, NM 87301-4707
Tel (505) 722-7711 *Founded/Ownrshp* 1958
Sales 84.1MM^E *EMP* 1,500
SIC 8211 Public elementary school; Public junior high school; Public senior high school; Public elementary school; Public junior high school; Public senior high school
CTO: David Oaks
IT Man: Danny John
IT Man: Deana Larson
IT Man: Moni Short
Pr Dir: Koreen Smith
Schl Brd P: Joe Menini
Teacher Pr: Ron Doonkerscoot
Teacher Pr: Judie Jaramillo
Instr Medi: Mary Lyndemeyer
Snr Mgr: Carol Burnett

GALLUS BIOPHARMACEUTICALS
See CENTOCOR BIOLOGICS LLC

D-U-N-S 13-108-6563
GALMAN GROUP LTD
261 York Rd Ste 110, Jenkintown, PA 19046
Tel (215) 886-2000 *Founded/Ownrshp* 1985
Sales 35.4MM^E *EMP* 95^E
SIC 6552 6513 6512 Subdividers & developers; Apartment building operators; Nonresidential building operators
Pr: Arnold Galman
**Pr:* Jerald Slipakoff
**CFO:* Samuel M Goldstein
VP: Salvatore Villanti
Dir IT: Kwame Yankson
Mktg Dir: Michelle Stuckey

GALMOR'S
See G & G STEAM SERVICE INC

D-U-N-S 92-630-6408 IMP
GALPERTI INC
(*Suby of* OFFICINE NICOLA GALPERTI E FIGLIO SPA)
160 Southbelt Indus Dr, Houston, TX 77047-7012
Tel (713) 433-0700 *Founded/Ownrshp* 1995
Sales 54.0MM^E *EMP* 111
SIC 3462 Flange, valve & pipe fitting forgings, ferrous; Flange, valve & pipe fitting forgings, ferrous
Pr: Rockleigh S Dawson Jr
VP: Andrea Galperti
Prd Mgr: Raul Sorola
VP Sls: Joey Diaz

GALPIN COUNTRY
See FORD GALPIN INC

GALPIN FORD
See GALPIN MOTORS INC

D-U-N-S 15-767-6164
GALPIN JAGUAR LINCOLN-MERCURY INC
15500 Roscoe Blvd, Van Nuys, CA 91406-1347
Tel (818) 892-3800 *Founded/Ownrshp* 1986
Sales 64.2MM^E *EMP* 220
SIC 5511 Automobiles, new & used; Automobiles, new & used
Pr: H F Boeckmann II
**Sec:* Phil H Marshall
**VP:* Karl L Boeckmann
Genl Mgr: Brian Allen
IT Man: Tony Nassif
Sales Asso: Galpin Martin

D-U-N-S 02-945-3131 EXP
GALPIN MOTORS INC
GALPIN FORD
15505 Roscoe Blvd, North Hills, CA 91343-6598
Tel (818) 787-3800 *Founded/Ownrshp* 1964
Sales 293.2MM^E *EMP* 1,000
SIC 5511 5521 7538 7515 7514 5531 Automobiles, new & used; Used car dealers; General automotive repair shops; Passenger car leasing; Passenger car rental; Automotive & home supply stores; Automobiles, new & used; Used car dealers; General automotive repair shops; Passenger car leasing; Passenger car rental; Automotive & home supply stores
Pr: Herbert F Boeckman II
**Treas:* Jane Boeckmann
Sr VP: Andrew Akavan
Sr VP: Cyndee Casey
**VP:* Bradley M Boeckmann
VP: Laura Espino
**VP:* Alan J Skobin
VP: Rose Tapia
Genl Mgr: Brian Allan
Genl Mgr: David Gillum
**Genl Mgr:* Phil Marshall

D-U-N-S 79-769-0039
GALSON LABORATORIES INC
(*Suby of* MINERALS SERVICES DIVISION) ★
6601 Kirkville Rd, East Syracuse, NY 13057-9817
Tel (315) 432-5227 *Founded/Ownrshp* 2014
Sales 22.3MM^E *EMP* 115
SIC 8734 Testing laboratories; Testing laboratories
Pr: Jeffrey McDonald
Pr: Ron McMahan
Pr: Ronald McMahon
**Treas:* Mark Connors
**VP:* Kevin Kuppel
**VP:* Joseph Unangst
**VP:* Mary Unangst
Dir Lab: Bill Crowley
Dir Lab: Lisa Swab
Genl Mgr: William Crowley
Genl Mgr: Rozlyn Luber

Board of Directors: Michael Briganti, Steven Dorry, Jeffrey McDonald

GALT ELEMENTARY SCHOOL DST
See GALT JOINT UNION SCHOOL DISTRICT

GALT HOUSE, THE
See AL J SCHNEIDER CO

D-U-N-S 07-879-6733
GALT JOINT UNION ELEMENTARY SCHOOL DISTRICT
1018 C St Ste 210, Galt, CA 95632-1771
Tel (209) 744-4545 *Founded/Ownrshp* 2013
Sales 19.0MM^E *EMP* 430^E
SIC 8211 Elementary & secondary schools
Prin: Karen Schauer
Teacher Pr: Tracy Stinson

D-U-N-S 94-248-1508
GALT JOINT UNION SCHOOL DISTRICT
GALT ELEMENTARY SCHOOL DST
1018 C St Ste 210, Galt, CA 95632-1771
Tel (209) 744-4545 *Founded/Ownrshp* 1911
Sales 18.0MM^E *EMP* 500
SIC 8211 Public elementary school; Public elementary school

D-U-N-S 02-219-2728
GALVA HOLSTEIN AG LLC
204 E 1st St, Holstein, IA 51025-7700
Tel (712) 368-4314 *Founded/Ownrshp* 1907
Sales 62.2MM *EMP* 30
Accts Gardiner Thomsen Pc
SIC 5153 5191 5172 Grains; Feed; Chemicals, agricultural; Fertilizer & fertilizer materials; Petroleum products; Grains; Feed; Chemicals, agricultural; Fertilizer & fertilizer materials; Petroleum products
Bd of Dir: Jerry Ruser
Bd of Dir: Jim Woods

D-U-N-S 00-344-8552 IMP/EXP
GALVAN INDUSTRIES INC
7320 Millbrook Rd, Harrisburg, NC 28075-7489
Tel (704) 455-5102 *Founded/Ownrshp* 1988
Sales 35.2MM^E *EMP* 150
SIC 3479 Galvanizing of iron, steel or end-formed products
Pr: Laurens Willard
COO: Brian Buchanan
**VP:* Roger Montambo

D-U-N-S 88-443-9670
GALVESTON AUTOPLEX LTD
SANDDOLLAR AUTOPLEX
2601 Palmer Hwy, Texas City, TX 77590-7003
Tel (409) 741-2222 *Founded/Ownrshp* 1994
Sales 35.4MM^E *EMP* 111
SIC 5511 Automobiles, new & used; Pickups, new & used; Vans, new & used; Automobiles, new & used; Pickups, new & used; Vans, new & used
Pt: Robert Y Pagan
Sls Dir: Ever Pereira

GALVESTON COUNTY DAILY NEWS
See GALVESTON NEWSPAPERS INC

D-U-N-S 07-939-7204
GALVESTON INDEPENDENT SCHOOL DISTRICT (TX)
3904 Avenue T, Galveston, TX 77550-8643
Tel (409) 765-2101 *Founded/Ownrshp* 1882
Sales 582.0M *EMP* 1,218
Accts Belt Harris Pechacek Lllp
SIC 8211 Public elementary school; Public junior high school; Public senior high school; Public elementary school; Public junior high school; Public senior high school
Dir Sec: Levoy Amador
Pr Dir: John Farrow
Instr Medi: Mariana Mueller
HC Dir: Zia Robinson

D-U-N-S 04-112-7911
GALVESTON NEWSPAPERS INC
GALVESTON COUNTY DAILY NEWS
(*Suby of* BRAZOSPORT FACTS) ★
8522 Teichman Rd, Galveston, TX 77554-9119
Tel (409) 683-5200 *Founded/Ownrshp* 1968
Sales 60.9MM^E *EMP* 687
SIC 2711 Newspapers, publishing & printing; Newspapers, publishing & printing
Pr: Martha Walls
**Pr:* Dolph Pillotson
**Sec:* Rosetta Bonnin
VP: Les Daughtry Jr
Web Dev: Matt Hurless
Web Dev: Israel Thompson
Advt Dir: Steve Paterson
Snr Mgr: Rachael Crider

D-U-N-S 02-648-7256
GALVESTON STANDARD AUTO PARTS INC
TEXAS CITY STANDARD AUTO PARTS
5601 Broadway St, Galveston, TX 77551-4440
Tel (409) 744-0402 *Founded/Ownrshp* 1960
Sales 23.7MM^E *EMP* 95
SIC 5531 5013 Automotive parts; Automotive accessories; Automotive supplies & parts
Pr: Lyle Honey
**Treas:* Jean Honey
**VP:* Warren Honey

D-U-N-S 10-363-1925
■ **GALYANS TRADING CO LLC**
(*Suby of* DICKS SPORTING GOODS INC) ★
300 Industry Dr, Pittsburgh, PA 15275-1001
Tel (724) 273-3400 *Founded/Ownrshp* 2004
Sales 199.7MM^E *EMP* 6,100
SIC 5941 5699 5661 Sporting goods & bicycle shops; Sports apparel; Footwear, athletic; Sporting goods & bicycle shops; Sports apparel; Footwear, athletic
CEO: Edwin J Holman
CFO: Donald P Lofe
**CFO:* Edward S Wozniak
**Chf Mktg O:* Richard Leto
**Ex VP:* C David Zoba

Sr VP: Charles Nelson
**Sr VP:* Lindsay Rice
**Sr VP:* Paul C Wagner
Sr VP: Edward Whitehead
VP: Matt Lynch

D-U-N-S 09-824-6601
GAMA AVIATION INC
(*Suby of* GAMA GROUP LIMITED)
480 Lordship Blvd Ste 2, Stratford, CT 06615-7149
Tel (203) 337-4600 *Founded/Ownrshp* 2008
Sales 37.9MM^E *EMP* 150^E
SIC 4729 Airline ticket offices; Airline ticket offices
CEO: Marwan Khalek
**COO:* Steve Wright

D-U-N-S 17-439-8321
GAMAY FOODS INC
2770 S 171st St, New Berlin, WI 53151-3510
Tel (262) 789-5104 *Founded/Ownrshp* 1987
Sales 28.4MM^E *EMP* 30
SIC 5169 2022 8731 Food additives & preservatives; Spreads, cheese; Food research
Pr: Aly Y Gamay
**Pr:* Terry Schneider
Sfty Mgr: Niel Risler
VP Mktg: Randy Cook

GAMBER 0687
See GAMBER-JOHNSON LLC

D-U-N-S 04-142-0308
GAMBER GLASS CONTAINER INC
BACON JUG COMPANY, THE
2220 Dutch Gold Dr, Lancaster, PA 17601-1941
Tel (717) 393-1716 *Founded/Ownrshp* 1967
Sales 24.1MM *EMP* 10
Accts Parentebeard Llc
SIC 5085 Glass bottles; Glass bottles
Ch: William R Gamber II
Pr: Nancy J Gamber

D-U-N-S 11-983-5218
■ **GAMBER-JOHNSON LLC**
GAMBER 0687
(*Suby of* LEGGETT & PLATT INC) ★
3001 Borham Ave, Stevens Point, WI 54481-5062
Tel (715) 344-3482 *Founded/Ownrshp* 2007
Sales 22.0MM^E *EMP* 85
SIC 3663 Mobile communication equipment
Pr: Brian Wagner
Pr: Jason Lewandowski
VP: Veronica Bruske
Exec: Cheryl Bikowski
IT Man: Mark Landin
IT Man: Jeremy Moore
Mfg Dir: Brian Lepak
Ql Cn Mgr: David Lamb
Manager: Dan Gimotty
Sales Asso: Nicky Molski
Snr PM: Gary Schmitz

D-U-N-S 06-894-6862
GAMBLE ELIZABETH DEACONESS HOME ASSOCIATION (INC)
2139 Auburn Ave, Cincinnati, OH 45219-2906
Tel (513) 751-4224 *Founded/Ownrshp* 1888
Sales 28.6MM *EMP* 2,900
Accts Barnes Dennig & Co Ltd Cin
SIC 8062 8082 General medical & surgical hospitals; Home health care services; General medical & surgical hospitals; Home health care services
Ch Bd: Thomas Petry
**Pr:* Theodore H Emmerich
Bd of Dir: Thomas R Gerdes
Bd of Dir: Michael Keating

D-U-N-S 80-629-6484
GAMBLER TRUCKING INC
500 Dennis Rd, Weatherford, TX 76087-9098
Tel (940) 627-0062 *Founded/Ownrshp* 2006
Sales 25.0MM *EMP* 60
SIC 4212 Local trucking, without storage; Local trucking, without storage
CEO: Roy Patterson
**Pr:* Charles Newcomb
**Treas:* Mike Skowronek
**VP:* Clinton Kilgour
**VP:* George Reese
Genl Mgr: Russ Liang

D-U-N-S 04-749-8134
GAMBLIN LLC
1047 Roosevelt Ave E, Enumclaw, WA 98022-9238
Tel (360) 825-3567 *Founded/Ownrshp* 2004
Sales 26.8MM^E *EMP* 70
SIC 5511

D-U-N-S 03-801-3157
GAMBONE BROS ENTERPRISES INC
GAMBONE GROUP, THE
1030 W Germantown Pike A, Norristown, PA 19403-3929
Tel (610) 539-4700 *Founded/Ownrshp* 1958
Sales 22.6MM^E *EMP* 90
SIC 1521 6552 1522 1542 1541 New construction, single-family houses; Land subdividers & developers, commercial; Multi-family dwelling construction; Commercial & office building, new construction; Industrial buildings, new construction
Pr: Joseph R Gambone Jr
**Pr:* Michael Gambone
**CFO:* Thomas F Hennigan
**Sec:* Anthony Gambone

GAMBONE GROUP, THE
See GAMBONE BROS ENTERPRISES INC

D-U-N-S 15-746-7085 IMP
GAMBRINUS CO
SHINER BOCK
14800 San Pedro Ave # 310, San Antonio, TX 78232-3735
Tel (210) 483-5100 *Founded/Ownrshp* 1986
Sales 296.1MM^E *EMP* 446
SIC 5181 2082 Beer & other fermented malt liquors; Beer (alcoholic beverage); Beer & other fermented malt liquors; Beer (alcoholic beverage)

Pr: Carlos Alvarez
**Pr:* James Bolz
CFO: Jim Bolz
**CFO:* James J O'Sullivan
**Sec:* John Horan
Exec: David Hutto
Genl Mgr: Luis Alvarez
CTO: Tim Crisp
Web Prj Mg: Ron Christensen
Opers Mgr: Karl Ockert

D-U-N-S 04-109-3923
■ **GAMBRO INC**
(*Suby of* GAMBRO AB)
9540 Maroon Cir Unit 400, Englewood, CO 80112-5731
Tel (800) 525-2623 *Founded/Ownrshp* 1964, 2008
Sales 310.2MM^E *EMP* 1,950
SIC 6719 Personal holding companies, except banks; Personal holding companies, except banks
COO: Juan Bosch
VP: Frank Corbin
VP: Tom Poholsky
VP: Jeff Weinert
Web Prj Mg: Panella Todd
Opers Mgr: David Fisher
Sls Mgr: Kimberly Hamilton
Sls Mgr: Steven Roth

D-U-N-S 82-904-2337 IMP/EXP
■ **GAMBRO RENAL PRODUCTS INC**
(*Suby of* GAMBRO INC) ★
9540 Maroon Cir Unit 400, Englewood, CO 80112-5731
Tel (303) 222-6500 *Founded/Ownrshp* 1990
Sales 138.6MM^E *EMP* 662
SIC 3842 Surgical appliances & supplies; Surgical appliances & supplies
Pr: Nick Mendez
Pr: Gary Strange
**CFO:* David Doerr
Sr VP: Juan Bosch
Sr VP: Javad Seyedzadeh
**VP:* Robert Belknapp
VP: Anne Boardman
VP: Luca Chiastra
VP: Tom Dielmann
VP: Andy Holley
VP: Russ Thornton

GAMCO
See GENERAL ALUMINUM MFG CO

D-U-N-S 05-454-5202
▲ **GAMCO INVESTORS INC**
1 Corporate Ctr, Rye, NY 10580-1485
Tel (914) 921-3700 *Founded/Ownrshp* 1977
Sales 440.3MM *EMP* 228^E
Tkr Sym GBL *Exch* NYS
SIC 6282 Investment advisory service; Investment advisory service
Ch Bd: Mario J Gabelli
Pr: Douglas R Jamieson
Pr: George Maldonado
Pr: Jeff Tate
COO: Bruce N Alpert
CFO: Joseph Egan
CFO: Robert S Zuccaro
Ofcr: Kevin V Dreyer
Ofcr: Mark Gambetta
Ofcr: Christopher J Marangi
Ex VP: Kevin Handwerker
Sr VP: Tom Bardik
Sr VP: Henry G Van Der Eb
Sr VP: Agnes Mullady
Sr VP: Paul Swirbul
VP: Carter Austin
VP: Brian Burke
VP: Heidi Koontz
VP: Nina Lobozza
VP: Scott Sadowski
VP: Marco Sampellegrini
Board of Directors: Edwin L Artzt, Raymond C Avansino Jr, Richard L Bready, Marc Gabelli, Eugene R McGrath, Robert S Prather Jr, Elisa M Wilson

D-U-N-S 03-934-7666
GAME & FISH COMMISSION ARKANSAS
AGFC
(*Suby of* EXECUTIVE OFFICE OF STATE OF ARKANSAS) ★
2 Natural Resources Dr, Little Rock, AR 72205-1572
Tel (501) 223-6300 *Founded/Ownrshp* 1944
Sales NA *EMP* 500
SIC 9512 Fish & wildlife conservation agency, government; ; Fish & wildlife conservation agency, government;
V Ch: George Dunklin Jr
CFO: David Kinnard
Ofcr: Matthew Baker
Ofcr: Tracey Blake
Ofcr: Crystal Blakley
Ofcr: Jeffrey Cowan
Ofcr: Andy Smith
Ofcr: Kenneth Taylor
Ofcr: Trent Whitehead
Ofcr: Joseph Williams
CTO: Steve Wilson

D-U-N-S 87-802-3282
GAME & PARKS COMMISSION NEBRASKA
(*Suby of* EXECUTIVE OFFICE OF STATE OF NEBRASKA) ★
2200 N 33rd St, Lincoln, NE 68503-1417
Tel (402) 471-0641 *Founded/Ownrshp* 1800
Sales NA *EMP* 500
SIC 9512 Land, mineral & wildlife conservation; ; Land, mineral & wildlife conservation;
VP: Mary Geibel
Exec: Justin Haag
Exec: Jerry Kane
IT Man: Tammy Crosby
IT Man: Toni Knust
Prd Mgr: Tina Rohrs
Snr Mgr: Gene Cotter
Snr Mgr: Lori Griggs
Snr Mgr: Clay Schutz
Snr Mgr: Tara Sprigler-Price
Snr Mgr: Shane Stutzman

D-U-N-S 80-991-5788
GAME AND FISH COMMISSION WYOMING
(*Suby of* EXECUTIVE OFFICE OF STATE OF WYOMING) ★
5400 Bishop Blvd, Cheyenne, WY 82009-3338
Tel (307) 777-4600 *Founded/Ownrshp* 1921
Sales NA *EMP* 400
SIC 9512 Wildlife conservation agencies; ; Wildlife conservation agencies;
IT Man: Pat Lewis
IT Man: Meredith Wood

GAME AND INLAND FISHERIES DEPT
See VIRGINIA DEPARTMENT OF GAME AND INLAND FISHERIES

D-U-N-S 79-657-3715
GAME COMMISSION PENNSYLVANIA
(*Suby of* EXECUTIVE OFFICE OF COMMONWEALTH OF PENNSYLVANIA) ★
2001 Elmerton Ave, Harrisburg, PA 17110-9762
Tel (717) 787-4250 *Founded/Ownrshp* 1895
Sales NA *EMP* 669
SIC 9512 Game & inland fish agency, government; ; Game & inland fish agency, government;
Ex Dir: Carl G Roe
Chf Inves: Anthony Clark
Rgnl Mgr: Terri Hopkins
Genl Couns: Sallie Rodgers
Counsel: M Nolan
Counsel: Sonja Zucker
Snr Mgr: Thomas Malesky
Snr Mgr: Frank Miller
Snr Mgr: Thomas Poploskie
Snr Mgr: Letitia Schubauer
Snr Mgr: Michael Stone

GAME QUEST
See CRESCENT MARKETING INC

GAME READY
See COOLSYSTEMS INC

D-U-N-S 13-159-2755
■ **GAME SHOW NETWORK LLC**
G S N
(*Suby of* LIBERTY ENTERTAINMENT INC) ★
2150 Colorado Ave Ste 100, Santa Monica, CA 90404-5514
Tel (310) 255-6800 *Founded/Ownrshp* 2012
Sales 78.0MM^E *EMP* 198^E
SIC 4841 Cable & other pay television services
CEO: David Goldhill
Pr: Frank Cartwright
CFO: Brent Williams
**Ofcr:* Andrew Pedersen
Ex VP: Peter Blacklow
Ex VP: Steven Brunell
Ex VP: Mark Feldman
Sr VP: Mark Cullinane
Sr VP: Kelly Goode
VP: Tara Briganti
VP: Kam Diba
VP: Nico Fasano
VP: Dennis K Gillespie
VP: Jessy Hanley
VP: Steve Leblang
VP: Chad Mallam
VP: Davin Miyoshi
VP: Steve Namm
VP: Stacey Odonnell
VP: Jonathan Small
VP: Ryan Tredinnick
Board of Directors: Rich Cronin, Jamie Roberts

D-U-N-S 07-940-0031
GAMECHANGE RACKING LLC
730 5th Ave Fl 16, New York, NY 10019-4105
Tel (212) 359-0200 *Founded/Ownrshp* 2012
Sales 26.0MM *EMP* 24
SIC 5074 Heating equipment (hydronic)
CEO: Andrew Worden
CFO: Olga Filippova

D-U-N-S 05-094-5155
GAMEDAY ENTERTAINMENT LLC
GAMEDAY MERCHANDISING
8100 Southpark Way Ste A3, Littleton, CO 80120-4525
Tel (720) 457-9485 *Founded/Ownrshp* 2009
Sales 72.1MM^E *EMP* 500^E
SIC 5699 Sports apparel; ; Sports apparel
CEO: Jeff Neal
Pr: Alan Fey
COO: Martin Garafalo
Ex VP: Jeff Newman
Genl Mgr: Michael Larson

GAMEDAY MERCHANDISING
See GAMEDAY ENTERTAINMENT LLC

D-U-N-S 62-223-6078
GAMEFLY INC
6080 Center Dr Fl 8, Los Angeles, CA 90045-9205
Tel (310) 568-8224 *Founded/Ownrshp* 2002
Sales 35.8MM^E *EMP* 135
SIC 7379 ;
Pr: Dave Hodess
**CFO:* Stacey M Peterson
Treas: Steve Hartmann
VP: Shosannah Bacura
VP: Neil Seth
Snr Sftwr: Chris Gee
Software D: Tommy Jiang
Software D: Christopher Tearpak
VP Mktg: Racheal Silverstien
Mktg Dir: Serene Chan

D-U-N-S 00-304-4679
GAMELOFT INC
45 W 25th St Fl 9, New York, NY 10010-2035
Tel (212) 993-3000 *Founded/Ownrshp* 2000
Sales 20.8MM^E *EMP* 50^E
SIC 5092 Video games
CEO: Michel Guillemot
**Pr:* Gerard Guillemot
CFO: Rimniceanu Mirela
VP: Baudouin Corman
**VP:* Gonzague De Vallois
Dir Bus: Alexandre Tan
Mng Dir: Alexis Gresoviac

IT Man: Vincent Coupal
Prd Mgr: Paul Friciu
Sls Mgr: Yann Fourneau
Sls Mgr: Sebastien Givry

D-U-N-S 19-687-7138
GAMER PACKAGING INC
330 2nd Ave S Ste 895, Minneapolis, MN 55401-2302
Tel (612) 788-4444 *Founded/Ownrshp* 1988
Sales 34.6MM^E *EMP* 32
SIC 5085 4225 Bins & containers, storage; Glass bottles; Plastic bottles; Bottler supplies; General warehousing
CEO: Ronald Gamer
**Pr:* Kenneth Gamer
**CFO:* Tim Kraus
VP: Christopher Lussier
Manager: Chip Barto
Manager: Jodi Reding
Sales Asso: Cheryl Bolin
Sales Asso: Alicia Johnson

D-U-N-S 13-611-8077 IMP
GAMERS FACTORY INC
10957 Mccormick Rd, Hunt Valley, MD 21031
Tel (410) 340-1051 *Founded/Ownrshp* 2003
Sales 27.7MM *EMP* 64
SIC 5092 Video games; Video games
Pr: Todd S Hays
**CFO:* Rodney Hillman
**VP:* John Hays

GAMERSFIRST
See K2 NETWORK INC

D-U-N-S 11-207-0334 IMP
GAMES WORKSHOP AMERICA INC
(*Suby of* GAMES WORKSHOP GROUP PLC)
6211 E Holmes Rd, Memphis, TN 38141-8310
Tel (901) 541-7700 *Founded/Ownrshp* 2002
Sales 58.1MM^E *EMP* 300
SIC 5092 Model kits; Model kits
CEO: John Stallard
**CFO:* Kevin J Smith

D-U-N-S 60-245-5839 IMP/EXP
GAMESA TECHNOLOGY CORP INC
GAMESA WIND
(*Suby of* GAMESA CORPORACION TECNOLOGICA SOCIEDAD ANONIMA)
1150 Northbrook Dr # 300, Feasterville Trevose, PA 19053-8443
Tel (215) 710-3100 *Founded/Ownrshp* 2005
Sales 152.5MM^E *EMP* 800^E
SIC 3621 6719 Windmills, electric generating; Investment holding companies, except banks; Windmills, electric generating; Investment holding companies, except banks
CEO: Dirk Matthys
Opers Mgr: Rich Rossi
Snr Mgr: Luis Fernandez

GAMESA WIND
See GAMESA TECHNOLOGY CORP INC

D-U-N-S 60-254-9680 EXP
GAMESA WIND PA LLC
(*Suby of* GAMESA TECHNOLOGY CORP INC) ★
1801 Market St Ste 2700, Philadelphia, PA 19103-1609
Tel (215) 665-9810 *Founded/Ownrshp* 2005
Sales 25.8MM^E *EMP* 140^E
SIC 3621 Windmills, electric generating; Windmills, electric generating

D-U-N-S 60-245-7686 IMP/EXP
GAMESA WIND US LLC
(*Suby of* GAMESA TECHNOLOGY CORP INC) ★
1150 Northbrook Dr # 300, Trevose, PA 19053-8443
Tel (215) 428-9750 *Founded/Ownrshp* 2005
Sales 63.6MM^E *EMP* 266^E
SIC 3621 Windmills, electric generating; Windmills, electric generating
Ch: Ignacio Martin San Vicente
Opers Mgr: Angel Lauzara
Snr Mgr: Jairo Arias

D-U-N-S 60-744-2428 IMP
▲ **GAMESTOP CORP**
625 Westport Pkwy, Grapevine, TX 76051-6740
Tel (817) 424-2000 *Founded/Ownrshp* 1996
Sales 9.3MMM *EMP* 18,000^E
Tkr Sym GME *Exch* NYS
SIC 5945 5734 5932 2721 Hobby, toy & game shops; Dolls & accessories; Computer & software stores; Software, computer games; Computer software & accessories; Used merchandise stores; Computers & accessories, secondhand; Magazines: publishing only, not printed on site; Hobby, toy & game shops; Dolls & accessories; Computer & software stores; Software, computer games; Computer software & accessories; Used merchandise stores; Computers & accessories, secondhand; Magazines: publishing only, not printed on site
CEO: J Paul Raines
**Ch Bd:* Daniel A Dematteo
COO: Tony D Bartel
CFO: Robert A Lloyd
Chf Mktg O: Frank Hamlin
Ex VP: Ronald Freeman
Ex VP: Michael P Hogan
Ex VP: Mike Hogan
Ex VP: Michael K Mauler
VP: A J Cobb
CIO: Todd Heeaton
Board of Directors: Jerome L Davis, R Richard Fontaine, Thomas N Kelly, Shane S Kim, Steven R Koonin, Stephanie M Shern, Gerald R Szczepanski, Kathy P Vrabeck, Lawrence S Zilavy

D-U-N-S 61-283-0653
■ **GAMESTOP HOLDINGS CORP**
(*Suby of* ELECTRONICS BOUTIQUE AMERICA INC) ★
625 Westport Pkwy, Grapevine, TX 76051-6740
Tel (956) 630-3043 *Founded/Ownrshp* 2005
Sales 34.8MM^E *EMP* 279

SIC 5961 5734 5932 2721 5092 Computer software, mail order; Computers & peripheral equipment, mail order; Computer & software stores; Software, computer games; Computer software & accessories; Used merchandise stores; Computers & accessories, secondhand; Magazines: publishing only, not printed on site; Video games; Computer software, mail order; Computers & peripheral equipment, mail order; Computer & software stores; Software, computer games; Computer software & accessories; Used merchandise stores; Computers & accessories, secondhand; Magazines: publishing only, not printed on site; Video games
CEO: R Richard Fontaine
**Ch Bd:* Daniel De Matteo
**CFO:* David W Carlson
**Sec:* Michael N Rosen
Sr Cor Off: Greg Dunlevy
Brnch Mgr: Brad Geoffor
Brnch Mgr: Mike Glotfelty
Brnch Mgr: Jesse Holaman
Brnch Mgr: Dan Moore
Genl Mgr: Angela Perkins
Off Mgr: Dawn Hofer

D-U-N-S 96-195-2728 IMP
■ GAMESTOP INC
(*Suby of* ELECTRONICS BOUTIQUE HOLDINGS CORP) ★
625 Westport Pkwy, Grapevine, TX 76051-6740
Tel (817) 424-2000 *Founded/Ownrshp* 1999
Sales 55.9MM^E *EMP* 279
SIC 5945 Hobby, toy & game shops; Hobby, toy & game shops
Pr: Tony Bartel
COO: Julian P Raines
CFO: Stanley Steinberg
Sr VP: Shawn D Freeman
Dist Mgr: Todd Andresen
Dist Mgr: Haresh Idnani
Dist Mgr: Cordell McDougald
Dist Mgr: Heath McIntyre
Dist Mgr: Sean McMahon
Dist Mgr: Ametria Sheard
Dist Mgr: Shane Walls
Board of Directors: Kathy Vrabeck

D-U-N-S 83-600-1321 IMP
GAMETECH INTERNATIONAL INC
8850 Double Diamond Pkwy, Reno, NV 89521-5908
Tel (775) 850-6000 *Founded/Ownrshp* 1994
Sales 30.8MM *EMP* 133^E
SIC 3944 3999

GAMETIME FABRICS
See AMES TEXTILE CORP

D-U-N-S 00-369-9861
GAMEWORKS ENTERTAINMENT LLC
6580 S Mccarran Blvd C, Reno, NV 89509-6140
Tel (206) 521-0952 *Founded/Ownrshp* 2012
Sales 16.8MM^E *EMP* 620
SIC 5812 7993 Eating places; Video game arcade; Eating places; Video game arcade
Ch Bd: Joseph Zarraveto

D-U-N-S 07-884-7988
GAMING AND LEISURE PROPERTIES INC
825 Berkshire Blvd # 200, Wyomissing, PA 19610-1247
Tel (610) 401-2900 *Founded/Ownrshp* 2013
Sales 33.7MM^E *EMP* 900
Tkr Sym GLPI *Exch* NGS
SIC 6519 Real property lessors; Real property lessors
CEO: Peter M Carlino
**CFO:* William J Clifford
Sr VP: Curtis Magleby
Pr Mgr: Joseph N Jaffoni

D-U-N-S 94-726-3828
GAMING CONTROL BOARD NEVADA
ADMINISTRATION DIVISION
(*Suby of* EXECUTIVE OFFICE OF STATE OF NEVADA) ★
1919 College Pkwy, Carson City, NV 89706-7941
Tel (775) 684-7713 *Founded/Ownrshp* 1955
Sales NA *EMP* 430
SIC 9311 Gambling control board, government; ; Gambling control board, government;
Ch: Dennis K Neilander
Bd of Dir: A G Burnett
Snr Mgr: Frank Streshley

D-U-N-S 60-661-3065
GAMING LABORATORIES INTERNATIONAL INC
G L I
600 Airport Rd, Lakewood, NJ 08701-5995
Tel (732) 942-3999 *Founded/Ownrshp* 1989
Sales 49.9MM^E *EMP* 273
SIC 8748 Testing services; Testing services
Pr: James Maida
Ofcr: Federica Fortuna
VP: Liz Bowen
**VP:* Paul Magno
**Prin:* James Lawrence
Genl Mgr: Peter Cercone
Dir IT: Tim Reigel
IT Man: Cory Nelson
Genl Couns: Angela Koutsouris

D-U-N-S 03-494-2193 IMP/EXP
▲ GAMING PARTNERS INTERNATIONAL CORP
1700 Industrial Rd, Las Vegas, NV 89102-2620
Tel (702) 384-2425 *Founded/Ownrshp* 1963
Sales 60.9MM *EMP* 726^E
Accts Moss Adams Llp San Diego Cal
Tkr Sym GPIC *Exch* NGM
SIC 3944 Games, toys & children's vehicles; Poker chips; Games, toys & children's vehicles; Poker chips
Pr: Gregory S Gronau
**Ch Bd:* Alain Thieffry
VP: Louis Degregorio
Area Mgr: Miguel Gonzalez
Board of Directors: Martin A Berkowitz, Eric P Endy, Charles R Henry, Robert J Kelly

D-U-N-S 15-163-3377
GAMKA SALES CO INC
983 New Durham Rd, Edison, NJ 08817-2253
Tel (732) 248-1400 *Founded/Ownrshp* 1986
Sales 24.3MM^E *EMP* 20
SIC 5082 7699 7359 7353 Construction & mining machinery; Masonry equipment & supplies; Industrial machinery & equipment repair; Construction equipment repair; Tool rental; Heavy construction equipment rental
Pr: Karl Weiss Sr
**VP:* Karl Weiss Jr
**VP:* Ronald Weiss

D-U-N-S 13-762-9911 IMP
GAMMA CONSTRUCTION CO INC
2808 Joanel St, Houston, TX 77027-5306
Tel (713) 963-0086 *Founded/Ownrshp* 1985
Sales 112.5MM^E *EMP* 190
Accts Kurt & Associates Pc Houst
SIC 1542 Commercial & office building contractors; Commercial & office building contractors
Pr: Keith Williams
**CFO:* Guy Windheim
**Sr VP:* Thomas R Hansen
**Sr VP:* Cecil Windsor
Dir IT: Jase Payne
Sfty Mgr: Roy Harris
Snr PM: Koy Scheiner

D-U-N-S 05-867-1504
GAMMA ENGINEERING INC
601 Airport Dr, Mansfield, TX 76063-2718
Tel (817) 477-2193 *Founded/Ownrshp* 1971
Sales 27.8MM^E *EMP* 110
SIC 3444 3469 3398 Forming machine work, sheet metal; Stamping metal for the trade; Metal heat treating
Pr: Sandra Bontke
**VP:* Nathan Bontke
**VP:* Kelli Savering
Genl Mgr: Rory Norrell

D-U-N-S 09-882-6501
GAMMA HEALTHCARE INC
1717 W Maud St, Poplar Bluff, MO 63901-4003
Tel (573) 727-5600 *Founded/Ownrshp* 1981
Sales 33.5MM^E *EMP* 470
SIC 8071 Blood analysis laboratory; Urinalysis laboratory; Blood analysis laboratory; Urinalysis laboratory
Pr: Jerry Murphy
COO: Jeff Qualls
CFO: Katie Caudel
CFO: Derik Rahlmann
Ex VP: Brent Davis
Sr VP: Andrea Latrasse
VP Bus Dev: Shannon Terrell
Rgnl Mgr: Nikita Featherstone
Rgnl Mgr: Jan Hiegert
Snr Sftwr: Brandon Clark
Dir IT: Lance Donze

D-U-N-S 09-593-7207
GAMMA III LTD
BURGER KING
4555 W Dickman Rd, Springfield, MI 49037-7328
Tel (269) 660-2800 *Founded/Ownrshp* 1977
Sales 9.2MM^E *EMP* 350
SIC 5812 Fast-food restaurant, chain; Fast-food restaurant, chain
Pr: Paul S Gregory
**VP:* Lawrence Gregory

D-U-N-S 11-341-9485 IMP
GAMMA SCIENTIFIC INC
ROAD VISTA
(*Suby of* KR ACQUISITION CORP) ★
9925 Carroll Canyon Rd, San Diego, CA 92131-1105
Tel (858) 635-9008 *Founded/Ownrshp* 1995
Sales 25.0MM *EMP* 48
SIC 3829 Spectrometers, liquid scintillation & nuclear; Photogrammetrical instruments
Pr: Richard Austin
COO: Kong G Loh
CFO: John Yiannakakis

D-U-N-S 80-526-5014 IMP/EXP
GAMMA SEAFOOD CORP
ALFA GAMMA SEAFOOD
7850 Nw South River Dr, Medley, FL 33166-2514
Tel (305) 804-0048 *Founded/Ownrshp* 1990
Sales 20.1MM^E *EMP* 35
SIC 5146 Seafoods
Pr: Antonio Alvarez Sr

D-U-N-S 02-405-5100 IMP
GAMMA USA INC (FL)
5600 Nw 37th Ave, Miami, FL 33142-2720
Tel (305) 633-2403 *Founded/Ownrshp* 1995, 2013
Sales 58.0MM^E *EMP* 175^E
SIC 1793 Glass & glazing work; Glass & glazing work
Pr: Matthew Baum
**Ch:* Elliott Kracko
**Sr VP:* Juan J Alpizar
**VP:* Jose M Rodriguez
**Sls Mgr:* Richard Kiefer

D-U-N-S 19-058-9986 IMP
GAMMATECH COMPUTER CORP
48303 Fremont Blvd, Fremont, CA 94538-6580
Tel (510) 824-6700 *Founded/Ownrshp* 1989
Sales 26.7MM^E *EMP* 55
SIC 5045 Computers
Pr: Steven Gau
Sr Cor Off: Bill Liu
VP: Tony Hua
Exec: Julie Meng
MIS Dir: Charlie Chen
S&M/VP: Paul Kim
Sls Mgr: Lester Crosbie
Sls Mgr: Rowena Gammatech
Sls Mgr: William Tang

D-U-N-S 03-113-8076 IMP
GAMMON EQUIPMENT CO INC
2918 E Blaine St, Springfield, MO 65803-5265
Tel (417) 866-3528 *Founded/Ownrshp* 1962
Sales 37.2MM^E *EMP* 85
SIC 5084 Industrial machinery & equipment; Industrial machinery & equipment
Pr: Gregory Gammon

GAMSE LITHO & GRAVURE
See GAMSE LITHOGRAPHING CO INC OF DELAWARE

D-U-N-S 00-306-1538 EXP
GAMSE LITHOGRAPHING CO INC OF DELAWARE
GAMSE LITHO & GRAVURE
(*Suby of* CANZONIERO CORP) ★
7413 Pulaski Hwy, Baltimore, MD 21237-2580
Tel (410) 866-4700 *Founded/Ownrshp* 1896
Sales 40.7MM^E *EMP* 148
SIC 2671 2752 2754 Packaging paper & plastics film, coated & laminated; Commercial printing, gravure; Commercial printing, lithographic; Packaging paper & plastics film, coated & laminated; Commercial printing, lithographic; Commercial printing, gravure
Pr: Daniel Canzoniero
CFO: James Canzoniero
VP: Mark Ledonne
Dir Risk M: Holly Helcamp
QA Dir: Matt Haynes
IT Man: Leroy Krempel

D-U-N-S 00-596-5363 IMP
GAMTEX INDUSTRIES LP (TX)
ASHMAN MEDALS & RECYCL COMANY
2600 Shamrock Ave, Fort Worth, TX 76107-1311
Tel (817) 334-0211 *Founded/Ownrshp* 1918
Sales 124.7MM *EMP* 90
SIC 5093 Metal scrap & waste materials; Metal scrap & waste materials
Pt: Arnold Gachman
Pt: Eric Gachman

D-U-N-S 05-220-3810
■ GAMUT SMART MEDIA FROM COX LLC
COXREPS
(*Suby of* CABLE REP ADVERTISING) ★
1 Dag Hammarskjold Plz, New York, NY 10017-2201
Tel (212) 588-2800 *Founded/Ownrshp* 2007
Sales 65.0MM *EMP* 100
SIC 7313 4899 Electronic media advertising representatives; Data communication services
Pr: Kim Guthrie
VP: Matt Murphy

D-U-N-S 03-799-8499
GANA-A YOO LIMITED
1205 E Intl Arprt Rd # 100, Anchorage, AK 99518-1409
Tel (907) 569-9599 *Founded/Ownrshp* 1978
Sales 20.3MM *EMP* 250
SIC 6512 Nonresidential building operators; Commercial & industrial building operation; Nonresidential building operators; Commercial & industrial building operation
CEO: Betty Huntington
**Ch Bd:* Michael Stickman
**Pr:* Ragine Pilot
**Treas:* Erica Frankson
Treas: Josephine Malemute
**VP:* Jennine Elias
Opers Mgr: Cheri Sullivan

D-U-N-S 79-512-9774
GANADO UNIFIED SCHOOL DISTRICT 20
Hwy 264 & 191, Ganado, AZ 86505
Tel (928) 755-1000 *Founded/Ownrshp* 1954
Sales 29.5MM^E *EMP* 450
SIC 8211 Public elementary & secondary schools; Public elementary school; Public junior high school; Public senior high school; Public elementary & secondary schools; Public elementary school; Public junior high school; Public senior high school
Schl Brd P: Silvia Etsitty

D-U-N-S 00-850-0159 IMP
GANAHL LUMBER CO
1220 E Ball Rd, Anaheim, CA 92805-5993
Tel (714) 772-5444 *Founded/Ownrshp* 1923
Sales 290.7MM *EMP* 625
SIC 5211

D-U-N-S 04-602-4964 EXP
GANCEDO LUMBER CO INC
GANCEDO REBAR
9300 Nw 36th Ave, Miami, FL 33147-2898
Tel (305) 836-7030 *Founded/Ownrshp* 1968
Sales 52.9MM *EMP* 110
Accts Prats Fernandez & Co Coral G
SIC 5031 5211 Lumber, plywood & millwork; Lumber & other building materials; Lumber, plywood & millwork; Lumber & other building materials
Ch Bd: Ignacio Perez Sr
**Pr:* Martin Perez
**VP:* Ignacio Perez Jr
**VP:* Ricardo Perez
**VP:* Ricky Perez
**VP:* Rolando Perez

GANCEDO REBAR
See GANCEDO LUMBER CO INC

GANDA
See GARCIA AND ASSOCIATES

D-U-N-S 08-745-0383
GANDARA MENTAL HEALTH CENTER INC
147 Norman St, West Springfield, MA 01089-5003
Tel (413) 736-8329 *Founded/Ownrshp* 1977
Sales 24.4MM *EMP* 250
Accts Lester Halpern & Company Pc
SIC 8093 8011 Alcohol clinic, outpatient; Mental health clinic, outpatient; Rehabilitation center, outpatient treatment; Offices & clinics of medical doctors; Alcohol clinic, outpatient; Mental health clinic, outpatient; Rehabilitation center, outpatient treatment; Offices & clinics of medical doctors
Pr: James F Donnelly
**Treas:* Sterling Hall
Ex Dir: Henry Easttrou
Genl Mgr: Joseph Gendreau

Pgrm Dir: Victor Griffiths
Snr Mgr: Frank Kostek

D-U-N-S 96-384-8650 IMP
GANDER MOUNTAIN CO
180 5th St E Ste 1300, Saint Paul, MN 55101-1664
Tel (651) 325-4300 *Founded/Ownrshp* 2010
Sales 1.1MMM^E *EMP* 5,605
SIC 5941 Sporting goods & bicycle shops; Hunting equipment; Fishing equipment; Camping & backpacking equipment; Sporting goods & bicycle shops; Hunting equipment; Fishing equipment; Camping & backpacking equipment
Ch Bd: David C Pratt
**Pr:* Michael Owens
**Ex VP:* Eric R Jacobsen
**Ex VP:* Lisa Schmidt
**Ex VP:* Derek Siddons
Sr VP: Mark A Bussard
VP: Greg Desch
VP: Pat Mauldin
VP: Alan Tague
Mng Dir: Shannon Roberson
Dist Mgr: Tim Miller
Board of Directors: Karen M Bohn, Marshall L Day, Richard C Dell, Gerald A Erickson, Ronald A Erickson

GANDRUD NISSAN
See IVAN GANDRUD CHEVROLET INC

D-U-N-S 09-262-6936
GANLEY AUTOMOTIVE INC (OH)
310 Broadway Ave, Bedford, OH 44146-2131
Tel (877) 639-6813 *Founded/Ownrshp* 1978
Sales 25.6MM^E *EMP* 52
SIC 5511 Automobiles, new & used
Pr: Thomas D Ganley
**Treas:* David Robinson
Genl Mgr: Tom Cinalli
Genl Mgr: Michael Friedman
Genl Mgr: Bob Ganley
Sls Mgr: Brett Clapham
Sls Mgr: Wayne Frejofsky
Sls Mgr: John Romeo

D-U-N-S 04-061-7826
GANLEY EAST INC
GANLEY SUBARU WICKLIFFE
28840 Euclid Ave, Wickliffe, OH 44092-2529
Tel (440) 585-1000 *Founded/Ownrshp* 2000
Sales 20.8MM^E *EMP* 40
SIC 5511 5531 Automobiles, new & used; Automotive parts
Pr: Tom Ganley
Genl Mgr: Jay Hoegler
Sls Mgr: Brandon Boro
Sales Asso: Andrew Anderson

GANLEY HONDA
See TD GANLEY INC

GANLEY LINCOLN MIDDLEBURG HTS
See BROADVUE MOTORS INC

GANLEY MERCEDES
See AKRON GANLEY INC

GANLEY SUBARU WICKLIFFE
See GANLEY EAST INC

D-U-N-S 12-700-6729
GANNAWAY WEB HOLDINGS LLC
WORLDNOW
(*Suby of* FRANKLY INC.)
2701 Queens Plz N Ste 502, Long Island City, NY 11101-4024
Tel (212) 931-1200 *Founded/Ownrshp* 2015
Sales 26.0MM *EMP* 100
SIC 7371 ; Computer software development & applications
CEO: Gary Gannaway
CFO: Inna Vartelsky
Ofcr: Craig Smith
Ex VP: Melissa Hatter
Ex VP: Sandhi Kozsuch
Sr VP: Frank Alfieri
Sr VP: Elizabeth Firalio
Sr VP: Stan Justice
VP: Allen Barney
VP: Rick Bentz
VP: Mike Cassetta
VP: Shevin Conway
VP: Denise Groover
VP: David Murphy
VP: Charlie Ponger

D-U-N-S 08-169-8342 IMP
■ GANNETT BROADCASTING INC
WXIA-TV
(*Suby of* TEGNA INC) ★
7950 Jones Branch Dr, Mc Lean, VA 22102-3302
Tel (703) 854-6000 *Founded/Ownrshp* 1995
Sales 370.3MM^E *EMP* 1,500^E
SIC 4833 Television broadcasting stations; Television broadcasting stations
Sr VP: Brooke Spectorsky
V Ch: James Johnson
**Sr VP:* Rob Mennie
Sr VP: Bob Sullivan
VP: Ellen Crooke
VP: Philip R Currie
VP: Gary Foy
VP: Dale Henn
VP: Abigail Horrigan
VP: Leslie Hurst
VP: James Jackson
VP: Kevin Lefew
VP: Lane Michaelsen
VP: Joshua Resnik
VP: Joel Rochon
Board of Directors: Douglas H Mc Corkindale

D-U-N-S 07-984-1977
GANNETT CO INC
7950 Jones Branch Dr, Mc Lean, VA 22102-3302
Tel (703) 854-6000 *Founded/Ownrshp* 2014
Sales 189.7MM^E *EMP* 19,600
Tkr Sym GCI *Exch* NYS
SIC 2711 7375 Newspapers; Information retrieval services
Pr: Robert J Dickey

*Ch Bd: John Jeffry Louis
CFO: Alison K Engel
Chf Cred: Joanne Lipman
VP: Kelly Andersen
Dir Sec: Maribel Perez Wadsworth
CTO: Jamshid Khazenie
Board of Directors: John E Cody, Stephen W Coll, Donald E Felsinger, Lila Ibrahim, Tony A Prophet, Debra A Sandler, Chloe R Sladden

D-U-N-S 02-811-9915
GANNETT FLEMING AFFILIATES INC
207 Senate Ave, Camp Hill, PA 17011-2316
Tel (717) 763-7211 Founded/Ownrshp 1981
Sales 331.9MM EMP 1,743
Accts Stambaugh Ness Pc Hanover P
SIC 8711 7374 6512 Engineering services; Data processing service; Commercial & industrial building operation; Engineering services; Data processing service; Commercial & industrial building operation
Ch Bd: William Stout
*Pr: Robert Scaer
*Treas: Lynn E Knepp
*Sr VP: Robert J Dietz

D-U-N-S 13-582-4808
GANNETT FLEMING ENGINEERS AND ARCHITECTS PC
209 Senate Ave Ste 100, Camp Hill, PA 17011-2332
Tel (717) 763-7212 Founded/Ownrshp 2004
Sales 23.7MM^E EMP 157^E
SIC 8711 Civil engineering
CEO: William M Stout
Treas: Kate Berrigan
*Treas: Joseph Botchie
*VP: Chester Allen
VP: Charles H Beauduy
VP: Charles Lynch
VP: Greg Nazarow
Off Mgr: Michelle Fitzmaurice
VP Opers: Paul Linahan

D-U-N-S 11-436-0899
GANNETT FLEMING PROJECT DEVELOPMENT CORP
(Suby of FLEMING GANNETT INC) ★
207 Senate Ave, Camp Hill, PA 17011-2316
Tel (717) 763-7270 Founded/Ownrshp 1998
Sales 22.8MM EMP 22
Accts Stambaugh Ness Pc Hanover P
SIC 1541 Industrial buildings & warehouses; Industrial buildings & warehouses
Pr: Donald Morosky
Treas: Marcello H Soto
VP: Lynn E Knepp
VP: Kambiz F Shadan
Mktg Dir: James Costello

D-U-N-S 00-713-3515
■ **GANNETT MISSOURI PUBLISHING INC**
SPRINGFIELD NEWS-LEADER
(Suby of TEGNA INC) ★
651 N Boonville Ave, Springfield, MO 65806-1005
Tel (417) 836-1100 Founded/Ownrshp 1933
Sales 52.7MM^E EMP 390
SIC 2711 2752 Newspapers, publishing & printing; Commercial printing, lithographic; Newspapers, publishing & printing; Commercial printing, lithographic
Pr: Tom Bookstaver
*Pr: Tom Brookstaver
Software D: Tyler Lane

D-U-N-S 00-634-2026 EXP
■ **GANNETT RIVER STATES PUBLISHING CORP**
(Suby of TEGNA INC) ★
7950 Jones Branch Dr, Mc Lean, VA 22102-3302
Tel (703) 284-6000 Founded/Ownrshp 1819
Sales 115.7MM^E EMP 1,300
SIC 2711 2741 Newspapers, publishing & printing; Miscellaneous publishing; Newspapers, publishing & printing; Miscellaneous publishing
Ch Bd: William T Malone
Pr: Craig A Moon
V Ch Bd: Hugh B Patterson
VP: Donald Davis
VP: Ronald Krengel
VP: Edgar Major
VP: N Suzanne Miles

D-U-N-S 01-424-9759 IMP
■ **GANNETT SATELLITE INFORMATION NETWORK INC**
USA TODAY
(Suby of TEGNA INC) ★
7950 Jones Branch Dr, Mc Lean, VA 22102-3302
Tel (703) 854-3400 Founded/Ownrshp 1980
Sales 263.9MM^E EMP 2,800
SIC 2711 Newspapers, publishing & printing; Newspapers, publishing & printing
CEO: Douglas H Mc Corkindale
Pr: Tom Beusse
*Pr: David Hunke
Ch: Dave Morgan
*Treas: Gracia Martore
*Ex VP: Susie Ellwood
Ex VP: Derek Murphy
Sr VP: Peter Lazarus
Sr VP: Sandra Cordova Micek
Sr VP: Michael Safran
Sr VP: Dan Thomas
VP: Maureen Consavage
VP: Laura Del Greco
VP: Lori Erdos
VP: Tony Hill
VP: Myron Maslowsky
VP: John Palmisano
VP: Scott R Singer

D-U-N-S 07-914-3598
■ **GANNETT SATELLITE INFORMATION NETWORK INC** (TN)
TENNESSEAN NEWSPAPER
(Suby of TEGNA INC) ★
1100 Broadway, Nashville, TN 37203-3116
Tel (615) 259-8000 Founded/Ownrshp 1980
Sales 107.2MM^E EMP 1,100
SIC 2711 Newspapers; Newspapers
Pr: Laura Hollingsworth

D-U-N-S 06-790-2189
■ **GANNETT SUPPLY CORP**
(Suby of TEGNA INC) ★
7950 Jones Branch Dr, Mc Lean, VA 22102-3302
Tel (703) 854-6000 Founded/Ownrshp 1970
Sales 21.0MM^E EMP 15
SIC 5111 5084 Printing & writing paper; Printing trades machinery, equipment & supplies
CEO: Gracia C Martore
*Pr: Frank O'Toole
*CFO: Victoria D Harker
*Sr VP: Maryam Banikarim
*Sr VP: William Behan
*Sr VP: Kevin Lord

D-U-N-S 07-215-9767
GANNON UNIVERSITY
109 University Sq, Erie, PA 16541-0002
Tel (814) 871-7000 Founded/Ownrshp 1944
Sales 86.6MM EMP 600
Accts Parentebeard Llc Pittsburgh
SIC 8221 University; University
Pr: Antoine Garibaldi
V Ch: Steven Ropski
COO: Tex Brieger
VP: Kaitlyn Roose
Assoc Dir: Catherine Gillespie
Assoc Dir: Catherine Oakley
Genl Mgr: Pete Mannarelli
CIO: Robert Cline
IT Man: Hamid Torab
Pgrm Dir: Anne O'Neill
Art Dir: Andrew Lapiska

D-U-N-S 01-420-5199
GANS COMMUNICATIONS LP
GMP CABLE TV
(Suby of HARRON COMMUNICATIONS LP) ★
911 N Market St, Berwick, PA 18603-3127
Tel (570) 802-5642 Founded/Ownrshp 1954, 2003
Sales 44.7MM^E EMP 150
SIC 4841 Cable television services; Cable television services
Genl Pt: Joseph Gans III
Pt: Irene Gans
VP: Terry Herron
Rgnl Mgr: Edward Merrill
Genl Mgr: Tom Carey
Netwrk Eng: J Donaldson
Netwrk Eng: Pete Garcia
Opers Mgr: Robert Curtis
Opers Mgr: John Wollett
Mktg Mgr: Kathleen Macleod

D-U-N-S 10-252-4803 IMP
GANT USA CORP
100 Wall St Ste 702, New York, NY 10005-3721
Tel (212) 230-1949 Founded/Ownrshp 1999
Sales 34.2MM^E EMP 75
SIC 5136 5611 Men's & boys' clothing; Men's & boys' clothing stores
CEO: Justin Cupps
Store Mgr: Taylor Ruckh
IT Man: Franklyn Calderon
VP Mktg: Rocco Venneri
Pr Mgr: Emily Schumann
Sls Mgr: Jaron Ross

D-U-N-S 01-719-3033
GANTECH INC
9175 Guilford Rd Ste 101, Columbia, MD 21046-2564
Tel (410) 464-1400 Founded/Ownrshp 1999
Sales 31.6MM^E EMP 89
SIC 8711 Consulting engineer
Pr: Thomas J Laskowski
*CFO: Jeff Furst
*VP: Mia Millette
*Prin: Michael Helmicki
IT Man: Amy Pierce
Netwrk Eng: Leo Bruni
Opers Mgr: Dana Goodrich
Snr Mgr: Chad Mathias

D-U-N-S 02-041-6921 IMP/EXP
GANTRADE CORP
210 Summit Ave Ste B2, Montvale, NJ 07645-1590
Tel (201) 476-5256 Founded/Ownrshp 1975
Sales 140.0MM EMP 22
SIC 5169 Organic chemicals, synthetic
Pr: Mahendra Parekh
*Treas: Joan Parekh
*VP: Jay Moorghy
*VP: Haron Parekh

D-U-N-S 03-503-5877 EXP
GANVT MOTORS INC
GWINNETT PLACE NISSAN
2555 Pleasant Hill Rd, Duluth, GA 30096-4117
Tel (770) 476-7771 Founded/Ownrshp 1999
Sales 51.3MM^E EMP 148
SIC 5511 Automobiles, new & used; Automobiles, new & used
CEO: Larry Van Tuyl
*CFO: Allan M Cady
Genl Mgr: Rick Williams
Off Mgr: Sylvia Wilder
Sls Mgr: Eric Carriveau
Sls Mgr: Julie Pazone

D-U-N-S 96-231-3446 IMP
GANZ USA HOLDING LLC
60 Industrial Pkwy Ste 43, Cheektowaga, NY 14227-2774
Tel (770) 973-0092 Founded/Ownrshp 2007
Sales 79.5MM^E EMP 351
SIC 5199 Gifts & novelties; Gifts & novelties
Ex Dir: Mike Palumbo

D-U-N-S 79-878-5242 IMP/EXP
GANZ USA LLC
(Suby of GANZ USA HOLDING LLC) ★
60 Industrial Pkwy Ste 43, Cheektowaga, NY 14227-2774
Tel (770) 973-0092 Founded/Ownrshp 2007
Sales 79.5MM^E EMP 350
SIC 5199 Gifts & novelties; Gifts & novelties
Ex Dir: Mike Palumbo
Dir IT: Moses Levy
Sls Dir: Doug Heck
Sls Mgr: Kelly Watson

D-U-N-S 18-361-0112 IMP/EXP
GANZCORP INVESTMENTS INC
MUSTANG DYNAMOMETER
2300 Pinnacle Pkwy, Twinsburg, OH 44087-2368
Tel (330) 963-5400 Founded/Ownrshp 1986
Sales 24.6MM^E EMP 60
SIC 3559 Automotive related machinery
Owner: Dean Ganzhorn
*Ex VP: Donald W Ganzhorn Jr
VP: Eser Manav
Exec: Jennifer Schwarzwalder
VP Mktg: Dean Ganvhorn
Sls Mgr: Michael Caldwell

D-U-N-S 04-862-6915 IMP
▲ **GAP INC**
2 Folsom St, San Francisco, CA 94105-1205
Tel (415) 427-0100 Founded/Ownrshp 1969
Sales 16.4MMM EMP 141,000
Accts Deloitte & Touche Llp San Fra
Tkr Sym GPS Exch NYS
SIC 5651 5641 5632 5621 5611 Family clothing stores; Jeans stores; Children's & infants' wear stores; Children's wear; Infants' wear; Women's accessory & specialty stores; Women's clothing stores; Men's & boys' clothing stores; Family clothing stores; Jeans stores; Children's & infants' wear stores; Children's wear; Infants' wear; Women's accessory & specialty stores; Women's clothing stores; Men's & boys' clothing stores
CEO: Arthur Peck
Pr: Deborah Lloyd
CFO: Tim Billups
CFO: Sabrina Simmons
Chf Cred: Michelle Banks
Ex VP: Nick Cullen
Ex VP: Patti Johnson
Ex VP: John T Keiser
Ex VP: Brian Pollitt
Ex VP: Sonia Syngal
Sr VP: Liz Meltzer
Sr VP: Stan Raggio
VP: Johnathon Baker
VP: Michael Corr
VP: Kevin Durrance
VP: Tom Lima
VP: Tess Roering
VP: Steve Rouman
VP: Mark Webb
VP Bus Dev: Jayne Greenberg
Exec: Jill Robertson
Board of Directors: Domenico De Sole, Robert J Fisher, William S Fisher, Isabella D Goren, Bob L Martin, Jorge P Montoya, Mayo A Shattuck III, Katherine Tsang

D-U-N-S 82-745-1050
GAP INC
40 1st St Ne, Rio Rancho, NM 87124-3589
Tel (505) 462-0034 Founded/Ownrshp 1988
Sales 124.8MM^E EMP 277^E
SIC 2326 Men's & boys' work clothing
CEO: Glenn K Murphy
*Treas: Jennifer Cho
*VP: Bryon Pollitt
*VP: Sabrina Simmons

D-U-N-S 15-379-7527
GAP INTERNATIONAL INC
700 Old Marple Rd, Springfield, PA 19064-1236
Tel (610) 328-0308 Founded/Ownrshp 1978
Sales 32.7MM^E EMP 130
SIC 8742 Management consulting services; Management consulting services
CEO: Pontish Yeramyan
*COO: Cindi Cooper
*COO: Cindy Fischer
*COO: Robert E Rothman
*VP: Mary Alice Benamy
VP: Jon Greenawalt
VP: Betsey Johnson
VP: Ije Nwokomah
VP: Sally S Richard
*VP: ARA Yeramyan
Genl Mgr: Aris Degirmenci

D-U-N-S 14-815-5971
GAP PARTNERS INC
400 Kellys Creek Rd # 105, Rabun Gap, GA 30568-2213
Tel (706) 746-4000 Founded/Ownrshp 2008
Sales 31.5MM^E EMP 94
SIC 3444 Sheet metalwork
CEO: Luke T Faulstick
*CFO: James J Murray
*Ch: Steve L Hollis
*Genl Mgr: David Bowes
Opers Mgr: David Williams

D-U-N-S 12-043-9869
GAP SOLUTIONS INC
GAPSI
12054 North Shore Dr, Reston, VA 20190-4991
Tel (703) 707-2090 Founded/Ownrshp 1998
Sales 49.8MM^E EMP 500
SIC 7379 Computer related consulting services
CEO: Eric Wolking
*Ex VP: Pat Flannery

D-U-N-S 96-518-9322
GAPP WIRELESS CORP
12312 95th Ave, South Richmond Hill, NY 11419-1424
Tel (212) 444-8288 Founded/Ownrshp 2009
Sales 23.5MM EMP 5
SIC 8748 Business consulting; Business consulting
Pr: Rajpreet Kaur

D-U-N-S 94-431-3428
GAPPA OIL CO INC
DICKS STANDARD SERVICE
211 S Otter Ave, Parkers Prairie, MN 56361-4999
Tel (218) 338-4391 Founded/Ownrshp 1995
Sales 30.3MM EMP 21
Accts Conway Deuth And Schmiesing
SIC 5541 Gasoline service stations; Gasoline service stations
CEO: Richard Gappa
*VP: Deborah Gappa

GAPSI
See GAP SOLUTIONS INC

D-U-N-S 92-698-6522 IMP
GAPVAX INC
575 Central Ave, Johnstown, PA 15902-2600
Tel (814) 535-6766 Founded/Ownrshp 1990
Sales 30.0MM EMP 100
SIC 3537 Industrial trucks & tractors
Pr: Gary Pobrosky
*Sec: Rose Pobrosky
*VP: James E Griffith
VP: Richard Lamm

D-U-N-S 00-850-4870
GAR ENTERPRISES (CA)
K G S ELECTRONICS
418 E Live Oak Ave, Arcadia, CA 91006-5619
Tel (626) 574-1175 Founded/Ownrshp 1960
Sales 30.3MM^E EMP 100
SIC 5045 3728 Anti-static equipment & devices; Aircraft assemblies, subassemblies & parts; Anti-static equipment & devices; Aircraft assemblies, subassemblies & parts
Pr: Nathan Sugimoto
Off Mgr: Corie Soto
Mktg Mgr: Elisa Aldape

D-U-N-S 02-897-3055
GAR TOOTELIAN INC
8246 Crawford Ave, Reedley, CA 93654-9550
Tel (559) 638-6311 Founded/Ownrshp 1949
Sales 57.8MM^E EMP 50
SIC 5191

D-U-N-S 36-192-2016
GAR-MONT OF PRAISE INC
ALL-TEMP REFRIGERATION
271 Highway 1085, Madisonville, LA 70447-3307
Tel (888) 626-1277 Founded/Ownrshp 2009
Sales 27.0MM^E EMP 64
SIC 5078 5075 Commercial refrigeration equipment; Air conditioning equipment, except room units
Pr: Bryan Krantz
Genl Mgr: George Nicoll
Opers Mgr: Eddie Montreuil
Sls Mgr: Mark Mayeux

D-U-N-S 10-709-7529 IMP/EXP
GARAGE DOOR GROUP INC
AMARR GARAGE DOORS
(Suby of AMARR CO) ★
3800 Greenway Cir, Lawrence, KS 66046-5443
Tel (785) 865-5500 Founded/Ownrshp 1983
Sales 117.3MM^E EMP 500
SIC 3442 Garage doors, overhead: metal; Garage doors, overhead: metal
CEO: Richard Brenner
Pr: Jim Ford
VP: Matt Hukill
Genl Mgr: Andrew Claxton
Genl Mgr: Cory Dayton
Genl Mgr: Jason Degroot
Genl Mgr: John Schwahn
VP Mfg: Delbert Phlipot
Sfty Dirs: Jake Trybom
Opers Mgr: David Davidson
Prd Mgr: Phillip Peek

D-U-N-S 00-693-8518
GARAGE DOOR SYSTEMS LLC
OVERHEAD DOOR CO INDIANAPOLIS
8811 Bash St, Indianapolis, IN 46256-1276
Tel (317) 842-7444 Founded/Ownrshp 1967
Sales 43.8MM^E EMP 190
SIC 5031 1742

D-U-N-S 07-770-5200
GARAGE MANAGEMENT CO LLC
RED BALL GARAGE
770 Lexington Ave Rm 1102, New York, NY 10065-8165
Tel (212) 888-7400 Founded/Ownrshp 1962
Sales 31.1MM^E EMP 550
SIC 7521 Parking garage; Parking garage
Pr: Richard Chapman
MIS Mgr: Dale Reynolds

D-U-N-S 00-149-5472
■ **GARAN INC** (VA)
(Suby of BERKSHIRE HATHAWAY INC) ★
200 Madison Ave Fl 4, New York, NY 10016-3905
Tel (212) 563-1292 Founded/Ownrshp 1941, 2002
Sales 657.0MM^E EMP 4,500
SIC 2361 2369 2331 2339 2321 T-shirts & tops: girls', children's & infants'; Slacks: girls' & children's; T-shirts & tops, women's: made from purchased materials; Shirts, women's & juniors': made from purchased materials; Jeans: women's, misses' & juniors'; Men's & boys' furnishings; Sport shirts, men's & boys': from purchased materials; T-shirts & tops: girls', children's & infants'; Slacks: girls' & children's; T-shirts & tops, women's: made from purchased materials; Shirts, women's & juniors': made from purchased materials; Jeans: women's, misses' & juniors'; Men's & boys' furnishings; Sport shirts, men's & boys': from purchased materials
CEO: Seymour Lichtenstein
*Pr: Jerald Kamiel
*CFO: David M Fligel
Treas: Alex J Sistarenik
VP: Wayne C Cooper
VP: Kathie Fiore
VP: Anthony Raffa
*VP: Marvin S Robinson
Plng Mgr: Jet Wang
Dir IT: Jason Wood
Info Man: Carmine Vizzero
Board of Directors: Warren Buffett, Marc Hamburg

D-U-N-S 07-425-0945
GARAN LUCOW MILLER PROFESSIONAL CORP
1155 Brewery Park Blvd, Detroit, MI 48207-2668
Tel (313) 446-1530 Founded/Ownrshp 1948
Sales 30.3MM^E EMP 250
SIC 8111 General practice law office; General practice law office
Ch: Roger A Smith
Sr Pt: John Gillooly
Sr Pt: Ian Simpson
Sr Pt: Peter Worden
Mng Pt: Gregory Bokota
*Pr: James Borin
Pr: Lisa Hoyt
Pr: Megan Thill
CTO: Scott Olson
Opers Mgr: Maureen Brogan

D-U-N-S 04-717-3976
GARB-KO INC
7-ELEVEN
(Suby of GRAD, INC.)
3925 Fortune Blvd, Saginaw, MI 48603-2287
Tel (989) 799-6937 Founded/Ownrshp 1982
Sales 76.9MM^E EMP 620
Accts Bdo Grand Rapids Michigan
SIC 5411 6794 Convenience stores, chain; Franchises, selling or licensing; Convenience stores, chain; Franchises, selling or licensing
Pr: Dan Abraham
COO: Robert Dement
*CFO: Pat Plumley
Off Mgr: Ginny Arnold
Off Mgr: Kelly Taylor
CIO: Kathy Jaure
MIS Dir: Kim Bivens
Dir IT: Nathan Fowler
IT Man: Monica Slater
Opers Mgr: Bob Demint
Board of Directors: Larry Hauck, Cathy Morris

D-U-N-S 05-777-1958
GARBADE CONSTRUCTION CORP
200 N Main St, Vestal, NY 13850-1635
Tel (607) 754-9609 Founded/Ownrshp 1986
Sales 27.8MM EMP 40
Accts Borelli & Mahonski Llp Vestal
SIC 1542 8741 Commercial & office building, new construction; Commercial & office buildings, renovation & repair; School building construction; Construction management; Commercial & office building, new construction; Commercial & office buildings, renovation & repair; School building construction; Construction management
Pr: Robert W Garbade

GARBAGE DISPOSAL SERVICE
See REPUBLIC SERVICES OF NORTH CAROLINA LLC

GARBAN INTERCAP
See ICAP SERVICES NORTH AMERICA LLC

GARBER AUTOMALL
See GARBER CHEVROLET-BUICK-PONTIAC-GMC TRUCK INC

D-U-N-S 01-920-9196
GARBER BROS INC
Kay Way Rr 139, Stoughton, MA 02072
Tel (781) 341-0800 Founded/Ownrshp 1947
Sales 221.8MM^E EMP 275
SIC 5194 5145 5141 5122 Tobacco & tobacco products; Cigarettes; Candy; Groceries, general line; Cosmetics, perfumes & hair products;Toiletries;Tobacco & tobacco products; Cigarettes; Candy; Groceries, general line; Cosmetics, perfumes & hair products; Toiletries
Pr: Harold Garber
*Treas: Amy Garber
Sales Exec: John Poulakis

D-U-N-S 79-522-7628
GARBER BUICK CO INC
GARBER BUICK OF SAGINAW
5925 State St, Saginaw, MI 48603-3422
Tel (989) 497-4444 Founded/Ownrshp 1907
Sales 26.4MM^E EMP 90
SIC 5511 Automobiles, new & used; Automobiles, new & used
Genl Mgr: Rich Perdue
Off Mgr: Stacey Buszka
Sls Mgr: Erica Fritzler
Sls Mgr: Mary Lynch
Sls Mgr: Thomas Ward
Sales Asso: Mark Gehringer
Sales Asso: Josh Kusterer
Sales Asso: Jeff Pacholka
Snr Mgr: Ryan Shepard

GARBER BUICK OF SAGINAW
See GARBER BUICK CO INC

D-U-N-S 01-724-1035
GARBER CHEVROLET GEO INC
GARBER GEO
(Suby of GARBER MANAGEMENT GROUP INC) ★
1700 N Saginaw Rd, Midland, MI 48640-2693
Tel (989) 839-9944 Founded/Ownrshp 1991
Sales 23.0MM^E EMP 60
SIC 5511 Automobiles, new & used; Automobiles, new & used
Pr: Richard J Garber Jr
Genl Mgr: Mike Weinert
Store Mgr: Darin Crook
Sls Mgr: Brian Strong
Sales Asso: Gary Ashley

D-U-N-S 86-109-7343
GARBER CHEVROLET-BUICK-PONTIAC-GMC TRUCK INC
GARBER AUTOMALL
3340 Highway 17, Green Cove Springs, FL 32043-9365
Tel (904) 264-4502 Founded/Ownrshp 1993
Sales 34.4MM^E EMP 106
SIC 5511 Automobiles, new & used; Automobiles, new & used
Pr: Richard J Garber
*Genl Mgr: Ron Harris
Sls Mgr: Daniel Devries
Sls Mgr: Mike Stringer

D-U-N-S 03-232-5870
GARBER CHRYSLER PLYMOUTH DODGE TRUCK INC
3408 Highway 17, Green Cove Springs, FL 32043-9306
Tel (904) 264-2442 Founded/Ownrshp 1957
Sales 21.6MM^E EMP 90
SIC 5511 7538 Automobiles, new & used; General automotive repair shops; Automobiles, new & used; General automotive repair shops
Pr: Richard J Garber
Genl Mgr: Frank Kuitkowski

GARBER GEO
See GARBER CHEVROLET GEO INC

D-U-N-S 08-983-9328
GARBER INDUSTRIES INC (LA)
OFFSHORE ENERGY
5900 Highway 90 E, Broussard, LA 70518-5701
Tel (337) 233-7442 Founded/Ownrshp 1977
Sales 47.8MM^E EMP 140
SIC 1389 7353 4492 4499 5169 Oil field services; Oil field equipment, rental or leasing; Marine towing services; Boat rental, commercial; Drilling mud; Oil field services; Oil field equipment, rental or leasing; Marine towing services; Boat rental, commercial; Drilling mud
CEO: Charles M Garber
Pr: Charles Garber
Board of Directors: Roy Garber

D-U-N-S 00-696-0686 EXP
GARBER MANAGEMENT GROUP INC
GARBER'S PRESTIGE AUTO SALES
999 S Washington Ave # 1, Saginaw, MI 48601-2573
Tel (989) 790-9090 Founded/Ownrshp 1980
Sales 419.8MM^E EMP 1,200
SIC 5511 Automobiles, new & used; Automobiles, new & used
Pr: Richard J Garber Jr
Treas: Michael Dicken
*Sec: Patrick Hengesbach
Sls Mgr: Craig Lang
Sales Asso: Justin Jarman
Sales Asso: Joseph Rau

GARBER'S PRESTIGE AUTO SALES
See GARBER MANAGEMENT GROUP INC

D-U-N-S 04-652-2686
GARBERVILLE GAS CORP
880 N Wright Rd, Santa Rosa, CA 95407-6606
Tel (707) 923-2188 Founded/Ownrshp 1948
Sales 53.3MM^E EMP 71
SIC 4923 5984 5722 Gas transmission & distribution; Propane gas, bottled; Gas household appliances; Gas transmission & distribution; Propane gas, bottled; Gas household appliances
Pr: William P Stewart
*Sec: Marlyn R Stewart
*VP: Jeff Stewart

GARBO'S
See MLH INC

D-U-N-S 07-840-8620
GARCADIA MOTORS LLC
405 S Main St Ste 1200, Salt Lake City, UT 84111-3412
Tel (801) 257-3400 Founded/Ownrshp 2008
Sales 72.1MM EMP 0^E
SIC 6719 Investment holding companies, except banks; Investment holding companies, except banks

D-U-N-S 08-004-9903
GARCADIA PARTNERS LLC
(Suby of GARFF ENTERPRISES INC) ★
405 S Main St Ste 1200, Salt Lake City, UT 84111-3412
Tel (801) 257-3400 Founded/Ownrshp 2015
Sales 28.4MM^E EMP 74^E
SIC 5511 6719 Automobiles, new & used; Investment holding companies, except banks

D-U-N-S 87-806-9459
GARCIA AND ASSOCIATES
GANDA
1 Saunders Ave, San Anselmo, CA 94960-1719
Tel (415) 458-5803 Founded/Ownrshp 1994
Sales 23.5MM^E EMP 175
SIC 8748 Environmental consultant; Environmental consultant
Owner: John C Garcia
VP: Samantha Hillaire
Rgnl Mgr: Patrick Oday
Snr Mgr: John Scott

D-U-N-S 60-356-4071
GARCIA CONSTRUCTION GROUP INC
HEARTLAND READY MIX
6002 Michigan Rd, Indianapolis, IN 46228-1163
Tel (317) 222-5329 Founded/Ownrshp 1989
Sales 22.7MM^E EMP 100
SIC 1542 7349 4225 Commercial & office buildings, renovation & repair; Building maintenance, except repairs; General warehousing; Commercial & office buildings, renovation & repair; Building maintenance, except repairs; General warehousing
Pr: Charles J Garcia

D-U-N-S 05-265-1783
GARCIA FOODS INC (TX)
ANDY GARCIA FOODS
1802 Jackson Keller Rd, San Antonio, TX 78213-2517
Tel (210) 349-6262 Founded/Ownrshp 1956
Sales 22.5MM^E EMP 120^E
SIC 2032 Sausages from purchased meat; Mexican foods: packaged in cans, jars, etc.
Ch Bd: Andy Garcia
*Pr: Louis R Garcia
*Pr: Yvonne Gottwald
*Sec: Andrew E Garcia
*VP: Kenneth D Garcia
*VP: Yvette Garcia

GARCIA HONDA
See GARCIA IMPORTS INC

D-U-N-S 09-797-2095
GARCIA IMPORTS INC (NM)
GARCIA HONDA
8301 Lomas Blvd Ne, Albuquerque, NM 87110-7908
Tel (505) 260-5000 Founded/Ownrshp 1971, 1996
Sales 31.7MM^E EMP 80
SIC 5511 Automobiles, new & used; Automobiles, new & used
Pr: Sheilah P Garcia
*VP: Edward Garcia
*VP: Toby E Garcia

GARCIA JAGUAR EL PASO
See GARCIA MOTORS EL PASO LLC

D-U-N-S 02-177-4576
GARCIA MOTORS EL PASO LLC
GARCIA JAGUAR EL PASO
1444 Airway Blvd, El Paso, TX 79925-2215
Tel (915) 881-1505 Founded/Ownrshp 2009
Sales 20.4MM^E EMP 70
SIC 5511 Automobiles, new & used

D-U-N-S 03-979-6495
GARCIA VIRGINIA MEMORIAL HEALTH CENTER (OR)
85 N 12th Ave, Cornelius, OR 97113-9029
Tel (503) 359-5564 Founded/Ownrshp 1974
Sales 37.8MM EMP 52
Accts Hoffman Stewart & Schmidt Pc
SIC 8011 Clinic, operated by physicians; Clinic, operated by physicians
Ex Dir: Gilles Munoz
*Pr: Robert Warner
*Treas: Joe Strom
Doctor: Laura R Byerly MD

D-U-N-S 10-288-5209
GARCO BUILDING SYSTEMS INC
2714 S Garfield Rd, Airway Heights, WA 99001-9595
Tel (509) 244-5611 Founded/Ownrshp 2010
Sales 29.0MM^E EMP 120
Accts Bdo Seidman Llp Spokane Was
SIC 3448 Prefabricated metal buildings; Prefabricated metal buildings
Pr: C William Savitz
Sec: Paul Millar
VP: John Pargman
VP: Mark Radmaker
Info Man: Dennis Wood
Cust Svc D: John Hundahl

D-U-N-S 09-368-4694 IMP
GARCO CONSTRUCTION INC
4114 E Broadway Ave, Spokane, WA 99202-4531
Tel (509) 536-1649 Founded/Ownrshp 1978
Sales 133.2MM^E EMP 275
SIC 1541 Steel building construction; Steel building construction
Pr: Clancy Welsh
CFO: Ben Leuty
*CFO: James Morrison
*Ch: James T Welsh
*Treas: Sharon Harkrader
Ofcr: Pete Subitch
*VP: Hollis E Barnett
*VP: Frank Etter
*VP: Jamie Welsh
*VP: Timothy J Welsh
Sfty Mgr: Mary Karrer

D-U-N-S 10-303-9178
GARCOA INC
GARCOA MARKETING
26135 Mureau Rd Ste 100, Calabasas, CA 91302-3184
Tel (818) 225-0375 Founded/Ownrshp 1975
Sales 77.9MM^E EMP 1,000
SIC 7389

GARCOA MARKETING
See GARCOA INC

GARDA CASH LOGISTICS
See GARDA CL TECHNICAL SERVICES INC

D-U-N-S 05-472-7995
GARDA CL ATLANTIC INC
GCL A
(Suby of GARDA CASH LOGISTICS) ★
4200 Governor Printz Blvd, Wilmington, DE 19802-2315
Tel (302) 762-5444 Founded/Ownrshp 1951, 1996
Sales 19.4MM^E EMP 297
SIC 7381 Armored car services; Armored car services
Pr: Stephan Cretier
*Pr: Chris W Jamroz
Ofcr: Vic Schnurstein
*Sr VP: Patrick Prince
VP: Rob Van Der Merwe
VP: Michael Middleton
VP: Jim Purcell
Brnch Mgr: Kevin Lee
IT Man: Edward Shank

D-U-N-S 07-443-4606
GARDA CL GREAT LAKES INC
UNITED ARMORED SERVICES
(Suby of GARDA CASH LOGISTICS) ★
201 Schofield Dr, Columbus, OH 43213-3831
Tel (561) 939-7000 Founded/Ownrshp 2005
Sales 15.1MM^E EMP 500
SIC 7381 7389 7359 Armored car services; Packaging & labeling services; Equipment rental & leasing; Armored car services; Packaging & labeling services; Equipment rental & leasing
Pr: Stephan Cretier
Pr: Chris W Jamroz
VP: Patrice Boily

D-U-N-S 04-018-4483
GARDA CL NORTHWEST INC
GCL NW
(Suby of GARDA CASH LOGISTICS) ★
1401 E Yesler Way, Seattle, WA 98122-5545
Tel (206) 322-8848 Founded/Ownrshp 1983
Sales 16.4MM^E EMP 800^E
SIC 7381 Armored car services; Armored car services
Pr: Stephan Cretier
*Pr: Chris W Jamroz

D-U-N-S 07-672-4392
GARDA CL SOUTHWEST INC
GCL SW
(Suby of GARDA CASH LOGISTICS) ★
3300 Matrix Dr, Richardson, TX 75082-2765
Tel (213) 383-3611 Founded/Ownrshp 1985
Sales 9.7MM^E EMP 300
SIC 7381 7389 4215 Armored car services; Courier or messenger service; Parcel delivery, vehicular; Armored car services; Courier or messenger service; Parcel delivery, vehicular
Pr: Stephan Cretier
*Pr: Chris W Jamroz

D-U-N-S 79-945-5480
GARDA CL TECHNICAL SERVICES INC
GARDA CASH LOGISTICS
(Suby of ATI SYSTEMS INTERNATIONAL INC) ★
700 S Federal Hwy Ste 300, Boca Raton, FL 33432-6128
Tel (561) 939-7000 Founded/Ownrshp 1996
Sales NA EMP 3,000
SIC 6099 7381 Safe deposit companies; Armored car services; Safe deposit companies; Armored car services
Pr: Stephan Cretier
V Ch: Richard Drutman
*Pr: Chris W Jamroz
Ofcr: Barbara Danzi
Sr VP: Thomas P Gross
Sr VP: Michael McSpadden
Sr VP: Rick Miller
VP: Jim Liggit
VP: Sophia Sas
VP: Malcolm Stokes
Assoc Dir: Peter Brzezinski

D-U-N-S 06-669-4621
GARDA CL WEST INC
GCL W
(Suby of GARDA CASH LOGISTICS) ★
1612 W Pico Blvd, Los Angeles, CA 90015-2410
Tel (213) 383-3611 Founded/Ownrshp 1947
Sales 41.2MM^E EMP 1,100
SIC 7381 Armored car services; Armored car services
Pr: Stephan Cretier
*Pr: Chris W Jamroz
VP: Jeb Bowdoin
VP: Linda Slattery

D-U-N-S 62-525-2465
GARDA CL WEST INC
PROSECURITY
3021 Gilroy St, Los Angeles, CA 90039-2819
Tel (323) 668-2712 Founded/Ownrshp 1988
Sales 16.6MM^E EMP 327
SIC 7381 Armored car services; Security guard service; Armored car services; Security guard service
Pr: Jacki Summerson
*VP: Tom Choate
*VP: Jerry Spain

GARDAWORLD
See GW CONSULTING INC

D-U-N-S 09-869-2213
GARDEN & ASSOCIATES INC T L
LIFE SFETY SLTIONS INTEGRATORS
7170 Gary Rd, Manassas, VA 20109-2649
Tel (703) 257-9506 Founded/Ownrshp 1978
Sales 21.9MM^E EMP 125
SIC 1731 Fire detection & burglar alarm systems specialization; Fire detection & burglar alarm systems specialization
Ch: Thomas L Garden
*Pr: Randal Garden
*Treas: Tamara L Feliciano
IT Man: Jennifer Corbin
Sls Mgr: Michael Crutchley

D-U-N-S 14-453-7867
GARDEN & VALLEY ISLE SEAFOOD INC
GARDEN ISLE SEAFOOD
225 N Nimitz Hwy Unit 3, Honolulu, HI 96817-5349
Tel (808) 524-4847 Founded/Ownrshp 1984
Sales 38.0MM^E EMP 36^E
SIC 5146 Seafoods
Pr: Robert Shields Fram
*Treas: David Marabella

GARDEN CITY
See GLASSCOCK CO IND SCH DISTRICT

GARDEN CITY CASINO & REST
See GARDEN CITY INC

D-U-N-S 00-694-2684
GARDEN CITY CO-OP INC
106 N 6th St, Garden City, KS 67846-5545
Tel (620) 275-6161 Founded/Ownrshp 1919
Sales 327.0MM^E EMP 66
Accts Lindburg Vogel Pierce Faris D
SIC 5153 5191 5172 Grains; Feed; Seeds: field, garden & flower; Fertilizer & fertilizer materials; Chemicals, agricultural; Petroleum products; Grains; Feed; Seeds: field, garden & flower; Fertilizer & fertilizer materials; Chemicals, agricultural; Petroleum products
Pr: John McClelland
V Ch: Thomas Mulville
*CFO: Brent Merz
Treas: Kendall Clark
VP: Barry Brant
*VP: Elevatorsken Jameson
VP: Pete Maestas
Creative D: Trevor Hands
Brnch Mgr: Juan Barron
Brnch Mgr: Beto Deleon
Brnch Mgr: Chris Martinez

GARDEN CITY FAN
See FAN GROUP INC

GARDEN CITY GROUP, INC., THE
See GARDEN CITY GROUP LLC

D-U-N-S 87-716-5860
■ GARDEN CITY GROUP LLC
GARDEN CITY GROUP, INC., THE
(*Suby of* CRAWFORD & CO) ★
1985 Marcus Ave Ste 200, New Hyde Park, NY 11042-2029
Tel (631) 470-5000 *Founded/Ownrshp* 1999
Sales 50.5MM^E *EMP* 262
SIC 8111 Specialized legal services; Specialized legal services
CEO: David A Isaac
**Pr:* Neil L Zola
**Ex VP:* Jennifer M Keough
Sr VP: Stephen Cirami
**Sr VP:* Richard Cohen
**Sr VP:* Jeanne Finegan
**Sr VP:* Lois Schnipper
VP: Lisa Buckser-Schulz
VP: Brian Burke
VP: Jeffrey N Leibell
VP: George Mallory
VP: Arun RAO
**VP:* Andrew Sommer
VP: Jeffrey S Stein
Exec: Danielle Campbell
**Exec:* Karen B Shaer

D-U-N-S 07-278-4002
GARDEN CITY HOSPITAL
ADVANCE NURSING CENTER
(*Suby of* PRIME HEALTHCARE SERVICES INC) ★
6245 Inkster Rd, Garden City, MI 48135-4001
Tel (734) 458-3300 *Founded/Ownrshp* 2013
Sales 127.0MM *EMP* 1,200
SIC 8062 General medical & surgical hospitals; General medical & surgical hospitals
Pr: Gary R Ley
**Chf Mktg O:* H Rex Ruettinger
VP: Kirsten Waarala
Exec: Lynn Giovannini
Dir Risk M: Alan Karcher
Dir Lab: Jerry Jordt
Chf Nrs Of: Karla Zarb
Off Mgr: Joan Campbell
Cmptr Lab: Andy Mazzara
VP Opers: Art Greenlee
QC Dir: Claudia Gering

D-U-N-S 17-734-5295
GARDEN CITY HOSPITAL FOUNDATION
6245 Inkster Rd Ste 210, Garden City, MI 48135-4001
Tel (734) 458-4421 *Founded/Ownrshp* 1986
Sales 129.3M *EMP* 2,100
SIC 8741 7389 Hospital management; Nursing & personal care facility management; Fund raising organizations; Hospital management; Nursing & personal care facility management; Fund raising organizations
CEO: Gary Ley
Ex Dir: Darla Parsons

D-U-N-S 10-683-2157
GARDEN CITY HOTEL LLC
45 7th St, Garden City, NY 11530-2890
Tel (516) 747-3000 *Founded/Ownrshp* 1982
Sales 30.3MM^E *EMP* 475
SIC 7011 Hotels; Hotels
Pr: Catherine Nelkin

D-U-N-S 01-092-0817
GARDEN CITY INC
GARDEN CITY CASINO & REST
1887 Matrix Blvd, San Jose, CA 95110-2309
Tel (408) 244-3333 *Founded/Ownrshp* 1993
Sales 13.0MM^E *EMP* 569
SIC 7999 Card rooms; Card rooms
CEO: Pete V Lunardi III
**Pr:* Eli Reinhard
**CFO:* Llene Brandon
**CFO:* Kathy Reiner
**Trst:* Frederick Wyle

GARDEN CITY PUBLIC SCHOOLS
See GARDEN CITY SCHOOL DISTRICT

GARDEN CITY PUBLIC SCHOOLS
See SCHOOL DISTRICT OF CITY OF GARDEN CITY

D-U-N-S 09-433-5320
GARDEN CITY PUBLIC SCHOOLS
1205 Fleming St, Garden City, KS 67846-4751
Tel (620) 805-7000 *Founded/Ownrshp* 1890
Sales 60.0MM *EMP* 1,100
SIC 8211 Public elementary & secondary schools; High school, junior or senior; School board; Public elementary & secondary schools; High school, junior or senior; School board
IT Man: Diana Lee
IT Man: Chris Sisk

D-U-N-S 01-271-9407
GARDEN CITY SAAB MOTORS CORP
HEMPSTEAD LINCOLN MERCURY
301 N Franklin St, Hempstead, NY 11550-1311
Tel (516) 483-7200 *Founded/Ownrshp* 1994
Sales 33.2MM^E *EMP* 98
SIC 5511

D-U-N-S 01-000-6310
GARDEN CITY SCHOOL DISTRICT
GARDEN CITY PUBLIC SCHOOLS
56 Cathedral Ave, Garden City, NY 11530-2819
Tel (516) 478-1000 *Founded/Ownrshp* 1911
Sales 31.5MM^E *EMP* 575
Accts Nawrocki Smith Llp Melville
SIC 8211 Public combined elementary & secondary school; Public combined elementary & secondary school
**Treas:* Dorothy Lasmeister
**VP:* Collen Foley
Dir IT: Pat Galano
IT Man: Tara Ferraro
Pr Dir: Catherine Knight
Teacher Pr: Maureen Appiarias
HC Dir: Lynette Abruzzo

GARDEN CITY TERMINAL
See GEORGIA PORTS AUTHORITY

D-U-N-S 07-831-4412
GARDEN CITY UNION FREE SCHOOL DISTRICT
56 Cathedral Ave, Garden City, NY 11530-2819
Tel (516) 478-1000 *Founded/Ownrshp* 2011
Sales 20.8MM^E *EMP* 615^E
SIC 8211 Kindergarten
Pr: Robert Elkins

GARDEN FRESH
See CONCORD FEED & FUEL INC

D-U-N-S 80-688-7027 IMP
GARDEN FRESH FRUIT MARKET INC
GARDEN FRESH MARKET
390 Townline Rd, Naperville, IL 60540
Tel (847) 520-1200 *Founded/Ownrshp* 1993
Sales 29.5MM^E *EMP* 146
SIC 5431 Fruit stands or markets
Pr: ADI Mor
Off Mgr: Andrea Cook
Store Mgr: Anna Ferenczak
Dir IT: Golan Mor
Mktg Dir: Julie Smolucha

D-U-N-S 14-473-0384
GARDEN FRESH HOLDINGS INC
SOUPPLANTATION SWEET TOMATOES
(*Suby of* SUN CAPITAL PARTNERS INC) ★
15822 Bernardo Center Dr A, San Diego, CA 92127-2362
Tel (858) 675-1600 *Founded/Ownrshp* 2005
Sales 21.0MM *EMP* 5,420
SIC 5812 Fast-food restaurant, chain; Fast-food restaurant, chain
CEO: John Morberg
**Pr:* David W Qualls

GARDEN FRESH MARKET
See GARDEN FRESH FRUIT MARKET INC

D-U-N-S 15-065-6932
GARDEN FRESH PRODUCE INC
390 Townline Rd, Mundelein, IL 60060-4225
Tel (847) 520-1200 *Founded/Ownrshp* 1983
Sales 33.2MM^E *EMP* 90
SIC 5148 5431 Fruits, fresh; Vegetables, fresh; Fruit stands or markets; Vegetable stands or markets; Fruits, fresh; Vegetables, fresh; Fruit stands or markets; Vegetable stands or markets
Pr: ADI Mor
Genl Mgr: Golan Mor

D-U-N-S 11-533-2637
GARDEN FRESH RESTAURANT CORP
SOUPLANTATION
(*Suby of* GARDEN FRESH HOLDINGS INC) ★
15822 Bernardo Center Dr A, San Diego, CA 92127-2362
Tel (858) 675-1600 *Founded/Ownrshp* 2004
Sales 21.0MM^E *EMP* 5,420
SIC 5812 Restaurant, family: chain; Restaurant, family: chain
CEO: John Morberg
Ch Bd: Robert A Gunst
Pr: Michael P Mack
CFO: David A Carr
Ofcr: Julie L Derry
Ofcr: Eric Rosenzweig
Sr VP: R Gregory Keller
VP: Walter Carucci
VP: Susan Hoffman
VP: Kenneth J Keane
VP: Rich Thompson

GARDEN GROVE HOSPITAL
See KENNETH CORP

GARDEN GROVE HOSPITAL MED CTR
See PRIME HEALTH CARE SERVICES GARDEN GROVE LLC

D-U-N-S 07-359-1760
GARDEN GROVE UNIFIED SCHOOL DISTRICT
10331 Stanford Ave, Garden Grove, CA 92840-6351
Tel (714) 663-6000 *Founded/Ownrshp* 1965
Sales 235.5MM^E *EMP* 5,000
SIC 8211 Public elementary & secondary schools; Public elementary & secondary schools
**Pr:* George West
**VP:* Lan Quoc Nguyen
Exec: Amy Stevens
Dir Risk M: Dianne Hansen
**Prin:* Coleen Cross
Off Admin: Kari Brown
Off Admin: Dayna Burt
Opers Mgr: Karen Landrum
Teacher Pr: Jason Bevacqua
Teacher Pr: Valerie Shedd

GARDEN HOMES DEVELOPMENT
See GARDEN HOMES MANAGEMENT CORP

D-U-N-S 12-214-7259
GARDEN HOMES INC
820 Morris Tpke Ste 301, Short Hills, NJ 07078-2624
Tel (973) 467-5000 *Founded/Ownrshp* 2006
Sales 795.8MM^E *EMP* 5,125
SIC 1531 6531 Condominium developers; Real estate agents & managers; Condominium developers; Real estate agents & managers
Pr: Zygmund Wilf
**VP:* Leonard Wilf
**Prin:* Mark Wilf

D-U-N-S 06-339-6451
GARDEN HOMES MANAGEMENT CORP
GARDEN HOMES DEVELOPMENT
29 Knapp St, Stamford, CT 06907-1799
Tel (203) 348-2200 *Founded/Ownrshp* 1965
Sales 23.0MM^E *EMP* 50^E
SIC 6799 Real estate investors, except property operators
Pr: Richard Freedman
VP: Joe Driscoll
**VP:* Joel E Freedman
**VP:* Kenneth I White
**VP:* Helene Stancato

GARDEN ISLE SEAFOOD
See GARDEN & VALLEY ISLE SEAFOOD INC

GARDEN NTURE STR AT RICH FARMS
See RICH FARMS INC

D-U-N-S 00-449-9492
GARDEN OF EDEN ENTERPRISES INC
220 E 23rd St Ste 605, New York, NY 10010-4661
Tel (212) 675-3365 *Founded/Ownrshp* 1999
Sales 51.3MM^E *EMP* 350
SIC 5499 Gourmet food stores; Gourmet food stores
CEO: Mustafa Coskun
**VP:* Celal Coskun

D-U-N-S 03-957-3720
■ GARDEN PARK COMMUNITY HOSPITAL LIMITED PARTNERSHIP
(*Suby of* HCA INC) ★
15200 Community Rd, Gulfport, MS 39503-3085
Tel (228) 575-7000 *Founded/Ownrshp* 1995
Sales 30.4MM^E *EMP* 380
SIC 8062 General medical & surgical hospitals; General medical & surgical hospitals
CEO: Jack Bovender
**Pr:* Tommy Frist MD
**CFO:* Regina Ramazani
Dir Bus: Michaela Moran
Doctor: Hugo Quintana

D-U-N-S 07-515-2090
GARDEN PROPERTIES CORP
SHORT HILLS OFFICE PLAZA
(*Suby of* GARDEN HOMES INC) ★
820 Morris Tpke Ste 102, Short Hills, NJ 07078-2619
Tel (973) 467-5000 *Founded/Ownrshp* 1986
Sales 176.0MM^E *EMP* 5,000
SIC 6531 Real estate managers; Real estate managers
VP: Anthony Moscaritolo
**Ch Bd:* Joseph Wilf
**Pr:* Leonard Wilf
Treas: Orin Wilf
VP: Scott Lobenthal
VP: Scott Loventhal
**VP:* Zygmund Wilf
Genl Mgr: Joseph Korn
Off Mgr: Irene Bartosh
Mktg Dir: Laura Perry

D-U-N-S 79-118-3106 IMP
GARDEN RIDGE CORP
1600 E Plano Pkwy, Plano, TX 75074-8124
Tel (972) 265-6227 *Founded/Ownrshp* 1992
Sales 64.4MM^E *EMP* 3,500
SIC 5719 5999 5945 Kitchenware; Glassware; Pictures, wall; Pottery; Artificial flowers; Candle shops; Picture frames, ready made; Hobby & craft supplies; Arts & crafts supplies

D-U-N-S 12-580-4950
GARDEN RIDGE HOLDINGS INC
1600 E Plano Pkwy, Plano, TX 75074-8124
Tel (832) 391-7201 *Founded/Ownrshp* 1992
Sales NA *EMP* 4,000
SIC 5719 5945 5992 5947 5999 Kitchenware; Glassware; Pictures, wall; Pottery; Hobby & craft supplies; Arts & crafts supplies; Flowers, fresh; Party favors; Artificial flowers; Candle shops; Picture frames, ready made

GARDEN RIDGE POTTERY
See AT HOME STORES LLC

D-U-N-S 87-896-7009
GARDEN SPOT VILLAGE
433 S Kinzer Ave Ofc, New Holland, PA 17557-9468
Tel (717) 355-6000 *Founded/Ownrshp* 1990
Sales 31.7MM *EMP* 320
Accts Parentebeard Llc Philadelphi
SIC 8051 6513 Skilled nursing care facilities; Apartment building operators; Skilled nursing care facilities; Apartment building operators
Ch Bd: Philip Hess
**Pr:* Steve Lindsey
**COO:* John Farber
**CFO:* Dale Beiler
Dir IT: Andrew Dietzel
Mktg Dir: Scott Miller
Nrsg Dir: Connie Fasnacht

D-U-N-S 03-395-4210 IMP
GARDEN STATE BULB CO LLC
2720 Industrial Way, Vineland, NJ 08360-1550
Tel (856) 205-9300 *Founded/Ownrshp* 1998, 2000
Sales 35.7MM^E *EMP* 34^E
SIC 5193 Nursery stock
Opers Mgr: Don Volpe

GARDEN STATE FARMS
See PROCACCI BROS SALES CORP

D-U-N-S 05-602-1462 IMP
GARDEN STATE GROWERS LLC
99 Locust Grove Rd, Pittstown, NJ 08867-4022
Tel (908) 730-8888 *Founded/Ownrshp* 1976
Sales 22.5MM^E *EMP* 100
SIC 5193 Flowers & florists' supplies
Area Mgr: Alison Gallagher
Opers Mgr: Doug Sumpman
Sls Mgr: Laura Masi

D-U-N-S 13-445-4891
■ GARDEN STATE LIFE INSURANCE CO INC
(*Suby of* AMERICAN NATIONAL INSURANCE CO INC) ★
2450 S Shore Blvd Ste 401, League City, TX 77573-2997
Tel (409) 763-4661 *Founded/Ownrshp* 1992
Sales NA *EMP* 60
SIC 6311 Life insurance; Life insurance
Ch Bd: Ronald J Welch
Pr: Chad Ferrell
**Pr:* Scott K Luchesi
**Sec:* John Mark Flippin
**VP:* John R Barrett
**VP:* Lee Chad Ferrell
**VP:* Lee C Horn
Creative D: Kawika Maszak

D-U-N-S 00-167-9661 IMP
GARDEN STATE LUMBER PRODUCTS CORP
22 Muller Rd, Oakland, NJ 07436
Tel (201) 337-7400 *Founded/Ownrshp* 1955, 1971
Sales 48.3MM^E *EMP* 70
SIC 5031 Molding, all materials; Molding, all materials
Pr: David Kulick
**Sec:* Lance Kulick
IT Man: Ted Hickey
Sales Asso: John Alessandro

GARDEN STATE NUTRITIONALS
See VITAQUEST INTERNATIONAL LLC

D-U-N-S 01-171-1744 IMP
GARDEN STATE TILE DISTRIBUTORS INC
1324 Wyckoff Rd Ste 101, Wall Township, NJ 07753-6809
Tel (732) 938-6675 *Founded/Ownrshp* 1997
Sales 50.3MM^E *EMP* 65
SIC 5032 5211 Ceramic wall & floor tile; Tile, ceramic
Pr: Stephen Fischer
VP: Nancy Scanlan

D-U-N-S 01-763-4775
GARDEN STREET IRON & METAL INC
2885 Spring Grove Ave, Cincinnati, OH 45225-2222
Tel (513) 853-3700 *Founded/Ownrshp* 1959
Sales 30.7MM^E *EMP* 40
SIC 4953 3341 3312 Recycling, waste materials; Secondary nonferrous metals; Blast furnaces & steel mills
Pr: Earl J Weber Jr
**VP:* Margaret Weber
Genl Mgr: Dave Hollbroke
Off Mgr: Sarah Weber

D-U-N-S 60-344-7285 IMP
GARDEN STREET IRON & METAL INC OF SW FLORIDA
3350 Old Metro Pkwy, Fort Myers, FL 33916-7521
Tel (239) 337-5865 *Founded/Ownrshp* 1989
Sales 29.0MM^E *EMP* 90
SIC 5093 Metal scrap & waste materials; Metal scrap & waste materials
Pr: Earl Weber Sr
**Pr:* Robert Weber
**Sec:* Margaret T Weber
**VP:* Earl James Weber Sr
Genl Mgr: John Hoving

GARDEN USA
See BIOMASS ONE LIMITED PARTNERSHIP

D-U-N-S 00-890-3809
GARDEN VALLEY TELEPHONE CO
201 Ross Ave, Erskine, MN 56535
Tel (218) 687-5251 *Founded/Ownrshp* 1906
Sales 23.1MM *EMP* 90
SIC 4813 Local telephone communications; Local telephone communications
Pr: Vernon Hamnes
Treas: Wayne Olson
**Treas:* Joe O Sandberg
Dir Bus: Joyce Burkel
**Prin:* Ronald Engelstad
**Prin:* Jerry Freitag
**Genl Mgr:* George Fish
Off Mgr: Carolyn Hultman
Off Mgr: John Reichert
Sls Mgr: Doug Laubenstein

GARDEN VILLAS
See DELMAR GARDENS OF LENEXA INC

GARDEN WATERING
See ROBERT BOSCH TOOL CORP

GARDEN WEASEL
See FAULTLESS STARCH/BON AMI CO

D-U-N-S 08-985-1638
GARDEN-FRESH FOODS INC (WI)
726 S 12th St, Milwaukee, WI 53204-1211
Tel (414) 645-1000 *Founded/Ownrshp* 1977
Sales 66.4MM^E *EMP* 85
SIC 5148 Vegetables, fresh; Vegetables, fresh
Pr: Thomas H Hughes
**VP:* MO Elahi
**VP:* Steve Mueller
Natl Sales: Kathy Fritz

GARDENA HONDA
See LLL SALES CO LLC

D-U-N-S 06-862-0400
GARDENER CARTON & DOUGLAS LLP
GARDNER, CARTON & DOUGLAS
191 N Wacker Dr Ste 3700, Chicago, IL 60606-1615
Tel (312) 223-1303 *Founded/Ownrshp* 1910
Sales 30.4MM^E *EMP* 430
SIC 8111 General practice law office; General practice law office
Ch Bd: Harold Kaplan
Pr: David Wolfe
COO: Helen Carroll

D-U-N-S 10-677-8715 IMP/EXP
GARDENER EASY INC
3022 Franklin Ave, Waco, TX 76710-7352
Tel (859) 987-5389 *Founded/Ownrshp* 1995
Sales 86.0MM *EMP* 40^E
SIC 2211 0782 3423 2875 Canvas & other heavy coarse fabrics: cotton; Lawn & garden services; Hand & edge tools; Fertilizers, mixing only; Canvas & other heavy coarse fabrics: cotton; Lawn & garden services; Hand & edge tools; Fertilizers, mixing only
Pr: David Jackson
**CEO:* Karen Bettege
VP: Dan Boxser
VP: Chuck Hayes
Brnch Mgr: Doug Austin

IT Man: Tricia Anderson
Info Man: Lee Fahlenkamp
VP Mfg: Andrew Loberger
VP Opers: Sheila Jones
VP Opers: Andy Loberger
Trfc Dir: Carey Patt

D-U-N-S 06-002-0104
GARDENER HEIGHTS INC
(*Suby of* FLORA AND MARY HEWITT MEMORIAL HOSPITAL INC) ★
172 Rocky Rest Rd, Shelton, CT 06484-4299
Tel (203) 929-1481 *Founded/Ownrshp* 1979
Sales 8.7MM^E *EMP* 290
SIC 8059 8051 Convalescent home; Skilled nursing care facilities; Convalescent home; Skilled nursing care facilities
Genl Mgr: Maggie Bucknall
Off Mgr: Melissa Evans

GARDENERS EDGE
See A M LEONARD INC

GARDENER'S SUPPLY COMPANY
See AMERICAS GARDENING RESOURCE INC

GARDENS, THE
See WESLEY HOMES

D-U-N-S 55-729-7348 IMP
GARDENS ALIVE INC
CATALOG
5100 Schenley Pl, Greendale, IN 47025-2100
Tel (513) 354-1482 *Founded/Ownrshp* 1990
Sales 54.1MM^E *EMP* 150^E
SIC 5961 Flowers, plants & bulbs: mail order; Flowers, plants & bulbs: mail order
CEO: Niles Kinerk
**Pr:* Eric Hamant
CFO: Laura Soos
VP: Felix Cooper
Manager: Matthew Horney
Mktg Mgr: Deborah Hill
Snr Mgr: Chetan Malhotra

D-U-N-S 06-425-5268
GARDENS REGIONAL HOSPITAL AND MEDICAL CENTER INC
TRI CITY REGIONAL MEDICAL CTR
21530 Pioneer Blvd, Hawaiian Gardens, CA 90716-2608
Tel (562) 860-0401 *Founded/Ownrshp* 1996
Sales 59.2MM *EMP* 450
Accts Yh Advisors Inc Huntington Be
SIC 8062 General medical & surgical hospitals; General medical & surgical hospitals
CEO: Jim Sherman
**CFO:* Terri Davis
**Ch:* Brian Walton
Ofcr: Daisy Schneidman
Dir Rad: David Donovan
Mtls Dir: Mert Ortaliza
Doctor: Yaming Shi MD
Pharmcst: Kathleen Chan
HC Dir: Teffey Meza

GARDENSCAPE
See TRI-STATE GARDEN SUPPLY INC

GARDENVIEW EGGS
See HILLANDALE FARMS OF PA INC

D-U-N-S 06-898-0754
GARDERE WYNNE SEWELL LLP
1601 Elm St Ste 3000, Dallas, TX 75201-4761
Tel (214) 999-3000 *Founded/Ownrshp* 1920
Sales 110.8MM^E *EMP* 700
SIC 8111 General practice attorney, lawyer; General practice attorney, lawyer
Ch: Holland N O'Neil
Pt: Michael A Abbott
Pt: Val J Albright
Pt: Jose A Berlanga
Pt: Geoffrey H Bracken
Pt: Fernando C Cardona
Pt: John G Caverlee
Pt: Alexander C Chae
Pt: Merritt B Chastain III
Pt: Daniel L Cohen
Pt: James Cooper
Pt: Allen B Craig III
Pt: Jeffrey S Davis
Pt: Jerry A Devault
Pt: William D Dunn
Pt: David R Earhart
Pt: Mark Edwards
Pt: John A Eliason
Pt: Douglas K Eyberg
Pt: Richard O Faulk
Pt: John S Gray

GARDETTO'S
See GARDETTOS BAKERY INC

D-U-N-S 02-338-7210 IMP
■ **GARDETTOS BAKERY INC**
GARDETTO'S
(*Suby of* GENERAL MILLS INC) ★
4625 S 6th St, Milwaukee, WI 53221-2410
Tel (414) 481-2517 *Founded/Ownrshp* 1999
Sales 21.8MM^E *EMP* 225
SIC 2052 2099 Bakery products, dry; Food preparations; Bakery products, dry; Food preparations
Pr: John B Gardetto
**Ex VP:* Nannette Gardetto
Dir IT: Michael Ulicki

D-U-N-S 04-662-7642
GARDINER SERVICE CO (OH)
GARDINER TRANE
31200 Bainbridge Rd Ste 1, Solon, OH 44139-2298
Tel (440) 349-5588 *Founded/Ownrshp* 1957
Sales 90.0MM^E *EMP* 160
Accts Mayer Hoffman Mccann Pc Ply
SIC 5075 1711 7623 Air conditioning & ventilation equipment & supplies; Plumbing, heating, air-conditioning contractors; Refrigeration service & repair; Air conditioning repair; Air conditioning & ventilation equipment & supplies; Plumbing, heating, air-conditioning contractors; Refrigeration service & repair; Air conditioning repair
CEO: William H Gardiner
**Pr:* Robert M Case
**Treas:* Michael R Reder
VP: Bob Mehling
Sls Mgr: Brent Jividen

GARDINER TRANE
See GARDINER SERVICE CO

GARDINERS FURNITURE
See GARDINERS HOME FURNISHINGS CENTER INC

D-U-N-S 02-248-6955 IMP
GARDINERS HOME FURNISHINGS CENTER INC
GARDINERS FURNITURE
4241 Brookhill Rd, Baltimore, MD 21215-2200
Tel (410) 358-1730 *Founded/Ownrshp* 1942
Sales 34.6MM^E *EMP* 200
SIC 5712

D-U-N-S 00-723-6946 IMP
GARDN-WISE DISTRIBUTORS INC
1515 E 29th St N, Wichita, KS 67219-4129
Tel (316) 838-6104 *Founded/Ownrshp* 1958
Sales 37.9MM^E *EMP* 70
SIC 5191 Garden supplies; Garden supplies
Ch Bd: Robert S Wise
**Pr:* Stephen T Wise
**Treas:* Marc Wise
**VP:* David Scott Wise
Sls Mgr: John Bruntzel

D-U-N-S 04-149-5490 IMP/EXP
GARDNER ASPHALT CORP
(*Suby of* GARDNER-GIBSON INC) ★
4161 E 7th Ave, Tampa, FL 33605-4601
Tel (813) 248-2441 *Founded/Ownrshp* 1973
Sales 113.3MM^E *EMP* 525
SIC 3531 Roofing equipment; Roofing equipment
Ch Bd: Raymond T Hyer
CFO: Sean Poole

GARDNER BENDER
See GB TOOLS AND SUPPLIES INC

GARDNER BENDER
See POWER PRODUCTS LLC

D-U-N-S 00-425-5915
GARDNER BUSINESS MEDIA INC (OH)
MAP YOUR SHOW
6915 Valley Ave, Cincinnati, OH 45244-3029
Tel (513) 527-8800 *Founded/Ownrshp* 1928
Sales 32.5MM *EMP* 125
SIC 2721 2731 2741

GARDNER, CARTON & DOUGLAS
See GARDENER CARTON & DOUGLAS LLP

D-U-N-S 01-766-8002 EXP
GARDNER CRYOGENICS DEPARTMENT OF AIR PRODUCTS AND CHEMICALS INC
2136 City Line Rd, Bethlehem, PA 18017-2128
Tel (610) 264-4523 *Founded/Ownrshp* 1988
Sales 22.3MM^E *EMP* 150
SIC 3559 Cryogenic machinery, industrial; Cryogenic machinery, industrial
Pr: Eric Schnable

D-U-N-S 18-818-6480
GARDNER DENVER HOLDINGS INC
(*Suby of* GARDNER DENVER INC) ★
1800 Gardner Expy, Quincy, IL 62305-9364
Tel (217) 222-5400 *Founded/Ownrshp* 1992
Sales 773.6MM^E *EMP* 6,000
SIC 3564 3563 Blowers & fans; Vacuum (air extraction) systems, industrial; Blowers & fans; Vacuum (air extraction) systems, industrial
Pr: Winfried Kaiser
VP: Duane Morgan
VP: Brent A Walters
Off Mgr: Paul Phillips
Dir IT: Russ Cook
IT Man: John Sharp
Prd Mgr: Angelo Deriggi
Ql Cn Mgr: Brian Gaffey
Ql Cn Mgr: Dan Pfister
Sls&Mrk Ex: Gary Gillespie
Mktg Mgr: Jennifer Green

D-U-N-S 02-159-7778 IMP/EXP
GARDNER DENVER INC (DE)
(*Suby of* GARDNER DENVER HOLDINGS INC) ★
100 Gardner Park, Peachtree City, GA 30269-3026
Tel (770) 632-5000 *Founded/Ownrshp* 1979, 1988
Sales 27.9MM^E *EMP* 120
SIC 3564 Blowers & fans; Blowers & fans
Pr: Peter Wallace
**Pr:* Jacques Le Page
**CFO:* Michael McGrath
**VP:* John Clarke
Tech Mgr: Jeff Massman
VP Mktg: Patrick James
Sls Mgr: Tim Shull

D-U-N-S 82-644-8615 IMP/EXP
GARDNER DENVER INC
(*Suby of* RENAISSANCE PARENT CORP.)
222 E Erie St Ste 500, Milwaukee, WI 53202-6062
Tel (414) 212-4700 *Founded/Ownrshp* 2013
Sales 1.9MMM^E *EMP* 6,800
SIC 3564 3561 3563 Air & gas compressors including vacuum pumps; Blowers & fans; Industrial pumps & parts; Pumps, oil well & field; Blowers & fans; Industrial pumps & parts; Air & gas compressors including vacuum pumps
CEO: Peter Wallace
**Pr:* Barry L Pennypacker
**CFO:* Michael M Larsen
CFO: Jeffrey Likosar
VP: Siva Balakrishnan
VP: Francois Estellon
**VP:* Susan A Gunn
VP: Ankush Kumar
VP: Kevin Mineard
VP: Kim Rubottom
**VP:* Brent A Walters

D-U-N-S 13-695-4497 IMP
GARDNER DENVER NASH LLC
(*Suby of* GARDNER DENVER INC) ★
2 Trefoil Dr, Trumbull, CT 06611-1330
Tel (203) 459-3923 *Founded/Ownrshp* 2004
Sales 483.7MM^E *EMP* 1,225
SIC 5084 3563 8711 3561 Compressors, except air conditioning; Air & gas compressors including vacuum pumps; Engineering services; Pumps & pumping equipment; Compressors, except air conditioning; Air & gas compressors including vacuum pumps; Engineering services; Pumps & pumping equipment
CEO: Barry Pennypacker
**CFO:* Helen Cornell
**VP:* Armando Castorena
**VP:* T Duane Morgan
**VP:* Brent A Walters

D-U-N-S 00-637-9317 IMP/EXP
GARDNER DENVER THOMAS INC
THOMAS PRODUCTS DIVISION
(*Suby of* GARDNER DENVER INC) ★
1419 Illinois Ave, Sheboygan, WI 53081-4821
Tel (920) 457-4891 *Founded/Ownrshp* 1859
Sales 486.9MM^E *EMP* 2,467
SIC 3563 Air & gas compressors including vacuum pumps; Vacuum pumps, except laboratory; Air & gas compressors including vacuum pumps; Vacuum pumps, except laboratory
VP: Mark McElhinny
Dir Bus: Scott Johnston
Area Mgr: Mike Humenik
Dir IT: Terry Roberts
Ql Cn Mgr: John Poker

D-U-N-S 15-722-7208 IMP
GARDNER DENVER WATER JETTING SYSTEMS INC
(*Suby of* GARDNER DENVER INC) ★
12300 N Huston Rosslyn Rd, Houston, TX 77086-3219
Tel (281) 448-5800 *Founded/Ownrshp* 1999
Sales 32.2MM^E *EMP* 101
SIC 3561 3829 Pumps & pumping equipment; Measuring & controlling devices; Pumps & pumping equipment; Measuring & controlling devices
Pr: Helen W Cornell
**VP:* Duane Morgan
**VP:* Brent A Walters
Exec: Peggy Snyder
QA Dir: David Gongora
Sls Mgr: Bill Guthrie

GARDNER DISTRIBUTING CO.
See PHILLIPS FEED AND PET SUPPLY NE LLC

D-U-N-S 03-981-4280
GARDNER EDGERTON UNIFIED SCHOOL DISTRICT 231
231 E Madison St, Gardner, KS 66030-1846
Tel (913) 856-7102 *Founded/Ownrshp* 1956
Sales 131.4MM *EMP* 800
Accts Lowenthal Singleton Webb & Wil
SIC 8211 Public elementary & secondary schools; Public elementary school; Public junior high school; Public senior high school; Public elementary & secondary schools; Public elementary school; Public junior high school; Public senior high school
Treas: Andrea Allenbrand
VP: Tim Rayburn
VP: Ron Raygan
Ex Dir: Chritsty Ziegler
MIS Dir: Andy Price
Pr Dir: Leann Northway
Teacher Pr: Jody Marshall
HC Dir: Katie Watkins
HC Dir: Jeremy Williams
Board of Directors: Eric Hansen

D-U-N-S 06-910-3083
GARDNER FAMILY HEALTH NETWORK INC (CA)
160 E Virginia St Ste 100, San Jose, CA 95112-5865
Tel (408) 918-2682 *Founded/Ownrshp* 1968
Sales 26.3MM^E *EMP* 300
SIC 8093 Specialty outpatient clinics; Specialty outpatient clinics
CEO: Reymundo C Espinoza
CFO: Joseph Demont
Dir: Richard Ajluni

D-U-N-S 62-056-2905
GARDNER FINANCIAL SERVICES LTD
LEGACY MUTUAL MORTGAGE
1635 Ne Loop 410, San Antonio, TX 78209-1625
Tel (210) 832-8622 *Founded/Ownrshp* 2005
Sales NA *EMP* 130
SIC 6162 Mortgage bankers & correspondents; Mortgage bankers & correspondents
Pt: Robert D Gardner
CFO: Patrick Bibb
Ex VP: Daniel Diepenhorst
VP: Don Kalbacher
VP Sls: Joshua Sigman

D-U-N-S 00-322-1462 IMP/EXP
GARDNER GLASS PRODUCTS INC (NC)
301 Elkin Hwy, North Wilkesboro, NC 28659-3444
Tel (336) 651-9300 *Founded/Ownrshp* 1961, 1999
Sales 107.1MM^E *EMP* 363
SIC 3231 Products of purchased glass; Mirrored glass; Products of purchased glass; Mirrored glass
Pr: Tommy Huskey
**COO:* Randy Brooks
**CFO:* Melissa Lackey
**Founder:* Edd Gardner
VP: Richard Finnie
Off Admin: Ashley George
MIS Dir: Ron Wood
Plnt Mgr: Ronnie Blevins

D-U-N-S 01-789-2803 IMP
GARDNER INC
3641 Interchange Rd, Columbus, OH 43204-1499
Tel (614) 351-1325 *Founded/Ownrshp* 1944
Sales 215.2MM^E *EMP* 300
Accts Deloitte & Touche Llp
SIC 5084 6512 Engines, gasoline; Nonresidential building operators; Engines, gasoline; Nonresidential building operators
CEO: John F Finn
**CFO:* John T Finn
Chf Mktg O: Don Thornton
**VP:* James P Finn
VP: Ted Finn
Dir IT: Matt Davis
IT Man: Chris Cooley
Plnt Mgr: Mark Hoffmann
Sls Mgr: Rick Jackson
Sls Mgr: Mark James
Sls Mgr: Bob Merkler

D-U-N-S 87-888-4196
GARDNER METAL SYSTEMS INC
4276 Cantrell Rd Nw, Acworth, GA 30101-3707
Tel (770) 966-1660 *Founded/Ownrshp* 1994
Sales 23.9MM^E *EMP* 50
SIC 3442 3449 3231 2394 Window & door frames; Miscellaneous metalwork; Products of purchased glass; Canvas & related products
Pr: C Wayne Gardner
COO: Herb Kieler
**VP:* Ralph Gardner

D-U-N-S 04-454-5960
GARDNER MILL CO (UT)
COUNTRY FURNITURE
1100 W 7800 S, West Jordan, UT 84088-3500
Tel (801) 566-8903 *Founded/Ownrshp* 1983
Sales 20.0MM^E *EMP* 120
SIC 5712 5947 Furniture stores; Gift, novelty & souvenir shop; Furniture stores; Gift, novelty & souvenir shop
Pr: Joe Long
Board of Directors: Harold Christenson

D-U-N-S 10-003-1566
GARDNER PUBLIC SCHOOLS
70 Waterford St, Gardner, MA 01440-2525
Tel (978) 632-1000 *Founded/Ownrshp* 1994
Sales 15.5MM^E *EMP* 310
SIC 8211 Public elementary & secondary schools; Public elementary & secondary schools
MIS Dir: Robert O'Keefe

D-U-N-S 78-793-1070
GARDNER TRUCKING INC
331 Premier Ct S, Franklin, TN 37067-8303
Tel (615) 778-0668 *Founded/Ownrshp* 1974
Sales 91.5MM^E *EMP* 500
SIC 4213 4212 Trucking, except local; Local trucking, without storage; Trucking, except local; Local trucking, without storage
CEO: Thomas J Lanting
**Pr:* Ron J Lanting
Treas: Doris Gardner
VP: Ramona Gill
VP: Cory Peters
Site Mgr: Larry Moore
Sfty Mgr: Anthony Lema
Sfty Mgr: Robert Mendoza
Board of Directors: Angie Caward

D-U-N-S 01-687-8670 IMP
GARDNER WHITE FURNITURE CO INC (MI)
GARDNER-WHITE FURNITURE
4445 N Atlantic Blvd, Auburn Hills, MI 48326-1580
Tel (586) 774-8853 *Founded/Ownrshp* 1987
Sales 99.5MM^E *EMP* 300
SIC 5712 Furniture stores; Furniture stores
Pr: Steven L Tronstein
Ex VP: Kathy Veltri
VP: Pamela Novak-George
**VP:* Barbara Tronstein

D-U-N-S 00-711-4788
GARDNER ZEMKE CO (NM)
6821 Academy Parkway W Ne, Albuquerque, NM 87109-4405
Tel (505) 881-0555 *Founded/Ownrshp* 1964, 2010
Sales 26.8MM *EMP* 110^E
Accts Atkinson & Co Ltd Albuquer
SIC 1731 1623 1711 General electrical contractor; Mechanical contractor; Electric power line construction; General electrical contractor; Electric power line construction; Mechanical contractor
Pr: Richard Zemke
VP: Nancy Reisbeck
VP: Wayne Zellner
VP: David Zemke
VP: Linda Zemke
Genl Mgr: Anna Trujeque
Snr Mgr: Steve Hickman

D-U-N-S 83-300-4067
GARDNER-CONNELL LLC
125 Constitution Blvd, Franklin, MA 02038-2584
Tel (508) 543-3600 *Founded/Ownrshp* 2009
Sales 51.3MM^E *EMP* 50^E
SIC 5191 5083 Garden supplies; Lawn & garden machinery & equipment
CFO: John T Finn
Genl Mgr: Alan Rodina
IT Man: Chris Silva
Opers Mgr: Paul Ochab
Sls Mgr: Raphael Andujar
Sls Mgr: John Joensen
Sls Mgr: Patrick Murray
Sls Mgr: Scott Pysher

D-U-N-S 06-591-7817 IMP/EXP
GARDNER-GIBSON INC
4161 E 7th Ave, Tampa, FL 33605-4601
Tel (813) 248-2101 *Founded/Ownrshp* 1993
Sales 230.7MM^E *EMP* 550
SIC 2951 2851 2952

D-U-N-S 16-478-8841 IMP/EXP
GARDNER-GIBSON MANUFACTURING INC
(Suby of GARDNER-GIBSON INC) ★
4161 E 7th Ave, Tampa, FL 33605-4601
Tel (813) 248-2101 Founded/Ownrshp 2000
Sales 93.0MM^E EMP 225
SIC 2951 2891 2952 Asphalt paving mixtures & blocks; Adhesives & sealants; Roof cement: asphalt, fibrous or plastic; Asphalt paving mixtures & blocks; Adhesives & sealants; Roof cement: asphalt, fibrous or plastic
Pr: Raymond T Hyer Jr
COO: Sean Hyer
*Sec: Sean W Poole
VP: Michael Lazuk
MIS Dir: Neil Loftie-Eaton
Dir IT: Neil Loftie
Dir IT: Roberta Loftie-Eaton
Sls&Mrk Ex: Tripp Hyer

D-U-N-S 07-450-6254
GARDNER-WEBB UNIVERSITY
110 S Main St, Boiling Springs, NC 28017-9797
Tel (704) 406-4000 Founded/Ownrshp 1905
Sales 64.0MM EMP 375
Accts Cherry Bekaert Llp Charlotte
SIC 8221 University; University
Pr: A Frank Bonner
CFO: Mike W Hardin
VP: Chuck Burch
CIO: Lou Gilliam

GARDNER-WHITE FURNITURE
See GARDNER WHITE FURNITURE CO INC

D-U-N-S 11-916-5538
GAREDA DIVERSIFIED BUSINESS SERVICES INC
GAREDA HOMEMAKER SERVICES
1431 Huntington Dr, Calumet City, IL 60409-5465
Tel (708) 868-1300 Founded/Ownrshp 1981
Sales 15.8MM^E EMP 832
SIC 7363 8082 Domestic help service; Medical help service; Home health care services; Domestic help service; Medical help service; Home health care services
Pr: Gwen C Duncan-James

GAREDA HOMEMAKER SERVICES
See GAREDA DIVERSIFIED BUSINESS SERVICES INC

D-U-N-S 00-143-0172 IMP
■ **GARELICK FARMS LLC** (MA)
(Suby of DEAN FOODS CO) ★
1199 W Central St Ste 1, Franklin, MA 02038-3160
Tel (508) 528-9000 Founded/Ownrshp 1902, 1997
Sales 322.1MM^E EMP 2,500
SIC 2026 Fluid milk; Buttermilk, cultured; Cottage cheese; Fluid milk; Buttermilk, cultured; Cottage cheese
Sales Exec: Chris Keyes
Sls Dir: Frank Whorfe

D-U-N-S 00-618-5607 IMP
■ **GARELICK MFG CO** (MN)
EEZ-IN
(Suby of MERCURY MARINE GROUP) ★
644 2nd St, Saint Paul Park, MN 55071-1852
Tel (651) 459-9795 Founded/Ownrshp 1956, 2015
Sales 20.2MM^E EMP 130
Accts Schechter Dokken Kanter Andrew
SIC 3429 3499 Marine hardware; Metal ladders; Marine hardware; Metal ladders
CEO: Kenneth Garelick
Treas: Richard J Garelick
Plnt Mgr: Jack Hauck

D-U-N-S 01-528-0956
GARELLI WONG & ASSOCIATES INC (IL)
(Suby of ADECCO TECHNICAL) ★
200 S Michigan Ave # 700, Chicago, IL 60604-2416
Tel (312) 583-9264 Founded/Ownrshp 2002, 2006
Sales 30.0MM EMP 40
SIC 7361 Executive placement; Executive placement
Pr: John Marshall

D-U-N-S 07-312-6732
GARFF ENTERPRISES INC
KEN GARFF AUTOMOTIVE GROUP
405 S Main St Ste 1200, Salt Lake City, UT 84111-3412
Tel (801) 257-3400 Founded/Ownrshp 1949
Sales 576.9MM EMP 855
Accts Mayer Hoffman Mc Cann Pc Sal
SIC 5511 6512 Automobiles, new & used; Nonresidential building operators; Automobiles, new & used; Nonresidential building operators
Ch: Robert Garff
Pr: John Garff
CFO: Philip Johnson
VP: Rick Fulkerson
CIO: Mark Boehlen
Dir IT: Kathy Blackley
Sls Mgr: Sam Jarvie
Sales Asso: Gordon Harry

D-U-N-S 05-719-3898
GARFF WARNER AUTOMOTIVE GROUP INC
KEN GAFF NISSAN
777 S West Temple, Salt Lake City, UT 84101-2746
Tel (801) 322-5663 Founded/Ownrshp 2001
Sales 20.1MM^E EMP 60
Accts Kpmg Peat Marwick Llp
SIC 5511 Automobiles, new & used; Automobiles, new & used
Pr: Bob Garff
Sls Mgr: Lee Deppe
Sls Mgr: Tyler Larson
Sls Mgr: Muhammed Mackie
Sls Mgr: Niyazi Shenkal
Sales Asso: Keith Blomsness
Sales Asso: Joe Ecker
Sales Asso: Greg Gibb
Sales Asso: Bill Lopez
Sales Asso: Charles Madon
Sales Asso: Brian Page
Board of Directors: Brad J Eichers Is Secretar

D-U-N-S 03-534-0983
GARFF-UC LLC
KEN GARFF AUTOMOTIVE GROUP
3455 N Digital Dr, Lehi, UT 84043
Tel (801) 374-1751 Founded/Ownrshp 1984
Sales 32.6MM^E EMP 100
SIC 5511 7538 Automobiles, new & used; General automotive repair shops; Automobiles, new & used; General automotive repair shops
Ch: Robert H Garff
*CEO: John Ken Garff
Genl Mgr: Tom Buckley
Opers Mgr: Christopher Barton
Sls Mgr: Ryan Brady
Sls Mgr: Carlos Iglesias
Sls Mgr: Brantley Reade
Sls Mgr: Shane Toponce

D-U-N-S 03-685-7381
GARFF-WARNER DODGE LLC
WEST VALLEY DODGE
4175 W 3500 S, Salt Lake City, UT 84120-3203
Tel (801) 955-7448 Founded/Ownrshp 1996
Sales 33.7MM^E EMP 120
SIC 5511 Automobiles, new & used; Automobiles, new & used
CEO: Robert H Garff
COO: Brad Eichers
CFO: Howard Lowe
VP: Matt Garff
Telecom Ex: Chad Rigby

D-U-N-S 05-991-2796
■ **GARFIELD BEACH CVS LLC**
(Suby of CVS HEALTH CORP) ★
1 Cvs Dr, Woonsocket, RI 02895-6146
Tel (401) 765-1500 Founded/Ownrshp 2010
Sales 60.3MM^E EMP 718^E
SIC 5912 Drug stores & proprietary stores
Pr: Larry J Merlo

D-U-N-S 02-478-9141
GARFIELD HEIGHTS CITY SCHOOL DISTRICT (OH)
BOARD OFFICE
5640 Briarcliff Dr, Cleveland, OH 44125-4158
Tel (216) 332-0742 Founded/Ownrshp 1919
Sales 25.9MM^E EMP 486
SIC 8211 Public elementary & secondary schools; Public elementary & secondary schools
Dir Sec: Gordon Dupree
Dir IT: Shari Bailey

D-U-N-S 04-522-0241
GARFIELD PUBLIC SCHOOL DISTRICT
34 Outwater Ln Ste 2, Garfield, NJ 07026-3868
Tel (973) 340-5000 Founded/Ownrshp 1897
Sales 35.5MM^E EMP 725
SIC 8211 Public elementary & secondary schools; High school, junior or senior; Public elementary & secondary schools; High school, junior or senior
Ofcr: Glenn Mati
Assoc Dir: Michael Alfonso
Dir IT: Debbie Rigoglioso
IT Man: Laura Dunning
Schl Brd P: Richard Giacomarro
Psych: Melissa Timochko
HC Dir: Tana Raymond

D-U-N-S 02-225-4403
GARFIELD SCHOOL DISTRICT NO RE-2
839 Whiteriver Ave, Rifle, CO 81650-3515
Tel (970) 665-7600 Founded/Ownrshp 1963
Sales 53.1MM^E EMP 750
Accts Mcmahan And Associates Llc A
SIC 8211 Public elementary & secondary schools; School board; Public elementary & secondary schools; School board
Schl Brd P: Chris Pearson
HC Dir: Sarah Bell-Wright

GARFIELDS RESTAURANT & PUB
See EATERIES INC

D-U-N-S 01-909-2477 EXP
GARGIULO INC
15000 Old Hwy 41 N, Naples, FL 34110
Tel (239) 597-3131 Founded/Ownrshp 1980
Sales 169.0MM^E EMP 400
SIC 5148 Fresh fruits & vegetables; Fresh fruits & vegetables
Pr: Christian Leleu
*Pr: Michael Sullivan
*Prin: Jeffrey D Gargiulo
Genl Mgr: Guillermo Fernandez
Off Mgr: Heather Didonato
IT Man: Daniel Subbert
Mtls Mgr: Mike Gorski
Opers Mgr: Mark Handschmann
Mktg Mgr: Robert Elliot

GARGUILO PRODUCE
See FRANK M GARGIULO & SON INC

D-U-N-S 06-615-2372
GARICH INC
THE TRISTAFF GROUP
6336 Greenwich Dr Ste A, San Diego, CA 92122-5922
Tel (858) 453-1331 Founded/Ownrshp 1971
Sales 40.3MM^E EMP 1,024
Accts Lipsey Millimaki & Co Llp
SIC 7361 8742 Employment agencies; Management consulting services; Employment agencies; Management consulting services
Pr: Gary O Van Eik
COO: Rick Kail
VP: Amy Moser
VP: Alex Papike
VP: Chris Papike
*VP: Richard N Papike
VP: Thomas Tanner
Ex Dir: Ben Chazen
Brnch Mgr: Patrick Burnside

D-U-N-S 02-673-0874
GARICK GROUP INC
GARICK MECHANICAL SERVICES
7181 Copperqueen Dr, El Paso, TX 79915-1226
Tel (915) 779-5727 Founded/Ownrshp 1977
Sales 21.9MM^E EMP 50
SIC 1731 1711 General electrical contractor; Plumbing contractors

GARICK MECHANICAL SERVICES
See GARICK GROUP INC

D-U-N-S 00-684-6372
GARIUP CONSTRUCTION CO INC
3965 Harrison St, Gary, IN 46408-2653
Tel (219) 887-5233 Founded/Ownrshp 1959
Sales 30.8MM^E EMP 125
SIC 1531 Operative builders; Operative builders
Pr: Alessandro Gariup
*Treas: Matthew Gariup
*VP: Alex A Griup
Off Mgr: Sunday Detamore

D-U-N-S 06-332-4255
GARKANE ENERGY COOPERATIVE INC
120 W 300 S, Loa, UT 84747
Tel (435) 836-2795 Founded/Ownrshp 1938
Sales 24.6MM EMP 15
Accts Marcus Lewis Greenwich Ut
SIC 4911 Generation, electric power; Generation, electric power
CEO: Carl Albrecht
IT Man: Stacee Blackburn

GARLAND CARPET & RUG
See GARLAND SALES INC

D-U-N-S 06-603-7409
GARLAND CO INC
(Suby of GARLAND INDUSTRIES INC) ★
3800 E 91st St, Cleveland, OH 44105-2197
Tel (216) 641-7500 Founded/Ownrshp 1988
Sales 182.1MM EMP 250
SIC 2952 2851

GARLAND COUNTY ROAD DEPT
See COUNTY OF GARLAND

D-U-N-S 07-837-0061
GARLAND INDEPENDENT SCHOOL DISTRICT
I S D
501 S Jupiter Rd, Garland, TX 75042-7108
Tel (972) 494-8201 Founded/Ownrshp 1897
Sales 543.5MM EMP 7,307
Accts Whitley Penn Llp Houston Tex
SIC 8211 Public elementary & secondary schools; Public elementary school; Public junior high school; Public senior high school; Public elementary & secondary schools; Public elementary school; Public junior high school; Public senior high school
Bd of Dir: Linda Griffin
Dir Sec: Pat Lamb
VP Mktg: Alan Smith
Schl Brd P: Rick Lambert
Teacher Pr: Jed Reed
HC Dir: Maggie Willis

D-U-N-S 19-935-4507
GARLAND INDUSTRIES INC
3800 E 91st St, Cleveland, OH 44105-2103
Tel (216) 641-7500 Founded/Ownrshp 1974
Sales 269.9MM^E EMP 500
SIC 2952 6512 8712 Roofing materials; Roofing felts, cements or coatings; Coating compounds, tar; Commercial & industrial building operation; Architectural services; Roofing materials; Commercial & industrial building operation; Architectural services
Pr: David Sokol
*CFO: Charles Ripepi
*VP: Melvin Chrostowski
*VP: Richard Debacco
*VP: William Oley
*VP: G Richard Olivier
*Sls Mgr: Joe Orlando

D-U-N-S 06-635-8003
GARLAND INSULATING LTD
10912 Sanden Dr, Dallas, TX 75238-5326
Tel (214) 341-0254 Founded/Ownrshp 1977
Sales 28.0MM^E EMP 150
SIC 1742 Insulation, buildings; Insulation, buildings
Pr: Ferrell D Drum
COO: Mike Horowitz
CFO: Gary Horowitz
Off Mgr: Cathy Clough
Opers Mgr: Cardice Gray-Howard
Opers Mgr: Jonathan Heathington

D-U-N-S 93-887-1381 EXP
GARLAND LLC
3330 Nw 60th St, Miami, FL 33142-2127
Tel (305) 636-1607 Founded/Ownrshp 2008
Sales 45.5MM^E EMP 72
SIC 5148 Vegetables

D-U-N-S 00-576-8521
GARLAND NISSAN LLC (KY)
2507 Campbell Blvd, Hopkinsville, KY 42240
Tel (270) 886-6681 Founded/Ownrshp 2007
Sales 44.1MM^E EMP 100
SIC 5511 Automobiles, new & used
Genl Mgr: Pat Hayes
Sls Mgr: Jim Bryan

D-U-N-S 08-217-2198 IMP/EXP
GARLAND SALES INC
GARLAND CARPET & RUG
1800 Antioch Rd, Dalton, GA 30721-4617
Tel (706) 278-7880 Founded/Ownrshp 1972
Sales 83.9MM^E EMP 345
SIC 2273 Carpets & rugs; Carpets & rugs
CEO: Garland Rick
*Pr: Richard Garland
*CFO: Greta Chandler
VP Mktg: Steve Snyder

GARLAND WHOLESALE HUNTSVILLE
See J W GARLAND WHOLESALE INC

D-U-N-S 83-084-6817
GARLAND/DBS INC
(Suby of GARLAND CO INC) ★
3800 E 91st St, Cleveland, OH 44105-2103
Tel (216) 641-7500 Founded/Ownrshp 2009
Sales 59.6MM EMP 250
Accts Meaden & Moore Ltd Cleveland
SIC 2952 6512 8712 Roofing materials; Roofing felts, cements or coatings; Coating compounds, tar; Commercial & industrial building operation; Architectural services; Roofing materials; Roofing felts, cements or coatings; Coating compounds, tar; Commercial & industrial building operation; Architectural services
Pr: Dave Sokol
CFO: Chuck Ripepi
VP: Melvin Chrostowski
VP: Richard Debacco

D-U-N-S 02-289-6179 IMP
GARLANDS INC
MATERIALS MANAGEMENT CO
2501 26th Ave S, Minneapolis, MN 55406-1250
Tel (612) 333-0646 Founded/Ownrshp 1948
Sales 37.9MM^E EMP 54
SIC 5084 Materials handling machinery
CEO: Robert Smith
Owner: Bob Smith
VP: Jerry Smith

GARLANDS OF BARRINGTON, THE
See BARRINGTON VENTURE HOLDING CO LLC

D-U-N-S 10-276-1186 IMP
GARLIC CO
18602 Zerker Rd, Bakersfield, CA 93314-9747
Tel (661) 393-4212 Founded/Ownrshp 1980
Sales 53.8MM EMP 125
Accts Fisher Keathley & Ross Llp
SIC 0139 2099 0191 Herb or spice farm; Food preparations; General farms, primarily crop; Herb or spice farm; Food preparations; General farms, primarily crop
Mng Pt: John Layous
*Pt: Joe Lane
CFO: Gordan Cook
Plnt Mgr: Bill Lane
Sls Mgr: Tiffany Manning
Sls Mgr: Corinne Sabovich

GARLOCK
See PLYMOUTH INDUSTRIES INC

GARLOCK BEARINGS
See COLTEC INDUSTRIES INC

D-U-N-S 79-128-2309
GARLOCK BEARINGS INC
700 Mid Atlantic Pkwy, Thorofare, NJ 08086
Tel (856) 848-3200 Founded/Ownrshp 2007
Sales 38.0MM^E EMP 62^E
SIC 5085 Industrial supplies
CEO: Al Lenac
VP: Larry Davis
VP: Anita Varacallo
VP: Kenneth Walker
Prd Dir: Serge Raineri
Ql Cn Mgr: Devika Ranganathan

D-U-N-S 00-647-8853 IMP
GARLOCK EQUIPMENT CO
(Suby of GARLOCK) ★
2601 Niagara Ln N, Plymouth, MN 55447-4720
Tel (763) 553-1935 Founded/Ownrshp 1990
Sales 40.2MM^E EMP 100
SIC 3531 3535 Roofing equipment; Conveyors & conveying equipment; Roofing equipment; Conveyors & conveying equipment
Ch Bd: Larry Hines
*Pr: Mark Hefly
*CEO: Randy Rollins
Natl Sales: Brian Palkovich
Mktg Dir: Jim Sidla

D-U-N-S 19-555-4514 IMP
GARLOCK PRINTING AND CONVERTING CORP
164 Fredette St, Gardner, MA 01440-3722
Tel (978) 630-1028 Founded/Ownrshp 1987
Sales 73.6MM^E EMP 250
SIC 2759 2679 3554 Flexographic printing; Screen printing; Paper products, converted; Bag & envelope making machinery, paper; Flexographic printing; Screen printing; Paper products, converted; Bag & envelope making machinery, paper
Pr: Peter Garlock
*Treas: Kevin W King
Board of Directors: Phil Ceryanek, James B Jones, Joseph Litchwell

D-U-N-S 04-307-5738 IMP/EXP
■ **GARLOCK SEALING TECHNOLOGIES LLC**
(Suby of ENPRO INDUSTRIES INC) ★
1666 Division St, Palmyra, NY 14522-9350
Tel (315) 597-4811 Founded/Ownrshp 1887
Sales 206.4MM^E EMP 1,500
SIC 3053 3585 3714

D-U-N-S 07-375-9755
GARMAR INDUSTRIES INC
WOOLWICH TWP
1625 Us Hwy 322, Swedesboro, NJ 08085
Tel (856) 241-9700 Founded/Ownrshp 1972
Sales 28.2MM^E EMP 45
SIC 5031 Lumber: rough, dressed & finished
Pr: Howard Bernard
*VP: Gary Bernard

GARMCO
See REPUBLIC FOIL INC

D-U-N-S 04-484-3274
GARMIN AT INC
(Suby of GARMIN INTERNATIONAL INC) ★
2345 Turner Rd Se, Salem, OR 97302-2059
Tel (503) 581-8101 Founded/Ownrshp 2003
Sales 66.3MM^E EMP 147

SIC 3812 Navigational systems & instruments; Navigational systems & instruments
Pr: Clifton A Pemble
Snr Sftwr: Michael Zendels
CTO: Eric Juntunen
Sftwr Eng: Brian Adams
Sls Mgr: Sam Seery

D-U-N-S 79-128-8004 IMP
GARMIN INTERNATIONAL INC
(Suby of GARMIN SWITZERLAND GMBH)
1200 E 151st St, Olathe, KS 66062-3426
Tel (913) 397-8200 Founded/Ownrshp 2001
Sales 2.7MMM EMP 3,000
SIC 3812 Search & navigation equipment; Search & navigation equipment
CEO: Clifton Pemble
COO: Mark Stephens
*CFO: Doug Boessen
CFO: Elle Desimone
CFO: Aimee Pearce
*Ch: Dr Min KAO
*VP: Andrew Etkind
Exec: Marsha Befort
Prgrm Mgr: Raj Sekar
Snr Sftwr: Jason Dilley
Snr Sftwr: John Estabrook

GARMONG CONSTRUCTION SERVICES
See C H GARMONG & SON INC

GARNER & TRUMP EYECARE
See MIDWEST EYE CONSULTANTS PC

D-U-N-S 05-355-4531 IMP
GARNER ENVIRONMENTAL SERVICES INC
1717 W 13th St, Deer Park, TX 77536-2531
Tel (281) 930-1200 Founded/Ownrshp 1981
Sales 142.7MM^E EMP 250
SIC 4959 Toxic or hazardous waste cleanup; Oil spill cleanup; Toxic or hazardous waste cleanup; Oil spill cleanup
Pr: L D Garner
*CFO: Cheryl Morvillo
*VP: John Pavlicek
Dir IT: Mikie Sopczak
IT Man: Edgar Rotundo
Opers Mgr: Casey Anderson
Opers Mgr: Juan Morales
Sls Mgr: Keith Emmons
Genl Couns: Bobbie Risner

D-U-N-S 00-727-3063 IMP
GARNER INDUSTRIES INC
BIN MASTER LEVEL CONTROLS
7201 N 98th St, Lincoln, NE 68507-9711
Tel (402) 434-9100 Founded/Ownrshp 1951
Sales 31.6MM^E EMP 100
SIC 3089 3544 3823 3699 3825 3625 Injection molded finished plastic products; Injection molding of plastics; Special dies, tools, jigs & fixtures; Industrial instrmnts msrmnt display/control process variable; Electrical equipment & supplies; Instruments to measure electricity; Relays & industrial controls
Pr: Scott McLain
*Treas: Linda Steele
Exec: Dewey Garner
IT Man: John Newkirch
Plnt Mgr: Dave Fiddes
Plnt Mgr: Todd Tyler
Ql Cn Mgr: Kathy Christensen
VP Mktg: Scott A McLain
Manager: Nathan Grube
Sls Mgr: Todd Peterson
Snr Mgr: Jenny Christensen

D-U-N-S 11-434-3502
GARNET FORD INC
GARNET VOLKSWAGEN
Rtes 1 & 202, Chadds Ford, PA 19317
Tel (610) 358-5600 Founded/Ownrshp 1984
Sales 23.7MM^E EMP 60
SIC 5511 5521 Automobiles, new & used; Used car dealers; Automobiles, new & used; Used car dealers
Pr: Bruce Hendrixson

D-U-N-S 08-125-7917 IMP
■ **GARNET HILL INC**
(Suby of CORNERSTONE BRANDS GROUP INC) ★
231 Main St, Franconia, NH 03580-4803
Tel (603) 823-5545 Founded/Ownrshp 2000
Sales 42.9MM^E EMP 175
SIC 5961 5621 Clothing, mail order (except women's); Women's apparel, mail order; Furniture & furnishings, mail order; Women's clothing stores; Clothing, mail order (except women's); Women's apparel, mail order; Furniture & furnishings, mail order; Women's clothing stores
VP: Diane Brush
*Sec: Patrick Vonderhaar
Sr VP: Sandi Summerson
VP: Mark Dimarzio
*VP: Christopher T Gassett
*VP: Harold Herman
VP: Sheila Howell
VP: Scott Johnson
VP: Amy Leighton
*VP: Bryant Purvis
Creative D: Charles Pates

D-U-N-S 07-367-0028
GARNET VALLEY SCHOOL DISTRICT (INC)
80 Station Rd, Glen Mills, PA 19342-1751
Tel (610) 579-7300 Founded/Ownrshp 1962
Sales 48.9MM^E EMP 800^E
Accts Bbd Llp Philadelphia Pennsyl
SIC 8211 Public elementary & secondary schools; High school, junior or senior; Elementary school; Public elementary & secondary schools; High school, junior or senior; Elementary school
*Treas: Thomas Delhaney
Bd of Dir: Barbara Shaw
Psych: Jane Bowers

GARNET VOLKSWAGEN
See GARNET FORD INC

D-U-N-S 07-306-2325
GARNEY COMPANIES INC (MO)
(Suby of GARNEY HOLDING CO) ★
1333 Nw Vivion Rd, Kansas City, MO 64118-4554
Tel (816) 741-4600 Founded/Ownrshp 1961
Sales 577.6MM^E EMP 1,100
Accts Mayer Hoffman Mccann Pc Lea
SIC 1623 1629 Sewer line construction; Water main construction; Underground utilities contractor; Highway & street construction; Waste water & sewage treatment plant construction; Sewer line construction; Water main construction; Underground utilities contractor; Waste water & sewage treatment plant construction
Pr: Mike Heitmann
COO: Wayne O'Brien
COO: Jason Seubert
CFO: Jeff Lacy
VP: Steve Ford
VP: Matt Foster
VP: Mike Gardner
VP: Greg Harris
VP: Tony Kempf
VP: Stephen McCandless
VP: Steve McCandless
VP: Wayne Obrien
VP: Scott Parrish

D-U-N-S 03-063-3663
GARNEY HOLDING CO
1333 Nw Vivion Rd, Kansas City, MO 64118-4554
Tel (816) 741-4600 Founded/Ownrshp 1994
Sales NA EMP 1,100
SIC 1623 1611 1629 Water main construction; Sewer line construction; Highway & street construction; Concrete construction: roads, highways, sidewalks, etc.; Waste water & sewage treatment plant construction; Water main construction; Sewer line construction; Highway & street construction; Concrete construction: roads, highways, sidewalks, etc.; Waste water & sewage treatment plant construction
CEO: Mike Heitmann
*COO: Wayne O'Brien
*COO: Jason Seubert
*CFO: Jeff Lacy
*Treas: Thomas J Dahl
Snr PM: Dave Hall

GARNIER THIEBAUT
See GARNIER-THIEBAUT INC

D-U-N-S 00-617-5516 IMP/EXP
GARNIER-THIEBAUT INC
GARNIER THIEBAUT
3000 S Eads St Ste 2000, Arlington, VA 22202-4022
Tel (703) 920-2448 Founded/Ownrshp 2007
Sales 27.0MM^E EMP 200^E
SIC 2511 Club room furniture: wood; Club room furniture: wood
Pr: Jean-Philippe Krukowicz
Sr VP: Thomas W Eales II
*VP: Lisa Aliano
*VP: Herve Perouse De Montclos
*VP: Tom Hall
*VP: Cedric Montagnana
IT Man: Katalin Budi
Mktg Dir: Rossie Metodieva
Manager: Camille Weber

GARPHYTTAN WIRE
See SUZUKI GARPHYTTAN CORP

D-U-N-S 12-414-9654
GARRARD CARPENTRY INC
GARRARD FRAMING AND DRYWALL
5578 Commercial Blvd, Winter Haven, FL 33880-1008
Tel (863) 967-3992 Founded/Ownrshp 2001
Sales 20.4MM^E EMP 80
SIC 1751 1742 Carpentry work; Drywall
Pr: Julie Garrard
VP: John Ridenour
Area Supr: Stephen Garrard

D-U-N-S 88-352-8473
GARRARD CONSTRUCTION GROUP INC
1960 Satellite Blvd, Duluth, GA 30097-4122
Tel (770) 822-1944 Founded/Ownrshp 1994
Sales 22.2MM^E EMP 43
Accts Moore Stephens Tiller Llc Du
SIC 1542 Commercial & office building contractors
CEO: Ronald H Garrard
CFO: Patty Storey

D-U-N-S 94-681-9760
GARRARD COUNTY BOARD OF EDUCATION
322 W Maple Ave, Lancaster, KY 40444-1170
Tel (859) 792-4677 Founded/Ownrshp 1950
Sales 22.8MM^E EMP 425^E
Accts Radwan Brown & Company Psc Cp
SIC 8211 Elementary & secondary schools; Public senior high school; School board; Elementary & secondary schools; Public senior high school; School board

D-U-N-S 07-923-6202
GARRARD COUNTY SCHOOLS
322 W Maple Ave, Lancaster, KY 40444-1170
Tel (859) 792-3018 Founded/Ownrshp 2013
Sales 40.5MM^E EMP 248^E
SIC 6799 Investors

GARRARD FRAMING AND DRYWALL
See GARRARD CARPENTRY INC

D-U-N-S 00-911-8340
GARRATT-CALLAHAN CO (CA)
50 Ingold Rd, Burlingame, CA 94010-2206
Tel (650) 697-5811 Founded/Ownrshp 1904, 1942
Sales 63.8MM^E EMP 275
SIC 2899 2911 Water treating compounds; Oils, lubricating; Water treating compounds; Oils, lubricating
CEO: Jeffrey L Garratt
*CFO: Matthew Colvin
*Ex VP: Matthew R Garratt
Genl Mgr: Nick Smith
Mktg Mgr: Manny Chargualaf
Sls Mgr: Jacob Creel
Sls Mgr: Jonathan Davis
Sls Mgr: Tyler Morton
Sls Mgr: Cal Quast
Sls Mgr: Jeremy Thompson
Snr PM: Colby Townsend

D-U-N-S 96-871-6790
GARRETSON FIRM RESOLUTION GROUP INC
GARRETSON RESOLUTION GROUP
6281 Tri Rdg Ste 300, Cincinnati, OH 45201
Tel (513) 794-0400 Founded/Ownrshp 2008
Sales 24.6MM^E EMP 200^E
SIC 8111 Bankruptcy law; Debt collection law; Taxation law; Corporate, partnership & business law; Bankruptcy law; Debt collection law; Taxation law; Corporate, partnership & business law
CEO: Matt Garretson
*Pr: Jason Wolf
*CFO: Shawn Kocher
Sr VP: Dan Docherty
Sr VP: Jeff Wolverton
VP: Mark Maughan
VP: Ellie Moss
Prgrm Mgr: Jon Paschal
Software D: Anthony Thomas
Opers Mgr: Matthew Long
Mktg Dir: Erin Hively

GARRETSON RESOLUTION GROUP
See GARRETSON FIRM RESOLUTION GROUP INC

D-U-N-S 06-940-3905
GARRETT COUNTY PHYSICIAN HOSPITAL ORGANIZATION INC
251 N 4th St, Oakland, MD 21550-1375
Tel (301) 533-4000 Founded/Ownrshp 1950
Sales NA EMP 335
SIC 8062

D-U-N-S 07-962-8834
GARRETT COUNTY PUBLIC SCHOOLS
40 S 2nd St, Oakland, MD 21550-1518
Tel (301) 334-8900 Founded/Ownrshp 2014
Sales 11.7MM^E EMP 536^E
SIC 8211 Public elementary & secondary schools
Dir IT: Lawrence McKenzie
Pr Dir: Jim Morris
Schl Brd P: Thomas Carr
Teacher Pr: Tim Thornburg
HC Dir: Phil Lauver

D-U-N-S 00-499-6112 IMP
GARRETT ELECTRONICS INC (TX)
GARRETT METAL DETECTORS
1881 W State St, Garland, TX 75042-6797
Tel (972) 494-6151 Founded/Ownrshp 1965
Sales 69.3MM^E EMP 180
Accts Saville Dodgen & Co Dallas
SIC 3669 Metal detectors; Metal detectors
Pr: Charles L Garrett
*VP: Eleanor Garrett
Prd Mgr: Terry Ludwig
Mktg Dir: Steve Moore

GARRETT ELEMENTARY SCHOOL
See HAZELWOOD SCHOOL DISTRICT

GARRETT INDUSTRIAL SUPPLY
See GARRETT MINE SUPPLY INC

D-U-N-S 18-601-3319
GARRETT MECHANICAL AND MAINTENANCE INC
11159 Lakeview Dr, Union, KY 41091-9511
Tel (859) 384-0392 Founded/Ownrshp 2004
Sales 55.8MM EMP 2
SIC 7349 7389 Building maintenance services; ; Building maintenance services;
Pr: Garry Strange
*VP: Karen M Strange

GARRETT METAL DETECTORS
See GARRETT ELECTRONICS INC

D-U-N-S 10-902-1543
GARRETT MINE SUPPLY INC
GARRETT INDUSTRIAL SUPPLY
104 Commerce Dr, Oakland, MD 21550-3932
Tel (301) 334-4136 Founded/Ownrshp 1983
Sales 20.1MM^E EMP 32
SIC 5084 7699 5082 Industrial machinery & equipment; Geophysical equipment repair; Mining machinery & equipment, except petroleum
Pr: Courtland J Helbig
*Pr: Steven P Tressler
Genl Mgr: Jeremy Radabaugh

GARRETT POPCORN SHOP
See CARAMELCRISP LLC

D-U-N-S 83-273-1959
GARRETT REGIONAL MEDICAL CENTER
251 N 4th St, Oakland, MD 21550-1375
Tel (301) 334-7843 Founded/Ownrshp 1950
Sales 43.3MM EMP 374
Accts Dixon Hughes Goodman Llp Tys
SIC 8062 General medical & surgical hospitals; General medical & surgical hospitals
Pr: Mark Boucot
*CEO: Donald P Battista
COO: Steven Peterson
CFO: Tracy Lipscomb
Treas: Robert Gorlaski
VP: Denise Liston
Dir Inf Cn: Linda Danjou
Dir Lab: Lois Frazee
Dir Rad: Mike Reed
Nurse Mgr: Jeff Hinebaugh
CIO: Sandy Swanson

D-U-N-S 04-960-0596
GARRETT-KEYSER-BUTLERCOMMUNITY SCHOOL DISTRICT
801 E Houston St, Garrett, IN 46738-1662
Tel (260) 357-3185 Founded/Ownrshp 1967
Sales 23.6MM^E EMP 300
SIC 8211 Public elementary & secondary schools; Public elementary & secondary schools
COO: Ryan Hathaway
Bd of Dir: Danny Weimer
Bd of Dir: Terry Yarde
VP: Anthony Griffin
Dir Sec: Gerrald Kline
Dir Sec: Jim Slain
Dir IT: Kyle Smith
Dir IT: Grant Surfus
Schl Brd P: Christopher Hoeffel

D-U-N-S 04-876-3494
GARRICK MOTORS INC
TOYOTA OF ESCONDIDO
231 E Lincoln Ave, Escondido, CA 92026-3078
Tel (760) 746-0601 Founded/Ownrshp 1978
Sales 98.6MM^E EMP 235^E
SIC 5511 Automobiles, new & used; Automobiles, new & used
Pr: Gary Myers
*VP: Rick Billuni
Mktg Dir: Damian Campos
Sls Mgr: Don Abadie
Sls Mgr: Kevin Edgett
Sls Mgr: Isaac Garcia
Sls Mgr: James Peters
Sls Mgr: Julie Whitehead
Sales Asso: Juan Zaragoza

GARRIGAN LYMAN
See LYMAN GARRIGAN GROUP INC

D-U-N-S 00-318-6277
GARRIS - EVANS LUMBER CO
701 W 14th St, Greenville, NC 27834-4043
Tel (252) 752-2106 Founded/Ownrshp 1919
Sales 47.6MM EMP 105
Accts Sullivan Shearin & Company G
SIC 5211 1521 6159 Lumber & other building materials; New construction, single-family houses; Loan institutions, general & industrial; Lumber & other building materials; New construction, single-family houses; Loan institutions, general & industrial
Pr: John Evans
*Treas: David A Evans Jr

GARRIS PLASTERING
See PADILLA CONSTRUCTION CO

GARRISON & TOWNSEND
See ADVANTA US INC

GARRISON BREWER CO
See STATIONERS INC

D-U-N-S 96-790-2243
GARRISON CAPITAL INC
1290 Ave Of The Americas, New York, NY 10104-0101
Tel (212) 372-9500 Founded/Ownrshp 2010
Sales NA EMP 10
SIC 6153 Working capital financing
CEO: Joseph Tansey
*CFO: Brian Chase

D-U-N-S 02-694-3993
GARRISON FRED OIL CO
ALL STAR FUEL
1107 Walter Griffin St, Plainview, TX 79072-5401
Tel (806) 296-6353 Founded/Ownrshp 1974
Sales 191.1MM EMP 50
SIC 5172 5541

D-U-N-S 79-653-5065
GARRISON INVESTMENT GROUP LP
1290 Avenue Of The Americ, New York, NY 10104-0008
Tel (212) 372-9500 Founded/Ownrshp 2007
Sales 198.9MM^E EMP 210
SIC 6282 Investment advisory service
Pt: Steven Stuart
Pt: Brian Chase
Sr VP: Mitchell Garrison
VP: Joshua Brandt
VP: Josh Dinstein
VP: Robert Feeney
VP: Jeff Fier
VP: Colm Flynn
VP: Matthew Lambert
VP: Nguyen Long
VP: Tom McGarrity
VP: Jason Morrow
VP: Jason Reeves
VP: Sloan Sutta

D-U-N-S 60-387-7333
GARRISON PROTECTIVE SERVICES INC
TRILOGY
120 Lake Ave S Ste 24, Nesconset, NY 11767-1060
Tel (631) 979-7000 Founded/Ownrshp 1977
Sales 18.4MM^E EMP 850
SIC 7381 4215 Security guard service; Courier services, except by air; Security guard service; Courier services, except by air
Pr: Mike Tenreiro
VP: Frank Hubert

D-U-N-S 03-483-1180 IMP
GARRISON SERVICE CO
HOIST & CRANE COMPANY
100 Fernco Dr, Nashville, TN 37207-3909
Tel (615) 350-6700 Founded/Ownrshp 1960
Sales 34.2MM^E EMP 80
SIC 5084 7359

D-U-N-S 94-007-3562
GARRISON STEEL ERECTORS INC
1122 Industrial Park Dr, Pell City, AL 35125-1592
Tel (205) 884-4766 Founded/Ownrshp 1994
Sales 30.3MM^E EMP 80
SIC 1791 Structural steel erection
Pr: John Garrison
*CFO: Keith Cornelius

D-U-N-S 00-403-7024
GARROTT BROTHERS CONTINOUS MIX INC (TN)
375 Red River Rd, Gallatin, TN 37066-3115
Tel (615) 452-2385 Founded/Ownrshp 1950
Sales 20.5MM^E EMP 60

SIC 3273 Ready-mixed concrete; Ready-mixed concrete
Pr: John B Garrott Jr
*VP: Pamela Garrott
Opers Mgr: Daniel Bugbee

D-U-N-S 07-091-9159
GARRY BRADFORD MANAGEMENT CO LTD
(Suby of G BRADFORD CO INC) ★
4646 Corona Dr Ste 105, Corpus Christi, TX 78411-4383
Tel (361) 852-6392 Founded/Ownrshp 2000
Sales 20.6MM^E EMP 1,675^E
SIC 8741 Management services
Prin: Garry Bradford

D-U-N-S 01-308-3985
GARSTEN MOTORS INC
APPLE HONDA
1375 Old Country Rd, Riverhead, NY 11901-2026
Tel (631) 727-0555 Founded/Ownrshp 1959
Sales 40.6MM^E EMP 72
SIC 5511 Automobiles, new & used; Automobiles, new & used
Ch Bd: Irwin Garsten
Pr: William Fields
Dir Bus: Eric Goetz
Dir Bus: Eric Nichols
Store Mgr: Dave Campbell
Sls Mgr: Bob Sullivan
Sales Asso: Jeffrey Schepps

GARSTON SIGN SCREEN PRTG SUPS
See GARSTON SIGN SUPPLIES INC

D-U-N-S 01-868-4233
GARSTON SIGN SUPPLIES INC
GARSTON SIGN SCREEN PRTG SUPS
570 Tolland St, East Hartford, CT 06108-2662
Tel (860) 289-3040 Founded/Ownrshp 1960
Sales 40.9MM^E EMP 70
SIC 5085 Signmaker equipment & supplies; Signmaker equipment & supplies
Pr: Steve Garston
*VP: Dean Garston

D-U-N-S 62-164-1018 IMP
GARTH O GREEN ENTERPRISES INC
SOUTHWEST PLUMBING SUPPLY
506 N 200 W, Cedar City, UT 84721-3544
Tel (435) 586-4972 Founded/Ownrshp 1989
Sales 59.3MM^E EMP 80
SIC 5074 5999 Plumbing fittings & supplies; Plumbing & heating supplies; Plumbing fittings & supplies; Plumbing & heating supplies
Pr: Michael Green
*Sec: Phillip T Green
*VP: Jeff Green
*VP: Ryan R Nelson

D-U-N-S 00-603-3302 IMP
GARTLAND FOUNDRY CO INC
330 Grant St, Terre Haute, IN 47802-3063
Tel (812) 232-0226 Founded/Ownrshp 1902, 1922
Sales 51.3MM^E EMP 110
SIC 3321 Gray iron castings; Gray iron castings
Pr: Bill Grimes
*Pr: William Grimes
*Sr VP: Steve Cass
*VP: Dave Grimes
*VP: David A Grimes
*VP: Don Powell
IT Man: Randy Hittle
QI Cn Mgr: Michelle Ring

D-U-N-S 09-722-0180
▲ GARTNER INC
56 Top Gallant Rd, Stamford, CT 06902-7700
Tel (203) 316-1111 Founded/Ownrshp 1979
Sales 2.0MMM EMP 6,759
Tkr Sym IT Exch NYS
SIC 8732 8742 8741 Commercial nonphysical research; Market analysis or research; Management consulting services; Business consultant; Management services; Commercial nonphysical research; Market analysis or research; Management consulting services; Business consultant; Management services
CEO: Eugene A Hall
COO: Kevin Volpe
CFO: Craig W Safian
CFO: Craig Safian
Sr VP: Madeline Hanewinckel
Sr VP: Darko Hrelic
Sr VP: Robin B Kranich
Sr VP: Lewis G Schwartz
Sr VP: Peter Sondergaard
Sr VP: Chris Thomas
Sr VP: Per Anders Waern
VP: Doug Laney
VP: Per Waern
Dir Bus: Dan Ahearn
Dir Bus: Kurt Calderone
Board of Directors: Michael J Bingle, Richard J Bressler, Raul E Cesan, Karen E Dykstra, Anne Sutherland Fuchs, William O Grabe, Stephen G Pagliuca, James C Smith

D-U-N-S 00-622-7813
GARTNER REFRIGERATION AND MANUFACTURING INC
13205 16th Ave N, Plymouth, MN 55441-4566
Tel (763) 559-5880 Founded/Ownrshp 1942
Sales 36.4MM^E EMP 78
Accts Gary R Nylund And Associates
SIC 1711 Refrigeration contractor
Pr: John Hendrickson
*VP: Don Faust
*VP: Todd Hendrickson
Board of Directors: Donald Faust, John Hendrickson, Todd Hendrickson, Julie Malek

D-U-N-S 03-643-9214 IMP/EXP
GARTNER STUDIOS INC (MN)
GARTNER STUDIOS INTERNATIONAL
(Suby of GARTNER COMPANIES)
220 Myrtle St E, Stillwater, MN 55082-5033
Tel (651) 351-7700 Founded/Ownrshp 1998
Sales 57.0MM EMP 100
Accts Lethert Skwira Schultz & Co
SIC 5112 Stationery & office supplies; Stationery & office supplies
CEO: Gregory Gartner
*CFO: Daron Johnson
*VP: Carl Monty
CTO: Matthew Fitzgerald
IT Man: Corey Culver
Sls Mgr: Cheri Elshaw
Art Dir: Heather Schmidt

GARTNER STUDIOS INTERNATIONAL
See GARTNER STUDIOS INC

D-U-N-S 02-955-7733 IMP
GARTON TRACTOR INC
KUBOTA
2400 N Golden State Blvd, Turlock, CA 95382-9408
Tel (209) 632-3931 Founded/Ownrshp 1953
Sales 111.9MM EMP 205
SIC 5999 Farm machinery; Farm machinery
Pr: William L Garton
*Treas: Thomas Garton
Dir IT: Jeff Degraff
Sales Asso: David Silva

D-U-N-S 04-448-5860
GARVER LLC
4701 Northshore Dr, North Little Rock, AR 72118-5325
Tel (501) 376-3633 Founded/Ownrshp 1970
Sales 38.8MM EMP 285
Accts Rasco Winter Abston Moore & As
SIC 8711 Consulting engineer; Consulting engineer
CFO: Dathan Gaskill
VP: Brode Morgan
VP: Herbert Parker
Exec: Larry Taylor
Snr PM: Gary Bennett
Board of Directors: Michael Griffin, Brock Hoskins, Stephen Jones, Frank McIlwain

GARVEY GROUP, THE
See ED GARVEY AND CO

GARVEY GROUP, THE
See GARVEY GROUP LLC

D-U-N-S 78-516-3119
GARVEY GROUP LLC
GARVEY GROUP, THE
7400 N Lehigh Ave, Niles, IL 60714-4024
Tel (847) 647-1900 Founded/Ownrshp 2001
Sales 101.1MM^E EMP 320^E
SIC 6719 Personal holding companies, except banks; Personal holding companies, except banks
*COO: Joe Kulis
CFO: Mike Leonard
*VP: David Nolte
Genl Mgr: Roxann Black
Dir IT: William Brady
VP Opers: Jim Oring
Mtls Mgr: Richard Zaccone
Opers Mgr: Dave Alden
Plnt Mgr: Bill Grosskreuz
Prd Mgr: Bob Garcia
Prd Mgr: Charlene Pajewski

GARVEY NUT & CANDY
See GENESIS FOODS CORP

D-U-N-S 07-964-6220
GARVEY SCHOOL DISTRICT
2730 Del Mar Ave, Rosemead, CA 91770-3099
Tel (626) 307-3400 Founded/Ownrshp 1892
Sales 39.1MM^E EMP 788
SIC 8211 Public elementary & secondary schools; Public elementary & secondary schools
Dir IT: Lupe Mesa
Schl Brd P: Tony Ramos
Genl Couns: Bonifacio Garcia
Board of Directors: Anita Chu, Bertha Mobassaly, Art Reynolds

D-U-N-S 05-830-9220
GARVEY SCHUBERT BARER A PROFESSIONAL SERVICES COR
GARVEY SCHUBERT BARER LAW
1191 2nd Ave Fl 18, Seattle, WA 98101-2996
Tel (206) 264-1349 Founded/Ownrshp 1964
Sales 32.5MM^E EMP 220
SIC 8111 General practice law office; General practice law office
Pr: Anne Preston
COO: Annemarie Brown
Ofcr: Jill Allyn
*VP: Bruce Robertson
Dir Soc: Amber Buntin
Genl Mgr: Andrew Palk
Corp Couns: Gary Swearingen
Counsel: Samuel Kauffman
Counsel: Ruth Walters

GARVEY SCHUBERT BARER LAW
See GARVEY SCHUBERT BARER A PROFESSIONAL SERVICES COR

D-U-N-S 01-267-8512
GARVEY VOLKSWAGEN INC
HAUNDAI
483 Quaker Rd, Queensbury, NY 12804-1516
Tel (518) 793-3488 Founded/Ownrshp 1978
Sales 24.1MM^E EMP 58
SIC 5511 Automobiles, new & used; Automobiles, new & used
Pr: J Peter Garvey III
*Treas: Sean Garvey
Off Mgr: Regina Leahy
Sls Mgr: Lee Garand
Sls Mgr: Lee Garrand
Sales Asso: Shane Labounty
Sales Asso: Alberto Lupia
Sales Asso: Claude Middleton

D-U-N-S 02-529-5619
GARVEYS OFFICE PRODUCTS INC (IL)
7500 N Caldwell Ave, Niles, IL 60714-3808
Tel (847) 588-1690 Founded/Ownrshp 1926, 1993
Sales 42.9MM^E EMP 45
SIC 5112 5021 Office supplies; Office furniture
Pr: Bernard C Garvey
*VP: Kenneth Garvey
VP Sls: Scott Larson
Sls Mgr: Jean Frank

D-U-N-S 01-920-9337
GARVIN CONSTRUCTION PRODUCTS INC (MA)
G C P
8 Bunker Hill Indus Park, Charlestown, MA 02129-1621
Tel (617) 242-2525 Founded/Ownrshp 1949, 1975
Sales 20.8MM^E EMP 27
SIC 5031 Building materials, exterior; Building materials, interior
Pr: Brendan R Garvin
*Pr: Brendan P Garvin

D-U-N-S 03-628-2598
GARVIN OIL CO INC
KENT'S KORNER
4154 Festival Trail Rd, Wagener, SC 29164-9717
Tel (803) 564-5944 Founded/Ownrshp 1985
Sales 20.6MM^E EMP 150
SIC 5411 5541 Convenience stores, independent; Filling stations, gasoline; Convenience stores, independent; Filling stations, gasoline
Ch: Kent G Ingram
Treas: Chad G Ingram
VP: Chase W Ingram

GARY & LEO'S IGA
See GARY AND LEOS INC

D-U-N-S 13-446-5608
GARY AND LEOS INC
GARY & LEO'S IGA
730 1st St, Havre, MT 59501-3702
Tel (406) 265-1404 Founded/Ownrshp 1986
Sales 35.8MM^E EMP 225
SIC 5411 Grocery stores; Grocery stores
Pr: Gary Leland
*Prin: Leo Job

D-U-N-S 79-178-0927
GARY BALE REDI-MIX CONCRETE INC
16131 Construction Cir W, Irvine, CA 92606-4410
Tel (949) 786-9441 Founded/Ownrshp 1968
Sales 26.7MM^E EMP 80
SIC 3273 Ready-mixed concrete
CEO: Kyle Goerlitz

D-U-N-S 08-205-8017
GARY C WYATT GENERAL CONTRACTOR LLC
245 Riverchase Pkwy E, Hoover, AL 35244-2903
Tel (205) 985-0121 Founded/Ownrshp 2003
Sales 24.0MM^E EMP 130
Accts Warren Averett Kimbrough & Ma
SIC 1542 Commercial & office building, new construction; Commercial & office building, new construction
Plnt Mgr: Rick Daniel
Snr PM: Bill Heath

D-U-N-S 06-862-2455
GARY COMMUNITY SCHOOLS CORP
1988 Polk St, Gary, IN 46407-2443
Tel (219) 886-6400 Founded/Ownrshp 1909
Sales 186.9MM^E EMP 3,278
SIC 8211 Public elementary school; Public junior high school; Public senior high school; Public elementary school; Public junior high school; Public senior high school
Pr: Gregory Fleming
Ofcr: Eric Johnson
*Prin: Dr Cheryl Pruitt
Dir IT: Lloyd Keith
IT Man: Bonita Gray
IT Man: Kevin Joseph
Pr Dir: Charmella Greer
Psych: Patricia Hudson
Psych: Bobbie Jones
Psych: Jacqueline Lafave
Psych: David Mucci

D-U-N-S 05-408-8760
GARY CROSSLEY FORD INC
8050 N Church Rd, Kansas City, MO 64158-1166
Tel (816) 781-4844 Founded/Ownrshp 1980
Sales 36.8MM^E EMP 75
SIC 5511 Automobiles, new & used; Pickups, new & used; Vans, new & used; Automobiles, new & used; Pickups, new & used; Vans, new & used
Prin: Todd Crossley
Off Mgr: Lisa Haffecke
Store Mgr: Leon Garrett
Sls Mgr: Howard Longsdale
Sales Asso: Gene Burgen
Sales Asso: Lisa Garcia

D-U-N-S 06-886-8652
GARY D NELSON ASSOCIATES INC
NELSON STAFFING SOLUTIONS
19080 Lomita Ave, Sonoma, CA 95476-5453
Tel (707) 935-6113 Founded/Ownrshp 1970
Sales 44.6MM^E EMP 267
SIC 7361 Employment agencies; Employment agencies
CEO: Donna Farrugia
Ch Bd: Gary D Nelson
Pr: Mark Nelson
CEO: Craig S Nelson
COO: Tony Bartenetti
CFO: Steve Furtado
Ofcr: Deb Mings
Sr VP: Courtney Dickson
VP: Beth Noseworthy
VP: Todd Witkin
Exec: Todd Nelson

D-U-N-S 62-657-8269
GARY E MILGARD FAMILY OFFICE
1701 Commerce St, Tacoma, WA 98402-3207
Tel (253) 274-0121 Founded/Ownrshp 2006
Sales 21.3MM EMP 5
SIC 8699 Charitable organization
Prin: Gary Gard
Ex Dir: Jim Sheehan

D-U-N-S 08-381-9292
GARY G DAY CONSTRUCTION CO INC
4480 W Nevso Dr, Las Vegas, NV 89103-3764
Tel (702) 873-4377 Founded/Ownrshp 1975
Sales 21.9MM EMP 150
Accts Swecker & Company Ltd Las V
SIC 1522 1521 Hotel/motel & multi-family home construction; New construction, single-family houses; Hotel/motel & multi-family home construction; New construction, single-family houses
Pr: Gary G Day
*Sec: Linda C Day

D-U-N-S 09-633-0134
GARY HALGRAN
INTERIM SERVICES
2833 Fairview Ave N, Roseville, MN 55113-1325
Tel (651) 917-3634 Founded/Ownrshp 2001
Sales 13.8MM^E EMP 350
SIC 7363 Temporary help service; Temporary help service
Ch Bd: Gary Halgran
*Treas: Kari Jarvi
Genl Mgr: Pat Skogen

GARY HOBART ROOFING SUPPLY
See GHR ENTERPRISES INC

D-U-N-S 78-021-5476
GARY JOB CORPS CENTER
2800 Airport Hwy 21, San Marcos, TX 78666
Tel (512) 396-6622 Founded/Ownrshp 1965
Sales 24.3MM^E EMP 525
SIC 8249 Vocational apprentice training; Vocational apprentice training
CEO: Lonnie Hall
Adm Dir: Kathy Eggers

D-U-N-S 04-568-8462
GARY LANG CHEVROLET INC
GARY LANG IMPORTS
1107 S Il Route 31, McHenry, IL 60050-8200
Tel (815) 385-2100 Founded/Ownrshp 1983
Sales 35.6MM^E EMP 65
SIC 5511 Automobiles, new & used; Automobiles, new & used
Pr: Gary Lang
*VP: Dixie Gilmore
*VP: Patricia Lang
CTO: Carrey Kilora
Sales Asso: Tony Feucht

GARY LANG IMPORTS
See GARY LANG CHEVROLET INC

GARY MATHEWS JEEP
See GARY MATHEWS MOTORS INC

D-U-N-S 08-584-3092
GARY MATHEWS MOTORS INC
GARY MATHEWS JEEP
1100 New Ashland City Rd, Clarksville, TN 37040
Tel (931) 552-7100 Founded/Ownrshp 1977
Sales 79.8MM^E EMP 250
SIC 5511 7538 5521 New & used car dealers; General automotive repair shops; Used car dealers; New & used car dealers; General automotive repair shops; Used car dealers
Pr: Gary Mathews
*Sec: Joyce Mathews
Genl Mgr: Terry Yarbourough
Opers Mgr: Greg Mathews
Sales Asso: Paul Horton

D-U-N-S 02-745-2689
GARY MERLINO CONSTRUCTION CO INC
STONEWAY CONSTRUCTION SUPPLY
9125 10th Ave S, Seattle, WA 98108-4600
Tel (206) 763-9552 Founded/Ownrshp 1961
Sales 168.4MM^E EMP 350
SIC 1611 1623 3273 Highway & street construction; Water main construction; Sewer line construction; Ready-mixed concrete; Highway & street construction; Water main construction; Sewer line construction; Ready-mixed concrete
Pr: Gary M Merlino
*Pr: Dan Raymond
*VP: Don Merlino
*VP: Charlie Oliver
Genl Mgr: Herb Allen
IT Man: Cong Nguyen
Sfty Mgr: Don Robertson

D-U-N-S 03-799-7574
GARY NELSON INC
OLYMPIC BRAKE SUPPLY
907 Thomas Ave Sw, Renton, WA 98057-2931
Tel (206) 575-8100 Founded/Ownrshp 1980
Sales 25.9MM^E EMP 80
SIC 5013 3714 Automotive supplies & parts; Motor vehicle brake systems & parts
Pr: Gary L Nelson

GARY PLASTIC
See VIELE MANUFACTURING CORP

D-U-N-S 00-161-9337 IMP
GARY PLASTIC PACKAGING CORP (NY)
GARYLINE
1340 Viele Ave, Bronx, NY 10474-7134
Tel (718) 893-2200 Founded/Ownrshp 1962
Sales 65.6MM^E EMP 400
SIC 3089 Plastic containers, except foam; Plastic containers, except foam
Ch Bd: Gary Hellinger
*Pr: Richard Hellinger
CFO: Harold King
VP: Scott Denny
IT Man: Robert Denny
Natl Sales: Rick Ledonne
Manager: David Granetz

GARY POOLS COMMERCIAL
See GARY POOLS INC

D-U-N-S 00-813-5527
GARY POOLS INC
GARY POOLS COMMERCIAL
438 Sandau Rd, San Antonio, TX 78216-3621
Tel (210) 341-3333 *Founded/Ownrshp* 1953
Sales 26.5MM^E *EMP* 140
SIC 1799 Swimming pool construction
Ch Bd: Leif A Zars
IT Man: Jeffery Farrell
Sls Mgr: Pete Herrera

D-U-N-S 04-882-0195
GARY SMITH FORD INC
1 Beal Pkwy Ne, Fort Walton Beach, FL 32548-4894
Tel (850) 244-4111 *Founded/Ownrshp* 1969
Sales 34.2MM^E *EMP* 85
SIC 5511 5521 Automobiles, new & used; Used car dealers; Automobiles, new & used; Used car dealers
Pr: Tim Smith
**Sec:* Jacqueline Skeen
Sls Mgr: Rusty Chambers

GARY SMITH HONDA
See BLACK-JACK INC

D-U-N-S 03-995-5638 EXP
GARY W CLEM INC
ALMACO
99 M Ave, Nevada, IA 50201-1549
Tel (515) 382-3506 *Founded/Ownrshp* 1978
Sales 30.5MM^E *EMP* 90
SIC 3523 Planting machines, agricultural; Combines (harvester-threshers)
Pr: Gary W Clem
**Sr VP:* Arlan Sandvik
VP: Brian Carr
Plnt Mgr: Scott Webster

GARY YEOMANS FORD
See TERRY TAYLOR FORD CO

GARYLINE
See GARY PLASTIC PACKAGING CORP

GAS & SUPPLY
See INDUSTRIAL WELDING SUPPLY CO OF HARVEY INC

GAS & WATER DEPT
See DYERSBURG CITY OF (INC)

D-U-N-S 01-502-7030
GAS ANALYTICAL SERVICES INC
(*Suby of* CRITICALCONTROL SOLUTIONS CORP)
8444 Water St, Stonewood, WV 26301-8006
Tel (304) 623-0020 *Founded/Ownrshp* 2009
Sales 52.8MM^E *EMP* 101
SIC 1389 Gas field services
Pr: Brenton Lawther
Off Mgr: Mark Nuzum

GAS AND SUPPLY
See BR WELDING SUPPLY LLC

D-U-N-S 06-348-6117
GAS BREAKER INC
17 Lee Blvd Ste D, Malvern, PA 19355-1234
Tel (610) 407-7200 *Founded/Ownrshp* 2000
Sales 100.0MM *EMP* 28
SIC 3491 Gas valves & parts, industrial; Gas valves & parts, industrial
CEO: John B McGowan Jr
**Pr:* C Dean McGowan

D-U-N-S 04-154-0238
GAS CITY LTD
STEEL CITY TRUCK & AUTO
401 S Old Woodward Ave # 340, Birmingham, MI 48009-6611
Tel (815) 469-9000 *Founded/Ownrshp* 1963
Sales 98.5MM^E *EMP* 500
SIC 5541 5411 5172 Filling stations, gasoline; Convenience stores; Gasoline; Fuel oil; Diesel fuel; Filling stations, gasoline; Convenience stores; Gasoline; Fuel oil; Diesel fuel
Pr: William McEnery
Sec: Ross Trovato
VP: Leonard Mc Mc Enery
VP: Leonard McEnery
Brnch Mgr: Kevin Anderson
Brnch Mgr: Lisa Baruer

D-U-N-S 02-144-7591
GAS CLIP TECHNOLOGIES INC
610 Uptown Blvd Ste 4100, Cedar Hill, TX 75104-3534
Tel (972) 775-7577 *Founded/Ownrshp* 2009
Sales 24.9MM *EMP* 30^E
Accts Milbern Ray And Company Grape
SIC 1799 Gas leakage detection
CEO: Bryan Bates
**CEO:* Fonda Bates
VP Mktg: Allen Daniell
Manager: Chad Bilger
Manager: Bob Hirth
Manager: Todd Holtz

D-U-N-S 13-388-1974 IMP
■ **GAS CO LLC**
HAWAII GAS
(*Suby of* MACQUARIE INFRASTRUCTURE CORP) ★
745 Fort Street Mall # 1800, Honolulu, HI 96813-3818
Tel (808) 594-5530 *Founded/Ownrshp* 2006
Sales 215.1MM^E *EMP* 317
SIC 4932 4925 5172 5984 Gas & other services combined; Gas production and/or distribution; Gases; Propane gas, bottled; Gas & other services combined; Gas production and/or distribution; Gases; Propane gas, bottled
CEO: Alicia Moy
**Pr:* Joseph Boivin
**Sr VP:* Joseph J Boivin Jr
VP: Stephanie C Ackerman
**VP:* Charles Mike Futrell
**VP:* Thomas K L M Young
VP Mktg: Greg Toth
VP Sls: Jill Tokunaga
S&M/VP: David Uchiyama

GAS COMPANY, THE
See SOUTHERN CALIFORNIA GAS CO

D-U-N-S 79-345-2863
■ **GAS CONNECTION LLC**
HOMETOWN HEARTH & GRILL
(*Suby of* SUBURBAN PROPANE PARTNERS LP) ★
9801 Se 82nd Ave, Portland, OR 97086-3730
Tel (503) 771-1750 *Founded/Ownrshp* 1999
Sales 427.6MM^E *EMP* 2,400
SIC 5984 5722 Propane gas, bottled; Gas household appliances; Propane gas, bottled; Gas household appliances

D-U-N-S 12-163-5929
GAS DEPOT OIL CO
8930 Waukegan Rd Ste 300, Morton Grove, IL 60053-2116
Tel (847) 470-1687 *Founded/Ownrshp* 2000
Sales 27.0MM^E *EMP* 14
SIC 5172 Gasoline
Pr: Fincy Nediyakalayil
**CFO:* Nick Tanglis

D-U-N-S 00-894-6733 IMP
GAS EQUIPMENT CO INC
11616 Harry Hines Blvd, Dallas, TX 75229-2203
Tel (972) 241-2333 *Founded/Ownrshp* 1937
Sales 186.9MM^E *EMP* 550
SIC 5084 5085 3823 3321 Instruments & control equipment; Pumps & pumping equipment; Hose, belting & packing; Valves & fittings; Industrial instrmnts msrmnt display/control process variable; Liquid level instruments, industrial process type; Pressure gauges, dial & digital; Temperature instruments: industrial process type; Ductile iron castings; Instruments & control equipment; Pumps & pumping equipment; Hose, belting & packing; Valves & fittings; Industrial instrmnts msrmnt display/control process variable; Liquid level instruments, industrial process type; Pressure gauges, dial & digital; Temperature instruments: industrial process type; Ductile iron castings
Pr: Milton Ladue III
**Pr:* M J La Due III
**VP:* C K La Due
VP: Wes Livermore
Dir IT: Stephen Montgomery
Dir IT: Lance Steckel
Opers Mgr: Bobby Couch
Ql Cn Mgr: Paul Trippett
Natl Sales: Lance Looper
Sls&Mrk Ex: Lori Kirk

D-U-N-S 07-147-6451
GAS FIELD SPECIALISTS INC
2107 State Route 44 S, Shinglehouse, PA 16748-4429
Tel (814) 698-2122 *Founded/Ownrshp* 2009
Sales 170.8MM^E *EMP* 218
Accts Lumsden & Mccormick Llp Buffa
SIC 1389 Oil field services; Gas field services; Oil field services; Gas field services
Pr: Gregory West
**VP:* Bradley A West
Dir IT: David Talada
Sfty Mgr: Kirk McDowell
Opers Mgr: Ken Russell

D-U-N-S 03-375-6800
GAS INC
77 Jefferson Pkwy, Newnan, GA 30263-5813
Tel (770) 502-8800 *Founded/Ownrshp* 1947
Sales 22.5MM^E *EMP* 125
SIC 5984 Butane gas, bottled; Butane gas, bottled
Ch Bd: Betty Mattox
**Pr:* Zachry Mattox
**CEO:* Kendrick W Mattox Jr
CFO: Ken J Mattox
CFO: T Perry
**Treas:* Forest Shephard
**VP:* Bob Hetzler
VP: Robert Hetzler
Brnch Mgr: Timothy Truman

GAS INNOVATIONS
See WILLINGHAM WELDING SOLUTIONS INC

GAS MART
See SAYLE OIL CO INC

GAS MART
See DICKERSON STATIONS INC

D-U-N-S 08-632-5388
GAS MART INC (NC)
MINUTE MAN FOOD MART
(*Suby of* CAMPBELL OIL & GAS) ★
301 1/2 E Broad St, Elizabethtown, NC 28337-9306
Tel (910) 862-4107 *Founded/Ownrshp* 1976
Sales 29.0MM^E *EMP* 100
Accts Thompson Price Scott Adams &
SIC 5541 5411 Filling stations, gasoline; Convenience stores, chain; Filling stations, gasoline; Convenience stores, chain
Pr: D M Campbell Jr
**Treas:* D McQueen Campbell III
**VP:* Chris Campbell
**VP:* Wesley S Campbell

GAS N GROCERIES
See HAYWOOD OIL CO INC

D-U-N-S 07-800-6459
GAS N SHOP INC
701 Marina Bay Pl, Lincoln, NE 68528-1443
Tel (402) 475-1101 *Founded/Ownrshp* 1974
Sales 37.4MM^E *EMP* 150
Accts Steven R Doolittle Pc Lin
SIC 5541 5411 5921 Filling stations, gasoline; Convenience stores, independent; Beer (packaged); Filling stations, gasoline; Convenience stores, independent; Beer (packaged)
Pr: Larry Coffey
**CFO:* Tom Vik

D-U-N-S 00-282-1890
▲ **GAS NATURAL INC** (OH)
1375 E 9th St Ste 3100, Cleveland, OH 44114-1797
Tel (440) 974-3770 *Founded/Ownrshp* 1909
Sales 132.5MM *EMP* 291^E
Accts Malonebailey Llp Houston Tex
Tkr Sym EGAS *Exch* ASE
SIC 4924 4911 5172 5984 Natural gas distribution; Distribution, electric power; Gases, liquefied petroleum (propane); Propane gas, bottled; Natural gas distribution; Distribution, electric power; Gases, liquefied petroleum (propane); Propane gas, bottled
Pr: Gregory J Osborne
**Ch Bd:* W E Argo
**COO:* Kevin J Degenstein
**CFO:* James E Sprague
Sr VP: Sheila M Rice
**VP Admn:* Jed D Henthorne
Opers Mgr: Jeff Heidnik
Board of Directors: Michael B Bender, Wade F Brooksby, James P Carney, Richard K Greaves, Robert B Johnston, Michael T Victor, Michael R Winter

GAS RECOVERY SYSTEMS ILLINOIS
See GAS RECOVERY SYSTEMS LLC

D-U-N-S 09-838-0504
GAS RECOVERY SYSTEMS LLC
GAS RECOVERY SYSTEMS ILLINOIS
(*Suby of* FORTISTAR LLC) ★
1 N Lexington Ave Ste 620, White Plains, NY 10601-1721
Tel (914) 421-4903 *Founded/Ownrshp* 2002
Sales 27.9MM^E *EMP* 112
SIC 1389 Removal of condensate gasoline from field (gathering) lines
Pr: Thomas Gesicki
VP: Anthony Albao

D-U-N-S 01-183-9352
GAS SENSING TECHNOLOGY CORP
WELLDOG PTY
1525 Industry Dr, Laramie, WY 82070-7038
Tel (307) 742-6340 *Founded/Ownrshp* 2007
Sales 26.4MM^E *EMP* 75^E
SIC 1382 Oil & gas exploration services
Prin: John Pope
Ex VP: James Walker
**Ex Dir:* Sandy Hunter

GAS TECHNOLOGY INSTITUTE
See INSTITUTE OF GAS TECHNOLOGY

D-U-N-S 13-582-7355
GAS TRANSMISSION SYSTEMS INC
GTS
130 Amber Grove Dr # 134, Chico, CA 95973-5880
Tel (530) 893-6711 *Founded/Ownrshp* 2001
Sales 37.2MM^E *EMP* 220
SIC 8711 Professional engineer; Professional engineer
Pr: Katie Clapp
**VP:* Robert Gross
Sfty Mgr: Kirk Jefferson

D-U-N-S 78-340-9993
GAS TURBINE EFFICIENCY INC
GTE
300 Sunport Ln, Orlando, FL 32809-8119
Tel (407) 304-5200 *Founded/Ownrshp* 2006
Sales 21.4MM^E *EMP* 50
SIC 3511 Turbines & turbine generator sets; Steam turbines
Prin: Steven Zwolinski
Pr: Bob Knott
**Prin:* Chris Watson
Prgrm Mgr: Navjot Salh
Dir IT: Devin Sullivan
Sls Dir: Jorge Cadena

D-U-N-S 01-078-5681
GAS UNLIMITED INC (TX)
15999 City Walk Ste 200, Sugar Land, TX 77479-6606
Tel (281) 295-5600 *Founded/Ownrshp* 1970
Sales 115.0MM^E *EMP* 10,000
SIC 7363 Engineering help service; Engineering help service
Pr: Leo M Glass
**CFO:* Guillermo Camargo
**Sec:* Karen T Glass
**VP:* David M Glass
IT Man: Michael Glass

D-U-N-S 02-601-0061
GAS-MART USA INC
10777 Barkley St Ste 200, Overland Park, KS 66211-1162
Tel (913) 599-5800 *Founded/Ownrshp* 1995
Sales 56.6MM^E *EMP* 275
SIC 5411 Convenience stores; Convenience stores
Ch Bd: Abe Gustin
**Pr:* David George
CFO: Jerry Heck
**VP:* Michael George
VP: Kevin Lott
Exec: Louise Tilghman
DP Exec: Marcus Morgan

GAS-N-GO
See CALDER BROTHERS CO INC

GAS-OIL PRODUCTS INC MARYLAND
See UNITED PROPANE INC

D-U-N-S 11-404-3094
GASAMAT OIL CORP OF COLORADO
3975 E 56th Ave Unit A7, Commerce City, CO 80022-3633
Tel (303) 442-2520 *Founded/Ownrshp* 1986
Sales 35.0MM *EMP* 150
SIC 5541 Gasoline service stations
CEO: Terrence P Gallagher Sr
**Pr:* Michael J Gallagher
**Sec:* Dan Gallagher

D-U-N-S 01-662-0080
GASAMERICA SERVICES INC
2700 W Main St, Greenfield, IN 46140-2739
Tel (317) 468-2515 *Founded/Ownrshp* 1983
Sales 154.3MM^E *EMP* 850
SIC 5541 5171 Filling stations, gasoline; Petroleum bulk stations; Filling stations, gasoline; Petroleum bulk stations
Pr: Stephanie White
**Ch:* Judy White
**Sr VP:* Keith White

D-U-N-S 06-683-8145 IMP
GASBARRE PRODUCTS INC
SINTERITE PRODUCTS DIVISION
590 Division St, Du Bois, PA 15801-2530
Tel (814) 371-3015 *Founded/Ownrshp* 1973
Sales 88.2MM^E *EMP* 218
SIC 3542 3567 3544 Presses: forming, stamping, punching, sizing (machine tools); Industrial furnaces & ovens; Special dies, tools, jigs & fixtures; Presses: forming, stamping, punching, sizing (machine tools); Industrial furnaces & ovens; Special dies, tools, jigs & fixtures
Pr: Thomas G Gasbarre
**Treas:* Carl Gasbarre
Genl Mgr: Alex Gasbarre
IT Man: Jeff Gasbarre
IT Man: Fred Gustafson
Mktg Mgr: Randy Bauer
Sls Mgr: Patrick Bowen

GASCARD
See WEST TEXAS GAS INC

GASCARD
See WTG FUELS INC

D-U-N-S 07-654-9174
■ **GASCO PRODUCTION CO**
(*Suby of* GASCO ENERGY, INC.)
7979 E Tufts Ave Ste 1150, Denver, CO 80237-2886
Tel (303) 483-0044 *Founded/Ownrshp* 2001
Sales 21.0MM *EMP* 21
SIC 1382 Oil & gas exploration services; Oil & gas exploration services
COO: Mike Decker
**CFO:* W King Grant
**VP:* Peggy Herald
**VP:* John Longwell

D-U-N-S 10-586-3443
GASETERIA OIL CORP
2318
275 Madison Ave Fl 37, New York, NY 10016-1101
Tel (718) 599-2963 *Founded/Ownrshp* 1975
Sales 30.5MM^E *EMP* 80
SIC 5541 Gasoline service stations
CEO: Oscar Porcelli
**Pr:* Marcello Porcelli

D-U-N-S 00-389-5623
GASFRAC INC
572 Rancho Grande, Floresville, TX 78114
Tel (281) 854-2022 *Founded/Ownrshp* 2009
Sales 30.5MM^E *EMP* 125
SIC 1389

D-U-N-S 05-957-6686
GASGO MARKETS INC
8102 W Military Dr Ste 2, San Antonio, TX 78227-1846
Tel (210) 673-6530 *Founded/Ownrshp* 1980
Sales 28.5MM^E *EMP* 85
SIC 5541 5411 Filling stations, gasoline; Convenience stores, chain
Pr: Fred Ghavidel
**VP:* Kurt Q Anderson

D-U-N-S 07-310-4437
GASHER-BRUM ENERGY PARTNERS CORP
13332 W Jewell Dr, Lakewood, CO 80228-4221
Tel (303) 988-9297 *Founded/Ownrshp* 1997
Sales 40.0MM *EMP* 10
SIC 7361 Employment agencies; Employment agencies
Pr: Molly Haefele

GASHO INN
See GASHO OF JAPAN INTERNATIONAL LTD

D-U-N-S 11-278-5100
GASHO OF JAPAN INTERNATIONAL LTD
GASHO INN
7675 Gilespie St, Las Vegas, NV 89123-1101
Tel (845) 928-2387 *Founded/Ownrshp* 1980
Sales 8.7MM^E *EMP* 295
Accts Goldstein Karlewicz & Goldste
SIC 5812 7011 Japanese restaurant; Hotels & motels; Japanese restaurant; Hotels & motels
Ch: Shiro Aoki
**VP:* Kazuko Aoki

D-U-N-S 00-553-7428 IMP
GASKA TAPE INC
1810 W Lusher Ave, Elkhart, IN 46517-1395
Tel (574) 294-5431 *Founded/Ownrshp* 1965
Sales 31.8MM^E *EMP* 100
SIC 3086 2821 3053 Insulation or cushioning material, foamed plastic; Thermoplastic materials; Gaskets, all materials; Insulation or cushioning material, foamed plastic; Thermoplastic materials; Gaskets, all materials
Pr: Jack Boyd Smith Jr
Genl Mgr: Cathy Ruff
Mfg Dir: Greg Szabo
Sls Mgr: Rica Holtzinger
Sls Mgr: Kate Liewald

D-U-N-S 00-714-2888 IMP
GASKET ENGINEERING CO INC
4500 E 75th Ter, Kansas City, MO 64132-2000
Tel (816) 363-8333 *Founded/Ownrshp* 1997
Sales 35.7MM^E *EMP* 100
SIC 3469 3053 3465 2891 Metal stampings; Gaskets, all materials; Automotive stampings; Adhesives & sealants
Pr: Robert Comfort
**Sec:* Stan McLerran
VP: Bert Bell
**VP:* Dave McLerran

D-U-N-S 14-724-2663 EXP
GASLLC LIMITED LIABILITY CO
GOLDEN ALASKA SEAFOODS
2200 Alaskan Way Ste 420, Seattle, WA 98121-1684
Tel (206) 441-7009 *Founded/Ownrshp* 1984
Sales 26.5MM^E *EMP* 115

SIC 2092 Seafoods, fresh: prepared; Seafoods, frozen: prepared; Seafoods, fresh: prepared; Seafoods, frozen: prepared
IT Man: Mark Franklin
CFO: Markna Franklyn
VP Opers: Larry Levien

D-U-N-S 05-999-8096
GASPER-ATKINSON TRUCK PLAZA INC
3325 County Road 211, Kingdom City, MO 65262-2110
Tel (573) 642-6641 *Founded/Ownrshp* 1965
Sales 25.2MM *EMP* 30
SIC 5541 Gasoline service stations; Gasoline service stations
Pr: Ron Atkinson
**Sec:* Cindy Atkinson
**VP:* Tommy J Atkinson

D-U-N-S 00-149-3774
GASSER & SONS INC (NY)
440 Moreland Rd, Commack, NY 11725-5778
Tel (631) 543-6600 *Founded/Ownrshp* 1916
Sales 25.2MM^E *EMP* 145
SIC 3469 Metal stampings; Metal stampings
Ch: Richard F Gasser
**VP:* Jack Gasser

D-U-N-S 00-416-7888 IMP
GASSER CHAIR CO INC (OH)
4136 Logan Way, Youngstown, OH 44505-1797
Tel (330) 534-2234 *Founded/Ownrshp* 1947
Sales 23.2MM^E *EMP* 130
SIC 2531 2521 Chairs, table & arm; Chairs, office: padded, upholstered or plain: wood; Chairs, table & arm; Chairs, office: padded, upholstered or plain: wood
CEO: Gary L Gasser
**Pr:* Mark E Gasser
VP: Cindy Gasser
VP: Frank Joy
Opers Mgr: Rick Williams
Mktg Dir: Jim Bush
Sls Mgr: Roger Gasser
Sls Mgr: Tina Humphries

D-U-N-S 03-187-4910
GAST CONSTRUCTION CO INC
1722 17th Ave N, Wahpeton, ND 58075-3109
Tel (701) 235-3454 *Founded/Ownrshp* 1971
Sales 25.0MM *EMP* 30
SIC 1542 1521 Commercial & office building contractors; Single-family housing construction
Pr: Darrell Gast
**Treas:* Marlene Gast
**VP:* Tim Gast
Genl Mgr: Micheal Casper

D-U-N-S 00-510-9392 IMP
■ **GAST MANUFACTURING INC** (MI)
(*Suby of* IDEX CORP) ★
2300 M 139, Benton Harbor, MI 49022-6114
Tel (269) 926-6171 *Founded/Ownrshp* 1921
Sales 76.5MM^E *EMP* 367
SIC 3563 3594 3621 3566 3561 Vacuum pumps, except laboratory; Air & gas compressors including vacuum pumps; Motors: hydraulic, fluid power or air; Motors & generators; Speed changers, drives & gears; Pumps & pumping equipment; Vacuum pumps, except laboratory; Air & gas compressors including vacuum pumps; Motors: hydraulic, fluid power or air; Motors & generators; Speed changers, drives & gears; Pumps & pumping equipment
Pr: Eric Ashelman
VP: Mike Fortier
VP: Fred Niemeier
VP: Del Thomas
VP Sls: Lisa Walsh

D-U-N-S 78-197-5573
▲ **GASTAR EXPLORATION INC**
1331 Lamar St Ste 650, Houston, TX 77010-3131
Tel (713) 739-1800 *Founded/Ownrshp* 2011
Sales 171.4MM *EMP* 57^E
Tkr Sym GST *Exch* ASE
SIC 1382 Oil & gas exploration services; Oil & gas exploration services
Pr: J Russell Porter
**Ch Bd:* Jerry R Schuyler
COO: Michael McCown
CFO: Michael A Gerlich
VP: Keith Blair
VP: Henry J Hansen
VP: Henry Hansen
VP: Patricia Livergood
Exec: Keith R Blair
Board of Directors: John H Cassels, Randolph C Coley, Stephen A Holditch, Robert D Penner, Jerry R Schuyler

D-U-N-S 80-863-6703
GASTAR EXPLORATION INC
1331 Lamar St Ste 650, Houston, TX 77010-3131
Tel (713) 739-1800 *Founded/Ownrshp* 1987
Sales 49.9MM *EMP* 41^E
SIC 1311

GASTAR EXPLORATION LIMITED
See GASTAR EXPLORATION TEXAS LP

D-U-N-S 18-987-0988
GASTAR EXPLORATION TEXAS LP
GASTAR EXPLORATION LIMITED
1331 Lamar St Ste 650, Houston, TX 77010-3131
Tel (713) 739-1800 *Founded/Ownrshp* 2004
Sales 49.9MM *EMP* 30
SIC 1311 1382

D-U-N-S 03-049-7689
GASTON COLLEGE
GASTON COLLEGE BOOKSTORE
(*Suby of* NORTH CAROLINA COMMUNITY COLLEGE SYSTEM) ★
201 Highway 321 S, Dallas, NC 28034-1499
Tel (704) 922-6552 *Founded/Ownrshp* 1963
Sales 24.6MM^E *EMP* 625^E
SIC 8222 9411 Community college; Administration of educational programs; Community college; Administration of educational programs
Pr: Patricia A Skinner
**Ex VP:* Don Ammons
VP: Ethel Glenn
**VP:* Linda Greer
**VP:* Ralph Huddin
**VP:* Cynthia McCrory
**Prin:* Kimberly Gelsinger
**Prin:* Dr Patricia Skinner
IT Man: Savonne McNeil
Mktg Dir: Stephanie Michael-Pickett
Mktg Dir: Rosalind Welder
Board of Directors: Kimberly Gelsinger, Stephanie Michael

GASTON COLLEGE BOOKSTORE
See GASTON COLLEGE

D-U-N-S 07-106-2186
GASTON COUNTY
COUNTY MANAGER OFFICE
128 W Main Ave, Gastonia, NC 28052-2306
Tel (704) 866-3100 *Founded/Ownrshp* 1846
Sales NA *EMP* 1,500
Accts Martin Starnes & Associates C
SIC 9111 County supervisors' & executives' offices; ; ; County supervisors' & executives' offices; ;

D-U-N-S 19-329-4840
GASTON COUNTY SCHOOL DISTRICT
943 Osceola St, Gastonia, NC 28054-5482
Tel (704) 866-6100 *Founded/Ownrshp* 1968
Sales 241.2MM *EMP* 3,848^E
Accts Anderson Smith & Wike Pllc Ga
SIC 8211 Public elementary & secondary schools; Public elementary school; Public junior high school; Public senior high school; Public elementary & secondary schools; Public elementary school; Public junior high school; Public senior high school
Bd of Dir: Kevin Collier
Opers Mgr: Tammy Wade
Pr Dir: Todd Hagans
Instr Medi: Grant Sparks
Psych: Allison McKee
HC Dir: Betty Worthy

D-U-N-S 01-351-1415
GASTON COUNTY YMCA
615 W Franklin Blvd, Gastonia, NC 28052-3828
Tel (704) 865-8551 *Founded/Ownrshp* 1957
Sales 13.1MM^E *EMP* 365
SIC 8641 7991 8351 7032 8322 Youth organizations; Physical fitness facilities; Child day care services; Youth camps; Individual & family services; Youth organizations; Physical fitness facilities; Child day care services; Youth camps; Individual & family services
CEO: Tony Sigmon
Ex Dir: Darren Dannelly
Ex Dir: Scott Mason
Ex Dir: Susan Mosk
VP Opers: Sharon Padgett

D-U-N-S 14-314-9388 IMP
GASTON ELECTRONICS LLC
1310 Chrles Rper Jnas Hwy, Mount Holly, NC 28120-1234
Tel (704) 822-5184 *Founded/Ownrshp* 2004
Sales 22.3MM^E *EMP* 90
SIC 3559 Electronic component making machinery
VP: Larry Brimer
Genl Mgr: David Sanders
IT Man: Jimmy Warren
Ql Cn Mgr: George Ballard
Snr Mgr: Dana Lucas

D-U-N-S 04-846-5736
■ **GASTON GAZETTE LLP**
(*Suby of* HALIFAX MEDIA GROUP LLC) ★
1893 Remount Rd, Gastonia, NC 28054-7413
Tel (704) 869-1700 *Founded/Ownrshp* 1969
Sales 23.3MM^E *EMP* 210
SIC 2711 Newspapers, publishing & printing; Newspapers, publishing & printing
Sales Exec: Titus L Workman

D-U-N-S 07-107-1682
GASTON MEMORIAL HOSPITAL INC
CAROMONT HEALTH
(*Suby of* CAROMONT HEALTH INC) ★
2525 Court Dr, Gastonia, NC 28054-2182
Tel (704) 333-9033 *Founded/Ownrshp* 1984
Sales 423.9MM *EMP* 1,849^E
Accts Dixon Hughes Goodman Llp Ashe
SIC 8062 General medical & surgical hospitals; General medical & surgical hospitals
Pr: Wayne F Shovelin
COO: Kathleen Besson
**COO:* Terry L Jones
**CFO:* David O Connor
VP: John Buerkert
VP: Jeffory Canose MD
**VP:* W Kathleen Harwell
**VP:* Robert F Henderson Jr
**VP:* Jerome Levine
Dir Lab: Vivian Mitchell
IT Man: Tom Parnelle

GASTON SWANSAE SCHOOL DISTRICT
See LEXINGTON SCHOOL DISTRICT 4

GASTONIA CHRYSLER
See SEVEN SIX AUTOMOTIVE INC

D-U-N-S 00-317-3671
GASTONIA SHEET METAL WORKS INC (NC)
GSM SERVICES
1535 W May Ave, Gastonia, NC 28052-1409
Tel (704) 864-0344 *Founded/Ownrshp* 1925
Sales 20.1MM *EMP* 100
Accts Butler & Stowe Cpas Gastonia
SIC 1761 1711 3444 Roofing contractor; Sheet metalwork; Heating & air conditioning contractors; Sheet metalwork; Roofing contractor; Sheet metalwork; Heating & air conditioning contractors; Sheet metalwork
Pr: Ronald J Long Jr
**CFO:* Steven D Long
Tech Mgr: Mark Benton
Sfty Mgr: Sam Vicknousey

D-U-N-S 95-704-6886
GASTRO HEALTH PL
9500 S Dadeland Blvd # 802, Miami, FL 33156-2824
Tel (305) 670-1420 *Founded/Ownrshp* 2003
Sales 21.0MM^E *EMP* 135
Accts Gelber And Company Miramar F
SIC 8011 Clinic, operated by physicians
Pr: James S Leavitt MD
Ex Dir: Eliot Appel

D-U-N-S 00-396-2950
GASTROCARE LLP
DIGESTIVE CARE
5431 N University Dr, Coral Springs, FL 33067-4639
Tel (954) 344-2522 *Founded/Ownrshp* 2008
Sales 23.7MM^E *EMP* 280^E
SIC 8011 Offices & clinics of medical doctors; Offices & clinics of medical doctors
Pt: Garry Luckman
Pt: Jay Adler
Pt: Edward Deutsch
Pt: David Silver
COO: Joni Brown

D-U-N-S 01-065-0096
GASTROENTEROLOGY DIVISION
SAN FRANCISCO GENERAL HOSPITAL
1001 Potrero Ave Ste 1e21, San Francisco, CA 94110-3518
Tel (415) 206-8823 *Founded/Ownrshp* 1998
Sales 34.3MM^E *EMP* 50
SIC 8011 Gastronomist
COO: Gene O'Connell
Dir Lab: Mary Clancy
Dir Lab: Joan Moore
IT Man: Scott Dowdee
Sfty Dirs: Tom Holton
Sfty Dirs: Janet Kosewic
Mktg Dir: Rachel Kagan
Pathlgst: Lisa Tai
Surgeon: Richard Coughlin
Obsttrcn: Teresa Depineres
Obsttrcn: Karen Meckstroth

D-U-N-S 03-920-5588
GASTRONOMY INC
MARKET STREET GRILL
48 W Market St Ste 250, Salt Lake City, UT 84101-2147
Tel (801) 322-2020 *Founded/Ownrshp* 1980
Sales 30.3MM^E *EMP* 700
SIC 5812 Grills (eating places); Grills (eating places)
Pr: John W Williams
CFO: Eldon Payne
**Sec:* Thomas L Guinney
VP: John W Illiams
Exec: Will Pllier

D-U-N-S 62-792-7130
GAT AIRLINE GROUND SUPPORT INC
8400 Airport Blvd, Mobile, AL 36608-9603
Tel (251) 633-3888 *Founded/Ownrshp* 1967
Sales 117.5MM^E *EMP* 1,000
SIC 4581 Airports, flying fields & services; Airfreight loading & unloading services; Airports, flying fields & services; Airfreight loading & unloading services
CEO: Jean Raines
**Pr:* Richard Thiel
**VP:* Dian Lensch
Ex Dir: Carl Schouw
Off Mgr: Urvi Kantharia

D-U-N-S 82-468-0888
■ **GATAN INC**
(*Suby of* ROPER TECHNOLOGIES INC) ★
5794 W Las Positas Blvd, Pleasanton, CA 94588-4083
Tel (925) 463-0200 *Founded/Ownrshp* 1996
Sales 55.7MM^E *EMP* 180
SIC 8711 3826 Designing: ship, boat, machine & product; Analytical optical instruments; Designing: ship, boat, machine & product; Analytical optical instruments
Pr: Benjamin Wood
**Treas:* Ed Morrissey
Sr VP: Sander Gubbens
VP: Tom Balutis
**VP:* Jack Buhsmer
VP: John Hunt
VP: Jennifer McKie
VP: Paul Spellward
**Prin:* Robert Buchanan
Ex Dir: Peter Gage
Brnch Mgr: Kevin Scudder

GATE
See GIBSON APPLIED TECHNOLOGY & ENGINEERING (TEXAS) INC

D-U-N-S 18-459-4190
GATE 1 TRAVEL
455 Maryland Dr Ste 100, Fort Washington, PA 19034-2510
Tel (215) 572-7676 *Founded/Ownrshp* 2011
Sales 29.8MM^E *EMP* 200^E
SIC 4725 Arrangement of travel tour packages, wholesale; Arrangement of travel tour packages, wholesale
Pr: Dani Pipano
Sr VP: Ilene Pipano
**VP:* Robin Dean
**VP:* Tal Pipano
Off Mgr: Valentina Pagliariccі
QA Dir: Sasha Jurchak
Info Man: Michael Curcio
Web Dev: Tim Kline
Opers Mgr: Louis Hagarty
Mktg Mgr: Kelly Gallagher
Sls Mgr: Aharoni Zisling

GATE CITY BEVERAGE BEAR TRCKG
See BEAR TRUCKING INC

D-U-N-S 00-285-4354 IMP
GATE CITY BEVERAGE DISTRIBUTORS (CA)
2505 Steele Rd, San Bernardino, CA 92408-3913
Tel (909) 799-0281 *Founded/Ownrshp* 1940
Sales 65.8MM^E *EMP* 324
SIC 5181 5149 5145 Beer & other fermented malt liquors; Soft drinks; Mineral or spring water bottling; Confectionery; Beer & other fermented malt liquors; Soft drinks; Mineral or spring water bottling; Confectionery
Pr: Leona Aronoff
**CFO:* Barry Aronoff
Genl Mgr: Mark Smith
Plnt Mgr: Greg Raco
Plnt Mgr: Ed Williams

D-U-N-S 84-071-2251
GATE CITY OF BURLINGTON INC
GCB STAFFING
2603 Holly Hill St, Burlington, NC 27215-5156
Tel (336) 584-1762 *Founded/Ownrshp* 1996
Sales 13.2MM *EMP* 825
SIC 7361 Employment agencies; Employment agencies
Pr: Donna Clubb
**Sec:* Jackie Chambers

GATE CITY QUIK STOP MARKET
See ADDINGTON OIL CORP

GATE FUEL SERVICE
See GATE PETROLEUM CO

D-U-N-S 19-836-1698 IMP
GATE GOURMET US INC
(*Suby of* GATEGROUP US HOLDING INC) ★
1880 Campus Commons Dr, Reston, VA 20191-1503
Tel (703) 964-2300 *Founded/Ownrshp* 2009
Sales 508.6MM^E *EMP* 8,000
SIC 5812 8742 Caterers; Industry specialist consultants; Caterers; Industry specialist consultants
CEO: Andrew Gibson
COO: David Kuhns
CFO: Ron Lindo
CFO: Barry Oshare
**Treas:* Douglas Goeke
VP: James Long
Exec: Dickson Alvarado
Exec: William Bauer
Exec: Derrick Chaulk
Exec: Giselle Miranda
Exec: Brian Smrcka

D-U-N-S 87-930-1190
GATE LANDS HOLDING CO INC
(*Suby of* GATE FUEL SERVICE) ★
9540 San Jose Blvd, Jacksonville, FL 32257-5432
Tel (904) 737-7220 *Founded/Ownrshp* 1983
Sales 57.0MM^E *EMP* 900
SIC 6552 7997 Subdividers & developers; Country club, membership; Golf club, membership; Subdividers & developers; Country club, membership; Golf club, membership
Pr: Joseph Luke
VP: Jack Lueders Jr
S&M/Mgr: David Dill

GATE OF HEAVEN CEMETERY
See TRUSTEES OF ST PATRICKS CATHEDRAL INC

D-U-N-S 04-239-1789
GATE PETROLEUM CO
GATE FUEL SERVICE
9540 San Jose Blvd, Jacksonville, FL 32257-5444
Tel (904) 737-7220 *Founded/Ownrshp* 1960
Sales 1.3MMM^E *EMP* 3,200
SIC 5541 3272 5411 7997 Gasoline service stations; Prestressed concrete products; Convenience stores, chain; Country club, membership; Gasoline service stations; Prestressed concrete products; Convenience stores, chain; Country club, membership
Ch Bd: Herbert H Peyton
Treas: Jack C Lueders
Sr VP: Scott Robinson
VP: Donald R Davis
VP: Buzz Hoover
VP: Wayne M Levitt
VP: Joseph C Luke
VP: James McCormack
VP: George Nail
VP: P Jeremy Smith Jr
Exec: Howard Weadon
Dir Risk M: Thomas Glavin

D-U-N-S 11-270-5244
GATE PRECAST CO
(*Suby of* GATE FUEL SERVICE) ★
9540 San Jose Blvd, Jacksonville, FL 32257-5432
Tel (904) 732-7668 *Founded/Ownrshp* 1989
Sales 133.1MM^E *EMP* 1,000
SIC 3272 Concrete stuctural support & building material; Concrete stuctural support & building material
CEO: Dean Gwin
**Treas:* Jack C Lueders Jr
**Sr VP:* Earl N Shimp
IT Man: Jane Martin

D-U-N-S 11-415-3336
GATE SAFE INC
(*Suby of* GATE GOURMET US INC) ★
1669 Phoenix Pkwy Ste 104, Atlanta, GA 30349-7225
Tel (770) 991-4512 *Founded/Ownrshp* 2007
Sales 16.9MM^E *EMP* 500^E
SIC 7381 Security guard service; Security guard service
Pr: Kevin Didion
Admn Mgr: James Bowling
Off Mgr: Lauraleigh Turner
VP Mktg: Larry White

D-U-N-S 06-179-3477
GATECO OIL CO
2200 E Bessemer Ave, Greensboro, NC 27405-7342
Tel (336) 273-8663 *Founded/Ownrshp* 1990
Sales 76.7MM *EMP* 7
Accts Costello Hill & Company Llp
SIC 5172 Petroleum products; Petroleum products
Pr: John W Fuquay
**Sec:* J B Reid
**VP:* Thomas A Berry

D-U-N-S 83-062-7209 IMP
GATEGROUP US HOLDING INC
(*Suby of* GATE GOURMET LUXEMBOURG III SARL)
11710 Plaza America Dr # 800, Reston, VA 20190-4742
Tel (703) 964-2300 *Founded/Ownrshp* 2008
Sales 508.6MM^E *EMP* 8,000^E
SIC 5812 8742 Caterers; Industry specialist consultants; Caterers; Industry specialist consultants
CEO: Andrew Gibson
**CFO:* Thomas Bucher
**Sr VP:* Jrg A Boder
**VP:* Jean-Luc Ferrazzini
**VP:* Mike Hargett
**VP:* Stein Tumert

D-U-N-S 96-779-4269
■ **GATEHOUSE MEDIA ILLINOIS HOLDINGS II INC**
STATE JOURNAL REGISTER, THE
(*Suby of* NEW MEDIA INVESTMENT GROUP INC) ★
1 Copley Plz, Springfield, IL 62701-1927
Tel (217) 788-1300 *Founded/Ownrshp* 2007
Sales 29.1MM^E *EMP* 375
SIC 2711 Newspapers, publishing & printing; Commercial printing & newspaper publishing combined
VP: Bryan Groves
**Prin:* Patrick Coburn
Mktg Mgr: Richard Sybert
Sls Mgr: Brad Ames

D-U-N-S 01-347-3116 IMP
■ **GATEHOUSE MEDIA LLC**
(*Suby of* NEW MEDIA INVESTMENT GROUP INC) ★
175 Sullys Trl Ste 300, Pittsford, NY 14534-4560
Tel (585) 598-0030 *Founded/Ownrshp* 1997, 2013
Sales 77.4MM^E *EMP* 70^E
Tkr Sym GHSEQ *Exch* OTO
SIC 2711 Newspapers; Commercial printing & newspaper publishing combined
CEO: Kirk Davis
Pr: Rick Daniels
Pr: Peter Newton
Pr: Bernie Szachara
**CFO:* Melinda A Janik
**Treas:* Mark Maring
**Ofcr:* Keri Curtis
Sr VP: Dave Arkin
**Sr VP:* Brad Dennison
**Sr VP:* Harry Jenkins
VP: Travis Engebretson
VP: Jay Fogarty
VP: Rick Martin
VP: Peter Meyer
VP: Laura Mimken
VP: Laura Passantino
VP: Wayne Pelland
VP: Patrick Peregrin
**VP:* Polly G Sack
VP: Polly Sack

D-U-N-S 03-057-7337
■ **GATEHOUSE MEDIA MASSACHUSETTS I INC**
COMMUNITY NEWSPAPER
(*Suby of* NEW MEDIA INVESTMENT GROUP INC) ★
75 Sylvan St Ste C105, Danvers, MA 01923-2765
Tel (585) 598-0030 *Founded/Ownrshp* 2013
Sales 139.9MM^E *EMP* 1,800
SIC 2711 Newspapers; Commercial printing & newspaper publishing combined
**Pr:* Kirk Davis
VP: Anne Dorsey
VP: Rebecca Roth
VP: Robert Saurer

D-U-N-S 03-738-4646 IMP
GATEKEEPER SYSTEMS INC
8 Studebaker, Irvine, CA 92618-2012
Tel (949) 268-1414 *Founded/Ownrshp* 1998
Sales 42.0MM *EMP* 76
Accts Windes & Mcclaughry Accountanc
SIC 3699 Security devices
CEO: Michael Lawler
Pr: Stephen Hannah
**Pr:* Erik Paulson
**VP:* R J Brandes
VP: Kris Merrill
Dir Bus: Richard Moreton
VP Admn: Vickie Byrd
Snr Sftwr: Kirk Wayland
Dir IT: Paul Kammerer
Tech Mgr: Ryan Harter

GATES BAR B QUE
See GATES MANAGEMENT CORP

D-U-N-S 00-798-6375
GATES CHEVY WORLD INC
GATES CHEVY WORLD OF MISHAWAKA
636 W Mckinley Ave, Mishawaka, IN 46545-5518
Tel (574) 256-3000 *Founded/Ownrshp* 1928
Sales 27.0MM^E *EMP* 90
SIC 5511 7538

GATES CHEVY WORLD OF MISHAWAKA
See GATES CHEVY WORLD INC

D-U-N-S 07-369-6684
GATES CHILI CENTRAL SCHOOL DISTRICT
3 Spartan Way, Rochester, NY 14624-1448
Tel (585) 247-5345 *Founded/Ownrshp* 1956
Sales 47.3MM^E *EMP* 850
SIC 8211 Public elementary & secondary schools; Elementary school; High school, junior or senior; Public elementary & secondary schools; Elementary school; High school, junior or senior
Treas: Michelle Barno
Dir Sec: John Soderman
MIS Dir: Bernadette Best
MIS Dir: Barbara Misiaszek
Cmptr Lab: Betty Backus
Schl Brd P: Lowell Benjamin
Psych: Alynn Dasta
Psych: Mike Fici
Psych: Nancy Mason
Psych: James Miller

D-U-N-S 04-977-2478
GATES CONSTRUCTION CO INC
2806 Charlotte Hwy, Mooresville, NC 28117-8051
Tel (704) 664-2121 *Founded/Ownrshp* 1969
Sales 22.9MM^E *EMP* 200
SIC 1741 Masonry & other stonework; Masonry & other stonework
Pr: Robert H Gates

D-U-N-S 05-543-3197 IMP
GATES CORP
1551 Wewatta St, Denver, CO 80202-6173
Tel (303) 744-1911 *Founded/Ownrshp* 2014
Sales 3.3MMM^E *EMP* 13,433
SIC 3052 3089 3568 5084 4789 Rubber belting; Rubber hose; Automobile hose, rubber; V-belts, rubber; Fiber, vulcanized; Pulleys, power transmission; Rubber belting; Rubber hose; Automobile hose, rubber; V-belts, rubber; Fiber, vulcanized; Pulleys, power transmission; Water pumps (industrial); Cargo loading & unloading services
CEO: Ivo Jurek
**Pr:* Ken Friedman
**Pr:* Jim Nicol
Pr: Al Stecklein
COO: Frank Diels
**CFO:* David Naemura
CFO: J M Riess
Ofcr: Matt Pascarella
**Ex VP:* Rasmani Bhattacharya
**Ex VP:* Dave Carroll
Ex VP: David Carroll
Ex VP: Rick Hale
**Sr VP:* Heather Dumas
VP: Harvey Mednicovy
VP: Antonio Teodoro
Exec: Bobby Bassett
Dir Bus: Kim Henderson

D-U-N-S 01-960-5752
GATES FAMILY FOUNDATION
1390 Lawrence St Ste 400, Denver, CO 80204-2081
Tel (303) 722-1881 *Founded/Ownrshp* 1946
Sales 32.3MM *EMP* 5
SIC 8322 8611 Individual & family services; Business associations; Individual & family services; Business associations
Ofcr: Mary Seawell

D-U-N-S 01-888-3108
GATES GMC TRUCK INC (CT)
143 Boston Post Rd, North Windham, CT 06256-1302
Tel (860) 456-0055 *Founded/Ownrshp* 1937, 1986
Sales 20.6MM^E *EMP* 45
SIC 5511 Pickups, new & used; Automobiles, new & used
Pr: Craig Gates
**VP:* Roland Toutant
Rgnl Mgr: Debbie Miller
Genl Mgr: Denny Gates
Sls Mgr: Tomas Gates
Sales Asso: Ralph Clement
Sales Asso: Robert Lussier
Sales Asso: Brian Philips

D-U-N-S 08-070-1444
GATES MANAGEMENT CORP
GATES BAR B QUE
4621 Paseo Blvd, Kansas City, MO 64110-1825
Tel (816) 923-0900 *Founded/Ownrshp* 1973
Sales 18.5MM^E *EMP* 285
SIC 8741 5812 Restaurant management; Eating places; Restaurant management; Barbecue restaurant
Pr: Ollie W Gates
**VP:* George Gates
**VP:* Maureen Gates

D-U-N-S 04-642-3489
GATES MCDONALD & CO INC
(*Suby of* NATIONWIDE CORP) ★
215 N Front St, Columbus, OH 43215-2255
Tel (614) 677-3700 *Founded/Ownrshp* 1969
Sales NA *EMP* 800
SIC 6411 Insurance claim processing, except medical; Insurance claim processing, except medical
Pr: William Evans
**Pr:* Danny Fullerton
**CFO:* John Mier
**VP:* Kate Gaynor
**VP:* Patrick Geyer
**VP:* Deborah Haueisen
**VP:* William Polston
**VP:* Sandy Wood

D-U-N-S 62-033-9473 IMP/EXP
GATES MECTROL INC
(*Suby of* GATES CORP) ★
9 Northwestern Dr, Salem, NH 03079-4809
Tel (603) 890-1515 *Founded/Ownrshp* 2004
Sales 32.0MM^E *EMP* 50
SIC 5169 2821 Chemicals & allied products; Plastics materials & resins
CEO: Jim Nicols
**CFO:* John Zimmerman
**Ex VP:* Dave Carroll
**Genl Mgr:* Chad Young
MIS Dir: Sheldon Tapley
Tech Mgr: Gerhard Fickenwirth
Ql Cn Mgr: Leonardo Vazquez
Manager: Jason Bathon
Manager: Jenny Dakos
Manager: Kevin McCue
Sls Mgr: Tony Maniscalco

D-U-N-S 16-011-6471
GATESTONE & CO INTERNATIONAL INC
455 N 3rd St Ste 260, Phoenix, AZ 85004-3937
Tel (602) 443-2920 *Founded/Ownrshp* 1998
Sales 22.0MM^E *EMP* 175
SIC 7322 Adjustment & collection services
CEO: Nicholas Wilson
**Pr:* Leigh Anderson
**Treas:* Boris Dybenko

D-U-N-S 00-453-9490
GATESVILLE INDEPENDENT SCHOOL DISTRICT
311 S Lovers Ln, Gatesville, TX 76528-1814
Tel (254) 865-7251 *Founded/Ownrshp* 1949
Sales 24.5MM *EMP* 360
Accts Lott Vernon & Company Pc
SIC 8211 Public elementary & secondary schools; Public elementary & secondary schools
HC Dir: Nancy Morgan

D-U-N-S 07-004-2940
GATESWAY FOUNDATION INC
GATESWAY INDUSTRIES
1217 E College St, Broken Arrow, OK 74012-4204
Tel (918) 258-3900 *Founded/Ownrshp* 1963
Sales 15.0MM *EMP* 500
Accts Hogantaylor Llp Tulsa Ok
SIC 8361 8322 Home for the mentally retarded; Individual & family services; Home for the mentally retarded; Individual & family services
Ex Dir: Judy Myers
**CFO:* Mike Owens
IT Man: Chris Douglas

GATESWAY INDUSTRIES
See GATESWAY FOUNDATION INC

GATEWAY ACADEMY
See GATEWAY GROUP INC

D-U-N-S 04-756-4922
■ **GATEWAY BANK & TRUST CO**
(*Suby of* GATEWAY FINANCIAL HOLDINGS, INC.)
1145 N Road St, Elizabeth City, NC 27909-3334
Tel (252) 334-1511 *Founded/Ownrshp* 1998
Sales NA *EMP* 300
SIC 6022 State trust companies accepting deposits, commercial; State trust companies accepting deposits, commercial
Pr: Daniel B Berry
Pr: Charles E Parker
Ch: Ronald K Bennett
**Sr VP:* Stephen C Skinner
Sr VP: Sarah B Stedfast
**Exec:* Donna C Kitchen
Snr Mgr: Suzette Ward

D-U-N-S 17-562-0723
GATEWAY BOBCAT OF MISSOURI INC
BOBCAT OF ST LOUIS
401 W Outer Rd, Valley Park, MO 63088-2031
Tel (636) 225-2900 *Founded/Ownrshp* 1990
Sales 41.8MM^E *EMP* 84
SIC 5082 5083 7699 Excavating machinery & equipment; Landscaping equipment; Industrial equipment services; Excavating machinery & equipment; Landscaping equipment; Industrial equipment services
Pr: Daniel J Anich
Brnch Mgr: Robert Halley
Store Mgr: Nathan Dyck
Telecom Ex: Mandy Greeno
Mktg Dir: Becky Mueller
Sales Asso: Steve Ruck

D-U-N-S 06-691-8657
GATEWAY BUICK GMC INC
(*Suby of* BEHLMANN AUTOMOTIVE HOLDING CO INC) ★
820 Jmes S Mcdonnell Blvd, Hazelwood, MO 63042-2306
Tel (314) 895-1600 *Founded/Ownrshp* 2000
Sales 71.8MM^E *EMP* 368
SIC 5511 5521 7538 7532 7515 Automobiles, new & used; Used car dealers; General automotive repair shops; Top & body repair & paint shops; Passenger car leasing; Automobiles, new & used; Used car dealers; General automotive repair shops; Top & body repair & paint shops; Passenger car leasing
Treas: Paul Behlmann
**Prin:* Brian Behlmann
**Prin:* Linda Behlmann

D-U-N-S 06-814-9319
GATEWAY BUILDING SYSTEMS INC (ND)
2138 Main Ave W, West Fargo, ND 58078-1346
Tel (701) 293-7202 *Founded/Ownrshp* 1958, 1977
Sales 128.2MM^E *EMP* 250
SIC 1542 5083 Nonresidential construction; Farm building construction; Silo construction, agricultural; Agricultural machinery & equipment; Nonresidential construction; Farm building construction; Silo construction, agricultural; Agricultural machinery & equipment
Pr: Kevin Johnson
Sfty Dirs: Jason Albertson
Mktg Dir: Susana Suk
Sls Mgr: Brian Shuck

GATEWAY CHARITABLE FOUNDATION
See GATEWAY FOUNDATION INC

D-U-N-S 00-797-9594
GATEWAY CHEVROLET INC
GATEWAY CHEVROLET-OLDSMOBILE
5373 N Milwaukee Ave, Chicago, IL 60630-1222
Tel (773) 353-6880 *Founded/Ownrshp* 1947, 1981
Sales 23.0MM^E *EMP* 100
SIC 5511 7538 Automobiles, new & used; General automotive repair shops; Automobiles, new & used; General automotive repair shops
Pr: Lee Drabek
**VP:* Craig Andrea

D-U-N-S 08-446-3199
GATEWAY CHEVROLET INC
GATEWAY COLLISION
9901 W Papago Fwy, Avondale, AZ 85323-5307
Tel (623) 932-4389 *Founded/Ownrshp* 1985
Sales 25.3MM^E *EMP* 50
SIC 5511 5521 Automobiles, new & used; Used car dealers; Automobiles, new & used; Used car dealers
Pr: Joseph A Gambino Sr
Sec: Donna Harland
VP: Janet Gambino
Off Mgr: Gail Leitner
Off Mgr: Nancy Turrell
Store Mgr: Jeremy Thompson

GATEWAY CHEVROLET-OLDSMOBILE
See GATEWAY CHEVROLET INC

D-U-N-S 02-046-1161
GATEWAY CHURCH
500 S Nolen Dr Ste 300, Southlake, TX 76092-9170
Tel (817) 328-1000 *Founded/Ownrshp* 2000
Sales 71.1MM^E *EMP* 1,500^E
SIC 8661 Non-denominational church; Non-denominational church
Assoc Dir: Marci Elliott
Dir IT: Jon Seale

GATEWAY CLIPPER FLEET
See GATEWAY CLIPPER INC

D-U-N-S 04-529-4097
GATEWAY CLIPPER INC
GATEWAY CLIPPER FLEET
350 W Station Square Dr, Pittsburgh, PA 15219-1162
Tel (412) 355-7980 *Founded/Ownrshp* 1958
Sales 37.1MM^E *EMP* 250
SIC 4489 Sightseeing boats; Sightseeing boats
Pr: Terrance Wirginis
Treas: Audrey Wirginis
VP: John E Connelly
VP: Pamela K Wirginis

GATEWAY CMNTY ACTION PARTNR
See TRI-COUNTY COMMUNITY ACTION AGENCY INC

GATEWAY COLLISION
See GATEWAY CHEVROLET INC

GATEWAY COLLISION CENTER
See HEARTLAND AUTOMOTIVE LLC

D-U-N-S 93-885-9472
GATEWAY COMMUNITY CHARTERS
5726 Dudley Blvd, McClellan, CA 95652-1034
Tel (916) 286-5129 *Founded/Ownrshp* 2003
Sales 33.8MM *EMP* 10
Accts Mann Urrutia Nelson Cpas & Ass
SIC 8211 Elementary & secondary schools; Elementary & secondary schools
CEO: Cindy Petersen
**Pr:* Lillie Campbell
**CFO:* Aaron Thornsberry
**Treas:* Mark Anderson
**VP:* Bruce Mangerich

D-U-N-S 12-911-0024
GATEWAY COMMUNITY HEALTH
1333 Brewery Ste 100, Detroit, MI 48207
Tel (313) 262-5050 *Founded/Ownrshp* 2002
Sales NA *EMP* 75^E
Accts Uhy Advisors Mi Inc Farmingto
SIC 6324 Hospital & medical service plans
CEO: Dr Radwan Khoury

D-U-N-S 61-356-8757
GATEWAY COMMUNITY HEALTH CENTER INC
1515 Pappas St, Laredo, TX 78041-1705
Tel (956) 795-8100 *Founded/Ownrshp* 1967
Sales 21.1MM *EMP* 186
SIC 8011 Offices & clinics of medical doctors; Offices & clinics of medical doctors
CEO: Mike Trevino
**CFO:* Cecilia Moreno
Ofcr: Margie Cortez
Exec: Miguel Madrigal
Exec: Maria Sifuentes
Dir Rx: Irasema Perez
Telecom Ex: Eddie Acosta
Dir IT: Vicki Ryan
Psych: Carmen Cardona
Surgeon: Carlos Garza
Surgeon: Roberto Gomez-Vazquez

D-U-N-S 02-450-1910
GATEWAY DISTRIBUTION INC (IL)
720 W Mc Allister St, Lebanon, IL 62254-2642
Tel (618) 537-6121 *Founded/Ownrshp* 2008
Sales 26.4MM^E *EMP* 150
SIC 5199 Art goods & supplies; Art goods & supplies
Pr: William Dowling

D-U-N-S 11-904-0988
■ **GATEWAY EDI LLC**
(*Suby of* TRIZETTO CORP) ★
501 N Broadway Ste 300, Saint Louis, MO 63102-2136
Tel (314) 802-6700 *Founded/Ownrshp* 1988
Sales NA *EMP* 67^E
SIC 6411 Medical insurance claim processing, contract or fee basis
CEO: Timothy Fogerty
Ex VP: Bob Strickland
Sr VP: Lynnette Helmle
Sr VP: James Laird
VP: Jackie Griffin
VP: John Marron
CIO: Dave Cheli
Dir IT: Brian Lawrencee
IT Man: Brian Lawrence
Mktg Mgr: Kelly Netherton
Manager: Denise Haire

D-U-N-S 01-387-6508
GATEWAY ENERGY SERVICES CORP (NY)
(*Suby of* DIRECT ENERGY LP) ★
400 Rella Blvd Ste 206, Suffern, NY 10901-4249
Tel (845) 503-5308 *Founded/Ownrshp* 1997, 2011
Sales 79.8MM^E *EMP* 138^E
Accts Grant Thornton Llp New York
SIC 4932 Gas & other services combined; Gas & other services combined
CEO: Don Whaley
**Ch Bd:* Cory Byzewski
Comm Dir: Darlene Hyde
Admn Mgr: James Reynolds
Off Mgr: Teresa Moran
CIO: Ethan Kagan
QA Dir: Chiam Rutenberg
IT Man: Seth Gluck
S&M/VP: William Cateno
Sls Dir: John Moran
Manager: Bill Moul

D-U-N-S 09-447-2115
GATEWAY FOODS INC
14928 Highway 278, Double Springs, AL 35553-2535
Tel (205) 489-8888 Founded/Ownrshp 1978
Sales 30.2MME EMP 310
SIC 5411 Grocery stores, independent; Grocery stores, independent
Pr: Harold Garrett
*CEO: William J Wadrop

GATEWAY FORD LINCOLN MAZDA
See GATEWAY FORD LINCOLN-MERCURY INC

D-U-N-S 03-464-7859
GATEWAY FORD LINCOLN-MERCURY INC
GATEWAY FORD LINCOLN MAZDA
1055 W Andrew Johnson Hwy, Greeneville, TN 37745-1437
Tel (423) 639-5151 Founded/Ownrshp 2009
Sales 23.7MME EMP 63
SIC 5511 New & used car dealers
Pr: Lenny Lawson

D-U-N-S 04-088-3779
GATEWAY FOUNDATION INC
GATEWAY CHARITABLE FOUNDATION
55 E Jackson Blvd # 1500, Chicago, IL 60604-4137
Tel (312) 663-1130 Founded/Ownrshp 1964
Sales 81.5MM EMP 1,500
Accts Mcgladrey Llp Chicago Illino
SIC 8093 Substance abuse clinics (outpatient); Substance abuse clinics (outpatient)
CEO: Michael Darcy
*Ch: Victor Fonseca
*Treas: Donal S Crossett
VP: Nike Gantes
Snr Mgr: Yolanda Johnson

D-U-N-S 62-160-2994
GATEWAY FS INC
221 E Pine St, Red Bud, IL 62278-1548
Tel (618) 282-4000 Founded/Ownrshp 1990
Sales 50.5MME EMP 105
SIC 5153 5191 5172 Grains; Farm supplies; Petroleum products; Grains; Farm supplies; Petroleum products
Pr: Ronald Fehr
*Treas: Kenneth Mc Conachie
*VP: Gary Leber
Genl Mgr: Carl Tebbe
Off Mgr: Elizabeth Beccue
Plnt Mgr: Jim Reinhold
Mktg Mgr: Dwight Asselmerie
Mktg Mgr: Mike Kuhn
Sls Mgr: Jeff Gillespie

D-U-N-S 86-937-0585
GATEWAY FUNDING DIVERSIFIED MORTGAGE SERVICES LP
(Suby of FINANCE OF AMERICA HOLDINGS LLC)
300 Welsh Rd, Horsham, PA 19044-2248
Tel (215) 591-0222 Founded/Ownrshp 2015
Sales NA EMP 1,200
SIC 6162 Mortgage bankers; Mortgage brokers, using own money; Mortgage bankers; Mortgage brokers, using own money
Pt: Bruno J Pasceri
Pt: Micheal Karp
VP: Jim Goldstein
CIO: Brian McGovern
Sls Mgr: Jerry Spence

D-U-N-S 78-793-9680
GATEWAY GETTYSBURG HOTEL AND CONFERENCE PARTNERS
95 Presidential Cir, Gettysburg, PA 17325-8397
Tel (717) 339-0020 Founded/Ownrshp 2006
Sales 5.9MME EMP 400
SIC 7011 Hotels & motels; Hotels & motels
Prin: Robert J Monahan Jr
IT Man: Karl Mincemoyer

GATEWAY GIFT SHOP
See SNYDERS GATEWAY INC

D-U-N-S 94-462-5524
GATEWAY GROUP INC
GATEWAY ACADEMY
791 Greenlawn Dr Ste 7, Columbia, SC 29209-2641
Tel (803) 776-8668 Founded/Ownrshp 1998
Sales 12.1MME EMP 450
SIC 8351 Child day care services; Child day care services
*Pr: David Jacobs

GATEWAY HEALTH CENTER
See DEACONESS HEALTH SYSTEM INC

D-U-N-S 80-443-2193
GATEWAY HEALTH PLAN INC
(Suby of GATEWAY HEALTH PLAN LP) ★
600 Grant St Fl 41, Pittsburgh, PA 15219-2713
Tel (412) 255-4640 Founded/Ownrshp 1997
Sales NA EMP 235
SIC 6324 Health maintenance organization (HMO), insurance only; Health maintenance organization (HMO), insurance only
CFO: C Eric Huss
VP Opers: Margaret Worek

D-U-N-S 80-076-9721
GATEWAY HEALTH PLAN LP
(Suby of HIGHMARK BLUE CRSS-BLUE SHIELD) ★
4 Gateway Ctr 444, Pittsburgh, PA 15222
Tel (412) 255-4640 Founded/Ownrshp 1992
Sales NA EMP 235
SIC 6324 Health maintenance organization (HMO), insurance only; Health maintenance organization (HMO), insurance only
Pr: Patricia J Darnley
Pr: Robert S Mirsky
Bd of Dir: Michael Blackwood
Ofcr: Mary Craig
VP: Kara House
VP: Austin Ifedirah
VP: Mark Lantzy
VP: Marcia Martin
VP: Cynthia Zydel

Genl Mgr: Andrea Maxwell
MIS Dir: David Guilinger

D-U-N-S 07-546-1004
GATEWAY HEALTH SYSTEM INC
CLARKSVILLE MEMORIAL HOSPITAL
651 Dunlop Ln, Clarksville, TN 37040-5015
Tel (931) 502-1000 Founded/Ownrshp 1954
Sales 179.3MME EMP 1,100
SIC 8062 General medical & surgical hospitals; General medical & surgical hospitals
Pr: Kim Puthoff
Dir Vol: Sandy Wooten
*Ch Bd: Walton Smith Jr
*Ch Bd: William H Wyatt
COO: Russell Pigg
*CFO: Lynn Lambert
CFO: George Sprinkel
VP: Duncan McKellar
VP: Cindy Sidebottom
Dir Inf Cn: Dana Sandefur
Chf Nrs Of: Faye Perry

D-U-N-S 04-008-4980
GATEWAY HEALTHCARE INC
249 Roosevelt Ave # 205, Pawtucket, RI 02860-2134
Tel (401) 724-8400 Founded/Ownrshp 1996
Sales 10.3MM EMP 400
SIC 8093 Mental health clinic, outpatient; Mental health clinic, outpatient
Ex Dir: Richard Leclerc
*VP: Scott Dichristofero

D-U-N-S 94-756-8945
GATEWAY HEALTHCARE INC
249 Roosevelt Ave # 205, Pawtucket, RI 02860-2134
Tel (401) 724-8400 Founded/Ownrshp 1995
Sales NA EMP 700
SIC 8361

D-U-N-S 04-368-1480 IMP
GATEWAY HOME CARE INC
1301 Armitage Ave, Melrose Park, IL 60160-1423
Tel (630) 693-3799 Founded/Ownrshp 1997
Sales 8.0MME EMP 500
SIC 8082 Home health care services; Home health care services
CFO: Gerald Paone
*Prin: Beth McGowen

GATEWAY HOME REALTY
See AMERICAN FINANCIAL NETWORK INC

D-U-N-S 55-747-6975
GATEWAY HOMES LTD
7676 Hillmont St, Houston, TX 77040-6400
Tel (713) 622-1468 Founded/Ownrshp 1990
Sales 22.3MM EMP 34
SIC 1521 New construction, single-family houses; New construction, single-family houses
Mng Pt: Tom Walker
VP: Alan Blackshear
VP: Tony Stancik
IT Man: Chris Mathis
IT Man: Robert Rizzetto

D-U-N-S 55-594-3349
GATEWAY HOTEL HOLDINGS INC
MILLENIUM HOTEL ST LOUIS
5775 Dtc Blvd Ste 315, Greenwood Village, CO 80111-3209
Tel (303) 220-2000 Founded/Ownrshp 1991
Sales 10.9MME EMP 455
SIC 7011 Hotels; Hotels
Pr: Paul T Underhill
*Sr VP: Lyle Boll
*Sr VP: Roberta L Griffen
*VP: David Kolar
IT Man: Paul Mitchell

D-U-N-S 15-513-1332
GATEWAY HYUNDAI INC
CARTER MYERS AUTOMOTIVE
(Suby of CARTER MYERS AUTOMOTIVE) ★
2200 Walthall Ctr Dr, Chester, VA 23831
Tel (804) 861-2020 Founded/Ownrshp 2003
Sales 50.8MM EMP 40
Accts Mitchell Wiggins & Company L
SIC 5511 Automobiles, new & used; Automobiles, new & used
Ch: H Carter Myers III
*Pr: Ed Nicol
*VP: Mark Wright
Sls Mgr: Kenny Cheatham
Sales Asso: Roger Cordle
Sales Asso: Anthony Hazelwood
Sales Asso: Anthony Tennyson

D-U-N-S 15-207-2849 IMP
GATEWAY INC
(Suby of ACER AMERICAN HOLDINGS CORP) ★
7565 Irvine Center Dr # 150, Irvine, CA 92618-4933
Tel (949) 471-7000 Founded/Ownrshp 2007
Sales 211.5MME EMP 1,700
SIC 3571 3577 Personal computers (microcomputers); Computer peripheral equipment; Personal computers (microcomputers); Computer peripheral equipment
CEO: Ed Coleman
Pr: Bradly Shaw
COO: Bryan Albrecht
COO: Peter Cohen
COO: Judy Sandberg
CFO: John Goldsberry
Treas: Craig Calle
Sr VP: Scott Bauhofer
Sr VP: Bart Brown
Sr VP: Edward R Fisher
Sr VP: Steve Phillips
Sr VP: Michael R Tyler
VP: John Carson
Exec: Joe Berkel
Exec: Stacy Brown
Exec: Peter Burns
Dir Surg: Kevin Shabow
Dir Surg: Gary Thomas
Assoc Dir: Lisa Takata

D-U-N-S 14-921-7874
GATEWAY INDUSTRIAL POWER INC
GATEWAY TRUCK AND RFRGN
921 Fournie Ln, Collinsville, IL 62234-7430
Tel (314) 531-3316 Founded/Ownrshp 1989
Sales 34.4MME EMP 131E
SIC 3585 7538 Refrigeration & heating equipment; Diesel engine repair: automotive; Refrigeration & heating equipment; Diesel engine repair: automotive
Pr: David M Keach
*Ch Bd: John Wagner
*Pr: Zach Wagner
VP: Robert Yost
Brnch Mgr: Dan Desalme

GATEWAY INN MOTEL
See RICHESON MANAGEMENT INC

D-U-N-S 08-794-9561
GATEWAY LOGISTICS GROUP INC
18201 Viscount Rd, Houston, TX 77032-5513
Tel (281) 443-7447 Founded/Ownrshp 2000
Sales 36.4MME EMP 75
SIC 4731 Freight forwarding
Pr: George J Smith
*Treas: Bill McCaughey
*Treas: William J McCaughey
*VP: Kahne D Smith
VP: Lisa Wright
Genl Mgr: Tony Faia
Genl Mgr: Karrie Staab
Opers Supe: Paul Jensen
Sfty Mgr: David Collins
Opers Mgr: Joe Morris
Opers Mgr: Carrie Staab

D-U-N-S 12-737-6684
GATEWAY MORTGAGE GROUP LLC
6910 E 14th St, Tulsa, OK 74112-6618
Tel (918) 712-9000 Founded/Ownrshp 2000
Sales NA EMP 600
SIC 6163 Mortgage brokers arranging for loans, using money of others; Mortgage brokers arranging for loans, using money of others
Pr: John Kevin Stitt
*Pr: Alan Ferree
*COO: Mike Goyer
*CFO: Patrick McGowan
*Ofcr: Scott Henley
Ofcr: Kristen Henry
Ofcr: Shana Longacre
Ex VP: Scott Gesell
Sr VP: Bill Clopton
Sr VP: G Todd White
Sr VP: Todd White
VP: Brian Ashlock
VP: Dane Basham
VP: Steve Frink
VP: Sherron Gomez
VP: Tonya Granberry
VP: John Matuszeski
VP: Kevin Osuna
VP: David Robinson

D-U-N-S 01-913-8858
GATEWAY MOTORS INC
HYUNDAI
190 Sykes Mountain Ave, White River Junction, VT 05001-2008
Tel (802) 295-3124 Founded/Ownrshp 1920
Sales 29.1MME EMP 64
SIC 5511 Automobiles, new & used; Automobiles, new & used
Pr: Charles Hall
VP: Allen Hall
*Prin: Ann Hall
Off Mgr: Martin Dole

D-U-N-S 10-319-9824 IMP
GATEWAY PACKAGING CO
100 S 4th St Ste 600, Saint Louis, MO 63102-1822
Tel (618) 451-0010 Founded/Ownrshp 1982
Sales 82.9MME EMP 290
SIC 2674 2679 Bags: uncoated paper & multiwall; Labels, paper: made from purchased material; Bags: uncoated paper & multiwall; Labels, paper: made from purchased material
Pr: Roger D Miller
*CFO: Greg Petermeyer
*VP: Rebecca J Miller
IT Man: Marshall Andersen
IT Man: Marshall Winslow
Prd Mgr: Robert Tiepelman
S&M/VP: Joseph Fiore

GATEWAY PACKAGING CO GRAN CY
See GATEWAY PACKAGING CO LLC

D-U-N-S 96-321-2258 IMP
GATEWAY PACKAGING CO LLC
GATEWAY PACKAGING CO GRAN CY
(Suby of GATEWAY PACKAGING CO) ★
20 Central Industrial Dr, Granite City, IL 62040-6801
Tel (618) 219-4447 Founded/Ownrshp 2010
Sales 73.2MME EMP 250
SIC 2674 3565 Bags: uncoated paper & multiwall; Bags: uncoated paper & multiwall; Packaging machinery
CEO: Omar Abuaita
*CFO: David Antonini
VP: Dave Cragen
IT Man: Marshall Andersen
IT Man: Marshall Winslow
Tech Mgr: Brian Schiermeier
Opers Mgr: Douglas Everson
Opers Mgr: Robert Tiepelman
Plnt Mgr: Vance Fortenberry
Prd Mgr: Bob Tiepelman
Ql Cn Mgr: Eboni Delaney

D-U-N-S 04-395-4445
GATEWAY PHARMACY OF PHOENIXVILLE INC
165 Nutt Rd, Phoenixville, PA 19460-3905
Tel (610) 933-2310 Founded/Ownrshp 1982
Sales 28.1MME EMP 110
SIC 5912 5999 5947 5411

D-U-N-S 05-082-5991 IMP
GATEWAY PLASTICS INC
5650 W County Line Rd, Mequon, WI 53092-4751
Tel (262) 242-2020 Founded/Ownrshp 1970
Sales 35.6MME EMP 110
SIC 3089 Injection molded finished plastic products
Pr: Carl W Vogel
*VP: Bob Proudfoot
*VP: John Samz
*VP: Mary R Vogel
Opers Mgr: Bill Martin
Sls Mgr: Steve Key

GATEWAY PRESS
See GATEWAY PUBLICATIONS

GATEWAY PRINTING
See ROHRER CORP

D-U-N-S 00-812-0727
GATEWAY PRINTING & OFFICE SUPPLY INC (TX)
JONES & COOK OFFICE SUPPLY
315 S Closner Blvd, Edinburg, TX 78539-4594
Tel (956) 383-3861 Founded/Ownrshp 1963
Sales 36.0MME EMP 215
SIC 5943 5712 2752

D-U-N-S 00-432-7573
GATEWAY PUBLICATIONS
GATEWAY PRESS
610 Beatty Rd Ste 2, Monroeville, PA 15146-1558
Tel (412) 856-7400 Founded/Ownrshp 1956, 2010
Sales 37.2MME EMP 627
SIC 2711 Commercial printing & newspaper publishing combined; Commercial printing & newspaper publishing combined
Pr: Scott Patterson
*VP: Thomas Bova

D-U-N-S 01-964-2345
GATEWAY REAL ESTATE LLC
REMAX POWERCENTRAL
1000 Lincoln Dr E, Marlton, NJ 08053-1566
Tel (856) 797-1550 Founded/Ownrshp 2005
Sales 25.0MME EMP 4
SIC 6531 Real estate agent, residential; Real estate agent, residential

D-U-N-S 07-287-8424
GATEWAY REGIONAL HEALTH SYSTEM INC
MARY CHILES HOSPITAL
50 Sterling Ave, Mount Sterling, KY 40353-1100
Tel (859) 498-1220 Founded/Ownrshp 1918
Sales 16.7MME EMP 350
SIC 8062 General medical & surgical hospitals; General medical & surgical hospitals
Ch: Michael Fiechter
Chf Rad: John Felker
*CEO: Eugene A Woods
Obsttrcn: Sheila Barnes
Phys Thrpy: Leslyn Spauldin

D-U-N-S 06-698-5391
GATEWAY REGIONAL SCHOOL DISTRICT
12 Littleville Rd, Huntington, MA 01050-9761
Tel (413) 667-0142 Founded/Ownrshp 1959
Sales 22.9MME EMP 429
SIC 8211 Public combined elementary & secondary school; School board; Public combined elementary & secondary school; School board
Prin: Donald Nicoletti
Exec: Stacy Stewart
Schl Brd P: Michelle Crane
HC Dir: Linda Dugas

D-U-N-S 07-497-4379
GATEWAY REHABILITATION CENTER
311 Rouser Rd, Moon Township, PA 15108-6801
Tel (412) 604-8900 Founded/Ownrshp 1971
Sales 32.8MM EMP 500
Accts Maherduessel Pittsburgh Penn
SIC 8093 8069 8361 Alcohol clinic, outpatient; Drug clinic, outpatient; Alcoholism rehabilitation hospital; Drug addiction rehabilitation hospital; Residential care; Alcohol clinic, outpatient; Drug clinic, outpatient; Alcoholism rehabilitation hospital; Drug addiction rehabilitation hospital; Residential care
Pr: Paul Bacharach
Ch Bd: James Rogal
Treas: Thomas Todd
V Ch Bd: Richard Grace
Ex VP: Richard Foster
VP: Alfreda Hampton
VP: Patricia Orangis
Genl Mgr: Frances Fry
Genl Mgr: Kenneth Ramsey
Genl Mgr: Lynda Smith
Board of Directors: Ronald A Owen, Kenneth S Ramsey, William R Yanakos

D-U-N-S 06-874-9373
GATEWAY SCHOOL DISTRICT
9000 Mosside Gateway Camp, Monroeville, PA 15146-3377
Tel (412) 372-5300 Founded/Ownrshp 1960
Sales 66.9MM EMP 648
Accts Sarp & Company Greensburg Pe
SIC 8211 Public elementary & secondary schools; Public elementary & secondary schools
*Pr: David Macgill
*Treas: Paul S Schott
Treas: Harvey Smith
Exec: Steve Delisle
Mng Dir: Chad Hensler
MIS Dir: Paul Hoffman
Opers Mgr: Jeremy Kostyak

D-U-N-S 11-307-6186
GATEWAY SECURITY INC
604 Market St 608, Newark, NJ 07105-2911
Tel (973) 465-8006 Founded/Ownrshp 1979
Sales 97.9MME EMP 3,500E
SIC 7381 Security guard service; Security guard service
Pr: James Dell'ermo
*Pr: James Dellermo

*CEO: Kurus Elavia
VP: Sunny Williams
Genl Mgr: Lisa Edwards
Genl Mgr: Mario Gonzalez
Genl Mgr: Xavier Merizalde
Opers Mgr: Kurt Ebler
Secur Mgr: Bill Whitley
Genl Couns: Roy Pitcoff

GATEWAY SERVICE CENTER
See GATEWAY TRUCK PLAZA INC

D-U-N-S 00-336-9048 EXP
GATEWAY SUPPLY CO INC (SC)
1312 Hamrick St, Columbia, SC 29201-4517
Tel (803) 771-7160 Founded/Ownrshp 1964
Sales 117.5MM^E EMP 130
Accts Bauknight Pietras & Stormer P
SIC 5075 5074 Warm air heating & air conditioning; Plumbing & hydronic heating supplies; Warm air heating & air conditioning; Plumbing & hydronic heating supplies
CEO: Sam Williams Jr
*Pr: Chris Williams
*VP: Leonard Moore Jr
VP: R Moore
Exec: Katheren Holmes
Exec: Kim Martin
Brnch Mgr: Lonnie McCall
Brnch Mgr: Kelly Powers
Opers Mgr: Chris Sholtis
Sls Mgr: Camille Cartee
Sls Mgr: John Skeppstrom

D-U-N-S 18-284-5172
GATEWAY TECHNICAL COLLEGE
(Suby of WISCONSIN TECHNICAL COLLEGE SYSTEM BOARD) ★
3520 30th Ave, Kenosha, WI 53144-1690
Tel (262) 564-2200 Founded/Ownrshp 2006
Sales 53.0MM EMP 600
Accts Schenck Green Bay Wisconsin
SIC 8222 Technical institute; Technical institute
Pr: Bryan D Albrecht
V Ch: Tom Niesen
*CFO: Mark Zlevor
*Ex VP: Zina Haywood
VP: William Nickolai
Exec: Ram Bhatia
Dir Bus: Kate Walker
VP Admn: Susan Debe
Dir Sec: Steve Pozorski
Psych: Damira Grady
Snr Mgr: Elizabeth Oplatka

GATEWAY TERMINAL
See WATERFRONT ENTERPRISES INC

D-U-N-S 60-366-5399
GATEWAY TICKETING SYSTEMS INC
445 County Line Rd, Gilbertsville, PA 19525-8822
Tel (610) 987-4000 Founded/Ownrshp 1988
Sales 20.4MM^E EMP 73^E
Accts Herbein & Company Inc Readi
SIC 7373 Computer integrated systems design
Pr: Michael M Andre
*Ex VP: Darryl L Moser
Sys/Mgr: Nancy Bohn

GATEWAY TIRE & SERVICE CENTER
See DUNLAP & KYLE CO INC

GATEWAY TIRE & SERVICE CENTER
See SOUTH GATEWAY TIRE CO INC

GATEWAY TIRE & SERVICE CENTERS
See DUNLAP AND KYLE TIRE CO INC

D-U-N-S 03-553-4569 IMP
GATEWAY TIRE OF ARKANSAS INC (AR)
301 Industrial Dr, Trumann, AR 72472-4045
Tel (870) 483-2660 Founded/Ownrshp 1963
Sales 28.7MM EMP 42
SIC 5014 5531 Tires & tubes; Automotive & home supply stores; Tires & tubes; Automotive & home supply stores
Pr: Robert H Dunlap
*Treas: Brent Nichols
*VP: Michael E Dunlap
IT Man: Joyce Powell

GATEWAY TIRES
See HESSELBEIN TIRE CO INC

GATEWAY TRUCK AND RFRGN
See GATEWAY INDUSTRIAL POWER INC

D-U-N-S 06-464-1319
GATEWAY TRUCK PLAZA INC
GATEWAY SERVICE CENTER
699 State Route 203, East Saint Louis, IL 62201-1608
Tel (618) 274-5900 Founded/Ownrshp 1973
Sales 20.4MM^E EMP 120
SIC 5541 5812 Truck stops; Eating places; Truck stops; Eating places
Pr: Douglas J Pratt

D-U-N-S 60-680-5612
GATEWAY UNIFIED SCHOOL DISTRICT
4411 Mountain Lakes Blvd, Redding, CA 96003-1446
Tel (530) 245-7900 Founded/Ownrshp 1990
Sales 24.2MM^E EMP 400
SIC 8211 Public elementary school; Public junior high school; Public senior high school; Public elementary school; Public junior high school; Public senior high school

D-U-N-S 78-102-3551
GATEWAY WOODSIDE INC
100 Midway Rd Ste 14, Cranston, RI 02920-5742
Tel (401) 942-2800 Founded/Ownrshp 1998
Sales 135.0MM EMP 6
SIC 6512 Shopping center, property operation only; Shopping center, property operation only
Genl Mgr: Douglas Gordon

D-U-N-S 15-043-0320 IMP
GATEWAYCDI INC
909 N 20th St, Saint Louis, MO 63106-3520
Tel (314) 535-1888 Founded/Ownrshp 2003
Sales 28.1MM EMP 80
Accts Brown Smith Wallace Llc St L
SIC 5199 Advertising specialties; Advertising specialties
CEO: Chuck Fandos
*COO: Ray Gross
CFO: Michael Dishian
*Chf Mktg O: Conrad Franey
VP: David Christoff
Store Mgr: Aimee Myers
Manager: Chris Miller
Manager: Cindy Rosen
Manager: Lisa Silver

GATEWAYS COMMUNITY SERVICES
See AREA AGENCY OF GREATER NASHUA INC

D-U-N-S 08-838-1983
GATEWAYS HOSPITAL AND MENTAL HEALTH CENTER INC (CA)
1891 Effie St, Los Angeles, CA 90026-1711
Tel (323) 644-2000 Founded/Ownrshp 1953
Sales 27.4MM EMP 280
Accts Vavrinektrineday & Co Llp Ran
SIC 8063 8093 Hospital for the mentally ill; Mental health clinic, outpatient; Hospital for the mentally ill; Mental health clinic, outpatient
CEO: Mara Pelsman
*CFO: Jeff Emery
Dir Lab: Anil Churana
Dir Rx: Joshua Ly
Brnch Mgr: Brett Morana
Off Mgr: Ebony Clarke
CIO: Charles Disliva
QA Dir: Phil Wong
IT Man: Rozelle De Vera
Opers Supe: Julie Feuer
Sls&Mrk Ex: Sandra Long

D-U-N-S 60-773-5677
GATEWAYS INTERNATIONAL INC
(Suby of PASHA FREIGHT) ★
2030 1st Ave Ste 200, Seattle, WA 98121-2187
Tel (206) 448-6317 Founded/Ownrshp 1997
Sales 76.8MM^E EMP 600
SIC 4731 Freight forwarding; Freight forwarding
Pr: Rick Curry
VP: Jackie Bailey

D-U-N-S 08-576-0148
GATEWAYS TO BETTER LIVING INC
6000 Mahoning Ave Ste 234, Youngstown, OH 44515-2225
Tel (330) 792-2854 Founded/Ownrshp 1972
Sales 14.6MM EMP 300
Accts Plante & Moran Pllc Cleveland
SIC 8361 Home for the mentally retarded; Home for the mentally retarded
Ex Dir: Gail Riess
CFO: James Linert
Ql Cn Mgr: Bob Wirtz

GATHERCO, INC.
See ASPIRE ENERGY OF OHIO LLC

D-U-N-S 02-523-8955
GATHRIGHT RACING INC
321 40th Ave, Greeley, CO 80634-1107
Tel (970) 672-9362 Founded/Ownrshp 2006, 2010
Sales 30.0MM EMP 55
SIC 7948 Race car owners; Race car owners
Pr: Bryan T Gathright

GATLINBURG SKI RESORT
See OBER GATLINBURG INC

D-U-N-S 05-718-2156
GATOR BOOSTERS INC
Gale Lemerand Dr, Gainesville, FL 32611-0001
Tel (352) 372-8489 Founded/Ownrshp 1940
Sales 40.9MM EMP 12
Accts James Moore & Co Pl Gainesvil
SIC 8399 8641 Fund raising organization, non-fee basis; Booster club; Fund raising organization, non-fee basis; Booster club
Ex Dir: John James
*Dir Surg: Phill Tharr

D-U-N-S 05-210-3231
GATOR CHRYSLER PLYMOUTH INC
GATOR CHRYSLR DDG JP SZKI ISZU
300 E Nasa Blvd, Melbourne, FL 32901-1940
Tel (321) 727-7711 Founded/Ownrshp 1992
Sales 41.3MM^E EMP 100
SIC 5511 5531 7538 5521 Automobiles, new & used; Vans, new & used; Trucks, tractors & trailers: new & used; Automotive parts; General automotive repair shops; Used car dealers; Automobiles, new & used; Vans, new & used; Trucks, tractors & trailers: new & used; Automotive parts; General automotive repair shops; Used car dealers
Treas: Gary Miller
*Genl Mgr: Joe Kelly Sr

GATOR CHRYSLR DDG JP SZKI ISZU
See GATOR CHRYSLER PLYMOUTH INC

D-U-N-S 06-467-6034
GATOR FORD TRUCK SALES INC
11780 Tampa Gateway Blvd, Seffner, FL 33584-3038
Tel (813) 980-3673 Founded/Ownrshp 1997
Sales 47.6MM^E EMP 74
SIC 5511 Automobiles, new & used; Automobiles, new & used
Pr: David Kilcoyne
Prin: Donald Fisch
Sales Asso: Frankie Morales

D-U-N-S 14-716-7022
GATOR FORE INC
DUTHLER'S FAMILY FOODS
1025 4 Mile Rd Nw, Grand Rapids, MI 49544-1504
Tel (616) 774-0788 Founded/Ownrshp 1990
Sales 20.6MM^E EMP 125
SIC 5411 Grocery stores
Pr: David Duthler
*Ch: Tom Duthler
*VP: John Duthler

D-U-N-S 11-542-9730
GATOR GYPSUM INC
GMS
(Suby of G M S) ★
3904 E Adamo Dr, Tampa, FL 33605-5902
Tel (813) 248-6393 Founded/Ownrshp 1984
Sales 29.0MM^E EMP 49
SIC 5031 5211 Wallboard; Wallboard (composition) & paneling
Pr: Richard K Mueller
*Treas: Richard Whitcomb
*VP: G Michael J Callahan
*VP: Longell Les
*VP: Gerald R Sweet

D-U-N-S 00-409-5113 IMP/EXP
GATOR OF FLORIDA INC (FL)
5002 N Howard Ave, Tampa, FL 33603-1416
Tel (813) 877-8267 Founded/Ownrshp 1955
Sales 36.8MM^E EMP 138
SIC 5137 Sportswear, women's & children's; Sportswear, women's & children's
Ch Bd: Sam Agliano
*Pr: Frank Agliano
*Sec: Josephine Agliano
Dept Mgr: Regina Brooks

D-U-N-S 18-802-8732
GATOR STAMPINGS INTERNATIONAL INC
6610 33rd St E, Sarasota, FL 34243-4123
Tel (941) 753-9598 Founded/Ownrshp 1987
Sales 25.2MM^E EMP 80
SIC 3469 Metal stampings
Pr: Paul Cronen
Sec: Christy Cornen
*Sec: Christie Borda Lescano
*VP: John Cronen

GATOR TIRE
See CHRISTENSEN ENTERPRISES INC

D-U-N-S 95-855-8132
GATOR VALVE INC
115 Thruway Park Rd, Broussard, LA 70518-3601
Tel (337) 837-8228 Founded/Ownrshp 1996
Sales 27.4MM^E EMP 40
SIC 5085 7699 Valves & fittings; Valve repair, industrial
Pr: Michael Gillen
Off Mgr: Sheila Gillen

D-U-N-S 85-856-1632 EXP
■ **GATORADE CO**
(Suby of QUAKER OATS CO) ★
555 W Monroe St Fl 1, Chicago, IL 60661-3700
Tel (312) 821-1000 Founded/Ownrshp 1990
Sales 150.5MM^E EMP 1,210
SIC 2086 5149 Bottled & canned soft drinks; Beverages, except coffee & tea; Bottled & canned soft drinks; Beverages, except coffee & tea
Pr: Charles I Maniscalco
Treas: Juanita Theodate
VP: Carla Hassan
VP: Victoria Ingram
Comm Dir: Mary Doherty
Mktg Mgr: Sarah Bild
Mktg Mgr: John Shumate
Snr Mgr: Gina Hardy

GATORLAND TOYOTA-KIA-ACURA
See GETTEL ENTERPRISES INC

D-U-N-S 05-448-4217
GATR OF SAUK RAPIDS INC (MN)
GATR VOLVO GMC CENTER
218 Stearns Dr, Sauk Rapids, MN 56379-2520
Tel (320) 251-7356 Founded/Ownrshp 1961
Sales 105.0MM^E EMP 240
SIC 5511 Automobiles, new & used; Automobiles, new & used
Pr: Robert Neitzke
*VP: Trevin Hartung
Genl Mgr: Jeff Schroder
IT Man: Paula Schmitz
Sls Mgr: Jon Pearson
Sales Asso: Zach Campion

GATR VOLVO GMC CENTER
See GATR OF SAUK RAPIDS INC

GATRA
See GREATER ATTLEBORO TAUNTON REGIONAL TRANSIT AUTHORITY

GATSBY
See KOMODIDAD DISTRIBUTORS INC

GATTI'S PIZZA
See MR GATTIS LP

D-U-N-S 06-996-0128
GATTO INDUSTRIAL PLATERS INC
4620 W Roosevelt Rd, Chicago, IL 60644-1430
Tel (773) 287-0100 Founded/Ownrshp 1974
Sales 25.9MM^E EMP 185
SIC 3471 Finishing, metals or formed products; Finishing, metals or formed products
Pr: George Gatto
COO: Juan Arroyo
*Treas: Dominick Gatto
*VP: Robert N Swanson
Ql Cn Mgr: Andy Gruda

D-U-N-S 00-516-1476
▲ **GATX CORP** (NY)
222 W Adams St, Chicago, IL 60606-5312
Tel (312) 621-6200 Founded/Ownrshp 1898
Sales 1.4MMM EMP 2,213
Accts Ernst & Young Llp Chicago Il
Tkr Sym GMT Exch NYS
SIC 4741 7359 4491 Rental of railroad cars; Equipment rental & leasing; Aircraft rental; Marine cargo handling; Marine loading & unloading services; Rental of railroad cars; Equipment rental & leasing; Aircraft rental; Marine cargo handling; Marine loading & unloading services
Ch Bd: Brian A Kenney
Pr: Stuart Southern
COO: Irma Dominguez
CFO: Robert C Lyons
CFO: Jack Stark
CFO: Janet Troher
Treas: Eric D Harkness
Ofcr: Paul F Titterton
Ofcr: Paul Titterton
Ex VP: Deborah A Golden
Ex VP: Mary Lawler
Sr VP: Michael T Brooks
Sr VP: James M Conniff
Sr VP: Jeffrey Muckian
Sr VP: William M Muckian
VP: Don Archiable
VP: Jack Arcurie
VP: Terrence G Heidkamp
VP: David Horwitz
VP: Brooks Laudin
VP: Bob Lyons
Board of Directors: Anne L Arvia, Ernst A Haberli, James B Ream, Robert J Ritchie, David S Sutherland, Casey J Sylla, Stephen R Wilson, Paul G Yovovich

D-U-N-S 78-691-2691
GATX LOGISTICS INC
APL LOGISTICS
(Suby of APL LOGISTICS WAREHOUSE MANAGEMENT SERVICES INC) ★
4300 Old Greensboro Rd, Winston Salem, NC 27101-6219
Tel (336) 852-6482 Founded/Ownrshp 1993
Sales 23.3MM^E EMP 330
SIC 4225 General warehousing & storage; General warehousing & storage
Pr: Joseph A Nicosia
VP: Gene Bannon
Genl Mgr: Roger Vogler

D-U-N-S 03-451-8118
GAUBERT OIL CO INC
1201 Saint Patrick St, Thibodaux, LA 70301-2541
Tel (985) 447-3811 Founded/Ownrshp 2006
Sales 236.7MM EMP 205
SIC 5172 5411

D-U-N-S 07-947-8707
GAUDENZIA INC (PA)
106 W Main St, Norristown, PA 19401-4716
Tel (610) 239-9600 Founded/Ownrshp 1968, 1969
Sales 69.8MM EMP 1,100
SIC 8361 8093 Rehabilitation center, residential: health care incidental; Drug clinic, outpatient; Alcohol clinic, outpatient; Rehabilitation center, residential: health care incidental; Drug clinic, outpatient; Alcohol clinic, outpatient
Pr: Michael B Harle
*CFO: Michael Coyle
*Treas: Charles McGeady
*VP: Michael Moyle
*Ex Dir: Robert P Kelly
Mktg Dir: Ken Dickinson
Pgrm Dir: Annamarie Carter

GAUDIN FORD
See SILVER STATE FORD

D-U-N-S 12-179-8164 IMP
GAUDIN JAGUAR PORSCHE OF LAS VEGAS
SILVER STATE FORD
6800 Redwood St, Las Vegas, NV 89118
Tel (702) 284-7000 Founded/Ownrshp 2004
Sales 24.2MM^E EMP 51
SIC 5511 5521 5531 7538 Automobiles, new & used; Automobiles, used cars only; Automotive parts; General automotive repair shops
Pr: Gary Ackerman
Genl Mgr: Jim Mooradian
Genl Mgr: Art Toombs

D-U-N-S 11-828-1450
GAUGHAN SOUTH
GOLD SPIKE HOTEL & CASINO
1 S Main St, Las Vegas, NV 89101-6370
Tel (702) 384-8444 Founded/Ownrshp 1983
Sales NA EMP 296
SIC 7011 Casino hotel

D-U-N-S 55-735-0910
GAUGHAN SOUTH LLC
SOUTH POINT HOTEL & CASINO SPA
9777 Las Vegas Blvd S, Las Vegas, NV 89183-4013
Tel (702) 796-7111 Founded/Ownrshp 2006
Sales 141.6MM^E EMP 2,400
SIC 7011 Casino hotel; Casino hotel
COO: Lawrence Vaughan
VP: Ruth Casino
VP: Richard Costa
VP: Scott Donar
Exec: George Noriye
Dir Risk M: Heather Hall
Dir Soc: Flo Serna
Dir Sec: Michael Bryant
Area Mgr: Darlene Ford
Area Mgr: John Munoz
Genl Mgr: Ryan Growney

D-U-N-S 00-225-4951
GAULT CHEVROLET CO INC (NY)
GAULT TOYOTA
2205 North St, Endicott, NY 13760-6124
Tel (607) 748-8244 Founded/Ownrshp 1955
Sales 121.0MM EMP 230^E
Accts Evans And Bennett Llp Syracu
SIC 5511 5012 Automobiles, new & used; Automobiles & other motor vehicles; Automobiles, new & used; Automobiles & other motor vehicles; Automobiles
Pr: Bob Gault
*Ch Bd: Robert J Gault Sr
*VP: Connie Gault

D-U-N-S 79-428-7185
GAULT CHEVROLET TOYOTA BMW INC
GAULT TOYOTA
2507 North St, Endicott, NY 13760-6105
Tel (607) 748-8244 Founded/Ownrshp 1955
Sales 26.7MM^E EMP 92

SIC 5511 7538 7532 7515 5531 Automobiles, new & used; General automotive repair shops; Top & body repair & paint shops; Passenger car leasing; Automotive & home supply stores; Automobiles, new & used; General automotive repair shops; Top & body repair & paint shops; Passenger car leasing; Automotive & home supply stores
Pr: Bob Gault
**VP:* Connie Gault
Off Mgr: Carla Hamilton
Dir IT: Robert Soto
Sls Mgr: Margaret Davis
Sls Mgr: Tom Fargo
Sls Mgr: Patrick Whited
Sales Asso: Badr Elhamraoui
Sales Asso: Tom Lavelle
Sales Asso: Jenna Saddlemire

GAULT TOYOTA
See GAULT CHEVROLET CO INC

GAULT TOYOTA
See GAULT CHEVROLET TOYOTA BMW INC

D-U-N-S 06-963-3428
GAUMER CO INC
GAUMER PROCESS
13616 Hempstead Rd, Houston, TX 77040-5816
Tel (713) 460-5200 *Founded/Ownrshp* 1974
Sales 48.3MM^E *EMP* 110
SIC 3533 3433 Gas field machinery & equipment; Heating equipment, except electric; Gas field machinery & equipment; Heating equipment, except electric
Pr: J L McClanahan
**VP:* Norman Bond
**VP:* Mark Buss
**VP:* Mark Crosby
**VP:* Jay McClanahan
**VP:* Craig Tiras
IT Man: Ammar Ahmed
IT Man: Lisette Strandh
Prd Mgr: Tony Kennon
Manager: Octavio Cedillo
Manager: Dean Strauser

GAUMER PROCESS
See GAUMER CO INC

GAUSS SALES CO
See ABRASIVE-TOOL CORP

D-U-N-S 04-170-7774
GAUTIER STEEL LTD
(*Suby of* RESERVE GROUP MANAGEMENT CO) ★
80 Clinton St, Johnstown, PA 15901-2200
Tel (814) 535-9200 *Founded/Ownrshp* 1998
Sales 26.5MM^E *EMP* 90
SIC 3312 3325 Blast furnaces & steel mills; Rolling mill rolls, cast steel; Blast furnaces & steel mills; Rolling mill rolls, cast steel
Pr: Darryl Diorio
**CFO:* Jackie Kulback
**CFO:* Jacqueline Kulback
VP: Richard M Hamlin Jr
**VP:* Jack Mazur
VP Opers: Ken Smith
Mtls Mgr: Tony Kassander
S&M/VP: Peter Thompson
Sls Mgr: Mark Groebel
Snr Mgr: Rob Gall

GAVIA
See F GAVINA & SONS INC

GAVIAL ENGINEERING & MFG
See GAVIAL HOLDINGS INC

D-U-N-S 06-527-3757
GAVIAL HOLDINGS INC
GAVIAL ENGINEERING & MFG
1435 W Mccoy Ln, Santa Maria, CA 93455-1002
Tel (805) 614-0060 *Founded/Ownrshp* 1995
Sales 27.3MM^E *EMP* 160
Accts Ginny Poketylo
SIC 3679 Electronic circuits; Electronic circuits
CEO: Morgan Maxwell Connor
Genl Mgr: Ken Hicks
Off Mgr: Cathy Castor
S&M/Mgr: Scott Barton

D-U-N-S 07-629-4941
GAVILAN JOINT COMMUNITY COLLEGE DISTRICT (INC)
5055 Santa Teresa Blvd, Gilroy, CA 95020-9578
Tel (408) 848-4800 *Founded/Ownrshp* 1963
Sales 11.2MM *EMP* 353
Accts Vavrinek Trine Day & Co Ll
SIC 8222 Community college; Community college
Pr: Rhonda Phenning
COO: Robert Overson
VP: Walt Glines
VP: Fred Harris
VP: Jose Rodriguez
VP: Kathleen Rose
Store Mgr: Alexis Bollin
Snr Mgr: Alicia Arias

D-U-N-S 07-966-1160
GAVILON AGRICULTURE HOLDINGS CO
(*Suby of* MARUBENI CORPORATION)
1331 Capitol Ave, Omaha, NE 68102-1106
Tel (402) 889-4000 *Founded/Ownrshp* 2013
Sales 1.4MMM^E *EMP* 930^E
SIC 5153 5191 Grain & field beans; Fertilizers & agricultural chemicals; Grain & field beans; Fertilizers & agricultural chemicals
Pr: Jim Anderson
**COO:* John Neppl
**CFO:* Kevin Lewis
**VP:* Corey Dencklau
**Prin:* Brian Harlander

D-U-N-S 07-944-4851
GAVILON AGRICULTURE INVESTMENT INC
(*Suby of* GAVILON AGRICULTURE HOLDINGS CO) ★
1331 Capitol Ave, Omaha, NE 68102-1106
Tel (402) 889-4000 *Founded/Ownrshp* 2012
Sales 1.4MMM^E *EMP* 500^E
SIC 5153 5191 ; Grain & field beans; Fertilizers & agricultural chemicals

CEO: Jim Anderson
**Pr:* Brian Harlander
**COO:* Greg Piper
**CFO:* John Neppl
**VP:* Corey Dencklau
**VP:* Ed Prosser
Opers Mgr: Scott Sorrows
Counsel: Yuichi Kono

D-U-N-S 07-837-3804 EXP
GAVILON AGRICULTURE LLC
(*Suby of* GAVILON GLOBAL AG HOLDINGS LLC) ★
1331 Capitol Ave, Omaha, NE 68102-1106
Tel (402) 889-4000 *Founded/Ownrshp* 2011
Sales 417.7MM^E *EMP* 1^E
SIC 0762 5153 5261 Citrus grove management & maintenance services; Grains; Fertilizer
CEO: Jim Anderson
**CFO:* John Neppl
**VP:* Corey Dencklau
**VP:* Greg Konsor
**VP:* Ed Prosser

D-U-N-S 78-759-8465 IMP/EXP
GAVILON FERTILIZER LLC
(*Suby of* GAVILON GROUP LLC) ★
5 Skidaway Village Walk # 201, Savannah, GA 31411-2905
Tel (912) 598-8392 *Founded/Ownrshp* 2008
Sales 67.0MM^E *EMP* 25^E
SIC 5191 Fertilizer & fertilizer materials; Fertilizers & agricultural chemicals
**CFO:* John Neppl
**VP:* Corey Dencklau
**VP:* Robert Gipson
**VP:* Greg Heckman
Opers Mgr: Kelly Pfitzer

D-U-N-S 07-932-9914
GAVILON GLOBAL AG HOLDINGS LLC
(*Suby of* GAVILON GROUP LLC) ★
1331 Capitol Ave, Omaha, NE 68102-1106
Tel (402) 889-4000 *Founded/Ownrshp* 2012
Sales 417.7MM^E *EMP* 1^E
SIC 6799 0762 Commodity investors; Farm management services
CEO: Jim Anderson

D-U-N-S 82-748-1479
GAVILON GRAIN LLC
GRAINSTORE
(*Suby of* GAVILON AGRICULTURE LLC) ★
1331 Capitol Ave, Omaha, NE 68102-1106
Tel (402) 889-4000 *Founded/Ownrshp* 2008
Sales 411.7MM^E *EMP* 653^E
SIC 6221 5153 4221 4226 Commodity contracts brokers, dealers; Grain & field beans; Farm product warehousing & storage; Special warehousing & storage
CEO: Jim Anderson
Pr: Brian Harlander
CFO: John Neppl
VP: Greg Konsor
VP: Dana Wright

D-U-N-S 12-893-8839 IMP/EXP
GAVILON GROUP LLC
(*Suby of* GAVILON INTERMEDIATE HOLDINGS LLC) ★
1331 Capitol Ave, Omaha, NE 68102-1106
Tel (402) 889-4000 *Founded/Ownrshp* 2008
Sales 1.2MMM^E *EMP* 930
SIC 5153 5191 Grain & field beans; Fertilizers & agricultural chemicals; Grain & field beans; Fertilizers & agricultural chemicals
Pr: Jim Anderson
COO: Tom Ramsey
**CFO:* John Neppl

D-U-N-S 02-095-7773
GAVILON HOLDINGS LLC
(*Suby of* GAVILON AGRICULTURE INVESTMENT INC) ★
1331 Capitol Ave, Omaha, NE 68102-1106
Tel (402) 889-4000 *Founded/Ownrshp* 2012
Sales 164.3MM^E *EMP* 930^E
SIC 6719 Public utility holding companies; Public utility holding companies

D-U-N-S 07-912-8549
GAVILON INTERMEDIATE HOLDINGS LLC
(*Suby of* GAVILON HOLDINGS LLC) ★
1331 Capitol Ave, Omaha, NE 68102-1106
Tel (402) 889-4000 *Founded/Ownrshp* 2008
Sales 1.2MMM^E *EMP* 930
SIC 6722 Management investment, open-end
CEO: Jim Anderson

D-U-N-S 15-555-0544
GAVIN DE BECKER & ASSOCIATES
11684 Ventura Blvd # 440, Studio City, CA 91604-2699
Tel (818) 760-4213 *Founded/Ownrshp* 1979
Sales 31.9MM^E *EMP* 180
SIC 8742 Management consulting services; Management consulting services
Pr: Gavin De Becker
**Ex VP:* Michael La Fever
Ex VP: Jeff Marquart

D-U-N-S 82-475-6733
GAVS TECHNOLOGIES NA INC
(*Suby of* GAVS TECHNOLOGIES LIMITED)
10901 W 120th Ave Ste 110, Broomfield, CO 80021-3419
Tel (303) 468-0250 *Founded/Ownrshp* 2008
Sales 68.5MM^E *EMP* 700
SIC 7371 Custom computer programming services; Custom computer programming services
CEO: Sumit Ganguli
Pt: Rajeev Srivastava
Pr: Avijit Kalita
**CFO:* Narasimha Shenoy D
**Sr VP:* Suresh Raman
**VP:* RAO Haridasu
**VP:* Srinivasan Sundararajan
CTO: Don Manuel
Sls Mgr: Vinoth Mariyappan
Snr Mgr: Amit Gupta

Board of Directors: Sanjay Balram

D-U-N-S 00-510-4393
GAW-OHARA ENVELOPE CO
500 N Sacramento Blvd, Chicago, IL 60612-1024
Tel (773) 638-1200 *Founded/Ownrshp* 1913
Sales 28.4MM^E *EMP* 150
SIC 2677

D-U-N-S 92-698-8460
GAWFCO ENTERPRISES INC
UNOCAL
587 Ygnacio Valley Rd, Walnut Creek, CA 94596-3801
Tel (925) 979-0560 *Founded/Ownrshp* 1995
Sales 37.6MM^E *EMP* 85
SIC 5541 5411 Gasoline service stations; Convenience stores
Pr: Mohammed Ahmadi
**Treas:* Nazeem Ahmadi
IT Man: Ahmadi Mike

D-U-N-S 18-234-9121
GAWKER MEDIA LLC
114 5th Ave Fl 2, New York, NY 10011-5611
Tel (212) 655-9524 *Founded/Ownrshp* 2004
Sales 29.4MM^E *EMP* 150
SIC 5963 Direct selling establishments
Pr: Nick Denton
COO: Gaby Darbyshire
CTO: Thomas Plunkett
VP Sls: Gabriela Giacoman
Assoc Ed: Kevin Kelly

D-U-N-S 10-119-6124
GAWVT MOTORS INC
MALL OF GEORGIA FORD
(*Suby of* V.T., INC.)
4525 Nelson Brogdon Blvd, Buford, GA 30518-3488
Tel (678) 318-2297 *Founded/Ownrshp* 2001
Sales 48.4MM *EMP* 98
SIC 5511 Automobiles, new & used; Automobiles, new & used
Genl Mgr: Bill Huseby
**CFO:* Allan M Cady
**Prin:* Kathy Miller
**Prin:* Christina Sharifi
Sls Mgr: Martin Gladstone
Sales Asso: Bryan Curran

D-U-N-S 03-322-6705
GAY & ROBINSON INC
1 Kaumakani Ave, Kaumakani, HI 96747
Tel (808) 335-3133 *Founded/Ownrshp* 1880
Sales 21.1MM *EMP* 200
SIC 0133 Sugarcane farm; Sugarcane farm
Ch: Warren S Robinson
**Pr:* E Alan Kennett
**Treas:* Clem Lum
**VP:* Bruce Robinson

D-U-N-S 02-634-0299
GAY BUICK GMC INC
GAY G M C
3033 Gulf Fwy, Dickinson, TX 77539-3230
Tel (281) 337-2521 *Founded/Ownrshp* 1950
Sales 48.4MM^E *EMP* 100
SIC 5511 Automobiles, new & used; Automobiles, new & used
Pr: Shane R Gay
**Sec:* Marie Gay
**VP:* Don Gay
**Genl Mgr:* Kevin Lardie

D-U-N-S 03-352-7490
GAY CONSTRUCTION CO
JASPER GRADING
2907 Log Cabin Dr Se, Atlanta, GA 30339-1513
Tel (404) 873-4941 *Founded/Ownrshp* 1973
Sales 79.6MM^E *EMP* 150
SIC 1542 1541 Commercial & office building, new construction; Industrial buildings, new construction; Commercial & office building, new construction; Industrial buildings, new construction
Pr: L Thomas Gay Jr
VP: Dave Carl
VP: David Drews
Snr PM: Charles Baxter
Snr PM: Joe Thompson

GAY G M C
See GAY BUICK GMC INC

D-U-N-S 05-236-8206
GAYLE MANUFACTURING CO INC
1455 E Kentucky Ave, Woodland, CA 95776-6121
Tel (707) 226-9136 *Founded/Ownrshp* 1968
Sales 90.6MM *EMP* 96
SIC 3441 1541 Fabricated structural metal; Industrial buildings & warehouses; Fabricated structural metal; Industrial buildings & warehouses
CEO: Andrew Stoll
**Pr:* Gary Glenn
**CFO:* James Deblasio
VP: David De Blasio
**VP:* David Deblasio
**VP:* Nelson Vieira
Genl Mgr: Gary Glen
IT Man: Efrain Calderon
Opers Mgr: Nelson Viera
Snr Mgr: Phil Suek
Board of Directors: David Deblasio, Lisa Deblasio, Gary Glenn, Andrew Stoll, Nelson Vieira

D-U-N-S 13-082-5185
GAYLOR ELECTRIC INC
5750 Castle Creek Parkway, Indianapolis, IN 46250-4337
Tel (317) 843-0577 *Founded/Ownrshp* 1984
Sales 173.5MM *EMP* 750
Accts Katz Sapper & Miller Indiana
SIC 1731 1542 General electrical contractor; Nonresidential construction; General electrical contractor; Nonresidential construction
Pr: John C Gaylor
COO: Paul Osland
VP: Justin Baker
VP: Chris Dice
VP: Andrew Foreman
VP: Craig Hopkins

VP: Tom Nesmith
Exec: Roger White
Dir Bus: Virginia Jones
Prin: Michael Fort
Prin: Johnny Giannuzzi

GAYLORD ARCHIVAL
See GAYLORD BROS INC

D-U-N-S 13-574-5219 EXP
GAYLORD BROS INC
GAYLORD ARCHIVAL
(*Suby of* DEMCO INC) ★
7282 William Barry Blvd, North Syracuse, NY 13212-3347
Tel (315) 457-5070 *Founded/Ownrshp* 2003
Sales 56.5MM^E *EMP* 125
SIC 5112 Stationery & office supplies; Stationery & office supplies
Pr: R Keith George
IT Man: Bill Schickling

D-U-N-S 10-003-5146
GAYLORD COMMUNITY SCHOOL DISTRICT
615 S Elm Ave, Gaylord, MI 49735-1253
Tel (989) 705-3080 *Founded/Ownrshp* 1900
Sales 27.0MM *EMP* 300
Accts Plante & Moran Pllc East Lan
SIC 8211 Public combined elementary & secondary school; Public combined elementary & secondary school
Prin: Betty Hartmann
Prin: Donna Polus
Prin: Ed Sandri
Prin: Dave Smethurst

D-U-N-S 96-305-9428
GAYLORD ENTERTAINMENT FOUNDATION
1 Gaylord Dr, Nashville, TN 37214-1207
Tel (615) 316-6767 *Founded/Ownrshp* 2005
Sales 600.0M *EMP* 653^E
SIC 8699 Charitable organization
VP: Gary Ettinger
Telecom Ex: Ed Thelusma

D-U-N-S 07-539-2134
GAYLORD FARM ASSOCIATION INC (CT)
GAYLORD HOSPITAL
50 Gaylord Farm Rd, Wallingford, CT 06492-2828
Tel (203) 284-2800 *Founded/Ownrshp* 1902
Sales 76.0MM *EMP* 682
SIC 8361 Rehabilitation center, residential: health care incidental; Rehabilitation center, residential: health care incidental
Pr: James Cullin
**CFO:* Janine Enright
**Chf Mktg O:* Louis Taba MD
Ofcr: John Carson
Ofcr: George Kyriacou
Nurse Mgr: Diane Giglio
CIO: Gerry Maroney
Secur Mgr: Carlos Neves
Manager: Geoffrey Blum
Nutrtnst: Brendan Coburn
Doctor: Iulian Benetato MD

GAYLORD HOSPITAL
See GAYLORD FARM ASSOCIATION INC

D-U-N-S 62-375-3857
GAYLORD HOSPITAL INC
Gaylord Farm Rd, Wallingford, CT 06492
Tel (203) 284-2800 *Founded/Ownrshp* 2006
Sales 74.2MM *EMP* 2
SIC 8361 Residential care; Residential care

GAYLORD HOTELS
See GAYLORD OPRYLAND USA INC

D-U-N-S 18-361-0984
GAYLORD NATIONAL LLC
(*Suby of* RYMAN HOSPITALITY PROPERTIES INC) ★
201 Waterfront St, Forest Heights, MD 20745-1135
Tel (301) 965-2000 *Founded/Ownrshp* 2012
Sales 38.8MM^E *EMP* 646
SIC 7011 Resort hotel; Resort hotel
CFO: David Kloeppel
Ex VP: James Olin
VP: Melissa Fraley Agguini
VP: Rod Connor
VP: Helmar Dahle
VP: Joanie Flynn
VP: Kemp Gallineau
VP: Rick Maradik
VP: Mike Mason
VP: Robert McPherrin
VP: Tina Sampson
VP: Sheldon Suga

D-U-N-S 11-870-3529
■ **GAYLORD OPRYLAND USA INC**
GAYLORD HOTELS
(*Suby of* MARRIOTT INTERNATIONAL INC) ★
2800 Opryland Dr, Nashville, TN 37214-1200
Tel (615) 889-6600 *Founded/Ownrshp* 2012
Sales 196.0MM^E *EMP* 4,000
SIC 7011 Resort hotel; Resort hotel
Ch Bd: Colin V Reed
VP: Pete Fisher
Dir Soc: David Furnish
Dir Soc: Michael Murgas
Dir Soc: Lori Story
Genl Mgr: Danna Hutton
Genl Mgr: Ben Levy
CIO: Matt Collins
Dir IT: Lee Rotholz
Dir IT: David Sacco
Netwrk Eng: Josh Gibbar

GAYLORD TXN RSRT & CNVNTN CTR
See RHP PROPERTY GT LP

D-U-N-S 00-211-1979 IMP
■ **GAYMAR INDUSTRIES INC** (NY)
(*Suby of* STRYKER CORP) ★
10 Centre Dr, Orchard Park, NY 14127-2280
Tel (800) 828-7341 *Founded/Ownrshp* 1956, 2010
Sales 43.4MM^E *EMP* 350
SIC 3841 Surgical & medical instruments; Surgical & medical instruments

CEO: Bradford L Saar
Prin: Kent J Davies
QA Dir: Pradeep Gupta

D-U-N-S 00-427-8156 IMP/EXP
GAYSTON CORP
721 Richard St, Miamisburg, OH 45342-1840
Tel (937) 743-6050 *Founded/Ownrshp* 1951
Sales 66.3MM^E *EMP* 200
SIC 3443 3999 3949 2813 Nuclear reactors, military or industrial; Military insignia; Baseball, softball & cricket sports equipment; Oxygen, compressed or liquefied; Nuclear reactors, military or industrial; Military insignia; Baseball, softball & cricket sports equipment; Oxygen, compressed or liquefied
Ch Bd: Mark W Stone
VP: Willard W Deey
VP: Willard W Dewey
VP: J G Heitz
VP: Connie G Hinkel
VP: John L Michael
Exec: Andrew Sheldrick
Prgrm Mgr: Neville Sheldrick
IT Man: Jerry Young
VP Mfg: Lester F Sonterre
Ql Cn Mgr: Dan Large

D-U-N-S 06-664-3834
GAYTAN FOODS
15430 Proctor Ave, City of Industry, CA 91745-1024
Tel (626) 330-4553 *Founded/Ownrshp* 1973
Sales 28.2MM^E *EMP* 100
SIC 2013 2099 2022 2011 Sausages & other prepared meats; Food preparations; Cheese, natural & processed; Meat packing plants; Sausages & other prepared meats; Food preparations; Cheese, natural & processed; Meat packing plants
CEO: Rudolph Gaytan
Prd Mgr: Chris Gonzalez
Sales Asso: Peter Diaz
Sales Asso: Tony Meraz
Sales Asso: Nick Monroy

D-U-N-S 83-730-5056
GAZELLE INC
300 A St Ste 3, Boston, MA 02210-1695
Tel (800) 429-3553 *Founded/Ownrshp* 1996
Sales 22.2MM^E *EMP* 95
SIC 5731 5065 Radio, television & electronic stores; Electronic parts & equipment
Pr: Israel Ganot
Pr: Marty Frenzel
CFO: Chris Sullivan
Chf Mktg O: Sarah Welch
Ofcr: Susan M McCuaig
Ex VP: Joseph Morrow
Sr VP: Roger Neal
VP: Debra Fleig
VP: Eliza Royal
Exec: Maria Manrique
CTO: Ben Katz

D-U-N-S 13-933-9295
GAZELLE TRANSPORTATION INC
34915 Gazelle Ct, Bakersfield, CA 93308-9618
Tel (661) 322-8868 *Founded/Ownrshp* 1992
Sales 45.1MM^E *EMP* 193
SIC 4212

GAZETTE, THE
See FREEDOM COLORADO INFORMATION INC

D-U-N-S 80-801-3432
GAZETTE
COLORADOSPRINGSCOM
30 E Pikes Peak Ave # 100, Colorado Springs, CO 80903-1580
Tel (719) 632-5511 *Founded/Ownrshp* 2007
Sales 22.3MM^E *EMP* 200
SIC 7313 Electronic media advertising representatives
Prin: Steve Pope
COO: Sharon Peters
CFO: Dan Dueber
VP: Heather Hale
VP: Brad Howard
VP: Kevin Miller
VP: Rich Williams
Genl Mgr: Dan Steever
CIO: Michael Heffern
Dir IT: Bradford B Shaw
Dir IT: Stephanie Weber

D-U-N-S 00-528-4393
GAZETTE CO (IA)
GFOC HOLDINGS,
500 3rd Ave Se, Cedar Rapids, IA 52401-1608
Tel (319) 398-8211 *Founded/Ownrshp* 1883
Sales 123.2MM^E *EMP* 600
SIC 2711 2752 4833 Newspapers, publishing & printing; Commercial printing, lithographic; Television broadcasting stations; Newspapers, publishing & printing; Commercial printing, lithographic; Television broadcasting stations
Pr: Chuck Peters
**CFO:* Ken Slaughter
**Ch:* Joe Hladky
**Treas:* Scott Grasso
VP: Mary Collins

D-U-N-S 62-759-0680
GAZETTE COMMUNICATIONS INC
(*Suby of* GAZETTE CO) ★
500 3rd Ave Se, Cedar Rapids, IA 52401-1608
Tel (319) 398-8211 *Founded/Ownrshp* 1999
Sales 64.9MM^E *EMP* 600
SIC 2711 Commercial printing & newspaper publishing combined; Commercial printing & newspaper publishing combined
Ch Bd: Joe Hladky
**Pr:* Charles M Peters
**CFO:* Ken Slaughter
**Treas:* Scott Grasso
Dir IT: Scott Barter

D-U-N-S 60-399-1550
GAZILLION INC
SLIPGATTE IRONWORKS
475 Concar Dr, San Mateo, CA 94402-2650
Tel (650) 393-6500 *Founded/Ownrshp* 2005
Sales 51.6MM^E *EMP* 300
SIC 7372 Publishers' computer software; Publishers' computer software
CEO: Robert Hutter
**Pr:* David Brevik
**COO:* Bhavin Shah
**CFO:* Eric Garay
CFO: Eric Russell
Chf Cred: Peter Hu
Sr VP: Christine Legg
VP: Dan Fiden
VP: Jeff Lind
Snr Sftwr: Brian Bazyk
QA Dir: William Busch

D-U-N-S 07-884-1540
GB AERO ENGINE LLC
555 Theodore Fremd Ave, Rye, NY 10580-1451
Tel (914) 925-9600 *Founded/Ownrshp* 2013
Sales 118.6MM^E *EMP* 390^E
SIC 3724 3541 3769 Aircraft engines & engine parts; Machine tools, metal cutting type; Guided missile & space vehicle parts & auxiliary equipment; Aircraft engines & engine parts; Machine tools, metal cutting type; Guided missile & space vehicle parts & auxiliary equipment

D-U-N-S 62-291-0255
GB AUCTIONS INC
D A A NORTHWEST
2215 S Hayford Rd, Spokane, WA 99224-9490
Tel (509) 244-4500 *Founded/Ownrshp* 1992
Sales 32.3MM^E *EMP* 250^E
SIC 5012 5521 Automobile auction; Used car dealers; Automobile auction; Used car dealers
Pr: Bob McConkey Jr
**VP:* Greg Mahugh
Dept Mgr: Joe Metzger
Dept Mgr: Mike Paulson
Dept Mgr: James Sloan
Dir IT: Scott Sinkle
Dir IT: Arron Wagner
IT Man: Aaron Smith
Opers Mgr: Lee Kelly
Opers Mgr: Kelly Lee
Sales Exec: Chris Legg

D-U-N-S 01-654-3055 IMP
GB BIOSCIENCES CORP
(*Suby of* SYNGENTA CORP) ★
2200 Concord Pike, Wilmington, DE 19803-2909
Tel (336) 632-6000 *Founded/Ownrshp* 1986, 2000
Sales 67.9MM^E *EMP* 320
SIC 2879 2834 2899 Pesticides, agricultural or household; Fungicides, herbicides; Pharmaceutical preparations; Druggists' preparations (pharmaceuticals); Chemical preparations; Pesticides, agricultural or household; Fungicides, herbicides; Pharmaceutical preparations; Druggists' preparations (pharmaceuticals); Chemical preparations
CEO: Robert Woods

D-U-N-S 08-121-8117 IMP
GB MANUFACTURING CO
1120 E Main St, Delta, OH 43515
Tel (419) 822-5323 *Founded/Ownrshp* 2005
Sales 33.5MM^E *EMP* 180
SIC 3469 Metal stampings
Pr: Nelson U Reyes
**CFO:* Michael Pechette
**VP:* Annette Y Petree
**VP:* Mark Ries
Ql Cn Mgr: Michael Rude

D-U-N-S 04-056-1664
GB SALES & SERVICE INC (MI)
FRAZA/FORKLIFTS
6865 Commerce Blvd, Canton, MI 48187
Tel (734) 455-5150 *Founded/Ownrshp* 1976
Sales 68.5MM^E *EMP* 150
SIC 5084 7359 7699 Lift trucks & parts; Materials handling machinery; Equipment rental & leasing; Industrial truck rental; Industrial truck repair; Industrial machinery & equipment repair; Lift trucks & parts; Materials handling machinery; Equipment rental & leasing; Industrial truck rental; Industrial truck repair; Industrial machinery & equipment repair
CEO: Gregory J Blackwood
Pr: Timothy J Blackwood
CFO: Roger E Runyan
Sls Mgr: Scott McGlone

D-U-N-S 83-068-3269
GB SHADES LLC
GOODWIN BROTHERS SHADING & SPC
100 Naamans Rd Ste 5f, Claymont, DE 19703-2700
Tel (302) 798-3028 *Founded/Ownrshp* 2005
Sales 20.3MM^E *EMP* 30
SIC 5023 Window furnishings
Pr: John Goodwin
CFO: Mark A Anchor
VP: Charles Goodwin

GB SHOES
See HOUSER SHOES INC

D-U-N-S 00-609-8370 IMP
GB TOOLS AND SUPPLIES INC
GARDNER BENDER
6200 N Baker Rd, Milwaukee, WI 53209-3736
Tel (414) 352-4160 *Founded/Ownrshp* 1988
Sales NA *EMP* 500
SIC 3699

GBC
See GRANITE BROADCASTING CORP

D-U-N-S 60-891-7964
GBC CONSTRUCTION LLC
2273 Nw Prof Dr Ste 200, Corvallis, OR 97330
Tel (541) 752-0381 *Founded/Ownrshp* 2005
Sales 22.0MM *EMP* 15
SIC 1542 Commercial & office building, new construction
CEO: Jason Pond
Pr: Gregory Goracke
Snr PM: Joel Freeman

D-U-N-S 08-220-9305
GBC INTERNATIONAL BANK
GUARANTEED BANKING CALIFORNIA
(*Suby of* G B C HOLDINGS INC) ★
5670 Wilshire Blvd Ph 1, Los Angeles, CA 90036-5644
Tel (310) 826-4228 *Founded/Ownrshp* 1991
Sales NA *EMP* 57
SIC 6022 State trust companies accepting deposits, commercial; State trust companies accepting deposits, commercial
CEO: Dennis Lam
Ex VP: Annie Pan
VP: Randy Cheng
VP: Betty Chien
VP: Todd Huynh
VP: Baryy Lee
VP: Eileen MA

D-U-N-S 80-850-0081 EXP
■ **GBC METALS LLC**
OLIN BRASS
(*Suby of* GLOBAL BRASS AND COPPER INC) ★
427 N Shamrock St, East Alton, IL 62024-1174
Tel (618) 258-2350 *Founded/Ownrshp* 2007
Sales 241.9MM^E *EMP* 1,900
SIC 3351 3341 3469 Brass rolling & drawing; Copper smelting & refining (secondary); Metal stampings; Brass rolling & drawing; Copper smelting & refining (secondary); Metal stampings
Pr: Bill Toler
**CEO:* John Walker
**COO:* John J Wasz
**CFO:* Robert Michelli
**VP:* Tom Werner
VP: Michael Wickenhauser
Mtls Mgr: Kristen Young
Sls Mgr: David Hagenbrock

D-U-N-S 78-189-7272
GBC TRADING INTERNATIONAL CORP
8475 Nw 29th St, Doral, FL 33122-1919
Tel (305) 395-7382 *Founded/Ownrshp* 2006
Sales 21.0MM *EMP* 12
SIC 5065 Electronic parts; Electronic parts
Pr: Mann Bazzi
**VP:* Faddy Bazzi
**Genl Mgr:* Bilal Bazzi

D-U-N-S 03-588-6332
GBF INC (NC)
GUILFORD BUSINESS FORMS
2427 Penny Rd, High Point, NC 27265-8120
Tel (336) 665-0205 *Founded/Ownrshp* 1964
Sales 32.3MM^E *EMP* 72
SIC 2835 2899 5112 In vitro & in vivo diagnostic substances; ; Business forms
Pr: Danny Bowman
COO: Jack Bedrosian
**VP:* Jason Bowman
**VP:* Coy Shields
IT Man: Eric Warshawsky
Sfty Mgr: John Fuller
Sls Dir: Steve Pippin

GBFB
See GREATER BOSTON FOOD BANK INC

D-U-N-S 96-351-0420
GBG ACCESSORIES GROUP LLC
(*Suby of* GBG USA INC) ★
350 5th Ave Lbby 9, New York, NY 10118-0109
Tel (646) 839-7000 *Founded/Ownrshp* 2010
Sales 165.6MM^E *EMP* 55^E
SIC 5137 Women's & children's clothing

D-U-N-S 06-597-4644 IMP/EXP
GBG USA INC
MAX LEATHER
(*Suby of* FUNG HOLDINGS (1937) LIMITED)
350 5th Ave Lbby 9, New York, NY 10118-0109
Tel (646) 839-7000 *Founded/Ownrshp* 1986
Sales 911.7MM^E *EMP* 1,722^E
SIC 5139 5137 5136 Sportswear, men's & boys'; Footwear; Sportswear, women's & children's; Footwear; Sportswear, women's & children's; Sportswear, men's & boys'
CEO: Spencer Fung
**Pr:* Henry Chan
**Pr:* Marc Compagnon
**CFO:* Ed Lam
**Chf Cred:* Lale Kesebi
Sr VP: James Baldwin
Sr VP: Heather Mee
VP: Antoinette Scarangella
VP Opers: Joseph Favuzza
VP Sls: Caroline Banks

GBI RESEARCH
See GLOBAL DATA PUBLICATIONS INC

D-U-N-S 78-530-7356 IMP
GBI TILE & STONE INC
QUARRY COLLECTION
3120 Airway Ave, Costa Mesa, CA 92626-4610
Tel (949) 567-1880 *Founded/Ownrshp* 1991
Sales 20.7MM^E *EMP* 50^E
SIC 5032 Brick, stone & related material
Pr: John Jeffrey Jones
**VP:* Marco A Gonzalez
VP: Vincent Moiso
VP Opers: Robert Gabrielson

D-U-N-S 03-398-5557 IMP
GBK CORP
KAISER-FRANCIS OIL COMPANY
6733 S Yale Ave, Tulsa, OK 74136-3302
Tel (918) 494-0000 *Founded/Ownrshp* 1976
Sales 777.4MM^E *EMP* 2,067^E
SIC 1311 Crude petroleum production; Natural gas production; Crude petroleum production; Natural gas production
Pr: George B Kaiser
**Ex VP:* James A Willis

D-U-N-S 06-823-6772
GBK SOLUTIONS INC (OH)
108 S Main St, Bowling Green, OH 43402-2909
Tel (419) 354-2110 *Founded/Ownrshp* 1988, 1997
Sales 49.8MM *EMP* 7
SIC 5734 Computer & software stores; Computer & software stores
Pr: William R Gross

GBM INTERNATIONAL
See GTM INTERNATIONAL LLC

D-U-N-S 18-962-8076
GBMC HEALTHCARE INC
6701 N Charles St, Baltimore, MD 21204-6808
Tel (443) 849-2000 *Founded/Ownrshp* 1986
Sales 42.3MM *EMP* 103
Accts Deloitte Tax Llp Mclean Va
SIC 8082 8051 Home health care services; Skilled nursing care facilities
Pr: John B Chessare
**COO:* Keith Poisson
**CFO:* Eric L Melchior
**Sr VP:* John W Ellis
**Sr VP:* Jody Porter
**VP:* George Bayless
**VP:* Richard Borschuk
**VP:* Carolyn L Candiello
**VP:* Jenny Coldiron
VP: John Ellis
**VP:* Michael A Forthman
**VP:* Cathy Hamel
VP: Robert Roca
VP: Mark Thomas
**VP:* Deloris Simpson Tuggle

D-U-N-S 13-447-0280
GBP MANAGEMENT INC
(*Suby of* GUARDIAN BUILDING PRODUCTS INC) ★
979 Batesville Rd, Greer, SC 29651-6819
Tel (864) 297-6101 *Founded/Ownrshp* 2002
Sales 733.8MM^E *EMP* 200^E
SIC 8741 Business management; Business management
Pr: Duane H Faulkner
**CFO:* David E Love
**VP:* Bruce Schneider

D-U-N-S 07-500-4366
GBQ HOLDINGS LLC
230 West St Ste 700, Columbus, OH 43215-2663
Tel (614) 221-1120 *Founded/Ownrshp* 2012
Sales 21.5MM^E *EMP* 120^E
SIC 8721 Accounting, auditing & bookkeeping
Prin: Darci Congrove
COO: Andrew Arend
Exec: Jeff Kovacs
Exec: Richard Schollaert
Dir IT: Robert Pyles
Snr Mgr: Jerry Cullins
Snr Mgr: Craig Hickey

D-U-N-S 87-926-2491
GBS BENEFITS INC
465 S 400 E Ste 300, Salt Lake City, UT 84111-3349
Tel (801) 364-7233 *Founded/Ownrshp* 1993
Sales NA *EMP* 112
SIC 6321 Health insurance carriers
Pr: Richard K Fielding
**VP:* Scott A Stewart
Mng Dir: Gary Bell
Board of Directors: Tyler Gee

GBS COMPUTER SOLUTIONS
See GBS CORP

D-U-N-S 05-466-8751 IMP
GBS CORP (OH)
GBS COMPUTER SOLUTIONS
135 W Adams Ave, Saint Louis, MO 63122-4022
Tel (314) 966-4692 *Founded/Ownrshp* 1971
Sales 173.4MM^E *EMP* 315
SIC 5045 5112 2675 2672 2761 2759 Computers, peripherals & software; Business forms; Folders, filing, die-cut: made from purchased materials; Labels (unprinted), gummed: made from purchased materials; Tape, pressure sensitive: made from purchased materials; Manifold business forms; Commercial printing; Computers, peripherals & software; Business forms; Folders, filing, die-cut: made from purchased materials; Labels (unprinted), gummed: made from purchased materials; Tape, pressure sensitive: made from purchased materials; Manifold business forms; Commercial printing
CEO: Eugene Calpria
**Pr:* Jeff Fusco
Pr: David Laughling
CFO: Michele Benson
**Ex VP:* James R Carey
VP: Jeff Merriman
VP: Dave Noble
VP Bus Dev: Allan Greer
Dir IT: Mark Galpin
Opers Mgr: Jody Doll
Sales Exec: Tom Yannarell

D-U-N-S 92-904-0079
▲ **GBS ENTERPRISES INC**
ROYAL LIMOUSINE SERVICE, A
125 Townpark Dr Nw # 300, Kennesaw, GA 30144-5803
Tel (404) 891-1711 *Founded/Ownrshp* 2010
Sales 31.9MM *EMP* 331
Tkr Sym GBSX *Exch* OTO
SIC 5045 7371 Limousine rental, with driver; Computer software; Computer software systems analysis & design, custom
CEO: Joerg Ott
**COO:* Mark Durst
**CFO:* Markus Ernst
**Chf Mktg O:* John Durst
Ex VP: Stefan Mehlhorn
Ex VP: Sheri Pierce
**VP:* Marion Betz
VP: Rafael Gomez
Genl Mgr: Scott Hooks

D-U-N-S 60-640-3210 IMP
GBS ENTERPRISES LLC
1006 E Maple St, Sutton, NE 68979-2149
Tel (402) 773-4601 *Founded/Ownrshp* 2011
Sales 22.0MM *EMP* 46
SIC 7389 Sewing contractor; Sewing contractor
CEO: Jeffrey McWey
**CFO:* Lawrence Mandras
Off Mgr: Merle Swartz

D-U-N-S 05-961-5583
GBS LUMBER INC
11 Geneva Ct, Greenville, SC 29607-5302
Tel (864) 288-6754 *Founded/Ownrshp* 1972
Sales 40.4MM *EMP* 100
Accts Greene Finney & Horton Llp M
SIC 5211 Lumber & other building materials; Millwork & lumber; Windows, storm: wood or metal; Doors, storm: wood or metal; Lumber & other building materials; Millwork & lumber; Windows, storm: wood or metal; Doors, storm: wood or metal
Pr: Olin R Mc Neely
**Sec:* Merridee J Harper
**VP:* M G Proffitt III
Board of Directors: John C Cothran, Richard Sumerel

D-U-N-S 61-476-4108 IMP
GBT INC
GIGA BITE TECHNOLOGY
(*Suby of* GIGA-BYTE TECHNOLOGY CO., LTD.)
17358 Railroad St, City of Industry, CA 91748-1023
Tel (626) 854-9333 *Founded/Ownrshp* 1990
Sales 34.4MM^E *EMP* 80
SIC 5045 Computers & accessories, personal & home entertainment
Pr: Eric C Lu
VP: Henry KAO
Dir Bus: Robert Sun
**Prin:* James Liao
Dir IT: Rock Lin
Opers Mgr: Maggie Lin
S&M/VP: Tony Liao

D-U-N-S 07-938-4795
■ **GBT US LLC**
AMERICAN EX GLOBL BUS TRVL
(*Suby of* AMERICAN EXPRESS TRAVEL RELATED SERVICES CO INC) ★
7 Times Sq Fl 44, New York, NY 10036-6508
Tel (212) 829-0942 *Founded/Ownrshp* 2013
Sales 53.8MM^E *EMP* 1
SIC 4724 Travel agencies
Prin: Stacke Haverty
Dir Bus: Kristyn Proeschel

D-U-N-S 07-495-9834
GBU FINANCIAL LIFE
G B U
4254 Saw Mill Run Blvd, Pittsburgh, PA 15227-3394
Tel (412) 884-5100 *Founded/Ownrshp* 1892
Sales NA *EMP* 26^E
SIC 6311 Fraternal life insurance organizations
CEO: James R Stoker
**Ch Bd:* Lea Ann Hazi
**VP:* Matthew Blistan
Dept Mgr: Debbie Morgan
Mktg Dir: Jim Laick

D-U-N-S 07-963-7735
GBW RAILCAR SERVICES LLC
1 Centerpointe Dr Ste 200, Lake Oswego, OR 97035-8612
Tel (503) 684-7000 *Founded/Ownrshp* 2014
Sales 202.5MM^E *EMP* 873^E
SIC 4789 Railroad car repair
CEO: Jim Cowan

D-U-N-S 82-476-8410
■ **GBW RAILCAR SERVICES LLC**
GREENBRIER RAIL SVCS-SPRNGFELD
(*Suby of* GUNDERSON LLC) ★
303 S 5th St Ste 195, Springfield, OR 97477-5477
Tel (620) 231-2230 *Founded/Ownrshp* 2005
Sales 34.2MM^E *EMP* 158
SIC 4789 Railroad car repair; Railroad car repair
VP: Paul Wostmann
Info Man: Judy Fleming

D-U-N-S 07-962-6191
GC ALLEGRA LLC
(*Suby of* DIALOGDIRECT INC) ★
13700 Oakland St, Highland Park, MI 48203-3173
Tel (313) 957-5100 *Founded/Ownrshp* 2014
Sales 18.7MM^E *EMP* 408^E
SIC 8742 Marketing consulting services
Snr Ntwrk: Philip Lincoln

D-U-N-S 00-547-3608 IMP/EXP
GC AMERICA INC (IL)
(*Suby of* GC CORPORATION)
3737 W 127th St, Alsip, IL 60803-1542
Tel (708) 597-0900 *Founded/Ownrshp* 1928
Sales 70.8MM^E *EMP* 250
SIC 3843 Dental equipment & supplies; Dental equipment & supplies
Pr: Yutaka Suzuki
**Pr:* M Dean Porter
**CFO:* Carolyn M Van Eck
**VP:* Richard Demke
VP: Beth Majka
**VP:* John O'Neill
Comm Man: Linda Bellisario
Rgnl Mgr: Tom Meintz
Dist Mgr: Terri Blatchford
Dist Mgr: Todd Cretors
Dist Mgr: Michael Furgason

GC ELECTRONICS
See WALDOM ELECTRONICS CORP

D-U-N-S 08-255-3041 IMP
GC PACKAGING LLC
877 N Larch Ave, Elmhurst, IL 60126-1114
Tel (630) 758-4100 *Founded/Ownrshp* 1976
Sales 63.0MM^E *EMP* 245
SIC 2754 7389 Cards, except greeting: gravure printing; Packaging & labeling services; Cards, except greeting: gravure printing; Packaging & labeling services
Ch: John Tinnon
Pr: Michael Tinnon
CFO: Joseph Yaney
Ex VP: Steve Skalski
VP: John Dean
Genl Mgr: John Hutcherson
MIS Mgr: Jim Spangler

D-U-N-S 96-843-0947
GC PIVOTAL LLC
GLOBAL CAPACITY
180 N La Salle St # 2430, Chicago, IL 60601-2704
Tel (312) 660-5000 *Founded/Ownrshp* 2010
Sales 35.5MM^E *EMP* 73^E
SIC 4813
Pr: Jack Lodge
**CFO:* Vic Pierni
Treas: Matthew McKinney
Sr VP: Andy Berquist
Sr VP: Wendell Nelson
VP: Tasha Davis
VP: Steve Starliper
CIO: Phil Doyle
IT Man: Angelica Chan
VP Mktg: Julie Dillenbeck
VP Sls: David Sperandeo

D-U-N-S 18-052-9323
GC SERVICES LIMITED PARTNERSHIP
6330 Gulfton St, Houston, TX 77081-1108
Tel (713) 777-4441 *Founded/Ownrshp* 1957
Sales 414.2MM^E *EMP* 9,000
Accts Ham Langston & Brezina Llp
SIC 7389 7322 7375 Information retrieval services; Financial services; Collection agency, except real estate; Financial services; Collection agency, except real estate; Information retrieval services
Pr: Frank A Taylor
**Ch Bd:* Jerold B Katz
**CFO:* Michael Jones
CFO: Michael D Jones
Treas: Linda M Spellicy
**Ex VP:* Daniel R Cook
**Ex VP:* Gary L Hopkins
**Ex VP:* Mark A Schordock
**Sr VP:* Craig M Cappelle
**Sr VP:* Scott Cole
VP: Robert D Wilson

D-U-N-S 07-955-2791
GC SHORE HOLDINGS LLC
(*Suby of* DIALOGDIRECT INC) ★
13700 Oakland St, Highland Park, MI 48203-3173
Tel (313) 957-5100 *Founded/Ownrshp* 2013
Sales 18.7MM^E *EMP* 408^E
SIC 8742 Marketing consulting services
Prin: Ronald Risher

G.C. ZARNAS
See ZARNAS INC

D-U-N-S 08-497-8514
GC&E SYSTEMS GROUP INC
5835 Peachtree Cors E A, Norcross, GA 30092-3413
Tel (770) 448-3908 *Founded/Ownrshp* 1999
Sales 24.3MM *EMP* 186
Accts Windham Brannon Pc Atlanta
SIC 7373 Systems integration services; Systems integration services
CEO: Dan O'Sullivan
**Pr:* Dennis Bristol
Pr: Wilt Corban
**CFO:* John Santacroce
Sls&Mrk Ex: Paula Simpkins
Sls Dir: Jim Mann

D-U-N-S 13-350-1127
GCA SERVICES GROUP INC
1350 Euclid Ave Ste 1500, Cleveland, OH 44115-1832
Tel (216) 535-4900 *Founded/Ownrshp* 2012
Sales 800.0MM *EMP* 32,000
SIC 7349 Janitorial service, contract basis; Janitorial service, contract basis
CEO: Robert Norton
Pr: Eric Hudgens
Pr: Alan Odom
**CFO:* Robert Gerber
Rgnl VP: Kevin Davis
VP: Jon Burney
VP: Glenn Essig
VP: Walt Griffin
VP: Dan Havelka
VP: George Kanganis
VP: Samuel Knezevic
VP: Cole Leitch
VP: Tom Martin
VP: Randall Twyman

D-U-N-S 00-147-5730
GCA SERVICES GROUP OF NORTH CAROLINA INC (NC)
ADVANTAGE STAFFING
(*Suby of* GCA SERVICES GROUP INC) ★
1 Centerview Dr Ste 109, Greensboro, NC 27407-3712
Tel (336) 294-9411 *Founded/Ownrshp* 1974
Sales 40.9MM^E *EMP* 4,000
SIC 7349 7363 Janitorial service, contract basis; Temporary help service; Janitorial service, contract basis; Temporary help service
CEO: Robert Norton
**Pr:* Cole Leitch
**Ch:* Tom Fivgerald

GCAS
See GOLD CROSS AMBULANCE SERVICE

D-U-N-S 04-986-5553 IMP
GCAT LLC
TARGET DISTRIBUTING
19560 Amaranth Dr, Germantown, MD 20874-1202
Tel (301) 296-9400 *Founded/Ownrshp* 2006
Sales 29.5MM^E *EMP* 40
SIC 5065 Telephone equipment; Communication equipment
CEO: Michael Momsen
**Pr:* Richard Warsaw
VP: Robert Warsaw
**VP:* Stephen Yablon
Opers Mgr: Joy Carter

GCB STAFFING
See GATE CITY OF BURLINGTON INC

GCC
See GHILOTTI CONSTRUCTION CO INC

D-U-N-S 79-145-4460
GCC ALLIANCE CONCRETE INC
412 8th St Sw, Orange City, IA 51041-1547
Tel (712) 722-1646 *Founded/Ownrshp* 2008
Sales 23.9MM^E *EMP* 205^E
SIC 3273 Ready-mixed concrete; Ready-mixed concrete
Pr: Enrique Escalante
**Pr:* Thomas L Slaughter
**Treas:* Martha Rodriguez

D-U-N-S 83-725-2246
GCC DACOTAH INC
DACOTAH CEMENT
(*Suby of* GRUPO CEMENTOS DE CHIHUAHUA, S.A.B. DE C.V.)
501 N Saint Onge St, Rapid City, SD 57702-0329
Tel (605) 721-7100 *Founded/Ownrshp* 1925
Sales 40.0MM^E *EMP* 180
SIC 3241 5032 Natural cement; Cement; Natural cement; Cement
Pr: Steve Zellmer
VP: Dan Baker
VP: Dave Rydquist
Plnt Mgr: Steve Post
Sls Mgr: Henry Mc Kitterick

D-U-N-S 08-737-1647
GCC ENERGY LLC
KING COAL MINE
6473 County Road 120, Hesperus, CO 81326-9633
Tel (970) 259-6175 *Founded/Ownrshp* 1977, 1995
Sales 28.0MM^E *EMP* 145
SIC 1222 Bituminous coal-underground mining; Underground mining, semibituminous; Bituminous coal-underground mining; Underground mining, semibituminous
VP: Trent Peterson
Fr: Ron Henley

D-U-N-S 12-194-1954
GCC OF AMERICA INC
(*Suby of* GRUPO CEMENTOS DE CHIHUAHUA, S.A.B. DE C.V.)
11783 New Mexico 337, Tijeras, NM 87059-8619
Tel (505) 281-3311 *Founded/Ownrshp* 1994
Sales 49.6MM^E *EMP* 144
SIC 3272 Concrete products
Pr: Enrique Escalante
**Treas:* Martha Rodrigues
MIS Dir: Francisco Meza

D-U-N-S 00-224-4999
GCC RIO GRANDE INC (NM)
G C C
(*Suby of* GCC OF AMERICA INC) ★
11783 New Mexico 337, Tijeras, NM 87059-8619
Tel (505) 281-3311 *Founded/Ownrshp* 1994
Sales 40.1MM^E *EMP* 144
SIC 3272 Concrete products; Concrete products
Pr: Enrique Escalante
**Treas:* Martha Rodrigues
**VP:* Jaime Fernandez
IT Man: Tony Flores

D-U-N-S 03-046-1409
GCC TECHNOLOGIES LLC
65 Enterprise Dr, Oakland, MD 21550-6372
Tel (301) 387-4848 *Founded/Ownrshp* 1997
Sales 21.0MM^E *EMP* 175^E
SIC 8711 8741 Engineering services; Management services; Engineering services; Management services
Pr: James D Bailey
Pt: Shirley Bailey
QA Dir: Chrissy Marucci

GCCCD
See GROSSMONT-CUYAMACA COMMUNITY COLLEGE DISTRICT

D-U-N-S 60-357-5015
GCDJ HOLDINGS INC
8505 Chancellor Row, Dallas, TX 75247-5519
Tel (214) 905-9500 *Founded/Ownrshp* 2004
Sales 44.6MM^E *EMP* 680
SIC 1799 2394 Building site preparation; Canvas & related products; Shades, canvas: made from purchased materials; Building site preparation; Canvas & related products; Shades, canvas: made from purchased materials
CEO: John Saunders
**CFO:* Jeffrey Sarembock
**Ch:* Basil Haymann

D-U-N-S 00-129-3224 IMP
GCE INTERNATIONAL INC (NY)
GREAT CHINA EMPIRE
1385 Broadway Fl 21, New York, NY 10018-6022
Tel (212) 704-4800 *Founded/Ownrshp* 1920
Sales 174.7MM^E *EMP* 400
Accts Cohnreznick Llp New York New
SIC 2253 2389 2331 5137 5136 Hats & headwear, knit; Scarves & mufflers, knit; Handkerchiefs, except paper; T-shirts & tops, women's: made from purchased materials; Blouses, women's & juniors': made from purchased material; Scarves, women's & children's; Gloves, women's & children's; Scarves, men's & boys'; Gloves, men's & boys'; Hats & headwear, knit; Scarves & mufflers, knit; Handkerchiefs, except paper; T-shirts & tops, women's: made from purchased materials; Blouses, women's & juniors': made from purchased material; Scarves, women's & children's; Gloves, women's & children's; Scarves, men's & boys'; Gloves, men's & boys'
Ch: Peter Markson
**Pr:* Donald Oberfield
**Treas:* Martin J Kelly
IT Man: Abe Anteby
IT Man: AVI Sivan
IT Man: Lisa Valdespino
Snr Mgr: Michael Miller

D-U-N-S 09-898-3471
GCG FINANCIAL INC
3 Parkway N Ste 500, Deerfield, IL 60015-2567
Tel (847) 457-3000 *Founded/Ownrshp* 1975
Sales NA *EMP* 150
SIC 6411 8742 6211 Insurance agents; Financial consultant; Security brokers & dealers
Pr: Alan Levitz
**Ch Bd:* Robert Levitz
Ofcr: Charles Melka
Ofcr: Mark Pietch
**Ex VP:* David Levitz
**Ex VP:* Rick Loudenback
**Ex VP:* Mark Pietsch
**Ex VP:* Matt Schlaepfer
**Ex VP:* Michael Smith
VP: Lauren Barnard
VP: Phillip Battin
VP: Jim Berman
VP: Kristi Brull
VP: Arthur Chantler
VP: Dina Collins
VP: Brian Crane
VP: Pam Davis
VP: Bob Janson
VP: Joseph Jonas
VP: Michael Kesner
VP: Mike Kesner

D-U-N-S 62-636-8518
GCGC FAIR CORP
MCDONALD'S
44425 Airport Rd Ste 205, California, MD 20619-2040
Tel (301) 866-5401 *Founded/Ownrshp* 1991
Sales 25.4MM^E *EMP* 700
SIC 5812 Fast-food restaurant, chain; Fast-food restaurant, chain
Pr: Gerald Fair
**VP:* Charlene Fair

D-U-N-S 60-473-2482
GCH INTERNATIONAL INC
330 Boxley Ave, Louisville, KY 40209-1845
Tel (502) 636-1374 *Founded/Ownrshp* 2012
Sales 22.0MM *EMP* 97
SIC 3531 3444 Forestry related equipment; Sheet metalwork
CEO: John Thornton
CFO: Lisa Burden-Bendixen
VP: Haldun Turgay
Mktg Mgr: Pat Giacone
Sales Asso: James Chaney

GCI
See CORRECTIONAL INDUSTRIES GEORGIA ADMINISTRATION

D-U-N-S 83-811-8420
■ **GCI CABLE INC**
(*Suby of* GENERAL COMMUNICATION INC) ★
5151 Fairbanks St, Anchorage, AK 99503-7443
Tel (907) 265-5400 *Founded/Ownrshp* 1996
Sales 100.9MM^E *EMP* 250
SIC 4841 7375 4812 Cable television services; Information retrieval services; Radio telephone communication; Cable television services; Information retrieval services; Radio telephone communication
VP: Bruce L Broquet
**CEO:* Ronald A Duncan
**CFO:* John M Lowber
**Ex VP:* Riley Snell
VP: Gary Haynes

D-U-N-S 62-370-4731 IMP
■ **GCI COMMUNICATION CORP**
(*Suby of* GENERAL COMMUNICATION INC) ★
2550 Denali St Ste 1000, Anchorage, AK 99503-2751
Tel (907) 265-5600 *Founded/Ownrshp* 1990
Sales 343.0MM^E *EMP* 850
SIC 4813 4841 4812 1731 Local telephone communications; Long distance telephone communications; Cable & other pay television services; Radio telephone communication; Electrical work; Local telephone communications; Long distance telephone communications; Cable & other pay television services; Radio telephone communication; Electrical work
CEO: Ronald A Duncan
**CFO:* John M Lowber
**CFO:* Peter Pounds
**Ex VP:* Wilson Hughes
**Sr VP:* William Binkey
**Sr VP:* Richard P Dowling
**Sr VP:* Dana Tindall
VP: Gina R Borland
**VP:* Gregory F Chapados
**VP:* Gary Haynes
**VP:* Wilson Huges
**VP:* Paul E Landes
**VP:* Landes Paul
**VP:* Alfred Walker
Exec: Hughes Wilson

D-U-N-S 79-164-4136
GCI CONSTRUCTION LLC
25101 Chagrin Blvd, Beachwood, OH 44122-5643
Tel (919) 851-0661 *Founded/Ownrshp* 2007
Sales 25.6MM^E *EMP* 300
SIC 1522 1521 Multi-family dwelling construction; Single-family housing construction
Pr: Larry Goldberg

D-U-N-S 02-360-6488
GCI INC
(*Suby of* SWEATT CONSTRUCTION INC) ★
720 S Texaco Rd, Hobbs, NM 88240-8630
Tel (575) 393-3180 *Founded/Ownrshp* 1992
Sales 60.0MM *EMP* 11
SIC 1794 Excavation work; Excavation work
Pr: William J Sweatt
**Sec:* Johnathan L Shuman
**VP:* Kendall S Livingston

D-U-N-S 55-619-1260
■ GCI INC
(*Suby of* GENERAL DYNAMICS CORP) ★
11111 Sunset Hills Rd # 400, Reston, VA 20190-5374
Tel (703) 453-7700 *Founded/Ownrshp* 1989
Sales 65.2MM^E *EMP* 570^E
SIC 8748 Telecommunications consultant; Telecommunications consultant
Pr: Joseph V Duffy
**CFO:* Richard McDonald
**Treas:* David H Fogg
**VP:* Vincent S Antonacci
VP: James Moorhead

D-U-N-S 79-679-8841 IMP
GCI INC
875 Battery St Fl 1, San Francisco, CA 94111-1547
Tel (415) 978-2790 *Founded/Ownrshp* 1992
Sales 130.3MM *EMP* 48
Accts Johnston Gremaux & Rossi Llp
SIC 1542 Commercial & office buildings, renovation & repair; Commercial & office buildings, renovation & repair
Pr: James Jenkins
CFO: John Lowber
Sr VP: Paul E Fearer
Sr VP: Wilson G Hughes
Sr VP: William Kelley
**VP:* Peter D Goldsmith
**VP:* Jon Helman
VP Opers: E Iniguez

GCIT
See GLOUCESTER COUNTY VOCATIONAL-TECHNICAL SCHOOL DISTRICT

D-U-N-S 18-534-8547
GCJ ENTERPRISES INC
RITZ FOOD STORES
926 N Ferdon Blvd, Crestview, FL 32536-1706
Tel (850) 682-8337 *Founded/Ownrshp* 1992
Sales 23.5MM^E *EMP* 200
SIC 5411 5541 Grocery stores; Filling stations, gasoline; Grocery stores; Filling stations, gasoline
CEO: Gary C Jones
**Pr:* Richard Twitty
**VP:* Thomas M Lalor

GCL A
See GARDA CL ATLANTIC INC

GCL NW
See GARDA CL NORTHWEST INC

GCL SW
See GARDA CL SOUTHWEST INC

GCL W
See GARDA CL WEST INC

GCM
See GRAHAM CAPITAL MANAGEMENT LP

D-U-N-S 09-707-9552 IMP/EXP
GCM MEDICAL & OEM DIVISION INC
GLOBAL CONTRACT MANUFACTURING
(*Suby of* HI-TECH MANUFACTURING LLC) ★
1350 Atlantic St, Union City, CA 94587-2004
Tel (510) 475-0404 *Founded/Ownrshp* 2014
Sales 27.9MM^E *EMP* 78
SIC 3444 3541 Sheet metalwork; Machine tools, metal cutting type
Pr: Seanus Meaghr
Mfg Mgr: Greg Snyder
Opers Mgr: Walt Webster
Sales Exec: Peter Peng

D-U-N-S 03-851-8817
■ GCM NORTH AMERICAN AEROSPACE LLC
KLUNE AEROSPACE
(*Suby of* KLUNE INDUSTRIES INC) ★
21719 84th Ave S, Kent, WA 98032-1969
Tel (253) 872-7488 *Founded/Ownrshp* 2011
Sales 27.3MM^E *EMP* 96
SIC 3728 3812 3643 3444 Aircraft parts & equipment; Search & navigation equipment; Current-carrying wiring devices; Sheet metalwork; Aircraft parts & equipment; Search & navigation equipment; Current-carrying wiring devices; Sheet metalwork

D-U-N-S 00-923-9450
GCO INC
27750 Industrial Blvd, Hayward, CA 94545-4043
Tel (510) 786-3333 *Founded/Ownrshp* 1949
Sales 120.1MM^E *EMP* 200
SIC 5074 5087 Pipe & boiler covering; Pipes & fittings, plastic; Plumbing & heating valves; Firefighting equipment; Sprinkler systems; Pipe & boiler covering; Pipes & fittings, plastic; Plumbing & heating valves; Firefighting equipment; Sprinkler systems
Ch Bd: Michael H Groeniger
**Treas:* Beverly J Groeniger
**Ex VP:* Richard Alexander
**VP:* Richard Old
**VP:* James Wunsche
Brnch Mgr: Gary Spring
S&M/VP: Dick Alexander

D-U-N-S 82-862-5900
■ GCP REIT II
(*Suby of* GREEN COURTE PARTNERS LLC) ★
840 S Waukegan Rd Ste 222, Lake Forest, IL 60045-2619
Tel (847) 582-9400 *Founded/Ownrshp* 2007
Sales 38.6MM^E *EMP* 294^E
SIC 6798 Real estate investment trusts; Real estate investment trusts
Prin: Randall Rowe

GCR
See GOVERNMENT CONTRACTING RESOURCES INC

D-U-N-S 36-240-5250
GCR ACQUISITIONS LLC
(*Suby of* PARKS XANTERRA & RESORTS INC) ★
6312 S Fiddlers Green Cir, Greenwood Village, CO 80111-4943
Tel (303) 600-3400 *Founded/Ownrshp* 2007
Sales 32.3MM *EMP* 300
SIC 5812 4111 Fast food restaurants & stands; Passenger rail transportation; Fast food restaurants & stands; Passenger rail transportation
Pr: Andrew N Todd
Off Mgr: Jessica Knoll

D-U-N-S 02-101-9674
GCR INC
GREGORY C RIGAMER & ASSOCIATES
2021 Lakeshore Dr Ste 500, New Orleans, LA 70122-3529
Tel (504) 304-2500 *Founded/Ownrshp* 2011
Sales 32.8MM *EMP* 117
Accts Laporte Covington La
SIC 7379 8742 ; Management consulting services; ; Management consulting services
Pr: Michael W Flores
Founder: Gregory C Rigamer
Chf Mktg O: Phillip D Brodt
VP: Todd Bouillion
VP: Angele C Romig
VP: Angele Romig
Dir Bus: Blair Cox
Prgrm Mgr: Denis Bechac
Plng Mgr: Nathan Cataline
Plng Mgr: Robert Edgecombe
Plng Mgr: Dwight Norton
Board of Directors: James Andersen, Paul Caliento, Michael Flores, Joseph Posewick, Gregory Rigamer, Mathias Rumilly

D-U-N-S 00-194-7852
■ GCS SYSTEMS INC
(*Suby of* ECOLAB INC) ★
370 Wabasha St N, Saint Paul, MN 55102-1323
Tel (651) 293-2134 *Founded/Ownrshp* 1892, 2002
Sales 108.3MM^E *EMP* 1,000
SIC 5046 7699

D-U-N-S 03-107-7628
GCS&I INC
1055 Montlimar Dr, Mobile, AL 36609-1708
Tel (251) 694-7012 *Founded/Ownrshp* 2008
Sales 49.1MM^E *EMP* 125
SIC 5211 Lumber & other building materials; Home centers
Prin: Toni Scott

GCSAP
See TATA CHEMICALS SODA ASH PARTNERS

GCSC
See GREENCASTLE COMMUNITY SCHOOLS

GCSEC
See GRUNDY COUNTY SPECIAL EDUCATION CO-OPERATIVE

GCSIT SOLUTIONS
See GOVERNMENT COMPUTER SALES INC

GCT NEW YORK
See NEW YORK CONTAINER TERMINAL INC

D-U-N-S 00-189-7839
GCT SEMICONDUCTOR INC
2121 Ringwood Ave Ste A, San Jose, CA 95131-1741
Tel (408) 325-8300 *Founded/Ownrshp* 1998, 1999
Sales 22.3MM *EMP* 210
Accts Pricewaterhousecoopers Llp Sa
SIC 5065 Telecommunications consultant; Semiconductor devices
CEO: John Schlaefer
**Ch Bd:* Kyeong Ho Lee
**CFO:* Gene Kulzer
VP: Sung Djoe
VP: Patricia Kim
VP: Ginger Lee
**VP:* David Yoon
CTO: Stephen Gold

GCWA
See GULF COAST WATER AUTHORITY

D-U-N-S 05-324-2632 IMP/EXP
GCX CORP (CA)
3875 Cypress Dr, Petaluma, CA 94954-5635
Tel (707) 773-1100 *Founded/Ownrshp* 1971, 1998
Sales 97.2MM *EMP* 300^E
SIC 3429

D-U-N-S 02-432-0997
GD COPPER (USA) INC
COPPER AND COPPER TUBE
(*Suby of* GOLDEN DRAGON PRECISE COPPER TUBE GROUP INC.)
405 General Delivery Dr, Pine Hill, AL 36769
Tel (334) 637-0200 *Founded/Ownrshp* 2007
Sales 200.0MM *EMP* 300
SIC 3351 3999 Metal mining services; Copper & copper alloy pipe & tube; Atomizers, toiletry
Pr: Xuhui Zhang
**Pr:* Mingxu Chen
**Prin:* Ming Xu

D-U-N-S 06-843-0597
GD DENTAL SERVICES LLC
(*Suby of* LINDEN CAPITAL PARTNERS II LP) ★
951 Broken Sound Pkwy Nw, Boca Raton, FL 33487-3507
Tel (561) 999-9650 *Founded/Ownrshp* 2012
Sales NA *EMP* 335
SIC 6719 Investment holding companies, except banks; Investment holding companies, except banks

D-U-N-S 79-637-8859
GD HEIL INC
1031 Segovia Cir, Placentia, CA 92870-7137
Tel (818) 997-7022 *Founded/Ownrshp* 1992
Sales 28.9MM^E *EMP* 160
SIC 1795 Demolition, buildings & other structures; Demolition, buildings & other structures
CEO: James A Langford
**Pr:* Gary Heil
**VP:* Steve Mc Clain
Brnch Mgr: Carl Crave
Mktg Mgr: Courtney Heil

D-U-N-S 17-959-3397
GDA TECHNOLOGIES INC
(*Suby of* LARSEN AND TOUBRO LIMITED)
25 Metro Dr Ste 300, San Jose, CA 95110-1340
Tel (408) 753-1191 *Founded/Ownrshp* 2007
Sales 24.6MM^E *EMP* 300
SIC 8711 Electrical or electronic engineering; Electrical or electronic engineering
CEO: Isaac Sundarajan
**Ex VP:* Gopa Periyadan
VP: Prakppash Bare
**VP:* Gopakumar K Periyadan
**VP:* Ravi Thummarukudy
Sls Mgr: Sandeep Mohan Kumar

D-U-N-S 80-729-4541
GDB INTERNATIONAL INC
1 Home News Row, New Brunswick, NJ 08901-3601
Tel (732) 246-3001 *Founded/Ownrshp* 1993
Sales 117.6MM *EMP* 100
Accts Withum Smith & Brown Cpa
SIC 4783 5162 5111 5198 5093 2851 Plastics scrap; Nonferrous metals scrap; Paints; Printing & writing paper; Plastics materials & basic shapes; Packing & crating; Packing & crating; Plastics materials & basic shapes; Printing & writing paper; Paints; Plastics scrap; Nonferrous metals scrap; Paints & paint additives
CEO: Sanjeev Bagaria
**Pr:* Sunil Bagaria
Ex VP: Robert Tsai
Sr VP: Mani Palani
Sr VP: Howard Schamach
VP: Kyle Koziczkowski
VP: Mohammed Liaquat
VP: Francisco Suarez
Opers Mgr: Rowena Arevalo
Secur Mgr: Tyrone Dean
Secur Mgr: Marcus Messias

D-U-N-S 16-175-5678
GDC ACQUISITIONS LLC
4707 32nd Pl, Long Island City, NY 11101-2409
Tel (212) 594-8869 *Founded/Ownrshp* 2003
Sales 60.0MM *EMP* 175
SIC 5063 5021 1731 Electrical apparatus & equipment; Furniture; General electrical contractor; Electrical apparatus & equipment; Furniture; General electrical contractor
CEO: Courtney Dupree

D-U-N-S 05-253-2962 IMP
GDC ENTERPRISES INC
WAHOO DOCKS
1604 Athens Hwy, Gainesville, GA 30507-7306
Tel (678) 971-4448 *Founded/Ownrshp* 2002
Sales 33.7MM^E *EMP* 100
SIC 3448 Docks: prefabricated metal
Pr: Harold M Hawkins III
**CFO:* Tim G Osby
VP: Jon Bailey
Sls Dir: Wayne Hilton

GDC HOMES
See ACHEN-GARDNER INC

D-U-N-S 00-524-5873 IMP
GDC INC
G D C
815 Logan St, Goshen, IN 46528-3508
Tel (574) 533-3128 *Founded/Ownrshp* 1955
Sales 25.8MM^E *EMP* 310
SIC 3086 3069 2891 2869 2822 Plastics foam products; Medical & laboratory rubber sundries & related products; Rubber floor coverings, mats & wallcoverings; Rubber coated fabrics & clothing; Air-supported rubber structures; Adhesives & sealants; Industrial organic chemicals; Synthetic rubber
Pr: Loretta Miller
COO: Lonnie Abney
Prgrm Mgr: Cody Troeger
IT Man: Wes Miller
Opers Mgr: Judy Bronge
Opers Mgr: Leroy Cox
Sls Dir: Chris Miller

GDC IT SOLUTIONS
See GLOBAL DATA CONSULTANTS LLC

D-U-N-S 93-882-5940 IMP
GDC TECHNICS LTD
GORE COMPLETIONS
607 N Frank Luke Dr, San Antonio, TX 78226-2005
Tel (210) 496-5614 *Founded/Ownrshp* 1988
Sales 54.5MM^E *EMP* 100
SIC 1799 Renovation of aircraft interiors
Pt: Kathy Gore
CFO: Rick Burr
CFO: Stephen Pierce
Exec: Rick Penshorn
Prgrm Mgr: Joseph Barrett
Prgrm Mgr: Neil Beard
Prgrm Mgr: Tim Bohrer
Prgrm Mgr: Richard Francey
IT Man: Milton Ramirez
Opers Mgr: Racie Dimerson
Pgrm Dir: Tracy Bartos

D-U-N-S 96-890-9739
GDF SUEZ ENERGY DEVELOPMENT NA INC
(*Suby of* GDF SUEZ ENERGY INTERNATIONAL) ★
1990 Post Oak Blvd # 1900, Houston, TX 77056-3818
Tel (713) 636-0000 *Founded/Ownrshp* 2011
Sales 91.2MM^E *EMP* 150
SIC 4911 Electric services; Electric services
Pr: Herman Schopman
CFO: Geert Peeters
Ex VP: Paul J Cavicchi
Ex VP: Kelly McGrath
Ex VP: Jean Nassau
Sr VP: Karim Barbir
Sr VP: Bart Clark
Sr VP: Mike Thompson
VP: Jorge Alvarez
VP: Guy Braden
VP: Newton Houston
VP: Jay Wilgar

GDF SUEZ ENERGY INTERNATIONAL
See GDF SUEZ ENERGY NORTH AMERICA INC

D-U-N-S 05-444-7164 IMP
GDF SUEZ ENERGY NORTH AMERICA INC
GDF SUEZ ENERGY INTERNATIONAL
(*Suby of* ENGIE)
1990 Post Oak Blvd # 1900, Houston, TX 77056-3818
Tel (713) 636-0000 *Founded/Ownrshp* 1970
Sales 1.0MMM^E *EMP* 387
SIC 1311 8741 1629 Natural gas production; Industrial management; Power plant construction; Industrial plant construction; Natural gas production; Industrial management; Power plant construction; Industrial plant construction
Pr: Zin Smati
Pr: Duncan McCaig
**Pr:* Werner Schattner
**CFO:* Patrick Gaussent
**Treas:* Rachel Kilpatrick
Ex VP: Karim Barbir
Ex VP: Paul Cavicchi
Sr VP: Guy Braden
Sr VP: Francis Katulak
**Sr VP:* Robert Minter
VP: Gerald Depatoul
**VP:* Steven R Gavin
Exec: Susan White

D-U-N-S 09-966-8332
GDF SUEZ ENERGY RESOURCES NA INC
(*Suby of* GDF SUEZ ENERGY INTERNATIONAL) ★
1990 Post Oak Blvd # 1900, Houston, TX 77056-3818
Tel (713) 636-0000 *Founded/Ownrshp* 2001
Sales 31.3MM^E *EMP* 190
SIC 8731 4911 Energy research; Generation, electric power; Energy research; Generation, electric power
Pr: Herman Schopman
Ofcr: Jim Hammelman
Ofcr: Naveen Rabie
VP: Hart Baker
VP: Alain Bechtel
VP: Jay Bell
VP: John Henderson
VP: Vikram Kulkarni
VP: Graham Leith
VP: Helen Lo
VP: Michael Pinion
VP: Danielle R Wilks

D-U-N-S 19-671-4414 IMP
GDF SUEZ GAS NA LLC
(*Suby of* GDF SUEZ ENERGY INTERNATIONAL) ★
1990 Post Oak Blvd # 1900, Houston, TX 77056-3818
Tel (713) 636-0000 *Founded/Ownrshp* 2007
Sales 39.3MM^E *EMP* 85
SIC 4924 Natural gas distribution; Natural gas distribution
CEO: Zin Smati
Pr: Chip Leckey
**CFO:* Patrick Gaussent
Sr VP: Rudy Adamiak
VP: Karthik Rajan
Dir IT: Sean McClure

D-U-N-S 03-908-7379
GDG HOLDINGS INC
2601 American Blvd E, Minneapolis, MN 55425-1321
Tel (952) 854-2044 *Founded/Ownrshp* 1975
Sales 450.1MM^E *EMP* 850^E
SIC 5084 Engines & transportation equipment; Engines & transportation equipment
CEO: Jeff Caswell
**CEO:* Gordon D Galarneau
**Sec:* Larry Schwartz
IT Man: Dave Walch
Netwrk Mgr: Scott Frasier

GDGSOC
See GENERAL DYNAMICS GOVERNMENT SYSTEMS OVERSEAS CORP

D-U-N-S 10-133-7660
GDH CONSULTING INC
4200 E Skelly Dr Ste 650, Tulsa, OK 74135-3244
Tel (918) 392-1600 *Founded/Ownrshp* 2001
Sales 97.8MM^E *EMP* 450
SIC 7371 7361 7379 Computer software systems analysis & design, custom; Employment agencies; Computer related consulting services; Computer software systems analysis & design, custom; Employment agencies; Computer related consulting services
CEO: Gerald Hurley
**Pr:* Charles L Snell Jr
**VP:* Steven Smith
Brnch Mgr: Marc Berlin

D-U-N-S 07-930-0867
GDI FACILITY SERVICES INC
(*Suby of* GDI OMNI INC) ★
24300 Southfield Rd # 220, Southfield, MI 48075-2820
Tel (248) 483-3170 *Founded/Ownrshp* 2012
Sales 7.0MM^E *EMP* 1,007^E
SIC 7349 Building maintenance services; Janitorial service, contract basis
Pr: Claude Bigras

D-U-N-S 07-876-5442
GDI OMNI INC
(*Suby of* 9268-4935 QUEBEC INC)
24300 Southfield Rd # 220, Southfield, MI 48075-2820
Tel (248) 483-3170 *Founded/Ownrshp* 2012
Sales 38.7MM^E *EMP* 1,150
SIC 7349 Building maintenance services; Janitorial service, contract basis; Building maintenance services; Janitorial service, contract basis
CEO: Ahmad Boomrod
Ex VP: Hassan Kadouh

D-U-N-S 07-948-4041
GDI SERVICES INC
780 5th Ave Ste 115, King of Prussia, PA 19406-4065
Tel (610) 584-0888 Founded/Ownrshp 2014
Sales 41.0MM^E EMP 1,700
SIC 7349 Building maintenance services; Building & office cleaning services; Janitorial service, contract basis; Building maintenance services; Building & office cleaning services; Janitorial service, contract basis
Pr: Peter Criville
*VP: George Mick

D-U-N-S 96-695-3940
GDIC GROUP LLC
1300 E 9th St Fl 20, Cleveland, OH 44114-1501
Tel (330) 468-0700 Founded/Ownrshp 2009
Sales 59.4MM^E EMP 210^E
SIC 6719 Personal holding companies, except banks; Personal holding companies, except banks
Pr: Steve White

GDIT
See GENERAL DYNAMICS INFORMATION TECHNOLOGY INC

D-U-N-S 16-768-1857
GDK DEVELOPMENT INC
BURGER KING
45 N 4th St, Shamokin, PA 17872-5205
Tel (570) 648-8634 Founded/Ownrshp 1982
Sales 14.9MM^E EMP 300
SIC 5812 Fast-food restaurant, chain; Fast-food restaurant, chain
Pr: Eugene Welsh Jr
*Sec: Denise Welsh

D-U-N-S 93-043-9047
GDK LEASING INC
AMPLEX
13100 34th St N, Clearwater, FL 33762-4246
Tel (727) 572-4546 Founded/Ownrshp 1985
Sales 38.4MM^E EMP 70
SIC 5193 Flowers & florists' supplies
Pr: George D Kostilnik
*VP: Tami McKnight

GDLS
See GENERAL DYNAMICS LAND SYSTEMS INC

GDM ELECTRONIC & MEDICAL
See G D M ELECTRONIC ASSEMBLY INC

D-U-N-S 15-101-2085
GDS ASSOCIATES INC
1850 Parkway Pl Se # 800, Marietta, GA 30067-8260
Tel (770) 425-8100 Founded/Ownrshp 1986
Sales 32.3MM EMP 170
Accts Frazier & Deeter Llc
SIC 8711 Consulting engineer; Consulting engineer
CEO: Richard F Spellman
*Pr: Daniel Heller
*Pr: William Jacobs Jr
*Pr: Jack Madden
Pr: Terry Myers
*Pr: J Steven Shurbutt
*Pr: Robert Smith
COO: James McGaughy
*CFO: David M Brian
VP: David Brian
*VP: James W Daniel
*VP: Kevin Mara
Board of Directors: Robert M Gross

GDS ENGINEERS
See SNC-LAVALIN ENGINEERS & CONSTRUCTORS INC

D-U-N-S 95-603-9015
GDS INTERNATIONAL LLC
GLOBAL DRILLING SUPPORT
9841 Windmill Park Ln, Houston, TX 77064-3300
Tel (713) 623-1449 Founded/Ownrshp 2008
Sales 32.2MM^E EMP 26
SIC 1389 Oil & gas wells: building, repairing & dismantling
Dir QC: Carlos Ramirez
Sls Mgr: Les Stewart

D-U-N-S 00-340-4308
GDT PROPERTIES INC (PA)
CNSLTD ELCTRCL DSTRIBUTOR
(Suby of C E D) ★
312 N 8th St, Lebanon, PA 17046-4717
Tel (717) 273-4514 Founded/Ownrshp 1935, 2011
Sales 173.6MM^E EMP 254
SIC 5063 Electrical supplies; Electrical supplies
Pr: G David Thomas
*Pr: Mark D Bucci
*Treas: John C Rodman
*VP: Richard A Firth
*VP: Stephen G Foley
*VP: John P Hagan II
*VP: Michael Klahr

GE
See G E REINSURANCE CORP

GE
See IDX SYSTEMS CORP

GE
See USA INSTRUMENTS INC

GE AERO ENERGY PRODUCTS
See GE ENERGY MANUFACTURING INC

D-U-N-S 01-663-5687 IMP
■ **GE AIRCRAFT ENGINES HOLDINGS INC**
(Suby of GENERAL ELECTRIC CO) ★
1 Neumann Way, Cincinnati, OH 45215-1915
Tel (513) 243-8251 Founded/Ownrshp 1992
Sales 340.6MM^E EMP 1,335
SIC 7699

D-U-N-S 12-140-6151 IMP
■ **GE ANALYTICAL INSTRUMENTS INC**
(Suby of GENERAL ELECTRIC CO) ★
6060 Spine Rd, Boulder, CO 80301-3323
Tel (303) 444-2009 Founded/Ownrshp 2005
Sales 30.3MM^E EMP 200
SIC 3823 3826 5049 Industrial instrmnts msrmnt display/control process variable; Laser scientific & engineering instruments; Scientific instruments; Industrial instrmnts msrmnt display/control process variable; Laser scientific & engineering instruments; Scientific instruments
CEO: David Gellison
*CFO: Tom Wallace
*VP: Wayne Brothers
*VP: Carmon Dillard
*VP: Steve Poirier
Sfty Mgr: Cathy West
Ql Cn Mgr: Damon Ford
Sales Exec: Frank Silvester
VP Sls: Carl Craig
Sls Mgr: Tom Daniels
Snr Mgr: David Alexander

GE APPLIANCE DIV
See ROPER CORP

D-U-N-S 18-003-1908
■ **GE ASSET MANAGEMENT INC**
GE INVESTMENTS
(Suby of GENERAL ELECTRIC CO) ★
1600 Summer St Ste 3, Stamford, CT 06905-5125
Tel (203) 326-2300 Founded/Ownrshp 1980
Sales 566.8MM^E EMP 2,200
SIC 6282 Investment advisory service; Investment advisory service
Pr: Dmitri Stockton
VP: Ben Ross
VP: Anthony Sirabella
Genl Mgr: Ralph R Layman
Dir IT: Terence Finn
IT Man: John Rossi

D-U-N-S 18-621-0134
■ **GE AUTO & HOME ASSURANCE CO**
(Suby of 21ST CENTURY CENTENNIAL INSURANCE CO) ★
500 Virginia Dr, Fort Washington, PA 19034-2707
Tel (800) 523-4040 Founded/Ownrshp 1986
Sales NA EMP 533^E
SIC 6411 Life insurance agents
Ch Bd: Oliver Lincoln Patrell
*Pr: Henry Harrison Wulsin
*CFO: Stephen Thomas List
*Treas: David Kohlman Sherman
*VP: Barbara Anne Herrman

D-U-N-S 87-994-0666 IMP
■ **GE AVIATION MUSKEGON**
(Suby of GE AIRCRAFT ENGINES HOLDINGS INC) ★
2034 Latimer Dr, Muskegon, MI 49442-6232
Tel (231) 777-2685 Founded/Ownrshp 1997
Sales 141.0MM^E EMP 600
SIC 3724 Turbines, aircraft type; Turbines, aircraft type
Pr: David Yacavone
Dir IT: Bennett Bassette
Dir IT: Mark Cybulski
IT Man: Bob McFalls
Pgrm Dir: John Friedli
Snr Mgr: Mark Anderson

D-U-N-S 00-424-4851 IMP
GE AVIATION SYSTEMS LLC
TDI
6800 Poe Ave, Dayton, OH 45414-2530
Tel (937) 898-9600 Founded/Ownrshp 1987, 2000
Sales 53.8MM^E EMP 150
SIC 3511 3724 Turbines & turbine generator sets & parts; Aircraft engines & engine parts; Turbines & turbine generator sets & parts; Aircraft engines & engine parts
QC Dir: Gail Boes

D-U-N-S 10-720-6559 IMP
■ **GE AVIATION SYSTEMS LLC**
(Suby of GENERAL ELECTRIC CO) ★
1 Neumann Way, Cincinnati, OH 45215-1915
Tel (513) 243-2000 Founded/Ownrshp 2006
Sales NA EMP 3,573
SIC 3812 Aircraft control systems, electronic; Aircraft control systems, electronic
Pr: R F Ehr
*Pr: J B Hines
Treas: David Martin
*Ex VP: Peter Page
VP: Charles P Blankenship Jr
Software D: Rebecca Seaberg
Sls Dir: Kent Lehmann
Snr Mgr: Asha Belarski
Snr Mgr: Kelly Townsley

D-U-N-S 00-972-2265 IMP/EXP
■ **GE BETZ INC**
GE WATER & PROCESS TECH
(Suby of GENERAL ELECTRIC CO) ★
4636 Somerton Rd, Trevose, PA 19053-6742
Tel (215) 355-3300 Founded/Ownrshp 2002
Sales 958.5MM^E EMP 4,000
SIC 2899 3826 5084 3823 Water treating compounds; Water testing apparatus; Pumps & pumping equipment; Industrial instrmnts msrmnt display/control process variable; Water treating compounds; Water testing apparatus; Pumps & pumping equipment; Industrial instrmnts msrmnt display/control process variable
Pr: Heiner Markhoff
*CEO: William R Cook
*Treas: Monica A Oconnor
*Treas: R D Voncanon
Chf Mktg O: Steve Watzeck
VP: Craig Hobkirk
IT Man: Robert Marsicano
Snr Mgr: Gary Kralik

D-U-N-S 06-902-8637
■ **GE BETZ INTERNATIONAL INC**
(Suby of GE BETZ INC) ★
4636 Somerton Rd, Langhorne, PA 19053-6742
Tel (215) 957-2200 Founded/Ownrshp 2002
Sales 23.8MM^E EMP 190
SIC 2899 Water treating compounds; Water treating compounds
Pr: Heinrich Markhoff
*VP: William W Booth

GE CAPITAL AVIATION SERVICES
See GECAS ASSET MANAGEMENT SERVICES INC

D-U-N-S 78-556-4688
■ **GE CAPITAL AVIATION SERVICES LLC**
GECAS
(Suby of GENERAL ELECTRIC CAPITAL CORP) ★
777 Long Ridge Rd, Stamford, CT 06902-1247
Tel (203) 585-2700 Founded/Ownrshp 1993
Sales 36.5MM^E EMP 500^E
SIC 7363 Pilot service, aviation; Pilot service, aviation
CEO: Norman C T Liu
Ofcr: Mark Malec
Ex VP: Jim Burke
*Ex VP: Sean Flannery
*Ex VP: Diarmuid Hogan
*Ex VP: Ted Kearns
*Ex VP: John Ludden
Sr VP: Greg Conlon
Sr VP: Liam Creaven
Sr VP: Gilberto Peralta
Sr VP: Roger Welaratne
VP: John Alexander
VP: Virginia Connolly
VP: Chris Corcino
VP: Jim Davis
VP: Ken Franzman
VP: Jeff Glaus
VP: Peter Hasslund
VP: Thomas McCauley
VP: Regina Rokosky
VP: Brian Sleigh

D-U-N-S 80-472-6552
■ **GE CAPITAL FINANCIAL INC**
(Suby of GENERAL ELECTRIC CAPITAL CORP) ★
170 W Election Rd Ste 125, Draper, UT 84020-6425
Tel (801) 816-4778 Founded/Ownrshp 1990
Sales NA EMP 700
SIC 6159 Loan institutions, general & industrial; Loan institutions, general & industrial
Ch Bd: Jeff Dye
*CFO: Brent Wallace
VP: Frank Willard III
IT Man: Mike Deboer

D-U-N-S 03-953-9713
■ **GE CAPITAL FRANCHISE FINANCE CORP**
(Suby of GENERAL ELECTRIC CAPITAL CORP) ★
8377 E Hartford Dr # 200, Scottsdale, AZ 85255-5687
Tel (480) 585-4500 Founded/Ownrshp 2001
Sales 34.0MM^E EMP 180^E
SIC 6512 Nonresidential building operators
CEO: Agustin Carcoba
*Ch Bd: Morton H Fleischer
Pr: Roel Longoria
Pr: Gary Naquin
*CFO: Max Axler
CFO: John R Barravecchia
*CFO: James Richards
Bd of Dir: Paul Bossidy
Bd of Dir: Thomas Fanelli
Bd of Dir: Christopher Jacob
*Ex VP: Dennis L Ruben
Ex VP: Dave Russell
Ex VP: Stephen Schmilz
*Ex VP: Stephen G Schmitz
Sr VP: Scott Andrews
*Sr VP: Catherine F Long
Sr VP: Jon K Taylor
VP: Shelly R Core
VP: R Scott Cowan
VP: Patrick Feltes
VP: Andrew Kent
Board of Directors: Willie R Barnes, Kelvin L Davis, Kathleen H Lucier, Dennis E Mitchem, Louis P Neeb, Kenneth B Roath, Casey J Sylla, Christopher H Volk, Shelby Yastro

D-U-N-S 15-995-3140
■ **GE CAPITAL INTERNATIONAL HOLDINGS CORP**
(Suby of GENERAL ELECTRIC CAPITAL SERVICES INC) ★
260 Long Ridge Rd, Stamford, CT 06927-1600
Tel (203) 357-4000 Founded/Ownrshp 1994
Sales 703.0MM^E EMP 10,000^E
SIC 6719 Investment holding companies, except banks; Investment holding companies, except banks
CEO: Mike Neil
Prgrm Mgr: Helen Miloslavsky
IT Man: Cathy Murphy

D-U-N-S 60-302-8325
■ **GE CAPITAL MONTGOMERY WARD**
(Suby of GENERAL ELECTRIC CAPITAL CORP) ★
3135 Easton Tpke, Stamford, CT 06927-0001
Tel (203) 357-4000 Founded/Ownrshp 1988
Sales NA EMP 2,300
SIC 6141 Consumer finance companies; Consumer finance companies
Pr: Marc Sheinbaum
V Ch: Suzanne Thomas
Sr VP: Eric Dull
VP: Charles M Crabtree
VP: Maria Dipietro
VP: Mike McMahon
VP: Joanne Stewart
Dir Risk M: William Strittmatter
Mng Dir: Todd Jones
Mng Dir: Steve Poulin

D-U-N-S 02-036-1697 IMP
■ **GE COMMERCIAL DISTRIBUTION FINANCE CORP**
(Suby of GENERAL ELECTRIC CAPITAL CORP) ★
5595 Trillium Blvd, Hoffman Estates, IL 60192-3405
Tel (847) 747-6800 Founded/Ownrshp 2002
Sales NA EMP 1,475
SIC 6153 6159 6141 Mercantile financing; Automobile finance leasing; Finance leasing, vehicles: except automobiles & trucks; Machinery & equipment finance leasing; Personal credit institutions; Mercantile financing; Automobile finance leasing; Finance leasing, vehicles: except automobiles & trucks; Machinery & equipment finance leasing; Personal credit institutions
Pr: Robert M Martin
Pr: Dan Long
*Pr: Geoffrey Lyon
Treas: W Steven Culp
Sr VP: P Frank Limbaugh
Sr VP: Richard L Shirley
VP: James Berry
VP: Timothy Bowen
VP: Leonard F Buchan
VP: Thomas J Grathwohl
VP: Richard M Hinton
VP: James J Keinze
VP: John F Kelly
VP: Ronald L Kozminske
VP: Dennis L V An Leeuwen
VP: Stephen R Leskovsky
VP: Stephen C Monahan
VP: Pat Natale
VP: James M Nolan
VP: Paul R Puma
VP: James D Russell

D-U-N-S 17-072-7304
■ **GE CONSUMER CORP**
G E APPLIANCES
(Suby of GENERAL ELECTRIC CAPITAL CORP) ★
140 Whittington Pkwy, Louisville, KY 40222-4930
Tel (203) 373-2211 Founded/Ownrshp 2004
Sales 27.1MM^E EMP 234^E
SIC 7389 Personal service agents, brokers & bureaus
CEO: Charles Blankenship

D-U-N-S 36-154-9657
■ **GE CONSUMER FINANCE INC**
GE MONEY
(Suby of GENERAL ELECTRIC CO) ★
777 Long Ridge Rd, Stamford, CT 06902-1247
Tel (203) 921-1443 Founded/Ownrshp 2006
Sales 247.7MM^E EMP 11,000^E
SIC 8742 Financial consultant
Prin: Mark Begor
*Pr: Margaret Keane
Pr: Deepak Luthra
Ofcr: Jane Wexton
Sr VP: Mike Macchia
VP: George Awad
VP: John Baraldi
VP: Diane Barone
VP: David Beebe
VP: Susan Bishop
VP: Dan Borchers
VP: Gautam Borooah
VP: David Caruso
VP: Donovan Goertzen
VP: Bob Rendine
VP: Bart Schaller
VP: Saby Sengupta
VP: Pete Tosches
VP Bus Dev: Steve Apesos
Comm Man: Mariane Ceballo

GE CRITICAL POWER
See LINEAGE POWER HOLDINGS INC

D-U-N-S 60-387-1083 IMP/EXP
■ **GE DRIVES & CONTROLS INC**
(Suby of GENERAL ELECTRIC CO) ★
1501 Roanoke Blvd, Salem, VA 24153-6422
Tel (540) 387-7000 Founded/Ownrshp 1955
Sales 122.1MM^E EMP 900
SIC 3612 Power transformers, electric; Power transformers, electric
Pr: Steven S Roy
Genl Mgr: Richard Rafalik
Dir IT: Laura Luchsinger

GE ENERGY
See GE OIL & GAS COMPRESSION SYSTEMS LLC

GE ENERGY
See MOTECH AMERICAS LLC

GE ENERGY
See BENTLY NEVADA INC

GE ENERGY
See GE PACKAGED POWER LP

D-U-N-S 06-020-4595 IMP
GE ENERGY
1 River Rd, Schenectady, NY 12305-2500
Tel (518) 385-2211 Founded/Ownrshp 2010
Sales 77.3MM^E EMP 296^E
SIC 3621 Electric motor & generator parts
Opers Mgr: Zachary Dorfman
Opers Mgr: Anthony Fiorenza
Sls Dir: Mike Joseph
Snr Mgr: Siva Chockalingam
Snr Mgr: John Mahar

D-U-N-S 16-278-4735
■ **GE ENERGY FINANCIAL SERVICES INC**
(Suby of GENERAL ELECTRIC CAPITAL CORP) ★
800 Long Ridge Rd, Stamford, CT 06902-1227
Tel (203) 357-6400 Founded/Ownrshp 2003
Sales NA EMP 284
SIC 6153 Working capital financing; Working capital financing
CEO: David Nason
*Pr: John A Urquhart
Sr VP: Vimal Chauhan
Sr VP: Joe Galan
Sr VP: Ankur Mathur
VP: Steve Taub
VP: Hagai Zaifman
Mng Dir: Gerald Friel
Mng Dir: Christopher Kratky
Mng Dir: Rink Smith

D-U-N-S 10-283-2131 IMP
GE ENERGY MANAGEMENT SERVICES INC
(*Suby of* GRID SOLUTIONS (US) LLC) ★
4200 Wildwood Pkwy, Atlanta, GA 30339-8402
Tel (678) 844-6000 *Founded/Ownrshp* 2002
Sales 2.0MMM^E *EMP* 4,008
SIC 4911 Electric services; Electric services
CEO: Mark Begor
**CFO:* Kenneth Schweer
Ofcr: Brian West
VP: Victor Abate
VP: Barbara A Cameron
VP: Happy R Pekins
VP: Keith Stentiford
Mng Dir: Robert Balletti
Mng Dir: Antti Kotisaari
Mng Dir: Anton Kubler
Prgrm Mgr: Brian Week

D-U-N-S 01-388-7554 IMP
■ **GE ENERGY MANUFACTURING INC**
GE AERO ENERGY PRODUCTS
(*Suby of* GENERAL ELECTRIC CO) ★
1333 West Loop S Ste 700, Houston, TX 77027-9117
Tel (713) 803-0900 *Founded/Ownrshp* 1998
Sales 1.5MMM^E *EMP* 3,800
SIC 3621 3568 5084 Power generators; Power transmission equipment; Power plant machinery; Power generators; Power transmission equipment; Power plant machinery
Pr: Charles Blakenship
**CFO:* Richard Kasson

GE ENERGY OILFIELD TECHNOLOGY
See REUTER-STOKES INC

D-U-N-S 03-875-0035 IMP/EXP
■ **GE ENERGY PARTS INC**
(*Suby of* GENERAL ELECTRIC CO) ★
4200 Wildwood Pkwy, Atlanta, GA 30339-8402
Tel (678) 844-6000 *Founded/Ownrshp* 1998
Sales 285.7MM^E *EMP* 500^E
SIC 5065 3612 Electronic parts & equipment; Autotransformers, electric (power transformers); Electronic parts & equipment; Autotransformers, electric (power transformers)
Pr: Karl Fessenden
COO: Ann McWhorter
Treas: Charles H Coffin
Treas: Kristopher McBright
VP: Stephanie Mains
VP: Margaret Morton
Snr Mgr: Martina Streiter

D-U-N-S 62-385-2030 IMP
■ **GE ENERGY POWER CONVERSION USA INC**
CONVERTEAM
(*Suby of* GENERAL ELECTRIC CO) ★
610 Epsilon Dr, Pittsburgh, PA 15238-2808
Tel (412) 967-0765 *Founded/Ownrshp* 2011
Sales 93.0MM^E *EMP* 325^E
SIC 3629 Power conversion units, a.c. to d.c.: static-electric; Power conversion units, a.c. to d.c.: static-electric
CEO: Joe Mastrangelo
**Pr:* Michael Archibald
COO: Garry Rauscher
CFO: Jane Liscio
**Treas:* Donald Grau
Mng Dir: Jim Morrison
Sls&Mrk Ex: Timothy Barnhart
Snr Mgr: Ian Davies
Board of Directors: Joseph Mastrangelo Theirry

D-U-N-S 11-845-3195 IMP
■ **GE ENGINE SERVICES - MCALLEN L P**
MCALLEN P&RS SERVICE CENTER
(*Suby of* GE AVIATION SYSTEMS LLC) ★
6200 S 42nd St, McAllen, TX 78503-8856
Tel (956) 971-5200 *Founded/Ownrshp* 1997
Sales 92.3MM^E *EMP* 575
SIC 3724 Aircraft engines & engine parts; Aircraft engines & engine parts
Genl Mgr: Daniel Campos

D-U-N-S 01-600-4702 IMP/EXP
■ **GE ENGINE SERVICES LLC**
(*Suby of* GENERAL ELECTRIC CO) ★
1 Neumann Way, Cincinnati, OH 45215-1915
Tel (513) 243-2000 *Founded/Ownrshp* 1997
Sales 460.5MM^E *EMP* 11,000
SIC 7699

D-U-N-S 07-858-0155 EXP
GE FAIRCHILD MINING EQUIPMENT
200 Fairchild Ln, Glen Lyn, VA 24093-3530
Tel (540) 921-8000 *Founded/Ownrshp* 2012
Sales 71.3MM^E *EMP* 271^E
SIC 3532 3535 Mining machinery; Conveyors & conveying equipment
Prin: Jack Fairchild
Ql Cn Mgr: Dewey Sibold
Snr Mgr: Kenneth Mosley

D-U-N-S 03-207-0364
■ **GE FINANCIAL ASSURANCE HOLDINGS INC**
(*Suby of* GENERAL ELECTRIC CAPITAL SERVICES INC) ★
6604 W Broad St, Richmond, VA 23230-1702
Tel (804) 281-6000 *Founded/Ownrshp* 2001
Sales NA *EMP* 6,250
SIC 6311 Life insurance; Life insurance carriers; Life insurance; Life insurance carriers
Ch Bd: Michael Fraizer
Sr VP: Michael S Laming
Sr VP: Kevin Schneider

GE FLEET SERVICES
See GELCO CORP

D-U-N-S 79-075-4167
GE FOUNDATION
3135 Easton Tpke, Fairfield, CT 06828-0002
Tel (203) 373-3216 *Founded/Ownrshp* 2013
Sales 132.8MM *EMP* 50^E
SIC 6722 Management investment, open-end; Management investment, open-end
Pr: Deb Elam
Dir Risk M: Derrick Ramsey
Dir Lab: Ravikanth Malladi
Admn Mgr: Andy Day
Dist Mgr: Ron Spielman
CIO: Tony Ross
CTO: Jeff Rademaekers
Dir IT: Sandesh Lal
Counsel: Joseph Noga
Counsel: Christine S Ricci
Counsel: Tony Walsh

GE FUNDING GROUP
See GIANNINO ENTERPRISES LLC

D-U-N-S 96-549-3591 IMP
■ **GE GAS TURBINES (GREENVILLE) LLC**
(*Suby of* GENERAL ELECTRIC CO) ★
300 Garlington Rd, Greenville, SC 29615-4614
Tel (864) 675-5866 *Founded/Ownrshp* 1999
Sales 32.9MM^E *EMP* 109^E
SIC 3511 Turbines & turbine generator sets
CEO: Steven Zwolinski
CIO: Gabor Olah
Plnt Mgr: William Sandera
Snr Mgr: Stephen Peck

D-U-N-S 05-081-2622 IMP
■ **GE GENERATORS (PENSACOLA) LLC**
G E GENERATORS
(*Suby of* GENERAL ELECTRIC CO) ★
8301 Scenic Hwy, Pensacola, FL 32514-7810
Tel (850) 474-4011 *Founded/Ownrshp* 2000
Sales 36.9MM^E *EMP* 200^E
SIC 3621 Power generators; Power generators
Snr Mgr: Teneeka Bass
Snr Mgr: Richard Bolden

GE GLOBAL EXCHANGE SERVICES
See GXS INC

D-U-N-S 07-986-6942
■ **GE GRID SOLUTIONS LLC**
(*Suby of* GENERAL ELECTRIC CO) ★
4200 Wildwood Pkwy, Atlanta, GA 30339-8402
Tel (877) 605-6777 *Founded/Ownrshp* 2015
Sales 1.0MMM *EMP* 900^E
SIC 3612 Transformers, except electric
Pr: John Lavelle

GE HEALTHCARE
See MEDI-PHYSICS INC

D-U-N-S 02-539-4172
■ **GE HEALTHCARE**
MEMBRANE SEPARATION GROUP
(*Suby of* GE HEALTHCARE BIO-SCIENCES CORP) ★
14 Walkup Dr, Westborough, MA 01581-1019
Tel (508) 366-1876 *Founded/Ownrshp* 2002
Sales 32.1MM^E *EMP* 130
Accts Rodman & Rodman
SIC 2836 2833 8731 8733 Culture media; Organic medicinal chemicals: bulk, uncompounded; Commercial research laboratory; Research institute; Culture media; Organic medicinal chemicals: bulk, uncompounded; Commercial research laboratory; Research institute
CEO: John Dineen
Pr: Attila Herczeg
Pr: Mike Swinford
CEO: Tom Gentile
Sls Mgr: Garry Ferency
Board of Directors: Mordechai Wiesller

D-U-N-S 07-866-9565
■ **GE HEALTHCARE**
(*Suby of* GENERAL ELECTRIC CO) ★
8200 W Tower Ave, Milwaukee, WI 53223-3219
Tel (414) 355-5000 *Founded/Ownrshp* 2012
Sales 42.4MM^E *EMP* 64^E
SIC 5047 Medical equipment & supplies
Prin: Melvin Newman
Sys Mgr: Howard Anstedt
Snr Mgr: Traci Bartolomei
Snr Mgr: Vivek Kapoor

D-U-N-S 80-978-5715 IMP
■ **GE HEALTHCARE**
GE MEDICAL SYSTEMS INFO TECH
(*Suby of* GE MEDICAL SYSTEMS INFORMATION TECHNOLOGIES INC) ★
3000 N Grandview Blvd, Waukesha, WI 53188-1615
Tel (262) 544-3011 *Founded/Ownrshp* 2008
Sales 166.4MM^E *EMP* 173^E
SIC 5047 Hospital equipment & furniture
VP: James Corrigan
VP: Michael Harsh
Exec: Kenneth Denison
Exec: Nancy Techel
Prgrm Mgr: Shreejay Mehta
Prgrm Mgr: Sudeep Nath
Prgrm Mgr: Bob Romnek
Genl Mgr: Paul Anderson
Genl Mgr: Agnes Berzsenyi
Genl Mgr: Tony Holland
Genl Mgr: Sandra Palbiski

D-U-N-S 01-165-8242
■ **GE HEALTHCARE BIO-SCIENCES CORP**
GE HEALTHCARE LIFE SCIENCES
(*Suby of* GE HEALTHCARE LIMITED)
350 Campus Dr, Marlborough, MA 01752-3082
Tel (800) 526-3593 *Founded/Ownrshp* 1997
Sales 932.4MM^E *EMP* 3,955
SIC 5122 Pharmaceuticals; Pharmaceuticals
CEO: Joseph M Hogan
**CEO:* Kieran Murphy
**CFO:* Henry Lyons
**Ex VP:* John Lynch
**Ex VP:* Mark Vachon
Sr VP: Anders Felt
VP: Glenn Melrose
**VP:* Andrew Rackear
Dir Rx: Rinsi Chacko
Prgrm Mgr: Benjamin Lhotka
Opers Mgr: Terry Taylor

D-U-N-S 14-475-6827
■ **GE HEALTHCARE FINANCIAL SERVICES INC**
(*Suby of* CAPITAL ONE NATIONAL ASSOCIATION) ★
500 W Monroe St Fl 19, Chicago, IL 60661-3759
Tel (312) 697-3999 *Founded/Ownrshp* 2015
Sales NA *EMP* 900
SIC 6141 Personal credit institutions; Personal credit institutions
Pr: Darren Alcus
VP: Jeremy Miller
Genl Mgr: Darren Kowalske

D-U-N-S 79-453-7043 IMP
■ **GE HEALTHCARE HOLDINGS INC**
(*Suby of* GE HEALTHCARE LIMITED)
3350 N Ridge Ave, Arlington Heights, IL 60004-1412
Tel (847) 398-8400 *Founded/Ownrshp* 1968
Sales 111.5MM^E *EMP* 1,498
SIC 2835 2833 5169 5122 In vitro & in vivo diagnostic substances; Radioactive diagnostic substances; Medicinals & botanicals; Chemicals & allied products; Medicinals & botanicals; In vitro & in vivo diagnostic substances; Radioactive diagnostic substances; Medicinals & botanicals; Chemicals & allied products; Medicinals & botanicals
Pr: Daniel Peters
**Ex VP:* William Clarke MD
VP: Russel P Mayer
VP: J E Reller
VP: Jack Waterman
QA Dir: Lori Sekera
Dir IT: Chris Vincent
VP Mktg: Jean-Michel Cossery
Board of Directors: W M Castell, W D Davies, R E Long

D-U-N-S 05-304-6579 IMP
■ **GE HEALTHCARE INC**
(*Suby of* GE HEALTHCARE LIMITED)
350 Campus Dr, Marlborough, MA 01752-3082
Tel (609) 514-6000 *Founded/Ownrshp* 1968
Sales 1.2MMM^E *EMP* 1,400
SIC 5122 2833 Medicinals & botanicals; Medicinals & botanicals; Medicinals & botanicals; Medicinals & botanicals
Pr: Jeffrey Freedman
**CFO:* Tamas Feitel
**VP:* Tom Giordano
**VP:* Vito Pulito
VP: Victor Reddick
**VP:* David Sager
**Prin:* Daniel Peters
Prgrm Mgr: Michael Passineau

D-U-N-S 07-943-5732
GE HEALTHCARE INC
235 N Executive Dr # 300, Brookfield, WI 53005-6032
Tel (608) 335-4958 *Founded/Ownrshp* 1994
Sales 8.7MM^E *EMP* 850
SIC 8099 ; Blood related health services

GE HEALTHCARE LIFE SCIENCES
See GE HEALTHCARE BIO-SCIENCES CORP

GE HELTHCARE BSCNCE BIOPROCESS
See DATEX-OHMEDA INC

D-U-N-S 03-738-3759
■ **GE HOLDINGS INC**
CABINET SUPPLY
(*Suby of* MASCO SERVICES GROUP CORP) ★
82545 Showcase Pkwy # 104, Indio, CA 92203-9653
Tel (760) 343-1299 *Founded/Ownrshp* 2007
Sales 17.9MM^E *EMP* 510
SIC 1751 5031 Finish & trim carpentry; Doors; Molding, all materials; Finish & trim carpentry; Doors; Molding, all materials
Pr: Guy Evans
**Sec:* Malia Evans
**VP:* Mark Croudy
Off Mgr: Jana Corbeil

D-U-N-S 15-781-0730 IMP
■ **GE INDUSTRIAL OF PR LLC**
CARIBE GE INTL RELAYS INC
(*Suby of* GENERAL ELECTRIC CO) ★
Km 1/5 Las Marias Rr 402, Anasco, PR 00610
Tel (787) 826-7338 *Founded/Ownrshp* 1995
Sales 43.7MM^E *EMP* 340
SIC 3625 Relays & industrial controls; Relays & industrial controls
Prin: Louis Orhardin

D-U-N-S 00-177-2060 IMP/EXP
GE INFRASTRUCTURE SENSING INC (OH)
GE SENSING & INSPECTION TECH
(*Suby of* GE ENERGY MANAGEMENT SERVICES INC) ★
1100 Technology Park Dr # 100, Billerica, MA 01821-4111
Tel (978) 437-1000 *Founded/Ownrshp* 1960, 2002
Sales NA *EMP* 800
SIC 3823 5084 3699 3674 3663 3625 Moisture meters, industrial process type; Industrial machinery & equipment; Electrical equipment & supplies; Semiconductors & related devices; Radio & TV communications equipment; Relays & industrial controls; Moisture meters, industrial process type; Industrial machinery & equipment; Electrical equipment & supplies; Semiconductors & related devices; Radio & TV communications equipment; Relays & industrial controls
Pr: Kristopher McBride
**VP:* Barbara A Cameron
IT Man: Christian Brauner
IT Man: Kristin Setser
Opers Mgr: Donald Sarazen
Sls Mgr: John Kerney
Snr Mgr: Greg Young

D-U-N-S 18-940-7674 EXP
■ **GE INFRASTRUCTURE SENSING INC**
GE WATER & PROCESS TECH
(*Suby of* GENERAL ELECTRIC CO) ★
4636 Somerton Rd, Feasterville Trevose, PA 19053-6742
Tel (617) 926-1749 *Founded/Ownrshp* 1968
Sales 260.4MM^E *EMP* 2,360
SIC 3589 2086 4941 3559 2899 3823 Water purification equipment, household type; Water filters & softeners, household type; Water treatment equipment, industrial; Water, pasteurized: packaged in cans, bottles, etc.; Water supply; Desalination equipment; Water treating compounds; Water quality monitoring & control systems; Water purification equipment, household type; Water filters & softeners, household type; Water treatment equipment, industrial; Water, pasteurized: packaged in cans, bottles, etc.; Water supply; Desalination equipment; Water treating compounds; Water quality monitoring & control systems
Pr: John G Rice
**Pr:* Joel A Berdine
**CFO:* John J Falconi
**Treas:* Andrew J Cring
**VP:* Barbara Cameron
**VP:* Matthew G Cribbins
IT Man: Joseph Halstead

GE INFRASTRUCTURE WATER & PROC
See GE MOBILE WATER INC

D-U-N-S 14-229-3856
■ **GE INSPECTION TECHNOLOGIES LP**
(*Suby of* GENERAL ELECTRIC CO) ★
50 Industrial Park Rd, Lewistown, PA 17044-9312
Tel (717) 242-0327 *Founded/Ownrshp* 2004
Sales 25.0MM^E *EMP* 250^E
SIC 3829 3844

D-U-N-S 82-465-6193 IMP
■ **GE INTELLIGENT PLATFORMS INC**
(*Suby of* GENERAL ELECTRIC CO) ★
2500 Austin Dr, Charlottesville, VA 22911-8319
Tel (434) 978-5000 *Founded/Ownrshp* 1986
Sales 330.8MM^E *EMP* 1,850
SIC 3625 3674 7371 Numerical controls; Computer logic modules; Custom computer programming services; Numerical controls; Computer logic modules; Custom computer programming services
CEO: Jody Markopoulos
**CEO:* Markopoulos Jody
**CFO:* Showman Roy
**CFO:* Roy Showman
Treas: Alex Siedlecki
VP: Amy Anderson
**VP:* Bernardo Anger
**VP:* Anger Bernardo
**VP:* William Estep
VP: Rick Freeman
VP: John Pina
VP: Erik Udstuen

GE INVESTMENTS
See GE ASSET MANAGEMENT INC

D-U-N-S 00-104-6325
■ **GE IONICS INC** (MA)
(*Suby of* GE INFRASTRUCTURE SENSING INC) ★
3 Burlington Woods Dr # 200, Burlington, MA 01803-4531
Tel (781) 359-7000 *Founded/Ownrshp* 1948, 2005
Sales 260.2MM^E *EMP* 2,350
SIC 3589 2086 4941 3559 2899 3823 Water purification equipment, household type; Water filters & softeners, household type; Water treatment equipment, industrial; Water, pasteurized: packaged in cans, bottles, etc.; Water supply; Desalination equipment; Water treating compounds; Water quality monitoring & control systems
Pr: David L Calhoun
Treas: John Bergeron
Sr VP: Erik Schoepke
VP: John F Curtis
VP: Lyman B Dickerson
VP: Edward Geishecker
VP: Brian Hernon
VP: John Sabol

GE LEASING SOLUTIONS
See COLONIAL PACIFIC LEASING CORP

D-U-N-S 80-894-3166 IMP/EXP
■ **GE LIGHTING LLC**
(*Suby of* GENERAL ELECTRIC CO) ★
1801 Edison Dr, Lexington, KY 40503-1359
Tel (859) 277-1161 *Founded/Ownrshp* 1947
Sales 63.4MM^E *EMP* 475
SIC 3641 6719 Sealed low-pressure gas lights; Investment holding companies, except banks; Sealed low-pressure gas lights; Investment holding companies, except banks
Plnt Mgr: Joel Fay
Snr Mgr: James May

D-U-N-S 08-403-1439 IMP/EXP
■ **GE LIGHTING SOLUTIONS LLC**
(*Suby of* GENERAL ELECTRIC CO) ★
1975 Noble Rd Ste 338e, Cleveland, OH 44112-1719
Tel (216) 266-4800 *Founded/Ownrshp* 1998
Sales 24.0MM^E *EMP* 76
SIC 3648 5063 Lighting equipment; Lighting fixtures; Lighting equipment; Lighting fixtures
Pr: Maryrose Sylvester
Pr: Agostino Renna
CFO: Kelly Novak
VP: Shin Kimura
Exec: Heather Wilson
IT Man: Keith Arbogast
IT Man: David Jenner
IT Man: Anne Rossoll
Mktg Mgr: Steven Reed
Sls Mgr: Jay Thompson
Snr Mgr: Abdoulaye Ndiaye

D-U-N-S 00-316-8374 IMP/EXP
■ GE LIGHTING SYSTEMS INC
(*Suby of* GENERAL ELECTRIC CO) ★
3010 Spartanburg Hwy, East Flat Rock, NC 28726-2926
Tel (828) 693-2000 *Founded/Ownrshp* 1997
Sales 221.8MM^E *EMP* 700
SIC 5063 Lighting fixtures; Lighting fixtures
Pr: Paul Morse
IT Man: Daniel Lefitz
Sls Mgr: Samson Lee

D-U-N-S 86-012-4465 IMP
■ GE MDS LLC
AFERGE MDS
(*Suby of* GENERAL ELECTRIC CO) ★
175 Science Pkwy, Rochester, NY 14620-4260
Tel (585) 242-9600 *Founded/Ownrshp* 2007
Sales 29.7MM^E *EMP* 201
SIC 3663 Radio & TV communications equipment; Radio & TV communications equipment
Exec: Stephen Pettis
Snr Sftwr: Paul Ruhland
Opers Mgr: Henry Garcia

GE MEASUREMENT & CONTROL
See DRUCK INC

GE MEDICAL SYSTEMS INFO TECH
See GE HEALTHCARE

D-U-N-S 00-658-0799 IMP
■ GE MEDICAL SYSTEMS INFORMATION TECHNOLOGIES INC
(*Suby of* GENERAL ELECTRIC CO) ★
9900 W Innovation Dr, Wauwatosa, WI 53226-4858
Tel (414) 355-5000 *Founded/Ownrshp* 1965
Sales 887.3MM^E *EMP* 5,361^E
SIC 3845 7352 7699 Patient monitoring apparatus; Electrocardiographs; Defibrillator; Respiratory analysis equipment, electromedical; Medical equipment rental; Medical equipment repair, non-electric; Patient monitoring apparatus; Electrocardiographs; Defibrillator; Respiratory analysis equipment, electromedical; Medical equipment rental; Medical equipment repair, non-electric
Pr: Dow Wilson
**CFO:* Scott F Schenkel
Ex VP: Mark Blair
VP: Russell Kidd
**VP:* Pamela S Krop
**VP:* Peter M Kuijper
Prgrm Mgr: Nandhini Anbarasan
Genl Mgr: Ted Dunham
Snr Sftwr: Scott Coursin
Dir IT: Tim Monday
IT Man: Lyle Steinberg

D-U-N-S 19-822-9291
■ GE MILITARY SYSTEMS
(*Suby of* GENERAL ELECTRIC CO) ★
1 Neumann Way, Cincinnati, OH 45215-1915
Tel (513) 243-2000 *Founded/Ownrshp* 1996
Sales 42.3MM^E *EMP* 812
SIC 3724 Aircraft engines & engine parts; Aircraft engines & engine parts
VP: Russ Sparks

D-U-N-S 06-341-4841 EXP
■ GE MOBILE WATER INC
GE INFRASTRUCTURE WATER & PROC
(*Suby of* GE IONICS INC) ★
4545 Patent Rd, Norfolk, VA 23502-5604
Tel (757) 855-9000 *Founded/Ownrshp* 2004
Sales 89.1MM^E *EMP* 350
SIC 3589 Water treatment equipment, industrial; Water treatment equipment, industrial
Ch: Thomas Johnston
**Pr:* Heinrich Markhoff
Ofcr: Dave Meissner
**VP:* Ashim Gupta
VP: William S Miller
Info Man: Jim Collister

GE MODULAR SPC/TRLR FLT SVCS
See TRANSPORT INTERNATIONAL POOL INC

GE MONEY
See GE CONSUMER FINANCE INC

GE OIL & GAS
See VETCO GRAY INC

D-U-N-S 07-944-9348
GE OIL & GAS COMPRESSION SYSTEMS LLC
GE ENERGY
16250 Port Nw, Houston, TX 77041-2667
Tel (713) 354-1900 *Founded/Ownrshp* 2014
Sales 123.7MM^E *EMP* 200^E
SIC 1389 Gas compressing (natural gas) at the fields; Gas compressing (natural gas) at the fields

D-U-N-S 10-246-5176 EXP
■ GE OIL & GAS ESP INC
E S P
(*Suby of* GE AERO ENERGY PRODUCTS) ★
5500 Se 59th St, Oklahoma City, OK 73135-4530
Tel (405) 670-1431 *Founded/Ownrshp* 2011
Sales 72.6MM^E *EMP* 200
SIC 7699 1389 7353 3479 Pumps & pumping equipment repair; Testing, measuring, surveying & analysis services; Oil field equipment, rental or leasing; Coating of metals & formed products; Pumps & pumping equipment repair; Testing, measuring, surveying & analysis services; Oil field equipment, rental or leasing; Coating of metals & formed products
Pr: Gary Ford
**CFO:* Stephen Ross
**Sr VP:* Mike Sackash
**VP:* Boris Aranovich
VP: P Hughes
VP: Dmichael Leonard
**VP:* Louis Misssel
**VP:* Joe Mitcho
**VP:* Brian Sevin
Dir IT: Jason Jansing
Mktg Mgr: Jack Semon

D-U-N-S 17-106-6546
GE OIL & GAS INC
4424 W Sam Houston Pkwy N # 700, Houston, TX 77041-8243
Tel (713) 683-2400 *Founded/Ownrshp* 1998
Sales 32.1MM^E *EMP* 99^E
SIC 3563 Air & gas compressors
Pr: Jay Wileman
**VP:* Mark E Buchanan
**VP:* Barbara A Cameron
**VP:* Jose Dumenigo
**VP:* John Eyen
**VP:* Henry Ware
Prgrm Mgr: Case Carstensen
Prgrm Mgr: Silvana Vitelli
Genl Mgr: David Lemier
CIO: Thomas Martin
Sfty Mgr: Dustin Drew

D-U-N-S 92-833-6924 EXP
■ GE OIL & GAS LOGGING SERVICES INC
(*Suby of* GE AERO ENERGY PRODUCTS) ★
16240 Port Nw Ste 100, Houston, TX 77041-2668
Tel (281) 579-9879 *Founded/Ownrshp* 2011
Sales 276.6MM^E *EMP* 500
SIC 1389 4789 Oil field services; Cargo loading & unloading services; Oil field services; Cargo loading & unloading services
Pr: John Paul Jones
Pr: Marco Rossi
**CFO:* Jon Piantez
**VP:* Grant Johnston
IT Man: Diana Glaze
Snr Mgr: Ronnie Russo

D-U-N-S 00-843-0456 IMP/EXP
■ GE OIL & GAS PRESSURE CONTROL LP (TX)
(*Suby of* GE AERO ENERGY PRODUCTS) ★
4424 W Sam Houston Pkwy N, Houston, TX 77041-8243
Tel (281) 398-8901 *Founded/Ownrshp* 1962, 2011
Sales 398.7MM^E *EMP* 1,500
SIC 3491 Industrial valves; Industrial valves
CEO: Daniel C Heintzelman
Genl Pt: Scott Bender
Pt: Thomas Adams
Pt: Joel Bender
Pt: Wendell Brooks
Pt: Craig Dewees
Pt: David Landry
Pt: Kent McAllister
Pt: Brian J Small
Pt: Ian Milne
Mktg Mgr: Linda M Knight

D-U-N-S 03-017-1196
■ GE ON WING SUPPORT INC
(*Suby of* GE ENGINE SERVICES LLC) ★
3010 Red Hawk Dr Ste B, Grand Prairie, TX 75052-7714
Tel (214) 960-3322 *Founded/Ownrshp* 2010
Sales 10.5MM^E *EMP* 1,474^E
SIC 7699 8711 Aviation propeller & blade repair; Aviation &/or aeronautical engineering
Prin: Joel Corbitt

D-U-N-S 79-013-2930 IMP/EXP
■ GE OSMONICS INC
(*Suby of* GE IONICS INC) ★
5951 Clearwater Dr, Minnetonka, MN 55343-8990
Tel (952) 933-2277 *Founded/Ownrshp* 2002
Sales 71.7MM^E *EMP* 300
SIC 3569 Filters; Filters
Prin: Heinrich Markhoff

D-U-N-S 01-388-8503 IMP/EXP
■ GE PACKAGED POWER INC
(*Suby of* GE AERO ENERGY PRODUCTS) ★
1330 West Loop S Ste 1000, Houston, TX 77027
Tel (713) 803-0900 *Founded/Ownrshp* 1997
Sales 121.3MM^E *EMP* 600
SIC 3511 Turbines & turbine generator sets; Turbines & turbine generator sets
Pr: Darryl L Wilson
**CFO:* Samuel R Aquillano
Counsel: Bryan Kay

D-U-N-S 16-838-8846 IMP/EXP
■ GE PACKAGED POWER LP
GE ENERGY
(*Suby of* GENERAL ELECTRIC CO) ★
16415 Jacintoport Blvd, Houston, TX 77015-6589
Tel (281) 452-3610 *Founded/Ownrshp* 1997
Sales 116.2MM^E *EMP* 375^E
SIC 3511 Turbines & turbine generator sets; Turbines & turbine generator sets
Prin: Ryan A Brown

D-U-N-S 62-390-6971
■ GE PARALLEL DESIGN INC
(*Suby of* GE MEDICAL SYSTEMS INFORMATION TECHNOLOGIES INC) ★
4313 E Cott Ctr Blvd Ste, Phoenix, AZ 85040
Tel (480) 966-6768 *Founded/Ownrshp* 2000
Sales 22.0MM^E *EMP* 280^E
SIC 3845 3841 3829 3541 Ultrasonic medical equipment, except cleaning; Surgical & medical instruments; Measuring & controlling devices; Machine tools, metal cutting type; Ultrasonic medical equipment, except cleaning; Surgical & medical instruments; Measuring & controlling devices; Machine tools, metal cutting type
Pr: John Schmeling
**VP:* Barbara A Cameron
**VP:* Ann-Marie McElligott
S&M/Mgr: Richard Amodei

D-U-N-S 18-121-4776 EXP
GE POWER CONVERSION
(*Suby of* ALSTOM INC) ★
610 Epsilon Dr, Pittsburgh, PA 15238-2808
Tel (412) 967-0765 *Founded/Ownrshp* 1970
Sales 22.1MM^E *EMP* 250
SIC 3612 3823 3672 Autotransformers, electric (power transformers); Power transformers, electric; Industrial instrmnts msrmnt display/control process variable; Printed circuit boards; Autotransformers, electric (power transformers); Power transformers, electric; Industrial instrmnts msrmnt display/control process variable; Printed circuit boards
Pr: Shoun Kerbaugh

D-U-N-S 00-779-3297 IMP
GE POWER ELECTRONICS INC (NV)
(*Suby of* GE ENERGY MANAGEMENT SERVICES INC) ★
601 Shiloh Rd, Plano, TX 75074-7210
Tel (972) 244-9288 *Founded/Ownrshp* 2000
Sales 358.8MM^E *EMP* 1,638^E
SIC 3661 Telephone & telegraph apparatus; Switching equipment, telephone; Telephone central office equipment, dial or manual; Telephone & telegraph apparatus; Switching equipment, telephone; Telephone central office equipment, dial or manual
CEO: Craig A Witsoe
Pr: Jeffrey P Schnitzer
CFO: Roxi Wen
Treas: Jason Garland
VP: Yafei Wen
Prgrm Mgr: Lauri Stapp
Tech Mgr: Raymond Rene
QI Cn Mgr: Maggy Swisulski
Snr Mgr: Eli Gueta

GE RICHARDS
See GE RICHARDS GRAPHIC SUPPLIES CO INC

D-U-N-S 94-244-7764 IMP
GE RICHARDS GRAPHIC SUPPLIES CO INC
GE RICHARDS
928 Links Ave, Landisville, PA 17538-1615
Tel (717) 892-4620 *Founded/Ownrshp* 1990
Sales 165.0MM^E *EMP* 180
SIC 5084 5045 Industrial machinery & equipment; Computers, peripherals & software; Industrial machinery & equipment; Computers, peripherals & software
Pr: Larry Wagner
**Treas:* Judith A Wagner
**VP:* Jeffrey E Wagner
Genl Mgr: Peter Vanheyst
CIO: Linda Rupp
Dir IT: Bob Shaunberger
IT Man: Horst Bernhard
IT Man: Hoyt Doyle
IT Man: Gary Houck
Sls Mgr: David Fickain

D-U-N-S 08-486-6003
GE RICHARDS GRAPHIC SUPPLIES MIDWEST INC
928 Links Ave, Landisville, PA 17538-1615
Tel (717) 898-3151 *Founded/Ownrshp* 1977
Sales 59.0MM^E *EMP* 230
SIC 5084 Printing trades machinery, equipment & supplies; Printing trades machinery, equipment & supplies
Pr: Larry Wagner
**Treas:* Judith Wagner
**Sec:* Linda Yost
**VP:* Jeffrey Wagner

GE SENSING & INSPECTION TECH
See GE INFRASTRUCTURE SENSING INC

GE SENSING & INSPECTION TECH
See AMPHENOL THERMOMETRICS INC

D-U-N-S 96-867-6523
■ GE SENSING ANASCO
(*Suby of* GENERAL ELECTRIC CAPITAL CORPORATION OF PUERTO RICO)
Km.1/3 Indus Park Rr 402, Anasco, PR 00610
Tel (787) 826-0222 *Founded/Ownrshp* 1998
Sales 25.4MM^E *EMP* 130
SIC 3829 3823 Thermometers & temperature sensors; Thermistors, industrial process type; Thermometers & temperature sensors; Thermistors, industrial process type
Plnt Mgr: Victor Balaguer

GE WATER & PROCESS TECH
See GE BETZ INC

GE WATER & PROCESS TECH
See GE INFRASTRUCTURE SENSING INC

D-U-N-S 11-650-5426 IMP
■ GE WIND ENERGY LLC
(*Suby of* GENERAL ELECTRIC CO) ★
13000 Jameson Rd, Tehachapi, CA 93561-8157
Tel (661) 823-6700 *Founded/Ownrshp* 2002
Sales 258.5MM^E *EMP* 1,700
SIC 3511 Turbines & turbine generator sets; Turbines & turbine generator sets
Comm Dir: Jim Spohm
IT Man: Angeie Lentz

D-U-N-S 06-744-8241
■ GE ZENITH CONTROLS INC
(*Suby of* GENERAL ELECTRIC CO) ★
830 W 40th St, Chicago, IL 60609-2535
Tel (773) 247-9202 *Founded/Ownrshp* 2000
Sales 81.8MM^E *EMP* 285
SIC 3613 Switchgear & switchgear accessories; Switchgear & switchgear accessories
Pr: Thomas Duffy
CFO: Jeffrey S Bornstein
VP: Robert Doherty
Prgrm Mgr: James Anderson
IT Man: Khalid Pervaiz
IT Man: Greg Sanchez
VP Mfg: Phillip Johnson
Plnt Mgr: David Garrison
Manager: Kathy McCarney
Snr Mgr: Patrick Moore

D-U-N-S 80-033-4570 EXP
■ GE-HITACHI NUCLEAR ENERGY AMERICA LLC
(*Suby of* GENERAL ELECTRIC CO) ★
3901 Castle Hayne Rd, Wilmington, NC 28401
Tel (910) 819-5073 *Founded/Ownrshp* 2007
Sales 488.0MM^E *EMP* 2,300
SIC 2819 Nuclear fuel & cores, inorganic; Nuclear fuel & cores, inorganic
CEO: Caroline Reda
CFO: Craig Steven
CFO: Mark R Sweeney
VP: Christopher J Monetta
VP: Kevin Walsh
Prin: Angela Thornhill
Snr Mgr: Robert Carr
Snr Mgr: Bobby Schultz

D-U-N-S 00-692-8584 IMP/EXP
GEA FARM TECHNOLOGIES INC
(*Suby of* GEA WESTFALIA SEPARATOR INC) ★
1880 Country Farm Dr, Naperville, IL 60563-1089
Tel (630) 548-8200 *Founded/Ownrshp* 1906, 1999
Sales 273.4MM^E *EMP* 450
SIC 5083 3523 2841 2842 Dairy machinery & equipment; Dairy equipment (farm); Detergents, synthetic organic or inorganic alkaline; Sanitation preparations; Dairy machinery & equipment; Dairy equipment (farm); Detergents, synthetic organic or inorganic alkaline; Sanitation preparations
Pr: Vern Foster
**Pr:* Matt Daley
**CFO:* Patrick Ferry
Mktg Dir: Linda Mrugacz

GEA FES SYSTEM
See GEA REFRIGERATION NORTH AMERICA INC

D-U-N-S 01-936-2610 IMP
GEA FOOD SOLUTIONS NORTH AMERICA INC
(*Suby of* GEA GROUP AG)
8000 Dallas Pkwy, Frisco, TX 75034-4057
Tel (214) 618-1100 *Founded/Ownrshp* 2001
Sales 54.7MM^E *EMP* 125^E
SIC 5084 Food industry machinery; Packaging machinery & equipment; Food industry machinery; Packaging machinery & equipment
Pr: Bob Bard
Top Exec: Neil Eccles
**VP:* Bryon Stricker
Area Mgr: Cecilie O'Gara
Sls Mgr: Peter Monte

D-U-N-S 07-915-2791
GEA MECHANICAL EQUIPMENT US INC
GEA TUCHENHAGEN DIVISION
(*Suby of* GEA NORTH AMERICA INC) ★
33 Mcalister Farm Rd, Portland, ME 04103-5946
Tel (207) 797-9500 *Founded/Ownrshp* 2010
Sales 40.0MM *EMP* 23
SIC 5085 Valves & fittings; Valves & fittings
Pr: Dave Medlar

D-U-N-S 96-667-0171 IMP
GEA MECHANICAL EQUIPMENT US INC
GEA WESTFALIA SEPARATOR DIV
(*Suby of* GEA NORTH AMERICA INC) ★
100 Fairway Ct, Northvale, NJ 07647-2401
Tel (201) 767-3900 *Founded/Ownrshp* 2010
Sales 187.9MM^E *EMP* 530^E
SIC 5084 7699 Industrial machinery & equipment; Industrial machinery & equipment repair; Industrial machinery & equipment; Industrial machinery & equipment repair
Pr: Michael Vick
CFO: Ronald Fitz
Ex VP: Michael Friis
**VP:* Joseph Pavlosky
**Prin:* Clement O'Donnell
Genl Mgr: Jim Dupree
Dir IT: Dale Miller
Genl Couns: Brian Casto

D-U-N-S 80-762-8425
GEA NORTH AMERICA INC
METALLGESELLSCHAFT
(*Suby of* GEA GROUP AG)
9165 Rumsey Rd, Columbia, MD 21045-1929
Tel (410) 997-8700 *Founded/Ownrshp* 1998
Sales 844.7MM^E *EMP* 530
SIC 7218 Industrial equipment launderers; Industrial equipment launderers
CEO: Anders Wilhjelm
**Pr:* Steve Kaplan
**VP:* Robert Johnson
**VP:* William McCarter

D-U-N-S 09-181-8930
GEA PROCESS ENGINEERING INC
(*Suby of* GEA NORTH AMERICA INC) ★
9165 Rumsey Rd, Columbia, MD 21045-1929
Tel (410) 772-5792 *Founded/Ownrshp* 2006
Sales 163.1MM^E *EMP* 327
SIC 8711 Industrial engineers; Industrial engineers
Pr: Steven M Kaplan
**Treas:* Robert E Johnson Jr
Treas: Peter McGivney
**Ex VP:* Steven Lancos
**VP:* Michael Bowers
**VP:* Ronald J Matzek
VP: Ronald Matzik
**VP:* Swami Sundaram
Rgnl Mgr: Navin Lakhanpaul

D-U-N-S 11-350-6443
GEA PT NORTH AMERICA INC
(*Suby of* GEA NORTH AMERICA INC) ★
9165 Rumsey Rd, Columbia, MD 21045-1929
Tel (410) 997-8700 *Founded/Ownrshp* 1997
Sales 76.6MM^E *EMP* 326
SIC 8748 Business consulting; Business consulting
Prin: Robert E Johnson
CFO: Patrick Ferry
Ex VP: Steven Lancos
Ex VP: Ronald Matzek
VP: William McCarter
IT Man: Brian Zwart

Trfc Mgr: Ron Hazel
Manager: Josh Eagan
Manager: Jeffrey Feller
Sls Mgr: Ronald Tuckner

D-U-N-S 00-722-7861 IMP
GEA RAINEY CORP
(*Suby of* GEA NORTH AMERICA INC) ★
5202 W Channel Rd, Catoosa, OK 74015-3057
Tel (918) 266-2706 *Founded/Ownrshp* 2007
Sales 81.3MM^E *EMP* 220
SIC 3443 Heat exchangers: coolers (after, inter), condensers, etc.; Heat exchangers: coolers (after, inter), condensers, etc.
CEO: Christine O'Connor
**CFO:* Bryan Fleming
CFO: Rodney Pratz
**CFO:* Robert Sellers
**VP Mfg:* Phil Snodgrass
**VP Sls:* Chris Jungers

D-U-N-S 79-973-4251 IMP
GEA REFRIGERATION NORTH AMERICA INC
GEA FES SYSTEM
(*Suby of* GEA PT NORTH AMERICA INC) ★
3475 Board Rd, York, PA 17406-8414
Tel (717) 767-6411 *Founded/Ownrshp* 2004
Sales 76.6MM^E *EMP* 250
SIC 3585 Refrigeration & heating equipment; Refrigeration & heating equipment
CEO: John Ansbro
Pr: Greg Klidonas
**Treas:* Glenn A Miller
**VP:* Dennis Halsey
VP: Gary Schrift
IT Man: Rohil Ratanpara
Web Prj Mg: Will Parshall

GEA TUCHENHAGEN DIVISION
See GEA MECHANICAL EQUIPMENT US INC

GEA WESTFALIA SEPARATOR DIV
See GEA MECHANICAL EQUIPMENT US INC

D-U-N-S 00-166-3012 IMP
GEA WESTFALIA SEPARATOR INC
(*Suby of* GEA NORTH AMERICA INC) ★
100 Fairway Ct, Northvale, NJ 07647-2401
Tel (201) 767-3900 *Founded/Ownrshp* 1950
Sales 273.4MM^E *EMP* 530
SIC 5083 5084 Milking machinery & equipment; Industrial machinery & equipment; Milking machinery & equipment; Industrial machinery & equipment
CEO: Michael J Vick
**Pr:* Clement O'Donnell
**VP:* Joseph Pavlosky
Sfty Mgr: Per Ralamb
Sls Mgr: Constantine Tricules

GEAC
See GOVERNMENTAL & EDUCATIONAL ASSISTANCE CORP

GEAR FOR SPORTS
See GFSI INC

D-U-N-S 00-924-7305 IMP
GEAR WORKS SEATTLE INC
500 S Portland St, Seattle, WA 98108-4329
Tel (206) 762-3333 *Founded/Ownrshp* 1982
Sales 40.5MM^E *EMP* 135
SIC 3566 3599 Gears, power transmission, except automotive; Machine shop, jobbing & repair; Gears, power transmission, except automotive; Machine shop, jobbing & repair
Pr: Sterling R Ramberg
Ch Bd: Roland S Ramberg
CFO: Karen A Roberts
VP: Manfred H CHI
Prin: Jay W Hamilton
QA Dir: Daniel Ross
Dir IT: Brad Failing
IT Man: Kevin Acheson

D-U-N-S 15-321-7844
GEARBOX SOFTWARE LLC
101 E Park Blvd Ste 1069, Plano, TX 75074-8823
Tel (972) 312-8202 *Founded/Ownrshp* 1999
Sales 37.5MM^E *EMP* 75
SIC 5045 Computer software
Pr: Randall Pitchford II
COO: John Antal
VP: David Eddings
QA Dir: Fred Echols
Sftwr Eng: Derek Escontrias

GEARHART CHEVROLET
See TILTON AUTOMOTIVE LLC

D-U-N-S 07-302-7187
GEARY COMMUNITY HOSPITAL
1102 Saint Marys Rd, Junction City, KS 66441-4196
Tel (785) 238-4131 *Founded/Ownrshp* 1913
Sales 45.0MM *EMP* 450
Accts Bkd Llp Wichita Kansas
SIC 8062 General medical & surgical hospitals; General medical & surgical hospitals
CEO: Joe Stratton
Chf Rad: Patrick Landes
CFO: Darrin Rumford
Ofcr: Joseph Stratton
Dir OR: Jody Hittle Jr
Dir Rad: Pat Small
Comm Man: Yolanda Bowyer
Prgrm Mgr: Dennis Sewell
Nurse Mgr: Dawn Engel
Cmptr Lab: Johnnie Hale
Mktg Dir: Harold Marion
Board of Directors: John Williams, Lynne Addair, Elaine Becker, Pat Benson, Al Bowyer, Dawn Engel, Lois Fegan, Brenda Stocklin- Smith, Randy Wagner, Terri Wahle

D-U-N-S 09-582-1419
GEARY COUNTY UNIFIED SCHOOL DISTRICT 475
123 N Eisenhower Dr, Junction City, KS 66441-3313
Tel (785) 717-4000 *Founded/Ownrshp* 1965
Sales 65.2MM^E *EMP* 1,200
SIC 8211 Public elementary school; Public junior high school; Public senior high school; Public elementary school; Public junior high school; Public senior high school
Bd of Dir: Belle Whaley
Schl Brd P: Becky Bramlage
HC Dir: Rebekah Helget

D-U-N-S 09-731-6033
GEARY LSF GROUP INC
LSF INTERACTIVE
332 Pine St Fl 6, San Francisco, CA 94104-3228
Tel (877) 616-8226 *Founded/Ownrshp* 2002
Sales 116.0MM^E *EMP* 210
SIC 4813 ;
Pr: Karen Kovaleski
**CFO:* Paul McKnight
**Ex VP:* Ramsay Crooks
Ex VP: Bob Rothenberg
**Ex VP:* Bob Yakominich
VP: Lauren Ferst
VP: Caroline Sherman
Mng Dir: Cary Johnson
Sales Asso: Lauren Helm
Art Dir: Tim Borillo

D-U-N-S 00-963-8198
GEARY PACIFIC CORP
GEARY PACIFIC SUPPLY
1908 N Enterprise St, Orange, CA 92865-4102
Tel (714) 279-2950 *Founded/Ownrshp* 1961
Sales 58.5MM^E *EMP* 128
SIC 5075

GEARY PACIFIC SUPPLY
See GEARY PACIFIC CORP

D-U-N-S 83-003-8993
GEARY PROPERTY HOLDINGS LLC
(*Suby of* GOLDEN LIVING) ★
1000 Fianna Way, Fort Smith, AR 72919-9008
Tel (479) 201-2000 *Founded/Ownrshp* 2005
Sales 38.7MM^E *EMP* 4,155^E
SIC 6531 Real estate managers

GEARY WHOLESALE CASH & CARRY
See GEARY WHOLESALE INC

D-U-N-S 02-919-0048
GEARY WHOLESALE INC
GEARY WHOLESALE CASH & CARRY
971 Crestview Dr, Millbrae, CA 94030-1510
Tel (650) 589-5669 *Founded/Ownrshp* 1978
Sales 24.1MM *EMP* 12
Accts Cote & Company Apc San Franc
SIC 5194 5145 5149 Tobacco & tobacco products; Candy; Groceries & related products; Tobacco & tobacco products; Candy; Groceries & related products
Pr: John Ganim
**VP:* Eisa Ganim

D-U-N-S 05-374-4926
GEATER MACHINING AND MANUFACTURING CO
901 12th St Ne, Independence, IA 50644-1016
Tel (319) 334-6026 *Founded/Ownrshp* 1962
Sales 22.9MM *EMP* 235
SIC 3444 3469 Sheet metalwork; Machine parts, stamped or pressed metal; Sheet metalwork; Machine parts, stamped or pressed metal
CEO: Jerry Bitterman
**Pr:* Scott Geater
Exec: Stacie Halverson
Ql Cn Mgr: John Miller

D-U-N-S 12-309-5309
GEAUGA COUNTY BOARD OF MENTAL RETARDATION & DEVELOPMENTAL DISABILITIES
8200 Cedar Rd, Chesterland, OH 44026-3550
Tel (440) 729-2370 *Founded/Ownrshp* 1963
Sales NA *EMP* 300
SIC 9431 Mental health agency administration, government; ; Mental health agency administration, government;

GEAUGA HOSPITAL ASSN INC, THE
See UNIVERSITY HOSPITALS GEAUGA MEDICAL CENTER

GEBBERS FARMS
See BREWSTER HEIGHTS PACKING & ORCHARDS LP

D-U-N-S 04-874-6911
GEBHARDT AUTOMOTIVE INC
GEBHARDT PORSCHE, BMW, VOLKSWA
4740 Valmont Rd, Boulder, CO 80301-2228
Tel (303) 447-8000 *Founded/Ownrshp* 1975
Sales 56.6MM^E *EMP* 150
SIC 5511 Automobiles, new & used; Automobiles, new & used
Pr: James P Gebhardt
**VP:* Paul E Gebhardt
Sls Mgr: Rich Moss
Snr Mgr: Courtney Snyder

GEBHARDT PORSCHE, BMW, VOLKSWA
See GEBHARDT AUTOMOTIVE INC

D-U-N-S 04-632-1840 IMP
GEBO DISTRIBUTING CO INC
GEBO'S
3109 Olton Rd, Plainview, TX 79072-6763
Tel (806) 293-4212 *Founded/Ownrshp* 1978
Sales 46.8MM *EMP* 165
Accts Robinson Burdette Martin & Ser
SIC 5261 5999 5531 5699 Lawn & garden supplies; Feed & farm supply; Automotive tires; Western apparel; Lawn & garden supplies; Feed & farm supply; Automotive tires; Western apparel
Ch Bd: Brent T Gebo
**Pr:* Mike McCarthy
CFO: Dennis Johnston
**VP:* Cheryl W Gebo

GEBO'S
See GEBO DISTRIBUTING CO INC

D-U-N-S 82-898-8477
GEC DURHAM INDUSTRIES INC
255 Samuel Barnet Blvd, New Bedford, MA 02745-1220
Tel (508) 995-2636 *Founded/Ownrshp* 1994
Sales 34.9MM^E *EMP* 338
SIC 3612 Transformers, except electric; Transformers, except electric
Pr: J Douglas Russel

GECAS
See GE CAPITAL AVIATION SERVICES LLC

D-U-N-S 06-165-6807 IMP
■ **GECAS ASSET MANAGEMENT SERVICES INC**
GE CAPITAL AVIATION SERVICES
(*Suby of* GENERAL ELECTRIC CAPITAL CORP) ★
3860 E Holmes Rd 108, Memphis, TN 38118-7710
Tel (203) 340-2523 *Founded/Ownrshp* 2006
Sales 29.6MM^E *EMP* 189
SIC 7389 7629 3728 5088 7699 Purchasing service; Aircraft electrical equipment repair; Aircraft parts & equipment; Aircraft engines & engine parts; Aircraft & heavy equipment repair services; Purchasing service; Aircraft electrical equipment repair; Aircraft parts & equipment; Aircraft engines & engine parts; Aircraft & heavy equipment repair services
Pr: Sean P Flannery
**COO:* Sharon Green
**CFO:* Cynthia Johnson
**VP:* John V Abbott
VP: Cathy Shea
VP: Cathy Williams
Dir IT: Paul Hughes
S&M/VP: Seamus Odonnell

GECIS
See GENPACT PROCESS SOLUTIONS LLC

D-U-N-S 19-008-8836
GECITS
IKON FINANCIAL SERVICES
1738 Bass Rd, Macon, GA 31210-1043
Tel (478) 405-4001 *Founded/Ownrshp* 2009
Sales NA *EMP* 99
SIC 6159 Miscellaneous business credit
Pr: Jeff Immelt

D-U-N-S 08-698-4937
GECOS INC
(*Suby of* EUROVIA)
1936 Lee Rd, Winter Park, FL 32789-7229
Tel (407) 645-5500 *Founded/Ownrshp* 1988
Sales 476.6MM^E *EMP* 1,400
SIC 1611 2951 1623 General contractor, highway & street construction; Asphalt & asphaltic paving mixtures (not from refineries); Sewer line construction; General contractor, highway & street construction; Asphalt & asphaltic paving mixtures (not from refineries); Sewer line construction
Pr: Jean Noel Vely
Sec: P Frederick O'Dea Jr
Board of Directors: Jacques Tavernier

GECU
See GENERAL ELECTRIC CREDIT UNION

D-U-N-S 06-897-2199
GECU
GREATER EL PASO'S CREDIT UNION
1225 Airway Blvd, El Paso, TX 79925-3620
Tel (915) 778-9221 *Founded/Ownrshp* 1933
Sales NA *EMP* 500
SIC 6062 State credit unions, not federally chartered; State credit unions, not federally chartered
CEO: Crystal Long
**CEO:* Harriet May
**CFO:* Steve Lutz
**Sr VP:* Fermin Acosta
**Sr VP:* Pierre Cardenas
Sr VP: Sarah Newman
VP: Fernando Ortega
VP: Art Perez
VP: Martin Sena
VP: Chris Tomkins
VP Mktg: Claudia Austin

D-U-N-S 06-530-6727
GED HOLDINGS INC
9280 Dutton Dr, Twinsburg, OH 44087-1967
Tel (330) 963-5401 *Founded/Ownrshp* 2000
Sales 20.2MM^E *EMP* 141
SIC 3559 3549 5084 Glass making machinery: blowing, molding, forming, etc.; Cutting & slitting machinery; Industrial machinery & equipment; Glass making machinery: blowing, molding, forming, etc.; Cutting & slitting machinery; Industrial machinery & equipment
Pr: William Weaver
CFO: Steve Lang

D-U-N-S 08-450-1345
GED INTEGRATED SOLUTIONS INC (OH)
9280 Dutton Dr, Twinsburg, OH 44087-1967
Tel (330) 963-5401 *Founded/Ownrshp* 1977, 2015
Sales 22.5MM^E *EMP* 90^E
SIC 5211 Glass making machinery: blowing, molding, forming, etc.; Cutting & slitting machinery; Industrial machinery & equipment; Door & window products
Pr: William Weaver
CFO: Steve Lang
Genl Mgr: Dennis Stonis

GEDNEY FOODS COMPANY
See MA GEDNEY CO

D-U-N-S 10-338-9771
GEE INVESTMENTS INC
GEORGE GEE AUTOMOTIVE CO.
21502 E George Gee Ave, Liberty Lake, WA 99019-7623
Tel (509) 927-1000 *Founded/Ownrshp* 1990
Sales 75.0MM *EMP* 90^E
SIC 5511 Automobiles, new & used; Automobiles, new & used
Pr: Ryan Gee

CFO: Valerie Christiansen
**Sec:* Molly Gee
**VP:* Edward Tabish
IT Man: Bruce Hanson
Sls Mgr: Stephen Robinson

GEEDING CONSTRUCTION
See FOUR G CONSTRUCTION INC

D-U-N-S 92-959-3630
■ **GEEK SQUAD INC**
(*Suby of* BEST BUY CO INC) ★
1213 Washington Ave N, Minneapolis, MN 55401-1036
Tel (612) 343-1028 *Founded/Ownrshp* 2002
Sales 111.7MM^E *EMP* 2,500
SIC 7379 Computer related consulting services; Computer related consulting services
CEO: Robert Stephens

D-U-N-S 83-643-4563
■ **GEEKNET INC**
(*Suby of* GAMESTOP CORP) ★
11216 Waples Ste 100, Fairfax, VA 22030
Tel (877) 433-5638 *Founded/Ownrshp* 2015
Sales 140.7MM^E *EMP* 125^E
Tkr Sym GKNT *Exch* NGM
SIC 5961 Computer software, mail order; Computers & peripheral equipment, mail order; Computer software, mail order; Computers & peripheral equipment, mail order
Pr: Kathryn K McCarthy
CFO: Julie A Pangelinan
Sr VP: Jenny Gillespie
VP: Sue McNeill
VP: Dave Nelson
Manager: Phil Guerra

GEEKS IN A FLASH
See MANUEL W LLOYD INC

D-U-N-S 07-831-5027 EXP
■ **GEFCO INC**
(*Suby of* ASTEC INDUSTRIES INC) ★
2215 S Van Buren St, Enid, OK 73703-8218
Tel (580) 237-7433 *Founded/Ownrshp* 2011
Sales 66.3MM^E *EMP* 176
SIC 3533 Drilling tools for gas, oil or water wells; Drilling tools for gas, oil or water wells
Pr: Dale Aaron Harmon
VP: Thomas Campbell
**VP:* Charles Cunningham
**VP:* Greg Hub
MIS Dir: Terry Washburn
Mktg Dir: Heidi Hughes

D-U-N-S 36-460-4876 IMP
■ **GEFEN LLC**
(*Suby of* NORTEK SECURITY & CONTROL LLC)
20600 Nordhoff St, Chatsworth, CA 91311-6114
Tel (818) 772-9100 *Founded/Ownrshp* 2006
Sales 44.0MM *EMP* 42
SIC 3699 High-energy particle physics equipment
CEO: Hagai Gefen
**Pr:* Tony Dowzall
**VP:* Jill Gefen
IT Man: Christopher Smith

D-U-N-S 02-957-0348 IMP
GEHAN HOMES LTD (TX)
15725 Dallas Pkwy Ste 300, Addison, TX 75001-3850
Tel (972) 383-4300 *Founded/Ownrshp* 1965, 2014
Sales 129.8MM^E *EMP* 300
Accts Grant Thornton Llp Dallas Te
SIC 1521 New construction, single-family houses; Speculative builder, single-family houses; Commercial & industrial building operation; New construction, single-family houses
CEO: Tim Gehan
Treas: Helen Gehan
VP: Shannon Powers
Area Mgr: Lee Olson
Div Mgr: Jeff McVean
IT Man: David Gallant
Mktg Mgr: Christina Lombardo
Sls Mgr: Angie Jenkins
Sales Asso: Jennifer Ellis
Sales Asso: Melodie Monroe

GEHL COMPANY
See MANITOU AMERICAS INC

D-U-N-S 00-608-7951 IMP
GEHL FOODS LLC (WI)
N116w15970 Main St, Germantown, WI 53022-2654
Tel (262) 251-8570 *Founded/Ownrshp* 1920, 2015
Sales 294.5MM^E *EMP* 726
SIC 2022 Natural cheese; Natural cheese
CEO: Eric Beringause
**Pr:* Andrew Gehl
Pr: Mike Sowieja
**CFO:* Tim Preuninger
Rgnl Mgr: Kristin Cullaz
IT Man: Will Liz
Sfty Mgr: John Ward
Opers Mgr: Brian Dederich
Plnt Mgr: Michael Betzhold
Ql Cn Mgr: Steven Treis
Sls Mgr: Dolli Garrison

D-U-N-S 18-310-1559 IMP
GEHL POWER PRODUCTS INC
(*Suby of* GEHL CO) ★
900 Ferdig St, Yankton, SD 57078-3208
Tel (605) 665-6500 *Founded/Ownrshp* 1997
Sales 135.5MM^E *EMP* 716
SIC 3537 3531 3535 Forklift trucks; Graders, road (construction machinery); Conveyors & conveying equipment; Forklift trucks; Graders, road (construction machinery); Conveyors & conveying equipment
Pr: William D Gehl
**Treas:* Kenneth P Hahn
Netwrk Mgr: Aaron Klimes
Mtls Mgr: Tom Bergeson
Plnt Mgr: David Ewald

D-U-N-S 07-998-8265
GEHR GROUP INC
7400 E Slauson Ave, Commerce, CA 90040-3308
Tel (323) 728-5558 *Founded/Ownrshp* 2012
Sales 52.1MM^E *EMP* 360^E
SIC 3315 5063 6512 6513 Wire & fabricated wire products; Electronic wire & cable; Nonresidential building operators; Apartment building operators
CEO: David Lifschitz
Pr: Alfred Somekh
COO: Mark Goldman
Ex VP: Carl Rosenthal

D-U-N-S 00-960-7839 IMP
GEHR INDUSTRIES INC (CA)
(*Suby of* GEHR GROUP INC) ★
7400 E Slauson Ave, Commerce, CA 90040-3300
Tel (323) 728-5558 *Founded/Ownrshp* 1965
Sales 45.2MM^E *EMP* 250
SIC 3357 5063 5072 5085 6512 6513 Nonferrous wiredrawing & insulating; Electrical apparatus & equipment; Hardware; Industrial supplies; Nonresidential building operators; Apartment building operators; Nonferrous wiredrawing & insulating; Electrical apparatus & equipment; Hardware; Industrial supplies; Nonresidential building operators; Apartment building operators
Pr: David Lifschitz
**COO:* Mark Goldman
**Ex VP:* Carl Rosenthal
**VP:* Saleem Baakza
**VP:* Carlton Tom

GEHRING TEXTILES
See GEHRING TRICOT CORP

D-U-N-S 00-154-4923 IMP
GEHRING TRICOT CORP (NY)
GEHRING TEXTILES
1225 Franklin Ave Ste 300, Garden City, NY 11530-1659
Tel (315) 429-8551 *Founded/Ownrshp* 1952, 1986
Sales 55.4MM^E *EMP* 204
SIC 2258 2262 Dyeing & finishing lace goods & warp knit fabric; Tricot fabrics; Finishing plants, manmade fiber & silk fabrics; Dyeing & finishing lace goods & warp knit fabric; Tricot fabrics; Finishing plants, manmade fiber & silk fabrics
Pr: George G Gehring Jr
CFO: Paul Gutowski
Bd of Dir: Samuel Ackerman
VP: Marie Bevilaqua
VP: George Kelnhofer
VP: George Kelnhoffer
VP: William J Rowan
Exec: Skip Gehring
Prin: Brenda Gehring
IT Man: Rich Patrick
Tech Mgr: Raj Suhag

D-U-N-S 11-434-1357 IMP
GEHRING-MONTGOMERY INC
(*Suby of* TER HELL & CO. GMBH)
710 Louis Dr, Warminster, PA 18974-2829
Tel (215) 957-3669 *Founded/Ownrshp* 1990
Sales 26.7MM^E *EMP* 25
SIC 5169 Industrial chemicals
CEO: Klaus C Westphal
**Mng Dir:* Larry Biss
**Mng Dir:* Ruth Gehring
Sls Mgr: Rocky Spear

D-U-N-S 03-359-6555 IMP
GEHRLICHER SOLAR AMERICA CORP
(*Suby of* M+W AMERICAS INC) ★
21 Fadem Rd Ste 7, Springfield, NJ 07081-3136
Tel (908) 219-4379 *Founded/Ownrshp* 2009
Sales 51.9MM^E *EMP* 72
Accts Deloitte & Touche Llp Parsipp
SIC 3433 Solar heaters & collectors
Pr: Jerry Shinn
Sr VP: David Larrick
**VP:* Peter Farlekas
**VP:* Andrew Nekus

D-U-N-S 09-399-3780
GEHRY PARTNERS LLP
12541 Beatrice St, Los Angeles, CA 90066-7001
Tel (310) 482-3000 *Founded/Ownrshp* 2001
Sales 22.4MM^E *EMP* 130
SIC 8712 Architectural services; Architectural services
Pt: Frank Gehry
Pt: Brian Aamoth
Pt: John Bowers
Pt: Anand Devarajan
Pt: Berta Gehry

GEI
See GENERAL EXTRUSIONS INC

D-U-N-S 05-782-4526
GEI CONSULTANTS INC
400 Unicorn Park Dr Ste 8, Woburn, MA 01801-3341
Tel (781) 721-4000 *Founded/Ownrshp* 1970
Sales 168.1MM^E *EMP* 520
SIC 8711 Engineering services; Structural engineering; Engineering services; Structural engineering
Pr: Raymond D Hart
Ch Bd: Naser J Bateni
**COO:* Ron Palmieri
CFO: Steve Poulos
Ch: Anne L Leifer
Treas: Thomas Kahl
Sr VP: Jim Chadwick
Sr VP: Michael Gatzow
VP: Jim Ash
VP: Jesus E Gomez
VP: Dan Johnson
VP: Tom Keller
VP: Jeremy Pratt

D-U-N-S 04-829-6636
GEIB INDUSTRIES INC
3220 Mannheim Rd, Franklin Park, IL 60131-1532
Tel (847) 455-4550 *Founded/Ownrshp* 1971
Sales 36.7MM^E *EMP* 25
SIC 5084 3498 3429 3052 Hydraulic systems equipment & supplies; Fabricated pipe & fittings; Manufactured hardware (general); Rubber & plastics hose & beltings
Pr: Robert Geib
**Pr:* Christopher Geib
Genl Mgr: Michael A Zalas
VP Sls: Thomas Geib
Sls Mgr: Peter Tinsley

GEICO
See GOVERNMENT EMPLOYEES INSURANCE CO INC

D-U-N-S 82-745-0032
■ **GEICO CASUALTY CO**
(*Suby of* GEICO CORP) ★
5260 Western Ave, Chevy Chase, MD 20815-3799
Tel (301) 986-3000 *Founded/Ownrshp* 1982
Sales NA *EMP* 103^E
SIC 6331 Fire, marine & casualty insurance; Fire, marine & casualty insurance
Ch Bd: Olza Nicely
Treas: Charles Gerard Schara
DP Exec: David Willis
Netwrk Eng: Hugh Golden

D-U-N-S 04-735-3364
GEICO CORP
1 Geico Blvd, Fredericksburg, VA 22412-9000
Tel (540) 752-4801 *Founded/Ownrshp* 2010
Sales NA *EMP* 122^E
SIC 6411 Insurance agents, brokers & service
Prin: Diane Elsey
Sr VP: Nancy Pierce
Telecom Ex: Bob Hager

D-U-N-S 09-656-3747
■ **GEICO CORP**
(*Suby of* BERKSHIRE HATHAWAY INC) ★
1 Geico Plz, Washington, DC 20076-0005
Tel (301) 986-3000 *Founded/Ownrshp* 1978
Sales NA *EMP* 28,000
SIC 6411 Insurance agents, brokers & service; Insurance agents, brokers & service
Pr: Tony Nicely
Pr: Louis A Simpson
CFO: Mike Campbell
Treas: Charles G Schara
Ex VP: Silva Franklin
Ex VP: Ron Guzinsky
Sr VP: Greg Kalinsky
Sr VP: David L Schindler
VP: John Ammendola
VP: Michelle Trindade
CIO: Harvey Demovick

D-U-N-S 80-824-3901
■ **GEICO GENERAL INSURANCE CO**
(*Suby of* GEICO) ★
1 Geico Plz, Washington, DC 20076-0005
Tel (301) 986-3000 *Founded/Ownrshp* 1983
Sales NA *EMP* 10,000
SIC 6411 Insurance agents, brokers & service; Insurance agents, brokers & service
Pr: Olza Nicely
Sr VP: Robert Miller
VP: Bill Dommasch
Prgrm Mgr: Craig Masterson
MIS Dir: Paul Lenk
Dir IT: Norman Johns
Dir IT: Debbie Nickell
Dir IT: Pete Olympia
Dir IT: Steve Vercoutter
IT Man: Henry Boone
IT Man: Richard Chan

D-U-N-S 00-691-9500
■ **GEICO INDEMNITY CO**
(*Suby of* GEICO CORP) ★
One Geico Plaza, Washington, DC 20047-0001
Tel (301) 986-3000 *Founded/Ownrshp* 1961
Sales NA *EMP* 22,889
SIC 6331 6411 Fire, marine & casualty insurance; Insurance agents, brokers & service; Fire, marine & casualty insurance; Insurance agents, brokers & service
Pr: Olza M Nicely
Treas: Charles G Schara
VP: Shawn Burklin
VP: R Cheek
VP: Richard Van Essendelft

D-U-N-S 00-605-2831
GEIGER & PETERS INC
761 S Sherman Dr, Indianapolis, IN 46203-1584
Tel (317) 322-7740 *Founded/Ownrshp* 1905
Sales 27.8MM^E *EMP* 62
Accts Charles Madden Pc Indianapol
SIC 3441 Fabricated structural metal; Fabricated structural metal
Pr: Stephen H Kitter
**Pr:* James Colzani
**Ch:* Carl Peters
VP: Robert Elsner
**VP:* Barry Hochstedler
**VP:* Steve Knitter
VP: Don Peterson
IT Man: Simon Corn
QI Cn Mgr: Frankie Donofrio

D-U-N-S 00-109-5686 IMP
GEIGER BROS
SUN GRAPHIX/DIV
70 Mount Hope Ave, Lewiston, ME 04240-1021
Tel (207) 755-2000 *Founded/Ownrshp* 1878
Sales 238.5MM^E *EMP* 400
SIC 5199 3993 2752 2782 2789 Advertising specialties; Gifts & novelties; Advertising novelties; Calendars, lithographed; Periodicals, lithographed; Blankbooks & looseleaf binders; Diaries; Bookbinding & related work; Bronzing, gilding, edging & deckling: books, cards, paper; Advertising specialties; Gifts & novelties; Advertising novelties; Calendars, lithographed; Periodicals, lithographed; Blankbooks & looseleaf binders; Diaries; Bookbinding & related work; Bronzing, gilding, edging & deckling: books, cards, paper
Ch Bd: Eugene G Geiger
**Ex VP:* Peter E Geiger
**Ex VP:* Ronald G Giard
**Ex VP:* Jo-An G Lantz
VP: Carrie Lautner
VP: Herb Miller
Off Mgr: Kerry Worden
Sales Exec: Denise Bates

D-U-N-S 60-610-3729
GEIGER GROUP INC
6095 Fulton Indus Blvd Sw, Atlanta, GA 30336-2806
Tel (404) 344-1100 *Founded/Ownrshp* 1989
Sales 32.5MM *EMP* 320
Accts Kpmg Peat Marwick Llp
SIC 2521 Wood office furniture; Wood office furniture
Ch: John Geiger
**Sec:* Frances Geiger

D-U-N-S 09-930-8603 IMP/EXP
■ **GEIGER INTERNATIONAL INC**
(*Suby of* HERMAN MILLER INC) ★
6095 Fulton Indus Blvd Sw, Atlanta, GA 30336-2806
Tel (404) 344-1100 *Founded/Ownrshp* 1999
Sales 85.7MM^E *EMP* 522
SIC 2521 Wood office furniture; Wood office furniture
Pr: Brian C Walker
CFO: Wendell E Jacobs III
Sr VP: Collin Maclean
VP: Jim Clemens
VP: Dianne Rich
MIS Dir: Charles Boden
Opers Mgr: Michael Glassford
Mktg Dir: Michael Matascik
Mktg Mgr: Carlton Poole
Sls Mgr: Doug Dreyer

D-U-N-S 10-147-4898 IMP
GEIGER PUMP AND EQUIPMENT CO
8924 Yellow Brick Rd, Baltimore, MD 21237-2304
Tel (410) 682-2660 *Founded/Ownrshp* 1996
Sales 32.1MM^E *EMP* 92
SIC 5084

D-U-N-S 00-715-9924
GEIGER READY-MIX CO INC (KS)
1333 S 2nd St, Leavenworth, KS 66048-3508
Tel (913) 772-4010 *Founded/Ownrshp* 1949
Sales 34.2MM^E *EMP* 180
SIC 3273 5211 Ready-mixed concrete; Masonry materials & supplies; Sand & gravel; Paving stones; Concrete & cinder block; Ready-mixed concrete; Masonry materials & supplies; Sand & gravel; Paving stones; Concrete & cinder block
Pr: Steve McDonald
**Ch:* Bill Geiger
**Sec:* Blaine Weeks
**VP:* Todd Geiger
**Prin:* E W Geiger III
CTO: Myrna Filley
Plnt Mgr: Jim Van Veghte
Plnt Mgr: Bill Yunghans

D-U-N-S 15-083-1709
GEIL ENTERPRISES INC
CIS SECURITY
1945 N Helm Ave Ste 102, Fresno, CA 93727-1670
Tel (559) 495-3000 *Founded/Ownrshp* 2006
Sales 36.2MM^E *EMP* 540^E
SIC 7381 7349 Protective services, guard; Janitorial service, contract basis; Building maintenance, except repairs; Protective services, guard; Janitorial service, contract basis; Building maintenance, except repairs
CEO: Sam Geil
**Pr:* Ryan Geil
Genl Mgr: Kyle Chaney
Genl Mgr: Tom Cordeiro
Genl Mgr: Roy Hernandez
Opers Supe: Michele Betancourt
Opers Supe: Aiyaz Buksh
Opers Supe: Sam Cabrera
Opers Supe: Xang Lee
Sls Mgr: Doug Cutts

GEIS COMPANY
See HIGHLAND SOM DEVELOPMENT

GEIS COMPANIES
See GEIS CONSTRUCTION INC

D-U-N-S 02-948-2887
GEIS CONSTRUCTION INC
GEIS COMPANIES
10020 Aurora Hudson Rd, Streetsboro, OH 44241-1621
Tel (330) 528-3500 *Founded/Ownrshp* 1999
Sales 40.9MM^E *EMP* 38
SIC 1541 1542 Industrial buildings & warehouses
Pr: Jeff Martin
CFO: Gary Murphy
VP: Katherine Geis
VP: Gregory Seifert
Sfty Mgr: Chad Schubah

GEISHA
See WORLD WIDE FOOD PRODUCTS INC

D-U-N-S 06-959-5031
GEISINGER - BLOOMSBURG HOSPITAL (PA)
BLOOMSBURG HEALTH SYSTEM, THE
549 Fair St, Bloomsburg, PA 17815-1419
Tel (570) 387-2124 *Founded/Ownrshp* 1905
Sales 43.5MM^E *EMP* 512
SIC 8062 8063 General medical & surgical hospitals; Psychiatric hospitals; General medical & surgical hospitals; Psychiatric hospitals
Pr: Regis P Cabonor
**CEO:* Lissa Bryan-Smith
COO: Melvin Martz
CFO: Erin Fitzgerald
VP: Michael Berger
**VP:* Clair Hock
CTO: Tom Conlin
DP Dir: Alex Cavallini
MIS Dir: Yeuping Chen
QA Dir: Vivek Darji
Dir IT: Marlin Moyer

D-U-N-S 07-916-1360
GEISINGER CLINIC
GEISINGER MEDICAL CENTER
(*Suby of* GEISINGER HEALTH SYSTEM FOUNDATION) ★
100 N Academy Ave, Danville, PA 17822-9800
Tel (570) 271-6211 *Founded/Ownrshp* 1962
Sales 849.4MM *EMP* 12,000
SIC 8011 8733 Clinic, operated by physicians; Health maintenance organization; Internal medicine, physician/surgeon; Physical medicine, physician/surgeon; Medical research; Clinic, operated by physicians Health maintenance organization; Internal medicine, physician/surgeon; Physical medicine, physician/surgeon; Medical research
CEO: Glenn D Steele Jr
Treas: Frank J Trembulak

D-U-N-S 13-076-7890
GEISINGER HEALTH PLAN
(*Suby of* GEISINGER HEALTH SYSTEM FOUNDATION) ★
100 N Academy Ave, Danville, PA 17822-9800
Tel (570) 271-8778 *Founded/Ownrshp* 1984
Sales 1.2MMM *EMP* 900
SIC 8011 Health maintenance organization; Health maintenance organization
Pr: Steve Yosu
CFO: Cinde Rouk
VP: Susan Fetterman
VP: Timothy Fitzgerald
VP: Michael Leighow
**VP:* Frank J Trembulak
VP: Teresa Willard
Dir IT: Peter Cassidy
Doctor: Susan Paolucci MD

D-U-N-S 07-958-2433
GEISINGER HEALTH SYSTEM FOUNDATION
GEISINGER MEDICAL CENTER
100 N Academy Ave, Danville, PA 17822-9800
Tel (570) 271-6211 *Founded/Ownrshp* 1915
Sales 4.3MMM^E *EMP* 13,000^E
SIC 8741 6512 7699 Management services; Nonresidential building operators; Hospital equipment repair services; Management services; Nonresidential building operators; Hospital equipment repair services
Pr: Glenn D Steele Jr
**Ch Bd:* Frank M Henry
**COO:* Frank J Trembulak
COO: Frank Trembulak
Sr Cor Off: Jane Kanyock
Ofcr: Susan W Alcorn
**Ofcr:* Albert Bothe Jr
Ex VP: Andrew M Deubler
Ex VP: Howard R Grant
Ex VP: Susan Hallick
**Ex VP:* Bruce H Hamory MD
Ex VP: David H Ledbetter
**Ex VP:* Lynn Miller
**Ex VP:* Ronald A Paulus
Ex VP: Steven B Pierdon
**Ex VP:* Joanne E Wade
Sr VP: Robert Spahr
VP: Lee Myers
VP: David Weader
VP: John Wiercinski
Exec: Peter Brooks

GEISINGER MEDICAL CENTER
See GEISINGER SYSTEM SERVICES

GEISINGER MEDICAL CENTER
See GEISINGER CLINIC

GEISINGER MEDICAL CENTER
See GEISINGER HEALTH SYSTEM FOUNDATION

D-U-N-S 06-959-1238
GEISINGER MEDICAL CENTER
(*Suby of* GEISINGER HEALTH SYSTEM FOUNDATION) ★
100 N Academy Ave, Danville, PA 17822-0001
Tel (570) 271-6211 *Founded/Ownrshp* 1915
Sales 999.6MM *EMP* 8,000
SIC 8062 General medical & surgical hospitals; General medical & surgical hospitals
Pr: Glenn D Steele Jr
**Pr:* Glenn D Steele
Chf Mktg O: Kenneth Wood
Ofcr: Daron McRee
**Ex VP:* Albert Bothe Jr
Ex VP: Bruce Hamory
**Ex VP:* Lynn Miller
Ex VP: Earl Steinberg
**Ex VP:* Frank J Trembulak
**Ex VP:* Joanne E Wade
VP: John R Boker
Assoc Dir: Brenda Finucane
Creative D: Patrick Pacacha
Dir Rx: Pamela Salwocki

D-U-N-S 06-133-1682
GEISINGER SOUTH WILKES-BARRE (PA)
(*Suby of* GEISINGER HEALTH SYSTEM FOUNDATION) ★
25 Church St, Wilkes Barre, PA 18765-0999
Tel (570) 808-3100 *Founded/Ownrshp* 1984
Sales 55.0MM^E *EMP* 679
SIC 8062 General medical & surgical hospitals; General medical & surgical hospitals
CEO: John Nespoli
**Pr:* Glenn D Steele Jr
**COO:* Synthiya Brylinsky
**Treas:* Frank J Trembulak

D-U-N-S 07-538-2077
GEISINGER SYSTEM SERVICES
GEISINGER MEDICAL CENTER
(*Suby of* GEISINGER HEALTH SYSTEM FOUNDATION) ★
100 N Academy Ave, Danville, PA 17822-9800
Tel (570) 271-6211 *Founded/Ownrshp* 1981
Sales 582.6MM *EMP* 344

SIC 8741 8082 Administrative management; Business management; Financial management for business; Personnel management; Home health care services; Administrative management; Business management; Financial management for business; Personnel management; Home health care services
Pr: Glenn D Steele Jr
**Treas:* Timothy Fitzgerald
**Treas:* Frank J Trembulak
Comm Man: Scott Singer
Dir IT: Chuck Gerst
Dir IT: Ann Korzenaskie
Plnt Mgr: Gloria Gerrity

D-U-N-S 02-795-0542
GEISINGER WYOMING VALLEY MEDICAL CENTER
(*Suby of* GEISINGER HEALTH SYSTEM FOUNDATION) ★
1000 E Mountain Dr, Wilkes Barre, PA 18711-0001
Tel (570) 808-7300 *Founded/Ownrshp* 1976
Sales 447.6MM *EMP* 15
SIC 8062 General medical & surgical hospitals; General medical & surgical hospitals
VP: Timothy Fitzgerald
Ch Bd: Glenn D Steele Jr
COO: Conrad Schintz
Treas: Frank J Trembulak
Opers Mgr: Michael Blazaskie
Ansthlgy: Samuel Lee
Ansthlgy: Samuel Plummer
Plas Surg: Anthony Bruno
Doctor: Rachel Chapman
Pharmcst: Michelle Butcher
Diag Rad: Arthur Liss

D-U-N-S 07-915-8812
GEISINGER-COMMUNITY MEDICAL CENTER
(*Suby of* GEISINGER HEALTH SYSTEM FOUNDATION) ★
1822 Mulberry St, Scranton, PA 18510-2369
Tel (570) 969-8000 *Founded/Ownrshp* 2012
Sales 99.6MM^E *EMP* 1,302^E
SIC 8062 General medical & surgical hospitals; Hospital, medical school affiliated with nursing & residency; General medical & surgical hospitals; Hospital, medical school affiliated with nursing & residency
Pr: Karl Stark
Dir Recs: Sean M Andrew
CFO: Ed Chabalowski
Treas: Felice J Freyer
Ofcr: Gina Mc Cabe
VP: Sean Mc Andrew
VP: Sean McAndrew
Dir Case M: Michelle Albright
Dir Rx: David Rowlands
Chf Nrs Of: Barbara Bossi
CIO: Bo Bobanic

D-U-N-S 01-884-6998
GEISSLERS SUPERMARKET INC
100 Bridge St, East Windsor, CT 06088-9585
Tel (860) 623-6336 *Founded/Ownrshp* 1949
Sales 76.1MM^E *EMP* 485^E
SIC 5411

GEIST GLOBAL
See GEIST MANUFACTURING INC

D-U-N-S 08-707-0124 IMP
GEIST MANUFACTURING INC
GEIST GLOBAL
(*Suby of* IT WATCHDOGS) ★
1821 Yolande Ave, Lincoln, NE 68521-1835
Tel (402) 474-3400 *Founded/Ownrshp* 1997
Sales 54.1MM^E *EMP* 150
SIC 3089 3643 3087 3612 Thermoformed finished plastic products; Power outlets & sockets; Custom compound purchased resins; Transformers, except electric; Thermoformed finished plastic products; Power outlets & sockets; Custom compound purchased resins; Transformers, except electric
Pr: Sam Featherston
**CFO:* Sheli Carpenter
Off Mgr: Cassandra Hayes
CTO: Mark Germagian
IT Man: Will Kerns
Opers Mgr: Vicki Merkle
Sls&Mrk Ex: Ranelle Rundquist
Mktg Dir: Sean Heyen
Mktg Dir: Dave Wilson
Manager: Drew Henderson
Sls Mgr: Kevin Joy

D-U-N-S 96-814-3482
GEISTLICH PHARMA NORTH AMERICA INC
(*Suby of* GEISTLICH PHARMA AG)
202 Carnegie Ctr Ste 103, Princeton, NJ 08540-6239
Tel (609) 779-6560 *Founded/Ownrshp* 2010
Sales 29.7MM *EMP* 39
SIC 3843 Dental equipment & supplies
CEO: Andreas Geistlich PHD
VP: Jeffrey Lord
Dir Soc: Maria Nyholm
Genl Mgr: David Swanson
Sls Mgr: Eric Gruosso
Sls Mgr: Lisa Jacobson
Sls Mgr: Laurie Meschke
Sls Mgr: Paul Philo

D-U-N-S 60-602-1442
GEL CORP
1200 S Leavitt Ave, Orange City, FL 32763-7114
Tel (386) 775-5385 *Founded/Ownrshp* 1985
Sales 20.1MM^E *EMP* 100
SIC 4953 Recycling, waste materials
Pr: Milton Eugene Evans Jr

D-U-N-S 03-009-9667
GEL GROUP INC (SC)
G E L
2040 Savage Rd, Charleston, SC 29407-4731
Tel (843) 556-8171 *Founded/Ownrshp* 1981, 2001
Sales 71.8MM^E *EMP* 330
SIC 8711 8734 8731 8744 1381 Consulting engineer; Pollution testing; Commercial physical research; Facilities support services; Drilling water intake wells; Consulting engineer; Pollution testing; Commercial physical research; Facilities support services; Drilling water intake wells
Pr: James M Stelling
**COO:* Carey J Bocklet
**CFO:* Douglas E Earnst
**Ch:* Kathleen Stelling
Snr PM: Craig McKenzie
Snr PM: Scott Smith
Snr Mgr: Michael Penny
Snr Mgr: Gregg Szymkowicz

D-U-N-S 13-740-4922
GEL LABORATORIES LLC
(*Suby of* G E L) ★
2040 Savage Rd, Charleston, SC 29407-4731
Tel (843) 556-8171 *Founded/Ownrshp* 2003
Sales 25.9MM^E *EMP* 330
SIC 8734 Testing laboratories; Testing laboratories
Prgrm Mgr: John Powell
QA Dir: Michael Penny
Dir IT: Russell Moser
Pgrm Dir: Larry Taake
Snr PM: Keith McCullock
Snr PM: Craig McKenzie
Snr Mgr: Vonda Fields
Snr Mgr: Tim Winters

D-U-N-S 01-236-4501 IMP/EXP
GEL SPICE CO INC
48 Hook Rd, Bayonne, NJ 07002-5007
Tel (201) 339-0700 *Founded/Ownrshp* 1955
Sales 75.0MM^E *EMP* 200^E
Accts Weiss & Company Llp New York
SIC 2099 5149 5145 Spices, including grinding; Spices & seasonings; Bakery products; Nuts, salted or roasted; Spices, including grinding; Spices & seasonings; Bakery products; Nuts, salted or roasted
Pr: Andre Engel
CFO: Sam Baum
**CFO:* Allan Gemberg
Sr VP: Steve Thomas
VP: Leon Nisenboym
VP: Pamela Sabo
VP: Aaron Stahl
VP Sls: Joe Mandel
Sls Mgr: Harry Blumenfeld
Snr Mgr: Richie Bonicioli
Snr Mgr: Jeff Strand

GEL-PAK
See DELPHON INDUSTRIES LLC

D-U-N-S 06-706-6860
GELBER GROUP LLC
350 N Orleans St Fl 7, Chicago, IL 60654-1601
Tel (312) 253-0005 *Founded/Ownrshp* 1982
Sales 86.7MM^E *EMP* 300
Accts Mcgladrey & Pullen Llp Chica
SIC 6221 Futures brokers & dealers, commodity; Futures brokers & dealers, commodity
Ch: Brian Gelber
CFO: Franklin A Gelber

D-U-N-S 00-621-2492
■ **GELCO CORP**
GE FLEET SERVICES
(*Suby of* GENERAL ELECTRIC CAPITAL CORP) ★
3 Capital Dr, Eden Prairie, MN 55344-3889
Tel (952) 828-1000 *Founded/Ownrshp* 1957, 1987
Sales NA *EMP* 2,730
SIC 6159

D-U-N-S 03-001-5333
GELCO INFORMATION NETWORK INC (MN)
(*Suby of* H-G HOLDINGS, INC)
10700 Prairie Lakes Dr, Eden Prairie, MN 55344-3858
Tel (952) 947-1500 *Founded/Ownrshp* 1894, 1994
Sales 23.9MM^E *EMP* 325
SIC 8741 Financial services; Management services
Pr: Karen T Beckwith
**COO:* Brian E Provost
COO: Brian Provost
**CFO:* Tom Goodmanson
**CFO:* Frank Pelzer
Treas: Craig Peterson
Ex VP: Melton Littlepage
VP: Sandra J Crowley
**VP:* Melton E Littlepage III
VP: Richard Switzky
**Prin:* Robert K Maeser

GELITA NORTH AMERICA
See GELITA USA INC

D-U-N-S 61-357-8335 IMP
GELITA NORTH AMERICA INC
(*Suby of* GELITA AG)
2445 Port Neal Rd, Sergeant Bluff, IA 51054-7728
Tel (712) 943-5516 *Founded/Ownrshp* 1977
Sales 225.0MM *EMP* 305
SIC 5169 2099 Gelatin; Food preparations; Gelatin; Food preparations
Pr: Robert Mayberry
VP: Heinrich Schmidt
Dir Lab: Jeff Abell
Genl Mgr: Lisa Barthole
IT Man: Mark Maslonka
Sfty Mgr: Susan Lowrey
Ql Cn Mgr: Carol Ostendorf
Sls Dir: Melissa Simon

D-U-N-S 00-206-4764 IMP
GELITA USA INC
GELITA NORTH AMERICA
(*Suby of* GELITA NORTH AMERICA INC) ★
2445 Port Neal Rd, Sergeant Bluff, IA 51054-7728
Tel (712) 943-5516 *Founded/Ownrshp* 1972, 2002
Sales 49.2MM^E *EMP* 250
SIC 2899 2099 Gelatin: edible, technical, photographic or pharmaceutical; Gelatin dessert preparations; Gelatin: edible, technical, photographic or pharmaceutical; Gelatin dessert preparations
Pr: Robert Mayberry
**Sec:* Sandy Wisecup

D-U-N-S 18-117-9953
GELLER & CO LLC
909 3rd Ave Fl 15, New York, NY 10022-4745
Tel (212) 583-6000 *Founded/Ownrshp* 1984
Sales 111.0MM^E *EMP* 370^E
SIC 8742 8721 Management consulting services; Certified public accountant; Management consulting services; Certified public accountant
CEO: Martin Geller
CEO: Joe Calabrese
COO: Steve Fadem
CFO: Paul Kasnetz
CFO: Aaron Testa
CFO: Kevin Worth
Chf Inves: Robert Wedeking
Ofcr: Jon Persson
Mng Dir: Steven Goldberg
CIO: Anthony Sirabella
CTO: Michelle Starker

D-U-N-S 00-534-1813 IMP
■ **GELMAN SCIENCES INC** (MI)
PALL LIFE SCIENCES
(*Suby of* PALL CORP) ★
674 S Wagner Rd, Ann Arbor, MI 48103-9793
Tel (734) 665-0651 *Founded/Ownrshp* 1980, 1996
Sales 98.8MM^E *EMP* 610
SIC 3821 3569 3564 3841 3845 3699 Laboratory apparatus, except heating & measuring; Filters, general line: industrial; Air purification equipment; Surgical instruments & apparatus; Electromedical apparatus; Insect lamps, electric; Laboratory apparatus, except heating & measuring; Filters, general line: industrial; Air purification equipment; Surgical instruments & apparatus; Electromedical apparatus; Insect lamps, electric
Ch Bd: Eric Krasnoff
Pr: Ricardo Alfonso
**COO:* Don Stevens
**CFO:* Lisa McDermott
VP: Jim Marshall
Sfty Mgr: Doug Preston
Plnt Mgr: Jeremy Surry
VP Sls: Edward Ignacio

D-U-N-S 00-129-2234 IMP
GELMART INDUSTRIES INC (DE)
48 W 38th St Fl 10, New York, NY 10018-0041
Tel (212) 743-6900 *Founded/Ownrshp* 1965, 1972
Sales 28.8MM^E *EMP* 35
Accts Rosen Seymour Shapss Martin &
SIC 5137 Women's & children's accessories
Pr: Yoseph Nasser
CFO: Kenneth Parage
**Treas:* Ronald Karger
Sr VP: Ralph Djemal

GELSON'S MARKETS
See ARDEN GROUP INC

D-U-N-S 02-813-5911
GELSONS MARKETS
(*Suby of* ARDEN-MAYFAIR INC) ★
2020 S Central Ave, Compton, CA 90220-5302
Tel (310) 638-2842 *Founded/Ownrshp* 1966
Sales 261.1MM^E *EMP* 2,264
SIC 5411 Supermarkets, chain; Supermarkets, chain
CEO: Rob McDougall
**Sr VP:* Brenda McDanile
VP: Doug Freund
Snr Mgr: Patricia Betance

D-U-N-S 00-702-7922
GEM AMBULANCE LLC
1750 Cedarbridge Ave # 2, Lakewood, NJ 08701-6921
Tel (732) 575-1700 *Founded/Ownrshp* 2007
Sales 36.1MM^E *EMP* 361^E
SIC 4119 Ambulances; Ambulance service; Ambulance service
CEO: Jacob Halpern
Brnch Mgr: Dawn Vanbrunt

GEM BUILDINGS
See GOLDEN EMPIRE MANUFACTURING INC

GEM CITY ENGINEERING & MFG
See GEM CITY ENGINEERING CO

D-U-N-S 00-424-0941
GEM CITY ENGINEERING CO (OH)
GEM CITY ENGINEERING & MFG
401 Leo St, Dayton, OH 45404-1009
Tel (937) 223-5544 *Founded/Ownrshp* 1936
Sales 37.1MM^E *EMP* 175
SIC 3544 3549 3569 Special dies & tools; Metalworking machinery; Assembly machines, non-metalworking; Special dies & tools; Metalworking machinery; Assembly machines, non-metalworking
CEO: James Whalen
**Pr:* David D Harry
COO: Roger Falcinelli
COO: Jerry Roerig
CFO: Bill Gallagher
**CFO:* William Gallagher
Bd of Dir: Randy Bear
Prgrm Mgr: Michael Alexander
Prgrm Mgr: Steve Bilderback
Prgrm Mgr: Dave Meyer
Prgrm Mgr: Prashanta Shrestha

D-U-N-S 79-041-0328
GEM CITY FORD INC
GEM CITY FORD LINCLON
5101 Broadway St, Quincy, IL 62305-9124
Tel (217) 222-8700 *Founded/Ownrshp* 1992
Sales 24.3MM^E *EMP* 65
SIC 5511 Automobiles, new & used; Trucks, tractors & trailers: new & used; Vans, new & used; Automobiles, new & used; Trucks, tractors & trailers: new & used; Vans, new & used
Pr: Stephen Brink
**Treas:* Don Bolin

GEM CITY FORD LINCLON
See GEM CITY FORD INC

D-U-N-S 88-343-1921
GEM CITY TIRES INC
(*Suby of* JTL ENTERPRISES LLC)
2531 Needmore Rd, Dayton, OH 45414-4203
Tel (513) 769-0007 *Founded/Ownrshp* 2000
Sales 60.3MM^E *EMP* 136
SIC 5531 Automotive tires; Automotive tires
Pr: Jeffrey Lecklider
**CFO:* Pat McMahon
Treas: Russell Jones
**Prin:* Thomas P Martin
Store Mgr: Josh Dobyns
Store Mgr: Steve Taylor
IT Man: John Welsh
Opers Mgr: Mike Hammond

D-U-N-S 04-708-7002 IMP
GEM EQUIPMENT OF OREGON INC
2150 Progress Way, Woodburn, OR 97071-9765
Tel (503) 845-1900 *Founded/Ownrshp* 1969
Sales 27.6MM^E *EMP* 150
SIC 3556 Food products machinery; Food products machinery
CEO: Steve Ross
**Pr:* Edward T Mc Kenney
**Sec:* Warren Bednarz
Off Mgr: Terri Hern
IT Man: Chris Imdieke
QC Dir: Tony Meehl
Sls Dir: Jerry Bell
Sls Mgr: Jim Caughlin

D-U-N-S 01-960-5104 IMP
GEM GROUP INC
GEMLINE
9 International Way, Lawrence, MA 01843-1066
Tel (978) 691-2000 *Founded/Ownrshp* 1958
Sales 66.0MM^E *EMP* 400^E
SIC 2759 Screen printing; Screen printing
Pr: Jonathan G Isaacson
CFO: Clyde Sylvia
Chf Mktg O: Bob Stoltz
VP: Bret Clemons
VP: Robert Leavitt
VP: Matt Millies
**VP:* Clyde W Sylvia
Dist Mgr: Jon Jackson
VP Opers: Frank Papa
Opers Mgr: Michael Braley
Opers Mgr: Debra Koppenaal

D-U-N-S 06-874-9217
GEM GROUP L P
(*Suby of* HEALTHPLAN HOLDINGS INC) ★
3 Gateway Ctr Ste 1200, Pittsburgh, PA 15222
Tel (412) 471-2885 *Founded/Ownrshp* 2010
Sales NA *EMP* 130
SIC 6371 Union welfare, benefit & health funds; Union welfare, benefit & health funds
Genl Pt: Leonard Spencer
Pt: William J Clair
Exec: Bill Clair

D-U-N-S 55-549-4327 IMP
GEM INDUSTRIES INC
(*Suby of* ITR INDUSTRIES INC) ★
Hwy 123 N, Toccoa, GA 30577
Tel (706) 886-8431 *Founded/Ownrshp* 1989
Sales 84.8MM^E *EMP* 700
SIC 3429 2531 2511 3446 2821 2515 Furniture hardware; Casket hardware; Public building & related furniture; Wood household furniture; Architectural metalwork; Plastics materials & resins; Mattresses & bedsprings; Furniture hardware; Casket hardware; Public building & related furniture; Wood household furniture; Architectural metalwork; Plastics materials & resins; Mattresses & bedsprings
CEO: D McVeigh
**Sec:* Adrienne Rolla
**Prin:* Steve Gaymor
Genl Mgr: Doug Hitchon

D-U-N-S 17-075-1619
GEM MANAGEMENT INC
2021 Cross Beam Dr, Charlotte, NC 28217-2856
Tel (704) 357-6000 *Founded/Ownrshp* 1991
Sales 17.3MM^E *EMP* 290
SIC 6531 Real estate agents & managers; Real estate agents & managers
Pr: Gary D Ellis
**Sec:* Timothy L Gunderman
**VP:* Melvin B Melton

D-U-N-S 00-117-2899 IMP
GEM MANUFACTURING CO INC (CT)
78 Brookside Rd, Waterbury, CT 06708-1402
Tel (203) 574-1466 *Founded/Ownrshp* 1943
Sales 23.3MM^E *EMP* 126
SIC 3469 Stamping metal for the trade; Stamping metal for the trade
Pr: Robert C Caulfield Jr
Treas: June Gemino
**VP:* Gerard Berthiaume
**VP:* Mark G Caulfield
Sls Mgr: Jeff McCasland

D-U-N-S 07-209-3248
GEM MECHANICAL SERVICES INC
G E M
1 Wellington Rd, Lincoln, RI 02865-4411
Tel (401) 867-5309 *Founded/Ownrshp* 2005
Sales 39.4MM^E *EMP* 300
SIC 1711 Plumbing contractors; Heating & air conditioning contractors; Plumbing contractors; Heating & air conditioning contractors
Pr: Leonard P Gemma
**CFO:* Elizabeth Gemma
**Treas:* Anthony Gemma
**VP:* Edward Gemma

D-U-N-S 01-977-4322 IMP/EXP
GEM MOBILE TREATMENT SERVICES INC (CA)
(*Suby of* GEM MOBILE TREATMENT SERVICES INC) ★
1196 E Willow St, Signal Hill, CA 90755-3441
Tel (562) 436-2999 *Founded/Ownrshp* 1994
Sales 25.7MM^E *EMP* 58^E

SIC 4959 Environmental cleanup services
CEO: Steve Ragiel
**COO:* Paul Anderson
**VP:* John Beale
**VP:* Steve Haskin
Opers Mgr: Leo Ramirez

D-U-N-S 02-391-5918
GEM MOBILE TREATMENT SERVICES INC
(*Suby of* EVERGREEN ENVIRONMENTAL SERVICES LLC) ★
2525 Cherry Ave Ste 105, Signal Hill, CA 90755-2054
Tel (562) 595-7075 *Founded/Ownrshp* 2015
Sales 27.8MM^E *EMP* 85^E
SIC 3822 1629 Vapor heating controls; Waste water & sewage treatment plant construction
COO: Paul Anderson
CFO: Shane Whittington

D-U-N-S 87-806-3312
GEM REALTY CAPITAL INC
900 N Michigan Ave # 1450, Chicago, IL 60611-1542
Tel (773) 244-0326 *Founded/Ownrshp* 1994
Sales 118.0MM^E *EMP* 666
SIC 6799 Real estate investors, except property operators
Pr: Barry Malkin
**CFO:* Michael A Elrad
**Ex VP:* Norman S Geller
VP: Jason Kalisman
VP: Tom Paulsen
Mng Dir: Denise Olson

D-U-N-S 08-481-8525 IMP
GEM SOUTHEAST INC
(*Suby of* GEM INDUSTRIES INC) ★
961 Highway 123, Toccoa, GA 30577-8798
Tel (706) 886-8431 *Founded/Ownrshp* 1974
Sales 50.4MM^E *EMP* 200
SIC 3495 3429 2514 2512 2542 Wire springs; Casket hardware; Beds, including folding & cabinet, household: metal; Upholstered household furniture; Partitions for floor attachment, prefabricated: except wood; Wire springs; Casket hardware; Beds, including folding & cabinet, household: metal; Upholstered household furniture; Partitions for floor attachment, prefabricated: except wood
CEO: P Rolla
**Pr:* Michael F Rolla
**CFO:* Rolla A M
**Sec:* Adrienne Rolla

D-U-N-S 03-399-0862
GEM STATE DISTRIBUTORS INC
350 Industrial Ln, Pocatello, ID 83201-4265
Tel (208) 237-5151 *Founded/Ownrshp* 1958
Sales 33.1MM^E *EMP* 70
SIC 5194 5145 5962

D-U-N-S 00-909-2198
GEM STATE PAPER & SUPPLY CO (ID)
1801 Highland Ave E, Twin Falls, ID 83301-7923
Tel (208) 733-6081 *Founded/Ownrshp* 1946
Sales 44.1MM^E *EMP* 84
SIC 5113 5087 5046 5169 Towels, paper; Paper & products, wrapping or coarse; Napkins, paper; Janitors' supplies; Restaurant equipment & supplies; Chemicals & allied products; Towels, paper; Paper & products, wrapping or coarse; Napkins, paper; Janitors' supplies; Restaurant equipment & supplies; Chemicals & allied products
Pr: John C Anderson
COO: Fred Alegria
Sales Asso: Sandy Mosbrucker

GEM STOP COMPANY
See A H SCHADE INC

D-U-N-S 04-988-8704 IMP/EXP
■ **GEMAIRE DISTRIBUTORS LLC**
JOHNSON CONTROLS
(*Suby of* WATSCO INC) ★
2151 W Hillsboro Blvd # 400, Deerfield Beach, FL 33442-1199
Tel (954) 246-2665 *Founded/Ownrshp* 1988
Sales 171.6MM^E *EMP* 325
SIC 5075 Air conditioning & ventilation equipment & supplies; Air conditioning & ventilation equipment & supplies
Pr: Kenneth F Connell
Pr: Chris Johnson
**Treas:* Lina C Mori
**VP:* Barry S Logan
**VP:* Ana M Menendez
VP: Lena Mori
VP: Douglas Mullins
**VP:* Kenbian Ng
VP: Mike Plathe
Rgnl Mgr: Gavin Bruno
Rgnl Mgr: Jesse Saldivar

D-U-N-S 93-354-1047 IMP
GEMALTO INC
(*Suby of* GEMALTO N.V.)
9442 Capital Of, Austin, TX 78759
Tel (512) 257-3872 *Founded/Ownrshp* 1990
Sales 211.9MM^E *EMP* 450
SIC 5045 Computers, peripherals & software; Computers, peripherals & software
CEO: Olivier Piou
**Pr:* Paul Beverly
**COO:* Philippe Valle
**CFO:* Jacques Tierny
Treas: Christophe Pouteau
Bd of Dir: France Sud
Ex VP: Philippe Cabanettes
Ex VP: Claude Dahan
Ex VP: Joletta Kaiser
VP: Philippe Cassagne
VP: Regniers Philippe
VP: Rodrigo Serna
Dir Risk M: Bastien Daire

D-U-N-S 55-671-4244 IMP
■ **GEMCHEM INC**
(*Suby of* AMERICAN VANGUARD CORP) ★
4695 Macarthur Ct # 1200, Newport Beach, CA 92660-8859
Tel (949) 476-1919 *Founded/Ownrshp* 1991
Sales 57.9MM^E *EMP* 23
SIC 5122 5169 5191 Pharmaceuticals; Chemicals & allied products; Fertilizers & agricultural chemicals
Pr: Eric G Wintemute
**Co-Ch Bd:* Herbert A Kraft
**Co-Ch Bd:* Glen A Wintemute
**Treas:* Robert F Gilbane

GEMCO MEDICAL
See EDWARDS GEM INC

D-U-N-S 16-687-7840
GEMCOR II LLC
100 Gemcor Dr, West Seneca, NY 14224-2055
Tel (716) 674-9300 *Founded/Ownrshp* 2004
Sales 35.4MM^E *EMP* 87
SIC 3542 Spinning, spline rolling & winding machines; Spinning, spline rolling & winding machines
CEO: William Mangus
COO: Tony Goddard
Exec: Gary Bakalike
IT Man: Brian Magnus
Info Man: Conrad Lesniak
Opers Mgr: Gary Szymkowiak
Plnt Mgr: Mike Kwieiniak

D-U-N-S 80-318-7475
GEMCRAFT HOMES GROUP INC
2205 Commerce Rd Ste A, Forest Hill, MD 21050-2576
Tel (410) 893-8458 *Founded/Ownrshp* 1993
Sales 180.0MM *EMP* 1
SIC 1522 Residential construction; Residential construction
Pr: Vickie Luther
**Pr:* Sharon Babcock
**VP:* Brian Fromme
Off Mgr: Sandi Duncan
Netwrk Mgr: Sean Smith

D-U-N-S 82-500-4666
GEMCRAFT HOMES INC
2205 Commerce Rd Ste A, Forest Hill, MD 21050-2576
Tel (410) 893-8458 *Founded/Ownrshp* 1995
Sales 38.7MM^E *EMP* 125
SIC 1522

D-U-N-S 18-635-0740 IMP
GEMINI COATINGS INC
(*Suby of* GEMINI INDUSTRIES INC) ★
421 Se 27th St, El Reno, OK 73036-5705
Tel (405) 262-5710 *Founded/Ownrshp* 1964
Sales 25.1MM^E *EMP* 137
SIC 2851 Lacquer: bases, dopes, thinner; Lacquer: bases, dopes, thinner
Pr: David P Warren
**CFO:* Richard A McGee
Opers Mgr: Brandon Bosler
Plnt Mgr: Scott Rott
VP Sls: Chris Hicks
Sls Mgr: Jeff Hendry
Sls Mgr: Larry Moore

D-U-N-S 61-732-7143
GEMINI ELECTRIC INC
POWER-UP GENERATOR SERVICES
8 Priscilla Ln Unit 1, Auburn, NH 03032-3747
Tel (603) 657-9080 *Founded/Ownrshp* 1990
Sales 21.3MM^E *EMP* 105^E
Accts Paul E Hendrickson Cpa Bedfo
SIC 1731 Electrical work; Electrical work
Pr: Matthew C Connors
VP: Ryan Corneau
VP Opers: Jeff Beaudin
Sales Exec: Stacey Oikle
Sales Asso: Peter Placet

D-U-N-S 60-645-3777
GEMINI EMPLOYEE LEASING INC
840 Enterprise Dr, Slinger, WI 53086-9135
Tel (262) 644-7480 *Founded/Ownrshp* 1981
Sales 10.5MM^E *EMP* 520^E
Accts Jannsen & Company Sc Pewaukee
SIC 8082 Home health care services; Home health care services
Pr: Kathy Rublee

D-U-N-S 94-379-4800 IMP
GEMINI FOOD CORP
251 Benton Ct, Walnut, CA 91789-5213
Tel (909) 839-0018 *Founded/Ownrshp* 1994
Sales 21.2MM^E *EMP* 30
SIC 5141 Groceries, general line
CEO: George Tong
**VP:* Jonathan Tong MD

D-U-N-S 84-210-3694
GEMINI GROUP INC
175 Thompson Rd Ste A, Bad Axe, MI 48413-8274
Tel (248) 435-7271 *Founded/Ownrshp* 1996
Sales 395.6MM^E *EMP* 480
SIC 8741 3089 Management services; Extruded finished plastic products; Management services; Extruded finished plastic products
VP: David Hyzer
CIO: Dawn Hurlburt
Plnt Mgr: Joe Copes
Plnt Mgr: Dennis Engelhart
Ql Cn Mgr: Wendy Barnes
Sls Dir: Frank Gerbig
Sls Mgr: Norma Hernandez

D-U-N-S 04-540-6589
GEMINI GROUP SERVICE CORP
5108 Pegasus Ct Ste A, Frederick, MD 21704-8328
Tel (301) 378-0294 *Founded/Ownrshp* 1998
Sales 11.0MM^E *EMP* 300
SIC 7349 Building maintenance services; Building maintenance services
CEO: Alan Dykstra
**Pr:* Thomas Ingersoll
Off Mgr: Rosa Cabrera

D-U-N-S 00-625-7430 IMP/EXP
GEMINI INC (MN)
BUYGEMINI.COM
103 Mensing Way, Cannon Falls, MN 55009-1185
Tel (507) 263-3957 *Founded/Ownrshp* 1962, 1963
Sales 68.4MM^E *EMP* 380
SIC 3089 3365 3366 3953 3993 3161

D-U-N-S 00-720-7129 IMP/EXP
GEMINI INDUSTRIES INC
421 Se 27th St, El Reno, OK 73036-5705
Tel (405) 262-5710 *Founded/Ownrshp* 1964
Sales 46.6MM^E *EMP* 155
SIC 2851 7389 Lacquer: bases, dopes, thinner; Packaging & labeling services; Lacquer: bases, dopes, thinner; Packaging & labeling services
Pr: David Warren
**CFO:* Richard McGee
**VP:* Rob Doman
**VP:* Sal Malgari
Genl Mgr: Scott Hunt
Sls Mgr: David Potter
Sls Mgr: Rodney Wickersham

D-U-N-S 05-594-2270 IMP
GEMINI PHARMACEUTICALS INC
87 Modular Ave Ste 1, Commack, NY 11725-5718
Tel (631) 543-3334 *Founded/Ownrshp* 1982
Sales 36.4MM *EMP* 150
SIC 2833 Vitamins, natural or synthetic: bulk, uncompounded; Vitamins, natural or synthetic: bulk, uncompounded
Pr: Andrew Finamore
**Treas:* Brian Finamore
Sr VP: Joni Foley
VP: John Donovan
VP: Bianca Eulloqui
**VP:* Michael Finamore
QC Dir: Clyde Granger

GEMINI PLASTICS
See PEPRO ENTERPRISES INC

GEMINI PLASTICS
See REGENCY PLASTICS - UBLY INC

GEMINI TRADING CO.
See SMITH FAMILY COMPANIES INC

GEMINUS
See SOUTHLAKE/TRI-CITY MANAGEMENT CORP

GEMLINE
See GEM GROUP INC

D-U-N-S 17-934-8164
■ **GEMMA POWER SYSTEMS LLC**
(*Suby of* ARGAN INC) ★
769 Hebron Ave, Glastonbury, CT 06033-5021
Tel (860) 659-0509 *Founded/Ownrshp* 1997
Sales 219.0MM^E *EMP* 239^E
SIC 1629 8711 Power plant construction; Construction & civil engineering; Power plant construction; Construction & civil engineering
CEO: William F Griffin Jr
Pr: Daniel L Martin
Sr VP: Joel W Canino
Sr VP: Bruce M Davis
Sr VP: Ronald W Polaske
Sr VP: Eric Whitehouse
VP: William Carter
VP: Ronald Cochran
VP: Bob Deitz
VP: John Gorzkowske
VP: John S Gorzkowski
VP: John S Gorzkowski Jr
VP: Christopher J Kollmer
VP: Christopher Kollmer
VP: Ron Polaske

D-U-N-S 00-373-7413 IMP
GEMMY INDUSTRIES CORP
VARIDESK
117 Wrangler Dr Ste 100, Coppell, TX 75019-4711
Tel (972) 538-4200 *Founded/Ownrshp* 1984
Sales 22.0MM^E *EMP* 105
SIC 3999 5045 Boutiquing: decorating gift items with sequins, fruit, etc.; Computer peripheral equipment
Ch: Daniel G Flaherty
**Pr:* Jason McCann
**CFO:* Dale Chen
Creative D: Lio Chang
Creative D: Jim Scheibel
Opers Mgr: Anup Dhruve

GEMOCO DIVISION
See CHROMALLOY GAS TURBINE LLC

GEMOLOGICAL INSTITUTE AMERICA
See GEMOLOGICAL INSTITUTE OF AMERICA INC

D-U-N-S 04-849-5378
GEMOLOGICAL INSTITUTE OF AMERICA INC
GEMOLOGICAL INSTITUTE AMERICA
5345 Armada Dr, Carlsbad, CA 92008-4602
Tel (760) 603-4000 *Founded/Ownrshp* 1943
Sales 255.0MM *EMP* 2,800
SIC 8249 8733 Vocational schools; Noncommercial research organizations; Vocational schools; Noncommercial research organizations
Pr: Susan M Jacques
COO: Allison Devlin
CFO: Carl Chilstrom
**CFO:* David Tearle
Treas: Robert Hord
VP: Katherine Palmer Andrews
VP: Frances Hanebrink
**VP:* Tom Moses
VP: Susan Petrich
VP: Michael Quinn
Mng Dir: Kenneth Scarratt
Board of Directors: John Green Chb

GEMS SENSORS & CONTROLS
See GEMS SENSORS INC

D-U-N-S 03-315-5693 IMP
■ **GEMS SENSORS INC**
GEMS SENSORS & CONTROLS
(*Suby of* DANAHER CORP) ★
1 Cowles Rd, Plainville, CT 06062-1107
Tel (860) 747-3000 *Founded/Ownrshp* 1959
Sales 110.4MM^E *EMP* 400
SIC 3824 5084 3812 3625 3613 Fluid meters & counting devices; Industrial machinery & equipment; Search & navigation equipment; Relays & industrial controls; Switchgear & switchboard apparatus; Fluid meters & counting devices; Industrial machinery & equipment; Search & navigation equipment; Relays & industrial controls; Switchgear & switchboard apparatus
Pr: Anne N De Greeg-Sasst
**Pr:* Muriel Bras-Jorge
**VP:* Evan Burns

D-U-N-S 02-293-6870
GEMVARA INC
121 High St Ste 400, Boston, MA 02110-2475
Tel (617) 443-2400 *Founded/Ownrshp* 2011
Sales 21.4MM^E *EMP* 31^E
SIC 5094 Jewelry
Chf Mktg O: S Chandler
**Chf Mktg O:* Matt Marcus
Software D: Jacob Story
Prd Mgr: Kate Hyland

D-U-N-S 10-912-1582
GEN III INC
(*Suby of* N WASSERSTROM & SONS INC) ★
100 Gen Iii Ave, Fountain Inn, SC 29644-2351
Tel (614) 228-5550 *Founded/Ownrshp* 1984
Sales 23.3MM^E *EMP* 150
SIC 3469 Kitchen fixtures & equipment: metal, except cast aluminum; Kitchen fixtures & equipment: metal, except cast aluminum
Pr: John Mc Cormick
**Sr VP:* Roger Sparks

D-U-N-S 06-024-5244
GEN POWER COMPONENTS
4311 W Oquendo Rd, Las Vegas, NV 89118-3086
Tel (702) 280-7777 *Founded/Ownrshp* 2013
Sales 34.7MM^E *EMP* 80
SIC 3452 Bolts, metal
Owner: Richard Lassater

D-U-N-S 11-533-7123
■ **GEN-PROBE INC**
(*Suby of* HOLOGIC INC) ★
10210 Genetic Center Dr, San Diego, CA 92121-4394
Tel (858) 410-8000 *Founded/Ownrshp* 2012
Sales 226.5MM^E *EMP* 1,391
SIC 8731 Biological research; Biological research
Pr: Carl W Hull
Pr: Henry L Nordhoff
CFO: Herm Rosenman
Ex VP: Daniel L Kacian PHD
Sr VP: R William Bowen
Sr VP: Diana De Walt
Sr VP: Jorgine Ellerbrock
Sr VP: Brian B Hansen
Sr VP: Christina C Yang
VP: Brad Blake
VP: N Conway
VP: Edward Cook
VP: Dave Dunn
VP: Kevin Herde
VP: Bruce Huebner
VP: Graham Lidgard
VP: Linda Merrill
VP: Eric Tardif
VP: Robin Vedova
VP: Michael Watts
VP: Michael J Watts
Board of Directors: John W Brown, Armin M Kessler, John C Martin Phd, Phillip M Schneider, Lucy Shapiro Phd, Abraham D Sofaer, Patrick J Sullivan

D-U-N-S 02-740-4248
GEN-TECH CONSTRUCTION LLC
(*Suby of* JE DUNN CONSTRUCTION CO) ★
9895 Harwin Dr Ste B12, Houston, TX 77036-1682
Tel (713) 681-8486 *Founded/Ownrshp* 2008
Sales 31.8MM^E *EMP* 60
SIC 1542 Commercial & office buildings, renovation & repair
CEO: Gordon Lansford III
**Ch:* William Dunn
Sr VP: Al Dyar
VP Opers: Daniel Marzilli

D-U-N-S 18-963-3667
GEN3 CONSTRUCTION LLC
1270 S Lipan St, Denver, CO 80223-3007
Tel (303) 274-6332 *Founded/Ownrshp* 2005
Sales 27.2MM^E *EMP* 85
SIC 1542 Commercial & office buildings, prefabricated erection; Commercial & office buildings, prefabricated erection

GENA
See GROUP ENTERPRISE OF NORTH AMERICA INC

D-U-N-S 00-661-6130 IMP
GENADYNE BIOTECHNOLOGIES INC (NY)
16 Midland Ave, Hicksville, NY 11801-1510
Tel (516) 487-8787 *Founded/Ownrshp* 1992
Sales 20.6MM^E *EMP* 35
SIC 5047 3841 Medical equipment & supplies; Surgical & medical instruments
Pr: Shahzad Pirzada
VP Sls: Bruce Schuchat

D-U-N-S 07-237-8292
GENATT ASSOCIATES INC
H L I
3333 New Hyde Park Rd, New Hyde Park, NY 11042-1204
Tel (516) 869-8666 *Founded/Ownrshp* 1967
Sales NA *EMP* 95
SIC 6411 Insurance agents
Pr: Stephen Genatt
**Ch Bd:* Leslie Genatt

VP: Kathy Damon
VP: Rob Grotsky
VP: Robin Kahn
VP: Marc Sacco
MIS Mgr: John Perazzo
Sls&Mrk Ex: Renee Guthart
Mktg Mgr: Jeff Kozarsky

D-U-N-S 07-438-1513 IMP
GENBAND US LLC
2801 Network Blvd Ste 300, Frisco, TX 75034-1881
Tel (972) 521-5800 *Founded/Ownrshp* 1999
Sales 514.0MM^E *EMP* 1,550
SIC 3661 Telephones & telephone apparatus; Telephones & telephone apparatus
Pr: David Walsh
Pr: Bg Kumar
CFO: Daryl Raiford
Treas: Karen Leopardi
Chf Mktg O: Mehmet N Balos
Chf Mktg O: Patrick Joggerst
Ofcr: Jan E Gaulding
Ofcr: Sean Huurman
Ex VP: Brad Bush
Ex VP: Barbara Dalibard
Ex VP: Daniel R Lakey
Ex VP: Keith Landau
Ex VP: John McCready
Ex VP: John McReady
Ex VP: Paul Pluschkell
Ex VP: Mark Pugerude
Ex VP: Jeff Townley
Ex VP: Darrin Whitney
Ex VP: Robin Wright
Sr VP: John Dannunzio
Sr VP: Patrick Dolan

GENCO ATC
See ATC LOGISTICS & ELECTRONICS INC

GENCO ATC
See GENCO DISTRIBUTION SYSTEM INC

GENCO ATC
See I GENCO INC

D-U-N-S 79-618-5445
■ **GENCO DISTRIBUTION SYSTEM INC**
GENCO ATC
(*Suby of* FEDEX CORP) ★
100 Papercraft Park, Pittsburgh, PA 15238-3274
Tel (412) 820-3922 *Founded/Ownrshp* 2015
Sales 1.5MMM^E *EMP* 8,612
SIC 4225 4731 General warehousing & storage; General warehousing; Freight transportation arrangement; General warehousing & storage; General warehousing; Freight transportation arrangement
CEO: Todd R Peters
Pr: John McGonigle III
Pr: Herb Shear
Pr: Mike Simpson
Pr: Andy Smith
Pr: Dwight Wyland
COO: Art Smuck
CFO: Rick Roadarmel
Treas: Rick L Roadarmel
Ex VP: John J Machota
Ex VP: Pete Rector
Ex VP: Joseph Salamunovichs
Sr VP: Mark Boyer
Sr VP: Ryan Kelly
VP: Venkat Avunoori
VP: Gene Bodenheimer
VP: Bob Devos
VP: Kevin Giles
VP: Jeff Gilmore
VP: Stephen Hertzer
VP: Young Joe

D-U-N-S 07-952-1913
GENCO ENERGY SERVICES INC
1701 W State Highway 107, McAllen, TX 78504-9550
Tel (956) 380-3710 *Founded/Ownrshp* 2011
Sales 29.8MM^E *EMP* 275^E
SIC 7359 Equipment rental & leasing; Equipment rental & leasing
Pr: Murray Meggison
Off Mgr: Becky Bergh

D-U-N-S 10-793-5207
GENCO MASONRY INC
4853 Cordell Ave, Bethesda, MD 20814-7055
Tel (301) 657-4420 *Founded/Ownrshp* 1986
Sales 40.0MM *EMP* 500
SIC 1741 Masonry & other stonework; Masonry & other stonework
Ch: Anthony Izzo Jr
Pr: Steve Sullivan
CEO: Anthony Izzo III
Treas: Edward Moore
VP: Dante J Marcario

D-U-N-S 13-119-2767
GENCO OF LEBANON INC
100 Papercraft Park, Pittsburgh, PA 15238-3200
Tel (412) 820-3747 *Founded/Ownrshp* 1995
Sales 314.5MM^E *EMP* 6,500
SIC 6512 Commercial & industrial building operation; Commercial & industrial building operation
Pr: Herbert Shear
COO: Terry Bentley
CFO: Rick Roadarmeo
Sr VP: Glenn Mauney
VP: Brad Feuerbacher
VP: Larry Schoeneberger
Genl Mgr: Kent Berry
Genl Mgr: Howard Hutt
Genl Mgr: George Pancake
Genl Mgr: Joe Pugar
Genl Mgr: Genco-Tom Scheitrum
Board of Directors: Eric Lange

D-U-N-S 36-321-3112
▲ **GENCO SHIPPING & TRADING LTD**
299 Park Ave Rm 1200, New York, NY 10171-3806
Tel (646) 443-8550 *Founded/Ownrshp* 2014
Sales 119.6MM^E *EMP* 1,564^E
Tkr Sym GNK *Exch* NYS
SIC 4412 Deep sea foreign transportation of freight; Deep sea foreign transportation of freight

Pr: John C Wobensmith
Ch Bd: Peter C Georgiopoulos
CFO: John Wobensmith
CFO: Apostolos Zafolias
Board of Directors: Ian Ashby, Eugene I Davis, James G Dolphin, Michael J Leffell, William Manuel

D-U-N-S 94-850-1101
■ **GENCO TRANSPORTATION MANAGEMENT LLC**
(*Suby of* GENCO ATC) ★
100 Papercraft Park, Pittsburgh, PA 15238-3200
Tel (412) 820-3700 *Founded/Ownrshp* 2003
Sales 56.0MM^E *EMP* 1,500
SIC 4225 4111 5045 4789 General warehousing & storage; Local & suburban transit; Computers, peripherals & software; Cargo loading & unloading services; General warehousing & storage; Local & suburban transit; Computers, peripherals & software; Cargo loading & unloading services
CEO: Todd R Peters
CFO: Rick Roadarmel
VP Sls: Dave Vehec

GENCO-ATC
See ATC TECHNOLOGY CORP

D-U-N-S 61-930-8307
GENCOM REAL ESTATE SERVICES CORP
10777 Westheimer Rd # 1000, Houston, TX 77042-3455
Tel (713) 952-7800 *Founded/Ownrshp* 1999
Sales 10.9MM^E *EMP* 700
SIC 7011 Hotels & motels; Hotels & motels
Pr: Karim Alibhai
Ex VP: Bahadur Alibhai
VP: Amir Alibhai

D-U-N-S 05-210-1409 EXP
▲ **GENCOR INDUSTRIES INC**
5201 N Orange Blossom Trl, Orlando, FL 32810-1038
Tel (407) 290-6000 *Founded/Ownrshp* 1968
Sales 39.2MM *EMP* 237
Tkr Sym GENC *Exch* NGM
SIC 3531 3823 3443 Asphalt plant, including gravel-mix type; Combustion control instruments; Heat exchangers, condensers & components; Asphalt plant, including gravel-mix type; Combustion control instruments; Heat exchangers, condensers & components
Ch Bd: E J Elliott
Pr: Marc G Elliott
CFO: Eric E Mellen
CFO: Scott W Runkel
Sr VP: Dennis B Hunt
Genl Mgr: Tim Bugler
Genl Mgr: Mike Dieli
Genl Mgr: Susan Hillard
Genl Mgr: Michael Ossler
Sftwr Eng: Jorge Felix
Sftwr Eng: Henry Marchese
Board of Directors: Cort J Dondero, Randolph H Fields, James P Sharp, David A Air

D-U-N-S 14-457-5763 IMP
■ **GENDEX CORP**
GENDEX DENTAL SYSTEMS
(*Suby of* DANAHER CORP) ★
1910 N Penn Rd, Hatfield, PA 19440-1960
Tel (800) 323-8029 *Founded/Ownrshp* 2003
Sales 24.0MM^E *EMP* 200
SIC 3844 X-ray apparatus & tubes; X-ray apparatus & tubes
Pr: Matt Reintjes
CFO: Frederick Gupta
VP: Robert Joyce Jr
VP: Chuck Ravetto
Mng Dir: Gary Sieckman
Rgnl Mgr: Erik Beard
Opers Mgr: Gordon Leahy

GENDEX DENTAL SYSTEMS
See GENDEX CORP

D-U-N-S 08-130-3562
GENE & PAUL ASSOCIATES
9 Moody Rd Ste 18, Enfield, CT 06082-3120
Tel (860) 749-1472 *Founded/Ownrshp* 1961
Sales 14.4MM^E *EMP* 650
SIC 7389 8743 Merchandise liquidators; Promotion service; Merchandise liquidators; Promotion service
Pt: Paul Cohen
Pt: Gene Rosenberg

D-U-N-S 01-640-4295
GENE B GLICK CO INC
CARRAIGE HOUSE OF COLUMBIA
8425 Woodfield Crossing B, Indianapolis, IN 46240-2590
Tel (317) 469-0400 *Founded/Ownrshp* 1947
Sales 240.4MM^E *EMP* 627
Accts Katz Sapper & Miller Llp In
SIC 1522 6531 6513 Multi-family dwelling construction; Real estate managers; Apartment building operators; Multi-family dwelling construction; Real estate managers; Apartment building operators
Pr: David O Barrett
Pr: Eugene B Glick
Treas: Anita Smith
Sr VP: James T Bisesi
Sr VP: Marilyn K Glick
Sr VP: Tom Grande
VP: Dennis Edmonds
Dir IT: Curtis Taylor

D-U-N-S 62-164-4991
GENE B GLICK FAMILY HOUSING FOUNDATION INC
8425 Wdfld Xing Blvd, Indianapolis, IN 46240-7315
Tel (317) 469-5898 *Founded/Ownrshp* 2009
Sales 42.2MM *EMP* 1
Accts Ksm Business Services Inc Ind
SIC 6513 Apartment building operators; Apartment building operators
VP: Kathleen Overbey

D-U-N-S 83-447-4454
GENE GLICK MANAGEMENT CO INC
RICHFELD APRTMNTS W LFAYETTE A
8425 Woodfld Crnng Blvd S Ste 300, Indianapolis, IN 46240
Tel (317) 469-0400 *Founded/Ownrshp* 1993
Sales 26.0MM *EMP* 80^E
SIC 8742 Management consulting services
VP: James Bisesi
VP: Linda Orange
VP: Brian Poor

D-U-N-S 96-697-8905
GENE HAAS FOUNDATION
2800 Sturgis Rd, Oxnard, CA 93030-8901
Tel (805) 278-1800 *Founded/Ownrshp* 2011
Sales 50.6MM *EMP* 2
Accts Cbiz Mhm Llc Los Angeles Ca
SIC 8699 Charitable organization; Charitable organization

D-U-N-S 02-611-7465
GENE HARRIS PETROLEUM INC
HARRIS, GENE PROPANE
12901 South Fwy, Burleson, TX 76028-7002
Tel (817) 295-1091 *Founded/Ownrshp* 1953
Sales 31.4MM^E *EMP* 55
SIC 5171 5984 Petroleum bulk stations; Propane gas, bottled; Petroleum bulk stations; Propane gas, bottled
Pr: Eugene L Harris
Treas: David Quisenberry
Treas: Paula Quisenberry
VP: Ron Smith

D-U-N-S 12-125-3397
GENE HUGGINS IMPORTS INC
HUGGINS HONDA
(*Suby of* PEARSON HONDA) ★
7551 Ne Loop 820, Fort Worth, TX 76180-6971
Tel (817) 485-7112 *Founded/Ownrshp* 1983
Sales 29.2MM^E *EMP* 60
SIC 5511 Automobiles, new & used; Automobiles, new & used
Pr: Ronald B Huggins
Treas: Brenda Dukeman
Treas: Dan Wilkins
VP: Max Pearson
Genl Mgr: Ronnie Huggins
Genl Mgr: Robert Raper
Genl Mgr: Ronnie Vaughin

D-U-N-S 05-651-4872
GENE JUAREZ SALONS LLC
3633 136th Pl Se Ste 200, Bellevue, WA 98006-1455
Tel (425) 748-1400 *Founded/Ownrshp* 2008
Sales 1.7MM^E *EMP* 4,000
SIC 7231 Beauty shops
CEO: Scott Missaca

D-U-N-S 04-623-8465 IMP
GENE LANGAN VOLKSWAGEN INC
816 New London Tpke, Glastonbury, CT 06033-3076
Tel (860) 633-0261 *Founded/Ownrshp* 1969
Sales 23.3MM^E *EMP* 70^E
SIC 5511 Automobiles, new & used; Automobiles, new & used
Pr: Carol Langan
VP: Kevin Langan

D-U-N-S 18-630-9621
GENE M FORBES ENTERPRISES INC
MCDONALD'S
120 Mcdonalds St, Tazewell, VA 24651-9326
Tel (276) 988-2558 *Founded/Ownrshp* 1983
Sales 18.4MM^E *EMP* 600
SIC 5812 Fast-food restaurant, chain; Fast-food restaurant, chain
Pr: Gene Forbes

D-U-N-S 10-678-0380
■ **GENE MESSER FORD OF AMARILLO INC**
EAGLE OF AMARILLO
(*Suby of* GROUP 1 AUTOMOTIVE INC) ★
3400 S Soncy Rd, Amarillo, TX 79119-6427
Tel (806) 331-0962 *Founded/Ownrshp* 1999
Sales 30.6MM^E *EMP* 91
SIC 5511 Automobiles, new & used; Pickups, new & used; Automobiles, new & used; Pickups, new & used
Pr: Greg Wessels
Genl Mgr: David Beer
Sales Exec: Gene Messer

D-U-N-S 02-063-2268
GENE R GLOVER INCOME TAX SERVICE
131 Chango Cir, Sacramento, CA 95835-2414
Tel (916) 804-1052 *Founded/Ownrshp* 2009
Sales 27.9MM *EMP* 1^E
SIC 8999 Services; Services
Prin: Gene R Glover

D-U-N-S 05-207-4028
GENE REED CHEVROLET INC
CHEVROLET OF NORTH CHARLESTON
8199 Rivers Ave, North Charleston, SC 29406-9238
Tel (843) 569-7700 *Founded/Ownrshp* 2005
Sales 27.9MM^E *EMP* 181
SIC 5511 Automobiles, new & used
Pr: Stephen R Jacobs
Genl Mgr: John Calcutt
Genl Mgr: Bill Walker
Sls Mgr: Chris Whittamore

D-U-N-S 05-961-4339 EXP
GENE REED TOYOTA INC
LEXUS OF CHARLESTON
7151 Rivers Ave, North Charleston, SC 29406-4608
Tel (843) 797-8000 *Founded/Ownrshp* 1983
Sales 32.0MM^E *EMP* 115
SIC 5511 5521 Automobiles, new & used; Used car dealers; Automobiles, new & used; Used car dealers
Pr: Gene Reed
Pr: Ed Brown
Genl Mgr: Scott Noblitt
IT Man: Angie Polk
Mktg Dir: Chris Sommer

Sls Mgr: Don Hesher
Sls Mgr: Joel Smith
Sls Mgr: Michael Warren

GENE SISKEL FILM CENTER
See ART INSTITUTE OF CHICAGO

D-U-N-S 01-743-5637
GENE SMYTH INC (NV)
DREYERS OF LAS VEGAS
3125 Losee Rd, North Las Vegas, NV 89030-4113
Tel (702) 657-8944 *Founded/Ownrshp* 1978, 1982
Sales 24.0MM^E *EMP* 72
SIC 5143 Ice cream & ices; Ice cream & ices
Pr: Gene Smyth
Sec: Marjorie Smyth

D-U-N-S 10-229-7579
GENE STEFFYS CHRYSLER CENTER INC
GENE STFFYS CHRYSLER JEEP EGLE
2545 E 23rd Ave S, Fremont, NE 68025-2478
Tel (402) 727-8550 *Founded/Ownrshp* 1981
Sales 22.6MM^E *EMP* 60
SIC 5511 Automobiles, new & used; Automobiles, new & used
Pr: Gene Steffensmeier
Treas: Chris Stefferstrter
Genl Mgr: Tim Hoshor
IT Man: Dan Larson
Sales Asso: Fred Cappellano
Sales Asso: Bryan Spilinek
Sales Asso: Ed Steffy
Sales Asso: Konner Tourek
Sales Asso: Gary Wiese

GENE STFFYS CHRYSLER JEEP EGLE
See GENE STEFFYS CHRYSLER CENTER INC

D-U-N-S 86-705-0031
GENE WATSON CONSTRUCTION A CALIFORNIA LIMITED PARTNERSHIP
801 Kern St, Taft, CA 93268-2734
Tel (661) 763-5254 *Founded/Ownrshp* 1993
Sales 12.4MM^E *EMP* 530
SIC 1389 1382 Oil field services; Oil & gas exploration services; Oil field services; Oil & gas exploration services
Ltd Pt: Gene Watson
Ltd Pt: Patricia Watson

D-U-N-S 09-747-2315 EXP
GENE WHEELER FARMS INC
220 W Avenue H6, Lancaster, CA 93534-1636
Tel (661) 951-2100 *Founded/Ownrshp* 2003
Sales 25.0MM *EMP* 250
Accts Fisher Keathley & Ross Llp
SIC 0191 General farms, primarily crop; General farms, primarily crop
Pr: Gene Wheeler

D-U-N-S 94-082-1213
GENE WHITLEY KELLY
44439 Fish Camp Rd, New London, NC 28127-9620
Tel (704) 984-0811 *Founded/Ownrshp* 1999
Sales 328.0MM *EMP* 6
SIC 5031 Lumber: rough, dressed & finished; Lumber: rough, dressed & finished
Owner: Kelly Gene Whitley

D-U-N-S 82-679-3981
GENEDX
481 Edward H Ross Dr, Elmwood Park, NJ 07407-3118
Tel (201) 791-2600 *Founded/Ownrshp* 2010
Sales 20.5MM *EMP* 120
SIC 8071 8011 Medical laboratories; Offices & clinics of medical doctors; Medical laboratories; Offices & clinics of medical doctors

GENENCOR INTERNATIONAL
See DANISCO US INC

D-U-N-S 08-012-9000 IMP
■ **GENENTECH INC**
(*Suby of* ROCHE HOLDINGS INC) ★
1 Dna Way, South San Francisco, CA 94080-4990
Tel (650) 225-1000 *Founded/Ownrshp* 1986, 2009
Sales 2.6MMM^E *EMP* 11,174
SIC 2834 Pharmaceutical preparations; Hormone preparations; Drugs acting on the cardiovascular system, except diagnostic; Drugs acting on the respiratory system; Pharmaceutical preparations; Hormone preparations; Drugs acting on the cardiovascular system, except diagnostic; Drugs acting on the respiratory system
CEO: Ian Clark
COO: Myrtle S Potter
COO: Pascal Soriot
CFO: Steve Krognes
CFO: Thomas Parker
Treas: Odette Go
Sec: Stephen G Juelsgaard
Sec: Aimee Markey
Chf Mktg O: Hal Barron
Ofcr: Rick Kentz
Ofcr: Richard Scheller
Top Exec: Sandra J Horning
Sr VP: Bruce C Cooper
Sr VP: Troy Cox
Sr VP: David A Ebersman
Sr VP: Robert L Garnick
Sr VP: Paula M Jardieu
Sr VP: Ann Karlon
Sr VP: Timothy L Moore
Sr VP: John Orwin
Sr VP: Richard H Scheller
Board of Directors: Aggie ADM Aisst, Frank J D'angelo, Frederick C Kentz III, Arthur D Levinson Phd

D-U-N-S 80-804-3678 IMP
■ **GENENTECH USA INC**
(*Suby of* GENENTECH INC) ★
1 Dna Way, South San Francisco, CA 94080-4990
Tel (650) 225-1000 *Founded/Ownrshp* 2007
Sales 205.9MM^E *EMP* 39^E
SIC 2834 Pharmaceutical preparations; Hormone preparations; Drugs acting on the cardiovascular system, except diagnostic; Drugs acting on the respiratory system
Prin: Ian T Clark

COO: William Young
Ex VP: David A Ebersman
Exec: Patrick Y Yang
**Prin:* Leonard Kanavy
**Prin:* Frederick C Kentz III
**Prin:* Steve Krognes
IT Man: Michele Redhair
IT Man: Maureen Sharkey

D-U-N-S 15-871-2997
▲ GENER8 MARITIME INC
299 Park Ave Fl 2, New York, NY 10171-0299
Tel (212) 763-5600 *Founded/Ownrshp* 1997
Sales 392.4MM *EMP* 42
Tkr Sym GNRT *Exch* NYS
SIC 4412 Deep sea foreign transportation of freight; Deep sea foreign transportation of freight
Ch Bd: Peter C Georgiopoulos
COO: John P Tavlarios
CFO: Leonard J Vrondissis
Treas: John Georgiopoulos
VP: Chris Allwin

D-U-N-S 80-087-0545 IMP
GENERA CORP
2800 Saturn St, Brea, CA 92821-6201
Tel (714) 522-6688 *Founded/Ownrshp* 1991
Sales 67.0MM^E *EMP* 125
SIC 5013 Automotive supplies; Automotive supplies
Ch Bd: Philo Shih-You Wang
**Pr:* Jackson Kwok
VP: Annie Wong
IT Man: Minchi Chen
IT Man: Peter Lai
IT Man: Chen Minchi
IT Man: Wu Vince
IT Man: Vince Wu

D-U-N-S 83-288-8155
▲ GENERAC HOLDINGS INC
S45w29290 Hwy 59, Waukesha, WI 53189-9071
Tel (262) 544-4811 *Founded/Ownrshp* 2006
Sales 1.4MMM *EMP* 3,587^E
Tkr Sym GNRC *Exch* NYS
SIC 3621 Motors & generators; Motors & generators
Pr: Aaron P Jagdfeld
**Pr:* Jeff Koepke
COO: Dawn Tabat
CFO: York A Ragen
Ex VP: Terry Dolan
Ex VP: Allen D Gillette
Ex VP: Russell S Minick
Ex VP: Roger F Pascavis
Sr VP: Roger Schaus Jr
VP: Shawn Fortune
Dir Bus: Bob Heller
Dir Bus: Jack Mandula
Board of Directors: Todd A Adams, John D Bowlin, Ralph W Castner, Robert D Dixon, Andrew G Lampereur, Bennett Morgan, David A Ramon, Timothy Walsh

D-U-N-S 19-962-3596 IMP/EXP
■ GENERAC MOBILE PRODUCTS LLC
(*Suby of* GENERAC POWER SYSTEMS INC) ★
215 Power Dr, Berlin, WI 54923-2420
Tel (920) 361-4442 *Founded/Ownrshp* 2011
Sales 62.4MM^E *EMP* 435^E
SIC 3646 3537 3621 3569 3648

D-U-N-S 00-610-3055 IMP/EXP
■ GENERAC POWER SYSTEMS INC
(*Suby of* GENERAC HOLDINGS INC) ★
S45 W 29290 State Rd 59 St S 45, Waukesha, WI 53189
Tel (262) 544-4811 *Founded/Ownrshp* 1959
Sales 404.2MM^E *EMP* 1,574
SIC 3621 Generator sets: gasoline, diesel or dual-fuel; Generator sets: gasoline, diesel or dual-fuel
Pr: Aaron Jagdfeld
**COO:* Dawn Tabat
**CFO:* York Ragen
VP: Kyle Raabe
Dir Lab: Jim Piquette
**Prin:* Joe Kavalary
Opers Supe: Mary Pick
Natl Sales: Chet Larson
Sls Dir: Ross Castner
Manager: Brandon Bassler
Sls Mgr: Bob Cramer

D-U-N-S 00-643-1878 EXP
GENERAC POWER SYSTEMS INC (WI)
BALDOR GENERATORS
(*Suby of* BALDOR ELECTRIC CO) ★
3815 Oregon St, Oshkosh, WI 54902-7100
Tel (262) 544-4811 *Founded/Ownrshp* 1973, 2000
Sales 1.5MMM^E *EMP* 3,400
SIC 3621 Generators & sets, electric; Generators & sets, electric
Pr: Ron Tucker
**Pr:* Ronald Tucker
Exec: Joel Luepke
Genl Mgr: Bill Magritz
Sfty Dirs: Rob Harris
Opers Mgr: Dean Zastrow
Plnt Mgr: Scott Sherwood

GENERAL & COLOGNE LIFE RE AMER
See GENERAL RE LIFE CORP

GENERAL ACCIDENT GROUP
See PENNSYLVANIA GENERAL INSURANCE CO INC

GENERAL AIR DIVISION
See PSB INDUSTRIES INC

D-U-N-S 05-122-7338
GENERAL AIR SERVICE & SUPPLY CO
1105 Zuni St, Denver, CO 80204-3399
Tel (303) 892-7003 *Founded/Ownrshp* 1984
Sales 86.8MM^E *EMP* 112^E
SIC 5169 5085 5084 5149 Industrial gases; Welding supplies; Welding machinery & equipment; Soft drinks; Industrial gases; Welding supplies; Welding machinery & equipment; Soft drinks
Pr: Gary E Armstrong
Pr: Bob Page
Ex VP: Brad Armstrong
VP: Mark Gregory
**VP:* Michael Owings
**VP:* Art Waskey
Store Mgr: Jeff Call
S&M/VP: Bonnie Blakesley
Sls Mgr: Steve Duren
Sales Asso: Kyle Killpack

D-U-N-S 19-433-7978
GENERAL ALUMINUM CO OF TEXAS LP
(*Suby of* MI WINDOWS AND DOORS INC) ★
1001 W Crosby Rd, Carrollton, TX 75006-6901
Tel (972) 242-5271 *Founded/Ownrshp* 2001
Sales 89.7MM^E *EMP* 600
SIC 3442 5031 Window & door frames; Casements, aluminum; Metal doors, sash & trim; Window & door frames; Casements, aluminum; Metal doors, sash & trim
Ch Bd: Dean P Guerin
Pr: Chris Rix
COO: John Russell
CFO: Mark Swoverland
IT Man: Charlie Hinkle
Sfty Dirs: Joe Jackson
S&M/VP: Curtis Jaska

D-U-N-S 00-415-2658 IMP
■ GENERAL ALUMINUM MFG CO (OH)
GAMCO
(*Suby of* PARK-OHIO INDUSTRIES INC) ★
6065 Parkland Blvd, Cleveland, OH 44124-6119
Tel (440) 947-2000 *Founded/Ownrshp* 1981, 1993
Sales 246.9MM^E *EMP* 900^E
SIC 3365 3369 Aluminum & aluminum-based alloy castings; Nonferrous foundries; Aluminum & aluminum-based alloy castings; Nonferrous foundries
CEO: Edward Crawford
Pr: Bob Paulenske
Sr VP: Neil Schneider
Dir IT: Timothy Ziegler
Ql Cn Mgr: Michele Bates
Ql Cn Mgr: Richard Burcham

D-U-N-S 62-709-8536
GENERAL AMERICA CORP
(*Suby of* SAFECO CORP) ★
1001 4th Ave, Seattle, WA 98154-1119
Tel (866) 844-4046 *Founded/Ownrshp* 1968
Sales 24.7MM^E *EMP* 400
SIC 6512 6411 Insurance building operation; Insurance brokers
Ch Bd: Roger H Eigsti
**Pr:* Boh Dickey
**CFO:* Rodney A Pierson

D-U-N-S 00-696-7541
■ GENERAL AMERICAN LIFE INSURANCE CO
(*Suby of* METLIFE INC) ★
13045 Tesson Ferry Rd, Saint Louis, MO 63128-3407
Tel (314) 843-8700 *Founded/Ownrshp* 1997
Sales NA *EMP* 1,067^E
Accts Deloitte & Touche Llp
SIC 6411 6311 Insurance agents, brokers & service; Education services, insurance; Life insurance; Insurance agents, brokers & service; Education services, insurance; Life insurance
Ex VP: Bernard H Wolzenski
COO: Sharpe Gregory
**CFO:* Steve Anderson
**CFO:* Tim Klopfenstein
**Ex VP:* Albert Greig Woodring
Sr VP: Jerry Mueller
VP: Karen Kotner
Dir IT: Debbie Youngs

D-U-N-S 03-686-1334
■ GENERAL AMERICAN MUTUAL HOLDING CO
(*Suby of* METLIFE) ★
700 Market St, Saint Louis, MO 63101-1829
Tel (314) 231-1700 *Founded/Ownrshp* 2000
Sales NA *EMP* 1,690
SIC 6311 Life insurance carriers; Life insurance carriers
Pr: Richard A Liddy

D-U-N-S 03-250-4037
GENERAL ASPHALT CO INC
4850 Nw 72nd Ave, Miami, FL 33166-5642
Tel (305) 592-6005 *Founded/Ownrshp* 1966
Sales 105.5MM^E *EMP* 150
SIC 3531 Asphalt plant, including gravel-mix type; Asphalt plant, including gravel-mix type
Pr: Robert A Lopez
**CFO:* Curtis Simpson
**VP:* Albert J Lopez
**VP:* Royal Webster Jr
VP: Royal S Webter

D-U-N-S 01-469-9243
GENERAL ASPHALT PAVING CO OF PHILADELPHIA
GENERAL ASPHALT PAVING CO PHIL
9301 Krewstown Rd, Philadelphia, PA 19115-3710
Tel (215) 673-7800 *Founded/Ownrshp* 1942
Sales 23.1MM^E *EMP* 50
SIC 1623 1611 Pipe laying construction; Highway & street paving contractor
Pr: Austin A Meehan Jr
**VP:* Austin A Meehan III
**VP:* Joseph P Meehan

GENERAL ASPHALT PAVING CO PHIL
See GENERAL ASPHALT PAVING CO OF PHILADELPHIA

GENERAL ASSEMBLY
See LEGISLATIVE OFFICE OF STATE OF GEORGIA

GENERAL ASSEMBLY
See LEGISLATIVE OFFICE OF STATE OF CONNECTICUT

GENERAL ASSEMBLY
See LEGISLATIVE OFFICE OF STATE OF INDIANA

D-U-N-S 92-680-7587 IMP
GENERAL ASSEMBLY CORP
1530 Goodyear Dr, El Paso, TX 79936-6062
Tel (915) 859-3118 *Founded/Ownrshp* 1992
Sales 85.8MM^E *EMP* 600^E
SIC 3679 Harness assemblies for electronic use: wire or cable; Harness assemblies for electronic use: wire or cable
Pr: Roman Brenner
**Treas:* George McPherson
**Sec:* Josef Bornbaum
**Sec:* Chris Karanicolas
**Genl Mgr:* Cesar Aguilera Saucedo
Opers Mgr: Jose Medina

D-U-N-S 16-989-3596
GENERAL ASSEMBLY MARYLAND
(*Suby of* STATE OF MARYLAND) ★
90 State Cir Rm 300, Annapolis, MD 21401-1914
Tel (410) 946-5025 *Founded/Ownrshp* 1789
Sales NA *EMP* 382
SIC 9121 Legislative bodies, state & local; ; Legislative bodies, state & local;
Ex Dir: Karl Aro
Off Mgr: Karen Cassidy
Sftwr Eng: Jagriti Nanda
Snr Mgr: Janice Hendra

D-U-N-S 80-958-2026
GENERAL ASSEMBLY NORTH CAROLINA
CONTROLLERS OFFICE
(*Suby of* LEGISLATIVE OFFICE OF NORTH CAROLINA) ★
16 W Jones St, Raleigh, NC 27601-1030
Tel (919) 733-4111 *Founded/Ownrshp* 1789
Sales NA *EMP* 800^E
SIC 9121 Legislative bodies, state & local; ; Legislative bodies, state & local;
Prin: George Hall
Exec: Mitch Gillespie
Exec: Joe Hackney
Opers Mgr: Pete Capriglione
Snr Mgr: Anna McHugh
Snr Mgr: Paul Stam

D-U-N-S 09-750-1357
GENERAL ATLANTIC CORP
3 Pickwick Plz Ste 200, Greenwich, CT 06830-5546
Tel (203) 629-8600 *Founded/Ownrshp* 1979
Sales 505.8MM^E *EMP* 3,298
SIC 6211 Security brokers & dealers; Security brokers & dealers
Pr: William Ford
Sr VP: Ronan Cunningham
Sr VP: Rich Gold
Sr VP: Patricia Hedley
VP: Steven A Denning
VP: Tracey Duff
VP: Shaw Joseph
VP: Amit Soni
Exec: Jason Currier
Mng Dir: Adrianne Cherpak
Mng Dir: Cory Eaves

D-U-N-S 36-126-6724
GENERAL ATLANTIC LLC
THREE PICKWICK PLAZA
600 Steamboat Rd Ste 105, Greenwich, CT 06830-7181
Tel (203) 629-8600 *Founded/Ownrshp* 1995
Sales 112.3MM^E *EMP* 536^E
SIC 6799 Investors; Investment clubs
CEO: William E Ford
**COO:* J Frank Brown
**CFO:* Thomas J Murphy
**Ex VP:* Richard Gold
**Ex VP:* Andy Papadakos
**Sr VP:* David Buckley
**Sr VP:* Paul Doran
Sr VP: Cory A Eaves
Prin: Gabriel Caillaux
Prin: Jan Hammer
Mng Dir: Rene Kern

D-U-N-S 05-097-1340
GENERAL ATLANTIC SERVICE CO LLC
600 Steamboat Rd Ste 105, Greenwich, CT 06830-7181
Tel (203) 629-8600 *Founded/Ownrshp* 2006
Sales 174.7MM^E *EMP* 962
SIC 8742 Management consulting services; Management consulting services
**Pr:* William E Ford
COO: Matthew Nimetz
**CFO:* Thomas J Murphy
**VP:* Lisa Dennis-Valvo

D-U-N-S 85-918-1984
GENERAL ATOMIC TECHNOLOGIES CORP
GENERAL ATOMICS
3550 General Atomics Ct, San Diego, CA 92121-1122
Tel (858) 455-3000 *Founded/Ownrshp* 1986
Sales 2.4MMM^E *EMP* 10,109
SIC 8731 3829 3443 7374 3499 2819 Commercial physical research; Nuclear radiation & testing apparatus; Nuclear reactors, military or industrial; Computer time-sharing; Magnets, permanent: metallic; Fuels & radioactive compounds; Commercial physical research; Nuclear radiation & testing apparatus; Nuclear reactors, military or industrial; Computer time-sharing; Magnets, permanent: metallic; Fuels & radioactive compounds
CEO: J Neal Blue
**Sec:* John E Jones
**VP:* Linden S Blue
CIO: Dave Nebo

GENERAL ATOMICS
See GENERAL ATOMIC TECHNOLOGIES CORP

D-U-N-S 06-763-8957 IMP
GENERAL ATOMICS
(*Suby of* GENERAL ATOMIC TECHNOLOGIES CORP) ★
3550 General Atomics Ct, San Diego, CA 92121-1194
Tel (858) 455-3000 *Founded/Ownrshp* 1986
Sales 1.4MMM^E *EMP* 9,000
SIC 3721 Aircraft; Aircraft
CEO: J Neal Blue
**CFO:* Ann Cole
**CFO:* John McGibbney
**CFO:* Tony Navarra
Treas: Karen Baldwin
Treas: Roseanne Hovey
Treas: Karen Nichols
**Sr VP:* Linden Blue
**Sr VP:* David O'Overskei
VP: Scott Forney
Exec: Beverly Moore

D-U-N-S 82-468-4229
GENERAL ATOMICS AERONAUTICAL SYSTEMS INC
GA-ASI
(*Suby of* AERONAUTICAL SYSTEMS INC) ★
14200 Kirkham Way, Poway, CA 92064-7103
Tel (858) 312-2810 *Founded/Ownrshp* 1993
Sales 978.0MM^E *EMP* 5,400
SIC 3721 Aircraft; Aircraft
CEO: Neal Blue
**Pr:* Lawrence Woolf
CFO: Max Kemp
**Treas:* Tony Navarra
**VP:* Brad Clark
**VP:* Stacy Jakuttis
VP: John Rawls
Dir Bus: Carl Fisher
Dir Bus: Mike Piersante
Prgrm Mgr: David Cain
Prgrm Mgr: Ron Carson

D-U-N-S 15-411-1892 IMP/EXP
GENERAL ATOMICS ELECTRONIC SYSTEMS INC
4949 Greencraig Ln, San Diego, CA 92123-1675
Tel (858) 522-8495 *Founded/Ownrshp* 1987
Sales NA *EMP* 300
SIC 3675

D-U-N-S 80-807-9529 IMP
GENERAL ATOMICS INTERNATIONAL SERVICES CORP
CRYOTECH
(*Suby of* GENERAL ATOMIC TECHNOLOGIES CORP) ★
3550 General Atomics Ct, San Diego, CA 92121-1122
Tel (858) 455-3000 *Founded/Ownrshp* 1955
Sales 23.0MM^E *EMP* 130
SIC 2899 Deicing or defrosting fluid; Deicing or defrosting fluid
Pr: Keith Johnson
**Treas:* Anthony Navarra

D-U-N-S 00-152-7688 IMP
GENERAL BEARING CORP (DE)
(*Suby of* SKF MOTION TECHNOLOGIES) ★
44 High St, West Nyack, NY 10994-2702
Tel (845) 358-6000 *Founded/Ownrshp* 1958, 2012
Sales 126.9MM^E *EMP* 971
SIC 3562 Ball & roller bearings; Ball bearings & parts; Roller bearings & parts; Ball & roller bearings; Ball bearings & parts; Roller bearings & parts
CEO: David L Gussack
**Pr:* Thomas J Uhlig
**CFO:* Rocky Cambrea
VP: Joseph Hoo
**VP:* Corby W Self
VP: Corby Self
Rgnl Mgr: Don Morris
CTO: Carol Schneider
Sfty Mgr: David Passariello
Opers Mgr: Bill Kurtz
Plnt Mgr: Joe Sassano

D-U-N-S 00-281-2949 IMP
GENERAL BEVERAGE SALES CO-MILWAUKEE (WI)
MASTER IMPORTS
6169 Mckee Rd, Fitchburg, WI 53719-5104
Tel (608) 271-1237 *Founded/Ownrshp* 1996
Sales 95.2MM^E *EMP* 124
SIC 5182 5181 Bottling wines & liquors; Beer & ale; Bottling wines & liquors; Beer & ale
Pr: Dan Weinstein
**Sec:* Richard J Karls
VP: Michael Gorst
**VP:* Joel Minkoff
**VP:* B Royko
**VP:* Arvin B Weinstein
Exec: Lynn Keiser
Mktg Dir: Bob Royko
Sls Mgr: Luke Bartelme
Sls Mgr: Jeffrey Calder
Sls Mgr: Daryl Hanson

D-U-N-S 88-486-0834 IMP
GENERAL BEVERAGE SALES CO-OSHKOSH INC
2855 Oregon St, Oshkosh, WI 54902-7135
Tel (920) 235-9130 *Founded/Ownrshp* 1926
Sales 49.4MM^E *EMP* 150
SIC 5182 Bottling wines & liquors; Bottling wines & liquors
Pr: Daniel Weinstein
VP: D Karls
**VP:* Joel Minkoff

D-U-N-S 00-514-4480
GENERAL BINDING CORP (DE)
G B C
4 Corporate Dr, Lake Zurich, IL 60047-8924
Tel (847) 541-9500 *Founded/Ownrshp* 1947
Sales NA *EMP* 3,600
SIC 5044 2782 3559 3589 7629 3579

D-U-N-S 07-685-6574
GENERAL BOARD OF PENSION AND HEALTH BENEFITS OF UNITED METHODIST
1901 Chestnut Ave, Glenview, IL 60025-1604
Tel (847) 869-4550 *Founded/Ownrshp* 1918
Sales NA *EMP* 250
SIC 6411 Pension & retirement plan consultants; Pension & retirement plan consultants
CEO: Barbara A Boigegrain
**CFO:* Tim Koch
**Ch:* Jeri Sutton

Comm Man: Mark Ornstein
Mng Dir: Jon Jones
QA Dir: Helen Exarhakos
QA Dir: Cindy Hwang
Genl Couns: Steven Clark
Genl Couns: Sheri Young

D-U-N-S 05-514-4414
GENERAL BODY MANUFACTURING CO
GENERAL TRUCK BODY
7110 Jensen Dr, Houston, TX 77093-8703
Tel (713) 692-5177 Founded/Ownrshp 1961
Sales 42.4MM[E] EMP 195
SIC 3713 3715 3711 Truck bodies (motor vehicles); Truck trailers; Motor vehicles & car bodies; Truck bodies (motor vehicles); Truck trailers; Motor vehicles & car bodies
Pr: Barbara L Paull
Pr: Jim Braden
*Pr: Barbara Paull
Off Mgr: Cedric Davis
IT Man: Tony Mitchell
Opers Mgr: Hector Rios
Sales Asso: Carlos Sotelo

D-U-N-S 05-371-2519 IMP
GENERAL BUILDERS SUPPLY CO INC
101 N Ann Arbor Ave, Oklahoma City, OK 73127-6303
Tel (405) 947-7227 Founded/Ownrshp 1970
Sales 23.8MM[E] EMP 74
SIC 5031 Lumber, plywood & millwork
Pr: J Jerome Kennedy
*Sec: Mary K Kennedy

D-U-N-S 05-533-2964
GENERAL BUSINESS CREDIT
110 E 9th St Ste A1126, Los Angeles, CA 90079-2154
Tel (213) 244-9500 Founded/Ownrshp 2001
Sales NA EMP 14
SIC 6141 Financing: automobiles, furniture, etc., not a deposit bank; Financing: automobiles, furniture, etc., not a deposit bank
Pr: Daniel Ko
Off Mgr: Justin Cha
Dir IT: Young Kim

GENERAL CABLE
See G K TECHNOLOGIES INC

D-U-N-S 84-791-4173 IMP/EXP
▲ GENERAL CABLE CORP
4 Tesseneer Dr, Highland Heights, KY 41076-9136
Tel (859) 572-8000 Founded/Ownrshp 1992
Sales 5.9MMM EMP 13,000
Tkr Sym BGC Exch NYS
SIC 3351 3357 Wire, copper & copper alloy; Communication wire; Aluminum wire & cable; Fiber optic cable (insulated); Wire, copper & copper alloy; Communication wire; Aluminum wire & cable; Fiber optic cable (insulated)
Pr: Michael T McDonnell
Recvr: Phil Parker
COO: Michael Rainville
CFO: Brian J Robinson
Chf Cred: Kurt L Drake
Bd of Dir: Charles McClure
Ofcr: Sonya Reed
Ex VP: Domingo Goenaga Campmany
Ex VP: Domingo Goenaga
Ex VP: Bob Kenny
Sr VP: Emerson C Moser
VP: Stephen R Messinger
Exec: Jay Lahman
Exec: Roderick Macdonald
Exec: Stu Parsons
Board of Directors: Sallie B Bailey, Edward Childs Hall III, Gregory E Lawton, Craig P Omtvedt, Patrick M Prevost, John E Weslsh III

D-U-N-S 79-346-3209 IMP/EXP
■ GENERAL CABLE INDUSTRIES INC
(Suby of GENERAL CABLE CORP) ★
4 Tesseneer Dr, Highland Heights, KY 41076-9136
Tel (859) 572-8000 Founded/Ownrshp 1979
Sales 352.9MM[E] EMP 4,200
SIC 3351 3315 3357

D-U-N-S 79-350-0448
■ GENERAL CABLE TECHNOLOGIES CORP
(Suby of GENERAL CABLE CORP) ★
4 Tesseneer Dr, Highland Heights, KY 41076-9136
Tel (859) 572-8000 Founded/Ownrshp 1994
Sales 356.6MM[E] EMP 3,800
SIC 3357 Building wire & cable, nonferrous; Aluminum wire & cable; Coaxial cable, nonferrous; Communication wire; Building wire & cable, nonferrous; Aluminum wire & cable; Coaxial cable, nonferrous; Communication wire
Pr: Gregory B Kenny
*Treas: Brian J Robinson
*Sec: Robert J Siverd
*VP: Jeffrey J Whelan
CIO: Elizabeth W Taliaferro

D-U-N-S 04-588-2651 IMP
GENERAL CARBIDE CORP
1151 Garden St, Greensburg, PA 15601-6417
Tel (724) 836-3000 Founded/Ownrshp 1968
Sales 37.7MM[E] EMP 160
SIC 3544 3568 3545 3312 2819 Special dies & tools; Power transmission equipment; Machine tool accessories; Blast furnaces & steel mills; Industrial inorganic chemicals; Special dies & tools; Power transmission equipment; Machine tool accessories; Blast furnaces & steel mills; Industrial inorganic chemicals
Pr: Mona L Pappafava
*Sec: L B Pappafava
QA Dir: Jessica Lenhart
QI Cn Mgr: Scott Carroll
Board of Directors: Edward Brinker, Paul McLaughlin, Marcy L Pappafava, Thomas Shearer

D-U-N-S 07-911-4682
GENERAL CASUALTY CO OF AMERICA
(Suby of QBE AMERICAS INC) ★
717 Green Valley Rd # 100, Greensboro, NC 27408-2156
Tel (334) 270-6000 Founded/Ownrshp 2005
Sales NA EMP 275
SIC 6331 6411 Fire, marine & casualty insurance & carriers; Insurance agents, brokers & service; Fire, marine & casualty insurance & carriers; Insurance agents, brokers & service
Pr: Peter McPartland
Treas: Rush Meriwether
Ofcr: Kip Kobussen
Ex VP: Rodger Drostee
Sr VP: Jim Blair
Sr VP: Richard Kalina
Sr VP: Paul Schulte
VP: Sharon Brown
VP: Lewis Culpepper
VP: Jack Hooks
VP: Carlene Payne
VP: Michael Roberts
VP: Bert Shephard
Exec: Carol Gambino

D-U-N-S 93-386-7629
GENERAL CASUALTY INSURANCE CO
(Suby of QBE HOLDINGS INC) ★
1 General Dr, Sun Prairie, WI 53596-0002
Tel (608) 837-4440 Founded/Ownrshp 1989
Sales NA EMP 1[E]
SIC 6411 Insurance agents, brokers & service
Sr VP: Paul Schulte
IT Man: Aaron Kuhl
Netwrk Eng: Nathan Guenther
Netwrk Eng: Terry Tiffany
Corp Couns: Joe Decker

D-U-N-S 18-963-1740
GENERAL CASUALTY INSURANCE GROUP
(Suby of CREDIT SUISSE GROUP AG)
8500 Keystone Xing # 200, Indianapolis, IN 46240-2458
Tel (317) 722-3838 Founded/Ownrshp 2004
Sales NA EMP 120
SIC 6331 6411 Fire, marine & casualty insurance; Insurance agents, brokers & service
Pr: Charles Taylor
*Pr: Joe Peterbon

D-U-N-S 05-043-0610
GENERAL CAULKING & COATINGS CO INC
G C C
101 Nw 176th St, Miami, FL 33169-5045
Tel (305) 652-1020 Founded/Ownrshp 1970
Sales 21.3MM[E] EMP 100[E]
SIC 1799 Caulking (construction); Waterproofing
Pr: Michael Engelke
*Pr: Horace S Andrews
*Sec: George Kanistras
*VP: Terry J Townson

GENERAL CHEMICAL
See CHEMTRADE CHEMICALS US LLC

D-U-N-S 60-672-1231 EXP
GENERAL CIGAR CO INC
(Suby of SWEDISH MATCH AB)
10900 Nuckols Rd Ste 100, Glen Allen, VA 23060-9277
Tel (860) 602-3500 Founded/Ownrshp 1906
Sales 40.4MM[E] EMP 1,061
SIC 2121 5199 0132 Cigars; Smokers' supplies; Lighters, cigarette & cigar; Tobacco; Cigars; Smokers' supplies; Lighters, cigarette & cigar; Tobacco
Pr: Austin T McNamara
COO: Dan Carr
Sr VP: John Rano
VP: W Brent Currier
VP: Robert Loftus

D-U-N-S 19-484-8735
■ GENERAL CINEMA BEVERAGES OF OHIO INC
PEPSI BOTTLE AND GROUP
(Suby of PEPSI-COLA METROPOLITAN BOTTLING CO INC) ★
1 Pepsi Way Ste 1, Somers, NY 10589-2212
Tel (914) 767-6000 Founded/Ownrshp 1989
Sales 83.5MM[E] EMP 1,200
SIC 2086 Soft drinks: packaged in cans, bottles, etc.; Soft drinks: packaged in cans, bottles, etc.
Pr: Craig Weatherup
Exec: Jodi Eldredge
IT Man: Christian Luther
Snr Mgr: Mike Becker

D-U-N-S 61-573-7822
■ GENERAL CINEMA CORP OF TEXAS
(Suby of A M C - G C T INC)
1300 Boylston St, Chestnut Hill, MA 02467-2112
Tel (617) 738-3513 Founded/Ownrshp 1994
Sales 12.5MM[E] EMP 3,259[E]
SIC 7832 Motion picture theaters, except drive-in
Prin: Paul Del Rossi
*Pr: Frank T Stryjewski
*Treas: G Gail Edwards
VP: Smith Robert A

GENERAL CNSTRCTONS MET FBRCTOR
See CONSOLIDATED SOUTHERN INDUSTRIES INC

D-U-N-S 02-390-4410
GENERAL CO INC
15 E Cary St, Richmond, VA 23219-3732
Tel (804) 649-1904 Founded/Ownrshp 1960
Sales 5.6MM[E] EMP 310
SIC 7349 5087 Janitorial service, contract basis; Window cleaning; Janitors' supplies; Janitorial service, contract basis; Window cleaning; Janitors' supplies
Pr: Norman Rosenbaum

D-U-N-S 14-637-6236
GENERAL COACH AMERICA INC
(Suby of ALLIED SPECIALTY VEHICLES INC) ★
275 Graham Rd, Imlay City, MI 48444-9738
Tel (810) 724-6474 Founded/Ownrshp 2013
Sales 20.9MM[E] EMP 300[E]
SIC 3711 Buses, all types, assembly of; Buses, all types, assembly of
Pr: John Resnik
*Treas: Dominic Romeo
*VP: Theresa Smith

D-U-N-S 17-913-5710
GENERAL COATINGS CORP
6711 Nancy Ridge Dr, San Diego, CA 92121-2231
Tel (858) 587-1277 Founded/Ownrshp 1987
Sales 96.7MM[E] EMP 500
SIC 1721 1799 Painting & paper hanging; Waterproofing; Painting & paper hanging; Waterproofing
CEO: Craig A Kinsman
*VP: Andrew Fluken
Opers Mgr: Jeff Haight
S&M/VP: Lou Donato

GENERAL COCOA CO
See COFFEE AMERICA (USA) CORP

D-U-N-S 80-939-8712
■ GENERAL COLOGNE CORP
(Suby of GENERAL REINSURANCE CORP) ★
120 Long Ridge Rd, Stamford, CT 06902-1839
Tel (203) 328-5000 Founded/Ownrshp 1989
Sales NA EMP 240
SIC 6411 Insurance agents, brokers & service; Insurance agents, brokers & service
Pr: Ronald E Ferguson
Board of Directors: Ronald E Ferguson

D-U-N-S 00-420-9839
GENERAL COLOR INVESTMENTS INC (OH)
PLASTIC COLOR DIVISION
350 Bridge St, Minerva, OH 44657-1561
Tel (330) 868-4161 Founded/Ownrshp 1938
Sales 21.1MM[E] EMP 100
SIC 2816 2899 2851 Color pigments; Frit; Paints & allied products; Color pigments; Frit; Paints & allied products
Pr: Carl W Gartner
*Sec: Martha Gartner
*VP: Keith W Gartner
Ex Dir: Holly Gartner

D-U-N-S 12-222-7937 EXP
■ GENERAL COMBUSTION CORP
(Suby of GENCOR INDUSTRIES INC) ★
5201 N Orange Blossom Trl, Orlando, FL 32810-1008
Tel (407) 290-6000 Founded/Ownrshp 1969
Sales 29.7MM[E] EMP 180
SIC 3567 Heating units & devices, industrial: electric; Heating units & devices, industrial: electric
Ch Bd: E J Elliott
*Pr: John E Elliott

D-U-N-S 01-119-9767
▲ GENERAL COMMUNICATION INC
2550 Denali St Ste 1000, Anchorage, AK 99503-2751
Tel (907) 868-5600 Founded/Ownrshp 1979
Sales 910.2MM EMP 2,255
Accts Grant Thornton Llp Anchorage
Tkr Sym GNCMA Exch NGS
SIC 4813 4841 4812 Telephone communication, except radio; Long distance telephone communications; ; Cable & other pay television services; Radio telephone communication; Telephone communication, except radio; Long distance telephone communications; ; Cable & other pay television services; Radio telephone communication
Pr: Ronald A Duncan
*Ch Bd: Stephen M Brett
COO: Gregory F Chapados
CFO: Peter J Pounds
CFO: Peter Pounds
Chf Cred: Tina M Pidgeon
Sr VP: William C Behnke
Sr VP: Paul E Landes
Sr VP: Richard D Westlund
VP: Gina Borland
VP: John M Lowber
VP: Craig Mollerstuen
VP: Terry Nidiffer
VP: Jim Sipes
VP: Brad Spees
VP: Gene Strid
Exec: Mark Moderow

D-U-N-S 00-691-9732 IMP/EXP
GENERAL CONFERENCE OF SEVENTH-DAY ADVENTISTS (DC)
12501 Old Columbia Pike, Silver Spring, MD 20904-6601
Tel (301) 680-6000 Founded/Ownrshp 1863
Sales 227.9MM EMP 550
Accts Maner Costerisan Pc Lansing
SIC 8661 Seventh Day Adventist Church; Seventh Day Adventist Church
Pr: Ted N C Wilson
*Treas: Robert Lemon
Assoc Dir: Mario Ceballos
Assoc Dir: Artour Vasmout
Ex Dir: Rajmund Dabrowski
Off Admin: Teru Fukui
Telecom Mg: Orion Gonzales
IT Man: Kimberly Terry
Pr Mgr: Michelle Oetman
Genl Couns: Thomas Wetmore

D-U-N-S 08-373-7403
GENERAL CONSTRUCTION CO
(Suby of KIEWIT INFRASTRUCTURE WEST CO) ★
33455 6th Ave S, Federal Way, WA 98003-6335
Tel (253) 943-4200 Founded/Ownrshp 2002
Sales 234.7MM[E] EMP 1,414
Accts Kpmg Llp
SIC 1622 1629 Bridge, tunnel & elevated highway; Bridge construction; Highway construction, elevated; Dams, waterways, docks & other marine construction; Dam construction; Dock construction; Pier construction; Bridge, tunnel & elevated highway; Bridge construction; Highway construction, elevated; Dams, waterways, docks & other marine construction; Dam construction; Dock construction; Pier construction
Pr: Ronald H Morford
*Treas: Stephen S Thomas
*Ex VP: Ken E Riley
*Sr VP: Parke D Ball
*Sr VP: A T Skoro
*VP: Jeffrey C Arviso
*VP: Kent A Boden
*VP: Paul H Guintini
*VP: Michael J Piechoski
*VP: Tobin A Schropp
*VP: Phillip C Wallace
*VP: Gregg F Woodward

D-U-N-S 06-089-5828
GENERAL CONTAINER (CA)
5450 Dodds Ave, Buena Park, CA 90621-1209
Tel (714) 562-8700 Founded/Ownrshp 1976
Sales 22.5MM[E] EMP 75
SIC 2653 Boxes, corrugated: made from purchased materials
Pr: Tim Black
VP: Jerry Monroe
Opers Mgr: Tabitha Fetherolf
Sls Mgr: Dan Winfrey

GENERAL CONTRACTING USA CO
See TAMLITE LIGHTING INC

GENERAL CONTRACTOR
See WELTY BUILDING CO LTD

GENERAL CONTRACTOR
See WRIGHT-RYAN CONSTRUCTION INC

GENERAL CONTRACTOR
See AETOS CONSTRUCTION CO

GENERAL CONTRACTOR
See FINCOR CONSTRUCTION INC

D-U-N-S 04-286-7390
GENERAL COUNCIL OF ASSEMBLIES OF GOD
1445 N Boonville Ave, Springfield, MO 65802-1894
Tel (417) 862-2781 Founded/Ownrshp 1914
Sales 70.6MM[E] EMP 895
SIC 8661 2731 Assembly of God Church; Books: publishing & printing; Pamphlets: publishing & printing; Assembly of God Church; Books: publishing & printing; Pamphlets: publishing & printing
Pr: George Wood
*Ch Bd: Scott Holmes
*Treas: Doug Clay
Treas: Jay Herndon
VP: Charles Crabtree
*VP: Alton Garrison
Ex Dir: George Garrison
Ex Dir: Greg Mundis
Ex Dir: Zollie L Smith Jr
Secur Mgr: Paul Griffin
Snr Mgr: M T Dillon
Board of Directors: Allen Chapin

GENERAL COURT, NEW HAMPSHIRE
See HOUSE OF REPRESENTATIVES NEW HAMPSHIRE

D-U-N-S 07-087-9630
GENERAL CRANE SERVICE INC (TX)
BAY AREA/GENERAL CRANE SVC CO
4206 Weslow St, Houston, TX 77087-2206
Tel (713) 649-4088 Founded/Ownrshp 1976, 2014
Sales 21.0MM[E] EMP 74
SIC 3536 7389 5084 Crane & aerial lift service; Lift trucks & parts; Cranes, overhead traveling; Cranes, overhead traveling; Crane & aerial lift service; Lift trucks & parts
Pr: Patrick Donahoe
*Sec: Allison Taylor
*VP: David Heinsley

D-U-N-S 03-961-0852 IMP
GENERAL DATA CO INC (PA)
4354 Ferguson Dr, Cincinnati, OH 45245-1667
Tel (513) 752-7978 Founded/Ownrshp 1980
Sales 68.1MM[E] EMP 280
SIC 2679 5046 5084 2759 3841 3081 Labels, paper: made from purchased material; Commercial equipment; Printing trades machinery, equipment & supplies; Commercial printing; Surgical & medical instruments; Unsupported plastics film & sheet; Labels, paper: made from purchased material; Commercial equipment; Printing trades machinery, equipment & supplies; Commercial printing; Surgical & medical instruments; Unsupported plastics film & sheet
Pr: Peter Wenzel
Pr: Chris Miller
*VP: Jim Burns
VP: Richard Cmar
VP: Walter Van Tilburg
Genl Mgr: Jim Bacho
IT Man: Don Brashear
VP Mfg: Dave Laurash
VP Opers: Jeffrey Kenny
Sfty Mgr: Rick Mullen
Opers Mgr: John Finger

D-U-N-S 17-546-5996
GENERAL DATATECH LP
999 Metro Media Pl, Dallas, TX 75247-4730
Tel (214) 857-6100 Founded/Ownrshp 1998
Sales 303.2MM[E] EMP 400
SIC 5065 Communication equipment
Genl Pt: John Roberts
Treas: Rhonda Hopper
Prgrm Mgr: Rob Foerster
CIO: Michael Gilbert
Dir IT: Johnathan Pendrich
IT Man: Tim Kempa
IT Man: Mario Saldivar
IT Man: Karl Sanford
Netwrk Eng: Jan Brooks
Netwrk Eng: Tim Kempka
Netwrk Eng: Jason Pilon

D-U-N-S 05-412-8525 IMP
GENERAL DIE CASTERS INC
2150 Highland Rd, Twinsburg, OH 44087-2229
Tel (330) 678-2528 Founded/Ownrshp 1995
Sales 37.1MM[E] EMP 150

SIC 3364 3363 3544 3369 3365 Zinc & zinc-base alloy die-castings; Aluminum die-castings; Special dies, tools, jigs & fixtures; Nonferrous foundries; Aluminum foundries; Zinc & zinc-base alloy die-castings; Aluminum die-castings; Special dies, tools, jigs & fixtures; Nonferrous foundries; Aluminum foundries
CEO: James M Mathias
**Pr:* Thomas J Lennon
Sfty Mgr: Dan Owens
Sls Mgr: Todd Jackovitc

D-U-N-S 00-624-1236
GENERAL DISTRIBUTING CO (MT)
G D
430 17th Ave Ne, Great Falls, MT 59404-1936
Tel (406) 454-1351 *Founded/Ownrshp* 1948
Sales 23.4MM^E *EMP* 52
SIC 5084 2813 5085 Welding machinery & equipment; Industrial gases; Industrial supplies; Welding supplies
Pr: Glenn Bliss Jr
**CFO:* Monte D Ruud
**VP:* Glenn F Bliss Sr
Genl Mgr: Juliann Bliss

D-U-N-S 04-611-3759
GENERAL DISTRIBUTING CO
5350 W Amelia Earhart Dr, Salt Lake City, UT 84116-2900
Tel (801) 531-7895 *Founded/Ownrshp* 1967
Sales 97.7MM^E *EMP* 157
SIC 5181 Beer & other fermented malt liquors; Beer & other fermented malt liquors
Pr: Andrew Z Zweber
**Sec:* Mark S Purdie
**Sec:* Kimberly Zweber
**VP:* Michael P Brennan
**VP:* Rebecca Ann Brennan

D-U-N-S 02-772-4996
GENERAL DISTRIBUTORS INC
13895 Fir St, Oregon City, OR 97045-7996
Tel (503) 656-9470 *Founded/Ownrshp* 1933
Sales 38.2MM^E *EMP* 104^E
SIC 5181 Beer & other fermented malt liquors
Pr: Charles Fick III
**VP:* Robert L Smart Sr
Dist Mgr: Greg Elledge
Dist Mgr: Mike Tomasco
Sales Exec: Rick Antonacci

D-U-N-S 19-491-6888
GENERAL DISTRIBUTORS INC
G D I
8225 Washington St Ne A, Albuquerque, NM 87113-1702
Tel (505) 798-4740 *Founded/Ownrshp* 1994
Sales 63.2MM^E *EMP* 75
SIC 5141 Groceries, general line; Groceries, general line
CEO: Marek Friederich
**CFO:* Annette Tixier
**Ch:* Jan Friederich

GENERAL DYNAMICS ADVANCED
See DIGITAL SYSTEM RESOURCES INC

D-U-N-S 00-309-1746
■ **GENERAL DYNAMICS ADVANCED INFORMATION SYSTEMS INC**
(*Suby of* GENERAL DYNAMICS CORP) ★
5440 Millstream Rd W300, Mc Leansville, NC 27301-9282
Tel (336) 698-8000 *Founded/Ownrshp* 1997
Sales 70.8MM^E *EMP* 1,138
SIC 8711 Engineering services; Engineering services
Pr: Charles E McQueary
VP: Harry Grant
VP: Edward A Timmes
VP: Debra Whited
Prgrm Mgr: Jim Unger

D-U-N-S 07-116-6839 IMP
■ **GENERAL DYNAMICS ADVANCED INFORMATION SYSTEMS INC**
(*Suby of* GENERAL DYNAMICS CORP) ★
10467 White Granite Dr # 304, Oakton, VA 22124-2782
Tel (703) 277-1315 *Founded/Ownrshp* 2004
Sales 47.0MM^E *EMP* 200
SIC 7379 7373 7372 Computer related consulting services; Systems integration services; Application computer software; Computer related consulting services; Systems integration services; Application computer software
Pr: Thomas W Kirchmaier
**VP:* Robert Draim
**VP:* Maura Dunn
**VP:* Edward Grecco
VP: Maryann Hale
**VP:* John Jolly
Prgrm Mgr: Paul Solosky
Snr Sftwr: Peter Burrell
Sftwr Eng: David Bartoe
Snr Mgr: Kevin Mangis

D-U-N-S 17-183-7730 IMP
■ **GENERAL DYNAMICS ADVANCED INFORMATION SYSTEMS INC**
GENERAL DYNAMICS ADVNCD
(*Suby of* GENERAL DYNAMICS GOVERNMENT SYSTEMS CORP) ★
12450 Fair Lakes Cir, Fairfax, VA 22033-3810
Tel (703) 263-2800 *Founded/Ownrshp* 2001
Sales 1.2MMM^E *EMP* 7,991
SIC 3571 Electronic computers; Electronic computers
Pr: Thomas W Kirchmaier
**VP:* Gregory Gallopoulos
Prgrm Mgr: Karen Chenaille
Prgrm Mgr: Joe Christy
Prgrm Mgr: Sandra Dye
Prgrm Mgr: David Fuhrmann
Prgrm Mgr: Brian Gollenberg
Prgrm Mgr: Joe Kubiak
Prgrm Mgr: Anthony McDonald
Prgrm Mgr: William New
Prgrm Mgr: Brian Roy

GENERAL DYNAMICS ADVNCD
See GENERAL DYNAMICS ADVANCED INFORMATION SYSTEMS INC

GENERAL DYNAMICS AMERICAN
See AMERICAN OVERSEAS MARINE CO LLC

D-U-N-S 10-205-0742
■ **GENERAL DYNAMICS AVIATION SERVICES**
(*Suby of* GULFSTREAM DELAWARE CORP) ★
500 Gulfstream Rd, Savannah, GA 31408-9643
Tel (912) 965-7372 *Founded/Ownrshp* 2010
Sales 24.4MM^E *EMP* 170^E
SIC 3721 7699 Aircraft; Aircraft & heavy equipment repair services; Aircraft; Aircraft & heavy equipment repair services
CEO: William Boisture
**Pr:* Phebe N Novakovic
**Ch:* Jay L Johnson
Ofcr: Jennifer Giffen
**VP:* John P Casey
**VP:* Gerard J Demuro
**VP:* David K Heebner
Mktg Dir: Scott McDonald

D-U-N-S 12-154-0038
■ **GENERAL DYNAMICS C4 SYSTEMS INC**
GENERAL DYNAMICS GOVT
(*Suby of* GENERAL DYNAMICS GOVERNMENT SYSTEMS CORP) ★
8201 E Mcdowell Rd, Scottsdale, AZ 85257-3812
Tel (480) 441-3033 *Founded/Ownrshp* 2002
Sales 975.2MM^E *EMP* 7,003
SIC 8711 Engineering services; Engineering services
Pr: Chris Marzilli
Pr: Dick Hanson
CFO: Edward M Secher Jr
**Treas:* David H Fogg
Ex VP: Ronald Boyd
Ex VP: Marvin Shoemake
**Sr VP:* Manny Mora
VP: Nolen Bivens
VP: Lou Dinunzio
**VP:* Devon Engel
**VP:* David Heebner
VP: Thomas Kreidler
VP: John Sciberras
VP: John Stoy
VP: John Weidman
**VP:* William Weiss

D-U-N-S 00-138-1284 IMP
▲ **GENERAL DYNAMICS CORP**
2941 Frview Pk Dr Ste 100, Falls Church, VA 22042
Tel (703) 876-3000 *Founded/Ownrshp* 1952
Sales 30.8MMM *EMP* 99,500
Tkr Sym GD *Exch* NYS
SIC 3721 3731 3795 3711 3812 Aircraft; Submarines, building & repairing; Combat vessels, building & repairing; Tanks, military, including factory rebuilding; Reconnaissance cars, assembly of; Search & navigation equipment; Search & detection systems & instruments; Aircraft; Submarines, building & repairing; Combat vessels, building & repairing; Tanks, military, including factory rebuilding; Reconnaissance cars, assembly of; Search & navigation equipment; Search & detection systems & instruments
Ch Bd: Phebe N Novakovic
CFO: Jason W Aiken
Ex VP: Gerard J Demuro
Ex VP: Mark C Roualet
Sr VP: Gregory S Gallopoulos
Sr VP: Walter M Oliver
VP: Kimberly A Kuryea
Corp Couns: Richard Lanzon
Board of Directors: William A Osborn, Mary T Barra, Laura J Schumacher, Nicholas D Chabraja, James S Crown, Rudy F Deleon, William P Fricks, John M Keane, Lester L Lyles, Mark Malcolm, James N Mattis

D-U-N-S 00-358-7024 IMP
■ **GENERAL DYNAMICS DEFENSE SYSTEMS INC**
(*Suby of* GENERAL DYNAMICS CORP) ★
100 Plastics Ave, Pittsfield, MA 01201-3985
Tel (413) 494-1110 *Founded/Ownrshp* 1996, 2001
Sales 99.2MM^E *EMP* 1,900
SIC 3812 3795 3625 Search & detection systems & instruments; Tanks & tank components; Relays & industrial controls; Search & detection systems & instruments; Tanks & tank components; Relays & industrial controls
Pr: Nicholas D Chabraja
CFO: Bob Plunkitt
MIS Dir: Charlie Banker
Dir IT: Carl Walser
Sftwr Eng: John Thier
Pr Dir: Christine McLaughlin

GENERAL DYNAMICS ELECTRIC BOAT
See ELECTRIC BOAT CORP

D-U-N-S 04-318-9620 IMP
■ **GENERAL DYNAMICS GLOBAL IMAGING TECHNOLOGIES INC**
(*Suby of* GENERAL DYNAMICS GOVERNMENT SYSTEMS CORP) ★
24 Simon St, Nashua, NH 03060-3025
Tel (603) 864-6300 *Founded/Ownrshp* 1959, 2009
Sales 256.2MM^E *EMP* 1,284
SIC 3827 3861 Optical instruments & apparatus; Aerial cameras; Optical instruments & apparatus; Aerial cameras
CEO: Stephen W Bershad
Pr: Scott B Conner
VP: Mark Bonney
VP: David Enos
VP: Bob McGill
Exec: Thomas Crafts
Exec: Dawn Emerson
Prgrm Mgr: Keith Spaley
Prgrm Mgr: Richard Williams
Genl Mgr: G J Roe
CTO: Bill Hurst

D-U-N-S 11-618-7758 IMP
■ **GENERAL DYNAMICS GOVERNMENT SYSTEMS CORP**
(*Suby of* GENERAL DYNAMICS CORP) ★
77 A St, Needham, MA 02494-2806
Tel (781) 449-2000 *Founded/Ownrshp* 1999
Sales 6.1MMM^E *EMP* 25,000
SIC 3661 Telephone & telegraph apparatus; Telephone & telegraph apparatus
Pr: Kenneth C Dahlberg
**VP:* Vincent Antonacci
**VP:* David Breen
**VP:* Michael Garrity
**VP:* Jim Knapp

D-U-N-S 78-495-9124
■ **GENERAL DYNAMICS GOVERNMENT SYSTEMS OVERSEAS CORP**
GDGSOC
(*Suby of* GENERAL DYNAMICS GOVERNMENT SYSTEMS CORP) ★
3211 Jermantown Rd, Fairfax, VA 22030-2844
Tel (703) 995-8666 *Founded/Ownrshp* 1991
Sales 5.0MM *EMP* 5,000
SIC 3663 Radio & TV communications equipment
VP: Vince Antonacci

GENERAL DYNAMICS GOVT
See GENERAL DYNAMICS C4 SYSTEMS INC

D-U-N-S 06-764-1597
■ **GENERAL DYNAMICS INFORMATION TECHNOLOGY INC** (VA)
GDIT
(*Suby of* GENERAL DYNAMICS GOVERNMENT SYSTEMS CORP) ★
3211 Jermantown Rd, Fairfax, VA 22030-2844
Tel (703) 995-8700 *Founded/Ownrshp* 1975, 2006
Sales 3.0MMM^E *EMP* 16,988
SIC 7379 8711 7373 Computer related maintenance services; Professional engineer; Computer systems analysis & design; Systems engineering, computer related; Computer related maintenance services; Professional engineer; Computer systems analysis & design; Systems engineering, computer related
Pr: S Daniel Johnson
**Treas:* David H Fogg
**VP:* Vincent S Antonacci
**VP:* David Breen
**VP:* Marcus Collier
**VP:* Gregory S Gallopoulos
**VP:* Spain Hall Jr
**VP:* Edward G Hudson Jr
**VP:* Thomas W Kirchmaler
**VP:* Zannie Smith
**VP:* Robert Toth
VP: Garry Waggoner
**VP:* Ray Whitehead
**VP:* Al Whitmore
VP Bus Dev: Paul Harrington
Dir Bus: Robert Case
Dir Bus: Laura Jones
Board of Directors: Gerard J Demuro, Gregory S Gallopoulos, S Daniel Johnson, L Hugh Redd

D-U-N-S 79-181-9535
■ **GENERAL DYNAMICS LAND SYSTEMS CUSTOMER SERVICE & SUPPORT CO**
(*Suby of* GDLS) ★
38500 Mound Rd, Sterling Heights, MI 48310-3260
Tel (586) 825-4000 *Founded/Ownrshp* 1978
Sales 11.2MM^E *EMP* 400
SIC 7699 Tank repair; Tank repair
**Pr:* Charles M Hall
Sftwr Eng: Larry Currie

D-U-N-S 13-126-6926 IMP
■ **GENERAL DYNAMICS LAND SYSTEMS INC**
GDLS
(*Suby of* GENERAL DYNAMICS CORP) ★
38500 Mound Rd, Sterling Heights, MI 48310-3200
Tel (586) 825-4000 *Founded/Ownrshp* 1982
Sales 3.8MMM^E *EMP* 6,900
SIC 5088 8711 Combat vehicles; Engineering services; Combat vehicles; Engineering services
Pr: Gary L Whited
CFO: Jason Aiken
CFO: Evelyn Milam
**CFO:* Evelyn Milan
**Treas:* David Fogg
Ofcr: Raymond Lafferty
**VP:* Peter Keating
VP: John W Osina
VP: Anne M Regling
VP: Gary Whitehead
Comm Dir: Marie Remboulis

GENERAL DYNAMICS NASSCO EARL
See EARL INDUSTRIES LLC

D-U-N-S 12-153-8859
■ **GENERAL DYNAMICS NETWORK SYSTEMS INC**
GENERAL DYNAMICS WIRELESS SVCS
(*Suby of* GENERAL DYNAMICS GOVERNMENT SYSTEMS CORP) ★
77 A St, Needham Heights, MA 02494-2806
Tel (781) 400-7669 *Founded/Ownrshp* 2002
Sales 408.4MM^E *EMP* 6,700
SIC 8711 Engineering services; Engineering services
Pr: Michael Chandler
Pr: Paul Hengst
CFO: Keith F Koon
Treas: David H Fogg
Ofcr: Ann Young
Ex VP: Raynor Reavis
VP: Bob Dutton
VP: Brian Harrington
VP: Victor Lanio
Prgrm Mgr: Pablo Estrada
Prgrm Mgr: Ryan Tomasetti

GENERAL DYNAMICS ORDNANCE
See GENERAL DYNAMICS OTS (PENNSYLVANIA) INC

GENERAL DYNAMICS ORDNANCE AND
See EBV EXPLOSIVES ENVIRONMENTAL CO

D-U-N-S 19-486-0813 IMP/EXP
■ **GENERAL DYNAMICS ORDNANCE AND TACTICAL SYSTEMS INC**
(*Suby of* GENERAL DYNAMICS CORP) ★
11399 16th Ct N Ste 200, Saint Petersburg, FL 33716-2322
Tel (727) 578-8100 *Founded/Ownrshp* 2001
Sales 418.7MM^E *EMP* 2,277
SIC 3483 3482 2892 3489 Ammunition, except for small arms; Small arms ammunition; Explosives; Ordnance & accessories; Ammunition, except for small arms; Small arms ammunition; Explosives; Ordnance & accessories
Pr: Michael S Wilson
Bd of Dir: David D Baier
Bd of Dir: John P Casey
Bd of Dir: Randy M Collins
Bd of Dir: Gerard J Demuro
Bd of Dir: Henry C Eickelberg
Bd of Dir: Larry R Flynn
Bd of Dir: Charles M Hall
Bd of Dir: David K Heebner
Bd of Dir: Preston A Henne
Bd of Dir: Peter J Lawrence
Bd of Dir: Joseph T Lombardo
Bd of Dir: Michael J Mulligan
Bd of Dir: Phebe N Novakovic
Bd of Dir: Walter M Oliver
Bd of Dir: Alfonso Ramonet
Bd of Dir: Raynor B Reavis
Bd of Dir: William O Schmieder
Bd of Dir: John W Schwartz
Bd of Dir: John F Shipway
Bd of Dir: Michael W Toner

D-U-N-S 00-948-0823
■ **GENERAL DYNAMICS OTS (AEROSPACE) INC**
GENERAL DYNAMICS OTS SEATTLE
(*Suby of* GENERAL DYNAMICS ORDNANCE AND TACTICAL SYSTEMS INC) ★
11714 N Creek Pkwy N # 200, Bothell, WA 98011-8250
Tel (425) 420-9311 *Founded/Ownrshp* 1997
Sales 68.7MM^E *EMP* 840
SIC 3825 3764 3823 Instruments to measure electricity; Test equipment for electronic & electrical circuits; Electrical power measuring equipment; Guided missile & space vehicle propulsion unit parts; Industrial instrmnts msrmnt display/control process variable; Instruments to measure electricity; Test equipment for electronic & electrical circuits; Electrical power measuring equipment; Guided missile & space vehicle propulsion unit parts; Industrial instrmnts msrmnt display/control process variable
Pr: Michael S Wilson
**Ch:* Mark Roualet
**Treas:* Firat Gezen
**VP:* Del S Dameron
**VP:* Gregory Gallopoulos
MIS Dir: Bob Pixley
IT Man: Tim Borland

D-U-N-S 07-793-5203 IMP
■ **GENERAL DYNAMICS OTS (DRI) INC**
(*Suby of* GENERAL DYNAMICS ORDNANCE AND TACTICAL SYSTEMS INC) ★
1425 Commerce Blvd, Anniston, AL 36207-9449
Tel (256) 835-1660 *Founded/Ownrshp* 1998
Sales 21.3MM^E *EMP* 180^E
SIC 3489 Ordnance & accessories; Ordnance & accessories
Genl Mgr: Dennis Degrenier
Ofcr: John Clausen
VP: Kirk Von Seelen
Exec: Toni Curtis
MIS Mgr: Jessica Frank
Plnt Mgr: David Hauseman

D-U-N-S 07-908-5410 IMP
■ **GENERAL DYNAMICS OTS (PENNSYLVANIA) INC**
GENERAL DYNAMICS ORDNANCE
(*Suby of* GENERAL DYNAMICS ORDNANCE AND TACTICAL SYSTEMS INC) ★
200 E High St, Red Lion, PA 17356-1426
Tel (717) 246-8208 *Founded/Ownrshp* 1974
Sales 20.7MM^E *EMP* 118
SIC 3483 Ammunition, except for small arms; Ammunition, except for small arms
VP: Dan Paul
Treas: Keith Brown

GENERAL DYNAMICS OTS SEATTLE
See GENERAL DYNAMICS OTS (AEROSPACE) INC

D-U-N-S 62-699-8314
■ **GENERAL DYNAMICS ROBOTIC SYSTEMS INC**
(*Suby of* GDLS) ★
1231 Tech Ct, Westminster, MD 21157-3029
Tel (410) 876-9200 *Founded/Ownrshp* 1991
Sales 47.0MM^E *EMP* 250^E
SIC 7373 3569 Computer-aided system services; Robots, assembly line: industrial & commercial; Computer-aided system services; Robots, assembly line: industrial & commercial
Pr: Dana Caro
**VP:* Edward K Mottern
Exec: Michael Barnes
Prgrm Mgr: Janet Rupp
Sftwr Eng: John Paul
Ql Cn Mgr: Bonnie Pennington

D-U-N-S 02-356-4888 IMP/EXP
■ **GENERAL DYNAMICS SATCOM TECHNOLOGIES INC**
(*Suby of* GENERAL DYNAMICS GOVERNMENT SYSTEMS CORP) ★
1500 Prodelin Dr, Newton, NC 28658-7819
Tel (828) 464-4141 *Founded/Ownrshp* 2004
Sales 265.0MM^E *EMP* 1,511
SIC 3663 Radio & TV communications equipment; Radio & TV communications equipment
Pr: Christopher Marzilli

Sr VP: Marvin Shoemaker
VP: Lou Dinunzio
**VP:* Gary Kanipe
Dir IT: Jim Barrett
Dir IT: Kevin Sutton
Opers Mgr: Robert Featherstone
Plnt Mgr: Brian Strother
Sls Dir: Michael Jackson

GENERAL DYNAMICS WIRELESS SVCS
See GENERAL DYNAMICS NETWORK SYSTEMS INC

D-U-N-S 16-737-7204 IMP
■ GENERAL DYNAMICS-OTS INC
(*Suby of* GENERAL DYNAMICS CORP) ★
11399 16th Ct N Ste 200, Saint Petersburg, FL 33716-2322
Tel (727) 578-8100 *Founded/Ownrshp* 1948
Sales 706.4MM^E *EMP* 5,000
SIC 3728 3812 Military aircraft equipment & armament; Search & navigation equipment; Military aircraft equipment & armament; Search & navigation equipment
Pr: Mike Wilson
Pr: Dan Chien
Ofcr: Bob Dunsage
Ofcr: Stephen Hetcko
**Ex VP:* Charles M Hall
VP: Catherine Luther
**VP:* Tim McAuliffe
**VP:* Mike Obrien
Exec: Garrett Dominy
**Comm Dir:* Karl Johnson
Comm Dir: Karl Johnson

GENERAL DYNMICS NASSCO-NORFOLK
See METRO MACHINE CORP

D-U-N-S 04-124-8451
GENERAL ECONOPAK INC
1725 N 6th St, Philadelphia, PA 19122-2997
Tel (215) 763-1832 *Founded/Ownrshp* 1999
Sales 21.8MM^E *EMP* 75
SIC 3842 Surgical appliances & supplies
Pr: James G Baxter
**CFO:* Jeffrey Markowitz
**Ch:* Harvey Kimmel
**Treas:* Edward Cahill
Mktg Mgr: John Sincavage
Sales Asso: David Shannon
Sales Asso: Jennifer Woodruff

D-U-N-S 07-842-4131 IMP
■ GENERAL ELECTRIC APPLIANCES AND LIGHTING
(*Suby of* GENERAL ELECTRIC CO) ★
4000 Buechel Bank Rd, Louisville, KY 40225-0001
Tel (502) 452-5658 *Founded/Ownrshp* 2001
Sales 40.9MM^E *EMP* 120^E
SIC 5722 Electric household appliances
CEO: Charles P Blankenship
Mng Dir: Daniel J Damon
Mng Dir: Joe Lee
Prgrm Mgr: Syndra Scherffius
Sftwr Eng: Byron Guernsey

D-U-N-S 03-751-9063
GENERAL ELECTRIC CAPITAL AUTO FINANCIAL SERVICES INC (DEL)
540 W Northwest Hwy, Barrington, IL 60010-3051
Tel (847) 277-4000 *Founded/Ownrshp* 1978
Sales NA *EMP* 600^E
SIC 6159

D-U-N-S 00-698-4256 IMP
■ GENERAL ELECTRIC CAPITAL CORP
(*Suby of* GENERAL ELECTRIC CO) ★
901 Main Ave, Norwalk, CT 06851-1168
Tel (203) 840-6300 *Founded/Ownrshp* 1932, 2012
Sales NA *EMP* 47,000
Accts Kpmg Llp Stamford Connecticu
Tkr Sym GEK *Exch* NYS
SIC 6159 6141 7359 Equipment & vehicle finance leasing companies; Machinery & equipment finance leasing; Financing: automobiles, furniture, etc., not a deposit bank; Installment sales finance, other than banks; Equipment rental & leasing; Equipment & vehicle finance leasing companies; Machinery & equipment finance leasing; Financing: automobiles, furniture, etc., not a deposit bank; Installment sales finance, other than banks; Equipment rental & leasing
Ch Bd: Keith S Sherin
**Pr:* Thomas C Gentile
**CFO:* Robert C Green
CFO: Robert Green
Treas: Kathryn A Cassidy
Chf Mktg O: Lee Cooper
Ofcr: Steve Dorman
Ofcr: Michael J Pilot
**Ofcr:* Ryan A Zanin
Sr VP: Douglas Cannaliato
Sr VP: Alex Dimitrief
Sr VP: Walter Ielusic
VP: Bruce Christensen
VP: Kanchan Deshmukh
VP: John Godin
VP: Pamela Grays
VP: Aris Kekedjian
VP: Ll Liu
VP: Xiaowei Luan
VP: Louis Natale
Dir Risk M: Dean Debroux
Board of Directors: Jeffrey S Bornstein, Jeffrey R Immelt

D-U-N-S 11-618-2890
■ GENERAL ELECTRIC CAPITAL SERVICES INC
(*Suby of* GENERAL ELECTRIC CO) ★
3135 Easton Tpke, Fairfield, CT 06828-0001
Tel (203) 373-2211 *Founded/Ownrshp* 1984
Sales NA *EMP* 55,000^E
SIC 6159 6141 7359 6162 Equipment & vehicle finance leasing companies; Machinery & equipment finance leasing; Consumer finance companies; Financing: automobiles, furniture, etc., not a deposit bank; Installment sales finance, other than banks; Equipment rental & leasing; Bond & mortgage companies; Equipment & vehicle finance leasing companies; Machinery & equipment finance leasing; Consumer finance companies; Financing: automobiles, furniture, etc., not a deposit bank; Installment sales finance, other than banks; Equipment rental & leasing; Bond & mortgage companies
Ch Bd: Jeffrey R Immelt
Pr: Stuart D Aronson
Pr: Michael E Chen
Pr: Margaret Keane
Pr: Dmitri Stockton
CEO: Robert Stefanowski
CFO: Stewart B Koenigsberg
CFO: Trevor A Schauenberg
CFO: Keith S Sherin
Chf Mktg O: Bob Morton
Chf Mktg O: Glenn Thomas
Ofcr: David Ringhausen
Sr VP: Ray Duggins
Sr VP: Andreas Hirsemann
Sr VP: Jamie S Miller
Sr VP: Tho Nghiem
Sr VP: Richard Rudolph
Sr VP: John Trentos
VP: Alec Burger
VP: Kristi Colburn
VP: William Dakin Jr
Board of Directors: Michael A Neal, Mark W Begor, Ronald R Pressman, Jeffrey S Bornstein, John M Samuels, William H Cary, Ryan A Zanin, Kathryn A Cassidy, Pamela Daley, Mark J Krakowiak, John Krenicki Jr, J Keith Morgan, David Nason

D-U-N-S 00-136-7960 EXP
▲ GENERAL ELECTRIC CO
3135 Easton Tpke, Fairfield, CT 06828-0001
Tel (203) 373-2211 *Founded/Ownrshp* 1892
Sales NA *EMP* 305,000
Tkr Sym GE *Exch* NYS
SIC 6159 3511 3724 3632 4833 3845 Equipment & vehicle finance leasing companies; Turbines & turbine generator sets; Steam turbines; Gas turbines, mechanical drive; Aircraft engines & engine parts; Refrigerators, mechanical & absorption: household; Freezers, home & farm; Television broadcasting stations; Electromedical equipment; Electromedical apparatus; Magnetic resonance imaging device, nuclear; Equipment & vehicle finance leasing companies; Turbines & turbine generator sets; Steam turbines; Gas turbines, mechanical drive; Aircraft engines & engine parts; Refrigerators, mechanical & absorption: household; Freezers, home & farm; Television broadcasting stations; Electromedical equipment; Electromedical apparatus; Magnetic resonance imaging device, nuclear
Ch Bd: Jeffrey R Immelt
Pr: Mark Begor
Pr: Alec Burger
Pr: John Flannery
COO: Ed Martin
CFO: Jeffrey S Bornstein
CFO: Tim Donovan
CFO: William Lacey
Chf Mktg O: Linda Boff
Chf Mktg O: Eric Labat
Ex VP: Lloyd G Trotter
Sr VP: Alexander Byers
Sr VP: Brackett B Denniston III
Sr VP: Mark Familo
VP: Chaker Chahrour
VP: Xiangli Chen
VP: Jorg F Debatin
VP: Christine Furstoss
VP: Michael Gosk
VP: Jan R Hauser
VP: Jaime A Irick
Board of Directors: James E Rohr, W Geoffrey Beattie, Mary L Schapiro, John J Brennan, Robert J Swieringa, James I Cash Jr, James S Tisch, Francisco D'souza, Douglas A Warner III, Susan J Hockfield, Andrea Jung, Robert W Lane, Rochelle B Lazarus, James J Mulva

D-U-N-S 06-893-7135
GENERAL ELECTRIC CREDIT UNION
GECU
10485 Reading Rd, Cincinnati, OH 45241-2580
Tel (513) 243-4328 *Founded/Ownrshp* 1954
Sales NA *EMP* 150
SIC 6062 State credit unions, not federally chartered; State credit unions, not federally chartered
CEO: Timothy D Ballinger
**CFO:* Joan Moore
DP Dir: Kevin Riede

D-U-N-S 96-450-8043
GENERAL ELECTRIC INSURANCE PLAN TRUST
1070 High Ridge Rd, Stamford, CT 06905-1122
Tel (203) 326-2300 *Founded/Ownrshp* 2010
Sales NA *EMP* 2^E
Accts Pricewaterhousecoopers Llp Ph
SIC 6411 Insurance agents, brokers & service; Insurance agents, brokers & service

D-U-N-S 06-492-3659
■ GENERAL ELECTRIC INTERNATIONAL INC
(*Suby of* GENERAL ELECTRIC CO) ★
3135 Easton Tpke, Fairfield, CT 06828-0001
Tel (203) 373-2039 *Founded/Ownrshp* 1961
Sales 12.8MMM *EMP* 125^E
Accts Kpmg Llp Stamford Ct
SIC 8711 Engineering services; Engineering services
Pr: Giuseppe Recchi
CFO: Stephen Sedita Jr
**Treas:* Michael J Geary
**VP:* Candace F Carson
**VP:* Daniel Janki
Mng Dir: Osman Tunagur
Prgrm Mgr: Mark Hachenski
Area Mgr: Chris Barnes
Dist Mgr: Brian Fitzgerald
Genl Mgr: Chuck Elias
CIO: John Maya

D-U-N-S 94-724-4943
■ GENERAL ELECTRIC INTERNATIONAL OPERATIONS CO INC
(*Suby of* GENERAL ELECTRIC CO) ★
2 Corporate Dr Fl 5, Shelton, CT 06484-6238
Tel (203) 944-3000 *Founded/Ownrshp* 1976
Sales 760.5MM *EMP* 26^E
Accts Kpmg Llp Stamford Ct
SIC 7389 Personal service agents, brokers & bureaus; Personal service agents, brokers & bureaus
Pr: Robert Smits

D-U-N-S 10-752-0470
■ GENERAL ELECTRIC RAILCAR REPAIR SERVICES CORP
(*Suby of* GENERAL ELECTRIC CAPITAL CORP) ★
161 N Clark St Fl 7, Chicago, IL 60601-3375
Tel (312) 853-5000 *Founded/Ownrshp* 2013
Sales 91.2MM^E *EMP* 937
SIC 4789 3743 5088 4741 Railroad car repair; Railroad car rebuilding; Transportation equipment & supplies; Rental of railroad cars; Railroad car repair; Railroad car rebuilding; Transportation equipment & supplies; Rental of railroad cars
CEO: Robert W Speetzen
Pr: Joseph Lattanzio
Pr: Ted Torbeck
CFO: Mandeep Johar
Ex VP: Sameer Gaur
Ex VP: Patrice Powers
Ex VP: Robert Tucker
Sr VP: Kristina Miller
Sr VP: Nick Muday
Sr VP: Gregory Taylor
VP: Frank Mantero

D-U-N-S 10-752-0769
GENERAL ELECTRIC RAILCAR SERVICES CORP
161 N Clark St Fl 7, Chicago, IL 60601-3375
Tel (312) 853-5000 *Founded/Ownrshp* 1983
Sales NA *EMP* 1,000
SIC 7359 3743 4789 3462

GENERAL EMPLOYEES PENSION
See CITY OF PLANTATION

D-U-N-S 00-553-9010
▲ GENERAL EMPLOYMENT ENTERPRISES INC (IL)
184 Shuman Blvd Ste 420, Naperville, IL 60563-8323
Tel (630) 954-0400 *Founded/Ownrshp* 1893
Sales 39.8MM *EMP* 130^E
Accts Friedman Llp New York New Y
Tkr Sym JOB *Exch* ASE
SIC 7361 Employment agencies; Employment agencies
Ch Bd: Derek Dewan
**CFO:* Andrew J Norstrud
VP: David Bond
VP: Kathleen Elston
Board of Directors: George A Bajalia, William Isaac, Arthur B Laffer, Peter Tanous, Thomas C Williams

D-U-N-S 06-540-9476
GENERAL ENGINEERING CO OF VIRGINIA
26485 Hillman Hwy, Abingdon, VA 24210-7681
Tel (276) 628-6068 *Founded/Ownrshp* 1948
Sales 22.5MM^E *EMP* 91
SIC 3593 3599 Fluid power cylinders, hydraulic or pneumatic; Custom machinery
Ch Bd: Donald W Tuckwiller
**Pr:* John E Owens
CFO: Michael Sanders

D-U-N-S 07-037-7457 IMP
▲ GENERAL ENVIRONMENTAL MANAGEMENT INC
4790 Irvine Blvd Ste 105, Irvine, CA 92620-1998
Tel (909) 444-9500 *Founded/Ownrshp* 2005
Sales 51.0MM^E *EMP* 186
Tkr Sym GEVI *Exch* OTO
SIC 4952 Sewerage systems; Sewerage systems
Ch Bd: Timothy J Koziol
Pr: William J Mitzel
**CFO:* Brett M Clark
**Ex VP:* Douglas B Edwards

D-U-N-S 03-181-8297
GENERAL EQUIPMENT & SUPPLIES INC
4300 Main Ave, Fargo, ND 58103-1128
Tel (701) 282-2662 *Founded/Ownrshp* 1984
Sales 48.7MM^E *EMP* 120
SIC 5082 7353 3799

D-U-N-S 15-187-6075
GENERAL EQUIPMENT & SUPPLY CO INC
3423 Fork Shoals Rd, Simpsonville, SC 29680-6815
Tel (864) 243-5452 *Founded/Ownrshp* 1986
Sales 21.6MM^E *EMP* 70
SIC 7359 5082 Tool rental; General construction machinery & equipment; Contractors' materials
Pr: Rob Hall
VP Sls: John Millener
Sls Mgr: Cindy Walker

D-U-N-S 09-207-1687
GENERAL EQUITIES INC
FOOD BAG
318 Main St, Kensington, CT 06037-2637
Tel (860) 828-6963 *Founded/Ownrshp* 1974
Sales 64.9MM^E *EMP* 500
SIC 5411 5541 5145 5194 Convenience stores, chain; Filling stations, gasoline; Candy; Tobacco & tobacco products; Convenience stores, chain; Filling stations, gasoline; Candy; Tobacco & tobacco products
Ch Bd: Raymond Hill
**Pr:* George Webb
**CFO:* William Walluk
**Treas:* John Sabol

D-U-N-S 00-447-0852
GENERAL EXTRUSIONS INC
GEI
4040 Lake Park Rd, Youngstown, OH 44512-1801
Tel (330) 783-0270 *Founded/Ownrshp* 1950
Sales 28.0MM^E *EMP* 58
SIC 3354 3471 Shapes, extruded aluminum; Polishing, metals or formed products
Pr: Herbert F Schuler
Plnt Mgr: Ted Allen
Sls&Mrk Ex: Eric Mc Mc Elroy
Sls Mgr: Elic McElroy

D-U-N-S 00-178-4875 IMP
GENERAL FABRICS CO (RI)
FABRICS BY SPECTRIX
45 Washington St, Pawtucket, RI 02860-3615
Tel (401) 728-4200 *Founded/Ownrshp* 1951
Sales 42.5MM^E *EMP* 60
SIC 5131 Piece goods & other fabrics; Textiles, woven
Pr: Edward P Odessa
**CFO:* Jack Berifo
**VP:* David Odessa

D-U-N-S 00-886-2005
GENERAL FACTORY SUPPLIES CO INC (OH)
GFWD SUPPLY
4811 Winton Rd, Cincinnati, OH 45232-1502
Tel (513) 864-6007 *Founded/Ownrshp* 2007
Sales 50.0MM *EMP* 40
SIC 5085 Industrial supplies
Pr: Teri Stautberg
**CFO:* Jeff Stautberg

D-U-N-S 01-687-9751 IMP/EXP
GENERAL FASTENERS CO
37584 Amrhein Rd Ste 150, Livonia, MI 48150-1090
Tel (734) 452-2400 *Founded/Ownrshp* 2002
Sales 67.5MM^E *EMP* 200
SIC 5072

D-U-N-S 60-738-4518 IMP
GENERAL FIBRE PRODUCTS CORP
170 Nassau Terminal Rd, New Hyde Park, NY 11040-4940
Tel (516) 358-7500 *Founded/Ownrshp* 2000
Sales 21.6MM^E *EMP* 70
SIC 2653 2675 2671 2679 Corrugated boxes, partitions, display items, sheets & pad; Die-cut paper & board; Packaging paper & plastics film, coated & laminated; Corrugated paper: made from purchased material
Pr: James Miller
CFO: Irene Miller
**VP:* Michael Petti
**VP:* Stuart Shrode
Plnt Mgr: Frank Anthony
Ql Cn Mgr: Ruth Cartegena

D-U-N-S 00-424-8407
GENERAL FILMS INC
645 S High St Ste 48, Covington, OH 45318-1182
Tel (937) 473-2051 *Founded/Ownrshp* 1938
Sales 32.0MM^E *EMP* 80
SIC 3081 2673 Polyethylene film; Plastic & pliofilm bags; Polyethylene film; Plastic & pliofilm bags
Ch: Roy J Weikert
Pr: Tim Weikert
VP: Tom Granata
Opers Mgr: Joseph Sprouse
Natl Sales: Wesley Hendley
Natl Sales: Marty Leonard

D-U-N-S 80-033-4430
▲ GENERAL FINANCE CORP
39 E Union St Ste 206, Pasadena, CA 91103-3929
Tel (626) 584-9722 *Founded/Ownrshp* 2007
Sales 303.8MM *EMP* 902^E
Tkr Sym GFN *Exch* NGM
SIC 7359 5085 Shipping container leasing; Bins & containers, storage; Shipping container leasing; Bins & containers, storage
Ch Bd: Ronald F Valenta
CFO: Charles E Barrantes
Ex VP: Jeffrey A Kluckman
VP: James Dunmyer
Sales Asso: Susie Osborne
Board of Directors: David M Connell, Susan L Harris, Manuel Marrero, James B Roszak, Larry D Tashjian

GENERAL FINDINGS
See EF LEACH & CO

D-U-N-S 80-761-2817 IMP
GENERAL FLOOR INDUSTRIES INC
190 Benigno Blvd, Bellmawr, NJ 08031-2516
Tel (856) 931-2288 *Founded/Ownrshp* 1993
Sales 43.9MM^E *EMP* 85
SIC 5023 Floor coverings; Floor cushion & padding; Floor coverings; Floor cushion & padding
Pr: David Cometz
**VP:* Michael Cometz
Brnch Mgr: Ed Johnson
Sales Asso: Keith Bradshaw

D-U-N-S 00-317-6385 IMP/EXP
GENERAL FOAM PLASTICS CORP (VA)
GFP PLASTICS
4429 Bonney Rd Ste 500, Virginia Beach, VA 23462-3881
Tel (757) 857-0153 *Founded/Ownrshp* 1957, 1960
Sales 347.1MM^E *EMP* 1,500
SIC 3089 Christmas trees, artificial; Swimming pools, plastic; Plastic processing; Ice chests or coolers (portable), foamed plastic; Plastic processing
CEO: Jack Hall
**Pr:* George Dieffenbach
COO: Wingate Sung
**CFO:* Stan Hobbs
CFO: Bob Scott
**Ch:* Bill Fields
**Ex VP:* Sandy Caprow
VP: Eva Austin
VP: Lamont D Kennedy II
**Prin:* Ascher Chase
Mng Dir: Tom Brandenburg

GENERAL FORMULATIONS
See CELIA CORP

D-U-N-S 03-032-4321
GENERAL GERMAN AGED PEOPLES HOME OF BALTIMORE
EDENWALD
800 Southerly Rd Ste 1, Towson, MD 21286-8488
Tel (410) 339-6000 *Founded/Ownrshp* 1881
Sales 23.4MM *EMP* 245
Accts Mclean Koehler Sparks & Hammon
SIC 8051 6513 Convalescent home with continuous nursing care; Retirement hotel operation; Convalescent home with continuous nursing care; Retirement hotel operation
Pr: Salvatore J Molite
Dir Recs: Eileen Devaney
**Ch:* Daniel Judge
Ex VP: William Garrett
Off Mgr: Bridgett Jones
Secur Mgr: Jason Spivey
Sls Dir: Diane Stinchcomb
Nrsg Dir: Susan Denning

GENERAL GLASS INTERNATIONAL
See GGI GLASS DISTRIBUTORS CORP

D-U-N-S 08-208-9368
GENERAL GRIND & MACHINE INC
2103 Se 5th St, Aledo, IL 61231-9473
Tel (309) 582-5959 *Founded/Ownrshp* 2002
Sales 53.6MM^E *EMP* 150
SIC 3599 Machine shop, jobbing & repair; Machine shop, jobbing & repair
Pr: Mark Bieri
**COO:* Blake Bieri
**CFO:* Michael Vipond
**Treas:* Todd Stone
**VP:* Schuyler Downey
**VP:* Charles Guldenzopf
Exec: Lisa Holtschlag
Ql Cn Mgr: Rob Long

GENERAL GROWTH PROPERTIES
See GGP LIMITED PARTNERSHIP

D-U-N-S 07-877-6876
▲ GENERAL GROWTH PROPERTIES INC
110 N Wacker Dr, Chicago, IL 60606-1526
Tel (312) 960-5000 *Founded/Ownrshp* 1986
Sales 2.5MMM *EMP* 1,500^E
Accts Deloitte & Touche Llp Chicago
Tkr Sym GGP *Exch* NYS
SIC 6798 Real estate investment trusts; Real estate investment trusts
CEO: Sandeep Mathrani
**Ch Bd:* J Bruce Flatt
COO: Shobi Khan
CFO: Michael B Berman
Bd of Dir: Mark Patterson
Ofcr: Marvin J Levine
Ex VP: Alan Barocas
Ex VP: Richard S Pesin
Sr VP: Sarah Alter
Sr VP: Tara Marszewski
VP: Erin Armendinger
VP: George Tanasijevich
Comm Dir: Lesley Cheers
Dir Bus: Nancy Barbary
Dir Bus: Jill Werner
Board of Directors: Richard B Clark, Mary Lou Fiala, John K Haley, Daniel B Hurwitz, Brian Kingston, David J Neithercut, Mark R Patterson

D-U-N-S 07-878-1003
GENERAL GROWTH SERVICES INC
GGSI
110 N Wacker Dr, Chicago, IL 60606-1526
Tel (312) 960-5826 *Founded/Ownrshp* 2012
Sales 31.6MM^E *EMP* 930
SIC 8741 Management services; Management services
CEO: Sandeep Mathrani
VP: James Harris

GENERAL HARDWARE DISTRIBUTORS
See ALASKA INDUSTRIAL HARDWARE INC

D-U-N-S 13-954-9901
GENERAL HEALTH SERVICES CORP
PRESBYTERIAN HOSPITAL DALLAS
(*Suby of* TEXAS HEALTH RESOURCES) ★
7515 Grnvlle Ave Ste 1000, Dallas, TX 75231
Tel (214) 345-8345 *Founded/Ownrshp* 1998
Sales 372.0MM^E *EMP* 15,000
SIC 6719 Investment holding companies, except banks; Investment holding companies, except banks
Pr: Douglas Hawthorne
**Sec:* Charles Boes
Opthamlgy: Gary E Fish

D-U-N-S 07-505-5160
GENERAL HEALTH SYSTEM
BATON ROUGE GENERAL
8585 Picardy Ave, Baton Rouge, LA 70809-3679
Tel (225) 387-7000 *Founded/Ownrshp* 1945
Sales 68.4MM *EMP* 3,400
Accts Postlethwaite & Netterville B
SIC 8741 6324 Hospital management; Hospital & medical service plans; Hospital management; Hospital & medical service plans
CEO: Mark F Slyter
**CFO:* Kendall Johnson
**Ex VP:* Anna Cazes
**Ex VP:* Dionne E Viator
**VP:* Paul Douglas
Dir Lab: Jerad Stutes

D-U-N-S 60-920-2742
GENERAL HEALTH SYSTEM
HEART & FITNESS CENTER
(*Suby of* BATON ROUGE GENERAL) ★
5757 Corp Blvd Ste 200, Baton Rouge, LA 70808
Tel (225) 237-1500 *Founded/Ownrshp* 1983
Sales 326.8MM *EMP* 5
SIC 8071 7991 Medical laboratories; Physical fitness facilities; Medical laboratories; Physical fitness facilities
Prin: Dr Milton Sietman
**Pr:* Drmilton Sietman
CFO: Patricia Thomas
**CFO:* Jack Wagner

D-U-N-S 17-371-9386
GENERAL HEALTH SYSTEM MANAGEMENT INC
(*Suby of* BATON ROUGE GENERAL) ★
8585 Picardy Ave, Baton Rouge, LA 70809-3679
Tel (225) 237-1700 *Founded/Ownrshp* 1986
Sales NA *EMP* 4,000
SIC 6324 Hospital & medical service plans; Hospital & medical service plans
VP: Don Shaw
Off Mgr: Carol Jackson

D-U-N-S 87-634-1272
GENERAL HEALTHCARE RESOURCES INC
GHR
2250 Hickory Rd Ste 240, Plymouth Meeting, PA 19462-2225
Tel (610) 834-1122 *Founded/Ownrshp* 1993
Sales 34.4MM^E *EMP* 1,000
SIC 8082 Home health care services; Home health care services
Pr: John I Quirk
Treas: John Cameron
**Sec:* Lawrence Palmer
Sr VP: Gloria Alfonsi
VP: Ron Deal
Mng Dir: Coley Murphy
Mng Dir: Brian Simpson
Genl Mgr: Jayne Suchora
Off Admin: Latoya Bailey
Mktg Dir: Kevin Saeger
Mktg Mgr: Erica Coley

D-U-N-S 02-332-1243
GENERAL HEATING & AIR CONDITIONING INC
(*Suby of* HOOPER CORP) ★
3002 Perry St, Madison, WI 53713
Tel (608) 271-3900 *Founded/Ownrshp* 1994
Sales 69.8MM *EMP* 120
Accts Mcgladrey Llp Madison Wiscon
SIC 1711 3444 Warm air heating & air conditioning contractor; Sheet metalwork; Warm air heating & air conditioning contractor; Sheet metalwork
Pr: Brad Werlein
**Ch:* Fred Davie
Treas: Richard Hanna
VP: Andy Chrisinger
VP: G Davie
**VP:* David Gillette
VP: Dan Kurtz
VP: Rob Weise
Sfty Mgr: Jeff Hanson

D-U-N-S 93-869-2944
GENERAL HEATING & PLUMBING CO
(*Suby of* AMERICAN RESIDENTIAL SERVICES OF INDIANA INC) ★
9070 Euclid Ave, Manassas, VA 20110-5308
Tel (703) 631-2690 *Founded/Ownrshp* 1999
Sales 15.8MM^E *EMP* 370
SIC 1711 Plumbing, heating, air-conditioning contractors; Plumbing, heating, air-conditioning contractors
Genl Mgr: Jack Beers
Treas: Stanley Zalik

GENERAL HOSPITAL, THE
See MASSACHUSETTS GENERAL HOSPITAL

GENERAL HOSPITAL
See M G H HEALTH SERVICES CORP

D-U-N-S 03-250-4136 IMP/EXP
GENERAL HOTEL & RESTAURANT SUPPLY CORP (FL)
13900 Nw 82nd Ave, Miami Lakes, FL 33016-1548
Tel (305) 885-8651 *Founded/Ownrshp* 1955
Sales 40.0MM^E *EMP* 70
SIC 5046 Restaurant equipment & supplies; Hotel equipment & supplies
Pr: Walter Simon
Pr: William Chables
**CFO:* John Orts
VP: Don Alloian
**VP:* William Chaples
**VP:* Glenda M Simon
**VP:* Jeffrey Simon
**VP:* Richard Stone
Off Mgr: Linda Lawal
Opers Mgr: Len Davis
Sls Mgr: Dave Katz

D-U-N-S 07-204-8523
GENERAL HOTELS CORP
2501 S High School Rd, Indianapolis, IN 46241-4919
Tel (317) 243-1000 *Founded/Ownrshp* 1969
Sales 20.4MM^E *EMP* 77
SIC 8741 Hotel or motel management
Pr: James E Dora Jr
**CFO:* Richard A Jett
**VP:* Glenn Brooks
VP: Larry Pianto
VP: Larry A Pinto
VP: Chuck Summers
Sls Dir: Danny Coffin
Sls Dir: Amanda Heminger
Sls Dir: Lonnette Neill
Sls Dir: Trina Woolfington
Sls Mgr: Patti Overton

D-U-N-S 18-344-6160
GENERAL HOUSING INC
2255 Industrial Blvd, Waycross, GA 31503-6969
Tel (912) 285-5068 *Founded/Ownrshp* 2005
Sales 49.1MM^E *EMP* 1,025
SIC 2451 Mobile homes; Mobile homes
Sec: J Wayne Roberts
VP: Tim Vinson
IT Man: Thomas Holland
Mfg Dir: Keith Graham

D-U-N-S 79-276-0907 IMP
GENERAL IMAGING CO
17239 S Main St, Gardena, CA 90248-3129
Tel (310) 328-7777 *Founded/Ownrshp* 2006
Sales 48.0MM *EMP* 22
SIC 5043 Cameras & photographic equipment; Cameras & photographic equipment
CEO: Shu-Yun KAO
Pr: Mike Fing
CFO: Tony Chang
CFO: Tammi Graham
Sr VP: Rene Buhay
Sr VP: Craig McManis
VP: Ann Szilagyi
Prd Mgr: Emily Wong
VP Mktg: Paul Meyhoefer
VP Sls: Jim Krodel

D-U-N-S 02-875-1337
GENERAL INDUSTRIAL TOOL & SUPPLY INC
GI TOOL
7649 N San Fernando Rd, Burbank, CA 91505-4348
Tel (818) 504-9333 *Founded/Ownrshp* 1955
Sales 23.9MM^E *EMP* 35^E
SIC 5085 5251 Tools; Abrasives; Tools
CEO: Kathleen Durbin
**Ch Bd:* Mary F Sawin
**Pr:* Karen Boyle
Genl Mgr: Tom Amick
Off Mgr: Wendy Koehnen
IT Man: Alan Nilsen
**VP Sls:* Joan Hoppock
Sales Asso: Lisa Christensen
Sales Asso: Manny Saucedo

GENERAL INDUSTRIES
See GENERAL MECHANICAL CONTRACTORS INC

D-U-N-S 04-310-9867
GENERAL INDUSTRIES OF TENNESSEE INC
5912 Quintus Loop, Chattanooga, TN 37421-2216
Tel (423) 894-6875 *Founded/Ownrshp* 1971
Sales 31.3MM^E *EMP* 404
SIC 8742 Management consulting services; Management consulting services
Pr: Patrick Owings
**Sec:* Lynn G Owings

D-U-N-S 94-188-0312
GENERAL INFORMATION SERVICES INC
GIS
917 Chapin Rd, Chapin, SC 29036-8875
Tel (800) 447-0798 *Founded/Ownrshp* 1996
Sales 77.8MM^E *EMP* 321
SIC 7375 7371 7373 Information retrieval services; Custom computer programming services; Systems software development services; Information retrieval services; Custom computer programming services; Systems software development services
CEO: Raymond Conrad
**Pr:* Albert Bueno
**CFO:* Sharon Mann
**Ex VP:* David Bartley
**Ex VP:* Chris Lemens
Sr VP: Frank Cory
**Sr VP:* Lori Webb
VP: Nate Gabelman
VP: Jamie Grimes
VP: Richard Scott
VP: Jack Snedecor

D-U-N-S 10-825-0663 IMP
■ GENERAL INJECTABLES & VACCINES INC
G I V
(*Suby of* HENRY SCHEIN INC) ★
80 Summit View Ln, Bastian, VA 24314-5299
Tel (276) 688-4121 *Founded/Ownrshp* 1999
Sales 49.7MM^E *EMP* 200
SIC 5122 5047 Drugs & drug proprietaries; Animal medicines; Proprietary (patent) medicines; Medical & hospital equipment; Dentists' professional supplies; Veterinarians' equipment & supplies; Drugs & drug proprietaries; Animal medicines; Proprietary (patent) medicines; Medical & hospital equipment; Dentists' professional supplies; Veterinarians' equipment & supplies
Pr: Stanley Bergman
**Pr:* James Breslawski
CFO: Dixon Low
**Ex VP:* Mark E Mlotek
**Ex VP:* Steven Paladino
Netwrk Mgr: Jason Pennington
Netwrk Eng: Adam Faulkner
Mktg Dir: Kim Crabtree
Sales Asso: Scot Shannon

D-U-N-S 00-100-8986 IMP
GENERAL INSULATION CO (MA)
278 Mystic Ave Ste 209, Medford, MA 02155-6330
Tel (781) 391-2070 *Founded/Ownrshp* 1927, 1981
Sales 269.0MM^E *EMP* 357
SIC 5033 Roofing, siding & insulation; Roofing, siding & insulation
Pr: Francis R Granara
Pr: Mark Snodgrass
**VP:* Rick McMullen
**VP:* Lawrence D Murphy
**VP:* Mark T Oneil
VP: Mark Oneil
**VP:* Gerry Towle
Genl Mgr: Robert De Boer
Genl Mgr: Brian Fabrizio
Genl Mgr: Michael Fritts
Genl Mgr: Raul Martinez

D-U-N-S 08-138-4281
GENERAL INSULATION INC
3555 Hurricane Bay Dr, Theodore, AL 36582-5251
Tel (251) 443-9002 *Founded/Ownrshp* 1989
Sales 29.5MM *EMP* 300
Accts Karen C Simmons Pc Mobile
SIC 1799 Insulation of pipes & boilers; Insulation of pipes & boilers
Pr: William Clark
IT Man: Gary Arnold

GENERAL INSURANCE, THE
See PERMANENT GENERAL COMPANIES INC

D-U-N-S 05-888-9965
GENERAL INVESTMENT & DEVELOPMENT CO
125 High St Ste 27, Boston, MA 02110-2704
Tel (617) 973-9680 *Founded/Ownrshp* 1969
Sales 15.9MM^E *EMP* 600
SIC 6531 Real estate managers; Real estate managers
Ch: W Gardner Wallace
**Pr:* Robert E Dewitt
**Treas:* Peter Martin
Sr VP: Kevin Baldridge
Sr VP: Robert Farington
Sr VP: John Gagnier
**VP:* Stuart R Johnson

D-U-N-S 05-942-5017 IMP/EXP
GENERAL IRON INDUSTRIES INC
1909 N Clifton Ave, Chicago, IL 60614-4803
Tel (773) 327-9600 *Founded/Ownrshp* 1955
Sales 41.4MM^E *EMP* 100
SIC 5051 5093

D-U-N-S 01-064-8533
GENERAL JOHN J PERSHING MEMORIAL HOSPITAL ASSOCIATION
130 E Lockling St, Brookfield, MO 64628-2337
Tel (660) 258-2222 *Founded/Ownrshp* 1960
Sales 17.9MM *EMP* 293
Accts Bkd Llp Kansas City Mo
SIC 8062 8051 Hospital, affiliated with AMA residency; Skilled nursing care facilities; Hospital, affiliated with AMA residency; Skilled nursing care facilities
CEO: Phil Hamilton
Chf Rad: Paul Williams
CFO: Aleta Boyd
**CFO:* Gary Tandy
CIO: Scott Thomason
Mktg Dir: Wendy Engberg
Mktg Dir: Stephanie Millford
Occ Thrpy: Gary Fite

D-U-N-S 00-507-2715 IMP/EXP
GENERAL KINEMATICS CORP
5050 Rickert Rd, Crystal Lake, IL 60014-7333
Tel (815) 455-3222 *Founded/Ownrshp* 1960
Sales 26.4MM^E *EMP* 135^E
SIC 3559

D-U-N-S 09-113-9324
GENERAL LAND OFFICE TEXAS
EXECUTIVE OFC OF THE STATE
(*Suby of* EXECUTIVE OFFICE OF STATE OF TEXAS) ★
1700 Congress Ave, Austin, TX 78701-1436
Tel (512) 305-9116 *Founded/Ownrshp* 1836
Sales NA *EMP* 570
SIC 9512 Land, mineral & wildlife conservation; ; Land, mineral & wildlife conservation;
Ofcr: Johnny Darcey
Area Mgr: Kim Griffith
Software D: Kenny Opara
Snr Mgr: Sterling Harris

D-U-N-S 09-570-6842
GENERAL MACHINERY CO INC
921 Frst Ave N Birmingham, Birmingham, AL 35203
Tel (205) 251-9243 *Founded/Ownrshp* 1967
Sales 37.6MM^E *EMP* 62
SIC 5084 5063 7359 7699

D-U-N-S 04-121-9437
GENERAL MAGNAPLATE CORP
1331 W Edgar Rd, Linden, NJ 07036-6496
Tel (908) 862-6200 *Founded/Ownrshp* 1959
Sales 23.5MM^E *EMP* 140
Accts Franklin Lobrace & Associates
SIC 3479 3471 Coating of metals & formed products; Coating, rust preventive; Electroplating of metals or formed products
Ch Bd: Candida C Aversenti
Pr: Edmund V Aversenti Jr
VP: Larry Campbell
Genl Mgr: Martin Chadwick
Genl Mgr: Jim Dedmon

D-U-N-S 15-130-2358
■ GENERAL MARITIME MANAGEMENT LLC
(*Suby of* GENER8 MARITIME INC) ★
299 Park Ave Fl 2, New York, NY 10171-0299
Tel (212) 763-5600 *Founded/Ownrshp* 2003
Sales 46.2MM^E *EMP* 30^E
SIC 8741 Business management
VP: Kevin Coyne
VP: Steinar Ropeid

D-U-N-S 02-353-9216
GENERAL MC LANE SCHOOL DISTRICT (INC)
11771 Edinboro Rd, Edinboro, PA 16412-1025
Tel (814) 273-1033 *Founded/Ownrshp* 1949
Sales 21.5MM^E *EMP* 335
Accts Buseck Barger Bleil & Co l
SIC 8211 Public elementary school; Public junior high school; Public senior high school; Public elementary school; Public junior high school; Public senior high school
IT Man: Jeffrey Fox

D-U-N-S 06-563-5930
GENERAL MECHANICAL CONTRACTORS INC
GENERAL INDUSTRIES
15 Arentzen Blvd, Charleroi, PA 15022-1060
Tel (724) 483-1600 *Founded/Ownrshp* 1973
Sales 31.5MM^E *EMP* 60
SIC 1542 1541 Commercial & office building, new construction; Commercial & office buildings, renovation & repair; Industrial buildings, new construction; Renovation, remodeling & repairs: industrial buildings
Pr: Donald J Ivill
VP: Russel Lyon

VP: Chad Vittone
Exec: Jerry Reed
VP Admn: Cynthia Grimm
Snr Mgr: John Helsley
Snr Mgr: Matthew Ivill

D-U-N-S 00-928-1098
GENERAL MECHANICAL INC
2701 S J St, Tacoma, WA 98409-8092
Tel (253) 627-8155 *Founded/Ownrshp* 1970
Sales 45.4MM^E *EMP* 135
SIC 1541 1711

GENERAL MEDICAL SURGICAL
See HARRISON MEDICAL CENTER

GENERAL METAL PRODUCTS
See GMP METAL PRODUCTS

D-U-N-S 09-689-0231
GENERAL MICRO SYSTEMS INC
G M S
8358 Maple Pl, Rancho Cucamonga, CA 91730-3839
Tel (909) 980-4863 *Founded/Ownrshp* 1979
Sales 24.6MM^E *EMP* 80^E
SIC 3571 Personal computers (microcomputers); Personal computers (microcomputers)
Pr: Benjamin K Sharfi
CTO: Udi Levin

D-U-N-S 02-138-8798 IMP
GENERAL MICROCIRCUITS INC (NC)
1133 N Main St, Mooresville, NC 28115-2359
Tel (704) 664-6913 *Founded/Ownrshp* 1980, 1998
Sales 52.5MM^E *EMP* 102
SIC 3672 Printed circuit boards; Printed circuit boards
Pr: David Dalton
**Ch Bd:* Rufus Dalton
**Pr:* Stanley Cox
**Treas:* Thomas Evans
VP: Jay Handley
**VP:* Nick Harris
Prgrm Mgr: Ann Hall
Prgrm Mgr: Kathy Johnson
Genl Mgr: Staton Williams
QC Dir: Tracy Bates
Sfty Mgr: Ralf Maier

D-U-N-S 12-117-2530
GENERAL MICROSYSTEMS INC
3220 118th Ave Se Ste 100, Bellevue, WA 98005-4140
Tel (425) 644-2233 *Founded/Ownrshp* 1983
Sales 26.5MM^E *EMP* 28
Accts Grant Thornton Llp Seattle W
SIC 5045 Computer peripheral equipment
Pr: Earl W Overstreet II
**Sec:* Barbara Overstreet
**VP:* Paul Overstreet

D-U-N-S 00-819-8863 IMP
GENERAL MILL SUPPLIES INC (LA)
751 Hill St, New Orleans, LA 70121-1017
Tel (504) 736-0404 *Founded/Ownrshp* 1979
Sales 24.5MM^E *EMP* 53
SIC 5085 5088 5072 Mill supplies; Fasteners, industrial: nuts, bolts, screws, etc.; Tools; Marine supplies; Hardware; Miscellaneous fasteners; Bolts
CEO: Dimitry Morvant Jr
**Pr:* Myra Robertson
**Treas:* Dracos Morvant
**VP:* Clarence Steeg
**VP:* Willis Williams
VP: Robert Winters
Exec: Benard Morvant

D-U-N-S 96-993-3956
GENERAL MILLS FOUNDATION
1 General Mills Blvd, Minneapolis, MN 55426-1348
Tel (763) 764-2211 *Founded/Ownrshp* 1954
Sales 27.4MM *EMP* 8
SIC 8699 Charitable organization; Charitable organization
Ex Dir: Ellen Goldberg Luger

D-U-N-S 00-625-0740 IMP/EXP
▲ **GENERAL MILLS INC**
1 General Mills Blvd, Minneapolis, MN 55426-1348
Tel (763) 764-7600 *Founded/Ownrshp* 1928
Sales 17.6MMM *EMP* 42,000
Accts Kpmg Llp Minneapolis Minnes
Tkr Sym GIS *Exch* NYS
SIC 2099 2041 2045 2064 2024 Dessert mixes & fillings; Frosting mixes, dry: for cakes, cookies, etc.; Potatoes, dried: packaged with other ingredients; Pasta, uncooked: packaged with other ingredients; Flour; Flour mixes; Prepared flour mixes & doughs; Cake mixes, prepared: from purchased flour; Biscuit mixes, prepared: from purchased flour; Fruit & fruit peel confections; Granola & muesli, bars & clusters; Yogurt desserts, frozen; Dessert mixes & fillings; Frosting mixes, dry: for cakes, cookies, etc.; Potatoes, dried: packaged with other ingredients; Pasta, uncooked: packaged with other ingredients; Flour; Flour mixes; Prepared flour mixes & doughs; Cake mixes, prepared: from purchased flour; Biscuit mixes, prepared: from purchased flour; Fruit & fruit peel confections; Granola & muesli, bars & clusters; Yogurt desserts, frozen
Ch Bd: Kendall J Powell
Pr: Kim Nelson
Pr: Chris Shea
CFO: Donal L Mulligan
Sr VP: Richard C Allendorf
Sr VP: Marc Belton
Sr VP: John Machuzick
Sr VP: Shawn P O'Grady
VP: Jerald A Young
Comm Man: Grant Moos
Dept Mgr: Traci Palm
Board of Directors: Steve Odland, Hilda Ochoa-Brillembourg, Michael D Rose, R Kerry Clark, Robert L Ryan, David M Cordani, Eric D Sprunk, Paul Danos, Dorothy A Terrell, Roger W Ferguson Jr, Henrietta H Fore, Raymond V Gilmartin, Judith Richards Hope, Heidi G Miller

D-U-N-S 03-428-6919
■ **GENERAL MILLS OPERATIONS LLC**
(*Suby of* GENERAL MILLS INC) ★
1 General Mills Blvd, Minneapolis, MN 55426-1348
Tel (763) 764-7600 *Founded/Ownrshp* 1996
Sales 175.8MM^E *EMP* 750
SIC 4221 Grain elevator, storage only; Grain elevator, storage only
**CEO:* Stephen Sanger
Mktg Mgr: Billie Norris

D-U-N-S 00-831-6929 IMP/EXP
■ **GENERAL MONITORS INC**
(*Suby of* MINE SAFETY APPLIANCES CO LLC) ★
26776 Simpatica Cir, Lake Forest, CA 92630-8128
Tel (949) 581-4464 *Founded/Ownrshp* 2011
Sales 62.7MM^E *EMP* 225
SIC 3669 1799 3812 Fire detection systems, electric; Gas leakage detection; Infrared object detection equipment; Fire detection systems, electric; Gas leakage detection; Infrared object detection equipment
VP: Nish Vartanian
**CFO:* Richard Lamishaw
Mng Dir: Steven Tan
Genl Mgr: Tom Dagerman
CTO: John Romero
IT Man: Randy Foy
Manager: Tom Chand
Sls Mgr: Jimmy Cheng
Sls Mgr: Abert Jao
Sls Mgr: Mitsuhiro Suda

D-U-N-S 82-969-5910
■ **GENERAL MOTORS CHINA INC**
(*Suby of* GENERAL MOTORS LLC) ★
300 Renaissance Ctr L1, Detroit, MI 48243-1403
Tel (313) 556-5000 *Founded/Ownrshp* 2009
Sales 82.0MM^E *EMP* 347^E
SIC 3714 Motor vehicle parts & accessories
CEO: Lillian Orth
Ex VP: Thomas Lasorda
**Ex VP:* Matthew Tsien
VP: Bryan Nesbitt
Exec: Jon Centurino
Ex Dir: John Murtagh
Tech Mgr: Peter Scott
Opers Mgr: Joe Beauchamp
Opers Mgr: Jim Vincent
Plnt Mgr: Scott Gaines
Plnt Mgr: Scott Williamson

D-U-N-S 83-244-7812 IMP
▲ **GENERAL MOTORS CO**
300 Renaissance Ctr L1, Detroit, MI 48243-1403
Tel (313) 556-5000 *Founded/Ownrshp* 1908
Sales 155.9MMM *EMP* 216,000^E
Tkr Sym GM *Exch* NYS
SIC 3711 3714 Motor vehicles & car bodies; Motor vehicle parts & accessories; Motor vehicles & car bodies; Motor vehicle parts & accessories
CEO: Mary T Barra
Pr: Daniel Ammann
CFO: Charles K Stevens III
Bd of Dir: Chris Gibson
Bd of Dir: Marty Heinzmann
Bd of Dir: Joe McHugh
Ofcr: Peter Komijn
Ex VP: James B Deluca
Ex VP: Stefan Jacoby
Ex VP: Roger Lewis
Ex VP: Michael P Millikin
Ex VP: Mark L Reuss
Sr VP: Randy Arickx
Sr VP: Mary Barra
Sr VP: Robert E Ferguson
Sr VP: Randall D Mott
Sr VP: John Quattrone
VP: Thomas S Timko
Comm Man: Lynn Speranzini
Board of Directors: Theodore M Solso, Joseph J Ashton, Carol M Stephenson, Stephen J Girsky, Linda R Gooden, Joseph Jimenez Jr, Kathryn V Marinello, Michael G Mullen, James J Mulva, Patricia F Russo, Thomas M Schoewe

GENERAL MOTORS CYBERWORKS
See CAMPBELL-EWALD CO

D-U-N-S 17-778-1390
■ **GENERAL MOTORS FINANCIAL CO INC**
AMERICREDIT
(*Suby of* GENERAL MOTORS HOLDINGS LLC) ★
801 Cherry St Ste 3500, Fort Worth, TX 76102-6854
Tel (817) 302-7000 *Founded/Ownrshp* 2010
Sales NA *EMP* 3,800
SIC 6141 Financing: automobiles, furniture, etc., not a deposit bank; Financing: automobiles, furniture, etc., not a deposit bank
Pr: Daniel E Berce
**Ch Bd:* Clifton H Morris Jr
Pr: Charles Berend
Pr: Joshua Blankenship
Pr: Denise Campbell
Pr: Dianne Doughty
Pr: Dan Heinrich
Pr: John Jones
Pr: Kelli Kennedy
Pr: Fred Kenney
Pr: Bill Livesey
Pr: Alan Newburn
Pr: Chuck Nix
Pr: Nicole Swaim
Pr: Brandi West
Pr: Lisa Wood
COO: Kyle Birch
CFO: Chris A Choate
Ofcr: Kyle R Birch
Assoc VP: Carrie Matthies
Ex VP: Robert Beatty

D-U-N-S 83-245-8033 IMP
■ **GENERAL MOTORS HOLDINGS LLC**
(*Suby of* GENERAL MOTORS CO) ★
300 Renaissance Ctr L1, Detroit, MI 48243-1403
Tel (313) 556-5000 *Founded/Ownrshp* 2009
Sales 4.8MMM^E *EMP* 4,085^E
SIC 3711 3714 Motor vehicles & car bodies; Motor vehicle parts & accessories
CEO: Robert A Lutz
**CFO:* Daniel Ammann
**CFO:* Ray G Young
**V Ch Bd:* Thomas G Stephens
**Ex VP:* Jaime Ardila
**Ex VP:* Mary T Barra
**Ex VP:* Michael P Millikin
**VP:* Alan Batey
VP: Ron Sobrerro
Sls Mgr: Paul Scott

D-U-N-S 07-957-3316
■ **GENERAL MOTORS LLC**
(*Suby of* GENERAL MOTORS CO) ★
30001 Van Dyke Ave, Warren, MI 48093-2350
Tel (586) 751-2784 *Founded/Ownrshp* 2014
Sales 64.4MM^E *EMP* 91^E
SIC 5511 Automobiles, new & used
CEO: Mary T Barra
Pr: Dan Ammann
CEO: Daniel E Berce
Ex VP: Jaime Ardila
Ex VP: Alan Batey
Ex Dir: Alberto Rejman
IT Man: Kenneth Koss
Snr Mgr: Dennis Dwyer
Snr Mgr: Michael Fitzgerel
Snr Mgr: Jeffrey Luke
Snr Mgr: Charles Rondeau

D-U-N-S 83-124-7536 EXP
■ **GENERAL MOTORS LLC**
(*Suby of* GENERAL MOTORS CO) ★
300 Renaissance Ctr L1, Detroit, MI 48243-1403
Tel (313) 556-5000 *Founded/Ownrshp* 2009
Sales 3.7MMM^E *EMP* 1,053^E
SIC 3714 3711 Motor vehicle parts & accessories; Motor vehicles & car bodies
CEO: Mary T Barra
**Pr:* Dan Ammann
COO: Leslie Bauer
CFO: Michael J Losh
CFO: Tom Okray
**CFO:* Ray G Young
**Ex VP:* Jaime Ardila
**VP:* Alan Batey
**VP:* Stephen J Girsky
**VP:* Melissa A Howell
**VP:* Timothy E Lee
**VP:* Daniel Nicholson
**VP:* Robert S Osborne
VP: Eric Peterson
Exec: Patricia F Bonderman
Dir Rx: Cynthia Kirman

D-U-N-S 80-452-7794 IMP/EXP
■ **GENERAL MOTORS OVERSEAS DISTRIBUTION LLC**
(*Suby of* GENERAL MOTORS LLC) ★
300 Renaissance Ctr, Detroit, MI 48243-1402
Tel (313) 556-5000 *Founded/Ownrshp* 1972
Sales 21.0MM^E *EMP* 59^E
SIC 5511 Automobiles, new & used

GENERAL MOTORS PLANWORKS
See STARCOM MEDIAVEST GROUP INC

D-U-N-S 05-560-7378 IMP
GENERAL NOVELTY LTD
COACH HOUSE GIFTS
420 E 58th Ave Ste 200, Denver, CO 80216-1400
Tel (303) 292-5537 *Founded/Ownrshp* 1969
Sales NA *EMP* 1,400
SIC 5947 Gift shop; Greeting cards

D-U-N-S 00-434-7936
GENERAL NUCLEAR CORP (PA)
3519 Wheeler St, New Stanton, PA 15672
Tel (724) 925-3565 *Founded/Ownrshp* 1966, 1995
Sales 20.1MM^E *EMP* 55
SIC 3599 3829 3823 Machine shop, jobbing & repair; Measuring & controlling devices; Industrial instrmnts msrmnt display/control process variable; Machine shop, jobbing & repair; Measuring & controlling devices; Industrial instrmnts msrmnt display/control process variable
Pr: Duane Lang
**Ex VP:* Geno Persio

D-U-N-S 79-252-5615
■ **GENERAL NUTRITION CENTERS INC**
GNC
(*Suby of* GNC HOLDINGS INC) ★
300 6th Ave, Pittsburgh, PA 15222-2514
Tel (412) 288-4600 *Founded/Ownrshp* 2007
Sales 2.6MMM^E *EMP* 13,800
SIC 5499 2023 Health & dietetic food stores; Health & dietetic food stores; Dietary supplements, dairy & non-dairy based
CEO: Michael G Archbold
**Sr VP:* Curt Larrimer
**Sr VP:* Michael Locke

D-U-N-S 60-671-0960 IMP
■ **GENERAL NUTRITION COMPANIES INC**
(*Suby of* GNC INC) ★
300 6th Ave, Pittsburgh, PA 15222-2514
Tel (412) 288-4600 *Founded/Ownrshp* 2003
Sales 672.5MM^E *EMP* 7,500
SIC 5499 Health & dietetic food stores; Health foods; Dietetic foods; Health & dietetic food stores; Health foods; Dietetic foods
Pr: Louis Mancini
**Pr:* Joseph Fortunato
**Treas:* J Kenneth Fox
**Ex VP:* Michael K Meyers
**Sr VP:* John A Dicecco
**VP:* David R Heilman
**VP:* Curtis J Larrimer
**VP:* Eileen D Scott
MIS Dir: Gerald Werner Jr
Sls Dir: Mike McNiel
Board of Directors: Ken Fox

D-U-N-S 01-496-0165 EXP
■ **GENERAL NUTRITION CORP**
GNC
(*Suby of* GENERAL NUTRITION CENTERS INC) ★
300 6th Ave, Pittsburgh, PA 15222-2514
Tel (412) 288-4600 *Founded/Ownrshp* 1989
Sales 1.3MMM^E *EMP* 7,000
SIC 5499 5999 5941 5699 6794 Health & dietetic food stores; Health foods; Dietetic foods; Cosmetics; Hair care products; Exercise equipment; Sports apparel; Franchises, selling or licensing; Health & dietetic food stores; Health foods; Dietetic foods; Cosmetics; Hair care products; Exercise equipment; Sports apparel; Franchises, selling or licensing
VP: Michael Nuzzo
CFO: William E Watts
**Treas:* Mary Ellen Costa
Treas: Edwin J Kozlowski
Ex VP: Paul Yater
Sr VP: Jay Kent
VP: Jennifer Brinker
VP: Lou Mancini
VP: Jeff Sieber
Dir Soc: Tony Kuniak
Off Admin: Brenda McGorrian

D-U-N-S 01-161-6778
GENERAL OFFICE ENVIRONMENTS INC
65 Clyde Rd Ste A, Somerset, NJ 08873-3485
Tel (732) 873-6900 *Founded/Ownrshp* 1933
Sales 34.5MM^E *EMP* 128
SIC 5044 5021 Office equipment; Furniture; Office equipment; Furniture
Pr: Steven Grillo
Ex VP: Ted Grillo
**VP:* Robert T Grillo
VP: Marge McCabe
VP: Rob Pfister

D-U-N-S 80-885-7106
GENERAL OFFICE PRODUCTS CO
G O P
4521 Highway 7, Minneapolis, MN 55416-4098
Tel (952) 925-7500 *Founded/Ownrshp* 1993
Sales 31.6MM *EMP* 64^E
SIC 5021

D-U-N-S 02-772-5068 EXP
GENERAL PACIFIC INC
(*Suby of* RURALITE SERVICES INC) ★
22414 Ne Townsend Way, Fairview, OR 97024-4623
Tel (503) 907-2900 *Founded/Ownrshp* 1965
Sales 54.3MM *EMP* 16^E
SIC 5063 Electrical apparatus & equipment; Electrical apparatus & equipment
Ch Bd: John Gerstenderger
Pr: Rick Hall
CFO: Bob Bingham
CFO: Robert Bingham
Sec: Russell Green
VP: Mike Crumbaker
Opers Mgr: Lance Hall
Sales Asso: John Busch
Sales Asso: Diane Carlson
Sales Asso: Lori D'Agostino
Sales Asso: Lori Dagostino

GENERAL PACKAGING AND EQP
See SIGMA SUPPLY INC

D-U-N-S 03-352-7722
GENERAL PAPER GOODS CO
3601 Suthside Indus Ct Se, Atlanta, GA 30354
Tel (404) 361-5500 *Founded/Ownrshp* 1999
Sales 52.9MM^E *EMP* 48
SIC 5113 2672 Industrial & personal service paper; Coated & laminated paper
CEO: Kevin M Florence
**CFO:* Jeffrey A Florence
VP: Daniel Florence
**VP:* W David Shivers
Genl Mgr: David Shivers
Sales Exec: Jeremy Bright
VP Sls: Lawrence Henry

GENERAL PARTS & SUPPLY
See GENERAL PARTS LLC

D-U-N-S 00-320-1480 IMP/EXP
■ **GENERAL PARTS INC** (NC)
CARQUEST AUTO PARTS
(*Suby of* ADVANCE AUTO PARTS INC) ★
2635 E Millbrook Rd Ste C, Raleigh, NC 27604-2989
Tel (919) 573-3000 *Founded/Ownrshp* 1960, 2014
Sales 2.2MMM^E *EMP* 17,000
SIC 5013 5531

D-U-N-S 18-426-7248
■ **GENERAL PARTS INTERNATIONAL INC**
CARQUEST
(*Suby of* ADVANCE AUTO PARTS INC) ★
2635 E Millbrook Rd Ste B, Raleigh, NC 27604-2989
Tel (919) 573-3000 *Founded/Ownrshp* 2014
Sales 2.4MMM^E *EMP* 18,000
SIC 5013

D-U-N-S 00-621-1320
GENERAL PARTS LLC (MN)
GENERAL PARTS & SUPPLY
11311 Hampshire Ave S, Minneapolis, MN 55438-2456
Tel (952) 944-5800 *Founded/Ownrshp* 1939, 1969
Sales 30.1MM^E *EMP* 200
SIC 7699 Industrial equipment services; Industrial equipment services
CEO: John F O'Shaughnessy
**Pr:* Bruce Hodge
**VP:* Jeff Weber
Rgnl Mgr: Guy Jones
Dir IT: Kevin Schoenheider
VP Opers: Gary Schermann
Sales Exec: Chuck Knuth
Manager: Erick Martinez

D-U-N-S 78-096-3968 IMP
GENERAL PATTERN CO INC
3075 84th Ln Ne, Minneapolis, MN 55449-7215
Tel (763) 780-3518 *Founded/Ownrshp* 1929
Sales 23.6MM^E *EMP* 125

SIC 3086 3334 Plastics foam products; Aluminum ingots & slabs; Plastics foam products; Aluminum ingots & slabs
CEO: Dennis J Reiland
MIS Dir: Duc Fortado
Sfty Mgr: Julian Otten

GENERAL PERFORMANCE PRODUCTS
See CHEMTRADE CHEMICALS CORP

D-U-N-S 00-397-0621
GENERAL PET SUPPLY INC
(*Suby of* MERCO GROUP INC) ★
7711 N 81st St, Milwaukee, WI 53223-3847
Tel (414) 365-3400 *Founded/Ownrshp* 1989
Sales 100.5MM^E *EMP* 220
SIC 5199 Pet supplies; Pet supplies
Pr: Bob Merar
Treas: Erwin Merar
Ex VP: David Merar
IT Man: Dan Henry
Sls Dir: B Cohn

D-U-N-S 02-934-5865 IMP
GENERAL PETROLEUM CORP
G P RESOURCES
(*Suby of* PECOS INC) ★
19501 S Santa Fe Ave, Compton, CA 90221-5913
Tel (562) 983-7300 *Founded/Ownrshp* 2006
Sales 79.6MM^E *EMP* 225
SIC 5172 Crude oil; Diesel fuel; Gasoline; Petroleum products
CEO: James A Halsam III
**Pr:* Michael Ruehring
CFO: Scott Smith
Sr VP: Charles McDaniel
Sr VP: Charles McDaniels
**VP:* Sean Kha
CTO: Kerry Cashman
IT Man: Kathleen Ross
S&M/VP: Anthony Mardesich
Sls Mgr: Chris Willig
Snr Mgr: John Zar

D-U-N-S 01-630-8066
GENERAL PETROLEUM INC
7404 Disalle Blvd, Fort Wayne, IN 46825-3369
Tel (260) 489-8504 *Founded/Ownrshp* 1978
Sales 27.0MM *EMP* 30
SIC 5172

D-U-N-S 15-325-8582 IMP
GENERAL PLASMA INC
546 E 25th St, Tucson, AZ 85713-1659
Tel (520) 882-5100 *Founded/Ownrshp* 2004
Sales 27.9MM^E *EMP* 65
SIC 3565 2851 Vacuum packaging machinery; Coating, air curing
Pr: John E Madocks
**Treas:* Jeffrey R Altman
**VP:* Marion D McEuen
**VP:* Phong Ngo
**VP:* Walter M Seaman

GENERAL PLASTICS
See PLASTIC SERVICES AND PRODUCTS INC

D-U-N-S 04-112-5402 EXP
GENERAL PLASTICS & COMPOSITES LP
GP&C
6910 E Orem Dr, Houston, TX 77075-5326
Tel (713) 644-1449 *Founded/Ownrshp* 1997
Sales 114.7MM^E *EMP* 150
SIC 3083 Laminated plastics plate & sheet; Laminated plastics plate & sheet
CEO: David Walstad
**Pr:* Simon Lawrie
CFO: Rob Degeyter
Mfg Mgr: Max Stormo
Ql Cn Mgr: Mark Cox
Sls&Mrk Ex: Jovita Cantu

D-U-N-S 00-924-1548 IMP/EXP
GENERAL PLASTICS MANUFACTURING CO
4910 S Burlington Way, Tacoma, WA 98409-2833
Tel (253) 473-5000 *Founded/Ownrshp* 1941
Sales 58.7MM^E *EMP* 134
SIC 3086 2821 Plastics foam products; Plastics materials & resins; Plastics foam products; Plastics materials & resins
CEO: Henry Schatz
**Pr:* Bruce Lind
CFO: Cherie Morgan
**VP:* Eric Hahn
**VP:* Kirk Lider
Genl Mgr: Dinorh Dorsey
QA Dir: Kyle Riddle
Dir IT: Walt Holman
IT Man: Bob Ciampi
IT Man: Mark Gust
QC Dir: Tod Maurmann

D-U-N-S 00-422-1693 IMP
GENERAL PLUG AND MANUFACTURING CO (OH)
455 Main St, Grafton, OH 44044-1257
Tel (440) 926-2411 *Founded/Ownrshp* 1955
Sales 33.3MM^E *EMP* 135
SIC 3494 3599 3643 Pipe fittings; Machine shop, jobbing & repair; Current-carrying wiring devices; Pipe fittings; Machine shop, jobbing & repair; Current-carrying wiring devices
Pr: D Wallace Weil
VP: Gerald L Jenkins
Exec: Megan Flanigan
Genl Mgr: Jim Tyree
VP Sls: Ron Richmond
Sales Asso: Juliette Blair

D-U-N-S 02-961-9772 IMP
GENERAL PLUMBING SUPPLY CO INC (CA)
1530 San Luis Rd, Walnut Creek, CA 94597-3114
Tel (925) 939-4622 *Founded/Ownrshp* 1965
Sales 52.5MM^E *EMP* 85
SIC 5074 5063 Plumbing & hydronic heating supplies; Electrical apparatus & equipment; Plumbing & hydronic heating supplies; Electrical apparatus & equipment

CEO: Richard P Amaro Jr
**Treas:* Evelyn Amaro
**VP:* Richard Amaro Jr
Brnch Mgr: Steve McDonald

D-U-N-S 01-108-3102
GENERAL PLUMBING SUPPLY INC
980 New Durham Rd, Edison, NJ 08817-2274
Tel (732) 248-1000 *Founded/Ownrshp* 1996
Sales 177.1MM^E *EMP* 140
Accts Rs Kaplan & Company Woodbri
SIC 5075 5074 Warm air heating & air conditioning; Plumbing & hydronic heating supplies; Warm air heating & air conditioning; Plumbing & hydronic heating supplies
Pr: Bruce Tucker
**VP:* Gary Kuperstein
**VP:* Joseph Novack
VP: Joe Novak
IT Man: Tom Mazzola
Mktg Dir: Justin Freedman
Sls Mgr: Ian Ebner
Sls Mgr: Brian Zeitler
Sales Asso: Ryan McLoughlin

D-U-N-S 04-454-6182
GENERAL POLYMERIC CORP
GENPORE
1136 Morgantown Rd, Reading, PA 19607-9522
Tel (610) 374-5171 *Founded/Ownrshp* 1968
Sales 20.7MM^E *EMP* 62
SIC 2821 2992 Plastics materials & resins; Lubricating oils & greases
Pr: Joseph E Ferri
**Sec:* Rose M Ferri
Exec: Matthew Kreska
Plnt Mgr: Ken Kreska
Ql Cn Mgr: Dan Hoellwarth

D-U-N-S 02-961-9780 EXP
GENERAL POOL & SPA SUPPLY INC
11285 Sunco Dr, Rancho Cordova, CA 95742-6517
Tel (916) 853-2401 *Founded/Ownrshp* 1985
Sales 27.4MM^E *EMP* 130
SIC 5091 Swimming pools, equipment & supplies; Spa equipment & supplies; Swimming pools, equipment & supplies; Spa equipment & supplies
Pr: Philip Gelhaus
**Sec:* Patty Gelhaus
**VP:* Mark Yomogida

D-U-N-S 96-357-6095 IMP
GENERAL PROCUREMENT INC
CONNECT COMPUTERS
800 E Dyer Rd, Santa Ana, CA 92705-5604
Tel (949) 679-7960 *Founded/Ownrshp* 1996
Sales 150.0MM *EMP* 50^E
Accts Jack Runke Cpa San Diego Ca
SIC 5045 Computers, peripherals & software
Pr: Imad Boukai
**VP:* Sam Boukai
Dir Bus: Janet Carmona
Rgnl Mgr: Alberto Sabogal
Off Mgr: Sandy Doukai
Mktg Dir: Yesenia Ocon
Sls Dir: Les Luzar

GENERAL PRODUCE
See V & L PRODUCE INC

D-U-N-S 00-886-1379 IMP/EXP
GENERAL PRODUCE CO A CALIFORNIA LIMITED PARTNERSHIP (CA)
1330 N B St, Sacramento, CA 95811-0605
Tel (916) 441-6431 *Founded/Ownrshp* 1933
Sales 105.4MM^E *EMP* 225
SIC 5148 Fruits, fresh; Vegetables, fresh; Fruits, fresh; Vegetables, fresh
CEO: Tom Chan
**Pr:* Dan Chan
VP: Willard Harrison
**VP:* Don Weersing
**VP:* Sheryl Weichert
VP: Chuck Wilkinson
Genl Mgr: Jerry Sharon
IT Man: Sam Rodandte
Snr Mgr: Gary Adams
Snr Mgr: Norm Avila

D-U-N-S 03-371-4775
GENERAL PRODUCE INC
(*Suby of* CASTELLINI CO LLC) ★
16 Forest Pkwy Bldg M, Forest Park, GA 30297-2001
Tel (404) 361-0215 *Founded/Ownrshp* 2014
Sales 135.7MM^E *EMP* 230
SIC 5148 Fresh fruits & vegetables; Fresh fruits & vegetables
Pr: Hiram C Folds Jr
CFO: Jeannie Springfield
Ex VP: Randy Lineberger
IT Man: Michelle Giles
Trfc Dir: Joe Thompson

D-U-N-S 07-944-4930
GENERAL PRODUCE LLC
16 Forest Pkwy Bldg M, Forest Park, GA 30297-2001
Tel (404) 366-8367 *Founded/Ownrshp* 2014
Sales 56.5MM^E *EMP* 238
SIC 5148 5431 Fresh fruits & vegetables; Fruit & vegetable markets; Fresh fruits & vegetables; Fruit & vegetable markets
Genl Mgr: Randy Lineberger
VP: Butch Nelson
VP: Timothy Slaughter

D-U-N-S 10-915-6922
GENERAL PRODUCTION SERVICE OF CALIFORNIA INC
G P S
1333 Kern St, Taft, CA 93268-9700
Tel (661) 765-5330 *Founded/Ownrshp* 1967
Sales 67.3MM^E *EMP* 180
SIC 1623 Oil & gas pipeline construction; Oil & gas pipeline construction
CEO: Charles Beard
Pr: Oreste Risi
Area Mgr: Mike Smith
Sfty Mgr: Mark Potaczala

GENERAL PRODUCTS
See BENCHMARK DOORS

D-U-N-S 15-066-1023 IMP
GENERAL PRODUCTS ANGOLA CORP
(*Suby of* GENERAL PRODUCTS DELAWARE CORP) ★
1411 Wohlert St, Angola, IN 46703-1062
Tel (260) 665-8441 *Founded/Ownrshp* 1989
Sales 22.0MM^E *EMP* 175
SIC 3714 Manifolds, motor vehicle; Axles, motor vehicle; Manifolds, motor vehicle; Axles, motor vehicle
Pr: Gerald Kyro
Dir IT: Tokuhiko Otani
Prd Mgr: Michael Ahlersmeyer
Ql Cn Mgr: Dave Raloff

D-U-N-S 02-058-1397
GENERAL PRODUCTS CORP
(*Suby of* GENERAL PRODUCTS DELAWARE CORP) ★
14137 Farmington Rd, Livonia, MI 48154-5422
Tel (260) 668-1475 *Founded/Ownrshp* 2003
Sales 48.1MM^E *EMP* 127
SIC 5051 Forgings, ferrous; Castings, rough: iron or steel; Forgings, ferrous; Castings, rough: iron or steel
Pr: David P Kelley

D-U-N-S 60-758-7920 IMP
GENERAL PRODUCTS DELAWARE CORP
1411 Wohlert St, Angola, IN 46703-1062
Tel (260) 668-1487 *Founded/Ownrshp* 2000
Sales 70.1MM^E *EMP* 335
SIC 3599 3462 3369 Machine shop, jobbing & repair; Iron & steel forgings; Nonferrous foundries; Machine shop, jobbing & repair; Iron & steel forgings; Nonferrous foundries
CFO: David P Kelley
Ql Cn Mgr: Dennis Ginder
Board of Directors: Hiroshi Harunari, James F Mason, Ronald Mininger

GENERAL PUMP
See GP COMPANIES INC

GENERAL PUMP & MACHINERY
See GENERAL PUMP AND MACHINERY INC

D-U-N-S 04-103-0693
GENERAL PUMP AND MACHINERY INC
GENERAL PUMP & MACHINERY
1044 W Olympia Dr, Peoria, IL 61615-2063
Tel (309) 693-7444 *Founded/Ownrshp* 1982
Sales 21.4MM^E *EMP* 21
SIC 5084 Pumps & pumping equipment
Pr: John Mahon
**Sec:* Roland Garland
Sales Asso: Ron Lagro

D-U-N-S 00-167-3409
■ **GENERAL RE CORP**
(*Suby of* GENERAL REINSURANCE CORP) ★
120 Long Ridge Rd, Stamford, CT 06902-1839
Tel (203) 352-3000 *Founded/Ownrshp* 1921
Sales NA *EMP* 1,000^E
SIC 6331 Fire, marine & casualty insurance; Fire, marine & casualty insurance
CEO: Franklin Tad Montross
**Pr:* John Cholnoky
Pr: Bill Guttman
Pr: Damon Vocke
CEO: Tad Montross
Treas: Steve Barbour
Treas: Eckhard A V Lkening
Treas: Trent Tosh
Ex VP: William Gasdaska Jr
Ex VP: Damon N Vocke
Sr VP: Janice Englesbe
Sr VP: Dan Lyons
**Sr VP:* Timothy Mc Caffrey
Sr VP: A Morris Tooker
Sr VP: James Whamon
VP: George Barson
VP: Uli Boing
VP: Francesco Bucciero
VP: Jacqueline Dimatteo
VP: Lynette Edmonds
VP: Justin Gardner
Board of Directors: Peter Lutke-Bornefeld, Salvatore R Curiale, William G Gasdaska, Winfried Heinen, Steven J Mannik, Tad Montross, Patricia H Roberts, Damon N Vocke

D-U-N-S 07-540-8641
■ **GENERAL RE LIFE CORP**
GENERAL & COLOGNE LIFE RE AMER
(*Suby of* GENERAL REINSURANCE AG)
120 Long Ridge Rd, Stamford, CT 06902-1839
Tel (203) 352-3000 *Founded/Ownrshp* 1975
Sales NA *EMP* 175
SIC 6311 Life reinsurance; Life reinsurance
Prin: Thomas West
Sr VP: Robert Costa
VP: Roberta Andriosi
VP: Joe Atamaniuk
VP: Ralph Barbieri
VP: Vincent A Demarco
VP: Barry D Eagle
VP: Tony Forte
VP: Kimberly Hanke
VP: Cliff Kozemchak
VP: Anne G Mitchell
VP: John V Najarian
VP: Jeremy Starr
VP: Jill Tumney
VP: Barbara White
Exec: Stephane Julien
Board of Directors: Conrad Ahrens, Peter Lutke-Bornefeld, Philip Dutter, Paul A Hermatt, John Loynes, William Slattery, Richard Toft, Fredric Weisberg

D-U-N-S 15-117-6062
■ **GENERAL RE-NEW ENGLAND ASSET MANAGEMENT INC**
(*Suby of* GENERAL REINSURANCE CORP) ★
76 Batterson Park Rd # 10, Farmington, CT 06032-2586
Tel (860) 676-8722 *Founded/Ownrshp* 1995
Sales 26.3MM^E *EMP* 90^E

SIC 6282 Investment advice
Pr: Gerard Lynch
Chf Inves: Vincent Delucia
Ofcr: Karen Morais
VP: James Bachman
VP: Stewart J Foley
VP: Michael J Gilotti
VP: Stacy Varney
Mng Dir: Alverne Bolitho
CIO: Calvin Clark
Web Dev: David Cover
Web Dev: Garry Thibodeau

D-U-N-S 03-046-8565
■ **GENERAL REINSURANCE CORP**
(*Suby of* BERKSHIRE HATHAWAY INC) ★
120 Long Ridge Rd, Stamford, CT 06902-1843
Tel (203) 328-5000 *Founded/Ownrshp* 1998
Sales NA *EMP* 2,513
SIC 6331 6351 6411 6321

D-U-N-S 80-102-6915 IMP
GENERAL RESOURCE TECHNOLOGY CORP
(*Suby of* MAPEI CORP) ★
2978 Center Ct, Saint Paul, MN 55121-1257
Tel (651) 454-4151 *Founded/Ownrshp* 2014
Sales 20.6MM^E *EMP* 29
SIC 5169 2899 Concrete additives; Chemical preparations
Genl Mgr: Travis Collins

D-U-N-S 05-655-2847
■ **GENERAL REVENUE CORP**
G R C
(*Suby of* NAVIENT CORP) ★
4660 Duke Dr Ste 300, Mason, OH 45040-8466
Tel (513) 469-1472 *Founded/Ownrshp* 2002
Sales 21.7MM^E *EMP* 500
SIC 7322 6141 Collection agency, except real estate; Personal credit institutions; Collection agency, except real estate; Personal credit institutions
CEO: John Kane
**Pr:* Brian Hill
**Treas:* Eric Kiss
Treas: John S McManus
**Treas:* John Terry
Ofcr: Ron Bernett
Ofcr: Jeff Wilmington
**VP:* Justen Gay
VP: Kendra McAnear
VP: Julie Mitchell-Barney
VP: Myron Rowland
VP: Ernest H Wickline Jr

D-U-N-S 00-954-3604 IMP
GENERAL RIBBON CORP
G R C
5775 E Ls Angls Ave Ste 2, Chatsworth, CA 91311
Tel (818) 709-1234 *Founded/Ownrshp* 1995
Sales 46.5MM^E *EMP* 500
Accts Tone Walling & Kissinger Cpas
SIC 3955 3861 Ribbons, inked: typewriter, adding machine, register, etc.; Photographic equipment & supplies; Ribbons, inked: typewriter, adding machine, register, etc.; Photographic equipment & supplies
Pr: Stephen R Morgan
**Ch Bd:* Robert W Daggs
VP: Lynn Robison
Mktg Mgr: James R Daggs

D-U-N-S 79-457-7015
GENERAL ROOFING SERVICES INC
(*Suby of* REPUBLIC FINANCIAL CORP) ★
3300 S Parker Rd Ste 500, Aurora, CO 80014-3522
Tel (303) 923-2200 *Founded/Ownrshp* 2004
Sales 79.5MM^E *EMP* 1,233^E
SIC 1761 Roofing contractor
Ch Bd: W Randal Dietrich
**Pr:* Robert Possehl
**Treas:* Ann D Hastings

D-U-N-S 09-327-4280
GENERAL RUBBER AND PLASTICS CO INC
1016 Majaun Rd, Lexington, KY 40511-1151
Tel (859) 254-6436 *Founded/Ownrshp* 1978
Sales 35.8MM^E *EMP* 48
SIC 5169 Synthetic resins, rubber & plastic materials
Pr: David G Stone

D-U-N-S 00-700-2140 IMP
GENERAL RUBBER AND PLASTICS OF PADUCAH INC (KY)
3118 Preston Hwy, Louisville, KY 40213-1100
Tel (502) 635-2605 *Founded/Ownrshp* 1943
Sales 50.0MM^E *EMP* 130
SIC 5085 Industrial supplies; Hose, belting & packing; Industrial supplies; Hose, belting & packing
Pr: Westman L Burnett
Dir IT: Brian Petrella
Sales Exec: Ken Etheridge
Sls Mgr: David Gardiner

D-U-N-S 00-653-5017
GENERAL RV CENTER INC (MI)
GENERAL TRAILER
25000 Assembly Park Dr, Wixom, MI 48393-0019
Tel (248) 349-0900 *Founded/Ownrshp* 1956
Sales 319.5MM^E *EMP* 400
SIC 5561 Recreational vehicle dealers; Travel trailers: automobile, new & used; Recreational vehicle parts & accessories; Recreational vehicle dealers; Travel trailers: automobile, new & used; Recreational vehicle parts & accessories
Pr: Robert S Baidas
COO: Chris Miller
**CFO:* Katie Short
VP: Stufft Wade
IT Man: Ron Slater
IT Man: Rudolph Vincent
Opers Mgr: Grant Baidas
Opers Mgr: Keith Lessner
Mktg Dir: Kevin Tosolt
Mktg Mgr: Dennis Anderson
Sls Mgr: Dan Broat

D-U-N-S 02-801-8653 IMP
GENERAL SEALANTS INC (CA)
300 Turnbull Canyon Rd, City of Industry, CA 91745-1009
Tel (626) 961-0211 *Founded/Ownrshp* 1964
Sales 38.6MME *EMP* 120
SIC 2891 Adhesives & sealants; Adhesives & sealants
Pr: Bradley Boyle
**Owner:* Patricia Boyle
**CFO:* Patrick Boyle
Exec: Cecilia Lara

D-U-N-S 05-860-5791
GENERAL SECRETARIAT OF ORGANIZATION OF AMERICAN STATES
GS OAS
1889 F St Nw, Washington, DC 20006-4401
Tel (202) 458-3000 *Founded/Ownrshp* 1890
Sales 42.6MME *EMP* 650
SIC 8399 Social change association; Social change association
CFO: Frank Almguer
Ex VP: William Berenson
Brnch Mgr: Orland Mason
MIS Dir: Alfonso Monera

D-U-N-S 19-330-1504
GENERAL SECURITY INC
ALARMS UNLIMITED
100 Fairchild Ave, Plainview, NY 11803-1710
Tel (516) 997-6464 *Founded/Ownrshp* 1984
Sales 35.9MME *EMP* 50
SIC 5072 1731 Security devices, locks; Fire detection & burglar alarm systems specialization
CEO: Edward M Minicozzi
Genl Mgr: Peter Allen
Off Mgr: Lisa Payne
Sls Dir: Al Staab
Sls Mgr: David Kunker

D-U-N-S 14-326-2579
GENERAL SECURITY NATIONAL INSURANCE
(*Suby of* SCOR REINSURANCE CO) ★
199 Water St Fl 21, New York, NY 10038-3536
Tel (212) 480-1900 *Founded/Ownrshp* 2004
Sales NA *EMP* 1E
SIC 6331 Fire, marine & casualty insurance & carriers
Prin: Alexis Ruset

D-U-N-S 04-539-8559
GENERAL SECURITY SERVICES CORP
MIDWEST PATROL DIVISION
9110 Meadowview Rd, Minneapolis, MN 55425-2458
Tel (952) 858-5000 *Founded/Ownrshp* 1946
Sales 56.9MME *EMP* 1,000
SIC 7381 Security guard service; Security guard service
CEO: Whitney Miller
CFO: David Speich
**VP:* Jackson Hall

D-U-N-S 07-949-9711
GENERAL SECURITY SYSTEMS INC (PA)
1339 Brandywine St, Philadelphia, PA 19123-3208
Tel (215) 627-7600 *Founded/Ownrshp* 1974
Sales 9.2MM *EMP* 430
SIC 7381 Protective services, guard; Private investigator; Security guard service; Protective services, guard; Private investigator; Security guard service
Ex VP: David W Gardner
**Pr:* Mark T Smylie
Treas: Richard Bongiovanni
Off Mgr: Gene Hymerce
Off Mgr: Joanne Snider

GENERAL SERVICES
See ICAFS INC

D-U-N-S 00-195-4700
■ **GENERAL SERVICES ADMINISTRATION US** (MD)
G S A
(*Suby of* EXECUTIVE OFFICE OF UNITED STATES GOVERNMENT) ★
1800 F St Nw Rm 6100, Washington, DC 20405-0001
Tel (202) 501-8880 *Founded/Ownrshp* 1949
Sales NA *EMP* 13,000
SIC 9199 General government administration; ; General government administration;
**CFO:* Kathleen M Turco
Adm Dir: Carla Bynum
Adm Dir: Leroy Wise
Genl Mgr: Lois Sather
Off Mgr: Gail Brush
CIO: Michael W Carleton
**CIO:* Casey Coleman
Counsel: Jeremiah Strack
Counsel: Adam Supple

D-U-N-S 86-808-6385
GENERAL SERVICES OF VA INC
3804 Cook Blvd Ste 15, Chesapeake, VA 23323-1633
Tel (757) 558-2220 *Founded/Ownrshp* 1995
Sales 22.1MME *EMP* 300
SIC 4789 4013 Freight car loading & unloading; Switching & terminal services; Freight car loading & unloading; Switching & terminal services
CEO: George M Barlow
**Pr:* Larry Taylor
Genl Mgr: Chris Columbus
Sfty Mgr: Robert Harris

D-U-N-S 00-338-3361 IMP
GENERAL SHALE BRICK INC (GA)
(*Suby of* WIENERBERGER AG)
3015 Bristol Hwy, Johnson City, TN 37601-1511
Tel (423) 282-4661 *Founded/Ownrshp* 1928, 1999
Sales 439.3MME *EMP* 1,900
SIC 5211 5031 Lumber & other building materials; Brick; Building materials, exterior; Building materials, interior; Lumber & other building materials; Brick; Building materials, exterior; Building materials, interior
Pr: Richard L Green

COO: Berry Ron
VP: Dan Green
VP: Mark Kinser
VP: Charles Smith
VP: Mark Stutz
Store Mgr: Matt Pratt
IT Man: Scott Clark
IT Man: Mike Downing
IT Man: Ken Sauls
VP Opers: J B Cooper

D-U-N-S 00-624-8009
GENERAL SHEET METAL CO LLC
2330 Louisiana Ave N, Minneapolis, MN 55427-3667
Tel (612) 221-0164 *Founded/Ownrshp* 2003
Sales 25.0MM *EMP* 80
SIC 1711 3444 Heating & air conditioning contractors; Ventilation & duct work contractor; Warm air heating & air conditioning contractor; Sheet metalwork; Heating & air conditioning contractors; Ventilation & duct work contractor; Warm air heating & air conditioning contractor; Sheet metalwork
Pr: James Krenik
**Sec:* Michael Jenson
Off Mgr: Cheryl Fischer

D-U-N-S 00-510-7735
GENERAL SHEET METAL WORKS INC
1902 S Main St, South Bend, IN 46613-2399
Tel (574) 288-0611 *Founded/Ownrshp* 1922
Sales 28.6MME *EMP* 210
SIC 7692 3469 3444 1799 Welding repair; Metal stampings; Sheet metalwork; Welding on site; Welding repair; Metal stampings; Sheet metalwork; Welding on site
Pr: John Axelberg
COO: Taylor Lewis
**CFO:* John Ryal
Dept Mgr: Kevin Ridenour
IT Man: Roger Ridenour
Plnt Mgr: Art Harrison
Ql Cn Mgr: Scott Gring

D-U-N-S 06-343-0771
GENERAL SHEET METAL WORKS INC
16345 Se Evelyn St, Clackamas, OR 97015-9515
Tel (503) 650-0405 *Founded/Ownrshp* 1972
Sales 28.3MME *EMP* 75
SIC 1711 1761 Heating systems repair & maintenance; Roofing, siding & sheet metal work; Architectural sheet metal work; Siding contractor
Pr: Carol Duncan
CFO: Greg Swartz
**Ex VP:* Kelly True
VP: Scott Murrill
**VP:* Michelle Waddell
Genl Mgr: Bill Cochran

D-U-N-S 00-637-9879
GENERAL SHOE LACE CO INC (NC)
108 Industrial Park Rd, Lincolnton, NC 28092-8358
Tel (704) 735-3276 *Founded/Ownrshp* 1919
Sales 21.2MME *EMP* 270
SIC 2241 3131 Laces, corset or shoe: textile; Braids, textile; Footwear cut stock; Laces, corset or shoe: textile; Braids, textile; Footwear cut stock
CEO: Michael H Raus

D-U-N-S 18-205-1805
GENERAL SOUTHERN INDUSTRIES INC
15825 Highway 243, Russellville, AL 35654-6514
Tel (256) 332-6652 *Founded/Ownrshp* 1985
Sales 39.1MM *EMP* 293
Accts Carr Riggs & Ingram Llc Birm
SIC 3441 Building components, structural steel; Building components, structural steel
Pr: Danny Gist
**Sec:* Patricia Gist
Sls Mgr: Jeff Harvin

D-U-N-S 05-341-7838 IMP
GENERAL SPORTS CORP (MN)
5025 France Ave S, Minneapolis, MN 55410-2091
Tel (612) 925-4010 *Founded/Ownrshp* 1962, 1976
Sales 22.7MME *EMP* 55
SIC 5091 5136 5941 5699 Sporting & recreation goods; Sportswear, men's & boys'; Sporting goods & bicycle shops; Sports apparel
Pr: John W Porter
**VP:* Craig Johnson

D-U-N-S 00-121-6449 IMP/EXP
GENERAL SPORTWEAR CO INC (NY)
2 Elting Ct Fl 4, Ellenville, NY 12428-1396
Tel (845) 647-4411 *Founded/Ownrshp* 1927
Sales 26.3MME *EMP* 120
SIC 2361 2369 2329 Jeans: girls', children's & infants'; T-shirts & tops: girls', children's & infants'; T-shirts & tops: girls', children's & infants'; Jeans: girls', children's & infants'; Men's & boys' sportswear & athletic clothing
Ch Bd: Herbert Rosenstock
**Sec:* David Rosensock
**Ex VP:* Jeffrey Rosenstock
Exec: Karen Rosselli
Sales Exec: Michael Rosenstock

D-U-N-S 62-080-5390
■ **GENERAL STAR INDEMNITY CO**
(*Suby of* GENERAL REINSURANCE CORP) ★
695 Main St Ste 1, Stamford, CT 06901-2141
Tel (203) 328-5000 *Founded/Ownrshp* 1971
Sales NA *EMP* 4
SIC 6321 Accident & health insurance; Accident & health insurance
Pr: Patricia Roberts
**Ch Bd:* Joseph Patrick Brandon
VP: Ernest C Frohboese
VP: Gary Korsak

D-U-N-S 00-590-2119
■ **GENERAL STAR NATIONAL INSURANCE CO**
(*Suby of* GENERAL RE CORP) ★
120 Long Ridge Rd, Stamford, CT 06902-1839
Tel (203) 328-5700 *Founded/Ownrshp* 1987
Sales NA *EMP* 66

SIC 6411 Insurance agents, brokers & service; Insurance agents, brokers & service
Pr: Patricia Roberts
VP: Robert Denis
VP: John Nunneley
VP: Frank Oleskiewicz
VP: Christine Snowberger
VP: Patricia Villegas

GENERAL STEAMSHIP AGENCIES
See GENERAL STEAMSHIP INTERNATIONAL LTD

D-U-N-S 00-387-1837
GENERAL STEAMSHIP INTERNATIONAL LTD (CA)
GENERAL STEAMSHIP AGENCIES
575 Rdwd Hwy Frntg Rd 200 Ste 200 Frontage, Mill Valley, CA 94941
Tel (415) 381-1694 *Founded/Ownrshp* 1975
Sales 45.7MME *EMP* 145
SIC 4731 Agents, shipping; Agents, shipping
Ch Bd: G Scott Jones
**Pr:* Scott M Jones
**CFO:* Michael Sabarese
**VP:* Janis R Mahoney
Dist Mgr: Carlos Garcia
Dist Mgr: Larry Ports
Dist Mgr: Jeff Robbins
Dist Mgr: Larry Stephens
Dist Mgr: Joseph Tabisola
Dist Mgr: Robert Toups
Off Admin: Rebecca Peralez

GENERAL STEEL
See TRIPLE-S STEEL OF GEORGIA LLC

D-U-N-S 93-778-6846 EXP
GENERAL STEEL DOMESTIC SALES LLC
10639 Bradford Rd, Littleton, CO 80127-4208
Tel (303) 904-4837 *Founded/Ownrshp* 2000
Sales 29.3MME *EMP* 140
SIC 1541 4724 3448 Steel building construction; Travel agencies; Prefabricated metal buildings; Steel building construction; Travel agencies; Prefabricated metal buildings
Pr: Jeff Knight
CFO: Michelle Aranyos
VP: Jonah Goldman
Sales Exec: Ken King
Sls Mgr: Dean Young

D-U-N-S 00-786-1230
GENERAL STEEL WAREHOUSE INC (TX)
3314 Clovis Rd, Lubbock, TX 79415-1504
Tel (806) 763-7327 *Founded/Ownrshp* 1948, 1992
Sales 37.6MME *EMP* 38
SIC 5051 Steel; Plates, metal; Bars, metal; Wire
Pr: Robert D Rogers
**CFO:* Peggy Rogers
Sales Asso: Keith Langenbeck
Board of Directors: Margaret D Rogers

D-U-N-S 18-712-6529
GENERAL STORE 2 INC
MARSH'S SUNFRESH SUPERMARKET
4001 Mill St, Kansas City, MO 64111-3008
Tel (816) 931-1505 *Founded/Ownrshp* 1978
Sales 35.0MM *EMP* 300
SIC 5411 Grocery stores; Grocery stores
Pr: Jim Marsh
**VP:* Gary Marsh

GENERAL SUPER PLATING
See UNY LLC

D-U-N-S 78-518-4206 IMP
GENERAL SUPPLY & SERVICES INC
GEXPRO
(*Suby of* REXEL HOLDINGS USA CORP) ★
1000 Bridgeport Ave 5-1, Shelton, CT 06484-4673
Tel (203) 925-2400 *Founded/Ownrshp* 2006
Sales 2.0MMME *EMP* 2,077
SIC 5063 8742 Electrical apparatus & equipment; Materials mgmt. (purchasing, handling, inventory) consultant; Electrical apparatus & equipment; Materials mgmt. (purchasing, handling, inventory) consultant
Pr: Brian P McNally
Ch Bd: Christopher P Hartmann
**CEO:* Mitchell D Williams
CFO: Douglas Seymour
**CFO:* Mark Testa
Treas: Gary Hibbs
VP: Mike Burke
VP: Robert Casagrande
VP: John Gschwind
VP: Amanda Malburg
Prgrm Mgr: Donald Dodson

D-U-N-S 00-340-0058
GENERAL SUPPLY CO (PA)
2651 Baglyos Cir, Bethlehem, PA 18020-8029
Tel (610) 882-2141 *Founded/Ownrshp* 1903
Sales 20.5MME *EMP* 86
SIC 5031 5211 Building materials, exterior; Building materials, interior; Lumber & other building materials; Building materials, exterior; Building materials, interior; Lumber & other building materials
Ch Bd: Aldo Braido
**Pr:* John J Simon
**Treas:* Kathy Hahn
**VP:* James E Csencsitz
Genl Mgr: Robert Mann
IT Man: Rick McCorrison
Sales Exec: Spiro Malitsis
Sales Asso: Michael Cipolloni

D-U-N-S 17-530-3536 IMP
GENERAL TECHNOLOGY INC
18022 Cowan Ste 200b, Irvine, CA 92614-6807
Tel (949) 861-8305 *Founded/Ownrshp* 1985
Sales 20.7MM *EMP* 17
SIC 5045 7373 Computer software; Computer integrated systems design; Computer software; Computer integrated systems design
Pr: Gerald Serra
**CFO:* Eileen Serra

D-U-N-S 00-423-8671 IMP
GENERAL TOOL CO (OH)
101 Landy Ln, Cincinnati, OH 45215-3495
Tel (513) 733-5500 *Founded/Ownrshp* 1947
Sales 40.9MM *EMP* 250
Accts Rudler Psc Ft Wright Kentu
SIC 3599 3443 3444 3544 7692 Machine shop, jobbing & repair; Fabricated plate work (boiler shop); Sheet metalwork; Special dies & tools; Welding repair; Machine shop, jobbing & repair; Fabricated plate work (boiler shop); Sheet metalwork; Special dies & tools; Welding repair
CEO: William J Kramer Jr
**COO:* John Cozad
CFO: Bradley Brezinski
**CFO:* William J Kramer III
**Treas:* Paul Kramer
**Ex VP:* Elliot Adams
Ql Cn Mgr: Sarah Vujevich

D-U-N-S 15-755-4916 IMP
GENERAL TOOL INC
2025 Alton Pkwy, Irvine, CA 92606-4904
Tel (949) 261-2322 *Founded/Ownrshp* 1984
Sales 44.5MME *EMP* 50
SIC 5085 Diamonds, industrial: natural, crude
CEO: Jae Woo Kim
CFO: Laura Kim
Prd Mgr: Corey Van Tran
Manager: Thomas Kruegar
Manager: Craig Steiner
Sls Mgr: Scott Seifert

D-U-N-S 19-477-1853
GENERAL TRADE CORP
745 Power Plant Rd, New Florence, PA 15944-7000
Tel (724) 235-2595 *Founded/Ownrshp* 1988
Sales 20.0MME *EMP* 42
SIC 5052 5093 Coal & coke; Metal scrap & waste materials
CEO: Clifford C Wise
**COO:* Allen Goldberg
**Treas:* Gregory Z Rudman

D-U-N-S 01-135-1681 IMP/EXP
GENERAL TRADING CO INC
455 16th St, Carlstadt, NJ 07072-1922
Tel (201) 935-7717 *Founded/Ownrshp* 1935
Sales 177.9MME *EMP* 420
SIC 5141

GENERAL TRAILER
See GENERAL RV CENTER INC

D-U-N-S 92-673-7719 EXP
GENERAL TRAILER PARTS LLC
1420 S B St, Springfield, OR 97477-5248
Tel (541) 746-2506 *Founded/Ownrshp* 1995
Sales 24.1MME *EMP* 80
SIC 5013 3715 5531 Trailer parts & accessories; Truck trailers; Truck equipment & parts
Genl Mgr: Jim Fritz

D-U-N-S 05-624-0708
GENERAL TRAILER SERVICES INC
2620 Campbell Blvd, Ellenwood, GA 30294-3422
Tel (404) 363-4387 *Founded/Ownrshp* 1990
Sales 35.3MM *EMP* 47
Accts Larson Allen Weishair & Co
SIC 5012 7539 7519 5013 Trailers for trucks, new & used; Trailer repair; Trailer rental; Trailer parts & accessories; Trailers for trucks, new & used; Trailer repair; Trailer rental; Trailer parts & accessories
Pr: James T Godwin
**VP:* Paul Ashworth
**VP:* Samuel H Hardman

GENERAL TRUCK BODY
See GENERAL BODY MANUFACTURING CO

D-U-N-S 05-319-6200 IMP
GENERAL TRUCK PARTS & EQUIPMENT CO
4040 W 40th St Rear, Chicago, IL 60632-3488
Tel (773) 247-6900 *Founded/Ownrshp* 1970
Sales 31.0MM *EMP* 95
SIC 5013 5531 Truck parts & accessories; Truck equipment & parts; Truck parts & accessories; Truck equipment & parts
CEO: Gregg Chudacoff
CFO: Barry Brave
Genl Mgr: John McNally
Sls Mgr: David Anderson

D-U-N-S 00-704-5172
GENERAL TRUCK SALES & SERVICE INC (TN)
1973 E Brooks Rd, Memphis, TN 38116-3601
Tel (901) 345-3270 *Founded/Ownrshp* 1965, 1993
Sales 30.8MME *EMP* 54
SIC 5511 5012 Trucks, tractors & trailers: new & used; Trucks, commercial; Trucks, tractors & trailers: new & used; Trucks, commercial
Pr: James McCullough
**Treas:* Vicki Mc Cullough

D-U-N-S 87-808-1413
GENERAL TRUCK SALES INC
4300 N Broadway Ave, Muncie, IN 47303-1016
Tel (765) 289-4481 *Founded/Ownrshp* 1990
Sales 20.9MME *EMP* 50E
SIC 5511 Trucks, tractors & trailers: new & used; Trucks, tractors & trailers: new & used
Pr: Steven R Bassett
CFO: Dave Hahn
CFO: Tina Rodgers
Store Mgr: Bryan Seagraves
Mktg Mgr: Tina Thompson

D-U-N-S 01-001-6913
GENERAL UTILITIES INC (NY)
100 Fairchild Ave, Plainview, NY 11803-1713
Tel (516) 349-8989 *Founded/Ownrshp* 1969
Sales 25.1MME *EMP* 110
SIC 5983 1711

D-U-N-S 14-373-3785
GENERAL VISION SERVICES LLC
G V S
520 8th Ave Fl 9, New York, NY 10018-4191
Tel (212) 594-2580 *Founded/Ownrshp* 2001
Sales 32.1MM^E *EMP* 150
SIC 5995 Optical goods stores
CEO: Robert Cohen
**Pr:* Alan Cohen
**CFO:* Darlene Cettina
Sls&Mrk Ex: Janet Kramer
VP Mktg: Ken Levin

D-U-N-S 06-301-2728
GENERAL VISION SERVICES OF NY INC
520 8th Ave Fl 9, New York, NY 10018-4191
Tel (212) 594-2580 *Founded/Ownrshp* 2002
Sales 21.8MM^E *EMP* 191
SIC 5995 5999 Optical goods stores; Hearing aids; Optical goods stores; Hearing aids
Ch Bd: Shaul Kopelowitz
**Sec:* Jerome Porter
**VP Mktg:* Ken Levin

GENERAL WAX & CANDLE CO
See GENERAL WAX CO INC

D-U-N-S 00-965-7586 IMP
GENERAL WAX CO INC
GENERAL WAX & CANDLE CO
6863 Beck Ave, North Hollywood, CA 91605-6206
Tel (818) 765-5800 *Founded/Ownrshp* 1988
Sales 21.6MM^E *EMP* 95
SIC 3999 Candles
CEO: Carol Lazar
**Pr:* Mike Tapp
**Sec:* Colton Lazar
Exec: Jerry Baker
Off Mgr: Martha Smith
Snr Mgr: John Ragsdale

GENERAL WHOLESALE BEER COMPANY
See GENERAL WHOLESALE CO

D-U-N-S 00-884-7089 IMP
GENERAL WHOLESALE CO
GENERAL WHOLESALE BEER COMPANY
1271 Tacoma Dr Nw, Atlanta, GA 30318-4145
Tel (404) 352-1041 *Founded/Ownrshp* 1982
Sales 107.3MM^E *EMP* 350
SIC 5182 5181 Liquor; Wine; Beer & other fermented malt liquors; Liquor; Wine; Beer & other fermented malt liquors
CEO: Jane H Young
**CFO:* William D Young Sr
**CFO:* William D Young Jr
**VP:* E Howard Young
VP: Howard E Young
Dist Mgr: Marlon Coleman
Dist Mgr: Ralph Lane
Sales Exec: Dale Lowenstein
Sls Mgr: Pete Hargita
Sls Mgr: Brad Jones

D-U-N-S 00-432-3556 IMP/EXP
GENERAL WIRE SPRING CO (PA)
1101 Thompson Ave, Mc Kees Rocks, PA 15136-3899
Tel (412) 771-6300 *Founded/Ownrshp* 1930, 1953
Sales 66.6MM^E *EMP* 179^E
SIC 3589 3495 3493 3423 Sewer cleaning equipment, power; Wire springs; Steel springs, except wire; Hand & edge tools
Pr: Lee Silverman
**Treas:* Steve Glick
Ex VP: David Silverman
**VP:* Arthur A Silverman
VP: Robert Silverman
Off Mgr: Dave Dunbar
Sls Mgr: Andy Zelazny

D-U-N-S 94-435-9595
GENERAL YELLOW PAGES CONSULTANTS INC
MARQUETTE GROUP
222 Ne Monroe St Ste 800, Peoria, IL 61602-1066
Tel (309) 677-0400 *Founded/Ownrshp* 1996
Sales 96.0MM^E *EMP* 225
SIC 7311 Advertising agencies; Advertising agencies
CEO: Chris Cummings
Pr: Troy Dowell
**Pr:* Eric Webb
**CFO:* Theresa Lafontaine
Treas: Jeff Corron
Ex VP: David Lenzen
VP: Chris Malone
Snr Sftwr: Mike Schaetz
CIO: Duane Timerson
IT Man: Josee Gosselin
Software D: Carrie Lennie

GENERAL-DYNAMICS-IT
See VANGENT INC

GENERALLY YOURS GIFT SHOP
See BRYAN HEALTH WEST CAMPUS

D-U-N-S 00-256-1140 IMP/EXP
GENERANT CO INC
1865 Route 23 S, Butler, NJ 07405
Tel (814) 337-0380 *Founded/Ownrshp* 1913, 1995
Sales 41.1MM^E *EMP* 150
SIC 3492 Control valves, fluid power: hydraulic & pneumatic; Control valves, fluid power: hydraulic & pneumatic
Pr: Ben Buren
CFO: Peter Regan
Manager: Dennis Prawl

D-U-N-S 01-192-7501
GENERATION 2000 LLC
101 Wendover Blvd, Wendover, NV 89883
Tel (775) 664-4508 *Founded/Ownrshp* 2001
Sales 21.0MM *EMP* 260
SIC 7993 7999 7011 5812 Gambling machines, coin-operated; Slot machines; Gambling establishment; Casino hotel; Eating places; Gambling machines, coin-operated; Slot machines; Gambling establishment; Casino hotel; Eating places

D-U-N-S 01-944-9849 IMP/EXP
GENERATION BRANDS CO
7400 Linder Ave, Skokie, IL 60077-3219
Tel (847) 410-4400 *Founded/Ownrshp* 2009
Sales 42.8MM^E *EMP* 69^E
SIC 5063 Lighting fixtures
CEO: Tom Sargeant
COO: Jim Brewer
CFO: Blake Bonyko
VP: Victor Smith
VP: Michael Wolf
Mktg Mgr: Brian Klein

D-U-N-S 00-596-0161
GENERATION COMPANIES LLC (NC)
4208 Six Forks Rd Ste 850, Raleigh, NC 27609-5738
Tel (919) 361-9000 *Founded/Ownrshp* 1996
Sales 6.9MM *EMP* 300
SIC 6513 6552 Apartment hotel operation; Subdividers & developers; Apartment hotel operation; Subdividers & developers
CFO: J Coupland

D-U-N-S 79-510-0085
GENERATION GROWTH CAPITAL INC
GGC
411 E Wiscnsn Ave 1710, Milwaukee, WI 53202
Tel (414) 291-8908 *Founded/Ownrshp* 2007
Sales 25.8MM^E *EMP* 166
SIC 6799 Investors; Investors
Ch: Cory L Nettles
**Pr:* John K Reinke
**VP:* Thomas P Nye
Genl Couns: Jennifer Johnson
Board of Directors: Paul Carbone, John K Reinke Cfa

D-U-N-S 14-141-8033
GENERATION HOMES INC
75 Park Creek Dr Ste 104, Clovis, CA 93611-4432
Tel (559) 323-9700 *Founded/Ownrshp* 2002
Sales 28.0MM *EMP* 15
SIC 1521 Single-family housing construction; Single-family housing construction
Pr: Robert Wood
**CFO:* C Scott Hulme
**VP:* John Olson

D-U-N-S 83-155-4915
GENERATION JEWELERS LLC
GOLD STANDARD, THE
150 Aerial Way, Syosset, NY 11791-5503
Tel (516) 513-0830 *Founded/Ownrshp* 2009
Sales 21.0MM *EMP* 12
SIC 5094 7389 5932 Bullion, precious metals; Brokers' services; Bullion, precious metals; Brokers' services; Pawnshop

D-U-N-S 78-825-7405
GENERATION MORTGAGE CO
CALIFORNIA RIVERSE MORTGAGE
3565 Pmtrd N 3 Pmt Cir, Atlanta, GA 30305
Tel (404) 995-5500 *Founded/Ownrshp* 2002
Sales NA *EMP* 143
SIC 6162 Mortgage bankers; Mortgage bankers
CEO: Colin A Cushman
**CFO:* Carl A Rojas
**CFO:* Sean Sievers
**Ex VP:* Luke Stehouwer
VP: Drew Benson
VP: Patrick Journy
IT Man: Gerald Owens
Sls Dir: Matthew Gregory
Counsel: Samira Martin

D-U-N-S 36-299-2351
GENERATIONAL EQUITY LLC
14241 Dallas Pkwy Ste 700, Dallas, TX 75254-2937
Tel (877) 213-1792 *Founded/Ownrshp* 2004
Sales 51.1MM^E *EMP* 180^E
SIC 6726 Management investment funds, closed-end; Management investment funds, closed-end
Pr: Ryan Binkley
Ofcr: David McCreary
Ex VP: Thomas Farrell
Ex VP: Dwight Jacobs
VP: Beth Little
Snr Mgr: Jason Varvel

D-U-N-S 00-575-2439
GENERATIONS BANK
(*Suby of* CHICAGO BANCORP)
7900 College Blvd, Overland Park, KS 66210-2194
Tel (913) 928-6181 *Founded/Ownrshp* 2000, 2011
Sales NA *EMP* 10
SIC 6021 National commercial banks
Pr: Roger Messner
**CFO:* William Morton

GENERATIONS CENTER OF SPENCER
See GENERATIONS HEALTH ASSOCIATION INC

D-U-N-S 07-692-5429
GENERATIONS COMMUNITY FEDERAL CREDIT UNION
9311 San Pedro Ave # 1100, San Antonio, TX 78216-4458
Tel (210) 229-1800 *Founded/Ownrshp* 1940
Sales NA *EMP* 240
SIC 6061 Federal credit unions; Federal credit unions
CEO: Steve Schipull
**CFO:* Geraldine Breeding
VP: Ashley Harris
VP: Andrew Wilson
Brnch Mgr: Kim Schaefer
VP Mktg: Wendy Beswick
VP Mktg: Steve Patti
Snr Mgr: Clay Thompson

D-U-N-S 00-980-3631
GENERATIONS CONSTRUCTION INC
15650 El Prado Rd, Chino, CA 91710-9108
Tel (909) 606-0370 *Founded/Ownrshp* 1986
Sales 39.0MM^E *EMP* 150
SIC 1542 Commercial & office buildings, renovation & repair; Commercial & office buildings, renovation & repair
Pr: Antwan De Paul
Off Mgr: Diana Simons

D-U-N-S 78-736-4744
GENERATIONS HEALTH ASSOCIATION INC
GENERATIONS CENTER OF SPENCER
406 N Spring St, McMinnville, TN 37110-2134
Tel (606) 549-1212 *Founded/Ownrshp* 1993
Sales 9.2MM *EMP* 500^E
Accts Totherow Haile & Welch Cpas Pl
SIC 8741 8051 Nursing & personal care facility management; Skilled nursing care facilities; Nursing & personal care facility management; Skilled nursing care facilities
CEO: David G Gaither
**Pr:* Kathy Campbell
**VP:* James Campbell
**VP:* Patricia W Gaither

D-U-N-S 87-829-7977
GENERATIONS LLC
8601 Se Causey Ave Ste 1, Portland, OR 97086-2628
Tel (503) 652-0750 *Founded/Ownrshp* 1994
Sales 21.8MM^E *EMP* 250
SIC 8059 Nursing home, except skilled & intermediate care facility; Nursing home, except skilled & intermediate care facility
Ch Bd: Wendell White
**Pr:* Robert White
**Treas:* Jennifer White
VP: Chip Gabriel
**VP:* Melody Gabriel

GENERATOR SERVICE COMPANY
See POWER PRO-TECH SERVICES INC

D-U-N-S 82-744-2281
GENERIC DRUG HOLDINGS INC
(*Suby of* COURT SQUARE CAPITAL PARTNERS LP) ★
31778 Enterprise Dr, Livonia, MI 48150-1960
Tel (734) 743-6000 *Founded/Ownrshp* 2010
Sales 489.0MM *EMP* 450
Accts Grant Thornton Llp Southfield
SIC 8734 5122 5047 Testing laboratories; Pharmaceuticals; Medical & hospital equipment; Testing laboratories; Pharmaceuticals; Medical & hospital equipment
CEO: Terry Haas
**Pr:* Jay Levine
**CFO:* David F Liming
VP: John H Heidel

D-U-N-S 01-110-3059 IMP
■ **GENERICS BIDCO I LLC**
QUALITEST PHARMACEUTICALS
(*Suby of* GENERICS INTERNATIONAL (US) INC) ★
130 Vintage Dr Ne, Huntsville, AL 35811-8216
Tel (256) 859-4011 *Founded/Ownrshp* 2007
Sales 68.3MM^E *EMP* 441^E
SIC 2834 5122 5961 Pharmaceutical preparations; Pharmaceuticals; Pharmaceuticals, mail order
Plnt Mgr: Aaron Ayres
S&M/VP: Trey Propst

D-U-N-S 15-122-8897 IMP/EXP
■ **GENERICS BIDCO II LLC**
QUALITEST PHARMACEUTICALS
(*Suby of* GENERICS INTERNATIONAL (US) INC) ★
3241 Woodpark Blvd, Charlotte, NC 28206-4212
Tel (704) 596-9440 *Founded/Ownrshp* 2007
Sales 47.0MM^E *EMP* 265^E
SIC 2834

D-U-N-S 60-966-4156
GENERICS GROUP INC
1601 Trapelo Rd Ste 154, Waltham, MA 02451-7349
Tel (617) 290-5606 *Founded/Ownrshp* 2002
Sales 25.0MM *EMP* 20
SIC 8748 8711 Business consulting; Engineering services
Pr: Peter Hyde
**Pr:* Geoff Waite

D-U-N-S 82-846-4474 IMP
■ **GENERICS INTERNATIONAL (US) INC**
QUALITEST PHARMACEUTICALS
(*Suby of* ENDO PHARMACEUTICALS INC) ★
130 Vintage Dr Ne, Huntsville, AL 35811-8216
Tel (256) 859-2575 *Founded/Ownrshp* 2010
Sales 360.7MM^E *EMP* 1,232
SIC 2834 Pharmaceutical preparations; Pharmaceutical preparations
Pr: Rajiv De Silva
Sr VP: Blaine Davis
VP: Carole Ben-Maimon
VP: Ted Leggett
VP: Margaret Richardson
Dir Surg: Diane Servello
Assoc Dir: Mohammed Chowdhury
Dir Sec: Adam Bryan
QA Dir: Kathryn Weingart
Plnt Mgr: Aaron Ayres
Prd Mgr: Mark Riegel

D-U-N-S 16-872-7204 IMP/EXP
GENERON IGS INC
(*Suby of* INNOVATIVE GAS SYSTEMS INC) ★
16250 State Highway 249, Houston, TX 77086-1014
Tel (713) 937-5200 *Founded/Ownrshp* 2001
Sales 32.8MM^E *EMP* 125
Accts Fpr Pc Houston Tx
SIC 3569 Separators for steam, gas, vapor or air (machinery); Separators for steam, gas, vapor or air (machinery)
Pr: Tom Jeffers
Pr: Bruce Graham
Pr: Chris Jeans
**CFO:* Edward J Devine
Genl Mgr: Tony Triano
Info Man: David Elmore

D-U-N-S 07-914-3867 EXP
GENERTEK POWER CORP
POWERTEAM
(*Suby of* MEGAWATT POWER HOLDINGS LIMITED)
1935 Industrial Park Rd, Mulberry, FL 33860-6605
Tel (863) 425-9000 *Founded/Ownrshp* 2013
Sales 41.8MM^E *EMP* 200
SIC 3621 Power generators; Power generators
CEO: Joseph Adir
Pr: John Sams
CFO: Sandy Vereb
Ex Dir: Mohammad Ayoub

GENE'S CHRYSLER
See GENES INC

D-U-N-S 03-541-4242
GENES INC
GENE'S CHRYSLER
3400 S Cushman St, Fairbanks, AK 99701-7522
Tel (907) 452-7117 *Founded/Ownrshp* 2004
Sales 28.6MM^E *EMP* 70
SIC 5511 7538 5531 Automobiles, new & used; General automotive repair shops; Automotive & home supply stores; Automobiles, new & used; General automotive repair shops; Automotive & home supply stores
Pr: Gregory Wagner
**VP:* Lane Nichols
Sls Mgr: Scott Graham
Sales Asso: Victor Anderson
Board of Directors: Lane Nichols, Gregory Wagner

GENE'S QUITO MARKET
See MIDTOWN FOOD STORES INC

D-U-N-S 04-856-5170
GENESAR INC
DUNES MOTEL, THE
2800 N Baltimore Ave, Ocean City, MD 21842-3442
Tel (410) 289-4414 *Founded/Ownrshp* 1966
Sales 20.5MM^E *EMP* 300
SIC 7011 Motels; Resort hotel; Motels; Resort hotel
Pr: Thelma C Conner
**Pr:* Bill Mariner
**Treas:* Patricia Swain Dufendach
**VP:* Jennifer Swain Clarke
Sls Dir: Marge Steele

D-U-N-S 00-136-7549 IMP/EXP
▲ **GENESCO INC** (TN)
1415 Murfreesboro Pike, Nashville, TN 37217-2829
Tel (615) 367-7000 *Founded/Ownrshp* 1934
Sales 2.8MMM *EMP* 27,325
Accts Ernst & Young Llp Nashville
Tkr Sym GCO *Exch* NYS
SIC 5661 5139 5961 Shoe stores; Footwear; Catalog & mail-order houses; Shoe stores; Footwear; Catalog & mail-order houses
Ch Bd: Robert J Dennis
CFO: Mimi Eckel Vaughn
Treas: Matthew N Johnson
Sr VP: Roger G Sisson
VP: Mara Kennedy
VP: Ted Macias
VP: Paul D Williams
Brnch Mgr: Jasmine Jones
Brnch Mgr: Melissa Sanford
Dist Mgr: Keith McKee
Genl Mgr: Debbie Hinson
Board of Directors: Joanna Barsh, James S Beard, Leonard L Berry, James W Bradford, Matthew C Diamond, Marty G Dickens, Thurgood Marshall Jr, Kathleen Mason

D-U-N-S 09-360-9113
▲ **GENESEE & WYOMING INC**
20 West Ave, Darien, CT 06820-4401
Tel (203) 202-8900 *Founded/Ownrshp* 1899
Sales 1.6MMM *EMP* 5,200^E
Tkr Sym GWR *Exch* NYS
SIC 4011 4013 Railroads, line-haul operating; Switching & terminal services; Railroads, line-haul operating; Switching & terminal services
Pr: John C Hellmann
Pr: Joe Arbona
Pr: Richard Christopher
Pr: Kristine Storm
COO: David A Brown
COO: Michael Holben
CFO: Neal Aronson
CFO: Timothy J Gallagher
CFO: Luis Pacheco
Bd of Dir: Oivind Lorentzen
Ofcr: Michael O Miller
Ex VP: Mark W Hastings
Sr VP: Charles W Chabot
Sr VP: Dave Ebbrecht
Sr VP: Louis Gravel
Sr VP: James E Irvin
Sr VP: Bill Jasper
Sr VP: Martin D Lacombe
Sr VP: Tony Long
Sr VP: Ronald G Russ
Sr VP: Dewayne Swindall
Board of Directors: Mark A Scudder, Richard H Allert, Hunter C Smith, Richard H Bott, Mortimer B Fuller III, Robert M Melzer, Albert Neupaver, Michael Norkus, Joseph Pyne, Ann N Reese, Philip J Ringo

D-U-N-S 05-798-5970
GENESEE COMMUNITY COLLEGE
(*Suby of* STATE UNIVERSITY OF NEW YORK) ★
1 College Rd, Batavia, NY 14020-9704
Tel (585) 343-0055 *Founded/Ownrshp* 1967
Sales 17.6MM^E *EMP* 300
Accts Freed Maxick & Battaglia Cpas
SIC 8222 Community college; Community college;
Pr: James Sunser
Ex VP: Kate Schiefen
VP: Kevin Hamilton
VP: Virginia Taylor
Exec: Gina Weaver
HC Dir: Tanya Lane-Martin
Pgrm Dir: Victoria Campbell

D-U-N-S 06-394-6651
GENESEE COUNTY OF (INC)
15 Main St, Batavia, NY 14020-2136
Tel (585) 344-2550 *Founded/Ownrshp* 1802
Sales NA *EMP* 1,000
Accts Freed Maxick Cpas Pc Batav
SIC 9111 ;
**Ch Bd:* Mary Pat Hancock
**Treas:* Scott German
Dir IT: Stephen Zimmer

D-U-N-S 00-335-9770
GENESEE FUEL & HEATING CO INC (WA)
BOMAN OIL
3616 S Genesee St, Seattle, WA 98118-1362
Tel (206) 722-1545 *Founded/Ownrshp* 1929
Sales 25.9MM^E *EMP* 27
SIC 5171 Petroleum bulk stations & terminals
Pr: Steven T Clark

D-U-N-S 19-998-5516
GENESEE GROUP INC
2595 Canyon Blvd Ste 420, Boulder, CO 80302-6737
Tel (972) 623-2004 *Founded/Ownrshp* 2007
Sales 27.0MM^E *EMP* 109^E
SIC 3469 Stamping metal for the trade; Machine parts, stamped or pressed metal
Pr: Daniel Fergus

D-U-N-S 14-020-7437
GENESEE HEALTH PLAN
2171 S Linden Rd, Flint, MI 48532-4175
Tel (810) 232-7740 *Founded/Ownrshp* 2003
Sales 25.7MM *EMP* 3
Accts Maner Costerisan Pc Lansing
SIC 8099 Health & allied services; Health & allied services
Pr: Al Tucker

D-U-N-S 10-651-2783
GENESEE HEALTH SYSTEM
725 Mason St, Flint, MI 48503-2421
Tel (810) 257-3736 *Founded/Ownrshp* 1963
Sales NA *EMP* 550
Accts Rehmann Robson Grand Rapids
SIC 9431 Mental health agency administration, government; Mental health agency administration, government
Ex Dir: Jeff Delay
Genl Mgr: Gust Baterakes
Psych: Audrey Hill

D-U-N-S 06-982-5826
GENESEE INTERMEDIATE SCHOOL DISTRICT
ELMER A KNOPF LEARNING CENTER
2413 W Maple Ave, Flint, MI 48507-3429
Tel (810) 591-4489 *Founded/Ownrshp* 1962
Sales 200.0MM *EMP* 1,500
SIC 8211 9411 School for physically handicapped; School for the retarded; Public vocational/technical school; Administration of educational programs; School for physically handicapped; School for the retarded; Public vocational/technical school; Administration of educational programs
Treas: Cindy Gansen
Bd of Dir: Paul Newman
VP: Jerry Ragsdale
MIS Dir: Beverly Knox-Pipes
IT Man: Barbara Stewart

GENESEE LAKE SCHOOL
See OCONOMOWOC DEVELOPMENTAL TRAINING CENTER OF WISCONSIN LLC

GENESEE PETRO
See MARATHON FLINT OIL CO INC

D-U-N-S 02-261-0718
GENESEE REGION HOME CARE ASSOCIATION INC
165 Court St, Rochester, NY 14647-0001
Tel (585) 238-4399 *Founded/Ownrshp* 2008
Sales 77.4MM *EMP* 2
SIC 8699 Membership organizations; Membership organizations
Prin: John Biemiller

D-U-N-S 07-969-7991
GENESEE REGION HOME CARE ASSOCIATION INC (NY)
LIFETIME CARE
3111 Winton Rd S, Rochester, NY 14623-2905
Tel (585) 214-1000 *Founded/Ownrshp* 1960
Sales 97.1MM *EMP* 925
SIC 8082 Home health care services; Home health care services
Pr: Patricia Heffernan
**VP:* John Cauvel
**VP:* Nancy Horn
**VP:* Terrence Tehan
Mng Dir: Guy Tommasi
Nurse Mgr: Raquel Hulster
MIS Dir: John Caubel

D-U-N-S 00-983-1983
GENESEE RESERVE SUPPLY INC
200 Jefferson Rd, Rochester, NY 14623-2136
Tel (585) 292-7040 *Founded/Ownrshp* 1952
Sales 28.2MM *EMP* 33
SIC 5031 5033 Lumber: rough, dressed & finished; Roofing, siding & insulation; Lumber: rough, dressed & finished; Roofing, siding & insulation
Ch Bd: John Harrower
**Pr:* Steven Perry
**Ex VP:* Thomas Sangiacomo
**VP:* Sarah Ferrara
Sales Asso: Rob Schott

GENESEE ROAD COMMISSION
See COUNTY OF GENESEE

D-U-N-S 07-994-1795
GENESEE VALLEY BOCES SCHOOL DISTRICT
BOARD COOPERATIVE EDUCTL SVCS
80 Munson St, Le Roy, NY 14482-8989
Tel (585) 344-7900 *Founded/Ownrshp* 1948
Sales 25.3MM^E *EMP* 500
SIC 8331 8211 Vocational training agency; Private special education school; Public adult education school; Vocational training agency; Private special education school; Public adult education school
Treas: Sally Sanford
**Prin:* Cahrles Dipasquale
**Prin:* Rick McInroy
**Prin:* Foster Miller
Off Admin: Sheila Sinclair
Netwrk Mgr: Larry Harvey
Teacher Pr: Stepehen Mahoney
HC Dir: Kim McLaughlin
Snr Mgr: Stephen Mahoney

D-U-N-S 07-367-1000
GENESEE VALLEY GROUP HEALTH ASSOCIATION
LIFETIME HEALTH
800 Carter St, Rochester, NY 14621-2604
Tel (585) 338-1400 *Founded/Ownrshp* 1972
Sales 107.9MM *EMP* 576
SIC 8011 Health maintenance organization; Health maintenance organization
Pr: Patricia L Bonino
CFO: Deke Duda
Prac Mgr: Janene Baase
Telecom Ex: Chris Olsen
IT Man: James Lesure
Doctor: Farokh Foroozesh-Banej
Doctor: Pradip Kadakia
Doctor: Clifford Katz
Doctor: David Kuranda
Doctor: David Lewin
Doctor: Edward Sassaman

D-U-N-S 00-677-3436
GENESEO COMMUNICATIONS INC
GENESEO TELEPHONE COMPANY
111 E 1st St, Geneseo, IL 61254-2123
Tel (309) 944-2103 *Founded/Ownrshp* 1905
Sales 30.5MM^E *EMP* 100
Accts Deloitte & Touche Llp Davenpo
SIC 4813 Local telephone communications; Local telephone communications
Pr: Scott Rubins
**Ch Bd:* Alan C Anderson
Pr: Bill Farb
**Sec:* Stanley Storm
Genl Mgr: Matt Storm

D-U-N-S 04-679-2669
GENESEO COMMUNITY UNIT SCHOOL DISTRICT 228
648 N Chicago St, Geneseo, IL 61254-1118
Tel (309) 945-0450 *Founded/Ownrshp* 1890
Sales 24.2MM *EMP* 343
SIC 8211 Public elementary & secondary schools; Public elementary & secondary schools
Bd of Dir: Jackie Mickley
Bd of Dir: John Puentes
Bd of Dir: Alan Vandewoestyne

GENESEO TELEPHONE COMPANY
See GENESEO COMMUNICATIONS INC

D-U-N-S 09-756-9136
GENESH INC
BURGER KING
8831 Long St, Lenexa, KS 66215-3586
Tel (913) 492-0007 *Founded/Ownrshp* 1999
Sales 47.2MM^E *EMP* 1,000
SIC 5812 Fast-food restaurant, chain; Fast-food restaurant, chain
Pr: Mukesh Dharod

GENESIS
See BREYUT CONVALESCENT CENTER INC

GENESIS
See CEDAR RIDGE NURSING HOME

D-U-N-S 82-810-6422
GENESIS
1273 W Derynne St, Le Center, MN 56057-4391
Tel (507) 357-6868 *Founded/Ownrshp* 2008
Sales 92.1MM *EMP* 2
Accts Carlson Highland & Co Llp
SIC 7359 Propane equipment rental; Propane equipment rental
Prin: Joe Spinler

GENESIS 10
See GENESIS CORP

D-U-N-S 18-043-8384 IMP/EXP
GENESIS ATTACHMENTS LLC
GENESIS EQUIPMENT & MFG
(*Suby of* PALADIN ATTACHMENTS) ★
1000 Genesis Dr, Superior, WI 54880-1351
Tel (715) 395-5252 *Founded/Ownrshp* 1990
Sales 35.2MM^E *EMP* 115
SIC 3531 3594 Construction machinery; Fluid power pumps & motors; Construction machinery; Fluid power pumps & motors
CEO: Steve Andrews
Genl Mgr: Jeff Adams
Tech Mgr: Tim Alseth
Mktg Mgr: Amy Burmeister

D-U-N-S 18-584-7902
GENESIS CENTER INC
587 Middle Tpke E, Manchester, CT 06040-3731
Tel (860) 646-3888 *Founded/Ownrshp* 2000
Sales 5.1MM^E *EMP* 400
Accts Hagget Longobardi Llp
SIC 8322 Rehabilitation services; Social services for the handicapped; Rehabilitation services; Social services for the handicapped
CEO: Heather Gates
CFO: Patrick Sidley
**Ch:* Penny Micci

D-U-N-S 07-741-2331
GENESIS CORP
GENESIS 10
950 3rd Ave Ste 2702, New York, NY 10022-2874
Tel (212) 688-5522 *Founded/Ownrshp* 1999
Sales 179.7MM *EMP* 2,105
Accts Cohn Reznick Llp New York Ne
SIC 7379 8742 Computer related consulting services; Management consulting services; Computer related consulting services; Management consulting services
CEO: Harley Lippman
Mng Pt: James Heller
COO: Michael Rapken
**CFO:* Glenn Klein
Ex VP: Matt McBride
Sr VP: Mark Murphy
VP: Remster Bingham
VP: Amy Moog
Exec: Valerie Miller
Dir Bus: Lauren Pavka
Dir Bus: Heather Pearson

D-U-N-S 96-631-5640 IMP
■ **GENESIS CRUDE OIL LP**
(*Suby of* GENESIS ENERGY LP) ★
919 Milam St Ste 2100, Houston, TX 77002-5417
Tel (713) 860-2500 *Founded/Ownrshp* 1996
Sales 105.7MM^E *EMP* 185
Accts Deloitte & Touche Llp Housto
SIC 4612 Crude petroleum pipelines; Crude petroleum pipelines
CEO: Grant E Sims
Pt: Mark Gorman
Pr: Steve Nathanson
COO: Joseph Mueller
CFO: Robert V Deere
Sr VP: Karen N Pape
VP: Astanley Stanley
CIO: Joseph Muller
IT Man: Duane Durham
Sales Exec: Paul Fowler

D-U-N-S 06-619-8730
GENESIS DEVELOPMENT
CUSTOMBOXESONLINE
401 W Mckinley St, Jefferson, IA 50129-1421
Tel (515) 386-3017 *Founded/Ownrshp* 1973
Sales 14.3MM *EMP* 390
Accts Gronewold Bell Kyhnn & Co
SIC 8331 Sheltered workshop; Sheltered workshop
CEO: Terry Johnson
Pr: Donovan Olson
**Pr:* Jefferson Steve Pope
Treas: Ken Putzier
**VP:* James Last
**VP:* Alta P Nelson
**Prin:* Donodan Olson
Mktg Dir: Betty Niles

GENESIS DIAGNOSTICS
See ABIRA MEDICAL LABORATORIES LLC

GENESIS DMNSNAL TLING SLUTIONS
See GENESIS SYSTEMS GROUP LLC

D-U-N-S 61-031-1557
GENESIS ELDER CARE REHABILATION SERVICES INC
(*Suby of* GENESIS HEALTHCARE CORP) ★
101 E State St, Kennett Square, PA 19348-3109
Tel (610) 925-4598 *Founded/Ownrshp* 1986
Sales 36.1MM^E *EMP* 2,100
SIC 8049 8093 Physical therapist; Rehabilitation center, outpatient treatment; Physical therapist; Rehabilitation center, outpatient treatment
Pr: George Hagger
IT Man: Maryann Kurowski

D-U-N-S 03-543-4356 IMP
GENESIS ELDERCARE NATIONAL CENTERS INC (FL)
(*Suby of* GENESIS HEALTHCARE CORP) ★
101 E State St, Kennett Square, PA 19348-3109
Tel (610) 444-6350 *Founded/Ownrshp* 1981, 2003
Sales 800.4MM^E *EMP* 35,000
SIC 8051 8361 Skilled nursing care facilities; Home for the aged; Skilled nursing care facilities; Home for the aged
Pr: George V Hager
CFO: George Hagar
**Treas:* Rick Edwards
Ex VP: George V Cathey
VP: Lewis Hoch
Prgrm Mgr: Joanne Ally-Steller
Dist Mgr: Raymond Haga
Obsttrcn: Marc Rubinbger

GENESIS ENERGY
See TDC LLC

D-U-N-S 13-384-7876
■ **GENESIS ENERGY INC**
(*Suby of* DENBURY ONSHORE LLC) ★
919 Milam St Ste 2100, Houston, TX 77002-5417
Tel (713) 860-2500 *Founded/Ownrshp* 1996
Sales 58.1MM^E *EMP* 260
SIC 5172 4612 Crude oil; Crude petroleum pipelines; Crude oil; Crude petroleum pipelines
Pr: Mark J Gorman
**Ch Bd:* Gareth Roberts
**CFO:* Ross A Benavides
**VP:* Kerry W Mazoch

D-U-N-S 96-296-5406
▲ **GENESIS ENERGY LP**
919 Milam St Ste 2100, Houston, TX 77002-5417
Tel (713) 860-2500 *Founded/Ownrshp* 1996
Sales 3.8MMM *EMP* 1,200^E
Tkr Sym GEL *Exch* NYS
SIC 4612 5171 4212 Crude petroleum pipelines; Petroleum bulk stations & terminals; Petroleum haulage, local; Crude petroleum pipelines; Petroleum bulk stations & terminals; Petroleum haulage, local
Ch Bd: Grant E Sims
Genl Pt: Genesis Energy
CFO: Robert V Deere
Sr VP: Paul A Davis
VP: Richard R Alexander
VP: Jeff Gifford
VP: Jim Glattly
VP: Firoz Jhaver
VP: John Millar
Dist Mgr: Norman Ncyman
CTO: Kenneth Farley

D-U-N-S 17-759-7564
GENESIS ENGINEERS INC
1850 Gravers Rd Ste 300, Plymouth Meeting, PA 19462-2837
Tel (610) 592-0280 *Founded/Ownrshp* 1997
Sales 98.4MM^E *EMP* 3,100
SIC 8711 8741 Engineering services; Construction management; Engineering services; Construction management
Pr: Bernard Friel
**Treas:* Anthony J Macchia
**VP:* Michael J Dapkunas
**VP:* Joseph W O'Donnell
Dir Bus: Harry Segner
Snr PM: Bernie Carroll

GENESIS EQUIPMENT & MFG
See GENESIS ATTACHMENTS LLC

D-U-N-S 02-123-2488
GENESIS FINANCIAL SOLUTIONS INC
GFS FINANCIAL SOLUTIONS
15220 Nw Greenbrier Pkwy, Beaverton, OR 97006-5744
Tel (503) 350-4300 *Founded/Ownrshp* 2001
Sales 30.3MM^E *EMP* 150
SIC 7322 Collection agency, except real estate
Pr: Bruce Weinstein
**Ch Bd:* Irving J Levin
**COO:* Patrick Moore
Ofcr: Jennifer Johnson
VP: Ellen Falbo
Prgrm Mgr: Tami Pearson
Prgrm Mgr: Patti Robinson
Prgrm Mgr: Angel Walton
Snr Sftwr: Shane Voelker
QA Dir: Dean Aoyama
QA Dir: Cheryl Roberts

D-U-N-S 36-441-0621 IMP
GENESIS FOODS CORP
GARVEY NUT & CANDY
(*Suby of* FIRSTSOURCE LLC) ★
8825 Mercury Ln, Pico Rivera, CA 90660-6707
Tel (323) 890-5890 *Founded/Ownrshp* 1984
Sales 50.6MM^E *EMP* 60^E
SIC 5145 5149 Confectionery; Cookies
Pr: Steven R Corri
VP Sls: Trisha Frazier

D-U-N-S 96-709-8661
GENESIS HEALTH CLUBS OF EMPORIA LLC
1007 Commercial St, Emporia, KS 66801-2918
Tel (620) 343-6034 *Founded/Ownrshp* 2011
Sales 12.0MM *EMP* 330
SIC 7997 Services; Membership sports & recreation clubs
CFO: Ryan Brooks

D-U-N-S 10-187-0251
GENESIS HEALTH INC
BROOKS HEALTH SYSTEM
3599 University Blvd S # 1, Jacksonville, FL 32216-4259
Tel (904) 858-7600 *Founded/Ownrshp* 1982
Sales 140.2MM *EMP* 1,400
Accts Dixon Hughes Goodman Llp Gre
SIC 8069 8011 8741 Specialty hospitals, except psychiatric; Medical centers; General & family practice, physician/surgeon; Management services; Specialty hospitals, except psychiatric; Medical centers; General & family practice, physician/surgeon; Management services
Pr: Douglas M Baer
**Ch Bd:* Bruce Johnson
**Pr:* Michael R Spigel
CFO: Odin Berg
Treas: Tim Reinschmidt
Bd of Dir: Frank Houser
Bd of Dir: Donald Wright
Sr VP: Karen Wright-Bennett
Ex Dir: Brian Fuller
CIO: Karen Green
IT Man: Janet Collins

D-U-N-S 10-738-2301
GENESIS HEALTH SYSTEM
1227 E Rusholme St, Davenport, IA 52803-2459
Tel (563) 421-1000 *Founded/Ownrshp* 1994
Sales 623.3MM^E *EMP* 5,000
SIC 8741 8399 7218 Hospital management; Nursing & personal care facility management; Fund raising organization, non-fee basis; Industrial launderers; Hospital management; Nursing & personal care facility management; Fund raising organization, non-fee basis; Industrial launderers
CEO: Doug Cropper
Dir Recs: Betsy Tibbitts
**Pr:* Leo A Bressanelli
**COO:* Wayne Diewald
**CFO:* Mark Rogers
**Treas:* Greg Bush
Ofcr: Kathy Bamman
**Sr VP:* Flo Spyrow
VP: Sarah Blessing
**VP:* Kenneth Croken
**VP:* Robert Frieden
**VP:* Peter Metcalf
VP: Judith Mondello
VP: Rob Nelson
VP: Judy Pranger
VP: Jackie A Rn-Bc
VP: Florence Spyrow
VP: Robert Travis
VP: Kevin Youmans
**Exec:* Jackie Anhalt
Exec: Myron Higgins

D-U-N-S 79-337-5932
GENESIS HEALTH SYSTEMS
CROSSTOWN SQUARE
1455 Hospital Rd, Silvis, IL 61282-1834
Tel (309) 281-3270 *Founded/Ownrshp* 1991
Sales 86.9MM *EMP* 75
Accts Mcgladrey Llp Davenport Ia
SIC 8051 8059 Skilled nursing care facilities; Nursing home, except skilled & intermediate care facility; Skilled nursing care facilities; Nursing home, except skilled & intermediate care facility

D-U-N-S 36-137-7245
GENESIS HEALTH VENTURES OF BLOOMFIELD INC
(*Suby of* GENESIS HEALTHCARE CORP) ★
1 Emerson Dr, Windsor, CT 06095-3204
Tel (860) 688-6443 *Founded/Ownrshp* 1985
Sales 11.8MM *EMP* 303

SIC 8059 8322 8051 Convalescent home; Individual & family services; Skilled nursing care facilities; Convalescent home; Individual & family services; Skilled nursing care facilities
Pr: David C Barr
CFO: George V Hager Jr
Treas: Kenneth R Kuhnle
VP: Lewis J Hoch
Board of Directors: Richard R Howard

GENESIS HEALTHCARE
See FC-GEN ACQUISITION INC

D-U-N-S 13-235-4460 IMP
GENESIS HEALTHCARE CORP
(*Suby of* FC-GEN ACQUISITION INC) ★
101 E State St, Kennett Square, PA 19348-3109
Tel (610) 444-6350 *Founded/Ownrshp* 2008
Sales 6.6MMM^E *EMP* 35,000
SIC 8051 8361 Skilled nursing care facilities; Extended care facility; Rehabilitation center, residential: health care incidental; Skilled nursing care facilities; Extended care facility; Home for the aged; Rehabilitation center, residential: health care incidental
Ch Bd: George V Hager Jr
Pr: Robert Reitz
CFO: James V McKeon
Chf Mktg O: Pat Crawford
Ofcr: Janice Rotondo
Ofcr: Mary Thomas
Sr VP: Eileen Coggins
Sr VP: Eileen M Coggins
Sr VP: Barbara J Hauswald
Sr VP: Richard Pell Jr
Sr VP: David Polakoff
VP: Joe Bourne
VP: Susan Coppola
VP: Thomas Divittorio
VP: Tom Divittorio
VP: Richard Edwards
VP: Sean Stevenson
VP: Sharon Warren
Exec: Marilyn Brennan
Exec: Jeff Govoni
Exec: Philips Jeanie

D-U-N-S 79-649-0493
▲ **GENESIS HEALTHCARE INC**
101 E State St, Kennett Square, PA 19348-3109
Tel (610) 444-6350 *Founded/Ownrshp* 2005
Sales 833.2MM *EMP* 95,000^E
Tkr Sym GEN *Exch* NYS
SIC 8051 8052 8059 8361 Skilled nursing care facilities; Convalescent home with continuous nursing care; Extended care facility; Personal care facility; Domiciliary care; Nursing home, except skilled & intermediate care facility; Personal care home, with health care; Rehabilitation center, residential: health care incidental; Skilled nursing care facilities; Convalescent home with continuous nursing care; Extended care facility; Personal care facility; Domiciliary care; Nursing home, except skilled & intermediate care facility; Personal care home, with health care; Rehabilitation center, residential: health care incidental
CEO: George V Hager Jr
**Ch Bd:* Steven Fishman
COO: Robert A Reitz
CFO: Thomas Divittorio
Sr VP: Michael S Sherman
VP: Cyndee Jackson
CIO: Dave Goff
Genl Couns: Zachary Larson

D-U-N-S 96-808-6376
■ **GENESIS HEALTHCARE LLC**
(*Suby of* FC-GEN OPERATIONS INVESTMENT, LLC)
101 E State St, Kennett Square, PA 19348-3109
Tel (610) 444-6350 *Founded/Ownrshp* 2010
Sales 5.0MMM *EMP* 15,050
SIC 8099 8051 8093 Medical services organization; Skilled nursing care facilities; Specialty outpatient clinics; Medical services organization; Skilled nursing care facilities; Specialty outpatient clinics
**VP:* Richard Edwards
Sls&Mrk Ex: Amy Covello
Mktg Dir: Kortez Kelly
HC Dir: Sharon Glaud

D-U-N-S 12-198-8745
GENESIS HEALTHCARE SYSTEM
BETHESDA CARE
2951 Maple Ave, Zanesville, OH 43701-1406
Tel (740) 454-5000 *Founded/Ownrshp* 1800
Sales 462.0MM *EMP* 3,500
SIC 8082 Home health care services; Home health care services
Pr: Matthew Perry
**COO:* Al Burns
COO: Mike Deming
**CFO:* Paul Masterson
Trst: Laura Wolf
Ofcr: Dan Scheerer
Trst Ofcr: Shirley Vanwye
VP: Edmund J Romuto
Exec: Cassandra Palmer
Dir Risk M: Deborah Trimble
Dir Lab: Tammy Bruner
Dir Rx: Gregory Hamilton

D-U-N-S 96-749-0897
GENESIS HEALTHCARE SYSTEM
2951 Maple Ave, Zanesville, OH 43701-1406
Tel (740) 454-4000 *Founded/Ownrshp* 1997
Sales 359.1MM *EMP* 2,500
SIC 8062 General medical & surgical hospitals; General medical & surgical hospitals
Pr: Tom Sieber
COO: Chuck Conner
COO: Alan Vierling
Dir Case M: Shellie Haegen
Dir Rad: Charles Muchnok
Dir Rad: Edmond Ru
Chf Nrs Of: Pat Campbell
Nurse Mgr: Barb Powell
VP Mktg: Craig Worstall

GENESIS HLTHCARE CTRS HOLDINGS
See MERIDIAN HEALTH INC

GENESIS HOUSE 1, 2 AND 3
See DETROIT RESCUE MISSION MINISTRIES INC

D-U-N-S 09-316-6031
GENESIS INC
980 Central Ave, Roselle, IL 60172-1742
Tel (630) 351-4400 *Founded/Ownrshp* 1977
Sales 25.9MM^E *EMP* 110
SIC 3444 Sheet metal specialties, not stamped
Pr: Marge P Stringfellow
**Pr:* William J Stringfellow
**VP:* Scott Stringfellow
**Genl Mgr:* Tom Stringfellow

D-U-N-S 15-705-3026 IMP
GENESIS INDUSTRIES INC
601 Project Dr, Elmwood, WI 54740-8748
Tel (715) 639-2435 *Founded/Ownrshp* 1985
Sales 62.2MM^E *EMP* 120
SIC 5162 3841 Plastics products; Veterinarians' instruments & apparatus; Plastics products; Veterinarians' instruments & apparatus
Pr: Mark L Anderson
Genl Mgr: Jill Peters
IT Man: Brian Delayer
Ql Cn Mgr: Carl Branshaw

D-U-N-S 80-939-8316
■ **GENESIS INSURANCE CO**
(*Suby of* GENERAL RE CORP) ★
120 Long Ridge Rd, Stamford, CT 06902-1839
Tel (800) 431-9994 *Founded/Ownrshp* 1983
Sales NA *EMP* 96^E
SIC 6411 Insurance agents, brokers & service
Pr: Roger Greiner
**Ch Bd:* Harry Richter
**Pr:* G Roger Greiner
COO: Robert Jones
**Treas:* Betsy Monrad
Sr VP: Barry Anderson
Sr VP: Pamela Davis
VP: Anthony Colucci
VP: David Erazmus
VP: Chris Golonka
VP: Cheryl Marczak
**VP:* Richard Gerard McCarty
VP: Lauren Oliver
VP: Joseph Proffitt
VP: Robert Sharrer
VP: Scott Wood

D-U-N-S 08-827-4720
GENESIS JANITORIAL SERVICES INC
4083 N Saint Peters Pkwy, Saint Peters, MO 63304-7396
Tel (636) 928-2164 *Founded/Ownrshp* 1997
Sales 11.2MM^E *EMP* 276
SIC 7349 Building maintenance services; Building maintenance services
CEO: Gary M Clifton
VP: Felecia Walker

D-U-N-S 05-580-4389 IMP
GENESIS MEDICAL CENTER
FIRST MED CLINIC
(*Suby of* GENESIS HEALTH SYSTEM) ★
1227 E Rusholme St, Davenport, IA 52803-2459
Tel (563) 421-6000 *Founded/Ownrshp* 1994
Sales 295.7MM^E *EMP* 2,397
Accts Mcgladrey Llp Davenport Ia
SIC 8062 Hospital, affiliated with AMA residency; Hospital, affiliated with AMA residency
Pr: Wayne A Diewald
**Pr:* Leo A Bressanelli
**CEO:* Doug Cropper
**VP:* George Kovach
VP: Judith Pranger
**VP:* Mike Sharp
Dept Mgr: Dan Bond
MIS Dir: Bob Hofmann
Dir IT: Dean Hiles
Prd Mgr: Steve Friedrich
Mktg Dir: Ken Croken

D-U-N-S 10-339-0717
GENESIS NETWORKS ENTERPRISES LLC
600 N Loop 1604 E, San Antonio, TX 78232-1268
Tel (210) 489-6600 *Founded/Ownrshp* 2001
Sales 73.4MM^E *EMP* 800
SIC 7373 Systems integration services; Systems integration services
CEO: James Goodman
**Pr:* Sean Nelson
**Pr:* Mark Viertel
**CEO:* Todd Richard
**CFO:* Cathy Kincy
**CFO:* Perry Uhles
**Treas:* Phil Schubert
Ex VP: Mark Wallhouser
**VP:* Steve Griffith
VP: Bashar Hajhamad
**VP:* John Homsey
VP: John Johnson
VP: Philip Kiser
VP: Rick Schiavinato
Dir Bus: Duwayne Tarrant

D-U-N-S 06-084-8753
GENESIS NETWORKS TELECOM SERVICES LLC
GENESIS-ATC
600 N Loop 1604 E, San Antonio, TX 78232-1268
Tel (210) 489-6600 *Founded/Ownrshp* 2011
Sales 846.0MM^E *EMP* 475
SIC 5065 Communication equipment; Communication equipment
CEO: James Goodman
**Pr:* Sean Nelson
**CEO:* Jesse Torres
**CFO:* Cathy Kincy
IT Man: Gina Baroni
VP Sls: Steve Seago

D-U-N-S 83-871-3659 IMP
GENESIS PLASTICS AND ENGINEERING LLC
640 N Wilson Rd, Scottsburg, IN 47170-7727
Tel (812) 752-6742 *Founded/Ownrshp* 1995
Sales 27.6MM^E *EMP* 110
SIC 3089 Injection molded finished plastic products
Pr: James Gladden
CFO: Chad Fawcett
Sls&Mrk Ex: Vince Schroeder

D-U-N-S 12-672-4983
GENESIS PRODUCTS INC
2608 Almac Ct, Elkhart, IN 46514-7628
Tel (574) 264-7189 *Founded/Ownrshp* 2002
Sales 64.4MM^E *EMP* 255
SIC 7389 2431 Laminating service; Doors, wood; Laminating service; Doors, wood
Pr: Jonathan Helmuth
CFO: Chad Barden
VP: Matt Hazelbaker
**VP:* Jonathan Wenger
Opers Mgr: Rick Berggren
Opers Mgr: Joe Campbell
Plnt Mgr: Dave Vanvooren
VP Sls: Braden McCormick
Sales Asso: Lori Chubb

D-U-N-S 83-294-2986
GENESIS PURE INC
GOYIN INTERNATIONAL
7164 Tech Dr Ste 100, Frisco, TX 75033
Tel (469) 213-2900 *Founded/Ownrshp* 2011
Sales 223.6MM^E *EMP* 90^E
SIC 5122 Vitamins & minerals; Drugs & drug proprietaries
Pr: Bobby Love
**COO:* Bill Shuler
**CFO:* Dave Bricker
**VP:* Brooks Gordon
**VP:* John Saldana
**VP:* Jinhee Woo
CIO: James Porter

D-U-N-S 07-855-6381
GENESIS RAIL SERVICES LLC
120 L E Barry Rd, Natchez, MS 39121
Tel (713) 860-2626 *Founded/Ownrshp* 2011
Sales 16.2MM^E *EMP* 940
SIC 4789 Cargo loading & unloading services; Cargo loading & unloading services
Sr VP: Karen Pape

D-U-N-S 04-421-5663
GENESIS REHABILITATION HOSPITAL INC
BROOKS REHABILITATION
3599 University Blvd S # 1, Jacksonville, FL 32216-4252
Tel (904) 858-7600 *Founded/Ownrshp* 1983
Sales 32.7MM^E *EMP* 422
Accts Pricewaterhousecoopers Llp Ja
SIC 8063 8069 8051 Hospital for the mentally ill; Specialty hospitals, except psychiatric; Skilled nursing care facilities; Hospital for the mentally ill; Specialty hospitals, except psychiatric; Skilled nursing care facilities
Ex Dir: Stephen K Wilson
**Pr:* Michael Spigel
Treas: Doug Baer
Exec: Karen Gallagher
**Prin:* Stanley Carter
**Prin:* Bruce M Johnson
IT Man: Jayne Shults
Web Prj Mg: Laurie Smith
Mtls Mgr: Debbie Edwards
Snr Mgr: Joann Gallichio

D-U-N-S 06-354-1323
GENESIS RESOURCES INC
1400 Fashion Island Blvd # 1000, San Mateo, CA 94404-2067
Tel (650) 577-3115 *Founded/Ownrshp* 2011
Sales 100.0MM^E *EMP* 4
SIC 8742 1021 5093 5052 Business planning & organizing services; Copper ores; Nonferrous metals scrap; Iron ore
CEO: Steven KAO
**CFO:* Steven Springer

GENESIS SEATING 0519
See GENESIS SEATING INC

D-U-N-S 95-881-6860 IMP/EXP
■ **GENESIS SEATING INC**
GENESIS SEATING 0519
(*Suby of* LEGGETT & PLATT INC) ★
5505 33rd St Se, Grand Rapids, MI 49512-2061
Tel (616) 954-1040 *Founded/Ownrshp* 2001
Sales 21.6MM^E *EMP* 80^E
SIC 5021 2521 2511 2426 Office & public building furniture; Wood office furniture; Wood household furniture; Hardwood dimension & flooring mills
Pr: John Walton
VP Opers: Jeff Agar
Mtls Mgr: Brenda Rider
Plnt Mgr: Mike Kuperus

D-U-N-S 55-562-9513
GENESIS SECURITIES LLC
1 Penn Plz Ste 5320, New York, NY 10119-5300
Tel (212) 668-0888 *Founded/Ownrshp* 1999
Sales 22.8MM^E *EMP* 153
SIC 6211 6231 Security brokers & dealers; Security & commodity exchanges; Security brokers & dealers; Security & commodity exchanges
Dir Bus: Serge Pustelnik
Mng Dir: Harry Eagens
Mng Dir: Alex Kravets
IT Man: Jian Zhen
Mktg Dir: Anthony Haney

D-U-N-S 04-718-2368
GENESIS SECURITY SERVICE
5900 Ave Isla Verde L, Carolina, PR 00979-5746
Tel (787) 701-2830 *Founded/Ownrshp* 2010
Sales 49.6MM^E *EMP* 4,700
SIC 7381 Detective & armored car services; Detective & armored car services
CEO: Roberto Morales
**Pr:* Emilio Morales

D-U-N-S 83-158-9200 IMP
■ **GENESIS SOLAR LLC**
(*Suby of* NEXTERA ENERGY RESOURCES LLC) ★
700 Universe Blvd, North Palm Beach, FL 33408-2657
Tel (561) 691-3062 *Founded/Ownrshp* 2011
Sales 774.6MM^E *EMP* 38^E
SIC 4911 Electric services

D-U-N-S 15-114-7931
GENESIS SYSTEMS GROUP LLC
GENESIS DMNSNAL TLING SLUTIONS
8900 N Harrison St, Davenport, IA 52806-7323
Tel (563) 445-5600 *Founded/Ownrshp* 1984
Sales 25.8MM^E *EMP* 130
SIC 3599 3699 3544 3829

D-U-N-S 55-600-2806
GENESIS TECHNOLOGIES INC
2942 Macarthur Blvd, Northbrook, IL 60062-2005
Tel (847) 498-0606 *Founded/Ownrshp* 1991
Sales 37.5MM^E *EMP* 54^E
SIC 5045 Computers, peripherals & software; Computer peripheral equipment
Pr: Michael J Kahn
VP: John Kaiser
Sls Dir: Robert Nelson
Mktg Mgr: Nancy Wasielewski
Sls Mgr: Jay Bellman
Sls Mgr: John Massouras

D-U-N-S 15-353-8488 IMP/EXP
GENESIS TODAY INC
6800 Burleson Rd Ste 180, Austin, TX 78744-2325
Tel (512) 389-1918 *Founded/Ownrshp* 2006
Sales 100.0MM^E *EMP* 127
SIC 5149 Health foods; Health foods
CEO: William Meissner
**Pr:* Nancy Manshum

D-U-N-S 10-106-6756
GENESIS WORLDWIDE II INC
(*Suby of* ANDRITZ (USA) INC) ★
130 Main St, Callery, PA 16024
Tel (724) 538-3180 *Founded/Ownrshp* 2014
Sales 57.2MM^E *EMP* 291
SIC 3541 Machine tools, metal cutting type; Machine tools, metal cutting type
Pr: Kip Mostowy
**CFO:* Randy Saputo
VP: Jim McKenna
Sfty Mgr: Russ Cline

GENESIS-ATC
See GENESIS NETWORKS TELECOM SERVICES LLC

GENESYS AEROSYSTEMS
See S-TEC CORP

D-U-N-S 07-947-3837
GENESYS AEROSYSTEMS GROUP INC
1 S Tec Way, Mineral Wells, TX 76067-9236
Tel (800) 872-7832 *Founded/Ownrshp* 2014
Sales 36.0MM^E *EMP* 130^E
SIC 3812 3728 Aircraft/aerospace flight instruments & guidance systems; Aircraft parts & equipment
Pr: Roger Smith
CFO: Tammy Crawford
**VP:* Tricia Crawford
**VP:* Gordon Pratt
**VP:* Ricardo Price

D-U-N-S 00-370-4830 IMP
■ **GENESYS CONFERENCING INC**
(*Suby of* INTERCALL EUROPE HOLDING SAS)
8020 Towers Crescent Dr # 900, Vienna, VA 22182-6224
Tel (703) 749-2500 *Founded/Ownrshp* 1996
Sales 90.6MM^E *EMP* 600
SIC 4813 Long distance telephone communications; Long distance telephone communications
Ch Bd: Francois Legros
**CFO:* Andrew G Lazarus
Treas: Jerome Pouvreau
VP: Clarissa A Peterson
VP: John D Polcari
VP: Gary G Vilardi
Dir Bus: Kurt Magdanz
Ex Dir: Joyce Finkenbiner
IT Man: Jonathan Cottingham
VP Sls: Kevin O'Brien
S&M/VP: Julius Anderson

GENESYS HEALTH CENTER
See GENESYS REGIONAL MEDICAL CENTER

D-U-N-S 96-141-8878 IMP
GENESYS HEALTH SYSTEM
PEDIATRIC SPECIALTY CLINIC
(*Suby of* ASCENSION HEALTH) ★
1 Genesys Pkwy, Grand Blanc, MI 48439-8065
Tel (810) 606-5710 *Founded/Ownrshp* 1980
Sales 419.0MM^E *EMP* 5,000
SIC 8062 General medical & surgical hospitals; General medical & surgical hospitals
Ch: Roger Samuel
Chf Rad: John Morrison
**Pr:* Young S Suh
**CEO:* Elizabeth Aderholbt
**Treas:* John Boles
**Treas:* William Lovejoy
Trst: Juan Mestas
Trst: Gerald Selke
VP: Dave Caudle
VP: Curtis Clark
VP: Joy Finkenbinder
VP: Ron Haase
Dir Rad: Michelle Newman

D-U-N-S 06-960-5194
GENESYS HOME HEALTH & HOSPICE INC
1000 Health Park Blvd B, Grand Blanc, MI 48439-7324
Tel (888) 246-6322 *Founded/Ownrshp* 1977
Sales 12.5MM *EMP* 300
SIC 8082 Home health care services; Home health care services
Pr: Larry Brothers

D-U-N-S 01-557-5038 IMP
GENESYS INDUSTRIAL CORP
GENESYS SYSTEMS INTEGRATOR
3210 E 85th St, Kansas City, MO 64132-2528
Tel (816) 525-7701 *Founded/Ownrshp* 1997
Sales 51.8MM *EMP* 85
Accts Mayer Hoffman Mccann Pc Lea
SIC 3535 Conveyors & conveying equipment; Conveyors & conveying equipment
Pr: Matthew Perry
CFO: Richard Scott Simkins III
Sys Mgr: Jay Williams

D-U-N-S 06-982-8507
GENESYS REGIONAL MEDICAL CENTER
GENESYS HEALTH CENTER
(*Suby of* GENESYS HEALTH SYSTEM) ★
1 Genesys Pkwy, Grand Blanc, MI 48439-8065
Tel (810) 606-5000 *Founded/Ownrshp* 2000
Sales 417.6MM *EMP* 3,739
Accts Deloitte Tax Lp Cincinnati O
SIC 8062 General medical & surgical hospitals; General medical & surgical hospitals
Pr: Mark Taylor
**CFO:* David Carrol
CFO: Nancy Haywood
Ofcr: Greg Murray
Sr VP: Denny Fischer
VP: Rick Felts
Dir Rad: Char Heeley
Dir Rx: Joy Finkenbinder
Dir Rx: Joy Finkenbiner
Adm Dir: Michael Thompson
Admn Mgr: Nancy Alton

GENESYS SYSTEMS INTEGRATOR
See GENESYS INDUSTRIAL CORP

GENESYS TELECOM LABS
See GENESYS TELECOMMUNICATIONS LABORATORIES INC

D-U-N-S 62-228-6318
GENESYS TELECOMMUNICATIONS LABORATORIES INC
GENESYS TELECOM LABS
(*Suby of* PERMIRA ADVISERS LLP)
2001 Junipero Serra Blvd, Daly City, CA 94014-3891
Tel (650) 466-1100 *Founded/Ownrshp* 2012
Sales 573.4MM^E *EMP* 3,500
SIC 7372 Computer software development; Business oriented computer software
Pr: Paul Segre
COO: James Budge
COO: James W Budge
Treas: Mark Alloy
Chf Mktg O: Reed Henry
Ofcr: Faiz Askari
Ofcr: Jim Ren
Ex VP: Thomas Eggemeier
Ex VP: Steve Pollock
VP: Brian Bischoff
VP: Madan Gadde
VP: Karl Holzthum
VP: Steve Rutledge
VP: Andy Zazzera
Exec: Mark Chambers
Creative D: Kady Wood

GENETICS & I V F INSTITUTE
See GENETICS & IVF INSTITUTE INC

D-U-N-S 17-518-9265 IMP
GENETICS & IVF INSTITUTE INC
GENETICS & I V F INSTITUTE
3015 Williams Dr Ste 202, Fairfax, VA 22031-4623
Tel (703) 698-7355 *Founded/Ownrshp* 1984
Sales 21.6MM^E *EMP* 350
SIC 8071 8093 8099 8011 Biological laboratory; Family planning & birth control clinics; Sperm bank; Offices & clinics of medical doctors; Biological laboratory; Family planning & birth control clinics; Sperm bank; Offices & clinics of medical doctors
Pr: Joseph D Schulman
**CEO:* Lewin Howard J
CFO: Sean Swindell
**Treas:* Swindell Sean
Brnch Mgr: Ed Fugger
Off Mgr: Linda Harley
CTO: Joseph Schulman
IT Man: Nafees Khan
IT Man: Hilario Rellos
Sftwr Eng: Waleed Malik
Mktg Dir: Lisa Brannick

D-U-N-S 86-740-8601
GENETIPORC USA LLC
4125 Minnesota St, Alexandria, MN 56308-3328
Tel (320) 834-7675 *Founded/Ownrshp* 1998
Sales 33.0MM *EMP* 47
SIC 0751 Breeding services, livestock; Breeding services, livestock
Sls Mgr: Todd Olson

D-U-N-S 04-861-6569
GENEVA AREA CITY SCHOOL DISTRICT
135 S Eagle St, Geneva, OH 44041-1513
Tel (440) 466-4831 *Founded/Ownrshp* 1961
Sales 35.7MM *EMP* 375
SIC 8211 School board; School board
Pr: David Foote Jr
**CFO:* Kevin Lillie
**VP:* Edward Brashaer
Prin: Melissa Doherty
Prin: Kaye E Haskins
Prin: Michael R Penzenik
Prin: John Spiesman
Schl Brd P: Ed Braschear
Teacher Pr: Terri Kush

D-U-N-S 10-005-5367
GENEVA CITY SCHOOL DISTRICT
400 W North St, Geneva, NY 14456-1314
Tel (315) 781-0489 *Founded/Ownrshp* 1839
Sales 26.0MM^E *EMP* 500
SIC 8211 Public elementary & secondary schools; Public elementary & secondary schools
Treas: Beverly Burrall
Ofcr: Steve Muzzi
VP: Pat Poole
Prin: Joseph L Demeis
Prin: John Natti
Prin: DT Scherer
Prin: Michael Simon
Dir IT: Tom Simpson
Mktg Mgr: Victor Cottengim
Psych: Heather Grasso

D-U-N-S 06-875-9851
GENEVA COLLEGE
3200 College Ave, Beaver Falls, PA 15010-3599
Tel (724) 846-5100 *Founded/Ownrshp* 1848
Sales 54.8MM *EMP* 290
Accts Schneider Downs & Co Inc Pitt
SIC 8221 College, except junior; College, except junior
Pr: Kenneth Smith
Ofcr: Janet Barlett
VP: Alex Winger
Dir: Diana Patterson
Prgrm Mgr: Colene Dawes
Sales Exec: Mary A Tondo
Psych: Rosa Feddersen
Psych: Kristina Graham
Pgrm Dir: Becky Case

D-U-N-S 02-144-0672
GENEVA COMMUNITY UNIT SCHOOL DISTRICT 304
227 N 4th St, Geneva, IL 60134-1307
Tel (630) 463-3000 *Founded/Ownrshp* 1953
Sales 101.9MM *EMP* 460
SIC 8211 Public elementary & secondary schools; Public elementary & secondary schools
COO: Jennifer Thill
VP: Kelly Nowak
Exec: Jessica Egan
Dir IT: Sheila Finch
Dir IT: Elizabeth Janowiak
Psych: Stefany Montgomery

D-U-N-S 10-410-6372
GENEVA COUNTY BOARD OF EDUCATION
200 N Commerce St, Geneva, AL 36340-2003
Tel (334) 684-5690 *Founded/Ownrshp* 1974
Sales 23.2MM *EMP* 500
SIC 8211 Public elementary & secondary schools; Public elementary & secondary schools
Bd of Dir: Mike Gillis

D-U-N-S 07-209-0558
GENEVA COUNTY HEALTHCARE AUTHORITY INC
WIREGRASS HOSP & NURSING HM
1200 W Maple Ave, Geneva, AL 36340-1642
Tel (334) 684-3655 *Founded/Ownrshp* 1955
Sales 28.3MM^E *EMP* 325
SIC 8062 8059 General medical & surgical hospitals; Nursing home, except skilled & intermediate care facility; General medical & surgical hospitals; Nursing home, except skilled & intermediate care facility
CEO: Sam Johnson
CFO: Vance Devane
Ofcr: Barbara Lawson
Ex Dir: Traci Kellner
Nrsg Dir: Kathy Ingalls

D-U-N-S 07-979-9020
GENEVA COUNTY SCHOOL DISTRICT
606 S Academy St, Geneva, AL 36340-2527
Tel (334) 684-5690 *Founded/Ownrshp* 2015
Sales 15.7MM^E *EMP* 337^E
SIC 8211 Public elementary & secondary schools
HC Dir: Carol Spivey

D-U-N-S 06-602-3057
GENEVA ENTERPRISES INC
1902 Association Dr, Reston, VA 20191-1502
Tel (703) 553-6570 *Founded/Ownrshp* 1986, 1990
Sales 276.0MM^E *EMP* 1,000
SIC 5511 New & used car dealers; New & used car dealers
Ch Bd: Robert Rosenthal
**Pr:* Donald Bavely
**CFO:* Steve Farouz
**VP:* Jerry Griffin
Dir IT: Aaresh Mufty

D-U-N-S 95-913-1194
GENEVA FOUNDATION
917 Pacific Ave Ste 600, Tacoma, WA 98402-4437
Tel (253) 383-1398 *Founded/Ownrshp* 1993
Sales 44.8MM *EMP* 87
Accts Mcgladrey Llp Olympia Wa
SIC 6732 8733 Trusts: educational, religious, etc.; Medical research; Trusts: educational, religious, etc.; Medical research
Ch: Michael W Hansch
**Treas:* David Blanford
**Prin:* David A Little
**Prin:* Scott M O'Halloran
Prgrm Mgr: Randal Leblanc
Dir IT: Jason McKinney
IT Man: Marjorie Osmer

GENEVA GENERAL HOSPITAL
See FINGER LAKES REGIONAL HEALTH SYSTEM INC

D-U-N-S 05-596-0710
GENEVA GENERAL HOSPITAL
196 North St, Geneva, NY 14456-1694
Tel (315) 787-4000 *Founded/Ownrshp* 1892
Sales 78.8MM *EMP* 870
Accts Bonadio & Co Llp Pittsford
SIC 8062 General medical & surgical hospitals; General medical & surgical hospitals
Pr: James Dooley
**CFO:* Lawrence Farnand
VP: Eileen Gage
Dir Rx: Ted Mitchell
Adm Dir: Rebecca Mack
Dir IT: Barbara Taney
Ansthlgy: Kermit McGinnis
Doctor: Susan Battisti
Doctor: Olaf Lieberg
Doctor: Ketul Patel
Doctor: Tamara Prull

D-U-N-S 09-922-8553 IMP
GENEVA HOLDINGS INC
8015 Piedmont Triad Pkwy, Greensboro, NC 27409-9407
Tel (336) 275-9936 *Founded/Ownrshp* 1979
Sales 105.7MM^E *EMP* 400
SIC 5084 5063

D-U-N-S 02-330-3423
GENEVA LAKE FOODS INC
PICK-N-SAVE
100 E Geneva Sq, Lake Geneva, WI 53147-9693
Tel (262) 248-8798 *Founded/Ownrshp* 1974
Sales 35.5MM^E *EMP* 290
SIC 5411 Supermarkets; Supermarkets
Pr: Mark Stinebrink
Mng Pt: Danny Michalove
**Sec:* Eleanor Stinebrink
**Prin:* Brett Stinebrink
Board of Directors: Brett Stinebrink, Jerry Stinebrink

D-U-N-S 00-341-6281
GENEVA MEMORIAL HOSPITAL
870 W Main St, Geneva, OH 44041-1219
Tel (440) 415-0159 *Founded/Ownrshp* 2000
Sales 36.8MM *EMP* 24^E
SIC 8062 General medical & surgical hospitals
Prin: Krishman Sundararajan

D-U-N-S 00-907-9302 IMP
GENEVA PIPE CO (UT)
1465 W 400 N, Orem, UT 84057-4444
Tel (801) 225-2416 *Founded/Ownrshp* 1956
Sales 22.5MM^E *EMP* 103
SIC 3272 Pipe, concrete or lined with concrete; Pipe, concrete or lined with concrete
Ch Bd: Aldo Bussio
**Pr:* Vince Bussio
VP: Fred Klug
Plnt Mgr: Tom Black
Prd Mgr: Derrick Wing
Ql Cn Mgr: Jeff Graffio
Sales Asso: Kirk Remund

D-U-N-S 04-283-5439
GENEVA ROCK PRODUCTS INC
(*Suby of* CLYDE COMPANIES INC) ★
302 W 5400 S Ste 201, Murray, UT 84107-8237
Tel (801) 765-7800 *Founded/Ownrshp* 1954
Sales 528.9MM^E *EMP* 1,000
SIC 5032 Concrete mixtures; Asphalt mixture; Gravel; Concrete mixtures; Asphalt mixture; Gravel
Pr: James Golding
**Treas:* Don Magee
**VP:* Carl C Clyde
VP: Carl Clyde
**VP:* Jay Ritchie
**VP:* Nathan Schellenberg

D-U-N-S 17-341-0267 IMP
GENEVA SCIENTIFIC INC
BARCO PRODUCTS COMPANY
24 N Washington Ave, Batavia, IL 60510-2614
Tel (630) 879-0084 *Founded/Ownrshp* 1986
Sales 25.0MM^E *EMP* 25
SIC 5084 Safety equipment; Safety equipment
Pr: Robert H Runke
Exec: Reeder John
IT Man: Shirley Garback
Sls&Mrk Ex: Susan Ross

GENEVA WATCH GROUP
See ADVANCE WATCH CO LTD

D-U-N-S 08-460-1610
GENEVA WOODS PHARMACY INC
GENEVA WOODS REHABILATION
501 W Intl Airport Rd 1a, Anchorage, AK 99518-1106
Tel (907) 565-6100 *Founded/Ownrshp* 1977
Sales 40.0MM *EMP* 222
SIC 5912 5999 Drug stores; Medical apparatus & supplies; Drug stores; Medical apparatus & supplies
CEO: W Thomas Gimple
**Pr:* Dan Afrasiabi
VP: Donna Cote
**VP:* Matthew Keith
VP: James C Morgan

GENEVA WOODS REHABILATION
See GENEVA WOODS PHARMACY INC

D-U-N-S 00-949-3664
GENEVA WORLDWIDE INC
256 W 38th St Fl 10, New York, NY 10018-9121
Tel (212) 398-0700 *Founded/Ownrshp* 1996
Sales 47.8MM^E *EMP* 600
SIC 8743 Public relations services; Public relations services
CEO: Craig Buckstein
**Pr:* Joel Buckstein
Trfc Dir: Maya Tompkins

D-U-N-S 05-667-7446
■ **GENEVE CORP**
(*Suby of* GENEVE HOLDINGS INC) ★
60 Thread Needle Ln, Stamford, CT 06902-7911
Tel (203) 358-8000 *Founded/Ownrshp* 1986
Sales 173.8MM^E *EMP* 1,150
SIC 5961 3483 6282 Educational supplies & equipment, mail order; Mail order house; Ammunition components; Investment counselors; Educational supplies & equipment, mail order; Mail order house; Ammunition components; Investment counselors
Pr: F Peter Zoch III
**Ch Bd:* Edward Netter
**Sr VP:* Robert T Keiser
**Sr VP:* Steven P Lapin
**VP:* Ronald G Strackbein

D-U-N-S 06-496-0966 IMP/EXP
▲ **GENEVE HOLDINGS INC**
96 Cummings Point Rd, Stamford, CT 06902-7919
Tel (203) 358-8000 *Founded/Ownrshp* 1971
Sales 707.7MM^E *EMP* 1,750
SIC 3462 6331 Ordnance forgings, ferrous; Fire, marine & casualty insurance & carriers; Ordnance forgings, ferrous; Fire, marine & casualty insurance & carriers
Ch Bd: Edward Netter
**Pr:* F Peter Zoch II
**VP:* Robert Keiser
VP: Douglas Moffitt
Doctor: Wendy Tsai

D-U-N-S 04-681-5234
GENEWIZ LLC
115 Corporate Blvd, South Plainfield, NJ 07080-2409
Tel (908) 222-0711 *Founded/Ownrshp* 1998
Sales 44.2MM^E *EMP* 150
SIC 8733 8731 Biotechnical research, noncommercial; Commercial physical research; Biotechnical research, noncommercial; Commercial physical research
Pr: Guojuan Liao
CEO: Zhong Ping Sun
VP: Conrad Leung
Software D: Supriya Salvi
Sales Exec: Willert Beth
Snr Mgr: Xuan Pan

D-U-N-S 13-494-6461
GENEX COOPERATIVE INC
(*Suby of* C R I) ★
100 Mbc Dr, Shawano, WI 54166-6095
Tel (715) 526-2141 *Founded/Ownrshp* 1999
Sales 142.2MM *EMP* 777
Accts Wipfli
SIC 0751 5159 Artificial insemination services, livestock; Artificial insemination services, livestock; Semen, bovine
CEO: Keith Heikes
**COO:* R Douglas Wilson
**VP:* Joel Amdall
**VP:* John Ruedinger
**VP:* Brown Swiss
**VP:* David Watkins
Natl Sales: Molly Zorn
Mktg Mgr: Briana Schumacher
Sls Mgr: Greg Hoffman

D-U-N-S 07-968-1544
GENEX LABORATORIES LLC (TX)
9301 Southwest Fwy # 365, Houston, TX 77074-1510
Tel (832) 982-2500 *Founded/Ownrshp* 2014
Sales 52.3MM *EMP* 3
SIC 8734 Testing laboratories
CEO: Joanna Davis
VP: Janell Russell

D-U-N-S 09-684-3842
GENEX SERVICES LLC
(*Suby of* APAX PARTNERS LP) ★
440 E Swedesford Rd # 1000, Wayne, PA 19087-1896
Tel (610) 964-5100 *Founded/Ownrshp* 2014
Sales NA *EMP* 2,075
SIC 6411 Advisory services, insurance; Advisory services, insurance
Pr: Peter C Madeja
**Treas:* John D Keohane
**Ex VP:* Delphia B Frisch
**Sr VP:* Stanley S Jakubowski
VP: Christopher G Darrell
**VP:* Paul E Neff
VP: Kevin Ufier
Exec: Erik Nilson
Ex Dir: Tammy Bledsoe
Prgrm Mgr: Marjorie Portnoy
Area Mgr: Kim Barbour

D-U-N-S 80-792-3271 EXP
GENEXIS CORP
1881 Nw 87th Ave, Doral, FL 33172-2609
Tel (305) 593-5388 *Founded/Ownrshp* 1993
Sales 52.7MM *EMP* 30
Accts Ida C Ovies Cpa Pa Coral Ga
SIC 5045 Computers, peripherals & software; Computers, peripherals & software
Pr: Alejandro Araujo
**Treas:* Jose L Malter
**VP:* Fernando Borrajo

D-U-N-S 07-848-1023
GENGHIS GRILL INC
18900 Dallas Pkwy Ste 125, Dallas, TX 75287-6922
Tel (214) 774-4240 *Founded/Ownrshp* 2012
Sales 19.7MM^E *EMP* 565^E
SIC 5812 Grills (eating places)
Pr: Al Bahkta
Chf Mktg O: Ron Parikh
**Prin:* Chet Bahkta
**Prin:* Ron Prahka
Genl Mgr: Amanda Willia
Dir IT: Marcin Kedzierski
Pr Dir: Liz Jones

D-U-N-S 07-888-2781
GENGOTEX CORP
12301 Old Columbia Pike, Silver Spring, MD 20904-1656
Tel (240) 753-5497 *Founded/Ownrshp* 2013
Sales 100.0MM *EMP* 1
SIC 7389 ;
CEO: Victor Igwe

GENGRAS CENTER
See UNIVERSITY OF ST JOSEPH

GENGRAS' VOLVO
See CCS GROUP INC

D-U-N-S 07-326-0197 IMP
GENICA CORP
43195 Business Park Dr, Temecula, CA 92590-3629
Tel (855) 433-5747 *Founded/Ownrshp* 1999
Sales 82.3MM^E *EMP* 334
SIC 5045 5734 Computer peripheral equipment; Modems, monitors, terminals & disk drives: computers; Printers & plotters: computers; Computer peripheral equipment; Modems, monitors, terminals & disk drives: computers; Printers & plotters: computers
Ch Bd: Frank Segler
**Pr:* Scott Kusel
**CFO:* Geoffrey Hildebrandt
**VP:* Greg Hansen
VP: Chris Herzog
**VP:* Randy Segler
**VP:* Patrick Thompson

Genl Mgr: Mel Turner
Snr Sftwr: Mehul Patel
IT Man: Shawn Badolian
IT Man: Shawn Vadolian

GENIE, A TEREX COMPANY
See GENIE HOLDINGS INC

GENIE COMPANY, THE
See GMI HOLDINGS INC

D-U-N-S 05-413-8433
GENIE ELECTRONICS CO INC
SECURITY FENCE CO DIVISION
710 Wise Ave, Red Lion, PA 17356-2515
Tel (717) 244-7653 *Founded/Ownrshp* 1972
Sales 25.7MM^E *EMP* 140
SIC 1799 5039 3446 5065 8741 3672 Fence construction; Wire fence, gates & accessories; Flagpoles, metal; Electronic parts & equipment; Management services; Printed circuit boards; Fence construction; Wire fence, gates & accessories; Flagpoles, metal; Electronic parts & equipment; Management services; Printed circuit boards
CEO: B Robert Snyder
**Pr:* William R Snyder
**Treas:* Lori A Noga
**VP:* Holly Seace
VP Admn: Holly Snyder
Genl Mgr: Barry J Seace

D-U-N-S 96-955-3424
▲ GENIE ENERGY LTD
550 Broad St Ste 1700, Newark, NJ 07102-4549
Tel (973) 438-3500 *Founded/Ownrshp* 2011
Sales 275.0MM *EMP* 103^E
Tkr Sym GNE *Exch* NYS
SIC 4911 4924 4931 Electric services; Distribution, electric power; Transmission, electric power; Natural gas distribution; Electric & other services combined; Electric services; Distribution, electric power; Transmission, electric power; Natural gas distribution; Electric & other services combined
Ch Bd: Howard S Jonas
Pr: Ira Greenstein
CFO: AVI Goldin
V Ch Bd: James A Courter
Ex VP: Michael Jonas
Sr VP: Claude Pupkin
VP: Daniel Falik
CTO: Alan K Burnham

D-U-N-S 16-008-0875
■ GENIE FINANCIAL SERVICES INC
(*Suby of* GENIE A TEREX CO) ★
18340 Ne 76th St, Redmond, WA 98052-5020
Tel (425) 881-1800 *Founded/Ownrshp* 1996
Sales NA *EMP* 300
SIC 6159 Machinery & equipment finance leasing; Machinery & equipment finance leasing
Pr: Robert Wilkerson

D-U-N-S 12-081-4178 IMP/EXP
■ GENIE HOLDINGS INC
GENIE, A TEREX COMPANY
(*Suby of* TEREX CORP) ★
18340 Ne 76th St, Redmond, WA 98052-5020
Tel (425) 881-1800 *Founded/Ownrshp* 2002
Sales 575.4MM^E *EMP* 2,800
SIC 3536 Hand hoists; Hoists; Hand hoists; Hoists
Pr: Ronald M Defeo
**Pr:* Tim Ford
**VP:* Kevin Bradley
**VP:* Eric I Cohen
**VP:* Robert Wylie

D-U-N-S 00-490-4041 IMP/EXP
■ GENIE INDUSTRIES INC (WA)
(*Suby of* GENIE A TEREX CO) ★
18340 Ne 76th St, Redmond, WA 98052-6710
Tel (425) 881-1800 *Founded/Ownrshp* 1960, 2002
Sales 467.7MM^E *EMP* 1,900
SIC 3536 Hand hoists; Hoists; Hand hoists; Hoists
Pr: Matthew S Fearon
**VP:* Ward Bushnell
**VP:* Gene Dougherty
**VP:* Eric I Cohen
VP: Dave Hubbell
VP: Steve Matuschak
VP: Kevin O'Rilly
**VP:* Robert Wylie
**Prin:* Tim Ford
IT Man: Jeff Porter
Software D: Daniel Fallou

D-U-N-S 12-092-4456 IMP
■ GENIE MANUFACTURING INC
(*Suby of* GENIE A TEREX CO) ★
18340 Ne 76th St, Redmond, WA 98052-5020
Tel (425) 881-1800 *Founded/Ownrshp* 2006
Sales 82.7MM^E *EMP* 1,800
SIC 3531 Aerial work platforms: hydraulic/elec. truck/carrier mounted; Aerial work platforms: hydraulic/elec. truck/carrier mounted
Pr: Robert Wilkerson
**Pr:* Tim Ford

D-U-N-S 07-632-4144
GENISYS CREDIT UNION
2100 Executive Hills Dr, Auburn Hills, MI 48326-2947
Tel (248) 322-9800 *Founded/Ownrshp* 1954
Sales NA *EMP* 117
SIC 6061 6163 Federal credit unions; Loan brokers; Federal credit unions; Loan brokers
Ch Bd: John Schulte
V Ch: Patrick Shaffer
**Pr:* Jackie Buchanan
**CFO:* Gerald Strausbaugh
CFO: Wilma Wells
**Ex VP:* Thomas H Alter
Sr VP: Chris Dewitt
Sr VP: Carolyn James
VP: Jerry McIlrath
IT Man: Lisa Tyrrell

GENISYS GROUP
See CARREKER CORP

D-U-N-S 17-978-0460
GENISYS SOFTWARE LTD
1345 Ave Of The Americas, New York, NY 10105-0302
Tel (732) 635-7132 *Founded/Ownrshp* 2000
Sales 44.9MM^E *EMP* 1,270^E
SIC 7371 7372 5734 Computer software development; Application computer software; Business oriented computer software; Computer & software stores; Computer software development; Application computer software; Business oriented computer software; Computer & software stores
CEO: Ashok J Raberu
**Pr:* Lingaraj URS
**CEO:* Ashok J Rabheru
**VP:* Jaspreet Bedi

D-U-N-S 06-459-4260
GENLABS
5568 Schaefer Ave, Chino, CA 91710-9041
Tel (909) 591-8451 *Founded/Ownrshp* 1973
Sales 20.5MM^E *EMP* 155
SIC 2842 2841

D-U-N-S 13-048-3597 IMP/EXP
GENLYTE GROUP INC
GLYT
(*Suby of* PHILIPS CONSUMER LIFESTYLE) ★
3000 Minuteman Rd, Andover, MA 01810-1032
Tel (781) 418-7900 *Founded/Ownrshp* 2008
Sales 472.0MM^E *EMP* 5,000^E
SIC 3646 3645 3648 Ceiling systems, luminous; Residential lighting fixtures; Lighting equipment; Ceiling systems, luminous; Residential lighting fixtures; Lighting equipment
Pr: Larry K Powers
**CFO:* William G Ferko
Treas: Rene Marineau
Sr VP: Bill Wilson
VP: Mitchell Bloomberg
**VP:* Zia Eftekhar
VP: William Fabbri
VP: Ronald D Schneider
Dir Surg: Leverda Wallace
Dir Lab: Ashok Tewari
Creative D: Paul Neervoort

D-U-N-S 03-309-4678 IMP/EXP
GENLYTE THOMAS GROUP LLC
PHILIPS ENTERTAINMENT LIGHTING
(*Suby of* GENLYTE GROUP INC) ★
200 Franklin Pk Dr, Somerset, NJ 08875
Tel (978) 659-4990 *Founded/Ownrshp* 1998, 2008
Sales 471.5MM^E *EMP* 4,070
SIC 3646 3648 3645 Commercial indusl & institutional electric lighting fixtures; Ceiling systems, luminous; Ornamental lighting fixtures, commercial; Fluorescent lighting fixtures, commercial; Residential lighting fixtures; Garden, patio, walkway & yard lighting fixtures: electric; Fluorescent lighting fixtures, residential; Outdoor lighting equipment; Decorative area lighting fixtures; Underwater lighting fixtures; Commercial indusl & institutional electric lighting fixtures; Ceiling systems, luminous; Ornamental lighting fixtures, commercial; Fluorescent lighting fixtures, commercial; Outdoor lighting equipment; Decorative area lighting fixtures; Underwater lighting fixtures; Residential lighting fixtures; Garden, patio, walkway & yard lighting fixtures: electric; Fluorescent lighting fixtures, residential
CFO: Bill Ferko
VP: George Preston
VP: Jeff Truax
Dir Surg: Leverda Wallace
VP Sls: Guy Petruccelli

GENMAK GENEVA LIBERTY
See LIBERTY GENEVA STEEL LTD

D-U-N-S 00-613-1205 EXP
GENMAR YACHT GROUP LLC
CARVER
790 Markham Dr, Pulaski, WI 54162
Tel (920) 822-3214 *Founded/Ownrshp* 2010
Sales 40.0MM *EMP* 310^E
SIC 3732

D-U-N-S 17-694-4718 IMP
GENMARK AUTOMATION
46723 Lakeview Blvd, Fremont, CA 94538-6528
Tel (408) 745-6520 *Founded/Ownrshp* 1985
Sales 59.0MM^E *EMP* 170
SIC 3569 Robots, assembly line: industrial & commercial; Robots, assembly line: industrial & commercial
CEO: Victor Lima Sales
**Ch Bd:* Mila Genov
Pr: Zlatko Sotirov
VP: Carl McMahon
**Prin:* Mike Klayko
Genl Mgr: Emill Natzkin
Ql Cn Mgr: Danny Hinckley
Sls Dir: Dennis Coulter
Manager: Yuhong Tay
Board of Directors: Mike Klayko

D-U-N-S 96-210-4217
▲ GENMARK DIAGNOSTICS INC
5964 La Place Ct Ste 100, Carlsbad, CA 92008-8829
Tel (760) 448-4300 *Founded/Ownrshp* 2010
Sales 30.5MM *EMP* 153^E
Tkr Sym GNMK *Exch* NGM
SIC 3841 Surgical & medical instruments; Surgical & medical instruments
Pr: Hany Massarany
**Ch Bd:* James Fox
CFO: Scott Mendel
Ex VP: Jorge Garces
Sr VP: Jon Faiz Kayyem
Sr VP: Eric Stier
Sr VP: Jennifer Willia
Sr VP: Jennifer Williams
VP: Tyler Jensen
VP: Alan Maderazo
Assoc Dir: Michele Wisniewski
Board of Directors: Daryl J Faulkner, Lisa M Giles, Michael S Kagnoff, Kevin C O'boyle

D-U-N-S 79-555-1782
GENOA A QOL HEALTHCARE CO LLC
18300 Cascade Ave S # 251, Tukwila, WA 98188-4746
Tel (253) 218-0830 *Founded/Ownrshp* 2013
Sales 578.4MM^E *EMP* 1,700^E
SIC 2834 Pharmaceutical preparations
CEO: John Figueroa

D-U-N-S 13-678-5768
GENOA AREA LOCAL SCHOOL DISTRICT
2810 N Genoa Clay Ctr Rd, Genoa, OH 43430-9730
Tel (419) 855-7741 *Founded/Ownrshp* 2003
Sales 23.1MM *EMP* 157^E
Accts Charles E Harris & Associates
SIC 8211 Public combined elementary & secondary school; Public combined elementary & secondary school
**Treas:* Mike Weis
Schl Brd P: Mitch Hoyles
Schl Brd P: Laura McInke

D-U-N-S 11-197-7265
GENOA HEALTHCARE LLC
(*Suby of* GENOA A QOL HEALTHCARE CO LLC) ★
18300 Cascade Ave S # 251, Tukwila, WA 98188-4746
Tel (253) 218-0830 *Founded/Ownrshp* 2002
Sales 248.8MM^E *EMP* 1,200
SIC 5912 Drug stores; Drug stores
CEO: John Figueroa
COO: David Vucurevich
CFO: Victor Breed
Ofcr: Ira Paligutan
Dir Rx: Gargey Bhatt
Dir Rx: Stacy Graham
Dir Rx: Sarah Jester
Dir Rx: Kevin Messier
Dir Rx: Jonathon Montag
Dir Rx: Christopher Rosario
Dir Rx: Rita Schille
Dir Rx: Courtney Tucker

D-U-N-S 01-883-7943
▲ GENOMIC HEALTH INC
301 Penobscot Dr, Redwood City, CA 94063-4700
Tel (650) 556-9300 *Founded/Ownrshp* 2000
Sales 275.7MM *EMP* 752^E
Accts Ernst & Young Llp Redwood Cit
Tkr Sym GHDX *Exch* NGS
SIC 8071 8731 Medical laboratories; Biotechnical research, commercial; Medical laboratories; Biotechnical research, commercial
CEO: Kimberly J Popovits
COO: G Bradley Cole
Bd of Dir: Hank Fuchs
Sr VP: Josh Gralapp
VP: Carl Yoshizawa
Assoc Dir: Allison Lai
Assoc Dir: RAO Parige
Assoc Dir: Randy Rudolph
Dir Sec: Steven Shak
Prgrm Mgr: Irena Petkovska
Rgnl Mgr: Pete Simchera
Board of Directors: Felix J Baker, Julian C Baker, Fred E Cohen, Henry J Fuchs, Ginger L Graham, Randall S Livingston

D-U-N-S 13-359-0328
■ GENON AMERICAS GENERATION LLC
(*Suby of* GENON AMERICAS INC) ★
211 Carnegie Ctr, Princeton, NJ 08540-6213
Tel (609) 524-4500 *Founded/Ownrshp* 1999
Sales 2.9MMM *EMP* 602^E
SIC 4911 Generation, electric power; Generation, electric power
Ex VP: Kirkland B Andrews
VP: Ronald B Stark

D-U-N-S 06-792-3297
■ GENON AMERICAS INC (GA)
(*Suby of* GENON ENERGY HOLDINGS INC) ★
1155 Perimeter Ctr # 100, Atlanta, GA 30338-5463
Tel (678) 579-5000 *Founded/Ownrshp* 2001
Sales 3.2MMM^E *EMP* 1,679
SIC 4924 Natural gas distribution; Natural gas distribution
CEO: J W Holden
Sr VP: Jason Few

D-U-N-S 12-609-4205
■ GENON CALIFORNIA NORTH LLC
(*Suby of* GENON NORTH AMERICA LLC) ★
1350 Treat Blvd Ste 500, Walnut Creek, CA 94597-8853
Tel (925) 287-3133 *Founded/Ownrshp* 1999
Sales 53.2MM^E *EMP* 150^E
SIC 4911 Generation, electric power; Generation, electric power

D-U-N-S 15-291-2291 IMP
■ GENON ENERGY HOLDINGS INC
(*Suby of* GENON ENERGY INC) ★
1000 Main St, Houston, TX 77002-6336
Tel (832) 357-3000 *Founded/Ownrshp* 2010
Sales 3.3MMM^E *EMP* 1,679
SIC 4911 Generation, electric power; ; ; Generation, electric power; ;
Pr: Edward R Muller
COO: John Deep
**CFO:* J William Holden III
Sr VP: James Garlick
**Sr VP:* Thomas E Legro
Sr VP: Jose P Leviste
Sr VP: Thomas Livengood
Sr VP: William P Von Blasingame
Sr VP: Lloyd Warnock
VP: Steve Astren
VP: Mark Durow
VP: Shawn McFarlane
VP: Robert Mickits
**VP:* Angela M Nagy
VP: Mathew Parker
VP: Terry Thompson

D-U-N-S 00-820-0680 IMP
■ GENON ENERGY INC
NRG
(*Suby of* NRG ENERGY INC) ★
211 Carnegie Ctr, Princeton, NJ 08540-6213
Tel (609) 524-4500 *Founded/Ownrshp* 2012
Sales 3.0MMM *EMP* 2,932
Accts Kpmg Llp Philadelphia Pennsy
SIC 4911 Electric services; Distribution, electric power; Generation, electric power; Transmission, electric power; Electric services; Distribution, electric power; Generation, electric power; Transmission, electric power
Pr: Mauricio Gutierrez
CEO: Maria Deouca
**CFO:* Kirkland B Andrews
Sr VP: Matthew Benner
Sr VP: Karen Dyson
Sr VP: Tom Gros
Sr VP: Dan Hannon
**VP:* Ronald B Stark
VP: Walter Stone
Prin: Heather Humalainen
Admn Mgr: Edie Good

D-U-N-S 13-384-3644
■ GENON ENERGY SERVICES LLC
(*Suby of* GENON AMERICAS INC) ★
211 Carnegie Ctr, Princeton, NJ 08540-6213
Tel (609) 524-4500 *Founded/Ownrshp* 2001
Sales 113.1MM^E *EMP* 299
SIC 4911 Generation, electric power
Off Mgr: Mark Jensen
CIO: James McDonald
IT Man: Glen Pierce

D-U-N-S 11-040-2893
■ GENON MID-ATLANTIC LLC
(*Suby of* GENON NORTH AMERICA LLC) ★
211 Carnegie Ctr, Princeton, NJ 08540-6213
Tel (609) 524-4500 *Founded/Ownrshp* 2000
Sales 1.0MMM *EMP* 451
SIC 4911 Distribution, electric power; Generation, electric power; Transmission, electric power; Distribution, electric power; Generation, electric power; Transmission, electric power
Ex VP: Kirkland B Andrews

D-U-N-S 17-719-8629 IMP
■ GENON NORTH AMERICA LLC
(*Suby of* GENON AMERICAS GENERATION LLC) ★
1155 Perimeter Ctr # 100, Atlanta, GA 30338-5463
Tel (678) 579-5000 *Founded/Ownrshp* 2000
Sales 1.1MMM^E *EMP* 798
SIC 4924 4911 6221 Natural gas distribution; Distribution, electric power; Commodity brokers, contracts; Natural gas distribution; Distribution, electric power; Commodity brokers, contracts
Pr: Robert E Driscoll
**Pr:* Edward R Muller
CFO: J William Holden III
**Sr VP:* Julia A Houston
VP: Angela M Nagy

D-U-N-S 96-492-9561
■ GENON POWER GENERATION LLC
(*Suby of* GENON AMERICAS INC) ★
1000 Main St, Houston, TX 77002-6336
Tel (832) 357-3000 *Founded/Ownrshp* 1996
Sales 54.6MM^E *EMP* 299^E
SIC 4911 Electric services
Pr: J William Holden III

D-U-N-S 78-672-2863
■ GENON POWER MIDWEST LP
(*Suby of* GENON POWER GENERATION ASSETS, LLC)
1000 Main St, Houston, TX 77002-6336
Tel (713) 497-3000 *Founded/Ownrshp* 2006
Sales 100.8MM^E *EMP* 337^E
SIC 4911 Electric services
Pt: David Freysinger

GENON REMA, LLC
See NRG REMA LLC

D-U-N-S 06-125-3907
GENOPTIX INC
GENOPTIX MEDICAL LABORATORY
(*Suby of* NOVARTIS FINANCE CORP) ★
1811 Aston Ave Ste 100, Carlsbad, CA 92008-7396
Tel (760) 268-6200 *Founded/Ownrshp* 2011
Sales 1.4MM^E *EMP* 440^E
SIC 8071 Medical laboratories; Medical laboratories
Pr: Tina S Nova PHD
COO: Samuel D Riccitelli
CFO: Douglas A Schuling
Sr VP: Jonathan Diver
VP: Bashar Dabas
VP: Allison Hooker
VP: Christian V Kuhlen MD
VP: Tyler Merritt
Dir Lab: Jonathan Lawson
Dir Lab: Anh Pham
Ex Dir: Marcy Graham

GENOPTIX MEDICAL LABORATORY
See GENOPTIX INC

D-U-N-S 02-402-1305 IMP
GENOS FORMAL AFFAIR INC (KY)
2016 Mercer Rd Ste 2, Lexington, KY 40511-2510
Tel (859) 259-2323 *Founded/Ownrshp* 1963, 1971
Sales 20.8MM^E *EMP* 52
SIC 5136 5699 7299 Men's & boys' clothing; Formal wear; Tuxedo rental
Pr: Gino R Guarnieri
Off Mgr: Tricia Wise

D-U-N-S 60-317-9581
GENOVA DIAGNOSTICS INC
GREAT SMOKIES DIAGNOSTIC LAB
63 Zillicoa St, Asheville, NC 28801-1038
Tel (828) 210-7455 *Founded/Ownrshp* 1987
Sales 49.0MM^E *EMP* 519^E
SIC 8071 Testing laboratories; Testing laboratories
Pr: Christopher S Smith
**CFO:* Andrew Church
CFO: Charles Thompson
Ofcr: Jim Kelton
VP: Bob Giles
VP: Daryl Landis
VP: Sarah Martin
Dir Lab: Theresa McBride

CIO: Ceco Ivanov
QA Dir: Larry Fowler
QA Dir: Pamela Robson

D-U-N-S 00-539-3103 IMP/EXP
GENOVA PRODUCTS INC (MI)
7034 E Court St, Davison, MI 48423-2504
Tel (810) 744-4500 *Founded/Ownrshp* 1962
Sales 175.2MM^E *EMP* 570
SIC 3089 2891 2911 3494 3084 2952 Gutters (glass fiber reinforced), fiberglass or plastic; Downspouts, plastic; Fittings for pipe, plastic; Glue; Solvents; Plumbing & heating valves; Plastics pipe; Asphalt felts & coatings; Gutters (glass fiber reinforced), fiberglass or plastic; Downspouts, plastic; Fittings for pipe, plastic; Glue; Solvents; Plumbing & heating valves; Plastics pipe; Asphalt felts & coatings
Ch Bd: Robert M Williams
**Pr:* Michael S Deboer
CFO: Barry Brang
**CFO:* Nicholas S Onica
**VP:* Donald Dinkgrave
**VP:* Jeanette M Kollias
VP: Nicholas Onica
IT Man: Carol Scott
Mktg Mgr: Mary Berklich
Sls Mgr: Brian Morey
Snr Mgr: Mark Case

D-U-N-S 10-154-0701
GENOX TRANSPORTATION INC
2000 Old Underwood Rd, La Porte, TX 77571-9637
Tel (281) 479-0338 *Founded/Ownrshp* 2001
Sales 62.9MM *EMP* 17
Accts Hancock & Dana Pc Omaha Nebr
SIC 4213 Trucking, except local; Trucking, except local
Ch: Russell L Mathews
**Pr:* Kevin L Mathews

D-U-N-S 12-056-0029
GENPACT
(*Suby of* GENPACT INDIA)
2004 Bassett Ave Pmb 2500, El Paso, TX 79901-1923
Tel (915) 225-2500 *Founded/Ownrshp* 2006
Sales 127.0MM^E *EMP* 2,500
SIC 7374 Data processing & preparation; Data processing & preparation
Pr: Frank Freeman
Sr VP: Michael Corning
VP: Tiger Tyagarajan
VP: Amit Yadav
IT Man: Rodolfo Aguinaga
IT Man: Sixto Rubio
Board of Directors: Ferdinando Beccalli-Falco

D-U-N-S 83-230-8352
GENPACT LIMITED
1155 Avenue Of The Americ, New York, NY 10036-2711
Tel (212) 896-6600 *Founded/Ownrshp* 2007
Sales 207.9MM^E *EMP* 325^E
SIC 8741 7372 Business management; Prepackaged software; Business management; Prepackaged software
CEO: NV Tiger Tyagarajan
**Ch Bd:* Robert G Scott
Sr VP: Mohit Bhatia
Sr VP: Scott McConnell
Sr VP: Anil Nanduru
VP: Christopher Acevedo
VP: Craig W Anderson
VP: Manoj Bajpai
VP: Diana L Boersma
VP: Michael Flammer
VP: David Hauser
VP: Rein Horst
VP: Brad Jolson
VP: Chetan Mehta
VP: Troy Merriman
VP: Tom Moran
VP: Doug Morehouse
VP: Jorge Moreno
VP: Umesh Pahwa
VP: Michael Plummer
VP: Michael Pommer

D-U-N-S 02-400-2549
GENPACT LLC
(*Suby of* GENPACT LIMITED)
42 Old Ridgebury Rd Ste 1, Danbury, CT 06810-5247
Tel (203) 730-5110 *Founded/Ownrshp* 1999
Sales 384.1MM *EMP* 2,300^E
Accts Kpmg Llp Gurgaon India
SIC 8742 Management consulting services; Management consulting services
Pr: NV Tiger Tyagarajan
Pr: David Petrucci
Treas: Ashish Shukla
VP: Craig Anderson
VP: Scott Cox
VP: Daniel English
VP: Hakan Franson
VP: Mary Hall
VP: Umacharan Iyer
VP: Amit Jindal
VP: Tanya Johnson
VP: ABI Karun
VP: Janice Kennedy
VP: Krishna Kumar
VP: Paul Loub
VP: Bhaskar Mandalaparthy
VP: Holly Neumann
VP: Ratnamala Palepu
VP: Kieran Quinn
VP: Mohd Qureshi
VP: Vivek Saxena

D-U-N-S 00-571-6154
GENPACT MORTGAGE SERVICES INC (CA)
MONEYLINE LENDING SERVICES
(*Suby of* GENPACT LIMITED)
15420 Laguna Canyon Rd, Irvine, CA 92618-2119
Tel (949) 417-5131 *Founded/Ownrshp* 1996
Sales NA *EMP* 85
Accts Kushner Smith Joanou Gregsonc
SIC 6162 6163 Mortgage brokers, using own money; Loan brokers
Pr: Evan Gentry
Pr: Maria Escarcega
Pr: Brett Fish
**CFO:* Richard Belliston
Treas: Chandan Goel
**Ex VP:* Bradley J Barber
**Ex VP:* Taylor Woods
VP: James Mealey
IT Man: Joffre Loor
VP Sls: Joe Puthur
Manager: Guru Prasad

D-U-N-S 60-258-2798
GENPACT PROCESS SOLUTIONS LLC
GECIS
(*Suby of* GENPACT LIMITED)
42 Old Ridgebury Rd Ste 1, Danbury, CT 06810-5247
Tel (203) 730-5100 *Founded/Ownrshp* 1999
Sales 69.3MM^E *EMP* 800
SIC 8748 Business consulting; Business consulting
Sr VP: V M Angles
Sr VP: Eileen Silvers
VP: Heather White

GENPAK
See GREAT PACIFIC ENTERPRISES (US) INC

D-U-N-S 05-405-4218
GENPAK LLC
(*Suby of* GENPAK) ★
68 Warren St, Glens Falls, NY 12801-4530
Tel (518) 798-9511 *Founded/Ownrshp* 1969
Sales 331.2MM^E *EMP* 1,295
SIC 3089 Plastic containers, except foam; Plastic containers, except foam
CEO: James Allen Pattison
Pr: Edward Rider
Exec: Brian Grant
Area Mgr: Mark Franz
Off Admin: Joan Taylor
CIO: Chris Walsh
CTO: Gordon Edge
Plnt Mgr: Amir Mustafa
Prd Mgr: Surinder Deol
Ql Cn Mgr: Barbara Allen
Ql Cn Mgr: Charity Campbell

GENPORE
See GENERAL POLYMERIC CORP

D-U-N-S 83-310-8934
GENPOWER HOLDINGS LP
85 Wells Ave Ste 300, Newton, MA 02459-3215
Tel (617) 340-4500 *Founded/Ownrshp* 2010
Sales 60.7MM^E *EMP* 159^E
SIC 4911 Electric services
VP: Charlie Huguenard
Off Admin: Phyllis Smith

D-U-N-S 01-335-8979
GENPOWER SERVICES LLC
966 Crafts Run Rd, Maidsville, WV 26541-8145
Tel (304) 599-0931 *Founded/Ownrshp* 2006
Sales 24.2MM^E *EMP* 75
SIC 4911 Generation, electric power; Generation, electric power

D-U-N-S 01-196-2763
GENSCAPE INC
(*Suby of* DMG INFORMATION INC) ★
445 E Market St Ste 200, Louisville, KY 40202-6105
Tel (502) 583-3435 *Founded/Ownrshp* 2001
Sales 54.6MM^E *EMP* 173
SIC 8711 7375 Energy conservation engineering; Information retrieval services; Energy conservation engineering; Information retrieval services
CEO: Matthew Burkley
**Pr:* Sterling Lapinski
**CFO:* David Deans
Chf Mktg O: David Francoeur
Sr VP: Jill Sampson
VP: Stephen Bannasch
**VP:* Jon Ecker
VP: Hudson Gilmer
VP: Susan Olson
**VP:* Bill Townsend
Exec: Daniel Haas
Dir Bus: Simon Toyne
Board of Directors: Sean O'leary

D-U-N-S 02-753-7596 IMP/EXP
GENSCO INC
4402 20th St E, Fife, WA 98424-1803
Tel (253) 620-8203 *Founded/Ownrshp* 1947
Sales 239.0MM^E *EMP* 500
SIC 5074 3444 Heating equipment (hydronic); Sheet metalwork; Ducts, sheet metal; Heating equipment (hydronic); Sheet metalwork; Ducts, sheet metal
Ch: Charles E Walters Sr
**Pr:* Charles E Walters Jr
**Treas:* Ken R Bell
VP: Sterling Hicks
Brnch Mgr: Jeff Black
VP Opers: John McKenna

D-U-N-S 07-922-3990
GENSER ENERGY HOLDINGS LLC
800 Haley St, Middletown, DE 19709-6122
Tel (302) 442-0312 *Founded/Ownrshp* 2007
Sales 10.0MM *EMP* 300
SIC 3612 Transformers, except electric; Transformers, except electric

D-U-N-S 55-737-8783
GENSERVE INC
100 Newtown Rd, Plainview, NY 11803-4302
Tel (631) 435-0437 *Founded/Ownrshp* 1990
Sales 29.1MM^E *EMP* 52
SIC 5063 7629 4911 3621 Generators; Generator repair; Generation, electric power; Generators & sets, electric
Ch: Bob Fortunato
**Pr:* Dennis Schneider
**CFO:* Joseph Flynn
**Sec:* Eric Sklar
**Ex VP:* Edward J Flannigan
VP: Phil Du Tot
**VP:* Phil Dutot
**VP:* Michael Vahling
Genl Mgr: Joseph Prizzi
Sls Mgr: Frank Spadafino

D-U-N-S 13-619-0654 EXP
GENSET SERVICES INC
3100 Gateway Dr, Pompano Beach, FL 33069-4872
Tel (954) 956-9252 *Founded/Ownrshp* 2003
Sales 26.3MM^E *EMP* 40
SIC 6063 Generators
Pr: Keith Friedman
**VP:* Walter Bacallao
**VP:* Jose Santos
Sales Asso: Scott Wilcox
Sales Asso: David Yeakle

D-U-N-S 17-323-4162 IMP
■ **GENSIA SICOR INC**
(*Suby of* TEVA PHARMACEUTICAL INDUSTRIES LIMITED)
19 Hughes, Irvine, CA 92618-1902
Tel (949) 455-4700 *Founded/Ownrshp* 2004
Sales 62.0MM^E *EMP* 1,851
SIC 2834 8731 Drugs acting on the cardiovascular system, except diagnostic; Medical research, commercial; Drugs acting on the cardiovascular system, except diagnostic; Medical research, commercial
V Ch: Carlo Salvi
CTO: Frank Becker

D-U-N-S 96-334-1636
GENSLER AND ASSOCIATES/INTERNATIONAL LTD
(*Suby of* M ARTHUR GENSLER JR & ASSOCIATES INC) ★
2 Harrison St Ste 400, San Francisco, CA 94105-1672
Tel (415) 433-3700 *Founded/Ownrshp* 1988
Sales 18.2MM^E *EMP* 350^E
SIC 8712 Architectural services; Architectural services
Pr: Arthur Gensler Jr

D-U-N-S 07-926-7539
GENSLER ARCHITECTURE DESIGN & PLANNING PC
(*Suby of* M ARTHUR GENSLER JR & ASSOCIATES INC) ★
2 Harrison St Fl 4, San Francisco, CA 94105-6127
Tel (415) 433-3700 *Founded/Ownrshp* 2014
Sales 1.6MM^E *EMP* 316
SIC 8712 Architectural services
Prin: Daniel W Winey
Prin: Joan Price

D-U-N-S 93-330-2499 IMP
GENSTAR CAPITAL LLC
4 Embarcadero Ctr # 1900, San Francisco, CA 94111-4191
Tel (415) 834-2350 *Founded/Ownrshp* 1991
Sales 926.4MM^E *EMP* 3,661
SIC 6799 Investors; Investors
**Pr:* J Ryan Clark
CFO: Melissa Dickerson
Ex VP: John Ryan
**VP:* David J Golde
VP: Roman A Margolin
VP: Jean Mayer
VP: James D Nadauld
VP: Gretchen Robinson
**VP:* Eli P Weiss
Exec: Hugh Lytle
Exec: Raj Parikh
Adv Bd Mbr: Harry Totonis

D-U-N-S 13-444-3089
GENSTAR CAPITAL LP
4 Embarcadero Ctr # 1500, San Francisco, CA 94111-4106
Tel (415) 834-2350 *Founded/Ownrshp* 1986
Sales 31.3MM^E *EMP* 560
SIC 6211 Security brokers & dealers; Security brokers & dealers
Pt: Jean-Pierre L Conte
Pt: Richard F Hoskins
Pt: Richard D Paterson

D-U-N-S 87-754-9097 IMP
GENTEK BUILDING PRODUCTS INC
REVERE BUILDING PRODUCTS
(*Suby of* ASSOCIATED MATERIALS LLC) ★
3773 State Rd, Cuyahoga Falls, OH 44223-2603
Tel (800) 548-4542 *Founded/Ownrshp* 2003
Sales 208.2MM^E *EMP* 1,000
SIC 3444 3089 Siding, sheet metal; Downspouts, sheet metal; Siding, plastic; Siding, sheet metal; Downspouts, sheet metal; Siding, plastic
CEO: Thomas Chieffe
**Pr:* Michael Caporale
**VP:* D Keith Lavanway

D-U-N-S 07-206-4418 IMP/EXP
GENTEK INC
90 E Halsey Rd Ste 301, Parsippany, NJ 07054-3709
Tel (973) 515-0900 *Founded/Ownrshp* 1999
Sales 218.6MM^E *EMP* 1,110
SIC 2869 2819 2844 3714 3496 Industrial organic chemicals; Industrial inorganic chemicals; Toilet preparations; Motor vehicle parts & accessories; Cable, uninsulated wire: made from purchased wire; Industrial organic chemicals; Industrial inorganic chemicals; Toilet preparations; Motor vehicle parts & accessories; Cable, uninsulated wire: made from purchased wire
Pr: William E Redmond Jr
**CFO:* Thomas B Testa
VP: Mark J Connor
VP: Greg Gilbert
**VP:* Douglas J Grierson
**VP:* James Imbriaco
VP: Michael J Murphy
VP: Vincent J Opalewski
Sls Mgr: Lenny Andia
Board of Directors: Henry L Druker, Kathleen R Flaherty, John G Johnson Jr, John F McGovern, Richard A Rubin

D-U-N-S 04-538-9988 IMP
GENTEX CORP
324 Main St, Simpson, PA 18407-1182
Tel (570) 282-3550 *Founded/Ownrshp* 1972
Sales 163.6MM^E *EMP* 575
SIC 3842 8731 2295 Surgical appliances & supplies; Helmets, space; Respiratory protection equipment, personal; Commercial physical research; Coated fabrics, not rubberized; Surgical appliances & supplies; Helmets, space; Respiratory protection equipment, personal; Commercial physical research; Coated fabrics, not rubberized
Pr: L Peter Frieder Jr
CFO: Steven Downing
VP: Dennis Alexejun
Prgrm Mgr: Jon Morey
Ql Cn Mgr: Christine Kistler
Snr Mgr: Ken Dejonge
Snr Mgr: Chuck Dryfhout

D-U-N-S 06-585-5363 IMP
▲ **GENTEX CORP**
600 N Centennial St, Zeeland, MI 49464-1374
Tel (616) 772-1800 *Founded/Ownrshp* 1974
Sales 1.3MMM *EMP* 4,196
Tkr Sym GNTX *Exch* NGS
SIC 3231 3714 3669 Mirrors, truck & automobile: made from purchased glass; Motor vehicle parts & accessories; Smoke detectors; Mirrors, truck & automobile: made from purchased glass; Motor vehicle parts & accessories; Smoke detectors
Ch Bd: Fred Bauer
CFO: Steve Downing
Bd of Dir: Eric Domke
Chf Mktg O: David Cammenga
VP: Neil Boehm
VP: Brad Bosma
VP: Joe Donato
VP: Joseph Matthews
Dir Lab: Ratchaneekorn Luten
Dir Lab: Paul Van Lente
Dept Mgr: Louis Bush
Board of Directors: Gary Goode, Pete Hoekstra, James Hollars, John Mulder, Richard Schaum, Frederick Sotok, James Wallace

D-U-N-S 55-540-3690 IMP/EXP
GENTEX OPTICS INC
(*Suby of* ESSILOR OF AMERICA INC) ★
324 Main St, Carbondale, PA 18407-1182
Tel (570) 282-8531 *Founded/Ownrshp* 1988
Sales 89.1MM^E *EMP* 500
SIC 3851 3842 Lenses, ophthalmic; Goggles: sun, safety, industrial, underwater, etc.; Surgical appliances & supplies; Lenses, ophthalmic; Goggles: sun, safety, industrial, underwater, etc.; Surgical appliances & supplies
Pr: Gerard Malledant
**CEO:* L P Frieder
**CEO:* Eric Javellaud
**CFO:* Heather M Acker
**VP:* Helene Greuzard
VP: Russell F Weymouth

D-U-N-S 00-245-2758
■ **GENTHERM (TEXAS) INC** (TX)
W.E.T. AUTOMOTIVE SYSTEMS AG
(*Suby of* GENTHERM CANADA LTD)
2121b Frontera Rd, Del Rio, TX 78840-8905
Tel (830) 774-3094 *Founded/Ownrshp* 1968
Sales 221.8MM^E *EMP* 500
SIC 5013 Motor vehicle supplies & new parts; Motor vehicle supplies & new parts
CEO: Klaus Wilhelm
Ch Bd: Dan Coker
CFO: Barry Steel

D-U-N-S 55-687-9252 IMP
▲ **GENTHERM INC**
21680 Haggerty Rd Ste 101, Northville, MI 48167-8994
Tel (248) 504-0500 *Founded/Ownrshp* 2000
Sales 811.3MM *EMP* 8,607^E
Tkr Sym THRM *Exch* NGS
SIC 3714 Motor vehicle parts & accessories; Motor vehicle electrical equipment; Motor vehicle parts & accessories; Motor vehicle electrical equipment
Pr: Daniel R Coker
**Ch Bd:* Oscar B Marx III
Pr: Darren Schumacher
CFO: Barry G Steele
CFO: William Wills
VP: Erin E Ascher
VP: Kenneth J Phillips
Prgrm Mgr: Elias Chidiac
Prgrm Mgr: Ed Marlovits
Genl Mgr: Klaus Wilhelm
Snr Sftwr: Simon Zheng
Board of Directors: Lewis Booth, Francois J Castaing, Sophie Desormiere, Maurice E P Gunderson, Carlos E Mazzorin, Franz Scherer, Byron T Shaw II

D-U-N-S 04-902-6321
GENTILE MOTOR GROUP
6801 Washington Ave, Mount Pleasant, WI 53406-3927
Tel (262) 886-5111 *Founded/Ownrshp* 1969
Sales 22.6MM^E *EMP* 80
SIC 5511 Automobiles, new & used; Automobiles, new & used
Pr: Ralph Gentile
**Ch Bd:* Frank Gentile
**Treas:* Thomas Pias
**VP:* Norma Gentile

D-U-N-S 83-255-4625
GENTILINI CHEVROLET LLC
500 John S Penn Blvd, Woodbine, NJ 08270-2636
Tel (609) 861-9000 *Founded/Ownrshp* 2008
Sales 21.8MM *EMP* 13
SIC 5511 Automobiles, new & used; Automobiles, new & used
Sales Asso: Rick Mead
Sales Asso: Jeff Saduk

D-U-N-S 12-974-1026 IMP
■ **GENTIVA HEALTH SERVICES INC**
(*Suby of* KINDRED HEALTHCARE INC) ★
3350 Riverwood Pkwy Se # 1400, Atlanta, GA 30339-3314
Tel (770) 951-6450 *Founded/Ownrshp* 2015
Sales 1.7MMM *EMP* 39,200
SIC 8082 Home health care services; Home health care services

CEO: Tony Strange
Pr: Stacy Bromell
**Pr:* David A Causby
Pr: Kathleen Cleary
Pr: Robert Koch
Pr: Richard Scrima
**CFO:* Eric R Slusser
VP: Jacquelin Blankenship
VP: Cara Burns
VP: Debbie Kearns
VP: Rosa Mascardi
VP: Danny Mullins
VP: Mari Pitcher
VP: April Price
VP: Maryjo Rinkewich
VP: Nancy Sciortino
VP: Todd Tyler
Assoc Dir: Ryan Sherer

D-U-N-S 01-064-1304
■ GENTIVA HOME HEALTH
(*Suby of* GENTIVA HEALTH SERVICES INC) ★
8502 N Nevada St, Spokane, WA 99208-7395
Tel (509) 464-4970 *Founded/Ownrshp* 2009
Sales 3.8MM^E *EMP* 572^E
SIC 8361 Residential care
Prin: John Hamilton

D-U-N-S 93-072-1295
GENTLE COMMUNICATIONS LLC
200 5th Ave Fl 3, Waltham, MA 02451-8759
Tel (781) 647-0772 *Founded/Ownrshp* 1997
Sales 36.9MM^E *EMP* 200
SIC 8742 Administrative services consultant; Administrative services consultant
**Treas:* Ronald Weissman
Info Man: Vinay Kaza

GENTLE DENTAL GROUP
See NORTHWESTERN MANAGEMENT SERVICES LLC

D-U-N-S 80-860-6326
GENTLE DENTAL SERVICE CORP
(*Suby of* HIG CAPITAL LLC) ★
9800 S La Cienega Blvd # 800, Inglewood, CA 90301-4440
Tel (310) 765-2400 *Founded/Ownrshp* 2007
Sales 583.6MM^E *EMP* 1,824^E
SIC 8021 Offices & clinics of dentists
CFO: Fred Vanerden
Exec: Wayne Cozy

D-U-N-S 16-186-8658
GENTLE GIANT MOVING CO INC
29 Harding St, Somerville, MA 02143-4204
Tel (617) 661-3333 *Founded/Ownrshp* 1980
Sales 32.9MM^E *EMP* 200^E
SIC 4214 4213 4212

D-U-N-S 80-055-4821
GENTOSI BUILDERS INC
WYOMING GENTOSI BUILDERS
1750 E Deere Ave, Santa Ana, CA 92705-5719
Tel (949) 474-2333 *Founded/Ownrshp* 2000
Sales 30.0MM *EMP* 30
SIC 1542 Nonresidential construction; Nonresidential construction
Pr: Paul Gentosi
CFO: Anne Amelung

D-U-N-S 96-285-4824
GENTRY MILLS INC
2035 Kingsley Dr, Albemarle, NC 28001-4473
Tel (704) 983-5555 *Founded/Ownrshp* 1992
Sales 34.0MM^E *EMP* 60
SIC 5131 3999 Textiles, woven; Atomizers, toiletry
Pr: Jan Berkovic
**Sec:* Emilio Kraizel
**VP:* Alvaro Kraizel
Sales Asso: Karen Griffin

GENTRY, SHAWN MD
See MURRAY REGIONAL HOSPITAL

GENTZ AERO
See MB AEROSPACE WARREN LLC

D-U-N-S 14-607-2793
GENTZLER ELECTRICAL SERVICES INC
11545 Pagemill Rd, Dallas, TX 75243-5508
Tel (214) 341-2890 *Founded/Ownrshp* 2004
Sales 56.0MM^E *EMP* 210
SIC 1731 Electric power systems contractors; Electric power systems contractors
Pr: Leah P Gentzler
**Ex VP:* Stan Gentzler
**VP:* Randy Johnson
**VP:* Ron Moore
VP: Monty Nairn
**VP:* Scott Newell
Off Mgr: Connie Franks
Prd Mgr: Rodney Tomlinson
Ql Cn Mgr: Ben Hernandez
Snr PM: Jeff Cary
Snr PM: Rodney Mash

D-U-N-S 01-488-1627
GENUARDIS FAMILY MARKETS LP
(*Suby of* SAFEWAY INC) ★
301 E Germantown Pike, Norristown, PA 19401-6517
Tel (610) 277-6000 *Founded/Ownrshp* 1930, 2001
Sales 421.6MM^E *EMP* 7,400
SIC 5912 5411 Drug stores; Supermarkets, independent; Drug stores; Supermarkets, independent
Genl Mgr: Don Ciotti

D-U-N-S 14-425-4054
GENUINE BUILDERS INC
301 S Highway 81, Arlington, SD 57212-2014
Tel (605) 983-3240 *Founded/Ownrshp* 2003
Sales 21.6MM^E *EMP* 136
SIC 1521 1542 New construction, single-family houses; Commercial & office building, new construction
Pr: James P Bunker

D-U-N-S 00-692-4948 IMP
▲ GENUINE PARTS CO
NAPA AUTO PARTS
2999 Circle 75 Pkwy Se, Atlanta, GA 30339-3050
Tel (770) 953-1700 *Founded/Ownrshp* 1928
Sales 15.3MMM *EMP* 39,000
Accts Ernst & Young Llp Atlanta Ge
Tkr Sym GPC *Exch* NYS
SIC 5013 5531 3714 5084 5085 5021 Motor vehicle supplies & new parts; Automotive & home supply stores; Automotive parts; Motor vehicle engines & parts; Industrial machine parts; Materials handling machinery; Industrial supplies; Bearings; Hose, belting & packing; Power transmission equipment & apparatus; Office furniture; Motor vehicle supplies & new parts; Automotive & home supply stores; Automotive parts; Motor vehicle engines & parts; Industrial machine parts; Materials handling machinery; Industrial supplies; Bearings; Hose, belting & packing; Power transmission equipment & apparatus; Office furniture
Ch Bd: Thomas C Gallagher
**Pr:* Paul D Donahue
CFO: Earl Dolive
CFO: Nix Jerry
CFO: Carol B Yancey
Sr VP: Treg S Brown
Sr VP: Charles A Chesnutt
Sr VP: Robert A Milstead
Sr VP: James R Neill
Sr VP: Michael D Orr
Sr VP: Robert J Susor
VP: Thomas K Davis
VP: Christopher T Galla
VP: Robert L Swann
Dir Risk M: Jessica George
Board of Directors: Jerry W Nix, Mary B Bullock, Gary W Rollins, Elizabeth W Camp, E Jenner Wood III, Jean Douville, Gary P Fayard, John R Holder, Donna W Hyland, John D Johns, Robert C Loudermilk Jr, Wendy B Needham

D-U-N-S 03-319-9696
■ GENUINE PARTS CO
NAPA DIST CENTER-HAWAII
(*Suby of* GENUINE PARTS CO) ★
94-141 Leowaena St, Waipahu, HI 96797-2226
Tel (808) 671-4081 *Founded/Ownrshp* 2003
Sales 30.0MM *EMP* 150
SIC 5531 Automobile & truck equipment & parts; Automobile & truck equipment & parts
Pr: Tom Galagher
Pr: Tim Brown

GENUINE PARTS DISTRIBUTORS
See TRACY INDUSTRIES INC

D-U-N-S 12-121-3185
GENWAL RESOURCES INC
UTAH AMERICAN ENERGY
(*Suby of* UTAHAMERICAN ENERGY INC) ★
794 N C Canyon Rd, East Carbon, UT 84520
Tel (435) 888-4000 *Founded/Ownrshp* 1995
Sales 13.8MM^E *EMP* 300
SIC 1222 Bituminous coal-underground mining; Bituminous coal-underground mining
Pr: David Hibbs
Info Man: Rinji Gregersen

D-U-N-S 60-255-8202
■ GENWOODS HOLDCO LLC
(*Suby of* BLOUNT INTERNATIONAL INC) ★
2606 S Il Route 2, Oregon, IL 61061-9685
Tel (815) 732-2141 *Founded/Ownrshp* 2011
Sales 53.8MM^E *EMP* 1,250
SIC 3523 Farm machinery & equipment; Farm machinery & equipment
CFO: Mike Goldberg
VP: Greg Malicki

D-U-N-S 04-322-2160
■ GENWORTH FINANCIAL CAPITAL INC
(*Suby of* GENWORTH FINANCIAL INC) ★
700 Main St, Lynchburg, VA 24504-1448
Tel (434) 845-0911 *Founded/Ownrshp* 1999, 2006
Sales NA *EMP* 2,000
SIC 6411 Insurance agents, brokers & service; Insurance agents, brokers & service
Pr: George Zippel

D-U-N-S 14-236-0416
▲ GENWORTH FINANCIAL INC
6620 W Broad St Ste 270, Richmond, VA 23230-1799
Tel (804) 281-6000 *Founded/Ownrshp* 2003
Sales NA *EMP* 5,300
Tkr Sym GNW *Exch* NYS
SIC 6311 6371 6351 Life insurance; Pensions; Mortgage guarantee insurance; Life insurance; Pensions; Mortgage guarantee insurance
Pr: Thomas J McInerney
Mng Pt: Floyd Franks
CFO: Kelly L Groh
Ofcr: Lori M Evangel
Ex VP: Ward E Bobitz
Ex VP: Scott J McKay
Ex VP: Kevin D Schneider
Ex VP: Daniel J Sheehan IV
Sr VP: Jim Bennison
Sr VP: Marcia A Dall
Sr VP: Cheryl C Whaley
VP: Robert Chinn
VP: Stephen Cooke
VP: Leslie Deich
VP: Paul Haley
VP: Sena Kwawu
VP: Linda Taylor
Dir Risk M: Sheila Klostermann

D-U-N-S 00-794-1198
■ GENWORTH LIFE AND ANNUITY INSURANCE CO (VA)
(*Suby of* GENWORTH LIFE INSURANCE CO) ★
6610 W Broad St, Richmond, VA 23230-1702
Tel (804) 281-6000 *Founded/Ownrshp* 1871, 2004
Sales NA *EMP* 1,200
Accts Kpmg Llp Richmond Virginia
SIC 6311 6211 Life insurance carriers; Investment certificate sales; Life insurance carriers; Investment certificate sales
Ch Bd: Pamela S Schutz
V Ch: Patsy Smith
CFO: Kelly L Groh
Sr VP: Paul A Haley
**Sr VP:* Ronald P Joelson
**Sr VP:* Leon E Roday
**Sr VP:* Geoffrey S Stiff
VP: Jac J Amerell
VP: Pamela C Asbury
MIS Dir: Jeff Peterson

D-U-N-S 06-954-7719
■ GENWORTH LIFE INSURANCE CO
(*Suby of* GENWORTH FINANCIAL INC) ★
6620 W Broad St, Richmond, VA 23230-1716
Tel (804) 281-6000 *Founded/Ownrshp* 2003
Sales NA *EMP* 2,120
SIC 6311 Life insurance carriers; Life insurance carriers
CEO: Thomas J McInerney
CFO: Kelly Groh
**CFO:* Martin P Klein
**CFO:* Richard McKenney
**Ex VP:* Kevin D Schneider
**Sr VP:* Leon Roday

D-U-N-S 03-751-2134
■ GENWORTH MORTGAGE INSURANCE CORP
(*Suby of* GENWORTH FINANCIAL INC) ★
8325 Six Forks Rd, Raleigh, NC 27615-6514
Tel (919) 846-4100 *Founded/Ownrshp* 2007
Sales NA *EMP* 1,000
SIC 6351 8741 Mortgage guarantee insurance; Management services; Mortgage guarantee insurance; Management services
Ch Bd: Thomas H Mann
**CFO:* Marcia A Dal
**Sr VP:* Gerhard A Miller
VP: Jim Bennison
**VP:* Deb Lely
VP: Chris Mock
Dir Risk M: Brenda King

D-U-N-S 14-848-3212
■ GENWORTH NORTH AMERICA CORP
(*Suby of* GENWORTH FINANCIAL INC) ★
6620 W Broad St Bldg 3, Richmond, VA 23230-1721
Tel (804) 281-6000 *Founded/Ownrshp* 2012
Sales NA *EMP* 5,000
SIC 6141 Personal credit institutions; Consumer finance companies; Automobile & consumer finance companies; Personal credit institutions; Consumer finance companies; Automobile & consumer finance companies
Pr: Patrick Kelleher
**Treas:* Gary T Prizzia
**Sr VP:* Ward E Bobitz
**Sr VP:* Leon E Roday
VP: Dan Erhard
**VP:* Scott McKay

GENYSIS BRAND SOLUTIONS
See VMI NUTRITION INC

D-U-N-S 02-301-0804
GENZ-RYAN PLUMBING AND HEATING CO
2200 Highway 13 W, Burnsville, MN 55337-6024
Tel (651) 423-1144 *Founded/Ownrshp* 1949
Sales 37.6MM^E *EMP* 175
SIC 1711 5999 Plumbing contractors; Warm air heating & air conditioning contractor; Plumbing & heating supplies; Plumbing contractors; Warm air heating & air conditioning contractor; Plumbing & heating supplies
CEO: Jon Ryan
**Pr:* Daniel Ryan
**Treas:* Bob Ryan
**VP:* Michael Ryan

D-U-N-S 02-532-2157 IMP
GENZYME CORP
GENZYME THERAPEUTICS DIVISION
(*Suby of* SANOFI US SERVICES INC) ★
500 Kendall St, Cambridge, MA 02142-1108
Tel (617) 252-7500 *Founded/Ownrshp* 2011
Sales 2.9MMM^E *EMP* 12,000
SIC 2835 2834 8071 3842 2836 5122 Enzyme & isoenzyme diagnostic agents; In vitro diagnostics; Pharmaceutical preparations; Biological laboratory; Surgical appliances & supplies; Biological products, except diagnostic; Drugs & drug proprietaries; Enzyme & isoenzyme diagnostic agents; In vitro diagnostics; Pharmaceutical preparations; Biological laboratory; Surgical appliances & supplies; Biological products, except diagnostic; Drugs & drug proprietaries
Pr: David Meeker
COO: Lorenzo Stefani
CFO: Marc Esteva
Bd of Dir: Anne Fitzgerald
Ofcr: Sanjay Rakhade
Assoc Dir: Doug Bornstein
Assoc Dir: Douglas Bornsteing
Assoc Dir: Gordon Brailsford
Assoc Dir: Jennifer Braly
Assoc Dir: Paul Brunelle
Assoc Dir: Claudia Buser
Assoc Dir: Tisha Delmore
Assoc Dir: Janet Deluca
Assoc Dir: Les Deluca
Assoc Dir: Michael Donovan
Assoc Dir: Jim Dougherty
Assoc Dir: Elizabeth Dunn
Assoc Dir: Tarek Ebrahim
Assoc Dir: Nataliya Einhorn
Assoc Dir: Glen Firth
Assoc Dir: Chris Glover

GENZYME THERAPEUTICS DIVISION
See GENZYME CORP

D-U-N-S 00-790-1671
GEO BYERS SONS HOLDING INC
BYERS CAR RENTALS
427 S Hamilton Rd, Columbus, OH 43213-2035
Tel (614) 228-5111 *Founded/Ownrshp* 1921
Sales 189.8MM^E *EMP* 450
SIC 5511 Automobiles, new & used; Pickups, new & used; Vans, new & used; Automobiles, new & used; Pickups, new & used; Vans, new & used
Ch: George W Byers Jr
**Pr:* George W Byers III
**Sec:* Don Grant
**Ex VP:* Frank M Byers Jr
**VP:* Blaine Byers
**VP:* D Jay Du Rivage Jr
VP: George Kauffman
Genl Mgr: Mark Ludwig
CIO: Joshua Lowe
Sls Mgr: Brian Smith
Sales Asso: Calvin Angel

D-U-N-S 07-981-5117
GEO CORRECTIONS AND DETENTION LLC
(*Suby of* G E O) ★
621 Nw 53rd St Ste 700, Boca Raton, FL 33487-8242
Tel (561) 999-7490 *Founded/Ownrshp* 2012
Sales NA *EMP* 10,431
SIC 9223 Correctional institutions; Detention center, government
Ch: George Zoley
CFO: Brian Evans
Treas: Shayn March
VP: James Black
VP: Ron Brack
VP: John Bulfin
VP: Louis Carrillo
VP: David Donahue
VP: Marcel Maier
VP: Amber Martin
VP: Kyle Schiller
VP: Reed Smith

D-U-N-S 07-924-2241
GEO CORRECTIONS HOLDINGS INC (FL)
G E O
(*Suby of* GEO GROUP INC) ★
1 Park Pl, Boca Raton, FL 33487-8235
Tel (432) 267-7911 *Founded/Ownrshp* 2012
Sales 376.2MM^E *EMP* 10,432^E
SIC 6719 Investment holding companies, except banks
CEO: George C Zoley
**Treas:* Marcel Maier
**VP:* Brian R Evans

D-U-N-S 02-934-4785 IMP
GEO DRILLING FLUIDS INC
1431 Union Ave, Bakersfield, CA 93305-5732
Tel (661) 325-5919 *Founded/Ownrshp* 1981
Sales 74.4MM^E *EMP* 75
SIC 5169 1389 7389 Chemicals & allied products; Servicing oil & gas wells; Grinding, precision: commercial or industrial; Chemicals & allied products; Servicing oil & gas wells; Grinding, precision: commercial or industrial
Pr: Jim Clifford
**Treas:* Don Boulet
**VP:* Tom Needham

GEO EROSION & TURF SOLUTIONS
See GETSCO

D-U-N-S 00-480-6659
GEO GRADEL CO (OH)
3135 Front St, Toledo, OH 43605-1009
Tel (419) 691-7123 *Founded/Ownrshp* 1903
Sales 28.5MM *EMP* 65
Accts Rayner Foos Kruse & Irwin Cp
SIC 1794 Excavation & grading, building construction; Excavation & grading, building construction
Pr: John F Gradel
**Treas:* Alan Raven
**VP:* Frederick T Sander
Sfty Dirs: Craig Chall

D-U-N-S 08-490-1776 IMP
GEO GRAPHICS INC (NC)
GEOGRAPHICS PRINTING & DESIGN
3450 Browns Mill Rd Se, Atlanta, GA 30354-2705
Tel (404) 762-3883 *Founded/Ownrshp* 1976
Sales 20.7MM^E *EMP* 110^E
SIC 2752 2791 2789 2759 Commercial printing, offset; Typesetting; Bookbinding & related work; Commercial printing; Commercial printing, offset; Typesetting; Bookbinding & related work; Commercial printing
Pr: Norvin C Hagan
COO: Paul Mullen
CFO: Alex Ruska
VP: Ron Lanio
Exec: Wanda Fincher
CTO: Marty Hynson
DP Exec: Kevin McHale
Manager: Lew Poteat
Snr PM: Sheila Dunn

D-U-N-S 61-270-6465
GEO GROUP INC
621 Nw 53rd St Ste 700, Boca Raton, FL 33487-8242
Tel (561) 893-0101 *Founded/Ownrshp* 2013
Sales 1.6MMM *EMP* 16,292
Accts Grant Thornton Llp Miami Flo
SIC 6798 Real estate investment trusts; Real estate investment trusts
Ch Bd: George C Zoley
Pr: Mark H Underwood
CFO: Brian R Evans
Treas: Shayn P March
Ofcr: Denise Harmon
Ofcr: Jonathan Johnson
Sr VP: John J Bulfin
Sr VP: Tom M Weidsma
VP: Blake Barras
VP: Ronald A Brack
VP: David C Cooper
VP: John G O'Rourke Jr
VP: Alfred P Ramon
VP: Gary Templeton

Exec: Cynthia Gutierrez
Dir Risk M: Kathy Chiarello
Board of Directors: Clarence E Anthony, Norman A Carlson, Anne N Foreman, Richard H Glanton, Christopher C Wheeler, Julie Myers Wood

D-U-N-S 04-164-6787
GEO H WILSON INC
250 Harvey West Blvd, Santa Cruz, CA 95060-2127
Tel (831) 423-9522 *Founded/Ownrshp* 1921
Sales 28.4MM^E *EMP* 85
Accts Burr Pilger Mayer San Jose Ca
SIC 1711 Plumbing, heating, air-conditioning contractors
CEO: James E Wilson
**Pr:* Richard J Wilson
**Treas:* Thomas G Akrop
**VP:* Thomas E Wilson
Dir IT: Tom Lackovic

D-U-N-S 17-640-5892 IMP
GEO HEAT EXCHANGERS LLC
3650 Cypress Ave, Saint Gabriel, LA 70776
Tel (225) 642-8900 *Founded/Ownrshp* 1997
Sales 21.0MM^E *EMP* 75
SIC 3443 Heat exchangers, condensers & components
Pr: Gene E Ohmstede Jr
**IT Man:* August Ohmstede
IT Man: Jason Outlaw
Prd Mgr: Kevin Hill

D-U-N-S 00-107-5555
■ **GEO J FOSTER & CO INC** (NH)
FOSTER'S DAILY DEMOCRAT
(*Suby of* NEW MEDIA INVESTMENT GROUP INC) ★
333 Central Ave, Dover, NH 03820-4127
Tel (603) 740-3400 *Founded/Ownrshp* 1968, 2014
Sales 23.3MM^E *EMP* 300
SIC 2711 Newspapers, publishing & printing; Newspapers, publishing & printing
Pr: Robert H Foster

D-U-N-S 00-796-5528
GEO M HUFF LUMBER CO (CA)
13535 Rosecrans Ave, Santa Fe Springs, CA 90670-5022
Tel (562) 921-1331 *Founded/Ownrshp* 1922
Sales 35.0MM *EMP* 36
SIC 5031

D-U-N-S 05-556-6851
GEO PACIFIC SERVICES INC (CA)
12721 Vicente View Dr, Lakeside, CA 92040-5910
Tel (619) 772-0009 *Founded/Ownrshp* 2011
Sales 24.2MM^E *EMP* 42^E
SIC 5511 Automobiles, new & used
Prin: Jodi Hamilton

D-U-N-S 07-980-5721
GEO REENTRY INC
(*Suby of* GEO GROUP INC) ★
1 Park Pl Ste 700621, Boca Raton, FL 33487-8235
Tel (561) 893-0101 *Founded/Ownrshp* 2015
Sales 22.1MM *EMP* 596
SIC 6798 Real estate investment trusts
Pr: George Zoley
**CFO:* Brian Evans
**Treas:* Shayn March
**VP:* John Bulfin
**VP:* John Hurley
**VP:* Marcel Maier
**VP:* Ann Schlarb
**VP:* David Venturella
**VP:* Tom Wierdsma

D-U-N-S 79-747-0549
GEO REENTRY INC
CORNELL COMPANIES INC
(*Suby of* GEO GROUP INC) ★
621 Nw 53rd St Ste 700, Boca Raton, FL 33487-8242
Tel (561) 893-0101 *Founded/Ownrshp* 2010
Sales 102.5MM^E *EMP* 4,407
SIC 8744 Correctional facility; Correctional facility
Pr: George C Zoley
VP: Blake Barras
VP: Ronald A Brack
VP: John J Bulfin
VP: Louis Carrillo
VP: Brian R Evans
VP: Loren Grayer
VP: Marcel Maier
VP: Shayn March
VP: Laura J Sabol
VP: Laura J Shol
Board of Directors: John Bulfin, Brian Evans, Ann Schlarb, George C Zoley

D-U-N-S 07-980-5752
GEO REENTRY SERVICES LLC
1 Park Pl Ste 700621, Boca Raton, FL 33487-8235
Tel (561) 893-0101 *Founded/Ownrshp* 2012
Sales 10.9MM^E *EMP* 440
SIC 6798 Real estate investment trusts
CEO: George Zoley
**Pr:* Ann Schlarb
**CFO:* Brian Evans
**Treas:* Shayn March
**VP:* Blake Barras
**VP:* John Bulfin
**VP:* Louis Carillo
**VP:* Loren Grayer
**VP:* Marcel Maier

D-U-N-S 04-300-2377
GEO S BUSH & CO INC
825 Ne Multnomah St # 910, Portland, OR 97232-2140
Tel (503) 228-6501 *Founded/Ownrshp* 1887
Sales 22.8MM^E *EMP* 50
SIC 4731 Customhouse brokers; Foreign freight forwarding
Pr: Brian J Welsh
**CEO:* Frank Dausz
**VP:* David J Perrin

GEO SALES-COURTESY CHEVROLET
See COURTESY CHEVROLET CENTER

D-U-N-S 61-070-5183 EXP
GEO SPECIALTY CHEMICALS INC
739 Independence Pkwy, Deer Park, TX 77536
Tel (281) 479-9525 *Founded/Ownrshp* 1993
Sales 24.9MM^E *EMP* 42^E
SIC 5169 Chemicals & allied products
Pr: George Ahearn
Plnt Mgr: Joe Schauef

D-U-N-S 80-131-4378 IMP
GEO SPECIALTY CHEMICALS INC
401 S Earl Ave Ste 3, Lafayette, IN 47904-3606
Tel (765) 448-9412 *Founded/Ownrshp* 1992
Sales 149.3MM^E *EMP* 290
Accts Crowe Chizek & Company Oak B
SIC 2819 Industrial inorganic chemicals; Industrial inorganic chemicals
CEO: Kenneth A Ghazey
VP: Dennis Grandle
VP: Larry Morris
Plnt Mgr: Brad Osborne
Plnt Mgr: Robert Zacker
Ql Cn Mgr: Jim Smith

D-U-N-S 00-173-0522
GEO W KISTLER INC (PA)
KISTLER-OBRIEN FIRE PROTECTION
2210 City Line Rd, Bethlehem, PA 18017-2130
Tel (610) 266-7100 *Founded/Ownrshp* 1933
Sales 86.4MM^E *EMP* 90
SIC 5063 7382 5087 7389 Fire alarm systems; Fire alarm maintenance & monitoring; Fire alarm systems; Fire alarm maintenance & monitoring; Sprinkler systems; Fire protection service other than forestry or public
Pr: George Kistler
**Pr:* Fred W Eberting
**Treas:* Thomas P Derkits
**VP:* Eric F Blasser
VP: Eric Blasser
IT Man: Irene Gutshall

D-U-N-S 03-617-8507 IMP
GEO W PARK SEED CO INC
PARK SEED COMPANY
1 Parkton Ave, Greenwood, SC 29647-0001
Tel (864) 223-8555 *Founded/Ownrshp* 2010
Sales 21.2MM^E *EMP* 200
SIC 5261 5961 5193 0723

D-U-N-S 94-730-8425
GEO-SOLUTIONS INC
1250 5th Ave, New Kensington, PA 15068-6106
Tel (724) 335-7273 *Founded/Ownrshp* 1996
Sales 70.9MM *EMP* 130
Accts Mcgladrey Llp Blue Bell Penn
SIC 1629 8711 Irrigation system construction; Construction & civil engineering; Irrigation system construction; Construction & civil engineering
Pr: Robert M Schindler
**Treas:* Michael F Daly
**VP:* Kenneth Andromalos
**VP:* Richard M Horowitz
**VP:* Peter C Maltese
Site Mgr: Robert Evans
Board of Directors: Michael F Daly, Robert A Fox, Richard M Horowitz, Robert M Schindler

D-U-N-S 02-580-8791 IMP
GEO-SYNTHETICS LLC (WI)
G S I
2401 Pewaukee Rd, Waukesha, WI 53188-6904
Tel (262) 524-7979 *Founded/Ownrshp* 1980, 1994
Sales 29.0MM *EMP* 120^E
SIC 5169 Manmade fibers; Manmade fibers
Pr: John O'Connell
Mtls Mgr: David Rosine
Sfty Mgr: Dan Vogt

D-U-N-S 14-700-9328
GEO-TECHNOLOGY ASSOCIATES INC
(*Suby of* GTA HOLDINGS INC) ★
3445 Box Hll Corp Ctr Dr, Abingdon, MD 21009-1256
Tel (410) 515-9000 *Founded/Ownrshp* 1985
Sales 21.8MM^E *EMP* 223
SIC 8711 Earth science services; Engineering services; Civil engineering; Geophysical exploration, oil & gas field; Engineering services; Civil engineering
Pr: Patrick J Klima
**Treas:* David A Quaranta
**VP:* Amin Rahman
VP: Thomas Wirth

D-U-N-S 02-238-4115
GEOCENT LLC
111 Veterans Memorial Blv, Metairie, LA 70005-3044
Tel (504) 831-1900 *Founded/Ownrshp* 2008
Sales 32.6MM *EMP* 203
SIC 8711 7371 7373 7374 Engineering services; Custom computer programming services; Computer integrated systems design; Data processing & preparation; Engineering services; Custom computer programming services; Computer integrated systems design; Data processing & preparation
IT Man: Cale Husted

D-U-N-S 60-982-2606 EXP
GEOCHEM INTERNATIONAL LLC
1900 Smt Twr Blvd Ste 900, Orlando, FL 32810-5925
Tel (407) 875-9595 *Founded/Ownrshp* 1990
Sales 42.2MM^E *EMP* 9^E
SIC 5169 Synthetic resins, rubber & plastic materials
Pr: David Der Hagopian

D-U-N-S 78-959-6749
GEOCON CONSULTANTS INC
6960 Flanders Dr, San Diego, CA 92121-3992
Tel (858) 558-6900 *Founded/Ownrshp* 1987
Sales 22.2MM^E *EMP* 129
SIC 8748 8711 Environmental consultant; Engineering services; Environmental consultant; Engineering services
CEO: Michael Chapin
**Pr:* Joe Vettel
COO: Joseph Vettel
**VP:* John Hoobs

**Prin:* Neal Berliner
**Prin:* John Juhrend

D-U-N-S 88-415-0165
GEOCONSTRUCTORS INC
GEOSTRUCTURES
413 Browning Ct, Purcellville, VA 20132-6171
Tel (703) 771-9844 *Founded/Ownrshp* 1997
Sales 20.2MM *EMP* 82
Accts Baker Tilly Virchow Krause Ll
SIC 8711 Excavation & grading, building construction; Engineering services; Land preparation construction; Foundation & retaining wall construction; Piles, foundation & marine construction: treated wood
Pr: Michael Cowell
**COO:* Kenneth Leahy
**CFO:* Pietro Sacripanti

D-U-N-S 13-320-3096 IMP/EXP
GEOCYCLE LLC
(*Suby of* HOLCIM (US) INC) ★
6211 N Ann Arbor Rd, Dundee, MI 48131-9527
Tel (734) 529-4380 *Founded/Ownrshp* 2002
Sales 41.1MM^E *EMP* 120
SIC 1629 Waste disposal plant construction
Pr: Rob Davies

D-U-N-S 14-613-6762
GEODESICX INC
616 Innovation Dr, Chesapeake, VA 23320-3846
Tel (757) 312-0790 *Founded/Ownrshp* 2004
Sales 20.3MM^E *EMP* 93
SIC 7371 8711 7373 Custom computer programming services; Engineering services; Computer integrated systems design
CEO: Charles A Schue III
CFO: Wayne Smith
**Ex VP:* Randall E Hall
Dir Surg: Jeff Schleicher
Snr Sftwr: Bill Woodward
DP Dir: Kevin Peterson
Dir Opers: Chris Stout

D-U-N-S 18-928-8710
GEODIGITAL INTERNATIONAL CORP
(*Suby of* GEODIGITAL INTERNATIONAL INC)
137 W Central Ave, Lompoc, CA 93436-2834
Tel (805) 740-0077 *Founded/Ownrshp* 2007
Sales 45.2MM *EMP* 100^E
Accts Deloitte Llp Burlington On C
SIC 7389 Pipeline & power line inspection service; Pipeline & power line inspection service
Pr: Alastair Jenkins
**Treas:* Trevor Kryt
**VP:* Ian Carwardine

D-U-N-S 17-439-4903
GEODIGM CORP
1740 Prior Ave N, Saint Paul, MN 55113-5554
Tel (952) 556-5657 *Founded/Ownrshp* 1996
Sales 98.8MM^E *EMP* 2,038
SIC 8731 Computer (hardware) development; Computer (hardware) development
CEO: Andrew Hofmeister
CFO: Dave Wohlberg
**VP:* Mike Marshall

D-U-N-S 96-225-6777
GEODIS GLOBAL SOLUTIONS
(*Suby of* GEODIS SCO)
4660 Trindle Rd Ste 300, Camp Hill, PA 17011-5610
Tel (717) 610-2737 *Founded/Ownrshp* 2009
Sales 63.0MM^E *EMP* 300
SIC 5045 Computers, peripherals & software; Computers, peripherals & software
CEO: Bertrand Augere

D-U-N-S 82-965-3299
GEODIS GLOBAL SOLUTIONS USA INC
(*Suby of* GEODIS WILSON HOLDING AB)
485c Us Highway 1 S, Iselin, NJ 08830-3037
Tel (732) 362-0600 *Founded/Ownrshp* 1981
Sales 27.3MM^E *EMP* 250
SIC 4731 Freight transportation arrangement; Freight transportation arrangement
CEO: Marie Christine Lombard
**Pr:* Marc Walbaum
COO: Laurence Arseniadis
COO: Nancy Costo
**CFO:* Vito Sicilia
**VP:* Denise Givens

D-U-N-S 02-422-7427
GEODIS WILSON USA INC
18800 8th Ave S Ste 2200, Seatac, WA 98148-1964
Tel (206) 834-9988 *Founded/Ownrshp* 1969
Sales 3.0MM *EMP* 450
SIC 4731 Freight forwarding
Pr: Michael Greco

D-U-N-S 08-566-7327 IMP/EXP
GEODIS WILSON USA INC
(*Suby of* GEODIS WILSON HOLDING AB)
485c Us Highway 1 S # 410, Iselin, NJ 08830-3037
Tel (732) 362-0600 *Founded/Ownrshp* 1999
Sales 610.2MM^E *EMP* 3,900
SIC 4731 4412 4225 Freight transportation arrangement; Deep sea foreign transportation of freight; General warehousing; Freight transportation arrangement; Customhouse brokers; Foreign freight forwarding; Freight consolidation; Deep sea foreign transportation of freight; General warehousing
Pr: John Gallahan
**Sec:* Vitaliano Sicilia
**VP:* Lou Policastro
CIO: Dean Devasia

D-U-N-S 18-357-8462 IMP
GEODYNAMICS INC
10500 W Interstate 20, Millsap, TX 76066-3135
Tel (817) 341-5300 *Founded/Ownrshp* 2003
Sales 85.5MM^E *EMP* 220
SIC 2892 3533 Explosives; Oil & gas field machinery; Explosives; Oil & gas field machinery
CEO: David Wesson
**COO:* Nathan Clark
**CFO:* Durg Kumar

Rgnl Mgr: Jeff Clinton
IT Man: Shaun Rohde
**VP Mfg:* Robert Davis
VP Opers: Pat Byrne
Ql Cn Mgr: Blake Slayton
**VP Sls:* Cameron Kirkpatrick
Sls Dir: Ted Price

D-U-N-S 01-898-2918
GEOENGINEERS INC
600 Stewart St Ste 1700, Seattle, WA 98101-1233
Tel (206) 728-2674 *Founded/Ownrshp* 1980
Sales 42.7MM *EMP* 297
Accts Sweeney Conrad Ps Bellevue
SIC 8711 Consulting engineer; Consulting engineer
Pr: Kurt R Fraese
**Ch Bd:* David P Sauls
**COO:* Dan Campbell
**CFO:* Carrie Rorem
**CIO:* Kurt S Anderson

D-U-N-S 82-484-2249
■ **GEOEYE IMAGERY COLLECTION SYSTEMS INC**
(*Suby of* DIGITALGLOBE INC) ★
2325 Dulle Corne Blvd Ste, Herndon, VA 20171
Tel (303) 684-4800 *Founded/Ownrshp* 2013
Sales 24.7MM^E *EMP* 484
SIC 8713 Photogrammetric engineering; Photogrammetric engineering
CEO: Jeffrey Tarr
**Pr:* James R Clapper
**Pr:* Martin C Faga
**Pr:* Lawrence A Hough
**Pr:* James M Simon Jr
**Pr:* William W Sprague
**COO:* William Schuster
Sr VP: Paolo Colombi
VP: Mg Chandrasekhar
VP: Lee Demitry
**Prin:* Joseph M Ahearn
Board of Directors: Joseph M Ahearn, Martin C Faga, Michael Horn, Lawrence A Hough, Roberta Lenczowski, James M Simon Jr, William W Sprague

D-U-N-S 79-788-4587
■ **GEOEYE LLC**
(*Suby of* DIGITALGLOBE INC) ★
2325 Dulles Corner Blvd # 1000, Herndon, VA 20171-6123
Tel (703) 480-7500 *Founded/Ownrshp* 2013
Sales 151.6MM^E *EMP* 743^E
SIC 4899 Satellite earth stations; Satellite earth stations
Pt: Tara Byrnes
Pt: Shaun Callaghan
**CEO:* Matthew M O Connell
CFO: Henry E Dubois
Sr VP: Steven P Wallach
VP: Steven R Balthazor
VP: James M Craig
VP: Dean Edmundson
VP: Chris Glanzmann
VP: Ramsey W Price
VP: Randall J Scherago

D-U-N-S 15-604-0847 IMP
GEOGLOBAL PARTNERS LLC
(*Suby of* OASE GMBH)
1727 Old Okeechobee Rd, West Palm Beach, FL 33409-5225
Tel (561) 598-6000 *Founded/Ownrshp* 2014
Sales 28.9MM *EMP* 53
SIC 5023 5191 Decorative home furnishings & supplies; Garden supplies; Decorative home furnishings & supplies; Garden supplies
Pr: Douglas Ward
**VP:* Daniel Owen

D-U-N-S 11-508-8874
GEOGRAPHIC EXPEDITIONS INC
INNERASIA TRAVEL GROUP
1008 General Kennedy Ave # 3, San Francisco, CA 94129-1731
Tel (415) 922-0448 *Founded/Ownrshp* 1982
Sales 30.0MM *EMP* 45
SIC 4725 8742 Tour operators; Transportation consultant; Tour operators; Transportation consultant
Ch Bd: George Doubleday
**Pr:* James D Sano
VP: Vassi Koutsaftis

D-U-N-S 82-670-6848
GEOGRAPHIC INFORMATION SERVICES INC
G/I/S
2100 Riverchase Ctr # 105, Hoover, AL 35244-1858
Tel (205) 941-0442 *Founded/Ownrshp* 1990
Sales 24.9MM *EMP* 112
SIC 7372 7379 7371 8711 Prepackaged software; Computer related consulting services; Custom computer programming services; Custom computer programming services; Engineering services
Pr: Lee Lichlyter
**Ch Bd:* Dale Dunham
**CFO:* Carrie Green
Treas: Geraldine Dunham
Exec: Joe Howell
Genl Mgr: Loretta Fowler
Genl Mgr: Katie Irwin
Genl Mgr: Keith King
Off Mgr: Tonya Brown
CTO: Dan Levine
DP Dir: Gary Melendez

GEOGRAPHICS PRINTING & DESIGN
See GEO GRAPHICS INC

D-U-N-S 00-200-0474 IMP
GEOKINETICS ACQUISITION CO (DE)
PGS ONSHORE
(*Suby of* PETROLEUM GEO-SERVICES ASA)
15150 Memorial Dr # 1009, Houston, TX 77079-4304
Tel (281) 509-8000 *Founded/Ownrshp* 1997
Sales 22.3MM^E *EMP* 150
SIC 1382 Seismograph surveys; Seismograph surveys
Pr: Eric Wersich

Pr: Sven O Havig
**VP:* Jerry Courtney

D-U-N-S 07-464-3768 IMP/EXP
GEOKINETICS INC
1500 Citywest Blvd # 800, Houston, TX 77042-2380
Tel (713) 850-7600 *Founded/Ownrshp* 1980
Sales 2.6MMM^E *EMP* 5,695^E
Accts Uhy Llp Houston Texas
SIC 1382 7374 Seismograph surveys; Data processing service; Seismograph surveys; Data processing service
Pr: David J Crowley
**CFO:* Gary L Pittman
Ex VP: Lee Parker
VP: James Bogardus
VP: Gerry Gilbert
VP: Tom Lewis
VP: Troy Matherne
VP: William L Moll Jr
VP: Arnaud Pham
VP: Hugh Shields
VP: Glenn Sniezek
VP: John Vance
VP: Alejandra Veltmann
VP: Richard Verm
Board of Directors: Robert L Cabes Jr, Christopher M Harte, Christopher D Strong, Anthony Tripodo, Steven A Webster, William R Ziegler

D-U-N-S 17-930-2021
GEOKINETICS MANAGEMENT INC
GRANT GEOPHYSICAL
(*Suby of* GEOKINETICS INC) ★
1500 City W Blvd Ste 800, Houston, TX 77042
Tel (281) 870-8506 *Founded/Ownrshp* 2006
Sales 178.1MM^E *EMP* 1,000
SIC 1382 Seismograph surveys; Seismograph surveys
Pr: Richard F Miles

D-U-N-S 09-550-8149 IMP
GEOKON INC
48 Spencer St, Lebanon, NH 03766-1363
Tel (603) 448-1562 *Founded/Ownrshp* 1979
Sales 30.3MM *EMP* 100
SIC 3829 Vibration meters, analyzers & calibrators; Vibration meters, analyzers & calibrators
Pr: James Barrie Sellers
**Treas:* Jack Taylor
**VP:* John B McRae
Dir IT: Colin Judd
IT Man: Kevin Brook
Sftwr Eng: Wayne Tucker
Mtls Mgr: Duane Perron
Prd Mgr: Stuart Crocker
Sales Exec: Martin Gradijan
Sales Asso: Chris Brun

D-U-N-S 79-804-2685
GEOLOGIC ASSOCIATES INC
2777 E Guasti Rd, Ontario, CA 91761-1251
Tel (909) 626-2282 *Founded/Ownrshp* 1991
Sales 25.7MM^E *EMP* 106
SIC 8711 8748 8999 Engineering services; Business consulting; Geological consultant; Engineering services; Business consulting; Geological consultant
CEO: Gary L Lass
Off Admin: Eden Paul

D-U-N-S 14-786-5604
GEOLOGICAL SURVEY OF ALABAMA
(*Suby of* STATE OF ALABAMA) ★
420 Hackberry Ln, Tuscaloosa, AL 35487-0001
Tel (205) 247-3592 *Founded/Ownrshp* 1848
Sales NA *EMP* 5,024^E
SIC 9199

D-U-N-S 62-172-3022
GEOLOGICS CORP
5285 Shawnee Rd Ste 300, Alexandria, VA 22312-2328
Tel (703) 750-1583 *Founded/Ownrshp* 1993
Sales 57.0MM *EMP* 600
Accts Cherry Bekaert Llp Tysons Cor
SIC 8748 8711 Systems analysis & engineering consulting services; Environmental consultant; Telecommunications consultant; Consulting engineer; Systems analysis & engineering consulting services; Environmental consultant; Telecommunications consultant; Consulting engineer
Pr: Fernando J Arroyo
VP: Don Fernandez
**VP:* Roberto Lopez-Aparicio
Software D: Devin Blakley
Software D: Tracey Fritz

D-U-N-S 79-429-8075 IMP
■ **GEOMENTUM INC**
INTERPUBLIC GROUP OF CO
(*Suby of* INTERPUBLIC GROUP OF COMPANIES INC) ★
3025 Highland Pkwy # 700, Downers Grove, IL 60515-5506
Tel (630) 729-7500 *Founded/Ownrshp* 2004
Sales 62.4MM^E *EMP* 325
SIC 2711 7311 Newspapers; Advertising agencies; Newspapers; Advertising agencies
CEO: Sean Finnegan
**Chf Mktg O:* Tony Bombacino
VP: Judi Crisileo
VP: Sean Seeling Dp
**VP:* Larry Fuchs
VP: Dan Gilmartin
VP: Karin Kasper
VP: Steve Muller
VP: Randy Novak
VP: Earl Potter
VP: Tim Rodriguez
**VP:* Robin Zeldin

D-U-N-S 84-500-5730
GEOMETRIC AMERICAS INC
GEOMETRIC ENGINEERING
(*Suby of* GEOMETRIC LIMITED)
50 Kirts Blvd Ste A, Troy, MI 48084-5257
Tel (248) 404-3500 *Founded/Ownrshp* 2008
Sales 68.2MM^E *EMP* 502^E
SIC 8711 Engineering services; Engineering services
Ch Bd: Jamshyd N Godrej
**Pr:* Michael M Pelkey
**CEO:* Manu M Parpia
Prgrm Mgr: Rick Blanchard
Prgrm Mgr: Amod Ghangurde

GEOMETRIC ENGINEERING
See GEOMETRIC AMERICAS INC

D-U-N-S 04-789-7533
GEOMETRICS INC
(*Suby of* OYO CORP USA) ★
2190 Fortune Dr, San Jose, CA 95131-1815
Tel (408) 428-4244 *Founded/Ownrshp* 1969
Sales 26.6MM *EMP* 80
SIC 3829 Geophysical or meteorological electronic equipment
Pr: Mark Prouty
**CFO:* Rod Bravo
VP: Linda Forkapa
VP: Ross Johnson
**VP:* Ron Royal
Sales Exec: Deborah Underwood
**VP Sls:* Robert Huggins
Sls Mgr: Craig Lippus

D-U-N-S 14-417-8683
GEONIX OPERATING LP
2008 N Longview St, Kilgore, TX 75662-6830
Tel (903) 983-3249 *Founded/Ownrshp* 2003
Sales 22.0MM^E *EMP* 20^E
SIC 5082 Oil field equipment
Genl Pt: Terry George

D-U-N-S 03-621-1758 IMP
GEOPHARMA INC
INNOVATIVE HEALTH PRODUCTS
6950 Bryan Dairy Rd, Largo, FL 33777-1606
Tel (727) 258-4830 *Founded/Ownrshp* 1985
Sales 33.7MM^E *EMP* 271
SIC 2834 8742 5912 Pharmaceutical preparations; Hospital & health services consultant; Drug stores & proprietary stores; Pharmaceutical preparations; Hospital & health services consultant; Drug stores & proprietary stores
Pr: George Stuart

D-U-N-S 05-782-1704
GEOPHYSICAL SURVEY SYSTEMS INC
GSSI
(*Suby of* OYO CORP USA) ★
40 Simon St Ste 1, Nashua, NH 03060-3075
Tel (603) 893-1109 *Founded/Ownrshp* 1990
Sales 23.4MM *EMP* 5^E
SIC 3812 Radar systems & equipment; Radar systems & equipment
Pr: Christopher C Hawekotte
**Treas:* Donald K Walczyk
IT Man: Cheryl Giroux
Sftwr Eng: Jake Kirk
Ql Cn Mgr: Laurie Hill

GEOPROBE SYSTEMS
See KEJR INC

D-U-N-S 00-719-4707 IMP/EXP
GEORG FISCHER CENTRAL PLASTICS LLC (OK)
(*Suby of* GEORG FISCHER AG)
39605 Independence St, Shawnee, OK 74804-9203
Tel (405) 273-6302 *Founded/Ownrshp* 1955, 2008
Sales 168.0MM *EMP* 530
SIC 3089

D-U-N-S 00-300-1435 IMP
GEORG FISCHER HARVEL LLC (PA)
GF HARVEL
(*Suby of* GEORG FISCHER AG)
300 Kuebler Rd, Easton, PA 18040-9290
Tel (610) 252-7355 *Founded/Ownrshp* 1964, 2012
Sales 51.3MM^E *EMP* 269
SIC 3084 Plastics pipe; Plastics pipe
Pr: Earl E Wismer
**COO:* Patrick M Foose
**Treas:* Virginia Happel
**Sr VP:* Evan Wismer
**VP:* John Mattavi
Plnt Mgr: Scott Happel
Sls Dir: Greg Martino

GEORG FISCHER PIPING
See GEORGE FISCHER LLC

D-U-N-S 00-833-6562 IMP
GEORG FISCHER SIGNET LLC (CA)
(*Suby of* GEORG FISCHER SPA)
3401 Aero Jet Ave, El Monte, CA 91731-2801
Tel (626) 572-9280 *Founded/Ownrshp* 1953
Sales 25.9MM^E *EMP* 90
SIC 3823 Industrial process control instruments; Industrial process control instruments
VP: Martin Neil

D-U-N-S 95-694-9788 IMP
GEORG FISCHER SLOANE LLC
(*Suby of* GEORGE FISCHER INC) ★
7777 Sloane Dr, Little Rock, AR 72206-3872
Tel (501) 490-7777 *Founded/Ownrshp* 2010
Sales 75.7MM^E *EMP* 150
SIC 3089 Fittings for pipe, plastic; Hardware, plastic; Plastic hardware & building products; Fittings for pipe, plastic; Hardware, plastic; Plastic hardware & building products
Pr: John Pregenzer
**CFO:* Mads Joergensen
Bd of Dir: Georg Fischer
**VP:* Paul Mastro
Sls Dir: Darryl Edwards
Mktg Mgr: Michael Neubert
Manager: Ornella Giraudo
Manager: Holger Hoffmann
Manager: Rich McArthur
Manager: Ryan Warner
Sls Mgr: Bob Manson

D-U-N-S 00-248-3667
GEORGE & LYNCH INC
150 Lafferty Ln, Dover, DE 19901-7205
Tel (302) 736-3031 *Founded/Ownrshp* 1923, 1994
Sales 114.0MM^E *EMP* 300^E
SIC 1623 1611 1629 1731 Water, sewer & utility lines; Highway & street construction; Marine construction; Environmental system control installation; Water, sewer & utility lines; Highway & street construction; Marine construction; Environmental system control installation
CEO: William B Robinson
**Pr:* Dennis J Dinger
**CFO:* Barry G Hudson
**VP:* Leonard Brooks
**VP:* Jeffrey I Norman
**VP:* David W McGuigan

D-U-N-S 03-238-0263
GEORGE A ISRAEL JR INC
144 Watts St, Jacksonville, FL 32204-1844
Tel (904) 355-7867 *Founded/Ownrshp* 1952
Sales 22.3MM^E *EMP* 33
SIC 5075 Fans, heating & ventilation equipment; Air conditioning equipment, except room units
Pr: George A Israel III
**VP:* Kevin Cordero
IT Man: Kim Kish
Sls Mgr: Kevin Sides

D-U-N-S 79-454-2084 EXP
GEORGE AMARAL RANCHES INC
25453 Iverson Rd, Gonzales, CA 93926-9403
Tel (831) 679-2977 *Founded/Ownrshp* 1989
Sales 41.0MM *EMP* 100
SIC 0161 Lettuce & leaf vegetable farms; Broccoli farm; Cabbage farm; Celery farm; Lettuce & leaf vegetable farms; Broccoli farm; Cabbage farm; Celery farm
Pr: George Amaral
Genl Mgr: Chris Amaral

D-U-N-S 03-518-6105
GEORGE BROTHERS PROPANE & FERTILIZER CORP
1001 S Saunders Ave, Sutton, NE 68979-2072
Tel (402) 773-5561 *Founded/Ownrshp* 1960
Sales 27.5MM^E *EMP* 45
SIC 5191 5984 5541 Fertilizer & fertilizer materials; Chemicals, agricultural; Propane gas, bottled; Gasoline service stations
Pr: Donald George
**VP:* Betty B George

D-U-N-S 04-957-6721
GEORGE BUTLER ASSOCIATES INC
9801 Renner Blvd Ste 300, Lenexa, KS 66219-8117
Tel (913) 492-0400 *Founded/Ownrshp* 1969
Sales 47.0MM *EMP* 160
SIC 8711 8712

D-U-N-S 03-997-5172
GEORGE C HOPKINS CONSTRUCTION CO INC
919 W Glenoaks Blvd, Glendale, CA 91202-2725
Tel (323) 245-1136 *Founded/Ownrshp* 1981
Sales 29.0MM *EMP* 17
Accts Russ & Allcroft Cpas Glendal
SIC 1542 Commercial & office building contractors; Commercial & office building contractors
Pr: Gary J Hopkins
**VP:* David Sparhawk
**VP:* Jeffery Ward
Sfty Mgr: John Camphouse
VP Sls: Bill Kane

D-U-N-S 02-790-2840
GEORGE CHEVROLET
17000 Lakewood Blvd, Bellflower, CA 90706-5594
Tel (562) 925-2500 *Founded/Ownrshp* 1961
Sales 43.3MM^E *EMP* 100
SIC 5511 7515 7538 Automobiles, new & used; Passenger car leasing; General automotive repair shops; Automobiles, new & used; Passenger car leasing; General automotive repair shops
Pr: Jeffery Estabrooks
**VP:* Patricia Estabrooks
IT Man: Judy Warner
Sls Mgr: Allen Bill
Sls Mgr: Jose Garcia
Sls Mgr: John Good
Sales Asso: Juana Araujo
Sales Asso: Andres Cestoni
Sales Asso: Jerry Martinez
Sales Asso: Frank Romero
Sales Asso: Richard Torres

D-U-N-S 17-390-8666
GEORGE CHIALA FARMS INC
CHIALA, GEORGE PACKING
15500 Hill Rd, Morgan Hill, CA 95037-9516
Tel (408) 778-0562 *Founded/Ownrshp* 1972
Sales 51.8MM^E *EMP* 120
SIC 0161 0723 Vegetables & melons; Vegetable crops market preparation services
Pr: George Chiala Sr
**CFO:* Alice Chiala
**VP:* George Chiala Jr
Exec: Soheila Guerin
Plnt Mgr: Pat Connelly

GEORGE COLEMAN FORD
See GEORGE COLEMAN MOTOR CO INC

D-U-N-S 03-627-8950
GEORGE COLEMAN MOTOR CO INC (SC)
GEORGE COLEMAN FORD
47 Plaza Dr, Travelers Rest, SC 29690-1683
Tel (864) 834-6060 *Founded/Ownrshp* 1939
Sales 20.4MM^E *EMP* 45
SIC 5511 7538 Automobiles, new & used; General automotive repair shops
Pr: Greg L Coleman
Off Mgr: Ann Mansfield

D-U-N-S 19-301-1046
GEORGE COUNTY SCHOOL DISTRICT
5152 Main St, Lucedale, MS 39452-6533
Tel (601) 947-6993 *Founded/Ownrshp* 1995
Sales 30.8MM *EMP* 400
SIC 8211 Public elementary & secondary schools; Public elementary & secondary schools
Teacher Pr: Sonia Hudson
HC Dir: Jodi McMillian

D-U-N-S 01-450-0441
GEORGE D MANDERBACH INC
MANDERBACH FORD
4450 5th Street Hwy, Temple, PA 19560-1741
Tel (610) 929-3683 *Founded/Ownrshp* 1947
Sales 32.6MM^E *EMP* 70
SIC 5511 New & used car dealers; Automobiles, new & used; Pickups, new & used; Trucks, tractors & trailers: new & used; New & used car dealers; Automobiles, new & used; Pickups, new & used; Trucks, tractors & trailers: new & used
Pr: George M Manderbach
**Treas:* Gary M Manderbach
**VP:* Lynn R Manderbach

D-U-N-S 01-424-5906
GEORGE DELALLO CO INC
DE LALLO ITALIAN FOODS
1 Delallo Way, Mount Pleasant, PA 15666-2773
Tel (724) 925-2222 *Founded/Ownrshp* 1954
Sales 176.1MM^E *EMP* 300
SIC 5149 Groceries & related products; Pasta & rice; Groceries & related products; Pasta & rice
Pr: Francis Delallo
**Pr:* Francis X Delallo
**Treas:* Philip M Polsinelli
Rgnl Mgr: Michele Sturdivant
IT Man: Jim Beranek
Natl Sales: Ron Martin
Sls Mgr: Larry Coon

D-U-N-S 05-295-6083
GEORGE E BOOTH CO INC
8202 W 10th St, Indianapolis, IN 46214-2432
Tel (317) 247-0100 *Founded/Ownrshp* 1966
Sales 28.2MM^E *EMP* 45
SIC 5084 Instruments & control equipment
Pr: George E Booth III
**VP:* John Liles
Tech Mgr: Douglas Manning
Sls Mgr: Troy Daves
Sls Mgr: Frank Traikovich
Sales Asso: Todd Eaton

D-U-N-S 00-695-3392 IMP
GEORGE E WARREN CORP
3001 Ocean Dr Ste 203, Vero Beach, FL 32963-1992
Tel (772) 778-7100 *Founded/Ownrshp* 1982
Sales 103.7MM *EMP* 35
Accts Grant Thornton Llp Orlando F
SIC 5171 Petroleum bulk stations; Petroleum bulk stations
Pr: Thomas L Corr
**Treas:* Mike George
Ofcr: Norma Mellor
VP: Joseph Corr
VP: Darrell Weakland
Admn Mgr: Richard Cobb

D-U-N-S 03-397-0062 IMP/EXP
GEORGE F BROCKE & SONS INC
901 Hwy 3, Kendrick, ID 83537
Tel (208) 289-4231 *Founded/Ownrshp* 1942
Sales 44.2MM *EMP* 35^E
SIC 0723

D-U-N-S 01-472-9974
GEORGE F KEMPF SUPPLY CO INC
5200 Grays Ave, Philadelphia, PA 19143-5817
Tel (215) 724-9941 *Founded/Ownrshp* 1950
Sales 83.2MM^E *EMP* 55
SIC 5039 Prefabricated structures; Glass construction materials
Pr: Robert W Kempf
**CFO:* John Savelloni
Sls Mgr: Tucker Lownes
Sales Asso: Brian Burke
Sales Asso: Mike Gadd

GEORGE FERN COMPANY
See FERN EXPOSITION SERVICES LLC

D-U-N-S 04-928-2908 IMP/EXP
GEORGE FISCHER INC
(*Suby of* GEORG FISCHER AG)
3401 Aero Jet Ave, El Monte, CA 91731-2801
Tel (626) 571-2770 *Founded/Ownrshp* 1972
Sales 259.3MM^E *EMP* 1,000^E
SIC 3599 5074 3829 3559 Pipes & fittings, plastic; Electrical discharge machining (EDM); Testing equipment: abrasion, shearing strength, etc.; Foundry machinery & equipment; Electrical discharge machining (EDM); Pipes & fittings, plastic; Testing equipment: abrasion, shearing strength, etc.; Foundry machinery & equipment
CEO: Chris Blumer
VP: Martin Neil
**VP:* Daniel Vaterlaus
IT Man: Tobias Auer
IT Man: Steve Wells
Opers Mgr: Joe Longoria

D-U-N-S 06-615-6001 IMP
GEORGE FISCHER LLC
GEORG FISCHER PIPING
(*Suby of* GEORGE FISCHER INC) ★
9271 Jeronimo Rd, Irvine, CA 92618-1906
Tel (714) 731-8800 *Founded/Ownrshp* 1967
Sales 100.0MM^E *EMP* 115
SIC 5051 5085 Pipe & tubing, steel; Valves & fittings; Pipe & tubing, steel; Valves & fittings
COO: Yves Studer
Ex VP: Oshaben Daniel
VP: Paul Galvin
VP: Keith Jansen
VP: Thomas Sixsmith
Mng Dir: Rocky Wade
Area Mgr: Gary Boushell

Area Mgr: Jon Cleveland
Area Mgr: Mendy Gordon
Area Mgr: Brett Hicks
Area Mgr: Greg Lange

D-U-N-S 03-408-1703
GEORGE FOUNDATION (TX)
215 Morton Pmb, Richmond, TX 77469
Tel (281) 342-6109 *Founded/Ownrshp* 1945
Sales 20.3MM^E *EMP* 19^E
SIC 6732 8699 Charitable trust management; Charitable trust management; Charitable organization
Ex Dir: Roger Adamson
Bd of Dir: Nell Ciancarelli
CTO: Jennifer Gilbert
Opers Mgr: Rocky Parr

D-U-N-S 01-075-5106
GEORGE FOX UNIVERSITY
414 N Meridian St, Newberg, OR 97132-2697
Tel (503) 538-8383 *Founded/Ownrshp* 1891
Sales 99.0MM *EMP* 450
Accts Moss Adams Llp Portland Ore
SIC 8221 College, except junior; College, except junior
Pr: Robin Baker
**CFO:* G Michael Goins
Assoc VP: Rebecca Hernandez
Ex VP: Ted Allen
VP: Brad Lau
VP: Rob Westervelt
Exec: Dianna McIntyre
Psych: William Buhrow
Doctor: Kathy Weiss
Art Dir: Darryl Brown

D-U-N-S 60-270-0262
■ **GEORGE G KERASOTES CORP**
(*Suby of* CARMIKE CINEMAS INC) ★
1301 1st Ave, Columbus, GA 31901-2109
Tel (706) 576-3400 *Founded/Ownrshp* 2005
Sales 3.2MM^E *EMP* 1,000
SIC 7832 Exhibitors, itinerant: motion picture; Exhibitors, itinerant: motion picture
Pr: Beth Kerasotes
Ex VP: Jeff Cole
Ex VP: Marge Kerasotes
Sys/Dir: Cyndi Fleck

D-U-N-S 06-252-0366
GEORGE G SHARP INC
160 Broadway Fl 8, New York, NY 10038-4230
Tel (212) 732-2800 *Founded/Ownrshp* 1983
Sales 74.2MM^E *EMP* 450
SIC 3731 4225 8712 Shipbuilding & repairing; Commercial cargo ships, building & repairing; Military ships, building & repairing; General warehousing; Architectural services; Shipbuilding & repairing; Commercial cargo ships, building & repairing; Military ships, building & repairing; General warehousing; Architectural services
Ch Bd: I Hilary Rolih
Pr: Allen Chin
COO: CHI-Cheng Yang
Treas: Al F Seneca
IT Man: Nagen Burra

GEORGE GEE AUTOMOTIVE CO.
See GEE INVESTMENTS INC

D-U-N-S 07-980-1296
GEORGE GUND FOUNDATION
45 W Prospect Ave # 1845, Cleveland, OH 44115-1008
Tel (216) 241-3114 *Founded/Ownrshp* 1952
Sales 43.5MM *EMP* 11
SIC 6732 Charitable trust management; Educational trust management; Charitable trust management; Educational trust management
Pr: Geoffrey Gund
Ofcr: John Mitterholzer
Ex Dir: Marjorie Carlson

D-U-N-S 95-637-5752
GEORGE HANCOCK INC
ELTECH ELECTRIC
2123 W Elmore St, Seattle, WA 98199-1238
Tel (206) 213-0048 *Founded/Ownrshp* 2005
Sales 44.7MM^E *EMP* 141
SIC 1731 Electrical work; Electrical work
CEO: George Hancock
**Pr:* Jordan Sinclair
Off Mgr: Jessica Jensen

D-U-N-S 04-694-0490
GEORGE HARMS CONSTRUCTION CO INC
HARMS EXCAVATING
62 Yellow Brook Rd, Freehold, NJ 07728-8428
Tel (732) 938-4004 *Founded/Ownrshp* 1960
Sales 55.7MM^E *EMP* 200
SIC 1611 1622 General contractor, highway & street construction; Highway construction, elevated; General contractor, highway & street construction; Highway construction, elevated
Pr: George Harms
**Pr:* Edward Nyland
VP: Robert Harms
IT Man: Bruce Kunz

D-U-N-S 07-169-6066
GEORGE HILLS CO INC (CA)
3043 Gold Canal Dr # 200, Rancho Cordova, CA 95670-6393
Tel (916) 859-4800 *Founded/Ownrshp* 1954
Sales NA *EMP* 55
SIC 6411 Insurance adjusters
Pr: Michael J Kielty
COO: John Chaquica
Brnch Mgr: Rodger Hayton
**Brnch Mgr:* Elizabeth Miller

D-U-N-S 00-433-2359
GEORGE I REITZ & SONS INC (PA)
BROOKVILLE TANKS
17214 Route 36, Brookville, PA 15825-4640
Tel (814) 849-2308 *Founded/Ownrshp* 1944
Sales 28.5MM^E *EMP* 45
Accts Mauthe Yutzey & Gabler Llc
SIC 5084 3443 7692 3714 3444 3441 Pumps & pumping equipment; Tanks, standard or custom fabricated: metal plate; Welding repair; Motor vehicle parts & accessories; Sheet metalwork; Fabricated structural metal
Pr: Alan L Reitz
Plnt Mgr: Larry Kirkman
Sls Mgr: Lisa Stair

D-U-N-S 00-837-8887
■ **GEORGE INDUSTRIES**
(*Suby of* VALMONT INDUSTRIES INC) ★
4116 Whiteside St, Los Angeles, CA 90063-1619
Tel (323) 264-6660 *Founded/Ownrshp* 1953
Sales 44.3MM^E *EMP* 380
SIC 3471 3479 Anodizing (plating) of metals or formed products; Cleaning & descaling metal products; Plating of metals or formed products; Aluminum coating of metal products; Anodizing (plating) of metals or formed products; Cleaning & descaling metal products; Plating of metals or formed products; Aluminum coating of metal products
Pr: Jeff Briggs
VP: Thomas Sanderson
Off Mgr: Miima Taddi

D-U-N-S 02-243-6554
GEORGE J FALTER CO
3501 Benson Ave, Baltimore, MD 21227-1098
Tel (410) 646-3641 *Founded/Ownrshp* 1935
Sales 83.0MM^E *EMP* 130
SIC 5194 5145 5141 5015 Tobacco & tobacco products; Confectionery; Candy; Food brokers; Automotive supplies, used; Tobacco & tobacco products; Confectionery; Candy; Food brokers; Automotive supplies, used
CEO: Frank H Falter Jr
**Pr:* Frank H Falter III
Sls Mgr: Buddy Bernstein
Sls Mgr: Dan Pepe

D-U-N-S 07-599-2743
GEORGE J HAYDEN INC
HAYDEN ELECTRIC
235 E Maple St, Hazleton, PA 18201-6000
Tel (570) 455-6109 *Founded/Ownrshp* 1975
Sales 36.3MM^E *EMP* 90
SIC 1731 General electrical contractor; General electrical contractor
Pr: George J Hayden Sr
**Sec:* Florence Hayden
**VP:* George S Hayden
IT Man: Sara McKinley
VP Sls: Andrea Martz
Pr Mgr: Nancy Collison

D-U-N-S 00-892-8764
GEORGE J IGEL & CO INC (OH)
2040 Alum Creek Dr, Columbus, OH 43207-1714
Tel (614) 445-8421 *Founded/Ownrshp* 1911
Sales 158.5MM^E *EMP* 892
SIC 1794 1623 6552 Excavation & grading, building construction; Sewer line construction; Water main construction; Subdividers & developers; Excavation & grading, building construction; Sewer line construction; Water main construction; Subdividers & developers
Pr: John B Igel
**CFO:* Jeffrey Fries
VP: George Igel
VP: Brian Van Deventer
**VP:* Ronald L Wallace
Sfty Dirs: Mary So
Sales Exec: Dave Downs
Snr Mgr: Brian Rinehart
Board of Directors: William Igel, William McCauley, Robert Werth

GEORGE J. SHAW CONSTRUCTION
See BEUTLER INC

D-U-N-S 01-416-5047 IMP
GEORGE JHOWE CO
HOWE COFFEE CO
629 W Main St, Grove City, PA 16127-1109
Tel (724) 458-9410 *Founded/Ownrshp* 1927
Sales 78.9MM^E *EMP* 100
SIC 5145 Nuts, salted or roasted; Candy; Nuts, salted or roasted; Candy
Pr: Dan Phillips
**Pr:* Ernest D May
**Treas:* Joseph A Trinch
**VP:* Richard Beech
Sls&Mrk Ex: Joe Klimchak

GEORGE JR RPUB UN PRSCHOOL DST
See WILLIAM GEORGE AGENCY FOR CHILDRENS SERVICES INC

D-U-N-S 06-872-9102
GEORGE JUNIOR REPUBLIC IN PENNSYLVANIA
233 George Junior Rd, Grove City, PA 16127-4417
Tel (724) 458-9330 *Founded/Ownrshp* 1909
Sales 38.4MM *EMP* 700
Accts Stillwaggon & Mcgill Llc Grov
SIC 8361 Juvenile correctional home; Home for the emotionally disturbed; Juvenile correctional home; Home for the emotionally disturbed
Prin: Richard Losasso
COO: Jeff Mooris
CFO: Michell Gerwick
Dir IT: Bryan Redfoot

GEORGE K. BAUM & COMPANY
See GEORGE K BAUM HOLDINGS INC

D-U-N-S 04-956-5385
GEORGE K BAUM & CO (MO)
(*Suby of* GEORGE K BAUM & CO) ★
4801 Main St Ste 500, Kansas City, MO 64112-2551
Tel (816) 474-1100 *Founded/Ownrshp* 1928, 1993
Sales 55.0MM^E *EMP* 220
SIC 6211 Investment bankers; Investment bankers
Ch: Jonathan E Baum
Pr: William H Coughlin
CFO: Dana L Bjornson
Ex VP: Nick J Quatrochi
Sr VP: Renie Lamkin
Sr VP: Neal Skiver
VP: Alan Gafford
VP: Alexandra Iseman
VP: Donna Locascio
VP: Debra Serino

D-U-N-S 00-710-0407
GEORGE K BAUM HOLDINGS INC
GEORGE K. BAUM & COMPANY
4801 Main St Ste 500, Kansas City, MO 64112-2551
Tel (816) 474-1100 *Founded/Ownrshp* 1993
Sales 66.4MM^E *EMP* 250
SIC 6211 Investment bankers; Investment bankers
Ch Bd: Jonathan Baum
**Pr:* William Coughlin
**CFO:* Dana Bjornson
Sr VP: Julie Villarreal
**VP:* Janice Bolin

D-U-N-S 87-442-2749
GEORGE KAISER FAMILY FOUNDATION
7030 S Yale Ave Ste 600, Tulsa, OK 74136-5749
Tel (918) 392-1612 *Founded/Ownrshp* 1999
Sales 154.3MM *EMP* 12
SIC 8641 Civic social & fraternal associations
Prin: Stanton Doyle
Chf Inves: Robert Thomas

D-U-N-S 05-445-7192
GEORGE KOCH SONS LLC
(*Suby of* KOCH ENTERPRISES INC) ★
10 S 11th Ave, Evansville, IN 47712-6800
Tel (812) 465-9600 *Founded/Ownrshp* 1998
Sales 85.1MM *EMP* 173^E
Accts Harding Shymanski And Company
SIC 3549 3567 3535 Metalworking machinery; Industrial furnaces & ovens; Conveyors & conveying equipment; Metalworking machinery; Industrial furnaces & ovens; Conveyors & conveying equipment
Pr: Robert L Koch II
CFO: Thomas Falkenstein
IT Man: Daniel Blue
Mfg Dir: Samuel Woehler
Sales Exec: Dean Holmes
Mktg Mgr: Don Chatmon
Manager: Koch-Mark Horton
Manager: Don Miller
Snr Mgr: Susan Parsons

GEORGE L MEE MEMORIAL HOSPITAL
See SOUTHERN MONTEREY COUNTY MEMORIAL HOSPITAL INC

D-U-N-S 12-267-4526
GEORGE M LEADER FAMILY CORP
COUNTRY MEADOWS
830 Cherry Dr, Hershey, PA 17033-2007
Tel (717) 520-0323 *Founded/Ownrshp* 2001
Sales 102.3MM^E *EMP* 2,200
SIC 8051 Skilled nursing care facilities; Skilled nursing care facilities
Pr: G Michael Leader
**COO:* David C Leader
**CFO:* Ted Janeczek
VP: Randy Hanson
**VP:* Theodore R Janeczeck
IT Man: Robin Gray
Sls&Mrk Ex: Tammy Sharp
Mktg Dir: Sara Agerton
Mktg Dir: Pat Hartman
Mktg Dir: John Loftus
Mktg Mgr: Kathy Cox

D-U-N-S 17-704-6620
GEORGE MASON MORTGAGE LLC
4100 Monu Crnr Dr Ste 100, Fairfax, VA 22030
Tel (703) 273-2600 *Founded/Ownrshp* 2004
Sales NA *EMP* 110
SIC 6162 Mortgage bankers; Mortgage bankers
CEO: D Gene Merrill
Ofcr: Julie Andre
Ofcr: Steve Brunett
Ofcr: Alicia Hollick
Ofcr: Cindy Kolencik
Ofcr: Timothy Phillips
Ofcr: Natalie Riffle
Ofcr: Chris Ryan
Ofcr: Chelsea Torrance
Ex VP: Matt Fox
Sr VP: Landon Bill
Sr VP: Jamie Bleakley
Sr VP: Chris Cusack
Sr VP: Joe Dunn
Sr VP: Brenna Dutton
Sr VP: Mark Ferguson
Sr VP: Ben Fox
Sr VP: Lea Frye
Sr VP: Mike Homberg
Sr VP: Susan Huber
Sr VP: Tom McLister

D-U-N-S 07-781-7450
GEORGE MASON UNIVERSITY
4400 University Dr, Fairfax, VA 22030-4444
Tel (703) 993-1000 *Founded/Ownrshp* 1963
Sales 588.2MM *EMP* 5,500
SIC 8221 University; University
Pr: Alan G Merten
CFO: Andrew M Bursten
Bd of Dir: Jean D Wu
Trst: Otis D Coston
Trst: Paul E Kyl
Ofcr: John Arnold
Ofcr: Christopher Ewald
Ofcr: David Green
Ofcr: Emily Ross
Assoc VP: John Blacksten
Assoc VP: Laura Gleason
Assoc VP: Arati Seth
VP: Marc Broderick
VP: Karen Petronis
Exec: Christina Lapel
Exec: Mary Levine
Exec: Carey McDaniel
Exec: Mark Stahley
Assoc Dir: Ilissa T Belanger
Assoc Dir: Amanda Meter

D-U-N-S 10-793-9563
GEORGE MASON UNIVERSITY FOUNDATION INC
4400 University Dr, Fairfax, VA 22030-4422
Tel (703) 993-8850 *Founded/Ownrshp* 1966
Sales 63.5MM *EMP* 30
SIC 6732 Educational trust management; Educational trust management
**Pr:* Judith Marshall Jobbitt
Pr: Sharon Pitt
**CFO:* David Roe
Bd of Dir: Lovey Hammel
Bd of Dir: Long Nguyen
Ofcr: Mary Vilhelmsen
VP: Beth Brock
VP: Marc Broderick
Assoc Dir: Bobbi Ritz
Comm Man: Heather Bailey
Ex Dir: Gregg Toney

D-U-N-S 04-179-4942
GEORGE MATICK CHEVROLET INC
14001 Telegraph Rd, Redford, MI 48239-2854
Tel (313) 531-7100 *Founded/Ownrshp* 1967
Sales 34.8MM^E *EMP* 70
SIC 5511 7538 7532 7515 5531 5521 New & used car dealers; General automotive repair shops; Top & body repair & paint shops; Passenger car leasing; Automotive & home supply stores; Used car dealers; Automobiles, new & used; General automotive repair shops; Top & body repair & paint shops; Passenger car leasing; Automotive & home supply stores; Used car dealers
Prin: John Peters
Store Mgr: Walter Smith
Snr Sftwr: Anna Shetler
Mktg Mgr: Ryan Esler
Sls Mgr: Dan Maloney
Sls Mgr: Tim Swinea
Sls Mgr: Paul Zimmerman
Sls Mgr: Paul Zimmermann
Sales Asso: Daniel Bible
Sales Asso: Rich Curran
Sales Asso: Tim Duncan

D-U-N-S 09-659-5293 EXP
GEORGE MOORE CHEVROLET INC (FL)
10979 Atlantic Blvd, Jacksonville, FL 32225-2921
Tel (904) 249-8282 *Founded/Ownrshp* 1986
Sales 22.5MM^E *EMP* 37
SIC 5511 Automobiles, new & used
Pr: George H Moore
**Sec:* Virginia M Moore
Sls Mgr: Frank Huth

D-U-N-S 00-387-7057
GEORGE MORLAN PLUMBING SUPPLY INC (OR)
2222 Nw Raleigh St, Portland, OR 97210-2631
Tel (503) 224-7000 *Founded/Ownrshp* 1927
Sales 27.4MM^E *EMP* 115
SIC 5999 5074 Plumbing & heating supplies; Plumbing fittings & supplies; Plumbing & heating supplies; Plumbing fittings & supplies
Pr: Rick Kramien
VP: Alex Kramien
Opers Mgr: Jeff Lofsted
Opers Mgr: Don Shimel
Advt Dir: Dave Charvet
Sales Asso: Chano Rocha

D-U-N-S 03-760-2620 IMP
GEORGE ODAYS INC
19 143rd St, Hammond, IN 46327-1313
Tel (219) 937-6670 *Founded/Ownrshp* 1980
Sales 22.0MM^E *EMP* 50
SIC 5021 Lockers
Pr: Steven J O'Day
**Ch:* George O'Day
**Sec:* Jeanne O'Day
Plnt Mgr: Jason Ladwig

D-U-N-S 00-484-9048
GEORGE P BANE INC (TX)
BANE MACHINERY TRACES
3402 N Northeast Loop 323, Tyler, TX 75708-5600
Tel (903) 597-6641 *Founded/Ownrshp* 1963, 1962
Sales 21.9MM^E *EMP* 55
SIC 5082 7699 Tractors, construction; Tractor repair
Prin: George Bane

D-U-N-S 00-537-8013 IMP
GEORGE P JOHNSON CO (MI)
INTAGLIO ASSOCIATES IN DESIGN
(*Suby of* PROJECT WORLDWIDE INC) ★
3600 Giddings Rd, Auburn Hills, MI 48326-1515
Tel (248) 475-2500 *Founded/Ownrshp* 1914
Sales 121.2MM^E *EMP* 500
SIC 3993 7389 Signs & advertising specialties; Advertising, promotional & trade show services; Signs & advertising specialties; Advertising, promotional & trade show services
Ch Bd: Robert G Vallee Jr
Pr: Tiffany Fong
Pr: Laurence S Vallee
Pr: Denise Wong
CFO: David Drews
CFO: Dave D Rews
Treas: Kurt Berry
Ex VP: Tara Higgins
Ex VP: Mike Rossi
VP: Scott Kellner
VP: Kenny Lauer
VP: Mark Mullen
VP: Dan Patterson
Exec: Amy Buchanan
Dir Soc: Isabella Gomide
Creative D: Keith Capobianco
Creative D: Joel McCall
Creative D: Edward Schowalter
Creative D: Michael Wood
Dir Bus: Scott West

D-U-N-S 00-712-2864
GEORGE P REINTJES CO INC (MO)
3800 Summit St, Kansas City, MO 64111
Tel (816) 756-2150 *Founded/Ownrshp* 1919
Sales 29.7MM^E *EMP* 250

SIC 1741

D-U-N-S 07-571-9211
GEORGE PATTON ASSOCIATES INC
DISPLAYS2GO
(*Suby of* TAKKT AG)
55 Broadcommon Rd, Bristol, RI 02809-2730
Tel (401) 247-0333 *Founded/Ownrshp* 2012
Sales 32.8MM[E] *EMP* 180
SIC 7389 3993 2821 2542 Design services; Displays & cutouts, window & lobby; Plastics materials & resins; Partitions & fixtures, except wood; Design services; Displays & cutouts, window & lobby; Plastics materials & resins; Partitions & fixtures, except wood
Pr: G Thomas Patton
**VP:* Christopher Patton

D-U-N-S 01-465-7936 IMP/EXP
GEORGE R CHABY INC (PA)
CHABY IMPORTS
10981 Decatur Rd Ste 2, Philadelphia, PA 19154-3213
Tel (215) 923-2400 *Founded/Ownrshp* 1963
Sales 29.3MM *EMP* 30[E]
SIC 5136 Umbrellas, men's & boys'
Pr: Allan G Chaby
**Treas:* John J Bonner Jr
**VP:* John Bonner
**Exec:* Allen Chaby
VP Sls: John Bonner

D-U-N-S 14-220-2733
GEORGE R NORRIS INC
NORRIS FORD
901 Merritt Blvd, Baltimore, MD 21222-1435
Tel (410) 282-7595 *Founded/Ownrshp* 1991
Sales 60.6MM[E] *EMP* 150
SIC 5511 Automobiles, new & used; Automobiles, new & used
CEO: George R Norris
COO: Ben Fenlon
**Treas:* Wendy Neiberlin
Sr Cor Off: Rick Fulco
**VP:* David Cook
VP: Jeff Grossman
Exec: Will Watson
Genl Mgr: Andy Franklin
Off Mgr: April Cherry
Sales Exec: Harvey Appleby
Sales Exec: Ray Snyder

D-U-N-S 88-418-0360
GEORGE REGIONAL HEALTH SYSTEM
859 Winter St, Lucedale, MS 39452-6603
Tel (601) 947-3161 *Founded/Ownrshp* 2009
Sales 46.4MM[E] *EMP* 100
Accts Horne Llp Ridgeland Mississi
SIC 8742 Hospital & health services consultant; Hospital & health services consultant
CEO: Paul Gardner
CFO: Deborah Brannan
Dir Lab: Joyce Rutherford
CIO: Anthony Fryfogle
Mktg Mgr: Stephanie Chisholm
Doctor: Ben Freeman
Doctor: Guy Rutledge
Doctor: James West
Nrsg Dir: Joel Turner

D-U-N-S 07-945-1217
GEORGE REGIONAL HOSPITAL
859 Winter St, Lucedale, MS 39452-6603
Tel (601) 947-3161 *Founded/Ownrshp* 1950
Sales 34.0MM *EMP* 325
Accts Horne Llp Ridgeland Mississi
SIC 8062 8011 General medical & surgical hospitals; Offices & clinics of medical doctors; General medical & surgical hospitals; Offices & clinics of medical doctors
CEO: Paul Gardner
Chf Rad: Leigh Cashwell
CFO: Denise Borroni
**CFO:* Debbie Brannan
Dir OR: Belva Hayden
Dir Rad: Christy Pope
CIO: Anthoney Fryfogle
Sfty Dirs: Bill Keys
Nrsg Dir: Joel Turner
Occ Thrpy: Johnnie Smith
HC Dir: Sherry Cooley
Board of Directors: Debbie Raines

D-U-N-S 96-308-0093
GEORGE S AND DOLORES DORE ECCLES FOUNDATION
79 S Main St Ste 1400, Salt Lake City, UT 84111-1946
Tel (801) 246-5351 *Founded/Ownrshp* 2010
Sales 26.4MM *EMP* 6
SIC 8699 Charitable organization
Pr: Lisa Eccles

D-U-N-S 01-466-7240 IMP
GEORGE S COYNE CHEMICAL CO INC
3015 State Rd, Croydon, PA 19021-6962
Tel (215) 785-4500 *Founded/Ownrshp* 1868
Sales 104.7MM[E] *EMP* 120
SIC 5169 Chemicals, industrial & heavy; Chemicals, industrial & heavy
Pr: Thomas H Coyne
Treas: Don C Helwig
VP: Thomas Holshue
VP: Jack C Mair
Dir Lab: Jennifer Logue
Genl Mgr: Chris Miriello
IT Man: Ruth Campos
Sfty Mgr: Terry Sturgis
Opers Mgr: Steve Baehser
VP Mktg: Gerald J Powel Jr
VP Mktg: Jerry Powel

D-U-N-S 96-294-9517
GEORGE S HALL INC
GSH GROUP
(*Suby of* GEORGE S HALL AMERICAS LIMITED)
4 Gatehall Dr Ste 2, Parsippany, NJ 07054-4522
Tel (877) 447-4255 *Founded/Ownrshp* 1996
Sales 40.0MM *EMP* 170
Accts Baker Tilly Stoke-On-Trent U
SIC 8711 1731 Electrical or electronic engineering; Electrical or electronic engineering; Energy management controls
Ch: Ian Scar Hall
**Pr:* Mark Thomas
**CFO:* Ian Davidson
Treas: Lawrence Resnick
**VP:* Kevin Okeeffe
VP: Jonathon Parker
Exec: Christopher Jones
IT Man: Stephen Plechy

GEORGE S HARRINGTON CO
See BARROW INDUSTRIES INC

D-U-N-S 00-552-7213
GEORGE S MAY INTERNATIONAL CO
303 S Northwest Hwy, Park Ridge, IL 60068
Tel (800) 999-3020 *Founded/Ownrshp* 1925
Sales 21.5MM[E] *EMP* 500
SIC 8742 Management consulting services; Management consulting services
CEO: Charles E Black Jr
**Pr:* Kerry S Jacobs
**Pr:* Israel Kushnir
CFO: Michael Hanrahanmichael
VP: Michael Bruening
**VP:* Dorothy May Campbell

D-U-N-S 03-109-4469
GEORGE SEEGER & SONS INC
SEEGER TOYOTA
12833 Olive Blvd, Saint Louis, MO 63141-6205
Tel (314) 434-5000 *Founded/Ownrshp* 1920
Sales 25.5MM[E] *EMP* 56
SIC 5511 5521 Automobiles, new & used; Used car dealers; Automobiles, new & used; Used car dealers
Pr: Tom Seeger
Dir IT: Gina Boucher
Sls Mgr: Ed Benton
Sales Asso: Randy Hixson
Sales Asso: Greg Riley
Sales Asso: Andy Seeger

D-U-N-S 00-798-0865
GEORGE SOLLITT CONSTRUCTION CO (IL)
790 N Cent Ave, Wood Dale, IL 60191
Tel (630) 860-7333 *Founded/Ownrshp* 1838, 1949
Sales 58.9MM[E] *EMP* 120
SIC 1542 1541

D-U-N-S 00-958-4111 IMP
GEORGE T HALL CO INC
1605 E Gene Autry Way, Anaheim, CA 92805-6730
Tel (909) 825-9751 *Founded/Ownrshp* 1975
Sales 26.0MM[E] *EMP* 55
SIC 5075 5085 3613 Warm air heating & air conditioning; Industrial supplies; Control panels, electric; Warm air heating & air conditioning; Industrial supplies; Control panels, electric
Pr: Charles Niemann
VP: Dina Harris
VP: Martin Jim
**VP:* James Martin
Brnch Mgr: Laurel Kellam
IT Man: Michael Smith
Sales Asso: Hulda Torres

D-U-N-S 00-742-9111
GEORGE T SANDERS CO
GTS
10201 W 49th Ave, Wheat Ridge, CO 80033-2211
Tel (303) 423-9660 *Founded/Ownrshp* 1950
Sales 96.2MM[E] *EMP* 140
SIC 5074 Plumbing fittings & supplies; Plumbing fittings & supplies; Heating equipment (hydronic)
Ch: Gary Sanders
**Pr:* Scott A Horner
**CFO:* Ted Batchelder
**VP:* Beverly Sanders

D-U-N-S 01-879-5075
GEORGE T SANDERS CO
10201 W 49th Ave, Wheat Ridge, CO 80033-2211
Tel (303) 940-4545 *Founded/Ownrshp* 1983
Sales 60.0MM *EMP* 160
SIC 5074 Plumbing fittings & supplies; Plumbing fittings & supplies
CEO: Gary T Sanders
**Treas:* Ted Batchelder

D-U-N-S 88-430-2993
GEORGE TEENY
NEW PHOENIX, THE
225 W 4th St, La Center, WA 98629-5427
Tel (360) 263-1221 *Founded/Ownrshp* 1988
Sales 7.4MM[E] *EMP* 300
SIC 7999 5813 5812 Card rooms; Drinking places; Eating places; Card rooms; Drinking places; Eating places
Owner: George Teeny

D-U-N-S 01-082-5044
GEORGE W BUSH PRESIDENTIAL LIBRARY FOUNDATION
6166 N Central Expy, Dallas, TX 75206
Tel (214) 890-9943 *Founded/Ownrshp* 2009
Sales 87.3MM *EMP* 13[E]
Accts Lockart Atchley & Associates
SIC 8231 Libraries; Libraries
Pr: Margaret Spellings

D-U-N-S 03-439-9592
GEORGE W GROETSCH INC
GROETSCH WHOLESALE GROCERS
5615 Jefferson Hwy, Harahan, LA 70123-5110
Tel (504) 733-9322 *Founded/Ownrshp* 1917
Sales 35.7MM[E] *EMP* 56
Accts Laporte Sehrt Romig Hand Covi
SIC 5141 5194 Food brokers; Cigarettes; Food brokers; Cigarettes
Pr: George J Groetsch Jr
**VP:* George W Groetsch
Sls Mgr: Michael Licciardi

GEORGE WAIKEM NISSAN
See WAIKEM GEORGE FORD INC

D-U-N-S 04-814-2983
GEORGE WASHINGTON CARVER ACADEMY
45 Broadway Fl 17, New York, NY 10006-3007
Tel (404) 841-2305 *Founded/Ownrshp* 1997
Sales NA *EMP* 2,000
SIC 8299 Educational services

D-U-N-S 04-399-0498
GEORGE WASHINGTON UNIVERSITY (DC)
2121 I St Nw Ste 601, Washington, DC 20052-0086
Tel (202) 242-6600 *Founded/Ownrshp* 1821
Sales 1.2MMM *EMP* 5,000
Accts Pricewaterhousecoopers Llp Mc
SIC 8221 University; University
Pr: Stephen Knapp
COO: Andre Cardim
**Treas:* Louis H Katz
Trst: Nelson A Carbonell
Trst: Eugene I Lambert
Ofcr: Sanjay Rupani
Ex VP: Tyler Coffey
**VP:* Dennis H Blumer
**VP:* Beverly Bond
**VP:* Robert Chernak
**VP:* Michael Freedman
**VP:* Donald R Lehman
**VP:* Richard N Sawaya
**VP:* John F Williams MD
Assoc Dir: Alexandra M Gomes
Assoc Dir: Christina Huszcza

GEORGE WASHINGTON'S MT VERNON
See MOUNT VERNON LADIES ASSOCIATION OF UNION

D-U-N-S 02-344-7667
GEORGE WEBB CORP
W229n1687 Westwood Dr A, Waukesha, WI 53186-1174
Tel (262) 547-4344 *Founded/Ownrshp* 1948, 1985
Sales 40.4MM[E] *EMP* 175
SIC 6794 5812 Franchises, selling or licensing; Restaurant, family: independent; Franchises, selling or licensing; Restaurant, family: independent
Pr: David M Stamm
CFO: Ryan Stam
**VP:* Ryan Stamm
Exec: Liz Anderson
Exec: Ann Bordeau

D-U-N-S 02-537-3788
GEORGE WEBER CHEVROLET CO
701 Old State Route 3, Columbia, IL 62236-2651
Tel (314) 487-4075 *Founded/Ownrshp* 1989
Sales 30.2MM[E] *EMP* 76
SIC 5511 Automobiles, new & used; Pickups, new & used; Automobiles, new & used; Pickups, new & used
Pr: George Weber III
**VP:* Mary Weber
Genl Mgr: Dave Vogel
Dir IT: Missy Lickteig
Sls Mgr: Joe Sewell
Sales Asso: John Belz
Sales Asso: Gary Christ
Sales Asso: Bill Emling
Sales Asso: Ron Filipiak
Sales Asso: Doug Johannes
Sales Asso: Joe Keilholz

D-U-N-S 02-039-1777 IMP
GEORGE WEINTRAUB & SONS INC
641 Lexington Ave Fl 11, New York, NY 10022-4503
Tel (212) 581-8708 *Founded/Ownrshp* 1975
Sales 62.7MM[E] *EMP* 60
SIC 5136 Men's & boys' clothing
Pr: Jeff A Weintraub
**Ex VP:* Roberta Tisser
**VP:* Greg Gordon
VP Sls: Brian Weintraub

GEORGE WESTON BAKERIES
See ARNOLD FOODS CO INC

D-U-N-S 05-068-7672
GEORGE WHITE CHEVROLET INC
WHITE GEORGE CHEVROLET PONTIAC
Hwy 30 & 69 S, Ames, IA 50010
Tel (515) 233-2211 *Founded/Ownrshp* 1970
Sales 20.6MM[E] *EMP* 60
SIC 5511 Automobiles, new & used; Trucks, tractors & trailers: new & used; Automobiles, new & used; Trucks, tractors & trailers: new & used
Pr: Robert W Parks

D-U-N-S 00-686-8947
GEORGE YOUNG CO
509 Heron Dr, Swedesboro, NJ 08085-1713
Tel (215) 467-2200 *Founded/Ownrshp* 1869
Sales 20.2MM[E] *EMP* 125
Accts Joseph P Melvin Company Wayn
SIC 1796 4214 Machine moving & rigging; Machinery installation; Millwright; Local trucking with storage; Machine moving & rigging; Machinery installation; Millwright; Local trucking with storage
Pr: George S Young
**Sec:* Meredith Dornenburg
**VP:* Steven F Scott
Snr PM: James Jordan

D-U-N-S 06-466-7371
GEORGE/MCKENNA ELECTRICAL CONTRACTORS INC
2319 E Grauwyler Rd, Irving, TX 75061-3313
Tel (972) 721-1950 *Founded/Ownrshp* 1981
Sales 32.6MM[E] *EMP* 61
SIC 1542 7382

D-U-N-S 15-969-9164
GEORGECO INC
2609 Willowbrook Rd, Dallas, TX 75220-4422
Tel (214) 352-9091 *Founded/Ownrshp* 1971
Sales 129.3MM[E] *EMP* 200
SIC 5032 Concrete building products; Concrete building products
Prin: G W White
**Pr:* Jeff L Barnes
**VP:* Gary A Barnes
**VP:* Shawn White

D-U-N-S 06-531-5194
GEORGES INC
402 W Robinson Ave, Springdale, AR 72764-6359
Tel (479) 927-7000 *Founded/Ownrshp* 1939
Sales 1.1MMM[E] *EMP* 4,180
SIC 2015 0254 0251 Poultry, processed; Chicken hatchery; Broiling chickens, raising of; Poultry, processed; Chicken hatchery; Broiling chickens, raising of
Pr: Carl George
**Ch Bd:* Gary George
**Pr:* Charles George
COO: Monty Henderson
CFO: Ancel McClaine
Treas: Ancel McClain
**Treas:* Angel McClane
**Ex VP:* Otto Jeck
VP: Matt Brown
Exec: Gary Clayton
CIO: John Delphon

GEORGE'S LIVE HAUL
See GEORGES PROCESSING INC

D-U-N-S 06-768-3557
GEORGES PROCESSING INC (AR)
GEORGE'S LIVE HAUL
(*Suby of* GEORGES INC) ★
402 W Robinson Ave, Springdale, AR 72764-6359
Tel (479) 927-7000 *Founded/Ownrshp* 1973
Sales 326.9MM[E] *EMP* 4,000[E]
SIC 2015 Poultry, processed; Poultry, processed
Ch: Eugene George
Pr: Monty Henderson
CEO: Gary George
Sec: Ancel McClane
Ex VP: Otto Jeck

D-U-N-S 01-203-3536
GEORGESON & CO INC (DE)
(*Suby of* COMPUTERSHARE LIMITED)
480 Washington Blvd Fl 26, Jersey City, NJ 07310-2056
Tel (212) 440-9800 *Founded/Ownrshp* 1940, 1992
Sales 28.2MM[E] *EMP* 150[E]
SIC 6282 Investment advice; Investment advice
Ch Bd: Alexander Miller
**Pr:* William M Crane
**CEO:* Alexander B Miller
**COO:* Sam Chandoha
Sr Cor Off: Ferdinand Von Ballestrem
Ofcr: Rosemary Depalma
Sr VP: Brian Permenter
VP: Eva Orecchio
Mng Dir: Donna Ackerly
Mng Dir: Leahruth Jemilo

D-U-N-S 79-143-8484
GEORGESON INC
(*Suby of* GEORGESON SECURITIES CORP) ★
1290 Avenue Of America, New York, NY 10104
Tel (212) 440-9800 *Founded/Ownrshp* 1999
Sales 27.1MM[E] *EMP* 150
SIC 6282 Investment advice; Investment advice
Ch Bd: William Crene
**Pr:* David Brake
Sr Cor Off: Michael Albert
Sr Cor Off: Michael Geffrard
Sr Cor Off: Jens Olsen
Sr VP: Patrick Tracey
VP: Frank Delillo
VP: Karen Lewis
Mng Dir: Christopher Dowd
Mng Dir: Richard Gottcent
Mng Dir: Christopher Hayden

D-U-N-S 07-860-6985
GEORGESON SECURITIES CORP (DE)
(*Suby of* COMPUTERSHARE LLC) ★
17 State St Fl 26, New York, NY 10004-1526
Tel (212) 805-7000 *Founded/Ownrshp* 1969, 2003
Sales 38.8MM[E] *EMP* 200
SIC 8742 Management consulting services; Management consulting services
Ch: William Crane
**Pr:* Ronald Boronkay
**CEO:* Jon Einsidler

GEORGETOWN CAREER CENTER
See GEORGETOWN COUNTY SCHOOL DISTRICT

D-U-N-S 07-678-2820
GEORGETOWN COLLEGE (KY)
400 E College St, Georgetown, KY 40324-1696
Tel (502) 863-8000 *Founded/Ownrshp* 1829
Sales 55.8MM *EMP* 350
SIC 8221 8611 University; Business associations; University; Business associations
Pr: William H Crouch Jr
VP: Todd Rasberry
Dir IT: Jane Higgins
HC Dir: Johnnie Johnson

D-U-N-S 10-066-9746
GEORGETOWN COUNTY SCHOOL DISTRICT
GEORGETOWN CAREER CENTER
2018 Church St, Georgetown, SC 29440-2604
Tel (843) 436-7000 *Founded/Ownrshp* 1878
Sales 77.7MM[E] *EMP* 1,544
Accts Mcgregor & Company Llp Columb
SIC 8211 Public elementary & secondary schools; Public elementary & secondary schools
**Ch:* Jim Dumm
**Bd of Dir:* Dr Arthur Lance Jr
Cmptr Lab: Kathleen Elmore
HC Dir: Michael Caviris

D-U-N-S 55-698-4730
GEORGETOWN COUNTY WATER & SEWER DISTRICT
456 Clearwater Dr, Pawleys Island, SC 29585
Tel (843) 237-9727 *Founded/Ownrshp* 1967
Sales 32.6MM[E] *EMP* 78
Accts Derrick Stubbs & Stith Llp C
SIC 4941 4952 Water supply; Sewerage systems

Ex Dir: Ray Gagnon

D-U-N-S 07-263-6210
GEORGETOWN DAY SCHOOL INC
4530 Macarthur Blvd Nw, Washington, DC 20007-4297
Tel (202) 295-6113 *Founded/Ownrshp* 1945
Sales 49.3MM *EMP* 212
Accts Mcgladrey Llp Mc Lean Va
SIC 8211 Public elementary & secondary schools; Public elementary & secondary schools
CFO: Kate Lindsey
Ofcr: Carolyn Lockie
CIO: Ashley Hair
CTO: Lisa Schneiderman
Dir IT: Dave Arnstein
HC Dir: Kim Scott
HC Dir: Lisa Shambaugh

D-U-N-S 83-315-2940
GEORGETOWN HEALTHCARE & REHAB INC
2715 South Island Rd, Georgetown, SC 29440-4415
Tel (843) 546-4123 *Founded/Ownrshp* 1994
Sales 395.2MM *EMP* 18ᴱ
SIC 8011 Offices & clinics of medical doctors; Offices & clinics of medical doctors

D-U-N-S 03-757-3818
GEORGETOWN HOSPITAL
3800 Reservoir Rd Nw, Washington, DC 20007-2113
Tel (202) 444-2000 *Founded/Ownrshp* 2001
Sales 28.4MMᴱ *EMP* 351ᴱ
SIC 8011 Medical centers
Prin: Gregory Milmoe
Ansthlgy: Lisa Bellil
Ansthlgy: Medhat Hannallah
Doctor: Amy Lu
Diag Rad: Angela Levy

GEORGETOWN HOSPITAL SYSTEM
See WACCAMAW COMMUNITY HOSPITAL

D-U-N-S 04-244-6765
GEORGETOWN INDEPENDENT SCHOOL DISTRICT
603 Lakeway Dr, Georgetown, TX 78628-2843
Tel (512) 943-5000 *Founded/Ownrshp* 1917
Sales 125.5MM *EMP* 1,700
Accts Maxwell Locke & Ritter Llp A
SIC 8211 Public elementary school; Public junior high school; Public senior high school; Public elementary school; Public junior high school; Public senior high school
Pr: Scott Alarcon
Bd of Dir: Sheila Carter
Bd of Dir: Mike Hewlett
Prin: Judy Johnston
Prin: Randy Weisinger
Pr Dir: Suzanne Machman
Teacher Pr: Cheryl Hoover

D-U-N-S 82-494-0824
GEORGETOWN INVESTING LLC
21 Georgetown Oval, New City, NY 10956-6803
Tel (845) 634-6689 *Founded/Ownrshp* 2008
Sales 25.0MM *EMP* 3
SIC 6513 Apartment building operators; Apartment building operators

D-U-N-S 80-958-7962
GEORGETOWN MAC HAIK DODGE CHRYSLER JEEP LTD
5255 S Interstate 35, Georgetown, TX 78626-7549
Tel (512) 930-7900 *Founded/Ownrshp* 2005
Sales 23.4MMᴱ *EMP* 70
SIC 5511 Automobiles, new & used; Automobiles, new & used
Pr: Mac Haik
CFO: Jeff Heath

GEORGETOWN MANOR HEALTH CARE C
See CHELTENHAM NURSING AND REHABILITATION CENTER

GEORGETOWN MANOR HEALTH CARE C
See AHF/KENTUCKY-IOWA INC

D-U-N-S 04-746-1660
GEORGETOWN MANOR INC
ROBERT JOSEPH INTERIORS
8353 Kempwood Dr, Houston, TX 77055-1096
Tel (713) 464-4460 *Founded/Ownrshp* 1968
Sales 26.1MMᴱ *EMP* 130
SIC 5712 Furniture stores
Co-Ch Bd: Joyce Chesnick
**Pr:* H Joseph Chesnick Jr
**Ch:* H Joseph Chesnick Sr
**Sec:* Bradley Chesnick
**VP:* Robert G Chesnick
Off Mgr: Steve Schulle

D-U-N-S 84-985-2298
GEORGETOWN MARINE INSTITUTE INC
ASSOCIATED MARINE INSTITUTES
5915 Benjamin Center Dr, Tampa, FL 33634-5239
Tel (813) 887-3300 *Founded/Ownrshp* 1989
Sales 57.8MM *EMP* 13
SIC 8322 Offender rehabilitation agency; Offender rehabilitation agency
CFO: William Griffin
Dir Risk M: Matt Frye
Comm Dir: MA Whelihan
Ex Dir: Reginald Jackson
Ex Dir: Robert Johnson
Ex Dir: Jimmie Lee
Ex Dir: Jerome Platt
Netwrk Mgr: Saray Thach

D-U-N-S 06-932-9647
GEORGETOWN MEMORIAL HOSPITAL
606 Black River Rd, Georgetown, SC 29440-3368
Tel (843) 626-9040 *Founded/Ownrshp* 1950
Sales 112.8MM *EMP* 1,300
SIC 8062 General medical & surgical hospitals; General medical & surgical hospitals
CEO: Jeannie Davis
V Ch: Charles A Moore
**Pr:* Bruce P Bailey
COO: Gayle L Resetar
Chf Mktg O: John Manning
Ofcr: Wanda Prevatte
VP: John Larochelle
VP: Gary Metcalfe
VP: Amy Stevens
Exec: James Harper
Dir Lab: Elizabeth D Gannon
Dir Rx: Ambrose Holiday

D-U-N-S 07-265-6077
GEORGETOWN PREPARATORY SCHOOL INC (MD)
10900 Rockville Pike, Rockville, MD 20852-3209
Tel (301) 493-5000 *Founded/Ownrshp* 1789
Sales 21.6MMᴱ *EMP* 146
SIC 8211 7999 Preparatory school; Recreation services
Pr: Father William George
Comm Man: Kim Yue
Mktg Dir: Patrick Coyle

D-U-N-S 04-951-5844 IMP
GEORGETOWN UNIVERSITY
37th & O Sts Nw, Washington, DC 20057-0001
Tel (202) 687-0100 *Founded/Ownrshp* 1789
Sales 1.1MMM *EMP* 9,700
Accts Pricewaterhousecoopers Llp Mc
SIC 8221 8062 University; General medical & surgical hospitals; University; General medical & surgical hospitals
Pr: John J Degioia
V Ch: Christopher Mulrooney
COO: Christopher Augostini
COO: Jack Chirikjian
CFO: Darryl Christmon
Ofcr: Emmanuel Alignay
Ofcr: Anthony Allen
Ofcr: David Blanco
Ofcr: Clark Browne
Ofcr: David Budd
Ofcr: David Dennison
Ofcr: Cat Glover-Bradford
Ofcr: Antony Johnson
Ofcr: Terence Mack
Ofcr: Rachel Pugh
**Ex VP:* Howard Federoff
**Ex VP:* Robert M Groves
Ex VP: William Treanor
**Sr VP:* Spiros Dimolitsas
**VP:* Lisa Brown
**VP:* Lisa Davis

GEORGETOWN UNIVERSITY HOSPITAL
See MEDSTAR-GEORGETOWN MEDICAL CENTER INC

D-U-N-S 61-989-5659
GEORGETOWNE GROUP LP
BURGER KING
55-77 Schanck Rd Ste B-1, Freehold, NJ 07728-2989
Tel (732) 303-1600 *Founded/Ownrshp* 1990
Sales 18.1MMᴱ *EMP* 400
SIC 5812 Fast-food restaurant, chain; Fast-food restaurant, chain
Pt: Joseph Angelo

D-U-N-S 92-600-6755
GEORGIA AIR ASSOCIATES INC
6135 Northbelt Dr Ste A, Norcross, GA 30071-4632
Tel (678) 736-5100 *Founded/Ownrshp* 2009
Sales 33.5MMᴱ *EMP* 35ᴱ
SIC 4911 Distribution, electric power
CEO: Larry M Douglas
VP: Rob Roux
Sales Asso: Lyle Baker

GEORGIA ALABAMA DEFENSE DST
See FT BENNING SCHOOL DISTRICT

D-U-N-S 12-926-6347 IMP
GEORGIA AQUARIUM INC
225 Baker St Nw, Atlanta, GA 30313-1809
Tel (404) 581-4000 *Founded/Ownrshp* 2000
Sales 78.7MM *EMP* 410ᴱ
Accts Moore Stephens Tiller Llc Dul
SIC 8422 Botanical garden; Botanical garden
Ch Bd: Bernie Marcus
Dir Vol: Pam Pate
**CFO:* Matt Hodgdon
CFO: Mark Schafer
VP: Heather McKeen
Genl Mgr: Alexander Polazzo
CTO: Keith Rose
Dir IT: Brenda Fairbanks
Sls&Mrk Ex: Roisin Florence
VP Mktg: Greg Rancone
Pr Dir: Meghann Gibbons

D-U-N-S 19-996-6656
■ **GEORGIA BANK & TRUST CO OF AUGUSTA**
(*Suby of* SOUTHEASTERN BANK FINANCIAL CORP) ★
3530 Wheeler Rd, Augusta, GA 30909-6710
Tel (706) 738-6990 *Founded/Ownrshp* 1988
Sales NA *EMP* 340
SIC 6022 State commercial banks; State commercial banks
Pr: R Daniel Blanton
Pr: Robert Osborne
Pr: Sherry Wiggins
CFO: Darrell Rains
**CFO:* Ronald L Thigpen
Trst Ofcr: Deirdre Clements
Ex VP: Denise Bargeron
Ex VP: Ronald Thiqpen
Sr VP: Patrick Kingsmill
**Sr VP:* Robert Strozier
VP: R Benjamin
VP: Wayne Bissell
**VP:* Sonya Hanson
VP: Regina Kennedy
**VP:* Tom McLaughlin
VP: Paula Mobley
VP: Jerry Rogers
VP: Larry Sides
VP: Paula Tankersley

D-U-N-S 80-956-1272
GEORGIA BANKERS ASSOCIATION INSURANCE TRUST INC
50 Hurt Plz Se Ste 1050, Atlanta, GA 30303-2955
Tel (404) 522-1501 *Founded/Ownrshp* 2011
Sales NA *EMP* 2ᴱ
Accts Moore Colson & Company Pc Mar
SIC 6411 Insurance agents, brokers & service; Insurance agents, brokers & service
Prin: Remer Y Brinson III

D-U-N-S 82-810-2827
GEORGIA BANKERS ASSOCIATION INSURANCE TRUST INC
50 Hurt Plz Se Ste 1050, Atlanta, GA 30303-2955
Tel (404) 522-1501 *Founded/Ownrshp* 2011
Sales NA *EMP* 2
Accts Moore Colson & Company Pc Mer
SIC 6411 Insurance agents, brokers & service
Sr VP: Dan Thomason

GEORGIA BAPTIST CONVENTION
See EXECUTIVE COMMITTEE OF BAPTIST CONVENTION OF STATE OF GEORGIA

D-U-N-S 07-588-3603
GEORGIA BAPTIST HEALTH CARE SYSTEM INC
100 10th St Nw Ste 700, Atlanta, GA 30309-3810
Tel (404) 814-4477 *Founded/Ownrshp* 1993
Sales 187.9MMᴱ *EMP* 1,300
Accts Ernst & Young Llp
SIC 8741 Hospital management; Nursing & personal care facility management; Hospital management; Nursing & personal care facility management
CEO: David E Harrell
**COO:* Robert Otwell
**CFO:* Ann Finlon

GEORGIA BATHWARE
See BATHCRAFT LLC

D-U-N-S 83-258-9498 IMP/EXP
GEORGIA BIOMASS LLC
(*Suby of* RWE AG)
3390 Industrial Blvd, Waycross, GA 31503-8730
Tel (912) 721-6105 *Founded/Ownrshp* 2009
Sales 64.9MMᴱ *EMP* 90
SIC 4911
CEO: James B Roecker
CFO: Sam Kang
Sr VP: Marcus W Gaddy
VP: James N Flowers Jr
VP: Jason Jakubsen
Plnt Mgr: Ken Ciarletta
Plnt Mgr: Brad Mayhew

GEORGIA BOARD OF REGENTS
See GEORGIA COLLEGE & STATE UNIVERSITY FOUNDATION INC

GEORGIA BOARD OF REGENTS
See CLAYTON STATE UNIVERSITY

GEORGIA BOARD OF REGENTS
See DALTON STATE FOUNDATION

GEORGIA BOARD OF REGENTS
See ABRAHAM BALDWIN AGRICULTURAL COLLEGE FOUNDATION INC

GEORGIA BOARD OF REGENTS
See BOARD OF REGENTS OF UNIVERSITY SYSTEM OF GEORGIA

D-U-N-S 13-105-4595
■ **GEORGIA BOOT LLC**
(*Suby of* EJ FOOTWEAR LLC)
39 E Canal St, Nelsonville, OH 45764-1247
Tel (740) 753-1951 *Founded/Ownrshp* 1995
Sales 21.4MMᴱ *EMP* 100
SIC 5139 3144 3143 3021 Shoes; Women's footwear, except athletic; Men's footwear, except athletic; Rubber & plastics footwear
CEO: Gerald M Cohn
Pr: Thomas R Morrison

D-U-N-S 80-859-7330
GEORGIA BUILDING AUTHORITY
(*Suby of* EXECUTIVE OFFICE OF STATE OF GEORGIA) ★
1 Martin Ave Se D, Atlanta, GA 30315
Tel (404) 656-3253 *Founded/Ownrshp* 1960
Sales NA *EMP* 300
SIC 9531 Building standards agency, government; ; Building standards agency, government;
Dir IT: Alan Perry
Opers Mgr: Sylvia Hatfield

D-U-N-S 87-997-6215
GEORGIA BUREAU OF INVESTIGATION
(*Suby of* EXECUTIVE OFFICE OF STATE OF GEORGIA) ★
3121 Panthersville Rd, Decatur, GA 30034-3830
Tel (404) 244-2600 *Founded/Ownrshp* 1940
Sales NA *EMP* 800
SIC 9221 Bureau of criminal investigation, government; ; Bureau of criminal investigation, government;
Dir Lab: George Herrin
Prgrm Mgr: Bradley Chester
Prgrm Mgr: Elizabeth Turner
Off Admin: Linda Jackson
Ql Cn Mgr: Lori Nix
Pr Dir: Sherry Lang
Snr Mgr: Amanda Bazzanini
Snr Mgr: Kevin Daniel

D-U-N-S 79-078-4599
GEORGIA CANCER SPECIALISTS I PC
1835 Savoy Dr Ste 300, Atlanta, GA 30341-1071
Tel (770) 496-9400 *Founded/Ownrshp* 1999
Sales 6.0MM *EMP* 500
SIC 8011 Medical centers; Oncologist; Medical centers; Oncologist
CEO: J B Lesesne MD
**Pr:* Wendy Hawke
**CFO:* Ronald W Fleming
Ex VP: Anthony Lagroon
VP: J D Pearlman
Area Mgr: Valerie Stephen
Genl Mgr: Sandy Englsh
CIO: Tom Gondesen

D-U-N-S 17-353-1203
GEORGIA CARPET FINISHERS INC
134 Highland Rd, Chatsworth, GA 30705-6328
Tel (706) 695-3600 *Founded/Ownrshp* 1986
Sales 35.7MMᴱ *EMP* 156
SIC 2273 Finishers of tufted carpets & rugs; Finishers of tufted carpets & rugs
Pr: Larry Oxford
**Sec:* Jean Phillips

D-U-N-S 04-758-5492
GEORGIA CASUALTY & SURETY CO
(*Suby of* COLUMBIA INSURANCE GROUP) ★
11138 State Bridge Rd # 200, Alpharetta, GA 30022-7465
Tel (770) 410-3720 *Founded/Ownrshp* 2008
Sales NA *EMP* 200
SIC 6331 Fire, marine & casualty insurance & carriers; Fire, marine & casualty insurance & carriers
Pr: Dianne Morris
**Ch Bd:* J M Robinson
**Ex VP:* Hilton H Howell
**Ex VP:* Craig Stufflet
VP: Jeanne Marshburn
VP: Christy Payne

D-U-N-S 02-044-8333
GEORGIA CENTRAL CREDIT UNION INC
6705 Sugarloaf Pkwy # 100, Duluth, GA 30097-4926
Tel (770) 476-9704 *Founded/Ownrshp* 1990
Sales NA *EMP* 48
Accts Orth Chakler Murnane And Co Cp
SIC 6062 State credit unions; State credit unions
Pr: Dave Preter
CFO: Amanda S Harrell

D-U-N-S 01-010-1020
GEORGIA COLLEGE & STATE UNIVERSITY FOUNDATION INC (GA)
GEORGIA BOARD OF REGENTS
(*Suby of* BOARD OF REGENTS OF UNIVERSITY SYSTEM OF GEORGIA) ★
231 W Hancock St, Milledgeville, GA 31061-3371
Tel (478) 445-5004 *Founded/Ownrshp* 1889
Sales 8.5MM *EMP* 800ᴱ
SIC 8221 College, except junior; College, except junior
Pr: Steve Dorman
**Pr:* Dr Paul Jones
**Pr:* Dorothy Leland
**VP:* Pete Shields
Off Mgr: Toi Franks
Off Admin: Renee Mosley
Off Admin: Justin Mundy
Off Admin: Lindy Ruark
Off Admin: Theodore Windish
CIO: James Carlose
Web Dev: Mark Misinco

D-U-N-S 00-326-4546 IMP
GEORGIA CRATE & BASKET CO INC
1200 Parnell St, Thomasville, GA 31792
Tel (229) 226-2541 *Founded/Ownrshp* 1979
Sales 23.6MM *EMP* 150
Accts Fletcher & Associates Pc T
SIC 2449 Food containers, wood: wirebound; Boxes, wood: wirebound; Food containers, wood: wirebound; Boxes, wood: wirebound
Ch Bd: Constance B Jones
**Pr:* Bolling Jones IV
**Sec:* Ellis E Fletcher

D-U-N-S 00-586-7643 IMP/EXP
GEORGIA CROWN DISTRIBUTING CO (GA)
ALABAMA CROWN DISTRIBUTING CO
100 Georgia Crown Dr, McDonough, GA 30253-9071
Tel (770) 302-3000 *Founded/Ownrshp* 1949, 1959
Sales 181.9MMᴱ *EMP* 475
SIC 5182 5181 Wine & distilled beverages; Beer & ale; Wine & distilled beverages; Beer & ale
CEO: Donald M Leebern
**CFO:* Orlene K Bovaird
CFO: Orlene Bovaird
Ex VP: Persall Buddy
VP: Mary Gibbon
VP: Brian Hendrick
Exec: Dave Leonard
Genl Mgr: Turner Hendricks
Genl Mgr: David Hubbard
Genl Mgr: Shane Mooney
Genl Mgr: Greg Rains

D-U-N-S 06-452-0190
GEORGIA CUMBERLAND CONFERENCE
(*Suby of* SOUTHERN UNION CONFERENCE ASSOCIATION OF SEVENTH-DAY ADVENTISTS) ★
255 Conference Rd Ne, Calhoun, GA 30701-9387
Tel (706) 629-7951 *Founded/Ownrshp* 1932
Sales 46.4MM *EMP* 405
SIC 8661 8211 Seventh Day Adventist Church; Private combined elementary & secondary school; Seventh Day Adventist Church; Private combined elementary & secondary school
Pr: Ed Wright
**Treas:* S Kurt Allen
Ofcr: Les Speer
VP: Kevin Kossick
VP: Victor Maddox

D-U-N-S 06-649-4436
GEORGIA DEPARTMENT OF AGRICULTURE
(*Suby of* EXECUTIVE OFFICE OF STATE OF GEORGIA) ★
19 Martin Luther King Jr, Atlanta, GA 30334-4200
Tel (404) 656-3600 *Founded/Ownrshp* 1874
Sales NA *EMP* 650
SIC 9641 Regulation & inspection of agricultural products, government; ; Regulation & inspection of agricultural products, government;
**Ofcr:* Tony Amberoso
VP: Derrick Lastinger
Dir Bus: Bo Warren
Adm Dir: Shirley King

CIO: David Rierson
Pr Dir: Sydne Smith

D-U-N-S 80-847-5792
GEORGIA DEPARTMENT OF AUDITS AND ACCOUNTS
(*Suby of* GENERAL ASSEMBLY) ★
270 Washntn St Sw 1156 Rm 1, Atlanta, GA 30334
Tel (404) 656-2180 *Founded/Ownrshp* 1990
Sales NA *EMP* 340
Accts Russell W Hinton Cpa Cgfm
SIC 9311 Public finance & monetary policy; ; Public finance & monetary policy;

D-U-N-S 80-747-9084
GEORGIA DEPARTMENT OF COMMUNITY AFFAIRS
(*Suby of* EXECUTIVE OFFICE OF STATE OF GEORGIA) ★
60 Executive Park S N, Atlanta, GA 30329-2296
Tel (404) 679-4940 *Founded/Ownrshp* 1975
Sales NA *EMP* 405
SIC 9441 Administration of social & manpower programs; ; Administration of social & manpower programs;
Ch: James Billy Croker
Ofcr: Willa Dudley
Ex Dir: Donnie Smith
Dir IT: William Rutherford
IT Man: Sally Mrus
Pr Dir: Kimberly King

D-U-N-S 80-747-9118
GEORGIA DEPARTMENT OF CORRECTIONS
(*Suby of* EXECUTIVE OFFICE OF STATE OF GEORGIA) ★
300 Patrol Rd, Forsyth, GA 31029-1868
Tel (404) 656-4593 *Founded/Ownrshp* 1943
Sales NA *EMP* 12,000
SIC 9223 Prison, government; ; Prison, government;
Ofcr: Shea Allen
Ofcr: Damien Ford
Ofcr: Tony Graham
Ofcr: Bradley Harp
Ofcr: Rob Hyde II
Mng Dir: Alan Adams
Opers Mgr: Gary Bell
Opers Mgr: William Driver
Psych: Timothy Sanders
Nrsg Dir: Martha Sheley
Snr PM: Lauren Salas

D-U-N-S 80-747-8946
GEORGIA DEPARTMENT OF DEFENSE
(*Suby of* EXECUTIVE OFFICE OF STATE OF GEORGIA) ★
1000 Halsey Ave Se, Marietta, GA 30060-4277
Tel (404) 624-6085 *Founded/Ownrshp* 1951
Sales NA *EMP* 467
SIC 9711 National security; ; National security;
Prin: Sam Olens

D-U-N-S 80-674-3159
GEORGIA DEPARTMENT OF EDUCATION
(*Suby of* EXECUTIVE OFFICE OF STATE OF GEORGIA) ★
205 Jesse Hill Jr Dr Se, Atlanta, GA 30334-9033
Tel (404) 656-2497 *Founded/Ownrshp* 1972
Sales 70.7MM^E *EMP* 1,000
SIC 8211 9411 Public elementary & secondary schools; Public elementary & secondary schools;
CIO: Mike Karl

D-U-N-S 80-674-3191
GEORGIA DEPARTMENT OF HUMAN RESOURCES
(*Suby of* EXECUTIVE OFFICE OF STATE OF GEORGIA) ★
2 Peachtree St Nw, Atlanta, GA 30303-3141
Tel (404) 651-9361 *Founded/Ownrshp* 2009
Sales NA *EMP* 23,000
SIC 9441 Administration of social & manpower programs; ; Administration of social & manpower programs;
CEO: Thomas Updike
Treas: Cathy McDade
Ofcr: Bobbie Bartlett
Ofcr: Gary Childers
Ofcr: Venkat Krishnan
CIO: John Stewart
Dir IT: Betsy Lerner
Dir IT: Andrew Miller
Software D: Douglas Simpson
Nrsg Dir: Kay Brooks
Pgrm Dir: Ebony Harris

D-U-N-S 00-973-5973
GEORGIA DEPARTMENT OF JUVENILE JUSTICE
(*Suby of* EXECUTIVE OFFICE OF STATE OF GEORGIA) ★
3408 Covington Hwy, Decatur, GA 30032-1513
Tel (404) 508-6500 *Founded/Ownrshp* 1996
Sales NA *EMP* 4,000
SIC 9222 ;
Ofcr: Jamyle Phillips
Dir IT: Doug Engle
IT Man: Jack Johnson
IT Man: Maleia Wilson
Genl Couns: Tracy Masters
Snr Mgr: John Pearson

D-U-N-S 80-747-9290
GEORGIA DEPARTMENT OF LABOR
LABOR, COMMISSIONER OF
(*Suby of* EXECUTIVE OFFICE OF STATE OF GEORGIA) ★
148 Andrew Yng Intl Blvd # 100, Atlanta, GA 30303-1751
Tel (404) 232-3540 *Founded/Ownrshp* 1911
Sales NA *EMP* 1,879
SIC 9651 Labor regulatory agency; ; Labor regulatory agency;
Treas: Patsy Morris
Ofcr: David Scherer
VP: Ed James
Exec: Sharon Baker
Prgrm Mgr: David Rollins
CIO: Linda Russell
IT Man: Don Cole
IT Man: Gregory Lane
Tech Mgr: David Kilbride
Sls Mgr: Linda Manis
Snr Mgr: Kenneth King
Board of Directors: Andrea Harper, Brooke Lucas

D-U-N-S 80-674-3399
GEORGIA DEPARTMENT OF MEDICAL ASSISTANCE
(*Suby of* GEORGIA DEPT OF COMMUNITY HEALTH) ★
2 Peachtree St Nw # 3950, Atlanta, GA 30303-3142
Tel (404) 651-5590 *Founded/Ownrshp* 1977
Sales NA *EMP* 510
SIC 9441 Administration of social & manpower programs; ; Administration of social & manpower programs;
Ql Cn Mgr: Arnita Watson

D-U-N-S 14-698-5544
GEORGIA DEPARTMENT OF NATURAL RESOURCES
(*Suby of* EXECUTIVE OFFICE OF STATE OF GEORGIA) ★
2 Martin Luther King Jr, Atlanta, GA 30334-9000
Tel (404) 656-3500 *Founded/Ownrshp* 1972
Sales NA *EMP* 1,900
SIC 9512

D-U-N-S 05-124-3074
GEORGIA DEPARTMENT OF PUBLIC HEALTH
(*Suby of* GEORGIA DEPARTMENT OF HUMAN RESOURCES) ★
2 Peachtree St Nw Fl 15, Atlanta, GA 30303-3142
Tel (404) 657-2700 *Founded/Ownrshp* 1972
Sales NA *EMP* 6,000
SIC 9431 Administration of public health programs; ; Administration of public health programs;
**COO:* Janie Brodnax
Dir Surg: Dafna Kanny
IT Man: Meshun Daniel
IT Man: Kathleen Robinson

D-U-N-S 80-674-3217
GEORGIA DEPARTMENT OF PUBLIC SAFETY
GA STATE PATROL
(*Suby of* EXECUTIVE OFFICE OF STATE OF GEORGIA) ★
959 E Confederate Ave Se, Atlanta, GA 30316-2531
Tel (404) 624-7739 *Founded/Ownrshp* 1937
Sales NA *EMP* 2,100
SIC 9229 Public order & safety statistics centers; ; Public order & safety statistics centers;
Ofcr: Winnis Preece
IT Man: Natalie Austin

D-U-N-S 80-674-3209
GEORGIA DEPARTMENT OF REVENUE
(*Suby of* EXECUTIVE OFFICE OF STATE OF GEORGIA) ★
1800 Century Blvd Ne # 1200, Atlanta, GA 30345-3202
Tel (877) 423-6711 *Founded/Ownrshp* 1923
Sales NA *EMP* 1,439
Accts State Of Georgia Department Of
SIC 9311 Finance, taxation & monetary policy; ; Finance, taxation & monetary policy;
VP: Massah David
Prgrm Mgr: Mary Anderson
Prgrm Mgr: John Coleman
CTO: Wes Brooks
QA Dir: Linda Waters
Netwrk Mgr: Geoffrey Catron
Netwrk Eng: Mark Sanders
Netwrk Eng: Steve Weatherby

D-U-N-S 80-738-2338
GEORGIA DEPARTMENT OF TRANSPORTATION
(*Suby of* EXECUTIVE OFFICE OF STATE OF GEORGIA) ★
600 W Peachtree St Nw, Atlanta, GA 30308-3607
Tel (404) 631-1014 *Founded/Ownrshp* 1972
Sales NA *EMP* 6,400
SIC 9621 Regulation, administration of transportation; ; Regulation, administration of transportation;
Ofcr: Shelia Smith
Comm Dir: Karlene Barron
Dir IT: Jeffrey Hill
IT Man: Theresa Ricks

D-U-N-S 12-341-2095
GEORGIA DEPT OF COMMUNITY HEALTH
(*Suby of* EXECUTIVE OFFICE OF STATE OF GEORGIA) ★
2 Peachtree St Nw Fl 5, Atlanta, GA 30303-3142
Tel (404) 656-4507 *Founded/Ownrshp* 1999
Sales NA *EMP* 550
SIC 9431 Administration of public health programs; ; Administration of public health programs;
COO: Debbie Hall
Ex Dir: Carol Snype
IT Man: Howard Leggett
Pgrm Dir: Ramona Clark
Snr Mgr: Ryan McNeal

D-U-N-S 03-364-2422
GEORGIA ELEVATOR CO
1807 1st Ave, Columbus, GA 31901-1001
Tel (706) 323-7070 *Founded/Ownrshp* 1951
Sales 40.0MM *EMP* 250
SIC 3534 Elevators & moving stairways; Elevators & moving stairways
CEO: Mark Boelhouwer
**Pr:* Henry L Barfield
**Sec:* Steve D Barfield
**VP:* David S Barfield

D-U-N-S 17-072-9227
GEORGIA ENERGY COOPERATIVE (AN ELECTRIC MEMBERSHIP CORP)
2100 E Exch Pl Ste 300, Tucker, GA 30084
Tel (770) 270-7500 *Founded/Ownrshp* 2001
Sales 232.0MM *EMP* 15
Accts Mcnair Mclemore Middlebrooks
SIC 4911 Electric services; Electric services
Pr: Glenn D Loomer
**VP:* Melissa Calzada
VP: Bill Verner
**VP:* John Winskie III
CTO: Louise Blackman
CTO: Roger Borkenhagen
CTO: Marty Williamson
DP Dir: John Broxson
Dir IT: Janet Katzenberger
Dir IT: Gary Williamson
IT Man: Ricky McGee

GEORGIA FARM BUREAU COMPANY
See GEORGIA FARM BUREAU MUTUAL INSURANCE CO

D-U-N-S 04-069-8284
GEORGIA FARM BUREAU FEDERATION INC
1620 Bass Rd, Macon, GA 31210-6503
Tel (478) 474-8411 *Founded/Ownrshp* 1937
Sales NA *EMP* 1,210
Accts Mcnair Mclemore Middlebrooks
SIC 6111 5154 8699 5191 Farmers Home Administration; Livestock; Farm bureau; Farm supplies; Farmers Home Administration; Livestock; Farm bureau; Farm supplies
Pr: Vincent Duvall
**Pr:* Zippy Duvall
**Sec:* Wayne Daniel
VP: Donald Childs
**VP:* Gerald Long

D-U-N-S 05-421-4093
GEORGIA FARM BUREAU MUTUAL INSURANCE CO
GEORGIA FARM BUREAU COMPANY
(*Suby of* GEORGIA FARM BUREAU FEDERATION INC) ★
1620 Bass Rd, Macon, GA 31210-6500
Tel (478) 474-0679 *Founded/Ownrshp* 1958
Sales NA *EMP* 1,210
Accts Porter Keadle Moore Llc Atla
SIC 6411 Insurance agents, brokers & service; Insurance agents, brokers & service
Pr: Vincent M Duvall
**Sec:* Carlos Wayne Daniel
Bd of Dir: Louis J Hunt
Bd of Dir: Gary H Paulk
Bd of Dir: Jimmy Perry
Bd of Dir: Marvin Ruark
Bd of Dir: Randy Ruff
Bd of Dir: James E Tate
Bd of Dir: Jeannie Tucker
Ofcr: Robert Puryear
VP: William Anderson
VP: Donald Childs
VP: Robert Fountain
VP: Gerald Long
VP: Larry Monroe

D-U-N-S 07-926-9089
GEORGIA FEDERAL RECOVERY AND AUTO AGENCY
GOVERNMENT
3581 Ivy Crest Way, Buford, GA 30519-4475
Tel (770) 945-5577 *Founded/Ownrshp* 1980
Sales NA *EMP* 457
SIC 9621 9111 9121 Regulation, administration of transportation; Executive offices, state & local; Legislative bodies, state & local; Regulation, administration of transportation; Executive offices, state & local; Legislative bodies, state & local

D-U-N-S 03-352-8076
GEORGIA GAS DISTRIBUTORS INC
6000 Lake Forrest Dr # 230, Atlanta, GA 30328-3824
Tel (404) 497-1600 *Founded/Ownrshp* 1974
Sales 24.6MM^E *EMP* 35
SIC 5172 Petroleum products
Pr: Gerald Misel Jr
Sls Mgr: Mark Mochowski

D-U-N-S 78-955-9478
GEORGIA GWINNETT COLLEGE
1000 University Center Ln, Lawrenceville, GA 30043-7409
Tel (678) 407-5000 *Founded/Ownrshp* 2006
Sales 30.1MM^E *EMP* 90
Accts Moore Stephens Tiller Llc Dul
SIC 8221 Colleges universities & professional schools
Pr: Daniel J Kaufman

D-U-N-S 36-074-9550
GEORGIA HARDWOODS INC
3061 Verona Ave, Buford, GA 30518-3572
Tel (770) 932-0640 *Founded/Ownrshp* 1990
Sales 24.1MM^E *EMP* 33
SIC 5031 Hardboard
CEO: Robert M Dyson
**Sec:* Joann K Dyson
Genl Mgr: Scott Wilson
IT Man: Connie Wiley
Mktg Dir: Billy Dyson

D-U-N-S 03-139-2124
GEORGIA HEART INSTITUTE INC
UNIVERSITY HOSPITAL
1350 Walton Way 10, Augusta, GA 30901-2612
Tel (706) 722-9011 *Founded/Ownrshp* 2001
Sales 44.1MM^E *EMP* 100
SIC 8062 General medical & surgical hospitals
COO: Marilyn Bowcutt
Dir Lab: Bobby Burnett
Dir Rad: Gip Young
Pathlgst: Kailash Sharma
Doctor: Agneta Troilius PHD
Pharmcst: Blair Bagwell
Pharmcst: Allen Hicks
Cert Phar: Sherri Carter

D-U-N-S 09-930-6029
GEORGIA HOUSING FINANCE AUTHORITY
60 Executive Pk S Ne Fl 2, Atlanta, GA 30329-2257
Tel (404) 679-4840 *Founded/Ownrshp* 1975
Sales NA *EMP* 196
Accts Reznick Group Pc Atlanta
SIC 6163 8322 Loan brokers; Individual & family services; Loan brokers; Individual & family services
Prin: Carmen Chubb
**Prin:* Marcia Paul

D-U-N-S 00-332-1619
GEORGIA INSTITUTE OF TECHNOLOGY
GEORGIA TECH
(*Suby of* BOARD OF REGENTS OF UNIVERSITY SYSTEM OF GEORGIA) ★
225 North Ave Nw, Atlanta, GA 30332-0002
Tel (404) 894-2000 *Founded/Ownrshp* 1885
Sales 1.1MMM *EMP* 5,932
SIC 8221

D-U-N-S 60-236-3905
GEORGIA KENWORTH INC
MHC KENWORTH - SAVANNAH
(*Suby of* MURPHY-HOFFMAN CO) ★
11120 Tomahawk Creek Pkwy, Leawood, KS 66211-2695
Tel (816) 483-6444 *Founded/Ownrshp* 2013
Sales 30.9MM^E *EMP* 94
SIC 5511 5531 7538 7532 Trucks, tractors & trailers: new & used; Truck equipment & parts; General automotive repair shops; Truck painting & lettering; Trucks, tractors & trailers: new & used; Truck equipment & parts; General automotive repair shops; Truck painting & lettering
CEO: Timothy R Murphy
**CFO:* Jeffrey W Johnson
Treas: Glenn Sikes
**Prin:* Lee Sikes

D-U-N-S 79-321-7527
■ GEORGIA L AMEDISYS L C
(*Suby of* AMEDISYS INC) ★
5959 S Shrwood Frest Blvd, Baton Rouge, LA 70816
Tel (225) 292-2031 *Founded/Ownrshp* 2007
Sales 11.8MM^E *EMP* 1,132^E
SIC 8082 Home health care services
Prin: Celeste Peiffer

D-U-N-S 01-454-0928 IMP
GEORGIA L SEJONG L C
(*Suby of* SEJONG INDUSTRIAL CO., LTD.)
1641 Lukken Indus Dr W, Lagrange, GA 30240-5703
Tel (706) 845-7091 *Founded/Ownrshp* 2009
Sales 138.0MM *EMP* 180
SIC 3714 Motor vehicle parts & accessories; Motor vehicle parts & accessories
Pr: Sungwoo OH
CFO: Jack Kim

D-U-N-S 80-289-2257
GEORGIA LOTTERY CORP
(*Suby of* EXECUTIVE OFFICE OF STATE OF GEORGIA) ★
250 Williams St Nw # 3000, Atlanta, GA 30303-1042
Tel (404) 215-5000 *Founded/Ownrshp* 1993
Sales 25.1MM^E *EMP* 260^E
SIC 7999 9199 Lottery operation; Lottery operation;
CEO: Debbie Dlugolenski Alford
Pr: Jeannie Lin
CFO: Joe Hong
Ex VP: Marty Greers
VP: Daniel Johnson
VP: Rosemarie Morse
VP: Teri Rosa
Ex Dir: Anabel Arellano
Ex Dir: Adrienne Gottlieb
Ex Dir: Maureen Greeley
Ex Dir: Betty Sharpe

D-U-N-S 06-760-5865
GEORGIA MASONRY SUPPLY
(*Suby of* OLDCASTLE INC) ★
125 Industrial Park Cir, Lawrenceville, GA 30046-4641
Tel (770) 963-5888 *Founded/Ownrshp* 2003
Sales 45.0MM *EMP* 50
SIC 5032

D-U-N-S 60-820-6835
GEORGIA MECHANICAL INC
5148 Carson Ct, Buford, GA 30518-5848
Tel (770) 614-9214 *Founded/Ownrshp* 1993
Sales 25.8MM^E *EMP* 65
SIC 1711 Warm air heating & air conditioning contractor
Pr: Kevin Reach
Pr: Jeff Dale
VP: Nic Ayoob
VP: Rick Northern
Sls Mgr: Thomas Cobb
Sls Mgr: Aisha Gillette

D-U-N-S 06-645-5924
GEORGIA MILITARY COLLEGE FOUNDATION INC
201 E Greene St, Milledgeville, GA 31061-3398
Tel (478) 445-0202 *Founded/Ownrshp* 1955
Sales 2.9MM *EMP* 450
Accts Mauldin & Jenkins Llc Bradent
SIC 8221 Colleges universities & professional schools; Colleges universities & professional schools
Pr: Mg Peter J Boylan
VP: Cynthia Allard
VP: Samuel Conn
VP: Jody Yearwood
Sls Mgr: Tina Lewis

D-U-N-S 94-090-0905
GEORGIA MOUNTAIN COMMUNITY SERVICES
AVITA COMMUNITY PARTNERS
4331 Thurmon Tanner Rd, Flowery Branch, GA 30542-2829
Tel (678) 513-5700 *Founded/Ownrshp* 1968
Sales 23.7MM^E *EMP* 400
Accts Robert Baker And Associates A
SIC 8093 Mental health clinic, outpatient; Mental health clinic, outpatient
CEO: Laura Tyler
**CFO:* Victor Bowers
IT Man: Cynthia Levi

D-U-N-S 07-937-5556
GEORGIA MUNICIPAL ASSOCIATION INC
GMA
201 Pryor St Sw, Atlanta, GA 30303-3606
Tel (404) 688-0472 *Founded/Ownrshp* 1969
Sales 109.0MM *EMP* 96E
Accts Crace Galvis Mcgrath Llc Ken
SIC 2711 2741 8611 Newspapers; Miscellaneous publishing; Trade associations; Newspapers; Miscellaneous publishing; Trade associations
Ex Dir: D Lamar Norton
Pr: Kelly Shields
Ex Dir: Jim Higdon
Mng Dir: Randy Meacham
Genl Couns: Alison Earles

GEORGIA NATURAL GAS
See SOUTHSTAR ENERGY SERVICES LLC

D-U-N-S 78-714-2447
■ **GEORGIA NATURAL GAS SERVICES INC**
(*Suby of* ATLANTA GAS LIGHT CO) ★
10 Peachtree Pl Ne, Atlanta, GA 30309-4497
Tel (404) 584-4000 *Founded/Ownrshp* 1964
Sales 33.5MME *EMP* 700
SIC 4924 Natural gas distribution; Natural gas distribution
Pr: Paula Rosput
**Pr:* Richard H Woodward
COO: Michael Braswell
**VP:* Stanley Price

D-U-N-S 06-149-4282
GEORGIA NORTH BRICK CO INC (GA)
N G B
2405 Oak St W, Cumming, GA 30041-6456
Tel (770) 886-6555 *Founded/Ownrshp* 1982
Sales 60.8MME *EMP* 142
SIC 5032 5082 Brick, except refractory; Masonry equipment & supplies; Brick, except refractory; Masonry equipment & supplies
CEO: John P Alvord
**Pr:* Keith Green
**CFO:* Forrest Green
VP: Larry Tarver
CIO: Dwaine Tony

D-U-N-S 03-383-8053
GEORGIA NORTH DISTRIBUTING CO (GA)
J & L VENTURES
3 Villa Dr Nw, Rome, GA 30165-1943
Tel (706) 232-2064 *Founded/Ownrshp* 1949, 1950
Sales 25.3MME *EMP* 50
SIC 5181 5182 Beer & other fermented malt liquors; Wine
Pr: Courtney Hizer
**Treas:* Villa S Hizer

D-U-N-S 17-353-0973
GEORGIA NORTH FOODS INC
BURGER KING
942 Tllah Fls Scnic Loop, Tallulah Falls, GA 30573
Tel (706) 754-5464 *Founded/Ownrshp* 1985
Sales 26.8MME *EMP* 621
SIC 5812 Fast-food restaurant, chain; Fast-food restaurant, chain
CEO: Johnny M Irvin
**Sec:* Irvin L David
Off Mgr: Jim Fridy

D-U-N-S 96-481-8467
GEORGIA NORTH TECHNICAL COLLEGE
1500 Highway 197 N, Clarkesville, GA 30523-4230
Tel (706) 754-7700 *Founded/Ownrshp* 1943
Sales 46.2MME *EMP* 426
SIC 8222 Technical institute; Technical institute
Pr: Gail Thaxton
**VP:* Carol Carson
Dir IT: James Watkins
Nrsg Dir: Melinda Shiflet
HC Dir: Amanda Mitchell
Snr Mgr: Michele Shirley

D-U-N-S 02-513-7076
GEORGIA NUT CO
LINDERHOUSE
7500 Linder Ave, Skokie, IL 60077-3270
Tel (847) 324-3600 *Founded/Ownrshp* 1945
Sales 24.3MME *EMP* 125
SIC 2064 5145

D-U-N-S 93-306-4404
GEORGIA OFFICE OF PLANNING AND BUDGET
(*Suby of* EXECUTIVE OFFICE OF STATE OF GEORGIA) ★
270 Washington St Sw # 8066, Atlanta, GA 30334-9056
Tel (404) 656-3820 *Founded/Ownrshp* 1999
Sales NA *EMP* 336
SIC 9199 General government administration; ; General government administration;
IT Man: Yvonne Turner

D-U-N-S 09-076-6890 IMP
GEORGIA OKEEFFE MUSEUM
217 Johnson St, Santa Fe, NM 87501-1826
Tel (505) 946-1000 *Founded/Ownrshp* 1995
Sales 58.9MM *EMP* 50
SIC 8412 Museums & art galleries
Mktg Mgr: Mara Harris

GEORGIA PACIFIC
See NEKOOSA PAPERS INC

D-U-N-S 82-930-1493
GEORGIA PACIFIC HOLDINGS INC
(*Suby of* KOCH INDUSTRIES INC) ★
13208 Hadley St Apt 1, Whittier, CA 90601-4531
Tel (626) 926-1474 *Founded/Ownrshp* 2008
Sales 13.4MMME *EMP* 46,275E
SIC 2676 2656 2435 2821 Sanitary paper products; Sanitary food containers; Hardwood veneer & plywood; Plastics materials & resins
CEO: Jorge Arroyo

D-U-N-S 92-929-3983
GEORGIA PACKAGING INC
918 8th Ave, Columbus, GA 31901-2830
Tel (706) 323-7316 *Founded/Ownrshp* 1995
Sales 30.0MM *EMP* 117
SIC 2671 Packaging paper & plastics film, coated & laminated; Packaging paper & plastics film, coated & laminated
Pr: Wesley P Swartout
**CFO:* Nichols Ruitenberg
**Treas:* Frederick L Ghent
**VP:* Stephen Sumption
Board of Directors: Howard East, Paul N Leitner, David M Thomas

D-U-N-S 80-476-2524
GEORGIA PERIMETER COLLEGE
(*Suby of* BOARD OF REGENTS OF UNIVERSITY SYSTEM OF GEORGIA) ★
3251 Panthersville Rd, Decatur, GA 30034-3832
Tel (678) 891-2300 *Founded/Ownrshp* 1964
Sales 55.8MM *EMP* 2,359
SIC 8222 Community college; Community college
Pr: Rob Watts
Ofcr: Heather Pharris
Ex VP: Ron Carrutch
**Ex VP:* Ron Carruth
VP: Diane Hickey
**VP:* Vincent June
**VP:* Ronald Stark
**VP:* Jeff Tarnowski
Exec: Lisa Lewis
Off Admin: Ganiyat Salami
Dir IT: Marisa Greenlee

D-U-N-S 61-708-1914
GEORGIA PIEDMONT TECHNICAL COLLEGE
(*Suby of* TCSG) ★
495 N Indian Creek Dr, Clarkston, GA 30021-2359
Tel (404) 297-9522 *Founded/Ownrshp* 1961
Sales 22.2MME *EMP* 550E
Accts Russell W Hinton Cpa Cgfm
SIC 8222 9411 Technical institute; ; Technical institute;
Pr: Robin W Hoffman
Ex VP: Larry Teems
VP: Cynthia Edwards
VP: Heather Pence

D-U-N-S 19-284-2222
GEORGIA PINES COMMUNITY SERVICE BOARD
1102 Smith Ave Ste K, Thomasville, GA 31792-5740
Tel (229) 225-4373 *Founded/Ownrshp* 2005
Sales 11.8MME *EMP* 312
SIC 8322 Individual & family services; Individual & family services
Ex Dir: Robert H Jones

D-U-N-S 19-601-1464
GEORGIA PIPE CO
(*Suby of* ALLIED TUBE & CONDUIT CORP) ★
1206 Sunset Dr, Thomasville, GA 31792-6355
Tel (229) 226-7337 *Founded/Ownrshp* 2006
Sales 72.1MME *EMP* 150
SIC 3084 Plastics pipe; Plastics pipe
CEO: John Williamson
**Pr:* Lelda Conner
**CFO:* James A Mallak
Genl Mgr: John Blust

GEORGIA PLANT
See MOBIS ALABAMA LLC

D-U-N-S 07-586-5469 IMP
GEORGIA PORTS AUTHORITY
GARDEN CITY TERMINAL
(*Suby of* EXECUTIVE OFFICE OF STATE OF GEORGIA) ★
2 Main St, Garden City, GA 31408-1403
Tel (912) 964-3811 *Founded/Ownrshp* 1945
Sales NA *EMP* 900
SIC 9621 Water vessels & port regulating agencies; Water vessels & port regulating agencies
Ex Dir: Curtis J Foltz
**COO:* Griffith Lynch
**Sec:* Alva Joseph Hopkins III
Rgnl Mgr: Pat Dinon
Admn Mgr: Betty Rappe
Dir IT: William Sutton
Info Man: Adam Lutz
Sales Exec: Robert Prescott
Manager: Thomas Wyville
Sls Mgr: Chip Hawkins
Sales Asso: Monica Garrett

D-U-N-S 00-692-4989 IMP
■ **GEORGIA POWER CO**
(*Suby of* SOUTHERN CO) ★
241 Ralph Mcgill Blvd Ne, Atlanta, GA 30308-3374
Tel (404) 506-6526 *Founded/Ownrshp* 1930
Sales 8.9MMM *EMP* 7,909
Tkr Sym GPEA *Exch* NYS
SIC 4911 Electric services; Distribution, electric power; Generation, electric power; Transmission, electric power; Electric services; Distribution, electric power; Generation, electric power; Transmission, electric power
Ch Bd: W Paul Bowers
CFO: W Ron Hinson
Chf Cred: Thomas P Bishop
Ex VP: W Craig Barrs
Ex VP: Horst Fanning
Ex VP: Eleanor Labrato
Ex VP: Joseph A Miller
Ex VP: Larry Westbrook
Ex VP: Anthony L Wilson
Sr VP: John L Pemberton
VP: Mark Berry
Exec: Susan Story
Board of Directors: Robert L Brown Jr, Anna R Cablik, Stephen S Green, Jimmy C Tallent, Charles K Tarbutton, Beverly Daniel Tatum, D Gary Thompson, Clyde C Tuggle, Richard W Ussery

GEORGIA PUBLIC BROADCASTING
See PUBLIC TELECOMMUNICATIONS COMMISSION GEORGIA

D-U-N-S 04-460-7708
GEORGIA PUBLIC WEB INC
1470 Riveredge Pkwy, Atlanta, GA 30328-4640
Tel (770) 661-2000 *Founded/Ownrshp* 2001
Sales 20.8MM *EMP* 33
SIC 4812 4813 Radio telephone communication; ; Radio telephone communication;
Pr: F David Muschamp
**CFO:* Eric Snell
**VP:* Jim Hendrickson
CIO: Karen Norwood
IT Man: Neil Fusillo
Netwrk Mgr: Jimmy Carey
VP Sls: Lew Griner

D-U-N-S 96-666-8691
GEORGIA REGENTS RESEARCH INSTITUTE INC
GRRI
(*Suby of* GEORGIA REGENTS UNIVERSITY) ★
1120 15th St Cj3301, Augusta, GA 30912-0004
Tel (706) 721-2592 *Founded/Ownrshp* 1980
Sales 59.4MM *EMP* 1
Accts Cherry Bekaert & Holland Llp
SIC 8731 Medical research, commercial; Medical research, commercial
Ex Dir: Sarah White
Ofcr: Stacey Kraemer
Assoc Dir: Lee A Merchen
Assoc Dir: John Thornton
Pathlgst: Rory Dalton
Pgrm Dir: David R Haburchak

D-U-N-S 06-534-8054
GEORGIA REGENTS UNIVERSITY
JOINT BOARD OF FAMILY PRACTICE
(*Suby of* BOARD OF REGENTS OF UNIVERSITY SYSTEM OF GEORGIA) ★
1120 15th St, Augusta, GA 30912-0004
Tel (800) 869-1113 *Founded/Ownrshp* 1828
Sales 522.5MM *EMP* 7,500
Accts Greg S Griffin State Auditor
SIC 8062 8221 Hospital, medical school affiliation; College, except junior; Hospital, medical school affiliation; College, except junior
Pr: Ricardo Azziz
**COO:* Robert Zeyfang
CFO: William Bowes
Ofcr: James Viebrock
Sr VP: Barry Goldstein
Sr VP: Douglas Miller
Sr VP: Sandra I McVcker
**VP:* Susan Barcus
DP Dir: Onley Howser
Dir IT: David Ernest
Dir IT: Shelley Mishoe

D-U-N-S 96-774-0445
GEORGIA REGENTS UNIVERSITY
(*Suby of* BOARD OF REGENTS OF UNIVERSITY SYSTEM OF GEORGIA) ★
1120 15th St, Augusta, GA 30912-0004
Tel (706) 721-0011 *Founded/Ownrshp* 2013
Sales 522.5MM *EMP* 5,000
Accts Greg S Griffin Atlanta Geor
SIC 8221 University; University
Pr: Ricardo Azziz
COO: Steven Scott
**CFO:* James Jones
Assoc VP: Christopher McKinney
Ex VP: David Hefner
Ex VP: Karla Leeper
Ex VP: Anthony Wagner
Sr VP: Mark Hamrick
VP: Ralph Alee
VP: William Bowes
VP: Kevin Dellsperger
VP: Franklin Smith
VP: Betty Wray

D-U-N-S 01-118-7002
GEORGIA REGENTS UNIVERSITY - SUMMERVILLE CAMPUS
(*Suby of* BOARD OF REGENTS OF UNIVERSITY SYSTEM OF GEORGIA) ★
2500 Walton Way, Augusta, GA 30904-4562
Tel (706) 721-1469 *Founded/Ownrshp* 2013
Sales 27.5MME *EMP* 520E
SIC 8221

D-U-N-S 95-679-2469
GEORGIA REGIONAL HOSPITAL AT SAVANNAH FOUNDATION INC
1915 Eisenhower Dr, Savannah, GA 31406-5027
Tel (912) 356-2011 *Founded/Ownrshp* 1970
Sales 9.9MME *EMP* 350
SIC 8063 Hospital for the mentally ill; Hospital for the mentally ill
Dir Rad: Helene Small
Nrsg Dir: Beth Jones
HC Dir: Merline Minott

D-U-N-S 17-710-5095
GEORGIA REHABILITATION INSTITUTE INC
1355 Independence Dr, Augusta, GA 30901-1037
Tel (706) 823-8505 *Founded/Ownrshp* 1985
Sales 36.5MME *EMP* 50
Accts Cherry Bekaert Llp Augusta G
SIC 8361 Residential care; Residential care for the handicapped; Home for the physically handicapped; Residential care; Residential care for the handicapped; Home for the physically handicapped
Pr: Dennis B Skelley
Dir Risk M: Doug Bryant
IT Man: Beth Miller

D-U-N-S 07-580-9660
GEORGIA SOUTHERN STAFFING INC
TROJAN LABOR
509 Saint Francis St, Tallahassee, FL 32301-2230
Tel (850) 222-2030 *Founded/Ownrshp* 1998
Sales 11.7MME *EMP* 500
SIC 7363 Temporary help service; Temporary help service
Pr: Amy L Freeland

D-U-N-S 06-536-1784
GEORGIA SOUTHERN UNIVERSITY
(*Suby of* BOARD OF REGENTS OF UNIVERSITY SYSTEM OF GEORGIA) ★
1582 Southern Dr, Statesboro, GA 30458
Tel (912) 681-5224 *Founded/Ownrshp* 1906
Sales 206.1MM *EMP* 1,700
Accts Greg S Griffin Atlanta Geor
SIC 8221 University; University
Pr: Brooks Keel
Ofcr: Dawn Oliver
Comm Dir: David Thompson
Opers Supe: Michael Mahon
Mktg Mgr: Tess Kiser
Snr Mgr: Beth Durodoye

D-U-N-S 07-587-3570
GEORGIA SOUTHWESTERN STATE UNIVERSITY
(*Suby of* BOARD OF REGENTS OF UNIVERSITY SYSTEM OF GEORGIA) ★
800 Gsw State Univ Dr, Americus, GA 31709-4376
Tel (229) 928-1273 *Founded/Ownrshp* 1908
Sales 29.2MME *EMP* 250
SIC 8221 University; University
Pr: Randolph A Barksdale
**Pr:* Dr Michael Hanes
Treas: Michelle Morton
Ofcr: Von D Bacon
VP: Brian Adler
VP: Anna Champion
VP: Gaye S Hayes
VP: Samuel Miller
VP: Helen Tate
IT Man: Beverly Carroll
IT Man: William Hackett

D-U-N-S 80-859-7223
GEORGIA STATE BOARD OF PARDONS & PAROLES
(*Suby of* EXECUTIVE OFFICE OF STATE OF GEORGIA) ★
2 Martn Lthr Kng Jr Se, Atlanta, GA 30334-9000
Tel (404) 656-5651 *Founded/Ownrshp* 1970
Sales 28.8MME *EMP* 900
Accts Claude L Vickers State Audito
SIC 8322 9223 Parole office; ; Parole office;
Ch: Walter Ray
VP: David Sheffield

D-U-N-S 80-859-7280
GEORGIA STATE BOARD OF WORKERS COMPENSATION
(*Suby of* EXECUTIVE OFFICE OF STATE OF GEORGIA) ★
270 Peachtree St Nw # 500, Atlanta, GA 30303-1299
Tel (404) 656-3875 *Founded/Ownrshp* 1970
Sales NA *EMP* 300
SIC 9441 Workmen's compensation office, government; ; Workmen's compensation office, government;
Prin: Jorge Carolin
Prin: Harold Dawkins

D-U-N-S 07-342-5951
GEORGIA STATE UNIVERSITY
(*Suby of* BOARD OF REGENTS OF UNIVERSITY SYSTEM OF GEORGIA) ★
140 Decatur St Se, Atlanta, GA 30303-3204
Tel (404) 413-2000 *Founded/Ownrshp* 1955
Sales 398.1MM *EMP* 5,500
SIC 8221

D-U-N-S 12-094-4509
GEORGIA STATE UNIVERSITY FOUNDATION INC
533 1 Park Pl Ste 533, Atlanta, GA 30303
Tel (404) 413-3402 *Founded/Ownrshp* 1958
Sales 38.1MM *EMP* 76
Accts Cherry Bekaert & Holland Llp
SIC 8399 Fund raising organization, non-fee basis; Fund raising organization, non-fee basis
Pr: Walter Massey
**Ch Bd:* Kenetth Bernhardt
**VP:* Dale Palmer

D-U-N-S 83-732-2494
GEORGIA STATE UNIVERSITY RESEARCH FOUNDATION INC
30 Courtland St Se, Atlanta, GA 30303-3011
Tel (404) 413-3529 *Founded/Ownrshp* 2004
Sales 62.7MM *EMP* 10
Accts Cherry Bekaert & Holland Llp
SIC 8732 Educational research; Educational research
Ch Bd: James Weyhenmeyer
**V Ch:* Monica Swahn
**Treas:* Jerry Rackliffe
CIO: Mary Casto
Dir IT: William Gruszka
Dir IT: Rob Poh
Info Man: Robin Dent

D-U-N-S 96-774-9933
GEORGIA STEVEDORE ASSOCIATION INTL LONGSHOREMENS ASSOC VACATION BENEFITS
10 Mersey Way, Savannah, GA 31405-1583
Tel (912) 233-0218 *Founded/Ownrshp* 2011
Sales 31.3MM *EMP* 2E
Accts Tjs Deemer Dana Llp Savannah
SIC 8699 Membership organizations; Membership organizations

D-U-N-S 96-030-8591
GEORGIA SYSTEM OPERATIONS CORP
2100 E Exchange Pl, Tucker, GA 30084-5342
Tel (770) 270-7200 *Founded/Ownrshp* 1996
Sales 77.3MM *EMP* 250
SIC 4911

GEORGIA TECH
See GEORGIA INSTITUTE OF TECHNOLOGY

D-U-N-S 36-412-4651
GEORGIA TECH APPLIED RESEARCH CORP
GTARC
(*Suby of* GEORGIA TECH RESEARCH CORP) ★
505 10th St Nw, Atlanta, GA 30318-5775
Tel (404) 894-4819 *Founded/Ownrshp* 1998
Sales 340.8MM *EMP* 1,100ᴱ
Accts Cherry Bekaert Llp Atlanta G
SIC 8731 Commercial physical research; Commercial physical research
CEO: Stephen Cross
**Pr:* G Wayne Clough
**Ch:* Leslie R Sibert
VP: Jilda D Garton

D-U-N-S 80-822-4815 IMP
GEORGIA TECH ATHLETIC ASSOCIATION
150 Bobby Dodd Way Nw, Atlanta, GA 30332-2500
Tel (404) 894-6668 *Founded/Ownrshp* 1934
Sales 66.6MM *EMP* 165
Accts James Moore & Co Pl Gainesvil
SIC 7941 Sports clubs, managers & promoters
CEO: Daniel Radakovich
**CFO:* James Franklin Hardymon
Brnch Mgr: Wayne Clough

D-U-N-S 09-779-6411
GEORGIA TECH FOUNDATION INC
760 Spring St Nw Ste 400, Atlanta, GA 30308-1028
Tel (404) 894-8345 *Founded/Ownrshp* 1932
Sales 174.5MM *EMP* 30
Accts Kpmg Llp Atlanta Ga
SIC 8399 6282 Fund raising organization, non-fee basis; Investment advice; Fund raising organization, non-fee basis; Investment advice
Pr: John B Carter Jr
**Ch Bd:* Charles Moseley
**CFO:* Mark W Long
CIO: James Taylor
Board of Directors: Hubert Harris

D-U-N-S 09-739-4084
GEORGIA TECH RESEARCH CORP
505 10th St Nw, Atlanta, GA 30318-5775
Tel (404) 894-4819 *Founded/Ownrshp* 1937
Sales 653.0MM *EMP* 2,210
SIC 8732

D-U-N-S 82-561-7202
GEORGIA TECHNOLOGY AUTHORITY
GTA
(*Suby of* EXECUTIVE OFFICE OF STATE OF GEORGIA) ★
47 Trinity Ave Sw, Atlanta, GA 30334-9006
Tel (404) 463-2300 *Founded/Ownrshp* 1990
Sales 142.4MMᴱ *EMP* 164ᴱ
SIC 4899 9199 Communication signal enhancement network system; ; Communication signal enhancement network system;
Ex Dir: Calvin Rhodes
**COO:* Dean Johnson
VP: Tom Fruman
Comm Dir: Paula Calhoun
Rgnl Mgr: Michael Carrick
CIO: Tom Wade
Software D: Arthur Broomes
Snr Mgr: Elliot Johnson
Snr Mgr: Gene Reardon
Snr Mgr: Mark Reardon
Snr Mgr: Doug Shaddix

D-U-N-S 01-704-1687
GEORGIA TENASKA PARTNERS L P
14302 Fnb Pkwy, Omaha, NE 68154-5212
Tel (402) 691-9500 *Founded/Ownrshp* 1998
Sales 53.0MM *EMP* 12
Accts Kpmg Llp Omaha Ne
SIC 4911 Generation, electric power; Generation, electric power
Pt: Howard Hawks

GEORGIA TRANSFORMER
See CARAVELS LLC

D-U-N-S 95-862-7903
GEORGIA TRANSMISSION CORP
GTC
2100 E Exchange Pl, Tucker, GA 30084-5342
Tel (770) 270-7400 *Founded/Ownrshp* 1996
Sales 263.2MM *EMP* 285
SIC 4911 Generation, electric power; Distribution, electric power; Generation, electric power; Distribution, electric power
Pr: Jerry Donovan
**CFO:* Barbara Hampton

D-U-N-S 78-891-6989 EXP
GEORGIA UNDERGROUND & SUPPLY INC
5158 Kennedy Rd Ste G, Forest Park, GA 30297-2002
Tel (404) 675-7999 *Founded/Ownrshp* 1991
Sales 42.0MMᴱ *EMP* 18ᴱ
SIC 5051 5082 Cable, wire; General construction machinery & equipment
CEO: Cindy Bartosh
**CFO:* David Bartosh

D-U-N-S 07-971-1280
GEORGIA UNITED CREDIT UNION
6705 Sugarloaf Pkwy # 100, Duluth, GA 30097-4926
Tel (770) 476-6400 *Founded/Ownrshp* 2010
Sales NA *EMP* 197ᴱ
Accts Schwartz Cole And Associates L
SIC 6062 State credit unions, not federally chartered
CEO: Warren Butler
Chf Mktg O: Jason Halperin
Ex VP: Todd Gustafson
Sr VP: Mike London
Brnch Mgr: Vonda Bledsoe
IT Man: Anthony Frazier
Opers Mgr: Doreen Blaha
Mktg Dir: Jamie Fristoe
Mktg Mgr: Nicole Simpson

D-U-N-S 80-987-2310
■ **GEORGIA WASTE SYSTEMS INC**
WASTE MANAGEMENT OF ATLANTA
(*Suby of* WASTE MANAGEMENT HOLDINGS INC) ★
1001 Fannin St Ste 4000, Houston, TX 77002-6711
Tel (713) 512-6200 *Founded/Ownrshp* 1999
Sales 83.4MMᴱ *EMP* 335
SIC 4953 Refuse collection & disposal services
Pr: David Steiner
**COO:* James Trevathan
**CFO:* James Fish Jr

D-U-N-S 83-317-4571
GEORGIA WEST MEDICAL CENTER INC
WEST GEORGIA HEALTH
1514 Vernon Rd, Lagrange, GA 30240-4131
Tel (706) 882-1411 *Founded/Ownrshp* 2006
Sales 160.2MM *EMP* 1,500
Accts Dixon Hughes Goodman Llp Atla
SIC 8062 General medical & surgical hospitals; General medical & surgical hospitals
CEO: Gerald N Fulks
Chf Rad: Aparna Velnat
**Sr VP:* Charis Acree
VP Admn: John Flock
Ex Dir: Susan Burdick
Dir Sec: John Whitney
IT Man: Sherry Holliday
Doctor: Clarence Alford
Doctor: William Ayers
Doctor: Robert Copeland MD
Doctor: Rod Duraski

D-U-N-S 13-255-2092
GEORGIA WORLD CONGRESS CENTER
CENTENNIAL OLYMPIC PARK
285 Andrew Young Intl, Atlanta, GA 30313-1591
Tel (404) 223-4000 *Founded/Ownrshp* 1976
Sales 66.6MMᴱ *EMP* 528
SIC 6512 7389 Property operation, auditoriums & theaters; Convention & show services; Property operation, auditoriums & theaters; Convention & show services
CEO: Dan Graveline
**COO:* Kevin Duvall
**CFO:* Sherrie Spinks
Treas: Anne Hennessy
Ofcr: Mercy Mbugua
Ofcr: Ken Snow
Ofcr: Annie Thomas
Exec: Charles Pridgen
Dir Soc: Jim Ridgway
Comm Dir: Jennifer Lemaster
Ex Dir: Daniel Grabeline

D-U-N-S 04-935-1419
GEORGIA-CAROLINA BANCSHARES INC
3527 Wheeler Rd, Augusta, GA 30909-6718
Tel (706) 731-6600 *Founded/Ownrshp* 1997
Sales NA *EMP* 165ᴱ
SIC 6022 State commercial banks

GEORGIA-PACIFIC
See COLOR-BOX LLC

D-U-N-S 80-787-1137 EXP
GEORGIA-PACIFIC BREWTON LLC
G P
(*Suby of* GEORGIA-PACIFIC LLC) ★
32224 Highway 31, Brewton, AL 36426-8191
Tel (251) 867-3622 *Founded/Ownrshp* 2007
Sales 174.7MMᴱ *EMP* 450
SIC 2611 2679 Pulp mills; Paper products, converted; Pulp mills; Paper products, converted
Pr: Darren Barker
COO: Maria Grasso
Sr VP: Mike E Adams
Genl Mgr: Jeff Joyce
Opers Mgr: Glenn Smith
Snr Mgr: Robert Diercks

D-U-N-S 80-821-4881 EXP
GEORGIA-PACIFIC CHEMICALS LLC
(*Suby of* GP OPERATIONS HOLDINGS LLC) ★
133 Peachtree St Ne, Atlanta, GA 30303-1804
Tel (404) 652-4000 *Founded/Ownrshp* 2007
Sales 22.0MMᴱ *EMP* 87ᴱ
SIC 2821 2869 Melamine resins, melamine-formaldehyde; Formaldehyde (formalin)
Pr: Rick Urschel
Sfty Dirs: Bob Schanaman
Snr Mgr: Cecil Rasmussen

D-U-N-S 80-821-5367
GEORGIA-PACIFIC CORRUGATED LLC
(*Suby of* GEORGIA-PACIFIC PACKAGING LLC) ★
133 Peachtree St Ne # 1, Atlanta, GA 30303-1812
Tel (404) 652-4000 *Founded/Ownrshp* 2007
Sales 43.1MMᴱ *EMP* 257ᴱ
SIC 2656 Paper cups, plates, dishes & utensils
VP: Garnet Roni
VP: Roni Garnet
IT Man: Denise Frosina

D-U-N-S 86-727-3609 IMP/EXP
GEORGIA-PACIFIC FOUNDATION INC
(*Suby of* KOCH INDUSTRIES INC) ★
133 Peachtree St Ne # 4810, Atlanta, GA 30303-1821
Tel (404) 652-4000 *Founded/Ownrshp* 2006
Sales 81.6MMᴱ *EMP* 365
SIC 5031 Lumber, plywood & millwork; Lumber, plywood & millwork
Pr: Curley M Dossman Jr

D-U-N-S 07-872-0693
GEORGIA-PACIFIC GYPSUM II LLC
(*Suby of* GEORGIA-PACIFIC LLC) ★
133 Peachtree St Ne, Atlanta, GA 30303-1804
Tel (404) 652-4000 *Founded/Ownrshp* 2013
Sales 22.7MMᴱ *EMP* 340
SIC 3275 Gypsum products; Gypsum products
Pr: Brent H Paugh

D-U-N-S 00-902-0777 EXP
GEORGIA-PACIFIC LLC
(*Suby of* GEORGIA PACIFIC HOLDINGS INC) ★
133 Peachtree St Ne # 4810, Atlanta, GA 30303-1821
Tel (404) 652-4000 *Founded/Ownrshp* 2005
Sales 13.4MMMᴱ *EMP* 46,270
SIC 2676 2656 2653 2435 2821 3275 Sanitary paper products; Sanitary food containers; Corrugated & solid fiber boxes; Hardwood veneer & plywood; Plastics materials & resins; Gypsum products; Sanitary paper products; Sanitary food containers; Corrugated & solid fiber boxes; Hardwood veneer & plywood; Plastics materials & resins; Gypsum products
Pr: James Hannan
Pr: Sean Fallmann
Pr: Brent Paugh
Pr: Rick Rising
Pr: Bill Sleeper
Pr: Lee M Thomas
COO: Clifford Nelson
CFO: Sharon Esposito-Mayer
**CFO:* Tyler Woolson
Bd of Dir: Estella McGriff
Ofcr: Mark Dejean
Ofcr: William A Nahill
**Ex VP:* W Wesley Jones
Ex VP: Wesley Jones
Ex VP: Steve Klinger
Ex VP: Mark Luetters
Ex VP: Dave Paterson
Ex VP: Kathleen Ann Walters
**Sr VP:* Michael E Adams
**Sr VP:* Julie Brehm
**Sr VP:* Tye Darland
Board of Directors: Steven J Feilmeier, Richard H Fink, Dale W Gibbens, Charles G Koch, John C Pittenger, David L Robertson

D-U-N-S 80-813-4006 EXP
GEORGIA-PACIFIC PACKAGING LLC
(*Suby of* GP OPERATIONS HOLDINGS LLC) ★
133 Peachtree St Ne # 700, Atlanta, GA 30303-1804
Tel (404) 652-4000 *Founded/Ownrshp* 2006
Sales 89.2MMᴱ *EMP* 864
SIC 2656 Paper cups, plates, dishes & utensils; Paper cups, plates, dishes & utensils

D-U-N-S 07-872-0683
GEORGIA-PACIFIC PANEL PRODUCTS LLC
(*Suby of* GEORGIA-PACIFIC LLC) ★
133 Peachtree St Ne, Atlanta, GA 30303-1804
Tel (404) 652-4000 *Founded/Ownrshp* 2013
Sales 49.3MMᴱ *EMP* 640
SIC 2675 Panels, cardboard, die-cut: made from purchased materials; Panels, cardboard, die-cut: made from purchased materials
Pr: Mark E Luetters

D-U-N-S 80-802-7945 EXP
GEORGIA-PACIFIC WOOD PRODUCTS SOUTH LLC
(*Suby of* GEORGIA-PACIFIC LLC) ★
133 Peachtree St Ne, Atlanta, GA 30303-1804
Tel (404) 652-4000 *Founded/Ownrshp* 2007
Sales 163.6MMᴱ *EMP* 2,425
SIC 2656 Paper cups, plates, dishes & utensils; Paper cups, plates, dishes & utensils
Pr: Mike Rehwinkel

D-U-N-S 03-120-9304 IMP
GEORGIAN AMERICAN ALLOYS INC
200 S Biscayne Blvd # 5500, Miami, FL 33131-2333
Tel (305) 375-7560 *Founded/Ownrshp* 2012
Sales 166.9MMᴱ *EMP* 425
SIC 1061 Manganese ores mining; Manganese ores mining
Pr: Mordechai Korf
**CFO:* Barry Nuss
Pr Dir: Zakaria Zalikashvili
Counsel: Robert Powell

D-U-N-S 08-095-1007
GEORGIAN COURT UNIVERSITY
900 Lakewood Ave, Lakewood, NJ 08701-2600
Tel (732) 987-2200 *Founded/Ownrshp* 1924
Sales 57.8MM *EMP* 854
Accts Grant Thornton Llp Philadelph
SIC 8221 Colleges & universities; Colleges & universities
Pr: Rosemary E Jeffries
**Treas:* Suzanne Elliott RSM
Trst: Edmund Bennett
Trst: Raymond F Shea
Ofcr: Stephanie Coutros
VP: Margaret Huber
VP: Mellissia Zanjani
CIO: Arlene Martinez
Dir IT: Jack Porcelli
IT Man: Peter Lisowsky
Doctor: Margaret Taylor-Ulizio

GEORGIAN MANOR APTS
See HARTMAN AND TYNER INC

D-U-N-S 08-008-7760
GEORGIAS OWN CREDIT UNION
1155 Peachtree St Ne # 400, Atlanta, GA 30309-7629
Tel (404) 874-1166 *Founded/Ownrshp* 1934
Sales NA *EMP* 211
SIC 6062 State credit unions, not federally chartered; State credit unions, not federally chartered
Pr: Charlotte S Ayers
**Ch Bd:* C Edward Heath
Pr: Lorenzo Brown
**CEO:* David Preter
COO: William Lusk
CFO: Linda Finch
**CFO:* William L Lusk
**Treas:* Patrick H Casey
Ofcr: Julie Andriano
Ofcr: Cedric Horton
VP: Dan Denning
VP: Amy Eagan
VP: Adam Marlowe
VP: Barbara J Takacs

GEORGIOU
See KOLONAKI

D-U-N-S 62-513-8102
GEORGIOU RETAIL STORES
ALEXIA NATURAL FASHIONS
(*Suby of* GEORGIOU) ★
135 Bluxome St, San Francisco, CA 94107-1507
Tel (415) 554-8000 *Founded/Ownrshp* 1988
Sales 22.6MMᴱ *EMP* 400
SIC 5621 Women's clothing stores; Women's clothing stores
Pr: George Georgiou
Dir Soc: Maureen Boyle

D-U-N-S 00-379-7776
GEOSOUTHERN ENERGY CORP
1425 Lake Front Cir # 200, The Woodlands, TX 77380-3631
Tel (281) 363-9161 *Founded/Ownrshp* 1981
Sales 27.1MMᴱ *EMP* 30
SIC 1311 Crude petroleum production; Natural gas production
Pr: George Bishop
**VP:* Margaret Woodward Molleston

D-U-N-S 03-924-7630 IMP/EXP
▲ **GEOSPACE TECHNOLOGIES CORP**
7007 Pinemont Dr, Houston, TX 77040-6601
Tel (713) 986-4444 *Founded/Ownrshp* 1980
Sales 84.8MM *EMP* 978
Accts Bdo Usa Llp Houston Texas
Tkr Sym GEOS *Exch* NGS
SIC 3829 3826 Seismographs; Seismometers; Seismoscopes; Thermal analysis instruments, laboratory type; Plastics film; Seismographs; Seismometers; Seismoscopes; Thermal analysis instruments, laboratory type
Pr: Walter R Wheeler
**Ch Bd:* Gary D Owens
CFO: Thomas T McEntire
Ex VP: Robbin B Adams
**Sr VP:* Michael J Sheen
VP: Joan Wheeler
Board of Directors: Thomas L Davis, Edgar R Giesinger, Tina M Langtry, Richard F Miles, William H Moody, Charles H Still

D-U-N-S 13-754-2788
GEOSTABILIZATION INTERNATIONAL LLC
GSI
543 31 Rd, Grand Junction, CO 81504-5772
Tel (970) 210-6170 *Founded/Ownrshp* 2002
Sales 35.0MMᴱ *EMP* 60ᴱ
SIC 1542 1611 Design & erection, combined: non-residential; General contractor, highway & street construction
CEO: Tim Ruckman
Pr: Colby Barrett
VP: Kim Ruckman

GEOSTRUCTURES
See GEOCONSTRUCTORS INC

D-U-N-S 12-249-2390
GEOSYNTEC CONSULTANTS INC
900 Broken Sound Pkwy Nw # 2, Boca Raton, FL 33487-3513
Tel (561) 995-0900 *Founded/Ownrshp* 1983
Sales 285.6MMᴱ *EMP* 850
Accts Grant Thornton Llp
SIC 8711 Engineering services; Engineering services
CEO: Rudolph Bonaparte
**CFO:* Jon Dickinson
**Ex VP:* Thierry Sanglerat
**Sr VP:* Peter Zeeb
VP: Mark Grivetti
Prin: Susan Hill
Snr PM: Steve Fitzwilliam

GEOTEC LABS
See ENPROTEC / HIBBS & TODD INC

D-U-N-S 07-624-4904 EXP
GEOTECH ENVIRONMENTAL EQUIPMENT INC
2650 E 40th Ave, Denver, CO 80205-3604
Tel (303) 320-4764 *Founded/Ownrshp* 1978
Sales 20.4MMᴱ *EMP* 80ᴱ
SIC 3823 Industrial instrmnts msrmnt display/control process variable; Water quality monitoring & control systems
CEO: Jerry L Popiel
**Sec:* Wes Allbritten
VP: Mickele Bragg
**VP:* Jeffrey Popiel
Off Mgr: David Hathaway
IT Man: Leonard Don
IT Man: Ladon Leonard
IT Man: Mike Pedrick
Prd Mgr: Frank Gonzales
Oper/Mgr: Janell Spiker
Natl Sales: Brett Krohn

D-U-N-S 11-904-5870
GEOTECHNOLOGY INC
11816 Lackland Rd Ste 150, Saint Louis, MO 63146-4263
Tel (314) 997-7440 *Founded/Ownrshp* 1984
Sales 20.2MM *EMP* 165
Accts Abeles And Hoffman Pc Saint
SIC 8711 Consulting engineer; Consulting engineer
CEO: Ed D Alizadeh
**CFO:* James Howe
VP: John Baker
**VP:* Frank Callanan
**VP:* Dominic Grana
**VP:* Jim Howe
**VP:* Rick Pershall
IT Man: Ed Dromgoole

D-U-N-S 07-884-6113
GEOTEK LLC
PUPI
1421 2nd Ave Nw, Stewartville, MN 55976-1615
Tel (507) 533-6076 *Founded/Ownrshp* 2008
Sales 54.5MMᴱ *EMP* 120
SIC 5033 Fiberglass building materials
CEO: Dale Nordquist
Pr: Steve Volkman
CFO: Amy Donahoe

VP: Dean Casad
Dir IT: Kar Harris
Mfg Mgr: Karl Clausen
Opers Mgr: Julie Underdahl
S&M/VP: Peter Surmak

D-U-N-S 18-504-9681
GEOTEMPS INC
970 Caughlin Xing Ste 102, Reno, NV 89519-0691
Tel (775) 746-7146 *Founded/Ownrshp* 1986
Sales 17.5MM^E *EMP* 400
SIC 7363 7361 8999 8742 1481

D-U-N-S 11-597-9031
GEOTRACE TECHNOLOGIES INC
12141 Wickchester Ln # 200, Houston, TX 77079-1238
Tel (281) 497-8440 *Founded/Ownrshp* 1989
Sales 58.0MM *EMP* 194
SIC 7374

D-U-N-S 17-126-9389
GEOWIRELESS INC
3125 Ashley Phosphate Rd # 110, North Charleston, SC 29418-8419
Tel (843) 277-1177 *Founded/Ownrshp* 2005
Sales 32.0MM *EMP* 20
SIC 4899 8322 Communication signal enhancement network system; Emergency social services
Pr: John Hearton
Bd of Dir: Rodger Johnson
IT Man: Anthony George

GEP
See NB VENTURES INC

D-U-N-S 16-831-2002
GEPA HOTEL OPERATOR DAYTONA BEACH LLC
HILTON DAYTONA BCH
100 N Atlantic Ave, Daytona Beach, FL 32118-4204
Tel (386) 254-8200 *Founded/Ownrshp* 2003
Sales NA *EMP* 500
SIC 7011

D-U-N-S 09-671-3490
GEPA HOTEL OWNER HOUSTON LLC
HOUSTON MARRIOTT WESTCHASE
2900 Briarpark Dr, Houston, TX 77042-3704
Tel (713) 978-7400 *Founded/Ownrshp* 2007
Sales 21.4MM^E *EMP* 400
SIC 7011 7389 Hotel, franchised; Office facilities & secretarial service rental; Hotel, franchised; Office facilities & secretarial service rental
Mng Dir: Harry Greenblatt
Sls Mgr: Pam Lewis

D-U-N-S 09-528-4550
GEPHART ELECTRIC CO INC
3550 Labore Rd Ste 11, Saint Paul, MN 55110-5113
Tel (651) 484-4900 *Founded/Ownrshp* 1983
Sales 51.7MM^E *EMP* 210^E
SIC 1731 Electrical work; Electrical work
Pr: Carol Heinsch
**CEO:* Lawrence Heinsch
**VP:* David Cords
Sfty Dirs: Claudia Pallansch
Mktg Dir: Scot Moser

D-U-N-S 00-385-6994
GERACE CONSTRUCTION CO INC (MI)
4055 S Saginaw Rd, Midland, MI 48640-8501
Tel (989) 496-2440 *Founded/Ownrshp* 1963
Sales 32.3MM^E *EMP* 100
SIC 1542 1541 1731

D-U-N-S 07-576-0843
GERALD A MARTIN LTD
GERALD MARTIN GENERAL CONTR
4901 Mcleod Rd Ne Ste A, Albuquerque, NM 87109-2158
Tel (505) 828-1144 *Founded/Ownrshp* 1974
Sales 30.7MM^E *EMP* 84
SIC 1542 Commercial & office building, new construction; Commercial & office building, new construction
Pr: Victoria E Martin
**Ch Bd:* Gerald A Martin
**Pr:* Fred Gorenz
**CFO:* Keri Adrian
**Treas:* Zane Martin
Sfty Mgr: Brian Costanzo
Board of Directors: Jonathan Bent, Jack Dicky, Gerald Martin, Victoria Martin, Zane Martin, Grant Warner

GERALD CHMPN REGIONAL MED CTR
See OTERO COUNTY HOSPITAL ASSOCIATION INC

D-U-N-S 01-820-9320
GERALD GRAIN CENTER INC
14540 County Road U, Napoleon, OH 43545-9747
Tel (800) 783-8015 *Founded/Ownrshp* 1931
Sales 22.0MM^E *EMP* 46
SIC 5153

D-U-N-S 00-577-7651
GERALD H PHIPPS INC
GH PHIPPS CNSTR COMPANIES
5995 Greenwood Ste 100, Greenwood Village, CO 80111
Tel (303) 571-5377 *Founded/Ownrshp* 1952
Sales 194.9MM^E *EMP* 350
Accts Eks&H Llp Fort Collins Color
SIC 1542 Commercial & office building, new construction; School building construction; Hospital construction; Commercial & office building, new construction; School building construction; Hospital construction
Pr: Kurt Klanderud
**CFO:* Rhonda Kay
**VP:* Kevin Barden
**VP:* Gary Constant
**VP:* Chris Pedersen
Dir Bus: Victoria Hatfield
Sls Dir: Matt Paull
Corp Couns: Danielle A Curtiss
Snr PM: Tim Feldmann

D-U-N-S 07-849-1499
GERALD HOLDINGS LLC
680 Washington Blvd Fl 9, Stamford, CT 06901-3727
Tel (203) 609-8550 *Founded/Ownrshp* 2007
Sales 154.4MM^E *EMP* 550^E
SIC 6221 Commodity brokers, contracts; Commodity brokers, contracts

D-U-N-S 95-801-3898 IMP
GERALD INDUSTRIES INC
625 W Industrial Dr, Gerald, MO 63037-2011
Tel (573) 764-2262 *Founded/Ownrshp* 1987
Sales 28.2MM^E *EMP* 320
SIC 3491 3585 3492 Process control regulator valves; Refrigeration & heating equipment; Fluid power valves & hose fittings; Process control regulator valves; Refrigeration & heating equipment; Fluid power valves & hose fittings
Pr: Jack Deutsch
Plnt Mgr: Jeff Siebert
Plnt Mgr: Rosalee Wells

D-U-N-S 06-759-6791
GERALD JONES VOLKSWAGEN INC
JONES, ANDY MAZDA
4022 Washington Rd, Augusta, GA 30907-2323
Tel (706) 738-2561 *Founded/Ownrshp* 1974
Sales 29.1MM^E *EMP* 46
SIC 5511 5531 7538 Automobiles, new & used; Automotive parts; General automotive repair shops
Pr: Anthony E Jones
**VP:* David W Jones
Off Mgr: Lisa Adkinson
IT Man: Jeremy Young
Sls Mgr: Wayne Cox
Sls Mgr: David Nowling
Sales Asso: Chris Johnson
Sales Asso: Travis White

GERALD MARTIN GENERAL CONTR
See GERALD A MARTIN LTD

D-U-N-S 01-203-3635 IMP/EXP
GERALD METALS LLC
(*Suby of* GERALD HOLDINGS LLC) ★
680 Washington Blvd Fl 9, Stamford, CT 06901-3727
Tel (203) 609-8300 *Founded/Ownrshp* 1962
Sales 131.9MM^E *EMP* 550^E
SIC 5051 Nonferrous metal sheets, bars, rods, etc.; Nonferrous metal sheets, bars, rods, etc.
CEO: Craig Dean
**Pr:* Fabio Calia
**CFO:* Thomas Restivo
Sr VP: Eric Sugerman
VP: Kory Marks
VP: Lisa Trell
Opers Mgr: Katia Solovieva
Genl Couns: Gary Lerner
Counsel: Howard Law

D-U-N-S 06-819-0008 IMP
GERALD MICHAEL LTD (CA)
12836 Alondra Blvd, Cerritos, CA 90703-2107
Tel (562) 921-9611 *Founded/Ownrshp* 1983
Sales 40.0MM^E *EMP* 35
SIC 5136 2329 3999 Sweaters, men's & boys'; Sweaters, men's & boys'; Men's & boys' sportswear & athletic clothing; Atomizers, toiletry
Ch Bd: Gerald D Barnes
Pr: Ben Cooper
VP: Danette Cubic
Rgnl Mgr: Gloria Cruz
Off Mgr: Gloria Santa Cruz
VP Opers: Cooper Ben

D-U-N-S 79-100-2173
GERALD NISSAN INC
1575 W Ogden Ave, Naperville, IL 60540-3906
Tel (630) 355-3337 *Founded/Ownrshp* 1992
Sales 31.0MM^E *EMP* 65
Accts Crowechisek Of Oakbrook
SIC 5511 Automobiles, new & used; Automobiles, new & used
Pr: Neil Gerald
**VP:* John Gerald
Genl Mgr: Dean Collins
Genl Mgr: Anthony Miceli
DP Dir: Paul Gawel
Sls Mgr: Anthony Triner
Sales Asso: Ervin Memushaj
Sales Asso: Keevan Pullen
Board of Directors: Alec McKean

D-U-N-S 01-615-5199
GERALD NISSAN OF NORTH AURORA INC
213 Hansen Blvd, North Aurora, IL 60542-8923
Tel (630) 907-0800 *Founded/Ownrshp* 1997
Sales 24.2MM^E *EMP* 50
SIC 5511 Automobiles, new & used
Pr: Neal Gerald
**Prin:* Deen Collins
**Prin:* Rene Peyton
**Prin:* Scott Wolf
Genl Mgr: Doug Gerald
Sls Dir: Nick Smiley
Sls Mgr: Sunny Gjinolli

GERALD PETERS GALLERY
See PETERS CORP

D-U-N-S 00-946-2094
GERALD SUBARU INC
1210 E Ogden Ave, Naperville, IL 60563-1604
Tel (630) 355-3900 *Founded/Ownrshp* 1980
Sales 32.2MM^E *EMP* 72
SIC 5511 5521 Automobiles, new & used; Used car dealers; Automobiles, new & used; Used car dealers
Pr: Neil Gerald
CFO: Lisa Collins
**VP:* Jeffrey Gerald
Sls Mgr: Jason Allen
Sales Asso: Dany Khochaba

GERARD DANIEL WORLDWIDE
See DANIEL GERARD WORLDWIDE INC

GERARD DANIEL WORLDWIDE
See G D C INTERNATIONAL INC

GERARD REALTY GROUP
See SERVING ST LOUIS REALTY LLC

GERARD ROOFING TECHNOLOGIES
See METALS USA BUILDING PRODUCTS L P

D-U-N-S 13-195-0557 IMP
GERAWAN FARMING INC
7108 N Fresno St Ste 450, Fresno, CA 93720-2961
Tel (559) 787-8780 *Founded/Ownrshp* 1973
Sales 59.2MM^E *EMP* 200
SIC 0721 4783 Tree orchards, cultivation of; Packing goods for shipping; Tree orchards, cultivation of; Packing goods for shipping
Pr: Daniel J Gerawan
CFO: Scott Grabau
**CFO:* Brent Hansston
**VP:* George Nikolich
IT Man: Jason Kabeary
IT Man: Tad Uhl
Tech Mgr: Prima Brand
Tech Mgr: Denver Schutz
Sls Mgr: George Papangellin

D-U-N-S 92-829-3737
GERAWAN FARMING PARTNERS INC
15749 E Ventura Ave, Sanger, CA 93657-9657
Tel (559) 787-8780 *Founded/Ownrshp* 1950
Sales 11.6MM^E *EMP* 300
SIC 0721 0172 Tree orchards, cultivation of; Grapes; Tree orchards, cultivation of; Grapes
Pr: Dan Gerawan

D-U-N-S 09-890-0434 IMP/EXP
GERBER AGRI INTERNATIONAL LLC
(*Suby of* GERBER GOLDSCHMIDT GROUP (S A) (PTY) LTD)
1000 Parkwood Cir Se # 335, Atlanta, GA 30339-2124
Tel (770) 952-4187 *Founded/Ownrshp* 2001
Sales 107.7MM *EMP* 18^E
SIC 5144 5147

GERBER AUTO COLLISON AND GLASS
See GERBER GROUP INC

D-U-N-S 15-725-6876 IMP/EXP
GERBER CHILDRENSWEAR LLC
(*Suby of* CHILDRENSWEAR LLC) ★
7005 Pelham Rd Ste D, Greenville, SC 29615-5782
Tel (864) 987-5200 *Founded/Ownrshp* 2013
Sales 29.3MM^E *EMP* 140
Accts Pricewaterhousecoopers Llp Sp
SIC 5641 Children's wear
CEO: Gary Simmons
VP: David Hamilton
VP: David Hammer
VP: Tom McRae
QA Dir: Matt McCullen
IT Man: Donna Campbell
VP Opers: Samuel Beason
Snr Mgr: Sandy White

D-U-N-S 07-308-9039
GERBER CONSTRUCTION INC
815 E 675 S, Lehi, UT 84043-3950
Tel (801) 407-2000 *Founded/Ownrshp* 1974
Sales 34.1MM *EMP* 120
Accts Tanner Llc Salt Lake City Ut
SIC 1771 1611 Concrete work; Highway & street maintenance; General contractor, highway & street construction; Guardrail construction, highways; Concrete work; Highway & street maintenance; General contractor, highway & street construction; Guardrail construction, highways
Pr: Allen Gerber
**Treas:* Shane Poulson
**Sr VP:* Scott Gerber
**VP:* Brandon Gerber Jr
Mtls Mgr: Steve Fox

D-U-N-S 07-946-9075
GERBER GLASS (DISTRICT 1) LLC
GERBER NATIONAL GLASS SERVICES
(*Suby of* BOYD GROUP U S INC) ★
500 W Lake St, Elmhurst, IL 60126-1400
Tel (800) 826-8682 *Founded/Ownrshp* 2011
Sales 22.6MM^E *EMP* 1,200^E
SIC 7549 High performance auto repair & service; High performance auto repair & service
CEO: Eddie Cheskis
Site Mgr: Diane Zatezalo

D-U-N-S 05-664-7357
GERBER GROUP INC
GERBER AUTO COLLISON AND GLASS
(*Suby of* THE BOYD GROUP INC)
8250 Skokie Blvd, Skokie, IL 60077-2543
Tel (847) 679-0510 *Founded/Ownrshp* 1971, 1998
Sales 44.2MM^E *EMP* 330
SIC 7532 Interior repair services; Paint shop, automotive; Exterior repair services; Interior repair services; Paint shop, automotive; Exterior repair services
CEO: Eddie Cheskis
Pr: Rick Paukstitus
Pr: Herb Rabatin
**COO:* Tim O'Day
Sr VP: Gary Bunce
VP: Kevin Burnett
Genl Mgr: Peter Callaway
Genl Mgr: Joe Faller
Genl Mgr: Gary Gulisano
Genl Mgr: Dean Hood
Off Mgr: Jamie Beatty

D-U-N-S 00-902-0447 IMP
GERBER LEGENDARY BLADES INC
(*Suby of* FISKARS BRANDS INC) ★
14200 Sw 72nd Ave, Portland, OR 97224-8010
Tel (503) 684-2495 *Founded/Ownrshp* 1946
Sales 28.8MM^E *EMP* 260
SIC 3421 Knife blades & blanks; Carving sets; Knives: butchers', hunting, pocket, etc.; Table cutlery, except with handles of metal; Knife blades & blanks; Carving sets; Knives: butchers', hunting, pocket, etc.; Table cutlery, except with handles of metal
Pr: Rob Cass
Rgnl Mgr: Marty Carlson
VP Opers: Bob Durdel

Natl Sales: Joe Marchant
Mktg Dir: Mark Schindel
Mktg Mgr: Andrew Gritzbaugh
Sls Mgr: Adam Suttle

D-U-N-S 07-272-5716
GERBER LIFE INSURANCE CO
(*Suby of* GERBER PRODUCTS CO) ★
1311 Mmroneck Ave Ste 350, White Plains, NY 10605
Tel (914) 272-4000 *Founded/Ownrshp* 1967
Sales NA *EMP* 200
SIC 6311 6321 Life insurance; Accident & health insurance; Life insurance; Accident & health insurance
Pr: Keith O'Reilly
Exec: John Craig
Sls&Mrk Ex: Deb Smith

D-U-N-S 01-149-5629
GERBER METAL SUPPLY CO
2 Boundary Rd, Somerville, NJ 08876-6038
Tel (908) 823-9150 *Founded/Ownrshp* 1986
Sales 54.7MM^E *EMP* 48
SIC 5051 Metals service centers & offices; Sheets, metal; Tubing, metal
Ch: Glenn A Gerber
**Pr:* Charles Calabrese
**Sec:* Joseph Trainor
**Ex VP:* Peter Morison
**Prin:* Michael Jacobellis
**Prin:* Joe La Rosa
**Prin:* Natalie Rodriguez

GERBER NATIONAL GLASS SERVICES
See GERBER GLASS (DISTRICT 1) LLC

GERBER PLUMBING FIXTURES
See CFPG LTD

D-U-N-S 96-903-8558
GERBER PLUMBING FIXTURES LLC
(*Suby of* GLOBE UNION GROUP INC) ★
2500 Intrntonale Pkwy, Woodridge, IL 60517-4073
Tel (630) 679-1420 *Founded/Ownrshp* 2003
Sales 113.2MM *EMP* 53
SIC 3261 Plumbing fixtures, vitreous china; Plumbing fixtures, vitreous china
Pr: Werner Michael

D-U-N-S 00-421-1041
GERBER POULTRY INC
5889 Kidron Rd, Kidron, OH 44636
Tel (330) 857-2731 *Founded/Ownrshp* 1952
Sales 5.5MM^E *EMP* 500
SIC 2015

D-U-N-S 00-601-9780 IMP
GERBER PRODUCTS CO
NESTLE INFANT NUTRITION
(*Suby of* NESTLE HOLDINGS INC) ★
12 Vreeland Rd Fl 2, Florham Park, NJ 07932-1521
Tel (973) 593-7500 *Founded/Ownrshp* 1867, 2007
Sales 495.2MM^E *EMP* 2,381
SIC 2023 2043 2037 2052 2086 2091 Baby formulas; Cereal breakfast foods; Fruit juices; Cookies & crackers; Pasteurized & mineral waters, bottled & canned; Canned & cured fish & seafoods; Baby formulas; Cereal breakfast foods; Fruit juices; Cookies & crackers; Pasteurized & mineral waters, bottled & canned; Canned & cured fish & seafoods
Pr: Kurt T Schmidt
Treas: Don W Gosline
VP: Kevin L Goldberg
VP: Kevin L Goldbert
VP: Craig Thompson
Dir Risk M: David Binder
Board of Directors: Dianne Jacobs, David Nieto

D-U-N-S 00-115-8195 IMP
GERBER SCIENTIFIC INC (CT)
GERBER SCIENTIFIC PRODUCTS
(*Suby of* VECTOR KNIFE HOLDINGS (CAYMAN) LTD)
24 Indl Pk Rd W, Tolland, CT 06084
Tel (860) 644-1551 *Founded/Ownrshp* 1948, 2011
Sales 365.7MM^E *EMP* 1,950
SIC 3993 7336 3851 7372 3577 Signs & advertising specialties; Commercial art & graphic design; Lenses, ophthalmic; Prepackaged software; Magnetic ink & optical scanning devices; Signs & advertising specialties; Commercial art & graphic design; Lenses, ophthalmic; Prepackaged software; Magnetic ink & optical scanning devices
Pr: Michael Elia
**Pr:* Thomas P Finn
COO: Pam Miller
**CFO:* John Capasso
**Sr VP:* James S Arthurs
**Sr VP:* William V Grickis Jr
VP: Bill Brewster
VP: Patti Burmahl
VP: Peter Doscas
**VP:* James Martin
VP: Bud McCann
VP: Theo Ostendorf
VP: Johnny Wang
**VP:* Karen Watson
Exec: Paul Soderburg
Dir Risk M: Theresa Kenny

D-U-N-S 04-771-3581
GERBER SCIENTIFIC INTERNATIONAL INC
(*Suby of* GERBER SCIENTIFIC INC) ★
24 Industrial Park Rd W, Tolland, CT 06084-2806
Tel (860) 871-8082 *Founded/Ownrshp* 1968
Sales 163.7MM^E *EMP* 915
SIC 3559 7371 Foundry machinery & equipment; Custom computer programming services; Foundry machinery & equipment; Custom computer programming services
CEO: Michael R Elia
**Sr Pt:* Patricia Burmahl
**CFO:* John Capasso
**CFO:* David Kralic
**Treas:* Victoria J Kenny
**VP:* Patricia L Burmahl
**VP:* Greg Collins
**VP:* Michael J Lyon
**VP:* Johnny Wang
IT Man: Peter Bollino

GERBER SCIENTIFIC PRODUCTS
See GERBER SCIENTIFIC INC

D-U-N-S 18-816-6664
GERBER SCIENTIFIC PRODUCTS INC
(*Suby of* GERBER SCIENTIFIC INC) ★
83 Gerber Rd W, South Windsor, CT 06074-3230
Tel (860) 648-8300 *Founded/Ownrshp* 1980
Sales 48.0MM^E *EMP* 300^E
SIC 3599 Custom machinery; Custom machinery
Pr: Greg Wolf
CFO: Edward G Jepsen
Sr VP: Bill Grickis Jr
VP: Bill Brewster
VP: Raf Cohen
Ex Dir: Bud McCann
Ex Dir: Richard F Treacy Jr
Ql Cn Mgr: Hope Janaitis
Sls Mgr: Steve Albert

GERBES SPRMKT / KING SOOPERS
See DILLON COMPANIES INC

D-U-N-S 14-043-7299
GERBIG SNELL/WEISHEIMER ADVERTISING LLC
GSW WORLDWIDE
(*Suby of* INVENTIV COMMUNICATIONS INC) ★
500 Olde Worthington Rd, Westerville, OH 43082-8913
Tel (614) 848-4848 *Founded/Ownrshp* 2001
Sales 38.2MM^E *EMP* 290
SIC 7311

GERDAU AMERISTEEL
See SHEFFIELD STEEL CORP

D-U-N-S 78-425-3564 IMP/EXP
GERDAU AMERISTEEL CORP
(*Suby of* GERDAU S/A)
4221 W Boy Scout Blvd # 600, Tampa, FL 33607-5760
Tel (813) 286-8383 *Founded/Ownrshp* 1956
Sales 1.3MMM^E *EMP* 7,850
SIC 3312 Blast furnaces & steel mills; Blast furnaces & steel mills
Pr: Mario Longhi
**Pr:* Guilherme C Gerdau Johannpeter
**COO:* Terry Sutter
**CFO:* Barbara Smith
**VP:* Peter Campo
**VP:* Carl Czarnik
VP: Paul J Lawrence
**VP:* Robert E Lewis
VP: J Neal McCullohs III
**VP:* Rodrigo Souza
**VP:* Yuan Wang
VP: Matthew Yeatman
VP: Matthew C Yeatman

GERDAU AMERISTEEL DINWIDDIE CO
See VIRGINIA CHAPARRAL INC

D-U-N-S 13-162-5084
GERDAU AMERISTEEL PERTH AMBOY INC
(*Suby of* GERDAU LONG STEEL AMERICA) ★
225 Elm St, Perth Amboy, NJ 08861-4503
Tel (732) 442-1600 *Founded/Ownrshp* 1999
Sales 60.8MM^E *EMP* 300
SIC 3312 Blast furnaces & steel mills; Rods, iron & steel: made in steel mills; Wire products, steel or iron; Blast furnaces & steel mills; Rods, iron & steel: made in steel mills; Wire products, steel or iron

D-U-N-S 14-003-8204 IMP
GERDAU AMERISTEEL SAYREVILLE INC
(*Suby of* GERDAU LONG STEEL AMERICA) ★
N Crossman Rd, Sayreville, NJ 08872
Tel (732) 721-6600 *Founded/Ownrshp* 1978
Sales 228.8MM^E *EMP* 45,000
SIC 3312 Blast furnaces & steel mills; Bars & bar shapes, steel, hot-rolled; Blast furnaces & steel mills; Bars & bar shapes, steel, hot-rolled
Pr: Peter Campo
**VP:* Carl Czarnik
**VP:* Jim Kerkvliet
**VP:* Andre Pires
VP: Mark Quiring
**VP:* Rodrigo Souza
**VP:* Yuan Wang
**VP:* Matthew Yeatman
Genl Mgr: Zilmar Cardoso
Dir IT: Shawn Barksdale
Sfty Mgr: Jeff Wawrzeni

D-U-N-S 00-409-3456 IMP/EXP
GERDAU AMERISTEEL US INC (FL)
GERDAU LONG STEEL NORTH AMER
(*Suby of* GERDAU LONG STEEL AMERICA) ★
4221 W Boy Scout Blvd # 600, Tampa, FL 33607-5760
Tel (813) 286-8383 *Founded/Ownrshp* 1956, 1999
Sales 6.6MMM^E *EMP* 45,000
SIC 3312 3449 3315 Hot-rolled iron & steel products; Bars & bar shapes, steel, hot-rolled; Structural shapes & pilings, steel; Bars, concrete reinforcing: fabricated steel; Spikes, steel: wire or cut; Welded steel wire fabric; Nails, steel: wire or cut; Hot-rolled iron & steel products; Bars & bar shapes, steel, hot-rolled; Structural shapes & pilings, steel; Bars, concrete reinforcing: fabricated steel; Spikes, steel: wire or cut; Welded steel wire fabric; Nails, steel: wire or cut
CEO: Peter J Campo
Pr: Guilherme G Johannpeter
CFO: Celtyn Hughes
Treas: George Beck
Treas: Santiago Gil
Ex VP: Paulo Vasconcellos
Sr VP: T Barker
Sr VP: D Bourdon
VP: Ricardo Anawate
VP: D Ballard
VP: Andr Beaudry
VP: Greg W Bott
VP: Yan Chang
VP: Jim Christina
VP: Jim Crompton
VP: Carl W Czarnik
VP: Andre Pires De Oliveira Dias
VP: Christopher Ervin
VP: James R Kerkvliet
VP: Alan Lamb
VP: Silvio Lemos
Board of Directors: Frederico Carlos Gerdau Jo, Andre Bier Johannpeter, Klaus Gerdau Johannpeter, Rick J Mills, Carlos Petry

D-U-N-S 19-274-0640 IMP/EXP
GERDAU AMERISTEEL US INC
(*Suby of* GERDAU AMERISTEEL US INC) ★
300 Ward Rd, Midlothian, TX 76065-9646
Tel (972) 775-8241 *Founded/Ownrshp* 2007
Sales 228.8MM^E *EMP* 1,450
SIC 3312 Blast furnaces & steel mills; Blast furnaces & steel mills
CEO: Mario Longhi
Pr: Glen Carlisle
**CFO:* Barbara Smith
**VP:* Robert E Lewis
Cmptr Lab: Amos Long
VP Opers: Dave Fournie
Sfty Dirs: David Witschorke
Sfty Mgr: Charlie Hall
Sfty Mgr: Ron Herring
Opers Mgr: Bob Frey
Opers Mgr: Gene Suslowicz

GERDAU LONG STEEL AMERICA
See GERDAU USA INC

GERDAU LONG STEEL NORTH AMER
See GERDAU AMERISTEEL US INC

D-U-N-S 82-632-9299 IMP/EXP
GERDAU MACSTEEL INC
NITRO STEEL
(*Suby of* GRUPO GERDAU DE EMPREENDIMENTOS LTDA.)
5591 Morrill Rd, Jackson, MI 49201-7084
Tel (517) 782-0415 *Founded/Ownrshp* 2008
Sales 309.6MM^E *EMP* 1,200
SIC 3312 3316 Bars & bar shapes, steel, cold-finished: own hot-rolled; Cold finishing of steel shapes; Bars & bar shapes, steel, cold-finished: own hot-rolled; Cold finishing of steel shapes
Pr: Jack Finlayson
Sr VP: Martin H Dodd
Sr VP: Glenn Harkness
VP: Renee Arze
VP: Paul Giddens
VP: Chris Knudstrup
VP: Fernando Peredo
VP: Arlan Piepho
**VP:* Rick Szink
Brnch Mgr: Forrest Fordham
Genl Mgr: Ron Ancevic

D-U-N-S 79-046-9717
GERDAU REINFORCING STEEL
(*Suby of* GERDAU AMERISTEEL US INC) ★
3880 Murphy Canyon Rd # 100, San Diego, CA 92123-4410
Tel (858) 737-7700 *Founded/Ownrshp* 2006
Sales 515.3MM^E *EMP* 1,000
SIC 1541 Steel building construction; Steel building construction
VP: Christopher Ervin
Treas: Steven Fellows
VP: Howard Bennion
VP: Jim Del RE
Dir Risk M: Jennifer Martin
Off Mgr: Kimberli Clement
Sls Mgr: Frank Sutera

D-U-N-S 62-757-1193
GERDAU STEEL
(*Suby of* GERDAU AMERISTEEL CORPORATION)
225 Elm St, Perth Amboy, NJ 08861-4503
Tel (732) 442-1600 *Founded/Ownrshp* 1986
Sales 64.5MM^E *EMP* 480
SIC 3312 Blast furnaces & steel mills; Blast furnaces & steel mills
VP: Mark Quiring

D-U-N-S 19-408-1451 IMP
GERDAU USA INC
GERDAU LONG STEEL AMERICA
(*Suby of* GERDAU AMERISTEEL CORPORATION)
4221 W Boy Scout Blvd, Tampa, FL 33607-5743
Tel (813) 286-8383 *Founded/Ownrshp* 2000
Sales 6.9MMM^E *EMP* 45,000
SIC 3312 3449 3315 Blast furnaces & steel mills; Hot-rolled iron & steel products; Bars & bar shapes, steel, hot-rolled; Structural shapes & pilings, steel; Bars, concrete reinforcing: fabricated steel; Spikes, steel: wire or cut; Welded steel wire fabric; Nails, steel: wire or cut; Blast furnaces & steel mills; Hot-rolled iron & steel products; Bars & bar shapes, steel, hot-rolled; Structural shapes & pilings, steel; Bars, concrete reinforcing: fabricated steel; Spikes, steel: wire or cut; Welded steel wire fabric; Nails, steel: wire or cut
Pr: Guilherme Johannpeter
**VP:* Peter J Campo
**VP:* Carl W Czarnik
**VP:* Rodrigo Ferreira De Souza
Info Man: Della Erickson
Ql Cn Mgr: Jim Trentadue
Snr PM: Stewart Whitehead
Board of Directors: Frederico Carlos Gerdau Jo, Andre Bier Johannpeter, Jorge Gerdau Johannpeter

D-U-N-S 87-814-5085
GERELCO ELECTRICAL CONTRACTORS INC
560 Nw Enterprise Dr, Port Saint Lucie, FL 34986-2203
Tel (772) 340-5998 *Founded/Ownrshp* 1993
Sales 52.8MM^E *EMP* 200
SIC 1731 General electrical contractor; General electrical contractor
Pr: Kenneth Geremia Sr
**VP:* Mark Buehler
**VP:* Kenneth Geremia Jr
Sfty Dirs: Dan Gadacz

GERFLOR NORTH AMERICA
See GERFLOR USA INC

D-U-N-S 11-537-5503 IMP
GERFLOR USA INC
GERFLOR NORTH AMERICA
595 Supreme Dr, Bensenville, IL 60106-1123
Tel (847) 394-3944 *Founded/Ownrshp* 2007
Sales 35.0MM *EMP* 265^E
SIC 5023 7389 Floor coverings; Interior design services; Floor coverings; Interior design services
CEO: Bertrand Chammas
Exec: Pierre Lienhard
**Prin:* Benjamin Bachman
Genl Mgr: Ken Chmura
IT Man: Eva Morello
Tech Mgr: Andrew Sedman
Mktg Mgr: Kurt Holler
Manager: Chris Mechler

D-U-N-S 15-142-3050
GERGEL-KELLEM CO INC
WATT PRINTERS
4544 Hinckley Indus Pkwy, Cleveland, OH 44109-6010
Tel (216) 398-2000 *Founded/Ownrshp* 1985
Sales 20.5MM^E *EMP* 80
Accts Hausser + Taylor Llp Clevelan
SIC 2752 Commercial printing, offset
Pr: John Gergel
**Treas:* Craig Kellem
**VP:* Mike Nakonek

GERHARD'S APPLIANCES
See GERHARDS INC

D-U-N-S 01-414-9934
GERHARDS INC (PA)
GERHARD'S APPLIANCES
290 N Keswick Ave, Glenside, PA 19038-4804
Tel (215) 884-8650 *Founded/Ownrshp* 1945
Sales 37.9MM *EMP* 85
Accts Sacco Sweeney Llp Cpas Horsh
SIC 5722 5731 Household appliance stores; Electric household appliances, major; Electric household appliances, small; Radio, television & electronic stores; Consumer electronic equipment; Household appliance stores; Electric household appliances, major; Electric household appliances, small; Radio, television & electronic stores; Consumer electronic equipment
Pr: Charles E Gerhard III
**VP:* Gerald Gerhard
Genl Mgr: Erik Meyer
Store Mgr: Pete Siegfried

D-U-N-S 03-500-3383
GERHOLD CONCRETE CO INC
(*Suby of* LYMAN-RICHEY CORP) ★
4315 Cuming St, Omaha, NE 68131-1014
Tel (402) 558-2727 *Founded/Ownrshp* 1989
Sales 26.0MM^E *EMP* 187
SIC 3271 3273 3241 5032 Concrete block & brick; Ready-mixed concrete; Cement, hydraulic; Concrete mixtures; Concrete block & brick; Ready-mixed concrete; Cement, hydraulic; Concrete mixtures
Pr: Patrick J Gorup
Treas: Mark Osborn
**Ex VP:* Kevin Schmidt
Site Mgr: Doug Carroll

GERI CARE
See GERI-CARE PHARMACEUTICALS CORP

D-U-N-S 62-236-7357
GERI-CARE INC
GLOUSTER MANOR HEALTH CARE
104 Pension Rd, Manalapan, NJ 07726-8400
Tel (732) 792-8121 *Founded/Ownrshp* 1988
Sales 13.9MM^E *EMP* 300
SIC 8051 8052 Skilled nursing care facilities; Intermediate care facilities; Skilled nursing care facilities; Intermediate care facilities
Pr: Marvin Beinhorn
**VP:* Eric Paniff

D-U-N-S 61-119-6254 IMP
GERI-CARE PHARMACEUTICALS CORP
GERI CARE
1650 63rd St, Brooklyn, NY 11204-2713
Tel (718) 382-5000 *Founded/Ownrshp* 1983
Sales 23.9MM^E *EMP* 100
SIC 5122 2834

D-U-N-S 01-934-1312
GERIATRIC MEDICAL & SURGICAL SUPPLY INC (MA)
28 Torrice Dr, Woburn, MA 01801-6220
Tel (617) 387-5936 *Founded/Ownrshp* 1945, 1980
Sales 34.4MM^E *EMP* 65
SIC 5047 Medical equipment & supplies; Surgical equipment & supplies
Pr: Arthur Siegal
**Treas:* Corey Peyser
Sfty Mgr: Robert Gomez
Sls Mgr: Gary Sklar

GERIATRIC OTRACH CLNC/CARE MGT
See HURLEY MEDICAL CENTER

D-U-N-S 10-004-8230
GERING PUBLIC SCHOOLS
1519 10th St, Gering, NE 69341-2818
Tel (308) 436-3125 *Founded/Ownrshp* 1976
Sales 13.4MM^E *EMP* 285
SIC 8211 Public elementary & secondary schools; School board; Public elementary & secondary schools; School board
Dir Sec: Kraig Weyrich
Dir IT: Lionel Newberry

D-U-N-S 78-107-9074
GERITOM MED INC
GERITOM MED PHARMACY
10501 Florida Ave S, Bloomington, MN 55438-2553
Tel (952) 854-1190 *Founded/Ownrshp* 1987
Sales 30.4MM^E *EMP* 140
SIC 5912 Drug stores; Drug stores
CEO: Thomas Smit
**Pr:* Shelley Psyhogios-Smith
**Ex VP:* Joe Keim
**VP:* John Feickert
VP: Drew Smith
Dir Rx: Jason Wachtl
Dir Bus: Matt Retterath
Dir IT: Tim Williams
Pharmcst: John Stites

GERITOM MED PHARMACY
See GERITOM MED INC

D-U-N-S 05-163-1588
GERKEN MATERIALS INC
9072 County Road 424, Napoleon, OH 43545-9732
Tel (419) 533-2421 *Founded/Ownrshp* 1959
Sales 68.4MM^E *EMP* 250
SIC 1611 2951

GERKIN WINDOW & DOORS
See GWD LTD

D-U-N-S 10-384-0831
GERLAND CORP
(*Suby of* 2ML REAL ESTATE INTERESTS INC) ★
3131 Pawnee St, Houston, TX 77054-3302
Tel (713) 746-3600 *Founded/Ownrshp* 2013
Sales 232.8MM^E *EMP* 1,500
SIC 5411 Grocery stores, chain; Grocery stores, chain
Pr: Kevin P Doris
**Ex VP:* Jeffrey K Reeder
Sr VP: Rick Noeth
**VP:* Donald Benefield
**VP:* Bill Bouquet
VP: Kathy Caton
VP: Lori Hall
Store Dir: Bill Pulido
Sls&Mrk Ex: Alex Vonsehrwald
Mktg Mgr: James Nesbitt

GERLAND'S FOOD FAIR
See GERLANDS REALTY INC

D-U-N-S 13-931-8992
GERLANDS REALTY INC
GERLAND'S FOOD FAIR
(*Suby of* GERLAND'S FOOD FAIR, INC.)
3131 Pawnee St, Houston, TX 77054-3302
Tel (713) 746-3600 *Founded/Ownrshp* 1982
Sales 40.0MM *EMP* 885
SIC 5411 Grocery stores, chain; Grocery stores, chain
Pr: Kevin Doris

D-U-N-S 04-460-2571 IMP
GERLER AND SON INC
ONLINESHOES.COM
1730 Minor Ave Ste 700, Seattle, WA 98101-1481
Tel (206) 812-7800 *Founded/Ownrshp* 1974, 2014
Sales 37.4MM^E *EMP* 170
SIC 5661 Shoe stores
CEO: Roger Hardy
VP: Jan Akin
CTO: Dominic Uy

D-U-N-S 00-167-0082 EXP
GERLI & CO INC
AMERICAN SILK MILLS
41 Madison Ave Ste 4101, New York, NY 10010-2203
Tel (212) 213-1919 *Founded/Ownrshp* 1883
Sales 29.9MM^E *EMP* 270
SIC 2211 2221 Cotton broad woven goods; Broadwoven fabric mills, manmade; Rayon broadwoven fabrics; Silk broadwoven fabrics; Cotton broad woven goods; Broadwoven fabric mills, manmade; Rayon broadwoven fabrics; Silk broadwoven fabrics
Pr: Robin L Slough
**CFO:* James Harowicz
**VP:* John M Sullivan Jr
Plnt Mgr: Russell Sokolas

D-U-N-S 80-202-9157 EXP
GERLING AND ASSOCIATES INC
138 Stelzer Ct, Sunbury, OH 43074-8528
Tel (740) 965-6200 *Founded/Ownrshp* 1988
Sales 35.4MM^E *EMP* 80
SIC 3711 Mobile lounges (motor vehicle), assembly of
Pr: Fred Gerling
Opers Mgr: Jennifer Myers
Opers Mgr: Zach Myers
Plnt Mgr: Jennifer Fenton
Sls Dir: Chris Devol
Sls Dir: Shannon McElroy
Sls Mgr: Chris Devoule

GERM GUARDIAN
See GUARDIAN TECHNOLOGIES LLC

D-U-N-S 04-081-8601
GERMAIN FORD LLC
7250 Sawmill Rd, Columbus, OH 43235-1942
Tel (614) 889-7777 *Founded/Ownrshp* 2000
Sales 46.6MM^E *EMP* 135
SIC 5511 7539 Automobiles, new & used; Automotive repair shops; Automobiles, new & used; Automotive repair shops
Sales Asso: Steve Hadley

GERMAIN LEXUS OF NAPLES
See GERMAIN OF NAPLES INC

D-U-N-S 17-991-1164
GERMAIN MOTOR CO
225 E Spring St, Columbus, OH 43215-2646
Tel (614) 416-3377 *Founded/Ownrshp* 1986
Sales 30.7MM^E *EMP* 45^E
SIC 5511 New & used car dealers
Prin: Sean Mc Carthy
Genl Mgr: Rodney Back
Genl Mgr: Mike Visocky
Sls Mgr: Mike Soles
Sales Asso: Dan Beveridge
Sales Asso: Seref Denizeri
Sales Asso: Erik Gordon
Sales Asso: Matthew Nolan

D-U-N-S 19-247-3577
GERMAIN NISSAN OF NEW ALBANY INC
4300 Morse Rd, Columbus, OH 43230-1524
Tel (614) 418-4500 *Founded/Ownrshp* 1997
Sales 20.7MM^E *EMP* 50
SIC 5511 5521 Automobiles, new & used; Used car dealers

Pr: Robert Germaine Sr
**VP:* Steve Germaine
Sls Mgr: Ralph Johnson
Sales Asso: Jeremy Ross

D-U-N-S 01-670-9966
GERMAIN OF ANN ARBOR INC
VOLKSWAGEN OF ANN ARBOR
2575 S State St, Ann Arbor, MI 48104-6145
Tel (734) 761-3200 *Founded/Ownrshp* 1965
Sales 27.9MM^E *EMP* 70
Accts Yeo & Yeo Cpa
SIC 5511 Automobiles, new & used; Automobiles, new & used
Pr: Howard J Cooper

D-U-N-S 79-337-9751
GERMAIN OF NAPLES INC
GERMAIN LEXUS OF NAPLES
13491 Tamiami Trl N, Naples, FL 34110-6338
Tel (239) 592-5533 *Founded/Ownrshp* 1992
Sales 36.1MM^E *EMP* 110
SIC 5511 Automobiles, new & used; Automobiles, new & used
Pr: Robert L Germain Sr
**VP:* Robert L Germain Jr
Genl Mgr: Evelyn Camilo
Genl Mgr: Dave Camposano
Off Mgr: Sherry Lentjes
Sls Mgr: Trish Cano
Sls Mgr: Chris Lilly
Sls Mgr: Vince Marcantonio
Sales Asso: B J Harris

D-U-N-S 05-216-3342
GERMAIN TOYOTA INC
GERMAIN TOYOTA OF COLUMBUS
4250 Morse Xing, Columbus, OH 43219-3024
Tel (239) 592-5550 *Founded/Ownrshp* 1988
Sales 133.2MM^E *EMP* 400
SIC 5511

GERMAIN TOYOTA OF COLUMBUS
See GERMAIN TOYOTA INC

D-U-N-S 78-181-3691
GERMAIN/MORRAND ENTERPRISES LLC
TOYOTA OF NORTHWEST ARKANSAS
411 S Metro Pkwy, Rogers, AR 72758-8530
Tel (479) 845-1444 *Founded/Ownrshp* 2004
Sales 24.3MM^E *EMP* 93
SIC 5511 Automobiles, new & used; Automobiles, new & used
Off Mgr: Carla Capron
Sls Mgr: Chris Powers
Sales Asso: Felix Gutierrez
Sales Asso: Michael Narx
Sales Asso: Brian Neisen

D-U-N-S 00-693-8849
■ **GERMAN AMERICAN BANCORP**
(*Suby of* GERMAN AMERICAN BANCORP INC) ★
711 Main St, Jasper, IN 47546-3042
Tel (812) 482-1314 *Founded/Ownrshp* 1910
Sales NA *EMP* 341
Accts Crowe Horwath Llp Indianapoli
SIC 6022 State commercial banks; State commercial banks
Pr: Kenneth Sendelweck
**CFO:* Brad Rust
**Sr VP:* Chris Melton

D-U-N-S 11-974-8101
▲ **GERMAN AMERICAN BANCORP INC**
711 Main St, Jasper, IN 47546-3042
Tel (812) 482-1314 *Founded/Ownrshp* 1982
Sales NA *EMP* 480^E
Tkr Sym GABC *Exch* NGS
SIC 6022 State commercial banks; State commercial banks
Ch Bd: Mark A Schroeder
Pr: Clay W Ewing
Pr: Kenneth L Sendelweck
CFO: Bradley M Rust
Chf Cred: Keith A Leinenbach
Trst Ofcr: Dave Mitchell
Ex VP: Joe Dedman
Sr VP: Randall L Braun
Sr VP: Jane Thoma
VP: Dale Altstadt
VP: Jane Balsmeyer
VP: Clay Barrett
VP: Jay Burch
VP: Dan Collignon
VP: Julie Donham
VP: John Gutgsell
VP: Lisa Matheis
VP: David Pleiss
VP: Donna Sholtis
Board of Directors: Michael J Voyles, Douglas A Bawel, Christina M Ernst, Marc D Fine, U Butch Klem, J David Lett, Chris A Ramsey, M Darren Root, Thomas W Seger, Raymond W Snowden

D-U-N-S 04-471-4132
GERMAN AUTO REPAIR LLC
ALEXANDER GROUPS
561 Watertown Ave, Waterbury, CT 06708-2200
Tel (203) 596-3505 *Founded/Ownrshp* 2000
Sales 30.0MM^E *EMP* 150
SIC 5511 5531 7538 Automobiles, new & used; Automotive parts; General automotive repair shops; Automobiles, new & used; Automotive parts; General automotive repair shops
Pr: Ashraf Hussein
**VP:* Mohamad Hussein

GERMAN CTR, SNR PLC, EDELWSS
See DEUTSCHES ALTENHEIM INC

D-U-N-S 96-808-9412
GERMAN MARSHALL FUND OF UNITED STATES
1744 R St Nw, Washington, DC 20009-2410
Tel (202) 683-2650 *Founded/Ownrshp* 2011
Sales 37.0MM *EMP* 68^E
Accts Mcgladrey Llp Mc Lean Va
SIC 6722 Management investment, open-end; Management investment, open-end
Pr: Craig Kennedy
Ofcr: Sara Coffey
Ofcr: Louise Langeby
IT Man: Kiarash Toossi

D-U-N-S 09-240-1843
GERMAN MARSHALL FUND OF UNITED STATES - A MEMORIAL TO
1744 R St Nw, Washington, DC 20009-2410
Tel (202) 745-6667 *Founded/Ownrshp* 1972
Sales 44.8MM *EMP* 126^E
Accts Rsm Mcgladrey Inc Vienna Va
SIC 8733 Educational research agency; Economic research, noncommercial; Educational research agency; Economic research, noncommercial
Pr: Craig Kennedy
**CFO:* Deborah R Iwig
Ofcr: Andrew Chrismer
Ofcr: Nicola Lightner

D-U-N-S 04-601-5194
GERMAN MOTORS CORP
BMW OF SAN FRANCISCO
1140 Harrison St, San Francisco, CA 94103-4525
Tel (415) 863-9000 *Founded/Ownrshp* 1964
Sales 112.2MM^E *EMP* 240^E
SIC 5511 7532 Automobiles, new & used; Top & body repair & paint shops; Automobiles, new & used; Top & body repair & paint shops
Pr: Henry Schmitt
**Sec:* Michael Greening
**VP:* Michele Schmitt
Exec: Evette Caceres
Off Mgr: Willis Kirk
Mktg Dir: Keith Howard
Sls Mgr: Jessy Custodio

D-U-N-S 01-368-1825
GERMANE SYSTEMS LC
3680 Centerview Dr # 100, Chantilly, VA 20151-3218
Tel (703) 502-8890 *Founded/Ownrshp* 1997
Sales 33.8MM^E *EMP* 74
SIC 3571 3572 Electronic computers; Computer storage devices; Electronic computers; Computer storage devices
CEO: Kerry O'Brien
Pr: Dan Connole
COO: Barry Altman
CFO: James Armstrong
Off Admin: Maryann Sullivan
QA Dir: Ali Khurram
IT Man: Isaac Stuart
Netwrk Eng: Jeremy Keen
VP Opers: Gregory Hall
Ql Cn Mgr: Tyson Edell
Sales Exec: Brian Hellems

D-U-N-S 07-940-3986
GERMANIA FARM MUTUAL INSURANCE ASSOCIATION
507 Highway 290 E, Brenham, TX 77833-5709
Tel (979) 836-5224 *Founded/Ownrshp* 1897
Sales NA *EMP* 366
SIC 6311 6331 Life insurance; Fire, marine & casualty insurance; Life insurance; Fire, marine & casualty insurance
Pr: Paul Ehlert
**Sec:* Derrell Krebs
**VP:* Gary Weiss
**Prin:* David Sommer
IT Man: Marcella Bennett
IT Man: Nancy Mahlmann
Board of Directors: William Boeer

D-U-N-S 87-650-9167
GERMANIA INSURANCE CO
(*Suby of* GERMANIA FARM MUTUAL INSURANCE ASSOCIATION) ★
507 Highway 290 E, Brenham, TX 77833-5709
Tel (979) 836-5224 *Founded/Ownrshp* 1985
Sales NA *EMP* 300
SIC 6411 Insurance agents, brokers & service; Insurance agents, brokers & service
Pr: Paul Ehlert
**Sec:* Derrell Gene Krebs
CIO: James Pharaon
Dir IT: Donna Kessler
IT Man: Dahmann Carl
IT Man: Carl Dahmann
IT Man: Nishant Gaikwad
IT Man: Tuttie Stiewert
Opers Mgr: Tim Tarnowski
Mktg Dir: Vicki Bergstrom
Sls Mgr: Steve Leftwich

GERMANN, JOSEPH R MD
See BAPTIST HEALTH CENTERS INC

GERMANTOWN ACADEMY
See PUBLIC SCHOOL OF GERMANTOWN

D-U-N-S 07-162-6576
GERMANTOWN COMMUNITY HEALTH SERVICES
(*Suby of* ALBERT EINSTEIN HEALTHCARE NETWORK) ★
1 Penn Blvd, Philadelphia, PA 19144-1476
Tel (215) 951-8000 *Founded/Ownrshp* 1863
Sales 16.1MM^E *EMP* 550
SIC 8062 General medical & surgical hospitals; General medical & surgical hospitals
CEO: Martin Goldsmith
**Ch Bd:* Francis R Strawbridge III
**Pr:* Cynthia A McGlone

D-U-N-S 07-145-4243
GERMANTOWN FRIENDS SCHOOL
31 W Coulter St, Philadelphia, PA 19144-2898
Tel (215) 951-2300 *Founded/Ownrshp* 1845
Sales 26.5MM^E *EMP* 230
Accts Doyle & Mcdonnell Pc Broom
SIC 8211 Private elementary school; Private elementary school
CFO: Mina Fader
VP: Michael E Dangelo
Psych: Craig Stevens

D-U-N-S 07-949-0479
GERMANTOWN MUNICIPAL SCHOOL DISTRICT
6685 Poplar Ave Ste 202, Germantown, TN 38138-3698
Tel (901) 752-7900 *Founded/Ownrshp* 2014
Sales 13.6MM^E *EMP* 280^E
SIC 8211 Public elementary & secondary schools
Dir Sec: Brandon Schiel
MIS Dir: John Pierce
Teacher Pr: Dan Haddow
Teacher Pr: Elissa Stratton

D-U-N-S 07-892-6771
GERMANTOWN MUTUAL INSURANCE CO
W209n11845 Insurance Pl, Germantown, WI 53022-1604
Tel (262) 251-6680 *Founded/Ownrshp* 1854
Sales NA *EMP* 50
SIC 6331 6411 Fire, marine & casualty insurance: mutual; Insurance agents, brokers & service; Fire, marine & casualty insurance: mutual; Insurance agents, brokers & service
Pr: Richard R Smith
VP: Thomas Galle
**VP:* Art Hintz
**VP:* Les Ibach
**VP:* Don Sturm
VP: Robert Viste
VP: Jim Weninger
Exec: Amanda Blank
Dept Mgr: Lisa Kindler
CTO: Joan Plato
VP Mktg: Ronald Vermillion

D-U-N-S 10-008-2809
GERMANTOWN SCHOOL DISTRICT
N104w13840 Donges Bay Rd, Germantown, WI 53022-4430
Tel (262) 253-3904 *Founded/Ownrshp* 1964
Sales 32.1MM^E *EMP* 500
Accts Reilly Penner & Benton Llp M
SIC 8211 Public elementary & secondary schools; Public elementary & secondary schools
CTO: Mark Gabrysiak

D-U-N-S 00-212-6449
GERNATT ASPHALT PRODUCTS INC (NY)
GERNATT COMPANIES
13870 Taylor Hollow Rd, Collins, NY 14034-9713
Tel (716) 532-3371 *Founded/Ownrshp* 1961
Sales 33.7MM^E *EMP* 80
SIC 2951 Asphalt paving mixtures & blocks; Asphalt paving mixtures & blocks
Ch Bd: Daniel R Gernatt Jr
**VP:* Randall Best
VP: Bill Schmitz
**Off Mgr:* Susan Degolier
Sfty Mgr: John Redman

GERNATT COMPANIES
See GERNATT ASPHALT PRODUCTS INC

D-U-N-S 00-439-0639 IMP
GEROME MANUFACTURING CO INC
80 Laurel View Dr, Smithfield, PA 15478-1643
Tel (724) 438-8544 *Founded/Ownrshp* 1957
Sales 26.5MM^E *EMP* 83
SIC 3444 3812 3699 3613 3469 3443 Sheet metalwork; Magnetic field detection apparatus; Electrical equipment & supplies; Switchgear & switchboard apparatus; Metal stampings; Fabricated plate work (boiler shop)
Pr: Joseph Putila
**VP:* Henry Gerome
Info Man: Fred Gantzhorn
Ql Cn Mgr: Chris Ramage
Board of Directors: Henry Gerome, Carol McDowell, Joseph Putila, Patricia Putila

D-U-N-S 07-263-2615
GERONTOLOGICAL SOCIETY OF AMERICA (INC)
1220 L St Nw Ste 901, Washington, DC 20005-4001
Tel (202) 842-1275 *Founded/Ownrshp* 1945
Sales 21.4MM *EMP* 24
SIC 8621 Professional membership organizations

D-U-N-S 07-985-4071
GEROTECH INC (MI)
HAAS FACTORY OUTLET
29220 Commerce Dr, Flat Rock, MI 48134-2749
Tel (734) 379-7788 *Founded/Ownrshp* 1970, 1987
Sales 28.4MM^E *EMP* 50
SIC 5084 Machine tools & accessories
Ch Bd: G Roger Gauthier
**Pr:* Jay Haas
Exec: Berenice Bruwer
Sls Mgr: Fred Schultz
Sls Mgr: Douglas Taber

GERRESHEIMER GLASS INC.
See CORNING PHARMACEUTICAL GLASS LLC

D-U-N-S 80-849-1211 IMP/EXP
GERRESHEIMER PEACHTREE CITY (USA) LP
(*Suby of* GERRESHEIMER GLAS GMBH)
650 Highway 74 S, Peachtree City, GA 30269-3002
Tel (770) 631-4939 *Founded/Ownrshp* 1993
Sales 26.0MM^E *EMP* 90
SIC 3089 Injection molding of plastics
CEO: Uwe Rohrhoff
**Pt:* Christian Lapka
**CFO:* Rainer Beaujean
Ql Cn Mgr: K Risley

D-U-N-S 01-914-1589
GERRISH CORP (VT)
GERRISH HONDA
369 Miracle Mile, Lebanon, NH 03766-2637
Tel (603) 448-5515 *Founded/Ownrshp* 1950, 1967
Sales 22.1MM *EMP* 38
Accts Tyler Simms & St Sauveur Pc
SIC 5511 Automobiles, new & used; Automobiles, new & used
Pr: Kurt D Gerrish
Sr VP: Stephen Perlowski
VP: Phyllis Gerrish
Genl Mgr: David Derrick
Mktg Mgr: Andrea Lessard
Sls Mgr: Daniel Ambrose
Sls Mgr: Peter Gordon
Sls Mgr: Jon Merrill

GERRISH HONDA
See GERRISH CORP

D-U-N-S 00-695-2212
GERRITY ENTERPRISES INC
63b Bedford St, Lakeville, MA 02347-1307
Tel (617) 916-0776 *Founded/Ownrshp* 1904, 1950
Sales 39.9MM^E *EMP* 45
SIC 6519 2448 5032 Real property lessors; Pallets, wood & wood with metal; Granite building stone; Marble building stone
Pr: James Gerrity III
**CFO:* Kevin W Moran
**Treas:* J Frank Gerrity II
**VP:* Peter F Gerrity
MIS Dir: Colleen O'fihelly

D-U-N-S 09-873-2654
GERRITYS SUPER MARKET INC
CITY PROVISION
950 N South Rd Ste 5, Scranton, PA 18504-1430
Tel (570) 342-4144 *Founded/Ownrshp* 1971
Sales 158.4MM *EMP* 1,100
Accts Mcgrail Merkel Quinn & Associa
SIC 5411 Grocery stores, independent; Grocery stores, independent
Pr: Joyce A Fasula
CFO: Anna Corcoran
IT Man: Tom Kaley
Mktg Mgr: Cindy Casciano

D-U-N-S 08-197-9759
GERRUS MAINTENANCE INC
95 Northfield Ave, Edison, NJ 08837-3806
Tel (732) 225-0662 *Founded/Ownrshp* 1973
Sales 7.0MM^E *EMP* 300
SIC 7349 5999 Building maintenance, except repairs; Cleaning equipment & supplies; Building maintenance, except repairs; Cleaning equipment & supplies
CEO: Gerald Cohen

D-U-N-S 83-495-2715
GERRY HOMES INC
HERITAGE VILLAGE
4570 Route 60, Gerry, NY 14740-9540
Tel (716) 985-4612 *Founded/Ownrshp* 1959
Sales 24.1MM^E *EMP* 586
SIC 8051 6513 Skilled nursing care facilities; Apartment building operators; Skilled nursing care facilities; Apartment building operators
Ch: William G Rushik
CFO: Robert Heller
**Treas:* Edwin Roorda
MIS Dir: Mark Guy

GERRY LANE CHEVROLET
See GERRY LANE ENTERPRISES INC

D-U-N-S 03-418-7534
GERRY LANE ENTERPRISES INC (MS)
GERRY LANE CHEVROLET
6505 Florida Blvd, Baton Rouge, LA 70806-4464
Tel (225) 926-4600 *Founded/Ownrshp* 1986, 1988
Sales 40.7MM *EMP* 250
SIC 5511

D-U-N-S 02-479-3309
GERRY WOOD AUTOMOTIVE LLC (NC)
GERRY WOOD CHRYSLER, DODGE
525 Jake Alexander Blvd S, Salisbury, NC 28147-9055
Tel (704) 637-9090 *Founded/Ownrshp* 1994
Sales 71.8MM^E *EMP* 130
SIC 5511 5521 Automobiles, new & used; Used car dealers; Automobiles, new & used; Used car dealers
Sls Dir: Ray Andersen
Sls Mgr: Jerry Bono
Sls Mgr: Steve Dibacco
Sls Mgr: Don Morgan
Sls Mgr: Curtis Trapp

GERRY WOOD CHRYSLER, DODGE
See GERRY WOOD AUTOMOTIVE LLC

D-U-N-S 08-938-5355
GERSHENSON CONSTRUCTION CO INC
2 Truitt Dr, Eureka, MO 63025-1920
Tel (636) 938-9595 *Founded/Ownrshp* 1977
Sales 26.7MM^E *EMP* 100
SIC 1611 1623 Highway & street paving contractor; Sewer line construction; Highway & street paving contractor; Sewer line construction
Pr: Edward N Gershenson
CTO: Chuck Risley
IT Man: Penny Stewart
IT Man: Jackie Van Noman

GERSHOW RECYCLING CENTERS
See GERSHOW RECYCLING CORP

D-U-N-S 04-447-6372 IMP
GERSHOW RECYCLING CORP
GERSHOW RECYCLING CENTERS
71 Peconic Ave, Medford, NY 11763-3201
Tel (631) 289-6188 *Founded/Ownrshp* 1964
Sales 137.9MM^E *EMP* 172
SIC 4953 Recycling, waste materials; Recycling, waste materials
CEO: Sam Gershowitz
**Pr:* Kevin Gershowitz
**VP:* Joseph Bertuccio
**Prin:* Elliot Gershowitz
Info Man: Ken Assenmacher
Sfty Dirs: Charles Keeling

D-U-N-S 00-122-3478 EXP
GERSON & GERSON INC (NY)
100 W 33rd St Ste 911, New York, NY 10001-2912
Tel (212) 244-6775 *Founded/Ownrshp* 1933
Sales 22.1MM^E *EMP* 120
Accts Weisermazars Llp New York Ny

SIC 2369 2361 Girls' & children's outerwear; Dresses: girls', children's & infants'; Girls' & children's outerwear; Dresses: girls', children's & infants'
Ch Bd: Matthew Gerson
Off Mgr: Scott Kassoff
Dir IT: Jack Dabby
Dir IT: Ken Dippold
Prd Mgr: Shelley Striar
Sls&Mrk Ex: Barbara Bowen
Sls Mgr: Kevin Gray

GERSON BAKAR & ASSOCIATES
See JALSON CO INC

D-U-N-S 00-890-6885 IMP/EXP
GERSON CO
GERSON COMPANIES, THE
1450 S Lone Elm Rd, Olathe, KS 66061-7256
Tel (913) 262-7400 *Founded/Ownrshp* 1942
Sales 55.5MM *EMP* 302E
SIC 5193 5199 5023 5094

GERSON COMPANIES, THE
See GERSON CO

D-U-N-S 83-196-3124
GERSON LEHRMAN GROUP INC
60 E 42nd St Fl 3, New York, NY 10165-1200
Tel (212) 223-0839 *Founded/Ownrshp* 1998
Sales 257.4MME *EMP* 300
SIC 6282 Investment research; Investment research
CEO: Alexander Saint-Amand
Pr: Zecki Dossal
Pr: Conrad Gorospe
COO: Alexander Saint-Mand
CFO: Michael Blumenstein
**CFO:* Bart Catalane
Top Exec: Alison Chan
Top Exec: John Donoghue
Sr VP: Craig Cinquina
Sr VP: Matthew Creedon
Sr VP: Nick Foster
Sr VP: Bartley O'Dwyer
VP: Dudley Brundige
VP: Christine Chapman
VP: Michael Daecher
VP: Jacquelyn Dille
VP: David Evans
VP: Marc Glennon
VP: Mark Haseltine
VP: Josh Hittman
VP: Thomas Hutzel

GERSTCO DIVISION
See ARTIFLEX MANUFACTURING LLC

D-U-N-S 19-196-5748
GERSTMAN HARVEY & ASSOC INC
QUEST
439 Oak St, Garden City, NY 11530-6453
Tel (516) 594-4400 *Founded/Ownrshp* 1979
Sales 23.1MME *EMP* 275
SIC 8742 Marketing consulting services; Marketing consulting services
CEO: Harvey Gerstman
**Pr:* Dan Gerstman
**Sec:* Carol Gerstman
Sr VP: Matilde Pennisi
VP: Micheal Beaudoin
Dir IT: Marc Langone

D-U-N-S 78-532-8860
GERSTMAN LLC
HGA QUEST
439 Oak St Ste 1, Garden City, NY 11530-6453
Tel (516) 594-4400 *Founded/Ownrshp* 2006
Sales 22.7MME *EMP* 700
SIC 8742 Merchandising consultant; Merchandising consultant
Pr: Glenn Ward
Ex VP: Linda Gerstman
Sr VP: Brian Bair
Sr VP: Gregg Gerstman
VP: Pete Wilson
Dist Mgr: John Baab
Sls Dir: Mike Shey
Sls Mgr: Denis Liakos
Sls Mgr: Joe Scherrer
Snr Mgr: Oscar Bailon
Snr Mgr: Sam Piunti

D-U-N-S 07-175-2414 IMP
GERTEN GREENHOUSES & GARDEN CENTER INC
5500 Blaine Ave, Inver Grove Heights, MN 55076-1206
Tel (651) 450-1501 *Founded/Ownrshp* 1952
Sales 105.5MME *EMP* 450E
SIC 5261 5193 Nursery stock; Nurseries & garden centers; Nurseries; Nursery stock, seeds & bulbs; Nurseries & garden centers; Nurseries; Nursery stock, seeds & bulbs; Nursery stock
Pr: Lewis Gerten
**Treas:* Gino Pitera
**VP:* Glen Gerten
IT Man: Scott Fischer

D-U-N-S 00-304-2991 IMP/EXP
GERTRUDE HAWK CHOCOLATES INC (PA)
9 Keystone Industrial Par, Dunmore, PA 18512-1544
Tel (570) 342-7556 *Founded/Ownrshp* 1936
Sales 224.8MME *EMP* 650
SIC 2064 2066 Gift shop; Candy & other confectionery products; Chocolate & cocoa products; Candy & other confectionery products; Chocolate & cocoa products
Pr: William E Auerey
**Ch Bd:* David W Hawk
**Pr:* William Aubrey
**CFO:* Steve Arling
VP: Bruce Cottle
VP: Christopher Cuneo
VP: Bill Hyndshaw
Rgnl Mgr: Sandy Williams
QA Dir: Alyssa Schweighofer

GERVAIS FORD
See GERVAIS INC

D-U-N-S 01-916-1702
GERVAIS INC
GERVAIS FORD
5 Littleton Rd, Ayer, MA 01432-1750
Tel (978) 772-6600 *Founded/Ownrshp* 1961
Sales 23.5MME *EMP* 60
SIC 5511

GES
See GRANITE ELECTRICAL SUPPLY INC

GES
See GROUNDWATER AND ENVIRONMENTAL SERVICES INC

D-U-N-S 04-515-5979
GES GLADIATOR ENERGY SERVICES TEXAS LLC
5983 Highway 80, Arcadia, LA 71001-5307
Tel (318) 263-2467 *Founded/Ownrshp* 2011
Sales 50.0MM *EMP* 173
SIC 1381 Drilling oil & gas wells; Drilling oil & gas wells
Dist Mgr: Todd Coburn

GES GLOBAL ENERGY SERVICES USA
See GES USA INC

D-U-N-S 04-831-8455
GES INC
EDWARDS FOOD GIANT
460 S Alabama St, Marianna, AR 72360-2753
Tel (870) 295-9311 *Founded/Ownrshp* 1968
Sales 63.6MME *EMP* 400
SIC 5411 Grocery stores; Grocery stores
Pr: Steve Edwards
**Sec:* Laura D Edwards
**VP:* Oral Edwards
VP: Gary Proffitt
VP: John Zelechoski
Genl Mgr: Mark Johnson
Netwrk Eng: John Ennis

D-U-N-S 78-408-8887
GES USA INC
GES GLOBAL ENERGY SERVICES USA
(*Suby of* GLOBAL ENERGY SERVICES SIEMSA SA)
9240 Belmont Ave Unit A, Franklin Park, IL 60131-2849
Tel (610) 940-6088 *Founded/Ownrshp* 2006
Sales 43.2MME *EMP* 250
SIC 1711 Solar energy contractor; Solar energy contractor
CEO: Hans Joern Rieks
COO: David Fernandez Garcia
**Treas:* Sergio Alonso
**Sec:* Berta Alvarez-Stuber
Off Mgr: Theresa Ciscar

D-U-N-S 09-983-3451
GESA CREDIT UNION
51 Gage Blvd, Richland, WA 99352-9700
Tel (509) 378-3100 *Founded/Ownrshp* 1953
Sales NA *EMP* 377
SIC 6062 State credit unions; State credit unions
Pr: Don Miller
COO: Raj Bandaru
VP: Bill Brandt
VP: Jeff Gegen
VP: Steve Oord
VP: Richard Waddle

D-U-N-S 02-040-6989 IMP
GESIPA FASTENERS USA INC
(*Suby of* GESIPA BLINDNIETTECHNIK GESELLSCHAFT MIT BESCHRANKTER HAFTUNG)
126 Quality Dr, Mocksville, NC 27028-4415
Tel (609) 208-1740 *Founded/Ownrshp* 1975
Sales 26.1MME *EMP* 120
SIC 5251 3542 3965 3599 Builders' hardware; Riveting machines; Fasteners; Machine shop, jobbing & repair
VP: Erik Olshall
**Pr:* Guy C Krone
VP: Dennis Buss
**VP:* Bill Schuler
Ql Cn Mgr: Tim Harris
Manager: Craig Donnville
Manager: Ron Valentine
Sls Mgr: Steve Rogers

D-U-N-S 09-271-0292
GESSLER CLINIC PROFESSIONAL ASSOCIATION
635 1st St N, Winter Haven, FL 33881-4191
Tel (863) 294-0670 *Founded/Ownrshp* 1972
Sales 35.0MME *EMP* 300
SIC 8011 Primary care medical clinic; Primary care medical clinic
Pr: John J McGetric MD
**Treas:* Joseph A Mancini
**VP:* Gordon J Rafool MD
Cmptr Lab: Barbara Bartels
Surgeon: Wojtek Aronski
Surgeon: Richard Honer
Surgeon: Fred Howard
Surgeon: Patrick Sullivan
Obsttrcn: Peter Verrill
Opthamlgy: Raymond A Chouinard
Opthamlgy: Alan G Gasner

D-U-N-S 17-121-9749 IMP
GESTAMP ALABAMA LLC
(*Suby of* GESTAMP NORTH AMERICA INC) ★
7000 Jefferson Metro Pkwy, Mc Calla, AL 35111-3956
Tel (205) 477-1412 *Founded/Ownrshp* 2012
Sales 147.9MME *EMP* 450E
SIC 3465 Automotive stampings; Body parts, automobile: stamped metal; Automotive stampings; Body parts, automobile: stamped metal
Pr: Francisco Riberas
Ex VP: James Barry
Dir IT: Andrew Stewart
IT Man: Josue Najera
Mtls Mgr: David Murrell
Mfg Mgr: Dan Fox
Ql Cn Mgr: John Nelson
Snr Mgr: Kris Colburn
Snr Mgr: David Minor
Snr Mgr: Andy Schwendner

GESTAMP AUTOMOCION
See GESTAMP CHATTANOOGA LLC

D-U-N-S 83-163-2505 IMP
GESTAMP CHATTANOOGA LLC
GESTAMP AUTOMOCION
(*Suby of* GESTAMP NORTH AMERICA INC) ★
3063 Hickory Valley Rd, Chattanooga, TN 37421-1266
Tel (423) 305-6300 *Founded/Ownrshp* 2009
Sales 123.2MM *EMP* 1,000
SIC 3465 Automotive stampings
CEO: Jeffrey Wilson
Pr: John Craig
CFO: James Barry
Mtls Mgr: Scott Willie

D-U-N-S 16-001-6291 IMP/EXP
GESTAMP MASON LLC
(*Suby of* GESTAMP NORTH AMERICA INC) ★
200 E Kipp Rd, Mason, MI 48854-9291
Tel (517) 244-8800 *Founded/Ownrshp* 2004
Sales 144.2MME *EMP* 489
SIC 3398 5013 3714 3711 3465 Metal heat treating; Motor vehicle supplies & new parts; Motor vehicle parts & accessories; Motor vehicles & car bodies; Automotive stampings; Metal heat treating; Motor vehicle supplies & new parts; Motor vehicle parts & accessories; Motor vehicles & car bodies; Automotive stampings
CEO: Jeffrey Wilson
**Pr:* John Craig
**CFO:* James Barry
Ex Dir: Debra Doyle
Plnt Mgr: Walter Hill

D-U-N-S 62-366-5333 IMP
GESTAMP NORTH AMERICA INC
(*Suby of* ACEK DESARROLLO Y GESTION INDUSTRIAL SL.)
2701 Troy Center Dr # 150, Troy, MI 48084-4755
Tel (248) 743-3400 *Founded/Ownrshp* 2004
Sales 1.1MMME *EMP* 1,057E
SIC 5013 Automotive supplies & parts; Automotive supplies & parts
Pr: Jeffrey Wilson
Pr: Roger Fuller
**CFO:* James Barry
VP: Eduardo Aguilar
**VP:* John Craig
VP: Thomas Lazer
Dir Bus: Garry Kasaczun
Prgrm Mgr: Thom Ball
Prgrm Mgr: Crystal Wiese
IT Man: Charlie Lee
IT Man: Gregory Lefler

D-U-N-S 78-798-0007 IMP
GESTAMP SOUTH CAROLINA LLC
(*Suby of* GESTAMP NORTH AMERICA INC) ★
1 Lsp Dr, Union, SC 29379-7785
Tel (864) 466-3960 *Founded/Ownrshp* 2009
Sales 252.7MM *EMP* 370
SIC 3465 Automotive stampings; Automotive stampings
CEO: Jeffrey Wilson
**Pr:* John Craig
**CFO:* James Barry

D-U-N-S 07-854-3536 IMP
GESTAMP WEST VIRGINIA LLC
(*Suby of* GESTAMP NORTH AMERICA INC) ★
3100 Maccorkle Ave Sw, South Charleston, WV 25303-1473
Tel (304) 744-4601 *Founded/Ownrshp* 2012
Sales 135.5MM *EMP* 351
SIC 3469 Stamping metal for the trade; Stamping metal for the trade
CEO: Jeffrey Wilson
**Pr:* John Craig
**CFO:* James Barry

G.E.T.
See GLOBAL ENTERPRISE TECHNOLOGIES CORP (DE)

G.E.T. ENTERPRISES
See G E T ENTERPRISES LLC

D-U-N-S 88-311-0983
GET FRESH PRODUCE INC
1441 Brewster Creek Blvd, Bartlett, IL 60103-1695
Tel (630) 837-9700 *Founded/Ownrshp* 1996
Sales 95.5MME *EMP* 61
SIC 5148 Fresh fruits & vegetables; Fresh fruits & vegetables
Pr: James Costabile
COO: Peter Sikorski
**CFO:* Sharon Costabile
**VP:* Eugenio Alimondi
IT Man: Randy Krahmer
Opers Mgr: Rick Buccola
Opers Mgr: Nick Cilfone
Opers Mgr: Joe Zeno
Sls Mgr: Ray Gutierrez

D-U-N-S 61-757-9149 IMP
GET FRESH SALES INC
FRESH CUTS
6745 Escondido St, Las Vegas, NV 89119-3858
Tel (702) 897-8522 *Founded/Ownrshp* 1990
Sales 190.0MME *EMP* 300
SIC 5148 Fresh fruits & vegetables; Fresh fruits & vegetables
Pr: Dominic Caldara
**CFO:* Scott Goldberg
Ql Cn Mgr: Karla Mendoza

GET N GO CONVENIENCE STORES
See RED HORSE OIL CO INC

GET ORGANIZED
See TAYLOR GIFTS INC

D-U-N-S 05-024-4529
GET SET MERCHANDISING SERVICES INC
1810 Durant Rd, Valrico, FL 33596-4526
Tel (813) 689-2767 *Founded/Ownrshp* 2000
Sales 22.0MME *EMP* 600
SIC 7319 Display advertising service; Display advertising service
Pr: Alan Gary

D-U-N-S 02-718-5121
GET YOU FOUND ONLINE MARKETING INC
301 S Elm St Ste 401, Greensboro, NC 27401-2636
Tel (336) 790-6735 *Founded/Ownrshp* 2008
Sales 284.9MM *EMP* 4
SIC 8742 Marketing consulting services; Marketing consulting services
Pr: Jessamyn Bean
**VP:* Peter Raines

GET-A-LIFT HANDICAP BUS TRNSP
See GOLDEN EMPIRE TRANSIT DISTRICT

D-U-N-S 92-877-9305 IMP
GETAC INC
(*Suby of* MITAC INTERNATIONAL CORPORATION)
400 Exchange Ste 100, Irvine, CA 92602-1340
Tel (949) 681-2900 *Founded/Ownrshp* 1997
Sales 24.4MME *EMP* 40
SIC 5045 Mainframe computers
CEO: Ming-Hang Hwang
**Pr:* Jim Rimay
Pr: Scott Shainman
Genl Mgr: Matt Tabatabai
Ql Cn Mgr: Ken Shima
Mktg Dir: John Lamb
Mktg Mgr: Jennifer Guba
Mktg Mgr: Han Ling
Manager: Duane Miller
Manager: Bill Rutan
Manager: Troy Ware

D-U-N-S 00-530-4266
GETHMANN CONSTRUCTION CO INC
313 Front St, Gladbrook, IA 50635-7707
Tel (641) 473-2180 *Founded/Ownrshp* 1937
Sales 23.9MME *EMP* 75
SIC 1541 1542 Industrial buildings, new construction; Commercial & office building, new construction
Pr: Jill D Craft
**Pr:* Jack Gethmann
**Treas:* Cornell Gethmann
**VP:* Bernard J Capesius
**VP:* John L Craft

D-U-N-S 12-851-3145 IMP
GETINGE SOURCING LLC
(*Suby of* GETINGE AB)
1777 E Henrietta Rd, Rochester, NY 14623-3133
Tel (585) 475-1400 *Founded/Ownrshp* 2002
Sales 23.7MME *EMP* 174
SIC 3842 Sterilizers, hospital & surgical; Sterilizers, hospital & surgical
Pr: John Aymong
CFO: Darren Soudan
Mtls Mgr: Michael Kotsch

D-U-N-S 05-577-8088 IMP
GETINGE USA INC
(*Suby of* GETINGE AB)
1777 E Henrietta Rd, Rochester, NY 14623-3133
Tel (585) 475-1400 *Founded/Ownrshp* 1997
Sales 95.6MME *EMP* 600
SIC 3842 3841 Sterilizers, hospital & surgical; Surgical & medical instruments; Sterilizers, hospital & surgical; Surgical & medical instruments
Pr: Charles Carrier
**Ch Bd:* Andrew Ray
Pr: John Hansson
**CFO:* Chris Dorsey
**VP:* Terry D Cooke
VP: Rudi Kober
VP: Gina Lubert
VP: Michael Treude
Ex Dir: Bo Engberg
Brnch Mgr: Jeff Carrig
Brnch Mgr: Charles Cash

GETIX HEALTH
See PATIENT ACCOUNTING SERVICE CENTER LLC

GETMEDLEGAL
See LEGAL SOLUTIONS HOLDINGS INC

D-U-N-S 80-915-0043
GETRAG TRANSMISSIONS CORP
(*Suby of* THI INVESTMENTS GMBH)
35885 Mound Rd, Sterling Heights, MI 48310-4777
Tel (586) 620-1338 *Founded/Ownrshp* 2012
Sales 26.0MME *EMP* 129
SIC 3714 Gears, motor vehicle
Pr: Tobias Hagenmeyer
**CEO:* Mihir Kotecha
**COO:* John McDonald
**CFO:* Michael McMillan
Prgrm Mgr: Sandeep Yadav

D-U-N-S 19-861-9459
GETRONICS US OPERATIONS INC
(*Suby of* GETRONICS USA INC) ★
100 Ames Pond Dr Ste 99, Tewksbury, MA 01876-1240
Tel (978) 625-5000 *Founded/Ownrshp* 2003
Sales 7.0MME *EMP* 1,140E
SIC 7373 Computer integrated systems design
CEO: Kevin Roach
Sfty Mgr: Frank Robinson

D-U-N-S 00-101-8167
GETRONICS USA INC (DE)
(*Suby of* COMPUCOM SYSTEMS INC) ★
290 Concord Rd, Billerica, MA 01821-3405
Tel (978) 625-5000 *Founded/Ownrshp* 1951, 2008
Sales 108.2MME *EMP* 2,600
SIC 7378 7373 7379 Computer & data processing equipment repair/maintenance; Local area network (LAN) systems integrator; Computer related consulting services; Computer related maintenance services; Computer & data processing equipment repair/maintenance; Local area network (LAN) systems integrator; Computer related consulting services; Computer related maintenance services
CEO: Mark Cook
**CEO:* Andreas Ziegenhain
**CFO:* Pom Burie

**Treas:* William Clark
**VP:* David Buka
MIS Dir: Roger Gilfert
Mktg Dir: Payton Chung

D-U-N-S 09-837-3756
GETRONICS WANG CO LLC
(*Suby of* GETRONICS USA INC) ★
8110 Anderson Rd Ste 100, Tampa, FL 33634-2424
Tel (813) 884-2500 *Founded/Ownrshp* 1997
Sales 13.7MM^E *EMP* 375
SIC 7371 5734 Computer software development; Modems, monitors, terminals & disk drives: computers; Computer software development; Modems, monitors, terminals & disk drives: computers
Genl Mgr: Bob Pike
VP: Jim Page
VP: Rena Thompson

D-U-N-S 94-773-8295
GETSCO
GEO EROSION & TURF SOLUTIONS
10791 E Finch Ave, Middlesex, NC 27557-9203
Tel (252) 235-5015 *Founded/Ownrshp* 2007
Sales 25.0MM *EMP* 30
SIC 5039 Soil erosion control fabrics
Pr: Gregory A Turnage
**Sec:* Turner Burn
**VP:* Greg Baker
**VP:* Coalter Paxton
Sls Mgr: John Parrish

D-U-N-S 05-844-8275
GETTEL AUTOMOTIVE INC
GETTEL TOYOTA
6423 14th St W, Bradenton, FL 34207-5330
Tel (941) 225-7567 *Founded/Ownrshp* 1990
Sales 58.8MM^E *EMP* 145
SIC 5511 7538 Automobiles, new & used; General automotive repair shops; Automobiles, new & used; General automotive repair shops
Pr: James Gettel
Sls Mgr: Sanjuan Gutierrez
Sls Mgr: Paul Trombley

D-U-N-S 03-231-7968
GETTEL ENTERPRISES INC
GATORLAND TOYOTA-KIA-ACURA
2985 N Main St, Gainesville, FL 32609-3002
Tel (352) 376-3262 *Founded/Ownrshp* 1994
Sales 39.9MM^E *EMP* 90
SIC 5511 Automobiles, new & used; Automobiles, new & used
Pr: James C Gettel
**Sec:* Robert E Bisplinghoff
Genl Mgr: Adam Rohlman
Dir IT: Brent Biehl
Sales Exec: Ryan Fischer
Sales Asso: Eddie Stockman

GETTEL NISSAN
See NISSAN GETTEL INC

GETTEL TOYOTA
See GETTEL AUTOMOTIVE INC

D-U-N-S 92-820-8503
■ **GETTHERE LP**
GETTHERE.COM
(*Suby of* SABRE HOLDINGS CORP) ★
3150 Sabre Dr, Southlake, TX 76092-2103
Tel (682) 605-1000 *Founded/Ownrshp* 1995
Sales 34.9MM^E *EMP* 390
SIC 4724 7375 5961 Travel agencies; Information retrieval services; Catalog & mail-order houses; Travel agencies; Information retrieval services; Catalog & mail-order houses
Prin: Jeff Palmer
VP: Chris Kroeger
VP: Steve Soto
CTO: Tom Murray
Software D: Clint Crocker
Site Mgr: Scott Pechous

GETTHERE.COM
See GETTHERE LP

GETTIER SECURITY
See JR GETTIER & ASSOCIATES INC

D-U-N-S 01-514-8588
GETTLE INC
2745 Black Bridge Rd, York, PA 17406-7920
Tel (717) 324-0433 *Founded/Ownrshp* 1984
Sales 68.8MM^E *EMP* 140
SIC 1731 General electrical contractor; General electrical contractor
Pr: George Buss
Treas: Bob Oettel
**VP:* Jeffrey Dubs
**VP:* Timothy Kinsley
Div Mgr: Randy Bush
Telecom Ex: Frank Snyder
IT Man: Tracy Barganier
Info Man: Tom Shoffner
Sfty Dirs: Garry Cornbower
Sfty Dirs: Royce Foltz
Sfty Dirs: Steve Miller

D-U-N-S 07-519-7665
■ **GETTY IMAGES (US) INC**
(*Suby of* GETTY IMAGES INC) ★
1 Hudson St, New York, NY 10013-3835
Tel (646) 613-4000 *Founded/Ownrshp* 1999
Sales 15.6MM^E *EMP* 301
SIC 7389 Photographic library service; Photographic library service
CEO: Jonathan Klein
VP: Joe Knudson
Sales Exec: Roshni Ray

D-U-N-S 02-846-4894 IMP
■ **GETTY IMAGES INC**
(*Suby of* CARLYLE GROUP L P) ★
605 5th Ave S Ste 400, Seattle, WA 98104-3887
Tel (206) 925-5000 *Founded/Ownrshp* 2012
Sales 65.2MM^E *EMP* 1,300
SIC 5961 Commercial photography; Commercial art & graphic design; Creative services to advertisers, except writers;
Pr: Jonathan Klein
COO: Nicholas E Evans-Lombe
CFO: Tara Comonte
Chf Mktg O: Susan Smith Ellis
Ofcr: Jeff Dunn
Ex VP: Linda Ranz
Sr VP: Matthew Bencke
Sr VP: James C Gurke
Sr VP: John J Lapham III
Sr VP: Lee Martin
VP: Jonathan Broad
VP: Carmen Cano
VP: Jim Gurke
VP: Shane Johnson
VP: Scott Miskimens
VP: Erin Sullivan
VP: Maged Zaher

GETTY PUBLICATIONS
See J PAUL GETTY TRUST

D-U-N-S 05-773-0202
▲ **GETTY REALTY CORP**
2 Jericho Plz Ste 110, Jericho, NY 11753-1681
Tel (516) 478-5400 *Founded/Ownrshp* 1955
Sales 99.8MM *EMP* 29^E
Accts Pricewaterhousecoopers Llp Ne
Tkr Sym GTY *Exch* NYS
SIC 6798 Real estate investment trusts; Real estate investment trusts
Pr: David B Driscoll
**Ch Bd:* Leo Liebowitz
COO: Mark J Olear
CFO: Christopher J Constant
Ex VP: Kevin C Shea
Sr VP: Joshua Dicker
Snr Mgr: Eugene Shnayderman
Board of Directors: Milton Cooper, Philip E Coviello, Richard E Montag, Howard B Safenowitz

D-U-N-S 19-677-8294
GETTYS GROUP INC
55 W Wacker Dr Ste 400, Chicago, IL 60601-1689
Tel (312) 836-1111 *Founded/Ownrshp* 1988
Sales 38.5MM^E *EMP* 80^E
SIC 7389 Interior design services
CEO: Roger Hill
**Pr:* Andrew Fay
CFO: Bradley Gookins
**CFO:* Dan Paul
Sr VP: Meg Prendergast
**Sr VP:* Ariane Steinbeck
VP: Duk Kim
VP: Jerry Zeitner

D-U-N-S 05-730-7043
GETTYSBURG AREA SCHOOL DISTRICT
900 Biglerville Rd, Gettysburg, PA 17325-7897
Tel (717) 334-6254 *Founded/Ownrshp* 1970
Sales 26.1MM^E *EMP* 466
SIC 8211 Public senior high school; Public junior high school; Public elementary school; Public senior high school; Public junior high school; Public elementary school
CFO: Patricia Simpson
Treas: Kathryn Hewitt
IT Man: John Ziegler
Prd Mgr: Brenda Larson

D-U-N-S 07-144-5134
GETTYSBURG COLLEGE (PA)
MAJESTIC THEATER
300 N Washington St, Gettysburg, PA 17325-1483
Tel (717) 337-6000 *Founded/Ownrshp* 1832
Sales 128.8MM *EMP* 95^E
Accts Kpmg Llp Harrisburg Pennsylv
SIC 8221 College, except junior; College, except junior
Pr: Janet M Riggs
Assoc VP: Michael Martys
VP: Christopher Delaney
VP: Barbara Fritze
**VP:* Daniel L Konstalid
VP: Rod Tosten
VP: Henning Wrage
Exec: Charles Stockman
Assoc Dir: Joshua Azer
Assoc Dir: Jill Titus
Board of Directors: James Wiltgen

D-U-N-S 10-804-8679
GETTYSBURG HEALTH CARE CORP
HOSPITAL
147 Gettys St, Gettysburg, PA 17325-2534
Tel (717) 339-2025 *Founded/Ownrshp* 1984
Sales 899.7M *EMP* 600
SIC 8062 General medical & surgical hospitals; General medical & surgical hospitals
Pr: Kevin Mosser
Opers Mgr: Dennis Shriner
Opers Mgr: Tom Young

GETTYSBURG HLTH ADMINISTRATORS
See GETTYSBURG INSURANCE SERVICES INC

D-U-N-S 07-118-6118
GETTYSBURG HOSPITAL (PA)
(*Suby of* WELLSPAN HEALTH) ★
147 Gettys St, Gettysburg, PA 17325-2536
Tel (717) 334-2121 *Founded/Ownrshp* 1919, 2001
Sales 140.5MM *EMP* 800
SIC 8062 General medical & surgical hospitals; General medical & surgical hospitals
Pr: Jane Hyde
Sr VP: Craig Long
VP: Maria Royce

D-U-N-S 15-880-6752
GETTYSBURG INSURANCE SERVICES INC
GETTYSBURG HLTH ADMINISTRATORS
404 Baltimore St, Gettysburg, PA 17325-2604
Tel (717) 334-9247 *Founded/Ownrshp* 1979
Sales NA *EMP* 89
SIC 6411 Medical insurance claim processing, contract or fee basis
Pr: Ronald Pack
CFO: Curtis Winger
Dir IT: Phillip Gomer
Sls&Mrk Ex: Hemler Jeff

D-U-N-S 10-522-4849
GETWELLNETWORK INC
7700 Old Georgetown Rd 4t, Bethesda, MD 20814-6100
Tel (240) 482-3200 *Founded/Ownrshp* 2013
Sales 81.6MM^E *EMP* 220^E
SIC 7371 Computer software development & applications; Computer software development & applications
CEO: Micheal O Neal Jr
COO: David D Bennett
CFO: Wellford Dillard
CFO: Bart Witteveen
Bd of Dir: Scott Frederick
Ofcr: John George
Ex VP: Bruce Matter
Sr VP: Jim Cato
Sr VP: Tony Cook
Sr VP: Karen Drenkard
Sr VP: Stephen Hiscott
Sr VP: Sharon Kaufman
VP: Greg Essler
VP: Jeff Fallon
VP: Cheryl Gnehm
VP: Lea Hackmann
VP: Dianne Johnson
VP: Pankaj Kulkarni
VP: Ellen Swartwout
VP: Vinnie Whibbs
Board of Directors: Anthony J Principi

GETZ EQUIPMENT INNOVATORS
See GETZ FIRE EQUIPMENT CO

D-U-N-S 00-176-1584
GETZ FIRE EQUIPMENT CO
GETZ EQUIPMENT INNOVATORS
1615 Sw Adams St, Peoria, IL 61602-1782
Tel (309) 673-0761 *Founded/Ownrshp* 1957
Sales 34.8MM^E *EMP* 95
SIC 5087 Firefighting equipment; Firefighting equipment
CEO: Rod Getz

GEUPEL DEMARS HAGERMAN, LLC
See HAGERMAN GROUP

D-U-N-S 92-756-3882
■ **GEVITY HR INC**
(*Suby of* TRINET GROUP INC) ★
9000 Town Center Pkwy, Lakewood Ranch, FL 34202-4101
Tel (941) 741-4300 *Founded/Ownrshp* 2009
Sales 27.4MM^E *EMP* 810
SIC 7363 8742 8721 Employee leasing service; Human resource consulting services; Payroll accounting service; Employee leasing service; Human resource consulting services; Payroll accounting service
CEO: Burton Goldfield
Pr: Edwin E Hightower
Pr: Maribeth Phillips
COO: Heath Byrd
CFO: Douglas Devlin
CFO: William Porter
Ex VP: Michael Ehresman
Ex VP: Karin Otto
Sr VP: Jim E Hardee
Sr VP: Gregory M Nichols
VP: William Grenier
VP: Janet Watson
VP: Brad Webb

D-U-N-S 13-967-4964
■ **GEVITY HR LP**
(*Suby of* GEVITY HR INC) ★
9000 Town Center Pkwy, Lakewood Ranch, FL 34202-4101
Tel (941) 748-4540 *Founded/Ownrshp* 1997
Sales 19.2MM^E *EMP* 782
SIC 7363 Employee leasing service; Employee leasing service
Pt: Erick Vonk
Pt: Peter Grabowski
VP: Helen Meola
CIO: Lisa Harris
Dir IT: Michael Clifford

D-U-N-S 60-863-9345
▲ **GEVO INC**
345 Inverness Dr S # 310, Englewood, CO 80112-5892
Tel (303) 858-8358 *Founded/Ownrshp* 2005
Sales 28.2MM *EMP* 112^E
Accts Deloitte & Touche Llp Denver
Tkr Sym GEVO *Exch* NGM
SIC 2869 8731 Butyl alcohol, butanol; Ethyl alcohol, ethanol; Commercial physical research
CEO: Patrick R Gruber
**Ch Bd:* Ruth Dreessen
Pr: Christopher Ryan
Chf Cred: Greg Roda
Ex VP: Mike Willis
VP: Jeff Scheib
Dir IT: Dean Kramer
IT Man: Debbie Dalrymple
Board of Directors: Ruth I Dreessen, Andy Marsh, Gary W Mize, Johannes Minho Roth

D-U-N-S 02-865-6437
GEWEKE CO
LARRY GEWEKE FORD
871 E Onstott Rd, Yuba City, CA 95991-3666
Tel (530) 821-2121 *Founded/Ownrshp* 1986
Sales 59.6MM^E *EMP* 130
SIC 5511 5531 Automobiles, new & used; Automobile & truck equipment & parts; Automobiles, new & used; Automobile & truck equipment & parts
Pr: Larry William Geweke
**CFO:* Dianne Vinson
**Sec:* Dale Geweke
Exec: Kim George

D-U-N-S 78-522-3264
GEWEKE MOTORS INC
GEWEKE TOYOTA SCION
1020 S Beckman Rd, Lodi, CA 95240-3152
Tel (209) 367-6500 *Founded/Ownrshp* 1991
Sales 37.0MM *EMP* 79
SIC 5511

GEWEKE TOYOTA SCION
See GEWEKE MOTORS INC

D-U-N-S 10-811-4542
■ **GEXA ENERGY LP**
(*Suby of* NEXTERA ENERGY INC) ★
20455 State Highway 249 # 200, Houston, TX 77070-2758
Tel (713) 961-9399 *Founded/Ownrshp* 2005
Sales 125.3MM^E *EMP* 300
SIC 4911 Electric services; Electric services
Pr: Brian Landrum
COO: Jason Lucia
Treas: Mark R Sorenson
VP: Larry Boisvert
VP: Jim Brown
VP: Kenny Matula
VP: Deena Morgan
VP: Allison Wall
Genl Mgr: Sabrina Garcia
Software D: Ryan Purcell
Software D: Jason Rivera

GEXPRO
See GENERAL SUPPLY & SERVICES INC

D-U-N-S 01-814-5987
GEYERS MARKETS INC
SUPER VALU
385 N Seltzer St Unit 5, Crestline, OH 44827-1400
Tel (419) 683-2925 *Founded/Ownrshp* 1946
Sales 60.0MM *EMP* 500
SIC 5411 Grocery stores, independent; Grocery stores, independent
Pr: Eric S Geyer
**VP:* Eric J Geyer

D-U-N-S 01-708-3510
GEZON MOTORS INC
GEZON NISSAN
3985 Plainfield Ave Ne, Grand Rapids, MI 49525-1673
Tel (616) 361-7361 *Founded/Ownrshp* 1913
Sales 22.8MM^E *EMP* 47
SIC 5511 Automobiles, new & used
CEO: Mary Gezon
Sales Asso: Michael Jenkins

GEZON NISSAN
See GEZON MOTORS INC

GF
See G FISHER CONSTRUCTION CO

GF HARVEL
See GEORG FISCHER HARVEL LLC

D-U-N-S 13-201-6168 IMP/EXP
GF HEALTH PRODUCTS INC
BASIC AMERICAN MEDICAL PDTS
2935 Northeast Pkwy, Atlanta, GA 30360-2808
Tel (770) 447-1609 *Founded/Ownrshp* 2003
Sales 81.7MM^E *EMP* 300^E
SIC 3841 5047 Medical instruments & equipment, blood & bone work; Medical equipment & supplies; Medical instruments & equipment, blood & bone work; Medical equipment & supplies
Pr: Kenneth Spett
CFO: Alan Monahan
CFO: Mike Poelking
**Sr VP:* Cherie Antoniazzi
**Sr VP:* Marc Bernstein
**Sr VP:* Ivan Bielik
**Sr VP:* Lawrence De La Haba
**Sr VP:* David Walton
VP: Harvey Cohen
VP: Tim Sheehan
VP: Alan Spett
Creative D: Dan Grieco

D-U-N-S 92-619-8610
GF INVESTORS LLC
U.S. GREENFIBER
60 E 42nd St Rm 4510, New York, NY 10165-0012
Tel (212) 457-1138 *Founded/Ownrshp* 2013
Sales 120.1MM^E *EMP* 539^E
SIC 1742 Insulation, buildings
CEO: Michael Green
Sr VP: Ben Kramer

D-U-N-S 10-762-6434 IMP
GF MACHINING SOLUTIONS LLC
AGIE CHARMILLES
(*Suby of* GEORGE FISCHER INC) ★
560 Bond St, Lincolnshire, IL 60069-4207
Tel (847) 913-5300 *Founded/Ownrshp* 1983
Sales 83.6MM^E *EMP* 189
SIC 5084 Machine tools & metalworking machinery; Machine tools & metalworking machinery
Pr: Glynn Fletcher
CFO: Gregg Denig
Treas: Donna Achs

D-U-N-S 02-239-1473
GF MANAGEMENT INC
1628 John F Kennedy Blvd # 2300, Philadelphia, PA 19103-2128
Tel (215) 972-2222 *Founded/Ownrshp* 1997
Sales 36.7MM^E *EMP* 100
SIC 8748 8741 Business consulting; Management services; Hotel or motel management; Hospital management
CEO: Ken Kochenour
V Ch: Bob Keith Jr
Pr: Paul Williamson
**Ex VP:* Barbara Evans
**Ex VP:* Stan Glander
**Ex VP:* Andrew S Tod
**Sr VP:* Jay Wellenbusher
VP: Dave Ditto
VP: Fred Grabosky
VP: Robert Trammell
**VP:* Joseph A Wellenbusher

D-U-N-S 60-718-7841
GF WIEDEMAN INTERNATIONAL INC
1715 S Joplin Ave Ste D, Joplin, MO 64804-0611
Tel (417) 206-0752 *Founded/Ownrshp* 2005
Sales 22.5MM *EMP* 42
Accts Mense Churchwell & Mense Pc
SIC 4789 Railroad maintenance & repair services; Railroad maintenance & repair services
Pr: Gaylon Jackson
**VP:* William Ryan Jackson

D-U-N-S 07-840-0647
GFA ALABAMA INC (AL)
GFA TRANSPORTATION
6211 Fairfax Byp, Valley, AL 36854-4550
Tel (334) 756-3035 *Founded/Ownrshp* 2010
Sales 27.4MM^E *EMP* 295^E
SIC 7549 4212 Automotive maintenance services; Local trucking, without storage; Automotive maintenance services; Local trucking, without storage
Pr: Steve Hong
**VP:* Glenn Macdonald
**Genl Mgr:* Daniel Skipworth

GFA TRANSPORTATION
See GFA ALABAMA INC

GFAS
See GLOBAL FINANCIAL AID SERVICES INC

GFC LEASING
See GORDON FLESCH CO INC

D-U-N-S 06-114-2089 IMP
GFF INC
GIRARD FOOD SERVICE
145 Willow Ave, City of Industry, CA 91746-2047
Tel (323) 232-6255 *Founded/Ownrshp* 1981
Sales 42.3MM^E *EMP* 89
SIC 2035 Pickles, sauces & salad dressings; Pickles, sauces & salad dressings
Ch: Jack Tucey
**Pr:* Bill Perry
**CEO:* Farrell Hirsch
VP Mktg: Ron Caplan

D-U-N-S 04-939-1156
GFG MANAGEMENT LLC
5555 Glenridge Connector # 850, Atlanta, GA 30342-4810
Tel (770) 514-4871 *Founded/Ownrshp* 2010
Sales 184.8MM^E *EMP* 2,308^E
SIC 8741 Management services

D-U-N-S 15-988-8999
GFI CAPITAL RESOURCES GROUP INC
140 Broadway Fl 41, New York, NY 10005-1033
Tel (212) 668-1444 *Founded/Ownrshp* 1993
Sales 26.0MM^E *EMP* 600
SIC 6513 Apartment building operators; Apartment building operators
Ch Bd: Allen I Gross
**CFO:* Jennifer McLean
**Ex VP:* Ilya Braz
**VP:* Abraham Eisner

GFI DIGITAL
See GIBBS TECHNOLOGY CO

D-U-N-S 15-235-9092
■ **GFI GROUP INC**
(*Suby of* BGC PARTNERS INC) ★
55 Water St, New York, NY 10041-0004
Tel (212) 968-4100 *Founded/Ownrshp* 2015
Sales 940.0MM^E *EMP* 2,087^E
Tkr Sym GFIG *Exch* OTO
SIC 6211 Security brokers & dealers; Security brokers & dealers
CEO: Colin Heffron

D-U-N-S 94-004-1176
■ **GFI GROUP LLC**
(*Suby of* GFI GROUP INC) ★
55 Water St Fl 10, New York, NY 10041-0002
Tel (212) 968-4100 *Founded/Ownrshp* 2000
Sales 36.9MM^E *EMP* 270^E
SIC 6211 Security brokers & dealers; Security brokers & dealers
CFO: Jim Pears
Mng Dir: Herv Alfon

D-U-N-S 82-465-4941
GFI MANAGEMENT SERVICES INC
G F I
50 Broadway Fl 4, New York, NY 10004-3856
Tel (212) 668-1444 *Founded/Ownrshp* 1993
Sales 185.6MM^E *EMP* 1,000^E
SIC 6513 6512 Apartment building operators; Nonresidential building operators
CEO: Abe Eisner
Mng Pt: Lon Rubackin
**Pr:* Allen I Gross
Pr: Ilya Braz
Pr: Tice Vieira
CFO: Judith Crook
CFO: Paul Glick
**Sr VP:* Brian Gross
VP: Deborah Holcombe
**VP:* Steven Hurwitz
VP: Amanda Pinto
VP: Randi Sherman
VP: William Watkins
**VP:* Michael Weiser
Assoc Dir: Daniel Shragaei

D-U-N-S 15-400-0020
GFI MORTGAGE BANKERS INC
50 Broadway Fl 4, New York, NY 10004-3856
Tel (212) 668-1444 *Founded/Ownrshp* 1983
Sales NA *EMP* 100
SIC 6162 Mortgage bankers & correspondents
CEO: Abraham Eisner
**Pr:* Edith Gross
Ofcr: Clara Ziri
Ex VP: Michael Weiser
Sr VP: Rafi Ohana
**VP:* Isaac Eisner
VP: Steven Hurwitz

Opers Mgr: Stacey Curran
Sls Dir: Aaron Rosenfeld

D-U-N-S 01-452-1590
GFI SECURITIES LLC
(*Suby of* JERSEY PARTNERS INC) ★
55 Water St Fl 10, New York, NY 10041-0002
Tel (212) 968-2073 *Founded/Ownrshp* 1997
Sales 35.0MM^E *EMP* 270
SIC 6211 Security brokers & dealers; Security brokers & dealers
Pr: Michael Gooch
CFO: Jim Pears

GFI SOFTWARE
See GFI USA INC

D-U-N-S 07-971-5557
GFI SOFTWARE INC
1005 Slater Rd Ste 300, Durham, NC 27703-8471
Tel (919) 379-3402 *Founded/Ownrshp* 1994
Sales 33.8MM^E *EMP* 70^E
SIC 7371 6719 Computer software development & applications; Investment holding companies, except banks
CEO: Walter Scott
CFO: Josef Calleja
Genl Mgr: Sergio Galindo

D-U-N-S 01-494-1020
GFI USA INC
GFI SOFTWARE
(*Suby of* GFI SOFTWARE INC) ★
1005 Slater Rd Ste 300, Durham, NC 27703-8471
Tel (919) 379-3397 *Founded/Ownrshp* 1997
Sales 33.8MM^E *EMP* 70^E
SIC 7372 Prepackaged software
Pr: Walter Scott
**CFO:* Paul Goodridge
**CFO:* Daniel J Kossmann
**Treas:* Mark Lessing
Sr VP: Patricia Hume
VP: Scott Hagenus
VP: Steve McAveeney
Comm Dir: Angelica M Trigona
**Prin:* Pierre-Michel Kronenberg
Mng Dir: Ian Clague
CIO: Sergio Galindo

D-U-N-S 07-870-4251 IMP
GFK CUSTOM RESEARCH LLC
(*Suby of* GFK NORTH AMERICA HOLDING GMBH)
200 Liberty St Fl 4, New York, NY 10281-4111
Tel (212) 240-5300 *Founded/Ownrshp* 2014
Sales 85.8MM^E *EMP* 900
SIC 8732 Market analysis or research; Opinion research; Market analysis or research; Opinion research
CEO: Matthias Hartmann
**CFO:* Pamela Knapp
Chf Cred: Thomas Finkle
Ex VP: Pat Pellegrini

D-U-N-S 78-510-4857
GFK HEALTHCARE LP
GFK MARKET MEASURES
(*Suby of* GFK CUSTOM RESEARCH LLC) ★
120 Eagle Rock Ave # 200, East Hanover, NJ 07936-3159
Tel (973) 599-3500 *Founded/Ownrshp* 2014
Sales 55.0MM *EMP* 175
SIC 8732 Market analysis or research; Market analysis or research
Sr VP: Michael Krangel
Assoc VP: David Hamming
Ex VP: Steve O'Hara
VP: Kimberly Ficarra
VP: Art Rome

GFK MARKET MEASURES
See GFK HEALTHCARE LP

D-U-N-S 78-530-7625
GFM LLC
101 The Grove Dr, Los Angeles, CA 90036-6221
Tel (323) 900-8100 *Founded/Ownrshp* 2002
Sales 45.0MM *EMP* 26
SIC 6552 Subdividers & developers; Subdividers & developers

D-U-N-S 96-172-0591
GFMCO LLC
600 12th St, Columbus, GA 31901-2634
Tel (706) 323-0471 *Founded/Ownrshp* 2009
Sales 45.0MM *EMP* 3
SIC 3321 Gray & ductile iron foundries; Gray & ductile iron foundries

D-U-N-S 82-851-5481
■ **GFN NORTH AMERICA CORP**
(*Suby of* GENERAL FINANCE CORP) ★
260 S Los Robles Ave # 217, Pasadena, CA 91101-2824
Tel (626) 584-9722 *Founded/Ownrshp* 2008
Sales 49.0MM^E *EMP* 229^E
SIC 7359 5085 Shipping container leasing; Bins & containers, storage; Shipping container leasing; Bins & containers, storage
Ch Bd: Lawrence Glascott
**CEO:* Ronald F Valenta
**CFO:* Charles Barrantes

GFOC HOLDINGS,
See GAZETTE CO

GFP PLASTICS
See GENERAL FOAM PLASTICS CORP

GFPS
See GREAT FALLS PUBLIC SCHOOLS DIST1

D-U-N-S 09-009-9854 IMP/EXP
GFR MEDIA LLC
EL NUEVO DIA
50 Carr 165 Ste 1, Guaynabo, PR 00968-8024
Tel (787) 641-8000 *Founded/Ownrshp* 1963
Sales 178.4MM *EMP* 837^E
Accts Pricewaterhousecoopers Llp Sa
SIC 7389 2711 5963 Newspapers, publishing & printing; Advertising, promotional & trade show services; Advertising, promotional & trade show services; Newspapers, publishing & printing; Newspapers, home delivery, not by printers or publishers
Pr: Maria Eugenia Ferre Rangel
**CFO:* Ana M Bonilla
VP: Gustavo A Cordova
**VP:* Jose M Espinal
VP: Antonio Ferre
**VP:* Luis Gautier
**VP:* Antonio Hidalgo
**VP:* Jorge Mercado
**VP:* Carlos Nido
Genl Mgr: Agustin Meisozo
IT Man: Marisol Diaz

GFS
See GLOBAL FINISHING SOLUTIONS LLC

D-U-N-S 03-992-5123
GFS CAPITAL HOLDINGS
6499 Havenwood Cir # 720, Huntington Beach, CA 92648-6621
Tel (714) 720-3918 *Founded/Ownrshp* 2001
Sales NA *EMP* 280
SIC 6162 Mortgage brokers, using own money

D-U-N-S 96-424-1462
GFS CENTRAL STATES DIVISION
342 Gordon Industrial Ave, Shepherdsville, KY 40165-8539
Tel (502) 215-1000 *Founded/Ownrshp* 2012
Sales 15.8MM^E *EMP* 400^E
SIC 8742 Distribution channels consultant; Distribution channels consultant
Pr: Dan Gordon
Sfty Dirs: Tony Lawson

D-U-N-S 00-428-4188 EXP
GFS CHEMICALS INC (OH)
3041 Home Rd, Powell, OH 43065-9710
Tel (740) 881-5501 *Founded/Ownrshp* 1928, 2004
Sales 21.5MM^E *EMP* 120
SIC 2819 2899 2869 2812 Chemicals, reagent grade: refined from technical grade; Chemical preparations; Industrial organic chemicals; Alkalies & chlorine; Chemicals, reagent grade: refined from technical grade; Chemical preparations; Industrial organic chemicals; Alkalies & chlorine
Pr: J Steel Hutchinson
**Sec:* Martha S Kiser
**VP:* M Robert Pierron
Dir Bus: Michael McBride
Genl Mgr: Chris Beasley
Genl Mgr: John Roof
Genl Mgr: Harry Ruska
VP Mfg: Richard Sheridan
Opers Mgr: John Reed
Ql Cn Mgr: Stephen Eckert
Sls&Mrk Ex: Liza Strong

GFS FINANCIAL SOLUTIONS
See GENESIS FINANCIAL SOLUTIONS INC

D-U-N-S 03-367-8462
GFSC INC
CLEAN AIR SYSTEMS
204 Camden Indus Pkwy Nw, Conyers, GA 30012-3952
Tel (770) 918-0527 *Founded/Ownrshp* 1991
Sales 10.7MM^E *EMP* 300
SIC 1711 Heating & air conditioning contractors; Heating & air conditioning contractors
Pr: Paul Green

D-U-N-S 16-200-9732
■ **GFSI HOLDINGS INC**
(*Suby of* HANESBRANDS INC) ★
9700 Commerce Pkwy, Shawnee Mission, KS 66219-2402
Tel (913) 693-3200 *Founded/Ownrshp* 1996
Sales 56.1MM^E *EMP* 850
SIC 2339 2329 Sportswear, women's; Men's & boys' sportswear & athletic clothing; Sportswear, women's; Men's & boys' sportswear & athletic clothing
Ch: Robert M Wolff
Pr: Larry D Graveel
Sr VP: Michael H Gary
Sr VP: Robert G Shaw
VP: Jim Keaton

D-U-N-S 06-796-3967 EXP
■ **GFSI INC**
GEAR FOR SPORTS
(*Suby of* GFSI HOLDINGS INC) ★
9700 Commerce Pkwy, Lenexa, KS 66219-2402
Tel (913) 693-3200 *Founded/Ownrshp* 1997
Sales 2.1MM^E *EMP* 802
Accts Walters Mccann Fanska Llc Mis
SIC 2339 2329 2396 2395 Sportswear, women's; Men's & boys' sportswear & athletic clothing; Automotive & apparel trimmings; Pleating & stitching; Sportswear, women's; Men's & boys' sportswear & athletic clothing; Automotive & apparel trimmings; Pleating & stitching
Pr: Larry D Graveel
CFO: Craig Peterson
**CFO:* J Craig Peterson
**Ex VP:* Mike Gary
Ex VP: Jim Malseed
Sr VP: Randall Stabenow
VP: Carl Allard
VP: Donna Hansen
VP: Gregory Johnson
VP: Ingrid Sanchez
Dir Soc: Jared Hunt
Creative D: Jay Clements
Creative D: Susan Wiedenmeyer

GFWC
See BROWN DEER JUNIOR WOMENS CLUB INC

GFWD SUPPLY
See GENERAL FACTORY SUPPLIES CO INC

D-U-N-S 00-512-2924
GFX INTERNATIONAL INC
333 Barron Blvd, Grayslake, IL 60030-1638
Tel (847) 543-7179 *Founded/Ownrshp* 1989
Sales 45.6MM^E *EMP* 205^E
SIC 7336 2759 7335 7812 Graphic arts & related design; Posters, including billboards: printing; Commercial photography; Commercials, television: tape or film; Graphic arts & related design; Posters, including billboards: printing; Commercial photography; Commercials, television: tape or film
CEO: Charles Huttinger
**CFO:* Frank Gulik
**Sr VP:* Jim McLaughlin
**VP:* Debbie Lofchie
VP: Willem Nieuboer
**VP:* Mark Taylor
Ex Dir: Jeff Kaiz

D-U-N-S 84-850-7315
GG MCGUIGGAN CORP
1085 Snelling Ave N, Saint Paul, MN 55108-2705
Tel (651) 646-4544 *Founded/Ownrshp* 1877
Sales 123.2MM^E *EMP* 480
SIC 2679 3993 2752 Labels, paper: made from purchased material; Displays & cutouts, window & lobby; Commercial printing, offset; Labels, paper: made from purchased material; Displays & cutouts, window & lobby; Commercial printing, offset
Pr: John P Hickey
COO: William J Hickey III
CFO: David Baumgardner

D-U-N-S 06-007-4101 IMP
■ **GGB NORTH AMERICA LLC**
(*Suby of* ENPRO INDUSTRIES INC) ★
700 Mid Atlantic Pkwy, Thorofare, NJ 08086
Tel (856) 848-3200 *Founded/Ownrshp* 2002
Sales 72.9MM^E *EMP* 325^E
SIC 3568 Bearings, bushings & blocks; Bearings, bushings & blocks
Pr: Susan Sweeney
VP: E Joseph Fults
**Genl Mgr:* Kenneth Walker
VP Sls: Al Lenac

GGC
See GENERATION GROWTH CAPITAL INC

D-U-N-S 96-870-0554
GGC ADMINISTRATION LLC
GOLDEN GATE CAPITAL
1 Embarcadero Ctr Fl 39, San Francisco, CA 94111-3735
Tel (415) 983-2700 *Founded/Ownrshp* 2010
Sales 1.1MMM^E *EMP* 8,590^E
SIC 2591 Drapery hardware & blinds & shades; Drapery hardware & blinds & shades; Curtain & drapery rods, poles & fixtures; Blinds vertical; Window shade rollers & fittings
Pr: Stephan Scholl

D-U-N-S 07-838-1663
GGC USS HOLDINGS LLC
8490 Progress Dr Ste 300, Frederick, MD 21701-4996
Tel (800) 345-6170 *Founded/Ownrshp* 2008
Sales 10.2MM^E *EMP* 701
SIC 1446 Silica mining; Silica mining; Silica sand mining

D-U-N-S 07-934-7281
GGG DEMOLITION INC
1130 W Trenton Ave, Orange, CA 92867-3536
Tel (714) 699-9350 *Founded/Ownrshp* 2012
Sales 22.9MM^E *EMP* 99^E
SIC 1542 Specialized public building contractors
IT Man: Celia Miller

D-U-N-S 05-215-1466
GGG FOODS INC (AL)
KFC
256 Honeysuckle Rd Ste 3, Dothan, AL 36305-1168
Tel (334) 793-0083 *Founded/Ownrshp* 1998
Sales 28.7MM *EMP* 750
SIC 5812 Fast-food restaurant, chain; Fast-food restaurant, chain
Pr: C Charles Nailen Jr
Sec: Kay G Nailen

D-U-N-S 11-072-3264
GGG OF MYRTLE BEACH LLC
500 Burning Ridge Rd, Conway, SC 29526-9073
Tel (843) 293-5202 *Founded/Ownrshp* 2000
Sales 14.1MM^E *EMP* 300
SIC 6531 7992 Real estate agents & managers; Public golf courses; Real estate agents & managers; Public golf courses
Sr VP: Tommy Smothers

D-U-N-S 78-277-5647 IMP
GGI GLASS DISTRIBUTORS CORP
GENERAL GLASS INTERNATIONAL
101 Venture Way, Secaucus, NJ 07094-1825
Tel (201) 553-1850 *Founded/Ownrshp* 1993
Sales 37.3MM^E *EMP* 100
SIC 5231 Glass
Pr: David Balik
Treas: Carol Balik
VP: Richard Balik
**VP:* Ronald Vance
VP Opers: John Bush
Ql Cn Mgr: Cristina Antunes
Manager: Scott Cook
Sls Mgr: Nick Barone
Snr PM: Muhammad Arif

D-U-N-S 05-557-6513
GGNSC HOLDINGS LLC
GOLDEN LIVING
(*Suby of* GOLDEN LIVING) ★
7160 Dallas Pkwy Ste 400, Plano, TX 75024-7111
Tel (972) 372-6300 *Founded/Ownrshp* 2011
Sales 584.2MM^E *EMP* 791^E
SIC 8059 Rest home, with health care
VP: Michael Yao

D-U-N-S 80-863-0284
GGNSC HOLDINGS LLC
GOLDEN LIVING
(*Suby of* GGNSC HOLDINGS LLC) ★
1000 Fianna Way, Fort Smith, AR 72919-9008
Tel (479) 201-2000 *Founded/Ownrshp* 2006
Sales 584.2MM^E *EMP* 700
Accts Ernst & Young Llp Rogers Ar
SIC 8059 8051 8082 8322 Nursing home, except skilled & intermediate care facility; Skilled nursing care facilities; Home health care services; Rehabilitation services; Nursing home, except skilled & intermediate care facility; Skilled nursing care facilities; Home health care services; Rehabilitation services
CEO: Ronald Silva
**Pr:* Neil Kurtz
**COO:* Wendy Susienka
**CFO:* Ruth Ann Harmon
Treas: Shelly Henson
Ofcr: Ann Harmon
Sr VP: Michael Karicher
VP: Pamela Hansen
VP: Kelly Hilmes
VP: Kevin P Morris
VP: Scott Norton
VP: Lisa Spears
Exec: Mickey Sellard

D-U-N-S 80-303-3943
■ **GGP INC**
(*Suby of* GENERAL GROWTH PROPERTIES INC) ★
110 N Wacker Dr, Chicago, IL 60606-1511
Tel (312) 960-5000 *Founded/Ownrshp* 1986
Sales 601.2MM^E *EMP* 1,500^E
Accts Deloitte & Touche Llp Chicago
SIC 6798 Real estate investment trusts; Real estate investment trusts
CEO: Sandeep Mathrani
Pt: Kate Sheehy
Pr: Gary Kahnke
Pr: Andrew Silberfein
COO: Bradley Dexter
COO: Shobi Khan
CFO: Michael B Berman
CFO: Gregory Hinton
Ex VP: Alan Barocas
Ex VP: Michael Berman
Sr VP: Sharon Palonia
Sr VP: Randy Richardson
VP: Michael McCall
VP: Thomas McCarthy
VP: Kevin Soule
VP: Linda White
Board of Directors: Richard B Clark, Mary Lou Fiala, Bruce J Flatt, John K Haley, Cyrus Madon, David J Neithercut, Mark R Patterson, John G Schreiber

D-U-N-S 02-649-4273
■ **GGP LIMITED PARTNERSHIP**
GENERAL GROWTH PROPERTIES
(*Suby of* GGP INC) ★
110 N Wacker Dr, Chicago, IL 60606-1511
Tel (312) 960-5000 *Founded/Ownrshp* 1993
Sales 41.6MM^E *EMP* 500^E
SIC 6531 Real estate agent, commercial; Real estate managers; Real estate agent, commercial; Real estate managers
CEO: Sandeep Mathrani
**Genl Pt:* General Growth Properties
**Ltd Pt:* John Bucksbaum
**COO:* Shobi Khan
**CFO:* Michael Berman
**Ch:* J Bruce Flatt
Sec: Marshall Eisenberg
**Ex VP:* Marvin Levine
**Sr VP:* Alan Barocas

D-U-N-S 83-039-9585
GGP-GATEWAY MALL LLC
110 N Wacker Dr, Chicago, IL 60606-1511
Tel (312) 960-5000 *Founded/Ownrshp* 2009
Sales 4.5MM^E *EMP* 300^E
SIC 6512 Shopping center, property operation only; Shopping center, property operation only
CEO: Sandy Mathrani
Pr: Robert Nolan
CEO: Adam Metz

D-U-N-S 01-956-2640
GGS CONSTRUCTION
13608 Bullick Hollow Rd, Austin, TX 78726-5005
Tel (512) 257-8075 *Founded/Ownrshp* 2008
Sales 50.0MM *EMP* 8
SIC 1521 Single-family housing construction; Single-family housing construction
Prin: Rolando Osario
Prin: Kenia Cubas
Prin: Rolando Osorio

D-U-N-S 09-423-2972
GGS INFORMATION SERVICES INC (PA)
G G S
3265 Farmtrail Rd, York, PA 17406-5602
Tel (717) 764-2222 *Founded/Ownrshp* 1988
Sales 56.5MM^E *EMP* 270
SIC 2796 2741 2791 8711 7389 7371 Color separations for printing; Catalogs: publishing only, not printed on site; Technical manuals: publishing only, not printed on site; Photocomposition, for the printing trade; Engineering services; Personal service agents, brokers & bureaus; Custom computer programming services; Color separations for printing; Catalogs: publishing only, not printed on site; Technical manuals: publishing only, not printed on site; Photocomposition, for the printing trade; Engineering services; Personal service agents, brokers & bureaus; Custom computer programming services
Pr: Paul V Kilker
VP: Bud Beal
VP: Bill Black
VP: Carl Fraser
**VP:* Rita A Hoover
**VP:* Lloyd D Kendall
VP: Donna Ogborn
VP: Joe Prastrek
Mng Dir: Joseph Aliason
Prgrm Mgr: Russ Moorman
Genl Mgr: Kevin Becker

GGSCA
See GLENMOUNT GLOBAL SOLUTIONS INC

GGSI
See GENERAL GROWTH SERVICES INC

D-U-N-S 00-110-2508 IMP
■ **GH BASS & CO**
(*Suby of* AM RETAIL GROUP INC) ★
200 Madison Ave, New York, NY 10016-3903
Tel (212) 381-3900 *Founded/Ownrshp* 1987, 2013
Sales 77.1MM^E *EMP* 4,100
SIC 3144 3143 3149 5661 Women's footwear, except athletic; Men's footwear, except athletic; Children's footwear, except athletic; Shoe stores; Women's footwear, except athletic; Men's footwear, except athletic; Children's footwear, except athletic; Shoe stores
Pr: Bill Hutchison
Sr VP: Howard Renner
Dir: Jeremy Goldenberg
Genl Mgr: Jannice Gomez
Store Mgr: Rebecca Ewens

D-U-N-S 80-657-3619
GH DAIRY
GH PROCESSING
14651 Grove Ave, Ontario, CA 91762-7704
Tel (909) 606-6455 *Founded/Ownrshp* 1987
Sales 130.7MM *EMP* 225
SIC 0241 Dairy farms; Dairy farms
Pt: Gerben Hettinga

D-U-N-S 01-863-8512
■ **GH FOODS CA LLC**
(*Suby of* RENAISSANCE FOOD GROUP LLC) ★
8425 Carbide Ct, Sacramento, CA 95828-5609
Tel (916) 844-1140 *Founded/Ownrshp* 2007
Sales 80.2MM^E *EMP* 350
SIC 2099 Salads, fresh or refrigerated; Salads, fresh or refrigerated

D-U-N-S 07-969-1078
GH HOLDINGS INC
(*Suby of* GULF OIL INTERNATIONAL UK LIMITED)
Madison & Van Buren Ave, Valley Forge, PA 19482
Tel (610) 666-4000 *Founded/Ownrshp* 2012
Sales 413.7MM^E *EMP* 1,900
SIC 2869 2992 Hydraulic fluids, synthetic base; Lubricating oils & greases
CEO: Paul De Vivo
CFO: Keller Arnold
**Sec:* Ali Ganjaei
VP: Fernanda G Clifford

GH PHIPPS CNSTR COMPANIES
See GERALD H PHIPPS INC

GH PROCESSING
See GH DAIRY

D-U-N-S 92-774-7907
GHA TECHNOLOGIES INC
8998 E Raintree Dr, Scottsdale, AZ 85260-7024
Tel (480) 951-6865 *Founded/Ownrshp* 1999
Sales 118.4MM *EMP* 103
Accts Johnson Lawdahl Pllc Cpa Ph
SIC 7373 Value-added resellers, computer systems; Value-added resellers, computer systems
Pr: George Hertzberg
VP: Tom Matson
**VP:* Steven Nevins
VP Sls: William Alger
VP Sls: Roy May
Manager: Jesse Abeyta
Manager: Dale Campbell
Manager: Tim Cleary
Manager: Timothy Dial
Manager: Barry Eisler
Manager: Daniel Gillespie

D-U-N-S 00-359-3030
GHAFARI ASSOCIATES LLC
17101 Michigan Ave, Dearborn, MI 48126-2736
Tel (313) 271-6280 *Founded/Ownrshp* 2000
Sales 108.1MM^E *EMP* 385
SIC 8711 Engineering services; Engineering services
V Ch: Rita Dunker
COO: Ali Solaksubasi
COO: Robert Stevenson
CFO: Glenn Cole
Ex VP: John Patelski
Ex VP: Michael Scimeca
Sr VP: Ted Oberlies
Sr VP: Mike Ryan
VP: Robert K Burgess
VP: Richard W Butwin
VP: Bill Herrmann
VP: Frank Larocca
VP: Robert Mauck
VP: Dearborn MI
VP: Eric Norman
VP: Steven Santucci
VP: Patrick J Smithbauer
Comm Man: Michelle Plawecki

D-U-N-S 96-159-9466 EXP
■ **GHC SPECIALTY BRANDS LLC**
LAB SAFETY SUPPLY
(*Suby of* WW GRAINGER INC) ★
401 S Wright Rd, Janesville, WI 53546-8729
Tel (608) 754-2345 *Founded/Ownrshp* 2010
Sales 142.3MM^E *EMP* 1,005^E
SIC 5961 Catalog sales; Catalog sales
Pr: M A Pulick
Ex VP: Phil West
VP: Bobette McGinty

D-U-N-S 18-943-5238
GHD INC
(*Suby of* GHD INTERNATIONAL PTY LTD)
4747 N 22nd St Ste 200, Phoenix, AZ 85016-4730
Tel (602) 216-7200 *Founded/Ownrshp* 2006
Sales 62.2MM^E *EMP* 300^E
SIC 8711 8712 8713 8748 Engineering services; Architectural services; Surveying services; Business consulting; Environmental consultant; Engineering services; Architectural services; Surveying services; Business consulting; Environmental consultant

Ch: Donoald F Graf
**CEO:* Ian Shepherd
**Genl Mgr:* Richard Wankmuller
Sls Mgr: Anthony Petroccitto
Snr PM: Ludwig Smeets
Snr Mgr: Sandy Tripp

D-U-N-S 15-350-8080
GHD SERVICES INC
CRA SERVICES
(*Suby of* CRA HOLDINGS INC)
2055 Niagara Falls Blvd, Niagara Falls, NY 14304-5702
Tel (716) 297-6150 *Founded/Ownrshp* 1976
Sales 233.6MM^E *EMP* 1,000
SIC 8748 Environmental consultant; Environmental consultant
Pr: Steve Quigley
**Treas:* Anthony Ying
**Ex VP:* Glenn Turchan
Mtls Mgr: Tony Manns
Snr PM: Judy Gilbert
Snr Mgr: Chuck Boller

D-U-N-S 00-681-7241
GHEMM CO INC
3861 Schacht St, Fairbanks, AK 99701-7362
Tel (907) 452-5191 *Founded/Ownrshp* 1952
Sales 38.6MM *EMP* 15
Accts Walsh Kelliher & Sharp Fairb
SIC 1542 Commercial & office building, new construction; Commercial & office building, new construction
Pr: Albert E Bell
**Ch:* Conrad G B Frank
Dir IT: Meg Ghemm
IT Man: Kim Mahaney

GHENT CHEVROLET CADILLAC
See GHENT MOTOR CO

GHENT MANUFACTURING
See GMI COMPANIES INC

D-U-N-S 18-917-4980
GHENT MOTOR CO
GHENT CHEVROLET CADILLAC
2715 35th Ave, Greeley, CO 80634-4125
Tel (970) 339-2438 *Founded/Ownrshp* 1989
Sales 57.4MM *EMP* 50
SIC 5511 Automobiles, new & used; Pickups, new & used; Trucks, tractors & trailers: new & used; Vans, new & used; Automobiles, new & used; Pickups, new & used; Trucks, tractors & trailers: new & used; Vans, new & used
Pr: Robert Ghent
**Sec:* Judy Roberts
Sls Mgr: Manny Canedo
Sls Mgr: Tim Ervin

GHF
See GROUP HOME FOUNDATION INC

D-U-N-S 10-352-4385
GHG CORP
960 Clear Lake City Blvd, Webster, TX 77598-6604
Tel (281) 461-6533 *Founded/Ownrshp* 1979
Sales 36.8MM^E *EMP* 340
SIC 7372 8711 8731 Application computer software; Engineering services; Engineering laboratory, except testing; Application computer software; Engineering services; Engineering laboratory, except testing
Pr: Israel Galvan
**VP:* John Denny
IT Man: Paige Glier

GHH
See GREENBRIAR HOLDINGS HOUSTON LTD

GHI
See GROUP HEALTH INC

D-U-N-S 15-806-6931
GHI HMO SELECT INC
789 Grant Ave, Lake Katrine, NY 12449-5360
Tel (845) 340-2200 *Founded/Ownrshp* 1999
Sales NA *EMP* 238
SIC 6324 Hospital & medical service plans
CEO: Frank J Branchini
**Pr:* Aran Ron

D-U-N-S 60-241-1444
GHI HOLDINGS INC
11300 N Cntl Expy Ste 200, Dallas, TX 75243
Tel (214) 750-6528 *Founded/Ownrshp* 1986
Sales 30.7MM^E *EMP* 175
SIC 6719 Investment holding companies, except banks; Investment holding companies, except banks
Pr: Stephen H Brooks

D-U-N-S 00-946-9701
GHILOTTI BROS INC (CA)
525 Jacoby St, San Rafael, CA 94901-5370
Tel (415) 454-7011 *Founded/Ownrshp* 1914, 1999
Sales 110.6MM^E *EMP* 290
SIC 1611 1794 1623 Surfacing & paving; Grading; Highway & street paving contractor; Excavation work; Water, sewer & utility lines; Surfacing & paving; Grading; Highway & street paving contractor; Excavation work; Water, sewer & utility lines
CEO: Dante W Ghilotti
**Pr:* Michael M Ghilotti
Pr: Dominic Nuccio
**CFO:* Daniel Y Chin
**VP:* Thomas G Barr
VP: Frank Palagi
Admn Mgr: Melissa Daniels
Off Mgr: Kelly Mollain
IT Man: Michael Maxson
IT Man: Maxson Mike
IT Man: Kelly Mullane

D-U-N-S 79-404-5542
GHILOTTI CONSTRUCTION CO INC
GCC
246 Ghilotti Ave, Santa Rosa, CA 95407-8152
Tel (707) 585-1221 *Founded/Ownrshp* 1992
Sales 136.6MM^E *EMP* 275^E

SIC 1629 Land preparation construction; Land preparation construction
CEO: Richard W Ghilotti
COO: Ali Yazdi
VP: Ali Mohaghegh

D-U-N-S 60-884-1342 IMP
GHIRARDELLI CHOCOLATE CO
(*Suby of* LINDT & SPRUNGLI (USA) INC) ★
1111 139th Ave, San Leandro, CA 94578-2616
Tel (510) 483-6970 *Founded/Ownrshp* 1852
Sales 154.4MM^E *EMP* 650
SIC 5441 2066 5812 5149 Candy, nut & confectionery stores; Chocolate; Soda fountain; Chocolate; Candy, nut & confectionery stores; Chocolate; Soda fountain; Chocolate
CEO: Martin Thompson
CFO: Martin Hug
Treas: Martin Thompson
VP: Tom Parent
VP: Yvo Smit
Rgnl Mgr: Cynthia Contreras
Dist Mgr: Lori Carrig
Dist Mgr: Eric Gepner
Genl Mgr: David Africa
Genl Mgr: Jennifer Beckstrand
Genl Mgr: David Castorena

D-U-N-S 18-742-5376
GHIRINGHELLI SPECIALTY FOODS INC
101 Benicia Rd, Vallejo, CA 94590-7003
Tel (707) 561-7670 *Founded/Ownrshp* 1984
Sales 40.7MM^E *EMP* 145
SIC 1541 Food products manufacturing or packing plant construction; Food products manufacturing or packing plant construction
Pr: Mike Ghiringhelli
**VP:* Ed Ferrero
Off Mgr: Margee Longnecker
Plnt Mgr: Al Rivas

D-U-N-S 02-037-8380
GHJ CONSTRUCTION INC
21800 Oxnard St Ste 220, Woodland Hills, CA 91367-3643
Tel (747) 888-3333 *Founded/Ownrshp* 2013
Sales 25.0MM *EMP* 12
SIC 1542 Commercial & office building, new construction
CEO: Tingting Han
**Treas:* Julie Zhu
**VP:* Yan Xing

GHJ&M
See GOLDNER HAWN JOHNSON & MORRISON INC

D-U-N-S 55-659-2426
GHM CORP
12700 Hillcrest Rd # 291, Dallas, TX 75230-2161
Tel (972) 840-1200 *Founded/Ownrshp* 1978
Sales 238.8MM^E *EMP* 1,500
SIC 3448 1799 5999 5561 Buildings, portable: prefabricated metal; Spa or hot tub installation or construction; Swimming pools, above ground; Recreational vehicle dealers; Buildings, portable: prefabricated metal; Spa or hot tub installation or construction; Swimming pools, above ground; Recreational vehicle dealers
Pr: Guy H Morgan
**Sec:* Hicks B Morgan
CIO: Ruven Ramirez
CTO: Peter Lewis
IT Man: Patrick Miller

GHN
See GALLAND HENNING NOPAK INC

D-U-N-S 14-790-5715
GHN INC
ONTARIO VOLVO
1300 Auto Center Dr, Ontario, CA 91761-2210
Tel (909) 605-5700 *Founded/Ownrshp* 1985
Sales 29.4MM^E *EMP* 72
SIC 5511 Automobiles, new & used; Automobiles, new & used
Pr: Gary H Sherman
**Sec:* Helga Sherman
IT Man: Mark Madrid
Sls Mgr: Tim Franklin
Sls Mgr: Scott Reed

D-U-N-S 78-971-1231
GHP MEDIA INC
475 Heffernan Dr, West Haven, CT 06516-4151
Tel (203) 479-7500 *Founded/Ownrshp* 1991
Sales 45.4MM^E *EMP* 145
SIC 2752 2796 Offset & photolithographic printing; Color separations for printing; Offset & photolithographic printing; Color separations for printing
CEO: John Robinson
**Mng Pt:* Fred Hoxsie
Sr VP: Wayne Bruno
VP: Marc Server
VP: Mike Zurolo
Sales Exec: Elizabeth Poore
VP Sls: Greg Santini
VP Sls: David Sweet
Sls Dir: Steve Bortner

GHR
See GENERAL HEALTHCARE RESOURCES INC

D-U-N-S 01-637-7723
GHR ENTERPRISES INC
GARY HOBART ROOFING SUPPLY
2520 W 37th Ave, Hobart, IN 46342-1830
Tel (219) 962-1173 *Founded/Ownrshp* 1947
Sales 20.8MM *EMP* 25
SIC 5033 Roofing & siding materials; Roofing & siding materials
CEO: John Ronneau
**VP:* Rodney Ruess

D-U-N-S 07-959-7657
GHS CORP (MI)
D'ANGELICO STRINGS
2813 Wilbur St, Springfield, MI 49037-7990
Tel (800) 388-4447 *Founded/Ownrshp* 1964

Sales 54.9MM^E *EMP* 108^E
SIC 3931 Strings, musical instrument
Pr: Russell S McFee
VP: Ray Rothlisberger
Mktg Dir: Connie McVee

D-U-N-S 13-029-5350 IMP
GHSP INC
(*Suby of* JSJ CORP) ★
1250 S Beechtree St, Grand Haven, MI 49417-2840
Tel (248) 588-5095 *Founded/Ownrshp* 1999
Sales 167.1MM^E *EMP* 825
SIC 3714 Motor vehicle parts & accessories; Motor vehicle parts & accessories
Ch: Jerry Scott
**Pr:* Paul Doyle
**Pr:* Jeff Smith
CFO: Ron Wallish
Snr Sftwr: Adam Bouwens
Snr Sftwr: Long Lee
IT Man: Rick Leffler
IT Man: Daine Shanahan
IT Man: Jack Sischo
Software D: Jeff Parks
Mtls Mgr: Bruce Hawkins

GHVFHC
See GREATER HUDSON VALLEY FAMILY HEALTH CENTER INC

D-U-N-S 00-808-0756 IMP
GHX INDUSTRIAL LLC
(*Suby of* UNITED DISTRIBUTORS GROUP INC) ★
3430 S Sam Houston Pkwy E, Houston, TX 77047-6531
Tel (713) 222-2231 *Founded/Ownrshp* 2012
Sales 190.0MM *EMP* 370
SIC 3053 3052 3061 Gaskets & sealing devices; Rubber hose; Oil & gas field machinery rubber goods (mechanical); Gaskets & sealing devices; Rubber hose; Oil & gas field machinery rubber goods (mechanical)
Ch Bd: Daniel Ahuero
Pr: Richard Harrison
CFO: Dan Maddox
VP: Roy Torres
Brnch Mgr: Byron Freeman
Brnch Mgr: Matt Hames
Brnch Mgr: John McCormick
Brnch Mgr: Graham Ryan
Genl Mgr: Don Presley
Off Mgr: Paul Breen
Off Mgr: Kimberly Moore

D-U-N-S 96-445-6110
GI ADVO OPCO LLC
ADVOSERV
2520 Wrangle Hill Rd # 210, Bear, DE 19701-3849
Tel (302) 365-8051 *Founded/Ownrshp* 2009
Sales 12.8MM^E *EMP* 600
SIC 8361 Residential care

GI CONSTRUCTION
See GUARANTEE INTERIORS INC

D-U-N-S 78-021-5237
GI PARTNERS FUND II LP
188 The Embarcadero # 700, San Francisco, CA 94105-1247
Tel (650) 233-3600 *Founded/Ownrshp* 2005
Sales 60.9MM^E *EMP* 451
SIC 7371 4813 Custom computer programming services; ; Custom computer programming services;
Mng Pt: Rick Magnuson

D-U-N-S 83-221-3214
GI PLASTEK CORP
GI PLASTEK WOLFEBORO
5 Wickers Dr, Wolfeboro, NH 03894-4323
Tel (603) 569-5100 *Founded/Ownrshp* 2015
Sales 25.9MM^E *EMP* 95
SIC 3089 Molding primary plastic
Pr: Daniel H Mills
VP: Gerry Gajewski
VP Mfg: Tad Vaughn
VP Sls: Rick Collopy

D-U-N-S 92-778-0072
GI PLASTEK LIMITED PARTNERSHIP
5 Wickers Dr, Wolfeboro, NH 03894-4323
Tel (603) 569-5100 *Founded/Ownrshp* 1995
Sales 42.5MM^E *EMP* 435
SIC 3089 Plastic processing; Plastic processing
Pt: James Lyman
Prin: Perry Ashley
Prin: Walter Beinecke Jr
Prin: Wayne Donohue
Prin: Graham Gund
Prin: Charles Lagasse Jr
Prin: Stephen Trapp
Prin: Shelly Trochemenko

D-U-N-S 12-674-2761 IMP
GI PLASTEK LLC
5 Wickers Dr, Wolfeboro, NH 03894-4323
Tel (603) 569-5100 *Founded/Ownrshp* 2002
Sales 60.6MM^E *EMP* 435
SIC 3089 Injection molded finished plastic products; Injection molded finished plastic products
IT Man: Brian Wheeler
Mfg Mgr: Bolton Jim
Plnt Mgr: Tad Vaughn
VP Sls: Rick Collopy

GI PLASTEK WOLFEBORO
See GI PLASTEK CORP

D-U-N-S 03-758-7805
GI PROPERTIES INC
CORRECT CONSTRUCTION
6610 Melton Rd, Portage, IN 46368-1236
Tel (219) 763-1177 *Founded/Ownrshp* 1977
Sales 100.4MM^E *EMP* 180
SIC 1623 3441 7353 Pipeline construction; Fabricated structural metal; Heavy construction equipment rental; Pipeline construction; Fabricated structural metal; Heavy construction equipment rental
Pr: Paul K Graegin
Treas: Joyce Starkey
IT Man: Mary Chaney
Sfty Mgr: Terry Graegin

GI TOOL
See GENERAL INDUSTRIAL TOOL & SUPPLY INC

D-U-N-S 07-662-5870
GIA ENTERPRISES
MCDONALD'S
1882 136th Pl Ne Ste 101, Bellevue, WA 98005-2338
Tel (425) 822-0356 *Founded/Ownrshp* 1975
Sales 23.0MM *EMP* 620
SIC 5812 Fast-food restaurant, chain; Fast-food restaurant, chain
Pr: Len Giannola
**Sec:* Mark Hansen

D-U-N-S 02-935-9820
GIA HOLDINGS CORP INC
3201 Griffin Rd Ste 202, Fort Lauderdale, FL 33312-6900
Tel (954) 985-1500 *Founded/Ownrshp* 2007
Sales 14.8MM^E *EMP* 501
SIC 4522 Flying charter service; Flying charter service
Pr: David F Hackett

D-U-N-S 36-291-2180
GIACALONE DESIGN SERVICES INC
6300 Monterey Rd, Gilroy, CA 95020-6603
Tel (408) 842-9655 *Founded/Ownrshp* 2000
Sales 22.2MM^E *EMP* 275
SIC 1731 General electrical contractor; General electrical contractor
Pr: Vincent Giacalone
**CFO:* Lisa Burns
**VP:* Lisa Giacalone

D-U-N-S 02-919-1038
GIAMPOLINI & CO
GIAMPOLINI/COURTNEY
1482 67th St, Emeryville, CA 94608-1016
Tel (415) 673-1236 *Founded/Ownrshp* 1949
Sales 21.4MM^E *EMP* 225
SIC 1721 1542 1742 Exterior commercial painting contractor; Interior commercial painting contractor; Commercial & office buildings, renovation & repair; Plastering, drywall & insulation; Exterior commercial painting contractor; Interior commercial painting contractor; Commercial & office buildings, renovation & repair; Plastering, drywall & insulation
Pr: Greg Quilici
**CFO:* Patrick Roland
**VP:* Tom Quilici
**Prin:* James Patrick Roland

GIAMPOLINI/COURTNEY
See GIAMPOLINI & CO

GIANELLI SAUSAGE
See G & L DAVIS MEAT CO INC

GIANNI VERSACE
See VERSACE USA INC

D-U-N-S 07-976-0707
GIANNINO ENTERPRISES LLC
GE FUNDING GROUP
40 Wall St, New York, NY 10005-1304
Tel (888) 554-5651 *Founded/Ownrshp* 2013
Sales 54.0MM *EMP* 35
SIC 8742 Banking & finance consultant

D-U-N-S 06-611-3952
GIANNOLAS INC
MCDONALD'S
601 W Grangeville Blvd, Hanford, CA 93230-2862
Tel (559) 582-9055 *Founded/Ownrshp* 1972
Sales 14.1MM^E *EMP* 360
SIC 5812 Fast-food restaurant, chain; Fast-food restaurant, chain
Pr: Frank Giannola
**Treas:* Belita Giannola
**VP:* Terrance Mergan

GIANT AUTOMOTIVE GROUP
See GIANT CHEVROLET CO

D-U-N-S 18-840-8702 IMP
GIANT BICYCLE INC
(*Suby of* GAIWIN B.V.)
3587 Old Conejo Rd, Newbury Park, CA 91320-2122
Tel (805) 267-4600 *Founded/Ownrshp* 1987
Sales 33.8MM^E *EMP* 80
SIC 5091 Bicycles; Bicycles
CEO: Elysa Walk
Genl Mgr: Scott Helvie
Dir IT: Dave Karneboge
IT Man: Jean Scott
Mktg Mgr: A N Le
Mktg Mgr: Russ Okawa
Sls Mgr: Colby Large
Sales Asso: Bevan Harris
Sales Asso: Keith Kettler

GIANT CAR & TRUCK RENTAL
See RON WESTPHAL CHEVROLET INC

D-U-N-S 10-190-4597
GIANT CEMENT CO
(*Suby of* CEMENTOS PORTLAND VALDERRIVAS, SA)
320 Midland Pkwy Ste D, Summerville, SC 29485-8113
Tel (843) 851-9898 *Founded/Ownrshp* 1985
Sales 43.7MM^E *EMP* 221
SIC 3241 Masonry cement; Portland cement; Masonry cement; Portland cement
CEO: Duncan Gage
CFO: Javier Martanez
**Ch:* Gary Pechota
**VP:* Robert B Thompson

D-U-N-S 86-956-3304
GIANT CEMENT HOLDING INC
(*Suby of* CEMENTOS PORTLAND VALDERRIVAS, SA)
320 Midland Pkwy Ste D, Summerville, SC 29485-8113
Tel (843) 851-9898 *Founded/Ownrshp* 1999
Sales 166.1MM^E *EMP* 649
Accts Deloitte & Touche Llp
SIC 3241 4953 Cement, hydraulic; Recycling, waste materials; Cement, hydraulic; Recycling, waste materials
CEO: Jose A Llontop
CFO: Angela Young
Bd of Dir: Robert Jones
**VP:* F William Biddix
**VP:* Richard A Familia
MIS Dir: Les Studebaker
Dir IT: Victor Llanso
IT Man: Cathy Lehr
Info Man: Thomas Baird

GIANT CENTER
See TOWNSHIP OF DERRY INDUSTRIAL AND COMMERCIAL DEVELOPMENT AUTHORITY

D-U-N-S 02-961-0680
GIANT CHEVROLET CO
GIANT AUTOMOTIVE GROUP
1001 S Ben Maddox Way, Visalia, CA 93292-3656
Tel (559) 733-1100 *Founded/Ownrshp* 1963
Sales 29.1MM^E *EMP* 70
SIC 5511 Automobiles, new & used; Pickups, new & used; Vans, new & used; Automobiles, new & used; Pickups, new & used; Vans, new & used
CEO: James Petty
**VP:* Catherine Petty
**VP:* Jack Petty
Genl Mgr: John Mudruga
Sls Mgr: John Madruga
Sls Mgr: Joe Sanchez
Sales Asso: Roger Pereira

D-U-N-S 11-442-3119
GIANT CREATIVE STRATEGY LLC
1700 Montgomery St # 485, San Francisco, CA 94111-1025
Tel (415) 227-4444 *Founded/Ownrshp* 2002
Sales 46.9MM^E *EMP* 230
SIC 7311 Advertising agencies; Advertising consultant; Advertising agencies; Advertising consultant
CEO: Steven Gold
**CFO:* Jeffrey Nemy
Sr VP: Christine Armstrong
Sr VP: Jonathan Pieschl
Sr VP: Kevin Stokes
Sr VP: Alyse Sukalski
Sr VP: Adena Svingos
VP: Michele Adams
VP: Vanya Akraboff
VP: Angela Busa
VP: Kevin Eddleman
VP: Kristine Ellis
**VP:* Adam Gelling
VP: Stacy Hall
VP: Joshua McCasland
VP: Sheri Neher
VP: Nelli Newman
VP: Kathleen Ralston
VP: George Sencl
VP: Jan Vennari
Creative D: Purr Drummey

GIANT DISCOUNT DRUG
See GIANT OF MARYLAND LLC

GIANT EAGLE
See MARCKISOTTO MARKETS INC

GIANT EAGLE
See P P H & K INC

GIANT EAGLE
See BUTLER REFRIGERATED MEATS INC

GIANT EAGLE
See DENNYS ENTERPRISES OF AMERICA INC

GIANT EAGLE
See ALTAGHENY INC

D-U-N-S 06-173-2798
GIANT EAGLE
IGA
907 W Maple St, Hartville, OH 44632-9671
Tel (330) 877-2293 *Founded/Ownrshp* 1972
Sales 47.7MM^E *EMP* 700
SIC 5411 5912 Supermarkets, chain; Drug stores & proprietary stores; Supermarkets, chain; Drug stores & proprietary stores
VP: Frieda Olszeski

D-U-N-S 19-614-6310
GIANT EAGLE
20111 Route 19 Ste 35, Cranberry Township, PA 16066-6225
Tel (724) 772-1030 *Founded/Ownrshp* 1993
Sales 23.0MM^E *EMP* 200
SIC 5411 5912 2051 Supermarkets, chain; Drug stores & proprietary stores; Bread, cake & related products; Supermarkets, chain; Drug stores & proprietary stores; Bread, cake & related products
Pr: Evelyn Sandonato
**VP:* Robert Sandonato

D-U-N-S 00-791-5713 IMP
GIANT EAGLE INC (PA)
101 Kappa Dr, Pittsburgh, PA 15238-2833
Tel (800) 362-8899 *Founded/Ownrshp* 1916
Sales 7.2MMM^E *EMP* 36,000
SIC 5411 5141 5147 5148 5143 6794 Supermarkets, chain; Groceries, general line; Meats, fresh; Fresh fruits & vegetables; Dairy products, except dried or canned; Franchises, selling or licensing; Supermarkets, chain; Groceries, general line; Meats, fresh; Fresh fruits & vegetables; Dairy products, except dried or canned; Franchises, selling or licensing
Pr: John R Lucot
Treas: Mark I Minnaugh
Treas: Phillip W Oliveri
Sr VP: Robert Garrity
Sr VP: John Tedesco
VP: James Bainbridge
VP: Raymond A Huber
VP: Craig Ignatz
VP: William Parry
VP: Ian Prisuta
VP: Russ Ross
VP: Raymond Smaltz
VP: Gene Tommasi
Exec: Jay Yardley

D-U-N-S 00-691-9757
GIANT FOOD LLC (MD)
(*Suby of* AFS) ★
8301 Prof Pl Ste 115, Hyattsville, MD 20785
Tel (301) 341-4100 *Founded/Ownrshp* 1935
Sales 2.2MMM^E *EMP* 27,835
SIC 5411 6512 5912 Drug stores; Supermarkets, chain; Supermarkets, 55,000-65,000 square feet (superstore); Shopping center, property operation only; Supermarkets, chain; Shopping center, property operation only; Drug stores
CEO: Richard A Baird
Pr: Mark Adamcik
**CFO:* Paula A Price
**Ex VP:* Dan Currie
**Ex VP:* Bill Holmes
**Sr VP:* Thomas Gandolfi
Sr VP: Walt Lentz
**Sr VP:* Stephen Neal
Sr VP: Shane Sampson
**Sr VP:* Eric Weiss
VP: Susan Bowen
VP: Stuart Brown
VP: Jodie Daubert
VP: Ira Kress
VP: Chris Kukay
VP: Steve Lerman
VP: Wayne Macleod
Exec: Heather Mundie
Exec: James Yanger

D-U-N-S 01-393-2165 IMP
GIANT FOOD STORES LLC
MARTIN'S FOOD MARKET
(*Suby of* AFS) ★
1149 Harrisburg Pike, Carlisle, PA 17013-1667
Tel (717) 249-4000 *Founded/Ownrshp* 1981
Sales 2.8MMM^E *EMP* 24,000
SIC 5411 Supermarkets, chain; Supermarkets, chain
Pr: Carl Schlicker
COO: James McCann
CFO: Rick Herring
Ofcr: Jim Ware
Ex VP: Robert Anderson
Ex VP: John Bussenger
Ex VP: Don Gabrys
Sr VP: Dan Glei
Sr VP: Laura Williams
VP: Jeff Beaulieu
VP: Jodie Daubert
VP: Steve Fanion
VP: Denny Hopkins
VP: Erik Keptner
VP: Chris Kukay
VP: Steve Lamontagne
VP: Kris Murphy
VP: Leigh Shirley
VP: William Shrader
VP: Larry Stover
Exec: Madeline Torres
Board of Directors: Fritz Ahlqvist, Marshall Collins Jr, Peter Van Dun, Robert Zwartendijk

D-U-N-S 60-628-7308 IMP/EXP
■ **GIANT INDUSTRIES INC**
(*Suby of* WESTERN REFINING INC) ★
1250 W Washington St # 101, Tempe, AZ 85281-1794
Tel (915) 534-1400 *Founded/Ownrshp* 2007
Sales 162.6MM^E *EMP* 881
SIC 2911 5541 5172 Petroleum refining; Gasoline service stations; Petroleum products; Petroleum refining; Gasoline service stations; Petroleum products
CEO: Jeff A Stevens
**Pr:* Morgan Gust
**Pr:* Mark J Smith
**CFO:* Mark B Cox
CFO: Gary Dalke
**Treas:* Jeffrey S Beyersdorfer
**Ex VP:* S Leland Gould
**Sr VP:* Kim H Bullerdick
**VP:* Dennis Calhoun

D-U-N-S 16-158-7548
GIANT INLAND EMPIRE RV CENTER INC
GIANT RV
9150 Benson Ave, Montclair, CA 91763-1688
Tel (909) 981-0444 *Founded/Ownrshp* 1986
Sales 108.5MM^E *EMP* 250
SIC 5561 7538 Recreational vehicle parts & accessories; Recreational vehicle repairs; Recreational vehicle parts & accessories; Recreational vehicle repairs
CEO: Behzad Barouti
CFO: Mark Hudson
**Treas:* Nasser Etebar
Off Mgr: Greg Chilcote
CIO: Mike Murphy
Dir IT: Tom Ashley
Sls Dir: Kevin McDannel
Sls Mgr: Darryl Wolford
Sales Asso: Scott Phares

GIANT MAGELLAN TELESCOPE ORGAN
See GMTO CORP

GIANT OF LANDOVER
See STOP & SHOP SUPERMARKET CO

D-U-N-S 04-672-5719
GIANT OF MARYLAND LLC
GIANT DISCOUNT DRUG
(*Suby of* AFS) ★
8301 Prof Pl Ste 115, Hyattsville, MD 20785
Tel (301) 332-5030 *Founded/Ownrshp* 1998
Sales 67.3MM^E *EMP* 629
SIC 5411 5912 5499 Supermarkets, chain; Supermarkets, 55,000-65,000 square feet (superstore); Drug stores; Gourmet food stores; Supermarkets, chain; Supermarkets, 55,000-65,000 square feet (superstore); Drug stores; Gourmet food stores
Pr: Richard Baird
VP: Esther Peterson
IT Man: Bradley Dayton
Board of Directors: Bradley Dayton

GIANT RECREATION WORLD
See RECREATION WORLD INC

GIANT RV
See GIANT INLAND EMPIRE RV CENTER INC

GIANT TRANSPORTATION DIV
See WESTERN REFINING SOUTHWEST INC

D-U-N-S 60-526-8598
GIBAR INC
TULLY'S GOOD TIMES
1 Technology Pl, East Syracuse, NY 13057-9735
Tel (315) 432-4546 *Founded/Ownrshp* 1988
Sales 9.0MM *EMP* 300
SIC 5812 American restaurant; American restaurant
Pr: John Giamartino
**Treas:* David Giamartino

D-U-N-S 07-207-8959
GIBAULT FOUNDATION INC
6401 S Us Highway 41 # 7, Terre Haute, IN 47802-4749
Tel (812) 299-1156 *Founded/Ownrshp* 1921
Sales 1.3MM *EMP* 300E
Accts Sacîroder & Company Inc Ter
SIC 8361 Juvenile correctional facilities; Juvenile correctional facilities
COO: Timothy Hayes
CFO: Amy Atchley
Ex Dir: Jacob Fish
Dir IT: Kevin Bielsk
Dir IT: Lee Brannon
IT Man: Kenneth Polky

D-U-N-S 79-892-9506
GIBAULT INC
EXCESS BAGGAGE SELF STORAGE
6401 S Us Highway 41, Terre Haute, IN 47802-4749
Tel (812) 298-3131 *Founded/Ownrshp* 1921
Sales 8.4MM *EMP* 350
Accts Sackrider & Company Inc Ute
SIC 8322 Child related social services; Child related social services
Pr: James Sinclair
**Ch Bd:* Dale J Heger
**VP:* Pamela Bowman
**VP:* Michele Madley
Dir IT: Lee Brannon
Dir IT: Kevin Ho
IT Man: Rebecca Jones

D-U-N-S 05-331-7087
GIBBON PACKING CO INC
TAMA PACKING
E Hwy 30, Gibbon, NE 68840
Tel (308) 468-5771 *Founded/Ownrshp* 1991
Sales 79.7MME *EMP* 710
SIC 2011 Meat packing plants; Meat packing plants
Ch Bd: Rick Elsman

GIBBONS BREWING CO
See LION BREWERY INC

D-U-N-S 06-823-6611
GIBBS & COX INC (NY)
253 W 35th St Fl 10, New York, NY 10001-1907
Tel (212) 366-3900 *Founded/Ownrshp* 1929, 1971
Sales 30.4MME *EMP* 322
SIC 8712 8711

D-U-N-S 08-200-0381
GIBBS CONSTRUCTION LLC
5736 Citrus Blvd Ste 200, Harahan, LA 70123-1698
Tel (504) 733-4336 *Founded/Ownrshp* 1998
Sales 93.9MME *EMP* 144E
SIC 1542 1541 Commercial & office building, new construction; Industrial buildings, new construction; Commercial & office building, new construction; Industrial buildings, new construction
VP: Mike Johnson
Ql Cn Mgr: Ryan Casteix
Snr PM: Doug Bruza
Snr PM: Lloyd Crochet
Snr PM: Lenny Held
Snr PM: Jimmy Wehrlin
Snr PM: Loren White
Snr Mgr: Jim Finklea
Snr Mgr: Marjean Gohd

D-U-N-S 04-994-6627 IMP
GIBBS DIE CASTING CORP (KY)
(*Suby of* KOCH ENTERPRISES INC) ★
369 Community Dr, Henderson, KY 42420-4397
Tel (270) 827-1801 *Founded/Ownrshp* 1965, 1969
Sales 190.0MM *EMP* 1,087
Accts Harding Shymanski And Company
SIC 3364 3363 3542 Magnesium & magnesium-base alloy die-castings; Aluminum die-castings; Die casting & extruding machines; Magnesium & magnesium-base alloy die-castings; Aluminum die-castings; Die casting & extruding machines
Ch Bd: Robert L Koch II
**Pr:* Steven A Church
Ofcr: Shannon Kavanaugh
VP: John Economou
VP: Steve Link
**VP:* James H Muehlbauer
Prgrm Mgr: Michael Clegg
Prgrm Mgr: Rachel French
Prgrm Mgr: Todd Sulawske
Prgrm Mgr: Wade Wallace
Dept Mgr: Darrell Moore
Board of Directors: Steven A Church, William Haeberle, Kevin R Koch, Thomas A Mowatt, James H Muehlbauer, Susan E Parsons

D-U-N-S 05-146-4873
GIBBS INTERNATIONAL INC
GIBBS INTERNATIONAL TRUCK CTRS
2201 E Ventura Blvd, Oxnard, CA 93036-7902
Tel (805) 485-0551 *Founded/Ownrshp* 1976
Sales 59.0MM *EMP* 135E
SIC 7538 5511 4212 Truck engine repair, except industrial; Trucks, tractors & trailers: new & used; Local trucking, without storage; Truck engine repair, except industrial; Trucks, tractors & trailers: new & used; Local trucking, without storage
Pr: Edward A Gibbs
Sls Mgr: Mark Rapin
Sales Asso: John Limoli

GIBBS INTERNATIONAL TRUCK CTRS
See GIBBS INTERNATIONAL INC

D-U-N-S 05-104-5664
GIBBS LANDSCAPE CO
4055 Atlanta Rd Se, Smyrna, GA 30080-5909
Tel (770) 432-7761 *Founded/Ownrshp* 1971
Sales 29.6MME *EMP* 180
SIC 0782 Landscape contractors
Ch: James H Gibbs
**Pr:* David M Gibbs
**Treas:* Sarah B Gibbs
Area Mgr: William Melendez

D-U-N-S 62-778-8037
GIBBS OIL CO LIMITED PARTNERSHIP
6 Kimball Ln Ste 400, Lynnfield, MA 01940-2685
Tel (617) 660-7430 *Founded/Ownrshp* 1991
Sales 44.0MME *EMP* 200
SIC 5541 5411 Gasoline service stations; Convenience stores; Gasoline service stations; Convenience stores
Pr: Gary Kaneb
Genl Pt: Chelsea M Corp
Genl Pt: Alice Kuhne
Sls Mgr: Joe Cafarelli

D-U-N-S 09-922-1363
GIBBS TECHNOLOGY CO
GFI DIGITAL
12163 Prichard Farm Rd, Maryland Heights, MO 63043-4202
Tel (314) 997-6300 *Founded/Ownrshp* 1999
Sales 53.9MME *EMP* 214
SIC 5999 7378 Facsimile equipment; Computer & data processing equipment repair/maintenance; Facsimile equipment; Computer & data processing equipment repair/maintenance
Pr: Bruce Gibbs
**VP:* Corey Backues
VP: Mark Kehoe
Dir IT: Matt Klaus
Sls Mgr: Jeremiah Essmyer
Sls Mgr: Dave Gift
Sls Mgr: Nick Morales
Sls Mgr: Spencer Overfelt
Sls Mgr: Paul Tripi
Sales Asso: Dana Brondel

D-U-N-S 62-144-2615
GIBBS WELDING SUPPLY INC
A L COMPRESSED GASES
875 Visco Dr, Nashville, TN 37210-2167
Tel (615) 254-1457 *Founded/Ownrshp* 1990
Sales 27.7MME *EMP* 19E
SIC 5169 5084 Chemicals & allied products; Welding machinery & equipment
Pr: Richard Gibbs Sr
**Sec:* Kathy Gibbs
Opers Mgr: Brady Bush
Opers Mgr: Corey Shipping
Sls&Mrk Ex: Donald Adcock

D-U-N-S 00-887-3929 IMP
GIBBS WIRE & STEEL CO INC
Metals Dr, Southington, CT 06489
Tel (860) 621-0121 *Founded/Ownrshp* 1956
Sales 83.0MME *EMP* 155
Accts Haggett Longobardi & Company
SIC 5051 Ferrous metals; Nonferrous metal sheets, bars, rods, etc.; Wire; Strip, metal; Ferrous metals; Nonferrous metal sheets, bars, rods, etc.; Wire; Strip, metal
Ch: C Wayne Gibbs
**CEO:* William J Torres
**CFO:* Mario Izzo
VP: Don Hennon
**VP:* Dick Lane
VP: Robert Lorio
VP: Thomas Molnar
**VP:* Shannon Riotto
Opers Mgr: Ben Leary
Ql Cn Mgr: Beverley Randle
VP Sls: Donald Gibbs
Board of Directors: Maurice Fitzmaurice, Gary Niederpruem, Paul Ruby

D-U-N-S 07-884-1293
GIBNEY ANTHONY & FLAHERTY LLP
665 5th Ave Fl 11, New York, NY 10022-5339
Tel (212) 546-7650 *Founded/Ownrshp* 1960
Sales 29.0MM *EMP* 130E
SIC 8111 General practice law office; General practice law office
CEO: Frederick W Anthony
Pt: Brian W Brokate
Pt: Peter Cousins
Pt: Joseph Di Cesare
Pt: Gerald J Dunworth Jr
Pt: John F Flaherty
Pt: Paolo S Grassi
Pt: Bertrand Gros
Pt: Melvin H Halper
Pt: John Macaluso
Pt: Chris Magrath
Pt: Stephen J O Maltby
Pt: Angelo Mazza
Pt: James H McGivney
Pt: Robert V Okulski
Pt: Ellen Poreda
Pt: Stephen F Ruffino
Pt: Kenneth N Sacks
Pt: Barry Zalaznick

D-U-N-S 06-137-2207
GIBRALTAR CONSTRUCTION CO INC (MD)
42 Hudson St Ste 107, Annapolis, MD 21401-8537
Tel (410) 573-1000 *Founded/Ownrshp* 1972
Sales 39.6MME *EMP* 120
Accts H David Dellumo Cockeysville
SIC 1522 Remodeling, multi-family dwellings; Remodeling, multi-family dwellings
CEO: Phillip Bernhardt
Treas: Elizabeth Fravel
**VP:* Robert Babbitt
VP: Steven Forman
Snr Mgr: Betsy Fravel

D-U-N-S 96-508-8446
GIBRALTAR CONSTRUCTION CORP
2932 N Webster Ave, Indianapolis, IN 46219-1015
Tel (317) 375-1588 *Founded/Ownrshp* 1995
Sales 38.0MM *EMP* 67
Accts Yount And Company Llc Ind
SIC 1542 Institutional building construction; Institutional building construction
Pr: Michael A Smith
**Sec:* Judy Smith
**VP:* Steve Smith

D-U-N-S 05-996-1847 IMP/EXP
▲ **GIBRALTAR INDUSTRIES INC**
3556 Lake Shore Rd # 100, Buffalo, NY 14219-1400
Tel (716) 826-6500 *Founded/Ownrshp* 1993
Sales 862.0MM *EMP* 2,416
Tkr Sym ROCK *Exch* NGS
SIC 3499 3316 3441 3398 Strapping, metal; Cold finishing of steel shapes; Strip steel, cold-rolled: from purchased hot-rolled; Sheet, steel, cold-rolled: from purchased hot-rolled; Bars, steel, cold finished, from purchased hot-rolled; Fabricated structural metal; Metal heat treating; Strapping, metal; Cold finishing of steel shapes; Strip steel, cold-rolled: from purchased hot-rolled; Sheet, steel, cold-rolled: from purchased hot-rolled; Bars, steel, cold finished, from purchased hot-rolled; Fabricated structural metal; Metal heat treating
Pr: Frank Heard
Pr: Andy Blanchard
Pr: Paul C Soucier
CFO: Kenneth W Smith
Treas: Timothy F Murphy
Ex VP: J A Rosenecker
Sr VP: Paul M Murray
VP: Gregory Leong
VP: Derek Paulsen
VP: Paul Plourde
Comm Dir: Peter Ciotta
Board of Directors: William J Colombo, Jane L Corwin, Craig Hindman, Vinod Khilnani, William P Montague, Robert E Sadler Jr

D-U-N-S 11-296-4267
GIBRALTAR PRIVATE BANK & TRUST
55 Alhambra Plz Ste 600, Coral Gables, FL 33134-5254
Tel (305) 476-1982 *Founded/Ownrshp* 1993
Sales NA *EMP* 150
SIC 6035 6029 Federal savings banks; Commercial banks; Federal savings banks; Commercial banks
Ch Bd: Adolfo Henriques
**Pr:* Gail Birks
**Pr:* Angel Medina
**CFO:* Tony Caron
**CFO:* Richard McCroskey
**Ch:* Bob Dickinson
Treas: Andrew Paluszek
Chf Inves: David Moore
Ofcr: Peter Quevedo
Ofcr: Natalia Tarazona
**Ex VP:* R Thomas Burge
**Ex VP:* Christopher V Damian
**Ex VP:* Jay Pelham
Ex VP: William Vandresser
Sr VP: Terri Castellano
Sr VP: Tania Dubats-Paulis
Sr VP: Terri Echarte
Sr VP: George Fernandez
Sr VP: Cathy Gradine
Sr VP: Robert Hebble
Sr VP: Michael Hill

D-U-N-S 07-426-2056
GIBRALTAR SCHOOL DISTRICT
19370 Vreeland Rd, Woodhaven, MI 48183-4460
Tel (734) 379-6350 *Founded/Ownrshp* 1930
Sales 17.3MME *EMP* 400
SIC 8211 Public elementary school; Public junior high school; Public senior high school; Public elementary school; Public junior high school; Public senior high school
**Prin:* Kathy Wayda
Schl Brd P: James Crapko
HC Dir: Pat Coluccia

D-U-N-S 05-457-3944 IMP
GIBRALTAR TRADE CENTER INC (MI)
237 N River Rd, Mount Clemens, MI 48043-1920
Tel (734) 287-2000 *Founded/Ownrshp* 1980
Sales 66.3MME *EMP* 209E
SIC 5199 General merchandise, non-durable; General merchandise, non-durable
Pr: James A Koester
**VP:* Robert A Koester
Genl Mgr: Craig Miller

D-U-N-S 15-052-7265
GIBSON & ASSOCIATES INC
11210 Ryliecrest Dr, Mesquite, TX 75180-3730
Tel (972) 557-1199 *Founded/Ownrshp* 1985
Sales 29.6MME *EMP* 90
SIC 1771 Concrete work; Blacktop (asphalt) work; Concrete pumping; Concrete repair
CEO: William E Gibson
**Pr:* William J Gibson
**Ex VP:* A J Johnston
IT Man: Robert Dodson

D-U-N-S 01-969-6920
GIBSON APPLIED TECHNOLOGY & ENGINEERING (TEXAS) INC
GATE
16360 Park Ten Pl Ste 206, Houston, TX 77084-5048
Tel (281) 398-5781 *Founded/Ownrshp* 2000
Sales 100.0MM *EMP* 150
SIC 8711 Engineering services; Engineering services
Pr: Grant T Gibson
CFO: Brian Deleney
Sr VP: Cody Moffitt

D-U-N-S 06-741-7980
GIBSON AREA HOSPITAL & HEALTH SERVICES
1120 N Melvin St, Gibson City, IL 60936-1477
Tel (217) 784-4251 *Founded/Ownrshp* 1952
Sales 71.0MM *EMP* 350E
SIC 8062 8051 General medical & surgical hospitals; Skilled nursing care facilities; General medical & surgical hospitals; Skilled nursing care facilities
CEO: Gary Petersen
**CFO:* Rob Schmitt
Sr Cor Off: Rose Robin
Bd of Dir: Jim Gulliford
Bd of Dir: Viola Kumpf
Bd of Dir: Frank Stocker
Bd of Dir: Melanie Warfield
Exec: Ty Royal
Dir Rx: Greg Beasley
Mng Ofcr: Katherine Austman
Chf Nrs Of: Robin Rose

D-U-N-S 15-200-8538 IMP
GIBSON BRANDS INC
GIBSON USA
309 Plus Park Blvd, Nashville, TN 37217-1005
Tel (615) 871-4500 *Founded/Ownrshp* 1974
Sales 749.9MME *EMP* 2,800
SIC 3931 Guitars & parts, electric & nonelectric
Ch Bd: Henry E Juszkiewicz
**Pr:* Dave Berryman
CFO: Anthony Crudele
**CFO:* Dan Krawczyk
Sr VP: Michael L Allen
Sr VP: Fred Greene
Natl Sales: Larry Urie
Mktg Dir: Reno Kling
Mktg Mgr: Jim Grundberg

D-U-N-S 11-934-5957
GIBSON COMMUNITY HOSPITAL PHARMACY INC
OWEN HEALTH CARE AND PHARMACY
1120 N Melvin St, Gibson City, IL 60936-1477
Tel (217) 784-2670 *Founded/Ownrshp* 1980
Sales 74.0MM *EMP* 5
SIC 5912 Drug stores & proprietary stores
Dir Recs: Candis Underwood
COO: Lisa Wilson
Bd of Dir: Frank Stocker
VP: Margo Martin
Dir Rx: Greg L Beesley
QA Dir: Sylvia Day
Doctor: Mark Spangler
Nrsg Dir: Kristy Elder
Pharmcst: Alli Braden
Pharmcst: Dave L Dawdy
Pharmcst: Sarah Wagner

D-U-N-S 06-908-5707
GIBSON CORRUGATED LLC
1920 E Main St, Tupelo, MS 38804-2937
Tel (662) 842-1862 *Founded/Ownrshp* 1999
Sales 32.4MME *EMP* 93
SIC 2653 Corrugated & solid fiber boxes; Corrugated & solid fiber boxes

D-U-N-S 09-999-4886
■ **GIBSON COUNTY COAL LLC**
(*Suby of* ALLIANCE COAL LLC) ★
2579 W Gibson Coal Rd, Princeton, IN 47670-8556
Tel (812) 385-1816 *Founded/Ownrshp* 1999
Sales 28.6MME *EMP* 290
SIC 1241 1221 Coal mining services; Bituminous coal surface mining; Coal mining services; Bituminous coal surface mining
Genl Mgr: Danny Durham

D-U-N-S 10-067-0801
GIBSON COUNTY SCHOOL DISTRICT
130 Trenton Hwy, Dyer, TN 38330-4239
Tel (731) 692-3803 *Founded/Ownrshp* 1981
Sales 20.0MM *EMP* 384
SIC 8211 Public elementary & secondary schools; School board; Public elementary & secondary schools; School board
**Prin:* Terry Cunningham

D-U-N-S 04-668-3173
GIBSON CTY-MELVIN-SIBLEY SCHOOL DISTRICT
307 N Sangamon Ave, Gibson City, IL 60936-1255
Tel (217) 784-8296 *Founded/Ownrshp* 1992
Sales 11.6MME *EMP* 287
SIC 8211 Elementary & secondary schools; Elementary & secondary schools
IT Man: Donald Worthington
Schl Brd P: Rod Cope
Instr Medi: Jessica Titus

GIBSON DUNN
See GIBSON DUNN & CRUTCHER LLP

D-U-N-S 07-796-3684
GIBSON DUNN & CRUTCHER LLP
GIBSON DUNN
333 S Grand Ave Ste 4400, Los Angeles, CA 90071-3197
Tel (213) 229-8063 *Founded/Ownrshp* 1880
Sales 358.3MME *EMP* 1,900
SIC 8111 General practice law office; General practice law office
Mng Pt: Ken Doran
**Pt:* Nicholas Aleksander
**Pt:* Peter Alexiadis
**Pt:* Lisa A Alfaro
**Pt:* Terrence R Allen
**Pt:* James Barabas
**Pt:* Joseph Barbeau
**Pt:* Hatef Behnia
**Pt:* Cyrus Benson
**Pt:* Ashlie Beringer
**Pt:* Karen E Bertero
**Pt:* J Keith Biancamano
**Pt:* Robert C Bonner
**Pt:* Michael D Bopp
**Pt:* Frederick Brown
**Pt:* Thomas M Budd
**Pt:* Gregory A Campbell

**Pt:* Candice Choh
**Pt:* Michael Collins
**Pt:* James A Cox
**Pt:* Jesse A Cripps

D-U-N-S 07-946-3401
GIBSON DUNN & CRUTCHER LLP
3 Ashton Rd Ph, Yonkers, NY 10705-2828
Tel (212) 351-4000 Founded/Ownrshp 2003
Sales 34.6MM^E EMP 421^E
SIC 8111 Specialized law offices, attorneys
Prin: Andrea Newman
Pr: Michelle Acuna
Pr: Kelly England
Pr: Pamela Santos
Exec: Susan Faga
Mng Ofcr: Zakiyyah Salim-Williams
Counsel: Michael Valek

GIBSON ELC & TECH SOLUTIONS
See GIBSON ELECTRIC CO INC

D-U-N-S 07-023-4836
■ **GIBSON ELECTRIC CO INC**
GIBSON ELC & TECH SOLUTIONS
(Suby of EMCOR GROUP INC) ★
3100 Woodcreek Dr, Downers Grove, IL 60515-5414
Tel (630) 288-3800 Founded/Ownrshp 1987
Sales 123.0MM^E EMP 300
SIC 1731 General electrical contractor; General electrical contractor
Pr: Daniel Fitzgibbons
CFO: Bob Springborn
Sr VP: Scott Rowe
VP: Scott Evensen
VP: Dan Fitzgibbons
VP: Carmen Manno
VP: Frank Mitter
VP: Francis Sikora
Exec: David Gelinas
Dir Bus: Marybeth Kulinski
Div Mgr: Mike Sugrue

D-U-N-S 00-792-3006
GIBSON ELECTRIC MEMBERSHIP CORP (TN)
1207 S College St, Trenton, TN 38382-3605
Tel (731) 855-4660 Founded/Ownrshp 1936
Sales 86.5MM EMP 85
Accts Alexander Thompson Arnold Pll
SIC 4911 Distribution, electric power; Distribution, electric power
Pr: Dan Rodamaker
COO: Anita Jones
VP: Richard Beden
Sfty Dirs: Billy Porter

D-U-N-S 96-291-6776
GIBSON ENERGY LLC
(Suby of GIBSON ENERGY ULC)
3819 Towne Crossing Blvd, Mesquite, TX 75150-2799
Tel (214) 461-5600 Founded/Ownrshp 2006
Sales 34.0MM^E EMP 130^E
SIC 4789 Cargo loading & unloading services
CEO: Dominic Maggiano
Ofcr: Erik Sherman
VP: Ralph Benson
VP: Don A Fowlis
VP: A Stewart Hanlon
VP: Michael McGowan
Area Mgr: Neil Carruthers
Area Mgr: Reed Siltala
Area Mgr: Stuart Sund
Dir IT: Jeff Hale
Sfty Dirs: Lisa Stoll

D-U-N-S 02-724-0811
GIBSON ENERGY MARKETING LLC
TAYLOR PROPANE GAS
3819 Towne Crossing Blvd, Mesquite, TX 75150-2799
Tel (214) 461-5600 Founded/Ownrshp 1998
Sales 147.0MM^E EMP 150
SIC 5172 5984 Butane gas; Gases, liquefied petroleum (propane); Butane gas, bottled; Propane gas, bottled; Butane gas; Gases, liquefied petroleum (propane); Butane gas, bottled; Propane gas, bottled
CEO: A Stewart Hanlon
*VP: Rodney J Bantle
*VP: Ralph Benson
*VP: Dominic Maggiano
*VP: Michael McGowan
Brnch Mgr: Les Carmichael

D-U-N-S 05-345-7552
GIBSON ENGINEERING CO INC
90 Broadway, Norwood, MA 02062-3519
Tel (781) 769-3600 Founded/Ownrshp 1945
Sales 39.6MM EMP 43
Accts Caras & Shulman Pc Burlington
SIC 5084 8711 Controlling instruments & accessories; Pneumatic tools & equipment; Engineering services; Controlling instruments & accessories; Pneumatic tools & equipment; Engineering services
CEO: Joseph F O'Brien Jr
*Pr: Daniel B O'Brien
Manager: Cristina Fein
Sales Asso: Steve Diflaminies
Sales Asso: Susan Sabin

GIBSON FAMILY HEALTH CENTER
See HELEN NEWBERRY JOY HOSPITAL & HEALTHCARE CENTER

D-U-N-S 03-490-2908
GIBSON FARMERS COOPERATIVE INC (TN)
1210 S Manufacturers Row, Trenton, TN 38382-3633
Tel (731) 855-1891 Founded/Ownrshp 1946
Sales 23.9MM^E EMP 70
SIC 5191 5014 5072

D-U-N-S 07-785-6748
GIBSON GENERAL HOSPITAL INC
LIFESTYLES DIABETES CENTER
1808 Sherman Dr, Princeton, IN 47670-1000
Tel (812) 385-3401 Founded/Ownrshp 1941
Sales 26.1MM EMP 300^E
SIC 8062 8052 General medical & surgical hospitals; Intermediate care facilities; General medical & surgical hospitals; Intermediate care facilities
CEO: Emmett Schuster
*CFO: Ron Harrington
CFO: Richard Stivers
Sr Cor Off: Wagih Satar
Dir Lab: Conda Welch
Dir Rx: Satya RAO
*Chf Nrs Of: Lori Phillips
Off Mgr: Nancy Dearing
Off Mgr: Brenda Kruper
Dir IT: Steve Paddock
Dir IT: Trish Ping
Board of Directors: Angie Bryant, Amy Drury, Deann Hunt, Jeff Jones, Michael Logan, Rick McKinney, Steve Rausch

D-U-N-S 07-981-5180
GIBSON HOTEL MANAGEMENT INC
409 Montbrook Ln, Knoxville, TN 37919-2704
Tel (865) 539-0588 Founded/Ownrshp 2006
Sales 53.0MM EMP 50
SIC 8741 Hotel or motel management
CEO: Michael Gibson

D-U-N-S 09-860-7401 IMP/EXP
GIBSON OVERSEAS INC
2410 Yates Ave, Commerce, CA 90040-1918
Tel (323) 725-8381 Founded/Ownrshp 1979
Sales 221.8MM^E EMP 400
Accts Kelman & Chan Llp Calabasas
SIC 5023 Glassware; China; Kitchen tools & utensils; Glassware; China; Kitchen tools & utensils
CEO: Sohail Gabbay
*COO: Darioush Gabbay
*CFO: Soloman Gabbay
VP: Connie Bowman
VP: Edmund Souder
VP: Alex Wittner
Dir IT: Steven Dabzadeh
Sls Mgr: Sylvia Hang
Sls Mgr: Jeffrey Nichols
Sls Mgr: Patty Toledo

D-U-N-S 10-261-0979
GIBSON SALES LP
DRUG EMPORIUM
2321a W Loop 281, Longview, TX 75604-2563
Tel (903) 297-0966 Founded/Ownrshp 1981
Sales 111.4MM EMP 440^E
SIC 5912 Drug stores; Drug stores
Genl Pt: Glen A Gibson
Pt: Sammy Culpepper
Pt: K Elaine Gibson
Dir Rx: Richard Magliolo
Div Mgr: Billy Speer
CIO: David Haney

D-U-N-S 13-385-7896 IMP
GIBSON TECHNICAL SERVICES INC
230 Mountain Brook Ct, Canton, GA 30115-9019
Tel (678) 493-3750 Founded/Ownrshp 1990
Sales 20.2MM EMP 75
Accts Babush Neiman Kornman & John
SIC 4899 Communication signal enhancement network system
CEO: Stuart V Gibson
*COO: Jon Martin
*CFO: Robert Moore
*CTO: Michael E McCracken
CTO: Michael E McCrackn
IT Man: William Brawley
Snr PM: Jerry Walker

GIBSON USA
See GIBSON BRANDS INC

GIBSON'S
See CHAFFIN ACQUISITION CO INC

D-U-N-S 18-052-3649
GIC REAL ESTATE INC
(Suby of PRIME PROPERTIES INC)
255 Shoreline Dr Ste 600, Redwood City, CA 94065-1433
Tel (650) 593-3122 Founded/Ownrshp 1985
Sales 38.9MM^E EMP 313
SIC 6799 6531 Real estate investors, except property operators; Real estate managers; Real estate investors, except property operators; Real estate managers
Pr: Mike Carp

GICHNER SHELTER SYSTEMS
See GICHNER SYSTEMS GROUP INC

D-U-N-S 80-803-7720
■ **GICHNER SYSTEMS GROUP INC**
GICHNER SHELTER SYSTEMS
(Suby of KRATOS UNMANNED SYSTEMS SOLUTIONS INC) ★
490 E Locust St, Dallastown, PA 17313-1902
Tel (717) 246-5430 Founded/Ownrshp 2007
Sales 107.2MM^E EMP 425^E
SIC 3795 Specialized tank components, military; Specialized tank components, military
Pr: Eric M Demarco
*COO: Richard Selvaggio
*CFO: Deanna H Lund
*Treas: Laura L Siegal
*VP: Michael W Fink
*VP: Thomas Mills
Mktg Mgr: Richard Smith

GICMH
See GOODWILL INDUSTRIES OF CENTRAL MICHIGANS HEARTLAND INC

D-U-N-S 09-605-9134 IMP
GICON PUMPS & EQUIPMENT LTD
AMERICAN W WINDMILL & SOLAR CO
1001 Texas Ave, Lubbock, TX 79401-3317
Tel (806) 401-8287 Founded/Ownrshp 1979
Sales 122.3MM^E EMP 75
SIC 5084 5074 5039 Water pumps (industrial); Pipes & fittings, plastic; Septic tanks; Water pumps (industrial); Pipes & fittings, plastic; Septic tanks
VP: Robert Mark
*Ltd Pt: Kim Ford
*Ltd Pt: Ken Grant
*Pt: Jerry Holton
*CFO: Vance Grant
*Prin: Mark Durham

D-U-N-S 15-096-5981
GID INVESTMENT ADVISERS LLC
125 High St 27th, Boston, MA 02110-2704
Tel (617) 973-9680 Founded/Ownrshp 1960
Sales 21.3MM^E EMP 100
SIC 6282 6531 Investment advice; Real estate managers; Investment advice; Real estate managers
VP: Gary Lovesky
VP: Brian T O'Herlihy

D-U-N-S 07-972-1821
GIDDENS HOLDINGS INC
(Suby of CADENCE AEROSPACE LLC) ★
2600 94th St Sw Ste 150, Everett, WA 98204-2151
Tel (425) 353-0405 Founded/Ownrshp 2008
Sales 50.7MM^E EMP 155^E
SIC 3728 Aircraft parts & equipment

D-U-N-S 08-373-4301
GIDDENS INDUSTRIES INC
(Suby of GIDDENS HOLDINGS INC) ★
2600 94th St Sw Ste 150, Everett, WA 98204-2151
Tel (425) 353-0405 Founded/Ownrshp 1974
Sales 50.7MM^E EMP 150
SIC 3728 Aircraft parts & equipment; Aircraft parts & equipment
Pr: Dale Peinecke
CFO: Mark Faller
*CFO: Paul Jackson
*Chf Mktg O: John Seguin
Prgrm Mgr: Tabitha Lewis
Prgrm Mgr: Jeff Merten
CTO: Larry Cooper
Dir IT: James Todd
QI Cn Mgr: Mike Stewart

D-U-N-S 11-925-0355
GIDDENS SECURITY CORP
528 Edgewood Ave S Ste 1, Jacksonville, FL 32205-5375
Tel (904) 384-8071 Founded/Ownrshp 1981
Sales 9.4MM^E EMP 315
SIC 7381 Protective services, guard; Protective services, guard
Pr: Darrell Giddens

GIDDINGS, CORBY, HYNES
See CAPAX MANAGEMENT & INSURANCE SERVICES

D-U-N-S 07-420-3522
GIDDINGS INDEPENDENT SCHL DST
GIDDINGS ISD
2337 N Main St, Giddings, TX 78942-1460
Tel (979) 542-2854 Founded/Ownrshp 1874
Sales 21.8MM^E EMP 300
SIC 8211 Public elementary & secondary schools; Public elementary & secondary schools
Exec: Benita Trujillo
Schl Brd P: Stan Degerolami
Schl Brd P: Mark Johnson
Psych: Debbie Lehmann

GIDDINGS ISD
See GIDDINGS INDEPENDENT SCHL DST

D-U-N-S 13-387-9572
GIDEON TOAL MANAGEMENT SERVICES INC
500 W 7th St Ste 1400, Fort Worth, TX 76102-4748
Tel (817) 335-4991 Founded/Ownrshp 1996
Sales 2.0MM EMP 276^E
SIC 8741 Management services
Pr: Randall Gideon
CFO: Debra Witherspoon

D-U-N-S 05-202-7273
GIELOW PICKLES INC
5260 Main St, Lexington, MI 48450-9393
Tel (810) 359-7680 Founded/Ownrshp 1970
Sales 62.3MM EMP 300
Accts Frohm Kelly Butler & Ryan Pc
SIC 2035 Cucumbers, pickles & pickle salting; Cucumbers, pickles & pickle salting
Pr: Douglas R Gielow
*VP: Craig Gielow

D-U-N-S 00-974-9946 IMP
GIESECKE & DEVRIENT AMERICA INC
G&D AMERICA
(Suby of GIESECKE & DEVRIENT GESELLSCHAFT MIT BESCHRANKTER HAFTUNG)
45925 Horseshoe Dr # 100, Dulles, VA 20166-6588
Tel (703) 480-2000 Founded/Ownrshp 1990
Sales 74.6MM^E EMP 308
SIC 2672 5044 Coated & laminated paper; Office equipment; Coated & laminated paper; Office equipment
Pr: Scott Marquardt
*CFO: Kevin J Fitzgerald
Sr VP: Marianne Arosenius
Sr VP: Vivek Shankar
VP: Jeff Bowers
VP: Lauri Pesonen
VP: Steve Rugen
VP: Brian Russell
Exec: Alexander Penaojas
Dir Bus: Thomas Kelly
Prgrm Mgr: Jyrki Penttinen

D-U-N-S 88-352-6485
GIESEN RESTAURANT ENTERPRISES LLC
ARBY'S
10 E Belleview Way, Greenwood Village, CO 80121-1408
Tel (303) 761-7498 Founded/Ownrshp 1991
Sales 20.6MM^E EMP 1,100
SIC 5812 Fast-food restaurant, chain; Fast-food restaurant, chain

D-U-N-S 96-384-8374
GIF NORTH AMERICA LLC
120 Kelly Ct, Monroeville, PA 15146-1352
Tel (703) 969-9243 Founded/Ownrshp 2009
Sales 64.8MM^E EMP 500
SIC 8711 3714 Engineering services; Engineering services; Motor vehicle parts & accessories
Pr: Peter G Hartmann

D-U-N-S 05-420-3468 IMP
GIFFIN INC
GIFFIN, INC. AND AFFILIATES
1900 Brown Rd, Auburn Hills, MI 48326-1701
Tel (248) 494-9600 Founded/Ownrshp 1980
Sales 75.0MM^E EMP 100
SIC 3559 Metal finishing equipment for plating, etc.; Metal finishing equipment for plating, etc.
Pr: Donald J P Giffin
*VP: Steven Smith
*VP: Gary T Zelinsky
Sfty Dirs: Jim Rice

GIFFIN, INC. AND AFFILIATES
See GIFFIN INC

D-U-N-S 03-210-2865
GIFFIN INTERIOR & FIXTURE INC
500 Scotti Dr, Bridgeville, PA 15017-2938
Tel (412) 221-1166 Founded/Ownrshp 1980
Sales 34.8MM^E EMP 150
SIC 2541 1542 2431 2511 Store & office display cases & fixtures; Commercial & office building, new construction; Millwork; Wood household furniture; Store & office display cases & fixtures; Commercial & office building, new construction; Millwork; Wood household furniture
Pr: Gordon Giffin

GIFFORD FAMILY HEALTH CENTER
See GIFFORD MEDICAL CENTER INC

D-U-N-S 07-398-3827
GIFFORD MEDICAL CENTER INC
GIFFORD FAMILY HEALTH CENTER
44 S Main St, Randolph, VT 05060-1381
Tel (802) 728-7000 Founded/Ownrshp 1905
Sales 58.2MM EMP 500
SIC 8062 8011 General medical & surgical hospitals; Offices & clinics of medical doctors; General medical & surgical hospitals; Offices & clinics of medical doctors
Ch Bd: Randy Garner
*Pr: Joseph Woodin
*CFO: David Sanville
VP: Alison White
Cmptr Lab: Jil Roger
Mktg Dir: Ashley Lincon
Pr Mgr: Phyllis Jensen
Doctor: Pamela Udomprasert MD
Nrsg Dir: Louis Dinicola
Diag Rad: Scott Smith
HC Dir: Cathy Traeglar

D-U-N-S 79-021-7652
GIFT CARD IMPRESSIONS LLC
415 Delaware St Ste B, Kansas City, MO 64105-1264
Tel (816) 421-0055 Founded/Ownrshp 2005
Sales 26.5MM^E EMP 52
SIC 5099

D-U-N-S 79-351-0454
GIFT COLLECTION INC
HMS HOST INTERNATIONAL
(Suby of HOST INTERNATIONAL INC) ★
6905 Rockledge Dr Fl 1, Bethesda, MD 20817-7826
Tel (240) 694-4100 Founded/Ownrshp 1988
Sales 108.7MM^E EMP 2,700
SIC 6512 5812 Nonresidential building operators; Eating places; Nonresidential building operators; Eating places
CEO: Steve Johnson
*Pr: William W McCarten
Treas: Douglas Ribbeck
Ex VP: Mall Maalouf
Sr VP: Donald Olinger
VP: Bernard Brown
VP: Steven Johnson
Opers Mgr: Justin Davidson

D-U-N-S 15-517-6506
GIFT OF HOPE ORGAN & TISSUE DONOR NETWORK
425 Spring Lake Dr, Itasca, IL 60143-2076
Tel (630) 758-2600 Founded/Ownrshp 1986
Sales 52.8MM EMP 250
Accts Mcgladrey Llp Rockford Il
SIC 8099 8071 Organ bank; Testing laboratories; Organ bank; Testing laboratories
CEO: J Kevin Cmunt
*CFO: Ross Raspopovich
VP: Mary Rosenberg
VP: Allison Smith
Mng Dir: Dara Griffin

GIFT OF LIFE DONOR PROGRAM
See GREATER DELAWARE VALLEY SOCIETY OF TRANSPLANT SURGEONS

GIFT OF LIFE MICHIGAN
See ORGAN PROCUREMENT AGENCY OF MICHIGAN

D-U-N-S 96-765-3494
GIFT SERVICES INC
GIFTTREE
1800 W Fourth Ste 120, Vancouver, WA 98660
Tel (360) 699-0772 Founded/Ownrshp 1996
Sales 40.0MM EMP 120^E
SIC 5961 Catalog & mail-order houses
Pr: Craig T Bowen
Ofcr: Neal Rose
*VP: Esther Diez
*VP: Scott Hippe
Creative D: Doug Anderson
Dir Bus: Michael Thomas
Mng Dir: Jessica Healy
Dir IT: Bill Meuler
VP Mktg: Micheal Thomas
Sls Dir: Jennine Zari
Sls Mgr: Erin Musgrove

GIFT SHOP
See MEMORIAL HEALTH CARE INC

D-U-N-S 00-640-3613
GIFTANGO LLC
INCOMM DIGITAL SOLUTIONS
(*Suby of* INCOMM HOLDINGS INC) ★
111 Sw 5th Ave Ste 900, Portland, OR 97204-3615
Tel (877) 443-8264 *Founded/Ownrshp* 2005, 2012
Sales 225.0MM^E *EMP* 89
SIC 5961 Cards, mail order; Cards, mail order
Pr: Michael Fletcher
COO: Christian Casebeer
VP: Kj Gunderfen
Sftwr Eng: Nicholas Brandon

D-U-N-S 01-901-4369 EXP
GIFTCRAFT INC
(*Suby of* GIFTCRAFT LTD)
300 International Dr # 100, Williamsville, NY 14221-5781
Tel (905) 790-2000 *Founded/Ownrshp* 1992
Sales 45.0MM *EMP* 115
SIC 5199 General merchandise, non-durable; General merchandise, non-durable
Pr: Trevor Cohen
**COO:* Ron Tomiuck
COO: Ron Tomiuk
**CFO:* Thomas Kydd
**VP:* Leslie Lepage
**VP:* Gary Polan
IT Man: Jim Gressmann
Manager: Ellen Sztogryn

GIFTED EXPRESSIONS
See AMERICAN GOURMET GROUP LLC

GIFTS FROM THE HEART
See PHOEBE PUTNEY MEMORIAL HOSPITAL INC

GIFTS FROM THE HEART
See PHOEBE PUTNEY MEMORIAL HOSPITAL INC

GIFTS IN KIND
See GOOD360

GIFTTREE
See GIFT SERVICES INC

GIGA BITE TECHNOLOGY
See GBT INC

GIGAAGE
See STEINER ELECTRIC CO

D-U-N-S 36-273-7251 IMP
▲ GIGAMON INC
3300 Olcott St, Santa Clara, CA 95054-3005
Tel (408) 831-4000 *Founded/Ownrshp* 2004
Sales 157.1MM *EMP* 352^E
Accts Pricewaterhousecoopers Llp S
Tkr Sym GIMO *Exch* NYS
SIC 3577 7372 Computer peripheral equipment; Prepackaged software; Computer peripheral equipment; Prepackaged software
CEO: Paul A Hooper
Ch Bd: Corey M Mulloy
CFO: Mike Burns
Chf Mktg O: Peter Finter
Sr VP: Sachi Sambandan
VP: David Cox
VP: Rich Jacquet
VP: Jennifer Miller
VP: Ananda Rajagopal
VP: Scott Sullivan
VP: Helmut Wilke
VP: Andy Zollo
Board of Directors: Kenneth A Goldman, Ted C Ho, John H Kispert, Paul J Milbury, Michael C Ruettgers

D-U-N-S 02-605-2209 IMP
GIGLIO DISTRIBUTING CO INC
155 S M L King Jr Pkwy, Beaumont, TX 77701-2788
Tel (409) 838-1654 *Founded/Ownrshp* 1955
Sales 35.0MM^E *EMP* 105^E
SIC 5181 5182 Beer & other fermented malt liquors; Wine; Liquor; Ale; Wine & distilled beverages
Pr: Charles J Giglio
**VP:* Frank A Crorey
Off Mgr: Carolyn Kirkpatrick

D-U-N-S 01-758-8224 IMP/EXP
▲ GIGOPTIX INC
130 Baytech Dr, San Jose, CA 95134-2302
Tel (408) 522-3100 *Founded/Ownrshp* 2007
Sales 32.9MM *EMP* 76^E
Accts Burr Pilger Mayer Inc San J
Tkr Sym GIG *Exch* ASE
SIC 3674 Semiconductors & related devices; Hybrid integrated circuits; Semiconductors & related devices; Hybrid integrated circuits
Ch Bd: AVI Katz
CFO: Darren MA
Sr VP: Andrea Betti-Berutto
Sr VP: Raluca Dinu
VP: Steve Choate
VP: Jorg Wieland
VP Bus Dev: Elie Massabki
VP Opers: Julie Tipton
Board of Directors: Joseph J Lazzara, John J Mikulsky, Neil J Miotto, Frank Schneider, Kimberly D C Trapp

D-U-N-S 07-947-3383
GII HOLDING I CORP
666 5th Ave Fl 36, New York, NY 10103-3102
Tel (212) 755-3131 *Founded/Ownrshp* 2014
Sales 32.4MM^E *EMP* 122^E
SIC 6719 5065 Investment holding companies, except banks; Electronic parts
Pr: John Garcia

D-U-N-S 00-729-0208
GIL HAUGAN CONSTRUCTION INC
200 E 60th St N, Sioux Falls, SD 57104-0433
Tel (605) 336-6082 *Founded/Ownrshp* 1961
Sales 60.7MM^E *EMP* 223
SIC 1542 1541 Commercial & office building, new construction; Industrial buildings, new construction; Commercial & office building, new construction; Industrial buildings, new construction
Pr: Gil Haugan Jr

D-U-N-S 02-842-3788 IMP
GIL-MAR MANUFACTURING CO
GM
7925 Ronda Dr, Canton, MI 48187-2456
Tel (248) 640-4303 *Founded/Ownrshp* 1982
Sales 21.8MM^E *EMP* 90
SIC 3599 Machine shop, jobbing & repair
Pr: Gildo Ruicci
**Treas:* Gary W Gorski
**VP:* William L Martin
**VP:* Joseph Ruicci
Genl Mgr: Mark Kosbe
Mfg Mgr: David Lavigne
Ql Cn Mgr: Robert Conley
Pgrm Dir: Robert A Zulker

GILA GROUP
See GILA LLC

D-U-N-S 78-643-8200
■ GILA LLC
GILA GROUP
(*Suby of* NAVIENT CORP) ★
8325 Tuscany Way Bldg 4, Austin, TX 78754-4734
Tel (512) 371-9995 *Founded/Ownrshp* 2015
Sales 55.1MM^E *EMP* 360
SIC 7322 Collection agency, except real estate; Collection agency, except real estate
CEO: Bruce Cummings
Sr VP: Doug Holt
VP: Gloria Martinez
VP: James Perasso
VP: Jason Schmer
VP: Patrick J Swanick
IT Man: Art Adams
Software D: Nick Parrillo
VP Opers: Elye Sackmary
Opers Mgr: Suzi Tanksley
Sales Exec: David Keim

D-U-N-S 07-509-0910
GILA REGIONAL MEDICAL CENTER (NM)
1313 E 32nd St, Silver City, NM 88061-7251
Tel (575) 538-4000 *Founded/Ownrshp* 1937, 1960
Sales 92.3MM^E *EMP* 1,178
Accts Redw Llc Albuquerque New Mex
SIC 8093 8062 8082 General medical & surgical hospitals; Home health care services; Rehabilitation center, outpatient treatment; Rehabilitation center, outpatient treatment; General medical & surgical hospitals; Home health care services
CEO: Brian Cunningham
COO: Jed Rudd
CFO: David Glassburn
CFO: Omaira Heakin
CFO: Craig Stewart
Bd of Dir: Jean Fortenberry
Bd of Dir: Ken Foster
Bd of Dir: Richard Lawyer
Bd of Dir: John P Saari
Ofcr: Ruth Pruitt
VP: James Burke
Dir Lab: Robert Eytalis
Dir Lab: Bob Eytallis
Dir Lab: David Harju
Dir Lab: Michael Honea
Dir Rx: Larry Rivkin

GILA RIVER CASINOS
See GILA RIVER GAMING ENTERPRISES INC

D-U-N-S 84-920-5091
GILA RIVER GAMING ENTERPRISES INC
GILA RIVER CASINOS
5040 W Wildhorse Pass Blvd, Chandler, AZ 85226-5404
Tel (800) 946-4452 *Founded/Ownrshp* 1994
Sales 94.1MM^E *EMP* 1,500
SIC 7993 5812 Slot machines; Eating places; Slot machines; Eating places
Pr: Kenneth Manuel
Ofcr: Deborah Carruthers
Dir Soc: Joe Guy
Dir Soc: Cameron Howard
Dir Soc: Leslie Lau
Dir Sec: Jeffrey Buckner
Genl Mgr: Mike Doocey
Genl Mgr: Michael Olujic
Dir IT: Robin Villareal
Mktg Dir: Martin Moore
Mktg Dir: Wendy Perez

D-U-N-S 10-219-3070
GILA RIVER SAND & GRAVEL CORP
2126 N Tanner Rd, Sacaton, AZ 85147
Tel (520) 418-2106 *Founded/Ownrshp* 2001
Sales 32.6MM^E *EMP* 96
SIC 5032 Sand, construction; Gravel; Sand, construction; Gravel
Genl Mgr: Michael Morago
CFO: Donna C Mitchell
Site Mgr: John Gonzales
Site Mgr: Wayne Patch

D-U-N-S 06-467-6240
GILBANE BUILDING CO
MILLS GILBANE
(*Suby of* GILBANE BUILDING CO) ★
8433 Entp Cir Ste 200, Bradenton, FL 34202
Tel (941) 758-6441 *Founded/Ownrshp* 2011
Sales 62.0MM^E *EMP* 200
SIC 1542 Commercial & office building contractors; Institutional building construction; Commercial & office building contractors; Institutional building construction
CEO: Thomas F Gilbane Jr
**Pr:* William J Gilbane Jr
**CFO:* John T Ruggieri
**Treas:* Richard R Roy
VP: Mark Kennell
Exec: Jason Burt
Off Mgr: Barbara Connor
CIO: Michael Caravello
Sls&Mrk Ex: Howard Camp
Mktg Dir: Heather Nye
Snr PM: Kathy Aquiola

D-U-N-S 09-628-7347
GILBANE BUILDING CO
(*Suby of* GILBANE INC) ★
7 Jackson Walkway Ste 2, Providence, RI 02903-3694
Tel (401) 456-5800 *Founded/Ownrshp* 1873
Sales 3.8MMM *EMP* 2,500
Accts Mcgladrey And Pullen Llp Bost
SIC 1542 Institutional building construction; Institutional building construction
Ch Bd: Thomas F Gilbane
**Pr:* Michael McKelvy
CFO: Ken Alderman
**Treas:* Michael Costello
Treas: Richard R Roy
**Ex VP:* Michael R Bohn
**Ex VP:* Dennis Cornick
**Ex VP:* Daniel Mc Conaghy
Sr VP: Andrew R Faber
Sr VP: Bruce Hoffman
Sr VP: Walter McKelvey
Sr VP: Alfred K Potter II
VP: Jim Busam
**VP:* Freddie T Bustillo
VP: John Fumosa
VP: Lori Giordano
VP: Mark Hill
VP: Joseph Hohman
VP: Dan Kelly
VP: Mike Kennedy
VP: Phillip Leffert

D-U-N-S 87-456-9015 IMP
GILBANE FEDERAL
(*Suby of* GILBANE BUILDING CO) ★
1655 Grant St Fl 12, Concord, CA 94520-2445
Tel (925) 946-3100 *Founded/Ownrshp* 2010
Sales 169.7MM^E *EMP* 500
SIC 8711 8748 Building construction consultant; Environmental consultant; Building construction consultant; Environmental consultant
CEO: Sarabjit Singh
CFO: Steve Schneider
VP: Subhash Pantakar
**VP:* Jon Verlinde
Prgrm Mgr: Dan Ledford
Sys Mgr: Randy Muir
VP Mktg: Dave Tenca

D-U-N-S 02-272-6165 IMP
GILBANE INC
7 Jackson Walkway, Providence, RI 02903-3638
Tel (401) 456-5800 *Founded/Ownrshp* 1908
Sales 3.8MMM^E *EMP* 2,500
SIC 1541 1542 8741 6513 6512 Industrial buildings, new construction; Renovation, remodeling & repairs: industrial buildings; Commercial & office building, new construction; Institutional building construction; Commercial & office buildings, renovation & repair; Construction management; Residential hotel operation; Commercial & industrial building operation; Industrial buildings, new construction; Renovation, remodeling & repairs: industrial buildings; Commercial & office building, new construction; Institutional building construction; Commercial & office buildings, renovation & repair; Construction management; Residential hotel operation; Commercial & industrial building operation
CEO: Thomas F Gilbane Jr
**Pr:* Michael E McKelvy
**CFO:* John Ruggieri
CFO: John T Ruggieri
Ex VP: Dennis Cornick
Ex VP: Thomas Laird
**VP:* Michael R Bohn
**VP:* Paul J Choquette Jr
**VP:* Robert V Gilbane
**VP:* William J Gilbane Jr
VP: Jason Pelkey

D-U-N-S 00-111-5245 IMP/EXP
■ GILBARCO INC (DE)
GILBARCO VEEDER-ROOT
(*Suby of* DANAHER CORP) ★
7300 W Friendly Ave, Greensboro, NC 27410-6200
Tel (336) 547-5000 *Founded/Ownrshp* 1865, 1987
Sales 528.7MM^E *EMP* 3,600
SIC 3586

GILBARCO VEEDER-ROOT
See GILBARCO INC

D-U-N-S 80-466-2810
GILBERT BARBEE MOORE & MCILVOY PSC
GRAVES-GILBERT CLINIC
201 Park St Fl 3, Bowling Green, KY 42101-1759
Tel (270) 781-5111 *Founded/Ownrshp* 1969
Sales 71.7MM^E *EMP* 450
SIC 8011 Offices & clinics of medical doctors; Offices & clinics of medical doctors
Pr: Christopher Thorn
Exec: Debbie Diamond
MIS Dir: Linda Pillow
Dir IT: Mike Smith
Opers Mgr: Marsha Clayton
Surgeon: Timothy Wierson
Obsttrcn: Todd Drexel
Obsttrcn: Nathan Stice
Doctor: Lin Charles
Doctor: Paul Cofoid
Doctor: Michelle Crowe

D-U-N-S 05-882-9888
GILBERT CENTRAL CORP
(*Suby of* KIEWIT CORP) ★
Kiewit Plz, Omaha, NE 68131
Tel (402) 342-2052 *Founded/Ownrshp* 1982
Sales 137.4MM^E *EMP* 282
SIC 1611 1622 Highway & street construction; Bridge construction; Highway & street construction; Bridge construction
Pr: Keith N Sasich
Treas: Stephen S Thomas
VP: Howard L Barton Jr
VP: William D Glaser
VP: Troy L Heckmaster
VP: Mark D Langford
VP: Michael J Piechoski
VP: John D Proskovec

D-U-N-S 03-259-8427
GILBERT CHEVROLET CO INC
3550 Us Highway 441 S, Okeechobee, FL 34974-6211
Tel (863) 763-3154 *Founded/Ownrshp* 1977
Sales 23.3MM^E *EMP* 50
SIC 5511 Automobiles, new & used
Pr: H Gilbert Culbreth Jr
**VP:* Jeremiah Culbreth
**Genl Mgr:* Christa Luna
Off Mgr: Becky Racine
Sls Dir: Bert Culbreth
Sls Mgr: Susan Hendershot

GILBERT COMPANY, THE
See GPR LOGISTICS LLC

D-U-N-S 12-192-1761
GILBERT DISPLAYS INC
110 Spagnoli Rd, Melville, NY 11747-3502
Tel (631) 577-1100 *Founded/Ownrshp* 1986
Sales 40.0MM *EMP* 185
SIC 7389 2499 Advertising, promotional & trade show services; Decorative wood & woodwork; Advertising, promotional & trade show services; Decorative wood & woodwork
Ch Bd: Barry Ballen
**CFO:* Anthony J Colombo
**CFO:* Ron Felber
VP: Steve Ballen
**VP:* Ron Bergida
Exec: Chris Silverman
Prd Mgr: Naomi Buck
VP Sls: Ryan Golden
Mktg Dir: Michael Schwartz

D-U-N-S 02-245-3138
GILBERT FOODS LLC
HEARN-KIRKWOOD
7251 Standard Dr, Hanover, MD 21076-1322
Tel (410) 712-6000 *Founded/Ownrshp* 1974
Sales 102.2MM^E *EMP* 148
SIC 5148 5147 5146 5142 Fruits, fresh; Vegetables, fresh; Meats, fresh; Seafoods; Packaged frozen goods; Fish, frozen: packaged; Meat, frozen: packaged; Fruits, fresh; Vegetables, fresh; Meats, fresh; Seafoods; Packaged frozen goods; Fish, frozen: packaged; Meat, frozen: packaged
Pr: Charles Gilbert
**Treas:* Patricia McCawley
Opers Mgr: Fred Taylor

D-U-N-S 83-319-3824
GILBERT GLOBAL EQUITY CAPITAL LLC
767 5th Ave Fl 15, New York, NY 10153-0028
Tel (212) 584-6200 *Founded/Ownrshp* 1997
Sales 265.1MM^E *EMP* 600^E
SIC 8741 Financial management for business; Financial management for business
Mng Dir: Paul Wallace

D-U-N-S 36-357-3341
GILBERT HOSPITAL LLC
8020 E Palm Ln, Mesa, AZ 85207-9759
Tel (480) 984-2000 *Founded/Ownrshp* 2005
Sales 20.7MM^E *EMP* 250
SIC 8062 General medical & surgical hospitals; General medical & surgical hospitals
Pt: Dr Kim John

D-U-N-S 87-648-0885
GILBERT HOSPITAL LLC
5656 S Power Rd Ste 133, Gilbert, AZ 85295-8490
Tel (480) 984-2000 *Founded/Ownrshp* 2003
Sales 100.0MM *EMP* 250
SIC 8062 General medical & surgical hospitals; General medical & surgical hospitals
CEO: Bryan J Hargis
**CFO:* Dennis Rutherford
**Ch:* Bradley L Newswander
Dir Lab: Donald Dover
Chf Nrs Of: Carolyn Masood
Mktg Dir: Amy Jascourt
Nutrtnst: Kristen Thurmond
Doctor: Vincent Hernandez
Doctor: Tim Johns
Snr Mgr: Debbi Madvig
Snr Mgr: Zubair Tahir

D-U-N-S 78-056-4998
GILBERT INTERNATIONAL INC
1001 Ave Of The Americas, New York, NY 10018-5460
Tel (212) 628-5305 *Founded/Ownrshp* 1992
Sales 21.0MM *EMP* 231
SIC 7389 Brokers, business: buying & selling business enterprises; Brokers, business: buying & selling business enterprises
Pr: Kevin Gilbert

D-U-N-S 04-407-3047 IMP
GILBERT MARTIN WOODWORKING CO INC (CA)
MARTIN FURNITURE
2345 Britannia Blvd, San Diego, CA 92154-8313
Tel (619) 449-1009 *Founded/Ownrshp* 1980
Sales 46.8MM^E *EMP* 400
SIC 2517 2511 2521 Home entertainment unit cabinets, wood; Stereo cabinets, wood; Television cabinets, wood; Wood household furniture; Wood office furniture; Home entertainment unit cabinets, wood; Stereo cabinets, wood; Television cabinets, wood; Wood household furniture; Wood office furniture
Pr: Gilbert Martin
**VP:* Mark Mitchell
VP: Mike Starkey

D-U-N-S 11-745-4173
GILBERT MAY INC
PHILLIPS/MAY
4861 Sharp St, Dallas, TX 75247-6617
Tel (214) 631-3331 *Founded/Ownrshp* 1990
Sales 63.0MM *EMP* 124
Accts Denke Cpa Pc Fort Worth Tx
SIC 1542 Commercial & office building contractors; Commercial & office building contractors
Pr: Gilbert May
VP: Christopher Escobedo
Sfty Dirs: Robert Baldivia
Sfty Mgr: Alex Mendoza

Ql Cn Mgr: Kendal Allman
Ql Cn Mgr: Alejandro Rivera

D-U-N-S 13-239-7394
GILBERT MECHANICAL CONTRACTORS INC
4451 W 76th St, Edina, MN 55435-5111
Tel (952) 835-3810 *Founded/Ownrshp* 2002
Sales 39.5MM *EMP* 145
Accts Cliftonlarsonallen Llp Minnea
SIC 1711 1731 Warm air heating & air conditioning contractor; Plumbing contractors; Fire sprinkler system installation; Mechanical contractor; General electrical contractor; Warm air heating & air conditioning contractor; Plumbing contractors; Fire sprinkler system installation; Mechanical contractor; General electrical contractor
CEO: P Dan Gilbert
**CFO:* Robyn Bitz
**VP:* Ed Dahlgren
**VP:* John Gorman
Genl Mgr: Dave Deshler
IT Man: Lynn Patch

GILBERT TEXAS CONSTRUCTION
See KIEWIT TEXAS CONSTRUCTION LP

D-U-N-S 09-365-6569
GILBERT UNIFIED SCHOOL DISTRICT 41
140 S Gilbert Rd, Gilbert, AZ 85296-1016
Tel (480) 497-3452 *Founded/Ownrshp* 1920
Sales 207.4MM^E *EMP* 4,800
SIC 8211 Public elementary school; Public junior high school; Public senior high school; Public elementary school; Public junior high school; Public senior high school
Dir Sec: Aziz Bukhari
Pr Dir: Irene Mahoney-Paige
Psych: Cara Albaugh
HC Dir: Lori Miller

GILBERT/K & M ELEC SYSTEMS DIV
See MINING CONTROLS LLC

D-U-N-S 17-419-6121
GILBERTON POWER CO A PARTNERSHIP
(*Suby of* NORTHERN STAR GENERATION SERVICES LLC) ★
81 Eleanor Ave Ofc, Frackville, PA 17931-2345
Tel (570) 874-4119 *Founded/Ownrshp* 2004
Sales 37.3MM^E *EMP* 42
SIC 4911 Generation, electric power
Genl Mgr: John Hart
Opers Mgr: Mark Fedorshak

D-U-N-S 00-324-0608
GILBERTSON RESTAURANTS LLC
BURGER KING
5812 Trailridge Dr, Parkville, MO 64152-6065
Tel (816) 505-9344 *Founded/Ownrshp* 1996
Sales 9.5MM^E *EMP* 400
SIC 5812 Fast-food restaurant, chain; Fast-food restaurant, chain

D-U-N-S 01-165-7712
■ **GILCHRIST & SOAMES HOLDINGS CORP**
(*Suby of* GUEST SUPPLY SERVICES) ★
2425 E Perry Rd, Plainfield, IN 46168-7620
Tel (317) 786-8286 *Founded/Ownrshp* 2007, 2015
Sales 27.2MM^E *EMP* 105^E
SIC 5999 Toiletries, cosmetics & perfumes
CEO: Kathie De Voe

D-U-N-S 05-268-3856 IMP/EXP
■ **GILCHRIST & SOAMES INC**
(*Suby of* GILCHRIST & SOAMES HOLDINGS CORP) ★
2425 E Perry Rd Ste 150, Plainfield, IN 46168-7620
Tel (317) 786-8286 *Founded/Ownrshp* 1988, 2015
Sales 27.2MM^E *EMP* 102^E
SIC 5699 Military goods & regalia
Pr: Cathy Devoe
COO: Josh Kirschbaum
Treas: Len Janssen
Ofcr: Karla Gosche
Ex VP: Brian Garrett
VP: Daniel Thomas
Genl Mgr: Robert Hunt
CTO: Kris Brenard
IT Man: Jason Pruett
VP Opers: Kurt Sendek
QC Dir: Christina Mavity

GILCHRIST AUTO CENTERS
See GILCHRIST CHEVROLET INC

D-U-N-S 00-895-8464
GILCHRIST CHEVROLET INC
GILCHRIST AUTO CENTERS
6030 South Tacoma Way, Tacoma, WA 98409-4124
Tel (253) 472-3311 *Founded/Ownrshp* 1988
Sales 31.3MM^E *EMP* 88
SIC 5511 5012 Automobiles, new & used; Trucks, commercial; Automobiles, new & used; Trucks, commercial
Pr: Gary Gilchrist
Sales Asso: David Shubladze
Board of Directors: John L Gilchrist Sr

D-U-N-S 06-264-0347
GILCHRIST CONSTRUCTION CO LLC
5709 New York Ave, Alexandria, LA 71302-2824
Tel (318) 448-3565 *Founded/Ownrshp* 1972, 1981
Sales 158.5MM^E *EMP* 700
SIC 1611 1771 Concrete construction: roads, highways, sidewalks, etc.; Concrete work; Concrete construction: roads, highways, sidewalks, etc.; Concrete work
Pr: David R Gilchrist
CFO: Michael Latiolais
VP: Shane Carter
Dir IT: Jason Mulea
Sfty Dirs: Kevin Grage

D-U-N-S 10-001-2798
GILCHRIST COUNTY SCHOOL DISTRICT
310 Nw 11th Ave, Trenton, FL 32693-3804
Tel (352) 463-3200 *Founded/Ownrshp* 1927
Sales 23.6MM^E *EMP* 400
SIC 8211 Public elementary & secondary schools; Public elementary & secondary schools
**V Ch Bd:* Robert Clemons
IT Man: Sam Hall
Schl Brd P: Julie Thomas

D-U-N-S 83-031-6308
GILCHRIST HOSPICE CARE INC
(*Suby of* GREATER BALTIMORE MEDICAL CENTER INC) ★
11311 Mccormick Rd # 350, Hunt Valley, MD 21031-8618
Tel (443) 849-8200 *Founded/Ownrshp* 1993
Sales 48.6MM *EMP* 99^E
Accts Deloitte Tax Llp Mclean Va
SIC 8051 Skilled nursing care facilities; Skilled nursing care facilities
Dir Vol: Patti Holbrook
**COO:* Catherine Hamel
Dir Bus: Anne Evans

D-U-N-S 01-279-7665
GILCREASE & PARTNERS LLC
8620 N New Braunfels Ave, San Antonio, TX 78217-6382
Tel (210) 824-0500 *Founded/Ownrshp* 2007
Sales 25.0MM *EMP* 165
SIC 8742 Business consultant; Business consultant
VP: Mark Pickering

D-U-N-S 00-798-8298
GILCREST/JEWETT LUMBER CO (IA)
PLUM BUILDING SYSTEMS
1100 Se Alices Rd, Waukee, IA 50263-9669
Tel (515) 987-3600 *Founded/Ownrshp* 1856
Sales 40.9MM^E *EMP* 220
SIC 5211 5713

D-U-N-S 09-622-7959 IMP
GILDAN ACTIVEWEAR (EDEN) INC (NC)
(*Suby of* LES VETEMENTS DE SPORT GILDAN INC)
602 E Meadow Rd, Eden, NC 27288-3426
Tel (336) 623-9555 *Founded/Ownrshp* 1985, 1998
Sales 79.8MM^E *EMP* 160
SIC 5136 5311 Men's & boys' clothing; Department stores; Department stores, non-discount; Men's & boys' clothing; Department stores; Department stores, non-discount
Pr: Glenn Chamandry
**CFO:* Laurence G Sellyn
Ofcr: Mark Juba
Sr VP: Anthony Corsano
Sr VP: Dave Gardner
Sr VP: Jonathan Roiter
Sr VP: Chuck Ward
Sr VP: Linda Weiss
VP: Jason Fragapane
VP: Alfredo Silva
Plng Mgr: Tony Kiser

D-U-N-S 87-906-8120
GILDAN APPAREL USA INC
(*Suby of* ANVIL HOLDINGS INC) ★
48 W 38th St Fl 8, New York, NY 10018-0043
Tel (212) 476-0341 *Founded/Ownrshp* 1995
Sales 715.1MM^E *EMP* 5,000
SIC 5137 2331 Women's & children's clothing; Women's & misses' blouses & shirts; Women's & children's clothing; Women's & misses' blouses & shirts
Ch Bd: Anthony Corsano
Ex VP: Jacob Hollander
Ex VP: Heather Stefani
VP: Chris Binnicker
VP: J Goldberg
VP: Ellen Singer
Ql Cn Mgr: Claudia Montenegro

D-U-N-S 78-744-7791 IMP
GILDAN USA INC
(*Suby of* GILDAN DELAWARE INC.)
1980 Clements Ferry Rd, Charleston, SC 29492-7723
Tel (843) 849-6191 *Founded/Ownrshp* 2007
Sales 375.7MM^E *EMP* 1,500^E
SIC 2252 2254 Socks; Underwear, knit; Socks; Underwear, knit
Pr: Michael Hoffman
VP: Luis Brito
VP: Alvaro Cereceda
VP: Ron Davis
**VP:* Doug Leroy
VP: Shannon Preston
VP: David Voizard
Dir Lab: Raymond Ratelle
Dir Sec: Ricardo Zavala
QA Dir: Kenia Martinez
Dir IT: Rafael Orellana

D-U-N-S 05-047-5029
GILDER GAGNON HOWE & CO LLC
3 Columbus Cir, New York, NY 10019-8760
Tel (212) 765-2500 *Founded/Ownrshp* 1968
Sales 26.5MM^E *EMP* 90
SIC 6211 Stock brokers & dealers; Stock brokers & dealers
Netwrk Mgr: Shafqat Ali

D-U-N-S 78-030-8404
GILEAD GROUP LLC
12444 Powerscort Dr # 375, Saint Louis, MO 63131-3630
Tel (314) 821-2500 *Founded/Ownrshp* 2003
Sales 15.0MM *EMP* 350
SIC 6722 Management investment, open-end; Management investment, open-end
VP: Diane Kopitsky
Mng Dir: Dave Barford

D-U-N-S 18-504-9848 IMP
▲ **GILEAD SCIENCES INC**
333 Lakeside Dr, Foster City, CA 94404-1147
Tel (650) 574-3000 *Founded/Ownrshp* 1987
Sales 24.8MMM *EMP* 6,100
Tkr Sym GILD *Exch* NGS
SIC 2836 Biological products, except diagnostic; Biological products, except diagnostic
Ch Bd: John C Martin
Pr: John F Milligan
CFO: Maggie Levy
CFO: Robin Washington
CFO: Robin L Washington
Ex VP: Gregg H Alton
Ex VP: Norbert Bischofberge
Ex VP: Norbert W Bischofberger
Ex VP: Paul R Carter
Ex VP: Andrew Cheng
Ex VP: William Lee
Ex VP: John G McHutchison
Ex VP: John McHutchison
Ex VP: Taiyin Yang
Sr VP: Philippe C Bishop
Sr VP: Crispin G S Eley
Sr VP: Michael K Inouye
Sr VP: Muzammil M Mansuri
Sr VP: John G McHutchison
Sr VP: A Bruce Montgomery
Sr VP: Nicole Onetto
Board of Directors: John F Cogan, Etienne F Davignon, Carla A Hills, Kevin E Lofton, John W Madigan, Nicholas G Moore, Per Wold-Olsen, Richard J Whitley, Gayle E Wilson

D-U-N-S 00-791-0417 IMP/EXP
GILES & RANSOME INC (PA)
RANSOME ENGINE POWER
2975 Galloway Rd, Bensalem, PA 19020-2399
Tel (215) 639-4300 *Founded/Ownrshp* 1916, 1946
Sales 174.1MM^E *EMP* 540
SIC 5082 5084 7353

D-U-N-S 06-468-7387
GILES AUTOMOTIVE INC
NISSAN OF OPELOUSAS
(*Suby of* GILES AUTOMOTIVE GROUP, INC)
6137 Johnston St, Lafayette, LA 70503-5618
Tel (337) 988-1920 *Founded/Ownrshp* 1998
Sales 63.9MM^E *EMP* 140
SIC 5511

D-U-N-S 06-812-6465
GILES CARILION COMMUNITY HOSPITAL (VA)
CARILLION GILES COMMUNITY HOSP
159 Hartley Way, Pearisburg, VA 24134-2471
Tel (540) 921-6000 *Founded/Ownrshp* 1949
Sales 26.2MM *EMP* 212
SIC 8062 General medical & surgical hospitals; General medical & surgical hospitals
Pr: James A Hartley
**Pr:* James A Harltey
**CEO:* James Tyler
**Treas:* Harlond Chafin
Pharmcst: Leland Lacy

D-U-N-S 82-599-1425
GILES CHEMICAL INDUSTRIES INC
SALTEX
102 Commerce St, Waynesville, NC 28786-5739
Tel (828) 452-4784 *Founded/Ownrshp* 1993
Sales 25.0MM *EMP* 9
SIC 8742 Marketing consulting services; Marketing consulting services
Pr: Richard Wrenn

D-U-N-S 83-321-9624
GILES COUNTY BOARD OF EDUCATION
270 Richland Dr, Pulaski, TN 38478-2616
Tel (931) 363-4558 *Founded/Ownrshp* 2012
Sales NA *EMP* 650
SIC 9411 County supervisor of education, except school board; ; County supervisor of education, except school board;
Prin: Beth Moore
Dir IT: Andy Chunn

GILES COUNTY BOARD SUPERVISORS
See COUNTY OF GILES

D-U-N-S 07-979-8803
GILES COUNTY PUBLIC SCHOOLS
151 School Rd, Pearisburg, VA 24134-2134
Tel (540) 921-1421 *Founded/Ownrshp* 2015
Sales 6.8MM^E *EMP* 363^E
SIC 8211 Public elementary & secondary schools
MIS Dir: Trisha Young
HC Dir: Mary Henderson

D-U-N-S 08-888-1594
GILES ENGINEERING ASSOCIATES INC
N8 W2235 Johns Dr Ste A, Waukesha, WI 53186
Tel (262) 544-0118 *Founded/Ownrshp* 1976
Sales 25.2MM^E *EMP* 145
SIC 8711 8734 Consulting engineer; Building construction consultant; Testing laboratories; Consulting engineer; Building construction consultant; Testing laboratories
Pr: Terry Giles
**Sec:* Joyce Giles
**VP:* Patrick Reuteman
Brnch Mgr: Darryl Keating

D-U-N-S 04-647-3948 IMP
GILES ENTERPRISES INC
GILES FOOD SERVICE EQUIPMENT
2750 Gunter Park Dr W, Montgomery, AL 36109-1098
Tel (334) 272-1457 *Founded/Ownrshp* 2009
Sales 25.7MM *EMP* 87
SIC 3589 Commercial cooking & foodwarming equipment; Commercial cooking & foodwarming equipment
Pr: David Byrd
**VP:* Sandra Passmore
Sls&Mrk Ex: Phil Coleman
Manager: Craig Comstock

GILES FOOD SERVICE EQUIPMENT
See GILES ENTERPRISES INC

D-U-N-S 00-636-7296
■ **GILES INDUSTRIES OF TAZEWELL INC**
(*Suby of* SOUTHERN ENERGY HOMES INC) ★
405 S Broad St, New Tazewell, TN 37825-7243
Tel (423) 626-7243 *Founded/Ownrshp* 1959, 2006
Sales 28.4MM^E *EMP* 300^E
SIC 2451 Mobile homes; Mobile homes
Pr: Alan Neely
Treas: Dorothy Neely
Sfty Mgr: Jim Turnblazer
Sls Mgr: Mike Comparato
Sls Mgr: Rex Richey

D-U-N-S 62-225-0181 IMP
GILFORD CORP
3001 Hamburg Pike, Jeffersonville, IN 47130-6724
Tel (812) 288-7900 *Founded/Ownrshp* 1991
Sales 25.1MM^E *EMP* 50
SIC 5131 5198 Upholstery fabrics, woven; Wallcoverings
Pr: Dennis Cook
**VP:* Scott Shanks
**VP:* Richard Wallingford
IT Man: Rick Bloom
IT Man: Shawn Frazier
S&M/VP: Rob Purkins
Manager: David Cullen
Manager: Jodie Doyle
Sls Mgr: Mike Brammer
Sls Mgr: Jim Croy
Sls Mgr: George Hammond

D-U-N-S 09-949-3512
GILFORD SECURITIES INC
750 3rd Ave Fl 9, New York, NY 10017-2718
Tel (212) 888-6400 *Founded/Ownrshp* 1979
Sales 34.6MM^E *EMP* 160
Accts Freedman & Co Cpa Pc New Yor
SIC 6211 Brokers, security; Dealers, security; Brokers, security; Dealers, security
Ch Bd: Ralph Worthington
CFO: Bonnie Sachs
Sr VP: Bob Baisch
Sr VP: Joseph Bialoglaw
Sr VP: Stephen Collins
Sr VP: Harvey Silvester
Sr VP: Joseph Sullivan
Sr VP: Robert V Tango
Sr VP: George Walsh
VP: Stanley Bartels
VP: Otis Bradley
VP: David Kaplan
**VP:* Lucinda Morrisey
VP: Robert Nyilas
VP: E Howard Perkins
VP: Madeline Rutinel

GILL ATHLETICS
See LITANIA SPORTS GROUP INC

D-U-N-S 00-601-8311 IMP
GILL CORP
GR SPRING & STAMPING, INC.
(*Suby of* GILL HOLDING CO INC.) ★
706 Bond Ave Nw, Grand Rapids, MI 49503-1434
Tel (859) 625-5284 *Founded/Ownrshp* 2014
Sales 128.9MM^E *EMP* 340
SIC 3469 3312 3495 3493 3496 3465 Metal stampings; Tool & die steel; Wire springs; Steel springs, except wire; Miscellaneous fabricated wire products; Automotive stampings; Metal stampings; Tool & die steel; Wire springs; Steel springs, except wire; Miscellaneous fabricated wire products; Automotive stampings
Pr: James J Zawacki
**Treas:* Ted Hohman
Prgrm Mgr: Dave Monterusso
Ql Cn Mgr: Chriss Niceley
Sls Mgr: Tom Gunn

D-U-N-S 00-831-7422 EXP
GILL CORP
4056 Easy St, El Monte, CA 91731-1054
Tel (626) 443-6094 *Founded/Ownrshp* 1945
Sales 217.1MM *EMP* 475
Accts Bdo Usa Llp
SIC 3089 Laminating of plastic; Panels, building: plastic; Laminating of plastic; Panels, building: plastic
Pr: Stephen E Gill
**CFO:* Bill Heinze
**VP:* Irv Freund
Ql Cn Mgr: Gene Schreiner
Board of Directors: Linda Gill, Nancy Gill, Phillip Gill, Stephen Gill

GILL ENERGY
See CREATIVE MANAGEMENT INC

D-U-N-S 18-792-9146
GILL GROUP INC
TRIMARK GILL MARKETING
(*Suby of* TRIMARK UNITED EAST) ★
1904 W Parkside Ln # 100, Phoenix, AZ 85027-1228
Tel (602) 943-7700 *Founded/Ownrshp* 2007
Sales 70.0MM *EMP* 90
SIC 5046 Commercial cooking & food service equipment; Commercial cooking & food service equipment
Pr: Kimberley Gill-Rimsza
Sec: Anton E Rimsza
Sr Cor Off: Richard Hoel
VP: Laura Gill Jacobsen
Rgnl Mgr: Melanie Kerns
VP Sls: Craig Anderson

D-U-N-S 07-933-7831
GILL HOLDING CO INC
5271 Plainfield Ave Ne, Grand Rapids, MI 49525-1046
Tel (616) 559-2700 *Founded/Ownrshp* 2011
Sales 304.5MM^E *EMP* 1,500^E
SIC 3465 3544 Automotive stampings; Special dies & tools; Automotive stampings; Special dies & tools
CEO: Richard Perreault
CFO: J Timothy Gargaro

D-U-N-S 92-618-5349 IMP
GILL INDUSTRIES GEORGIA INC
(*Suby of* GILL INDUSTRIES INC) ★
505 N Industrial Blvd, Trenton, GA 30752-2233
Tel (706) 657-2130 *Founded/Ownrshp* 1995
Sales 26.2MM^E *EMP* 185
SIC 3469 Metal stampings; Metal stampings
Pr: Richard Perreault

D-U-N-S 00-640-9080 IMP
GILL INDUSTRIES INC
GILL MANUFACTURING CO.
(Suby of GILL HOLDING CO INC) ★
5271 Plainfield Ave Ne, Grand Rapids, MI 49525-1046
Tel (616) 559-2700 Founded/Ownrshp 1964
Sales 175.6MM^E EMP 700
SIC 3465 3544 Automotive stampings; Special dies & tools; Automotive stampings; Special dies & tools
CEO: Rita Williams
*Pr: Richard Perrault
Treas: Matthew Hale
*VP: Joe Gill
VP: Dimitri Moustakeas
*VP: Tom Popma
*VP: Charles Scholfield
*VP: Rita Woodruff
Prgrm Mgr: Craig Dedamos
Prgrm Mgr: Tony Graber
Prgrm Mgr: David-Peter Herczeg

GILL MANUFACTURING CO.
See GILL INDUSTRIES INC

D-U-N-S 06-869-4835
GILL ST BERNARDS SCHOOL
St Bernards Rd, Gladstone, NJ 07934
Tel (908) 234-1611 Founded/Ownrshp 1972
Sales 25.0MM EMP 100
SIC 8211 Private elementary & secondary schools; Private elementary & secondary schools
Prin: Sidney Rowell
IT Man: Ryan Roque

D-U-N-S 03-133-7231 EXP
GILL STUDIOS INC (KS)
GILL-LINE
10800 Lackman Rd, Shawnee Mission, KS 66219-1200
Tel (913) 888-4422 Founded/Ownrshp 1934
Sales 56.7MM^E EMP 441
SIC 2752 3993 2679

D-U-N-S 79-653-4688
GILL TRANSPORT LLC
1051 Pacific Ave, Oxnard, CA 93030-7254
Tel (805) 240-1979 Founded/Ownrshp 2005
Sales 21.4MM^E EMP 400
SIC 4213 Trucking, except local; Trucking, except local

GILL-LINE
See GILL STUDIOS INC

GILL-ROY'S HARDWARE
See R L MORGAN CO INC

D-U-N-S 00-282-8283
GILL-SIMPSON INC
2834 Loch Raven Rd, Baltimore, MD 21218-4220
Tel (410) 467-3335 Founded/Ownrshp 1932
Sales NA EMP 430
SIC 1731

GILLAND CHEVROLET PONTIAC GMC
See GILLAND PONTIAC-GMC TRUCK INC

D-U-N-S 19-457-9348
GILLAND PONTIAC-GMC TRUCK INC
GILLAND CHEVROLET PONTIAC GMC
3071 S Us Highway 231, Ozark, AL 36360-0855
Tel (334) 774-9030 Founded/Ownrshp 1991
Sales 24.8MM^E EMP 60
SIC 5511 Automobiles, new & used; Pickups, new & used; Vans, new & used; Automobiles, new & used; Pickups, new & used; Vans, new & used
Pr: John E Gilland
*Sec: Betty Gilland
*VP: Tim Gilland
Off Mgr: Faye Johnson

D-U-N-S 15-444-4152
GILLELAND CHEVROLET CADILLAC INC
ST CLOUD COLLISION CENTER
3019 W Division St, Saint Cloud, MN 56301-3832
Tel (320) 281-4290 Founded/Ownrshp 1986
Sales 74.5MM EMP 143
SIC 5511 5531 7538

D-U-N-S 04-146-9396
GILLETTE AIR CONDITIONING CO INC
1215 San Francisco, San Antonio, TX 78201-4639
Tel (210) 735-9235 Founded/Ownrshp 1959
Sales 47.0MM^E EMP 181
SIC 1711 Heating & air conditioning contractors; Warm air heating & air conditioning contractor; Ventilation & duct work contractor; Heating & air conditioning contractors; Warm air heating & air conditioning contractor; Ventilation & duct work contractor
Ch Bd: Vincent A Gillette Sr
*Pr: Vincent J Gillette Jr
*Treas: Sharon Walls
*VP: Thomas Gillette
Exec: Kevin Hays
DP Exec: Maureen Elyea

D-U-N-S 03-733-5882
GILLETTE CHILDRENS SPECIALTY HEALTHCARE
200 University Ave E, Saint Paul, MN 55101-2507
Tel (651) 291-2848 Founded/Ownrshp 1898
Sales 208.0MM EMP 623
SIC 8069 Children's hospital; Children's hospital
Pr: Margaret Perryman
*CFO: James Haddican
*VP: Jon Galloway
*VP: Christine Milbrath
*VP: Kathryn Wardrop
IT Man: Colette Salmonowicz
Surgeon: Robert Acton
Surgeon: Arnold Leonard
Surgeon: Robert Rich
Surgeon: Daniel Saltzman
Doctor: Thomas Rieser

GILLETTE CHLDRN SPCLTY HLTH
See PEDIATRIC RHEUMATOLOGY

D-U-N-S 00-102-5931
■ **GILLETTE CO**
(Suby of PROCTER & GAMBLE CO) ★
1 Gillette Park, Boston, MA 02127-1096
Tel (617) 463-3000 Founded/Ownrshp 1901
Sales 4.4MMM^E EMP 28,700
SIC 3421 3691 3634 2844 3951 2899 Razor blades & razors; Storage batteries; Alkaline cell storage batteries; Electric housewares & fans; Razors, electric; Food mixers, electric: household; Toilet preparations; Cosmetic preparations; Pens & mechanical pencils; Ball point pens & parts; Fountain pens & fountain pen desk sets; Pencils & pencil parts, mechanical; Correction fluid; Razor blades & razors; Storage batteries; Alkaline cell storage batteries; Electric housewares & fans; Razors, electric; Food mixers, electric: household; Toilet preparations; Cosmetic preparations; Pens & mechanical pencils; Ball point pens & parts; Fountain pens & fountain pen desk sets; Pencils & pencil parts, mechanical; Correction fluid
Pr: Edward F Degraan
*Pr: Mark M Leckie
*Treas: Gail Sullivan
VP: Kara Baker
VP: Cathleen J Chizauskas
*VP: Terry Overbey
Opers Mgr: Tim Wilde
Plnt Mgr: Mar Arsenault
Ql Cn Mgr: Dan Labelle
Mktg Dir: Brenda Bynarowicz
Snr Mgr: Mark Cerce

GILLETTE CREAMERY
See PHYLJOHN DISTRIBUTORS INC

D-U-N-S 95-866-1654
■ **GILLETTE DE PUERTO RICO INC**
(Suby of GILLETTE CO) ★
Metro Office Park Ste 3, Guaynabo, PR 00968-1704
Tel (787) 706-4800 Founded/Ownrshp 1959
Sales 60.0MM EMP 75
Accts Kpmg Llp San Juan Pr
SIC 5122

D-U-N-S 08-654-6496
GILLIARD HEALTH SERVICES INC
EVERGREEN MEDICAL CENTER
3091 Carter Hill Rd, Montgomery, AL 36111-1801
Tel (334) 265-5009 Founded/Ownrshp 1977
Sales 41.1MM^E EMP 309
SIC 8062 General medical & surgical hospitals; General medical & surgical hospitals
Pr: William G McKenzie

D-U-N-S 13-081-9535
GILLIATTE GENERAL CONTRACTORS INC
2515 Bloyd Ave, Indianapolis, IN 46218-3666
Tel (317) 638-3355 Founded/Ownrshp 1985
Sales 21.8MM^E EMP 40
SIC 1542 Commercial & office building, new construction
Pr: Thomas J Ritman
*Treas: Brenda S Wagoner
Treas: Nala Wolfe
*VP: Adam W Gilliate
VP: Adam Gilliatte
*VP: Jacob A Gilliatte
VP: Travis McIntyre
Off Mgr: Diane Willsey
Sfty Mgr: Mark Bowling
Snr Mgr: Howard Dugan

D-U-N-S 02-603-1765
GILLIE HYDE FORD LINCOLN INC
610 Happy Valley Rd, Glasgow, KY 42141-1500
Tel (270) 651-2125 Founded/Ownrshp 1983
Sales 26.6MM^E EMP 60^E
SIC 5511 Automobiles, new & used; Automobiles, new & used
Pr: Michael Hyde
*Sec: Anne Hyde
Genl Mgr: Wes Gentry
Genl Mgr: Ruben Kinslow
Off Mgr: Stephanie Logsdon
Sales Exec: Ray Bradley
Mktg Dir: Alex Patterson
Sls Mgr: Michael Campbell
Sls Mgr: Ronnie Wilson

D-U-N-S 06-655-7182 IMP
GILLIG LLC
(Suby of CC INDUSTRIES) ★
25800 Clawiter Rd, Hayward, CA 94545-3213
Tel (510) 785-1500 Founded/Ownrshp 2008
Sales 186.8MM^E EMP 700^E
SIC 3713 Truck & bus bodies; Truck & bus bodies
Pr: Dennis Howard
Pr: Jerry Sheehan
VP: Stephen Bender
VP: Chris Turner
Area Mgr: Dan Pereira
Div Mgr: Steve Davis
MIS Dir: Chuck Smith
IT Man: Jeri Ward
Mtls Mgr: Richard Dykes
Plnt Mgr: Javier Hernandez
Sls&Mrk Ex: Steve Hasson

GILLMAN CONSTRUCTION
See GILLMAN INC

GILLMAN HONDA
See GILLMAN INC

GILLMAN HONDA
See GILLMAN IMPORTS OF AUSTIN INC

GILLMAN HONDA OF SAN ANTONIO
See GILLMAN OF SAN ANTONIO INC

D-U-N-S 62-759-9996
GILLMAN IMPORTS OF AUSTIN INC
GILLMAN HONDA
16044 Interstate 35 N, Selma, TX 78154-1208
Tel (210) 651-5533 Founded/Ownrshp 1990
Sales 31.1MM^E EMP 137
SIC 5511 Automobiles, new & used; Automobiles, new & used
Pr: Ramsay H Gillman

*VP: Jason Gillman
VP: Stacey G Wimbish

D-U-N-S 00-448-2584
GILLMAN INC
GILLMAN CONSTRUCTION
271 State Road 129 S, Batesville, IN 47006-7104
Tel (812) 934-4140 Founded/Ownrshp 1953
Sales 36.4MM^E EMP 150
SIC 5251 5211 Hardware; Lumber & other building materials
Pr: Gillman Charles
Store Mgr: Keith Hart

D-U-N-S 13-233-1455
GILLMAN INC
GILLMAN HONDA
(Suby of GILLMAN INTERESTS INC) ★
10575 W Sam Huston Pkwy S, Houston, TX 77099-2844
Tel (713) 776-7020 Founded/Ownrshp 1982
Sales 66.1MM^E EMP 152
SIC 5511 Automobiles, new & used; Automobiles, new & used
Pr: Stacey Gillman Wimbish
*Ch Bd: Ramsay H Gillman
*COO: Patrick York
*CFO: Bart McAndrews
*Ex VP: Christopher R Gillman
VP: Barton Gillman

D-U-N-S 17-373-1647
GILLMAN INTERESTS INC
10595 W Sam Huston Pkwy S, Houston, TX 77099-2844
Tel (713) 776-7000 Founded/Ownrshp 1980
Sales 121.7MM^E EMP 450
SIC 5511 Automobiles, new & used; Pickups, new & used; Automobiles, new & used; Pickups, new & used
Pr: Ramsay H Gillman
*Ofcr: Bart Andrews

D-U-N-S 13-932-3356
GILLMAN OF SAN ANTONIO INC
GILLMAN HONDA OF SAN ANTONIO
10595 W Sam Huston Pkwy S, Houston, TX 77099-2844
Tel (713) 776-7000 Founded/Ownrshp 1984
Sales 20.4MM^E EMP 80
SIC 5511 Automobiles, new & used; Automobiles, new & used
Pr: Ramsay H Gillman
VP: Stacey G Wimbish

D-U-N-S 06-337-8101
GILLMANN SERVICES INC
11848 Rock Landing Dr # 102, Newport News, VA 23606-4425
Tel (757) 873-0527 Founded/Ownrshp 2007
Sales 13.0MM EMP 350^E
SIC 7363 Employee leasing service; Employee leasing service
Pr: Jeff Mann
*COO: Brian Gillespie
Brnch Mgr: Brian Dayton
Genl Mgr: David Gillespie

D-U-N-S 02-738-2589
GILLOTA INC
415 E Hines Hill Rd, Hudson, OH 44236-1119
Tel (330) 656-2158 Founded/Ownrshp 1978
Sales 21.6MM^E EMP 24
SIC 5172 5983 Petroleum products; Fuel oil dealers
Pr: John L Gillota Sr
*Pr: John L Gillota Jr

D-U-N-S 82-737-8928 IMP
GILLS ONIONS LLC
1051 Pacific Ave, Oxnard, CA 93030-7254
Tel (805) 240-1983 Founded/Ownrshp 1983
Sales 24.6MM^E EMP 55
SIC 0161 Onion farm
Ql Cn Mgr: Carson Ludwig
Ql Cn Mgr: Nivia Santiago
Manager: Teri Trost

GILMAN BUILDING PRODUCTS
See FITZGERALD LLC

GILMAN BUILDING PRODUCTS
See BLACKSHEAR LLC

GILMAN BUILDING PRODUCTS
See MAXVILLE LLC

D-U-N-S 12-297-3741
GILMAN BUILDING PRODUCTS LLC
2500 Saint Marys Rd, Saint Marys, GA 31558-4141
Tel (912) 576-0300 Founded/Ownrshp 1999
Sales 237.5MM EMP 788
Accts Pricewaterhousecoopers Llp At
SIC 2421 Building & structural materials, wood; Building & structural materials, wood
Pr: Victor Garrett
*VP: Daniel Kurtz
VP Mfg: Victor Garnett

D-U-N-S 00-608-6599
GILMAN CHEESE CORP (WI)
300 S Riverside Dr, Gilman, WI 54433-9300
Tel (715) 447-8241 Founded/Ownrshp 1946, 2000
Sales 33.3MM EMP 100
SIC 2022 Processed cheese; Processed cheese
Pr: Thomas P Hand

D-U-N-S 10-826-6966
■ **GILMAN CIOCIA INC**
(Suby of NATIONAL HOLDINGS CORP) ★
11 Raymond Ave, Poughkeepsie, NY 12603-2349
Tel (888) 673-0402 Founded/Ownrshp 2013
Sales 67.8MM^E EMP 139^E
Tkr Sym GTAX Exch OTO
SIC 8742 7291 6163 Financial consultant; Tax return preparation services; Mortgage brokers arranging for loans, using money of others; Financial consultant; Tax return preparation services; Mortgage brokers arranging for loans, using money of others

Pr: Michael Ryan
*Ch: James Ciocia
*Treas: Maureen Abbate
VP: Daniel Bengio
*VP: Ted Finkelstein
Exec: Timothy Bodner
Exec: Gerald Hoenigs
Mktg Mgr: Samantha Santana

D-U-N-S 07-492-7807
GILMAN SCHOOL INC
5407 Roland Ave Ste 1, Baltimore, MD 21210-1990
Tel (410) 323-3800 Founded/Ownrshp 1897
Sales 39.5MM EMP 230
SIC 8211

GILMER CO SCHOOL DISTRICT
See GILMER COUNTY BOARD OF EDUCATION

D-U-N-S 00-819-0340
GILMER COUNTY BOARD OF EDUCATION
201 N Court St Rm 201, Glenville, WV 26351-1273
Tel (304) 462-7386 Founded/Ownrshp 1965
Sales 16.3MM^E EMP 310
SIC 8211 Public elementary & secondary schools; Public elementary & secondary schools
Ch Bd: Dorothy Rhodes

D-U-N-S 10-001-3754
GILMER COUNTY BOARD OF EDUCATION
GILMER CO SCHOOL DISTRICT
134 Industrial Blvd, Ellijay, GA 30540-3713
Tel (706) 276-5000 Founded/Ownrshp 1945
Sales 32.5MM^E EMP 695
SIC 8211 Public elementary & secondary schools; Public elementary & secondary schools
CFO: Julie Swindle
Exec: Jim Parmer
Schl Brd P: James Waters
HC Dir: Mary Fuller

D-U-N-S 07-979-9705
GILMER COUNTY CHARTER SCHOOLS
134 Industrial Blvd, Ellijay, GA 30540-3713
Tel (706) 276-5000 Founded/Ownrshp 2015
Sales 17.0MM^E EMP 480^E
SIC 8211 Public elementary & secondary schools

D-U-N-S 01-059-7045
GILMER INDEPENDENT SCHOOL DISTRICT (INC)
500 S Trinity St, Gilmer, TX 75644-2536
Tel (903) 841-7400 Founded/Ownrshp 1880
Sales 18.4MM^E EMP 365
SIC 8211 Public elementary & secondary schools; Public elementary & secondary schools
*Prin: Joni Elms
Schl Brd P: Jeff Rash
Schl Brd P: Todd Tefteller

D-U-N-S 02-335-2060 IMP
GILMER WAREHOUSE & LOGISTICS LLC
801 Valley Dr, Perry, GA 31069-2432
Tel (478) 987-1516 Founded/Ownrshp 1997
Sales 25.9MM^E EMP 60^E
SIC 1541 Industrial buildings & warehouses; Paper/pulp mill construction

GILMORE & ASSOCIATES
See D GILMORE ROBERT & ASSOCIATES INC

D-U-N-S 00-695-9936
GILMORE BROTHERS INC
210 Farmers Aly, Kalamazoo, MI 49007-4854
Tel (616) 345-3541 Founded/Ownrshp 1881
Sales 14.9MM^E EMP 350
SIC 5311 5632 5611 5621 Department stores, non-discount; Women's accessory & specialty stores; Men's & boys' clothing stores; Women's clothing stores
Pr: Stephen Phillips
*Ch Bd: Martha G Parfet
CFO: James Hallan
CFO: James Walsh
*Treas: Ray T Parfet Jr
Treas: Larry Sherman
Bd of Dir: Larry Mullins
Ex VP: Jean Sarasin
VP: Kathy Breyfogle
VP: Jim Fiebig
VP: Stacey Davis Furgaso
VP: Dorothy A Lierman
VP: John Mayleben
VP: Joseph McCurry
VP: Tom Scott
VP: Barb Tronstein

D-U-N-S 80-014-7027
GILMORE HEALTH SYSTEM INC
GILMORE MEMORIAL HOSPITAL
1105 Earl Frye Blvd, Amory, MS 38821-5500
Tel (662) 256-7111 Founded/Ownrshp 1992
Sales 1.9M EMP 500
SIC 8741 6552 Hospital management; Subdividers & developers; Hospital management; Subdividers & developers
CEO: Danny Spreitler
Dir Lab: Thomas Gann
Dir Lab: Jerry Walden
*Prin: Danny Speitler
Off Mgr: Lee Frans
CIO: Jeff Wideman
Mktg Dir: Lorie Bryant

GILMORE MEMORIAL HOSPITAL
See GILMORE HEALTH SYSTEM INC

D-U-N-S 00-809-7602 IMP
GILMORE VALVE CO
PROSERV - GILMORE VALVE
1231 Lumpkin Rd, Houston, TX 77043-4101
Tel (713) 468-8778 Founded/Ownrshp 2006
Sales 40.0MM EMP 90^E
SIC 3491 3494 3492

D-U-N-S 07-674-9399
GILMOUR ACADEMY INC
34001 Cedar Rd, Gates Mills, OH 44040-9356
Tel (440) 442-1104 Founded/Ownrshp 1946

Sales 21.4MM^E *EMP* 150
SIC 8211 Preparatory school
**CFO:* Kelly Carney
Ofcr: Amy Boyle
Ofcr: Kathleen Kenny
Ex Dir: John Young
Info Man: Greg Nagle

GILPIN HOTEL CASINO
See GILPIN VENTURES INC

D-U-N-S 79-922-4357
GILPIN VENTURES INC
GILPIN HOTEL CASINO
(*Suby of* BLACK HAWK GAMING & DEVELOPMENT CO INC) ★
111 Main St, Black Hawk, CO 80422
Tel (303) 582-1133 *Founded/Ownrshp* 1998
Sales 30.0MM *EMP* 250
SIC 7999 Gambling establishment; Gambling establishment
Pr: Steve Roark
**Treas:* Stan Politano
Genl Mgr: John East

D-U-N-S 06-069-8800
GILROY UNIFIED SCHOOL DISTRICT
7810 Arroyo Cir, Gilroy, CA 95020-7309
Tel (408) 847-2700 *Founded/Ownrshp* 1975
Sales 43.2MM^E *EMP* 424
SIC 8211 Public elementary & secondary schools; Public elementary & secondary schools
Trst: Rhoda Bress
MIS Dir: Kermit Schrock
IT Man: James Fletcher
Schl Brd P: Jaime Rosso
HC Dir: Cindy Spangler

GILSA DAIRY PRODUCTS
See LALA BRANDED PRODUCTS INC

D-U-N-S 07-194-6966
GILSBAR INC
2100 Covington Centre, Covington, LA 70433-2981
Tel (985) 892-3520 *Founded/Ownrshp* 1959
Sales NA *EMP* 330
SIC 6411 Insurance information & consulting services; Insurance brokers; Insurance information & consulting services; Insurance brokers
Pr: Henry J Miltenberger Jr
COO: Wendy King
**Chf Mktg O:* Douglas Layman
**VP:* Shelley P Lampard
Off Mgr: Rebecca Wright
CIO: Gene Knoblock
CTO: Chris Drake
CTO: Kingsley Skinner
DP Exec: Jeremy Welch
IT Man: John Cueva
IT Man: Anthony Moore

D-U-N-S 00-602-1166
GILSON GRAPHICS INC
NORTHSTAR TEACHERS RESOURCES
2000 Oak Industrial Dr Ne, Grand Rapids, MI 49505-6012
Tel (616) 459-4539 *Founded/Ownrshp* 1948
Sales 32.0MM^E *EMP* 165
SIC 2791 2752

D-U-N-S 00-610-6090
GILSON INC (WI)
3000 Parmenter St, Middleton, WI 53562-1617
Tel (608) 836-1551 *Founded/Ownrshp* 1947
Sales 59.8MM^E *EMP* 425
SIC 3826

GILSTER-MARY LEE
See MARY LEE PACKAGING CORP

D-U-N-S 05-774-4039 EXP
GILSTER-MARY LEE CORP
(*Suby of* GILSTER-MARY LEE) ★
1037 State St, Chester, IL 62233-1657
Tel (618) 826-2361 *Founded/Ownrshp* 1971
Sales 880.4MM^E *EMP* 4,200
SIC 2043 2098 2099 2045 3089 Cereal breakfast foods; Macaroni products (e.g. alphabets, rings & shells), dry; Popcorn, packaged: except already popped; Blended flour: from purchased flour; Plastic containers, except foam; Cereal breakfast foods; Macaroni products (e.g. alphabets, rings & shells), dry; Popcorn, packaged: except already popped; Blended flour: from purchased flour; Plastic containers, except foam
Pr: Donald E Welge
**Ex VP:* Michael W Welge
Sr VP: Sheldon Geitelman
**VP:* Delbert Dethrow
**VP:* Ron Tretter
**VP:* Tina Welcher
**VP:* Tom Welge
Genl Mgr: Timothy Petzolt
CIO: Stephanie Siegmund
QA Dir: Matt Keim
Sfty Mgr: Eric Asselmeier

D-U-N-S 00-188-5326
GILSTON ELECTRICAL CONTRACTING CORP
338 E 95th St, New York, NY 10128-5703
Tel (212) 410-7800 *Founded/Ownrshp* 1926
Sales 20.5MM^E *EMP* 95
Accts Nadell Franco Weinberger & Ass
SIC 1731 General electrical contractor
Ch Bd: Craig Gilston
**VP:* Richard Gilston
Off Mgr: Patty Fessmann
Snr Mgr: Stephen Yan

D-U-N-S 07-845-1336 IMP
GILT GROUPE HOLDINGS INC
GILT
2 Park Ave Fl 4, New York, NY 10016-5602
Tel (877) 445-8692 *Founded/Ownrshp* 2011
Sales 294.1MM^E *EMP* 1,200
SIC 5611 Clothing accessories: men's & boys'; Clothing accessories: men's & boys'
Ch: Kevin P Ryan
Pr: Andy Page
CEO: Michelle Peluso
COO: Tracey Weber
CFO: Tom Sansone
Ex VP: Jyothi RAO
Sr VP: Kristel Kearney
Prgrm Mgr: Dana Romano
Area Mgr: Jason Flener
Snr Sftwr: Mike Chimirev
Snr Sftwr: Peter Gram
Board of Directors: Adrianne Shapira

D-U-N-S 07-882-9080 IMP/EXP
GILT GROUPE INC
GILT MAN
(*Suby of* G I L T) ★
2 Park Ave Fl 4, New York, NY 10016-5602
Tel (646) 679-1656 *Founded/Ownrshp* 2012
Sales 293.9MM^E *EMP* 1,100
SIC 5961 ;
Ch Bd: Michelle Peluso
**COO:* Tracey Weber
**CFO:* Tom Sansone
**Chf Mktg O:* Clay Cowan
Chf Mktg O: Lizzie Francis
**Sr VP:* Jennifer Miller
VP: Brooke Cundiff
VP: Alex Ogof
VP: Anthony Lo Pinto
VP: Benjamin Singer
Creative D: Bradley Browder

GILT MAN
See GILT GROUPE INC

GILTNER LOGISTICS
See PROGRESSIVE LOGISTICS INC

D-U-N-S 80-820-3777
GILTNER LOGISTICS SERVICES INC
834 Falls Ave Ste 1250, Twin Falls, ID 83301-3364
Tel (208) 644-9090 *Founded/Ownrshp* 2007
Sales 32.2MM^E *EMP* 58^E
SIC 4213 Refrigerated products transport
Pr: Doug Blevins
Opers Mgr: Amanda Porter

D-U-N-S 04-486-3223
GILTON SOLID WASTE MANAGEMENT INC
755 S Yosemite Ave # 106, Oakdale, CA 95361-4991
Tel (209) 527-3781 *Founded/Ownrshp* 1961
Sales 36.4MM^E *EMP* 136
Accts Priest Amistadi Creedon Oakda
SIC 4953 Rubbish collection & disposal; Recycling, waste materials; Rubbish collection & disposal; Recycling, waste materials
Pr: Richard Gilton
**VP:* Tedford Gilton
**VP:* Karen Gilton Hardister
**VP:* Donna Gilton Love

D-U-N-S 00-894-4605
GILVIN-TERRILL LTD
CHOW, TIMOTHY
6000 Fm 2373, Claude, TX 79019-3638
Tel (806) 944-5200 *Founded/Ownrshp* 1947
Sales 32.7MM^E *EMP* 102^E
Accts Ault & Associates Amarillo T
SIC 1611 8711 Highway & street paving contractor; Consulting engineer
Pr: Tim C Chow
**Sec:* Elizabeth Dodson
**VP:* F C Raymond Chow
**VP:* Martha Chow

D-U-N-S 15-457-2374
GINCOP INC
GINNY'S PRINTING
(*Suby of* ONETOUCHPOINT CORP) ★
8410 Tuscany Way Ste B, Austin, TX 78754-4824
Tel (512) 454-6874 *Founded/Ownrshp* 2012
Sales 42.5MM^E *EMP* 235
SIC 2752 7334 2759 Commercial printing, offset; Photocopying & duplicating services; Commercial printing; Commercial printing, offset; Photocopying & duplicating services; Commercial printing
CEO: Michael Martin
**CFO:* Cheryl Degan
Off Mgr: Connie Hilburn
IT Man: Pat Rezabek
VP Sls: Larry Bolden
Snr Mgr: Erin Dessain

D-U-N-S 96-593-6466
GINDI MAIMONIDES ACADEMY
310 Huntley Dr, West Hollywood, CA 90048-1919
Tel (310) 659-2456 *Founded/Ownrshp* 2010
Sales 21.7MM *EMP* 11^E
Accts Magidov Cpa Los Angeles Ca
SIC 8211 Academy; Academy
Prin: Allan Enigy

GINGER COVE
See ANNAPOLIS LIFE CARE INC

GINGER-MAE FINANCIAL SERVICES
See GMFS LLC

GINN
See GOSPEL OF PEACE INC

D-U-N-S 36-420-6839
GINN GROUP INC
200 Westpark Dr Ste 100, Peachtree City, GA 30269-3527
Tel (404) 669-9214 *Founded/Ownrshp* 1997
Sales 25.0MM *EMP* 300
SIC 8742 Management consulting services; Management consulting services
CEO: James P Ginn
COO: Jerry Ginn
CFO: Michael J Reagan
Sr VP: Ron Packard
VP: Billy Greg

D-U-N-S 03-366-0986
GINN MOTOR CO
8153 Access Rd Nw, Covington, GA 30014-2099
Tel (770) 786-3421 *Founded/Ownrshp* 1922
Sales 44.9MM^E *EMP* 80
SIC 5511 5531 7538 Automobiles, new & used; Automotive parts; General automotive repair shops; Automobiles, new & used; Automotive parts; General automotive repair shops
Pr: William D Fortson Jr
**VP:* T Rucker Ginn
Mng Dir: Richard Carnes
Sales Exec: Scott Simmons
Sls Mgr: Phil Neal
Sales Asso: Lucy Cherry

GINNY'S PRINTING
See GINCOP INC

D-U-N-S 07-188-8440
GINO MORENA ENTERPRISES LLC
111 Starlite St, South San Francisco, CA 94080-6398
Tel (800) 227-6905 *Founded/Ownrshp* 1943
Sales 50.4MM^E *EMP* 2,500
SIC 7241 7231 Barber shops; Beauty shops; Barber shops; Beauty shops
Off Mgr: Jan Vandevere

D-U-N-S 13-159-6058
GINO/GIUSEPPE INC
G & G CONSTRUCTION CO
700 Enterprise Ct Ste A, Atwater, CA 95301-9512
Tel (209) 358-0556 *Founded/Ownrshp* 1983
Sales 35.9MM^E *EMP* 250
SIC 1771 Concrete work; Concrete work
CEO: Giuseppe Castiglione
**CEO:* Giuseppe Castiglione
**CFO:* Gino Graziano

D-U-N-S 01-669-5942
GINOP SALES INC
KUBOTA
11274 W M 68 Hwy, Alanson, MI 49706-9699
Tel (231) 548-2272 *Founded/Ownrshp* 1959
Sales 28.9MM *EMP* 31
Accts Hill Schroderus & Co Llp P
SIC 5999 Farm equipment & supplies; Farm tractors; Farm machinery; Farm equipment & supplies; Farm tractors; Farm machinery
Pr: Larry Ginop
**Sec:* Cindy Bowen
**VP:* Leonard Ginop
**Prin:* Ken Ginop
**Prin:* Jim Thompson

GINO'S EAST RESTAURANT
See BRAVO RESTAURANTS INC

GINO'S PIZZA
See BETTER FOODS INC

D-U-N-S 78-762-3107
GINSAN LIQUIDATING CO LLC
TRUSCO
3611 3 Mile Rd Nw, Grand Rapids, MI 49534-1231
Tel (616) 791-8100 *Founded/Ownrshp* 1992
Sales 21.7MM^E *EMP* 95
SIC 3589 2899 Car washing machinery; Water treating compounds; Car washing machinery; Water treating compounds
Pr: Sigrid Valk-Feeney
Sales Exec: Doug Empie

GINSBERG FOODS
See GINSBERGS INSTITUTIONAL FOODS INC

D-U-N-S 01-274-6715
GINSBERGS INSTITUTIONAL FOODS INC
GINSBERG FOODS
29 Ginsburg Ln, Hudson, NY 12534-3431
Tel (518) 828-4004 *Founded/Ownrshp* 1909
Sales 161.4MM *EMP* 225
SIC 5148 5147 5142 5141 5143 Vegetables, fresh; Meats, fresh; Packaged frozen goods; Groceries, general line; Dairy products, except dried or canned; Vegetables, fresh; Meats, fresh; Packaged frozen goods; Groceries, general line; Dairy products, except dried or canned
Pr: David Ginsberg
**CFO:* Edward M Maziejka Jr
VP: Ira Ginsberg
**VP:* Nancy Ginsberg
VP: Joe Ordway
Mktg Mgr: Tracy Cantele
Sls Mgr: Hans Dennie
Sls Mgr: Richard Heinke
Sales Asso: Carlo Carlini
Sales Asso: Peter Clair
Sales Asso: Josie Dunbar

D-U-N-S 00-238-7520
GINSBURG BAKERY INC
300 N Tennessee Ave, Atlantic City, NJ 08401-3257
Tel (609) 345-2265 *Founded/Ownrshp* 1903
Sales 39.4MM^E *EMP* 125
SIC 5149 Bakery products; Bakery products
Pr: John Mulloy Sr
**COO:* John Mulloy Jr
**CFO:* Daniel Mulloy
**VP:* Christopher Mulloy
**VP:* Marie J Mulloy
**VP:* Michael Mulloy
Plnt Mgr: Wally Palmer

D-U-N-S 04-357-4367 IMP
GINSEY INDUSTRIES INC
2078 Center Square Rd, Swedesboro, NJ 08085-1703
Tel (856) 933-1300 *Founded/Ownrshp* 1965
Sales 30.7MM^E *EMP* 75
SIC 2499 Seats, toilet
Pr: Herbert Briggs
**CFO:* George Valletti
VP: Christopher Greco
Dir IT: Sam Dimaria
IT Man: Bridget Crozier
IT Man: Dave Sullenberger
Sls&Mrk Ex: Elizabeth Stevenson
VP Sls: Kathleen Walsh
Sls Mgr: Elizabeth Sarson
Art Dir: Tracy Downing

D-U-N-S 04-318-7954
GIOIA SAILS INC
1951 Rutgers Blvd, Lakewood, NJ 08701-4538
Tel (732) 901-6770 *Founded/Ownrshp* 1967
Sales 31.4MM^E *EMP* 85
SIC 5199 5999 Canvas products; Canvas products
Pr: Donald T Gioia
Board of Directors: Rita Gioia, Robert Stacy

D-U-N-S 06-658-3477
GIOIOSO BROS INC
50 Sprague St Ste 2, Hyde Park, MA 02136-2175
Tel (617) 364-5800 *Founded/Ownrshp* 1959
Sales 23.6MM^E *EMP* 175
Accts Shuman & Epstein
SIC 7353 Heavy construction equipment rental; Heavy construction equipment rental
Pr: Luigi Gioioso
**Treas:* Francesco Gioioso
VP: Joseph Bettencourt

D-U-N-S 00-679-5702
GIORDANO CONSTRUCTION CO INC
1155 Main St, Branford, CT 06405-3799
Tel (203) 488-7264 *Founded/Ownrshp* 1946
Sales 26.2MM^E *EMP* 50
SIC 1542 6552 5211 5031 7389 8741 Commercial & office building, new construction; Subdividers & developers; Lumber & other building materials; Lumber, plywood & millwork; Office facilities & secretarial service rental; Construction management; Commercial & office building, new construction; Subdividers & developers; Lumber & other building materials; Lumber, plywood & millwork; Office facilities & secretarial service rental; Construction management
Pr: Michael F Giordano
**Ex VP:* Vincent S Giordano Jr

GIORDANO RECYCLING
See GIORDANO VINELAND SCRAP MATERIAL LLC

D-U-N-S 09-164-4872
GIORDANO VINELAND SCRAP MATERIAL LLC
GIORDANO RECYCLING
110 N Mill Rd, Vineland, NJ 08360-3437
Tel (856) 696-2068 *Founded/Ownrshp* 1940
Sales 38.1MM^E *EMP* 80
SIC 5093 Scrap & waste materials
Owner: Joseph Giordano Jr
**Owner:* Brian Giordano

D-U-N-S 36-435-5271
GIORDANOS ENTERPRISES INC
740 N Rush St Ste 414, Chicago, IL 60611-2521
Tel (312) 641-6500 *Founded/Ownrshp* 1988
Sales NA *EMP* 800
SIC 5812 2099 6794 5813

D-U-N-S 04-453-6324 IMP
GIORGI MUSHROOM CO
GIORGIO FRESH CO
347 June Ave, Blandon, PA 19510-9550
Tel (610) 926-2800 *Founded/Ownrshp* 1957
Sales 74.3MM^E *EMP* 550
SIC 0182 Mushrooms grown under cover; Mushrooms grown under cover
Pr: David A Carroll
**VP:* Thomas Versagli

D-U-N-S 55-689-4319 IMP
GIORGIO ARMANI CORP
(*Suby of* GIORGIO ARMANI SPA)
450 W 15th St 3, New York, NY 10011-7097
Tel (212) 209-3500 *Founded/Ownrshp* 1983
Sales 334.4MM^E *EMP* 850
SIC 5136 5137 5122 5611 5621 5632 Men's & boys' clothing; Women's & children's clothing; Cosmetics, perfumes & hair products; Clothing, sportswear, men's & boys'; Clothing accessories: men's & boys'; Women's clothing stores; Apparel accessories; Men's & boys' clothing; Women's & children's clothing; Cosmetics, perfumes & hair products; Clothing, sportswear, men's & boys'; Clothing accessories: men's & boys'; Women's clothing stores; Apparel accessories
Ch Bd: Giorgio Armani
CFO: Tom Chan
Ex VP: Martin Coronel
Ex VP: Alessandro Valenti
VP: Lorenzo Bighi
VP: Rosana Cassano
VP: Alessandro Monti
VP: Bruce Weldyn
Creative D: Florence Lee
Comm Man: Sophie Hedley
Dept Mgr: Ikeisha Bugg

GIORGIO FOODS
See DIGIORGIO MUSHROOM CORP

D-U-N-S 00-250-9065 IMP
GIORGIO FOODS INC (PA)
(*Suby of* DIGIORGIO MUSHROOM CORP) ★
1161 Park Rd, Reading, PA 19605
Tel (610) 926-2139 *Founded/Ownrshp* 1960
Sales 90.2MM^E *EMP* 278^E
SIC 2033 2037 5148 2038 Mushrooms: packaged in cans, jars, etc.; Vegetables, quick frozen & cold pack, excl. potato products; Vegetables, fresh; Frozen specialties; Mushrooms: packaged in cans, jars, etc.; Vegetables, quick frozen & cold pack, excl. potato products; Vegetables, fresh; Frozen specialties
Pr: John Majaewski
CFO: Mike Butto
CFO: Robert Erisman
CFO: Phil Impink
Sec: Philip M Impink
VP: Ron Broomhall
VP: Chris Groff
VP: Ginaro Quaglia
Genl Mgr: Tom Czerpak
CIO: Gary Burkert
QA Dir: Gary Zanecosky

D-U-N-S 12-976-9139 IMP
GIORGIO FOODS INTERNATIONAL INC
1161 Park Rd, Temple, PA 19560
Tel (610) 926-2139 *Founded/Ownrshp* 2006
Sales 23.2MM^E *EMP* 40
SIC 5148 Vegetables, fresh
Pr: John Majaewski

CFO: Robert Erisman
**Sec:* Frederick Giorgi
Bd of Dir: Thomas Madden
Ex VP: Mark Kimmel
Ex VP: Brian Threllfall
**VP:* Ginaro Quagilia
Comm Man: Bruce Johnston
Genl Mgr: David Carol
DP Exec: Githens Rick
IT Man: Max Romulus

GIORGIO FRESH CO
See GIORGI MUSHROOM CO

D-U-N-S 14-586-5379
GIORGIO FRESH CO
(*Suby of* GIORGI MUSHROOM CO) ★
347 June Ave, Blandon, PA 19510-9550
Tel (610) 926-2800 *Founded/Ownrshp* 2001
Sales 19.5MM^E *EMP* 550
SIC 0182 Field crops, except cash grains, market preparation services; Mushrooms grown under cover
Pr: David Carroll
**Treas:* Thomas Versagli
Sales Exec: Audrey Rothermel

GIORGIO'S PIZZA HOUSE
See FULLFILLMENT SYSTEMS INC

GIOVANNI RANA
See RANA MEAL SOLUTIONS LLC

D-U-N-S 02-413-6822
GIPE AUTOMOTIVE INC (KY)
A P W WAREHOUSE DIVISION
510 W 4th St, Owensboro, KY 42301-0784
Tel (270) 685-2901 *Founded/Ownrshp* 1931, 1944
Sales 22.1MM^E *EMP* 63
SIC 5013 5531 Automotive supplies & parts; Automotive parts
VP: Thomas H Gipe
**CFO:* Larry R McDaniel
VP: Donald E Gip
IT Man: David Wright

D-U-N-S 07-051-4609
GIPSON STEEL INC (MS)
G S
2770 Sellers Dr, Meridian, MS 39301-1736
Tel (601) 482-5131 *Founded/Ownrshp* 1976
Sales 27.9MM^E *EMP* 75
SIC 3441 Bridge sections, prefabricated highway
Pr: R Scott Gipson
**Pr:* Keith Gipson
**Treas:* Mishelle Hollan
**VP:* J Keith Gipson
**VP:* Mark Gipson
Sls Mgr: Elton Hogan

D-U-N-S 96-599-7062 IMP
GIRAFFE HOLDING INC
500 Howard St, San Francisco, CA 94105-3000
Tel (415) 278-7000 *Founded/Ownrshp* 2010
Sales 1.2MMM^E *EMP* 14,716^E
SIC 5641 Children's & infants' wear stores; Children's & infants' wear stores
VP: Jordan Hitch

D-U-N-S 05-203-0546
GIRARD ENVIRONMENTAL SERVICES INC
701 Codisco Way, Sanford, FL 32771-5701
Tel (407) 708-5856 *Founded/Ownrshp* 1998
Sales 53.5MM^E *EMP* 200
Accts Falconetti & Groomes Cpa Pa
SIC 0781 Landscape services; Landscape services
CEO: Richard A Girard
**Pr:* William R Girard
**VP:* Kenneth E Doyle
VP: Mike Guthrie
VP: Brian Weatherby
Brnch Mgr: Wes Cleaves
Brnch Mgr: Mark Higbee
Off Mgr: David Simmons
IT Man: Sarah Mazzie

D-U-N-S 00-173-9572
GIRARD ESTATE FEE (PA)
21 S 12th St, Philadelphia, PA 19107-3614
Tel (215) 787-2600 *Founded/Ownrshp* 1869
Sales 80.0MM^E *EMP* 360
Accts Deloitte & Touche Llp Philade
SIC 6732 8211 Educational trust management; Boarding school; Educational trust management; Boarding school
Pr: Autumn Adkins
**CFO:* David S Smith
VP: Melvin C Howell

GIRARD FOOD SERVICE
See GFF INC

D-U-N-S 04-519-6391
GIRARD INDUSTRIES I LTD
6531 N Eldridge Pkwy, Houston, TX 77041-3599
Tel (713) 466-3100 *Founded/Ownrshp* 1968
Sales 20.1MM^E *EMP* 25^E
SIC 4619 Slurry pipeline operation
Pr: J David Henry III
Prd Mgr: Kiet Trinh
Sls Mgr: Jim Burris

GIRARD, KERRY
See PRIMARY CARE AFFILIATES

GIRARD MEDICAL CENTER
See PHILADELPHIA NORTH HEALTH SYSTEM

D-U-N-S 03-631-1041
GIRARD NATIONAL BANK
(*Suby of* GN BANKSHARES, INC.)
100 E Forest Ave, Girard, KS 66743-1311
Tel (620) 724-8223 *Founded/Ownrshp* 1929
Sales NA *EMP* 20
SIC 6021 National commercial banks; National commercial banks
Pr: Martin Schifferdecker
Ofcr: John Vulgamore
**VP:* Jeff Smith
VP: Bradley Ulbrich
Dir IT: Richard Baxter

GIRARD TOYOTA-BMW
See CAR SERVICE INC

D-U-N-S 04-018-7895
GIRARDS GARAGE DOOR SERVICES
5962 Keystone Dr, Bath, PA 18014-8898
Tel (610) 837-4738 *Founded/Ownrshp* 1998
Sales 26.8MM^E *EMP* 2,011^E
SIC 7699 Garage door repair; Garage door repair
Owner: Jim Gerard

D-U-N-S 60-959-7450 IMP
GIRI CORP
STONE CREEK COFFEE
422 N 5th St, Milwaukee, WI 53203-3005
Tel (414) 270-1008 *Founded/Ownrshp* 1993
Sales 38.7MM^E *EMP* 100^E
SIC 5149 5812 Coffee, green or roasted; Coffee shop
Pr: Eric Resch
Prd Mgr: Joe Erdman

D-U-N-S 10-913-1037
GIRL SCOUTS CONNECTICUT TRAILS COUNCIL INC
20 Washington Ave Ste 300, North Haven, CT 06473-2341
Tel (203) 239-2922 *Founded/Ownrshp* 1964
Sales 5.5MM^E *EMP* 300
SIC 8641 Girl Scout organization; Girl Scout organization
Ex Dir: Jeannette A Simons
Ofcr: Renee Oliwa

D-U-N-S 00-698-4447
GIRL SCOUTS OF UNITED STATES OF AMERICA
GSUSA
420 5th Ave Fl 13, New York, NY 10018-2729
Tel (212) 852-8000 *Founded/Ownrshp* 1915
Sales 43.8MM^E *EMP* 500
Accts Grant Thornton Llp New York
SIC 8641 5137 6794 2721 Girl Scout organization; Uniforms, women's & children's; Women's & children's accessories; Copyright buying & licensing; Magazines: publishing only, not printed on site; Girl Scout organization; Uniforms, women's & children's; Women's & children's accessories; Copyright buying & licensing; Magazines: publishing only, not printed on site
CEO: Kathy Cloninger
**Ch Bd:* Connie Lindsey
**CEO:* Anna Maria Chavez
**CFO:* Daniel Boockvar
**CFO:* Florence Corsello
CFO: Angela Olden
Ofcr: Barry Horowitz
**Ofcr:* Krista Kokjohn-Poehler
Ofcr: Nhadine Leung
Sr VP: Delphia Y Duckens
Sr VP: Courtney Q Shore
VP: Sharon H Mattews
VP: Harriet Mosatche
VP: Denise Pesich
**VP:* Susan Peters
**VP:* Davia Temin

D-U-N-S 02-155-8143
GIRLING HEALTH CARE INC (TX)
(*Suby of* HARDEN HEALTHCARE SERVICES LLC) ★
1703 W 5th St Fl 7, Austin, TX 78703-4895
Tel (512) 452-5781 *Founded/Ownrshp* 1967, 2007
Sales 235.8MM^E *EMP* 15,000
SIC 8082 Home health care services; Home health care services
Pr: Lew Little
Area Mgr: Nanci Baggett

D-U-N-S 01-049-3112
GIRLING HEALTH CENTER
(*Suby of* GIRLING HEALTH CARE INC) ★
1920 Birdcreek Dr, Temple, TX 76502-1001
Tel (254) 778-4210 *Founded/Ownrshp* 1975
Sales 19.6MM^E *EMP* 2,000
SIC 8082 Visiting nurse service; Visiting nurse service
Pr: Ronda Van Meter

D-U-N-S 00-598-6237 IMP
GIROUX GLASS INC (CA)
850 W Washington Blvd, Los Angeles, CA 90015-3359
Tel (213) 747-7406 *Founded/Ownrshp* 1946
Sales 25.2MM *EMP* 173
Accts Singer Lewak Llp Irvine Cali
SIC 1793 Glass & glazing work; Window frames, all materials; Glass & glazing work
CEO: Nataline Lomedico
**Ch Bd:* Anne-Merelie Murrell
Exec: Richard Mausolf
IT Man: Jerod Allen
Opers Mgr: Chris Lamb
Sls Mgr: Robert Burkhammer
Snr PM: Doug Bade

D-U-N-S 11-870-4436
GIRTMAN AND ASSOCIATES INC
345 Mason Rd, La Vergne, TN 37086-3606
Tel (615) 350-6000 *Founded/Ownrshp* 1993
Sales 45.3MM^E *EMP* 85
SIC 5031 Lumber, plywood & millwork; Doors; Door frames, all materials
Pr: Charles Girtman
**Treas:* Rich West
**VP:* T Michael Harris
Snr PM: Amy Baker

D-U-N-S 03-120-8150
GIRTON PROPANE SERVICE INC
1156 Bridge St, Clay Center, KS 67432-3607
Tel (785) 632-6273 *Founded/Ownrshp* 1954
Sales 57.2MM^E *EMP* 80
SIC 5172 4212 Gases, liquefied petroleum (propane); Liquid transfer services; Gases, liquefied petroleum (propane); Liquid transfer services
Pr: Barry Girton
**VP:* Brad Girton

GIRTZ ENGINEERING
See GIRTZ INDUSTRIES INC

D-U-N-S 04-029-8044 IMP
GIRTZ INDUSTRIES INC
GIRTZ ENGINEERING
5262 N East Shafer Dr, Monticello, IN 47960-7313
Tel (574) 278-7510 *Founded/Ownrshp* 1981
Sales 29.4MM^E *EMP* 100
SIC 3444 Sheet metalwork
Pr: David A Girtz
Dir IT: Michael Lichtenstein

GIS
See GENERAL INFORMATION SERVICES INC

GISD
See GREENVILLE INDEPENDENT SCHOOL DISTRICT

GISI MARKETING GROUP
See GRAPHIC INFORMATION SYSTEMS INC

D-U-N-S 05-559-0582
GIT-N-GO CONVENIENCE STORES INC
2716 Indianola Ave, Des Moines, IA 50315-2377
Tel (515) 288-8565 *Founded/Ownrshp* 1972
Sales 108.3MM *EMP* 203
SIC 5411 5541 6722 Convenience stores, chain; Filling stations, gasoline; Management investment, open-end; Convenience stores, chain; Filling stations, gasoline; Management investment, open-end
Pr: Dennis Flora
Off Mgr: Sarah Jenkins
Dir Opers: Pete Klinbt

D-U-N-S 01-887-1875
GITANJALI - INTERNATIONAL
1212 Johnson St, Pasadena, TX 77506-4622
Tel (713) 475-0856 *Founded/Ownrshp* 2008
Sales 45.0MM *EMP* 7
SIC 6733 Trusts, except educational, religious, charity: management; Trusts, except educational, religious, charity: management
CEO: Govinda Vishnu
**Ch Bd:* Neetu Sehgal
**Pr:* Smita Mehata

D-U-N-S 61-053-7974 IMP
GITI TIRE (USA) LTD
(*Suby of* GITI TIRE GLOBAL ENTERPRISE PTE. LTD.)
10404 6th St, Rancho Cucamonga, CA 91730-5831
Tel (909) 527-8800 *Founded/Ownrshp* 2005
Sales 80.5MM^E *EMP* 55^E
SIC 5014 Automobile tires & tubes
CEO: Enki Tan
Ex VP: Armand Allaire
Ex VP: Tom McNamara
Ex Dir: Enk Tan
**Mng Dir:* Lei Huai Chin
Opers Mgr: Raymond Zhang
Sls Dir: David Myers

D-U-N-S 00-286-1052
GITO INC
NELLO CONSTRUCTION
100 Houston Sq Ste 200, Canonsburg, PA 15317-1469
Tel (724) 746-1900 *Founded/Ownrshp* 1960
Sales 39.8MM^E *EMP* 90
Accts Schneider Downs
SIC 1542 1541 Commercial & office building, new construction; Industrial buildings, new construction; Commercial & office building, new construction; Industrial buildings, new construction
Pr: George Leasure
**Sec:* Janet Torriero
VP: Bob Skrzyniarz
**VP:* Gino Torriero
Snr Mgr: Martin Donahoe

D-U-N-S 79-293-4234 IMP
■ **GITS MANUFACTURING CO INC**
(*Suby of* ACTUANT CORP) ★
9250 Sepulveda Blvd # 202, North Hills, CA 91343-3907
Tel (641) 782-2105 *Founded/Ownrshp* 1986
Sales 31.3MM^E *EMP* 114
SIC 3714 3625 3469 Lubrication systems & parts, motor vehicle; Actuators, industrial; Metal stampings; Lubrication systems & parts, motor vehicle; Actuators, industrial; Metal stampings
Pr: Daryl Lilly
**VP:* Michael Taylor
Sfty Mgr: Sherry Lund

D-U-N-S 00-218-5858
GITTLIN COMPANIES INC (NJ)
740 S Powerline Rd 4a, Deerfield Beach, FL 33442-8113
Tel (212) 244-4646 *Founded/Ownrshp* 1910
Sales 33.9MM^E *EMP* 161
SIC 2752 Commercial printing, lithographic; Commercial printing, lithographic
CEO: Bruce Gittlin
**Ch Bd:* Sam Gittlin
**Pr:* B Morton Gittlin
**Prin:* Bob Gittlin

D-U-N-S 11-792-9307 IMP/EXP
GIUFFRE BUICK INC
GIUFFRE BUICK-ISUZU-VOLVO
1030 S Dirksen Pkwy, Springfield, IL 62703-2119
Tel (217) 788-2400 *Founded/Ownrshp* 1954
Sales 20.5MM^E *EMP* 50
SIC 5511 Automobiles, new & used
Pr: Roger C Sables
**VP:* Jan G Sables
Exec: Patrick Devlain
Sales Asso: David Hahn
Sales Asso: Jeff Hassinger

GIUFFRE BUICK-ISUZU-VOLVO
See GIUFFRE BUICK INC

D-U-N-S 06-088-7379
GIULIANO-PAGANO CORP (CA)
GIULIANO'S BAKERY
1264 E Walnut St, Carson, CA 90746-1319
Tel (310) 537-7700 *Founded/Ownrshp* 1952
Sales 27.0MM^E *EMP* 100
SIC 2051 Bakery: wholesale or wholesale/retail combined
Ch Bd: Nancy Ritmire Giuliano
**Pr:* Gregory Ritmire
QA Dir: Alice Fu

GIULIANO'S BAKERY
See GIULIANO-PAGANO CORP

D-U-N-S 00-954-3810 IMP
GIUMARRA BROS FRUIT CO INC
GIUMARRA INTERNATIONAL BERRY
1601 E Olympic Blvd # 408, Los Angeles, CA 90021-1943
Tel (213) 627-2900 *Founded/Ownrshp* 1950
Sales 60.6MM^E *EMP* 75
SIC 5148 Fresh fruits & vegetables; Fresh fruits & vegetables
CEO: Donald Corsaro
**Pr:* John Corsaro
**Treas:* John Giumarra Jr
VP: T I Riley
VP: Craig Uchizono
Div Mgr: Chuck Anunciation
Trfc Dir: Margarita Juarez
Sales Asso: Adolfo Zesati

GIUMARRA COMPANIES
See RIO VISTA VENTURES LLC

GIUMARRA INTERNATIONAL BERRY
See GIUMARRA BROS FRUIT CO INC

D-U-N-S 04-309-8896 EXP
GIUMARRA VINEYARDS CORP (CA)
11220 Edison Hwy, Edison, CA 93220
Tel (661) 395-7000 *Founded/Ownrshp* 1946
Sales 162.4MM *EMP* 3,000
SIC 0172 2084 2086 Grapes; Wines; Fruit drinks (less than 100% juice): packaged in cans, etc.; Tea, iced: packaged in cans, bottles, etc.; Grapes; Wines; Fruit drinks (less than 100% juice): packaged in cans, etc.; Tea, iced: packaged in cans, bottles, etc.
Pr: John G Giumarra Jr
**VP:* George Giumarra Jr
IT Man: Craig Bowers
VP Sls: Randy Giumarra

D-U-N-S 00-916-6190 IMP
GIUSTOS SPECIALTY FOODS LLC
344 Littlefield Ave, South San Francisco, CA 94080-6103
Tel (650) 873-6566 *Founded/Ownrshp* 2007
Sales 24.0MM *EMP* 47
SIC 2041 Flour mills, cereal (except rice); Grain mills (except rice); Flour mills, cereal (except rice); Grain mills (except rice)
COO: Jarjeet Bahia
CFO: Ann Moore
Plnt Mgr: Ed Hirle

D-U-N-S 96-335-4951
GIVAUDAN FLAVORS AND FRAGRANCES INC
(*Suby of* GIVAUDAN ROURE (UNITED STATES) INC) ★
1199 Edison Dr, Cincinnati, OH 45216-2265
Tel (513) 948-8000 *Founded/Ownrshp* 2004
Sales 434.7MM^E *EMP* 2,500
SIC 2869 2087 Flavors or flavoring materials, synthetic; Perfume materials, synthetic; Flavoring extracts & syrups; Flavors or flavoring materials, synthetic; Perfume materials, synthetic; Flavoring extracts & syrups
CFO: Stefan Giezendanner

D-U-N-S 60-759-2920 IMP/EXP
GIVAUDAN FLAVORS CORP
(*Suby of* GIVAUDAN FLAVORS AND FRAGRANCES INC) ★
1199 Edison Dr, Cincinnati, OH 45216-2265
Tel (513) 948-8000 *Founded/Ownrshp* 2000
Sales 111.9MM^E *EMP* 700
SIC 2869 2087

D-U-N-S 00-215-6354 IMP
GIVAUDAN FRAGRANCES CORP
(*Suby of* GIVAUDAN FLAVORS AND FRAGRANCES INC) ★
1199 Edison Dr Ste 1-2, Cincinnati, OH 45216-2265
Tel (513) 948-3428 *Founded/Ownrshp* 2000
Sales 322.7MM^E *EMP* 1,800
SIC 2869 Perfume materials, synthetic; Flavors or flavoring materials, synthetic; Perfume materials, synthetic; Flavors or flavoring materials, synthetic
CEO: Gilles Andrier
Sr VP: Cathy Torelli
Dir IT: Peter Becker

D-U-N-S 00-780-4680 IMP/EXP
GIVAUDAN ROURE (UNITED STATES) INC
GIVAUDAN US
(*Suby of* GIVAUDAN SA)
1199 Edison Dr, Cincinnati, OH 45216-2265
Tel (513) 948-8000 *Founded/Ownrshp* 2000
Sales 434.7MM^E *EMP* 2,737
SIC 2869 2087 Perfume materials, synthetic; Flavors or flavoring materials, synthetic; Flavoring extracts & syrups; Perfume materials, synthetic; Flavors or flavoring materials, synthetic; Flavoring extracts & syrups
Pr: Michael Davis
Sr VP: Robert Sherwood
Sr VP: Cathy Torelli
VP: Roger Elkin
VP: Albert Lopez
IT Man: Pat Morgan
VP Sls: Jeff Peppet

GIVAUDAN US
See GIVAUDAN ROURE (UNITED STATES) INC

GIVE KIDS THE WORLD VILLAGE
See GIVE KIDS WORLD INC

D-U-N-S 60-951-6596
GIVE KIDS WORLD INC
GIVE KIDS THE WORLD VILLAGE
210 S Bass Rd, Kissimmee, FL 34746-6099
Tel (407) 396-1114 *Founded/Ownrshp* 1986
Sales 50.7MM *EMP* 130
Accts Cross Fernandez & Riley Llp O
SIC 8322 7011 Child related social services; Hotels & motels
Pr: Pamela Landwirth
**Ch Bd:* Michael Short
**CFO:* Robert Cook
**Treas:* Micheal Cassara
VP: Shannon Gravitte

D-U-N-S 78-766-7005 IMP
GIVE SOMETHING BACK INC
GIVE SOMETHING BACK OFF SUPS
7730 Pardee Ln Ste A, Oakland, CA 94621-1555
Tel (510) 635-5500 *Founded/Ownrshp* 1991
Sales 98.9MM^E *EMP* 90
SIC 5112 Stationery & office supplies; Stationery & office supplies
CEO: Sean Marx
**Pr:* Mike Hannigan
IT Man: Verna Carter
Sales Exec: Chareen Mejia
Mktg Mgr: Cheryl Pallas
Manager: Christian Westbrook

GIVE SOMETHING BACK OFF SUPS
See GIVE SOMETHING BACK INC

D-U-N-S 06-626-6334
GIVE2ASIA
340 Pine St Ste 501, San Francisco, CA 94104-3237
Tel (415) 967-6300 *Founded/Ownrshp* 2000
Sales 30.2MM *EMP* 15
Accts Ghrnt Thornton Llp San Franci
SIC 8733 8322 Noncommercial research organizations; Individual & family services
Pr: Birger Stamperdahl
**CFO:* Pamela Calvert
CFO: Henry Tang
Trst: Edwin Go
Ofcr: Nishita Bakshi
Ofcr: Scott Sugiura
Ofcr: Kalsang Tashi
Ofcr: Uyen Tran
VP: David Andrews
VP: Jennifer Lofing
Mng Dir: Michael REA

D-U-N-S 09-007-3722
■ **GIVEN IMAGING INC**
(*Suby of* MEDTRONIC PUBLIC LIMITED COMPANY)
3950 Shackleford Rd # 500, Duluth, GA 30096-1852
Tel (770) 662-0870 *Founded/Ownrshp* 2001, 2015
Sales 86.8MM^E *EMP* 130
SIC 5047 Medical equipment & supplies; Medical equipment & supplies
CEO: Nachum Shamir
CFO: Alan Bond
VP: Johnathan Bissinger
VP: Ed Cordell
VP: Nestor Zelico
Exec: Eric Shapiro
Rgnl Mgr: Dean Gillitzer
Mtls Mgr: Stewart Conner
VP Sls: Tari Allen
VP Sls: Jennifer Barraza
VP Sls: Beth Putnam

D-U-N-S 02-138-7212
GIVENS ESTATES INC
2360 Sweeten Creek Rd, Asheville, NC 28803-2030
Tel (828) 274-4800 *Founded/Ownrshp* 1975
Sales 44.2MM *EMP* 270^E
Accts Dixon Hughes Goodman Llp Ashe
SIC 8361 Home for the aged; Home for the aged
Ex Dir: Kenneth M Partin
Bd of Dir: David C Whilden
VP: Mary Donnelly
Dir IT: Chris Snyder
HC Dir: Tabitha Hinman

D-U-N-S 05-099-8889
GIVENS INC
1720 S Military Hwy, Chesapeake, VA 23320-2612
Tel (757) 233-4300 *Founded/Ownrshp* 1980
Sales 34.7MM^E *EMP* 100
SIC 4225 General warehousing
Pr: Edward J Reed
COO: Robert McNichols
**Sec:* Janice G Reed
**Ex VP:* Keith Helton
**VP:* Jeri G Long
Admn Mgr: Charlotte Ange
Opers Mgr: Susie Herron
Natl Sales: Michael Thomas

D-U-N-S 03-373-4716 IMP/EXP
GIW INDUSTRIES INC
GIW MINERALS
(*Suby of* KSB AMERICA CORP) ★
5000 Wrightsboro Rd, Grovetown, GA 30813-2842
Tel (706) 863-1011 *Founded/Ownrshp* 1996
Sales 114.6MM^E *EMP* 464
SIC 3561 3559 Industrial pumps & parts; Foundry machinery & equipment; Industrial pumps & parts; Foundry machinery & equipment
CEO: Dennis Ziegler
**CFO:* Enrico Handrick
**VP:* Thomas Mueller
**VP:* Charlie Stone
**VP:* Robert Visintainer
Exec: Lee Whitlock
Dir IT: Bryan Bronson
Mktg Mgr: Richard Inglett
Board of Directors: Carmelo Fernandes Moldes

GIW MINERALS
See GIW INDUSTRIES INC

D-U-N-S 00-685-0010
GJ HOPKINS INC (VA)
(*Suby of* BRANCH GROUP INC) ★
714 5th St Ne, Roanoke, VA 24016-2124
Tel (540) 982-1873 *Founded/Ownrshp* 1958
Sales 23.1MM *EMP* 230^E
Accts Kpmg Llp Roanoke Virginia
SIC 1731 1761 5087 1711 Electrical work; Sheet metalwork; Service establishment equipment; Mechanical contractor; Electrical work; Sheet metalwork; Service establishment equipment; Mechanical contractor
VP: Eddie Caldwell
**Treas:* Melanie Wheeler
**VP:* Mike Bowling
**VP:* Ernie Caldwell
**VP:* Terry Keffer
Board of Directors: William McAdams

D-U-N-S 04-390-5785
GJOVIK CHEVROLET-BUICK-GMC INC
GJOVIK OLDSMOBILE
2780 E Church St, Sandwich, IL 60548-1985
Tel (815) 786-2177 *Founded/Ownrshp* 1968
Sales 28.3MM^E *EMP* 81
SIC 5511 7515 7539 Automobiles, new & used; Pickups, new & used; Passenger car leasing; Automotive repair shops; Automobiles, new & used; Pickups, new & used; Passenger car leasing; Automotive repair shops
Prin: Olaf Gjovik
**Sec:* Florence Gjovik
**VP:* Scott Gjovik
Sales Asso: James Friday
Sales Asso: Carla Horsley

GJOVIK OLDSMOBILE
See GJOVIK CHEVROLET-BUICK-GMC INC

D-U-N-S 02-133-3203
GJR SERVICES LLC
OFS
7804 Foothill Blvd, Rock Springs, WY 82901-3472
Tel (307) 382-4168 *Founded/Ownrshp* 2000
Sales 35.0MM^E *EMP* 96
SIC 5085 3533 Industrial tools; Oil & gas field machinery
CEO: Gary Roberts
**COO:* Brad Hayden
**CFO:* Gay Stanley Mayeux
Treas: Robert Baker

D-U-N-S 08-580-9770
GJS HOLDING LLC
JUAREZ SALONS & SPAS
(*Suby of* EVERGREEN PACIFIC PARTNERS MANAGEMENT CO INC) ★
3633 136th Pl Se Ste 200, Bellevue, WA 98006-1455
Tel (425) 748-1400 *Founded/Ownrshp* 2006
Sales 38.6MM^E *EMP* 1,300
SIC 7231 Beauty shops; Beauty schools; Beauty shops; Beauty schools
VP: Jerry Ahern
Creative D: Christophe Soltane
MIS Dir: Janice Smith
Dir IT: George Jones
IT Man: Debbie Brown
Mktg Mgr: Sheri Rearick

GK
See GAFFNEY-KROESE SUPPLY CORP

D-U-N-S 06-183-8443
GK HOLDINGS INC
9000 Regency Pkwy Ste 500, Cary, NC 27518-8520
Tel (800) 268-7737 *Founded/Ownrshp* 2011
Sales 323.0MM *EMP* 1,314
SIC 6719 Investment holding companies, except banks; Investment holding companies, except banks
Pr: Brian K Branson
**Treas:* Robert Kalainikas

D-U-N-S 11-933-7827
GK NEVADA LLC
CENTENNIAL TOYOTA
6551 Centennial Ctr Blvd, Las Vegas, NV 89149-4553
Tel (702) 942-3800 *Founded/Ownrshp* 2001
Sales 28.3MM^E *EMP* 85
SIC 5511 Automobiles, new & used; Automobiles, new & used
Exec: Michelle Bredin
Genl Mgr: Anthony Woods
Sls Mgr: Randy Brooks
Sls Mgr: Peter Cornish
Sls Mgr: James Gardiner
Sales Asso: Eldon Brown
Sales Asso: Varoujan Buduzyan

D-U-N-S 11-259-3595 IMP
GK PACKAGING INC
PLAIN CITY MOLDING
7680 Commerce Pl, Plain City, OH 43064-9222
Tel (614) 873-9823 *Founded/Ownrshp* 1983
Sales 26.4MM^E *EMP* 95^E
SIC 3085 Plastics bottles
Pr: Gene J Kuzma
CFO: Bob Kellerman
**Treas:* Jeff Kuzma
**Prin:* Betty Jo Jerome
Opers Mgr: Ted Niswonger
Plnt Mgr: Ron Marion
Plnt Mgr: Edward Stevenson

D-U-N-S 11-323-7437
GK TECHSTAR LLC
802 W 13th St, Deer Park, TX 77536-3166
Tel (281) 884-8257 *Founded/Ownrshp* 2001
Sales 27.6MM^E *EMP* 70
SIC 3823 Pressure gauges, dial & digital; Industrial flow & liquid measuring instruments; Industrial process measurement equipment
Pr: Kyle Kuhlow
VP: Dave Bigalke
Sls Mgr: Wes Mayfield
Sales Asso: Josh Gill
Sales Asso: Nathan Sheen

GKA
See GOODWILL KEYSTONE AREA

D-U-N-S 10-183-4588 IMP
GKD-USA INC
(*Suby of* GKD - GEBR. KUFFERATH AG)
825 Chesapeake Dr, Cambridge, MD 21613-9401
Tel (410) 221-0542 *Founded/Ownrshp* 1982
Sales 21.1MM^E *EMP* 30
SIC 5131 5051 Nylon piece goods, woven; Yard goods, woven; Steel
Pr: Tom Powley
Pt: Theilig Kaufmann
VP: Mike Spangler
Dir Bus: Steven Culver
Sls Mgr: James Jones
Sls Mgr: Will Linthicum

D-U-N-S 03-878-1159
GKI FOODS LLC
GRANOLA KITCHENS
(*Suby of* CENTRAL INVESTMENT LLC) ★
7926 Lochlin Dr, Brighton, MI 48116-8329
Tel (248) 486-0055 *Founded/Ownrshp* 1974, 2012
Sales 23.0MM^E *EMP* 100
SIC 2064 Candy & other confectionery products
Pr: Manny Zapata
Sec: Carl Myers

D-U-N-S 78-310-4888
GKK CORP
GKKWORKS
2355 Main St Ste 220, Irvine, CA 92614-4251
Tel (949) 250-1500 *Founded/Ownrshp* 1991
Sales 117.5MM *EMP* 210
Accts Kushner Smith Joanou & Gregson
SIC 8712 8711 Architectural engineering; Building construction consultant; Architectural engineering; Building construction consultant
Pr: Praful Kulkarni
CFO: James Staley
**VP:* David Hunt
VP: Charles G Merrick
Genl Mgr: Vanessa Ozzano
Snr Mgr: Amit Bhargava

GKKWORKS
See GKK CORP

D-U-N-S 79-065-6768
GKKWORKS CONSTRUCTION SERVICES
2355 Main St Ste 220, Irvine, CA 92614-4251
Tel (949) 250-1500 *Founded/Ownrshp* 1997
Sales 24.7MM^E *EMP* 200
SIC 8712 1542 Industrial buildings & warehouses; Architectural services; Commercial & office building, new construction
Pr: Praful Kulkarni
**Sr VP:* Mike Helton
**Sr VP:* David Hunt
**Sr VP:* Charlie Merrick
**VP:* Juan Caldentey
**VP:* William Line
**VP:* Naila Moloo
**Prin:* Rachel Morgan

D-U-N-S 06-765-5985
GKN AEROSPACE CHEM-TRONICS INC (CA)
(*Suby of* GKN PLC)
1150 W Bradley Ave, El Cajon, CA 92020-1504
Tel (619) 448-2320 *Founded/Ownrshp* 1953, 2001
Sales 202.8MM^E *EMP* 683
SIC 3724 7699 Aircraft engines & engine parts; Aircraft & heavy equipment repair services; Aircraft engines & engine parts; Aircraft & heavy equipment repair services
Pr: Michael A Beck
**CEO:* Marcus J Bryson
CFO: Les Emanuel
VP: Bill Beard
VP: Stacey Clapp
VP: Dale Derischebourg
VP: Paul Gutierrez
VP: Neal Montany
VP: Peter Wazlawek
Dir IT: Kirt Hymin
Dir IT: Jim McGhee

D-U-N-S 00-425-1757 IMP
GKN AEROSPACE CINCINNATI INC
AEROSPACE MFG GROUP-OHIO
(*Suby of* GKN PLC)
11230 Deerfield Rd, Blue Ash, OH 45242-2024
Tel (513) 489-9800 *Founded/Ownrshp* 1986
Sales 54.1MM^E *EMP* 250^E
SIC 3599 Electrical discharge machining (EDM); Machine shop, jobbing & repair; Electrical discharge machining (EDM); Machine shop, jobbing & repair
CEO: Phil Swash
**Sr VP:* Tom Battagli
VP: Larry Alexandre
**VP:* Mike Beck
VP: Robert Cohen
Genl Mgr: Floyd McConnell
Genl Mgr: Tim Orr
Dir IT: Richard Groch
IT Man: Ronnie Patton
Sfty Mgr: Brandon Cox

D-U-N-S 02-156-3359 IMP/EXP
GKN AEROSPACE INC
142 Jmes S Mcdonnell Blvd, Hazelwood, MO 63042-3102
Tel (314) 264-3000 *Founded/Ownrshp* 1997
Sales 68.6MM^E *EMP* 171^E
SIC 3365 Aerospace castings, aluminum
Pr: Phil Swash
Treas: Hugo Perez
Dir Sec: Gary Bledsoe
Genl Mgr: Josh Laughlin
Dir IT: Rich Dobyns
IT Man: Jeff Hutson
IT Man: Siglinda Mayer

D-U-N-S 00-204-4162 IMP
GKN AEROSPACE MONITOR INC (NY)
(*Suby of* GKN PLC)
1000 New Horizons Blvd, Amityville, NY 11701-1138
Tel (562) 619-8558 *Founded/Ownrshp* 1947, 2006
Sales 89.8MM^E *EMP* 275
SIC 3728 3769 Aircraft assemblies, subassemblies & parts; Guided missile & space vehicle parts & auxiliary equipment
CEO: Daniele Cagnatel
**Ch Bd:* Kevin L Cummings
**Pr:* Fran Novak
VP: Gary Kahrau
**VP:* Paul Kowack
VP: Stephen Marshall
**VP:* Patrick Powers
**VP:* Dave Sylvain
Genl Mgr: David Maguire
Genl Mgr: Charles Paterson
MIS Mgr: Dianne Burcyk

D-U-N-S 18-784-8619 IMP
GKN AEROSPACE NEWINGTON LLC
(*Suby of* GKN AEROSPACE SWEDEN AB)
183 Louis St, Newington, CT 06111
Tel (860) 667-8502 *Founded/Ownrshp* 2012
Sales 20.9MM^E *EMP* 150
SIC 3724 3728 Aircraft engines & engine parts; Aircraft parts & equipment
CEO: Kevin Cummings
Opers Mgr: Sergio Moren
Sls Mgr: Bruce L Fiedorowicz

D-U-N-S 78-811-9142 IMP
GKN AEROSPACE PRECISION MACHINING INC
(*Suby of* GKN PLC)
429 N West Rd, Wellington, KS 67152-8047
Tel (620) 326-5952 *Founded/Ownrshp* 1999
Sales 30.8MM^E *EMP* 255
SIC 7539 Machine shop, automotive; Machine shop, automotive
CEO: Marcus Bryson
**Pr:* Kevin Cummings
**Pr:* Brian Decant
**Pr:* Stephen A Marshall
**Pr:* Mike McCann
**Pr:* Phil Swash
Sr VP: Tom Bataglia
Genl Mgr: Roger Emley
IT Man: Rick Henderson
IT Man: Joanna Williams

D-U-N-S 00-957-8162 IMP
GKN AEROSPACE TRANSPARENCY SYSTEMS INC
(*Suby of* GKN AMERICA CORP) ★
12122 Western Ave, Garden Grove, CA 92841-2915
Tel (714) 893-7531 *Founded/Ownrshp* 2003
Sales 78.2MM^E *EMP* 360^E
SIC 3089 3231 3827 3728 3081 2821 Windows, plastic; Windshields, plastic; Mirrors, truck & automobile: made from purchased glass; Optical instruments & lenses; Aircraft parts & equipment; Unsupported plastics film & sheet; Plastics materials & resins; Windows, plastic; Windshields, plastic; Mirrors, truck & automobile: made from purchased glass; Optical instruments & lenses; Aircraft parts & equipment; Unsupported plastics film & sheet; Plastics materials & resins
Ch Bd: Dr John Foster
CEO: Ronald Kato
CFO: Michael Kaalund
CFO: Nick Waters
Sr Cor Off: Joe McCollough
Ex VP: Mike Beck
Sr VP: Tom Battaglia
Prin: Kevin Cummings
Mng Dir: Jeff Armitage
Genl Mgr: Tony Salerno
Sfty Dirs: Mike Baumeister
Board of Directors: Benjamin A Cosgrove, T Allan Maartor, Michael Schwabero

D-U-N-S 83-806-7718
GKN AEROSPACE TRANSPARENCY SYSTEMS-FORT WORTH
A C T
(*Suby of* GKN PLC)
3220 S Grove St, Fort Worth, TX 76110-4303
Tel (817) 921-2220 *Founded/Ownrshp* 2006
Sales 36.5MM^E *EMP* 346
SIC 3369 3365 Aerospace castings, nonferrous: except aluminum; Aerospace castings, aluminum; Aerospace castings, nonferrous: except aluminum; Aerospace castings, aluminum
CEO: Chris Hall

D-U-N-S 14-423-3608 IMP
GKN AMERICA CORP
(*Suby of* G.K.N. INDUSTRIES LIMITED)
2715 Davey Rd Ste 300, Woodridge, IL 60517-5064
Tel (630) 972-9300 *Founded/Ownrshp* 2001
Sales 585.3MM^E *EMP* 3,000
SIC 3714 Universal joints, motor vehicle; Drive shafts, motor vehicle; Universal joints, motor vehicle; Drive shafts, motor vehicle
Pr: Grey Denham
**Treas:* Hugo Perez
**VP:* John A Giannangeli

D-U-N-S 00-530-9349 IMP
GKN ARMSTRONG WHEELS INC
ARMSTRONG RIM & WHEEL MFG CO
(*Suby of* GKN HOLDINGS PLC)
5453 6th Ave, Armstrong, IA 50514-7573
Tel (712) 362-4934 *Founded/Ownrshp* 1998
Sales 68.3MM^E *EMP* 300
SIC 3714 Motor vehicle wheels & parts; Motor vehicle wheels & parts
Pr: Doug Jacowski
**Pr:* Steven Norgrove
**Treas:* Hugo Perez
Plnt Mgr: Wilson Alan
Plnt Mgr: Kenneth Glaser
Plnt Mgr: Adrian Hagebock
Board of Directors: Brian Newman

D-U-N-S 14-735-4476 IMP/EXP
GKN DRIVELINE NEWTON LLC
(*Suby of* GKN DRIVELINE NORTH AMERICA INC) ★
1848 Gkn Way, Newton, NC 28658-9072
Tel (828) 428-1591 *Founded/Ownrshp* 2011

Sales 185.1MM^E *EMP* 650
SIC 3462 3714 Iron & steel forgings; Gears, motor vehicle; Iron & steel forgings; Gears, motor vehicle
Pr: Max Owens
Ex VP: Mike McMillan

D-U-N-S 09-452-9401 IMP
GKN DRIVELINE NORTH AMERICA INC
(*Suby of* GKN AMERICA CORP) ★
2200 N Opdyke Rd, Auburn Hills, MI 48326-2389
Tel (248) 296-7000 *Founded/Ownrshp* 1977
Sales 404.1MM^E *EMP* 1,800
SIC 3714 5013 Universal joints, motor vehicle; Drive shafts, motor vehicle; Automotive engines & engine parts; Universal joints, motor vehicle; Drive shafts, motor vehicle; Automotive engines & engine parts
Pr: Robert Willig
COO: Al Rivard
**CFO:* Craig Connop
VP: Ramon Kuczera
Div Mgr: Dan Twomley
Opers Mgr: Jason Holland
Counsel: Capri Pelshaw

D-U-N-S 12-513-6270
GKN FREIGHT SERVICES INC
(*Suby of* GKN AMERICA CORP) ★
1202 Industrial Dr Ste 4, Van Wert, OH 45891-2483
Tel (419) 232-3821 *Founded/Ownrshp* 2002
Sales 23.2MM^E *EMP* 52
SIC 4731 Freight transportation arrangement
Pr: Dennis Morris
**Ex VP:* Patrick Byrne
VP: Juan Perez
Dir IT: Andy Uttley
Snr Mgr: Rolando Torres

D-U-N-S 07-175-4337
GKN NORTH AMERICA INC
(*Suby of* GKN HOLDINGS PLC)
2200 N Opdyke Rd, Auburn Hills, MI 48326-2389
Tel (248) 296-7200 *Founded/Ownrshp* 1981
Sales 228.8MM^E *EMP* 5,580
SIC 3714 5013 7359 Motor vehicle transmissions, drive assemblies & parts; Transmissions, motor vehicle; Universal joints, motor vehicle; Drive shafts, motor vehicle; Motor vehicle supplies & new parts; Equipment rental & leasing
Pr: Robert Willig
VP: Richard Best
VP: A George
Genl Couns: John O'Donnell
Board of Directors: Herbert Galant, David Rood

D-U-N-S 80-816-6946 IMP/EXP
GKN NORTH AMERICA SERVICES INC
(*Suby of* GKN PLC)
2715 Davey Rd Ste 300, Woodridge, IL 60517-5064
Tel (630) 737-1456 *Founded/Ownrshp* 2005
Sales 144.8MM^E *EMP* 698
SIC 3714 5013 7359 Motor vehicle transmissions, drive assemblies & parts; Transmissions, motor vehicle; Motor vehicle supplies & new parts; Equipment rental & leasing; Motor vehicle transmissions, drive assemblies & parts; Transmissions, motor vehicle; Motor vehicle supplies & new parts; Equipment rental & leasing
CEO: Daniele Cagnatel
**Treas:* Hugo Perez

D-U-N-S 09-077-7558 IMP
GKN SINTER METALS LLC
(*Suby of* GKN PLC)
2200 N Opdyke Rd, Auburn Hills, MI 48326-2389
Tel (248) 296-7832 *Founded/Ownrshp* 1991
Sales 424.5MM^E *EMP* 2,825
SIC 3714 3568 3369 3366 Motor vehicle engines & parts; Motor vehicle transmissions, drive assemblies & parts; Gears, motor vehicle; Bearings, motor vehicle; Power transmission equipment; Sprockets (power transmission equipment); Bearings, plain; Nonferrous foundries; Copper foundries; Motor vehicle engines & parts; Motor vehicle transmissions, drive assemblies & parts; Gears, motor vehicle; Bearings, motor vehicle; Power transmission equipment; Sprockets (power transmission equipment); Bearings, plain; Nonferrous foundries; Copper foundries
Pr: David J Turner
Pr: Rich McCorry
Sr VP: Peter M Lgg
**VP:* Trevor C Bonner Cbe
VP: Richard Gough
VP: Stuart Greidanus
**VP:* Rufus A Oglivie Smals
Exec: Ian Gibson
Genl Mgr: Terry Shutter
CTO: Jim Wilmes
IT Man: Jason Holland

D-U-N-S 00-642-3594
GKN SINTER METALS-GERMANTOWN INC
(*Suby of* GKN SINTER METALS LLC) ★
N112w18700 Mequon Rd, Germantown, WI 53022-3142
Tel (262) 255-9050 *Founded/Ownrshp* 2002
Sales 55.5MM^E *EMP* 514
SIC 3312 Sinter, iron; Sinter, iron
COO: Greg Kern
Board of Directors: Joanne Roseberg

D-U-N-S 07-069-4328 IMP
GKN WALTERSCHEID INC
(*Suby of* GKN WALTERSCHEID GMBH)
2715 Davey Rd, Woodridge, IL 60517-5064
Tel (630) 972-9300 *Founded/Ownrshp* 1978
Sales 39.0MM *EMP* 139
SIC 5083 3568 Agricultural machinery & equipment; Power transmission equipment; Agricultural machinery & equipment; Power transmission equipment
Pr: Peter Roettgen
**CFO:* Ernie Balogh
**Mng Dir:* Phil Brown

D-U-N-S 60-991-3538 IMP
GKN WESTLAND AEROSPACE INC
(*Suby of* GKN PLC)
3951 Al Highway 229 S, Tallassee, AL 36078-4733
Tel (334) 283-9200 *Founded/Ownrshp* 1998
Sales 231.3MM^E *EMP* 980
SIC 3728 Aircraft body & wing assemblies & parts; Aircraft propellers & associated equipment; Aircraft body & wing assemblies & parts; Aircraft propellers & associated equipment
CEO: Kevin Cummings
**CFO:* John Michaels
CFO: William Seeger
VP: Roger Emley
VP: John Herthum
Genl Mgr: Daniele Cagnatel
Dir IT: Robert Mask
IT Man: Dianne Burcyk
IT Man: Jolene Butler
Opers Mgr: Chris Wilson

D-U-N-S 15-722-3892
GKR SYSTEMS INC
VENTURE TECHNOLOGIES
860 Centre St, Ridgeland, MS 39157-4501
Tel (601) 956-5440 *Founded/Ownrshp* 1986
Sales 172.0MM^E *EMP* 108
Accts Horne Llp Ridgeland Mississi
SIC 5045 7373 Computers, peripherals & software; Computer systems analysis & design; Computers, peripherals & software; Computer systems analysis & design
CEO: Gerard R Gibert
COO: Joe Rucker
**COO:* Joseph Rucker
**Sec:* Norman P Katool
**VP:* Mark Frye
**VP:* Wayne Gilbert
**CTO:* John Little
IT Man: Gary Campbell
IT Man: Glen Mire
Info Man: Allison Fryant
Sftwr Eng: Jason Guilbeau

GKV COMMUNICATION
See GRAY KIRK/VANSANT ADVERTISING INC

D-U-N-S 12-337-6654
GL CAPITAL PARTNERS LLC
YORK STREET CAPITAL PARTNERS
364 Main St Ste 2, Bedminster, NJ 07921-2592
Tel (928) 526-2735 *Founded/Ownrshp* 2002
Sales NA *EMP* 12
SIC 6159 Small business investment companies; Small business investment companies
Mng Pt: Robert Golding
CFO: David Tahan
VP: Glenn T Kim

D-U-N-S 06-960-8560
GL DODGE CITY LLC
STEW HANSEN DODGE CT CHRYSLER
12103 Hickman Rd, Des Moines, IA 50323-1801
Tel (515) 331-2900 *Founded/Ownrshp* 1974
Sales 61.4MM^E *EMP* 172
SIC 5511 5521 Automobiles, new & used; Used car dealers; Automobiles, new & used; Used car dealers
Genl Mgr: Dan Boettcher
Sls Mgr: James Hansen
Sls Mgr: Jason Levang
Sls Mgr: Bob McKeehan
Sales Asso: Rhonda Marx

D-U-N-S 05-919-2914 IMP
GL GROUP INC
JAFFE BOOK SOLUTIONS
5111 Southwest Ave, Saint Louis, MO 63110-3429
Tel (314) 647-0600 *Founded/Ownrshp* 1974
Sales 231.6MM^E *EMP* 160
SIC 5192 2789 Bookbinding & related work; Books; Books; Bookbinding & related work
CEO: Gary Jaffe
**Pr:* Sanford Jaffe
**CFO:* Mark Rygelski
**VP:* Donna Jaffe
**VP:* Neil Jaffe
VP: Mary McCarthy
Dir IT: Greg Bonebrake
IT Man: Nick Dreyer
IT Man: Scott Hankins
IT Man: Adam Schell
Software D: Evan Haas

D-U-N-S 03-807-5008
GL HMH LLC
HAMER MOTORS
(*Suby of* GARFF ENTERPRISES INC) ★
11041 Sepulveda Blvd, Mission Hills, CA 91345-1413
Tel (661) 254-3344 *Founded/Ownrshp* 2011
Sales 62.1MM^E *EMP* 200
SIC 5511 Automobiles, new & used; Automobiles, new & used
Pr: Robert Garff
**Sec:* Shirley Cheri
**VP:* Don Redding
Exec: Adriana Martinez
Genl Mgr: Dave Gilman
Sls Mgr: Shawn Gilmartin
Sls Mgr: Darwin Ribadeneira
Sls Mgr: Abdul Salahieh
Sales Asso: Charles Belton
Sales Asso: Jerry Riboli

D-U-N-S 03-268-9442
GL NOBLE DENTON INC
DNV GL
(*Suby of* DNV GL GROUP AS)
1155 Dairy Ashford Rd # 315, Houston, TX 77079-3007
Tel (713) 586-7000 *Founded/Ownrshp* 2000
Sales 67.8MM^E *EMP* 400
SIC 8711 8734 7371 8742 1389 Marine engineering; Calibration & certification; Product certification, safety or performance; Computer software development & applications; Quality assurance consultant; Gas field services; Oil field services; Marine engineering; Calibration & certification; Product certification, safety or performance; Computer software development & applications; Quality assurance consultant; Gas field services; Oil field services
Pr: Arthur Stoddart
Pr: Guy Eng
Snr PM: Danny Seal

D-U-N-S 62-518-9055 IMP
GL SEAMAN & CO OF HOUSTON
DEBNERCOMPANY
8020 Katy Fwy, Houston, TX 77024-1908
Tel (713) 782-1300 *Founded/Ownrshp* 1991
Sales 46.6MM^E *EMP* 75
SIC 5021 Office furniture; Office furniture
Pr: Tim R Debner
**VP:* Cody Debner Jr
**Prin:* R Cody Debner Jr

D-U-N-S 12-543-4832
GL STAFFING SERVICES INC
1709 Banks Rd Bldg A, Margate, FL 33063-7744
Tel (954) 973-8350 *Founded/Ownrshp* 2001
Sales 30.6MM^E *EMP* 1,000
SIC 7361 Employment agencies; Employment agencies
Pr: Gerry Califano
**Sec:* Lawrence J Minei
**VP:* Robert Conde

GL TRADING
See GLOBAL LION INC

D-U-N-S 00-460-7235 IMP
GL&V USA INC
(*Suby of* GLV US HOLDING INC) ★
1 Cellu Dr Ste 200, Nashua, NH 03063-1008
Tel (603) 882-2711 *Founded/Ownrshp* 2000, 2010
Sales 59.9MM^E *EMP* 300
SIC 3554 Paper industries machinery; Paper industries machinery
Pr: Laurent Verreault
**Treas:* Dave Lemoine
**VP:* William Mahoney
**VP:* Richard Verreault
Snr PM: Alexander Berman

D-U-N-S 79-062-6449
GLACIAL ENERGY HOLDINGS
24 Route 6a, Sandwich, MA 02563-1862
Tel (508) 833-3500 *Founded/Ownrshp* 2005
Sales 147.2MM^E *EMP* 620
Accts Deloitte & Touche British Vir
SIC 4911 Distribution, electric power; Distribution, electric power
CEO: Gary Mole
**Pr:* Mark Finley
**CFO:* Ben Esposito
**VP:* Jessica Evans

D-U-N-S 02-296-7210
GLACIAL PLAINS COOPERATIVE
543 Van Norman Ave, Murdock, MN 56271-8027
Tel (320) 875-2810 *Founded/Ownrshp* 1999
Sales 89.1MM^E *EMP* 60
SIC 5153 5191 Grain elevators; Farm supplies; Feed; Seeds: field, garden & flower; Grain elevators; Farm supplies; Feed; Seeds: field, garden & flower
Genl Mgr: Tom Traen

D-U-N-S 80-100-4383
▲ GLACIER BANCORP INC
49 Commons Loop, Kalispell, MT 59901-2679
Tel (406) 756-4200 *Founded/Ownrshp* 1990
Sales NA *EMP* 2,030^E
Tkr Sym GBCI *Exch* NGS
SIC 6022 State commercial banks; State commercial banks
Pr: Michael J Blodnick
**Ch Bd:* Dallas I Herron
Pr: Judy Overcast
Pr: Sonal Shah
CFO: Ron J Copher
Ofcr: Don J Chery
Sr VP: Marcia Johnson
VP: Todd Grande
VP: Karin Hergesheimer
VP: April Kelso
VP: Don Lloyd
VP: Bill McCarthy
VP: Grant Orr
VP: Michael Smith
VP: Leslie Thompson
Board of Directors: Sherry L Cladouhos, James M English, Annie M Goodwin, Craig A Langel, Douglas J McBride, John W Murdoch, Mark J Semmens

D-U-N-S 06-555-9742
■ GLACIER BANK
BANK OF THE SAN JUANS
(*Suby of* GLACIER BANCORP INC) ★
202 Mn St, Kalispell, MT 59901
Tel (406) 756-4200 *Founded/Ownrshp* 1990
Sales NA *EMP* 210
SIC 6022 State commercial banks; State commercial banks
Pr: Randall M Chesler
Top Exec: Bob Nystuen
Ex VP: Dennis Beams
Ex VP: Donald Chery
Ex VP: James Strosahl
Sr VP: Duane Kechter
Sr VP: Don Lloyd
Sr VP: Paul Peterson
Sr VP: Robert Taylor
VP: Tammy Lawler
VP: Sharon Procopio
VP: Gary Sparr
VP: Roxanne Swartzenberger
VP: Cheryl Zobenica

D-U-N-S 17-639-9475
GLACIER CONSTRUCTION CO INC
5460 S Quebec St Ste 200, Greenwood Village, CO 80111-1917
Tel (303) 221-5383 *Founded/Ownrshp* 1997
Sales 57.6MM^E *EMP* 115^E
Accts Bauerle & Company Pc
SIC 1521 1629 Single-family housing construction; Industrial plant construction; Single-family housing construction; Industrial plant construction
Pr: Randall L Wambsgnass
VP: Steve Stephenson
Sfty Dirs: Vicente Rodriguez

D-U-N-S 00-886-5292 IMP/EXP
GLACIER FISH CO LLC
GLACIER SEAFOODS INTERNATIONAL
2320 W Commodore Way # 200, Seattle, WA 98199-1287
Tel (206) 298-1200 *Founded/Ownrshp* 1997
Sales 57.6MM^E *EMP* 350
SIC 0912 Finfish; Finfish
CEO: Mike Breivik
**Pr:* Jim Johnson
COO: Jonathan Lockwood
**CFO:* Rob Wood
**VP:* Merle Knapp
IT Man: Bart Lovejoy
Tech Mgr: Vebjorn Antonsen

GLACIER FOODS DIVISION
See DOLE PACKAGED FOODS LLC

D-U-N-S 02-010-8007
GLACIER HILLS INC
GLACIER HILLS RETIREMENT CTR
1200 Earhart Rd, Ann Arbor, MI 48105-2768
Tel (734) 769-6410 *Founded/Ownrshp* 1973
Sales 34.1MM *EMP* 320
Accts Rehmann Robson Llc Ann Arbor
SIC 8051 8361 Skilled nursing care facilities; Home for the aged; Skilled nursing care facilities; Home for the aged
Pr: Ray Rabidoux
**COO:* Sally Schaden
CFO: Bill Colburn
**CFO:* Jim Hume
CFO: Cathering Schmidt
Treas: George Borel
Ex Dir: Macmillan Shelley
Mktg Mgr: Julia Van De Car
Mktg Mgr: Julia Van Car

GLACIER HILLS RETIREMENT CTR
See GLACIER HILLS INC

D-U-N-S 18-329-8678 IMP/EXP
GLACIER NORTHWEST INC
SNOQUALMIE SAND & GRAVEL
(*Suby of* ARIZONA PORTLAND CEMENT) ★
5975 E Marginal Way S, Seattle, WA 98134-2414
Tel (206) 764-3000 *Founded/Ownrshp* 1990
Sales 65.2MM^E *EMP* 740
SIC 3273 3272 5032

D-U-N-S 09-903-8317 EXP
GLACIER SALES INC
316 N 3rd St, Yakima, WA 98901-2341
Tel (509) 248-2866 *Founded/Ownrshp* 2001
Sales 32.1MM^E *EMP* 15
SIC 5142 Packaged frozen goods
Pr: Bruce Bacon
**Sec:* Doug Kanyer
**VP:* Mark Cherry
**VP:* Christopher Prohska

GLACIER SEAFOODS INTERNATIONAL
See GLACIER FISH CO LLC

D-U-N-S 17-822-1391
GLACIER TECHNOLOGIES LLC
(*Suby of* BBNC) ★
1200 Golden Key Cir # 400, El Paso, TX 79925-5820
Tel (915) 757-1487 *Founded/Ownrshp* 2004
Sales 57.3MM *EMP* 75
SIC 8711 Engineering services; Engineering services
VP: Bennie Haberlein
Prgrm Mgr: Nancy Kurtyka
Prgrm Mgr: Myron Rone
Ql Cn Mgr: Norman Ontiveros

D-U-N-S 10-627-0861 IMP
▲ GLACIER WATER SERVICES INC
1385 Park Center Dr, Vista, CA 92081-8338
Tel (760) 560-1111 *Founded/Ownrshp* 1983
Sales 105.5MM^E *EMP* 400^E
Tkr Sym GWSV *Exch* OTO
SIC 5962 Automatic vending machines; Cold drinks vending machines
Pr: Brian H McInerney
**Ch Bd:* Charles A Norris
COO: Steve Murphy
**COO:* Steven L Murphy
**CFO:* Steve Stringer
**V Ch Bd:* Peter H Neuwirth
VP: Thomas Conti
VP: David Porcelli
Exec: Kris Anderson
Dist Mgr: Brian Vega
Dist Mgr: Brian Wencka

D-U-N-S 14-492-7597 IMP
■ GLAD PRODUCTS CO
(*Suby of* CLOROX CO) ★
1221 Broadway Ste A, Oakland, CA 94612-1837
Tel (510) 271-7000 *Founded/Ownrshp* 1999
Sales 500.1MM^E *EMP* 4,800
SIC 3081 2673 2842 3295 Plastic film & sheet; Plastic bags: made from purchased materials; Automobile polish; Waxes for wood, leather & other materials; Cat box litter; Plastic film & sheet; Plastic bags: made from purchased materials; Automobile polish; Waxes for wood, leather & other materials; Cat box litter
Ch Bd: William V Stephenson
**Pr:* Thomas H Rowland
**CFO:* Donald A De Santis
**VP:* Joseph B Furey

Genl Mgr: Beth Springer
MIS Dir: Cathy Savage

D-U-N-S 02-259-9187
GLADDING CHEVROLET INC
J B A CHEVROLET
7327 Ritchie Hwy, Glen Burnie, MD 21061-3104
Tel (410) 766-6300 *Founded/Ownrshp* 1955
Sales 48.6MM^E *EMP* 130
SIC 5511 Automobiles, new & used; Pickups, new & used; Vans, new & used; Automobiles, new & used; Pickups, new & used; Vans, new & used
Pr: Joseph Aiello
**VP:* Mark Aiello
**VP:* Mathew Aiello
Off Mgr: Nora Warren
Sales Asso: Carlo Florio
Sales Asso: Kelly Paris
Sales Asso: Matt Weibel
Board of Directors: Rene Bradley, Joe Kircher

D-U-N-S 04-824-6375
GLADE RUN LUTHERAN SERVICES (PA)
70 W Beaver St, Zelienople, PA 16063-1582
Tel (724) 452-4453 *Founded/Ownrshp* 1854
Sales 25.1MM *EMP* 525
Accts Grossman Yanak & Ford Llp Pit
SIC 8322 8361 8093 Multi-service center; Child related social services; Residential care; Mental health clinic, outpatient; Multi-service center; Child related social services; Residential care; Mental health clinic, outpatient
Pr: Charles T Lockwood

D-U-N-S 02-284-3387
GLADEN CONSTRUCTION INC
40739 Us 71, Laporte, MN 56461-4278
Tel (218) 224-2237 *Founded/Ownrshp* 1974
Sales 22.1MM *EMP* 65
SIC 1611 Grading; Grading
Pr: Clayton Gladen
CFO: Mark Frosaker
**Treas:* Connie Gladen
**VP:* Tim Gladen
VP: Greg Hall

D-U-N-S 00-479-4749
GLADES ELECTRIC COOPERATIVE INC (FL)
26733 Us Highway 27, Moore Haven, FL 33471-6226
Tel (863) 946-0061 *Founded/Ownrshp* 1945
Sales 43.2MM *EMP* 66
Accts Jackson Thornton & Co Pc Mont
SIC 4911 Distribution, electric power; Distribution, electric power
CEO: Jeffrey Brelington
COO: Jeff Brewington
**CFO:* Jennifer Manning
Ex Dir: Tracy Whirls
IT Man: Naomi Snowden
Sfty Mgr: Christy Caputo

GLADES GENERAL HOSPITAL
See LAKESIDE MEDICAL CENTER

D-U-N-S 10-768-8103 EXP
GLADES PARTS CO INC
ORIGINAL EQUIPMENT
1348 S Main St, Belle Glade, FL 33430-4914
Tel (561) 996-2202 *Founded/Ownrshp* 1974
Sales 23.7MM^E *EMP* 50
SIC 5013 5531 Automotive supplies & parts; Automotive parts
Pr: Jose M Antuna II
**VP:* Juan C Antuna
Genl Mgr: Jose Antuna III

GLADES SUGAR HOUSE
See SUGAR CANE GROWERS COOPERATIVE OF FLORIDA

D-U-N-S 19-329-4659
GLADEWATER INDEPENDENT SCHOOL DISTRICT
500 W Quitman Ave, Gladewater, TX 75647-2143
Tel (903) 845-6991 *Founded/Ownrshp* 1930
Sales 18.7MM *EMP* 341
Accts Karen A Jacks & Associates P
SIC 8211 Public elementary & secondary schools; Public elementary & secondary schools
Psych: Dawn Kirkindoll

D-U-N-S 79-035-0826
GLADIATOR CORP
2882 Sand Hill Rd Ste 280, Menlo Park, CA 94025-7057
Tel (650) 233-2900 *Founded/Ownrshp* 2006
Sales 81.3MM^E *EMP* 338
SIC 7372 Prepackaged software; Prepackaged software
Pr: Benjamin Ball

D-U-N-S 18-818-7298
GLADIEUX TRADING AND MARKETING CO LP
4133 New Haven Ave, Fort Wayne, IN 46803-1643
Tel (260) 423-4477 *Founded/Ownrshp* 1987
Sales 161.4MM^E *EMP* 97
SIC 5171 Petroleum terminals; Petroleum terminals
Pt: James Gladieux
Pt: David Sordelet
Pt: Steven Uebelhoer
Exec: Robert Hayes

D-U-N-S 13-256-7736
GLADSTONE AUTOMOTIVE INC
GLADSTONE DODGE CHRYSLER
5610 N Oak Trfy, Kansas City, MO 64118-5237
Tel (816) 455-3500 *Founded/Ownrshp* 1987
Sales 33.5MM^E *EMP* 81
SIC 5511 7532 Automobiles, new & used; Vans, new & used; Pickups, new & used; Top & body repair & paint shops; Automobiles, new & used; Vans, new & used; Pickups, new & used; Top & body repair & paint shops
Pr: Tom Doherty
**Sec:* Frances Doherty
Sls Mgr: Gerald Bentley
Sls Mgr: Adam Cash

D-U-N-S 03-008-7402
▲ **GLADSTONE CAPITAL CORP**
1521 Westbranch Dr # 200, Mc Lean, VA 22102-3204
Tel (703) 287-5800 *Founded/Ownrshp* 2001
Sales 38.0MM *EMP* 60^E
Tkr Sym GLAD *Exch* NGS
SIC 6211 Investment bankers; Investment bankers
Ch Bd: David Gladstone
Pr: Robert L Marcotte
COO: Terry Lee Brubaker
CFO: Melissa Morrison
Chf Inves: George Stelljes

D-U-N-S 13-263-6502
▲ **GLADSTONE COMMERCIAL CORP**
1521 Westbranch Dr # 200, Mc Lean, VA 22102-3204
Tel (703) 287-5800 *Founded/Ownrshp* 2003
Sales 73.7MM *EMP* 5^E
Accts Pricewaterhousecoopers Llp M
Tkr Sym GOOD *Exch* NGS
SIC 6798 Real estate investment trusts; Real estate investment trusts
Ch Bd: David Gladstone
**V Ch:* Terry L Brubaker
Pr: Robert Cutlip
CFO: Harry Brill
CFO: Danielle Jones
CFO: David Watson
**Ex VP:* David A R Dullum
Mng Dir: Arthur Cooper
Mng Dir: Robert Corry
Mng Dir: Chris Daniel
Mng Dir: Chris Massey

GLADSTONE DODGE CHRYSLER
See GLADSTONE AUTOMOTIVE INC

D-U-N-S 61-164-4159
▲ **GLADSTONE INVESTMENT CORP**
1521 Westbranch Dr # 200, Mc Lean, VA 22102-3210
Tel (703) 287-5800 *Founded/Ownrshp* 2005
Sales 41.6MM *EMP* 315
Tkr Sym GAIN *Exch* NGS
SIC 6726 Management investment funds, closed-end; Management investment funds, closed-end
Ch Bd: David Gladstone
V Ch: Terry L Brubaker
V Ch: George Stelljes
Pr: David A R Dullum
CFO: Mark Perrigo
CFO: Julia Ryan
Ofcr: Jack Dellafiora
Mng Dir: Michael Brown
Mng Dir: Bill Frisbie
Board of Directors: Paul W Adelgren, Michela A English, Caren D Merrick, John H Outland, Anthony W Parker, John Reilly, Walter H Wilkinson Jr

D-U-N-S 36-176-6467
GLADSTONE MANAGEMENT CORP
1521 Westbranch Dr # 200, Mc Lean, VA 22102-3204
Tel (703) 287-5800 *Founded/Ownrshp* 2002
Sales 32.0MM *EMP* 48^E
SIC 8742 Business planning & organizing services; Business planning & organizing services
CEO: David Gladstone
**Pr:* Terry Brubaker
**CFO:* Harry Brill
CFO: Danielle Jones
Treas: Melissa Morrison
Ofcr: Jack Dellafiora
Ofcr: Jennifer Smith
Exec: Greg Bowie
Exec: Erika Highland
Genl Couns: Catherine Klaus
Snr Mgr: Paula Novara

D-U-N-S 13-712-7916
GLADSTONE SCHOOL DISTRICT 115
17789 Webster Rd, Gladstone, OR 97027-1498
Tel (503) 655-2777 *Founded/Ownrshp* 1908
Sales 25.1MM *EMP* 234
Accts Talbot Korvola & Warwick Llp
SIC 8211 Public elementary & secondary schools; Public elementary school; Public junior high school; Public senior high school; Public elementary & secondary schools; Public elementary school; Public junior high school; Public senior high school
Teacher Pr: Tammy Tracy

D-U-N-S 08-971-5700
GLADWIN COMMUNITY SCHOOLS
401 N Bowery Ave, Gladwin, MI 48624-1409
Tel (989) 426-9255 *Founded/Ownrshp* 1896, 2005
Sales 16.4MM^E *EMP* 325
SIC 8211 Public elementary school; Public junior high school; Public senior high school; Public elementary school; Public junior high school; Public senior high school
**Pr:* Paul Graveline
**Treas:* Kelly Gower
Treas: Chuck Hinman
**VP:* Greg Alward

D-U-N-S 07-425-6975
GLADWIN HOSPITAL INC (MI)
MIDMICHIGAN MEDICAL CENTER-GLA
515 Quarter St, Gladwin, MI 48624-1959
Tel (989) 246-0128 *Founded/Ownrshp* 1937
Sales 27.4MM *EMP* 180
SIC 8062 General medical & surgical hospitals
Ex VP: Mark Bush
**Ex VP:* Sherry Taung
Dir Rad: Charles A Guidot
CTO: Kim Krahn
QA Dir: Carolyn Vanwert
Mktg Dir: Cal McIntosh
Doctor: Christy Gary
HC Dir: Lisa Schnieder

D-U-N-S 06-476-0333
GLADWIN MACHINERY & SUPPLY CO
5170 Main St Ne, Minneapolis, MN 55421-1528
Tel (763) 574-9000 *Founded/Ownrshp* 1973
Sales 23.4MM^E *EMP* 54
SIC 5051 Sheets, metal
CEO: Thomas W Gladwin
**VP:* Todd King
Sls Dir: Dave Hintze
Sls Mgr: Dave King
Sales Asso: Adam Hegedus

D-U-N-S 02-702-8968
GLADWIN PAINT CO AUSTIN LTD
2000 Broadway St, San Antonio, TX 78215-1100
Tel (512) 420-9400 *Founded/Ownrshp* 1954
Sales 65.8MM^E *EMP* 100
SIC 5198 5231 Paints; Paint; Paints; Paint
Pr: Larry Pyle

D-U-N-S 00-134-4902 IMP/EXP
GLAMORISE FOUNDATIONS INC (NY)
MAIDWELL
135 Madison Ave Fl 3, New York, NY 10016-6793
Tel (212) 684-5025 *Founded/Ownrshp* 1955
Sales 28.5MM^E *EMP* 250
SIC 2342

D-U-N-S 10-305-4912
GLAMOUR INDUSTRIES CO
AMERICAN INTERNATIONAL INDS
2220 Gaspar Ave, Commerce, CA 90040-1516
Tel (323) 728-2999 *Founded/Ownrshp* 1971
Sales 53.6MM^E *EMP* 300
SIC 5122 Cosmetics; Cosmetics
Pr: Zvi Ryzman
**Ex VP:* Theresa Cooper

D-U-N-S 00-907-6225 IMP
GLANBIA FOODS INC (ID)
(*Suby of* GLANBIA INC) ★
121 4th Ave S, Twin Falls, ID 83301-6223
Tel (208) 733-7555 *Founded/Ownrshp* 1947, 1990
Sales 63.6MM^E *EMP* 400
SIC 2022 2023

D-U-N-S 62-664-6848
GLANBIA INC
(*Suby of* GLANBIA PUBLIC LIMITED COMPANY)
121 4th Ave S, Twin Falls, ID 83301-6223
Tel (208) 733-7555 *Founded/Ownrshp* 1966
Sales 272.9MM^E *EMP* 700
SIC 2022 Natural cheese; Whey, raw or liquid; Natural cheese; Whey, raw or liquid
Pr: David Thomas
**CFO:* Daragh Maccabee
CFO: Mark Short
VP: Brendan Britton
VP: Mike Brown
Dir IT: Bob Link
Doctor: Geoffrey Meagher

D-U-N-S 05-099-0324 IMP/EXP
GLANBIA NUTRITIONALS (NA) INC
(*Suby of* GLANBIA PUBLIC LIMITED COMPANY)
2840 Loker Ave E Ste 100, Carlsbad, CA 92010-6677
Tel (760) 438-0089 *Founded/Ownrshp* 2006
Sales 85.1MM^E *EMP* 165^E
SIC 5169 2833 8099

D-U-N-S 06-481-7181 IMP
GLANBIA NUTRITIONALS INC
2840 Loker Ave E Ste 100, Carlsbad, CA 92010-6677
Tel (760) 438-0089 *Founded/Ownrshp* 2003
Sales 26.1MM^E *EMP* 51^E
SIC 5169 Chemicals & allied products
Pr: Jerry O'Dea
VP: Deedee Bennett
VP: Lynda Doyle
VP: Kevin Meyer
Off Admin: Barbara Levitt
Dir IT: Rick Schulze
Plnt Mgr: Diana Plumey

D-U-N-S 92-944-4826 IMP/EXP
GLANBIA PERFORMANCE NUTRITION INC
COSTELLO'S HEALTH DISTRIBUTORS
(*Suby of* GLANBIA INC) ★
975 Meridian Lake Dr, Aurora, IL 60504-4929
Tel (630) 236-0097 *Founded/Ownrshp* 1989
Sales 93.8MM^E *EMP* 280
SIC 2833 5149 5122 Vitamins, natural or synthetic: bulk, uncompounded; Health foods; Vitamins & minerals; Vitamins, natural or synthetic: bulk, uncompounded; Health foods; Vitamins & minerals
CEO: Thomas Tench
V Ch: Jim Manion
**CEO:* Anthony P Costello
**CEO:* Hugh McGuire
COO: Frank Stephenson
**CFO:* T J Kelly
VP: Robert Gollias
VP: Timothy Hennessy
VP: Peter Poteres
VP: Jonathan Thompson
CTO: Craig Martin

D-U-N-S 36-080-5261
GLANT PACIFIC INC
2230 4th Ave S, Seattle, WA 98134-1515
Tel (206) 628-6222 *Founded/Ownrshp* 1987
Sales 83.9MM^E *EMP* 260^E
SIC 5949 5093 5094 5945 Knitting goods & supplies; Fabric stores piece goods; Sewing supplies; Scrap & waste materials; Precious metals; Hobby, toy & game shops; Knitting goods & supplies; Fabric stores piece goods; Sewing supplies; Scrap & waste materials; Precious metals; Hobby, toy & game shops
Pr: Douglas F Glant
**Ex VP:* Bruce Glant

D-U-N-S 01-203-6422 IMP
GLANTZ HOLDINGS INC
16 Court St Ste 3000, Brooklyn, NY 11241-1013
Tel (502) 271-5560 *Founded/Ownrshp* 1906
Sales 134.8MM^E *EMP* 158
SIC 5046 Neon signs; Neon signs
Pr: Herbert Glantz
**Ch Bd:* Joseph Hartman

GLAS-COL DIV
See TEMPLETON COAL CO INC

D-U-N-S 18-970-0966
GLASER WEIL FINK JACOBS HOWARD AVCHEN & SHAPIRO LLP
10250 Constellation Blvd # 1900, Los Angeles, CA 90067-6229
Tel (310) 553-3000 *Founded/Ownrshp* 1988
Sales 36.5MM^E *EMP* 180
SIC 8111 General practice law office; General practice law office
Mng Pt: Terry Christensen
**Pt:* Barry E Fink
**Pt:* Patricia L Glaser
Pt: John Mason
**Pt:* Peter Weil
Pr: Eunice Jung
COO: Charles Cohen
**COO:* Allen Gilbert
Genl Couns: James Schreier
Counsel: Clare Bronowski
Counsel: Gerry Ginsberg

D-U-N-S 00-185-6400
GLASFLOSS INDUSTRIES INC (OH)
2168 Commerce St, Lancaster, OH 43130-9363
Tel (740) 687-1100 *Founded/Ownrshp* 1956, 1964
Sales 54.3MM^E *EMP* 308
SIC 3564 Filters, air: furnaces, air conditioning equipment, etc.; Filters, air: furnaces, air conditioning equipment, etc.
Pr: Scott Lange
**VP:* Donald Kingston
Exec: Susan Goodman
**Prin:* Cheryl Thompson
Natl Sales: Chris Zaker

D-U-N-S 00-731-7746
GLASFLOSS INDUSTRIES INC
400 S Hall St, Dallas, TX 75226-1976
Tel (214) 741-7056 *Founded/Ownrshp* 1956
Sales 51.4MM^E *EMP* 220
SIC 3564 Filters, air: furnaces, air conditioning equipment, etc.; Filters, air: furnaces, air conditioning equipment, etc.
Pr: K Scott Lange
**Treas:* Steve Wilson
**VP:* Don Kingston
Dist Mgr: Wynn Yamamoto
IT Man: Alexander Juby
Sfty Mgr: Carlos Manrique
Plnt Mgr: Brian McGarity
Plnt Mgr: Efrain Mondragon
Plnt Mgr: Tim Teska
VP Mktg: Mark Filewood
Mktg Mgr: Jessica Garcia

D-U-N-S 09-261-9220 EXP
■ **GLASFORMS INC**
(*Suby of* POLYONE CORP) ★
3850 Pinson Valley Pkwy, Birmingham, AL 35217-1854
Tel (205) 856-0033 *Founded/Ownrshp* 2012
Sales 35.0MM^E *EMP* 225
SIC 3229 Glass fiber products; Glass fiber products
CEO: Daniel J O'Bryon
Board of Directors: Ken Bass

D-U-N-S 10-835-4275
GLASGOW BOARD OF EDUCATION
711 S L Rogers Wells Blvd, Glasgow, KY 42141-1041
Tel (270) 651-6757 *Founded/Ownrshp* 1940
Sales 11.3MM^E *EMP* 288
Accts Campbell Myers & Rutledge Gl
SIC 8211 Public elementary & secondary schools; Public elementary & secondary schools

GLASGOW ELECTRIC PLANT BOARD
See ELECTRIC PLANT BOARD

D-U-N-S 00-791-0979
GLASGOW INC (PA)
104 Willow Grove Ave, Glenside, PA 19038-2110
Tel (215) 884-8800 *Founded/Ownrshp* 1975
Sales 107.8MM^E *EMP* 425
SIC 2951 1611 1623 Road materials, bituminous (not from refineries); General contractor, highway & street construction; Cable laying construction; Sewer line construction; Underground utilities contractor; Road materials, bituminous (not from refineries); General contractor, highway & street construction; Cable laying construction; Sewer line construction; Underground utilities contractor
Pr: Bruce B Rambo
COO: Rachel McCool
**Treas:* Lois Ann Glasgow
VP: Jim Bagley
**VP:* John Rath
Prgrm Mgr: Franklin Smith
Telecom Ex: Karen Brislin
DP Exec: Tim Call
Sfty Mgr: Bob Conrad
Plnt Mgr: Howard Pennell
Snr Mgr: Joe Edgar

D-U-N-S 92-702-7813
GLASGOW SPRAY-DRY INC
BLUEGRASS DAIRIES
1117 Cleveland Ave, Glasgow, KY 42141-1011
Tel (270) 651-2146 *Founded/Ownrshp* 1995
Sales 22.1MM^E *EMP* 100
SIC 2023 2034 Dry, condensed, evaporated dairy products; Dehydrated fruits, vegetables, soups; Dry, condensed, evaporated dairy products; Dehydrated fruits, vegetables, soups
Pr: Billy Joe Williams
VP: Kerry Williams
VP: Kirk Williams
Board of Directors: Kevin Williams

D-U-N-S 06-983-0771
GLASS & DOOR INTERNATIONAL I LLC
2002 Brittmoore Rd, Houston, TX 77043-2209
Tel (713) 690-8282 *Founded/Ownrshp* 1995
Sales 55.2MM^E *EMP* 128
SIC 5031 5039 Doors; Glass construction materials; Doors; Glass construction materials

D-U-N-S 18-140-6591
GLASS AMERICA MIDWEST INC
977 N Oaklawn Ave Ste 200, Elmhurst, IL 60126-1028
Tel (877) 743-7237 *Founded/Ownrshp* 2004
Sales 20.8MM^E *EMP* 200
SIC 7536 3231 Automotive glass replacement shops; Windshields, glass: made from purchased glass; Automotive glass replacement shops; Windshields, glass: made from purchased glass
CEO: Michael G Barry
**CFO:* Scott Wills
VP: Nik Frye
Genl Mgr: Bob Simpson
Off Mgr: Tim Trepanier
Sales Exec: Ben Herndon
Sales Exec: Brad Naiser
Sales Exec: Debbie Torrey
Mktg Dir: Ron Burns
Mktg Dir: Deborah Geiger
Mktg Dir: Joy Houston

GLASS CLASS
See VVP HOLDINGS LLC

D-U-N-S 15-199-7517 IMP/EXP
GLASS ENERGY CO INC
ARKANSAS GLASS CONTAINER
516 W Johnson Ave, Jonesboro, AR 72401-1982
Tel (870) 932-0168 *Founded/Ownrshp* 1967
Sales 66.4MM^E *EMP* 353
SIC 3221 Bottles for packing, bottling & canning: glass; Bottles for packing, bottling & canning: glass
CEO: Anthony Rampley
**Pr:* Tony Rampley
**Pr:* Carl Rosenbaum
**Treas:* Vicki Rampley
VP: Sandy Lilly
**VP:* Charles Rosenbaum
**VP:* Joel Sharp
Dir IT: Steve Bailey
IT Man: David Shaw
Sls Dir: Lee Aspinwall

D-U-N-S 10-656-5435 IMP
GLASS GALLERY LTD
CRYSTAL ODYSSEY
10300 Lake Bluff Dr, Saint Louis, MO 63123-7244
Tel (314) 416-4200 *Founded/Ownrshp* 1975
Sales 8.9MM *EMP* 1,100
SIC 5947 5199 Gift shop; Glassware, novelty; Gift shop; Glassware, novelty
Pr: George Ottensmeyer
**VP:* Kirby Boyd

D-U-N-S 01-170-6504
GLASS GARDENS INC
SHOP RITE OF ROCHELLE PARK
220 W Passaic St, Rochelle Park, NJ 07662-3118
Tel (201) 843-1364 *Founded/Ownrshp* 1955
Sales 107.2MM^E *EMP* 781
SIC 5411 5921 Supermarkets, chain; Liquor stores; Supermarkets, chain; Liquor stores
Pr: Irving Glass
VP: Terry Glass
Exec: Lori Bettineschi
Sls&Mrk Ex: Ed Restaino

D-U-N-S 12-629-1512 IMP/EXP
GLASS HOLDINGS CORP
3802 Robert Porcher Way, Greensboro, NC 27410-2190
Tel (336) 545-0011 *Founded/Ownrshp* 1988
Sales 42.2MM^E *EMP* 799
SIC 2221 Glass broadwoven fabrics; Glass broadwoven fabrics
CEO: Philippe Porcher

D-U-N-S 06-528-4846
GLASS MTN PUMICE INC
3400 Kauai Ct Ste 206, Reno, NV 89509-4828
Tel (775) 826-3399 *Founded/Ownrshp* 1977
Sales 350.0MM *EMP* 15
SIC 5032 Aggregate; Aggregate
Pr: Niilo Hyytinen
**Treas:* Elene Hyytinen

D-U-N-S 18-214-0314
GLASS OPERATING LLC
PORTLAND GLASS
(*Suby of* DWYER GROUP LLC) ★
1020 N Univ Parks Dr, Waco, TX 76707-3866
Tel (207) 774-9851 *Founded/Ownrshp* 2004
Sales 33.1MM^E *EMP* 190
SIC 5231 Glass; Glass
Pr: Samuel Katz
VP: Michael Bidwell
VP: Nathan Chandrasekaran
VP: Dina Dwyer-Owens
VP: Vladimir Gutin
VP: James M Johnston Jr

GLASS SPORTS CYLINDER WORKS
See TRI-STATE HYDRAULICS INC

D-U-N-S 12-091-5988
GLASS SYSTEMS INC
6655 Marbut Rd, Lithonia, GA 30058-5233
Tel (770) 482-5232 *Founded/Ownrshp* 1984
Sales 20.9MM^E *EMP* 65^E
SIC 1793 Glass & glazing work
Pr: Luther R Hudson
**CFO:* Franklin D McCoy Jr
**Sec:* Linda G Hudson
**VP:* Frank McCoy

D-U-N-S 05-958-6263
GLASSBORO PUBLIC SCHOOLS
560 Joseph Bowe Mem Blvd, Glassboro, NJ 08028
Tel (856) 652-2700 *Founded/Ownrshp* 1880
Sales 16.9MM^E *EMP* 300
SIC 8211 Public elementary school; Public junior high school; Public senior high school; Public special education school; Public elementary school; Public junior high school; Public senior high school; Public special education school

D-U-N-S 09-275-2823
GLASSCOCK CO INC
GLASSCOCK READY-MIX
5070 Broad St, Sumter, SC 29154
Tel (800) 800-6840 *Founded/Ownrshp* 1978
Sales 25.0MM^E *EMP* 142
SIC 4213 3273 Heavy hauling; Ready-mixed concrete; Heavy hauling; Ready-mixed concrete
Pr: James T Glasscock Jr
**Ex VP:* Mark Coleman
DP Dir: Spence Rowe

D-U-N-S 04-388-9385
GLASSCOCK CO IND SCH DISTRICT (TX)
GARDEN CITY
240 W Bearkat Ave, Garden City, TX 79739
Tel (432) 354-2230 *Founded/Ownrshp* 1929
Sales 36.8MM *EMP* 166
SIC 8211 Public elementary & secondary schools; Public elementary & secondary schools
Schl Brd P: James Eggemeyer

GLASSCOCK READY-MIX
See GLASSCOCK CO INC

D-U-N-S 11-284-1093 IMP
GLASSCRAFT DOOR MANUFACTURING CORP
(*Suby of* GLASS & DOOR INTERNATIONAL I LLC) ★
2002 Brittmoore Rd, Houston, TX 77043-2209
Tel (713) 934-9820 *Founded/Ownrshp* 1982
Sales 51.5MM^E *EMP* 128
SIC 5031 5039 3231 2431 Doors; Glass construction materials; Products of purchased glass; Millwork; Doors; Glass construction materials; Products of purchased glass; Millwork
Pr: John Plummer
**VP:* John M Hart
**VP:* David Miller
**VP:* Mark O'Neil
**VP:* Lisa Swchwarz

D-U-N-S 05-244-1680
■ **GLASSEAL PRODUCTS INC**
(*Suby of* HCC INDUSTRIES INC) ★
485 Oberlin Ave S, Lakewood, NJ 08701-6996
Tel (732) 370-9100 *Founded/Ownrshp* 1983
Sales 21.0MM^E *EMP* 130
SIC 3643 3679 3471 3812 3678 Connectors & terminals for electrical devices; Hermetic seals for electronic equipment; Plating of metals or formed products; Search & navigation equipment; Electronic connectors; Connectors & terminals for electrical devices; Hermetic seals for electronic equipment; Plating of metals or formed products; Search & navigation equipment; Electronic connectors
Pr: Ian McGavisk
**VP:* William Hubbard
Opers Mgr: Renato Madarang

GLASSELL SCHOOL OF ART
See MUSEUM OF FINE ARTS OF HOUSTON

GLASSFORM
See VANTAGE ASSOCIATES INC

D-U-N-S 08-377-3783
GLASSHOUSE TECHNOLOGIES INC
352 Turnpike Rd Ste 200, Southborough, MA 01772-1756
Tel (508) 879-5729 *Founded/Ownrshp* 2000
Sales NA *EMP* 550^E
SIC 7373

D-U-N-S 05-567-7199
GLASSMAN AUTOMOTIVE GROUP INC
GLASSMAN OLDSMOBILE
28000 Telegraph Rd, Southfield, MI 48034-1955
Tel (248) 354-3300 *Founded/Ownrshp* 1969
Sales 43.6MM^E *EMP* 95^E
SIC 5511 Automobiles, new & used; Automobiles, new & used
Pr: George Glassman
Exec: Kandra Kreger
Sls Mgr: Adam Germain
Sls Mgr: Tom Kalmeta
Sls Mgr: Michael Parziale

D-U-N-S 03-931-4307
GLASSMAN CORP
900 Commerce Pkwy, Hays, KS 67601-9342
Tel (785) 625-6600 *Founded/Ownrshp* 1980
Sales 20.0MM^E *EMP* 60
SIC 1711 Plumbing contractors; Warm air heating & air conditioning contractor
CEO: Joseph Glassman
**CFO:* Christy Phlieger
**VP:* Curt Unrein

GLASSMAN OLDSMOBILE
See GLASSMAN AUTOMOTIVE GROUP INC

D-U-N-S 01-400-4873
GLASSMERE FUEL SERVICE INC
535 Freeport Rd, Tarentum, PA 15084
Tel (724) 265-4646 *Founded/Ownrshp* 1952
Sales 49.1MM^E *EMP* 65
SIC 5172 5541 5983 5411 Gasoline; Diesel fuel; Filling stations, gasoline; Fuel oil dealers; Grocery stores; Gasoline; Diesel fuel; Filling stations, gasoline; Fuel oil dealers; Grocery stores
Pr: Dell M Cromie
**VP:* Linda J Cromie
Sales Exec: Chris Gardner
Art Dir: Shayna R Atkinson

D-U-N-S 00-791-0809
GLASSPOINT SOLAR INC
46421 Landing Pkwy, Fremont, CA 94538-6496
Tel (415) 778-2800 *Founded/Ownrshp* 2009
Sales 27.0MM^E *EMP* 61^E
SIC 5074 Heating equipment & panels, solar
Pr: Rod Macgregor
Pr: Ben Bierman
**CFO:* David Allsworth
**CFO:* David Dreessen
Top Exec: Lisette Rauwendaal
VP: Glenn Griffith

VP: John Odonnell
**CTO:* Pete Von Behrens

D-U-N-S 05-416-6293 IMP
GLASSTECH INC
995 4th St, Perrysburg, OH 43551-4321
Tel (419) 661-9500 *Founded/Ownrshp* 1995
Sales 26.3MM^E *EMP* 115
SIC 3211 3229 3231 Tempered glass; Structural glass; Glass tubes & tubing; Tubing, glass; Glass sheet, bent: made from purchased glass; Tempered glass; Structural glass; Glass tubes & tubing; Tubing, glass; Glass sheet, bent: made from purchased glass
Pr: Mark D Christman
**CFO:* Diane Tymiak
Sr VP: Eric Fintel
VP: Ashoka Jinka
**VP:* Ken Wetmore
Plnt Mgr: Mark Musselman
Sls Dir: Randy Croson

GLASSTEEL PARTS AND SERVICES
See PFAUDLER INC

GLASSWERKS GROUP
See GLASSWERKS LA INC

D-U-N-S 02-807-7048 IMP
GLASSWERKS LA INC (CA)
GLASSWERKS GROUP
(*Suby of* GWLA ACQUISITION CORP) ★
8600 Rheem Ave, South Gate, CA 90280-3333
Tel (323) 789-7800 *Founded/Ownrshp* 1949, 1980
Sales 48.8MM^E *EMP* 300
SIC 3231 3211 Mirrored glass; Tempered glass: made from purchased glass; Furniture tops, glass: cut, beveled or polished; Flat glass; Mirrored glass; Tempered glass: made from purchased glass; Furniture tops, glass: cut, beveled or polished; Flat glass
Pr: Randy Steinberg
**VP:* Edwin Rosengrant
IT Man: Saul Sosa
S&M/VP: John Medel
Sales Asso: Crystal Jones

GLASTEEL
See STABILIT AMERICA INC

D-U-N-S 07-635-7961 IMP
GLASTENDER INC (MI)
5400 N Michigan Rd, Saginaw, MI 48604-9700
Tel (989) 752-4275 *Founded/Ownrshp* 1969
Sales 40.9MM^E *EMP* 180
SIC 3589 2542 3585 Dishwashing machines, commercial; Bar fixtures, except wood; Refrigeration & heating equipment; Dishwashing machines, commercial; Bar fixtures, except wood; Refrigeration & heating equipment
Pr: Jon D Hall Sr
**Pr:* Todd Hall
**Pr:* Kim Norris
**VP:* Mark Norris
Sfty Mgr: Melvin Kuhl
Ql Cn Mgr: Walt Wojciechowski
Sls Mgr: John Wilson

D-U-N-S 07-463-4445 IMP/EXP
GLASTON AMERICA INC
(*Suby of* GLASTON SERVICES LTD. OY)
6000 Commerce Pkwy Ste D, Mount Laurel, NJ 08054-2226
Tel (856) 780-3001 *Founded/Ownrshp* 1982
Sales 40.4MM^E *EMP* 83
SIC 5084 Industrial machinery & equipment
VP Sls: Scott Steffy
Sls Mgr: Dan Thompson

GLASTONBURY GAGE
See ALPHA Q INC

D-U-N-S 78-748-0326
GLASTONBURY PUBLIC SCHOOL SYSTEM
628 Agbron Ave, Glastonbury, CT 06033
Tel (860) 652-7951 *Founded/Ownrshp* 1994
Sales 37.8MM^E *EMP* 970
SIC 8211 Public combined elementary & secondary school; Public combined elementary & secondary school
HC Dir: Annmarie Colebrook

D-U-N-S 03-179-7692 EXP
GLASTRON LLC
925 Frisbie St, Cadillac, MI 49601-9259
Tel (800) 354-3141 *Founded/Ownrshp* 2010
Sales 20.6MM^E *EMP* 450
SIC 3732 Boat building & repairing; Boat building & repairing

GLATFELTER INSURANCE GROUP
See ARTHUR J GLATFELTER AGENCY INC

D-U-N-S 06-388-0355 IMP
■ **GLATFELTER PULP WOOD CO INC**
(*Suby of* P H GLATFELTER CO) ★
228 S Main St, Spring Grove, PA 17362-1000
Tel (717) 225-4711 *Founded/Ownrshp* 1947
Sales 1.3MMM^E *EMP* 3,545^E
SIC 5099 2411 2621 Pulpwood; Cases, carrying; Pulpwood contractors engaged in cutting; Paper mills; Pulpwood; Cases, carrying; Pulpwood contractors engaged in cutting; Paper mills
CEO: Dante C Parrini
**Pr:* T C Norris
**Treas:* M A Johnson II
**Sr VP:* Christopher W Astley
**Sr VP:* John P Jacunski
VP: Steve Basom
**VP:* Jonathan Bourget
**VP:* David C Elder
**VP:* C F Glattfelder
VP: Tim Hess
**VP:* Kent K Matsumoto
VP: Amy Wannemacher
VP: William T Yanavitch II
Board of Directors: Richard C III

D-U-N-S 79-022-0628 IMP
GLATT AIR TECHNIQUES INC
(*Suby of* GLATT GESELLSCHAFT MIT BESCHRANKTER HAFTUNG)
20 Spear Rd, Ramsey, NJ 07446-1288
Tel (201) 825-6308 *Founded/Ownrshp* 1973
Sales 163.2MM^E *EMP* 155
SIC 5084 Industrial machinery & equipment; Industrial machinery & equipment
CEO: Reinhard Nowak
Ex VP: William Bundenthal
Ex VP: Ivo Nowak
VP: Bill Bundenthal
**VP:* Richard E Davis
**VP:* Diane Lancaster
VP: Paul Portje
VP: Steve Sirabian
Exec: Leah Jungkind
Exec: John Woods
Assoc Dir: Tom Bonitz
Board of Directors: Todd Brinberg, George Ferrito, Werner Glatt, Reinhard Nowak

D-U-N-S 01-372-6666
GLAUBER EQUIPMENT CORP
1600 Commerce Pkwy, Lancaster, NY 14086-1731
Tel (716) 681-1234 *Founded/Ownrshp* 2011
Sales 46.8MM^E *EMP* 50
SIC 5084 Compressors, except air conditioning; Pumps & pumping equipment
Ch: Peter W Glauber
**VP:* Pj Glauber
Opers Mgr: Diane Glauber
Sales Asso: Brandon Coxhead
Sales Asso: Dale Feringer

D-U-N-S 04-773-8281
GLAUS PYLE SCHOMER BURNS & DEHAVEN INC
GPD GROUP
520 S Main St Ste 2531, Akron, OH 44311-1073
Tel (330) 572-2100 *Founded/Ownrshp* 1986
Sales 90.2MM *EMP* 550
Accts Bcg & Company Akron Oh
SIC 8711 8712 Consulting engineer; Architectural services; Commercial art & graphic design; Consulting engineer; Architectural services
Pr: Darrin Kotecki
Treas: James Shives
Sr VP: Jeff Evans
VP: Jose Hoffmann
Dir: MO Darwish
Genl Mgr: Trever Powers
Dir IT: Kenny Koltas
Netwrk Eng: Jon Shannon
Sls&Mrk Ex: Dan Klecha
Mktg Dir: Joe Kidder
Genl Couns: Jackie Bennett
Board of Directors: Jeff Evans, David Martin, Mark Salopek, James Shives, Angela Wells

GLAUSER MERCEDES-BENZ
See MERCEDES BENZ OF WESTMINSTER

D-U-N-S 07-940-7973
GLAXOSMITHKLINE (USAL)
GSK
709 Swedeland Rd, King of Prussia, PA 19406-2711
Tel (888) 825-5249 *Founded/Ownrshp* 2014
Sales 48.9MM^E *EMP* 264^E
SIC 2834 Pharmaceutical preparations
CEO: Sir Andrew Witty
**Pr:* Deirdre Connelly
**VP:* Simon Bicknell
VP: Peter Kirkby
**Prin:* Roger Connor
Dist Mgr: Tim Dean
Snr Mgr: Janet Grogg
Snr Mgr: Melissa Szymczak

GLAXOSMITHKLINE BIO N AMER
See CORIXA CORP

D-U-N-S 82-892-4212 IMP/EXP
GLAXOSMITHKLINE CONSUMER HEALTHCARE LP
(*Suby of* G S K) ★
1000 Gsk Dr, Moon Township, PA 15108-1330
Tel (412) 200-4000 *Founded/Ownrshp* 1992
Sales 1.0MMM^E *EMP* 1,700
SIC 5122 Drugs, proprietaries & sundries; Drugs, proprietaries & sundries
Pr: Roger Scarlett Smith
Sr Cor Off: Mike Amburgey
Sr Cor Off: Janet Slack
VP: Gregg R Brandyberry
VP: Jacqueline Carsanaro
**VP:* Raymond D Rise
Exec: John Nashette
Ex Dir: Chris Britten
Ex Dir: Joseph Kiceina
Ex Dir: Mark Levy
Ex Dir: Neil McCrae

D-U-N-S 00-138-1342 IMP/EXP
GLAXOSMITHKLINE HOLDINGS (AMERICAS) INC (DE)
(*Suby of* GLAXOSMITHKLINE FINANCE PLC)
1105 N Market St Ste 622, Wilmington, DE 19801-1216
Tel (302) 656-5280 *Founded/Ownrshp* 1830, 2009
Sales 4.6MMM^E *EMP* 24,000
SIC 2834 2836 2833 2844 8071 Cough medicines; Vaccines & other immunizing products; Vaccines; Antibiotics; Face creams or lotions; Suntan lotions & oils; Oral preparations; Toothpastes or powders, dentifrices; Medical laboratories; Cough medicines; Vaccines & other immunizing products; Vaccines; Antibiotics; Face creams or lotions; Suntan lotions & oils; Oral preparations; Toothpastes or powders, dentifrices; Medical laboratories
Pr: Deirdre Connelly
**CFO:* Julian S Heslop
Mktg Mgr: Katrina L Brown
Mktg Mgr: Isha M Williams

D-U-N-S 00-230-0077
GLAXOSMITHKLINE LLC
G S K
(*Suby of* GLAXOSMITHKLINE HOLDINGS (AMERICAS) INC) ★
5 Crescent Dr, Philadelphia, PA 19112-1001
Tel (215) 751-4000 *Founded/Ownrshp* 1967
Sales 3.5MMM^E *EMP* 11,900
SIC 2834 Pharmaceutical preparations; Pharmaceutical preparations
CEO: Sir Andrew Witty
Pr: Deirdre Connelly
Pr: Roger Connor
CFO: Simon Dingemans
Treas: Sarah J Chilverstainer
Ex VP: Beth Spanninger
Sr VP: Simon Bicknell
Sr VP: Nick Hirons
Sr VP: Bill Louv
VP: Mike Corrigan
Exec: John Bolla
Exec: Robert Denton
Dir Lab: Robert Sanchez
Dir Bus: Charlotte Blanchard

D-U-N-S 07-879-1771
GLAXOSMITHKLINE LLC
2512 S Tricenter Blvd, Durham, NC 27713-1852
Tel (919) 483-3187 *Founded/Ownrshp* 2009
Sales 127.2MM^E *EMP* 976^E
SIC 1541 Pharmaceutical manufacturing plant construction

D-U-N-S 79-100-8162 IMP
GLAZ-TECH INDUSTRIES INC
2207 E Elvira Rd, Tucson, AZ 85756-7026
Tel (520) 629-0268 *Founded/Ownrshp* 1990
Sales 67.6MM^E *EMP* 200
SIC 5039 Glass construction materials; Glass construction materials
Pr: Peter Fazlollah
**VP:* Alex J Miramontez
Genl Mgr: Luis Medina
Off Mgr: Tammie Valdenegro
VP Mktg: Linda Salazar
Sales Asso: Nashie Sexton

D-U-N-S 03-087-3942
■ **GLAZED INVESTMENTS LLC**
KRISPY KREME DONUTS
(*Suby of* KRISPY KREME DOUGHNUTS INC) ★
1211 W 22nd St Ste 700, Oak Brook, IL 60523-3220
Tel (630) 928-6161 *Founded/Ownrshp* 2000
Sales 61.6MM^E *EMP* 977
SIC 5461 Doughnuts; Pies; Pastries; Doughnuts; Pies; Pastries
CEO: Lawrence Jaro
**COO:* Don Stahurski
**VP:* Joel Aaseby
Admn Mgr: Carolyn Estes

D-U-N-S 00-385-4197 IMP
GLAZERS DISTRIBUTORS OF INDIANA LLC
OLINGER DISTRIBUTING COMPANY
(*Suby of* GLAZERS DISTRIBUTORS OF TEXAS INC) ★
5337 W 78th St, Indianapolis, IN 46268-4148
Tel (317) 876-1188 *Founded/Ownrshp* 1947, 1980
Sales 135.4MM^E *EMP* 200
SIC 5182 Liquor; Wine; Wine coolers, alcoholic; Liquor; Wine; Wine coolers, alcoholic
**Pr:* Jim Oliver
VP: Dan Novack
CIO: Roger Smith
VP Sls: Jim Dixon
VP Sls: Bill Stevens
Mktg Mgr: Rob Meinzer
Sls Mgr: Jason Booth

D-U-N-S 00-799-4460 IMP
GLAZERS DISTRIBUTORS OF LOUISIANA INC (LA)
NEW ORLEANS BEVERAGE AGENCY
111 Riverbend Dr, Saint Rose, LA 70087-3318
Tel (504) 443-8600 *Founded/Ownrshp* 1944
Sales 63.3MM^E *EMP* 270
SIC 5182 Wine & distilled beverages; Wine & distilled beverages
Pr: Bennett Glazer
COO: Tim Wood
**CFO:* Cary Rossell
VP Bus Dev: Mike Lakusta
Exec: Darla Gullett
Admn Mgr: John Berry
Dist Mgr: Josh Perschall

D-U-N-S 79-142-2389 IMP
GLAZERS DISTRIBUTORS OF OHIO INC
GLAZER'S OF OHIO
(*Suby of* GLAZERS DISTRIBUTORS OF TEXAS INC) ★
4800 Poth Rd, Columbus, OH 43213-1332
Tel (614) 552-7900 *Founded/Ownrshp* 2012
Sales 94.2MM^E *EMP* 270^E
SIC 5181 5182 Beer & ale; Wine; Beer & ale; Wine
Pr: Bennett Glazer
**COO:* Mike Maxwell
VP: Stanton Robins
**VP:* Scott Westerman
Opers Mgr: Brian Thimling
Sls Mgr: Kimberly Rosenbaum

D-U-N-S 00-792-6538 IMP/EXP
GLAZERS DISTRIBUTORS OF TEXAS INC (IA)
GLAZERS WHOLESALE DISTRIBUTORS
(*Suby of* GLAZERS OF CANADA LLC) ★
14911 Quorum Dr Ste 150, Dallas, TX 75254-7003
Tel (972) 392-8200 *Founded/Ownrshp* 1909
Sales 2.7MMM^E *EMP* 6,000
SIC 5199 2082 2086 Wine & distilled beverages; Wine; Liquor; Beer (alcoholic beverage); Ale (alcoholic beverage); Carbonated beverages, nonalcoholic: bottled & canned; General merchandise, non-durable; Art goods & supplies; Gifts & novelties; Beer (alcoholic beverage); Ale (alcoholic beverage); Carbonated beverages, nonalcoholic: bottled & canned
Pr: Bennett Glazer
**Pr:* Sheldon Stein
**COO:* Robert Swartz
COO: Robert M Swartz
Ex VP: Pete Carr
Ex VP: Alan Greenspan
Ex VP: Mike Maxwell
Ex VP: Mike McLaughlin
Sr VP: Jim Oliver
VP: Orman Anderson
VP: Tom Brannen
VP: Stephen Cohen
VP: Ron Flanary
VP: Louis Leibs
VP: Cheri Pieringer
VP: Ben Rowell
**VP:* Betty Silverman
**VP:* Barkley Stuart
VP: Louis Zweig
Exec: Tracy Kosub
Exec: Lisa Pierce

D-U-N-S 07-943-3425
GLAZERS OF CANADA LLC
14911 Quorum Dr Ste 150, Dallas, TX 75254-7003
Tel (972) 392-8200 *Founded/Ownrshp* 2014
Sales 2.7MMM^E *EMP* 6,000^E
SIC 5963 Beverage services, direct sales
CEO: Sheldon Stein
COO: Robert Swartz
CFO: Thomas Greenlee
Ex VP: Pete Carr
Ex VP: Mike McLaughlin

GLAZER'S OF OHIO
See GLAZERS DISTRIBUTORS OF OHIO INC

GLAZER'S OF OKLAHOMA
See GLAZERS OF OKLAHOMA INC

D-U-N-S 07-241-4618 IMP
GLAZERS OF OKLAHOMA INC
GLAZER'S OF OKLAHOMA
3800 Harmon Ave, Oklahoma City, OK 73179-8604
Tel (405) 943-3833 *Founded/Ownrshp* 1974
Sales 40.0MM *EMP* 49
SIC 5182 Wine; Wine
Pr: Bennett Glazer
**Treas:* Betty Glazer Silverman
**Ex VP:* Michael Glazer
**Ex VP:* Barkley Stuart
Mktg Dir: John Burdge

GLAZERS WHOLESALE DISTRIBUTORS
See GLAZERS DISTRIBUTORS OF TEXAS INC

D-U-N-S 00-983-0837 IMP
GLAZIER FOODS CO
(*Suby of* GORDON FOOD SERVICE INC) ★
11303 Antoine Dr, Houston, TX 77066-4429
Tel (713) 869-6411 *Founded/Ownrshp* 2014
Sales 983.1MM^E *EMP* 550
SIC 5142 5141 Packaged frozen goods; Groceries, general line; Packaged frozen goods; Groceries, general line
Pr: John Miller
VP: Tom Dring
VP: Amelia A McStravick
VP: Judith Spring
Manager: David Gerow
VP Mktg: Troy Small
Manager: Deanne Robuck
Sls Mgr: Greg Bohnsack
Sls Mgr: David Curren
Sls Mgr: Jeff Smith
Sls Mgr: Ron Vaudt

D-U-N-S 05-460-3709
GLAZIER STEEL INC
650 Sandoval Way, Hayward, CA 94544-7129
Tel (510) 471-5300 *Founded/Ownrshp* 1982
Sales 30.4MM^E *EMP* 75
SIC 1794 Excavation & grading, building construction
CEO: Craig Glazier
**Pr:* Harold Glazier

D-U-N-S 02-740-8986
GLAZIERS FOOD MARKETPLACE INC
8525 W Warm Springs Rd, Las Vegas, NV 89113-3625
Tel (267) 446-6588 *Founded/Ownrshp* 2008
Sales 22.6MM^E *EMP* 175
SIC 5411 Grocery stores; Grocery stores
Pr: William R Glazier

D-U-N-S 08-757-8576
GLAZING SADDLES LTD
KRISPY KREME
12201 Tech Ridge Blvd, Austin, TX 78753
Tel (512) 744-4000 *Founded/Ownrshp* 2000
Sales 28.7MM^E *EMP* 187
SIC 5461 Doughnuts; Doughnuts

GLC
See GREAT LAKES COILS LLC

D-U-N-S 80-906-9131
GLC BUSINESS SERVICES INC
28 Prince St, Rochester, NY 14607-1406
Tel (585) 258-3910 *Founded/Ownrshp* 1992
Sales 14.5MM *EMP* 285
Accts Bonadio & Co Llp
SIC 8742 7359 Business consultant; Business consultant; Office machine rental, except computers
Ch: Gerard J Chambers
**Pr:* John Hayes
**CEO:* Gerard J Chambers
**CFO:* John A Falco
Sr VP: John Imperiale Sr
**VP:* Matthew Cosby
**VP:* John Solomon
Area Mgr: Mark Starnes
Off Mgr: Nicole Fargnoli
Site Mgr: Jerry Ramos
Sales Asso: Gerard Chambers

D-U-N-S 83-239-5136
GLC BUSINESS SERVICES INC
225 W 34th St Ste 1703, New York, NY 10122-1701
Tel (516) 510-9878 *Founded/Ownrshp* 2002
Sales 6.1MM^E *EMP* 350
SIC 7363 Office help supply service; Office help supply service
Pr: John Hayes

D-U-N-S 60-389-3392
■ **GLCC LAUREL LLC**
(*Suby of* CHEMTURA CORP) ★
1 Geddes Way, West Lafayette, IN 47906-5394
Tel (765) 497-6100 *Founded/Ownrshp* 2005
Sales 30.1MM^E *EMP* 200
SIC 2819 Bromine, elemental; Bromine, elemental
Pr: Robert Wood
**VP:* Billie S Flaherty

D-U-N-S 00-208-8607
GLEACHER & CO (NY)
677 Broadway Ste 2, Albany, NY 12207-2953
Tel (212) 273-7178 *Founded/Ownrshp* 1953, 1985
Sales 33.2MM^E *EMP* 220^E
Accts Pricewaterhousecoopers Llp
SIC 6282 6211 Investment advisory service; Investment research; Security brokers & dealers; Brokers, security; Dealers, security; Traders, security; Investment advisory service; Investment research; Security brokers & dealers; Brokers, security; Dealers, security; Traders, security
Ch: Homas Hughes
COO: Gordon J Fox
CFO: Brian Coad
Assoc VP: Dorothy Pasco
Assoc VP: George Wolf
Sr VP: Mark Ellis
Sr VP: Daniel F Marciano
VP: Jason Avilio
VP: Etan Ayalon
VP: Kevin Berg
VP: Charles Bricker
VP: John Cramer
VP: Denise Dicerce
VP: Eric Hagen
VP: Craig Irwin
VP: Seth Kaufman
VP: Gabrielle Kivitz
VP: Catherine Moore
VP: Susan Morris
VP: Audrey Mydosh
VP: Oleg Pohotsky

GLEAMNS HEAD START
See GLEAMS HUMAN RESOURCE COMMISSION

D-U-N-S 07-807-0497
GLEAMS HUMAN RESOURCE COMMISSION (SC)
GLEAMNS HEAD START
237 Hospital St N, Greenwood, SC 29646-2962
Tel (864) 223-8434 *Founded/Ownrshp* 1966
Sales 22.4MM *EMP* 400
SIC 8322 Individual & family services; Individual & family services
Ex Dir: Joe Patton

D-U-N-S 04-056-7471
GLEANER LIFE INSURANCE SOCIETY INC
5200 W Us Highway 223, Adrian, MI 49221-9461
Tel (517) 263-2244 *Founded/Ownrshp* 1894
Sales NA *EMP* 62
Accts Andrews Hooper Pavlik Plc Oke
SIC 6311 Life insurance; Life insurance
Pr: Ellsworth L Stout
Bd of Dir: Frank Dick
VP: Arell Chapman
VP: Daniel Gordon
VP: Jeff Patterson
Snr Mgr: Kevin Marti

GLEANERS COM FOOD BANK SE MI
See GLEANERS COMMUNITY FOOD BANK INC

D-U-N-S 08-429-7738
GLEANERS COMMUNITY FOOD BANK INC
GLEANERS COM FOOD BANK SE MI
2131 Beaufait St, Detroit, MI 48207-3410
Tel (313) 923-3535 *Founded/Ownrshp* 1977
Sales 51.6MM *EMP* 95^E
Accts Rehmann Robson Llc Troy Mi
SIC 8399 Council for social agency; Council for social agency
CEO: Gerald Brisson
Dir Vol: Delores Watters
Pt: Beth Macleod
Pt: Elaine Teuscher
**Ch Bd:* Katy Locker
**V Ch:* Catherine Schmitt
**Treas:* Jim Tompkins
IT Man: Gwen Breskl
Software D: Darren Boyd
Mktg Mgr: Stacy Averill
Mktg Mgr: Stacy Kessel

D-U-N-S 83-198-4062
GLEANERS COMMUNITY FOOD BANK OF SOUTHEASTERN MICHIGAN
5924 Sterling Dr, Howell, MI 48843-8861
Tel (313) 923-3535 *Founded/Ownrshp* 2009
Sales 66.2MM *EMP* 57
Accts Rehmann Robson Troy Mi
SIC 8322 Individual & family services; Individual & family services
Ex Dir: Dewayne Wells

D-U-N-S 04-515-8938
GLEANERS FOOD BANK OF INDIANA INC
SECOND HARVEST GLEANERS IND
3737 Waldemere Ave, Indianapolis, IN 46241-7234
Tel (317) 856-9764 *Founded/Ownrshp* 2010
Sales 54.7MM *EMP* 70
Accts Greenwall Cpas Inc Indianap
SIC 8322 Individual & family services; Individual & family services
Pr: Cythia Hubert
Dir Vol: Jessica Shive
Mktg Dir: Todd Clevenger
Board of Directors: James Browning, Martha L Durall, Carrie Petty, John T Wortman

D-U-N-S 09-933-3598
GLEANING FOR WORLD INC
7539 Stage Rd, Concord, VA 24538-3590
Tel (434) 993-3600 *Founded/Ownrshp* 1998
Sales 31.6MM *EMP* 10
SIC 8699 Charitable organization; Charitable organization
Pr: Rev Ronald T Davisdon
Chf Mktg O: Mike Tilley
VP: Jeane Smiley-Mason
Comm Dir: Daphne Inge

D-U-N-S 00-607-8398
GLEASON CORP (CA)
10474 Santa Monica Blvd # 400, Los Angeles, CA 90025-6932
Tel (310) 470-6001 *Founded/Ownrshp* 1946
Sales 47.3MM^E *EMP* 250
SIC 2393 2399 5399 Textile bags; Hammocks & other net products; Surplus & salvage goods; Textile bags; Hammocks & other net products; Surplus & salvage goods
CEO: Mort M Kay
**Pr:* Gary Magoda
**COO:* Howard Seinman
VP: Naghea Gary
**VP:* Shirley Kotler
VP: Garry Nagata
VP: Garry Nagta

D-U-N-S 11-878-9825 IMP/EXP
GLEASON CORP
1000 University Ave, Rochester, NY 14607-1286
Tel (585) 473-1000 *Founded/Ownrshp* 2000
Sales 853.4MM^E *EMP* 2,508
SIC 3541 3829 Machine tools, metal cutting type; Gear cutting & finishing machines; Numerically controlled metal cutting machine tools; Machine tool replacement & repair parts, metal cutting types; Physical property testing equipment; Machine tools, metal cutting type; Gear cutting & finishing machines; Numerically controlled metal cutting machine tools; Machine tool replacement & repair parts, metal cutting types; Physical property testing equipment
Ch: James S Gleason
Pr: John J Perrotti
Treas: John W Pysnack
Sr VP: Robert P Phillips
VP: Douglas C Beerck
VP: Edward J Pelta
VP: Brian M Perry
VP: William J Simpson
VP: Hermann J Stadtfeld
VP: Udo Stolz
Mng Dir: Karl-Heinz K Bler

D-U-N-S 16-140-5014 IMP
GLEASON CUTTING TOOLS CORP
(*Suby of* GLEASON CORP) ★
1351 Windsor Rd, Loves Park, IL 61111-4235
Tel (815) 877-8900 *Founded/Ownrshp* 1997
Sales 4.1MM^E *EMP* 360
SIC 3545 3541

D-U-N-S 60-225-3796 IMP
GLEASON INDUSTRIAL PRODUCTS INC
MILWAUKEE HAND TRUCK
612 E Reynolds St, Goshen, IN 46526-4097
Tel (574) 533-1141 *Founded/Ownrshp* 1964
Sales 42.9MM^E *EMP* 200
SIC 3537 Industrial trucks & tractors; Industrial trucks & tractors
CEO: Morton Kay
CFO: William Malone

D-U-N-S 15-187-1597 IMP
■ **GLEASON REEL CORP**
(*Suby of* HUBBELL INC) ★
605b 4th St, Mayville, WI 53050-1802
Tel (920) 387-4120 *Founded/Ownrshp* 1996
Sales 34.1MM^E *EMP* 160
SIC 3823 Industrial process control instruments; Industrial process control instruments
Pr: Th Powers
Ofcr: Jeff Dietzler
Exec: Steve Dubrava
Dir Bus: Richard Leissring
Ql Cn Mgr: Robert Dehond
Ql Cn Mgr: John Meredith
Ql Cn Mgr: Amy Rozin
VP Sls: Steve Loeck
Manager: Lance Bell
Manager: Tom McMahon
Sls Mgr: Paul Giblin
Board of Directors: R W Davies, T H Powers

D-U-N-S 12-134-5912
GLEASON RESEARCH ASSOCIATES INC
5537 Twin Knolls Rd, Columbia, MD 21045-3270
Tel (410) 730-1400 *Founded/Ownrshp* 1982
Sales 25.0MM^E *EMP* 128
Accts Beason & Nalley Inc Huntsvi
SIC 8711 Engineering services; Engineering services
CEO: Robert E Yates
**Pr:* Charles M Vessels
**CFO:* Jimmy Kelley
Brnch Mgr: Marie Bentley
Dir IT: Sharlene Hicks

D-U-N-S 00-220-5755 IMP/EXP
GLEASON WORKS (NY)
(*Suby of* GLEASON CORP) ★
1000 University Ave, Rochester, NY 14607-1286
Tel (585) 473-1000 *Founded/Ownrshp* 1865, 1984
Sales 159.7MM^E *EMP* 926

SIC 3714 3728 3566 3541 3829 3469 Gears, motor vehicle; Gears, aircraft power transmission; Gears, power transmission, except automotive; Gear cutting & finishing machines; Numerically controlled metal cutting machine tools; Machine tool replacement & repair parts, metal cutting types; Physical property testing equipment; Metal stampings; Gears, motor vehicle; Gears, aircraft power transmission; Gears, power transmission, except automotive; Gear cutting & finishing machines; Numerically controlled metal cutting machine tools; Machine tool replacement & repair parts, metal cutting types; Physical property testing equipment; Metal stampings
Ch Bd: James S Gleason
**Pr:* John J Perrotti
**VP:* Nanci Malin Peck
**VP:* Edward J Pelta
**VP:* John W Pysnack
Snr Mgr: Craig Ronald

D-U-N-S 14-627-1858
GLEESON CONSTRUCTORS & ENGINEERS LLC
(*Suby of* KLINGER COMPANIES INC) ★
2015 7th St, Sioux City, IA 51101-2003
Tel (712) 258-9300 *Founded/Ownrshp* 2004
Sales 100.3MM^E *EMP* 150
SIC 1542 Commercial & office building contractors; Commercial & office building contractors
Pr: Harlan Vandezandschulp
**CFO:* Robert Desmidt
**Ex VP:* Ron Rens
Ex VP: Ronald Rens
**VP:* James Black
VP: Ronald L Rens
Genl Mgr: Scott Chamberlain

GLEIM ENVIRONMENTAL GROUP DIV
See JOHN W GLEIM JR INC

D-U-N-S 08-570-3874
GLEN BLOOMING CONTRACTORS INC (PA)
HANDWORK CONTRACTORS
901 Minsi Trl, Blooming Glen, PA 18911
Tel (215) 257-9400 *Founded/Ownrshp* 1971
Sales 91.0MM^E *EMP* 300
SIC 1611 1794 Highway & street paving contractor; Excavation work; Highway & street paving contractor; Excavation work
Pr: John B Haines IV
**Sec:* John R Kibblehouse
Snr Mgr: Doug McManus

GLEN COVE CITY HALL
See CITY OF GLEN COVE

D-U-N-S 07-336-3616
GLEN COVE HOSPITAL
101 Saint Andrews Ln, Glen Cove, NY 11542-2263
Tel (516) 674-7300 *Founded/Ownrshp* 1921
Sales 43.8MM^E *EMP* 1,000
SIC 8062 General medical & surgical hospitals; General medical & surgical hospitals
CEO: Michael Dowling
Ansthlgy: Katrina Sabater

GLEN COVE MARINE
See GLENCOVE MARINA LLC

GLEN ELLYN CLINIC
See DU PAGE MEDICAL GROUP LTD

D-U-N-S 10-391-8678
GLEN ELLYN SCHOOL DISTRICT 41
BOARD OF EDUCATION DIST 41
793 N Main St, Glen Ellyn, IL 60137-3999
Tel (630) 534-7221 *Founded/Ownrshp* 2003
Sales 52.1MM *EMP* 452
Accts Baker Tilly Virchow Krause Ll
SIC 8211 Public elementary school; Public junior high school; Public elementary school; Public junior high school
MIS Dir: Gill Minkus
Psych: Sharon Dunham
Psych: Jennifer Rose

GLEN EYRIE CHRSTN CNFRENCE CTR
See NAVIGATORS

GLEN GERY BRICK
See GLEN-GERY CORP

D-U-N-S 07-550-5289
GLEN MILLS SCHOOLS
185 Glen Mills Rd, Glen Mills, PA 19342-1743
Tel (610) 459-8100 *Founded/Ownrshp* 1826
Sales 40.9MM *EMP* 540
Accts Grant Thornton Llp Philadelph
SIC 8361 Training school for delinquents; Training school for delinquents
Pr: Curtis Johnson
**Treas:* Harvey Ellis
**VP:* Frank Davis
**VP:* Carolyn Seagraves
Ex Dir: Garrison Ipock
Info Man: Richards Danelutti
Psych: Israel Delgado

D-U-N-S 01-454-5693 IMP
GLEN OAK LUMBER & MILLING INC (WI)
2885 N County Rd F, Montello, WI 53949
Tel (608) 297-2161 *Founded/Ownrshp* 1980
Sales 54.9MM^E *EMP* 350
SIC 2426 2435 2431 Dimension, hardwood; Hardwood veneer & plywood; Millwork; Dimension, hardwood; Hardwood veneer & plywood; Millwork
Pr: Tom Talbot
**CFO:* Richard Allen
**VP:* Ron Lindquist

D-U-N-S 16-729-4060 IMP/EXP
GLEN RAVEN CUSTOM FABRICS LLC
(*Suby of* GLEN RAVEN INC) ★
1831 N Park Ave, Burlington, NC 27217-1137
Tel (336) 227-6211 *Founded/Ownrshp* 1999
Sales 24.3MM^E *EMP* 150^E
SIC 5949 Fabric stores piece goods
CEO: Allan Gant Jr
Pr: Harold Hill Jr
Pr: Leib Oehmig
CFO: Gary Smith
VP: Sue Rich

D-U-N-S 00-323-0158 IMP/EXP
GLEN RAVEN INC
GLENRAVEN.COM
1831 N Park Ave, Burlington, NC 27217-1137
Tel (336) 227-6211 *Founded/Ownrshp* 1880
Sales 463.8MM^E *EMP* 3,000
SIC 2221 2281 2261 2211

D-U-N-S 16-962-2003 EXP
GLEN RAVEN TECHNICAL FABRICS LLC
GLENRAVEN.COM
(*Suby of* GLEN RAVEN INC) ★
1831 N Park Ave, Burlington, NC 27217-1137
Tel (336) 227-6211 *Founded/Ownrshp* 1999
Sales 27.8MM^E *EMP* 150
SIC 2221 Broadwoven fabric mills, manmade; Broadwoven fabric mills, manmade
Pr: Allen E Gant Jr
**Pr:* Harold W Hill Jr
**Pr:* Leib Oehmig
**Sr VP:* Gary Smith
**Sr VP:* Carl E Wally Wallace
VP: William E Bordin Jr

D-U-N-S 09-619-2265
GLEN ROCK BOARD OF EDUCATION
620 Harristown Rd, Glen Rock, NJ 07452-2328
Tel (201) 445-7700 *Founded/Ownrshp* 1894
Sales 21.4MM^E *EMP* 260
SIC 8211 Public elementary & secondary schools; High school, junior or senior; Public elementary & secondary schools; High school, junior or senior
VP: Rona McNabola

GLEN ROCK HAM
See AL & JOHN INC

D-U-N-S 96-792-6895
GLEN ROCK SCHOOL DISTRICT
380 Harristown Rd, Glen Rock, NJ 07452-2812
Tel (201) 445-7700 *Founded/Ownrshp* 2011
Sales 11.6MM^E *EMP* 466^E
SIC 8211 Elementary & secondary schools

D-U-N-S 04-626-5773
GLEN ROSE INDEPENDENT SCHOOL DISTRICT
1102 Stadium Dr, Glen Rose, TX 76043
Tel (254) 897-2517 *Founded/Ownrshp* 1910
Sales 38.8MM *EMP* 271
SIC 8211 Public elementary & secondary schools; Public elementary & secondary schools
Schl Brd P: Kelley Snodgrass

GLEN ROSE MEAT CO
See ROSE MEAT SERVICES INC

D-U-N-S 07-316-9310
GLEN ROSE MEDICAL CENTER EMPLOYEE CORP
GLEN ROSE NURSING HOME
1021 Holden St, Glen Rose, TX 76043-4937
Tel (254) 897-2215 *Founded/Ownrshp* 1994
Sales 25.0MM^E *EMP* 203
SIC 8059 8051 8052 Nursing home, except skilled & intermediate care facility; Skilled nursing care facilities; Intermediate care facilities; Nursing home, except skilled & intermediate care facility; Skilled nursing care facilities; Intermediate care facilities
CEO: Gary Marks
**Ch Bd:* Larry Shaw
**Ch Bd:* Gary Whittle
COO: MO Sheldon
**CFO:* Michael Honea
**Prin:* Sharon Boone
**Prin:* Deborah Gray
Prac Mgr: Candace Martinez

GLEN ROSE NURSING HOME
See GLEN ROSE MEDICAL CENTER EMPLOYEE CORP

D-U-N-S 07-941-9370
GLEN WESLEY INC (OH)
WESLEY RIDGE
5155 N High St, Columbus, OH 43214-1525
Tel (614) 888-7492 *Founded/Ownrshp* 1967
Sales 21.4MM *EMP* 100
Accts Plante & Moran Pllc Columbus
SIC 8051 6513 8361 Skilled nursing care facilities; Apartment building operators; Retirement hotel operation; Geriatric residential care; Home for the aged; Rehabilitation center, residential: health care incidental
Prin: Africa Thomas
**CEO:* Margeret Carmany
**CFO:* Robert Wehner
Treas: Robert Rouse
VP: Patricia Banzhof
VP: Charles Leader III
**Prin:* Tina Cassady
**Prin:* Lauren Croman

D-U-N-S 00-235-5857 IMP
GLEN-GERY CORP
GLEN GERY BRICK
(*Suby of* OLDCASTLE INC) ★
1166 Spring St, Reading, PA 19610-1721
Tel (610) 374-4011 *Founded/Ownrshp* 1979
Sales 142.7MM^E *EMP* 900
SIC 3251 Brick clay: common face, glazed, vitrified or hollow; Brick clay: common face, glazed, vitrified or hollow
Ch Bd: Steve Matsick
**VP:* George Robinson
VP: Ray Staub
Mktg Mgr: Tim Leese

D-U-N-S 00-838-5312
GLENAIR INC
1211 Air Way, Glendale, CA 91201-2497
Tel (818) 247-6000 *Founded/Ownrshp* 1956
Sales 216.8MM^E *EMP* 1,100^E
SIC 3643 3825 3357

D-U-N-S 09-677-5358
GLENBARD TOWNSHIP HIGH SCHOOL DISTRICT 87
596 Crescent Blvd, Glen Ellyn, IL 60137-4200
Tel (630) 469-9100 *Founded/Ownrshp* 1920
Sales 52.9MM^E *EMP* 1,039
SIC 8211 Public senior high school; Public senior high school
Schl Brd P: Rich Heim

D-U-N-S 01-630-7332
GLENBROOK DODGE INC
GLENBROOK HYUNDAI
100 W Coliseum Blvd, Fort Wayne, IN 46805-1044
Tel (260) 484-1533 *Founded/Ownrshp* 1964, 1979
Sales 49.7MM^E *EMP* 95
SIC 5511 5521 7538 Automobiles, new & used; Used car dealers; General automotive repair shops; Automobiles, new & used; Used car dealers; General automotive repair shops
Pr: Douglas Mc Kibben
**VP:* Christine Mc Kibben
Store Mgr: Todd Bonecutter
Sls Mgr: Nick Castillo
Sls Mgr: Matt McKibben
Sls Mgr: Ryan Tuttle
Sales Asso: Angel Bahena
Sales Asso: Jason Campos
Sales Asso: Jon Hartman
Sales Asso: Chad Holzinger
Sales Asso: Zach Hunter

GLENBROOK HYUNDAI
See GLENBROOK DODGE INC

GLENBROOK NORTH HIGH SCHOOL
See NORTHFIELD TOWNSHIP HIGH SCHOOL DISTRICT 225 (INC)

D-U-N-S 06-998-4771
GLENBROOK SECURITY SERVICES INC
1400 S Wolf Rd Ste 300, Wheeling, IL 60090-6525
Tel (847) 279-6465 *Founded/Ownrshp* 1959
Sales 5.6MM^E *EMP* 290
SIC 7381 Security guard service; Security guard service
Ch Bd: Thomas Bucklin
**Pr:* Steve Bucklin
Ex VP: John Sorman Jr
**Sr VP:* Roy Bucklin

D-U-N-S 14-012-6041
GLENCOE LIMITED LLC
227 W Monroe St Ste 3880, Chicago, IL 60606-5097
Tel (312) 795-6300 *Founded/Ownrshp* 1998
Sales 20.2MM^E *EMP* 142
SIC 6799 Venture capital companies

D-U-N-S 88-313-3035
GLENCOE MANAGEMENT INC
BURGER KING
7548 W Sahara Ave Ste 102, Las Vegas, NV 89117-2779
Tel (702) 254-7400 *Founded/Ownrshp* 1987
Sales 11.8MM^E *EMP* 370
SIC 5812 8741 Fast-food restaurant, chain; Management services; Fast-food restaurant, chain; Management services
Pr: Thomas McDonald

GLENCOE MEDICAL CLINIC
See GLENCOE REGIONAL HEALTH SERVICES

D-U-N-S 07-642-0095
GLENCOE REGIONAL HEALTH SERVICES
GLENCOE MEDICAL CLINIC
1805 Hennepin Ave N, Glencoe, MN 55336-1416
Tel (320) 864-3121 *Founded/Ownrshp* 1999
Sales 5.0MM *EMP* 360
SIC 8011 Offices & clinics of medical doctors; Medical centers; Offices & clinics of medical doctors; Medical centers
Pr: Jon D Braband
Chf Path: John H Uecker
Dir Vol: Denise Lemke
CFO: Cheryl Trippel
Ofcr: Kelly Wouters
VP: Julie Schmidt
Dir OR: Carmen Forcier
Dir Risk M: Cindy Noga
Dir Case M: Barb Jaskowiak
Dir Lab: Lee Springer
Dir Rx: Amy Dittmer
Dir Rx: Gina Jennissen

D-U-N-S 19-426-6870
GLENCORE LTD
(*Suby of* GLENCORE AG)
301 Tresser Blvd Ste 1500, Stamford, CT 06901-3255
Tel (203) 328-4900 *Founded/Ownrshp* 1985
Sales 237.7MM^E *EMP* 170^E
SIC 6221 Commodity contracts brokers, dealers; Commodity contracts brokers, dealers
Treas: David Porter
**VP:* Blandine Lewine
IT Man: RAO Uppuluri
Software D: Jacques Ipyam
Software D: John Shea
Opers Mgr: Jeffrey Henderson
VP Sls: Alan Johnson
Snr Mgr: Cyril Reol

D-U-N-S 06-912-4717 IMP
GLENCORE RECYCLING INC
(*Suby of* GLENCORE CANADA CORPORATION)
1695 Monterey Hwy, San Jose, CA 95112-6113
Tel (408) 998-4930 *Founded/Ownrshp* 2013
Sales 21.5MM^E *EMP* 75
SIC 5093

D-U-N-S 11-541-4971
GLENCOVE MARINA LLC
GLEN COVE MARINE
147 Glencove Blvd, Lake Ozark, MO 65049-5652
Tel (573) 365-4001 *Founded/Ownrshp* 1995
Sales 23.6MM^E *EMP* 72
SIC 5551 Boat dealers
Pr: Janice Thompson

**VP:* Sherry Jackson
IT Man: Brynda Waller

GLENCROFT
See FRIENDSHIP RETIREMENT CORP

D-U-N-S 07-623-2735
GLENDALE ADVENTIST MEDICAL CENTER INC
1509 Wilson Ter, Glendale, CA 91206-4007
Tel (818) 409-8000 *Founded/Ownrshp* 1905
Sales 403.7MM *EMP* 2,600
SIC 8062 8093 8011 General medical & surgical hospitals; Mental health clinic, outpatient; Freestanding emergency medical center; General medical & surgical hospitals; Mental health clinic, outpatient; Freestanding emergency medical center
CEO: Warren L Tetz
Chf Rad: Robert McKay
**Ch Bd:* Frank Dupper
**Pr:* Fred Manchur
**CEO:* Kevin Roberts
CFO: Jon Giese
CFO: Douglas Rebok
Bd of Dir: Christine Friestad
Ofcr: Gail Shannon
**Sr VP:* Judy Blair
**Sr VP:* Kelly Turner
**VP:* Karen Brandt
VP: Michael Cann
VP: Sharon Correa
VP: Dennis Deleon
VP: Rob Marchuk
VP: Gwen Mathews
VP: Arby Nahapetian
Exec: Nancy Cruz
Dir Lab: Cruisma Merinda
Dir Rad: Clayton Lau

GLENDALE CHRYSLER, DODGE & RAM
See MERLO AUTOMOTIVE GROUP INC

D-U-N-S 07-881-9539
GLENDALE COMMUNITY COLLEGE DIST
1500 N Verdugo Rd, Glendale, CA 91208-2894
Tel (818) 240-1000 *Founded/Ownrshp* 1927
Sales 10.3MM^E *EMP* 1,500
Accts Vavrinek Trine Day & Co Ll
SIC 8222 Community college; Community college
Pr: Dr David Viar
**Pr:* Audre Levy
**CFO:* Larry Serot
Trst: Tony Tartaglia
Ofcr: Rony Aharonian
Assoc VP: Jack Raubolt
Ex VP: Lawrence Serot
VP: Wayne Keller
**VP:* Mary Mirch
**VP:* Ron Nakasone
VP: Vicki Nicholson
VP: Arnel Pascua

D-U-N-S 05-197-2214
GLENDALE DODGE LLC
JACK ELLIS' GLENDALE DODGE
900 S Brand Blvd, Glendale, CA 91204-2398
Tel (323) 245-2333 *Founded/Ownrshp* 1981
Sales 32.3MM^E *EMP* 60
SIC 5511 Automobiles, new & used; Automobiles, new & used
Pr: David Ellis
Sls Mgr: Evan Ellis

D-U-N-S 12-280-0238
GLENDALE ELEMENTARY SCHOOL DISTRICT
7301 N 58th Ave, Glendale, AZ 85301-1893
Tel (623) 237-4000 *Founded/Ownrshp* 1913
Sales 65.1MM^E *EMP* 1,700
SIC 8211 Public elementary school; Public elementary school
Prgrm Mgr: Sharon Reed
CIO: Nancy Radz
MIS Dir: Matthew Peterson
IT Man: Jill Winn
Pr Dir: Tim Cummings
Instr Medi: Janet Gironda
Psych: Frank Dais
Psych: Alice Hoesch

D-U-N-S 11-379-3710
GLENDALE INDUSTRIAL SUPPLY LLC
UNICOA INDUSTRIAL SUPPLY
2121 N 23rd Ave, Phoenix, AZ 85009-2711
Tel (602) 254-4666 *Founded/Ownrshp* 2002
Sales 54.2MM^E *EMP* 90
SIC 5085 Industrial supplies; Industrial supplies
Brnch Mgr: Abraham Erazo
Sales Asso: Ruben Diaz

GLENDALE INFINITI
See GLENDALE NISSAN/INFINITI INC

GLENDALE MEMORIAL CENTER
See GLENDALE MEMORIAL HEALTH CORP

D-U-N-S 06-380-2136
GLENDALE MEMORIAL HEALTH CORP
GLENDALE MEMORIAL CENTER
(*Suby of* C H W) ★
1420 S Central Ave, Glendale, CA 91204-2508
Tel (818) 502-1900 *Founded/Ownrshp* 1995
Sales 2.6MM *EMP* 1,245
SIC 8062 General medical & surgical hospitals; General medical & surgical hospitals
CEO: David S Parkin
**Pr:* Jack Ivie
**COO:* Patrick A Petre
Nurse Mgr: Carol Cogswell
Prd Mgr: Jesus Ahedo
Pathlgst: Kenneth Frankel
Pharmcst: Young S Kim
Pharmcst: Kevin Lee

GLENDALE MITSUBISHI
See UNIVERSAL AUTO GROUP

D-U-N-S 78-992-5385
GLENDALE NISSAN/INFINITI INC
GLENDALE INFINITI
(*Suby of* SAGE HOLDING CO) ★
812 S Brand Blvd, Glendale, CA 91204-2106
Tel (818) 543-5000 *Founded/Ownrshp* 1995
Sales 63.9MM^E *EMP* 180^E
SIC 5511 7514 Automobiles, new & used; Rent-a-car service; Automobiles, new & used; Rent-a-car service
Pr: Morris Schrage
Genl Mgr: Mike Reed
Sls Mgr: Charlie Park

GLENDALE NURSING HOME
See GLENDALE UPTOWN HOME

D-U-N-S 16-752-3245
GLENDALE PLUMBING & FIRE SUPPLY INC
GPFS
723 Sonora Ave, Glendale, CA 91201-2431
Tel (818) 550-8444 *Founded/Ownrshp* 2006
Sales 27.2MM^E *EMP* 31^E
SIC 5087 Sprinkler systems
CEO: Armond Sarkisian
Off Mgr: Edwld Nozsheyen

D-U-N-S 80-846-0286
GLENDALE STEEL SUPPLY LLC
5743 W Bethany Home Rd, Glendale, AZ 85301-7755
Tel (623) 937-5290 *Founded/Ownrshp* 1998
Sales 26.7MM^E *EMP* 21
SIC 5051 Steel

D-U-N-S 07-723-9929
GLENDALE UNIFIED SCHOOL DISTRICT
223 N Jackson St, Glendale, CA 91206-4380
Tel (818) 241-3111 *Founded/Ownrshp* 1887
Sales 238.0MM^E *EMP* 4,000
Accts Vicenti Lloyd & Stutzman Llp
SIC 8211 Public elementary & secondary schools; High school, junior or senior; Kindergarten; Specialty education; Public elementary & secondary schools; High school, junior or senior; Kindergarten; Specialty education
Ex VP: Henrietta Movsessian
VP: Christine Walters
Exec: Kelly Velasquez
Ex Dir: Marina Garabedyan
Ex Dir: Camille Levee
CIO: Katie Warren
CTO: Mack Dugger
IT Man: Bruce Dalton
IT Man: Ed McBreen
IT Man: Angelica Reyes
Pr Dir: Steven Frasher

D-U-N-S 09-711-5539
GLENDALE UNION HIGH SCHOOL DISTRICT
GUHSD
7650 N 43rd Ave, Glendale, AZ 85301-1661
Tel (623) 435-0152 *Founded/Ownrshp* 1910
Sales 88.1MM^E *EMP* 1,800
Accts Heinfeld Meech & Co Pc P
SIC 8211 Public senior high school; Public senior high school

D-U-N-S 80-957-3459
GLENDALE UPTOWN HOME
GLENDALE NURSING HOME
(*Suby of* PRESTIGE HEALTHCARE) ★
7800 Bustleton Ave, Philadelphia, PA 19152-3812
Tel (215) 722-2300 *Founded/Ownrshp* 2010
Sales 12.0MM^E *EMP* 315
SIC 8059 Nursing home, except skilled & intermediate care facility; Nursing home, except skilled & intermediate care facility
Dir Soc: Lauren Polito

D-U-N-S 07-972-3292
GLENDIVE MEDICAL CENTER INC
EASTERN MONTANA VETERANS HOME
202 Prospect Dr, Glendive, MT 59330-1999
Tel (406) 345-2654 *Founded/Ownrshp* 1965
Sales 37.4MM *EMP* 430
Accts Eide Badly Lp Minneapolis Mn
SIC 8062 8051 General medical & surgical hospitals; Skilled nursing care facilities; General medical & surgical hospitals; Skilled nursing care facilities
CEO: Scott A Duke
Dir Vol: Laurie Kurtz
V Ch: Jeanne Seifert
**Pr:* David Linn
**CFO:* Barbara Markham
**Treas:* Steve Scheitlin
**VP:* Laura Glueckert
VP: Tige Vester
Exec: Mona Humphrey
Exec: Samuel Mintz
CIO: Matthew Shahan

D-U-N-S 87-990-5065
■ **GLENDORA CHEVROLET INC**
(*Suby of* GENERAL MOTORS LLC) ★
1959 Auto Centre Dr, Glendora, CA 91740-6714
Tel (626) 815-1147 *Founded/Ownrshp* 2009
Sales 34.5MM^E *EMP* 65
SIC 5511 5521 Automobiles, new & used; Pickups, new & used; Trucks, tractors & trailers: new & used; Automobiles, used cars only; Automobiles, new & used; Pickups, new & used; Trucks, tractors & trailers: new & used; Automobiles, used cars only
Pr: Michael Martin
Genl Mgr: Mike McGuire

D-U-N-S 96-490-2782
GLENDORA GRAND INC
805 W Arrow Hwy, Glendora, CA 91740-5413
Tel (626) 966-2924 *Founded/Ownrshp* 2007
Sales 25.8MM *EMP* 41^E
SIC 8062 General medical & surgical hospitals
Pr: William Nelson

D-U-N-S 07-619-1527
GLENDORA UNIFIED SCHOOL DISTRICT
500 N Loraine Ave, Glendora, CA 91741-2964
Tel (626) 963-1611 *Founded/Ownrshp* 1961
Sales 38.3MM^E *EMP* 650
SIC 8211 Public elementary school; Public junior high school; Public senior high school; Public elementary school; Public junior high school; Public senior high school
IT Man: Lavonia Margalla

D-U-N-S 08-613-4145
GLENELG COUNTRY SCHOOL INC (MD)
12793 Folly Quarter Rd, Ellicott City, MD 21042-1271
Tel (410) 531-2898 *Founded/Ownrshp* 1954
Sales 22.5MM *EMP* 170
Accts Nardone Pridgeon & Company Pa
SIC 8211 Preparatory school; Preparatory school
Ch Bd: James R Moxley III
Top Exec: Anne Wooleyhand
Dir IT: William Pickett

D-U-N-S 04-899-0669
GLENEWINKEL CONSTRUCTION CO LLC
3104 S Andrews Ave, Fort Lauderdale, FL 33316-4126
Tel (954) 990-8091 *Founded/Ownrshp* 2010
Sales 28.0MM *EMP* 13
SIC 1521 General remodeling, single-family houses; General remodeling, single-family houses
Pr: Gary Glenewinkel
**Pt:* David L Brennan
**Pt:* Maura F Corrigan
**Pt:* Kent J Darragh
**Ch Bd:* Kathryn Glenewinkel

GLENFALLS ELECTRIC SUPPLY
See GREEN MOUNTAIN ELECTRIC SUPPLY INC

D-U-N-S 06-801-4521
GLENGARIFF CORP
141 Dosoris Ln, Glen Cove, NY 11542-1225
Tel (516) 676-1100 *Founded/Ownrshp* 2009
Sales 34.0MM *EMP* 320
SIC 8051 Skilled nursing care facilities; Skilled nursing care facilities
Ch Bd: Sanjay Ahuja
Telecom Ex: Douglas Kiernan
IT Man: Barbara Bifone

D-U-N-S 02-003-5267
GLENKIRK
3504 Commercial Ave, Northbrook, IL 60062-1821
Tel (847) 272-5111 *Founded/Ownrshp* 1954
Sales 15.0MM *EMP* 300
Accts Miller Cooper & Co Ltd De
SIC 8361 8331 Home for the mentally retarded; Vocational training agency; Home for the mentally retarded; Vocational training agency
Pr: Alan Spector
CFO: Linda Coleman
Treas: Edward W Forsberg
Sr Cor Off: Thomas Mason
Sr Cor Off: Larry Menaker
Sr Cor Off: Robert Stein
Sr Cor Off: Bernie Sykes
Pgrm Dir: Stacy Roe
Pgrm Dir: Linse Varughese

D-U-N-S 10-364-7673
GLENMARK CONSTRUCTION CO INC
951 Western Dr, Indianapolis, IN 46241-1434
Tel (317) 244-3659 *Founded/Ownrshp* 1983
Sales 22.8MM^E *EMP* 100
SIC 1542 Commercial & office building, new construction; Commercial & office buildings, renovation & repair; Commercial & office building, new construction; Commercial & office buildings, renovation & repair
Pr: Mark E Smith

D-U-N-S 60-760-6167
GLENMARK INDUSTRIES LTD
4545 S Racine Ave Ste 1, Chicago, IL 60609-3384
Tel (773) 927-4800 *Founded/Ownrshp* 1988
Sales 65.0MM *EMP* 250
SIC 2013 Sausages & other prepared meats; Sausages & other prepared meats
Pr: Dave Van Kampen
Treas: George Krzesinski
QC Dir: Sharon Birkett
Board of Directors: Gerald Kolschowsky, Sheldon Lavin, David McDonald

D-U-N-S 13-059-7813 IMP/EXP
GLENMARK PHARMACEUTICALS INC USA
(*Suby of* GLENMARK PHARMACEUTICALS LIMITED)
750 Corporate Dr, Mahwah, NJ 07430-2009
Tel (201) 684-8000 *Founded/Ownrshp* 2002
Sales 34.0MM^E *EMP* 91^E
SIC 5122 Pharmaceuticals
Pr: Robert Mapsuk
**CFO:* Prakash Chainani
**Ex VP:* Vijay Soni
VP: Axel Perlwitz
Exec: Ivor Almeida
Exec: Sandeep Battan
Exec: Ganesh Bharambe
Exec: Sandeep Bist
Exec: Prashant Daspute
Exec: Sandeep Ghule
Exec: Umesh Jadhav
Exec: Anil Jakhar
Exec: Pankaj Kanungo
Exec: Sneha Kharangate
Exec: Ajit Mandal
Exec: Rekha Mishra
Exec: Prabhakar Niphade
Exec: Santosh Panda
Exec: Ravindra Pandit
Exec: Deepak Pant
Exec: Priya Parab

D-U-N-S 96-908-5666
GLENMARK THERAPEUTICS INC USA
(*Suby of* GLENMARK PHARMACEUTICALS LIMITED)
750 Corporate Dr, Mahwah, NJ 07430-2009
Tel (201) 684-8000 *Founded/Ownrshp* 2007
Sales 75.3MM^E *EMP* 468^E
SIC 2834 Pharmaceutical preparations
VP: Dereck Lobo

D-U-N-S 79-180-5401
GLENMEDE CORP
1650 Market St Ste 1200, Philadelphia, PA 19103-7311
Tel (215) 419-6000 *Founded/Ownrshp* 1983
Sales 130.2MM *EMP* 250
SIC 6733 6732 Personal investment trust management; Charitable trust management; Personal investment trust management; Charitable trust management
Pr: Gordon B Fowler
**Treas:* Laura A Williamson
Ofcr: Michael Cervasio
Ofcr: Richard Gale
Ofcr: Maria McGarry
Trst Ofcr: Barbara Hill
Sr VP: Susan P Mucciarone
VP: Matthew Beardwood
**VP:* James R Belanger
VP: John Carson
VP: Matthew Cross
VP: Deborah Cugel
VP: Letitia Ewing
VP: Scott Gilleland
VP: Frederick Haack
VP: Margaret Kelly
VP: Paul Keperling
VP: Robert Kiep
VP: William Krauss
VP: Jerry Littenberg
VP: Robert Maxwell

D-U-N-S 62-499-6109
GLENMEDE FUND INC
GLENMEDE LARGE CAP VALUE
1650 Market St Ste 1200, Philadelphia, PA 19103-7311
Tel (215) 419-6021 *Founded/Ownrshp* 2006
Sales 21.0MM *EMP* 1
SIC 6722 Management investment, open-end
Pr: Mary Ann Wirts
VP: Phyllis Simirglia
Exec: Mary Hoffman
IT Man: Jeff Bllew
MIS Mgr: John Peiffer

GLENMEDE LARGE CAP VALUE
See GLENMEDE FUND INC

D-U-N-S 07-547-9766
GLENMEDE TRUST CO NATIONAL ASSOCIATION
(*Suby of* GLENMEDE CORP) ★
1650 Market St Ste 1200, Philadelphia, PA 19103-7391
Tel (215) 419-6000 *Founded/Ownrshp* 1956, 1983
Sales 61.4MM^E *EMP* 242
SIC 6733 6732 6282 6726 Administrator of private estates, non-operating; Charitable trust management; Investment advisory service; Investment offices; Administrator of private estates, non-operating; Charitable trust management; Investment advisory service; Investment offices
Pr: Theodore Flocco
Mng Pt: Gordon Fowler
Pr: Philip Wachs
**CFO:* Laura A Williamson
Ofcr: Isabel Albuquerque
Ofcr: Anten Kraemer
Ex VP: Howard Wilson
Sr VP: James Belanger
Sr VP: Katherine Koch
Sr VP: Lisa Whitcomb
VP: Thomas Angers
VP: Charles Aulino
VP: John Carson
VP: Bill Christy
VP: Diana Deane
VP: Glenn Deibert
VP: Christine Dragoun
VP: Fred Haack
VP: Rekha Hagen
VP: Christopher Jcolarik
VP: Tracy Jemison
Board of Directors: Joseph N Pew V

D-U-N-S 05-851-7786 IMP
GLENMORE DISTILLERIES CO
2001 E 4th St, Owensboro, KY 42303-0147
Tel (270) 926-1110 *Founded/Ownrshp* 2001
Sales 26.6MM^E *EMP* 180
SIC 2085 Distilled & blended liquors; Distilled & blended liquors
Pr: John Goldring
IT Man: Craig Cunningham

GLENMORE PLASTIC INDUSTRIES
See SENDAR PLASTICS INC

D-U-N-S 01-683-9536
GLENMOUNT GLOBAL SOLUTIONS INC
GGSCA
3101 Bee Caves Rd Ste 220, Austin, TX 78746-5574
Tel (219) 762-0700 *Founded/Ownrshp* 2008
Sales 31.3MM *EMP* 148
SIC 8711 Engineering services; Engineering services
CEO: Ralph Carter
VP: Brad Hendrickson

D-U-N-S 05-478-2008
GLENN A RICK ENGINEERING AND DEVELOPMENT CO (CA)
RICK ENGINEERING COMPANY
5620 Friars Rd, San Diego, CA 92110-2513
Tel (619) 291-0708 *Founded/Ownrshp* 1955
Sales 60.1MM^E *EMP* 224
SIC 8711 Civil engineering; Civil engineering
Pr: Roger Ball
Pr: William B Rick
**CFO:* Deborah B Ragione
**VP:* Dennis C Bowling
**VP:* Paul J Iezzi
VP: Michael Kenney
**VP:* Robert A Stockton
VP: Kathy Tegeler
Dir: Colleen Stoetzel
**Prin:* James C Kuhlken
**Prin:* Bruce Paton
Board of Directors: Roger L Ball, Paul Iezzi, Robert A Stockton

D-U-N-S 02-402-1461
GLENN BUICK GMC TRUCKS INC (KY)
GLENN G M C
3340 Richmond Rd, Lexington, KY 40509-1835
Tel (859) 263-5022 *Founded/Ownrshp* 1940, 1962
Sales 41.7MM^E *EMP* 80
SIC 5511 7538 7532 7515 5521 Automobiles, new & used; General automotive repair shops; Top & body repair & paint shops; Passenger car leasing; Used car dealers; Automobiles, new & used; General automotive repair shops; Top & body repair & paint shops; Passenger car leasing; Used car dealers
Pr: Cyrus A Dicken
**Treas:* Steven L Goldsberry

D-U-N-S 19-321-0937
GLENN COUNTY OFFICE OF EDUCATION
311 S Villa Ave, Willows, CA 95988-2959
Tel (530) 934-6575 *Founded/Ownrshp* 1870
Sales 13.1MM^E *EMP* 300^E
SIC 8211 Public special education school; Public special education school
CFO: Nancy Osborne
Ex Dir: Joy Amaro
Ex Dir: Joy North
IT Man: Bobby Shoutz
Schl Brd P: Judy Holzapfel
Teacher Pr: Judy Corum
Instr Medi: Anna Lane

D-U-N-S 02-757-6420
GLENN DISTRIBUTOR INC
1301 N Wenatchee Ave, Wenatchee, WA 98801-1537
Tel (509) 663-7173 *Founded/Ownrshp* 1966
Sales 137.2MM *EMP* 19
SIC 5172 5541 7359 Fuel oil; Petroleum brokers; Filling stations, gasoline; Equipment rental & leasing; Fuel oil; Petroleum brokers; Filling stations, gasoline; Equipment rental & leasing
Pr: Ray Glenn
**Sec:* Pegi Glenn
**VP:* Ed Glenn

GLENN G M C
See GLENN BUICK GMCTRUCKS INC

D-U-N-S 92-929-8008 EXP
GLENN HUNTER & ASSOCIATES INC
1222 County Road 6, Delta, OH 43515-9644
Tel (419) 822-3744 *Founded/Ownrshp* 1993
Sales 22.7MM^E *EMP* 75
SIC 3559 Recycling machinery
Pr: Glenn Hunter
**Ch Bd:* James Clark
Exec: Sue Pollitt
Genl Mgr: Dean Daenens
Web Dev: Colby Hunter
Sales Asso: Dan McMurray
Sales Asso: Jeff Pilliod

D-U-N-S 09-005-0212 IMP/EXP
GLENN INTERNATIONAL INC (FL)
Vela Acosta Ave Bldg, Carolina, PR 00987
Tel (787) 757-6000 *Founded/Ownrshp* 1967
Sales 22.0MM^E *EMP* 42
Accts Victoria E Canellas San Juan
SIC 5063 Electrical construction materials
Pr: Carlos Diaz
**Sec:* Raul Rodriguez
**VP:* Ignazio Diaz

D-U-N-S 10-243-3133
GLENN LEGE CONSTRUCTION INC
1339 Fortune Rd, Youngsville, LA 70592-5436
Tel (337) 233-3406 *Founded/Ownrshp* 1995
Sales 36.0MM^E *EMP* 180^E
Accts Darnall Sikes Gardes & Frede
SIC 1794 1611 Excavation work; Highway & street paving contractor; Excavation work; Highway & street paving contractor
Pr: Glenn W Lege
**Sec:* Patricia Guilbeau Lege
**Sec:* Patricia Lege
**VP:* Stacy Landry
**VP:* Andree St Andre

GLENN MITSUBISHI
See GLENN MOTORS INC

D-U-N-S 61-453-1267
GLENN MOTORS INC
GLENN MITSUBISHI
3380 Richmond Rd, Lexington, KY 40509-1835
Tel (859) 263-5880 *Founded/Ownrshp* 1989
Sales 43.6MM^E *EMP* 150
SIC 5511 Automobiles, new & used; Automobiles, new & used
Pr: Cy Dicken Jr
IT Man: Shannon Jones
Sales Asso: James Anderson

D-U-N-S 01-459-8460
GLENN O HAWBAKER INC
1952 Waddle Rd Ste 203, State College, PA 16803-1649
Tel (814) 237-1444 *Founded/Ownrshp* 1966
Sales 300.0MM *EMP* 1,200
Accts Parent Beard Llc State Colleg
SIC 2951 3281 1622 1794 1611 1422 Asphalt & asphaltic paving mixtures (not from refineries); Stone, quarrying & processing of own stone products; Bridge construction; Excavation work; Highway & street paving contractor; Crushed & broken limestone; Asphalt & asphaltic paving mixtures (not from refineries); Stone, quarrying & processing of own stone products; Bridge construction; Excavation work; Highway & street paving contractor; Crushed & broken limestone
Pr: Daniel R Hawbaker
COO: Robert Hall
**Treas:* Patrick G Hawbaker
VP: Hal Gee
**VP:* D Michael Hawbaker
VP: Steve Taylor
IT Man: Jim Molloy
VP Opers: Ivan Hassinger
Sfty Mgr: Curtis Moore

Sales Exec: Donald Liedl
Sales Exec: Robert McDaniel

D-U-N-S 00-643-8436 EXP
GLENN RIEDER INC
3420 W Capitol Dr, Milwaukee, WI 53216-2547
Tel (414) 449-2888 *Founded/Ownrshp* 1965
Sales 21.9MM^E *EMP* 124
SIC 2431 1541 1542 1522 Woodwork, interior & ornamental; Industrial buildings, new construction; Renovation, remodeling & repairs: industrial buildings; Commercial & office building, new construction; Commercial & office buildings, renovation & repair; Residential construction
CEO: Michael Floyd
VP Opers: Jeff Heckman

D-U-N-S 05-741-1415
GLENN THURMAN INC
3180 S Belt Line Rd, Balch Springs, TX 75181-3086
Tel (972) 286-6333 *Founded/Ownrshp* 1978
Sales 109.5MM^E *EMP* 278
SIC 1611 4212 General contractor, highway & street construction; Local trucking, without storage; General contractor, highway & street construction; Local trucking, without storage
Pr: Glenn C Thurman
**Pr:* Gary R Maynor

D-U-N-S 10-301-9139
GLENN WALTERS NURSERY INC
(*Suby of* AMERISCAPE INC) ★
7375 Nw Roy Rd, Cornelius, OR 97113-6303
Tel (503) 693-1125 *Founded/Ownrshp* 2006
Sales 19.6MM^E *EMP* 500
SIC 0181 Nursery stock, growing of; Nursery stock, growing of
CEO: Pat Blake
**CFO:* Greg Grasso
Board of Directors: Joyce O'connell, Edward Sredenburgh

D-U-N-S 04-333-1065 IMP
GLENNY GLASS CO (OH)
209 Castleberry Ct, Milford, OH 45150-1193
Tel (513) 248-0307 *Founded/Ownrshp* 1851, 1989
Sales 21.1MM^E *EMP* 40
SIC 5039 Glass construction materials
Pr: R Braxton Smith
Treas: April Shinkle
Div Mgr: Ralph Sabato
Plnt Mgr: Chris Hawkins

D-U-N-S 07-230-6459
GLENOAKS CONVALESCENT HOSPITAL (LP)
409 W Glenoaks Blvd, Glendale, CA 91202-2916
Tel (818) 240-4300 *Founded/Ownrshp* 1984
Sales 473.1MM *EMP* 85
SIC 8062 General medical & surgical hospitals; General medical & surgical hospitals
Pt: Elaine Levine

D-U-N-S 00-136-0122 EXP
GLENOIT LLC
(*Suby of* EXCELL HOME FASHIONS) ★
1500 N Carolina St, Goldsboro, NC 27530-1210
Tel (919) 735-7111 *Founded/Ownrshp* 1995
Sales 39.0MM^E *EMP* 250
SIC 2392 Household furnishings; Household furnishings
Pr: Marc Navarre
**Pr:* Joe Granger
Ex VP: Mike McCullough
Off Mgr: Mary Jones

D-U-N-S 83-194-8588 IMP
GLENOIT UNIVERSAL LTD
EXCELL HOME FASHIONS
1 Excell Linde Dr, Goldsboro, NC 27533
Tel (919) 735-7111 *Founded/Ownrshp* 1994
Sales 42.8MM^E *EMP* 250^E
SIC 2273 2392 Rugs, tufted; Cushions & pillows; Shower curtains: made from purchased materials; Tablecloths & table settings; Rugs, tufted; Cushions & pillows; Shower curtains: made from purchased materials; Tablecloths & table settings
CEO: Barry Leonard
**Treas:* Cliff Campbell

GLENPOOL HIGH SCHOOL
See GLENPOOL PUBLIC SCHOOL DISTRICT 013

D-U-N-S 02-166-0444
GLENPOOL PUBLIC SCHOOL DISTRICT 013
GLENPOOL HIGH SCHOOL
461 E 146th St S, Glenpool, OK 74033-3900
Tel (918) 322-9500 *Founded/Ownrshp* 1919
Sales 25.0MM^E *EMP* 401
SIC 8211 9411 Public elementary & secondary schools; Administration of educational programs; Public elementary & secondary schools; Administration of educational programs
**Pr:* Rick Rice
Treas: Mark Bilby

GLENRAVEN.COM
See GLEN RAVEN INC

GLENRAVEN.COM
See GLEN RAVEN TECHNICAL FABRICS LLC

D-U-N-S 04-317-3645
GLENRIDGE ON PALMER RANCH INC (FL)
7333 Scotland Way, Sarasota, FL 34238-8530
Tel (941) 552-5300 *Founded/Ownrshp* 1997
Sales 31.3MM *EMP* 290
Accts Bobbitt Pittenger & Company Pa
SIC 8361 Residential care; Residential care
CEO: Jim Cater
Bd of Dir: Donald Featherman
Ex Dir: John Knox
Dir IT: David Lemon
Sls&Mrk Ex: Cari Owens
Nrsg Dir: Kim Runyen
Nrsg Dir: Cookie Salter

D-U-N-S 00-178-0899 IMP
GLENROY INC (WI)
EVERWHITE
W158n9332 Norxway Ave, Menomonee Falls, WI 53051-1561
Tel (262) 255-4422 *Founded/Ownrshp* 1965
Sales 55.0MM *EMP* 191
SIC 2759 2671 Flexographic printing; Plastic film, coated or laminated for packaging; Flexographic printing; Plastic film, coated or laminated for packaging
CEO: Richard Buss
CFO: Dan Ihde
CFO: Daniel Ihde
Rgnl Mgr: Rich Myklebust
QA Dir: Justine Christopherson
IT Man: Amanda Dahlby
IT Man: John Mawby
VP Mfg: Mike Dean
Opers Mgr: Jim Costello
Prd Mgr: Steve Weis
Mktg Mgr: Barbara Woodruff

D-U-N-S 10-037-5609
GLENS FALLS CITY SCHOOL DISTRICT
15 Quade St, Glens Falls, NY 12801-2799
Tel (518) 792-1212 *Founded/Ownrshp* 1881
Sales 16.5MM^E *EMP* 320
Accts Flynn Walker Diggin Cpa
SIC 8211 Public elementary & secondary schools; Public elementary & secondary schools
Bd of Dir: Shirley Berger
Bd of Dir: Kathleen Burton
Bd of Dir: Peter Casertino
Bd of Dir: Suzanne Spector-Tougas
VP: Matthew Conrick
**Dir Bus:* Stephen Meier
Prin: Harriet Finch
Prin: Jeffery L Ziegler
IT Man: Jodene Eyer
IT Man: Gay Jarvis
Psych: Heather Ovitt

D-U-N-S 06-054-0382 IMP
GLENS FALLS HOSPITAL (NY)
100 Park St, Glens Falls, NY 12801-4447
Tel (518) 926-1000 *Founded/Ownrshp* 1897, 1984
Sales 289.0MM *EMP* 2,726
SIC 8011 8062 8221 Offices & clinics of medical doctors; General medical & surgical hospitals; Colleges universities & professional schools; Offices & clinics of medical doctors; General medical & surgical hospitals; Colleges universities & professional schools
Pr: Dianne Shugrue
**Pr:* David G Kruczlnicki
**COO:* James W Connolly
COO: Dianne Shugrue
**CFO:* Mitchell J Amado III
CFO: Daniel Burke
CFO: Donna Leroux
**CFO:* D Michael Niles
Bd of Dir: Brenda Albertson
Sr VP: Jeffrey Treasure Sr
VP: Douglas Barry
**VP:* Kyle Brock
VP: Cindy Gage
**VP:* Edward Hanchett
VP: James Hungerford
VP: Cindy Sherwood
VP: Celeste Steele
Dir Rad: Ed Hanchett
Dir Rx: Nancy Huntington

D-U-N-S 00-697-7441
■ GLENS FALLS NATIONAL BANK & TRUST CO
(*Suby of* ARROW FINANCIAL CORP) ★
250 Glen St, Glens Falls, NY 12801-3505
Tel (518) 793-4121 *Founded/Ownrshp* 1851
Sales NA *EMP* 481
SIC 6021 National commercial banks; National commercial banks
Ch Bd: Thomas L Hoy
Pr: David S Demarco
Pr: Michael Jacobs
Pr: Susan Kenneally
**Pr:* Thomas J Murphy
Pr: Martin West
CFO: Terry Goodemote
Chf Cred: David Kaiser
Ofcr: Harrison Sangster
Ofcr: Craig Seybolt
Ofcr: Charles Veeder
Sr VP: Kathleen Kelleher
Sr VP: Peter Lareau
Sr VP: Charles R Petit
VP: Jim Brown
VP: Patricia Bryant
VP: Lynn Crayford
VP: Mary Rabin
VP: David Riihimaki
VP: Paul Wersten
Board of Directors: Michael B Clarke, Kenneth Hopper MD, David Kruczlnicki, Elizabeth Little, Michael F Massiano Chb, David Moynehan, Bill Owens, Richard Reisman

GLENVIEW AT PELICAN BAY
See PELICAN BAY COOPERATIVE HOUSING CORP

D-U-N-S 00-386-0376
GLENVIEW COMMUNITY CONSOLIDATED SCHOOL DISTRICT 34 (IL)
1401 Greenwood Rd, Glenview, IL 60026-1511
Tel (847) 998-5000 *Founded/Ownrshp* 1840
Sales 79.9MM *EMP* 700
Accts Evoy Kamschulte Jacobs & Co
SIC 8211 Public combined elementary & secondary school; Public junior high school; Public combined elementary & secondary school; Public junior high school
Pr: Chris Northwick
**VP:* Sue Ellen Bohac Galligan
Teacher Pr: Brett Clark

D-U-N-S 36-109-7012
GLENVIEW PUBLIC SCHOOL DISTRICT
1401 Greenwood Rd, Glenview, IL 60026-1511
Tel (847) 998-5000 *Founded/Ownrshp* 2005
Sales 76.6MM *EMP* 16
SIC 8211 Public elementary & secondary schools; Public elementary & secondary schools
Prin: Scott Martin

D-U-N-S 05-192-6764
GLENVIEW STATE BANK
(*Suby of* CUMMINS - ALLISON CORP) ★
800 Waukegan Rd Ste 1, Glenview, IL 60025-4310
Tel (847) 729-1900 *Founded/Ownrshp* 1965
Sales NA *EMP* 210
SIC 6022 State commercial banks; State commercial banks
Ch Bd: Paul A Jones
**CFO:* John Diedrich
Sr Cor Off: Indra Ramdass
Ofcr: Paul Hodolitz
Ofcr: Randy Nys
Ex VP: Scott Limper
Sr VP: Peter Dedes
Sr VP: Karen Forgette
Sr VP: Mark Frighetto
Sr VP: Susan Schroll
Sr VP: John Tofano
Sr VP: Elizabeth Wexler
VP: Pamela Aho
VP: Jane Boiko
VP: Jim Cooper
VP: Ilene Eckert
VP: Timothy Gaida
VP: Pat Grimes
VP: Nancy Jarmusz
VP: Marimel Lim
VP: Elaine Nicholson
Board of Directors: Pam Alto

D-U-N-S 07-232-9048
GLENVIEW TERRACE NURSING CENTER
1511 Greenwood Rd, Glenview, IL 60026-1597
Tel (847) 729-9090 *Founded/Ownrshp* 1974
Sales 28.2MM *EMP* 285
SIC 8051 Skilled nursing care facilities; Skilled nursing care facilities
Pr: Mark Hollander
Genl Pt: Yosef Davis
Genl Pt: Bernard B Hollander
Genl Pt: Jack Rajchenbach

D-U-N-S 80-293-4872
GLENVILLE BANK HOLDING CO INC
201 Mohawk Ave, Schenectady, NY 12302-2128
Tel (518) 370-7200 *Founded/Ownrshp* 2006
Sales NA *EMP* 145^E
SIC 6712 Bank holding companies; Bank holding companies
CEO: Lh Buhrmaster

D-U-N-S 09-790-9274
GLENWOOD CAPITAL INVESTMENTS LLC
(*Suby of* MAN STRATEGIC HOLDINGS LTD)
123 N Wacker Dr Fl 20, Chicago, IL 60606-1753
Tel (312) 881-6500 *Founded/Ownrshp* 1985
Sales NA *EMP* 100
SIC 6371

D-U-N-S 07-210-4060
GLENWOOD INC
150 Glenwood Ln, Birmingham, AL 35242-5700
Tel (205) 969-2880 *Founded/Ownrshp* 1974
Sales 18.5MM *EMP* 300
Accts Yeage & Boyd Llc Birmingham
SIC 8211 Elementary & secondary schools; Elementary & secondary schools
Pr: Lee Yount
CFO: Ned Blum
Ex VP: Bob Mutschink
**VP:* Greg Carlson
**VP:* Joe Carter
**VP:* Barbara Murbach
Dir IT: Blain Harrison
IT Man: Sonja Holder
Info Man: Pete McCalla

D-U-N-S 15-984-2384 IMP
GLENWOOD LLC
GLENWOOD-PALISADES
111 Cedar Ln, Englewood, NJ 07631-4803
Tel (201) 569-0050 *Founded/Ownrshp* 1997
Sales 25.9MM^E *EMP* 194
SIC 2834 Pharmaceutical preparations; Pharmaceutical preparations

D-U-N-S 04-187-1062
GLENWOOD MANAGEMENT CORP
1200 Union Tpke, New Hyde Park, NY 11040-1708
Tel (718) 343-6400 *Founded/Ownrshp* 1961
Sales 82.6MM^E *EMP* 228
SIC 5083 Landscaping equipment; Landscaping equipment
Pr: Leonard Litwin
Ex VP: Maureen Dowell
Ex VP: Gary Jacob
Sr VP: Charlie Dorego
**Sr VP:* Morton Sanders
VP: George Finegold
VP: Steve Maschi
IT Man: Fran Mekhanik
Info Man: Michael Honig

GLENWOOD REGIONAL MEDICAL CTR
See GLENWOOD RESOLUTION AUTHORITY INC

D-U-N-S 07-137-3625 IMP
GLENWOOD RESOLUTION AUTHORITY INC
GLENWOOD REGIONAL MEDICAL CTR
503 Mcmillan Rd, West Monroe, LA 71291-5327
Tel (318) 329-4200 *Founded/Ownrshp* 1961
Sales 136.5MM^E *EMP* 1,156
SIC 8062 General medical & surgical hospitals; General medical & surgical hospitals
CEO: Ron Elder
**VP:* Jan Walker

D-U-N-S 03-206-9494
GLENWOOD SPRINGS FORD INC
55 Storm King Rd, Glenwood Springs, CO 81601-2540
Tel (970) 945-2317 *Founded/Ownrshp* 1978
Sales 37.0MM^E *EMP* 95
SIC 5511 7538 5521 Automobiles, new & used; General automotive repair shops; Used car dealers; Automobiles, new & used; General automotive repair shops; Used car dealers
Pr: Jeff Carlson
**Treas:* Eric Carlson
Sls Mgr: Zach Carlson
Sales Asso: Chet Garling
Sales Asso: Amanda Radov

D-U-N-S 36-097-4906
GLENWOOD TREE EXPERTS
21457 Milwaukee Ave, Deerfield, IL 60015-5322
Tel (847) 459-0200 *Founded/Ownrshp* 1981
Sales 99.3MM^E *EMP* 351^E
SIC 0783 0782 Ornamental shrub & tree services; Lawn & garden services; Ornamental shrub & tree services; Lawn & garden services
Owner: Jim Sackelman

GLENWOOD-PALISADES
See GLENWOOD LLC

D-U-N-S 00-958-3311
GLESBY BUILDING MATERIALS CO INC
GLESBY WHOLESALE
15119 Oxnard St, Van Nuys, CA 91411-2615
Tel (323) 873-1593 *Founded/Ownrshp* 1960
Sales 68.1MM^E *EMP* 90
SIC 5031 Building materials, exterior; Building materials, interior; Building materials, exterior; Building materials, interior
Pr: George Gottesman
**Sec:* Richard Gottesman
Ex VP: Doyle Shipley
**VP:* D E Shepley
Sls Mgr: Mark McMahon
Sales Asso: Valerie Karr

GLESBY WHOLESALE
See GLESBY BUILDING MATERIALS CO INC

D-U-N-S 80-273-7833 IMP/EXP
GLF CONSTRUCTION CORP
(*Suby of* GRANDI LAVORI FINCOSIT SPA)
80 Sw 8th St Ste 2201, Miami, FL 33130-3047
Tel (305) 371-5228 *Founded/Ownrshp* 1993
Sales 255.0MM^E *EMP* 450
SIC 1611 1622 1542 1541 1522 Highway & street construction; Bridge, tunnel & elevated highway; Commercial & office building, new construction; Industrial buildings, new construction; Condominium construction; Highway & street construction; Bridge, tunnel & elevated highway; Commercial & office building, new construction; Industrial buildings, new construction; Condominium construction
CEO: Francesco Senis
**COO:* Joseph M Beaird
CFO: Vincent Perciani
**CFO:* Vincent L Persiani
Sr VP: Sebastian Gunningham
VP: Corrado Difabio
VP: James Gassenhemier
VP: Alejandro Gonzalez
**VP:* Ernest Howard Jr
**VP:* William E Junkin
**VP:* Michael J Miles
VP: Susan Serrats

GLI
See GREAT LAKES INTEGRATED INC

GLI DISTRIBUTING
See GLI INC

D-U-N-S 02-706-9889 IMP
GLI INC
GLI DISTRIBUTING
803 S Medina St, San Antonio, TX 78207-5610
Tel (210) 226-4376 *Founded/Ownrshp* 1982
Sales 1.0MM^E *EMP* 11,040^E
SIC 5181

D-U-N-S 08-758-2107
GLICK LLC
415 W Main St, Rochester, NY 14608-1944
Tel (716) 235-1595 *Founded/Ownrshp* 2001
Sales 164.1MM^E *EMP* 1,200
SIC 6719 Investment holding companies, except banks; Investment holding companies, except banks
MIS Dir: Melva Boren

GLIDDEN PROFESSIONAL PAINT CTR
See AKZO NOBEL PAINTS LLC

GLIDE-WRITE
See MARBURG TECHNOLOGY INC

GLIDEAWAY BED CARRIAGE MFG CO
See FREDMAN BROS FURNITURE CO INC

D-U-N-S 14-538-5758 IMP/EXP
GLIDEPATH LLC
BEUMER GLIDEPATH
(*Suby of* BEUMER GROUP GMBH & CO. KG)
2241 S Watson Rd Ste 151, Arlington, TX 76010-8121
Tel (972) 641-4200 *Founded/Ownrshp* 2002
Sales 41.8MM^E *EMP* 69
SIC 3535 Conveyors & conveying equipment
Pr: Finn Lyng Pedersen
**Ch Bd:* Kenneth Stevens
**Pr:* Thomas Dalstein
VP: Klaus Fremmeley
**VP:* David Mead
Site Mgr: Ken Nunn
Mfg Mgr: Vince Avirett
Snr PM: Tom Ball

D-U-N-S 03-549-6066
GLIDEWELL DISTRIBUTING CO (AR)
5705 Steep Hill Rd, Fort Smith, AR 72916-8197
Tel (479) 649-3999 *Founded/Ownrshp* 1946
Sales 60.5MM^E *EMP* 72
SIC 5141 5921 5541

GLIDEWELL LABORATORIES
See JAMES R GLIDEWELL DENTAL CERAMICS INC

D-U-N-S 00-401-4742 IMP
GLIDEWELL SPECIALTIES FOUNDRY CO
600 Foundry Rd, Calera, AL 35040
Tel (205) 668-1972 Founded/Ownrshp 1963
Sales 24.3MM^E EMP 80
SIC 3321 3325 3322 3599 Gray & ductile iron foundries; Alloy steel castings, except investment; Malleable iron foundries; Machine shop, jobbing & repair
Pr: David Glidewell
*CFO: Brannon Brooks
*VP: William Bell
*VP: John C Hendrix
*VP: Rebecca Richey
Sfty Dirs: Dave Harring
Sfty Dirs: John Ortman
Sfty Dirs: Chris Weas
Plnt Mgr: Tad Littleton

D-U-N-S 02-560-8480
GLIK CO
GLIK'S
3248 Nameoki Rd, Granite City, IL 62040-5014
Tel (618) 876-1065 Founded/Ownrshp 1897
Sales 17.2MM EMP 500
Accts Scheffel Boyle Edwardsville
SIC 5651 Family clothing stores; Family clothing stores
Pr: Joseph W Glik
*Treas: Judith Glik
*VP: James Glik
*Prin: Joe Glik

GLIK'S
See GLIK CO

D-U-N-S 83-931-9738
■ **GLIMCHER PROPERTIES LIMITED PARTNERSHIP**
INDIAN MOUND MALL
(Suby of WP GLIMCHER INC) ★
180 E Broad St Fl 22, Columbus, OH 43215-3714
Tel (614) 621-9000 Founded/Ownrshp 1994
Sales 30.7MM^E EMP 800
SIC 6512 Commercial & industrial building operation; Commercial & industrial building operation
Pt: Herbert Glimcher

D-U-N-S 07-502-3036
GLIMCHER REALTY TRUST (MD)
180 E Broad St Fl 20, Columbus, OH 43215-3714
Tel (614) 621-9000 Founded/Ownrshp 1993
Sales 381.8MM EMP 981^E
SIC 6512 Commercial & industrial building operation

D-U-N-S 03-807-6787 IMP
GLK FOODS LLC
158 E Northland Ave, Appleton, WI 54911-2125
Tel (715) 752-4105 Founded/Ownrshp 1997
Sales 31.6MM^E EMP 110
SIC 2035 Sauerkraut, bulk; Sauerkraut, bulk
*Ch Bd: Ryan A Downs
*CFO: Tom Palmer

D-U-N-S 07-829-3828 IMP/EXP
GLOBAL ADVANCED METALS USA INC
CABOT SUPERMETALS
1223 County Line Rd, Boyertown, PA 19512
Tel (610) 367-2181 Founded/Ownrshp 2011
Sales 58.0MM^E EMP 174^E
SIC 3339 Tantalum refining
CEO: Bryan Ellis
Genl Mgr: Andrew O'Donovan

D-U-N-S 16-727-5713
GLOBAL ADVISORY GROUP INC
MORTGAGE ADVISORY GROUP
2902 Colby Ave, Everett, WA 98201-4011
Tel (425) 317-8000 Founded/Ownrshp 2004
Sales NA EMP 170
SIC 6162 Mortgage bankers & correspondents; Mortgage bankers; Mortgage bankers & correspondents; Mortgage bankers
CEO: David D Wortham
*Pr: Anthony Blodgett
*CEO: Lee J Dionne
*Treas: Mary Loarie
Opers Mgr: Carol Coletta
Snr PM: Tyler Wortham

D-U-N-S 00-402-8366
■ **GLOBAL AEROSPACE INC**
(Suby of GLOBAL AEROSPACE UNDERWRITING MANAGERS LTD)
1 Sylvan Way Ste 3, Parsippany, NJ 07054-3879
Tel (973) 490-8500 Founded/Ownrshp 2001
Sales NA EMP 271^E
SIC 6411 Insurance agents, brokers & service; Insurance agents, brokers & service
CEO: Tony Medniuk
*CEO: Nick Brown
Ofcr: Ann-Marie Friedman
Ofcr: Marilena Sharpell
Assoc VP: Eileen Cashman-Jermak
Ex VP: Jeffrey Bruno
Sr VP: Mike Falcone
Sr VP: Joseph Taccetta
VP: Karen D'Amico
VP: Michael Happe
VP: Steven Ivans
VP: John Meehan
VP: David Nelson
VP: Michael Pechloff
Board of Directors: Nick Brown, Jeffrey Bruno, Michael Falcone, Sharon Holahan, John Kelly, Alan Tasker, Stephen Walsh

D-U-N-S 07-262-0797
GLOBAL AGGREGATE LLC
AWIZEBUY.COM
8901 E Mountain View Rd, Scottsdale, AZ 85258-4422
Tel (480) 414-9400 Founded/Ownrshp 1999
Sales 600.0MM EMP 163
SIC 6798 7389 5045 Real estate investment trusts; Financial services; Computer peripheral equipment

D-U-N-S 01-731-9886 IMP
GLOBAL AGRI-TRADE CORP
320 Golden Shore Ste 350, Long Beach, CA 90802-4297
Tel (562) 320-8550 Founded/Ownrshp 2006
Sales 76.8MM EMP 15
SIC 5199 Oils, animal or vegetable; Oils, animal or vegetable
Pr: Haresh Kumar Bhatt
*VP: Jignesh Bhatt
VP: Jurgen Godau
Sls Mgr: Ken Colgan
Sls Mgr: Dustin Nelson
Sls Mgr: Benjamin Perez

GLOBAL AIRCRAFT TOOL
See DEWITT TOOL CO INC

D-U-N-S 80-712-9684
GLOBAL AIRTECH INTERNATIONAL
AOG SHIPPING
(Suby of GLOBAL AIRTECH MFG INC) ★
16539 Saticoy St, Van Nuys, CA 91406-1739
Tel (818) 933-6100 Founded/Ownrshp 1993
Sales 26.7MM^E EMP 35
SIC 5088 Aeronautical equipment & supplies
Pr: James R Chiamulon
*Pr: Adam Chiamulon
Ofcr: Steve Summers
VP: Saisuree Satchawitwisal
VP: Sisca Tesoro
Sales Exec: Maria Aguilar
Sales Exec: Ivan Collado
Sales Exec: Ashley Elliott
Sales Exec: Cresencia Nakamura
Sales Exec: Shian Tsao
Sls Dir: Frank Collado
Board of Directors: Rowena Montoya

D-U-N-S 62-755-3514
GLOBAL AIRTECH MFG INC
16539 Saticoy St, Van Nuys, CA 91406-1739
Tel (818) 933-6100 Founded/Ownrshp 1989
Sales 51.7MM^E EMP 75
Accts Anthony & Associates Cpa S Br
SIC 5088 Aircraft & parts; Aircraft engines & engine parts; Aircraft equipment & supplies; Aircraft & parts; Aircraft engines & engine parts; Aircraft equipment & supplies
Pr: James R Chiamulon

D-U-N-S 36-155-1026
GLOBAL ALUMINA CORP
277 Park Ave Fl 40, New York, NY 10172-2902
Tel (212) 351-0000 Founded/Ownrshp 2005
Sales 26.0MM^E EMP 500^E
SIC 3297 Alumina fused refractories
CEO: Bruce J Wrobel
*Pr: Graham Morrey
*CFO: Michael J Cella
*Sr VP: Tony McCabe

D-U-N-S 11-222-7173
GLOBAL ALUMINA SERVICES CO
(Suby of GLOBAL ALUMINA CORP) ★
277 Park Ave Fl 40, New York, NY 10172-2902
Tel (212) 309-8060 Founded/Ownrshp 1999
Sales 25.8MM^E EMP 500
SIC 3297 Alumina fused refractories; Alumina fused refractories
Ch Bd: Bruce Wrobel
*Pr: Bernie Cousineau
*CFO: Michael Cella
CFO: Hamsa Shadaksharappa
Bd of Dir: Craig A Huff
Ex VP: Dirk Straussfeld
Sr VP: Jim McGowan
VP: Thomas Boehlert
VP: Thomas Boelhert
VP: David Crouse
VP: Robert Fernandez
VP: William Geiser
VP: Rafael Herz
VP: Merritt James
VP: Thomas Johns
VP: Glen Krapf
VP: Brian Kubeck
VP: Donald Lockett
VP: Sharon Moore
VP: Nathans Plagens
VP: Steve Poje

D-U-N-S 12-673-3422
GLOBAL ASSOCIATION OF RISK PROFESSIONALS INC
G A R P
111 Town Square Pl # 1215, Jersey City, NJ 07310-1755
Tel (201) 719-7210 Founded/Ownrshp 2003
Sales 23.1MM EMP 50^E
Accts Rsm Mcgladrey Inc New York
SIC 8611 Business associations
Pr: Richard Apostolik
VP: Carol McGall
VP Opers: Frank Weber

D-U-N-S 07-881-6994
GLOBAL ATLANTIC FINANCIAL CO
GLOBAL ATLANTIC FINCL GROUP
(Suby of GLOBAL ATLANTIC FINANCIAL GROUP LIMITED)
250 Greenwich St Fl 47, New York, NY 10007-2369
Tel (508) 460-2414 Founded/Ownrshp 2013
Sales 37.4MM^E EMP 95^E
SIC 6282 Investment advice
CEO: Allan Lavine
VP: Fayez Ali

GLOBAL ATLANTIC FINCL GROUP
See GLOBAL ATLANTIC FINANCIAL CO

GLOBAL AUTO MALL
See GLOBAL MOTORS CORP

GLOBAL AUTO PARTS GROUP
See GLOBAL AUTOMOTIVE PARTS GROUP LLC

D-U-N-S 02-332-0729 IMP
GLOBAL AUTOMOTIVE PARTS GROUP LLC
GLOBAL AUTO PARTS GROUP
(Suby of WALKER PRODUCTS) ★
525 W Congress St, Pacific, MO 63069-1924
Tel (636) 257-2190 Founded/Ownrshp 2000
Sales 21.6MM^E EMP 180
SIC 3053 Gaskets, packing & sealing devices; Gaskets, packing & sealing devices
Genl Mgr: Tim Weaver

D-U-N-S 61-489-7440
GLOBAL AUTOMOTIVE SYSTEMS LLC
(Suby of DURA AUTOMOTIVE SYSTEMS LLC) ★
1780 Pond Run, Auburn Hills, MI 48326-2752
Tel (248) 299-7230 Founded/Ownrshp 2005
Sales 244.3MM^E EMP 1,000
SIC 3469 Metal stampings; Metal stampings
CEO: Lynn Tilton
*COO: Martin Becker
*CFO: Jim Gregory
*Ex VP: Franois Stouvenot
*Ex VP: Nizar Trigui

D-U-N-S 80-564-1847
GLOBAL AVIATION HOLDINGS INC
101 World Dr, Peachtree City, GA 30269-6965
Tel (770) 632-8000 Founded/Ownrshp 2012
Sales NA EMP 2,012
SIC 4522 Air passenger carriers, nonscheduled

D-U-N-S 01-082-7298
GLOBAL AVIATION INC
2250 Ne 25th Ave, Hillsboro, OR 97124-5960
Tel (503) 648-6403 Founded/Ownrshp 1995
Sales 27.4MM EMP 80
SIC 4522 4581 5172 Air transportation, nonscheduled; Aircraft maintenance & repair services; Aircraft cleaning & janitorial service; Aircraft fueling services; Air transportation, nonscheduled; Aircraft maintenance & repair services; Aircraft cleaning & janitorial service; Aircraft fueling services
Pr: Flo Newton
*VP: Brian Lockhart
Exec: Elaine Frances
*Prin: Ephraim Ingals
Snr Mgr: Del Kaufmann
Snr Mgr: Rob Lien
Snr Mgr: A J Orlando

D-U-N-S 11-880-6108
GLOBAL AXCESS CORP
7800 Belfort Pkwy Ste 165, Jacksonville, FL 32256-6915
Tel (904) 395-1149 Founded/Ownrshp 1984
Sales 31.1MM EMP 45^E
Tkr Sym GAXCQ Exch OTO
SIC 7389 Process serving service; Process serving service
Pr: Kevin L Reager
*Ch Bd: Joseph M Loughry III
*CFO: Michael J Loiacono
Ex VP: John C Rawlins
Sales Exec: Robert Colabrese
Board of Directors: Robert Landis, Eric S Weinstein

D-U-N-S 07-948-8344
GLOBAL BRANDS GROUP HOLDING LIMITED
Empire State Building # 350, New York, NY 10118
Tel (646) 839-7000 Founded/Ownrshp 2005
Sales 3.4MMM EMP 1
Accts Pricewaterhousecoopers Cpa H
SIC 5136 5137 Men's & boys' clothing; Women's & children's clothing; Footwear
Ch: William Fung Kwok Lun
*CFO: Ronald Ventricelli
*CFO: Leong Kwok Yee
*Ex Dir: Hau Leung Lee

D-U-N-S 80-849-9920
▲ **GLOBAL BRASS AND COPPER HOLDINGS INC**
475 N Marti Rd Ste 1050, Schaumburg, IL 60173
Tel (847) 240-4700 Founded/Ownrshp 2007
Sales 1.7MMM EMP 1,896
Tkr Sym BRSS Exch NYS
SIC 3351 3341 3469 Copper rolling & drawing; Brass rolling & drawing; Copper smelting & refining (secondary); Metal stampings; Copper rolling & drawing; Brass rolling & drawing; Copper smelting & refining (secondary); Metal stampings
Pr: John J Wasz
Pr: Kevin W Bense
Pr: Devin K Denner
Pr: William G Toler
CFO: Robert T Micchelli

D-U-N-S 80-850-0032
■ **GLOBAL BRASS AND COPPER INC**
(Suby of GLOBAL BRASS AND COPPER HOLDINGS INC) ★
305 Lewis And Clark Blvd, East Alton, IL 62024-1177
Tel (618) 258-5000 Founded/Ownrshp 2007
Sales 1.6MMM^E EMP 1,900
SIC 3351 3341 3469 1542 Brass rolling & drawing; Copper smelting & refining (secondary); Metal stampings; Commercial & office building, new construction; Brass rolling & drawing; Copper smelting & refining (secondary); Metal stampings; Commercial & office building, new construction
Pr: John Wasz
*Ch Bd: Michael Psaros
Chf Mktg O: Ann Pipkin
VP: Joseph Wickenhauser
Prd Mgr: Terry McDaniel

D-U-N-S 16-192-3149
GLOBAL BUILDING SERVICES INC
25129 The Old Rd Ste 102, Stevenson Ranch, CA 91381-2287
Tel (661) 288-5733 Founded/Ownrshp 1986
Sales 39.5MM^E EMP 1,100^E
SIC 7349 Janitorial service, contract basis; Janitorial service, contract basis
Pr: Julio Belloso

D-U-N-S 80-799-8500
GLOBAL BUSINESS SOLUTIONS INC
600 Anton Blvd Ste 1050, Costa Mesa, CA 92626-7055
Tel (714) 257-1488 Founded/Ownrshp 2002
Sales 23.9MM^E EMP 258
SIC 7379 8741 8742 Computer related consulting services; Construction management; Construction project management consultant; Computer related consulting services; Construction management; Construction project management consultant
CEO: Johnnie R Carlin
*CEO: John R Carlin
COO: David H Gleit

GLOBAL CAPACITY
See GC PIVOTAL LLC

D-U-N-S 80-079-2876
GLOBAL CAPITAL RESOURCES GROUP LLC
1201 Broadway Ste 608, New York, NY 10001-5405
Tel (646) 221-1898 Founded/Ownrshp 2007
Sales 100.0MM EMP 2
SIC 6722 Management investment, open-end; Management investment, open-end
Pr: Benedictus D K Ayitey
Pt: Michael Megalli
VP: James E Moore

GLOBAL CARE TRAVEL
See CUSTOMIZED SERVICES ADMINISTRATORS INC

D-U-N-S 79-501-6380
GLOBAL CASH CARD INC
7 Corporate Park Ste 130, Irvine, CA 92606-5154
Tel (949) 751-0360 Founded/Ownrshp 2002
Sales 21.8MM^E EMP 165
SIC 5947 Greeting cards
Pr: Joe Purcell
Sr VP: Joe Tumbarello
Mng Dir: Sloan Purcell
IT Man: Tara Williams
Sales Exec: Megan Lazar
Manager: Christine Derose
Manager: Bill Doody
Manager: Renee Erickson
Manager: Tonya Kowalczyk
Manager: Bernard Nolan
Manager: Anthony Purcell

D-U-N-S 01-537-9402 IMP/EXP
GLOBAL CELLULAR INC (GA)
CELLAIRIS
6485 Shiloh Rd Ste B100, Alpharetta, GA 30005-1605
Tel (678) 513-4020 Founded/Ownrshp 1999
Sales 147.4MM^E EMP 476^E
SIC 5065 Mobile telephone equipment; Mobile telephone equipment
CEO: Konstantine Skouras
*Pr: Ken Taylor
*COO: Richard Motilal
*Ofcr: Joseph Brown
*VP: Jason Adler
*VP: Valerie Brunson
VP: Michael Duarte
VP: Carlos Gonzalez
VP: Marty Welch
*CTO: Rob Jackness
VP Mktg: Beth Ciardullo

D-U-N-S 02-522-3149
GLOBAL CELLUTIONS DISTRIBUTORS INC (CA)
218 W Palm Ave, Burbank, CA 91502-1835
Tel (818) 847-2266 Founded/Ownrshp 2012
Sales 70.0MM EMP 5
SIC 5731 Consumer electronic equipment
CEO: Greg Kiselyuk

D-U-N-S 82-899-7432
GLOBAL CLIENT SOLUTIONS LLC
4500 S 129th East Ave # 17, Tulsa, OK 74134-5801
Tel (918) 492-0386 Founded/Ownrshp 2003
Sales 26.5MM^E EMP 228
SIC 8741 Financial management for business; Financial management for business
VP: Kristie Howes
VP: Allison Keltner
QA Dir: Mimi Tran
Dir IT: Grant Teakell
Software D: Travis Stapleton
Sftwr Eng: Chris Hallum
Sls Dir: Allison Filenko

GLOBAL CLOUD XCHANGE
See RELIANCE GLOBALCOM SERVICES INC

D-U-N-S 83-258-3210 EXP
GLOBAL COAL SALES GROUP LLC
41 S High St Ste 2240, Columbus, OH 43215-6104
Tel (614) 221-0101 Founded/Ownrshp 2008
Sales 36.7MM^E EMP 9^E
SIC 1241 Coal mining services

D-U-N-S 01-300-7336
GLOBAL COMMUNICATION SEMICONDUCTORS LLC
G C S
23155 Kashiwa Ct, Torrance, CA 90505-4026
Tel (310) 530-7274 Founded/Ownrshp 1997
Sales 41.6MM^E EMP 155
SIC 3674 Semiconductors & related devices; Semiconductors & related devices
Pr: Bau-Hsing Ann
*Ch: Ta-Lun Huang
VP: Sam Wang
VP: Wing Yau
Mng Dir: Armando Gutierrez
Prgrm Mgr: Dhiraj Kumar
QA Dir: Debbie Collins
Sfty Mgr: Steve Saunders
Prd Mgr: Mark Alvarado

GLOBAL COMMUNITIES
See COOPERATIVE HOUSING FOUNDATION (INC)

D-U-N-S 01-917-7757 IMP
■ GLOBAL COMPANIES LLC
(*Suby of* GLOBAL OPERATING LLC) ★
800 South St Ste 500, Waltham, MA 02453-1483
Tel (800) 542-0778 *Founded/Ownrshp* 2005
Sales 661.9MM^E *EMP* 229^E
SIC 5172 5171 Fuel oil; Gasoline; Diesel fuel; Kerosene; Petroleum bulk stations & terminals
Pr: Eric Slifka
**COO:* Thomas J Hollister
CFO: Caroline Dorsa
**Ex VP:* Edward J Faneuil
**Ex VP:* Charles A Rudinsky
Genl Mgr: Karnig Ekizian
Mktg Mgr: Joe De Stefano

D-U-N-S 36-290-1493
GLOBAL COMPOSITES INC
GLOBAL MOULDING
58190 County Road 3, Elkhart, IN 46517-9007
Tel (574) 522-9956 *Founded/Ownrshp* 1981
Sales 51.3MM^E *EMP* 180
SIC 3229 Glass fibers, textile; Glass fibers, textile
Pr: Gary L Beck
Genl Mgr: Todd Jones
Sls Dir: Jerry Healey
Sls Mgr: Greg Schossau

D-U-N-S 61-783-0518
■ GLOBAL COMPUTER SUPPLIES INC
(*Suby of* SYSTEMAX INC) ★
11 Harbor Park Dr, Port Washington, NY 11050-4656
Tel (516) 403-2800 *Founded/Ownrshp* 1995
Sales 38.6MM^E *EMP* 550
SIC 7379 Data processing consultant; Data processing consultant
Genl Mgr: James Fritz
**Ch Bd:* Richard Leeds
Bd of Dir: Carlos Gonzalez
Sales Exec: Amanda Crawford
Sls Mgr: Jason Cohen
Sls Mgr: Stephen Grubstein

D-U-N-S 00-280-1079 IMP
GLOBAL CONCEPTS ENTERPRISE INC (MI)
785 Waverly Ct, Holland, MI 49423-9387
Tel (616) 355-7657 *Founded/Ownrshp* 1995
Sales 25.3MM^E *EMP* 65
SIC 5021 5084 Office furniture; Industrial machinery & equipment
CEO: Jay Kang
**Pr:* Robert Rynbrandt
**Sr VP:* Rudy Broekhuis
Off Mgr: Jannelle Geertman
Mtls Mgr: Bill Grit
Prd Mgr: Barry Slinkman
Ql Cn Mgr: Pete Mitchell
Board of Directors: Sang Kang

D-U-N-S 03-699-1438
GLOBAL CONNECTIONS INC
GLOBAL VACATIONS
5360 College Blvd Ste 200, Leawood, KS 66211-1641
Tel (913) 498-0960 *Founded/Ownrshp* 1996
Sales 30.0MM^E *EMP* 100^E
SIC 4724 Travel agencies
Pr: Tom Lyons
**COO:* Frank Zawojski
**CFO:* Richard Washburn
**VP:* Dave Dawson
**VP:* Melanie Gring
**VP:* Cathy Wunder
Dir IT: Brian Stearns

D-U-N-S 04-108-2754
GLOBAL CONSTRUCTION SERVICES LLC
934 N University Dr 453, Coral Springs, FL 33071-7029
Tel (954) 688-6255 *Founded/Ownrshp* 2010
Sales 700.0MM *EMP* 7
SIC 1522 Apartment building construction; Apartment building construction
Off Mgr: Cindy Owen

D-U-N-S 10-400-2865
GLOBAL CONTACT SERVICES LLC
118b S Main St B, Salisbury, NC 28144-4942
Tel (312) 604-5017 *Founded/Ownrshp* 2001
Sales 46.0MM^E *EMP* 1,600
SIC 7389 Telephone services; Telephone answering service; Telephone services; Telephone answering service
CEO: Greg Alcorn
**COO:* Bryan Overcash
**Sr VP:* Frank Camp
VP: Bucky Cline
**VP:* Mark Petty
Dir IT: Richard Johnson

GLOBAL CONTRACT MANUFACTURING
See GCM MEDICAL & OEM DIVISION INC

D-U-N-S 14-183-0724
GLOBAL CONTRACT PROFESSIONALS INC
4000 Sandshell Dr, Fort Worth, TX 76137-2422
Tel (817) 847-6673 *Founded/Ownrshp* 2003
Sales 20.8MM^E *EMP* 300
SIC 8711 Engineering services; Engineering services
Pr: Paul Milligan
**Treas:* Gene Rhoades
**VP:* Kenny Boner
CIO: Scott Kostelecky

D-U-N-S 15-469-1328
■ GLOBAL CROSSING BANDWIDTH INC
(*Suby of* LEVEL 3 COMMUNICATIONS INC) ★
225 Kenneth Dr, Rochester, NY 14623-4277
Tel (212) 920-8201 *Founded/Ownrshp* 2011
Sales 166.9MM^E *EMP* 2,000
SIC 4813 7373 7374 Telephone communication, except radio; Computer integrated systems design; Data processing & preparation; Telephone communication, except radio; Computer integrated systems design; Data processing & preparation
Pr: David R Carey
**CFO:* John Kritzmacher
**Treas:* Mark Gottlieb
**VP:* Mitchell C Sussis
IT Man: James Harney

D-U-N-S 00-699-4065 IMP
■ GLOBAL CROSSING NORTH AMERICA INC
ROCHESTER TELEPHONE
(*Suby of* GLOBAL CROSSING NORTH AMERICAN HOLDINGS INC) ★
200 Park Ave Ste 300, Florham Park, NJ 07932-1026
Tel (973) 937-0100 *Founded/Ownrshp* 1999
Sales 161.7MM^E *EMP* 570
SIC 4813 Local & long distance telephone communications; Data telephone communications; Voice telephone communications; Local & long distance telephone communications; Data telephone communications; Voice telephone communications
CEO: John J Legere
Pt: Alan Rosenberg
Pr: Christopher Conley
Pr: Dennis Morton
**CFO:* Jean Mandeville
**Chf Mktg O:* Anthony Christie
Ex VP: David R Caey
**Ex VP:* David R Carey
**Ex VP:* Daniel Enright
Ex VP: Matias Heinrich
**Ex VP:* John B McShane
Ex VP: John R Mulhearn
Ex VP: Paul O'Brien
Sr VP: Paul O Brien
VP: Neil Barua
VP: Mike Benjamin
VP: Ricky Chau
VP: Mike Cromwell
VP: Steve Cross
VP: Terrence Dugan
VP: Maria Funkhouser
Board of Directors: Mitchell Sussis

D-U-N-S 15-443-6914
■ GLOBAL CROSSING NORTH AMERICAN HOLDINGS INC
(*Suby of* LEVEL 3 COMMUNICATIONS INC) ★
200 Park Ave Ste 300, Florham Park, NJ 07932-1026
Tel (973) 937-0100 *Founded/Ownrshp* 2011
Sales 421.8MM^E *EMP* 3,155
SIC 4813 Telephone communication, except radio; Telephone communication, except radio
CEO: John Legere
**Chf Mktg O:* Gary Breauninger
Sr VP: Michael Toplisek
**VP:* Mitchell C Sussis

D-U-N-S 05-489-3409
■ GLOBAL CROSSING TELECOMMUNICATIONS INC
(*Suby of* GLOBAL CROSSING NORTH AMERICA INC) ★
200 Park Ave Ste 300, Florham Park, NJ 07932-1026
Tel (973) 937-0100 *Founded/Ownrshp* 2003
Sales 69.5MM^E *EMP* 390
SIC 4813 Long distance telephone communications; Long distance telephone communications
Pr: John Leger
Treas: Mark Gottlibe
VP: David Carey
Prin: Rachel Kleier
Board of Directors: Joseph P Clayton, Robert A Klug, Mitchell C Sussis

D-U-N-S 84-480-8639
■ GLOBAL CUSTOM COMMERCE INC
BLINDS.COM
(*Suby of* HOME DEPOT INC) ★
10255 Richmond Ave # 300, Houston, TX 77042-4175
Tel (800) 505-1905 *Founded/Ownrshp* 2001
Sales 71.0MM^E *EMP* 260
SIC 5714 Drapery & upholstery stores; Drapery & upholstery stores
CEO: Jay Steinfield
CFO: Jerome Smalley
**Sec:* Marilynne Franks
VP: Steve Riddell
VP Sls: Jeff Miller
Sls Dir: Sean Graham
Pr Mgr: Katie Laird
Sls Mgr: Chris Blair
Sls Mgr: Sharon Scheckter

D-U-N-S 14-440-7462
GLOBAL DATA CONSULTANTS LLC
GDC IT SOLUTIONS
1144 Kennebec Dr, Chambersburg, PA 17201-2809
Tel (717) 262-2080 *Founded/Ownrshp* 2003
Sales 66.8MM^E *EMP* 275
SIC 7371 7373 Custom computer programming services; Systems software development services; Computer systems analysis & design; Systems integration services; Local area network (LAN) systems integrator; Custom computer programming services; Systems software development services; Computer systems analysis & design; Systems integration services; Local area network (LAN) systems integrator
Pr: Mike Coons
Bd of Dir: Greg Courtney
**Ex VP:* Thomas Trgovac
VP: Dan Logan
CTO: Tommy Mowen
IT Man: Nicole Staretz
Netwrk Mgr: Cynthia Dixon
Netwrk Mgr: Kurt Hoffeditz
Netwrk Mgr: Tim Wetzel

D-U-N-S 80-788-9022
GLOBAL DATA PUBLICATIONS INC
GBI RESEARCH
441 Lexington Ave Fl 3, New York, NY 10017-3950
Tel (646) 395-5460 *Founded/Ownrshp* 2007
Sales 68.6MM^E *EMP* 1,000
SIC 7379 8732 8748 Data processing consultant; Market analysis or research; Business consulting; Data processing consultant; Market analysis or research; Business consulting
Pr: Ben Slattery
**CEO:* Wayne Lloyd
Sr VP: Marc Elichman
Dir Bus: Daniel Aminipour
Dir Bus: Michael Glover
Dir Bus: K Khan
Dir Bus: Andrew Suri
VP Sls: Janet Dresher

D-U-N-S 62-648-6237
GLOBAL DATA SYSTEMS INC
310 Laser Ln, Lafayette, LA 70507-5325
Tel (337) 291-6500 *Founded/Ownrshp* 1987
Sales 75.9MM^E *EMP* 115
SIC 5065 3572 Telephone equipment; Telephone equipment; Computer storage devices
Pr: Chris Vincent
**CEO:* Chuck Vincent
CEO: Joseph Young
**CFO:* Mark Ditsious
Chf Mktg O: Ned Fasullo
VP: David Heximer
Dir Bus: Dean Davis
**CTO:* Robert Guidry
IT Man: Scott Harris
Opers Mgr: Les Henderson
Pr Dir: Greg Oloughlin

GLOBAL DEVELOPMENT
See SHREDDERHOTLINE.COM CO INC

D-U-N-S 11-420-6076 IMP
GLOBAL DISPLAY SOLUTIONS INC
(*Suby of* GLOBAL DISPLAY SOLUTIONS SPA)
5217 28th Ave, Rockford, IL 61109-1722
Tel (815) 282-2328 *Founded/Ownrshp* 1997
Sales 24.9MM^E *EMP* 50
SIC 3679 Liquid crystal displays (LCD)
Ch Bd: Thomas Lentz
**Pr:* Giovanni Cariolato
Treas: Emmanuel Grodzinski
**Genl Mgr:* Robert Heise

GLOBAL DISTRIBUTION CENTER
See JACINTOPORT INTERNATIONAL LLC

GLOBAL DISTRIBUTION SERVICES
See BOWTIE INC

D-U-N-S 09-852-6775
GLOBAL DISTRIBUTORS INC (FL)
2161 Nw 25th Ave, Miami, FL 33142-7120
Tel (305) 638-8954 *Founded/Ownrshp* 1977
Sales 26.3MM^E *EMP* 35
SIC 5147 5141 Meats, fresh; Groceries, general line
Pr: Felipe Valls Jr
VP: Jose Maria Bravo

D-U-N-S 03-973-8281 IMP
GLOBAL DIVING & SALVAGE INC
3840 W Marginal Way Sw, Seattle, WA 98106-1163
Tel (206) 623-0621 *Founded/Ownrshp* 1980
Sales 209.7MM^E *EMP* 443^E
SIC 4959 1629 7389 Oil spill cleanup; Marine construction; Divers, commercial; Oil spill cleanup; Marine construction; Divers, commercial
Pr: Devon Grennan
Bd of Dir: John Graham
VP: Martin Anderson
VP: David Devilbiss
VP: Jennifer Jensen
**VP:* Trinity Ng-Yeung
Div Mgr: Bruce Humberstone
Off Mgr: Connie Alvarez
Off Mgr: Kathy Kaae
IT Man: Jeffery Chin
IT Man: Kurt Vancampen

GLOBAL DOSIMETRY SOLUTIONS
See MIRION TECHNOLOGIES (GDS) INC

D-U-N-S 02-589-2480 IMP/EXP
GLOBAL DRILLING SUPPLIERS INC
12101 Centron Pl, Cincinnati, OH 45246-1704
Tel (513) 671-8700 *Founded/Ownrshp* 1981
Sales 49.2MM *EMP* 35
SIC 5082 Construction & mining machinery; Construction & mining machinery
Pr: Mark Kuenning
**VP:* Jim Rupert
**VP:* Ted Walker
Brnch Mgr: Brian Walker

GLOBAL DRILLING SUPPORT
See GDS INTERNATIONAL LLC

D-U-N-S 78-346-0566
■ GLOBAL EAGLE ENTERTAINMENT INC
ROW 44, INC.
(*Suby of* GLOBAL EAGLE ENTERTAINMENT INC) ★
4353 Park Terrace Dr # 100, Westlake Village, CA 91361-4638
Tel (818) 706-3111 *Founded/Ownrshp* 2013
Sales 30.1MM^E *EMP* 27^E
SIC 4813
CEO: John Lavalle
V Ch: Louis Martin
Pr: Simon McLellan
**CFO:* Dave Davis
**Chf Cred:* Doug Walner
Bd of Dir: Larry Kellner
Sr VP: Aditya Chatterjee
**Sr VP:* Pierre Steffen
VP: Jags Burhm
**VP:* Jim Costello
VP: Nancy Hood
VP: Mike Pigott
**VP:* Steve Redford
Dir Bus: Frederick Amour

D-U-N-S 96-730-2865
▲ GLOBAL EAGLE ENTERTAINMENT INC
4553 Glencoe Ave Ste 300, Marina Del Rey, CA 90292-7914
Tel (310) 437-6000 *Founded/Ownrshp* 2013
Sales 387.7MM *EMP* 730^E
Tkr Sym ENT *Exch* NAS
SIC 7371 4813 4899 Custom computer programming services; Software programming applications; ; ; Data communication services; Custom computer programming services; Software programming applications; ; ; Data communication services
CEO: David M Davis
Ch Bd: Edward L Shapiro
V Ch: Louis Martin
CFO: Michael Zemetra
Ofcr: Pierre Steffen
Ex VP: Wal Adepoju
Sr VP: Zant Chapelo
Sr VP: Mike Douglass
Sr VP: Jim Griffiths
Sr VP: Jay Itzkowitz
VP: Julian Gorniok
VP: Chris Jeffries
VP: Charles Wong
Board of Directors: Jeffrey E Epstein, Steve Hasker, Jeffrey A Leddy, Louis Belanger-Martin, Robert W Reding, Jeff Sagansky, Harry E Sloan

D-U-N-S 00-115-9292 IMP
GLOBAL EDM SUPPLIES INC (OH)
7697 Innovation Way # 400, Mason, OH 45040-9605
Tel (513) 701-0468 *Founded/Ownrshp* 1944, 1995
Sales 37.8MM^E *EMP* 81
SIC 5084 Industrial machinery & equipment; Industrial machinery & equipment
Ch: Ramesh Malthrotra
**Pr:* Christopher Frost
CFO: Sunil Bhirani
**Prin:* Thomas D Shackleford

D-U-N-S 00-484-4242
GLOBAL EDUCATIONAL EXCELLENCE LLC
2455 S Industrial Hwy A, Ann Arbor, MI 48104-6122
Tel (734) 369-9500 *Founded/Ownrshp* 1998
Sales 58.7MM^E *EMP* 600
SIC 8748 Educational consultant; Educational consultant
IT Man: Deborah Reynolds

D-U-N-S 78-424-6790
GLOBAL EMPLOYMENT HOLDINGS INC
10375 Park Meadows Dr # 375, Littleton, CO 80124-6735
Tel (303) 216-9500 *Founded/Ownrshp* 2006
Sales 175.0MM^E *EMP* 15,000^E
SIC 7363 6719 Temporary help service; Investment holding companies, except banks; Temporary help service; Investment holding companies, except banks
Pr: Howard Brill
**Pr:* Terry Koch
**CFO:* Wayne Cavanaugh
Ex VP: Michael Devlieger
Ex VP: John Evans
VP: Kimberly Lepre
VP: Gavin Meacham
VP: Ken Michaels
**VP:* Ashley Notthoff
Brnch Mgr: Denise Hernandez
Off Mgr: Maureen Standing
Board of Directors: Richard Goldman, Charles Gwirtsman

GLOBAL EMPLOYMENT SOLUTIONS
See FRIENDLY ADVANCED SOFTWARE TECHNOLOGY INC

D-U-N-S 02-613-6288
GLOBAL EMPLOYMENT SOLUTIONS INC
(*Suby of* GLOBAL EMPLOYMENT HOLDINGS INC) ★
10375 Park Meadows Dr # 475, Littleton, CO 80124-6735
Tel (303) 216-9500 *Founded/Ownrshp* 2009
Sales 86.6MM^E *EMP* 2,000
SIC 7363 Temporary help service; Temporary help service
Pr: Howard Brill
Pr: Wayne Cavanaugh
CFO: Daniel Hollenbach
Div Pres: Tom Bodeep
Assoc VP: Rose Chu
Ex VP: John Evans
Ex VP: Joe Verroca
Ex VP: Susan Zingaro
VP: Russ Abraham
VP: Miguel Boland
VP: Kevin Kelly
VP: Kevin Lecompte
VP: Ashley Notthoff
VP: Zach Schnell
Dir Risk M: Debra Roberts

D-U-N-S 07-850-2030
GLOBAL ENERGY CONTRACTORS LLC
1400 Preston Rd Ste 400, Plano, TX 75093-5189
Tel (972) 665-9763 *Founded/Ownrshp* 2011
Sales 40.0MM *EMP* 5
SIC 1389 Bailing, cleaning, swabbing & treating of wells; Bailing, cleaning, swabbing & treating of wells

D-U-N-S 83-140-3238
■ GLOBAL ENERGY MARKETING LLC
(*Suby of* GLOBAL OPERATING LLC) ★
800 South St Ste 500, Waltham, MA 02453-1439
Tel (781) 894-8800 *Founded/Ownrshp* 2009
Sales 107.5MM^E *EMP* 1,000^E
SIC 5172 4924 Fuel oil; Natural gas distribution
Pr: Eric Slifka
**COO:* Thomas J Hollister
**Ex VP:* Edward J Faneuil
**Ex VP:* Charles A Rudinsky

D-U-N-S 18-818-7710
GLOBAL ENERGY SERVICES INC
10307 Wallisville Rd, Houston, TX 77013-4117
Tel (281) 447-9000 *Founded/Ownrshp* 1996
Sales 129.9MM^E *EMP* 605
SIC 3533 Oil field machinery & equipment; Oil field machinery & equipment
CEO: Paul Deweese
**Pr:* Michael Stansberry
**CFO:* Chris Ruffner
Dir IT: Mark Johns
VP Sls: Lance Vogelsang
Sls Dir: Ryan Canter

GLOBAL ENERGY SOLUTIONS
See GLOBAL ENVIRONMENTAL SOLUTIONS INC

D-U-N-S 10-511-7506
GLOBAL ENGINEERING & CONSTRUCTION LLC
4904 Lake Wash Blvd Ne, Renton, WA 98056-1057
Tel (425) 255-3111 *Founded/Ownrshp* 1999
Sales 28.1MM^E *EMP* 261
SIC 8711 1541 7349 Engineering services; Engineering services; Renovation, remodeling & repairs: industrial buildings; Building maintenance services
IT Man: John Boe
Opers Mgr: David Fernandes
Snr PM: Darrell Hoppe

D-U-N-S 79-516-4953
GLOBAL ENGINEERING & TECHNOLOGY INC
1720 S 151st St W, Goddard, KS 67052-9449
Tel (316) 729-9232 *Founded/Ownrshp* 1991
Sales 25.9MM^E *EMP* 145
SIC 3728 2434 7389 Aircraft parts & equipment; Wood kitchen cabinets; Design services; Aircraft parts & equipment; Wood kitchen cabinets; Design services
CEO: Delores A Nevin
**Pr:* Finley Nevin
COO: Darren Moore
Ql Cn Mgr: Bill Hudnall

D-U-N-S 92-942-6005
GLOBAL ENTERPRISE TECHNOLOGIES CORP (DE)
G.E.T.
230 3rd Ave Ste 6, Waltham, MA 02451-7542
Tel (781) 890-6700 *Founded/Ownrshp* 1986
Sales 25.6MM^E *EMP* 220
SIC 7373 Systems integration services; Systems integration services
CEO: Gary Christelis
**Ch Bd:* Maysoon Jamal
IT Man: Lawrence Ashiku

D-U-N-S 96-703-7743 EXP
GLOBAL ENTERPRISE WORLDWIDE LLC
1201 N Orange St Ste 700, Wilmington, DE 19801-1186
Tel (713) 260-9687 *Founded/Ownrshp* 2010
Sales 22.8MM^E *EMP* 70^E
SIC 5099 Wood chips

GLOBAL ENTERPRISES
See POLYMERICA LTD

D-U-N-S 96-789-0521 IMP
GLOBAL ENVIRONMENTAL PRODUCTS INC
GLOBAL SWEEPING SOLUTIONS
5405 Industrial Pkwy, San Bernardino, CA 92407-1803
Tel (909) 713-1600 *Founded/Ownrshp* 2011
Sales 26.6MM^E *EMP* 67
SIC 3711 Street sprinklers & sweepers (motor vehicles), assembly of
Pr: Walter Pusic
**Pr:* Sebastian Mentelski
**VP:* Chad Bormann
Opers Mgr: Naomi Thompson

D-U-N-S 82-604-3718
GLOBAL ENVIRONMENTAL SOLUTIONS INC
GLOBAL ENERGY SOLUTIONS
707 Sable Oaks Dr Ste 150, South Portland, ME 04106-6954
Tel (207) 541-9421 *Founded/Ownrshp* 2008
Sales 37.1MM *EMP* 36
Accts Berry Dunn & Mcneil & Parker
SIC 1629 Land clearing contractor; Land clearing contractor
Pr: Kevin B Pomerleau
**CFO:* Pamela Wright
**VP:* Gregory Pomerleau

D-U-N-S 00-147-2216 EXP
■ **GLOBAL EQUIPMENT CO INC** (NY)
GLOBAL INDUSTRIAL EQUIPMENT
(*Suby of* SYSTEMAX INC) ★
11 Harbor Park Dr, Port Washington, NY 11050-4646
Tel (516) 608-7000 *Founded/Ownrshp* 1951, 2001
Sales 188.8MM^E *EMP* 400
SIC 5085 Industrial supplies; Industrial supplies
Ch Bd: Richard Leeds
Pr: Michael Haskins
**Treas:* Steven Goldschein
**VP:* Dennis Gerard
**VP:* Bruce Leeds
Exec: Yaminah Graves
Natl Sales: Carl Schaaf
Mktg Mgr: Anne Miu
Sls Mgr: Vincent Zirrillo

D-U-N-S 02-173-2202 IMP
GLOBAL EQUIPMENT SERVICES AND MANUFACTURING INC
2372 Qume Dr Ste F, San Jose, CA 95131-1843
Tel (408) 441-0682 *Founded/Ownrshp* 2006
Sales 40.3MM^E *EMP* 105
SIC 5046 Commercial equipment
Pr: Don Tran
VP Sls: Marty Mason

D-U-N-S 08-377-2749 IMP
■ **GLOBAL EXPERIENCE SPECIALISTS INC**
G E S GLOBAL EXPERIENCE
(*Suby of* VIAD CORP) ★
7000 Lindell Rd, Las Vegas, NV 89118-4702
Tel (702) 515-5500 *Founded/Ownrshp* 1976
Sales 539.0MM^E *EMP* 2,800
SIC 7389 Convention & show services; Convention & show services
Ch Bd: Robert H Bohannon
**Pr:* Steve Moster
**COO:* Damian Morgan
**CFO:* Dave Hall
Treas: Elyse A Newman
Ofcr: Jeff Quade
Ex VP: Bruce H Baum
Ex VP: Chuck Grouzard
Ex VP: Shirley R Kerfoot
**Ex VP:* Eddie Newqu
Ex VP: Eddie Newquist
Ex VP: John Patronski
Ex VP: Jason Popp
Ex VP: Heather Ronnow
Ex VP: Vin Saia
Ex VP: Gary C Sain
Ex VP: Thomas W Vogt
Sr VP: Terry Campanaro
**Sr VP:* Chris Elam
Sr VP: Dan Hilbert
Sr VP: Paul Wedesky

D-U-N-S 19-605-9430 EXP
GLOBAL EXPORT MARKETING CO LTD
25 W 31st St Fl 8, New York, NY 10001-4450
Tel (212) 268-9930 *Founded/Ownrshp* 1988
Sales 26.0MM^E *EMP* 8^E
SIC 5141 Groceries, general line
Pr: Morty Fazal
**VP:* Kevin Egan

D-U-N-S 82-903-6420 EXP
GLOBAL FABRICATION INC
235 Beaver Dr, Du Bois, PA 15801-2517
Tel (814) 372-1500 *Founded/Ownrshp* 2009
Sales 30.0MM^E *EMP* 65
SIC 3441 Fabricated structural metal
Pr: Dennis V Raybuck
**CFO:* Molly Kelsey
**VP:* Kenneth J Mitchell
**VP:* Rebecca F Raybuck
Genl Mgr: Todd Gorden

D-U-N-S 86-149-9432 IMP/EXP
GLOBAL FABRICATION SERVICES INC
GLOBAL STL & FLAMECUTTING SVCS
9400 Forest Ln, Conroe, TX 77385-5108
Tel (281) 367-9333 *Founded/Ownrshp* 1994
Sales 39.1MM^E *EMP* 110
SIC 3441 Fabricated structural metal; Fabricated structural metal for ships; Fabricated structural metal; Fabricated structural metal for ships
CEO: Karl W Oswald
**Pr:* Ron Borg
**CFO:* Larry Keeler

GLOBAL FABRICATORS
See MCM FABRICATORS INC

D-U-N-S 80-834-4621
GLOBAL FACILITY MANAGEMENT & CONSTRUCTION INC
525 Broadhollow Rd # 100, Melville, NY 11747-3736
Tel (631) 617-6500 *Founded/Ownrshp* 2007
Sales 70.0MM *EMP* 160
SIC 7349 Building maintenance services; Building maintenance services
CEO: Lauryn Blank
VP: Mike Russo
Sls Dir: Sean Blank
Sls Mgr: Arun Dayaram
Sls Mgr: Lexi Pisciotto
Snr Mgr: Ashley Orfini

D-U-N-S 96-630-0873
GLOBAL FINANCIAL AID SERVICES INC
GFAS
10467 Corporate Dr, Gulfport, MS 39503-4634
Tel (228) 523-1000 *Founded/Ownrshp* 1996
Sales 23.9MM^E *EMP* 320
SIC 7389 Financial services; Financial services
Pr: Edward J Addison Jr
**COO:* Chyrl R Ayers
**CFO:* Leo J Romano
**VP:* Brian Duckworth
**VP:* Matthew Johnner
Software D: Tina Metcalf
Sales Exec: Justin Allen

D-U-N-S 96-827-1734
GLOBAL FINANCIAL SERVICES
2500 N Federal Hwy # 201, Fort Lauderdale, FL 33305-1618
Tel (954) 568-4400 *Founded/Ownrshp* 1995
Sales NA *EMP* 5
SIC 6163 Loan brokers; Loan brokers
Pr: Ed Rowland
**VP:* Volkmar Darksen

D-U-N-S 13-037-5991
GLOBAL FINISHING SOLUTIONS LLC
(*Suby of* CURRAN GROUP INC) ★
1625 W Crosby Rd Ste 124, Carrollton, TX 75006-6694
Tel (800) 468-5872 *Founded/Ownrshp* 2003
Sales 16.5MM^E *EMP* 300
SIC 3448 Prefabricated metal buildings
Pr: Carlos Pippa
VP: Mike Reese
CIO: Jeanne Perdue

D-U-N-S 13-735-2576 IMP
GLOBAL FINISHING SOLUTIONS LLC
GFS
(*Suby of* CURRAN GROUP INC) ★
12731 Norway Rd, Osseo, WI 54758-7780
Tel (715) 597-8007 *Founded/Ownrshp* 1998
Sales 94.0MM *EMP* 360
SIC 3444 Booths, spray: prefabricated sheet metal; Booths, spray: prefabricated sheet metal
CEO: Michael Curran
**Pr:* James Fargher
**CFO:* Joshua Eager
Sfty Mgr: John Vonasek
VP Sls: Gary Hammerling

D-U-N-S 80-780-2660
GLOBAL FITNESS HOLDINGS LLC
URBAN ACTIVE
1056 Wellington Way # 200, Lexington, KY 40513-2000
Tel (859) 252-5993 *Founded/Ownrshp* 2000
Sales 34.1MM^E *EMP* 1,500
SIC 7991 Athletic club & gymnasiums, membership; Athletic club & gymnasiums, membership
CFO: Denver Pratt
Dist Mgr: Jeremy Alexander
CIO: Keith Trawick

GLOBAL FITTINGS & FLANGES
See DODSON GLOBAL INC

D-U-N-S 16-597-4002 EXP
GLOBAL FLEET SALES LLC
24725 W 12 Mile Rd # 114, Southfield, MI 48034-8345
Tel (248) 327-6483 *Founded/Ownrshp* 2004
Sales 23.7MM^E *EMP* 8
SIC 5012 8711 3621 Automobiles & other motor vehicles; Engineering services; Generators & sets, electric; Automobiles & other motor vehicles; Engineering services; Generators & sets, electric
Pr: Kevin R Whitcraft
CFO: Alexander Brenneisen
Treas: Mark I Whitcraft
VP: Carol Grakul
Genl Mgr: Carol Zrakul
IT Man: Clark Farmer
Sls Mgr: Chris Grakul
Sls Mgr: Ken Young

D-U-N-S 79-115-2304 IMP
■ **GLOBAL FLOW TECHNOLOGIES INC**
(*Suby of* FORUM ENERGY TECHNOLOGIES INC) ★
12735 Dairy Ashford Rd, Stafford, TX 77477-3612
Tel (281) 340-5400 *Founded/Ownrshp* 2010
Sales 45.1MM^E *EMP* 223^E
SIC 5085 Valves & fittings; Valves & fittings
Pr: Steve Twellman
CFO: Greg Obrien
**VP:* Greg O'Brien
Dir IT: Karen Godec
Sales Asso: Kathy Farris

D-U-N-S 96-549-2416 IMP
GLOBAL FOODS INC
5435 S Durango Dr, Las Vegas, NV 89113-1849
Tel (702) 870-7600 *Founded/Ownrshp* 1995
Sales 44.9MM^E *EMP* 35
SIC 5141 Groceries, general line
Pr: Sean Cook
Off Mgr: Erika Ruffin
IT Man: William Sherman
Mfg Dir: Sandra Sanoh
VP Sls: Wendy Shanks
Sls Mgr: Liz Fetherolf
Sls Mgr: Dwight Gardner
Sls Mgr: Rhonda Mengert
Sls Mgr: Victoria Newman

D-U-N-S 80-630-1362
GLOBAL FOODS PROCESSING INC
1826 Chicago Ave, Sioux City, IA 51106-5810
Tel (712) 255-6000 *Founded/Ownrshp* 2011
Sales 29.8MM^E *EMP* 160
SIC 2013 2011 Prepared pork products from purchased pork; Meat packing plants; Prepared pork products from purchased pork; Meat packing plants
Pr: David Guest
**Sec:* Dolores M Guest

GLOBAL FOUNDRIES
See GLOBALFOUNDRIES US INC

D-U-N-S 80-078-6696
GLOBAL FRANCHISE GROUP LLC
PRETZEL TIME
(*Suby of* GFG MANAGEMENT LLC) ★
5555 Glenridge Connector # 850, Atlanta, GA 30342-4810
Tel (770) 514-4500 *Founded/Ownrshp* 2010
Sales 184.8MM^E *EMP* 961^E
SIC 5461 6794 Bakeries; Franchises, selling or licensing; Bakeries; Franchises, selling or licensing
Pr: Chris Dull
**CFO:* Lewis Loeb
**Ofcr:* John Barber
VP: Andrew Kmiec
VP: John Peddar
VP Inf Sys: Gerald Brouilette
Mktg Mgr: Andrea Walker
Snr Mgr: Kevin Lind

D-U-N-S 13-489-9009 IMP/EXP
GLOBAL FURNITURE USA INC
47 Sixth St, East Brunswick, NJ 08816-5701
Tel (732) 613-0001 *Founded/Ownrshp* 2003
Sales 23.7MM^E *EMP* 35
SIC 5021 Furniture
CEO: Alex Vaysman
VP: Bill Brady
Genl Mgr: Elan Gershman
Off Mgr: Joseph Lomangino
Sales Exec: John Turano

D-U-N-S 80-374-2345 IMP
GLOBAL GEAR & MACHINING LLC
(*Suby of* IMS COMPANIES LLC) ★
2500 Curtiss St, Downers Grove, IL 60515-4058
Tel (630) 969-9400 *Founded/Ownrshp* 1991
Sales 43.5MM^E *EMP* 127
SIC 3714 Gears, motor vehicle; Gears, motor vehicle
Pr: Mark Simington
QA Dir: Etelvina Garcia

D-U-N-S 18-036-3611
GLOBAL GEOPHYSICAL SERVICES INC
13927 S Gessner Rd, Missouri City, TX 77489-1021
Tel (713) 972-9200 *Founded/Ownrshp* 2003
Sales 288.6MM *EMP* 1,500^E
SIC 1382 Oil & gas exploration services; Geophysical exploration, oil & gas field; Seismograph surveys; Oil & gas exploration services; Geophysical exploration, oil & gas field; Seismograph surveys
Ch Bd: Richard C White
COO: Earl Snyder
COO: P Mathew Verghese
CFO: Sean M Gore
Sr VP: James E Brasher
Sr VP: Thomas J Fleure
VP: Tony Clark
VP: Raymond Dobrosky
VP: Maurice Flynn
VP: Kirk Girouard
VP: Carolan Laudon
VP: Bill McLain
VP: Victoria Sublette
VP: Charles Yanez
VP: George Yapuncich

Board of Directors: Michael S Bahorich, Michael C Forrest, Karl F Kurz, George E Matelich, Joseph P McCoy, Stanley De J Osborne

GLOBAL GOLF
See GLOBAL VALUE COMMERCE INC

D-U-N-S 14-006-3152
■ **GLOBAL GOVERNMENT EDUCATION SOLUTIONS INC**
(*Suby of* SYSTEMAX INC) ★
6450 Poe Ave Ste 200, Dayton, OH 45414-2655
Tel (937) 368-2308 *Founded/Ownrshp* 1997
Sales 36.0MM *EMP* 70
SIC 5045 Computers, peripherals & software; Computer peripheral equipment; Printers, computer; Computers & accessories, personal & home entertainment; Computers, peripherals & software; Computer peripheral equipment; Printers, computer; Computers & accessories, personal & home entertainment
Pr: Richard Leeds
**Treas:* Curt Rush
**VP:* Steve Goldschein
IT Man: Penny Musser
Sls Mgr: Nicki Williams
Sales Asso: Michael Fast
Snr Mgr: Mark Wentworth

D-U-N-S 07-019-3854 IMP
GLOBAL GRANITE & MARBLE LLC
GLOBAL GRANITE & STONE
10800 Linpage Pl Bldg 1, Saint Louis, MO 63132-1008
Tel (314) 426-1466 *Founded/Ownrshp* 1998
Sales 26.1MM^E *EMP* 60
SIC 5032 Marble building stone
Pr: David Havens
**CFO:* Robert C Ballard

GLOBAL GRANITE & STONE
See GLOBAL GRANITE & MARBLE LLC

GLOBAL GRAPHICS SOLUTION
See WRIGHT OF THOMASVILLE INC

D-U-N-S 17-686-6937 EXP
■ **GLOBAL GROUND SUPPORT LLC**
(*Suby of* T AIR INC) ★
540 E Highway 56, Olathe, KS 66061-4640
Tel (913) 780-0300 *Founded/Ownrshp* 1997
Sales 24.4MM^E *EMP* 70
SIC 3728 5088 Deicing equipment, aircraft; Aircraft & parts
COO: Michael Moore
**CFO:* Kurt Hinrichs
Ex VP: J Martin
IT Man: Bill Dempsey
VP Opers: Leo Ruhlman
Prd Mgr: Charles Preston

GLOBAL GROUP, THE
See GLOBAL STAINLESS SUPPLY INC

D-U-N-S 19-616-5711
GLOBAL HARNESS SYSTEMS INC
3304 Danley Rd, Philadelphia, PA 19154-1410
Tel (609) 815-2100 *Founded/Ownrshp* 2001
Sales 173.9MM^E *EMP* 845
SIC 3679 Harness assemblies for electronic use: wire or cable; Harness assemblies for electronic use: wire or cable
CEO: Saul Epstein
**Pr:* Chad London
Manager: John Herider

GLOBAL HEALTH INDUSTRIES
See PRO PAC LABS INC

D-U-N-S 96-489-2553
GLOBAL HEALTH SOLUTIONS INC
325 Swanton Way, Decatur, GA 30030-3001
Tel (404) 592-1430 *Founded/Ownrshp* 2010
Sales 1.7MMM *EMP* 2
SIC 8099 Health & allied services; Health & allied services
VP: T Rosenberger
VP: Thomas Rosenberger

D-U-N-S 04-638-4171
GLOBAL HEALTHCARE EXCHANGE INC
1315 W Century Dr, Louisville, CO 80027-9560
Tel (720) 887-7000 *Founded/Ownrshp* 1999
Sales 33.8MM^E *EMP* 350
SIC 8099 Blood related health services; Blood related health services
CEO: Bruce Johnson

D-U-N-S 12-487-9334
GLOBAL HEALTHCARE EXCHANGE LLC
1315 W Century Dr Ste 100, Louisville, CO 80027-9560
Tel (720) 887-7000 *Founded/Ownrshp* 2014
Sales 219.5MM^E *EMP* 500
SIC 4813 7371 ; Computer software development & applications; ; Computer software development & applications
CEO: Bruce Johnson
CFO: Richard Hunt
Ex VP: Kurt W Blasena
VP: John Gaither
VP: Dale Locklair
VP: Sloane Stricker
Dir Bus: Sherry Jennings
Ex Dir: Stacey Breeden
Ex Dir: Lori Cook
Ex Dir: Alan Findley
Ex Dir: Robert Phinney

GLOBAL HOBBY DISTRIBUTORS
See HOBBY SHACK

D-U-N-S 11-892-0417
GLOBAL HORIZONS INC
DOMESTIC HORIZONS
468 N Camden Dr Ste 200, Beverly Hills, CA 90210-4507
Tel (310) 234-8475 *Founded/Ownrshp* 1997
Sales 18.1MM^E *EMP* 400
SIC 7361 Labor contractors (employment agency); Labor contractors (employment agency)

Pr: Mordechai Orian
**CFO:* Robert Rutt

D-U-N-S 00-475-8025
GLOBAL HOSPITALITY
FLEISCHER ENTERPRISES
1000 Lions Ridge Loop, Vail, CO 81657-4412
Tel (970) 476-2929 *Founded/Ownrshp* 1992
Sales 27.2MM *EMP* 33
SIC 6531 8741 Real estate managers; Hotel or motel management; Real estate managers; Hotel or motel management
CEO: William Fleischer
CFO: Nancy Byington

D-U-N-S 78-199-0796
GLOBAL HUNTER SECURITIES LLC
400 Poydras St Ste 3100, New Orleans, LA 70130-6911
Tel (504) 410-8010 *Founded/Ownrshp* 2007
Sales 50.7MM[E] *EMP* 134[E]
SIC 6211 Security brokers & dealers
Ch Bd: Daniel O Conwill IV
**Pr:* Edward R Lainfiesta
**CFO:* Mary Johnson
Ofcr: David Zack
Sr VP: Drew Adderly
Sr VP: Eric Krogius
Sr VP: James O'Donnell
Sr VP: Christopher Pollard
Sr VP: John P Songer
VP: Michael Monahan
VP: Patrick Rigamer
VP: Brad Steele
VP: Kevin Stone
VP: Ary Zomorodi
Exec: Bernard Colson

D-U-N-S 13-885-7789
GLOBAL HVAC DISTRIBUTORS INC
900 Spreckels Rd, Manteca, CA 95336-8940
Tel (209) 239-6446 *Founded/Ownrshp* 2002
Sales 21.0MM[E] *EMP* 24
SIC 1711 5075 Heating & air conditioning contractors; Warm air heating & air conditioning; Heating & air conditioning contractors; Warm air heating & air conditioning
Pr: Michael Druyanoff

D-U-N-S 88-388-2615 IMP
GLOBAL IMAGING INC
2011 Cherry St Unit 116, Louisville, CO 80027-3090
Tel (303) 673-9773 *Founded/Ownrshp* 1995
Sales 48.5MM[E] *EMP* 175
SIC 5045 3953

D-U-N-S 84-985-2389
■ **GLOBAL IMAGING SYSTEMS INC**
(*Suby of* XEROX CORP) ★
3903 Northdale Blvd 200w, Tampa, FL 33624-1854
Tel (813) 960-5508 *Founded/Ownrshp* 2007
Sales 2.5MMM[E] *EMP* 5,553
SIC 5044 5045 7629 Office equipment; Computers, peripherals & software; Computer peripheral equipment; Business machine repair, electric; Office equipment; Computers, peripherals & software; Computer peripheral equipment; Business machine repair, electric
CEO: Thomas Salierno Jr
**Pr:* Russell Peacock
**CFO:* R Edward Bass
Bd of Dir: Terry Smith
Ex VP: Daniel Robert Cooper
Sr VP: Dick Peterson
Sr VP: Mike Pietrunti
VP: Denny Houseman
**VP:* Roxanne Kosarzycki
VP: Dawn North
VP: Debra Patsky
Exec: Judy Schmidt
Dir Risk M: George Achin
Dir Bus: Wayne E Wilson

GLOBAL IMPORTS BMW
See SONIC-GLOBAL IMPORTS LP

D-U-N-S 83-320-8528
GLOBAL INDEMNITY GROUP INC
(*Suby of* GLOBAL INDEMNITY PUBLIC LIMITED COMPANY)
3 Bala Plz Ste 300, Bala Cynwyd, PA 19004-3406
Tel (610) 664-1500 *Founded/Ownrshp* 2003
Sales NA *EMP* 1,080[E]
SIC 6351 Surety insurance
Pr: Robert Fishman
CFO: Thomas McGeehan
VP: John Curry
VP: James Genghini
Snr Mgr: Cindy Valko

D-U-N-S 83-553-6749 IMP
GLOBAL INDUSTRIAL COMPONENTS INC
G I C
705 College St, Woodbury, TN 37190-1627
Tel (615) 563-5120 *Founded/Ownrshp* 1994
Sales 21.3MM[E] *EMP* 35
SIC 5085 5013 Fasteners & fastening equipment; Automotive supplies & parts
Pr: Gerald Toledo
**Sec:* Martha Whitmore
IT Man: Zachary Cannon
IT Man: Greg Parker
Sls Mgr: Steve Deberry

GLOBAL INDUSTRIAL EQUIPMENT
See GLOBAL EQUIPMENT CO INC

D-U-N-S 79-252-1445 IMP/EXP
GLOBAL INDUSTRIAL TECHNOLOGIES INC
(*Suby of* AP GREEN REFRACTORIES) ★
1305 Chrrington Pkwy Moon, Coraopolis, PA 15108
Tel (412) 375-6600 *Founded/Ownrshp* 2013
Sales 117.1MM[E] *EMP* 895[E]
SIC 3297 3255 1459 3546 3272 3589 Nonclay refractories; Crucibles: graphite, magnesite, chrome, silica, etc.; Graphite refractories: carbon bond or ceramic bond; Cement, magnesia; Clay refractories; Fire clay blocks, bricks, tile or special shapes; Foundry refractories, clay; Magnesite mining; Clays, except kaolin & ball; Power-driven handtools; Drills, portable, except rock: electric or pneumatic; Solid containing units, concrete; Battery wells or boxes, concrete; Shredders, industrial & commercial
CEO: Steven M Delo
CFO: Frances Winfield
Sr VP: Douglas Hall
Sr VP: Carol Jackson
VP: Stephen B Spolar

D-U-N-S 04-990-8403 IMP
GLOBAL INDUSTRIES INC
EVOLVE FURNITURE GROUP
17 W Stow Rd, Marlton, NJ 08053-3116
Tel (856) 596-3390 *Founded/Ownrshp* 1972
Sales 147.0MM[E] *EMP* 356
SIC 2522 5021 Office furniture, except wood; Furniture; Office furniture, except wood; Furniture
Ch Bd: Joel Appel
**Ex VP:* Jon Abraham
**Ex VP:* Jon Soll
Sr VP: Byron Baker
Sr VP: Eddie Evans
Sr VP: Andrew Smith
VP: Allan Bartolini
VP: Todd Holderness
VP: Bob Kohls
Opers Mgr: Scott Paden
Manager: Rich Oliver

D-U-N-S 96-461-1578 IMP/EXP
GLOBAL INDUSTRIES INC
MFS/YORK/STORMOR
2928 E Us Highway 30, Grand Island, NE 68801-8318
Tel (308) 384-9320 *Founded/Ownrshp* 1996
Sales 62.8MM[E] *EMP* 613
SIC 7992 3589 3444 5084 5083 3535 Public golf courses; Water treatment equipment, industrial; Metal housings, enclosures, casings & other containers; Materials handling machinery; Agricultural machinery & equipment; Conveyors & conveying equipment; Bucket type conveyor systems; Public golf courses; Water treatment equipment, industrial; Metal housings, enclosures, casings & other containers; Materials handling machinery; Agricultural machinery & equipment; Conveyors & conveying equipment
Pr: Jack R Henry
**CFO:* Douglas D Fargo
VP: John Haugh
VP: Randy Langen
Genl Mgr: Steve Back
Genl Mgr: Steve Beck
Genl Mgr: Jesse Depriest
Genl Mgr: Scott Stuhmiller
QA Dir: Gard Frerichs
Sfty Dirs: Jamie Lemburg
Mfg Mgr: Shannon Hinrichs

D-U-N-S 10-010-4376
GLOBAL INDUSTRY ANALYSTS INC
6150 Hellyer Ave Ste 100, San Jose, CA 95138-1072
Tel (408) 528-9966 *Founded/Ownrshp* 1992
Sales 29.5MM[E] *EMP* 700
SIC 8732 Market analysis or research; Market analysis or research
CEO: Kalakoti S Reddy

D-U-N-S 00-819-4974
GLOBAL INFOTECH CORP (DE)
2890 Zanker Rd Ste 202, San Jose, CA 95134-2118
Tel (408) 567-0600 *Founded/Ownrshp* 1995
Sales 46.1MM *EMP* 550
SIC 8748 Systems analysis & engineering consulting services; Systems analysis & engineering consulting services
Pr: Atul Sharma
**VP:* Nitin Prasad

D-U-N-S 79-077-4199
GLOBAL INFRASTRUCTURE MANAGEMENT LLC
GLOBAL INFRASTRUCTURE PARTNERS
12 E 49th St, New York, NY 10017-1028
Tel (212) 315-8100 *Founded/Ownrshp* 2006
Sales 47.4MM[E] *EMP* 51
SIC 6726 Management investment funds, closed-end
Mng Pt: Adebayo Ogunlesi
Mng Pt: Bayo Ogunlesi
**COO:* Mark Levitt
Ofcr: Lori Gish
VP: Jason Baer
VP: Jessica Ciardulli
VP: Andy Froberg
VP: Dan Galanter
VP: Nick Hume
VP: James Lee
VP: Sharad Malhotra
VP: Tom Price
VP: David Robinson

GLOBAL INFRASTRUCTURE PARTNERS
See GLOBAL INFRASTRUCTURE MANAGEMENT LLC

D-U-N-S 08-365-7713 IMP
GLOBAL INNOVATION CORP
901 Hensley Ln, Wylie, TX 75098-4909
Tel (214) 291-1427 *Founded/Ownrshp* 1990
Sales 29.9MM[E] *EMP* 179
SIC 3672 Printed circuit boards; Printed circuit boards
Ch Bd: Brad Jacoby
Pr: J Brent Nolan
CFO: Joe Dwyer
CFO: Brad J Peters
Ch: Jim Campbell
VP: Douglas McBride
VP: Frank Nieto
IT Man: Scott Mapes
VP Opers: Brett Whitman
QC Dir: Kara Walker
Opers Mgr: Al Wilson

GLOBAL INNOVATION PARTNER
See CBRE GLOBAL INVESTORS LLC

GLOBAL INTEGRATED LOGISTICS
See AGILITY LOGISTICS CORP

D-U-N-S 96-582-6931
GLOBAL INTEGRATED SECURITY (USA) INC
12950 Worldgate Dr # 550, Herndon, VA 20170-6038
Tel (703) 394-5100 *Founded/Ownrshp* 2011
Sales 11.0MM[E] *EMP* 350
SIC 7381 Detective & armored car services; Detective & armored car services
Pr: Michael Roberts
**CEO:* Greg Buckis
Sr VP: John Ayers
**VP:* Larry Vawter
IT Man: Rob Neale

D-U-N-S 80-104-1922 IMP
GLOBAL INVESTMENT RECOVERY INC
G I R
(*Suby of* SIMS RECYCLING SOLUTIONS HOLDINGS INC) ★
5806 N 53rd St Ste A, Tampa, FL 33610-4817
Tel (813) 620-1507 *Founded/Ownrshp* 2008
Sales 715.7M[E] *EMP* 340
SIC 5093 Metal scrap & waste materials; Metal scrap & waste materials
Pr: Stephen Skurnac

GLOBAL INVESTOR DISRIBUTORS
See ALLIANZ GLOBAL INVESTORS NY HOLDINGS LLC

D-U-N-S 94-131-9345
GLOBAL KNOWLEDGE TRAINING LLC
(*Suby of* GK HOLDINGS INC) ★
9000 Regency Pkwy Ste 400, Cary, NC 27518-8520
Tel (919) 388-1064 *Founded/Ownrshp* 1995
Sales 323.7MM *EMP* 462[E]
SIC 8243 Business training services; Software training, computer; Data processing schools
Pr: Brian Branson
**Treas:* Robert Kalainikas
VP: Bryan L Pickett
VP: Bruce Ryan
VP: Robert Schaffner
Exec: Priscilla Cooney
Prgrm Mgr: Nikki Anderson
IT Man: Ava Hines
Opers Mgr: Tom Krause
VP Sls: Jonathan Hensley
Mktg Mgr: Michelle Gray

D-U-N-S 94-632-1903
GLOBAL LION INC
GL TRADING
145 S Anderson St, Los Angeles, CA 90033-3219
Tel (323) 262-9969 *Founded/Ownrshp* 2005
Sales 25.0MM *EMP* 8
SIC 5199 General merchandise, non-durable
Pr: Bosco Kwon
Sls Mgr: James Song

D-U-N-S 62-410-1239
GLOBAL LOGISTICAL CONNECTIONS INC
475 W Manville St, Compton, CA 90220-5619
Tel (310) 603-2100 *Founded/Ownrshp* 2006
Sales 27.6MM[E] *EMP* 60
SIC 4731 Customhouse brokers
Pr: Derek Scarbrough

D-U-N-S 03-820-8427
■ **GLOBAL LOSS PREVENTION INC** (DE)
AIG
(*Suby of* AMERICAN INTERNATIONAL GROUP INC) ★
180 Maiden Ln Fl 27, New York, NY 10038-4925
Tel (212) 770-7000 *Founded/Ownrshp* 1978
Sales 78.3MM[E] *EMP* 150
SIC 8748 Environmental consultant; Systems analysis & engineering consulting services; Environmental consultant; Systems analysis & engineering consulting services
Pr: Stephen J Cook
Pr: Lily Fong
COO: Randy Epright
CFO: Richard Butler
CFO: Grace A Laforgia
Treas: Steven J Bersinger
Sec: Donald S Clark
Sec: Elizabeth M Tuck
Ex Ofcr: Robert Lang
Ex Ofcr: Fan Lin
Ex Ofcr: Michael Manire
Ex Ofcr: Jian Miao
Ex VP: Eugene Raitt
Ex VP: Nicholas Rasmussen
Sr VP: Charles Benda
Sr VP: Joseph Charlack
Sr VP: Jack Graham
Sr VP: Marc Joseph
Sr VP: Melissa Kerns
Sr VP: Kathleen McCutcheon
Sr VP: Paul Rix

D-U-N-S 17-704-7677
GLOBAL MAIL INC
DHL SMART AND GLOBAL MAIL
(*Suby of* DEUTSCHE POST AG)
2700 S Comm Pkwy Ste 300, Weston, FL 33331
Tel (800) 805-9306 *Founded/Ownrshp* 1999
Sales 75.9MM[E] *EMP* 261
SIC 4513 Letter delivery, private air; Package delivery, private air; Letter delivery, private air; Package delivery, private air
CEO: Lee Spratt
Recvr: Robert Morris
Ch Bd: S David Fineman
**CFO:* Terry Hilsman
**Sr VP:* Dave Loonam
**Sr VP:* Paul Tessy
VP: Mark Backes
VP: Sergio Cravedi
VP: Kevin Eggart
VP Bus Dev: Craig Morris
Genl Mgr: Anne-Marie Bernardin

D-U-N-S 82-895-4636
GLOBAL MANAGEMENT SOLUTIONS INC
507 Mecklem Ln, Ellwood City, PA 16117-3005
Tel (724) 758-4199 *Founded/Ownrshp* 1991
Sales 8.2MM[E] *EMP* 400
SIC 7349

D-U-N-S 03-443-9500
GLOBAL MANUFACTURING & ASSEMBLY CORP
1801 Wildwood Ave, Jackson, MI 49202-4044
Tel (517) 789-8116 *Founded/Ownrshp* 2001
Sales 27.0MM[E] *EMP* 331
SIC 3089 Plastic containers, except foam; Plastic containers, except foam
CEO: Armida Pearse
**Pr:* Travis Pearse Jr

D-U-N-S 00-690-7299
■ **GLOBAL MARINE INC** (DE)
TRANSOCEAN
(*Suby of* TRANSOCEAN INC) ★
4 Greenway Plz Ste 100, Houston, TX 77046-0403
Tel (713) 232-7500 *Founded/Ownrshp* 1955, 1964
Sales 216.1MM[E] *EMP* 700[E]
Accts Ernst & Young Llp Houston Te
SIC 1381 1311 Drilling oil & gas wells; Crude petroleum production; Natural gas production; Drilling oil & gas wells; Crude petroleum production; Natural gas production
Pr: Gregory L Cauthen
**CEO:* Steven L Newman
**COO:* John Stobart
**Treas:* Ramon Yi
Ofcr: Mike Munro
**Ex VP:* ESA Ikheimonen
Ex VP: Mark Mey
VP: Myrtle Penelton
Dir Risk M: Keith Avery
Dir Risk M: Todd Jordan
Dir Risk M: Ben Murrell

GLOBAL MARINE INSURANCE
See OLD KENT INSURANCE GROUP INC

D-U-N-S 12-998-9286
GLOBAL MARITEK SYSTEMS INC
GMSI
5251 Nw 33rd Ave, Fort Lauderdale, FL 33309-6302
Tel (954) 766-9999 *Founded/Ownrshp* 2003
Sales 33.7MM[E] *EMP* 160
SIC 8711 Marine engineering; Marine engineering
Pr: C H Gillenwater
**Ch:* John Douglas
**VP:* Cynthia K Cercone
**VP:* Roger P Mitchell

D-U-N-S 11-107-1218
GLOBAL MARKET INSITE INC
GLOBALTESTMARKET.COM
(*Suby of* KANTAR GROUP) ★
600 108th Ave Ne Ste 202, Bellevue, WA 98004-5110
Tel (206) 315-9300 *Founded/Ownrshp* 2011
Sales 21.5MM[E] *EMP* 225
SIC 8732 Market analysis or research; Market analysis or research
Pr: Michael Brochu
**Ch Bd:* Enrique Godreau III
**CEO:* David Day
**COO:* Andrew Cayton
**CFO:* T Mitchell McCauley
**CFO:* David Parker
**Chf Mktg O:* Luis J Salazar
Ofcr: Efrain Ribeiro
Assoc Dir: Stefanie Mackenzie
Mng Dir: Matt Shepherd
**CTO:* Mitch Eggers

GLOBAL MARKETING CONSULTANCE
See ZORAN ADVERTISING & DESIGN INC

GLOBAL MARKETING SERVICE
See TRAVEL CLICK INC

D-U-N-S 80-648-9089
GLOBAL MARKETS INC
HORIZONTAL INTEGRATION
9800 Bren Rd E Ste 450, Minnetonka, MN 55343-4740
Tel (612) 392-7582 *Founded/Ownrshp* 1994
Sales 32.4MM[E] *EMP* 230
SIC 7379 7371 ; Computer software development & applications; ; Computer software development & applications
Pr: Sabin Ephrem
VP: Chris Moore
**Prin:* Chris Staley

D-U-N-S 79-291-9842
GLOBAL MATERIAL HANDLING INC
LAMBERT MATERIAL HANDLING
14 Orchard Park Dr, Geneva, NY 14456-9789
Tel (315) 789-7630 *Founded/Ownrshp* 2006
Sales 40.0MM *EMP* 42
SIC 5084 Materials handling machinery; Materials handling machinery
Pr: Robert Manion
**VP:* Jeffrey Gambrill
VP: Sally Manion

D-U-N-S 00-121-0616 IMP
GLOBAL MATERIAL TECHNOLOGIES INC (NY)
GMT
750 W Lake Cook Rd # 480, Buffalo Grove, IL 60089-2074
Tel (847) 495-4700 *Founded/Ownrshp* 1977
Sales 99.6MM[E] *EMP* 316
SIC 3291 Steel wool; Steel wool
Pr: Norman Soep
**CFO:* Robert Krebs
**VP:* Alex Krupnik
VP: Alan Pads
**VP Admn:* Edwin Jones
Genl Mgr: Dave Colbert
Opers Mgr: Alex Krupink
VP Sls: David Colbert
Sls Mgr: Paul Bonn

D-U-N-S 19-289-2433 IMP
GLOBAL MED SERVICES INC
EASTWEST
11818 South St Ste 201a, Cerritos, CA 90703-6831
Tel (562) 207-6970 *Founded/Ownrshp* 2003
Sales 10.0MM^E *EMP* 600
SIC 8082 Home health care services; Home health care services
Pr: Kwang Chang
Ofcr: Janet Chang

D-U-N-S 10-689-1984 EXP
GLOBAL MEDICAL IMAGING LLC
G M I
222 Rampart St, Charlotte, NC 28203-4932
Tel (877) 761-7589 *Founded/Ownrshp* 2015
Sales 42.1MM^E *EMP* 68
SIC 5047 8071 Medical & hospital equipment; Ultrasound laboratory
CEO: Jon Perry

D-U-N-S 16-986-9067
GLOBAL MEDICAL SOLUTIONS LTD
14140 Ventura Blvd Frnt, Sherman Oaks, CA 91423-2750
Tel (818) 783-2915 *Founded/Ownrshp* 2004
Sales 50.0MM *EMP* 2
SIC 2834 5122 Pharmaceutical preparations; Pharmaceuticals; Pharmaceutical preparations; Pharmaceuticals
CEO: Haig S Bagerdjian
**Pr:* Jay Simon
**CFO:* Neal Cannon

GLOBAL METAL SOLUTIONS
See USA TANK SALES AND ERECTION CO INC

D-U-N-S 94-466-6056
GLOBAL MILITARY MARKETING INC
1288 Country Club Rd # 1001, Gulf Breeze, FL 32563-1403
Tel (850) 934-0715 *Founded/Ownrshp* 1996
Sales 40.1MM *EMP* 62
Accts Scott G Hamilton Cpa Pa Pe
SIC 8732 Market analysis or research; Market analysis or research
Pr: Paul Stagner
**CFO:* Kim Stagner

D-U-N-S 13-161-5978 IMP
GLOBAL MINERALS CORP
G M C
6701 Democracy Blvd # 300, Bethesda, MD 20817-1572
Tel (301) 571-2449 *Founded/Ownrshp* 2002
Sales 20.4MM^E *EMP* 75
SIC 5052 Metallic concentrates
Pr: Michael Xu
**VP:* Dan Itter

D-U-N-S 78-530-7310
GLOBAL MOBILITY SOLUTIONS LLC
FAS RELOCATION NETWORK
(*Suby of* GLOBAL MS, INC.)
15333 N Pima Rd Ste 240, Scottsdale, AZ 85260-7303
Tel (480) 922-0700 *Founded/Ownrshp* 2006
Sales 61.9MM *EMP* 30
SIC 6531 4214 8742 Buying agent, real estate; Rental agent, real estate; Household goods moving & storage, local; Human resource consulting services; Buying agent, real estate; Rental agent, real estate; Household goods moving & storage, local; Human resource consulting services
Pr: Christopher Bloedel
Pr: Sam Hoey
Pr: Amanda Rakofsky
CFO: Lehman Vaughn
Ofcr: Fayette Wester
Ex VP: Michael Setze
VP: John Fernandez
VP: Samantha Hodges
Dir Soc: Steven Wester
Dir Soc: Steve Ziomek
Dir Bus: Whitney Gagle
Dir Bus: Tim Rambo

D-U-N-S 13-938-7450
■ **GLOBAL MONTELLO GROUP CORP**
GLOBAL PARTNER
(*Suby of* GLOBAL OPERATING LLC) ★
800 South St Ste 500, Waltham, MA 02453-1483
Tel (800) 542-0778 *Founded/Ownrshp* 2006
Sales 53.3MM^E *EMP* 55^E
SIC 5172 Gases, liquefied petroleum (propane); Diesel fuel; Gasoline; Fuel oil
Pr: Eric Slifka
**CFO:* Thomas J Hollister
**Treas:* Daphne Foster
**Ex VP:* Charles A Rudinsky
Exec: Alexis Sohr

D-U-N-S 01-166-3408 IMP
GLOBAL MOTORS CORP
GLOBAL AUTO MALL
1099 Us Highway 22, North Plainfield, NJ 07060-6614
Tel (908) 757-4000 *Founded/Ownrshp* 1977
Sales 60.9MM^E *EMP* 120
SIC 5511 Automobiles, new & used; Automobiles, new & used
Pr: Robert Nitabach
CFO: Cherly Giles
**CFO:* Marvin Schell
**VP:* William S Feinstein
**Genl Mgr:* Anthony Ferrara
Sls Mgr: Pete Metzger

GLOBAL MOTORSPORT GROUP
See DAE-IL USA INC

GLOBAL MOULDING
See GLOBAL COMPOSITES INC

GLOBAL NAB
See GLOBAL NORTHAMERICAN BUSINESS LLC

D-U-N-S 16-507-2161
GLOBAL NET ACCESS LLC
NETDEPOT
(*Suby of* GNAX HOLDINGS, LLC) ★
1100 White St Sw, Atlanta, GA 30310-2636
Tel (404) 230-9150 *Founded/Ownrshp* 2003
Sales 20.0MM^E *EMP* 50
SIC 4813 7379 ; Computer related consulting services
CEO: Jeff Hinkle
Pr: William D Souder
**COO:* Erik Blumenau
VP: William Souder
**Dir Sec:* Frankie Rios
VP Sls: George A Robbie

D-U-N-S 07-948-9905
GLOBAL NORTHAMERICAN BUSINESS LLC
GLOBAL NAB
1701 Jacaman Rd Ste Rp4, Laredo, TX 78041-6211
Tel (956) 999-6469 *Founded/Ownrshp* 2013
Sales 38.0MM *EMP* 7
SIC 5147 Meats & meat products
Genl Mgr: Ileana Bravo

D-U-N-S 82-993-8716 IMP
■ **GLOBAL OILFIELD SERVICES INC**
INTERNATIONAL TOOL & SUPPLY
(*Suby of* HALLIBURTON CO) ★
2150 Town Square Pl # 410, Sugar Land, TX 77479-1465
Tel (713) 977-5900 *Founded/Ownrshp* 1979
Sales 29.6MM^E *EMP* 170
SIC 3561 Pumps, domestic: water or sump; Pumps, domestic: water or sump
Pr: Wayne Richards
**CFO:* Stuart Spence
**Treas:* Gary Kasper
Sls Mgr: Luis Cristobal

D-U-N-S 78-625-1988
■ **GLOBAL OPERATING LLC**
(*Suby of* GLOBAL PARTNERS LP) ★
800 South St Ste 500, Waltham, MA 02453-1439
Tel (800) 542-0778 *Founded/Ownrshp* 2006
Sales 983.0MM^E *EMP* 933^E
SIC 4924 4911 Natural gas distribution; Electric services
Pr: Eric Slifka
**COO:* Thomas J Hollister
**Ex VP:* Edward J Faneuil
**Ex VP:* Charles A Rudinsky

D-U-N-S 88-306-7548
GLOBAL OPERATIONS AND DEVELOPMENT/GIVING CHILDREN HOPE
8332 Commonwealth Ave, Buena Park, CA 90621-2526
Tel (714) 523-4454 *Founded/Ownrshp* 1979
Sales 63.1MM *EMP* 11
SIC 8322 Individual & family services; Individual & family services
Pr: John A Ditty Jr
Dir Vol: Angie Brock
VP: Pat Power

D-U-N-S 05-875-8595 IMP/EXP
GLOBAL ORGANIC/SPECIALTY SOURCE INC
6284 Mcintosh Rd, Sarasota, FL 34238-2965
Tel (941) 924-8728 *Founded/Ownrshp* 2001
Sales 50.8MM^E *EMP* 85
SIC 5148 Fruits; Vegetables; Fruits; Vegetables
Pr: Mitch D Blumenthal
**VP:* Rhonda Blumenthal
**VP:* Richard Blumenthal

D-U-N-S 13-303-2826 EXP
GLOBAL PACIFIC PRODUCE INC
11500 S Eastern Ave # 160, Henderson, NV 89052-7400
Tel (702) 898-8051 *Founded/Ownrshp* 2000
Sales 315.3MM *EMP* 250^E
SIC 5148 Fruits

D-U-N-S 19-247-0524 IMP
GLOBAL PACKAGING INC
G P
209 Brower Ave, Oaks, PA 19456
Tel (610) 666-1608 *Founded/Ownrshp* 2000
Sales 44.3MM^E *EMP* 250^E
SIC 2759 Flexographic printing; Flexographic printing
CEO: Anthony J Maginnis
Pr: Peter Constantinidis
**Pr:* Michael Frost
**VP:* Jim Princivalle
IT Man: Myron Kolodiy
Ql Cn Mgr: Phyllis Kerr

D-U-N-S 80-680-5516 IMP
GLOBAL PACKAGING SOLUTIONS INC
1605 Pacific Rim Ct Ste A, San Diego, CA 92154-7522
Tel (619) 710-2661 *Founded/Ownrshp* 2006
Sales 6.3MM^E *EMP* 280
SIC 2653 3089 Corrugated & solid fiber boxes; Injection molding of plastics; Corrugated & solid fiber boxes; Injection molding of plastics
CEO: Jawed Ghias
**Treas:* Rajnikanth Parikh
**Prin:* Anila Parikh

D-U-N-S 02-499-9786
GLOBAL PARATRANSIT INC (CA)
400 W Compton Blvd, Gardena, CA 90248-1700
Tel (310) 715-7550 *Founded/Ownrshp* 2000
Sales 16.2MM^E *EMP* 300
SIC 4119 Local passenger transportation; Local passenger transportation
Pr: Reza Nasrollahy
COO: Edward Muncy
Dir Risk M: Luis Preciado

GLOBAL PARTNER
See GLOBAL MONTELLO GROUP CORP

D-U-N-S 60-258-0867 IMP
▲ **GLOBAL PARTNERS LP**
800 South St Ste 200, Waltham, MA 02453-1483
Tel (781) 894-8800 *Founded/Ownrshp* 2005
Sales 17.2MMM *EMP* 1,154^E
Tkr Sym GLP *Exch* NYS
SIC 5172 5171 Petroleum bulk stations & terminals; Petroleum terminals; Petroleum products; Petroleum products; Petroleum bulk stations & terminals; Petroleum terminals
Pr: Eric Slifka
Genl Ptr: Global GP LLC
CFO: Daphne H Foster
Treas: Richard Liska
Ofcr: Charles A Rudinsky
Sr VP: Bill Gifford
VP: Perry Bernstein
VP: Dennis Bowersox
VP: Audrey Deleskey
VP: Joseph Destefano
VP: Robert Fraczkiewicz
VP: Tom Keefe
VP: Mary McCarty
VP: Scott McIlroy
VP: Katherine McManmon
VP: Bob Reicher
VP: Barbara Rosenbloom
VP: Steve Spensley
VP: Carl Stoffi
VP Bus Dev: Bruce Atkins
VP Bus Dev: Jennifer Culver

D-U-N-S 79-938-6255 IMP/EXP
GLOBAL PARTS & MAINTENANCE LLC
6112 E Executive Dr, Westland, MI 48185-1937
Tel (734) 326-7600 *Founded/Ownrshp* 1997
Sales 20.2MM^E *EMP* 17
SIC 5085 Industrial supplies

GLOBAL PARTS AERO
See GLOBAL PARTS INC

D-U-N-S 16-565-7607 IMP/EXP
GLOBAL PARTS DISTRIBUTORS LLC
OMEGA ACQUISITION
(*Suby of* AUTO AIR EXPORT INC) ★
3279 Avendale Milroad, Macon, GA 31216
Tel (478) 785-6400 *Founded/Ownrshp* 2012
Sales 35.0MM *EMP* 55
SIC 5013 Automotive supplies & parts

D-U-N-S 07-945-2895
GLOBAL PARTS GROUP INC (KS)
901 Industrial Rd, Augusta, KS 67010-9565
Tel (316) 733-9240 *Founded/Ownrshp* 2013
Sales 59.7MM^E *EMP* 90
SIC 5088 Aircraft & parts
Pr: Troy Palmer
**COO:* Malissa Nesmith

D-U-N-S 14-883-3804 IMP/EXP
GLOBAL PARTS INC
GLOBAL PARTS AERO
(*Suby of* GLOBAL PARTS GROUP INC) ★
901 Industrial Rd, Augusta, KS 67010-9565
Tel (316) 733-9240 *Founded/Ownrshp* 2003
Sales 59.0MM^E *EMP* 78^E
SIC 5088 Aircraft & parts
Pr: Troy Palmer
**VP:* Malissa Nesmith
QA Dir: Nin George
Dir IT: Brian Edwards
Ql Cn Mgr: Derek Herrell
Manager: Bruce Batson
Sales Asso: Shane Eldringhoff
Sales Asso: Steve Mayer
Sales Asso: Heath Myers
Sales Asso: Patrick Ryan
Snr Mgr: Dylan Lamb

D-U-N-S 94-726-2226
■ **GLOBAL PAYMENT SYSTEMS LLC**
(*Suby of* GLOBAL PAYMENTS INC) ★
4 Corporate Blvd Ne, Brookhaven, GA 30329-2022
Tel (404) 235-4400 *Founded/Ownrshp* 2001
Sales 25.8MM *EMP* 555
SIC 7389 Credit card service; Credit card service
CFO: James Kelly
VP: Jeff Hackling
Opers Mgr: Gary Phillips
Sls Dir: Christine Anderson

D-U-N-S 60-298-9944
■ **GLOBAL PAYMENTS DIRECT INC**
(*Suby of* GLOBAL PAYMENTS INC) ★
10 Glenlake Pkwy Ste 130, Atlanta, GA 30328-3495
Tel (770) 829-8000 *Founded/Ownrshp* 2001
Sales 28.6MM^E *EMP* 400^E
SIC 7389 Credit card service; Credit card service
Pr: Jeffrey Sloan
**Treas:* James G Kelly
Ex VP: Morgan Schuessler Jr

D-U-N-S 00-504-7290
▲ **GLOBAL PAYMENTS INC**
GLOBALPAYMENTS
10 Glenlake Pkwy, Atlanta, GA 30328-3495
Tel (770) 829-8000 *Founded/Ownrshp* 1967
Sales 2.7MMM *EMP* 4,438^E
Accts Deloitte & Touche Llp Atlant
Tkr Sym GPN *Exch* NYS
SIC 7389 Credit card service; Credit card service
CEO: Jeffrey S Sloan
**Ch Bd:* William I Jacobs
**Pr:* David E Mangum
**CFO:* Cameron M Bready
Ofcr: Morgan Schuesslea
Ex VP: G Balas
**Ex VP:* David L Green
Sr VP: Andra Milender
Sr VP: Erik Mogelgaard
Sr VP: Joanne Rill
VP: Bill Gaskin
Exec: Jennifer Bozeman
Comm Man: Laura Coerper
Board of Directors: John G Bruno, Alex W Hart, Ruth Ann Marshall, John M Partridge, Alan M Silberstein, Michael W Trapp, Gerald J Wilkins

GLOBAL PC DIRECT
See ST CYBERLINK CORP

D-U-N-S 60-377-4142
GLOBAL PCCI (GPC)
4695 Macarthur Ct Ste 950, Newport Beach, CA 92660-1841
Tel (757) 637-9000 *Founded/Ownrshp* 1995
Sales 23.3MM^E *EMP* 175
SIC 3469 4499 Metal stampings; Salvaging, distressed vessels & cargoes; Metal stampings; Salvaging, distressed vessels & cargoes
Pt: Sherri Bovino
VP: Reka Marginean

D-U-N-S 17-592-8043 IMP
GLOBAL PET INC
145 Malbert St, Perris, CA 92570-8624
Tel (951) 657-5466 *Founded/Ownrshp* 1996
Sales 44.3MM^E *EMP* 100
SIC 5093 4953 Plastics scrap; Recycling, waste materials; Plastics scrap; Recycling, waste materials
Pr: Nadim Salim Bahou
VP: Carl Bettis
**VP:* Patti Gilmour
VP Sls: Paul Bahau

D-U-N-S 06-116-7842 IMP
GLOBAL PETROLEUM CORP (MA)
800 South St Ste 500, Waltham, MA 02453-1483
Tel (781) 894-6920 *Founded/Ownrshp* 1974
Sales 179.3MM^E *EMP* 210
SIC 4924 5172 4911 Natural gas distribution; ; Fuel oil; Gasoline; Diesel fuel; Kerosene; ; Natural gas distribution; ; Fuel oil; Gasoline; Diesel fuel; Kerosene;
Ch Bd: Alfred A Slifka
**CFO:* Thomas Mc Manmon
CFO: Thomas McMannon
**Treas:* Richard Slifka
Ex VP: Thomas Hollister
Ex VP: Gregory Rudoy
VP: Jack Frost
VP: William Patten
VP: Lisa Vanhemert
Snr Ntwrk: Aaron Thompson
Opers Mgr: Derek Reynolds
Board of Directors: Richard B Slifka

D-U-N-S 79-824-5239
GLOBAL PLASTICS INC
6739 Guion Rd, Indianapolis, IN 46268-4810
Tel (317) 299-2345 *Founded/Ownrshp* 1992
Sales 33.3MM^E *EMP* 100
SIC 3089 3544 Injection molding of plastics; Special dies, tools, jigs & fixtures
Pr: J R Spitznogle

D-U-N-S 83-508-8720
GLOBAL PLASTICS LP
21 Downing St Frnt 1, New York, NY 10014-0836
Tel (800) 417-4605 *Founded/Ownrshp* 2008
Sales 90.0MM^E *EMP* 11^E
SIC 2821 Plastics materials & resins; Plastics materials & resins
Mng Pt: Chris Guimond
Pt: David Guimond

D-U-N-S 96-587-9836
GLOBAL POLYMER INDUSTRIES INC
702 N Industrial Ave, Arlington, SD 57212-8100
Tel (605) 983-2830 *Founded/Ownrshp* 1995
Sales 32.8MM^E *EMP* 80
SIC 2821 Molding compounds, plastics
Pr: Todd Hintimer
**VP:* Dan Palli

GLOBAL POWER COMPONENTS
See BHP LLC

D-U-N-S 01-380-1746
▲ **GLOBAL POWER EQUIPMENT GROUP INC**
400 Las Colinas Blvd E, Irving, TX 75039-5579
Tel (214) 574-2000 *Founded/Ownrshp* 1998
Sales 538.5MM *EMP* 1,244^E
Accts Bdo Usa Llp Dallas Texas
Tkr Sym GLPW *Exch* NYS
SIC 3568 1796 7699 Power transmission equipment; Power generating equipment installation; Industrial equipment services; Power transmission equipment; Power generating equipment installation; Industrial equipment services
Pr: Terence J Cryan
**Ch Bd:* Charles Macaluso
Pr: Stanley Breitweiser
Pr: Peter W Dawes
Pr: Neil Riddle
Pr: Tedd Sellers
Pr: Penny Sherrod-Campanizzi
CFO: Raymond K Guba
Ofcr: Keri Jolly
Ofcr: Tracy D Pagliara
Sr VP: Craig E Holmes
Sr VP: Scott Snow
VP: Bill Kirk
VP: Gary R McCloskey
VP: Lee Nguyen
VP: Mark Wolfe
Board of Directors: Carl Bartoli, David L Keller, Robert B Mills, Michael E Rescoe, Michael E Salvati, Gary J Taylor

D-U-N-S 16-676-3917 IMP
GLOBAL POWER SUPPLY LLC
G P S
136 W Canon Perdido St # 200, Santa Barbara, CA 93101-3242
Tel (805) 683-3828 *Founded/Ownrshp* 2004
Sales 46.6MM^E *EMP* 30
SIC 5063 Electrical apparatus & equipment
CEO: Ron Zamir
VP: David Mossman
VP: Sandy Tubis
**VP:* Mike Wolfe
Sales Asso: Callie Gillett

GLOBAL PRINTER SERVICES
See GPS HOLDINGS LLC

D-U-N-S 06-928-5526
GLOBAL PRINTING INC
3670 Wheeler Ave, Alexandria, VA 22304-6403
Tel (703) 751-3611 Founded/Ownrshp 1979
Sales 41.8MM^E EMP 135
SIC 2752 7331 Commercial printing, lithographic; Mailing service; Commercial printing, lithographic; Mailing service
Pr: Jonathan Budington
*VP: Gerhard Dreo
Prd Mgr: Robert Brown
Snr PM: Kevin Fay

D-U-N-S 07-162-3383 IMP
GLOBAL PRODUCE SALES INC
1018 E Oleander St, Lakeland, FL 33801-2012
Tel (863) 682-7163 Founded/Ownrshp 2000
Sales 42.8MM^E EMP 20
Accts Hamic Jones Hamic & Sturworld
SIC 5148 Fruits, fresh; Vegetables, fresh; Fruits, fresh; Vegetables, fresh
CEO: Lee Allen J Wroten
CFO: Richard Sellers
*VP: Mark A Elliott
*VP: Michael V Nichols
*VP: Stephen R Nichols
*VP: Richard L Sellers
*VP: Gerald T Stephens
*Prin: Gerry Stephens

D-U-N-S 11-085-7955
GLOBAL PRODUCTIVITY SOLUTIONS LLC
19176 Hall Rd, Clinton Township, MI 48038-6914
Tel (586) 412-9609 Founded/Ownrshp 2000
Sales 26.6MM EMP 4
SIC 8742 Management consulting services; Management consulting services
Mng Pt: Bob Wexler
IT Man: Edward Kim

D-U-N-S 78-583-0563 IMP/EXP
GLOBAL PRODUCTS INC
21 Cherokee Dr, Saint Peters, MO 63376-3927
Tel (636) 939-1622 Founded/Ownrshp 1976
Sales 20.6MM^E EMP 80
SIC 2752 2395 2353 Commercial printing, lithographic; Pleating & stitching; Hats, caps & millinery
Pr: Rebecca L Herwick
VP: Andrew Popper
IT Man: Marc Roark
Sls Mgr: Shirley Rehm

D-U-N-S 01-818-6192
GLOBAL PROTECTIVE SERVICES INC
2508 Pendergrass Ln, Ellenwood, GA 30294-6241
Tel (404) 962-4454 Founded/Ownrshp 1999
Sales 2.4MM EMP 300
SIC 7381 7382 Security guard service; Security systems services; Security guard service; Security systems services
Pr: Reginald L Lindsay
*VP: Phillip Lindsay

D-U-N-S 96-829-2511 IMP
GLOBAL QUALITY FOODS INC
3524 Investment Blvd, Hayward, CA 94545-3707
Tel (510) 783-8999 Founded/Ownrshp 2011
Sales 26.0MM EMP 30
SIC 5421 Seafood markets; Seafood markets
Pr: Minh Thi Vo
*VP: Tan Vo

D-U-N-S 07-101-7362
GLOBAL REINSURANCE CORP OF AMERICA
(Suby of WINSOR VERWALTUNGS-GMBH)
125 Broad St Lbby 5, New York, NY 10004-2440
Tel (212) 754-7500 Founded/Ownrshp 2007
Sales NA EMP 300
SIC 6321 Reinsurance carriers, accident & health; Reinsurance carriers, accident & health
Pr: Volker Weisbrodt
Pr: Volker Wiesbrodt
CFO: Burton Henry
Sr VP: Barry Keough
Genl Couns: David Smith

D-U-N-S 88-301-8822
GLOBAL RESOURCE MANAGEMENT INC
5400 Laurel Springs Pkwy # 902, Suwanee, GA 30024-6037
Tel (770) 888-6404 Founded/Ownrshp 1993
Sales 29.4MM^E EMP 310
SIC 7379 7371 Computer related consulting services; Computer software systems analysis & design, custom; Computer related consulting services; Computer software systems analysis & design, custom
Pr: Naheed Syed
Pr: Michael Sharp
VP: Tariq Sultan
*VP: Nuzhath Syed
IT Man: John Solomon
Opers Mgr: Nuzzu Syed

D-U-N-S 61-097-4201
GLOBAL RESOURCE SOLUTIONS INC
3701 Pender Dr Ste 320, Fairfax, VA 22030-6045
Tel (703) 364-5700 Founded/Ownrshp 2005
Sales 21.7MM EMP 120
SIC 8742 Management consulting services; Management consulting services
CEO: Anthony D Williams
CFO: Michelle Rubie-Smith
Sec: Tina Williams
Prin: J Richard Knop
Prgrm Mgr: Terrance Bradford

D-U-N-S 02-141-3778 IMP
GLOBAL RESPONSE CORP
777 S State Road 7, Margate, FL 33068-2803
Tel (954) 973-7300 Founded/Ownrshp 1974
Sales 101.3MM^E EMP 900^E
SIC 7389

D-U-N-S 13-878-8067 IMP
GLOBAL ROLLFORMING CORP
(Suby of VOESTALPINE AG)
1070 Brooks Industrial Rd, Shelbyville, KY 40065-9141
Tel (502) 633-4435 Founded/Ownrshp 2012
Sales 33.8MM^E EMP 401
SIC 3449 7389 Miscellaneous metalwork; Custom roll formed products; Miscellaneous metalwork; Custom roll formed products; Financial services
CEO: Ray Leathers
*CFO: Dan Ahern

D-U-N-S 01-348-1033 IMP
GLOBAL SAFETY TEXTILES LLC
(Suby of GLOBAL SAFETY TEXTILES GMBH)
1556 Montgomery St, South Hill, VA 23970-3919
Tel (434) 447-2378 Founded/Ownrshp 2009
Sales 228.8MM^E EMP 2,500
SIC 3714 3496 2211 Motor vehicle parts & accessories; Miscellaneous fabricated wire products; Automotive fabrics, cotton; Motor vehicle parts & accessories; Miscellaneous fabricated wire products; Automotive fabrics, cotton
CEO: Georg Saint Denis
*Pr: Frank Goehring
*Pr: Joseph Gorga
*COO: Michael Ambler
*CFO: Anthony Forman
VP: Rob Deutsch
VP Sls: Paul L Sullivan

D-U-N-S 09-482-6716
■ **GLOBAL SANTA FE DRILLING CO**
(Suby of GLOBAL MARINE INC) ★
4 Greenway Plz Ste 100, Houston, TX 77046-0403
Tel (281) 925-6821 Founded/Ownrshp 2006
Sales 29.9MM^E EMP 550
SIC 1381 Drilling oil & gas wells; Drilling oil & gas wells
Pr: Charles M Striedel
Treas: L Craig Williams
VP: Steven J Gangelhoff
VP: Mark E Monroe

D-U-N-S 18-781-2680
■ **GLOBAL SANTA FE INC**
(Suby of GLOBAL MARINE INC) ★
4 Greenway Plz Ste 100, Houston, TX 77046-0403
Tel (281) 925-6000 Founded/Ownrshp 2002
Sales 27.7MM^E EMP 485
SIC 1381 Drilling oil & gas wells; Drilling oil & gas wells
Pr: Jon Marshall
Pr: Steve Gangelhoff
Off Mgr: Sharon Cole
CTO: Steve Cosby
CTO: Doug Freede
CTO: Mark Monroe
Plnt Mgr: Marion M Woolie

D-U-N-S 83-035-6577
GLOBAL SCAFFOLD CONSTRUCTION SERVICES INC
EXCEL MODULAR SCAFFORD
39459 John Lanier Rd, Walker, LA 70785-2302
Tel (225) 777-4157 Founded/Ownrshp 2009
Sales 26.1MM^E EMP 200
SIC 1629 8741 Chemical plant & refinery construction; Construction management; Chemical plant & refinery construction; Construction management
Pr: Bruce R Bartlett
VP: Carl Barksdale
Site Mgr: Johnnie Dupont
Site Mgr: Justin Papania

D-U-N-S 80-372-1679
GLOBAL SCIENCE & TECHNOLOGY INC
GST
7855 Walker Dr Ste 200, Greenbelt, MD 20770-3239
Tel (301) 474-9696 Founded/Ownrshp 1990
Sales 47.1MM^E EMP 230
SIC 8711 Engineering services; Consulting engineer; Engineering services; Consulting engineer
Pr: Chieh-San Cheng
Pr: Brian Bell
Pr: Michael Wooster
*COO: Celeste Jarvis
*CFO: Jack Kelly
CFO: Joan Long
VP: John C Chehansky
*VP: Norm Gundersen
*Prin: Darrel Williams
Prgrm Mgr: Samir Chettri
Prgrm Mgr: Paul Heppner

D-U-N-S 16-800-7222
GLOBAL SCRAP MANAGEMENT INC
G S M
4340 Batavia Rd, Batavia, OH 45103-3342
Tel (513) 576-6600 Founded/Ownrshp 2003
Sales 30.0MM^E EMP 40
SIC 4953 Recycling, waste materials
Pr: Chris Hamm
*CFO: Kathy Luccasen
*VP: Pat Bowden
*VP: Dave Chodos
Opers Mgr: Ryan Hamm

GLOBAL SECURITY GLAZING
See GAAG LLC

GLOBAL SECURITY SERVICES
See DELUCA ASSOCIATES INC

D-U-N-S 17-851-3826
GLOBAL SERVICES CORP
245 Westlake Rd Ste 101, Fayetteville, NC 28314-4866
Tel (910) 868-5500 Founded/Ownrshp 1997
Sales 47.0MM EMP 125
SIC 8711 Engineering services; Engineering services
Pr: Phil Mearing
*VP: Dennis Walko
Prgrm Mgr: Stephen Kinder

D-U-N-S 02-974-6919
■ **GLOBAL SIGNAL INC**
(Suby of CROWN CASTLE INTERNATIONAL CORP) ★
301 N Cattlemen Rd # 200, Sarasota, FL 34232-6430
Tel (941) 364-8886 Founded/Ownrshp 1995
Sales 21.6MM^E EMP 293
SIC 6798 4899 4813 Real estate investment trusts; Communication signal enhancement network system; Wire telephone; Real estate investment trusts; Communication signal enhancement network system; Wire telephone
Ch Bd: Wesley Edens
CFO: William T Freeman
Ex VP: Ronald Bizrick III
Ex VP: Jeffrey Langdon
Sr VP: Jeffrey H Foster
VP: David Zahn

D-U-N-S 06-172-0173
GLOBAL SOFTWARE INC
3201 Beechleaf Ct Ste 170, Raleigh, NC 27604-1547
Tel (919) 872-7800 Founded/Ownrshp 1994
Sales 22.0MM EMP 90
SIC 7371 7372 Custom computer programming services; Application computer software; Business oriented computer software; Custom computer programming services; Application computer software; Business oriented computer software
CEO: Ronald Kupferman
Pr: Becky Kaufman
*Pr: Matthew Kupferman
*VP: Spencer Kupferman
VP: David Oakes
VP: Paul Zunker
Mng Dir: Larry Cucchi
QA Dir: Carol Bauldree
QA Dir: Catherine Holley
IT Man: Rob Keller
Software D: Thearon Willis

D-U-N-S 96-899-5985 IMP
GLOBAL SOLAR ENERGY INC
(Suby of HANERGY HOLDING GROUP LIMITED)
8500 S Rita Rd, Tucson, AZ 85747-9142
Tel (520) 546-6313 Founded/Ownrshp 2013
Sales 59.0MM^E EMP 162
SIC 3674 4911 3861 Semiconductors & related devices; Electric services; Photographic equipment & supplies; Semiconductors & related devices; Electric services; Photographic equipment & supplies
CEO: Jeffrey Britt
*CFO: Stephen Alexander
*Treas: Sandra Wallach
VP: Jeff Britt
VP: Jean-Noel Poirier
*VP: Timothy Teich
VP: Tim Telch
VP: Robert G Wendt
QA Dir: Diana Pees

D-U-N-S 82-811-2909
GLOBAL SOURCE LLC
MFP TECHNOLOGY SERVICES
65 Trap Falls Rd, Shelton, CT 06484-4666
Tel (203) 761-9944 Founded/Ownrshp 2001
Sales 30.0MM EMP 17
SIC 5734 5045 Personal computers; Computer peripheral equipment
Pr: Steve Nickle
*Pt: Scott Coyne

D-U-N-S 61-531-0471
GLOBAL SPECIALTY CONTRACTORS INC
3220 Terminal Dr, Eagan, MN 55121-1609
Tel (651) 406-8232 Founded/Ownrshp 1990
Sales 31.8MM^E EMP 70^E
SIC 1541 1611 1623 1629 Industrial buildings & warehouses; Highway & street sign installation; Guardrail construction, highways; Transmitting tower (telecommunication) construction; Dams, waterways, docks & other marine construction
Pr: Todd V Johnson
*VP: C Ron Brazier
VP: Ron Brazier
*VP: Joel Ecker
VP: Thomas Heinrich

D-U-N-S 96-069-1707
■ **GLOBAL SPECTRUM LP**
(Suby of COMCAST SPECTACOR INC) ★
3601 S Broad St Ste 1, Philadelphia, PA 19148-5250
Tel (215) 952-5216 Founded/Ownrshp 1999
Sales 44.4MM^E EMP 289
SIC 8741 Management services; Management services
Pt: John Page
*Pt: Kenneth Wajda
*Sr VP: Hank Abate
*Sr VP: Todd Glickman
Sr VP: Thomas M Mobley
Sr VP: Frank E Russo
VP: Lewis Bostic
VP: Brock Jones
VP: Brett Mitchell
VP: Tim Murphy
VP: Kenneth J Wajda
VP: Meghan Webb

GLOBAL SPORTS
See GSI COMMERCE INC

D-U-N-S 01-590-0323 IMP
GLOBAL STAINLESS SUPPLY
17006 S Figueroa St, Gardena, CA 90248-3019
Tel (310) 525-1865 Founded/Ownrshp 2009
Sales 19.9MM^E EMP 300
SIC 5099 Firearms & ammunition, except sporting
Pr: Art Shelton
Manager: Spencer Elliott
Sales Asso: Kyle Levesque

D-U-N-S 10-834-8546 IMP
GLOBAL STAINLESS SUPPLY INC
GLOBAL GROUP, THE
(Suby of SUMITOMO CORP OF AMERICAS) ★
8900 Railwood Dr Unit A, Houston, TX 77078-4535
Tel (713) 980-0733 Founded/Ownrshp 2003
Sales 192.5MM^E EMP 300
SIC 5051 Pipe & tubing, steel; Pipe & tubing, steel
Pr: Art Shelton
Sales Asso: Angie Belmore
Sales Asso: Jason Von Haefen

D-U-N-S 07-239-5262 IMP/EXP
GLOBAL STEEL PRODUCTS CORP
(Suby of ITR INDUSTRIES INC) ★
95 Marcus Blvd, Deer Park, NY 11729-4501
Tel (631) 586-3455 Founded/Ownrshp 1978
Sales 20.5MM^E EMP 187
SIC 2542 3446 3443 3442 Partitions for floor attachment, prefabricated: except wood; Architectural metalwork; Fabricated plate work (boiler shop); Metal doors, sash & trim
Pr: Peter Rolla
*Treas: Adrienne Rolla
Genl Mgr: Max Moore

D-U-N-S 82-994-8368 IMP
GLOBAL STEERING SYSTEMS LLC
G S S
156 Park Rd, Watertown, CT 06795-1616
Tel (860) 945-5400 Founded/Ownrshp 2009
Sales 52.5MM^E EMP 215^E
SIC 3714 Motor vehicle steering systems & parts; Motor vehicle steering systems & parts
CEO: Larry Finnell
CFO: David Schramm
VP: Scott Filion
VP: Gabe Rosa
Prgrm Mgr: Charlie Fritz
Prgrm Mgr: Victor Lesniewski
Plnt Mgr: Joe Carry
Ql Cn Mgr: Monique Embelton
Ql Cn Mgr: Craig Young
VP Sls: Julio Costa

GLOBAL STL & FLAMECUTTING SVCS
See GLOBAL FABRICATION SERVICES INC

D-U-N-S 92-853-8677
GLOBAL STRATEGY GROUP LLC
215 Park Ave S Fl 15, New York, NY 10003-1612
Tel (212) 260-8813 Founded/Ownrshp 1994
Sales 20.4MM^E EMP 85
SIC 8742 8732 Marketing consulting services; Commercial sociological & educational research
Mng Pt: Marc Litvinoff
Pr: Alex Flores
Sr VP: Risa Heller
Sr VP: Justin Lapatine
VP: Eily Hayes
VP: Ethan Schwartz

D-U-N-S 11-004-9850
GLOBAL SUPPLY CHAIN SOLUTIONS LLC
GSCS
11494 Luna Rd Ste 100, Dallas, TX 75234-9429
Tel (972) 401-4727 Founded/Ownrshp 2010
Sales 25.0MM^E EMP 40
SIC 5045 Computers, peripherals & software
CEO: Katherine Sepich
*Pr: Leon J Backes
*Pr: Philip Odette
*CEO: Paul Peck
*VP: John Backes
Prgrm Mgr: Jason Petzel
Sls Mgr: Angie Odette
Snr Mgr: Terry Gonzalez

D-U-N-S 17-222-0571
GLOBAL SUPPLY SOLUTIONS LLC
GSS GEAR
2037 Laskin Rd, Virginia Beach, VA 23454-4266
Tel (757) 227-6757 Founded/Ownrshp 2011
Sales 21.2MM^E EMP 35^E
Accts Michael R O Neal Cpa Pc Che
SIC 5091 Hunting equipment & supplies; Ammunition, sporting; Archery equipment; Athletic goods; Hunting equipment & supplies; Ammunition, sporting; Archery equipment; Athletic goods
Store Mgr: Crystal Smith

GLOBAL SWEEPING SOLUTIONS
See GLOBAL ENVIRONMENTAL PRODUCTS INC

D-U-N-S 15-255-5368
GLOBAL SWITCHING INC
34 Franklin Ave Ste 220, Brooklyn, NY 11205-1221
Tel (718) 889-1100 Founded/Ownrshp 1999
Sales 122.2MM^E EMP 55
Accts Saul N Friedman & Company Br
SIC 4813 Telephone communications broker; Telephone communications broker
Pr: Moses Greenfield

D-U-N-S 96-796-8959
GLOBAL SYSTEMS INC
TOMCO
7208 Weil Ave Unit A, Saint Louis, MO 63119-3404
Tel (314) 646-5300 Founded/Ownrshp 1996
Sales 20.5MM^E EMP 65
SIC 8711 3465 3053 3592 7371 3714 Engineering services; Automotive stampings; Gaskets, all materials; Carburetors, pistons, rings, valves; Computer software development; Fuel systems & parts, motor vehicle
Pr: Bob Killion
CFO: David Killion

D-U-N-S 07-916-1346
GLOBAL TECH CENTER CORP
TECHNOLOGY CENTER
4 Calle B, Barranquitas, PR 00794-1911
Tel (787) 857-6620 Founded/Ownrshp 2013
Sales 27.4MM EMP 3
SIC 5045 Computers & accessories, personal & home entertainment
Pr: Carlos R Vazquez Berrios

D-U-N-S 17-189-8732
GLOBAL TECH INC
EGLOBALTECH
3865 Wilson Blvd Ste 500, Arlington, VA 22203-1781
Tel (703) 652-0991 Founded/Ownrshp 2004
Sales 40.6MM^E EMP 250^E

SIC 7371 7373 7379 8742 Computer software systems analysis & design, custom; Computer integrated systems design; Computer related maintenance services; Management consulting services
Pr: Sonya K Jain
**COO:* Sal Fazzolari
**VP:* Sanjiv Jain
**VP:* Branko Primetica

GLOBAL TECHNICAL SYSTEMS
See MANAGEMENT SERVICES GROUP INC

D-U-N-S 12-819-3245
GLOBAL TECHNICAL TALENT INC
28 Deer St Ste 201, Portsmouth, NH 03801-7704
Tel (603) 433-9911 *Founded/Ownrshp* 1999
Sales 21.3MM^E *EMP* 75
SIC 7361 8742 8732 7382 7371 8741 Executive placement; Management information systems consultant; Quality assurance consultant; Business analysis; Security systems services; Computer software development & applications; Management services
CEO: Vishnu Doraiswamy
Pr: Phil Psareas
Pr: Joseph Yukica
CFO: Gary Cebula
VP: Daniel Kehoe
VP: David Simpson
Dir Bus: George Riggs

GLOBAL TECHNOLOGIES DIV
See ANGUIL ENVIRONMENTAL SYSTEMS INC

D-U-N-S 79-046-7778
GLOBAL TECHNOLOGY ASSOCIATES LLC
1890 Preston White Dr # 150, Reston, VA 20191-5471
Tel (703) 476-8999 *Founded/Ownrshp* 2006
Sales 42.9MM^E *EMP* 389
SIC 8748 Telecommunications consultant; Telecommunications consultant
Pr: Omer Hassan
VP: Aman Udani

D-U-N-S 18-775-6523 IMP
GLOBAL TECHNOLOGY GROUP LTD
206 E 38th St, New York, NY 10016-2705
Tel (212) 490-2186 *Founded/Ownrshp* 1987
Sales 40.4MM^E *EMP* 50
SIC 5084 5085 1796 Industrial machinery & equipment; Industrial supplies; Installing building equipment
Pr: Simas Velonskis
**VP:* Edwin Velonskis
Genl Mgr: Darren Iliachev

D-U-N-S 05-534-2690
GLOBAL TECHNOLOGY RESOURCES INC
GTRI
990 S Broadway Ste 300, Denver, CO 80209-4274
Tel (303) 455-8800 *Founded/Ownrshp* 1998
Sales 139.6MM^E *EMP* 177
Accts Mcgladrey Llp Denver Colorad
SIC 7373 Local area network (LAN) systems integrator; Local area network (LAN) systems integrator
CEO: Greg C Byles
**Pr:* Glenn B Smith
**COO:* Steve Foster
**CFO:* Eric Toler
Sr VP: Craig Andrie
VP: Tim Rod
CTO: Glenn Veach
Dir IT: Roman Slaybaugh
Sls Mgr: Josh Sheets

D-U-N-S 19-614-7391
GLOBAL TEL LINK CORP
(*Suby of* GTEL HOLDINGS INC) ★
2609 Cameron St, Mobile, AL 36607-3104
Tel (251) 479-4500 *Founded/Ownrshp* 2011
Sales 222.7MM^E *EMP* 835
SIC 4813 Telephone communication, except radio; Telephone communication, except radio
CEO: Brian Oliver
CFO: Steve Yow
Sr VP: Gary Cato
VP: Robert Fragola
VP Opers: Bob Fragola
Prd Mgr: Danny Cravey
Sls Dir: Chris Moore

D-U-N-S 04-541-0110
■ **GLOBAL TELECOM & TECHNOLOGY AMERICAS INC**
(*Suby of* GTT COMMUNICATIONS INC) ★
7900 Tysons One Pl, Mc Lean, VA 22102-5971
Tel (703) 442-5500 *Founded/Ownrshp* 2005
Sales 185.9MM^E *EMP* 250
SIC 4813 Telephone communication, except radio; Telephone communication, except radio
CEO: Richard D Calder Jr
**Ch Bd:* H Brian Thompson
**CFO:* Michael R Bauer
**CFO:* Eric A Swank
**Chf Mktg O:* Corey Eng
**Ex VP:* Layne Levine
Sr VP: Bob Burris
Sr VP: Geoffrey K Hicks
Sr VP: Mike Hollander
VP: Joel Eidelberg
**VP:* Andrew Goldsmith
**VP:* Gary Hale
**VP:* John G Hendler
Board of Directors: Theodore B Smith

D-U-N-S 02-631-3737
GLOBAL TELECOM GROUP INC
43488 White Birch Way, Ashburn, VA 20147-5205
Tel (571) 291-9631 *Founded/Ownrshp* 2011
Sales 22.5MM^E *EMP* 4^E
SIC 2079 Edible fats & oils
Prin: Ahmed Farrukh

D-U-N-S 19-947-8327
GLOBAL TELESOURCING LLC
4301 Fairfax Dr Ste 320, Arlington, VA 22203-1652
Tel (703) 684-1141 *Founded/Ownrshp* 2003
Sales 25.8MM^E *EMP* 400
SIC 7389 3663 Telemarketing services; ;Telemarketing services;
Pr: Thomas Cannon
Sr VP: Brett Byers

D-U-N-S 05-353-8682
GLOBAL TERMINAL & CONTAINER SERVICES INC
(*Suby of* GCT GLOBAL CONTAINER TERMINALS INC)
302 Port Jersey Blvd, Jersey City, NJ 07305-4569
Tel (201) 451-5200 *Founded/Ownrshp* 2007
Sales 21.0MM^E *EMP* 49
SIC 4491 4731 Loading vessels; Unloading vessels; Freight consolidation
Pr: Michael Byan
COO: John Atkins
**Ch:* Paul Tellier
VP: Richard Ceci
**VP:* James Kukucka
CTO: Ing Peter
VP Opers: Joseph Battipaglia

D-U-N-S 04-068-5737 EXP
GLOBAL TEXTILE SERVICES LLC
TEXTILE COATING PLANT
124 Global Dr, Dalton, GA 30720-5997
Tel (706) 226-5647 *Founded/Ownrshp* 1976
Sales 52.8MM^E *EMP* 190
SIC 2273 Finishers of tufted carpets & rugs; Finishers of tufted carpets & rugs
Plng Mgr: Andy Henderson
Plng Mgr: Clinton Poole
Netwrk Eng: Nathan Henson
Plnt Mgr: David Brown

D-U-N-S 85-877-4651 IMP
GLOBAL TOBACCO LLC
2861 Congressman Ln # 300, Dallas, TX 75220-1407
Tel (214) 357-6653 *Founded/Ownrshp* 2007
Sales 37.7MM^E *EMP* 65
SIC 5194 Tobacco & tobacco products; Tobacco & tobacco products
Pr: Munir M Meghani
**VP:* Sultan Ali
Sls Mgr: Fred Gajiani

D-U-N-S 11-216-0952 EXP
GLOBAL TOOLING SYSTEMS LLC
(*Suby of* AIP AEROSPACE) ★
16445 23 Mile Rd, Macomb, MI 48042-4005
Tel (586) 726-0500 *Founded/Ownrshp* 2012
Sales 65.0MM *EMP* 265
SIC 3545 3569 Machine tool accessories; Gas producers, generators & other gas related equipment; Machine tool accessories; Gas producers, generators & other gas related equipment
Pr: Paul Walsh
**CFO:* Dan Nowicki
Prgrm Mgr: John Cesarz
Prgrm Mgr: Larry Rosecki
DP Exec: Joe Kozlowski
IT Man: Richard Tracy
Ql Cn Mgr: Jamie Franz

D-U-N-S 14-102-8964 IMP
■ **GLOBAL TOWER LLC**
G T P
(*Suby of* AMERICAN TOWER CORP) ★
750 Park Of Commerce Blvd # 300, Boca Raton, FL 33487-3605
Tel (561) 995-0320 *Founded/Ownrshp* 2003
Sales 45.8MM^E *EMP* 126
SIC 4812 6519 1623 Radio telephone communication; Real property lessors; Communication line & transmission tower construction; Radio telephone communication; Real property lessors; Communication line & transmission tower construction
CEO: Marc Ganzi
**Pr:* Alexander L Gellman
**CFO:* Ronald L Rubin
CFO: Ronald Rubin
CFO: Jane Salter
Sr VP: Shawn R Ruben
VP: Jeremy Martin
VP: Jim McCulloch
VP: Barry Rosson
VP: Jose Sola
Netwrk Eng: David Kupperman

D-U-N-S 01-511-4154
GLOBAL TPA LLC (FL)
5403 N Church Ave, Tampa, FL 33614-5611
Tel (813) 506-6000 *Founded/Ownrshp* 2004
Sales 44.0MM^E *EMP* 250
SIC 8741 Administrative management; Administrative management

D-U-N-S 12-155-2137
GLOBAL TRADE CORP
4240 Embassy Park Dr Nw, Washington, DC 20016-3619
Tel (202) 298-5995 *Founded/Ownrshp* 1982
Sales 42.6MM^E *EMP* 500
SIC 6211 6221 Oil & gas lease brokers; Commodity brokers, contracts; Oil & gas lease brokers; Commodity brokers, contracts
Ch Bd: William Goffe
**Sec:* Jeffrey Joyce
Board of Directors: Terry Donelli, Michael Infante

D-U-N-S 78-732-6362 IMP
GLOBAL TRADING AND SOURCING CORP
GTS
1587 Cllege Pk Bus Ctr Rd, Orlando, FL 32804-6000
Tel (407) 532-7600 *Founded/Ownrshp* 1991
Sales 27.8MM^E *EMP* 20
SIC 5084 Industrial machinery & equipment
Pr: Andrew Vandendriessche
Sales Exec: Andrew Vandendriessch
Sales Asso: Priscilla Oquendo

D-U-N-S 12-765-2951 IMP/EXP
GLOBAL TRADING ENTERPRISES LLC
RASTELLI GLOBAL
504 Sharptown Rd, Swedesboro, NJ 08085-3161
Tel (856) 223-9966 *Founded/Ownrshp* 2001
Sales 124.9MM^E *EMP* 150
Accts Herbein & Company Inc Readi
SIC 5147 Meats & meat products; Meats & meat products
Pr: Anthony Rastelli
**VP:* Paul Zaun
Genl Mgr: James Haverstick
Dir IT: Barry Hanna

D-U-N-S 92-826-7566
GLOBAL TRANSPORT LOGISTICS INC
208 Harristown Rd Ste 201, Glen Rock, NJ 07452-3306
Tel (201) 251-7333 *Founded/Ownrshp* 1995
Sales 36.0MM^E *EMP* 26
SIC 4731 4225 Freight transportation arrangement; General warehousing; Freight transportation arrangement; General warehousing
CEO: Eileen Matarazzo
**Pr:* Anthony F Matarazzo

D-U-N-S 10-670-2470 IMP/EXP
GLOBAL TRANSPORTATION SERVICES INC
1930 Sith Ave Ste 401, Seattle, WA 98134
Tel (206) 624-4354 *Founded/Ownrshp* 2001, 2006
Sales 21.1MM *EMP* 149
SIC 4731 8742

D-U-N-S 15-690-2751
GLOBAL TRANSPORTATION SERVICES INC
(*Suby of* JFT MANAGEMENT ACQUISITIONS INC.)
18209 80th Ave S Ste A, Kent, WA 98032-2505
Tel (425) 207-1500 *Founded/Ownrshp* 2013
Sales 68.8MM^E *EMP* 140
SIC 4731 Freight forwarding; Freight forwarding
CEO: Jason Totah
**CFO:* Jack Ingleq
Sec: Carol Yi
VP: Marty Howard

D-U-N-S 83-625-3989
GLOBAL TRAVEL INTERNATIONAL INC
1060 Maitland Ctr, Maitland, FL 32751
Tel (407) 660-7800 *Founded/Ownrshp* 1994
Sales 30.8MM^E *EMP* 125
SIC 4724 Travel agencies
Pr: Michael A Gross
**VP:* Randall J Warren
S&M/VP: Anthony Barbera
Sls Mgr: Mary Brautigan

D-U-N-S 82-697-3740 IMP/EXP
GLOBAL TUBING LLC
501 County Road 493, Dayton, TX 77535-8149
Tel (713) 265-5000 *Founded/Ownrshp* 2007
Sales 134.8MM^E *EMP* 175^E
SIC 1382 Oil & gas exploration services; Oil & gas exploration services

D-U-N-S 82-746-7866 IMP
GLOBAL TUNGSTEN & POWDERS CORP
GTP
(*Suby of* PLANSEE HOLDING AG)
1 Hawes St, Towanda, PA 18848-2134
Tel (570) 268-5000 *Founded/Ownrshp* 2008
Sales 500.0MM *EMP* 680
SIC 3291 3313 Tungsten carbide abrasive; Tungsten carbide powder; Tungsten carbide abrasive; Tungsten carbide powder; Molybdenum silicon, not made in blast furnaces
CEO: Andreas Lackner MD
Pr: Robert Fillnow
**Pr:* Karlheinz Wax
Board of Directors: Eric Rowe, Andreas Schwenninger

GLOBAL UNDERGROUND SOLUTIONS
See SECURED NETWORK SOLUTIONS INC

GLOBAL VACATIONS
See GLOBAL CONNECTIONS INC

D-U-N-S 12-731-9973
GLOBAL VALUE COMMERCE INC
GLOBAL GOLF
7320 Acc Blvd, Raleigh, NC 27617-8407
Tel (919) 719-7940 *Founded/Ownrshp* 2001
Sales 41.4MM^E *EMP* 55
SIC 5091 Golf equipment
Pr: Edward Byman
CFO: Dave Hunt
CFO: Mark Larson
Chf Mktg O: Zack Veasey
Ex VP: Rick Oldach
**VP:* Glenn Mersereau
**VP:* Mitesh Patel
Dir IT: Mike Slock
IT Man: Brouck McCall
Opers Mgr: Matthew Chase
Opers Mgr: Chris Condon

D-U-N-S 79-895-0270
GLOBAL VIBRATION INC
MSEO.COM
1250 Conn Ave Nw Ste 200, Washington, DC 20036-2643
Tel (202) 787-3989 *Founded/Ownrshp* 2006
Sales 52.6MM *EMP* 135
SIC 7389 Translation services; Translation services
Pr: Mathias Levarek
**VP:* Marc Schneider
**CIO:* Martin Larson
CTO: Sandra Schlosser

D-U-N-S 12-131-1471
GLOBAL VIDEO LLC
GUIDANCE CHANNEL
(*Suby of* SCHOOL SPECIALTY INC) ★
1000 Woodbury Rd Ste 1, Woodbury, NY 11797-2530
Tel (516) 222-2600 *Founded/Ownrshp* 2004
Sales 17.1MM^E *EMP* 375
SIC 2741 5961 5092 6719 Catalogs: publishing & printing; Book club, mail order; Educational toys; Investment holding companies, except banks
Pr: David Rust

D-U-N-S 03-690-9794 IMP
GLOBAL VIEWS LP
7301 Ambassador Row, Dallas, TX 75247-4801
Tel (214) 956-0030 *Founded/Ownrshp* 1997
Sales 84.3MM^E *EMP* 135
SIC 5023 Decorative home furnishings & supplies; Decorative home furnishings & supplies
Pr: David Gebhart
**COO:* Frederick Rayner
**CFO:* Lois G Del Negro
Mktg Dir: Rachel Burgess
Sls Dir: Josh Jarboe

D-U-N-S 16-010-5375
GLOBAL WIRELESS SOLUTIONS INC
23475 Rock Haven Way # 165, Dulles, VA 20166-4448
Tel (703) 661-7000 *Founded/Ownrshp* 1996
Sales 35.6MM^E *EMP* 170
SIC 8748 Systems engineering consultant, ex. computer or professional; Systems engineering consultant, ex. computer or professional
Pr: Paul Carter
Sftwr Eng: Wretvic Awasthi
Netwrk Eng: Bill Crabill
Opers Mgr: Drissa Coulibaly

D-U-N-S 78-517-9891
GLOBAL WORKPLACE SOLUTIONS LLC
G W S
9823 Cincinnati Dayton Rd, West Chester, OH 45069-3825
Tel (513) 759-6000 *Founded/Ownrshp* 2005
Sales 20.3MM^E *EMP* 69
SIC 4213 Trucking, except local
Pr: Jim Hellier
**Pr:* John Sabatalo
**CFO:* Robert Faillo
**Sr VP:* Jeff Ankenbauer
**VP:* Stephen Sabatalo

D-U-N-S 04-574-7409
GLOBAL X-RAY & TESTING CORP
INTERTEK COMPANY
(*Suby of* INTERTEK GROUP PLC)
112 E Service Rd, Amelia, LA 70340
Tel (985) 631-2426 *Founded/Ownrshp* 2013
Sales 45.0MM *EMP* 300
SIC 8734 Testing laboratories; Testing laboratories
Pr: Chris Moreau
CFO: Duke Gallagher
Ofcr: Lee Fanguy
VP: Thaddeus Zeringue

D-U-N-S 02-514-4358 IMP
GLOBAL-PAK INC (OH)
1387 County Road 440, Columbiana, OH 44408-9485
Tel (330) 482-1993 *Founded/Ownrshp* 1998
Sales 32.1MM^E *EMP* 28^E
SIC 5199 Packaging materials
Pr: Kevin Channell
**VP:* James Foster
Sls Mgr: Brock Beatty
Sales Asso: Nate Gotschall

D-U-N-S 11-855-8191
GLOBALCOM HOLDINGS INC
(*Suby of* FIRST COMMUNICATIONS LLC) ★
200 E Randolph St # 5135, Chicago, IL 60601-6436
Tel (312) 895-8818 *Founded/Ownrshp* 2008
Sales 42.2MM^E *EMP* 213
SIC 4813 Long distance telephone communications; Long distance telephone communications
Pr: John T Shave
Ex VP: Chris Forte
Ex VP: Eric Wince

D-U-N-S 95-830-6490
GLOBALCOM INC
(*Suby of* GLOBALCOM HOLDINGS INC) ★
200 E Randolph St Fl 23, Chicago, IL 60601-6434
Tel (312) 895-8818 *Founded/Ownrshp* 1993
Sales 42.2MM^E *EMP* 210
SIC 4813 Long distance telephone communications; Long distance telephone communications
Pr: John T Shave
Pr: Kieran Athy
Ex VP: Chris Forte
Ex VP: Eric Wince

D-U-N-S 79-436-9983
GLOBALFOUNDRIES AMERICAS INC
(*Suby of* GLOBALFOUNDRIES SINGAPORE PTE. LTD.)
2600 Great America Way, Santa Clara, CA 95054-1169
Tel (408) 462-3900 *Founded/Ownrshp* 1991
Sales 70.3MM^E *EMP* 132
SIC 5065 Semiconductor devices; Semiconductor devices
CEO: Ajit Manocha
**Ch Bd:* Jim Norling
**Ch Bd:* Barry Waite
COO: Stephen Beebe
**COO:* Chia Song Hwee
**CFO:* Daniel Durn
**Ex VP:* Alexie Lee
**Sr VP:* Kay Chai Ang
**Sr VP:* Gregg Bartlett
Sr VP: Kathleen Borneman
**Sr VP:* Terry Daly
**Sr VP:* Mike Rekuc
**VP:* Michael Buehler-Garcia
**VP:* Tom Guernee
VP: Subramani Kengeri
VP: Kevin Kimball

D-U-N-S 96-500-6773
GLOBALFOUNDRIES DRESDEN MODULE ONE LLC
(*Suby of* GLOBAL FOUNDRIES) ★
1050 E Arques Ave, Sunnyvale, CA 94085-4601
Tel (408) 462-3900 *Founded/Ownrshp* 2004
Sales 23.8MM^E *EMP* 218^E
SIC 3674 3369 Integrated circuits, semiconductor networks, etc.; Nonferrous foundries
VP: Bo Cheng
VP: Subi Kengeri
Exec: Tony Tsai
Prgrm Mgr: Warren Edwards
IT Man: Michael Cheong
Netwrk Eng: Jeannette Schreiber

D-U-N-S 83-041-7593 IMP
GLOBALFOUNDRIES US INC
GLOBAL FOUNDRIES
(*Suby of* GLOBALFOUNDRIES DRESDEN MODULE ONE LIMITED LIABILITY COMPANY & CO. KG)
2600 Great America Way, Santa Clara, CA 95054-1169
Tel (408) 462-3900 *Founded/Ownrshp* 2007
Sales 1.1MMM^E *EMP* 3,000^E
SIC 3369 Nonferrous foundries; Nonferrous foundries
CEO: Sanjay Jha
**CFO:* Young H Kim
CEO: Alexie Lee
Ofcr: RAO Baskar
**Ofcr:* Louis Lupin
Ofcr: Jeff Worth
**Ex VP:* Daniel Durn
**Ex VP:* Alexie H Lee
**Ex VP:* Michael Noonen
**Sr VP:* Kay Chai Ang
**Sr VP:* Gregg Bartlett
Sr VP: Kathy Borneman
**Sr VP:* Thomas Caulfield
**Sr VP:* Mojy Chian
**Sr VP:* Terry Daly
**Sr VP:* William Davidson Jr
Sr VP: Robert Stear
**VP:* Ibrahim Ajami
**VP:* Norm Armour
VP: Jon Carvill
VP: Paul Koch

D-U-N-S 02-134-3657
GLOBALGIVING FOUNDATION INC
1110 Vermont Ave Nw # 550, Washington, DC 20005-3544
Tel (202) 232-5784 *Founded/Ownrshp* 2002
Sales 27.1MM *EMP* 30
Accts Gelman Rosenberg & Freedman
SIC 8699 Charitable organization
Pr: Mari Kuraishi
VP: Jennifer Sigler
Prgrm Mgr: Michael Gale
Off Mgr: Sombit Mishra

D-U-N-S 18-554-9201
GLOBALHUE ASIAN INC
4000 Town Ctr Ste 1600, Southfield, MI 48075-1400
Tel (248) 223-8900 *Founded/Ownrshp* 1988
Sales 31.1MM^E *EMP* 300
SIC 7311 8743 Advertising agencies; Sales promotion; Public relations & publicity; Advertising agencies; Sales promotion; Public relations & publicity
CEO: Donald A Coleman
Ch: Sibyl Smith
Treas: Gaye Miller
Ofcr: Vida Cornelious
Ofcr: Michael Jacobs
Ex VP: Elcid Choi
Ex VP: Robert Fitzgerald
Ex VP: Allen Pugh
Sr VP: Robert Chavis
VP: Angela Ford
VP: Tony Hidalgo
VP: Matt Lee
VP: Najoh Reid
Exec: Publicis Sanchez

GLOBALINX
See 5LINX ENTERPRISES INC

D-U-N-S 10-169-2858
GLOBALLOGIC INC
1741 Tech Dr Ste 400, San Jose, CA 95110
Tel (408) 273-8900 *Founded/Ownrshp* 2002
Sales 532.8MM^E *EMP* 8,000
SIC 7371 7379 7373 Computer software development & applications; Computer software development & applications; Computer related consulting services; Systems engineering, computer related
CEO: Shashank Samant
**COO:* Jim Dellamore
**CFO:* Doug Ahrens
**CFO:* Anna Brunelle
**CFO:* Charles Wayne Grubbs
**CFO:* Wayne Grubbs
**Ch:* Mike Daniels
**V Ch Bd:* Peter Harrison
**Chf Mktg O:* Mike Devries
**Ofcr:* Bonnie Helton
Assoc VP: Michael Lesk
Assoc VP: Rohit Nagpal
Ex VP: Sanjay Singh
Sr VP: Manoj Agarwala
**Sr VP:* Yuri Goliyad
Sr VP: Andrew Nash
**Sr VP:* Boris Shnayder
VP: Sebastian Gryngarten
VP: Andrew Kalinovsky
VP: Roman Khmil
VP: Yuri Landgraf
Board of Directors: Steve Pusey

D-U-N-S 18-036-7257
GLOBALOGIX INC
13831 Nw Fwy Ste 600, Houston, TX 77040-5217
Tel (713) 987-7630 *Founded/Ownrshp* 2004
Sales 28.9MM^E *EMP* 60
SIC 1389 Construction, repair & dismantling services
CEO: Charles Drobny Jr
Pr: Wayne Salsiccia
**Sr VP:* Jim Fererro
Admn Mgr: Valerie Henning
Opers Mgr: Shawn Lain

D-U-N-S 96-392-3557
GLOBALOPTIONS SERVICES INC
5955 T G Lee Blvd Ste 600, Orlando, FL 32822-4431
Tel (407) 859-0997 *Founded/Ownrshp* 2010
Sales 12.7MM^E *EMP* 370
SIC 7381 Private investigator; Private investigator
CEO: Franklin B Pinder III
CFO: Kevin McGinn
Ex VP: Scott Cornelison
Ex VP: David D Finney
Ex VP: Bobby Gracey
Ex VP: Douglass Hock
CIO: Wesley Clark
Software D: Joe Paolini

GLOBALPAYMENTS
See GLOBAL PAYMENTS INC

D-U-N-S 94-978-5455
▲ GLOBALSCAPE INC
4500 Lockhill Selma Rd, San Antonio, TX 78249-2073
Tel (210) 308-8267 *Founded/Ownrshp* 1996
Sales 26.7MM *EMP* 105^E
Tkr Sym GSB *Exch* ASE
SIC 7372 Prepackaged software; Prepackaged software
Pr: James L Bindseil
**Ch Bd:* Thomas W Brown
COO: Matthew C Goulet
CFO: James W Albrecht Jr
Board of Directors: David L Mann, Frank M Morgan, Phillip M Renfro

D-U-N-S 07-587-0886
GLOBALSPEC INC
30 Tech Valley Dr Ste 102, East Greenbush, NY 12061-4129
Tel (518) 880-0200 *Founded/Ownrshp* 1996
Sales 29.5MM^E *EMP* 240
SIC 7379 5084 7375 Computer related consulting services; Industrial machinery & equipment; Information retrieval services; Computer related consulting services; Industrial machinery & equipment; Information retrieval services
Ch Bd: Jeffrey M Killeen
CFO: Mike Chittom
**CFO:* William Hollyer
Treas: Galen Kooten
Bd of Dir: Peter Derow
Sr VP: Brian Heller
**Sr VP:* Angela Hribar
Sr VP: Guy Maser
**VP:* Tom Brownell
VP: Tammy Mihalic
VP: Kate Reynolds
VP: Andi Schneiter
VP: Sarabjit Singh
Exec: Luke Mazza
Dir Bus: Bruce Bergwall
Board of Directors: Alex Berzofsky, Mark Colodny, Cary J Davis, Peter A Derow, Roland W Schmitt

D-U-N-S 14-830-1935 IMP
▲ GLOBALSTAR INC
300 Holiday Square Blvd # 300, Covington, LA 70433-6147
Tel (985) 335-1500 *Founded/Ownrshp* 2003
Sales 90.0MM *EMP* 282^E
Tkr Sym GSAT *Exch* ASE
SIC 4813 Voice telephone communications; Voice telephone communications
Ch Bd: James Monroe III
Pr: Frank J Bell II
CFO: Rebecca Clary
CFO: Rebecca S Clary
CFO: John Shay
VP: Walter Debus
VP: Jim Mandala
VP: Paul A Monte
VP: Barbee Ponder
VP: L Barbee Ponder IV
VP Admn: Jim Seese
Board of Directors: William A Hasler, John Kneuer, James F Lynch, J Patrick McIntyre, Kenneth M Young

D-U-N-S 93-393-3681 IMP
GLOBALTECH INDUSTRIES INC
418 441 Business Hwy, Cornelia, GA 30531-2181
Tel (706) 776-1912 *Founded/Ownrshp* 1995
Sales 71.6MM^E *EMP* 289
SIC 3999 Candles; Candles
CEO: D Rush Mauney
**Pr:* James L Bruce Jr

GLOBALTESTMARKET.COM
See GLOBAL MARKET INSITE INC

D-U-N-S 13-194-4493
GLOBALTRANZ ENTERPRISES INC
5415 E High St Ste 460, Phoenix, AZ 85054-5476
Tel (480) 339-5600 *Founded/Ownrshp* 2001
Sales 270.7MM *EMP* 424
SIC 4731 Freight transportation arrangement; Freight transportation arrangement
CEO: Andrew Leto
Mng Pt: Thom Evans
**Pr:* Michael Leto
**Pr:* Marty Sinicrope
**CFO:* Greg Roeper
**Ex VP:* Michael Bookout
Sr VP: Rick Werner
VP: Todd Lafond
Exec: Renee Krug
Dir Bus: Grant Glasser
Dir Bus: Eric Lenze
Dir Bus: Teresa Turner

D-U-N-S 78-328-4169
GLOBALWARE SOLUTIONS - CALIFORNIA
(*Suby of* GLOBALWARE SOLUTIONS INC) ★
30300 Whipple Rd, Union City, CA 94587-1525
Tel (650) 363-2200 *Founded/Ownrshp* 2000
Sales 15.9MM^E *EMP* 300^E
SIC 7379 Disk & diskette conversion service; Disk & diskette conversion service
CEO: Tony Rudston
CFO: Brenda Olivera
CFO: Tim Tropp
Comm Man: Bodie Haungs
Genl Mgr: Bill Moreland
IT Man: Eddie Way
Netwrk Mgr: Ingo Azarvand

D-U-N-S 62-810-3272
GLOBALWARE SOLUTIONS INC
(*Suby of* MEZZANINE MANAGEMENT UK LIMITED)
200 Ward Hill Ave, Haverhill, MA 01835-6972
Tel (978) 469-7500 *Founded/Ownrshp* 2000
Sales 23.9MM^E *EMP* 350
SIC 7389 4225 4813 Subscription fulfillment services: magazine, newspaper, etc.; General warehousing & storage; ; Subscription fulfillment services: magazine, newspaper, etc.; General warehousing & storage;

Pr: David I Beatson
**Ch Bd:* Bob Roche
CFO: Timothy Losik
**Sec:* John P Viliesis
VP Sls: Douglas Brittin

D-U-N-S 80-699-9368
GLOBALWIDE ELECTRONICS GROUP LLC
116 Wilbur Pl, Bohemia, NY 11716-2402
Tel (631) 677-2400 *Founded/Ownrshp* 2007
Sales 22.2MM^E *EMP* 75^E
SIC 5065 5999 Electronic parts & equipment; Electronic parts & equipment

D-U-N-S 05-178-2404
GLOBANT LLC
(*Suby of* GLOBANT SA.)
1212 New York Ave Nw # 900, Washington, DC 20005-3987
Tel (508) 544-2829 *Founded/Ownrshp* 2003
Sales 22.6MM *EMP* 60
SIC 7371 Computer software development & applications
CEO: Martn Migoya
**COO:* Guillermo Marsicovetere
**CFO:* Alejandro Scannapieco
Ex VP: Bob Kerner
**Ex VP:* Daniel Kuperstein
**Ex VP:* Nestor Nocetti
**Comm Dir:* Wanda Weigert
**Dir Sec:* Andres Angelani
**CIO:* Gustavo Barreiro
**CTO:* Guillermo Bodnar
**CTO:* Guibert Englebienne

D-U-N-S 07-828-8044
GLOBANT LLC
875 Howard St Fl 3, San Francisco, CA 94103-3027
Tel (877) 798-8104 *Founded/Ownrshp* 2003
Sales 100.0MM *EMP* 67
SIC 7371 Computer software development; Computer software development
CEO: Martin Migoya
**Dir Sec:* Andres Angelani

D-U-N-S 05-255-1413
■ GLOBE COMMUNICATIONS LLC
(*Suby of* DYCOM INDUSTRIES INC) ★
950 48th Ave N Ste 100, Myrtle Beach, SC 29577-5434
Tel (843) 839-5544 *Founded/Ownrshp* 1992
Sales 20.3MM^E *EMP* 125
SIC 4841 Cable & other pay television services; Cable & other pay television services
Pr: Victor R Lundy III
Treas: Melinda Beacham
Ex VP: L David Fugate
VP: Jeffrey Scott Hamrick

D-U-N-S 00-127-9017 IMP
GLOBE DIE CUTTING PRODUCTS INC
76 Liberty St, Metuchen, NJ 08840-1237
Tel (732) 494-7744 *Founded/Ownrshp* 1961
Sales 34.9MM^E *EMP* 200
SIC 3544 2675 Special dies, tools, jigs & fixtures; Cardboard cut-outs, panels & foundations: die-cut; Special dies, tools, jigs & fixtures; Cardboard cut-outs, panels & foundations: die-cut
Pr: Irwin Brody
**Sec:* Bruce Brody
Genl Mgr: Peter Hodgson
Sfty Mgr: John Appaluccio
Plnt Mgr: Joe Mahoney
Sales Exec: Jim Doherty
Sales Exec: Joe Negler
Mktg Dir: Joel Nagler
Sls Mgr: Sheana Carden

GLOBE DIRECT
See GLOBE SPECIALTY PRODUCTS LLC

D-U-N-S 55-744-7096 EXP
GLOBE ENERGY SERVICES LLC
3204 W Highway 180, Snyder, TX 79549-7858
Tel (325) 573-1310 *Founded/Ownrshp* 2010
Sales 2.7MMM^E *EMP* 1,900^E
SIC 1382 Oil & gas exploration services; Oil & gas exploration services
Bd of Dir: Richard Ellis
**Sr VP:* Philip Wright

D-U-N-S 00-723-5229
GLOBE ENGINEERING CO INC
1539 S Saint Paul St, Wichita, KS 67213-1797
Tel (316) 943-1266 *Founded/Ownrshp* 2000
Sales 44.5MM *EMP* 160
SIC 3728 Aircraft body assemblies & parts; Aircraft body assemblies & parts
Pr: Jeff Teague
Pr: Ronald Ross
CFO: Gerald Campbell
Snr Sftwr: Richard Crisp
Sys Mgr: Jason Rohr
Plnt Mgr: Curtis Roberts
Prd Mgr: Donald Ford
Prd Mgr: S Knuth
Prd Mgr: James Larkin
Ql Cn Mgr: Andy Chambers

D-U-N-S 80-695-2990
GLOBE EXPRESS SERVICES LTD
8025 Arrowridge Blvd, Charlotte, NC 28273-5604
Tel (704) 525-1758 *Founded/Ownrshp* 1990
Sales 51.0MM^E *EMP* 110
SIC 4731 Freight forwarding; Freight forwarding
CEO: Ziad Korban
CFO: Steve Hankins
Sr VP: Chris Slotten
VP: Regina Cross
Exec: Eliane Hall
Mng Dir: Mustapha Kawam
Mng Dir: Wolfgang Rohdenburg
Brnch Mgr: Linda Hastings
Genl Mgr: Henri Azar
Genl Mgr: Irina Tsyrlin
Off Mgr: Brenda Lynch

D-U-N-S 04-055-9312 IMP/EXP
GLOBE FIRE SPRINKLER CORP
4077 Airpark Dr, Standish, MI 48658-9533
Tel (989) 846-4583 *Founded/Ownrshp* 1987
Sales 26.7MM^E *EMP* 177^E
SIC 3569 3494 3491 Sprinkler systems, fire: automatic; Valves & pipe fittings; Industrial valves
CEO: Robert C Worthington
**Pr:* Steven R Worthington
CFO: Tayna Peterson
**CFO:* Tonya Peterson
**Ex VP:* Buck Buchanan
VP: Brian T Hoening
VP Opers: Terry Bovee
Opers Mgr: Angela Gould
Plnt Mgr: Fred Echstaedt
Ql Cn Mgr: Susan Kozero
Manager: Scott Bea

D-U-N-S 55-590-1925 IMP
GLOBE FOOD EQUIPMENT CO
2153 Dryden Rd, Moraine, OH 45439-1739
Tel (937) 299-5493 *Founded/Ownrshp* 1991
Sales 23.4MM^E *EMP* 39
SIC 5046 Commercial cooking & food service equipment
Pr: Hilton Garner
IT Man: Bruce Habegger
S&M/VP: Kevin Woods
Manager: Tony Quesenberry
Sls Mgr: Josh Compton

D-U-N-S 82-520-1697
GLOBE HOLDING CO LLC
37 Loudon Rd, Pittsfield, NH 03263-3604
Tel (603) 435-8323 *Founded/Ownrshp* 1890
Sales 81.5MM^E *EMP* 400
SIC 6519 Real property lessors; Real property lessors
Pr: Donald D Welch II
**VP:* George E Freese III
**VP:* Robert A Freese

D-U-N-S 00-720-4951
■ GLOBE LIFE & ACCIDENT INSURANCE CO
(*Suby of* TORCHMARK CORP) ★
204 N Robinson Ave, Oklahoma City, OK 73102-7001
Tel (972) 540-6542 *Founded/Ownrshp* 1980
Sales NA *EMP* 500
SIC 6311 6321 Life insurance carriers; Health insurance carriers; Life insurance carriers; Health insurance carriers
CEO: Chuck Hudson
**Treas:* Gary Coleman
**Sr VP:* Brian Mitchell
**VP:* Rosemary Montgomery
**Prin:* Mark S McAndrew
Sls&Mrk Ex: Rick Coleman

D-U-N-S 00-925-3782 IMP
GLOBE MACHINE MANUFACTURING CO
701 E D St, Tacoma, WA 98421-1811
Tel (253) 383-2584 *Founded/Ownrshp* 1917
Sales 44.3MM^E *EMP* 250
SIC 3553 3537 Woodworking machinery; Lift trucks, industrial: fork, platform, straddle, etc.; Woodworking machinery; Lift trucks, industrial: fork, platform, straddle, etc.
Ch Bd: Calvin D Bamford Jr
Pr: Thomas Scott
**Treas:* Jeffrey Peterson
**VP:* Ronald Jacobsen
CIO: Tom Spaulding
Dir IT: Kendra Spaulding
Opers Mgr: John Barnes
Plnt Mgr: George Richard
Prd Mgr: Tom Woodward
VP Sls: Mark Allen
Sls Mgr: Susan Greenberg

D-U-N-S 00-108-0886
GLOBE MANUFACTURING CO-OK LLC (NH)
(*Suby of* GLOBE HOLDING CO LLC) ★
37 Loudon Rd, Pittsfield, NH 03263-3604
Tel (603) 435-8323 *Founded/Ownrshp* 1887, 1890
Sales 77.6MM^E *EMP* 375
SIC 3842 Clothing, fire resistant & protective; Clothing, fire resistant & protective
Pr: Donald D Welch II
**Sr VP:* Gef Freese
**Sr VP:* George E Freese III
**Sr VP:* Robert A Freese
Tech Mgr: Pat Freeman
VP Mktg: Doug Towle
VP Sls: Rick Barr

GLOBE MANUFACTURING SALES CO
See A K STAMPING CO INC

D-U-N-S 88-448-7406
■ GLOBE MARKETING SERVICES INC
(*Suby of* GLOBE LIFE & ACCIDENT INSURANCE CO) ★
133 Nw 122nd St, Oklahoma City, OK 73114-7214
Tel (405) 755-8282 *Founded/Ownrshp* 1994
Sales 72.9MM^E *EMP* 350
SIC 2752 Commercial printing, lithographic; Commercial printing, lithographic
Sr VP: Chuck B Hudson

D-U-N-S 13-040-5871
GLOBE MECHANICAL INC
20 W 7th St, New Albany, IN 47150-5912
Tel (812) 949-2001 *Founded/Ownrshp* 1985
Sales 55.4MM *EMP* 99
SIC 3498 Fabricated pipe & fittings; Fabricated pipe & fittings
Pr: Marlin Andres
**Pr:* Bryan Kruer
S&M/Dir: Steve Chappars

D-U-N-S 12-168-7032 IMP/EXP
■ GLOBE METALLURGICAL INC
GLOBE SPECIALTY METALS
(*Suby of* GLOBE SPECIALTY METALS INC) ★
1595 Sparling Rd, Waterford, OH 45786-6104
Tel (740) 984-2361 *Founded/Ownrshp* 2006
Sales 136.3MM^E *EMP* 440

SIC 3339 3313 2819 Silicon refining (primary, over 99% pure); Silicon, epitaxial (silicon alloy); Ferrosilicon, not made in blast furnaces; Industrial inorganic chemicals; Silicon refining (primary, over 99% pure); Silicon, epitaxial (silicon alloy); Ferrosilicon, not made in blast furnaces; Industrial inorganic chemicals
Ch: Alan Kestenbaum
*Pr: Jeff Bradley
*CFO: Joe Ragan
VP: Phillip Gardner
*VP: Marlin Perkins
VP: Jeff Watson
Admn Mgr: Jim Holly
Off Admin: Sarah Bonse
Sfty Mgr: Gary Obrien
Sfty Mgr: Judy Paquette
Opers Mgr: Harold Odell

D-U-N-S 01-114-1645
GLOBE MOTOR CAR CO (NJ)
GLOBE MOTOR CAR LEASING
7 Pillar Dr, Rockaway, NJ 07866-1318
Tel (973) 227-3600 Founded/Ownrshp 1967
Sales 42.5MM^E EMP 103
SIC 5511 5012 Automobiles, new & used; Automobiles & other motor vehicles; Automobiles, new & used; Automobiles & other motor vehicles
Pr: Joseph P Chnapko
*Prin: Joseph Defransesco
*Prin: Aprilann Laduca
*Prin: David Morrison

GLOBE MOTOR CAR LEASING
See GLOBE MOTOR CAR CO

D-U-N-S 18-170-9775 IMP
■ GLOBE MOTORS INC
(Suby of ALLIED MOTION TECHNOLOGIES INC) ★
2275 Stanley Ave, Dayton, OH 45404-1226
Tel (334) 983-3542 Founded/Ownrshp 2013
Sales 105.7MM^E EMP 418
SIC 3621 Motors & generators; Motors & generators
CEO: Steven McHenry
*CFO: William Gillespie
VP: Dennis Mueller
Dir Bus: Daryl Bogan
Prgrm Mgr: Greg Malenich
Prgrm Mgr: Don Morris
VP Opers: Mauricio Clarke
Mtls Mgr: Joe Mueller
Opers Mgr: Lee Henderson
Prd Mgr: Fernando Lima
Ql Cn Mgr: Chad Bryan

GLOBE SHOES
See OSATA ENTERPRISES INC

GLOBE SPECIALTY CO DIV
See TRIPLEX MANUFACTURING CO

GLOBE SPECIALTY METALS
See GLOBE METALLURGICAL INC

D-U-N-S 78-284-7391
▲ GLOBE SPECIALTY METALS INC
600 Brickell Ave Ste 3100, Miami, FL 33131-3089
Tel (786) 509-6900 Founded/Ownrshp 2006
Sales 800.7MM EMP 1,684^E
Accts Deloitte & Touche Llp Miami
Tkr Sym GSM Exch NGS
SIC 3339 3313 Primary nonferrous metals; Silicon refining (primary, over 99% pure); Silicon, epitaxial (silicon alloy); Ferrosilicon, not made in blast furnaces; Primary nonferrous metals; Silicon refining (primary, over 99% pure); Silicon, epitaxial (silicon alloy); Ferrosilicon, not made in blast furnaces
CEO: Jeff Bradley
*Ch Bd: Alan Kestenbaum
CFO: Joseph Ragan
Sr VP: Theodore A Heilmn
Snr Mgr: Sarah Mower
Board of Directors: Donald G Barger Jr, Bruce Crockett, Stuart E Eizenstat, Franklin L Lavin, Alan Schriber

D-U-N-S 87-883-3821
GLOBE SPECIALTY PRODUCTS LLC
GLOBE DIRECT
(Suby of NE MEDIA GROUP INC) ★
9 Latti Farm Rd, Millbury, MA 01527-2132
Tel (508) 871-1900 Founded/Ownrshp 1996
Sales 50.0MM EMP 74
SIC 7331 Direct mail advertising services; Direct mail advertising services
Brnch Mgr: Susan Wilson
Plnt Mgr: Charles Hourvitz

GLOBE SUPERMARKET
See RICHANN LTD

GLOBE TIRE & MOTOR SPORTS
See GLOBE TIRE & MOTORSPORTS CORP

D-U-N-S 02-850-7861 IMP
GLOBE TIRE & MOTORSPORTS CORP
GLOBE TIRE & MOTOR SPORTS
2450 S La Cienega Blvd, Los Angeles, CA 90034-2216
Tel (310) 836-0804 Founded/Ownrshp 1961
Sales 28.4MM^E EMP 51
SIC 5014 5531 Automobile tires & tubes; Automotive tires
CEO: Arnold Sperling

D-U-N-S 07-729-5355 EXP
GLOBE TRAILER MANUFACTURING INC
GLOBE TRAILERS
3101 59th Avenue Dr E, Bradenton, FL 34203-5311
Tel (941) 753-2199 Founded/Ownrshp 2004
Sales 57.8MM^E EMP 80
SIC 5012 3715 Trailers for trucks, new & used; Truck trailers; Trailers for trucks, new & used; Truck trailers
Pr: Jeffrey K Walters
*VP: Steve Walters
Plnt Mgr: Jeff Coomber

GLOBE TRAILERS
See GLOBE TRAILER MANUFACTURING INC

D-U-N-S 12-463-1214 EXP
GLOBE UNION GROUP INC
(Suby of GLOBE UNION INDUSTRIAL CORP.)
2500 Internationale Pkwy, Woodridge, IL 60517-5090
Tel (630) 679-1420 Founded/Ownrshp 2002
Sales 169.5MM^E EMP 233
SIC 3261 3432 7699 Plumbing fixtures, vitreous china; Plumbers' brass goods: drain cocks, faucets, spigots, etc.; General household repair services; Plumbing fixtures, vitreous china; Plumbers' brass goods: drain cocks, faucets, spigots, etc.; General household repair services
Prin: Dennis Dugas
VP: Joe Sell
VP: Keith Yurko
IT Man: Julius Szabo
Natl Sales: John Gummersall
Natl Sales: Chris Jajko
Natl Sales: Bill Tipps
VP Sls: Jeff Pratt
Mktg Mgr: Shane Ouyang
Sls Mgr: Ray Moulsdale

D-U-N-S 07-134-5375
GLOBE UNIVERSITY INC
8089 Globe Dr, Saint Paul, MN 55125-3388
Tel (651) 730-5100 Founded/Ownrshp 1948
Sales 58.6MM EMP 46
Accts Bomberg Roach & Hanson Pllc W
SIC 8244 Business college or school
Pr: Terry L Myhre
*VP: Kathryn Myhre
Netwrk Mgr: Adam Craft

D-U-N-S 61-531-3079 IMP
GLOBE WIRELESS LLC
INMARSAT
(Suby of INMARSAT PLC)
1571 Robert J Conlan Blvd, Palm Bay, FL 32905-3562
Tel (321) 309-1300 Founded/Ownrshp 2013
Sales 34.0MM^E EMP 107
SIC 4822 Telegraph & other communications; Electronic mail; Telegraph & other communications; Electronic mail
Pr: Robert Knudson
CFO: Tom Black
CFO: Darrin Eldridge
CFO: Roland Minnis
VP: Mike McNally
VP: Don Wamsley
Exec: Steve Goldberg
Exec: Carla Simmons
Snr Sftwr: Sean Butler
Snr Sftwr: Mark Simmons
CTO: Mark Witsaman

D-U-N-S 17-794-5870 IMP
GLOBECAST AMERICA INC
(Suby of ORANGE)
10525 Washington Blvd, Culver City, CA 90232-3311
Tel (212) 373-5140 Founded/Ownrshp 1993
Sales 94.4MM^E EMP 400^E
SIC 4841 Satellite master antenna systems services (SMATV); Satellite master antenna systems services (SMATV)
CEO: Michele Gosetti
*CEO: Lisa Coelho
*VP: Batrice De Lagrevol
*VP: Elisabeth Mazurie
Off Mgr: Sharon Dacosta

D-U-N-S 87-891-5701 IMP/EXP
GLOBECOMM SYSTEMS INC
(Suby of WASSERSTEIN COSMOS CO-INVEST LP) ★
45 Oser Ave, Hauppauge, NY 11788-3808
Tel (631) 231-9800 Founded/Ownrshp 2013
Sales 319.6MM EMP 500
Accts Ernst & Young Llp Jericho Ne
SIC 3663 4813 Satellites, communications; Telephone communication, except radio; Satellites, communications; Telephone communication, except radio
CEO: Keith A Hall
*CFO: Kevin Coffey
*Treas: Catherine Cantasano
*Ex VP: Thomas C Coyle
*Sr VP: Julia Hanft
Sr VP: Dwight R Hunsicker
*Sr VP: Paul J Johnson
Sr VP: Brian Morris
*Sr VP: Andrew Silberstein
VP: Ed Behan
VP: Dov Cydulkin
*VP: Kristen Harrison
VP: Scott Herschander
VP: Gerard Johnston
VP: Paul Knudsen
VP: Kenneth Maynard
*VP: Paul Scardino
VP: Walter Scharpf
Dir Soc: Terry Wieland
Dir Bus: Morshed Ali

D-U-N-S 84-892-1482
GLOBEFLEX CAPITAL LP
4365 Executive Dr Ste 720, San Diego, CA 92121-2126
Tel (858) 658-9060 Founded/Ownrshp 1994
Sales 20.4MM EMP 22
Accts Deloitte & Touche Llp Los Ang
SIC 6799 Investors; Investors
*CFO: Jennifer O'Connell

D-U-N-S 16-060-1923
GLOBENET CABOS SUBMARINOS AMERICA INC
5355 Town Center Rd # 1102, Boca Raton, FL 33486-1005
Tel (561) 314-0500 Founded/Ownrshp 2014
Sales 200.0MM EMP 57
SIC 4813 Local & long distance telephone communications; Data telephone communications; Local & long distance telephone communications; Data telephone communications
COO: Erick W Contag
IT Man: Marc Fortin
Netwrk Eng: Husam Eldawi
Netwrk Eng: Patrick Patric
Opers Mgr: Fernando Kato
Sls Dir: Sandy Tejera

D-U-N-S 01-013-4679
■ GLOBEOP FINANCIAL SERVICES LLC
(Suby of SS&C TECHNOLOGIES INC) ★
1 South Rd, Harrison, NY 10528-3309
Tel (914) 670-3600 Founded/Ownrshp 1999
Sales 59.1MM^E EMP 793^E
SIC 7372 Prepackaged software
CEO: William Stone
*COO: Vernon Barback
*CFO: Martin Veilleux
Ofcr: Zaslow Bryan
Sr VP: Dawn Giovi
Exec: Robert McGilvray
Exec: Yuliva Moskivina
Assoc Dir: Robert Borukhov
Assoc Dir: Stephanie Camp
Assoc Dir: Marcus Couture
Assoc Dir: Patti Griffin
Assoc Dir: Jonathan Hinkley
Assoc Dir: Michael Klein
Assoc Dir: Lean Lim
Assoc Dir: John McGurk
Assoc Dir: Caroline Stalley
Dir Bus: Johnine Kilgallon
Dir Bus: Louis Morgantini

D-U-N-S 08-754-9986
GLOBETROTTERS ENGINEERING CORP
300 S Wacker Dr Ste 200, Chicago, IL 60606-6672
Tel (312) 583-0816 Founded/Ownrshp 1973
Sales 35.1MM^E EMP 150
SIC 8711 8712 Civil engineering; Structural engineering; Mechanical engineering; Architectural engineering; Civil engineering; Structural engineering; Mechanical engineering; Architectural engineering
Pr: Niranjan Shah
VP: Rose Jennings
Sfty Mgr: John Paulius
Snr PM: Robert Hegstrom

D-U-N-S 07-418-6797
GLOBITECH INC
(Suby of SINO-AMERICAN SILICON PRODUCTS INC.)
200 W Fm 1417, Sherman, TX 75092-8002
Tel (903) 957-1999 Founded/Ownrshp 2008
Sales 47.4MM^E EMP 150
SIC 3674 Semiconductors & related devices; Semiconductors & related devices
Pr: Mark England
COO: Jeff Sheridan
VP: Rick Boston
VP: Steve Courtney
VP: Danny Kenney
Ql Cn Mgr: Kelly Davis
Sls Mgr: Robert Royalty

D-U-N-S 88-440-1845
GLOBIX CORP
2200 W Park Dr Ste 110, Westborough, MA 01581-3961
Tel (508) 616-7800 Founded/Ownrshp 1989
Sales 66.4MM EMP 199
SIC 4813 ;
Pr: Kurt Van Wagenen
Ch Bd: Ted S Lodge
COO: Henry Holcombe
CFO: Eric J Sandman
Sec: Gene M Bauer
VP: John P Stack

D-U-N-S 88-493-7215
GLOBOFORCE INC
(Suby of GLOBOFORCE GROUP PUBLIC LIMITED COMPANY)
144 Turnpike Rd Ste 310, Southborough, MA 01772-2127
Tel (508) 229-1500 Founded/Ownrshp 2007
Sales 25.5MM^E EMP 80
SIC 7371 Computer software development & applications
Pr: Eric Mosley
*CFO: Steve Cromwell
*Treas: Stephen Cromwell
*Chf Mktg O: Jennifer Smith
*Chf Mktg O: Charlie Ungashick
*VP: Grant Beckett
VP: Neal Bruce
VP: Kieran Conlon
VP: Brian Corey
VP: Chris French
VP: Gene Gainey
VP: Dave Haskell
*VP: Benedetto Miele
VP: Jessica Miller-Merrell
VP: Thad Peterson
VP: Jennifer Reimert
VP: John Smith

D-U-N-S 12-718-9124
GLOBTEK INC
186 Veterans Dr, Northvale, NJ 07647-2303
Tel (201) 784-1000 Founded/Ownrshp 1982
Sales 59.0MM^E EMP 400^E
SIC 3612 Specialty transformers; Specialty transformers
CEO: Anna Kaplan
COO: David Rakovsky
Rgnl Mgr: Julius Hirsch
IT Man: Gina Krakovyak
VP Mfg: Gino Cardillo
Mtls Mgr: John McNicol
VP Sls: Edward Seaman
Mktg Dir: Alix Paultre

D-U-N-S 13-910-5691
▲ GLOBUS MEDICAL INC
2560 Gen Armistead Ave, Audubon, PA 19403-5214
Tel (610) 930-1800 Founded/Ownrshp 2003
Sales 474.3MM EMP 900
Tkr Sym GMED Exch NYS
SIC 3841 Surgical & medical instruments; Surgical & medical instruments
Ch Bd: David C Paul
*Pr: David M Demski
Pr: A Brett Murphy
Pr: Anthony L Williams
CFO: Daniel T Scavilla
*Sr VP: David D Davidar
Area Mgr: Steve Kassis

Snr Sftwr: Jeffrey Forsyth
Snr Sftwr: Xun Qu
Sftwr Eng: John Garczynski
Sales Asso: Christine Boyd
Board of Directors: Daniel T Lemaitre, Robert W Liptak, Ann D Rhoads, James R Tobin, Kurt C Wheeler

D-U-N-S 14-475-9797
GLOBUS RELIEF
SUPPLY RESOURCE NETWORK
1775 W 1500 S, Salt Lake City, UT 84104-3832
Tel (801) 977-0444 Founded/Ownrshp 1996
Sales 34.7MM EMP 32
Accts Shaw & Co Bountiful Ut
SIC 8322 Individual & family services; Individual & family services
Pr: Ashley Robinson

D-U-N-S 14-809-9450 IMP/EXP
GLOCK INC
(Suby of GLOCK GESELLSCHAFT M.B.H.)
6000 Highlands Pkwy Se, Smyrna, GA 30082-7204
Tel (770) 432-1202 Founded/Ownrshp 1985
Sales 84.8MM^E EMP 220
SIC 3484 Pistols or pistol parts, 30 mm. & below; Pistols or pistol parts, 30 mm. & below
Pr: Gaston H Glock
Pr: Carlos Guevara
*CEO: Chad Mathis
*VP: Josh Dorsey
*VP: Gary Fletcher
VP: Paul Jannuzzo
Rgnl Mgr: Beau Phillips
Dist Mgr: Kyle Aspinwall
Dist Mgr: John Copeland
Dist Mgr: Dan Henderson
Dist Mgr: Jeff Jones

D-U-N-S 01-827-5156
GLOCKNER CHEVROLET CO
GLOCKNER CHEVY OLDS CADDY
4368 Us Route 23, Portsmouth, OH 45662
Tel (740) 353-2161 Founded/Ownrshp 1927
Sales 96.6MM EMP 181
SIC 5013 5172 5511

GLOCKNER CHEVY OLDS CADDY
See GLOCKNER CHEVROLET CO

D-U-N-S 18-857-3950
GLOCKNER OIL CO INC
(Suby of GLOCKNER CHEVROLET CO) ★
4407 Us Highway 23, Piketon, OH 45661-9703
Tel (740) 289-2979 Founded/Ownrshp 1975
Sales 50.1MM EMP 44
SIC 5172

D-U-N-S 78-402-3132
GLODYNE TECHNOSERVE INC
2700 Augustine Dr Ste 190, Santa Clara, CA 95054-2926
Tel (408) 340-5017 Founded/Ownrshp 2006
Sales 88.4MM^E EMP 1,600^E
SIC 7373 Computer integrated systems design
Pr: Haneef Sheikh
Sr VP: Vijay Sonawane

GLOPROFESSIONAL
See HAYDEN CALEEL LLC

D-U-N-S 94-358-6073 EXP
GLORIA APPAREL INC
256 W 38th St Fl 700, New York, NY 10018-9124
Tel (212) 947-0869 Founded/Ownrshp 1994
Sales 59.0MM EMP 10
SIC 2386 Coats & jackets, leather & sheep-lined; Coats & jackets, leather & sheep-lined
Pr: Young H Lee

GLORIA FERRER
See FREIXENET USA INC

GLORIA JEANS COFFEE USA
See GLORIA JEANS GOURMET COFFEES CORP

D-U-N-S 01-997-5200
GLORIA JEANS GOURMET COFFEES CORP
GLORIA JEANS COFFEE USA
(Suby of PRAISE INTERNATIONAL NORTH AMERICA INC) ★
14071 Stage Rd, Santa Fe Springs, CA 90670-5225
Tel (949) 413-2081 Founded/Ownrshp 2009
Sales 21.2MM^E EMP 140
SIC 5499 5149 Coffee; Groceries & related products
Pr: Carl Mount
*VP: Edward Apffel
VP: Steve Leach
*VP: Michael Zorehkey
Sls&Mrk Ex: Linda Eldridge

D-U-N-S 14-810-3257
GLORIANN FARMS INC
4600 S Tracy Blvd Ste 102, Tracy, CA 95377-8105
Tel (209) 834-0010 Founded/Ownrshp 2001
Sales 36.8MM EMP 250^E
SIC 0723 Vegetable packing services; Vegetable packing services
Pr: Mark R Bacchetti
*CFO: Jim Thoming

D-U-N-S 01-886-8872 IMP
GLORY GLOBAL SOLUTIONS INC
(Suby of GLORY LTD.)
3333 Warrenville Rd # 310, Lisle, IL 60532-9831
Tel (630) 577-1000 Founded/Ownrshp 2012
Sales 146.4MM^E EMP 267
SIC 5087 5046 5044 Service establishment equipment; Vending machines & supplies; Coin counters; Coin-operated equipment; Vending machines, coin-operated; Office equipment; Service establishment equipment; Vending machines & supplies; Coin counters; Coin-operated equipment; Vending machines, coin-operated; Office equipment
CEO: Chris Reagan
Treas: Shigeru Komastsubara
Ex VP: Masaki Kurabayashi
S&M/Dir: Joseph Ganorski

GLORYBEE FOODS
See GLORYBEE NATURAL SWEETENERS INC

D-U-N-S 80-822-9491 IMP
GLORYBEE FOODS INC
120 N Seneca Rd, Eugene, OR 97402-6524
Tel (541) 689-0913 *Founded/Ownrshp* 1975
Sales 28.7MM^E *EMP* 163
SIC 5499 Health & dietetic food stores
Prin: Richard T Turanski
COO: Jamie Stoller
QA Dir: Gary Powell
Dir IT: Joseph Cioffi
Netwrk Eng: Doug Boyer
Opers Mgr: Alan Turanski
Mktg Mgr: Bonnie Larson
Manager: Darrin West

D-U-N-S 07-072-7698 IMP/EXP
GLORYBEE NATURAL SWEETENERS INC
GLORYBEE FOODS
120 N Seneca Rd, Eugene, OR 97402-6524
Tel (541) 689-0913 *Founded/Ownrshp* 1975
Sales 31.1MM^E *EMP* 57^E
SIC 5149 5499 Honey; Health & dietetic food stores
Pr: Richard T Turanski
**Sec:* Patricia Turanski

D-U-N-S 87-745-9271
GLOTEL INC
(*Suby of* GORES GROUP LLC) ★
8700 W Bryn Mawr Ave 400n, Chicago, IL 60631-3642
Tel (312) 612-7480 *Founded/Ownrshp* 2012
Sales 37.7MM^E *EMP* 350
SIC 7363 Temporary help service
CEO: Michele Casey
Sales Exec: Rachel Ferguson
Sales Exec: Julia Heath
Natl Sales: Heather Walsh
Sls Dir: Lilah Wagner
Sales Asso: Arelis Baden

D-U-N-S 04-993-3641 IMP
GLOTFELTY ENTERPRISES INC (MD)
14161 Garrett Hwy, Oakland, MD 21550-4047
Tel (301) 334-3911 *Founded/Ownrshp* 1954
Sales 33.1MM *EMP* 120
Accts The Rodeheaver Group Pc Oak
SIC 5531 7534 5013 5014 Automotive & home supply stores; Automotive tires; Tire retreading & repair shops; Automotive supplies; Tires & tubes; Automobile tires & tubes; Truck tires & tubes
Pr: Gene H Glotfelty
**Sec:* Roger Glotfelty Jr
**VP:* Garth Glotfelty
**VP:* George Glotfelty
**VP:* Scott Glotfelty
**VP:* Steven Glotfelty

D-U-N-S 04-874-4692
GLOUCESTER CITY BOARD OF EDUCATION
520 Cumberland St, Gloucester City, NJ 08030-1923
Tel (856) 456-4250 *Founded/Ownrshp* 1900
Sales 22.9MM^E *EMP* 455
SIC 8211 9111 Public elementary school; Public senior high school; Mayors' offices; Public elementary school; Public senior high school; Mayors' offices
IT Man: Susan McComb

D-U-N-S 86-905-5145
GLOUCESTER CITY SCHOOL DIST
MARY ETHEL CASTELO SCHOOL
520 Cumberland St, Gloucester City, NJ 08030-1923
Tel (856) 456-7000 *Founded/Ownrshp* 1995
Sales 13.5MM^E *EMP* 300^E
SIC 8211 8741 School board; Management services; School board; Management services

GLOUCESTER COUNTY PUB SCHOOLS
See GLOUCESTER COUNTY SCHOOLS

D-U-N-S 15-957-4755
GLOUCESTER COUNTY SCHOOLS
GLOUCESTER COUNTY PUB SCHOOLS
6099 T C Walker Rd, Gloucester, VA 23061-4403
Tel (804) 693-5300 *Founded/Ownrshp* 1851
Sales 52.6MM^E *EMP* 1,100
Accts Robinson Farmer Cox Associat
SIC 8211 Public elementary & secondary schools; School board; Public elementary & secondary schools; School board
Dir Sec: Shirley Chirch

D-U-N-S 80-054-0325
GLOUCESTER COUNTY SPECIAL SERVICES SCHOOL DISTRICT
1340 Tanyard Rd, Sewell, NJ 08080-4220
Tel (856) 468-6530 *Founded/Ownrshp* 2007
Sales 56.3M *EMP* 563^E
SIC 8211 Elementary & secondary schools; Public elementary & secondary schools
Top Exec: Patrick Mulvenna
Pr Dir: Eileen Shute

D-U-N-S 12-267-2512
GLOUCESTER COUNTY VOCATIONAL-TECHNICAL SCHOOL DISTRICT
GCIT
1360 Tanyard Rd, Sewell, NJ 08080-4261
Tel (856) 468-1445 *Founded/Ownrshp* 1972
Sales 12.2MM^E *EMP* 300^E
SIC 8249 Vocational schools; Vocational schools

D-U-N-S 00-105-1473 IMP/EXP
GLOUCESTER ENGINEERING CO INC
G E C
(*Suby of* DAVIS-STANDARD LLC) ★
11 Dory Rd, Gloucester, MA 01930-2236
Tel (978) 281-1800 *Founded/Ownrshp* 1961, 2015
Sales 37.0MM^E *EMP* 100^E
SIC 3559 Plastics working machinery; Plastics working machinery
CEO: Rick Tattersfield
Pr: Carl Johnson
CFO: Bill Schmidt
VP: Mark Jones
VP Opers: Amanda Oelschlegel

D-U-N-S 17-654-7867
GLOUCESTER MARINE TERMINAL INC
101 S King St, Gloucester City, NJ 08030-1947
Tel (856) 742-3103 *Founded/Ownrshp* 1994
Sales 21.0MM^E *EMP* 350
SIC 4491 Marine terminals; Marine terminals
Pr: Leo Holt

GLOUCESTER PHARMACEUTICALS
See CELGENE CORP

D-U-N-S 07-979-9215
GLOUCESTER PUBLIC SCHOOLS
2 Blackburn Dr, Gloucester, MA 01930-2227
Tel (978) 281-9800 *Founded/Ownrshp* 2015
Sales 25.3MM^E *EMP* 620^E
SIC 8211 Public elementary & secondary schools
Teacher Pr: Michelle Harvey

D-U-N-S 12-321-6322
GLOUCESTER TERMINALS LLC
101 S King St, Gloucester City, NJ 08030-1947
Tel (856) 742-3000 *Founded/Ownrshp* 2001
Sales 34.1MM^E *EMP* 350
SIC 4491 4222 Docks, piers & terminals; Warehousing, cold storage or refrigerated; Docks, piers & terminals; Warehousing, cold storage or refrigerated
Sfty Dirs: Charles Gamel

D-U-N-S 07-553-6060
GLOUCESTER TOWNSHIP (INC)
MUNICIPAL HALL
1261 Chews Landing Rd, Clementon, NJ 08021-2807
Tel (856) 228-4000 *Founded/Ownrshp* 1695
Sales NA *EMP* 300^E
SIC 9111 Mayors' offices; Mayors' offices;
**Pr:* Glen Bianchini
CFO: Christie Ehret
Treas: Joan Hinski
Treas: Candace Prince
VP: Jim Forte

D-U-N-S 04-215-5028
GLOUCESTER TOWNSHIP BOARD OF EDUCATION
GLOUCESTER TOWNSHIP SCHOOL DST
17 Erial Rd, Blackwood, NJ 08012-3964
Tel (856) 227-1400 *Founded/Ownrshp* 1890
Sales 63.6MM^E *EMP* 1,400
SIC 8211 Public elementary & secondary schools; Public elementary & secondary schools
IT Man: Carl Gross

D-U-N-S 07-979-9129
GLOUCESTER TOWNSHIP PUBLIC SCHOOLS
17 Erial Rd, Blackwood, NJ 08012-3964
Tel (856) 227-1400 *Founded/Ownrshp* 2015
Sales 10.4MM^E *EMP* 1,115^E
SIC 8211 Public elementary & secondary schools

GLOUCESTER TOWNSHIP SCHOOL DST
See GLOUCESTER TOWNSHIP BOARD OF EDUCATION

GLOUSTER MANOR HEALTH CARE
See GERI-CARE INC

D-U-N-S 00-319-6813
GLOVER CONSTRUCTION CO INC (NC)
4493 Us Highway 301, Pleasant Hill, NC 27866-9687
Tel (252) 536-2660 *Founded/Ownrshp* 1954
Sales 26.1MM^E *EMP* 90
SIC 1794 1623

D-U-N-S 03-245-4167
GLOVER OIL CO INC
3109 Main St, Melbourne, FL 32901-8021
Tel (321) 723-7461 *Founded/Ownrshp* 1967
Sales 53.8MM^E *EMP* 25
SIC 5171 5172

GLOVER TRUCK PARTS & EQUIPMENT
See GLOVERS TRANSMISSION AND REAR END INC

D-U-N-S 09-341-7780
GLOVERS TRANSMISSION AND REAR END INC
GLOVER TRUCK PARTS & EQUIPMENT
1200 Baucum Industrial Dr, North Little Rock, AR 72117-5274
Tel (501) 945-2000 *Founded/Ownrshp* 1979
Sales 33.3MM^E *EMP* 70
SIC 5012 5015 7538 7532 Automobiles & other motor vehicles; Motor vehicle parts, used; Truck engine repair, except industrial; General truck repair; Top & body repair & paint shops; Automobiles & other motor vehicles; Motor vehicle parts, used; Truck engine repair, except industrial; General truck repair; Top & body repair & paint shops
Pr: James H Glover
**Sec:* Rus Carlley
**VP:* Rustin W Glover
**VP:* Armin Turner
Off Mgr: Theresa Hull

D-U-N-S 10-005-5391
GLOVERSVILLE ENLARGED SCHOOL DISTRICT
234 Lincoln St, Gloversville, NY 12078-1935
Tel (518) 775-5700 *Founded/Ownrshp* 1968
Sales 29.9MM^E *EMP* 550
SIC 8211 Public elementary & secondary schools; Public elementary & secondary schools
**Treas:* Cathy Meher
Schl Brd P: Robert Curtis
Psych: Mary Lockwood
HC Dir: Michael Demagistris

D-U-N-S 06-054-1513
GLOVERSVILLE EXTENDED CARE & NURSING HOME CO INC (NY)
99 E State St, Gloversville, NY 12078-1203
Tel (518) 773-5665 *Founded/Ownrshp* 1970
Sales 18.8M *EMP* 800
SIC 8059 Nursing home, except skilled & intermediate care facility; Nursing home, except skilled & intermediate care facility

D-U-N-S 16-899-2159 EXP
GLOVIS ALABAMA LLC
300 Hyundai Blvd, Montgomery, AL 36105-9616
Tel (334) 244-2025 *Founded/Ownrshp* 2009
Sales 29.2MM^E *EMP* 50^E
SIC 5013 Automotive engines & engine parts

D-U-N-S 11-540-7525
GLOVIS AMERICA INC
(*Suby of* HYUNDAI GLOVIS CO., LTD.)
17305 Von Karman Ave # 200, Irvine, CA 92614-6674
Tel (714) 435-2960 *Founded/Ownrshp* 2002
Sales 32.7MM^E *EMP* 80
SIC 4731 Freight forwarding; Freight forwarding
Pr: Kyung B Kim
**COO:* Glenn Clift
Dir IT: Art Lim
Ql Cn Mgr: David Molina
Snr Mgr: Herbert Lee
Snr Mgr: Jason Woo

D-U-N-S 02-026-4172 IMP/EXP
GLOW INDUSTRIES INC (OH)
12962 Eckel Junction Rd, Perrysburg, OH 43551-1309
Tel (419) 872-4772 *Founded/Ownrshp* 1974
Sales 27.3MM^E *EMP* 58
SIC 5199 5331 Variety store merchandise; Variety stores
Pr: David P Glowacki
**VP:* Jason Glowacki

D-U-N-S 78-243-8253
▲ GLOWPOINT INC
1776 N Lincoln St # 1300, Denver, CO 80203-1017
Tel (303) 640-3838 *Founded/Ownrshp* 2000
Sales 32.1MM *EMP* 126
Tkr Sym GLOW *Exch* ASE
SIC 4899 4813 Data communication services; Data telephone communications; Voice telephone communications; ; Data communication services; Data telephone communications; Voice telephone communications;
Pr: Peter Holst
**Ch Bd:* Patrick J Lombardi
CFO: David Clark
Sr VP: Gary Iles

D-U-N-S 79-265-5826
GLP ASPHALT LLC
ASPHALT HAWAII
91-550 Malakole St, Kapolei, HI 96707-1809
Tel (808) 864-7000 *Founded/Ownrshp* 2006
Sales 40.0MM *EMP* 5
SIC 1771 Blacktop (asphalt) work
Pr: D Ick Levins

GLR
See GREAT LAKES ADVANCED RECYCLING CORP

GLS
See GREAT LAKES SYNERGY CORP

D-U-N-S 05-545-8780
GLS COMPANIES
1280 Energy Park Dr, Saint Paul, MN 55108-5106
Tel (651) 917-9927 *Founded/Ownrshp* 1971
Sales 28.2MM^E *EMP* 100
SIC 2752 Commercial printing, offset; Commercial printing, offset
Pr: Gary Garner
Pr: Duane Pogue
Chf Mktg O: Jason Reynolds
IT Man: Mike McCarron
Netwrk Mgr: Terry Peterson
Sales Exec: Greg King
Sales Exec: Ralph Tuff

D-U-N-S 13-063-1864
GLS COMPANIES
6845 Winnetka Cir, Brooklyn Park, MN 55428-1537
Tel (763) 535-7277 *Founded/Ownrshp* 1984
Sales 94.3MM^E *EMP* 292^E
SIC 2752 Commercial printing, offset; Commercial printing, offset
CEO: Gary Garner
CFO: Mike McPartland
Treas: Keith Sweat
Chf Mktg O: Randy Peterson
VP: Doug Hammerseng
VP: Jeanne Haro
VP: Mike Koshiol
VP: Nancy Kunkel
VP: Frank Salamone
VP: Jayme Wisely
CTO: Frank Powell

D-U-N-S 07-847-7159
GLS COMPOSITES DISTIBUTION CORP (IL)
COMPOSITES ONE
(*Suby of* GLS) ★
85 W Algonquin Rd Ste 600, Arlington Heights, IL 60005-4421
Tel (800) 621-8003 *Founded/Ownrshp* 1997
Sales 112.3MM^E *EMP* 372
SIC 5169 Chemicals & allied products; Chemicals & allied products
Pr: Steven L Dehmlow
Sls Mgr: Mark Kirk

D-U-N-S 84-977-2207 EXP
GLSD FLORIDA HOLDINGS INC
OCEAN POTION
851 Greensboro Rd, Cocoa, FL 32926-4516
Tel (321) 633-4644 *Founded/Ownrshp* 2012
Sales 75.0MM^E *EMP* 180
SIC 2844 Suntan lotions & oils; Suntan lotions & oils
CEO: Steve Taylor
**CFO:* Gerald Woelcke

GLT INTERNATIONAL
See GREAT LAKES TAPE CORP

GLT PACKAGING
See GREAT LAKES-TRIAD PLASTIC PACKAGING CORP

D-U-N-S 10-147-4505
▲ GLU MOBILE INC
500 Howard St Ste 300, San Francisco, CA 94105-3027
Tel (415) 800-6100 *Founded/Ownrshp* 2001
Sales 223.1MM *EMP* 653^E
Tkr Sym GLUU *Exch* NGS
SIC 7371 3944 Custom computer programming services; Computer software writing services; Computer code authors; Electronic games & toys; Custom computer programming services; Computer software writing services; Computer code authors; Electronic games & toys
Pr: Niccolo M De Masi
Ch Bd: William J Miller
Pr: Nick Earl
COO: Eric R Ludwig
Ofcr: Tim Wilson
Sr VP: Spencer Tucker
VP: Kal Iyer
VP: Scott J Leichtner
VP: Christian Limon
VP: Sheila Ryan
Dir Bus: Juan He
Board of Directors: Lorne Abony, Eric R Ball, Greg Brandeau, Ann Mather, Benjamin T Smith IV

GLUEK BREWING COMPANY
See COLD SPRING BREWING CO

D-U-N-S 07-186-8509
GLUMAC
150 California St Fl 3, San Francisco, CA 94111-4567
Tel (415) 398-7667 *Founded/Ownrshp* 1977
Sales 50.9MM^E *EMP* 195
Accts Perkins & Company Pc Portl
SIC 8711 Consulting engineer; Consulting engineer
CEO: Steven A Straus
**CFO:* Richard Thomas
**VP:* Angela Sheehan
Mng Dir: Paul Tia A

D-U-N-S 05-725-0912 IMP
GLUNT INDUSTRIES INC
319 N River Rd Nw, Warren, OH 44483-2248
Tel (330) 399-7585 *Founded/Ownrshp* 1971
Sales 32.7MM^E *EMP* 125
SIC 3599 3549 3444 Machine shop, jobbing & repair; Custom machinery; Metalworking machinery; Sheet metalwork; Machine shop, jobbing & repair; Custom machinery; Metalworking machinery; Sheet metalwork
Pr: Dennis Glunt
**CFO:* Stuart Gladstone
**VP:* Harold Glunt
**Prin:* Gary Shells

D-U-N-S 79-092-3119 IMP
GLUTENFREEDA FOODS INC
200 E Washington Ave, Burlington, WA 98233-1729
Tel (360) 755-1300 *Founded/Ownrshp* 2006
Sales 26.7MM^E *EMP* 65
SIC 5149 Natural & organic foods
CEO: Yvonne Gifford
Chf Mktg O: Jessica Hale

D-U-N-S 86-883-3851
GLUTH CONTRACT FLOORING LLC
12201 Cyrus Way Ste 102, Mukilteo, WA 98275-5735
Tel (425) 493-9100 *Founded/Ownrshp* 2007
Sales 500.0MM *EMP* 3
SIC 1752 Floor laying & floor work; Floor laying & floor work

D-U-N-S 80-848-1977
GLV US HOLDING INC
(*Suby of* GL&V CANADA INC)
1 Cellu Dr, Nashua, NH 03063-1008
Tel (603) 882-2711 *Founded/Ownrshp* 2010
Sales 64.6MM^E *EMP* 355
SIC 3554 Paper industries machinery; Paper industries machinery
Pr: Laurent Verreault
**Treas:* Marc Barbeau
**VP:* Richard Verreauot

D-U-N-S 02-743-1444
GLY CONSTRUCTION INC
G L Y
200 112th Ave Ne Ste 300, Bellevue, WA 98004-5878
Tel (425) 451-8877 *Founded/Ownrshp* 2001
Sales 227.4MM *EMP* 600
Accts Berntson Porter & Company Pll
SIC 1542 Commercial & office building, new construction; Commercial & office building, new construction
Pr: Jim Karambelas
**CFO:* Steve Peterson
**Ex VP:* Ted Herb
**Ex VP:* Mark Kane
VP: Joni Baker
VP: Bob Irwin
**VP:* Dale King
Exec: Marc Everson
Exec: Bryce Taylor
**Prin:* Bill Dejarlais
**Prin:* Jim Elliott

D-U-N-S 18-977-9135
GLY-TECH SERVICES INC
2054 Paxton St, Harvey, LA 70058-5905
Tel (504) 348-8566 *Founded/Ownrshp* 1987
Sales 52.7MM^E *EMP* 90
SIC 1389 7353 8742 5084 5169 Bailing, cleaning, swabbing & treating of wells; Oil field equipment, rental or leasing; Management consulting services; Petroleum industry machinery; Chemicals & allied products
Pr: Mark Middleton
**Pr:* Rockwell Buras

D-U-N-S 01-331-4952
GLYNLYON INC
300 N Mckemy Ave, Chandler, AZ 85226-2618
Tel (480) 940-0801 *Founded/Ownrshp* 2008
Sales 89.6MM^E *EMP* 500
SIC 3999 Education aids, devices & supplies
Pr: Robert J Campbell Jr
Pr: Ken Roberts
Pr: Jen Salta
**Treas:* Beth Te Grotenhuis
VP: David Austin
VP: Alan Christopherson
VP: Leonor Sebastia
Snr Ntwrk: Isaac Carbajal
IT Man: Patrick Smith
IT Man: Boyue Tipp

D-U-N-S 19-321-5704
GLYNN COUNTY BOARD OF EDUCATION
1313 Egmont St, Brunswick, GA 31520-7244
Tel (912) 267-4100 *Founded/Ownrshp* 1873
Sales 100.8MM^E *EMP* 1,800
Accts Karp Ronning & Tindol Pc
SIC 8211 Public elementary & secondary schools; School board
Ch Bd: Hank Yeargan
HC Dir: Susan Barber

D-U-N-S 96-802-1712
GLYNN COUNTY SCHOOL SYSTEM
1313 Egmont St, Brunswick, GA 31520-7244
Tel (912) 267-4100 *Founded/Ownrshp* 2011
Sales 70.1MM^E *EMP* 1,806^E
SIC 8211 Public elementary & secondary schools
MIS Dir: Debbie James
Dir IT: Michael Hall
IT Man: Francis Harris
Pr Dir: Jim Weidhaas

D-U-N-S 60-292-3922
GLYNN DEVINS INC
GLYNNS DEVINS ADVERTISING AND
11230 College Blvd, Overland Park, KS 66210-2797
Tel (913) 491-0600 *Founded/Ownrshp* 1987
Sales 34.8MM *EMP* 130
SIC 7311

D-U-N-S 60-837-8105
GLYNN ELECTRIC INC
11 Resnik Rd Ste 1, Plymouth, MA 02360-7231
Tel (508) 732-8933 *Founded/Ownrshp* 1986
Sales 43.5MM^E *EMP* 130
Accts Feeley & Driscoll Pc Bosto
SIC 1731 General electrical contractor; General electrical contractor
Pr: Matthew P Glynn
**Sec:* Michael Glynn
Dir Bus: Andrew Sheehan
Off Admin: Susan Curley
Trfc Dir: Amanda Williams
Opers Mgr: Alex Rodriguez
Board of Directors: Karen Mahoney

GLYNN JOHNSON
See VON DUPRIN LLC

D-U-N-S 03-407-1993
GLYNN SMITH CHEV INC (AL)
GLYNN SMITH CHVLET- JEEP EAGLE
600 Columbus Pkwy, Opelika, AL 36801-5934
Tel (334) 749-7970 *Founded/Ownrshp* 1918
Sales 21.2MM^E *EMP* 50
SIC 5511 Automobiles, new & used; Automobiles, new & used
Pr: Roger D McCreless
**VP:* Glynn Smith
Admn Mgr: Jody Noles
Sls Mgr: Mike Core
Sls Mgr: Marc Jeter
Sls Mgr: Mike Lee
Sales Asso: Harold Bonner
Sales Asso: Kevin Holloway
Sales Asso: Steve Moore

GLYNN SMITH CHVLET- JEEP EAGLE
See GLYNN SMITH CHEV INC

GLYNNS DEVINS ADVERTISING AND
See GLYNN DEVINS INC

GLYT
See GENLYTE GROUP INC

GM
See GIL-MAR MANUFACTURING CO

GM
See GRANT COUNTY MEMORIAL HOSPITAL (INC)

D-U-N-S 14-827-6900
GM & R CONSTRUCTION CO INC
2208 Mclaurin St, Waveland, MS 39576-2664
Tel (228) 467-0872 *Founded/Ownrshp* 1984
Sales 24.4MM *EMP* 4
SIC 1542 1623 Commercial & office building, new construction; Water, sewer & utility lines
Pr: Henry Martinez
Sec: Darlene Martinez

D-U-N-S 83-123-2371 IMP
■ **GM COMPONENTS HOLDINGS LLC**
GMCH
(*Suby of* GENERAL MOTORS LLC) ★
300 Renaissance Ctr, Detroit, MI 48243-1402
Tel (313) 556-5000 *Founded/Ownrshp* 2009
Sales 285.9MM^E *EMP* 1,053^E
SIC 3711 3714 Automobile assembly, including specialty automobiles; Truck & tractor truck assembly; Military motor vehicle assembly; Motor vehicle parts & accessories; Automobile assembly, including specialty automobiles; Truck & tractor truck assembly; Military motor vehicle assembly; Motor vehicle parts & accessories
COO: Jean-Claude Ghiotti
CFO: Archie Turner
Ofcr: Chester N Watso
**VP:* Niharika Taskar Ramdev
Dir Risk M: Rick Satawa
Assoc Dir: Mike Hegener
Assoc Dir: Michael Schmehl
Comm Man: Matthew Rattray-Wood
Area Mgr: Sherrell Kovach
Area Mgr: Michael Sager
Area Mgr: Felix Wu

GM FINANCIAL
See AMERICREDIT FINANCIAL SERVICES INC

D-U-N-S 06-235-4642
GM FREIGHT INC
J.D.S. TRANSPRTN/LOG ADV
25299 Brest, Taylor, MI 48180-6850
Tel (734) 946-1007 *Founded/Ownrshp* 1984
Sales 21.8MM^E *EMP* 100
SIC 4213 4212 Trucking, except local; Local trucking, without storage
Pr: Gary D Mc Cloe
**VP:* Ann Marie Mc Cloe
Genl Mgr: Chris Barnston

D-U-N-S 18-629-6062
■ **GM GLOBAL TECHNOLOGY OPERATIONS INC**
GMGTO
(*Suby of* GENERAL MOTORS LLC) ★
300 Renaissance Ctr, Detroit, MI 48243-1402
Tel (313) 665-3988 *Founded/Ownrshp* 2009
Sales 15.1MM^E *EMP* 300
SIC 8711 Engineering services; Engineering services
Ch: Tom Stephens

D-U-N-S 78-726-3904
GM JOHNSON COMPANIES INC
655 Landmark Dr, Arnold, MO 63010-4626
Tel (636) 296-3300 *Founded/Ownrshp* 1991
Sales 62.1MM^E *EMP* 250^E
SIC 1622 1629 Bridge construction; Dams, waterways, docks & other marine construction; Bridge construction; Dams, waterways, docks & other marine construction
Pr: William S Johnson

D-U-N-S 00-925-5423 IMP
GM NAMEPLATE INC
SUPERGRAPHICS
13725 Sw Millikan Way, Beaverton, OR 97005-2322
Tel (206) 284-2200 *Founded/Ownrshp* 1954
Sales 213.5MM^E *EMP* 1,200
SIC 3479 2679 3679

GM2
See GROUP MANAGEMENT 0002 LLC

GMA
See GEORGIA MUNICIPAL ASSOCIATION INC

D-U-N-S 55-746-0623 IMP
GMA ACCESSORIES INC
CAPELLI OF NY
1 E 33rd St Fl 9, New York, NY 10016-5011
Tel (212) 684-3344 *Founded/Ownrshp* 1986
Sales 110.2MM *EMP* 250
Accts Holtz Rubenstein Reminick Llp
SIC 5137 5139 Women's & children's accessories; Shoes; Women's & children's accessories; Shoes
Pr: George Altirs
**CFO:* Salvatore Mancino
**VP:* Masoud Altirs
Telecom Ex: Hani Afif

D-U-N-S 02-274-8961
GMA CONSTRUCTION INC
16460 Sw 72nd Ave Bldg 6, Portland, OR 97224-7752
Tel (503) 352-1971 *Founded/Ownrshp* 1978
Sales 21.0MM^E *EMP* 45^E
SIC 1752 Access flooring system installation; Access flooring system installation
Pr: Gregory Allen
Off Mgr: Craig Johnisee

GMAC
See BEDFORD WEAVING INC

GMAC
See ALLY INSURANCE HOLDINGS INC

GMAC
See GRADUATE MANAGEMENT ADMISSION COUNCIL INC

GMAC
See AMINMADANI FAID

D-U-N-S 07-462-7428
■ **GMAC HOME SERVICES INC**
(*Suby of* BROOKFIELD RESIDENTIAL SERVICES LTD)
4 Walnut Grove Dr, Horsham, PA 19044-2201
Tel (215) 682-4600 *Founded/Ownrshp* 2008
Sales 17.2MM^E *EMP* 350
SIC 6531 7389 Real estate brokers & agents; Relocation service; Real estate brokers & agents; Relocation service
Pr: John B Bearden
**CFO:* Brian Peterson
**VP:* Lynn Grassonoon
Off Mgr: Kendra Lutz
Snr Mgr: Adrienne Fox

GMAC INSURANCE
See BRADLEY & PARKER INC

GMAC INSURANCE
See MID HUTSON VALLEY CREDIT UNION

GMAC INSURANCE
See MORSTAN GENERAL INSURANCE AGENCY INC

GMAC INSURANCE
See W WELLS HAROLD & SON INC

GMAC INSURANCE
See LAWLEY SERVICE INC

GMAC INSURANCE
See FIRST NIAGARA RISK MANAGEMENT INC

GMAC INSURANCE
See CHARLES L CRANE AGENCY CO

GMAC INSURANCE
See CYI HOLDINGS INC

GMAC INSURANCE
See NATIONAL GENERAL INSURANCE CO

GMAC INSURANCE
See BAILEY & HASKELL ASSOCIATES INC

GMAC INSURANCE
See SENN DUNN MARSH & ROLAND LLC

GMAC INSURANCE
See AL BOENKER INSURANCE AGENCY INC

GMAC INSURANCE
See AAA SOUTHERN PENNSYLVANIA

GMAC INSURANCE
See NATIONAL GENERAL MANAGEMENT CORP

GMAC INSURANCE
See SOVEREIGN INSURANCE GROUP

D-U-N-S 13-920-6783
■ **GMAC MORTGAGE GROUP LLC**
(*Suby of* ALLY FINANCIAL INC) ★
4 Walnut Grove Dr, Horsham, PA 19044-2201
Tel (215) 682-1000 *Founded/Ownrshp* 2006
Sales 612.4MM^E *EMP* 10,300
SIC 6211 Dealers, security; Dealers, security
CEO: David M Applegate
Sales Asso: Geralyn Behring
Sales Asso: Donna Matheis

D-U-N-S 04-396-7496
■ **GMAC MORTGAGE LLC**
(*Suby of* GMAC MORTGAGE GROUP LLC) ★
4 Walnut Grove Dr, Horsham, PA 19044-2201
Tel (215) 682-1000 *Founded/Ownrshp* 1985
Sales NA *EMP* 7,500
Accts Pricewaterhousecoopers Llp Ne
SIC 6162 Mortgage bankers; Mortgage bankers
Comm Dir: Jeannine Bruin
Area Mgr: Frank Dimaio

D-U-N-S 18-908-8768
■ **GMAC MORTGAGE SECURITIES INC**
(*Suby of* GMAC MORTGAGE GROUP LLC) ★
1100 Virginia Dr, Fort Washington, PA 19034-3204
Tel (215) 682-1000 *Founded/Ownrshp* 2011
Sales 92.5MM^E *EMP* 500
SIC 6211 Dealers, security; Dealers, security
Pr: Michael O'Brien
Pr: Michael Brien
Rgnl Mgr: Scott Medrow

D-U-N-S 13-246-2391
■ **GMAC RE CORP**
(*Suby of* M I C) ★
6000 Midlantic Dr 200s, Mount Laurel, NJ 08054-1516
Tel (856) 359-2400 *Founded/Ownrshp* 1990
Sales NA *EMP* 130
SIC 6321 Reinsurance carriers, accident & health; Reinsurance carriers, accident & health
Pr: Arturo M Raschbaum
**Ex VP:* David L Adams
**Ex VP:* Stephen Diperi
**Ex VP:* John Marshaleck
**Ex VP:* Karen Schmitt
**Sr VP:* Thomas Hyghet
VP: Ed Halligan
Genl Couns: William Solomon

D-U-N-S 82-825-9239
▲ **GMACCH INVESTOR LLC**
9 W 57th St, New York, NY 10019-2701
Tel (212) 750-8300 *Founded/Ownrshp* 2008
Sales 1.0MMM^E *EMP* 2,003
SIC 6799 Real estate investors, except property operators; Real estate investors, except property operators

D-U-N-S 08-839-5165 IMP/EXP
GMB NORTH AMERICA INC
GMB WEST
(*Suby of* GMB CORPORATION)
100 Herrod Blvd, Dayton, NJ 08810-1528
Tel (609) 655-2422 *Founded/Ownrshp* 2004
Sales 37.5MM^E *EMP* 80
SIC 5013 5084 Truck parts & accessories; Industrial machinery & equipment; Water pumps (industrial)
CEO: Bongjip Koo
**Ch Bd:* Karl Yazaki
CFO: Thomas Kreimer
CFO: Senya Nishijima
**Ex VP:* Ted Matsumoto
Sr VP: Babuji Ambikapathy
QA Dir: Edward Gullans
IT Man: Hector Guevara
IT Man: Kiran Salgarkar
Sls Mgr: Rodrigo Ajates
Snr Mgr: Stella Kaplansky

GMB WEST
See GMB NORTH AMERICA INC

D-U-N-S 01-939-6795 EXP
GMC HARDWOODS INC
30 Springdale Ave, Dover, MA 02030-2374
Tel (508) 785-1140 *Founded/Ownrshp* 1965
Sales 22.4MM *EMP* 12^E
SIC 5031

GMC TRUCK
See ALLEN USED CARS LLC

GMC TRUCKS
See SCRANTON MOTORS INC

GMCH
See GM COMPONENTS HOLDINGS LLC

GMCS
See GREEN MTN CONCERT SERVICES INC

D-U-N-S 03-252-9778
GMF INDUSTRIES INC (FL)
G M F
4600 Drane Field Rd, Lakeland, FL 33811-1216
Tel (863) 646-5081 *Founded/Ownrshp* 1982
Sales 23.6MM^E *EMP* 90
SIC 3449 3599 Miscellaneous metalwork; Machine shop, jobbing & repair
Pr: Vincent Larry Norman
VP: Andy Norman
**VP:* Spencer A Norman
Dir IT: Larry Norman
Prd Mgr: Tommy Newberry
Prd Mgr: Jeremy Turner
Ql Cn Mgr: Greg Brakefield
Sls Mgr: Jason Hall

D-U-N-S 08-854-4296
■ **GMFS LLC**
GINGER MAE FINANCIAL SERVICES
(*Suby of* ZFC HONEYBEE TRS LLC) ★
7389 Florida Blvd 200a, Baton Rouge, LA 70806-4657
Tel (225) 214-5000 *Founded/Ownrshp* 2014
Sales NA *EMP* 140^E
SIC 6163 Mortgage brokers arranging for loans, using money of others; Mortgage brokers arranging for loans, using money of others
Ofcr: Robin Campbell
Sr VP: Jeff Weston
Sr VP: Molly Wills
VP: Raul Murria
Opers Mgr: Mike Sorrells
Ql Cn Mgr: Robert McGimsey
Genl Couns: Byron Kantrow

D-U-N-S 18-682-3316
GMG HEALTH SYSTEMS LTD
GONZABA MEDICAL GROUP
720 Pleasanton Rd, San Antonio, TX 78214-1306
Tel (210) 334-2800 *Founded/Ownrshp* 2000
Sales 31.0MM^E *EMP* 215
SIC 8011 Surgeon; Surgeon
Prin: William Gonzaba
COO: Ruben Cardenas
COO: Mark Mehlen
CFO: Cristina Arredondo
CFO: Elva Artega
CFO: Marshall Odowd
VP: Larry Norman
VP: Mary Unger
Exec: Belinda Fernandez
Ex Dir: Patrick Looney
Dir IT: Robin Syring

D-U-N-S 83-180-7594
GMG HOLDINGS LLC
5275 Sinclair Rd, Columbus, OH 43229-5042
Tel (614) 841-4500 *Founded/Ownrshp* 2008
Sales 34.3MM^E *EMP* 650^E
SIC 6719 Investment holding companies, except banks
CFO: Tim Seils

D-U-N-S 05-571-2707
■ **GMG MOTORS INC** (CA)
BMW OF SAN DIEGO
(*Suby of* PENSKE AUTOMOTIVE GROUP INC) ★
5090 Kearny Mesa Rd, San Diego, CA 92111-2101
Tel (858) 560-5050 *Founded/Ownrshp* 1971, 2001
Sales 42.4MM^E *EMP* 120
SIC 5511 Automobiles, new & used; Automobiles, new & used
Pr: Roger Penske
Genl Mgr: Skip Gartin
Sls Mgr: Mike Gartin

GMGTO
See GM GLOBAL TECHNOLOGY OPERATIONS INC

D-U-N-S 12-477-5359
■ **GMH COMMUNITIES TRUST**
(*Suby of* AMERICAN CAMPUS COMMUNITIES INC) ★
10 Campus Blvd, Newtown Square, PA 19073-3200
Tel (610) 355-8000 *Founded/Ownrshp* 2008
Sales 10.3MM^E *EMP* 1,084
SIC 6798 6513 8742 Real estate investment trusts; Apartment building operators; Real estate consultant; Real estate investment trusts; Apartment building operators; Real estate consultant
Ch Bd: Gary M Holloway Sr
Pr: Joseph M Coyle
Pr: John Deriggi
Pr: Bruce F Robinson
CFO: Dennis J O'Leary
Trst: James W Eastood
Ex VP: Joseph Macchione
Mktg Dir: Michele Cohen

D-U-N-S 96-179-0461
GMH VENTURES LLC
10 Campus Blvd, Newtown Square, PA 19073-3200
Tel (610) 355-8087 *Founded/Ownrshp* 2008
Sales 38.3MM^E *EMP* 161^E
SIC 6799 Investors; Investors
Pr: Dennis J Oleary
VP: Anthony D'Elia

GMI, A DIVISION OF AVAR
See AVAR CONSTRUCTION INC

D-U-N-S 06-409-7637 IMP
GMI COMPANIES INC
GHENT MANUFACTURING
2999 Henkle Dr, Lebanon, OH 45036-9260
Tel (513) 932-3445 *Founded/Ownrshp* 1976
Sales 20.7MM^E *EMP* 160
SIC 2531 2493 2599 2541 2521 2522 Blackboards, wood; Bulletin boards, wood; Bulletin boards, cork; Boards: planning, display, notice; Showcases, except refrigerated: wood; Panel systems & partitions (free-standing), office: wood; Panel systems & partitions, office: except wood; Blackboards, wood; Bulletin boards, wood; Bulletin boards, cork; Boards: planning, display, notice; Showcases, except refrigerated: wood; Panel systems & partitions (free-standing), office: wood; Panel systems & partitions, office: except wood
Ch: George L Leasure
VP: Mark Leasure
IT Man: Barb McDaniel
Manager: Frank Digiovanni
Sls Mgr: Fred Napier
Sls Mgr: Connie Ollish

D-U-N-S 00-601-9947
GMI COMPOSITES INC (MI)
1355 W Sherman Blvd, Muskegon, MI 49441-3538
Tel (231) 755-1611 Founded/Ownrshp 1920, 1984
Sales 25.4MME EMP 62
SIC 3089 Molding primary plastic
Pr: Bob Brady
*Sec: Jerry Dykstra
*Prin: Charles Brady
*Prin: Louis Simoncini
Genl Mgr: John Barlow
Sls Mgr: Aidan Brady

D-U-N-S 19-465-4422 IMP
GMI HOLDINGS INC
GENIE COMPANY, THE
(Suby of OVERHEAD DOOR CORP) ★
1 Door Dr, Mount Hope, OH 44660
Tel (330) 821-5360 Founded/Ownrshp 1994
Sales 97.0MME EMP 1,000
SIC 3699 3635 Door opening & closing devices, electrical; Household vacuum cleaners; Door opening & closing devices, electrical; Household vacuum cleaners
Pr: Mike Kridel
VP: Kim Blair
*VP: Craig Smith
*Prin: Carl Adrien

D-U-N-S 15-420-6932
GMK ASSOCIATES INC
1201 Main St Ste 2100, Columbia, SC 29201-3230
Tel (803) 256-0000 Founded/Ownrshp 1977
Sales 40.0MME EMP 125
SIC 8712 Architectural engineering; Architectural engineering
Pr: Tripp Berry
*Ch Bd: Thomas P Monahan
*Pr: Bruce Barragan
*Ex VP: P M Berry
VP: Bryant Brown
Adv Bd Mbr: Jerome Simons
Mktg Dir: Jeff Neuman
Art Dir: Cheryl Jackson
Snr PM: John Caruk
Snr Mgr: John Whetstone

GMKS AQUISITION
See SCHEBLER CO

GMLAW.COM
See GREENSPOON MARDER PA

D-U-N-S 18-486-1235
GMMB INC
3050 K St Nw Ste 100, Washington, DC 20007-5161
Tel (202) 338-8700 Founded/Ownrshp 1983
Sales 35.7MME EMP 180
SIC 8743 8742 Public relations & publicity; Management consulting services; Public relations & publicity; Management consulting services
Pr: James Margolis
COO: Stephens Brad
*CFO: Bill Brocato
Treas: David Mitchell
*Sr VP: Siobhan McCready Bunaes
Sr VP: Siobhan Bunaes
*Sr VP: Kelly Carey
*Sr VP: Adam Ferrari
Sr VP: Ellen Frawley
Sr VP: Christopher Keefe
Sr VP: Alison Kruzel
Sr VP: Jeff Martin
Sr VP: Alyson McColl
Sr VP: Susan D Michels
Sr VP: Chrissy Russillo
Sr VP: Delacey Skinner
VP: Michelle Austin
VP: Maru Becker
VP: Jen Farber
VP: Christine Glunz
VP: Terrance Green

GMO
See GRANTHAM MAYO VAN OTTERLOO & CO LLC

GMP CABLE TV
See GANS COMMUNICATIONS LP

D-U-N-S 01-052-2910
GMP EMPLOYERS RETIREE TRUST
5245 Big Pine Way Ste 200, Fort Myers, FL 33907-5924
Tel (239) 936-6242 Founded/Ownrshp 1968
Sales 51.5MM EMP 23
Accts Hill Barth & King Llc Fort My
SIC 6733 Trusts, except educational, religious, charity: management; Trusts, except educational, religious, charity: management
Ex Dir: Jim Chitwood

D-U-N-S 87-675-4375 IMP
GMP LABORATORIES OF AMERICA INC
2931 E La Jolla St, Anaheim, CA 92806-1306
Tel (714) 630-2467 Founded/Ownrshp 1994
Sales 21.9MME EMP 92
SIC 2834 Pharmaceutical preparations
CEO: Mohammad Ishaq
*Pr: Suhail Ahmad
VP: Shakil Ahmad
QA Dir: Victor Wilson
Prd Mgr: Adrian Cardenas
Ql Cn Mgr: Asim Ali
Sls Mgr: Andrea Groncy

GMP METAL PRODUCTS
See WOZNIAK INDUSTRIES INC

D-U-N-S 00-627-3718
GMP METAL PRODUCTS
GENERAL METAL PRODUCTS
(Suby of GMP METAL PRODUCTS) ★
3883 Delor St, Saint Louis, MO 63116-3327
Tel (314) 481-0300 Founded/Ownrshp 1986
Sales 53.8MME EMP 300
SIC 3469 3444 3544 Stamping metal for the trade; Sheet metalwork; Special dies, tools, jigs & fixtures; Stamping metal for the trade; Sheet metalwork; Special dies, tools, jigs & fixtures
CEO: Michael Wozniak
Pr: Brad McKean
*CFO: Michael Powers

D-U-N-S 10-672-6797
■ **GMR MARKETING LLC**
FRESHWIRE
(Suby of OMNICOM GROUP INC) ★
5000 S Towne Dr, New Berlin, WI 53151-7956
Tel (262) 786-5600 Founded/Ownrshp 1998
Sales 147.9MME EMP 550
SIC 8743

D-U-N-S 18-786-1468
GMR TRANSPORTATION INC
680 7th Ave Ne, West Fargo, ND 58078-1057
Tel (701) 492-3450 Founded/Ownrshp 2000
Sales 52.8MME EMP 95
SIC 4731 4213 Truck transportation brokers; Trucking, except local; Truck transportation brokers; Trucking, except local
Pr: Dennis Gustafson
*VP: Rick Johnson
*VP: Michael Podratz

D-U-N-S 05-210-2555 EXP
■ **GMRI INC**
RED LOBSTER
(Suby of DARDEN RESTAURANTS INC) ★
1000 Darden Center Dr, Orlando, FL 32837-4032
Tel (407) 245-4000 Founded/Ownrshp 1995
Sales 3.6MMME EMP 112,350
SIC 5812 Eating places; Italian restaurant; Seafood restaurants
Ch Bd: Joe R Lee
Mng Pt: Steven Weaver
Pr: Michael Dean
*Pr: Stephen Judge
*Pr: William R White III
Treas: Pam Denham
Ex VP: Valerie Insignares
Sr VP: Ron Bojalad
Sr VP: Chip Brown
Sr VP: John Caron
Sr VP: Bill Holmes
Sr VP: Kathy Nahlovsky
Sr VP: Suk Singh
Sr VP: Rob Viveros
VP: Valerie K Collins
Exec: Peter Olsacher
Board of Directors: Sherry Pears - Contrl

GMS
See GATOR GYPSUM INC

D-U-N-S 12-222-0577
GMS CONCRETE SPECIALISTS INC
5325 W Mohave St, Phoenix, AZ 85043-8036
Tel (602) 269-8341 Founded/Ownrshp 1984
Sales 28.7MME EMP 275
Accts Christopher Slayter Cpa Pc
SIC 1771 Foundation & footing contractor; Foundation & footing contractor
Pr: Guadalupe Medina
*CFO: Andrea Carbine
*Sr VP: Paul Medina
VP: Jonathan Medina
VP Admn: Catherine Medina

D-U-N-S 00-877-1979
GMS FLORIDA WEST COAST INC
15320 Amberly Dr Ste A, Tampa, FL 33647-1647
Tel (813) 977-0733 Founded/Ownrshp 1997
Sales 21.2MME EMP 220E
SIC 8011 General & family practice, physician/surgeon; General & family practice, physician/surgeon
Pr: Mark M Weissman MD
*COO: Jeffrey Kovalski
*CFO: Peter Bitchakas
*Treas: Christophe Blazejowski MD
*VP: Peter A Jacobson MD
Off Mgr: Sandy Allen
Mktg Mgr: Daniel Frazier

D-U-N-S 80-179-2602
GMS GROUP HOLDINGS CORP
5 Regent St Ste 513, Livingston, NJ 07039-1694
Tel (973) 535-5000 Founded/Ownrshp 2003
Sales 26.6MME EMP 150
SIC 6211 Brokers, security; Dealers, security; Brokers, security; Dealers, security
Pr: Paul Konsig
*COO: Timothy Donohue
*CFO: Jerry Korn
*Ex VP: Michael McKenna
*Ex VP: Paul A Steets
Sales Exec: Peter Demarco

D-U-N-S 06-154-9069
GMS GROUP L L C
(Suby of GMS GROUP HOLDINGS CORP) ★
5 Regent St Ste 513n, Livingston, NJ 07039-1682
Tel (973) 535-5000 Founded/Ownrshp 2003
Sales 26.8MME EMP 150
Accts Weisermazars Llp Woodbury Ny
SIC 6211 Brokers, security; Dealers, security; Brokers, security; Dealers, security
Pr: Paul Konsig
*Pr: Paul A Steets
*CFO: Jerry Korn
*Ex VP: Michael McKenna
Sr VP: Melvin Feldman
Sr VP: James Reiss
Sr VP: Marc Spurr
VP: Jack Baber
VP: Seema Balwada
VP: Scott Bart
VP: Tu Dang
VP: Tom Dunn
VP: Rhonda Dupree
VP: Paul Mante
VP: Cormac Maughan
VP: Daniel McCarthy
VP: Christopher Oelz
VP: Tammy Villoresi

D-U-N-S 82-894-1088 IMP
GMS MINE REPAIR AND MAINTENANCE INC
170 Leon White Rd, Oakland, MD 21550-6326
Tel (301) 334-8186 Founded/Ownrshp 1995
Sales 28.7MME EMP 180
SIC 7699 3599 7363 3542 3444 3443 Industrial machinery & equipment repair; Machine shop, jobbing & repair; Industrial help service; Machine tools, metal forming type; Sheet metalwork; Fabricated plate work (boiler shop); Industrial machinery & equipment repair; Machine shop, jobbing & repair; Industrial help service; Machine tools, metal forming type; Sheet metalwork; Fabricated plate work (boiler shop)
Pr: Courtland Helbig
*VP: Steve Tressler
Genl Mgr: Mike Thomas
Snr Mgr: Matt Brennan

GMSI
See GWINNETT MEDICAL SERVICES INC

GMSI
See GLOBAL MARITEK SYSTEMS INC

GMT
See GLOBAL MATERIAL TECHNOLOGIES INC

GMT
See G M T CORP

D-U-N-S 06-520-9694 IMP
GMT CORP
2116 E Bremer Ave, Waverly, IA 50677-4021
Tel (319) 352-1509 Founded/Ownrshp 1973
Sales 52.1MME EMP 350
SIC 3599 3449

D-U-N-S 80-148-2212
GMT EXPLORATION CO LLC
1560 Broadway Ste 2000, Denver, CO 80202-5138
Tel (720) 946-3028 Founded/Ownrshp 2005
Sales 28.3MM EMP 15
Accts Bdo Usa Llp Houston Texas
SIC 1382 Oil & gas exploration services; Oil & gas exploration services
CEO: Thomas E Claugus
*Pr: William D Lancaster
*CFO: Guy K Bradfield
VP: Keith Kress
*VP: Phillip G Wood

D-U-N-S 13-185-2084
GMT POWER INC
WOLVERINE POWER SYSTEMS
3229 80th Ave, Zeeland, MI 49464-9583
Tel (616) 820-0503 Founded/Ownrshp 2002
Sales 25.4MME EMP 30
SIC 5063 Generators
Pr: Glenn Emmert
*CFO: Aj Bosch
*Sec: Mike Dekock
*VP: Tim Emmert
Brnch Mgr: David Cronce

D-U-N-S 00-494-2829
GMTO CORP
GIANT MAGELLAN TELESCOPE ORGAN
251 S Lake Ave Ste 300, Pasadena, CA 91101-3055
Tel (626) 204-0500 Founded/Ownrshp 2007
Sales 27.7MM EMP 25
Accts Grant Thornton Llp Los Angele
SIC 8733 Scientific research agency
Ex Dir: Patrick McCarthy
*Pr: Edward I Moses
*CFO: Steven Dolmseth

D-U-N-S 07-123-4592
GMVT MOTORS LLC
DAVID MAUS CHEVROLET
972 Towne Center Blvd, Sanford, FL 32771-7435
Tel (407) 547-2600 Founded/Ownrshp 2011
Sales 71.1MME EMP 300
SIC 5511 Automobiles, new & used; Automobiles, new & used
Owner: David Maus
Sec: Delwyn T James

D-U-N-S 17-381-4856 IMP
GN HEARING CARE CORP
RESOUND
(Suby of GN US HOLDINGS INC) ★
8001 E Bloomington Fwy, Bloomington, MN 55420-1036
Tel (800) 248-4327 Founded/Ownrshp 1984
Sales 175.9MME EMP 828
SIC 3841 Surgical & medical instruments; Surgical & medical instruments
Pr: Kimberly S Herman
Pr: Sarah Aesop
Pr: Kevin Mensink
Pr: Tom Wood
COO: Alan P Dozier
COO: Rich Swanson
VP: Keith Lewis
Opers Mgr: Brian Tsuchiya
Manager: Shaun Erdmann
Manager: Kevin Haslam
Manager: Leslie Kelley

D-U-N-S 15-726-9697 IMP
GN NETCOM INC
G N NETCOM UNEX
(Suby of GN NETCOM A/S)
900 Chelmsford St # 313, Lowell, MA 01851-8313
Tel (603) 598-1100 Founded/Ownrshp 1996
Sales 84.0MME EMP 540
SIC 3661 Headsets, telephone; Headsets, telephone
CEO: Toon Bouten
*Pr: Peter Fox
COO: Michael Davis
*CFO: Dean G Kacos
*Treas: Anna Johnson
VP: James Lucivero
VP: David Snow
*Prin: Hanf Hendric Lund
Mng Dir: Steen Boge
Dir IT: Henric Jorgensen
VP Mktg: Stephan Petix

D-U-N-S 07-766-3271
GN US HOLDINGS INC
(Suby of GN RESOUND A/S)
8001 E Bloomington Fwy, Minneapolis, MN 55420-1036
Tel (952) 769-8000 Founded/Ownrshp 1999
Sales 175.9MME EMP 870E
Accts Kpmg Llp
SIC 3842 Hearing aids; Hearing aids
CEO: Alan Dozier
*VP: Bob Meekin
*VP: Rich Swanson

GNADEN HUETTEN MEMORIAL HOSP
See BLUE MOUNTAIN HEALTH SYSTEM INC

D-U-N-S 12-720-3185
GNADEN HUETTEN MEMORIAL HOSPITAL
(Suby of BLUE MOUNTAIN HEALTH SYSTEM INC) ★
211 N 12th St, Lehighton, PA 18235-1138
Tel (610) 377-7001 Founded/Ownrshp 2003
Sales 332.5ME EMP 900
Accts Parentebeard Llc Williamsport
SIC 8062 General medical & surgical hospitals; General medical & surgical hospitals
Pr: Andrew Harris
VP: Frank Debiaso
VP: Sue Lazar
*VP: Terry Purcell
VP: Mary Susko
*Prin: Sylvia Goal
Genl Mgr: Diane Pennington
CIO: Mary Davis
CIO: George Sanchez
Ansthlgy: William Goldstein
Ansthlgy: Robert Hahn

GNC
See GENERAL NUTRITION CORP

GNC
See GENERAL NUTRITION CENTERS INC

D-U-N-S 79-576-9541
▲ **GNC HOLDINGS INC**
300 6th Ave Fl 2, Pittsburgh, PA 15222-2528
Tel (412) 288-4600 Founded/Ownrshp 1935
Sales 2.6MMM EMP 16,500E
Tkr Sym GNC Exch NYS
SIC 5499 Health & dietetic food stores; Health & dietetic food stores
CEO: Michael G Archbold
*Ch Bd: Michael F Hines
CFO: Tricia K Tolivar
CFO: Tricia Tolivar
Chf Mktg O: Jeffrey R Hennion
Ofcr: Daisy L Vanderlinde
Ex VP: Michael D Dzura
Ex VP: Carmine Fortino
Sr VP: Robert M Chessen
Sr VP: Christine Clark
Sr VP: Darryl Green
Sr VP: Lee Karayusuf
Sr VP: Robert M Kral
Sr VP: Michael Locke
Sr VP: Anthony T Phillips
Sr VP: Guru Ramanathan
Board of Directors: Jeffrey P Berger, Alan D Feldman, Amy B Lane, Philip E Mallott, Robert F Moran, C Scott O'hara, Richard J Wallace

D-U-N-S 15-107-6630
■ **GNC INC**
(Suby of GENERAL NUTRITION CENTERS INC) ★
300 6th Ave Fl 2, Pittsburgh, PA 15222-2528
Tel (412) 288-4600 Founded/Ownrshp 1976
Sales 1.5MMME EMP 12,240
SIC 5499 Health & dietetic food stores; Health & dietetic food stores
Ch Bd: Robert J Dinicola
Pr: Amanda Skov
*CFO: Curtis J Larrimer
Chf Mktg O: Jeffrey Hennion
Ofcr: Gavin O'Connor
Ofcr: Gerald J Stubenhofer
Ex VP: Tom Dowd
*Sr VP: Darryl Green
Sr VP: Robert M Kral
Sr VP: Anthony Phillips
Sr VP: Guru Ramanathan
Sr VP: Carl Seletz
Sr VP: Gerald Stubenhofer
VP: Shawn Cupples
VP: Ted Deitrick
VP: Ronald Hallock

D-U-N-S 82-985-5852
GNH SERVICES INC
600 Trade Center Blvd, Chesterfield, MO 63005-1227
Tel (636) 728-0446 Founded/Ownrshp 2008
Sales 39.6MME EMP 150
SIC 1542 Nonresidential construction; Nonresidential construction
Pr: James Granger
*Ex VP: Mat Levinson
Dir IT: Mike Goodman
Opers Mgr: Diana Burgin

D-U-N-S 62-358-3296 IMP
GNI WATERMAN LLC
(Suby of SUMMIT INVESTMENT MANAGEMENT I LLC) ★
25500 Road 204, Exeter, CA 93221-9655
Tel (559) 562-4000 Founded/Ownrshp 2005
Sales 27.1MME EMP 129E
SIC 3589 Water treatment equipment, industrial; Water treatment equipment, industrial
CEO: Ken Mikesell

D-U-N-S 94-899-5019 IMP
GNLD INTERNATIONAL LLC
3500 Gateway Blvd, Fremont, CA 94538-6584
Tel (510) 651-0405 Founded/Ownrshp 2008
Sales 126.4MME EMP 478E
SIC 5122 Vitamins & minerals
CEO: Jerry Brassfield
*Pr: Roget Uys
COO: Edward Ng
*Ex VP: George Casale
Dir IT: Ben Britz

IT Man: Ryan Vo
Opers Mgr: Cecilia Balleza

D-U-N-S 05-531-1708 IMP
GNN INVESTOR LLC
(*Suby of* GEORGIA-PACIFIC LLC) ★
133 Peachtree St Ne, Atlanta, GA 30303-1804
Tel (404) 652-4000 *Founded/Ownrshp* 1990
Sales 104.7MM^E *EMP* 2,482
SIC 2621 2611 2631 2653 5111 2677 Paper mills; Business form paper; Newsprint paper; Bond paper; Kraft (sulfate) pulp; Container board; Corrugated boxes, partitions, display items, sheets & pad; Printing & writing paper; Envelopes; Paper mills; Business form paper; Newsprint paper; Bond paper; Kraft (sulfate) pulp; Container board; Corrugated boxes, partitions, display items, sheets & pad; Printing & writing paper; Envelopes
CEO: A D Correll
**CFO:* Danny W Huff
Board of Directors: James E Bostic Jr, William A Mamrack, Davis K Mortensen, James E Terrell

D-U-N-S 10-867-4763
GNP CO
GOLD 'N PLUMP POULTRY
(*Suby of* MASCHHOFFS LLC) ★
4150 2nd St S Ste 200, Saint Cloud, MN 56301-3994
Tel (320) 251-3570 *Founded/Ownrshp* 2013
Sales 172.1MM^E *EMP* 1,000
SIC 2015 Chicken, processed; Chicken, processed
CEO: Michael Helgeson
**Ex VP:* Steve Jurek
**Ex VP:* Tim Wensman
VP: Brian Roelofs
Mktg Mgr: Tom Janssen
Sls Mgr: Wayne Krone
Sales Asso: Kelli Schuh
Snr Mgr: Crystal Ganz
Snr Mgr: Angela Johnson
Snr Mgr: Lucas Peterson
Snr Mgr: Matthew Schlicht

D-U-N-S 83-162-2258 IMP
GNS AMERICA CO
(*Suby of* GNS HOLDING INC) ★
13341 Quincy St, Holland, MI 49424-9460
Tel (616) 796-0433 *Founded/Ownrshp* 2009
Sales 45.0MM *EMP* 2
SIC 3469 Perforated metal, stamped; Perforated metal, stamped
Pr: Sukje Lee
Ql Cn Mgr: Michele Robarge
VP Sls: Richard Ambler
Snr Mgr: Kenny Shelton

D-U-N-S 07-864-6076
GNS HOLDING INC (MI)
13341 Quincy St, Holland, MI 49424-9460
Tel (616) 796-0433 *Founded/Ownrshp* 2009
Sales 45.0MM^E *EMP* 2^E
SIC 3469 Perforated metal, stamped
Pr: Moon Gyu-Kong

D-U-N-S 13-191-9524 IMP
GNUTTI CARLO USA
WELLES MANUFACTURING DIVISION
140 Ludlow Ave, Northvale, NJ 07647-2305
Tel (201) 768-8200 *Founded/Ownrshp* 2012
Sales 41.7MM^E *EMP* 210
SIC 3714 Motor vehicle engines & parts; Motor vehicle engines & parts
CEO: Paolo Groff
**Ch Bd:* Piercarlo Gnutti
**CFO:* Nicola Morelli

GNY INSURANCE COMPANIES
See GREATER NEWYORK MUTUAL INSURANCE CO

GNY INSURANCE COMPANIES
See INSURANCE CO OF GREATER NEWYORK (INC)

GNYHA
See GREATER NEWYORK HOSPITAL ASSOCIATION SERVICES INC

GO 2 LOGISTICS
See GO TO LOGISTICS INC

GO AIRPORT SHUTTLE
See GO GROUP LLC

D-U-N-S 07-075-2123
GO BY TRUCK INC
6565 N Macarthur Blvd # 470, Irving, TX 75039-2497
Tel (417) 501-8919 *Founded/Ownrshp* 2012
Sales 55.0MM *EMP* 16^E
SIC 4212 4213 Local trucking, without storage; Trucking, except local
CEO: Dawn Strobel
Pr: Kevin Hiller
COO: Bill Hale
VP: Cole Hamels

D-U-N-S 14-897-2768
GO CORP I
GO FRESH
2521 E Hennepin Ave, Minneapolis, MN 55413-2911
Tel (612) 256-1770 *Founded/Ownrshp* 2003
Sales 20.8MM^E *EMP* 120
SIC 2099 Food preparations; Food preparations
Pr: Patricia G Greene
**COO:* M L Owen
**CFO:* Joyce Lupinek
Genl Mgr: Bob Matthews
CTO: Anna Yang

GO COURTESY FORD
See A N C F ACQUISITION CORP

D-U-N-S 13-572-8546
GO DADDY GROUP INC
14455 N Hayden Rd Ste 226, Scottsdale, AZ 85260-6947
Tel (480) 505-8800 *Founded/Ownrshp* 2001
Sales 513.3MM^E *EMP* 4,500
SIC 7371 Computer software development; Computer software development
CEO: Blake Irving
**Pr:* Robert R Parsons
COO: Scott W Wagner
**CFO:* Scott Wagner
CFO: Michael Zimmerman
CFO: Michael J Zimmerman
Ex VP: Christine N Jones
VP: Mike Chadwick
VP: Marianne Curran
VP: Theresa D'Hooge
VP: Lane Jarvis
VP: Miguel Lopez
**VP:* Elissa Murphy
VP: Robert Olson

D-U-N-S 07-888-9444
■ **GO DADDY OPERATING CO LLC**
(*Suby of* GODADDY INC) ★
14455 N Hayden Rd Ste 219, Scottsdale, AZ 85260-6947
Tel (480) 505-8877 *Founded/Ownrshp* 2011
Sales 5.0MM^E *EMP* 4,308^E
SIC 7373 7374 Systems integration services; Computer graphics service
CEO: Blake Irving
COO: Scott Wagner
Chf Mktg O: Barb Rechterman
Ex VP: Phil Bienert
Ex VP: James Carroll
Ex VP: Nima Kelly
Ex VP: Elissa Murphy
Sr VP: Steven Aldrich
Sr VP: Jeff King
Sr VP: David Popowitz

GO FER FOOD
See MONUMENT OIL CO

D-U-N-S 96-860-2396
■ **GO FIDO INC**
(*Suby of* US AUTO PARTS NETWORK INC) ★
225 N Michigan Ave, Chicago, IL 60601-7757
Tel (312) 431-6000 *Founded/Ownrshp* 2010
Sales 51.3MM^E *EMP* 500^E
SIC 5013 Automotive supplies & parts; Automotive supplies & parts
CEO: Shane Evangelist

D-U-N-S 94-950-4880
GO FORWARD OPERATING LP
SHANTY CREEK RESORT
5780 Shanty Creek Rd, Bellaire, MI 49615-8311
Tel (231) 533-8621 *Founded/Ownrshp* 1992
Sales 33.6MM^E *EMP* 300^E
SIC 5813 5812 7011 7999 Drinking places; Eating places; Resort hotel; Ski lodge; Golf services & professionals; Drinking places; Eating places; Resort hotel; Ski lodge; Golf services & professionals
Pt: Terry Schieber
Genl Pt: Zucco Resort Properties LLC
Pt: Lavanway Resort Properties LLC
Pt: Shanty C LLC
CFO: Kevin Fitzpatrick
Treas: Chris Hale
VP: Andrew Reh
Genl Mgr: Lynn Blanchard
Sls Mgr: Judi Young

D-U-N-S 07-827-7504
GO FRAC LLC
GOFRAC
350 Dennis Rd, Weatherford, TX 76087-9094
Tel (817) 731-0301 *Founded/Ownrshp* 2011
Sales 34.4MM^E *EMP* 30^E
SIC 1389 Oil field services
CEO: Richard Crawford
**COO:* Buddy Petersen
**CFO:* Kevin McGlinch
**VP:* Harlan Foster
Opers Mgr: Jerry Grimes

GO FRESH
See GO CORP I

GO FRESH TULSA FRUIT
See TULSA FRUIT CO

D-U-N-S 05-574-6175
GO GREEN JANITORIAL SERVICES LLC
8448 Crossland Loop, Montgomery, AL 36117-0950
Tel (334) 277-5880 *Founded/Ownrshp* 2011
Sales 88.0MM *EMP* 1
SIC 7699 Cleaning services; Cleaning services
Owner: Mekeisha T Thomas

D-U-N-S 07-951-9184
GO GROUP LLC
GO AIRPORT SHUTTLE
1200 W 35th St, Chicago, IL 60609-1305
Tel (844) 787-1670 *Founded/Ownrshp* 2014
Sales 26.3MM^E *EMP* 2,500
SIC 4111 Airport transportation; Airport transportation

D-U-N-S 83-282-3426
GO TO LOGISTICS INC
GO 2 LOGISTICS
165 W Lake St, Northlake, IL 60164-2427
Tel (708) 338-0303 *Founded/Ownrshp* 2006
Sales 41.2MM^E *EMP* 200
SIC 4789 Cargo loading & unloading services; Cargo loading & unloading services
Pr: Gregorz Rzedzian
**CFO:* Tomasz Rzedzian
VP Opers: Nicholas Meyers
VP Opers: Adrian Szuster

D-U-N-S 15-130-0675
GO WEST INSURANCE SERVICES INC
2386 Fair Oaks Blvd Ste 2, Sacramento, CA 95825-4741
Tel (916) 487-1102 *Founded/Ownrshp* 1998
Sales NA *EMP* 5
SIC 6411 Insurance brokers; Insurance brokers
Pr: John McNally

D-U-N-S 87-959-6724
GO WEST TOURS INC
790 Eddy St, San Francisco, CA 94109-7806
Tel (415) 837-0154 *Founded/Ownrshp* 1992
Sales 64.2MM *EMP* 50
Accts Woo & Shum Llp San Francisco
SIC 4725 Tour operators; Tour operators
Pr: Stephan Forget
**VP:* Julia Matheson
**VP:* Florence Solal
Exec: David Nicoletti
**Genl Mgr:* Benoit Demonsant
Genl Mgr: Emmanuelle Legoff
**Genl Mgr:* Emmanuelle Legoss
**Off Mgr:* Art Mischeaux

D-U-N-S 79-854-5356 IMP
GO WIRELESS INC
9970 W Cheyenne Ave # 100, Las Vegas, NV 89129-7700
Tel (702) 853-6200 *Founded/Ownrshp* 1994
Sales 190.7MM^E *EMP* 850
SIC 5999 Mobile telephones & equipment; Mobile telephones & equipment
Pr: Kevin Elder
Pr: Gordon Gober
**Pr:* Rob Murray
**Treas:* Paul Huether
Dist Mgr: Brandon Daigle
Dist Mgr: Jason Dean
Dist Mgr: Rahul Paul
Dist Mgr: Doron Shiff
Store Mgr: Amanda Austin
Store Mgr: John Bellomo
Store Mgr: Matthew Boesz

D-U-N-S 02-109-5264
GO-HIRE EMPLOYMENT AND DEVELOPMENT
1116 Main St, Jackson, KY 41339-1134
Tel (606) 666-2747 *Founded/Ownrshp* 2012
Sales 23.6MM *EMP* 3
Accts Craft Noble & Company Pllc Ri
SIC 7361 Employment agencies; Employment agencies
Prin: Raymond Hurst

D-U-N-S 00-586-9227
GO-MART INC (WV)
U-PAK
915 Riverside Dr, Gassaway, WV 26624-1127
Tel (304) 364-8000 *Founded/Ownrshp* 1966
Sales 209.3MM^E *EMP* 1,200
SIC 5411 5541 Convenience stores, independent; Gasoline service stations; Convenience stores, independent; Gasoline service stations
Pr: John D Heater
**Treas:* Sam Heater
**VP:* Betty J Heater
Div Mgr: Phil Shuman
Div Mgr: Glenna Stephenson
Dir IT: Mike Lafferty
Board of Directors: Laurie O Malley

D-U-N-S 02-844-1405
GO-STAFF INC
G S I
8798 Complex Dr, San Diego, CA 92123-1402
Tel (858) 292-8562 *Founded/Ownrshp* 2001
Sales 46.8MM^E *EMP* 2,500^E
SIC 7363 8721 Temporary help service; Payroll accounting service; Temporary help service; Payroll accounting service
CEO: Scott Crumrine
**VP:* Stacey Crumrine
Rgnl Mgr: Brooke Velazquez
Div Mgr: Jacques Albarran

D-U-N-S 16-663-3490
GO-TO TRANSPORT INC
1320 Washington Ave, Bay City, MI 48708-5711
Tel (989) 893-9941 *Founded/Ownrshp* 2003
Sales 50.3MM^E *EMP* 160
SIC 4213 Trucking, except local; Trucking, except local
CEO: Allison Short
**Pr:* Gary Short
**CFO:* Ed Dean

GO2 PARTNERS
See PRINT MANAGEMENT PARTNERS INC

D-U-N-S 83-273-9358
GOAL ACADEMY
GUIDED ONLINE ACADEMIC
223 N Santa Fe Ave, Pueblo, CO 81003-4132
Tel (877) 776-4625 *Founded/Ownrshp* 2009
Sales 22.0MM *EMP* 187^E
Accts John Cutler & Ssociates Llc D
SIC 8211 Academy; Academy
Pr: Richard Mestas
Ofcr: Kris Enright
Comm Dir: Janelle Quick
**Ex Dir:* Ken Crowell
IT Man: Ronald Ericson
Psych: Joseph Devita

D-U-N-S 09-737-6292
GOAL FINANCIAL LLC
401 W A St Ste 1300, San Diego, CA 92101-7906
Tel (858) 731-9000 *Founded/Ownrshp* 2004
Sales NA *EMP* 250
SIC 6162 Loan correspondents; Loan correspondents
VP: Matthew Myers
Sls Mgr: Eley Cruz

D-U-N-S 06-276-0269
GOAL FOODS INC
MCDONALD'S
4923 Lincoln Way Ste 101, Ames, IA 50014-3616
Tel (515) 292-1388 *Founded/Ownrshp* 1971
Sales 10.3MM^E *EMP* 400
SIC 5812 Fast-food restaurant, chain; Fast-food restaurant, chain
CEO: John Dasher
**VP:* Linda Dasher

D-U-N-S 02-512-2115
GOAL INC
1746 N Richmond St, Chicago, IL 60647-5124
Tel (773) 278-8200 *Founded/Ownrshp* 1991
Sales 21.4MM^E *EMP* 120
SIC 1731 Electrical work
Pr: Tom Rivi

D-U-N-S 00-936-8285 IMP/EXP
■ **GOAL ZERO LLC**
GOAL0
(*Suby of* NRG ENERGY INC) ★
675 W 14600 S, Bluffdale, UT 84065-4831
Tel (888) 794-6250 *Founded/Ownrshp* 2009, 2014
Sales 22.2MM^E *EMP* 90
SIC 3433 3825 Solar heaters & collectors; Meters: electric, pocket, portable, panelboard, etc.
CEO: Robert Workman
**CFO:* Robert Peay
VP: Rob Gardner
VP: Keyvan Vasefi
**Prin:* Lee Fromson
IT Man: Nate Baker
Mktg Mgr: Patrick Grewe
Mktg Mgr: Stacie Larsen
Sls Mgr: Cody Thomas
Sls Mgr: Dale Wood

GOAL0
See GOAL ZERO LLC

GOBIERNO MUNICIPAL AU
See CAROLINA MUNICIPALITY

D-U-N-S 10-899-6885
GOBLE & ASSOCIATES INC
GA COMMUNICATION GROUP
1 E Wacker Dr Ste 3200, Chicago, IL 60601-2002
Tel (312) 245-9520 *Founded/Ownrshp* 2001
Sales 26.1MM^E *EMP* 93
Accts Grossman Cohen & Diamond Llc
SIC 7311 Advertising agencies; Advertising agencies
CEO: Joseph Kuchta
**Pr:* Nancy Finigan
**COO:* Mark Goble
Bd of Dir: Deborah D Rath
Ex VP: Geoff Melick
**Sr VP:* Jody L Cahill
Sr VP: Ryan Pelt
VP: Steve Buecking
**VP:* Michael McCartney
VP: Barclay Missen
Creative D: Soyoon Bolton
Creative D: Anthony Diorio

D-U-N-S 02-134-7930
GOC LTD
801 Riderwood Dr, Butler, AL 36904-3501
Tel (205) 459-2727 *Founded/Ownrshp* 1997
Sales 31.1MM^E *EMP* 200
SIC 5411 Convenience stores, chain; Convenience stores, chain
CEO: Sam Gibson
Opers Mgr: Glenn Eldridge

D-U-N-S 07-942-9992
■ **GODADDY INC**
GODADDY.COM
(*Suby of* DESERT NEWCO LLC) ★
14455 N Hayden Rd Ste 100, Scottsdale, AZ 85260-6947
Tel (480) 505-8800 *Founded/Ownrshp* 2014
Sales 962.1MM^E *EMP* 4,908
Tkr Sym GDDY *Exch* NYS
SIC 4813
CEO: Blake J Irving
**Ch Bd:* Charles J Robel
COO: Scott W Wagner
Chf Mktg O: Philip H Bienert
Ex VP: Nima Kelly
Sr VP: Lauren Antonoff
VP: Jill Schoolenberg
Board of Directors: Herald Y Chen, Richard H Kimball, Gregory K Mondre, John I Park, Bob Parsons, Elizabeth S Rafael, Lee E Wittlinger

GODADDY.COM
See GODADDY INC

D-U-N-S 96-776-9167
GODADDY.COM LLC
(*Suby of* GO DADDY GROUP INC) ★
14455 N Hayden Rd Ste 219, Scottsdale, AZ 85260-6947
Tel (480) 505-8800 *Founded/Ownrshp* 2011
Sales 498.8MM^E *EMP* 3,300
SIC 7379 ;
CEO: Bob Parsons
**Pr:* Warren Adelman
**CFO:* Michael Zimmerman
VP: Carmelia Hackson
Snr Ntwrk: Michael Racki
Web Dev: Jody Johnson
Sftwr Eng: Jeff Kershner

D-U-N-S 00-583-3686 EXP
GODBERSEN-SMITH CONSTRUCTION CO INC
GOMACO MANUFACTURING CO
121 E State Highway 175, Ida Grove, IA 51445-1139
Tel (712) 364-3388 *Founded/Ownrshp* 1946
Sales 91.3MM *EMP* 450
SIC 3531 1622 Pavers; Finishers, concrete & bituminous: powered; Bituminous, cement & concrete related products & equipment; Bridge construction; Pavers; Finishers, concrete & bituminous: powered; Bituminous, cement & concrete related products & equipment; Bridge construction
Pr: Gary L Godbersen
COO: Wayne Hansen
**Treas:* Sharon K Godbersen
**VP:* Richard E Smith

D-U-N-S 06-844-0163
GODDARD PUBLIC SCHOOLS
201 S Main St, Goddard, KS 67052-8763
Tel (316) 794-4230 *Founded/Ownrshp* 1965
Sales 26.0MM^E *EMP* 320^E

SIC 8211 Public combined elementary & secondary school; Public combined elementary & secondary school
**Pr:* Larry Belcher
**Treas:* Eileen Bieker
**VP:* Frank Johnson
Dir Sec: Ronny Lieurance
Pr Dir: Dane Baxa

D-U-N-S 06-022-6859
GODDARD RIVERSIDE COMMUNITY CENTER INC
593 Columbus Ave Frnt 1, New York, NY 10024-1998
Tel (212) 873-6600 *Founded/Ownrshp* 1961
Sales 27.5MM *EMP* 100^E
Accts N Cheng & Co Pc New York Ny
SIC 8322 Community center
Ex Dir: Stephen Russo

GODFATHER'S PIZZA
See G-F FOUR INVESTMENTS INC

GODFATHER'S PIZZA
See PACIFIC PIZZA CO INC

D-U-N-S 15-063-9979
GODFATHERS PIZZA INC
2808 N 108th St, Omaha, NE 68164-3702
Tel (402) 391-1452 *Founded/Ownrshp* 1988
Sales 94.0MM^E *EMP* 2,500
SIC 5812 6794 Pizzeria, chain; Franchises, selling or licensing; Pizzeria, chain; Franchises, selling or licensing
Ch: Herman Cain
**Pr:* Ronald Gartlan
**CFO:* Richard W Ramm
Admn Mgr: John Callaghan
VP Mktg: Dawn Drazdys

D-U-N-S 06-045-2232
GODFREY & KAHN S C
780 N Water St Ste 1500, Milwaukee, WI 53202-3590
Tel (414) 273-3500 *Founded/Ownrshp* 1957
Sales 50.3M *EMP* 420
SIC 8111 General practice law office; General practice law office
Mng Pt: Nicholas P Wahl
Mng Pt: Rochelle Klaskin
Pr: Paula Cartwright
Pr: Mary Laluzerne
**VP:* Richard J Bliss
**VP:* Peter M Sommerhauser
Telecom Mg: Scott Bingenheimer
Mktg Dir: Susan Steberl
Counsel: Marvin Bynum
Counsel: Terrence Knudsen
Counsel: Helge Lee

D-U-N-S 05-150-3928
GODFREY & WING INC
IMPCO
27 Dexter Rd, East Providence, RI 02914-2045
Tel (401) 521-2490 *Founded/Ownrshp* 2014
Sales 28.9MM^E *EMP* 175
SIC 2821 3599 3471 2295 Polyesters; Machine & other job shop work; Machine shop, jobbing & repair; Plating & polishing; Coated fabrics, not rubberized
Pr: Chris Gilmore
**Treas:* Bradford Welch
**VP:* Karen Gilmore
IT Man: Peter Gebhard
IT Man: Paula Greene

D-U-N-S 01-716-7164
GODFREY BROS INC
JOHN DEERE
1166 E Chicago Rd, Jonesville, MI 49250-8200
Tel (517) 849-9966 *Founded/Ownrshp* 1974
Sales 25.0MM *EMP* 16
SIC 7699 5999 5083 Agricultural equipment repair services; Farm equipment & supplies; Farm & garden machinery; Lawn & garden machinery & equipment; Farm implements; Agricultural equipment repair services; Farm equipment & supplies; Farm & garden machinery; Lawn & garden machinery & equipment; Farm implements
Pr: W Jack Godfrey
**Pr:* Kevin W Godfrey
**Sec:* John Prater
**VP:* Kevin Clark
**Prin:* Roger Godfrey

D-U-N-S 00-546-9531 EXP
GODFREY CONVEYOR CO INC
GODFREY MARINE
4500 Middlebury St, Elkhart, IN 46516-9068
Tel (574) 522-8381 *Founded/Ownrshp* 2006
Sales 28.4MM^E *EMP* 144^E
SIC 5551

GODFREY MARINE
See GODFREY CONVEYOR CO INC

GODFREY MARINE
See HIGHWATER MARINE LLC

D-U-N-S 05-243-0501
GODFREY TRUCKING INC
6173 W 2100 S, West Valley City, UT 84128-6402
Tel (801) 972-0660 *Founded/Ownrshp* 1974
Sales 35.1MM^E *EMP* 150^E
Accts Daines Goodwin Cpas Salt Lak
SIC 4213 4214 Trucking, except local; Local trucking with storage; Trucking, except local; Local trucking with storage
Pr: Scott Godfrey
**CFO:* Kirk Greenhalgh
**VP:* Mike Williams
Exec: Erma Thompson
Dir IT: Dave Keller

D-U-N-S 03-378-6922
GODFREYS WAREHOUSE INC
255 W Jefferson St, Madison, GA 30650-1043
Tel (706) 342-0264 *Founded/Ownrshp* 1935
Sales 56.7MM *EMP* 31
SIC 5999 5191

D-U-N-S 04-964-4321
GODIVA CHOCOLATIER INC
(*Suby of* YILDIZ HOLDING ANONIM SIRKETI)
333 W 34th St Fl 6, New York, NY 10001-2566
Tel (212) 984-5900 *Founded/Ownrshp* 1966
Sales 400.8MM^E *EMP* 2,200
SIC 2066 5149 5441 2064 Chocolate candy, solid; Chocolate; Candy; Candy & other confectionery products; Chocolate candy, solid; Chocolate; Candy; Candy & other confectionery products
Pr: Jim Goldman
**CFO:* David Marberger
CFO: David S Marberger
Treas: Bill Oshea
Treas: William J Shea
Sr Cor Off: Roger Stier
Chf Mktg O: Lauri K Kotcher
Ofcr: Mike Hoehl
Sr VP: Mike Giresi
VP: Brett Barnello
VP: Doug Caldwell
VP: Anthony Disilvestro
VP: Linda Lombardi
VP: Dora Lu
VP: Debra Maher
VP: Mahender Nathan
VP: Rick Paschal
VP: James Ricciardi
VP: Sharon Rothstein
Exec: Erica Coletta
Comm Dir: Emily Kapusta
Board of Directors: Stefan Heidenreich

D-U-N-S 02-878-8891
GODLEY INDEPENDENT SCHOOL DISTRICT
313 N Pearson St, Godley, TX 76044-3738
Tel (817) 389-2265 *Founded/Ownrshp* 1925
Sales 26.4MM *EMP* 125
SIC 8211 Public elementary & secondary schools; Public elementary school; Public junior high school; Public senior high school; Public elementary & secondary schools; Public elementary school; Public junior high school; Public senior high school
Teacher Pr: Sonda McLellan
HC Dir: Carrie Owen

D-U-N-S 18-716-7234
GODS LOVE WE DELIVER INC
166 Avnue Of The Americas, New York, NY 10013-1291
Tel (212) 625-6300 *Founded/Ownrshp* 1987
Sales 24.7MM *EMP* 85
Accts Loeb & Troper Llp New York N
SIC 8322 Meal delivery program; Meal delivery program
Pr: Karen Pearl
Mktg Dir: Bruce Schwartz

D-U-N-S 16-683-7294
GODS PANTRY FOOD BANK
1685 Jaggie Fox Way, Lexington, KY 40511-1084
Tel (859) 255-6592 *Founded/Ownrshp* 1955
Sales 35.8MM *EMP* 23^E
SIC 5812 Food bars; Food bars
VP: Keith Peel
Ex Dir: Debbie Long

D-U-N-S 06-570-3670
GODSHALLS QUALITY MEATS INC
KUTZTOWN BOLOGNA
675 Mill Rd, Telford, PA 18969-2411
Tel (215) 256-8867 *Founded/Ownrshp* 1945
Sales 108.0MM^E *EMP* 200
SIC 5147 5421 Meats & meat products; Meat markets, including freezer provisioners; Meats & meat products; Meat markets, including freezer provisioners
Pr: Mark B Godshall
Pr: Ralph Bittel
**Sec:* Kendal Godshall
Ofcr: Chris Bruno
**VP:* Floyd Kratz
IT Man: Jeffrey Hunsinger
IT Man: Kevin Miller
Plnt Mgr: Mike Tice

D-U-N-S 19-132-5232
GODWIN CORP
1835 University Blvd E # 224, Hyattsville, MD 20783-4657
Tel (301) 434-3111 *Founded/Ownrshp* 1988
Sales 11.8MM^E *EMP* 400^E
SIC 8021 8031 8042 8043 8062 8069 Offices & clinics of dentists; Offices & clinics of osteopathic physicians; Offices & clinics of optometrists; Offices & clinics of podiatrists; General medical & surgical hospitals; Specialty hospitals, except psychiatric; Offices & clinics of dentists; Offices & clinics of osteopathic physicians; Offices & clinics of optometrists; Offices & clinics of podiatrists; General medical & surgical hospitals; Specialty hospitals, except psychiatric
Pr: Marcus Balogun III
IT Man: Barbara Winston

D-U-N-S 01-143-3687
GODWIN HEIGHTS PUBLIC SCHOOL DISTRICT
15 36th St Sw, Grand Rapids, MI 49548-2101
Tel (616) 245-0091 *Founded/Ownrshp* 1867
Sales 27.0MM *EMP* 378
Accts Maner Costerisan Pc Lansing
SIC 8211 Public elementary school; Public junior high school; Public senior high school; Public elementary school; Public junior high school; Public senior high school
MIS Dir: Bill Schafer

D-U-N-S 02-451-7831 IMP
GODWIN MANUFACTURING CO INC (NC)
17666 Us Highway 421 S, Dunn, NC 28334
Tel (910) 897-4995 *Founded/Ownrshp* 1966
Sales 48.8MM^E *EMP* 258^E
SIC 3713 3714 Truck bodies (motor vehicles); Dump truck lifting mechanism; Truck bodies (motor vehicles); Dump truck lifting mechanism
Pr: James P Godwin Sr
**CFO:* Mark Fentress
**Sec:* Pam Faircloth
**VP:* James P Godwin Jr
Sales Exec: David Wood

D-U-N-S 09-731-1070 IMP
GODWIN-SBO LLC
28825 Highway Blvd, Katy, TX 77494-8296
Tel (281) 371-5400 *Founded/Ownrshp* 1998
Sales 65.0MM *EMP* 175
SIC 3599 Machine shop, jobbing & repair; Machine shop, jobbing & repair
Pr: Michael Corliss
**Pt:* Colleen Rejcek
**Pt:* Larry Uren
Pgrm Dir: James Hyder

D-U-N-S 00-618-4907 IMP
GOEBEL FIXTURE CO
ENVIRONMENTS
528 Dale St Sw, Hutchinson, MN 55350-2397
Tel (320) 587-2112 *Founded/Ownrshp* 1935
Sales 23.7MM^E *EMP* 110
SIC 2541 Store fixtures, wood
CEO: Virgil Goebel
**Pr:* Robert Croatt
VP: Matt Field
**VP:* Richard Goebel
Plnt Mgr: Troy Rohach

D-U-N-S 05-123-8991
GOEL SERVICES INC
6201 Dix St Ne, Washington, DC 20019-2880
Tel (202) 457-0111 *Founded/Ownrshp* 2001
Sales 34.7MM^E *EMP* 87
SIC 1542 1795 1623 Commercial & office buildings, renovation & repair; Wrecking & demolition work; Water, sewer & utility lines
CEO: Piyush J Goel

D-U-N-S 00-507-3846
GOELITZ CONFECTIONERY CO INC
(*Suby of* JELLY BELLY CANDY CO) ★
1501 Morrow Ave, North Chicago, IL 60064-3200
Tel (847) 689-2225 *Founded/Ownrshp* 1898, 1978
Sales 22.4MM^E *EMP* 180
SIC 2064 Candy & other confectionery products; Jellybeans; Candy & other confectionery products; Jellybeans
Ch Bd: Herman G Rowland Sr
**Pr:* William H Kelley
QC Dir: Val Abrahamson

D-U-N-S 10-915-7227
GOELLNER INC
ADVANCED MACHINE AND ENGRG
2500 Latham St, Rockford, IL 61103-3963
Tel (815) 962-6076 *Founded/Ownrshp* 1999
Sales 93.2MM^E *EMP* 450
SIC 3599 Machine & other job shop work; Machine & other job shop work
CEO: Willy Goellner
**Pr:* Dietmiar Goellner
**CFO:* David Leezer
Sls Dir: Nick Goellner
Sls Dir: Dan Lapp

D-U-N-S 15-118-7366 IMP
GOELZER INDUSTRIES INC
201 E Trinity Blvd, Grand Prairie, TX 75050-8048
Tel (214) 524-6700 *Founded/Ownrshp* 1986
Sales 21.5MM^E *EMP* 65
SIC 2677 Envelopes
Pr: Paul Goelzer Sr
**VP:* Paul Goelzer Jr
Mktg Mgr: Shawn M Scott

D-U-N-S 02-894-4671
GOENGINEER INC
1787 E Fort Union Blvd # 200, Salt Lake City, UT 84121-2886
Tel (801) 359-6100 *Founded/Ownrshp* 1988
Sales 53.5MM^E *EMP* 114
SIC 7372 Prepackaged software; Prepackaged software
Pr: Ken Coburn
**CFO:* Brad Hansen
VP: Mike Coleman
Off Mgr: Sharon Brooks
Off Mgr: Flavia Chatterjee
Off Mgr: Heather Fronk
Off Mgr: Miguel Gallardo
Off Mgr: Debbie Howe
Off Mgr: Julia Pearson
Off Mgr: Lauren West
Dir IT: Nathan Gunderson

D-U-N-S 87-845-4094 IMP
GOERTZ+SCHIELE CORP
1750 Summit Dr, Auburn Hills, MI 48326-1780
Tel (248) 393-0414 *Founded/Ownrshp* 1999
Sales 20.1MM^E *EMP* 148
SIC 3462 Automotive forgings, ferrous: crankshaft, engine, axle, etc.; Automotive forgings, ferrous: crankshaft, engine, axle, etc.
Pr: Roland Schiele
**VP:* Hans Jung
VP: Peter Loetzner
**VP:* Wolsgang Speck
Genl Mgr: Peter Eggers

GOETTLE CONSTRUCTION
See GOETTLE HOLDING CO INC

D-U-N-S 00-448-5348
GOETTLE HOLDING CO INC
GOETTLE CONSTRUCTION
12071 Hamilton Ave, Cincinnati, OH 45231-1032
Tel (513) 825-8100 *Founded/Ownrshp* 1956
Sales 76.0MM^E *EMP* 130
SIC 1799 1629 1771 1794 Shoring & underpinning work; Pile driving contractor; Foundation & footing contractor; Excavation work; Shoring & underpinning work; Pile driving contractor; Foundation & footing contractor; Excavation work
Prin: Roger W Healey
**Ch Bd:* Larry P Rayburn
**Pr:* Terrence Tucker
**Sec:* Dan Baker
VP: Brent Grow
**VP:* Douglas Keller
**Prin:* Janet E Goettle
**Prin:* Richard J Goettle III

D-U-N-S 01-279-2289
GOETZ ENERGY CORP (NY)
KURK FUEL COMPANY
1319 Military Rd, Buffalo, NY 14217-1530
Tel (716) 824-1298 *Founded/Ownrshp* 1929
Sales 23.9MM^E *EMP* 30
SIC 5172 Fuel oil; Diesel fuel; Gasoline
VP: Roger L Schintzius

GOETZE DENTAL CO.
See GOETZE-NIEMER CO

D-U-N-S 02-984-0378
GOETZE-NIEMER CO
GOETZE DENTAL CO.
3939 Ne 33rd Ter Ste J, Kansas City, MO 64117-2689
Tel (816) 459-9900 *Founded/Ownrshp* 1884
Sales 47.2MM^E *EMP* 130
SIC 5047 Dental equipment & supplies; Dental equipment & supplies
CEO: Don Brunker
**CFO:* Bart Miller
VP: Benjamin Brunker
**VP:* Janet Brunker
VP: Jeff Erickson
VP: Bill Henning
Brnch Mgr: Jay McConnell
Off Mgr: Michelle Mitchell
IT Man: Keith Lister
IT Man: Ben Poese
Software D: Brad Jamison

D-U-N-S 00-306-0431 IMP
GOETZES CANDY CO INC (MD)
3900 E Monument St, Baltimore, MD 21205-2980
Tel (410) 342-2010 *Founded/Ownrshp* 1895
Sales 22.7MM^E *EMP* 90
SIC 2064 Chewing candy, not chewing gum
CEO: Spaulding A Goetze Sr
**Pr:* Randle M Goetze III
**Ch:* R Melvin Goetze Jr
**VP:* Mitchell T Goetze
**VP:* David Long
Exec: Debbie Maryman
Sftwr Eng: Perry Broyles
Opers Mgr: Matthew Tary
Trfc Mgr: Patricia Swagert
S&M/VP: Cynthia Goetze
Mktg Mgr: Meghan Brody

D-U-N-S 61-292-6915
GOEX CORP
802 E Us Highway 14, Janesville, WI 53545-8832
Tel (608) 754-3303 *Founded/Ownrshp* 1990
Sales 46.2MM^E *EMP* 130
SIC 3081 Packing materials, plastic sheet; Packing materials, plastic sheet
Ch: Joseph T Pregont
**Pr:* Joshua D Gray
VP: Don Waddell
Sales Exec: Ivan Lee
Sls&Mrk Ex: Marlon Knittel

D-U-N-S 05-690-4436 IMP
GOFFA INTERNATIONAL CORP
PLUSH TOYS
200 Murray Hill Pkwy # 1, East Rutherford, NJ 07073-2144
Tel (718) 361-8883 *Founded/Ownrshp* 1981
Sales 22.5MM^E *EMP* 50
SIC 5092 5099 5199 Toys; Sunglasses; General merchandise, non-durable
Pr: Douglas Song
Mktg Dir: Lily Song

D-U-N-S 62-353-0933
GOFFSTOWN SCHOOL DISTRICT
11 School St, Goffstown, NH 03045-1908
Tel (603) 497-4818 *Founded/Ownrshp* 2014
Sales 8.7MM^E *EMP* 419^E
SIC 8211 Public elementary & secondary schools; Public elementary school; Public junior high school; Public senior high school

D-U-N-S 00-960-8555 IMP
GOFORTH & MARTI
G/M BUSINESS INTERIORS
110 W A St Ste 140, San Diego, CA 92101-3702
Tel (951) 684-0870 *Founded/Ownrshp* 1986
Sales 78.0MM^E *EMP* 158
SIC 5021 Office furniture; Office furniture
Pr: Stephen L Easley
**VP:* William F Easley
Exec: Michael Lafond
Dir Bus: Daniel Hickey
Mktg Dir: Lisa McClinton
Snr PM: Ellen Miles

GOFRAC
See GO FRAC LLC

D-U-N-S 13-666-4096
GOG FOUNDATION INC
2127 Espey Ct Ste 100, Crofton, MD 21114-2489
Tel (410) 721-7126 *Founded/Ownrshp* 2002
Sales 27.7MM *EMP* 37
SIC 8011 Oncologist; Oncologist
Pr: Philip J Disaia
Treas: Oleg Klapovsky
**Prin:* Mary Sharp

GOGAS
See K E AUSTIN CORP

D-U-N-S 08-646-6559 IMP
GOGGIN WAREHOUSING LLC
111 Eaton Dr, Shelbyville, TN 37160-9156
Tel (931) 684-8971 *Founded/Ownrshp* 1998
Sales 27.4MM^E *EMP* 55
SIC 4225 4214 General warehousing & storage; Local trucking with storage
Ch Bd: Tommy Hodges
Pr: Keith Bellenfant
CEO: Jack Coop
Manager: Susan Pearson

D-U-N-S 12-229-5736 IMP/EXP
GOGLANIAN BAKERIES INC
(*Suby of* RICH PRODUCTS CORP) ★
3401 W Segerstrom Ave, Santa Ana, CA 92704-6404
Tel (714) 549-1524 *Founded/Ownrshp* 2012
Sales 558.2MM^E *EMP* 400
SIC 5149 Bakery products; Bakery products
CEO: William G Gisel
CFO: Albert Altro
Plnt Mgr: Javier Avila
Sls Mgr: Eric Porat

D-U-N-S 07-887-5378
▲ GOGO INC
1250 N Arlington Rd, Itasca, IL 60143
Tel (630) 647-1400 *Founded/Ownrshp* 1991
Sales 408.4MM *EMP* 891^E
Tkr Sym GOGO *Exch* NGS
SIC 4899 Communication signal enhancement network system; Communication signal enhancement network system
Pr: Michael J Small
**Ch Bd:* Ronald T Lemay
COO: Ben Murphy
CFO: Norman Smagley
Ex VP: Anand K Chari
Ex VP: Ash A Eldifrawi
Ex VP: Marguerite M Elias
Exec: Ruth Ruffino
Board of Directors: Robert L Crandall, Michael S Gilliland, Sam Gilliland, Robert H Mundheim, Christopher D Payne, Christopher Payne, Oakleigh Thorne, Charles C Townsend, Harris N Williams

D-U-N-S 07-950-6318
■ GOGO INTERMEDIATE HOLDINGS LLC
(*Suby of* GOGO INC) ★
1250 N Arlington Rd, Itasca, IL 60143
Tel (630) 647-1400 *Founded/Ownrshp* 2012
Sales 274.7MM^E *EMP* 689^E
SIC 3663 Radio & TV communications equipment; Radio & TV communications equipment

D-U-N-S 80-913-1733
■ GOGO LLC
(*Suby of* GOGO INTERMEDIATE HOLDINGS LLC) ★
111 N Canal St, Chicago, IL 60606-7218
Tel (630) 647-1400 *Founded/Ownrshp* 2012
Sales 229.0MM^E *EMP* 689
SIC 3663 4812 4813 4899 Radio & TV communications equipment; Cellular radio telephone; Cellular telephone services; Telephone communication, except radio; Data communication services; Radio & TV communications equipment; Cellular radio telephone; Cellular telephone services; Telephone communication, except radio; Data communication services
Ex VP: Margee Elias
**Pr:* Michael J Small
**CFO:* Norman Smagley
Treas: Varvara Alva
Treas: William Sawitz
Ex VP: Ash A Eldifrawi
Ex VP: John Wade
Sr VP: Marguerite M Elias
Sr VP: Mark Malosh
Sr VP: Rama Prasad
Sr VP: David Russell
Sr VP: Arbela Takhsh
VP: Andrew Kemmetmueller
VP: Nehad Leonardson
VP: Timothy Maxwell
VP: Joe Meszaro
VP: Clint Quanstrom
VP: Linda Ramsey
VP: Mike Syverson
VP: Gabriella Vacca
Board of Directors: Robert L Crandall, Lawrence N Lavine, Christopher Minnetian, Robert H Mundheim, Oakleigh Thorne, Charles C Townsend, Harris N Williams

D-U-N-S 09-735-9504
GOGRID LLC
COLOSERVE
(*Suby of* DATAPIPE INC) ★
2 Harrison St Ste 200, San Francisco, CA 94105-6141
Tel (415) 869-7000 *Founded/Ownrshp* 2015
Sales 60.8MM^E *EMP* 112^E
SIC 4813 7374 7375 7371 ; ; Data processing & preparation; Computer graphics service; ; ; Data processing & preparation; Computer graphics service; Data base information retrieval; Computer software development & applications
CFO: Brett Newsome
Chf Mktg O: Jeff Samuels
CIO: Mark Worsey
Mktg Dir: Andy Nester

D-U-N-S 00-637-3443
GOH A&C INC
(*Suby of* GOH CON INC) ★
1630 Broadway St, Clarksville, IN 47129-7712
Tel (812) 282-1349 *Founded/Ownrshp* 1950
Sales 43.2MM^E *EMP* 200
SIC 1611 1622 Highway & street maintenance; Bridge construction; Highway & street maintenance; Bridge construction
CEO: Jame Micheal Gohman
**Pr:* Annette G Dezelan
**CFO:* Richard L Cripe
**Ch:* John R Gohmann
**Treas:* Keith Kramer

D-U-N-S 04-292-3438
GOH CON INC
GOHMANN ASPHALT & CONSTRUCTION
1630 Broadway St, Clarksville, IN 47129-7712
Tel (812) 282-1349 *Founded/Ownrshp* 1998
Sales 95.9MM^E *EMP* 350
SIC 2951 1611 1622 4212 8734 Asphalt & asphaltic paving mixtures (not from refineries); General contractor, highway & street construction; Bridge construction; Local trucking, without storage; Testing laboratories; Asphalt & asphaltic paving mixtures (not from refineries); General contractor, highway & street construction; Bridge construction; Local trucking, without storage; Testing laboratories
Ch: J M Gohmann
**Pr:* Richard L Cripe
**Treas:* Keith A Kramer
Treas: Keith Kramer
**VP:* Annette G Dezelan
VP: Don Franks
**VP:* John R Gohmann
VP: Fred Sullivan
VP: Jason Yeager
IT Man: Diane Green
Sfty Mgr: Melony Geary

GOHEALTH INSURANCE
See NVX HOLDINGS INC

GOHMANN ASPHALT & CONSTRUCTION
See GOH CON INC

D-U-N-S 07-186-2452
■ GOINDUSTRY DOVEBID INC (MD)
(*Suby of* GOINDUSTRY-DOVEBID LIMITED)
11425 Cronhill Dr Ste A, Owings Mills, MD 21117-2268
Tel (410) 654-7500 *Founded/Ownrshp* 1937, 2008
Sales 69.6MM^E *EMP* 200
SIC 7389

D-U-N-S 96-952-8363
GOING OUT INC
US MEXICO TRADING
3515 Main St Ste 201, Chula Vista, CA 91911-5897
Tel (619) 422-9999 *Founded/Ownrshp* 1997
Sales 44.2MM^E *EMP* 200
SIC 5611 5136 Men's & boys' clothing stores; Men's & boys' clothing; Men's & boys' clothing stores; Men's & boys' clothing
CEO: Steven Maman
**COO:* Jacob Risman
**CFO:* Danny Maman
Board of Directors: Danny Maman, Steven Maman, Jake Risman

D-U-N-S 62-651-8158
GOIZUETA FOUNDATION
4401 Northside Pkwy Nw # 520, Atlanta, GA 30327-5279
Tel (404) 239-0390 *Founded/Ownrshp* 2000
Sales 23.5MM *EMP* 7
SIC 8699 Charitable organization; Charitable organization

D-U-N-S 00-416-2038 IMP/EXP
GOJO INDUSTRIES INC
1 Gojo Plz Ste 500, Akron, OH 44311-1085
Tel (330) 255-6000 *Founded/Ownrshp* 1946
Sales 286.1MM^E *EMP* 550
SIC 2842 3586 2844 Specialty cleaning, polishes & sanitation goods; Measuring & dispensing pumps; Toilet preparations; Specialty cleaning, polishes & sanitation goods; Measuring & dispensing pumps; Toilet preparations
Pr: Mark Lerner
**Ch Bd:* Joseph Kanfer
VP: Keith Dare
VP: Dan Edwards
VP: Dennis Gladin
VP: Brad Helfman
Exec: Stephanie Payne
CIO: Janet Kosar
QA Dir: Suzanne Crossen
IT Man: Ashley Blair
IT Man: Tom Johnson

D-U-N-S 95-791-5135
GOJO INTERNATIONAL HOLDINGS INC
1 Gojo Plz Ste 500, Akron, OH 44311-1085
Tel (330) 252-9916 *Founded/Ownrshp* 1990
Sales 26.4MM^E *EMP* 100^E
SIC 6719 Personal holding companies, except banks
Pr: Joseph Kanfer
VP: Natalie Adler
**VP:* Mark Lerner
Counsel: Jeffery Vengrow

D-U-N-S 07-970-7631
GOLD AND DIAMOND CENTER INC
FANCY CUT DIAMONDS
576 5th Ave Fl 4, New York, NY 10036-4807
Tel (212) 575-3655 *Founded/Ownrshp* 2009
Sales 85.0MM *EMP* 14
SIC 5094 5944 Diamonds (gems); Jewelry, precious stones & precious metals
Pr: Saumil Kothari

D-U-N-S 04-310-9222 IMP/EXP
GOLD BOND INC (TN)
5485 Hixson Pike, Hixson, TN 37343-3235
Tel (423) 842-5844 *Founded/Ownrshp* 1947, 1979
Sales 35.0MM^E *EMP* 250
SIC 3993 Advertising novelties; Advertising novelties
**Treas:* Mitch Henderson
Plnt Mgr: Mark Phurrough
Natl Sales: Mark Tipton
Mktg Dir: Matt Hodges
Sls Mgr: Rich Curtiss
Sls Mgr: Danny Morgan
Sls Mgr: Devon Stansbury
Sales Asso: Sarah Hovsepian

GOLD BUG
See GOLD INC

D-U-N-S 95-986-5903 IMP
GOLD BUYERS OF AMERICA LLC
2790 Windham Ct, Delray Beach, FL 33445-7109
Tel (877) 721-8033 *Founded/Ownrshp* 2009
Sales 38.0MM^E *EMP* 198^E
SIC 1041 Gold ore milling
Prin: Matthew K Zvacek

D-U-N-S 96-943-3275 IMP
GOLD CANYON INTERNATIONAL LLC
6205 S Arizona Ave, Chandler, AZ 85248-6399
Tel (480) 449-0900 *Founded/Ownrshp* 1997
Sales 69.2MM^E *EMP* 300
SIC 3999 5199 Candles; Candles; Candles; Candles
CEO: Thomas F Kelly
CFO: Kenneth Wallace
**Ex VP:* Curt Waisath
Prd Mgr: Sara Parent
Ql Cn Mgr: Malia Chavez
Mktg Dir: Lynae Parrott
Sls Mgr: Kevin Cooke
Sls Mgr: Janice Ogrady
Snr Mgr: Terrie Robinson
Snr Mgr: Curt Waisatch

GOLD CIRCLE ENTERTAINMENT
See WAITT MEDIA INC

GOLD COAST BAKERIES
See GOLD COAST BAKING CO INC

D-U-N-S 60-605-1670
GOLD COAST BAKING CO INC
GOLD COAST BAKERIES
1590 E Saint Gertrude Pl, Santa Ana, CA 92705-5310
Tel (714) 545-2253 *Founded/Ownrshp* 2003
Sales 75.5MM^E *EMP* 213^E
SIC 2051 Bakery: wholesale or wholesale/retail combined; Bakery: wholesale or wholesale/retail combined
CEO: Daniel W Giraudo
**Pr:* Mark Press
**VP:* Michael Zitelli
Prd Mgr: Frank Aranda

GOLD COAST BEVERAGE
See RMET HOLDINGS INC

D-U-N-S 07-963-8791
GOLD COAST BEVERAGE LLC
(*Suby of* REYES HOLDINGS LLC) ★
10055 Nw 12th St, Doral, FL 33172-2761
Tel (305) 591-9800 *Founded/Ownrshp* 2013
Sales 1.2MMM^E *EMP* 1,500
SIC 5181 Beer & other fermented malt liquors; Beer & other fermented malt liquors

D-U-N-S 03-274-2041 IMP
GOLD COAST EAGLE DISTRIBUTING LIMITED PARTNERSHIP
7051 Wireless Ct, Lakewood Ranch, FL 34240-4800
Tel (941) 355-7685 *Founded/Ownrshp* 2002
Sales 100.0MM *EMP* 168
SIC 5181 Beer & ale; Beer & other fermented malt liquors
Pt: John W Saputo
Pt: Andrea Saputo Cox
Pt: Bethany Saputo
Dir IT: John Lewis
S&M/VP: Pat Bruenning
Sls Dir: Devyn Dugger
Sls Mgr: Mike Rhode

D-U-N-S 14-742-9666
GOLD COAST FREIGHTWAYS INC
12250 Nw 28th Ave, Miami, FL 33167-2521
Tel (305) 687-3560 *Founded/Ownrshp* 1985
Sales 56.5MM^E *EMP* 170
SIC 4213 Trucking, except local; Trucking, except local
CEO: Patrick J Maxwell
COO: Ed Loeffler
**VP:* Dale T Maxwell
**VP:* Robert D Maxwell Jr
Genl Mgr: Bobby Rolland

D-U-N-S 13-011-5017 IMP
GOLD COAST INGREDIENTS INC
2429 Yates Ave, Commerce, CA 90040-1917
Tel (323) 724-8935 *Founded/Ownrshp* 1985
Sales 33.7MM^E *EMP* 53
SIC 5149 2087 Baking supplies; Flavourings & fragrances; Flavoring extracts & syrups
CEO: Clarence H Brasher
**Pr:* James A Sgro
**VP:* Laurie Goddard
IT Man: Haitao Yu

D-U-N-S 13-507-1728
GOLD COAST LINCOLN MERCURY
POTAMKIN MITSUBISHI
21111 S Dixie Hwy, Miami, FL 33189-2742
Tel (305) 238-0000 *Founded/Ownrshp* 1982
Sales 20.0MM^E *EMP* 100
SIC 5511 Automobiles, new & used; Automobiles, new & used
Pr: Allen Potamkin

D-U-N-S 18-924-2162 IMP
GOLD COAST MOTOR CARS INC
PERILLO SAAB
1035 N Clark St, Chicago, IL 60610-2809
Tel (312) 269-1111 *Founded/Ownrshp* 1997
Sales 51.7MM^E *EMP* 100
SIC 5511 5521 Automobiles, new & used; Used car dealers; Automobiles, new & used; Used car dealers
Pr: Joe Perrillo
CFO: Roy Lundquist
Sales Exec: Jim Demeter
Sales Exec: Don Mariano
Sales Exec: Alan Sahagian
Sls&Mrk Ex: Joe Perillo
Sls Mgr: Chris Car
Sls Mgr: Sam Destefano
Sls Mgr: Sean Dwyer
Sls Mgr: Peter Mers
Sales Asso: Frank Billman

D-U-N-S 02-184-9443
GOLD COAST PACKING INC
1259 Furukawa Way, Santa Maria, CA 93458-4929
Tel (805) 928-2593 *Founded/Ownrshp* 1979
Sales 57.1MM *EMP* 25^E
SIC 5148

GOLD COAST SALAD
See RADNO INC

D-U-N-S 80-919-8807
GOLD COAST TICKETS LTD
GOLDCOASTTICKETS.COM
908 W Madison St Fl 1, Chicago, IL 60607-2633
Tel (312) 644-6446 *Founded/Ownrshp* 1994
Sales 30.0MM^E *EMP* 25
SIC 7999 7922 Ticket sales office for sporting events, contract; Ticket agency, theatrical; Ticket sales office for sporting events, contract; Ticket agency, theatrical
Pr: Max Waisvisz
CFO: Mary Driscoll
**VP:* Daniel Finkel
Dir Soc: Jerry Richardson

GOLD COUNTRY CASINO
See TYME MAIDU TRIBE-BERRY CREEK

D-U-N-S 14-334-9988 EXP
GOLD CREEK FOODS LLC
686 Highway 9 N, Dawsonville, GA 30534-3576
Tel (706) 216-8640 *Founded/Ownrshp* 2003
Sales 256.3MM^E *EMP* 800^E
SIC 5144 Poultry products; Poultry products
Pr: Sonny Arrington
CFO: Craig Goodman
VP: Thomas Frankland
Off Mgr: Kellie Bearden
Ql Cn Mgr: Juan Lomas

GOLD CROSS AMBULANCE
See SCHAEFER AMBULANCE SERVICE INC

GOLD CROSS AMBULANCE
See GOLD CROSS SERVICES INC

D-U-N-S 96-774-9123
GOLD CROSS AMBULANCE INC
200 1st St Sw, Rochester, MN 55905-0001
Tel (507) 538-1297 *Founded/Ownrshp* 2011
Sales 43.0MM *EMP* 2
SIC 4119 Ambulance service; Ambulance service
Pr: Scott Seinola

D-U-N-S 04-480-3450
GOLD CROSS AMBULANCE SERVICE
GCAS
501 6th Ave Nw, Rochester, MN 55901-2673
Tel (507) 255-2230 *Founded/Ownrshp* 1962
Sales 18.6MM^E *EMP* 390
SIC 4119 8249 Ambulance service; Medical training services; Ambulance service; Medical training services
Pr: Paul Anderson
**CFO:* Bob Perez
Sr VP: Jack Hill

D-U-N-S 04-369-9636
GOLD CROSS SERVICES INC
GOLD CROSS AMBULANCE
1717 S Redwood Rd, Salt Lake City, UT 84104-5110
Tel (801) 972-1211 *Founded/Ownrshp* 1968
Sales 44.0MM^E *EMP* 329
SIC 4119 Ambulance service; Ambulance service
Ch Bd: Gene Moffitt
**Pr:* Mike Moffitt
**Sec:* Julie Moffitt
Ofcr: Justin Mellor
S&M/VP: Todd Peterson

D-U-N-S 00-512-3211 IMP/EXP
GOLD EAGLE CO (IL)
4400 S Kildare Ave Front, Chicago, IL 60632-4372
Tel (773) 376-4400 *Founded/Ownrshp* 1932
Sales 88.8MM^E *EMP* 236^E
SIC 5013 Tools & equipment, automotive; Tools & equipment, automotive
Pr: Marc Blackman
**Ch Bd:* Robert F Hirsch
Pr: Howard Donnally
Pr: Randy Levy
**CFO:* Randall Levy
**Treas:* Richard M Hirsch
Bd of Dir: Don Quigley
VP: Tim Stitt
Genl Mgr: Darlene Pouk
MIS Dir: Rick Klaus
Plnt Mgr: Jonathan Yawson

GOLD GUYS, THE
See GOLD GUYS HAWAII LLC

D-U-N-S 03-114-8428
GOLD GUYS HAWAII LLC
GOLD GUYS, THE
7900 Intl Dr Ste 955, Bloomington, MN 55425
Tel (952) 236-6380 *Founded/Ownrshp* 2010
Sales 22.4MM^E *EMP* 75
SIC 5094 Precious stones & metals; Precious metals

D-U-N-S 36-106-0452 IMP/EXP
GOLD HARBOR COMMODITIES INC
(*Suby of* RED RIVER FOODS GROUP, INC.)
9750 3rd Ave Ne Ste 302, Seattle, WA 98115-2022
Tel (206) 527-3494 *Founded/Ownrshp* 1988
Sales 40.0MM *EMP* 8
SIC 5141 Groceries, general line
Pr: Mark Cooke
**Pr:* James J Golden
**Treas:* Keith Dickerson
**VP:* James Golden
**VP:* James A Phipps

D-U-N-S 04-540-7707 IMP/EXP
GOLD INC
GOLD BUG
18245 E 40th Ave, Aurora, CO 80011-0805
Tel (303) 371-2535 *Founded/Ownrshp* 1968
Sales 28.5MM^E *EMP* 115
SIC 3149 2369 2221 2361 Children's footwear, except athletic; Girls' & children's outerwear; Comforters & quilts, manmade fiber & silk; Girls' & children's dresses, blouses & shirts; Children's footwear, except athletic; Girls' & children's outerwear; Comforters & quilts, manmade fiber & silk; Girls' & children's dresses, blouses & shirts
Pr: William Gold III
**Co-CEO:* Katherine Semler
**Ex VP:* Robert Eschino
VP: Lynn Rosen

*Prin: Bill Gold
Info Man: Calvin Voss
Mktg Dir: Scott Tallman

D-U-N-S 01-166-2199 IMP
GOLD KEY PROCESSING INC
(Suby of HEXPOL AB)
14910 Madison Rd, Middlefield, OH 44062-8403
Tel (440) 632-0901 Founded/Ownrshp 1997
Sales 74.3MM^E EMP 170
SIC 3069 2891 Reclaimed rubber & specialty rubber compounds; Adhesives & sealants; Reclaimed rubber & specialty rubber compounds; Adhesives & sealants
Pr: Tracy Garrison
*COO: Randy Simpson
*VP: Don Picard
Tech Mgr: Kevin Dominic

GOLD LEAF PUBLISHERS
See NEWS AND OBSERVER PUBLISHING CO

D-U-N-S 06-676-8557
GOLD LINE INC
GRAY LINE SIGHTSEEING
(Suby of FRANK MARTZ COACH CO) ★
5500 Tuxedo Rd, Hyattsville, MD 20781-1389
Tel (301) 386-8300 Founded/Ownrshp 1975
Sales 30.7MM^E EMP 283
Accts Parent Randolph Orlando Ker
SIC 4131 Interstate bus line; Interstate bus line
Pr: Frank Henry
*Prin: Douglas Forbes
Genl Mgr: David Snyder
IT Man: Dave Connell

D-U-N-S 08-436-2599
GOLD MECH INC
1559 Broad St, Augusta, GA 30904-3911
Tel (706) 722-1559 Founded/Ownrshp 1977
Sales 27.2MM EMP 175
SIC 1711

D-U-N-S 17-784-5914
GOLD MECHANICAL INC
GOLD SERVICE
4735 W Division St, Springfield, MO 65802-1006
Tel (417) 873-9770 Founded/Ownrshp 1987
Sales 34.9MM EMP 145^E
Accts Roberts Mckenzie Mangan & Co
SIC 1711 Plumbing contractors; Warm air heating & air conditioning contractor; Plumbing contractors; Warm air heating & air conditioning contractor
Pr: Dwain Gold
*CFO: Gary Glad
*VP: Ronald Bogart
Exec: Karen Erickson

D-U-N-S 00-140-6859
GOLD MEDAL BAKERY INC
21 Penn St, Fall River, MA 02724-1276
Tel (508) 679-8958 Founded/Ownrshp 1912
Sales 129.1MM^E EMP 500
SIC 2051 Bread, all types (white, wheat, rye, etc): fresh or frozen; Rolls, bread type: fresh or frozen; Bread, all types (white, wheat, rye, etc): fresh or frozen; Rolls, bread type: fresh or frozen
Pr: Roland S Lecomte
*Sec: Brian R Lecomte
VP: Roland Comte
VP: Tirdad Riahi
VP: Kevin Waters
Dir Bus: Mark Strausser
Dir IT: Kevin Watters
IT Man: Joe Walsh
Prd Mgr: Matt Lecomte
Sls&Mrk Ex: Carl Culotta
S&M/VP: Carl Culota
Board of Directors: Leonidas Lecomte Family

D-U-N-S 94-999-0113
GOLD MEDAL ENVIRONMENTAL OF PA INC
1770 Hurffville Rd, Sewell, NJ 08080-4260
Tel (856) 537-6093 Founded/Ownrshp 1994
Sales 43.7MM^E EMP 160
SIC 5722 Garbage disposals; Garbage disposals
Pr: Glen Miller
*Pr: Lisa Adams
*VP: Willie Adams

GOLD MEDAL INTERNATIONAL
See PREGER & WERTENTEIL INC

D-U-N-S 00-837-2083
GOLD MEDAL PLUMBING HEATING COOLING ELECTRIC INC
GOLD MEDAL SERVICE
11 Cotters Ln, East Brunswick, NJ 08816-2002
Tel (732) 246-4714 Founded/Ownrshp 1994
Sales 21.9MM^E EMP 92^E
SIC 1731 Electrical work
Pr: Robert Zadotti
VP: Adam Belitz

D-U-N-S 79-910-7292
GOLD MEDAL PRODUCE INC
163-168 Ny Cy Trml Mkt, Bronx, NY 10474
Tel (718) 893-5554 Founded/Ownrshp 1999
Sales 21.9MM^E EMP 40
SIC 5148 Fresh fruits & vegetables
Ch Bd: Michael Bonino

D-U-N-S 00-423-3797 IMP/EXP
GOLD MEDAL PRODUCTS CO
GOLD MEDAL-CAROLINA
10700 Medallion Dr, Cincinnati, OH 45241-4807
Tel (513) 769-7676 Founded/Ownrshp 1931
Sales 80.6MM^E EMP 365
SIC 3556 3589 5145 3581

GOLD MEDAL SERVICE
See GOLD MEDAL PLUMBING HEATING COOLING ELECTRIC INC

GOLD MEDAL-CAROLINA
See GOLD MEDAL PRODUCTS CO

D-U-N-S 09-822-4111
GOLD MEDALLION SENIOR HOUSING & HEALTHCARE INC
4609 E 91st St, Tulsa, OK 74137-2852
Tel (918) 523-0222 Founded/Ownrshp 1981
Sales 14.0MM^E EMP 300
SIC 8741 Nursing & personal care facility management; Nursing & personal care facility management
Pr: Diane Hambric

D-U-N-S 09-896-2111 EXP
GOLD METAL RECYCLERS LTD
(Suby of EMR GOLD RECYCLING LLC) ★
4305 S Lamar St, Dallas, TX 75215-4199
Tel (214) 421-0247 Founded/Ownrshp 1976
Sales 137.4MM^E EMP 150^E
SIC 5093 Metal scrap & waste materials; Metal scrap & waste materials
Pr: Kenneth Goldberg
CFO: Andrew Cooley
VP: Neil Goldberg
Sfty Dirs: Eloisa Medina
Mtls Mgr: Jesse Trevino
Sfty Mgr: Laura Myers
Opers Mgr: Chad Goldberg

GOLD MINE
See NICKELS AND DIMES INC

D-U-N-S 04-002-0039
GOLD MOUNTAIN MEDIA INC
2188 Monmouth Dr, Ventura, CA 93001-3822
Tel (818) 501-7744 Founded/Ownrshp 2000
Sales 40.0MM EMP 11
SIC 7313 Television & radio time sales; Television & radio time sales
Pr: George Leon
*VP: Mark Knudsen

D-U-N-S 93-769-5401 IMP
GOLD N DIAMONDS INC
G N D
250 Ted Turner Dr Nw 6e323b, Atlanta, GA 30303-6152
Tel (404) 522-4027 Founded/Ownrshp 1995
Sales 31.3MM^E EMP 93
SIC 5094 Jewelry & precious stones; Jewelry & precious stones
CEO: Amin K Jiwani
*CFO: Sultan Jiwani

GOLD 'N PLUMP POULTRY
See GNP CO

D-U-N-S 93-771-5373
GOLD POINT TRANSPORTATION INC
1621 E Opp St, Wilmington, CA 90744-3946
Tel (310) 518-2570 Founded/Ownrshp 1995
Sales 48.8MM EMP 32
SIC 4213 4731 Trucking, except local; Freight transportation arrangement; Trucking, except local; Freight transportation arrangement
Pr: Peter Ys Kim
Genl Mgr: C J Park
Sfty Mgr: Eva Vasquez

D-U-N-S 61-304-0505
▲ **GOLD RESOURCE CORP**
2886 Carriage Manor Pt, Colorado Springs, CO 80906-3656
Tel (303) 320-7708 Founded/Ownrshp 1998
Sales 115.4MM EMP 167^E
Accts Kpmg Llp Denver Colorado
Tkr Sym GORO Exch ASE
SIC 1041 1044 Gold ores; Silver ores; Gold ores; Silver ores
Ch Bd: Bill Conrad
Pr: Jason Reid
COO: Richard M Irvine
CFO: John Labate
CFO: Joe Rodriguez
Treas: David C Reid
VP: Jessica Browne
VP: Gregory A Patterson
Exec: Barry D Devlin
Genl Mgr: Jesus Rivera
Board of Directors: Isac Burstein, Tor Falck, Gary Huber

GOLD RUSH CHEVROLET-SUBARU
See RUSH GOLD CHEVROLET INC

D-U-N-S 07-911-2323
GOLD RUSH REFINERS USA INC
75 Mendel Dr Sw Ste J, Atlanta, GA 30336-2023
Tel (877) 565-3535 Founded/Ownrshp 2013
Sales 24.0MM EMP 23
SIC 3341 Platinum group metals, smelting & refining (secondary); Platinum group metals, smelting & refining (secondary)
CEO: Joel Natrio

GOLD SERVICE
See GOLD MECHANICAL INC

GOLD SPIKE HOTEL & CASINO
See GAUGHAN SOUTH

D-U-N-S 05-444-4069
GOLD SPUR TRUCKING LLC
902 Kitty Hawk Rd, Universal City, TX 78148-3825
Tel (210) 424-3890 Founded/Ownrshp 2008
Sales 22.7MM^E EMP 240
Accts Weaver & Tidwell Llp San Ant
SIC 1311 Natural gas production; Natural gas production
Owner: Andrew McClellan
*Owner: Brady McClellan

GOLD STANDARD, THE
See GENERATION JEWELERS LLC

D-U-N-S 96-662-6087
GOLD STANDARD BAKING INC
3700 S Kedzie Ave, Chicago, IL 60632-2768
Tel (773) 523-2333 Founded/Ownrshp 2015
Sales 50.6MM^E EMP 150
SIC 2051 Bakery: wholesale or wholesale/retail combined; Bakery: wholesale or wholesale/retail combined
Pr: Yianny Caparos
Genl Mgr: Constantin Caparos
Opers Mgr: Stuart Cryder
Plnt Mgr: Alex Salgado
Prd Mgr: Ed Gamble
Sls Dir: Jim Keyes

D-U-N-S 08-474-5819
GOLD STANDARD ENTERPRISES INC
CHALET WINE & CHEESE SHOP
5100 Dempster St, Skokie, IL 60077-1801
Tel (847) 674-4200 Founded/Ownrshp 1949
Sales 82.9MM^E EMP 400
SIC 5921 5451 5421 Liquor stores; Wine; Beer (packaged); Cheese; Meat & fish markets; Liquor stores; Wine; Beer (packaged); Cheese; Meat & fish markets
CEO: Michael Binstein
*Pr: Walter Fornek
Ex VP: Kyle Fornek
Dir Soc: Zenas Dass
Genl Mgr: Barbara Baskin
Genl Mgr: Ryan Krehbiel
Genl Mgr: Jim Olsen
Store Mgr: Charlie Gilbert
Sftwr Eng: Chris Durbin
Opers Mgr: Dennis Mullin
Mktg Mgr: Dale Maple

D-U-N-S 08-092-8187
GOLD STAR CHILI INC (OH)
650 Lunken Park Dr, Cincinnati, OH 45226-1800
Tel (513) 231-4541 Founded/Ownrshp 1965
Sales 65.3MM^E EMP 170
SIC 2099 Food preparations; Food preparations
Pr: John F Sullivan
*VP: Raymond P Peterson
Off Mgr: Maryann Williger

D-U-N-S 09-861-4118 IMP
GOLD STAR FOODS INC
3781 E Airport Dr, Ontario, CA 91761-1558
Tel (909) 843-9600 Founded/Ownrshp 2014
Sales 221.8MM^E EMP 210
SIC 5142 Packaged frozen goods; Packaged frozen goods
CEO: George Thorsen
Pr: Leonard Amato
COO: Cindy Yvanez
CFO: Greg Johnson
VP: Sean Leer
Ql Cn Mgr: Pedro Osorios

D-U-N-S 00-797-8752
GOLD STAR FS INC (IL)
101 N East St, Cambridge, IL 61238-1156
Tel (309) 937-3369 Founded/Ownrshp 1929
Sales 224.2MM EMP 120
SIC 5171 5153 5039 5191

D-U-N-S 78-384-1450 IMP/EXP
GOLD STAR METALS LLC
(Suby of PERFECT ENTERPRISES INC) ★
7944 Dockal Rd, Houston, TX 77028-3330
Tel (713) 633-6800 Founded/Ownrshp 2007
Sales 42.2MM^E EMP 48
SIC 5093 Scrap & waste materials; Scrap & waste materials
Pr: Manoj Ratani
*VP: Salim Dharani

GOLD STRIKE CASINO RESORTS
See MGM RESORTS MISSISSIPPI INC

GOLD STRIKE HT & GAMBLING HALL
See JEAN DEVELOPMENT CO LLC

D-U-N-S 19-705-4740 IMP
GOLD TOE MORETZ HOLDINGS CORP
(Suby of LES VETEMENTS DE SPORT GILDAN INC)
139 E Broad St, Statesville, NC 28677-5853
Tel (828) 464-0751 Founded/Ownrshp 2011
Sales 106.5MM^E EMP 706
SIC 5136 5137 5699 Hosiery, men's & boys'; Children's goods; Stockings: men's, women's & children's; Hosiery, men's & boys'; Children's goods; Stockings: men's, women's & children's
Pr: Steve Lineberger
*CFO: Chuck J Ward
Ofcr: John M Mortez
*VP: Greg D Huffman

D-U-N-S 09-642-9956 IMP
GOLD VENTURE INC
NORTH AMERICAN FOAM & PACKG
(Suby of FUTURE FOAM INC) ★
1395 E Lexington Ave # 102, Pomona, CA 91766-5506
Tel (909) 623-1810 Founded/Ownrshp 2009
Sales 21.7MM^E EMP 150
SIC 3086 Plastics foam products; Plastics foam products
CEO: Bruce Schnieder

D-U-N-S 00-798-8744
GOLD-EAGLE COOPERATIVE
GOLD-EAGLE FEED MILL
415 Locust St, Goldfield, IA 50542-5092
Tel (515) 825-3161 Founded/Ownrshp 1908, 1983
Sales 161.5MM^E EMP 215
SIC 5153 5191 Grains; Feed; Fertilizer & fertilizer materials; Seeds: field, garden & flower; Grains; Feed; Fertilizer & fertilizer materials; Seeds: field, garden & flower
Genl Mgr: Brad Davis
Treas: Jon Nissen
Treas: Clay Tompson
VP: Paul Rafmussen
VP: Paul Rasmussen
Ex Dir: William Cruise
CIO: Rod Heiden

GOLD-EAGLE FEED MILL
See GOLD-EAGLE COOPERATIVE

D-U-N-S 96-793-1903
GOLDBELT GLACIER HEALTH SERVICES LLC
(Suby of GOLDBELT INC) ★
5510 Cherokee Ave Ste 150, Alexandria, VA 22312-2320
Tel (703) 871-2091 Founded/Ownrshp 2011
Sales 21.1MM EMP 128
Accts Bdo Usa Llp Anchorage Alask
SIC 8322 8099 Individual & family services; Blood related health services; Individual & family services; Blood related health services
Dir Bus: Virginia Torsch

D-U-N-S 09-676-3800
GOLDBELT INC
3075 Vintage Blvd Ste 200, Juneau, AK 99801-7109
Tel (907) 790-4990 Founded/Ownrshp 1974
Sales 176.7MM^E EMP 800
Accts Bdo Usa Llp Anchorage Alask
SIC 4489 6512 Excursion boat operators; Commercial & industrial building operation; Excursion boat operators; Commercial & industrial building operation
Ch Bd: Joseph Kahklen
*Pr: Richard Irwin
CFO: Craig Molyneaux
Treas: Karen Taug
*V Ch Bd: Randy Wanamaker
Bd of Dir: Derek Duncan
Genl Mgr: Jim Duncan
Genl Mgr: Ron Hauck

D-U-N-S 36-126-9715
GOLDBERG & OSBORNE
4423 E Thomas Rd Ste 1, Phoenix, AZ 85018-7615
Tel (602) 808-6200 Founded/Ownrshp 1989
Sales 27.8MM^E EMP 300
SIC 8111 1521 General practice law office; Single-family housing construction; General practice law office; Single-family housing construction
Pt: Mark Goldberg
Pt: John E Osborne
COO: Bruce Squire
Dir IT: Justin Horne

D-U-N-S 07-229-2782
■ **GOLDBERG AND SOLOVY FOODS INC**
G AND S FOODS
(Suby of SYSCO CORP) ★
5925 Alcoa Ave, Vernon, CA 90058-3955
Tel (323) 581-6161 Founded/Ownrshp 2011
Sales 186.5MM^E EMP 285
SIC 5141 5149 5046 5169 Groceries, general line; Groceries & related products; Restaurant equipment & supplies; Chemicals & allied products; Groceries, general line; Groceries & related products; Restaurant equipment & supplies; Chemicals & allied products
CEO: Paul Paget
*Pr: Earl Goldberg
Genl Mgr: Paul Padgett
QA Dir: Matt Breenan
Opers Mgr: Greg Irvine

D-U-N-S 09-645-8856
GOLDBERG KOHN LTD
55 E Monroe St Ste 3300, Chicago, IL 60603-5792
Tel (312) 201-4000 Founded/Ownrshp 1976
Sales 22.7MM^E EMP 155
SIC 8111 General practice law office; Corporate, partnership & business law; Bankruptcy law; Real estate law; General practice law office; Corporate, partnership & business law; Bankruptcy law; Real estate law
Ex Dir: Sherry Jini
Mng Pt: Michael Sullivan
Pr: Elaine Kowalkowski
Pr: Kerri Ruether
Pr: Tina Tassone
COO: Robert Oberlies
*VP: Steve Bell
*VP: Dennis Black
*VP: Denise Caplan
*VP: Natalia Celgado
*VP: David Chizewer
*VP: Fred Cohn
*VP: David Dranoff
*VP: Barbara Flom
*VP: Michael D Karpeles
*VP: Frederic Klein
*VP: Stephen Levy
*VP: Michael Manuel
*VP: David Masan
*VP: Terry Moritz
*VP: Gerald Munitz
Board of Directors: Steven Levy, Michael Manuel, Nora Naughton, Douglas Taber, Ken Ulrich

D-U-N-S 07-506-2583
GOLDBERG LINDSAY & CO LLC
LINDSAY GOLDBERG
630 5th Ave Fl 30, New York, NY 10111-0204
Tel (212) 651-1100 Founded/Ownrshp 2002
Sales 709.5MM^E EMP 5,080
SIC 6799 8711 8712 Investors; Building construction consultant; Architectural services; Investors; Building construction consultant; Architectural services
VP: Krishna Agrawal

D-U-N-S 03-269-1169
GOLDBERG SEGALLA LLP
665 Main St Ste 400, Buffalo, NY 14203-1425
Tel (716) 566-5400 Founded/Ownrshp 2001
Sales 39.9MM^E EMP 250
SIC 8111 Legal services; Legal services
Sr Pt: Frank Ciano
Trst: Deanna Nelson
CIO: Les Page
Dir IT: Colleen Javenettio
Mktg Mgr: Jennifer Weintraub
Counsel: John Freedenberg

D-U-N-S 03-957-5261
GOLDCO LLC
BURGER KING
117 Hidden Glen Way, Dothan, AL 36303-2951
Tel (334) 793-0997 Founded/Ownrshp 2013
Sales 70.8MM^E EMP 1,700

Accts Jackson Thornton & Co Pc Dot
SIC 5812 Fast-food restaurant, chain; Fast-food restaurant, chain

GOLDCOASTTICKETS.COM
See GOLD COAST TICKETS LTD

GOLDE CIRCL FORD LINCO MERCU S
See GOLDEN CIRCLE FORD LINCOLN INC

GOLDEN 1 CHEVY
See A W GOLDEN CHEVROLET CADILLAC

D-U-N-S 08-613-0804
GOLDEN 1 CREDIT UNION
8945 Cal Center Dr, Sacramento, CA 95826-3239
Tel (916) 732-2900 *Founded/Ownrshp* 1933
Sales NA *EMP* 1,292
SIC 6062 State credit unions, not federally chartered; State credit unions, not federally chartered
Pr: Teresa Halleck
CFO: Barbara Kwan
CFO: Dustin Luton
Ofcr: Richard Alfaro
Ofcr: Walter Cunningham
Ofcr: Adrianne Pitts
Sr VP: Elizabeth A Freeman
Sr VP: Tom R Genessy
Sr VP: Charles Goss
VP: Greg Brown
VP: James Deas
VP: Christian Diaz
VP: Kimberly Dyer
VP: Elaine Flores
VP: Robert Garrison
VP: Adriana Godinez
VP: Sherry Greathouse
VP: Allyson Hill
VP: Kate Hines
VP: Amanda Holder
VP: Cheryl Landrus

D-U-N-S 03-061-8268
GOLDEN AGE NURSING HOME OF GUTHRIE INC
419 E Oklahoma Ave, Guthrie, OK 73044-3316
Tel (405) 282-6285 *Founded/Ownrshp* 1961
Sales 548.9MM *EMP* 231
SIC 8051 8361 Skilled nursing care facilities; Residential care; Skilled nursing care facilities; Residential care
Pr: Holly Chappell
**VP:* Mary Lou Chappell

GOLDEN ALASKA SEAFOODS
See GASLLC LIMITED LIABILITY CO

D-U-N-S 18-350-0891
GOLDEN ALUMINUM EXTRUSION LLC
1650 Alumax Cir, Plant City, FL 33566-8461
Tel (330) 372-2300 *Founded/Ownrshp* 2000
Sales 60.0MM *EMP* 275
SIC 3354 Shapes, extruded aluminum; Shapes, extruded aluminum
Pr: Tom Ploughe

D-U-N-S 13-791-6321 IMP/EXP
GOLDEN ALUMINUM INC
(*Suby of* LUPTON VENTURES INC) ★
1405 14th St, Fort Lupton, CO 80621-2718
Tel (800) 838-1004 *Founded/Ownrshp* 2004
Sales 92.5MM *EMP* 153
SIC 3353 Aluminum sheet, plate & foil; Aluminum sheet, plate & foil
CEO: Jeffery A Frim
Opers Mgr: David Voigt

D-U-N-S 07-570-7984
GOLDEN ARCH ENTERPRISES LLC
MCDONALD'S
1332 Fall River Ave, Seekonk, MA 02771-5927
Tel (508) 336-6230 *Founded/Ownrshp* 1980
Sales 20.9MM^E *EMP* 650
SIC 5812 Fast-food restaurant, chain; Fast-food restaurant, chain
Owner: Louis Provenzano

D-U-N-S 09-990-1159 IMP/EXP
GOLDEN ARTIST COLORS INC
188 Bell Rd, New Berlin, NY 13411-3616
Tel (607) 847-6154 *Founded/Ownrshp* 1980
Sales 29.3MM^E *EMP* 125
SIC 3952 Paints, except gold & bronze: artists'; Paints, gold or bronze: artists'; Paints, except gold & bronze: artists'; Paints, gold or bronze: artists'
Ch Bd: Mark Golden
**Pr:* Barbara J Schindler
**Treas:* Barbara Golden
Bd of Dir: Nancy Root
VP: Carol Diters
Creative D: Christopher Farrell
Sfty Mgr: Ben Gavett
Opers Mgr: Edward Holmquist
Mktg Dir: Jennifer McDowall
Mktg Dir: Howard Thaller
Sls Dir: Bill Hartman

D-U-N-S 96-841-2341
GOLDEN AUTOMOTIVE GROUP HOLDINGS LLC
15601 W Colfax Ave, Golden, CO 80401-3937
Tel (303) 215-4200 *Founded/Ownrshp* 2000
Sales 50.8MM^E *EMP* 115
SIC 5511 Automobiles, new & used; Automobiles, new & used

D-U-N-S 95-874-1472
GOLDEN AUTOMOTIVE GROUP LLC
PLANET HONDA
(*Suby of* GOLDEN AUTOMOTIVE GROUP HOLDINGS LLC) ★
15701 W Colfax Ave, Golden, CO 80401-7424
Tel (303) 215-4200 *Founded/Ownrshp* 1996
Sales 50.8MM^E *EMP* 115
SIC 5511 Automobiles, new & used; Automobiles, new & used
Genl Mgr: Ed Safko
Genl Mgr: Joe Soubasis
VP Mktg: Cindy Swanson
VP Mktg: Jill Unfried
Sales Asso: Stephen Keitel

D-U-N-S 13-141-9590
GOLDEN B ENTERPRISES LTD
BURGER KING
1111 Central Ave Ste 300, Charlotte, NC 28204-2257
Tel (704) 376-0975 *Founded/Ownrshp* 1979
Sales 18.0MM^E *EMP* 500
SIC 5812 Fast-food restaurant, chain; Fast-food restaurant, chain
Pr: Hugh E Bigham Jr
**VP:* William J Branstrom

D-U-N-S 19-462-0159
GOLDEN BAKE FOOD PRODUCTS INC
12120 Park St, Cerritos, CA 90703-1842
Tel (562) 404-8158 *Founded/Ownrshp* 2001
Sales 22.2MM^E *EMP* 30
SIC 5149 5046 Bakery products; Bakery equipment & supplies
CEO: Keng T Taing
**Prin:* Robert Chau

D-U-N-S 11-809-6783
GOLDEN BANK NATIONAL ASSOCIATION
9315 Bellaire Blvd, Houston, TX 77036-4503
Tel (713) 777-3838 *Founded/Ownrshp* 2007
Sales NA *EMP* 110
SIC 6021 National commercial banks; National commercial banks
Ch Bd: Henry Wu
**Pr:* Walter Syers
CFO: Kerry Stone
Ex VP: Herbert Ng
Sr VP: Syed Ahmed
**Sr VP:* Richard Fagert
Sr VP: Selina Hsieh
Sr VP: Paul Law
Sr VP: Karen Liu
Sr VP: John Song
**Sr VP:* Thomas Tsao
VP: Judith Chang
VP: Billie Garfield
VP: Suzi Kuo
VP: Mark Lai

D-U-N-S 87-992-2821
GOLDEN BEVERAGE CO LLC
2361 B Ave, Ogden, UT 84401-1201
Tel (801) 399-3773 *Founded/Ownrshp* 1994
Sales 31.4MM^E *EMP* 44
SIC 5181 5149 Beer & ale; Beverages, except coffee & tea; Juices; Mineral or spring water bottling
Genl Mgr: Brett Birt
**Prin:* John McCormick
**Prin:* Justin Neel
**Prin:* Stephen Schwab
**Prin:* Heather Wright
Sls Mgr: Kyle Decorso

D-U-N-S 15-074-2401 IMP
GOLDEN BROTHERS INC
GOLDEN TECHNOLOGIES
401 Bridge St, Old Forge, PA 18518-2323
Tel (570) 457-0867 *Founded/Ownrshp* 1985
Sales 66.1MM^E *EMP* 250
SIC 2512 5021 3842 Chairs: upholstered on wood frames; Beds; Surgical appliances & supplies; Chairs: upholstered on wood frames; Beds; Surgical appliances & supplies
Pr: Robert Golden
**Treas:* Fred Kiwak
VP: Jason Davis
**VP:* Richard J Golden
CIO: David Vanzee
IT Man: John Goleneski
Trfc Mgr: John Eremo
Sls Mgr: Carl Lloyd

GOLDEN CIRCLE FINANCIAL SVCS
See OAKWOOD ACCEPTANCE CORP LLC

D-U-N-S 03-466-8814
GOLDEN CIRCLE FORD LINCOLN INC
GOLDE CIRCL FORD LINCO MERCU S
1432 Highway 45 Byp, Jackson, TN 38305-2710
Tel (731) 554-9090 *Founded/Ownrshp* 1979
Sales 28.4MM^E *EMP* 70
SIC 5511 5521 Automobiles, new & used; Pickups, new & used; Used car dealers; Automobiles, new & used; Pickups, new & used; Used car dealers
Genl Mgr: Douglas Lewis
**Pr:* George White
**Sec:* Nancy White
IT Man: Sean Travis

D-U-N-S 02-739-5792
GOLDEN CONSTRUCTION LLC (AL)
2212 1st Ave S, Birmingham, AL 35233-2331
Tel (205) 322-7726 *Founded/Ownrshp* 1997
Sales 40.9MM^E *EMP* 50
SIC 1542 Commercial & office building, new construction
Pr: Geoffrey S Golden
VP: Brad Condray
Snr PM: John Godwin

GOLDEN CORRAL
See INVESTORS MANAGEMENT CORP

GOLDEN CORRAL
See CORRAL OF COLUMBUS LLC

GOLDEN CORRAL
See NORTHERN GC LLC

GOLDEN CORRAL
See PLATINUM CORRAL LLC

GOLDEN CORRAL
See GOLDEN PARTNERS INC

GOLDEN CORRAL
See G C PARTNERS INC

GOLDEN CORRAL
See MOUNTAIN WEST CORRAL

GOLDEN CORRAL
See METRO CORRAL PARTNERS INC

D-U-N-S 06-178-5465
GOLDEN CORRAL CORP
(*Suby of* GOLDEN CORRAL) ★
5151 Glenwood Ave Ste 300, Raleigh, NC 27612-3240
Tel (919) 781-9310 *Founded/Ownrshp* 1982
Sales 527.6MM^E *EMP* 9,000
Accts Dixon Hughes Cpa By Fax On Au
SIC 5812 Restaurant, family: chain; Restaurant, family: chain
Pr: Lance Trenary
VP: Beverly Lynch
VP: Donna Mercer
Dir Soc: Shelly Sack
Dir Bus: Carl Padgett
Rgnl Mgr: Jerome Kelley
Rgnl Mgr: Ian Worthington
Genl Mgr: Jeff Summey
Genl Mgr: Suresh Tummala
Genl Mgr: Linda Walls
Genl Mgr: Mike Wolf
Board of Directors: Paul A Delacourt, John Farquharson, Wayman O Leftwich Jr, James H Maynard, John W Pope

D-U-N-S 79-697-3592
GOLDEN CORRAL FRANCHISING SYSTEMS INC
(*Suby of* GOLDEN CORRAL CORP) ★
5151 Glenwood Ave Ste 300, Raleigh, NC 27612-3240
Tel (919) 781-9310 *Founded/Ownrshp* 1985
Sales 25.9MM^E *EMP* 250
Accts Kpmg Peat Marwick Llp
SIC 6794 5812 Franchises, selling or licensing; Restaurant, family: chain; Franchises, selling or licensing; Restaurant, family: chain
Pr: Theodore M Fowler
**VP:* Larry Tate

D-U-N-S 07-442-3476 IMP/EXP
GOLDEN COUNTRY ORIENTAL FOOD LLC
2355 S Blue Island Ave, Chicago, IL 60608-4227
Tel (773) 847-1700 *Founded/Ownrshp* 1998
Sales 50.0MM *EMP* 60
SIC 5149 Groceries & related products; Groceries & related products
Pr: Raymond B Lee
**VP:* Jean Lee
S&M/VP: Joanna Taylor

D-U-N-S 78-144-8667
GOLDEN COUNTY FOODS INC
300 Moore Rd, Plover, WI 54467-3152
Tel (800) 489-7783 *Founded/Ownrshp* 1991
Sales 163.8MM^E *EMP* 360
SIC 2099 Food preparations; Food preparations
Pr: Jim Reed
**CEO:* Patrick Oray
**CFO:* Bob Lampo
**CFO:* Douglas Reed
Chf Mktg O: Amanda Jones
VP: Tina Check
**VP:* Marc A Gaddis
**VP:* Mark Pulchinski
CTO: Kristi Arend
Dir IT: Robert Woods
Mtls Mgr: Shane Hoffman

D-U-N-S 19-006-4621 IMP
GOLDEN CRISP PREMIUM FOOD
251 15th St Ne, Sioux Center, IA 51250-2120
Tel (712) 722-3675 *Founded/Ownrshp* 2005
Sales 38.7MM^E *EMP* 300
SIC 2013 Bacon, side & sliced: from purchased meat; Bacon, side & sliced: from purchased meat
Plnt Mgr: Brant Lane
**Plnt Mgr:* Larry Raulie

D-U-N-S 18-052-5768
GOLDEN DESIGN GROUP INC
5592 S Nevada St Unit 103, Littleton, CO 80120-1922
Tel (303) 986-7398 *Founded/Ownrshp* 1987
Sales 57.0MM *EMP* 23
Accts Christensen Tyng & Hjelmstad
SIC 1521 1531 New construction, single-family houses; Speculative builder, single-family houses
Pr: Peter Capra Sr

GOLDEN D'OR FABRICS
See MURRAY A GOLDENBERG TEXTILES INC

D-U-N-S 94-685-5251
GOLDEN EAGLE CASINO
1121 Goldfinch Rd, Horton, KS 66439-9537
Tel (785) 486-6601 *Founded/Ownrshp* 1996
Sales 13.9MM^E *EMP* 400
SIC 7999 5812 7011 5813 Gambling establishment; Gambling machines, operation; Eating places; Casino hotel; Drinking places; Gambling establishment; Gambling machines, operation; Eating places; Casino hotel; Drinking places
Ofcr: Ivan Taff
Mktg Dir: Jarrod Simon

D-U-N-S 00-922-4130 IMP
GOLDEN EAGLE DISTRIBUTING CORP
1251 Tinker Rd, Rocklin, CA 95765-1311
Tel (916) 645-6600 *Founded/Ownrshp* 1946
Sales 29.5MM^E *EMP* 45
SIC 5084 Chainsaws; Pumps & pumping equipment
CEO: Gary Bussell
**VP:* Steven L Clark
VP: Dallas Eto
Brnch Mgr: Pat Wehrle
Genl Mgr: Jim Pugh
Dir IT: Mark Saks
Mktg Dir: Jerry Kobza
Sls Mgr: Chris Seeman
Sls Mgr: Dan Sumner
Sales Asso: Michael Advincula

D-U-N-S 03-588-5367 IMP/EXP
GOLDEN EAGLE DISTRIBUTORS INC
705 E Ajo Way, Tucson, AZ 85713-5011
Tel (520) 884-5999 *Founded/Ownrshp* 1982
Sales 113.2MM^E *EMP* 300
SIC 5181 5149 Beer & other fermented malt liquors; Groceries & related products; Beer & other fermented malt liquors; Groceries & related products
CEO: Christopher Clements
**Pr:* Kimberly A Clements
**Pr:* James Grimes
CFO: Jay Meridew
**Ch:* Virginia Clements
Sr VP: Bill Osteen
VP: Braddock Jack
**VP:* Craig McFarland
VP: Bill O Steen
**VP:* Cyndy A Valdez
Brnch Mgr: Mike Oglesbee
Board of Directors: Christopher Clements, Kimberly Clements

D-U-N-S 00-209-5698
GOLDEN EAGLE INSURANCE CORP
(*Suby of* LIBERTY MUTUAL INSURANCE CO) ★
525 B St Ste 1300, San Diego, CA 92101-4421
Tel (619) 744-6000 *Founded/Ownrshp* 1997
Sales NA *EMP* 500
SIC 6331 Fire, marine & casualty insurance; Property damage insurance; Fire, marine & casualty insurance; Property damage insurance
CEO: J Paul Condrin III
**Pr:* Frank J Kotarba
Treas: Robert Kennedy
VP: John Davis
VP: Mitsu Diley
Exec: Peter Wallick
Sls Mgr: Lonnie Burks
Sls Mgr: Suzanne Hartenstine

D-U-N-S 04-143-2576
GOLDEN EAGLE OF ARKANSAS INC
1900 E 15th St, Little Rock, AR 72202-5708
Tel (501) 372-2800 *Founded/Ownrshp* 2002
Sales 29.7MM^E *EMP* 90
SIC 5181 5145 Beer & other fermented malt liquors; Snack foods; Beer & other fermented malt liquors; Snack foods
Pr: Robby Vogel
Sec: Phil McLaughlin
Sec: Robert Vogel
VP: Sam Vogel
VP: Bill Wilkerson

D-U-N-S 18-123-2661
GOLDEN EMPIRE MANUFACTURING INC
GEM BUILDINGS
1025 Watery Ln, Brigham City, UT 84302-1513
Tel (435) 723-5000 *Founded/Ownrshp* 2006
Sales 29.3MM^E *EMP* 70
SIC 3448 Prefabricated metal buildings; Prefabricated metal buildings
Pr: Kyle Hansen
CFO: Bridget Mitchell
**VP:* John Rice
Sfty Mgr: Lance Balls
Opers Mgr: Brian Bowen

D-U-N-S 62-614-2991
GOLDEN EMPIRE MORTGAGE
1200 Discovery Dr Ste 300, Bakersfield, CA 93309-7036
Tel (661) 328-1600 *Founded/Ownrshp* 2006
Sales NA *EMP* 500
SIC 6162 Mortgage bankers; Mortgage bankers
Ex VP: Rick Roper
Brnch Mgr: Alex Lopez
Genl Mgr: Tim Silva
IT Man: Jeremy Romero
Sales Exec: Gerald Young

D-U-N-S 78-489-4438
GOLDEN EMPIRE MORTGAGE INC
2130 Chester Ave, Bakersfield, CA 93301-4471
Tel (661) 328-1600 *Founded/Ownrshp* 1987
Sales NA *EMP* 500
SIC 6162 Mortgage bankers & correspondents; Mortgage bankers & correspondents
CEO: Howard Kootstra
Ex VP: Rebecca Wegman
Brnch Mgr: Alex Lopez

D-U-N-S 07-530-2935
GOLDEN EMPIRE TRANSIT DISTRICT
GET-A-LIFT HANDICAP BUS TRNSP
1830 Golden State Ave, Bakersfield, CA 93301-1012
Tel (661) 869-2438 *Founded/Ownrshp* 1973
Sales 30.3MM^E *EMP* 240
SIC 4111 Bus line operations; Bus line operations
CEO: Steven Woods
**Pr:* Karen King
Sls&Mrk Ex: Gina Hayden
Mktg Dir: Jill Smith

D-U-N-S 00-400-8975
▲ GOLDEN ENTERPRISES INC
1 Golden Flake Dr, Birmingham, AL 35205-3312
Tel (205) 458-7316 *Founded/Ownrshp* 1946
Sales 131.7MM *EMP* 744^E
Accts Dudley Hopton-Jones Sims & F
Tkr Sym GLDC *Exch* NGM
SIC 2096 Potato chips & similar snacks; Corn chips & other corn-based snacks; Tortilla chips; Cheese curls & puffs; Potato chips & similar snacks; Corn chips & other corn-based snacks; Tortilla chips; Cheese curls & puffs
Ch Bd: Mark W McCutcheon
CFO: Patty Townsend
CTO: Ronald Mauldin
Board of Directors: John S Stein III, Joann F Bashinsky, Paul R Bates, David A Jones, John P McKleroy Jr, William B Morton Jr, J Wallace Nall Jr, Edward R Pascoe, F Wayne Pate, John S P Samford

D-U-N-S 04-842-1437
▲ GOLDEN ENTERTAINMENT INC
130 Cheshire Ln Ste 101, Minnetonka, MN 55305-1052
Tel (952) 449-9092 *Founded/Ownrshp* 1998
Sales 55.1MM *EMP* 504^E
Tkr Sym GDEN *Exch* NGM
SIC 7999 Gambling establishment; Gambling establishment
CEO: Lyle Berman
Pr: Timothy J Cope
Pr: Mark Sicilia
VP: Dick Bienapfl

VP: Scott Just
VP: Ronald Kramer
VP: Diane Stone
Mng Dir: Lisa Jolicoeur
Genl Mgr: Tracy Mimno
IT Man: Eric Strand
Board of Directors: Larry C Barenbaum, Ray M Moberg, Neil I Sell

D-U-N-S 14-726-3362 EXP
GOLDEN EQUIPMENT CO
721 Candelaria Rd Ne, Albuquerque, NM 87107-2122
Tel (505) 345-7811 *Founded/Ownrshp* 1984
Sales 23.4MM^E *EMP* 47
SIC 5082 7353 7699 General construction machinery & equipment; Mining machinery & equipment, except petroleum; Heavy construction equipment rental; Industrial machinery & equipment repair; General construction machinery & equipment; Mining machinery & equipment, except petroleum; Heavy construction equipment rental; Industrial machinery & equipment repair
Pr: William Golden
**VP:* Jessica Golden
Admn Mgr: Karl Smith
Brnch Mgr: Brian Saitta
Genl Mgr: Micheal Bahramma
Genl Mgr: Karen Hornick
Off Mgr: Barbara Gilbert
Dir IT: Marcus Luke
Mktg Mgr: Lisa Guinn
Sls Mgr: Judd Segal

D-U-N-S 09-318-0586 EXP
■ **GOLDEN FLAKE SNACK FOODS INC**
(*Suby of* GOLDEN ENTERPRISES INC) ★
1 Golden Flake Dr, Birmingham, AL 35205-3312
Tel (205) 323-6161 *Founded/Ownrshp* 1976
Sales 129.0MM^E *EMP* 729^E
SIC 2096 Potato chips & other potato-based snacks; Tortilla chips; Corn chips & other corn-based snacks; Pork rinds
Ch Bd: John Stein
**Pr:* Mark Mc Cutcheon
**CFO:* Patty Townsend
VP: Randy Bates
Mktg Dir: Julie McLaughlin
Sls Mgr: Bud Miller

D-U-N-S 82-764-8820 IMP
GOLDEN FLEECE MANUFACTURING GROUP LLC
SOUTHWICK
(*Suby of* BROOKS BROTHERS GROUP INC) ★
25 Computer Dr, Haverhill, MA 01832-1236
Tel (978) 738-0855 *Founded/Ownrshp* 2008
Sales 104.8MM^E *EMP* 900
SIC 2329 Men's & boys' sportswear & athletic clothing; Men's & boys' sportswear & athletic clothing
Pr: Claudio Del Vecchio
**CFO:* Edward J Ponto
**VP:* John Martynec
Sls Mgr: Craig Lickliter

D-U-N-S 05-602-6511
GOLDEN FOODS INC
1707 Shannon St, Monroe, LA 71201-4936
Tel (318) 387-8631 *Founded/Ownrshp* 1967
Sales 6.1MM^E *EMP* 331
SIC 5812 Fast-food restaurant, chain; Fast-food restaurant, chain
Pr: Alex George
**Sec:* Jimmie George

D-U-N-S 13-511-1610 IMP
GOLDEN FORTUNE IMPORT & EXPORT CORP
55 Hook Rd, Bayonne, NJ 07002-5006
Tel (201) 243-9880 *Founded/Ownrshp* 2000
Sales 28.8MM^E *EMP* 40
SIC 5122 Medical rubber goods
Pr: Wong Ng
Sales Exec: Frank Ng

D-U-N-S 14-781-3760
GOLDEN FURROW FERTILIZER INC
311 Elm St, Eldon, IA 52554-9619
Tel (641) 652-3535 *Founded/Ownrshp* 1978
Sales 34.4MM^E *EMP* 100
SIC 0711 5191 2875 Fertilizer application services; Seeds: field, garden & flower; Fertilizer & fertilizer materials; Fertilizers, mixing only
Pr: Thomas Fullenkamp

D-U-N-S 93-098-2442
GOLDEN GAMING LLC
GOLDEN ROUTE OPERATIONS
6595 S Jones Blvd, Las Vegas, NV 89118-3337
Tel (702) 893-7777 *Founded/Ownrshp* 2001
Sales 49.2MM^E *EMP* 600
SIC 7993 Slot machines; Slot machines
Pr: Blake L Sartini
**COO:* Steve Arcana
**CFO:* Matthew Flandermeyer
VP: Christopher Abraham
VP: Jay Fennel
VP: Sheila M Pankas
VP: Sheila Parmley
Genl Mgr: Jen Owens
CTO: Leonard Faircloth
Dir IT: James Bishop
Dir IT: Ruby Manuel

D-U-N-S 00-891-1042
GOLDEN GATE
GOLDEN GATE CASINO
1 Fremont St, Las Vegas, NV 89101-5601
Tel (702) 385-1906 *Founded/Ownrshp* 1983
Sales 12.9MM^E *EMP* 320
SIC 7993 7999 5813 5812 7011 Gambling machines, coin-operated; Slot machines; Gambling establishment; Bar (drinking places); Eating places; Casino hotel; Gambling machines, coin-operated; Slot machines; Gambling establishment; Bar (drinking places); Eating places; Casino hotel
Owner: Mark Brandenburg

D-U-N-S 05-841-7718
GOLDEN GATE BRIDGE HIGHWAY & TRANSPORTATION DISTRICT
Toll Plz, San Francisco, CA 94129
Tel (415) 921-5858 *Founded/Ownrshp* 1928
Sales 13.2MM^E *EMP* 854
Accts Vavrinek Trine Day & Co Ll
SIC 4785 4131 4482 4111 Toll bridge operation; Interstate bus line; Ferries operating across rivers or within harbors; Bus transportation; Toll bridge operation; Interstate bus line; Ferries operating across rivers or within harbors; Bus transportation
Pr: James C Eddie
Bd of Dir: Mike Kerns
VP: Geoff Jarvis
Genl Mgr: Denis J Mulligan
Genl Mgr: Donnalei Sumner
**Genl Mgr:* James Swindler
**Genl Mgr:* Kary H Witt
IT Man: Pamela Quattrochi
Netwrk Mgr: Tomasz Klys
Sls Mgr: James Keegan
Sls Mgr: Gary Meyring

GOLDEN GATE CAPITAL
See GOLDEN GATE PRIVATE EQUITY INC

GOLDEN GATE CAPITAL
See GGC ADMINISTRATION LLC

D-U-N-S 05-794-7454
GOLDEN GATE CAPITAL LP (CA)
1 Embarcadero Ctr Fl 39, San Francisco, CA 94111-3735
Tel (415) 983-2700 *Founded/Ownrshp* 2000
Sales 10.2MM^E *EMP* 28,860
SIC 6211 Investment firm, general brokerage; Investment firm, general brokerage
Mng Dir: David Dominik
**Genl Pt:* Harold O Shattuck
CFO: Patrice Prodda
Ex VP: Felix Lo
VP: Doug Ceto
VP: Brian Gornick
VP: Mike Montgomery
VP: Marcello Pantuliano
VP: Nick Stangl
Mng Dir: Josh Cohen
Mng Dir: Jake Mizrahi

D-U-N-S 83-076-2709
GOLDEN GATE CAPITOL
1 Embarcadero Ctr # 3900, San Francisco, CA 94111-3628
Tel (415) 983-2700 *Founded/Ownrshp* 2009
Sales 11.6MM^E *EMP* 500
SIC 8748 Business consulting; Business consulting
Prin: Jacob Mizrahi
Sr VP: Alan Dillsaver

GOLDEN GATE CASINO
See GOLDEN GATE

GOLDEN GATE FIELDS
See PACIFIC RACING ASSOCIATION

D-U-N-S 08-660-7900
GOLDEN GATE FREIGHTLINER INC
GOLDEN GATE TRUCK CENTER
(*Suby of* FRESNO TRUCK CENTER) ★
8200 Baldwin St, Oakland, CA 94621-1910
Tel (559) 486-4310 *Founded/Ownrshp* 1983
Sales 132.6MM^E *EMP* 422
SIC 5511 5531 7538 Trucks, tractors & trailers: new & used; Truck equipment & parts; General truck repair; Trucks, tractors & trailers: new & used; Truck equipment & parts; General truck repair
Pr: Gary L Howard
Pr: Mark Cook
**CFO:* Brian Nicholson
**VP:* Doug Howard
Store Mgr: Dave Lozano
Mktg Dir: Bob Baldwin

D-U-N-S 62-158-0943
GOLDEN GATE MEAT CO INC
550 7th St, San Francisco, CA 94103-4710
Tel (415) 861-3800 *Founded/Ownrshp* 1990
Sales 27.0MM^E *EMP* 50^E
SIC 5147 5144 Meats & meat products; Poultry & poultry products; Meats & meat products; Poultry & poultry products
Pr: James Offenbach
**VP:* Patricia Offenbach
Genl Mgr: Justin Offenbach
Sls Mgr: Jeremy Lemos

D-U-N-S 55-550-0453
GOLDEN GATE NATIONAL PARKS CONSERVANCY
Fort Mason Bldg 201, San Francisco, CA 94123
Tel (415) 561-3000 *Founded/Ownrshp* 1981
Sales 50.0MM *EMP* 514
SIC 8999 Natural resource preservation service; Natural resource preservation service
CEO: Greg Moore
Trst: David H Courtney
Trst: Alexander H Scilling
**Ex VP:* Nicolas Elsishans
**VP:* Cathie Barner

D-U-N-S 87-860-2742
GOLDEN GATE NATIONAL SENIOR CARE LLC
GOLDEN LIVING
(*Suby of* GOLDEN LIVING) ★
1000 Fianna Way, Fort Smith, AR 72919-9008
Tel (479) 201-2000 *Founded/Ownrshp* 2006
Sales 12.1MM^E *EMP* 650
SIC 8051 Skilled nursing care facilities; Skilled nursing care facilities
CFO: Richard D Skelly

D-U-N-S 00-923-9427
GOLDEN GATE PETROLEUM CO
1340 Arnold Dr Ste 231, Martinez, CA 94553-4189
Tel (925) 335-3700 *Founded/Ownrshp* 1979
Sales 100.7MM^E *EMP* 257
SIC 5172 Gasoline; Diesel fuel; Lubricating oils & greases; Gasoline; Diesel fuel; Lubricating oils & greases
Pr: Dennis M O'Keefe
CFO: John Bailey
Sales Asso: Rick Leroux

D-U-N-S 02-225-2022
GOLDEN GATE PRIVATE EQUITY INC
GOLDEN GATE CAPITAL
1 Embarcadero Ctr Fl 39, San Francisco, CA 94111-3735
Tel (415) 983-2706 *Founded/Ownrshp* 2000
Sales 1.5MM^E *EMP* 54,453^E
SIC 8741 5621 Management services; Ready-to-wear apparel, women's; Management services; Ready-to-wear apparel, women's
Mng Dir: Prescott Ashe
Mng Dir: Ken Diekroeger
Snr Ntwrk: Brandon Marrs

D-U-N-S 05-469-4245
GOLDEN GATE REGIONAL CENTER INC (CA)
1355 Market St Ste 220, San Francisco, CA 94103-1314
Tel (415) 546-9222 *Founded/Ownrshp* 1966
Sales 228.6MM *EMP* 210
Accts Lautze & Lautze San Francisco
SIC 8322 Referral service for personal & social problems; Outreach program; Referral service for personal & social problems; Outreach program
CEO: Ron Fell
Treas: Robert Ramirez
IT Man: Rudy Barroco
IT Man: Chris Trujillo

D-U-N-S 04-080-9071
GOLDEN GATE REHABILITATION & HEALTH CARE CENTER INC
(*Suby of* GOLDEN GATE REHABILITATION AND HEALTH CARE CENTER LLC) ★
191 Bradley Ave, Staten Island, NY 10314-5166
Tel (718) 698-8800 *Founded/Ownrshp* 2000
Sales 25.2MM *EMP* 250
Accts Martin Friedman Cpa Pc
SIC 8051 Skilled nursing care facilities; Skilled nursing care facilities
Prin: Michael Albano

D-U-N-S 13-072-5877
GOLDEN GATE REHABILITATION AND HEALTH CARE CENTER LLC
191 Bradley Ave, Staten Island, NY 10314-5166
Tel (718) 698-8800 *Founded/Ownrshp* 2000
Sales 25.2MM^E *EMP* 250^E
SIC 8051 8011 8071 Skilled nursing care facilities; Specialized medical practitioners, except internal; Medical laboratories; Skilled nursing care facilities; Specialized medical practitioners, except internal; Medical laboratories

D-U-N-S 60-299-2851
GOLDEN GATE SERVICE INC
2812 Old Lee Hwy Ste 300, Fairfax, VA 22031-4315
Tel (703) 425-6200 *Founded/Ownrshp* 1991
Sales 22.5MM^E *EMP* 500
SIC 7349 Janitorial service, contract basis; Janitorial service, contract basis
Pr: Ki Oup Hong
Mng Pt: Gregory Firestone
**VP:* Tery Hong
Opers Mgr: Juan Galindo

GOLDEN GATE SET PETROLEUM
See GOLDEN GATE/SET PETROLEUM PARTNERS OF NEVADA LLC

GOLDEN GATE TRUCK CENTER
See GOLDEN GATE FREIGHTLINER INC

D-U-N-S 05-459-5731
GOLDEN GATE UNIVERSITY (CA)
536 Mission St, San Francisco, CA 94105-2968
Tel (415) 442-7000 *Founded/Ownrshp* 1901
Sales 58.7MM *EMP* 330
Accts Hood & Strong Llp San Jose C
SIC 8221 University; University
Pr: Dan Angel
V Ch: Kenneth Weeman
**CFO:* Jeff Bialik
Ofcr: Lisa Frenkiel
VP: Elena Covo
Assoc Dir: David Kaufman
Assoc Dir: Kathleen Kelly
CIO: Scott Ciliberti
IT Man: Miro Costa
IT Man: Sandy Farmer
IT Man: Mladena Kotchmalarska

D-U-N-S 01-099-9586
GOLDEN GATE/SET PETROLEUM PARTNERS OF NEVADA LLC
GOLDEN GATE SET PETROLEUM
16580 Wedge Pkwy Ste 300, Reno, NV 89511-3258
Tel (775) 850-3010 *Founded/Ownrshp* 2007
Sales 34.0MM^E *EMP* 24^E
SIC 5172 Petroleum products

D-U-N-S 13-744-2617
GOLDEN GRAIN ENERGY LLC
1822 43rd St Sw, Mason City, IA 50401-7071
Tel (641) 423-8525 *Founded/Ownrshp* 2002
Sales 289.1MM *EMP* 47
SIC 2869 Industrial organic chemicals; Ethyl alcohol, ethanol; Industrial organic chemicals; Ethyl alcohol, ethanol
CEO: Curtis Strong
**Ch Bd:* Dave Sovereign
COO: Chad E Kuhlers
CFO: Christine A Marchand
**V Ch Bd:* Steve Sukup
Dir Lab: Donna Haugen
Board of Directors: Jim Boeding, Marion Cagley, Jerry Calease, Leslie M Hansen, Stanley Laures, Duane Lynch, Dave Reinhart, Roger Shaffer

D-U-N-S 83-541-7759
GOLDEN GROWERS COOPERATIVE
1002 Main Ave W Ste 5, West Fargo, ND 58078-1421
Tel (701) 281-0468 *Founded/Ownrshp* 1994
Sales 61.1MM *EMP* 2
SIC 5153 Corn; Corn
CFO: Scott Stofferahn
**Ch Bd:* Jason Medhaug
**Treas:* Leslie O Nesvig

D-U-N-S 04-276-0835
GOLDEN HARVEST FOOD BANK INC
3310 Commerce Dr, Augusta, GA 30909-4417
Tel (706) 261-0185 *Founded/Ownrshp* 1982
Sales 32.0MM *EMP* 46
Accts Cherry Bekaert & Holland Llp
SIC 8322 Meal delivery program; Meal delivery program
Ex Dir: Michael Firmin
CFO: Carolyn Pfotzer
Opers Mgr: Craig Garner
Snr Mgr: Judy Bishop

D-U-N-S 92-904-8296
GOLDEN HOME CARE PLUS INC
6 N Minnesota St, New Ulm, MN 56073-1728
Tel (507) 359-2756 *Founded/Ownrshp* 1992
Sales 3.2MM^E *EMP* 300
SIC 8082 Home health care services; Visiting nurse service
Pr: Kenneth Gulden

D-U-N-S 09-411-5875
GOLDEN HOUR DATA SYSTEMS INC (CA)
10052 Mesa Ridge Ct # 200, San Diego, CA 92121-2971
Tel (858) 768-2500 *Founded/Ownrshp* 1997
Sales 31.8MM^E *EMP* 120
SIC 4731 Transportation agents & brokers; Transportation agents & brokers
Pr: Kevin Hutton
CFO: Bill Dow
**VP:* Charles Haczewski
VP: Rick Mosteller
IT Man: Eric Angle
Opers Mgr: Jennifer Surban

D-U-N-S 19-404-3659
GOLDEN INTERNATIONAL
36720 Palmdale Rd, Rancho Mirage, CA 92270-2232
Tel (760) 568-1912 *Founded/Ownrshp* 1947
Sales 158.3MM^E *EMP* 3,000
SIC 6799 Investors; Investors
Owner: Howard Golden

D-U-N-S 10-285-3314 IMP
GOLDEN INTERNATIONAL IMPORT & EXPORT CORP
300 Sw 41st St, Renton, WA 98057-4929
Tel (206) 722-2888 *Founded/Ownrshp* 1977
Sales 22.0MM *EMP* 35
SIC 5141 5045 Groceries, general line; Computers, peripherals & software; Groceries, general line; Computers, peripherals & software
Pr: Shuchi Hou

GOLDEN ISLES TERMINAL RAILROAD
See RAIL LINK INC

GOLDEN JERSEY INN
See YOUNGS JERSEY DAIRY INC

D-U-N-S 11-118-7295
GOLDEN KEY GROUP LLC
11400 Comme Prk Dr Ste 25, Reston, VA 20191
Tel (703) 815-0290 *Founded/Ownrshp* 2002
Sales 20.8MM^E *EMP* 130
SIC 8741 8742 Personnel management; Management consulting services; Corporation organizing; Human resource consulting services; Programmed instruction service
Mng Pt: Larry McCracken
**Pt:* Gretchen McCracken
**Pt:* Bruce Tarpinian
**Mng Pt:* Valerie Langstaff

D-U-N-S 61-158-3212 IMP
GOLDEN KRUST CARIBBEAN BAKERY INC
3958 Park Ave, Bronx, NY 10457-8014
Tel (718) 655-7878 *Founded/Ownrshp* 1988
Sales 26.6MM *EMP* 142
Accts Thompson & Company Pllc Broo
SIC 5149 Bakery products; Bakery products
Pr: Lowell Hawthorne
**Sec:* Lauris Campbell
VP: Steve Ament
VP: Leroy Hawthorne
**VP:* Lloyd Hawthorne
VP: Lorraine Morrison
VP Mfg: Haywood Hawthorne

D-U-N-S 83-029-6260
GOLDEN LEAF FOUNDATION
301 N Winstead Ave, Rocky Mount, NC 27804-2228
Tel (252) 442-7474 *Founded/Ownrshp* 2009
Sales 57.2MM *EMP* 2
SIC 8611 Business associations; Business associations
Prin: Valeria Lee
COO: Terri Bryant
Ofcr: Marilyn Chism
Ofcr: Marquis Crews
Ofcr: Barbara Smith
VP: Patricia Cabe
VP: Ted Lord
VP: Mark Sorrells

GOLDEN LIVING
See GGNSC HOLDINGS LLC

GOLDEN LIVING
See PEARL SENIOR CARE LLC

GOLDEN LIVING
See GGNSC HOLDINGS LLC

GOLDEN LIVING
See GOLDEN GATE NATIONAL SENIOR CARE LLC

GOLDEN LIVING CTRS COMMUNITIES
See GOLDEN LIVING LLC

D-U-N-S 03-927-0371 IMP
GOLDEN LIVING LLC
GOLDEN LIVING CTRS COMMUNITIES
7160 Dallas Pkwy Ste 400, Plano, TX 75024-7111
Tel (972) 372-6300 *Founded/Ownrshp* 2006
Sales 1.1MMM^E *EMP* 34,298
SIC 8051 8082 8731 8093 Skilled nursing care facilities; Home health care services; Commercial physical research; Rehabilitation center, outpatient treatment; Skilled nursing care facilities; Home health care services; Commercial physical research; Rehabilitation center, outpatient treatment
Pr: Neil Kurtz M D
Dir Vol: Jennifer Sanabria
Pr: Michelle Hediger
Pr: Andrea Lynch
Pr: Cheryl Metrick
Pr: Salena Nikolaisen
Pr: James Palmer
Pr: David Stordy
**Pr:* Julianne Williams
**COO:* Cindy Susienka
CFO: Jeanne Butterworth
**CFO:* Ann Harmon
**Chf Cred:* David Friend
Chf Mktg O: Hal Price
**Ex VP:* David Beck
**Sr VP:* Michael Yao M D
Board of Directors: Demetrius Freeman

D-U-N-S 08-953-5397
GOLDEN MANUFACTURING CO INC
125 Highway 366, Golden, MS 38847-9702
Tel (662) 454-3428 *Founded/Ownrshp* 1978
Sales 137.7MM^E *EMP* 400
SIC 2311 2325 2321 2326 Military uniforms, men's & youths': purchased materials; Trousers, dress (separate): men's, youths' & boys'; Uniform shirts: made from purchased materials; Jackets, overall & work; Military uniforms, men's & youths': purchased materials; Trousers, dress (separate): men's, youths' & boys'; Uniform shirts: made from purchased materials; Jackets, overall & work
Pr: James Fennell
**Sec:* William H Thorn

D-U-N-S 12-213-9694
GOLDEN MAPLE OF DULUTH INC
RAPIDS COUNTY MARKET
5694 Miller Trunk Hwy, Duluth, MN 55811-1231
Tel (715) 682-8475 *Founded/Ownrshp* 1984
Sales 13.3MM^E *EMP* 300
SIC 5411 Supermarkets, independent; Supermarkets, independent
Pr: Robert Paulson
Treas: James Paulson Jr
VP: Gary Paulson
Board of Directors: James Paulson Sr

D-U-N-S 11-489-5290
GOLDEN MARDI GRAS INC
MARDI GRAS CASINO
300 Main St, Black Hawk, CO 80422
Tel (303) 582-1650 *Founded/Ownrshp* 2005
Sales 16.3MM^E *EMP* 340
SIC 7011 5812 Casino hotel; American restaurant; Casino hotel; American restaurant
Pr: Plake Sartini
IT Man: Cris Griffiths
Mktg Dir: Kelly Horton

D-U-N-S 13-331-0610
▲ GOLDEN MINERALS CO
350 Indiana St Ste 800, Golden, CO 80401-5099
Tel (303) 839-5060 *Founded/Ownrshp* 2009
Sales 235.0M *EMP* 293
Tkr Sym AUMN *Exch* ASE
SIC 1031 1041 1044 Lead & zinc ores; Gold ores; Silver ores
Pr: Warren M Rehn
**Ch Bd:* Jeffrey G Clevenger
CFO: Robert P Vogels
Sr VP: Deborah J Friedman
VP: Donald Ratcliff
Dir IT: Jeff Newcome

D-U-N-S 02-932-5032 IMP
GOLDEN NEO-LIFE DIAMITE INTERNATIONAL INC
3500 Gateway Blvd, Fremont, CA 94538-6584
Tel (510) 651-0405 *Founded/Ownrshp* 1992
Sales 25.1MM^E *EMP* 90
SIC 5122 Cosmetics, perfumes & hair products; Cosmetics, perfumes & hair products
CEO: Roget Uys
COO: Kevin Fox
**COO:* Daniel L Lewis
Chf Mktg O: Kendra Brassfield
Ex VP: George Casale
Ex VP: Anjana Srivastava
VP: Ricco Brown
**VP:* Robert Galano
VP: John Miller
CIO: Darin Mason
Dir IT: Jason Sperske

GOLDEN NUGGET CASINO & HOTEL
See GOLDEN NUGGET LLC

D-U-N-S 80-288-1482
■ GOLDEN NUGGET FINANCE CORP
(*Suby of* MGMRESORTS) ★
129 Fremont St, Las Vegas, NV 89101-5677
Tel (702) 385-7111 *Founded/Ownrshp* 1949
Sales 6.2MM^E *EMP* 3,951^E
SIC 7011 Casino hotel
Pr: Stephen A Wynn
**Pr:* Tilman Pergitta

GOLDEN NUGGET HOTEL AND CASINO
See GOLDEN NUGGET INC

D-U-N-S 03-875-7993
GOLDEN NUGGET INC
GOLDEN NUGGET HOTEL AND CASINO
(*Suby of* LANDRYS GAMING INC) ★
129 Fremont St, Las Vegas, NV 89101-5677
Tel (702) 385-7111 *Founded/Ownrshp* 2003
Sales 215.5MM^E *EMP* 3,145^E
SIC 5812 7011 Eating places; Casino hotel; Eating places; Casino hotel
Pr: Tilman J Fertitta
COO: Brett Kellerman
**Treas:* Rick H Liem
Ex VP: Tom Pohlman
Sr VP: Mike Leonard
Sr VP: William Sylvester
VP: Amy Chasey
VP: R Demman
VP: James Friesen
VP: James Prete
Exec: Tony Canicosa
Dir Soc: Christine Haberle
Dir Soc: Shelley Roberts

D-U-N-S 05-390-5325
GOLDEN NUGGET LLC
GOLDEN NUGGET CASINO & HOTEL
2550 Golden Nugget Blvd, Lake Charles, LA 70601-9031
Tel (337) 508-7777 *Founded/Ownrshp* 2014
Sales 43.3MM^E *EMP* 3,000
SIC 7011 Casino hotel

GOLDEN OAK
See WHALEN LLC

D-U-N-S 00-193-3977 IMP
GOLDEN OPTICAL CORP
SEE OPTICAL
19800 W 8 Mile Rd, Southfield, MI 48075-5730
Tel (248) 354-7100 *Founded/Ownrshp* 1945
Sales 66.1MM^E *EMP* 1,000^E
SIC 5995 6794 Eyeglasses, prescription; Contact lenses, prescription; Opticians; Franchises, selling or licensing; Eyeglasses, prescription; Contact lenses, prescription; Opticians; Franchises, selling or licensing
Ch: Donald L Golden Od
**Pr:* Richard S Golden
**CFO:* James E Lies
**VP:* Randal E Golden
VP: Catherine M Walker

D-U-N-S 83-266-1982
GOLDEN PACIFIC BANCORP INC
980 9th St Ste 100, Sacramento, CA 95814-2743
Tel (916) 444-2450 *Founded/Ownrshp* 2007
Sales NA *EMP* 75
SIC 6712 Bank holding companies
CEO: Virginia A Varela
Chf Cred: Carol Corsetti
**Chf Cred:* Edmund Gee
VP: Benson Louie
VP: Heather Luzzi
VP: Gayle Matsuoka
Sls&Mrk Ex: Crystal Bullard

D-U-N-S 04-793-0011
GOLDEN PANTRY FOOD STORES INC
1150 Wall St, Watkinsville, GA 30677-7712
Tel (706) 549-4945 *Founded/Ownrshp* 1965
Sales 102.8MM^E *EMP* 825
SIC 5411 5541

D-U-N-S 80-017-6430
GOLDEN PARTNERS INC
GOLDEN CORRAL
1820 S Zero St, Fort Smith, AR 72901-8414
Tel (479) 649-9224 *Founded/Ownrshp* 1992
Sales 14.1MM *EMP* 400
SIC 5812 Restaurant, family: chain; Restaurant, family: chain
Pr: K Brent McGruder
**VP:* Jon Dyer

D-U-N-S 18-146-4210
GOLDEN PASS LNG LLC
333 Clay St Ste 800, Houston, TX 77002-4115
Tel (713) 860-6361 *Founded/Ownrshp* 2003
Sales 23.5MM^E *EMP* 105^E
SIC 1799 Petroleum storage tanks, pumping & draining
Pr: Barton P Cahir
VP: Jos G Evens
VP: Christopher L Golden
IT Man: Earle Stubbs

D-U-N-S 83-591-7402 EXP
GOLDEN PEANUT & TREE NUTS
HARRELL NUT COMPANY
275 Industrial Blvd, Camilla, GA 31730-3911
Tel (229) 336-7282 *Founded/Ownrshp* 1994
Sales 94.0MM^E *EMP* 250
SIC 5159 2068 Nuts & nut by-products; Salted & roasted nuts & seeds; Nuts & nut by-products; Salted & roasted nuts & seeds
Pr: Marty R Harrell
**CFO:* Paula Johnson

GOLDEN PEANUT AND TREE NUTS
See GOLDEN PEANUT CO LLC

D-U-N-S 16-176-5425 IMP/EXP
■ GOLDEN PEANUT CO LLC
GOLDEN PEANUT AND TREE NUTS
(*Suby of* ARCHER-DANIELS-MIDLAND CO) ★
100 N Point Ctr E Ste 400, Alpharetta, GA 30022-8262
Tel (770) 752-8160 *Founded/Ownrshp* 2011
Sales 4.6MMM^E *EMP* 1,000
SIC 0723

GOLDEN PETERBILT
See E M THARP INC

GOLDEN PHOENIX CENTER
See PAMPA REGIONAL MEDICAL CENTER AUXILIARY

GOLDEN PLAINS COMMUNITY HOSP
See GPCH LLC

GOLDEN PLAINS FOODS
See OS SALESCO INC

D-U-N-S 60-546-1912
GOLDEN PLATTER FOODS INC
37 Tompkins Point Rd, Newark, NJ 07114-2814
Tel (973) 344-8770 *Founded/Ownrshp* 1989
Sales 30.0MM *EMP* 50
SIC 2015 Poultry, processed: frozen; Prepared beef products from purchased beef; Poultry, processed: frozen
CEO: Scott Bennett
Ex VP: William Louttit
Off Mgr: Susan Barich

D-U-N-S 79-472-4146
GOLDEN PUMP POULTRY INC
(*Suby of* GNP CO) ★
4150 2nd St S Ste 200, Saint Cloud, MN 56301-3994
Tel (320) 240-6234 *Founded/Ownrshp* 1993
Sales 68.7MM^E *EMP* 1,200
SIC 2015 0251 Chicken, processed; Broiling chickens, raising of; Chicken, processed; Broiling chickens, raising of
CEO: Michael Helgeson

D-U-N-S 04-324-2502
GOLDEN RAIN FOUNDATION OF WALNUT CREEK
ROSSMOOR
1001 Golden Rain Rd, Walnut Creek, CA 94595-2441
Tel (925) 988-7700 *Founded/Ownrshp* 1963
Sales 26.0MM^E *EMP* 350^E
SIC 6531 8011 2711 7997 Real estate managers; Offices & clinics of medical doctors; Newspapers; Golf club, membership; Real estate managers; Offices & clinics of medical doctors; Newspapers; Golf club, membership
CEO: Stephen Adams
Treas: Craig Miller
Bd of Dir: Paul Rosenzweig
VP: Lyle Brown
VP: Ronald Giblin
VP: Barbara Gilbert
VP: Mari Ventura
IT Man: Debi Tallerico

D-U-N-S 05-936-0990
■ GOLDEN ROAD MOTOR INN INC
ATLANTIS CASINO RESORT
(*Suby of* MONARCH CASINO & RESORT INC) ★
3800 S Virginia St, Reno, NV 89502-6005
Tel (775) 825-4700 *Founded/Ownrshp* 1972
Sales 101.5MM^E *EMP* 1,000
SIC 7011 5812 5813 7299 Casino hotel; American restaurant; Bar (drinking places); Banquet hall facilities; Casino hotel; American restaurant; Bar (drinking places); Banquet hall facilities
Ch Bd: John Farahi
**Pr:* Bahram Farahi
**CFO:* Ronald Rowan
Treas: Michele Hayden
Ofcr: Antonio Mulei
Ofcr: Aaron Theis
Exec: Robert Katausky
Off Mgr: Tom Maloney
Dir IT: Zak Gulling
Dir IT: Tom Koerner
Dir IT: Jesse Smith

GOLDEN ROUTE OPERATIONS
See GOLDEN GAMING LLC

D-U-N-S 07-195-4291
■ GOLDEN RULE FINANCIAL CORP
(*Suby of* UNITEDHEALTH GROUP INC) ★
7440 Woodland Dr, Indianapolis, IN 46278-1720
Tel (317) 297-4123 *Founded/Ownrshp* 1964
Sales NA *EMP* 1,100
SIC 6321 6311 Accident insurance carriers; Health insurance carriers; Life insurance carriers; Accident insurance carriers; Health insurance carriers; Life insurance carriers
Pr: Larry D Jones
**Ch Bd:* Therese A Rooney
**CFO:* Patrick F Carr

D-U-N-S 07-199-4651
■ GOLDEN RULE LIFE INSURANCE CO
(*Suby of* GOLDEN RULE FINANCIAL CORP) ★
7440 Woodland Dr, Indianapolis, IN 46278-1720
Tel (317) 297-4123 *Founded/Ownrshp* 1964
Sales NA *EMP* 990
SIC 6321 6311 Accident insurance carriers; Health insurance carriers; Life insurance carriers; Accident insurance carriers; Health insurance carriers; Life insurance carriers
Ch Bd: Therese A Rooney
**Pr:* John M Whelan
**CFO:* Patrick F Carr
Assoc Dir: Kathryn Powers
Comm Man: Dave Wilson
Mng Dir: Ashley Neice
Snr Sftwr: Peggy Garrett
IT Man: Tim Budd
IT Man: Bryan Hubbard
Sls Mgr: Tamika Bullock
Genl Couns: Adam Carroll

GOLDEN RULE STORES
See EMERY-WATERHOUSE CO

D-U-N-S 87-762-5772
GOLDEN SANDS GENERAL CONTRACTORS INC
2500 Nw 39th St Ste 102, Miami, FL 33142-5227
Tel (305) 633-3336 *Founded/Ownrshp* 1993
Sales 75.0MM *EMP* 191
SIC 1542 Commercial & office building contractors; Commercial & office building contractors
Ch Bd: Mary F Maguire
Pr: Peter Fedele
CEO: John Fedele
COO: Ken Fedele
Adm Dir: Maria A Cruz

D-U-N-S 07-695-7596
GOLDEN SLIPPER CLUB UPTOWN HOME FOR AGED
GOLDEN SLIPPER UPTOWN HOME
7800 Bustleton Ave, Philadelphia, PA 19152-3812
Tel (215) 722-2300 *Founded/Ownrshp* 1913
Sales 5.3MM^E *EMP* 300
SIC 8051 Convalescent home with continuous nursing care; Convalescent home with continuous nursing care
Ex Dir: Kenneth Keegan
Mktg Mgr: Elizabeth Green

GOLDEN SLIPPER UPTOWN HOME
See GOLDEN SLIPPER CLUB UPTOWN HOME FOR AGED

D-U-N-S 18-647-0779
GOLDEN SPREAD ELECTRIC COOPERATIVE INC
905 S Fillmore St Ste 300, Amarillo, TX 79101-3541
Tel (806) 379-7766 *Founded/Ownrshp* 1984
Sales 459.4MM *EMP* 80
SIC 4911

D-U-N-S 00-714-2896 IMP/EXP
GOLDEN STAR INC (MO)
6445 Metcalf Ave, Overland Park, KS 66202-3927
Tel (816) 842-0233 *Founded/Ownrshp* 1908, 1987
Sales 51.7MM^E *EMP* 115
SIC 5199 2392

D-U-N-S 88-307-3538
GOLDEN STAR RESOURCES LTD
10901 W Toller Dr Ste 300, Littleton, CO 80127-6312
Tel (303) 830-9000 *Founded/Ownrshp* 1985
Sales 550.5MM *EMP* 2,360^E
SIC 1041

D-U-N-S 15-128-0260 IMP
GOLDEN STAR TECHNOLOGY INC
G S T
12881 166th St Ste 100, Cerritos, CA 90703-2159
Tel (562) 345-8700 *Founded/Ownrshp* 1992
Sales 100.0MM^E *EMP* 98
SIC 5734 7378 5045 Computer peripheral equipment; Computer software & accessories; Computer maintenance & repair; Computers, peripherals & software
CEO: Jia Peir Wang
Pr: Alice Wang
CEO: Albert Wang
COO: Dennis Wang
VP: Larry Roelofs
Exec: Dan Martens
Snr Ntwrk: Jim Thorp
Dir IT: Jason Wang
Mktg Dir: James Gonzalez
Sls Mgr: Kevin Patel
Sales Asso: Katie Lolong

GOLDEN STATE ACTIVEWEAR
See GOLDEN STATE TS INC

D-U-N-S 18-759-5553
GOLDEN STATE BRIDGE INC
3701 Mallard Dr, Benicia, CA 94510-1246
Tel (925) 372-8000 *Founded/Ownrshp* 2004
Sales 60.7MM^E *EMP* 90
Accts Gallina Llp Walnut Creek Cal
SIC 1622 Bridge construction; Bridge construction
Pr: David Riccitiello
**CFO:* Annmarie Talbot
**VP:* Paul Lukaszewicz
**VP:* William Reames
Sfty Dirs: David Blohm

D-U-N-S 02-798-4079 EXP
GOLDEN STATE BULB GROWERS INC
3060 Hilltop Rd, Moss Landing, CA 95039-9692
Tel (831) 728-0500 *Founded/Ownrshp* 1910
Sales 30.0MM^E *EMP* 175
SIC 0181

GOLDEN STATE CARE CENTER
See GOLDEN STATE HABILITATION CONVALESCENT CENTER

GOLDEN STATE CONTAINER
See VICTORY PACKAGING LP

D-U-N-S 04-441-1866
GOLDEN STATE ENGINEERING INC
15338 Garfield Ave, Paramount, CA 90723-4092
Tel (562) 634-3125 *Founded/Ownrshp* 1968
Sales 29.1MM^E *EMP* 120
SIC 3549 3541 3451 8711 3452 Metalworking machinery; Grinding, polishing, buffing, lapping & honing machines; Screw machine products; Engineering services; Bolts, nuts, rivets & washers; Metalworking machinery; Grinding, polishing, buffing, lapping & honing machines; Screw machine products; Engineering services; Bolts, nuts, rivets & washers
CEO: Alexandra Rostovski
**Pr:* Eugenio Rostovski
**CEO:* Mary Saguini
**VP:* Tom Scroggin

D-U-N-S 07-881-9466 IMP
■ GOLDEN STATE FC LLC
AMAZON
(*Suby of* AMAZON.COM INC) ★
535 Terry Ave N, Seattle, WA 98109-4361
Tel (206) 266-2335 *Founded/Ownrshp* 2011
Sales 33.9MM^E *EMP* 84^E
SIC 5999 Alarm & safety equipment stores
Ofcr: Chris Layman
Prgrm Mgr: Sarah Delaney
Prgrm Mgr: Ken Eggers
Prgrm Mgr: Josh Leavitt
Prgrm Mgr: Heather Warner
Netwrk Eng: Kalyan Sam
Netwrk Eng: David Sinn
Opers Mgr: Michael Foley
Opers Mgr: Ron Snyder
Mktg Mgr: Jill Fagan
Corp Couns: Jordan Elsas

GOLDEN STATE FENCE CO.
See FENCEWORKS INC

D-U-N-S 62-513-9902
GOLDEN STATE FIRE APPARATUS INC
7400 Reese Rd, Sacramento, CA 95828-3706
Tel (916) 330-1638 *Founded/Ownrshp* 1989
Sales 25.0MM *EMP* 10
SIC 5012 Fire trucks; Fire trucks
Pr: Harold Wright
CFO: Daron Wright
Sales Asso: Nick Russo

GOLDEN STATE FLOORING
See H - INVESTMENT CO

D-U-N-S 02-850-8703 EXP
GOLDEN STATE FOODS CORP
GSF FOUNDATION
18301 Von Karman Ave # 1100, Irvine, CA 92612-0133
Tel (949) 252-2000 *Founded/Ownrshp* 2004
Sales 3.2MM *EMP* 3,000
SIC 5147 2087 5142 5148 5149 Meats & meat products; Meats, cured or smoked; Syrups, drink; Packaged frozen goods; Vegetables; Vegetables, fresh; Condiments; Meats & meat products; Meats, cured or smoked; Syrups, drink; Packaged frozen goods; Vegetables; Vegetables, fresh; Condiments
Ch Bd: Mark Wetterau
**Pr:* Larry McGill
**CFO:* Bill Sanderson
**Ex VP:* Neil Cracknell
Ex VP: Neil G Cracknell
Ex VP: Frank Listi
Sr VP: Amy McAngus
Sr VP: Susan Petrose
VP: John Broekhuis
**VP:* Philip Crane
VP: Brian Dick
VP: Joe Heffington
VP: Mike Labosky
**VP:* John Pooley
VP: Nancy Shepherd
VP: Jeff Steiner
VP: Larry Tandoi
VP: Amy Zurburg
Exec: Charles Browne

GOLDEN STATE FRUIT
See CALFORNIA FRUIT EXCHANGE LLC

D-U-N-S 62-609-6556
GOLDEN STATE HABILITATION CONVALESCENT CENTER
GOLDEN STATE CARE CENTER
1758 Big Dalton Ave, Baldwin Park, CA 91706-5910
Tel (626) 962-3274 *Founded/Ownrshp* 1991
Sales 9.4MM^E *EMP* 400
SIC 8051 8361 8052 Skilled nursing care facilities; Residential care; Intermediate care facilities; Skilled nursing care facilities; Residential care; Intermediate care facilities
Pr: Eden Salceda
**VP:* Claudio Hernandez

D-U-N-S 04-933-4311
GOLDEN STATE HEALTH CENTERS INC
13347 Ventura Blvd, Sherman Oaks, CA 91423-3979
Tel (818) 385-3200 *Founded/Ownrshp* 1984
Sales 62.1MM *EMP* 800^E
Accts Muennichow & Associates Llp
SIC 8051 Skilled nursing care facilities; Skilled nursing care facilities
CEO: Martin J Weiss
**CFO:* Ronald Mayer
**Ch:* David B Weiss
VP: Jacob Kasirer

D-U-N-S 13-034-2202
GOLDEN STATE HOLDING GROUP CORP
23624 Falcons View Dr, Diamond Bar, CA 91765-3335
Tel (909) 860-7668 *Founded/Ownrshp* 1993
Sales 14.6MM^E *EMP* 700^E
SIC 4412 4731 8711 Deep sea foreign transportation of freight; Agents, shipping; Engineering services; Deep sea foreign transportation of freight; Agents, shipping; Engineering services
Pr: Peter Jiang
Treas: Meng Yu
Genl Couns: Henry F Hsieh

D-U-N-S 13-113-7481
GOLDEN STATE LUMBER INC
855 Lakeville St Ste 200, Petaluma, CA 94952-7329
Tel (707) 206-4100 *Founded/Ownrshp* 1985
Sales 235.0MM *EMP* 400
Accts Johnston Gremaux Rossi Llp
SIC 5031 5211 Lumber: rough, dressed & finished; Building materials, exterior; Building materials, interior; Lumber & other building materials; Lumber: rough, dressed & finished; Building materials, exterior; Building materials, interior; Lumber & other building materials
CEO: Jessica L Scerri
Pr: Rick Zaslove
COO: Paul Nobbman
CFO: Bob Bowler
Exec: Wendi Storm
Div Mgr: Larry Jynes
MIS Mgr: Mark Eglin
Sfty Mgr: Brandon Deering
Sales Asso: Steve Campodonico

D-U-N-S 60-318-4490
GOLDEN STATE MEDICAL SUPPLY INC
5187 Camino Ruiz, Camarillo, CA 93012-8601
Tel (805) 477-9866 *Founded/Ownrshp* 1989
Sales 27.7MM^E *EMP* 100
SIC 2834 Pharmaceutical preparations; Pharmaceutical preparations
CEO: James L Stroud
**Pr:* Benjamin Hall
**CFO:* Shad Weaver
**Sr VP:* Jim McManimie
**Sr VP:* Anita Wrublevski
**VP:* Nancy Carranza
Dir IT: Aaron Valance
VP Opers: Wanda Stroud

D-U-N-S 00-690-7315
GOLDEN STATE MUTUAL LIFE INSURANCE CO INC
1999 W Adams Blvd, Los Angeles, CA 90018-3500
Tel (713) 526-4361 *Founded/Ownrshp* 1925
Sales NA *EMP* 298
SIC 6311 Mutual association life insurance; Life insurance carriers; Life reinsurance; Mutual association life insurance; Life insurance carriers; Life reinsurance
Pr: Larkin Teasley
Opers Mgr: John Harrington

D-U-N-S 83-513-6268
GOLDEN STATE OVERNIGHT DELIVERY SERVICE INC
7901 Stnridge Dr Ste 400, Pleasanton, CA 94588
Tel (800) 322-5555 *Founded/Ownrshp* 1993
Sales 179.1MM^E *EMP* 1,200
SIC 4215

D-U-N-S 96-982-3160
GOLDEN STATE SEA FOOD INC
512 Stanford Ave, Los Angeles, CA 90013-2123
Tel (213) 688-7650 *Founded/Ownrshp* 2001
Sales 34.8MM^E *EMP* 46
SIC 5146 Fish & seafoods
CEO: Harut Kavoukjian
**Pr:* Sirvart Kavoukjian

D-U-N-S 13-806-0012 EXP
■ **GOLDEN STATE SUPPLY INC**
CAR QUEST DISTRIBUTION CENTER
(*Suby of* CARQUEST AUTO PARTS) ★
34928 Mcmurtrey Ave, Bakersfield, CA 93308-9578
Tel (919) 573-3892 *Founded/Ownrshp* 2003
Sales 47.5MM^E *EMP* 100
SIC 5013 Automotive supplies & parts
Pr: David Mc Cartney
**Treas:* John Cumo

D-U-N-S 79-209-4963
GOLDEN STATE TS INC
GOLDEN STATE ACTIVEWEAR
2070 S 7th St Ste E, San Jose, CA 95112-6032
Tel (408) 278-1212 *Founded/Ownrshp* 1992
Sales 22.0MM^E *EMP* 35
SIC 5136 Sportswear, men's & boys'
CEO: Scott Prestine
**VP:* Laurie Prestine

D-U-N-S 03-313-6946
■ **GOLDEN STATE UTILITY CO**
(*Suby of* DYCOM INDUSTRIES INC) ★
4425 Farm Supply Dr, Ceres, CA 95307-7597
Tel (209) 579-3400 *Founded/Ownrshp* 2012
Sales 24.3MM^E *EMP* 150
SIC 1623

D-U-N-S 00-910-8671 EXP
GOLDEN STATE VINTNERS NAPA
607 Airpark Rd, NAPA, CA 94558-6272
Tel (707) 254-4900 *Founded/Ownrshp* 1996
Sales 55.2MM^E *EMP* 220
SIC 2084 Wines; Brandy
Pr: Jeffrey B O'Neill
**Ch Bd:* Jeffrey J Brown
CFO: David Johnson
**CFO:* John G Kelleher
VP: Michael Drobnick
**VP:* Jon M Powell

D-U-N-S 00-690-8859
■ **GOLDEN STATE WATER CO**
(*Suby of* AMERICAN STATES WATER CO) ★
630 E Foothill Blvd, San Dimas, CA 91773-1212
Tel (909) 394-3600 *Founded/Ownrshp* 1929
Sales 361.0MM *EMP* 552^E
Accts Pricewaterhousecoopers Llp Lo
SIC 4941 4911 Water supply; Distribution, electric power; Water supply; Distribution, electric power
Pr: Robert J Sprowls
Pr: Patrick Scanlon
CFO: Eva G Tang
Ex VP: Michael George
Sr VP: Susan Conway
Sr VP: Tang Eva
Sr VP: Denise Kruger
VP: Diane Rentfrow
VP: Keith Switzer
Dir Risk M: Robert Fansler
Genl Mgr: Henric Szopinski
Board of Directors: James L Anderson, Sarah J Anderson, Diana M Bonita, John R Fielder, Anne M Holloway, James F McNulty, Janice F Wilkins

D-U-N-S 06-982-6902
GOLDEN STOCK ENTERPRISES INC
MCDONALD'S
1458 Peterman Dr, Alexandria, LA 71301-3432
Tel (318) 619-9567 *Founded/Ownrshp* 1995
Sales 8.2MM^E *EMP* 300
Accts Julia P Byrne Cpa Pc The
SIC 5812 Fast-food restaurant, chain; Fast-food restaurant, chain
Pr: Glenda Stock
**Sec:* David V Stock

GOLDEN TECHNOLOGIES
See GOLDEN BROTHERS INC

D-U-N-S 01-009-9427 IMP/EXP
GOLDEN TOO INC
1410 Broadway Fl 8, New York, NY 10018-9362
Tel (212) 239-4657 *Founded/Ownrshp* 2000
Sales 30.6MM^E *EMP* 150
SIC 5137 Sweaters, women's & children's; Sweaters, women's & children's
Pr: Bruce Fisher
**Ch Bd:* Paul Fischer
**VP:* Jeff Fisher
**VP:* Richard Fleet

GOLDEN TOUCH
See PLANET GOLD CLOTHING CO INC

D-U-N-S 07-884-0394 IMP
GOLDEN TOUCH IMPORTS INC
PLANET GOLD
1410 Broadway Fl 8, New York, NY 10018-5001
Tel (212) 239-4657 *Founded/Ownrshp* 1975
Sales 52.6MM^E *EMP* 77
SIC 5137 2339 Sportswear, women's & children's; Sportswear, women's; Sportswear, women's & children's; Sportswear, women's
Pr: Bruce Fischer
**CFO:* Scott Adelsberg
Genl Mgr: Gene Sawaya
Dir IT: James Feliton

D-U-N-S 00-286-0252
GOLDEN TRIANGLE CONSTRUCTION CO INC (PA)
8555 Old Strubenville Pik, Imperial, PA 15126
Tel (724) 828-2800 *Founded/Ownrshp* 1952
Sales 120.9MM^E *EMP* 300
SIC 1623 1611 Sewer line construction; Highway & street paving contractor; Sewer line construction; Highway & street paving contractor
Pr: Belinda Bucci
Sr VP: Brian Laartz
**VP:* Charles Niederriter
**VP:* David Sciullo
Exec: Terilyn Havelka
Mtls Mgr: Brad Abbott
Sfty Mgr: Michael Rieber

D-U-N-S 08-867-5087
GOLDEN TRIANGLE CONSTRUCTION INC
700 Weaver Park Rd Ste E, Longmont, CO 80501-6034
Tel (303) 772-4051 *Founded/Ownrshp* 1993
Sales 41.4MM^E *EMP* 85
Accts Bauerle And Company Pc Den
SIC 1542 1541 Commercial & office building, new construction; Industrial buildings & warehouses; Commercial & office building, new construction; Industrial buildings & warehouses
CEO: Jeff Dingwall
**VP:* Brian Laartz
VP: Joe Vasbinder
Exec: Lynn Clark
VP Sls: Glenn Rouse

GOLDEN TROPHY STEAKS
See BRUSS CO

D-U-N-S 00-284-8588 IMP
GOLDEN VALLEY ELECTRIC ASSOCIATION INC
758 Illinois St, Fairbanks, AK 99701-2919
Tel (907) 452-1151 *Founded/Ownrshp* 1946
Sales 239.8MM *EMP* 270
Accts Bdo Usa Llp Anchorage Alask
SIC 4911 Generation, electric power; Transmission, electric power; Distribution, electric power; Generation, electric power; Transmission, electric power; Distribution, electric power
CEO: Cory Borgeson
V Ch: Daniel Osborne
Treas: Susan Redlin
Ofcr: Kristen Dubois
Ofcr: David Rich
Ofcr: Peter Sarauer
**VP:* Tom Hartnell
VP: Kate Lamal
VP: Gene Therriault
**VP:* Lynn Thompson
**VP:* Mike Wright
VP: Jeff Yauney
Exec: Corinne Bradish
Exec: Nancy Lee

D-U-N-S 07-879-3486
GOLDEN VALLEY HEALTH CENTERS
737 W Childs Ave, Merced, CA 95341-6805
Tel (209) 383-1848 *Founded/Ownrshp* 1972
Sales 83.6MM *EMP* 850
Accts Tca Partners Lp Fresno Ca
SIC 8093 Specialty outpatient clinics; Specialty outpatient clinics
CEO: Tony Weber
CFO: Lue Thao
Ofcr: Lisa Swenson
Exec: Marc Smith
CIO: Ray Parris
IT Man: Jerome Stehr
Site Mgr: Brian Capizzi
Doctor: Muhammad Arif
Doctor: Jeannette Ayala
Doctor: Anupam Khandelwal
Doctor: Pat Limpiado

D-U-N-S 83-164-2801 IMP
GOLDEN VALLEY IMPORT/EXPORT CO
10911 Valley View Rd, Eden Prairie, MN 55344-3730
Tel (952) 769-7235 *Founded/Ownrshp* 2009
Sales 50.0MM *EMP* 5
SIC 5199 Art goods & supplies; Art goods & supplies
CEO: Michael O'Shaughnessy
**VP:* Vlad Kazhdan

GOLDEN VALLEY MEM HEALTHCARE
See GOLDEN VALLEY MEMORIAL HOSPITAL

D-U-N-S 79-997-2930
GOLDEN VALLEY MEMORIAL HOSPITAL
GOLDEN VALLEY MEM HEALTHCARE
1600 N 2nd St, Clinton, MO 64735-1297
Tel (660) 885-5511 *Founded/Ownrshp* 1972
Sales 80.8MM *EMP* 500
Accts Bkd Llp Springfield Missour
SIC 8062 General medical & surgical hospitals; General medical & surgical hospitals
CEO: Randy S Wertz
Chf Rad: Kenneth Jones
**CFO:* Gordon Glass
CFO: Derek Jones
Exec: Anthony Velazquez
Dir Lab: Ann Kraft
Dir Rx: David Shultz
Off Mgr: Kyle Adkins
Off Mgr: Ken Lanning
IT Man: Paula Lewis
Sys Mgr: Steve Ballou

D-U-N-S 05-903-3092 IMP
GOLDEN VALLEY SUPPLY CO
1000 Zane Ave N, Minneapolis, MN 55422-4681
Tel (763) 544-8907 *Founded/Ownrshp* 1985
Sales 21.2MM^E *EMP* 24
SIC 5031 Building materials, interior
Pr: Connie Larson
**VP:* Gary Larson

D-U-N-S 07-992-8695
GOLDEN VALLEY TCA A LLC
AUDI MINNEAPOLIS
9393 Wayzata Blvd, Minneapolis, MN 55426-1862
Tel (763) 744-9393 *Founded/Ownrshp* 2012
Sales 106.5MM *EMP* 120
SIC 5511 New & used car dealers

GOLDEN WEST COMMUNICATIONS CO.
See VIVIAN TELEPHONE CO INC

D-U-N-S 06-415-9833
■ **GOLDEN WEST FINANCIAL CORP**
(*Suby of* WELLS FARGO & CO) ★
301 S College St, Charlotte, NC 28202-6000
Tel (704) 374-6565 *Founded/Ownrshp* 2008
Sales NA *EMP* 11,604
SIC 6035 Federal savings & loan associations; Federal savings & loan associations
Ch Bd: G Kennedy Thompson
**Pr:* Russell W Kettell
Ex VP: Gary R Badley
Ex VP: Gary R Bradley
Sr VP: Carl M Andersen
Sr VP: William C Nunan
VP: Scott Schultz
VP: Ted Tomblison
Exec: James T Judd
Genl Mgr: Maryellen Cattani
Genl Couns: Ray W West Jr

D-U-N-S 18-124-1282 EXP
GOLDEN WEST PAPER CONVERTING CORP
G W
16500 Worthley Dr, San Lorenzo, CA 94580-1812
Tel (510) 317-0646 *Founded/Ownrshp* 1984
Sales 23.8MM^E *EMP* 129^E
SIC 3565 2657 Carton packing machines; Folding paperboard boxes; Carton packing machines; Folding paperboard boxes
Pr: Shirley Hooi
**VP:* David Hooi
**Prin:* Henry Hooi

D-U-N-S 17-933-1830
GOLDEN WEST RESTAURANTS INC
APPLEBEE'S
555 W Redondo Beach Blvd, Gardena, CA 90248-1612
Tel (310) 532-3181 *Founded/Ownrshp* 1995
Sales 15.6MM^E *EMP* 670
SIC 8742 8748 Restaurant & food services consultants; Business consulting; Restaurant & food services consultants; Business consulting
Pr: Anand D Gala

GOLDEN WEST SPECIALTY FOODS
See AMES FINE FOOD INC

D-U-N-S 04-123-8437
GOLDEN WEST TECHNOLOGIES INC
(*Suby of* GOLDEN WEST TELECOMMUNICATIONS COOPERATIVE INC) ★
2727 N Plaza Dr, Rapid City, SD 57702-9391
Tel (605) 348-6529 *Founded/Ownrshp* 1985
Sales 65.8MM^E *EMP* 340
SIC 5999 7373 4812 7363 7359 Telephone equipment & systems; Computer integrated systems design; Paging services; Help supply services; Equipment rental & leasing; Telephone equipment & systems; Computer integrated systems design; Paging services; Help supply services; Equipment rental & leasing
CEO: Denny Law
Bd of Dir: Clayton Wright
Dir Bus: Gabe Doney
Genl Mgr: Mark Gustaf
IT Man: Marie Tyburec
IT Man: Marian Wescott-Toth
Opers Mgr: Ben Grupe
Sales Asso: Kristen Rush

D-U-N-S 00-482-5873
GOLDEN WEST TELECOMMUNICATIONS COOPERATIVE INC (SD)
415 Crown St, Wall, SD 57790
Tel (605) 279-2161 *Founded/Ownrshp* 1952
Sales 130.0MM^E *EMP* 340
SIC 4813 Local & long distance telephone communications; Local & long distance telephone communications
CEO: Denny Law
**CFO:* Jordy Kreut
Ofcr: Greg Goddickson
Dist Mgr: George Strandall
Genl Mgr: Jim Haar
Genl Mgr: Nick Rogness
Sls Mgr: James Vanloan

D-U-N-S 80-605-9606 IMP
GOLDEN WEST TRADING INC
ROYAL POULTRY
4401 S Downey Rd, Vernon, CA 90058-2518
Tel (323) 581-3663 *Founded/Ownrshp* 1992
Sales 217.3MM^E *EMP* 180
SIC 5147 5142 Meats & meat products; Meat, frozen: packaged; Meats & meat products; Meat, frozen: packaged
CEO: Erik Litmanovich
**Ch Bd:* Levi Litmanovich
**Pr:* Tony Cimolino
Pr: Greg Davis
**Pr:* Josh Solovy
Ex VP: Daniel Dehy
**Sr VP:* Zack Levenson
VP: Ray Domingo
VP: Neil Johnson
IT Man: Mak Abbasi
VP Sls: Armen Soghomonian

D-U-N-S 08-677-9535
GOLDEN-HELVEY HOLDINGS INC
27217 County Road 6, Elkhart, IN 46514-5601
Tel (574) 266-4500 Founded/Ownrshp 1975
Sales 25.0MM^E EMP 80
SIC 3728 3842 Aircraft parts & equipment; Implants, surgical
Pr: Russell Golden
*VP: Steve Helvey
CTO: Larry Sowell
QC Dir: Charles Russell
Prd Mgr: Rob Frank
Ql Cn Mgr: Kent Hurley

GOLDENRAM
See UPGRADEDETECT INC

D-U-N-S 00-330-3146 IMP
GOLDENS FOUNDRY AND MACHINE CO
600 12th St, Columbus, GA 31901-2634
Tel (706) 323-0471 Founded/Ownrshp 1882, 1915
Sales 25.5MM^E EMP 210^E
SIC 3714 3321

D-U-N-S 79-116-7190
GOLDENSOURCE CORP
115 Broadway Frnt 4, New York, NY 10006-1640
Tel (212) 798-7100 Founded/Ownrshp 1994
Sales 59.4MM^E EMP 240
SIC 7371 Computer software development; Computer software development
CEO: John H Eley
COO: John Priddy
*COO: Mark Zill
*CFO: Dave Goodman
Ex VP: Bob Wolfert
*Sr VP: Stephen Engdahl
VP: Rob Flatley
VP: Tim Lee
VP: Chids Mahadevan
VP: Michelle McGuinness
VP: Frank Piraino
VP: Joseph S Reddy
VP: Weibel Sam
VP: Samir Shah
VP: Tim Timple

GOLDENSTAR ELECTRONICS
See WESTINGHOUSE DIGITAL LLC

D-U-N-S 17-439-5686
GOLDENTREE ASSET MANAGEMENT LP
300 Park Ave Fl 21, New York, NY 10022-7403
Tel (212) 847-3500 Founded/Ownrshp 2000
Sales 71.6MM^E EMP 175^E
SIC 6722 Money market mutual funds; Money market mutual funds
Mng Pt: Steven A Tana
Treas: Elena Miteva
Ofcr: George Hartigan
Ofcr: George Travers
VP: Brian McNamara
Exec: Omar Mallick
Exec: Jennifer Ponico
Mng Dir: Robert Rediker
Netwrk Eng: James Barry
Mktg Dir: William Cisneros
Mktg Dir: Laurie Katz

D-U-N-S 07-311-1247
GOLDENWEST FEDERAL CREDIT UNION
5025 Adams Ave, Ogden, UT 84403-4102
Tel (801) 621-4550 Founded/Ownrshp 1936
Sales NA EMP 119
SIC 6061 Federal credit unions; Federal credit unions
Ch: Don Dinsdale
*CEO: Kerry H Wahlen
*VP: Darren J Godfrey

D-U-N-S 78-556-9992
GOLDENWEST FEDERAL CREDIT UNION
5025 Adams Ave, Ogden, UT 84403-4102
Tel (801) 621-4550 Founded/Ownrshp 2006
Sales NA EMP 4^E
SIC 6061 Federal credit unions; Federal credit unions
Prin: Jeanne Jones
IT Man: Lori Hickey

D-U-N-S 05-687-9182
GOLDER ASSOCIATES INC
(Suby of GOLDER ASSOCIATES CORPORATION)
3730 Chamblee Tucker Rd, Atlanta, GA 30341-4414
Tel (770) 496-1893 Founded/Ownrshp 1980
Sales 262.9MM EMP 1,200^E
Accts Pricewaterhousecoopers Llp On
SIC 8711 Consulting engineer; Consulting engineer
Pr: Hisham Mahmoud
*CFO: Michael J Strain
Ex VP: Charles Haury
Sr VP: Oliver Liu
VP: Paul Jjc
VP: Rick Keenan
VP: Stephen Wilson
Exec: Warren Krompf
Dir Lab: Henry Mock
Comm Man: Raaj Chandran
Rgnl Mgr: Kevin K Beechinor

D-U-N-S 03-029-0993
GOLDEY-BEACOM COLLEGE INC
4701 Limestone Rd, Wilmington, DE 19808-1993
Tel (302) 998-8814 Founded/Ownrshp 1886
Sales 34.0MM EMP 200
Accts Belfint Lyons & Shuman Pa W
SIC 8244 Business college or school; Business college or school
Pr: Gary Wirt
*Pr: Mohammad Ilyas
VP: Mark Berry
VP: Kris Santomauro
*VP: Kristine Santomauro
IT Man: Stephanie Foster
Netwrk Mgr: Peter Rysavy
Opers Supe: Lisa Shaffner
HC Dir: Larry EBY
Pgrm Dir: Jeffery Thurley

D-U-N-S 05-210-1185
▲ GOLDFIELD CORP DEL
1684 W Hibiscus Blvd, Melbourne, FL 32901-3082
Tel (321) 724-1700 Founded/Ownrshp 1906
Sales 98.3MM EMP 418^E
Accts Kpmg Llp Orlando Florida
Tkr Sym GV Exch ASE
SIC 1623 1731 Electric power line construction; Fiber optic cable installation; Electric power line construction; Fiber optic cable installation
Ch Bd: John H Sottile
Pr: John W Davis III
CFO: Stephen R Wherry
Board of Directors: David P Bicks, Harvey C Eads Jr, John P Fazzini

D-U-N-S 84-912-5976
GOLDFIELD TELECOM LC
611 N Main St, Goldfield, IA 50542-5045
Tel (515) 825-3400 Founded/Ownrshp 1993
Sales 26.6MM EMP 31
SIC 5065 Communication equipment; Communication equipment
Pr: Darrell Seaba
Pr: David Rich
VP: Troy Seaba
IT Man: Duane Sampson
Sls Dir: John Poulin
Manager: Mike Loecker
Sls Mgr: Jason Beisel
Sales Asso: Wayne Anderson
Sales Asso: Cari Sisson

D-U-N-S 00-683-4592
GOLDFINCH BROTHERS INC
2812 Rucker Ave, Everett, WA 98201-3425
Tel (425) 258-4662 Founded/Ownrshp 1961
Sales 20.2MM^E EMP 60
SIC 1793

GOLDIE'S PATIO GRILLS
See CROW CORP

D-U-N-S 96-791-3299
GOLDING BARGE LINE INC
101 Lee St, Vicksburg, MS 39180-4992
Tel (601) 629-9800 Founded/Ownrshp 2001
Sales 26.2MM^E EMP 125
SIC 4449 Canal barge operations; Canal barge operations
Pr: Steve Golding
*CFO: Cindy Howington
*VP: Austin Golding
*VP: Randy Martin-Nez
*VP: Rusty Moore

D-U-N-S 07-365-4287
GOLDIS ENTERPRISES INC
I K O
120 Hay Rd, Wilmington, DE 19809-3509
Tel (302) 764-3100 Founded/Ownrshp 1979
Sales 48.4MM^E EMP 100
SIC 2952 5033 Roofing materials; Roofing, asphalt & sheet metal; Roofing materials; Roofing, asphalt & sheet metal
Pr: Henry Koschitzky
*VP: Saul Koschitzky
VP: Mike Pinder
Plnt Mgr: Michael Horner

D-U-N-S 78-816-9886
GOLDIS HOLDINGS INC
I K O PRODUCTIONS
120 Hay Rd, Wilmington, DE 19809-3509
Tel (302) 764-3100 Founded/Ownrshp 1992
Sales 36.5MM^E EMP 194
SIC 2952 5033 Roofing materials; Roofing & siding materials; Roofing materials; Roofing & siding materials
Pr: Sarena Koschitzky

D-U-N-S 78-322-4066
■ GOLDLEAF FINANCIAL SOLUTIONS INC
PROFITSTARS
(Suby of JACK HENRY & ASSOCIATES INC) ★
350 Technology Pkwy # 200, Norcross, GA 30092-2998
Tel (678) 966-0844 Founded/Ownrshp 2009
Sales 106.3MM^E EMP 493^E
SIC 8721 8741 Billing & bookkeeping service; Financial management for business; Billing & bookkeeping service; Financial management for business
CEO: John F Prim
*Pr: Henry M Baroco
*Pr: G Lynn Boggs
CFO: Scott Mayeshoff
*CFO: Dan Owens
*CFO: Kevin D Williams
*Ex VP: Matthew W Pribus
*Ex VP: W Todd Shiver
Sr VP: Rick Cusimano
Sr VP: Cheryl Schiltz
VP: Ian Culling

D-U-N-S 08-081-4551 IMP
GOLDLINE CONTROLS INC (RI)
(Suby of HAYWARD FLOW CONTROL) ★
61 Whitecap Dr, North Kingstown, RI 02852-7444
Tel (401) 583-1100 Founded/Ownrshp 1975, 2004
Sales 21.3MM^E EMP 150
SIC 3822 Temperature controls, automatic; Temperature controls, automatic
Pr: Gilbert Conover
*CFO: Douglas Pickard
Board of Directors: Ralph Goudreau, Helmut Thielsch

D-U-N-S 80-676-7174
GOLDLINE INTERNATIONAL LLC
GOLDLINE PRECIOUS METALS
1601 Cloverfield Blvd 100s, Santa Monica, CA 90404-4162
Tel (310) 587-1423 Founded/Ownrshp 2005
Sales 35.4MM^E EMP 200
SIC 5999 Coins; Coins
Chf Mktg O: Brian Crumbaker
*Pr: Robert Fazio
*COO: Joseph P Ozaki
Ex VP: Scott Nmi
VP: Scott Burns
VP: Joel Gabrelow
Genl Mgr: Scott Carter
IT Man: Mark Albarian
VP Opers: Keyth Pengal
Opers Mgr: Alfonso Montero

D-U-N-S 03-234-9292
■ GOLDLINE LABORATORIES INC
(Suby of IVAX PHARMACEUTICALS LLC) ★
650 Cathill Rd, Sellersville, PA 18960-1512
Tel (215) 591-3000 Founded/Ownrshp 1995
Sales 20.4MM^E EMP 200
SIC 5122 Pharmaceuticals; Pharmaceuticals
Pr: Rafick Henein
Treas: Mark Durand

GOLDLINE PRECIOUS METALS
See GOLDLINE INTERNATIONAL LLC

D-U-N-S 16-817-1544
GOLDMAN EQUIPMENT LLC
JOHN DEERE
3270 Highway 568, Waterproof, LA 71375-4004
Tel (318) 749-3205 Founded/Ownrshp 1983
Sales 27.7MM^E EMP 80
SIC 5999 Farm machinery
*VP: Ken Vines
IT Man: Kally Dennig
IT Man: Blaine Merriett

D-U-N-S 01-615-8714
GOLDMAN JO ANN TRUSTEE
CHAPTER 13 STANDING TRUSTEE
7 Shackleford West Blvd, Little Rock, AR 72211-3886
Tel (501) 537-4400 Founded/Ownrshp 2001
Sales 20.5MM EMP 27
SIC 6733 Trusts, except educational, religious, charity: management; Trusts, except educational, religious, charity: management
Owner: Jo Ann Goldman

GOLDMAN SACHS
See GOLDMAN SACHS & CO

D-U-N-S 00-698-4561
■ GOLDMAN SACHS & CO (NY)
GOLDMAN SACHS
(Suby of GOLDMAN SACHS GROUP INC) ★
200 West St Bldg 200, New York, NY 10282-2102
Tel (212) 346-5440 Founded/Ownrshp 1991
Sales 10.3MMM^E EMP 32,400
SIC 6211 6221 6282 6153 Security brokers & dealers; Brokers, security; Dealers, security; Underwriters, security; Commodity traders, contracts; Investment advisory service; Purchasers of accounts receivable & commercial paper; Security brokers & dealers; Brokers, security; Dealers, security; Underwriters, security; Commodity traders, contracts; Investment advisory service; Purchasers of accounts receivable & commercial paper
Ch Bd: Lloyd C Blankfein
*COO: Gary D Cohn
CFO: Sam Agnew
CFO: Jennifer Barbetta
*CFO: Harvey M Schwartz
*CFO: David A Viniar
Ex VP: John F Rogers
Ex VP: Kristian Vinther
Sr VP: Anthony Vitalone
VP: Irina Blokh
VP: Robert Boardman
VP: Juan Carlos
VP: Jenny Chan
VP: Sanjay Chojar
VP: Carmine Falco
VP: Jeff Freund
VP: Mary Henry
VP: Magdalene Ho
VP: Kevin Joy
VP: Susan Kuller
VP: Angela Leung

D-U-N-S 15-366-5067
■ GOLDMAN SACHS (ASIA) LLC
(Suby of GOLDMAN SACHS GROUP INC) ★
200 West St Bldg 200, New York, NY 10282-2102
Tel (212) 902-1000 Founded/Ownrshp 1991
Sales 324.4MM^E EMP 650^E
SIC 6211 Security brokers & dealers; Security brokers & dealers
CEO: Lloyd C Blankfein
Pr: Gary D Cohn
Bd of Dir: Eric S Schwartz
VP: Carlos Arena
VP: Jeff Brown
VP: Alan M Cohen
VP: Edith W Cooper
VP: Doug Cornell
VP: Joseph Deluca
VP: Catalina Hayata
VP: Richard Horn
VP: Andrea Kirk
VP: Stuart Leigh
VP: Tom Osmond
VP: Yorke Rhodes
VP: Harvey M Schwartz
VP: Joe Todd
VP: Cassandra Tok
Exec: Christopher Babick
Exec: Gerhard Doetsch
Exec: David Geen

D-U-N-S 78-581-4661
■ GOLDMAN SACHS ASSET MANAGEMENT LP
(Suby of GOLDMAN SACHS GROUP INC) ★
200 West St Bldg 200, New York, NY 10282-2102
Tel (212) 902-1000 Founded/Ownrshp 1990
Sales 27.3MM^E EMP 40^E
SIC 6282 Investment advisory service
CEO: Lloyd C Blankfein
VP: Christopher Biasotti
VP: Bunty Bohra
VP: Roderick Chisholm
VP: Tamara Conway
VP: Joe Hornback
VP: Justin Mauskopf
VP: Adam Sall
VP: Jenna Shen
VP: Nadine Singer
Dir Risk M: Ahmad Farah

D-U-N-S 82-758-0320
■ GOLDMAN SACHS BANK USA HOLDINGS LLC
(Suby of GOLDMAN SACHS GROUP INC) ★
200 West St Bldg 200, New York, NY 10282-2102
Tel (212) 357-2882 Founded/Ownrshp 2008
Sales NA EMP 6
SIC 6029 Commercial banks; Commercial banks
V Ch: Alastair Lucas

D-U-N-S 07-872-5615
GOLDMAN SACHS BDC INC
200 West St Bldg 200, New York, NY 10282-2102
Tel (212) 902-1000 Founded/Ownrshp 2012
Sales 73.2MM EMP 8^E
Accts Pricewaterhousecoopers Llp Bo
SIC 6726 Investment offices
Pr: Brendan McGovern
*Ch Bd: Ashok N Bakhru
COO: Jon Yoder
CFO: Jonathan Lamm
Ofcr: Alison Conn
VP: Jason Cirrito
VP: Ida Hoghooghi
VP: Russ Hutchinson
VP: Rajeev Kasthuri
VP: Debbie Kemp
VP: Tracy McCaffrey
VP: Ruth Pan
VP: David Rmonk

D-U-N-S 96-933-5582
GOLDMAN SACHS CHARITABLE GIFT FUND
200 West St Fl 29, New York, NY 10282-2102
Tel (212) 902-4223 Founded/Ownrshp 2011
Sales 145.9MM EMP 1
Accts Pricewaterhousecoopers Llp
SIC 5947 Gift shop; Gift shop
CEO: Dina H Powell

D-U-N-S 93-259-0870
■ GOLDMAN SACHS EXECUTION CLEARING LP
(Suby of GOLDMAN SACHS GROUP INC) ★
30 Hudson St, Jersey City, NJ 07302-4600
Tel (201) 332-3577 Founded/Ownrshp 2001
Sales 38.2MM^E EMP 340
SIC 6211 Security brokers & dealers; Security brokers & dealers
Pt: Lloyd C Blankfein
Pt: John H Bryan
VP: Meghan Herrmann

D-U-N-S 78-563-9613
GOLDMAN SACHS FOUNDATION
375 Park Ave Ste 1002, New York, NY 10152-0002
Tel (212) 902-6875 Founded/Ownrshp 2006
Sales 314.5MM EMP 1
SIC 8748 Business consulting; Business consulting
Prin: Alastair Lucas
VP: Lloyd Ucko

D-U-N-S 05-916-4314 IMP
▲ GOLDMAN SACHS GROUP INC
200 West St Bldg 200, New York, NY 10282-2198
Tel (212) 902-1000 Founded/Ownrshp 1869
Sales 34.5MMM EMP 34,000
Tkr Sym GS Exch NYS
SIC 6211 Security brokers & dealers; Security brokers & dealers; Investment bankers
Ch Bd: Lloyd C Blankfein
*Pr: Gary D Cohn
Pr: Ken Hitchner
COO: Jim Esposito
COO: Eri Kakuta
CFO: Harvey M Schwartz
Ch: Jack Levy
Ofcr: Steven Kerr
Ofcr: Stephen M Scherr
Ofcr: Barry L Zubrow
Ex VP: Alan M Cohen
Ex VP: Edith W Cooper
Ex VP: Gregory K Palm
Ex VP: John F Rogers

D-U-N-S 95-801-9754
■ GOLDMAN SACHS REALTY MANAGEMENT LP
ARCHON HOSPITALITY
(Suby of GOLDMAN SACHS GROUP INC) ★
6011 Connection Dr, Irving, TX 75039-2607
Tel (972) 368-2200 Founded/Ownrshp 1996
Sales 87.6MM^E EMP 614
SIC 8741 Financial management for business; Financial management for business
Pt: James L Lozier Jr
Ofcr: Saleh Igal
VP: Curtis Ambrose
VP: Tanya Davis
VP: Curtis Harrison
VP: Mark Ricketts
VP: Chris Semple
VP: Ryan Stutz
VP: Chris Zertuchewong
Dir Risk M: Tom Bergstrom
Dir Risk M: Caroline Riskey

D-U-N-S 02-417-4182
GOLDMAN SCHOOL OF DENTAL MEDICINE
100 East Newton St, Roxbury, MA 02118-2308
Tel (617) 638-4778 Founded/Ownrshp 1955
Sales 2.0MM EMP 400
SIC 8249 8221 Medical & dental assistant school; University; Medical & dental assistant school; University
Prin: Spencer Frankl

D-U-N-S 00-498-9695 IMP
GOLDNER ASSOCIATES INC (TN)
231 Venture Cir, Nashville, TN 37228-1603
Tel (615) 244-3007 Founded/Ownrshp 1969, 1990
Sales 33.1MM^E EMP 62
SIC 5199 Advertising specialties

CEO: James Straus
**Sec:* Norma Neaderthal
**VP:* Andrew Straus
**VP:* Elise N Straus
Off Mgr: Phyllis Knight
Prd Mgr: Ricky Garrigus
Mktg Dir: Laurie Aronoff

D-U-N-S 78-708-2304
GOLDNER HAWN JOHNSON & MORRISON INC
GHJ&M
3700 Wells Fargo Ctr # 90, Minneapolis, MN 55402
Tel (612) 338-5912 *Founded/Ownrshp* 1989
Sales 165.2MM^E *EMP* 616
SIC 6211 Investment firm, general brokerage; Investment firm, general brokerage
Mng Dir: John L Morrison
**CFO:* Aaron J Goldstein
**VP:* Jason T Brass
**VP:* Van Zandt Hawn
**VP:* Michael E Healy
**VP:* Joseph M Heinen
VP: Joseph Helms
**VP:* Timothy D Johnson
Mng Dir: Chad Cornell
Mng Dir: John Jack
Mng Dir: Gary Obermiller

GOLDNER, HERMAN COMPANY
See HERMAN GOLDNER CO INC

D-U-N-S 87-852-7365
GOLDPOINT MORTGAGE BANKERS INC
60 Cuttermill Rd Ste 200, Great Neck, NY 11021-3132
Tel (516) 829-5353 *Founded/Ownrshp* 1994
Sales NA *EMP* 23
SIC 6162 Mortgage bankers; Mortgage bankers
Pr: John Lamendola
**VP:* Lenora Bakey

D-U-N-S 36-061-2808
GOLDRICH & KEST INDUSTRIES LLC
5150 Overland Ave, Culver City, CA 90230-4914
Tel (310) 204-2050 *Founded/Ownrshp* 1957
Sales 221.8MM^E *EMP* 885
SIC 6552 Subdividers & developers; Subdividers & developers

D-U-N-S 05-224-7418
GOLDRICH AND KEST CONSTRUCTION MANAGEMENT CORP A CALIFORNIA CORP
5150 Overland Ave, Culver City, CA 90230-4914
Tel (310) 204-2050 *Founded/Ownrshp* 1963
Sales 1.3MM *EMP* 276
SIC 6552 Land subdividers & developers, commercial; Land subdividers & developers, commercial
Pr: Jona Goldrich
**VP:* Sol Kest

D-U-N-S 00-509-7901
GOLDRUSH LLC
575 Lynnhven Pkwy Ste 260, Virginia Beach, VA 23452
Tel (757) 248-2506 *Founded/Ownrshp* 2008
Sales 56.0MM *EMP* 610
SIC 7389 Financial services

GOLDS GYM
See BODY FIRM AEROBICS INC

GOLDS GYM
See MUSCLEBOUND INC

D-U-N-S 09-306-9797
GOLDS GYM INTERNATIONAL INC
(*Suby of* OMNI HOTELS) ★
125 E J Carpentr Fwy 13, Irving, TX 75062
Tel (972) 444-8527 *Founded/Ownrshp* 1979, 2004
Sales 136.8MM^E *EMP* 2,000
SIC 7991 6794 Physical fitness facilities; Franchises, selling or licensing; Physical fitness facilities; Franchises, selling or licensing
Pr: David Schnabel
**COO:* Mike Feinman
COO: Mustafa Ibrahim
CFO: Randall R Schultz
CFO: Gene Snowden
**Chf Mktg O:* Michael Cobb
Ex VP: Todd Scartozzi
Sr VP: Aaron Watkins
VP: Kay Corio
VP: Scott Corless
VP: Bill Wade
Comm Man: Rosalynn Vasquez

D-U-N-S 06-192-8505
GOLDS HOLDING CORP
4001 Maple Ave Ste 200, Dallas, TX 75219-3249
Tel (214) 574-4653 *Founded/Ownrshp* 1999
Sales 107.6MM^E *EMP* 426^E
SIC 6719 Investment holding companies, except banks
CEO: James D Caldwell
**Pr:* James Snow
**VP:* Michael Smith

D-U-N-S 79-436-1212
GOLDS MARKET INC
GOLD'S PICK N SAVE
301 Falls Rd Stop 1, Grafton, WI 53024-2620
Tel (262) 375-1628 *Founded/Ownrshp* 1994
Sales 25.4MM^E *EMP* 600
SIC 5411 2051 Grocery stores; Bread, cake & related products; Grocery stores; Bread, cake & related products
Pr: Robert Gold

GOLD'S PICK N SAVE
See GOLDS MARKET INC

GOLDSBORO IRON & METAL
See RALEIGH RECYCLING NC SCRAP METAL LLC

GOLDSBORO MIL & GRN STOR CO
See GOLDSBORO MILLING CO

D-U-N-S 00-319-7142
GOLDSBORO MILLING CO (NC)
GOLDSBORO MIL & GRN STOR CO
938 Millers Chapel Rd, Goldsboro, NC 27534-7772
Tel (919) 778-3130 *Founded/Ownrshp* 1916, 1951
Sales 175.8MM^E *EMP* 800^E
SIC 2048 Poultry feeds; Livestock feeds; Poultry feeds; Livestock feeds
Ch Bd: J L Maxwell Jr
**Pr:* Hugh Gordon Maxwell III
**CFO:* Thomas Howell
**Sec:* J L Maxwell III
VP: Jere Pelletier
**VP:* J W Pelletier III
VP: Walter Pelletier
MIS Dir: Eric Letchworth
Prd Mgr: Lorenz Falls

D-U-N-S 83-150-7954
GOLDSHIELD FIBERGLASS INC
(*Suby of* ALLIED SPECIALTY VEHICLES INC) ★
2004 Patterson St, Decatur, IN 46733-1867
Tel (260) 728-2476 *Founded/Ownrshp* 2009
Sales 32.7MM^E *EMP* 150
SIC 2221 Fiberglass fabrics
Pr: Jeff Newport
Genl Mgr: Peter Stephenson
Mtls Mgr: Rodger Cornett
Sls Dir: Bryan Smith

GOLDSIGN
See CITIZENS OF HUMANITY LLC

GOLDSMITH SEEDS
See SYNGENTA CROP PROTECTION LLC

GOLDSTEIN BUICK
See ALAN BUICK INC

GOLDSTEIN CHRYSLER JEEP
See GOLDSTEIN CHRYSLER-PLYMOUTH INC

D-U-N-S 09-835-0762
GOLDSTEIN CHRYSLER-PLYMOUTH INC
GOLDSTEIN CHRYSLER JEEP
(*Suby of* GOLDSTEIN ENTERPRISES INC)
613 Loudonville Rd, Latham, NY 12110
Tel (518) 785-4156 *Founded/Ownrshp* 1979
Sales 22.6MM^E *EMP* 60
SIC 5511 Automobiles, new & used; Automobiles, new & used
Owner: Alan Goldstein
Genl Mgr: Tom Grindstaff
Genl Mgr: Ed Serian

D-U-N-S 12-819-1033
GOLDSTEIN GROUP INC
2117 State St, Bettendorf, IA 52722-6040
Tel (563) 344-5000 *Founded/Ownrshp* 2002
Sales 48.4MM^E *EMP* 850
SIC 4449 5093 River transportation, except on the St. Lawrence Seaway; Scrap & waste materials; River transportation, except on the St. Lawrence Seaway; Scrap & waste materials
CEO: Jeff Goldstein
**Ch Bd:* Bernard Goldstein
**Pr:* Jeffrey D Goldstein
**Ex VP:* Richard A Goldstein
**VP:* Tom Streight

D-U-N-S 06-378-8210
GOLDSTEIN MOTORS INC
GOLDSTEIN SUBARU
(*Suby of* GOLDSTEIN ENTERPRISES INC)
1754 Central Ave, Albany, NY 12205-4789
Tel (518) 869-1250 *Founded/Ownrshp* 1965
Sales 20.8MM^E *EMP* 50
SIC 5511 Automobiles, new & used
Pr: Alan Goldstein
**VP:* Stefanie Goldstein

GOLDSTEIN SUBARU
See GOLDSTEIN MOTORS INC

GOLDSTEIN, SWANK & GORDON
See HANNOUSH JEWELERS INC

GOLDSTEINS FURNITURE
See M N GOLDSTEIN CO

GOLDSTON'S BUILDING SUPPLY
See BUILDERS FIRSTSOURCE - RALEIGH LLC

D-U-N-S 03-695-0462
GOLDSTREAM INC
(*Suby of* SC FUELS) ★
1800 W Katella Ave # 400, Orange, CA 92867-3449
Tel (714) 744-7140 *Founded/Ownrshp* 2010
Sales 33.4MM^E *EMP* 254^E
SIC 1311 Crude petroleum & natural gas; Crude petroleum & natural gas
Pr: Frank P Greinke
**Treas:* Mimi S Taylor
**Sec:* Robert W Bollar

D-U-N-S 00-235-8463 IMP/EXP
GOLDTOEMORETZ LLC
514 W 21st St, Newton, NC 28658-3763
Tel (828) 464-0751 *Founded/Ownrshp* 1990
Sales NA *EMP* 500
SIC 2251 2252

D-U-N-S 80-950-6137
GOLDWORTH FINANCIAL INC
21820 Burbank Blvd # 325, Woodland Hills, CA 91367-7459
Tel (818) 444-7103 *Founded/Ownrshp* 1999
Sales 47.0MM *EMP* 17
SIC 5944 Jewelry, precious stones & precious metals; Jewelry, precious stones & precious metals
Pr: Teresa Panameno
VP: Alex Panameno

D-U-N-S 04-095-5502
GOLETA UNION SCHOOL DISTRICT
401 N Fairview Ave, Goleta, CA 93117-1796
Tel (805) 681-1200 *Founded/Ownrshp* 1900
Sales 36.0MM *EMP* 500
SIC 8211 Public elementary school; Public elementary school

Pr: Susan Epstein
**VP:* Dean Nevins
Psych: Joe Isaacson

D-U-N-S 80-017-3791
GOLETA VALLEY COMMUNITY HOSPITAL
(*Suby of* COTTAGE HOSPITAL CHILDRENS CTR) ★
351 S Patterson Ave, Santa Barbara, CA 93111-2403
Tel (805) 967-3411 *Founded/Ownrshp* 1972
Sales 74.9MM *EMP* 2
Accts Department Of Charitable Trust
SIC 7389 Fund raising organizations
VP: Wende Cappeta
VP: Lisa Moore
VP: Tiana Riskowski
VP: Ed Wroblewski
Exec: John Colt
CIO: Alberto Kiwi

D-U-N-S 04-645-1209
GOLETA VALLEY COTTAGE HOSPITAL
COTTAGE HEALTH SYSTEM
351 S Patterson Ave, Santa Barbara, CA 93111-2403
Tel (805) 967-3411 *Founded/Ownrshp* 1983
Sales 74.9MM *EMP* 275
SIC 8062 General medical & surgical hospitals; General medical & surgical hospitals
Pr: Ronald C Werft
**Ch Bd:* Robert Knight
**CFO:* Joan Bricher
VP: Jeff Allen
**VP:* Diane Wisby
Exec: Christine Gutierrez
Dir Rad: Michael A Trambert
Dir Rx: Allan Cohen
Chf Nrs Of: Herbert Gary
CTO: Albert Okywi
Doctor: David Gillon
Board of Directors: Robert Reid

D-U-N-S 07-879-8386
GOLETA WATER DISTRICT (CORP)
4699 Hollister Ave, Goleta, CA 93110-1999
Tel (805) 964-6761 *Founded/Ownrshp* 1944
Sales 29.8MM *EMP* 63
SIC 4941

D-U-N-S 12-864-7299
GOLF & TENNIS PRO SHOP INC
PGA TOUR SUPERSTORE
1801 Old Alabama Rd # 150, Roswell, GA 30076-2764
Tel (770) 640-0933 *Founded/Ownrshp* 2003
Sales 106.3MM^E *EMP* 700
SIC 5699 5941 Sports apparel; Golf goods & equipment; Tennis goods & equipment; Sports apparel; Golf goods & equipment; Tennis goods & equipment
CEO: Richard L Sullivan
**CFO:* Alan E Kessok
Chf Mktg O: Matt Corey
VP: Grady Stewart
Genl Mgr: Dustin Mahoney
Genl Mgr: Randy Ramsey
Genl Mgr: David Seckler
Genl Mgr: Mark Sternfels
Genl Mgr: Bridget Zuri
Store Mgr: Scott Warman
CIO: Stephen McDonnold

GOLF CENTER AT KINGS ISLAND
See GRIZZLY GOLF CENTER INC

GOLF CHANNEL, THE
See TGC INC

D-U-N-S 05-041-3568
GOLF CHANNEL LLC
7580 Golf Channel Dr, Orlando, FL 32819-8947
Tel (407) 355-4171 *Founded/Ownrshp* 2012
Sales 72.3MM^E *EMP* 416^E
SIC 7999 Golf services & professionals
Exec: Jeff Hill
Assoc Dir: Corbett Compel
Creative D: David Piccolo
**Prin:* Page Boudreau
Off Mgr: Patricia Anderson
Off Admin: Flora Szivos
CTO: Jenn Alter
Dir IT: Mike Aellig
Pr Mgr: Jeremy Friedman
Art Dir: Paul Devault
Snr Mgr: Matthew Shiles

GOLF CLUB AT DESERT MOUNTAIN
See DESERT MOUNTAIN PROPERTIES LIMITED PARTNERSHIP

GOLF CLUB AT NEW CASTLE
See NEW CASTLE GOLF LLC

GOLF CNTRY CLB ADM FOR VLLAGES
See GOLF MANAGEMENT SOLUTIONS

GOLF COURSE
See DUNDEE TOWNSHIP PARK DISTRICT

GOLF COURSES AT INCLINE VLG
See INCLINE VILLAGE GENERAL IMPROVEMENT DISTRICT

D-U-N-S 08-128-1636 IMP
■ **GOLF GALAXY GOLFWORKS INC**
(*Suby of* GOLF GALAXY INC) ★
4820 Jacksontown Rd, Newark, OH 43056-9377
Tel (740) 328-4193 *Founded/Ownrshp* 2006
Sales 76.0MM^E *EMP* 150
SIC 5091 2731 3949 5941 Golf & skiing equipment & supplies; Books: publishing only; Golf equipment; Shafts, golf club; Golf, tennis & ski shops; Golf & skiing equipment & supplies; Books: publishing only; Golf equipment; Shafts, golf club; Golf, tennis & ski shops
CEO: Mark McCormick
**CFO:* Jerry Datz
**VP:* Mark Wilson
**Prin:* Richard C Nordvoid
Genl Mgr: Jon O'Coin
VP Mktg: Todd Humphreys

D-U-N-S 96-121-5894
■ **GOLF GALAXY INC**
(*Suby of* DICKS SPORTING GOODS INC) ★
345 Court St, Coraopolis, PA 15108-3817
Tel (724) 273-3400 *Founded/Ownrshp* 2007
Sales 117.8MM^E *EMP* 1,460
SIC 5941 Golf goods & equipment; Golf goods & equipment
CEO: Edward W Stack
**Pr:* Schmidt Joseph
**COO:* Gregory B Maanum
**Treas:* Kullman Timothy
Bd of Dir: Gregg S Newmark
VP: Lee Belitsky
VP: Gregory Guentzel
**VP:* Oliver Joseph
Off Mgr: Caroleen Greenwood

D-U-N-S 16-884-7619
GOLF MANAGEMENT SOLUTIONS
GOLF CNTRY CLB ADM FOR VLLAGES
1000 Main St Ste 248, The Villages, FL 32159-7737
Tel (352) 753-3396 *Founded/Ownrshp* 2004
Sales 18.2MM^E *EMP* 900
SIC 7999 Golf services & professionals; Golf services & professionals
Owner: Kan Creely

GOLF MILL FORD
See GOLF MILL MOTOR SALES INC

D-U-N-S 55-608-7935
GOLF MILL MOTOR SALES INC
GOLF MILL FORD
9401 N Milwaukee Ave, Niles, IL 60714-1209
Tel (847) 470-9800 *Founded/Ownrshp* 2005
Sales 60.2MM^E *EMP* 102
SIC 5511 Automobiles, new & used; Automobiles, new & used
Pr: Gus Kreatsoulas
**VP:* Mario Sosnowski
Sales Exec: Art Wierzbicki
Sls Mgr: Craig Burton
Sls Mgr: Bryan Fulton
Sls Mgr: Ray Lacey
Sls Mgr: Barry Parsons
Sls Mgr: Joseph Smith
Sls Mgr: Frank Villalobos

D-U-N-S 17-408-9417
GOLF VENTURES INC
(*Suby of* MEADOWBROOK GOLF GROUP INC) ★
5385 Gateway Blvd Ste 12, Lakeland, FL 33811-1785
Tel (863) 665-5800 *Founded/Ownrshp* 1998
Sales 22.5MM^E *EMP* 49
SIC 5191 5091 Fertilizer & fertilizer materials; Insecticides; Seeds: field, garden & flower; Golf equipment
CEO: Ron E Jackson
**Ch Bd:* Arnold Rosenstein
**CFO:* K Eric Burk
CFO: Calvin C Sellers III
**Ex VP:* Walt McMahon
**VP:* Garry Callahan
**VP:* Debbie Nipper
IT Man: Tom Talley
Sls Mgr: Jeff Brown
Sls Mgr: Chad Nixon

GOLF VISTA ESTATES
See MHC OPERATING LIMITED PARTNERSHIP

D-U-N-S 03-612-0769 EXP
GOLF WAREHOUSE INC
BASEBALLSAVINGS.COM
(*Suby of* NORTHERN TOOL & EQUIPMENT CATALOG CO INC) ★
8851 E 34th St N, Wichita, KS 67226-2624
Tel (316) 838-5551 *Founded/Ownrshp* 1999, 2012
Sales 37.9MM^E *EMP* 250^E
SIC 5941 Golf goods & equipment; Golf goods & equipment
CEO: Jon Bernstein
**Pr:* R Michael Marney
**CFO:* Marie Daley
CFO: Brett Hamrick
Dir IT: Christine Morgan
Web Dev: Jeremy Yenser
VP Opers: Ray Arnoult

GOLFLAND/SUNSPLASH
See MESA GOLFLAND LTD AN ARIZONA LIMITED PARTNERSHIP

GOLFSMITH GOLF & TENNIS
See GOLFSMITH INTERNATIONAL INC

D-U-N-S 06-641-3931 IMP
GOLFSMITH INTERNATIONAL HOLDINGS INC
(*Suby of* GOLF TOWN USA HOLDINGS INC)
11000 N Interstate 35, Austin, TX 78753-3195
Tel (512) 837-8810 *Founded/Ownrshp* 2012
Sales 191.3MM^E *EMP* 1,621^E
SIC 5941 5699 5661 5961 Golf goods & equipment; Sports apparel; Footwear, athletic; Catalog & mail-order houses; Golf goods & equipment; Sports apparel; Footwear, athletic; Catalog & mail-order houses
CFO: Martin E Hanaka
Pr: Steven Larkin
**COO:* Sue E Gove
COO: Sue Gove
CFO: David Spence
Bd of Dir: James Grover
**Chf Mktg O:* Matthew Corey
Chf Mktg O: Lisa Zoellner
**Ex VP:* Ron Hornbaker
Sr VP: Eli Getson
Sr VP: Steven M Larkin
VP: Ashlee Aldridge
VP: Rick Hill
VP: Matt McCabe
VP: Ron Partridge
VP: Andrew Spratt

D-U-N-S 04-908-7307 IMP
GOLFSMITH INTERNATIONAL INC
GOLFSMITH GOLF & TENNIS
(*Suby of* GOLFSMITH INTERNATIONAL HOLDINGS INC) ★
11000 N Interstate 35, Austin, TX 78753-3195
Tel (512) 837-8810 *Founded/Ownrshp* 2003
Sales 23.9MM^E *EMP* 100^E
SIC 5941 Golf goods & equipment; Tennis goods & equipment
Pr: Sue Gove
**CFO:* David Spence
**Prin:* Ariel Ignacio

D-U-N-S 00-585-3799
GOLFVISIONS MANAGEMENT INC
2501 N Midlothian Rd, Mundelein, IL 60060-1037
Tel (708) 562-5247 *Founded/Ownrshp* 2001
Sales 25.8MM^E *EMP* 500^E
SIC 8741 Management services; Management services
Pr: Timothy J Miles Sr

D-U-N-S 00-840-7831
GOLIATH GAMES LLC (TX)
(*Suby of* GOLIATH B.V.)
3701 W Plano Pkwy Ste 100, Plano, TX 75075-7836
Tel (214) 295-2953 *Founded/Ownrshp* 2008
Sales 65.3MM^E *EMP* 119^E
SIC 5092 Toys & hobby goods & supplies
Pr: David Norman
Off Mgr: Julie Doverspike

GOLICK-MARTIN
See MARTINS GOLICK INC

D-U-N-S 05-057-1801
■ **GOLIN/HARRIS INTERNATIONAL INC**
GOLINHARRIS
(*Suby of* INTERPUBLIC GROUP OF COMPANIES INC) ★
875 N Michigan Ave # 2700, Chicago, IL 60611-1822
Tel (312) 729-4000 *Founded/Ownrshp* 2005
Sales 109.1MM^E *EMP* 830
SIC 8743 Public relations & publicity; Public relations & publicity
Ch Bd: Alvin Golin
**CEO:* Fred Cook
**CFO:* Brian J Beck
Sr Cor Off: Tom Harris
**Chf Mktg O:* Ellen Ryan Mardiks
Ex VP: Jeffrey Burnett
Ex VP: Kathy Carliner
Ex VP: David Duschene
Ex VP: Stephen Jones
Ex VP: Wendy Simmons
Ex VP: Tina Vennegaard
Ex VP: Tracy Weisman
Ex VP: David Zitlow
Sr VP: Kurt Markva
VP: Forrest Anderson
VP: Barret Buss
VP: Cristal Cole
VP: Holly Gillentine
VP: Douglas Hart
**VP:* Steve Holli
VP: Jeff Leshay

GOLINHARRIS
See GOLIN/HARRIS INTERNATIONAL INC

D-U-N-S 10-918-5801
GOLLING CHRYSLER DODGE JEEP RAM INC
2405 S Telegraph Rd, Bloomfield Hills, MI 48302-0256
Tel (248) 334-3600 *Founded/Ownrshp* 1983
Sales 45.1MM^E *EMP* 104
SIC 5511 5521

GOLLING G M C TRUCK
See GOLLING PONTIAC GMC TRUCK INC

D-U-N-S 01-718-6115
GOLLING PONTIAC GMC TRUCK INC (MI)
GOLLING G M C TRUCK
1491 S Lapeer Rd, Lake Orion, MI 48360-1438
Tel (248) 693-5900 *Founded/Ownrshp* 1955
Sales 20.5MM^E *EMP* 45
SIC 5511 5087 Automobiles, new & used; Firefighting equipment
Pr: A William Golling III
VP: John Buttermore
**VP:* Edwin J Levy
CTO: Michael Cook
CTO: Robert Ford
CTO: Alan Manduzzi
Sls Mgr: Darin Young
Sales Asso: Harvey Blitz
Sales Asso: John Hopper
Sales Asso: Dave Johnson
Sales Asso: Ken Seay

D-U-N-S 05-434-0419
GOLUB & CO LLC
625 N Michigan Ave, Chicago, IL 60611-3110
Tel (312) 440-8800 *Founded/Ownrshp* 1961
Sales 42.6MM^E *EMP* 63
SIC 6552 6799 6531 6519

D-U-N-S 96-226-5018
▲ **GOLUB CAPITAL BDC INC**
150 S Wacker Dr Ste 800, Chicago, IL 60606-4102
Tel (312) 205-5050 *Founded/Ownrshp* 2007
Sales 119.9MM *EMP* 5^E
Tkr Sym GBDC *Exch* NGS
SIC 6726 Investment offices; Management investment funds, closed-end
CEO: David B Golub
**Ch Bd:* Lawrence E Golub
CFO: Ross A Teune
Chf Cred: Joshua M Levinson
Mng Dir: Gregory A Robbins

D-U-N-S 00-699-4339 IMP/EXP
GOLUB CORP (DE)
PRICE CHOPPER SUPERMARKETS
461 Nott St, Schenectady, NY 12308-1812
Tel (518) 355-5000 *Founded/Ownrshp* 1930
Sales 3.4MMM *EMP* 21,741
SIC 5411 Supermarkets, chain; Convenience stores, chain; Supermarkets, chain; Convenience stores, chain
Pr: Jerel Golub
Pr: Russ Greenlaw
**COO:* Scott Grimmett
**CFO:* John J Endres Jr
**Treas:* Christina Maltbie
**Sr VP:* Blaine R Bringhurst
**Sr VP:* Margaret Davenport
**Sr VP:* David Golub
**Sr VP:* Willliam Kenneally
**Sr VP:* Dean A Little
**Sr VP:* Donald L Orlando
Sr VP: Daniel Riccio
Sr VP: Leo Taylor
VP: Daniela Allen
VP: Thomas Bird
VP: Mark Bourcher
VP: Mark Brown
**VP:* Christine Daniels
VP: Mike Davidson
**VP:* Robert Doyle
VP: Steven Duffy
Board of Directors: Robert C Blattberg, Lee A Brathwaite, Lita Cunningham, Mike Defabis, Edward S Dunn Jr, Carl Glick, Robert W Schwartz

D-U-N-S 12-772-3307
GOM SHELF LLC
2000 Post Oak Blvd # 100, Houston, TX 77056-4499
Tel (713) 296-6000 *Founded/Ownrshp* 2003
Sales 14.8MM^E *EMP* 600
SIC 0919 Whale oil production, crude; Whale oil production, crude
VP: Becky Hoyt

GOMACO MANUFACTURING CO
See GODBERSEN-SMITH CONSTRUCTION CO INC

D-U-N-S 03-077-6942
GOMEZ CONSTRUCTION CO
7100 Sw 44th St, Miami, FL 33155-4611
Tel (305) 661-7660 *Founded/Ownrshp* 1974
Sales 26.3MM^E *EMP* 50
SIC 1542 Commercial & office building, new construction; Commercial & office buildings, renovation & repair
Pr: Orlando J Gomez
**Treas:* Juan Carlos Gomez
Sr VP: Marc McIntee

D-U-N-S 95-856-0674
GOMEZ FLOOR COVERING INC
G F C
3816 Binz Engleman Rd, San Antonio, TX 78219-2236
Tel (210) 651-5002 *Founded/Ownrshp* 1996
Sales 26.7MM *EMP* 64
Accts Akin Doherty Klein & Feuge P
SIC 1752 Carpet laying; Carpet laying
Pr: Linda Gomez-Whitener
CFO: Steve Whitener

D-U-N-S 83-937-7256 IMP
GON-REY LLC
(*Suby of* CORPORATE OFFICE) ★
230 N Harbor Blvd, Santa Ana, CA 92703-3337
Tel (714) 265-9394 *Founded/Ownrshp* 2008
Sales 63.5MM^E *EMP* 600
SIC 5411 Grocery stores; Grocery stores
Mng Dir: Jared Stone

D-U-N-S 96-480-1690
GONGCO FOODS
FOOD 4 LESS
2025 N Dinuba Blvd Ste J, Visalia, CA 93291-2012
Tel (559) 734-0134 *Founded/Ownrshp* 1992
Sales 56.6MM^E *EMP* 320
SIC 5411 Supermarkets, chain; Grocery stores; Supermarkets
CEO: Joe Gong
**Pr:* Tom Gong

D-U-N-S 00-512-0803 IMP
GONNELLA BAKING CO
1117 Wiley Rd, Schaumburg, IL 60173-4337
Tel (312) 733-2020 *Founded/Ownrshp* 1886
Sales 192.3MM^E *EMP* 350
SIC 2051 5812 2099 2038 Bread, all types (white, wheat, rye, etc): fresh or frozen; Eating places; Food preparations; Frozen specialties; Bread, all types (white, wheat, rye, etc): fresh or frozen; Eating places; Food preparations; Frozen specialties
Pr: Nick Marcucci
Pr: Bob Gonnella
**Pr:* Robert Gonnella Jr
COO: Scott Smith
CFO: Timothy Madda
**Treas:* Thomas J Mazukelli
**VP:* Daniel Herzog
**VP:* Dennis Marcucci
VP: Meg McDonnell
VP: Bob Wolff
Exec: Amy Freshwater
Board of Directors: Katherine Roseen

D-U-N-S 00-509-8520
GONNELLA FROZEN PRODUCTS LLC (IL)
(*Suby of* GONNELLA BAKING CO) ★
1117 Wiley Rd, Schaumburg, IL 60173-4337
Tel (847) 884-8829 *Founded/Ownrshp* 1886, 1980
Sales 65.7MM^E *EMP* 350
SIC 2051 Bread, all types (white, wheat, rye, etc): fresh or frozen; Rolls, bread type: fresh or frozen; Bread, all types (white, wheat, rye, etc): fresh or frozen; Rolls, bread type: fresh or frozen
Pr: Nicholas Marcucci
VP: Roy Marcucci
Dir IT: Bruce Birky
Sales Exec: Ron Lucchesi
Sls Mgr: Anthony Mazukelli

D-U-N-S 02-804-0509
GONSALVES & SANTUCCI INC
CONCO CEMENT COMPANY
5141 Commercial Cir, Concord, CA 94520-8523
Tel (925) 685-6799 *Founded/Ownrshp* 1961
Sales 215.5MM^E *EMP* 1,000
SIC 1771 Concrete work; Concrete work
Ch Bd: Mathew Gonsalves
**Pr:* Steven Gonsalves
**CFO:* Barry Silberman
**VP:* Holly Bertuccelli
**VP:* Joseph Santucci
**VP:* Karen Watson
**Prin:* Mariah Panza Garcia
Opers Mgr: Hector Vargas
Prd Mgr: Arjaye Wroten

GONZABA MEDICAL GROUP
See GMG HEALTH SYSTEMS LTD

D-U-N-S 11-784-9356
GONZALES CONSULTING SERVICES INC
5200 Dtc Pkwy Ste 540, Greenwood Village, CO 80111-2720
Tel (303) 383-5500 *Founded/Ownrshp* 1990
Sales 15.0MM *EMP* 280
SIC 7382 Security systems services; Security systems services
Pr: Albert C Gonzales
COO: Brian Johnson

D-U-N-S 88-308-2182 IMP
GONZALES ENTERPRISES INC
AZTLAN GRAPHICS
495 Ryan Ave, Chico, CA 95973-8846
Tel (530) 343-8725 *Founded/Ownrshp* 1995
Sales 116.0MM^E *EMP* 174
SIC 5136 Shirts, men's & boys'; Shirts, men's & boys'
CEO: Daniel Gonzales
Pr: Randy Cook
COO: Lindsey Hoag
Treas: Dawn Gonzales
VP: B J Larossa
IT Man: Gery Gaffney
IT Man: Nestor Ramirez
Natl Sales: Stacy Santa
Sls Mgr: Julie Arndt

D-U-N-S 07-848-0738
GONZALES HEALTHCARE SYSTEMS (TX)
MEMORIAL HOSPITAL
1110 N Sarah Dewitt Dr, Gonzales, TX 78629-3311
Tel (830) 672-7581 *Founded/Ownrshp* 1922
Sales 28.1MM^E *EMP* 226
SIC 8062 General medical & surgical hospitals; General medical & surgical hospitals
CEO: Chuck Norris
Chf Path: Brent S Scheffer
COO: Steve Poteet
CFO: Patty Stewart
Ofcr: Julie Clay
Dir Soc: Sandra Johnston
Dir Rx: Melissa McAlroy
IT Man: Connie Kacir
Mktg Dir: Sascha Kardosz
Doctor: Roland A Medellin MD
Cert Phar: Deane Novosad

D-U-N-S 07-461-9305
GONZALES INDEPENDENT SCHOOL DISTRICT
926 Saint Lawrence St, Gonzales, TX 78629-4151
Tel (830) 672-9551 *Founded/Ownrshp* 1913
Sales 27.3MM^E *EMP* 665
Accts Floyd And Gindler Pc Gonzal
SIC 8211 Public elementary & secondary schools; Public elementary & secondary schools
Bd of Dir: Thomas Lester
**VP:* Gloria Torres
Exec: Ronald Darilek
Cmptr Lab: Peggy Janota

D-U-N-S 60-183-9582
GONZALES LABOR SYSTEMS INC
JAKE'S HOUSE
112 W Randol Mill Rd # 100, Arlington, TX 76011-5782
Tel (817) 261-5005 *Founded/Ownrshp* 1991
Sales 2.6MM *EMP* 500
SIC 7363 Temporary help service; Temporary help service
Pr: Cruz Gonzales
**Sec:* Nelda Gonzales
**VP:* Cecilia Gonzales

D-U-N-S 10-064-4244
GONZALES UNIFIED SCHOOL DISTRICT
600 Elko St, Gonzales, CA 93926
Tel (831) 675-2495 *Founded/Ownrshp* 1997
Sales 21.5MM^E *EMP* 429
SIC 8211 Public senior high school; Public senior high school

D-U-N-S 17-436-7128 IMP/EXP
GONZALEZ & SONS EQUIPMENT INC
G & S
9401 Nw 109th St, Medley, FL 33178-1226
Tel (305) 822-5455 *Founded/Ownrshp* 1984
Sales 76.5MM^E *EMP* 187^E
SIC 1623 4213 1611 Oil & gas pipeline construction; Heavy hauling; Concrete construction: roads, highways, sidewalks, etc.; Highway & street paving contractor; Oil & gas pipeline construction; Heavy hauling; Concrete construction: roads, highways, sidewalks, etc.; Highway & street paving contractor
CEO: Juan I Gonzalez
**Pr:* Juan C Gonzalez
Snr PM: Jonathan Slaton

GONZALEZ AND TAPANES FOODS
See LA FE FOODS INC

D-U-N-S 92-668-8102
GONZALEZ CONTRACT SERVICES INC
G C S
1670 Highwood E, Pontiac, MI 48340-1235
Tel (248) 548-6010 *Founded/Ownrshp* 1988
Sales 51.3MM^E *EMP* 1,000
SIC 7361 Employment agencies; Employment agencies
Pr: Gary H Gonzalez

D-U-N-S 06-943-8422
GONZALEZ DE CASTILLA INC (TX)
NAVISTAR MEXICO SA DE CV
11929 Sara Rd, Laredo, TX 78045-1803
Tel (956) 237-1336 *Founded/Ownrshp* 1974
Sales 21.3MM^E *EMP* 53
SIC 4731 Freight forwarding
Ch Bd: M Decastilla Ruiz
**Pr:* D Gonzalez De Castilla

D-U-N-S 94-611-5524
GONZALEZ PALLETS INC
1261 Yard Ct, San Jose, CA 95133-1048
Tel (408) 999-0280 *Founded/Ownrshp* 1994
Sales 21.0MM^E *EMP* 69
SIC 4953 Recycling, waste materials
CEO: Rafael Gomez
**Treas:* Jaime Silva

D-U-N-S 80-704-5331
GONZALEZ SAGGIO & HARLAN LLP
111 E Wisconsin Ave # 1000, Milwaukee, WI 53202-4806
Tel (414) 277-8500 *Founded/Ownrshp* 1989
Sales 34.8MM^E *EMP* 161
SIC 8111 General practice law office; General practice law office
Pt: Gerardo H Gonzalez
Pt: Emery K Harlan
Pt: Shelly Ranus
Pt: David Saggio
Pt: Werner E Scherr
CTO: Jennifer Bolger
IT Man: Ozzy Ornelas
Sys Mgr: Steve McCullough
Mktg Dir: Marieke Westerman
Counsel: Felix Chevalier
Counsel: Ed Fallone

D-U-N-S 05-178-1011
GOOBY INDUSTRIES CORP
CENTURY BOX
45 Chase St Ste 45, Methuen, MA 01844-3771
Tel (978) 689-0100 *Founded/Ownrshp* 1978
Sales 36.5MM^E *EMP* 125
SIC 2657 Folding paperboard boxes; Folding paperboard boxes
Pr: Joanna Kagan
**Treas:* Alvin Kagan
QA Dir: Arnold Hilliard

GOOCHLAND COUNTY BOARD OF SUPE
See COUNTY OF GOOCHLAND

D-U-N-S 15-957-5422
GOOCHLAND COUNTY PUBLIC SCHOOLS
2938 River Rd W, Goochland, VA 23063-3229
Tel (804) 556-5601 *Founded/Ownrshp* 1900
Sales 23.8MM^E *EMP* 420
SIC 8211 Public elementary & secondary schools; Public elementary & secondary schools
Bd of Dir: Elizabeth Hardy
Bd of Dir: Kevin Hazzard
Bd of Dir: John Lumpkins
Ex Dir: Jamie Beatty
Ex Dir: Amy Bowles
Ex Dir: Patrick Brook
Ex Dir: Susan Duty
Ex Dir: Barbara Evans
Ex Dir: Wes Farkas
Ex Dir: Elizabeth Ford
Ex Dir: Bethany Gordon

D-U-N-S 07-912-2822
GOOD & ROBERTS LLC
(*Suby of* C W DRIVER INC) ★
2455 Impala Dr, Carlsbad, CA 92010-7227
Tel (760) 598-7614 *Founded/Ownrshp* 2013
Sales 35.0MM *EMP* 46
SIC 1542 Commercial & office building, new construction; Commercial & office building, new construction
Pr: Joseph Grosshart

GOOD APPLE MEDIA
See GOOD APPLE PUBLISHING LLC

D-U-N-S 82-891-3884
GOOD APPLE PUBLISHING LLC
GOOD APPLE MEDIA
200 Park Ave S Ste 1603, New York, NY 10003-1521
Tel (646) 374-0156 *Founded/Ownrshp* 2006
Sales 36.0MM *EMP* 25
SIC 7311 Advertising agencies; Advertising agencies
VP: Nedim Aruz

D-U-N-S 07-972-1794
GOOD BUDDY BUDDY GOOD LLC
300 Anacostia Rd Se # 103, Washington, DC 20019-7184
Tel (240) 532-0031 *Founded/Ownrshp* 2015
Sales 100.0MM *EMP* 3
SIC 7389 Music recording producer;

GOOD CHEVROLET AND OLDSMOBILE
See GOOD CHEVROLET INC

D-U-N-S 05-931-8550
GOOD CHEVROLET INC
GOOD CHEVROLET AND OLDSMOBILE
325 Sw 12th St, Renton, WA 98057-3154
Tel (425) 235-2000 *Founded/Ownrshp* 1972
Sales 33.6MM^E *EMP* 86
SIC 5511 Automobiles, new & used; Trucks, tractors & trailers: new & used; Automobiles, new & used; Trucks, tractors & trailers: new & used
Pr: Howard Sheridan
**VP:* Greg Shenidan
Genl Mgr: Greg Sheridan
Sls Mgr: Karl Harrison
Sls Mgr: David Sheridan

D-U-N-S 02-976-1673 IMP
GOOD EARTH TOOLS INC
4 Industrial Dr, Crystal City, MO 63019
Tel (636) 937-3330 *Founded/Ownrshp* 1964
Sales 69.4MM^E *EMP* 130
SIC 3531 3398 Railroad related equipment; Brazing (hardening) of metal; Railroad related equipment; Brazing (hardening) of metal
Pr: Keith Williams
**Treas:* Edward Williams
**VP:* Jonathan G Williams
Sls Dir: Ned Williams

D-U-N-S 80-792-8098
GOOD EATS HOLDING CO INC
12200 N Stemmons Fwy, Dallas, TX 75234-5888
Tel (972) 247-6762 Founded/Ownrshp 1991
Sales 17.9MME EMP 900
SIC 5812 6719 Eating places; Personal holding companies, except banks; Eating places; Personal holding companies, except banks
Pr: E Gene Street
CFO: Sue Wyman
*VP: Franklin Bernard

D-U-N-S 18-884-6927
GOOD EATS RESTAURANT GROUP INC
MOTHER MESQUITE'S RESTAURANT
(Suby of GOOD EATS HOLDING CO INC) ★
12200 N Stemmons Fwy, Dallas, TX 75234-5888
Tel (972) 888-8172 Founded/Ownrshp 1993
Sales 17.4MME EMP 625
SIC 5812 American restaurant; American restaurant
VP: Frank Jones
*CEO: Gene Street
*VP: Frank Barnard
VP: Mark Czaus

D-U-N-S 06-867-0933
GOOD EGGS INC
901 Rankin St, San Francisco, CA 94124-1626
Tel (415) 483-7344 Founded/Ownrshp 2011
Sales 25.0MME EMP 37E
SIC 5144 Eggs
CEO: Rob Spiro
Bd of Dir: Adam Flynn
Mktg Mgr: Jessica Kramer

D-U-N-S 82-817-2622 IMP
GOOD FOODS GROUP LLC
CHEF EARL'S
10100 88th Ave, Pleasant Prairie, WI 53158-2217
Tel (262) 465-6900 Founded/Ownrshp 2008
Sales 95.4MME EMP 350
SIC 2038 5149 Frozen specialties; Breakfasts, frozen & packaged; Dinners, frozen & packaged; Lunches, frozen & packaged; Natural & organic foods; Frozen specialties; Breakfasts, frozen & packaged; Dinners, frozen & packaged; Lunches, frozen & packaged; Natural & organic foods
CEO: Kurt Penn
*Pr: John Fitzgerald
Opers Mgr: Charles Herrig
VP Sls: Kristyn Lawson

D-U-N-S 07-909-0639
GOOD FRIENDS OF NY INC (NY)
JOEUN CALL TAXI
16210 Crocheron Ave Fl 2, Flushing, NY 11358-1631
Tel (201) 666-2222 Founded/Ownrshp 2012
Sales 7.1MME EMP 520
SIC 4111 Airport limousine, scheduled service; Airport limousine, scheduled service
CEO: Charles Bai

D-U-N-S 05-606-5208
GOOD HARBOR FINANCIAL LLC
(Suby of CEDAR CAPITAL LLC) ★
155 N Wacker Dr Ste 850, Chicago, IL 60606-1723
Tel (312) 224-8150 Founded/Ownrshp 2010
Sales 22.1MME EMP 100
SIC 6282 Investment advice; Investment advice
CFO: David Boon
Ofcr: Cami Kirschner
Assoc VP: Sean Whalen
Ex VP: Thomas Hines
Sr VP: Stuart Browne
Mng Dir: Hugh Asher
Mng Dir: Bobby Carlson
Mng Dir: Peter Driscoll
Mng Dir: James Duddey
Mng Dir: Christopher Hultquist
Mng Dir: Jake Hutchinson

GOOD HART BRND SPECIALTY FOODS
See BLUEBONNET FOODS LP

D-U-N-S 80-234-9480
GOOD HEALTH HMO INC
(Suby of BLUE CROSS AND BLUE SHIELD OF KANSAS CITY) ★
2301 Main St, Kansas City, MO 64108-2429
Tel (816) 395-2222 Founded/Ownrshp 1988
Sales 4.8MME EMP 500
SIC 8011 Health maintenance organization; Health maintenance organization
Pr: Tom Bowser
CFO: Marilyn T Romans

D-U-N-S 93-151-9631 IMP
GOOD HEALTH NATURAL PRODUCTS INC
(Suby of UTZ QUALITY FOODS INC) ★
115 Pomona Dr, Greensboro, NC 27407-1617
Tel (336) 285-0735 Founded/Ownrshp 2013
Sales 22.0MM EMP 45
SIC 2096 Potato chips & other potato-based snacks; Corn chips & other corn-based snacks
Pr: Jeff Martin
*CEO: Dylan Lissette

D-U-N-S 79-969-4315
GOOD HEALTH SERVICES INC
18151 W Catawba Ave, Cornelius, NC 28031-5641
Tel (919) 676-9796 Founded/Ownrshp 1987
Sales 6.8MME EMP 400
SIC 8082 7361 Home health care services; Employment agencies; Home health care services; Employment agencies
Owner: Tony McCurdy
Bd of Dir: Gary Massey
*VP: Sandy Massey
*VP: Lisa McCurdy

D-U-N-S 00-226-3432
GOOD LAD CO (PA)
PETE'S PARTNERS
431 E Tioga St, Philadelphia, PA 19134-1118
Tel (215) 739-0200 Founded/Ownrshp 1944
Sales 28.5MME EMP 400
SIC 2369 Girls' & children's outerwear; Girls' & children's outerwear

CEO: Peter J Sheintoch
*Pr: Kenneth Sheintoch
VP: Henry Eichenbaum
*VP: Everett Sheintoch
Exec: Darnella Lane
Info Man: Mike Polaski

GOOD MEADOW HOMEMADES
See UKROPS HOMESTYLE FOODS LLC

GOOD NEIGHBOR PHARMACY
See SKAG-WAY DISCOUNT DEPARTMENT STORES INC

GOOD NEIGHBOR PHARMACY
See NORTHERN PHARMACY AND MEDICAL EQUIPMENT INC

GOOD NEIGHBOR PHARMACY
See DON QUIJOTE (USA) CO LTD

GOOD NEIGHBOR PHARMACY
See LOUISIANA WHOLESALE DRUG CO INC

GOOD NEIGHBOR PHARMACY
See OCEAN BREEZE PHARMACY INC

D-U-N-S 00-739-8421
GOOD NEIGHBOR PHARMACY
AMERISOURCE BERGEN
6305 Lasalle Dr, Lockbourne, OH 43137-9280
Tel (614) 409-6000 Founded/Ownrshp 2009
Sales 22.5MME EMP 169E
SIC 5912 Drug stores
Owner: Antony Neda
Sr VP: Terry Haas
Exec: Tim Beck
Exec: Sheila Harper
Exec: Michelle Westervelt
Dir IT: Christina Harris
VP Sls: Greg Arnold
VP Sls: Gregg Bollinger
Manager: Tracy Schakett
Sls Mgr: Tracey Larsen

D-U-N-S 00-519-9146 IMP/EXP
GOOD NEWS PUBLISHERS
CROSSWAY BIBLES, NFP
1300 Crescent St, Wheaton, IL 60187-5883
Tel (630) 868-6025 Founded/Ownrshp 1938
Sales 27.5MM EMP 50
Accts Capin Crouse Llp Wheaton Ill
SIC 2731 Pamphlets: publishing only, not printed on site; Textbooks: publishing only, not printed on site; Pamphlets: publishing only, not printed on site; Textbooks: publishing only, not printed on site
Pr: Lane T Dennis
VP: Paul Thomas

D-U-N-S 07-891-4090
GOOD OIL CO INC
1201 N Us Highway 35, Winamac, IN 46996-8003
Tel (574) 946-4863 Founded/Ownrshp 1941
Sales 56.3MME EMP 110
SIC 5541 5171 5411 6512 Filling stations, gasoline; Petroleum bulk stations; Convenience stores; Property operation, retail establishment; Filling stations, gasoline; Petroleum bulk stations; Convenience stores; Property operation, retail establishment
CEO: Don Good
*VP: Dean Good
IT Man: Wally Johanning

D-U-N-S 05-262-9359 IMP/EXP
GOOD ROADS AUTO SYSTEM INC
5360 Nw 35th Ave, Fort Lauderdale, FL 33309-6314
Tel (954) 771-5767 Founded/Ownrshp 1982
Sales 20.9MME EMP 70
SIC 5013

GOOD SAM
See AFFINITY GROUP HOLDING LLC

D-U-N-S 79-012-7109
GOOD SAM ENTERPRISES LLC
GSE
(Suby of AFFINITY GROUP HOLDING LLC) ★
250 Parkway Dr Ste 270, Lincolnshire, IL 60069-4346
Tel (847) 229-6720 Founded/Ownrshp 1986
Sales 481.4MM EMP 1,704E
SIC 5561 7997 2721 Recreational vehicle parts & accessories; Membership sports & recreation clubs; Magazines: publishing only, not printed on site; Recreational vehicle parts & accessories; Membership sports & recreation clubs; Magazines: publishing only, not printed on site
Ch Bd: Stephen Adams
*Pr: Marcus A Lemonis
*CFO: Thomas F Wolfe
*Chf Mktg O: Tamara Ward
Ex VP: Steve Albert
*Ex VP: Matthew Baden
*Ex VP: Brent Moody
*Ex VP: John A Sirpilla
Sr VP: Michael Blumer
VP: Mark Dowis
VP: Dale Hendrix
VP: David Scifres

D-U-N-S 14-765-2671
GOOD SAMARITAN COMMUNITY HEALTHCARE INC
407 14th Ave Se, Puyallup, WA 98372-3770
Tel (253) 848-6661 Founded/Ownrshp 1952
Sales 418.4MM EMP 300
SIC 8062 General medical & surgical hospitals; General medical & surgical hospitals
Pr: John Long
Chf Rad: Dan Martin
Obsttrcn: Laurie Morris
Doctor: Dan Nguyen MD

D-U-N-S 96-631-6262
GOOD SAMARITAN HEALTH CENTER OF MERRILL WISCONSIN INC
601 S Center Ave, Merrill, WI 54452-3404
Tel (715) 536-5511 Founded/Ownrshp 2011
Sales 22.5MM EMP 2E
SIC 8099 Health & allied services; Health & allied services

Prin: Kristine M McGarigle
CTO: David Seehafer

D-U-N-S 93-942-8512
GOOD SAMARITAN HEALTH SERVICES FOUNDATION
259 S 4th St Fl 2, Lebanon, PA 17042-6112
Tel (717) 270-7864 Founded/Ownrshp 1985
Sales 556.9M EMP 2,000
Accts Grant Thornton Llp Philadelph
SIC 8741 7389 8721 Hospital management; Fund raising organizations; Accounting, auditing & bookkeeping; Hospital management; Fund raising organizations; Accounting, auditing & bookkeeping
Pr: Robert J Longo
Dir Vol: Carol Seeley
*Ch: Darwin Glick
*Treas: Frederick S Wolfson

GOOD SAMARITAN HOSPITAL
See KNOX COUNTY HOSPITAL

GOOD SAMARITAN HOSPITAL
See SAMARITAN HEALTH SERVICES INC

D-U-N-S 04-310-6277
GOOD SAMARITAN HOSPITAL (CA)
901 Olive Dr, Bakersfield, CA 93308-4144
Tel (661) 399-4461 Founded/Ownrshp 1955, 1989
Sales 62.6MME EMP 400
SIC 8062 8063 8069 General medical & surgical hospitals; Psychiatric hospitals; Specialty hospitals, except psychiatric; General medical & surgical hospitals; Psychiatric hospitals; Specialty hospitals, except psychiatric
CEO: Andrew B Leeka
*Pt: David Huff
*Pr: Sakrepatna Manohara
*CEO: Anand Manohara
*CFO: Canesh Acharya
CFO: Raul Lopez
CFO: Vicki Nguyen
CIO: Stan Burkert
CTO: Richard Mamula
CTO: Kristine Mase
CTO: Evan Rayner

D-U-N-S 05-238-9657 IMP
GOOD SAMARITAN HOSPITAL
1225 Wilshire Blvd, Los Angeles, CA 90017-1901
Tel (213) 977-2121 Founded/Ownrshp 1885
Sales 208.9MME EMP 1,500E
SIC 8062 General medical & surgical hospitals; General medical & surgical hospitals
CEO: Andrew B Leeka
Dir Recs: Marcia Stein
Dir Vol: Esther Duenas
*Ch Bd: Charles Munger
COO: Dan McLaughlin
COO: Lynne Whaley-Welty
*CFO: Alan Ino
Ofcr: Barry Mangels
VP: Dean Campbell
VP: Susan Harlow
VP: Lynn Whalen
Dir Lab: Kathy Yoshimura
Dir Rad: Ralph Corbino
Dir Rx: Mark Holdych

D-U-N-S 06-194-9058
GOOD SAMARITAN HOSPITAL
600 Witmer St, Los Angeles, CA 90017
Tel (213) 977-2121 Founded/Ownrshp 1887
Sales 320.8MM EMP 1
SIC 8062 General medical & surgical hospitals; General medical & surgical hospitals
Pr: Andrew Leeka
Chf OB: Stephen N Pine
CFO: Alan Ino
VP: Sammy Feuerlicht
VP: Susan Harlow
VP: Dan McLaughlin
Dir Inf Cn: Joan Finney
Dir Risk M: Denise Faught
Dir Case M: Kelvin Matute
Dir Lab: Kathy Yoshimura
Dir Rad: Sukhvinder Puri
Dir Rx: Mark Holdych
Dir Env Sv: Jahn Butler

D-U-N-S 06-398-5261
GOOD SAMARITAN HOSPITAL
(Suby of SAMARITAN HEALTH PARTNERS) ★
2222 Philadelphia Dr, Dayton, OH 45406-1891
Tel (937) 278-2612 Founded/Ownrshp 1932
Sales 232.9MME EMP 2,000
SIC 8062 Hospital, affiliated with AMA residency; Hospital, affiliated with AMA residency
Pr: Mark S Shaker
*CFO: Scott Schelton
VP: Carol Bauer
VP: Sammy Feuerlicht
VP: Craig Self
Dir Rad: Roger Staton
Nurse Mgr: Susan Macy
IT Man: Lisa Smith
Ansthlgy: Thaiduc T Nguyen
Doctor: Dennis Brown
Doctor: Gary Fishbein

D-U-N-S 08-250-5900
GOOD SAMARITAN HOSPITAL
(Suby of ALLENMORE HOSPITAL) ★
401 15th Ave Se, Puyallup, WA 98372-3795
Tel (253) 697-4000 Founded/Ownrshp 2006
Sales 418.4MME EMP 1,600
SIC 8062 8069 General medical & surgical hospitals; Substance abuse hospitals; General medical & surgical hospitals; Substance abuse hospitals
Pr: Diane Cecchetini
*Pr: Bishop David Wold
COO: Marcia Johnson
CFO: Tim Maurice
*VP: Marcus S Gaspard
Ex Dir: Marianne Bastin
Mktg Dir: Mike Peterson
Podiatrist: Michael J Frazier
Podiatrist: William Hahn

D-U-N-S 12-152-1665
GOOD SAMARITAN HOSPITAL
PARENT ASSISTANCE NETWORK
4503 2nd Ave Ste 209, Kearney, NE 68847-2432
Tel (308) 865-2009 Founded/Ownrshp 2002
Sales 227.7MM EMP 1
SIC 8062 General medical & surgical hospitals; General medical & surgical hospitals
Ch: Sheila Meyer

D-U-N-S 07-651-3985
GOOD SAMARITAN HOSPITAL ASSOCIATION
HEART AMERICA MEDICAL CENTER
800 S Main Ave, Rugby, ND 58368-2118
Tel (701) 776-5261 Founded/Ownrshp 1905
Sales 24.4MM EMP 360
SIC 8062 8051 General medical & surgical hospitals; Skilled nursing care facilities; General medical & surgical hospitals; Skilled nursing care facilities
CEO: Jeffrey Lingerfelt
*CFO: Bonnie Kuehnemund
Sls&Mrk Ex: Kevin Schepp
Mktg Dir: Danni Schell
Pharmcst: Erik Christenson

D-U-N-S 03-803-2756
GOOD SAMARITAN HOSPITAL AUXILIARY
1225 Wilshire Blvd, Los Angeles, CA 90017-1901
Tel (213) 977-2121 Founded/Ownrshp 2001
Sales 309.6MM EMP 1,500
Accts Deloitte Tax Llp Costa Mesa
SIC 8011 Medical centers; Medical centers
CEO: Andrew Leeka
COO: Claus Von Zychlin
VP: Donna Nienaber
Dir Rad: Mike Gombar

D-U-N-S 05-361-5548
GOOD SAMARITAN HOSPITAL CORVALLIS
GOOD SMARITAN REGIONAL MED CTR
3600 Nw Samaritan Dr, Corvallis, OR 97330-3700
Tel (541) 757-5111 Founded/Ownrshp 1986
Sales 312.0MME EMP 900
SIC 8062 General medical & surgical hospitals; General medical & surgical hospitals
Pr: Becky Rose
COO: Steven Jasperson
*VP: Ronald S Stevens
Dir Soc: Sandy Taylor
*Prin: Larry Mullins
Off Mgr: Don Fucillo
Dir IT: Manuel Amaez
Opers Mgr: Ron Schreiner
Orthpdst: Luis Vela
Doctor: Shawn Hathaway

D-U-N-S 07-800-5824
GOOD SAMARITAN HOSPITAL KEARNEY NEBRASKA
VOLUNTEER SERVICES OF GOOD SAM
10 E 31st St, Kearney, NE 68847-2926
Tel (308) 865-7997 Founded/Ownrshp 1923
Sales 238.0MM EMP 1,300
Accts Catholic Health Initiatives E
SIC 8062 General medical & surgical hospitals; General medical & surgical hospitals
Pr: Michael H Schnieders
CFO: Bill Luke
*VP: George Harms
Dir Lab: Tyler Schwartz
Comm Dir: Marsha Wilkerson
IT Man: Stacy John
Mktg Dir: Robert Smoot
Pathlgst: Mark Mowry
Nrsg Dir: Janelle Mizell
HC Dir: Heather Lockhart

D-U-N-S 14-754-0298
■ **GOOD SAMARITAN HOSPITAL LP**
(Suby of HCA INC) ★
2425 Samaritan Dr, San Jose, CA 95124-3985
Tel (408) 559-2011 Founded/Ownrshp 1996
Sales 211.7MME EMP 1,800
SIC 8062 General medical & surgical hospitals; General medical & surgical hospitals
CEO: Paul Beaupre
V Ch: Sandra Hickok
COO: Jordan Herget
CFO: Lana Arad
CFO: Darrel Neuenschwander
Ofcr: Paul Deaupre
VP: Frank Hirano
VP: Jim Lamar
Chf Nrs Of: Dian Adams
CIO: Ravi Ramswamy
MIS Dir: Shelia Sol

D-U-N-S 06-801-8175
GOOD SAMARITAN HOSPITAL MEDICAL CENTER
1000 Montauk Hwy, West Islip, NY 11795-4927
Tel (631) 376-3000 Founded/Ownrshp 1997
Sales 488.1MM EMP 3,037
SIC 8062 8051 8092 General medical & surgical hospitals; Skilled nursing care facilities; Kidney dialysis centers; General medical & surgical hospitals; Skilled nursing care facilities; Kidney dialysis centers
VP: Nancy Simmons
Dir Recs: Paul Gaudio
Dir Recs: Nina Gore
*Pr: Richard J Murphy
*CFO: William E Allison
*Ch: Henry Schreiber
*Sec: Pascal Mercurio
Ofcr: Charles Bov
QA Dir: Elaine Shaw
IT Man: Geri Neber
Opers Mgr: Christopher Ross

D-U-N-S 17-492-1338
GOOD SAMARITAN HOSPITAL OF CINCINNATI
(Suby of CATHOLIC HEALTH INITIATIVES) ★
375 Dixmyth Ave, Cincinnati, OH 45220-2489
Tel (513) 569-6251 Founded/Ownrshp 1852
Sales 551.4MM EMP 3,452
Accts Bkd Llp Cincinnati Oh

SIC 8062 8082 8011 General medical & surgical hospitals; Home health care services; Offices & clinics of medical doctors; General medical & surgical hospitals; Home health care services; Offices & clinics of medical doctors
Pr: John S Prout
**COO:* Gerald Oliphant
**CFO:* Craig Rucker
**Ch:* Robert L Walker
**Sr VP:* John R Robinson
Dir OR: Mary Gilligan
Sfty Dirs: Tim Walters
Obsttrcn: Jack Basil

D-U-N-S 83-026-1173
GOOD SAMARITAN HOSPITAL OF LEBANON PENNSYLVANIA
252 S 4th St, Lebanon, PA 17042-6111
Tel (717) 270-7500 *Founded/Ownrshp* 2009
Sales 178.2MM *EMP* 99ᴱ
Accts Grant Thornton Llp Philadelph
SIC 8062 General medical & surgical hospitals; General medical & surgical hospitals
CEO: Robert J Longo
CFO: Bob Richards
VP: Renee Carpenter
Dir Lab: Anita McKulik
Ex Dir: Mary Reppert
Dir Sec: Larry Phillips
Off Mgr: Susan Smith
QA Dir: Vivian Mayopoulos
Sfty Dirs: Terrence Brandt
Sfty Dirs: Brad Foltz
VP Mktg: William Mulligan

D-U-N-S 07-494-5320 IMP
GOOD SAMARITAN HOSPITAL OF MD INC
MEDSTAR HEALTH VNA
(*Suby of* MEDSTAR HEALTH INC) ★
5601 Loch Raven Blvd, Baltimore, MD 21239-2945
Tel (443) 444-3780 *Founded/Ownrshp* 1968
Sales 318.3MM *EMP* 2,146
Accts Kpmg Llp Baltimore Maryland
SIC 8062 8741 General medical & surgical hospitals; Management services; General medical & surgical hospitals; Management services
Pr: Jeffrey A Matton
CFO: Deana Stout
Ch: Anthony Read
Off Mgr: Carol Grap
Off Mgr: Mary A Salango
MIS Dir: Mike Hebronk

D-U-N-S 96-581-1040
GOOD SAMARITAN HOSPITAL PHYSICIAN SERVICES INC
520 S 7th St, Vincennes, IN 47591-1038
Tel (812) 885-8040 *Founded/Ownrshp* 2010
Sales 29.0MM *EMP* 17ᴱ
SIC 8062 General medical & surgical hospitals
Prin: Robert McLin

GOOD SAMARITAN MEDICAL CENTER
See TENET GOOD SAMARITAN HOSPITAL INC

D-U-N-S 14-909-7821
GOOD SAMARITAN MEDICAL CENTER FOUNDATION
(*Suby of* EXEMPLA LUTHERAN MEDICAL CTR) ★
200 Exempla Cir, Lafayette, CO 80026-3370
Tel (303) 689-4000 *Founded/Ownrshp* 2004
Sales 860.5M *EMP* 1,200
SIC 8062 General medical & surgical hospitals; General medical & surgical hospitals
CEO: Dave Ham
VP: Bert Torres
VP: Lisa Wetherbee
Dir Lab: Dianne Beesley
Chf Nrs Of: Susan Kerschen
Doctor: Ellina Liptsen MD
Pharmcst: Nancy McClew
Dir Health: Karen Smith

D-U-N-S 03-071-1824
■ **GOOD SAMARITAN NURSING HOME**
(*Suby of* DIVERSICARE HEALTHCARE SERVICES INC) ★
403 W Main St, Cole Camp, MO 65325-1144
Tel (660) 668-4515 *Founded/Ownrshp* 1967
Sales 267.8MM *EMP* 75
SIC 8052 Intermediate care facilities; Intermediate care facilities
Nrsg Dir: Kyle Luetjen

D-U-N-S 14-765-2614
GOOD SAMARITAN OUTREACH SERVICE
401 15th Ave Se, Puyallup, WA 98372-3795
Tel (253) 848-6661 *Founded/Ownrshp* 1983
Sales 21.0MM *EMP* 300
SIC 8063 Psychiatric hospitals; Psychiatric hospitals
Pr: Diane Cecchettini
Ex VP: Robert Smith

D-U-N-S 06-978-1896
GOOD SAMARITAN PHYSICIAN SERVICES (PA)
HYMAN KAPLAN PAVILLION
(*Suby of* GOOD SAMARITAN HEALTH SERVICES FOUNDATION) ★
4th & Walnut St, Lebanon, PA 17042
Tel (717) 270-7500 *Founded/Ownrshp* 1889
Sales 219.0Mᴱ *EMP* 1,450
SIC 8062 General medical & surgical hospitals; General medical & surgical hospitals
Pr: Robert J Longo
CFO: Bill Luke
VP: Mikki Clancy
VP Bus Dev: Sammy Feuerlicht
Dir Lab: Kathy Yoshimura
Dir Sec: William Fagan
Obsttrcn: Roger Hine

D-U-N-S 79-967-5690
GOOD SAMARITAN REGIONAL HEALTH CENTER
(*Suby of* SSM HEALTH CARE CORP) ★
1 Good Samaritan Way, Mount Vernon, IL 62864-2402
Tel (618) 242-4600 *Founded/Ownrshp* 1988
Sales 85.8MMᴱ *EMP* 900
SIC 8062 General medical & surgical hospitals; General medical & surgical hospitals
Pr: Michael Warren
Ex VP: William Jennings
VP: Richard Huntington
Dir Risk M: Jeralee Sargent
Dir Lab: Matt Livengood
CIO: Steve Murphy

D-U-N-S 01-562-4091
GOOD SAMARITAN REGIONAL MEDICAL CENTER
255 Lafayette Ave, Suffern, NY 10901-4812
Tel (845) 368-5000 *Founded/Ownrshp* 1996
Sales 138.8MMᴱ *EMP* 1,600
SIC 8062 General medical & surgical hospitals; General medical & surgical hospitals
CEO: Philip Patterson
**CEO:* Mary Leahy
**CEO:* Dominick Stanzione
CFO: Stephen Majetich
CFO: Anthony Puorro
Ex VP: Michael Schneiders
Ex VP: Michael Schnieders
**Sr VP:* Jeff Reilly

GOOD SAMARITAN, THE
See CHRISTIAN AID MINISTRIES

GOOD SHEPHERD AMBULATORY SURGE
See GSHS ENTERPRISES INC

GOOD SHEPHERD CENTER
See HOUSE OF GOOD SHEPHERD OF CITY OF BALTIMORE

D-U-N-S 10-095-4270
GOOD SHEPHERD CENTER FOR EXCEPTIONAL CHILDREN
17314 Kedzie Ave, Hazel Crest, IL 60429-1619
Tel (708) 335-0020 *Founded/Ownrshp* 1963
Sales 1.1MM *EMP* 300
SIC 8351 8322 Preschool center; Individual & family services
Ex Dir: Brendan P McCormack

GOOD SHEPHERD COMMUNITIES
See GOOD SHEPHERD LUTHERAN HOME OF WEST

D-U-N-S 07-584-8275
GOOD SHEPHERD GERIATRIC CENTER INC
GOOD SHEPHERD HEALTH CENTER
302 2nd St Ne, Mason City, IA 50401-3412
Tel (641) 424-1740 *Founded/Ownrshp* 1946
Sales 16.6MM *EMP* 335
Accts Mcgladrey Llp Mason City Io
SIC 8051 6513 Skilled nursing care facilities; Retirement hotel operation; Skilled nursing care facilities; Retirement hotel operation
CEO: Diane Horning

D-U-N-S 04-980-3760
GOOD SHEPHERD HEALTH CARE SYSTEM
GOOD SHEPHERD MEDICAL CENTER
610 Nw 11th St, Hermiston, OR 97838-6601
Tel (541) 567-6483 *Founded/Ownrshp* 1954
Sales 88.3MM *EMP* 450
Accts Eide Bailly Lp Minneapolis Mn
SIC 8062 8082 General medical & surgical hospitals; Home health care services; General medical & surgical hospitals; Home health care services
CEO: Dennis E Burke
Pr: Molly Hansen
COO: Dennis E Burk
COO: E Burke
**Ex VP:* David Hughes
**VP:* Theresa L Brock
**VP:* Jan D Peter
**VP:* Kelly B Sanders
Dir Rx: Paul Stone
Dir IT: Rob Schaal
Psych: Olusola Olofnlade

GOOD SHEPHERD HEALTH CENTER
See GOOD SHEPHERD GERIATRIC CENTER INC

D-U-N-S 96-254-5443
GOOD SHEPHERD HEALTH SYSTEM INC
700 E Marshall Ave, Longview, TX 75601-5580
Tel (903) 315-2000 *Founded/Ownrshp* 1984
Sales 95.9MM *EMP* 2,900
SIC 8062 General medical & surgical hospitals; General medical & surgical hospitals
Pr: Kenneth Cunningham
**CFO:* Pat Keel
VP: Keith Creel
Off Mgr: Michelle Holeman
Off Mgr: Missy McKee
CIO: Chris Blakemore
CTO: Scott Mix
CTO: Deborah Terry
Dir IT: Kevin Covert
Dir IT: Wiley Thomas
Cert Phar: Cassie Hogan

D-U-N-S 00-760-8086
GOOD SHEPHERD HOME-LONG TERM CARE FACILITY INC
GOOD SHEPHERD REHAB HOSPITAL
6th & St John Sts, Allentown, PA 18103
Tel (610) 776-3111 *Founded/Ownrshp* 1982
Sales 21.5MM *EMP* 900
SIC 8361 Rehabilitation center, residential: health care incidental; Rehabilitation center, residential: health care incidental
CEO: Dale Sandstrom
**Pr:* Sally Gammon
CFO: Larry Deal
Ex VP: Carol Smith
VP: Maureen Rath
CIO: Mike Surba
Dir Health: Deb Grzelak

D-U-N-S 96-766-9388
GOOD SHEPHERD LUTHERAN HOME OF SAUK RAPIDS MINNESOTA
1115 4th Ave N, Sauk Rapids, MN 56379-2201
Tel (320) 252-6525 *Founded/Ownrshp* 2011
Sales 20.1MM *EMP* 9ᴱ
Accts Larsonallen Llp Minneapolis
SIC 8641 Civic social & fraternal associations; Civic social & fraternal associations
Prin: Bruce A Glanzer
Bd of Dir: Renee Frauendienst

D-U-N-S 07-736-8967
GOOD SHEPHERD LUTHERAN HOME OF WEST
GOOD SHEPHERD COMMUNITIES
119 N Main St, Porterville, CA 93257-3713
Tel (559) 791-2000 *Founded/Ownrshp* 1952
Sales 14.2MMᴱ *EMP* 1,100ᴱ
SIC 8361 Residential care for the handicapped; Residential care for the handicapped
CEO: David Geske

GOOD SHEPHERD MEDICAL CENTER
See SHEPHERD GOOD HOSPITAL INC

GOOD SHEPHERD MEDICAL CENTER
See GOOD SHEPHERD HEALTH CARE SYSTEM

GOOD SHEPHERD PLAZA
See SHEPHERD GOOD REHABILITATION NETWORK

GOOD SHEPHERD REHAB HOSPITAL
See GOOD SHEPHERD HOME-LONG TERM CARE FACILITY INC

GOOD SHEPHERD REHABILITATION
See SHEPHERD GOOD HOME INC

D-U-N-S 83-591-8798
GOOD SHEPHERD REHABILITATION HOSPITAL INC
850 S 5th St, Allentown, PA 18103-3308
Tel (610) 776-3100 *Founded/Ownrshp* 1909
Sales 81.3MM *EMP* 675
SIC 8361 8051 8093 8069 Rehabilitation center, residential: health care incidental; Skilled nursing care facilities; Specialty outpatient clinics; Specialty hospitals, except psychiatric; Rehabilitation center, residential: health care incidental; Skilled nursing care facilities; Specialty outpatient clinics; Specialty hospitals, except psychiatric
Pr: Sally Gammon
CFO: Dan Confalone
Chf Mktg O: Phillip Bryant
Sr VP: Samuel Miranda
VP: Clifford Trumbo
Mng Dir: Bob Shuminski
Rgnl Mgr: Dennis Duerring
QA Dir: Susan Lee
Sfty Dirs: Kimberly Pentland
Site Mgr: Donna Kelley
Psych: Rodney Schall

D-U-N-S 07-327-4292
GOOD SHEPHERD SERVICES
305 7th Ave Fl 9, New York, NY 10001-6161
Tel (212) 243-7070 *Founded/Ownrshp* 1947
Sales 86.2MM *EMP* 1,200
Accts Marks Paneth Llp New York Ny
SIC 8322 General counseling services; General counseling services
CEO: James J Sullivan
**Pr:* Paulette Lomonaco
**VP:* Adel Ayad
**Prin:* David A Barr
**Prin:* Denise M Kelly
**Prin:* Sheila Rule
Off Mgr: Chivonne Lloyd

GOOD SMARITAN REGIONAL MED CTR
See GOOD SAMARITAN HOSPITAL CORVALLIS

GOOD SMARITAN REGIONAL MED CTR
See SCHUYLKILL MEDICAL CENTER - EAST NORWEGIAN STREET

D-U-N-S 15-811-0697 IMP
GOOD SOURCE SOLUTIONS INC
GOODSOURCE SOLUTION
3115 Melrose Dr Ste 160, Carlsbad, CA 92010-6690
Tel (858) 455-4800 *Founded/Ownrshp* 1999
Sales 44.2MMᴱ *EMP* 130
SIC 5963 Beverage services, direct sales
CEO: Richard Friedlen
Pr: Alan Clarke
**CFO:* Bryon Borgardt
**CFO:* Eric Shiring
Ofcr: Rene Flohr
VP: Alan Clark
**VP:* Matt Fitzgerald
**VP:* Steve Guy
VP: Van Hooper
**VP:* Paul Ladouceur
VP: Brandon Marvin
**VP:* Andrew McCluskey
**VP:* Laurie McCluskey
VP: Alex Smith

D-U-N-S 19-836-1813
GOOD SPORTS PLUS LTD
ARC
370 Amapola Ave Ste 208, Torrance, CA 90501-7241
Tel (310) 671-4400 *Founded/Ownrshp* 2002
Sales 7.5MM *EMP* 300
SIC 7371 7997 Custom computer programming services; Outdoor field clubs; Custom computer programming services; Outdoor field clubs
Pr: Brad Lupien
**Pr:* Gary Lipsky
**VP:* Kitty Cohen

D-U-N-S 12-316-1197 IMP/EXP
GOOD SPORTSMAN MARKETING LLC
GSM OUTDOORS
3385 Roy Orr Blvd Ste B, Grand Prairie, TX 75050-4208
Tel (877) 269-8490 *Founded/Ownrshp* 1999
Sales 35.0MM *EMP* 40
SIC 5199 Variety store merchandise; Variety store merchandise
CEO: Timothy D Schnell
**Pr:* Edward Castro
CFO: Alex Castro
Manager: Harold Black

D-U-N-S 96-181-0723
GOOD START GENETICS INC
237 Putnam Ave Ste 2, Cambridge, MA 02139-3844
Tel (617) 714-0800 *Founded/Ownrshp* 2009
Sales 21.3MMᴱ *EMP* 100
SIC 8731 Commercial physical research; Commercial physical research
CEO: Don Hardison
CFO: Jean Franchi
Top Exec: WEI Zhang
Admn Mgr: Bunny Silverstein
Snr Sftwr: Giridhar Pottepalem
CIO: Mark Adams
CIO: R Mark Adams
Dir IT: Gregory Porreca
Opers Mgr: Laura Sullivan
Ql Cn Mgr: Bernard Braun
Ql Cn Mgr: Patricia Cerulle
Board of Directors: Charles F Wagner Jr

GOOD STUFF, THE
See RSB TOBACCO INC

D-U-N-S 03-655-3550
GOOD TECHNOLOGY CORP
(*Suby of* BLACKBERRY LIMITED)
430 N Mary Ave Ste 200, Sunnyvale, CA 94085-2923
Tel (408) 212-7500 *Founded/Ownrshp* 1996, 2015
Sales 160.3MM *EMP* 799
SIC 7371 7382 Prepackaged software; Computer software development & applications; Custom computer programming services; Protective devices, security
Pr: Christy Wyatt
CFO: Ronald J Fior
Treas: Ira Cook
Sr VP: Cheryln Chin
Sr VP: Fr D Ric ARI S
VP: Aira Cook
VP: Laura Fay
VP: Craig Gordon
VP: William Morris
VP: Julie O'Brien
VP: Karen Reynolds
VP: Chris Roberts
VP: Allen Spence
VP: Ted Tudor
Exec: Robert Curley
Dir Bus: Jonathan Dakin

D-U-N-S 15-797-9613
GOOD TECHNOLOGY SOFTWARE INC
(*Suby of* GOOD TECHNOLOGY CORP) ★
430 N Mary Ave Ste 200, Sunnyvale, CA 94085-2923
Tel (408) 212-7500 *Founded/Ownrshp* 2000
Sales 65.1MMᴱ *EMP* 600
SIC 7372 3661 Prepackaged software; Telephones & telephone apparatus; Prepackaged software; Telephones & telephone apparatus
Pr: Christy Wyatt
CFO: Ron Fior
Treas: Doug Whitman
Sr VP: Andrew Jacques
VP: Ginny Follen
VP: John Herrema III
VP: Ron Vaisbort

GOOD TIDINGS
See COMMERCE LLC

D-U-N-S 61-409-7145
▲ **GOOD TIMES RESTAURANTS INC**
141 Union Blvd Ste 400, Lakewood, CO 80228-1879
Tel (303) 384-1400 *Founded/Ownrshp* 1987
Sales 28.0MM *EMP* 583ᴱ
Tkr Sym GTIM *Exch* NAS
SIC 5812 Eating places; Drive-in restaurant; Eating places; Drive-in restaurant
Pr: Boyd E Hoback
**Ch Bd:* Robert J Stetson
CFO: James Zielke
VP: Scott G Lefever
IT Man: Tim Taylor
VP Sls: Robert D Turill
Board of Directors: Geoffrey R Bailey, Gary J Heller, Steven M Johnson, Eric W Reinhard, Alan A Teran

D-U-N-S 01-631-6046 IMP/EXP
GOOD TIMES USA LLC
8408 Temple Terrace Hwy, Tampa, FL 33637-5808
Tel (813) 621-8702 *Founded/Ownrshp* 2008
Sales 21.7MMᴱ *EMP* 45
Accts Sebree Accounting & Tax Servic
SIC 5194 Tobacco & tobacco products
VP: Greg Dana
Genl Mgr: Sam Saleh

D-U-N-S 05-762-0759 IMP/EXP
GOOD TIRE SERVICE INC
401 S Water St, Kittanning, PA 16201-1712
Tel (724) 543-2010 *Founded/Ownrshp* 1971
Sales 41.8MMᴱ *EMP* 95
SIC 5531 5014 Automotive tires; Automobile tires & tubes; Truck tires & tubes
Pr: Denton J Good
**VP:* Jack J Conte
**VP:* Tony Pouliot
Software D: Aaron White

D-U-N-S 62-578-4988 IMP/EXP
GOOD WATER WAREHOUSE INC
1700 E Walnut Ave, Fullerton, CA 92831-4800
Tel (714) 441-2893 *Founded/Ownrshp* 1989
Sales 53.5MMᴱ *EMP* 50ᴱ
SIC 5074 5999 Water purification equipment; Water purification equipment
Prin: James P Good
Brnch Mgr: Jason Schell
Off Admin: Tammy Strocel

GOOD WILL
See GOODWILL INDUSTRIES OF VALLEYS INC

D-U-N-S 00-316-8770 IMP
GOOD WILL PUBLISHERS INC (NC)
1520 S York Rd, Gastonia, NC 28052-6138
Tel (704) 853-3237 *Founded/Ownrshp* 1949

Sales 22.0MM^E *EMP* 140
SIC 2731 5942 Books: publishing only; Book stores; Books: publishing only; Book stores
Pr: John Briody
**CEO:* Robert M Gallagher
**Bd of Dir:* Richard Hoefling
VP: Joe Bentley
Exec: Kelly Ballard
Exec: Kelly Nichols
Div Mgr: Johnathan Crittenden
IT Man: Ed Gallagher
Natl Sales: Jay Barnes
Sls&Mrk Ex: Edward Gallager
VP Sls: David Moore
Board of Directors: Patrick L Gallagher, Daniel J Gardner Jr, Harry J Grim, Robert H King, Rev Alfred McBride

D-U-N-S 87-461-6683
GOOD-NITE INN INC
11500 W Olympic Blvd # 345, Los Angeles, CA 90064-1528
Tel (310) 235-2745 *Founded/Ownrshp* 1994
Sales 20.9MM^E *EMP* 260
SIC 7011 Motels; Motels
Pr: Philip Ho
**Treas:* Patrick Kataoka

D-U-N-S 05-197-4327 IMP
GOOD-WEST RUBBER CORP
GOODYEAR RBR CO SOUTHERN CAL
9615 Feron Blvd, Rancho Cucamonga, CA 91730-4503
Tel (909) 987-1774 *Founded/Ownrshp* 1961
Sales 35.7MM^E *EMP* 146
SIC 3069 3061 Molded rubber products; Liner strips, rubber; Mechanical rubber goods; Molded rubber products; Liner strips, rubber; Mechanical rubber goods
Pr: Christian Groche
**VP:* Fred Ledesma
**VP:* Harold W Sears
**VP:* Patrick Sears
Exec: Carol Sears
Plnt Mgr: Frank Ramos
Ql Cn Mgr: Kiet Tran
Sls Mgr: Julia Pope

D-U-N-S 17-423-1654
GOOD360
GIFTS IN KIND
675 N Washington St # 330, Alexandria, VA 22314-1939
Tel (703) 836-2121 *Founded/Ownrshp* 1984
Sales 310.0MM *EMP* 36^E
Accts Bdo Usa Llp Bethesda Md
SIC 8399 Community development groups; Community development groups
Pr: Cindy Hallberlin
Mng Pt: Bob Schwartz
**Ch Bd:* Carly Fiorina
COO: Kim Baich
**COO:* Don Miller
CFO: Michael Avis
**CFO:* Gerald Borenstein
CFO: David Maland
Ofcr: Mikel Durham
Ofcr: Elie Hollander
VP: John Connolly
**VP:* Kevin Hagan
**VP:* Melissa Trumpower

GOODBY SILVERSTEIN & PARTNERS
See GOODBY SILVERSTEIN & PARTNERS INC

D-U-N-S 13-017-1002
■ **GOODBY SILVERSTEIN & PARTNERS INC**
GOODBY SILVERSTEIN & PARTNERS
(*Suby of* OMNICOM GROUP INC) ★
720 California St, San Francisco, CA 94108-2440
Tel (415) 392-0669 *Founded/Ownrshp* 1983
Sales 25.8MM^E *EMP* 200^E
SIC 7311 Advertising agencies; Advertising agencies
CEO: Rich Silverstein
**Pr:* Jeff Goodby
**CFO:* Jerry Barnhart
Creative D: Brady Baltezore
Creative D: Paul Caiozzo
Creative D: Kate Catalinac
Creative D: Nathan Frank
Creative D: Danny Gonzalez
Creative D: Nick Klinkert
Creative D: Mike Landry
Creative D: Justin Moore
Creative D: David Suarez

GOODCENTS SOLUTIONS
See ENERTOUCH INC

D-U-N-S 00-952-2969
GOODCRANE CORP
TRIYARDS
12221 Almeda Rd, Houston, TX 77045-3725
Tel (713) 434-3322 *Founded/Ownrshp* 2007
Sales 26.2MM^E *EMP* 80
SIC 3531 Cranes, locomotive
Pr: Levi Romero

D-U-N-S 03-543-4526
GOODE INDUSTRIES INC
M. COOPER WINSUPPLY
(*Suby of* WINSUPPLY INC) ★
8605 Spring Lake Dr, Mokena, IL 60448-8164
Tel (708) 444-1600 *Founded/Ownrshp* 1938, 2015
Sales 28.6MM^E *EMP* 75
SIC 5074 Plumbing & hydronic heating supplies; Plumbing & hydronic heating supplies
Pr: Tom Schleisner
VP: Greg Goode
VP: Dave Poteete

GOODE MOTOR AUTO GROUP
See GOODE MOTOR INC

D-U-N-S 03-399-8634
GOODE MOTOR INC
GOODE MOTOR AUTO GROUP
1096 E Main St, Burley, ID 83318-2045
Tel (208) 878-5611 *Founded/Ownrshp* 1953
Sales 27.9MM^E *EMP* 66
SIC 5511 7538 Automobiles, new & used; General automotive repair shops; Automobiles, new & used; General automotive repair shops
Pr: Buster Goode
**Sec:* Ruth Goode
**VP:* Irene G Thornburg
Genl Mgr: Williams Garth
Genl Mgr: Nick Sfikas
Mktg Dir: Caitlyn Lancaster
Sls Mgr: Kurt Archibald

D-U-N-S 18-973-7146
GOODE PARTNERS LLC
767 3rd Ave Fl 22, New York, NY 10017-9007
Tel (646) 722-9450 *Founded/Ownrshp* 2005
Sales 120.0MM^E *EMP* 371^E
SIC 6282 Investment advice; Investment advice
Mng Pt: David Oddi
**CFO:* Paula Semelmacher
Genl Couns: Jason Berger

D-U-N-S 79-396-5997
GOODENOW BANCORPORATION
BANK MIDWEST
1017 Highway 71 S, Okoboji, IA 51355-2544
Tel (712) 332-2800 *Founded/Ownrshp* 1979
Sales NA *EMP* 41
SIC 6022 State commercial banks; State commercial banks
Pr: Stephen J Goodenow
**Ch:* John E Goodenow

D-U-N-S 00-794-3996 IMP/EXP
GOODFELLOW BROS INC (WA)
1407 Walla Walla Ave, Wenatchee, WA 98801-1530
Tel (509) 667-9095 *Founded/Ownrshp* 1921
Sales 203.0MM *EMP* 1,050
Accts Moss Adams Llp Spokane Washi
SIC 1611 General contractor, highway & street construction; General contractor, highway & street construction
Pr: Chad S Goodfellow
**Treas:* Daniel Reisenauer
Ex VP: Richard Dunn
**VP:* Daniel Goodfellow
Dir Risk M: Glenn Imanaka

D-U-N-S 02-837-0211 IMP
GOODFELLOW CORP
GOODFELLOW CRUSHERS
12451 Us 95, Boulder City, NV 89005
Tel (702) 293-7504 *Founded/Ownrshp* 1972
Sales 55.5MM^E *EMP* 50^E
SIC 5082 General construction machinery & equipment
Pr: Lynn Goodfellow
**Treas:* Curtis Goodfellow
IT Man: McKay Stevens
Sales Asso: Trevor Brindley

GOODFELLOW CRUSHERS
See GOODFELLOW CORP

D-U-N-S 60-989-8960
GOODFELLOW TOP GRADE CONSTRUCTION LLC
(*Suby of* GOODFELLOW BROS INC) ★
50 Contractors St, Livermore, CA 94551-4863
Tel (925) 449-5764 *Founded/Ownrshp* 2012
Sales 57.7MM^E *EMP* 300^E
SIC 8711 Engineering services; Construction & civil engineering; Engineering services; Construction & civil engineering
Pr: William L Gates
COO: Brian L Gates
CFO: Scott Blaine
Ex VP: Robert L Fisher
Ex VP: Brian Gates
VP: John Copriviza
VP: Frank Williams

D-U-N-S 02-450-0813
GOODGUIDE INC (NY)
(*Suby of* UL ENVIRONMENT)
98 Battery St Ste 400, San Francisco, CA 94111-5512
Tel (415) 732-7722 *Founded/Ownrshp* 2010, 2012
Sales 316.5M^E *EMP* 700^E
SIC 7299 Information services, consumer
CEO: George Consagra
Dir Sec: Dara O'Rourke
Snr Sftwr: Nathan Amick

GOODGUYS TIRE & AUTO REPAIR
See GOODGUYS TIRE CENTERS INC

D-U-N-S 07-877-1268 IMP
GOODGUYS TIRE CENTERS INC (CA)
GOODGUYS TIRE & AUTO REPAIR
6770 N Blackstone Ave, Fresno, CA 93710-3506
Tel (559) 498-7705 *Founded/Ownrshp* 1976
Sales 31.4MM^E *EMP* 85
SIC 5531 5014

D-U-N-S 01-429-0258
GOODHART SONS INC
2515 Horseshoe Rd, Lancaster, PA 17601-5998
Tel (717) 656-2404 *Founded/Ownrshp* 1953
Sales 23.9MM *EMP* 160
Accts Reinsel Kuntz Lesher Llp Lanc
SIC 3443 3441 1796 1731 3599 Fabricated plate work (boiler shop); Fabricated structural metal; Pollution control equipment installation; Electrical work; Machine shop, jobbing & repair; Fabricated plate work (boiler shop); Fabricated structural metal; Pollution control equipment installation; Electrical work; Machine shop, jobbing & repair
CEO: Gary W Goodhart
Treas: Randy A Goodhart
**Div Pres:* Chad E Goodhart
**VP:* Michael B Goodhart
VP: Ronald Mundy
Board of Directors: Chad E Goodhart, David R Goodhart, Frank G Goodhart III, Gary W Goodhart, Marc W Goodhart, Matthew S Goodhart, Michael B Goodhart, Randy A Goodhart, Richard J Goodhart Jr

GOODHUE COUNTY GOVERNMENT CTR
See COUNTY OF GOODHUE

D-U-N-S 00-890-4260 IMP
GOODIN CO
2700 N 2nd St, Minneapolis, MN 55411-1679
Tel (612) 588-7811 *Founded/Ownrshp* 1937
Sales 171.8MM *EMP* 405
Accts Mcgladrey Llp Minneapolis Mn
SIC 5074 5075 Pipes & fittings, plastic; Boilers, hot water heating; Radiators & parts, except electric; Furnaces, warm air; Air conditioning equipment, except room units; Pipes & fittings, plastic; Boilers, hot water heating; Radiators & parts, except electric; Furnaces, warm air; Air conditioning equipment, except room units
CEO: Greg Skagerberg
**Pr:* Steven Kelly
**CFO:* Mike Grunklee
**Treas:* Brian Sand
Ofcr: Mylo Gustafson
**Ex VP:* Gerard Melgaard
**VP:* Joel Skagerberg
Brnch Mgr: Dale Bley
Brnch Mgr: Barry Jenson
Brnch Mgr: Bruce Oelfke
Brnch Mgr: Bob Petersen

D-U-N-S 02-557-4310 IMP
GOODING RUBBER INC
(*Suby of* UC) ★
10321 Werch Dr Ste 200, Woodridge, IL 60517-4813
Tel (630) 685-2100 *Founded/Ownrshp* 1948, 2011
Sales 27.2MM^E *EMP* 57
SIC 5085 Industrial supplies
Pr: Dean W Goldbeck
**VP:* Kim Heis
**VP:* Dennis D Monarch
**VP:* Randall L Wagner
QA Dir: George Manderson

D-U-N-S 10-386-3861
GOODLAND HOLDINGS INC
FORM
8330 W 3rd St, Los Angeles, CA 90048-4311
Tel (323) 782-4981 *Founded/Ownrshp* 2001
Sales 50.0MM *EMP* 24
SIC 7819 Directors, independent: motion picture; Directors, independent: motion picture
Pr: Jesse Dylan
CFO: Kim Mackaye
**VP:* Craig Rodgers

D-U-N-S 08-178-2708 IMP/EXP
GOODMAN AND DOMINGUEZ INC
TRAFFIC SHOE
10701 Nw 127th St, Medley, FL 33178-3198
Tel (305) 571-9511 *Founded/Ownrshp* 1983
Sales 41.8MM^E *EMP* 650
SIC 5661 Shoe stores; Shoe stores
Pr: David Goodman
IT Man: Nory Orellana
IT Man: Manny Perez
Mktg Dir: Afroza Khan
Snr Mgr: Janiris Leonardo

D-U-N-S 03-352-9058
GOODMAN DECORATING CO INC
3400 Atlnta Indus Pkwy Nw, Atlanta, GA 30331-1038
Tel (404) 965-3626 *Founded/Ownrshp* 1986
Sales 32.9MM *EMP* 150
Accts Rosenthal & Kaplin Pc Atlan
SIC 1721 1742 Residential painting; Commercial painting; Wallcovering contractors; Drywall; Residential painting; Commercial painting; Wallcovering contractors; Drywall
CEO: Jeffrey M Diamond
**CFO:* Joseph G Pritchard
VP: Mike Schaffer
**VP:* Charles M Terrell
Sfty Mgr: Gerald Lee

D-U-N-S 00-192-6922 IMP/EXP
GOODMAN DISTRIBUTION INC (TX)
(*Suby of* GOODMAN GLOBAL HOLDINGS INC) ★
1426 Ne 8th Ave, Ocala, FL 34470-4250
Tel (352) 620-2727 *Founded/Ownrshp* 1955
Sales 221.2MM^E *EMP* 450
SIC 5075 Warm air heating & air conditioning; Warm air heating & air conditioning
CEO: David L Swift
**CEO:* Charles Carroll
**CFO:* Larry Blackburn
**VP:* Peter Alexander
Brnch Mgr: Scott McPeak

D-U-N-S 00-634-1002 IMP
GOODMAN FOOD PRODUCTS INC (CA)
DON LEE FARMS
200 E Beach Ave Fl 1, Inglewood, CA 90302-3404
Tel (310) 674-3180 *Founded/Ownrshp* 1982
Sales 87.6MM^E *EMP* 256
SIC 2038 Frozen specialties; Frozen specialties
CEO: Donald Goodman
CFO: Barry Drinkward
Sr VP: Jean Harris
CIO: Delores Rose

D-U-N-S 13-346-8210 IMP
GOODMAN GLOBAL HOLDINGS INC
(*Suby of* GOODMAN GLOBAL INC) ★
5151 San Felipe St # 500, Houston, TX 77056-3607
Tel (713) 861-2500 *Founded/Ownrshp* 2004
Sales 489.8MM^E *EMP* 4,401
SIC 3585 3564 Air conditioning equipment, complete; Heating equipment, complete; Heating & air conditioning combination units; Blowers & fans; Air conditioning equipment, complete; Heating equipment, complete; Heating & air conditioning combination units; Blowers & fans
Pr: Charles A Carroll
**CFO:* Lawrence M Blackburn
**Treas:* Mark M Dolan
**Sec:* Ben D Campbell
**Sec:* Cynthia Smith
**Ex VP:* Donald R King

D-U-N-S 62-389-4990 IMP
GOODMAN GLOBAL INC
(*Suby of* CHILL HOLDINGS INC) ★
5151 San Felipe St # 500, Houston, TX 77056-3607
Tel (713) 861-2500 *Founded/Ownrshp* 2008
Sales 1.5MMM^E *EMP* 8,732
SIC 3585 3564 Air conditioning equipment, complete; Heating equipment, complete; Heating & air conditioning combination units; Blowers & fans; Air conditioning equipment, complete; Heating equipment, complete; Heating & air conditioning combination units; Blowers & fans
Pr: David L Swift
**CFO:* Lawrence M Blackburn
CFO: Lawrence Blackburn
Ex VP: Ben D Campbell
Sr VP: Terrance M Smith
Sr VP: William H Topper
VP: Richard J Baenski
VP: Samuel Bikman
VP Sls: Michael J Bride
Counsel: Michael Pancherz

D-U-N-S 07-135-1977
GOODMAN GROUP INC
1107 Hazeltine Blvd # 200, Chaska, MN 55318-2564
Tel (952) 361-8000 *Founded/Ownrshp* 1970
Sales 24.2MM^E *EMP* 566
SIC 6513 8741 6512 6515 Residential hotel operation; Retirement hotel operation; Nursing & personal care facility management; Restaurant management; Business management; Shopping center, property operation only; Mobile home site operators; Residential hotel operation; Retirement hotel operation; Nursing & personal care facility management; Restaurant management; Business management; Shopping center, property operation only; Mobile home site operators
CEO: John B Goodman
COO: Lisa Reddick
VP: Craig Edinger
**VP:* Sidney A Goodman
Dir Risk M: Steve Weros
Comm Man: Sharon Widmer
Rgnl Mgr: Sue Perlich
Rgnl Mgr: Cathy Schumacher
CIO: Barry Reichmann
VP Sls: Dave Schempp
Mktg Dir: Helen Roettger

D-U-N-S 01-080-3013 IMP/EXP
GOODMAN MANUFACTURING CO LP
GOODMAN SALES COMPANY
(*Suby of* GOODMAN GLOBAL INC) ★
5151 San Felipe St # 500, Houston, TX 77056-3650
Tel (713) 861-2500 *Founded/Ownrshp* 2004
Sales 1.0MMM^E *EMP* 4,000
Accts Ernst & Young Llp Houston Te
SIC 3585 Air conditioning units, complete: domestic or industrial; Heating equipment, complete; Parts for heating, cooling & refrigerating equipment; Air conditioning units, complete: domestic or industrial; Heating equipment, complete; Parts for heating, cooling & refrigerating equipment
Pr: David Swift
Pt: Lawrence Blackburn
Pr: Jeffrey Ellingham
CTO: Larry B Urn
VP: Mike Froman
Ex Dir: Sandra Van De Walle
Ex Dir: Marc Marino
Area Mgr: Scott Carreiro
Area Mgr: Joe Hamilton
Area Mgr: Ted Harriman
Area Mgr: Gary Scott

D-U-N-S 17-097-7552
GOODMAN NETWORKS INC
6400 Intl Pkwy Ste 1000, Plano, TX 75093
Tel (972) 406-9692 *Founded/Ownrshp* 2000
Sales 1.2MMM *EMP* 3,925^E
Accts Kpmg Llp Dallas Texas
SIC 4899 Communication signal enhancement network system; Communication signal enhancement network system; Data communication services
Pr: Ron B Hill
Pr: Cari Shyiak
COO: Ernest J Carey
CFO: Joy L Brawner
CFO: Geoffrey Miller
Ex VP: Steven M Bell
Ex VP: Caren Gates
Ex VP: Jimmy Hulett
Ex VP: Ajay Ramaswami
VP: Darrell Collier
VP: Tim Enright
VP: Luis Garza
VP: Joseph Hart
VP: Shakeeb Mir
VP: Carol Murdock
VP: Gary Smith
VP: Bill Zeller
Board of Directors: J Samuel Crowley, Steven L Elfman, John A Goodman, Larry Haynes

GOODMAN PLUMBING
See NATIONAL HEAT & POWER CORP

GOODMAN SALES COMPANY
See GOODMAN MANUFACTURING CO LP

D-U-N-S 93-764-8467
GOODMAN TANK LINES INC
463 Old Reading Pike, Stowe, PA 19464-3729
Tel (610) 970-9250 *Founded/Ownrshp* 1995
Sales 23.9MM^E *EMP* 105
SIC 4212 Local trucking, without storage
Pr: Craig D Goodman
**Pr:* D Craig Goodman

GOODMAN THEATRE, THE
See CHICAGO THEATRE GROUP INC

D-U-N-S 02-363-6269
GOODMAN TRUCK & TRACTOR CO INC
17020 Patrick Henry Hwy, Amelia Court House, VA 23002-5047
Tel (804) 561-2141 *Founded/Ownrshp* 1951
Sales 23.5MM^E *EMP* 46

SIC 5511 Trucks, tractors & trailers: new & used
Pr: Charles B Goodman Jr
**Treas:* Clem W Goodman

D-U-N-S 03-588-7355
GOODMANS INC
GOODMAN'S INTERIOR STRUCTURES
1400 E Indian School Rd, Phoenix, AZ 85014-4983
Tel (602) 263-1110 *Founded/Ownrshp* 1968
Sales 79.5MM^E *EMP* 250
SIC 5712 Office furniture; Office furniture
CEO: Murray Goodman
**Pr:* Adam Goodman
CFO: Doug Klein
CFO: Clarke REA
VP: Tracy Peaya
VP: Tracy Pena
CIO: Steve Miller
Opers Mgr: Tarrell Babers
Sls&Mrk Ex: Rachel Dahl
VP Sls: Jacqui Sabo
Sales Asso: Colleen Geretti

GOODMAN'S INTERIOR STRUCTURES
See GOODMANS INC

D-U-N-S 78-107-5205
GOODNESS GREENESS INC
5959 S Lowe Ave, Chicago, IL 60621-2832
Tel (773) 224-4411 *Founded/Ownrshp* 1991
Sales 39.4MM^E *EMP* 50
SIC 5148 Fresh fruits & vegetables
Pr: Robert Scaman
CFO: Mike McDermott
**VP:* Rick Scaman

D-U-N-S 00-737-3038
GOODPASTURE LTD (TX)
214 S 6th St, Brownfield, TX 79316-4206
Tel (806) 637-2541 *Founded/Ownrshp* 1932
Sales 28.3MM *EMP* 23
Accts Sam Chaffin
SIC 5191 2873 Fertilizer & fertilizer materials; Ammonium nitrate, ammonium sulfate; Fertilizer & fertilizer materials; Ammonium nitrate, ammonium sulfate
Pr: H Ken Muldrow
**Treas:* Donnie R Wade
Bd of Dir: John Mayo
Bd of Dir: Mike McDonald
Bd of Dir: Rita Muldrow
**VP:* Sam Chaffin

GOODRICH
See UNIVERSAL PROPULSION CO INC

GOODRICH AEROSTRUCTURES
See GOODRICH CORP

GOODRICH AEROSTRUCTURES GROUP
See ROHR INC

GOODRICH ARCFT WHEELS & BRAKES
See GOODRICH CORP

D-U-N-S 00-446-7452
■ **GOODRICH CORP** (NY)
GOODRICH ARCFT WHEELS & BRAKES
(*Suby of* UNITED TECHNOLOGIES CORP) ★
4 Coliseum Ctr 2730 W, Charlotte, NC 28217
Tel (704) 423-7000 *Founded/Ownrshp* 1912, 2012
Sales 9.8MMM^E *EMP* 28,000
SIC 7372 3724 3728 Prepackaged software; Aircraft engines & engine parts; Aircraft parts & equipment; Aircraft landing assemblies & brakes; Aircraft body & wing assemblies & parts; Aircraft assemblies, subassemblies & parts; Prepackaged software; Aircraft engines & engine parts; Aircraft parts & equipment
Pr: David Gitlin
Pr: Tom Bergeron
Pr: Marc Duvall
Pr: Mike Gardiner
**Pr:* Greg Watson
Pr: Bob Yancey
COO: David Price
COO: Jerry Witowski
CFO: William Dries
**CFO:* Scott E Kuechle
CFO: Thomas Snead
**Treas:* Richard S Caswell
Div Pres: Bill Ashworth
Chf Mktg O: John Sims
Ex VP: Terrence G Linnert
Ex VP: Gerald T Witowski
**Sr VP:* Jennifer Pollino
VP: Scott Cottrill
Dir Bus: Peter Stein

D-U-N-S 07-171-0264 IMP
GOODRICH CORP
GOODRICH AEROSTRUCTURES
850 Lagoon Dr, Chula Vista, CA 91910-2001
Tel (619) 691-4111 *Founded/Ownrshp* 2011
Sales 20.4MM^E *EMP* 167^E
SIC 3324 Aerospace investment castings, ferrous
CFO: Kenneth Wood
VP: Paul Farsetta
Dir Bus: Barry Strauss
Prgrm Mgr: Mike Doyle
Prgrm Mgr: Frank Giglio
Dir IT: Jerry Kapcis
IT Man: Sandy Bailey
IT Man: Geoff Fox
IT Man: Jeff Fryhling
IT Man: Jan Messina
IT Man: John Nava

D-U-N-S 60-344-7744
■ **GOODRICH CORP**
UTC AEROSPACE SYSTEMS
(*Suby of* GOODRICH ARCFT WHEELS & BRAKES) ★
14300 Judicial Rd, Burnsville, MN 55306-4890
Tel (952) 892-4000 *Founded/Ownrshp* 1934
Sales 138.0MM^E *EMP* 150^E
SIC 5088 Aircraft equipment & supplies
Pr: Gerald T Witowski
**Pr:* David Gitlin
CFO: John Pain
VP: Jan Mathiesen
VP: Phil Rosnik
VP: Mark Skarohlid
VP: Tom Wiegele
Dir Bus: Chris Cojocar
Dir Bus: Mark Herion
Prgrm Mgr: Judy Keefe
Genl Mgr: Ross Rutledge

D-U-N-S 82-788-8277
GOODRICH CORP
GOODRICH ISR SYSTEMS
7 Technology Park Dr, Westford, MA 01886-3141
Tel (978) 303-6700 *Founded/Ownrshp* 1912
Sales 20.6MM^E *EMP* 119
SIC 5946 Cameras
Ch Bd: Marshall O Larsen
VP: Jeffrey Brown
**VP:* Sally L Geib
Exec: Joanne Conrad
Dir Bus: Glen Senkowski
Prgrm Mgr: Philip Giguere
Prgrm Mgr: David Hammond
Prgrm Mgr: Janice Price
Prgrm Mgr: Susan Raisbeck
Prgrm Mgr: Michael Schulze
Genl Mgr: Torri Blaire

D-U-N-S 00-896-7176
GOODRICH DAIRY INC
GOODRICH ICE CREAM
11223 Z St, Omaha, NE 68137-4662
Tel (402) 592-3910 *Founded/Ownrshp* 1982
Sales 27.7MM^E *EMP* 250
SIC 2024 Ice cream & frozen desserts; Ice cream & frozen desserts
Treas: John Houlihan

GOODRICH ICE CREAM
See GOODRICH DAIRY INC

GOODRICH INTERIORS SPECIALTY
See AMI INDUSTRIES INC

GOODRICH ISR SYSTEMS
See GOODRICH CORP

D-U-N-S 92-820-9287 IMP
▲ **GOODRICH PETROLEUM CORP**
801 Louisiana St Ste 700, Houston, TX 77002-4936
Tel (713) 780-9494 *Founded/Ownrshp* 1995
Sales 208.5MM *EMP* 105
Tkr Sym GDP *Exch* NYS
SIC 1311 1382 Crude petroleum & natural gas; Oil & gas exploration services; Crude petroleum & natural gas; Oil & gas exploration services
Ch Bd: Walter G Goodrich
V Ch: Gil Goodrich
**Pr:* Robert C Turnham Jr
CFO: Joseph T Leary
CFO: Jan L Schott
Ex VP: Mark E Ferchau
Sr VP: Clarke A Denney
Sr VP: Bret Hammett
Sr VP: Michael J Killelea
Sr VP: James G Marston III
VP: Timothy D Lane
VP: Rusty Mondelli
Board of Directors: Josiah T Austin, Peter D Goodson, Michael J Perdue, Arthur A Seeligson, Stephen M Straty, Gene Washington

D-U-N-S 60-938-4789
GOODRICH QUALITY THEATERS INC
4417 Broadmoor Ave Se, Grand Rapids, MI 49512-5367
Tel (616) 698-7733 *Founded/Ownrshp* 1989
Sales 88.5MM^E *EMP* 1,200
Accts Plante & Moran Pllc Grand Ra
SIC 7832 Motion picture theaters, except drive-in; Motion picture theaters, except drive-in
Pr: Robert Emmett Goodrich
Mng Pt: Kevin Morgan
COO: Martin Betz
CFO: Martin Bette
CFO: Sue Howard
**CFO:* Ross Pettinga
Area Mgr: Heath Thomas
Genl Mgr: Brian Wester
Web Dev: Chris Rannow
Mktg Mgr: Matt Johnson

GOODRICH SENSORS AND INTEGRATE
See ATLANTIC INERTIAL SYSTEMS INC

GOODRICH TURBOMACHINERY PDTS
See WALBAR INC

D-U-N-S 13-970-3219 IMP
GOODRIDGE USA INC
(*Suby of* GOODRIDGE LIMITED)
529 Van Ness Ave, Torrance, CA 90501-1424
Tel (310) 533-1924 *Founded/Ownrshp* 1991
Sales 27.5MM^E *EMP* 70
SIC 5013 Automotive supplies & parts
CEO: Celso Pierre
Ofcr: Joyce Lee
VP: Nick Heathershaw
VP: Jamie Ramsden
Sls Mgr: Jon Hourihan

D-U-N-S 14-487-8030
GOODRUM ENTERPRISES INC
MCDONALD'S
1176 Ralph David Avernath, Atlanta, GA 30310-1756
Tel (404) 755-4489 *Founded/Ownrshp* 1982
Sales 8.0MM *EMP* 300
SIC 5812 Fast-food restaurant, chain; Fast-food restaurant, chain
Pr: Leon Goodrum

GOOD'S DISTRIBUTION
See GOODS STORE INC

GOOD'S HOME FURNISHINGS
See MGL PARTNERS LLC

D-U-N-S 04-903-6726 IMP
GOODS STORE INC
GOOD'S DISTRIBUTION
165 Earland Dr, New Holland, PA 17557-1502
Tel (717) 355-0571 *Founded/Ownrshp* 1968
Sales 31.4MM *EMP* 190
Accts Weinhold Nickel & Company Ll
SIC 5311 Department stores; Department stores
Pr: Kenneth N Burkholder
CFO: Lloyd Kuhn
**VP:* Clinton Burkholder
VP: Amos Martin
**VP:* Ernest G Martin
IT Man: Craig Zimmerman
Site Mgr: Troy Hoover

D-U-N-S 07-768-1609
GOODSILL ANDERSON QUINN & STIFEL A LIMITED LIABILITY LAW PARTNERSHIP LLP
999 Bishop St Ste 1600, Honolulu, HI 96813-4440
Tel (808) 547-5600 *Founded/Ownrshp* 1942
Sales 28.6MM^E *EMP* 190
SIC 8111 General practice law office; General practice law office
Pt: Miki Okumura
Pt: Robert Fricke
Pt: John R Lacy
Mng Pt: Ronald Lum
COO: Debra B Marple
Trst: Martin Anderson
Ofcr: Rebecca Dayhuff
Exec: Bruce Lamon
Dir IT: Peter Kikuta
IT Man: Eric Fleckles

GOODSON ACURA
See GOODSON IMPORTS INC

D-U-N-S 05-188-9665
■ **GOODSON AUTO GROUP INC**
SPRING BRANCH HONDA
(*Suby of* PENSKE AUTOMOTIVE GROUP INC) ★
10250 Katy Fwy, Houston, TX 77043-5208
Tel (713) 464-7482 *Founded/Ownrshp* 1967
Sales 41.3MM^E *EMP* 175
SIC 5511 7538 Automobiles, new & used; General automotive repair shops; Automobiles, new & used; General automotive repair shops
Pr: Tena Fontenot
Sales Asso: Tim Chow

GOODSON HONDA
See GOODSON NORTH LLC

D-U-N-S 15-154-4046
GOODSON IMPORTS INC
GOODSON ACURA
1750 E Airport Fwy, Irving, TX 75062-4825
Tel (972) 554-0505 *Founded/Ownrshp* 1986
Sales 39.3MM^E *EMP* 120
SIC 5511 Automobiles, new & used; Automobiles, new & used
Pr: Clark Richardson
CFO: Christopher Morrow
**Sec:* Bobbie Woods
Exec: Richard Schindler
Genl Mgr: Richard Schneider
Sales Asso: Leonard Johnson
Sales Asso: Mark Laurenzi
Sales Asso: Israel Velasquez

D-U-N-S 00-894-9570
GOODSON NORTH LLC
GOODSON HONDA
17350 North Fwy, Houston, TX 77090-5010
Tel (832) 601-4000 *Founded/Ownrshp* 1976
Sales 47.0MM^E *EMP* 150
SIC 5511 5531 7538 Automobiles, new & used; Pickups, new & used; Automotive accessories; General automotive repair shops; Automobiles, new & used; Pickups, new & used; Automotive accessories; General automotive repair shops
Sls Mgr: Michael Capps
Sales Asso: Paul Morgan

GOODSONS' SUPERMARKET 1
See GOODSONS SUPERMARKETS INC

D-U-N-S 03-013-6493
GOODSONS SUPERMARKETS INC (WV)
GOODSONS' SUPERMARKET 1
U S Rte 52, Welch, WV 24801
Tel (304) 436-8481 *Founded/Ownrshp* 1976
Sales 20.6MM *EMP* 105
SIC 5411 Supermarkets, independent; Supermarkets, independent
Pr: Jeffrey S Goodson
**Treas:* W M Goodson
**VP:* Donald Goodson
VP: Danny Thornsbury
Board of Directors: Margaret B Goodson

GOODSOURCE SOLUTION
See GOOD SOURCE SOLUTIONS INC

GOODSPEED DISTRIBUTING
See R E GOODSPEED AND SONS DISTRIBUTING INC

GOODW INDUS OF ERIE, HURON, OT
See GOODWILL INDUSTRIES OF ERIE HURON OTTAWA AND SANDUSKY COUNTIES INC

D-U-N-S 15-203-1733
GOODWATER HEALTH CENTER CARE LLC
16 Jones Hill Rd, Goodwater, AL 35072-9463
Tel (256) 839-6711 *Founded/Ownrshp* 2004
Sales 196.2MM *EMP* 75
SIC 8059 Nursing & personal care; Nursing & personal care

D-U-N-S 06-904-9302
GOODWAY GRAPHICS INC
IGI PRINTING
261 York Rd Ste 930, Jenkintown, PA 19046
Tel (215) 887-5700 *Founded/Ownrshp* 1974
Sales 38.0MM^E *EMP* 350
SIC 2752 7336 7331 8743 3577 Lithographing on metal; Graphic arts & related design; Direct mail advertising services; Promotion service; Graphic displays, except graphic terminals; Lithographing on metal; Graphic arts & related design; Direct mail advertising services; Promotion service; Graphic displays, except graphic terminals
Ch Bd: Donald L Wolk
Pr: Noel Doherty
Pr: Robert Perotti
Pr: David Wolk
Sr VP: Christopher Fisher

D-U-N-S 06-115-3011
GOODWAY GROUP INC
261 Old York Rd Ste 930, Jenkintown, PA 19046-3711
Tel (215) 887-5700 *Founded/Ownrshp* 1975
Sales 34.7MM^E *EMP* 230
SIC 7311 Advertising agencies
VP: David Wolk
**COO:* Jay Friedman
**CFO:* Mark Meade
**Treas:* Beryl J Wolk
**Ex VP:* Dan Mauch
VP: Andrew S Vitek
**VP:* Donald Wolk
CTO: Sam Goldstein

D-U-N-S 07-967-4632
GOODWELL WIND PROJECT LLC
(*Suby of* ENEL GREEN POWER NORTH AMERICA INC) ★
2142 Rd Hh, Goodwell, OK 73939
Tel (978) 681-1900 *Founded/Ownrshp* 2003, 2013
Sales 224.7M^E *EMP* 360
SIC 4931 1796 4911 ; Power generating equipment installation; Generation, electric power
Ex VP: Michael Storch
CFO: Gianfranco Butera

GOODWILL CENTER
See GOODWILL INDUSTRIES OF DELAWARE & DELAWARE COUNTY INC

D-U-N-S 07-632-1520
GOODWILL CENTRAL COAST
350 Encinal St, Santa Cruz, CA 95060-2198
Tel (831) 423-8611 *Founded/Ownrshp* 1953
Sales 26.5MM *EMP* 525
SIC 5932 8322

GOODWILL COLUMBUS
See GOODWILL INDUSTRIES OF CENTRAL OHIO INC

D-U-N-S 96-409-4663
GOODWILL COMMUNITY FOUNDATION INC
4808 Chin Page Rd, Durham, NC 27703-8476
Tel (919) 941-9600 *Founded/Ownrshp* 2010
Sales 37.6MM *EMP* 2
Accts Batchelor Tillery & Roberts
SIC 8399 Social services; Social services
Pr: Dennis N McLain

GOODWILL IND OF SO NJ
See GOODWILL INDUSTRIES OF SOUTHERN NEW JERSEY & PHILADELPHIA INC

GOODWILL INDS NEW BRAUNFELS
See GOODWILL INDUSTRIES OF SAN ANTONIO

GOODWILL INDUSTRIES
See GOODWILL OF GREAT PLAINS

GOODWILL INDUSTRIES
See HANDI SKILLS INC

GOODWILL INDUSTRIES
See GOODWILL OF CENTRAL AND COASTAL VIRGINIA INC

D-U-N-S 07-490-1455
GOODWILL INDUSTRIES - KNOXVILLE INC
5307 Kingston Pike, Knoxville, TN 37919-5020
Tel (865) 588-1033 *Founded/Ownrshp* 1971
Sales 21.7MM *EMP* 275
SIC 8331 5331 Vocational rehabilitation agency; Variety stores; Vocational rehabilitation agency; Variety stores
Pr: Elizabeth Nother
VP: Meaghan Johnson
IT Man: David White

D-U-N-S 06-282-3638
GOODWILL INDUSTRIES INC
EASTER SEAL MINNESOTA
553 Fairview Ave N, Saint Paul, MN 55104-3080
Tel (651) 379-5800 *Founded/Ownrshp* 1990
Sales 57.7MM *EMP* 22,000
Accts Baker Tilly Virchow Krause Ll
SIC 4953 8331 8322 5932 4226 Recycling, waste materials; Job training services; Family service agency; Used merchandise stores; Special warehousing & storage; Recycling, waste materials; Job training services; Family service agency; Used merchandise stores; Special warehousing & storage
Pr: Michael Wirth-Davis
Dir Vol: Sara Triplett
CFO: Jason Seifert
Bd of Dir: John Bergstrom
VP: Sheila Olson
Genl Mgr: Jim Churchill
Genl Mgr: Emily Clancy
Genl Mgr: Kristen Faber
Genl Mgr: Alan Hurd
Genl Mgr: Donna Knicker
Genl Mgr: Katie Mild

D-U-N-S 09-339-3080
GOODWILL INDUSTRIES INC
4805 N 72nd St, Omaha, NE 68134-2304
Tel (402) 341-4609 *Founded/Ownrshp* 1933
Sales 24.5MM *EMP* 500
Accts Kpmg Llp Omaha Nebraska
SIC 8331 7349 5932 Vocational rehabilitation agency; Building maintenance services; Used merchandise stores; Vocational rehabilitation agency; Building maintenance services; Used merchandise stores
Pr: Frank J McGree
**CFO:* Pauli Bishop
**Treas:* Robert J Mitchell
Treas: Robert Mitchell
Ex VP: Andy Bradley
VP: Linda Kizzier
VP: Linda McLain
VP: Todd Milbrandt

VP: Ken Moler
VP: Lorri Molli
VP: Gary Oos
VP: Neil Parks
VP: Glen Travis

D-U-N-S 07-479-9800
GOODWILL INDUSTRIES INTERNATIONAL INC
15810 Indianola Dr, Rockville, MD 20855-2674
Tel (301) 530-6500 Founded/Ownrshp 1902
Sales 46.0MM EMP 100E
Accts Tate And Tryon Washington Dc
SIC 8331 8399 Job training & vocational rehabilitation services; Community development groups; Job training & vocational rehabilitation services; Community development groups
Pr: Jim Gibbions
*Ch Bd: A Gidget Hopf
*Ch Bd: Larry Ishol
V Ch: Don Steger
Pr: Dean Saketos
COO: Andrea Salinas
COO: Alexander M Sanchez
CFO: Claudia Dupont
Sr VP: Renee Weippert
*VP: Dave Barringer
*VP: Linda Chandellor
*VP: John Costopoulof
*VP: Harry Furukawa
VP: Anita Hill
VP: Kimberly B Lewis
VP: Linda Matthews
VP: Bob Reese
VP: Marisa Rohn
VP: Cathy Rudzinski
VP: Leanne Sommers
VP: Jill Wallace

GOODWILL INDUSTRIES MICHIANA
See GOODWILL INDUSTRIES OF MICHIANA INC

D-U-N-S 07-689-7743
GOODWILL INDUSTRIES OF AKRON OHIO INC
570 E Waterloo Rd, Akron, OH 44319-1223
Tel (330) 724-6995 Founded/Ownrshp 1929
Sales 18.0MM EMP 320
Accts Brockman Coats Gedelian & Co
SIC 8331 Vocational rehabilitation agency; Vocational rehabilitation agency
CEO: Nancy Ellis McClenaghan
*Treas: Brent R Thompson
Treas: Jorge Villacampa
VP: Hester Allison
*VP: Janet Morrison
*VP: Greg Morton
Exec: Joyce Estock
Exec: Pam Moreno
*Prin: M M Montis
Brnch Mgr: Deborah Childs
Brnch Mgr: Luis Garcia

D-U-N-S 07-565-0846
GOODWILL INDUSTRIES OF ARKANSAS INC
7400 Scott Hamilton Dr, Little Rock, AR 72209-3175
Tel (501) 244-2486 Founded/Ownrshp 1927
Sales 27.7MM EMP 480
Accts Bkd Llp Little Rock Arkansa
SIC 5932 8051 Used merchandise stores; Skilled nursing care facilities; Used merchandise stores; Skilled nursing care facilities
CEO: Brian Itzkowitz
Ex Dir: Johnnie Taylor

D-U-N-S 07-246-0678
GOODWILL INDUSTRIES OF CENTRAL ARIZONA FOUNDATION INC
GOODWILL OF CENTRAL ARIZONA
2626 W Beryl Ave, Phoenix, AZ 85021-1668
Tel (602) 535-4000 Founded/Ownrshp 1947
Sales 118.8MM EMP 2,100
Accts Mayer Hoffman Mccann Pc Phoe
SIC 8331 Vocational rehabilitation agency; Vocational rehabilitation agency
Pr: James Teter
Pr: Tim Oneal
Pr: Richmond J Vincent
CFO: Tanya Perry
Ofcr: Larry Betz
Sr VP: Nobu Hara
Exec: Valerie Brown
Dir Soc: Sherry Baker
CIO: Neal Goodrich
Dir IT: Amy Rodriguez
Sales Exec: Jackie Halleen
Board of Directors: Steve Kedzior

D-U-N-S 07-322-8728
GOODWILL INDUSTRIES OF CENTRAL FLORIDA INC
7531 S Orange Blossom Trl, Orlando, FL 32809-6901
Tel (407) 857-0659 Founded/Ownrshp 1959
Sales 48.3MM EMP 1,200
SIC 8331 8741 Skill training center; Management services; Skill training center; Management services
Ch Bd: Laurence Hames
*Pr: William G Oakley
*CFO: Curtis Ramsey
*Ch: Maximiano Brito
*Treas: Michael Clary
Bd of Dir: Michael Smith
Prgrm Mgr: Gene Heflin
IT Man: Todd Russell
Trfc Dir: Chris Hughes
Sfty Mgr: Kate Pile
Ql Cn Mgr: Lee Ciccone

D-U-N-S 03-056-2425
GOODWILL INDUSTRIES OF CENTRAL ILLINOIS INC
2319 E War Memorial Dr, Peoria, IL 61614-8041
Tel (309) 682-1113 Founded/Ownrshp 1934
Sales 12.4MM EMP 350
Accts Gordon Stockman & Waugh Pc
SIC 8331 Job training & vocational rehabilitation services; Job training & vocational rehabilitation services

Pr: Patrice W Fuchs

D-U-N-S 00-693-8278
GOODWILL INDUSTRIES OF CENTRAL INDIANA INC
1635 W Michigan St, Indianapolis, IN 46222-3852
Tel (317) 564-4313 Founded/Ownrshp 1930
Sales 128.9MM EMP 1,200
Accts Greenwalt Cpas Inc Indianap
SIC 5932 4783 8331 4953 Clothing, secondhand; Home furnishings, secondhand; Packing & crating; Job training services; Recycling, waste materials; Clothing, secondhand; Home furnishings, secondhand; Packing & crating; Job training services; Recycling, waste materials
Pr: James M McClelland
*Ch Bd: Perry Griffith
*Ch Bd: Fred C Tucker III
COO: Scott Bess
*Treas: Jean Wojtowicz
VP: Betsy Delgado
VP: Ken File
VP: Keith Reissaus
*VP: Daniel J Riley
VP: Aaron Roberts
VP: Eric Schlegel
Exec: Debbie Parvis
Dir Risk M: Matthew Pearsey

D-U-N-S 07-840-8630
GOODWILL INDUSTRIES OF CENTRAL MICHIGAN INC
617 N Mechanic St, Jackson, MI 49202-3342
Tel (517) 787-4448 Founded/Ownrshp 1950
Sales 65.9MM EMP 127
SIC 8331 Vocational rehabilitation agency; Job training services; Vocational rehabilitation agency; Job training services
Pr: Larry Jones

D-U-N-S 07-929-4989
GOODWILL INDUSTRIES OF CENTRAL MICHIGANS HEARTLAND INC
GICMH
4820 Wayne Rd, Battle Creek, MI 49037-7324
Tel (269) 788-6500 Founded/Ownrshp 1953
Sales 22.6MM EMP 450
Accts Plante & Moran Pllc Portage
SIC 8331 5651 5712 7349 Job training & vocational rehabilitation services; Family clothing stores; Furniture stores; Janitorial service, contract basis; Job training & vocational rehabilitation services; Family clothing stores; Furniture stores; Janitorial service, contract basis
Pr: Kenneth Bauer
*CFO: Susan Burdick
VP: John Bauer
IT Man: Doug Ivey

D-U-N-S 00-196-3982
GOODWILL INDUSTRIES OF CENTRAL OHIO INC
GOODWILL COLUMBUS
1331 Edgehill Rd, Columbus, OH 43212-3123
Tel (614) 294-5181 Founded/Ownrshp 1939
Sales 45.9MM EMP 610
Accts Schneider Downs & Co Inc C
SIC 8331 5399 Job training services; Vocational rehabilitation agency; Surplus & salvage goods; Job training services; Vocational rehabilitation agency; Surplus & salvage goods
Pr: Marjory Pizzuti
*COO: Anthony Hartley
*Treas: Fred G Pressley
Treas: Donna Teach
*VP: Hartley Anthony
*VP: Michael Goldbeck
*VP: Beth Kowalski
*VP: Tim Salvato
*VP: Mary Vail
Dir IT: Todd Laber
Site Mgr: Melania Massey

D-U-N-S 08-847-5835
GOODWILL INDUSTRIES OF CENTRAL TEXAS
1015 Norwood Park Blvd, Austin, TX 78753-6608
Tel (512) 637-7100 Founded/Ownrshp 1958
Sales 69.2MME EMP 1,200
SIC 8331 Vocational rehabilitation agency; Vocational training agency; Vocational rehabilitation agency; Vocational training agency
Pr: Gerald L Davis
CFO: Tracy Lintz
VP: Frank Holland
VP: Paul Padilla
Dir Risk M: Charles Briscoe
Comm Man: Ana Rummer
Dist Mgr: Robyn Jividen
Store Mgr: Sherry Cox
QA Dir: Gustavo Jimenez
IT Man: Beth Smyer
Web Dev: Amy Wood

D-U-N-S 07-745-7752
GOODWILL INDUSTRIES OF CHESAPEAKE INC
222 E Redwood St, Baltimore, MD 21202-3312
Tel (410) 282-8750 Founded/Ownrshp 1919
Sales 53.0MM EMP 550E
SIC 8699 8331 Charitable organization; Job training & vocational rehabilitation services; Charitable organization; Job training & vocational rehabilitation services
Ch Bd: Francis Taylor
*Pr: Lisa Rusyniak
*VP: Gerald Grasso
VP: Karen Pearson
Dir Bus: Catharine Fleming

D-U-N-S 07-585-5452
GOODWILL INDUSTRIES OF COASTAL EMPIRE INC (GA)
7220 Sallie Mood Dr, Savannah, GA 31406-3921
Tel (912) 354-6611 Founded/Ownrshp 1965
Sales 4.6MM EMP 500
SIC 5932 8322

D-U-N-S 01-020-2679
GOODWILL INDUSTRIES OF COLUMBIA INC
815 N Kellogg St Ste A, Kennewick, WA 99336-8007
Tel (509) 735-0400 Founded/Ownrshp 1969
Sales 20.5MME EMP 175E
Accts Baker & Giles Ps Cpas Pasco
SIC 8742 8741 Retail trade consultant; Management services
Pr: John Paetel
*Treas: Sue Supplee
*VP: Steve Palmer
*Ex Dir: Gordon Comfort

D-U-N-S 05-095-7372
GOODWILL INDUSTRIES OF COLUMBIA WILLAMETTE
1943 Se 6th Ave, Portland, OR 97214-4508
Tel (503) 238-6100 Founded/Ownrshp 1978
Sales 135.4MM EMP 1,950
Accts Jarrard Seibert Pollard & Co L
SIC 8331 Sheltered workshop; Vocational training agency; Sheltered workshop; Vocational training agency
Pr: John Paetel
CFO: Richard Knox
*VP: Steve Palmer
Dir IT: Marvin Aultman
IT Man: Carl Trachtenberg
Advt Mgr: Gilbert Vizon

D-U-N-S 07-137-9317
GOODWILL INDUSTRIES OF DALLAS INC
3020 N Westmoreland Rd, Dallas, TX 75212-3647
Tel (214) 638-2800 Founded/Ownrshp 1928
Sales 20.7MM EMP 400
SIC 7349 5399 Janitorial service, contract basis; Surplus & salvage goods; Janitorial service, contract basis; Surplus & salvage goods
Pr: Rodney Ginther
CFO: Ellison Daniels
*CFO: Nina Jones
*Treas: Robert Brooks Cullum Jr
VP: Chris Simms

D-U-N-S 80-437-7976
GOODWILL INDUSTRIES OF DELAWARE & DELAWARE COUNTY INC
GOODWILL CENTER
300 E Lea Blvd, Wilmington, DE 19802-2354
Tel (302) 761-4640 Founded/Ownrshp 1921
Sales 39.3MM EMP 425
Accts Whisman Giordano & Associates
SIC 5932 8331 Used merchandise stores; Vocational training agency; Used merchandise stores; Vocational training agency
Pr: Ted Van Name
*Ch Bd: Chris Quintanilla
Treas: Thomas Black
VP: Patrick Clancy
VP: Allison David
Area Mgr: Hillary Joseph
Opers Mgr: Chris Morris
VP Sls: Sue Murray

D-U-N-S 08-195-7110
GOODWILL INDUSTRIES OF DENVER
6850 Federal Blvd, Denver, CO 80221-2628
Tel (303) 650-7700 Founded/Ownrshp 1918
Sales 66.3MM EMP 1,300
Accts Eks&H Lllp Denver Co
SIC 8399 Council for social agency; Council for social agency
CEO: Stuart Davie
*CFO: Mike Pritchard
*VP: Jeff Ayers
*VP: Randy Dohne
VP: Joyce Schlose
VP: Bob Schow
*VP: Robert Tallmadge
*Ex Dir: Jesse Wolff

D-U-N-S 07-201-3592
GOODWILL INDUSTRIES OF EAST CENTRAL NORTH CAROLINA INC
4808 Chin Page Rd, Durham, NC 27703-8476
Tel (919) 941-9600 Founded/Ownrshp 1964
Sales 17.1MM EMP 350
Accts Batchelor Tillery & Roberts
SIC 8331 Vocational rehabilitation agency; Vocational rehabilitation agency
Pr: Dennis N McLain
*CFO: Dan Hawley
*VP: Linda Mc Lain
VP: Linda McLain

D-U-N-S 07-137-9119 IMP
GOODWILL INDUSTRIES OF EAST TEXAS INC
409 W Locust St, Tyler, TX 75702-5695
Tel (903) 593-8438 Founded/Ownrshp 1975
Sales 15.7MM EMP 500
SIC 5932 Used merchandise stores; Used merchandise stores
Pr: David J Walton
Brnch Mgr: Beverly Hamilton
IT Man: Jeff Littrell
Board of Directors: Mary Cowan

D-U-N-S 01-083-6823
GOODWILL INDUSTRIES OF ERIE HURON OTTAWA AND SANDUSKY COUNTIES INC
GOODW INDUS OF ERIE, HURON, OT
419 W Market St, Sandusky, OH 44870-2411
Tel (419) 625-4744 Founded/Ownrshp 1973
Sales 10.4MM EMP 280
Accts Barnes Wendling Cpas Llc Sand
SIC 8322 5932 Individual & family services; Clothing, secondhand; Individual & family services; Clothing, secondhand
Pr: Robert Talcott
*CEO: Eric Kochendoerfer
CFO: Bill Carroll
CFO: Mark Stratton
Treas: Don Hanck
VP: Barbara Hanck
Mktg Mgr: Steven Timmerman

D-U-N-S 07-079-8764
GOODWILL INDUSTRIES OF FORT WORTH
4005 Campus Dr, Fort Worth, TX 76119-5529
Tel (817) 332-7866 Founded/Ownrshp 1949
Sales 11.1MM EMP 900E
Accts Hartman Leito & Bolt Llp Fort
SIC 5932 8331 Used merchandise stores; Job training & vocational rehabilitation services; Used merchandise stores; Job training & vocational rehabilitation services
Pr: David Bostick

D-U-N-S 07-675-0330
GOODWILL INDUSTRIES OF GREATER CLEVELAND AND EAST CENTRAL OHIO INC
408 9th St Sw, Canton, OH 44707-4714
Tel (330) 454-9461 Founded/Ownrshp 1917
Sales 25.6MM EMP 485
Accts Bober Markey Fedorovich Akron
SIC 8331 Vocational rehabilitation agency; Vocational rehabilitation agency
CEO: Kenneth Weber
*CFO: Craig Chaffinch
VP: Marcie Bragg
Dir IT: Bill Crossen
Dir IT: William Crossen
Dir IT: Tom Whitfield
Board of Directors: Gladys V Hall

D-U-N-S 00-491-3364
GOODWILL INDUSTRIES OF GREATER DETROIT FOUNDATION
3111 Grand River Ave, Detroit, MI 48208-2962
Tel (313) 964-3900 Founded/Ownrshp 1921
Sales 37.9MM EMP 220
Accts Uhy Llp Farmington Hills Mic
SIC 8331 Vocational rehabilitation agency; Vocational rehabilitation agency
Pr: Lorna G Utley
*Ex VP: Felicia Hunter
*VP: Delois W Caldwell
*VP: Kathleen Laird
*VP: Karen Sanford
*VP: William Wimsatt

D-U-N-S 00-398-5140
GOODWILL INDUSTRIES OF GREATER EAST BAY INC (CA)
1301 30th Ave, Oakland, CA 94601-2208
Tel (510) 698-7200 Founded/Ownrshp 1919
Sales 25.6MM EMP 600
SIC 5932 8331 Clothing, secondhand; Job training & vocational rehabilitation services; Clothing, secondhand; Job training & vocational rehabilitation services
Pr: John Latchford
*COO: Virginia Robbins
*CFO: Michael Conlon
*CFO: Patrick Schmalz
*Treas: John Schorman
VP: Mathew Hoffman
*VP: Patricia Salmon
*Prin: Linda Chew
Area Mgr: Heather McInnes
Dir IT: Tom Clougher
IT Man: Jesse Foster

D-U-N-S 04-456-6982
GOODWILL INDUSTRIES OF GREATER GRAND RAPIDS INC
3035 Prairie St Sw, Grandville, MI 49418-2064
Tel (616) 532-4200 Founded/Ownrshp 1966
Sales 34.2MM EMP 535
Accts Rehmann Robson Llc Grand Rapi
SIC 8331 5932 Vocational rehabilitation agency; Used merchandise stores; Vocational rehabilitation agency; Used merchandise stores
Pr: Kathy Crosby
*CFO: Michael Fee
Chf Mktg O: Jill Wallace
VP: Dave Brinca
VP: Sue Cloutier
*VP: Reginald Graham
VP: Nancy Volpe
Store Mgr: Dora Sanchez
Telecom Ex: Chris Lane
IT Man: David Buchan
IT Man: Scott Dillard

D-U-N-S 07-853-4765
GOODWILL INDUSTRIES OF GREATER NEW YORK INC
421 27th Ave, Astoria, NY 11102-4175
Tel (718) 728-5400 Founded/Ownrshp 1920
Sales 115.1MM EMP 2,000
Accts Marks Paneth & Shron Llp New
SIC 8331 Vocational rehabilitation agency; Work experience center; Vocational rehabilitation agency; Work experience center
CEO: William Forrester
*Treas: Henry Gooss
Ofcr: Joan Meinking
Sr VP: Karen Means
*VP: Gillian Attfield
VP: Deborah Harrison
VP: Linda Turner
Area Mgr: Rick Ressler
CIO: Andre Bromes

D-U-N-S 06-628-1809
GOODWILL INDUSTRIES OF HAWAII INC
GOODWILL VOCATIONAL TRAINING C
2610 Kilihau St, Honolulu, HI 96819-2020
Tel (808) 836-0313 Founded/Ownrshp 1959
Sales 25.9MM EMP 500
Accts Wikoff Combs & Co Llc Honolul
SIC 8331 Vocational training agency; Vocational rehabilitation agency; Vocational training agency; Vocational rehabilitation agency
Pr: Laura Robertson
Ofcr: Katy Chen
Dir IT: Rick Stark

D-U-N-S 04-110-4977
GOODWILL INDUSTRIES OF HEARTLAND
1410 S 1st Ave, Iowa City, IA 52240-6038
Tel (319) 337-4158 *Founded/Ownrshp* 1965
Sales 30.5MM *EMP* 975
SIC 5932 8331

D-U-N-S 05-110-7506 IMP
GOODWILL INDUSTRIES OF HOUSTON FOUNDATION
1140 West Loop N, Houston, TX 77055-7218
Tel (713) 692-6221 *Founded/Ownrshp* 1993
Sales 900.9M *EMP* 850
Accts Abip Pc Houston Tx
SIC 5932 Used merchandise stores; Used merchandise stores
Pr: Steven P Lufburrow
CFO: Tony Van Slyke
**CFO:* Tony Vanslyke
Prgrm Mgr: Linda Girdner
Admn Mgr: Rachel Perry
IT Man: William Sala
Info Man: Leslie Ferguson
VP Opers: Charles Canton
Sls Mgr: Chris Eppner

D-U-N-S 07-663-6745
GOODWILL INDUSTRIES OF INLAND NORTHWEST
130 E 3rd Ave, Spokane, WA 99202-1491
Tel (509) 838-4246 *Founded/Ownrshp* 1939
Sales 25.9MM *EMP* 558
Accts Cliftonlarsonallen Llp Spokan
SIC 8331 8322 Job training & vocational rehabilitation services; Association for the handicapped; Job training & vocational rehabilitation services; Association for the handicapped
Pr: Clark Brekke
**CFO:* Merrilee Plowman
Sales Exec: Clark Breke
Sales Exec: Jim Stailey

D-U-N-S 05-984-3821
GOODWILL INDUSTRIES OF KANAWHA VALLEY INC
209 Virginia St W, Charleston, WV 25302-2210
Tel (304) 346-0811 *Founded/Ownrshp* 1950
Sales 9.9MM *EMP* 336
Accts Gray Griffith & Mays Ac
SIC 8331 5311 5932 Work experience center; Department stores; Used merchandise stores; Work experience center; Department stores; Used merchandise stores
Pr: David L Acord
Pr: Cheryl Bever
CFO: Patricia L Riley
VP: Tim Morris
VP Opers: Jesse Payne

D-U-N-S 06-879-0898
GOODWILL INDUSTRIES OF LANE AND SOUTH COAST COUNTIES
1010c Green Acres Rd, Eugene, OR 97408
Tel (541) 345-1801 *Founded/Ownrshp* 1968
Sales 19.9MM *EMP* 425
Accts Moss Adams Llp Eugene Or
SIC 8331 Vocational rehabilitation agency; Vocational rehabilitation agency
Ex Dir: Jim Martin
**CEO:* Jim Nelson
**CFO:* Kristy Langworthy

D-U-N-S 09-987-5700
GOODWILL INDUSTRIES OF LOWER SOUTH CAROLINA INC
2150 Eagle Dr Bldg 100, North Charleston, SC 29406-4803
Tel (843) 566-0072 *Founded/Ownrshp* 1980
Sales 45.1MM *EMP* 900
SIC 8331 7349 5932 Vocational rehabilitation agency; Janitorial service, contract basis; Clothing & shoes, secondhand; Vocational rehabilitation agency; Janitorial service, contract basis; Clothing & shoes, secondhand
CEO: Robert Smith
**CFO:* Gerald Romaine
**Treas:* Robert Phillips
**Treas:* Michael Saboe
Treas: Keith Vincent
VP: Hester Allison
VP: Rick Shelley
**VP:* Peggy Smith
Mktg Mgr: Matthew Spath
Snr PM: Rodney Mack

D-U-N-S 07-431-5508
GOODWILL INDUSTRIES OF MICHIANA INC
GOODWILL INDUSTRIES MICHIANA
1805 W Western Ave, South Bend, IN 46619-3555
Tel (574) 472-7300 *Founded/Ownrshp* 1936
Sales 28.6MM *EMP* 510
Accts Weidner And Company Pc Ply
SIC 8331 Vocational rehabilitation agency; Vocational rehabilitation agency
Pr: Debie M Coble
**Treas:* Thomas Kuhar
Sr Cor Off: Larry Neff
Ofcr: Otto Schlatter
VP: Debie Coble
VP: Arden Floran
VP: Mike Kinzie
VP: Ron Webb
IT Man: Jay Schlatter
Sfty Mgr: Beth Hoctel
VP Sls: Mike Mansbach

D-U-N-S 07-279-1304
GOODWILL INDUSTRIES OF MID-MICHIGAN INC
YOUR FASHION SECRET
501 S Averill Ave, Flint, MI 48506-4009
Tel (810) 762-9960 *Founded/Ownrshp* 1938
Sales 24.2MM *EMP* 400
Accts Plante & Moran Pllc Flint Mi
SIC 8331 Vocational rehabilitation agency; Vocational rehabilitation agency
Pr: Gary Smith
CFO: Laura Wilson
**Treas:* Mona L Hendrickson
Treas: Mark Piper
**VP:* Shawn M Jandernoa
**VP:* Rene M McMann
**VP:* D Angella Thompson
**VP:* Laura L Welsh
Rgnl Mgr: Timothy Cyrus
IT Man: Rene McMann
Psych: Conrad Bontrager
Board of Directors: Mona L Hendrickson, Michael A Siradakis, R Edward Berryman, A R Hobson Jr, Richard D Skaff, Dennis R Brooks, Kevin J Keane, Gary F Smith, Thomas Bryson, Thomas G Landaal, Arthur Thomas, James E Carlson, Jeffrey M Love, Martin A Tyckoski, Roland C Chavey, William C Loving, Delores M Williams, William P Daniel, Edward A Mitchell, Anne N Gregory, Valerie M Nelson, David Gunneson, Shirley J Prater, Dale S Harris, Madonna L Prusac

D-U-N-S 10-668-2289
GOODWILL INDUSTRIES OF MIDDLE GEORGIA INC
5171 Eisenhower Pkwy, Macon, GA 31206-5309
Tel (478) 475-9995 *Founded/Ownrshp* 1975
Sales 41.8MM *EMP* 700
SIC 8331

D-U-N-S 06-073-6816
GOODWILL INDUSTRIES OF MIDDLE TENNESSEE INC (TN)
1015 Herman St, Nashville, TN 37208-3143
Tel (615) 742-4151 *Founded/Ownrshp* 1957
Sales 77.0MM *EMP* 2,200
SIC 8641

D-U-N-S 04-714-2591
GOODWILL INDUSTRIES OF NEW MEXICO
5000 San Mateo Blvd Ne, Albuquerque, NM 87109-2499
Tel (505) 881-6401 *Founded/Ownrshp* 1941
Sales 18.5MM *EMP* 450
SIC 5932 8331 Used merchandise stores; Vocational rehabilitation agency; Used merchandise stores; Vocational rehabilitation agency
Pr: Patrick Michaels
Ex Dir: Charles Lynn
Admn Mgr: Leigh Penfold
Dist Mgr: Matt Melzer
Mktg Dir: Shauna O'Cleireachain
Mktg Dir: Shauna Ocleireachain

D-U-N-S 07-748-3998
GOODWILL INDUSTRIES OF NORTH CENTRAL PENNSYLVANIA INC
131 Preston Way, Falls Creek, PA 15840-9749
Tel (814) 371-2821 *Founded/Ownrshp* 2008
Sales 12.3MM *EMP* 480
Accts Joseph M Lazore Cpa Dubois P
SIC 8331 Job training & vocational rehabilitation services; Job training & vocational rehabilitation services
V Ch: Ross Donahue
CFO: Tom Glasl

D-U-N-S 07-384-9044
GOODWILL INDUSTRIES OF NORTH CENTRAL WISCONSIN INC
1800 Appleton Rd, Menasha, WI 54952-1195
Tel (920) 731-6601 *Founded/Ownrshp* 1971
Sales 95.1MM *EMP* 1,400
SIC 5932 7389 8331 Used merchandise stores; Packaging & labeling services; Job training & vocational rehabilitation services; Used merchandise stores; Packaging & labeling services; Job training & vocational rehabilitation services
Pr: Robert A Pedersen
CIO: Nancy Coonen
Snr Mgr: Doug Bergan
Snr Mgr: Keith Wilk

D-U-N-S 06-590-3296
GOODWILL INDUSTRIES OF NORTH FLORIDA INC
JOB JUNCTION
4527 Lenox Ave, Jacksonville, FL 32205-5417
Tel (904) 384-1361 *Founded/Ownrshp* 1940
Sales 27.3MM *EMP* 325
Accts Lba Certified Public Accountan
SIC 5932 8331 Clothing, secondhand; Household appliances, used; Book stores, secondhand; Vocational training agency; Clothing, secondhand; Household appliances, used; Book stores, secondhand; Vocational training agency
CEO: Robert H Thayer
**CFO:* Paige Christini
**CFO:* Mark Stephenson
**Treas:* Eric Eastland
Treas: Art Stites
Ex Dir: Liz Howe
Pr Dir: Beverly Jelinek

D-U-N-S 07-938-3378
GOODWILL INDUSTRIES OF NORTH GEORGIA INC
235 Peachtree St Ne # 2300, Atlanta, GA 30303-1406
Tel (404) 420-9914 *Founded/Ownrshp* 1925
Sales 13.0MM *EMP* 1,650
SIC 8331

D-U-N-S 04-500-2870
GOODWILL INDUSTRIES OF NORTH LOUISIANA INC
800 W 70th St, Shreveport, LA 71106-2550
Tel (318) 869-2575 *Founded/Ownrshp* 1926
Sales 15.2MM *EMP* 500
Accts Heard Mcelroy Vestal Shrevepo
SIC 8331 Vocational rehabilitation agency; Vocational rehabilitation agency
Pr: John M Rankin
CFO: Karen Peters
**Sr VP:* Carl G Mayer

D-U-N-S 07-430-6721
GOODWILL INDUSTRIES OF NORTHEAST IOWA INC
2640 Falls Ave, Waterloo, IA 50701-5722
Tel (319) 234-4626 *Founded/Ownrshp* 1960
Sales 13.0MM *EMP* 500
SIC 8331 5932 Vocational rehabilitation agency; Used merchandise stores; Clothing & shoes, secondhand; Vocational rehabilitation agency; Used merchandise stores; Clothing & shoes, secondhand
Ex Dir: David E Boyd
**CFO:* Robert W Hughes
CFO: Nicole Knudtson
Exec: Steve Tisue
**Prin:* Trish Johnson

D-U-N-S 01-023-9127
GOODWILL INDUSTRIES OF NORTHERN ILLINOIS AND WISCONSIN STATELINE AREA INC
ABILITIES CENTER
615 N Longwood St Fl 1, Rockford, IL 61107-4264
Tel (815) 987-6200 *Founded/Ownrshp* 1936
Sales 16.4MM *EMP* 300
SIC 8331 8243 5651 5932 Community service employment training program; Vocational rehabilitation agency; Operator training, computer; Family clothing stores; Furniture, secondhand; Community service employment training program; Vocational rehabilitation agency; Operator training, computer; Family clothing stores; Furniture, secondhand
Ex Dir: Samuel J Schmitz

D-U-N-S 07-746-1432
GOODWILL INDUSTRIES OF NORTHERN NEW ENGLAND
75 Washington Ave Ste 300, Portland, ME 04101-2665
Tel (207) 774-6323 *Founded/Ownrshp* 1933
Sales 71.5MM *EMP* 1,200
Accts Macdonald Page & Co Llc South
SIC 8331 2392 Vocational rehabilitation agency; Household furnishings; Vocational rehabilitation agency; Household furnishings
CEO: Anne Roosevelt
COO: David Crossman
CFO: Robert Moore
CFO: Steve Tselikis
Ofcr: Lynne Gaudette
Dir Sec: Craig Grugel
Dir IT: Mark Weatherbee
IT Man: Rich Cantz
IT Man: David Wong

D-U-N-S 00-323-1784
GOODWILL INDUSTRIES OF NORTHWEST NORTH CAROLINA INC (NC)
2701 University Pkwy, Winston Salem, NC 27105-4223
Tel (336) 724-3621 *Founded/Ownrshp* 1926
Sales 83.4MM *EMP* 1,100
Accts Dixon Hughes Goodman Llp Wins
SIC 5932 8331 Used merchandise stores; Vocational rehabilitation agency; Used merchandise stores; Vocational rehabilitation agency
Ch: Francine Madrey
Pr: Bill Haymore
**CEO:* Art Gibel
**CFO:* Curtis Bland
**Ch:* Sherry Polonsky
**Sec:* Rip Ford
**VP:* Dan Bradshaw
**VP:* Sherry Carpenter
**VP:* John Cunningham
CTO: Keith Perrel
Mktg Dir: Jaymie Eichorn

D-U-N-S 07-815-6551
GOODWILL INDUSTRIES OF ORANGE COUNTY CALIFORNIA
410 N Fairview St, Santa Ana, CA 92703-3412
Tel (714) 547-6308 *Founded/Ownrshp* 1926
Sales 69.6MM *EMP* 1,200
Accts Kushner Smith Joanou & Gregson
SIC 5932 Used merchandise stores; Used merchandise stores
CEO: Steven M Coyne
**COO:* Kim Seebach
CFO: Donald Voska
**V Ch Bd:* Cheryl Barrett
**VP:* Corrine Allen
**VP:* Joe Burke
**VP:* Kathy Copeland
Sls&Mrk Ex: Marlena Jiminez

D-U-N-S 06-697-6085
GOODWILL INDUSTRIES OF PIONEER VALLEY INC
570 Cottage St Ste 3, Springfield, MA 01104-3354
Tel (413) 233-5200 *Founded/Ownrshp* 1925
Sales 6.7MM *EMP* 625
SIC 5932 8322 8331 Used merchandise stores; Social services for the handicapped; Job training services; Vocational rehabilitation agency; Used merchandise stores; Social services for the handicapped; Job training services; Vocational rehabilitation agency
Pr: Steve Mundahl
Treas: Nancy Russell
VP: Derek Morris

D-U-N-S 07-738-1358 IMP
GOODWILL INDUSTRIES OF REDWOOD EMPIRE
651 Yolanda Ave, Santa Rosa, CA 95404-6324
Tel (707) 523-0550 *Founded/Ownrshp* 1974
Sales 17.3MM *EMP* 300
SIC 5932 8331 Clothing, secondhand; Furniture, secondhand; Household appliances, used; Vocational rehabilitation agency; Clothing, secondhand; Furniture, secondhand; Household appliances, used; Vocational rehabilitation agency
Pr: Mark Ihde
VP: Anne Martin
Prgrm Mgr: Amy Breckenridge

D-U-N-S 07-612-2639
GOODWILL INDUSTRIES OF SACRAMENTO VALLEY & NORTHERN NEVADA INC
GOODWLL INDUSTRS SACRAMENTO VL
8001 Folsom Blvd, Sacramento, CA 95826-2621
Tel (916) 395-9000 *Founded/Ownrshp* 1933
Sales 54.2MM *EMP* 500
Accts Gallina Llp Rancho Cordova C
SIC 5932 Home furnishings, secondhand; Clothing, secondhand; Home furnishings, secondhand; Clothing, secondhand
Pr: Joseph Mendez
**Ch Bd:* Julius Cherry
**COO:* Bob Dugas
**CFO:* Connie Schulze
**Ch:* Pete Little
**Treas:* Brett Huston
**VP:* Mark Klingler
**VP:* Larry Peterson

D-U-N-S 05-757-9807
GOODWILL INDUSTRIES OF SAN ANTONIO
GOODWILL INDS NEW BRAUNFELS
406 W Commerce St, San Antonio, TX 78207-3102
Tel (210) 924-8581 *Founded/Ownrshp* 1946
Sales 36.4MM *EMP* 1,024
Accts Bdo Usa Llp
SIC 8331 Vocational rehabilitation agency; Vocational rehabilitation agency
Pr: Marla Jackson
**CFO:* Stephanie Parker
Bd of Dir: Laura Hernandez
VP: Patti Black
**VP:* Lisa Brunsvold
VP: Julian Cruz
**VP:* Greg Eads
**VP:* Donna Lazzari
**VP:* Mark McKeever
**Prin:* Robert Dugas
Ex Dir: David Palmer

D-U-N-S 07-861-1177
GOODWILL INDUSTRIES OF SAN ANTONIO CONTRACT SERVICES
406 W Commerce St, San Antonio, TX 78207-3102
Tel (210) 924-8581 *Founded/Ownrshp* 2012
Sales 27.9MM *EMP* 15
SIC 0782 Mowing services, lawn
CEO: Robert Dugas

D-U-N-S 07-338-7045
GOODWILL INDUSTRIES OF SAN DIEGO COUNTY
3663 Rosecrans St, San Diego, CA 92110-3226
Tel (619) 225-2200 *Founded/Ownrshp* 1929
Sales 75.9MM *EMP* 1,350
Accts Cohn Reznick Llp San Diego C
SIC 8331 Job training & vocational rehabilitation services; Job training & vocational rehabilitation services
Ex Dir: Michael S Rowan
Rgnl Mgr: David Raver
Dir IT: Daniel Bossert
Mktg Dir: Sharon Corrigan

D-U-N-S 07-877-2951 IMP
GOODWILL INDUSTRIES OF SAN FRANCISCO SAN MATEO AND MARIN COUNTIES INC
1500 Mission St, San Francisco, CA 94103-2513
Tel (415) 575-2101 *Founded/Ownrshp* 1916
Sales 62.0MM *EMP* 710
Accts Armanino Llp San Ramon Ca
SIC 5932 8331 8641 Clothing, secondhand; Furniture, secondhand; Home furnishings, secondhand; Skill training center; Civic social & fraternal associations; Clothing, secondhand; Furniture, secondhand; Home furnishings, secondhand; Skill training center; Civic social & fraternal associations
Pr: Maureen Sedonaen
Mng Pt: Sharon Kittredje
COO: William Rogers
**CFO:* Terry Fitzpatrick
VP: David Downes
Ex Dir: Alan Sandler
Genl Mgr: Fred Stitt
Dir IT: Bhawin Mistry
Ql Cn Mgr: Sunny Suppa
S&M/VP: Sheryl Alexander

D-U-N-S 06-885-2029
GOODWILL INDUSTRIES OF SAN JOAQUIN VALLEY INC
129 S Grant St, Stockton, CA 95202-3103
Tel (209) 466-2311 *Founded/Ownrshp* 1937
Sales 35.6MM *EMP* 300
Accts Bowman & Company Llp Stockto
SIC 5932 8322 Used merchandise stores; Helping hand service (Big Brother, etc.); Used merchandise stores; Helping hand service (Big Brother, etc.)
Pr: David L Miller
VP: Emmett Dunn
**VP:* Linda Huntley

D-U-N-S 96-656-5942
GOODWILL INDUSTRIES OF SANTA CLARA COUNTY INC
1080 N 7th St, San Jose, CA 95112-4425
Tel (408) 998-5774 *Founded/Ownrshp* 2011
Sales 25.4MM *EMP* 1
Accts Petrinovich Pugh & Company Llp
SIC 3999 Manufacturing industries; Manufacturing industries
Prin: Hugh Barnet

D-U-N-S 07-699-6065
GOODWILL INDUSTRIES OF SOUTH FLORIDA INC
2121 Nw 21st St, Miami, FL 33142-7382
Tel (305) 325-9114 *Founded/Ownrshp* 1959
Sales 92.8MM *EMP* 2,600
SIC 8331 Work experience center; Management services; Work experience center
CEO: David Landsberg
**CFO:* Beatriz Anazco
**Ch:* Joseph Lacher
**Treas:* Ronald Murfin

*Sr VP: Bridget Pallango
*VP: Sherri Scyphers Hungate
VP: Lourdes D La Mata-Little
VP: Lourdes Little
*VP: Manny Lopez
*VP: Diana Valencia
*Prin: Dennis Pastrana

D-U-N-S 96-757-0685
GOODWILL INDUSTRIES OF SOUTHEASTERN LA SUPPORTING FOUNDATION
3400 Tulane Ave, New Orleans, LA 70119-7160
Tel (504) 482-4173 Founded/Ownrshp 2011
Sales 24.1MM EMP 1
Accts Laporte Apac Metairie La
SIC 3999 Manufacturing industries
Prin: Warren Benoit

D-U-N-S 02-338-9380
GOODWILL INDUSTRIES OF SOUTHEASTERN WISCONSIN INC
5400 S 60th St, Greendale, WI 53129-1404
Tel (414) 847-4200 Founded/Ownrshp 1919
Sales 282.7MM EMP 3,391
Accts Grant Thornton Llp Appleton
SIC 8331 7349 Job training & vocational rehabilitation services; Building cleaning service; Job training & vocational rehabilitation services; Building cleaning service
Pr: Jacqueline Hallberg
Pr: Dwight Ferguson
*VP: Mike Boelter
*VP: Pat Boelter
*VP: Timothy Christian
*VP: Dan Depies
VP: Catherine Girard
CIO: Jim Andreoni
Mktg Dir: Laura Sanders

D-U-N-S 07-445-8654
GOODWILL INDUSTRIES OF SOUTHERN ARIZONA INC
1940 E Silverlake Rd # 405, Tucson, AZ 85713-3872
Tel (520) 623-5174 Founded/Ownrshp 1969
Sales 24.0MM EMP 195
Accts Beachfleischman Pc Tucson Az
SIC 5932 8331 8641 Used merchandise stores; Vocational rehabilitation agency; Civic social & fraternal associations; Used merchandise stores; Vocational rehabilitation agency; Civic social & fraternal associations
Ch: Ron Robinette
COO: Lisa Allen
CFO: David Lewandowski
Rgnl Mgr: Mel Chambers
Off Mgr: Mary Castaneda
Dir IT: Warren Young
Sfty Mgr: Todd Waltz

D-U-N-S 00-958-2305 IMP
GOODWILL INDUSTRIES OF SOUTHERN CALIFORNIA
342 N San Fernando Rd, Los Angeles, CA 90031-1730
Tel (323) 223-1211 Founded/Ownrshp 1919
Sales 198.5MM EMP 2,100
Accts Grant Thornton Llp Los Angele
SIC 5331 8331 Variety stores; Vocational rehabilitation agency; Vocational training agency; Community service employment training program; Variety stores; Vocational rehabilitation agency; Vocational training agency; Community service employment training program
Pr: Craig Smith
VP: Lavalle Bullard
VP: Forrest Callahan
VP: Dennis Ciolli
VP: Jessica Cruz
VP: Mario Haug
VP: Sasha Itzikman
VP: Donna Snell
VP: Craig Stone
VP: Ray Tellez
CTO: John Quach

D-U-N-S 06-953-4758
GOODWILL INDUSTRIES OF SOUTHERN LOUISIANA INC
3400 Tulane Ave 1000, New Orleans, LA 70119-7160
Tel (504) 364-5625 Founded/Ownrshp 1947
Sales 38.8MM^E EMP 450
Accts Laporte Sehrt Romig & Hand Me
SIC 8699 Charitable organization; Charitable organization
Pr: William L Jessee
*VP: Jodee Daroca
VP: Bob Reese
Pr Mgr: Jan Gunter

D-U-N-S 62-140-9440
GOODWILL INDUSTRIES OF SOUTHERN NEVADA INC
GOODWILL OF SOUTHERN NEVADA
1280 W Cheyenne Ave, North Las Vegas, NV 89030-7818
Tel (702) 597-1107 Founded/Ownrshp 1975
Sales 32.1MM EMP 640
Accts Piercy Bowler Taylor & Kern L
SIC 8699 Charitable organization; Charitable organization
Pr: Steve Chartrand
*Treas: Josh Dobbins
Brnch Mgr: Marie Robinson
IT Man: Walter Lescano
Opers Mgr: Ray Granger
Opers Mgr: Dan Haugseth

D-U-N-S 07-145-9085 EXP
GOODWILL INDUSTRIES OF SOUTHERN NEW JERSEY & PHILADELPHIA INC
GOODWILL IND OF SO NJ
2835 Route 73 S, Maple Shade, NJ 08052-1627
Tel (856) 439-0200 Founded/Ownrshp 1948
Sales 2.0MM EMP 600
Accts Fischer Dorwart Pc Audubon N
SIC 5932 8331 Used merchandise stores; Job training & vocational rehabilitation services; Used merchandise stores; Job training & vocational rehabilitation services
Pr: Mark Boyd
Pr: Wes Hughes
*COO: Michael Shaw
*CFO: Steven Castro
*VP: Deb Eckenhoff
*VP: Bob Hain
*VP: Rick Lindsay
*VP: Jennifer Mauro
Board of Directors: Jennifer Mauro

D-U-N-S 03-049-7176
GOODWILL INDUSTRIES OF SOUTHERN PIEDMONT INC
2122 Freedom Dr, Charlotte, NC 28208-5154
Tel (704) 372-3434 Founded/Ownrshp 1949
Sales 50.8MM EMP 450
Accts Mcgladrey Llp Greensboro Nor
SIC 8331 5932 Job training services; Vocational rehabilitation agency; Used merchandise stores; Job training services; Vocational rehabilitation agency; Used merchandise stores
Pr: Micheal Elder
*Ch: Marilynn Bowler
*Ch: Laura Hampton
*Sec: Jim Skibbens
VP: Gary Barrett
VP: Paulette Griffin
VP: Anne Ibekwe
VP: Barbara Maida-Stolle
VP: Barbara Stolle
Genl Mgr: Donna Dysart
Genl Mgr: Brian Otto

D-U-N-S 15-282-3662 EXP
GOODWILL INDUSTRIES OF SOUTHWEST FLORIDA INC
5100 Tice St, Fort Myers, FL 33905-5203
Tel (239) 995-2106 Founded/Ownrshp 1966
Sales 154.6MM^E EMP 875
Accts Barton Gonzalez & Myers Pa La
SIC 5932 5087 Building materials, secondhand; Vending machines & supplies; Tire shredding machinery; Building materials, secondhand; Vending machines & supplies
Pr: Tom Feurig
V Ch: Raymond T Holland
*Pr: Rick Evanchyk
Treas: Sharlene Dozier
Bd of Dir: Sherri Denning
*VP: William J Barrett
VP: Carolyn Johnson
VP: Robert Randall
VP: Fred Richards
VP: Jennifer Swift
Exec: Tiffany Peterson
Dir Bus: Pat Smith

D-U-N-S 07-866-1550
GOODWILL INDUSTRIES OF TULSA INC
2800 Southwest Blvd, Tulsa, OK 74107-3817
Tel (918) 584-7291 Founded/Ownrshp 1927
Sales 22.5MM EMP 525
Accts Hogan Taylor Llp Tulsa Ok
SIC 8331 Vocational rehabilitation agency; Vocational rehabilitation agency
Pr: David E Oliver
*Sec: Terry D Blain

D-U-N-S 07-806-0555
GOODWILL INDUSTRIES OF UPSTATE MIDLANDS SOUTH CAROLINA INC
115 Haywood Rd, Greenville, SC 29607-3422
Tel (864) 351-0100 Founded/Ownrshp 1973
Sales 43.6MM EMP 751
Accts Dixon Hughes Goodman Llp Ashe
SIC 8331 Vocational rehabilitation agency; Vocational rehabilitation agency
CEO: Patrick Micheals
*VP: Stephanie Estarada
Off Mgr: Linda Oward
IT Man: Stephanie Estrada

D-U-N-S 07-792-6277
GOODWILL INDUSTRIES OF VALLEYS INC
GOOD WILL
2502 Melrose Ave Nw Ste A, Roanoke, VA 24017-3910
Tel (540) 581-0620 Founded/Ownrshp 1966
Sales 17.5MM EMP 500
Accts Cherry Bekaert Llp Roanoke V
SIC 8331 5399 3412 2449 2441 Job training & vocational rehabilitation services; Job training services; Surplus & salvage goods; Metal barrels, drums & pails; Wood containers; Nailed wood boxes & shook; Job training & vocational rehabilitation services; Job training services; Surplus & salvage goods; Metal barrels, drums & pails; Wood containers; Nailed wood boxes & shook
CEO: Bruce Phipps
*COO: Jackson Green
*Ch: John Coker
*Treas: Howard Lyon
Treas: Harlod McLeod
*Sr VP: Phil Jones
*VP: Jim Shaver
*VP: Lori Stohlmann
Div Mgr: Debbie Williams

D-U-N-S 04-589-0605
GOODWILL INDUSTRIES OF WEST MICHIGAN INC
271 E Apple Ave, Muskegon, MI 49442-3490
Tel (231) 722-7871 Founded/Ownrshp 1950
Sales 20.1MM EMP 500
Accts Rehmann Muskegon Michigan
SIC 8331 5932 Vocational rehabilitation agency; Used merchandise stores; Vocational rehabilitation agency; Used merchandise stores
Ex Dir: Richard J Carlson
*COO: James Moore
*CFO: Rick Snellenberger
*Ch: Bonnie Krueger

D-U-N-S 07-113-1288
GOODWILL INDUSTRIES REHABILITATION CENTER INC
408 9th St Sw, Canton, OH 44707-4799
Tel (330) 454-9461 Founded/Ownrshp 1920
Sales 24.3MM EMP 276
Accts Bober Markey Fedorovich & Co
SIC 8322 8331 Rehabilitation services; Community service employment training program; Rehabilitation services; Community service employment training program
CEO: Ken Weber
*CFO: Gene Dechellis
*Ex Dir: Harold G Oswald
IT Man: David Schollaert

D-U-N-S 08-068-6751
GOODWILL INDUSTRIES-BIG BEND INC
300 Mabry St, Tallahassee, FL 32304-3813
Tel (850) 576-7145 Founded/Ownrshp 1967
Sales 27.4MM^E EMP 400
SIC 8331 5932 Vocational rehabilitation agency; Used merchandise stores; Vocational rehabilitation agency; Used merchandise stores
Pr: Fred G Sheifer Jr
*CFO: Randy Jones
Treas: James Scarboro
VP: Jovita Bakker
VP: Pam Byrd
Exec: Rebecca Christmas
CTO: William Graham
Mktg Dir: Stephen Wagner

D-U-N-S 11-432-8123
GOODWILL INDUSTRIES-MANASOTA INC
GOODWILL MANASOTA
2705 51st Ave E, Bradenton, FL 34203-3937
Tel (941) 355-2721 Founded/Ownrshp 1981
Sales 43.2MM EMP 1,000
Accts Chnstophersmithleonard Etal B
SIC 8331 Work experience center; Work experience center
CEO: Donald L Roberts
*VP: Amy Confer
*VP: Peggy Roberts
Dir IT: Gray Vudenka
VP Opers: Mary England
Sfty Mgr: Christopher Georgoulis
VP Mktg: Yen Reed
Snr Mgr: Kelly Gardner

D-U-N-S 05-519-5176
GOODWILL INDUSTRIES-SUNCOAST INC
10596 Gandy Blvd N, Saint Petersburg, FL 33702-1427
Tel (727) 523-1512 Founded/Ownrshp 1954
Sales 62.7MM EMP 1,334
Accts Gregory Sharer & Stuart Pa
SIC 5932 8093 Used merchandise stores; Rehabilitation center, outpatient treatment; Used merchandise stores; Rehabilitation center, outpatient treatment
Ch Bd: Marty Gladysz
Pr: Deborah A Passerini
Pr: R Lee Waits
CFO: Gary R Hebert
VP: Jacqueline R Miller
VP: Debbie Passerini
VP: Kris A Rawson
VP: James D Williams
Dir IT: Lee Bice
Opers Mgr: Jason Martino

D-U-N-S 02-086-2694
GOODWILL INDUSTRIES/EASTER SEALS OF GULF COAST INC
ALABAMA EASTER SEAL SOCIETY
(Suby of EASTER SEALS ALABAMA, INC.)
2448 Gordon Smith Dr, Mobile, AL 36617-2319
Tel (251) 433-4900 Founded/Ownrshp 1956
Sales 21.8MM EMP 172
Accts Smith Dukes And Buckalew Llp
SIC 8331 Vocational rehabilitation agency; Vocational rehabilitation agency
Ch: Bradford Ladd
*CEO: Frank Harkins
*COO: John McCain
*VP: Terri Bolin
*VP: Bill Dillman
*VP: John N McCain

D-U-N-S 07-283-8212
GOODWILL KEYSTONE AREA
GKA
1150 Goodwill Dr, Harrisburg, PA 17101-2400
Tel (610) 777-7875 Founded/Ownrshp 1948
Sales 56.5MM EMP 3,000
Accts Brown Schultz Sheridan & Fritz
SIC 8331 Work experience center; Work experience center
CEO: Ronald Kratofil
*Ch: Anthony Byrne
Store Mgr: Rob Gaber
Prd Mgr: Matthew Logan
Mktg Mgr: John McHenry

GOODWILL MANASOTA
See GOODWILL INDUSTRIES-MANASOTA INC

D-U-N-S 09-844-1959
GOODWILL OF CENTRAL AND COASTAL VIRGINIA INC
GOODWILL INDUSTRIES
6301 Midlothian Tpke, Richmond, VA 23225-5707
Tel (804) 745-6300 Founded/Ownrshp 1923
Sales 59.4MM EMP 1,100
Accts Keiter Certified Public Accoun
SIC 8331 Job counseling; Job counseling
Pr: Charles D Layman
*VP: William Carlson
VP: Robert Hicks
Site Mgr: Maxine Mason

GOODWILL OF CENTRAL ARIZONA
See GOODWILL INDUSTRIES OF CENTRAL ARIZONA FOUNDATION INC

D-U-N-S 00-209-9645
GOODWILL OF FINGER LAKES INC
422 Clinton Ave S, Rochester, NY 14620-1103
Tel (585) 232-1111 Founded/Ownrshp 2010
Sales 26.3MM EMP 500^E
Accts Mengel Metzger Barr & Co Llp
SIC 8399 Fund raising organization, non-fee basis; Fund raising organization, non-fee basis
CEO: Gidget Hopf
IT Man: Monika Robertson

D-U-N-S 02-018-3059
GOODWILL OF GREAT PLAINS
GOODWILL INDUSTRIES
3100 W 4th St, Sioux City, IA 51103-3202
Tel (712) 258-4511 Founded/Ownrshp 1896
Sales 23.0MM^E EMP 500
Accts King Reinsch Prosser & Co L
SIC 8331 Vocational rehabilitation agency; Sheltered workshop; Vocational rehabilitation agency; Sheltered workshop
Pr: John Hantla
*COO: Vilay Keokenchanh
*CFO: Julie Klein
*VP: Betty Durfee
VP: Harry Furukawa
*VP: Paul Kellen
*Ex Dir: Jan Poulson
IT Man: Kathy Bousquet

GOODWILL OF GREATER WASHINGTON
See DAVIS MEMORIAL GOODWILL INDUSTRIES INC

D-U-N-S 79-227-6235
GOODWILL OF NORTH GEORGIA INC
235 Peachtree St Ne # 2300, Atlanta, GA 30303-1406
Tel (404) 420-9900 Founded/Ownrshp 2007
Sales 117.1MM EMP 1,650^E
Accts Grant Thornton Llp Atlanta G
SIC 5932 8331 Used merchandise stores; Job training & vocational rehabilitation services; Used merchandise stores; Job training & vocational rehabilitation services
Pr: Raymond W Bishop
*Ch Bd: Nicholas Hoffman
VP: Cheryl Cornett
VP: Cheryl Cornett-Earley
VP: Paul Jordan
Prgrm Mgr: Marylee Putnam
VP Mktg: James Caponigro
Advt Dir: Nicole McIntosh
Mktg Dir: Courtney Eskridge

D-U-N-S 07-818-9909 IMP/EXP
GOODWILL OF OLYMPICS AND RAINIER REGION (WA)
TACOMA GOODWILL INDUSTRIES
714 S 27th St, Tacoma, WA 98409-8130
Tel (253) 573-6500 Founded/Ownrshp 1922
Sales 71.6MM EMP 925
Accts Clark Nuber Ps Bellevue Wa
SIC 5932 8331 Used merchandise stores; Vocational rehabilitation agency; Used merchandise stores; Vocational rehabilitation agency
Pr: Don Johnson
*CEO: Terry Hayes
*CFO: Jef Veilleux
*Treas: C W Herchold
Sr VP: Mark Holcomb
VP: Gloria Eubanks
Exec: Stephanie Staylen
Dir Bus: Mike Shields
Ex Dir: Dean Hanks
IT Man: Kenneth Gibbon
Info Man: Ashley Taulbee
Board of Directors: Cheryl Bidleman, Mark Holcomb, Chris Politakis, Michael Secright

D-U-N-S 04-272-7883
GOODWILL OF SILICON VALLEY
INSTITUTE FOR CAREER DEVELOPME
1080 N 7th St, San Jose, CA 95112-4425
Tel (408) 998-5774 Founded/Ownrshp 1937
Sales 39.4MM EMP 700
Accts Petrinovich Pugh & Company Llp
SIC 7363 5932 Help supply services; Used merchandise stores; Help supply services; Used merchandise stores
CEO: Michael E Fox
*CEO: Frank Kent
*COO: Christopher King
*CFO: Christopher Baker
*Treas: Dale Achabal
Bd of Dir: Jeanice Owens
*VP: Phil Boyce
CTO: Sheery He
Tech Mgr: Nandor Fejer
Sfty Dirs: Ryan Gleason
Snr PM: Shawn Brundge

GOODWILL OF SOUTHERN NEVADA
See GOODWILL INDUSTRIES OF SOUTHERN NEVADA INC

D-U-N-S 07-498-1721
GOODWILL OF SOUTHWESTERN PENNSYLVANIA
118 52nd St, Pittsburgh, PA 15201-2593
Tel (412) 481-9005 Founded/Ownrshp 1965
Sales 53.0MM EMP 1,250
Accts Schneider Downs & Co Inc Pitt
SIC 8331 Vocational rehabilitation agency; Vocational rehabilitation agency
Pr: Michael Smith
Pr: Kathy Hrala
CFO: Suzanne Hribik
Ch: Gary Claus
Treas: John Mills
VP: Ella Holsinger
Prgrm Mgr: Jaime Tracktenberg
CIO: Francis Kosmoski
Dir IT: Jim Bouplon
IT Man: John Obritz

D-U-N-S 07-214-7432
GOODWILL OF WESTERN & NORTHERN CONNECTICUT INC
165 Ocean Ter, Bridgeport, CT 06605-2719
Tel (203) 368-6511 *Founded/Ownrshp* 1909
Sales 49.2MM *EMP* 802
SIC 8331

D-U-N-S 02-984-0634 IMP
GOODWILL OF WESTERN MISSOURI & EASTERN KANSAS
1817 Campbell St, Kansas City, MO 64108-1739
Tel (816) 220-1779 *Founded/Ownrshp* 1894
Sales 22.0MM *EMP* 340
SIC 8331 3441 5932 3444 7349 Job training services; Fabricated structural metal; Clothing, secondhand; Sheet metalwork; Janitorial service, contract basis; Job training services; Fabricated structural metal; Clothing, secondhand; Sheet metalwork; Janitorial service, contract basis
CEO: Stefany Williams
**Pr:* Larry Jones
CFO: Williams Stefany
**VP:* Kevin Bentley
**VP:* Tom Dooley
VP: Jenice Elley
**VP:* Stewart Hoffman
**VP:* Shirley Johnson
**VP:* Anne Maloney
**VP:* Jennifer Owens
**VP:* Ralph Smith
**VP:* Jessica Sulzen

D-U-N-S 60-802-2976
GOODWILL RETAIL SERVICES INC
(*Suby of* GOODWILL INDUSTRIES OF SOUTHEASTERN WISCONSIN INC) ★
5400 S 60th St, Greendale, WI 53129-1404
Tel (414) 847-4200 *Founded/Ownrshp* 2001
Sales 138.4MM *EMP* 2,129
SIC 5651 4226 Family clothing stores; Household goods, warehousing; Family clothing stores; Household goods, warehousing
Pr: Jacqueline L Hallberg
**Sr VP:* Vickie Volpano

D-U-N-S 80-355-7818
GOODWILL SERVICES INC
6301 Midlothian Tpke, Richmond, VA 23225-5707
Tel (804) 745-6300 *Founded/Ownrshp* 1994
Sales 6.1MM *EMP* 480
SIC 7349 Building maintenance services; Building maintenance services
Pr: Charles D Layman
**CFO:* Scott Warren
**VP:* Derby Brackett
**VP:* Rick Carr
VP: Norm Doucette
**VP:* Liz Rountree
Sls&Mrk Ex: Stephen Jones

D-U-N-S 02-843-6491
GOODWILL SERVING PEOPLE OF SOUTHERN LOS ANGELES COUNTY
LINKS SIGN LANGUAGE INTERPRETI
800 W Pacific Coast Hwy, Long Beach, CA 90806-5243
Tel (562) 435-3411 *Founded/Ownrshp* 1939
Sales 25.2MM *EMP* 300
Accts Harrington Group Pasadena Ca
SIC 5399 8331 Surplus & salvage goods; Vocational training agency; Surplus & salvage goods; Vocational training agency
CEO: Janet McCarthy
IT Man: Scott Darling

D-U-N-S 07-360-1718
GOODWILL SOUTHERN CALIFORNIA
INLAND CAREER CENTER
8120 Palm Ln, San Bernardino, CA 92410-4961
Tel (909) 885-3831 *Founded/Ownrshp* 1928
Sales 130.3MM *EMP* 200
SIC 5932 8331 Used merchandise stores; Job training & vocational rehabilitation services; Used merchandise stores; Job training & vocational rehabilitation services
Pr: Doug Barr
VP: John Kennedy

GOODWILL VOCATIONAL TRAINING C
See GOODWILL INDUSTRIES OF HAWAII INC

D-U-N-S 00-829-1445 IMP
GOODWIN AMMONIA CO
12102 Industry St, Garden Grove, CA 92841-2814
Tel (770) 995-9481 *Founded/Ownrshp* 1922
Sales 34.7MM^E *EMP* 150
SIC 2842 Specialty cleaning, polishes & sanitation goods; Automobile polish; Specialty cleaning, polishes & sanitation goods; Automobile polish
Pr: Tom Goodwin
**Sec:* Janice Fleet
**VP:* Gary Goodwin

D-U-N-S 02-806-9722
GOODWIN AND SONS INC
GOODWIN'S MARKET
24089 Lake Gregory Dr, Crestline, CA 92325
Tel (909) 338-1705 *Founded/Ownrshp* 1946
Sales 21.7MM^E *EMP* 130
SIC 5411 5734 Grocery stores, independent; Computer software & accessories; Grocery stores, independent; Computer software & accessories
Ch Bd: George Goodwin
**Pr:* David M Goodwin
**VP:* Martin Goodwin
Off Mgr: Larry Matias

D-U-N-S 00-783-7214 IMP
GOODWIN BROS CONSTRUCTION CO (MO)
1766 Hwy 61 S, Crystal City, MO 63019
Tel (636) 931-6084 *Founded/Ownrshp* 1947
Sales 20.9MM *EMP* 100
SIC 1541 1542 1629 Industrial buildings, new construction; Warehouse construction; Commercial & office building, new construction; Industrial buildings, new construction; Warehouse construction; Commercial & office building, new construction; Waste water & sewage treatment plant construction
Pr: Larry W Goodwin
**Sec:* Barbara Young
**VP:* Charlie Goodwin
**VP:* Brian Vestal
Sfty Mgr: Lee Acre

GOODWIN BROTHERS SHADING & SPC
See GB SHADES LLC

D-U-N-S 08-506-6157
GOODWIN COLLEGE INC
1 Riverside Dr, East Hartford, CT 06118-1837
Tel (860) 895-8000 *Founded/Ownrshp* 1981
Sales 106.4MM *EMP* 115
Accts Cohnreznick Llp Glastonbury
SIC 8221 Colleges & universities; Colleges & universities
Ch: Maria Ellis
**CFO:* Jerry Emlet
**Treas:* Raymond Madorin
**VP:* Bryant Harrell
CTO: Steven Michaud
Dir IT: Dan Rego
Info Man: David Ehler

GOODWIN HOUSE ALEXANDRIA
See GOODWIN HOUSE INC

D-U-N-S 07-779-8627
GOODWIN HOUSE INC
GOODWIN HOUSE ALEXANDRIA
4800 Fillmore Ave Ofc, Alexandria, VA 22311-5053
Tel (703) 379-2376 *Founded/Ownrshp* 1955
Sales 77.4MM *EMP* 635
Accts Cliftonlarsonallen Llp Boston
SIC 8051 8361 8322 Convalescent home with continuous nursing care; Geriatric residential care; Geriatric social service; Convalescent home with continuous nursing care; Geriatric residential care; Geriatric social service
CEO: Kathleen S Anderson
Dir Vol: Amy Conradt
**CFO:* Richard T Carter
Exec: Pierre Cummings

D-U-N-S 07-171-5676
GOODWIN PROCTER LLP
53 State St, Boston, MA 02109-2820
Tel (617) 570-1000 *Founded/Ownrshp* 1996
Sales 307.1MM^E *EMP* 1,324
SIC 8111 Corporate, partnership & business law; Patent, trademark & copyright law; Product liability law; Real estate law; Corporate, partnership & business law; Patent, trademark & copyright law; Product liability law; Real estate law
Pt: Bob Bishop
Pt: Mark J Abate
Pt: April E Abele
Pt: John D Aldock
Pt: Gina M Atwood
Pt: Gregory S Bishop
Pt: Dave Cappillo
Pt: Mitzi Chang
Pt: Derek A Cohen
Pt: Byron W Cooper
Pt: William Davisson
Pt: Kevin Dennis
Pt: Michael S Devincenzo
Pt: Amber R Dolman
Pt: John Egan
Pt: Steven A Ellis
Pt: Brian A Fairchild
Pt: Lewis G Feldman
Pt: Stephen C Ferruolo
Pt: Kathy Fields
Pt: Thomas F Fitzpatrick

D-U-N-S 01-899-8138
GOODWINS CHEVROLET CO (ME)
GOODWINS CHEVROLET-MAZDA
195 Pleasant St, Brunswick, ME 04011-2212
Tel (207) 729-1611 *Founded/Ownrshp* 1929, 1960
Sales 23.9MM^E *EMP* 45
SIC 5511 Automobiles, new & used
Pr: Frank Goodwin
VP: Jeanette Downing
Exec: Jennifer Downing
Sls Mgr: Jason Harrington
Sls Mgr: Mark Hranicky

GOODWINS CHEVROLET-MAZDA
See GOODWINS CHEVROLET CO

GOODWIN'S MARKET
See GOODWIN AND SONS INC

GOODWISH INDUSTRIES
See LONE STAR FASHIONS INC

GOODWLL INDUSTRS SACRAMENTO VL
See GOODWILL INDUSTRIES OF SACRAMENTO VALLEY & NORTHERN NEVADA INC

GOODWRENCH SERVICE CENTER
See DEMONTROND BUICK CO

D-U-N-S 00-311-2406
GOODWYN & SONS INC N B
2550 Bellwood Rd, North Chesterfield, VA 23237-1308
Tel (804) 748-5859 *Founded/Ownrshp* 1960
Sales 21.4MM^E *EMP* 106
SIC 5211 2421 Lumber products; Masonry materials & supplies; Lumber: rough, sawed or planed
Pr: Russow R Beck III
**Treas:* Maurice O Beck Jr
**VP:* David R Beck
**Prin:* Mike Beck

D-U-N-S 05-015-9953
GOODWYN MILLS & CAWOOD INC
2701 1st Ave S Ste 100, Birmingham, AL 35233-2723
Tel (205) 879-4462 *Founded/Ownrshp* 1975
Sales 48.1MM *EMP* 330
SIC 8711 8712 Engineering services; Architectural services; Engineering services; Architectural services
Pr: Steve Cawood
**VP:* Jeffrey Brewer
**VP:* Cathy Gerachis
**VP:* Galen Thackston

D-U-N-S 02-624-3436 IMP
GOODY GOODY LIQUOR INC
BUCKEYE LIQUOR
10370 Olympic Dr, Dallas, TX 75220-4436
Tel (214) 765-6853 *Founded/Ownrshp* 1964
Sales 53.9MM^E *EMP* 290
SIC 5921 5181 5182

D-U-N-S 00-134-0876
■ **GOODY PRODUCTS INC** (DE)
(*Suby of* NEWELL RUBBERMAID INC) ★
3 Glenlake Pkwy, Atlanta, GA 30328-3447
Tel (770) 418-7300 *Founded/Ownrshp* 1933
Sales 143.3MM^E *EMP* 800
SIC 3999 3089 3069 Hair & hair-based products; Barrettes; Combs, except hard rubber; Combs, plastic; Cases, plastic; Boxes, plastic; Rubber hair accessories; Curlers, hair, rubber; Combs, hard rubber; Brushes, rubber; Hair & hair-based products; Barrettes; Combs, except hard rubber; Combs, plastic; Cases, plastic; Boxes, plastic; Rubber hair accessories; Curlers, hair, rubber; Combs, hard rubber; Brushes, rubber
Pr: David Klatt
Ex VP: John Creel
VP Sls: Ric L Kern Jr
VP Sls: Richard L Kern

GOODYEAR
See MOORES RETREAD & TIRE OF ARK-LA-TEX INC

GOODYEAR
See YOUNGSTEDT INC

GOODYEAR
See MASON TIRE & AUTO SERVICE INC

GOODYEAR
See D W CAMPBELL INC

GOODYEAR
See MOUNTAIN VIEW TIRE & SERVICE INC

GOODYEAR COML TIRE & SVC CTRS
See WINGFOOT COMMERCIAL TIRE SYSTEMS LLC

D-U-N-S 11-832-7162 IMP/EXP
■ **GOODYEAR DUNLOP TIRES NORTH AMERICA LTD**
(*Suby of* GOODYEAR TIRE & RUBBER CO) ★
200 John Jmes Adubon Pkwy, Buffalo, NY 14228-1120
Tel (716) 639-5200 *Founded/Ownrshp* 1999
Sales 315.1MM^E *EMP* 1,153
SIC 5531 Automotive tires; Automotive tires
Pr: James Galoppo
Treas: Mary Kasprzak
VP: Michael Buckley
VP: Robert Schrecongost
Plnt Mgr: Tim Frossell

GOODYEAR ENGINEERED PRODUCTS
See VEYANCE TECHNOLOGIES INC

D-U-N-S 07-455-1201 EXP
■ **GOODYEAR INTERNATIONAL CORP**
(*Suby of* GOODYEAR TIRE & RUBBER CO) ★
200 E Innovation Way, Akron, OH 44316-0001
Tel (330) 796-2121 *Founded/Ownrshp* 1922
Sales 34.6MM^E *EMP* 23^E
SIC 5014 Tires & tubes
Pr: William J Sharp
**CFO:* Laura Thompson
**Treas:* Tom Kaczynski
**VP:* Damon J Audia
**VP:* Sylvain G Balensi
**VP:* CHI K Liang
**VP:* Richard Padante

GOODYEAR RBR CO SOUTHERN CAL
See GOOD-WEST RUBBER CORP

D-U-N-S 00-446-7924 IMP
▲ **GOODYEAR TIRE & RUBBER CO** (OH)
200 E Innovation Way, Akron, OH 44316-0001
Tel (330) 796-2121 *Founded/Ownrshp* 1898
Sales 18.1MMM *EMP* 67,000
Accts Pricewaterhousecoopers Llp C
Tkr Sym GT *Exch* NGS
SIC 3011 3052 7534 7538 7539 5013 Tires & inner tubes; Inner tubes, all types; Pneumatic tires, all types; Tire & inner tube materials & related products; Rubber & plastics hose & beltings; Automobile hose, rubber; Rubber belting; Tire retreading & repair shops; Rebuilding & retreading tires; General automotive repair shops; Truck engine repair, except industrial; Automotive repair shops; Brake services; Shock absorber replacement; Tune-up service, automotive; Motor vehicle supplies & new parts; Automotive servicing equipment; Automotive supplies & parts; Tires & inner tubes; Inner tubes, all types; Pneumatic tires, all types; Tire & inner tube materials & related products; Rubber & plastics hose & beltings; Automobile hose, rubber; Rubber belting; Tire retreading & repair shops; Rebuilding & retreading tires; General automotive repair shops; Truck engine repair, except industrial; Automotive repair shops; Brake services; Shock absorber replacement; Tune-up service, automotive; Motor vehicle supplies & new parts; Automotive servicing equipment; Automotive supplies & parts
Ch Bd: Richard J Kramer
Pr: Chris Delaney
CFO: Laura K Thompson
Treas: Damon Audia
Sr VP: John D Fish
Sr VP: Paul Fitzhenry
Sr VP: John T Lucas
Sr VP: Gregory L Smith
Sr VP: Joe Zekoski
VP: Kathleen Geier
VP: Michael McNulty
VP: Richard J Noechel
VP: Roy Sutfin
Exec: Eric Brown
Board of Directors: Stephanie A Streeter, William J Conaty, Thomas H Weidemeyer, James A Firestone, Michael R Wessel, Werner Geissler, Peter S Hellman, Laurette T Koellner, W Alan McCollough, John E McGlade, Michael J Morell, Roderick A Palmore

D-U-N-S 07-971-5438
GOOGLE CAPITAL MANAGEMENT CO LLC
1600 Amphitheatre Pkwy, Mountain View, CA 94043-1351
Tel (415) 640-1425 *Founded/Ownrshp* 2015
Sales 25.9MM^E *EMP* 47^E
SIC 6726 Investment offices

D-U-N-S 07-834-4713
■ **GOOGLE FIBER INC** (CA)
(*Suby of* GOOGLE INC) ★
1600 Amphitheatre Pkwy, Mountain View, CA 94043-1351
Tel (650) 253-0000 *Founded/Ownrshp* 2010
Sales 21.4MM^E *EMP* 75
SIC 4813
VP: Milo Medin

D-U-N-S 06-090-2413 IMP
■ **GOOGLE INC**
(*Suby of* ALPHABET INC) ★
1600 Amphitheatre Pkwy, Mountain View, CA 94043-1351
Tel (650) 253-0000 *Founded/Ownrshp* 1998
Sales 66.0MMM *EMP* 53,600
Tkr Sym GOOG *Exch* NGS
SIC 4813 7375 ; Information retrieval services; Data base information retrieval; On-line data base information retrieval; ; Information retrieval services; Data base information retrieval; On-line data base information retrieval
CEO: Sundar Pichai
**Ch Bd:* Eric Schmidt
CFO: Ruth M Porat
Sr VP: Nikesh Arora
Sr VP: Salar Kamangar
Sr VP: Sridhar Ramaswamy
Sr VP: Andy Rubin
Sr VP: Susan Wojcicki
VP: Ted Fike
Exec: Jon Venverloh
Creative D: Alexander Chen
Dir Bus: Michael Haswell
Board of Directors: L John Doerr, Diane B Greene, John L Hennessy, Ann Mather, Alan R Mulally, Paul S Otellini, K Ram Shriram, Shirley M Tilghman

D-U-N-S 62-260-4416 EXP
■ **GOOGLE INTERNATIONAL LLC**
(*Suby of* GOOGLE INC) ★
1600 Amphitheatre Pkwy, Mountain View, CA 94043-1351
Tel (650) 253-0000 *Founded/Ownrshp* 2002
Sales 286.7MM^E *EMP* 143^E
SIC 4813 7375 ; ; Information retrieval services
Ch Bd: Eric Schmidt
**CEO:* Larry Page
**Sr VP:* David C Drummond
Sftwr Eng: Chris Hayes
Pr Mgr: Michael Mayzel
Corp Couns: Andrew McLaughlin

D-U-N-S 55-648-4509
GOOLD HEALTH SYSTEMS
(*Suby of* MEDIFAX-EDI LLC) ★
45 Commerce Dr Ste 5, Augusta, ME 04330-7889
Tel (207) 622-7153 *Founded/Ownrshp* 2013
Sales 24.0MM^E *EMP* 209
Accts Albin Randall & Bennett Port
SIC 8742 7371 Drug stores & proprietary stores; Primary care medical clinic; Mailing & messenger services; Employment agencies; Data processing service; Management consulting services; Hospital & health services consultant; Management information systems consultant; Custom computer programming services; Computer software development & applications
CEO: James Clair
**Ch Bd:* William G Waldron Jr
**Pr:* Victoria Mulkern
VP: Jeffery Barkin
**Exec:* John Grotton
Dir Bus: Jude Walsh
Software D: Michael Dusoe
Sftwr Eng: Neal Bartley
Sftwr Eng: Jason Brown
Sftwr Eng: William Gehring
Sftwr Eng: Mitchell McVay

D-U-N-S 02-225-1367
GOOSE CREEK CONSOLIDATED INDEPENDENT SCHOOL DISTRICT
4544 Interstate 10 E, Baytown, TX 77521-8881
Tel (281) 420-4800 *Founded/Ownrshp* 1919
Sales 242.0MM *EMP* 3,000
SIC 8211

D-U-N-S 06-818-3631
GOOSENECK IMPLEMENT CO
JOHN DEERE
810 Highway 5 E, Mohall, ND 58761-9700
Tel (701) 756-6825 *Founded/Ownrshp* 1975
Sales 23.9MM^E *EMP* 90
SIC 5083 7699 Agricultural machinery; Farm machinery repair; Agricultural machinery; Farm machinery repair
Pr: Carl Larson
Off Mgr: Barb Otto

D-U-N-S 00-810-3095
GOOSENECK TRAILER MFG CO INC
4400 Highway 21 E, Bryan, TX 77808-0947
Tel (979) 778-0034 *Founded/Ownrshp* 1962
Sales 31.6MM^E *EMP* 120
SIC 3715 Trailer bodies; Trailer bodies
Pr: David Carrabba
**VP:* Mark Carrabba
Plnt Mgr: Pat McIntyne
Plnt Mgr: Pat McIntyre

D-U-N-S 78-713-6720
GOOTEE CONSTRUCTION INC
2400 N Arnoult Rd, Metairie, LA 70001-1813
Tel (504) 831-1909 Founded/Ownrshp 1991
Sales 28.1MM EMP 85
Accts Macaluso And Vignes
SIC 1711 Plumbing, heating, air-conditioning contractors; Plumbing, heating, air-conditioning contractors
Pr: Benjamin Gootee
*Ch Bd: Ken Gootee
*CFO: Kathleen T Gootee
*VP: Kyle Sharbonno
IT Man: Chris Fagot
VP Mktg: Brett Cook

D-U-N-S 00-621-9752
GOPHER ELECTRONICS CO
222 Little Canada Rd E Bsmt, Saint Paul, MN 55117-1378
Tel (651) 490-4900 Founded/Ownrshp 1952
Sales 50.0MM^E EMP 45
SIC 5065 Electronic parts & equipment
CEO: Mike Treece
*Pr: Norris Carnes Jr
CTO: Chris O'Donnell
IT Man: Rick Kosiarek
Mktg Dir: Tammy Cain
Sales Asso: Sheila Dougherty
Sales Asso: Jennifer Fluhrer
Sales Asso: Cory Hoveland
Sales Asso: Mike Lalone
Sales Asso: Pete McMerty
Sales Asso: Bob Schneiderhan

GOPHER RESOURCE
See LO NIDY CO INC

D-U-N-S 05-502-5527 IMP
GOPHER RESOURCE LLC
GOPHER SMELTING & REFINING
(Suby of GOPHER RESOURCE) ★
2900 Lone Oak Pkwy 140b, Eagan, MN 55121-1594
Tel (651) 454-3310 Founded/Ownrshp 1946
Sales 40.3MM^E EMP 150
SIC 3339 Lead smelting & refining (primary); Lead smelting & refining (primary)
MIS Dir: Maier Kutoff
IT Man: Joe Tappainer

GOPHER SMELTING & REFINING
See GOPHER RESOURCE LLC

GOPHER SPORT AND PLAY
See PROPHET CORP

D-U-N-S 14-607-0854 IMP
▲ **GOPRO INC**
3000 Clearview Way, San Mateo, CA 94402-3710
Tel (650) 332-7600 Founded/Ownrshp 2004
Sales 1.3MMM EMP 970
Tkr Sym GPRO Exch NGS
SIC 3861 7372 Photographic equipment & supplies; Prepackaged software; Photographic equipment & supplies; Prepackaged software
Ch Bd: Nicholas Woodman
*Pr: Anthony Bates
CFO: Jack Lazar
Sr VP: Zander Lurie
VP: Greg Patti
Comm Dir: Lara Sasken
Prgrm Mgr: Barrie Dickinson
Prgrm Mgr: Karen Makay
Prgrm Mgr: Heath Westbrook
Off Mgr: Jaime Dioli
Off Mgr: Joe Scuooy
Board of Directors: Edward Gilhuly, Kenneth Goldman, Peter Gotcher, Michael Marks

D-U-N-S 00-416-9991
GORANT CHOCOLATIER LLC (OH)
GORANT'S YUM YUM TREE
8301 Market St, Boardman, OH 44512-6257
Tel (330) 726-8821 Founded/Ownrshp 1946, 2009
Sales 65.2MM^E EMP 550
SIC 5441 5947 5145 3999 2066 Candy, nut & confectionery stores; Greeting cards; Gift shop; Candy; Candles; Chocolate & cocoa products; Candy, nut & confectionery stores; Greeting cards; Gift shop; Candy; Candles; Chocolate & cocoa products
Pr: Gary Weiss
Plnt Mgr: Jack Peluse

GORANT'S YUM YUM TREE
See GORANT CHOCOLATIER LLC

D-U-N-S 08-328-5445 IMP
GORBEL INC (NY)
600 Fishers Run, Fishers, NY 14453
Tel (585) 924-6262 Founded/Ownrshp 1977, 1985
Sales 72.3MM^E EMP 250
SIC 3536 Hoists, cranes & monorails; Cranes, industrial plant; Hoists, cranes & monorails; Cranes, industrial plant
Ch Bd: Brian D Reh
*CEO: David Reh
*VP: David Butwid
Genl Mgr: Gay Card
Sls Mgr: Pete Friedrich

D-U-N-S 86-872-9716
GORDIAN GROUP INC
30 Patewood Dr Ste 350, Greenville, SC 29615-6810
Tel (864) 467-9333 Founded/Ownrshp 2012
Sales 42.8MM^E EMP 170^E
SIC 7372 Prepackaged software; Prepackaged software
CEO: William Pollak
*Pr: Robert Coffey
*Ex VP: Daniel Black
*Ex VP: Eunice Cho
*Ex VP: Matthew Gormly
*Ex VP: Craig Klosk
*Ex VP: Daniel Kortick
Sr VP: Kristina Enlow
VP: Thomas J Digangi
VP: Greg Hanson
VP: Michael C Jones
*VP: Robert Kelbe
VP: David Mahler
Board of Directors: William K Flemming

D-U-N-S 96-473-9838
GORDIAN MEDICAL INC
AMERICAN MEDICAL TECHNOLOGIES
17595 Cartwright Rd, Irvine, CA 92614-5847
Tel (714) 556-0200 Founded/Ownrshp 2007
Sales 71.5MM^E EMP 290
SIC 5047 Medical equipment & supplies; Medical equipment & supplies
Pr: Gerald Del Signore
*CFO: James Sorenson
IT Man: James Sorensen

D-U-N-S 07-895-4963
GORDIE BOUCHER FORD LINCOLN OF JANESVILLE INC (WI)
BOUCHER, GORDIE LINCOLN
2727 E Us Hwy 14, Janesville, WI 53545
Tel (608) 754-5511 Founded/Ownrshp 1992
Sales 29.4MM^E EMP 78^E
SIC 5511 7538 Automobiles, new & used; General automotive repair shops; Automobiles, new & used; General automotive repair shops
Pr: Frank Boucher
*Ch Bd: Gordie Boucher
VP: Pat Meyers
*Prin: Shane Lott
Genl Mgr: Terry Nordness
Sales Asso: Charles Anderson

D-U-N-S 10-229-4774 IMP
GORDMANS INC
1926 S 67th St, Omaha, NE 68106-2800
Tel (402) 691-4000 Founded/Ownrshp 2008
Sales 1.0MMM^E EMP 5,200
SIC 5311

D-U-N-S 96-253-7895 IMP
GORDMANS MANAGEMENT CO INC
(Suby of GORDMANS INC) ★
1926 S 67th St, Omaha, NE 68106-2800
Tel (402) 691-4000 Founded/Ownrshp 2004
Sales 21.6MM^E EMP 150^E
SIC 5311 Department stores, discount
CFO: James Brown
*CFO: Mike James

D-U-N-S 96-612-6638 IMP
■ **GORDMANS STORES INC**
(Suby of SUN GORDMANS LLC) ★
1926 S 67th St, Omaha, NE 68106-2800
Tel (402) 691-4000 Founded/Ownrshp 2008
Sales 634.6MM EMP 5,500^E
Tkr Sym GMAN Exch NGS
SIC 5651 5963 Family clothing stores; Home related products, direct sales; Family clothing stores; Home related products, direct sales
Pr: Andrew T Hall
*Ch Bd: T Scott King
COO: Michael E Wirkkala
CFO: James B Brown
CFO: Michael D James
Chf Mktg O: Michael Morand
Sr VP: Geoffrey B Ayoub
Sr VP: Richard H Heyman
VP: Stacey M Townsend
Board of Directors: Mark E Brody, Stewart M Kasen, Donald V Roach, James A Shea, Kenneth I Tuchman, Brian J Urbanek

D-U-N-S 04-377-2680
GORDON ALUMINUM INDUSTRIES INC
PURPOSE EXTRUDED ALUMINUM
1000 Mason St, Schofield, WI 54476-1847
Tel (715) 359-6101 Founded/Ownrshp 1958
Sales 49.1MM^E EMP 150
SIC 3354 3441 3442 3471 Aluminum extruded products; Rods, extruded, aluminum; Fabricated structural metal; Window & door frames; Anodizing (plating) of metals or formed products; Aluminum extruded products; Rods, extruded, aluminum; Fabricated structural metal; Window & door frames; Anodizing (plating) of metals or formed products
Pr: Alfred J Gordon II
*Sec: James Liebner
Opers Mgr: Jeff Sandberg
Sls Mgr: Bruce Pregont

D-U-N-S 93-376-3849
GORDON AUTOMOTIVE GROUP INC
QUALITY TOYOTA
1700 W 6th St, Corona, CA 92882-2954
Tel (951) 734-6020 Founded/Ownrshp 1995
Sales 61.7MM^E EMP 185^E
SIC 5511 5521 Automobiles, new & used; Automobiles, used cars only; Automobiles, new & used; Automobiles, used cars only
CEO: Arthur E Gordon Jr
Genl Mgr: Biff Gordon
Sls Mgr: Matt Danner

D-U-N-S 18-750-1499 IMP
GORDON BIERSCH BREWING CO
3987 Paradise Rd, Las Vegas, NV 89169-4607
Tel (702) 221-4752 Founded/Ownrshp 1987
Sales 83.2MM^E EMP 848
SIC 5813 Tavern (drinking places); Tavern (drinking places)
CFO: William Bullard
*CFO: Paul Michels
Exec: Aaron Moir

GORDON BROS
See GORDON BROTHERS GROUP LLC

GORDON BROS
See GORDON BROTHERS RETAIL PARTNERS LLC

D-U-N-S 02-514-1789
GORDON BROS STEEL WAREHOUSE INC
1340 W 43rd St, Chicago, IL 60609-3308
Tel (773) 447-2696 Founded/Ownrshp 1910
Sales 20.3MM^E EMP 17
SIC 5051 5093 Steel; Ferrous metal scrap & waste
Pr: Lester Gordon
*VP: Richard M Gordon

D-U-N-S 01-438-1995 IMP
GORDON BROTHERS GROUP LLC
GORDON BROS
800 Boylston St Ste 27, Boston, MA 02199-7016
Tel (888) 424-1903 Founded/Ownrshp 1998
Sales 169.3MM^E EMP 250
SIC 6722 Management investment, open-end; Management investment, open-end
Pr: Kenneth S Frieze
Pt: Brian Cooper
Pt: Lisa F Galeota
Pt: Andrew Murphy
Ch Bd: Michael G Frieze
Pr: Neill J Kelly
Pr: Gary M Talarico
CEO: Mark T Dufton
COO: Malcolm Macaulay
CFO: John M Kelliher
CFO: Michael P Muldowney
CFO: Robert Pagia
CFO: Robert Paglia
Ofcr: Don Hancock
Ofcr: Jeffrey T Lerner
VP: Eli Appelbaum
VP: Andrew B Becker
VP: Michael Guelfo
VP: Jo-Ann Jackson
VP: Ronald W Liese
VP: Jim Lightburn
Board of Directors: Richard W Thaler Jr

D-U-N-S 01-669-8198
GORDON BROTHERS RETAIL PARTNERS LLC
GORDON BROS
(Suby of GORDON BROS) ★
101 Huntington Ave Fl 10, Boston, MA 02199-7607
Tel (888) 424-1903 Founded/Ownrshp 1997
Sales 31.5MM EMP 250
SIC 8741 Management services; Management services
VP: Suzan Cronin
VP: Andrew Murphy

D-U-N-S 10-352-1613
GORDON CHEVROLET INC
(Suby of STEWART MANAGEMENT GROUP INC) ★
31850 Ford Rd, Garden City, MI 48135-1569
Tel (734) 427-6200 Founded/Ownrshp 1983
Sales 41.7MM^E EMP 105^E
SIC 5511 7538 7532 5531 Automobiles, new & used; Trucks, tractors & trailers: new & used; Vans, new & used; General automotive repair shops; Top & body repair & paint shops; Automotive & home supply stores; Automobiles, new & used; Trucks, tractors & trailers: new & used; Vans, new & used; General automotive repair shops; Top & body repair & paint shops; Automotive & home supply stores
Pr: Gordon L Stewart
VP: Sandy Beach
*Genl Mgr: Susan Ianni
Genl Mgr: Andrew Stewart
Store Mgr: Steve Tesner
Sls Mgr: Al Denomme

D-U-N-S 79-720-9616
GORDON CHEVROLET INC
1166 Blanding Blvd, Orange Park, FL 32065-7714
Tel (904) 272-2200 Founded/Ownrshp 1991
Sales 58.0MM EMP 102
SIC 5511 5521 Automobiles, new & used; Used car dealers; Automobiles, new & used; Used car dealers
Pr: Gordon L Stewart
Off Mgr: Karen Rinker
Sls Mgr: Kurt Barnthouse
Sls Mgr: Mike Meszaros
Sls Mgr: James Schram
Sales Asso: Stephen Maurer
Sales Asso: Alex Pugh
Sales Asso: Steven Rees
Sales Asso: Terry Smith
Sales Asso: Tom Wright

GORDON CHEVROLET-GEO
See GORDON STEWART CHEVROLET INC

D-U-N-S 07-661-6176
GORDON COLLEGE
255 Grapevine Rd, Wenham, MA 01984-1899
Tel (978) 927-2300 Founded/Ownrshp 1914
Sales 61.0MM EMP 496
Accts Grant Thornton Llp Boston Ma
SIC 8221 University; University
Pr: D Michael Lindsay
Ofcr: John Soucy
Ofcr: Mark Stowell
VP: Lynn Brown
VP: James McDonald
VP: Richard D Sweeney Jr
Mng Dir: Tatyana Parsons
Genl Mgr: Kiki Dole
Off Mgr: Rebecca Whetsel
Off Admin: Karis Roper
CTO: Katie Breitigan

D-U-N-S 80-973-4098
GORDON COLLEGE
(Suby of BOARD OF REGENTS OF UNIVERSITY SYSTEM OF GEORGIA) ★
419 College Dr, Barnesville, GA 30204-1762
Tel (678) 359-5103 Founded/Ownrshp 1976
Sales 16.8MM^E EMP 350^E
SIC 8222 Junior colleges & technical institutes; Junior colleges & technical institutes
Pr: Shelly C Nickel
*Pr: Max Burns
*Pr: Shelly Nickel
VP: Dennis Chamberlain
VP: Lee Fruitticher
Genl Mgr: Kiki Dole
Nrsg Dir: Patsy H Brown

D-U-N-S 84-124-8730 IMP
GORDON COMPANIES INC
DAVE'S MKT CHRSTMAS WONDERLAND
85 Innsbruck Dr, Cheektowaga, NY 14227-2703
Tel (716) 706-0320 Founded/Ownrshp 1977
Sales 24.0MM EMP 200
Accts Bonadio & Co Llp Cpas Will
SIC 5092 5947 Arts & crafts equipment & supplies; Artcraft & carvings; Arts & crafts equipment & supplies; Artcraft & carvings
Ch Bd: David M Gordon
*VP: Nathan Gordon
*VP: Paulette Gordon

D-U-N-S 11-303-5500 IMP
GORDON CONTRACTORS INC
9010 Edgeworth Dr, Capitol Heights, MD 20743-3706
Tel (301) 350-6600 Founded/Ownrshp 2002
Sales 26.5MM^E EMP 125
SIC 1799 1761 Waterproofing; Roofing contractor
Pr: Paul Gordon
VP: Steve Wilt
Snr PM: Brett Kiah

D-U-N-S 09-962-5758
GORDON COUNTY BOARD OF EDUCATION
205 Warrior Path Ne, Calhoun, GA 30701-9266
Tel (706) 629-7366 Founded/Ownrshp 1925
Sales 40.3MM^E EMP 770
Accts Russell W Hinton Cpa Cgfm-D
SIC 8211 Boarding school; Public combined elementary & secondary school; Boarding school; Public combined elementary & secondary school

D-U-N-S 07-979-9696
GORDON COUNTY SCHOOL DISTRICT
205 Warrior Path Ne, Calhoun, GA 30701-9266
Tel (706) 629-7366 Founded/Ownrshp 2014
Sales 10.1MM^E EMP 1,027^E
SIC 8211 Public elementary & secondary schools
Pr Dir: Amy Parker
HC Dir: Mike Evelti

D-U-N-S 08-261-7846
GORDON FEINBLATT ROTHMAN HOFFBERGER & HOLLANDER LLC (MD)
233 E Redwood St, Baltimore, MD 21202-3332
Tel (410) 576-4000 Founded/Ownrshp 1953
Sales 29.9MM^E EMP 180
SIC 8111 General practice attorney, lawyer; General practice attorney, lawyer
Sr Pt: Bradley Swallow
Pr: Gina Dangelo
Pr: Nancy Wheeler
CTO: Barry Rosen
Mktg Mgr: Patrick Reardon
Counsel: Sander Wise

D-U-N-S 02-331-8074
GORDON FLESCH CO INC
GFC LEASING
2675 Research Park Dr, Fitchburg, WI 53711-4906
Tel (608) 271-2100 Founded/Ownrshp 1956
Sales 126.0MM^E EMP 600
SIC 5044 5045 5065 7359 7378 7372

D-U-N-S 00-640-9908 IMP/EXP
GORDON FOOD SERVICE INC
1300 Gezon Pkwy Sw, Wyoming, MI 49509-9302
Tel (888) 437-3663 Founded/Ownrshp 1942
Sales 2.3MMM^E EMP 10,600
Accts Hungerford Aldrin Nichols & Ca
SIC 5149 5142 5147 5146 5144 5143 Groceries & related products; Packaged frozen goods; Meats & meat products; Fish & seafoods; Poultry & poultry products; Dairy products, except dried or canned; Groceries & related products; Packaged frozen goods; Meats & meat products; Fish & seafoods; Poultry & poultry products; Dairy products, except dried or canned
Ch: Daniel A Gordon
*CEO: James Gordon
*CFO: Jeff Maddox
CFO: Steve Whitteberry
*Sec: John Gordon Jr
Ex VP: Tony Grohle
VP: Gopaul Aggarwal
VP: Cheryl Carter
VP: Clif Charles
VP: Chuck Mountjoy
VP: Robert Smit
VP: Ken Vink
Comm Man: Richard Van Dyke

GORDON HOSPITAL
See ADVENTIST HEALTH SYSTEM GEORGIA INC

D-U-N-S 02-818-9587
GORDON INDUSTRIAL SUPPLY CO
207 Van Ness Ave, Fresno, CA 93721-3123
Tel (559) 264-5931 Founded/Ownrshp 1962
Sales 24.8MM^E EMP 19
SIC 5085 Industrial supplies
Pr: Darol Hoffman
*CFO: Robert Hoffman
IT Man: Greg Hoffman

D-U-N-S 15-542-6828
GORDON INVESTMENTS INC
ORR'S JEWELERS
5857 Forbes Ave, Pittsburgh, PA 15217-1601
Tel (412) 421-6777 Founded/Ownrshp 1985
Sales 24.2MM EMP 17
Accts Schneider Downs & Co Inc P
SIC 5944 Jewelry stores; Jewelry stores
Pr: David Gordon
*VP: Marcia Orr Gordon
Sales Exec: Duane McConeghy
Mktg Dir: Bob Sittig

D-U-N-S 04-585-8479
GORDON L SEAMAN INC
29 Old Dock Rd, Yaphank, NY 11980-9702
Tel (631) 345-0479 Founded/Ownrshp 1968
Sales 35.9MM EMP 150
Accts Grassi & Co Cpas Pc Jerich
SIC 1731 Electrical work; Electrical work
Ch Bd: Gordon L Seaman Sr
*Pr: Gordon L Seaman Jr
VP: Edgardo Reyes
IT Man: Tracy Mees
Snr Mgr: Andrew Okula

D-U-N-S 00-832-8619 IMP
GORDON LABORATORIES INC
751 E Artesia Blvd, Carson, CA 90746-1202
Tel (310) 327-5240 *Founded/Ownrshp* 2004
Sales 26.7MM^E *EMP* 45
SIC 2844 Cosmetic preparations
CEO: Nabil Chartouni
**COO:* Anthony Robertson
VP: Judy Arbour-Fall
VP: Vladi Berman
Off Admin: Alvia Maciel

GORDON LAWN & GARDEN CO
See PBI-GORDON CORP

D-U-N-S 00-893-0521
GORDON LUMBER CO
GORDON MODULAR HOME DIVISION
1515 Croghan St, Fremont, OH 43420-2742
Tel (419) 333-5444 *Founded/Ownrshp* 1868
Sales 36.7MM *EMP* 100
SIC 5031 5211

D-U-N-S 12-770-7227
GORDON MCCOWN CONSTRUCTION LLC
422 Admiral Blvd, Kansas City, MO 64106-1560
Tel (816) 960-1111 *Founded/Ownrshp* 1999
Sales 94.9MM^E *EMP* 150^E
SIC 1542 Commercial & office building contractors; Commercial & office building contractors
CFO: Jeffery Placek
Off Mgr: Andrea Murdock
IT Man: Dustin Burns
Snr PM: Leed Brown
Snr PM: Calvin Hobbs

GORDON MODULAR HOME DIVISION
See GORDON LUMBER CO

D-U-N-S 80-359-3693
GORDON PAINTING & HOME REPAIR LLC
2560 Baywood Ct, Greenwood, IN 46143-9397
Tel (317) 496-7767 *Founded/Ownrshp* 2004
Sales 50.0MM *EMP* 2
SIC 1721 7622 Commercial painting; Home entertainment repair services; Commercial painting; Home entertainment repair services

D-U-N-S 00-318-1484 IMP
GORDON PAPER CO INC
5713 Ward Ave, Virginia Beach, VA 23455-3310
Tel (757) 464-3581 *Founded/Ownrshp* 1964
Sales 21.6MM^E *EMP* 108
SIC 2679 Paper products, converted; Paper products, converted
Pr: Gordon Avia F
**Sec:* Daniel Gordon
**VP:* Gordon Mark
**VP:* Gordon Steven
Ex Dir: Jon Weinstein
Dir IT: Steven Gordon
Dir IT: Joyce Robinson
Plnt Mgr: Gregory Butts
Sls Dir: Mark Gordon

D-U-N-S 94-358-1520
GORDON PHYSICIAN HOSPITAL ORGANIZATION INC
1035 Red Bud Rd Ne, Calhoun, GA 30701-6010
Tel (706) 629-2895 *Founded/Ownrshp* 1996
Sales 5.6MM^E *EMP* 450
SIC 8011 Offices & clinics of medical doctors; Offices & clinics of medical doctors
Pr: David Brannon MD
**CFO:* Will Theus MD

D-U-N-S 00-147-1221
GORDON PRILL INC (CA)
310 E Caribbean Dr, Sunnyvale, CA 94089-1148
Tel (408) 745-7164 *Founded/Ownrshp* 1989, 2001
Sales 21.3MM^E *EMP* 45
SIC 1542 8741 8712 8711 1541 Commercial & office building contractors; Construction management; Architectural services; Engineering services; Industrial buildings, new construction; Commercial & office building contractors; Construction management; Architectural services; Engineering services; Industrial buildings, new construction
Pr: Patrick Dolci
Treas: Gopal Aggarwal
Dir IT: Joe Ford

D-U-N-S 93-079-0337 IMP
GORDON RECYCLERS INC
L GORDON IRON & METAL COMPANY
1300 Salisbury Rd, Statesville, NC 28625-6256
Tel (704) 873-9004 *Founded/Ownrshp* 1997
Sales 99.3MM *EMP* 97
Accts Bernard Robinson & Company L
SIC 5093 4953 Metal scrap & waste materials; Recycling, waste materials; Metal scrap & waste materials; Recycling, waste materials
CEO: Barry Gordon
**Pr:* Kalman Gordon
**CFO:* Louis Gordon
**VP:* Richard Gordon

D-U-N-S 07-571-2877
GORDON RESEARCH CONFERENCES INC
512 Liberty Ln, West Kingston, RI 02892-1502
Tel (401) 783-7644 *Founded/Ownrshp* 1931
Sales 40.0MM *EMP* 39^E
Accts Kpmg Llp Providence Ri
SIC 8733 Scientific research agency; Scientific research agency
Bd of Dir: Heidi Appel
Bd of Dir: Karl Hansen
Trst: Sarah Ades
Trst: Phillip Britt
Trst: Mary Heng
Trst: Scott Keeney
Trst: Stephen King
Trst: Joseph Mindell
Trst: James Salzer
Trst: David Sibley
Trst: Steven Son

D-U-N-S 10-735-5000
GORDON SEVIG TRUCKING CO
GSTC
400 Highway 151 E, Walford, IA 52351-5459
Tel (319) 846-5500 *Founded/Ownrshp* 1984
Sales 21.7MM^E *EMP* 100
SIC 4213 Contract haulers
Pr: Gordon C Sevig
VP: Janelle M Schmidt
VP: Thomas Schmidt
VP: Bruce G Sevig
Board of Directors: Colleen Kosmach, Christine Schrader, Shirley Sevig

D-U-N-S 55-688-2181
GORDON STEWART CHEVROLET INC
GORDON CHEVROLET-GEO
16414 N Dale Mabry Hwy, Tampa, FL 33618-1343
Tel (813) 969-2600 *Founded/Ownrshp* 1991
Sales 32.0MM^E *EMP* 80
SIC 5511 7538 7532 7515 5531 5521 Automobiles, new & used; General automotive repair shops; Top & body repair & paint shops; Passenger car leasing; Automotive & home supply stores; Used car dealers; Automobiles, new & used; General automotive repair shops; Top & body repair & paint shops; Passenger car leasing; Automotive & home supply stores; Used car dealers
Pr: Gordon L Stewart
Exec: Agnes Prescott
**Genl Mgr:* Art Smith
IT Man: Ben Ruenger

D-U-N-S 00-433-3944
GORDON TERMINAL SERVICE CO OF PA
1000 Ella St, Mckees Rocks, PA 15136
Tel (412) 331-9410 *Founded/Ownrshp* 1982
Sales 41.2MM^E *EMP* 160
SIC 4789 4226 2992 4613 Pipeline terminal facilities, independently operated; Petroleum & chemical bulk stations & terminals for hire; Lubricating oils; Refined petroleum pipelines; Pipeline terminal facilities, independently operated; Petroleum & chemical bulk stations & terminals for hire; Lubricating oils; Refined petroleum pipelines
Pr: Robert N Gorden
**Pr:* Robert M Gordon Jr
**Treas:* Ralph Castelucci
**VP:* Thomas P Gordon
Plnt Mgr: Timothy Fiedler

D-U-N-S 06-771-5391
■ **GORDON TRUCKING INC** (WA)
(*Suby of* HEARTLAND EXPRESS INC) ★
151 Stewart Rd Sw, Pacific, WA 98047-2108
Tel (253) 863-7777 *Founded/Ownrshp* 1946, 2013
Sales 241.9MM^E *EMP* 2,000
SIC 4213

D-U-N-S 02-905-4723
GORDON TURNER MOTORS
TURNER VOLVO
2535 Arden Way, Sacramento, CA 95825-2413
Tel (916) 488-2400 *Founded/Ownrshp* 1948
Sales 35.9MM^E *EMP* 166
SIC 5511 5531 7538 Automobiles, new & used; Automotive parts; General automotive repair shops; Automobiles, new & used; Automotive parts; General automotive repair shops
CEO: Patrick G Turner
**VP:* Casey Turner
Genl Mgr: Chuck Houston
Sls Mgr: Jorgen Eiremo
Sales Asso: Art Spina

D-U-N-S 07-212-3409 IMP
GORDON-CONWELL THEOLOGICAL SEMINARY INC
130 Essex St, South Hamilton, MA 01982-2325
Tel (978) 468-7111 *Founded/Ownrshp* 1970
Sales 35.5MM *EMP* 167
Accts Berry Dunn Mcneil & Parker Ll
SIC 8221 Theological seminary; Theological seminary
Ch: Richard A Armstrong
**Pr:* Dennis P Hollinger
**CFO:* Robert S Landrebe
**Treas:* Herbert Hess
**Ex Dir:* Thomas Colatosti
IT Man: Ted Kang

D-U-N-S 10-689-8968
GORDON-DARBY INC
2410 Ampere Dr, Louisville, KY 40299-1572
Tel (502) 266-5795 *Founded/Ownrshp* 1982
Sales 45.1MM^E *EMP* 525
SIC 7549 Emissions testing without repairs, automotive; Emissions testing without repairs, automotive
Pr: S Jay Gordon Jr
**Sec:* Randall Hockensmith
**VP:* Cliff Mahaffey
Software D: Sean Abbey
Sftwr Eng: Jesse Campbell

GORDON'S MARKET
See THURLAND REAY FAMILY INVESTMENT CO

GORDONS OF KENNER
See ERICS OF METAIRIE INC

GORDY'S COUNTY MARKET
See GORDYS FOOD & LIQUOR INC

D-U-N-S 02-318-4799
GORDYS FOOD & LIQUOR INC
GORDY'S COUNTY MARKET
17158 County Highway J, Chippewa Falls, WI 54729-7114
Tel (715) 726-2505 *Founded/Ownrshp* 1966
Sales 23.3MM^E *EMP* 100^E
SIC 5411 5921 Grocery stores, independent; Liquor stores
Pr: Gordon Schafer
**VP:* Donna Schafer
Genl Mgr: Jeff Schafer

GORE COMPLETIONS
See GDC TECHNICS LTD

D-U-N-S 82-703-2467
GORELL ENTERPRISES INC
GORELL WINDOWS & DOORS
10250 Philipp Pkwy, Streetsboro, OH 44241-4765
Tel (724) 465-1800 *Founded/Ownrshp* 1993
Sales 16.4MM^E *EMP* 370
SIC 3089 5031 Plastic hardware & building products; Doors & windows; Plastic hardware & building products; Doors & windows
Ch Bd: Wayne C Gorell
**Pr:* Brian Zimmerman
**CFO:* Arnold S Levitt
**VP:* Michael A Rempel
VP: Tyson Schwartz
Sfty Mgr: Amy Romeo

GORELL WINDOWS & DOORS
See GORELL ENTERPRISES INC

D-U-N-S 62-520-9460
GORES ENT HOLDINGS INC
6260 Lookout Rd, Boulder, CO 80301-3685
Tel (303) 531-3100 *Founded/Ownrshp* 2005
Sales 1.5MM *EMP* 1,150
SIC 3577 7373 3357 Computer peripheral equipment; Local area network (LAN) systems integrator; Communication wire; Coaxial cable, nonferrous; Fiber optic cable (insulated); Computer peripheral equipment; Local area network (LAN) systems integrator; Communication wire; Coaxial cable, nonferrous; Fiber optic cable (insulated)
Pr: Donald Gruidel

D-U-N-S 13-713-7878
GORES GROUP LLC
9800 Wilshire Blvd, Beverly Hills, CA 90212-1804
Tel (310) 209-3010 *Founded/Ownrshp* 2004
Sales 7.2MMM^E *EMP* 19,800
SIC 6211 Investment firm, general brokerage; Investment firm, general brokerage
CEO: Alec Gores
COO: Joseph Page
Ex VP: Frank Stefanik
Sr VP: Kurt Hans
Sr VP: Jeremy Rossen
Sr VP: Dewey Turner III
VP: Paul Cottey
VP: Kari Harmon
VP: Desmond Nugent
VP: Gil Vassoly
Mng Dir: Saad Hammad

GORES IDEA HOLDING
See ASTADIA INC

D-U-N-S 05-463-9521
GORES INC
1300 E Mill Ave, Comanche, TX 76442
Tel (325) 356-3045 *Founded/Ownrshp* 1949
Sales 22.5MM^E *EMP* 170
SIC 5999 5191 Feed & farm supply; Farm supplies; Feed & farm supply; Farm supplies
Ch Bd: Joe T Gore
**Pr:* Kenneth Harvick
**CFO:* Richard Hill
**VP:* Jerry Gore
**VP:* Vickie Harvick

D-U-N-S 80-784-7020
GORES RADIO HOLDINGS LLC
(*Suby of* GORES GROUP LLC) ★
10877 Wilshire Blvd # 1805, Los Angeles, CA 90024-4341
Tel (310) 209-3010 *Founded/Ownrshp* 2007
Sales 70.9MM^E *EMP* 1,501
SIC 3699 7382 Security devices; Security systems services; Security devices; Security systems services
Pr: Alex Gores

D-U-N-S 03-513-2083
GORGES OF OMAHA INC
GORGES VOLVO
17665 Burt St, Omaha, NE 68118-3315
Tel (402) 359-1500 *Founded/Ownrshp* 1981
Sales 34.1MM *EMP* 41
SIC 5511 Automobiles, new & used; Automobiles, new & used
Pr: Dan Gorges
Sls Mgr: Craig Fischer

GORGES VOLVO
See GORGES OF OMAHA INC

D-U-N-S 00-452-4575
GORHAM MIDDLESEX CENTRAL SCHOOL DISTRICT
MARCUS WHITMAN CENTRAL SCHOOLS
4100 Baldwin Rd, Rushville, NY 14544-9738
Tel (585) 554-4848 *Founded/Ownrshp* 1969
Sales 17.6MM^E *EMP* 350
SIC 8211 Public elementary & secondary schools; Public elementary & secondary schools
CFO: Donna House
Brnch Mgr: Susan Wissick
Dir IT: Maureen Lee
Dir IT: Brenda Reynolds
IT Man: Bruce Penten
Schl Brd P: Sheila Brown

D-U-N-S 08-318-5116
GORHAM SAVINGS BANK
64 Main St, Gorham, ME 04038-1304
Tel (207) 839-4450 *Founded/Ownrshp* 1868
Sales NA *EMP* 110
SIC 6036 State savings banks, not federally chartered; State savings banks, not federally chartered
Pr: Christopher W Emmons
**COO:* Daniel P Hunter
**Sr VP:* Irene M Oldfield
**Sr VP:* Gregory R Palmer
**VP:* Matt Early
**VP:* Jack Lufkin

D-U-N-S 17-171-5563
GORHAM SCHOOL DEPARTMENT
75 South St Fl 2, Gorham, ME 04038-1713
Tel (207) 222-1002 *Founded/Ownrshp* 2004
Sales 30.0MM *EMP* 730
SIC 8211 Public elementary school; Public junior high school; Public senior high school; Public elementary school; Public junior high school; Public senior high school
Dir IT: Mark Fryover

D-U-N-S 06-768-5578
GORHAM/SCHAFFLER INC (TN)
3095 Stonebrook Cir, Memphis, TN 38116-1891
Tel (901) 345-6100 *Founded/Ownrshp* 1971
Sales 21.3MM^E *EMP* 30
SIC 5075 1711 Electrical heating equipment; Ventilating equipment & supplies; Air conditioning equipment, except room units; Plumbing, heating, air-conditioning contractors
Pr: Gary A Gorham
**CFO:* Brian D Schaffler

D-U-N-S 07-717-1577 IMP
GORILLA CIRCUITS
1445 Oakland Rd, San Jose, CA 95112-1203
Tel (408) 294-9897 *Founded/Ownrshp* 2000
Sales 36.2MM^E *EMP* 198^E
SIC 3672 Printed circuit boards; Printed circuit boards
Mng Pt: Fermin Aviles
**Pr:* Hershel Petty
**VP:* Jaime Gutierrez
CTO: Jose Borjon

D-U-N-S 00-425-1914 IMP
GORILLA GLUE CO (OH)
4550 Red Bank Rd, Cincinnati, OH 45227-2118
Tel (513) 271-3169 *Founded/Ownrshp* 1904, 1983
Sales 20.5MM^E *EMP* 49^E
SIC 3423 3991 3541 Hand & edge tools; Brooms & brushes; Machine tools, metal cutting type
Pr: Alvin Press
**Pr:* Howard N Ragland III
COO: Joe Ragland
Sr VP: Scott Vilagi
VP: Matt Kemme
**VP:* Michael F Ragland
**Prin:* William J Keating Jr
**Prin:* Joseph P Rouse
**Prin:* S K Von Hoene
Info Man: Gary Salazar
Plnt Mgr: Dave Kumpf

D-U-N-S 61-673-2470
GORILLA OFFROAD LIGHTS LLC
(*Suby of* EVOLVE MEDIA HOLDINGS LLC) ★
5140 W Goldleaf Cir Fl 3, Los Angeles, CA 90056-1655
Tel (310) 449-1890 *Founded/Ownrshp* 1999
Sales 81.6MM^E *EMP* 225^E
SIC 4813 ;
CFO: Bill Foltz
VP: ARI Lee Bayme

GORITEWAY
See RITEWAY BUS SERVICE INC

D-U-N-S 16-101-9534
GORMAN & CO INC
200 N Main St, Oregon, WI 53575-1447
Tel (608) 835-3900 *Founded/Ownrshp* 1984
Sales 95.8MM^E *EMP* 135
SIC 6552 6531 Land subdividers & developers, residential; Real estate managers
CEO: Gary Gorman
Rgnl Mgr: Sonja Droste

D-U-N-S 00-389-3963
GORMAN BROS INC (NY)
200 Church St, Albany, NY 12202-1965
Tel (518) 462-5401 *Founded/Ownrshp* 1900, 1968
Sales 67.0MM^E *EMP* 180
SIC 1611 General contractor, highway & street construction; General contractor, highway & street construction
Ch Bd: A Mark Gorman
VP: John Dearborn
**VP:* P Anthony Gorman

D-U-N-S 80-473-5132
GORMAN MANUFACTURING CO INC
492 Koller St, San Francisco, CA 94110
Tel (650) 555-0000 *Founded/Ownrshp* 1985
Sales 20.8MM *EMP* 125
SIC 2752

D-U-N-S 05-464-1345
GORMAN MILLING CO INC (TX)
302 E Lauderbock St, Gorman, TX 76454
Tel (254) 734-2252 *Founded/Ownrshp* 1969
Sales 35.0MM *EMP* 88
SIC 2048 Prepared feeds; Prepared feeds
Pr: Harold Fritts
**Sec:* Martha Guthrie
VP: John Fritts
**VP:* Darrell V Nay

D-U-N-S 00-415-4308
▲ **GORMAN-RUPP CO** (OH)
600 S Airport Rd, Mansfield, OH 44903-7831
Tel (419) 755-1011 *Founded/Ownrshp* 1933
Sales 434.9MM *EMP* 1,247^E
Accts Ernst & Young Llp Cleveland
Tkr Sym GRC *Exch* ASE
SIC 3561 3594 Pumps & pumping equipment; Industrial pumps & parts; Pumps, oil well & field; Pumps, domestic: water or sump; Fluid power pumps & motors; Pumps & pumping equipment; Industrial pumps & parts; Pumps, oil well & field; Pumps, domestic: water or sump; Fluid power pumps & motors
Pr: Jeffrey S Gorman
**Ch Bd:* James C Gorman
CFO: Wayne L Knabel
VP: Ronald D Pittenger
Dir IT: Pat Wischmeier
IT Man: Gary Lauderbaugh
VP Opers: Mark Kreinbihl
Sls Mgr: Dean Kastran
Board of Directors: M Ann Harlan, Thomas E Hoaglin, Christopher H Lake, Kenneth R Reynolds, Rick R Taylor, W Wayne Walston

D-U-N-S 08-393-2343 IMP
GORMANS FURNITURE INC
23231 Industrial Park Dr A, Farmington Hills, MI 48335-2844
Tel (248) 473-9131 *Founded/Ownrshp* 1976
Sales 24.0MM^E *EMP* 130
SIC 5712 7389 Furniture stores; Interior designer; Interior decorating
Ch: Bernard D Moray
**Pr:* Tom Lias
CFO: Mike Otto
**Ex VP:* Jeffrey B Roberts
**VP:* John Moray

D-U-N-S 01-742-2056
GORNO BROS INC
GORNO FORD
22025 Allen Rd, Woodhaven, MI 48183-2205
Tel (734) 676-0031 *Founded/Ownrshp* 1980
Sales 45.6MM^E *EMP* 115
SIC 5511 Automobiles, new & used; Automobiles, new & used
Pr: George M Gorno
**Sec:* Monica Southward
**VP:* Edwin Jolliffe

GORNO FORD
See GORNO BROS INC

GORTITE
See DYNATECT MANUFACTURING INC

D-U-N-S 00-176-3333 IMP
GORTON SLADE & CO INC (MA)
(*Suby of* SG SEAFOOD HOLDINGS INC) ★
225 Southampton St, Boston, MA 02118-2715
Tel (617) 442-5800 *Founded/Ownrshp* 1928
Sales 166.6MM^E *EMP* 192
SIC 5146 Fish, fresh; Fish, frozen, unpackaged; Seafoods; Fish, fresh; Fish, frozen, unpackaged; Seafoods
CEO: Kimberly Gorton
**Ch Bd:* Mike Gorton Sr
**COO:* Michael Richard
CFO: Joshua Bernstein
CFO: James Stauffer
Ex VP: Patrice Flanagan
**VP:* Dana Bartholomew Jr
**VP:* Ron Beane
VP: Dennis Newman
VP: Matthew Simpson
QA Dir: Bob Lafreniere

GORTONS
See GORTONS INC

D-U-N-S 05-124-2258 IMP
GORTONS INC
GORTONS
(*Suby of* NIPPON SUISAN (USA) INC) ★
128 Rogers St, Gloucester, MA 01930-5005
Tel (978) 283-3000 *Founded/Ownrshp* 1849
Sales 219.7MM^E *EMP* 975
SIC 2092 2091 Fresh or frozen packaged fish; Seafood products: packaged in cans, jars, etc.; Fresh or frozen packaged fish; Seafood products: packaged in cans, jars, etc.
Pr: Judson Reis
Rgnl Mgr: Michael Cahalan
QA Dir: Paula Decaro
QA Dir: Rita Nobile
QA Dir: Robert Shumaker
IT Man: Nancy Smithm
Ql Cn Mgr: Allison Williamson
Mktg Dir: Sue Prakken
Mktg Mgr: Jan Velco
Sls Mgr: Paul Raguso

GOSCH FORD LINCOLN MERCURY
See JACK GOSCH FORD INC

D-U-N-S 78-142-2761
GOSH ENTERPRISES INC
CHARLEY'S STEAKERY
2500 Farmers Dr 140, Columbus, OH 43235-5706
Tel (614) 923-4700 *Founded/Ownrshp* 1986
Sales 66.6MM^E *EMP* 185
Accts Gbq Partners Llc Columbus Oh
SIC 6794 5812 Franchises, selling or licensing; Grills (eating places); Franchises, selling or licensing; Grills (eating places)
Pr: Charley Shin
Mng Pt: Joe Hoock
**Pr:* Bob Wright
COO: John Hughes
**CFO:* Candra Alisiswanto
VP: Kris Miotke
Creative D: Ben Laplaca
Genl Mgr: Nelson Colon
Genl Mgr: Cody Garner
Genl Mgr: Rick Long
Genl Mgr: Cizo Nieto

D-U-N-S 03-096-2666
GOSHEN BOARD OF EDUCATION
GOSHEN LOCAL SCHOOL DISTRICT
6694 Goshen Rd, Goshen, OH 45122-9273
Tel (513) 722-2222 *Founded/Ownrshp* 1878
Sales 27.2MM *EMP* 325
SIC 8211 Elementary & secondary schools; Public combined elementary & secondary school; Elementary & secondary schools; Public combined elementary & secondary school
**Treas:* Todd Shinkle

D-U-N-S 10-037-5690
GOSHEN CENTRAL SCHOOL DISTRICT
227 Main St, Goshen, NY 10924-2195
Tel (845) 615-6740 *Founded/Ownrshp* 1998
Sales 53.7MM *EMP* 510
Accts Nugent & Haeussler Pc Mont
SIC 8211 Public elementary & secondary schools; Public elementary school; Public elementary & secondary schools; Public elementary school
Dir IT: James Sterett

D-U-N-S 11-441-9521
GOSHEN COLLEGE INC
1700 S Main St, Goshen, IN 46526-4794
Tel (574) 535-7000 *Founded/Ownrshp* 2002
Sales 28.1MM *EMP* 340^E
Accts Crowe Horwath Llp South Bend
SIC 8221 University; University
Pr: James E Brenneman
**CFO:* James L Histand
Ofcr: David Janzen
VP: Anita Stalter
Ex Dir: John Roth
Off Mgr: Marge Brandeberry
Pr Dir: Richard Aguirre
Pr Mgr: Rachel Lapp

D-U-N-S 07-433-2388
GOSHEN COMMUNITY SCHOOLS
613 E Purl St, Goshen, IN 46526-4044
Tel (574) 533-8631 *Founded/Ownrshp* 1895
Sales 65.0MM^E *EMP* 1,300
SIC 8211 Public elementary school; Public junior high school; Public senior high school; Public elementary school; Public junior high school; Public senior high school
Bd of Dir: Jane Devoe
VP: Michelle Smart
VP: Sharese Swafford
Prin: Jose Boza
Prin: Don Jantzi
Prin: Sue Olinghouse
Prin: Michael Springer
Prin: Denise Tahara
Genl Mgr: Marilyn Groves
Psych: Leon Bauman
Psych: Jan Holsopple

D-U-N-S 04-372-9409
GOSHEN COUNTY SCHOOL DISTRICT 1
626 W 25th Ave, Torrington, WY 82240-1809
Tel (307) 532-2171 *Founded/Ownrshp* 1972
Sales 23.0MM^E *EMP* 450
Accts Porter Muirhead Cornia & How
SIC 8211 Public elementary school; Public junior high school; Public senior high school; Public elementary school; Public junior high school; Public senior high school
MIS Dir: Bryan Foster
Schl Brd P: Charlie Marshberger

GOSHEN GENERAL HOSPITAL
See GOSHEN HOSPITAL ASSOCIATION INC

D-U-N-S 96-139-9367
GOSHEN HEALTH SYSTEM INC
200 High Park Ave, Goshen, IN 46526-4810
Tel (574) 533-2141 *Founded/Ownrshp* 1995
Sales 36.1MM *EMP* 1,100
SIC 5912 Drug stores; Drug stores
CEO: Randal E Christophel
Chf Rad: Michael Holt
Dir Vol: Karla Beasley
VP: Pamela Karsen
VP: James Vancuren
VP: Alan Weldy
Dir Rx: Amy Kemery
Dir Rx: Kent Schreck
Dir IT: Art Wager
IT Man: Charlene Bell
IT Man: Mark Lindemood

D-U-N-S 07-433-2453
GOSHEN HOSPITAL ASSOCIATION INC
GOSHEN GENERAL HOSPITAL
200 High Park Ave, Goshen, IN 46526-4810
Tel (574) 533-2141 *Founded/Ownrshp* 1908
Sales 216.9MM *EMP* 736
Accts Deloitte Tax Llp Indianapolis
SIC 8062 General medical & surgical hospitals; General medical & surgical hospitals
COO: Sheryl Lewis Blake
COO: Randy Cammenga
**CFO:* Amy Floria
Mtls Dir: Paul Lyons
Ansthlgy: Jon Horsch
Doctor: Keith Barkow
Doctor: Eric Beachy
Doctor: Daniel Bruetman
Doctor: Andrew Kuhn
Doctor: Benjamin Nelson
Nrsg Dir: Vicki Yoder

GOSHEN LOCAL SCHOOL DISTRICT
See GOSHEN BOARD OF EDUCATION

GOSHEN MEDICAL CENTER FAISON
See GOSHEN MEDICAL CENTER INC

D-U-N-S 11-042-3050
GOSHEN MEDICAL CENTER INC
GOSHEN MEDICAL CENTER FAISON
444 Sw Center St, Faison, NC 28341-8820
Tel (910) 267-1942 *Founded/Ownrshp* 1979
Sales 24.7MM *EMP* 109
Accts Nunn Brashear And Company Pa
SIC 8011 8021 General & family practice, physician/surgeon; Dentists' office; General & family practice, physician/surgeon; Dentists' office
Ex Dir: Greg Bounds
**Pr:* Chester Aycock
CFO: Brenda Goodrich

D-U-N-S 00-790-2497 IMP/EXP
GOSIGER INC
108 Mcdonough St, Dayton, OH 45402-2267
Tel (937) 228-5174 *Founded/Ownrshp* 1922
Sales 178.1MM^E *EMP* 435
SIC 5084 Machine tools & accessories; Machine tools & accessories
Pr: Peter G Haley
**Mng Pt:* John Haley
COO: Dan Neely
**CFO:* Jerry Presell
CFO: Gerry Preser
CFO: Jerry R Pressel
**Ch:* Jane Haley
**Ex VP:* Jerry L Gecowets
VP: Dan Butler
VP: Roger Oconnor
Prgrm Mgr: James Vanhise

Board of Directors: Hank Bachmann, Daniel Duvall, Charles Faruki, James Mc Swiney

D-U-N-S 15-533-8916 IMP
GOSNOLD INC
GOSNOLD ON CAPECOD
200 Ter Heun Dr, Falmouth, MA 02540-2525
Tel (508) 540-6550 *Founded/Ownrshp* 1972
Sales 22.9MM^E *EMP* 398
SIC 8093 8063 Substance abuse clinics (outpatient); Rehabilitation center, outpatient treatment; Mental health clinic, outpatient; Psychiatric hospitals; Substance abuse clinics (outpatient); Rehabilitation center, outpatient treatment; Mental health clinic, outpatient; Psychiatric hospitals
Pr: Raymond V Tamasi
**CEO:* Raymond Tamasi
**COO:* Alisa Galazzi
**COO:* James R Kane
CFO: Kathy Clay
**CFO:* Peter Gallitano
**Treas:* Ronald Garcia
Psych: Robert Blanchard
Psych: Linda Hanson

GOSNOLD ON CAPECOD
See GOSNOLD INC

D-U-N-S 00-830-7514 IMP
GOSPEL LIGHT PUBLICATIONS
1923 Eastman Ave 200, Ventura, CA 93003-7383
Tel (805) 644-9721 *Founded/Ownrshp* 1933
Sales 21.9MM^E *EMP* 90
SIC 2731 3999 Books: publishing & printing; Pamphlets: publishing & printing; Education aids, devices & supplies
CEO: William T Greig III
CFO: David Hutchinson
Bd of Dir: Elaine Montefu
VP: Michael Phawks
CTO: Al Harvey
Natl Sales: Ben Unseth
VP Sls: Robert Bever
Mktg Dir: Mario Pacifici

D-U-N-S 05-002-0911 IMP
GOSPEL OF PEACE INC
GINN
215 Celebration Pl # 200, Kissimmee, FL 34747-5400
Tel (321) 939-4700 *Founded/Ownrshp* 1998
Sales NA *EMP* 1,400
SIC 6552

D-U-N-S 09-693-1274
GOSS DODGE INC
1485 Shelburne Rd, South Burlington, VT 05403-7748
Tel (802) 658-0120 *Founded/Ownrshp* 1979
Sales 29.4MM *EMP* 51
SIC 5511 Automobiles, new & used; Pickups, new & used; Automobiles, new & used; Pickups, new & used
Pr: Douglas Hoar
**VP:* Cheryl Hoar
Genl Mgr: Brian Hoar
Genl Mgr: Todd Tarte
Off Mgr: Bob Poczabut
IT Man: Mark Ploof
Sales Asso: Vince Dober

D-U-N-S 09-774-5962
GOSS ELECTRIC INC
137 Woodall Rd, Decatur, AL 35601-7437
Tel (256) 353-8751 *Founded/Ownrshp* 1976
Sales 27.8MM^E *EMP* 200
SIC 1731 Electrical work; Electrical work
Pr: Carl Goss
Telecom Ex: Sharon Terry
Board of Directors: Ruth B Goss

D-U-N-S 10-187-5631 IMP
GOSS INTERNATIONAL AMERICAS INC
121 Technology Dr, Durham, NH 03824-4716
Tel (603) 749-6600 *Founded/Ownrshp* 2015
Sales 134.4MM^E *EMP* 950
SIC 7699 3555 Printing trades machinery & equipment repair; Printing presses; Printing trades machinery & equipment repair; Printing presses
Pr: Richard Nichols
COO: Leonardo Clavijo
Treas: Dan Dillman
Sr VP: Art Judson
Sr VP: Mark Oggero
VP: Thomas Clarke
VP: Dan Machaj
VP: Pascal Orliac
VP: Torben Rasmussen
VP: Richard Schultz
VP: Jeff Upchurch

D-U-N-S 10-446-9619 IMP/EXP
GOSS INTERNATIONAL CORP
(*Suby of* SHANGHAI ELECTRIC (GROUP) CO., LTD.)
9018 Heritage Pkwy # 1200, Woodridge, IL 60517-5136
Tel (630) 796-7560 *Founded/Ownrshp* 2010
Sales 241.9MM^E *EMP* 2,000
SIC 3555 5084 Printing presses; Printing trades machinery, equipment & supplies; Printing presses; Printing trades machinery, equipment & supplies
CEO: Richard Nichols
**Pr:* Jochen Meissner
Sr VP: Richard F Schultz
VP: Don Huppe
VP: Jacques Navarre
Genl Mgr: Matt Sharkady
Opers Mgr: Allan Phillips
Genl Couns: Shane Lancaster
Snr Mgr: Jack Noe

D-U-N-S 01-848-4907
GOSS SUPPLY CO (OH)
620 Marietta St, Zanesville, OH 43701-3633
Tel (740) 454-2571 *Founded/Ownrshp* 1954
Sales 30.3MM^E *EMP* 55
SIC 5085 Industrial supplies; Hose, belting & packing; Tools; Abrasives
Pr: Terry L Goss
**CFO:* Stacy Erwine
**VP:* Andy Goss
VP: David Goss

VP: Jeff Totman
**Prin:* Pasquale Gallina
**Prin:* Clarence A Goss
**Prin:* Don J Hollingsworth
IT Man: Henry Cornett
Sfty Mgr: Roger Witt
Sales Asso: Steve Atkins

D-U-N-S 14-774-4940 EXP
GOSSEN CORP
2030 W Bender Rd, Milwaukee, WI 53209-3727
Tel (414) 228-9800 *Founded/Ownrshp* 1985
Sales 75.1MM^E *EMP* 300
SIC 3089 2431 2452 Molding primary plastic; Moldings, wood: unfinished & prefinished; Prefabricated wood buildings; Molding primary plastic; Moldings, wood: unfinished & prefinished; Prefabricated wood buildings
Pr: Frank Butterfield Jr
COO: John Green
CFO: John Glayson
**Ex VP:* Bob Simon
**VP:* Frank Butterfield
Brnch Mgr: Jeff Mann
IT Man: John Gleason
Opers Mgr: Fred Inlenfeld
Plnt Mgr: Michael Detlefsen

GOSSETT MITSUBISHI
See GOSSETT MOTOR CARS INC

D-U-N-S 13-044-4961 IMP
GOSSETT MOTOR CARS INC
GOSSETT MITSUBISHI
1901 Covington Pike, Memphis, TN 38128-6980
Tel (901) 363-6556 *Founded/Ownrshp* 1985
Sales 146.0MM^E *EMP* 315
SIC 5511 5012 Automobiles, new & used; Pickups, new & used; Vans, new & used; Automobiles & other motor vehicles; Automobiles, new & used; Pickups, new & used; Vans, new & used; Automobiles & other motor vehicles
Owner: Al Gossett
**Sec:* George Roser
**VP:* David Gossett
Off Mgr: Pamela Trainor
IT Man: Dan Fields
Sls Mgr: Dustin Smith
Sales Asso: Patrick Butler
Sales Asso: Cherrie Granada
Sales Asso: Samantha Johnson
Sales Asso: David Towers
Snr Mgr: David Graham

D-U-N-S 00-910-1874 EXP
GOSSNER FOODS INC (UT)
1051 N 1000 W, Logan, UT 84321-6852
Tel (435) 713-6100 *Founded/Ownrshp* 1941
Sales 139.3MM^E *EMP* 360
SIC 2022 2026 2021 Natural cheese; Processed cheese; Milk, ultra-high temperature (longlife); Creamery butter; Natural cheese; Processed cheese; Milk, ultra-high temperature (longlife); Creamery butter
CEO: Dolores Gossner Wheeler
**Sec:* Dixie W Udy
**VP:* Greg Rowley

D-U-N-S 62-315-0294 IMP
GOTEC PLUS SUN LLC
107 Industrial Rd, Williamstown, KY 41097-9502
Tel (859) 824-5004 *Founded/Ownrshp* 2006
Sales 22.4MM^E *EMP* 115
SIC 3714 Steering mechanisms, motor vehicle; Tie rods, motor vehicle
Pr: Joerg Balzer
Brnch Mgr: Joerg Belzer
CTO: Richard Ider
Plnt Mgr: Don Fitzgerald

D-U-N-S 03-855-9253
GOTHAM TECHNOLOGY GROUP LLC
1 Paragon Dr Ste 200, Montvale, NJ 07645-1728
Tel (201) 802-9600 *Founded/Ownrshp* 2001
Sales 145.1MM^E *EMP* 80
SIC 5045 7361 5932 Computers, peripherals & software; Employment agencies; Computers & accessories, secondhand; Computers, peripherals & software; Employment agencies; Computers & accessories, secondhand
CEO: Ira Silverman
Prac Mgr: David Kim
Prac Mgr: Pablo Vidal
Dir IT: Christopher Passaretti
Software D: Matthew Dallicardillo
Opers Supe: Lisa Garcia
Sales Exec: Chris Passaretti
Sales Exec: Jerry Reid
VP Sls: Lee Shulz
Mktg Mgr: Lindsey Bohm
Mktg Mgr: Lauren Rodabaugh

D-U-N-S 07-803-4121
GOTHENBURG MEMORIAL HOSPITAL INC (NE)
910 20th St, Gothenburg, NE 69138-1253
Tel (308) 537-3661 *Founded/Ownrshp* 1970
Sales 29.5MM^E *EMP* 119
SIC 8062 General medical & surgical hospitals
CEO: Mick Brant
**CFO:* Taci Bartlett
Dir Rad: Julie Koehler
Mtls Dir: Kris Kleinknecht
Nrsg Dir: Kayleen Dudley
Nrsg Dir: Carolyn Evenson

GOTHIC GROUND MANAGEMENT
See GOTHIC LANDSCAPING INC

D-U-N-S 11-880-1414
GOTHIC LANDSCAPING INC
GOTHIC GROUND MANAGEMENT
27502 Avenue Scott, Valencia, CA 91355-3965
Tel (661) 257-1266 *Founded/Ownrshp* 1997
Sales 119.6MM^E *EMP* 600
SIC 0782 Landscape contractors; Lawn services; Landscape contractors; Lawn services
Pr: Jon S Georgio
**VP:* Ronald Georgio

VP: Perry Jones
**Prin:* Mike Georgio
VP Admn: Nick Arena
Sfty Dirs: Frankie Mata
Snr Mgr: John Gordon

D-U-N-S 12-651-6004
GOTTESMAN & SCHUCHAT
1818 N St Nw Ste 700, Washington, DC 20036-2477
Tel (202) 785-2727 *Founded/Ownrshp* 1984
Sales 20.9MM *EMP* 2
SIC 8111 Legal services; General practice attorney, lawyer; Legal services; General practice attorney, lawyer
Pt: Michael A Schuchat

D-U-N-S 10-391-1418
GOTTLIEB HEALTH RESOURCES INC
701 W North Ave, Melrose Park, IL 60160-1612
Tel (708) 681-3200 *Founded/Ownrshp* 1982
Sales 135.0MM *EMP* 1,200
SIC 8741 Hospital management; Hospital management
CEO: John Morgan
CFO: Andy Knauff
**VP:* Brett Wakefield

D-U-N-S 00-767-6554
GOTTLIEB MARTIN & ASSOCIATES LLC (FL)
4932 Sunbeam Rd Ste 100, Jacksonville, FL 32257-6128
Tel (904) 346-3088 *Founded/Ownrshp* 1997
Sales 22.9MM^E *EMP* 190
SIC 8741 8742 Financial management for business; Hospital & health services consultant; Financial management for business; Hospital & health services consultant
CEO: Melvin Gottlieb
Genl Mgr: Lisa Floyd
CIO: Delroy Walwyn

D-U-N-S 07-233-4287
GOTTLIEB MEMORIAL HOSPITAL (IL)
GOTTLIEB MEMORIAL HOSPITAL HOM
701 W North Ave, Melrose Park, IL 60160-1699
Tel (708) 681-3200 *Founded/Ownrshp* 1956
Sales 156.1MM *EMP* 900
SIC 8062 General medical & surgical hospitals; General medical & surgical hospitals
Pr: John Morgan
CFO: Ellen Chin
VP: Connie Clark
Dir Risk M: Bev Mc Adam
Dir Rx: Gary Hanson
Dir Sec: Irwin Olef
Dept Mgr: Gottlieb Murillo
Nurse Mgr: Kim Haukland
CIO: Mitty Addker
QA Dir: Judy Laube
IT Man: Jill Nelson

GOTTLIEB MEMORIAL HOSPITAL HOM
See GOTTLIEB MEMORIAL HOSPITAL

D-U-N-S 15-741-0648
GOTTSTEIN CONTRACTING CORP
39 Elm Rd, Hazle Township, PA 18202-9711
Tel (570) 233-2113 *Founded/Ownrshp* 1984
Sales 28.1MM^E *EMP* 100
SIC 1799 1796 Service station equipment installation & maintenance; Rigging & scaffolding; Artificial turf installation; Food service equipment installation; Installing building equipment; Machine moving & rigging; Millwright
Pr: Kenneth Gottstein
**Sec:* Barbara Gottstein
**VP:* Scott Gottstein

D-U-N-S 05-395-0564
GOUCHER COLLEGE
1021 Dulaney Valley Rd, Baltimore, MD 21204-2780
Tel (410) 337-6000 *Founded/Ownrshp* 1885
Sales 95.7MM *EMP* 500
SIC 8221 College, except junior; College, except junior
Pr: Sanford J Ungar
CFO: Renae Feyer
VP: Donna Frithsen
Dir Lab: Jaclyn Kellon
Genl Mgr: Norman Zwagil

GOUDY HONDA
See ALHAMBRA MOTORS INC

D-U-N-S 62-607-7218
GOUGEON HOLDING CO
100 Patterson Ave, Bay City, MI 48706-4136
Tel (989) 684-7286 *Founded/Ownrshp* 1969
Sales 26.1MM^E *EMP* 202
SIC 2851 Epoxy coatings; Epoxy coatings
Ch: Meade Gougeon
Pr: Robert H Monroe
Sec: Joanne R Gradowski
VP: Grant W Urband

D-U-N-S 01-686-6316
■ **GOULD & LAMB LLC**
(*Suby of* G&L INTERMEDIATE HOLDINGS INC) ★
2397 Huntcrest Way # 200, Lawrenceville, GA 30043-6309
Tel (941) 798-2098 *Founded/Ownrshp* 2014
Sales NA *EMP* 230
SIC 6411 Insurance information & consulting services; Insurance information & consulting services
CEO: Deborah Pfeifle
Pr: Scott Huber
**CFO:* John McDonough
Ofcr: Mark Masson
VP: Diane Haberman
VP: Russell S Whittle
VP Opers: William Brock

D-U-N-S 08-600-8430
GOULD ELECTRIC INC (CA)
12975 Brookprinter Pl # 280, Poway, CA 92064-8895
Tel (858) 486-1727 *Founded/Ownrshp* 1976
Sales 37.5MM^E *EMP* 125
SIC 1731 General electrical contractor; General electrical contractor
Pr: Russ Thurman
**Treas:* John Meyers
**VP:* Donn Lowrey

D-U-N-S 00-615-7747 IMP/EXP
GOULD ELECTRONICS INC
34929 Curtis Blvd Ste 100, Eastlake, OH 44095-4056
Tel (440) 953-5000 *Founded/Ownrshp* 1988
Sales 143.6MM^E *EMP* 2,730
SIC 3825 3497 3613 3691 3674 Instruments to measure electricity; Logic circuit testers; Oscillographs & oscilloscopes; Copper foil; Power circuit breakers; Storage batteries; Semiconductors & related devices; Instruments to measure electricity; Logic circuit testers; Oscillographs & oscilloscopes; Copper foil; Power circuit breakers; Storage batteries; Semiconductors & related devices
VP: D P Burgess
VP: Kerji Kataqiri
VP: John L Monaco

D-U-N-S 00-844-6130
GOULD EVANS P C
4041 Mill St Ste A, Kansas City, MO 64111-3700
Tel (816) 931-6655 *Founded/Ownrshp* 1974
Sales 27.3MM^E *EMP* 120
SIC 8712 8742 7336 0781 Architectural services; Management consulting services; Commercial art & graphic design; Landscape counseling & planning; Architectural services; Management consulting services; Commercial art & graphic design; Landscape counseling & planning
Pr: Anthony Rohr
**Treas:* Trudi Hummel
Assoc VP: Rachel Bias
Assoc VP: Rich Kniss
Assoc VP: Randall Kronblad
**VP:* Robert Baum
VP: Jackson Clark
VP: John Curran
VP: John Dimmel
VP: Henry Dougherty
VP: Brian Hamilton
VP: Everett Henderson
VP: Greg Hugeback
VP: Tim Woofter
VP: Dan Zeller
Dir Bus: Liz Thelen-Torres

D-U-N-S 00-698-9503
GOULD PAPER CORP (NY)
(*Suby of* JAPAN PULP & PAPER (USA) CORP) ★
99 Park Ave Fl 10, New York, NY 10016-1500
Tel (212) 301-0000 *Founded/Ownrshp* 1924, 2010
Sales 1.2MMM *EMP* 452
SIC 5113 5111 3523 Industrial & personal service paper; Fine paper; Harvesters, fruit, vegetable, tobacco, etc.; Industrial & personal service paper; Fine paper; Harvesters, fruit, vegetable, tobacco, etc.
CEO: David Berkowitz
CFO: Edward Silver
Treas: Pat Mullen
Treas: Patrick Mullen
Ex VP: Jim Costenbader
Ex VP: Takahiro Miyata
Ex VP: Joseph Ryan
Ex VP: Michael Trachtenberg
VP: Gary Bishop
VP: Robert Bunsick
VP: Joseph Cali
VP: Todd Chimoff
VP: Paul Collins
VP: Warren Connor
VP: John Cooper
VP: Michael Duncan
VP: Leena Etelalahti
VP: Vincent Eugenio
VP: Jim Gold
VP: Robert Hartman
VP: Marion Hindenburg

D-U-N-S 07-982-8150
GOULD PAPER CORP
(*Suby of* JAPAN PULP & PAPER (USA) CORP) ★
99 Park Ave Fl 10, New York, NY 10016-1500
Tel (212) 301-0000 *Founded/Ownrshp* 2015
Sales 1.0MMM *EMP* 500
SIC 5111 2759 Fine paper; Commercial printing
Pr: David H Berkowitz

D-U-N-S 03-043-1191
GOULDS DAY SPA & SALON INC
1203 Park Place Ctr # 204, Memphis, TN 38119-5319
Tel (901) 682-3737 *Founded/Ownrshp* 1932
Sales 7.5MM^E *EMP* 400
SIC 7231 Cosmetology & personal hygiene salons; Facial salons; Cosmetology & personal hygiene salons; Facial salons
CEO: Phillip Gould
**VP:* David Gould

D-U-N-S 84-131-5708
GOULDS DISCOUNT MEDICAL INC
3901 Dutchmans Ln Ste 100, Louisville, KY 40207-4726
Tel (502) 491-2000 *Founded/Ownrshp* 1990
Sales 30.0MM^E *EMP* 100
SIC 5999 7699 Hospital equipment & supplies; Hospital equipment repair services
Pr: Edmund Gould
**CFO:* Lonnie Oliver
**Treas:* Kenneth Gould
**VP:* David Gould
**VP:* Sharon Gould
IT Man: Thomas Shaffer
Mktg Dir: Shelly Satton

GOULDS PUMPS
See ITT WATER TECHNOLOGY INC

D-U-N-S 00-222-5100 IMP
■ **GOULDS PUMPS INC**
(*Suby of* ITT FLUID TECHNOLOGY CORP) ★
240 Fall St, Seneca Falls, NY 13148-1573
Tel (315) 568-2811 *Founded/Ownrshp* 1984
Sales 840.9MM^E *EMP* 4,500
SIC 3561 5084 Pumps & pumping equipment; Industrial pumps & parts; Pumps, oil well & field; Pumps, domestic: water or sump; Industrial machinery & equipment; Pumps & pumping equipment; Industrial pumps & parts; Pumps, oil well & field; Pumps, domestic: water or sump; Industrial machinery & equipment
Pr: Aris Chicles
**Ch Bd:* Robert Pagano
**Pr:* Ken Napolitano
Opers Mgr: Stan Knecht
Opers Mgr: Brad Larsen
Ql Cn Mgr: Patrick Torres
Manager: Jeff Fishel
Manager: Brian Verdehem
Sls Mgr: Steve George

GOULET SUPPLY COMPANY
See GRANITE GROUP WHOLESALERS LLC

GOULSTON & STORRS
See GOULSTORRS AND CO INC

D-U-N-S 00-104-7786 IMP/EXP
GOULSTON TECHNOLOGIES INC
(*Suby of* TAKEMOTO OIL & FAT CO.,LTD.)
700 N Johnson St, Monroe, NC 28110-2650
Tel (704) 289-6464 *Founded/Ownrshp* 1988
Sales 28.2MM^E *EMP* 120^E
Accts Grant Thornton Charlotte
SIC 2843 Soluble oils or greases; Soluble oils or greases
Pr: Gordon Magee
**Treas:* Alan Gold
Ofcr: George Massey
Ex VP: Tatsuya Endo
**Ex VP:* Hisao Yamamoto
**VP:* Andrew Starzecki
Dir IT: Srinivasan Ranganathan
Tech Mgr: Jeff Elvington
Info Man: Walter Pietrowski
Ql Cn Mgr: Katie Hall
Ql Cn Mgr: Armi Vero

D-U-N-S 07-951-1846
GOULSTORRS AND CO INC (MA)
GOULSTON & STORRS
400 Atlantic Ave, Boston, MA 02110-3331
Tel (617) 482-1776 *Founded/Ownrshp* 1990
Sales 54.6MM^E *EMP* 400
SIC 8111 General practice law office; General practice law office
Pr: Thomas G Sitzmann
**Treas:* Alan W Rottenberg
Bd of Dir: J Casey
Dir IT: Christopher Mann
Counsel: William O Flannery
Counsel: Timothy Watkins

D-U-N-S 01-235-5582 IMP
GOURMET BOUTIQUE LLC
14402 158th St, Jamaica, NY 11434-4214
Tel (718) 977-1200 *Founded/Ownrshp* 1995
Sales 64.0MM *EMP* 368
SIC 2099 Food preparations; Food preparations
COO: Robert Liberto
Genl Mgr: David Andersen
Genl Mgr: Jason Sussman
Info Man: Andrew Ghibaudi
Opers Mgr: Jedd Savel
Prd Mgr: Roger Hughes
VP Sls: Jere Dudley

GOURMET CULINARY
See BALBOA CULINARY INC

D-U-N-S 01-154-4737
GOURMET EXPRESS ACQUISITION FUND LLC
(*Suby of* ILEX CAPITAL GROUP LLC) ★
138 West St, Annapolis, MD 21401-2859
Tel (410) 897-0701 *Founded/Ownrshp* 2007
Sales 38.1MM^E *EMP* 137^E
SIC 6799 Investors

D-U-N-S 82-972-6483 IMP
GOURMET EXPRESS LLC
(*Suby of* GOURMET EXPRESS ACQUISITION FUND LLC) ★
600 Green Dr, Greenville, KY 42345
Tel (270) 377-0201 *Founded/Ownrshp* 1997
Sales 38.1MM^E *EMP* 135
SIC 2038 Frozen specialties; Frozen specialties
COO: Bradley Jackson
Ql Cn Mgr: Julia Mulhollen
Sls Dir: Dan Mellyn

GOURMET FACTORY
See KANGADIS FOOD INC

GOURMET FOODS
See HUG CO

D-U-N-S 15-751-3680 IMP
GOURMET FOODS INC
2910 E Harcourt St, Compton, CA 90221-5502
Tel (310) 632-3300 *Founded/Ownrshp* 1986
Sales 101.9MM^E *EMP* 215^E
SIC 5141 5812 2099 Food brokers; Eating places; Food preparations; Food brokers; Eating places; Food preparations
Pr: Heinz Naef
**CFO:* Gary David
**Sec:* Ursina Naef
Exec: Karen McCullough
Mng Dir: Norman Staley
Off Mgr: Rose Wallace
CTO: Michael Baumgart
IT Man: Karen Smith
Plnt Mgr: Rene Fraga
Sls Dir: Tom Buck
Mktg Mgr: Marcel Lagnez

GOURMET GARAGE
See JAN SERVICES CORP

D-U-N-S 83-587-9016
GOURMET GURU INC
1123 Worthen St, Bronx, NY 10474-6223
Tel (718) 842-2828 *Founded/Ownrshp* 1994
Sales 20.3MM^E *EMP* 50
SIC 2099 Food preparations
Pr: Jeff Lichtenstein
CFO: Kim Lichtenstein
IT Man: Brandon Lee
Snr Mgr: Iida Korhonen
Snr Mgr: Essi Liljama
Snr Mgr: Jonathan Moyer
Snr Mgr: Jen Pletscher

GOURMET JOSE
See GROEB FARMS INC

D-U-N-S 36-464-9822 IMP
GOURMET KITCHEN LLC
1238 State Route 33, Neptune, NJ 07753-5069
Tel (732) 775-5222 *Founded/Ownrshp* 2001
Sales 28.6MM^E *EMP* 140
SIC 2099 Food preparations; Food preparations
Pr: Micheal Lacey
**VP:* Pat Duffey
**Prin:* Ray Walsh

D-U-N-S 07-032-4744 IMP
GOURMET SERVICES INC
G S I
260 Peachtree St Nw # 1500, Atlanta, GA 30303-1245
Tel (404) 876-5700 *Founded/Ownrshp* 1974
Sales 40.0MM^E *EMP* 900
SIC 5812 Commissary restaurant; Caterers; Commissary restaurant; Caterers
Ch Bd: N R Goldston III
**Ch Bd:* Nathaniel R Goldston III
**Pr:* Bill Sims
CFO: Gil Jones
Sr VP: Al Baker
Sr VP: Valarie Goldston
Area Mgr: Gavin Moon
VP Mktg: Kristen Hoffman

D-U-N-S 15-095-1903
GOURMET SYSTEMS OF KANSAS INC
APPLEBEE'S
4551 W 107th St Ste 100, Shawnee Mission, KS 66207-4037
Tel (913) 967-4000 *Founded/Ownrshp* 2013
Sales 28.4MM^E *EMP* 1,000
SIC 5812 5813 Restaurant, family: chain; Bar (drinking places); Restaurant, family: chain; Bar (drinking places)
Ch Bd: Lloyd Hill
Pt: Shelly Gagen
Pr: Tammy Buplantis
Ex VP: Louis A Kucic
Ex VP: George Shadid
VP: Janell Jones
VP: David R Pasley
VP: Samuel M Rothschild
VP: Rohan M St George
**VP:* Robert Steinkamp
Ex Dir: Thomas Weaver

GOURMET TRADING COMPANY
See NZG SPECIALTIES INC

D-U-N-S 04-451-0840
GOUVERNEUR CENTRAL SCHOOL DISTRICT I
133 E Barney St, Gouverneur, NY 13642-1100
Tel (315) 287-4870 *Founded/Ownrshp* 1941
Sales 31.5MM *EMP* 350
Accts Dragon Benware Crowley & Co
SIC 8211 Public elementary & secondary schools; Public elementary & secondary schools

D-U-N-S 80-967-8782
■ **GOVCONNECTION INC**
(*Suby of* PC CONNECTION INC) ★
7503 Standish Pl, Rockville, MD 20855-2731
Tel (301) 340-1100 *Founded/Ownrshp* 1999
Sales 38.9MM^E *EMP* 180
SIC 5734 Computer peripheral equipment; Computer peripheral equipment
Pr: Robert Howard
VP: Nemeroff Ed
VP: Weintraub Stan
VP: Jennifer Tekin
**VP:* Stan Weintraub
Genl Mgr: Bob Howard
Opers Mgr: Stuart Hipwell
Opers Mgr: Janet Smithe
Sales Exec: Jeffrey Trent
Sls Dir: Robert Marconi
Mktg Mgr: Montanez Carlos

GOVERNER'S OFFICE
See PUEBLO OF ISLETA

GOVERNER'S OFFICE
See EXECUTIVE OFFICE OF STATE OF WISCONSIN

GOVERNERS OFFICE, THE
See EXECUTIVE OFFICE OF STATE OF ARKANSAS

GOVERNMENT
See GEORGIA FEDERAL RECOVERY AND AUTO AGENCY

D-U-N-S 00-325-1949
■ **GOVERNMENT ACCOUNTABILITY OFFICE**
(*Suby of* CONGRESS UNITED STATES) ★
441 G St Nw, Washington, DC 20548-0001
Tel (202) 512-3000 *Founded/Ownrshp* 1921
Sales NA *EMP* 3,275
SIC 9311 Budget agency, government; ; Budget agency, government;
Prin: Gene L Dodaro
Pr: Marlin McCrae
CFO: Richard Brown
Ofcr: Ray Dimm
Exec: William Wadsworth
Mng Dir: David Clark
Dir Sec: Robert Dacey
Dir IT: Teresa Tucker
IT Man: Brenda Thomas
Sales Exec: Jean Nazzaro
Genl Couns: Barbara Grewe

D-U-N-S 60-381-4054
GOVERNMENT ACQUISITIONS INC
720 E Pete Rose Way # 360, Cincinnati, OH 45202-3576
Tel (513) 721-8700 *Founded/Ownrshp* 1989
Sales 68.6MM[E] *EMP* 35
SIC 5045 7378 3577 Computers, peripherals & software; Computer software; Computer maintenance & repair; Computer peripheral equipment
CFO: Bobby Brown
**Owner:* Roger Brown
Pr: Ashley Lehman
**CFO:* Stan Jones
Ex VP: Jay Lambke
Prgrm Mgr: Bill Wyche
Netwrk Eng: Rick Kuhn
VP Sls: Carolyn Hyde
Mktg Dir: Leslie Egan
Sls Dir: William Wyche

GOVERNMENT AND LIBRARY SECTOR
See INFOUSA MARKETING INC

GOVERNMENT CENTER
See WASHINGTON TOWNSHIP MONTGOMERY COUNTY

GOVERNMENT CENTER COMMISSION
See CITY OF MALDEN

D-U-N-S 93-194-5299
GOVERNMENT COMPUTER SALES INC
GCSIT SOLUTIONS
1654 20th Ave, Seattle, WA 98122-2806
Tel (907) 474-8306 *Founded/Ownrshp* 1989
Sales 20.1MM *EMP* 23
SIC 5045 Computers, peripherals & software; Computers, peripherals & software
CEO: John Powers
**CFO:* Sara Powers
Manager: Jenson Isham

D-U-N-S 61-415-5380
GOVERNMENT CONTRACTING RESOURCES INC
GCR
315 Page Rd 7, Pinehurst, NC 28374-8751
Tel (910) 215-1900 *Founded/Ownrshp* 2008
Sales 27.5MM[E] *EMP* 167[E]
SIC 8744 Facilities support services
CEO: J Don Albritton
**Pr:* Paul Walden
**Treas:* Kimberly J Cherrix
Treas: Kimberly Cherrix
**VP:* Mike Albritton
Dir IT: Kevin Jernigan
Sfty Mgr: James Dick
Sfty Mgr: Mark Gapetz
Snr PM: Duane Maslowski

D-U-N-S 09-027-7047
GOVERNMENT DEVELOPMENT BANK FOR PUERTO RICO
BANCO GOVERNMENT DEV BNK PR
Cond De Diego Stop 22, San Juan, PR 00924-3840
Tel (787) 722-2525 *Founded/Ownrshp* 1942
Sales NA *EMP* 437
SIC 9111 8732 7389 Executive offices; Executive offices; Business economic service; Financial services
Pr: Juan Carlos Batlle
**Ch Bd:* Alfredo Salazar
**Acting Pr:* Jorge Irizarry
Ex VP: Luis I Alfaro-Martinez
Sr VP: Camille Toro
VP: Julio Caraballo
VP: Jesus G Rivera
VP: Gabriel R Serrano

D-U-N-S 07-627-9850
GOVERNMENT EMPLOYEES HEALTH ASSOCIATION INC (MO)
G E H A
310 Ne Mulberry St, Lees Summit, MO 64086-5861
Tel (816) 257-5500 *Founded/Ownrshp* 1939
Sales NA *EMP* 1,318
Accts Bkd Llp Kansas City Missour
SIC 6321 Health insurance carriers; Health insurance carriers
Ex Dir: Richard G Miles
**CFO:* Eileen Hutchinson
Bd of Dir: William Dawson
VP: Cynthia Anderson
VP: Julie Browne
**VP:* Larry McEnroe
VP: Chad Mills
CIO: Joseph Acosta
Dir IT: Brian Franke
IT Man: Bruce Brown
IT Man: Chastity Brown

D-U-N-S 00-691-9781
■ **GOVERNMENT EMPLOYEES INSURANCE CO INC** (MD)
GEICO
(*Suby of* GEICO CORP) ★
5260 Western Ave, Chevy Chase, MD 20815-3701
Tel (301) 986-2500 *Founded/Ownrshp* 1937, 1979
Sales NA *EMP* 10,000
SIC 6411 Insurance agents, brokers & service; Insurance agents, brokers & service
Ch Bd: Olza Nicely
Pr: Bill Roberts
Pr: John Zinno
CFO: Thomas M Wells
Treas: Charles Gerard Schara
Assoc VP: Howard Dickstein
Ex VP: W Alvin Sparks Jr
Sr VP: George Rogers
**VP:* Charles Davies
VP: Eve Exarhakis
VP: Richard Guertin
VP: Warren Klawitter
VP: Kirk La
VP: Luigi Lazzari
VP: Rhett Rayburn
VP: Daniel Schechter
VP: Ryan West
Board of Directors: James M Hitt, Seth Ingall, Donald Lyons, Robert Morton Miller, William Roberts, David Schindler

D-U-N-S 13-607-3298
GOVERNMENT EXECUTIVE
600 New Hampshire Ave Nw # 4, Washington, DC 20037-2403
Tel (202) 739-8500 *Founded/Ownrshp* 2001
Sales 34.0MM *EMP* 150
SIC 2721 Periodicals; Periodicals
Pr: Steve Vito
Prin: Timothy Clark
Ex Dir: Steven Vito

D-U-N-S 03-702-3640 EXP
■ **GOVERNMENT LIQUIDATION**
(*Suby of* GOINDUSTRY DOVEBID INC) ★
15051 N Kierland Blvd # 300, Scottsdale, AZ 85254-8162
Tel (480) 367-1100 *Founded/Ownrshp* 2001
Sales 69.0MM *EMP* 72[E]
SIC 5099 Ammunition, except sporting; Firearms, except sporting; Lifesaving & survival equipment (non-medical); Fireproof clothing; Ammunition, except sporting; Firearms, except sporting; Lifesaving & survival equipment (non-medical); Fireproof clothing
CIO: Eric Dean
Site Mgr: Lonny Jenderson

D-U-N-S 05-859-2122 IMP/EXP
GOVERNMENT OF DISTRICT OF COLUMBIA
OFFICE CONTG & PROCUREMENT
441 4th St Nw, Washington, DC 20001-2714
Tel (202) 727-2277 *Founded/Ownrshp* 1790
Sales NA *EMP* 34,600
Accts Kpmg Llp Washington Dc
SIC 9111 Mayors' offices; ; Mayors' offices;
**CFO:* Natawar Gandhi
Ofcr: Ray Davidson
Ofcr: Larry McCoy
**Ofcr:* George Schutter
VP: Natasha Ballentine
VP: Greg Bargeman
Prgrm Mgr: Pam Taylor
Brnch Mgr: Rob Mancini
CIO: Mahnaz Choobineh
CIO: Derek Sharp
Dir IT: Glenn Minter

D-U-N-S 16-190-6193
▲ **GOVERNMENT OF UNITED STATES**
U S GOVERNMENT
1600 Pennsylvania Ave Nw, Washington, DC 20500-0003
Tel (202) 456-1414 *Founded/Ownrshp* 1787
Sales NA *EMP* 2,768,886[E]
SIC 9111 ;
Pr: Barack H Obama
**VP:* Joseph R Biden
Exec: Jessica Carter
Exec: Betsy Hawkings
Comm Dir: Emily Davis
Comm Dir: Marisol Garibay
Comm Dir: Brian Robinson
Ex Dir: Jim Zoia
Prgrm Mgr: Linda Crosslin
**CTO:* Megan Smith
MIS Dir: Brian Deguzman

D-U-N-S 09-114-7678
GOVERNMENT OF US VIRGIN ISLANDS
21-22 Kongens Gade, Charlotte Amalie, VI 00802
Tel (340) 774-0001 *Founded/Ownrshp* 1917
Sales NA *EMP* 2,500
SIC 9111 Governors' offices; ; Governors' offices;

D-U-N-S 04-627-7034
GOVERNMENT PERSONNEL MUTUAL LIFE INSURANCE CO
GPM LIFE INSURANCE
2211 Ne Loop 410, San Antonio, TX 78217-4630
Tel (210) 357-2222 *Founded/Ownrshp* 1934
Sales NA *EMP* 101
SIC 6311 Life insurance carriers; Life insurance carriers
Pr: Peter Hennessey III
Ch Bd: Peter J Hennessey Jr
Pr: Kay Goodlett
Pr: Kelly Woodcock
Ofcr: Betty Kuhn
Sr VP: James Manley Denton
Sr VP: Charles Alan Ferguson
Sr VP: Victor Gerleman
Sr VP: Pam Hutchins
Sr VP: Pamela Hutchins
VP: Robert Draper
VP: William M Hoffman
VP: Kama Schilson

D-U-N-S 82-970-8408
GOVERNMENT PROPERTIES INCOME TRUST
255 Washington St Ste 300, Newton, MA 02458-1634
Tel (617) 219-1440 *Founded/Ownrshp* 2009
Sales 251.0MM *EMP* 407
SIC 6798 Real estate investment trusts; Real estate investment trusts
Pr: David M Blackman
Mng Trst: Barry Portnoy
CFO: Mark L Kleifges
Board of Directors: Barbara D Gilmore, John L Harrington, Adam D Portnoy, Barry M Portnoy, Jeffrey P Somers

D-U-N-S 78-563-3348
GOVERNMENT RELATIONS LLC
9259 Old Keene Mill Rd, Burke, VA 22015-4202
Tel (703) 644-4557 *Founded/Ownrshp* 1985
Sales 15.5MM[E] *EMP* 500
SIC 8748 Business consulting; Business consulting
Pr: Donald E Ellison
**VP:* David Ellison

GOVERNMENT RESEARCH OFFICE
See NATIONAL ANIMAL DISEASE CENTER

D-U-N-S 78-580-7611
GOVERNMENT SCIENTIFIC SOURCE INC
G S S
12351 Sunrise Valley Dr, Reston, VA 20191-3415
Tel (703) 734-1805 *Founded/Ownrshp* 1991
Sales 182.0MM *EMP* 90
Accts Lydon Fetterolf Corydon Pa
SIC 5049 5047 Scientific & engineering equipment & supplies; Medical equipment & supplies; Scientific & engineering equipment & supplies; Medical equipment & supplies
Pr: Wayne B Bardsley
**VP:* Smith James
VP: James Smith
**VP:* Sellentin Steve
Sls&Mrk Ex: Scott Stackhouse
Sales Asso: Kip Evoy
Snr Mgr: Chris Kinkaid

D-U-N-S 96-867-3546
GOVERNMENT SECURE SOLUTIONS CGI INC
(*Suby of* CGI FEDERAL INC) ★
9700 Capital Ct Ste 200, Manassas, VA 20110-2046
Tel (703) 227-6068 *Founded/Ownrshp* 2011
Sales 80.0MM *EMP* 200
SIC 7379 Computer related consulting services; Computer related consulting services
Pr: Tom Kirk

D-U-N-S 13-324-9941
GOVERNMENT SERVICE CENTER
315 High St Fl 10, Hamilton, OH 45011-6069
Tel (513) 887-3000 *Founded/Ownrshp* 2003
Sales NA *EMP* 1,000
SIC 9199 ;

D-U-N-S 09-346-6287
GOVERNMENT SUPPORT SERVICES INC
G S I
5999 Stevenson Ave, Alexandria, VA 22304-3302
Tel (703) 751-1300 *Founded/Ownrshp* 1999
Sales 21.2MM *EMP* 400
Accts Durham Aukemp & Rhodes Plc
SIC 4225 General warehousing & storage; General warehousing & storage
Pr: Cheng Yu Huang
**VP:* John K Coburn

GOVERNMENT TECHNOLOGY
See EREPUBLIC INC

D-U-N-S 18-384-2132
GOVERNMENTAL & EDUCATIONAL ASSISTANCE CORP
GEAC
7900 Excelsior Blvd, Hopkins, MN 55343-3445
Tel (952) 837-0540 *Founded/Ownrshp* 1997
Sales 29.9MM *EMP* 600
Accts Johnson West & Co Plc Saint P
SIC 8699 8741 Charitable organization; Management services; Charitable organization; Management services
Pr: Morris Knopf
Ex Dir: Emily Shelstad

D-U-N-S 04-248-5418
GOVERNMENTAL EDUCATIONAL ASSISTANCE CORP LLC
7900 Excelsior Blvd # 250, Hopkins, MN 55343-3445
Tel (952) 837-0540 *Founded/Ownrshp* 2012
Sales 31.3MM *EMP* 14[E]
SIC 8322 Adult day care center; Adult day care center
Prin: Tom Doran

D-U-N-S 14-497-3562
GOVERNMENTAL SUPPLY INTERNATIONAL LLC
301 Clematis St Ste 3000, West Palm Beach, FL 33401-4609
Tel (561) 659-1601 *Founded/Ownrshp* 2004
Sales 32.0MM[E] *EMP* 250
SIC 5085 5047 5065 1623 Industrial supplies; Medical equipment & supplies; Communication equipment; Water, sewer & utility lines; Industrial supplies; Medical equipment & supplies; Communication equipment; Water, sewer & utility lines

D-U-N-S 03-877-8536
GOVERNOR BUSINESS SOLUTIONS INC
15260 S Commerce Dr, Dearborn, MI 48120-1263
Tel (313) 441-4600 *Founded/Ownrshp* 1979
Sales 38.5MM[E] *EMP* 44
SIC 5112 5045 Computer paper; Data processing supplies; Laserjet supplies; Printers, computer
Pr: William Cullinan
COO: Jeff Candea
**VP:* Michael Cullinan

D-U-N-S 04-379-6924 IMP/EXP
GOVERNOR CONTROL SYSTEMS INC
3101 Sw 3rd Ave, Fort Lauderdale, FL 33315-3317
Tel (954) 462-7404 *Founded/Ownrshp* 1998
Sales 33.3MM *EMP* 60[E]
Accts Howard N Fink Cpa Pa Aventura
SIC 5084 Engines & parts, diesel; Engines & parts, diesel
Pr: Are Friesecke
**VP:* Benjamin Lozano
Genl Mgr: Lynn Bell
Opers Mgr: Cullette Harvin
Manager: Diane White
Sales Asso: Tamara Nunez

D-U-N-S 08-158-3353
GOVERNOR DUMMER ACADEMY
1 Elm St Unit 99, Byfield, MA 01922-2739
Tel (978) 465-1763 *Founded/Ownrshp* 1980
Sales 31.3MM *EMP* 130
Accts Kirkland Albrecht & Fredrickso
SIC 8211 Boarding school; Preparatory school; Boarding school; Preparatory school
**CFO:* Richard Savage
**CFO:* Christopher V Wejchert
Treas: Steven Shapiro

D-U-N-S 94-837-8567 EXP
GOVERNOR JUAN F LUIS HOSPITAL & MEDICAL CENTER
4007 Estate Diamond Ruby, Christiansted, VI 00820-4435
Tel (340) 778-6311 *Founded/Ownrshp* 1988
Sales 129.6MM[E] *EMP* 624
SIC 8062 General medical & surgical hospitals; General medical & surgical hospitals
CEO: Kendall Griffith MD
CFO: Anthony G Saul

D-U-N-S 08-161-7052
GOVERNOR MIFFLIN SCHOOL DISTRICT
10 S Waverly St, Reading, PA 19607-2642
Tel (610) 775-1461 *Founded/Ownrshp* 1953
Sales 36.2MM[E] *EMP* 600
SIC 8211 Public elementary school; Public junior high school; Public senior high school; Public elementary school; Public junior high school; Public senior high school
Pr: James Ulrich
Bd of Dir: Elaine Fiant
Dir IT: Rachel Hetzel
Dir IT: Brian Patton
IT Man: Britt Reed
Pr Dir: Melissa Fullerton

D-U-N-S 19-354-5027
GOVERNOR WENTWORTH REGIONAL SCHOOL DISTRICT
140 Pine Hill Rd, Wolfeboro Falls, NH 03896
Tel (603) 569-1658 *Founded/Ownrshp* 1964
Sales 22.1MM[E] *EMP* 527
Accts Vachon Clukay & Co Pc Cpa S
SIC 8211 Public elementary & secondary schools; Public adult education school; Public combined elementary & secondary school; Public junior high school; Public elementary & secondary schools; Public adult education school; Public combined elementary & secondary school; Public junior high school

GOVERNORS CENTER
See NORTHEAST HEALTH GROUP INC

D-U-N-S 96-858-0253
GOVERNORS ISLAND CORP
TRUST FOR GOVERNORS ISLAND
10 South St Frnt Slip7, New York, NY 10004-1939
Tel (212) 440-2200 *Founded/Ownrshp* 2011
Sales 116.4MM *EMP* 12
Accts Marks Paneth Llp New York Ny
SIC 6733 Trusts
Prin: Leslie Koch

GOVERNORS OFFICE
See STATE OF UTAH

GOVERNOR'S OFFICE
See STATE OF ARIZONA

GOVERNOR'S OFFICE
See STATE OF WASHINGTON

GOVERNORS OFFICE
See EXECUTIVE OFFICE OF STATE OF COLORADO

GOVERNOR'S OFFICE, THE
See EXECUTIVE OFFICE OF COMMONWEALTH OF PENNSYLVANIA

GOVERNOR'S OFFICE
See EXECUTIVE OFFICE OF STATE OF MINNESOTA

GOVERNOR'S OFFICE
See LEGISLATIVE OFFICE OF STATE OF NEW JERSEY

GOVERNOR'S OFFICE
See EXECUTIVE OFFICE OF STATE OF VERMONT

GOVERNORS OFFICE
See LEGISLATIVE STATE OF IOWA OFFICE OF

D-U-N-S 00-355-3190
GOVERNORS OFFICE
(*Suby of* EXECUTIVE OFFICE OF STATE OF NORTH CAROLINA) ★
20301 Mail Service Ctr, Raleigh, NC 27699-0300
Tel (919) 733-4240 *Founded/Ownrshp* 2000
Sales NA *EMP* 280
SIC 9111 Executive offices; ; Executive offices;
Pt: Lou Kost
Ex Dir: Sandra Babb
Ex Dir: Al Deitch
Admn Mgr: Karen Randolph
Genl Couns: McLaughlin Kevin
Genl Couns: Mary Penny
Genl Couns: Mary Thompson

D-U-N-S 87-814-7099
GOVERNORS OFFICE OF ECONOMICS DEVELOPMENT
(*Suby of* EXECUTIVE OFFICE OF STATE OF UTAH) ★
60 E South Temple Fl 3, Salt Lake City, UT 84111-1004
Tel (801) 538-8680 *Founded/Ownrshp* 2002
Sales NA *EMP* 550
SIC 9611 Administration of general economic programs; ; Administration of general economic programs;
Exec: Tony Yapias
**Ex Dir:* Spencer Eccles
Sales Exec: Val Finlayson
Sales Exec: Michael Glenn
Sales Exec: Edith Nidco
Sales Exec: Ron Richins

D-U-N-S 83-540-7354
GOVERNORS OFFICE STATE OF CONNECTICUT
(*Suby of* STATE OF CONNECTICUT) ★
210 Capitol Ave Ste 202, Hartford, CT 06106-1535
Tel (860) 566-4840 *Founded/Ownrshp* 1788
Sales NA *EMP* 35,970
SIC 9111 Executive offices; ; Executive offices;
CFO: Michael Last

GOVERNOR'S OFFICE
See LEGISLATIVE OFFICE OF STATE OF NEW HAMPSHIRE

D-U-N-S 06-998-2130
GOVERNORS STATE UNIVERSITY
1 University Pkwy, University Park, IL 60484-3165
Tel (708) 534-5000 *Founded/Ownrshp* 1969
Sales 76.5MM^E *EMP* 1,100
SIC 8221

D-U-N-S 95-705-0883 IMP
GOVPLACE
1886 Metro Center Dr # 100, Reston, VA 20190-5289
Tel (703) 435-6195 *Founded/Ownrshp* 1995
Sales 75.5MM *EMP* 50
SIC 5045 7373 Computers, peripherals & software; Computer peripheral equipment; Systems integration services; Computers, peripherals & software; Computer peripheral equipment; Systems integration services
CEO: Adam Robinson
**CFO:* Mark A Serway
VP: Jerry Calley
**VP:* Ryan McCullough
Exec: Peggy Overby
Ex Dir: Carole Zavala
CIO: Janice Stonebreaker
IT Man: Christine Arroyo
Sls Mgr: Steve Devereux
Sls Mgr: Wayne Hwang

D-U-N-S 96-160-0272
GOVSMART INC
706 Forest St Ste C, Charlottesville, VA 22903-5231
Tel (434) 326-1771 *Founded/Ownrshp* 2009
Sales 69.3MM *EMP* 20
Accts Robinson Farmer Cox Associat
SIC 5734 Computer peripheral equipment; Computer peripheral equipment
CEO: Brent Lillard
**CFO:* Hamza Durrani
**VP:* Adam Deane
**VP:* Glenn Willard
Off Mgr: Emily Lincoln
Snr Ntwrk: Malcolm Ewing
Sales Asso: Shaun Kennedy

GOWAN
See YORICK INC

GOWAN AGRO CANADA
See GOWAN CO LLC

D-U-N-S 82-745-0722
GOWAN CO INC
5550 Airline Dr, Houston, TX 77076-4998
Tel (713) 696-5400 *Founded/Ownrshp* 1992
Sales 32.8MM^E *EMP* 700
SIC 7389 ;
Pr: Mark Froman

D-U-N-S 17-863-1966 IMP
GOWAN CO LLC
GOWAN AGRO CANADA
370 S Main St, Yuma, AZ 85364-2312
Tel (928) 783-8844 *Founded/Ownrshp* 1996
Sales 37.6MM^E *EMP* 106^E
SIC 0781 5191 Chemicals, agricultural; Pesticides; Horticulture services; Herbicides; Insecticides
CEO: Juli Jessen
Pr: Steve Petersen
CFO: Robert Zonneveld
VP Inf Sys: Mike Tessmer
Sfty Mgr: Kathy Scott
Mktg Dir: Andy Morgan

D-U-N-S 18-931-4719
GOWAN CONSTRUCTION INC
3596 15th St Ne, Oslo, MN 56744-9108
Tel (701) 699-5171 *Founded/Ownrshp* 1994
Sales 36.8MM *EMP* 75^E
Accts Brady Martz & Associates Pc
SIC 1611 Grading; Grading
Pr: Milton Gowan
**VP:* Mark Gowan
IT Man: Steven Mack
Opers Mgr: Curt Horner
Opers Mgr: Bob Sween

D-U-N-S 83-542-3690 IMP
GOWAN MILLING CO LLC
12300 E County 8th St, Yuma, AZ 85365-9014
Tel (928) 344-1014 *Founded/Ownrshp* 1993
Sales 30.0MM *EMP* 350
SIC 2879 Pesticides, agricultural or household; Pesticides, agricultural or household
**VP:* Richard Messinger
Comm Man: Regina Carey

D-U-N-S 05-511-6818
GOWANDA CENTRAL SCHOOL DISTRICT
10674 Prospect St, Gowanda, NY 14070-1384
Tel (716) 532-3325 *Founded/Ownrshp* 1890
Sales 18.4MM^E *EMP* 300
Accts Lumsden & Mccormick Llp Buff
SIC 8211 Public elementary & secondary schools; Public elementary & secondary schools
Psych: Melissa Davis
Psych: Sandy Tomczak

D-U-N-S 00-335-5393
GOWER CORP (SC)
355 Woodruff Rd Ste 106, Greenville, SC 29607-3419
Tel (864) 458-3114 *Founded/Ownrshp* 1912, 1955
Sales 93.3MM^E *EMP* 250
SIC 3535 5051 7373 Unit handling conveying systems; Metals service centers & offices; Computer integrated systems design; Unit handling conveying systems; Metals service centers & offices; Computer integrated systems design
Pr: Mark Dullea
**VP:* Robert Parrott
**Prin:* Russell Park

D-U-N-S 10-125-8341
GOWRIE GROUP INSURANCE
MARITIME GENERAL AGENCY
70 Ectex Rd Ste 1, Westbrook, CT 06498
Tel (860) 399-5945 *Founded/Ownrshp* 1988
Sales NA *EMP* 70
SIC 6411 Insurance agents
Pr: Michael Brett
Pr: Damon Pesce
VP: Chris Brodeur
VP: Marc Mercier
VP: Steve Prime
Dir IT: Donald Bardinelli
Sls Mgr: Denis Schmelzer

D-U-N-S 09-008-3387 IMP
GOYA DE PUERTO RICO INC
Esq Calle 5 Rr 28, Bayamon, PR 00961
Tel (787) 740-4900 *Founded/Ownrshp* 1967
Sales 92.6MM^E *EMP* 500
SIC 2032 2033 Ethnic foods: canned, jarred, etc.; Vegetables & vegetable products in cans, jars, etc.; Ethnic foods: canned, jarred, etc.; Vegetables & vegetable products in cans, jars, etc.
Pr: Carlos Unaune
**VP:* Jorge Unaune
VP Mfg: Manolo Fernandez

D-U-N-S 00-169-4777 IMP
GOYA FOODS INC
350 County Rd, Jersey City, NJ 07307-4503
Tel (201) 348-4900 *Founded/Ownrshp* 1973
Sales 605.9MM^E *EMP* 725
SIC 5142 Frozen vegetables & fruit products; Frozen vegetables & fruit products
Pr: Robert Unanue
CFO: Hilda Galimberti
**Sec:* Frank Unanue
Ofcr: Maria Perez
**Ex VP:* Peter J Unanue
**Sr VP:* Joseph F Perez
**VP:* Conrad Colon
**VP:* David Kinkela
VP: Rebecca Rodriguez
VP: Jorge Unanue
Exec: Fernando DESA

D-U-N-S 16-160-4467 IMP
GOYA FOODS OF CALIFORNIA INC
(*Suby of* GOYA FOODS INC) ★
14500 Proctor Ave, La Puente, CA 91746-2911
Tel (626) 961-6161 *Founded/Ownrshp* 1951
Sales 43.7MM^E *EMP* 40
SIC 5141 8742 5812 Groceries, general line; Restaurant & food services consultants; Contract food services
CEO: Robert Unanue
**Prin:* Joseph A Unanue
Sls Mgr: David Pimentel

GOYA FOODS OF FLORIDA
See DIANA FOODS INC

GOYA FOODS OF TEXAS
See CARDET WHOLESALE INC

D-U-N-S 00-653-1859
GOYETTE MECHANICAL CO INC (MI)
3842 Gorey Ave, Flint, MI 48506-4100
Tel (810) 743-6883 *Founded/Ownrshp* 1928
Sales 35.0MM^E *EMP* 100
SIC 1711 Mechanical contractor; Mechanical contractor
Owner: Dominic Goyette
**Treas:* Jeffrey Kellerman
**VP:* Carl M Burke
**VP:* Kurt Lalonde
Genl Mgr: Tim Goyette
IT Man: Amy Morehouse
Counsel: Paul Goyette

GOYIN INTERNATIONAL
See GENESIS PURE INC

GOZZER RANCH GOLF AND LAKE CLB
See DISCOVERY COEUR DALENE INVESTMENTS

D-U-N-S 13-963-8923 IMP/EXP
GP CELLULOSE LLC
(*Suby of* KOCH INDUSTRIES INC) ★
133 Peachtree St Ne # 1, Atlanta, GA 30303-1804
Tel (404) 652-6630 *Founded/Ownrshp* 2003
Sales NA *EMP* 782
SIC 2611 Pulp mills; Pulp mills
Ofcr: Wesley Jones
**Ofcr:* Patrick Boushka
**Ofcr:* William Frerking
**Ofcr:* Richard King
**Ofcr:* Cato Rodgers
**Ofcr:* Marsha Seekins
Prd Mgr: Dwayne Hooper

D-U-N-S 60-585-1047
GP CHEMICALS EQUITY LLC
(*Suby of* GEORGIA-PACIFIC LLC) ★
55 Park Pl Ne, Atlanta, GA 30303-2529
Tel (404) 652-4000 *Founded/Ownrshp* 1984
Sales 120.9MM^E *EMP* 1,300
SIC 5169 Chemicals & allied products; Chemicals & allied products
VP: Carl Wilson
IT Man: Alan Guibord

D-U-N-S 07-407-5342 IMP/EXP
GP COMPANIES INC
GENERAL PUMP
(*Suby of* INTERPUMP GROUP SPA)
1174 Northland Dr, Mendota Heights, MN 55120-1167
Tel (651) 454-6500 *Founded/Ownrshp* 1982
Sales 34.7MM^E *EMP* 55
SIC 5084 5087 3451 3561 Water pumps (industrial); Cleaning & maintenance equipment & supplies; Screw machine products; Pumps & pumping equipment
CEO: Kristin Sanders
Mktg Dir: Troy Benike

D-U-N-S 09-145-1112 EXP
GP HARMON RECYCLING LLC
(*Suby of* GEORGIA-PACIFIC LLC) ★
2 Jericho Plz Ste 200, Jericho, NY 11753-1681
Tel (516) 997-3400 *Founded/Ownrshp* 2000
Sales 195.7MM^E *EMP* 185
SIC 5093 Waste paper; Waste paper
Pr: Marc Forman
**COO:* Mark Forman
**Treas:* Joyce Harvey
**VP:* Vince Bonfanti
**VP:* Ernst A Haverli
**VP:* Dan Maddox
VP: Eric Schnell
**VP:* Rick Torbeck
Genl Mgr: Ted Gloeckler

D-U-N-S 04-290-1939
GP INDUSTRIAL CONTRACTORS INC (TX)
400 Gulfway Dr, Port Arthur, TX 77640-3441
Tel (409) 982-8343 *Founded/Ownrshp* 1998
Sales 21.9MM^E *EMP* 125
SIC 1623 1542 7389 1751 7349 8711 Pipeline construction; Nonresidential construction; Drafting service, except temporary help; Carpentry work; Building maintenance services; Engineering services; Pipeline construction; Nonresidential construction; Drafting service, except temporary help; Carpentry work; Building maintenance services; Engineering services
Pr: Roosevelt Petry Jr
**CFO:* Pat S Guillory
Sfty Mgr: Ronnie Walston

GP OF ARIES FREIGHT SYSTEMS
See ARIES WORLDWIDE INC

D-U-N-S 80-802-8513
GP OPERATIONS HOLDINGS LLC
(*Suby of* GEORGIA-PACIFIC LLC) ★
133 Peachtree St Ne, Atlanta, GA 30303-1804
Tel (404) 652-4000 *Founded/Ownrshp* 2007
Sales 120.7MM^E *EMP* 865
SIC 2656 Paper cups, plates, dishes & utensils; Paper cups, plates, dishes & utensils

D-U-N-S 04-779-9267
▲ GP STRATEGIES CORP
11000 Broken Land Pkwy # 200, Columbia, MD 21044-3555
Tel (443) 367-9600 *Founded/Ownrshp* 1959
Sales 501.8MM *EMP* 3,300
Accts Kpmg Llp Baltimore Maryland
Tkr Sym GPX *Exch* NYS
SIC 8742 8711 8748 Management consulting services; Training & development consultant; Engineering services; Environmental consultant; Management consulting services; Training & development consultant; Engineering services; Environmental consultant
CEO: Scott N Greenberg
**Ch Bd:* Harvey P Eisen
Pr: Douglas E Sharp
CFO: Sharon Esposito-Mayer
Ex VP: Karl Baer
Sr VP: Kenneth L Crawford
Snr Sftwr: Vanessa Lincoln
Board of Directors: Daniel M Friedberg, Marshall S Geller, Laura L Gurski, Sue W Kelly, Richard C Pfenniger Jr, A Marvin Strait

GP&C
See GENERAL PLASTICS & COMPOSITES LP

GPA
See GROUP & PENSION ADMINISTRATORS INC

D-U-N-S 00-594-1075 IMP/EXP
GPA ACQUISITION CO INC
(*Suby of* FEDRIGONI SPA)
8740 W 50th St, Mc Cook, IL 60525-3149
Tel (800) 395-9000 *Founded/Ownrshp* 2004, 2015
Sales 90.1MM^E *EMP* 80
SIC 5113 Industrial & personal service paper; Industrial & personal service paper
CEO: Thomas G Brooker
**Pr:* Bob Niesen
**CFO:* Anne Tuzik
**Sr VP:* David Maucieri
VP: Jim Bender
VP: Kevin Cooper
VP: Mary Ann Geers
VP: Mike McConville
VP Opers: Gil Chavez

D-U-N-S 36-288-9284 IMP
GPA HOLDING CO INC
8740 W 50th St, Mc Cook, IL 60525-3149
Tel (773) 650-2020 *Founded/Ownrshp* 2004
Sales 29.2MM^E *EMP* 83
SIC 5113 Industrial & personal service paper; Industrial & personal service paper

GPB
See GRABER POST BUILDINGS INC

D-U-N-S 12-623-2771 IMP
GPC A JOINT VENTURE ESSM
1st St, Williamsburg, VA 23187
Tel (757) 637-9000 *Founded/Ownrshp* 2000
Sales 31.2MM^E *EMP* 175
SIC 1623 Underground utilities contractor; Underground utilities contractor
Pt: Loyed Saner

D-U-N-S 11-184-8748
GPC CAPITAL CORP II
(*Suby of* GRAHAM PACKAGING HOLDINGS CO) ★
2401 Pleasant Valley Rd # 2, York, PA 17402-9600
Tel (717) 849-8500 *Founded/Ownrshp* 1998
Sales 202.5MM^E *EMP* 4,100
SIC 3089 Blow molded finished plastic products; Extruded finished plastic products; Blow molded finished plastic products; Extruded finished plastic products
Ch Bd: Philip R Yates
Pr: Roger M Prevot
CFO: Mark Buches
CFO: John E Hamilton
VP: Jay W Hereford

D-U-N-S 13-928-1927
GPC INTERNATIONAL INC
510 Broadhollow Rd # 205, Melville, NY 11747-3606
Tel (631) 752-9600 *Founded/Ownrshp* 1989
Sales 21.9MM^E *EMP* 117
SIC 3861 Graphic arts plates, sensitized
Pr: Steven Roth
**CFO:* Don Fleisheiar

D-U-N-S 82-741-9537
GPCH LLC
GOLDEN PLAINS COMMUNITY HOSP
100 Medical Dr, Borger, TX 79007-7579
Tel (806) 467-5700 *Founded/Ownrshp* 2007
Sales 37.8MM^E *EMP* 200
Accts Bkd Llp Dallas Tx
SIC 8062 General medical & surgical hospitals; General medical & surgical hospitals
CEO: Kevin Storey
**COO:* Melody Henderson
**CFO:* Dina Hermes
Dir Lab: Zela Young
Dir Soc: Pamela Smith
Dir Rad: Stephen Brown
Off Mgr: Kim Charles
Pharmcst: Lance Richards
Pharmcst: Derek Smith
Phys Thrpy: Colleen Stidham
Dir Health: Kimberly Hogan

GPD GROUP
See GLAUS PYLE SCHOMER BURNS & DEHAVEN INC

D-U-N-S 82-813-2691 IMP
GPDE SILVA SPICES INCORPORATION
PETERSON'S SPICES
8531 Lochlomond Dr, Pico Rivera, CA 90660
Tel (562) 407-2643 *Founded/Ownrshp* 2008
Sales 28.0MM^E *EMP* 20
SIC 5149 2099 Spices & seasonings; Chili pepper or powder; Spices, including grinding
CEO: Ravi De Silva
**Pr:* Rupa De Silva
**CFO:* Nalin Kulasoogriya

GPFS
See GLENDALE PLUMBING & FIRE SUPPLY INC

GPHA
See GREAT PLAINS HEALTH ALLIANCE INC

D-U-N-S 94-379-0725
■ GPI HOLDINGS INC
GRAPHIC PACKAGING INTL
(*Suby of* GRAPHIC PACKAGING HOLDING CO) ★
1500 Riveredge Pkwy # 100, Atlanta, GA 30328-4642
Tel (770) 240-7200 *Founded/Ownrshp* 1995
Sales 228.8MM^E *EMP* 9,000
SIC 2631 2653 2449 4922 Container, packaging & boxboard; Container board; Folding boxboard; Boxes, corrugated: made from purchased materials; Wood containers; Containers, plywood & veneer wood; Pipelines, natural gas; Container, packaging & boxboard; Container board; Folding boxboard; Boxes, corrugated: made from purchased materials; Wood containers; Containers, plywood & veneer wood; Pipelines, natural gas
Pr: Stephen M Humphrey
**CFO:* Daniel J Blount
**Sr VP:* Wayne Juby
**Sr VP:* Steven D Saucier
Sls Mgr: Juan Gil

D-U-N-S 79-366-1518
GPI SC-A LLC
AUDI COLUMBIA
(*Suby of* AUDI OF CHARLOTTE) ★
6301 Two Notch Rd, Columbia, SC 29223-7311
Tel (803) 786-6601 *Founded/Ownrshp* 2010
Sales 27.8MM^E *EMP* 103^E
SIC 5511 Automobiles, new & used

D-U-N-S 80-644-0830
GPI TX-EPGM INC
SHAMALEY BUICK-GMC
955 Crockett St, El Paso, TX 79922-1363
Tel (915) 584-8419 *Founded/Ownrshp* 1997
Sales 22.6MM^E *EMP* 80
SIC 5511 Automobiles, new & used; Automobiles, new & used
Pr: Hector Rico

D-U-N-S 03-938-4263
GPI-ATLANTA INC
WORLD TOYOTA
5800 Peachtree Indus Blvd, Atlanta, GA 30341-1629
Tel (678) 547-9000 *Founded/Ownrshp* 2000
Sales 51.6MM^E *EMP* 135
SIC 5511 Automobiles, new & used; Automobiles, new & used
Pr: Kevin McHugh
Genl Mgr: Jack Brennan
Sls Mgr: Chris Clay
Sls Mgr: Courtney Donaldson
Sales Asso: Larry Bassett
Sales Asso: Hasan Choudhoury
Sales Asso: Danny Huang

GPISD
See GRAND PRAIRIE INDEPENDENT SCHOOL DISTRICT

D-U-N-S 05-903-0528
GPK PRODUCTS INC
1601 43rd St N, Fargo, ND 58102-2806
Tel (701) 277-3225 *Founded/Ownrshp* 1971
Sales 30.1MM^E *EMP* 165^E
SIC 3089 Fittings for pipe, plastic; Fittings for pipe, plastic
Pr: Spencer Hildre
**CFO:* Jeff Pflugrath
**Treas:* Brad Keller
**VP:* Tim Pflugrath
Exec: Mark Jacobs
Off Mgr: Pat Rerick
IT Man: Jeff Lothspeich
VP Opers: Brian McConnell

D-U-N-S 13-235-5574
GPM INVESTMENTS LLC
FAS MART
8565 Magellan Pkwy # 400, Richmond, VA 23227-1167
Tel (804) 266-1363 *Founded/Ownrshp* 2003
Sales 488.7MM^E *EMP* 1,300^E
Accts Grant Thornton Llp Raleigh

SIC 5541 5411 5172 Filling stations, gasoline; Convenience stores; Gasoline; Filling stations, gasoline; Convenience stores; Gasoline
CEO: Dave McComas
**COO:* Chris Giacobone
**CFO:* Mark King
Ex VP: Eyal Nuchamovitz
Sr VP: Bill Reilly
VP: Peter Meyer
VP: Kevin Perlowski
Dir IT: Barry Khosropanah
Site Mgr: Darlene Buchanan
Snr PM: Fred Howland

GPM LIFE INSURANCE
See GOVERNMENT PERSONNEL MUTUAL LIFE INSURANCE CO

GPMI COMPANY
See GPMI CO

D-U-N-S 18-790-4297 IMP
GPMI CO
GPMI COMPANY
1224 N Hobson St, Gilbert, AZ 85233-1214
Tel (480) 503-0006 *Founded/Ownrshp* 1989
Sales 54.5MM^E^ *EMP* 120
SIC 5169 Specialty cleaning & sanitation preparations; Specialty cleaning & sanitation preparations
Pr: Yarron Bendor
CFO: Jon Deiter
VP: Donna Barker

D-U-N-S 06-798-5747
GPOD OF IDAHO
865 E 1400 N, Shelley, ID 83274-5142
Tel (208) 357-7646 *Founded/Ownrshp* 1968, 1986
Sales 32.1MM *EMP* 140
SIC 5148 Potatoes, fresh; Potatoes, fresh
Pt: Kevin Searle

D-U-N-S 07-828-7249 IMP/EXP
GPR LOGISTICS LLC
GILBERT COMPANY, THE
1000 Riverside Dr, Keasbey, NJ 08832-1213
Tel (732) 709-5330 *Founded/Ownrshp* 2011
Sales 36.7MM^E^ *EMP* 115
SIC 4214 4225 Local trucking with storage; General warehousing
COO: Michael Cadero
VP: Tim Margotta
VP: Ron RAC
IT Man: Gary Sanchez
Sls Mgr: Taylor Christy

D-U-N-S 07-977-6099
GPS HOLDINGS LLC (WI)
GLOBAL PRINTER SERVICES
(*Suby of* LASERMASTERS LLC) ★
5315 Paulson Rd, Mc Farland, WI 53558-9137
Tel (608) 838-5070 *Founded/Ownrshp* 2014
Sales 22.0MM^E^ *EMP* 100
SIC 5084 Printing trades machinery, equipment & supplies
Pr: Bruce Andre
IT Man: Rebecca Auten
IT Man: John Macaulay
Sales Asso: Dan Wilson

D-U-N-S 04-329-3122
GPS HOSPITALITY LLC (GA)
5500 Interstate North Pkwy, Atlanta, GA 30328-4662
Tel (770) 933-5023 *Founded/Ownrshp* 2012
Sales 300.0MM *EMP* 270^E^
SIC 5812 Fast-food restaurant, chain
CEO: Thomas A Garrett
CFO: Scott Jasinski
CFO: Amelia McDonald
VP: Brian Arnold
VP: Mike Kovac
Prin: Attorney Foltz

D-U-N-S 55-540-3570
GPS INSIGHT LLC
7201 E Henkel Way 400, Scottsdale, AZ 85255-9678
Tel (480) 663-9454 *Founded/Ownrshp* 2005
Sales 25.0MM *EMP* 91
SIC 3596 3663 Communication signal enhancement network system; ;Truck (motor vehicle) scales;
CEO: Robert Donat
Pr: Elliot Batcheller
VP: Elliot Bachelor
**Prin:* Shawn Nordmann
Web Dev: Daniel Gray
Software D: Grant Anderson
Software D: Jennifer Dearing
VP Opers: Elliott Batchellor
Sales Exec: Evelyn Lawson
Sales Exec: Jason Walker
**Mktg Mgr:* Ryan Driscoll

GPS WORLD SUPPLY COMPANY
See JOLIET AVIONICS INC

D-U-N-S 94-950-3569
GPX CORP
300 S 4th St Ste 1100, Las Vegas, NV 89101-6028
Tel (702) 386-4789 *Founded/Ownrshp* 1995
Sales 23.7MM^E^ *EMP* 1,500
SIC 7389 Personal service agents, brokers & bureaus; Personal service agents, brokers & bureaus
Pr: Gary G Garrison

D-U-N-S 01-931-2594 IMP/EXP
GPX INTERNATIONAL TIRE CORP
124 Washington St Ste 101, Foxboro, MA 02035-1368
Tel (781) 321-3910 *Founded/Ownrshp* 1974
Sales 228.8MM^E^ *EMP* 2,500
SIC 3011 Tires & inner tubes; Tires & inner tubes
Pr: Craig A Steinke
**Ch Bd:* Robert Sherkin
**Pr:* Bryan Ganz
**Treas:* Jeffrey Lucas
Off Mgr: Maureen Brooks
Board of Directors: Bryan Ganz, Eric Ganz, Neil Ganz

D-U-N-S 09-767-4410
GR BIRDWELL CONSTRUCTION LP
BIRDWELL CONTRUCTION
9721 Derrington Rd, Houston, TX 77064-5807
Tel (281) 890-4981 *Founded/Ownrshp* 1977
Sales 88.0MM^E^ *EMP* 240
SIC 1542

GR GIBSON
See CR GIBSON LLC

GR SPRING & STAMPING, INC.
See GILL CORP

D-U-N-S 09-469-2316 IMP
■ **GRA-GAR INC**
(*Suby of* WERNER ENTERPRISES INC) ★
14507 Frontier Rd, Omaha, NE 68138-3808
Tel (402) 895-6640 *Founded/Ownrshp* 1978
Sales 26.1MM^E^ *EMP* 425
SIC 7538 Truck engine repair, except industrial; Truck engine repair, except industrial
VP: Dwayne Haug
**Treas:* John Steele
VP: Robert E Synowicki Jr
**VP:* Robert E Synowkci Jr

D-U-N-S 02-962-3329 IMP/EXP
GRABBER CONSTRUCTION PRODUCTS INC (NV)
5255 W 11000 N Ste 100, Highland, UT 84003-8955
Tel (801) 492-3880 *Founded/Ownrshp* 1965, 1967
Sales 88.2MM^E^ *EMP* 250
SIC 5072 5211

D-U-N-S 07-408-3346
GRABER POST BUILDINGS INC
GPB
7716 N 900 E, Montgomery, IN 47558-5114
Tel (812) 687-7508 *Founded/Ownrshp* 1973
Sales 70.5MM^E^ *EMP* 160
SIC 5211 1542

D-U-N-S 00-542-1441
GRABILL CABINET CO INC
13844 Sawmill Dr, Grabill, IN 46741-9481
Tel (260) 207-5500 *Founded/Ownrshp* 1946
Sales 37.7MM^E^ *EMP* 210
SIC 2431 2434 2511 Panel work, wood; Wood kitchen cabinets; Wood household furniture; Panel work, wood; Wood kitchen cabinets; Wood household furniture
Pr: Martin Heiney

D-U-N-S 16-166-8173
GRABOYES COMMERCIAL WINDOW CO
4050 S 26th St, Philadelphia, PA 19112-1613
Tel (215) 625-8810 *Founded/Ownrshp* 1984
Sales 29.6MM^E^ *EMP* 75
SIC 5031 Windows
Pr: Terry Graboyes
**CFO:* Joe Angbony
**VP:* Anthony Quinn
**VP:* John Scott
Off Admin: Diane Zborowski

GRACE AMBULATORY SURGERY CTR
See GRACE CLINIC MANAGEMENT LLC

D-U-N-S 60-605-5010
GRACE BAKING CO
(*Suby of* MAPLE LEAF FOODS INC)
3200 Regatta Blvd Ste G, Richmond, CA 94804-6401
Tel (510) 525-2253 *Founded/Ownrshp* 2002
Sales 24.5MM^E^ *EMP* 200
SIC 2051 Bread, all types (white, wheat, rye, etc): fresh or frozen; Bread, all types (white, wheat, rye, etc): fresh or frozen
Prin: Sandra Crinnion

GRACE BOOK SHACK
See GRACE COMMUNITY CHURCH OF VALLEY

D-U-N-S 15-915-8195
GRACE CHURCH SCHOOL
86 4th Ave, New York, NY 10003-5297
Tel (212) 475-5609 *Founded/Ownrshp* 1894
Sales 24.3MM *EMP* 95
Accts Marks Paneth Llp New York Ny
SIC 8211 Private elementary & secondary schools; Private elementary & secondary schools
Prin: George P Davison

D-U-N-S 78-853-9158
GRACE CLINIC MANAGEMENT LLC
GRACE AMBULATORY SURGERY CTR
4515 Marsha Sharp Fwy, Lubbock, TX 79407-2520
Tel (806) 740-8223 *Founded/Ownrshp* 2005
Sales 47.7MM^E^ *EMP* 425^E^
SIC 8093 Specialty outpatient clinics; Specialty outpatient clinics
Obsttrcn: Duncan Burkholder
Ansthlgy: Robert V Johnston
Doctor: Jared Brinker
Doctor: Brent Nall
Doctor: Obie Stalcup

D-U-N-S 07-890-8803
GRACE COLLEGE & THEOLOGICAL SEMINARY
200 Seminary Dr, Winona Lake, IN 46590-1224
Tel (574) 372-5100 *Founded/Ownrshp* 1940
Sales 40.9MM *EMP* 175
Accts Bkd Llp Fort Wayne Indiana
SIC 8221 Religious organizations; College, except junior; Theological seminary
Pr: John Katip
COO: Tom Dunn
**CFO:* Paul Blair
Ex VP: John Lillis
Exec: Mark Bragg
Assoc Dir: Rhoda Palmer

D-U-N-S 07-622-6232
GRACE COMMUNITY CHURCH OF VALLEY
GRACE BOOK SHACK
13248 Roscoe Blvd, Sun Valley, CA 91352-3798
Tel (818) 782-5920 *Founded/Ownrshp* 1968
Sales 24.6MM *EMP* 200
Accts Capincrouse Llp Tarzana Ca
SIC 8661 8211 5942 Non-denominational church; Private elementary school; Books, religious; Non-denominational church; Private elementary school; Books, religious
**Ch:* Chris Hamilton
**Treas:* John Bates
**Ex Dir:* Rob Iverson
Cmptr Lab: Duane Pinkham

D-U-N-S 82-474-1297
GRACE CONSTRUCTION MANAGEMENT CO LLC
1530 Glen Ave Ste 4, Moorestown, NJ 08057-1249
Tel (856) 755-0041 *Founded/Ownrshp* 2007
Sales 49.4MM *EMP* 31^E^
SIC 1542 Commercial & office building contractors; Commercial & office building contractors
CEO: Joseph K Barbara
CFO: Wayne Habard
Dir Bus: Audrey Campise-Schmidt
Off Mgr: Rachel Fisler

GRACE DVSON DISCOVERY SCIENCES
See ALLTECH ASSOCIATES INC

D-U-N-S 02-971-9093
GRACE ENERGY CORP
FASTRIP
2485 W Old 66 Blvd, Carthage, MO 64836-8823
Tel (417) 624-4045 *Founded/Ownrshp* 1974
Sales 35.1MM^E^ *EMP* 200
SIC 5171 5541 5411 Petroleum bulk stations; Filling stations, gasoline; Convenience stores; Petroleum bulk stations; Filling stations, gasoline; Convenience stores
Pr: Jerry Perry
**Treas:* Tahne R Barnett
**VP:* Nancy D Perry

D-U-N-S 04-376-9900 IMP
GRACE ENGINEERING CORP
34775 Potter St, Memphis, MI 48041-4613
Tel (810) 392-2181 *Founded/Ownrshp* 1966
Sales 20.6MM^E^ *EMP* 90
SIC 3544 3841 3577 3568 Punches, forming & stamping; Surgical & medical instruments; Printers, computer; Shafts, flexible
Pr: Louis Grace Jr
VP: Matthew Grace
Exec: Janet Hull
Mfg Mgr: Kenneth Walsh
Plnt Mgr: Russ Sarrine
Prd Mgr: Jeremiah Collins
Ql Cn Mgr: Jeff White
Sls&Mrk Ex: Joel Harris

D-U-N-S 79-696-9889 IMP
GRACE FOOD DISTRIBUTION INC
5646a Shattalon Dr, Winston Salem, NC 27105
Tel (336) 661-0291 *Founded/Ownrshp* 1991
Sales 23.7MM^E^ *EMP* 75
SIC 5046 Restaurant equipment & supplies; Restaurant equipment & supplies
Pr: Ben Chiu
Genl Mgr: Loy Lee

D-U-N-S 80-342-4431
GRACE FOODS INC
SAFEWAY FOODS
2153 Barth Ave, Indianapolis, IN 46203-4017
Tel (317) 780-5070 *Founded/Ownrshp* 1990
Sales 29.4MM^E^ *EMP* 230
SIC 5411 Supermarkets, independent; Supermarkets, independent
Pr: Daniel V McClure
**VP:* Corey Rowland
Dir IT: Dave Parsley

D-U-N-S 80-989-0882
GRACE HEALTH CARE
(*Suby of* CONSULATE HEALTH CARE CHESWICK) ★
3425 Knight Dr, Whites Creek, TN 37189-9189
Tel (615) 876-2754 *Founded/Ownrshp* 2003
Sales 423.5MM *EMP* 100
SIC 8051 Skilled nursing care facilities; Skilled nursing care facilities
Nrsg Dir: Mary Renfroe
HC Dir: Kathy Norman
HC Dir: Mary Smith

D-U-N-S 60-295-4034
GRACE HEALTH INC
FHCBC
181 Emmett St W, Battle Creek, MI 49037-2963
Tel (269) 965-8866 *Founded/Ownrshp* 1986
Sales 20.8MM *EMP* 270
Accts Plante & Moran Pllc
SIC 8011 Offices & clinics of medical doctors
Pr: A J Jones
**Treas:* Ann K Gallagher
**VP:* Scott Hutchings
Doctor: Emily Pala-Bandeen

D-U-N-S 09-019-2811
GRACE HEALTHCARE LLC
801 Broad St Ste 300, Chattanooga, TN 37402-2668
Tel (423) 308-1830 *Founded/Ownrshp* 1999
Sales 41.9MM^E^ *EMP* 95^E^
SIC 8741 Nursing & personal care facility management
COO: Jeff Schulz
Exec: Bethany McCoy
Genl Mgr: Loretha Barnes
Genl Mgr: Karen McGrath
IT Man: Adam Lloyd
Nrsg Dir: Julie Cottrell
Nrsg Dir: Mary Renfroe
Genl Couns: Dan Koliadko
Snr Mgr: Debbie Jones

GRACE HILL
See AFFINIA HEALTHCARE

D-U-N-S 80-444-2671
GRACE HOLMES INC
(*Suby of* J CREW OPERATING CORP) ★
770 Broadway Fl 11, New York, NY 10003-9512
Tel (212) 209-2500 *Founded/Ownrshp* 1997
Sales 71.8MM^E^ *EMP* 3,000
SIC 5611 5621 Men's & boys' clothing stores; Clothing accessories: men's & boys'; Clothing, men's & boys': everyday, except suits & sportswear; Clothing, sportswear, men's & boys'; Women's specialty clothing stores; Women's sportswear; Ready-to-wear apparel, women's; Teenage apparel; Men's & boys' clothing stores; Clothing accessories: men's & boys'; Clothing, men's & boys': everyday, except suits & sportswear; Clothing, sportswear, men's & boys'; Women's specialty clothing stores; Women's sportswear; Ready-to-wear apparel, women's; Teenage apparel
CEO: Millard Drexler
**COO:* Scott Gilbertson
**CFO:* Scott Rosen

D-U-N-S 82-811-4418 IMP
GRACE HOME FASHIONS LLC
COLORFUL GREENS
(*Suby of* GHCL LIMITED)
295 5th Ave Ste 515, New York, NY 10016-7103
Tel (212) 273-0760 *Founded/Ownrshp* 2008
Sales 52.5MM *EMP* 1
Accts Knav Pa Duluth Ga
SIC 5023 Linens & towels; Linens & towels

D-U-N-S 92-839-3391
GRACE HOSPICE LLC
500 Kirts Blvd Ste 250, Troy, MI 48084-4135
Tel (248) 824-6011 *Founded/Ownrshp* 2006
Sales 22.0MM *EMP* 600^E^
SIC 8052 Personal care facility; Personal care facility
CEO: Mark Mitchell

D-U-N-S 07-112-7112
GRACE HOSPITAL
2307 W 14th St, Cleveland, OH 44113-3698
Tel (216) 687-1500 *Founded/Ownrshp* 1910
Sales 21.1MM^E^ *EMP* 344
SIC 8062

D-U-N-S 80-838-3678
GRACE I W2007 LLC
85 Broad St Fl 15, New York, NY 10004-2434
Tel (212) 902-1000 *Founded/Ownrshp* 2007
Sales 179.6MM^E^ *EMP* 147
SIC 7011 Hotels & motels
COO: Ned Thompson

D-U-N-S 95-687-9746
GRACE INDUSTRIES INC
7171 Airport Rd, Bath, PA 18014-8802
Tel (610) 837-4100 *Founded/Ownrshp* 1991
Sales 30.5MM^E^ *EMP* 70
SIC 1541 Warehouse construction
Pr: Ronald C Check Jr
**Treas:* Todd A Check
Ex VP: Elizabeth Rusin
**VP:* Ronald C Check Sr

D-U-N-S 80-053-0706
GRACE INDUSTRIES LLC
11 Commercial St, Plainview, NY 11803-2401
Tel (718) 762-0200 *Founded/Ownrshp* 2006
Sales 53.2MM^E^ *EMP* 112
SIC 1622 1611 1731 1629 Bridge, tunnel & elevated highway; Highway & street construction; Electrical work; Dams, waterways, docks & other marine construction; Bridge, tunnel & elevated highway; Highway & street construction; Electrical work; Dams, waterways, docks & other marine construction
Ch: William J Haugland
**VP:* John Reynolds
VP: Edward Tackenberg
**VP:* Ed Takenberg
IT Man: Jay Able

GRACE LIVING CENTERS
See AMITY CARE LLC

D-U-N-S 02-212-4887
GRACE LOCKE MARINE LLC
L & M COMPANIES, INC.
(*Suby of* GRACELOCK INDUSTRIES LLC) ★
3402 Se Convenience Blvd, Ankeny, IA 50021-9431
Tel (515) 964-4205 *Founded/Ownrshp* 2012
Sales 31.0MM *EMP* 60^E^
SIC 5088

GRACE LUTHERAN FOUNDATION
See AMERICAN LUTHERAN HOMES INC

D-U-N-S 11-849-2834
GRACE MANAGEMENT INC
6225 42nd Ave N, Minneapolis, MN 55422-1603
Tel (763) 544-9934 *Founded/Ownrshp* 1984
Sales 37.5MM^E^ *EMP* 650
SIC 6513 6512 Retirement hotel operation; Apartment hotel operation; Commercial & industrial building operation; Retirement hotel operation; Apartment hotel operation; Commercial & industrial building operation
Pr: Eugene W Grace
CFO: Stephanie Grant
Ex VP: Mari Grace
**VP:* Jody Boedigheimer
**VP:* Mari Jo Grac

D-U-N-S 82-702-9633
GRACE MANAGEMENT INC
5335 Meadows Rd Ste 385, Lake Oswego, OR 97035-3153
Tel (503) 430-1270 *Founded/Ownrshp* 2015
Sales 8.9MM *EMP* 315
SIC 5812 Contract food services
CEO: Jennifer Chambers
COO: Dennis Chambers

D-U-N-S 60-790-3382 IMP
GRACE MANUFACTURING INC
614 Sr 247, Russellville, AR 72802-8408
Tel (479) 880-8901 Founded/Ownrshp 1966
Sales 23.3MM^E EMP 130
SIC 3577 3599 3479 3545 3841 Computer peripheral equipment; Chemical milling job shop; Etching, photochemical; Precision measuring tools; Surgical & medical instruments; Computer peripheral equipment; Chemical milling job shop; Etching, photochemical; Precision measuring tools; Surgical & medical instruments
Pr: Chris Grace
*Pr: Richard L Grace
*CEO: Christopher Grace
*CFO: Sylvia Blaty
*Treas: Josh Behjat
*Sec: Clarice Grace
*VP: Sandra Grace
IT Man: Johnny Henderson
IT Man: Syble Pool
Sfty Mgr: Ashley Anhalt
Sfty Mgr: Rachel Wade

GRACE MEDICAL CENTER
See LUBBOCK HERITAGE HOSPITAL LLC

D-U-N-S 01-059-6356 IMP
GRACE PACIFIC CORP
(Suby of GRACE PACIFIC LLC) ★
110 Puuhale Rd, Honolulu, HI 96819-2231
Tel (808) 845-3991 Founded/Ownrshp 1931
Sales 39.6MM^E EMP 350
SIC 1611 2951 3272 Highway & street construction; Asphalt paving mixtures & blocks; Concrete products; Highway & street construction; Asphalt paving mixtures & blocks; Concrete products
VP: William A Paik
*Pr: Robert F Wilkinson
*VP: Robert M Creps
Div/Sub He: William Wilson
IT Man: Bernalyn Werner

D-U-N-S 00-922-7851 IMP/EXP
GRACE PACIFIC LLC (HI)
949 Kamokila Blvd Ste 100, Kapolei, HI 96707-2046
Tel (808) 674-8383 Founded/Ownrshp 1921, 1975
Sales 180.1MM^E EMP 500
SIC 1611 1429 3272 Surfacing & paving; Igneous rock, crushed & broken-quarrying; Concrete products; Surfacing & paving; Igneous rock, crushed & broken-quarrying; Concrete products
CEO: David H Hulihee
*Sr VP: Robert M Creps
VP: Darrell Goo
VP: Rusty Niau
VP: Robert Singlehurst
VP Opers: Louis Fuatagavi
Mtls Mgr: Raymond Pauline
Sls Mgr: James Valdez
Board of Directors: Walter Dodds, Joseph Miccio, Bill Mills, Jeffrey Watanabe, Robert Wo

D-U-N-S 12-409-3720
GRACE SINAI HOSPITAL
6701 W Outer Dr, Detroit, MI 48235
Tel (313) 966-3333 Founded/Ownrshp 2002
Sales 16.4MM^E EMP 5,000
SIC 8062 General medical & surgical hospitals
Pr: Paula Autry

D-U-N-S 07-949-2994
GRACEKENNEDY FOODS (USA) LLC
LA FE FOODS
(Suby of GRACEKENNEDY LTD.)
230 Moonachie Ave, Moonachie, NJ 07074-1831
Tel (201) 329-6260 Founded/Ownrshp 2014
Sales 80.0MM EMP 300^E
SIC 5141 Groceries, general line; Groceries, general line
Ch: Don Wehby
CFO: Sarath Lankege
Sr VP: Gregory Solomon
VP: Derrick Reckord
VP Sls: Marino Roa

GRACELAND CARE CENTER PONTOC
See GRACELAND MANAGEMENT CO INC

D-U-N-S 87-820-6937
GRACELAND COLLEGE CENTER FOR PROFESSIONAL DEVELOPMENT AND LIFELONG LEARNING INC
SKILLPATH / NAT SMNARS TRINING
6900 Squibb Rd, Shawnee Mission, KS 66202-3247
Tel (913) 362-3900 Founded/Ownrshp 1995
Sales 49.1MM EMP 250
SIC 8299 Educational services; Educational services
CEO: Jack Cave
*CFO: Raymond D Liggett
Ex VP: Shane Snider
VP: Torre Bookout
*VP: William Cowles
VP: Lynn Jackson
VP: Steve Newbold
*VP: Eric Snider
*Prin: Robb Garr
Dir IT: Jason Spainhour
Web Dev: Tyson Kelley

D-U-N-S 06-587-9918 IMP/EXP
GRACELAND FRUIT INC
1123 Main St, Frankfort, MI 49635-9341
Tel (231) 352-7181 Founded/Ownrshp 1973
Sales 45.1MM^E EMP 180
Accts Dennis Gartland & Niergarth P
SIC 2034 2037 Fruits, dried or dehydrated, except freeze-dried; Fruits, quick frozen & cold pack (frozen); Fruits, dried or dehydrated, except freeze-dried; Fruits, quick frozen & cold pack (frozen)
Pr: Donald Nugent
*CEO: Alan Devore
*COO: Steve Nugent
*CFO: Troy Terwilliger
*Ch: James Nugent
*Treas: John Blight
*VP: Brent Bradley
*VP: Dr Nirmal Sinha

D-U-N-S 07-538-1988
GRACELAND MANAGEMENT CO INC
GRACELAND CARE CENTER PONTOC
1212 Adams Ave, Oxford, MS 38655-3213
Tel (662) 234-8311 Founded/Ownrshp 1971
Sales 14.4MM^E EMP 470
SIC 8051 Convalescent home with continuous nursing care; Convalescent home with continuous nursing care
Pr: W Larry Overstreet

GRACELAND MANSION
See ELVIS PRESLEY ENTERPRISES INC

D-U-N-S 07-807-5645
GRACELAND UNIVERSITY (IA)
1 University Pl, Lamoni, IA 50140-1699
Tel (641) 784-5000 Founded/Ownrshp 1895
Sales 94.7MM EMP 350
Accts Mcgladrey Llp Cedar Rapids I
SIC 8221 College, except junior; College, except junior
Pr: John D Sellars
*VP: Janice Tiffany
Off Mgr: Candy Fulton
CIO: Kam Mahi

D-U-N-S 07-953-0038
GRACELOCK INDUSTRIES LLC
4119 Guardian St, Simi Valley, CA 93063-3382
Tel (714) 632-9500 Founded/Ownrshp 2011
Sales 31.0MM^E EMP 60^E
SIC 5088 Marine crafts & supplies

D-U-N-S 08-261-0648
■ **GRACENOTE INC**
(Suby of TRIBUNE MEDIA CO) ★
2000 Powell St Ste 1500, Emeryville, CA 94608-1820
Tel (510) 428-7200 Founded/Ownrshp 2014
Sales 89.7MM^E EMP 350^E
SIC 7371 Software programming applications; Software programming applications
Pr: Stephen White
COO: Dominique Schurman
Sr VP: Eric Allen
Sr VP: Tal Ball
Sr VP: Desmond Cussen
Sr VP: Brian Hamilton
VP: R O Blanchard
VP: Don Gordon
VP Bus Dev: Julie Davenport
Dir Bus: Sheela Chandrasekhara
Prgrm Mgr: Bruce Hagen

GRACEPOINT
See MENTAL HEALTH CARE INC

GRACE'S MARKETPLACE
See DORIA ENTERPRISES INC

D-U-N-S 07-469-1015
GRACEWORKS LUTHERAN SERVICES
6430 Inner Mission Way, Dayton, OH 45459-7400
Tel (937) 433-2140 Founded/Ownrshp 1926
Sales 46.8MM EMP 609
Accts Battelle Rippe Kingston Llp D
SIC 8051 Skilled nursing care facilities; Skilled nursing care facilities
Pr: Willis O Serr II
VP: Michael W Allen
VP: Jim Bosse
Off Mgr: Sandra Jimison
CTO: Prashant Athalye
Dir IT: Dave Morgan

D-U-N-S 00-289-8492
GRACIANO CORP (PA)
209 Sigma Dr, Pittsburgh, PA 15238-2826
Tel (412) 963-8400 Founded/Ownrshp 1916, 1948
Sales 20.1MM^E EMP 150
SIC 1741 Masonry & other stonework; Masonry & other stonework
Pr: Glenn M Foglio
CFO: David Kearney
*Sec: Donna Lee Zuzich
*VP: Don Mc Devitt
*VP: Dan McIntyre
CTO: Larry Tielsch
VP Sls: Kevin Schaffer
Board of Directors: Kathleen Graciano, Richard A Graciano Jr, Richard A Graciano

D-U-N-S 96-312-2432
GRACIOUS HOME LLC
(Suby of AMERICAS RETAIL FLAGSHIP FUND LLC) ★
158 W 27th St Fl 12, New York, NY 10001-6378
Tel (212) 517-6300 Founded/Ownrshp 2010
Sales 59.8MM^E EMP 300
SIC 5722 5719 Household appliance stores; Wicker, rattan or reed home furnishings; Household appliance stores; Wicker, rattan or reed home furnishings
CFO: Davinder Somal
Chf Mktg O: Amy Chernoff
Area Mgr: Sabbir Ahmed
Genl Mgr: Bruce Buckler
*CIO: Jim Linsalata
Dir IT: Chandresh Patel
Sales Asso: Pami Albala
Sales Asso: Tom Spantopanagos

D-U-N-S 08-324-7510 IMP/EXP
■ **GRACO CHILDRENS PRODUCTS INC**
CENTURY PRODUCTS
(Suby of NEWELL RUBBERMAID INC) ★
3 Glenlake Pkwy, Atlanta, GA 30328-3447
Tel (770) 418-7200 Founded/Ownrshp 1995
Sales 122.2MM^E EMP 1,420
SIC 2514 Juvenile furniture, household: metal; Juvenile furniture, household: metal
CEO: William A Burke
*Pr: Howard Heckes
*CFO: Ronald L Hardnock
CFO: John Jordan
MIS Mgr: Allan Rabenau

D-U-N-S 04-694-4666
GRACO FISHING & RENTAL TOOLS INC
GRACO OILFIELD SERVICES
5300 Town And Cntry Blvd, Frisco, TX 75034-6894
Tel (214) 618-3930 Founded/Ownrshp 1978
Sales 46.5MM^E EMP 50
SIC 1389 Fishing for tools, oil & gas field
CEO: Dan Rambo
*Pr: Jonathan E Rambo
*COO: Mark Mixon
*CFO: Ed McKernan
*Sr VP: Steve Ferris
*VP: Mark Eason
*VP: Jason Rambo
Exec: Kelly Perkins
Off Mgr: Krista Berry

D-U-N-S 00-625-3223 IMP
▲ **GRACO INC** (MN)
88 11th Ave Ne, Minneapolis, MN 55413-1829
Tel (612) 623-6000 Founded/Ownrshp 1926
Sales 1.2MMM EMP 3,100^E
Accts Deloitte & Touche Llp Minneap
Tkr Sym GGG Exch NYS
SIC 3594 3563 3491 3823 3569 Fluid power pumps & motors; Motors: hydraulic, fluid power or air; Spraying outfits: metals, paints & chemicals (compressor); Industrial valves; Automatic regulating & control valves; Pressure valves & regulators, industrial; Industrial instrmnts msrmnt display/control process variable; Industrial flow & liquid measuring instruments; Fluidic devices, circuits & systems for process control; Lubricating equipment; Lubricating systems, centralized; Lubrication equipment, industrial; Lubrication machinery, automatic; Fluid power pumps & motors; Motors: hydraulic, fluid power or air; Spraying outfits: metals, paints & chemicals (compressor); Industrial valves; Automatic regulating & control valves; Pressure valves & regulators, industrial; Industrial instrmnts msrmnt display/control process variable; Industrial flow & liquid measuring instruments; Fluidic devices, circuits & systems for process control; Lubricating equipment; Lubricating systems, centralized; Lubrication equipment, industrial; Lubrication machinery, automatic
Pr: Patrick J McHale
Ch Bd: Lee R Mitau
CFO: James A Graner
Treas: Christian Rothe
VP: Caroline M Chambers
VP: Karen Park Gallivan
Comm Dir: Todd Safgren
Dist Mgr: Arvind Singh
Dist Mgr: Kent Streicher
Dist Mgr: Robert Zamarripa
CTO: Bernard Ortt
Board of Directors: William J Carroll, Eric P Etchart, Jack W Eugster, J Kevin Gilligan, Martha A Morfitt, R William Van Sant

D-U-N-S 13-932-9502
GRACO INTERESTS INC
5910 Schumacher Ln, Houston, TX 77057-7124
Tel (713) 978-7000 Founded/Ownrshp 1958
Sales 36.7MM^E EMP 280
SIC 1711 3444 Plumbing contractors; Warm air heating & air conditioning contractor; Sheet metal specialties, not stamped; Plumbing contractors; Warm air heating & air conditioning contractor; Sheet metal specialties, not stamped
Pr: James R Graves Sr
COO: Kermit Pittman
CFO: James A Graner
Sfty Dirs: Mark Kimmel

D-U-N-S 07-777-7670 IMP
■ **GRACO OHIO INC** (OH)
LIQUID CONTROL
(Suby of GRACO INC) ★
8400 Port Jackson Ave Nw, North Canton, OH 44720-5464
Tel (330) 494-1313 Founded/Ownrshp 1978
Sales 24.3MM^E EMP 150
SIC 3824 3586 5251 Predetermining counters; Measuring & dispensing pumps; Pumps & pumping equipment; Predetermining counters; Measuring & dispensing pumps; Pumps & pumping equipment
Ch Bd: William C Schiltz
*Pr: Kenneth Jacobs
*Treas: Barbara Schiltz
VP: Mac Larsen
*Prin: Ronald W Dougherty
Area Mgr: Theron Sherman

GRACO OILFIELD SERVICES
See GRACO FISHING & RENTAL TOOLS INC

D-U-N-S 02-643-0645 IMP
GRACO SUPPLY CO
1001 Miller Ave, Fort Worth, TX 76105-1798
Tel (817) 535-3200 Founded/Ownrshp 2015
Sales 22.6MM^E EMP 35
SIC 5088 Aircraft equipment & supplies
Pr: Steve Novakovich
COO: Charles Holland
VP: Blaine Gray
VP: Jeff Hazelrigg
VP: Rodney Phillips
QI Cn Mgr: Clarlene Lenderman
VP Sls: Hank ABT
Manager: Ed Ball
Sales Asso: Deon Tomlin
Sales Asso: Anne Winsor-Ash

D-U-N-S 18-611-8725
GRACON CONSTRUCTION INC
4343 Lasater Rd, Mesquite, TX 75181-3222
Tel (972) 222-8533 Founded/Ownrshp 1987
Sales 25.0MM^E EMP 75
SIC 1629 Waste water & sewage treatment plant construction; Waste water & sewage treatment plant construction
Pr: Kenneth A Graves
*VP: Joel G Graves

GRACY TITLE, A STEWART COMPANY
See GRACY TITLE CO LC

D-U-N-S 07-460-7656
■ **GRACY TITLE CO LC**
GRACY TITLE, A STEWART COMPANY
(Suby of STEWART TITLE CO) ★
524 N Lamar Blvd Ste 200, Austin, TX 78703-5422
Tel (512) 472-8421 Founded/Ownrshp 2003
Sales NA EMP 173
SIC 6361 Title insurance; Title insurance
Ch Bd: Larry Molinare
Pr: Donna Simmons
Sr VP: Bob Roberts
VP: Bill Bradshaw
Creative D: Pablo Berrios
Sales Exec: Denise Moody

GRACYWOODS NURSING CENTER
See HARDEN HEALTHCARE TEXAS LP

D-U-N-S 00-494-8191 IMP
■ **GRADALL INDUSTRIES INC**
(Suby of ALAMO GROUP INC) ★
406 Mill Ave Sw, New Philadelphia, OH 44663-3835
Tel (330) 339-2211 Founded/Ownrshp 1992, 2006
Sales 103.7MM^E EMP 400^E
SIC 3537 3531 Industrial trucks & tractors; Construction machinery; Industrial trucks & tractors; Construction machinery
Pr: Michael Haberman
*VP: Daniel Kaltenbaugh
*VP: Joseph H Keller

D-U-N-S 06-280-4430
GRADEX INC
12900 N Meridian St # 120, Carmel, IN 46032-5402
Tel (317) 573-3970 Founded/Ownrshp 1981
Sales 72.3MM^E EMP 350
SIC 1794 1623 1611 Excavation work; Sewer line construction; Concrete construction: roads, highways, sidewalks, etc.; Guardrail construction, highways; Airport runway construction; Excavation work; Sewer line construction; Concrete construction: roads, highways, sidewalks, etc.; Guardrail construction, highways; Airport runway construction
CEO: Thomas E Dapp
*Pr: Jason T Dapp
*CFO: Kyle Weitholter
*VP: Scott Sweeney
Sfty Dirs: Josh Rigdon

GRADIMAGES
See EVENT PHOTOGRAPHY GROUP INC

D-U-N-S 10-304-9185
GRADUATE MANAGEMENT ADMISSION COUNCIL INC
GMAC
11921 Freedom Dr Ste 300, Reston, VA 20190-5670
Tel (703) 668-9600 Founded/Ownrshp 1998
Sales 93.2MM EMP 142
Accts Cliftonlarsonallen Llp Arling
SIC 8748 Testing service, educational or personnel; Testing service, educational or personnel
Ch: Dina Dommett
*Pr: Sangeet Chowfla
Pr: Jennifer Garfinkel
*Pr: David A Wilson
*COO: Shelli Arnold
*COO: Nicole Chestang
*CFO: Samuel Reimer
Bd of Dir: Ralph S Sheridan
*Chf Mktg O: Betty Su
*Ex VP: Margaret Jobst
Sr VP: Peg Fagan
VP: Alan Levine
VP: Susan Motz
VP: Ramesh Thadani
VP: Julia Tyler
Assoc Dir: Daniel Eyob
Board of Directors: James W Bradford, James M Danko, Stacey Kole, Peggy Bishop Lane, Rosemarie Mecca, Christine Poon, Ajit Rangnekar, Alfons Sauquet, Alexander Sevilla

D-U-N-S 12-272-0485 IMP
GRADUATE PLASTICS INC
QUANTUM STORAGE SYSTEMS
15800 Nw15th Ave, Miami, FL 33169
Tel (305) 687-0405 Founded/Ownrshp 1973
Sales 44.3MM^E EMP 226
SIC 3089 Injection molding of plastics; Injection molding of plastics
Pr: Laurent Groll
*VP: Anthony Cohen

D-U-N-S 04-675-4206
GRADUATE RESTAURANTS INC
WILDCAT HOUSE
990 Industrial Way, San Luis Obispo, CA 93401-7699
Tel (805) 541-0700 Founded/Ownrshp 1971
Sales 25.0MM^E EMP 300
SIC 5813 5812 Night clubs; Fast-food restaurant, independent; Night clubs; Fast-food restaurant, independent
Pr: William S Everett

D-U-N-S 04-053-5536
GRADUATE SCHOOL
600 Maryland St, Washington, DC 20024
Tel (215) 861-4700 Founded/Ownrshp 1921
Sales 33.2MM EMP 260
Accts Cliftonlarsonallen Llp Luther
SIC 8249 Civil service training school; Civil service training school
Pr: Elaine Ryan
Ofcr: Victor Duncan
Ofcr: Hayley Kanlyn
Ofcr: Carolyn Nelson
Ofcr: Desiree Williamson
*VP: Lynn Edwards
VP: Sharon Fratta-Hill
VP: Jack Maykoski
VP: Kimberly Robinson
*Ex Dir: Jerry Ice
Prgrm Mgr: Dilnoza Abduganieva

GRADUATE SCHOOL WICHITA STATE
See WICHITA STATE UNIVERSITY

GRADY AUTOMOTIVE
See GRADY BUICK CO INC

D-U-N-S 03-402-5221 EXP
GRADY BUICK CO INC
GRADY AUTOMOTIVE
4420 Rangeline Rd, Mobile, AL 36619-9534
Tel (251) 476-2550 *Founded/Ownrshp* 1950
Sales 30.0MM *EMP* 75E
SIC 5511 Automobiles, new & used; Automobiles, new & used
Pr: Don Grady
CFO: Chip Mayer
**Sec:* A H Maier Jr
**VP:* Gary Grady
**VP:* Kelly Grady

D-U-N-S 07-979-8868
GRADY COUNTY SCHOOLS
122 N Broad St, Cairo, GA 39828-2105
Tel (229) 377-3701 *Founded/Ownrshp* 2015
Sales 6.8MME *EMP* 511E
SIC 8211 Public elementary & secondary schools
Owner: Brian Fannon

D-U-N-S 01-011-7026
GRADY COUNTY SCHOOLS BOARD OF EDUCATION
122 N Broad St, Cairo, GA 39828-2105
Tel (229) 377-3701 *Founded/Ownrshp* 1940
Sales 36.2MME *EMP* 730
SIC 8211 Public elementary & secondary schools; Public elementary & secondary schools

D-U-N-S 08-655-3674 IMP
GRADY CRAWFORD CONSTRUCTION CO INC OF BATON ROUGE
12290 Greenwell Sprng Rd, Baton Rouge, LA 70814-6335
Tel (225) 275-7334 *Founded/Ownrshp* 1976
Sales 62.6MM *EMP* 217
Accts Thomas W Kleinpeter Jr Bat
SIC 1623 8748 Water, sewer & utility lines; Telecommunications consultant; Water, sewer & utility lines; Telecommunications consultant
Pr: Hugh Jimmie Johnson
**Sec:* Grady H Crawford Jr
**VP:* Grady H Crawford III
**VP:* Richard Casey Crawford
VP: Trey Crawford

D-U-N-S 00-692-5655
GRADY ELECTRIC MEMBERSHIP CORP
1499 Us Highway 84 W, Cairo, GA 39828-1500
Tel (229) 377-4182 *Founded/Ownrshp* 1937
Sales 37.9MM *EMP* 65
Accts Nichols Cauley & Associates Ll
SIC 4911 Distribution, electric power; Distribution, electric power
Pr: Thomas Rosser
VP: Pat Reed
Opers Mgr: Todd Gibbs
Opers Mgr: Donnie Prince

D-U-N-S 04-705-8359
GRADY ELIZABETH FACE FIRST INC
222 Boston Ave, Medford, MA 02155-4248
Tel (781) 391-9380 *Founded/Ownrshp* 1990
Sales 28.0MME *EMP* 150
SIC 5999 7231 7299 Toiletries, cosmetics & perfumes; Beauty schools; Personal appearance services
Mktg Mgr: Jennifer Dorovan
**Pr:* John P Walsh

GRADY HEALTH SYSTEM
See FULTON DEKALB HOSPITAL AUTHORITY

D-U-N-S 96-161-5700
GRADY HEALTH SYSTEM
(*Suby of* FULTON DEKALB HOSPITAL AUTHORITY) ★
80 Jesse Hill Jr Dr Se, Atlanta, GA 30303-3050
Tel (404) 616-4360 *Founded/Ownrshp* 2007
Sales 1.0MMM *EMP* 4,500
Accts Kpmg Llp Greensboro Nc
SIC 8062 General medical & surgical hospitals; General medical & surgical hospitals
Pr: John M Haupert
V Ch: Thomas W Dortch Jr
**CFO:* Mark Meyer
Chf Mktg O: Robert Rohr
**Ex VP:* Timothy Jefferson
**Ex VP:* Curtis Lewis
**Ex VP:* Christopher R Mosley
Sr VP: Calvin Thomas IV
Off Mgr: Rebecca Daniel

D-U-N-S 07-264-6151
GRADY MANAGEMENT INC
8630 Fenton St Ste 625, Silver Spring, MD 20910-3876
Tel (301) 587-3330 *Founded/Ownrshp* 1965
Sales 16.1MM *EMP* 430
Accts Berman Goldman & Ribakow Llp
SIC 6531 Real estate managers; Real estate managers
Ch Bd: Kevin Grady
**Pr:* Gary Campbell
VP: Brian Alford
**Prin:* Erwin Gudelsky
Dir IT: John Hanle
Mktg Dir: Stacy Whyte
Board of Directors: Jonathan Duffie, Erwin Gudelsky, John Gudelsky, Martin Seldeen

D-U-N-S 05-137-0419
GRADY MEMORIAL HOSPITAL
561 W Central Ave, Delaware, OH 43015-1489
Tel (740) 615-1000 *Founded/Ownrshp* 1904
Sales 35.7MME *EMP* 348E
SIC 8062 General medical & surgical hospitals; General medical & surgical hospitals
CEO: David Blom
**Sr VP:* Johnni Beckel
Exec: Beth Crow
Ansthlgy: Richard Belch
Ansthlgy: Sandra Thrasher
Nrsg Dir: Sean Troub

D-U-N-S 07-733-6659
GRADY MEMORIAL HOSPITAL AUTHORITY
2220 W Iowa Ave, Chickasha, OK 73018-2700
Tel (405) 224-2300 *Founded/Ownrshp* 1959
Sales 39.2MM *EMP* 482
Accts Bkd Llp Tulsa Ok
SIC 8062 General medical & surgical hospitals; General medical & surgical hospitals
CEO: Warren Kean Spellman
**CFO:* Linda Hart
Dir OR: Rick Warden
Dir Lab: Debbie Cave
Dir Env Sv: Leslie Pendarvis
MIS Dir: Sylvia Ho
Mktg Mgr: Lesta Voegeli
Doctor: Jack Beller
Doctor: Bill Crowell
Doctor: Thomas Essex

D-U-N-S 82-506-8112
GRADY RENTALS LLC
2745 S Highway 171, Cleburne, TX 76031-0756
Tel (817) 556-3200 *Founded/Ownrshp* 2007
Sales 54.4MME *EMP* 250
SIC 7353 Heavy construction equipment rental; Heavy construction equipment rental
Exec: Brad Grady
VP: Kevin Grove

D-U-N-S 17-420-4818
GRAE-CON CONSTRUCTION INC
GRAE-CON CONTRUCTIONS
880 Kingsdale Rd, Steubenville, OH 43952-4361
Tel (740) 282-6830 *Founded/Ownrshp* 1987
Sales 30.4MME *EMP* 80E
SIC 1542 Commercial & office building, new construction; Commercial & office buildings, renovation & repair
Pr: Robert A Gribben Jr
**Sec:* Shirley Gribben
**VP:* Robert A Gribben III
**VP:* John A Humpe III

GRAE-CON CONTRUCTIONS
See GRAE-CON CONSTRUCTION INC

GRAEBEL 925
See GRAEBEL/AMERICAN MOVERS INC

D-U-N-S 15-730-2324
GRAEBEL COMPANIES INC
(*Suby of* GRAEBEL HOLDINGS INC) ★
16346 Airport Cir, Aurora, CO 80011-1558
Tel (303) 214-6683 *Founded/Ownrshp* 2001
Sales 85.3MM *EMP* 1,771E
Accts Wipfli Llp Wausau Wisconsin
SIC 4213 4225 Trucking, except local; General warehousing & storage; Trucking, except local; General warehousing & storage
CEO: Bill Graebel
Ch Bd: Dave Graebel
Pr: Gene Carpenter
CEO: Terri Drapal
CEO: Deborah Keeton
COO: Ron Dunlap
CFO: Brad Siler
Ch: Debra Fox
Ofcr: Dale Collins
Sr VP: William Borgman
Sr VP: Phil Burton
Sr VP: Mary Dymond
Sr VP: Myrla J Lance
Sr VP: Scott Snead
VP: Craig Chapman
VP: Tana C Gilmore
VP: Ed Schiefelbein
Exec: Linzey Schindel
Dir Bus: Zachary Atwell

D-U-N-S 04-146-5720
GRAEBEL HOLDINGS INC
16346 Airport Cir, Aurora, CO 80011-1558
Tel (303) 214-6683 *Founded/Ownrshp* 2000
Sales 85.3MM *EMP* 1,771
SIC 4213 4225 6719 Trucking, except local; General warehousing & storage; Investment holding companies, except banks; Trucking, except local; General warehousing & storage; Investment holding companies, except banks
Ch Bd: David W Graebel
**Pr:* Craig Broback
**CEO:* Bill Graebel
**COO:* William Graebel
**CFO:* Brad Siler
QA Dir: Elvis Machado

D-U-N-S 04-653-4871
GRAEBEL MOVERS INC
(*Suby of* GRAEBEL MOVING SERVICES) ★
16346 Airport Cir, Aurora, CO 80011-1558
Tel (303) 214-6683 *Founded/Ownrshp* 2014
Sales 181.9MME *EMP* 1,771
SIC 4213 4214

D-U-N-S 00-644-2438
GRAEBEL MOVING AND STORAGE LLC (WI)
(*Suby of* GRAEBEL COMPANIES INC) ★
7333 Stewart Ave, Wausau, WI 54401-9326
Tel (715) 845-4281 *Founded/Ownrshp* 1954, 2006
Sales 42.0MME *EMP* 430
SIC 4214 4213 Local trucking with storage; Trucking, except local; Local trucking with storage; Trucking, except local
Pr: Craig Brock
Pr: Benjamin D Graebel
Ex VP: William H Graebel
Trfc Dir: Aaron Newhouse

GRAEBEL MOVING SERVICES
See GRAEBEL VANLINES HOLDINGS LLC

GRAEBEL MOVING SERVICES
See VAN GRAEBEL LINES LLC

D-U-N-S 07-969-9003
GRAEBEL VANLINES HOLDINGS LLC
GRAEBEL MOVING SERVICES
15455 Dallas Pkwy Ste 600, Addison, TX 75001-6760
Tel (972) 694-0400 *Founded/Ownrshp* 2014
Sales 270.0MM *EMP* 1,550
SIC 4213 4214 4212 Contract haulers; Household goods transport; Household goods moving & storage, local; Moving services
Pr: Brent Snyder
**Ch Bd:* Vasilia Peterson
**CFO:* David Allen

D-U-N-S 04-895-3285
GRAEBEL/AMERICAN MOVERS INC
GRAEBEL 925
(*Suby of* GRAEBEL MOVERS INC) ★
1011 Asbury Dr, Buffalo Grove, IL 60089-4539
Tel (847) 808-8400 *Founded/Ownrshp* 2006
Sales 88.3MME *EMP* 1,421E
SIC 4213 4214 Trucking, except local; Local trucking with storage
Ch Bd: David W Graebel
Pr: Benjamin D Graebel
Ex VP: William H Graebel
Genl Mgr: Jim Bender
Opers Mgr: Michael Dammer

D-U-N-S 00-425-1302
GRAETERS MANUFACTURING CO (OH)
1175 Regina Graeter Way, Cincinnati, OH 45216-1998
Tel (513) 721-3323 *Founded/Ownrshp* 1870
Sales 107.4MME *EMP* 500
SIC 2024 2051 2064 2066 Ice cream, packaged: molded, on sticks, etc.; Bread, cake & related products; Candy & other confectionery products; Chocolate & cocoa products; Ice cream, packaged: molded, on sticks, etc.; Bread, cake & related products; Candy & other confectionery products; Chocolate & cocoa products
Pr: Richard Graeter II
Treas: James Cahill
VP: Chip Graeter
**VP:* Tom Kunzelman
Prin: Eric T Schulze
Off Mgr: Tacey Westerkamm
Store Mgr: Carol Pfau
Store Mgr: John Wilson
MIS Dir: Richard Grater

GRAF BROS FLOORING AND LUMBER
See GRAF BROTHERS FLOORING INC

D-U-N-S 16-491-9263 IMP
GRAF BROTHERS FLOORING INC
GRAF BROS FLOORING AND LUMBER
679 Johnson Ln, South Shore, KY 41175-7890
Tel (606) 932-3117 *Founded/Ownrshp* 2002
Sales 46.2MME *EMP* 124
SIC 5023 Floor coverings; Floor coverings
Pr: David R Graf
**VP:* Gregory P Graf

D-U-N-S 06-247-8649
GRAF-AIR FREIGHT INC
550 W Taylor St, Chicago, IL 60607-4499
Tel (312) 987-9960 *Founded/Ownrshp* 1971
Sales 23.2MME *EMP* 120
SIC 4731 Freight forwarding; Freight forwarding
Ch Bd: Patrick Fitzgerald
**Pr:* Michael Fitzgerald
**VP:* Cynthia Moore

D-U-N-S 79-344-4738
■ **GRAFCO INDUSTRIES LIMITED PARTNERSHIP**
(*Suby of* BERRY PLASTICS GROUP INC) ★
7447 Candlewood Rd, Hanover, MD 21076-3102
Tel (410) 691-9828 *Founded/Ownrshp* 1978
Sales 36.6MME *EMP* 120
SIC 3089 Plastic containers, except foam; Food casings, plastic
Pt: Timothy Frank
V Ch: Joseph Piccirilli
Pr: Virginia L Campbell
VP: Peter Amirault
VP: Dennis Dedmond
VP: John Guthrie
VP: Edward Logue
VP: George Petrie
IT Man: George Brooks
Netwrk Mgr: Jeffrey Lacey

GRAFF CHEVROLET
See GUARDIAN AUTO LEASING LLC

D-U-N-S 02-651-3465
GRAFF CHEVROLET CO
1405 E Main St, Grand Prairie, TX 75050-5939
Tel (972) 264-0700 *Founded/Ownrshp* 1952
Sales 55.5MME *EMP* 140
SIC 5511 Automobiles, new & used; Automobiles, new & used
Pr: Stanley V Graff
Genl Mgr: Robert Rippy
Sls Mgr: Sandra Sullivan

D-U-N-S 05-061-6325
GRAFF MOTOR SALES INC
1100 W Cedar Ave, Gladwin, MI 48624-1816
Tel (989) 426-9292 *Founded/Ownrshp* 1936
Sales 24.5MME *EMP* 70
SIC 5511 Automobiles, new & used; Automobiles, new & used
Pr: Max H Graff
**VP:* John Kirby
IT Man: Diane Backus

GRAFFAM BROS SEAFOOD MARKET
See PENOBSCOT BAY ICE CO INC

D-U-N-S 01-906-8097
GRAFFMANS INC
MOTOR SUPPLY
203 Madison Ave, Skowhegan, ME 04976-1369
Tel (207) 474-3327 *Founded/Ownrshp* 1976
Sales 22.7MME *EMP* 95
SIC 5013 5531 Automotive supplies & parts; Automotive parts; Automotive accessories; Automotive supplies & parts; Automotive parts; Automotive accessories
Pr: Robert J York
**VP:* Valerie McCarty
**VP:* Thomas J York
Genl Mgr: Tim Williams

D-U-N-S 61-522-9994
GRAFIKA COMMERCIAL PRINTING INC
710 Johnston St, Reading, PA 19608-1437
Tel (610) 678-8630 *Founded/Ownrshp* 1963
Sales 49.8MME *EMP* 258
SIC 2759 2752 2789 2672 2396 Commercial printing; Screen printing; Flexographic printing; Letterpress printing; Commercial printing, offset; Bookbinding & related work; Coated & laminated paper; Automotive & apparel trimmings; Commercial printing; Screen printing; Flexographic printing; Letterpress printing; Commercial printing, offset; Bookbinding & related work; Coated & laminated paper; Automotive & apparel trimmings
Pr: Bernard J Elzer Jr
**COO:* Bernard J Elzer III
**CFO:* Robert Zedaker
VP: Ken Drudy
Genl Mgr: Mike Kauffman
VP Mfg: Scott Morgan
Plnt Mgr: John Hess
Sales Asso: Erik Stothart
Sales Asso: Stephen Thompson

GRAFT OIL CO
See O C I INC

D-U-N-S 36-111-7534 IMP
■ **GRAFTECH INTERNATIONAL HOLDINGS INC**
UCAR CARBON
(*Suby of* GRAFTECH INTERNATIONAL LTD) ★
6100 Oak Tree Blvd # 300, Independence, OH 44131-2544
Tel (216) 676-2000 *Founded/Ownrshp* 1996
Sales 145.1MME *EMP* 661
SIC 3624 Carbon & graphite products; Electrodes, thermal & electrolytic uses: carbon, graphite; Carbon & graphite products; Electrodes, thermal & electrolytic uses: carbon, graphite
CEO: Joel Hawthorne
VP: Ivor Lewis
Dir Bus: Travis Wood
Dir IT: David Hilmer
Dir IT: Julian Norley
IT Man: Joe Paris
Sys Mgr: Peter Duncanson
Site Mgr: Andrew Winseck
Ql Cn Mgr: Gary Mills
Mktg Dir: Allen Frydenberg
Manager: Dave King

D-U-N-S 87-717-6578 IMP
■ **GRAFTECH INTERNATIONAL LTD**
(*Suby of* BROOKFIELD ASSET MANAGEMENT INC)
6100 Oak Tree Blvd # 300, Independence, OH 44131-6970
Tel (216) 676-2000 *Founded/Ownrshp* 2015
Sales 1.0MMME *EMP* 3,034E
Tkr Sym GTI *Exch* NYS
SIC 3624 Carbon & graphite products; Carbon & graphite products
Pr: Joel L Hawthorne
Pr: Lionel Batty
Pr: Hermanus L Pretorius
CFO: Erick R Asmussen
Treas: Quinn Coburn
Bd of Dir: Betsy Keck
VP: Darrell Blair
VP: John D Moran
VP: John Wetula
CTO: Adrian Nuta
QA Dir: Miranda Ery
Board of Directors: Thomas A Danjczek, Karen Finerman, David R Jardini, Nathan Milikowsky, M Catherine Morris

D-U-N-S 13-209-4934 IMP
■ **GRAFTECH USA LLC**
GRAPHITE ELECTRODE MFG FCILTY
(*Suby of* GRAFTECH INTERNATIONAL LTD) ★
800 Theresia St, Saint Marys, PA 15857-1831
Tel (814) 781-2478 *Founded/Ownrshp* 2001
Sales 59.3MME *EMP* 160
SIC 3624 3823 3567 Carbon & graphite products; Industrial instrmnts msrmnt display/control process variable; Industrial furnaces & ovens; Carbon & graphite products; Industrial instrmnts msrmnt display/control process variable; Industrial furnaces & ovens
COO: Norman D Struble

D-U-N-S 06-874-5744
GRAFTON CITY HOSPITAL INC
1 Hospital Plz, Grafton, WV 26354-1283
Tel (304) 265-0400 *Founded/Ownrshp* 1915
Sales 20.2MM *EMP* 253
Accts Lb Arnett Carbis Toothman Llp
SIC 8062 8051 Hospital, affiliated with AMA residency; Skilled nursing care facilities; Hospital, affiliated with AMA residency; Skilled nursing care facilities
CEO: Patrick Shaw
CIO: Anna White
QA Dir: Lisa Povroznik
Dir IT: Jim Harris
Dir IT: Ann Rexroad

GRAFTON COUNTY JAIL
See COUNTY OF GRAFTON

D-U-N-S 13-948-0115
GRAFTON INC
GRAFTON STAFFING COMPANIES
4501 College Blvd Ste 160, Leawood, KS 66211-2337
Tel (913) 498-0701 *Founded/Ownrshp* 1990
Sales 8.4MM *EMP* 1,100
SIC 7363 7361 Help supply services; Employment agencies; Help supply services; Employment agencies
CEO: Carol Carroll
**CFO:* Jeffrey Hagen
**Sr VP:* Richard Carroll
Off Mgr: Karla Degginger

D-U-N-S 12-043-3289
GRAFTON PUBLIC SCHOOLS
30 Providence Rd Ste 2, Grafton, MA 01519-1193
Tel (508) 839-5421 *Founded/Ownrshp* 2010
Sales 23.5MM^E *EMP* 450^E
SIC 8211 Elementary & secondary schools; Elementary & secondary schools
Ch: Kathleen Halloran
Dir IT: Andrew Marcinek
Schl Brd P: Donna Stock

D-U-N-S 07-494-7649
GRAFTON SCHOOL INC
120 Bellview Ave, Winchester, VA 22601-3142
Tel (540) 542-0200 *Founded/Ownrshp* 1960
Sales 52.3MM *EMP* 900
Accts Yount Hyde & Barbour Pc Wi
SIC 8211 8361 Private special education school; Residential care; Private special education school; Residential care
Pr: James G Gaynor II
**CFO:* David Applewood
**Ch:* Janice L Label
**Treas:* Demetrius Carmichael
Ex VP: James H Stewart
Ex Dir: Kimberly Sanders
IT Man: John Zeiter

GRAFTON STAFFING COMPANIES
See GRAFTON INC

D-U-N-S 06-991-5726
GRAFTON TOWN OF INC
TOWN CLERK
30 Providence Rd Ste 2, Grafton, MA 01519-1511
Tel (508) 839-8500 *Founded/Ownrshp* 1735
Sales NA *EMP* 862
SIC 9111 City & town managers' offices; ; City & town managers' offices;
Ch: Christopfer Lemay
**Ch:* Christopher Lamey
**Treas:* Deborah Fox
Treas: Jessica Gomez

D-U-N-S 08-243-9191
GRAHAM ARCHITECTURAL PRODUCTS CORP
1551 Mount Rose Ave, York, PA 17403-2909
Tel (717) 845-5097 *Founded/Ownrshp* 1986
Sales 119.2MM^E *EMP* 330
SIC 3442 Metal doors, sash & trim; Metal doors, sash & trim
Pr: Brian Hurley
**Ch Bd:* William Kerlin
**Pr:* Georges Thiret
CFO: Frederick Trimmer
**Treas:* Frederick R Trimmer
**VP:* Dennis Kelly
VP: Karen Lehr
VP Mfg: Greg Codner
Mtls Mgr: Eric Hartlieb
Plnt Mgr: John Hilbert
Plnt Mgr: Trevor Manahan

D-U-N-S 15-744-2435
GRAHAM BROTHERS ENTERTAINMENT INC
GRAHAM COMPANIES
6999 E Business 20, Odessa, TX 79762-5483
Tel (432) 362-0401 *Founded/Ownrshp* 1992
Sales 181.3MM^E *EMP* 2,000
SIC 5813 Night clubs; Night clubs
Ch Bd: Herbert Graham
**Pr:* Roger Gearhart
**CEO:* Phillip Graham
**VP:* Terry Graham
**Prin:* W Phillip Graham
**Prin:* Mehdi Shokraeifaro

D-U-N-S 88-495-0254
GRAHAM C-STORES CO
33978 N Us Highway 45, Grayslake, IL 60030-1714
Tel (847) 223-3710 *Founded/Ownrshp* 1992
Sales 35.7MM^E *EMP* 110^E
Accts Fgmk Llc Bannockburn Illinoi
SIC 5172 5411 Petroleum products; Convenience stores, independent; Petroleum products; Convenience stores, independent
Pr: John Graham

D-U-N-S 84-938-2270
GRAHAM CAPITAL MANAGEMENT LP
GCM
40 Highland Ave, Norwalk, CT 06853-1510
Tel (203) 899-3400 *Founded/Ownrshp* 1994
Sales 63.3MM^E *EMP* 140
SIC 6282 Investment advice; Investment advice
Ch: Kenneth G Tropin
Mng Pt: Peter Gakos
**Pr:* Pablo Calderini
**CEO:* Robert E Murray
**COO:* Paul Sedlack
Ofcr: Mark Werner
Ex VP: Robert Griffith
Ex VP: Tom Schneider
Sr VP: Bob Vrooman
VP: Alex Mucelli
Dir Risk M: Brian Aldershoff
Assoc Dir: Brad Evans
Assoc Dir: Robert Galeano

D-U-N-S 05-232-2351
GRAHAM CHEVROLET-CADILLAC CO
FORD
1515 W 4th St, Ontario, OH 44906-1857
Tel (419) 529-1800 *Founded/Ownrshp* 1957
Sales 64.2MM^E *EMP* 147^E
SIC 5511 7515 7513 5521 5012 Automobiles, new & used; Passenger car leasing; Truck rental & leasing, no drivers; Used car dealers; Automobiles & other motor vehicles; Automobiles, new & used; Passenger car leasing; Truck rental & leasing, no drivers; Used car dealers; Automobiles & other motor vehicles
Pr: James Graham
**Treas:* Clay Graham
**VP:* Ken Williams
CTO: Cody Hughes
VP Mktg: Richard Haines
VP Mktg: Mike Myers
Sls Mgr: Art Holcomb
Sls Mgr: K Pauley
Sales Asso: Tom Thomas

GRAHAM COMPANY, THE
See WILLIAM A GRAHAM CO

GRAHAM COMPANIES
See GRAHAM BROTHERS ENTERTAINMENT INC

D-U-N-S 04-118-1447 IMP
GRAHAM COMPANIES
MIAMI LAKER
6843 Main St, Miami Lakes, FL 33014-2048
Tel (305) 821-1130 *Founded/Ownrshp* 1955
Sales 137.6MM^E *EMP* 650
SIC 1531 7011 0212 6552 6512 2711 Operative builders; Resort hotel; Beef cattle except feedlots; Land subdividers & developers, residential; Commercial & industrial building operation; Newspapers; Operative builders; Resort hotel; Beef cattle except feedlots; Land subdividers & developers, residential; Commercial & industrial building operation; Newspapers
Pr: Stuart S Wyllie
**Sec:* Edwin E Feathers
VP: Robert Whitehead

D-U-N-S 60-342-9267
GRAHAM COMPANIES INC
6843 Main St, Miami Lakes, FL 33014-2048
Tel (305) 821-1130 *Founded/Ownrshp* 1988
Sales 490.0MM^E *EMP* 800^E
SIC 6552 Land subdividers & developers, residential; Land subdividers & developers, residential
Pr: Stewart Wyllie
CFO: Andre Teixeira
CFO: Andre Teixeira

D-U-N-S 16-147-0638
GRAHAM CONSTRUCTION & MANAGEMENT INC
(*Suby of* GRAHAM GROUP LTD)
331 N Fancher Rd, Spokane Valley, WA 99212-0831
Tel (509) 534-1030 *Founded/Ownrshp* 2001
Sales 32.9MM^E *EMP* 140
SIC 1542 1541 Commercial & office building, new construction; Commercial & office building, renovation & repair; Industrial buildings, new construction; Commercial & office building, new construction; Commercial & office building, renovation & repair; Industrial buildings, new construction
CEO: Grant Beck
**Pr:* Wayne Henderson
**CFO:* Daryl Ferko
**Ch:* Brian Lueken
**Treas:* Doug Bespalko
VP: Bob Askins
**VP:* John Connolly
**Prin:* Kees Cusveller
IT Man: Lorraine Lucas
Mtls Mgr: Tim Potts

D-U-N-S 07-488-5898
GRAHAM CONSTRUCTION CO
(*Suby of* GRAHAM GROUP INC) ★
421 Grand Ave, Des Moines, IA 50309-2309
Tel (515) 244-1279 *Founded/Ownrshp* 1981
Sales 37.9MM^E *EMP* 150
SIC 1542 2434 2431 Commercial & office building, new construction; Commercial & office buildings, renovation & repair; Wood kitchen cabinets; Millwork; Commercial & office building, new construction; Commercial & office buildings, renovation & repair; Wood kitchen cabinets; Millwork
Pr: George Milligan
**Pr:* Steve Hauschilt
Sr VP: Mark Hasek
Mktg Dir: Kevin Tubbs

D-U-N-S 13-665-9690
GRAHAM CONSTRUCTION SERVICES INC
(*Suby of* GRAHAM GROUP LTD)
2995 Lone Oak Cir Ste 1, Eagan, MN 55121-1431
Tel (651) 687-0648 *Founded/Ownrshp* 2003
Sales 27.0MM^E *EMP* 70
SIC 1542 1622 1541 Commercial & office building, new construction; Bridge construction; Industrial buildings, new construction
CEO: Scott D Fowler
**Pr:* Grant Beck
**CFO:* Michael Slapman
**Prin:* Doug Sherrow
Rgnl Mgr: Scott Fowler

GRAHAM CONTRACTING
See GRAHAM MANAGEMENT SERVICE

D-U-N-S 11-878-4305 IMP/EXP
▲ GRAHAM CORP
20 Florence Ave, Batavia, NY 14020-3318
Tel (585) 343-2216 *Founded/Ownrshp* 1936
Sales 135.1MM *EMP* 395^E
Accts Deloitte & Touche Llp Rochest
Tkr Sym GHM *Exch* NYS
SIC 3563 3585 3443 Vacuum pumps, except laboratory; Compressors for refrigeration & air conditioning equipment; Condensers, refrigeration; Heat exchangers, condensers & components; Heat exchangers, plate type; Heat exchangers: coolers (after, inter), condensers, etc.; Vacuum pumps, except laboratory; Compressors for refrigeration & air conditioning equipment; Condensers, refrigeration; Heat exchangers, condensers & components; Heat exchangers, plate type; Heat exchangers: coolers (after, inter), condensers, etc.
Pr: James R Lines
Pr: Stephen Northru
COO: Christy Sabatino
CFO: Jeffrey F Glajch
CFO: Hcpe Novosad
VP: Alan E Smith
CIO: Ann Lever
QA Dir: David Wojtkowiak
IT Man: Lisa Bernard
S&M/VP: Joseph P Gorman
Board of Directors: James J Barber, Helen H Berkeley, Alan Fortier, James J Malvaso, Gerard T Mazurkiewicz, Jonathan W Painter, Lisa M Schnorr

D-U-N-S 09-366-2443
GRAHAM COUNTY COMMUNITY COLLEGE DISTRICT
EASTERN ARIZONA COLLEGE
615 N Stadium Ave, Thatcher, AZ 85552-5545
Tel (928) 428-8233 *Founded/Ownrshp* 1888
Sales 8.5MM *EMP* 575
Accts Debra K Davenport Cpa Phoen
SIC 8222 8221 Community college; Colleges universities & professional schools; Community college; Colleges universities & professional schools
Pr: Mark Bryce
COO: Patrick Lukens
CFO: Timothy Curtis
CIO: Thomas Thompson
Snr Mgr: Karen Coppola
Snr Mgr: Mike McEven

D-U-N-S 06-840-7980
GRAHAM COUNTY ELECTRIC COOPERATIVE INC
9 W Ctr, Pima, AZ 85543
Tel (928) 485-2451 *Founded/Ownrshp* 1946
Sales 20.3MM *EMP* 37
SIC 4911 Distribution, electric power; Transmission, electric power; Distribution, electric power; Transmission, electric power
Genl Mgr: Steve Lines

D-U-N-S 05-414-3516 IMP
GRAHAM ENGINEERING CORP
1203 Eden Rd, York, PA 17402-1965
Tel (717) 848-3755 *Founded/Ownrshp* 1960
Sales 49.4MM^E *EMP* 175
SIC 3559 Plastics working machinery; Plastics working machinery
CEO: Bill Kerlin
Pr: Wayne Leidy
**Pr:* Wolfgang Liebertz
**Founder:* Donald Graham
VP: Gina Haines
**VP:* Dave Yenor
Sls Mgr: Brian Dowler

D-U-N-S 88-495-0304
GRAHAM ENTERPRISE INC
446 Morris Ave, Mundelein, IL 60060-1919
Tel (847) 393-7724 *Founded/Ownrshp* 1990
Sales 866.8MM *EMP* 350
Accts Fgmk Llc Bannockburn Illinoi
SIC 5172 5411 Petroleum products; Convenience stores, independent; Petroleum products; Convenience stores, independent
Pr: John C Graham
**Treas:* Patrick T Graham
**VP:* Eugene W Graham III
Mktg Dir: Suresh Bhatia

D-U-N-S 07-809-4380
GRAHAM GROUP INC
505 5th Ave Ste 200, Des Moines, IA 50309-2449
Tel (515) 244-0387 *Founded/Ownrshp* 1962
Sales 38.8MM^E *EMP* 170
SIC 6512 1542 Commercial & industrial building operation; Commercial & office building, new construction
Ch: Antisdel Melinda
**Pr:* George Milligan
CFO: Jeff Houten
**CFO:* Jeff Van Houten
Sr VP: Mark Larson
**VP:* Frank Coffman
**VP:* Jeff Hatfield
**VP:* Richard L Hein
VP: Kevin McIlhon

D-U-N-S 00-324-5768
▲ GRAHAM HOLDINGS CO
1300 17th St N Ste 1700, Arlington, VA 22209-3816
Tel (703) 345-6300 *Founded/Ownrshp* 1877
Sales 3.5MMM *EMP* 14,500
Tkr Sym GHC *Exch* NYS
SIC 8299 4833 4841 2721 Tutoring school; Television broadcasting stations; Cable television services; Magazines: publishing only, not printed on site; Tutoring school; Television broadcasting stations; Cable television services; Magazines: publishing only, not printed on site
Ch Bd: Donald E Graham
**Pr:* Timothy J O'Shaughnessy
CEO: Boisfeuillet Jones
CEO: David Rothkopf
CFO: Hal S Jones
Treas: Daniel Lynch
Ex VP: Andrew S Rosen
Sr VP: Ann L McDaniel
VP: Nicole Maddrey
Prin: Christian Swezey
Dir IT: Gary Lattimores
Board of Directors: G Richard Wagoner Jr, Lee C Bollinger, Katherine Weymouth, Christopher C Davis, Barry Diller, Thomas S Gayner, David Goldberg, Anne M Mulcahy, Ronald L Olson, James H Shelton, Larry D Thompson

D-U-N-S 07-142-9567 IMP
GRAHAM HOSPITAL ASSOCIATION
210 W Walnut St, Canton, IL 61520-2497
Tel (309) 647-5240 *Founded/Ownrshp* 1905
Sales 70.5MM *EMP* 700
Accts Mcgladrey Llp Davenport Iowa
SIC 8062 General medical & surgical hospitals; General medical & surgical hospitals
Pr: Robert Senneff
V Ch: Mike Renner
**CFO:* Eric T Franz
Treas: Robert Bobell
VP: Mike Freeman
**VP:* Carolyn Jacobus
**VP:* Teresa McConkey
**VP:* James Schreiner
Exec: Janet Jackson
Dir Rx: Matt Vogel
Off Admin: Val Albrecht

D-U-N-S 02-895-4837
GRAHAM MANAGEMENT SERVICE
GRAHAM CONTRACTING
9709 3rd Ave Ne Ste 300, Seattle, WA 98115-2027
Tel (206) 729-8844 *Founded/Ownrshp* 1992
Sales 49.1MM^E *EMP* 110
SIC 1541 Industrial buildings & warehouses; Industrial buildings & warehouses
Pr: Doug Sherrow
**Ch Bd:* Ron Graham
**Pr:* Grant Beck
**Sr VP:* John Connolly
Dist Mgr: Greg Ritke
Mtls Mgr: Tony Koziel

D-U-N-S 92-775-5389
■ GRAHAM MARINE INC
(*Suby of* SEACOR HOLDINGS INC) ★
7910 Main St Ste 200, Houma, LA 70360-3427
Tel (985) 876-5400 *Founded/Ownrshp* 1995
Sales 36.8MM^E *EMP* 1,500
SIC 4499 Boat rental, commercial; Boat rental, commercial
Pr: Milton Rose
**Treas:* Lenny Dantin
**VP:* Timothy Mc Keand

D-U-N-S 87-991-9157 IMP
■ GRAHAM MEDIA GROUP HOUSTON INC
KPRC-TV CHANNEL 2
(*Suby of* GRAHAM HOLDINGS CO) ★
8181 Southwest Fwy, Houston, TX 77074-1705
Tel (713) 222-2222 *Founded/Ownrshp* 1994
Sales 31.1MM^E *EMP* 180
SIC 4833 Television broadcasting stations; Television broadcasting stations
Pr: Alan Frank
Dir Vol: Mary Alice
**VP:* Larry Blackerby

D-U-N-S 04-549-4721
■ GRAHAM MEDIA GROUP MICHIGAN INC
WDIV CHANNEL 4
(*Suby of* GRAHAM HOLDINGS CO) ★
550 W Lafayette Blvd Fl 2, Detroit, MI 48226-3123
Tel (313) 222-0444 *Founded/Ownrshp* 1978
Sales 77.4MM^E *EMP* 525
SIC 4833 Television broadcasting stations; Television broadcasting stations
Pr: Alan Frank
**CFO:* Marcy Etienne
VP: Charles Chunn
VP: Neil Goldstein
VP: Barbara Reising
Genl Mgr: Joseph Berwanger
Corp Couns: Jane Marshall

D-U-N-S 01-918-0715
■ GRAHAM MEDIA GROUP ORLANDO INC
POST-NEWSWEEK STNS ORLANDO INC
(*Suby of* GRAHAM HOLDINGS CO) ★
4466 N John Young Pkwy, Orlando, FL 32804-1939
Tel (407) 291-6000 *Founded/Ownrshp* 1997
Sales 21.0MM^E *EMP* 150
SIC 4833 Television broadcasting stations
Pr: Emily Barr
**VP:* Fredrick Valet
**Genl Mgr:* Skip Walet
Web Dev: Scott Flowers
Natl Sales: Todd Weissman

D-U-N-S 02-491-9581
GRAHAM OLESON OF COLORADO INC
525 Communication Cir, Colorado Springs, CO 80905-1736
Tel (719) 635-7335 *Founded/Ownrshp* 1980
Sales 61.5MM *EMP* 48
SIC 7311 Advertising agencies
Ch: Jerry Graham
**CEO:* Kirk Oleson
**CFO:* Linda Harl

D-U-N-S 96-161-1642 IMP/EXP
GRAHAM PACKAGING CO EUROPE LLC
(*Suby of* REYNOLDS GROUP HOLDINGS LIMITED)
2401 Pleasant Valley Rd # 2, York, PA 17402-9600
Tel (717) 849-8500 *Founded/Ownrshp* 2011
Sales 1.7MMM^E *EMP* 8,300
SIC 3089 Plastic containers, except foam; Plastic containers, except foam
CEO: Mark S Burgess
**CFO:* David W Bullock
**Treas:* William E Hennessey
**Ofcr:* Michael L Korniczky
**Sr VP:* Peter T Lennox
Admn Mgr: Beth Knarr
Plnt Mgr: Steve Quandt
Sls Mgr: Neil Kerrod

D-U-N-S 00-744-2040 IMP
GRAHAM PACKAGING CO INC
(*Suby of* REYNOLDS GROUP HOLDINGS LIMITED)
2401 Pleasant Valley Rd # 2, York, PA 17402-9600
Tel (717) 849-1166 *Founded/Ownrshp* 2011
Sales 3.7MMM^E *EMP* 4,915^E
SIC 5199 3089 5162 Packaging materials; Plastic containers, except foam; Plastics materials; Packaging materials; Plastic containers, except foam; Plastics materials
CFO: David W Bullock
Admn Mgr: Laura Geier
Admn Mgr: Barb Polglaze-Carter
Admn Mgr: Anthony Saltaformaggio
Dir IT: Diego Hagino
IT Man: Edward Roubal
Corp Couns: Doug Cassel

D-U-N-S 36-354-6698 EXP
GRAHAM PACKAGING CO LP
(*Suby of* GRAHAM PACKAGING CO INC) ★
2401 Pleasant Valley Rd, York, PA 17402-9600
Tel (717) 849-8500 *Founded/Ownrshp* 2011
Sales 859.1MM^E *EMP* 4,915
Accts Deloitte & Touche Llp Philade
SIC 3089 Plastic containers, except foam; Plastic containers, except foam
CEO: Philip R Yates
Pr: Stacie Rampe

COO: Roger M Prevot
Treas: Paul Wannemaher
Sr VP: Scott G Booth
VP: Mitch Mankosa
VP: Paul J Young
Off Mgr: Jolene Little
CIO: Jeff Rishel
Plnt Mgr: Carlos Romero
Ql Cn Mgr: Jaime Isaac

D-U-N-S 10-739-2172 IMP/EXP
GRAHAM PACKAGING HOLDINGS CO
(*Suby of* GRAHAM PACKAGING CO LP) ★
2401 Pleasant Valley Rd # 2, York, PA 17402-9600
Tel (717) 849-8500 *Founded/Ownrshp* 2015
Sales 621.1MM^E *EMP* 4,915
SIC 3089 Plastic containers, except foam; Plastic containers, except foam
CEO: Mark S Burgess
CFO: David W Bullock
Ch: Mr Chinh E Chu
Sr VP: David W Cargile
Sr VP: George Lane
Sr VP: Peter T Lennox
Sr VP: Martin F Sauer
VP: Paul J Young
Admn Mgr: Scott Sheraw
Plnt Mgr: Pekka Sokka
Ql Cn Mgr: Angie Craddock
Board of Directors: Angelo G Acconcia, John R Chiminski, Charles E Kiernan, Gary G Michael, John R Murphy

D-U-N-S 12-181-6805
GRAHAM PACKAGING PLASTIC PRODUCTS INC
(*Suby of* REXAM PLC)
1 Seagate Ste 10, Toledo, OH 43604-1563
Tel (717) 849-8500 *Founded/Ownrshp* 2008
Sales 184.0MM^E *EMP* 2,500
SIC 3089 Plastic containers, except foam; Plastic containers, except foam
Ch Bd: Joseph H Lemieux

D-U-N-S 60-393-9492
GRAHAM PACKAGING PLASTIC PRODUCTS INC
(*Suby of* GRAHAM PACKAGING CO LP) ★
170 Stanford Pkwy, Findlay, OH 45840-1732
Tel (419) 423-3271 *Founded/Ownrshp* 2005
Sales 52.6MM^E *EMP* 200
SIC 5199 Packaging materials; Packaging materials
Plnt Mgr: John Lindy
Admn Mgr: Ken Flick
Plnt Mgr: Cris Ricker
Sls Dir: Ron Pfenning

D-U-N-S 62-680-4934 IMP
GRAHAM PARTNERS INC
3811 West Chester Pike # 200, Newtown Square, PA 19073-2325
Tel (610) 408-0500 *Founded/Ownrshp* 1988
Sales 208.3MM^E *EMP* 831
SIC 8742 6799

GRAHAM PROFESSIONAL PRODUCTS
See LITTLE RAPIDS CORP

D-U-N-S 15-345-4830
GRAHAM TIRE CO
(*Suby of* T GRAHAM COMPANIES) ★
711 W 41st St, Sioux Falls, SD 57105-6405
Tel (605) 332-9033 *Founded/Ownrshp* 1948
Sales 70.0MM^E *EMP* 300
SIC 5531 5014 Automotive tires; Automobile tires & tubes; Automotive tires; Automobile tires & tubes
Pr: David Mickelson
VP: Lyle Christensen
Sales Exec: Randy Reich

D-U-N-S 02-233-6226 IMP
GRAHAM TIRE CO OF SPENCER INC
1905 Highway Blvd, Spencer, IA 51301-2213
Tel (712) 262-3700 *Founded/Ownrshp* 1966
Sales 41.3MM^E *EMP* 100
SIC 5531 5722 Automotive tires; Household appliance stores
Pr: Robert C Graham
**Sec:* Martha Graham

D-U-N-S 96-961-3830
GRAHAM WINDHAM
33 Irving Pl Fl 4, New York, NY 10003-2385
Tel (212) 529-6445 *Founded/Ownrshp* 1977
Sales 55.1MM *EMP* 57^E
Accts O Connor Davies Munns & Dobbin
SIC 8699 Charitable organization; Charitable organization
CFO: Francis X Spain
**Pr:* Jess Dannhauser
**CEO:* Paul Jensen

D-U-N-S 06-824-9622
GRAHAM WINDHAM CHILDREN SERVICES (NY)
33 Irving Pl Fl 7, New York, NY 10003-2332
Tel (212) 529-6445 *Founded/Ownrshp* 1806
Sales 17.2MM^E *EMP* 450
SIC 8351 8361 8322 Child day care services; Residential care; Social service center; Child day care services; Residential care; Social service center
Pr: Jess Dannhauser
**Pr:* Poul Jensen
**CFO:* Francis X Spain
**VP:* Sandra April
**VP:* Sharmeela Mediratta
Dir IT: Raymond Maldonado

D-U-N-S 00-312-7610 IMP
GRAHAM-WHITE MANUFACTURING CO
(*Suby of* FAIVELEY TRANSPORT)
1242 S Colorado St, Salem, VA 24153-6993
Tel (540) 387-5600 *Founded/Ownrshp* 2012
Sales 47.9MM^E *EMP* 255^E
SIC 3743 3321 Railroad equipment, except locomotives; Gray iron castings; Railroad equipment, except locomotives; Gray iron castings
Pr: Jim Frantz

CFO: Rob Cassell
Ofcr: Mindy Conner
VP: Bruce W Stewart
Dir IT: Guenther Walker
QC Dir: Cole Semones
S&M/VP: W S Bruce Jr
Snr Mgr: David Carper

D-U-N-S 00-711-9357
GRAIN BELT SUPPLY CO INC (KS)
217 E Diamond Dr, Salina, KS 67401-8624
Tel (785) 827-4491 *Founded/Ownrshp* 1950
Sales 42.1MM^E *EMP* 134
SIC 3441 3523 3444 3535 Fabricated structural metal; Farm machinery & equipment; Sheet metalwork; Conveyors & conveying equipment; Fabricated structural metal; Farm machinery & equipment; Sheet metalwork; Conveyors & conveying equipment
CEO: Dl Sampson
**Pr:* Marc Wingo
CFO: Monty Brown
Mktg Dir: Dave Walker
Board of Directors: Cherie Keefer

GRAIN CRAFT
See CEREAL FOOD PROCESSORS INC

D-U-N-S 62-154-6753
GRAIN CRAFT INC
MILNER MILLING
201 W Main St 203, Chattanooga, TN 37408-1137
Tel (423) 265-2313 *Founded/Ownrshp* 1990
Sales 179.0MM^E *EMP* 428
SIC 2041 Flour & other grain mill products
CEO: Peter Thomas Frederick
**CFO:* Jonh Robert Noland

GRAIN D'OR
See ANDERSEN BAKERY INC

D-U-N-S 92-933-2443
■ **GRAIN INSPECTION PACKERS & STOCKYARDS ADMINISTRATION**
(*Suby of* U S D A) ★
1400 Independence Ave Sw, Washington, DC 20250-0002
Tel (202) 720-0219 *Founded/Ownrshp* 1976
Sales NA *EMP* 2,000
SIC 9641 Food inspection agency, government; ; Food inspection agency, government;
**Prin:* Julian Waterfield
Tech Mgr: Steven Tanner

D-U-N-S 08-536-5294 IMP
GRAIN MILLERS DAIRY PRODUCTS INC
(*Suby of* GRAIN MILLERS INC) ★
10400 Viking Dr Ste 301, Eden Prairie, MN 55344-7268
Tel (952) 944-9512 *Founded/Ownrshp* 2004
Sales 36.6MM^E *EMP* 14^E
SIC 5143 Dairy products, except dried or canned
Pr: Mark A Welch
**VP:* Patrick Pautz

D-U-N-S 15-382-0402 IMP
GRAIN MILLERS INC
GRAIN MILLERS SPECIALTY PDTS
10400 Viking Dr Ste 301, Eden Prairie, MN 55344-7268
Tel (952) 829-8821 *Founded/Ownrshp* 1975
Sales 268.9MM^E *EMP* 450
SIC 2041 5084 Flour & other grain mill products; Oat flour; Flour & other grain mill products; Oat flour; Dairy products manufacturing machinery
Pr: Steven J Eilertson
**Treas:* Patrick Pautz
VP: Randal Baker
VP: Dan Beck
VP: Tom Giel
**VP:* Christian P Kongsore
**VP:* Rick L Schwein
CTO: Roger Mortenson
Software D: Brian Ecker
Sfty Mgr: Grant McCallum
Opers Mgr: Ian Slimmon

GRAIN MILLERS SPECIALTY PDTS
See GRAIN MILLERS INC

D-U-N-S 19-848-4180 IMP/EXP
GRAIN PROCESSING CORP
(*Suby of* KENT CORP) ★
1600 Oregon St, Muscatine, IA 52761-1404
Tel (563) 264-4211 *Founded/Ownrshp* 1943
Sales 151.1MM^E *EMP* 656^E
SIC 2869 2085 2082 Grain alcohol, industrial; Grain alcohol for beverage purposes; Malt beverages; Grain alcohol, industrial; Grain alcohol for beverage purposes; Malt beverages
Pr: J C Thorpe
Pr: Kevin Halstead
**Pr:* Doyle Tubant
COO: John Taylor
**Ch:* Gage A Kent
VP: Douglas M Dermid
VP: Patrick Homoelle
VP: Rick Miller
VP: Mark Ricketts
VP: Kevin Schilling
VP: Osama Shihadeh
VP: Jeffrey Stone
VP: Rani Thomas
**VP:* E J Thomsen
**VP:* Eric Thomsen
VP: Carter Van Hemert
VP: Tom Wiesner
VP: Ralph Wilkinson

GRAIN SYSTEMS
See GSI GROUP LLC

D-U-N-S 09-392-1302
GRAIN VALLEY R-V SCHOOL DISTRICT
31606 E Pink Hill Rd, Grain Valley, MO 64029-9296
Tel (816) 847-5006 *Founded/Ownrshp* 1895
Sales 30.8MM^E *EMP* 450
SIC 8211 Public elementary & secondary schools; Public elementary school; Public elementary & secondary schools; Public elementary school
HC Dir: Denise Beach

D-U-N-S 05-415-3036
GRAINCO FS INC
3107 N State Route 23, Ottawa, IL 61350-9645
Tel (815) 434-0131 *Founded/Ownrshp* 1971
Sales 43.2MM^E *EMP* 60
SIC 5191 5171 Chemicals, agricultural; Feed; Fertilizer & fertilizer materials; Seeds: field, garden & flower; Petroleum bulk stations
Genl Mgr: Michael Builta
Treas: Monty Whipple
Genl Mgr: Joe Callan
Genl Mgr: Damon Neiggemann
Plnt Mgr: Brian Hettel
Plnt Mgr: Brett Hulmes
Mktg Mgr: Doug Larson
Mktg Mgr: Scott Reel

GRAINCORP MALT
See GREAT WESTERN MALTING CO

D-U-N-S 15-694-7657 EXP
GRAINGER COMPANIES INC
GRAINGER HONDA
1596 Chatham Pkwy, Savannah, GA 31408-3024
Tel (912) 790-5444 *Founded/Ownrshp* 1997
Sales 50.7MM^E *EMP* 70
SIC 5511 7538 Automobiles, new & used; General automotive repair shops; Automobiles, new & used; General automotive repair shops
CEO: William L Grainger
**CFO:* Michelle H Nelson
Genl Mgr: Damon Grainger
Sls Dir: Spencer Thomas
Sls Mgr: Ronny Moore
Sales Asso: Eric Brogan
Sales Asso: Jonathan Smith
Sales Asso: Tim Yount
Snr Mgr: Don Holloway

GRAINGER COUNTY BOARD EDUCATN
See GRAINGER COUNTY SCHOOL DISTRICT

D-U-N-S 04-372-1695
GRAINGER COUNTY SCHOOL DISTRICT
GRAINGER COUNTY BOARD EDUCATN
7850 Rutledge Pike, Rutledge, TN 37861-3000
Tel (865) 828-3611 *Founded/Ownrshp* 1920
Sales 18.0MM^E *EMP* 450
SIC 8211 9411 Public elementary & secondary schools; Administration of educational programs; Public elementary & secondary schools; Administration of educational programs
MIS Dir: James Atkins

GRAINGER HONDA
See GRAINGER COMPANIES INC

D-U-N-S 05-361-8240
■ **GRAINGER INTERNATIONAL INC**
(*Suby of* WW GRAINGER INC) ★
100 Grainger Pkwy, Lake Forest, IL 60045-5202
Tel (847) 535-1000 *Founded/Ownrshp* 1994
Sales 228.5MM^E *EMP* 271
SIC 5074 5084 5085 5072 Heating equipment (hydronic); Industrial machinery & equipment; Electric tools; Power tools & accessories; Heating equipment (hydronic); Industrial machinery & equipment; Electric tools; Power tools & accessories
Pr: Donald G Macpherson
**VP:* Bonnie McIntyre

D-U-N-S 00-742-9038
GRAINLAND COOPERATIVE
421 S Colorado Ave, Haxtun, CO 80731-2708
Tel (970) 774-6166 *Founded/Ownrshp* 1919, 1997
Sales 137.1MM *EMP* 40
SIC 5191 4221 5531 5541 Fertilizers & agricultural chemicals; Animal feeds; Seeds: field, garden & flower; Grain elevator, storage only; Automotive tires; Automotive accessories; Filling stations, gasoline; Fertilizers & agricultural chemicals; Animal feeds; Seeds: field, garden & flower; Grain elevator, storage only; Automotive tires; Automotive accessories; Filling stations, gasoline
Pr: Rick Unrein
**Ch Bd:* Robert Shaffer
V Ch: Gary Wemsman
VP: Jan Workman

D-U-N-S 00-979-8216
GRAINLAND COOPERATIVE
927 County Highway 3, Eureka, IL 61530-9457
Tel (309) 467-2355 *Founded/Ownrshp* 1904
Sales 55.5MM *EMP* 50
SIC 5153 Grain elevators; Grain elevators
Genl Mgr: Jeffery K Brooks
Opers Mgr: Lance Gehlbach

GRAINSTORE
See GAVILON GRAIN LLC

GRAINSTORE ELEVATORS
See GALESBURG ORDER BUYERS INC

D-U-N-S 03-740-9125 IMP
GRAKON LLC
1911 S 218th St, Des Moines, WA 98198-8370
Tel (206) 824-6000 *Founded/Ownrshp* 2007
Sales 77.0MM^E *EMP* 350^E
SIC 3714 Motor vehicle electrical equipment; Motor vehicle electrical equipment
Mktg Dir: Dennis Graham
CFO: David Olson
VP: Mark Brainard
Prgrm Mgr: David Speiser
Prgrm Mgr: Dwayne Trivax
Dir IT: Clint Arney
IT Man: Robert Hill
Ql Cn Mgr: Ryan Blosser

GRAM LUMBER COMPANY
See RSG FOREST PRODUCTS INC

GRAM MOTORS
See STEVE AUSTINS AUTO GROUP INC

D-U-N-S 61-183-0709
GRAMARBLE CO
RANIMEX
5002 Wareham Dr, Arlington, TX 76017-2726
Tel (817) 419-8792 *Founded/Ownrshp* 2004
Sales 67.5MM *EMP* 747
SIC 3281 5032 5031 Granite, cut & shaped; Marble, building: cut & shaped; Granite building stone; Marble building stone; Composite board products, woodboard; Granite, cut & shaped; Marble, building: cut & shaped; Granite building stone; Marble building stone; Composite board products, woodboard
CEO: Peter Nguyen
**CFO:* Tina Vu
**Sr VP:* Nhat Nguyen
**VP:* Vu Nguyen
**Ex Dir:* Thu Nga Vu
**S&M/Dir:* Hoang Nguyen

GRAMATAN MANAGEMENT
See DAVID BRADLEY MANAGEMENT INC

D-U-N-S 93-985-5565
GRAMBLING STATE UNIVERSITY
403 Main St, Grambling, LA 71245-2761
Tel (318) 274-2558 *Founded/Ownrshp* 1965
Sales 78.4MM^E *EMP* 900
SIC 8221 9411 Service academy; Administration of educational programs; ; Service academy; Administration of educational programs;
Pr: Cynthia Warrick
Top Exec: Igwe Udeh
Assoc VP: Nettie Daniels
Ex VP: Leslie Randle
VP: Monica Bradley
VP: Rashon Carruthers
VP: Beverly Crawford
VP: Lavoyd Dudley
VP: Stacey Duhon
VP: Anthony Johnson
VP: Norman Jones
VP: Melvin Mims
VP: Damon Wade
Exec: Destinee Westmoreland
Assoc Dir: Tremell Turner

D-U-N-S 01-513-9919
GRAMEEN AMERICA INC
150 W 30th St Fl 8, New York, NY 10001-4151
Tel (212) 735-4043 *Founded/Ownrshp* 2008
Sales 21.8MM^E *EMP* 175
Accts Pricewaterhousecoopers Llp Ne
SIC 8699 8732 Charitable organization; Market analysis, business & economic research
Pr: Andrea Jung
Pr: Katherine Rosenberg
Sr VP: Howard Axel
Sr VP: Diana Sacchi
VP: Molly McGrath
Assoc Dir: Victoria Adkinson
Comm Man: Rebecca Asch
Prin: Antonia Hernandez
Prin: Hope Knight
Genl Mgr: Shah Newaz

D-U-N-S 13-200-6730
GRAMERCY FINANCIAL GROUP LLC
20 Dayton Ave Ste 1, Greenwich, CT 06830-6499
Tel (203) 552-1900 *Founded/Ownrshp* 2000
Sales 25.3MM^E *EMP* 87^E
SIC 6211 Security brokers & dealers
Mng Pt: Robert Koenigsberger
Pr: Milton Koenigsberger
Sr VP: Joseph Griffin
Sr VP: Lacie Smith
Mng Dir: Jose Cerritelli
Mng Dir: Kelly Griffin
Mng Dir: Stephen Laversa
Mng Dir: Timothy Mahoney

D-U-N-S 12-696-3920
GRAMERCY GROUP INC
3000 Burns Ave, Wantagh, NY 11793-3202
Tel (516) 876-0020 *Founded/Ownrshp* 1989
Sales 27.2MM^E *EMP* 75
SIC 1795 1799 Wrecking & demolition work; Asbestos removal & encapsulation
Ch Bd: Vincent A Parziale
Snr Mgr: Richard Peterson

D-U-N-S 17-041-3319
GRAMERCY PROPERTY TRUST INC
521 5th Ave Fl 30, New York, NY 10175-3001
Tel (212) 297-1000 *Founded/Ownrshp* 2004
Sales 107.9MM *EMP* 103^E
SIC 6798 Real estate investment trusts; Real estate investment trusts
CEO: Gordon F Dugan
**Ch Bd:* Allan J Baum
Pr: Benjamin P Harris
CFO: Jon W Clark
Ex VP: Edward J Matey Jr
Sr VP: Joseph Romano
Sr VP: Wayne Stevens
IT Man: Prudence Duke
Board of Directors: Gregory F Hughes, Jeffrey E Kelter, Charles S Laven, William H Lenehan

GRAMERCYONE
See BOOKER SOFTWARE INC

D-U-N-S 00-697-3580
GRAMMER DEMPSEY & HUDSON INC
212 Rome St, Newark, NJ 07105-3920
Tel (973) 589-8000 *Founded/Ownrshp* 1935
Sales 33.5MM^E *EMP* 185
SIC 5051 Iron & steel (ferrous) products; Steel; Iron & steel (ferrous) products; Steel
Pr: James F Hudson
**Ex VP:* J Morgan Hudson
**VP:* John S Feeney

D-U-N-S 08-025-3438 IMP
GRAMMER INC
(*Suby of* GRAMMER AG)
2305 Willis Miller Dr, Hudson, WI 54016-7999
Tel (864) 672-0702 *Founded/Ownrshp* 2001
Sales 66.6MM^E *EMP* 100

SIC 5013 2396 Motor vehicle supplies & new parts; Automotive trimmings, fabric
Pr: Thomas Schleuchardt
CFO: Beal James
*Prin: Ed Nelson
Ex Dir: Bautista Patricia
Dir IT: Wolfgang Enders
Ql Cn Mgr: Doug Sitko
Sls Mgr: Maik Hanuschik
Sls Mgr: Dan Wallberg

D-U-N-S 02-137-0929
GRAMMER INDUSTRIES INC
18375 E 345 S, Elizabethtown, IN 47236-9720
Tel (812) 579-5655 Founded/Ownrshp 1972
Sales 29.5MM^E EMP 125
SIC 4213 Trucking, except local
Pr: Charles L Whittington
*VP: John S Whittington

D-U-N-S 10-395-5022 IMP
GRAMMER INDUSTRIES INC
(Suby of GRAMMER AG)
3505 Pelham Rd Ste C, Greenville, SC 29615-4154
Tel (864) 284-9616 Founded/Ownrshp 1999
Sales 36.7MM^E EMP 83
SIC 5013 Seat covers
VP: Richard Westwood
VP: Mario Borelli
Ql Cn Mgr: Denise Chapman

D-U-N-S 80-815-5910 IMP
GRAN QUARTZ LP
4963 S Royal Atlanta Dr, Tucker, GA 30084-3006
Tel (770) 621-5200 Founded/Ownrshp 1998
Sales 67.3MM^E EMP 132
SIC 5169 3291 Concrete additives; Synthetic abrasives; Concrete additives; Synthetic abrasives
Pt: Alan E Rauber
Dist Mgr: Matthew Smith
Store Mgr: Tony Dibartolo
IT Man: Michael Hook
Tech Mgr: Mike Brown
VP Opers: Rick Hudson
Manager: Robert Tait
Sales Asso: Vicente Ruiz

D-U-N-S 17-442-6924 IMP
GRAN QUARTZ TRADING INC
4963 S Royal Atlanta Dr, Tucker, GA 30084-3006
Tel (770) 621-9777 Founded/Ownrshp 1971
Sales 25.4MM^E EMP 75^E
Accts Moore Colson & Company
SIC 5085 3559 Industrial supplies; Stone working machinery
CEO: Peter Dekok
*CFO: C M Durham
IT Man: Michael Hook

D-U-N-S 36-279-5080
GRANADA HILLS CHARTER HIGH SCHOOL
10535 Zelzah Ave, Granada Hills, CA 91344-5902
Tel (818) 360-2361 Founded/Ownrshp 2003
Sales 39.4MM EMP 450
SIC 8211 High school, junior or senior; High school, junior or senior
CEO: Brian Bauer
*CFO: Walter Wallace
Adm Dir: Jennifer Dacosta
Adm Dir: Lori Zaragoza
Ex Dir: Elisa Ragus
Off Admin: Lindsey Dooley
Off Admin: Karina Gonzalez
Off Admin: Vanessa Vazquez
Off Admin: Beth Wallace
Plnt Mgr: William Minton
Psych: Dale Alpert

D-U-N-S 05-295-3783
■ **GRANBURY HOSPITAL CORP** (TX)
CHS
(Suby of COMMUNITY HEALTH SYSTEMS INC) ★
1310 Paluxy Rd, Granbury, TX 76048-5655
Tel (817) 573-2273 Founded/Ownrshp 1972
Sales 137.3MM EMP 185
SIC 8062 General medical & surgical hospitals; General medical & surgical hospitals
Ch: Robert Burns
*Owner: Di CK Carey
*Pr: Martin G Schweinhart
*CFO: W Larry Cash
*VP: T Mark Buford
*VP: James W Doucette
Dir Rx: Julie Rudd
Doctor: Susan M Davis
Doctor: Jennifer Smith MD
Phys Thrpy: Christy Snowdon

D-U-N-S 09-521-1801
GRANBURY INDEPENDENT SCHOOL DISTRICT
600 W Pearl St, Granbury, TX 76048-2046
Tel (817) 408-4000 Founded/Ownrshp 1900
Sales 71.7MM EMP 900
Accts Snowgarrett Williams Weatherf
SIC 8211 Public elementary & secondary schools; School board; Public elementary & secondary schools; School board
*CFO: Bobie Williams
IT Man: Carrie Knight-Mapes
Pr Dir: Jeff Meador

D-U-N-S 62-164-0630
GRANCARE LLC
(Suby of MARINER HEALTH CARE INC) ★
1 Ravinia Dr Ste 1400, Atlanta, GA 30346-2112
Tel (770) 393-0199 Founded/Ownrshp 1997
Sales 99.7MM^E EMP 13,800
SIC 8051 8052 8093 8071 Skilled nursing care facilities; Extended care facility; Intermediate care facilities; Rehabilitation center, outpatient treatment; Testing laboratories; Pathological laboratory; Skilled nursing care facilities; Extended care facility; Intermediate care facilities; Rehabilitation center, outpatient treatment; Testing laboratories; Pathological laboratory
Ch Bd: Keith B Pitts

Pr: Dennis Sarcasa
VP: Ken Tabler
Board of Directors: Charles Carden, Susan Thomas Whittle

GRANCELL VILLAGE
See LOS ANGELES JEWISH HOME FOR AGING

D-U-N-S 18-561-3887
GRANCOR ENTERPRISES INC
2121 Menaul Blvd Ne, Albuquerque, NM 87107-1714
Tel (505) 872-0005 Founded/Ownrshp 2004
Sales 26.1MM^E EMP 95
SIC 1542 1795 4959 Nonresidential construction; Demolition, buildings & other structures; Toxic or hazardous waste cleanup; Nonresidential construction; Demolition, buildings & other structures; Toxic or hazardous waste cleanup
Pr: Maria Cornay
Ql Cn Mgr: Micheal Lam

D-U-N-S 02-774-4911
GRAND & BENEDICTS INC
GRAND & BENEDICTS LIQUIDATION
6140 Sw Macadam Ave, Portland, OR 97239-3648
Tel (503) 232-1988 Founded/Ownrshp 1980
Sales 38.9MM^E EMP 90
SIC 5046 Store fixtures; Store equipment; Store fixtures; Store equipment
Pr: John V Phillips
*Ch Bd: Henry F Phillips
*COO: Frank Phillips IV
Manager: David Denike

GRAND & BENEDICTS LIQUIDATION
See GRAND & BENEDICTS INC

D-U-N-S 07-615-1000
GRAND AERIE OF FRATERNAL ORDER OF EAGLES
1623 Gateway Cir, Grove City, OH 43123-9309
Tel (614) 883-2200 Founded/Ownrshp 1898
Sales 11.6MM EMP 2,338
Accts Baker Tilly Virchow Krause Llp
SIC 8641 Fraternal associations; Fraternal associations
Ch: Chris Lainas Jr
*Ch Bd: Edgar L Bollenbacher
*Pr: Bill Losser
Treas: Bob Larsen

GRAND AMERICA HOTEL, THE
See GRAND AMERICA HOTELS & RESORTS INC

D-U-N-S 60-357-5338
GRAND AMERICA HOTELS & RESORTS
555 S Main St, Salt Lake City, UT 84111-4100
Tel (801) 258-6000 Founded/Ownrshp 1999
Sales 6.3MM^E EMP 800
SIC 7011 Hotels; Hotels
CEO: Bruce Fery
*Pr: Robert E Holding
*Treas: Charles E Barlow
*VP: Mark Sykes

D-U-N-S 78-501-4858
GRAND AMERICA HOTELS & RESORTS INC
GRAND AMERICA HOTEL, THE
555 S Main St, Salt Lake City, UT 84111-4100
Tel (801) 596-5717 Founded/Ownrshp 2005
Sales 226.9MM^E EMP 2,700^E
SIC 7011 Hotels & motels; Hotels & motels
Pr: S E Holding
*Pr: Bruce T Fery
*VP: B T Fery
*VP: M A Sykes
Exec: Fernando Soberanis
Ex Dir: Frank Harris
Genl Mgr: Bruce Ferry
CTO: Ali Afati
Dir IT: Matt Ballif
Natl Sales: Scott Farmery
Sls Mgr: Landon Anderson

GRAND APPLIANCE & TV
See GRAND APPLIANCE INC

D-U-N-S 02-590-2560
GRAND APPLIANCE INC
GRAND APPLIANCE & TV
3300 16th St, Zion, IL 60099-1417
*Tel (847) 746-6000 Founded/Ownrshp 1988
Sales 25.3MM^E EMP 129
SIC 5722

D-U-N-S 60-375-6701
GRAND AUTO INC
GRAND PONTIAC BUICK G M C KIA
2000 W 104th Ave, Denver, CO 80234-3604
Tel (303) 460-8000 Founded/Ownrshp 1989
Sales 35.0MM^E EMP 90
SIC 5511 Automobiles, new & used; Automobiles, new & used
Pr: Douglas Moreland
*Genl Mgr: Alex Jannicelli
Sales Asso: Zack Itehad

D-U-N-S 03-339-7141
GRAND AVENUE CHAUFFEURED TRANSPORTATION (TN)
GRAND AVENUE LIMOUSINE
186 N 1st St, Nashville, TN 37213-1102
Tel (615) 714-5466 Founded/Ownrshp 2010
Sales 55.0MM EMP 50
SIC 4119 Limousine rental, with driver
Pr: Carl Haley
Ex VP: Janna Landry
Genl Mgr: Russell Brashear
Genl Mgr: Terrie Lane

GRAND AVENUE LIMOUSINE
See GRAND AVENUE CHAUFFEURED TRANSPORTATION

D-U-N-S 10-281-1205
GRAND AVENUE PRODUCE CO INC
8990 W Windsor Dr, Peoria, AZ 85381-6152
Tel (602) 254-8643 Founded/Ownrshp 1946

Sales 47.2MM^E EMP 60
SIC 5148 Fresh fruits & vegetables; Fresh fruits & vegetables
Pr: John W New
*Sec: Mona Post
Genl Mgr: Chad Huddle

D-U-N-S 10-528-9628 EXP
GRAND BANK NA INC
1 Edinburg Rd, Trenton, NJ 08619-1709
Tel (609) 631-0540 Founded/Ownrshp 1999
Sales NA EMP 355
SIC 6021 National commercial banks; National commercial banks
CEO: Rich P Rosa
Ofcr: Barry Weed
Sr VP: Lauretta Lucchesi
*VP: Dave Metzheiser
VP: Martha Morley
*VP: Debra Morreale

D-U-N-S 06-984-1526
GRAND BLANC COMMUNITY SCHOOLS
11920 S Saginaw St, Grand Blanc, MI 48439-1402
Tel (810) 591-6000 Founded/Ownrshp 1919
Sales 85.9MM EMP 900
Accts Lewis & Knopf Pc Flint-Bri
SIC 8211 Public elementary school; Public junior high school; Public senior high school; Public elementary school; Public junior high school; Public senior high school
Netwrk Mgr: Rich Kuehnle

GRAND BOHEMIAN HOTEL ASHEVILLE
See KESSLER ASHEVILLE LLC

D-U-N-S 14-951-5913
▲ **GRAND CANYON EDUCATION INC**
3300 W Camelback Rd, Phoenix, AZ 85017-3030
Tel (602) 639-7500 Founded/Ownrshp 1949
Sales 691.0MM EMP 3,100^E
Accts Kpmg Llp Phoenix Arizona
Tkr Sym LOPE Exch NGS
SIC 8221 Colleges universities & professional schools; University; Colleges universities & professional schools; University
Pr: Brian E Mueller
*Ch Bd: Brent D Richardson
COO: W Stan Meyer
CFO: Daniel E Bachus
Sr VP: Brian M Roberts
VP: Richard Volk
CIO: Joseph N Mildenhall
CTO: Mike Lacrosse
Software D: Ben Sexton
Opers Mgr: Caroline Jones
Board of Directors: Bradley A Casper, Sara R Dial, Jack A Henry, David J Johnson, Kevin F Warren

D-U-N-S 83-134-6353
GRAND CANYON RAILWAY LLC
233 N Grand Canyon Blvd, Williams, AZ 86046-2563
Tel (928) 773-1976 Founded/Ownrshp 2009
Sales 24.9MM^E EMP 600
SIC 4111 Commuter rail passenger operation; Commuter rail passenger operation
VP: Gordon Taylor
CFO: Kevin Call
Genl Mgr: Bob Baker

GRAND CANYON RESORT
See HUALAPAI ENTERPRISES

D-U-N-S 05-367-7779
GRAND CANYON TITLE AGENCY INC
2720 E Camelback Rd # 100, Phoenix, AZ 85016-4394
Tel (602) 468-7777 Founded/Ownrshp 1986
Sales 41.9MM^E EMP 165
SIC 6541 6531 Title & trust companies; Escrow agent, real estate
Ch Bd: Robert A Lawler
Pr: Stanley A Feffer
CFO: Alan D Hunter
Sales Exec: Michelle Simpson

D-U-N-S 07-445-0750
■ **GRAND CANYON UNIVERSITY INC** (AZ)
(Suby of GRAND CANYON EDUCATION INC) ★
3300 W Camelback Rd, Phoenix, AZ 85017-1097
Tel (602) 639-7500 Founded/Ownrshp 1949
Sales 511.2MM^E EMP 4
Accts Kpmg Llp Phoenix Arizona
SIC 8221 University; University
Pr: Gil Stafford
*Ch Bd: Brent Richardson
*Pr: Brian Mueller
*COO: Stan Meyer
*CFO: Dan Bachus
Assoc VP: Jaime Leonard
Ex VP: Kate Hogan
Sr VP: Scott Fehrenbacher
Sr VP: Chanelle Ison
Sr VP: Scott Raleigh
VP: Tacy Ashby
VP: Star EBY
VP: Jennifer Lech
VP: Chris Linderson
VP: Fran Roberts
Assoc Dir: Robert Gay
Comm Man: Janie Magruder

GRAND CASINO MILLE LACS
See CORPORATE COMMISSION OF MILLE LACS BAND OF CHIPPEWA INDIANS

D-U-N-S 78-042-8900
GRAND CASINOS INC
ISLAND VIEW CASINO RESORT
3300 W Beach Blvd, Gulfport, MS 39501-1800
Tel (228) 314-2100 Founded/Ownrshp 2005
Sales 337.7MM^E EMP 7,300^E
SIC 7011 Casino hotel; Casino hotel
Pt: Lindsey Inman
*Pt: Terry Green
*Pt: Rick Harder
Bd of Dir: Kim Garris
Ex VP: John Bakley
Dir Risk M: Tony Vanderslice

D-U-N-S 86-007-2198
GRAND CENTRAL BAKERY INC
GRAND CENTRAL BAKING COMPANY
4634 E Marginal Way S C110, Seattle, WA 98134-2398
Tel (206) 768-0320 Founded/Ownrshp 1972
Sales 34.6MM^E EMP 110^E
SIC 5149 5461 5812 Bakery products; Bakeries; Cafeteria; Delicatessen (eating places); Bakery products; Bakeries; Cafeteria; Delicatessen (eating places)
Pr: Gwen Bassetti
VP: Piper Davis
Exec: Rosemary Kennedy
Genl Mgr: Gillian Allen-White
Genl Mgr: Gillian White
IT Man: Bob Kerr

GRAND CENTRAL BAKING COMPANY
See GRAND CENTRAL BAKERY INC

D-U-N-S 12-215-3898
GRAND CENTRAL INC
CENTRAL MARKET
310 Frazee St E, Detroit Lakes, MN 56501-3604
Tel (218) 847-4401 Founded/Ownrshp 2002
Sales 32.0MM EMP 200
SIC 5411 Supermarkets; Supermarkets
Pr: Cathy Dickson
*VP: John Losberg

D-U-N-S 07-887-2652
GRAND CENTRAL PUBLISHING
(Suby of HACHETTE BOOK GROUP INC) ★
1290 Ave Of The Americas, New York, NY 10104-0101
Tel (212) 364-1200 Founded/Ownrshp 1960, 1996
Sales 38.1MM^E EMP 400
SIC 2731 Books: publishing only; Books: publishing only
Ch Bd: David Young
CFO: Thomas Maciag
*Prin: Beth Ford
*Prin: Lawrence Kirshbaum

D-U-N-S 61-348-2173
GRAND CHARTER GROUP INC
810 7th Ave, New York, NY 10019-5818
Tel (212) 977-0614 Founded/Ownrshp 1990
Sales 54.6MM EMP 285^E
Accts Price Waterhouse Llp New York
SIC 6211 Brokers, security; Dealers, security; Brokers, security; Dealers, security
CEO: Stephen Schwartz
*Pr: Mark W Ronda
Sys/Mgr: Prince Polius

D-U-N-S 05-355-5256
GRAND CIRCLE LLC
GRAND CIRCLE TRAVEL
347 Congress St Ste 2, Boston, MA 02210-1222
Tel (617) 350-7500 Founded/Ownrshp 1985
Sales 73.2MM^E EMP 500^E
SIC 4725 Tour operators; Tour operators
CEO: Alan E Lewis
CFO: Nick Lento
CFO: Sean Stover
Ex VP: Joe Kelly
VP: Andre Atemasov
VP: Anne Bala
VP: Thomas Cauchon
VP: Susan Coakley
VP: Vinod George
VP: Heather Heverling
VP: Simon Horsburgh
VP: Ted Kenney
VP: Nancy Lakebody
VP: Nancy Lightbody
VP: David Lubchansky
VP: Kelly Niehoff
VP: Jonathan Quint
VP: Diane Rooney
VP: Mark Shionis
VP: Garrett Tight
VP: George Trant

GRAND CIRCLE TRAVEL
See GRAND CIRCLE LLC

GRAND CROWNE RESORTS
See SURREY GRAND CROWNE OWNERS ASSOCIATION CORP

GRAND CROWNE RESORTS
See SURREY VACATION RESORTS INC

D-U-N-S 78-784-3465
GRAND CYPRESS FLORIDA LP
GRAND CYPRESS RESORT
(Suby of KYO-YA HOTELS & RESORTS LP) ★
1 N Jacaranda St, Orlando, FL 32836-6618
Tel (407) 239-4700 Founded/Ownrshp 1990
Sales 33.6MM^E EMP 400^E
SIC 7011 Hotels & motels; Hotels & motels
Pr: Takamasa Osano
Treas: Mike Iwue
Ex VP: Ernest K Nishhizaki
Genl Mgr: Mark Cox
Sls Mgr: Kelly Dudek
Sales Asso: Martin Carroll

D-U-N-S 07-849-7114
GRAND CYPRESS ORLANDO LLC (FL)
VILLAS OF GRAND CYPRESS, THE
1 N Jacaranda St, Orlando, FL 32836-6618
Tel (407) 239-4700 Founded/Ownrshp 2012
Sales 11.8MM^E EMP 350
SIC 7997 Membership sports & recreation clubs; Membership sports & recreation clubs

GRAND CYPRESS RESORT
See GRAND CYPRESS FLORIDA LP

D-U-N-S 80-348-2368
GRAND DEL MAR RESORT L P
5300 Grand Del Mar Ct, San Diego, CA 92130-4901
Tel (858) 314-2000 Founded/Ownrshp 2005
Sales 44.8MM^E EMP 570
SIC 7011 Resort hotel; Resort hotel
Pt: Tom Voss
Exec: Christina Delcastillo
Dir Sec: Michael Vinson
Off Mgr: Adam Goffin

CTO: Jay Pak
IT Man: Edward Castillo
Natl Sales: Julie Francis
Natl Sales: Joanna Halpin
Natl Sales: Lisa Ray
Sls Dir: Indy Newsom

D-U-N-S 03-732-4061
GRAND DESIGN RV LLC
BLACK BEAR RECRTL VEHICLES
11333 County Road 2, Middlebury, IN 46540-9632
Tel (574) 825-8000 *Founded/Ownrshp* 2012
Sales 49.2MM^E *EMP* 625
SIC 7519 3799 Recreational vehicle rental; Recreational vehicles
Prin: Grant Williams
**Owner:* Donald Clark
Genl Mgr: Nate Goldenberg
Genl Mgr: Marc Hauser
Genl Mgr: Micah Staley
Manager: Jordan Struble

D-U-N-S 00-616-8389
■ **GRAND FORKS HERALD INC**
AGWEEK MAGAZINE
(*Suby of* MCCLATCHY CO) ★
375 2nd Ave N, Grand Forks, ND 58203-3707
Tel (701) 780-1100 *Founded/Ownrshp* 1897, 2006
Sales 24.0MM^E *EMP* 130
SIC 2711 2721 Commercial printing & newspaper publishing combined; Magazines: publishing & printing
Pr: Michael Maidenberg
CFO: Anita Geffre
VP: Kevin Kephart
VP: Jeff Slaby
**Prin:* Mike Jacobs
Dir Sec: Tina Chisholm

D-U-N-S 10-066-5041
GRAND FORKS PUBLIC SCHOOLS
2400 47th Ave S, Grand Forks, ND 58201-3405
Tel (701) 746-2200 *Founded/Ownrshp* 1881
Sales 73.1MM^E *EMP* 1,500
SIC 8211 Public elementary & secondary schools; Public elementary & secondary schools
Genl Mgr: Rosanne Momm
Dir IT: Darin King

D-U-N-S 00-586-7718 IMP
GRAND FURNITURE
SOFA'S ETC
1305 Baker Rd, Virginia Beach, VA 23455-3317
Tel (757) 460-3800 *Founded/Ownrshp* 1946
Sales 50.6MM *EMP* 300
Accts Wall Einhorn & Chernitzer Pc
SIC 5712 5713 5722 5731 Furniture stores; Carpets; Electric household appliances, major; Radio, television & electronic stores; Television sets; Furniture stores; Carpets; Electric household appliances, major; Radio, television & electronic stores; Television sets
Co-CEO: Craig Stein

D-U-N-S 16-911-1858
GRAND GENEVA LLC
GRAND GENEVA RESORT & SPA
7036 Grand Geneva Way, Lake Geneva, WI 53147-5105
Tel (262) 248-8811 *Founded/Ownrshp* 2000
Sales 76.7MM^E *EMP* 867
SIC 7011 Resort hotel; Resort hotel
Exec: Michael Sawin
Dir Soc: Rhonda Baior
Dir Soc: Kate Hartz
Mng Dir: Leslie Johnson
Dir Sec: David Bergsma
Dir Sec: Toby Jensen
Genl Mgr: Stephanie Ashley
Genl Mgr: Dave Hallenbeck
Genl Mgr: Amy Kelly
CTO: Vicki Jacobs
IT Man: Jared Boulden

GRAND GENEVA RESORT & SPA
See GRAND GENEVA LLC

D-U-N-S 09-593-7827
GRAND GREETINGS INC
7800 Clyde Park Ave Sw, Byron Center, MI 49315-9390
Tel (616) 878-3338 *Founded/Ownrshp* 1979
Sales 24.2MM^E *EMP* 51
SIC 5112 Greeting cards
Pr: Peter Haaksma
**VP:* Chris Holwerda

D-U-N-S 04-789-0595
GRAND HAVEN AREA PUBLIC SCHOOLS
1415 S Beechtree St, Grand Haven, MI 49417-2899
Tel (616) 850-5000 *Founded/Ownrshp* 1836
Sales 69.0MM *EMP* 776
Accts Rehman Robson Llc Muskegon M
SIC 8211 Public elementary school; Public junior high school; Public senior high school; Public elementary school; Public junior high school; Public senior high school
VP: John Siemion
Prin: Paul Kunde
Pr Dir: Ann Haruki Shelton

D-U-N-S 15-580-2002
GRAND HAVEN BOARD OF LIGHT & POWER
1700 Eaton Dr, Grand Haven, MI 49417-2820
Tel (616) 842-2241 *Founded/Ownrshp* 1896
Sales 37.8MM *EMP* 68
Accts Vredeveld Haefner Llc Grand R
SIC 4911 Generation, electric power; Generation, electric power
Ch Bd: Jack R Smant
**Genl Mgr:* Annette Allen

D-U-N-S 02-551-8471
GRAND HAVEN CUSTOM MOLDING LLC
1500 S Beechtree St, Grand Haven, MI 49417-2846
Tel (616) 935-3160 *Founded/Ownrshp* 2010
Sales 24.6MM^E *EMP* 47^E
SIC 3089 Molding primary plastic
Prin: Karl R Chapel
CFO: Michelle Hanks
Plnt Mgr: Dale Harken
Plnt Mgr: Paul Zelenka

GRAND HAVEN NURSERY PRODUCTS
See WEST MICHIGAN MOLDING INC

D-U-N-S 09-227-4534
GRAND HERITAGE HOTEL PORTLAND (MD)
HAMPTON INN
39 Bay Dr, Annapolis, MD 21403-4511
Tel (410) 280-9800 *Founded/Ownrshp* 1998
Sales 11.0MM^E *EMP* 800
SIC 7011 Hotels & motels; Hotels & motels
Prin: John Cullen
Off Mgr: Debby Devries

GRAND HOME FURNISHINGS
See GRAND PIANO & FURNITURE CO

GRAND HOMES
See GRAND TEXAS HOMES INC

D-U-N-S 17-664-5810
GRAND HOMES 99 LP
15455 Dallas Pkwy # 1000, Addison, TX 75001-6772
Tel (214) 750-6528 *Founded/Ownrshp* 1996
Sales 10.0MM^E *EMP* 350
SIC 1521 Single-family housing construction; Single-family housing construction
Pr: Edward Toole

D-U-N-S 00-696-0249
GRAND HOTEL LLC (MI)
286 Grand Ave, Mackinac Island, MI 49757
Tel (906) 847-3331 *Founded/Ownrshp* 1887, 1960
Sales 54.2MM^E *EMP* 650^E
SIC 7011 5947 5621 5994 Resort hotel; Gift shop; Women's sportswear; Newsstand; Resort hotel; Gift shop; Women's sportswear; Newsstand
Pr: Daniel Musser III
VP: Kim Styburski
Genl Mgr: Jennifer King
Sls Mgr: Jackie Hoskins
Sls Mgr: Rachel Pullman

GRAND HYATT CONVENTION CENTER
See HOTEL INVESTMENTS LP

GRAND HYATT DENVER
See 1750 WELTON STREET INVESTORS LLC

GRAND HYATT DENVER
See HYATT HOTELS CORP

GRAND HYATT DFW INTL ARPRT
See HYATT CORP

GRAND HYATT WASHINGTON
See HYATT CORP AS AGENT OF CCHH GHDC LLC A DELAWARE LIMITED LIABILITY CO

D-U-N-S 07-402-4928
GRAND ISLAND CENTRAL SCHOOL DISTRICT
1100 Ransom Rd, Grand Island, NY 14072-1460
Tel (716) 773-8800 *Founded/Ownrshp* 1879
Sales 31.1MM^E *EMP* 525
SIC 8211 9411 Public elementary school; Public junior high school; Public senior high school; School board; Administration of educational programs; Public elementary school; Public junior high school; Public senior high school; School board; Administration of educational programs
VP: Sharyn Mudd
Psych: Christina Kensy
Psych: Joan Portik

D-U-N-S 19-377-5368
GRAND ISLAND EXPRESS INC
432 S Stuhr Rd, Grand Island, NE 68801-8569
Tel (308) 384-8555 *Founded/Ownrshp* 1983
Sales 27.3MM^E *EMP* 158^E
Accts Contryman Associates Pc Gr
SIC 4213 Refrigerated products transport; Refrigerated products transport
Pr: Thomas J Pirnie
**Sec:* Susan D Pirnie
VP: Bob Caldwell
**VP:* Keith Pirnie
VP: Mike Young
Exec: Strano Andrea
IT Man: Patty Moore
IT Man: Matt Ostrander
IT Man: Matt Ostrender
Sfty Dirs: Mark Egger
Opers Mgr: Philip Burt

GRAND ISLAND PUBLIC SCHOOLS
See HALL COUNTY SCHOOL DISTRICT 2

D-U-N-S 96-277-0579
■ **GRAND ISLAND PUBLISHING CO INC**
(*Suby of* MIDLANDS NEWSPAPERS INC) ★
422 W 1st St, Grand Island, NE 68801-5802
Tel (308) 382-1000 *Founded/Ownrshp* 2010
Sales 24.4MM^E *EMP* 578^E
SIC 2711 Newspapers
Pr: Dun Smith
Sales Exec: Sonya Schultz
Snr Mgr: Barrett Stinson

D-U-N-S 00-817-7321 IMP
GRAND ISLE SHIPYARD INC
(*Suby of* NANA DEVELOPMENT CORP) ★
18838 Highway 3235, Galliano, LA 70354-4038
Tel (985) 475-5238 *Founded/Ownrshp* 2011
Sales 554.8MM^E *EMP* 1,050
SIC 1389 Oil field services; Oil field services
Pr: Robert C Pregeant
**Treas:* Richard Pregeant
**VP:* Bryan Pregeant
Mktg Dir: Brian Danos
Snr PM: Sonny Daigrepont

D-U-N-S 07-150-4377
GRAND ITASCA CLINIC AND HOSPITAL
1601 Golf Course Rd, Grand Rapids, MN 55744-8648
Tel (218) 326-3401 *Founded/Ownrshp* 1918
Sales 78.7MM *EMP* 380
SIC 8062 8011 General medical & surgical hospitals; Offices & clinics of medical doctors; General medical & surgical hospitals; Offices & clinics of medical doctors
Ch: Marva Jean Hutchens
**CEO:* Steve Feldman
CFO: Bruce Lorenz
Treas: Edwin Anderson
Dir OR: Brenda McIntyre
Dir Rad: Jeanette Olson
Dir Rx: Theresa Fox
Dir Rx: Melissa Walters
CIO: Cindy Chambers
Dir IT: Jon Pederson
Sls&Mrk Ex: Colleen Swanson

D-U-N-S 00-742-7685 IMP
GRAND JUNCTION CONCRETE PIPE CO INC
GRAND JUNCTION PIPE & SUP CO
(*Suby of* SUMMIT MATERIALS LLC) ★
2868 I 70 Bus Loop, Grand Junction, CO 81501-4712
Tel (970) 243-4604 *Founded/Ownrshp* 1966, 2011
Sales 45.9MM^E *EMP* 160
SIC 5074 3273 3272

D-U-N-S 00-708-0286
GRAND JUNCTION MEDIA INC
GRAND JUNCTION NEWSPAPERS INC
(*Suby of* MANHATTAN MERCURY) ★
734 S 7th St, Grand Junction, CO 81501-7737
Tel (970) 242-5050 *Founded/Ownrshp* 2009
Sales 23.1MM^E *EMP* 195
SIC 2711 Newspapers, publishing & printing; Newspapers, publishing & printing
Pr: George Orbanek
CFO: Sheryl Huffaker
VP: Preston B Barnett
VP: J R Smith

GRAND JUNCTION NEWSPAPERS INC
See GRAND JUNCTION MEDIA INC

GRAND JUNCTION PIPE & SUP CO
See GRAND JUNCTION CONCRETE PIPE CO INC

GRAND JUNCTION PIPE AND SUPPLY
See ELAM CONSTRUCTION INC

D-U-N-S 06-513-0353
GRAND LABORATORIES INC
44130 279th St, Freeman, SD 57029-5800
Tel (605) 925-7611 *Founded/Ownrshp* 1971
Sales 26.7MM *EMP* 20
SIC 2836 Vaccines; Serums; Vaccines; Serums
Treas: Dr Duane Pankratz
Advt Mgr: Jonetta Berta

GRAND LAKE HEALTH SYSTEM
See JOINT TOWNSHIP DISTRICT MEMORIAL HOSPITAL

D-U-N-S 08-887-3302
GRAND LEDGE PUBLIC SCHOOLS
220 Lamson St, Grand Ledge, MI 48837-1760
Tel (517) 925-5400 *Founded/Ownrshp* 1885
Sales 23.3MM^E *EMP* 429
SIC 8211 Public elementary school; Public junior high school; Public senior high school; Public adult education school; Public elementary school; Public junior high school; Public senior high school; Public adult education school
Pr: Jay Bennett
Opers Supe: John Piper

D-U-N-S 08-368-8564
GRAND LODGE OF FREE & ACCEPTED MASONS OF STATE OF MICHIGAN
MASONIC CENTER
233 Fulton St E Ste 110, Grand Rapids, MI 49503-3262
Tel (616) 459-6401 *Founded/Ownrshp* 2002
Sales 1.3MM^E *EMP* 314
SIC 8641 8051 Fraternal associations; Skilled nursing care facilities; Fraternal associations; Skilled nursing care facilities

D-U-N-S 11-733-8608
GRAND LODGE OF INDIANA F & A M SCHOLARSHIP BOARD INC
INDIANA MASONIC HOME
525 N Illinois St, Indianapolis, IN 46204-1209
Tel (317) 634-7904 *Founded/Ownrshp* 1818
Sales 82.4M *EMP* 352
Accts Ksm Business Services Inc I
SIC 8641 8059 Fraternal associations; Personal care home, with health care; Fraternal associations; Personal care home, with health care
**Treas:* John Grein

D-U-N-S 00-813-2649
GRAND LODGE OF ORDER OF SONS OF HERMANN
HERMANN SONS OF TEXAS
515 S Saint Marys St, San Antonio, TX 78205-3430
Tel (210) 226-9261 *Founded/Ownrshp* 1890
Sales NA *EMP* 55
SIC 6311 8361 7032 Fraternal life insurance organizations; Home for the aged; Sporting & recreational camps; Fraternal life insurance organizations; Home for the aged; Sporting & recreational camps
Pr: Buddy Cruz
**Pr:* Leroy Muehlstein
**VP:* Mary Beam
**VP:* Stephen R Prewitt
VP: Howard Saatahoff
VP: Harry Werland
Dir IT: Matt Walker

D-U-N-S 09-417-2272 IMP
■ **GRAND LUX CAFE LLC**
(*Suby of* CHEESECAKE FACTORY RESTAURANTS INC) ★
26901 Malibu Hills Rd, Calabasas, CA 91301-5354
Tel (818) 871-8300 *Founded/Ownrshp* 1999
Sales 12.1MM^E *EMP* 600
SIC 5812 American restaurant; Ethnic food restaurants; American restaurant; Ethnic food restaurants
Pr: David Overton
**VP:* Gerald Deitchle

D-U-N-S 04-367-6352
GRAND MANOR FURNITURE INC
929 Harrisburg Dr Sw, Lenoir, NC 28645-6126
Tel (828) 758-5521 *Founded/Ownrshp* 1963
Sales 23.0MM^E *EMP* 100
SIC 2512 Chairs: upholstered on wood frames; Couches, sofas & davenports: upholstered on wood frames; Recliners: upholstered on wood frames
CEO: William R Johnson
Sr VP: Eric Roseman
VP: Harold Clarkson

D-U-N-S 15-128-1144
GRAND MATERIALS AND SUPPLY INC
12912 W Santa Fe Dr, Surprise, AZ 85378-4190
Tel (623) 875-7000 *Founded/Ownrshp* 1985
Sales 28.0MM^E *EMP* 54
SIC 5032 Brick, stone & related material
Pr: Chaim Avraham
**Pr:* Evelyn Worden

D-U-N-S 05-995-5930 IMP/EXP
GRAND NORTHERN PRODUCTS LLC
9000 Byron Commerce Dr Sw, Byron Center, MI 49315-8077
Tel (616) 583-5000 *Founded/Ownrshp* 1997
Sales 37.0MM *EMP* 30
SIC 5085 5084 Abrasives; Refractory material; Industrial machinery & equipment; Abrasives; Refractory material; Industrial machinery & equipment
CEO: William Currie
**COO:* Michael Currie
**CFO:* Pam Bishop
IT Man: James Bauer
Opers Mgr: Dale Munger
Manager: Wayne Lawrence

D-U-N-S 13-956-0593 IMP
GRAND OPENINGS INC
1959 W Northwest Hwy, Dallas, TX 75220-2313
Tel (972) 484-8855 *Founded/Ownrshp* 1983
Sales 40.6MM^E *EMP* 100
SIC 5031 Door frames, all materials; Window frames, all materials; Millwork; Door frames, all materials; Window frames, all materials; Millwork
Pr: Tracy Edgemon
**Sec:* Karan Edgemon

D-U-N-S 01-588-8380
GRAND PACIFIC CARLSBAD HOTEL LP
SHERATON CARLSBAD RESORT & SPA
5480 Grand Pacific Dr, Carlsbad, CA 92008-4723
Tel (760) 827-2400 *Founded/Ownrshp* 2008
Sales 24.9MM^E *EMP* 272
SIC 7011 Hotels & motels; Hotels & motels
CFO: Tim Shinkle
Exec: Steven Patrick
Genl Mgr: Chris Draper
Sls Dir: Richard Honea
Mktg Mgr: Leah Loyer
Sls Mgr: Cathy Boxley
Sls Mgr: Katie Cambell
Sls Mgr: Tamara Gilbert
Sls Mgr: Sonja Matina

D-U-N-S 87-915-8608
GRAND PACIFIC RESORTS INC
5900 Pasteur Ct Ste 200, Carlsbad, CA 92008-7336
Tel (760) 431-8500 *Founded/Ownrshp* 1993
Sales 229.0MM^E *EMP* 800
SIC 6531 7011 Time-sharing real estate sales, leasing & rentals; Hotels & motels; Time-sharing real estate sales, leasing & rentals; Hotels & motels
CEO: Timothy J Stripe
CFO: Tim Shinkle
**VP:* David Brown
VP: Jeff Farr
VP: Sitka Morelli
Exec: Brenda Caughran
Exec: Sherri Weeks
Ex Dir: Eric Siegel
Rgnl Mgr: Mary Dieckmann
Genl Mgr: Joshua Short
Genl Mgr: Ben Sjodin

D-U-N-S 36-461-1822 IMP
GRAND PACKAGING INC
COMMAND PACKAGING
3840 E 26th St, Vernon, CA 90058-4107
Tel (323) 980-0918 *Founded/Ownrshp* 1989
Sales 98.8MM^E *EMP* 200
SIC 2673 Bags: plastic, laminated & coated; Bags: plastic, laminated & coated
CEO: Pete Grande
**COO:* Albert Halimi

D-U-N-S 13-323-8225
GRAND PEAKS PROPERTY MANAGEMENT INC
4582 S Ulster St Ste 1200, Denver, CO 80237-2639
Tel (720) 889-9200 *Founded/Ownrshp* 2003
Sales 23.3MM^E *EMP* 190
SIC 6531 Rental agent, real estate; Rental agent, real estate
CEO: Luke Simpson
**Pr:* James B Phelps
Treas: Nick Simpson
Sr VP: Paul Herskowitz
VP: Diane Medina
Dir IT: Andrew Smukler

D-U-N-S 00-895-6823 IMP
GRAND PIANO & FURNITURE CO
GRAND HOME FURNISHINGS
4235 Electric Rd Ste 100, Roanoke, VA 24018-8445
Tel (540) 776-7000 *Founded/Ownrshp* 1946
Sales 123.0MM *EMP* 650
Accts J A Johnson Pc Cpas Conyers
SIC 5712 5021 Furniture stores; Furniture stores; Beds & bedding
CEO: George B Cartledge Jr
**Pr:* George B Cartledge III
CFO: Randy Lundy
**Treas:* Randall W Lundy
**Ex VP:* Robert G Bennett

VP: Steve Davis
VP: Alan Zeigler
Store Mgr: Christopher Rhodes
VP Merchng: Fred Flora
Sls Mgr: Ray Graham
Snr Mgr: Nancy Neal

GRAND PONTIAC BUICK G M C KIA
See GRAND AUTO INC

D-U-N-S 07-151-1232
GRAND PORTAGE RESERVATION BUSINESS COMMITTEE
83 Stevens Rd, Grand Portage, MN 55605-3080
Tel (218) 475-2239 *Founded/Ownrshp* 1934
Sales NA *EMP* 475
SIC 9131 Indian reservation; ; Indian reservation;
Ch: Norman Deschampe
**Sec:* Gilbert Caribou

D-U-N-S 01-059-7169
GRAND PRAIRIE CITY OF (INC)
317 College St, Grand Prairie, TX 75050-5636
Tel (972) 237-8000 *Founded/Ownrshp* 1909
Sales NA *EMP* 1,000
Accts Weaver And Tidwell Llp Dalla
SIC 9111 City & town managers' offices; Mayors' offices; City & town managers' offices; Mayors' offices
COO: Anna Doll
CFO: Vivian Parker
Bd of Dir: Greg Giessner
Ofcr: John Brimmer
Ofcr: Randy Holton
Ofcr: Leon Roddy
Ofcr: Lauren Sossi
Ofcr: Joshua Stelter
Exec: Diane Castillo
Exec: Susan Faulkner
Exec: Cami McKillop

D-U-N-S 14-755-3932
GRAND PRAIRIE FOODS INC
1400 N Cleveland Ave, Sioux Falls, SD 57103-6114
Tel (605) 334-5332 *Founded/Ownrshp* 2006
Sales 37.0MM^E^ *EMP* 70
SIC 5149 Specialty food items
Pr: Kurt Loudenback
**CFO:* Tim Koch

D-U-N-S 02-651-2541
GRAND PRAIRIE FORD LP
701 E Palace Pkwy, Grand Prairie, TX 75050-2343
Tel (972) 859-5400 *Founded/Ownrshp* 1986, 1990
Sales 56.1MM^E^ *EMP* 140
SIC 5511 Automobiles, new & used; Automobiles, new & used
Genl Pt: Larry V Tuyl
**Pt:* Allan Cady
**Pt:* Patricia V Tuyl
Sls Dir: Shawn Leggett
Sls Mgr: Tony Terrazas
Sales Asso: Brandon Hanigan
Sales Asso: Demonte Young

D-U-N-S 07-933-2763
GRAND PRAIRIE INDEPENDENT SCHOOL DISTRICT (TX)
GPISD
2602 S Belt Line Rd, Grand Prairie, TX 75052-5344
Tel (972) 264-6141 *Founded/Ownrshp* 1925
Sales 290.2MM *EMP* 3,500
Accts Hereford Lynch Sellars & Kir
SIC 8211 Public elementary school; Public junior high school; Public senior high school; Public elementary school; Public junior high school; Public senior high school
Ofcr: Mark Ramsey
VP: Melissa Hagood
CTO: Matt Yeager
VP Sls: Tina Stewart
Psych: Crystal Torres

GRAND PRIZE CHVRLET-OLDSMOBILE
See GRAND PRIZE MOTORS INC

D-U-N-S 85-919-8574 IMP/EXP
GRAND PRIZE MOTORS INC
GRAND PRIZE CHVRLET-OLDSMOBILE
11701 Sw 152nd St, Miami, FL 33177-1601
Tel (305) 235-8200 *Founded/Ownrshp* 1992
Sales 33.9MM^E^ *EMP* 90^E^
Accts Illegible
SIC 5511 Automobiles, new & used; Automobiles, new & used
Pr: Ralph W Sifford
**CFO:* Louis Izquierdo

D-U-N-S 13-087-2534 IMP/EXP
GRAND PRODUCTS INC
1718 Hampshire Dr, Elk Grove Village, IL 60007-2760
Tel (800) 621-6101 *Founded/Ownrshp* 1985
Sales 25.1MM^E^ *EMP* 325
SIC 3999 3679 Coin-operated amusement machines; Harness assemblies for electronic use: wire or cable; Coin-operated amusement machines; Harness assemblies for electronic use: wire or cable
Pr: David Marofske Jr
Pr: Nicholas Kallas
Ch: David Marofske Sr

D-U-N-S 11-746-1236
GRAND RAPIDS AREA MEDICAL EDUCATION CONSORTIUM INC
GRAND RAPIDS MEDICAL EDUCAT
945 Ottawa Ave Nw, Grand Rapids, MI 49503-1431
Tel (616) 732-6200 *Founded/Ownrshp* 1971
Sales 33.3MM *EMP* 340
Accts Rehmann Robson Llc Grand Rapi
SIC 8249 Medical & dental assistant school; Medical & dental assistant school
Pr: Peter Coggan MD
Surgeon: Paul Butler

D-U-N-S 84-964-1238 IMP
GRAND RAPIDS CHAIR CO
1250 84th St Sw, Byron Center, MI 49315-8048
Tel (616) 774-0561 *Founded/Ownrshp* 1991
Sales 28.2MM^E^ *EMP* 120
SIC 2511 Wood household furniture
CEO: Dave Miller
**CFO:* Greg Bremer
VP: Jill Alison
**VP:* Geoffrey Miller
**VP:* Tom Southwell
VP: Mike Yost
VP Opers: Dave Overholt
Mtls Mgr: Jerry Baker
Mtls Mgr: Pete Weiblen
Mktg Dir: Jill Frey
Mktg Mgr: Tammy Fulcher-Muraski

D-U-N-S 07-257-8099
GRAND RAPIDS CHRISTIAN SCHOOLS
1508 Alexander St Se, Grand Rapids, MI 49506-3200
Tel (616) 574-6000 *Founded/Ownrshp* 1969
Sales 22.0MM *EMP* 295
SIC 8211 Private elementary & secondary schools; Private elementary & secondary schools
Pr: Jill Bielema
COO: Holly Haan
**CFO:* Jim Primus
**Prin:* Paul Jeltema
Ex Dir: John Blakemore
Genl Mgr: Teresa Quiggle
Psych: Renee Hartman

D-U-N-S 78-042-7324
GRAND RAPIDS COMMUNITY COLLEGE
GRCC
143 Bostwick Ave Ne, Grand Rapids, MI 49503-3201
Tel (616) 234-4000 *Founded/Ownrshp* 1963
Sales 57.8MM *EMP* 154
Accts Plante & Moran Pllc Grand Rap
SIC 8222 Community college; Community college
Pr: Steven Ender
**Pr:* Juan Olivarez
**Treas:* Ellen M James
Ofcr: Paul Coulson
Ex VP: Bob Partridge
**VP:* Donald Boyer
VP: David Custer
VP: John Doane
VP: Lisa Freiburger
**VP:* Kathy Mullins
**VP:* Cynthia Springer
Assoc Dir: Paul Doane

D-U-N-S 01-708-4237 IMP
GRAND RAPIDS FOAM TECHNOLOGIES INC
GRFT
2788 Remico St Sw, Wyoming, MI 49519-2410
Tel (616) 726-1677 *Founded/Ownrshp* 1949
Sales 213.5MM^E^ *EMP* 250
SIC 5199 Foam rubber; Foam rubber
Pr: Ben Amann
VP: Paul Vanderlaan
Plnt Mgr: Scott Miller
Sls Mgr: Jeff Leech

D-U-N-S 00-640-8538
GRAND RAPIDS GRAVEL CO
PORT CITY REDI-MIX
2700 28th St Sw, Grand Rapids, MI 49519-2110
Tel (616) 538-9000 *Founded/Ownrshp* 1986
Sales 23.6MM^E^ *EMP* 135
SIC 3273 1422 8741 1442 Ready-mixed concrete; Calcareous tufa, crushed & broken-quarrying; Cement rock, crushed & broken-quarrying; Management services; Construction sand & gravel; Ready-mixed concrete; Calcareous tufa, crushed & broken-quarrying; Cement rock, crushed & broken-quarrying; Management services; Construction sand & gravel
Pr: Andrew Dykema
Ql Cn Mgr: Jim English

GRAND RAPIDS HOUSING COMMISION
See LEONARD TERRACE APARTMENTS

D-U-N-S 08-947-6139
GRAND RAPIDS INDEPENDENT SCHOOL DISTRICT NO 318
820 Nw 1st Ave, Grand Rapids, MN 55744-2701
Tel (218) 327-5700 *Founded/Ownrshp* 1969
Sales 17.3MM^E^ *EMP* 351
SIC 8211 Public combined elementary & secondary school; School board; Public combined elementary & secondary school; School board
HC Dir: Angela Elhard

GRAND RAPIDS MEDICAL EDUCAT
See GRAND RAPIDS AREA MEDICAL EDUCATION CONSORTIUM INC

D-U-N-S 01-708-4492
GRAND RAPIDS METROLOGY INC (MI)
4215 Stafford Ave Sw, Grand Rapids, MI 49548-3055
Tel (616) 538-7080 *Founded/Ownrshp* 1922, 1963
Sales 33.8MM^E^ *EMP* 65
SIC 5046 Scales, except laboratory; Scales, except laboratory
Ch: Marisa Fahnenstiel
**Pr:* Richard Spruit
CFO: Anna Hickman
Ql Cn Mgr: Terry Benjamin

D-U-N-S 06-945-4965
GRAND RAPIDS OPHTHALMOLOGY PC
750 E Beltline Ave Ne # 100, Grand Rapids, MI 49525-6046
Tel (616) 949-2600 *Founded/Ownrshp* 1982
Sales 15.6MM^E^ *EMP* 300
SIC 8011 Ophthalmologist
Pr: Larry J Gerbens
**Pr:* David Barrett
Treas: Gerard Van Wesep
**VP:* Kenyon S Kendall Do
**VP:* Gilbert Vander Veen
Off Mgr: Toni Elkins
Board of Directors: Russell Weber

D-U-N-S 61-486-7880
GRAND RAPIDS PLASTICS INC
3910 R B Chaffee Mem Dr, Grand Rapids, MI 49548
Tel (616) 531-5455 *Founded/Ownrshp* 2005
Sales 58.4MM^E^ *EMP* 210
SIC 3089 Injection molding of plastics; Injection molding of plastics
Pr: Arthur J Bott Jr
Genl Mgr: Jerry Bott
Plnt Mgr: Jim Newman
Ql Cn Mgr: Rodney Marshall

D-U-N-S 80-940-9225
GRAND REALTY OF AMERICA CORP
19300 W Dixie Hwy Unit 12, Miami, FL 33180-2201
Tel (305) 931-7878 *Founded/Ownrshp* 2006
Sales 17.0MM^E^ *EMP* 714
SIC 6531 Real estate brokers & agents; Real estate brokers & agents
Pr: Eduardo Funes

D-U-N-S 11-746-2762
GRAND RIVER CONSTRUCTION INC
GRC
5025 40th Ave, Hudsonville, MI 49426-9481
Tel (616) 669-5611 *Founded/Ownrshp* 1984
Sales 48.0MM^E^ *EMP* 100
SIC 1771 1542 Concrete work; Commercial & office building, new construction; Concrete work; Commercial & office building, new construction
CEO: William Kersaan
**Pr:* Stanley Buell
**CFO:* David Coates
**Treas:* John Kersaan Jr
Sfty Dirs: John Spavale

D-U-N-S 07-426-4391 IMP
GRAND RIVER DAM AUTHORITY
GRDA
226 W Dwain Willis Ave, Vinita, OK 74301-4654
Tel (918) 256-5545 *Founded/Ownrshp* 1935
Sales 430.4MM *EMP* 468
Accts Deloitte & Touche Llp Tulsa
SIC 4911 1629 Generation, electric power; Transmission, electric power; Distribution, electric power; Dams, waterways, docks & other marine construction; Generation, electric power; Transmission, electric power; Distribution, electric power; Dams, waterways, docks & other marine construction
CEO: Dan Sullivan
COO: Tim Brown
COO: Holly Moore
CFO: Carolyn Dougherty
Ofcr: Derrick Bidleman
Ofcr: Scott Cox
Ofcr: Jason Littlefield
Genl Mgr: Chester Rothhammer
IT Man: Ray Flaming
Web Dev: John Lovell
Software D: Tim Kirby

GRAND RIVER FABRICATING
See CAPARO VEHICLE COMPONENTS INC

D-U-N-S 07-577-0644
GRAND RIVER HOSPITAL DISTRICT
GRAND RIVER MEDICAL CENTER
501 Airport Rd, Rifle, CO 81650-8510
Tel (970) 625-1514 *Founded/Ownrshp* 1962
Sales 42.4MM^E^ *EMP* 244
SIC 8062 8051 General medical & surgical hospitals; Skilled nursing care facilities; General medical & surgical hospitals; Skilled nursing care facilities
CEO: Patrick Howery
**Ch Bd:* Bruce Mills
**Pr:* Sam Potter
**CEO:* Jim Coombs
**CEO:* Michael J Raymond
CFO: Lasca Schrina
**Treas:* Marcia Kent
Ofcr: Martie Wisdom
**VP:* Kip Costanzo
Dir Lab: Cindy Baxter
Dir Lab: Scott Dooling

GRAND RIVER MEDICAL CENTER
See GRAND RIVER HOSPITAL DISTRICT

D-U-N-S 00-784-8773
GRAND RIVER MUTUAL TELEPHONE CORP
1001 Kentucky St, Princeton, MO 64673-1074
Tel (660) 748-2250 *Founded/Ownrshp* 1951, 1986
Sales 24.4MM^E^ *EMP* 98
SIC 4813 4812 Telephone communication, except radio; Cellular telephone services
**Treas:* John McCloud
Genl Mgr: Ron Hinds

D-U-N-S 08-014-9263 IMP/EXP
GRAND RIVER RUBBER & PLASTICS CO (OH)
2029 Aetna Rd, Ashtabula, OH 44004-6298
Tel (440) 998-2900 *Founded/Ownrshp* 1976
Sales 34.0MM^E^ *EMP* 200^E^
SIC 3069 3053

GRAND RPIDS THLOGICAL SEMINARY
See CORNERSTONE UNIVERSITY

GRAND SIERRA RESORT AND CASINO
See MEI-GSR HOLDINGS LLC

D-U-N-S 78-225-1016 IMP
GRAND SIERRA RESORT CORP
2500 2nd St, Reno, NV 89595-1201
Tel (800) 501-2651 *Founded/Ownrshp* 2011
Sales 130.5MM^E^ *EMP* 1,500
SIC 7011 Resort hotel; Casino hotel; Resort hotel; Casino hotel
Pr: Thomas J Schrade
CFO: Craig Robinson
**CFO:* Andrew Tammen
Sr VP: Rod Luck
Sr VP: Jeff Miller
VP: Ralph Burdick
VP: Corey Gene
VP: Vaughan Kent
VP: Jim Latser
VP: Jean Pace
VP: Kent Vaughan
Exec: Jerry Ignatich

D-U-N-S 80-014-4128
■ **GRAND SLAM HOLDINGS LLC**
BLACKSTONE GROUP
(*Suby of* BLACKSTONE CAPITAL PARTNERS V LP) ★
345 Park Ave Bsmt Lb4, New York, NY 10154-0004
Tel (212) 583-5000 *Founded/Ownrshp* 2006
Sales 1.2MMM^E^ *EMP* 5,470^E^
SIC 3842 Surgical appliances & supplies; Implants, surgical; Surgical appliances & supplies; Implants, surgical
CEO: Stephen A Schwarzman

GRAND STAND REGIONAL MED CTR
See GRAND STRAND REGIONAL MEDICAL CENTER LLC

D-U-N-S 60-374-8042
GRAND STRAND REGIONAL MEDICAL CENTER LLC
GRAND STAND REGIONAL MED CTR
809 82nd Pkwy, Myrtle Beach, SC 29572-4607
Tel (843) 449-4411 *Founded/Ownrshp* 2005
Sales 265.2MM *EMP* 1,000
SIC 8062 General medical & surgical hospitals; General medical & surgical hospitals
CEO: Mark Sims
Pr: Doug White
CFO: Robert Grace
Prin: Susan Satterfield
Mktg Dir: Joan Carroza
Doctor: James Brannon
Doctor: Kenneth Houghton
Doctor: Charles Tarbert
Doctor: Mark Waggener

D-U-N-S 07-373-0079
GRAND STRAND WATER & SEWER AUTHORITY
GSWSA
166 Jackson Bluff Rd, Conway, SC 29526-8750
Tel (843) 443-8200 *Founded/Ownrshp* 1970
Sales 74.8MM *EMP* 282
Accts Elliott Davis Columbia South
SIC 4941 4952 Water supply; Sewerage systems; Water supply; Sewerage systems
CEO: Fred R Richardson
**COO:* Irvin Wooley
**CFO:* Marguerite Carroll
**Ch:* Sidney F Thompson
**Prin:* Robert M Floyd Jr
**Prin:* Wilbur M James
**Prin:* Arnold Johnson
**Prin:* Robert Rabon
**Prin:* Richard Singleton
**Prin:* Liston Wells
Ex Dir: Fred R Ichadson

D-U-N-S 19-656-4848 IMP
GRAND SUPERCENTER INC
HANAHREUM GROUP
300 Chubb Ave, Lyndhurst, NJ 07071-3502
Tel (201) 507-9900 *Founded/Ownrshp* 2003
Sales 113.4MM^E^ *EMP* 70^E^
Accts Choi Kim & Park Llp Irvine
SIC 5141 Groceries, general line; Groceries, general line
Pr: Ilyeon Kwon
Store Mgr: Min Hans

D-U-N-S 11-912-4530
GRAND TARGHEE RESORT LLC
3300 E Skihill Rd, Alta, WY 83414-4570
Tel (307) 353-2300 *Founded/Ownrshp* 1973
Sales 19.6MM^E^ *EMP* 300
SIC 7011 Resort hotel; Resort hotel
VP: Heath Nielsen
Dir Soc: Andy Williams
IT Man: Frank Richey
VP Mktg: Susie Barnett-Bushong
Mktg Mgr: Jake Hawkes

D-U-N-S 02-919-3661
■ **GRAND TETON LODGE CO**
JACKSON HOLE GOLF & TENNIS
(*Suby of* VAIL RESORTS INC) ★
Highway 89 5 Mls N Moran, Moran, WY 83013
Tel (307) 543-2811 *Founded/Ownrshp* 1997
Sales 12.0MM *EMP* 1,100
SIC 7011 Vacation lodges; Vacation lodges
CEO: Alex Klein
Treas: Mark Schoppet
Sr VP: Mark Bigalke

D-U-N-S 60-835-4601
GRAND TEXAS HOMES INC
GRAND HOMES
(*Suby of* GHI HOLDINGS INC) ★
15455 Dallas Pkwy # 1000, Addison, TX 75001-6772
Tel (972) 387-6000 *Founded/Ownrshp* 1986
Sales 80.1MM^E^ *EMP* 174
SIC 1521 New construction, single-family houses; New construction, single-family houses
CEO: Stephen H Brooks
CFO: David Abbott
**CFO:* Tim Litinas
VP: Beau Brooks
VP: Marsue Heffner
VP: Alan Luna
Div Mgr: Craig Barrow
Div Mgr: Jim Monk
Prd Mgr: Shane Child
Prd Mgr: Scott Houck
Prd Mgr: Mike Pearce

GRAND THEATER, THE
See SOUTHERN THEATRES LLC

D-U-N-S 07-217-6105
GRAND TRAVERSE BAND ECONOMIC DEVELOPMENT CORP
GRAND TRAVERSE RESORT CASINOS
2331 N West Bay Shore Dr, Suttons Bay, MI 49682-9365
Tel (231) 534-8000 *Founded/Ownrshp* 1998
Sales 46.8MM^E^ *EMP* 1,024

SIC 7011 7993 5812 Casino hotel; Gambling establishments operating coin-operated machines; Gambling machines; Gambling machines, coin-operated; Eating places; Casino hotel; Gambling establishments operating coin-operated machines; Gambling machines; Gambling machines, coin-operated; Eating places
Pr: Richard Bailey
**CFO:* Richard Andrew

D-U-N-S 10-674-8833
GRAND TRAVERSE BAND LLC
TURTLE CREEK CASINO
2605 N West Bay Shore Dr, Suttons Bay, MI 49682-9275
Tel (231) 534-7750 *Founded/Ownrshp* 1980
Sales 56.0MM^E *EMP* 1,100
SIC 7011 Resort hotel; Resort hotel
Ch Bd: Robert Kewaygashcum
**Ch:* Derek J Bailey
**Ch:* Sandra Witherspoon
Telecom Ex: Evans Sam
IT Man: Katrina Smith

GRAND TRAVERSE CONTAINER
See GRAND TRAVERSE REELS INC

GRAND TRAVERSE COUNTY 911
See COUNTY OF GRAND TRAVERSE

D-U-N-S 07-927-3876
GRAND TRAVERSE PAVILIONS FOUNDATION INC
1000 Pavillions Cir, Traverse City, MI 49684-3198
Tel (231) 932-3000 *Founded/Ownrshp* 1959
Sales 292.9M *EMP* 415
SIC 8051 Extended care facility; Extended care facility
VP: Richard Marion Jr
Ofcr: Korvyn Hansen

D-U-N-S 92-616-6794
GRAND TRAVERSE REELS INC
GRAND TRAVERSE CONTAINER
1050 Business Park Dr, Traverse City, MI 49686-8372
Tel (231) 946-1057 *Founded/Ownrshp* 1995
Sales 26.6MM^E *EMP* 104
Accts Plante & Moran Pllc Traverse
SIC 2653 Corrugated & solid fiber boxes; Corrugated & solid fiber boxes
Owner: Thomas Schofield
**Treas:* Vince Balog
**VP:* Mike Chereskin

D-U-N-S 80-879-1024
GRAND TRAVERSE RESORT AND SPA LLC
(*Suby of* GRAND TRAVERSE BAND LLC) ★
100 Grand Trvrse Vlg Blvd, Acme, MI 49610
Tel (231) 534-6000 *Founded/Ownrshp* 2003
Sales 42.5MM^E *EMP* 500^E
SIC 7991 Spas; Spas
Pr: Donald Ponniah
Ex VP: Channing Grant
Comm Man: Jmichael Deagostino
Off Mgr: Michelle Trumble
Natl Sales: Kelly J Bowman
Natl Sales: Brenda McLellan
Natl Sales: Rex Oeconnor

GRAND TRAVERSE RESORT CASINOS
See GRAND TRAVERSE BAND ECONOMIC DEVELOPMENT CORP

D-U-N-S 07-424-1217
GRAND TRUNK CORP
(*Suby of* COMPAGNIE DES CHEMINS DE FER NATIONAUX DU CANADA)
2800 Livernois Rd Ste 110, Troy, MI 48083-1257
Tel (248) 740-6004 *Founded/Ownrshp* 1970
Sales 155.1M *EMP* 2,000
SIC 4011 Railroads, line-haul operating; Railroads, line-haul operating
Pr: Paul M Tellier
VP: Robert A Walker

D-U-N-S 13-547-6328
GRAND TRUNK WESTERN RAILROAD CO
CN
(*Suby of* GRAND TRUNK CORP) ★
17641 Ashland Ave, Homewood, IL 60430-1339
Tel (708) 332-3500 *Founded/Ownrshp* 1992
Sales 147.3M^E *EMP* 1,900^E
SIC 4011 Railroads, line-haul operating
Pr: Claude Mongeau
**COO:* Jim Vena
**CFO:* Luc Jobin
**Ex VP:* Sean Finn
**Sr VP:* Jeff Liepelt

GRAND UNION FAMILY MARKETS
See GU MARKETS LLC

D-U-N-S 11-030-0279
GRAND UNION HEALTHCARE LLC
MONROE MANNOR
226 E Monore St, Jay, OK 74346
Tel (918) 253-4500 *Founded/Ownrshp* 2000
Sales 205.4MM *EMP* 60
SIC 8059 Nursing home, except skilled & intermediate care facility; Nursing home, except skilled & intermediate care facility

D-U-N-S 06-213-0166
GRAND VALLEY HEALTH PLAN INC
JENISON HEALTH CENTER
829 Forest Hill Ave Se, Grand Rapids, MI 49546-2387
Tel (616) 949-2410 *Founded/Ownrshp* 1982
Sales 21.3MM^E *EMP* 150
SIC 8011 Health maintenance organization
Pr: Roland E Palmer
Dir Rx: Anne Kozal
Dir IT: Jeff Neese

GRAND VALLEY POWER
See GRAND VALLEY RURAL POWER LINES INC

D-U-N-S 00-387-0029
GRAND VALLEY RURAL POWER LINES INC
GRAND VALLEY POWER
845 22 Rd, Grand Junction, CO 81505-9729
Tel (970) 242-0040 *Founded/Ownrshp* 1936
Sales 31.4MM *EMP* 42
SIC 4911 Distribution, electric power; Distribution, electric power
Genl Mgr: Tom Walch
Opers Mgr: Pat Oglesby

D-U-N-S 05-969-2996
GRAND VALLEY STATE UNIVERSITY
MEADOWS GOLF CLUB , THE
1 Campus Dr, Allendale, MI 49401-9403
Tel (616) 331-5000 *Founded/Ownrshp* 1960
Sales 342.1MM *EMP* 2,000
Accts Plante & Moran Pllc Grand Ra
SIC 8221 University; University
Pr: Thomas J Haas
COO: Linda Masselink
**Treas:* Timothy O Schad
Bd of Dir: Caitlin Cusack
Bd of Dir: Patricia Stephenson
Trst: Kate P Wolters
Assoc VP: Julia Guevara
VP: Briand Copeland
**VP:* Gayle R Davis
**VP:* Matthew E McLogan
VP: Maribeth Wardrop
Dir Lab: Dell Paielli
Assoc Dir: Amy Campbell
Assoc Dir: Breeann Gorham
Assoc Dir: Jenna Poll
Assoc Dir: Bobby Springer

GRAND VICTORIA CASINO
See ELGIN RIVERBOAT RESORT-RIVERBOAT CASINO

GRAND VIEW HEALTH
See GRAND VIEW HOSPITAL

D-U-N-S 96-723-6220
GRAND VIEW HEALTH SYSTEM INC
10561 Grand View Ln, Ironwood, MI 49938
Tel (906) 932-6215 *Founded/Ownrshp* 2011
Sales 37.3MM *EMP* 45^E
Accts Eide Bailly Llp Minneapolis
SIC 8062 General medical & surgical hospitals; General medical & surgical hospitals
Prin: Bonnie Ozzello
CIO: Mary Babb
Pharmcst: Christopher Pogliano
Phys Thrpy: Nancy Levra
Snr Mgr: Donna Cataldo

D-U-N-S 86-125-0868 IMP
GRAND VIEW HOSPITAL
GRAND VIEW HEALTH
700 Lawn Ave, Sellersville, PA 18960-1548
Tel (215) 453-4000 *Founded/Ownrshp* 1913
Sales 203.5MM *EMP* 1,600
Accts Crowe Horwath Llp Louisville
SIC 8062 General medical & surgical hospitals; General medical & surgical hospitals
CEO: Stuart Fine
CFO: Gregory Wuerstle
Treas: Mitchell P Barrer
Ofcr: David Lightfoot
VP: Jane Ferrymd
VP: Jean Keeler
VP: Linda Lavin
Dir Rx: Brian Plajer
Dir Sec: Tom Hennink
Off Mgr: John Detweiler
Off Admin: Debbie Alles

D-U-N-S 08-349-3726
GRAND VIEW UNIVERSITY
1200 Grandview Ave, Des Moines, IA 50316-1529
Tel (515) 263-2800 *Founded/Ownrshp* 1896
Sales 34.6MM *EMP* 247
Accts Mcgladrey Llp Des Moines Iow
SIC 5942 8221 College book stores; College, except junior; College book stores; College, except junior
Pr: Kent L Henning
Assoc VP: Jason Bauer
Ex VP: Ronald Taylor
VP: Debbie Barger
VP: Carol Hall
**VP:* Mary E Stivers
Assoc Dir: Joy Brandt
Sls&Mrk Ex: Kati Bainter
Sls Mgr: Adam Voigts

D-U-N-S 94-367-7328
GRAND WAREHOUSE AND DISTRIBUTION CORP
4350 W Ohio St, Chicago, IL 60624-1051
Tel (773) 265-0403 *Founded/Ownrshp* 1994
Sales 85.7MM^E *EMP* 1,000
SIC 4225 General warehousing & storage; General warehousing & storage
Pr: David Schulman
**COO:* Rick Ehrensast

D-U-N-S 07-871-8049
■ **GRANDBRIDGE REAL ESTATE CAPITAL LLC**
(*Suby of* BB&T CORP) ★
20975 Swenson Dr Ste 325, Waukesha, WI 53186-4064
Tel (704) 379-6992 *Founded/Ownrshp* 2007
Sales 5.3MM^E *EMP* 300
SIC 6531 Real estate agent, commercial; Real estate agent, commercial
VP: Deborah Storts

D-U-N-S 88-427-9134
■ **GRANDBRIDGE REAL ESTATE CAPITAL LLC**
(*Suby of* BB&T) ★
200 S College St, Charlotte, NC 28202-2012
Tel (704) 379-6900 *Founded/Ownrshp* 2000
Sales 14.8MM^E *EMP* 300
SIC 6531 Real estate agents & managers; Real estate agents & managers

Sr VP: George V Atkison III
Sr VP: John Fenoglio
Sr VP: Shelley Magoffin
Sr VP: Anne McPhail
Sr VP: Carl Olzawski
Sr VP: Michael Ortlip
Sr VP: John M Stewart
VP: Michael Balan
VP: Robert Balderson
VP: Richard Brinson
VP: Michael Dunn
VP: Miki Eide
VP: Mary Funderburk III
VP: George Lander
VP: Robert Larue
VP: Jin Lin
VP: Kathleen Lomuscio
VP: Annie Martin
VP: Kelly Martone
VP: Patricia Muse
VP: Penny A Newton

GRANDE CENTRAL SHOWROOM
See CENTRAL PLUMBING SPECIALITIES CO INC

D-U-N-S 00-611-0274 IMP
GRANDE CHEESE CO
GRANDE CSTM INGREDIENTS GROUP
Dairy Rd, Brownsville, WI 53006
Tel (920) 583-3122 *Founded/Ownrshp* 1941
Sales 259.5MM^E *EMP* 760
SIC 2022 Natural cheese; Whey, raw or liquid; Natural cheese; Whey, raw or liquid
Pr: Wayne Matzke
**CFO:* Todd Koss
VP Opers: Mike Nelson

D-U-N-S 04-353-7849
GRANDE COMMUNICATIONS CLEARSOURCE INC (TX)
(*Suby of* RIO HOLDINGS INC) ★
401 Carlson Cir, San Marcos, TX 78666-6730
Tel (512) 381-7300 *Founded/Ownrshp* 1998
Sales 18.8MM^E *EMP* 700
SIC 7389 4841 4813 Telephone services; Cable television services; ;Telephone services; Cable television services
CEO: Scott Ferguson
**CFO:* Michael Wilfley

D-U-N-S 62-311-5701
GRANDE COMMUNICATIONS NETWORKS LLC
(*Suby of* RIO HOLDINGS INC) ★
401 Carlson Cir, San Marcos, TX 78666-6730
Tel (512) 878-4000 *Founded/Ownrshp* 2000
Sales 119.2MM^E *EMP* 10^E
SIC 4841 Cable & other pay television services; Cable & other pay television services
Sr VP: C Matthew Rohre
Treas: Douglas T Brannagan
Sr VP: W K Ferguson Jr
VP: Brady Adams
VP: Jared P Benson
VP: J Lyn Findley
**VP:* Lamar Horton
VP: James Jordan
VP: Mark Machen
**VP:* Shane Schilling
VP: Kay Stroman
VP: Frank R Wink

GRANDE CSTM INGREDIENTS GROUP
See GRANDE CHEESE CO

D-U-N-S 06-853-7278
GRANDE DEALER DEL GROUP
CAPITOL VOLKSWAGEN
911 Cptl Expy Aut Mall, San Jose, CA 95136-1103
Tel (408) 265-4400 *Founded/Ownrshp* 1999
Sales 66.8MM^E *EMP* 150^E
SIC 5511 New & used car dealers; New & used car dealers
CEO: Kevan Del Grande
**Pr:* Shaun Del Grande
Genl Mgr: Scott Jobe
Sls Mgr: Dave Rubenstein
Sls Mgr: Mclver Wicker

D-U-N-S 04-393-2334 EXP
GRANDE FORD TRUCK SALES INC
GRANDE TRUCK CENTER
4562 Interstate 10 E, San Antonio, TX 78219-4205
Tel (210) 666-7382 *Founded/Ownrshp* 1969
Sales 66.4MM^E *EMP* 135^E
SIC 5511 5012 Automobiles, new & used; Trucks, tractors & trailers: new & used; Trucks, commercial; Truck tractors; Automobiles, new & used; Trucks, tractors & trailers: new & used; Trucks, commercial; Truck tractors
CEO: David R Keck
**Pr:* R S Kane
VP: Terry Anderson
Sls Mgr: Larry Wilson

D-U-N-S 10-602-5328
GRANDE MASONRY LLC
780 Allens Ave, Providence, RI 02905-5424
Tel (401) 781-9800 *Founded/Ownrshp* 1999
Sales 23.8MM *EMP* 100
Accts Stowe & Degon Llc Westborough
SIC 1741 Masonry & other stonework
VP: Alexander F Grande
Exec: Timothy Withers
Snr Mgr: James Delsanto

D-U-N-S 78-650-3693
GRANDE PRODUCE LTD CO
109 W Dicker Rd Ste A, San Juan, TX 78589-4796
Tel (956) 283-7770 *Founded/Ownrshp* 2002
Sales 41.4MM^E *EMP* 62
SIC 5148 Fresh fruits & vegetables
Pr: Juan R Cano
**Prin:* Raul Cano

D-U-N-S 05-497-2211
GRANDE RONDE HOSPITAL INC
GRH
900 Sunset Dr, La Grande, OR 97850-1387
Tel (541) 963-8421 *Founded/Ownrshp* 1966
Sales 71.1MM *EMP* 509
Accts Dingus Zarecor & Associates Pl
SIC 8062 General medical & surgical hospitals; General medical & surgical hospitals
Pr: James Mattes
Chf Rad: Daniel Kirkham
CFO: Bob Whinery
Dir Lab: Sharon Butler
Dir Lab: John Sanchez
Dir Rad: Randy Siltanen
Chf Nrs Of: Doug Romer
**Adm Dir:* Wendy Roberts
Off Mgr: Rondyann Gerst
Off Mgr: Karli Wright
Pr Mgr: Mardi Ford

GRANDE TRUCK CENTER
See GRANDE FORD TRUCK SALES INC

D-U-N-S 06-800-8374
GRANDELL REHABILITATION AND NURSING CENTER INC
645 W Broadway, Long Beach, NY 11561-2902
Tel (516) 889-1100 *Founded/Ownrshp* 1996
Sales 22.0MM^E *EMP* 300
SIC 8051 Skilled nursing care facilities; Skilled nursing care facilities
Pr: Abraham Klein
**CEO:* Leibel Rubin
Nrsg Dir: Mary McGill
HC Dir: Allison Anchin

D-U-N-S 03-001-0417
GRANDMAS INC (MN)
GRANDMA'S SALOON & GRILL
525 S Lake Ave Ste 201, Duluth, MN 55802-2300
Tel (218) 727-2250 *Founded/Ownrshp* 1976
Sales 24.3MM^E *EMP* 600
SIC 5812 5947 5813 Steak restaurant; Gift shop; Bar (drinking places); Steak restaurant; Gift shop; Bar (drinking places)
CEO: Andy L Borg Jr
Pr: Michael Melbi
**Ch:* Michael Paulucci
Exec: Dave Rowell
IT Man: Thor Linnum

GRANDMA'S SALOON & GRILL
See GRANDMAS INC

D-U-N-S 07-138-3772
GRANDOR CORP
OIL CITY IRON WORKS
814 S Main St, Corsicana, TX 75110-7231
Tel (903) 872-6571 *Founded/Ownrshp* 1987
Sales 30.7MM^E *EMP* 270^E
SIC 3321 Gray & ductile iron foundries; Gray & ductile iron foundries
Pr: Eric Meyers
**CFO:* Stephen Spradlin
**VP:* Willard Cox
VP: Rebecca Kinkade
**VP:* Eric Ryan Meyers
QA Dir: Ana Alvarado
Trfc Mgr: Mike Cotten
Mktg Mgr: Glen Oliver
Snr Mgr: Christopher Cofer

GRANDOVER RESORT
See KOURY VENTURES LP

D-U-N-S 96-918-0603
GRANDOVER RESORT & CONFERENCE CENTER
DI VALLETTA RESTAURANT
1000 Club Rd, Greensboro, NC 27407-8286
Tel (336) 294-1800 *Founded/Ownrshp* 1996
Sales 11.9MM^E *EMP* 390
SIC 7011 7997 7299 5813 Resort hotel; Golf club, membership; Banquet hall facilities; Bar (drinking places); Resort hotel; Golf club, membership; Banquet hall facilities; Bar (drinking places)
Ex VP: MO Milani

D-U-N-S 78-826-8865
GRANDPOINT BANK
(*Suby of* GRANDPOINT CAPITAL INC) ★
355 S Grand Ave Ste 2400, Los Angeles, CA 90071-1589
Tel (213) 626-0085 *Founded/Ownrshp* 2006
Sales NA *EMP* 78
SIC 6022 State commercial banks; State commercial banks
CEO: Don M Griffith
Pr: Ana Gomezgil
**Pr:* Dan C Yates
**Treas:* David Scarbrough
Ex VP: David Anderson
Ex VP: R Bianchini
**Ex VP:* Anthony Q Evans
Ex VP: Jim Hackbarth
Ex VP: John Nixon
Ex VP: Jerry Otsuki
**Ex VP:* David J Ross
**Ex VP:* Loraine White
**Ex VP:* Anthony J Xinis
VP: Mackenzie Chambers
VP: Jonathan David
VP: C A Jennings
VP: Pat Lualngeaktrakul
VP: Phil Soh
VP: Harrison Tsai
VP: Mindy Webb
VP: Terry Zippwald

D-U-N-S 80-877-3472
GRANDPOINT CAPITAL INC
333 S Grand Ave Ste 4250, Los Angeles, CA 90071-1587
Tel (213) 542-4410 *Founded/Ownrshp* 2012
Sales 171.8MM^E *EMP* 181^E
SIC 6799 Investors; Investors
CEO: Don M Griffith
**COO:* Deborah A Marsten

CFO: Dave Dayton
**CFO:* Jerro Otsuki

GRANDS TOURS
See RIDGE ROAD EXPRESS INC

D-U-N-S 13-357-5048
▲ GRANDSOUTH BANCORPORATION
381 Halton Rd, Greenville, SC 29607-3405
Tel (864) 770-1000 *Founded/Ownrshp* 2000
Sales NA *EMP* 69^E
Tkr Sym GRRB *Exch* OTO
SIC 6022 State commercial banks
Ch Bd: Mason Garrett
**Pr:* Ronald K Earnest
CFO: J B Garrett
VP: Josh Kimbrell
VP: Trina Smith
IT Man: David Switzer

D-U-N-S 03-012-0286
■ GRANDSOUTH BANK
(*Suby of* GRANDSOUTH BANCORPORATION) ★
381 Halton Rd, Greenville, SC 29607-3405
Tel (864) 770-1000 *Founded/Ownrshp* 2000
Sales NA *EMP* 25
SIC 6022 State commercial banks; State commercial banks
Pr: Ronald K Earnest
**Ch Bd:* Mason Garrett
Sr VP: Michael Dean
VP: Bob Hoffman
VP: Tom Musante

GRANDVIE OUTLETS
See GRANDVIEW BUILDINGS & SUPPLY INC

D-U-N-S 62-211-9782
GRANDVIEW BUILDINGS & SUPPLY INC
GRANDVIE OUTLETS
1840 County Road 1, South Point, OH 45680-8849
Tel (740) 377-9229 *Founded/Ownrshp* 1985
Sales 29.6MM^E *EMP* 150
SIC 5211 Lumber & other building materials; Lumber & other building materials
Pr: Donald J Ashworth
**Sec:* Sandy Tomblin

D-U-N-S 06-794-7267
GRANDVIEW C-4 SCHOOL DISTRICT (MO)
GRANDVIEW SCHOOL DISTRICT
13015 10th St, Grandview, MO 64030-2401
Tel (816) 316-5000 *Founded/Ownrshp* 1914
Sales 50.0MM *EMP* 600
SIC 8211 Public elementary school; Public junior high school; Public senior high school; Public elementary school; Public junior high school; Public senior high school
Schl Brd P: Cindy Bastian

D-U-N-S 62-048-4006
GRANDVIEW CHRISTIAN MINISTRIES
135 Fern St N, Cambridge, MN 55008-1098
Tel (763) 689-4477 *Founded/Ownrshp* 1963
Sales 1.1MM *EMP* 400
SIC 8322 Individual & family services; Individual & family services
CEO: Greg Carlson
**CFO:* Julie Tooker

D-U-N-S 05-708-3610
GRANDVIEW ENTERPRISES INC
7708 Ne 99th St, Vancouver, WA 98662-1343
Tel (360) 254-0181 *Founded/Ownrshp* 1974
Sales 23.0MM^E *EMP* 85
SIC 4731 4213 Truck transportation brokers; Refrigerated products transport
Pr: Terryl Hass
**Pr:* Victoria Grant
**VP:* Shawn Stoller
Genl Mgr: Jim Hilts

D-U-N-S 01-512-9629 IMP
GRANDVIEW GALLERY LLC
5185 Hickory Hill Rd, Memphis, TN 38141-8209
Tel (901) 505-0191 *Founded/Ownrshp* 2009
Sales 28.0MM *EMP* 25
SIC 3641 5021 Electric lamps; Furniture; Electric lamps; Furniture

GRANDVIEW HOSPITAL
See STRESS CARE/BRIDGES

GRANDVIEW HOSPITAL & MED CTR
See KETTERING MEDICAL CENTER

D-U-N-S 04-959-9637
GRANDVIEW MEDICAL CENTER
(*Suby of* CHARLES F KETTERING MEM HOSP) ★
405 W Grand Ave, Dayton, OH 45405-4720
Tel (937) 226-3312 *Founded/Ownrshp* 2001
Sales 292.0MM^E *EMP* 4
SIC 8062 General medical & surgical hospitals; General medical & surgical hospitals
CEO: Fred Manchur
Pr: Roy Chew
Pr: Terri Day
CFO: Russell Wetherell
Sr VP: Terry Burns
Sr VP: Wally Sackett
Dir Lab: Lois Rudzienski

D-U-N-S 01-624-3735
GRANDVIEW PHARMACY INC
HEALTH MART
2230 N Park Rd, Connersville, IN 47331-2903
Tel (765) 827-0847 *Founded/Ownrshp* 1969
Sales 22.3MM^E *EMP* 100
SIC 5912 5047 Drug stores; Medical equipment & supplies
Ch Bd: Howard Eldridge
**CEO:* Mark Prifogle
**CFO:* Jeremy Eldridge
**Sr VP:* Lori King
**VP:* Glenn Eldridge
**Prin:* Betty Eldridge
Pharmcst: Dave Bushman

D-U-N-S 00-717-7330
GRANDVIEW PRODUCTS CO INC
1601 Superior Dr, Parsons, KS 67357
Tel (620) 421-6950 *Founded/Ownrshp* 1946
Sales 34.0MM *EMP* 291
Accts Stafford & Westervelt Parsons
SIC 2434 2541 Wood kitchen cabinets; Table or counter tops, plastic laminated; Wood kitchen cabinets; Table or counter tops, plastic laminated
Pr: Sophia Zetmeir
**Ex VP:* Teresa Hays
DP Dir: Dan Shields
Prd Mgr: Nicole Titus
Ql Cn Mgr: Mark McElroy

GRANDVIEW SCHOOL DISTRICT
See GRANDVIEW C-4 SCHOOL DISTRICT

D-U-N-S 02-473-5060
GRANDVIEW SCHOOL DISTRICT
913 W 2nd St, Grandview, WA 98930-1202
Tel (509) 882-8500 *Founded/Ownrshp* 1908
Sales 21.9MM^E *EMP* 400
SIC 8211 Public elementary & secondary schools; Public elementary & secondary schools
IT Man: Kevin Chase
IT Man: Pat Bonnell
Schl Brd P: Paul Jepson

GRANDVIEW TERRACE
See ROSKAMP/SUN HEALTH RESIDENTIAL SERVICES LLP

D-U-N-S 04-456-3617 EXP
GRANDVILLE PRINTING CO
4719 Ivanrest Ave Sw, Grandville, MI 49418-9141
Tel (616) 534-8647 *Founded/Ownrshp* 1956
Sales 65.4MM^E *EMP* 222
SIC 2752 Commercial printing, offset; Commercial printing, offset
Ch Bd: Jeffrey C Brewer
**Pr:* Patrick J Brewer
**CFO:* Curtis J Cooke
**VP:* Rickard A Durham
QA Dir: Amy Sloboda
Dir IT: Ken Boer
Prd Mgr: Alan Kebless
Ql Cn Mgr: Bob Estes
Sales Exec: Dave Crofoot
Sales Exec: Daniel James
Sales Exec: Tami Kring

D-U-N-S 08-589-8757
GRANDVILLE PUBLIC SCHOOL DISTRICT
3839 Prairie St Sw, Grandville, MI 49418-1648
Tel (616) 254-6550 *Founded/Ownrshp* 1867
Sales 62.5MM *EMP* 645
Accts Maner & Costerisan Lansing M
SIC 8211 Public elementary school; Public junior high school; Public senior high school; School board; Public elementary school; Public junior high school; Public senior high school; School board
VP: Barbara Palmer
Pr Dir: Jayne Johnson

GRANDY PRATT
See ARTHUR J GALLAGHER & CO OF IOWA INC

GRANDY'S
See RED APPLE CORP

D-U-N-S 11-537-5826
GRANE DISTRIBUTION SERVICES LLC
GRANE TRANSPORTATION
703 Foster Ave Frnt A, Bensenville, IL 60106-4500
Tel (630) 451-2000 *Founded/Ownrshp* 2005
Sales 48.7MM^E *EMP* 500
SIC 4213 4225 4212 7363 Trucking, except local; General warehousing; Delivery service, vehicular; Manpower pools; Trucking, except local; General warehousing; Delivery service, vehicular; Manpower pools
Pr: Allan Grane
**VP:* Tim Wells
Genl Mgr: Rick Duran

GRANE TRANSPORTATION
See GRANE DISTRIBUTION SERVICES LLC

D-U-N-S 94-690-1535
GRANELLO BAKERY INC
5045 W Mardon Ave, Las Vegas, NV 89139-5521
Tel (702) 361-0311 *Founded/Ownrshp* 1996
Sales 22.0MM^E *EMP* 60
SIC 5149 Groceries & related products
Pr: Laurie Steed

D-U-N-S 00-904-3555
GRANGE COOPERATIVE SUPPLY ASSOCIATION
PET COUNTRY
2833 N Pacific Hwy, Medford, OR 97501-1361
Tel (541) 773-7087 *Founded/Ownrshp* 1934
Sales 58.7MM *EMP* 175
Accts Moss Adams Llp Yakima Washin
SIC 5999 5171 2048 5261 Feed & farm supply; Pet supplies; Petroleum terminals; Prepared feeds; Lawn & garden supplies; Feed & farm supply; Pet supplies; Petroleum terminals; Prepared feeds; Lawn & garden supplies
CEO: Barry Robino
COO: Bill Christie
**CFO:* David Deyoung
Sls&Mrk Ex: John Jack

D-U-N-S 00-794-2725
GRANGE INSURANCE ASSOCIATION INC (WA)
200 Cedar St, Seattle, WA 98121-1223
Tel (206) 448-4911 *Founded/Ownrshp* 1894
Sales NA *EMP* 200
SIC 6411 Property & casualty insurance agent; Property & casualty insurance agent
Pr: Ryan M Dudley
Pr: Ralph Carlisle
CFO: Sean McGourty
**CFO:* Sean I McGourty
**VP:* Todd C Merkley
**VP:* Steven W Stogner
**VP:* James L Van Farowe
Snr Ntwrk: Mike Patriche
IT Man: Glen Beard
Software D: Doug Walker
Sftwr Eng: Michael Edgar

GRANGE INSURANCE COMPANIES
See GRANGE MUTUAL CASUALTY CO

D-U-N-S 00-232-8248
GRANGE INVESTMENTS INC
6105 Monarch Rd, Longmont, CO 80503-8818
Tel (720) 890-1555 *Founded/Ownrshp* 2000
Sales 42.5MM^E *EMP* 150
SIC 5149 Natural & organic foods; Natural & organic foods
Pr: Mark R Clapp

D-U-N-S 07-937-6515
GRANGE LIFE INSURANCE CO
671 S High St, Columbus, OH 43206-1066
Tel (800) 445-3030 *Founded/Ownrshp* 2014
Sales NA *EMP* 48^E
SIC 6311 Life insurance
CEO: Thomas Welch
VP Mktg: Steve Stogner
Manager: Kate Tobin

D-U-N-S 00-790-1861
GRANGE MUTUAL CASUALTY CO
GRANGE INSURANCE COMPANIES
671 S High St, Columbus, OH 43206-1049
Tel (800) 422-5050 *Founded/Ownrshp* 1935
Sales NA *EMP* 1,450
SIC 6331 Automobile insurance; Fire, marine & casualty insurance: mutual; Automobile insurance; Fire, marine & casualty insurance: mutual
CEO: Tom Welch
Pr: David Berentz
Pr: John Delucia
Pr: Patricia Eshman
Pr: Phil Fcas
Pr: Gary Irvine
Pr: Brent Lombardi
Pr: Brad Sorensen
Pr: Glenn Watson
CFO: J Paul McCaffrey
Assoc VP: Ken Kozek
VP: David Ackermann
VP: Elizabeth Dinnin
VP: Margaret Wildi
Exec: Philip Urban

D-U-N-S 07-635-0230
GRANGER ASSOCIATES INC
16980 Wood Rd, Lansing, MI 48906-1044
Tel (517) 372-2800 *Founded/Ownrshp* 1974
Sales 81.3MM^E *EMP* 119
SIC 4953 1794 6552

GRANGER BUILDING SERVICES
See GRANGER CONSTRUCTION CO INC

D-U-N-S 00-385-6804
GRANGER CONSTRUCTION CO INC (MI)
GRANGER BUILDING SERVICES
6267 Aurelius Rd, Lansing, MI 48911-4296
Tel (517) 393-1670 *Founded/Ownrshp* 1960
Sales 218.6MM *EMP* 215
SIC 1542 1541

D-U-N-S 10-912-5869
GRANGER CONSTRUCTION CO INC
6701 Manlius Center Rd # 215, East Syracuse, NY 13057-3091
Tel (315) 463-2700 *Founded/Ownrshp* 2002
Sales 20.0MM^E *EMP* 44
SIC 1542 Nonresidential construction
Pr: Les Granger
**Ex VP:* Walter Bok

D-U-N-S 14-795-6445
GRANGER MANAGEMENT CORP
R W GRANGER & SONS
415 Boston Tpke, Shrewsbury, MA 01545-3446
Tel (508) 842-8961 *Founded/Ownrshp* 1982
Sales 29.2MM^E *EMP* 148
SIC 1542 1541 1522 Nonresidential construction; Industrial buildings & warehouses; Residential construction; Nonresidential construction; Industrial buildings & warehouses; Residential construction
Pr: Tom Frederick
**Treas:* Robert W Granger Jr
**VP:* Emil Boudreau
**VP:* Stephen J Granger

D-U-N-S 07-301-2197
GRANGER MEDICAL CLINIC
GRANGER MEDICAL WEST VALLEY
3725 W 4100 S, West Valley City, UT 84120-5530
Tel (801) 965-3600 *Founded/Ownrshp* 1960
Sales 50.0MM *EMP* 300
SIC 8011 Clinic, operated by physicians; Clinic, operated by physicians
CEO: David Tanner
**Pr:* Mary Jane Penington
**COO:* John O'Donnell
**CFO:* Krista Beauchat
Dir IT: Gil McDougald
Surgeon: Dean Walker
Plas Surg: Robert Rodrigues
Doctor: Dale Chapman
Doctor: Christopher Hutchison

GRANGER MEDICAL WEST VALLEY
See GRANGER MEDICAL CLINIC

D-U-N-S 09-651-3981
GRANGER MOTORS INC (IA)
1708 Sycamore St, Granger, IA 50109-9752
Tel (515) 999-2224 *Founded/Ownrshp* 1918, 1978
Sales 21.9MM^E *EMP* 51
SIC 5511 Automobiles, new & used
Pr: Timothy H Westrum
DP Dir: Albert Schmitz
Sls Mgr: Trent Muhlenbruck

D-U-N-S 07-874-7433
GRANGETTOS FARM & GARDEN SUPPLY CO (CA)
1105 W Mission Ave, Escondido, CA 92025-1664
Tel (760) 745-4671 *Founded/Ownrshp* 1952
Sales 23.3MM^E *EMP* 47
SIC 5191 5261 Farm supplies; Nurseries & garden centers
CEO: Kevin M Grangetto
**Treas:* Edward Grangetto Jr

D-U-N-S 07-607-3691
GRANI INSTALLATION INC
5411 Commercial Dr, Huntington Beach, CA 92649-1231
Tel (714) 898-0441 *Founded/Ownrshp* 1973
Sales 43.2MM^E *EMP* 125
SIC 1542 1742 Commercial & office buildings, renovation & repair; Acoustical & ceiling work; Commercial & office buildings, renovation & repair; Acoustical & ceiling work
CEO: Gregory A Grani

D-U-N-S 12-910-6469
GRANICUS INC
707 17th St Ste 4000, Denver, CO 80202-3432
Tel (415) 357-3618 *Founded/Ownrshp* 1999
Sales 61.1MM^E *EMP* 136^E
SIC 4813 7371 ; Computer software development; ; Computer software development
CEO: Tom Spengler
**CFO:* Emery Jones
**VP:* Sherif Agib
**VP:* Thao Hill
Off Mgr: Jim Pham
Board of Directors: Peter Arrowsmith

D-U-N-S 14-797-7198 IMP
GRANISER LLC
GRANISER TILE KITCHEN BATH
(*Suby of* GRANISER GRANIT SERAMIK SANAYIVE TICARET ANONIM SIRKETI)
5650 General Wash Dr, Alexandria, VA 22312-2415
Tel (703) 256-5650 *Founded/Ownrshp* 2006
Sales 105.4MM^E *EMP* 860
SIC 5032 Tile & clay products; Tile & clay products

GRANISER TILE KITCHEN BATH
See GRANISER LLC

GRANIT-BRONZ DIV
See COLD SPRING GRANITE CO INC

D-U-N-S 95-899-1507
GRANITE ASSOCIATES LP
1 Cablvision Ctr Rd Ste 4, Liberty, NY 12754
Tel (845) 295-2400 *Founded/Ownrshp* 1995
Sales 23.5MM^E *EMP* 75
SIC 6282 Investment advice
Pt: Alan Gerry
Pr: Chris Grillo
Pr: Keith Suehnholz
VP: Philip Dropkin
Dir IT: Robert Adams
Dir IT: Karin Kanaar
IT Man: Paul Hein

D-U-N-S 16-649-7057
GRANITE BROADCASTING CORP
GBC
767 3rd Ave Fl 34, New York, NY 10017-2083
Tel (212) 826-2530 *Founded/Ownrshp* 1988
Sales 204.5MM^E *EMP* 749
SIC 4833 Television broadcasting stations; Television broadcasting stations
CEO: Don Cornwell
**Pr:* Craig Coane
Pr: Kemp Nichol
**COO:* John Deushane
**COO:* Duane Lammers
**CFO:* Lawrence I Wills
**Ch:* Peter Markham
VP: Herbert Hardt
VP: Marcy Timpone
**Prin:* Kirk W Aubry
**Prin:* Stuart J Beck

D-U-N-S 09-153-1574
GRANITE CITY COMMUNITY UNIT SCHOOL DISTRICT 9
1947 Adams St, Granite City, IL 62040-3311
Tel (618) 451-5800 *Founded/Ownrshp* 1900
Sales 47.4MM^E *EMP* 750
SIC 8211 Public elementary & secondary schools; Elementary school; Vocational high school; Public elementary & secondary schools; Elementary school; Vocational high school

D-U-N-S 01-512-4345
GRANITE CITY ELECTRIC SUPPLY CO
10 Lowell Junction Rd, Andover, MA 01810-5906
Tel (978) 470-1300 *Founded/Ownrshp* 1923
Sales 43.4MM^E *EMP* 250
SIC 5063 Electrical supplies; Electrical supplies
Pr: William Raney
Sls Mgr: Mike Muray
Sales Asso: Sarah Stickney
Sales Asso: Curtis Stoker

D-U-N-S 00-799-8933
GRANITE CITY ELECTRIC SUPPLY CO INC (MA)
19 Quincy Ave, Quincy, MA 02169-6750
Tel (617) 472-0404 *Founded/Ownrshp* 1931
Sales 263.3MM^E *EMP* 180
SIC 5063 5719 Electrical supplies; Lighting fixtures; Lamps & lamp shades; Lighting fixtures; Electrical supplies; Lighting fixtures; Lamps & lamp shades; Lighting fixtures
CEO: Phyllis Papani Godwin
**Pr:* Steven Helle
**Pr:* Nicholas V Papani
**CFO:* Mark Anderson
**Prin:* Nicholas Papani
Brnch Mgr: Nate Wood
Site Mgr: Melissa Welch
Sls Mgr: Ellis Cole
Sales Asso: Rich Bartleman

Sales Asso: Joe Faulkner
Sales Asso: John Foisy

D-U-N-S 07-632-3927 IMP
■ **GRANITE CITY FOOD & BREWERY LTD**
(*Suby of* CONCEPT DEVELOPMENT PARTNERS LLC) ★
701 Xenia Ave S Ste 120, Minneapolis, MN 55416-3593
Tel (952) 215-0660 *Founded/Ownrshp* 2011
Sales 134.1MM *EMP* 3,153^E
Accts Schechter Dokken Kanter And
Tkr Sym GCFB *Exch* OTO
SIC 5812 5813 Eating places; Drinking places; Eating places; Drinking places
CEO: Robert J Doran
Mng Pt: Neil Johnson
Mng Pt: Jill Woodford
**Ch Bd:* Fouad Z Bashour
CFO: James G Gilbertson
Ofcr: Dean S Oakey
Genl Mgr: Weston Baril
Genl Mgr: Ann Riesner
Genl Mgr: Jon Stryker
Mktg Mgr: Crista Demers-Dean

D-U-N-S 07-197-6096
■ **GRANITE CITY HOSPITAL CORP LLC**
CHS
(*Suby of* COMMUNITY HEALTH SYSTEMS INC) ★
2100 Madison Ave, Granite City, IL 62040-4701
Tel (618) 798-3000 *Founded/Ownrshp* 2002
Sales 120.2MM *EMP* 920
Accts Scott Oney Cpa Granite City
SIC 8062 8071 Hospital, affiliated with AMA residency; Testing laboratories; Hospital, affiliated with AMA residency; Testing laboratories
CEO: Ed Cunningham
**CEO:* Mark Benz
**COO:* David Orcutt
CFO: Dennis Lutz
**CFO:* Michelle McKee
Ofcr: Robin Anderson

D-U-N-S 04-478-8552
GRANITE CITY JOBBING CO INC
2731 Clearwater Rd, Saint Cloud, MN 56301-5999
Tel (320) 252-1782 *Founded/Ownrshp* 2005
Sales 21.1MM^E *EMP* 45
SIC 5194 5145 Tobacco & tobacco products; Confectionery; Tobacco & tobacco products; Confectionery
CEO: Michael Smith

GRANITE COMPANIES
See GRANITE LOAN MANAGEMENT OF DELAWARE LLC

D-U-N-S 00-691-4642
■ **GRANITE CONSTRUCTION CO** (CA)
(*Suby of* GRANITE CONSTRUCTION INC) ★
585 W Beach St, Watsonville, CA 95076-5123
Tel (831) 724-1011 *Founded/Ownrshp* 1922
Sales 705.6MM^E *EMP* 1,500
Accts Pricewaterhousecoopers Llp Sa
SIC 1611 1622 Highway & street construction; General contractor, highway & street construction; Bridge construction; Tunnel construction; Highway & street construction; General contractor, highway & street construction; Bridge construction; Tunnel construction
Pr: James H Roberts
**Ex VP:* Christopher S Miller
**Sr VP:* Thomas S Case
**Sr VP:* Laurel Krzeminski
**Sr VP:* Richard A Watts
VP: Kim Mattos

D-U-N-S 62-282-6360
▲ **GRANITE CONSTRUCTION INC**
585 W Beach St, Watsonville, CA 95076-5123
Tel (831) 724-1011 *Founded/Ownrshp* 1922
Sales 2.2MMM *EMP* 3,000
Tkr Sym GVA *Exch* NYS
SIC 1611 1622 1629 1442 Highway & street construction; General contractor, highway & street construction; Bridge construction; Tunnel construction; Dam construction; Canal construction; Land leveling; Construction sand & gravel; Highway & street construction; General contractor, highway & street construction; Bridge construction; Tunnel construction; Dam construction; Canal construction; Land leveling; Construction sand & gravel
Pr: James H Roberts
**Ch Bd:* William H Powell
COO: Christopher S Miller
CFO: Laurel J Krzeminski
Sr VP: Michael F Donnino
Sr VP: Martin P Matheson
Sr VP: James D Richards
VP: Travis Carter
Dir IT: Chris Kennedy
IT Man: Bruce Kootstra
Sftwr Eng: John Sieraski
Board of Directors: Claes G Bjork, James W Bradford Jr, Gary M Cusumano, William G Dorey, David H Kelsey

D-U-N-S 78-707-7080
■ **GRANITE CONSTRUCTION NORTHEAST INC**
(*Suby of* GRANITE CONSTRUCTION INC) ★
120 White Plains Rd, Tarrytown, NY 10591-5526
Tel (914) 606-3600 *Founded/Ownrshp* 2001
Sales 47.6MM^E *EMP* 389^E
Accts Pricewaterhousecoopers Llp Sa
SIC 1611 1623 1794 1771 General contractor, highway & street construction; Water main construction; Sewer line construction; Excavation & grading, building construction; Concrete work
Ch Bd: James H Roberts
**CFO:* Laurel J Krzeminski
**Sr VP:* Michael F Donnino
**VP:* Thomas S Case
**VP:* John A Franich

D-U-N-S 05-908-2409
GRANITE CONTRACTING LLC
18606 Northline Dr, Cornelius, NC 28031-9321
Tel (704) 892-0341 *Founded/Ownrshp* 1999
Sales 22.6MM^E *EMP* 70^E
SIC 1611 General contractor, highway & street construction
Pr: Steve Cosper
Mtls Mgr: Doug Barker
Plnt Mgr: Fred Reese

D-U-N-S 13-134-3902
GRANITE ELECTRICAL SUPPLY INC
GES
1701 National Dr Ste 200, Sacramento, CA 95834-2951
Tel (916) 648-3900 *Founded/Ownrshp* 2003
Sales 54.9MM *EMP* 75
Accts Rina Accountancy Corporation
SIC 5063 Electrical supplies; Electrical supplies
Ch: Al Russello
**Pr:* Bob Powers
**VP:* Brian Flynn
**VP:* Matt Rusello
Brnch Mgr: Ken Olson
**Off Mgr:* Bobbie Baldwin

D-U-N-S 78-548-6403
GRANITE EQUITY PARTNERS LLC
122 12th Ave N Ste 201, Saint Cloud, MN 56303-4893
Tel (320) 251-1800 *Founded/Ownrshp* 2006
Sales 21.0MM^E *EMP* 101
SIC 6726 Investment offices; Investment offices
Off Admin: Laura Larson
Dir IT: Tracy Schulte
Snr Mgr: Dennis Gregory

D-U-N-S 15-082-3172 IMP/EXP
GRANITE EXPRESS INC
1055 Se 9th Ter, Hialeah, FL 33010-5804
Tel (305) 889-1011 *Founded/Ownrshp* 2004
Sales 30.4MM^E *EMP* 126^E
SIC 5032 Granite building stone
Pr: Cornelio Costa
Sls Mgr: Felipe Lerma

D-U-N-S 10-912-7378
GRANITE FALLS ENERGY LLC
15045 Highway 23 Se, Granite Falls, MN 56241-1946
Tel (320) 564-3100 *Founded/Ownrshp* 2000
Sales 300.9MM *EMP* 75^E
Accts Boulay Pllp Minneapolis Min
SIC 2869 2085 2046 Ethyl alcohol, ethanol; Distillers' dried grains & solubles & alcohol; Corn oil, refined; Ethyl alcohol, ethanol; Distillers' dried grains & solubles & alcohol; Corn oil, refined
CEO: Steve Christensen
**Ch Bd:* Paul Enstad
CFO: Stacie Schuler
**V Ch Bd:* Rodney R Wilkison
Board of Directors: Leslie Bergquist, Dean Buesing, Kenton Johnson, Bruce Lavigne, Michael Lund, Myron D Peterson, Martin Seifert, David Thompson

D-U-N-S 04-093-1124
GRANITE FALLS LTC LLC
1435 Highway 258n, Kinston, NC 28504-7208
Tel (252) 523-9094 *Founded/Ownrshp* 2010
Sales 35.1MM^E *EMP* 627
SIC 1799 Counter top installation; Counter top installation

D-U-N-S 96-773-6575
GRANITE FALLS MUNICIPAL HOSPITAL AND MANOR
345 10th Ave, Granite Falls, MN 56241-1442
Tel (320) 564-3111 *Founded/Ownrshp* 1964
Sales 40.4MM^E *EMP* 280
SIC 8062 General medical & surgical hospitals; General medical & surgical hospitals
Chf Rad: Barry Sewall
**CFO:* Larry Lee
Nurse Mgr: April Walker
Pharmcst: Jason Linden

D-U-N-S 07-889-0806
GRANITE GEAR LLC
950 Technology Way # 120, Libertyville, IL 60048-5361
Tel (847) 737-3568 *Founded/Ownrshp* 2013
Sales 21.4MM^E *EMP* 45^E
SIC 5092 5941 Toys; Backpacking equipment
CEO: Bryan Kinsley
CFO: Mike Cruikshank
Sr VP: Rob Coughlin
VP: Zee Zhuang

D-U-N-S 05-573-9577
GRANITE GROUP WHOLESALERS LLC
GOULET SUPPLY COMPANY
6 Storrs St, Concord, NH 03301-4856
Tel (603) 224-1901 *Founded/Ownrshp* 1971
Sales 255.4MM^E *EMP* 369
SIC 5074 5075 Heating equipment (hydronic); Plumbing fittings & supplies; Warm air heating equipment & supplies; Heating equipment (hydronic); Plumbing fittings & supplies; Warm air heating equipment & supplies
Sr VP: Karen Rosenau
VP: Jesse King
VP: Scott Morris
VP: Matthew Spangler
VP: Jacob Williams
Comm Dir: Brad Dupuis
Comm Man: Dave Buck
Brnch Mgr: Richard Cooke
Brnch Mgr: Robert Ellis
Brnch Mgr: Tim Palmer
Brnch Mgr: Joseph Ruffo

D-U-N-S 96-510-7274
GRANITE HENSEL PHELPS JV
420 6th Ave, Greeley, CO 80631-2332
Tel (970) 352-6565 *Founded/Ownrshp* 2010
Sales 650.0MM *EMP* 1,000
SIC 1541 1542 Industrial buildings & warehouses; Nonresidential construction; Industrial buildings & warehouses; Nonresidential construction
VP: Jon W Ball
VP: John A Franich

D-U-N-S 07-838-0655
GRANITE HOLDINGS INC
2580 28th St Sw, Grand Rapids, MI 49519-2106
Tel (616) 532-2375 *Founded/Ownrshp* 2003
Sales 131.7MM^E *EMP* 370^E
SIC 5169 Gases, compressed & liquefied; Gases, compressed & liquefied
Pr: Gary Nyhuis

D-U-N-S 01-437-6706
GRANITE LOAN MANAGEMENT OF DELAWARE LLC
GRANITE COMPANIES
10770 E Briarwood Ave # 280, Centennial, CO 80112-3801
Tel (303) 488-0300 *Founded/Ownrshp* 1992
Sales NA *EMP* 70
Accts Ehrhardt Keefe Steiner Hottman
SIC 6141 Personal credit institutions
Pr: William S Cobb

D-U-N-S 06-773-1323
GRANITE MEDICAL GROUP INC
500 Congress St Ste 3a, Quincy, MA 02169-0919
Tel (617) 471-0033 *Founded/Ownrshp* 1972, 1997
Sales 67.4MM *EMP* 70
SIC 8011 Internal medicine, physician/surgeon; Internal medicine, physician/surgeon
Pr: Guy Spinelli
COO: Bob Calway
Exec: Mary Hopwood
Exec: Laura Murphy
Exec: Stephen Tarpy
**Prin:* Kenneth Einstein
**Prin:* Dennis Goldin
**Prin:* Charles Schwartz
**Prin:* Robert Sipzener
Podiatrist: George Ducach
Doctor: Eric H Awtry
Board of Directors: Kenneth Einstein MD, Dennis Goldin MD, Charles Schwartz MD, Robert Sipzener MD

GRANITE MOUNTAIN QUAR NUMBER 1
See MCGEORGE CONTRACTING CO INC

D-U-N-S 08-570-0086
GRANITE PACKAGING SUPPLY CO
SUPPLY ONE PLASTICS
(*Suby of* SUPPLYONE HOLDINGS CO INC) ★
111 Whittendale Dr, Moorestown, NJ 08057-1364
Tel (856) 727-1010 *Founded/Ownrshp* 1999
Sales 33.9MM^E *EMP* 100
SIC 5199 3086 5113 5085 2652 Packaging materials; Packaging & shipping materials, foamed plastic; Industrial & personal service paper; Industrial supplies; Setup paperboard boxes
Sec: Brian Cassano

GRANITE PROPERTIES
See SF REALTY INC

D-U-N-S 19-950-1110
GRANITE RIDGE ENERGY LLC
21 N Wentworth Ave, Londonderry, NH 03053-7437
Tel (603) 432-9114 *Founded/Ownrshp* 2004
Sales 37.6MM^E *EMP* 30
SIC 4911 Generation, electric power

D-U-N-S 00-922-1961
GRANITE ROCK CO
350 Technology Dr, Watsonville, CA 95076-2488
Tel (831) 768-2000 *Founded/Ownrshp* 1900
Sales 1.1MMM^E *EMP* 700
SIC 1442 3273 5032 2951 1611 3271 Gravel mining; Construction sand mining; Ready-mixed concrete; Sand, construction; Stone, crushed or broken; Asphalt & asphaltic paving mixtures (not from refineries); Highway & street paving contractor; Concrete block & brick; Gravel mining; Construction sand mining; Ready-mixed concrete; Sand, construction; Stone, crushed or broken; Asphalt & asphaltic paving mixtures (not from refineries); Highway & street paving contractor; Concrete block & brick
CEO: Thomas H Squeri
**V Ch:* Bruce G Woolpert
**Ch:* Mary E Woolpert
VP: Greg Diehl
VP: Steve Snodgrass
Area Mgr: Karl Philipovitch
Off Admin: Jessica Snow
CIO: Steve Hogg
IT Man: Katlin Johnston
Netwrk Mgr: Rick Boston
Sfty Dirs: Lisa Gallagher

D-U-N-S 07-299-8743
GRANITE SCHOOL DISTRICT
2500 S State St, Salt Lake City, UT 84115-3164
Tel (385) 646-5000 *Founded/Ownrshp* 1904
Sales 415.1MM^E *EMP* 8,000
Accts Squire & Company Pc Orem Ut
SIC 8211 Public elementary & secondary schools; Public elementary & secondary schools
Bd of Dir: Janet Bryner
Bd of Dir: Michelle Hall
Bd of Dir: Dan Lofgren
Bd of Dir: Audrey Price
Bd of Dir: Karyn Winder
Bd of Dir: Carla Wonder-Mcdowell
VP: Julene M Jolley
VP: Julene Oliver
Assoc Dir: Brandy Moon
Assoc Dir: Shauna Park
Assoc Dir: Karen Robinson

D-U-N-S 62-255-6884
GRANITE SECURITY PRODUCTS INC
WINCHESTER SAFES
4801 Esco Dr, Fort Worth, TX 76140-2211
Tel (817) 483-0910 *Founded/Ownrshp* 1991
Sales 30.2MM^E *EMP* 50
SIC 3499 Safes & vaults, metal
Pr: Kyle F Walters
VP: Patrick McDonald

D-U-N-S 04-932-3534
GRANITE SERVICES INC
1302 N 19th St, Tampa, FL 33605-5230
Tel (813) 242-7400 *Founded/Ownrshp* 2002
Sales 22.8MM^E *EMP* 147^E
SIC 1799 Counter top installation
Pr: Stanley Harvell
**CFO:* Morgan Williams

D-U-N-S 19-275-2996
■ **GRANITE SERVICES INTERNATIONAL INC**
(*Suby of* GENERAL ELECTRIC CO) ★
201 N Franklin St # 1000, Tampa, FL 33602-5218
Tel (813) 242-7400 *Founded/Ownrshp* 2006
Sales 230.5MM^E *EMP* 2,000
SIC 7363 Help supply services; Help supply services
Pr: Randy Willis
COO: Lacey Marcks
**Treas:* Morgan Williams
Exec: Joyce Guerra
Prgrm Mgr: Michael Morrow
QA Dir: Connor Vanderbogart
Dir IT: Amit Shankar
IT Man: Juan Galeano
Netwrk Eng: Ken Czerwinski
Netwrk Eng: Rob Nicol
Sfty Mgr: Angel Alejandro

GRANITE STATE ELECTRIC COMPANY
See LIBERTY UTILITIES (GRANITE STATE ELECTRIC) CORP

D-U-N-S 08-341-0415
■ **GRANITE STATE GAS TRANSMISSION INC**
(*Suby of* UNITIL CORP) ★
300 Friberg Pkwy, Westborough, MA 01581-3900
Tel (508) 836-7000 *Founded/Ownrshp* 2008
Sales 46.6MM^E *EMP* 301
SIC 4922 Pipelines, natural gas; Pipelines, natural gas
Pr: Glen Kettering
COO: David Monte

GRANITE STATE GLASS
See MARBUCCO CORP

D-U-N-S 11-808-4276
GRANITE STATE INDEPENDENT LIVING
GSIL
21 Chenell Dr, Concord, NH 03301-8539
Tel (603) 228-9680 *Founded/Ownrshp* 1980
Sales 15.8MM *EMP* 550
Accts Melanson Heath And Company Pc
SIC 8322 Social services for the handicapped; Social services for the handicapped
Pr: Clyde Terry
Treas: Mark Lore
VP: Kevin Walsh
Web Dev: Chad Carter

GRANITE STATE MANUFACTURING
See ALLARD NAZARIAN GROUP INC

D-U-N-S 80-140-9561
■ **GRANITE STATE PLUMBING & HEATING LLC**
(*Suby of* COMFORT SYSTEMS USA INC) ★
10 N Riverdale Rd, Weare, NH 03281-5545
Tel (603) 529-3322 *Founded/Ownrshp* 1984
Sales 29.5MM^E *EMP* 130
SIC 1711 Plumbing contractors; Plumbing contractors
Pr: Gerard Perron

D-U-N-S 11-177-7939
GRANITE TELECOMMUNICATIONS LLC
100 Newport Avenue Ext # 1, Quincy, MA 02171-2126
Tel (617) 933-5500 *Founded/Ownrshp* 2002
Sales 865.8MM *EMP* 650
SIC 4813 Local & long distance telephone communications; Local & long distance telephone communications
CEO: Robert Hale Jr
**COO:* Rand Currier
**CFO:* Richard Wurman
**VP:* Paul Stutzman
Exec: Christopher Barbaro
Exec: Matthew Cotter
Exec: Judy Parsons
Exec: Jennifer Pilato
CTO: Bennett McCarthy
Dir IT: Mike Russo
Dir IT: Olga Volansky

GRANITE VALLEY FOREST PRODUCTS
See FOREST WELTER PRODUCTS INC

D-U-N-S 00-830-2960 IMP/EXP
GRANITIZE PRODUCTS INC
11022 Vulcan St, South Gate, CA 90280-7621
Tel (562) 861-1349 *Founded/Ownrshp* 1985
Sales 26.2MM^E *EMP* 75
SIC 2842 Automobile polish; Cleaning or polishing preparations
CEO: Tony Raymondo
**Sec:* Betty Raymondo
VP: Lisa Garcia
VP: John Hughes
VP: Mike Long
Genl Mgr: Randy Bair
Genl Mgr: Robert Mayson
IT Man: Joe Bartoli
IT Man: Randy Bear
IT Man: Donald Horn
Sfty Mgr: Ken Scholefield

GRANNAS BROS CONTRACTING CO
See GRANNAS BROS STONE & ASPHALT CO INC

D-U-N-S 00-285-8959
GRANNAS BROS STONE & ASPHALT CO INC (PA)
GRANNAS BROS CONTRACTING CO
157 Grannas Rd, Hollidaysburg, PA 16648-7156
Tel (814) 695-5021 *Founded/Ownrshp* 1944
Sales 23.6MM^E *EMP* 70

SIC 2951 1423 Asphalt paving mixtures & blocks; Crushed & broken granite
Pr: Samuel P Grannas
**VP:* Scott Grannas

D-U-N-S 04-999-2241
GRANNYS KITCHENS LLC
(*Suby of* KEYSTONE BAKERY HOLDINGS LLC) ★
178 Industrial Park Dr, Frankfort, NY 13340-4798
Tel (315) 735-5000 *Founded/Ownrshp* 1981
Sales 62.4MM^E *EMP* 280
SIC 2053 2051 Doughnuts, frozen; Bread, cake & related products; Doughnuts, frozen; Bread, cake & related products
Pr: Kevin McDonough
VP: Barry J Thaler
Prd Mgr: Francis Kauth
Ql Cn Mgr: Thomas Kopa

GRANOLA KITCHENS
See GKI FOODS LLC

D-U-N-S 08-839-5207 IMP
GRANT & WEBER
GRANT & WEBER TRAVEL
26610 Agoura Rd Ste 209, Calabasas, CA 91302-2975
Tel (818) 878-7700 *Founded/Ownrshp* 1976
Sales 28.4MM^E *EMP* 250^E
SIC 7322 Collection agency, except real estate; Collection agency, except real estate
CEO: Jimi Bingham
**CFO:* Spencer Weinerman
VP: Kim Mehr
VP: Omar Perez
**CIO:* Mary Kempski
**Genl Couns:* Reid Steinfeld

GRANT & WEBER TRAVEL
See GRANT & WEBER

D-U-N-S 80-888-1882
GRANT AVENUE DEVELOPMENT INC
ARBY'S
161 Genesee St Ste 200, Auburn, NY 13021-3498
Tel (315) 255-1559 *Founded/Ownrshp* 1988
Sales 8.0MM *EMP* 400
SIC 5812 Fast-food restaurant, chain; Fast-food restaurant, chain
Pr: R Daniel Soules
Sr VP: Bob Kelley
**VP:* Mark Dunn
Dist Mgr: Sandy Parker
Off Mgr: Carmella Dixon

D-U-N-S 10-124-8938
GRANT CADARET & CO INC
1 Lincoln Rd Fl 5, Syracuse, NY 13212-3612
Tel (315) 471-2191 *Founded/Ownrshp* 1988
Sales 161.5MM *EMP* 120
SIC 6211 Brokers, security; Dealers, security; Brokers, security; Dealers, security
Pr: Arthur F Grant
**CFO:* Donald J Taylor
**Sr VP:* Beda L Johnson
Sr VP: Norlyn Popo
**Sr VP:* Arnold Taylor
VP: Sharon Deperro
VP: Donna Farrell
VP: Kevin Makowski
Mktg Dir: Michelle Werth
Sales Asso: Grace Frost
Board of Directors: Megan Grant

D-U-N-S 11-579-3259
GRANT COMMUNITY CLINIC SC
GRANT REGIONAL HEALTH CENTER
507 S Mineral St, Lancaster, WI 53813
Tel (608) 723-2131 *Founded/Ownrshp* 1952
Sales 24.1MM *EMP* 30
SIC 8011 8069 Physicians' office, including specialists; Surgeon; Orthopedic hospital
CEO: Nicole Klapp
**Pr:* Glen Hillery

D-U-N-S 03-127-6319
GRANT CONSTRUCTION INC (CA)
7702 Meany Ave Ste 103, Bakersfield, CA 93308-5199
Tel (661) 588-4586 *Founded/Ownrshp* 1994
Sales 31.0MM *EMP* 230
SIC 1751 1771 Framing contractor; Concrete work; Framing contractor; Concrete work
Pr: Grant Fraysier
CFO: Cezar Florin
VP: Anthony Yannotta
Exec: Julio Vega
Genl Mgr: Robert Lundberg

GRANT COUNTY BANK, THE
See HIGHLANDS BANKSHARES INC

D-U-N-S 02-387-7574
GRANT COUNTY BOARD OF EDUCATION
GRANT COUNTY SCHOOL DIST
820 Arnie Risen Blvd, Williamstown, KY 41097-9459
Tel (859) 824-3323 *Founded/Ownrshp* 1900
Sales 25.0MM^E *EMP* 375
Accts Denise M Keene By Fax On Janua
SIC 8211 Public elementary & secondary schools; Public elementary & secondary schools
**CFO:* Matthew Morgan

GRANT COUNTY CLERK
See COUNTY OF GRANT

D-U-N-S 07-126-7421
GRANT COUNTY FOODS LLC
(*Suby of* CASTELLINI HOLDING CO LLC) ★
1125 Dry Ridge Rd, Dry Ridge, KY 41035-7417
Tel (859) 428-1903 *Founded/Ownrshp* 1974
Sales 26.5MM^E *EMP* 100
SIC 5148 Fruits, fresh; Vegetables, fresh
Ch Bd: Robert H Castellini
**Pr:* William Schuler
**Treas:* Christopher Fister
**VP:* William Piper
**VP:* Timothy Slaughter
Exec: Daryl Wolking

D-U-N-S 07-492-5306
GRANT COUNTY MEMORIAL HOSPITAL (INC)
GM
117 Hospital Dr, Petersburg, WV 26847-9566
Tel (304) 257-1026 *Founded/Ownrshp* 1958
Sales 34.0MM *EMP* 300
Accts Parentebeard Llc Philadelphia
SIC 8062 General medical & surgical hospitals; General medical & surgical hospitals
CEO: Mary Beth
Chf Rad: James Kim
IT Man: Joe Barnes
Surgeon: Joey M Hahn
Doctor: Oleg Glushkov MD
HC Dir: Ann Smith

D-U-N-S 60-185-3682
GRANT COUNTY MULCH INC
635 Highway Rr 42, Arthur, WV 26847
Tel (304) 379-1252 *Founded/Ownrshp* 1986
Sales 33.2MM^E *EMP* 150
SIC 2499 3423 2421 Mulch, wood & bark; Mulch or sawdust products, wood; Hand & edge tools; Sawmills & planing mills, general; Mulch, wood & bark; Mulch or sawdust products, wood; Hand & edge tools; Sawmills & planing mills, general
Pr: Larry Berg
**VP:* Janie Berg
IT Man: Ben Judy

D-U-N-S 08-334-8771
GRANT COUNTY PUBLIC HOSPITAL DISTRICT 2
QUINCY VALLEY MEDICAL CENTER
908 10th Ave Sw, Quincy, WA 98848-1376
Tel (509) 787-3531 *Founded/Ownrshp* 1958
Sales 31.1MM^E *EMP* 111
SIC 8062 8052 8011 5999 General medical & surgical hospitals; Intermediate care facilities; Offices & clinics of medical doctors; Hearing aids
CEO: Mehdi Merred
Dir Recs: Nancy Lynn
Dir Risk M: Glenda Bishop
Dir Lab: Nancy Lewendowski
Dir Rx: Matt Walker
Off Mgr: Abigail Dominguez
Off Mgr: Lela Kunkel
**Mktg Dir:* Michelle Wurl
Psych: Coralee Gill
Psych: Darlene Gottschalk
Phys Thrpy: Amy York

D-U-N-S 08-192-8376
GRANT COUNTY PUBLIC HOSPITAL DISTRICT 3
COLUMBIA BASIN HOSPITAL
220 Nat Washington Way, Ephrata, WA 98823-1982
Tel (509) 754-3330 *Founded/Ownrshp* 1950
Sales 23.7MM^E *EMP* 200
SIC 8361 8051 8062 Residential care; Skilled nursing care facilities; General medical & surgical hospitals; Residential care; Skilled nursing care facilities; General medical & surgical hospitals
CFO: Ronda Hamley
Dir Rx: Doug Crafton
Off Mgr: Lisa McWilliams
IT Man: Michael Dutcher
Plnt Mgr: Ty Sween
Mktg Dir: Alayna Lodi
Mktg Mgr: Susan Scheib
Doctor: Brian Kirkham MD

D-U-N-S 07-573-2461
GRANT COUNTY PUBLIC HOSPITAL DISTRICT NO 1
SAMARITAN HOSPITAL
801 E Wheeler Rd, Moses Lake, WA 98837-1820
Tel (509) 765-5606 *Founded/Ownrshp* 1953
Sales 67.7MM *EMP* 480^E
SIC 8062 8011 General medical & surgical hospitals; Offices & clinics of medical doctors; General medical & surgical hospitals; Offices & clinics of medical doctors
CEO: Tom Thompson
COO: Theresa Sullivan
Bd of Dir: Chera Anderson
Dir OR: Desiree Hamilton
Dir OR: Terri Ottmar
Dir Inf Cn: Kelly Odermann
Dir Risk M: Richard Donaldson
Dir Lab: Pat Harrington
Dir Rx: Lloyd Stever
Off Mgr: Janet Green
Dir IT: Rainier Wolfcastle

GRANT COUNTY SCHOOL DIST
See GRANT COUNTY BOARD OF EDUCATION

D-U-N-S 07-982-7287
GRANT COUNTY SCHOOLS
820 Arnie Risen Blvd, Williamstown, KY 41097-9459
Tel (859) 824-3323 *Founded/Ownrshp* 2015
Sales 13.3MM^E *EMP* 448^E
SIC 8211 Public elementary & secondary schools
Prin: Nancy Howe

GRANT GEOPHYSICAL
See GEOKINETICS MANAGEMENT INC

D-U-N-S 80-814-4778
GRANT GLEN CHEVROLET/GEO SOUTH INC
PARKLAND CHEVROLET
11011 Pacific Ave S, Tacoma, WA 98444-5737
Tel (253) 539-1000 *Founded/Ownrshp* 1992
Sales 38.8MM *EMP* 77
SIC 5511 5521 Automobiles, new & used; Used car dealers; Automobiles, new & used; Used car dealers
Pr: Doug Grant
**VP:* Tom Grant

D-U-N-S 05-343-4015
GRANT INDUSTRIAL CONTROLS INC
220 Industry St, Pittsburgh, PA 15210
Tel (412) 787-9770 *Founded/Ownrshp* 1981
Sales 24.1MM^E *EMP* 28
SIC 5063 Motor controls, starters & relays: electric
Pr: William G Harrington
**VP:* William E Harrington
Div Mgr: Joseph Stumpf
Info Man: David Abbott
Opers Mgr: David Nemcsik

D-U-N-S 00-640-3471
GRANT INDUSTRIES INC
33415 Groesbeck Hwy, Fraser, MI 48026-4203
Tel (586) 293-9200 *Founded/Ownrshp* 1964
Sales 21.0MM^E *EMP* 90
SIC 3465 3469 3452 3429 3316 3312 Automotive stampings; Metal stampings; Bolts, nuts, rivets & washers; Manufactured hardware (general); Cold finishing of steel shapes; Blast furnaces & steel mills
Pr: Robert Grant
Ex VP: James Lefler
**VP:* Timothy Schley
Sfty Mgr: Rich Maziasz
Prd Mgr: Kent Thompson
Ql Cn Mgr: Kim Hewitt

D-U-N-S 08-550-5196 IMP
GRANT INDUSTRIES INC
125 Main Ave, Elmwood Park, NJ 07407-3203
Tel (201) 791-6700 *Founded/Ownrshp* 1972
Sales 30.4MM^E *EMP* 100
SIC 2834 Pharmaceutical preparations; Pharmaceutical preparations
CEO: Steven Grant
**Pr:* Michael Granatell
**VP:* David Granatell
VP: Chand Mehta
VP: Jim Scotkowski
Off Mgr: Bethany Ranno
Tech Mgr: Tania Viana
Plnt Mgr: Bob Horan
Mktg Dir: Grace Kelly
Sls Dir: Lori Rosenstreich
Board of Directors: Charles Granatell

D-U-N-S 17-329-8787
GRANT INTL CO INC
GRANT SUPPLIES
3915 21st St, Long Island City, NY 11101-6121
Tel (718) 729-2373 *Founded/Ownrshp* 1986
Sales 81.8MM^E *EMP* 70^E
SIC 5063 5211 Electrical supplies; Electrical construction materials; Electrical supplies; Electrical construction materials
Pr: Hark Lee
**Prin:* Jinwook Kim
Brnch Mgr: Paul Kim
Genl Mgr: Anna Lee
IT Man: David Im
Sls Mgr: Young Yoo
Sales Asso: Andy Choi
Sales Asso: Howard Ferdine
Sales Asso: David Lee
Sales Asso: Carlos Maldonado
Sales Asso: Kaz Sadighi

D-U-N-S 04-640-4729 IMP
GRANT J HUNT CO
7307 Edgewater Dr Ste A, Oakland, CA 94621-3015
Tel (510) 569-0304 *Founded/Ownrshp* 1934
Sales 81.2MM *EMP* 16
Accts Shea Labagh Dobberstein San F
SIC 5148 Fruits, fresh; Vegetables, fresh; Fruits, fresh; Vegetables, fresh
Pr: Grant M Hunt
**Ex VP:* Salvatore Rizzo
**VP:* Maurice Protzen

D-U-N-S 62-790-1044
GRANT PAPER CO
(*Suby of* AARON GROUP OF COMPANIES) ★
161 Wshington St Ste 1150, Conshohocken, PA 19428
Tel (610) 940-0900 *Founded/Ownrshp* 1990
Sales 38.4MM^E *EMP* 50
SIC 5111 8742 Printing & writing paper; Management consulting services
Ch Bd: Eugene Aaron
Sr VP: Franco Darazio
**VP:* Brent Aaron
**VP:* Drew Aaron

D-U-N-S 19-745-1982
GRANT PARISH SCHOOL BOARD
512 Main St, Colfax, LA 71417-1523
Tel (318) 627-2777 *Founded/Ownrshp* 1800
Sales 22.4MM^E *EMP* 470^E
SIC 8211 Public elementary & secondary schools; Public elementary & secondary schools
CTO: Janet Lincecum
Dir IT: Kecia Nugent
IT Man: Diana Patterson

D-U-N-S 07-980-2911
GRANT PARISH SCHOOLS
512 Main St, Colfax, LA 71417-1523
Tel (318) 627-3274 *Founded/Ownrshp* 2015
Sales 11.6MM^E *EMP* 291^E
SIC 8211 Public elementary & secondary schools
HC Dir: Melissa Steelman

GRANT PARK CARE CENTER
See GRANT PARK NURSING HOME LIMITED PARTNERSHIP

D-U-N-S 00-686-4821
GRANT PARK CO-OP GRAIN CO INC (IL)
116 S Main St, Grant Park, IL 60940-7114
Tel (815) 465-6551 *Founded/Ownrshp* 1920
Sales 31.0MM^E *EMP* 4
Accts Illinois Agricultural Auditing
SIC 5153 Grain elevators; Grain elevators
Pr: Richard Riechers
**Treas:* Robert Schilling
**Genl Mgr:* Daniel Stadt

GRANT PARK CUSTOM MEATS
See GRANT PARK SAUSAGE INC

D-U-N-S 10-393-2356
GRANT PARK NURSING HOME LIMITED PARTNERSHIP
GRANT PARK CARE CENTER
(*Suby of* CENTENNIAL HEALTHCARE CORP) ★
5000 Nannie H Burrough Av, Washington, DC 20019
Tel (202) 399-7504 *Founded/Ownrshp* 1983
Sales 12.2MM^E *EMP* 325
SIC 8051 8052 Skilled nursing care facilities; Intermediate care facilities; Skilled nursing care facilities; Intermediate care facilities
Pt: J Stephen Eaton
Dir Soc: Ryan Byrd
Mktg Mgr: Saveienne Mitchell
Nrsg Dir: Denise Gastos

D-U-N-S 96-553-6985
GRANT PARK SAUSAGE INC
GRANT PARK CUSTOM MEATS
3434 Runge St, Franklin Park, IL 60131-1315
Tel (847) 451-1231 *Founded/Ownrshp* 2002
Sales 38.5MM^E *EMP* 60
SIC 5147 Meats & meat products
CEO: Joseph Maffei
**Pr:* Vince Maffei

D-U-N-S 00-285-3240
■ **GRANT PRIDECO INC**
ATLAS BRADFORD DIVISION
(*Suby of* NATIONAL OILWELL VARCO INC) ★
400 N Sam Houston Pkwy E # 900, Houston, TX 77060-3531
Tel (281) 878-8000 *Founded/Ownrshp* 1960, 2008
Sales 634.7MM^E *EMP* 4,857
SIC 3533 Oil & gas field machinery; Oil & gas drilling rigs & equipment; Bits, oil & gas field tools: rock; Drilling tools for gas, oil or water wells; Oil & gas field machinery; Oil & gas drilling rigs & equipment; Bits, oil & gas field tools: rock; Drilling tools for gas, oil or water wells
Pr: John D Deane
Pr: David R Black
**Pr:* Jim Breihan
**CFO:* Matthew D Fitzgerald
**VP:* Greg L Boane
VP: Gary W Childress
**VP:* Philip Choyce
VP: Philip A Choyce
**VP:* Quintin V Kneen
VP: Tom McGrann
IT Man: Casey Lambright
Board of Directors: David J Butters, Eliot M Fried, Gordon T Hall, Dennis R Hendrix, Harold E Layman, Robert K Moses, Joseph E Reid, David A Trice

GRANT REGIONAL HEALTH CENTER
See GRANT COMMUNITY CLINIC SC

D-U-N-S 79-412-4693
GRANT REGIONAL HEALTH CENTER INC
507 S Monroe St, Lancaster, WI 53813-2099
Tel (608) 723-2143 *Founded/Ownrshp* 1995
Sales 24.9MM *EMP* 220
SIC 8062 General medical & surgical hospitals; General medical & surgical hospitals
Pr: Nicole Clapp
Chf Rad: Robert Smith
**CFO:* Scott Mitchell
CFO: Barbara Tabor
Treas: Mary Bausch
Bd of Dir: Erin Huebschman
**VP:* Jennifer Rutkowski
Exec: Sheri Fischer
Dir Inf Cn: Jenny Pritchett
Dir Rx: Avis Davis
Off Mgr: Joan Kruser

D-U-N-S 01-971-9850
GRANT STREET GROUP INC
339 6th Ave Ste 1400, Pittsburgh, PA 15222-2517
Tel (412) 391-5555 *Founded/Ownrshp* 1997
Sales 23.1MM^E *EMP* 150
SIC 7371 Computer software development
CEO: Myles Harrington
**CFO:* William Haskins
**Ex VP:* Dan Veres
Sr VP: John McCarthy
**CTO:* Fred Burnette
MIS Dir: David Hewett
IT Man: Craig Deering
IT Man: Jim Grattan
IT Man: Craig Walling
Software D: Graham Barr
Software D: Adam Boyers

GRANT SUPPLIES
See LEE & LEE SUPPLIES INC

GRANT SUPPLIES
See GRANT INTL CO INC

D-U-N-S 00-175-2971
GRANT THORNTON LLP
(*Suby of* GRANT THORNTON INTERNATIONAL LIMITED)
175 W Jackson Blvd Fl 20, Chicago, IL 60604-2687
Tel (312) 856-0200 *Founded/Ownrshp* 1924
Sales 734.0MM^E *EMP* 4,588
SIC 8721 8742 Accounting, auditing & bookkeeping; Auditing services; Accounting services, except auditing; Management consulting services; Accounting, auditing & bookkeeping; Auditing services; Accounting services, except auditing; Management consulting services
Pt: Dave Wedding
Pt: Terrance Bilbo
Pt: Deron Curliss
Pt: Allen Davidson
Pt: Thomas J English
Pt: Steve Finkelstein
Pt: Spencer E Golden
Pt: Lou Grabowsky
Pt: Lou J Grabowsky
Pt: Doreen Griffith
Pt: John T Harmeling
Pt: Glenn James
Pt: C Morgan Kinghorn
Pt: Brian E Lucas
Pt: Jim Maurer

Pt: Anne McGeorge
Pt: Mike Mleko
Pt: Gary A Samuels
Pt: Richard A Soukup
Pt: Richard A Stewart
Pt: Russ Wieman

D-U-N-S 07-808-6808
GRANT WOOD AREA EDUCATION AGENCY
GWAEA
4401 6th St Sw, Cedar Rapids, IA 52404-4432
Tel (319) 399-6704 *Founded/Ownrshp* 1975
Sales NA *EMP* 508
Accts Hogan-Hansen Mason City Iowa
SIC 9411 Education office, non-operating; ; Education office, non-operating;
CEO: Joseph Crozier
Dir IT: Dave Brousard
IT Man: Heath Ayers
IT Man: Mike Hauer
Instr Medi: Char Haddy
Psych: Stephanie Anthony
Psych: Tamara Beener
Psych: Austin Beer
Psych: Sharon Clark
Psych: Greg Feldmann
Psych: Tracy Liebermann

D-U-N-S 03-261-2509 IMP
GRANTHAM DISTRIBUTING CO INC
2685 Hansrob Rd, Orlando, FL 32804-3385
Tel (407) 299-6446 *Founded/Ownrshp* 1956
Sales 20.3MM^E *EMP* 53
SIC 5182 5181 Liquor; Beer & ale
Pr: H Varley Grantham Jr
**Prin:* Henry Varley J Grantham

D-U-N-S 00-180-4991
GRANTHAM EDUCATION CORP (MO)
GRANTHAM UNIVERSITY
7200 Nw 86th St Ste M, Kansas City, MO 64153-2262
Tel (816) 595-5759 *Founded/Ownrshp* 1999
Sales 43.3MM^E *EMP* 419
SIC 8221 Colleges universities & professional schools
CEO: Thomas M Macon
**Pr:* John Lanearl
Chf Mktg O: Lori Turec
Ofcr: Audrey Craig
Ofcr: Mary Mulloy
Ofcr: Katherine Tracey
**Ex VP:* Christine A Shelly
VP: Cheryl Hayek
VP: Karan Krna
VP: Roman Yagnitinsky
VP: Roman Yagnitinsky

D-U-N-S 08-851-6380
GRANTHAM MAYO VAN OTTERLOO & CO LLC
GMO
40 Rowes Wharf Ste 600, Boston, MA 02110-3361
Tel (617) 330-7500 *Founded/Ownrshp* 1977
Sales 366.7MM^E *EMP* 600
SIC 6282 6722 Investment counselors; Mutual fund sales, on own account; Investment counselors; Mutual fund sales, on own account
**Ch Bd:* Arjun Divecha
**CEO:* Brad Hilsabeck
COO: Jean-Pierre Mittaz
CFO: Shep Burnett
Ofcr: Kelly Donovan
Ofcr: Carolyn Haley
Ofcr: Judith Lyden
Ofcr: John McGinty
VP: Cheryl Wakeham
Exec: Drew Tamoney
Assoc Dir: Paul Chadwick

GRANTHAM UNIVERSITY
See GRANTHAM EDUCATION CORP

D-U-N-S 07-410-9158
GRANTHAM UNIVERSITY INC
(*Suby of* GRANTHAM EDUCATION CORP) ★
16025 W 113th St, Lenexa, KS 66219-5105
Tel (816) 595-5759 *Founded/Ownrshp* 1951
Sales 35.8MM^E *EMP* 414^E
SIC 8221 Colleges universities & professional schools
Pr: Joseph McGrath
**CFO:* Ed Sammarco
Ofcr: Laura Modick
**VP:* Alex Bach
VP: Jeffrey Cropsey
**VP:* Jared Parlette
**VP:* Roman Yagnitinsky
Off Mgr: Geri Krumsick
CIO: Anthony Schlinsog
IT Man: James Peckham
Web Dev: Paul Knopp

D-U-N-S 06-063-2940
GRANTS CIBOLA COUNTY SCHOOL DISTRICT
401 N Second St, Grants, NM 87020-2507
Tel (505) 285-2600 *Founded/Ownrshp* 1937
Sales 35.2MM^E *EMP* 653
SIC 8211 Public elementary & secondary schools; Public elementary & secondary schools
**Pr:* William Estaban
**VP:* Dione Sandoval
Prin: Rick Horacek
Prin: Greg Rockhold

D-U-N-S 03-000-6530
GRANTS MECHANICAL INC (ND)
3239 15th St S, Fargo, ND 58104-6147
Tel (701) 232-8891 *Founded/Ownrshp* 1975
Sales 27.7MM^E *EMP* 125
Accts Gary Anderson Cpa
SIC 1711 1623 Plumbing, heating, air-conditioning contractors; Warm air heating & air conditioning contractor; Ventilation & duct work contractor; Pipeline construction; Plumbing, heating, air-conditioning contractors; Warm air heating & air conditioning contractor; Ventilation & duct work contractor; Pipeline construction
Pr: Grant E Johnson

**COO:* George Fenwick
**Treas:* Paul Corcoran
**VP:* Paul Linstad
Sfty Dirs: Cody Hedberg

D-U-N-S 05-360-1217
GRANTS PASS CLINIC
495 Sw Ramsey Ave, Grants Pass, OR 97527-5681
Tel (541) 476-6644 *Founded/Ownrshp* 1949
Sales 30.7MM^E *EMP* 135
SIC 8011 Clinic, operated by physicians
CEO: Ross Gassaway
Pt: Thomas R Brandes MD
Pt: Elbert Collins MD
Pt: J S Countiss MD
Pt: Monika Froehlich DPM
Pt: Haitham B Haddad MD
Pt: William Kohn MD
Pt: Andrew Luther MD
Pt: Thomas J Morris MD
Pt: P B Murray MD
Pt: Theo H Powell MD Surgery
Pt: Stephen E Pratt MD
Pt: Daniel S Selinger MD
Pt: Ronald S Sinclair MD
Pt: Bruce Stowell MD
Pt: Martin K Young MD
Dir Lab: Denise King

D-U-N-S 03-979-2247
GRANTS PASS SCHOOL DISTRICT 7
725 Ne Dean Dr, Grants Pass, OR 97526-1649
Tel (541) 474-5700 *Founded/Ownrshp* 1900
Sales 35.7MM^E *EMP* 525
SIC 8211 Public elementary & secondary schools; Public elementary & secondary schools
MIS Dir: Jonathan Russ
Teacher Pr: Ernest Baldwin

GRANVILLE HEALTH SYSTEM
See GRANVILLE MEDICAL CENTER

D-U-N-S 07-556-5424
GRANVILLE HEALTH SYSTEM FOUNDATION INC
1010 College St, Oxford, NC 27565-2507
Tel (919) 690-3000 *Founded/Ownrshp* 1938
Sales 53.6MM *EMP* 641^E
SIC 8062 General medical & surgical hospitals; General medical & surgical hospitals
Ch: Gary Bowman
**COO:* Cristina Carroll
**CFO:* M Jeffery Armstrong
CFO: Sherry Jenson
Dir Lab: Jan Hart
Prin: Linda Roberson
Adm Dir: Jason Brand
Mtls Mgr: Betty Watson
HC Dir: Renita Timberlake

D-U-N-S 07-951-9511
GRANVILLE MEDICAL CENTER
GRANVILLE HEALTH SYSTEM
1010 College St, Oxford, NC 27565-2507
Tel (919) 690-3405 *Founded/Ownrshp* 2014
Sales 54.8MM *EMP* 41^E
SIC 8062 General medical & surgical hospitals
CFO: Marvin Armstrong
Chf Rad: Michael Stoll
CEO: Lee Isley
CFO: Jeff Armstrong
Ex Dir: Melissa Starr
CIO: Linda Roberson
IT Man: Geoff Tanthorey
Mktg Dir: Scott Thomas
Doctor: Sally Gilliland
Doctor: Peter Tocci
Snr Mgr: Stephan Baum

D-U-N-S 07-065-0668 IMP
GRAPEMAN FARMS LP
STEVECO
9777 Wilshire Blvd # 918, Beverly Hills, CA 90212-1910
Tel (310) 273-9540 *Founded/Ownrshp* 2011
Sales 144.8MM^E *EMP* 100^E
SIC 0172

D-U-N-S 00-353-6104
GRAPEVINE - COLLYVILLE INDEPENDENT SCHOOL DIST
VISTA ALTERNATIVE CAMPUS
3051 Ira E Woods Ave, Grapevine, TX 76051-3817
Tel (817) 251-5466 *Founded/Ownrshp* 1994
Sales 181.2MM *EMP* 11
Accts Hankins Eastup Deaton Tonn
SIC 8211 Public combined elementary & secondary school; Public combined elementary & secondary school

GRAPEVINE CHRYSLER
See GRAPEVINE DCJ LLC

D-U-N-S 04-943-0692
GRAPEVINE DCJ LLC
GRAPEVINE CHRYSLER
2601 William D Tate Ave, Grapevine, TX 76051-3984
Tel (817) 410-7500 *Founded/Ownrshp* 1970
Sales 25.2MM^E *EMP* 70
SIC 5511 Automobiles, new & used; Automobiles, new & used
Pr: Mohammad A Khan
**Mng Pt:* William Tennant
Genl Mgr: Bill Tennant
IT Man: Scott Davis
Sls Mgr: Chad Ivie
Sls Mgr: Dennis Thomas
Sls Mgr: Kirk Wilson
Sls Mgr: Christena Yates
Sales Asso: John Ward

D-U-N-S 96-004-2331
GRAPEVINE IMPORTS LTD
TEXAS TOYOTA OF GRAPEVINE
701 E State Highway 114, Grapevine, TX 76051-7689
Tel (817) 329-5949 *Founded/Ownrshp* 1996
Sales 69.2MM^E *EMP* 190^E
SIC 5511 Automobiles, new & used; Automobiles, new & used

Pt: Grapevine Imports
CFO: Tommy Lee
Off Admin: Linda Blasdel
Sales Exec: Floyd Goatcher
Sls Mgr: Muhammad Ahmed
Sls Mgr: Babatunde Ogundele
Sls Mgr: Jonathan Williams

D-U-N-S 02-032-7755
GRAPEVINE/COLLEYVILLE INDEPENDENCE SCHOOL DISTRICT
3051 Ira E Woods Ave, Grapevine, TX 76051-3817
Tel (817) 251-5200 *Founded/Ownrshp* 1920, 2004
Sales 181.2MM *EMP* 1,800
Accts Hankins Eastup Deaton Tonn
SIC 8211 Public elementary & secondary schools; Public elementary & secondary schools

GRAPH-PAK
See GRAPHIC PACKAGING CORP

GRAPHALLOY
See GRAPHITE METALLIZING CORP

D-U-N-S 00-447-8707
GRAPHEL CORP (OH)
CARBON PRODUCTS
(*Suby of* GRAPHALLOY) ★
6115 Centre Park Dr, West Chester, OH 45069-3869
Tel (513) 759-1477 *Founded/Ownrshp* 1965
Sales 64.8MM^E *EMP* 140
SIC 5052 3599 3624 Coal & other minerals & ores; Machine shop, jobbing & repair; Electrodes, thermal & electrolytic uses: carbon, graphite; Coal & other minerals & ores; Machine shop, jobbing & repair; Electrodes, thermal & electrolytic uses: carbon, graphite
Pr: Cliff Kerkser
**CFO:* Mark Grammer
Sales Asso: Dawn Brostrom

GRAPHIC ART SALES
See WATERHOUSE INC

D-U-N-S 00-905-1665
■ **GRAPHIC ARTS CENTER INC** (DE)
GACSC
(*Suby of* CENVEO CORP) ★
2000 Nw Wilson St, Portland, OR 97209-1884
Tel (503) 224-7777 *Founded/Ownrshp* 1901, 1995
Sales 188.0MM *EMP* 450
SIC 2752 Color lithography; Color lithography
Pr: Frank Stammers
**Pr:* Ron Jensen
CFO: Pat Hevrdjs
VP: Fim Fetherston
VP: Keith Larson
VP: Vince Schaller
**VP:* Steven M Williamson
Board of Directors: Ron Jensen, Jerry Mahoney, Paul Riley, Rodger Willmer

D-U-N-S 05-277-1664
GRAPHIC ARTS MUTUAL INSURANCE CO INC
180 Genesee St, New Hartford, NY 13413-2200
Tel (315) 734-2000 *Founded/Ownrshp* 1914
Sales NA *EMP* 1,325
Accts Pricewaterhousecoopers Llp Bo
SIC 6331 Property damage insurance; Reciprocal interinsurance exchanges: fire, marine, casualty; Property damage insurance; Reciprocal interinsurance exchanges: fire, marine, casualty
Ch Bd: W Craig Heston
CFO: Anthony Paolozzi
**Treas:* John R Zapisek
**Ex VP:* Jay Douglas Robinson

D-U-N-S 02-589-0045
GRAPHIC CENTER GROUP CORP
OFFICE GRAPHIC DESIGN
2150 Coral Way Fl 1, Coral Gables, FL 33145-2629
Tel (305) 961-1649 *Founded/Ownrshp* 2010
Sales 500.0MM *EMP* 8
SIC 7372 7336 Prepackaged software; Graphic arts & related design; Prepackaged software; Graphic arts & related design
CEO: Oliver Moreno

D-U-N-S 14-751-1612
■ **GRAPHIC COMMUNICATIONS HOLDINGS INC**
(*Suby of* ROLLSOURCE PAPERS) ★
5700 Darrow Rd Ste 110, Hudson, OH 44236-5026
Tel (330) 650-5522 *Founded/Ownrshp* 2003
Sales 317.1MM^E *EMP* 110^E
SIC 5111 7389 Fine paper; Printing broker; Fine paper; Printing broker
CEO: Mary A Laschinger
**Pr:* Matt Dawley
Pr: Mike Nash
**CEO:* Allan Dragone
**COO:* Ken Flajs
**CFO:* David Earney
**Sr VP:* Bill King
**Sr VP:* John Patneau
VP: George Fellner
VP: Steven Finzer
VP: Mark Keener

D-U-N-S 00-211-1896 IMP
GRAPHIC CONTROLS ACQUISITION CORP
400 Exchange St, Buffalo, NY 14204-2064
Tel (716) 853-7500 *Founded/Ownrshp* 2004
Sales 117.5MM^E *EMP* 280
SIC 2752 2679 Tag, ticket & schedule printing: lithographic; Paper products, converted; Tag, ticket & schedule printing: lithographic; Paper products, converted
CEO: Sam Heleba
COO: Jeffrey A Blair
**CFO:* Gary M Toomey
VP: John Bellotti
VP: Jon Bollie
VP Bus Dev: Eric Saenger
Exec: Janis Reicis
Admn Mgr: Theodore Sucher
Genl Mgr: Sam Haleba

Dir IT: Karl Shoot
IT Man: Karl Shoop

D-U-N-S 93-267-6484 IMP
GRAPHIC CONVERTING INC
877 N Larch Ave, Elmhurst, IL 60126-1114
Tel (630) 758-4100 *Founded/Ownrshp* 1976
Sales 96.8MM^E *EMP* 300
SIC 2675 Die-cut paper & board; Die-cut paper & board
Pr: John R Tinnon
**CFO:* Joe Yaney
**Prin:* Stibi Skalaski
Board of Directors: Jessica Prost

GRAPHIC EDGE, THE
See GRAPHIC EDGE INC

D-U-N-S 60-967-0625 EXP
GRAPHIC EDGE INC
GRAPHIC EDGE, THE
743 E Us Highway 30, Carroll, IA 51401-2615
Tel (712) 792-7777 *Founded/Ownrshp* 1989
Sales 37.7MM *EMP* 270
Accts Olsen Muhlbauer & Co Llp C
SIC 2396 2395 Screen printing on fabric articles; Embroidery & art needlework; Screen printing on fabric articles; Embroidery & art needlework
Pr: John Reglein
**VP:* Rich Hartley
**VP:* Donna Reglein
**VP:* Mike Riddle
Genl Mgr: Pat Venteicher

D-U-N-S 05-358-4967 IMP
GRAPHIC ENTERPRISES INC
(*Suby of* VISUAL EDGE TECHNOLOGY INC) ★
3874 Highland Park Nw, North Canton, OH 44720-4538
Tel (800) 553-6616 *Founded/Ownrshp* 2003
Sales 24.1MM^E *EMP* 54
SIC 5044 Copying equipment
Pr: Brian Frank
**CFO:* Yvonne Brown
Dir IT: John Sedlak
IT Man: Terry Kikkert
VP Opers: Michael Brigner
Opers Mgr: Troy Sacco
Sales Exec: George Zambie
VP Sls: Chip Reihl
Mktg Mgr: Denise Dennewitz
Sls Mgr: Tony Simeone

D-U-N-S 04-980-1285
GRAPHIC INFORMATION SYSTEMS INC
GISI MARKETING GROUP
17400 Sw Upper Boones, Portland, OR 97224
Tel (503) 598-0636 *Founded/Ownrshp* 1968
Sales 23.5MM^E *EMP* 200
SIC 7334 2752 7374 2759 3823 7336 Photocopying & duplicating services; Commercial printing, offset; Data processing & preparation; Commercial printing; Digital displays of process variables; Commercial art & graphic design; Photocopying & duplicating services; Commercial printing, offset; Data processing & preparation; Commercial printing; Digital displays of process variables; Commercial art & graphic design
Pr: Eben Swett
COO: Chris Babbitt
**CFO:* Audrey Swett
IT Man: Agbey Loui

D-U-N-S 61-985-8897
■ **GRAPHIC INFORMATION SYSTEMS INC**
FLOWERS BAKERY
(*Suby of* FLOWERS BAKERIES LLC) ★
1919 Flowers Cir, Thomasville, GA 31757-1137
Tel (229) 226-9110 *Founded/Ownrshp* 1978
Sales 68.2MM^E *EMP* 137
SIC 2051 Bread, cake & related products
CEO: Amos R McMullian

D-U-N-S 78-509-2024 IMP/EXP
GRAPHIC INNOVATORS INC
855 Morse Ave, Elk Grove Village, IL 60007-5105
Tel (847) 718-1516 *Founded/Ownrshp* 1991
Sales 30.8MM *EMP* 50
SIC 3555 5084 Printing trades machinery; Printing presses; Printing trades machinery, equipment & supplies; Printing trades machinery; Printing presses; Printing trades machinery, equipment & supplies
Pr: Scott J Kiley
**CEO:* Michael J Kiley
**CFO:* David J Kiley
**VP:* Paul Minasian
VP Opers: Irena Rybka
Plnt Mgr: Brian Blackmore

D-U-N-S 08-294-5452
GRAPHIC PACKAGING CORP
GRAPH-PAK
11250 Addison Ave, Franklin Park, IL 60131-1199
Tel (847) 451-7400 *Founded/Ownrshp* 1976
Sales 44.0MM^E *EMP* 120
SIC 2631 2752 Folding boxboard; Commercial printing, offset; Folding boxboard; Commercial printing, offset
Pr: John Hewitt
Plnt Mgr: Jess Bucaro
Plnt Mgr: Steve Farley
Prd Mgr: Irma Diaz
Trfc Mgr: Suzanne Hewitt

D-U-N-S 94-378-6657 IMP/EXP
▲ **GRAPHIC PACKAGING HOLDING CO**
1500 Riveredge Pkwy # 100, Atlanta, GA 30328-4658
Tel (770) 240-7200 *Founded/Ownrshp* 2008
Sales 4.2MMM *EMP* 12,900
Accts Ernst & Young Llp Atlanta Ge
Tkr Sym GPK *Exch* NYS

SIC 2631 2653 2671 Container, packaging & boxboard; Container board; Folding boxboard; Coated & treated board; Boxes, corrugated: made from purchased materials; Plastic film, coated or laminated for packaging; Container, packaging & boxboard; Container board; Folding boxboard; Coated & treated board; Boxes, corrugated: made from purchased materials; Plastic film, coated or laminated for packaging
Ch Bd: David W Scheible
**COO:* Michael P Doss
CFO: Stephen R Scherger
Ex VP: Donald Sturdivant
Sr VP: James M Aikins
Sr VP: Carla J Chaney
Sr VP: Alan R Nichols
Sr VP: Steven D Saucier
Sr VP: Stephen Scherger
Sr VP: Robert M Simko
Sr VP: Robert W Spiller
Sr VP: Michael S Ukropina
Sr VP: Michael Ukropina
VP: David Drennan
VP: Mollie Tankersley
Exec: Kelly Williams
Dir Bus: Gary McMahon
Board of Directors: G Andrea Botta, David D Campbell, Paul D Carrico, Jeffrey H Coors, Robert A Hagemann, Harold R Logan Jr, Philip R Martens, Lynn A Wentworth

D-U-N-S 79-702-4411
GRAPHIC PACKAGING INTERNATIONAL CORP
1795 Dogwood St Unit 100, Louisville, CO 80027-3131
Tel (303) 215-4600 *Founded/Ownrshp* 1992
Sales 1.0MMM *EMP* 4,200
SIC 2657 2671 2655 Folding paperboard boxes; Packaging paper & plastics film, coated & laminated; Fiber cans, drums & containers; Folding paperboard boxes; Packaging paper & plastics film, coated & laminated; Fiber cans, drums & containers
Ch Bd: Jeffrey H Coors
**COO:* David W Scheible
CFO: Gail Constancio
**CFO:* Luis E Leon
Treas: Beth Parish
CIO: Ron Bettencourt
Mill Mgr: Mark Shumate
Plnt Mgr: Roger Kuhl
Pr Dir: Paddy Broughton
Board of Directors: John D Beckett, William K Coors, Harold R Logan, James K Peterson, John Hoyt Stookey

D-U-N-S 80-883-9062 EXP
■ **GRAPHIC PACKAGING INTERNATIONAL INC**
(*Suby of* GRAPHIC PACKAGING HOLDING CO) ★
1500 Riveredge Pkwy # 100, Atlanta, GA 30328-4658
Tel (770) 240-7200 *Founded/Ownrshp* 1982
Sales 2.3MMM^E *EMP* 8,735
SIC 2657 2631 Folding paperboard boxes; Paperboard mills; Folding paperboard boxes; Paperboard mills
CEO: David W Scheible
**Pr:* Michael P Doss
Pr: Mitch Lowe
**CFO:* Daniel J Blount
**Sr VP:* Carla J Chaney
Sr VP: Michael R Schmal
VP: Jim Barutt
VP: Aaron Bates
**VP:* Deborah R Frank
Dir Risk M: William Frye
Dept Mgr: Toby Bowman

GRAPHIC PACKAGING INTL
See GPI HOLDINGS INC

D-U-N-S 01-998-4822 IMP
GRAPHIC PALLET & TRANSPORT INC
10225 Bode St, Plainfield, IL 60585-6903
Tel (630) 904-4951 *Founded/Ownrshp* 1995
Sales 23.0MM *EMP* 20
SIC 2448 5085 Wood pallets & skids; Industrial supplies
Pr: Christy Furmaniak
**Sec:* John Krawisz

D-U-N-S 93-354-9008 IMP
GRAPHIC PAPER INC
31 Windsor Pl, Central Islip, NY 11722-3301
Tel (631) 761-9700 *Founded/Ownrshp* 1989
Sales 100.5MM *EMP* 120
Accts Marcum Llp Melville Ny
SIC 5111 Printing & writing paper; Printing & writing paper
Ch Bd: Leonard Aronica Jr
**Ch Bd:* Anthony Aronica
**Pr:* Michael Aronica

D-U-N-S 05-221-8609
GRAPHIC PRODUCTS INC
6445 Sw Fallbrook Pl # 125, Beaverton, OR 97008-5480
Tel (503) 644-5572 *Founded/Ownrshp* 1970
Sales 33.5MM^E *EMP* 93^E
SIC 5045 5084 Computers; Industrial machinery & equipment
Pr: Claire Smart
**VP:* Edwin E Smart
Prgrm Mgr: Laura Parker
QA Dir: Mike Venneri
IT Man: Shane Johnson
Software D: Mihaela Gaspar
Software D: Giancarlo Villanueva
Sftwr Eng: Sasha Demyanik
Mktg Dir: Steve Stephenseon
Sls Dir: Miguel Luna
Mktg Mgr: Kevin Kahle

D-U-N-S 02-630-6829 IMP
GRAPHIC SOLUTIONS GROUP INC (TX)
JHD
4601 Spring Valley Rd, Dallas, TX 75244-3902
Tel (214) 748-3271 *Founded/Ownrshp* 1966
Sales 99.9MM^E *EMP* 97

SIC 5084 Printing trades machinery, equipment & supplies; Printing trades machinery, equipment & supplies
Pr: Randall M Granberry
**Pr:* Mark Grandberry
COO: Chuck Maulsby
**Treas:* Brandon Granberry
Treas: Glenn Wilson
**VP:* Anthony Bruckler
VP: Tony Bruckler
**VP:* Larry Rogers
Genl Mgr: Jason Freeman
Dir IT: John Dawson
Mktg Dir: Matt Smith

D-U-N-S 85-868-7346
GRAPHIC SPECIALTIES INC
G S I
2350 Brton Indus Pk Dr Se, Grand Rapids, MI 49508-1548
Tel (616) 247-4705 *Founded/Ownrshp* 1989
Sales 35.4MM^E *EMP* 40^E
SIC 3497 2675 2759 2796 2789 Metal foil & leaf; Die-cut paper & board; Embossing on paper; Platemaking services; Bookbinding & related work
Pr: Dale Hutchins
**VP:* Mathew Hutchins

GRAPHIC SYSTEMS DIVISION
See FUJIFILM NORTH AMERICA CORP

GRAPHICS ATLANTA
See GA COMMUNICATIONS INC

D-U-N-S 08-053-2211 IMP/EXP
GRAPHIK DIMENSIONS LIMITED (NC)
PICTUREFRAMES.COM
2103 Brentwood St, High Point, NC 27263-1807
Tel (336) 289-7954 *Founded/Ownrshp* 1966
Sales 38.0MM^E *EMP* 100
SIC 3499 2499 7379 Picture frames, metal; Picture & mirror frames, wood; Computer related consulting services
Pr: Lauri Feinsod
**COO:* Mike Keyes
**CFO:* Dave Shelton
**Sec:* Joan Feinsod
Web Dev: Stephen Paschall
Sls Dir: Bob Battista
Art Dir: Casey Rexrode

GRAPHITE ELECTRODE MFG FCILTY
See GRAFTECH USA LLC

D-U-N-S 06-188-2569 IMP
GRAPHITE MACHINING INC (MI)
240 N Main St, Topton, PA 19562-1419
Tel (610) 682-0080 *Founded/Ownrshp* 1973, 2000
Sales 28.4MM^E *EMP* 51
SIC 3624 Carbon & graphite products; Carbon & graphite products
Pr: Franklin C Schoch
Treas: Erica Schoch
**Treas:* Erica L Schochshane
**VP:* Timothy Bearss

D-U-N-S 00-156-0879
GRAPHITE METALLIZING CORP (NY)
GRAPHALLOY
1050 Nepperhan Ave, Yonkers, NY 10703-1432
Tel (914) 968-8400 *Founded/Ownrshp* 1913, 1941
Sales 64.8MM^E *EMP* 190^E
SIC 3624 Carbon & graphite products; Brushes & brush stock contacts, electric; Carbon & graphite products; Brushes & brush stock contacts, electric
Ch Bd: Eben T Walker
**CFO:* Mark R Grammer
VP: John Loconte
**VP Mfg:* Giovanni B Loconte

D-U-N-S 07-272-1111 IMP
GRAPHNET INC
60 Hudson St Rm 1014, New York, NY 10013-3315
Tel (212) 994-1100 *Founded/Ownrshp* 2004
Sales 20.2MM^E *EMP* 100
SIC 4822 4813 Nonvocal message communications; Telephone communication, except radio; Nonvocal message communications; Telephone communication, except radio
Pr: Yaakov Elkon
**COO:* Idan Elkon
Top Exec: Yin Chiu
**Sr VP:* Donna Tomasino
**VP:* Guy Conte
**Prin:* Steve Furman
IT Man: Jacques Liberti
Netwrk Mgr: Jim Gehrsitz
VP Sls: Joe Sciberras

D-U-N-S 02-377-0665
GRAPHXKIDS
24 Antis St, Pemberton, NJ 08068-1127
Tel (856) 296-9386 *Founded/Ownrshp* 2012
Sales 35.0MM *EMP* 2
SIC 7374 Computer graphics service; Computer graphics service
Owner: Lane Solomon

GRAPPONE AUTOMOTIVE GROUP
See GRAPPONE DISTRIBUTION INC

D-U-N-S 78-853-7095
GRAPPONE DISTRIBUTION INC
GRAPPONE AUTOMOTIVE GROUP
506 Route 3a, Bow, NH 03304-3100
Tel (603) 224-9912 *Founded/Ownrshp* 1987
Sales 26.2MM^E *EMP* 320
SIC 5531 Automotive tires; Automotive tires
Pr: Larry K Haynes
Dir IT: Linda Krieger
Sales Asso: Ricky Ryan

GRAPPONE FORD
See JOHN GRAPPONE INC

D-U-N-S 14-782-3215
GRAPPONETS INC
594 Route 3a, Bow, NH 03304-3217
Tel (603) 224-9912 *Founded/Ownrshp* 1984
Sales 21.2MM^E *EMP* 82

SIC 5511 7538 7532 7515 5531 5521 Automobiles, new & used; General automotive repair shops; Top & body repair & paint shops; Passenger car leasing; Automotive & home supply stores; Used car dealers; Automobiles, new & used; General automotive repair shops; Top & body repair & paint shops; Passenger car leasing; Automotive & home supply stores; Used car dealers
Pr: Robert Grappone
Board of Directors: Larry Haynes

D-U-N-S 03-393-8796
GRASMICK PRODUCE CO INC
215 E 42nd St, Boise, ID 83714-6398
Tel (208) 376-3981 *Founded/Ownrshp* 1985
Sales 45.5MM^E *EMP* 75
SIC 5148 Fresh fruits & vegetables; Fresh fruits & vegetables
CEO: Henry J Grasmick
**Pr:* Angela Grasmick

D-U-N-S 08-544-0592 IMP/EXP
GRASS AMERICA INC
(*Suby of* WURTH GROUP OF NORTH AMERICA INC) ★
1202 Nc Highway 66 S, Kernersville, NC 27284-3537
Tel (336) 996-4041 *Founded/Ownrshp* 2004
Sales 102.0MM *EMP* 201
SIC 3429 Cabinet hardware; Cabinet hardware
Pr: Tom Kipp
CFO: Kemenns Tollin
VP: George Domenig
Dir Bus: Jan Fitzpatrick
QA Dir: Kristy Kiser
QA Dir: Mark Shore
IT Man: Tom Mitchell
VP Opers: Juergen Ahlfeld
VP Opers: Hartmut Voght
Mtls Mgr: Larry Moore
Ql Cn Mgr: Marcus Pegram

D-U-N-S 15-613-9268
GRASS FAMILY PRACTICE
227 Riverside Dr W, Madison, WV 25130-1027
Tel (304) 687-5895 *Founded/Ownrshp* 2002
Sales 13.5MM^E *EMP* 500
SIC 8011 Clinic, operated by physicians; Clinic, operated by physicians
Owner: James Lee Grass

GRASS HOPPER COMPANY
See MORIDGE MANUFACTURING INC

D-U-N-S 00-103-7779 EXP
■ **GRASS INSTRUMENT CO** (MA)
ASTRO MED
(*Suby of* ASTRO-MED INC) ★
600 E Greenwich Ave, West Warwick, RI 02893-7526
Tel (401) 828-4000 *Founded/Ownrshp* 1935, 1994
Sales 20.7MM^E *EMP* 250
SIC 3841 Diagnostic apparatus, medical; Diagnostic apparatus, medical
Pr: Everett Pizzuti

D-U-N-S 06-531-2902
GRASS PAD INC
425 N Rawhide Dr, Olathe, KS 66061-3695
Tel (913) 764-4100 *Founded/Ownrshp* 1983
Sales 39.7MM^E *EMP* 90
SIC 5191 5193 5261 Seeds: field, garden & flower; Fertilizer & fertilizer materials; Nursery stock; Sod; Nursery stock, seeds & bulbs; Fertilizer; Seeds: field, garden & flower; Fertilizer & fertilizer materials; Nursery stock; Sod; Nursery stock, seeds & bulbs; Fertilizer
Pr: Michael J Mc Dermott
**COO:* Don Bain
Store Mgr: Billy Dupras
Sales Exec: Wes Lane

GRASS TEX
See CONTROLLED PRODUCTS LLC

D-U-N-S 60-685-7134
GRASS VALLEY
MIRANDA
(*Suby of* GRASS VALLEY CANADA)
125 Crown Point Ct, Grass Valley, CA 95945-9515
Tel (530) 265-1000 *Founded/Ownrshp* 2008
Sales 25.5MM^E *EMP* 130^E
SIC 3663 Radio & TV communications equipment; Radio & TV communications equipment
CEO: Strath Goodship
**Pr:* Marco Lopez
**Pr:* Charles Meyer
**COO:* Luc St-Georges
VP: Mitchell Yantis
Dir Soc: Martine Genereux
**Prin:* Mario Settinio
**Prin:* Patrick St Yges
Snr Sftwr: Luke Manis
Mktg Mgr: Frederic Jacques
Mktg Mgr: Suzie McSherry

D-U-N-S 12-368-1111 IMP
GRASS VALLEY INC
(*Suby of* GRASS VALLEY CANADA)
125 Crown Point Ct, Grass Valley, CA 95945-9515
Tel (530) 478-3000 *Founded/Ownrshp* 2002
Sales 131.5MM^E *EMP* 750
SIC 3663 Radio & TV communications equipment
Pr: Marc Valentine
COO: Dave Perillo
Sr VP: Patrick Montliaud
VP: Mark Hilton
VP: Jean-Marc Hoffer
VP: Tim Ordaz
Prgrm Mgr: Brian Kodai
Snr Sftwr: Nanyu Cao
CTO: Fredrick Schmidt
IT Man: Thomas Oates
IT Man: Dixie Rock

D-U-N-S 96-576-7945 IMP
■ **GRASS VALLEY USA LLC**
(*Suby of* BELDEN INC) ★
125 Crown Point Ct, Grass Valley, CA 95945-9515
Tel (800) 547-8949 *Founded/Ownrshp* 2014

Sales 164.3MM^E *EMP* 650
SIC 3651 3661 3663 Household audio & video equipment; Television receiving sets; Radio receiving sets; Video cassette recorders/players & accessories; Telephone sets, all types except cellular radio; Radio & TV communications equipment; Household audio & video equipment; Television receiving sets; Radio receiving sets; Video cassette recorders/players & accessories; Telephone sets, all types except cellular radio; Radio & TV communications equipment
Pr: Marco Lopez
Sr VP: Said Bacho
Sr VP: Aengus Linehan
Sr VP: Steve Ronneberg
VP: Kara Martin
Plng Mgr: David Meltz
CTO: Fredrick Schmidt
QA Dir: Larry Fleischman
QA Dir: James Wong
Netwrk Mgr: Thomas Oates
Sftwr Eng: Adam Bobek

D-U-N-S 00-198-7986
GRASSI & CO CERTIFIED PUBLIC ACCOUNTANTS PC
50 Jericho Quadrangle # 200, Jericho, NY 11753-2729
Tel (516) 256-3500 *Founded/Ownrshp* 1995
Sales 22.2MM^E *EMP* 130
SIC 8721 Accounting, auditing & bookkeeping; Accounting, auditing & bookkeeping
CEO: Louis Grassi
CFO: Michael A Caggiano
Dir Bus: Joseph Micara
Prin: Gary Purwin
Dir IT: Fred Hoffmann

D-U-N-S 00-608-0204 IMP/EXP
GRASSLAND DAIRY PRODUCTS INC (WI)
N8790 Fairground Ave, Greenwood, WI 54437-7668
Tel (715) 267-6182 *Founded/Ownrshp* 1904
Sales 118.3MM^E *EMP* 200^E
SIC 2021 5143 Creamery butter; Cheese; Creamery butter; Cheese
Pr: Dallas Wuethrich
Pr: Goedhart Westers
**VP:* Tayt Wuethrich
VP: Tayt Wuetrich
Telecom Ex: Stacy Petkovsek
QC Dir: Roger Mielke
Sfty Mgr: Ryan Martin
Plnt Mgr: Kevin Lucas
Plnt Mgr: Jeff Miller
Prd Mgr: Jim Heck
VP Sls: Rich Phillips

D-U-N-S 01-281-7995
GRASSLAND EQUIPMENT AND IRRIGATION CORP
892-898 Troy Schnctady Rd, Latham, NY 12110-1698
Tel (518) 785-5841 *Founded/Ownrshp* 1961
Sales 25.1MM^E *EMP* 70
SIC 5083 Garden machinery & equipment
Pr: Kirk Pogge
**Ex VP:* Hans Pogge
CTO: Edward Cody

GRASSMID TRANSPORT
See BORCULO GARAGE INC

GRASSROOTS STUDIOS
See WESTON ENTERTAINMENT LP

D-U-N-S 78-314-6046
GRATECH CO LLC
8201 282nd St Nw, Berthold, ND 58718-9602
Tel (701) 453-3434 *Founded/Ownrshp* 1990
Sales 45.0MM *EMP* 240
Accts Clifton Larson Allen Llp St
SIC 1611 1629 Grading; Earthmoving contractor; Grading; Earthmoving contractor
Pr: Harley Neshem
**Sec:* Nancy Neshem
**VP:* Terry Burke

D-U-N-S 05-800-0712 IMP
GRATING PACIFIC INC
3651 Sausalito St, Los Alamitos, CA 90720-2436
Tel (562) 598-4314 *Founded/Ownrshp* 1971
Sales 21.7MM^E *EMP* 60
SIC 3441 3446 Fabricated structural metal; Architectural metalwork
Pr: Ronald S Robertson
**VP:* Jeffrey Robertson
Plnt Mgr: Javier Ruiz

GRATIOT COMMUNITY HOSPITAL
See MIDMICHIGAN MEDICAL CENTER-GRATIOT

GRATIS CARD
See SERVE VIRTUAL ENTERPRISES INC

D-U-N-S 05-628-4606
GRATON ECONOMIC DEVELOPMENT AUTHORITY
(*Suby of* FEDERATED INDIANS OF GRATON RANCHERIA) ★
915 Golf Course Dr, Rohnert Park, CA 94928-1818
Tel (707) 800-7616 *Founded/Ownrshp* 2013
Sales NA *EMP* 1,122^E
SIC 9311 Gambling control board, government
Bd of Dir: Greg M Sarris
**Bd of Dir:* Jeannette E Anglin
**Bd of Dir:* Robert F Baguio Sr

GRATON RESORT & CASINO
See FEDERATED INDIANS OF GRATON RANCHERIA

GRAVA CHRYSLER, PLYMOUTH, JEEP
See GRAVA OF MEDFORD INC

D-U-N-S 15-725-3899
GRAVA OF MEDFORD INC
GRAVA CHRYSLER, PLYMOUTH, JEEP
29 Mystic Ave, Medford, MA 02155-4620
Tel (781) 391-8950 *Founded/Ownrshp* 1983
Sales 25.3MM^E *EMP* 58

SIC 5511 7538 7514 7532 7515 5521 Automobiles, new & used; General automotive repair shops; Passenger car rental; Top & body repair & paint shops; Passenger car leasing; Used car dealers; Automobiles, new & used; General automotive repair shops; Passenger car rental; Top & body repair & paint shops; Passenger car leasing; Used car dealers
Pr: Peter M Grava
**Exec:* Ralph Grava
**Prin:* Carl Bartalini
**Prin:* Michael Clarke
**Prin:* Nick Dicarlo
Store Mgr: James Murdock

D-U-N-S 05-708-6159
GRAVEL PRODUCTS INC
2920 Railway Ave, Minot, ND 58703-5003
Tel (701) 852-4751 *Founded/Ownrshp* 1970
Sales 50.5MM^E *EMP* 100
SIC 1442 1611 5211 Gravel mining; General contractor, highway & street construction; Sand & gravel
Ch Bd: William G Schriock Jr
**Pr:* Joel Schriock
**Treas:* Percy Schriock
**VP:* Todd Schriock
Exec: Eileen Muus

D-U-N-S 80-823-8083 IMP
■ GRAVER TECHNOLOGIES LLC
LIQUID FILTER DIVISION
(*Suby of* MARMON INDUSTRIAL LLC) ★
200 Lake Dr, Newark, DE 19702-3327
Tel (302) 731-1700 *Founded/Ownrshp* 1993
Sales 59.6MM^E *EMP* 220
SIC 5999 5074 3589 Water purification equipment; Water purification equipment; Water treatment equipment, industrial; Water purification equipment; Water purification equipment; Water treatment equipment, industrial
Pr: John Schroeder
**CFO:* Robert K Lorch
**VP:* Michael Butz
VP: John McPeak
**VP:* Angelo V Pantaleo
Sftwr Eng: Anand Harohalli
Mfg Dir: Jim Sheridan
Mtls Mgr: Walter Salamon
Mtls Mgr: Thomas Simmons
Sfty Mgr: Brian Velon
Ql Cn Mgr: Mark Johnson

D-U-N-S 09-212-0724
GRAVES AND GRAVES CONSTRUCTION CO INC
1267 W Main St, Parsons, TN 38363-2862
Tel (731) 847-6391 *Founded/Ownrshp* 1955
Sales 50.1MM^E *EMP* 150
SIC 1542 1794 1623 Commercial & office building, new construction; Excavation & grading, building construction; Water main construction; Sewer line construction; Commercial & office building, new construction; Excavation & grading, building construction; Water main construction; Sewer line construction
Pr: Danny L Graves
**VP:* John Graves

D-U-N-S 17-415-0748
GRAVES COUNTY SCHOOL DISTRICT
2290 State Route 121 N, Mayfield, KY 42066-6760
Tel (270) 328-2656 *Founded/Ownrshp* 1900
Sales 32.5MM^E *EMP* 700
SIC 8211 Public elementary & secondary schools; Public elementary & secondary schools
Adm Dir: Bobby Galloway

D-U-N-S 07-372-7237
GRAVES HOSPITALITY CORP
1934 Hennepin Ave Ste 201, Minneapolis, MN 55403-4035
Tel (320) 252-6034 *Founded/Ownrshp* 1996
Sales 27.4MM^E *EMP* 550
SIC 7011 Hotels; Hotels
CEO: James Graves
**Pr:* Ben Graves
VP: Matthew Mering
IT Man: Ronald Smith
Mktg Mgr: Jeremy Keippela
Mktg Mgr: Lisa Zollars
Sls Mgr: Sarah Peltier

D-U-N-S 00-422-9720 IMP
GRAVES LUMBER CO (OH)
1315 S Clvland Msslion Rd, Copley, OH 44321-2175
Tel (330) 666-1115 *Founded/Ownrshp* 1899
Sales 52.1MM^E *EMP* 115
SIC 5211 5031

GRAVES MENU MAKER FOODS
See MENU MAKER FOODS INC

D-U-N-S 02-205-0074
GRAVES OIL CO
RASCAL'S CONVENIENCE STORE
226 Pearson St, Batesville, MS 38606-2428
Tel (662) 563-4604 *Founded/Ownrshp* 1968
Sales 275.8MM *EMP* 146
Accts J Gary Kornegay Batesville
SIC 5171 5541 5411 Petroleum bulk stations; Filling stations, gasoline; Convenience stores, independent; Petroleum bulk stations; Filling stations, gasoline; Convenience stores, independent
Pr: C Fred Graves III
**VP:* Charlie B Graves
VP: Gary M Stiles
MIS Dir: Ben Graves
Sfty Mgr: Don Kilgore
Sls Mgr: Sue Grantham

GRAVES' SHOP N SAVE
See GRAVES SUPER MARKETS INC

D-U-N-S 01-903-4073
GRAVES SUPER MARKETS INC
GRAVES' SHOP N SAVE
797 Main St, Presque Isle, ME 04769-2201
Tel (207) 764-0946 *Founded/Ownrshp* 1955
Sales 36.7MM^E *EMP* 400
SIC 5411 5912 Grocery stores; Drug stores & proprietary stores; Grocery stores; Drug stores & proprietary stores
Pr: Robert D Graves
**VP:* Gregory V Graves
Board of Directors: Robert D Graves Sr

GRAVES SUPPLY
See WOMACK ELECTRIC & SUPPLY CO INC

GRAVES-GILBERT CLINIC
See GILBERT BARBEE MOORE & MCILVOY PSC

D-U-N-S 07-785-6698
GRAVES-GILBERT CLINIC HOLDING CO INC
201 Park St, Bowling Green, KY 42101-1759
Tel (270) 781-5111 *Founded/Ownrshp* 1937
Sales 40.6MM^E *EMP* 349
SIC 8011 Clinic, operated by physicians; Clinic, operated by physicians
**Pr:* Paul Cofoid
**VP:* Pippa Pinckley-Stewart
Dir Bus: William Harrigan
Opers Supe: Jennifer Merkle
Surgeon: Amber Hurt
Nutrtnst: Sandeep Chhabra

D-U-N-S 78-498-7104
GRAVICK GROUP LLC
4985 Fm 1017, San Isidro, TX 78588-1503
Tel (956) 330-5676 *Founded/Ownrshp* 2001
Sales 1.3MM *EMP* 1,178
SIC 8742 7371 7389 Management consulting services; Computer software development & applications;

D-U-N-S 13-178-4329
GRAVITAS INC
475 Park Ave S Fl 32, New York, NY 10016-6901
Tel (212) 607-8200 *Founded/Ownrshp* 2002
Sales 20.5MM^E *EMP* 75^E
SIC 7379 Computer related consulting services
Ch Bd: Jayesh Punater
Board of Directors: Bob Magee Joanna Peters Ca

D-U-N-S 00-724-6776
■ GRAVITY FINANCIAL LLC
(*Suby of* SS&C TECHNOLOGIES HOLDINGS INC) ★
1 New Boston Dr Ste 7, Canton, MA 02021-2859
Tel (781) 828-7800 *Founded/Ownrshp* 2012
Sales 138.9MM^E *EMP* 846^E
SIC 6282 Investment advice

D-U-N-S 08-600-8195 EXP
GRAVOIS ALUMINUM BOATS LLC
METAL SHARK
6816 E Admiral Doyle Dr, Jeanerette, LA 70544-6510
Tel (337) 365-2155 *Founded/Ownrshp* 2000
Sales 36.2MM^E *EMP* 71
SIC 3732 Boat building & repairing
Pr: Chris Allard
CEO: Carol J Gravois Jr
CFO: Donna Gravois
Prd Mgr: John Albert
Natl Sales: Jimmy Gravois
Natl Sales: Dean Jones

D-U-N-S 83-220-9741
GRAVOTECH US HOLDING LLC
(*Suby of* GRAVOTECH PARTICIPATIONS)
2200 Northmont Pkwy, Duluth, GA 30096-5895
Tel (770) 623-0331 *Founded/Ownrshp* 2007
Sales 20.6MM^E *EMP* 136
SIC 6719 Personal holding companies, except banks; Personal holding companies, except banks
CEO: Gerard Guyard
CFO: Carol D Franklin
**VP:* Victoria Ganes

GRAY
See ICE BUILDERS INC

D-U-N-S 05-708-5656 IMP/EXP
■ GRAY & CO
(*Suby of* SENECA FOODS CORP) ★
3325 W Polk Rd, Hart, MI 49420-8149
Tel (231) 873-5628 *Founded/Ownrshp* 2015
Sales 60.0MM^E *EMP* 325
SIC 2033 Maraschino cherries: packaged in cans, jars, etc.; Maraschino cherries: packaged in cans, jars, etc.
CEO: James G Reynolds
Ex VP: Joshua E Reynolds
Sr VP: Jacqueline Case
Plnt Mgr: Coy Petross

D-U-N-S 00-820-5429
GRAY & CO INC
3625 N I 10 Service Rd W, Metairie, LA 70002-7029
Tel (504) 888-7790 *Founded/Ownrshp* 1948
Sales NA *EMP* 200
SIC 6331 Fire, marine & casualty insurance & carriers; Fire, marine & casualty insurance & carriers
Pr: Michael Gray
CFO: Robert Hughes
**VP:* Eric V Gray
**VP:* Walter Gray
**VP:* David W Pixberg

D-U-N-S 00-342-3803
GRAY & SON INC (MD)
430 W Padonia Rd, Lutherville Timonium, MD 21093-2274
Tel (410) 771-4311 *Founded/Ownrshp* 1908, 1966
Sales 108.7MM^E *EMP* 350
Accts Jones Hall Advisors
SIC 1611 1623 1794 General contractor, highway & street construction; Water, sewer & utility lines; Excavation & grading, building construction; General contractor, highway & street construction; Water, sewer & utility lines; Excavation & grading, building construction
CEO: George V Palmer
**CEO:* Robert F Webbert
COO: Les Preble
**CFO:* Rick Scheetz
**Treas:* Barbara Webbert
Sr VP: William Donlet
VP: Christopher Eisenhart
**VP:* Jay Hergenroeder
VP: Mike Little
**VP:* Peter Placke
**VP:* Joel Stockbridge
VP: Paul Swank
Comm Man: Katie McLnnes

D-U-N-S 09-182-0811 IMP/EXP
GRAY AMERICA CORP
3050 Dryden Rd, Moraine, OH 45439-1620
Tel (937) 293-9313 *Founded/Ownrshp* 1978
Sales 52.5MM^E *EMP* 125^E
SIC 3312 3452

GRAY CHERVOLT OLDSMBL CADDLC
See RINE MOTORS INC

D-U-N-S 00-700-2181 IMP
GRAY CONSTRUCTION INC
(*Suby of* GRAY INC) ★
10 Quality St, Lexington, KY 40507-1450
Tel (859) 281-5000 *Founded/Ownrshp* 1960
Sales 183.9MM^E *EMP* 300
SIC 1541 1542 8712

GRAY DANIELS FORD LINCOLN
See ASBURY MS WIMBER LLC

D-U-N-S 78-027-6296
GRAY ENERGY SERVICES LLC
1912 West Ave, Levelland, TX 79336
Tel (806) 894-6008 *Founded/Ownrshp* 2006
Sales 7.3MM^E *EMP* 540
SIC 1389 Well logging; Well logging

GRAY ENTERPRISES
See POMPANETTE LLC

D-U-N-S 60-577-5998
GRAY FLEX SYSTEMS INC
232 N Ida St, Coats, NC 27521-8626
Tel (910) 897-3539 *Founded/Ownrshp* 1997
Sales 22.2MM^E *EMP* 150^E
SIC 3444 Ducts, sheet metal; Ducts, sheet metal
Pr: William R Gray
Treas: Carole L Gray
Off Mgr: Christy Holland
IT Man: Reid Taylor
Prd Mgr: McKinley Butler

D-U-N-S 10-834-9234
GRAY INC
10 Quality St, Lexington, KY 40507-1443
Tel (859) 281-5000 *Founded/Ownrshp* 1960
Sales NA *EMP* 450
SIC 1541 1542

D-U-N-S 36-291-5113
GRAY INSURANCE CO INC
(*Suby of* GRAY & CO INC) ★
3601 N I 10 Service Rd W, Metairie, LA 70002-7051
Tel (504) 888-7790 *Founded/Ownrshp* 2005
Sales NA *EMP* 112
SIC 6411 Insurance agents
Pr: Michael Gray
CFO: Robert M Hughes
Sr VP: Wallace Paletou
**VP:* Eric Gray
VP: Mark Mega
Snr Ntwrk: Brian Lejeune
CTO: Bruce Wilson
IT Man: Carleton Ellsworth
Software D: Clint Anderson
Software D: Jacob Schoen
Snr Mgr: Thomas Neely

D-U-N-S 78-363-1336
GRAY KIRK/VANSANT ADVERTISING INC
GKV COMMUNICATION
1500 Whetstone Way Fl 4, Baltimore, MD 21230-4768
Tel (410) 539-5400 *Founded/Ownrshp* 1993
Sales 20.8MM^E *EMP* 66
SIC 7311 Advertising agencies
Pr: Roger Gray
**CFO:* Cathy Kowaleski
CFO: Cathy Kowalewski
Treas: Emon McGeady
Sr VP: David Blum
Sr VP: Dan Collins
**Sr VP:* Jeff Millman
Sr VP: Alexei Yukna
VP: Brian Burkhart
VP: Dean Kenderdine
VP: Garry Raim
VP: Philip Scharper
Assoc Dir: Heather Woolford
Comm Man: Tina Heckner

D-U-N-S 02-818-9785
GRAY LIFT INC (CA)
WAREHOUSE SYS
4646 E Jensen Ave, Fresno, CA 93725-1699
Tel (559) 268-6621 *Founded/Ownrshp* 1957
Sales 37.8MM^E *EMP* 86^E
SIC 5084 7699 7359 Industrial machinery & equipment; Materials handling machinery; Lift trucks & parts; Stackers, industrial; Industrial equipment services; Equipment rental & leasing; Industrial machinery & equipment; Materials handling machinery; Lift trucks & parts; Stackers, industrial; Industrial equipment services; Equipment rental & leasing
Pr: John L Waugh Jr
**VP:* Richard Waugh
Sfty Mgr: Bill Stromer
Sales Exec: Raoul Rodriguez

GRAY LINE HAWAII
See POLYNESIAN ADVENTURE TOURS INC

GRAY LINE OF DALLAS
See KERRVILLE BUS CO INC

D-U-N-S 60-939-1755
GRAY LINE OF SEATTLE
4500 W Marginal Way Sw, Seattle, WA 98106-1511
Tel (206) 624-5077 *Founded/Ownrshp* 2005
Sales 8.2MM^E *EMP* 280
SIC 4141 Local bus charter service; Local bus charter service
Genl Mgr: Joshua Gatherum
VP: Oconnor Chris
VP: Bobby Hill

GRAY LINE SIGHTSEEING
See GOLD LINE INC

GRAY LINE/CITY SIGHTS
See TWIN AMERICA LLC

D-U-N-S 00-712-3953 EXP
GRAY MANUFACTURING CO INC (MO)
3501 S Leonard Rd, Saint Joseph, MO 64503-1756
Tel (816) 233-6121 *Founded/Ownrshp* 1952, 1965
Sales 61.6MM^E *EMP* 172
SIC 3569 3537 Jacks, hydraulic; Industrial trucks & tractors; Jacks, hydraulic; Industrial trucks & tractors
CEO: Joseph L Gray
**Ch Bd:* Joseph P Gray
**Pr:* Sterett W Schanze
**Treas:* Michael W Hurst
QA Dir: Ron Lasley
Dir IT: Jeanine Riddle
IT Man: Eric Worsham
Natl Sales: Doug Fletchall
Sls Mgr: Jack Bidding

D-U-N-S 78-761-4676
GRAY METAL SOUTH INC
600 N Powell Ave, Dunn, NC 28334
Tel (910) 892-2119 *Founded/Ownrshp* 1908
Sales 21.5MM^E *EMP* 140^E
SIC 3444 Sheet metalwork; Sheet metalwork
Pr: Marguerite Gray
**VP:* Joseph Gray
Manager: John Copeland
Board of Directors: Carole L Gray, Richard E Gray Sr

D-U-N-S 08-835-1002
GRAY OIL CO INC
804 Denver Ave, Fort Lupton, CO 80621-2164
Tel (303) 857-2288 *Founded/Ownrshp* 1978
Sales 102.0MM *EMP* 60
SIC 5171 5541 5411

GRAY PLANT MOOTY
See GRAY PLANT MOOTY MOOTY & BENNETT PA

D-U-N-S 08-025-0004
GRAY PLANT MOOTY MOOTY & BENNETT PA (MN)
GRAY PLANT MOOTY
80 S 8th St Ste 500, Minneapolis, MN 55402-3796
Tel (612) 632-3000 *Founded/Ownrshp* 1866
Sales 41.5MM^E *EMP* 338
SIC 8111 General practice law office; General practice law office
CEO: David C Bahls
**Treas:* William D Klein
**Prin:* Sarah Duniway
Prin: Stephen F Grinnel
**Prin:* Bruce W Mooty
Counsel: Lebedoff David
Counsel: Sharon Mackereth

D-U-N-S 60-343-8078
GRAY SUPPLY CORP
199 Franklin Rd, Randolph, NJ 07869-1612
Tel (973) 366-2290 *Founded/Ownrshp* 1952
Sales 82.7MM^E *EMP* 180
SIC 1623 7359 5084 Construction & mining machinery; Underground utilities contractor; Stores & yards equipment rental; Engines, gasoline; Underground utilities contractor; Stores & yards equipment rental; Engines, gasoline
Pr: Rudolph Herms Jr
**Pr:* Peter S Herms
**Sec:* Heidi Herms
Off Mgr: Judi Knapp

D-U-N-S 17-591-4456
■ GRAY TELEVISION GROUP INC
WCTV 6
(*Suby of* VOLUNTEER TV.COM) ★
4370 Peachtree Rd Ne # 500, Brookhaven, GA 30319-3056
Tel (404) 266-8333 *Founded/Ownrshp* 1996
Sales 291.0MM^E *EMP* 2,015^E
SIC 4833 Television broadcasting stations; Television broadcasting stations
CEO: Hilton H Howell Jr
Pr: James Ocon
**Pr:* Nick Waller
CFO: James Ryan
Bd of Dir: Howell Newton
VP: Lisa Bishop
VP: Mike Braun
**VP:* Mike Smith
Snr Ntwrk: Kraig Beahn
VP Opers: Julia Campbell
VP Prd: Lisa Guill

D-U-N-S 04-297-3875
▲ GRAY TELEVISION INC (GA)
4370 Peachtree Rd Ne # 500, Brookhaven, GA 30319-3056
Tel (404) 504-9828 *Founded/Ownrshp* 1897
Sales 508.1MM *EMP* 2,248
Accts Mcgladrey Llp West Palm Beach
Tkr Sym GTN *Exch* NYS
SIC 4833 Television broadcasting stations; Television broadcasting stations
Pr: Hilton H Howell Jr
CFO: James C Ryan
Ofcr: Jackson S Cowart IV
Sr VP: Jason Effinger
Sr VP: Kevin P Latek
Sr VP: Bob Smith
Sr VP: Nick Waller
VP: Greg Conklin
CIO: Joshua Schipmann
DP Exec: Eric J Goedde

D-U-N-S 80-603-5143
GRAY TRANSPORTATION INC
2459 Gt Dr, Waterloo, IA 50703-9434
Tel (319) 234-3930 *Founded/Ownrshp* 1984

Sales 27.8MM^E *EMP* 150
SIC 4213 Trucking, except local; Trucking, except local
Pr: Darrin Gray
**Treas:* Caroline Gray
Exec: Rita Lubbers
Opers Mgr: Mindy Stone

D-U-N-S 08-151-5988 IMP/EXP
GRAY VESTAR INVESTORS LLC
17622 Armstrong Ave, Irvine, CA 92614-5728
Tel (949) 863-1171 *Founded/Ownrshp* 1999
Sales 487.9MM^E *EMP* 5,860
SIC 2253 2339 2335 2337 3961 2387 Dresses, knit; Skirts, knit; Pants, slacks or trousers, knit; T-shirts & tops, knit; Sportswear, women's; Scarves, hoods, headbands, etc.: women's; Jackets, untailored: women's, misses' & juniors'; Slacks: women's, misses' & juniors'; Women's, juniors' & misses' dresses; Bridal & formal gowns; Women's & misses' suits & coats; Suits: women's, misses' & juniors'; Jackets & vests, except fur & leather: women's; Skirts, separate: women's, misses' & juniors'; Costume jewelry; Apparel belts; Dresses, knit; Skirts, knit; Pants, slacks or trousers, knit; T-shirts & tops, knit; Sportswear, women's; Scarves, hoods, headbands, etc.: women's; Jackets, untailored: women's, misses' & juniors'; Slacks: women's, misses' & juniors'; Women's, juniors' & misses' dresses; Bridal & formal gowns; Women's & misses' suits & coats; Suits: women's, misses' & juniors'; Jackets & vests, except fur & leather: women's; Skirts, separate: women's, misses' & juniors'; Costume jewelry; Apparel belts

D-U-N-S 00-190-3202 IMP/EXP
GRAYBAR ELECTRIC CO INC (NY)
34 N Meramec Ave, Saint Louis, MO 63105-1678
Tel (314) 573-9200 *Founded/Ownrshp* 1925
Sales 5.9MMM *EMP* 8,297
SIC 5063 5065

D-U-N-S 11-246-2408
GRAYBEARD CAPITAL LLC
1133 La Ave Ste 100, Winter Park, FL 32789
Tel (407) 622-5925 *Founded/Ownrshp* 2002
Sales 25.0MM *EMP* 3
SIC 6726 6282 Management investment funds, closed-end; Investment advisory service; Management investment funds, closed-end; Investment advisory service

D-U-N-S 07-333-4328
GRAYBILL MEDICAL GROUP INC
225 E 2nd Ave, Escondido, CA 92025-4249
Tel (866) 228-2236 *Founded/Ownrshp* 1977
Sales 40.6MM^E *EMP* 300
SIC 8011 General & family practice, physician/surgeon; General & family practice, physician/surgeon
CEO: Floyd Farley
**Pr:* Marvin V Beddoe
**CEO:* David Borecky
CFO: Leslie Chapman
**VP:* George A Pleitez
Exec: Jackie Craw
Off Mgr: Kathy Onorato
Off Mgr: Nicole Rivas
Off Mgr: Julie Robinson
Mktg Dir: Veronica Lozano
Doctor: Linden Burzell

D-U-N-S 13-959-9679
GRAYCLIFF ENTERPRISES INC
3300 Battleground Ave # 100, Greensboro, NC 27410-2447
Tel (336) 288-9464 *Founded/Ownrshp* 2003
Sales 40.0MM^E *EMP* 125
SIC 1623 Transmitting tower (telecommunication) construction; Telephone & communication line construction; Transmitting tower (telecommunication) construction; Telephone & communication line construction
Pr: Raymond Galtelli
**CFO:* Patsy Kesler
**VP:* James F Robertson

D-U-N-S 07-842-3727
GRAYCLIFF PARTNERS LP
500 5th Ave Fl 47, New York, NY 10110-4703
Tel (212) 300-2900 *Founded/Ownrshp* 2011
Sales 40.7MM^E *EMP* 70^E
SIC 6726 Investment offices; Management investment funds, closed-end
Prin: Will Henderson
CFO: Steven Schaefer
VP: Katherine Anderson
VP: Carl Barcoma
VP: Alberto Gomez
VP: Katherine Taylor
**Prin:* Duke Punhong

GRAYCO
See BEAUFORT MUFFLER AND AUTO SUPPLY CO INC

D-U-N-S 00-978-6427
GRAYCO HOME CENTER INC
22 Sams Point Rd, Beaufort, SC 29907-2000
Tel (843) 522-9994 *Founded/Ownrshp* 1984
Sales 34.5MM^E *EMP* 170
SIC 5211 Lumber & other building materials; Lumber & other building materials
CEO: Herb Gray
**COO:* Richard L Gray Jr

D-U-N-S 06-707-7065
GRAYCOR CONSTRUCTION CO INC
(*Suby of* GRAYCOR INC) ★
2 Mid America Plz Ste 400, Oakbrook Terrace, IL 60181-4714
Tel (630) 684-7110 *Founded/Ownrshp* 1982
Sales 52.1MM^E *EMP* 100^E
SIC 1542 1541 Commercial & office building, new construction; Hospital construction; Shopping center construction; Industrial buildings & warehouses; Commercial & office building, new construction; Hospital construction; Shopping center construction; Industrial buildings & warehouses
Pr: David Wing
**V Ch Bd:* Kenneth Isaacs
**Ex VP:* David McAllen
Sr VP: Jack Carlson
VP: Penny Emerson
**VP:* Steven Gray

D-U-N-S 04-957-5371
GRAYCOR INC
2 Mid America Plz Ste 400, Oakbrook Terrace, IL 60181-4714
Tel (630) 684-7110 *Founded/Ownrshp* 1996
Sales 704.7MM^E *EMP* 1,500
SIC 1541 1542 Industrial buildings & warehouses; Commercial & office building, new construction; Hospital construction; Shopping center construction; Industrial buildings & warehouses; Commercial & office building, new construction; Hospital construction; Shopping center construction
Ch: Gray Melvin
**CFO:* Steven Gray
**Ex VP:* Matthew Gray
VP: Lee Petcu
Dir Bus: Dean Andrisevic
VP Admn: Dave Wing
Off Mgr: Angela Tatta
Off Mgr: Roberta Wagner
Off Admin: Rebecca Salinas
Dir IT: Sergio Ruiz
Opers Mgr: Eric Gerlach

D-U-N-S 00-693-0341
GRAYCOR INDUSTRIAL CONSTRUCTORS INC
(*Suby of* GRAYCOR INC) ★
2 Mid America Plz Ste 400, Oakbrook Terrace, IL 60181-4714
Tel (630) 684-7110 *Founded/Ownrshp* 1921
Sales 420.3MM^E *EMP* 1,000
SIC 1542 1541 Commercial & office building, new construction; Industrial buildings, new construction; Commercial & office building, new construction; Industrial buildings, new construction
Ch Bd: Melvin Gray
**Pr:* Sam Potter
**CFO:* Steven Gray
VP: Tim Dace
Dir Bus: Greg Glidden
**Prin:* Bradley Teckenbrock
Sfty Mgr: Camron Day

D-U-N-S 93-394-4019
GRAYDAZE CONTRACTING INC
11495 N Fulton Indus Blvd, Alpharetta, GA 30009-4841
Tel (770) 752-7010 *Founded/Ownrshp* 1991
Sales 21.9MM *EMP* 50^E
Accts Williams Benator & Libby Llp
SIC 1721 Commercial painting; Industrial painting; Commercial painting; Industrial painting
Pr: Gary Otis Gray II
**VP:* David Henry

D-U-N-S 82-935-0029
GRAYHAWK CAPITAL LLC
5050 N 40th St Ste 310, Phoenix, AZ 85018-2153
Tel (602) 956-8700 *Founded/Ownrshp* 2002
Sales 25.0MM^E *EMP* 120^E
SIC 6799 Investors
Pt: Sherman Chu
Pt: Brian Burns

D-U-N-S 82-935-0052
GRAYHAWK LEGACY PARTNERS LLC
(*Suby of* GRAYHAWK CAPITAL LLC) ★
5050 N 40th St Ste 310, Phoenix, AZ 85018-2153
Tel (602) 956-8700 *Founded/Ownrshp* 2007
Sales 25.0MM^E *EMP* 120^E
SIC 6799 Investors

D-U-N-S 00-518-9790 IMP
GRAYHILL INC
561 W Hillgrove Ave, La Grange, IL 60525-5997
Tel (708) 354-1040 *Founded/Ownrshp* 1940
Sales 170.9MM^E *EMP* 800
SIC 3613 3625 3679 3643 3575 Switches, electric power except snap, push button, etc.; Switches, electric power; Switches, electronic applications; Electronic switches; Electric switches; Keyboards, computer, office machine; Switches, electric power except snap, push button, etc.; Switches, electric power; Switches, electronic applications; Electronic switches; Electric switches; Keyboards, computer, office machine
Ch: Gene R Hill
**Pr:* Brian May
**CFO:* Jerome J Klingenberger
**VP:* Jamie Dobravec
**VP:* Keith Hansen
**VP:* James Happel
**VP:* Michael Raleigh
VP: Mike Raleigh
Comm Man: Angie Panos
Mng Dir: Judy Williams
Snr Sftwr: Torsten Chase

D-U-N-S 61-291-1714
GRAYLINE NEW YORK TOURS I
(*Suby of* GRAY LINE/CITY SIGHTS) ★
777 8th Ave, New York, NY 10036-7009
Tel (212) 445-0848 *Founded/Ownrshp* 2009
Sales 154.3MM^E *EMP* 674^E
SIC 4725 Tours, conducted
Prin: Ira Berg

GRAYLINE OF ATLANTA
See AMERICAN COACH LINES OF ATLANTA INC

D-U-N-S 15-769-0926
GRAYLING CORP
CHILI'S
(*Suby of* BURGER KING) ★
4220 Edison Lkes Pkwy 100, Mishawaka, IN 46545
Tel (856) 384-1212 *Founded/Ownrshp* 1986
Sales 30.2MM^E *EMP* 1,100
SIC 5812 5813 6531 Restaurant, family: chain; Bar (drinking places); Real estate agents & managers; Restaurant, family: chain; Bar (drinking places); Real estate agents & managers
Pr: Daniel B Fitzpatrick
**Sr VP:* James Fitzpatrick
**VP:* Christoper Collier

D-U-N-S 14-759-2398 IMP
GRAYLING INDUSTRIES INC
(*Suby of* ILC DOVER LP) ★
2 Moonwalker Rd, Frederica, DE 19946-2080
Tel (770) 751-9095 *Founded/Ownrshp* 2013
Sales 25.8MM^E *EMP* 25
SIC 5169 2673 3081 2869 Polyurethane products; Plastic bags: made from purchased materials; Unsupported plastics film & sheet; Industrial organic chemicals
Pr: Kurt David Ross
**CFO:* Carlos Rubio
Admn Mgr: Dorothy Pahner
Netwrk Eng: Vanessa Gonzalez
Mfg Mgr: Manuel Gallarzo
Mktg Dir: Lynda Duke
Sls Dir: Raymond Joyner
Mktg Mgr: Randy Sullinger
Sls Mgr: David Larsen
Sls Mgr: Ryan Thaxton

GRAYMONT
See WESTERN LIME CORP

D-U-N-S 15-075-1725 EXP
GRAYMONT (PA) INC
(*Suby of* GRAYMONT INC) ★
965 E College Ave, Pleasant Gap, PA 16823-6823
Tel (814) 353-4613 *Founded/Ownrshp* 1998
Sales 29.3MM^E *EMP* 185
SIC 3274 1422 Agricultural lime; Hydrated lime; Quicklime; Limestones, ground; Agricultural limestone, ground; Agricultural lime; Hydrated lime; Quicklime; Limestones, ground; Agricultural limestone, ground
Pr: William Dodge
Chf Mktg O: Herb Herman
VP: Randy Pletcher
Admn Mgr: Steve Boucher
IT Man: Cynthia Gehringer
Manager: Charles Lucostic

D-U-N-S 00-617-9774 EXP
GRAYMONT (WI) INC
C L M
(*Suby of* GRAYMONT LIMITED)
800 Hill Ave, Superior, WI 54880-1369
Tel (218) 722-3981 *Founded/Ownrshp* 1946
Sales 167.5MM^E *EMP* 1,500^E
SIC 3274 Lime; Hydrated lime; Lime; Hydrated lime
Pr: William Dodge
**CFO:* Jim Hetimovich
**CFO:* Robert Kanuit
VP: David La Liberte
**VP:* Dana Stone
Sfty Mgr: Keith Miller
Sls Mgr: Terry Spooner

D-U-N-S 02-551-0413
GRAYMONT COOPERATIVE ASSOCIATION (INC) (IL)
313 N Main St, Graymont, IL 61743-7511
Tel (815) 743-5701 *Founded/Ownrshp* 1904, 1998
Sales 26.1MM^E *EMP* 30^E
SIC 5153 5191 5031 5211 5999 Grain elevators; Fertilizer & fertilizer materials; Feed; Lumber: rough, dressed & finished; Lumber products; Feed & farm supply
Pr: Edward Hoerner
Genl Mgr: Alan Zehr

D-U-N-S 18-295-5120 IMP
GRAYMONT INC
301 S 700 E 3950, Salt Lake City, UT 84102
Tel (801) 262-3942 *Founded/Ownrshp* 1943
Sales 237.2MM^E *EMP* 336
SIC 1429 2951 3273 Grits mining (crushed stone); Asphalt paving mixtures & blocks; Ready-mixed concrete; Grits mining (crushed stone); Asphalt paving mixtures & blocks; Ready-mixed concrete
CEO: Stephane Godin
**CFO:* Kenneth Lahti
**VP:* Marc Dagenais
VP: Bryan Nielson
VP: Thomas Wakefield
Plnt Mgr: Jim Otis

D-U-N-S 00-207-9960
GRAYMONT MATERIALS (NY) INC (NV)
(*Suby of* GRAYMONT INC) ★
111 Quarry Rd, Plattsburgh, NY 12901-6215
Tel (518) 561-5321 *Founded/Ownrshp* 1943
Sales 25.8MM^E *EMP* 84
SIC 1429 3273 2951 Grits mining (crushed stone); Ready-mixed concrete; Asphalt & asphaltic paving mixtures (not from refineries)
CEO: Stephane Godin
**Pr:* Todd Kempainen
**Treas:* Debora L Richards
Genl Mgr: Dennis Tsuchida
IT Man: Martin Beausoleil
Site Mgr: Jim Wossar
Sls Mgr: Mark Coombs

D-U-N-S 96-539-6427 IMP/EXP
GRAYMONT WESTERN US INC
(*Suby of* CLI HOLDINGS INC) ★
3950 S 700 E Ste 301, Salt Lake City, UT 84107-1303
Tel (801) 262-3942 *Founded/Ownrshp* 1989
Sales 166.2MM^E *EMP* 190
SIC 1411 Limestone, dimension-quarrying; Limestone, dimension-quarrying
Pr: Stephane Godin
**Pr:* William E Dodge
**Pr:* Gary A Poole
**CFO:* Kenneth J Lahti
**Ex VP:* Wayne J Wagner
VP: Mike Brown
**VP:* Jeff Higgs

D-U-N-S 04-657-6864
GRAYS FOODS INC
1630 N Alpine Rd, Rockford, IL 61107-1436
Tel (815) 397-4225 *Founded/Ownrshp* 1968
Sales 25.0MM^E *EMP* 250
SIC 5411 Grocery stores, independent; Grocery stores, independent
Pr: Clifford Gray
**Sec:* Joan Gray
**VP:* Jeff Gray
**VP:* Steve Whitney

D-U-N-S 08-192-6776
GRAYS HARBOR COLLEGE
1620 Edward P Smith Dr, Aberdeen, WA 98520-7599
Tel (360) 532-9020 *Founded/Ownrshp* 1934
Sales 54.1MM^E *EMP* 700
SIC 8221 8222 Colleges universities & professional schools; Community college; Colleges universities & professional schools; Community college
Pr: Ed Brewster
VP: Laurie Clary
VP: Jason Hoseney
**VP:* Arlene Porgerson
VP: Arlene Torgerson
Exec: Dave Halverstadt
Ex Dir: Wes Peterson
Prgrm Mgr: D Winkelman
CIO: Sandy Loyd
IT Man: Darrelyn Miller
Psych: Brian Shook

D-U-N-S 96-546-9260
GRAYS HARBOR COMMUNITY HOSPITAL
1006 N H St, Aberdeen, WA 98520-2599
Tel (360) 532-8330 *Founded/Ownrshp* 1983
Sales 114.9MM *EMP* 99
Accts Moss Adams Llp Everett Wa
SIC 8062 General medical & surgical hospitals; General medical & surgical hospitals
Pr: Tim Kuhn
COO: Thomas Hightower
COO: Larry Kahl
CFO: Art Tanner
**Treas:* Jim Manenica
Chf Mktg O: Brent Rowe
**VP:* Ty Palmer
IT Man: Brandon Ford
Obsttrcn: Carey Martens

D-U-N-S 07-926-5476
GRAYS HARBOR COMMUNITY HOSPITAL FOUNDATION
915 Anderson Dr, Aberdeen, WA 98520-1097
Tel (360) 537-5000 *Founded/Ownrshp* 1940
Sales 89.2MM *EMP* 594
Accts Moss Adams Llp Everett Wa
SIC 8062 General medical & surgical hospitals; General medical & surgical hospitals
Pr: Sharon Schermer
VP: Marilyn Guy
Dir Rx: Tom Kloepping
Surgeon: David Parks
Surgeon: Matthew Shepherd

GRAYS HARBOR PUD
See PUBLIC UTILITY DISTRICT NO 1 OF GRAYS HARBOR COUNTY

GRAY'S INVESTIGATIVE SERVICES
See GRAYS SECURITY SERVICE INC

GRAY'S ORNAMENTALS II
See GRAYS ORNAMENTALS INC

D-U-N-S 14-482-3259 EXP
GRAYS ORNAMENTALS INC
GRAY'S ORNAMENTALS II
15321 One Lions Rd, Delray Beach, FL 33446
Tel (561) 496-6442 *Founded/Ownrshp* 1985
Sales 33.4MM^E *EMP* 85
SIC 5193 0181 Nursery stock; Nursery stock, growing of
Pr: Lionel Gray
Off Mgr: Pam Halberg

D-U-N-S 08-264-1044
GRAYS SECURITY SERVICE INC (FL)
GRAY'S INVESTIGATIVE SERVICES
1742 Manning St, Jacksonville, FL 32207-8697
Tel (904) 346-0810 *Founded/Ownrshp* 1933, 1944
Sales 6.7MM^E *EMP* 312
SIC 7381 Guard services; Detective agency; Guard services; Detective agency
Pr: James E Gray Jr
**Sec:* Fay Gray

D-U-N-S 08-982-3496
GRAYSLAKE COMMUNITY HIGH SCHOOL DISTRICT 127
400 N Lake St, Grayslake, IL 60030-1430
Tel (847) 986-3300 *Founded/Ownrshp* 1945
Sales 25.1MM^E *EMP* 347
SIC 8211 Public junior high school; Public senior high school; Public junior high school; Public senior high school
**Pr:* Ann Dingman
**VP:* Suzanne Swanson

D-U-N-S 02-679-9742
GRAYSON COUNTY BOARD OF EDUCATION
790 Shaw Station Rd, Leitchfield, KY 42754-8150
Tel (270) 259-4011 *Founded/Ownrshp* 1903
Sales 37.6MM *EMP* 625
Accts Buckles Travis Vanmeter & Ha
SIC 8211 Elementary & secondary schools; Elementary & secondary schools

D-U-N-S 08-504-9112
GRAYSON COUNTY HOSPITAL FOUNDATION INC (KY)
TWIN LAKES REGIONAL MED CTR
910 Wallace Ave, Leitchfield, KY 42754-2414
Tel (270) 259-9400 *Founded/Ownrshp* 1956
Sales 39.7MM *EMP* 350
Accts Buckles Travis Vanmeter & Har

SIC 8062 8011 General medical & surgical hospitals; Offices & clinics of medical doctors; General medical & surgical hospitals; Offices & clinics of medical doctors
Pr: Brett Abney
**CEO:* Stephen Meredith
COO: Alan Alexander
**CFO:* Scott Arndall
CFO: Scott Arndell
Ofcr: Carey Sims
**VP:* Trevor Ray
Dir Lab: Matt Smith
Dir Rad: Jarrad Davis
Genl Mgr: Letta Hayes
CIO: Mandy Bryant

D-U-N-S 07-979-8858
GRAYSON COUNTY PUBLIC SCHOOLS
412 E Main St, Independence, VA 24348-3954
Tel (276) 773-2832 *Founded/Ownrshp* 2015
Sales 11.3MM^E *EMP* 322^E
SIC 8211 Public elementary & secondary schools

D-U-N-S 10-007-9664
GRAYSON COUNTY SCHOOL BOARD
PUBLIC SCHOOLS
412 E Main St, Independence, VA 24348-3954
Tel (276) 773-2832 *Founded/Ownrshp* 2007
Sales 19.8MM^E *EMP* 325^E
SIC 8211 Public elementary & secondary schools; Public elementary & secondary schools

D-U-N-S 07-982-7316
GRAYSON COUNTY SCHOOLS
790 Shaw Station Rd, Leitchfield, KY 42754-8150
Tel (270) 259-4011 *Founded/Ownrshp* 2015
Sales 15.9MM^E *EMP* 527^E
SIC 8211 Public elementary & secondary schools

GRAYSON JEEP
See GRAYSON PONTIAC INC

D-U-N-S 04-735-8205
GRAYSON PONTIAC INC
GRAYSON JEEP
8729 Kingston Pike, Knoxville, TN 37923-5100
Tel (865) 693-4550 *Founded/Ownrshp* 1978
Sales 28.1MM^E *EMP* 75
SIC 5511 5521 7538 7532 7515 5531 Automobiles, new & used; Used car dealers; General automotive repair shops; Top & body repair & paint shops; Passenger car leasing; Automotive & home supply stores; Automobiles, new & used; Used car dealers; General automotive repair shops; Top & body repair & paint shops; Passenger car leasing; Automotive & home supply stores
Store Mgr: Bill Partin
**Pr:* Arthur Grayson

D-U-N-S 00-985-1809
GRAYSON RURAL ELECTRIC COOPERATIVE CORP
109 Bagby Park St, Grayson, KY 41143-1203
Tel (606) 474-5136 *Founded/Ownrshp* 1950
Sales 34.4MM *EMP* 44
Accts Alan Zumstein Lexington Ky
SIC 4911 Distribution, electric power; Distribution, electric power
Pr: Carol Fraley

D-U-N-S 00-895-3812 IMP
GRAYSON-COLLIN ELECTRIC CO-OP INC
902 N Waco St, Van Alstyne, TX 75495
Tel (903) 482-7100 *Founded/Ownrshp* 1937
Sales 104.7MM *EMP* 100
Accts Bolinger Segars Gilbert And Mo
SIC 4911 Distribution, electric power; Distribution, electric power
Pr: Charles Rice
CFO: Mike Roland
**Sec:* Steve Robinson
**VP:* Mark Brown

D-U-N-S 00-221-1209
GRAYWOOD COMPANIES INC (NY)
JASCO CUTTING TOOLS
1390 Mount Read Blvd, Rochester, NY 14606-2820
Tel (585) 254-7000 *Founded/Ownrshp* 2005
Sales 107.2MM^E *EMP* 620
SIC 3541 3545 3544 3398 Machine tools, metal cutting type; Boring mills; Countersinking machines; Deburring machines; Machine tool accessories; Drill bits, metalworking; Taps, machine tool; Reamers, machine tool; Special dies, tools, jigs & fixtures; Metal heat treating; Machine tools, metal cutting type; Boring mills; Countersinking machines; Deburring machines; Machine tool accessories; Drill bits, metalworking; Taps, machine tool; Reamers, machine tool; Special dies, tools, jigs & fixtures; Metal heat treating
Ch Bd: John M Summers
**Pr:* Eugene Baldino
**CFO:* Diane Simon
**VP:* Dave Krigeer

D-U-N-S 08-442-3045
GRAZIANO PRODUCE CO (INC)
GRAZIANO'S
9243 N Rivergate Blvd, Portland, OR 97203-6615
Tel (503) 285-0992 *Founded/Ownrshp* 1988
Sales 24.9MM^E *EMP* 275
SIC 5148 Fresh fruits & vegetables; Fresh fruits & vegetables
Pr: Joe Graziano
**VP:* James Albaugh
VP: Bob Swartwout

GRAZIANO'S
See GRAZIANO PRODUCE CO (INC)

D-U-N-S 00-977-0728
GRAZZINI BROTHERS AND CO (MN)
1175 Eagan Industrial Rd, Saint Paul, MN 55121-1205
Tel (651) 452-2700 *Founded/Ownrshp* 1923
Sales 41.7MM^E *EMP* 200
SIC 1743 Terrazzo work; Tile installation, ceramic; Terrazzo work; Tile installation, ceramic
Pr: Eugene Grazzini Jr
**Pr:* Greg Grazzini
**CFO:* James Byrne
**VP:* Guido Gliori
Snr PM: Tom Palmer

D-U-N-S 15-154-9797
GRB SERVICE SYSTEMS INC
SOUTHWESTERN SERVICES
2901 Suffolk Dr Ste 100, Fort Worth, TX 76133-1152
Tel (817) 921-2466 *Founded/Ownrshp* 1999
Sales 22.8MM^E *EMP* 25
Accts Hanner & Associates Pc Bedfo
SIC 1542 Commercial & office buildings, renovation & repair
Pr: Clifton J Bruner
**Pr:* John S Lee
**VP:* Terry Easley
**VP:* Gary C Wortham
VP: Gary Wortham
Sfty Dirs: John Ario
Snr PM: Gary Tucker

GRC
See GRAND RIVER CONSTRUCTION INC

D-U-N-S 79-142-4617
GRC HOLDING INC
(*Suby of* RGP HOLDING INC) ★
1 Bala Ave Ste 310, Bala Cynwyd, PA 19004-3210
Tel (610) 667-6640 *Founded/Ownrshp* 1992
Sales 45.1MM^E *EMP* 340
SIC 3255 1741 1499 Firebrick, clay; Castable refractories, clay; Foundry refractories, clay; Refractory or acid brick masonry; Diatomaceous earth mining; Perlite mining; Firebrick, clay; Castable refractories, clay; Foundry refractories, clay; Refractory or acid brick masonry; Diatomaceous earth mining; Perlite mining
Pr: Raymond G Perelman

GRCC
See GRAND RAPIDS COMMUNITY COLLEGE

D-U-N-S 07-199-8244
GRD BROKERAGE INC
(*Suby of* G. R. DANIELS TRUCKING, INC.)
19258 Turner Ave, Hutchinson, MN 55350-4357
Tel (320) 587-4002 *Founded/Ownrshp* 1988
Sales 36.0MM *EMP* 7
SIC 4731 Brokers, shipping; Brokers, shipping
Pr: Gary R Daniels
**Sec:* Sharon M Daniels
Sec: Sharon Daniels

GRDA
See GRAND RIVER DAM AUTHORITY

D-U-N-S 96-794-6232
GRDG HOLDINGS LLC
19411 Atrium Pl Ste 170, Houston, TX 77084-6024
Tel (281) 578-2334 *Founded/Ownrshp* 1999
Sales 71.8MM^E *EMP* 3,510
SIC 5945 Hobby & craft supplies; Hobby & craft supplies; Arts & crafts supplies

GREASE LIGHTNING
See UNITY FUELS LLC

GREAT AMERICAN
See VIDA TRIPLE-S INC

D-U-N-S 16-799-9361 IMP
GREAT AMERICAN APPETIZERS INC
216 8th St N, Nampa, ID 83687-3029
Tel (208) 465-5111 *Founded/Ownrshp* 2004
Sales 131.0MM^E *EMP* 700
SIC 2038 Frozen specialties; Frozen specialties
Pr: Ellen Meyer
**COO:* Marco Meyer
VP Opers: Steve Cordova
Sfty Mgr: Maria Hernandez
Plnt Mgr: Kevin Tucker
Ql Cn Mgr: Heather Memmelaar
Sls Mgr: Nate Burke

D-U-N-S 01-361-1924 IMP/EXP
GREAT AMERICAN BEAUTY INC
PALM BEACH BEAUTE
124 N Swinton Ave, Delray Beach, FL 33444-2634
Tel (561) 496-2730 *Founded/Ownrshp* 2001
Sales 83.0MM *EMP* 14
SIC 5122 2844 Perfumes; Perfumes & colognes; Perfumes; Perfumes & colognes
Pr: Harold Ickovics
**CFO:* Paul Smith
VP: Dyann Davis
Opers Mgr: Sherling Mereus

D-U-N-S 93-375-9219 IMP
GREAT AMERICAN COIL LLC
1704 Cherokee Trce, White Oak, TX 75693-3510
Tel (903) 297-4700 *Founded/Ownrshp* 1996
Sales 26.0MM^E *EMP* 75
SIC 3585 Refrigeration & heating equipment
VP: Scott Nichols
**Pr:* Dion Faucheux

GREAT AMERICAN COOKIE CO
See TRI-CITY COOKIE CO INC

D-U-N-S 08-482-8599
GREAT AMERICAN COOKIE CO INC
(*Suby of* GLOBAL FRANCHISE GROUP LLC) ★
4685 Frederick Dr Sw, Atlanta, GA 30336-1807
Tel (404) 505-3500 *Founded/Ownrshp* 2010
Sales 136.6MM^E *EMP* 1,027^E
SIC 5461 Cookies
Pr: Steve Russo
**CFO:* Sandra Buffa

D-U-N-S 01-431-4802
GREAT AMERICAN DELI
(*Suby of* H T HACKNEY CO) ★
5828 Main St, Ooltewah, TN 37363-8714
Tel (423) 238-5492 *Founded/Ownrshp* 2009
Sales 7.8MM^E *EMP* 1,258^E
SIC 5812 Delicatessen (eating places)
Ch Bd: W B Sansom

GREAT AMERICAN DISPOSAL CO
See GREAT AMERICAN ENVIRONMENTAL SERVICES INC

D-U-N-S 07-479-3969
GREAT AMERICAN ENVIRONMENTAL SERVICES INC
GREAT AMERICAN DISPOSAL CO
1005 East Blvd, Iron Mountain, MI 49802-4444
Tel (906) 774-9006 *Founded/Ownrshp* 1975
Sales 21.0MM^E *EMP* 37
SIC 4953 Garbage: collecting, destroying & processing
Pr: David J Brisson
**VP:* Terry Barnes

D-U-N-S 18-005-2144
■ **GREAT AMERICAN FINANCIAL RESOURCES INC**
(*Suby of* AFG) ★
250 E 5th St Ste 1000, Cincinnati, OH 45202-4127
Tel (513) 333-5300 *Founded/Ownrshp* 1987
Sales NA *EMP* 1,422
SIC 6371 Pension, health & welfare funds; Union welfare, benefit & health funds; Pension, health & welfare funds; Union welfare, benefit & health funds
Pr: S Craig Lindner
Ch Bd: Carl H Lindner
COO: Charles R Scheper
CFO: Christopher P Miliano
Assoc VP: James Niehaus
Ex VP: John B Berding
Ex VP: Ernest T Giambra
Ex VP: Keith A Jensen
Ex VP: Mark F Muething
Ex VP: Mark Nielsen
Ex VP: David B Rich
Ex VP: Bill Thaxton
Ex VP: David Vickers
Ex VP: Brad Wolfram
Sr VP: Mathew T Dukiewicz
Sr VP: Richard L Magoteaux
Sr VP: Michael J Prager
VP: Richard E Beavers
VP: Becky Birch
VP: Paul Britzky
VP: Anne Elmore
Board of Directors: Kenneth C Ambrecht, L Thomas Hiltz, Ronald G Joseph, John T Lawrence III, William R Martin, Joseph P Tomain

D-U-N-S 03-972-0131
GREAT AMERICAN FOODS CORP
DAVID BEARD'S CATFISH KING
3684 Fm 161 N, Hughes Springs, TX 75656-6487
Tel (903) 968-6520 *Founded/Ownrshp* 1980
Sales 12.0MM^E *EMP* 281
SIC 5812 Seafood restaurants

D-U-N-S 79-405-7641 EXP
GREAT AMERICAN FOODS INC
PIK-NIK FOODS USA
(*Suby of* ALLIANCE GLOBAL GROUP, INC.)
433 Airport Blvd Ste 404, Burlingame, CA 94010-2014
Tel (650) 282-4444 *Founded/Ownrshp* 2000
Sales 24.1MM *EMP* 7
SIC 2096 Potato chips & similar snacks
CEO: Alma Dacanay
**Pr:* Alex Gabaldon
Opers Mgr: Carlo Dacanay

D-U-N-S 04-386-2390
GREAT AMERICAN HOLDING CO INC
BURGER KING
943 E Fort King St, Ocala, FL 34471-2354
Tel (352) 732-8060 *Founded/Ownrshp* 1978
Sales 16.2MM^E *EMP* 350
SIC 5812 Fast-food restaurant, chain; Fast-food restaurant, chain
Pr: Gene B Camp
**VP:* Merritt C Fore
Off Mgr: Laura Estes

D-U-N-S 07-827-2717
■ **GREAT AMERICAN HOLDING INC** (OH)
(*Suby of* AFG) ★
301 E 4th St, Cincinnati, OH 45202-4245
Tel (513) 369-3000 *Founded/Ownrshp* 2002
Sales 244.6MM^E *EMP* 5,100^E
SIC 6719 Investment holding companies, except banks; Investment holding companies, except banks
Pr: Carl H Lindner III

D-U-N-S 00-606-5187 IMP
GREAT AMERICAN HOME STORE II INC
7171 Appling Farms Pkwy, Memphis, TN 38133-4732
Tel (901) 260-5900 *Founded/Ownrshp* 2007
Sales 26.0MM *EMP* 86
SIC 5712 2519 Furniture stores; Lawn & garden furniture, except wood & metal; Furniture stores; Lawn & garden furniture, except wood & metal
Pr: Vick Etheridge
**VP:* Ron Becker

D-U-N-S 16-848-7705 IMP
GREAT AMERICAN HOME STORE INC
GAHS
5295 Pepper Chase Dr, Southaven, MS 38671-9690
Tel (662) 996-1000 *Founded/Ownrshp* 2003
Sales 28.2MM^E *EMP* 90
SIC 5712 Furniture stores
Pr: Vick L Etheridge
**Sec:* Billy Caperton
Genl Mgr: Ron Becker
Sls Mgr: Matt Klinger

D-U-N-S 00-136-8497 IMP/EXP
GREAT AMERICAN INDUSTRIES INC (DE)
(*Suby of* PUBLIC LOAN CO INC) ★
300 Plaza Dr, Vestal, NY 13850-3647
Tel (607) 729-9331 *Founded/Ownrshp* 1928, 1985
Sales 92.0MM^E *EMP* 400
SIC 3086 5031 5074 3442 3069 5091 Plastics foam products; Building materials, interior; Plumbing fittings & supplies; Metal doors, sash & trim; Metal doors; Wet suits, rubber; Watersports equipment & supplies; Diving equipment & supplies; Plastics foam products; Building materials, interior; Plumbing fittings & supplies; Metal doors, sash & trim; Metal doors; Wet suits, rubber; Watersports equipment & supplies; Diving equipment & supplies
Ch Bd: Burton I Koffman
**Sr VP:* Richard E Koffman

D-U-N-S 05-735-6909 IMP/EXP
■ **GREAT AMERICAN INSURANCE CO**
(*Suby of* AFG) ★
301 E 4th St Ste 2800, Cincinnati, OH 45202-4257
Tel (513) 369-5000 *Founded/Ownrshp* 1999
Sales NA *EMP* 4,000
SIC 6331 Fire, marine & casualty insurance; Automobile insurance; Property damage insurance; Agricultural insurance; Fire, marine & casualty insurance; Automobile insurance; Property damage insurance; Agricultural insurance
CEO: Carl H Lindner III
Pr: Jeffrey Lloyd
Pr: Terry Miesse
Pr: Lisa Pennekamp
Pr: David L Thompson
COO: Donald D Larson
COO: Mark F Muething
CFO: Jennifer Meyer
CFO: David Witzgall
Div Pres: Jim Muething
Div Pres: Timothy C Weber
Ex VP: Jane Korenesczuk
Sr VP: Kenneth Cavanagh
Sr VP: Frank Ceraolo
Sr VP: Karen H Horrell
Sr VP: Aaron Latto
Sr VP: Chester Nalepa
Sr VP: James R Niehaus
Sr VP: Vito C Peraino
Sr VP: Chad D Stewart
Sr VP: Michael E Sullivan Jr

D-U-N-S 06-074-9892
GREAT AMERICAN OPPORTUNITIES INC
SOUTH WESTERN
(*Suby of* SOUTHWESTERN CO) ★
2451 Atrium Way, Nashville, TN 37214-5102
Tel (615) 391-2717 *Founded/Ownrshp* 1982
Sales 30.1MM^E *EMP* 402^E
SIC 7389 Fund raising organizations; Fund raising organizations
Pr: John Davis
**CFO:* Tim Underwood
Ql Cn Mgr: Randy Strubhar
Sls Mgr: Jeff Adams
Sls Mgr: Ryan Colmer
Sls Mgr: Jon Decker
Sls Mgr: Ross Hemsley
Sls Mgr: Scott Neumann
Sls Mgr: Chris Rubel
Sls Mgr: Chad Svendson
Sales Asso: Robert Gibson

D-U-N-S 07-886-6556
GREAT AMERICAN PAPER INC
251 Carolina Best Dr, Inman, SC 29349-7367
Tel (864) 472-8022 *Founded/Ownrshp* 1995
Sales 21.4MM^E *EMP* 150
SIC 7389 2679 8742 Packaging & labeling services; Building, insulating & packaging paper; Administrative services consultant
CEO: Kenneth Garcia Jr
Sales Exec: Frank Harris
Sales Exec: Ryan Smyth

D-U-N-S 82-895-3401
GREAT AMERICAN PLAN ADMINISTRATORS INC
525 Vine St Fl 7, Cincinnati, OH 45202-3138
Tel (513) 412-2316 *Founded/Ownrshp* 2008
Sales NA *EMP* 55
SIC 6371 Pension, health & welfare funds
Pr: Mark Muething
VP: Robert Berg
VP: Peter Nerone

GREAT AMERICAN PUZZLE FACTORY
See FUNDEX GAMES LTD

D-U-N-S 96-692-3377
GREAT AMERICAN REAL FOOD FAST INC
GREAT AMERICAN RESTAURANTS
132 Riverside Ave, Bristol, CT 06010-6311
Tel (860) 583-1752 *Founded/Ownrshp* 1996
Sales 10.3MM^E *EMP* 350
SIC 5812 Eating places; Eating places
Pr: Michael Ouimet

GREAT AMERICAN RESTAURANTS
See GREAT AMERICAN REAL FOOD FAST INC

D-U-N-S 03-899-5445 IMP
GREAT AMERICAN RESTAURANTS INC
ARTIE'S
3066 Gate House Plz, Falls Church, VA 22042-1028
Tel (703) 645-0700 *Founded/Ownrshp* 1976
Sales 48.8MM^E *EMP* 425
SIC 5813 5812 Bar (drinking places); Restaurant, family: independent; Bar (drinking places); Restaurant, family: independent
Ch Bd: Howard Rand Norton
**CEO:* Jonathan R Norton
**Sec:* James Farley
**Sec:* Dave Morgan
**VP:* Michael Ranney
Exec: Todd Pozinsky
Dir IT: David Warner

GREAT AMERICAN SEAFOOD
See SOUTHWIND FOODS LLC

D-U-N-S 85-857-7554
GREAT AMERICAN TITLE AGENCY INC
7720 N 16th St Ste 450, Phoenix, AZ 85020-7400
Tel (602) 445-5525 *Founded/Ownrshp* 1998
Sales 28.5MM^E *EMP* 96

SIC 6541 Title abstract offices
Pr: Tom Konniker
Ofcr: Ellen Purtill
Ofcr: Nicole Zorn
VP: Gina Helbling
Brnch Mgr: Carolyn Hubbard
Brnch Mgr: Toni Jaeger
Brnch Mgr: Kim Leitz
Brnch Mgr: Carrie Persons
Brnch Mgr: Carol Schmidt
Brnch Mgr: Sheryl Stone
Brnch Mgr: Donna Walt

D-U-N-S 95-968-2324
GREAT AMERICAN TITLE CO
5910 Fm 2920 Rd, Spring, TX 77388-3666
Tel (281) 353-9865 *Founded/Ownrshp* 2009
Sales NA *EMP* 75E
SIC 6361 Title insurance
Prin: Peggy Godail

D-U-N-S 18-043-4623
GREAT AMERICAN TITLE OF GREENE COUNTY INC
506 W Battlefield St A, Springfield, MO 65807-4122
Tel (417) 823-0800 *Founded/Ownrshp* 1993
Sales NA *EMP* 120
SIC 6361 Title insurance
Pr: Peggy Barton
VP: Marcia Baker
Exec: Earl Johnson

GREAT AMERICAN TRUCKING SHOW
See RANDALL-REILLY LLC

GREAT AMERICAN WOODIES
See COMPETITOR SWIM PRODUCTS INC

D-U-N-S 00-136-7366 IMP
GREAT ATLANTIC & PACIFIC TEA CO INC
A & P
2 Paragon Dr, Montvale, NJ 07645-1718
Tel (201) 573-9700 *Founded/Ownrshp* 1859
Sales 7.0MMME *EMP* 39,000
SIC 5411 Supermarkets, chain; Supermarkets, 55,000-65,000 square feet (superstore); Supermarkets, chain; Supermarkets, 55,000-65,000 square feet (superstore)
Ch Bd: Greg Mays
Owner: Douglas Palmer
Pr: Paul Hertz
COO: Eric Kanterman
CFO: David Casali
CFO: Raymond P Silcock
Chf Mktg O: Ajay Kanwar
Ofcr: Nirup Krishnamurthy
Ex VP: Harry Giglio
Ex VP: George Graham
Ex VP: Thomas O'Boyle
Ex VP: Rebecca Pahilbert
Sr VP: William Costantini
Sr VP: John Harlow
Sr VP: Hans Heer
VP: Gerry Baskin
VP: Marina Chassap
VP: Kevin Clark
VP: Anthony Dispaltro
VP: Gary McQuillan
VP: Dan Slavin
Board of Directors: John D Barline, Maureen Tart-Bezer, Thomas Casey, Andreas Guldin, Christian W E Haub, Dan Kourkoumelis, Edward Lewis, Gregory Rayburn, Terrence J Wallock

D-U-N-S 60-823-0736 IMP
GREAT ATLANTIC NEWS LLC
NEWS GROUP-SOUTHEAST, THE
(*Suby of* JIM PATTISON INDUSTRIES LTD)
1962 Highway 160 W # 102, Fort Mill, SC 29708-8057
Tel (803) 802-8630 *Founded/Ownrshp* 1989
Sales 337.2MME *EMP* 1,654
SIC 5192 Magazines; Periodicals; Books; Magazines; Periodicals; Books
Pr: Terry Moser
Exec: Rochelle Hurse
Board of Directors: Nick Desmarais, Jim Pattison Jr, John Seebach

D-U-N-S 07-474-0598
GREAT ATLANTIC PROPERTIES CORP
999 Waterside Dr Ste 410, Norfolk, VA 23510-3344
Tel (804) 824-9401 *Founded/Ownrshp* 1963
Sales 7.6MME *EMP* 300E
SIC 6531 6513 Real estate managers; Apartment building operators
CEO: Adrianne Ryder Joseph
**Pr:* Aubrey L Layne Jr
CIO: Janis Meil

D-U-N-S 82-874-8116
GREAT BASIN INDUSTRIAL LLC
1284 Flint Meadow Dr A, Kaysville, UT 84037-9590
Tel (801) 543-2100 *Founded/Ownrshp* 2007
Sales 169.8MME *EMP* 375
SIC 3443 7699 Water tanks, metal plate; Industrial vessels, tanks & containers; Tank repair & cleaning services
Pr: Dan Clegg
CFO: James David Oldham
Treas: Jamie Astle
VP: Scott Kent
VP: Jesse Memmott
VP: Jeff Murray

D-U-N-S 04-305-4774 IMP
GREAT BAY DISTRIBUTORS INC
2750 Eagle Ave N, Saint Petersburg, FL 33716-4106
Tel (727) 584-8626 *Founded/Ownrshp* 1967
Sales 164.9MME *EMP* 575
SIC 5181 Beer & other fermented malt liquors; Beer & other fermented malt liquors
Pr: Ronald Petrini
COO: Mike Coleman
**CFO:* Craig Rubright
**VP:* Bill Carmen
Mktg Dir: Bill Carman

D-U-N-S 00-773-2964
GREAT BEAR LODGE OF SANDUSKY LLC
GREAT WOLF LODGE
4600 Milan Rd, Sandusky, OH 44870-5840
Tel (419) 609-6000 *Founded/Ownrshp* 2000
Sales 4.0MME *EMP* 300E
SIC 7011
CEO: John Emery
**CFO:* Jim Calder
**Treas:* Alex Lombardo
Exec: Teresa Schwieferg

D-U-N-S 03-125-0947
GREAT BEND COOPERATIVE ASSOCIATION
606 Main St, Great Bend, KS 67530-5406
Tel (620) 793-3531 *Founded/Ownrshp* 1959
Sales 137.7MM *EMP* 82
Accts Lindburg Vogel Pierce Faris H
SIC 5153 5191 5171 4221 Grains; Feed; Fertilizer & fertilizer materials; Petroleum bulk stations; Grain elevator, storage only; Grains; Feed; Fertilizer & fertilizer materials; Petroleum bulk stations; Grain elevator, storage only
Pr: Frank Riedl
Treas: Rick Hiss
Board of Directors: Brian Anshutz, Eric Batman, John De Werff, Randy Fanshier, Rick Hiss, Ron Koelsch, Dale Maneth, Kevin Mauler, Robert Standish

D-U-N-S 08-742-3513
GREAT BEND UNIFIED SCHOOL DISTRICT 428
201 S Patton Rd, Great Bend, KS 67530-4613
Tel (620) 793-1500 *Founded/Ownrshp* 1966
Sales 22.7MME *EMP* 500
SIC 8211 Public elementary & secondary schools; High school, junior or senior; Public senior high school; Public elementary & secondary schools; High school, junior or senior; Public senior high school

GREAT BREWERS
See L KNIFE & SON INC

D-U-N-S 00-787-1510
GREAT CENTRAL LUMBER CO INC (MO)
9264 Manchester Rd, Saint Louis, MO 63144-2697
Tel (314) 968-1700 *Founded/Ownrshp* 1946
Sales 42.6MM *EMP* 260
SIC 5211 Lumber & other building materials; Lumber & other building materials
Ch: Robert James Millman
**Pr:* Richard G Millman
**CFO:* Randolph Russo
**VP:* Daniel Millman

GREAT CHINA EMPIRE
See GCE INTERNATIONAL INC

D-U-N-S 07-711-9329
GREAT CIRCLE
13160 County Road 3610, Saint James, MO 65559-9151
Tel (573) 265-3251 *Founded/Ownrshp* 1948
Sales 44.2MM *EMP* 800
SIC 8361 Boys' Towns; Boys' Towns
Ch: Steve Bowles
**CEO:* Vincent Hillyer
**CFO:* Leroy Nunn
VP: Patrick Brookhouser
**VP:* John Money
**VP:* Barbara Shepard
Exec: Mary Martin
Comm Man: Annie Meagle
**Prin:* Clark Davis
**Prin:* Jim Hill
IT Man: Tammy Andrews

GREAT CLIPS
See SPRINGLINE CORP

D-U-N-S 10-229-0079
GREAT CLIPS INC
4400 W 78th St Ste 700, Minneapolis, MN 55435-5023
Tel (952) 831-1073 *Founded/Ownrshp* 1982
Sales 75.7MM *EMP* 191
Accts Grant Thornton Llp Minneapoli
SIC 7231 Unisex hair salons; Unisex hair salons
Ch Bd: Ray Barton
**Pr:* Steve Hockett
**Pr:* Charlie Simpson
**CEO:* Rhoda Olsen
**CFO:* Steve Overholser
Ofcr: Sandra Anderson
Rgnl VP: Yvone Mercer
**Ex VP:* Dean A Wieber
**VP:* Rob Goggins
**VP:* Terri Miller
VP: Michelle Sack
**VP:* Nancy Uden
**VP:* Kathy Wetzel
Comm Man: Tammy Nienaber

D-U-N-S 07-994-2685
GREAT DANE AIRLINES
9466 Margo Ann Ln, Saint Louis, MO 63134-3928
Tel (503) 888-1088 *Founded/Ownrshp* 1995
Sales 45.0MME *EMP* 56
SIC 3721 Aircraft
CEO: Michael Thien

D-U-N-S 03-753-5556
GREAT DANE COLUMBUS INC
(*Suby of* GREAT DANE LIMITED PARTNERSHIP) ★
4080 Lyman Dr, Hilliard, OH 43026-1287
Tel (614) 876-0666 *Founded/Ownrshp* 1997
Sales 26.0MM *EMP* 45
SIC 5012 Trailers for trucks, new & used; Trailers for trucks, new & used
Pr: Henry T Skipper Jr
**VP:* Donald L Ottney

GREAT DANE DIVISION OFFICE
See GREAT DANE TRAILERS INC

D-U-N-S 96-482-2860 EXP
GREAT DANE LIMITED PARTNERSHIP
GREAT DANE TRAILERS
(*Suby of* CC INDUSTRIES) ★
222 N Lasalle St Ste 920, Chicago, IL 60601
Tel (773) 254-5533 *Founded/Ownrshp* 1996
Sales 466.7MME *EMP* 1,483
SIC 3715 Truck trailers; Demountable cargo containers; Truck trailers; Demountable cargo containers
Pr: William H Crown
Ex VP: Dean Engelage
Ex VP: Jim Pines
VP: Chris Adkins
VP: Michael Canmann
VP: Jeff Orban
VP Mktg: Brandie Fuller

GREAT DANE TRAILERS
See GREAT DANE LIMITED PARTNERSHIP

D-U-N-S 00-332-6840
GREAT DANE TRAILERS INC
GREAT DANE DIVISION OFFICE
(*Suby of* GREAT DANE LIMITED PARTNERSHIP) ★
602 E Lathrop Ave, Savannah, GA 31415-1062
Tel (912) 644-2100 *Founded/Ownrshp* 1985, 2007
Sales 205.0MME *EMP* 1,000E
SIC 5013 5012 Trailer parts & accessories; Trailers for trucks, new & used; Trailer parts & accessories; Trailers for trucks, new & used
CEO: Bill Crown
Treas: Susan Nyberg
Ex VP: Dean Engelage
Admn Mgr: Jon Weitman
QA Dir: Ronald Gordy
QA Dir: Robert Maharrey
VP Mktg: Brandie Fuller

D-U-N-S 96-695-4245
GREAT DAY IMPROVEMENTS LLC
PATIO ENCLOSURES
(*Suby of* GDIC GROUP LLC) ★
700 Highland Rd E, Macedonia, OH 44056-2160
Tel (330) 468-0700 *Founded/Ownrshp* 2010
Sales 34.1MME *EMP* 210E
SIC 3231 3448 3444 5712 5719 Products of purchased glass; Prefabricated metal buildings; Sunrooms, prefabricated metal; Sheet metalwork; Outdoor & garden furniture; Window furnishings; Products of purchased glass; Prefabricated metal buildings; Sunrooms, prefabricated metal; Sheet metalwork; Outdoor & garden furniture; Window furnishings
CEO: Steve White
**Pr:* Craig Cox
**CFO:* Kevin Dow
CFO: Larry Napolitan
VP: Tony Bouquot
Genl Mgr: John Fitzpatrick
Genl Mgr: Brian Hejmanowski
Genl Mgr: Aaron Laport
IT Man: Brian Perry
Plnt Mgr: Kent Nusser
VP Sls: Bill Goddard

D-U-N-S 78-765-9549
■ **GREAT DIVIDE INSURANCE CO**
NAUTILUS INSURANCE GROUP
(*Suby of* NAUTILUS INSURANCE CO INC) ★
7233 E Butherus Dr, Scottsdale, AZ 85260-2410
Tel (480) 951-0905 *Founded/Ownrshp* 1991
Sales NA *EMP* 5
SIC 6411 Insurance agents, brokers & service; Insurance agents, brokers & service
Pr: Thomas M Kuzma
VP: Wendy Markham
VP: Cynthia Roa
VP: Debbie Savoie
**VP Mktg:* Steve Franke

D-U-N-S 04-000-0507 IMP
GREAT EASTERN SEAFOOD INC
14 Food Mart Rd, Boston, MA 02118-2802
Tel (617) 428-9400 *Founded/Ownrshp* 1982
Sales 37.4MME *EMP* 80
SIC 5146 Seafoods; Seafoods
Pr: Robert C Brandano
**Treas:* Douglas Nucatola

D-U-N-S 02-966-6633 IMP
GREAT ESCAPE AMUSEMENT PARK
1172 State Route 9, Queensbury, NY 12804-1372
Tel (518) 792-3500 *Founded/Ownrshp* 1996
Sales 47.8MME *EMP* 1,900
SIC 7996 Theme park, amusement; Theme park, amusement
Pr: Six Flags
Mktg Dir: Jennifer Mance

GREAT ESCAPE OF ILLINOIS, THE
See UNIVERSAL POOL CO INC

D-U-N-S 17-957-0353
GREAT EXPERIMENT L L C
LANDROVER ALEXANDRIA
2712 Duke St, Alexandria, VA 22314-4511
Tel (703) 370-6565 *Founded/Ownrshp* 1997
Sales 28.0MM *EMP* 45
SIC 5511 5521 New & used car dealers; Used car dealers; New & used car dealers; Used car dealers
Genl Mgr: John Altman
Sls Mgr: Amanda Haight

D-U-N-S 14-797-2277
GREAT EXPRESSIONS DENTAL CENTERS PC
GREAT EXPRESSIONS DENTAL CTR
(*Suby of* OMERS PRIVATE EQUITY USA INC) ★
300 E Long Lake Rd # 311, Bloomfield Hills, MI 48304-2377
Tel (248) 203-2330 *Founded/Ownrshp* 2011
Sales 77.3MME *EMP* 1,665E
SIC 8021 8741 Dental clinics & offices; Business management
CEO: Richard E Beckman
Pr: Kurt Harvey
Pr: Ken Strohschein
**COO:* Vito Dacchille
**CFO:* Greg Nodland
**Ch:* Walter Knysz Jr
VP: Eric Chenoweth
**VP:* Jack Falvo
VP: Cotton Hawes
VP: Kristy Loomis
VP: Thomas Montefinese
VP: Ryan Torresan

GREAT EXPRESSIONS DENTAL CTR
See GREAT EXPRESSIONS DENTAL CENTERS PC

D-U-N-S 36-140-7476
GREAT FAITH PROGRESSIVE MISSIONARY BAPTIST CHURCH INC
4769 N 38th St, Milwaukee, WI 53209-5949
Tel (414) 616-7269 *Founded/Ownrshp* 1989
Sales 10.3MME *EMP* 369
SIC 8661 Churches, temples & shrines; Churches, temples & shrines

D-U-N-S 03-581-8488
GREAT FALLS CLINIC LLP
1400 29th St S, Great Falls, MT 59405-5353
Tel (406) 454-2171 *Founded/Ownrshp* 1995
Sales 22.1MME *EMP* 40
SIC 8011 Clinic, operated by physicians
CEO: Vicki Newmiller
**Pt:* Jose C De Souza
**Pt:* Robert M Grassechi
**Pt:* Stephen D Hennessey
**Pt:* Chu Shei Hong
**Pt:* William Labunetz
**Pt:* Brian J Malloy
**Pt:* Shari K Marx
**Pt:* Craig C Matelich
**Pt:* Bobby L Maynard
**Pt:* Nancy J Maynard
**Pt:* Daniel G McAllister
**Pt:* Robert J McClure
**Pt:* John M McCraney
**Pt:* Petra M Messick
**Pt:* Frederick G Miller
**Pt:* Angela L Mills
**Pt:* John T Molloy
**Pt:* Michael B Orcutt
**Pt:* Gregg D Pike
**Pt:* Thomas W Rosenbaum

D-U-N-S 06-372-2342
GREAT FALLS CLINIC REALTY LLP
IMMEDIATE CARE CENTER
1400 29th St S, Great Falls, MT 59405-5353
Tel (406) 454-2171 *Founded/Ownrshp* 1917
Sales 53.9MME *EMP* 830
Accts Douglas Wilson & Co Pc Great
SIC 8011 Clinic, operated by physicians; Clinic, operated by physicians
CEO: Vicki Newmiller
Pt: Carey J Welsh
COO: Mary Frieling

D-U-N-S 82-531-6821
GREAT FALLS PUBLIC SCHOOLS DIST1
GFPS
1100 4th St S, Great Falls, MT 59405-4301
Tel (406) 268-6052 *Founded/Ownrshp* 1884
Sales 410.0ME *EMP* 1,768
Accts Junkermierclarkcampanellasteve
SIC 8211 Public elementary & secondary schools; Public elementary & secondary schools
IT Man: Katie Allen
IT Man: Pamela Ramsted

D-U-N-S 88-460-8147 IMP
GREAT FLOORS LLC
524 E Sherman Ave, Coeur D Alene, ID 83814-2731
Tel (208) 664-5405 *Founded/Ownrshp* 2000
Sales 126.9MME *EMP* 450
SIC 1752 5713 Floor laying & floor work; Carpets; Floor laying & floor work; Carpets
Pr: Doug Chadderdon
**VP:* Ken Chadderdon
Sales Exec: Jeff Anderson
Mktg Dir: Teresa Gavin

GREAT HARVEST ORGANICS
See BECKS SUPERIOR HYBRIDS INC

D-U-N-S 79-040-5679
GREAT HEALTHWORKS INC
4150 Sw 28th Way, Fort Lauderdale, FL 33312-5201
Tel (866) 449-9679 *Founded/Ownrshp* 2003
Sales 20.0MME *EMP* 340
SIC 5999 Health & dietetic food stores; Medical apparatus & supplies
CEO: Ken Meares
COO: Miles Dupree
CFO: David Spanos
VP: Ileana Dupree
Dept Mgr: Peter Pulgar
Dir IT: Jose Kudja
IT Man: Renee Williams
Web Dev: Chris Lagowski
Sftwr Eng: Aleksander Maros
Mktg Dir: Toni Negas

D-U-N-S 61-723-0094
GREAT HEARTS ACADEMIES
3102 N 56th St Ste 300, Phoenix, AZ 85018-6606
Tel (602) 438-7045 *Founded/Ownrshp* 2004
Sales 10.3MM *EMP* 1,000
Accts Fester & Chapman Pc Scottsdal
SIC 8211 Academy; Academy
CEO: Christine Jones
**Pr:* Reed Porter
**Pr:* Daniel Scoggin
**CFO:* Ward Huseth
Ofcr: Jerilyn Olson
Sr VP: Katie Cobb
**Sr VP:* Lisa Handley
**VP:* Jessica Pacheco
**Prin:* Peter Bezanson

D-U-N-S 05-422-9096
GREAT HILL PARTNERS LLC
(*Suby of* QUALIFACTS SYSTEMS INC) ★
1 Liberty Sq Fl 13, Boston, MA 02109-4841
Tel (617) 790-9400 *Founded/Ownrshp* 2014
Sales 79.0MME *EMP* 835

SIC 6799 4813 Venture capital companies; ;Venture capital companies;
VP: Craig Byrnes

D-U-N-S 15-397-0280
GREAT INNS OF ROCKIES INC
700 Homestead Dr, Midway, UT 84049-6409
Tel (435) 654-1102 *Founded/Ownrshp* 1986
Sales 13.0MM^E *EMP* 691
SIC 5812 7997 7011 American restaurant; Golf club, membership; Bed & breakfast inn; American restaurant; Golf club, membership; Bed & breakfast inn
Pr: Britt R Mathwich
**Ch Bd:* Kevin Shannon
**Sec:* Henry Weeks
Board of Directors: Vibert Kesler, Frank Shannon

GREAT ISLAND ENERGY
See GULF OIL LIMITED PARTNERSHIP

D-U-N-S 06-148-5371 EXP
GREAT LAKE WOODS INC
3303 John F Donnelly Dr, Holland, MI 49424-9207
Tel (616) 399-3300 *Founded/Ownrshp* 1988
Sales 38.2MM^E *EMP* 150
SIC 2851 2431 Vinyl coatings, strippable; Moldings, wood: unfinished & prefinished; Vinyl coatings, strippable; Moldings, wood: unfinished & prefinished
CEO: Keith Malmstadt
Dir IT: Brian Harkema
IT Man: Keith Kaniewski
Manager: Ryan Vandenbosch

D-U-N-S 04-496-8600
GREAT LAKES ADVANCED RECYCLING CORP
GLR
30835 Groesbeck Hwy, Roseville, MI 48066-1510
Tel (586) 779-1310 *Founded/Ownrshp* 1969
Sales 47.3MM^E *EMP* 80
SIC 5093 3341 2611 Waste paper; Metal scrap & waste materials; Plastics scrap; Secondary nonferrous metals; Pulp mills
CEO: Sandy Rosen
**Pr:* Benjamin M Rosen
**Sec:* Ilene Rosen-Walker
**VP:* Jerald Rosen

D-U-N-S 14-496-9644
GREAT LAKES AGGREGATES LLC
SYLVANIA MINERALS
5699 Ready Rd, South Rockwood, MI 48179-9592
Tel (734) 379-0311 *Founded/Ownrshp* 2003
Sales 84.5MM^E *EMP* 120^E
SIC 1422 Lime rock, ground
Pr: Chris Kinney
Ql Cn Mgr: Keith Childress

GREAT LAKES AIR TECHNOLOGIES
See ROBOVENT PRODUCTS GROUP INC

GREAT LAKES AIRLINES
See GREAT LAKES AVIATION LTD

D-U-N-S 17-748-4065
GREAT LAKES ASSEMBLIES LLC
(*Suby of* MODULAR ASSEMBLY INNOVATIONS)
11590 Tr 298, East Liberty, OH 43319
Tel (937) 645-3900 *Founded/Ownrshp* 2005
Sales 75.6MM^E *EMP* 70
SIC 3711 Automobile assembly, including specialty automobiles
Pr: Billy R Vickers

GREAT LAKES AUTOMATION SUPPLY
See KENDALL ELECTRIC INC

D-U-N-S 06-866-5827
▲ GREAT LAKES AVIATION LTD
GREAT LAKES AIRLINES
1022 Airport Pkwy, Cheyenne, WY 82001-1551
Tel (307) 432-7000 *Founded/Ownrshp* 1979
Sales 59.1MM *EMP* 1,159^E
Tkr Sym GLUX *Exch* OTO
SIC 4512 Air passenger carrier, scheduled; Air cargo carrier, scheduled; Air passenger carrier, scheduled; Air cargo carrier, scheduled
CEO: Charles R Howell IV
**Ch Bd:* Douglas G Voss
CFO: Stan Gadek
CFO: Michael O Matthews
Treas: Michael L Tuinstra
VP: Norma Courtney
VP: Kurt Franklin
Mng Dir: Larry Graff
Dir IT: Wes Cure
IT Man: Cory Andrews
Snr Mgr: Aaron Bowers
Board of Directors: Albert L Maxson, Vernon A Mickelson, Allan R Moulton III, Ivan L Simpson

GREAT LAKES BEVERAGE
See WOLPIN CO

D-U-N-S 18-053-8639 IMP
GREAT LAKES BREWING CO
2516 Market Ave, Cleveland, OH 44113-3434
Tel (216) 771-4404 *Founded/Ownrshp* 1988
Sales 32.4MM^E *EMP* 85
SIC 2082 5813 5812 Beer (alcoholic beverage); Bar (drinking places); American restaurant
Pr: Patrick F Conway
COO: Steven Eilerman
**Sec:* Daniel J Conway
Exec: Amanda Hodge
Area Mgr: Lisa Farmer
Area Mgr: Matt Roth
Area Mgr: Connie Tucci
Area Mgr: Mark Weinmann
Genl Mgr: Jonathon Satayathum
IT Man: Greg Tuttle
Opers Mgr: Bruce Cornish

D-U-N-S 78-632-1067 IMP
GREAT LAKES CARPET & TILE LLC
13553 N Us Highway 441, Lady Lake, FL 32159-8906
Tel (352) 753-7502 *Founded/Ownrshp* 1991
Sales 22.6MM *EMP* 48
SIC 5713 1752 Floor covering stores; Floor laying & floor work; Floor covering stores; Floor laying & floor work
**Sec:* Dawn Cary
**VP:* Daniel J Hearns
Sls Mgr: Tim Myers
Sls Mgr: Tom Urban

D-U-N-S 15-378-3022 IMP/EXP
GREAT LAKES CASE & CABINET CO INC
4193 Route 6n, Edinboro, PA 16412-1736
Tel (814) 734-7303 *Founded/Ownrshp* 1990
Sales 20.6MM^E *EMP* 102
SIC 3499 Fire- or burglary-resistive products
Pr: Carrie L Lowther
VP: Kevin Holzwart
VP: Jeff Markle
VP: Krista Mastrangelo
**VP:* Robert I Lowther
VP: Rick Trombetta
Exec: Leslie Bartley
Mng Dir: Terry Murphy
IT Man: Aaron Conley
Mktg Dir: Dan Adamus
Mktg Dir: Loretta Swartwood

D-U-N-S 00-601-6935
GREAT LAKES CASTINGS LLC
(*Suby of* RESERVE GROUP MANAGEMENT CO) ★
800 N Washington Ave, Ludington, MI 49431-1500
Tel (231) 843-2501 *Founded/Ownrshp* 1945, 2013
Sales 35.0MM^E *EMP* 210
SIC 3321 Gray & ductile iron foundries; Gray & ductile iron foundries
Pr: Robert Killips
Dir IT: Steven Giammalva
VP Mktg: Eric Bansch
S&M/VP: Bob Delbarker
Sales Asso: Jackie Ginter

D-U-N-S 10-559-0868 IMP
GREAT LAKES CHEESE
(*Suby of* GREAT LAKES CHEESE CO INC) ★
780 W 1400 S, Fillmore, UT 84631-5130
Tel (435) 743-5000 *Founded/Ownrshp* 2001
Sales 47.7MM^E *EMP* 120^E
SIC 2022 Natural cheese
Pr: Gary Vanic
**Treas:* Kurt L Epprecht

D-U-N-S 01-821-9808 IMP/EXP
GREAT LAKES CHEESE CO INC
17825 Great Lakes Pkwy, Hiram, OH 44234-9677
Tel (440) 834-2500 *Founded/Ownrshp* 1958
Sales 1.2MMM^E *EMP* 1,700
SIC 5143 2022 Cheese; Natural cheese; Cheese; Natural cheese
Pr: Gary Vanic
CFO: Russell Mullins
**Sec:* John Epprecht
VP: Kurt Epprecht
VP: Craig Filkouski
VP: Brian Gamier
VP: Mazur Mark
**Prin:* Marcel Dasen
**Prin:* Hans Epprecht
**Prin:* Albert Z Meyers
Off Mgr: Barbara Martucci

D-U-N-S 96-318-2258
GREAT LAKES CHEESE OF LA CROSSE WISCONSIN INC
(*Suby of* GREAT LAKES CHEESE CO INC) ★
2200 Enterprise Ave, La Crosse, WI 54603-1712
Tel (608) 781-2800 *Founded/Ownrshp* 1995
Sales 78.5MM^E *EMP* 300
SIC 2022 5143 Processed cheese; Cheese; Processed cheese; Cheese
Pr: Hans Epprecht
**Sec:* John Epprecht
IT Man: Josh Weber
Plnt Mgr: Walter Ehret

D-U-N-S 12-179-0794
GREAT LAKES CHEESE OF NEW YORK INC
(*Suby of* GREAT LAKES CHEESE CO INC) ★
23 Phelps St, Adams, NY 13605-1096
Tel (315) 232-4511 *Founded/Ownrshp* 1967
Sales 26.1MM^E *EMP* 79
SIC 2022 Cheese, natural & processed; Cheese, natural & processed
Ch Bd: Gary Vanic
**Pr:* Hans Epprecht
**VP:* John Epprecht
Opers Mgr: John Jennings

D-U-N-S 06-205-6072
GREAT LAKES CHEESE OF WISCONSIN INC (WI)
(*Suby of* GREAT LAKES CHEESE CO INC) ★
2602 County Road Pp, Plymouth, WI 53073-4242
Tel (920) 893-1121 *Founded/Ownrshp* 1982
Sales 30.5MM^E *EMP* 310
SIC 7389 5143 Packaging & labeling services; Cheese; Packaging & labeling services; Cheese
CEO: Hans Epprecht
**Pr:* John Epprecht
**Exec:* S Heidi Eller
IT Man: Wes Huibregtse
Plnt Mgr: Dick Metzler
Prd Mgr: Mary Ann Schultz

D-U-N-S 07-847-8421
GREAT LAKES CHEESE SEYMOUR INC
SEYMOUR DAIRY PRODUCTS
(*Suby of* GREAT LAKES CHEESE CO INC) ★
124 E Bronson Rd, Seymour, WI 54165-1001
Tel (920) 833-2900 *Founded/Ownrshp* 2012
Sales 23.0MM^E *EMP* 85^E
SIC 2022 Cheese, natural & processed
Pr: Michael Brennenstuhl

D-U-N-S 00-521-2808 IMP/EXP
■ GREAT LAKES CHEMICAL CORP (DE)
(*Suby of* CHEMTURA CORP) ★
199 Benson Rd, Middlebury, CT 06762-3218
Tel (203) 573-2000 *Founded/Ownrshp* 1932
Sales 492.1MM^E *EMP* 3,300
SIC 2899 2842 Fire retardant chemicals; Oxidizers, inorganic; Water treating compounds; Sanitation preparations, disinfectants & deodorants; Degreasing solvent; Fire retardant chemicals; Oxidizers, inorganic; Water treating compounds; Sanitation preparations, disinfectants & deodorants; Degreasing solvent
CEO: Craig Rogerson
**Pr:* Anne Noonan
VP: Eric Wisnefsky

D-U-N-S 07-968-8489
■ GREAT LAKES COCA-COLA DISTRIBUTION LLC
(*Suby of* COCA-COLA REFRESHMENTS USA INC) ★
1 Coca Cola Plz Nw, Atlanta, GA 30313-2420
Tel (404) 374-8969 *Founded/Ownrshp* 2015
Sales 37.3MM^E *EMP* 1,000
SIC 5149 Beverages, except coffee & tea

D-U-N-S 79-744-0455
GREAT LAKES COILS LLC
GLC
4650 W Us Highway 223, Adrian, MI 49221-8494
Tel (517) 264-2222 *Founded/Ownrshp* 2006
Sales 21.5MM^E *EMP* 27^E
SIC 5051 5065 Steel; Coils, electronic
Pr: Christopher H Lake
**CFO:* Matt Wilson

D-U-N-S 16-130-2591 IMP
GREAT LAKES COMPUTER SOURCE INC
5555 Corporate Exch Ct Se, Grand Rapids, MI 49512-5503
Tel (800) 488-2587 *Founded/Ownrshp* 2003
Sales 24.6MM^E *EMP* 80
SIC 5932 5045 Computers & accessories, secondhand; Computers
Ch Bd: Keith Harrold
**Pr:* Frank Kwiatek
**VP:* Jeff Stevens
CIO: Dave Britten
IT Man: Robert Sipka
Netwrk Eng: Christopher Conley
Netwrk Eng: Tyler Dykema
Opers Mgr: Matthew Evans
Mktg Mgr: Joel Ippel
Mktg Mgr: Katy Vandewaa
Sls Mgr: Jeff Schmidt

D-U-N-S 01-776-1115
GREAT LAKES CONSTRUCTION CO
TGLCC
(*Suby of* GREAT LAKES COMPANIES INC)
2608 Great Lakes Way, Hinckley, OH 44233-9590
Tel (330) 220-3900 *Founded/Ownrshp* 1946, 1985
Sales 67.2MM^E *EMP* 125
SIC 1611 1629

D-U-N-S 06-800-0355
GREAT LAKES CREDIT UNION
2525 Green Bay Rd, North Chicago, IL 60064-3012
Tel (847) 578-7000 *Founded/Ownrshp* 1938
Sales NA *EMP* 155
Accts Mcgladrey Llp Minneapolis Mn
SIC 6062 State credit unions, not federally chartered; State credit unions, not federally chartered
Pr: Vikki Kaiser
CFO: Kamil Sakici
Bd of Dir: Rich Durante
Admn Mgr: Kathy Carney
Brnch Mgr: Gloria Turner
Site Mgr: Sarah Cobb
Sls Mgr: Brian Bockholdt
Sls Mgr: Joseph Lagiglia
Snr Mgr: Carol Eberhart

D-U-N-S 03-300-6532
GREAT LAKES DELTA INSURANCE CO
(*Suby of* DELTA DENTAL PLAN OF MICHIGAN INC) ★
4100 Okemos Rd, Okemos, MI 48864-3215
Tel (517) 349-6000 *Founded/Ownrshp* 1998
Sales 12.0MM^E *EMP* 500
SIC 8021 Dental insurance plan; Dental insurance plan
Pr: Thomas Fleszar
**Pr:* Richard Seitz
VP: Sherry Crisp
VP: Nancy Hostetler
IT Man: Brenda Laird
Software D: Penny Parker

D-U-N-S 78-877-3708
GREAT LAKES DENTAL LLC
GREAT LAKES DENTAL USA
10101 W Innovation Dr # 700, Wauwatosa, WI 53226-4860
Tel (262) 966-2428 *Founded/Ownrshp* 2005
Sales 2.2MM *EMP* 1,553
SIC 8021 Dental clinics & offices; Dental clinics & offices

GREAT LAKES DENTAL USA
See GREAT LAKES DENTAL LLC

D-U-N-S 07-259-3254 IMP
GREAT LAKES DIE CAST CORP (MI)
701 W Laketon Ave, Muskegon, MI 49441-2925
Tel (231) 726-4002 *Founded/Ownrshp* 2002
Sales 40.1MM^E *EMP* 140^E
SIC 3363 3089 Aluminum die-castings; Injection molded finished plastic products; Aluminum die-castings; Injection molded finished plastic products
Pr: Con J Nolan
Pr: Bob Johnson
COO: Marilyn Miller
Ex VP: Tim Yarde
Prgrm Mgr: Mike Bosset
IT Man: Wayne Degner
Ql Cn Mgr: Ken Knowles
Mktg Dir: John Rowe

D-U-N-S 05-295-0529 IMP
GREAT LAKES DIVERSIFIED GROUP INC (MI)
800 Tech Row, Madison Heights, MI 48071-4678
Tel (586) 979-0022 *Founded/Ownrshp* 1999, 1998
Sales 20.8MM *EMP* 82
Accts Bonwell Kelley & Associates P
SIC 5051 Cable, wire; Cable, wire
Pr: Scott Edgar
CFO: Joseph Minaudo
VP Sls: Oscar Ferrari
Sls Mgr: Darla Abu-Shanab
Sls Mgr: Greg Hansen

D-U-N-S 00-693-0358 IMP/EXP
■ GREAT LAKES DREDGE & DOCK CO LLC (GA)
(*Suby of* GREAT LAKES DREDGE & DOCK CORP) ★
2122 York Rd Ste 200, Oak Brook, IL 60523-1981
Tel (630) 574-3000 *Founded/Ownrshp* 1890, 2003
Sales 629.2MM *EMP* 500
Accts Deloitte & Touche Llp Chicago
SIC 1629 Dredging contractor; Marine construction; Dredging contractor; Marine construction
CEO: Jonathan W Berger
**Pr:* David E Simonelli
**CFO:* Mark Marinko
**Treas:* Katherine M Hayes
**Sr VP:* Kyle D Johnson
**Sr VP:* John F Karas

D-U-N-S 36-289-9130 IMP/EXP
▲ GREAT LAKES DREDGE & DOCK CORP
2122 York Rd Ste 200, Oak Brook, IL 60523-1981
Tel (630) 574-3000 *Founded/Ownrshp* 1890
Sales 806.8MM *EMP* 785^E
Tkr Sym GLDD *Exch* NGS
SIC 1629 1741 Dams, waterways, docks & other marine construction; Dredging contractor; Marine construction; Foundation building; Dams, waterways, docks & other marine construction; Dredging contractor; Marine construction; Foundation building
CEO: Jonathan W Berger
**Ch Bd:* Nathan D Leight
COO: Kyle D Johnson
CFO: Mark W Marinko
Treas: Katie Hayes
Sr VP: William S Steckel
VP: Steven W Becker
VP: Bob Bisal
VP: Rick Dennis
VP: J Gillespie
VP: Bradley Tj Hansen
VP: William Hanson
VP: Katie Lavoy
VP: Sam Morrison
VP: Steven F O'Hara
VP: Steven F Ohara
VP: William F Pagendarm
VP: Stephen E Pegg
VP: Thomas C Roberts
VP: Russell F Zimmerman
Dir Bus: Hanson William
Board of Directors: Carl A Albert, Peter R Deutsch, Denise E Dickins, Michael J Walsh, Jason G Weiss

D-U-N-S 96-737-9496
GREAT LAKES EDUCATIONAL LOAN SERVICES INC
GREAT LKES HIGHER EDUCATN CORP
(*Suby of* GREAT LAKES HIGHER EDUCATION CORP) ★
2401 International Ln, Madison, WI 53704-3121
Tel (608) 246-1800 *Founded/Ownrshp* 1996
Sales NA *EMP* 725
Accts Ernst & Young Llp Milwaukee
SIC 6111 Federal & federally sponsored credit agencies; Federal & federally sponsored credit agencies
Pr: Jess Crosby
CFO: Kyle Kary
CFO: Nancy Seifert
Sr VP: Greg Stringer
VP: Mary Boisen
VP: Richard George
**Prin:* Paul Thornburgh
Prgrm Mgr: Alex Gagnon
Prgrm Mgr: Tou Khang
Prgrm Mgr: Nikki Wachter
QA Dir: Erin Starkey

D-U-N-S 05-477-5705
GREAT LAKES ENERGY COOPERATIVE
1323 Boyne Ave, Boyne City, MI 49712-8940
Tel (888) 485-2537 *Founded/Ownrshp* 1938
Sales 199.7MM *EMP* 235
SIC 4911 Distribution, electric power; Distribution, electric power
VP: Brian Wierenga
Dir Bus: Donald E Black
Dir IT: Missy Hall
Dir IT: Missy Thenikl
VP Opers: Daniel Nelson
VP Mktg: Pat Anzell
Mktg Dir: Kristy Beyer

D-U-N-S 11-452-9956
GREAT LAKES ENERGY GAS SERVICES LLC
1323 Boyne Ave, Boyne City, MI 49712-8940
Tel (231) 582-6521 *Founded/Ownrshp* 1999
Sales 49.3MM^E *EMP* 235
Accts Eide Bailly Llp Fargo North
SIC 4911 4932 Electric services; Gas & other services combined; Electric services; Gas & other services combined
Prin: Steve Boeckman
Comm Dir: Dave Guzniczak

GREAT LAKES FASTENERS & SUPPLY
See GREAT LAKES FASTENERS CORP

D-U-N-S 06-018-9586 IMP
GREAT LAKES FASTENERS CORP
GREAT LAKES FASTENERS & SUPPLY
5075 Clay Ave Sw Ste A, Grand Rapids, MI 49548-5502
Tel (616) 534-7200 *Founded/Ownrshp* 1976
Sales 25.0MM *EMP* 60
SIC 5072 5085 Bolts; Nuts (hardware); Industrial supplies; Bolts; Nuts (hardware); Industrial supplies
Ch: Gordon Vandermeulen
**Pr:* Kenneth Bott
**Treas:* Elaine Vandermeulen
IT Man: Bryan Schultz
Ql Cn Mgr: Scott Dunderman

Ql Cn Mgr: Jim Walker
Sales Asso: Wes Lamb
Sales Asso: Jake Lang
Sales Asso: Marty Shaw

D-U-N-S 11-803-7956
GREAT LAKES FINANCIAL MANAGEMENT GROUP INC
2033 Marinette Ave, Marinette, WI 54143-3864
Tel (715) 732-9955 *Founded/Ownrshp* 2001
Sales 100.0MM *EMP* 100
SIC 6211 8742 6282 6411 Security brokers & dealers; Financial consultant; Investment advisory service; Insurance agents, brokers & service; Security brokers & dealers; Financial consultant; Investment advisory service; Insurance agents, brokers & service
Pr: Michael Messer

D-U-N-S 07-424-7255
GREAT LAKES FISHERY COMMISSION
2100 Commonwealth Blvd, Ann Arbor, MI 48105-1593
Tel (734) 662-3209 *Founded/Ownrshp* 1955
Sales 30.4MM *EMP* 12
SIC 8742 8748 Management consulting services; Business consulting; Management consulting services; Business consulting
Off Mgr: Jennifer Jazwiec
Web Dev: Hao Zhuang
Software D: Jeff McAulay

D-U-N-S 00-974-3647
GREAT LAKES FOODS LLC
1230 48th Ave, Menominee, MI 49858-1002
Tel (906) 863-5503 *Founded/Ownrshp* 2004
Sales 75.7MM^E *EMP* 100
SIC 5149 Groceries & related products
**CFO:* Phil Strohl
**VP Sls:* Gene Mylender
Mktg Dir: Gene Mylener

D-U-N-S 11-872-1208
GREAT LAKES FORD INC
2469 E Apple Ave, Muskegon, MI 49442-4498
Tel (231) 777-2750 *Founded/Ownrshp* 1984
Sales 24.9MM^E *EMP* 55
SIC 5511 Automobiles, new & used; Pickups, new & used; Vans, new & used
Pr: Frederick Lafontaine
**VP:* Mark Lafontaine
Sales Asso: Jim Baughman
Sales Asso: Donald Sullivan
Sales Asso: Cherie Wandling

D-U-N-S 60-641-1247
GREAT LAKES FOREST PRODUCTS INC
21658 Buckingham Rd, Elkhart, IN 46516-9703
Tel (574) 389-9663 *Founded/Ownrshp* 1989
Sales 55.7MM^E *EMP* 75^E
SIC 5031 Lumber: rough, dressed & finished; Lumber: rough, dressed & finished
Pr: Mark E Smith
VP: Jennifer L Smith
Sfty Dirs: David Knight

D-U-N-S 04-607-7343
GREAT LAKES GAS TRANSMISSION LIMITED PARTNERSHIP
(*Suby of* TRANSCANADA PIPELINES LIMITED)
717 Texas St Ste 2400, Houston, TX 77002-2834
Tel (832) 320-5000 *Founded/Ownrshp* 1990
Sales 65.8MM^E *EMP* 172^E
Accts Kpmg Llp Houston Texas
SIC 4922 Pipelines, natural gas; Pipelines, natural gas
Pr: Lee Hobbs
Pt: Julie Willett
Genl Couns: Catharine Davis
Counsel: Eugene R Morabito

D-U-N-S 10-150-6921
GREAT LAKES GROUP
GREAT LAKES TOWING
4500 Division Ave, Cleveland, OH 44102-2228
Tel (216) 621-4854 *Founded/Ownrshp* 1978
Sales 21.5MM^E *EMP* 120
SIC 3731 4492 Shipbuilding & repairing; Marine towing services
Ch Bd: Sheldon Guren
**Pr:* Ronald Rasmus
**VP:* George Sogar
Board of Directors: Ernest Tallisman

GREAT LAKES HEATING, COOLNG
See GREAT LAKES MECHANICAL CORP

D-U-N-S 12-159-8791
GREAT LAKES HIGHER EDUCATION CORP
2401 International Ln, Madison, WI 53704-3121
Tel (608) 246-1800 *Founded/Ownrshp* 1967
Sales NA *EMP* 900
Accts Ernst & Young Us Llp Indianap
SIC 6111 Federal & federally sponsored credit agencies; Federal & federally sponsored credit agencies
Ch Bd: Richard D George
**CFO:* Nancy Seifert
VP: Paul Thornbugh
Netwrk Mgr: Tom Jacobs
Netwrk Mgr: Nancy Michalski
Sales Exec: Mary Winchell

D-U-N-S 93-020-6920
GREAT LAKES HIGHER EDUCATION SERVICING CORP
(*Suby of* GREAT LAKES HIGHER EDUCATION CORP) ★
2401 International Ln, Madison, WI 53704-3192
Tel (608) 246-1800 *Founded/Ownrshp* 1996
Sales NA *EMP* 700
SIC 6111 Federal & federally sponsored credit agencies; Federal & federally sponsored credit agencies
CEO: Richard George
Ofcr: Maureen Harrill
Ex Dir: Jane Hojan

D-U-N-S 83-705-9179
GREAT LAKES HOME HEALTH SERVICES INC
GREAT LAKES HOSPICE
900 Cooper St, Jackson, MI 49202-3398
Tel (517) 780-9500 *Founded/Ownrshp* 1994
Sales 35.9MM^E *EMP* 500
SIC 8082 Home health care services; Home health care services
CEO: William Deary
Dir Vol: Sonya Neeb
Dir Vol: Dana Perrin
CFO: Sundaram Lakshu
Sr VP: Jan Vanburen
**VP:* Trisha Crissman
VP: Adam Nielsen
Dir Bus: Mike Brookins
**CIO:* Sheri Lyn Deary
IT Man: Canis Arbrouet
Netwrk Mgr: Katy Solak

GREAT LAKES HONDA
See D I P AKRON INC

GREAT LAKES HOSPICE
See GREAT LAKES HOME HEALTH SERVICES INC

D-U-N-S 96-039-4294
GREAT LAKES HOSPITALITY CORP
525 Junction Rd Ste 6000, Madison, WI 53717-2153
Tel (608) 273-4677 *Founded/Ownrshp* 1993
Sales 11.4MM^E *EMP* 500
SIC 6531 Fiduciary, real estate; Fiduciary, real estate
CEO: John Emery

GREAT LAKES HUMMER
See TIM TYLER MOTORS INC

GREAT LAKES HYDRAULICS
See HAGUE EQUIPMENT CO OF MICHIGAN INC

D-U-N-S 06-848-3163 IMP
GREAT LAKES ICE CREAM INC
12355 S Kedvale Ave, Chicago, IL 60803-1816
Tel (708) 371-1999 *Founded/Ownrshp* 1966
Sales 31.2MM^E *EMP* 80
SIC 5143 5963 Ice cream & ices; Ice cream wagon; Ice cream & ices; Ice cream wagon
Pr: Josh Carpenter

GREAT LAKES INSURANCE ASSOC
See GREAT LAKES INSURANCE SERVICES GROUP LLC

D-U-N-S 78-682-6727
GREAT LAKES INSURANCE SERVICES GROUP LLC
GREAT LAKES INSURANCE ASSOC
3205 Peach St, Erie, PA 16508-2735
Tel (814) 456-0498 *Founded/Ownrshp* 2010
Sales NA *EMP* 30^E
SIC 6411 Insurance agents, brokers & service
Sales Exec: John Zaphiris

D-U-N-S 00-415-4472 IMP
GREAT LAKES INTEGRATED INC (OH)
GLI
4005 Clark Ave, Cleveland, OH 44109-1128
Tel (216) 651-1500 *Founded/Ownrshp* 1931
Sales 26.1MM^E *EMP* 155
SIC 2752 2796 2789 Commercial printing, lithographic; Lithographic plates, positives or negatives; Bookbinding & related work; Commercial printing, lithographic; Lithographic plates, positives or negatives; Bookbinding & related work
Pr: James R Schultz
Pr: Carrie Spence
VP: Joe Chinnici
VP: Paul Doerfler
**VP:* Anthony Sanson
**VP:* Robert J Schultz
CTO: Robert Kozel
IT Man: Robert Cullison
IT Man: Jamie Kosempa
Tech Mgr: David Eckhardt
QC Dir: Paul Schlund

GREAT LAKES KRAUT
See FLANAGAN BROTHERS TRUCKING INC

D-U-N-S 00-116-9692
GREAT LAKES LASER DYNAMICS INC (MI)
LASER-DYNAMICS
4881 Allen Park Dr, Allendale, MI 49401-8625
Tel (616) 892-7070 *Founded/Ownrshp* 1999
Sales 25.3MM^E *EMP* 60
SIC 3443 3444 3499 Fabricated plate work (boiler shop); Sheet metalwork; Machine bases, metal; Metal household articles
Pr: William Herberg
**VP:* Ken Koster
Plnt Mgr: Shawn Walton
Ql Cn Mgr: Chad Hindley
Ql Cn Mgr: Ric Woods

GREAT LAKES MAINTENANCE
See GREAT LAKES PETROLEUM CORP

D-U-N-S 04-895-4135
GREAT LAKES MAINTENANCE & SECURITY CORP
8734 S Cottage Grove Ave, Chicago, IL 60619-6924
Tel (773) 994-1899 *Founded/Ownrshp* 1965
Sales 3.0MM^E *EMP* 300
SIC 7381 7349 Security guard service; Janitorial service, contract basis; Security guard service; Janitorial service, contract basis
Pr: Leonard Waters

D-U-N-S 03-197-1570
GREAT LAKES MANUFACTURING INC
1521 Enterprise Rd, Corry, PA 16407-8575
Tel (814) 734-2436 *Founded/Ownrshp* 1997
Sales 22.3MM^E *EMP* 120
SIC 3444 Sheet metal specialties, not stamped
Pr: Carrie L Lowther
CFO: Tom Pakulski
**VP:* Robert I Lowther Jr
VP Sls: Rick Trombetta

GREAT LAKES MARINE
See KMW GROUP INC

D-U-N-S 01-680-5889
GREAT LAKES MECHANICAL CORP
GREAT LAKES HEATING, COOLNG
3800 Maple St, Dearborn, MI 48126-3672
Tel (313) 581-1400 *Founded/Ownrshp* 1955
Sales 38.3MM^E *EMP* 200
SIC 1711 3444 Mechanical contractor; Sheet metalwork; Mechanical contractor; Sheet metalwork
Pr: Mark Perpich
**Ch:* Harold J Perpich
**VP:* George Perpich II

D-U-N-S 83-612-0006
GREAT LAKES MEDICAL SUPPLY LLC
(*Suby of* SANARE LLC) ★
3613 N 29th Ave, Hollywood, FL 33020-1003
Tel (586) 501-1000 *Founded/Ownrshp* 2011
Sales 28.9MM^E *EMP* 140
SIC 5047 Medical equipment & supplies; Medical equipment & supplies
CEO: Tim Hargarten
**Pr:* Erika Thrubis

D-U-N-S 04-253-5708
GREAT LAKES MILK PRODUCTS INC
3000 W North Ave, Melrose Park, IL 60160-1124
Tel (708) 544-1692 *Founded/Ownrshp* 1967
Sales 40.0MM^E *EMP* 14
SIC 5143 Dairy depot; Dairy depot
Pr: Frank O'Toole
**CFO:* Brian McLaughlin
**Ch:* Douglas Bestole

D-U-N-S 04-185-4332 IMP
GREAT LAKES ORTHODONTICS LTD
GREAT LKES ORTHDONTIC LABS DIV
200 Cooper Ave, Tonawanda, NY 14150-6607
Tel (716) 871-1161 *Founded/Ownrshp* 1967
Sales 37.2MM^E *EMP* 200
SIC 5047 8071

D-U-N-S 00-609-8735
GREAT LAKES PACKAGING CORP
(*Suby of* GREEN BAY PACKAGING INC) ★
W190n11393 Carnegie Dr, Germantown, WI 53022-3064
Tel (262) 255-4024 *Founded/Ownrshp* 1963, 2014
Sales 22.7MM^E *EMP* 124
SIC 2653 Boxes, corrugated: made from purchased materials; Display items, corrugated: made from purchased materials; Boxes, corrugated: made from purchased materials; Display items, corrugated: made from purchased materials
CEO: Glen Arnold
VP: Bob Boden
**VP:* Kenneth J Ferron
**VP:* James M Nelson
IT Man: Colleen Brushaber
Natl Sales: Mark Lavin

GREAT LAKES PETERBILT
See GREAT LAKES TRUCK & EQUIPMENT INC

D-U-N-S 08-030-9516
GREAT LAKES PETROLEUM CO (OH)
4500 Renaissance Pkwy, Cleveland, OH 44128-5702
Tel (216) 478-0501 *Founded/Ownrshp* 1997
Sales 146.9MM^E *EMP* 100
SIC 5171 Petroleum bulk stations & terminals; Petroleum bulk stations & terminals
CEO: Tom Arcoria
**Pr:* Anthony Arcoria
**COO:* Jeff Platko
**CFO:* Louise A Kirk
IT Man: Ron Jaworski
Sls Mgr: Scott Dejohn
Sls Mgr: Clay Livengood
Sls Mgr: Mike Renn

D-U-N-S 80-562-8518
GREAT LAKES PETROLEUM CORP
GREAT LAKES MAINTENANCE
6525 N Jerome Rd, Alma, MI 48801-9706
Tel (989) 463-4654 *Founded/Ownrshp* 1992
Sales 180.5MM^E *EMP* 161
SIC 5172 Petroleum products; Petroleum products
Pr: Jeffrey Plott
VP: Jennifer Brown

GREAT LAKES PLASTICS DIVISION
See EVANS INDUSTRIES INC

D-U-N-S 00-195-9931
GREAT LAKES PLUMBING & HEATING CO (IL)
4521 W Diversey Ave, Chicago, IL 60639-1925
Tel (773) 489-0400 *Founded/Ownrshp* 1946
Sales 52.8MM^E *EMP* 200
SIC 1711 Plumbing contractors; Fire sprinkler system installation; Warm air heating & air conditioning contractor; Mechanical contractor; Plumbing contractors; Fire sprinkler system installation; Warm air heating & air conditioning contractor; Mechanical contractor
Pr: Kevin J Condon
**CFO:* Nicholas C Marino
**Ch:* George W Treutelaar
**Sec:* Debra Poole
**Ex VP:* Brian G Conway
**VP:* John G Devine

D-U-N-S 01-310-9004 IMP
GREAT LAKES PLUMBING SUPPLY INC (NY)
3025 Winton Rd S, Rochester, NY 14623-2931
Tel (585) 458-2930 *Founded/Ownrshp* 1959, 1973
Sales 28.0MM *EMP* 60
Accts Daitz Rice Gillette & Sardo
SIC 5074 5085 Plumbing fittings & supplies; Industrial supplies; Plumbing fittings & supplies; Industrial supplies
Pr: Charles Kiner
**CFO:* Donald Peggs
**VP:* Stephen Kiner
**VP Sls:* Mark A Coccia

D-U-N-S 06-409-2356 IMP
GREAT LAKES POWER PRODUCTS INC
JOHN DEERE
7455 Tyler Blvd, Mentor, OH 44060-8389
Tel (440) 951-5111 *Founded/Ownrshp* 1973
Sales 31.8MM^E *EMP* 90
SIC 5085 5084 3566 Power transmission equipment & apparatus; Materials handling machinery; Speed changers (power transmission equipment), except auto; Power transmission equipment & apparatus; Materials handling machinery; Speed changers (power transmission equipment), except auto
CEO: Harry Allen Jr
**Ch Bd:* Harry L Allen Jr
**Pr:* Richard J Pennza
**VP:* David Bell
**VP:* Sam Profio
Sfty Mgr: Paul Shope
Ql Cn Mgr: Keith Sargent
Sales Exec: Doug Frank
Sales Asso: Charlie Rother

GREAT LAKES PULP & FIBRE
See FIBREK RECYCLING US INC

D-U-N-S 61-055-0043
GREAT LAKES QUICK LUBE LIMITED PARTNERSHIP
VALVOLINE INSTANT OIL CHANGE
10150 W National Ave # 325, Milwaukee, WI 53227-2145
Tel (414) 755-0066 *Founded/Ownrshp* 2005
Sales 28.9MM^E *EMP* 670
SIC 7549 Automotive maintenance services; Automotive maintenance services
Pt: Jimmy Wheat
CFO: Dorothy Ramsey
Mktg Dir: Christina Roth

D-U-N-S 92-680-7272
GREAT LAKES REIT
823 Commerce Dr Ste 300, Oak Brook, IL 60523-8824
Tel (708) 848-5216 *Founded/Ownrshp* 1992
Sales 105.2MM *EMP* 20^E
Accts Ernst & Young Llp Chicago Il
SIC 6798 6531 Real estate investment trusts; Real estate agents & managers; Real estate investment trusts; Real estate agents & managers
Ch Bd: Richard May
**Pr:* Patrick R Hunt
CFO: James Hicks
Chf Inves: Raymond Braun
Ex VP: Richard Rasley
Sr VP: Brett Brown
Sr VP: Kim Mills
Sr VP: Edith M Scurto
VP: Joe Gianforte

GREAT LAKES SELECT
See GREAT LAKES WHOLESALE & MARKETING LLC

GREAT LAKES SHIPYARD
See GREAT LAKES TOWING CO

D-U-N-S 00-552-4731 IMP
GREAT LAKES SYNERGY CORP
GLS
85 W Algonquin Rd Ste 600, Arlington Heights, IL 60005-4421
Tel (847) 437-0200 *Founded/Ownrshp* 1965
Sales 118.8MM^E *EMP* 540
SIC 5084 4226 4213

D-U-N-S 61-791-8750 IMP
GREAT LAKES TAPE CORP
GLT INTERNATIONAL
2961 Bond St, Rochester Hills, MI 48309-3517
Tel (248) 537-3335 *Founded/Ownrshp* 1990
Sales 26.5MM^E *EMP* 30
SIC 5113 Pressure sensitive tape
Pr: John Chayka
**Sec:* Ryan Chayka
**VP:* Aric Petker

D-U-N-S 80-747-8920
GREAT LAKES TISSUE CO INC
437 S Main St, Cheboygan, MI 49721-1999
Tel (231) 627-0200 *Founded/Ownrshp* 1993
Sales 25.4MM^E *EMP* 100
SIC 2621 Towels, tissues & napkins: paper & stock; Towels, tissues & napkins: paper & stock
CEO: Clarence Roznowski
**Pr:* Kent Hogan
**CFO:* Doug Deeter

GREAT LAKES TOWING
See GREAT LAKES GROUP

D-U-N-S 06-603-2749
GREAT LAKES TOWING CO
GREAT LAKES SHIPYARD
4500 Division Ave, Cleveland, OH 44102-2228
Tel (216) 621-4854 *Founded/Ownrshp* 1973
Sales 29.4MM^E *EMP* 99
SIC 4492 3731

D-U-N-S 83-300-8407
GREAT LAKES TRANSPORTATION HOLDING LLC
METRO CARS
24957 Brest, Taylor, MI 48180-4027
Tel (734) 946-1700 *Founded/Ownrshp* 2009
Sales 26.9MM^E *EMP* 200^E
SIC 8742 Transportation consultant; Transportation consultant
CEO: Daniel Ret
**Sr VP:* Mark Hayden
**Sr VP:* Jeff Pardonnet
**VP:* Paula Mikola
**VP:* Dave Satawa
VP: Steve Walz
**Prin:* Gregory Eaton
**Prin:* Gary Sakwa
Rgnl Mgr: Jan Croft
Sls Mgr: Denny Verstrat

D-U-N-S 01-634-4350
GREAT LAKES TRUCK & EQUIPMENT INC
GREAT LAKES PETERBILT
5900 Southport Rd, Portage, IN 46368-6407
Tel (219) 763-7227 *Founded/Ownrshp* 1994
Sales 71.6MM^E *EMP* 120^E
SIC 5511 5531 7538 7513 Trucks, tractors & trailers: new & used; Automobile & truck equipment & parts; General automotive repair shops; Truck rental & leasing, no drivers
Pr: Stephen Buha
**VP:* Robert Buha
IT Man: Bob Buha
Mktg Dir: Charlie Flickner
Sls Mgr: Scott McIntyre
Board of Directors: Dave Bencze

D-U-N-S 12-092-5065
GREAT LAKES UTILITIES
1323 S 7th St, Manitowoc, WI 54221
Tel (920) 686-4342 *Founded/Ownrshp* 2000
Sales 91.6MM *EMP* 11
Accts Schenck Sc Green Bay Wiscon
SIC 7539 Electrical services; Electrical services
Ch: Jem Brown
**Prin:* Joe Pacovsky

D-U-N-S 19-342-4397 EXP
GREAT LAKES VENEER INC
(*Suby of* MARION PLYWOOD CORP) ★
222 S Parkview Ave, Marion, WI 54950-9698
Tel (715) 754-2501 *Founded/Ownrshp* 1894
Sales 24.4MM^E *EMP* 250
SIC 5031 2435 Veneer; Hardwood veneer & plywood; Veneer; Hardwood veneer & plywood
Pr: Peter T Rogers
CFO: Wendy O'Brien
VP: Dave Williams
VP Sls: Michael Burkart

D-U-N-S 36-192-5498 IMP/EXP
GREAT LAKES WHOLESALE & MARKETING LLC
GREAT LAKES SELECT
3100 Ivanrest Ave Sw # 107, Grandville, MI 49418-1489
Tel (616) 261-9393 *Founded/Ownrshp* 2003
Sales 23.6MM^E *EMP* 5
Accts Crowe Horwarth Llp Grand Rapi
SIC 5149 Groceries & related products
Sls Mgr: Eric Brandstatter

GREAT LAKES WHOLESALE GROUP
See ILLINOIS INDUSTRIAL TOOL INC

D-U-N-S 01-887-6789
■ **GREAT LAKES WINDOW INC**
(*Suby of* PLY GEM INDUSTRIES INC) ★
30499 Tracy Rd, Walbridge, OH 43465-9794
Tel (419) 666-5555 *Founded/Ownrshp* 2004
Sales 126.7MM^E *EMP* 600
SIC 3089 5211 Windows, plastic; Doors, folding: plastic or plastic coated fabric; Lumber & other building materials; Windows, plastic; Doors, folding: plastic or plastic coated fabric; Lumber & other building materials
Pr: Lynn Morstadt
Top Exec: Mike Riccotto
VP: Hans Vetter
VP: Greg Wolf
Dir IT: Eric Roberts
Netwrk Eng: Marty Szczublewski

D-U-N-S 01-685-1776 IMP
GREAT LAKES WINE & SPIRITS LLC
J. LEWIS COOPER CO.
373 Victor St, Highland Park, MI 48203-3117
Tel (313) 278-5400 *Founded/Ownrshp* 1946
Sales 393.9MM^E *EMP* 850
SIC 5182 2084 Wine & distilled beverages; Wine coolers, alcoholic; Liquor; Wine & distilled beverages; Wine coolers, alcoholic; Liquor; Wines, brandy & brandy spirits
Ch Bd: J Lewis Cooper Jr
**CEO:* Lew Cooper III
**CEO:* Syd Ross
**CFO:* John Queen
CFO: John Ricco
**Ex VP:* Ernie Almeranti
**Ex VP:* Lou Grech-Cumbo
Dist Mgr: Brian Coseo
Dist Mgr: Stephanie Kane
Dist Mgr: Guy Verderese
Dir IT: Ruch Steve

GREAT LAKES WINE COMPANY
See BAUM WINE IMPORTS INC

D-U-N-S 07-259-6737
GREAT LAKES-TRIAD PLASTIC PACKAGING CORP
GLT PACKAGING
3939 36th St Se, Grand Rapids, MI 49512-2917
Tel (616) 241-6441 *Founded/Ownrshp* 1974
Sales 41.4MM^E *EMP* 85
SIC 5113 Corrugated & solid fiber boxes; Corrugated & solid fiber boxes
CFO: Steven White
**Pr:* Brian Burns
**Sec:* Kevin Burns
MIS Dir: James Burns
IT Man: John Lauderback

GREAT LKES HIGHER EDUCATN CORP
See GREAT LAKES EDUCATIONAL LOAN SERVICES INC

GREAT LKES ORTHDONTIC LABS DIV
See GREAT LAKES ORTHODONTICS LTD

D-U-N-S 07-678-3927
GREAT MIAMI VALLEY YMCA
FAIRFIELD YMCA
105 N 2nd St, Hamilton, OH 45011-2701
Tel (513) 887-0001 *Founded/Ownrshp* 1889
Sales 13.6MM *EMP* 650
Accts Kirch Cpa Group Llc Fairfield
SIC 8641 7991 8351 7032 8322 Youth organizations; Physical fitness facilities; Child day care services; Youth camps; Individual & family services; Youth organizations; Physical fitness facilities; Child day care services; Youth camps; Individual & family services
Pr: Daven W Fippon
COO: Karen Staley
CFO: Jenny McGinnis
VP: Kim Phillips
Mktg Dir: Lindsey Mithoefer

D-U-N-S 00-643-9525
GREAT MIDWEST BANK SSB
15900 W Bluemound Rd, Brookfield, WI 53005-6065
Tel (262) 784-4400 *Founded/Ownrshp* 1935
Sales NA *EMP* 125
SIC 6036 6035 Savings & loan associations, not federally chartered; Savings institutions, federally chartered; Savings & loan associations, not federally chartered; Savings institutions, federally chartered
Pr: Dennis P Doyle
**Sec:* Andrew J Doyle
Ofcr: Cyndie Higgins
**VP:* Daniel C Doyle
**VP:* Mark Loeffel
**VP:* Jeffrey J Meser

D-U-N-S 04-397-2199
GREAT NECK PUBLIC SCHOOLS
345 Lakeville Rd, Great Neck, NY 11020-1639
Tel (516) 441-4001 *Founded/Ownrshp* 1814
Sales 213.2MM *EMP* 1,500
SIC 8211 Public elementary & secondary schools; Public elementary & secondary schools
Dir Sec: Christopher Tevlin
IT Man: Eleanor Demarco
Schl Brd P: Barbara Berkowitz

D-U-N-S 00-204-0277 EXP
GREAT NECK SAW MANUFACTURERS INC (NY)
BUCK BROS DIVISION
165 E 2nd St, Mineola, NY 11501-3523
Tel (800) 457-0600 *Founded/Ownrshp* 1930, 1940
Sales 221.5MM^E *EMP* 700
SIC 5072 Hand tools; Hand tools
Pr: Sydney Jacoff
**CFO:* Richard Hollingsworth
**Ex VP:* Daniel Jacoff
Sr VP: Bob Jacoff
Creative D: Roberta Daar
IT Man: George Brando
VP Sls: Braden Bazilus
VP Sls: Shlomi Bohbot
VP Sls: Rob Ronis
S&M/VP: Peter Hagicostas

D-U-N-S 05-976-9380 IMP
GREAT NORTH AMERICAN COMPANIES INC
GREAT WESTERN SUPPLY
2828 Forest Ln Ste 2000, Dallas, TX 75234-7517
Tel (972) 481-6100 *Founded/Ownrshp* 2009
Sales 21.4MM^E *EMP* 80
SIC 5112 5199 Office supplies; Advertising specialties
Pr: Dixon G Schafer
**Treas:* H J Schafer III
**VP:* Michael N Shelton

GREAT NORTH FOODS
See ALPENA WHOLESALE GROCER CO

D-U-N-S 00-612-6742 IMP
GREAT NORTHERN CORP
395 Stroebe Rd, Appleton, WI 54914-8782
Tel (920) 739-3671 *Founded/Ownrshp* 1961
Sales 392.5MM *EMP* 1,032
Accts Grant Thornton Llp Milwaukee
SIC 2653 5199 2671 Boxes, corrugated: made from purchased materials; Plastics foam; Paper coated or laminated for packaging; Boxes, corrugated: made from purchased materials; Plastics foam; Paper coated or laminated for packaging
CEO: John R Davis
**Ch Bd:* William Raaths
**CFO:* Terry A Abraham
Sr VP: Mike Schliesmann
VP: Martin Maher
Exec: Mike Tworozeck
IT Man: Robert Cramer
IT Man: Mark Orendorff
VP Mfg: Gary Weber
Mtls Mgr: Ron Hermes
Plnt Mgr: Josh Coldiron

D-U-N-S 04-548-9119
GREAT NORTHERN DODGE INC
24542 Fortune Trl, Westlake, OH 44145-4194
Tel (440) 777-4635 *Founded/Ownrshp* 1980
Sales 25.0MM^E *EMP* 65
SIC 5511 Automobiles, new & used; Automobiles, new & used
Pr: Edwin J Schartman
**Treas:* Tim Higgins

D-U-N-S 18-296-2126 IMP
GREAT NORTHERN EQUIPMENT DISTRIBUTING INC
K & M MANUFACTURING CO.
20195 S Diamond Lake Rd # 100, Rogers, MN 55374-4863
Tel (763) 428-2237 *Founded/Ownrshp* 1987
Sales 58.0MM^E *EMP* 95^E
SIC 5084 5063 5999 Engines, gasoline; Generators; Banners; Engines, gasoline; Generators; Banners
CEO: Alan Kotula
VP: Chris Brown
Assoc Dir: Steve Mason
**Prin:* Don Kotula
Dept Mgr: Harold Embry
Dept Mgr: John Schluender
Genl Mgr: Matt Clemens
Dir IT: Greg Clemens
Mktg Dir: Chris Osgood
Merch Mgr: Randy McCabe
Sls Mgr: David Agnew

D-U-N-S 60-129-1883 IMP/EXP
GREAT NORTHERN PRODUCTS LTD
NORTHERN SEA PRODUCTS
2700 Plainfield Pike, Cranston, RI 02921-2070
Tel (401) 821-2400 *Founded/Ownrshp* 1989
Sales 35.6MM^E *EMP* 41
SIC 5146 Fish & seafoods; Seafoods
Pr: George A Nolan
**Ex VP:* Peter Bruno
**VP:* Dan Mallek
VP: David Sussman
Prin: Ravshan Rakimov

D-U-N-S 61-929-1300
GREAT NORTHERN STAFF ADMINISTRATORS LLC
(*Suby of* AURELIUS HOLDINGS INC)
6915 Sw Mcdam Ave Ste 245, Portland, OR 97219
Tel (503) 972-1944 *Founded/Ownrshp* 1999
Sales NA *EMP* 25
SIC 6411 Insurance agents & brokers; Insurance agents & brokers
VP: Ralph Sanchez

D-U-N-S 09-288-4980
GREAT NORTHWEST INC
2975 Van Horn Rd, Fairbanks, AK 99709-5418
Tel (907) 479-0410 *Founded/Ownrshp* 1976
Sales 54.3MM *EMP* 197
SIC 1794 Excavation & grading, building construction; Excavation & grading, building construction
Pr: John Minder
**Sec:* Lori McCarter
**VP:* Randolph Brand
**VP:* Steve Geraghty
**VP:* Anton K Johansen

D-U-N-S 96-416-3430
GREAT NORTHWEST RESTAURANTS INC
TGI FRIDAY'S
3001 Lava Ridge Ct # 300, Roseville, CA 95661-3094
Tel (916) 786-8080 *Founded/Ownrshp* 1997
Sales 12.8MM^E *EMP* 550
SIC 5812 5813 Restaurant, family: chain; Bars & lounges; Restaurant, family: chain; Bars & lounges
Pr: Mike Alizadeh

D-U-N-S 05-637-9306
GREAT OAKS INSTITUTE OF T
P.O. Box 62627 (45262-0627)
Tel (513) 771-8840 *Founded/Ownrshp* 2013
Sales 34.7MM^E *EMP* 483^E
SIC 8733 Noncommercial research organizations
Prin: Harold Carr
Schl Brd P: Sue Steele

D-U-N-S 06-894-3075
GREAT OAKS INSTITUTE OF TECHNOLOGY & CAREER DEVELOPMENT
3254 E Kemper Rd, Cincinnati, OH 45241-6421
Tel (513) 771-8840 *Founded/Ownrshp* 1971
Sales 67.1MM *EMP* 482
Accts Plattenburg & Associates Inc
SIC 8211 8299 8331 8249 Public vocational/technical school; Educational service, nondegree granting: continuing educ.; Job training & vocational rehabilitation services; Vocational schools; Public vocational/technical school; Educational service, nondegree granting: continuing educ.; Job training & vocational rehabilitation services; Vocational schools
Pr: Harry Snyder
**CFO:* Robert Giuffre
**VP:* Jon Quatman
**VP:* Michelle Means Walker
Pr Dir: Rebecca Beckstedt
Teacher Pr: Michelle Means-Walker
HC Dir: Al Gille

GREAT OPENINGS
See METALWORKS INC

D-U-N-S 03-403-0783
GREAT OUTDOOR PROVISION CO (NC)
LAYERS
2017 Cameron St, Raleigh, NC 27605-1310
Tel (919) 833-1741 *Founded/Ownrshp* 1972
Sales 20.1MM^E *EMP* 175
SIC 5941 Sporting goods & bicycle shops; Backpacking equipment; Camping equipment; Fishing equipment
Pr: Thomas F Valone
**VP:* Bill Mauney

GREAT OUTDOORS
See BEAVER VALLEY SUPPLY CO INC

D-U-N-S 09-525-3530 IMP
GREAT PACIFIC ENTERPRISES (US) INC
GENPAK
(*Suby of* GREAT PACIFIC ENTERPRISES INC)
68 Warren St, Glens Falls, NY 12801-4530
Tel (518) 761-2593 *Founded/Ownrshp* 1983
Sales 396.7MM^E *EMP* 2,000
SIC 3089 Plastic containers, except foam; Plastic containers, except foam
Ch Bd: James Pattison
**CEO:* Michael Korenberg
**Ch:* James Reilly
**VP:* Nick Geer
Mktg Mgr: Michele Quirk

GREAT PACIFIC PATAGONIA
See PATAGONIA INC

D-U-N-S 08-001-2865
GREAT PARKS CO USA LLC (FL)
1707 Highlands Vw Se, Smyrna, GA 30082-5223
Tel (305) 517-7643 *Founded/Ownrshp* 2011
Sales 556.5MM^E *EMP* 400
SIC 7996 Amusement parks
CEO: Carlos Aragon
Treas: Mildred Salas

GREAT PASSION PLAY
See ELNA M SMITH FOUNDATION

D-U-N-S 05-043-2798
GREAT PERFORMANCES/ARTISTS AS WAITRESSES INC (NY)
304 Hudson St Fl 2, New York, NY 10013-1027
Tel (212) 727-2424 *Founded/Ownrshp* 1979
Sales 17.2MM^E *EMP* 300
SIC 7299 5812 Party planning service; Caterers; Party planning service; Caterers
Ch Bd: Lizbeth Neumark
**Pr:* Dean Martinus
**VP:* Linda Abbey
VP: Stephen Segaller
Dir Soc: Forrest Hedden
Dir Soc: Heather Pfeiffer
Dir Soc: Jodi Smith
Dir Soc: Lauren Tregor
Creative D: Josh Tierney
**Prin:* Ronnie Davis
Mng Dir: Brianne MAI

GREAT PLAINS AREA VO TECH
See GREAT PLAINS TECHNOLOGY CENTER

D-U-N-S 09-955-6359
■ **GREAT PLAINS COCA COLA BOTTLING CO**
COCA-COLA
(*Suby of* COCA-COLA REFRESHMENTS USA INC) ★
600 N May Ave, Oklahoma City, OK 73107-6324
Tel (405) 280-2000 *Founded/Ownrshp* 2011
Sales 85.6MM^E *EMP* 297
SIC 2086 Bottled & canned soft drinks; Bottled & canned soft drinks
Ch Bd: Robert F Browne
COO: Don Bischoff
CFO: Carie Monsey
CFO: Clayton Sliger
Ex VP: Henry W Browne Jr
Dist Mgr: Scott Kahmeyer
Div Mgr: Mike Hale
Dir IT: Steve Murphy
IT Man: Jeff Hands
IT Man: Jim Preslar
VP Opers: Bill McClure

D-U-N-S 00-682-1391
GREAT PLAINS COMMUNICATIONS INC
1600 Great Plains Ctr, Blair, NE 68008
Tel (402) 426-9511 *Founded/Ownrshp* 1984
Sales 55.6MM *EMP* 217^E
SIC 4813 Telephone communication, except radio; Telephone communication, except radio
Pr: Todd A Foje
**CFO:* Janelle Allison
CFO: Gerry Powell
VP: Ken Pfister
Dist Mgr: Shanon Morris
Div Mgr: Mike Tipton
Dir IT: John Greene
IT Man: Jeremy Tramp
Mktg Mgr: Iris Kennedy
Snr Mgr: Tom Randall

D-U-N-S 60-160-5892
GREAT PLAINS COMPANIES INC
15925 4th Ave N, Plymouth, MN 55447-3614
Tel (763) 208-9760 *Founded/Ownrshp* 1989
Sales 45.5MM^E *EMP* 346
SIC 5211 1521 Structural wood members; Trusses, wooden roof; Lumber & other building materials; Single-family housing construction; Residential construction; Millwork; Lumber & other building materials; Single-family housing construction
CEO: Michael R Wigley
CFO: David Franze

D-U-N-S 06-473-9076
▲ **GREAT PLAINS ENERGY INC**
1200 Main St, Kansas City, MO 64105-2122
Tel (816) 556-2200 *Founded/Ownrshp* 2001
Sales 2.5MMM *EMP* 2,964^E
Tkr Sym GXP *Exch* NYS
SIC 4911 Electric services; Distribution, electric power; Generation, electric power; Transmission, electric power; Electric services; Distribution, electric power; Generation, electric power; Transmission, electric power
Ch Bd: Terry Bassham
V Ch: James Gilligan
COO: Scott H Heidtbrink
CFO: James C Shay
Chf Cred: Ellen E Fairchild
Ofcr: Bob Nicholas
Ofcr: Bill Riggins
Sr VP: Barbara B Curry
Sr VP: Stephen Easley
Sr VP: Heather A Humphrey
VP: Duane Anstaett
VP: Steven P Busser
VP: Chuck Caisley
VP: Dana Crawford
VP: Maria R Jenks
VP: Charles King
VP: Kevin Noblet
VP: Russ Wiley
VP: Lori A Wright
Board of Directors: David L Bodde, Randall C Ferguson Jr, Gary D Forsee, Scott D Grimes, Thomas D Hyde, James A Mitchell, Ann D Murtlow, John J Sherman, Linda H Talbott

D-U-N-S 13-019-4280
■ **GREAT PLAINS ENERGY SERVICES INC**
(*Suby of* GREAT PLAINS ENERGY INC) ★
1201 Walnut St, Kansas City, MO 64106-2149
Tel (816) 556-2200 *Founded/Ownrshp* 2003
Sales 444.4MM^E *EMP* 395
SIC 4911 Generation, electric power; Transmission, electric power; Distribution, electric power; Generation, electric power; Transmission, electric power; Distribution, electric power
Pr: Mike Chesser
**Pr:* Terry Bassham
**CEO:* Michael Chesser
**Ex VP:* Scott Heidtbrink
Ex VP: John Marshall
Sr VP: Barbara Curry
**Sr VP:* Jim Shay
VP: Kevin Bryant

VP: William Herdegen
VP: Marvin Rollison
IT Man: Susan Bartlett

D-U-N-S 03-134-1543
GREAT PLAINS GAS COMPRESSION INC
210 E 1st St, Hugoton, KS 67951-2502
Tel (620) 544-3578 *Founded/Ownrshp* 2001
Sales 51.8MM^E *EMP* 131
SIC 1389 Gas compressing (natural gas) at the fields
Pr: Jim Wilson
**Treas:* Bob Passmore
**VP:* Stacy Smith
**Prin:* Terry McBride

GREAT PLAINS HEALTH
See NORTH PLATTE NEBRASKA HOSPITAL CORP

D-U-N-S 07-332-3586
GREAT PLAINS HEALTH ALLIANCE INC
GPHA
625 3rd St, Phillipsburg, KS 67661-2138
Tel (785) 543-2111 *Founded/Ownrshp* 1950
Sales 116.7MM^E *EMP* 1,097
Accts Bkd Llp Wichita Ks
SIC 8742 Productivity improvement consultant; Productivity improvement consultant
Ch: Steve Carlson
Pr: Curt Colson
**Pr:* Roger S John
**CFO:* Dave Dellasega
CFO: Dennis L Fredrickson
Treas: Thomas E Keller
**Sec:* Robert E Hamilton
VP: Tim Kerr
**VP:* Beth Meyeres
VP: Brenda Olson
**VP:* Logan Sprunger
Dir Rx: Deanna Culbertson
Dir Rx: Nancy Molzahn

D-U-N-S 78-753-7356
GREAT PLAINS HOSPITAL INC
HEARTLAND BEHAVIORAL HLTH SVCS
1500 W Ashland St, Nevada, MO 64772-1710
Tel (417) 667-2666 *Founded/Ownrshp* 2003
Sales 26.7MM^E *EMP* 230
SIC 8069 8062 Drug abuse counselor, nontreatment; Specialty hospitals, except psychiatric; Specialty hospitals, except psychiatric; General medical & surgical hospitals
Ofcr: Alyson Harder
Dir Rx: Tami Jones
CIO: Carri Compton
Mktg Dir: Betsy Curtis
Doctor: David Morrsion
Nrsg Dir: Nathan Taylor
HC Dir: Corie Daulton

D-U-N-S 09-770-7285 IMP
GREAT PLAINS INDUSTRIES INC
G P I
(*Suby of* GREAT PLAINS VENTURES INC) ★
5252 E 36th St N, Wichita, KS 67220-3205
Tel (316) 219-1106 *Founded/Ownrshp* 1972
Sales 55.4MM *EMP* 280
SIC 3586 3824 Measuring & dispensing pumps; Gasoline pumps, measuring or dispensing; Liquid meters; Gasoline dispensing meters; Measuring & dispensing pumps; Gasoline pumps, measuring or dispensing; Liquid meters; Gasoline dispensing meters
Pr: Victor Lukic
CFO: Jeanette Dreiling
Treas: Deborah Rix
Genl Mgr: Greg Gibson
IT Man: Gregg Collard
Ql Cn Mgr: Jamal Ahmed
Manager: Greg Alonzo
Manager: Gary Johnson
Manager: Ed Wiley

D-U-N-S 55-541-0851
GREAT PLAINS INTERNATIONAL INC
4511 N Cliff Ave, Sioux Falls, SD 57104-0449
Tel (605) 336-3820 *Founded/Ownrshp* 1987
Sales 25.7MM *EMP* 25
Accts Abdo Eick & Meyers Llp Mank
SIC 5511 Trucks, tractors & trailers: new & used; Trucks, tractors & trailers: new & used
Pr: Al Buresh
**Sec:* Rick Bye
**VP:* Robert Bye

D-U-N-S 03-061-2634 EXP
GREAT PLAINS MANUFACTURING INC
LAND PRIDE
1525 E North St, Salina, KS 67401-8562
Tel (785) 823-3276 *Founded/Ownrshp* 1976
Sales 418.6MM^E *EMP* 1,500^E
SIC 3523 Farm machinery & equipment; Planting, haying, harvesting & processing machinery; Hulling machinery, agricultural; Farm machinery & equipment; Planting, haying, harvesting & processing machinery; Hulling machinery, agricultural
Pr: Roy Applequist
**Pr:* Daniel Rauchholz
**COO:* Linda Salem
Sr VP: Linda Otte
VP: Curt Carpenter
VP: Lana Gant
VP: Todd Haddock
VP: Bob Warkentin
Exec: Vance Stinnett
Brnch Mgr: Tom Johnson
CIO: Mark Marcott

D-U-N-S 03-635-2490
GREAT PLAINS NATIONAL BANK
120 W Jones St, Hollis, OK 73550-3004
Tel (580) 688-3323 *Founded/Ownrshp* 1929
Sales NA *EMP* 100
SIC 6022 State commercial banks; State commercial banks
Ch Bd: W B Nell Jr
**Pr:* Jason McQueen
**Pr:* Terry Shelby
**CEO:* Art Harris
Sr VP: Mandy Bryant
Sr VP: Clay Carr
Sr VP: Carla Hoggard
**Sr VP:* Jr Mills
**Sr VP:* Dayle Penington
Sr VP: Ronda Smith
Sr VP: Jeff Waters
**VP:* Tammy Bynum
VP: Ashley Davis
VP: Marty Maddox
**VP:* Terri Mefford
VP: Mark Russell
**VP:* Lynda Shaver

D-U-N-S 05-593-9203
■ **GREAT PLAINS OILFIELD RENTAL LLC**
(*Suby of* SEVENTY SEVEN OPERATING LLC) ★
6100 N Western Ave, Oklahoma City, OK 73118-1044
Tel (405) 608-7777 *Founded/Ownrshp* 2006
Sales 120.8MM^E *EMP* 179^E
SIC 5084 Petroleum industry machinery
CEO: Jerry Winchester
Pr: Jerome Loughridge
COO: Karl Blanchard
CFO: Cary Baetz

GREAT PLAINS PACKAGING
See PAPERWORKS PACKAGING GROUP

GREAT PLAINS REGIONAL MED CTR
See FARMERS UNION HOSPITAL ASSOCIATION (INC)

GREAT PLAINS REGIONAL MEDICAL
See FARMERS UNION HOSPITAL ASSOCIATION

D-U-N-S 07-427-1818
GREAT PLAINS TECHNOLOGY CENTER
GREAT PLAINS AREA VO TECH
4500 Sw Lee Blvd, Lawton, OK 73505-8304
Tel (580) 355-6371 *Founded/Ownrshp* 1971
Sales 20.6MM^E *EMP* 260
SIC 8211 Public vocational/technical school; Public vocational/technical school
IT Man: Leah Fultz
Psych: Nancy Hasley
Snr Mgr: Jennifer Tuttle

D-U-N-S 05-657-7042
GREAT PLAINS VENTURES INC
3504 N Great Plains Dr # 100, Wichita, KS 67220-3407
Tel (316) 684-1540 *Founded/Ownrshp* 1972
Sales 73.2MM *EMP* 300
Accts Allen Gibbs & Houlik Lc Cpa
SIC 6719 Investment holding companies, except banks; Investment holding companies, except banks
CEO: Susayn Brandes
**CFO:* Jeanette Dreiling
**VP:* Jack Kratzer

GREAT PLANES MODEL DISTRS
See HOBBICO INC

D-U-N-S 06-454-5312
GREAT PLANES SALES INC
340 Airport Dr, Grove, OK 74344-4108
Tel (918) 786-6499 *Founded/Ownrshp* 1971
Sales 40.0MM *EMP* 10
SIC 5599 5088 Aircraft, self-propelled; Aircraft & parts; Aircraft, self-propelled; Aircraft & parts
Pr: Gary P Conklin
**Sec:* Ellen Conklin

GREAT PLATTE RIVER RD ARCHWAY
See GREAT PLATTE RIVER ROAD MEMORIAL FOUND

D-U-N-S 01-757-6625
GREAT PLATTE RIVER ROAD MEMORIAL FOUND
GREAT PLATTE RIVER RD ARCHWAY
1 Archway Pkwy, Kearney, NE 68847-7910
Tel (308) 237-1000 *Founded/Ownrshp* 2000
Sales 20.9MM *EMP* 2
SIC 8412 Museum
Genl Mgr: Ronniel Obrin

D-U-N-S 04-060-6014
GREAT PRAIRIE AREA EDUCATION AGENCY
2814 N Court St, Ottumwa, IA 52501-1163
Tel (319) 753-6561 *Founded/Ownrshp* 1975
Sales 15.0MM *EMP* 320
SIC 8299 Educational services; Educational services
Pr: Jon Sheleahl
CFO: Dennis Gourley
Dir IT: Julie Barwick
Teacher Pr: R Greg Manske

D-U-N-S 04-766-4649 IMP
GREAT RIVER ENERGY
12300 Elm Creek Blvd N, Maple Grove, MN 55369-4718
Tel (763) 445-5000 *Founded/Ownrshp* 1998
Sales 1.0MMM *EMP* 850
Accts Deloitte & Touche Llp
SIC 4911 Generation, electric power; Transmission, electric power; Generation, electric power; Transmission, electric power
Pr: David Saggau
CFO: Larry Schmid
Ch: Michael Thorson
Treas: Clay V De Bogart
Treas: Robert Thompson
VP: Jon Breke
VP: Jim Jones
VP: Will Kaul
VP: Rick Lancaster
VP: Eric Olsen
VP: Kandance Olsen
VP: Greg Ridderbusch
VP: Laureen Rossmccalib

D-U-N-S 80-033-5221
GREAT RIVER ENTERTAINMENT LLC
FUN CITY
3001 Winegard Dr, Burlington, IA 52601-2061
Tel (319) 753-2946 *Founded/Ownrshp* 2007
Sales 40.0MM *EMP* 500
SIC 7011 Casino hotel
CEO: Gary L Hoyer
COO: Jerry Baum
Dir IT: Scott Anderson
Pr Mgr: Jennifer Holliday

GREAT RIVER FOOD
See DEREK AND CONSTANCE LEE CORP

D-U-N-S 10-233-2301
GREAT RIVER HEALTH SYSTEMS INC
1221 S Gear Ave, West Burlington, IA 52655-1679
Tel (319) 768-1000 *Founded/Ownrshp* 1982
Sales 2.6M *EMP* 1,170
SIC 8062 General medical & surgical hospitals; General medical & surgical hospitals
Pr: Mark Richardson
CFO: Todd Sladky
**VP:* Ron Halligan
VP: Tony Hayes
VP: John Mercer
CTO: Michael Abouassaly
Doctor: Joseph Marshall
Doctor: Jonathan Snow

D-U-N-S 07-830-5142
GREAT RIVER INDUSTRIES LLC
21 Moran Rd, Natchez, MS 39120-4074
Tel (601) 442-7568 *Founded/Ownrshp* 2011
Sales 23.7MM^E *EMP* 61^E
SIC 3449 Bars, concrete reinforcing: fabricated steel

GREAT RIVER MARINE SERVICE DIV
See INGRAM BARGE CO

GREAT RIVER MEDICAL CENTER
See AMERIS OF ARKANSAS LLC

D-U-N-S 05-804-2961
GREAT RIVER MEDICAL CENTER
GREAT RVER HM HLTH CARE HSPICE
1221 S Gear Ave, West Burlington, IA 52655-1681
Tel (319) 768-1000 *Founded/Ownrshp* 1895
Sales 165.6MM^E *EMP* 1,400
Accts Cliftonlarsonallen Llp Minnea
SIC 8062 General medical & surgical hospitals; General medical & surgical hospitals
Pr: Mark Richardson
**Pr:* Kent Gaudian
Bd of Dir: Connee Stevens
Ofcr: Sandy Sacora
VP: Tony Hayes
Dir Lab: Nancy Mathahs
Dir Rad: Jay Radhakrishnan
Genl Mgr: Chris Reed
Tech Mgr: Mark Brown
Sls&Mrk Ex: Craig Vouchard
Ansthlgy: Jose Calderon

GREAT RIVER OLDS-NISSAN-GMC
See TILLMAN AUTOMOTIVE GROUP INC

GREAT RIVER PHYSICIANS GROUP -
See MISSISSIPPI COUNTY HOSPITAL SYSTEM

GREAT RVER HM HLTH CARE HSPICE
See GREAT RIVER MEDICAL CENTER

D-U-N-S 03-160-1131
GREAT SALT LAKE ELECTRIC INC (UT)
GSL ELECTRIC
8540 S Sandy Pkwy, Sandy, UT 84070-6422
Tel (801) 565-0088 *Founded/Ownrshp* 1981
Sales 45.0MM *EMP* 350
SIC 1731

GREAT SALT LAKE MINERALS
See G S L CORP

GREAT SALT LAKE MINERALS CORP
See COMPASS MINERALS OGDEN INC

D-U-N-S 01-802-3622 IMP
GREAT SCOT INC
(*Suby of* FRESH ENCOUNTER) ★
317 W Main Cross St, Findlay, OH 45840-3364
Tel (419) 422-8090 *Founded/Ownrshp* 1996
Sales 32.8MM^E *EMP* 300
SIC 5411 Supermarkets, independent; Supermarkets, independent
Ch Bd: Michael S Needler
**Prin:* Todd Terry

GREAT SMOKIES DIAGNOSTIC LAB
See GENOVA DIAGNOSTICS INC

D-U-N-S 05-281-6436
GREAT SOUTH METALS CO (GA)
2670 Hickory Grove Rd Nw, Acworth, GA 30101-3643
Tel (770) 917-9000 *Founded/Ownrshp* 1981
Sales 35.9MM^E *EMP* 38
SIC 5051 Metals service centers & offices
Ch Bd: Steven D Friedman
**Pr:* John Kingery
**VP:* Mark Farmer
Off Mgr: Lori Henson
Opers Mgr: Jack Williams
Ql Cn Mgr: Joey Brannon
Trfc Mgr: Charlie Oliver

D-U-N-S 60-580-0408
▲ **GREAT SOUTHERN BANCORP INC**
1451 E Battlefield St, Springfield, MO 65804-3701
Tel (417) 887-4400 *Founded/Ownrshp* 1989
Sales NA *EMP* 1,163^E
Tkr Sym GSBC *Exch* NGS
SIC 6022 State commercial banks; State commercial banks
Pr: Joseph W Turner
**Ch Bd:* William V Turner
Treas: Rex A Copeland
Ofcr: Laura Beaver
Ofcr: Gary Lewis
Ofcr: Lois McPhetridge
Ofcr: Melanie Pulscher
Ofcr: Carrie Rossow
Ofcr: Laura Smith
Ex VP: Barby Pohl
VP: Tammy Baurichter
VP: Scott Brekke
VP: Brian Fogle
VP: Bob Ogden
VP: Matt Snyder
VP: Linton J Thomason
VP: Ann Turner
Exec: Kent Lammers
Exec: Joseph Urner
Creative D: Nathan Williams
Board of Directors: William E Barclay, Julie T Brown, Thomas J Carlson, Larry D Frazier, Grant Q Haden, Douglas M Pitt, Earl A Steinert Jr

D-U-N-S 07-625-3855
■ **GREAT SOUTHERN BANK**
(*Suby of* GREAT SOUTHERN BANCORP INC) ★
1451 E Battlefield St, Springfield, MO 65804-3701
Tel (417) 888-5880 *Founded/Ownrshp* 1989
Sales NA *EMP* 740
SIC 6036 4724 6712 Savings & loan associations, not federally chartered; Travel agencies; Bank holding companies; Savings & loan associations, not federally chartered; Travel agencies; Bank holding companies
Ch Bd: William V Turner
Pr: Joseph W Turner
VP: Teresa S Chasteen
VP: Debbie Flowers
VP: Linton Thomason
CTO: Bart Evans
Board of Directors: Douglas M Pitt

D-U-N-S 00-793-1421
GREAT SOUTHERN LIFE INSURANCE CO (TX)
(*Suby of* UNITED FIDELITY LIFE INSURANCE CO INC) ★
300 W 11th St, Kansas City, MO 64105-1618
Tel (816) 391-2000 *Founded/Ownrshp* 1909, 1993
Sales NA *EMP* 300
SIC 6311 Life insurance carriers; Life insurance carriers
Pr: Gary Muller
**Ch Bd:* Michael A Merriman
CEO: Julie Briski
**COO:* Bill Marden

D-U-N-S 05-721-1823 IMP
GREAT SOUTHERN WOOD PRESERVING INC
1100 Us Highway 431 S, Abbeville, AL 36310-2079
Tel (334) 585-2291 *Founded/Ownrshp* 1971
Sales 357.7MM^E *EMP* 900
SIC 2491 Structural lumber & timber, treated wood; Structural lumber & timber, treated wood
Pr: Jimmy Rane
**COO:* Mark Callender
CFO: William Ray
Ofcr: Chris Bonner
**VP:* Michael Rane
**Prin:* Don McCullough
Genl Mgr: Chuck Dickert
Genl Mgr: Jeremy Doyle
Genl Mgr: Bill Freeman
Dir IT: Cris Anderson
Dir IT: Godwin Chris

D-U-N-S 09-357-2279 IMP
GREAT SOUTHWEST PAPER CO INC
5707 Harvey Wilson Dr, Houston, TX 77020-8025
Tel (713) 223-5050 *Founded/Ownrshp* 1990
Sales 35.0MM^E *EMP* 40
SIC 5113 Industrial & personal service paper
Pr: Michael J Vannatta
**VP:* Katherine Chandur
**VP:* Andrew M Vannatta
Sales Asso: Deneille Noah

D-U-N-S 13-972-3357
■ **GREAT SOUTHWESTERN CONSTRUCTION INC**
(*Suby of* MYR GROUP INC) ★
1100 Topeka Way, Castle Rock, CO 80109-3105
Tel (303) 688-5816 *Founded/Ownrshp* 2000
Sales 91.9MM^E *EMP* 184^E
SIC 1623 Electric power line construction; Communication line & transmission tower construction; Electric power line construction; Communication line & transmission tower construction
Pr: Brandon Lark
Treas: Greg Medici
**Treas:* Frank P Volpe
VP: Phil Connor
Opers Mgr: Heath Ferrell
Sls Mgr: Robert Agnew
Sls Mgr: Salvador Olivas

D-U-N-S 01-893-5692 IMP
GREAT STATE BEVERAGES INC
BETTER BRANDS
1000 Quality Dr, Hooksett, NH 03106-2625
Tel (603) 644-2337 *Founded/Ownrshp* 1957
Sales 115.1MM^E *EMP* 120
SIC 5181 5149 5145 Beer & other fermented malt liquors; Soft drinks; Snack foods; Fountain supplies; Beer & other fermented malt liquors; Soft drinks; Snack foods; Fountain supplies
Pr: Robert James Koslowsky
**Ch Bd:* Robert Koslowsky Sr
**Pr:* Robert Koslowsky Jr
**Prin:* Michael McGinn

GREAT STEAK & FRY
See NICAR MANAGEMENT INC

D-U-N-S 19-411-3270
GREAT TEXAS FOOD CORP
CAFE DEL RIO
8568 S Us Highway 59, Nacogdoches, TX 75964-8390
Tel (936) 564-5757 *Founded/Ownrshp* 1988
Sales 15.0MM^E *EMP* 450
SIC 5812 Steak & barbecue restaurants; Steak & barbecue restaurants
Ch Bd: Don Davis
**Pr:* Don Burdette
**Sec:* Maria Davis
**VP:* Warren Hutson

D-U-N-S 08-078-3624
GREAT VALLEY SCHOOL DISTRICT (INC)
47 Church Rd, Malvern, PA 19355-1539
Tel (610) 889-2100 *Founded/Ownrshp* 1969
Sales 33.3MM^E *EMP* 380

Accts Herbein & Company Inc Readi
SIC 8211 Public combined elementary & secondary school; Public combined elementary & secondary school
VP: Nicholas Vastardis
Dir Sec: Kenneth Stewart
Schl Brd P: David Barrett

D-U-N-S 17-072-7197 IMP
GREAT WALL SEAFOOD LA CORP
15854 Ornelas St, Irwindale, CA 91706-2030
Tel (626) 452-0908 *Founded/Ownrshp* 2011
Sales 48.6MM^E^ *EMP* 30
SIC 5146 Fish & seafoods
CEO: Yu Zhou Zheng
Pr: Guan Ll Liu
Genl Mgr: Jasmine Ni

D-U-N-S 14-462-6442 IMP
GREAT WALL SEAFOOD SUPPLY INC
1661 S Great Sw Pkwy 30, Grand Prairie, TX 75051-2515
Tel (972) 623-2900 *Founded/Ownrshp* 2003
Sales 77.0MM *EMP* 22
SIC 5146 5812 5421 Fish & seafoods; Seafood restaurants; Fish & seafood markets
Pr: Bo Chuan Wong
**Treas:* Nancy Yeung
**VP:* Yuk P Cheng

D-U-N-S 10-995-0852
■ **GREAT WEST CASUALTY**
(*Suby of* OLD REPUBLIC INTERNATIONAL CORP) ★
1100 W 29th St, South Sioux City, NE 68776-3130
Tel (402) 494-2411 *Founded/Ownrshp* 1956
Sales NA *EMP* 708
SIC 6331 Fire, marine & casualty insurance & carriers; Fire, marine & casualty insurance & carriers
Pr: Al Johnson
Ex VP: Philip Mahoney
**VP:* Mary Anderson
VP: Chuck Bean
VP: Bob Brodersen
VP: Dena Cochran
VP: Gary Frey
VP: Sarah Hansen
VP: John Joines
VP: David Kasprzyk
VP: Terry Keime
VP: Jim Klemme
VP: Rick Larson
VP: Randy Miller
VP: Steve Olson
VP: Eric Rosenbaum
VP: Robert Todd
VP: Rich Wright

D-U-N-S 00-749-8769
■ **GREAT WEST CASUALTY CO**
(*Suby of* GREAT WEST CASUALTY) ★
1100 W 29th St, South Sioux City, NE 68776-3130
Tel (402) 494-2411 *Founded/Ownrshp* 1956, 1985
Sales NA *EMP* 702
SIC 6331 Fire, marine & casualty insurance & carriers; Property damage insurance; Fire, marine & casualty insurance & carriers; Property damage insurance
Ch Bd: Scott Rager
**Pr:* Jim Jensen
**CFO:* Gaylen Tenhulzen
**Treas:* Mary Anderson
Treas: Mark Laurusevage
Ex VP: P Kuehl
**VP:* Dena M Cochran

GREAT WEST FINANCIAL
See GWL&A FINANCIAL INC

GREAT WEST FINANCIAL
See GREAT-WEST LIFE & ANNUITY INSURANCE CO

D-U-N-S 07-723-8830 EXP
GREAT WEST PRODUCE CO INC
2600 S Eastern Ave, Commerce, CA 90040-1402
Tel (323) 869-0200 *Founded/Ownrshp* 1962
Sales 60.0MM^E^ *EMP* 30
SIC 5148 Fresh fruits & vegetables; Fresh fruits & vegetables
CEO: Paul A Villa
**Pr:* Sean Villa
**VP:* Barbara Villa
Opers Mgr: Stacy Parks

D-U-N-S 07-289-9552
■ **GREAT WESTERN BANCORPORATION INC**
(*Suby of* NATIONAL AUSTRALIA BANK LIMITED)
100 N Phillips Ave # 100, Sioux Falls, SD 57104-6725
Tel (605) 334-2548 *Founded/Ownrshp* 2008
Sales NA *EMP* 786
Tkr Sym GWB *Exch* NYS
SIC 6712 6022 Bank holding companies; State commercial banks; Bank holding companies; State commercial banks
Pr: Ken Karels
**Pr:* Daniel A Hamann
Pr: Paul Thronson
Ofcr: Sonya Frickenstein
VP: John Bade
VP: Bill Fajen
VP: Pete Jardine
VP: Brad Larson
VP: Jeff Phillips
Exec: Kirk Cisler
Exec: Jeremy Douglas
Exec: Tom Fischer
Exec: John Jennett

GREAT WESTERN BANK
See NORTH CENTRAL BANCSHARES INC

D-U-N-S 00-697-0123
■ **GREAT WESTERN BANK**
(*Suby of* GREAT WESTERN BANCORPORATION INC) ★
6015 Nw Radial Hwy, Omaha, NE 68104-3425
Tel (402) 952-6021 *Founded/Ownrshp* 1932
Sales NA *EMP* 375
SIC 6022 State commercial banks; State commercial banks
Ch Bd: Deryl F Hamann
**Pr:* Daniel Brabec
**CFO:* David Henricksen
**Ex VP:* Craig Wilkins
**Ex VP:* Drew Williams
**VP:* Peggy J Blake
Exec: Brad Botos
Site Mgr: Wesley Graffius
VP Mktg: Harlan O Falk

D-U-N-S 00-894-2211
■ **GREAT WESTERN BANK (WATERTOWN)** (SD)
(*Suby of* GREAT WESTERN BANCORPORATION INC) ★
35 1st Ave Ne, Watertown, SD 57201-2452
Tel (605) 886-8401 *Founded/Ownrshp* 1935, 2003
Sales NA *EMP* 500
SIC 6022 State commercial banks; State commercial banks
CEO: Ken Karels
Pr: Jeff Erickson
COO: Bryan Kindopp
Ofcr: Paul Moore
Sr VP: Dean Devos
VP: David Hinderaker
VP: Doug Tribble
Telecom Mg: Gene Slouka
Site Mgr: Rebecca Brown
Opers Mgr: Cheryl Moe

D-U-N-S 78-964-9084
GREAT WESTERN DINING SERVICE INC
111 W Moniteau St, Tipton, MO 65081-8253
Tel (660) 433-2298 *Founded/Ownrshp* 1990
Sales 18.3MM *EMP* 650
SIC 5812 Contract food services; Caterers; Contract food services
Ch Bd: Warren Hunt
**Pr:* Fred Fiffer
Dist Mgr: Rick Vandiver

D-U-N-S 00-793-4664
GREAT WESTERN DRILLING CO (TX)
700 W Louisiana Ave, Midland, TX 79701-3249
Tel (432) 682-5241 *Founded/Ownrshp* 1936, 1951
Sales 25.0MM^E^ *EMP* 51
SIC 1311 1382 Crude petroleum production; Natural gas production; Oil & gas exploration services
Ch Bd: Kenneth W Davis Jr
**Pr:* Bruce M Brady
Treas: Beth Kaufmann
**Treas:* Elizabeth K Kaufmann
**VP:* Dennis L Hendrix
IT Man: Randy Hardin

D-U-N-S 13-955-1014
GREAT WESTERN ERECTORS LLC
9207 Sovereign Row, Dallas, TX 75247-4513
Tel (214) 637-2500 *Founded/Ownrshp* 1984
Sales 22.0MM^E^ *EMP* 250
SIC 1791 Structural steel erection; Structural steel erection
Pt: M R Duggan
Dir IT: Jamie Walker

GREAT WESTERN EXPRESS
See LISA MOTOR LINES INC

D-U-N-S 18-551-9741
GREAT WESTERN INSURANCE CO INC
3434 Washington Blvd # 100, Ogden, UT 84401-4128
Tel (801) 621-5688 *Founded/Ownrshp* 1983
Sales NA *EMP* 73
SIC 6411 Insurance agents
Pr: John E Lindquist
**CFO:* Nathan Felix
CFO: Fred L Meese
**Treas:* Fred Meese
Ofcr: Leanne Shay
**VP:* Ken Knauss
**VP:* Michael Scott
Rgnl Mgr: Chad Iverson
Rgnl Mgr: Doris McRae
Dir IT: Curtis Steab

D-U-N-S 06-534-8444
GREAT WESTERN MALTING CO
GRAINCORP MALT
1666 Kraft Rd, Pocatello, ID 83204-2425
Tel (360) 699-6759 *Founded/Ownrshp* 1989
Sales 49.6MM^E^ *EMP* 190^E^
SIC 2083 Malt
Plnt Mgr: Amy Mercy
Plnt Mgr: Tevis Vance

D-U-N-S 18-331-4053 IMP/EXP
GREAT WESTERN MALTING CO
(*Suby of* GRAINCORP MALT) ★
1705 Nw Harborside Dr, Vancouver, WA 98660-1026
Tel (360) 693-3661 *Founded/Ownrshp* 2014
Sales 49.6MM^E^ *EMP* 150
SIC 2083 Malt; Malt
Pr: Mike O'Toole
CFO: Mike Sullivan
IT Man: Bob Silva

D-U-N-S 00-713-6872 IMP/EXP
GREAT WESTERN MANUFACTURING CO INC (KS)
2017 S 4th St, Leavenworth, KS 66048-3928
Tel (913) 682-2291 *Founded/Ownrshp* 1358
Sales 24.9MM^E^ *EMP* 84
SIC 3556 Flour mill machinery
Pr: Jim Schroeder
Sfty Mgr: Doug Price
Prd Mgr: David Schroeder
Sls Mgr: Bob Ricklefs

D-U-N-S 07-926-0865
GREAT WESTERN PACIFIC INC (WA)
PIRATE'S PLUNDER
1301 Alaskan Way Pier 57, Seattle, WA 98101-2057
Tel (206) 624-5673 *Founded/Ownrshp* 1974
Sales 21.8MM^E^ *EMP* 500
SIC 5812 5813 5331 Restaurant, family: chain; Cocktail lounge; Variety stores; Restaurant, family: chain; Cocktail lounge; Variety stores
Pr: Harold Griffith Jr
**VP:* Kyle Griffith

D-U-N-S 06-993-6862 IMP
GREAT WESTERN SALES INC
MEGA WESTERN SALES
16200 S Maple Ave, Gardena, CA 90248-2828
Tel (310) 323-7900 *Founded/Ownrshp* 1982
Sales 20.6MM^E^ *EMP* 70
SIC 5074

GREAT WESTERN SUPPLY
See GREAT NORTH AMERICAN COMPANIES INC

D-U-N-S 19-270-4500
GREAT WESTERN SUPPLY INC
2626 Industrial Dr, Ogden, UT 84401-3206
Tel (801) 621-5412 *Founded/Ownrshp* 1988
Sales 98.1MM^E^ *EMP* 96
SIC 5074 5051 5999 1711 Plumbing fittings & supplies; Pipe & tubing, steel; Plumbing & heating supplies; Plumbing contractors
Pr: Mark Jenkins
**VP:* Glen G Jenkins
Sls Mgr: Don McFarland

GREAT WHITE ENERGY SERVICES
See ARCHER PRESSURE PUMPING LLC

D-U-N-S 79-500-0038
GREAT WHITE ENERGY SERVICES LLC
14201 Caliber Dr Ste 300, Oklahoma City, OK 73134-1017
Tel (405) 285-5812 *Founded/Ownrshp* 2006
Sales NA *EMP* 490
SIC 1381

D-U-N-S 79-079-8891
GREAT WHITE PRESSURE CONTROL LLC
(*Suby of* ARCHER WELL CO) ★
4500 Se 59th St, Oklahoma City, OK 73135-3326
Tel (405) 605-2700 *Founded/Ownrshp* 2006
Sales 44.9MM^E^ *EMP* 490
SIC 7353 3533 1381 Heavy construction equipment rental; Oil & gas field machinery; Drilling oil & gas wells; Heavy construction equipment rental; Oil & gas field machinery; Drilling oil & gas wells
VP: Nelson Britton
Sfty Dirs: Charlie Rumble

GREAT WOLF KANSAS CITY
See GREAT WOLF KANSAS SPE LLC

D-U-N-S 13-284-1409
GREAT WOLF KANSAS SPE LLC
GREAT WOLF KANSAS CITY
(*Suby of* GREAT WOLF LODGE) ★
10401 Cabela Dr, Kansas City, KS 66111-1954
Tel (913) 299-7001 *Founded/Ownrshp* 2004
Sales 14.1MM^E^ *EMP* 300
SIC 7011 7999 Hotels; Tourist attractions, amusement park concessions & rides; Hotels; Tourist attractions, amusement park concessions & rides
Exec: Pat Naime
Exec: Bryan Smith
Ex Dir: Derick Bickford
Genl Mgr: Karina Addari
Sls Mgr: Craig Scholz

GREAT WOLF LDGE WSCONSIN DELLS
See CLP GW WI-DEL TENANT LP

GREAT WOLF LODGE
See GREAT BEAR LODGE OF SANDUSKY LLC

GREAT WOLF LODGE
See GREAT WOLF RESORTS HOLDINGS INC

GREAT WOLF LODGE
See MASON FAMILY RESORTS LLC

GREAT WOLF LODGE
See CLP GW SANDUSKY TENANT LP

GREAT WOLF LODGE
See CTGW LLC

D-U-N-S 01-440-6811
GREAT WOLF LODGE OF CAROLINAS LLC
(*Suby of* GREAT WOLF LODGE) ★
10175 Weddington Road Ext, Concord, NC 28027-4413
Tel (704) 549-8206 *Founded/Ownrshp* 2007
Sales 25.8MM^E^ *EMP* 500
SIC 7011 Resort hotel; Resort hotel
IT Man: Kevin Oconnor
IT Man: Omar Sidak

D-U-N-S 80-963-0259
GREAT WOLF LODGE OF GRAPEVINE LLC
(*Suby of* GREAT WOLF LODGE) ★
100 Great Wolf Dr, Grapevine, TX 76051-0962
Tel (817) 488-6510 *Founded/Ownrshp* 2005
Sales 17.9MM^E^ *EMP* 500
SIC 7011 Hotels & motels; Hotels & motels
CEO: John Emery
Ch Bd: Joseph V Vittoria
COO: Kimberly Schaefer
CFO: Jim Calder
Treas: Alexander Lombardo
Genl Mgr: Jack D Bateman

D-U-N-S 16-603-0861
GREAT WOLF RESORTS HOLDINGS INC
GREAT WOLF LODGE
525 Junction Rd Ste 6000, Madison, WI 53717-2153
Tel (608) 662-4700 *Founded/Ownrshp* 2015
Sales 444.7MM^E^ *EMP* 4,900
SIC 7011 Hotels & motels; Resort hotel; Hotels & motels; Resort hotel
Ofcr: Kimberly K Schaefer
COO: Timothy D Black
Bd of Dir: Phil Cunningham
VP: Franceen Gonzales
Exec: Thom Bennett
Exec: Christopher Hood
Creative D: Tristen Schill
Comm Dir: Susan Storey
Ex Dir: Sharon Allen
Genl Mgr: James Anderson
Genl Mgr: Angie Brown

D-U-N-S 96-928-1252
GREAT WOLF RESORTS LLC
(*Suby of* GREAT WOLF LODGE) ★
1400 Great Wolf Dr, Wisconsin Dells, WI 53965
Tel (608) 253-2222 *Founded/Ownrshp* 2006
Sales 14.9MM^E^ *EMP* 350
SIC 5812 5813 7999 7011 Eating places; Drinking places; Waterslide operation; Hotels & motels; Eating places; Drinking places; Waterslide operation; Hotels & motels
VP: Helen Wick
Genl Mgr: James Anderson
Genl Mgr: Angela Brown
Genl Mgr: Robert Lowe
Genl Mgr: Craig Wilkinson
IT Man: Michael Fischbeck
Web Prj Mg: Jacques Heiner
Sls Dir: Christine Hinson
Sls Mgr: Kristin Vomhof

D-U-N-S 83-255-9301
GREAT-WEST CAPITAL MANAGEMENT LLC
(*Suby of* GREAT WEST FINANCIAL) ★
8515 E Orchard Rd, Greenwood Village, CO 80111-5002
Tel (303) 737-3817 *Founded/Ownrshp* 1994
Sales 69.4MM *EMP* 12
Accts Deloitte & Touche Llp Denver
SIC 6282 Investment advisory service; Investment advisory service
Pr: SM Corbett
**CFO:* Mc Maiers
**Ch:* Ba Byrne
**Ofcr:* Jl Terwilliger
**Sr VP:* Cs Tocher
**VP:* L Allbritten
**VP:* Ea Hampton
**Mng Dir:* Dg McLeod
**Snr Mgr:* Tl Gdovin

D-U-N-S 13-368-8627
GREAT-WEST FINANCIAL RETIREMENT PLAN SERVICES LLC
(*Suby of* GREAT WEST FINANCIAL) ★
11500 Outlook St, Overland Park, KS 66211-1804
Tel (847) 857-3000 *Founded/Ownrshp* 2014
Sales NA *EMP* 2,900
SIC 6411 Pension & retirement plan consultants; Pension & retirement plan consultants
CEO: Robert L Reynolds
Ex Dir: Bill Burton

D-U-N-S 05-805-7022
GREAT-WEST FUNDS INC
(*Suby of* GREAT WEST FINANCIAL) ★
8515 E Orchard Rd, Greenwood Village, CO 80111-5002
Tel (303) 737-3000 *Founded/Ownrshp* 1981
Sales 30.2MM^E^ *EMP* 1^E^
SIC 6282 Manager of mutual funds, contract or fee basis
Pr: Mtg Graye
**CFO:* Mc Maiers
**Ofcr:* Jl Terwilliger
**Mng Dir:* Dg McLeod
**Counsel:* Ba Byrne

D-U-N-S 19-679-0166
GREAT-WEST LIFE & ANNUITY INSURANCE CO
GREAT WEST FINANCIAL
(*Suby of* GREAT WEST FINANCIAL) ★
8515 E Orchard Rd, Greenwood Village, CO 80111-5002
Tel (303) 737-3000 *Founded/Ownrshp* 1907
Sales 2.5MMM *EMP* 3,300
SIC 6211 6311 Investment firm, general brokerage; Life insurance; Investment firm, general brokerage; Life insurance
CEO: Robert L Reynolds
**Ch Bd:* Raymond L McFeetors
Pr: Kevin Delaney
Ofcr: David Aspinwall
Ofcr: John R Gabbert
Ex VP: S Mark Corbett
Ex VP: Robert K Shaw
Ex VP: Robert Shaw
Sr VP: Charles B Childs Jr
Sr VP: Glenn R Derback
Sr VP: Wayne T Hoffman
Sr VP: James L McCallen
Sr VP: Scot A Miller
Sr VP: Martin Rosenbaum
Sr VP: Richard G Schultz
Sr VP: Neil Waldron
VP: Christopher R Bergeon
VP: Miles R Edwards
VP: Joseph S Greene
VP: James Harmelen
VP: Steven Hickman
Board of Directors: T Timothy Ryan Jr, Michel Plessis-Belair, Jerome J Selitto, John L Bernbach, Gregory D Tretiak, Andre Desmarais, Brian E Walsh, Paul Desmarais Jr, Alain Louvel, Raymond L McFeetors, Jerry E A Nickerson, R Jeffrey Orr, Raymond Royer

D-U-N-S 04-235-7959
GREAT-WEST LIFE & ANNUITY INSURANCE CO OF NEW YORK
(*Suby of* GREAT WEST FINANCIAL) ★
50 Main St, White Plains, NY 10606-1901
Tel (914) 682-3611 *Founded/Ownrshp* 1997
Sales NA *EMP* 1
Accts Deloitte & Touche Llp Denver
SIC 6411 Insurance agents, brokers & service; Insurance agents, brokers & service
Pr: Mtg Graye
**Pr:* CP Nelson
**Ch:* Rl McFeetors
**Treas:* Jh Van Harmelen
**Ofcr:* DC Aspinwall
**Ofcr:* Ba Byrne
**Ex VP:* SM Corbett
**Ex VP:* Rk Shaw
**Sr VP:* Ch Cumming

*Sr VP: Ws Harmon
*Sr VP: Rj Laeyendecker
*Sr VP: Dg McLeod
*Sr VP: RG Schultz
*Sr VP: GE Seller

D-U-N-S 61-347-8486
GREATAMERICA FINANCIAL SERVICES CORP
625 1st St Se Ste 800, Cedar Rapids, IA 52401-2031
Tel (319) 365-8000 Founded/Ownrshp 1992
Sales NA EMP 425
Accts Kpmg Llp Des Moines Ia
SIC 6159 Machinery & equipment finance leasing; Machinery & equipment finance leasing
CEO: Tony Golobic
*Pr: Stanley Herkelman
*COO: David Pohlman
*CFO: Joe Terfler
*V Ch Bd: Douglas Olson
Sr VP: Brian Bjella
*Sr VP: Marty Klees
VP: Jim House
VP: Terry L Robertson
VP: Greg Vandewalker
VP Bus Dev: Jon Krekelberg

D-U-N-S 17-874-4632 IMP
▲ GREATBATCH INC
2595 Dallas Pkwy Ste 310, Frisco, TX 75034-8530
Tel (716) 759-5600 Founded/Ownrshp 1970
Sales 687.7MM EMP 3,690
Tkr Sym GB Exch NYS
SIC 3675 3692 3691 Electronic capacitors; Primary batteries, dry & wet; Storage batteries; Electronic capacitors; Primary batteries, dry & wet; Storage batteries
Pr: Thomas J Hook
*Ch Bd: Bill R Sanford
CFO: Michael Dinkins
Ex VP: Mauricio Arellano
Ex VP: Thomas K Hickman
Ex VP: Andrew P Holman
Sr VP: George M Cintra
Sr VP: Michelle Graham
Sr VP: Timothy G McEvoy
Exec: Frank J Forkl
Ex Dir: Sean Curry
Board of Directors: Pamela G Bailey, Joseph W Dziedzic, Jean Hobby, M Craig Maxwell, Filippo Passerini, Peter H Soderberg, William B Summers Jr

D-U-N-S 00-625-3488
■ GREATBATCH LTD (MN)
GREATBATCH-GLOBE TOOL
(Suby of GREATBATCH INC) ★
730 24th Ave Se, Minneapolis, MN 55414-2604
Tel (612) 676-7200 Founded/Ownrshp 1954, 2002
Sales 40.0MM^E EMP 215
SIC 3469 Metal stampings; Metal stampings
CEO: Thomas Hook

D-U-N-S 04-882-2659 IMP
■ GREATBATCH LTD
MICRO POWER ELECTRONICS
(Suby of ELECTROCHEM SOLUTIONS INC) ★
13955 Sw Millikan Way, Beaverton, OR 97005-2800
Tel (503) 693-7600 Founded/Ownrshp 2011
Sales 44.5MM^E EMP 300
SIC 3691 Storage batteries; Storage batteries
CEO: Mike Dubose
*CFO: Steve Stewart
CTO: Brad Crackler
CTO: Ken Wilheimi
Snr Mgr: Healther Park

D-U-N-S 05-865-0102
■ GREATBATCH LTD
GREATBATCH MEDICAL
(Suby of GREATBATCH INC) ★
10000 Wehrle Dr, Clarence, NY 14031-2086
Tel (612) 331-6750 Founded/Ownrshp 1997
Sales 126.7MM^E EMP 680
SIC 5047 3692 Orthopedic equipment & supplies; Primary batteries, dry & wet; Orthopedic equipment & supplies; Primary batteries, dry & wet
Pr: Thomas J Hook
*CFO: Michael Dinkins
*Ex VP: Mauricio Arellano
*Sr VP: George M Cintra
VP: V W Brinkerhoff III
VP: Elizabeth Cowell
VP: Thomas Mazza
VP: Robert C Rusin
VP: Peter E Samek
VP: Eshter S Takeuchi
Admn Mgr: Denise Kellerman
Board of Directors: David L Jaffe, Robert E Rich Jr, Douglas E Rogers, Henry Wendt, David Wittels

GREATBATCH MEDICAL
See GREATBATCH LTD

GREATBATCH-GLOBE TOOL
See GREATBATCH LTD

D-U-N-S 07-605-0434
■ GREATBATCH-SIERRA INC
(Suby of GREATBATCH INC) ★
2701 Conestoga Dr Ste 115, Carson City, NV 89706-0487
Tel (775) 881-3655 Founded/Ownrshp 2001
Sales 22.7MM^E EMP 122^E
SIC 3675 Electronic capacitors
Pr: Kenneth F Potashner

D-U-N-S 60-991-9936
GREATCALL INC
10935 Vista Sorrento Pkwy # 200, San Diego, CA 92130-8698
Tel (858) 720-7501 Founded/Ownrshp 2005
Sales 60.2MM^E EMP 100
SIC 5999 4812 Cellular telephone services; Mobile telephones & equipment; Cellular telephone services
Pr: David Inns
Pr: Susan Weaver
*CFO: Bill Kuncz
VP: Dean Williams
Prgrm Mgr: Jana Bayad
Off Mgr: Lia Brown
Snr Sftwr: Varsheet Sharma
Snr Sftwr: Kevin Whalley
QA Dir: Ann Summerlin
IT Man: Laurent Gousset
Sftwr Eng: Adam Hansen

D-U-N-S 03-708-0520
GREATER ALBANY PUBLIC SCHOOL DISTRICT 8 J
718 7th Ave Sw, Albany, OR 97321-2320
Tel (541) 967-4501 Founded/Ownrshp 1950
Sales 78.2MM^E EMP 1,100
SIC 8211 Public elementary & secondary schools; Public elementary school; Public junior high school; Public senior high school; Public elementary & secondary schools; Public elementary school; Public junior high school; Public senior high school
CTO: Martha Highfill
Dir IT: Richard Thomas
HC Dir: Jeannie Watts

GREATER AMSTERDAM SCHOOL DST
See ENLARGED GREATER AMSTERDAM SCH DIST

D-U-N-S 82-464-9438
■ GREATER ARIZONA AUTO AUCTIONS INC
GREATER AUTO AUCTION PHOENIX
(Suby of COX AUTOMOTIVE INC) ★
201 N 83rd Ave, Tolleson, AZ 85353-3304
Tel (623) 907-7000 Founded/Ownrshp 1996
Sales 16.7MM^E EMP 325
SIC 7389 Auction, appraisal & exchange services; Auction, appraisal & exchange services
Pr: Sanford H Schwartz
*VP: Maria Friedman
*VP: Richard J Jacobson
Genl Mgr: Eric Farmer
*Genl Mgr: Butch Slack

D-U-N-S 09-779-5611
GREATER ATLANTA BAR-B-Q LLC
SONNY'S REAL PIT BAR-B-Q
5078 Brstol Indus Way 2, Buford, GA 30518-1743
Tel (770) 368-1653 Founded/Ownrshp 1998
Sales 12.0MM EMP 400
SIC 5812 Barbecue restaurant; Barbecue restaurant
Dir Soc: Janie Sutler

D-U-N-S 07-247-3960
GREATER ATLANTA CHRISTIAN SCHOOLS INC (GA)
1575 Indian Trail Lilbrn, Norcross, GA 30093-2614
Tel (770) 243-2000 Founded/Ownrshp 1961
Sales 48.4MM EMP 350
Accts Smith & Howard Atlanta Ga
SIC 8661 8211 Religious organizations; Private elementary & secondary schools; Religious organizations; Private elementary & secondary schools
Ch: James Combee
*Pr: David Fincher
COO: Marsha Horne
*VP: Randall Jackson
Exec: Scott Harsh
MIS Dir: Dan Voelzke
IT Man: Julia Osteen
Pr Dir: Jill Morris
Psych: Lori Davis

D-U-N-S 16-871-2131
GREATER ATTLEBORO TAUNTON REGIONAL TRANSIT AUTHORITY
GATRA
10 Oak St Ste 2, Taunton, MA 02780-3950
Tel (508) 823-8828 Founded/Ownrshp 1976
Sales 27.9MM EMP 26^E
Accts Bruce D Norling Cpa Pc S
SIC 4111 Local & suburban transit; Local & suburban transit
Exec: John Wilks

GREATER AUTO AUCTION PHOENIX
See GREATER ARIZONA AUTO AUCTIONS INC

D-U-N-S 06-487-4050 IMP
GREATER BALTIMORE MEDICAL CENTER INC
(Suby of GBMC HEALTHCARE INC) ★
6701 N Charles St, Baltimore, MD 21204-6808
Tel (410) 849-2000 Founded/Ownrshp 1986
Sales 117.4MM^E EMP 357^E
Accts Deloitte Tax Llp Mclean Va
SIC 8062 8011 Hospital, medical school affiliated with residency; Offices & clinics of medical doctors
Pr: John Chessare
CFO: Eric Melchior
Ofcr: Harold Tucker
Ofcr: Deloris S Tuggle
VP: Carolyn L Candiello
VP: Genny Selby
Exec: Renee Tankersley
Dir Risk M: Susanne Martielli
Div/Sub He: George Apostolides
Dir Rx: Christopher Kruft
Ex Dir: Michael Stein

D-U-N-S 96-960-7550
GREATER BALTIMORE MEDICAL CENTER LAND CORP
6701 N Charles St, Baltimore, MD 21204-6881
Tel (443) 849-2000 Founded/Ownrshp 2011
Sales 413.5MM EMP 14
Accts Deloitte Tax Llp Mc Lean Va
SIC 8062 General medical & surgical hospitals
Pr: John Chessare
Chf Rad: Alexander Munitz
Dir Vol: Cynthia Fager
Ex VP: Helen McCollum
Dir Lab: Janis Smith
Adm Dir: Lynn Bullock
Adm Dir: Cate O'Connor-Devlin
Off Mgr: Tara Holicky
Off Mgr: Debbie Magness
Off Mgr: Kristen Stamathis
MIS Dir: David Hynson

D-U-N-S 61-331-9938
GREATER BATON ROUGE FOOD BANK INC
10600 S Choctaw Dr, Baton Rouge, LA 70815-1826
Tel (225) 359-9940 Founded/Ownrshp 1985
Sales 20.7MM EMP 15
Accts Postlethwaite & Netterville B
SIC 8699 Food co-operative; Food co-operative
Pr: Durward Casteel
*Treas: Darin Arceneaux
VP: Gail M Johnson
VP: Rashmi Venugopal
*Prin: Fran Bussie
*Prin: Patricia Faxon
*Prin: Kathleen Howell
*Prin: Allen Posey
*Ex Dir: Carl Stages

D-U-N-S 16-133-1087
GREATER BOSTON FOOD BANK INC
GBFB
70 S Bay Ave, Boston, MA 02118-2704
Tel (617) 427-5200 Founded/Ownrshp 1981
Sales 82.9MM EMP 80
Accts Cohn Reznick Llp Boston Mass
SIC 8399 Antipoverty board; Antipoverty board
Pr: Catherine D'Amato
Pr: Paul G Swindlehurst
*COO: Carol Tienken
*CFO: David S Noymer
*Treas: John J Wallace
VP: Suzanne Battit
Mktg Dir: Courtney Johanson
Mktg Mgr: Mekea Harvey

D-U-N-S 79-667-0842
■ GREATER BUFFALO AUTO AUCTION LLC
ADESA AUCTIONS BUFFALO
(Suby of ADESA AUCTIONS) ★
12200 Main Rd, Akron, NY 14001-9306
Tel (716) 542-3300 Founded/Ownrshp 1992
Sales 60.5MM^E EMP 380
SIC 5012 Automobile auction; Automobile auction
Genl Mgr: Warren Clauss
*Prin: Michael Phillips
Genl Mgr: Gregg Maidment
Mktg Mgr: Paul Diebold

GREATER BURLINGTON YMCA
See GREATER BURLINGTON YOUNG MENS CHRISTIAN ASSOCIATION INC

D-U-N-S 06-052-5276
GREATER BURLINGTON YOUNG MENS CHRISTIAN ASSOCIATION INC
GREATER BURLINGTON YMCA
266 College St, Burlington, VT 05401-8318
Tel (802) 862-9622 Founded/Ownrshp 1866
Sales 8.7MM EMP 350
Accts Wallace W Tapia Pc Burlington
SIC 8641 7991 8351 7032 8322 Youth organizations; Physical fitness facilities; Child day care services; Youth camps; Individual & family services; Youth organizations; Physical fitness facilities; Child day care services; Youth camps; Individual & family services
Pr: Mary Burns
*CFO: Luanne Cantor
*Ch: James M Mooney
*Treas: Dirk A Aube
Treas: Dirk A Ube
VP: Marsha Faryniarz
*VP: Glenn Kelsey
VP: Alexander Martin
VP: Jan Riordan
Dir Bus: Stewart Jensen
MIS Dir: Lori Trieb-Smith

D-U-N-S 18-052-4605
GREATER CHICAGO FINANCIAL CORP
5645 W Lake St, Chicago, IL 60644-1956
Tel (773) 854-2900 Founded/Ownrshp 1986
Sales NA EMP 140
SIC 6712 Bank holding companies; Bank holding companies
Pr: Sam Scott
Chf Mktg O: Angela Preston
IT Man: Cheryl Johnston

D-U-N-S 09-476-2572
GREATER CHICAGO FOOD DEPOSITORY
4100 W 42nd Pl, Chicago, IL 60632-3920
Tel (773) 247-3663 Founded/Ownrshp 1978
Sales 106.0MM EMP 95
Accts Plante & Moran Pllc Chicago
SIC 8322 Individual & family services; Individual & family services
Pr: Katherine R Maehr
Dir Vol: Mark Barnfield
*COO: Caroline Howe
CFO: Donald Tusek
*VP: Bob Dolgan
*VP: Gerry Maguire
*VP: Steven McCullough
VP: Doug Schenkelberg
VP: Jill Zimmerman
*Prin: Scott Davis
Dir IT: Muhammad Khan
Board of Directors: Scott Davis

GREATER CHICAGOLAND CLOSEOUTS
See RICHARDS BUILDING SUPPLY CO

D-U-N-S 96-200-0253 IMP
GREATER CHINA INDUSTRIES INC
14205 Se 36th St Ste 210, Bellevue, WA 98006-1574
Tel (425) 643-6576 Founded/Ownrshp 1993
Sales 25.0MM^E EMP 45
SIC 5199 8741 Advertising specialties; Management services
Pr: Ben Zhang
*CFO: Thomas Boydell
*Ex VP: Mel Cutter
*VP: Michael Parks
VP: Gary Shaffer
Exec: Aaron Jones
*Prin: Mervin Olieslager
Opers Mgr: Paul McNabb
VP Sls: Chris Ritchie
Snr Mgr: Fiona Loughrey

D-U-N-S 07-472-6472
GREATER CINCINNATI BEHAVIORAL HEALTH SERVICES
1501 Madison Rd, Walnut Hills, OH 45206-1706
Tel (513) 354-7000 Founded/Ownrshp 1971
Sales 21.9MM EMP 325
Accts Barnes Dennig & Co Ltd Cincin
SIC 8322 Social service center; Social service center
CEO: Jeff O'Neil
Prgrm Mgr: Gregg Pieples
Dir QC: Diane Wright
Info Man: Pamela Martini
VP Opers: Roger Rosenberger
Pr Mgr: Andrea Paul-Taylor
Psych: Gary Lukens

D-U-N-S 36-150-9375
GREATER CINCINNATI FOUNDATION
200 W 4th St Fl 1, Cincinnati, OH 45202-2775
Tel (513) 241-2880 Founded/Ownrshp 1963
Sales 88.7MM EMP 20
Accts Deloitte & Touche Llp
SIC 6732 Charitable trust management; Charitable trust management
Pr: Kathryn E Merchant
V Ch: David W Ellis III
*CFO: Amy Cheney
Bd of Dir: Frank Fletcher
Ofcr: Margaret Gaither
Ofcr: Julia Mace
Ofcr: Kristina Moster
Ofcr: Molly Robertshaw
Ofcr: Laura Shamp
Ofcr: Ray Watson
VP: Elizabeth Benson
VP: Beth Reiter
VP: Shiloh Turner

D-U-N-S 07-132-9338
GREATER CLARK COUNTY SCHOOLS
2112 Utica Sellersburg Rd, Jeffersonville, IN 47130-8506
Tel (812) 283-0701 Founded/Ownrshp 2005
Sales 88.9MM^E EMP 1,400
SIC 8211 8741 Public elementary & secondary schools; Secondary school; Management services; Public elementary & secondary schools; Secondary school; Management services
Bd of Dir: Robert Valentine
Ofcr: Kevin Simms
VP: Mark Pavey
Exec: Joanne Caperton
Psych: Terry Burger
Psych: Elizabeth Eckler
Psych: Jane Sonntag

D-U-N-S 07-982-7313
GREATER CLARK COUNTY SCHOOLS
2112 Utica Sellersburg Rd, Jeffersonville, IN 47130-8506
Tel (812) 283-0701 Founded/Ownrshp 2015
Sales 7.0MM^E EMP 1,257^E
SIC 8211 Public elementary & secondary schools

D-U-N-S 10-151-5708
GREATER CLEVELAND FOOD BANK INC
15500 S Waterloo Rd, Cleveland, OH 44110-3800
Tel (216) 738-2265 Founded/Ownrshp 1999
Sales 67.3MM EMP 106
Accts Ss&G Inc Cleveland Oh
SIC 8399 8322 Community development groups; Individual & family services; Community development groups; Individual & family services
Pr: Anne Goodman
COO: Jeff Jones
*CFO: Bonnie Barrett
Dir IT: Neil Haffey

D-U-N-S 07-775-9447
GREATER CLEVELAND PARTNERSHIP
CLEVELAND DEV FOUNDATION
1240 Huron Rd E Ste 300, Cleveland, OH 44115-1722
Tel (216) 621-3300 Founded/Ownrshp 1848
Sales 30.2MM EMP 110
Accts Mcgladrey Llp Cleveland Oh
SIC 8611 Chamber of Commerce
Ch Bd: William Christopher
*Pr: Joe Roman
COO: Steve Millard
Ofcr: Hazel S Boyd
*Ex VP: Vette Ittu
*Sr VP: Carol Caruso
*Sr VP: Andrew Jackson
*Sr VP: Deb Janik
Sr VP: Quentin L McCorvey Sr
Sr VP: Martin McGann
VP: Nick Gattozzi
VP: Susan Olson
VP: Nancy Pokorny
Exec: Debbie Gebelle
Dir Soc: Angela Presutti

D-U-N-S 07-113-6071
GREATER CLEVELAND REGIONAL TRANSIT AUTHORITY
R T A
1240 W 6th St, Cleveland, OH 44113-1302
Tel (216) 566-5100 Founded/Ownrshp 1975
Sales 53.7MM EMP 2,700
SIC 4111

D-U-N-S 07-501-4209
GREATER COLUMBUS CONVENTION CENTER (OH)
400 N High St Fl 4, Columbus, OH 43215-2078
Tel (614) 827-2500 Founded/Ownrshp 1974
Sales 21.1MM^E EMP 189
SIC 6512 Commercial & industrial building operation; Commercial & industrial building operation
Genl Mgr: Craig Liston
Dir Soc: Jasmine Hardy
Dir Soc: Anne Schmitz
Sls Mgr: Lisa Harrison
Sls Mgr: Kaitlin Hayhurst
Sls Mgr: Kathy Lutz
Sls Mgr: Kristy Yonyon

D-U-N-S 19-504-5018
GREATER DAYTON CONSTRUCTION LTD
OBERER THOMPSON CO
4197 Research Blvd, Beavercreek, OH 45430-2203
Tel (937) 458-6501 *Founded/Ownrshp* 1988
Sales 36.1MM *EMP* 74
Accts Goldshot Lamb & Hobbs Inc
SIC 1542 1521 1522 Commercial & office building contractors; Specialized public building contractors; New construction, single-family houses; Residential construction; Apartment building construction; Multi-family dwellings, new construction; Remodeling, multi-family dwellings; Commercial & office building contractors; Specialized public building contractors; New construction, single-family houses; Residential construction; Apartment building construction; Multi-family dwellings, new construction; Remodeling, multi-family dwellings
Pt: Greg Thompson
**Pt:* Robin Collier
**Pt:* Kevin Hess
**Pt:* Gene Tartell
VP: Tom Mahan
Snr Mgr: Matt Prenatt

D-U-N-S 05-911-3589
GREATER DAYTON REGIONAL TRANSIT AUTHORITY
R T A
4 S Main St Ste C, Dayton, OH 45402-2052
Tel (937) 425-8310 *Founded/Ownrshp* 1971
Sales 9.3MM *EMP* 614
Accts Charles E Harris & Associates
SIC 4111 Bus line operations; Bus line operations
CEO: Mark Donaghy
**CFO:* Mary K Stanforth
IT Man: Robert Ruzinsky
IT Man: Sue Szymczak
Mktg Mgr: Sabrina Pritchett
Snr Mgr: Bill Ingram
Snr Mgr: John Thomas

D-U-N-S 15-821-9571
GREATER DAYTON RTA
4 S Main St, Dayton, OH 45402-2055
Tel (937) 425-8400 *Founded/Ownrshp* 2004
Sales 36.2MM^E^ *EMP* 680
Accts Charles E Harris & Associates
SIC 4131 Intercity & rural bus transportation; Intercity & rural bus transportation
CFO: Mary Stanforth
Dir: James Foster
Ex Dir: Mark Donaghy
Info Man: Hank Trimble
Mktg Dir: Anthony Whitmore

D-U-N-S 08-880-0701
GREATER DELAWARE VALLEY SOCIETY OF TRANSPLANT SURGEONS
GIFT OF LIFE DONOR PROGRAM
401 N 3rd St, Philadelphia, PA 19123-4106
Tel (215) 599-2025 *Founded/Ownrshp* 1972
Sales 60.0MM *EMP* 105
Accts Parentebeard Llc Philadelphia
SIC 8099 Medical services organization; Medical services organization
Pr: Howard M Nathan
**VP:* Richard Hasz
**VP:* Jan Weinstock
QA Dir: Kimberly Kauffman

D-U-N-S 60-663-8435
GREATER DICKSON GAS AUTHORITY
605 E Walnut St, Dickson, TN 37055-2505
Tel (615) 441-2830 *Founded/Ownrshp* 1989
Sales 26.6MM *EMP* 66
Accts Frazier & Deeter Llc Nashvil
SIC 4924 5984 Natural gas distribution; Propane gas, bottled; Natural gas distribution; Propane gas, bottled
Genl Mgr: Robert Durham
**Ch Bd:* Donald Richardson
V Ch: Robert N Milam Sr
**Sec:* John Duke
Bd of Dir: Don Weiss Jr

D-U-N-S 00-481-6559
GREATER EGG HARBOR REGIONAL HIGH SCHOOL DISTRICT (NJ)
1824 Dr Dennis Foreman Dr, Mays Landing, NJ 08330-2206
Tel (609) 625-1399 *Founded/Ownrshp* 1957
Sales 70.1MM *EMP* 400
Accts Ford Scott & Associates Ll
SIC 8211 Public senior high school; Public senior high school
Prin: John Keenan Supt

GREATER EL MONTE CMNTY HOSP
See AHM GEMCH INC

GREATER EL PASO'S CREDIT UNION
See GECU

D-U-N-S 01-044-4453
GREATER ERIE COMMUNITY ACTION COMMITTEE
G E C A C
18 W 9th St, Erie, PA 16501-1343
Tel (814) 459-4581 *Founded/Ownrshp* 1965
Sales 25.9MM *EMP* 478
Accts Root Spitznas & Smiley Inc
SIC 8322 Multi-service center; Multi-service center
CEO: Ronald A Steele
**CFO:* Dianne M Presogna
Sr VP: Abram Howzw
**VP:* Linda Madara
VP: Gertrude Simmons
Dir: Edward Sitter
Div Mgr: G Burrell
VP Opers: Georgia Freo
Pgrm Dir: Sandra Hansbrew

D-U-N-S 06-875-0108
GREATER ERIE Y M C A
DOWNTOWN Y M C A
31 W 10th St, Erie, PA 16501-1401
Tel (814) 452-3261 *Founded/Ownrshp* 1860
Sales 8.2MM^E^ *EMP* 450
SIC 8641 7991 8351 7032 8322 Youth organizations; Physical fitness facilities; Child day care services; Youth camps; Individual & family services; Youth organizations; Physical fitness facilities; Child day care services; Youth camps; Individual & family services
Ch Bd: Everette Walker
**Pr:* Gerry Van Demerwe
Ex Dir: Christine Fracassi

GREATER GOOD NETWORK
See CHARITY USA.COM LLC

D-U-N-S 07-479-4546
GREATER GREEN BAY YMCA
235 N Jefferson St, Green Bay, WI 54301-5126
Tel (920) 435-1541 *Founded/Ownrshp* 1925
Sales 11.8MM *EMP* 625
Accts Schenck Sc Green Bay Wi
SIC 8641 8351 8322 7997 7032 Youth organizations; Child day care services; Individual & family services; Membership sports & recreation clubs; Sporting & recreational camps; Youth organizations; Child day care services; Individual & family services; Membership sports & recreation clubs; Sporting & recreational camps
Pr: Steve Harty
Sr Cor Off: Glenn Whipp
Ex Dir: Korst Dave
Dir IT: Tenhaken Mark
MIS Mgr: Mark Ten Haken
Sls&Mrk Ex: Sherri Valitchka
Pgrm Dir: Reineking Amy

D-U-N-S 07-885-6507
GREATER HARLEM NURSING HOME AND REHABILITATION CENTER FOUNDATION (NY)
30 W 138th St, New York, NY 10037-1710
Tel (212) 690-7400 *Founded/Ownrshp* 1976
Sales 23.4MM *EMP* 205
Accts Loeb & Troper Llp New York N
SIC 8051 Skilled nursing care facilities; Skilled nursing care facilities
CEO: Thomas Foristall
**Pr:* Rodney Alexander
**CFO:* Steven Cohen
**CFO:* Joseph Giacomo
**Treas:* Jaime Lawson

D-U-N-S 07-731-3286
GREATER HARTFORD ASSOCIATION FOR RETARDED CITIZENS INC
900 Asylum Ave, Hartford, CT 06105-1901
Tel (860) 278-4272 *Founded/Ownrshp* 1951
Sales 15.7MM *EMP* 300
Accts Anquillare Roucco Traester A
SIC 8322 Association for the handicapped; Association for the handicapped
Pr: Stephen Becker
**Ch Bd:* Linda Nawrot
**CFO:* Robert Bowsza
**Ch:* Seth Fierston
**Sec:* Ceil McAculloch

D-U-N-S 96-457-8020
GREATER HORIZONS
1055 Broadway Blvd # 130, Kansas City, MO 64105-1595
Tel (816) 842-0944 *Founded/Ownrshp* 2010
Sales 199.0MM *EMP* 28^E^
Accts Bkd Llp Kansas City Mo
SIC 8399 Social services
CEO: Laura McKnight

D-U-N-S 19-153-6135
GREATER HOUSTON ANESTHESIOLOGY PA
2411 Fountain View Dr, Houston, TX 77057-4817
Tel (713) 620-4000 *Founded/Ownrshp* 1996
Sales 71.3MM^E^ *EMP* 260
SIC 8011 Anesthesiologist; Anesthesiologist
Pr: Steve Boozalis
CEO: Ronald Booker
**Treas:* Malcolm Donnell MD
**VP:* Jackie Ralston MD
Pathlgst: Dorothy Willis
Ansthlgy: Fariha Ahsan
Ansthlgy: Maria Alvarado
Ansthlgy: Madalina Andrei
Ansthlgy: Laura Aquino
Ansthlgy: Matthew S Arceneaux
Ansthlgy: Edward Ashmore

GREATER HOUSTON CNSTR SVCS
See GREATER HOUSTON POOL MANAGEMENT INC

D-U-N-S 96-639-6574
GREATER HOUSTON COMMUNITY FOUNDATION
5120 Woodway Dr Ste 6000, Houston, TX 77056-1791
Tel (713) 333-2200 *Founded/Ownrshp* 1971
Sales 125.0MM *EMP* 9
Accts Harper & Pearson Houston Tx
SIC 8733 Noncommercial research organizations
Pr: Stephen Maislin
**VP:* Emelda J Douglas
**VP:* Robert W Paddock
Ex Dir: Carol Shattuck

D-U-N-S 80-446-9158
GREATER HOUSTON POOL MANAGEMENT INC
GREATER HOUSTON CNSTR SVCS
12227 Old Huffmeister Rd, Cypress, TX 77429-3219
Tel (713) 771-7665 *Founded/Ownrshp* 1999
Sales 27.4MM^E^ *EMP* 300
SIC 1799 Swimming pool construction; Swimming pool construction
Pr: Eric Belyea
**VP:* Michelle Belyea
VP: Paul Clapper
VP: Judi Larkin
**Prin:* Daniel McInnis
Genl Mgr: Brian Zielinski

GREATER HOUSTON TAXI CO
See YELLOW CAB SERVICE CORP

D-U-N-S 17-514-0201
GREATER HUDSON VALLEY FAMILY HEALTH CENTER INC
GHVFHC
2570 Us Highway 9w, Cornwall, NY 12518-1323
Tel (845) 563-8000 *Founded/Ownrshp* 1981
Sales 25.7MM *EMP* 125
Accts Cohnreznickllp New York New
SIC 8011 8059 General & family practice, physician/surgeon; Personal care home, with health care; General & family practice, physician/surgeon; Personal care home, with health care
CEO: Linda S Muller
**CFO:* Patrick R Murphy
Snr Mgr: AVI Silber

D-U-N-S 02-737-2395
GREATER ILLINOIS TITLE CO INC
120 N La Salle St Ste 900, Chicago, IL 60602-2782
Tel (312) 236-7300 *Founded/Ownrshp* 1985
Sales NA *EMP* 60
SIC 6361 8111 Title insurance; Legal services
Pr: Gregory Kosin
IT Man: Bill Shanahan
Manager: Beth Hohman
Manager: Sara Hulsebus

D-U-N-S 07-499-0243
GREATER JOHNSTOWN SCHOOL DISTRICT
1091 Broad St, Johnstown, PA 15906-2437
Tel (814) 533-5650 *Founded/Ownrshp* 1900
Sales 42.1MM^E^ *EMP* 847
SIC 8211 Public elementary & secondary schools; Elementary school; High school, junior or senior; Public elementary & secondary schools; Elementary school; High school, junior or senior
**Pr:* Richard Unger
**Treas:* Thomas Kalinyak
Ofcr: Chad Miller
**VP:* John Berzinsky
Prin: Darren Buchko
Sfty Dirs: Michael Dadey
HC Dir: Lisa Miller

D-U-N-S 10-005-5839
GREATER JOHNSTOWN SCHOOL DISTRICT
GREATER JOHNSTOWN SCHOOL DST
1 Sir Bills Cir Ste 101, Johnstown, NY 12095-2035
Tel (518) 762-4611 *Founded/Ownrshp* 1869
Sales 25.8MM^E^ *EMP* 605
Accts Marvin & Co Schenectady Ny
SIC 8211 Public elementary school; Public junior high school; Public senior high school; School board; Public elementary school; Public junior high school; Public senior high school; School board
**Treas:* Alice Dillenbeck
**Prin:* Peter Brabant
**Prin:* Richard Santelli

GREATER JOHNSTOWN SCHOOL DST
See GREATER JOHNSTOWN SCHOOL DISTRICT

GREATER KALAMAZOO AUTO AUCTION
See SCHOOLCRAFT AUTO AUCTION INC

GREATER KANS CY CMNTY FNDATION
See COMMUNITY FOUNDATION OF WYANDOTTE COUNTY

D-U-N-S 78-271-1550
GREATER KANSAS CITY COMMUNITY FOUNDATION AND AFFILIATED TRUSTS
1055 Broadway Blvd # 130, Kansas City, MO 64105-1575
Tel (816) 842-0944 *Founded/Ownrshp* 1978
Sales 127.9MM *EMP* 46^E^
Accts Bkd Llp Kansas City Mo
SIC 6732 7941 Charitable trust management; Baseball club, professional & semi-professional; Charitable trust management; Baseball club, professional & semi-professional
CEO: Laura McKnight
V Ch: Pam Gradinger
Treas: Robert A Pearson
Bd of Dir: Carl L Chinnery
Bd of Dir: Gregory M Glore
Bd of Dir: Wallace S Hartfield
Bd of Dir: Jennifer Krizek
Bd of Dir: Linda Lenza
Bd of Dir: Lynn Mitchelson
Bd of Dir: Leisa Reid
Bd of Dir: Robin Sterneck
VP: George Bittner
VP: Jean-Paul Chaurand
VP: Brenda Chumley
VP: Randy James
VP: Roxanne Jurde
VP: Deborah L Wilkerson

D-U-N-S 07-598-4344
GREATER LAFAYETTE HEALTH SERVICES
ST ELIZABETH REGIONAL HEALTH
1501 Hartford St, Lafayette, IN 47904-2134
Tel (765) 423-6011 *Founded/Ownrshp* 1895
Sales 66.9MM^E^ *EMP* 2,200
SIC 8062 General medical & surgical hospitals; General medical & surgical hospitals
Pr: Terry Wilson
**VP:* Keith Lauter
Surgeon: Cathy Newman
Ansthlgy: William Tilt

D-U-N-S 08-253-5274
GREATER LAFAYETTE HEALTH SERVICES INC
SAINT JAMES HOSPITAL
(*Suby of* FRANCISCAN ALLIANCE INC) ★
1501 Hartford St, Lafayette, IN 47904-2134
Tel (765) 423-6011 *Founded/Ownrshp* 1999
Sales 156.6MM^E^ *EMP* 2,660
SIC 8062 General medical & surgical hospitals; General medical & surgical hospitals
CEO: Terry Wilson
**CFO:* Keith Lauter
Dir Rx: Jim Rawlings
Telecom Ex: Gina Spinelli

D-U-N-S 06-876-0099
GREATER LATROBE SCHOOL AUTHORITY
GREATER LATROBE SCHOOL DST
1816 Lincoln Ave, Latrobe, PA 15650-3038
Tel (724) 539-4200 *Founded/Ownrshp* 1962
Sales 29.0MM^E^ *EMP* 400
Accts Horner Wible & Terek Pc Gre
SIC 8211 Public elementary school; Public junior high school; Public senior high school; Public elementary school; Public junior high school; Public senior high school
Pr: Susan J Mains
Bd of Dir: Eric Hauser
Bd of Dir: Heidi Kozar
**VP:* Kathryn M Elder
Dir IT: Scott Marker
Psych: Jennifer Hartman
HC Dir: Lucinda Soltys

GREATER LATROBE SCHOOL DST
See GREATER LATROBE SCHOOL AUTHORITY

D-U-N-S 08-464-7817
GREATER LAWRENCE COMMUNITY ACTION COUNCIL INC
G L C A C
305 Essex St Fl 1, Lawrence, MA 01840-1445
Tel (978) 681-4900 *Founded/Ownrshp* 1965
Sales 29.0MM *EMP* 300^E^
SIC 8322 Social service center; Social service center
Pr: Thomas S Perrault Sr
**Pr:* Jesse Ramirez
COO: Rosa Talero
**CFO:* Richard Robichaud
**Treas:* Natalie Coon
**VP:* Cheryl Ann Matthews
Exec: Barry Finegold
Ex Dir: Isabel Melendez
Off Mgr: Pura Lopez
Pgrm Dir: Marie Finelli
Pgrm Dir: Kelly Fitzpatrick

D-U-N-S 11-493-7477
GREATER LAWRENCE FAMILY HEALTH CENTER INC
34 Haverhill St, Lawrence, MA 01841-2884
Tel (978) 686-0090 *Founded/Ownrshp* 1980
Sales 42.9MM^E^ *EMP* 450
Accts Alexander Aronson Finning & Co
SIC 8011 Medical centers; Medical centers
Pr: Robert Ingala
Pr: Robert Beals
**COO:* Saifur Rahman
CFO: Bob Urquhart
**CFO:* Robert Urquhart
**Sr VP:* Ann Marie Borgesi
**Sr VP:* Dean Cleghorn
**Sr VP:* Joseph Gravel
**Sr VP:* Patrick Grotton
**Sr VP:* Richard Napolitano Jr
**Sr VP:* Donna Rivera
Exec: Ann Borgesi
Exec: Evan Teplow

D-U-N-S 07-658-2576
GREATER LAWRENCE REGIONAL VOCATIONAL TECHNICAL HIGH SCHOOL
57 River Rd, Andover, MA 01810-1144
Tel (978) 686-0194 *Founded/Ownrshp* 2006
Sales 26.3MM^E^ *EMP* 251
SIC 8211 Vocational high school; Vocational high school
Ofcr: Sean O'Day
Prin: Marine Duca- Gilpert
Dir IT: William Jakubec
Tech Mgr: Ann Marie Fiore

D-U-N-S 96-905-0884
GREATER LAWRENCE REGIONAL VOCATIONAL TECHNICAL SCHOOL DISTRICT
57 River Rd, Andover, MA 01810-1144
Tel (978) 686-0194 *Founded/Ownrshp* 1965
Sales 7.3MM^E^ *EMP* 300
Accts Melanson Heath & Company Pc
SIC 8211 Public elementary & secondary schools; Public elementary & secondary schools
Teacher Pr: Annmarie T Mahan

D-U-N-S 94-747-9630
GREATER LOUISIANA STAFFING INC
SPHERION STAFFING
102 Amaryllis Dr, Lafayette, LA 70503-3215
Tel (337) 442-6203 *Founded/Ownrshp* 1981
Sales 9.8MM *EMP* 500
Accts Kolder Champagne Slaven & Co
SIC 7361 Employment agencies; Employment agencies
CEO: Thomas Zaunbrecher
Sales Exec: Bob Moore

D-U-N-S 07-380-7653
GREATER LOWELL TECHNICAL HIGH SCHOOL
250 Pawtucket Blvd, Tyngsboro, MA 01879-2214
Tel (978) 441-0990 *Founded/Ownrshp* 1976
Sales 27.4MM^E^ *EMP* 300
SIC 8249 8331 8211 Vocational schools; Job training & vocational rehabilitation services; Elementary & secondary schools; Vocational schools; Job training & vocational rehabilitation services; Elementary & secondary schools
Ofcr: John Callahan
Dir Sec: Ron Arsenault
IT Man: Steve Murphy
Pr Dir: Michael McGovern
Teacher Pr: Kathy Tierney

D-U-N-S 09-918-5985
GREATER LYNN SENIOR SERVICES INC
LYNN COUNCIL ON AGING
8 Silsbee St, Lynn, MA 01901-1404
Tel (781) 592-7540 *Founded/Ownrshp* 1975

Sales 55.9MM *EMP* 450ᴱ
Accts Anstiss & Co Pc Lowell Ma
SIC 8322 Homemakers' service; Outreach program; General counseling services; Adult day care center; Homemakers' service; Outreach program; General counseling services; Adult day care center
CEO: Paul Crowly
**CFO:* Kenneth Halkin
Ex Dir: Paul Crowley
Off Mgr: Betsy Miller
Dir IT: Mark Speziale
Opers Supe: Richard Deveau
Pgrm Dir: Keith Jones
Board of Directors: Richard Bane, Nelson Chang

GREATER MAMI JEWISH FEDERATION
See GREATER MIAMI JEWISH FEDERATION INC

GREATER MANCH MENTAL HEALTH
See MENTAL HEALTH CENTER OF GREATER MANCHESTER INC

D-U-N-S 05-130-8195
GREATER MEDIA INC
35 Braintree Hill Park # 300, Braintree, MA 02184-8762
Tel (781) 348-8600 *Founded/Ownrshp* 1956
Sales 123.6MMᴱ *EMP* 864
SIC 2711 8999 4832

D-U-N-S 00-244-8280
GREATER MEDIA NEWSPAPERS (NJ)
(*Suby of* GREATER MEDIA INC) ★
3499 Route 9 N Ste 1b, Freehold, NJ 07728-3281
Tel (732) 358-5200 *Founded/Ownrshp* 1888
Sales 36.1MMᴱ *EMP* 800
SIC 2711 Newspapers: publishing only, not printed on site; Newspapers: publishing only, not printed on site
Pr: Peter Smyth
**Prin:* John Zielinski
Div Mgr: Gregory Bean
Dir IT: Jeff Messeroll
Dir IT: Troy Tomaselli
Advt Dir: Kate Rochelle

D-U-N-S 78-183-2829
GREATER METROPLEX INTERIORS INC
G M I
2020 E Continental Blvd, Southlake, TX 76092-9768
Tel (817) 481-0029 *Founded/Ownrshp* 1990
Sales 48.5MMᴱ *EMP* 112
SIC 1542 Commercial & office building contractors; Commercial & office building contractors
Pr: G Mikal Mike Darden
**COO:* Douglas Nies
**CFO:* Kirk Challgren
**VP:* T Mikal Darden
Genl Mgr: Mikal Darden
Sfty Dirs: Barry Corey
Opers Mgr: John Wicker

D-U-N-S 83-711-6706
GREATER METROPOLITAN HOUSING CORP
15 S 5th St Ste 710, Minneapolis, MN 55402-1058
Tel (612) 339-0601 *Founded/Ownrshp* 1970
Sales 22.3MM *EMP* 27
Accts Olsen Thielen & Co Ltd St
SIC 6552 Subdividers & developers; Subdividers & developers
Pr: Carolyn Olson
VP: Corey Haaland
Prgrm Mgr: Jennifer Camacho
Prgrm Mgr: Denise Eloundou
Opers Mgr: Lynda Duncan

D-U-N-S 13-150-0365
GREATER MIAMI CONVENTION AND VISITORS BUREAU FOUNDATION INC
701 Brickell Ave Ste 2700, Miami, FL 33131-2851
Tel (305) 539-3000 *Founded/Ownrshp* 1985
Sales 28.7MM *EMP* 68
Accts Mcgladrey Llp West Palm Beach
SIC 7389 Convention & show services; Promoters of shows & exhibitions; Tourist information bureau; Convention & show services; Promoters of shows & exhibitions; Tourist information bureau
Pr: William D Talbert
Pr: Melina Martinez
**Ch:* Steven Hash
Assoc VP: Josie Llado
Assoc VP: Gisela Marti
Assoc VP: Barry Moskowitz
Sr VP: Ita Moriarty
Sr VP: Alvin West
VP: Rolando Aedo
VP: Robert Polk
VP: Jeanne Sullivan
**VP:* Joe Yarzabal

D-U-N-S 07-387-0271
GREATER MIAMI JEWISH FEDERATION INC
GREATER MAMI JEWISH FEDERATION
4200 Bisca Blvd Stanl C M Stanley C Myers, Miami, FL 33137
Tel (305) 576-4000 *Founded/Ownrshp* 1938
Sales 224.4MMᴱ *EMP* 92ᴱ
SIC 8661 Religious organizations; Religious organizations
Pr: Jacob Solomon
CFO: Stephen M Schwartz
Sr Inv Off: Alon Ozer
**VP:* John Bussel

D-U-N-S 14-981-8838
GREATER MILWAUKEE AUTO AUCTION LLC
BDA SALES
8711 W Brown Deer Rd, Milwaukee, WI 53224-2116
Tel (414) 362-1049 *Founded/Ownrshp* 2004
Sales 20.4MMᴱ *EMP* 90
SIC 5012 Automobile auction; Automobile auction
Pr: Kristie Griffin
Genl Mgr: Dan Pieroni
Opers Mgr: Jaime Ross

D-U-N-S 78-248-1550
GREATER MILWAUKEE FOUNDATION
101 W Pleasant St Ste 210, Milwaukee, WI 53212-3963
Tel (414) 272-5805 *Founded/Ownrshp* 1915
Sales 87.3MM *EMP* 35
Accts Kpmg Llp
SIC 8699 8733 Charitable organization; Noncommercial research organizations
Pr: Douglas M Jansson
VP: Rob Guilbert
VP: Timothy Larson
Comm Dir: Laura Mullen

D-U-N-S 02-442-1654
GREATER MOBILE URGENT CARE PC
7943 Moffett Rd, Semmes, AL 36575-5409
Tel (251) 633-0123 *Founded/Ownrshp* 2008
Sales 32.1MMᴱ *EMP* 57ᴱ
SIC 5065 Mobile telephone equipment
Prin: Darren Waters

D-U-N-S 02-591-8717
GREATER MOBILE WASHINGTON CNTY
BAYPOINTE BEHAVIORAL HEALTH
5800 Southland Dr, Mobile, AL 36693-3313
Tel (251) 660-1439 *Founded/Ownrshp* 2010
Sales 33.9MM *EMP* 5
SIC 8099 Health & allied services; Health & allied services
Prin: Stephanie H Bassenger
Brnch Mgr: Connie Pugh

D-U-N-S 06-051-6374
GREATER NANTICOKE AREA SCHOOL DISTRICT (INC)
427 Kosciuszko St, Nanticoke, PA 18634-2623
Tel (570) 735-7783 *Founded/Ownrshp* 1967
Sales 15.9MMᴱ *EMP* 336
SIC 8211 Public senior high school; Public junior high school; Public elementary school; Public senior high school; Public junior high school; Public elementary school
VP: M Bernatovich
VP: R Czarnecki
VP: K Levandowski
Prin: J Ruchinski
IT Man: Angelo Cipriani

D-U-N-S 16-449-6127
GREATER NEW ORLEANS FOUNDATION
1055 Saint Charles Ave # 100, New Orleans, LA 70130-3941
Tel (504) 598-4663 *Founded/Ownrshp* 2009
Sales 36.6MM *EMP* 21
Accts Laporte Sehrt Romig & Hand Me
SIC 8699 Charitable organization; Charitable organization
Pr: Albert Ruesta
VP: Alice Parkerson
Prin: Susan Vaugn

D-U-N-S 00-253-4998
GREATER NEW YORK COUNCILS BOY SCOUTS OF AMERICA (NY)
350th Ave Ste 7820, New York, NY 10118
Tel (212) 651-2432 *Founded/Ownrshp* 1927
Sales 17.0MM *EMP* 400
Accts Condon O Meara Mcginty & Donne
SIC 8641 Boy Scout organization; Boy Scout organization
CEO: Ethan V Draddy
**Pr:* Raymond Quartararo
CFO: Robert Madsen

D-U-N-S 01-500-3589
GREATER NEW YORK HOME CARE
535 Kent Ave Apt 1d, Brooklyn, NY 11249-6639
Tel (718) 388-4100 *Founded/Ownrshp* 2008
Sales 7.7MMᴱ *EMP* 500
SIC 8059 Personal care home, with health care; Personal care home, with health care
Prin: Shlomie Weiss

D-U-N-S 07-860-4832
GREATER NEW YORK HOSPITAL ASSOCIATION SERVICES INC
GNYHA
555 W 57th St Fl 15, New York, NY 10019-2925
Tel (212) 246-7100 *Founded/Ownrshp* 1904
Sales 37.9MM *EMP* 150
Accts Kpmg Llp New York Ny
SIC 8621 7389 Health association; Purchasing service; Health association; Purchasing service
Pr: Kenneth E Raske
Pr: Kristin Stephens
CFO: Elizabeth Barrett
**CFO:* Lee H Perlman
Ofcr: Lisa Krieger
Assoc VP: D V Fitts Jr
Ex VP: David Rich
Sr VP: Dave Mancione
Sr VP: Susan C Waltman
VP: Michelle Byalick
VP: Jonathan Cooper
**VP:* David Rosenfeld

D-U-N-S 00-698-4793
GREATER NEW YORK MUTUAL INSURANCE CO
GNY INSURANCE COMPANIES
200 Madison Ave Frnt 2, New York, NY 10016-3903
Tel (212) 683-9700 *Founded/Ownrshp* 1927
Sales NA *EMP* 350
SIC 6411 Property & casualty insurance agent; Property & casualty insurance agent
Ch Bd: Warren W Heck
**Pr:* Elizebeth Heck
Pr: Lillian Lent
Pr: Joan Simon
Bd of Dir: Richard Mauro
Sr VP: John Reda
Sr VP: Jeff Turrisi
VP: Steve Cangelosi
VP: Geraldine Gould
VP: Elliot Marcus
VP: John Racyzk
VP: Jeff Turisi

D-U-N-S 00-726-9871
GREATER OMAHA PACKING CO INC
TREX
3001 L St, Omaha, NE 68107-1409
Tel (402) 731-1700 *Founded/Ownrshp* 1952
Sales 2.0MM *EMP* 690
SIC 2011 5147 Meat by-products from meat slaughtered on site; Meats & meat products; Meat by-products from meat slaughtered on site; Meats & meat products
Pr: Henry A Davis
**Ex VP:* Angelo Fili
**VP:* David L Davis
**VP:* Dan Jensen
VP: Dean Johnson
**VP:* Roy Wiggs
Genl Mgr: Frank Albright
Dir IT: Lavonne Misner
IT Man: Tom Kelley
Sfty Mgr: Ross Ashbacher
Sfty Mgr: Jeff Lucas

D-U-N-S 94-305-8230
GREATER OREGON BEHAVIORAL HEALTH INC
309 E 2nd St, The Dalles, OR 97058-2107
Tel (541) 298-2101 *Founded/Ownrshp* 1994
Sales NA *EMP* 7
Accts Nichols & Mitchell Cpas Pc Ba
SIC 6324 Health maintenance organization (HMO), insurance only; Health maintenance organization (HMO), insurance only
CEO: Kevin Campbell

D-U-N-S 00-132-3344
GREATER ORLANDO AVIATION AUTHORITY
ORLANDO INTERNATIONAL AIRPORT
1 Jeff Fuqua Blvd, Orlando, FL 32827-4392
Tel (407) 825-2001 *Founded/Ownrshp* 1957
Sales 399.2MM *EMP* 650ᴱ
Accts Moore Stephens Lovelace Pa O
SIC 4581 Airports, flying fields & services; Airports, flying fields & services
Ch: Frank Kruppenbacher
V Ch: Stan Anderson
Treas: Domingo Sanchez
Bd of Dir: Jason Pirozzolo
Dir Risk M: Maury Remmers
Ex Dir: Phillip N Brown
Genl Mgr: Pam L'Heureux
Genl Mgr: Brad Middlebrook
Dir IT: John Newsome
Secur Mgr: Ken Harwood
Snr PM: Anne Arnold

D-U-N-S 96-452-1616
GREATER PENNSYLVANIA CARPENTERS MEDICAL PLAN
650 Ridge Rd Ste 300, Pittsburgh, PA 15205-9503
Tel (412) 922-5330 *Founded/Ownrshp* 2010
Sales 73.5MM *EMP* 3
Accts Henry Rossi & Co Monroeville
SIC 8631 Trade union; Trade union
Exec: James Klein

D-U-N-S 06-572-6523
GREATER PHILADELPHIA HEALTH ACTION INC (PA)
WILSON PARK MEDICAL
432 N 6th St, Philadelphia, PA 19123-4004
Tel (215) 238-9025 *Founded/Ownrshp* 1970
Sales 36.8MM *EMP* 350
Accts Brown & Company Cpas Pllc Upp
SIC 8093 Specialty outpatient clinics; Drug clinic, outpatient; Alcohol clinic, outpatient; Specialty outpatient clinics; Drug clinic, outpatient; Alcohol clinic, outpatient
CEO: Ronald E Heiglerr
**Ch Bd:* Royal E Brown
**CEO:* Ronald E Heigler
Ofcr: Barbara Veitch
Off Mgr: Dennis Carter
Off Mgr: Christina Christian
CIO: Eric Rios
MIS Dir: Josephine Mojica
Mktg Dir: Maggie Lyons
Psych: Hind Eljaali
Psych: Kristin Gratz

D-U-N-S 03-029-1801
GREATER PHILADELPHIA RADIO INC (DE)
GREATER PHILADELPHIA RDO GROUP
(*Suby of* GREATER MEDIA INC) ★
1 Bala Plz Ste 339, Bala Cynwyd, PA 19004-1424
Tel (610) 667-8500 *Founded/Ownrshp* 1973, 1995
Sales 21.8MMᴱ *EMP* 100ᴱ
SIC 4832 Radio broadcasting stations
Ch Bd: John Bordes
**COO:* Thomas J Millewski
**Treas:* John W Zielinski
Exec: Cynthia Lucas
CIO: Joseph Harris
Dir IT: Patrick Couch
Dir IT: Sofia Sosangelis
IT Man: Michelle Carroll
IT Man: Roy Perry
IT Man: Keith Weinberg
Sales Exec: Tina Costello
Board of Directors: Peter Smice

GREATER PHILADELPHIA RDO GROUP
See GREATER PHILADELPHIA RADIO INC

D-U-N-S 11-913-6885
GREATER PITTSBURGH COMMUNITY FOOD BANK
1 N Linden St, Duquesne, PA 15110-1097
Tel (412) 460-3663 *Founded/Ownrshp* 1982
Sales 43.9MM *EMP* 101
Accts Schneider Downs Pittsburgh P
SIC 8399 0139 Antipoverty board; Food crops; Antipoverty board; Food crops
CEO: Lisa Scales
Recvr: Sam Pozzuto
**Ch Bd:* Amy Lewis
**Ch Bd:* Melvin Steals
**COO:* Laura Randolph
**CFO:* Donald Lutovsky
**Treas:* Henry Gorman
**Treas:* Greg Lintner
**V Ch Bd:* George McGrady
**Chf Cred:* Ron Cichowicz
Bd of Dir: Anthony Brady
Bd of Dir: Deb Crosby
Bd of Dir: Debra Doerr
Bd of Dir: Kevin Holden
Bd of Dir: George Matta
Bd of Dir: William McCloy
VP: Mark Gray

D-U-N-S 07-469-3631
GREATER PITTSBURGH FOOD BROKERAGE CO INC
911 Washington Ave, Carnegie, PA 15106-3215
Tel (412) 429-8833 *Founded/Ownrshp* 1982
Sales 30.0MM *EMP* 30
SIC 5141 Food brokers; Food brokers
Pr: Randy Buczynski

GREATER PORTLAND YMCA
See CUMBERLAND COUNTY YMCA

D-U-N-S 07-572-4245
GREATER PROVIDENCE YOUNG MENS CHRISTIAN ASSOCIATION
YMCA
371 Pine St, Providence, RI 02903-4515
Tel (401) 521-9622 *Founded/Ownrshp* 1853
Sales 23.2MM *EMP* 1,250
SIC 8641 7991 8351 7032 8322 Youth organizations; Physical fitness facilities; Child day care services; Youth camps; Individual & family services; Youth organizations; Physical fitness facilities; Child day care services; Youth camps; Individual & family services
Pr: Karen Leslie
Pr: Carl Brown
CFO: Cheryl Bongivengo
Bd of Dir: Phil Gaeber
**VP:* Michael Fournier
VP: Jill Nosach
Ex Dir: Joe Martino
Dir Opers: Regina Raffa
Pgrm Dir: Joelle Beyer
Pgrm Dir: Luca Borgo

D-U-N-S 96-264-8643
GREATER PROVIDENCE YOUNG MENS CHRISTIAN ASSOCIATION
YMCA
371 Pine St, Providence, RI 02903-4515
Tel (401) 521-9622 *Founded/Ownrshp* 2010
Sales 22.5MM *EMP* 25
Accts Sullivan & Company Cpas Llp P
SIC 8641 Civic social & fraternal associations; Civic social & fraternal associations
Pr: Karen Leslie

D-U-N-S 07-807-4739
GREATER REGIONAL MEDICAL CENTER AUXILIARY
GREATER REGIONAL MEDICAL CTR
1700 W Townline St, Creston, IA 50801-1054
Tel (641) 782-7091 *Founded/Ownrshp* 1890
Sales 67.7MMᴱ *EMP* 298
SIC 8062 General medical & surgical hospitals; General medical & surgical hospitals
CEO: Monte Neitzel
**CFO:* Matt McCutchan
CFO: Matthew McCutchan
**Treas:* Lores Stewart
VP: Ellen Kearney
Dir OR: Jackie Whitson
Dir Lab: Barb Kenyon
Dir Rad: J R Rockhold
Dir Rx: Larry Richardson
Chf Nrs Of: Gwen Buck
**Ex Dir:* Joan Chubick

GREATER REGIONAL MEDICAL CTR
See GREATER REGIONAL MEDICAL CENTER AUXILIARY

D-U-N-S 14-821-4489
GREATER RICHMOND BUSINESS INC
COLONIAL FORD
1833 Commerce Rd, Richmond, VA 23224-7801
Tel (804) 232-3492 *Founded/Ownrshp* 1984
Sales 94.9MMᴱ *EMP* 215
SIC 5511 5013 5531 7513 Automobiles, new & used; Automotive supplies & parts; Truck parts & accessories; Automotive & home supply stores; Truck leasing, without drivers; Automobiles, new & used; Automotive supplies & parts; Truck parts & accessories; Automotive & home supply stores; Truck leasing, without drivers
Ch Bd: George R Barkley
**Pr:* George R Barkley Jr
**Ch:* George Bob Barkely
**Sec:* Warren Schoening

D-U-N-S 10-172-4474 IMP
GREATER RICHMOND TRANSIT CO
GRTC
301 E Belt Blvd, Richmond, VA 23224-1701
Tel (804) 358-4782 *Founded/Ownrshp* 1973
Sales 46.7MMᴱ *EMP* 450
SIC 4111 Bus transportation; Bus transportation
CEO: Rollo Axton
**Pr:* Linda G Broady-Meyers
**CEO:* Eldridge F Coles
**CEO:* John Lewis
**COO:* Charles E Mitchell
CFO: Hal Davis
**Sec:* James M Johnson
**VP:* David W Mathews
Exec: Kurt Pastuszak
Dir IT: Zeb Elliot
IT Man: Erica Dent

D-U-N-S 07-871-4817
GREATER ROCHESTER HEALTH FOUNDATION
150 State St Ste 100, Rochester, NY 14614-1353
Tel (585) 258-1700 *Founded/Ownrshp* 2013

Sales 30.3MM EMP 2
SIC 8699 Charitable organization; Charitable organization
CEO: John Urban
VP: Bonnie Devinney

D-U-N-S 10-912-2577
GREATER ROCHESTER INDEPENDENT PRACTICE ASSOCIATION INC
GREATER ROCHESTER IPA
100 Kings Hwy S Ste 2500, Rochester, NY 14617-5509
Tel (585) 922-1500 Founded/Ownrshp 1996
Sales 170.0MM EMP 49
SIC 8011 Offices & clinics of medical doctors; Offices & clinics of medical doctors
Pr: Gregg Coughlin
Sr VP: Richard Gangemi
Sr VP: Hugh Thomas
VP: Jeanette Altavela
Exec: Mary Lorei

GREATER ROCHESTER IPA
See GREATER ROCHESTER INDEPENDENT PRACTICE ASSOCIATION INC

GREATER SOUTHERN TIER BOCES
See SCHUYLER STEUBEN CHEMUNG TIOGA ALLEGANY BOCES

D-U-N-S 16-494-1460
GREATER SOUTHWEST ENTERPRISES INC
CRAZY LADY, THE
3701 N Interstate 35, Austin, TX 78722-1802
Tel (512) 478-2444 Founded/Ownrshp 1976
Sales 1.0MM EMP 315
SIC 5813 Night clubs; Night clubs
Pr: Sidney Tregre
*Sec: Celeste Tregre

D-U-N-S 07-922-4572
GREATER SPRINGFIELD SENIOR SERVICES INC
66 Industry Ave Ste 9, Springfield, MA 01104-3243
Tel (413) 781-8800 Founded/Ownrshp 1972
Sales 24.1MM EMP 136
Accts Adelson Moynihan Kowalczyk Pc
SIC 8322 Geriatric social service; Geriatric social service
Pr: Dorothy Hooper
*Bd of Dir: William Caplin
*Bd of Dir: William Sheehan
*Ex Dir: Elaine Massery
IT Man: Dan Piquette
Pr Dir: Karen Martin

D-U-N-S 07-026-8800
GREATER TWIN CITIES UNITED WAY (MN)
404 S 8th St Ste 100, Minneapolis, MN 55404-1027
Tel (612) 340-7400 Founded/Ownrshp 1919
Sales 96.2MM EMP 140
Accts Ryan J Terry Ltd St Paul Mn
SIC 8322 Individual & family services
Ex Dir: Sarah Caruso
Ofcr: Craig Warren
Sr VP: Barb Beard
Sr VP: Frank Forsberg
Sr VP: Andy Goldman-Gray
VP: Diane Hummon
VP: Lezlie Taylor
Dir Soc: Emily Peterson
Ex Dir: Doris Pagelkopf
Prgrm Mgr: Naomi Zuk-Fisher
CIO: Beth Jacob

D-U-N-S 00-585-4849
GREATER WASHINGTON EDUCATIONAL TELECOMMUNICATIONS ASSOCIATION INC
WETA TV 26
3939 Campbell Ave, Arlington, VA 22206-3440
Tel (703) 998-2600 Founded/Ownrshp 1953
Sales 75.6MM EMP 236
Accts Bdo Usa Llp Bethesda Md
SIC 4833 4832 Television broadcasting stations; Radio broadcasting stations; Television broadcasting stations; Radio broadcasting stations
CEO: Sharon Percy Rockefeller
V Ch: Ann Jordan
COO: Rick Schneider
*CFO: James Bond
Bd of Dir: J R Heller
Ofcr: Anna Berke
Ofcr: Jen Brake
VP: Jeff Bieber
VP: Dan Devany
VP: Karen Fritz
VP: Chris Lane
VP: Elaine Laughlin
VP: Jeff Regen
VP: Jim Schneider
VP: Mary Stewart

D-U-N-S 84-236-3637
GREATER WASHINGTON PUBLISHING LLC
(Suby of NASH HOLDINGS LLC) ★
1150 15th St Nw, Washington, DC 20071-0001
Tel (202) 334-6000 Founded/Ownrshp 2013
Sales 19.8MM^E EMP 552^E
SIC 2721 4813 Magazines: publishing & printing;
Pr: Becky Loker
Admn Mgr: Kris Wilber

D-U-N-S 17-435-4951
GREATER WATERBURY HEALTH NETWORK INC
64 Robbins St, Waterbury, CT 06708-2613
Tel (203) 573-6000 Founded/Ownrshp 1985
Sales 566.4M EMP 1,826^E
SIC 8741 8093 8011 Hospital management; Specialty outpatient clinics; Offices & clinics of medical doctors; Hospital management; Specialty outpatient clinics; Offices & clinics of medical doctors
Ch Bd: John Micheals
*Pr: John H Tobin

D-U-N-S 02-046-4517
GREATER WATERTOWN COMMUNITY HEALTH FOUNDATION INC
WATERTOWN AREA HEALTH SERVICES
125 Hospital Dr, Watertown, WI 53098-3303
Tel (920) 261-4210 Founded/Ownrshp 1958
Sales 104.0MM EMP 840
Accts Wipfli Llp Milwaukee Wiscons
SIC 8062 8011 8059 General medical & surgical hospitals; Clinic, operated by physicians; Nursing home, except skilled & intermediate care facility; General medical & surgical hospitals; Clinic, operated by physicians; Nursing home, except skilled & intermediate care facility
CEO: Richard Keddington
CFO: John A Graf
VP: Jacklyn Lesniak
Ex Dir: John Bardenwerper

GREATER WICHITA YMCA
See YOUNG MENS CHRISTIAN ASSOCIATION OF WICHITA KANSAS

D-U-N-S 11-113-3117
GREATER WISCONSIN AGENCY ON AGING RESOURCES INC
1414 Macarthur Rd A, Madison, WI 53714-1318
Tel (715) 677-6723 Founded/Ownrshp 1973
Sales 30.9MM EMP 35
SIC 8699 Charitable organization; Charitable organization

D-U-N-S 07-884-5425
GREATERGOOD KIDS LLC
3939 E 46th St, Minneapolis, MN 55406-3906
Tel (800) 353-0710 Founded/Ownrshp 2013
Sales 29.0MM^E EMP 241^E
SIC 5092 Toys & hobby goods & supplies; Toys & hobby goods & supplies
Pr: Roberta Bonoff

GREATESCAPES
See ADVANTAGE TRAVEL LC

GREATEST SHOW ON EARTH, THE
See RNGLNG BRS BRNM & BLY COMB SHO

GREATL LAKES FAMILY CARE
See BALDWIN FAMILY HEALTH CARE

D-U-N-S 02-089-3400
GREATLAND CORP
NELCO
2480 Walker Ave Nw, Grand Rapids, MI 49544-1300
Tel (616) 791-0100 Founded/Ownrshp 1974
Sales 37.4MM^E EMP 175
SIC 5961 5963 7372

D-U-N-S 83-079-4454
GREATWIDE DEDICATED TRANSPORT I LLC
(Suby of GREATWIDE DEDICATED TRANSPORT LLC) ★
12404 Park Central Dr # 300, Dallas, TX 75251-1800
Tel (972) 228-7344 Founded/Ownrshp 2008
Sales 24.9MM^E EMP 404
SIC 4213 4731 Trucking, except local; Truck transportation brokers; Trucking, except local; Truck transportation brokers
Pr: Leo Suggs
Treas: Robert C Larose
Sr VP: John Hove
VP: Dan Curtis
VP: Jeff Lester
VP: Michael Skipworth

D-U-N-S 83-079-6400
GREATWIDE DEDICATED TRANSPORT III LLC
(Suby of GREATWIDE DEDICATED TRANSPORT LLC) ★
12404 Park Central Dr 300s, Dallas, TX 75251-1800
Tel (972) 228-7344 Founded/Ownrshp 2008
Sales 21.5MM^E EMP 490^E
SIC 4213 4731 Trucking, except local; Truck transportation brokers; Trucking, except local; Truck transportation brokers
Pr: Leo Suggs
Treas: Robert C Larose
Sr VP: John Hove
VP: Dan Curtis
VP: Jeff Lester
VP: Michael Skipworth

D-U-N-S 83-078-1584
GREATWIDE DEDICATED TRANSPORT LLC
(Suby of GREATWIDE LOGISTICS SERVICES LLC) ★
12404 Park Central Dr # 300, Dallas, TX 75251-1803
Tel (972) 228-7344 Founded/Ownrshp 2008
Sales 111.1MM^E EMP 1,500
SIC 4213 4731 Trucking, except local; Truck transportation brokers; Trucking, except local; Truck transportation brokers
Ch Bd: Leo H Suggs
CFO: Edward Barnes
*Treas: Robert C Larose
*Ex VP: Bob Larose
*Sr VP: John Hove
*VP: Dan Curtis
*VP: Jeff Lester
*VP: Michael Skipworth

D-U-N-S 83-081-6786
GREATWIDE DISTRIBUTION LOGISTICS LLC
(Suby of GREATWIDE LOGISTICS SERVICES LLC) ★
12404 Park Central Dr # 300, Dallas, TX 75251-1803
Tel (972) 224-0072 Founded/Ownrshp 2008
Sales 22.1MM^E EMP 181^E
SIC 4225 4731 General warehousing & storage; Freight transportation arrangement
Pr: Leo H Suggs
*Treas: Robert C Larose
*Sr VP: John Hove
*VP: Jeff Lester
*VP: Dave Shatto
*VP: Michael Skipworth

D-U-N-S 96-823-1055
GREATWIDE LOGISTICS MANAGEMENT INC
GREATWIDE TRUCKLOAD MANAGEMENT
(Suby of GREATWIDE LOGISTICS SERVICES LLC) ★
2150 Cabot Blvd W, Langhorne, PA 19047-1852
Tel (215) 428-4800 Founded/Ownrshp 2009
Sales 38.2MM^E EMP 90^E
SIC 4213 Trucking, except local
Pr: Joe Chandler
*Pr: Jerry Bowman
*CFO: Ed Barnes
Ex VP: David Patti
VP: John Mullins
VP: Don Wrege
Dir Risk M: Stephen Kossayian
Mtls Mgr: Kathy Ilczuk

D-U-N-S 82-946-7187
GREATWIDE LOGISTICS SERVICES LLC
(Suby of CARDINAL LOGISTICS HOLDINGS LLC) ★
5333 Davidson Hwy, Concord, NC 28027-8478
Tel (972) 224-0072 Founded/Ownrshp 2008
Sales 405.1MM^E EMP 2,800
SIC 4213 4731 Trucking, except local; Truck transportation brokers; Trucking, except local; Truck transportation brokers
CEO: John Tague
*COO: William G Doherty
*Ofcr: Jeffrey Lester
*Ex VP: Bob Larose
*Sr VP: Tyler Ellison
*Sr VP: John Hove
VP: Thomas Sheehy
*VP: Michael Skipworth
VP Bus Dev: Kevin Wicks
Brnch Mgr: Bob Lemon
Brnch Mgr: Julie Sams

GREATWIDE TRUCKLOAD MANAGEMENT
See GREATWIDE LOGISTICS MANAGEMENT INC

GRECIAN DELIGHT FOODS, INC DEL
See DELIGHT GRECIAN FOODS INC

D-U-N-S 61-900-5382 IMP
GRECO & SONS INC
1550 Hecht Dr, Bartlett, IL 60103-1697
Tel (630) 668-1000 Founded/Ownrshp 1990
Sales 221.8MM^E EMP 200
SIC 5149 Pizza supplies; Pizza supplies
Pr: Pasquale Greco
Pr: Jeremy Sadler
CFO: Brian Barrett
CFO: Brian Barrette
*VP: Edwardo Greco
Opers Mgr: Tony Zarco
VP Sls: Lino Greco

D-U-N-S 00-609-7125 IMP/EXP
GREDE FOUNDRIES INC
4000 Town Ctr Ste 500, Southfield, MI 48075-1419
Tel (248) 440-9500 Founded/Ownrshp 1946
Sales 442.1MM^E EMP 4,000
SIC 3321 Gray iron castings; Ductile iron castings; Gray iron castings; Ductile iron castings
Pr: Thomas F Walker Sr
*Ch Bd: W Stewart Davis
COO: Peter E Sohlden
*CFO: Raymond F Lowery
Grp VP: John Haas
Grp VP: Randy Priem
VP: Ed Kaczmarek
IT Man: Tim Davis
Board of Directors: Thomas Davis, Gordon Gunnlaugsson, Susan Insley, Allen Kinzer, John Mellowes, James Rulesh, Mary York

D-U-N-S 96-170-5873
■ **GREDE HOLDINGS LLC**
(Suby of METALDYNE PERFORMANCE GROUP INC) ★
4000 Town Ctr Ste 500, Southfield, MI 48075-1419
Tel (248) 440-9500 Founded/Ownrshp 2014
Sales 520.7MM^E EMP 2,766
SIC 3321 Gray iron castings; Ductile iron castings; Gray iron castings; Ductile iron castings
Pr: Douglas J Grimm
*COO: Todd Heavin
*CFO: Louis Lavorata
*VP: William R Goodin
*VP: Anthony Lovell
*VP: Paul Suber

D-U-N-S 07-796-6950 IMP
■ **GREDE II LLC**
(Suby of GREDE HOLDINGS LLC) ★
4000 Town Ctr Ste 500, Southfield, MI 48075-1419
Tel (248) 522-4500 Founded/Ownrshp 2010
Sales 283.1MM^E EMP 1,600
SIC 3321 Ductile iron castings; Gray iron castings; Ductile iron castings; Gray iron castings
Pr: Douglas J Grimm
*CFO: Louis Lavorata
*VP: Stephen Busby
DP Exec: Leonard Jennings
Opers Mgr: Stan Galyen

D-U-N-S 96-171-7886 IMP
■ **GREDE LLC**
(Suby of GREDE HOLDINGS LLC) ★
4000 Town Ctr Ste 500, Southfield, MI 48075-1419
Tel (248) 522-4500 Founded/Ownrshp 2010
Sales 190.2MM^E EMP 750
SIC 3321 Gray iron castings; Ductile iron castings; Gray iron castings; Ductile iron castings
CEO: Douglas J Grimm
*CFO: Louis Lavorata
Dir Bus: Jeffrey Nichols
Mng Dir: Raul Lopez
IT Man: Aaron Weekes
Sales Exec: Anthony Lovell

D-U-N-S 07-845-3639
■ **GREDE RADFORD LLC**
(Suby of GREDE HOLDINGS LLC) ★
1701 W Main St, Radford, VA 24141-1684
Tel (540) 639-0199 Founded/Ownrshp 2012
Sales 39.6MM^E EMP 197
SIC 3321 Cast iron pipe & fittings; Cast iron pipe & fittings
CEO: Douglas J Grimm

D-U-N-S 15-084-6715 EXP
■ **GREDE WISCONSIN SUBSIDIARIES LLC**
CITATION BERLIN
(Suby of GREDE II LLC) ★
242 S Pearl St, Berlin, WI 54923-2071
Tel (920) 361-2220 Founded/Ownrshp 1995
Sales 54.9MM^E EMP 350
SIC 3321 Gray iron castings; Ductile iron castings; Gray iron castings; Ductile iron castings
Ch: Douglas J Grimm
*Pr: Mike Dowling
CFO: Chuck Bloome
*Sr VP: Todd Heavin
*Sr VP: Louis Lavorata
*VP: William R Goodin
*VP: Paul Suber
Sfty Mgr: Daniel Burlich

D-U-N-S 08-595-4493
GREDE-PRYOR INC
(Suby of GREDE FOUNDRIES INC) ★
Mid America Industrial Pa, Pryor, OK 74362
Tel (918) 476-8321 Founded/Ownrshp 1974, 1994
Sales 27.9MM^E EMP 365
SIC 3321 Ductile iron castings; Ductile iron castings
Pr: Bruce E Jacobs
VP: Stewarts Davis
*VP: W Stewart Davis

D-U-N-S 05-468-5552
GREDE-ST CLOUD INC
5200 Foundry Cir, Saint Cloud, MN 56303-2032
Tel (320) 255-5200 Founded/Ownrshp 2001
Sales 31.6MM^E EMP 330
SIC 3089 Automotive parts, plastic; Automotive parts, plastic
Pr: John Haas

D-U-N-S 15-730-2977
GREDE-VASSAR INC (MI)
(Suby of GREDE FOUNDRIES INC) ★
9898 W Bluemound Rd, Milwaukee, WI 53226-4319
Tel (414) 257-3600 Founded/Ownrshp 1986
Sales 22.0MM EMP 267
SIC 3321

D-U-N-S 06-678-6082
GREE INTERNATIONAL INC
(Suby of GREE, INC.)
185 Berry St Ste 590, San Francisco, CA 94107-9105
Tel (415) 409-5159 Founded/Ownrshp 2011
Sales 40.1MM^E EMP 250
SIC 7371 Computer software development & applications; Computer software systems analysis & design, custom; Software programming applications
CEO: Naoki Aoyagi
Pr: Neil Haldar
*COO: Andrew Sheppard
Sr VP: Eiji Araki
*Sr VP: Shanti Bergel
Prgrm Mgr: Midori Takeda
Dir IT: Rafael Assumpcao
Pr Mgr: Noemi Esparza
Pr Mgr: Akiko Thayer

D-U-N-S 02-972-7238 IMP
GREE USA INC
(Suby of GREE ELECTRIC APPLIANCES, INC. OF ZHUHAI)
20035 E Walnut Dr N, City of Industry, CA 91789-2922
Tel (909) 718-0478 Founded/Ownrshp 2010
Sales 154.1MM EMP 20
SIC 5075 Air conditioning & ventilation equipment & supplies; Air conditioning & ventilation equipment & supplies
Pr: Charley Loh
*CFO: Jian Chen
VP: Teresa Kamiya

D-U-N-S 06-791-5991
GREECE CENTRAL SCHOOL DISTRICT
750 Maiden Ln, Rochester, NY 14615-1230
Tel (585) 966-2000 Founded/Ownrshp 1928
Sales 102.2MM^E EMP 2,073
SIC 8211 Public elementary & secondary schools; Public elementary & secondary schools
Dir Sec: Steven Chatterton
Schl Brd P: Sean McCabe
HC Dir: Sandra McCormick

GREEHECK GROUP, THE
See GREENHECK FAN CORP

GREEK GODS
See HAIN REFRIGERATED FOODS INC

D-U-N-S 07-920-1459
GREEK PEAK HOLDINGS LLC
HOPE LAKE HOLDINGS
2000 State Route 392, Cortland, NY 13045-9556
Tel (607) 835-6111 Founded/Ownrshp 2013
Sales 18.4MM^E EMP 350
SIC 7999 Tourist attractions, amusement park concessions & rides; Tourist attractions, amusement park concessions & rides
Genl Mgr: Dwayne Spitzer

D-U-N-S 05-395-0544 IMP
GREEKTOWN CASINO LLC
OPA'S
555 E Lafayette Blvd, Detroit, MI 48226-2924
Tel (313) 223-2999 Founded/Ownrshp 1997
Sales 71.8MM^E EMP 2,200
SIC 5812 7011 Greek restaurant; Casino hotel; Greek restaurant; Casino hotel
Pr: Michael Puggi
*COO: Craig Ghelfi
CFO: Bruce Dall
VP: Norm Howard
VP: Allen Kerridge
VP: Bill Williams
Dir Risk M: Crystal Ford
Comm Man: Lloryn Love
CIO: Jason Baxter

MIS Dir: John Holloway
Netwrk Eng: Dino Panagiotopoulos

D-U-N-S 96-250-9274
GREEKTOWN SUPERHOLDINGS INC
555 E Lafayette Blvd, Detroit, MI 48226-2924
Tel (313) 223-2999 *Founded/Ownrshp* 2010
Sales 331.7MM *EMP* 2
Accts Ernst & Young Llp Detroit M
SIC 6719 Investment holding companies, except banks; Investment holding companies, except banks
Prin: Tony Williams
CFO: Glen Tomaszewski
Exec: Jessica Pondell
Mktg Mgr: Scott Rutledge

D-U-N-S 04-569-9949
GREELEY AND HANSEN LLC
100 S Wacker Dr Ste 1400, Chicago, IL 60606-4000
Tel (312) 558-9000 *Founded/Ownrshp* 1914
Sales 87.5MM^E *EMP* 325
SIC 8711 Consulting engineer; Consulting engineer
CEO: Andrew Richardson
**Pr:* John C Robak
CFO: Theresa Grace
Prin: Ana Dutra
Prin: Fernando Sarmiento
Prin: Nicole Spieles
Board of Directors: Ana Dutra

GREELEY COMPANY
See HCPRO INC

D-U-N-S 05-543-2660
GREELEY MEDICAL CLINIC P C
1900 16th St, Greeley, CO 80631-5114
Tel (970) 353-1551 *Founded/Ownrshp* 1985
Sales 21.4MM^E *EMP* 350
SIC 8011 Physicians' office, including specialists; Physicians' office, including specialists
CEO: Barbara Yosses
**Pr:* Daniel Zenk MD
**Treas:* James Ley MD
VP: Randy Bussey
**VP:* Robert L Cash MD
VP: Glenn Hewitt
VP: David McNaul
VP: Marj Wiedeman
Ex Dir: Dale Anderson
Off Mgr: Julie Netherton
Sls&Mrk Ex: Linda Fitzsimons

D-U-N-S 03-559-7491
GREEN & CHAPMAN INC
8301 Faulkner Lake Rd, North Little Rock, AR 72117-9440
Tel (501) 945-4555 *Founded/Ownrshp* 1956
Sales 30.5MM *EMP* 14
Accts Denman Hamilton & Associates
SIC 5172 Petroleum products; Petroleum products
Pr: Steve Green
**Treas:* Rick Green
**VP:* Tim Green

D-U-N-S 07-132-0456
GREEN ACQUISITION CORP (PA)
(*Suby of* CRR HOLDINGS LLC) ★
2001 Market St, Philadelphia, PA 19103-7044
Tel (215) 209-2000 *Founded/Ownrshp* 1997
Sales 200.4MM^E *EMP* 7,414
SIC 4011 Railroads, line-haul operating
Pr: Timothy T O'Toole

D-U-N-S 07-497-7604
GREEN ACRES CONTRACTING CO INC
148 Pennsylvania Dr, Scottdale, PA 15683-7768
Tel (724) 887-8096 *Founded/Ownrshp* 1975
Sales 40.4MM *EMP* 149
Accts Carbis Walker Llp New Castle
SIC 1611 0782 1799 Guardrail construction, highways; Highway lawn & garden maintenance services; Fence construction; Sign installation & maintenance; Guardrail construction, highways; Highway lawn & garden maintenance services; Fence construction; Sign installation & maintenance
Pr: Gregory M Pisula
**VP:* James F Humberston
VP: Doug Riley
Dir IT: Dave Lafrankie

D-U-N-S 07-550-5768
GREEN ACRES HEALTH SYSTEMS INC
4 Ivybrook Blvd, Warminster, PA 18974-1700
Tel (215) 357-6055 *Founded/Ownrshp* 1946
Sales 22.1MM^E *EMP* 1,000
SIC 8741 8051 Nursing & personal care facility management; Skilled nursing care facilities
Pr: Allen Segal
**CFO:* Gary Segal
Board of Directors: Jane Segal

D-U-N-S 13-403-3302 IMP
GREEN ACRES NURSERY & SUPPLY LLC
604 Sutter St, Folsom, CA 95630-2575
Tel (916) 782-2273 *Founded/Ownrshp* 2002
Sales 47.6MM^E *EMP* 90
SIC 5083 5261 Irrigation equipment; Nursery stock, seeds & bulbs; Irrigation equipment; Nursery stock, seeds & bulbs
Site Mgr: Mark Gill

GREEN ALTERNATIVE SYSTEMS
See CREATIVE BUS SALES INC

D-U-N-S 13-504-9158
GREEN APPLE LLC
APPLEBEE'S
164 Wind Chime Ct, Raleigh, NC 27615-6433
Tel (919) 846-2577 *Founded/Ownrshp* 2000
Sales 41.4MM^E *EMP* 1,000
SIC 5812 Restaurant, family: chain; Restaurant, family: chain
CFO: John Sook
Genl Mgr: Jared Noble

GREEN ART ENTERPRISE
See OKIN-WALLACK CORP

D-U-N-S 03-297-0428
GREEN AUTOMOTIVE LP (OK)
MILO GORDON AUTO MALL
4455 Nw Cache Rd, Lawton, OK 73505-3401
Tel (580) 355-1213 *Founded/Ownrshp* 1940, 2003
Sales 27.9MM^E *EMP* 94
SIC 5511 Automobiles, new & used; Pickups, new & used; Vans, new & used; Automobiles, new & used; Pickups, new & used; Vans, new & used
Pt: Scott Combs

D-U-N-S 79-121-2314
▲ GREEN BANCORP INC
4000 Greenbriar St, Houston, TX 77098-5204
Tel (713) 275-8220 *Founded/Ownrshp* 2004
Sales NA *EMP* 272
Tkr Sym GNBC *Exch* NGS
SIC 6021 National commercial banks; National commercial banks
Ch Bd: Manuel J Mehos
Pr: Geoffrey D Greenwade
CFO: John P Durie
Chf Cred: Donald S Perschbacher

D-U-N-S 96-369-2673
GREEN BANK NATIONAL ASSOCIATION
4000 Greenbriar St, Houston, TX 77098-5204
Tel (713) 275-8200 *Founded/Ownrshp* 2008
Sales NA *EMP* 292^E
SIC 6029 Commercial banks; Commercial banks
Ch Bd: Manuel J Mehos
**Pr:* Geoffrey Greenwade
**COO:* Sylvia Gonzales
**CFO:* John P Durie
Ofcr: Ermelinda Ortiz
Ex VP: Glen Bell
Ex VP: John Durie
Ex VP: Paco Rivera
Sr VP: Rebecca Dozier
Sr VP: Shelley Harrington
Sr VP: Ray Kembel
Sr VP: Cory Leboutf
Sr VP: Kenneth Montag
Sr VP: Tim Teske
VP: Adam Campbell
VP: Kevin Coffman
VP: Cindy Dorton
VP: Denise Doughtie
VP: Kay Moore
Exec: Diana Morgan

D-U-N-S 00-338-6497
■ GREEN BANKSHARES INC (TN)
(*Suby of* CAPITAL BANK FINANCIAL CORP) ★
100 N Main St, Greeneville, TN 37743-4920
Tel (423) 639-5111 *Founded/Ownrshp* 1985, 2011
Sales NA *EMP* 1,540
SIC 6022 State commercial banks; State commercial banks
Ch Bd: R Eugene Taylor
Pr: Lloyd L Montgomery III
**CFO:* Christopher G Marshall
Ex VP: Adams Bill
**Ex VP:* R Bruce Singletary
Sr VP: J Robert Grubbs
Sr VP: William Uscategui
VP: Michael Fowler
VP: Josh Howell
VP: Trisha Lamb
Netwrk Eng: Tim Feathers
Board of Directors: Martha M Bachman, Peter N Foss, William A Hodges, Samuel E Lynch

D-U-N-S 13-484-7177
GREEN BAY AREA PUBLIC SCHOOL DISTRICT
200 S Broadway, Green Bay, WI 54303-1516
Tel (920) 448-2101 *Founded/Ownrshp* 1847
Sales 130.9MM^E *EMP* 3,000
Accts Schenck Sc Greenbay Wisconsi
SIC 8211 Public elementary & secondary schools; Public elementary & secondary schools
**Pr:* Jean Marsch
**Pr:* Brenda Warren
Treas: Chris Wagner
Sr Cor Off: Ray Kopesh
**VP:* Katie Maloney
Assoc Dir: Amy Wachewicz
Adm Dir: Michael Donart
Dir IT: Tony Jaworski
IT Man: Gary Wojtowski
Counsel: Melissa Collar
Snr Mgr: Diane Doersch

D-U-N-S 00-683-5946
GREEN BAY CHEESE CO INC
(*Suby of* SAPUTO CHEESE USA INC) ★
13190 Velp Ave, Suamico, WI 54313-8040
Tel (920) 434-3233 *Founded/Ownrshp* 1948, 2013
Sales 58.1MM^E *EMP* 200
SIC 5143 Cheese; Cheese
Pr: Lino Saputo
**Prin:* Thomas R Vorpahl
Plnt Mgr: Dean Zaretzke

D-U-N-S 07-751-9929 IMP
GREEN BAY CONVERTING INC
2200 Larsen Rd, Green Bay, WI 54303-4810
Tel (920) 498-5100 *Founded/Ownrshp* 1999
Sales 131.1MM^E *EMP* 120^E
SIC 5113 Towels, paper; Paper tubes & cores; Towels, paper; Paper tubes & cores
Pr: Gregory Santaga
**Sr VP:* Pamela Vincent
VP: Cameron Moyer
Opers Mgr: Bruce Van Haren

D-U-N-S 05-492-7108
GREEN BAY DRESSED BEEF LLC
(*Suby of* AMERICAN FOODS GROUP LLC) ★
544 Acme St, Green Bay, WI 54302-1807
Tel (920) 436-4220 *Founded/Ownrshp* 1985
Sales 228.8MM^E *EMP* 1,400
SIC 2011 2013 Meat packing plants; Beef products from beef slaughtered on site; Boxed beef from meat slaughtered on site; Sausages from purchased meat; Luncheon meat from purchased meat; Meat packing plants; Beef products from beef slaughtered on site; Boxed beef from meat slaughtered on site; Sausages from purchased meat; Luncheon meat from purchased meat
CEO: Tom Rosen
CFO: Doug Hagen
VP: Steve Giroux
Prd Mgr: Daniel Klaus

D-U-N-S 08-617-7060
GREEN BAY METROPOLITAN SEWERAGE DISTRICT
2231 N Quincy St, Green Bay, WI 54302-1248
Tel (920) 432-4893 *Founded/Ownrshp* 1931
Sales 23.9MM^E *EMP* 101
Accts Virchow Krause & Company Madi
SIC 4952 Sewerage systems
Ex Dir: Thomas W Sigmund
VP: James Blumreich
VP: Lee Hoffmann
VP: Mark Turnpach
Sys/Dir: Rita Arwine
IT Man: Jeff Czyopinsky
Sfty Mgr: Jeremy Klingbeil
Opers Mgr: Pat Wescott
Snr Mgr: Bruce Bartel
Snr Mgr: Craig Lawiniczak
Snr Mgr: Marty Pyke

D-U-N-S 00-614-6997 IMP/EXP
GREEN BAY PACKAGING INC
1700 N Webster Ave, Green Bay, WI 54302-1196
Tel (920) 433-5111 *Founded/Ownrshp* 1919
Sales 506.2MM^E *EMP* 3,373
SIC 2631 2672 2653 2491

D-U-N-S 06-831-6538 EXP
GREEN BAY PACKERS INC
PACKERS PRO SHOP
1265 Lombardi Ave, Green Bay, WI 54304-3997
Tel (920) 569-7500 *Founded/Ownrshp* 1935
Sales 37.5MM^E *EMP* 160
SIC 7941 Football club
CEO: Mark Murphy
CFO: Vicki Vannieuwenhove
**Treas:* Mark McMullen
Treas: Herman Reckelberg
Treas: John Underwood
Ex VP: John Jones
VP: Marty Briggs
VP: Denny Tattum
**VP:* Larry Weyers
VP: Christine Wilbert
Exec: Winston Moss

D-U-N-S 82-888-2774
GREEN BOILER TECHNOLOGIES INC
SELLERS ENG'G COMPANY
918 W Walnut St, Danville, KY 40422-1359
Tel (859) 209-2003 *Founded/Ownrshp* 1931
Sales 21.4MM^E *EMP* 80
SIC 3433 Heating equipment, except electric
CEO: Stuart Miller
**Pr:* Tim Meador
Plnt Mgr: Randy Woolum
Sls Dir: Ray Larson

GREEN BRIAR NURSING CENTER
See INTERGRATED HEALTH SVCS OF GREEN BRIAR INC

D-U-N-S 80-040-0892
▲ GREEN BRICK PARTNERS INC
2805 Dallas Pkwy Ste 400, Plano, TX 75093-8722
Tel (469) 573-6755 *Founded/Ownrshp* 2014
Sales 246.1MM^E *EMP* 150
Tkr Sym GRBK *Exch* NAS
SIC 1531 6531 Operative builders; Real estate agents & managers
CEO: James R Brickman
**Ch Bd:* David Einhorn
COO: John Jason Corley
CFO: Richard A Costello

GREEN BROOK G M C
See GREENBROOK PONTIAC-GMC INC

GREEN BROOK TWNSHIP PUB SCHOLS
See GREEN BROOK TWP SCH DISTRICT

D-U-N-S 79-475-4445
GREEN BROOK TWP SCH DISTRICT
GREEN BROOK TWNSHIP PUB SCHOLS
132 Jefferson Ave, Green Brook, NJ 08812-2608
Tel (732) 968-1171 *Founded/Ownrshp* 2007
Sales 24.0MM *EMP* 135^E
SIC 8211 Public elementary & secondary schools; High school, junior or senior; Public elementary & secondary schools; High school, junior or senior

D-U-N-S 83-055-9287
GREEN BUILDING CERTIFICATION INSTITUTE
2101 L St Nw Ste 500, Washington, DC 20037-1599
Tel (202) 828-1145 *Founded/Ownrshp* 2007
Sales 41.5MM *EMP* 20^E
Accts Rsm Mcgladrey Inc Gaithersbur
SIC 8222 Technical institute; Technical institute
Pr: Peter Templeton
**Sec:* Nicole Ehardt
Genl Couns: Susan Dorn

GREEN CHEVROLET
See WARREN CHEVROLET INC

GREEN CHEVROLET
See GREEN HOLDING CO INC

GREEN CHEVROLET HUMMER
See GREEN CHEVROLET INC

D-U-N-S 06-523-3397
GREEN CHEVROLET INC
GREEN CHEVROLET HUMMER
8017 N Knoxville Ave, Peoria, IL 61615-2148
Tel (309) 691-1100 *Founded/Ownrshp* 1973
Sales 35.6MM^E *EMP* 90
SIC 5511 5013

GREEN CHIMNEY CHILDREN SVCS
See GREEN CHIMNEYS CHILDRENS SERVICES INC

D-U-N-S 15-054-7917
GREEN CHIMNEYS CHILDRENS SERVICES INC
GREEN CHIMNEY CHILDREN SVCS
400 Doansburg Rd 719, Brewster, NY 10509-5902
Tel (845) 279-2995 *Founded/Ownrshp* 1947
Sales 4.0MM *EMP* 450
SIC 8361 Children's home; Home for the emotionally disturbed; Children's home; Home for the emotionally disturbed
Pr: Mark Lescault
**Ch Bd:* Walter Leinhardt
CFO: Rafi Kalman
**Ch:* Rick Macrae
**VP:* Wayne Cutler
Admn Mgr: Joan O'Connell
Dir IT: Jay Singh
Mktg Dir: Jennifer Milillo
Psych: Bethany Burrows
Psych: Patricia Debiase
Psych: Martin Vigdor

D-U-N-S 06-930-4475
GREEN CHIMNEYS SCHOOL FOR LITTLE FOLK A CORP
FRIENDS OF GREEN CHIMNEYS, THE
400 Doansburg Rd 719, Brewster, NY 10509-5902
Tel (845) 279-2995 *Founded/Ownrshp* 1947
Sales 1.6MM *EMP* 400
SIC 8211 Private special education school; Private special education school
Pr: Jules Schwimmer
**Treas:* George Neuhaus Jr
Dir Soc: Kristin Boyle
**Prin:* Roderick Macrae
**Ex Dir:* Joseph Whalen

D-U-N-S 01-335-9230
GREEN CIRCLE BIO ENERGY INC
2500 Green Circle Pkwy, Cottondale, FL 32431-7450
Tel (850) 557-7357 *Founded/Ownrshp* 2006
Sales 25.0MM^E *EMP* 75
SIC 8711 Energy conservation engineering
CEO: Morten Neraas
**CEO:* Olaf Roed
**CFO:* Joe Koscik
IT Man: Kevin Daniel
Opers Mgr: J W Cole
Sls Dir: Todd Bush

D-U-N-S 05-906-3107 IMP
GREEN CIRCLE GROWERS INC
51051 Us Highway 20, Oberlin, OH 44074-9637
Tel (440) 775-1411 *Founded/Ownrshp* 1972
Sales 90.6MM^E *EMP* 600^E
SIC 0181 Flowers: grown under cover (e.g. greenhouse production); Plants, potted: growing of; Flowers: grown under cover (e.g. greenhouse production); Plants, potted: growing of
Pr: John Van Wingerden
**CFO:* Norman Daxter
CFO: Tony Lucarell
**VP:* Dawn Van Wingerden
Exec: John O"donnell
Plnt Mgr: Jeff Harbin
Natl Sales: Debbie Straub
Sls&Mrk Ex: Scott Giesbrecht
Sls Dir: Chris Ricci
Manager: Jason Smith
Sales Asso: Tyler Camp

D-U-N-S 78-458-0610 IMP
GREEN CIRCUITS INC
1130 Ringwood Ct, San Jose, CA 95131-1726
Tel (408) 526-1700 *Founded/Ownrshp* 2006
Sales 28.9MM^E *EMP* 71^E
SIC 3679 Electronic circuits
CEO: Ted Park
Pr: Michael Nguyen
Prgrm Mgr: John Kim
Prgrm Mgr: Eva Ye
QC Dir: Duane Barber

D-U-N-S 19-936-5347
GREEN CLINIC L L C
1200 S Farmerville St, Ruston, LA 71270-5941
Tel (318) 255-3690 *Founded/Ownrshp* 1948
Sales 31.7MM^E *EMP* 230
SIC 8011 Clinic, operated by physicians; Clinic, operated by physicians
CEO: Robert Goodwill
**Pr:* Charles W Tanner
CFO: India Carroll
Dir Lab: Timmy Singleton
Telecom Ex: Robert Volentine
**Dir IT:* India Carol
Surgeon: Marvin T Green
Doctor: Cordy Harrington
Doctor: Thomas Smith
Doctor: Jeff Weeks

D-U-N-S 06-357-9670
GREEN CLOUD TECHNOLOGIES LLC
411 University Rdg # 201, Greenville, SC 29601-3765
Tel (864) 990-5843 *Founded/Ownrshp* 2011
Sales 27.5MM^E *EMP* 108^E
SIC 7373 Computer integrated systems design
Pr: Eric Hester

D-U-N-S 02-205-0066
GREEN COMPANIES INC
HR GREEN DEVELOPMENT
8710 Earhart Ln Sw, Cedar Rapids, IA 52404-8947
Tel (319) 841-4000 *Founded/Ownrshp* 1953
Sales 101.3MM^E *EMP* 390
SIC 8711 8748 8713 4911 1623 Consulting engineer; Business consulting; Surveying services; Electric services; Water, sewer & utility lines; Consulting engineer; Business consulting; Surveying services; Electric services; Water, sewer & utility lines
CEO: Steven R Heyer
COO: Dave Maxwell
**Treas:* Michelle Byard

VP: Richard Cammarata
VP: Rick Cammarata
VP: Steven Heyer
**VP:* David Moermond
VP: Bill Moran
**VP:* Jason Poppen
**VP:* Richard White
Exec: Ajay Jain
Exec: Jill Kennedy
Board of Directors: Steven Heyer, Patrick Hogan, David Moermond, Jason Poppen, Eliot Protsch, Douglas Tholo, Richard White

D-U-N-S 00-282-8366
GREEN CONTRACTING CO INC
G C C
8837 Yellow Brick Rd, Baltimore, MD 21237-2301
Tel (410) 780-0500 *Founded/Ownrshp* 1999
Sales 35.4MM^E *EMP* 100
Accts Uhy Llp Columbia Maryland
SIC 1711 1791 1541 Mechanical contractor; Structural steel erection; Industrial buildings & warehouses; Mechanical contractor; Structural steel erection; Industrial buildings & warehouses
Pr: Charles Helm
**CFO:* Margaret Deletis
**Ch:* Marcia A Roof
**VP:* Charles Fauer
VP: Craig Kinnear
Genl Mgr: Gena D'Elia
Snr Mgr: Kevin McDermott

D-U-N-S 00-568-8416
GREEN COUCH CORP (IL)
231 S La Salle St Fl 8, Chicago, IL 60604-1472
Tel (312) 263-1177 *Founded/Ownrshp* 2001
Sales 89.2MM^E *EMP* 300^E
SIC 7379 7371 Computer related consulting services; Custom computer programming services; Computer related consulting services; Custom computer programming services
Pr: Andrew Sieja
COO: Steve Robertson
CFO: Keith Lieberman
Snr Sftwr: Don Frey
Snr Sftwr: Doug Osborne
Snr Sftwr: Scott Parillo
Snr Sftwr: Kayla Snell
Snr Sftwr: George Yaconi
Snr Ntwrk: Chris Stolp
QA Dir: Mason May
IT Man: Shaun McPeck

D-U-N-S 16-744-7759
■ **GREEN COUNTRY ENERGY LLC**
(*Suby of* COGENTRIX ENERGY POWER MANAGEMENT LLC) ★
12307 S Florence, Jenks, OK 74037-9703
Tel (918) 299-5689 *Founded/Ownrshp* 1999
Sales 31.7MM^E *EMP* 29
SIC 4911 Electric services
Off Mgr: Carol Wilson
Plnt Mgr: Rick Shackleford

D-U-N-S 09-663-9539
GREEN COUNTRY INTERIORS INC
G C I
9727 E 54th St, Tulsa, OK 74146-5716
Tel (918) 663-5713 *Founded/Ownrshp* 1979
Sales 26.2MM^E *EMP* 220^E
SIC 1742 Drywall; Acoustical & ceiling work; Drywall; Acoustical & ceiling work
Pr: David Hannagan
**CFO:* Paul Hannagan
VP: Tim McGuire
VP: Jason Stone
Off Mgr: Trish Schmitt

GREEN COUNTY FISCAL COURT
See COUNTY OF GREEN

D-U-N-S 07-904-2545
GREEN COUNTY GOVERNMET OF TENNESEE (TN)
GREENE COUNTY HIGHWAY DEPARTME
Greene County Courthouse, Greeneville, TN 37745
Tel (423) 798-1703 *Founded/Ownrshp* 1794
Sales NA *EMP* 1,876
Accts Justin P Wilson Nashville T
SIC 9111 Executive offices; ; Executive offices;
**Trst:* Dan Walker

GREEN, COUNTY OF
See COUNTY OF GREEN

D-U-N-S 14-485-4077
▲ **GREEN COURTE PARTNERS LLC**
303 W Madison St, Chicago, IL 60606-3309
Tel (847) 615-1631 *Founded/Ownrshp* 2002
Sales 113.8MM^E *EMP* 294
SIC 6798 Real estate investment trusts; Real estate investment trusts
Ch: Randall K Rowe
V Ch: James Goldman
**COO:* David B Lentz
Ofcr: James R Golfman
VP: Antonia Anagnostopoulos
**VP:* Chad V Gardner
VP: Tom Jasica
**VP:* Matthew J Pyzyk
VP: Susi Rowe
VP: Braden L Rudolph
**VP:* Cheri M Scully
VP: Thru A Shivakumar
VP: Kian H Wagner

D-U-N-S 13-939-8523
GREEN CROW CORP
727 E 8th St, Port Angeles, WA 98362-6448
Tel (360) 452-3325 *Founded/Ownrshp* 1983
Sales 20.4MM^E *EMP* 50
SIC 5099 Timber products, rough
Pr: Randall S Johnson
**Ch Bd:* David Crow
**VP:* John D Crow

D-U-N-S 11-448-4665
GREEN CUISINE INC
2021 1st St, San Fernando, CA 91340-2611
Tel (818) 837-7774 *Founded/Ownrshp* 1998
Sales 24.9MM^E *EMP* 48
SIC 5141 Groceries, general line
CEO: Hector Martinez
**Pr:* Terry Sanderson
**VP:* Spencer Sanderson

D-U-N-S 01-283-1553
▲ **GREEN DOT CORP**
3465 E Foothill Blvd, Pasadena, CA 91107-6071
Tel (626) 765-2000 *Founded/Ownrshp* 1999
Sales 601.5MM *EMP* 857^E
Accts Ernst & Young Llp Los Angeles
Tkr Sym GDOT *Exch* NYS
SIC 7389 6141 Credit card service; Credit card service; Personal credit institutions
Ch Bd: Steven W Streit
COO: Kuan Archer
CFO: Mark Shifke
CFO: Brandon Soto
CFO: Grace T Wang
Ofcr: Christina Hunt-Fuhr
Ofcr: Jeff Ross
Ofcr: Konstantinos Sgoutas
Ofcr: Kostas Sgoutas
Sr VP: Ralph Calvano
VP: Kathy Clark
VP: Jose Gomez
VP: Suzanne Rickards
VP Bus Dev: Ryan Rossow
Comm Man: Kevin Ireland
Board of Directors: Kenneth C Aldrich, Samuel Altman, Mary J Dent, Timothy R Greenleaf, Michael J Moritz, George T Shaheen

D-U-N-S 07-968-2468
GREEN DOT PUBLIC SCHOOLS CALIFORNIA
ANIMO ELLEN OCHOA CHRTR MIDDLE
5156 Whittier Blvd, Los Angeles, CA 90022-3932
Tel (323) 565-1600 *Founded/Ownrshp* 2014
Sales 3.7MM^E *EMP* 1,184
SIC 8211 Public special education school
Pr: Marco Petruzzi
**CEO:* Cristina De Jesus

D-U-N-S 07-842-5207
GREEN ENERGY OILFIELD SERVICES LLC (TX)
335 Indl Pk Rd, Fairfield, TX 75840
Tel (903) 389-0110 *Founded/Ownrshp* 2011
Sales 57.6MM^E *EMP* 170
SIC 1381 Drilling oil & gas wells; Drilling oil & gas wells
Pr: Roger Nevill
**CFO:* Kent Kendall
**VP:* Marla Aaron Collins
**VP:* J R Nevill
**VP:* John Renger
**Prin:* Joe Monroe

D-U-N-S 78-175-6267
GREEN EQUITY INVESTORS III L P
11111 Santa Monica Blvd # 2000, Los Angeles, CA 90025-3333
Tel (310) 954-0444 *Founded/Ownrshp* 1989
Sales 47.6MM^E *EMP* 1,115
SIC 6211 Investment bankers; Investment bankers
Pt: Jonathan D Sokoloff
Genl Pt: Leonald G LP

D-U-N-S 62-408-6265
GREEN EQUITY INVESTORS IV LP
11111 Santa Monica Blvd, Los Angeles, CA 90025-3333
Tel (310) 954-0444 *Founded/Ownrshp* 2002
Sales 2.2MMM^E *EMP* 15,000^E
SIC 6719 Investment holding companies, except banks

D-U-N-S 10-218-8034
GREEN FAMILY STORES INC
GREEN TOYOTA
3901 Wabash Ave, Springfield, IL 62711-9690
Tel (217) 698-3100 *Founded/Ownrshp* 1983
Sales 20.3MM^E *EMP* 36
SIC 5511 Automobiles, new & used
Pr: Todd Green
Sls Mgr: Tim Hanson
Sls Mgr: Josh Wagoner
Sales Asso: Dan Koeppel

D-U-N-S 94-576-5063
GREEN FARMS INC
WORLDWIDE PRODUCE
1661 Mcgarry St, Los Angeles, CA 90021-3116
Tel (213) 747-4411 *Founded/Ownrshp* 1995
Sales 209.9MM^E *EMP* 278^E
SIC 5148 Vegetables; Vegetables
CEO: Stuart Weisfeld
**Ofcr:* Ron Warenkiewicz
CTO: Lenny Nash
IT Man: Walter Xinico

GREEN FEED
See MORROW COUNTY GRAIN GROWERS INC

D-U-N-S 06-139-1686 IMP
GREEN FOODS CORP
2220 Camino Del Sol, Oxnard, CA 93030-8905
Tel (805) 983-7470 *Founded/Ownrshp* 1969
Sales 29.5MM^E *EMP* 110^E
SIC 5149 Health foods
CEO: Sadanori Abe
VP: Jason Nava
Off Mgr: Brenda Ulery
Mktg Dir: Stephanie Furukawa

GREEN GIFFORD NISSAN
See GREEN-GIFFORD INC

GREEN GUARD FIRST AID & SAFETY
See GREENGUARD

GREEN HILL RESIDENCE
See COMMUNITY PARTNERS INC

D-U-N-S 03-923-6476
GREEN HILLS AEA
A A SEARCHING
24997 Highway 92, Council Bluffs, IA 51503-5747
Tel (712) 366-0503 *Founded/Ownrshp* 2007
Sales 30.5MM *EMP* 260^E
Accts Schnurr & Company Llp Fort D
SIC 8331 Vocational training agency; Vocational training agency
Prin: James Blietz
Prin: Randy Brown
Software D: Andy Raczynski
Mktg Mgr: Lori Ahrends
Mktg Mgr: Carissa Otto
Psych: Elena Anson
Psych: Ellen Dosen
Psych: Stephanie Dredge

GREEN HILLS FARM STAND
See GREEN HILLS FARM STORES INC

D-U-N-S 01-292-3330 IMP
GREEN HILLS FARM STORES INC
GREEN HILLS FARM STAND
5933 S Salina St, Syracuse, NY 13205-3300
Tel (315) 469-1722 *Founded/Ownrshp* 1953
Sales 23.1MM^E *EMP* 200
SIC 5411 5812 Grocery stores, independent; Eating places; Grocery stores, independent; Eating places
Pr: Keith G Hawkins
**VP:* Gary E Hawkins
VP: Sterling Hawkins
Store Mgr: Bud Kennedy
IT Man: Benjamin Fenner

D-U-N-S 10-572-2854
GREEN HILLS SOFTWARE INC
30 W Sola St, Santa Barbara, CA 93101-2599
Tel (805) 965-6044 *Founded/Ownrshp* 1872
Sales 75.6MM^E *EMP* 185
SIC 5013 Motor vehicle supplies & new parts; Motor vehicle supplies & new parts
CEO: Daniel O Dowd
Pr: Michael W Liacko
**CEO:* Daniel O'Dowd
**CFO:* Jeffrey Hazarian
CFO: Bob Hull
**Ch:* Jack Douglas
**Sr VP:* David Chandler
**VP:* Tim Reed
VP: David Sequino
**VP:* Christopher Smith
VP: Dom Stroud
Dir Bus: Gregory Rudy
Board of Directors: Daniel P Burnham

D-U-N-S 19-693-0077
GREEN HOLDING CO INC
GREEN CHEVROLET
1700 W Morton Ave, Jacksonville, IL 62650-2720
Tel (217) 245-4117 *Founded/Ownrshp* 1985
Sales 33.8MM^E *EMP* 165
SIC 5511 Automobiles, new & used; Automobiles, new & used
Pr: Ramon J Green

D-U-N-S 00-235-2466 IMP
GREEN HORSE MEDIA LLC
EVERGREEN PRINTING COMPANY
101 Haag Ave, Bellmawr, NJ 08031-2506
Tel (856) 933-0222 *Founded/Ownrshp* 1955, 2008
Sales 22.0MM *EMP* 141
SIC 2752 Commercial printing, lithographic; Commercial printing, lithographic
Ex VP: Jack Ricciuti
VP: Steve Danifo
CTO: James Doughten
Prd Dir: Jim Hager
Opers Mgr: Tanya Erickson
Prd Mgr: Chris Geimer
VP Mktg: John Dreisbach

D-U-N-S 07-828-2718
GREEN HORSE MEDIA LLC
EVERGREEN PRINTING AND PUBG CO
101 Haag Ave, Bellmawr, NJ 08031-2506
Tel (856) 933-0222 *Founded/Ownrshp* 2007
Sales 20.5MM^E *EMP* 141
SIC 2752 Commercial printing, lithographic

D-U-N-S 80-827-9082
GREEN HOUSE DATA INC
304 Progress Cir Ste A, Cheyenne, WY 82007-9667
Tel (307) 459-0304 *Founded/Ownrshp* 2007
Sales 21.2MM^E *EMP* 57^E
SIC 7374 Data processing & preparation
Pr: Shawn Mills
Off Mgr: Jodee McClure

D-U-N-S 14-732-4086 IMP
GREEN INDUSTRIAL SUPPLY INC
1525 Innovation Dr, Dubuque, IA 52002-9624
Tel (563) 557-5125 *Founded/Ownrshp* 2002
Sales 45.8MM^E *EMP* 48
SIC 5083 Landscaping equipment
Pr: Mary Sue Green

D-U-N-S 09-814-2417 IMP
GREEN LEAF INC
9490 N Baldwin St, Fontanet, IN 47851
Tel (812) 877-1546 *Founded/Ownrshp* 1980
Sales 29.4MM^E *EMP* 144
SIC 3089 3498 Fittings for pipe, plastic; Injection molding of plastics; Electrical equipment & supplies; Farm machinery & equipment; Fabricated pipe & fittings; Fittings for pipe, plastic; Injection molding of plastics; Fabricated pipe & fittings
Pr: Pete A Goda
**CFO:* Angela Vikstko
CFO: Angela Virostko
VP: Dave Goda
**VP:* Curt Owens
VP: Gary Smith
IT Man: Robert Depasse
Advt Dir: Kevin Payton
Art Dir: Kara Cress

D-U-N-S 06-184-1901
GREEN LEAF POWER LLC
2600 Capitol Ave, Sacramento, CA 95816-5927
Tel (916) 596-2500 *Founded/Ownrshp* 2012
Sales 23.7MM^E *EMP* 60^E
SIC 4911 Generation, electric power
CEO: Hugh Smith
VP: Russell Huffman

D-U-N-S 60-240-7103
GREEN LIGHT CAPITAL INC
140 E 45th St Fl 24, New York, NY 10017-7142
Tel (212) 922-9370 *Founded/Ownrshp* 1996
Sales 631.6MM^E *EMP* 9,300
SIC 6726 Management investment funds, closed-end; Management investment funds, closed-end
Pr: David Einhorn
COO: Daniel Roitman
CFO: Harry Brendler
Sr Cor Off: Dennis Ho
Admn Mgr: Jeff Keswin
Admn Mgr: Eric Streisand
Snr Mgr: Sean Farrell

D-U-N-S 05-974-7286
GREEN LIGHT ENERGY SOLUTIONS CORP
220 Lombard St Apt 823, San Francisco, CA 94111-1159
Tel (415) 834-9434 *Founded/Ownrshp* 2010
Sales 50.0MM *EMP* 20
SIC 7389 Translation services; Translation services
CEO: Alex Feerer

D-U-N-S 04-257-6348 EXP
GREEN LINE EQUIP INC (NE)
JOHN DEERE
4050 W Stolley Park Rd, Grand Island, NE 68803-5505
Tel (308) 384-8777 *Founded/Ownrshp* 1967
Sales 25.4MM^E *EMP* 110
SIC 5083 7699 Farm implements; Tractors, agricultural; Harvesting machinery & equipment; Planting machinery & equipment; Farm machinery repair; Tractor repair; Farm implements; Tractors, agricultural; Harvesting machinery & equipment; Planting machinery & equipment; Farm machinery repair; Tractor repair
Pr: Russ Rerucha
**Treas:* Darrel Anderson
**Sec:* Greg Rerucha
Site Mgr: Ed Bauer

D-U-N-S 02-442-8864
GREEN LOCAL SCHOOLS INC (OH)
1900 Greensburg Rd, Green, OH 44232
Tel (330) 896-7500 *Founded/Ownrshp* 1915
Sales 34.7MM *EMP* 450
SIC 8211 Public elementary & secondary schools; Vocational high school; Public elementary & secondary schools; Vocational high school
COO: Duane Kortze
**Treas:* Roy Swartz
Bd of Dir: Allie Anenson
IT Man: Pam Matiatizo

D-U-N-S 00-691-7454
GREEN MANOR CORP (CT)
JOURNAL INQUIRER
306 Progress Dr, Manchester, CT 06042-9011
Tel (860) 643-8111 *Founded/Ownrshp* 1950
Sales 35.8MM^E *EMP* 560
SIC 2711 Newspapers, publishing & printing; Newspapers, publishing & printing
Pr: Neil H Ellis
**Sec:* Elizabeth Ellis

D-U-N-S 00-890-1290
GREEN MEADOW FARMS INC
6400 N Hollister Rd, Elsie, MI 48831-9702
Tel (989) 862-5134 *Founded/Ownrshp* 1951
Sales 23.4MM^E *EMP* 70
SIC 0241 Dairy farms
Pr: Velmar Green
**Sec:* Charles Green
**VP:* Craig Green

GREEN MOUNTAIN BEVERAGES
See VERMONT HARD CIDER CO LLC

D-U-N-S 08-047-5379
GREEN MOUNTAIN COLLEGE
1 Brennan Cir, Poultney, VT 05764-1199
Tel (802) 287-8000 *Founded/Ownrshp* 1958
Sales 29.5MM *EMP* 140
Accts O Brien Shortle Reynolds & Sab
SIC 8221 College, except junior; College, except junior
Pr: Paul Fontaeyn
**CFO:* Joseph A Manning II
**Treas:* Catherine V Parker
VP: Joseph Petrick
VP: William Throop
**VP:* Lorene F Wilbur
Comm Dir: Kevin Coburn
Comm Dir: Ronald Steffens
Dir Sec: Gary Paolillo
Store Mgr: Heather Lyng
Ql Cn Mgr: Victor Garza

D-U-N-S 83-933-0685
GREEN MOUNTAIN COMMUNICATIONS INC
702 Riverwood Dr, Pembroke, NH 03275-3700
Tel (603) 717-7117 *Founded/Ownrshp* 1995
Sales 24.5MM^E *EMP* 77
SIC 1731 1799 8711 Communications specialization; Telephone & telephone equipment installation; Antenna installation; Engineering services
Pr: Victor Drouin
**VP:* Catherine Drouin
Dir IT: Will Panek
Sls Dir: Jose Burgos
Snr PM: Jason Lander

D-U-N-S 07-602-9545 EXP
GREEN MOUNTAIN CORP
PETER GLENN SKI AND SPORTS
2901 W Oakland Park Blvd, Oakland Park, FL 33311-1243
Tel (954) 484-7800 *Founded/Ownrshp* 1975
Sales 30.9MM^E *EMP* 200
SIC 5941 Skiing equipment; Skiing equipment
CEO: Edward J Hamilton Jr
**Pr:* Peter G Hamilton
**Sec:* Lori Underwood
**VP:* Carolyn T Hamilton
**VP:* Martin Underwood
Exec: Connie Miller
Dir IT: David Libby
Mktg Dir: Ned Hamilton

D-U-N-S 01-911-8595
GREEN MOUNTAIN ELECTRIC SUPPLY INC
GLENFALLS ELECTRIC SUPPLY
5452 Us Route 5 Ste G, Newport, VT 05855-9037
Tel (802) 334-7963 *Founded/Ownrshp* 1977
Sales 39.5MM^E *EMP* 30
SIC 5063 Electrical supplies
Pr: Gregg Laber
**Treas:* Scott Laber
Sr VP: Brian Allard
**VP:* Josh Laber

D-U-N-S 17-687-1481 IMP
■ **GREEN MOUNTAIN ENERGY CO**
BEGREEN
(*Suby of* NRG ENERGY INC) ★
300 W 6th St Ste 1600, Austin, TX 78701-4521
Tel (512) 691-6100 *Founded/Ownrshp* 2010
Sales 184.4MM^E *EMP* 240
SIC 4911 ; ; ;
Pr: Paul Thomas
**Pr:* Scott Hart
**CFO:* Bryan M Decordova
**Ofcr:* Gillan Taddune
Ofcr: Robert Thomas
**Sr VP:* Paul N Markovich
**Sr VP:* Ron Prater
**Sr VP:* Robert P Thomas
VP: Jeff Bettison
VP: Michael Current
VP: Mark McShane
VP: Bridgett Neely
VP: Gary Phillips
VP: Mary L Shields
VP: Craig Trupo
Dir Risk M: Leonard Gardner

D-U-N-S 07-416-8332
GREEN MOUNTAIN MESSENGER INC (VT)
54 Echo Pl Unit 1, Williston, VT 05495-9302
Tel (802) 862-7662 *Founded/Ownrshp* 1991
Sales 25.8MM^E *EMP* 140
SIC 4513 4215 Air courier services; Courier services, except by air; Air courier services; Courier services, except by air
Pr: Doug Haser
Trfc Dir: Patrick Webb

GREEN MOUNTAIN POWER
See VERMONT ELECTRIC POWER CO INC

GREEN MOUNTAIN POWER
See CENTRAL VERMONT PUBLIC SERVICE CORP

D-U-N-S 00-793-9531 IMP
GREEN MOUNTAIN POWER CORP (VT)
(*Suby of* NORTHERN NEW ENGLAND ENERGY CORP) ★
163 Acorn Ln, Colchester, VT 05446-6611
Tel (888) 835-4672 *Founded/Ownrshp* 1893
Sales 171.0MM^E *EMP* 190
Accts Deloitte & Touche Llp Boston
SIC 4911 1623 1731 Distribution, electric power; Transmission, electric power; ; Electric power line construction; Electric power systems contractors; Distribution, electric power; Transmission, electric power; ; Electric power line construction; Electric power systems contractors
Pr: Mary G Powell
Ch Bd: Robert Tessier
Pr: Dawn Bugbee
CFO: Dawn D Bugbee
CFO: Bob Griffin
Ex VP: Norman Terreri
VP: Robert Griffin
VP: Donald J Rendall
VP: Donald Rendall
VP: Mary Saul
VP: Stephen Terry
VP: Steve Terry
Dir Bus: Kirk Shields
Board of Directors: Elizabeth A Bankowski, William H Bruett, Merrill O Burns, David R Coates, Kathleen C Hoyt, Euclid A Irving, Marc A Vanderheyden

D-U-N-S 79-132-2964
GREEN MTN CONCERT SERVICES INC
GMCS
25 Wentworth Dr, Williston, VT 05495-9733
Tel (802) 662-1210 *Founded/Ownrshp* 1995
Sales 1.0MM^E *EMP* 350
SIC 7381 Guard services; Burglary protection service; Protective services, guard; Security guard service; Guard services; Burglary protection service; Protective services, guard; Security guard service
Pr: Kevin Cheney
COO: Kenneth Schneider
**CFO:* Robert Sinkewicz
Rgnl Mgr: Jason Clifford
Rgnl Mgr: Mike Rhilinger
Board of Directors: Jefferson Goodrich

D-U-N-S 16-090-2201
GREEN OAKS AT MEDICAL CITY DALLAS
GREEN OAKS HOSPITAL
7808 Clodus Fields Dr, Dallas, TX 75251-2206
Tel (972) 991-9504 *Founded/Ownrshp* 1983
Sales 36.3MM^E *EMP* 350
SIC 8063 Psychiatric hospitals; Psychiatric hospitals
CEO: Tom Collin
CFO: Scott Cook
Ofcr: Sherry Cusumano
Sls&Mrk Ex: John Dornheim

D-U-N-S 03-553-8771
■ **GREEN OAKS BEHAVIORAL HEALTH CARE**
(*Suby of* HCA INC) ★
7808 Clodus Fields Dr, Dallas, TX 75251-2206
Tel (972) 991-9504 *Founded/Ownrshp* 1998
Sales 7.2MM^E *EMP* 300
SIC 8063 Psychiatric hospitals; Psychiatric hospitals
Pr: Tom Collins
Doctor: Mickey Gotham

D-U-N-S 19-249-9408 IMP
GREEN OAKS BEHAVIORAL HEALTHCARE SERVICES
HCA GREEN OAKS
7808 Clodus Fields Dr, Dallas, TX 75251-2206
Tel (972) 991-9504 *Founded/Ownrshp* 1983
Sales 8.7MM^E *EMP* 310
SIC 8062 General medical & surgical hospitals; General medical & surgical hospitals
Prin: Pam Whitley
**CEO:* Tom Collins
CFO: Jason Tillman

GREEN OAKS HOSPITAL
See GREEN OAKS AT MEDICAL CITY DALLAS

D-U-N-S 01-453-7943
GREEN PARK GROUP LLC
(*Suby of* WARBURG PINCUS LLC) ★
3010 Old Ranch Pkwy # 330, Seal Beach, CA 90740-2764
Tel (562) 446-4100 *Founded/Ownrshp* 1997
Sales 30.0MM *EMP* 20
SIC 6531 Real estate agents & managers; Real estate agents & managers

D-U-N-S 07-888-7136
■ **GREEN PLAINS ATKINSON LLC**
(*Suby of* GREEN PLAINS INC) ★
49131 Highway 20, Oneill, NE 68763-4693
Tel (402) 315-1658 *Founded/Ownrshp* 2013
Sales 150.0MM *EMP* 40
SIC 2869 Ethyl alcohol, ethanol; Ethyl alcohol, ethanol

D-U-N-S 18-638-0718
▲ **GREEN PLAINS INC**
450 Regency Pkwy Ste 400, Omaha, NE 68114-3701
Tel (402) 884-8700 *Founded/Ownrshp* 2004
Sales 3.2MMM *EMP* 710
Accts Kpmg Llp Omaha Nebraska
Tkr Sym GPRE *Exch* NGS
SIC 2869 2046 Ethyl alcohol, ethanol; Corn oil products; Ethyl alcohol, ethanol; Corn oil products
Pr: Todd A Becker
**Ch Bd:* Wayne Hoovestol
COO: Jeff S Briggs
CFO: Jerry L Peters
Treas: George P Simpkins
Bd of Dir: Jim Anderson
Bd of Dir: Michael Walsh
Ex VP: Steve Bleyl
Ex VP: Steve Blyeyl
Ex VP: Michelle S Mapes
Ex VP: Edgar Seward
VP: David Borcyk
VP: Kirk Johnson
VP: Michael Metzler
VP: Jim Stark
Dir Lab: Toria Clausen
Dir Lab: Mark Maybon
Comm Dir: Steve Duhn

D-U-N-S 84-898-4915
■ **GREEN PLAINS TRADE GROUP LLC**
(*Suby of* GREEN PLAINS INC) ★
450 Regency Pkwy Ste 400, Omaha, NE 68114-3701
Tel (402) 884-8700 *Founded/Ownrshp* 2008
Sales 30.2MM^E *EMP* 66^E
SIC 2819 Industrial inorganic chemicals
Pr: Todd Becker
COO: Jeff Briggs
CFO: Jerry Peters
Ex VP: Steve Bleyl

GREEN READY MIX OF MISSOURI
See PENNYS CONCRETE INC

D-U-N-S 87-746-1608 IMP
GREEN RESOURCE LLC
5204 Highgreen Ct, Colfax, NC 27235-9800
Tel (336) 855-6363 *Founded/Ownrshp* 2004
Sales 61.5MM^E *EMP* 64^E
SIC 5191 Fertilizer & fertilizer materials; Fertilizer & fertilizer materials
**CFO:* Ben Holcomb
Sls Dir: Abel G Mateu
Sls Mgr: Jim Davis

D-U-N-S 01-123-3629
GREEN RIDGE SERVICES LLC
6185 Industrial Way, Livermore, CA 94551-9750
Tel (925) 245-5500 *Founded/Ownrshp* 1998
Sales 23.8MM^E *EMP* 60
SIC 4911 Electric services; Electric services

D-U-N-S 07-925-6442
GREEN RIVER COMMUNITY COLLEGE (WA)
12401 Se 320th St, Auburn, WA 98092-3622
Tel (253) 833-9111 *Founded/Ownrshp* 1965
Sales 5.8MM *EMP* 1,041
Accts Peterson Sullivan Llp Seattle
SIC 8222 8299 8221 Community college; Educational service, nondegree granting: continuing educ.; Colleges universities & professional schools; Community college; Educational service, nondegree granting: continuing educ.; Colleges universities & professional schools
Pr: Eileen Ely
Pr: T I Vuong
**VP:* Rick Drumfield
Off Admin: Melissa Comeau
Dir IT: Tim Mason
HC Dir: Ross Jennings

D-U-N-S 07-966-8257
GREEN RIVER REGIONAL MENTAL HEALTH MENTAL RETARDATION BOARD INC
RIVER VALLEY BEHAVIORIAL HEALTH
1100 Walnut St Ste 46, Owensboro, KY 42301-2976
Tel (270) 689-6500 *Founded/Ownrshp* 1968
Sales 35.8MM *EMP* 835
Accts Bkd Llp Evansville In
SIC 8051 8052 8093 Mental retardation hospital; Home for the mentally retarded, with health care; Specialty outpatient clinics; Mental retardation hospital; Home for the mentally retarded, with health care; Specialty outpatient clinics
Pr: Gayle J Di Cesare
COO: James Stein
**COO:* Kenneth Stein
**CFO:* J Michael Mountain
HC Dir: Anne Parrott

D-U-N-S 61-744-8287 IMP/EXP
GREEN RUBBER-KENNEDY AG LP
1310 Dayton St, Salinas, CA 93901-4416
Tel (831) 753-6100 *Founded/Ownrshp* 1990
Sales 50.8MM^E *EMP* 99
SIC 5083 5085 Agricultural machinery & equipment; Industrial supplies; Agricultural machinery & equipment; Industrial supplies
Pt: John H Green
Pt: Patricia Green
Pt: Mark D Kennedy
Sls Mgr: Terry Chatelle
Sales Asso: Ronnie Mena

D-U-N-S 96-355-4444
GREEN STREAM CO
29414 Phillips St, Elkhart, IN 46514-1022
Tel (574) 293-1949 *Founded/Ownrshp* 2010
Sales 27.5MM^E *EMP* 90
SIC 4953 Recycling, waste materials
Pr: Amit Shah

D-U-N-S 04-351-2284 IMP
GREEN SUPPLY INC
GSI LAW ENFORCEMENT
3059 Audrain Road 581, Vandalia, MO 63382-4104
Tel (573) 594-6771 *Founded/Ownrshp* 1967
Sales 40.0MM *EMP* 95
SIC 5091 Firearms, sporting; Archery equipment; Ammunition, sporting
Pr: Robert L Green
**VP:* Karolyn Green
Mktg Dir: Edna Wheeler

D-U-N-S 02-945-3180 IMP
GREEN THUMB INTERNATIONAL INC
7105 Jordan Ave, Canoga Park, CA 91303
Tel (818) 340-6400 *Founded/Ownrshp* 1965
Sales 52.4MM^E *EMP* 349
SIC 5261 Nursery stock, seeds & bulbs; Lawn & garden supplies; Lawn & garden equipment; Nursery stock, seeds & bulbs; Lawn & garden supplies; Lawn & garden equipment
Pr: Max D Bergquist
**Treas:* Robert D Bergquist

GREEN THUMB NURSERY
See SUPER GARDEN CENTERS INC

D-U-N-S 93-973-0941
GREEN THUMB PRODUCE
2648 W Ramsey St, Banning, CA 92220-3716
Tel (951) 849-4711 *Founded/Ownrshp* 1996
Sales 93.4MM^E *EMP* 250
SIC 5148 Fresh fruits & vegetables; Fresh fruits & vegetables
Pr: Lonnie Saverino

D-U-N-S 18-004-2129 IMP
GREEN TOKAI CO LTD
GTC
(*Suby of* TOKAI KOGYO CO.,LTD.)
55 Robert Wright Dr, Brookville, OH 45309-1931
Tel (937) 833-5444 *Founded/Ownrshp* 1987
Sales 133.1MM^E *EMP* 825
SIC 3714 3069 Motor vehicle body components & frame; Rubber automotive products; Motor vehicle body components & frame; Rubber automotive products
Pr: Nobuaki Kimura
**CEO:* Fumi Kazu Hosada
VP: Dan Dowers
VP Opers: Dan Bowers
Ql Cn Mgr: Jerome Scott
Sls Mgr: Jeremy Journell
Snr Mgr: Thomas Hemmerick

D-U-N-S 01-768-3335
GREEN TOWNSHIP HOSPITALITY LLC
HOLIDAY INN
5505 Rybolt Rd, Cincinnati, OH 45248-1029
Tel (513) 574-6000 *Founded/Ownrshp* 2002
Sales 13.2MM^E *EMP* 294
SIC 7011 5812 Hotels & motels; Eating places; Hotels & motels; Eating places

GREEN TOYOTA
See GREEN FAMILY STORES INC

GREEN TREE
See GTCS HOLDINGS LLC

D-U-N-S 13-989-4690
■ **GREEN TREE SERVICING LLC**
DITECH FINANCIAL
(*Suby of* GREEN TREE) ★
345 Sint Peter St Ste 300, Saint Paul, MN 55102
Tel (651) 293-4800 *Founded/Ownrshp* 1994
Sales NA *EMP* 1,800
SIC 6162 Loan correspondents; Loan correspondents
Genl Couns: Brian Corey
Pr: Mark Kosanke
Pr: Jeff Moore
CFO: Cheryl Colins
Chf Cred: Ron Siemers
Ex VP: Jeff Hilligoss
Sr VP: Jim Breakey
Sr VP: David Slear
VP: Bill Ashley
VP: Alan Delman
VP: Matthew Detwiler
VP: Chip Hidinger
VP: Randy Shannon
VP: Michael Yedlicka
Exec: Barbara Didrikson

D-U-N-S 05-168-0739
GREEN VALLEY CO-OP INC
219 3rd St, Marietta, OH 45750-3002
Tel (740) 374-7741 *Founded/Ownrshp* 2002
Sales 34.4MM *EMP* 63
SIC 5191 Farm supplies; Feed; Fertilizers & agricultural chemicals; Garden supplies

D-U-N-S 94-583-6518
■ **GREEN VALLEY COAL CO**
(*Suby of* APPALACHIA HOLDING CO) ★
Rr 20, Leivasy, WV 26676
Tel (304) 846-6600 *Founded/Ownrshp* 1912
Sales 28.7MM^E *EMP* 500
SIC 1221 1241 1222 Coal preparation plant, bituminous or lignite; Coal mining services; Bituminous coal-underground mining; Coal preparation plant, bituminous or lignite; Coal mining services; Bituminous coal-underground mining
Pr: Jeffery L Griffith
**Pr:* Jon C Brown
**Treas:* G Scott Cole

D-U-N-S 05-051-4496
GREEN VALLEY CORP (CA)
SWENSON, BARRY BUILDER
777 N 1st St Fl 5, San Jose, CA 95112-6350
Tel (408) 287-0246 *Founded/Ownrshp* 1961
Sales 90.3MM^E *EMP* 120
SIC 1542 1522 6512 Commercial & office building, new construction; Multi-family dwelling construction; Commercial & industrial building operation; Commercial & office building, new construction; Multi-family dwelling construction; Commercial & industrial building operation
Pr: C Barron Swenson
**CFO:* Lee Ann Woodard
**Sr VP:* Steven W Andrews
**Sr VP:* Ronald L Cot
**Sr VP:* David A Gibbons
**VP:* Steven Andrews
**VP:* Ron Cote
**VP:* Jeffrey Current
**VP:* David Gibbons
**VP:* Jesse Nickell
**VP:* William Ryan

D-U-N-S 10-829-6039
■ **GREEN VALLEY DISPOSAL CO INC**
(*Suby of* AMERICAN SANITATION) ★
300 Raemisch Rd, Waunakee, WI 53597-9665
Tel (608) 849-8778 *Founded/Ownrshp* 1982
Sales 29.5MM^E *EMP* 100
SIC 4953 Refuse collection & disposal services

D-U-N-S 05-002-1547
GREEN VALLEY FARM SUPPLY INC
GVFS
10 Gonzales River Rd, Gonzales, CA 93926
Tel (831) 675-0168 *Founded/Ownrshp* 1999
Sales 24.7MM^E *EMP* 22
SIC 5191 Farm supplies; Fertilizers & agricultural chemicals
Pr: Michael Kennedy
**Sec:* Sam McKinsey
**VP:* Stan Pura

GREEN VALLEY GROCERY
See MIDJIT MARKET INC

D-U-N-S 07-957-5302
GREEN VALLEY HOSPITAL LLC (AZ)
9237 E Via De Ventura, Scottsdale, AZ 85258-3370
Tel (520) 808-2382 *Founded/Ownrshp* 2011
Sales 39.8MM^E *EMP* 316^E
SIC 8062 General medical & surgical hospitals; General medical & surgical hospitals
CEO: David Wanger

D-U-N-S 00-439-1207
GREEN VALLEY PACKING INC
ALBERT'S MEATS
2992 Green Valley Rd, Claysville, PA 15323-1360
Tel (724) 948-3321 *Founded/Ownrshp* 1974
Sales 22.6MM *EMP* 55
SIC 2011 2013

D-U-N-S 87-624-4737
GREEN VALLEY RANCH GAMING LLC
GREEN VLY RNCH RESORT & SPAS
2300 Paseo Verde Pkwy, Henderson, NV 89052-2672
Tel (702) 617-7777 *Founded/Ownrshp* 2000
Sales 49.4MM^E *EMP* 1,500
SIC 7011 Casino hotel; Casino hotel
Genl Mgr: Bob Finch
**VP:* Joe Hasson
Natl Sales: Dana Levin
Sls Mgr: Jose Rodriguez

GREEN VLY RNCH RESORT & SPAS
See GREEN VALLEY RANCH GAMING LLC

D-U-N-S 82-815-3853
GREEN WORLDWIDE SHIPPING LLC
619 E College Ave Ste F, Decatur, GA 30030-5330
Tel (404) 974-2910 *Founded/Ownrshp* 2008
Sales 26.4MM^E *EMP* 50
Accts Mj Porter & Associates Ll
SIC 4731 Freight transportation arrangement
**VP:* Peter Aaro-Hansen
**VP:* Edward Chambers
VP: Niel Landeg
**VP:* Rex Sherman

D-U-N-S 02-383-9392
GREEN-GIFFORD INC
GREEN GIFFORD NISSAN
6440 N Military Hwy, Norfolk, VA 23518-5249
Tel (757) 855-2091 *Founded/Ownrshp* 1939
Sales 29.7MM^E *EMP* 120
Accts Mcphillips Roberts & Deans P

SIC 5511 Automobiles, new & used; Automobiles, new & used
Pr: Michael E Galloway
**VP:* John Woodall

D-U-N-S 18-296-2472 IMP/EXP
GREEN-TEK INC
3708 Enterprise Dr, Janesville, WI 53546-8737
Tel (608) 754-7336 Founded/Ownrshp 1987
Sales 30.9MM^E EMP 40
SIC 5191 Greenhouse equipment & supplies
Pr: Paul Jacobson
**CFO:* Eli Bracha
**VP:* Linda Bracha

D-U-N-S 00-696-2948
GREEN-WAY COOPERATIVE SERVICE CO
3520 E River Rd Ne, Rochester, MN 55906-5407
Tel (507) 289-4086 Founded/Ownrshp 1929
Sales 143.9MM EMP 150
SIC 5541 5171 5191 Filling stations, gasoline; Petroleum bulk stations & terminals; Fertilizer & fertilizer materials; Chemicals, agricultural; Seeds: field, garden & flower; Filling stations, gasoline; Petroleum bulk stations & terminals; Fertilizer & fertilizer materials; Chemicals, agricultural; Seeds: field, garden & flower
Pr: David Eickdoff
**CEO:* Tim Clemens
VP: Bob Wiggins

D-U-N-S 79-475-4812
GREENACRES FOUNDATION
8255 Spooky Hollow Rd, Cincinnati, OH 45242-6518
Tel (513) 891-4227 Founded/Ownrshp 1989
Sales 20.2MM EMP 20^E
SIC 8699 Personal interest organization; Personal interest organization
Ex VP: Carter Randolph
CFO: Brianna Cole
Exec: Anne Lyon

GREENALL
See E B STONE & SON INC

D-U-N-S 16-756-5337
GREENBACK CAPITAL MORTGAGE CORP
1086 Teaneck Rd Ste 4e, Teaneck, NJ 07666-4857
Tel (201) 837-6400 Founded/Ownrshp 1989
Sales 60.0MM EMP 3
SIC 6211 Mortgages, buying & selling; Mortgages, buying & selling
Pr: Carl Guzman
Pr: Robyn Safier
VP: Robert Meyer

D-U-N-S 62-644-4202
■ **GREENBACKS INC**
ALL A DOLLAR
(Suby of DOLLAR TREE INC) ★
2369 W Orton Cir, Salt Lake City, UT 84119-7679
Tel (801) 977-7777 Founded/Ownrshp 2003
Sales 152.9MM^E EMP 1,600
SIC 5331 Variety stores; Variety stores
Pr: Brent L Bishop
VP: Terry Green
**VP:* Richard Wolfley
Art Dir: Joe Norwood

D-U-N-S 08-716-6591 IMP
GREENBALL CORP
TOWMASTER TIRE & WHEEL
222 S Harbor Blvd Ste 700, Anaheim, CA 92805-3730
Tel (714) 782-3060 Founded/Ownrshp 1976
Sales 57.7MM^E EMP 170
SIC 5014 5013 3999 Tires & tubes; Wheels, motor vehicle; Tires & tubes; Wheels, motor vehicle; Atomizers, toiletry
CEO: Chris S H Tsai
**VP:* Jenny Tsai
Sls Mgr: Doug Shultz

D-U-N-S 78-425-3382
■ **GREENBANK**
(Suby of GREEN BANKSHARES INC) ★
100 N Main St, Greeneville, TN 37743-4920
Tel (423) 639-5111 Founded/Ownrshp 2002
Sales NA EMP 789^E
SIC 6022 State commercial banks; State commercial banks
Pr: Stan R Puckett
VP: Telena Sizemore

D-U-N-S 02-078-4922
GREENBAUM ROWE SMITH & DAVIS LLP
99 Wood Ave S Ste 400, Iselin, NJ 08830-2715
Tel (732) 549-5600 Founded/Ownrshp 1914
Sales 24.2MM^E EMP 194^E
SIC 8111 General practice law office; General practice law office
Pt: Paul A Rowe
Pt: Alan Davis
Pt: Arthur M Greenbaum
Pt: Michael Himmel
Dir Bus: Diana Parker
Counsel: Maura E Blau
Counsel: Michele A Daitz
Counsel: Christine F Marks
Counsel: Franklin Sachs
Counsel: Robert S Underhill

D-U-N-S 00-791-9251
GREENBAX ENTERPRISES INC (SC)
884 Johnnie Dodds Blvd B, Mount Pleasant, SC 29464-3140
Tel (866) 891-1195 Founded/Ownrshp 1955
Sales 400.0MM EMP 200
Accts Ernst & Young Llp Greenville
SIC 7389 6159 6512 Trading stamp promotion & redemption; Small business investment companies; Nonresidential building operators; Trading stamp promotion & redemption; Small business investment companies; Nonresidential building operators
Pr: David Schools
Ex VP: William Edenfield
Sr VP: Robert Masche

D-U-N-S 00-983-3856
GREENBELT ELECTRIC COOPERATIVE INC (TX)
706 10th St, Wellington, TX 79095-3204
Tel (806) 447-2536 Founded/Ownrshp 1938
Sales 23.9MM EMP 37
Accts Bolinger Segars Gilbert & Moss
SIC 4911 Distribution, electric power; Distribution, electric power
Treas: Walter Camp
VP: T B Henderson
Genl Mgr: Stan McClendon
Off Mgr: Debra Belew
Off Mgr: Vickie Porter

D-U-N-S 08-435-0214
GREENBERG FARROW ARCHITECTURE INC (GA)
1430 W Peachtree St Nw # 200, Atlanta, GA 30309-2932
Tel (404) 601-4000 Founded/Ownrshp 1974, 2000
Sales 42.0MM^E EMP 200
SIC 8711 8712 Engineering services; Architectural services; Engineering services; Architectural services
Pr: Essie Ghadrdan
**Sec:* Margaret Brinkley
**Sr VP:* John Clifford
**Sr VP:* Navid Maqami
**Sr VP:* Hughes Thompson
**VP:* John Norzad Sr
Dir Bus: Ruth Chase
Dir Bus: Alan Pinsker
Snr PM: Charles Beadles
Snr PM: Larry Diehl
Snr PM: Michael Morgan

D-U-N-S 07-412-1989
GREENBERG GLUSKER FIELDS CLAMAN & MACHTINGER LLP
1900 Avenue Of The Stars 21f, Los Angeles, CA 90067-4301
Tel (310) 553-3610 Founded/Ownrshp 1959
Sales 40.7MM^E EMP 200
SIC 8111 General practice attorney, lawyer; General practice attorney, lawyer
Prin: Jonathan R Fitzgarrald
Pt: ARI B Brumer
Pt: Ricardo P Cestero
Pt: Stephen Claman
Pt: Bert Fields
Pt: Matt Galsor
Pt: Arthur N Greenberg
Pt: Jill A Cossman
COO: Henry Finkelstein
Prin: David Neesen
Ex Dir: Kimberly Lahs

D-U-N-S 94-714-6171
GREENBERG TRAURIG LLP
(Suby of GREENBERG TRAURIG PA) ★
200 Park Ave Fl 39, New York, NY 10166-1400
Tel (212) 801-9200 Founded/Ownrshp 1999
Sales 241.1MM^E EMP 3,500
SIC 8111 General practice attorney, lawyer; General practice attorney, lawyer
Mng Pt: Richard Rosenbaum
Sr Pt: Cliff Neimeth
Mktg Dir: Jill Perry
Corp Couns: Benjamin Adams
Corp Couns: Andrew Cosentino
Corp Couns: Jay Gordon
Corp Couns: James Leshaw
Corp Couns: Roderick Macleish
Corp Couns: Keith Reich
Counsel: Tami Cowden
Counsel: James Dempsey

D-U-N-S 07-130-4984
GREENBERG TRAURIG PA (FL)
333 Se 2nd Ave Ste 4400, Miami, FL 33131-2184
Tel (305) 579-0500 Founded/Ownrshp 1969
Sales 312.3MM^E EMP 3,500
SIC 8111 General practice law office; General practice law office
CEO: Richard A Rosenbaum
Pt: Richard Melnick
**Pr:* Matthew B Gorson
**Ch:* Larry J Hoffman
Ch: Paul Schindler
**VP:* Richard G Garrett
**Prin:* David E Hirsch
IT Man: Eric Scheele

D-U-N-S 07-640-1124
GREENBERRY INDUSTRIAL LLC
600 Se Maritime Ave # 190, Vancouver, WA 98661-8044
Tel (360) 567-0006 Founded/Ownrshp 1999
Sales 64.1MM^E EMP 350^E
SIC 1711 1541 3443 3441

D-U-N-S 01-412-1292
GREENBRIAR EQUITY GROUP LLC
555 Theodore Fremd Ave A201, Rye, NY 10580-1437
Tel (914) 925-9600 Founded/Ownrshp 1999
Sales 282.2MM^E EMP 800^E
SIC 4789 6799 Cargo loading & unloading services; Cargo loading & unloading services; Investors
Mng Pt: Reginald L Jones III
Mng Dir: Raynard D Benvenuti
Mng Dir: Jill C Raker
Off Mgr: Francine Vitale
IT Man: Scott Parkis

D-U-N-S 05-238-2848
GREENBRIAR HOLDINGS HOUSTON LTD
GHH
2911 Turtle Creek Blvd, Dallas, TX 75219-6247
Tel (214) 520-0056 Founded/Ownrshp 1994
Sales 22.0MM^E EMP 151
SIC 6719 Investment holding companies, except banks

D-U-N-S 02-500-4318
▲ **GREENBRIER COMPANIES INC**
1 Centerpointe Dr Ste 200, Lake Oswego, OR 97035-8612
Tel (503) 684-7000 Founded/Ownrshp 1981
Sales 2.2MMM EMP 9,244^E
Tkr Sym GBX Exch NYS
SIC 3743 4789 Railroad equipment, except locomotives; Railroad maintenance & repair services; Railroad equipment, except locomotives; Railroad maintenance & repair services
Ch Bd: William A Furman
CFO: Mark J Rittenbaum
Chf Cred: Martin R Baker
Ofcr: Walter T Hannan
Ex VP: Martin Graham
Ex VP: Victoria McManus
Sr VP: Adrian J Downes
VP: Chuck Garman
VP: Zara Horn
VP: Anne T Manning
VP: Glenn Rosebrook
VP: Tim Schitter
VP: Duane Turnes
VP: Paul Wostmann
Exec: Walter Hannan
Dir Bus: Ryan Roecker
Board of Directors: Thomas B Fargo, Graeme A Jack, Duane C McDougall, A Daniel O'neal Jr, Charles J Swindells, Wendy L Teramoto, Donald A Washburn, Kelly M Williams

D-U-N-S 19-308-0207
GREENBRIER COUNTY BOARD OF EDUCATION
202 Chestnut St, Lewisburg, WV 24901-1108
Tel (304) 647-6470 Founded/Ownrshp 1800
Sales 28.5MM^E EMP 740
SIC 8211 Public elementary & secondary schools; Administration of educational programs; School board
Pr: Jeanie Wyatt
IT Man: Christy Clemons-Rodgers
Pr Dir: Patty Gray

D-U-N-S 07-979-9744
GREENBRIER COUNTY SCHOOLS
202 Chestnut St, Lewisburg, WV 24901-1108
Tel (304) 647-6470 Founded/Ownrshp 2015
Sales 11.4MM^E EMP 904^E
SIC 8211 Public elementary & secondary schools
Dir Sec: Chris Sienkiewicz
Pr Dir: Christy Rodgers
Teacher Pr: Douglas Clemons
HC Dir: Paula McCoy

D-U-N-S 16-158-0337
GREENBRIER DODGE OF CHESAPEAKE INC
1717 S Military Hwy, Chesapeake, VA 23320-2611
Tel (757) 420-2800 Founded/Ownrshp 1991
Sales 23.0MM^E EMP 60
SIC 5511 Automobiles, new & used; Automobiles, new & used
Pr: Ray L Kantowski Jr
**VP:* Thurston I Watkins III
Genl Mgr: Rob Jones

GREENBRIER G M C TRUCKS
See GREENBRIER OLDSMOBILE GMC TRUCKS INC

D-U-N-S 00-794-5520
GREENBRIER HOTEL CORP (WV)
(Suby of JUSTICE FAMILY GROUP LLC) ★
300 W Main St, Wht Sphr Spgs, WV 24986-2498
Tel (304) 536-1110 Founded/Ownrshp 1946, 2014
Sales 100.2MM^E EMP 1,000
SIC 7011 Resort hotel; Resort hotel
CEO: James C Justice III
**Pr:* Jeff Kmiec
Pr: Bill Zimmerman
**Treas:* Michael McGovern
**Treas:* James T Miller
VP: Doug Balsley
Exec: Bryan Skelding
Adm Dir: Ginny Owens
Genl Mgr: Monte Hansen
Sales Exec: Hayes Beard
Sales Exec: Josh Hardy

D-U-N-S 00-634-6254
GREENBRIER INC
TIGER FUEL COMPANY
200 Carlton Rd, Charlottesville, VA 22902-5926
Tel (434) 817-2611 Founded/Ownrshp 1982
Sales 275.0MM EMP 200
SIC 6719 Investment holding companies, except banks; Investment holding companies, except banks
Pr: David G Sutton
**CFO:* Michael Johns

D-U-N-S 10-655-1500
■ **GREENBRIER LEASING CO LLC**
(Suby of GREENBRIER COMPANIES INC) ★
1 Centerpointe Dr Ste 200, Lake Oswego, OR 97035-8612
Tel (503) 684-7000 Founded/Ownrshp 1991
Sales 72.3MM^E EMP 100
SIC 5088 Railroad equipment & supplies; Railroad equipment & supplies
COO: Kevin Maughan
CFO: Larry Stanley
Ofcr: Martin Baker

D-U-N-S 07-885-3812
GREENBRIER OF VIRGINIA INC
SOUTHERN CHRYSLER JEEP
1414 S Military Hwy, Chesapeake, VA 23320-2604
Tel (757) 424-4600 Founded/Ownrshp 1978
Sales 29.7MM^E EMP 75^E
SIC 5521 Automobiles, used cars only
CEO: Shepherd William R
**Treas:* King Michael J
Ofcr: Holly Stoeckeler
Genl Mgr: Cameron Shaw

D-U-N-S 96-399-3824
GREENBRIER OF VIRGINIA INC
SOUTHERN DODGE CHRSLR JEEP RAM
2747 N Military Hwy, Norfolk, VA 23518-5606
Tel (757) 855-2277 Founded/Ownrshp 1978
Sales 25.0MM^E EMP 80
SIC 5511 Automobiles, new & used; Automobiles, new & used
CEO: William R Shepherd Jr
**Pr:* James J Moore III
**Treas:* Michael J King

D-U-N-S 06-342-0012
GREENBRIER OLDSMOBILE GMC TRUCKS INC
GREENBRIER G M C TRUCKS
1300 S Military Hwy, Chesapeake, VA 23320-2514
Tel (757) 424-6380 Founded/Ownrshp 1989
Sales 30.1MM^E EMP 91
SIC 5511 Automobiles, new & used; Pickups, new & used; Automobiles, new & used; Pickups, new & used
Pr: William R Shepherd Jr
Comm Man: Robert Rice

D-U-N-S 61-726-8594
GREENBRIER PUBLIC SCHOOLS
4 School Dr, Greenbrier, AR 72058-9267
Tel (501) 679-4808 Founded/Ownrshp 1994
Sales 10.8MM^E EMP 300
SIC 8621 Education & teacher association; Education & teacher association
Psych: Sherry Hogg

GREENBRIER RAIL SERVICES
See MERIDIAN RAIL ACQUISITION CORP

GREENBRIER RAIL SVCS-SPRNGFELD
See GBW RAILCAR SERVICES LLC

D-U-N-S 19-694-4409
■ **GREENBRIER RAILCAR LLC**
(Suby of GREENBRIER LEASING CO LLC) ★
1 Centerpointe Dr Ste 200, Lake Oswego, OR 97035-8612
Tel (503) 684-7000 Founded/Ownrshp 1987
Sales 32.7MM^E EMP 153^E
SIC 4789 Railroad car repair
**VP:* Robin Bisson
Genl Mgr: William A Furman

D-U-N-S 78-330-8935
GREENBRIER RESORT AND CLUB MANAGEMENT CO
300 W Main St, Wht Sphr Spgs, WV 24986-2498
Tel (304) 536-1110 Founded/Ownrshp 2009
Sales 84.2MM^E EMP 900
SIC 8741 Management services; Management services
Pr: James C Justice III
Pr: Jeff Kmiec
Treas: James T Miller
VP: Bruce Rosenberger
VP: Jerry Wayne
Exec: Rich Rosendale
Dir Sec: Jim Belka
IT Man: Robin Mieras

D-U-N-S 15-934-7699
GREENBRIER SCHOOL DISTRICT
4 School Dr, Greenbrier, AR 72058-9267
Tel (501) 679-4808 Founded/Ownrshp 1878
Sales 16.5MM^E EMP 290
SIC 8211 Public elementary & secondary schools; Public elementary & secondary schools

D-U-N-S 07-681-2536
■ **GREENBRIER VALLEY MEDICAL CENTER LLC**
(Suby of COMMUNITY HEALTH SYSTEMS INC) ★
202 Maplewood Ave, Ronceverte, WV 24970-1334
Tel (304) 647-6042 Founded/Ownrshp 2000
Sales 74.6MM^E EMP 475
SIC 8062 General medical & surgical hospitals; General medical & surgical hospitals
CEO: Rob Followell
CFO: Joy Fergie
Dir Lab: Nancy Hyre
Dir Lab: Nancy Scurlock
Dir Rx: Ruth Bartenslager
Chf Nrs Of: Molly Scarborough
Prin: Mark Nosacka
Software D: Paul Hanna
Software D: Mendy Paxton
Pr Mgr: Todd Jackson
Surgeon: Jefferson Casto

D-U-N-S 01-166-6765
GREENBROOK PONTIAC-GMC INC
GREEN BROOK G M C
101 Us Highway 22, Green Brook, NJ 08812-2128
Tel (732) 752-3000 Founded/Ownrshp 1999
Sales 69.3MM^E EMP 75
SIC 5511 7532 Automobiles, new & used; Body shop, automotive; Automobiles, new & used; Body shop, automotive
Pr: David Ferraez
**CFO:* Jennifer Moylan
**VP:* Bryan Ferraez
**Off Mgr:* Angela Clemens
Sls Mgr: Sarah Donnini
Sales Asso: Ernie Baptista
Sales Asso: Mike Nixon
Sales Asso: Garry Santos
Sales Asso: Michael Santucci
Sales Asso: Jim Sheehan
Sales Asso: Brani Vasiljevic

D-U-N-S 11-279-0738
GREENBURGH 11 UNION FREE SCHOOL DISTRICT
Childrens Vlg, Dobbs Ferry, NY 10522
Tel (914) 693-8500 Founded/Ownrshp 1928
Sales 12.3MM^E EMP 474
SIC 8211 Public elementary & secondary schools; Public elementary & secondary schools

D-U-N-S 07-272-1665
GREENBURGH CENTRAL SCHOOL DISTRICT
475 W Hartsdale Ave, Hartsdale, NY 10530-1367
Tel (914) 761-6000 Founded/Ownrshp 1928
Sales 26.4MM^E EMP 440

SIC 8211 Public combined elementary & secondary school; Public senior high school; Kindergarten; Public combined elementary & secondary school; Public senior high school; Kindergarten
Pr: Lloyd Newland
**VP:* David Warner
Prin: John B Murphy
Cmptr Lab: Diego Rendon
Dir IT: Miriam Bernabei
IT Man: Stanley Bronski

D-U-N-S 01-094-9055
GREENBURGH-NORTH CASTLE UNION FREE SCHOOL DISTRICT
71 Broadway, Dobbs Ferry, NY 10522-2834
Tel (914) 693-3030 *Founded/Ownrshp* 1969
Sales 18.7MM[E] *EMP* 450
SIC 8211 Public special education school; Public special education school
CIO: Denise Rivera
Schl Brd P: Nona Joseph

GREENBUSH
See SOUTHEAST KANSAS EDUCATION SERVICE CENTER

D-U-N-S 60-424-1385
GREENBUSH LOGISTICS INC
(*Suby of* GREAT SOUTHERN WOOD PRESERVING INC) ★
445 Singletary Rd, Abbeville, AL 36310
Tel (334) 585-0069 *Founded/Ownrshp* 2004
Sales 45.3MM[E] *EMP* 201
SIC 4731 Freight transportation arrangement; Freight transportation arrangement
Pr: James W Rane

D-U-N-S 07-144-3394
GREENCASTLE ANTRIM SCHOOL DISTRICT
500 Leitersburg St, Greencastle, PA 17225-1138
Tel (717) 597-3226 *Founded/Ownrshp* 1956
Sales 22.3MM[E] *EMP* 375
SIC 8211 Public combined elementary & secondary school; Public senior high school; Public combined elementary & secondary school; Public senior high school
IT Man: Jolinda Wilson
Schl Brd P: Brian Hissong
Teacher Pr: Tina Clever

D-U-N-S 07-205-7672
GREENCASTLE COMMUNITY SCHOOLS
GCSC
711 S Central Ave, Greencastle, IN 46135-2085
Tel (765) 653-9771 *Founded/Ownrshp* 1974
Sales 18.4MM[E] *EMP* 280
SIC 8211 Public elementary & secondary schools; Public elementary & secondary schools
**CFO:* Clayton Slaughter
**Treas:* Jayme Barber
Dir IT: Tamra Walker
Schl Brd P: Michael White

GREENCORE
See SCHAU SOUTHEAST SUSHI INC

D-U-N-S 06-703-6159
GREENCORE US HOLDINGS INC
(*Suby of* GREENCORE GROUP PUBLIC LIMITED COMPANY)
222 Rosewood Dr Ste 240, Danvers, MA 01923-4520
Tel (508) 586-8418 *Founded/Ownrshp* 2008
Sales 370.8MM[E] *EMP* 500[E]
SIC 2043 Oatmeal: prepared as cereal breakfast food; Oatmeal: prepared as cereal breakfast food
Pr: Liam McClennon
**Treas:* Jonathan Hall
**Treas:* Paul Kenny
Sr VP: Christopher Calitri
Sfty Mgr: Richard McGowan
Opers Mgr: Ron Tomacchio
VP Sls: Stephen Young

D-U-N-S 19-646-2220 IMP
GREENCORE USA INC
(*Suby of* GREENCORE US HOLDINGS INC) ★
222 Rosewood Dr Fl 4, Danvers, MA 01923-4502
Tel (978) 716-2530 *Founded/Ownrshp* 2012
Sales 136.3MM[E] *EMP* 490
SIC 2099 Sandwiches, assembled & packaged: for wholesale market; Salads, fresh or refrigerated; Ready-to-eat meals, salads & sandwiches; Sandwiches, assembled & packaged: for wholesale market; Salads, fresh or refrigerated; Ready-to-eat meals, salads & sandwiches
CEO: Liam McClennon
CFO: Paul Kenny

D-U-N-S 96-488-2349
GREENCROFT GOSHEN INC
1603 Eisenhower Dr N, Goshen, IN 46526-5382
Tel (574) 537-4000 *Founded/Ownrshp* 2010
Sales 33.5MM *EMP* 24[E]
Accts Plante & Moran Pllc Southfiel
SIC 8361 Home for the aged; Home for the aged
Prin: Sandra Yoder

D-U-N-S 06-975-2293
GREENCROFT RETIREMENT COMMUNITIES INC
GREENCROFT SENIOR CENTER
1721 Greencroft Blvd, Goshen, IN 46526-5175
Tel (574) 537-4000 *Founded/Ownrshp* 1967
Sales 3.9MM *EMP* 550[E]
Accts Plante & Moran Pllc Southfiel
SIC 8741 8322 6513 8051 Nursing & personal care facility management; Senior citizens' center or association; Retirement hotel operation; Skilled nursing care facilities; Nursing & personal care facility management; Senior citizens' center or association; Retirement hotel operation; Skilled nursing care facilities
Pr: Mark King
**Ch Bd:* Burl Troyer
**CFO:* Robert Gibson
**VP:* Jennifer Hayes
**VP:* Karen Lehman
Off Mgr: Ruth Esh

GREENCROFT SENIOR CENTER
See GREENCROFT RETIREMENT COMMUNITIES INC

D-U-N-S 07-116-2002
GREENDALE SCHOOL DISTRICT
6815 Southway, Greendale, WI 53129-2428
Tel (414) 423-2700 *Founded/Ownrshp* 1939
Sales 33.9MM *EMP* 660
Accts Virchow Krause & Company Milw
SIC 8211 Public elementary & secondary schools
IT Man: Keith Bohlin
Pr Dir: Julie Grotophorst
Schl Brd P: Joe Crapitto
Instr Medi: Mike Robertson

GREENE ARLES CAULKING CONTRS
See ABG CAULKING CONTRACTORS INC

D-U-N-S 03-412-8223
GREENE BEVERAGE CO INC
6000 Grover Burchfield Dr, Tuscaloosa, AL 35401-9328
Tel (205) 345-6950 *Founded/Ownrshp* 1937
Sales 30.0MM *EMP* 85
SIC 5181 Beer & other fermented malt liquors; Beer & other fermented malt liquors
Pr: Spencer Burchfield

GREENE CO TECH PRE-SCHOOL
See GREENE COUNTY TECHNICAL SCHOOL DISTRICT

GREENE CONCRETE CUTTING
See GREENES INC

D-U-N-S 06-894-8348
GREENE COUNTY
GREENE COUNTY GOVERNMENT
35 Greene St, Xenia, OH 45385-3101
Tel (937) 562-5006 *Founded/Ownrshp* 1850
Sales NA *EMP* 1,117
Accts Dave Yost Columbus Ohio
SIC 9111 Executive offices; ; Executive offices;
Sls&Mrk Ex: Vicki Abel

D-U-N-S 03-561-2402
■ **GREENE COUNTY BANCORP INC**
(*Suby of* GREENE COUNTY BANCORP MHC) ★
302 Main St, Catskill, NY 12414-1801
Tel (518) 943-2600 *Founded/Ownrshp* 1998
Sales NA *EMP* 136
Accts Bdo Usa Llp Harrisburg Penn
Tkr Sym GCBC *Exch* NAS
SIC 6036 State commercial banks; Savings & loan associations, not federally chartered
Pr: Donald E Gibson
COO: Michelle M Plummer

D-U-N-S 07-606-4166
▲ **GREENE COUNTY BANCORP MHC**
302 Main St, Catskill, NY 12414-1801
Tel (518) 943-2600 *Founded/Ownrshp* 1998
Sales NA *EMP* 149
SIC 6712 Bank holding companies; Bank holding companies
Pr: J Bruce Whitaker
CFO: Michelle Plummer
VP: Timothy Bartholomew
VP Opers: Shauna Bellich

D-U-N-S 02-087-6033
GREENE COUNTY BOARD OF EDUCATION
GREENE COUNTY SCHOOL DISTRICT
528 Oak St, Leakesville, MS 39451-2998
Tel (601) 394-2364 *Founded/Ownrshp* 1940
Sales 13.0MM *EMP* 350
SIC 8211 Public elementary & secondary schools; Public elementary & secondary schools

D-U-N-S 07-811-6100
GREENE COUNTY BOARD OF EDUCATION (GA)
101 E Third St, Greensboro, GA 30642-1440
Tel (706) 453-7688 *Founded/Ownrshp* 1817
Sales 20.8MM[E] *EMP* 386
Accts Russell W Hinton Cpa Cgfm
SIC 8211 Public elementary & secondary schools; High school, junior or senior; Public elementary & secondary schools; High school, junior or senior
IT Man: Maxwell Anderson

D-U-N-S 07-911-7891
GREENE COUNTY BOARD OF EDUCATION
220 Main St, Eutaw, AL 35462-1002
Tel (205) 372-3161 *Founded/Ownrshp* 1950
Sales 15.2MM[E] *EMP* 300
SIC 8211 Public elementary & secondary schools; Public elementary & secondary schools

D-U-N-S 10-001-3804
GREENE COUNTY BOARD OF EDUCATION
201 Main St, Greensboro, GA 30642
Tel (706) 453-7688 *Founded/Ownrshp* 1872
Sales 11.4MM[E] *EMP* 367
Accts Department Of Audits And Accou
SIC 8211 Public elementary & secondary schools; Public elementary & secondary schools
Adm Dir: Morris Miller

D-U-N-S 10-067-0827
GREENE COUNTY BOARD OF EDUCATION
910 W Summer St, Greeneville, TN 37743-3016
Tel (423) 639-4194 *Founded/Ownrshp* 1940
Sales 48.3MM[E] *EMP* 900
SIC 8211 Public elementary & secondary schools; School board; Public elementary & secondary schools; School board
Ch Bd: Rick Tipton

GREENE COUNTY GOVERNMENT
See GREENE COUNTY

GREENE COUNTY HIGHWAY DEPARTME
See GREEN COUNTY GOVERNMET OF TENNESEE

D-U-N-S 60-951-0300
GREENE COUNTY PUBLIC SCHOOLS
GREENE COUNTY SCHOOLS
40 Celt Rd, Stanardsville, VA 22973-3001
Tel (434) 985-5254 *Founded/Ownrshp* 1871
Sales 27.0MM *EMP* 500
SIC 8211 Public elementary & secondary schools; Public elementary & secondary schools

GREENE COUNTY SCHOOL DISTRICT
See GREENE COUNTY BOARD OF EDUCATION

D-U-N-S 07-979-6349
GREENE COUNTY SCHOOL DISTRICT
528 Oak St, Leakesville, MS 39451-2998
Tel (601) 394-2364 *Founded/Ownrshp* 2015
Sales 11.7MM[E] *EMP* 280[E]
SIC 8211 Public elementary & secondary schools

D-U-N-S 10-040-6149
GREENE COUNTY SCHOOL DISTRICT
301 Kingold Blvd, Snow Hill, NC 28580-1305
Tel (252) 747-3425 *Founded/Ownrshp* 1960
Sales 32.0MM *EMP* 500
SIC 8211 Public elementary & secondary schools; Public senior high school; Public elementary & secondary schools; Public senior high school
MIS Dir: Josa Garcia
Teacher Pr: Raymond Smith

GREENE COUNTY SCHOOLS
See GREENE COUNTY PUBLIC SCHOOLS

D-U-N-S 07-979-8801
GREENE COUNTY SCHOOLS
910 W Summer St, Greeneville, TN 37743-3016
Tel (423) 639-4194 *Founded/Ownrshp* 2015
Sales 9.6MM[E] *EMP* 769[E]
SIC 8211 Public elementary & secondary schools
Opers Mgr: Laurie Jewell

D-U-N-S 07-979-9678
GREENE COUNTY SCHOOLS
101 E Third St, Greensboro, GA 30642-1440
Tel (706) 453-7688 *Founded/Ownrshp* 2015
Sales 5.1MM[E] *EMP* 289[E]
SIC 8211 Public elementary & secondary schools
MIS Dir: Michael Powell
Pr Dir: Robyn Brunson

D-U-N-S 10-000-4084
GREENE COUNTY TECHNICAL SCHOOL DISTRICT
GREENE CO TECH PRE-SCHOOL
5413 W Kingshighway, Paragould, AR 72450-3368
Tel (870) 236-2762 *Founded/Ownrshp* 1994
Sales 18.7MM[E] *EMP* 353
Accts William R Baum Cpa Cfe
SIC 8211 9411 Public elementary & secondary schools; School board; Administration of educational programs; Public elementary & secondary schools; School board; Administration of educational programs

GREENE GROUP
See SOUTHWEST GREENE INTERNATIONAL INC

D-U-N-S 15-067-7920
GREENE HEALTH PARTNERS
1141 N Monroe Dr, Xenia, OH 45385-1619
Tel (937) 352-2000 *Founded/Ownrshp* 1983
Sales 1.3MM *EMP* 880
SIC 8741 Hospital management; Nursing & personal care facility management; Hospital management; Nursing & personal care facility management
Ex Dir: Michael Stephens

D-U-N-S 07-287-8358
GREENE MEMORIAL HOSPITAL INC
(*Suby of* GREENE HEALTH PARTNERS) ★
1141 N Monroe Dr, Xenia, OH 45385-1600
Tel (937) 352-2000 *Founded/Ownrshp* 1983
Sales 932.4M[E] *EMP* 630
SIC 8062 Hospital, affiliated with AMA residency; Hospital, affiliated with AMA residency
CEO: Michael R Stephens
CFO: Jim Pollard
**CFO:* Timothy Pollard
Dir IT: William Hall
Pr Dir: Robert Jackson
Pathlgst: Pushpa Makkar
Pharmcst: Michelle Sutton
Phys Thrpy: Lori L Stemmer

D-U-N-S 06-655-7109
GREENE MOTORS INC
AVERY GREENE MOTORS
800 Admiral Callaghan Ln, Vallejo, CA 94591-3651
Tel (707) 551-3200 *Founded/Ownrshp* 1963
Sales 65.7MM *EMP* 90
SIC 5511 Automobiles, new & used; Automobiles, new & used
Pr: Avery H Greene
**Sec:* Joan Greene
**VP:* Christopher Greene

D-U-N-S 00-142-2435 IMP
GREENE RUBBER CO INC (MA)
20 Cross St, Woburn, MA 01801-5606
Tel (781) 937-9909 *Founded/Ownrshp* 1931, 1957
Sales 74.2MM[E] *EMP* 100
Accts Kennedy Hentoff & Patterson
SIC 5085 3053 3061 3052 Gaskets; Seals, industrial; Rubber goods, mechanical; Hose, belting & packing; Gaskets, all materials; Automotive rubber goods (mechanical); Rubber hose; Rubber belting
Pr: John F Connors
**Treas:* Abraham Ponn
VP: Sheila Morton
Exec: Paul Okeefe
**VP Mfg:* David Ponn
VP Opers: Richard Sage
Mktg Mgr: Steve Watras

GREENEBAUM DOLL & MCDONALD
See BINGHAM GREENEBAUM DOLL LLP

D-U-N-S 15-428-8716
GREENELL CORP
KITCHEN MAGIC
4243 Lonate Dr, Nazareth, PA 18064-8403
Tel (908) 387-1440 *Founded/Ownrshp* 1980
Sales 24.0MM[E] *EMP* 150
Accts William P Reiss Allentown P
SIC 5712 Cabinet work, custom; Cabinet work, custom
Ch Bd: Reine C Fleck
Pr: Brett W Bacho
Chf Mktg O: Linda Fennessy
VP: Lieselotte Bacho
VP: Cindy L Buck
Dir Soc: Marianne Baehr
Mfg Mgr: Troy Bowers

D-U-N-S 88-377-0398
GREENER PASTURES LANDSCAPE INC
2525 Manana Dr, Dallas, TX 75220-1241
Tel (214) 634-0806 *Founded/Ownrshp* 1992
Sales 31.4MM[E] *EMP* 200
SIC 0782 1711 Landscape contractors; Irrigation sprinkler system installation; Landscape contractors; Irrigation sprinkler system installation
Pr: Audrey Brown
**Sec:* John Brown
**VP:* Martin Glenn

D-U-N-S 06-701-2294
GREENERY INC
960 William Hilton Pkwy, Hilton Head Island, SC 29928-3302
Tel (843) 785-3848 *Founded/Ownrshp* 1973
Sales 25.0MM *EMP* 350
SIC 0781 1629 5261 Landscape services; Irrigation system construction; Nursery stock, seeds & bulbs; Landscape services; Irrigation system construction; Nursery stock, seeds & bulbs
CEO: William Lee Edwards
**CFO:* Scott Slawson
**Ex VP:* William Davoli
VP: Dennis Hensley
Brnch Mgr: Clay Kinard
Off Admin: Melissa Brock
Opers Mgr: Miles Graves
Opers Mgr: Joshua Smith

D-U-N-S 80-942-6088 IMP
GREENERY NORTH AMERICA INC
(*Suby of* GREENERY PRODUCE B.V.)
614 Highland Dr Ste 614, Westampton, NJ 08060
Tel (856) 735-1500 *Founded/Ownrshp* 2006
Sales 24.4MM[E] *EMP* 39
SIC 5148 0161 Vegetables; Tomato farm
CEO: William Ison
**Treas:* Maureen Osborne

GREENE'S ENERGY GROUP
See OLD GES INC

D-U-N-S 82-939-9836
GREENES ENERGY GROUP LLC
1610 Saint Etienne Rd, Broussard, LA 70518-7904
Tel (337) 232-1830 *Founded/Ownrshp* 2004
Sales 24.2MM[E] *EMP* 65
SIC 3999 Permanent wave equipment & machines
CEO: Robert Vilyus
CFO: Mark Yuille
**Sr VP:* Maury Dumba
**Sr VP:* Eugene Garber
**Sr VP:* Gene Garber
VP: Guy Comeaux
Exec: Dwayne Doucet
Ex Dir: Tommy Brinkman
Dir IT: Edwin Martin
Mktg Dir: Kay Carlisle
Mktg Mgr: Ray Keller

D-U-N-S 00-953-9516
GREENES ENERGY SERVICES INC
3037 Yellowstone Rd, Rock Springs, WY 82901-2835
Tel (307) 382-7470 *Founded/Ownrshp* 1998
Sales 22.9MM *EMP* 80
SIC 1389 1799 1542 Construction, repair & dismantling services; Welding on site; Nonresidential construction; Construction, repair & dismantling services; Welding on site; Nonresidential construction
Pr: Rick Greene
**Sec:* Rhonda Greene
Sfty Mgr: Ricky Gardea
Sfty Mgr: Randy McConnell

D-U-N-S 78-256-2565
GREENES INC
GREENE CONCRETE CUTTING
1065 W 750 S, Woods Cross, UT 84087-2083
Tel (801) 544-1000 *Founded/Ownrshp* 1990
Sales 20.6MM[E] *EMP* 110
Accts Hansen Bradshaw Malmrose & E
SIC 1771 1799 Concrete repair; Epoxy application
Pr: Mike Greene
**Sec:* Kristin Waters
**VP:* Kelly Downs
VP: Trevor Kidd
Off Mgr: Kellie McDonough
Mktg Mgr: Nicole Lawrence

D-U-N-S 78-020-8661
GREENEVILLE CITY SCHOOLS
129 W Depot St Ste 4, Greeneville, TN 37743-1103
Tel (423) 787-8000 *Founded/Ownrshp* 2006
Sales 401.6M *EMP* 357
Accts Adams & Plucker Cpas Pllp Gre
SIC 8699 Charitable organization
Ex Dir: Amanda Waddell

D-U-N-S 07-901-7414
GREENEVILLE LIGHT & POWER SYSTEM (INC) (TN)
110 N College St, Greeneville, TN 37743-5608
Tel (423) 636-6200 *Founded/Ownrshp* 1945
Sales 90.6MM[E] *EMP* 80
SIC 4911 Distribution, electric power; Distribution, electric power
Ch Bd: Willie Anderson
Genl Mgr: Bill Carroll

Genl Mgr: William M Carroll
Store Mgr: T J Freshour
DP Exec: John Skillman
Dir IT: Dwayne Wells
IT Man: Phil Bradley
Sfty Dirs: Charlie Spears

D-U-N-S 86-825-8724
GREENEVILLE OIL & PETROLEUM INC
QUICK STOP
860 W Andrew Johnson Hwy, Greeneville, TN 37745-1293
Tel (423) 638-3145 *Founded/Ownrshp* 1994
Sales 163.2MM^E *EMP* 125
SIC 5172 5411 5541 Crude oil; Convenience stores, chain; Filling stations, gasoline; Crude oil; Convenience stores, chain; Filling stations, gasoline
Pr: Allen Johnson
**CFO:* Nickie Rhoads
IT Man: Becky Ricker
Sls Mgr: Lyn Crum

GREENEVILLE TOWN HALL
See TOWN OF GREENEVILLE

D-U-N-S 00-384-8498
GREENFIBER ALBANY INC (NY)
US GREENFIBER
(*Suby of* US GREENFIBER LLC) ★
78 N Pawling St, Hagaman, NY 12086
Tel (518) 842-1470 *Founded/Ownrshp* 1986
Sales 26.4MM^E *EMP* 76^E
SIC 2679 Building, insulating & packaging paperboard
Ch Bd: Dennis Barrineau

GREENFIELD AREA MEDICAL CENTER
See ADENA HEALTH SYSTEM

D-U-N-S 07-957-4901
GREENFIELD CENTRAL COMMUNITY SCHOOL CORP
110 W North St, Greenfield, IN 46140-2172
Tel (317) 462-4434 *Founded/Ownrshp* 1965
Sales 33.1MM^E *EMP* 574
SIC 8211 Public elementary & secondary schools; High school, junior or senior; Public elementary & secondary schools; High school, junior or senior
Schl Brd P: Retta Livengood
Psych: Elizabeth Fortuna
Psych: Tim Horsman
Psych: Sarah Knecht
HC Dir: Dawn Hanson

D-U-N-S 87-804-2423
GREENFIELD COMMUNITY COLLEGE
G C C
(*Suby of* MASSACHUSETTS BOARD OF HIGHER EDUCATION SYSTEM) ★
1 College Dr, Greenfield, MA 01301-9755
Tel (413) 775-1000 *Founded/Ownrshp* 1962
Sales 25.0MM *EMP* 300
SIC 8221 9199 College, except junior; ; College, except junior;
Pr: Dr Robert Pura
**CFO:* Tim Braim
**CFO:* Richard Hillier
CFO: Christopher Pile
Ofcr: Ilie Taraburca
CIO: Michael Assaf
Dir IT: Kenneth Ketchum
S&M/VP: Amber Scoon
Pr Mgr: Allan Davis
Psych: Ellie Goodman
Psych: Dave Johnson

D-U-N-S 00-536-3718
■ **GREENFIELD DIE & MANUFACTURING CORP** (MI)
CANTON MANUFACTURING
(*Suby of* SHILOH INDUSTRIES INC) ★
7295 N Haggerty Rd Rf, Canton, MI 48187-2452
Tel (734) 454-4000 *Founded/Ownrshp* 1955
Sales 31.9MM^E *EMP* 250
SIC 3544 3469 Special dies & tools; Metal stampings; Special dies & tools; Metal stampings
Pr: James Fanello

D-U-N-S 80-358-8818
GREENFIELD HOLDINGS LLC
19881 Brownstown Ctr Dr, Brownstown, MI 48183-1680
Tel (734) 530-5600 *Founded/Ownrshp* 2007
Sales 32.4MM^E *EMP* 475
SIC 2531 Seats, automobile; Seats, automobile
CFO: Leslie Stansbery

D-U-N-S 83-131-5952 IMP
GREENFIELD INDUSTRIES INC
(*Suby of* DALIAN TOP-EASTERN GROUP CO., LTD.)
2501 Davis Creek Rd, Seneca, SC 29678-1315
Tel (864) 654-4922 *Founded/Ownrshp* 2009
Sales 70.0MM *EMP* 350
SIC 3545 Drill bits, metalworking
CEO: Jeff Chee
**Pr:* Tyrone Taylor
**CFO:* Anthony Tosti
**VP:* Bonnie Sun
Plnt Mgr: Mike Szumlas

D-U-N-S 07-576-1924
GREENFIELD MANAGEMENT SERVICE INC
COLUMBINE CARE CENTER EAST
947 Worthington Cir, Fort Collins, CO 80526-1841
Tel (970) 482-0198 *Founded/Ownrshp* 1971
Sales 8.9MM *EMP* 300
SIC 8051 Skilled nursing care facilities; Skilled nursing care facilities
Pr: J R Wilson
Ex Dir: James Kant

GREENFIELD ONLINE
See TOLUNA USA INC

D-U-N-S 78-305-7870
GREENFIELD PLACE LLC
2575 W 5th St, Greenville, NC 27834-7813
Tel (252) 830-9100 *Founded/Ownrshp* 1999
Sales 771.4MM *EMP* 145
SIC 8051 8052 8059 Skilled nursing care facilities; Intermediate care facilities; Rest home, with health care; Skilled nursing care facilities; Intermediate care facilities; Rest home, with health care

GREENFIELD PONTIAC BUICK GMC
See GREENFIELD PONTIAC-BUICK INC

D-U-N-S 04-467-4885
GREENFIELD PONTIAC-BUICK INC
GREENFIELD PONTIAC BUICK GMC
3615 S 108th St, Milwaukee, WI 53228-1205
Tel (414) 545-7000 *Founded/Ownrshp* 1968, 1997
Sales 47.4MM^E *EMP* 130
SIC 5511 5013 Automobiles, new & used; Automotive supplies & parts; Automobiles, new & used; Automotive supplies & parts
Pr: Cathy L Jones
Ofcr: Karen Kirsanoff
VP: Philip Jones
Off Mgr: Helene Poetz
Store Mgr: Jay Gesell
Sls Mgr: Paul Woodson

D-U-N-S 78-669-3531
GREENFIELD PUBLIC SCHOOLS
141 Davis St, Greenfield, MA 01301-2504
Tel (413) 772-1300 *Founded/Ownrshp* 2010
Sales 13.7MM^E *EMP* 317^E
SIC 8211 Elementary & secondary schools

D-U-N-S 04-333-4150 EXP
GREENFIELD RESEARCH INC (OH)
347 Edgewood Ave, Greenfield, OH 45123-1149
Tel (937) 981-7763 *Founded/Ownrshp* 1966
Sales 33.5MM^E *EMP* 300
SIC 2396 Automotive & apparel trimmings; Automotive trimmings, fabric; Automotive & apparel trimmings; Automotive trimmings, fabric
Pr: Michael Penn
**Sec:* Robert Snider
VP: Gary Pristas
Sls Mgr: Jim Pristas

D-U-N-S 00-695-4523
GREENFIELD SAVINGS BANK
400 Main St, Greenfield, MA 01301-3323
Tel (413) 775-8160 *Founded/Ownrshp* 1869
Sales NA *EMP* 130
SIC 6036 Savings institutions, not federally chartered; Savings institutions, not federally chartered
Pr: Joseph A Poirier
**CFO:* Margaret Hopkins
Ofcr: Prudence Blond
Ofcr: Karen Cartier
Ofcr: Sandra A Laude
Assoc VP: Cathy Roberts
**Ex VP:* Rebecca B Caplice
**Sr VP:* Denise Coyne
Sr VP: Lori Grover
Sr VP: Mark Grumoli
Sr VP: Stephen Hamlin
VP: Christopher Caouette
VP: Maura Guzik
VP: Philip Lemere
VP: Ruth Root
VP: Mark Russo

GREENFIELD TRANSPORT
See FIELD GREEN TRANSPORT CO INC

D-U-N-S 01-312-3419
GREENFIELD UNION SCHOOL DISTRICT
493 El Camino Real, Greenfield, CA 93927-4915
Tel (831) 674-2840 *Founded/Ownrshp* 1912
Sales 25.2MM^E *EMP* 250
Accts Perry-Smith Llp Sacramento
SIC 8211 Public elementary & secondary schools; Public elementary & secondary schools
Dir Bus: Melanie Kennedy
Ex Dir: Kimberly Berman
Schl Brd P: Arthur Salvagno
Teacher Pr: Richard Rabtke

D-U-N-S 10-000-6071
GREENFIELD UNION SCHOOL DISTRICT
1624 Fairview Rd, Bakersfield, CA 93307-5512
Tel (661) 837-6000 *Founded/Ownrshp* 1900
Sales 68.6MM^E *EMP* 1,400
SIC 8211 9411 Public elementary school; Administration of educational programs; Public elementary school; Public junior high school; Administration of educational programs
Netwrk Mgr: Cody Bowman

D-U-N-S 10-837-0524 IMP/EXP
GREENFIELD WORLD TRADE INC
J COBO & ASSOCIATES
3355 Entp Ave Ste 160, Fort Lauderdale, FL 33331
Tel (954) 202-7419 *Founded/Ownrshp* 1999
Sales 120.0MM *EMP* 150^E
SIC 5046 Commercial cooking & food service equipment; Commercial cooking & food service equipment
Pr: Oscar N Asbury
CFO: Jason Green
**VP:* Jonathan Vadnos
Opers Mgr: Tyler Helms
Opers Mgr: Alex Rojas
VP Mktg: Meagan Bradley
Manager: Brenden Wright

D-U-N-S 00-834-3521
GREENGATE FRESH LLLP
3255 S Avenue 3 1/2 E # 31, Yuma, AZ 85365-8032
Tel (928) 783-7374 *Founded/Ownrshp* 2009
Sales 52.0MM^E *EMP* 100
SIC 5142 Packaged frozen goods; Packaged frozen goods
CEO: Toby Jones

GREENGUARD
See KINGSPAN INSULATION LLC

D-U-N-S 17-652-8040
■ **GREENGUARD**
GREEN GUARD FIRST AID & SAFETY
(*Suby of* UNIFIRST CORP) ★
4159 Shoreline Dr, Earth City, MO 63045-1217
Tel (314) 344-1100 *Founded/Ownrshp* 1984
Sales 74.0MM^E *EMP* 175
SIC 5122 Bandages; Medicine cabinet sundries; Bandages; Medicine cabinet sundries
VP: Todd Lewis
Sls Dir: Josh Dubois
Manager: Scott Radvin
Sls Mgr: Jason Euston
Sls Mgr: Susan Hare
Sls Mgr: Laura Krainas
Sls Mgr: Rick Poole

D-U-N-S 06-203-6884 IMP
GREENHEART FARMS INC
902 Zenon Way, Arroyo Grande, CA 93420-5807
Tel (805) 481-2234 *Founded/Ownrshp* 1979
Sales 41.8MM^E *EMP* 350^E
SIC 0182 Vegetable crops grown under cover; Vegetable crops grown under cover
CEO: Hoy Buell
**Treas:* Leo Wolf
**VP:* Henry Katzenstein
IT Man: Melody Fair
Opers Mgr: Brian Monte
Ql Cn Mgr: Edgard Ramirez

D-U-N-S 00-613-6360 IMP
GREENHECK FAN CORP (WI)
GREEHECK GROUP, THE
1100 Greenheck Dr, Schofield, WI 54476-1889
Tel (715) 359-6171 *Founded/Ownrshp* 1947, 1957
Sales 650.0MM *EMP* 2,500
SIC 3564 3444 Sheet metalwork; Blowers & fans; Blowers & fans; Sheet metalwork
CEO: James McIntyre
**Ofcr:* Gary M Stroyny
Ex VP: Craig Hofferber
Area Mgr: Becky Gatzke
Genl Mgr: Dave Kallstrom
Genl Mgr: Gary Lochner
Genl Mgr: Ken Tokarz
Dir IT: Bob Koshalek
Mfg Dir: Jeff Lamer
Opers Mgr: Josh Holtz
Plnt Mgr: Tim Leith

D-U-N-S 14-465-6308
▲ **GREENHILL & CO INC**
300 Park Ave Fl 23, New York, NY 10022-7402
Tel (212) 389-1500 *Founded/Ownrshp* 1996
Sales 275.2MM *EMP* 305^E
Tkr Sym GHL *Exch* NYS
SIC 6211 Investment bankers; Underwriters, security; Investment bankers; Underwriters, security
CEO: Scott L Bok
**Ch Bd:* Robert F Greenhill
Pr: Kevin M Costantino
Pr: David A Wyles
COO: Harold J Rodriguez Jr
CFO: Christopher T Grubb
Top Exec: Bill Thompson
Top Exec: Daniel Wainstein
Mng Dir: Pieter Bouten
Mng Dir: Fredrik Elwing
Mng Dir: Philip Horn
Board of Directors: Robert T Blakely, Steven F Goldstone, Stephen L Key, Karen P Robards

D-U-N-S 07-511-8455
GREENHILL SCHOOL
4141 Spring Valley Rd, Addison, TX 75001-3683
Tel (972) 628-5400 *Founded/Ownrshp* 1950
Sales 45.7MM *EMP* 250
Accts Grant Thornton Llp Dallas T
SIC 8211 Private combined elementary & secondary school; Preparatory school; Private combined elementary & secondary school; Preparatory school
Ch Bd: Mike Halloran
COO: Angie Manning
CFO: Melissa Orth
Trst: Gail Griswold
Trst: Asif Masod
Exec: Rachel Brodie
Exec: Darlene Caraway
Exec: Jean Duncan
Exec: Aditya Malhotra
Exec: Martha Parker
Exec: John Simpson
Exec: Michelle Smith

D-U-N-S 04-476-0510
GREENHORNE & OMARA INC
6110 Frost Pl, Laurel, MD 20707-2927
Tel (301) 982-2800 *Founded/Ownrshp* 2012
Sales NA *EMP* 568^E
SIC 8711

GREENHOUSE CENTER
See EMERGE INC

D-U-N-S 80-979-8395
▲ **GREENHUNTER RESOURCES INC**
909 Lake Carolyn Pkwy, Irving, TX 75039-3908
Tel (972) 410-1044 *Founded/Ownrshp* 2005
Sales 27.1MM *EMP* 234
Tkr Sym GRH *Exch* ASE
SIC 1389 Hydraulic fracturing wells; Haulage, oil field; Hydraulic fracturing wells; Haulage, oil field
Ch Bd: Gary C Evans
COO: Kirk J Trosclair
CFO: Ronald McClung
Sr VP: Morgan F Johnston
VP: Bruce Baughman
VP: Melissa Pagen
Board of Directors: Roy E Easley, Julie Silcock, Ronald H Walker

D-U-N-S 00-682-7091
GREENHUT CONSTRUCTION CO INC (FL)
23 S A St, Pensacola, FL 32502-5595
Tel (850) 433-5421 *Founded/Ownrshp* 1946
Sales 24.6MM^E *EMP* 60
SIC 1542 1541 Commercial & office building, new construction; Industrial buildings & warehouses
Pr: Bill Greenhut
**Ch Bd:* Dudley H Greenhut
**CFO:* Racheal Reyes
**CFO:* Rachel Reyes
**Ex VP:* Lawrence Northrup
**Ex VP:* Larry Northup
**VP:* Connie J Greenhut
**VP:* Ryan H Greenhut
VP: Ryan Greenhut
**VP:* Kevin Spellman

GREENLEAF
See OAKVILLE PRODUCE PARTNERS LLC

D-U-N-S 96-548-5530
GREENLEAF ADVERTISING & MEDIA INC
IVIE
(*Suby of* IVIE & ASSOCIATES INC) ★
601 Silveron Ste 200, Flower Mound, TX 75028-4030
Tel (972) 899-8750 *Founded/Ownrshp* 2010
Sales 169.1MM *EMP* 12
SIC 7311 Advertising agencies; Advertising agencies
Pr: Warren C Ivie
**VP:* Jim Garrison

D-U-N-S 80-660-9574
GREENLEAF CO
GREENLEAF ESTIMATING
26 Worlds Fair Dr Ste A, Somerset, NJ 08873-1359
Tel (908) 272-0100 *Founded/Ownrshp* 1996
Sales 33.3MM^E *EMP* 25^E
SIC 1541 1542 7349 Industrial buildings & warehouses; Commercial & office building, new construction; Building maintenance services
Pr: Samuel N Prisco
**Treas:* Deanie Olsen

D-U-N-S 00-434-1335 IMP
GREENLEAF CORP
18695 Greenleaf Dr, Saegertown, PA 16433-4429
Tel (814) 763-2915 *Founded/Ownrshp* 1966
Sales 102.2MM^E *EMP* 450
SIC 3545 3541 Cutting tools for machine tools; Machine tools, metal cutting type; Cutting tools for machine tools; Machine tools, metal cutting type
Ch Bd: Walter J Greenleaf Jr
Ch Bd: James M Greenleaf
Treas: Dave Galey
Treas: Ray Seth
Area Mgr: Scot Hayden
Ql Cn Mgr: Elizabeth Jemetz
Ql Cn Mgr: Tom Payne
Manager: Terry Moore
Genl Couns: James Kyper

GREENLEAF ESTIMATING
See GREENLEAF CO

D-U-N-S 82-884-5599
GREENLEAF HOSPITALITY GROUP INC
SYDNEY AT THE RADISSON
100 W Michigan Ave # 100, Kalamazoo, MI 49007-3963
Tel (269) 567-7691 *Founded/Ownrshp* 1999
Sales 43.9MM^E *EMP* 1,000
SIC 7011 5813 Hotels & motels; Tavern (drinking places); Hotels & motels; Tavern (drinking places)
Pr: William Johnston

D-U-N-S 08-076-7999 EXP
GREENLEAF INC
951 S Pine St Ste 100, Spartanburg, SC 29302-3370
Tel (864) 573-7341 *Founded/Ownrshp* 1976
Sales 34.6MM^E *EMP* 149
SIC 5199 Gifts & novelties
Pr: Robert E Caldwell
**VP:* Sylvia R Caldwell

D-U-N-S 03-299-2778
GREENLEAF NURSERY CO
28406 Highway 82, Park Hill, OK 74451-2845
Tel (918) 457-5172 *Founded/Ownrshp* 1960
Sales 73.2MM *EMP* 1,100
Accts Moffitt Parker And Company I
SIC 0181 Nursery stock, growing of; Nursery stock, growing of
Pr: Randy Davis
**Ch Bd:* Austin F Kenyon
**CFO:* Tom Bearer
**Co-Ch Bd:* John T Nickel
Ex VP: Bruce Ringleb
Ex VP: Richard Young
VP: Larry Ahrens
VP: Greg Wes
**Prin:* Harold R Nickel
**Prin:* Rebecca A Nickel
CIO: Mike Edwards

GREENLEAF PRODUCTS
See OLDCASTLE NEW FRONTIERS INC

D-U-N-S 15-123-8362
GREENLEAF VENTURES II INC
RADISSON PLAZA HOTEL
100 W Michigan Ave Ofc, Kalamazoo, MI 49007-3965
Tel (269) 343-3333 *Founded/Ownrshp* 2003
Sales 14.8MM^E *EMP* 380
SIC 7011 Hotels & motels; Hotels & motels
Pr: William Johnston
**CFO:* Barry Bedford

D-U-N-S 04-418-4570
GREENLEAF WHOLESALE FLORIST INC
540 E Bridge St Ste A, Brighton, CO 80601-2171
Tel (303) 659-8000 *Founded/Ownrshp* 2003
Sales 90.9MM^E *EMP* 250
SIC 5193 Flowers, fresh; Flowers, fresh; Flowers & nursery stock
Pr: Scott Kitayama
**Ch Bd:* Dennis Kitayama
Off Mgr: Jane Cimo
Dir IT: Tim Matsuno
Sls Dir: Dana Sprayberry

GREENLEAF/A PPR CONVERTING CO
See MOOR PRODUCTS INC

D-U-N-S 00-720-2638 IMP
■ GREENLEE TEXTRON INC
(*Suby of* TEXTRON INC) ★
4455 Boeing Dr, Rockford, IL 61109-2932
Tel (815) 397-7070 *Founded/Ownrshp* 1866
Sales 212.3MM[E] *EMP* 1,010
SIC 3549 3541 3546 Metalworking machinery; Machine tools, metal cutting type; Power-driven handtools; Metalworking machinery; Machine tools, metal cutting type; Power-driven handtools
Pr: J Scott Hall
CFO: Jesus Guevara
Ofcr: Frank Connor
VP: Jason Butchko
VP: Scott Fenton
**VP:* Joe Mallak
**VP:* Bill Shulha
VP: Matt Sisco
**VP:* Dan Wilkinson
**Prin:* Dzura Mike
Rgnl Mgr: Klever Keltner

D-U-N-S 17-735-6805
■ GREENLINE FOODS INC
(*Suby of* APIO INC) ★
12700 S Dixie Hwy, Bowling Green, OH 43402-9697
Tel (419) 354-1149 *Founded/Ownrshp* 2012
Sales 68.6MM[E] *EMP* 106[E]
SIC 5148 Vegetables, fresh
CEO: George Benson
**CFO:* Mervyn McCulloch
QA Dir: Ginger Povenmire
Opers Mgr: Kevin Stapleton
Prd Mgr: Jason Frost
Sls Mgr: Bill Otley

D-U-N-S 06-593-5132
GREENMAN-PEDERSEN INC
G P I
325 W Main St Bldg 1, Babylon, NY 11702-3414
Tel (631) 587-5060 *Founded/Ownrshp* 1966
Sales 192.7MM[E] *EMP* 100[E]
SIC 8711 Civil engineering; Civil engineering
Pr: Ralph Csogi
Pr: Barbara Idhaw
Treas: Michael Buoncore
VP: Christer Ericsson
VP: Thomas Gibbons
VP: Andes Harry
VP: Suzanne Heilpern
VP: Dan Jackson
VP: Robert Kundrick
VP: Lenny Lembersky
VP: Fred Mastroianni
VP: Susan Morog
VP: James Noyes
VP: Kirk Shields
Dir Bus: Robert Kaplan

D-U-N-S 08-035-0176
GREENMARK EQUIPMENT INC (MI)
JOHN DEERE
4098 M 40, Holland, MI 49423
Tel (269) 751-5141 *Founded/Ownrshp* 1978
Sales 31.1MM[E] *EMP* 240
SIC 7359 5083 Equipment rental & leasing; Farm & garden machinery; Equipment rental & leasing; Farm & garden machinery
Pr: Dave Timmerman
**Sec:* Kenneth Timmerman
Rgnl Mgr: Todd Niermeyer
Dist Mgr: William Rhoda
Prd Dir: Dennis Dominiak

D-U-N-S 06-879-5326 IMP
GREENPAC MILL LLC
(*Suby of* NORAMPAC INDUSTRIES INC) ★
4400 Royal Ave, Niagara Falls, NY 14303-2128
Tel (716) 299-0560 *Founded/Ownrshp* 2010
Sales 152.1MM[E] *EMP* 135
SIC 2631 Linerboard

D-U-N-S 78-640-3113
GREENPAGES INC
GREENPAGES TECH SOLUTIONS
33 Badgers Is W, Kittery, ME 03904-1688
Tel (207) 439-7310 *Founded/Ownrshp* 1992
Sales 130.0MM *EMP* 185
SIC 7379 Computer related maintenance services; Computer related consulting services; Computer related maintenance services; Computer related consulting services
CEO: Ron Dupler
**Pr:* Drew Lally
**CFO:* Stephen Manero
**Ofcr:* Kevin Hall
VP: Randy Becker
**VP:* Glen Jodoin
Exec: John Marzi
Exec: Chris Thurber
Dir Soc: Jessica Egan
Creative D: Elvis Zukovic
Prac Mgr: William Kane

GREENPAGES TECH SOLUTIONS
See GREENPAGES INC

GREENPATH DEBT SOLUTIONS
See GREENPATH INC

D-U-N-S 07-277-3500
GREENPATH INC
GREENPATH DEBT SOLUTIONS
36500 Corporate Dr, Farmington Hills, MI 48331-3553
Tel (248) 553-5400 *Founded/Ownrshp* 1967
Sales 38.1MM[E] *EMP* 228[E]
SIC 7299 Debt counseling or adjustment service, individuals; Debt counseling or adjustment service, individuals
Pr: Jane E McNamara
**COO:* Donna McNeill
**CFO:* Kurt Murphy
**Ch:* Read Dunn
**Treas:* Tony Zambelli
Ofcr: Danielle Crane
**Ex VP:* Rick Bialobrzeski
QA Dir: Katie Swehla
IT Man: Ben Graziano
Netwrk Eng: John Deegan
Mktg Dir: Eve Pridgeon
Board of Directors: Delores C Tripp

D-U-N-S 07-854-8832
GREENPATH RECOVERY WEST INC
330 W Citrus St Ste 250, Colton, CA 92324-1422
Tel (909) 954-0686 *Founded/Ownrshp* 2012
Sales 38.8MM[E] *EMP* 60
SIC 5093 3089 2821 Scrap & waste materials; Plastic processing; Injection molding of plastics; Plastics materials & resins; Molding compounds, plastics
Pr: Joe Castro

D-U-N-S 18-530-7241 IMP/EXP
GREENPEACE INC
(*Suby of* GREENPEACE LICENSING B.V.)
702 H St Nw Ste 300, Washington, DC 20001-3876
Tel (202) 462-1177 *Founded/Ownrshp* 1987
Sales 33.5MM *EMP* 88
Accts Rogers & Company Pllc Vienna
SIC 8641 8748 Environmental protection organization; Business consulting
Ch: Karen Topakian
Dir Vol: Janika Gelinek
**Pr:* John Passacantando
COO: Ramesh Singh
Bd of Dir: Janet Dalziell
Ofcr: Diego Creimer
Ofcr: Molly Dorozenski
Ofcr: Jane Kochersperger
Ofcr: Joe Smyth
Ofcr: Jessica Wilson
Comm Dir: Martin Baker
Comm Dir: David Barre
Comm Dir: Kiko Brito
Comm Dir: Gene Hashmi
Comm Dir: Polina Malysheva
Comm Dir: Mike Townsley
Comm Dir: Spencer Tripp

D-U-N-S 06-858-4662
GREENPOINT AG
3350 Players Club Pkwy, Memphis, TN 38125-8926
Tel (901) 758-1341 *Founded/Ownrshp* 2012
Sales 586.0MM[E] *EMP* 249[E]
SIC 5191 Fertilizers & agricultural chemicals; Chemicals, agricultural; Seeds: field, garden & flower

D-U-N-S 19-843-1496 IMP
GREENPOINT TECHNOLOGIES INC
(*Suby of* ZODIAC AEROSPACE CS20001)
4600 Carillon Pt, Kirkland, WA 98033-7344
Tel (425) 828-2777 *Founded/Ownrshp* 2014
Sales 69.1MM[E] *EMP* 450
SIC 1799

D-U-N-S 87-891-7876
GREENPOINT TECHNOLOGY SERVICES LLC
1407 Broadway Rm 1220, New York, NY 10018-5132
Tel (212) 913-0500 *Founded/Ownrshp* 2001
Sales 24.4MM[E] *EMP* 366
SIC 8741 Management services; Management services
Snr Mgr: Vinesh Shanbhag

D-U-N-S 03-262-6335
GREENS ENERGY SERVICES INC
GREENS FUEL OIL
186 N Goldenrod Rd, Orlando, FL 32807-8204
Tel (407) 282-5000 *Founded/Ownrshp* 1957
Sales 24.0MM[E] *EMP* 50
Accts Averett Warmus Durkee Osburn H
SIC 5983 1711 Fuel oil dealers; Warm air heating & air conditioning contractor
Pr: John T Green Jr
**Treas:* Rebecca M Green
**VP:* John W Green

D-U-N-S 01-013-5861
GREENS FARMS ACADEMY INC (CT)
35 Beachside Ave, Greens Farms, CT 06838
Tel (203) 256-0717 *Founded/Ownrshp* 1925
Sales 34.9MM *EMP* 155
Accts Blum Shapiro & Company Pc W
SIC 8211 Private combined elementary & secondary school; Private combined elementary & secondary school
Pr: Janet M Hartwell
Ex Dir: Raluca Cocianga
Prgrm Mgr: Monique Rutledge
Dir IT: Jesse Robinson
Snr Mgr: Russ Friedson

D-U-N-S 14-707-8471
GREENS FORK ALIGNMENT AND SERVICE
2441 N Centerville Rd, Centerville, IN 47330-9608
Tel (765) 855-2772 *Founded/Ownrshp* 1986
Sales 27.1MM[E] *EMP* 60
SIC 5531 7538 7539 Automotive tires; General automotive repair shops; Wheel alignment, automotive
Pr: Thomas Goble

GREENS FUEL OIL
See GREENS ENERGY SERVICES INC

GREEN'S SUZUKI
See LEXINGTON LINCOLN-MERCURY INC

GREENS TOYOTA
See CURTIS GREEN AND CLAY GREEN INC

D-U-N-S 14-867-0466
GREENSBORO AUTO AUCTION INC
G A A
3907 W Wendover Ave, Greensboro, NC 27407-1902
Tel (336) 299-7777 *Founded/Ownrshp* 1985
Sales 117.0MM[E] *EMP* 850
SIC 5012

D-U-N-S 07-782-5982
GREENSBORO COLLEGE INC
3254 Dahlia St, Denver, CO 80207-1952
Tel (336) 272-7102 *Founded/Ownrshp* 1838
Sales 30.2MM *EMP* 295
SIC 8221 College, except junior; College, except junior
Pr: Lawrence D Czarda
**VP:* Paul Leslie
**VP Admn:* Marci Peace

D-U-N-S 00-321-3824
■ GREENSBORO NEWS & RECORD LLC (NC)
(*Suby of* BH MEDIA GROUP INC) ★
200 E Market St, Greensboro, NC 27401-2950
Tel (336) 373-7000 *Founded/Ownrshp* 2013
Sales 49.3MM[E] *EMP* 600
SIC 2711 2791 2796 2752 Newspapers, publishing & printing; Typesetting; Platemaking services; Commercial printing, lithographic; Newspapers, publishing & printing; Typesetting; Platemaking services; Commercial printing, lithographic
Pr: Robin Saul
Advt Mgr: Tanya Roberts
Sls Mgr: Betty Pitchford

D-U-N-S 02-459-0838
GREENSBORO PLUMBING SUPPLY CO
501 E Washington St, Greensboro, NC 27401-2932
Tel (336) 274-7615 *Founded/Ownrshp* 1949, 1986
Sales 25.2MM[E] *EMP* 38
SIC 5074 Plumbing & hydronic heating supplies
Pr: Robert Skirboll
**CFO:* Michael Spohn
**Sec:* Frank Brenner
**VP:* Clark Oaks
Genl Mgr: Mark Wieselquist
Genl Mgr: Mark Wieselquist
Sales Exec: Charles Whitehurst
Sales Asso: Mike Clougher
Sales Asso: Travis Tomlinson

D-U-N-S 05-464-8183
GREENSCAPE INC (NC)
2360 Broad St, Holly Springs, NC 27540-8563
Tel (919) 552-7742 *Founded/Ownrshp* 1979
Sales 70.8MM[E] *EMP* 95
SIC 0782

D-U-N-S 60-415-6935
GREENSCAPE LAND DESIGN INC
16 Commerce Blvd Ste C, Middleboro, MA 02346-1085
Tel (508) 977-9100 *Founded/Ownrshp* 1987
Sales 85.3MM[E] *EMP* 300
SIC 0782 4959 Landscape contractors; Snowplowing; Landscape contractors; Snowplowing
Pr: Joseph N Ciffolillo
COO: Karen Sanborn
Snr Mgr: Derek Durgin
Snr Mgr: Mark Neves

D-U-N-S 05-972-2756 IMP
GREENSCAPES HOME AND GARDEN PRODUCTS INC
200 Union Grove Rd Se, Calhoun, GA 30701-3685
Tel (706) 629-6652 *Founded/Ownrshp* 2000
Sales 32.0MM[E] *EMP* 45
SIC 3524 Lawn & garden equipment; Lawn & garden equipment
Pr: Sage Ralston
**CEO:* R E Ralston
**CFO:* Randy Jones
VP: Matt Gagliardi

GREENSFELDER, ATTORNEYS AT LAW
See GREENSFELDER HEMKER GALE PC

D-U-N-S 07-198-3118
GREENSFELDER HEMKER GALE PC
GREENSFELDER, ATTORNEYS AT LAW
10 S Broadway Ste 2000, Saint Louis, MO 63102-1747
Tel (314) 241-9090 *Founded/Ownrshp* 1997
Sales 32.4MM[E] *EMP* 280
SIC 8111 General practice law office; General practice law office
Pr: Tim Thornton
Pr: Beverly Holtmann
Pr: Louise Vogt
**CFO:* Dean Poeschen
Chf Mktg O: Mike Andrews
Ofcr: Kara Cenar
Ofcr: Christopher Pickett
**VP:* Vince Garozzo
Off Mgr: Daniel Rizzo
Software D: Ginny Bauza
Counsel: Kay Sherman
Board of Directors: Lawrence Holmes

GREENSHEET
See HELEN GORDON INTERESTS LTD

GREENSHILSS COURT
See BROOKSIDE PROPERTIES INC

D-U-N-S 02-278-6914
GREENSKIES RENEWABLE ENERGY LLC
10 Main St Ste E, Middletown, CT 06457-3407
Tel (860) 398-5408 *Founded/Ownrshp* 2008
Sales 80.0MM *EMP* 30[E]
SIC 1711 Plumbing, heating, air-conditioning contractors; Plumbing, heating, air-conditioning contractors
Bd of Dir: Arthur Linares
Sr VP: Andrew Chester
VP: Nick Denegre

D-U-N-S 00-546-1627
GREENSKY TRADE CREDIT LLC (GA)
1797 Northeast Expy Ne, Brookhaven, GA 30329-7803
Tel (404) 832-4000 *Founded/Ownrshp* 2006
Sales 38.3MM[E] *EMP* 148[E]
SIC 7323 Credit reporting services
Prin: David Zalik
Ex VP: Mark Davis
CIO: Marty Smith

GREENSLEEVES
See ALLIES INC

D-U-N-S 84-793-0880 IMP
GREENSOURCE BRAND APPAREL INC
APPAREL SOURCE, THE
1020 Sw 34th St, Renton, WA 98057-4813
Tel (425) 656-9123 *Founded/Ownrshp* 1999
Sales 50.3MM[E] *EMP* 50
Accts Moss Adams Llp Seattle Wash
SIC 5136 5137 Men's & boys' clothing; Women's & children's clothing
Pr: Brady Hill
**Pr:* David Basson
**CFO:* William Gould
**Sec:* Patty Barile
**VP:* John Flynn
VP Sls: Scott Lemaster

D-U-N-S 07-103-4008
GREENSPAN CO
GREENSPAN CORP ADJUSTERS INTL
16542 Ventura Blvd # 200, Encino, CA 91436-2092
Tel (213) 387-5335 *Founded/Ownrshp* 1960
Sales NA *EMP* 100
SIC 6411 Insurance adjusters
CEO: William G Rake
**Pr:* Bill Rake
VP: Martin Altman
VP: Susy Kim
VP: William Raffart
VP: Gordon Scott
Exec: Dan D Tambrosia
IT Man: Jeff Fox

GREENSPAN CORP ADJUSTERS INTL
See GREENSPAN CO

D-U-N-S 87-901-0148
GREENSPOINT PLAZA LTD PARTNERSHIP
HIENS
16825 Northchase Dr, Houston, TX 77060-6024
Tel (281) 873-2988 *Founded/Ownrshp* 1994
Sales 40.0MM *EMP* 1
SIC 6531 Real estate agent, commercial; Real estate agent, commercial

D-U-N-S 05-254-6264
GREENSPOON MARDER PA (FL)
GMLAW.COM
100 W Cypress Creek Rd # 700, Fort Lauderdale, FL 33309-2195
Tel (954) 491-1120 *Founded/Ownrshp* 1981
Sales 42.7MM[E] *EMP* 250
SIC 8111 Legal services; Legal services
Pr: Gerald Greenspoon
Pr: Emily Pigula
CFO: Kathryn Bass
Bd of Dir: Beth-Ann Krimsky
Chf Mktg O: Anne Hendricks
**VP:* William Berger
**VP:* Richard W Epstein
**VP:* Neil Hirschfeld
**VP:* Michael Marder
**VP:* Michael S Ross
CTO: William Riley

D-U-N-S 96-584-2243
GREENSPRING VILLAGE INC
7440 Spring Village Dr, Springfield, VA 22150-4446
Tel (703) 313-7800 *Founded/Ownrshp* 2010
Sales 84.5MM *EMP* 1,000
SIC 8059 Personal care home, with health care; Personal care home, with health care
Ex Dir: Robin Gliboff

GREENSPUN THE
See GREENSPUN CORP

D-U-N-S 78-556-2476
GREENSPUN CORP
GREENSPUN THE
2275 Corp Cir Ste 300, Henderson, NV 89074
Tel (702) 259-4023 *Founded/Ownrshp* 1990
Sales 74.8MM[E] *EMP* 612
SIC 8741 Management services; Management services
Pr: Bruce Deifik
**Pr:* Paul Hamilton
**Treas:* Brian L Greenspun
Ex VP: Keith Redmond

D-U-N-S 80-629-6781
■ GREENSTAR MID-AMERICA LLC
(*Suby of* WM RECYCLE AMERICA LLC) ★
1001 Fannin St Ste 4000, Houston, TX 77002-6711
Tel (713) 512-6200 *Founded/Ownrshp* 2013
Sales 382.3MM[E] *EMP* 600
SIC 4953 Recycling, waste materials; Recycling, waste materials
CEO: Marcelo Figueira
**CFO:* Lorna Conn
**Sr VP:* Eamonn Medley
**Sr VP:* Conor Roche
VP: Brian Gaughan
**VP:* Robert Pickens
VP: Rusty Waldrup
VP: Jeff Wiewiura
Genl Mgr: Ryan Baldwin
Opers Mgr: Jose Herrera
VP Sls: Tim Herman

D-U-N-S 80-825-0810
GREENSTAR NORTH AMERICA HOLDINGS INC
(*Suby of* ALTAS INVESTMENTS PUBLIC LIMITED COMPANY)
3411 Richmond Ave Ste 700, Houston, TX 77046-3417
Tel (713) 965-0005 *Founded/Ownrshp* 2007
Sales 38.9MM[E] *EMP* 600
SIC 4953 3229 8741 2611 Recycling, waste materials; Glassware, industrial; Management services; Pulp mills; Recycling, waste materials; Glassware, industrial; Management services; Pulp mills
CEO: Matt Delnick
**CFO:* Dan Crociata
VP: Robert Pickens
VP: Rusty Waldrup
VP: Jeff Wiewiura
IT Man: John Cisar
VP Sls: Tim Herman

D-U-N-S 82-995-4275
■ GREENSTAR SERVICES CORP
(*Suby of* TUTOR PERINI CORP) ★
30 N Macquesten Pkwy, Mount Vernon, NY 10550-1841
Tel (914) 776-8000 *Founded/Ownrshp* 2011

Sales 517.3MM^E *EMP* 155
SIC 1521 New construction, single-family houses; New construction, single-family houses
CEO: Gary Segal
V Ch: Stephen Kornfeld
CFO: Anthony Bonica

GREENSTONE FARM CREDIT SERVICE
See FARM CREDIT SERVICE OF SOUTHEAST MICHIGAN FLCA

D-U-N-S 15-252-1829
GREENSTONE FARM CREDIT SERVICES ACA
PRODUCTION CREDIT ASSOCIATION
3515 West Rd, East Lansing, MI 48823-7312
Tel (517) 324-0213 *Founded/Ownrshp* 2000
Sales NA *EMP* 380
Accts Pricewaterhousecoopers Llp Mi
SIC 6159 Agricultural credit institutions; Agricultural credit institutions
Pr: David B Armstrong
**Chf Cred:* Paul Anderson
Ofcr: Michelle Backhaus
Ofcr: Travis Bratschi
Ofcr: Erica Burke
Ofcr: Jeana Carlson
Ofcr: Melissa Humphrey
Ofcr: Ann Klemp
Ofcr: Jay Laanen
Ofcr: Brandon Leep
Ofcr: Karen Messer
Ofcr: Courtney Neubauer
Ofcr: Brian Peariso
Ofcr: Emelee Rajzer
Ofcr: Laurie Schetter
Ofcr: Brent Voss
Ofcr: Scott Welden
**Ex VP:* Travis Jones
**Ex VP:* Jack W Kelly
**Ex VP:* Peter Lemmer
**Ex VP:* Melissa Stolicker

D-U-N-S 82-556-0733
■ **GREENSTONE LLC**
(*Suby of* PFIZER INC) ★
100 Rte 206 N, Peapack, NJ 07977
Tel (800) 447-3360 *Founded/Ownrshp* 2010
Sales 105.1MM^E *EMP* 1,200
SIC 5122 Pharmaceuticals
CEO: Jack Jackson
**Pr:* Gregory Schofield
**Treas:* Debra Houston
**VP:* Sheri Staak

D-U-N-S 07-979-9732
GREENSVILLE COUNTY PUBLIC SCHOOLS
105 Ruffin St, Emporia, VA 23847-1320
Tel (434) 634-3748 *Founded/Ownrshp* 2015
Sales 4.3MM^E *EMP* 355^E
SIC 8211 Public elementary & secondary schools

GREENTEAM OF SAN JOSE
See WASTE CONNECTIONS OF CALIFORNIA INC

D-U-N-S 07-852-0252 IMP
GREENTECH AUTOMOTIVE CORP
GTA
(*Suby of* WM INDUSTRIES CORP) ★
1600 Tysons Blvd Ste 1150, Mc Lean, VA 22102-4883
Tel (703) 666-9001 *Founded/Ownrshp* 2012
Sales 23.2MM^E *EMP* 100^E
SIC 3711 Motor vehicles & car bodies
CEO: Charles Wang
**Ch Bd:* Terry McAuliffe
Sr VP: Richard Xiaoyun LI
Snr Mgr: Youssef Daou
Snr Mgr: Chris McClear

D-U-N-S 01-674-6782 IMP
GREENTECH AUTOMOTIVE INC
(*Suby of* GREENTECH AUTOMOTIVE CORP) ★
1 Greentech Dr, Robinsonville, MS 38664-6002
Tel (662) 996-1118 *Founded/Ownrshp* 2009
Sales 22.0MM^E *EMP* 92
SIC 3711 Automobile assembly, including specialty automobiles
CEO: Charles Wang
**Ex VP:* Gary Tang

GREENTREE LINCOLN MERCURY
See GREENTREE MOTORS OF DANBURY INC

D-U-N-S 01-863-5409
GREENTREE MOTORS OF DANBURY INC
GREENTREE LINCOLN MERCURY
87 Federal Rd, Danbury, CT 06811-4039
Tel (203) 730-4040 *Founded/Ownrshp* 1976
Sales 32.3MM^E *EMP* 65
SIC 5511 7515 7538 5932 5541 5521 Automobiles, new & used; Pickups, new & used; Vans, new & used; Passenger car leasing; General automotive repair shops; Used merchandise stores; Gasoline service stations; Used car dealers; Automobiles, new & used; Pickups, new & used; Vans, new & used; Passenger car leasing; General automotive repair shops; Used merchandise stores; Gasoline service stations; Used car dealers
Pr: Harold Tananbaum
**CFO:* Craig Bonoff
**Treas:* Maxwell Tananbaum
**VP:* George Haber
**VP:* Charles Monaco
**VP:* Christopher Morgado
**VP:* Jose Sabillon
**VP:* Brenda Tananbaum
Sales Exec: Ken Britton
VP Mktg: Bruce Mowery
Sls Mgr: Brian Dwyer

D-U-N-S 01-160-5896
GREENTREE PACKING INC
(*Suby of* J A O MEAT PACKING CO INC) ★
65 Central Ave, Passaic, NJ 07055-8406
Tel (212) 675-2868 *Founded/Ownrshp* 1985
Sales 48.5MM^E *EMP* 88
SIC 5147 Meats & meat products; Meats & meat products

Pr: Michael P Waters
**VP:* Don Waters

GREENTREE TOYOTA
See JEFF WYLER CLARKSVILLE INC

D-U-N-S 03-804-8984
GREENUP COUNTY SCHOOL DISTRICT
45 Musketeer Dr, Greenup, KY 41144-6412
Tel (606) 473-9819 *Founded/Ownrshp* 2000
Sales 25.0MM *EMP* 475
SIC 8211 Elementary & secondary schools; Elementary & secondary schools
**CFO:* Scott Burchett

GREENUP LAWN CARE
See MASSEY SERVICES INC

D-U-N-S 62-398-6705
GREENVIEW REGIONAL HOSPITAL
1801 Ashley Cir, Bowling Green, KY 42104-3362
Tel (270) 793-1000 *Founded/Ownrshp* 2006
Sales 87.3MM *EMP* 18^E
SIC 8011 Offices & clinics of medical doctors
CEO: Mark Marsh
Chf Path: Donna Boden
Dir Recs: Shannon Dixon
**CEO:* Nashville Tenn
COO: Jarrett Millsaps
VP: Mary Brasseaux
Chf Nrs Of: Bill Singletary

D-U-N-S 15-187-2991
■ **GREENVILLE AUTOMOTIVE INC**
VOLVO
(*Suby of* ASBURY AUTOMOTIVE GROUP INC) ★
2668 Laurens Rd, Greenville, SC 29607-3818
Tel (864) 288-7575 *Founded/Ownrshp* 2010
Sales 46.9MM^E *EMP* 200
SIC 5511 Automobiles, new & used; Automobiles, new & used
Pr: Terry F Wall
**VP:* Charles R Turk
Genl Mgr: David Ossi
Sales Asso: Angel Magliano

D-U-N-S 00-323-3921
GREENVILLE CENTRAL SCHOOL DISTRICT
4982 State Route 81, Greenville, NY 12083
Tel (518) 966-5065 *Founded/Ownrshp* 1930
Sales 18.0MM *EMP* 280
SIC 8211 Public elementary school; Public junior high school; Public senior high school; Public elementary school; Public junior high school; Public senior high school
Pr: Wilton Bear
Teacher Pr: Donna Accuosti

GREENVILLE CENTRAL SVCS FCILTY
See GREENVILLE PUBLIC SCHOOLS

D-U-N-S 15-795-1534
GREENVILLE CHR LLC
GREENVLLE CHRYSLER CASH CORRAL
5401 Interstate Hwy 30, Greenville, TX 75402-7514
Tel (903) 454-0283 *Founded/Ownrshp* 1999
Sales 33.9MM^E *EMP* 75
SIC 5511 5521 Automobiles, new & used; Vans, new & used; Pickups, new & used; Used car dealers; Automobiles, new & used; Vans, new & used; Pickups, new & used; Used car dealers
Pr: Mark Daniels
Sls Mgr: Clyde Hux

D-U-N-S 06-772-3437
GREENVILLE CITY OF (INC)
340 Main St, Greenville, MS 38701-4039
Tel (662) 378-1501 *Founded/Ownrshp* 1886
Sales NA *EMP* 425
Accts Bridgers & Goodman Pllc Vick
SIC 9111 City & town managers' offices; ; City & town managers' offices;
Dir IT: Al Scarbrough

D-U-N-S 03-457-9854
GREENVILLE CITY SCHOOLS
GREENVILLE CITY SCHOOLS BOARD
215 W 4th St, Greenville, OH 45331-1423
Tel (937) 548-3185 *Founded/Ownrshp* 1850
Sales 36.1MM *EMP* 410
Accts Mary Taylor Cpa Dayton Oh
SIC 8211 Public elementary & secondary schools; School board; Public elementary & secondary schools; School board
**Treas:* Carla Surber
IT Man: Linda Allread
Schl Brd P: James Summer

GREENVILLE CITY SCHOOLS BOARD
See GREENVILLE CITY SCHOOLS

D-U-N-S 07-711-8222
GREENVILLE COLLEGE
315 E College Ave, Greenville, IL 62246-1145
Tel (618) 664-2800 *Founded/Ownrshp* 1892
Sales 36.9MM *EMP* 294
Accts Capin Crouse Llp Greenwood I
SIC 8221 College, except junior; College, except junior
Pr: Ivan Silby
**CFO:* Dana T Funderburk
Treas: Mark Whitlock
VP: Scott Giffen
VP: Norman Hall
Dir IT: Rob Younker

D-U-N-S 18-593-6445 IMP
GREENVILLE COLORANTS LLC
20 Linden Ave E, Jersey City, NJ 07305-4727
Tel (201) 595-0200 *Founded/Ownrshp* 2005
Sales 53.3MM^E *EMP* 80
SIC 5131 5999 8712 Dyes, synthetic organic; Piece goods & other fabrics; Plastic piece goods, woven; Artists' supplies & materials; Architectural services
Dir Lab: Barbara Andreassen
VP Sls: Peter Rumore

D-U-N-S 07-987-7652
GREENVILLE COUNTY SCHOOL DISTRICT
301 E Camperdown Way, Greenville, SC 29601-2910
Tel (864) 355-3100 *Founded/Ownrshp* 2015
Sales 293.4MM^E *EMP* 9,600^E
SIC 8211 Public elementary & secondary schools
Pr Dir: Oby Lyle
Teacher Pr: Lynn Gibbs
HC Dir: Catherine Storey

D-U-N-S 80-755-3508 IMP
GREENVILLE HEALTH CORP
UPSTATE HM & FUSION THERAPIES
(*Suby of* G H S) ★
701 Grove Rd Ste 1, Greenville, SC 29605-4210
Tel (864) 455-6220 *Founded/Ownrshp* 1986
Sales 31.7MM^E *EMP* 407
SIC 8011 8059 4119 5912 Offices & clinics of medical doctors; Personal care home, with health care; Ambulance service; Drug stores & proprietary stores; Offices & clinics of medical doctors; Personal care home, with health care; Ambulance service; Drug stores & proprietary stores
CEO: Michael C Riordan
**Sec:* Susan Bichel
**Ex VP:* Gregory J Rusnak
**VP:* Terri T Newsom

D-U-N-S 07-799-0745
GREENVILLE HEALTH SYSTEM
G H S
701 Grove Rd, Greenville, SC 29605-4210
Tel (864) 455-7000 *Founded/Ownrshp* 1947
Sales 1.0MMM *EMP* 7,200
SIC 8069 8051 Specialty hospitals, except psychiatric; Skilled nursing care facilities; Specialty hospitals, except psychiatric; Skilled nursing care facilities
CEO: Michael C Riordan
Chf Path: Jesse Stafford
Chf Path: Phillip Vanhale
Dir Vol: Rebecca Crown
V Ch: Harry A Chapman Jr
CFO: Susan J Bichel
Trst: Jerry E Dempsey
**Ex VP:* Gregory J Rusnak
VP: Joe J Blake
**VP:* Joseph J Blake Jr
**VP:* Malcolm W Isley
**VP:* Terri T Newsom
VP: Michelle Taylor Smith
VP: Suzanne K White
Dir Lab: Ginger Smith

D-U-N-S 06-497-9842
GREENVILLE HOSPITAL
391 Grand St, Jersey City, NJ 07302-4238
Tel (201) 547-6100 *Founded/Ownrshp* 1990
Sales 8.5MM^E *EMP* 290
SIC 8062 General medical & surgical hospitals; General medical & surgical hospitals
CEO: Jonathan M Metsch
**Ex VP:* Stephen Kirby

D-U-N-S 01-491-9625
■ **GREENVILLE HOSPITAL CORP**
L V STABLER MEMORIAL HOSPITAL
(*Suby of* COMMUNITY HEALTH SYSTEMS INC) ★
29 L V Stabler Dr, Greenville, AL 36037-3850
Tel (334) 382-2671 *Founded/Ownrshp* 1986
Sales 24.9MM *EMP* 225
SIC 8062 General medical & surgical hospitals; General medical & surgical hospitals
CEO: Connie Nicholas
Pr: Rena McNeil
Dir Rad: Dena Bedunah
Mktg Dir: David Norrell

GREENVILLE HOUSING AUTHORITY
See HOUSING AUTHORITY OF GREENVILLE INC

D-U-N-S 02-671-7728
GREENVILLE INDEPENDENT SCHOOL DISTRICT
4004 Moulton St, Greenville, TX 75401-5840
Tel (903) 457-0702 *Founded/Ownrshp* 1901
Sales 47.1MM *EMP* 640
Accts Rutherford Taylor & Company P
SIC 8211 Public elementary & secondary schools; Public elementary & secondary schools
CFO: Billy Myers
Ex Dir: Edith Ashford
IT Man: Gary Sorrells
Pr Dir: Sidney Philips
Teacher Pr: Ralph Sanders

D-U-N-S 02-365-6359
GREENVILLE INDEPENDENT SCHOOL DISTRICT
GISD
3703 Templeton St, Greenville, TX 75401-5098
Tel (903) 457-2658 *Founded/Ownrshp* 2009
Sales 45.0MM *EMP* 800
SIC 8211 Public elementary & secondary schools
Pr: Anne Haynes

D-U-N-S 02-999-5276
GREENVILLE MEATS INC
845 White Horse Rd, Greenville, SC 29605-3557
Tel (864) 277-5570 *Founded/Ownrshp* 2004
Sales 33.8MM^E *EMP* 75^E
SIC 5147 Meats & meat products; Meats & meat products
Owner: Dan Sloan
**VP:* Jerry Sloan
Genl Mgr: Joe Monroe
Sls Mgr: David Straitiff

D-U-N-S 11-274-0568 IMP
■ **GREENVILLE METALS INC**
PCC FORGED PRODUCTS
(*Suby of* PCC SPS FASTENER DIVISION) ★
99 Crestview Drive Ext, Transfer, PA 16154-1709
Tel (724) 509-1861 *Founded/Ownrshp* 1998
Sales 33.1MM^E *EMP* 83
SIC 3313 Alloys, additive, except copper: not made in blast furnaces; Alloys, additive, except copper: not made in blast furnaces

Pr: Joseph Snowden
**Treas:* Geoffrey A Hawkes
**VP:* William D Larsson
**Prin:* Robert H Elwell

GREENVILLE NOLAND
See NOLAND CO

D-U-N-S 04-650-4866
GREENVILLE OFFICE SUPPLY CO INC
G O S
310 E Frontage Rd, Greer, SC 29651-6913
Tel (864) 233-5346 *Founded/Ownrshp* 1989
Sales 37.0MM^E *EMP* 48
Accts Elliott Davis Llc Greenvill
SIC 5112 7389 5712 5932 2752 Stationery & office supplies; Interior design services; Office furniture; Office furniture, secondhand; Commercial printing, lithographic
Pr: Charles Scales
**VP:* Robert M Carpenter
VP: Tammy Dankovich
**VP:* Scott Hart
Admn Mgr: Murray Dodd
Dir IT: Keith Hagerty
Opers Mgr: Dave Wester
Sls Mgr: Melonie Estridge

D-U-N-S 06-017-9603
GREENVILLE PUBLIC SCHOOLS
GREENVILLE CENTRAL SVCS FCILTY
1414 Chase St, Greenville, MI 48838-7147
Tel (616) 754-3686 *Founded/Ownrshp* 1861
Sales 26.2MM^E *EMP* 450
Accts Plante & Moran Llp
SIC 8211 Public elementary & secondary schools; Public elementary & secondary schools
CFO: Nancy Hadley

D-U-N-S 12-620-7224
GREENVILLE PUBLIC SCHOOLS INC
412 S Main St, Greenville, MS 38701-4747
Tel (662) 334-7000 *Founded/Ownrshp* 1890
Sales 63.0MM^E *EMP* 1,413
SIC 8211 9411 Public elementary & secondary schools; School board; Administration of educational programs; Public elementary & secondary schools; School board; Administration of educational programs
IT Man: Scottie Saulter
Pr Dir: Everett Chen
Schl Brd P: Betsy Alexander

GREENVILLE RDYMX DPD TEAM CON
See GREENVILLE READY MIX CONCRETE INC

D-U-N-S 06-311-3617
GREENVILLE READY MIX CONCRETE INC
GREENVILLE RDYMX DPD TEAM CON
5039 Nc 11 S, Winterville, NC 28590-7764
Tel (252) 756-0119 *Founded/Ownrshp* 1982
Sales 35.1MM^E *EMP* 57
SIC 5032 3273 Concrete mixtures; Ready-mixed concrete
Pr: Derek P Dunn
**Treas:* Elizabeth K Dunn
VP: R Messick
Genl Mgr: Marshall Tatum
VP Opers: Finley Messick

D-U-N-S 08-373-9362
GREENVILLE REGIONAL HEALTHCARE INC
UTLAUT MEMORIAL FOUNDATION
200 Health Care Dr, Greenville, IL 62246-1154
Tel (618) 664-1230 *Founded/Ownrshp* 1983
Sales NA *EMP* 375
Accts Cliftonlarsonallen Llp Saint
SIC 6324 Hospital & medical service plans; Hospital & medical service plans
CEO: Brian Nall
**Pr:* James M Hayes
**Pr:* Michael Zilm
CFO: Cassie Beesley
**Ch:* Buddy Bond
VP: Veronica Forbis
Dir Lab: Jim Schnarre
Chf Nrs Of: Tammy Lett

D-U-N-S 07-711-7661
GREENVILLE REGIONAL HOSPITAL INC
(*Suby of* GREENVILLE REGIONAL HEALTHCARE INC) ★
200 Health Care Dr, Greenville, IL 62246-1154
Tel (618) 664-1230 *Founded/Ownrshp* 1960
Sales 8.2MM^E *EMP* 325
Accts Cliftonlarsonallen Llp St Lo
SIC 8062 8051 Hospital, affiliated with AMA residency; Extended care facility; Hospital, affiliated with AMA residency; Extended care facility
Ex Dir: Morris Bond
**CFO:* Sherry Koehler
**Ch:* Buddy Bond
Dir Soc: Mary Massena
Doctor: Barb Strieker

D-U-N-S 94-959-0806
GREENVILLE RIVERBOAT LLC
LIGHT HOUSE POINT CASINO
240 S Walnut St, Greenville, MS 38701-4003
Tel (662) 335-5490 *Founded/Ownrshp* 1996
Sales 11.9MM^E *EMP* 400
SIC 7011 Hotels; Hotels

D-U-N-S 07-371-4743
GREENVILLE TECHNICAL COLLEGE PUBLIC FACILITIES CORP
506 S Pleasantburg Dr, Greenville, SC 29607-2439
Tel (864) 250-8000 *Founded/Ownrshp* 1962
Sales 40.2MM^E *EMP* 1,200
Accts Cline Brandt Kochenower & Co
SIC 8222 8211 8221 Technical institute; Elementary & secondary schools; Colleges universities & professional schools; Technical institute; Elementary & secondary schools; Colleges universities & professional schools
Pr: Thomas E Barton Jr PHD
**Pr:* Dr Keith Miller
**VP:* Jacqueline Dimaggio

VP: Lenna Young
Ex Dir: Jennie Johnson
Psych: Kelly Avigliano
Psych: Erica Brantley

D-U-N-S 14-721-6394 IMP
GREENVILLE TECHNOLOGY INC
(*Suby of* MORIROKU HOLDINGS COMPANY,LTD.)
5755 State Route 571, Greenville, OH 45331-9692
Tel (937) 548-3217 *Founded/Ownrshp* 1986
Sales 133.3MM^E *EMP* 700
SIC 3089 Injection molded finished plastic products; Injection molded finished plastic products
Pr: Kiyoshi Sato
Treas: Akihiko Hirano
Treas: Kazuhiko Tani
Ex VP: James Heiser
Ex VP: William Laframboise

D-U-N-S 00-602-4582 IMP
GREENVILLE TOOL & DIE CO
1215 S Lafayette St, Greenville, MI 48838-9386
Tel (616) 754-5693 *Founded/Ownrshp* 2005
Sales 24.6MM *EMP* 140
Accts Windham Brannon Pc Atlanta
SIC 3544 Special dies & tools; Special dies & tools
CEO: Dale Hartway
**Pr:* Larry Caverley
**Ex VP:* Ted Bush
Prgrm Mgr: Ronald Brimmer
Prgrm Mgr: Jim Buskirk
Snr Mgr: Kurt Laux
Snr Mgr: Brad Throop

D-U-N-S 55-670-4062
GREENVILLE TOYOTA
CRAIG F GOESS
3615 S Memorial Dr, Greenville, NC 27834-6768
Tel (252) 321-3000 *Founded/Ownrshp* 1991
Sales 30.1MM^E *EMP* 62
SIC 5511 7538 Automobiles, new & used; General automotive repair shops; Automobiles, new & used; General automotive repair shops
Pr: Craig Goess Sr
Advt Dir: Ricky Atencia
Sls Mgr: Alex Barletta
Sls Mgr: Jimmy Merendino
Sales Asso: Richard Atencia
Sales Asso: Todd Bond
Sales Asso: Derrick Kinsey

D-U-N-S 04-430-7114
■ **GREENVILLE TUBE CO LLC**
(*Suby of* PCC) ★
2505 Foster Ave, Janesville, WI 53545-0814
Tel (608) 531-3140 *Founded/Ownrshp* 1950, 2006
Sales 23.5MM^E *EMP* 198
SIC 3317 Tubes, seamless steel; Tubes, seamless steel
VP: H R Holstead

D-U-N-S 07-201-2818
GREENVILLE UTILITIES COMMISSION
401 S Greene St, Greenville, NC 27834-1977
Tel (252) 551-3315 *Founded/Ownrshp* 1905
Sales NA *EMP* 435
Accts Mcgladrey & Pullen Llp Moreh
SIC 9631 Public utility commission, government; ; Public utility commission, government;
Genl Mgr: Ron Elks
Ofcr: Jim Rapin
IT Man: David Garris

GREENVILLE WATER
See COMMISSIONERS OF PUBLIC WORKS OF CITY OF GREENVILLE (INC)

D-U-N-S 07-371-7431 IMP/EXP
GREENVILLE-SPARTANBURG AIRPORT COMMISSION INC
GSP INTERNATIONAL
2000 Gsp Dr Ste 1, Greer, SC 29651-6633
Tel (864) 877-7426 *Founded/Ownrshp* 1962
Sales 26.6MM *EMP* 100^E
Accts Cherry Bekaert Llp Greenvill
SIC 4581 Airport; Airport
Ch: Minor Shaw
**Pr:* David N Edwards Jr
**COO:* Kevin Howell
**CFO:* Jack G Murrin
**VP:* Rosylin Weston
Ex Dir: David Edwards
IT Man: Dan Ingram

GREENVLLE CHRYSLER CASH CORRAL
See GREENVILLE CHR LLC

GREENWALL PAVILION
See JEWISH HOME LIFECARE MANHATTAN

D-U-N-S 78-944-3116
GREENWASTE RECOVERY INC
625 Charles St, San Jose, CA 95112-1402
Tel (408) 283-4800 *Founded/Ownrshp* 1991
Sales 125.4MM^E *EMP* 170^E
SIC 4953 Rubbish collection & disposal; Waste materials, disposal at sea; Rubbish collection & disposal; Waste materials, disposal at sea
Pr: Richard Christina
**COO:* Frank Weigel
**CFO:* Don Dean
**Sec:* Jesse Weigel
**VP:* Murray Hall

D-U-N-S 02-758-7211
GREENWAY AUTO PLAZA INC
BOB HALL LYNCH HONDA GMC
1700 E Yakima Ave, Yakima, WA 98901-2140
Tel (509) 248-7600 *Founded/Ownrshp* 1989
Sales 22.4MM^E *EMP* 70
SIC 5511 Automobiles, new & used; Automobiles, new & used
Pr: Robert Hall
Sales Asso: Peter Grayson

GREENWAY CHRYSLER DODGE JEEP
See GREENWAY CHRYSLER-JEEP-DODGE INC

D-U-N-S 09-302-0597
GREENWAY CHRYSLER-JEEP-DODGE INC (FL)
GREENWAY CHRYSLER DODGE JEEP
9051 E Colonial Dr, Orlando, FL 32817-4176
Tel (407) 275-3200 *Founded/Ownrshp* 2000
Sales 50.6MM^E *EMP* 75^E
SIC 5511 Automobiles, new & used
Pr: Frank J Rodriguez
**Treas:* Edward M Alden
**Prin:* Carl R Atkinson
Genl Mgr: Conrad Letson
Sls Dir: Alvin Davis
Sls Dir: Ricky Lopez
Sls Mgr: William Leigh
Sls Mgr: Orlando Soto
Sales Asso: Joseph Borrero
Sales Asso: Nader Herz
Sales Asso: Jacob Scott

D-U-N-S 09-870-7706
GREENWAY ENTERPRISES INC
608 Lincoln Rd W, Helena, MT 59602-8146
Tel (406) 458-9411 *Founded/Ownrshp* 1978
Sales 25.0MM *EMP* 75
SIC 1542 Commercial & office building, new construction; Commercial & office building, new construction
Pr: Yuvonne D Hooverstal
Ofcr: Palmer Hoovestal
**VP:* Gary E Hooverstal

D-U-N-S 08-758-3907
GREENWAY EQUIPMENT INC
JOHN DEERE
(*Suby of* CONMAC INVESTMENTS INC) ★
412 S Van Buren, Weiner, AR 72479
Tel (870) 684-7740 *Founded/Ownrshp* 1999
Sales 90.5MM^E *EMP* 350^E
SIC 5999 Farm equipment & supplies; Farm equipment & supplies
CEO: John L Connor
Pr: Marshall Stewart
CFO: Stephen Smith
Sr VP: Rick Bormann
VP: Chad Sandoval
VP: Steve Shepard

D-U-N-S 15-902-8443
GREENWAY GROUP ASSOCIATES LLC
ALEXANDRIA VOLKSWAGON
107 W Glebe Rd, Alexandria, VA 22305-2625
Tel (703) 535-3528 *Founded/Ownrshp* 1998
Sales 25.3MM^E *EMP* 80
SIC 5511 5521 Automobiles, new & used; Automobiles, used cars only; Automobiles, new & used; Automobiles, used cars only
CFO: Ene Pakasaar
Sls Mgr: Andy Benone
Sales Asso: Sedeke Dunzo

D-U-N-S 79-079-5616
GREENWAY HEALTH LLC
4301 W Boy Scout Blvd, Tampa, FL 33607-5709
Tel (813) 202-5000 *Founded/Ownrshp* 2011
Sales 70.5MM^E *EMP* 500
SIC 5734 Computer & software stores; Computer & software stores
CEO: Matthew J Hawkins
CFO: Laurens Albada
Ex VP: Kermit Randa
Sr VP: Steven Holmquist
Sr VP: Mark Janiszewski
Sr VP: Jeremy Muench
Sr VP: Shantanu Paul
VP: James Brooks
VP: Jeff Cummings
VP: Bud Meadows
VP: Lara Caldwell Stout
VP: Ron Taylor
VP: Todd Treiber

D-U-N-S 04-900-4968
GREENWAY MEDICAL TECHNOLOGIES INC (GA)
(*Suby of* VCG HOLDINGS, LLC)
100 Greenway Blvd, Carrollton, GA 30117-4338
Tel (770) 836-3100 *Founded/Ownrshp* 1998, 2013
Sales 172.5MM^E *EMP* 810
SIC 7373 7371 Computer integrated systems design; Custom computer programming services; Computer integrated systems design; Custom computer programming services
CEO: Wyche T Green III
**Pr:* Matthew Hawkins
**COO:* Gregory H Schulenburg
**CFO:* James A Cochran
CFO: Dave Morgan
Chf Mktg O: Robin Hackney
**Chf Mktg O:* Bob Kneeley
**Ofcr:* James Ingram
Ex VP: Michael Hairston
Ex VP: Mark Janiszewski
Ex VP: Shantanu Paul
**Ex VP:* Jonathan Samples
VP: John Ayers
**VP:* William G Esslinger Jr
VP: Eric Grunden
VP: Randy Mancherian
VP: Rob Newman
VP: Chris Riddle
VP: Scott Snapp
**Dir Risk M:* David Wirta
Comm Dir: Mac McKinsey

GREENWAY PRMIUM WD FUEL PLLETS
See HASSELL & HUGHES LUMBER CO INC

D-U-N-S 07-852-2340
GREENWELL ENERGY SOLUTIONS LLC (TX)
2000 Edwards St Unit B, Houston, TX 77007-4433
Tel (713) 993-7772 *Founded/Ownrshp* 2012
Sales 43.6MM^E *EMP* 90
SIC 1389 Oil field services
CEO: Peter Shaper
Pr: Ron Wagnon
VP: David Kippie
VP: Ron Long

VP: Parel Patel
VP Mktg: Christy Hartman

D-U-N-S 07-540-7650
GREENWICH ACADEMY INC
200 N Maple Ave, Greenwich, CT 06830-4799
Tel (203) 625-8900 *Founded/Ownrshp* 1827
Sales 52.2MM *EMP* 210
Accts Kpmg Llp Hartford Ct
SIC 8211 Private combined elementary & secondary school; Private combined elementary & secondary school
Ch Bd: Richard L Chilton Jr
**CFO:* Donna Matheson
Comm Dir: Marylou Evans
Comm Dir: Asha Marsh
Netwrk Mgr: Leesa Singleton

D-U-N-S 82-893-2710
GREENWICH AEROGROUP INC
475 Steamboat Rd Fl 2, Greenwich, CT 06830-7144
Tel (203) 618-4861 *Founded/Ownrshp* 2009
Sales 368.9MM^E *EMP* 273^E
SIC 4581 5088 7699 5085 Airports, flying fields & services; Airport terminal services; Aircraft maintenance & repair services; Airport hangar rental; Transportation equipment & supplies; Caliper, gauge & other machinists' instrument repair; Industrial supplies; Airports, flying fields & services; Airport terminal services; Aircraft maintenance & repair services; Airport hangar rental; Transportation equipment & supplies; Caliper, gauge & other machinists' instrument repair; Industrial supplies
Pr: Jim Ziegler
**CFO:* Gene Juris
**Ex VP:* Gerald A Goguen
**VP:* Frank Medici
VP: D Meier
IT Man: Mark Gomes
**VP Mktg:* Daniel Lafrance

D-U-N-S 07-539-0641
GREENWICH ASSOCIATES LLC
6 High Ridge Park, Stamford, CT 06905-1327
Tel (203) 629-1200 *Founded/Ownrshp* 1972
Sales 56.6MM^E *EMP* 200
SIC 8742 8732 8748 Management consulting services; Business research service; Business consulting; Management consulting services; Business research service; Business consulting
CFO: John Delly
VP: Gaurav Arora
VP: John Feng
VP: Andrew Grant
VP: Bryan Kozlowski
VP: Tobias Miarka
VP: Bruce Paul
VP: William E Russell
VP: David Stryker
VP: Anthony Tarzia
VP: Jim Voros

D-U-N-S 79-924-9263
GREENWICH BANK AND TRUST CO
(*Suby of* ASSOCIATED COMMUNITY BANCORP INC)
1495 Post Rd E, Westport, CT 06880-5510
Tel (203) 319-6260 *Founded/Ownrshp* 1997
Sales NA *EMP* 15
SIC 6029 Commercial banks; Commercial banks
Pr: James McLean
**CFO:* William Laudano
**Sr VP:* Richard Muskus

D-U-N-S 07-538-9437
GREENWICH COUNTRY DAY SCHOOL INC
401 Old Church Rd, Greenwich, CT 06830-4809
Tel (203) 863-5600 *Founded/Ownrshp* 1926
Sales 31.3MM *EMP* 210
Accts Dylewsky Goldberg & Brenner Ll
SIC 8211 Private elementary school; Private junior high school; Kindergarten; Private elementary school; Private junior high school; Kindergarten
CFO: Gail Epstein
Exec: Marc Roman
Assoc Dir: Deidre Orsino
Ex Dir: Anna Munoz
Dir IT: Leon Martinez

D-U-N-S 55-542-7954
GREENWICH HEALTH CARE SERVICES INC
5 Perryridge Rd, Greenwich, CT 06830-4608
Tel (203) 661-5330 *Founded/Ownrshp* 1986
Sales 0.1 *EMP* 1,600^E
Accts Ernst & Young Llp Ny Ny
SIC 8062 General medical & surgical hospitals; General medical & surgical hospitals
Pr: Frank A Corvino
**COO:* Quinton Friesen
**CFO:* Eugene Colucci
VP: Christine Beechner
Doctor: Maria Massimi

D-U-N-S 01-013-8097 IMP
GREENWICH HOSPITAL
(*Suby of* GREENWICH HEALTH CARE SERVICES INC) ★
5 Perryridge Rd, Greenwich, CT 06830-4697
Tel (203) 863-3000 *Founded/Ownrshp* 1986
Sales 312.9MM *EMP* 1,600
SIC 8062 General medical & surgical hospitals; General medical & surgical hospitals
Pr: Frank A Corvino
Pr: Stephen Carbery
**CFO:* Eugene Colucci
Bd of Dir: Edward Jacobson
Ofcr: Fahad Ahmed
Ofcr: Cynthia Catterson
Ofcr: Helen Welch
**Ex VP:* Brian J Doran
**Sr VP:* Susan Brown
Sr VP: Michael Marino
**VP:* Christine Beechner
VP: Jack Mahoney
Dir Rad: Ralph Sgambato

D-U-N-S 15-532-6655
GREENWICH HOTEL LIMITED PARTNERSHIP
HYATT HOTEL
1800 E Putnam Ave, Old Greenwich, CT 06870-1320
Tel (203) 698-9350 *Founded/Ownrshp* 1985
Sales 22.9MM^E *EMP* 320^E
SIC 7011 Hotels & motels; Hotels & motels
Genl Mgr: Tom Delaney

D-U-N-S 01-866-5117
GREENWICH IMAGING SERVICES LLC
THRIFT SHOP, THE
5 Perryridge Rd, Greenwich, CT 06830-4608
Tel (203) 863-3220 *Founded/Ownrshp* 1903, 2000
Sales NA *EMP* 500
SIC 6324 Hospital & medical service plans; Hospital & medical service plans
Genl Couns: Frederick Thomas

D-U-N-S 94-834-1367
GREENWICH SCHOOL DISTRICT
GREENWICH WESTERN MIDDLE SCHL
290 Greenwich Ave, Greenwich, CT 06830-6508
Tel (203) 625-7400 *Founded/Ownrshp* 1962
Sales 40.6MM^E *EMP* 1,982
SIC 8211 Public junior high school; Public junior high school
**Prin:* Stacey Gross
Dir Sec: Thomas Bobkowski
Pr Dir: Kimberley Eves
HC Dir: Mary Keller

D-U-N-S 13-466-0831
GREENWICH TERMINALS LLC
3301 S Columbus Blvd, Philadelphia, PA 19148-5115
Tel (215) 923-5000 *Founded/Ownrshp* 2001
Sales 27.1MM^E *EMP* 300
SIC 4491 Stevedoring; Stevedoring
IT Man: Kurt Ferry

D-U-N-S 16-162-3087 IMP
GREENWICH VILLAGE FISH CO INC
CITARELLA
2135 Broadway, New York, NY 10023-1709
Tel (631) 324-9190 *Founded/Ownrshp* 1980
Sales 116.5MM^E *EMP* 600
SIC 5411 Grocery stores, independent; Grocery stores, independent
Ch Bd: Gaspare Catanzaro
**Pr:* Joseph R Gurrera
COO: Jenny Herman
Mktg Dir: Ray Payne

GREENWICH WESTERN MIDDLE SCHL
See GREENWICH SCHOOL DISTRICT

GREENWOOD & HALL
See PCS LINK INC

D-U-N-S 01-847-3090
GREENWOOD CHEVROLET INC
4695 Mahoning Ave, Youngstown, OH 44515-1687
Tel (330) 270-1299 *Founded/Ownrshp* 1980
Sales 71.0MM^E *EMP* 146
SIC 5511 7538 5521 Automobiles, new & used; Trucks, tractors & trailers: new & used; General automotive repair shops; Used car dealers; Automobiles, new & used; Trucks, tractors & trailers: new & used; General automotive repair shops; Used car dealers
Pr: Gregory Greenwood
**VP:* Wayne C Greenwood Jr
Genl Mgr: Denny Denoi
Genl Mgr: Dave Roberts
Dir IT: Roger Kordes
Dir IT: Marilyn Wurst
Sls&Mrk Ex: Teri Simon
Sls Mgr: Kyle English
Sales Asso: Shawn Sweitzer

D-U-N-S 06-449-6474
GREENWOOD COMMUNITIES AND RESORTS INC
(*Suby of* GREENWOOD MILLS INC) ★
104 Maxwell Ave, Greenwood, SC 29646-2641
Tel (864) 941-4044 *Founded/Ownrshp* 1978
Sales 70.0MM^E *EMP* 325
SIC 6552 7992 7999 Subdividers & developers; Public golf courses; Tennis club, non-membership; Subdividers & developers; Public golf courses; Tennis club, non-membership
Pr: Julian J Nexsen
Pr: Bill Watkins
**CFO:* Ronald R Poole
**VP:* Charles W Pigg
**VP:* Bubba Self
IT Man: Art Fousek

D-U-N-S 09-323-0126
GREENWOOD COMMUNITY SCHOOL BUILDING CORP
605 W Smith Valley Rd, Greenwood, IN 46142-3048
Tel (317) 889-4060 *Founded/Ownrshp* 1870
Sales NA *EMP* 500
SIC 9411 8211 Administration of educational programs; Public elementary & secondary schools; Administration of educational programs; Public elementary & secondary schools
**Treas:* Stephanie Cobele
MIS Dir: Rebecca Rinehart

D-U-N-S 96-732-4844
GREENWOOD COMMUNITY SCHOOL CORP
605 W Smith Valley Rd, Greenwood, IN 46142-3048
Tel (317) 889-4060 *Founded/Ownrshp* 2011
Sales 25.8MM^E *EMP* 489^E
SIC 8211 Elementary & secondary schools

GREENWOOD COUNTY HOSPITAL
See SELF REGIONAL HEALTHCARE

GREENWOOD COUNTY HOSPITAL
See SELF MEDICAL GROUP

D-U-N-S 15-420-9282 IMP
GREENWOOD FABRICATING & PLATING LLC
G F P
215 Mill Ave, Greenwood, SC 29646-2252
Tel (864) 229-1225 *Founded/Ownrshp* 2005
Sales 31.1MM^E *EMP* 200
SIC 3471 3443

D-U-N-S 13-859-2568
GREENWOOD FARMERS COOPERATIVE
MIDWEST FARMERS COOP
304 S 3rd St, Elmwood, NE 68349-6114
Tel (402) 994-2585 *Founded/Ownrshp* 2003
Sales 170.7MM *EMP* 75
SIC 5191 Farm supplies; Farm supplies
Pr: Dale Piper

D-U-N-S 07-804-7966
GREENWOOD GENETIC CENTER INC (SC)
SELF RESEARCH INSTITUTE
106 Gregor Mendel Cir, Greenwood, SC 29646-2315
Tel (864) 941-8100 *Founded/Ownrshp* 1974
Sales 20.2MM *EMP* 170
SIC 8731

D-U-N-S 61-874-5137
GREENWOOD INC
160 Milestone Way Ste A, Greenville, SC 29615-6628
Tel (864) 288-5510 *Founded/Ownrshp* 1993
Sales 220.2MM^E *EMP* 786
Accts Dixon Hughes Pllc Greenville
SIC 1541 7349 Industrial buildings & warehouses; Building & office cleaning services; Industrial buildings & warehouses; Building & office cleaning services
Ch Bd: John Wood
**Pr:* Brad Wood
**CFO:* Chris Hemmings
**VP:* Laura Lipscomb
IT Man: Kevin Crittendon

D-U-N-S 80-654-0910
GREENWOOD INDUSTRIES INC
640 Lincoln St, Worcester, MA 01605-2058
Tel (508) 865-4040 *Founded/Ownrshp* 1992
Sales 62.6MM *EMP* 230
Accts Marcum Llp New Haven Ct
SIC 1761 Roofing contractor; Roofing contractor
Pr: David S Klein
VP: John D'Elia

D-U-N-S 07-355-3661
GREENWOOD LEFLORE HOSPITAL
1401 River Rd, Greenwood, MS 38930-4030
Tel (662) 459-7000 *Founded/Ownrshp* 1950
Sales 120.0MM *EMP* 890
Accts Horne Llp Ridgeland Mississi
SIC 8062 General medical & surgical hospitals; General medical & surgical hospitals
Ofcr: Jim Jackson
Chf OB: Edwin M Meek Jr
**CFO:* Dawne Holmes
Dir Inf Cn: Allison Harris
Dir Risk M: Karen B Upchurch
Dir Lab: Jerry Ruffin
Dir Rad: Monica Flowers
Dir Rx: Dean Kidd
Dir Env Sv: Mike Fleetwood
Chf Nrs Of: Rebecca Edward
Dir Pat Ac: Terri Ashworth

D-U-N-S 00-334-8521 IMP
GREENWOOD MILLS INC (SC)
300 Morgan Ave, Greenwood, SC 29646-4552
Tel (864) 227-2121 *Founded/Ownrshp* 1889
Sales 124.0MM^E *EMP* 325
SIC 2211 2221 2241 2261 2262 6552 Broadwoven fabric mills, cotton; Acetate broadwoven fabrics; Poplin, manmade fiber; Twills, manmade fiber; Shirting fabrics, manmade fiber & silk; Narrow fabric mills; Dyeing cotton broadwoven fabrics; Dyeing: manmade fiber & silk broadwoven fabrics; Subdividers & developers; Broadwoven fabric mills, cotton; Acetate broadwoven fabrics; Poplin, manmade fiber; Twills, manmade fiber; Shirting fabrics, manmade fiber & silk; Narrow fabric mills; Dyeing cotton broadwoven fabrics; Dyeing: manmade fiber & silk broadwoven fabrics; Subdividers & developers
Pr: James C Self III
**Ex VP:* Thomas J Davis
**VP:* W Eddie Gaither
**VP:* H Doyle Kidd
**VP:* Warren L Moore
**VP:* Gary Niederauer
Dir IT: Glenn Pinnel
Board of Directors: Virginia S Brennan, Sally S Harley

D-U-N-S 00-379-3072
GREENWOOD MOTOR LINES INC (SC)
R & L CARRIERS
(*Suby of* R & L CARRIERS INC) ★
600 Gilliam Rd, Wilmington, OH 45177-9089
Tel (937) 382-1494 *Founded/Ownrshp* 1954, 1992
Sales 61.8MM^E *EMP* 700
SIC 4213 4212

D-U-N-S 10-629-2311
GREENWOOD PUBLIC SCHOOL DISTRICT
401 Howard St, Greenwood, MS 38930-4337
Tel (662) 453-4231 *Founded/Ownrshp* 1910
Sales 23.9MM^E *EMP* 490^E
Accts Cunningham Cpas Pllc Belzoni
SIC 8211 9411 Public elementary & secondary schools; High school, junior or senior; Administration of educational programs; Public elementary & secondary schools; High school, junior or senior; Administration of educational programs
**CFO:* Deirdre R Mayes
IT Man: Aubrey Reynolds

D-U-N-S 07-375-0283
GREENWOOD RACING INC
PARX CASINO
(*Suby of* INTERNATIONAL TURF INVESTMENT CO INC) ★
299 Street Rd, Bensalem, PA 19020
Tel (215) 639-9000 *Founded/Ownrshp* 1973, 1990
Sales 66.3MM^E *EMP* 690
SIC 7948 Race track operation; Race track operation
CEO: Harold Handel
**Pr:* Robert Green
CFO: Bryan Bartlett
**Sec:* Anthony Ricci
Chf Mktg O: Marc Oppenheimer
Ofcr: Brandon Bach
Ofcr: James Cahill
Ofcr: James Cloman
Ofcr: Ward Rooney
Ofcr: Aziza Wilson
Exec: Donna Lane
Exec: Francis Perko

D-U-N-S 07-806-3203
GREENWOOD SCHOOL DISTRICT 50
1855 Calhoun Rd, Greenwood, SC 29649-9102
Tel (864) 941-5400 *Founded/Ownrshp* 1900
Sales 75.8MM^E *EMP* 1,200
SIC 8211 Public elementary & secondary schools; Public elementary & secondary schools
V Ch: Tony Bowers
V Ch: Mark Lowe
**CFO:* Henry Teague
Trst: Curtis Hensley
Trst: Claude Wright
Ofcr: Gary Moore
MIS Dir: Zach Lloyd
Info Man: Terese Grant
Psych: Allison Rice II

GREENWOOD VILLAGE SOUTH
See WESTMINSTER VILLAGE GREENWOOD INC

D-U-N-S 00-690-1003
GREER AUTRY & SONS INC
GREER'S
2850 W Main St, Mobile, AL 36612-2043
Tel (251) 342-7964 *Founded/Ownrshp* 1916
Sales 124.4MM^E *EMP* 700
SIC 5411 Grocery stores; Grocery stores
Ch Bd: J Barton Greer Jr
**Treas:* Jack V Greer Jr
**VP:* Robert A Greer
**VP:* O M Otts III

D-U-N-S 04-338-8594
GREER COMMISSION OF PUBLIC WORKS
GREER COMMISSION PUBLIC WORKS
301 Mccall St, Greer, SC 29650-2024
Tel (864) 848-2150 *Founded/Ownrshp* 1913
Sales 29.4MM^E *EMP* 130
SIC 4939 Combination utilities; Combination utilities
Ch: Jeffrey M Howell
VP: Wilton Bradley
Dir Lab: Pete Davis
Genl Mgr: Kandi Powell
**Genl Mgr:* Nick W Stegall
**Genl Mgr:* Jeffrey M Tuttle

GREER COMMISSION PUBLIC WORKS
See GREER COMMISSION OF PUBLIC WORKS

D-U-N-S 00-446-1927
GREER INDUSTRIES INC
GREER LIMESTONE CO DIV
570 Canyon Rd, Morgantown, WV 26508-9065
Tel (304) 296-2549 *Founded/Ownrshp* 1920
Sales 128.1MM^E *EMP* 450
SIC 3316 3272 2951 1422 3274 1446 Strip steel, cold-rolled: from purchased hot-rolled; Concrete products; Asphalt & asphaltic paving mixtures (not from refineries); Agricultural limestone, ground; Lime rock, ground; Dolomite, crushed & broken-quarrying; Lime; Industrial sand; Strip steel, cold-rolled: from purchased hot-rolled; Concrete products; Asphalt & asphaltic paving mixtures (not from refineries); Agricultural limestone, ground; Lime rock, ground; Dolomite, crushed & broken-quarrying; Lime; Industrial sand
Ch: Charles McGill
**Pr:* John R Raese
**Ex VP:* David A Raese
VP: James M Goff
VP: Robert Henn
**VP:* James M Troy
VP: James Troy
VP: Duane Walls
Genl Mgr: Fred Persinger
Dir IT: Brad Hadley
Dir IT: Matt Smith

D-U-N-S 02-467-1414 IMP
GREER LABORATORIES INC (NC)
(*Suby of* ALBION MEDICAL HOLDINGS INC)
639 Nuway Cir, Lenoir, NC 28645-3646
Tel (828) 754-5327 *Founded/Ownrshp* 1946
Sales 43.9MM^E *EMP* 214
SIC 2836 8734 2834 Vaccines; Testing laboratories; Pharmaceutical preparations; Vaccines; Testing laboratories; Pharmaceutical preparations
Pr: Rick Russell
COO: David Burney
**CFO:* Anthony Palombo
CFO: Tony Palombo
CFO: Tony Palumbo
**Ofcr:* Terrance C Coyne
**Ex VP:* Robert E Esch
VP: Charles Bolyard
VP: Robert Phipps
Dir Lab: Edward Patt
Assoc Dir: Kimberly Davis
Board of Directors: Charles Dobbin

GREER LIMESTONE CO DIV
See GREER INDUSTRIES INC

D-U-N-S 78-689-3990
GREER STEEL CO
(*Suby of* GREER INDUSTRIES INC) ★
624 Boulevard St, Dover, OH 44622-2027
Tel (330) 343-8811 *Founded/Ownrshp* 1991
Sales 51.6MM^E *EMP* 150
SIC 3316 Strip steel, cold-rolled: from purchased hot-rolled; Strip steel, cold-rolled: from purchased hot-rolled
Pr: John R Raese
**CFO:* James M Troy
VP: David Matisko
VP: Charles Maul
Dir Bus: Curtis Lamar

D-U-N-S 08-518-8571
GREER TANK INC
3140 Lakeview Dr, Fairbanks, AK 99701-7833
Tel (907) 452-1711 *Founded/Ownrshp* 1972
Sales 25.0MM^E *EMP* 55
SIC 3441 5051 3443 Fabricated structural metal; Steel; Tanks, standard or custom fabricated: metal plate
Pr: Stephen Helms
**Sec:* Linda D Helms
**VP:* David M Greer
Sls Dir: Michelle Jensen

GREER'S
See GREER AUTRY & SONS INC

D-U-N-S 62-801-4151
GREG BARNETT
SHAKES SALES
4912 Mill Creek Rd, Edmond, OK 73025-2818
Tel (405) 341-2648 *Founded/Ownrshp* 1991
Sales 24.0MM *EMP* 2
SIC 5031 5033

D-U-N-S 13-520-6733
GREG BEECHE LOGISTICS LLC
356 Hudson River Rd, Waterford, NY 12188-1914
Tel (518) 664-5255 *Founded/Ownrshp* 2002
Sales 20.1MM^E *EMP* 104^E
SIC 8741 Business management

D-U-N-S 17-421-5863
GREG HASYN
NORTH POLE PHOTO
103 Winter Dr, North Wales, PA 19454-1720
Tel (215) 855-8123 *Founded/Ownrshp* 1982
Sales 14.7MM^E *EMP* 400
SIC 7335 Commercial photography; Commercial photography
Owner: Greg Hasyn

GREG HUBLER CHEVROLET
See ECS INC

GREG NORMAN COLLECTION
See THARANCO LIFESTYLES LLC

D-U-N-S 02-591-2296
GREG WEEKS INC
WEEKS CHEVROLET PONTIAC GEO
10881 State Highway 149, West Frankfort, IL 62896-4173
Tel (618) 937-2446 *Founded/Ownrshp* 1957
Sales 32.8MM^E *EMP* 80
SIC 5511 Automobiles, new & used; Automobiles, new & used
Pr: Greg Weeks
Store Mgr: Doug Thomas
Sls Mgr: Randy Minton

D-U-N-S 80-821-4530
GREG WELTEROTH HOLDING INC
G W A
356 Laurens Rd, Montoursville, PA 17754-8329
Tel (570) 433-3366 *Founded/Ownrshp* 1990
Sales 23.9MM^E *EMP* 130
SIC 7319 Media buying service; Media buying service
Pr: Lauri Welteroth
**VP:* Gregory Welteroth
Opers Mgr: Sam Shaheen
Sls Mgr: Joe Rechel

D-U-N-S 01-641-1043 IMP
■ **GREGG APPLIANCES INC**
H.H. GREGG
(*Suby of* HHGREGG INC) ★
4151 E 96th St, Indianapolis, IN 46240-1442
Tel (317) 848-8710 *Founded/Ownrshp* 1955, 2007
Sales 537.7MM^E *EMP* 2,800
SIC 5731 5722 5719 Television sets; Radios, two-way, citizens' band, weather, short-wave, etc.; Consumer electronic equipment; Electric household appliances, major; Electric household appliances, small; Bedding (sheets, blankets, spreads & pillows); Linens; Television sets; Radios, two-way, citizens' band, weather, short-wave, etc.; Consumer electronic equipment; Electric household appliances, major; Electric household appliances, small; Bedding (sheets, blankets, spreads & pillows); Linens
CFO: Robert J Riesbeck
**Pr:* Dennis L May
**COO:* Troy H Risch
VP: Kelli Slavin
CIO: Stephen Nelson
Sls Mgr: Joshua Kirsten
Board of Directors: Lawrence P Castellani, Benjamin D Geiger, John M Roth, Charles P Rullman, Michael L Smith, Peter M Starrett

D-U-N-S 18-705-6775 IMP
GREGG DRILLING & TESTING INC
2726 Walnut Ave, Signal Hill, CA 90755-1832
Tel (562) 427-6899 *Founded/Ownrshp* 1985
Sales 36.3MM *EMP* 133
Accts Glenn M Gelman & Associates
SIC 1799 1781 Core drilling & cutting; Water well drilling; Core drilling & cutting; Water well drilling
Pr: John M Gregg
**VP:* Chris Christensen
**VP:* Patrick Keating
Board of Directors: John Gregg

D-U-N-S 00-786-0158
GREGG ELECTRIC INC (CA)
608 W Emporia St, Ontario, CA 91762-3709
Tel (909) 983-1794 *Founded/Ownrshp* 1961, 1957
Sales 28.7MM^E *EMP* 150
SIC 1731 General electrical contractor; General electrical contractor
Pr: Randall F Fehlman
**CFO:* Victoria Mensen
**VP:* James Fehlman

D-U-N-S 06-768-3359
GREGG FARM SERVICES INC (AR)
DO IT BEST
6135 Hwy 126 S, Midway, AR 72651
Tel (870) 481-5165 *Founded/Ownrshp* 1974, 1998
Sales 25.0MM *EMP* 12
SIC 5251 2048 5261 5211 Farm supplies; Feed; Prepared feeds; Fertilizer; Garden supplies & tools; Lumber & other building materials; Hardware; Prepared feeds; Fertilizer; Garden supplies & tools; Lumber & other building materials
Pr: Douglas E Gregg
Store Mgr: Tammy Daffron

D-U-N-S 08-513-0664
GREGG INDUSTRIAL INSULATORS INC
(*Suby of* GREGG INDUSTRIES INC) ★
201 Estes Dr, Longview, TX 75602-6100
Tel (903) 757-5754 *Founded/Ownrshp* 1989
Sales 58.2MM^E *EMP* 450
SIC 1799 2493 Insulation of pipes & boilers; Insulating board, hard pressed; Insulation board, cellular fiber; Insulation of pipes & boilers; Insulating board, hard pressed; Insulation board, cellular fiber
Pr: CHI N Swallo
**Treas:* Ames R Billingsley
**Treas:* Mike Merritt
**VP:* David Brooks
**Prin:* Thomac C Merritt
Opers Mgr: Ray Barnett

D-U-N-S 00-831-8586
■ **GREGG INDUSTRIES INC**
(*Suby of* NEENAH FOUNDRY CO) ★
2121 Brooks Ave, Neenah, WI 54956-4756
Tel (920) 725-7000 *Founded/Ownrshp* 1946
Sales 40.3MM^E *EMP* 450
SIC 3321 Gray & ductile iron foundries; Ductile iron castings; Gray iron castings; Gray & ductile iron foundries; Ductile iron castings; Gray iron castings
Pr: William M Barrett
Genl Mgr: Dave Bash
MIS Dir: Dan Barahona
MIS Dir: Aydin Taskin

D-U-N-S 80-542-6145 IMP
GREGG INDUSTRIES INC
(*Suby of* BRAND ENERGY & INFRASTRUCTURE SERVICES INC) ★
201 Estes Dr, Longview, TX 75602-6100
Tel (903) 757-5754 *Founded/Ownrshp* 2013
Sales 58.2MM^E *EMP* 750
SIC 1742 7359 1721 1731 1799 Insulation, buildings; Equipment rental & leasing; Industrial painting; Electrical work; Scaffolding construction; Insulation, buildings; Equipment rental & leasing; Industrial painting; Electrical work; Scaffolding construction
Pr: Thomas C Merritt
Sec: A P Merritt Jr
VP: David Brooks
VP: Mike Merritt

D-U-N-S 05-125-6824
GREGG YOUNG CHEVROLET INC
17750 Burt St, Omaha, NE 68118-3311
Tel (402) 572-8080 *Founded/Ownrshp* 2000
Sales 48.0MM^E *EMP* 95
SIC 5511

D-U-N-S 07-941-0207
GREGG YOUNG CHEVROLET OF NORWALK INC
HOLMES AUTOMOTIVE GROUP
28 Foster Dr, Des Moines, IA 50312-2563
Tel (515) 256-4010 *Founded/Ownrshp* 2014
Sales 21.4MM^E *EMP* 45
SIC 5511 Automobiles, new & used
Pr: Gregory B Young
Off Mgr: Bobbi Hartfield

D-U-N-S 00-797-2151
GREGGO & FERRARA INC
4048 New Castle Ave, New Castle, DE 19720-1498
Tel (302) 658-5241 *Founded/Ownrshp* 1946
Sales 56.1MM^E *EMP* 200
SIC 1611 1622 1542

D-U-N-S 15-202-4956
GREGMAR INC
4312 S Georgia Pl, Oklahoma City, OK 73129-7972
Tel (405) 677-6633 *Founded/Ownrshp* 1980
Sales 53.2MM^E *EMP* 300
SIC 4212 4213 Petroleum haulage, local; Liquid petroleum transport, non-local; Petroleum haulage, local; Liquid petroleum transport, non-local
Pr: Greg Price
**Sec:* Margaret Price
**VP:* Tim M Rains

D-U-N-S 07-596-5855
GREGORY & APPEL INC
GREGOY AND APPEL INSURANCE
1402 N Capitol Ave # 400, Indianapolis, IN 46202-6148
Tel (317) 634-7491 *Founded/Ownrshp* 1940
Sales NA *EMP* 115
SIC 6411 Life insurance agents
Pr: Daniel C Appel
CFO: David Riley
Bd of Dir: Susan Rider
**Ex VP:* David M Riley
Sr VP: Sheryl Alexander
Sr VP: Jeffrey Webster
VP: Andy Brown
VP: Jean Casolaro
VP: Brad Dumbauld
VP: Cindy English

VP: Reba Ericksen
VP: Scott Gray
VP: Lee Hauser
VP: Janet McClure
VP: Mary Schmid
VP: Kelly Witt

D-U-N-S 00-615-8450
GREGORY B LURING
MCDONALD'S
110 S 4th Ave, Yakima, WA 98902-3428
Tel (509) 248-2176 *Founded/Ownrshp* 1980
Sales 11.0MM *EMP* 300
SIC 5812 Fast-food restaurant, chain; Fast-food restaurant, chain
Owner: Greg Luring

GREGORY C RIGAMER & ASSOCIATES
See GCR INC

GREGORY CONSTRUCTION COMPANY
See SAGINAW BAY DEVELOPMENT II INC

D-U-N-S 36-342-0951
GREGORY CONSULTING INC
6350 Leland St, Ventura, CA 93003-8585
Tel (805) 642-0111 *Founded/Ownrshp* 1986
Sales 12.0MM *EMP* 335
SIC 5511 7538 5521 New & used car dealers; General automotive repair shops; Used car dealers; New & used car dealers; General automotive repair shops; Used car dealers
Pr: Robert Gregory
**VP:* Nancy Gregory

D-U-N-S 00-336-4395
GREGORY ELECTRIC CO INC (SC)
2124 College St, Columbia, SC 29205-1023
Tel (803) 748-1122 *Founded/Ownrshp* 1949
Sales 65.0MM^E *EMP* 250
SIC 1731 General electrical contractor; General electrical contractor
Pr: Robert E Livingston Jr
**VP:* Glenn W Greer
**VP:* Lisa M Philips
**VP:* Jack Royal
Exec: Beth Wright
Admn Mgr: Connie Vaughn
Snr PM: Scott Webber

D-U-N-S 00-446-8856 IMP/EXP
GREGORY INDUSTRIES INC (OH)
4100 13th St Sw, Canton, OH 44710-1464
Tel (330) 477-4800 *Founded/Ownrshp* 1957
Sales 24.1MM^E *EMP* 100
SIC 3499 Metal household articles; Metal household articles
CEO: T Stephen Gregory
**CFO:* Joseph Weaver
IT Man: Corey Paulus
Sfty Mgr: Mike Quirin
Plnt Mgr: Thomas Brem
Plnt Mgr: Brian Lester
Mktg Mgr: Rick Mauer
Manager: Tom Close
Sls Mgr: Bob Chufar
Sls Mgr: FT Zalenski
Sales Asso: Jim Dehnke

D-U-N-S 84-446-1983
GREGORY LOGISTICS INC
2844 Fair St, Poplar Bluff, MO 63901-7016
Tel (573) 785-1088 *Founded/Ownrshp* 1999
Sales 514.0MM *EMP* 100
SIC 4213 4212 Trucking, except local; Local trucking, without storage
Pr: Larry Gregory
**CFO:* Carol Bounds

D-U-N-S 06-104-3832
GREGORY MANUFACTURING CO
2512 Henry Ladyn Dr, Fort Madison, IA 52627-2519
Tel (319) 463-7700 *Founded/Ownrshp* 1968
Sales 75.7MM^E *EMP* 330
SIC 3446 3537 3469 2542 Architectural metalwork; Industrial trucks & tractors; Metal stampings; Partitions & fixtures, except wood; Architectural metalwork; Industrial trucks & tractors; Metal stampings; Partitions & fixtures, except wood
Pr: Michael Walker
Genl Mgr: Mike Straw
Plnt Mgr: Michael Strawhacker
Sls&Mrk Ex: Bill Coppage

D-U-N-S 07-370-8422
GREGORY PEST CONTROL INC
GREGORY PEST SOLUTIONS
1313 Miller Rd, Greenville, SC 29607-5711
Tel (864) 675-6226 *Founded/Ownrshp* 1972
Sales 20.7MM^E *EMP* 187
SIC 7342 Exterminating & fumigating; Exterminating & fumigating
CEO: Phillip Gregory
**Pr:* Sarah Gregory
**Pr:* Benjamin Walker
Dist Mgr: Derek Johnson
Dir IT: Brad Baker

GREGORY PEST SOLUTIONS
See GREGORY PEST CONTROL INC

D-U-N-S 18-844-0614
GREGORY PHARMACEUTICAL HOLDINGS INC
UPM PHARMACEUTICALS
6200 Seaforth St Ste 1, Baltimore, MD 21224-6536
Tel (423) 989-8000 *Founded/Ownrshp* 1997
Sales 25.9MM^E *EMP* 48^E
SIC 8731 2834 Medical research, commercial; Pharmaceutical preparations
CEO: John M Gregory
Pr: Richard Green
**Pr:* James E Gregory
Pr: Ed Scholtz
**CFO:* Greg Tebeau
**CFO:* Gregory J Tebeau
**Treas:* Susan K Gregory
Ofcr: Gary Hollenbeck
VP: John Bowles
**VP:* Frances Spaven
Ql Cn Mgr: Mike Gipprich

D-U-N-S 00-699-7241 EXP
GREGORY POOLE EQUIPMENT CO
CATERPILLAR
(*Suby of* PANTHER SUMMIT INDUSTRIES INC) ★
4807 Beryl Rd, Raleigh, NC 27606-1493
Tel (919) 828-0641 *Founded/Ownrshp* 1946
Sales 522.5MM^E *EMP* 900
SIC 5082 Road construction equipment; General construction machinery & equipment; Road construction equipment; General construction machinery & equipment
Ch Bd: J Gregory Poole III
**CFO:* Kathy Morris
CFO: Michael Tew
**Ex VP:* Richard F Donnelly
VP: Paul Eberhart
VP: Hal Ingram
VP: Eddie Williford
IT Man: Joe Owen
Sls Mgr: Chris Beckman

D-U-N-S 04-533-9462
GREGORY PORTLAND INDEPENDENT SCHOOL DISTRICT
GREGORY PORTLAND ISD
608 College St, Portland, TX 78374-2021
Tel (361) 777-1091 *Founded/Ownrshp* 1940
Sales 37.4MM *EMP* 598
Accts Lovvorn & Kieschnick Llp Cor
SIC 8211 Public elementary & secondary schools; Public elementary & secondary schools
CFO: Ronald Wilson
VP: Randy Eulenfeld
Dir IT: Tena Walls

GREGORY PORTLAND ISD
See GREGORY PORTLAND INDEPENDENT SCHOOL DISTRICT

D-U-N-S 03-798-0042 IMP
GREGORY PRICE INTERNATIONAL INC
PRICE GREGORY
920 Mmrial Cy Way Ste 600, Houston, TX 77024
Tel (713) 780-7500 *Founded/Ownrshp* 1980
Sales 353.8MM^E *EMP* 1,000
SIC 1623

D-U-N-S 01-051-6383
GREGORYS FOODS INC (MN)
1301 Trapp Rd, Saint Paul, MN 55121-1247
Tel (651) 454-0277 *Founded/Ownrshp* 1980
Sales 25.6MM^E *EMP* 40
SIC 5149 2051 2053 2052 2045 2038 Bakery products; Bakery: wholesale or wholesale/retail combined; Frozen bakery products, except bread; Cookies & crackers; Prepared flour mixes & doughs; Frozen specialties
Pr: Greg Helland
Dir Lab: Tom Hoebbel
Sales Exec: Gary Morstad
Sls Dir: Mike Reineck

GREGOY AND APPEL INSURANCE
See GREGORY & APPEL INC

D-U-N-S 00-104-1656 IMP
GREGSTROM CORP (MA)
64 Holton St, Woburn, MA 01801-5288
Tel (781) 935-6600 *Founded/Ownrshp* 1946, 1959
Sales 20.2MM^E *EMP* 75
SIC 3089 Thermoformed finished plastic products
Ch Bd: Paul J Didonato
**Pr:* Jeffrey Didonato
Treas: Paul D Donato
**Sec:* Judy Didonato
Dir Bus: Rick Wicker
IT Man: Mark Catanesu
IT Man: Drew Stellmach
Mtls Mgr: Drew Stelmach
Plnt Mgr: Dave Hoskinson
Prd Mgr: Vincent Abraham
Ql Cn Mgr: Thomas Kelley

D-U-N-S 00-428-2661
▲ **GREIF INC** (DE)
425 Winter Rd, Delaware, OH 43015-8903
Tel (740) 549-6000 *Founded/Ownrshp* 1877
Sales 3.6MMM *EMP* 13,325
Accts Deloitte & Touche Llp Columbu
Tkr Sym GEF *Exch* NYS
SIC 2653 2449 2655 3412 3089 2674 Corrugated & solid fiber boxes; Boxes, corrugated: made from purchased materials; Shipping cases & drums, wood: wirebound & plywood; Barrels, wood: coopered; Fiber cans, drums & similar products; Drums, fiber: made from purchased material; Fiber cans, drums & containers; Drums, shipping: metal; Plastic containers, except foam; Paper bags: made from purchased materials; Corrugated & solid fiber boxes; Boxes, corrugated: made from purchased materials; Shipping cases & drums, wood: wirebound & plywood; Barrels, wood: coopered; Fiber cans, drums & similar products; Drums, fiber: made from purchased material; Fiber cans, drums & containers; Drums, shipping: metal; Plastic containers, except foam; Paper bags: made from purchased materials
Pr: David B Fischer
**Ch Bd:* Michael J Gasser
COO: Peter G Watson
CFO: Lawrence A Hilsheimer
CFO: Robert McNutt
Treas: Nadeem S Ali
Ofcr: Andrew Pruzinsky
Ex VP: Gary R Martz
Sr VP: Karen P Lane
Sr VP: Deeanne Marlow
Sr VP: Ivan Signorelli
VP: Kenneth Andre
VP: Michael Barilla
VP: John Dergentis
VP: John Dieker
VP: Matthew Gay
VP: Myron Gramelspacher
VP: Scott R Griffin
VP: Travis Groff
VP: Addison P Kilibarda
VP: Adry Kooyman
Board of Directors: Vicki L Avril, Bruce A Edwards, Mark A Emkes, John F Finn, Daniel J Gunsett, Judith D Hook, John W McNamara, Patrick J Norton

D-U-N-S 61-727-2856 IMP
■ **GREIF PACKAGING LLC**
(*Suby of* GREIF INC) ★
366 Greif Pkwy, Delaware, OH 43015-8260
Tel (740) 549-6000 *Founded/Ownrshp* 2004
Sales 296.5MM^E *EMP* 250^E
SIC 3086 Packaging & shipping materials, foamed plastic; Packaging & shipping materials, foamed plastic
CEO: Brian Dum
**Ch:* Michael J Gasser

D-U-N-S 80-803-9551
■ **GREIF PAPER PACKAGING & SERVICES LLC**
(*Suby of* GREIF INC) ★
425 Winter Rd, Delaware, OH 43015-8903
Tel (740) 549-6000 *Founded/Ownrshp* 2004
Sales 26.1MM^E *EMP* 99
SIC 2631 Paperboard mills
Snr Mgr: Pam Price

D-U-N-S 07-995-5784
■ **GREIF USA LLC**
(*Suby of* GREIF PACKAGING LLC) ★
366 Greif Pkwy, Delaware, OH 43015-8260
Tel (740) 549-6000 *Founded/Ownrshp* 2005
Sales 296.5MM^E *EMP* 231^E
SIC 5093 Barrels & drums

D-U-N-S 00-426-8020 IMP
GREINER BIO-ONE NORTH AMERICA INC
GREINER-BIO-ONE
(*Suby of* GREINER BIO-ONE GMBH)
4238 Capital Dr, Monroe, NC 28110-7681
Tel (704) 261-7883 *Founded/Ownrshp* 1997
Sales 84.4MM^E *EMP* 205
SIC 5047 Medical equipment & supplies; Medical equipment & supplies
Pr: Rainer Perneker
Exec: Diane Ban
VP Mfg: Joses Sellfoser
VP Sls: Carol D'Ance
Board of Directors: Wolfgang Hock, Franz Konard

D-U-N-S 01-718-1251
GREINER ELECTRIC LLC
12456 Dumont Way, Littleton, CO 80125-9755
Tel (303) 470-9702 *Founded/Ownrshp* 1997
Sales 35.0MM *EMP* 185
Accts Bkd Denver Colorado
SIC 1731 Electrical work; Electrical work
Owner: David Greiner
Treas: Laura Gwinn
VP: Sharleen Rogers
Rgnl Mgr: Steve Foote
Sfty Dirs: Susie Klune
Opers Mgr: Jerry Carlson

GREINER FORD LINCOLN MERCURY
See GREINER/SCHMIDT MOTOR CO INC

D-U-N-S 01-057-0034 EXP
GREINER INDUSTRIES INC
1650 Steel Way, Mount Joy, PA 17552-9515
Tel (717) 653-8111 *Founded/Ownrshp* 1979
Sales 44.0MM *EMP* 275
SIC 3441 1799 7353 1731 Fabricated structural metal; Mechanical contractor; Cranes & aerial lift equipment, rental or leasing; Fabricated structural metal; Food service equipment installation; Cranes & aerial lift equipment, rental or leasing; General electrical contractor
Pr: Franklin Greiner Jr

GREINER-BIO-ONE
See GREINER BIO-ONE NORTH AMERICA INC

D-U-N-S 05-271-7840
GREINER/SCHMIDT MOTOR CO INC
GREINER FORD LINCOLN MERCURY
3333 Cy Ave, Casper, WY 82604-3482
Tel (307) 266-1680 *Founded/Ownrshp* 1970, 1972
Sales 51.4MM^E *EMP* 110^E
SIC 5511 7532 5531 Automobiles, new & used; Pickups, new & used; Top & body repair & paint shops; Automotive tires; Automobiles, new & used; Pickups, new & used; Top & body repair & paint shops; Automotive tires
Pr: Philip A Schmidt
**VP:* Richard Greiner
**Prin:* Bob Dixon
**Prin:* Brant Rothfuss
Off Admin: Krystal Roberts
Sales Asso: Alicia Cope
Sales Asso: Sherry Haines

D-U-N-S 00-568-5807
GREKA INC
1791 Sinton Rd, Santa Maria, CA 93458-9708
Tel (805) 347-8700 *Founded/Ownrshp* 1997
Sales 40.0MM *EMP* 150
SIC 1241 1081 Coal mining services; Metal mining services; Coal mining services; Metal mining services
Pr: Andy Devegvar
**CEO:* Randeep Grewal

D-U-N-S 05-880-0959 IMP
GREKA INTEGRATED INC
1700 Sinton Rd, Santa Maria, CA 93458-9708
Tel (805) 347-8700 *Founded/Ownrshp* 2001
Sales 97.3MM^E *EMP* 145^E
SIC 1382 Oil & gas exploration services; Oil & gas exploration services
CEO: Randeep S Grewal
**CFO:* Ken Miller
**VP:* Susan Whalen

D-U-N-S 05-871-6432
GRELTON ELEVATOR INC
6944 County Road M, Grelton, OH 43523-1000
Tel (419) 256-6381 *Founded/Ownrshp* 1972
Sales 35.0MM *EMP* 11
SIC 5153 5191 Grain elevators; Farm supplies; Grain elevators; Farm supplies
Pr: Michael Beck
**Treas:* Tom Beck

D-U-N-S 00-622-1899 IMP
GREMADA INDUSTRIES INC (ND)
BUTLER REMANUFACTURING
825 28th St S Ste E, Fargo, ND 58103-2325
Tel (701) 282-5294 *Founded/Ownrshp* 1962
Sales 22.6MM^E *EMP* 110
SIC 3599 3531 Machine shop, jobbing & repair; Construction machinery; Machine shop, jobbing & repair; Construction machinery
Ch Bd: Gregory F Butler
**CEO:* Steven F Walker
CFO: Kimberly Glidden
VP Sls: James Kowske

D-U-N-S 00-540-0681
GRENADA ADULT HEALTH CARE CLINIC PC
GRENADA LAKE MEDICAL CENTER
965 Avent Dr Ste 106, Grenada, MS 38901-5045
Tel (662) 227-6450 *Founded/Ownrshp* 2008
Sales 47.5MM *EMP* 5
SIC 8011 Offices & clinics of medical doctors; Offices & clinics of medical doctors

GRENADA LAKE MEDICAL CENTER
See GRENADA ADULT HEALTH CARE CLINIC PC

GRENADA LIVING CENTER
See COMMUNITY CARE CENTER OF GRENADA LLC

D-U-N-S 17-925-6149
GRENADA SALES MANAGEMENT INC
635 Highway 332, Grenada, MS 38901-8056
Tel (662) 226-1161 *Founded/Ownrshp* 2005
Sales 21.7MM^E *EMP* 175
SIC 3469 Appliance parts, porcelain enameled; Appliance parts, porcelain enameled
Ch Bd: Howard Ice
**Pr:* Paul Bishop
**CFO:* Jeff Boger

D-U-N-S 05-177-2457
GRENADA SCHOOL DISTRICT
253 S Main St, Grenada, MS 38901-3213
Tel (662) 226-1606 *Founded/Ownrshp* 1920
Sales 34.3MM *EMP* 675
Accts Fortenberry And Ballard Pc B
SIC 8211 Public elementary & secondary schools; Public elementary & secondary schools
IT Man: Rodney Murphy
Pr Dir: Gail Daigneault

D-U-N-S 61-078-0517 IMP
GRENADA STAMPING AND ASSEMBLY INC
(*Suby of* ICE INDUSTRIES INC) ★
635 Highway 332, Grenada, MS 38901-8056
Tel (662) 226-1161 *Founded/Ownrshp* 2003
Sales 23.5MM^E *EMP* 130
SIC 3469 Metal stampings
Ch Bd: Howard Ice
**Pr:* Paul Bishop
**CFO:* Jeff Boger
**Prin:* Jeffrey Snavely

D-U-N-S 03-334-1316
GRENCO SCIENCE INC (CA)
7095 Hollywood Blvd, Los Angeles, CA 90028-8903
Tel (800) 948-7480 *Founded/Ownrshp* 2012
Sales 25.0MM *EMP* 25
SIC 5064 Humidifiers, portable; Humidifiers, portable
CEO: Anthony Efren Barron
CFO: Sean Wilcox
**Founder:* Chris Folkerts
**Mng Dir:* Anthony Marino

D-U-N-S 78-542-9861
GRENE VISION GROUP LLC
G.V.G
1851 N Webb Rd, Wichita, KS 67206-3413
Tel (316) 691-4444 *Founded/Ownrshp* 1996
Sales 22.7MM^E *EMP* 200
SIC 8011 Eyes, ears, nose & throat specialist: physician/surgeon; Eyes, ears, nose & throat specialist: physician/surgeon
**COO:* Kayli Smith
**CFO:* Crystal Page
Off Mgr: Sherry Moore
IT Man: Jason Morris
**IT Man:* Brian Pond
Sls Mgr: Robert Moore
Doctor: Robin Agpoon
Doctor: F Depenbusch

D-U-N-S 61-523-8482 IMP
GRENZEBACH CORP
10 Herring Rd, Newnan, GA 30265-1006
Tel (770) 253-4980 *Founded/Ownrshp* 2004
Sales 30.9MM^E *EMP* 115
SIC 3537 3535 3559 Glass making machinery: blowing, molding, forming, etc.; Industrial trucks & tractors; Unit handling conveying systems; Industrial trucks & tractors; Unit handling conveying systems; Glass making machinery: blowing, molding, forming, etc.
CEO: Stefan Grenzebach
**Pr:* Joe Chuhran
**Pr:* John Fluker
Ex VP: Martina Eberwein
**VP:* Martin Pleyer
VP: Peter Richter
QA Dir: Kevin Newman
Dir IT: Craig Nilson
IT Man: Keon Copeland
Mfg Mgr: Chris Bishop
Opers Mgr: Steffen Schmidt

D-U-N-S 04-582-3283
GRESCO UTILITY SUPPLY INC
1135 Rumble Rd, Forsyth, GA 31029-6350
Tel (478) 315-0800 *Founded/Ownrshp* 1960
Sales 161.7MM *EMP* 105

Accts Mcnair Mclemore Middlebrooks
SIC 5063 Electrical apparatus & equipment; Electrical apparatus & equipment
CEO: Jere T Thorne
**CFO:* Steve Gramling
Ex VP: Steve Grambling

GRESGAM NONDA
See EBB AUTO CO INC

GRESHAM FORD
See MC ROBERT MOTOR CO INC

D-U-N-S 03-333-3998
GRESHAM PETROLEUM CO
415 Pershing Ave, Indianola, MS 38751-3150
Tel (662) 887-2160 *Founded/Ownrshp* 1958
Sales 188.5MM *EMP* 38
SIC 5171 5984

D-U-N-S 05-915-3676
GRESHAM SMITH AND PARTNERS MS PC
GS&P
511 Union St Ste 1400, Nashville, TN 37219-1710
Tel (615) 770-8100 *Founded/Ownrshp* 1967
Sales 97.6MM^E *EMP* 600
SIC 8712

D-U-N-S 05-221-2503
GRESHAM TOYOTA INC
OWN A CAR
950 Ne Hogan Dr, Gresham, OR 97030-5899
Tel (503) 667-1135 *Founded/Ownrshp* 1970
Sales 39.3MM^E *EMP* 145
SIC 5511

D-U-N-S 05-097-3437
GRESHAM TRANSFER INC
GRESHAM TRUCK REPAIR
24001 Ne Sandy Blvd, Wood Village, OR 97060-9652
Tel (503) 255-7900 *Founded/Ownrshp* 1922
Sales 34.8MM^E *EMP* 150
SIC 4212 4213 Local trucking, without storage; Heavy hauling; Local trucking, without storage; Heavy hauling
Pr: Rick Ulmer
**VP:* David Ulmer
Sales Exec: Neil Skovholt

GRESHAM TRUCK REPAIR
See GRESHAM TRANSFER INC

D-U-N-S 03-839-6057
GRESHAM WOFTAM INC
(*Suby of* AMWINS GROUP INC) ★
1 Gresham Lndg, Stockbridge, GA 30281-6341
Tel (770) 389-1600 *Founded/Ownrshp* 2013
Sales NA *EMP* 215
SIC 6411 Insurance brokers; Insurance brokers
Ch: James V Gresham
**Pr:* Tony Gresham
**Ch:* George L Abernathy
**Sec:* Gail S Gresham
**Sr VP:* James A Gresham
VP: Lisa Cupp
VP: Jenny Driskell
VP: Andrea Ford
VP: Sandy Foster
VP: Art Hays
VP: Ed Hrabovsky
VP: Lil Hullinghorst
VP: Janis Jenkins

D-U-N-S 07-978-4773
GRESHAM-BARLOW SCHOOL DISTRICT
GRESHAM-BARLOW SCHOOL DST 10J
1331 Nw Eastman Pkwy, Gresham, OR 97030-3896
Tel (503) 618-2470 *Founded/Ownrshp* 1918
Sales 119.9MM *EMP* 1,003
Accts Pauly Rogers And Co PcT
SIC 8211 Public senior high school; Public senior high school
**CFO:* Jerry Jones
Pr Dir: Athena Vadnais
Snr Mgr: Michael Lindblad

GRESHAM-BARLOW SCHOOL DST 10J
See GRESHAM-BARLOW SCHOOL DISTRICT

D-U-N-S 04-725-2580 IMP
GRESSER COMPANIES INC
GRESSER CONCRETE
3 Checkered Flag Blvd, Shakopee, MN 55379-8967
Tel (651) 454-5976 *Founded/Ownrshp* 1969
Sales 31.5MM^E *EMP* 240
SIC 1771 1741 Concrete work; Masonry & other stonework; Concrete work; Masonry & other stonework
Pr: Michael J Gresser
CFO: Katie Landwehr
Bd of Dir: Dennis Doyle
Ofcr: Justin Wagner

GRESSER CONCRETE
See GRESSER COMPANIES INC

GRETZ BEER CO
See GRETZ BEVERAGE MONTCO INC

D-U-N-S 01-488-3581
GRETZ BEVERAGE MONTCO INC
GRETZ BEER CO
710 E Main St, Norristown, PA 19401-4102
Tel (610) 272-3530 *Founded/Ownrshp* 1996
Sales 48.8MM^E *EMP* 150
SIC 5181 Beer & other fermented malt liquors; Beer & other fermented malt liquors
Pr: Robert J Gretz Jr
**Ch Bd:* Robert Gretz Sr
VP: John Radliff
Sales Asso: Jon Courtney

GREY ADVERTISING
See GREY GLOBAL GROUP LLC

GREY EAGLE DISTRIBUTORS
See D & D DISTRIBUTORS LLLP

D-U-N-S 00-698-4876
GREY GLOBAL GROUP LLC
GREY ADVERTISING
(*Suby of* WPP PLC)
200 5th Ave Bsmt B, New York, NY 10010-3372
Tel (212) 546-2000 *Founded/Ownrshp* 1917, 1969
Sales 526.9MM^E *EMP* 10,000
SIC 7311 Advertising agencies; Advertising agencies
Ch Bd: Jim Heekin
**V Ch:* Joe Celia
V Ch: Steven G Felsher
**V Ch:* Tim Mellors
Pr: Alain Groenendaal
Pr: Meldy Warren
**COO:* Owen Dougherty
**CFO:* Robert Oates
CFO: Mabel Tan
**Ofcr:* Pele Cortizo-Burgess
Ofcr: Owen J Dougherty
**Ofcr:* Tor Myhren
Ofcr: Ali Shabaz
Ex VP: Millicent Badillo
Ex VP: Josh Golden
Ex VP: Robert Kaufman
Ex VP: Suresh Nair
**Sr VP:* John A Grudzina
Sr VP: John Gurdzina
VP: Courtney Engel
VP: Courtney Jacobs

D-U-N-S 09-367-2665
GREY HEALTHCARE GROUP INC
G H G
200 5th Ave Ste 500, New York, NY 10010-4286
Tel (212) 886-3000 *Founded/Ownrshp* 1997
Sales NA *EMP* 512
SIC 7311

D-U-N-S 07-933-0442
GREY HEALTHCARE GROUP LLC
(*Suby of* GREY ADVERTISING) ★
200 5th Ave Ste 500, New York, NY 10010-4286
Tel (212) 886-3000 *Founded/Ownrshp* 2013
Sales 36.8MM^E *EMP* 512
SIC 7311 Advertising agencies; Advertising agencies
CEO: Lynn O'Connor Vos
Mng Pt: John Dietz
Ch Bd: John Anthony Gradzina
COO: John Hegquist
Ex VP: Erin Byrne
Ex VP: Laura Fusco
Sr VP: Bryan Archambault
Sr VP: Jennifer Bagnall
Sr VP: Jessica Cini
Sr VP: Christine Finamore
Sr VP: Joe Magnemi
Sr VP: Hudson Plumb
Sr VP: Eric Ratinetz
Sr VP: Dan Relton
Sr VP: Roseann Roccaro
VP: Bonnie Baker
VP: Jonathan Bloom
VP: Ralph Gabay
VP: Bud Pusposuharto
VP: Brian Reilly
VP: Elisa Wright

D-U-N-S 17-838-9958
GREY MOUNTAIN PARTNERS LLC
1470 Walnut St Ste 400, Boulder, CO 80302-5371
Tel (303) 449-5692 *Founded/Ownrshp* 2006
Sales 484.8MM^E *EMP* 1,192
SIC 6726 Investment offices; Investment offices
VP: Dan Crouse
VP: Brad Starkweather
Mng Dir: Jeff Vincent
Off Mgr: Tania Martin

D-U-N-S 15-119-7878 IMP
GREYHOUND LINES INC
(*Suby of* FIRSTGROUP PLC)
350 N Saint Paul St # 300, Dallas, TX 75201-4285
Tel (214) 849-8000 *Founded/Ownrshp* 1987
Sales 1.3MMM^E *EMP* 8,000
SIC 4111 4215 4142

D-U-N-S 11-923-5364
GREYLOCK FEDERAL CREDIT UNION
150 West St, Pittsfield, MA 01201-9150
Tel (413) 236-4000 *Founded/Ownrshp* 1935
Sales NA *EMP* 240
SIC 6061 Federal credit unions; Federal credit unions
CEO: Marilyn Sperling
**CEO:* Marylin Sperling
COO: Dan Dillon
Ofcr: Stephanie Carlson
Ofcr: John Masten
**Sr VP:* John Bissell
Sr VP: Nancy Howcroft
**Sr VP:* Kent Hudson
**Sr VP:* John S Rys
VP: Michael Jerome
VP: Joel Scussel

D-U-N-S 83-937-5797
GREYSTAR CORP
PENSPEN
10375 Richmond Ave # 900, Houston, TX 77042-4190
Tel (713) 953-7007 *Founded/Ownrshp* 1995
Sales 233.7MM^E *EMP* 700
SIC 1389 Gas field services; Gas field services
Pr: John D Patton
**CFO:* Jeff Powers
**VP:* Michael Kneale
Genl Mgr: Michael McGovern
IT Man: Tracy Brandes
IT Man: Beejan Vessali
Sfty Mgr: Barry Poston
Opers Mgr: John Dunn

D-U-N-S 09-519-3496
GREYSTAR DEVELOPMENT AND CONSTRUCTION LP
750 Bering Dr Ste 300, Houston, TX 77057-2132
Tel (713) 535-9512 *Founded/Ownrshp* 1993
Sales 42.5MM^E *EMP* 60
SIC 1522 1542 Apartment building construction; Hotel/motel, new construction; Commercial & office building contractors
CEO: Bob Faith
COO: Bill Maddux
VP: Debbie Webre

D-U-N-S 61-415-3265
GREYSTAR MANAGEMENT SERVICES
CAS RESIDENTIAL
1201 Elm St Ste 1600, Dallas, TX 75270-2038
Tel (214) 290-7300 *Founded/Ownrshp* 2014
Sales 493.0MM^E *EMP* 4,500^E
SIC 8741 Management services; Management services
Pr: Terry Danner
**COO:* Marysusan Wanich
**CFO:* Pal Ottesen
Chf Mktg O: Katie Sibbern
Ofcr: Peggy Bertsch
Ofcr: Hoffman Michael
Assoc VP: Tami Greene
Ex VP: Dave Denslow
Ex VP: Lisa Ellis
Ex VP: Stephanie Fuhrman
Ex VP: Loyal Proffitt
Sr VP: Lydia Bishop
Sr VP: Gail Duke
Sr VP: Jeff Kimes
VP: Kate Barber
VP: Christina Castleberry
VP: Cindy Defrancesco
VP: Richard Friedman
VP: Mary Golaboff
VP: Mark McElvain
VP: Lisa Nerheim

D-U-N-S 05-383-9911
GREYSTAR MANAGEMENT SERVICES LP
18 Broad St Ste 300, Charleston, SC 29401-3012
Tel (704) 332-0404 *Founded/Ownrshp* 2003
Sales 26.3MM^E *EMP* 15^E
SIC 6531 Real estate agent, commercial
CEO: Bob Faith
**Pt:* Ken Oldham
**Ex Dir:* Stacy Hunt
**Ex Dir:* Andrew Livingstone
**Ex Dir:* Bill Maddux
**Ex Dir:* Derek Ramsey
**Ex Dir:* Scott Wise
Snr Mgr: Susan Northcutt

D-U-N-S 83-879-2158
GREYSTAR MANAGEMENT SERVICES LP
GREYSTAR MULTI-FAMILY SERVICES
750 Bering Dr Ste 300, Houston, TX 77057-2132
Tel (713) 966-5000 *Founded/Ownrshp* 1993
Sales 264.3MM^E *EMP* 5,000
SIC 6513 6531 1522 Apartment hotel operation; Real estate brokers & agents; Remodeling, multi-family dwellings; Apartment hotel operation; Real estate brokers & agents; Remodeling, multi-family dwellings
CEO: Bob Faith
Genl Pt: Greystar Holdings
COO: Bill Maddux
CFO: Eddie Fletcher
CFO: Derek Ramsey
Ex Dir: Stacy Hunt
Ex Dir: Andrew Livingstone

GREYSTAR MULTI-FAMILY SERVICES
See GREYSTAR MANAGEMENT SERVICES LP

D-U-N-S 08-316-9735
GREYSTAR REAL ESTATE PARTNERS LLC
18 Broad St Ste 300, Charleston, SC 29401-3012
Tel (843) 579-9400 *Founded/Ownrshp* 1999
Sales 454.2MM^E *EMP* 4,600
SIC 6531 Real estate brokers & agents; Real estate brokers & agents
CEO: Robert Faith
**COO:* Bill Maddux
**CFO:* Derek Ramsey
Off Mgr: Lynn Gibson
Off Mgr: Bekah Sutter
Mktg Dir: Trisha Peters

D-U-N-S 18-741-3083 IMP/EXP
GREYSTON BAKERY INC
(*Suby of* GREYSTON FOUNDATION INC) ★
104 Alexander St, Yonkers, NY 10701-2535
Tel (914) 375-1510 *Founded/Ownrshp* 1982
Sales 22.1MM^E *EMP* 130
SIC 2051 Cakes, pies & pastries; Cakes, pies & pastries
Ch Bd: Michael Brady
**Pr:* Julius Walls
Treas: Joan Binstock
**VP:* Joan Cotter
Plnt Mgr: Harry Kraklow
Prd Mgr: Rodney Johnson
Ql Cn Mgr: Eileen Wachowski

D-U-N-S 01-402-8760
GREYSTON FOUNDATION INC (NY)
21 Park Ave, Yonkers, NY 10703-3401
Tel (914) 376-3900 *Founded/Ownrshp* 1993
Sales 23.6MM^E *EMP* 130
SIC 8322 Individual & family services
Pr: Steven Brown
**CFO:* Alexandra Dyer
Sr VP: Matthew Shelley
VP: Jonathan Greengrass

GREYSTONE
See INDUPLATE INC

D-U-N-S 36-185-4219 IMP
GREYSTONE & CO INC
152 W 57th St Fl 60, New York, NY 10019-3413
Tel (212) 649-9700 *Founded/Ownrshp* 1993
Sales 71.7MM^E *EMP* 200
Accts Deloitte & Touche Llp
SIC 6211 Investment bankers; Bond dealers & brokers; Investment bankers; Bond dealers & brokers
CEO: Stephen Rosenberg
**COO:* Curtis Pollock
**CFO:* Bruce Bolick
Ofcr: Robert Barolak
**Ofcr:* Darryl Speach
Ex VP: Sharon Briskman
**Ex VP:* Marty Lanigan
**Sr VP:* Matt Grodd
Sr VP: Sharon Schneeman
Sr VP: Jason Stein
**VP:* Kerry Brewer
VP: Raphael Inzlicht
VP: Tom Ryan
VP: Andrew Shedlock
VP: Christopher Utz
VP: Jeffrey Yachmetz
Exec: Robert Culnane

D-U-N-S 05-168-7130
GREYSTONE HEALTHCARE MANAGEMENT CORP
4042 Park Oaks Blvd # 300, Tampa, FL 33610-9539
Tel (813) 635-9500 *Founded/Ownrshp* 2001
Sales 222.1MM^E *EMP* 3,000
SIC 8741 Nursing & personal care facility management; Nursing & personal care facility management
CEO: Bessler Connie
CFO: Ron Swartz
**VP:* Mando William
Off Mgr: Bryan Gureck
Phys Thrpy: Mike Spillane
Occ Thrpy: Erin Shetter
HC Dir: Michele Thorny
Board of Directors: Schwartz Lisa SEC, David Ridel

D-U-N-S 79-186-0943
■ **GREYSTONE HOMES INC**
(*Suby of* LENNAR CORP) ★
25 Enterprise, Aliso Viejo, CA 92656-2708
Tel (949) 349-8000 *Founded/Ownrshp* 1997
Sales 69.0MM^E *EMP* 584
SIC 1521 New construction, single-family houses; New construction, single-family houses
Pr: Jeff Roos
**CFO:* Bruce D Gross
Pr Dir: Ed McQuiston

GREYSTONE LOGISTICS
See GREYSTONE MANUFACTURING LLC

D-U-N-S 93-932-5114
▲ **GREYSTONE LOGISTICS INC**
1613 E 15th St, Tulsa, OK 74120-6007
Tel (918) 583-7441 *Founded/Ownrshp* 1969
Sales 22.2MM *EMP* 83^E
Accts Hogantaylor Llp Tulsa Oklaho
Tkr Sym GLGI *Exch* OTO
SIC 3089 Pallets, plastic; Pallets, plastic
Pr: Warren F Kruger
COO: Robert Noland
CFO: William W Rahhal

D-U-N-S 14-910-5913 IMP
GREYSTONE MANUFACTURING LLC
GREYSTONE LOGISTICS
2601 Shoreline Dr, Bettendorf, IA 52722-5550
Tel (563) 332-0052 *Founded/Ownrshp* 2003
Sales 26.7MM^E *EMP* 85
SIC 2821 Molding compounds, plastics
CEO: Warren F Kruger
CFO: Bill Rahhal
**CFO:* William Rahhal
Sfty Mgr: Scott Ramsey

D-U-N-S 94-395-4701 IMP
GREYSTONE OF LINCOLN INC
INDUPLATE
7 Wellington Rd, Lincoln, RI 02865-4411
Tel (401) 333-0444 *Founded/Ownrshp* 1995
Sales 73.1MM^E *EMP* 300
SIC 3451 3462 Screw machine products; Iron & steel forgings; Automotive & internal combustion engine forgings; Screw machine products; Iron & steel forgings; Automotive & internal combustion engine forgings
Pr: Everett Fernald Jr
**Ex VP:* David Lippy
Tech Mgr: Rick Carvalho

D-U-N-S 00-692-6000
GREYSTONE POWER CORP AN ELECTRIC MEMBERSHIP CORP (GA)
4040 Bankhead Hwy 78, Douglasville, GA 30134-4313
Tel (770) 942-6576 *Founded/Ownrshp* 1936
Sales 140.4MM^E *EMP* 260
SIC 4911 Electric services; Electric services
Pr: Gary Miller
**Ch:* Calvin Earwood
**V Ch Bd:* Charles Rutland
Ofcr: Jerry Donovan
VP: Tim Williams
Board of Directors: J Calvin Earwood, Ed Haley, William Parks, W McSel Pearson, Fred E Wallace

D-U-N-S 05-751-1057
GREYSTONE PROGRAMS INC
36 Violet Ave, Poughkeepsie, NY 12601-1521
Tel (845) 454-7158 *Founded/Ownrshp* 1979
Sales 14.7MM *EMP* 280
Accts Bdo Seidman Llp New York Ne
SIC 8361 Residential care for the handicapped; Residential care for the handicapped
CEO: Catherine Doyle

D-U-N-S 55-690-1163
GREYSTONE SERVICING CORP INC
419 Belle Air Ln, Warrenton, VA 20186-4368
Tel (540) 341-2100 *Founded/Ownrshp* 1988
Sales NA *EMP* 80
SIC 6163 Mortgage brokers arranging for loans, using money of others
Pr: Stephen Rosenberg
**COO:* Robert R Barolak
**COO:* Curtis A Pollock
**CFO:* J Bruce Bolick
**CFO:* Sharon Briskman
**Ex VP:* Betsy Vartanian
**Sr VP:* Deborah Cook
**Sr VP:* Mary Lenser
VP: Leslie Dominy
VP: Jeanne Endsley
VP: Sheila Jenkins
VP: Debi Martin
**VP:* Leona Sanders
VP: Michael Wall
Exec: Garry Ryan

D-U-N-S 18-890-3397
GREYSTONE STAFFING INC
48 S Service Rd Ste 101w, Melville, NY 11747-2335
Tel (516) 797-1000 *Founded/Ownrshp* 1987
Sales 23.8MM^E *EMP* 500
SIC 7361 Employment agencies; Employment agencies
Pr: Philip N Missirlian
**VP:* Barbara E Missirlian

GRFT
See GRAND RAPIDS FOAM TECHNOLOGIES INC

GRH
See GRANDE RONDE HOSPITAL INC

D-U-N-S 14-212-3202 IMP/EXP
GRI ENGINEERING & DEVELOPMENT LLC
(*Suby of* MAT HOLDINGS INC) ★
6700 Wildlife Way, Long Grove, IL 60047
Tel (847) 383-8478 *Founded/Ownrshp* 2003
Sales 230.8MM^E *EMP* 22
Accts Bdo Seidman Llp
SIC 5013 Motor vehicle supplies & new parts; Motor vehicle supplies & new parts
CFO: Greg Purse
Treas: Heather Korsvik

D-U-N-S 13-040-8347
GRIBBINS INSULATION CO INC
1400 E Columbia St, Evansville, IN 47711-5222
Tel (812) 422-3340 *Founded/Ownrshp* 1985
Sales 34.8MM *EMP* 140
Accts Harding Shymanski & Company
SIC 1742 Insulation, buildings; Insulation, buildings
Pr: Jim Gribbins
**Sec:* Patrick Wahl
**VP:* Leslee Gribbins
**VP:* Mark Gribbins
**VP:* Brian Willett
Off Admin: Traci Weber
Sfty Mgr: Trevor Atherton

D-U-N-S 83-123-0813
GRID ALTERNATIVE
1171 Ocean Ave 200, Emeryville, CA 94608-1147
Tel (510) 731-1310 *Founded/Ownrshp* 2009
Sales 21.0MM *EMP* 15
SIC 1711 Solar energy contractor; Solar energy contractor
Prin: Erica Mackie

D-U-N-S 07-999-7072
GRID SOLUTIONS (US) LLC
4200 Wildwood Pkwy # 2018, Atlanta, GA 30339-8402
Tel (877) 605-6777 *Founded/Ownrshp* 2015
Sales 2.0MMM^E *EMP* 3,086^E
SIC 4911 Electric services
CEO: Mark W Begor

D-U-N-S 12-352-8494
GRIDIRON CAPITAL LLC
220 Elm St, New Canaan, CT 06840-5322
Tel (203) 972-1100 *Founded/Ownrshp* 2004
Sales 181.8MM^E *EMP* 1,100^E
SIC 6726 Investment offices; Investment offices
Mng Dir: Scott Harrison

D-U-N-S 93-160-6511
GRIDIRON TRADING MANAGEMENT CO LLC
81 Hemlock Hill Rd, New Canaan, CT 06840-3002
Tel (704) 872-5231 *Founded/Ownrshp* 1996
Sales 121.9MM^E *EMP* 260
SIC 6221 Commodity contracts brokers, dealers; Commodity contracts brokers, dealers

D-U-N-S 17-787-3937
GRIDPOINT INC
(*Suby of* TWENTY FIRST CENTURY UTILITIES LLC) ★
2801 Clarendon Blvd # 100, Arlington, VA 22201-2868
Tel (703) 667-7000 *Founded/Ownrshp* 2015
Sales 44.7MM^E *EMP* 130
SIC 8711 Energy conservation engineering; Energy conservation engineering
Pr: Todd M Raba
CFO: Joseph R Chinnici
Ex VP: Denis A Curran
Sr VP: Mark Danzenbaker
Sr VP: Jeffrey B Hatef
Sr VP: Laurene M Mitchell
VP: Perry Fabi
VP: Jennifer Faulkner
VP: Ben Harris
VP: John Haynes
VP: Stewart Ken
VP: David Lowman
VP: Michael Peterson
VP: John Richmond

GRIECO MAZDA OF DELRAY BEACH
See FLORIDA MAG ENTERPRISES INC

GRIEF CENTER
See HOSPICE & PALLIATIVE CARE CENTER

D-U-N-S 01-666-1571
GRIEGERS MOTOR SALES INC
1756 Morthland Dr, Valparaiso, IN 46385-5445
Tel (219) 462-4117 *Founded/Ownrshp* 1967
Sales 23.0MM^E *EMP* 65
SIC 5511 5521 7538 7515 7513 5013 New & used car dealers; Used car dealers; General automotive repair shops; Passenger car leasing; Truck rental & leasing, no drivers; Motor vehicle supplies & new parts
Pr: Barb Pappas

D-U-N-S 04-570-2057 IMP
GRIER ABRASIVE CO INC
123 W Taft Dr, South Holland, IL 60473-2034
Tel (708) 333-6445 *Founded/Ownrshp* 1988
Sales 22.3MM^E *EMP* 120
SIC 3291 7389 Wheels, abrasive; Wheels, abrasive;
VP: Virginia Yaksic
COO: David Yaksic
VP: Roberta Dubuc
VP: William Humphrey
Genl Mgr: Chris Price
Sfty Mgr: Sandra Mangel
Sales Asso: Elsie Cheffer

D-U-N-S 00-514-0926 EXP
GRIEVE CORP
500 Hart Rd, Round Lake, IL 60073-2898
Tel (847) 546-8225 *Founded/Ownrshp* 1949
Sales 28.3MM^E *EMP* 90
SIC 3567 3821 3433 Industrial furnaces & ovens; Ovens, laboratory; Furnaces, laboratory; Heating equipment, except electric
CEO: D V Grieve
**Pr:* Pat J Calabrese
Sls Mgr: Frank P Calabrese

D-U-N-S 01-744-9778 IMP
GRIFFIN BEVERAGE CO
1901 Dam Rd, West Branch, MI 48661-9344
Tel (989) 345-0883 *Founded/Ownrshp* 1963
Sales 40.4MM^E *EMP* 100
SIC 5181 5182 5149 Beer & other fermented malt liquors; Wine; Soft drinks; Beer & other fermented malt liquors; Wine; Soft drinks
Pr: Robert T Griffin
**Sec:* Nancy Griffin

D-U-N-S 83-103-1612
GRIFFIN BROTHERS TIRES INC
19141 W Catawba Ave, Cornelius, NC 28031-5602
Tel (704) 896-8473 *Founded/Ownrshp* 1999
Sales 23.3MM^E *EMP* 90
SIC 5531 Automotive tires
Pr: Larry Griffin Sr
**Sec:* Mike Griffin

D-U-N-S 11-806-6356 IMP
GRIFFIN CARE LLC
80 Manheim Ave, Bridgeton, NJ 08302-2113
Tel (856) 455-6870 *Founded/Ownrshp* 2012
Sales 40.3MM^E *EMP* 75^E
SIC 5047 Incontinent care products & supplies
Pr: Mark Naim
Pr: David Kenny
COO: Shawn Naim
Treas: Margaret Basile
VP: Jeff Basile
VP Sls: Neal O'Brien
S&M/VP: Hugh Robison
Mktg Mgr: James Bennett

D-U-N-S 01-442-8358
GRIFFIN CHRYSLER DODGE JEEP INC
GRIFFIN DODGE
961 E Us Highway 74, Rockingham, NC 28379-7541
Tel (910) 582-1200 *Founded/Ownrshp* 1997
Sales 21.3MM^E *EMP* 50
SIC 5511 Automobiles, new & used
Pr: Michael Griffin
Genl Mgr: Joe Brown
Opers Mgr: Jim Tanski

D-U-N-S 04-926-9780
GRIFFIN DEWATERING CORP
(*Suby of* GRIFFIN HOLDCO LLC) ★
5306 Clinton Dr, Houston, TX 77020-7912
Tel (713) 676-8000 *Founded/Ownrshp* 1992
Sales 33.3MM^E *EMP* 120
SIC 1799 7359 3561 Dewatering; Equipment rental & leasing; Pumps & pumping equipment; Dewatering; Equipment rental & leasing; Pumps & pumping equipment
Pr: Kazem Khonsari
**Ex VP:* Daisy Suit
VP: Harry Bagherzadeh
IT Man: Greg Jordan
Mktg Dir: Terry Aylward
Mktg Dir: Harry Bagheradh

GRIFFIN DODGE
See GRIFFIN CHRYSLER DODGE JEEP INC

GRIFFIN DODGE MITSUBISHI
See GRIFFIN SALES INC

GRIFFIN FERTILIZER CO
See BEN HILL GRIFFIN INC

D-U-N-S 01-958-8672
GRIFFIN GREENHOUSE SUPPLIES INC
1619 Main St, Tewksbury, MA 01876-2047
Tel (978) 851-4346 *Founded/Ownrshp* 1967
Sales 106.4MM^E *EMP* 220
SIC 5191 Greenhouse equipment & supplies; Seeds: field, garden & flower; Fertilizer & fertilizer materials; Greenhouse equipment & supplies; Seeds: field, garden & flower; Fertilizer & fertilizer materials
Pr: Richard T Hyslip
**COO:* Craig S Hyslip
**Treas:* Kenneth M Hyslip Sr
Sr VP: Dave Morin
Brnch Mgr: Bill Hotz
IT Man: Bob Brackbill
Info Man: Alex Ho
Sfty Mgr: Rick Lane
Opers Mgr: Guy Gallant
Mktg Mgr: Matthew Munafo
Sales Asso: Stephen Dick

D-U-N-S 00-540-5551
GRIFFIN GROUP LLC (CA)
4 Rebelo Ln Ste D, Novato, CA 94947-3629
Tel (415) 892-4569 *Founded/Ownrshp* 2007
Sales 30.0MM^E *EMP* 110^E
SIC 8741 Business management
CEO: Keith Greggor
**CFO:* Crystal Marty
**Ch:* Tony Foglio
**VP:* Lynn Lackey
**CTO:* Chad Farmer
**Counsel:* Graham Taylor

D-U-N-S 07-975-0398
GRIFFIN HOLDCO LLC
5306 Clinton Dr, Houston, TX 77020-7912
Tel (713) 671-7000 *Founded/Ownrshp* 2013
Sales 41.2MM^E *EMP* 120
SIC 1629 1794 Dams, waterways, docks & other marine construction; Excavation & grading, building construction
CEO: David Singleton

D-U-N-S 96-542-3572
GRIFFIN HOLDINGS LLC
2121 Avenue Of The Stars, Los Angeles, CA 90067-5010
Tel (424) 245-4423 *Founded/Ownrshp* 2004
Sales 99.2MM^E *EMP* 325^E
SIC 8741 Business management; Business management
Prin: Dan Gabbay

D-U-N-S 07-212-8424
GRIFFIN HOSPITAL INC (CT)
MEDSOURCE
130 Division St, Derby, CT 06418-1326
Tel (203) 735-7421 *Founded/Ownrshp* 1901, 1984
Sales 135.9MM *EMP* 1,100
SIC 8062 General medical & surgical hospitals; General medical & surgical hospitals
Pr: Patrick Charmel
Chf Rad: Douglas Silin
Dir Vol: Tricia Ness-Brister
Pr: Paul Toburn
**CFO:* Mark O'Neill
VP: Frederick Browne
VP: James Haswell
VP: Bill Powanda
VP: Barbara Stumpo
Assoc Dir: Joseph Gnanaraj
Dir Soc: Haq Nawaz
Dir Rx: Lisa Jaser

D-U-N-S 05-138-3511 EXP
GRIFFIN INC
6562 Highway 178, Byhalia, MS 38611-9442
Tel (662) 838-2128 *Founded/Ownrshp* 1994
Sales 32.6MM^E *EMP* 70
SIC 3713 3499 3711 3442 Truck bodies (motor vehicles); Fire- or burglary-resistive products; Doors, safe & vault: metal; Motor vehicles & car bodies; Metal doors, sash & trim
Pr: Greg McKay
MIS Dir: Gregory McKay
Plnt Mgr: David Talley
Natl Sales: Bill Hurst

D-U-N-S 05-550-7677
▲ GRIFFIN INDUSTRIAL REALTY INC
1 Rockefeller Plz, New York, NY 10020-2003
Tel (212) 218-7910 *Founded/Ownrshp* 1970
Sales 24.2MM *EMP* 99^E
Accts Mcgladrey Llp New Haven Conn
Tkr Sym GRIF *Exch* NGM
SIC 6512 Nonresidential building operators; Nonresidential building operators
Ch Bd: Frederick M Danziger
Pr: Michael S Gamzon
CFO: Anthony J Galici
VP: Scott Bosco
Board of Directors: Winston J Churchill Jr, David M Danziger, Thomas C Israel, John J Kirby Jr, Jonathan P May, Albert H Small Jr

D-U-N-S 00-425-6509 EXP
■ GRIFFIN INDUSTRIES LLC
BAKERY FEEDS
(*Suby of* DARLING INGREDIENTS INC) ★
4221 Alexandria Pike, Cold Spring, KY 41076-1897
Tel (859) 781-2010 *Founded/Ownrshp* 1999, 2010
Sales 405.1MM^E *EMP* 1,800
SIC 2077 Grease rendering, inedible; Tallow rendering, inedible; Grease rendering, inedible; Tallow rendering, inedible
Pr: Robert A Griffin
**Pr:* John M Griffin
**CFO:* Steven Blair
**CFO:* Anthony Griffin
Ex VP: Rick Elrod
VP: Spike Chronowski
**VP:* Martin W Griffin
Exec: Wayne Stanberry
Exec: Tammy Wagner
Dir Lab: Alicia Moore
Dist Mgr: Terry Paschall

D-U-N-S 00-331-1248 IMP/EXP
■ GRIFFIN LLC VALDOSTA GEORGIA (DELAWARE)
(*Suby of* E I DU PONT DE NEMOURS AND CO) ★
2509 Rocky Ford Rd, Valdosta, GA 31601-1575
Tel (229) 242-8635 *Founded/Ownrshp* 1936, 2003
Sales 47.8MM^E *EMP* 600
SIC 2879 Insecticides, agricultural or household; Pesticides, agricultural or household; Fungicides, herbicides; Insecticides, agricultural or household; Pesticides, agricultural or household; Fungicides, herbicides
VP: J Jette Campbell

D-U-N-S 00-328-2365
GRIFFIN LUMBER CO (GA)
1603 Drayton Rd, Cordele, GA 31015-8943
Tel (229) 273-3113 *Founded/Ownrshp* 1948
Sales 20.1MM^E *EMP* 80
SIC 2421 5211 Sawmills & planing mills, general; Planing mill, independent: except millwork; Wood chips, produced at mill; Lumber & other building materials
Pr: W H Griffin III
**Sec:* Larry Lewis
VP: Wayne Ward
Sfty Mgr: Jay Sudduth
Opers Mgr: David Robinson
Plnt Mgr: Jesse Griffin
Sales Asso: B I Thornton

D-U-N-S 60-760-7454 EXP
GRIFFIN MANAGEMENT CO INC
LEXUS OF GREENWICH
19 Railroad Ave, Greenwich, CT 06830-6302
Tel (203) 869-6700 *Founded/Ownrshp* 1986
Sales 127.5MM^E *EMP* 386
SIC 5511 Automobiles, new & used; Automobiles, new & used
Pr: Samuel R Scatterday
**Treas:* Anthony Mazza
**VP:* William J Griffin III
Genl Mgr: Eric Pagan
Store Mgr: Robert Merturi
Dir IT: Matthew Sposato
Sls Mgr: John Annunziato
Sls Mgr: Ched Gelb
Sls Mgr: John McCaffrey
Sls Mgr: Chris Scatterday
Sls Mgr: Dave Sturm

D-U-N-S 80-243-9588 IMP
GRIFFIN MANUFACTURING CO INC
502 Bedford St, Fall River, MA 02720-4855
Tel (508) 677-0048 *Founded/Ownrshp* 1991
Sales 25.0MM^E *EMP* 200
SIC 2329 2339 Athletic (warmup, sweat & jogging) suits: men's & boys'; Athletic clothing: women's, misses' & juniors'; Athletic (warmup, sweat & jogging) suits: men's & boys'; Athletic clothing: women's, misses' & juniors'
Pr: Gene Laudon

D-U-N-S 62-534-2837
GRIFFIN MASONRY INC
11301 Blair Rd, Mint Hill, NC 28227-6871
Tel (704) 545-2722 *Founded/Ownrshp* 1990
Sales 40.4MM^E *EMP* 220
SIC 1741 Masonry & other stonework; Masonry & other stonework
Pr: Scott Griffin
**VP:* Tony Griffin

D-U-N-S 05-675-8436 IMP
GRIFFIN MOTORWERKE INC
1146 6th St, Berkeley, CA 94710-1246
Tel (510) 524-7447 *Founded/Ownrshp* 1981
Sales 26.4MM^E *EMP* 1,011
SIC 7538 5531 General automotive repair shops; Automotive parts; General automotive repair shops; Automotive parts
Pr: John Griffin

GRIFFIN OIL CO
See RIP GRIFFIN TRUCK SERVICE CENTER INC

D-U-N-S 18-659-8298
GRIFFIN PARTNERS INC
1177 West Loop S Ste 1750, Houston, TX 77027-9060
Tel (713) 622-7714 *Founded/Ownrshp* 1986
Sales 34.0MM^E *EMP* 100
SIC 6552 Land subdividers & developers, commercial
Pr: Edward Griffin
CFO: Jacquie McCombs
**Ch:* Fred Griffin
Ex VP: Wayne Axtell
Ex VP: Andrew Montgomery
**Ex VP:* Lee Moreland
Sr VP: Stephen Montgomery
**Sr VP:* Richard Selke
**Sr VP:* Janie Snider
Sr VP: Joe Veytia
Exec: Betsy Griffin

D-U-N-S 82-604-3593 IMP
GRIFFIN PIPE PRODUCTS CO INC
10 Adams St, Lynchburg, VA 24504-1446
Tel (434) 845-8021 *Founded/Ownrshp* 2005
Sales 215.3MM^E *EMP* 750
SIC 3317 Steel pipe & tubes; Steel pipe & tubes
Pr: Mark S Shirely
**Treas:* D J Litwin
**VP:* M J Hower
**Prin:* Glenn E Chamberlin
CTO: John Blankenship
Mfg Dir: Dave Hoffman

D-U-N-S 82-686-4576 IMP
GRIFFIN PIPE PRODUCTS CO LLC
(*Suby of* U S PIPE) ★
1011 Warrenville Rd # 550, Lisle, IL 60532-0903
Tel (630) 719-6500 *Founded/Ownrshp* 2014
Sales 45.6MM^E *EMP* 206^E
SIC 4619 Slurry pipeline operation
Pr: M S Shirley
CFO: Tim Lehman
Treas: G E Chamberlin
Sr VP: T E Bergmann
VP: Norb Gross
VP: Norbert V Gross
VP: T A Temple
Admn Mgr: Tom Freer
MIS Dir: Mike Widicus
Mktg Dir: Mark Wooten
Snr Mgr: Joe Gobeille

D-U-N-S 08-144-5801 IMP
GRIFFIN PRODUCE CO INC
MISSION PACKING COMPANY
33155 Gloria Rd, Gonzales, CA 93926-9401
Tel (831) 675-5100 *Founded/Ownrshp* 1976
Sales 45.2MM^E *EMP* 52
SIC 5148 0723 Vegetables, fresh; Vegetable packing services
Pr: Stephen Griffin
Pr: Dick Farmer
**CFO:* Tony Murphy
VP: Ed Fitzgerald
Genl Mgr: Trinidad Ogs
Dir IT: Brian Metz
Ql Cn Mgr: Leticia Reyes
Mktg Mgr: Alicia Blanco

GRIFFIN RACING RADIATOR
See GRIFFIN THERMAL ACQUISITION CO

D-U-N-S 02-335-0739
GRIFFIN SALES INC
GRIFFIN DODGE MITSUBISHI
5700 S 27th St, Milwaukee, WI 53221-4129
Tel (262) 251-8898 *Founded/Ownrshp* 1998
Sales 21.0MM^E *EMP* 75
SIC 5511 7538 7532 5521 Automobiles, new & used; General automotive repair shops; Top & body repair & paint shops; Used car dealers; Automobiles, new & used; General automotive repair shops; Top & body repair & paint shops; Used car dealers
Pr: Jim Griffin
**VP:* Geoff Slomann

IT Man: Kathy Disalvo
Sls Mgr: Warren Haase

D-U-N-S 88-309-3817
GRIFFIN TECHNOLOGY INC
2030 Lindell Ave, Nashville, TN 37203-5509
Tel (615) 399-7000 *Founded/Ownrshp* 1996
Sales 58.5MM^E *EMP* 65^E
SIC 8711 7377 Engineering services; Computer peripheral equipment rental & leasing
Pr: Paul Griffin
**Pr:* Mark Rowan
COO: Connie Wendzicki
VP: Holly Hixson
VP: Van Thompson
Creative D: Clay James
Genl Mgr: Chris Paterson
Snr Ntwrk: Patrick Ip
QA Dir: J R Cary
QA Dir: Todd Fisher
IT Man: Currey May

D-U-N-S 61-168-5629
GRIFFIN TELEVISION OKC LLC
KWTV-CHANNEL 9
7401 N Kelley Ave, Oklahoma City, OK 73111-8420
Tel (405) 843-6641 *Founded/Ownrshp* 1989
Sales 69.0MM^E *EMP* 216^E
SIC 4833 Television broadcasting stations; Television broadcasting stations
CEO: David F Griffin
COO: Robert Krier
**VP:* Steve Foerster
VP: Kevin Fullbright
**VP:* Kathy Haney
**VP:* Rob Krier
**VP:* Tedd Strickland
Comm Man: Alex Cameron
IT Man: Brian Caudle
VP Mktg: Houston Hunt
Sls Dir: Shawn Jordan

D-U-N-S 11-917-3219
GRIFFIN THERMAL ACQUISITION CO
GRIFFIN RACING RADIATOR
750 Estes Dr, Piedmont, SC 29673-8824
Tel (864) 845-5000 *Founded/Ownrshp* 2006
Sales 26.4MM^E *EMP* 150
SIC 3714 Radiators & radiator shells & cores, motor vehicle; Radiators & radiator shells & cores, motor vehicle
Pr: Thomas Beebe
**VP:* Thomas Knottek
Mktg Dir: Steve Beebe

GRIFFIN UTILITIES
See CITY OF GRIFFIN

D-U-N-S 03-140-1583
GRIFFIN WHEEL CO
(*Suby of* AMSTED INDUSTRIES INC) ★
7111 Griffin Rd, Kansas City, KS 66111-2497
Tel (913) 299-2223 *Founded/Ownrshp* 2010
Sales 20.9MM^E *EMP* 97^E
SIC 3462 5015 Iron & steel forgings; Automotive parts & supplies, used
Pr: Robert W Reum
IT Man: Ron Wright
Mtls Mgr: David Boegh
Mtls Mgr: John James
Mtls Mgr: Duane Monroe
Sfty Mgr: Linda Olderman
Opers Mgr: Michael Decola
Opers Mgr: Aaron McCrady
Mktg Dir: Cathy Strup
Snr Mgr: Theo Bradshaw

D-U-N-S 10-064-6132
GRIFFIN-SPALDING COUNTY SCHOOLS SYSTEM
216 S 6th St, Griffin, GA 30224-3420
Tel (770) 229-3700 *Founded/Ownrshp* 1953
Sales 108.7MM *EMP* 1,700
Accts Robinson Grimes & Company Pc
SIC 8211 Public elementary & secondary schools; Public elementary & secondary schools
Ch: James Westbury
Pr Dir: Judy Parker

D-U-N-S 00-690-7380
GRIFFITH CO (CA)
3050 E Birch St, Brea, CA 92821-6248
Tel (714) 984-5500 *Founded/Ownrshp* 1922
Sales 160.5MM^E *EMP* 194
SIC 1611 Highway & street construction; Highway & street construction
CEO: Thomas L Foss
**Ch Bd:* Jim Waltze
**COO:* Jaimie Angus
**CFO:* Gordon Csutak
VP: Dave Diaz
VP: Craig Huss
VP: Dan Muns
Rgnl Mgr: Luke Walker
Off Mgr: Mary McGee
IT Man: Eric Frid
Sfty Dirs: John Baham

D-U-N-S 00-251-3075
GRIFFITH ELECTRIC SUPPLY CO INC
5 2nd St, Trenton, NJ 08611-2293
Tel (609) 695-6121 *Founded/Ownrshp* 1938
Sales 25.3MM^E *EMP* 60
SIC 8711 3999 Electrical supplies; Electrical construction materials; Electrical or electronic engineering; Atomizers, toiletry
Pr: Meta Griffith
**Ex VP:* Margaret Kline
**Prin:* William Goodwin
Sales Asso: Vinny Cavigliano
Sales Asso: Carolyn Woodruff

GRIFFITH ENERGY
See SUPERIOR PLUS ENERGY SERVICES INC

D-U-N-S 04-184-6598
■ **GRIFFITH ENERGY SERVICES INC**
(*Suby of* STAR GAS PARTNERS LP) ★
6996 Columbia Gateway Dr, Columbia, MD 21046-3303
Tel (443) 430-8800 *Founded/Ownrshp* 2014
Sales 67.9MM^E *EMP* 500
SIC 5983 Fuel oil dealers; Fuel oil dealers
Pr: W Randolph Groft
**CFO:* Mark Wagus
Exec: Elizabeth Hudak
Dir IT: Minna Miranda
IT Man: Miles Kevin
Sls Mgr: Kevin Spain

D-U-N-S 19-283-7495
GRIFFITH HOLDINGS INC
(*Suby of* SUPERIOR PLUS CORP)
760 Brooks Ave Fl 2, Rochester, NY 14619-2259
Tel (585) 328-3930 *Founded/Ownrshp* 2010
Sales 67.8MM^E *EMP* 530
SIC 5171 5983 5172 Petroleum terminals; Petroleum bulk stations; Fuel oil dealers; Petroleum products; Petroleum terminals; Petroleum bulk stations; Fuel oil dealers; Petroleum products
Pr: John Hamilton
**VP:* Chris Modesti
**VP:* William Pfeiffer

D-U-N-S 08-709-5360
GRIFFITH INC (PA)
ALPHA SYSTEMS
(*Suby of* DATABANK IMX LLC) ★
458 Pike Rd, Huntingdon Valley, PA 19006-1610
Tel (215) 322-8100 *Founded/Ownrshp* 1977, 2014
Sales 31.7MM^E *EMP* 225
SIC 7389 7379 3861 3577 3572 Microfilm recording & developing service; Disk & diskette conversion service; Photographic equipment & supplies; Computer peripheral equipment; Computer storage devices; Microfilm recording & developing service; Disk & diskette conversion service; Photographic equipment & supplies; Computer peripheral equipment; Computer storage devices
Pr: Brett Griffith
COO: Stephanie Wright
**Treas:* Scott Griffith
Dept Mgr: Cindy Donnelly
Genl Mgr: Vince Ireland
Snr Sftwr: Vincent Sasso
IT Man: Chris Palmerio
IT Man: Tony White
Tech Mgr: Connie Lynch
Prd Mgr: Lisa Hoopes
Secur Mgr: Timothy Cohen

D-U-N-S 02-191-7265
GRIFFITH JACK GAS UP INC
GRIFFITH, JACK GAS-UP
312 S Duck St, Stillwater, OK 74074-3218
Tel (405) 372-7665 *Founded/Ownrshp* 1974
Sales 22.3MM^E *EMP* 125
SIC 5541 5411 Filling stations, gasoline; Convenience stores, chain; Filling stations, gasoline; Convenience stores, chain
Pr: Jim Griffith
**Pr:* Jack A Griffith
**CFO:* Steve James
**Treas:* Janet Griffith

GRIFFITH, JACK GAS-UP
See GRIFFITH JACK GAS UP INC

D-U-N-S 00-510-5788 IMP/EXP
GRIFFITH LABORATORIES INC (IL)
1 W Griffith Ctr, Alsip, IL 60803-4701
Tel (708) 371-0900 *Founded/Ownrshp* 1919
Sales 763.2MM^E *EMP* 2,500
SIC 2099 Seasonings: dry mixes; Spices, including grinding; Seasonings: dry mixes; Spices, including grinding
Ch Bd: D L Griffith
V Ch: Brian Griffith
CFO: Joe Maslick
**CFO:* Joseph R Maslick
Treas: Nancy Rossmiller
VP: Michael Plichta
VP: Darren Richmond
VP: Christopher Woods
Exec: Alfredo Del Pozzo
Exec: Gail Higgins
Mng Dir: Shyam Mohan

D-U-N-S 62-213-7644 IMP
GRIFFITH LABORATORIES INTERNATIONAL INC
(*Suby of* GRIFFITH LABORATORIES INC) ★
1 W Griffith Ctr, Alsip, IL 60803-4701
Tel (708) 371-0900 *Founded/Ownrshp* 1978
Sales 249.0MM^E *EMP* 2,500^E
SIC 2099 7389 Seasonings: dry mixes; Spices, including grinding; Inspection & testing services; Seasonings: dry mixes; Spices, including grinding; Inspection & testing services
Pr: D L Griffith
CFO: J R Maslick
Ex VP: Herve De La Vauvre
Sr VP: William C Frost
VP: Drew M Bandusky
VP: James S Legg
Board of Directors: Lois J Griffith, Dr Ben Johnson, Dr Susan Lind, Norman H Mc Millan, Albert C Schauer

D-U-N-S 09-316-9738 IMP
GRIFFITH LABORATORIES USA INC
(*Suby of* GRIFFITH LABORATORIES WORLDWIDE INC) ★
12200 S Central Ave, Alsip, IL 60803-3493
Tel (708) 371-0900 *Founded/Ownrshp* 1990
Sales 124.0MM^E *EMP* 440
SIC 2099 Seasonings: dry mixes; Spices, including grinding; Seasonings: dry mixes; Spices, including grinding
Ch Bd: Dean L Griffith
**Pr:* Jennifer Convery
**CFO:* Joseph R Maslick

D-U-N-S 96-847-9188
GRIFFITH LABORATORIES WORLDWIDE INC
(*Suby of* GRIFFITH LABORATORIES INTERNATIONAL INC) ★
12200 S Central Ave, Alsip, IL 60803-3408
Tel (708) 371-0900 *Founded/Ownrshp* 1996
Sales 140.8MM^E *EMP* 2,000
SIC 2099 Seasonings: dry mixes; Spices, including grinding; Seasonings: dry mixes; Spices, including grinding
Pr: Herve De La Vauvre
**Ch Bd:* Dean L Griffith
VP: Paul Hubner
IT Man: Dave Herring
VP Mktg: Christine Carr

D-U-N-S 02-992-7076
GRIFFITH MOTOR CO (MO)
1300 W Harmony St, Neosho, MO 64850-1637
Tel (417) 451-2626 *Founded/Ownrshp* 1938
Sales 21.5MM^E *EMP* 70
SIC 5511 5521 Automobiles, new & used; Pickups, new & used; Used car dealers; Automobiles, new & used; Pickups, new & used; Used car dealers
Pr: Jerry Griffith
**VP:* Nadine Griffith
Genl Mgr: James Craig
Sls Mgr: Evan Griffith

D-U-N-S 02-779-8669
GRIFFITH MOTORS INC
523 E 3rd St, The Dalles, OR 97058-2503
Tel (541) 296-2271 *Founded/Ownrshp* 2001
Sales 22.3MM^E *EMP* 73
SIC 5511 Automobiles, new & used; Automobiles, new & used
Pr: David Griffith
Genl Mgr: Nancy Bowlds
Off Mgr: Tammy Eane
Off Mgr: Brittany Loomis
Sls Mgr: Steve Leavitt

GRIFFITH MOTORS TOYOTA HONDA L
See DG MOTORS LLC

D-U-N-S 03-900-8917
GRIFFITH PUBLIC SCHOOLS
602 N Raymond St, Griffith, IN 46319-2041
Tel (219) 924-4250 *Founded/Ownrshp* 1907
Sales 18.4MM^E *EMP* 319
SIC 8211 Public elementary school; Public junior high school; Public senior high school; Public elementary school; Public junior high school; Public senior high school
Schl Brd P: Raymond White
HC Dir: Jen Kolon

D-U-N-S 00-902-7491
GRIFFITH RUBBER MILLS (OR)
2625 Nw Indul St, Portland, OR 97210
Tel (503) 226-6971 *Founded/Ownrshp* 1900, 1988
Sales 109.7MM^E *EMP* 300
SIC 3061 3069 Mechanical rubber goods; Molded rubber products; Mechanical rubber goods; Molded rubber products
Prin: Jill Jarrett Laney
**Pr:* Jennifer Chacon
Pr: Max Gregory
CFO: Richard Hahnert
VP: Forrest Gragg
VP: Candy Scott
**Prin:* Jennifer Laney
VP Opers: Forrest Gregg

D-U-N-S 00-648-0875
GRIFFITHS CORP
(*Suby of* GRIFFITHS HOLDING CORP) ★
2717 Niagara Ln N, Minneapolis, MN 55447-4844
Tel (763) 557-8935 *Founded/Ownrshp* 1963
Sales 101.0MM^E *EMP* 700
SIC 3544 3469 3444 3451 Special dies, tools, jigs & fixtures; Stamping metal for the trade; Sheet metal specialties, not stamped; Screw machine products; Special dies, tools, jigs & fixtures; Stamping metal for the trade; Sheet metal specialties, not stamped; Screw machine products
Ch Bd: Harold F Griffiths
**Pr:* Kenneth H Griffiths
**VP:* Keith A Griffiths

D-U-N-S 07-842-5496
GRIFFITHS HOLDING CORP
2717 Niagara Ln N, Minneapolis, MN 55447-4844
Tel (763) 557-8935 *Founded/Ownrshp* 2001
Sales 109.3MM^E *EMP* 700
SIC 3544 3469 Special dies, tools, jigs & fixtures; Stamping metal for the trade; Special dies, tools, jigs & fixtures; Stamping metal for the trade
Ch Bd: Harold F Griffiths
**Pr:* Kenneth H Griffiths
**VP:* Keith A Griffiths
**VP:* Arthur A Hahn

D-U-N-S 03-049-2227
GRIFFITHS INC
GRIFFITH'S SECURITY
357 1st Ave Nw, Hickory, NC 28601-6122
Tel (828) 327-4354 *Founded/Ownrshp* 1968
Sales 4.7MM *EMP* 300
SIC 7381 6282 Security guard service; Investment advice; Security guard service; Investment advice
Pr: Britt Griffith
**Treas:* Brad Griffith
Board of Directors: Brad Griffith, Brian Griffith, Britt Griffith

GRIFFITH'S SECURITY
See GRIFFITHS INC

D-U-N-S 05-059-0710 IMP/EXP
▲ **GRIFFON CORP**
712 5th Ave Fl 18, New York, NY 10019-4108
Tel (212) 957-5000 *Founded/Ownrshp* 1959
Sales 2.0MMM *EMP* 6,000
Accts Grant Thornton Llp New York
Tkr Sym GFF *Exch* NYS
SIC 3442 2431 1751 1799 3083 3663 Garage doors, overhead: metal; Garage doors, overhead: wood; Garage door, installation or erection; Home/office interiors finishing, furnishing & remodeling; Prefabricated fireplace installation; Laminated plastics plate & sheet; Laminated plastic sheets; Radio & TV communications equipment; Garage doors, overhead: metal; Garage doors, overhead: wood; Garage door, installation or erection; Home/office interiors finishing, furnishing & remodeling; Prefabricated fireplace installation; Laminated plastics plate & sheet; Laminated plastic sheets; Radio & TV communications equipment
CEO: Ronald J Kramer
Pr: Eugene C Colleran
Pr: Les H Ireland
Pr: Alan H Koblin
Pr: Robert F Mehmel
COO: Kevin McSweeney
CFO: Brian G Harris
Treas: Thomas Gibbons
Sr VP: Seth L Kaplan
VP: Leonard Fuld
VP: Michael Hansen
VP: Denise Lueders

D-U-N-S 09-269-4538 IMP
GRIFOLS BIOLOGICALS INC (CA)
(*Suby of* GRIFOLS SHARED SERVICES NORTH AMERICA INC) ★
5555 Valley Blvd, Los Angeles, CA 90032-3520
Tel (323) 227-7028 *Founded/Ownrshp* 2003
Sales 121.5MM^E *EMP* 450^E
SIC 2836 2834 Plasmas; Pharmaceutical preparations; Plasmas; Pharmaceutical preparations
CEO: Greg Rich
**CFO:* Max Debrouwer
**VP:* David Bell
Mfg Mgr: Manuel Acosta
Prd Mgr: Peter Pawlik
Prd Mgr: Robert Rodriguez
Secur Mgr: Bob Yates
Mktg Dir: Anand Vairavan
Board of Directors: Alfredo Arroyo, Tomas Daga, Thomas Glanzmann Chb, Victor Grifols, Ramon Riera, Dr Marla Salmon, Juan Ignacio Twose

D-U-N-S 05-657-0085
GRIFOLS DIAGNOSTIC SOLUTIONS INC
(*Suby of* GRIFOLS SA)
4560 Horton St, Emeryville, CA 94608-2916
Tel (323) 225-2221 *Founded/Ownrshp* 2013
Sales 39.1MM^E *EMP* 200^E
SIC 8071 Testing laboratories; Biological laboratory; Blood analysis laboratory; Pathological laboratory; Testing laboratories; Biological laboratory; Blood analysis laboratory; Pathological laboratory
Ex VP: David Bell
Assoc Dir: Jessica Dines
Assoc Dir: Susan Kader
Assoc Dir: Alyshia Martin
Assoc Dir: Chris Michalik

D-U-N-S 03-482-9038
GRIFOLS INC
8368 Us 70 Bus Hwy W, Clayton, NC 27520-9464
Tel (919) 553-5011 *Founded/Ownrshp* 2003
Sales 71.2MM^E *EMP* 115^E
SIC 5122 Biotherapeutics
CEO: Gregory Gene Rich
**VP:* David Bell
Genl Mgr: Jackie Wall
Mfg Dir: Ray Blaner
Opers Mgr: Jenny Harrell
Corp Couns: Samuel Talarico
Snr PM: Mike McCormick

D-U-N-S 14-114-9950 IMP
GRIFOLS SHARED SERVICES NORTH AMERICA INC
(*Suby of* GRIFOLS SA)
2410 Lillyvale Ave, Los Angeles, CA 90032-3514
Tel (323) 225-2221 *Founded/Ownrshp* 1987
Sales 5.2MMM^E *EMP* 9,000^E
SIC 5122 2834 Drugs, proprietaries & sundries; Druggists' preparations (pharmaceuticals); Drugs, proprietaries & sundries; Druggists' preparations (pharmaceuticals)
CEO: Gregory Rich
**CFO:* Max Debrouwer
**VP:* David Bell
VP: Dave Dew
Rgnl Mgr: Jon Pieja
Genl Mgr: William Stopher
QA Dir: Nathaniel Holston
Dir IT: Ramon Bertran
Dir IT: Dan Davis
IT Man: Gisela Bartolome
IT Man: Adrienne Bouie
Board of Directors: Alfredo Arroyo, Tomas Daga, Thomas Glanzmann Chb, Victor Grifols, Ramon Riera, Dr Marla Salmon, Juan Ignacio Twose

D-U-N-S 83-973-1507 IMP
GRIFOLS THERAPEUTICS INC
(*Suby of* GRIFOLS SHARED SERVICES NORTH AMERICA INC) ★
79 Tw Alexander Dr, Durham, NC 27709-0152
Tel (919) 316-6300 *Founded/Ownrshp* 2011
Sales 753.4MM^E *EMP* 4,763
SIC 2836 Blood derivatives; Blood derivatives
CEO: Greg Rich
**CFO:* Max Debrouwer
CFO: Debra Newman
Sr VP: Keith Kosinski
VP: Lori Antieau
**VP:* David Bell
VP: Karen Kelly
VP: Gerald Klein
Assoc Dir: Anna McSorley
Dir IT: Krista Davila
Dir IT: Rose Mattiace
Board of Directors: Alfredo Arroyo, Tomas Daga, Thomas Glanzmann Chb, Victor Grifols, Ramon Riera, Dr Marla Salmon, Juan Ignacio Twose

D-U-N-S 04-898-7452 IMP
GRIFOLS USA LLC
(*Suby of* GRIFOLS SHARED SERVICES NORTH AMERICA INC) ★
2410 Lillyvale Ave, Los Angeles, CA 90032-3514
Tel (800) 421-0008 *Founded/Ownrshp* 1995
Sales 1.7MMM^E *EMP* 9,000
Accts Goldman Juda & Martin Cpa S
SIC 5047 Diagnostic equipment, medical; Diagnostic equipment, medical
CEO: Gregory Rich
CFO: Max Debrouwer
Treas: Montserrat Lloveras
**VP:* David Bell
Mfg Dir: Kenneth Whitlow
Sls Dir: Ralph Muniz
Snr Mgr: Donna Lee

D-U-N-S 02-050-3715
GRIGGS ENTERPRISES INC
MCDONALD'S
330 Marshall St Ste 711, Shreveport, LA 71101-3016
Tel (318) 424-9748 *Founded/Ownrshp* 2000
Sales 18.8MM^E *EMP* 500
SIC 5812 Fast-food restaurant, chain; Fast-food restaurant, chain
Pr: Roy Griggs

GRILL CONCEPTS
See GRILL ON ALLEY THE INC

D-U-N-S 17-330-4999
GRILL CONCEPTS INC
DAILY GRILL ENCINO PLACE
6300 Canoga Ave Ste 600, Woodland Hills, CA 91367-8022
Tel (818) 251-7000 *Founded/Ownrshp* 1987
Sales 71.2MM^E *EMP* 1,470^E
SIC 5812 Restaurant, family: independent; Restaurant, family: independent
CEO: Bob Spivak
**Ch Bd:* Robert Spivak
**Ch Bd:* Michael Weinstock
**CFO:* Wayne Lipschitz
**Sr VP:* Louie Feinstein
**Sr VP:* John Sola
VP: Tammy Billings

D-U-N-S 60-967-1516
GRILL CONCEPTS-DC INC
DAILY GRILL
(*Suby of* DAILY GRILL ENCINO PLACE) ★
11661 San Vicente Blvd, Los Angeles, CA 90049-5103
Tel (310) 820-5559 *Founded/Ownrshp* 1987
Sales 27.9MM^E *EMP* 1,300
SIC 5812 Grills (eating places); Grills (eating places)
Pr: Robert Spivak
CFO: John Bayley
VP: Terri Henry

D-U-N-S 04-940-9738
GRILL ON ALLEY THE INC (CA)
GRILL CONCEPTS
11661 San Vicente Blvd # 404, Los Angeles, CA 90049-5103
Tel (310) 820-5559 *Founded/Ownrshp* 1995
Sales 28.7MM^E *EMP* 1,300
SIC 5812 Grills (eating places); Grills (eating places)
Pr: Robert Spivak

D-U-N-S 05-397-7724 IMP/EXP
GRIMCO INC (MO)
1585 Fencorp Dr, Fenton, MO 63026-2942
Tel (636) 305-0088 *Founded/Ownrshp* 1875, 1978
Sales 106.0MM^E *EMP* 200
SIC 3469 2759 3993 3429 3312 Patterns on metal; Screen printing; Signs & advertising specialties; Manufactured hardware (general); Blast furnaces & steel mills; Patterns on metal; Screen printing; Signs & advertising specialties; Manufactured hardware (general); Blast furnaces & steel mills
CEO: Robert Hummert
**Pr:* John Burkemper
**Pr:* Dale Kleinheider
Ex VP: Urse Haug
Rgnl Mgr: Mike Bolinger
Brnch Mgr: Nick Allen
Brnch Mgr: Brad Pye
Brnch Mgr: Nathan Walsh
Art Dir: Christine Jokerst

D-U-N-S 00-418-9262 IMP
■ **GRIMES AEROSPACE CO**
HONEYWELL
(*Suby of* HONEYWELL INTERNATIONAL INC) ★
550 State Route 55, Urbana, OH 43078-9482
Tel (937) 484-2000 *Founded/Ownrshp* 1923, 1997
Sales 93.9MM^E *EMP* 1,025
SIC 3728 3647 3646 3645 3577 3571

GRIMES COMPANIES, THE
See GRIMES LOGISTICS SERVICES INC

GRIMES COMPANIES, THE
See GRIMES TRUCKING SERVICES INC

D-U-N-S 05-848-8545
GRIMES LOGISTICS SERVICES INC
GRIMES COMPANIES, THE
600 Ellis Rd N, Jacksonville, FL 32254-2801
Tel (904) 786-5711 *Founded/Ownrshp* 1920
Sales 37.8MM^E *EMP* 104
SIC 4225 4214 4222 General warehousing; Local trucking with storage; Refrigerated warehousing & storage
Pr: Thomas L Grimes
**Ch:* Michael S O'Leary

GRIMES TRUCK CENTER
See JAMES S GRIMES INC

D-U-N-S 82-988-2690
GRIMES TRUCKING SERVICES INC
GRIMES COMPANIES, THE
(*Suby of* GRIMES COMPANIES) ★
600 Ellis Rd N, Jacksonville, FL 32254-2801
Tel (904) 786-5711 *Founded/Ownrshp* 1977
Sales 20.6MM^E *EMP* 80
SIC 4225 4212 4222 General warehousing & storage; Local trucking, without storage; Refrigerated warehousing & storage
**Pr:* Michael S O'Leary
QI Cn Mgr: Edward McDowell

D-U-N-S 08-634-2003
GRIMM CONSTRUCTION CO INC
(*Suby of* GARNEY HOLDING CO) ★
1333 Nw Vivion Rd, Kansas City, MO 64118-4554
Tel (816) 278-5950 *Founded/Ownrshp* 1977
Sales 41.9MM^E *EMP* 230
SIC 1623 1629 Water main construction; Waste water & sewage treatment plant construction; Water main construction; Waste water & sewage treatment plant construction
Pr: Mike Heitmann
**Pr:* Joey Perrell
**Sec:* Jeffery Lacy
Mtls Mgr: Nathan Church

D-U-N-S 04-576-4263
GRIMM INDUSTRIES INC
7070 W Ridge Rd, Fairview, PA 16415-2096
Tel (814) 474-2648 *Founded/Ownrshp* 1968
Sales 42.2MM^E *EMP* 200
SIC 3089 Injection molding of plastics; Injection molding of plastics
Pr: Beatus Grimm
CFO: Butch Drimm
**Sec:* Beatrice Grimm
**VP:* Steven Grimm
IT Man: Karl Kenyon
Opers Mgr: Erich Zech

D-U-N-S 03-356-0509 EXP
GRIMMWAY ENTERPRISES INC
GRIMMWAY FARMS
14141 Di Giorgio Rd, Arvin, CA 93203-9518
Tel (661) 854-6250 *Founded/Ownrshp* 1992
Sales 1.4MMM^E *EMP* 4,000
SIC 0723 Vegetable packing services; Vegetable packing services
Pr: Jeff Meger
**CFO:* Steve Barnes
Ex VP: Jeff Huckaby
VP: Mike Anspach
VP: Lisa McNeece
Genl Mgr: Steve Roodzant
Telecom Mg: Mandy Harris
Sfty Dirs: Edward Gerding
Sfty Dirs: Mark Rodriguez
Opers Mgr: Eddie Rosson
Opers Mgr: Kevin Tibbett

GRIMMWAY FARMS
See GRIMMWAY ENTERPRISES INC

D-U-N-S 79-515-8799
GRINDER & HAIZLIP CONSTRUCTION INC
1746 Thomas Rd, Memphis, TN 38134-6313
Tel (901) 377-1000 *Founded/Ownrshp* 1992
Sales 20.6MM^E *EMP* 90
SIC 1541 Industrial buildings & warehouses
Owner: Greg Grinder
**Owner:* Henry Haizlip
**VP:* Brad Burford
VP: Chris McDermott
Sls&Mrk Ex: Dorothy Jones

GRINDING SZING LLC FORMER NAME
See PRINCE ENERGY LLC

D-U-N-S 05-427-7462 IMP
GRINDMASTER CORP
CRATHCO
4003 Collins Ln, Louisville, KY 40245-1602
Tel (502) 357-2284 *Founded/Ownrshp* 1933, 1985
Sales 67.5MM^E *EMP* 300
SIC 3589 3585 Coffee brewing equipment; Cold drink dispensing equipment (not coin-operated); Coffee brewing equipment; Cold drink dispensing equipment (not coin-operated)
CEO: Nestor Ibrahim
Pr: Greg Immell
**CFO:* David Dudding
**CFO:* Robert A Poe
VP: Joseph Defrancisci
**VP:* David Haimes
**VP:* Rich Tosi
Prgrm Mgr: Katie Eason
QC Dir: Steve Fortier
Mtls Mgr: Angela Coler
Sfty Mgr: Craig Armstrong

GRINDSTAFF CHEVROLET C-P-D-J-E
See GRINDSTAFF INC

D-U-N-S 03-462-9428
GRINDSTAFF INC
GRINDSTAFF CHEVROLET C-P-D-J-E
2224 W Elk Ave, Elizabethton, TN 37643-3714
Tel (423) 547-7020 *Founded/Ownrshp* 1987
Sales 56.5MM^E *EMP* 154
SIC 5511 Automobiles, new & used; Automobiles, new & used
Pr: Steven G Grindstaff
Bd of Dir: Holly Shields
Genl Mgr: Adam Mullins
Dir IT: Rob Foster

D-U-N-S 03-391-0688
GRINER AUTOMOTIVE GROUP INC (GA)
TOMMY GRINER NISSAN
3685 Inner Perimeter Rd, Valdosta, GA 31602-1048
Tel (229) 242-7325 *Founded/Ownrshp* 1954, 1982
Sales 29.4MM^E *EMP* 70
SIC 5511 7532 Automobiles, new & used; Body shop, automotive; Automobiles, new & used; Body shop, automotive
Pr: Joseph T Griner
**Sec:* Janis Patterson
**Ex VP:* Eric C Griner
Genl Mgr: Craig Griner
Genl Mgr: Craig Phillip
Sls Mgr: Scott Avant
Sls Mgr: Arthur Bradford
Sls Mgr: Nick Dejohn

D-U-N-S 03-327-7161
GRINER DRILLING SERVICE INC
1014 Highway 98 Byp, Columbia, MS 39429-9190
Tel (601) 731-1853 *Founded/Ownrshp* 1966
Sales 23.1MM^E *EMP* 110
SIC 1781 Water well drilling
Pr: Charles H Griner Jr
**VP:* Brenda Griner
Exec: Rachael Darby

D-U-N-S 05-135-2938
GRINER ENGINEERING INC
2500 N Curry Pike, Bloomington, IN 47404-1431
Tel (812) 332-2220 *Founded/Ownrshp* 1976
Sales 20.9MM^E *EMP* 75
SIC 3714 Motor vehicle parts & accessories
Pr: John Griner
VP: Betty Lee
VP: Dana Riiska
VP Mfg: John Elmore
Opers Mgr: Richard Kleis
VP Sls: Dan Bucek

D-U-N-S 94-570-5119
GRINGO VENTURES LLC
DOS GRINGOS
3260 Corporate Vw, Vista, CA 92081-8528
Tel (760) 477-7999 *Founded/Ownrshp* 1995
Sales 24.2MM^E *EMP* 354
SIC 5193

GRINGOS MEXICAN KITCHEN
See GRINGOS MEXICAN KITCHEN NO 1 INC

D-U-N-S 80-504-3130
GRINGOS MEXICAN KITCHEN NO 1 INC
GRINGOS MEXICAN KITCHEN
2202 Broadway St, Pearland, TX 77581-6404
Tel (281) 485-3844 *Founded/Ownrshp* 1993
Sales 19.8MM^E *EMP* 800
SIC 5812 Mexican restaurant; Mexican restaurant
Pr: Russell Ybarra
**CFO:* Joe L Aguilar
**Sec:* Monica Ybarra

D-U-N-S 07-533-4446 EXP
GRINNELL CONCRETE PAVINGSTONES INC
482 Houses Corner Rd, Sparta, NJ 07871-3404
Tel (973) 383-9300 *Founded/Ownrshp* 1986
Sales 20.3MM^E *EMP* 100
SIC 3272 Stone, cast concrete
CEO: Margaret A Cofrancesco
**Pr:* Craig Austin
**VP:* Jason N Cofrancesco
Sls Mgr: Jason Georgevich

GRINNELL FIRE PRTCTION SYSTEMS
See TYCO SIMPLEXGRINNELL

D-U-N-S 60-710-2241
GRINNELL LIFE INSURANCE CO
(*Suby of* GRINNELL MUTUAL REINSURANCE CO) ★
4215 Highway 146, Grinnell, IA 50112-8110
Tel (641) 236-6121 *Founded/Ownrshp* 1984
Sales NA *EMP* 298^E
SIC 6411 Insurance agents & brokers
Pr: Larry Jansen
**VP:* Steve Crawford

D-U-N-S 00-694-1652
GRINNELL MUTUAL REINSURANCE CO
4215 Highway 146, Grinnell, IA 50112-8110
Tel (641) 269-8000 *Founded/Ownrshp* 1909
Sales NA *EMP* 740
SIC 6411 Insurance agents, brokers & service; Insurance agents, brokers & service
Pr: Larry Jansen
Pr: Martina Schubert
**CFO:* David Wingert
**VP:* Thomas Bachmann
**VP:* Dennis G Day
**VP:* Shirley Linn
**VP:* Willard McDonald
**VP:* Mike Ward
**CIO:* Dennis Mehmen
Board of Directors: William J Lampe, John McMahon, Paul G Stueven

D-U-N-S 01-024-5835
GRINNELL REGIONAL MEDICAL CENTER
210 4th Ave, Grinnell, IA 50112-1886
Tel (641) 236-7511 *Founded/Ownrshp* 1967
Sales 57.6MM^E *EMP* 420
SIC 8062 8011 General medical & surgical hospitals; Offices & clinics of medical doctors; General medical & surgical hospitals; Offices & clinics of medical doctors
Pr: Todd Linden
Chf Rad: Marvin Walker
COO: David Ness
**VP:* Suzanne Cooner
VP: David Cranston
**VP:* Jack Fritts
**VP:* David L Ness
**VP:* Doris J Rindels
Dir OR: Deb Reding
Dir Lab: Gregg Hawkins
Dir Rad: Kevin Kincaid

GRIPHOIST DIVISION
See TRACTEL INC

D-U-N-S 09-895-4183
GRISANTI INC
9300 Shelbyville Rd # 508, Louisville, KY 40222-5145
Tel (502) 429-0341 *Founded/Ownrshp* 1989
Sales 6.4MM^E *EMP* 300
SIC 5812 Italian restaurant; Italian restaurant
Pr: Michael Grisanti

D-U-N-S 06-844-2417
GRISELL MEMORIAL HOSPITAL ASSOCIATION
210 S Vermont Ave, Ransom, KS 67572-9525
Tel (785) 731-2231 *Founded/Ownrshp* 1936
Sales 3.7MM *EMP* 286
SIC 8062 General medical & surgical hospitals; General medical & surgical hospitals

D-U-N-S 19-656-6822
GRISHAM FARM PRODUCTS INC
7364 Newkirk Rd, Mountain Grove, MO 65711-2540
Tel (417) 746-0242 *Founded/Ownrshp* 1980
Sales 44.7MM^E *EMP* 300
SIC 2048 Poultry feeds; Poultry feeds
Pr: Lexie Grisham
**Sec:* Annabelle Grisham
**VP:* Rick Grisham

D-U-N-S 00-427-6515 IMP
GRISMER TIRE CO (OH)
1099 S Main St, Centerville, OH 45458-3840
Tel (937) 643-2526 *Founded/Ownrshp* 1932, 1975
Sales 24.5MM^E *EMP* 70
SIC 5531 7538 5014 7534 Automotive tires; General automotive repair shops; Automobile tires & tubes; Truck tires & tubes; Rebuilding & retreading tires
Pr: Charles L Marshall II
**Treas:* Robert Hupp

D-U-N-S 04-679-9318 IMP/EXP
GRISTEDES FOODS INC
GRISTEDES SUPERMARKETS
(*Suby of* RED APPLE GROUP INC) ★
800 3rd Ave Fl 5, New York, NY 10022-7655
Tel (212) 956-5770 *Founded/Ownrshp* 1986
Sales 339.5MM^E *EMP* 2,180
SIC 5411 Grocery stores; Grocery stores
Ch Bd: John Catsimatidis
**CFO:* Mark Kassner
Ex VP: Jim Monos
VP: Carmine Napolitano
Exec: Deborah Clusan

GRISTEDES SUPERMARKETS
See GRISTEDES FOODS INC

D-U-N-S 05-747-7994 IMP/EXP
GRISWOLD INDUSTRIES
CLA-VAL CO
1701 Placentia Ave, Costa Mesa, CA 92627-4416
Tel (949) 722-4800 *Founded/Ownrshp* 1975
Sales 98.6MM^E *EMP* 410
SIC 3492 3365 3366

D-U-N-S 10-466-5328
GRISWOLD PUBLIC SCHOOLS
267 Slater Ave, Griswold, CT 06351-2533
Tel (860) 376-7600 *Founded/Ownrshp* 1845
Sales 17.7MM^E *EMP* 320^E
SIC 8211 Public elementary & secondary schools; Public elementary & secondary schools
**Ch Bd:* Norman Gileau
**V Ch Bd:* Stewart Norman

D-U-N-S 01-021-3700
GRITMAN MEDICAL CENTER INC
700 S Main St, Moscow, ID 83843-3046
Tel (208) 882-4511 *Founded/Ownrshp* 1939
Sales 49.8MM *EMP* 500
SIC 8062 General medical & surgical hospitals; General medical & surgical hospitals
CEO: Kara Besst
Dir Recs: Robin Fike
Pr: Cheryl Ardrey
Pr: Justin Bonner
COO: Jeffery Martin
Bd of Dir: Nancy Kure
Dir OR: Becky McLeod
Dir Lab: Mary Graden
Dir Rx: Bill Nash
Chf Nrs Of: Deena Rauch
CIO: Kane Francetich

D-U-N-S 03-095-5538
■ **GRIZZLY GOLF CENTER INC**
GOLF CENTER AT KINGS ISLAND
(*Suby of* GREAT AMERICAN INSURANCE CO) ★
6042 Fairway Dr, Mason, OH 45040-2006
Tel (513) 398-5200 *Founded/Ownrshp* 1990
Sales 8.0MM^E *EMP* 300
SIC 7992 5812 5941 0782 Public golf courses; Eating places; Golf goods & equipment; Landscape contractors; Public golf courses; Eating places; Golf goods & equipment; Landscape contractors
Genl Mgr: Peter Ryan
Sr VP: Andrea Polan

D-U-N-S 10-288-5035 IMP
GRIZZLY INDUSTRIAL INC
1821 Valencia St, Bellingham, WA 98229-4746
Tel (360) 676-6090 *Founded/Ownrshp* 1983
Sales 82.1MM^E *EMP* 300
SIC 5251 Tools, power; Tools; Tools, power
CEO: Shiraz Balolia
**CFO:* Colleen Lahr
VP: Darrell Bozarth
**VP:* Don Osterloh
Admn Mgr: Matt Washkow
CTO: Renee Showalter
Dir IT: Justin McCuiston
Netwrk Eng: Krundish Grewal
Opers Mgr: Jean Turner
Mktg Mgr: Melinda Sweet

D-U-N-S 78-729-3398
GRM INFORMATION MANAGEMENT SERVICES INC
GUARANTEE RECORDS MANAGEMENT
215 Coles St, Jersey City, NJ 07310-1301
Tel (201) 798-7100 *Founded/Ownrshp* 1988
Sales 82.9MM *EMP* 500
SIC 4226 7389 Document & office records storage; Document storage service; Document & office records storage; Document storage service
Pr: Jerry Glatt
**CEO:* Moishe Mana
**CFO:* Amyn Maskati
Ex VP: Yossi Harel
VP: Peter Hamilton
VP: Dan Quinn
Genl Mgr: Walter Perez
Genl Mgr: Dan O Reilly
Off Mgr: Amy Bowen
Dir IT: Peter D'Souza
Opers Mgr: Maurice Ebanks

D-U-N-S 01-647-0126
GRM INNOVATIONS LLC
STAINLESS INNOVATIONS
3501 Tulsa St, Fort Smith, AR 72903-6809
Tel (479) 783-1900 *Founded/Ownrshp* 2007
Sales 43.1MM^E *EMP* 40^E
SIC 5046 Commercial cooking & food service equipment
Pr: Randy Mullikin
IT Man: Gerald Mullikin

D-U-N-S 01-438-6700
GRO-GREEN CORP
ASHCOMBE FARM & GREENHOUSES
906 W Grantham Rd, Mechanicsburg, PA 17055-5327
Tel (717) 766-7611 *Founded/Ownrshp* 1956
Sales 22.8MM^E *EMP* 120
SIC 5261 5431 5193 5947 Nurseries & garden centers; Lawn & garden supplies; Fruit & vegetable markets; Plants, potted; Gift shop
Pr: Glenn M Gross
**Sec:* Mary Ellen Gross
**VP:* John H Bear

GRO-WELL BRANDS
See WESTERN ORGANICS INC

D-U-N-S 96-179-2707
GRO-WELL BRANDS INC
420 E Southern Ave, Tempe, AZ 85282-5212
Tel (602) 792-0275 *Founded/Ownrshp* 2005
Sales 26.6MM^E *EMP* 156
SIC 5032 5191 Brick, stone & related material; Farm supplies; Aggregate; Beekeeping supplies (nondurable)
CEO: James Porter

D-U-N-S 00-678-9804
GROATHOUSE CONSTRUCTION INC
1050 N 3rd St Ste A, Laramie, WY 82072-2590
Tel (307) 745-4119 *Founded/Ownrshp* 1954
Sales 21.6MM^E *EMP* 60
SIC 1542 1541 Commercial & office building, new construction; Industrial buildings, new construction
Pr: Fred Bronnenerg
**Pr:* Danial Groathouse
**CFO:* Jim Mackey
**CFO:* Ray McElwee
**Sec:* Kenneth Groathouse
Sfty Mgr: Wendy Bruntmyer

D-U-N-S 07-407-0988 IMP/EXP
GROB SYSTEMS INC
MACHINE TOOL DIVISION
(*Suby of* GROB-WERKE BURKHART GROB E.K.)
1070 Navajo Dr, Bluffton, OH 45817-9666
Tel (419) 358-9015 *Founded/Ownrshp* 1993
Sales 161.3MM^E *EMP* 198
SIC 3535 7699 Robotic conveyors; Industrial equipment services; Robotic conveyors; Industrial equipment services
CEO: Ralf Bronnenmeier
Pr: Jason Cartright
**Pr:* Michael Hutecker
VP: Bill Vejnovic
IT Man: Douglas L Gesler
Sls Mgr: Darrin Lanasky
Sls Mgr: Mark Schem
Snr Mgr: Herb Maehle
Snr Mgr: David Stall

GROBBELS
See E W GROBBEL SONS INC

D-U-N-S 18-198-3425
GROCERS ICE AND COLD STORAGE CO
CREATION GARDENS
2055 Nelson Miller Pkwy, Louisville, KY 40223-2185
Tel (502) 584-4112 *Founded/Ownrshp* 1906
Sales 30.2MM^E *EMP* 45^E
SIC 5148 2097 Fresh fruits & vegetables; Block ice
Pr: Mollie Turnier
COO: Rob Webber
**VP:* Ron Turnier
**VP:* Jim Walker
Opers Mgr: George Punter

D-U-N-S 78-566-9201
GROCERS INSURANCE GROUP INC
ARGO SELECT
(*Suby of* ARGO GROUP US INC) ★
6400 Se Lake Rd Ste 190, Portland, OR 97222-2189
Tel (503) 833-1600 *Founded/Ownrshp* 1998
Sales NA *EMP* 180
SIC 6411 Property & casualty insurance agent; Property & casualty insurance agent
Pr: William Meisen
**Pr:* Ross E Dwinell
**VP:* Tom Newton

D-U-N-S 01-955-4633 IMP
GROCERS SPECIALTY CO
G S C BALL
(*Suby of* UNIFIED GROCERS INC) ★
5200 Sheila St, Commerce, CA 90040-3906
Tel (323) 264-5200 *Founded/Ownrshp* 1981
Sales 93.8MM^E *EMP* 200
SIC 5141 Groceries, general line; Groceries, general line
Pr: Joe Falvey
**CFO:* Rich Martin
**Treas:* Christine Neal

D-U-N-S 00-385-4122 IMP
GROCERS SUPPLY CO INC
4310 Stout Field North Dr, Indianapolis, IN 46241-4000
Tel (317) 243-6000 *Founded/Ownrshp* 2008
Sales 73.9MM^E *EMP* 65
SIC 5141 5145 5113 Groceries, general line; Candy; Bags, paper & disposable plastic; Groceries, general line; Candy; Bags, paper & disposable plastic
Pr: Scott Weaver
Treas: Patric McClarnon
VP: Jack Mumbower

D-U-N-S 05-446-0522
GROCERS SUPPLY PRODUCE CO INC
(*Suby of* 2ML REAL ESTATE INTERESTS INC) ★
3000 Hicks St, Houston, TX 77007-3816
Tel (713) 747-5000 *Founded/Ownrshp* 1990
Sales 53.0MM^E *EMP* 170
SIC 5148

D-U-N-S 07-940-8264
GROCERY DELIVERY E-SERVICES USA INC
HELLOFRESH
85 Broad St Fl 18, New York, NY 10004-2783
Tel (800) 733-2414 *Founded/Ownrshp* 2012
Sales 59.1MM^E *EMP* 28^E
SIC 5148 5149 Fresh fruits & vegetables; Groceries & related products
CEO: Seth Goldman

D-U-N-S 00-826-3522
GROCERY HAULERS INC
581 Main St Ste 510, Woodbridge, NJ 07095-1144
Tel (732) 499-3745 *Founded/Ownrshp* 1992
Sales 41.0MM^E *EMP* 260^E
SIC 4213 Trucking, except local; Trucking, except local
Pr: Mark Jacobson
Pr: Bob Helmer
VP: Michael Omalley
Dir: Mary Ruotolo

D-U-N-S 04-135-3293
GROCERY MANUFACTURERS ASSOCIATION
G M A
1350 Eye I St Nw, Washington, DC 20005
Tel (202) 639-5900 *Founded/Ownrshp* 1909
Sales 41.3MM *EMP* 125
Accts Raffa Pc Washington Dc
SIC 8611 Trade associations; Trade associations
Pr: Pamela Bailey
**Ch Bd:* Richard G Wolford
CFO: J Steven McCroddan
Ex VP: Roger Lowe
Sr VP: Robert Brackett
Sr VP: Stephen Sibert
Sr VP: Mary Sophos
VP: Bill Pappas
VP: James Skiles
Board of Directors: J S Brown III, J Alexander M Douglas Jr, Tom Ferriter, Melanie Healey, Michael Mendes

GROCERY OUTLET
See FORSTER & HOWELL INC

D-U-N-S 02-916-1585 IMP/EXP
GROCERY OUTLET INC
CANNED FOODS GROCERY OUTLET
5650 Hollis St Ste 100, Emeryville, CA 94608-2505
Tel (510) 845-1999 *Founded/Ownrshp* 2014
Sales 154.7MM^E *EMP* 315
SIC 5411

GROCERY STORE
See H & S DEVELOPERS INC

D-U-N-S 82-932-7548
■ **GROCERY SUPPLY ACQUISITION CORP**
GROCERY SUPPLY CO SOUTHEAST
(*Suby of* NASH-FINCH CO) ★
7600 France Ave S, Minneapolis, MN 55435-5924
Tel (952) 832-0534 *Founded/Ownrshp* 2008
Sales 142.1MM^E *EMP* 600
SIC 5141 5149 Groceries, general line; Groceries & related products; Groceries, general line; Groceries & related products
Pr: Robert B Dimond
VP: Peter O'Donnell
Board of Directors: Alec C Covington

GROCERY SUPPLY COMPANY
See GSC ENTERPRISES INC

GROCERY SUPPLY CO SOUTHEAST
See GROCERY SUPPLY ACQUISITION CORP

D-U-N-S 11-522-2366 IMP
GROEB FARMS INC
GOURMET JOSE
10464 Bryan Hwy, Onsted, MI 49265-9551
Tel (517) 467-2065 *Founded/Ownrshp* 1973
Sales 33.4MM^E *EMP* 110
SIC 5149 2099

GROEN
See UNIFIED BRANDS INC

D-U-N-S 00-790-5748
GROENDYKE TRANSPORT INC
2510 Rock Island Blvd, Enid, OK 73701-1342
Tel (580) 234-4663 *Founded/Ownrshp* 1932
Sales 217.4MM^E *EMP* 1,350
SIC 4213

D-U-N-S 03-298-5830
GROESBECK INDEPENDENT SCHOOL DISTRICT BAND BOOSTERS
1202 N Ellis St, Groesbeck, TX 76642-2111
Tel (254) 729-4100 *Founded/Ownrshp* 2009
Sales 27.4MM *EMP* 270
Accts Anderson Marx & Bohl Pc C
SIC 8211 Public elementary & secondary schools; Public junior high school; Public senior high school; School board; Public elementary & secondary schools; Public junior high school; Public senior high school; School board
Psych: Susan Swick
HC Dir: Jenny Flower

GROETSCH WHOLESALE GROCERS
See GEORGE W GROETSCH INC

D-U-N-S 00-195-3918 EXP
GROFF TRACTOR & EQUIPMENT INC
6779 Carlisle Pike, Mechanicsburg, PA 17050-1712
Tel (717) 766-7671 *Founded/Ownrshp* 1956
Sales 59.7MM^E *EMP* 185^E
SIC 5082

GROGANS TOWNE
See TOLEDO CHARLIES INC

D-U-N-S 01-836-2707 EXP
GROGANS TOWNE CHRYSLER INC
6100 Telegraph Rd, Toledo, OH 43612-4575
Tel (419) 476-0761 *Founded/Ownrshp* 1998
Sales 40.4MM^E *EMP* 105
SIC 5511 7515 7513 7538 7532 5521 Automobiles, new & used; Passenger car leasing; Truck leasing, without drivers; General automotive repair shops; Top & body repair & paint shops; Used car dealers; Automobiles, new & used; Passenger car leasing; Truck leasing, without drivers; General automotive repair shops; Top & body repair & paint shops; Used car dealers
Pr: Mark Floyd
**Treas:* Ed J Lishewski
**VP:* Denny Amrhiem
Sls Mgr: Marc Ray
Sales Asso: John Baertschi
Sales Asso: Fuller David
Sales Asso: Russell Irvine
Sales Asso: Allen Laurel
Sales Asso: Freddie Mason
Sales Asso: Steven Merritt
Sales Asso: Richard Nearhood

GROJEAN TRANSPORTATION
See HIRSCHBACH & SON INC

D-U-N-S 14-768-4583 IMP
GROLINK PLANT CO INC
4107 W Gonzales Rd, Oxnard, CA 93036-7783
Tel (805) 984-7958 *Founded/Ownrshp* 1985
Sales 59.1MM^E *EMP* 150
SIC 5193 0181 Flowers & florists' supplies; Ornamental nursery products; Flowers & florists' supplies; Ornamental nursery products
CEO: Anthony Vollering
**Sec:* Jerry Van Wingerden
**Prin:* Art Gordijin
**Prin:* Ton Vallering

D-U-N-S 84-356-5110
GROM ASSOCIATES INC
1 Main St, Flemington, NJ 08822-1420
Tel (908) 284-2200 *Founded/Ownrshp* 1982
Sales 32.7MM^E *EMP* 250
SIC 7371 8742 7379 Custom computer programming services; Training & development consultant; Computer related consulting services; Custom computer programming services; Custom computer programming services; Training & development consultant; Computer related consulting services
CEO: Robert Grom
COO: Tom Eineker
Sr VP: Michael Nusser
VP: Paul Gover
VP: John Levasseur
VP: Mike Nusser
VP: Mark Vesper
Dir IT: A J Brown
Software D: Henk Bakker
Mktg Mgr: Sean Grom

GRONDIN'S HAIR CENTERS
See GRONDINS INC

D-U-N-S 11-927-9586
GRONDINS INC
GRONDIN'S HAIR CENTERS
350 N Court St Ste 300, Lapeer, MI 48446-2263
Tel (810) 664-5903 *Founded/Ownrshp* 1970
Sales 9.9MM^E *EMP* 350
SIC 7231 Unisex hair salons; Unisex hair salons
CEO: Paul N Grondin
**Pr:* Carl J Grondin
**Sec:* Mary Cloutier
Sls Mgr: Terry Town

D-U-N-S 04-953-0884
GROOM & SON HARDWARE AND LUMBER INC
1310 S 3rd St, Mabank, TX 75147-7604
Tel (903) 887-7581 *Founded/Ownrshp* 1972
Sales 31.6MM^E *EMP* 120
SIC 5211 5251 Lumber & other building materials; Hardware
Ch Bd: Estle H Groom
**Pr:* Roger Groom
**Prin:* Terry Groom
**Prin:* Michael Rosen
Store Mgr: Sherry Weaver

D-U-N-S 16-110-3429
GROOM CONSTRUCTION CO INC
96 Swampscott Rd Ste 6, Salem, MA 01970-7004
Tel (781) 592-3135 *Founded/Ownrshp* 1979
Sales 32.1MM^E *EMP* 100
Accts John F Murphy Cpa
SIC 5211 1521 Masonry materials & supplies; Single-family housing construction
Pr: Thomas Groom
**COO:* Graeme Poole
**Treas:* David Groom
**Sr VP:* Scott Faulkner
**Sr VP:* Dwight Groom
VP: Rob Davis
Brnch Mgr: Ryan Levorson
Off Mgr: Lissa Brownlee
IT Man: Erik Levorson
VP Opers: Bob Kirby
Sfty Dirs: Kevin Pessolano

D-U-N-S 02-395-4951
GROOME TRANSPORTATION INC
5500 Lewis Rd, Sandston, VA 23150-1924
Tel (804) 222-7226 *Founded/Ownrshp* 1985
Sales 51.3MM^E *EMP* 204
SIC 4141 Local bus charter service; Local bus charter service
CEO: C Franklin Flanary II
**Pr:* Harold V Groome III
**CFO:* Brad Hungate
**VP:* Christopher Groome

D-U-N-S 17-759-0239
GROOMERS SEAFOOD OF SAN ANTONIO INC
SUPERIOR SEAFOOD
9801 Mccullough Ave, San Antonio, TX 78216-4610
Tel (210) 377-3474 *Founded/Ownrshp* 1982
Sales 34.4MM^E *EMP* 65
SIC 5146 Fish, fresh; Fish, frozen, unpackaged; Fish, fresh; Fish, frozen, unpackaged
Pr: Richard Groomer
**Sec:* Michael Groomer
**VP:* Russell Groomer

D-U-N-S 00-284-9941
GROOT INDUSTRIES INC
2500 Landmeier Rd, Elk Grove Village, IL 60007-2627
Tel (847) 734-6400 *Founded/Ownrshp* 1944, 1978
Sales 257.5MM^E *EMP* 300
SIC 4953 Rubbish collection & disposal; Street refuse systems; Rubbish collection & disposal; Street refuse systems
Pr: Larry Groot
**VP:* Lee Brandsma
Dir IT: Vlad Dukhovyy
Sfty Dirs: Ryan Brandsma
Sales Exec: Ted Payton

D-U-N-S 00-284-9925
GROOT RECYCLING & WASTE SERVICE INC
(*Suby of* GROOT INDUSTRIES INC) ★
2500 Landmeier Rd, Elk Grove Village, IL 60007-2627
Tel (773) 686-0900 *Founded/Ownrshp* 1960
Sales 34.8MM^E *EMP* 300
SIC 4953 4212 Garbage: collecting, destroying & processing; Recycling, waste materials; Local trucking, without storage; Garbage: collecting, destroying & processing; Recycling, waste materials; Local trucking, without storage
Pr: Larry Groot
**VP:* Lee Brandsma

GROOVE FORD
See VISTA FD LLC

D-U-N-S 04-102-2997 IMP/EXP
GROSOUTH INC
MONTGOMERY SEED & SUPPLY
620 N Mcdonough St, Montgomery, AL 36104-2623
Tel (334) 265-8241 *Founded/Ownrshp* 1945
Sales 24.0MM^E *EMP* 47
SIC 5191 5261 5999 Farm supplies; Seeds: field, garden & flower; Insecticides; Garden supplies; Nursery stock, seeds & bulbs; Garden supplies & tools; Insecticides; Feed & farm supply
Pr: John W Morgan
**CFO:* Walter Catching
**VP:* Cecil Dorsey Jr
**VP:* Arthur L Morgan Jr
**VP:* J Scott Morgan

GROSS BUILDERS
See I & M J GROSS CO

D-U-N-S 00-541-7993
GROSS ELECTRIC INC (OH)
2807 N Reynolds Rd, Toledo, OH 43615-2080
Tel (419) 392-2214 *Founded/Ownrshp* 1910
Sales 46.0MM^E *EMP* 55
SIC 5063 5719 Electrical supplies; Lighting fixtures; Lighting fixtures
Ch Bd: Richard J Gross
**Pr:* Laurie Gross
**Treas:* H C Reinhard
**VP:* Joseph Gross
Mktg Dir: Sue Sweeney
Sls Mgr: Collen Braham
Sales Asso: Samantha Collins
Sales Asso: Frank Sopko

D-U-N-S 00-614-9942 IMP
GROSS GIVEN MANUFACTURING CO
75 Plato Blvd W, Saint Paul, MN 55107-2005
Tel (651) 225-8117 *Founded/Ownrshp* 1935
Sales 47.8MM^E *EMP* 325
SIC 3581 Automatic vending machines; Automatic vending machines
Ch Bd: John B Edgerton Jr
**CEO:* Alan Suitor
**Treas:* Richard Gross
Bd of Dir: Mike Denoma
**Sr VP:* Scott Edgerton
IT Man: Kevin Baltus
IT Man: Vince Thomas
Mtls Mgr: Randy Wourms

D-U-N-S 15-525-4147
GROSS MECHANICAL CONTRACTORS INC
3622 Greenwood Blvd, Saint Louis, MO 63143-4100
Tel (314) 644-6000 *Founded/Ownrshp* 1985
Sales 26.2MM^E *EMP* 100
SIC 1711 Mechanical contractor
Pr: Hanford Gross
**CFO:* Larry Scheller
**Treas:* Geoffrey Gross

D-U-N-S 02-346-5313
GROSS MOTORS INC
404 E Division St, Neillsville, WI 54456-2111
Tel (715) 743-3207 *Founded/Ownrshp* 1956
Sales 23.2MM^E *EMP* 66
SIC 5511 Automobiles, new & used; Automobiles, new & used
Pr: Wayne Gross
**VP:* Gerald Gross
Sls Mgr: Mike Gro
Sls Mgr: Mike Gross

D-U-N-S 00-197-2421 IMP
GROSS-YOWELL & CO (TX)
3720 Franklin Ave, Waco, TX 76710-7330
Tel (254) 754-5475 *Founded/Ownrshp* 1946
Sales 20.2MM^E *EMP* 45
SIC 5031 5211 Lumber, plywood & millwork; Lumber & other building materials
Pr: Barry Gross
**VP:* Robert Alan Gross
**VP:* W O Gross

D-U-N-S 06-983-7672
GROSSE POINTE PUBLIC SCHOOL SYSTEM (MI)
389 Saint Clair St, Grosse Pointe, MI 48230-1501
Tel (313) 432-3000 *Founded/Ownrshp* 1919
Sales 108.1MM *EMP* 1,200
Accts Plante & Moran Pllc Clinton
SIC 8211 Public elementary school; Public junior high school; Public senior high school; Public elementary school; Public junior high school; Public senior high school
Prin: Glenn Croydon
Prin: Deborah Hubbell
Prin: Patricia J Meek
Prin: Elaine Middlekauff
Prin: Joan Robie
Prin: Jean Rusing
Prin: Kathy Satut
Prin: Ronald D Wardie

D-U-N-S 02-439-6541 IMP
GROSSENBURG IMPLEMENT INC (NE)
JOHN DEERE
31341 Us Highway 18, Winner, SD 57580-6484
Tel (605) 842-2040 *Founded/Ownrshp* 1937
Sales 60.7MM^E *EMP* 150
Accts Morey A Monk & Associates Wi
SIC 5083 7699 Agricultural machinery & equipment; Agricultural equipment repair services; Agricultural machinery & equipment; Agricultural equipment repair services
Pr: Barry Grossenburg
**Treas:* Charlie Grossenburg
**VP:* Gene Grossenburg

D-U-N-S 07-857-7481
GROSSENBURG IMPLEMENT INC
JOHN DEERE
(*Suby of* GROSSENBURG IMPLEMENT INC) ★
88189 Highway 57, Hartington, NE 68739-4626
Tel (402) 254-3908 *Founded/Ownrshp* 1937
Sales 25.0MM *EMP* 80
SIC 5083 7699 Farm implements; Farm machinery repair; Farm implements; Farm machinery repair
Pr: Barry Grossenburg

D-U-N-S 93-156-3951
GROSSINGER AUTOPLEX INC
6900 N Mccormick Blvd # 1, Lincolnwood, IL 60712-2757
Tel (847) 674-9000 *Founded/Ownrshp* 1930
Sales 81.3MM^E *EMP* 200^E
SIC 5511 Automobiles, new & used; Automobiles, new & used
Pr: Caroline Grossinger
Genl Mgr: Charlie Hanmeyer
Dir IT: Robert Pandev
Sls Mgr: Donnie Avramov
Sls Mgr: Courtney Collins
Sls Mgr: Angel Delfi
Sls Mgr: Joseph Jamilkowski

D-U-N-S 02-493-9514
GROSSINGER CHEVROLET INC
151 E Lake Cook Rd, Palatine, IL 60074-9375
Tel (847) 359-7700 *Founded/Ownrshp* 2000
Sales 23.2MM^E *EMP* 55
SIC 5511

D-U-N-S 04-759-9720
GROSSINGER CITY AUTOCORP INC
GROSSINGER CITY TOYOTA
1561 N Fremont St, Chicago, IL 60642-2527
Tel (312) 707-9500 *Founded/Ownrshp* 1997
Sales 25.5MM^E *EMP* 70
SIC 5511 Automobiles, new & used; Automobiles, new & used
Pr: Gary Grossinger
**VP:* Caroline Grossinger
Sls Mgr: Darwin Brown

GROSSINGER CITY TOYOTA
See GROSSINGER CITY AUTOCORP INC

D-U-N-S 17-448-3016
GROSSINGER MOTORCORP INC
CADILLAC GROSSINGER
6900 N Mccormick Blvd # 1, Lincolnwood, IL 60712-2775
Tel (847) 675-8300 *Founded/Ownrshp* 1963
Sales 62.1MM^E *EMP* 215
SIC 5511 7538 7532 5531 Automobiles, new & used; General automotive repair shops; Top & body repair & paint shops; Automotive & home supply stores; Automobiles, new & used; General automotive repair shops; Top & body repair & paint shops; Automotive & home supply stores
Pr: Sharon B Grossinger
**VP:* Gary Grossinger
**Prin:* Antonio Camacho
**Prin:* Francisco Gallegos

D-U-N-S 07-723-4151
GROSSLIGHT INSURANCE INC
KEMPER INSURANCE
1333 Westwood Blvd # 200, Los Angeles, CA 90024-4949
Tel (310) 473-9611 *Founded/Ownrshp* 1950
Sales NA *EMP* 60
SIC 6411 Insurance agents, brokers & service
CEO: Gilbert F Grosslight
**Pr:* Steven Schiewe
VP: Margo Milman
Dir IT: John Durand
Sales Exec: Joan Schiewe
VP Mktg: Joanne Blentzas

D-U-N-S 01-879-1327
GROSSMAN CHEVROLET-NISSAN-GEO INC
GROSSMAN NISSAN
300 Middlesex Tpke, Old Saybrook, CT 06475-4208
Tel (860) 388-5785 *Founded/Ownrshp* 1991
Sales 26.4MM^E *EMP* 60
SIC 5511 Automobiles, new & used; Automobiles, new & used
Pr: Jon Grossman
**VP:* Linda Grossman
**VP:* Craig W Katko
Store Mgr: Duane Chenette
Sls Mgr: Kenneth Britton
Sls Mgr: Phil Greenwood
Sls Mgr: Tim Scamporino
Sales Asso: Brian Filipowski
Sales Asso: Tony Garcia
Sales Asso: Greg Grabulis

D-U-N-S 03-104-2443 IMP
GROSSMAN IRON AND STEEL CO
5 N Market St, Saint Louis, MO 63102-1488
Tel (314) 231-9423 *Founded/Ownrshp* 1918
Sales 100.0MM *EMP* 90
SIC 5093 Metal scrap & waste materials; Ferrous metal scrap & waste; Nonferrous metals scrap; Wire & cable scrap; Metal scrap & waste materials; Ferrous metal scrap & waste; Nonferrous metals scrap; Wire & cable scrap
Pr: David Grossman
**Ex VP:* Sidney Grossman Jr
Off Mgr: Cindy Muehlhauser
Sfty Dirs: Harry Garber

GROSSMAN NISSAN
See GROSSMAN CHEVROLET-NISSAN-GEO INC

D-U-N-S 07-334-1562
GROSSMONT HOSPITAL CORP
SHARP REES-STEALY PHARMACY
(*Suby of* SHARP HEALTHCARE) ★
5555 Grossmont Center Dr, La Mesa, CA 91942-3077
Tel (619) 740-6000 *Founded/Ownrshp* 1953
Sales 596.8MM *EMP* 2,697
SIC 8062 General medical & surgical hospitals; General medical & surgical hospitals
CEO: Dan Gross
Chf Rad: Tere Trout
Dir Rx: Hoangmy Nguyen
IT Man: Chris Ortiz
Opers Mgr: Suzie Warner
Pr Mgr: Karalyn King
Plthlgst: Daniel Molden
Plas Surg: Michael Halls
Pharmcst: Cliff Keltner

D-U-N-S 01-052-0422
GROSSMONT HOSPITAL FOUNDATION
(*Suby of* SHARP HEALTHCARE) ★
5555 Grossmont Center Dr, La Mesa, CA 91942-3077
Tel (619) 740-4200 *Founded/Ownrshp* 1985
Sales 673.8MM *EMP* 6
Accts Ernst & Young Us Llp San Dieg
SIC 8399 Fund raising organization, non-fee basis; Fund raising organization, non-fee basis
Ex Dir: Elizabeth Morgante
Chf Path: Octavio Armas
Dir OR: Suzie Warner
Dir Case M: Mike Murphey
Dir Rx: Patrick Craychee
Chf Nrs Of: Janet Hanley
Pr Mgr: Sandy Pugliese

D-U-N-S 07-873-3086
GROSSMONT UNION HIGH SCHOOL
1100 Murray Dr, El Cajon, CA 92020-5664
Tel (619) 644-8000 *Founded/Ownrshp* 1920
Sales 248.7MM *EMP* 1,887
Accts Christywhite Accountancy Corpo
SIC 8211 Public elementary & secondary schools; Public elementary & secondary schools
**Prin:* Terry Ryan
HC Dir: Teresa Kemper
Board of Directors: Scott Patterson

D-U-N-S 08-000-9310
GROSSMONT-CUYAMACA COMMUNITY COLLEGE DISTRICT
GCCCD
8800 Grossmont College Dr, El Cajon, CA 92020-1765
Tel (619) 644-7010 *Founded/Ownrshp* 2015
Sales 54.0MM *EMP* 2,000^E
SIC 8221 Colleges universities & professional schools

D-U-N-S 11-295-8137
GROSVENOR BUILDING SERVICES INC
3398 Parkway Center Ct, Orlando, FL 32808-1032
Tel (407) 292-3383 *Founded/Ownrshp* 1983
Sales 24.5MM^E *EMP* 700
SIC 7349 Building cleaning service; Janitorial service, contract basis; Building cleaning service; Janitorial service, contract basis
Pr: Rita T Mc Cauley
**VP:* Bernard McCauley
IT Man: Rita McCauley

D-U-N-S 82-908-1616
GROSVENOR CAPITAL MANAGEMENT HOLDINGS LLLP
900 N Michigan Ave # 1850, Chicago, IL 60611-1542
Tel (312) 263-7777 *Founded/Ownrshp* 2005
Sales 73.0MM^E *EMP* 250^E
SIC 6719 Investment holding companies, except banks; Investment holding companies, except banks
Prin: Richard Elden
Sr VP: Karen Sesin
Prin: Allen R Thorpe

D-U-N-S 55-604-5144
GROSVENOR CAPITAL MANAGEMENT LLC
900 N Michigan Ave # 1100, Chicago, IL 60611-6558
Tel (312) 506-6500 *Founded/Ownrshp* 1971
Sales 24.7MM^E *EMP* 60^E
SIC 6282 6722 Investment advisory service; Management investment, open-end
VP: Eliane Studer

D-U-N-S 06-903-4031
■ **GROSVENOR INVESTMENT MANAGEMENT US INC**
LEGG MASON
(*Suby of* LEGG MASON INC) ★
10 New King St Ste 214, White Plains, NY 10604-1211
Tel (914) 683-3710 *Founded/Ownrshp* 1990
Sales NA *EMP* 220
SIC 6411 Pension & retirement plan consultants; Pension & retirement plan consultants
Pr: M Walter Dalessio
**Treas:* Elliott Huesken
**VP:* Arthur Judson
**VP:* Eugene Veneziale

D-U-N-S 07-186-5950
GROSVENOR PROPERTIES LTD
222 Front St Fl 7, San Francisco, CA 94111-4421
Tel (415) 421-5940 *Founded/Ownrshp* 1972
Sales 11.0MM^E *EMP* 824
SIC 6531 Real estate managers; Real estate managers
Pr: Todd Werby
**Ex VP:* Susan Gallagher
**Sr VP:* Dan Croley
**VP:* Steve Nokes

D-U-N-S 00-638-2840 IMP/EXP
GROTE INDUSTRIES INC
2600 Lanier Dr, Madison, IN 47250-1797
Tel (812) 273-2121 *Founded/Ownrshp* 1901
Sales 324.6MM^E *EMP* 1,200
Accts Deloitte Cincinnatiohio
SIC 3231 3647 Vehicular lighting equipment; Mirrors, truck & automobile: made from purchased glass; Mirrors, truck & automobile: made from purchased glass; Vehicular lighting equipment
Ch Bd: William D Grote III
**Pr:* Dominic Grote
**CEO:* William Dominic Grote IV
COO: Keith Grote
**Treas:* Michael R Grote
**VP:* Michael T Adams
Genl Mgr: Dave Poppell
QA Dir: Richard Ll
Dir IT: Lynn Kipper
Dir IT: Mike Routh
Sfty Mgr: Barry Duff

D-U-N-S 08-008-9913
GROTE INDUSTRIES LLC
2600 Lanier Dr, Madison, IN 47250-1797
Tel (812) 265-8273 *Founded/Ownrshp* 1996
Sales 22.6MM^E *EMP* 1,200
SIC 3647 3231 Vehicular lighting equipment; Mirrors, truck & automobile: made from purchased glass
Pr: William Grote IV
CFO: James Braun

GROTENHUIS
See G G T INC

D-U-N-S 00-194-3695 IMP
GROTH CORP (MO)
(*Suby of* CONTINENTAL DISC CORP) ★
13650 N Promenade Blvd, Stafford, TX 77477-3972
Tel (281) 295-6800 *Founded/Ownrshp* 1960, 1999
Sales 24.9MM^E *EMP* 75
SIC 3491 2676 Industrial valves; Sanitary paper products
VP: C J Hagemann
VP: Robert A Robison
Sales Asso: Groth-Michael Couts
Board of Directors: Tony Raguirre, Mark Simmons

D-U-N-S 09-305-5536
■ **GROTH EQUIPMENT CORP OF LOUISIANA**
(*Suby of* CURTISS-WRIGHT FLOW CONTROL CORP) ★
37056 Cornerview Rd, Geismar, LA 70734-3358
Tel (225) 673-6132 *Founded/Ownrshp* 1972
Sales 29.8MM^E *EMP* 78
SIC 5084 5085 7699 Industrial machinery & equipment; Valves & fittings; Valve repair, industrial
CEO: Edward Groth Jr
**Pr:* Gary Gandolfi
**Pr:* David J Linton
**Treas:* Harry Jakubowitz
**VP:* John Brennan
VP: Frank Ditomasso
**VP:* Glenn Tynan

D-U-N-S 05-757-4097
GROTHUES BROTHERS HOLDINGS LTD
2651 Sw Military Dr, San Antonio, TX 78224-1048
Tel (830) 569-1131 *Founded/Ownrshp* 1999
Sales 211.5MM^E *EMP* 905
SIC 5031 5211 Lumber: rough, dressed & finished; Building materials, exterior; Building materials, interior; Lumber & other building materials; Millwork & lumber; Lumber: rough, dressed & finished; Building materials, exterior; Building materials, interior; Lumber & other building materials; Millwork & lumber
Pr: Larry Grothues
**CFO:* Kevin Solomon
IT Man: Marvin Palacios

GROTON BOARD OF EDUCATION
See GROTON PUBLIC SCHOOL DISTRICT

D-U-N-S 01-796-7209
GROTON EQUITIES ASSOCIATES LLC
FAIRFIELD VILLAGE
538 Hallow Rd 3rd Fl E, Melville, NY 11747
Tel (631) 499-6660 *Founded/Ownrshp* 1972
Sales 22.4MM^E *EMP* 150
SIC 6512 6513 Commercial & industrial building operation; Apartment building operators
Opers Mgr: David Nobile

D-U-N-S 19-330-8681
GROTON PUBLIC SCHOOL DISTRICT
GROTON BOARD OF EDUCATION
1300 Flanders Rd, Mystic, CT 06355-1042
Tel (860) 572-2100 *Founded/Ownrshp* 1900
Sales 47.0MM^E *EMP* 800
SIC 8211 Public elementary & secondary schools; Public elementary & secondary schools
MIS Dir: Kevin Lemoi

D-U-N-S 14-400-9149
GROTON UTILITIES
295 Meridian St, Groton, CT 06340-4012
Tel (860) 446-4000 *Founded/Ownrshp* 1904
Sales 20.9MM^E *EMP* 102
SIC 4941 4911 Water supply; Electric services; Water supply; Electric services
Opers Mgr: Randall Surprenant

D-U-N-S 18-985-1389
GROTON-DUNSTABLE REGIONAL SCHOOL DISTRICT
145 Main St, Groton, MA 01450-1272
Tel (978) 448-5192 *Founded/Ownrshp* 1976
Sales 22.6MM^E *EMP* 480
SIC 8211 Public combined elementary & secondary school; Public combined elementary & secondary school
**Pr:* Craig Young
**Treas:* Maryanne Squeglia
VP: Dawn Dorr
Exec: Linda Crewe
Cmptr Lab: Lois Goldstein
Cmptr Lab: Daphne Gowland
Schl Brd P: Jim Frey
Schl Brd P: Alison Manugin

GROTTO
See LANDRYS SEAFOOD INN & OYSTER BAR II INC

D-U-N-S 00-595-1637
GROTTO PIZZA INC
20376 Coastal Hwy, Rehoboth Beach, DE 19971-8015
Tel (302) 227-3567 *Founded/Ownrshp* 1970
Sales 27.8MM^E *EMP* 500
SIC 5812 5813 Pizzeria, independent; Cocktail lounge; Pizzeria, independent; Cocktail lounge
Pr: Dominick Pulieri
**Sec:* Joseph A Paglianite
VP: Jeff Gosnear
Genl Mgr: Dan Jefferis
Genl Mgr: Russ Wiedenmann

D-U-N-S 07-869-8984
GROUND EFFECTS LLC
(*Suby of* GROUND EFFECTS LTD)
3302 Kent St, Flint, MI 48503-4484
Tel (810) 250-5560 *Founded/Ownrshp* 2012
Sales 64.6MM^E *EMP* 700^E
SIC 3429 Motor vehicle hardware
Pt: Greg Lanoue

D-U-N-S 17-150-3100 IMP
GROUND/WATER TREATMENT & TECHNOLOGY LLC
627 Mount Hope Rd, Wharton, NJ 07885-2807
Tel (973) 983-0901 *Founded/Ownrshp* 2014
Sales 35.0MM *EMP* 89
SIC 1629 Waste water & sewage treatment plant construction; Waste water & sewage treatment plant construction
Pr: Robert Kunzel
**Sec:* Bryan P Lamphear
**VP:* Matthew C Phillips

GROUNDSKEEPER, THE
See ENVIRONMENTAL EARTHSCAPES INC

GROUNDSPRING
See NETWORK FOR GOOD INC

D-U-N-S 14-841-3602
GROUNDWATER AND ENVIRONMENTAL SERVICES INC
GES
1340 Campus Pkwy Bldg B, Wall Township, NJ 07753-6829
Tel (800) 220-3068 *Founded/Ownrshp* 1985
Sales 124.3MM^E *EMP* 711
SIC 8748

D-U-N-S 78-731-1265
GROUNDWATER ENVIRONMENTAL SERVICES INC
1750 Kraft Dr Ste 2700, Blacksburg, VA 24060-6161
Tel (540) 552-0685 *Founded/Ownrshp* 1988
Sales 70.0MM *EMP* 12^E
SIC 8748 7371 5045 8741 8711 Environmental consultant; Computer software development; Computer software; Management services; Consulting engineer; Environmental consultant; Computer software development; Computer software; Management services; Consulting engineer
Pr: Ed Vanwoudenburg

GROUP
See UNIVERSITY OF NORTH TEXAS SYSTEM

D-U-N-S 08-271-5707
GROUP & PENSION ADMINISTRATORS INC
GPA
12770 Merit Dr Ste 200, Dallas, TX 75251-1233
Tel (972) 238-7900 *Founded/Ownrshp* 1968
Sales NA *EMP* 150
SIC 6411 Insurance information & consulting services; Pension & retirement plan consultants
Pr: Jerry Mc Peters
CFO: Thomas McDaniel
Ex VP: Kathy Enochs
VP: Edna Geer-Hudgins
VP: Mac McIntyre
VP: Neal Stanley
Dir IT: Terry Hamilton
IT Man: Marsha Hamm
Sales Exec: Matt McCuen
Mktg Dir: Clyde New

D-U-N-S 83-967-2748 IMP
▲ **GROUP 1 AUTOMOTIVE INC**
800 Gessner Rd Ste 500, Houston, TX 77024-4498
Tel (713) 647-5700 *Founded/Ownrshp* 1995
Sales 9.9MMM *EMP* 11,978^E
Tkr Sym GPI *Exch* NYS
SIC 5511 6141 7538 7532 5531 Automobiles, new & used; Automobile loans, including insurance; Engine repair; Collision shops, automotive; Automotive parts; Automobiles, new & used; Automobile loans, including insurance; Engine repair; Collision shops, automotive; Automotive parts
Pr: Earl J Hesterberg
Pr: Gigi Myung
CFO: Robert Kennedy
CFO: Matthew McGovern
CFO: Paul Reinhart

CFO: John C Rickel
CFO: Pete Ruiz
CFO: Christie Steverson
CFO: Douglas Stewart
VP: Darryl M Burman
VP: Peter C Delongchamps
VP: James R Druzbik
VP: Frank Grese Jr
VP: David W Hult
VP: Mark Iuppenlatz
VP: Daryl Kenningham
VP: Ian Twinley
Board of Directors: John L Adams, Doyle L Arnold, Lincoln Pereira, Stephen D Quinn, J Terry Strange, Max P Watson Jr, Maryann Wright

D-U-N-S 05-575-7439 IMP
GROUP 1 MILLER AUTOMOTIVE
MERCEDES BENZ OF BEVERLY HILLS
400 Foothill Rd, Beverly Hills, CA 90210-3603
Tel (310) 659-2980 *Founded/Ownrshp* 2004
Sales 46.0MM^E *EMP* 175^E
SIC 5511 Automobiles, new & used; Automobiles, new & used
Genl Mgr: Bruce Schulman
Mng Pt: Kevin Steward
VP: Maureen Lowery
IT Man: Ron Robertson
Software D: Assaf Haim
Sales Asso: Lindsay Goldberg

D-U-N-S 13-120-9033
GROUP ADMINISTRATORS LTD
915 National Pkwy Ste F, Schaumburg, IL 60173-5120
Tel (847) 519-1880 *Founded/Ownrshp* 1985
Sales NA *EMP* 85^E
Accts Blumenfeld Weiser Friedman &
SIC 6411 Insurance brokers
CEO: David Dorfman
**Ex VP:* William E Webbe IV
**Ex VP:* Barb Wieda
Dir IT: Anthony Willard
MIS Mgr: Brett Webbe

D-U-N-S 01-178-0874
GROUP AFFILIATES LLP
5717 Legacy Dr Ste 250, Plano, TX 75024-4246
Tel (214) 573-2430 *Founded/Ownrshp* 2009
Sales 15.6MM^E *EMP* 276
SIC 8712 8711 Architectural services; Engineering services; Architectural services; Engineering services
Pt: Marjorie Simmons

D-U-N-S 07-929-4382
GROUP BELLA LLC PORTA
38 W 34th St, New York, NY 10001-3004
Tel (212) 239-7380 *Founded/Ownrshp* 2012
Sales 33.0MM *EMP* 350^E
SIC 5611 Men's & boys' clothing stores; Men's & boys' clothing stores
Pt: Karl Ashmawy

D-U-N-S 02-175-3843
GROUP BUILDERS INC
511 Mokauea St, Honolulu, HI 96819-3232
Tel (808) 832-0888 *Founded/Ownrshp* 1979
Sales 44.1MM *EMP* 280
SIC 1742 1751 1799 Plastering, plain or ornamental; Drywall; Acoustical & ceiling work; Insulation, buildings; Carpentry work; Fireproofing buildings; Plastering, plain or ornamental; Drywall; Acoustical & ceiling work; Insulation, buildings; Carpentry work; Fireproofing buildings
Pr: Anacleto R Alcantra
**Sec:* Charles Cook
**VP:* Robert Farmer

D-U-N-S 95-860-1528
GROUP CBS INC
1315 Columbine Dr, Gainesville, TX 76240-2010
Tel (940) 665-4484 *Founded/Ownrshp* 1990
Sales 20.5MM^E *EMP* 83
SIC 3643 Current-carrying wiring devices
Pr: Finley Ledbetter

D-U-N-S 95-792-5225
GROUP CONTRACTORS LLC
15055 Jefferson Hwy, Baton Rouge, LA 70817-6230
Tel (225) 752-2500 *Founded/Ownrshp* 1996
Sales 67.8MM *EMP* 120^E
Accts Hannis T Bourgeois Llp Bato
SIC 1771 Concrete work; Concrete work
Pr: David Arrighi
**CFO:* Dane Falgout
**Ex VP:* Shane Kirkpatrick
**VP:* Don Petersonn

D-U-N-S 07-970-5079
GROUP DEEP FOUNDATIONS LLC
15055 Jefferson Hwy, Baton Rouge, LA 70817-6230
Tel (225) 778-5550 *Founded/Ownrshp* 2015
Sales 40.0MM *EMP* 100
SIC 1629 Pile driving contractor
CEO: David Arrighi
Pr: Kevin Gourgues
CFO: Dane Falgout

D-U-N-S 80-801-4042
GROUP DEKKO HOLDINGS INC
(*Suby of* DEKKO ACQUISITION PARENT INC) ★
2505 Dekko Dr, Garrett, IN 46738-1886
Tel (260) 347-0700 *Founded/Ownrshp* 2006
Sales 126.0MM^E *EMP* 1,267
SIC 3496 Miscellaneous fabricated wire products; Miscellaneous fabricated wire products
CEO: John R May
**Pr:* Timothy White
**VP:* Gerald Whiteford
Genl Mgr: Shawnna Dillinger
Info Man: Ron Jennett

D-U-N-S 79-696-5168 IMP
■ **GROUP DEKKO INC**
(*Suby of* GRAHAM HOLDINGS CO) ★
2505 Dekko Dr, Garrett, IN 46738-1886
Tel (260) 357-3621 *Founded/Ownrshp* 2015
Sales 110.5MM^E *EMP* 356
SIC 3479 3469 3643 3315 3089 Coating of metals & formed products; Painting of metal products; Metal stampings; Current-carrying wiring devices; Wire & fabricated wire products; Molding primary plastic; Coating of metals & formed products; Painting of metal products; Metal stampings; Current-carrying wiring devices; Wire & fabricated wire products; Molding primary plastic
CEO: John R May
**Pr:* Jon Jensen
VP: Larry Colestock
Exec: Theresa Bajgrowicz
Exec: Steve Dwarica
Prgrm Mgr: Josh Ambrose
Prgrm Mgr: Dan Filley
Prgrm Mgr: Kelly Schurr
CIO: Christopher Edwards
Mfg Mgr: Mark McCue
Opers Mgr: Stephen Herson

GROUP DELPHI
See DELPHI PRODUCTIONS INC

D-U-N-S 79-496-7414
GROUP ENTERPRISE OF NORTH AMERICA INC
GENA
10509 Route 68, Rimersburg, PA 16248-7005
Tel (814) 473-3362 *Founded/Ownrshp* 1985
Sales 10.5MM^E *EMP* 300
SIC 8741 5812 Management services; Eating places; Management services; Eating places
Pr: Barry B George
**Sec:* Dan Lewis

D-U-N-S 17-132-1693
GROUP EXCELLENCE LTD
13111 N Cntl Expy Ste 230, Dallas, TX 75243
Tel (214) 570-3140 *Founded/Ownrshp* 2004
Sales 7.4MM^E *EMP* 454^E
SIC 8299 Educational services; Educational services
Pt: Carl G Dorvil
VP: Byron Sanders
Creative D: Jeremy Biggers

D-U-N-S 61-262-4437
GROUP FIVE PRODUCTIONS
55 N 300 W, Salt Lake City, UT 84101-3502
Tel (801) 575-5733 *Founded/Ownrshp* 1990
Sales 16.5MM^E *EMP* 350
SIC 3663 Studio equipment, radio & television broadcasting; Studio equipment, radio & television broadcasting
Pr: Jack Adamson

D-U-N-S 02-045-2850
GROUP HEALTH CO-OPERATIVE OF SOUTH CENTRAL WISCONSIN
GROUP HEALTH COOPERATIVE HMO
1265 John Q Hammons Dr # 200, Madison, WI 53717-1962
Tel (608) 251-4156 *Founded/Ownrshp* 1972
Sales NA *EMP* 500
SIC 6324

D-U-N-S 07-819-8520
GROUP HEALTH COOPERATIVE
320 Westlake Ave N # 100, Seattle, WA 98109-5233
Tel (206) 448-4141 *Founded/Ownrshp* 1945
Sales NA *EMP* 9,300
Accts Kpmg Llp Seattle Wa
SIC 6324 5999 8093 6321 Health maintenance organization (HMO), insurance only; Medical apparatus & supplies; Hearing aids; Weight loss clinic, with medical staff; Accident & health insurance; Health maintenance organization (HMO), insurance only; Medical apparatus & supplies; Hearing aids; Weight loss clinic, with medical staff; Accident & health insurance
Pr: Scott Armstrong
COO: James Hereford
CFO: Scott Boyd
**CFO:* Richard Magnuson
CFO: Rick Magnuson
Sr Cor Off: John Long
Trst: Phyllis C Best
Trst: Jerry Campbell
Trst: Ann Daley
Trst: Ira Fielding
Trst: Tracy Garland
Trst: Jennifer Joly
Trst: Bob Margulis
Trst: Changmook Sohn
Assoc VP: Chris Taylor
Ex VP: Greg Swint
Ex VP: Mark Szalwinski
Ex VP: Marc West
**Ex VP:* Rick Woods
VP: John Harris
Assoc Dir: Mark Johnson

D-U-N-S 01-709-0617
GROUP HEALTH COOPERATIVE ADMINISTRATION
1265 John Q Hammons Dr # 200, Madison, WI 53717-1962
Tel (608) 251-4156 *Founded/Ownrshp* 2008
Sales 313.5MM *EMP* 50
SIC 8099 Health & allied services; Health & allied services
Sales Exec: Al Wearing
CIO: Bruce Quade

GROUP HEALTH COOPERATIVE HMO
See GROUP HEALTH CO-OPERATIVE OF SOUTH CENTRAL WISCONSIN

D-U-N-S 07-313-4157
GROUP HEALTH INC
GHI
(*Suby of* EMBLEMHEALTH INC) ★
441 9th Ave Frnt, New York, NY 10001-1642
Tel (212) 615-0000 *Founded/Ownrshp* 1946
Sales NA *EMP* 2,354
Accts Bdo Seidman Llp New York Ne
SIC 6324 Hospital & medical service plans; Hospital & medical service plans
Pr: Frank Branchini
Pr: Daniel P Finke
CFO: Arthur J Byrd
Bd of Dir: Gregory Floyd
Bd of Dir: Susan M Mathews
Ofcr: Mitchell Goldberg
Ex VP: Draran Ron
Ex VP: John Steber
Sr VP: George Babitsch
Sr VP: Phillip Berman
Sr VP: Jeffrey D Chansler
VP: Mariann E Drohan
VP: Vince Hartmann
VP: William Mastro
VP: Michael Palmateer
VP: Karen Smith-Hagman
Board of Directors: Harry Nespoli, Howard Berliner, Daniel Rubino Esq, Frank J Branchini, Dennis Sullivan, Jerome S Breslaw MD, Roger Toussaint, Ethelyn A Chase, Rosa Mgill Dsw, Jay E Russ Equire, John Gerrick Esq, James F Gill Esq, Bernard Schayes Mdpc

D-U-N-S 11-301-4161
GROUP HEALTH NORTHWEST (INC)
5615 W Sunset Hwy, Spokane, WA 99224-9454
Tel (509) 838-9100 *Founded/Ownrshp* 1977
Sales 21.6MM^E *EMP* 400
SIC 8011 Health maintenance organization; Health maintenance organization
Pr: Sharon Fairchild
**Treas:* James Truess
VP: Kelly Stanford
Doctor: Brad Pope

D-U-N-S 00-189-7649 IMP
GROUP HEALTH PERMANENTE
320 Westlake Ave N # 100, Seattle, WA 98109-5233
Tel (206) 448-4491 *Founded/Ownrshp* 1998
Sales 44.2MM^E *EMP* 1,100
SIC 8011 Offices & clinics of medical doctors; Offices & clinics of medical doctors
Pr: Hugh Streley MD
**Pr:* Gary Feldbau
**Pr:* Hugh Stralay
Pr: Edith Weller
**CFO:* Mark West
Bd of Dir: Mike Wanderer
VP: Dorothy F Teeter
Ex Dir: William L Akers
Doctor: Paul Gott
Doctor: Rachel Opel
Doctor: Wendy Siu

D-U-N-S 05-459-0344
GROUP HOME FOUNDATION INC (ME)
GHF
61 Little River Dr, Belfast, ME 04915-6035
Tel (207) 338-2080 *Founded/Ownrshp* 1975
Sales 28.6MM *EMP* 257
Accts Pfbfcpas Oakland Me
SIC 8331 8361 Sheltered workshop; Home for the mentally retarded; Sheltered workshop; Home for the mentally retarded
Ex Dir: Harold Siefken
Ex Dir: Salvatore Garozzo

GROUP HOSPITAL & MEDICAL SVC
See CAREFIRST INC

D-U-N-S 05-518-5862
GROUP HOSPITALIZATION AND MEDICAL SERVICES INC
CAREFIRST BLUECROSS BLUESHIELD
(*Suby of* CAREFIRST INC) ★
10455 Mill Run Cir, Owings Mills, MD 21117-4208
Tel (202) 479-8000 *Founded/Ownrshp* 1939
Sales NA *EMP* 2,000
Accts Ernst And Young Llp Baltimore
SIC 6324 Group hospitalization plans; Group hospitalization plans
Pr: Chet Burrell
Treas: Jeff Clasper
VP: Sam Bennet
VP: Helen Struck
Dir IT: Christi C Snyder
IT Man: Ann Doyle
IT Man: Ken Fritsch
IT Man: Boenig Sandy
IT Man: Art Smith
Netwrk Mgr: Pete Longden
S&M/VP: Anne Gallant

GROUP II COMMUNICATIONS
See INTEGRATED MERCHANDISING SYSTEMS LLC

D-U-N-S 19-972-2922
GROUP M WORLDWIDE LLC
GROUPM
(*Suby of* WPP GROUP USA INC) ★
498 7th Ave, New York, NY 10018-6798
Tel (212) 297-8181 *Founded/Ownrshp* 1999
Sales 213.3MM^E *EMP* 30^E
SIC 7319 Media buying service
Ch: Irwin Gotlieb
Sr Pt: Jamie Considine
Sr Pt: Evan Schweitzer
Mng Pt: Michael Erlinger
Mng Pt: John Miles
**Pr:* Dominic Proctor
**CEO:* Kelly Clark
CEO: Brian Lesser
**COO:* Colin Barlow
**CFO:* Stuart Diamond
Treas: Mary E Howe
Chf Inves: Rino Scanzoni
VP: Jason Blake
Assoc Dir: Doreen Crupi
Dir Rx: Prasanna Raman
Dir Rx: Sheila Shanmugam
Comm Man: Bori Frisch

D-U-N-S 05-650-7405
GROUP MANAGEMENT 0002 LLC
GM2
1321 Upland Dr 3966, Houston, TX 77043-4718
Tel (716) 998-3386 *Founded/Ownrshp* 2010
Sales NA *EMP* 3,400
SIC 6411 Insurance information & consulting services
Genl Mgr: Victoria Conde

D-U-N-S 96-172-0476 IMP
GROUP MONTANA INC
1 Sterling Ln, Columbus, MT 59019-7611
Tel (406) 322-4555 *Founded/Ownrshp* 2004
Sales 21.9MM^E *EMP* 200^E
SIC 3911 Jewelry, precious metal; Jewelry, precious metal
Pr: George Branca
**CFO:* David Stimmel
VP: Curt Robbins
Off Mgr: Bev Newman
Plnt Mgr: Wayne Gransbery

D-U-N-S 09-731-7663
GROUP O INC
(*Suby of* GROUP O INC) ★
120 4th Ave E, Milan, IL 61264-2803
Tel (309) 736-8660 *Founded/Ownrshp* 1992
Sales 108.5MM^E *EMP* 280
Accts Crippen Reid & Bowen Llc
SIC 5085 5013 3479 Industrial supplies; Bearings; Automotive supplies; Painting of metal products; Industrial supplies; Bearings; Automotive supplies; Painting of metal products
Pr: Robert Ontiveros
**CEO:* Gregg Ontiveros
**CFO:* Bob Marriott
**VP:* Kim Fox
VP: Bob Ontiveros
**VP:* Alfred Ramirez

D-U-N-S 80-278-7937
GROUP O INC
4905 77th Ave E, Milan, IL 61264-3250
Tel (309) 736-8100 *Founded/Ownrshp* 1992
Sales 708.2MM *EMP* 1,520
Accts Honkamp Krueger & Co Pc Mo
SIC 7389 Packaging & labeling services; Packaging & labeling services
CEO: Gregg Ontiveros
**Pr:* Charles Wetzel
**CFO:* Bob Marriott
**Ch:* Robert Ontiveros
Sr VP: Mike De La Cruz
VP: Mike De Cruz
VP: Tony Lopez
VP: Kevin Mainoe
VP: Kevin Maione
**VP:* Chris Ontiveros
VP: Matt Ontiveros
VP: Alfred Ramirez
VP: Debbie Storey
VP: Dorothy Tubbs
Exec: Jennifer Cole
Dir Bus: Mark Herbert

D-U-N-S 19-255-6582
GROUP ONE INVESTMENTS LLC
614 Frelinghuysen Ave # 30, Newark, NJ 07114-1346
Tel (973) 854-0956 *Founded/Ownrshp* 2002
Sales 29.1MM^E *EMP* 750
SIC 8741 Business management; Business management
CFO: Rishi Hinduja
Opers Mgr: Mike Welch

D-U-N-S 79-211-0017
GROUP ONE TRADING LTD
440 S La Salle St # 3232, Chicago, IL 60605-5021
Tel (312) 431-2840 *Founded/Ownrshp* 1989
Sales 43.8MM^E *EMP* 180
SIC 6211 Stock option dealers; Traders, security; Stock option dealers; Traders, security
Pr: Steven Robinson
**Treas:* Alan Suslow
**VP:* Gary Sparks

D-U-N-S 08-835-4196 IMP
GROUP PUBLISHING INC
1515 Cascade Ave, Loveland, CO 80538-8681
Tel (970) 669-3836 *Founded/Ownrshp* 1977
Sales 72.9MM^E *EMP* 320
SIC 2731 2721 8661 Book publishing; Magazines: publishing & printing; Religious instruction; Book publishing; Magazines: publishing & printing; Religious instruction
Pr: Thom Schultz
**CFO:* Jeff Loop
**VP:* Joel Fay
VP: Kirk Gilmore
VP: Joani Schultz
CTO: Brandon Kelley
Dir IT: David Schuett
IT Man: Sherry Greener
Netwrk Eng: Alan Strand
VP Opers: Rocky Gilmore
Mktg Dir: Vaughan Jon

D-U-N-S 06-117-7853
GROUP RESOURCES INC
3080 Premiere Pkwy # 100, Duluth, GA 30097-8911
Tel (770) 623-8383 *Founded/Ownrshp* 1981
Sales NA *EMP* 130
SIC 6411 Insurance brokers
Pr: Tom Byrd
**Sr VP:* Andy Willoughby
VP: Sheila Autry
**VP:* Robby Kerr
IT Man: Steve Kemp
Sales Asso: Pat Lund

D-U-N-S 83-771-1027
GROUP TRANSPORTATION SERVICES INC
GTS
5876 Darrow Rd, Hudson, OH 44236-3864
Tel (330) 342-8700 *Founded/Ownrshp* 1995
Sales 26.0MM^E *EMP* 69
SIC 8742 Transportation consultant
Pr: Michael Valentine
**VP:* Paul Kithcart
Snr Mgr: Denise Stryker
Board of Directors: James Cahill

D-U-N-S 10-114-4327 IMP
GROUP USA INC
FIRST TRADING
25 Enterprise Ave N Ste 1, Secaucus, NJ 07094-2583
Tel (201) 867-6005 *Founded/Ownrshp* 1997
Sales 67.0MM^E *EMP* 470
SIC 5621 5632 Ready-to-wear apparel, women's; Apparel accessories; Ready-to-wear apparel, women's; Apparel accessories
CEO: Mahyar Amirsaleh
**Pr:* Denise Viotti
**COO:* Ali Amirnirounand
**CFO:* Raffi Allahverdian
VP: Behshid Zandi
Dir IT: Jacqueline Puig

D-U-N-S 05-049-6447
GROUP VOYAGERS INC
AVALON WATERWAYS
5301 S Federal Cir, Littleton, CO 80123-2980
Tel (303) 703-7000 *Founded/Ownrshp* 1997
Sales 89.0MM^E *EMP* 295
SIC 4725 Tour operators; Tour operators
Ch Bd: Philip Gordon
**Pr:* Scott Nisbet
**CFO:* Kevin F Ford
VP: Pam Hoffee
VP: Ken Migaki
Snr Sftwr: Damon Flynn
QA Dir: Krista McClure
QA Dir: Kate Vogl
IT Man: Jeff Canterbury
Software D: Eric Bonney
Software D: Todd Cone

D-U-N-S 05-696-3945
GROUP360 INC
GROUP360 WORLDWIDE
1227 Washington Ave, Saint Louis, MO 63103-1903
Tel (314) 260-6360 *Founded/Ownrshp* 2003
Sales 38.6MM^E *EMP* 350
SIC 7335 7389 7319 7336

GROUP360 WORLDWIDE
See GROUP360 INC

GROUPAERO
See AEROSPACE HOLDINGS INC

D-U-N-S 00-403-6778 IMP/EXP
GROUPE LACASSE LLC
222 Merchandise Mart Plz # 1042, Chicago, IL 60654-1103
Tel (312) 670-9100 *Founded/Ownrshp* 1981, 2012
Sales 37.5MM^E *EMP* 232
SIC 2522 2521 2512 Desks, office: except wood; Chairs, office: padded or plain, except wood; Cabinets, office: except wood; Bookcases, office: except wood; Desks, office: wood; Chairs, office: padded, upholstered or plain: wood; Cabinets, office: wood; Panel systems & partitions (free-standing), office: wood; Upholstered household furniture; Desks, office: except wood; Chairs, office: padded or plain, except wood; Cabinets, office: except wood; Bookcases, office: except wood; Desks, office: wood; Chairs, office: padded, upholstered or plain: wood; Cabinets, office: wood; Panel systems & partitions (free-standing), office: wood; Upholstered household furniture
Pr: Sylvain Garneau
Ex VP: Kevin Glynn
VP: Bob Bishop
VP: Roy Jean

D-U-N-S 18-035-7795
GROUPE SEB HOLDINGS INC
(*Suby of* SEB INTERNATIONALE SAS)
1105 N Market St Ste 1142, Wilmington, DE 19801-1216
Tel (973) 736-0300 *Founded/Ownrshp* 2005
Sales 98.4MM^E *EMP* 272
SIC 5064 Electrical appliances, television & radio; Electrical appliances, television & radio
Ch: Francois Duley
**Pr:* Jacques Alexandre

D-U-N-S 78-540-6141 IMP/EXP
GROUPE SEB USA
T-FAL WEAREVER
(*Suby of* GROUPE SEB HOLDINGS INC) ★
5 Woodhollow Rd Ste 2, Parsippany, NJ 07054-2832
Tel (973) 736-0300 *Founded/Ownrshp* 1990
Sales 78.1MM^E *EMP* 250
SIC 5023

GROUPE STAHL
See STAHLS INC

GROUPM
See GROUP M WORLDWIDE LLC

D-U-N-S 19-721-1993
GROUPM WORLDWIDE INC
498 Fashion Ave Fl 4, New York, NY 10018-6798
Tel (212) 297-7000 *Founded/Ownrshp* 1991
Sales 188.5MM^E *EMP* 1,000
SIC 3993 Signs & advertising specialties; Signs & advertising specialties
CEO: Kelly Clark
**Pr:* Mark Golestein
**Prin:* Scott Neslund

D-U-N-S 83-154-7612
▲ GROUPON INC
600 W Chicago Ave Ste 400, Chicago, IL 60654-2067
Tel (312) 334-1579 *Founded/Ownrshp* 2008
Sales 3.1MMM *EMP* 11,843
Accts Ernst & Young Llp Chicago Il
Tkr Sym GRPN *Exch* NGS
SIC 7311 7319 Advertising agencies; Display advertising service; Advertising agencies; Display advertising service
CEO: Rich Williams
Ch Bd: Eric Lefkofsky
CFO: Jason E Child
Sr VP: Carol Campagnolo
Area Mgr: Sean Murphy
Area Mgr: John Neal
Plng Mgr: Jessica Barker
CTO: SRI Viswanath

Board of Directors: Peter J Barris, Robert J Bass, Daniel T Henry, Jeffrey T Housenbold, Bradley A Keywell, Ann E Ziegler

D-U-N-S 96-793-1270
GROUPWARE INTERNATIONAL INC
995 W Kennedy Blvd Ste 47, Orlando, FL 32810-6139
Tel (727) 462-5743 *Founded/Ownrshp* 1999
Sales 37.1MM^E *EMP* 450
SIC 1731 Cable television installation; Cable television installation
CEO: Ron Dean

D-U-N-S 07-352-3750
GROUPWARE TECHNOLOGY INC
511 Division St, Campbell, CA 95008-6932
Tel (408) 540-0090 *Founded/Ownrshp* 1992
Sales 516.9MM^E *EMP* 200
SIC 5045 7373 Computers, peripherals & software; Computer software; Computer-aided system services; Computers, peripherals & software; Computer software; Computer-aided system services
CEO: Mike Thompson
**Ex VP:* Scott Sutter
**VP:* Josh Avila
**VP:* John Barnes
**VP:* Anthony Miley
Genl Mgr: Tim Carver
Mktg Mgr: Renee Thompson
Sales Asso: Cassidy Johnson

GROVE, THE
See GROVE AQUATIC FITNESS CENTER

D-U-N-S 10-798-7633
GROVE AQUATIC FITNESS CENTER
GROVE, THE
8055 Barbara Ave, Inver Grove Heights, MN 55077-3430
Tel (651) 450-2480 *Founded/Ownrshp* 1996
Sales 9.3MM^E *EMP* 400
SIC 7991 Physical fitness facilities; Physical fitness facilities
Snr Mgr: Franklin Martin

D-U-N-S 09-287-0948
GROVE AVON SCHOOL DISTRICT
375 S Jennersville Rd, West Grove, PA 19390-8401
Tel (610) 869-2441 *Founded/Ownrshp* 1928
Sales 41.5MM^E *EMP* 670
SIC 8211 Public elementary & secondary schools; Public junior high school; Public senior high school; Public elementary school; Public elementary & secondary schools; Public junior high school; Public senior high school; Public elementary school
Prin: Augustus J Massaro
Prin: Marie Digiulio
MIS Dir: Gary Mattei
Teacher Pr: Wendi L Kraft
HC Dir: Louis Chance

D-U-N-S 07-749-0290
GROVE CITY AREA SCHOOL DIISTRICT
511 Highland Ave, Grove City, PA 16127-1107
Tel (724) 458-6733 *Founded/Ownrshp* 1958
Sales 33.0MM *EMP* 327
Accts Paparone Stillwaggon & Mcgill
SIC 8211 Public elementary & secondary schools; Public elementary & secondary schools
**Prin:* James Anderson
**Prin:* Jennifer Connelly
**Prin:* Lawrence Connelly
**Prin:* Rae-Lin Howard
**Prin:* Tammi Martin
Cmptr Lab: Heather Hough
Dir IT: Judy Dennis
Instr Medi: Laura Wienand

D-U-N-S 07-496-9304
GROVE CITY COLLEGE
100 Campus Dr, Grove City, PA 16127-2104
Tel (724) 458-2000 *Founded/Ownrshp* 1875
Sales 68.3MM *EMP* 385^E
Accts Grossman Yanak & Ford Llp Pit
SIC 8221 College, except junior; College, except junior
Pr: Richard G Jewell
**CFO:* Roger Towle
**Ch:* David R Rathburn
**Treas:* Charlotte Zuschlag
VP Opers: Tom Gregg

D-U-N-S 08-967-0251
GROVE CITY HEALTH SYSTEM
631 N Broad Street Ext, Grove City, PA 16127-4603
Tel (724) 450-7000 *Founded/Ownrshp* 1978
Sales 45.1MM *EMP* 475
Accts Bkd Llp Springfield Missouri
SIC 8062 General medical & surgical hospitals; General medical & surgical hospitals
CEO: Robert C Jackson Jr
Dir Lab: Kim Young
Dir Rx: Tony Patterson
Off Mgr: Linda Skillwaggon
Dir IT: Phil Swartwood
Mtls Mgr: Michael Kearns
Obsttrcn: Francis J Bassani

D-U-N-S 05-248-4306
GROVE CITY MEDICAL CENTER
631 N Broad Street Ext, Grove City, PA 16127-4603
Tel (724) 450-7000 *Founded/Ownrshp* 2010
Sales 47.5MM *EMP* 28^E
SIC 8062 General medical & surgical hospitals; General medical & surgical hospitals
Ch Bd: Timothy Bonner
CFO: Edward Rice
Off Mgr: Mary A Kane
Off Mgr: Linda Skillwaggon
Mtls Mgr: Mike Kearns

D-U-N-S 01-361-7204
GROVE ELK UNIFIED SCHOOL DISTRICT
EGUSD
9510 Elk Grove Florin Rd, Elk Grove, CA 95624-1801
Tel (916) 686-5085 *Founded/Ownrshp* 1959
Sales 417.1MM^E *EMP* 5,600
Accts Perry-Smith Llp Sacramento C

SIC 8211 Public elementary school; Public junior high school; Public senior high school; Public special education school; Public elementary school; Public junior high school; Public senior high school; Public special education school
Dir Risk M: Scott Nelson
Dir Sec: Rick Ewing
Pr Dir: Elizabeth Graswich
Teacher Pr: Evelyn Lahuan
HC Dir: Carl Steinauer

D-U-N-S 03-927-8577
GROVE HILL MEDICAL CENTER PC
300 Kensington Ave Ste 1, New Britain, CT 06051-3916
Tel (860) 224-6215 *Founded/Ownrshp* 1947
Sales 43.1MM^E *EMP* 500
SIC 8093 Specialty outpatient clinics; Specialty outpatient clinics
Pr: Earle Sittambalam
**CEO:* Michael G Genovesi
**CFO:* Jacqueline Cahill
**VP:* Robert Napoletano
**VP:* Neil Wasserman
**Ex Dir:* Alan McGinnes
Prac Mgr: Alan Meyerjack
Dir IT: Carl Labbadia
Software D: Christine Speight
Mktg Mgr: Joel McClelland
Surgeon: Robert Belniak

D-U-N-S 00-980-4444 IMP
GROVE INC
3 Westbrook Corporate Ctr # 500, Westchester, IL 60154-5796
Tel (708) 531-1694 *Founded/Ownrshp* 1981
Sales 53.0MM^E *EMP* 350
SIC 5441 5451 Candy; Nuts; Dairy products stores; Candy; Nuts; Dairy products stores
Pr: Michelle Dukler
**COO:* Paul Loupakos
**CFO:* Robert L Ireland

D-U-N-S 10-006-5606
GROVE INDEPENDENT SCHOOL DISTRICT
517 W 10th St, Grove, OK 74344
Tel (918) 786-3003 *Founded/Ownrshp* 1900
Sales 10.3MM^E *EMP* 300
SIC 8211 Elementary & secondary schools; Elementary & secondary schools

D-U-N-S 83-291-5065
GROVE INTERNATIONAL PARTNERS LLP
126 E 56th St Ste 1120, New York, NY 10022
Tel (212) 308-6025 *Founded/Ownrshp* 2005
Sales 24.7MM^E *EMP* 89^E
SIC 6798 6799 8741 Real estate investment trusts; Investors; Management services
Mng Pt: Richard Georgi
Genl Couns: David Noakes
Snr Mgr: John McHugh

D-U-N-S 11-875-8598
GROVE INVER HEIGHTS COMMUNITY SCHOOLS
INVER GROVE HTS PUB SCHOOLS
2990 80th St E, Inver Grove Heights, MN 55076-3232
Tel (651) 306-7800 *Founded/Ownrshp* 1958
Sales 26.7MM^E *EMP* 525
SIC 8211 Public combined elementary & secondary school; Public combined elementary & secondary school
Exec: Belle Sarff

D-U-N-S 03-911-6913
GROVE INVESTORS INC
1542 Buchanan Trl E, Greencastle, PA 17225-9511
Tel (717) 597-8121 *Founded/Ownrshp* 2001
Sales 88.8MM^E *EMP* 1,300
SIC 3531 Cranes; Cranes
Pr: Jeff Bust

D-U-N-S 07-873-3276
GROVE LEMON SCHOOL DISTRICT
8025 Lincoln St, Lemon Grove, CA 91945-2515
Tel (619) 825-5600 *Founded/Ownrshp* 1893
Sales 32.3MM^E *EMP* 500
SIC 8211 Public elementary school; Public elementary school
Genl Mgr: Eric Stigall
IT Man: Darryl Lagace

D-U-N-S 10-006-6018
GROVE LOCUST PUBLIC SCHOOLS
LOCUST GROVE PUBLIC SCHOOLS
419 N Broadway, Locust Grove, OK 74352-5020
Tel (918) 479-5243 *Founded/Ownrshp* 1910
Sales 11.7MM *EMP* 375
SIC 8211 Public combined elementary & secondary school; Public combined elementary & secondary school
Dir IT: Bill Hix

D-U-N-S 07-457-2538 IMP/EXP
GROVE LONG CONFECTIONERY CO
MANGEL & CO
333 Lexington Dr, Buffalo Grove, IL 60089-6934
Tel (847) 459-3100 *Founded/Ownrshp* 1971
Sales 21.9MM^E *EMP* 120
SIC 5441 2064 Confectionery; Candy & other confectionery products
CEO: John Mangel II
**VP:* John Mangel III
**VP:* W David Mangel
Sls Mgr: Nick Quartano

D-U-N-S 09-470-9011
GROVE LUMBER & BUILDING SUPPLIES INC (CA)
1300 S Campus Ave, Ontario, CA 91761-4378
Tel (909) 947-0277 *Founded/Ownrshp* 1979
Sales 203.0MM^E *EMP* 240
SIC 5031 5211 Lumber, plywood & millwork; Lumber products; Lumber, plywood & millwork; Lumber products
Pr: Raymond G Croll Jr
VP Sls: Bob Lucarelli

D-U-N-S 85-840-3694
GROVE MEDICAL INC
1089 Park West Blvd, Greenville, SC 29611-6124
Tel (864) 269-0283 *Founded/Ownrshp* 1988
Sales 48.6MM^E *EMP* 70
SIC 5047 5021 Medical equipment & supplies; Beds, hospital; Hospital furniture; Office furniture
Pr: Larry Lollis
**CFO:* Melissa Selig
**Ex VP:* Scott Williams
**VP:* Michael Laico
**VP:* David York
Mfg Dir: Robert Hoyt

D-U-N-S 00-578-1059
GROVE MONONA SCHOOL DISTRICT INC
MONONA GROVE ALTERNATIVE HS
5301 Monona Dr, Monona, WI 53716-3126
Tel (608) 221-7660 *Founded/Ownrshp* 1962
Sales 42.9MM *EMP* 365
Accts Wegner Cpas Llp Madison Wisc
SIC 8211 Public elementary & secondary schools; Public elementary school; Public junior high school; Public senior high school; Public elementary & secondary schools; Public elementary school; Public junior high school; Public senior high school
Treas: Susan Manning
VP: Linda Ammann
Prin: Connie Haessly
Prin: Judie Lehman
Prin: Thomas Vanwinkle
Psych: Christa Macomber

D-U-N-S 01-093-2713
GROVE OAK SCHOOL DISTRICT
6578 Santa Teresa Blvd, San Jose, CA 95119-1297
Tel (408) 227-8300 *Founded/Ownrshp* 1861
Sales 71.4MM^E *EMP* 1,000
Accts Vavrinek Trine Day & Co Ll
SIC 8211 Public elementary school; Public junior high school; Public elementary school; Public junior high school
Bd of Dir: Carolyn Bauer
**VP:* Jacquelyn Adams
VP: Dennis Hawkins
Dir Rx: Keiko Mizuno

GROVE PARK INN, THE
See OMNI GROVE PARK LLC

D-U-N-S 05-438-6214
GROVE PARK INN RESORT INC
290 Macon Ave, Asheville, NC 28804-3799
Tel (828) 252-2711 *Founded/Ownrshp* 2012
Sales NA *EMP* 1,000
SIC 7011 5812 5813 7992 7991 7299

D-U-N-S 05-656-1749
GROVE PUBLIC SCHOOL DISTRICT 2
310 S Broadway St, Grove, OK 74344-3310
Tel (918) 786-3003 *Founded/Ownrshp* 1900
Sales 12.8MM^E *EMP* 300
SIC 8211 Public elementary & secondary schools; Public elementary & secondary schools
**Prin:* Julie Bloss

D-U-N-S 16-988-4546
GROVE RESOURCE SOLUTIONS INC
GRSI
5235 Westview Dr Ste 101, Frederick, MD 21703-8397
Tel (240) 236-0800 *Founded/Ownrshp* 2000
Sales 29.3MM^E *EMP* 200
SIC 7371 7379 7373 8711 Custom computer programming services; Computer related consulting services; Computer integrated systems design; Engineering services; Custom computer programming services; Computer related consulting services; Computer integrated systems design; Engineering services
CEO: Deborah Grove
**Pr:* David Affeldt
Dir Bus: Greg Galanos
Genl Mgr: Jose Umpierre
Dir IT: Danny Swett

D-U-N-S 07-833-9799
GROVE SERVICES (UKRAINE) LLC (MA)
(*Suby of* GROVE SERVICES INC) ★
100 William St Ste 210, Wellesley, MA 02481-3702
Tel (617) 558-1991 *Founded/Ownrshp* 2009
Sales 350.0MM *EMP* 2
SIC 5144 Poultry & poultry products; Poultry & poultry products
Pr: Gene Spivak
**CFO:* Victor Spivak

D-U-N-S 87-777-0375 IMP/EXP
GROVE SERVICES INC
100 William St Ste 210, Wellesley, MA 02481-3702
Tel (781) 772-1187 *Founded/Ownrshp* 2001
Sales 350.0MM^E *EMP* 14
Accts Mcgladrey & Pullen Llp Burli
SIC 5141 Food brokers
Pr: Victor Spivak
**CFO:* Gene Spivak
Opers Mgr: Felix Gurevich
Sls Dir: Paulo M Trindade

D-U-N-S 18-786-9891
GROVE SHADY ADVENTIST HOSPITAL
9901 Medical Center Dr, Rockville, MD 20850-3395
Tel (240) 826-6000 *Founded/Ownrshp* 1981
Sales 306.9MM *EMP* 49
SIC 8062 General medical & surgical hospitals; General medical & surgical hospitals
Pr: John Sackett
**CFO:* Daniel Cochran
CFO: Victor Newinski
Bd of Dir: Philip A Besler
Bd of Dir: Robert G Brewer Jr
Bd of Dir: Peter H Plamondon
VP: Robin Toomey
VP: Rhodora Vaflor
Dir Lab: Rob Sanluis
Prin: Benson Klein
**Ex Dir:* Shelvan Arunan

GROVE STAFFING
See GROVE TEMPORARY SERVICE INC

GROVE STONE & SAND DIVISION
See B V HEDRICK GRAVEL & SAND CO

D-U-N-S 00-248-5092
GROVE SUPPLY INC (PA)
106 Steamboat Dr, Warminster, PA 18974-4854
Tel (215) 659-0666 Founded/Ownrshp 1948, 1970
Sales 71.9MM^E EMP 120
SIC 5074 Plumbing & hydronic heating supplies; Plumbing & hydronic heating supplies
Pr: Robert Hamilton
*Treas: Karl Wieland
*Prin: Carl M Wolfe
VP Sls: Clem Ciocca

D-U-N-S 16-466-5648
GROVE TEMPORARY SERVICE INC
GROVE STAFFING
608 W Interstate 30, Garland, TX 75043-5732
Tel (972) 226-1234 Founded/Ownrshp 1973
Sales 6.8MM^E EMP 313
SIC 7361 Employment agencies; Employment agencies
Pr: Margie Howard
*Sec: Mike Howard
*VP: Debbie Comp

D-U-N-S 01-971-0289 IMP/EXP
■ **GROVE US LLC**
MANITOWOC CRANE GROUP
(Suby of MANITOWOC CRANES LLC) ★
1565 Buchanan Trl E, Shady Grove, PA 17256
Tel (717) 597-8121 Founded/Ownrshp 1998, 2002
Sales 131.7MM^E EMP 19^E
SIC 3531 3537 Cranes; Platforms, cargo
Pr: Eric Etchart
*Pr: Glen E Tellock
VP: Karine Gagne
*VP: Larry Weyers
Prgrm Mgr: Stacy Beck
IT Man: Christine Teh
Ql Cn Mgr: Clay Nunemaker
Ql Cn Mgr: Michael Seville
VP Sls: Robert Hixon

D-U-N-S 02-027-3566 IMP/EXP
■ **GROVE WORLDWIDE LLC**
(Suby of MANITOWOC CO INC) ★
1565 Buchanan Trl E, Shady Grove, PA 17256
Tel (717) 597-8121 Founded/Ownrshp 1989, 2002
Sales 66.8MM^E EMP 99^E
SIC 3536 Hoists, cranes & monorails

D-U-N-S 03-340-1308
GROVE-MADSEN INDUSTRIES
390 E 6th St, Reno, NV 89512-3361
Tel (775) 322-3400 Founded/Ownrshp 1981
Sales 41.2MM^E EMP 60
SIC 5063 Electrical supplies
Pr: Mike Madsen
*Pr: Michael C Madsen
*Sec: William Newberg
*VP: Vickie Combs
*VP: Bill Newberg
Sls Mgr: Robert Lacy
Sales Asso: Craig Foster
Sales Asso: Chuck Hodson

GROVER CLEVELAND MIDDLE SCHOOL
See BOARD OF EDUCATION CALDWELL-WEST CALDWELL

GROVER PAY & PACK ELC & PLBG
See G & G ELECTRIC AND PLUMBING DISTRIBUTORS INC

D-U-N-S 05-718-7916
GROVES INDUSTRIAL SUPPLY CORP
(Suby of DGI SUPPLY) ★
7301 Pinemont Dr, Houston, TX 77040-6607
Tel (713) 675-4747 Founded/Ownrshp 1990
Sales 213.7MM^E EMP 153^E
SIC 5085 5084 5198 Industrial supplies; Safety equipment; Paints
Pr: David Crawford
*VP: Timothy P Moran
*VP: Jeff Waller
IT Man: Mike Mays
Software D: Shannon Riley-Silessi
Mfg Dir: Scott Salminen
Trfc Dir: Don Williams
Sales Asso: Roland Almendarez
Sales Asso: Andy Attaway
Sales Asso: Jackie Barger
Sales Asso: Patrick Bellmyer

D-U-N-S 03-802-9609
GROW FINANCIAL FEDERAL CREDIT UNION
9927 Delaney Lake Dr, Tampa, FL 33619-5071
Tel (813) 837-2451 Founded/Ownrshp 1955
Sales NA EMP 525
SIC 6061 Federal credit unions; Federal credit unions
CEO: Robert L Fisher
COO: Jean Hopstetter
CFO: Gail Wean
Ofcr: Willy Asab
Ofcr: Nick Decosola
Ofcr: Jennifer Evans
Ofcr: Carol McCann
Ofcr: Naomi Tillman
Ofcr: Jennifer Truman
Ofcr: Lisa Wolf
Sr VP: Dona Svehla
VP: Chase Clelland
VP: Dongenevie Genevie
VP: Robert Keatts
VP: Jose Perez
Exec: Sherry Demoranville
Exec: Alex Huggins
Exec: Anthony Weston

D-U-N-S 16-358-9406 IMP/EXP
GROWER DIRECT NUT CO INC
2288 Geer Rd, Hughson, CA 95326-9614
Tel (209) 883-4890 Founded/Ownrshp 2004
Sales 37.4MM^E EMP 50
SIC 0723 Walnut hulling & shelling services
Pr: Aaron Martella
*COO: Kevin Chiesa
*VP: Lucio Salazar
Ql Cn Mgr: Jeremiah Sasser

GROWERS AG
See TREMONT GROUP INC

D-U-N-S 07-899-7129
GROWERS CO INC
15834 S Avenue G, Somerton, AZ 85350-7010
Tel (928) 627-8080 Founded/Ownrshp 1976
Sales 20.0MM EMP 900
SIC 0722 Field crops, except cash grains, machine harvesting services; Field crops, except cash grains, machine harvesting services
Pr: Joseph A Rodriguez
*VP: Mark Rodriguez
Sales Exec: Quintana Mini

D-U-N-S 19-936-2393 EXP
GROWERS EXPRESS LLC
150 Mn St Ste 210, Salinas, CA 93901
Tel (831) 757-9951 Founded/Ownrshp 2004
Sales 51.4MM^E EMP 90^E
SIC 5148 Vegetables; Vegetables
CFO: Kathleen McInnis
Opers Mgr: Martin Sotelo

D-U-N-S 00-409-5121
GROWERS FERTILIZER CORP
312 N Buena Vista Dr, Lake Alfred, FL 33850-2006
Tel (863) 956-1101 Founded/Ownrshp 1934
Sales 36.8MM EMP 52
Accts Hoskins Quiros Osborne & Lebea
SIC 2874 2879 2873 Phosphatic fertilizers; Insecticides, agricultural or household; Nitrogenous fertilizers; Phosphatic fertilizers; Insecticides, agricultural or household; Nitrogenous fertilizers
Pr: Brent W Sutton
*Sec: Rick O Steen
*VP: Harvey B Snively
*VP: John Strang
IT Man: Rick Steen

D-U-N-S 07-883-7492
GROWERS SALES AND MARKETING LLC
FARM FRESH DIRECT OF AMERICA
15 Washington St Ste 207, Monte Vista, CO 81144-1406
Tel (719) 852-2600 Founded/Ownrshp 2012
Sales 121.1MM EMP 35
SIC 5148 Fresh fruits & vegetables; Fresh fruits & vegetables
CEO: James Knutzon
*CFO: Alex Miller
Board of Directors: John Artaechevarria, Keith McGovern, Marty Myers, Jerry Smith, Virgil Valdez, Dave Warsh

D-U-N-S 03-267-0655 IMP
GROWERS TRANSPLANTING INC (CA)
(Suby of MONTEREY PENINSULA HORTICULTURE INC) ★
360 Espinosa Rd, Salinas, CA 93907-8895
Tel (831) 449-3440 Founded/Ownrshp 1981
Sales 30.9MM^E EMP 267
SIC 0182 Vegetable crops grown under cover; Vegetable crops grown under cover
CEO: Charles I Kosmont
*CFO: Leslie Surber
*VP: Kevin Doyle
*VP: Bill Rover

D-U-N-S 10-797-1736
GROWING CHILD PEDIATRICS
500 Gateway Dr, Clayton, NC 27520-2158
Tel (919) 585-9001 Founded/Ownrshp 2000
Sales 4.1MM^E EMP 300
SIC 0781 8011 Landscape services; Offices & clinics of medical doctors; Landscape services; Offices & clinics of medical doctors
Owner: Jim Poole

D-U-N-S 12-134-5532 EXP
GROWMARK FS LLC
MILFORD FERTILIZER
(Suby of GROWMARK INC) ★
308 Ne Front St, Milford, DE 19963-1434
Tel (302) 422-3001 Founded/Ownrshp 2002
Sales 68.6MM^E EMP 300
SIC 2875 2873 2874 5191 Fertilizers, mixing only; Nitrogenous fertilizers; Nitrogen solutions (fertilizer); Phosphatic fertilizers; Pesticides; Seeds: field, garden & flower; Fertilizers, mixing only; Nitrogenous fertilizers; Nitrogen solutions (fertilizer); Phosphatic fertilizers; Pesticides; Seeds: field, garden & flower
Brnch Mgr: Keith Keily
Genl Mgr: Paul Masula
Dir IT: Bill Walton
IT Man: Sarah Cawley
VP Opers: Larry Lee
Prd Mgr: Norman Hamstead
Sls Mgr: Denis Shaffer

D-U-N-S 00-521-3335 IMP
GROWMARK INC (DE)
1701 Towanda Ave, Bloomington, IL 61701-2057
Tel (309) 557-6000 Founded/Ownrshp 1962
Sales 8.7MMM EMP 1,036
Accts Ernst & Young Llp Chicago I
SIC 5191 Fertilizer & fertilizer materials; Feed; Seeds: field, garden & flower; Fertilizer & fertilizer materials; Feed; Seeds: field, garden & flower
Ch Bd: John Reifsteck
V Ch: John Reifsteck
*CEO: Jim Spradlin
CFO: Jeff Price
*CFO: Mike Woods
Treas: Dan Irving
Treas: Karen Ohliger
*VP: Brent Bostrom
*VP: Steve Buckalew
*VP: Kevin Carroll
VP: Tom Dowell
*VP: Brent Ericson
*VP: Shelly Kruse
*VP: Mark Orr
*VP: Barry Schmidt
*VP: Denny Worth
Board of Directors: Ron Pierson, Jim Anderson, John Reifsteck, Chet Esther, Allen Tanner, Kim Fysh, David Uhlman, Warren Jibb, David Watt, Kevin Malchine, Jack McCormick, Rick Nelson, Dennis Neuhaus, Bob Phelps

D-U-N-S 13-162-2347
GROWTH DEVELOPMENT MARKETING INC
5963 Freedom Dr, Chino, CA 91710-7015
Tel (909) 627-0200 Founded/Ownrshp 2002
Sales 33.3MM EMP 100
Accts Porte Brown Llc Elk Grove Vil
SIC 1771 7353 5084 1623 1731 1794 Concrete work; Heavy construction equipment rental; Industrial machinery & equipment; Cable laying construction; Electrical work; Excavation work; Concrete work; Heavy construction equipment rental; Industrial machinery & equipment; Cable laying construction; Electrical work; Excavation work
CEO: Gregory Alan Gates
*VP: Terry Devins

D-U-N-S 96-629-2810
GROWTH ENERGY
777 N Capitol St Ne # 805, Washington, DC 20002-4294
Tel (202) 545-4000 Founded/Ownrshp 2008
Sales 25.6MM^E EMP 19
Accts Larsonallen Llp Mesa Az
SIC 8999 Earth science services; Earth science services
CEO: Tom Buis
VP: Jim Miller
Creative D: Houston Ruck

D-U-N-S 07-917-2379
GROWTH HORIZONS INC
23 Walker Ave, Baltimore, MD 21208-4004
Tel (410) 653-0944 Founded/Ownrshp 1978
Sales 17.0MM EMP 400
SIC 8399

D-U-N-S 04-668-7893
GROWTH MANAGEMENT CORP
AMIGOS
3201 Pioneers Blvd # 112, Lincoln, NE 68502-5963
Tel (402) 488-8500 Founded/Ownrshp 1980
Sales 29.9MM^E EMP 1,000
SIC 5812 5411 Mexican restaurant; Convenience stores; Mexican restaurant; Convenience stores
Pr: Roger D Moore

D-U-N-S 04-172-9331
GROWTH PROPERTIES INVESTMENT MANAGERS INC
1608 Spruce St, Philadelphia, PA 19103-6788
Tel (215) 546-5980 Founded/Ownrshp 1981
Sales 11.4MM^E EMP 475
SIC 7011 Hotels & motels; Hotels & motels
Pr: Ronald Gilbert

D-U-N-S 09-495-1019 IMP
GROZ-BECKERT USA INC (SC)
(Suby of GROZ-BECKERT KG)
3480 Lakemont Blvd, Fort Mill, SC 29708-9243
Tel (803) 548-4769 Founded/Ownrshp 1952, 1985
Sales 24.4MM^E EMP 51
SIC 5131 Sewing accessories
Pr: Phillipe Champagne
*Treas: Karen Fwicegood
*Sec: Paul I Folger
*VP: Henry Tio
Exec: Karen Swicegood
IT Man: Manuel Rojas

D-U-N-S 00-386-0361
GRP INC (NC)
1823 Boone Trail Rd, Sanford, NC 27330-8662
Tel (919) 776-9940 Founded/Ownrshp 2010
Sales 68.3MM^E EMP 2,200
SIC 2281 Cotton yarn, spun; Cotton yarn, spun

D-U-N-S 00-682-9014
GRP MECHANICAL CO INC
1 Mechanical Dr, Bethalto, IL 62010
Tel (618) 258-9000 Founded/Ownrshp 1950
Sales 46.6MM EMP 50
SIC 1711 1623 1629 1542

GRPHICS GRAFEK
See MATT INDUSTRIES INC

GRRI
See GEORGIA REGENTS RESEARCH INSTITUTE INC

GRSI
See GROVE RESOURCE SOLUTIONS INC

GRTC
See GREATER RICHMOND TRANSIT CO

GRTC TRANSIT SYSTEMS
See OLD DOMINION TRANSIT MANAGEMENT CO

GRU
See GAINESVILLE REGIONAL UTILITIES (INC)

D-U-N-S 01-177-2053
GRU
301 Se 4th Ave, Gainesville, FL 32601-6857
Tel (352) 334-3434 Founded/Ownrshp 2010
Sales 370.4MM EMP 13^E
Accts Ernst & Young Llp Orlando Fl
SIC 4813 ;

D-U-N-S 00-922-8198 IMP/EXP
GRUBB & ELLIS CO
1551 N Tustin Ave Ste 300, Santa Ana, CA 92705-8638
Tel (714) 667-8252 Founded/Ownrshp 2012
Sales NA EMP 4,500
SIC 6531 8742 6162

D-U-N-S 05-353-7234
GRUBB & ELLIS MANAGEMENT SERVICES INC
1551 N Tustin Ave Ste 300, Santa Ana, CA 92705-8638
Tel (412) 201-8200 Founded/Ownrshp 2000
Sales NA EMP 1,800
SIC 6531

D-U-N-S 00-465-1985
GRUBB & ELLIS REALTY INVESTORS LLC
1551 N Tustin Ave Ste 200, Santa Ana, CA 92705-8693
Tel (714) 667-8252 Founded/Ownrshp 1998, 2007
Sales 102.6MM^E EMP 458
SIC 6799 6531 Investors; Real estate managers; Investors; Real estate managers
Pr: Jeffrey T Hanson
Bd of Dir: Richard Voast
Assoc VP: Ellen Cullinan
Assoc VP: Sean McNulty
Assoc VP: Tom Oldham
Ex VP: Christopher Becker
Ex VP: Rick Burnett
Ex VP: Branson Edwards
Ex VP: Jerry Geiger
Sr VP: Richard Abdulian
Sr VP: Gregory Albertini
Sr VP: Charmaine Ali
Sr VP: Conrad Anderson
Sr VP: Benton Benalcazar
Sr VP: Paul Buckingham
Sr VP: Jerry Eggleston
Sr VP: Benjamin Greazel
Sr VP: Al Haworth
Sr VP: Alex Jelepis
Sr VP: Michael Kammerling
Sr VP: Anne Klein
Board of Directors: Louis Rogers

GRUBB W O CRANE RENTAL
See W O GRUBB STEEL ERECTION INC

D-U-N-S 36-256-1623
GRUBBS INFINITI LTD
1661 Airport Fwy, Euless, TX 76040-4020
Tel (817) 318-1200 Founded/Ownrshp 1989
Sales 53.2MM^E EMP 47
SIC 5511 5521 Automobiles, new & used; Automobiles, used cars only
Pt: George Grubbs Jr
Exec: Denise Jones
Sls Mgr: Chris Stiles
Sls Mgr: Justin Villa

D-U-N-S 11-510-7229 IMP
GRUBER INDUSTRIES INC
21439 N 2nd Ave, Phoenix, AZ 85027-2916
Tel (602) 863-2655 Founded/Ownrshp 1984
Sales 21.2MM EMP 178
Accts Estes/Avellone Cpas Ltd Pho
SIC 5065 3357 7359 Communication equipment; Modems, computer; Nonferrous wiredrawing & insulating; Electronic equipment rental, except computers; Communication equipment; Modems, computer; Nonferrous wiredrawing & insulating; Electronic equipment rental, except computers
Pr: Peter M Gruber
*VP: Stephen Korf
Exec: Hope Gruber
IT Man: Irwin Drootman
Manager: Shawn Jones
Natl Sales: Christopher Such
S&M/VP: Bruce Vanallen
S&M/Dir: Michael Mast
Sls Mgr: Tony Palmer
Sls Mgr: Gary Toon
Sales Asso: Evan Entze

D-U-N-S 05-356-4866
▲ **GRUBHUB INC**
111 W Washington St # 2100, Chicago, IL 60602-2783
Tel (877) 585-7878 Founded/Ownrshp 1999
Sales 253.8MM EMP 1,090^E
Tkr Sym GRUB Exch NYS
SIC 5961 Food, mail order; Food, mail order
CEO: Matthew Maloney
Ch Bd: Brian McAndrews
CFO: Adam Dewitt
Sr VP: Margo Drucker
CTO: Brian Lanier
Board of Directors: David Fisher, Lloyd Frink, J William Gurley, Girish Lakshman, Justin L Sadrian, Benjamin Spero

D-U-N-S 07-996-6641
GRUDEN ACQUISITION INC
4041 Park Oaks Blvd # 200, Tampa, FL 33610-9531
Tel (800) 282-2031 Founded/Ownrshp 2015
Sales 32.8MM^E EMP 4,342
SIC 4213 Trucking, except local

D-U-N-S 08-003-1039
▲ **GRUDEN ACQUISITION INC**
601 Lexington Ave Fl 53, New York, NY 10022-4630
Tel (212) 753-6300 Founded/Ownrshp 2015
Sales 892.5MM^E EMP 4,342^E
SIC 6282 4213 Investment advisory service; Trucking, except local
CEO: Martin Halusa

D-U-N-S 00-177-8752 IMP
GRUETTS INC (WI)
101 W Main, Potter, WI 54160
Tel (920) 853-3516 Founded/Ownrshp 1958
Sales 25.9MM EMP 40
Accts Suttner Accounting Inc Chil
SIC 5083 3523 Farm implements; Barn, silo, poultry, dairy & livestock machinery; Farm implements; Barn, silo, poultry, dairy & livestock machinery
Pr: Steve Gruett
*Sec: Dave Gruett
Genl Mgr: Tom Gruett
*VP Mfg: Lloyd Gruett

D-U-N-S 03-873-5890 IMP
GRUMA CORP
MISSION FOODS
(*Suby of* GRUMA, S.A.B. DE C.V.)
1159 Cottonwood Ln # 200, Irving, TX 75038-6107
Tel (972) 232-5000 *Founded/Ownrshp* 1983
Sales 2.0MMM *EMP* 7,000
SIC 0723 2096 2099 Flour milling custom services; Tortilla chips; Food preparations; Flour milling custom services; Tortilla chips; Food preparations
Pr: Javier Velez Bautista
Ch: Juan A Gonzalez Moreno
**Treas:* Dan Burke
Ex VP: Michael Crane
VP: Marco Casillas
**VP:* Felipe Rubio Lamas
VP: Miguel Trejo
Area Mgr: Guillermo Garza
Area Mgr: Chris Oberbroeckling
Genl Mgr: William Buffington
CIO: Edgar Sosa
Board of Directors: Homero Huerta Moren

D-U-N-S 00-896-1047
GRUNAU CO INC
(*Suby of* API GROUP INC) ★
1100 W Anderson Ct, Oak Creek, WI 53154-1472
Tel (414) 216-6900 *Founded/Ownrshp* 2006
Sales 96.4MM *EMP* 400
Accts Kpmg Llp Minneapolis Mn
SIC 1711 Mechanical contractor; Fire sprinkler system installation; Mechanical contractor; Fire sprinkler system installation
Pr: Larry Loomis
CFO: Jeffrey A Hintze
Treas: Greg Keup
Ex VP: Ted Angelo
VP: Mark Gall
VP: Bob Harlow
VP: Ron Kwiatkowski
VP: Randy Rubesa
Exec: Jeff Kuhnke
Dir Bus: Chris Miller
Dir Bus: Robyn Minarik
Dir Bus: John Ostrowski

D-U-N-S 62-310-7427 IMP
GRUNDFOS CBS INC
PACO PUMPS BY GRUNDFOS
(*Suby of* GRUNDFOS HOLDING AG)
902 Koomey Rd, Brookshire, TX 77423-8216
Tel (281) 994-2700 *Founded/Ownrshp* 2006
Sales 64.9MM^E *EMP* 270^E
SIC 3561 Pumps & pumping equipment; Pumps & pumping equipment
Pr: Gregers Johansen

D-U-N-S 07-878-9518 IMP/EXP
GRUNDFOS PUMPS CORP
(*Suby of* GRUNDFOS HOLDING AG)
17100 W 118th Ter, Olathe, KS 66061-6599
Tel (913) 227-3400 *Founded/Ownrshp* 1973
Sales 78.0MM^E *EMP* 160
SIC 5084

D-U-N-S 93-847-3345 IMP/EXP
GRUNDFOS PUMPS MANUFACTURING CORP
(*Suby of* GRUNDFOS HOLDING AG)
5900 E Shields Ave, Fresno, CA 93727-8612
Tel (559) 292-8000 *Founded/Ownrshp* 1973
Sales 38.7MM^E *EMP* 270
SIC 3561

GRUNDY COUNTY CLERK OFFICE
See COUNTY OF GRUNDY

GRUNDY COUNTY COURT HOUSE
See COUNTY OF GRUNDY

D-U-N-S 17-102-7204
GRUNDY COUNTY SPECIAL EDUCATION COOPERATIVE
GCSEC
725 School St, Morris, IL 60450-1218
Tel (815) 942-5780 *Founded/Ownrshp* 1969
Sales 13.3MM^E *EMP* 280
SIC 8211 Specialty education; Specialty education
Psych: Lacey Anderson

D-U-N-S 00-741-3857
GRUNDY WORLDWIDE INC
400 Horsham Rd Ste 150, Horsham, PA 19044-2147
Tel (888) 647-8639 *Founded/Ownrshp* 2001
Sales NA *EMP* 5,200^E
SIC 6331 Automobile insurance
Pr: James Grundy
IT Man: Heather Marr
Mktg Dir: William Hoffer

D-U-N-S 09-367-1063 IMP/EXP
GRUNER + JAHR USA GROUP INC
GRUNER JAHR USA PUBLISHING DIV
1745 Broadway Fl 16, New York, NY 10019-4640
Tel (866) 323-9336 *Founded/Ownrshp* 1978
Sales 636.2MM^E *EMP* 5,058
SIC 2721 2754 Periodicals: publishing & printing; Magazines: publishing & printing; Commercial printing, gravure; Periodicals: publishing & printing; Magazines: publishing & printing; Commercial printing, gravure
Pr: Mike Amundson
**Ex VP:* Gregg Black
**Ex VP:* Larry Hawkey
**Ex VP:* Dan Nitz
VP: Yvette Miller
VP: Scott Seltz

GRUNER JAHR USA PUBLISHING DIV
See GRUNER + JAHR USA GROUP INC

D-U-N-S 18-868-6778
GRUNLEY CONSTRUCTION CO INC
15020 Shady Ste 500, Rockville, MD 20850
Tel (240) 399-2000 *Founded/Ownrshp* 1988
Sales 350.0MM *EMP* 310
Accts Baker Tilly Virchow Krause Ll
SIC 1542 Specialized public building contractors; Commercial & office buildings, renovation & repair; Commercial & office buildings, new construction; Specialized public building contractors; Commercial & office buildings, renovation & repair; Commercial & office buildings, new construction
Pr: Kenneth M Grunley
Pr: Sonya Brown
Pr: Gregory M Druga
Ofcr: Courtney Eaton
Sr VP: Bh Scott II
VP: John Greenwill
VP: George Rusk
VP: Tom Walker
Exec: Bill Six
Dir Bus: Michelle Honey
Dir Bus: Timothy Hudak

D-U-N-S 00-811-1296
GRUNWALD PRINTING CO
1418 Morgan Ave, Corpus Christi, TX 78404-3350
Tel (361) 882-5654 *Founded/Ownrshp* 1946
Sales 4.1MM^E *EMP* 300
SIC 2752 Commercial printing, offset; Commercial printing, offset
Pr: John E Grunwald
Prd Mgr: Julian Figueroa

D-U-N-S 00-538-4334
GRUNWELL-CASHERO CO (MI)
1041 Major St, Detroit, MI 48217-1376
Tel (313) 843-8440 *Founded/Ownrshp* 1950
Sales 22.4MM^E *EMP* 70
SIC 1542 8711 Commercial & office buildings, renovation & repair; Engineering services
Pr: Scott Cashero
**CFO:* Mark Schneider
**Ex VP:* Joseph M Dapkus
VP: Larry Darling
**VP:* Jelane Raycraft
**VP:* Tony Sabo
Sfty Dirs: Rich Sumner

D-U-N-S 00-946-7002
GRUPE CO (CA)
3255 W March Ln Ste 400, Stockton, CA 95219-2352
Tel (209) 473-6000 *Founded/Ownrshp* 1960, 1988
Sales 82.9MM^E *EMP* 400
SIC 6531 1542 Real estate agent, residential; Real estate brokers & agents; Commercial & office building, new construction; Real estate agent, residential; Real estate brokers & agents; Commercial & office building, new construction
Pr: Frank A Passadore
**Ch Bd:* Greenlaw Grupe Jr
COO: Frank Paadore
VP: Niem Dang
VP: Anna Depedrini
VP: Julie Dzubak
VP: Ron Reganni
VP: Ron Rugani
Prgrm Mgr: Katie Falconer
Brnch Mgr: Stephanie Miller
Sls Mgr: Tina Brodston

D-U-N-S 60-382-1104
GRUPO ANTOLIN ILLINOIS INC
(*Suby of* GRUPO ANTOLIN-IRAUSA SA)
642 Crystal Pkwy, Belvidere, IL 61008-4065
Tel (815) 544-8020 *Founded/Ownrshp* 2005
Sales 27.6MM^E *EMP* 180
SIC 8741 3714 Management services; Motor vehicle parts & accessories
Prin: Joseph Maximilan Rogers
Ex VP: Russ Goemaere
Exec: Melissa Gary
Dir IT: Pascal Bacue
IT Man: David Bassols
IT Man: David Cornelius
IT Man: James Cramer
Plnt Mgr: Diego Vizcaino
Ql Cn Mgr: Andrew Paul
Ql Cn Mgr: Jeremy Walker
Ql Cn Mgr: Linda Ward

D-U-N-S 80-865-9114 IMP
GRUPO ANTOLIN KENTUCKY INC
(*Suby of* GRUPO ANTOLIN-IRAUSA SA)
208 Commerce Ct, Hopkinsville, KY 42240-6806
Tel (270) 885-2703 *Founded/Ownrshp* 1993
Sales 96.4MM^E *EMP* 502
SIC 3559 2399 Motor vehicle body components & frame; Tops, motor vehicle; Seat covers, automobile; Automotive related machinery; Seat covers, automobile
Ch: Ernesto Antoln Arribas
**Pr:* Ken Carter
**Pr:* Max Rogers
**CEO:* Jess Pascual Santos
COO: Eric Rucker
Treas: Juan Martinez
**Sec:* Pablo Ruiz
**VP:* Ernesto Molina
**VP:* Roberto Monteros
**Prin:* Mike Sewell
IT Man: Thomas Eickhoff

D-U-N-S 13-271-3012 IMP
GRUPO ANTOLIN MICHIGAN INC
(*Suby of* GRUPO ANTOLIN-NORTH AMERICA INC) ★
6300 Euclid St, Marlette, MI 48453-1424
Tel (989) 635-5055 *Founded/Ownrshp* 2003
Sales 48.7MM^E *EMP* 200
SIC 3714 Motor vehicle body components & frame; Motor vehicle body components & frame
Plnt Mgr: Jesus Tome
CIO: David Kropp

D-U-N-S 07-880-2177 IMP
GRUPO ANTOLIN MISSOURI LLC
(*Suby of* GRUPO ANTOLIN-NORTH AMERICA INC) ★
1601 Southern Rd, Kansas City, MO 64120-1125
Tel (248) 373-1517 *Founded/Ownrshp* 2013
Sales 51.9MM^E *EMP* 130
SIC 3714 Tops, motor vehicle; Tops, motor vehicle
VP: Roberto Monteros

D-U-N-S 07-350-2903 IMP
GRUPO ANTOLIN PRIMERA AUTOMOTIVE SYSTEMS LLC
GRUPO ANTOLIN WAYNE
(*Suby of* GRUPO ANTOLIN-IRAUSA SA)
47440 Michigan Ave # 150, Canton, MI 48188-2219
Tel (734) 495-9180 *Founded/Ownrshp* 1998
Sales 34.3MM^E *EMP* 280
SIC 3714 Motor vehicle body components & frame; Motor vehicle body components & frame
Pr: William Pickard
IT Man: Ken Zook
Plnt Mgr: Bret Southern
Ql Cn Mgr: Michael Ferasolis

GRUPO ANTOLIN WAYNE
See GRUPO ANTOLIN PRIMERA AUTOMOTIVE SYSTEMS LLC

D-U-N-S 00-649-4129 IMP
GRUPO ANTOLIN-NORTH AMERICA INC
(*Suby of* GRUPO ANTOLIN-IRAUSA SA)
1700 Atlantic Blvd, Auburn Hills, MI 48326-1504
Tel (248) 373-1437 *Founded/Ownrshp* 2005
Sales 675.7MM^E *EMP* 3,000
SIC 8741 8711 Management services; Engineering services; Management services; Engineering services
Pr: Pablo Baroja
**Pr:* Carlos Araujo
CFO: Maria Manuel
Ex VP: Maria Hidalgo
VP: Carl Guething
VP: Marta Martin
Prgrm Mgr: David Hinman
Prgrm Mgr: Brian Miscovich
Prgrm Mgr: John Taras
IT Man: Marc Merren
IT Man: Chris Wald

D-U-N-S 83-106-2018
GRUPO EDUK INC
EDUK GROUP
Marginal Rd 20 Km 2 3, Guaynabo, PR 00966
Tel (787) 982-3000 *Founded/Ownrshp* 2004
Sales 34.7MM^E *EMP* 2,000
SIC 8249 8244 8243 8222 7231 Banking school, training; Business & secretarial schools; Data processing schools; Technical institute; Cosmetology school; Banking school, training; Business & secretarial schools; Data processing schools; Technical institute; Cosmetology school
Pr: Guillermo Nigaglioni
Pr: Melissa Rosario

D-U-N-S 80-612-6111
GRUPO HIMA-SAN PABLO INC
HIMA SAN PABLO HOSPITAL
100 Calle Munoz Rivera, Caguas, PR 00725-3629
Tel (787) 653-3434 *Founded/Ownrshp* 2005
Sales 481.7MM *EMP* 4,200
SIC 8062 General medical & surgical hospitals; General medical & surgical hospitals
Pr: Joaquin Rodriguez Sr
VP: Francisco Cardona
VP: Francisco Medina
**VP:* Carlos Pineiro
**VP:* Dennis Tristan

GRUPO MEXICO
See ASARCO LLC

GRUPO PHOENIX
See PHOENIX PACKAGING LLC

GRUPO PHOENIX
See PHOENIX PACKAGING OPERATIONS LLC

GRUPOEX
See MEJICO EXPRESS INC

D-U-N-S 05-183-3994
GRW ENGINEERS INC
801 Corporate Dr Ste 400, Lexington, KY 40503-5404
Tel (615) 366-1600 *Founded/Ownrshp* 1972
Sales 26.0MM *EMP* 246
SIC 8713 8711 Surveying services; Engineering services; Surveying services; Engineering services
Pr: Ron Gilkerson
**CFO:* Charles Baker
Bd of Dir: Jim Laskowski
**VP:* Ben Fister
**VP:* Harvey Helm
VP: Robert Hench
**VP:* Ralph Johanson
**VP:* Bob Smallwood
Dir IT: Erin Smith
Board of Directors: Ben Fister, Ron Gilkerson, Ralph Johanson

D-U-N-S 07-485-7264 IMP
GRW TECHNOLOGIES INC
(*Suby of* SOHNERGROUP GMBH)
4460 44th St Se Ste B, Grand Rapids, MI 49512-4096
Tel (616) 575-8119 *Founded/Ownrshp* 2008
Sales 29.0MM *EMP* 160
SIC 3544 3089 Special dies, tools, jigs & fixtures; Injection molding of plastics; Special dies, tools, jigs & fixtures; Injection molding of plastics
Pr: Rosemarie Soehner
**VP:* Joechim Hollimius

D-U-N-S 96-153-8790 IMP
GRYPHON INVESTORS INC
1 Maritime Plz Ste 2300, San Francisco, CA 94111-3513
Tel (415) 217-7400 *Founded/Ownrshp* 1995
Sales 1.7MMM^E *EMP* 11,715
SIC 6799 Venture capital companies; Venture capital companies
CEO: R David Andrews
CEO: Bob Myers
VP: Tim Bradley

D-U-N-S 94-220-7838
GRYPHON TECHNOLOGIES LLC
80 M St Se Ste 600, Washington, DC 20003-3544
Tel (202) 621-2000 *Founded/Ownrshp* 1995
Sales 109.0MM *EMP* 622
SIC 7371 8742 8741 8711 8731 Management consulting services; Computer software development & applications; Engineering services; Financial management for business; Biological research; Computer software development & applications; Management consulting services; Financial management for business; Engineering services; Biological research
Pr: P J Braden
**Pr:* Dudley Berthold
**Sr VP:* Carol Davis

D-U-N-S 19-667-5706 IMP
■ **GS BLODGETT CORP**
BLODGETT OVEN CO
(*Suby of* MIDDLEBY CORP) ★
44 Lakeside Ave, Burlington, VT 05401-5242
Tel (802) 860-3700 *Founded/Ownrshp* 2001
Sales 37.5MM^E *EMP* 167
SIC 3631 3589 Household cooking equipment; Cooking equipment, commercial; Household cooking equipment; Cooking equipment, commercial
Pr: Selim A Bassoul
**Treas:* Martin Lindsay
**VP:* Timothy J Fitzgerald
**Prin:* Gary Mick
IT Man: Simon Wade

D-U-N-S 80-103-5825
GS BROTHERS INC
2215 N Gaffey St, San Pedro, CA 90731-1238
Tel (310) 833-1369 *Founded/Ownrshp* 1963
Sales 21.9MM^E *EMP* 200
SIC 0782 Landscape contractors; Landscape contractors
Pr: Alan M Gaudenti
**Sec:* Robert M Gaudenti
Opers Mgr: Steve Rogers

D-U-N-S 03-894-6625
GS ELECTRIC GENERATING COOPERATIVE INC
GSEGC
(*Suby of* GOLDEN SPREAD ELECTRIC COOPERATIVE INC) ★
905 S Fillmore St Ste 300, Amarillo, TX 79101-3541
Tel (806) 379-7766 *Founded/Ownrshp* 1995
Sales 24.1MM *EMP* 4
Accts Bolinger Segars Gilbert & Mo
SIC 4911 Electric services; Electric services
Pr: Mark W Schwirtz
**Ch:* James Driver
**Sec:* Stephen R Louder
VP Mktg: Delbert Smith

D-U-N-S 60-585-0908 IMP
GS EQUIPMENT INC
1023 S 50th St, Tampa, FL 33619-3629
Tel (866) 586-8956 *Founded/Ownrshp* 1989
Sales 34.7MM^E *EMP* 68
SIC 5082 5084 Contractors' materials; Industrial machinery & equipment
**Sec:* Laura Dibenedetto
**VP:* Bruce Bowers
IT Man: Anthony Bryant
IT Man: Marc Young

D-U-N-S 05-606-8968 IMP
GS GLOBAL RESOURCES INC
5050 S Towne Dr, New Berlin, WI 53151-7956
Tel (262) 786-0100 *Founded/Ownrshp* 1971
Sales 85.2MM^E *EMP* 120
SIC 5084 Hydraulic systems equipment & supplies; Hydraulic systems equipment & supplies
Pr: John Thornton
**CEO:* Kishor Patel
Sls Mgr: Bob Klinter
Sls Mgr: Bill Pope
Sales Asso: Tamara Higgins
Snr Mgr: Bob Zastrow

D-U-N-S 18-116-3007 EXP
GS METALS CORP
3764 Longspur Rd, Pinckneyville, IL 62274-3103
Tel (618) 357-5353 *Founded/Ownrshp* 1987
Sales 25.0MM^E *EMP* 170
SIC 3446 Gratings, tread: fabricated metal; Gratings, tread: fabricated metal
Pr: Kenneth W Coco

GS OAS
See GENERAL SECRETARIAT OF ORGANIZATION OF AMERICAN STATES

GS&P
See GRESHAM SMITH AND PARTNERS MS PC

D-U-N-S 11-322-8204
GS1 US INC
1009 Lenox Dr Ste 202, Lawrenceville, NJ 08648-2321
Tel (937) 435-3870 *Founded/Ownrshp* 1971
Sales 55.8MM *EMP* 325^E
SIC 8699 8748 Personal interest organization; Business consulting; Personal interest organization; Business consulting
CEO: Bob Carpenter
**Ch Bd:* Barry H Beracha
**Pr:* Michael E DiYeso
**Pr:* Katy Klenk Theroux
**CFO:* Alex Jervis
**CFO:* Yegneswaran Kumar
Ex VP: Christophe Beck
Sr VP: Bob Noe
Sr VP: Siobhan O'Bara
VP: Greg Bylo
VP: Ruben Castano
**VP:* Glenn Dubois
VP: Michael Innes
Dir Bus: Alan Garton

D-U-N-S 12-518-2225
■ **GSA CFO OFFICE OF BUDGET (BBO)**
GSA OFFICE OF THE CHIEF FIN OF
(*Suby of* GSA OFFICE OF CHIEF FINANCIAL OFFICER) ★
1800 F St Nw, Washington, DC 20405-0001
Tel (202) 501-1700 *Founded/Ownrshp* 2003
Sales NA *EMP* 667^E
SIC 9199 General government administration;

Prin: Sunny Kwa

D-U-N-S 80-145-1514
■ GSA FAS OFFICE OF GENERAL SUPPLIES AND SERVICES (QS)
(*Suby of* GSA FEDERAL ACQUISITION SERVICE (Q)) ★
2200 Crystal Dr Rm 904, Arlington, VA 22202-3730
Tel (703) 605-5515 *Founded/Ownrshp* 2007
Sales NA *EMP* 504^E
SIC 9199 General government administration;
Prin: Joseph H Jeu

D-U-N-S 80-145-2439
■ GSA FAS OFFICE OF INTEGRATED TECHNOLOGY SERVICES (QT)
(*Suby of* GSA FEDERAL ACQUISITION SERVICE (Q)) ★
10304 Eaton Pl Rm 3-1005, Fairfax, VA 22030-2238
Tel (703) 282-3459 *Founded/Ownrshp* 2007
Sales NA *EMP* 430^E
SIC 9199 General government administration;
Prin: John C Johnson

D-U-N-S 12-816-1408
■ GSA FAS OFFICE OF TRAVEL AND TRANSPORTATION SERVICES
(*Suby of* FEDERAL SUPPLY SERVICE)
2200 Crystal Dr Ste 300, Arlington, VA 22202-3730
Tel (703) 605-9184 *Founded/Ownrshp* 2003
Sales NA *EMP* 445^E
SIC 9199 General government administration;
Prin: Betho Vogelsinger

D-U-N-S 80-142-6839
■ GSA FEDERAL ACQUISITION SERVICE (Q)
(*Suby of* G S A) ★
2200 Crystal Dr Rm 1100, Arlington, VA 22202-3730
Tel (703) 605-5400 *Founded/Ownrshp* 2007
Sales NA *EMP* 1,261^E
SIC 9199 General government administration;

D-U-N-S 93-788-0995
■ GSA GREATER SOUTHWEST REGION OFC OF REGIONAL ADMINISTRATOR
(*Suby of* G S A) ★
819 Taylor St Rm 11a00, Fort Worth, TX 76102-6124
Tel (817) 978-2321 *Founded/Ownrshp* 2003
Sales NA *EMP* 1,200^E
SIC 9199 General government administration; ; General government administration;
CEO: Scott Armey

D-U-N-S 15-440-3877
■ GSA HEARTLAND REGION OFC OF REGIONAL ADMINISTRATOR (6A)
(*Suby of* G S A) ★
1500 E Bannister Rd Ste B, Kansas City, MO 64131-3201
Tel (816) 926-7201 *Founded/Ownrshp* 2005
Sales NA *EMP* 800^E
SIC 9199 General government administration; ; General government administration;

D-U-N-S 12-811-2666
■ GSA MID-ATLANTIC REGION OFC OF REGIONAL ADMINISTRATOR (3A)
(*Suby of* G S A) ★
20 N 8th St, Philadelphia, PA 19107-3101
Tel (215) 446-4900 *Founded/Ownrshp* 2003
Sales NA *EMP* 1,000
SIC 9199 General government administration; ; General government administration;
Prin: Margaret Moore

D-U-N-S 12-811-3086
■ GSA NATIONAL CAPITAL AREA REGION OF REGIONAL ADMINISTRATOR (11A)
(*Suby of* G S A) ★
7 & D St Sw Ste 7022th, Washington, DC 20407-0001
Tel (202) 708-9100 *Founded/Ownrshp* 2003
Sales NA *EMP* 1,500^E
SIC 9199 ;

D-U-N-S 12-661-8417
■ GSA NATIONAL CAPITAL REGION
GSA NATIONAL CAPTL AREA REGION
(*Suby of* GSA NATIONAL CAPITAL AREA REGION OF REGIONAL ADMINISTRATOR (11A)) ★
7 & D St Sw Rm 1065th, Washington, DC 20407-0001
Tel (202) 708-5891 *Founded/Ownrshp* 2003
Sales NA *EMP* 1,490^E
SIC 9199

D-U-N-S 13-094-4726
■ GSA NATIONAL CAPITAL REGION PUBLIC BUILDINGS SERVICE - RWA
FINANCIAL MANAGEMENT DIV WPL
(*Suby of* GSA NATIONAL CAPITAL REGION) ★
7th And D Streets Sw Fl-7, Washington, DC 20407-0001
Tel (202) 260-8495 *Founded/Ownrshp* 2003
Sales NA *EMP* 653^E
SIC 9199 General government administration;
Prin: William Nelson

GSA NATIONAL CAPTL AREA REGION
See GSA NATIONAL CAPITAL REGION

D-U-N-S 10-335-4585
■ GSA NORTHWEST ARCTIC REGION OFFICE OF REGIONAL ADMINISTRATOR 10A
REAL PRPRTY DSPSAL OFFC-AUBURN
(*Suby of* G S A) ★
400 15th St Sw, Auburn, WA 98001-6599
Tel (253) 931-7000 *Founded/Ownrshp* 2000
Sales NA *EMP* 500^E
SIC 9199 General government administration; ; General government administration;
Prin: Cami Tarr
Ofcr: Heather Bowden

D-U-N-S 12-661-8383
■ GSA NORTHWEST/ARCTIC REGION OFC OF ASST REG ADMINISTRATOR (10P)
(*Suby of* GSA NORTHWEST ARCTIC REGION OFFICE OF REGIONAL ADMINISTRATOR 10A) ★
400 15th St Sw, Auburn, WA 98001-6599
Tel (253) 931-7200 *Founded/Ownrshp* 2003
Sales NA *EMP* 531^E
SIC 9199 General government administration;

GSA OFFICE OF THE CHIEF FIN OF
See GSA CFO OFFICE OF BUDGET (BBO)

D-U-N-S 05-742-4298
■ GSA OFFICE OF CHIEF FINANCIAL OFFICER
(*Suby of* G S A) ★
1800 F St Nw Rm 2140, Washington, DC 20405-0001
Tel (202) 501-1721 *Founded/Ownrshp* 2003
Sales NA *EMP* 1,000^E
SIC 9199 General government administration; ; General government administration;
CFO: Kathleen Turko
Ofcr: Carl Brown
Ofcr: Jennifer Kauffmann
Ofcr: Jeff Seria
Exec: Kristi Tunstall
Adm Dir: Herman Clemmons
Adm Dir: Gino Combi
Adm Dir: Roger Schulte
Adm Dir: Kristie Srabian
Ex Dir: Catherine Lee
Area Mgr: Donald Crawford

D-U-N-S 12-661-8334
■ GSA PACIFIC RIM REGION OFFICE OF ASSISTANT REGIONAL ADMINISTRATOR (9P)
GSA PUBLIC BUILDING SVC REG 9
(*Suby of* GSA PACIFIC RIM REGION OFFICE OF REGIONAL ADMINISTRATOR) ★
450 Golden Gate Ave, San Francisco, CA 94102-3661
Tel (415) 522-3100 *Founded/Ownrshp* 2003
Sales NA *EMP* 701^E
SIC 9199 General government administration;
Pr: Pamela Collins
**Prin:* Jeffrey Neely

D-U-N-S 12-811-2922
■ GSA PACIFIC RIM REGION OFFICE OF REGIONAL ADMINISTRATOR
(*Suby of* G S A) ★
450 Golden Gate Ave Fl 5, San Francisco, CA 94102-3405
Tel (415) 522-3001 *Founded/Ownrshp* 2005
Sales NA *EMP* 1,000^E
SIC 9199 General government administration; ; General government administration;

GSA PUBLIC BUILDING SVC REG 9
See GSA PACIFIC RIM REGION OFFICE OF ASSISTANT REGIONAL ADMINISTRATOR (9P)

D-U-N-S 12-661-8136
■ GSA ROCKY MOUNTAIN REGION OFFICE OF ASSISTANT REGIONAL ADMINISTRATOR
GSA ROCKY MOUNTAIN REGN OFC OF
(*Suby of* GSA ROCKY MOUNTAIN REGION OFFICE OF REGIONAL ADMINISTRATOR (8A)) ★
1 Denver Federal Ctr, Denver, CO 80225-0001
Tel (303) 236-7245 *Founded/Ownrshp* 2003
Sales NA *EMP* 316^E
SIC 9199 General government administration;

D-U-N-S 79-142-8469
■ GSA ROCKY MOUNTAIN REGION OFFICE OF REGIONAL ADMINISTRATOR (8A)
(*Suby of* G S A) ★
1 Denver Federal Ctr, Lakewood, CO 80225-0001
Tel (303) 236-7329 *Founded/Ownrshp* 1950
Sales NA *EMP* 300^E
SIC 9199 General government administration; ; General government administration;

D-U-N-S 13-094-3611
■ GSA ROCKY MOUNTAIN REGION PUBLIC
GSA ROCKY MTN RGN OFC OF ASST
(*Suby of* GSA ROCKY MOUNTAIN REGION OFFICE OF ASSISTANT REGIONAL ADMINISTRATOR) ★
1 Denver Federal Ctr 41, Denver, CO 80225-0001
Tel (303) 236-7245 *Founded/Ownrshp* 2003
Sales NA *EMP* 300
SIC 9199 General government administration; ; General government administration;

GSA ROCKY MOUNTAIN REGN OFC OF
See GSA ROCKY MOUNTAIN REGION OFFICE OF ASSISTANT REGIONAL ADMINISTRATOR

GSA ROCKY MTN RGN OFC OF ASST
See GSA ROCKY MOUNTAIN REGION PUBLIC

D-U-N-S 02-712-1532
GSC ENTERPRISES INC
GROCERY SUPPLY COMPANY
130 Hillcrest Dr, Sulphur Springs, TX 75482
Tel (903) 885-7621 *Founded/Ownrshp* 1972
Sales 870.0MM *EMP* 575^E
SIC 5141 6099 Groceries, general line; Money order issuance; Groceries, general line; Money order issuance
Ch Bd: Michael K McKenzie
**CEO:* Michael J Bain
**COO:* Ryan McKenzie
**CFO:* Kerry Law
**VP:* Janet Price
Brnch Mgr: David Simmons
Div Mgr: Dirk Francis
DP Dir: Larry Smith
Telecom Mg: John Bradberry
Mfg Dir: Mark Pope
Opers Mgr: Lloyd Kelley

GSC FOUNDRIES
See WYMAN-GORDON INVESTMENT CASTINGS INC

D-U-N-S 19-673-5666
GSC LOGISTICS INC
530 Water St Fl 5, Oakland, CA 94607-3532
Tel (510) 844-3700 *Founded/Ownrshp* 1988
Sales 27.3MM^E *EMP* 120^E
SIC 4214 4225 4213 Local trucking with storage; General warehousing; Trucking, except local
CEO: Scott E Taylor
Pr: Clement Chin
COO: Richard Norton
**CFO:* Joel Lesser
CFO: Norman Robert
Ex VP: Andres Garcia
**VP:* Garcia Andres
VP: Marc Jensen
VP: Joseph Zepko
Genl Mgr: Sean Winker
Trfc Dir: Kevan Clayton

GSCS
See GLOBAL SUPPLY CHAIN SOLUTIONS LLC

D-U-N-S 93-016-9789
■ GSD&M IDEA CITY LLC
(*Suby of* OMNICOM GROUP INC) ★
828 W 6th St, Austin, TX 78703-5420
Tel (512) 242-4736 *Founded/Ownrshp* 1971
Sales 88.7MM^E *EMP* 515
SIC 7311 Advertising agencies; Advertising agencies
Ch: Roy Spence
**Pr:* Marianne Malina
**CEO:* Duff M Stewart
Ofcr: Jay Russell
VP: Maryellen Bruno
Creative D: Matthew Barker
Creative D: Gene Brenek
Creative D: Barry Brothers
Creative D: Ryan Carroll
Creative D: Joel Davis
Creative D: Mike Ferrer
Creative D: Joel Guidry
Creative D: Tom Hamling
Creative D: Sean Labounty
Creative D: Jeff Maki
Creative D: Andy Miller
Creative D: Bryan Pudder
Creative D: Haven Simmons
Creative D: Shane Starr

GSE
See GOOD SAM ENTERPRISES LLC

D-U-N-S 03-990-0469
GSE CONSTRUCTION CO INC
6950 Preston Ave, Livermore, CA 94551-9545
Tel (925) 447-0292 *Founded/Ownrshp* 1980
Sales 66.3MM^E *EMP* 140^E
Accts Gallina Llp Rancho Cordova C
SIC 1623 1542 Water & sewer line construction; Pipe laying construction; Pipeline construction; Nonresidential construction; Water & sewer line construction; Pipe laying construction; Pipeline construction; Nonresidential construction
CEO: Orlando Gutierrez

GSE ENVIRONMENTAL
See GSE HOLDING INC

D-U-N-S 16-167-6986
■ GSE ENVIRONMENTAL INC
(*Suby of* GSE ENVIRONMENTAL) ★
19103 Gundle Rd, Houston, TX 77073-3515
Tel (281) 443-8564 *Founded/Ownrshp* 2004
Sales 391.7MM^E *EMP* 603^E
SIC 3081 1799 Plastic film & sheet; Protective lining installation, underground (sewage, etc.); Plastic film & sheet; Protective lining installation, underground (sewage, etc.)
CEO: Charles A Sorrentino
**Ch Bd:* Daniel J Hennessy
**Pr:* Mark Arnold
**CFO:* Ernest C English Jr
VP: Wayne Case
VP: Boyd Ramsey
Tech Mgr: Adam Maskal
Tech Mgr: Dhani B Narejo
VP Sls: Gary Joachim
Manager: Abhijit Khare
Sls Mgr: Manish Kushwaha
Board of Directors: Michael G Evans, Marcus J George, Richard E Goodrich, Brian P Simmons

D-U-N-S 18-308-4805 IMP/EXP
■ GSE ENVIRONMENTAL LLC
(*Suby of* GSE ENVIRONMENTAL) ★
19103 Gundle Rd, Houston, TX 77073-3515
Tel (281) 443-8564 *Founded/Ownrshp* 2002
Sales 391.7MM^E *EMP* 603
SIC 3081 Polyethylene film; Polyethylene film
Pr: Charles A Sorrentino
**Pr:* Peter McCourt
**Pr:* Mark Whitney
CFO: Roger Klatt
Ex VP: Joellyn Champagne
**Ex VP:* Mike Kirksey
**Ex VP:* Jeffery Nigh
**Sr VP:* Daniel Storey
VP: Daniel A Daluise
VP: Gary Joachim
VP: Lee D Leggett
VP: Scott Lucas
VP: Richard S Schaefer
VP: William T Sharkey
VP: Terrance G Sheridan
**VP:* Gregg Taylor

D-U-N-S 14-797-1902 EXP
■ GSE HOLDING INC
GSE ENVIRONMENTAL
(*Suby of* LITTLEJOHN & CO LLC) ★
19103 Gundle Rd, Houston, TX 77073-3515
Tel (281) 443-8564 *Founded/Ownrshp* 2014
Sales 395.0MM *EMP* 608
Tkr Sym GSEH *Exch* OTO
SIC 3081 6719 Plastic film & sheet; Investment holding companies, except banks; Plastic film & sheet; Investment holding companies, except banks
Ch Bd: Robert Preston
**Pr:* Peter McCourt
**CFO:* Daniel C Storey
**Ex VP:* Jeffery D Nigh
**VP:* Giovanna Capra
**VP:* Steve Eckhart
**VP:* Edward Zimmel

D-U-N-S 05-127-1278 IMP
■ GSE HOLDINGS INC
ITW MILITARY GSE
(*Suby of* ILLINOIS TOOL WORKS INC) ★
11001 Us Highway 41 N, Palmetto, FL 34221-7700
Tel (941) 721-1000 *Founded/Ownrshp* 2007
Sales 28.7MM^E *EMP* 158
SIC 7699 7629 5088 Aircraft & heavy equipment repair services; Aircraft electrical equipment repair; Aircraft equipment & supplies; Aircraft & heavy equipment repair services; Aircraft electrical equipment repair; Aircraft equipment & supplies
CEO: William Sullivan
VP: Jack Campbell
Genl Mgr: Richard Hansen

D-U-N-S 96-211-0300
■ GSE INTERNATIONAL INC
(*Suby of* GSE ENVIRONMENTAL INC) ★
19103 Gundle Rd, Houston, TX 77073-3515
Tel (281) 443-8564 *Founded/Ownrshp* 1992
Sales 392.4M^E *EMP* 482^E
SIC 3081 1799 Plastic film & sheet; Protective lining installation, underground (sewage, etc.)
CEO: Samir T Badawi
Treas: Charles McCullough
Ex VP: Robert Otto

D-U-N-S 82-643-3658
▲ GSE SYSTEMS INC
1332 Londontown Blvd, Sykesville, MD 21784-6587
Tel (410) 970-7800 *Founded/Ownrshp* 1994
Sales 37.9MM *EMP* 335^E
Tkr Sym GVP *Exch* ASE
SIC 7372 Prepackaged software; Prepackaged software
Pr: Kyle J Loudermilk
**Ch Bd:* Roger L Hagengruber
**COO:* Christopher D Sorrells
CFO: Jeffery G Hough
Sr VP: Lawrence M Gordon
Sr VP: Gill R Grady
Sr VP: Phillip M Polefrone
VP: Santosh Joshi
VP Bus Dev: Alex Lekich
Prgrm Mgr: Jamie Camp
Prgrm Mgr: Scott Zepplin
Board of Directors: Sheldon L Glashow, Joseph W Lewis, Jane Bryant Quinn

GSEGC
See GS ELECTRIC GENERATING COOPERATIVE INC

GSF FOUNDATION
See GOLDEN STATE FOODS CORP

D-U-N-S 88-300-9425
GSF MORTGAGE CORP
15430 W Capitol Dr # 100, Brookfield, WI 53005-2626
Tel (262) 373-0790 *Founded/Ownrshp* 1995
Sales NA *EMP* 225
SIC 6163 Mortgage brokers arranging for loans, using money of others; Mortgage brokers arranging for loans, using money of others
Pr: Chad Jampedro
Sr VP: Brian Fiskum
VP: David Butcher
Brnch Mgr: Jim Ahlin
Brnch Mgr: Kim Bos
Brnch Mgr: Bill Compton
Brnch Mgr: Sam Fisher
Brnch Mgr: Ronald Gardner
Brnch Mgr: John Maliska
Brnch Mgr: Dana Tiltrague
Brnch Mgr: Stephen Trye

D-U-N-S 62-394-1853
GSF USA INC
G S F
(*Suby of* GROUPE SERVICES FRANCE)
107 S Penn St Ste 300, Indianapolis, IN 46204-3684
Tel (317) 262-4958 *Founded/Ownrshp* 1987
Sales 21.8MM^E *EMP* 1,100
Accts Crowe Horwath Llp Indianapoli
SIC 7349 Janitorial service, contract basis; Janitorial service, contract basis
CEO: Regis Bernard
Pr: Troy Bargmann
Sales Exec: Michael Johnsen

D-U-N-S 06-168-3892 IMP
GSG CORP
DIAMOND LIL'S CARD CASINO
361 Rainier Ave S, Renton, WA 98057-2404
Tel (425) 226-2763 *Founded/Ownrshp* 1976
Sales 6.2MM^E *EMP* 335
SIC 7999 5812 5813 Card & game services; Eating places; Cocktail lounge; Card & game services; Eating places; Cocktail lounge
Pr: Lori K Bender
**Sec:* Karen Bell
VP: Herb Frie
**VP:* Keith Quale
Off Mgr: Matt Hew

D-U-N-S 07-830-4916 IMP
GSG FASTENERS LLC
SCOVILL FASTENERS
(*Suby of* MORITO CO., LTD.)
1802 Scovill Dr, Clarkesville, GA 30523-6348
Tel (706) 754-1000 *Founded/Ownrshp* 2011, 2014
Sales 35.3MM^E *EMP* 230^E
SIC 3965 Fasteners; Fasteners
CEO: Craig Stoudt
CFO: Gary Reinert
Ex VP: Robert Feltz
VP: Jim Overwyck

VP Sls: Shane McEntyre
Sls Mgr: Sunny Chan

GSH GROUP
See GEORGE S HALL INC

D-U-N-S 83-182-2452
GSHS ADMINISTRATIVE SERVICES ORGANIZATION INC
700 E Marshall Ave, Longview, TX 75601-5580
Tel (903) 315-1811 *Founded/Ownrshp* 2005
Sales 51.6MM *EMP* 99
SIC 8011 Offices & clinics of medical doctors; Offices & clinics of medical doctors
CEO: Edward Banos

D-U-N-S 82-637-2864
GSHS ENTERPRISES INC
GOOD SHEPHERD AMBULATORY SURGE
700 E Marshall Ave, Longview, TX 75601-5580
Tel (903) 315-4880 *Founded/Ownrshp* 1993
Sales 41.9MM *EMP* 80
SIC 8011 Surgeon; Surgeon
Ch: Tom Mobley
**Pr:* Steve Altmiller

GSI
See GULFSTREAM SERVICES INC

GSI
See GEOSTABILIZATION INTERNATIONAL LLC

D-U-N-S 79-138-4329
■ **GSI COMMERCE CALL CENTER INC**
(*Suby of* GLOBAL SPORTS) ★
915 S Babcock St, Melbourne, FL 32901-1850
Tel (321) 309-9800 *Founded/Ownrshp* 2002
Sales 20.0MM^E *EMP* 649
SIC 7389 Telephone services; Telephone services
Pr: Hartmann Tobias
IT Man: Paul N Collado

D-U-N-S 17-818-5393 IMP
■ **GSI COMMERCE INC**
GLOBAL SPORTS
(*Suby of* EBAY INC) ★
935 1st Ave, King of Prussia, PA 19406-1342
Tel (610) 491-7000 *Founded/Ownrshp* 2011
Sales 1.1MMM^E *EMP* 5,848
SIC 5961 7371 7379 Catalog & mail-order houses; Computer equipment & electronics, mail order; Clothing, mail order (except women's); Cosmetics & perfumes, mail order; Custom computer programming services; ; Catalog & mail-order houses; Computer equipment & electronics, mail order; Clothing, mail order (except women's); Cosmetics & perfumes, mail order; Custom computer programming services
Pr: Chris Saridakis
**Pr:* Tobias Hartmann
COO: Mark Reese
CFO: Jordan Copland
CFO: Phillip Depaul
CFO: Adam Livingston
Ex VP: Dan Dobson
**Ex VP:* Jim Flanagan
**Ex VP:* Scott Hardy
**Ex VP:* Damon Mintzer
Sr VP: Gregg McNulty
VP: Mark Kirschner
VP: Mark Lavelle
VP: Conn R Michael
Exec: David Guzman

D-U-N-S 00-169-4256 IMP
GSI EXIM AMERICA INC (NY)
(*Suby of* GSI HOLDING CORP) ★
1065 Avenue Of The Am, New York, NY 10018
Tel (212) 684-5760 *Founded/Ownrshp* 1955
Sales 77.0MM *EMP* 24
SIC 5169 5051 5085 Chemicals & allied products; Wire; Industrial supplies
Pr: Tadaaki Yoshinaga
COO: Lori Wong
**VP:* Hiroyuki Matsuura
**Prin:* Shigenori Nishiguchi

D-U-N-S 04-376-9173 IMP
■ **GSI GROUP CORP**
(*Suby of* GSI GROUP INC) ★
125 Middlesex Tpke, Bedford, MA 01730-1409
Tel (781) 266-5700 *Founded/Ownrshp* 1989
Sales 325.1MM^E *EMP* 1,264^E
SIC 3699 Laser systems & equipment; Laser systems & equipment
CEO: John A Roush
**Pr:* Jamie B Bader
**Pr:* Matthijs Glastra
**CFO:* Robert Buckley
**VP:* Peter Chang
**VP:* Deborah A Mulryan
Board of Directors: Stephen W Bershad, Harry Bosco, Dennis J Fortino, Ira J Lamel, Dominic Romeo, John A Roush, Thomas Secor

D-U-N-S 78-780-3761
▲ **GSI GROUP INC**
125 Middlesex Tpke, Bedford, MA 01730-1409
Tel (781) 266-5700 *Founded/Ownrshp* 1968
Sales 364.7MM *EMP* 1,418^E
Tkr Sym GSIG *Exch* NGS
SIC 3699 3845 Laser systems & equipment; Laser welding, drilling & cutting equipment; Laser systems & equipment, medical; Laser systems & equipment; Laser welding, drilling & cutting equipment; Laser systems & equipment, medical
CEO: John A Roush
COO: Matthijs Glastra
CFO: Robert Buckley
VP: Manjit Daniel
VP: Mike Foley
VP: Scott Rehner
VP Bus Dev: Felix I Stukalin
Admn Mgr: Jodie Morris
Snr Mgr: Lydia Nguyen
Assoc Ed: Dens Milne
Board of Directors: Harry L Bosco, Dennis J Fortino, Ira J Lamel, Dominic A Romeo, Thomas N Secor

D-U-N-S 02-492-8343 IMP/EXP
■ **GSI GROUP LLC**
GRAIN SYSTEMS
(*Suby of* AGCO CORP) ★
1004 E Illinois St, Assumption, IL 62510-9529
Tel (217) 226-4421 *Founded/Ownrshp* 2011
Sales 257.4MM^E *EMP* 2,029
SIC 3523

D-U-N-S 01-911-9820 IMP
GSI HOLDING CORP
(*Suby of* GSI CREOS CORPORATION)
461 5th Ave Fl 16, New York, NY 10017-7718
Tel (212) 684-5760 *Founded/Ownrshp* 1998
Sales 66.0MM *EMP* 38
SIC 5169 5084 5131 Chemicals & allied products; Industrial machinery & equipment; Piece goods & notions; Chemicals & allied products; Industrial machinery & equipment; Piece goods & notions
Pr: Tadaaki Yoshinaga
**Sec:* Kenny Ono

D-U-N-S 61-801-9215 EXP
■ **GSI HOLDINGS CORP**
(*Suby of* AGCO CORP) ★
1004 E Illinois St, Assumption, IL 62510-9529
Tel (217) 226-4421 *Founded/Ownrshp* 2011
Sales 119.8MM^E *EMP* 2,029
SIC 3523 Crop storage bins; Driers (farm): grain, hay & seed; Poultry brooders, feeders & waterers; Hog feeding, handling & watering equipment; Crop storage bins; Driers (farm): grain, hay & seed; Poultry brooders, feeders & waterers; Hog feeding, handling & watering equipment
CEO: Scott Clawson

GSI LAW ENFORCEMENT
See GREEN SUPPLY INC

D-U-N-S 06-604-1695
■ **GSI LEGACY HOLDINGS INC**
(*Suby of* EBAY INC) ★
1075 1st Ave, King of Prussia, PA 19406-1396
Tel (610) 491-7000 *Founded/Ownrshp* 2001
Sales NA *EMP* 300
SIC 6719 Investment holding companies, except banks; Investment holding companies, except banks
Pr: Michael Rubin

D-U-N-S 07-945-0553
GSI SERVICE GROUP INC
(*Suby of* NATIVE HAWAIIAN COMMUNITY DEVELOPMENT CORPORATION)
181 S Kukui St, Honolulu, HI 96813-2329
Tel (808) 864-5050 *Founded/Ownrshp* 2014
Sales 6.6MM^E *EMP* 325
SIC 7363 Employee leasing service; Employee leasing service
Pr: Derek Sakaguchi

D-U-N-S 13-971-7557 IMP
GSI TECHNOLOGIES LLC
311 Shore Dr, Burr Ridge, IL 60527-5859
Tel (630) 325-8181 *Founded/Ownrshp* 1985
Sales 27.3MM^E *EMP* 60
Accts Mcgladrey & Pullen
SIC 2791 2759 Typesetting; Letterpress & screen printing; Typesetting; Letterpress & screen printing; Screen printing; Flexographic printing
CEO: David G Austin
Treas: Edward Leahy
**VP:* Dominic Robert Zaccone II
**VP:* Suzanne M Zaccone
VP: Bob Zaconne
**CTO:* Gordon Smith
Prd Mgr: Gary Gresko
Prd Mgr: Ed Stropus
Mktg Dir: Kathy Welsh

D-U-N-S 83-541-8898
▲ **GSI TECHNOLOGY INC**
1213 Elko Dr, Sunnyvale, CA 94089-2211
Tel (408) 331-8800 *Founded/Ownrshp* 1995
Sales 53.5MM *EMP* 138
Tkr Sym GSIT *Exch* NGS
SIC 3674 3572 Semiconductors & related devices; Computer storage devices; Semiconductors & related devices; Computer storage devices
Pr: Lee-Lean Shu
CFO: Douglas Schirle
VP: Suengliang Lee
VP: Bor-Tay Wu
VP: Ping Wu
Prd Mgr: Gary Gresko
VP Mktg: David Chapman
VP Sls: Didier Lasserre
Board of Directors: Jack A Bradley, E Thomas Hart, Haydn Hsieh, Ruey L Lu, Arthur O Whipple

GSIL
See GRANITE STATE INDEPENDENT LIVING

GSK
See GLAXOSMITHKLINE (USAL)

GSK CONSUMER HEALTHCARE
See NOVARTIS CONSUMER HEALTH INC

GSL ELECTRIC
See GREAT SALT LAKE ELECTRIC INC

GSM - WALKER PRODUCTS
See HEARING LAB TECHNOLOGY LLC

D-U-N-S 02-402-8123
GSM AUTO GROUP II LLC (CA)
INFINITI OF MISSION VIEJO
28471 Marguerite Pkwy, Mission Viejo, CA 92692-3707
Tel (949) 916-4200 *Founded/Ownrshp* 2000
Sales 26.6MM^E *EMP* 70
SIC 5511 Automobiles, new & used; Automobiles, new & used
Mktg Dir: Dimitri Anagnostopoulos
Sls Mgr: Karim Tejani
Sales Asso: Trace Donaldson
Sales Asso: Tyler Sendelbach

D-U-N-S 10-621-8001 IMP
GSM INDUSTRIAL INC
3249 Hempland Rd, Lancaster, PA 17601-6913
Tel (717) 207-8985 *Founded/Ownrshp* 1983
Sales 32.7MM^E *EMP* 112
SIC 3444 1711 Sheet metalwork; Mechanical contractor
Ch Bd: John S Gooding
**Pr:* Brian Dombach
**Sec:* William H Gooding
VP: John Kleinfelter
**VP:* Jeffrey Ream
Sfty Dirs: Randy Kauffman
Sls Mgr: Jeff Ream

D-U-N-S 00-898-3785
GSM INVESTMENTS INC
2524 Austin Ave, Waco, TX 76710-7418
Tel (254) 753-7367 *Founded/Ownrshp* 1972
Sales 17.9MM^E *EMP* 500
SIC 8741 Nursing & personal care facility management; Nursing & personal care facility management
Pr: Scott Marwitz
**Prin:* Gary Marwitz

GSM OUTDOORS
See GOOD SPORTSMAN MARKETING LLC

GSM SERVICES
See GASTONIA SHEET METAL WORKS INC

D-U-N-S 01-722-4705
GSM WIRELESS INC
CINGULAR WIRELESS
8871 Research Dr, Irvine, CA 92618-4236
Tel (949) 425-1300 *Founded/Ownrshp* 1998
Sales 64.2MM^E *EMP* 545
SIC 4813 Telephone communication, except radio; Telephone communication, except radio
CEO: Mohammad Honarkar

D-U-N-S 79-095-0146
GSMA LTD
(*Suby of* GSM CONFERENCE SERVICES LIMITED)
1000 Abernathy Rd Ste 450, Atlanta, GA 30328-5623
Tel (678) 281-6600 *Founded/Ownrshp* 2006
Sales 164.0MM *EMP* 105^E
Accts Smith & Howard Pc Atlanta Ga
SIC 7389 Convention & show services; Convention & show services
CEO: John Hoffman
**Ch Bd:* Bill Hague
**CFO:* Jeremy Sewell
Off Mgr: Cindy Elliott

D-U-N-S 62-037-1034
GSMGLOBE.COM INC
134 Ne 1st St, Miami, FL 33132-2502
Tel (305) 372-9590 *Founded/Ownrshp* 2007
Sales 40.0MM *EMP* 12
SIC 5065 Mobile telephone equipment; Mobile telephone equipment
Pr: Allauddin M Panjwani
**VP:* Madatali M Panjwani

D-U-N-S 60-671-0171
■ **GSO CAPITAL PARTNERS LP**
BLACKSTONE GROUP
(*Suby of* BLACKSTONE GROUP L P) ★
345 Park Ave Ste 1100, New York, NY 10154-1703
Tel (212) 583-5000 *Founded/Ownrshp* 2008
Sales 280.8MM^E *EMP* 900
SIC 6722 7389 Management investment, open-end; Financial services; Management investment, open-end; Financial services
Genl Pt: Douglas I Ostrover
**Pt:* Bennett Goodman
**Pt:* Tripp Smith
Mng Pt: Lee Shaiman
Pr: Chris Striano
Sr VP: Amy Chen
Sr VP: Leanne Gonzalez
Sr VP: Nick Tassell
VP: Allan Barja
VP: Anthony Borreca
VP: Claudio Chappell
VP: Jana Douglas
VP: Mary Eubanks
VP: Emma Fleming
VP: Heiko Freitag
VP: Michael Garrow
VP: David Goldberg
VP: Andrew Jordan
VP: Russell Lamb
VP: Verena Letzerich
VP: Brian Morris

D-U-N-S 13-926-9372
GSOLUTIONZ INC
625 E Santa Clara St # 100, Ventura, CA 93001-2820
Tel (805) 662-1500 *Founded/Ownrshp* 2002
Sales 31.8MM^E *EMP* 45
SIC 5065 Communication equipment
CEO: Allen Pugh
Rgnl Mgr: Jay Licata

GSP INTERNATIONAL
See GREENVILLE-SPARTANBURG AIRPORT COMMISSION INC

D-U-N-S 09-297-7727
GSP MARKETING TECHNOLOGIES INC
5400 140th Ave N, Clearwater, FL 33760-3763
Tel (727) 532-0647 *Founded/Ownrshp* 1978
Sales 44.8MM^E *EMP* 195
SIC 8713 Surveying services; Surveying services
CEO: Geoff Neuhoff
**Pr:* Paul Neuhoff
VP: Hartmut Dalheimer
Sfty Mgr: John Gallo

D-U-N-S 61-233-3695 IMP
GSP NORTH AMERICA CO INC
298 Commercial Rd, Spartanburg, SC 29303-6303
Tel (864) 578-6900 *Founded/Ownrshp* 2005
Sales 21.3MM^E *EMP* 135
SIC 3714 Axles, motor vehicle; Axles, motor vehicle
Pr: Richard G Lovely
**CFO:* Xia Lei

D-U-N-S 05-985-2532
GSR RESTAURANTS LLC
12660 S Kirkwood Rd, Stafford, TX 77477-2915
Tel (281) 565-9779 *Founded/Ownrshp* 2010
Sales 13.2MM^E *EMP* 291^E
SIC 5812 Eating places

GSS CONSTRUCTION & OILFLD SUP
See GSS TRANSPORT LLC

GSS GEAR
See GLOBAL SUPPLY SOLUTIONS LLC

D-U-N-S 09-310-6198
GSS INFOTECH INC (IL)
(*Suby of* GSS INFOTECH LIMITED)
2050 Bruns Plz State Hwy, North Brunswick, NJ 08902
Tel (866) 726-0520 *Founded/Ownrshp* 1999
Sales 27.4MM^E *EMP* 366^E
SIC 7371 Custom computer programming services; Custom computer programming services
CEO: Bhargav Marepally
**Pr:* Ramesh Yerramsetti
**CFO:* Ravi S Chivukula
**Ch:* Pvrk Prasad
VP: Sanford Cohn

D-U-N-S 96-170-8703
GSS TRANSPORT LLC
GSS CONSTRUCTION & OILFLD SUP
4809 Hazel Jones Rd, Bossier City, LA 71111-5321
Tel (318) 742-5881 *Founded/Ownrshp* 2008
Sales 63.9MM^E *EMP* 106^E
SIC 1389 Oil consultants

GSSI
See GEOPHYSICAL SURVEY SYSTEMS INC

GST
See GLOBAL SCIENCE & TECHNOLOGY INC

D-U-N-S 61-032-7082 IMP/EXP
GST AUTOLEATHER INC
20 Oak Hollow St Ste 300, Southfield, MI 48033-7491
Tel (248) 436-2300 *Founded/Ownrshp* 2008
Sales 805.8MM^E *EMP* 2,100
SIC 3111 Leather tanning & finishing; Cutting of leather; Leather tanning & finishing; Cutting of leather
Pr: Dennis E Hiller
**CFO:* Eric Evans
**Sr VP:* Cesar Hugo Escobedo
Sr VP: Cysar H Escobedo
**Sr VP:* Stephen Jeske
**VP:* Francisco Ros Jimnez
VP: Eric Kozlowski
VP: Allen Shaw
VP Bus Dev: Francisco Jimenez
Ex Dir: Francisco R Jimynez
Ex Dir: Francisco R Jim Nez

D-U-N-S 13-181-4449
GST MANUFACTURING LTD
CLEMENS SHEET METAL WORKS
4201 Janada St, Haltom City, TX 76117-1231
Tel (817) 335-1401 *Founded/Ownrshp* 2000
Sales 40.6MM^E *EMP* 165
SIC 3444 Sheet metalwork; Sheet metalwork
CEO: George Lamberth
Pr: Sherri Lamberth
CFO: Daniel Gray
VP: Tye Lamberth
Genl Mgr: Josh Ward
IT Man: Joseph Warren
Sls Mgr: Sam Kerbel

GSTC
See GORDON SEVIG TRUCKING CO

GSUSA
See GIRL SCOUTS OF UNITED STATES OF AMERICA

D-U-N-S 60-577-9925 IMP
GSW MANUFACTURING INC
(*Suby of* G S WIRING SYSTEMS INC) ★
1801 Production Dr, Findlay, OH 45840-5446
Tel (419) 423-7111 *Founded/Ownrshp* 1989
Sales 141.5MM^E *EMP* 412
SIC 3714 3694 Automotive wiring harness sets; Engine electrical equipment; Automotive wiring harness sets; Engine electrical equipment
Pr: Yukinobu Ukai
CIO: William Brown
Ql Cn Mgr: Jeffrey Marok

GSW WORLDWIDE
See GERBIG SNELL/WEISHEIMER ADVERTISING LLC

GSWSA
See GRAND STRAND WATER & SEWER AUTHORITY

D-U-N-S 15-133-6393
GT & T CORP
24262 Broadway Ave, Cleveland, OH 44146-6333
Tel (440) 232-5511 *Founded/Ownrshp* 1983
Sales NA *EMP* 120
Accts Deloitte & Touche Llp Clevela
SIC 6361 Title insurance; Guarantee of titles
CEO: Louis Frank
Treas: Paula Knodel
**VP:* Mike Mc Donald

D-U-N-S 82-772-7814 IMP
GT ADVANCED TECHNOLOGIES INC
243 Daniel Webster Hwy, Merrimack, NH 03054-4807
Tel (603) 883-5200 *Founded/Ownrshp* 2006
Sales 298.9MM^E *EMP* 541^E
SIC 3674 Semiconductors & related devices; Photovoltaic devices, solid state; Semiconductors & related devices; Photovoltaic devices, solid state
CEO: David Keck
**Ch Bd:* Matthew E Massengill
COO: Daniel W Squiller
CFO: Kenwardev Raja Singh Bal
CFO: Raja Bal
Ofcr: Hoil Kim

Ex VP: David W Keck
VP: David Gray
VP: Christine Richardson
Prgrm Mgr: James Lovenstein
Prgrm Mgr: Joe Sevigny
Board of Directors: J Michal Conaway, Kathleen A Cote, Ernest L Godshalk, Richard E Newsted, John J Ray III, Robert E Switz, Noel G Watson, Thomas Wroe Jr

D-U-N-S 02-935-0695
GT COMMODITIES LLC
(*Suby of* GERALD HOLDINGS LLC) ★
680 Washington Blvd Fl 9, Stamford, CT 06901-3727
Tel (203) 609-8300 *Founded/Ownrshp* 1960
Sales 22.4MM^E *EMP* 75
SIC 6221 Commodity brokers, contracts
CEO: Craig Dean
**CFO:* Thomas Restivo

D-U-N-S 03-062-2780
GT EXHAUST INC
(*Suby of* I A C) ★
3901 W Kearney St, Lincoln, NE 68524-2201
Tel (402) 323-7272 *Founded/Ownrshp* 2012
Sales 24.9MM^E *EMP* 70^E
SIC 3444 Metal ventilating equipment
Pr: Ed Osborn
**CFO:* Rob Gregersen
Sfty Mgr: John Bilka
Mktg Mgr: Andrew Boellstorff

GT NEXUS
See GTNX INC

D-U-N-S 04-551-6085 IMP
GT PRECISION INC
ALARD MACHINE PRODUCTS
1629 W 132nd St, Gardena, CA 90249-2005
Tel (310) 323-4374 *Founded/Ownrshp* 1984
Sales 26.0MM^E *EMP* 107
SIC 3451 Screw machine products; Screw machine products
CEO: Gregg Thompson
Ql Cn Mgr: Efren Costales

D-U-N-S 60-562-6548 IMP
GT TECHNOLOGIES I INC
PRECISION ENGINE PRODUCTS CORP
(*Suby of* GENTEK INC) ★
2919 Commonwealth Blvd, Tallahassee, FL 32303-3156
Tel (850) 575-8181 *Founded/Ownrshp* 2006
Sales 31.2MM^E *EMP* 200
SIC 3714 Motor vehicle engines & parts; Motor vehicle engines & parts
CEO: William E Redmond Jr
**CFO:* Douglas J Grierson
**CFO:* Mike Spadarotto
**CFO:* Thomas Testa
**VP:* Robert Novo
**Genl Mgr:* Mark Mueller

D-U-N-S 14-734-8346
GT TECHNOLOGIES INC
(*Suby of* GENTEK INC) ★
5859 E Executive Dr, Westland, MI 48185-1932
Tel (734) 467-8371 *Founded/Ownrshp* 1985
Sales 87.5MM^E *EMP* 500
SIC 8711 3714 3545 3089 Designing: ship, boat, machine & product; Motor vehicle engines & parts; Machine tool attachments & accessories; Injection molded finished plastic products; Designing: ship, boat, machine & product; Motor vehicle engines & parts; Machine tool attachments & accessories; Injection molded finished plastic products
Pr: Paul Schwarzbaum
CFO: John Cattell
**Sr VP:* Daniel Brinker
VP: Dan Brinker
VP: Jim Porcaro
**Prin:* William Redmond Jr
Tech Mgr: Paul Szymanski
Board of Directors: James E Heighway, George H Lewis III, Richard W Lock, John D Ong, Scott Roulston, Thomas H Roulston II Chb

D-U-N-S 16-993-2535 IMP
GT&S INC
5275 Tilghman St, Allentown, PA 18104-9378
Tel (610) 398-2211 *Founded/Ownrshp* 2004
Sales 280.4MM^E *EMP* 700
Accts Beard Miller Company Llp Read
SIC 4925 5169 5084 5085 2813 5172 Gas production and/or distribution; Industrial gases; Carbon dioxide; Gases, compressed & liquefied; Dry ice; Welding machinery & equipment; Safety equipment; Welding supplies; Industrial gases; Carbon dioxide; Dry ice, carbon dioxide (solid); Nitrous oxide; Gases, liquefied petroleum (propane); Gas production and/or distribution; Industrial gases; Carbon dioxide; Gases, compressed & liquefied; Dry ice; Welding machinery & equipment; Safety equipment; Welding supplies; Industrial gases; Carbon dioxide; Dry ice, carbon dioxide (solid); Nitrous oxide; Gases, liquefied petroleum (propane)
Pr: Bryan R Gentry
**CFO:* Michael A Masha
**Treas:* John D Karpinski
Off Mgr: Donna Kline

GTA
See GREENTECH AUTOMOTIVE CORP

D-U-N-S 10-330-5793
GTA AMERICAS LLC
GULLIVERS TRAVEL ASSOCIATES
(*Suby of* DONVAND LIMITED)
5 Penn Plz Fl 5, New York, NY 10001-1810
Tel (212) 376-5400 *Founded/Ownrshp* 2011
Sales 63.0MM^E *EMP* 210
SIC 4725 Tour operators; Arrangement of travel tour packages, wholesale; Tour operators; Arrangement of travel tour packages, wholesale
CEO: Ralph Schraforth
Pr: Richie Karaburan
CFO: Manjit Heyer
Ex VP: Michael Fisher
VP: Sean Bayliss
VP: Missy Zacks
Exec: Elena Acuna
Exec: Ketty Celifie
Exec: Maritza Troiano
Comm Man: Elliott Frisby
Ex Dir: Nancy Castro

D-U-N-S 96-796-4516
GTA HOLDINGS INC
3445a Box Hl, Abingdon, MD 21009
Tel (410) 515-9000 *Founded/Ownrshp* 2008
Sales 21.9MM^E *EMP* 223
Accts Weyrich Cronin & Sorra Chart
SIC 8711 8999 Engineering services; Earth science services; Engineering services; Earth science services
Pr: James P Klima
**CFO:* David Quaranta
**VP:* Amin Rahman

D-U-N-S 17-184-2128
GTA NORTH AMERICA INC
GULLIVER'S TRAVEL ASSOCIATES
510 Penn Plz Ste 5, New York, NY 10012
Tel (212) 334-1350 *Founded/Ownrshp* 1982
Sales 28.9MM^E *EMP* 263
SIC 4724 Travel agencies; Travel agencies
Pr: Elizabeth Crabill
VP: Adrienne Gillespie
VP: Barry Kaplan

GTA TELEGUAM
See TELEGUAM HOLDINGS LLC

D-U-N-S 02-100-8206 IMP/EXP
■ **GTA-NHT INC**
VENTURE TAPE
(*Suby of* 3M CO) ★
30 Commerce Rd, Rockland, MA 02370-1053
Tel (781) 331-5900 *Founded/Ownrshp* 2007
Sales 61.7MM^E *EMP* 300
SIC 2672 3842 2671 2295 2241 Tape, pressure sensitive: made from purchased materials; Surgical appliances & supplies; Packaging paper & plastics film, coated & laminated; Coated fabrics, not rubberized; Narrow fabric mills; Tape, pressure sensitive: made from purchased materials; Surgical appliances & supplies; Packaging paper & plastics film, coated & laminated; Coated fabrics, not rubberized; Narrow fabric mills
Pr: Mark Hurowitz
COO: Mark Hurwitz
**Treas:* Manuel Pardo
Treas: Brian Solimini
VP: Ed Wagner
VP: Brett Webster
Genl Mgr: Terry Pikul
Dir IT: Brian Dean
Prd Mgr: Alex Adamopoulos
Ql Cn Mgr: Marie Casey
Ql Cn Mgr: Gary Littman

D-U-N-S 62-521-6424
GTA-USA GULLIVERS TRAVEL ASSOCIATES
(*Suby of* KUONI REISEN HOLDING AG)
5 Penn Plz Fl 5, New York, NY 10001-1810
Tel (212) 843-9778 *Founded/Ownrshp* 2006
Sales 25.3MM^E *EMP* 150
SIC 4724 Travel agencies
Pr: Richie Karaburn
CFO: Bill Keneally

GTARC
See GEORGIA TECH APPLIED RESEARCH CORP

D-U-N-S 84-985-7784 IMP
GTAT CORP
(*Suby of* GT ADVANCED TECHNOLOGIES INC) ★
243 Daniel Webster Hwy, Merrimack, NH 03054-4807
Tel (603) 883-5200 *Founded/Ownrshp* 2002
Sales 168.2MM^E *EMP* 332
Accts Ernst & Young Llp Manchester
SIC 3674 3567 Photovoltaic devices, solid state; Vacuum furnaces & ovens; Photovoltaic devices, solid state; Vacuum furnaces & ovens
VP: Hoil Kim
**COO:* Dan Squiller
**CFO:* Raja Bal
**CFO:* Rick Gaynor
**VP:* Jeffrey J Ford
VP: Michele Rayos
VP: Ed Samaha
VP: Susan Sulesky
VP: John Tattersfield
VP: Rick Tattersfield
Admn Mgr: Keith Matthei
Board of Directors: J Michal Conaway

GTC
See GREEN TOKAI CO LTD

D-U-N-S 92-945-6614
GTC SYSTEMS INC
504 W Mission Ave Ste 203, Escondido, CA 92025-1604
Tel (858) 560-5800 *Founded/Ownrshp* 1995
Sales 34.5MM^E *EMP* 30
SIC 5045 7373 8742 Computers, peripherals & software; Computer systems analysis & design; Training & development consultant
CEO: Keith M Esshaki
CFO: Cathy Wang
Chf Mktg O: Daniel Lappert
CIO: Mike L Chase
CTO: Thaniel Noles
IT Man: Seth Wilensky
Opers Mgr: Ben Silver
Mktg Mgr: Paul Alvarez
Sls Mgr: Kimberly Cobb
Sls Mgr: Jay Irvine

D-U-N-S 96-200-5299
GTC TECHNOLOGY US LLC
(*Suby of* GTC MEXICO, S. DE R.L. DE C.V.)
1001 S Dairy Ashford Rd # 500, Houston, TX 77077-2333
Tel (281) 597-4800 *Founded/Ownrshp* 2009
Sales 22.8MM^E *EMP* 99^E
SIC 8711 Engineering services
CFO: Edward Chen
Mng Dir: Sam Kumar
Off Mgr: Amanda Bishop
Tech Mgr: Bryant Slimp

D-U-N-S 02-272-5282
GTCR GOLDER RAUNER LLC
300 N La Salle Dr # 5600, Chicago, IL 60654-5410
Tel (312) 329-0225 *Founded/Ownrshp* 1998
Sales 749.6MM^E *EMP* 2,550
SIC 6726 Investment offices; Investment offices
CFO: Anna Trala
VP: Sean Cunningham
VP: Justin Dupere
VP: Lawrence Fey
VP: Jeffrey Heh
VP: Stephen Jeschke
VP: Benjamin Remmert
VP: Lesly Schlender
VP: Neil Willis
Exec: Aimee Broderick
**Prin:* Aaron D Cohen

D-U-N-S 01-639-5792
GTCR LLC
300 N La Salle Dr # 5600, Chicago, IL 60654-5410
Tel (312) 382-2200 *Founded/Ownrshp* 2009
Sales 246.4MM^E *EMP* 505^E
SIC 5049 Laboratory equipment, except medical or dental
VP: Josh Earl
VP: Travis Krueger
Exec: Jeanette Lesniak
Mng Dir: Sean Cunningham
CIO: Jim Lott
Dir IT: Justin Sheppard
Snr Mgr: Mike Hollander
Snr Mgr: Pat Nola

D-U-N-S 07-943-5151
GTCR VALOR COMPANIES INC
300 N La Salle Dr # 5600, Chicago, IL 60654-5410
Tel (312) 382-2200 *Founded/Ownrshp* 2014
Sales 304.6MM^E *EMP* 1,273^E
SIC 7389 Financial services; Financial services

D-U-N-S 96-875-0856
■ **GTCS HOLDINGS LLC**
GREEN TREE
(*Suby of* WALTER INVESTMENT MANAGEMENT CORP) ★
345 Saint Peter St, Saint Paul, MN 55102-1211
Tel (651) 293-4800 *Founded/Ownrshp* 2011
Sales 220.5MM^E *EMP* 1,900^E
SIC 6719 Investment holding companies, except banks; Investment holding companies, except banks
**Pr:* Keith Anderson
VP: Al Rudnickas

GTE
See GAS TURBINE EFFICIENCY INC

D-U-N-S 00-129-3950 IMP
■ **GTE CORP** (NY)
(*Suby of* VERIZON COMMUNICATIONS INC) ★
140 West St, New York, NY 10007-2141
Tel (212) 395-1000 *Founded/Ownrshp* 1935
Sales 8.8MMM^E *EMP* 111,285
SIC 4813 4812 3661 3663 4899 2741 Telephone communication, except radio; Local telephone communications; Local & long distance telephone communications; Voice telephone communications; Cellular telephone services; Telephones & telephone apparatus; Toll switching equipment, telephone; Data sets, telephone or telegraph; Mobile communication equipment; Airborne radio communications equipment; Satellite earth stations; Directories, telephone: publishing only, not printed on site; Telephone communication, except radio; Local telephone communications; Local & long distance telephone communications; Voice telephone communications; Cellular telephone services; Telephones & telephone apparatus; Toll switching equipment, telephone; Data sets, telephone or telegraph; Mobile communication equipment; Airborne radio communications equipment; Satellite earth stations; Directories, telephone: publishing only, not printed on site
Ch Bd: Roy H Chestnut
**VP:* David H Benson
**Prin:* John W Diercksen
IT Man: James Scoffield
Board of Directors: Marianne Drost

D-U-N-S 09-445-5573
GTE INDUSTRIES INC
4121 Nw 37th St, Lincoln, NE 68524-1921
Tel (402) 323-7272 *Founded/Ownrshp* 2007
Sales 40.8MM^E *EMP* 149
Accts Bkd Llp Lincoln Ne
SIC 3564 Exhaust fans: industrial or commercial; Exhaust fans: industrial or commercial
Pr: Ed Osborne
Pr: Kathy Plunkett
**CFO:* Robert Gregson
VP: John Meola

D-U-N-S 86-132-0992
■ **GTE MIDWEST INC**
VERIZON MIDWEST
(*Suby of* GTE CORP) ★
600 Hidden Rdg, Irving, TX 75038-3809
Tel (972) 718-1856 *Founded/Ownrshp* 1992
Sales 56.1MM^E *EMP* 1,000
SIC 4813 Telephone communication, except radio; Telephone communication, except radio
Pr: M Michael Foster
**Pr:* Lawrence R Whitman
**VP:* John C Appel

D-U-N-S 00-793-5885
■ **GTE SOUTHWEST INC**
VERIZON SOUTHWEST
(*Suby of* GTE CORP) ★
700 Hidden Rdg, Irving, TX 75038-3811
Tel (972) 718-5600 *Founded/Ownrshp* 1926, 2000
Sales 846.0MM^E *EMP* 6,948
SIC 4813 Local & long distance telephone communications; Local telephone communications; Local & long distance telephone communications; Local telephone communications
Ex VP: John C Appel
**CFO:* Michael T Stefanski
**Treas:* Gregory D Jacobson
**Treas:* Neil D Olson
**Sr VP:* Gerald K Dinsmore
**VP:* Quentin E Bredeweg
**VP:* Charles H Carrathers
**VP:* William M Edwards III
VP: Wael Faheem
**VP:* Robert G McCoy
**VP:* William G Mundy
**VP:* Barry W Paulson
**VP:* Richard L Schaulin
**VP:* Larry J Sparrow
**VP:* Lawrence R Whitman

D-U-N-S 82-954-8788 IMP
■ **GTE WIRELESS INC**
(*Suby of* GTE CORP) ★
1 Verizon Way, Basking Ridge, NJ 07920-1025
Tel (908) 559-7000 *Founded/Ownrshp* 1981
Sales 236.3MM^E *EMP* 2,714^E
SIC 4813 Telephone communication, except radio
VP: John Townsend

D-U-N-S 60-820-8286 IMP/EXP
■ **GTECH HOLDINGS CORP**
(*Suby of* LOTTOMATICA SPA)
10 Memorial Blvd Ste 101, Providence, RI 02903-1125
Tel (401) 392-1000 *Founded/Ownrshp* 1981
Sales 156.1MM^E *EMP* 5,300
SIC 7999 7371 Lottery operation; Computer software development & applications; Lottery operation; Computer software development & applications
Pr: Jaymin Patel
**Treas:* William M Pieri
Bd of Dir: Philip Lochner
Chf Mktg O: Connie Oconnor
Ofcr: Steve Fiedler
Sr VP: Stefano Bortoli
Sr VP: David J Calabro
Sr VP: Stephen Davidson
Sr VP: Jean-Pierre Desbiens
**Sr VP:* Walter G Desocio
Sr VP: Kathleen E McKeough
VP: Tom Caffrey
VP: Marc A Crisafulli
VP: Joseph Nadan
VP: Robert J Plourde
VP: Michael Prescott
VP: Francis Ward
VP: Lavaz Watson
Comm Man: Hamilton Henderson

D-U-N-S 62-223-9937
GTECH SERVICES INC
G-TECH PROFESSIONAL STAFFING
17101 Michigan Ave, Dearborn, MI 48126-2736
Tel (313) 441-3600 *Founded/Ownrshp* 1986
Sales 44.4MM^E *EMP* 830
SIC 7363 Temporary help service; Temporary help service
Pr: Theresa Ghafari
VP: James Davis
VP: Alex Evangelista
**VP:* Kouhaila G Hammer
VP: Bob Kelley
Sys Mgr: Willie Hilliard
Sls Mgr: Jennifer Bouwkamp

D-U-N-S 96-841-6219
GTEL HOLDINGS INC
2609 Cameron St, Mobile, AL 36607-3104
Tel (251) 479-4500 *Founded/Ownrshp* 1999
Sales 222.7MM^E *EMP* 714^E
SIC 3661 7389 Telephone sets, all types except cellular radio; Telephone services

D-U-N-S 96-841-6250
GTEL HOLDINGS LLC
(*Suby of* VERITAS CAPITAL FUND III L P) ★
590 Madison Ave, New York, NY 10022-2524
Tel (212) 415-6700 *Founded/Ownrshp* 1999
Sales NA *EMP* 361
SIC 6719 Personal holding companies, except banks; Personal holding companies, except banks

D-U-N-S 96-524-8560 IMP
GTFM LLC
FUBU THE COLLECTION
350 5th Ave Ste 6617, New York, NY 10118-6617
Tel (212) 273-3300 *Founded/Ownrshp* 1998
Sales 40.4MM^E *EMP* 62
Accts Schissel & Cohen Cpa S
SIC 5136 5137 Sportswear, men's & boys'; Men's & boys' outerwear; Sportswear, women's & children's; Women's & children's outerwear
Sls&Mrk Ex: Leslie Short
Snr Mgr: Vadim Shalencov

D-U-N-S 82-863-5909
GTJ REIT INC
60 Hempstead Ave Ste 718, West Hempstead, NY 11552-2158
Tel (516) 881-3535 *Founded/Ownrshp* 2008
Sales 39.3MM *EMP* 2
Accts Bdo Usa Llp New York New Yo
SIC 6798 Real estate investment trusts; Real estate investment trusts
Prin: Dennis Connor

D-U-N-S 02-046-3128
GTL (USA) INC
GTL AMERICAS
(*Suby of* GTL LIMITED)
5200 Tennyson Pkwy # 200, Plano, TX 75024-7147
Tel (972) 464-0561 *Founded/Ownrshp* 2008
Sales 28.1MM^E *EMP* 134
Accts Israeloff Trattner & Co Pc G
SIC 8711 8748 Engineering services; Telecommunications consultant; Engineering services; Telecommunications consultant
Ch: Manoj Tirodkar
**COO:* S K Roy

*CFO: Rajiv Kamat
*Sr VP: Urmeet Juneja
VP: Sabyasachi Basu

GTL AMERICAS
See GTL (USA) INC

D-U-N-S 11-522-6698
GTL INVESTMENTS INC
JOHN ADAMS MORTGAGE COMPANY
25800 Northwestern Hwy, Southfield, MI 48075-8403
Tel (248) 208-3900 Founded/Ownrshp 1971
Sales NA EMP 100
SIC 6163 Mortgage brokers arranging for loans, using money of others; Mortgage brokers arranging for loans, using money of others
Pr: Jess Monticello
Brnch Mgr: Brad Silvius
Board of Directors: Richard S Elsea

D-U-N-S 83-793-4897
GTL PUBLIC COMMUNICATIONS INC
(Suby of GLOBAL TEL LINK CORP) ★
2609 Cameron St, Mobile, AL 36607-3104
Tel (251) 471-3680 Founded/Ownrshp 2010
Sales 31.6MM^E EMP 405^E
SIC 7389 Financial services
CEO: Brian Oliver

D-U-N-S 10-230-5786
■ **GTL TRUCK LINES INC**
(Suby of NASH-FINCH CO) ★
4228 S 72nd St, Omaha, NE 68127-1803
Tel (402) 339-7300 Founded/Ownrshp 1983
Sales 27.9MM^E EMP 300
SIC 4213 Contract haulers; Contract haulers
Pr: Norman R Soland

D-U-N-S 80-542-2581 IMP/EXP
GTM INTERNATIONAL LLC
GBM INTERNATIONAL
2000 West Loop S Ste 2020, Houston, TX 77027-3591
Tel (713) 993-0900 Founded/Ownrshp 2014
Sales 88.6MM EMP 14
Accts Mcconnell & Jones Llp Housto
SIC 5169 Chemicals, industrial & heavy; Chemicals, industrial & heavy
CEO: Michael Van Marle
*Pr: Jorge C Squier

D-U-N-S 00-178-2887
GTM SERVICE INC (OH)
PARTS PRO AUTOMOTIVE WAREHOUSE
1366 Rockefeller Rd, Wickliffe, OH 44092-1973
Tel (440) 944-5099 Founded/Ownrshp 1981, 1995
Sales 72.3MM^E EMP 170
SIC 5013 Automotive supplies & parts; Automotive supplies & parts
Pr: Michael McPhee
*VP: Laura McPhee
Sls Mgr: Sue Naght

G.T.M. SPORTSWEAR
See ITS GREEK TO ME INC

D-U-N-S 11-341-5962
GTM WHOLESALE LIQUIDATORS INC
GTM'S DISCOUNT GENERAL STORES
1462 Corporate Center Dr, San Diego, CA 92154-6662
Tel (619) 596-7486 Founded/Ownrshp 1980
Sales 24.2MM EMP 130
SIC 5719 5411 5621 5999

GTM'S DISCOUNT GENERAL STORES
See GTM WHOLESALE LIQUIDATORS INC

D-U-N-S 11-961-8705
GTNX INC
GT NEXUS
(Suby of INFOR INC) ★
1111 Broadway 5f, Oakland, CA 94607-4139
Tel (510) 808-2222 Founded/Ownrshp 2015
Sales 38.2MM^E EMP 85^E
SIC 4813
CEO: Sean Feeney
COO: Guy Rey-Herme
Ex VP: Andreas Stinnes
Ex VP: John Urban
VP: Cary Dittmann
VP: Michael Hubbard
VP: Jenny Nevin
VP: Gary Schneider
Mng Dir: Andy Stinnes
Dir Sec: Kurt Cavano
CTO: Nestor Zwyhun

D-U-N-S 61-523-0430
GTO 2000 INC
2555 Flintridge Rd, Gainesville, GA 30501-7426
Tel (800) 966-0801 Founded/Ownrshp 1975
Sales 23.5MM^E EMP 40
SIC 4731 Freight transportation arrangement
CEO: G Thomas Cornett
*Pr: Gregg Gordon
*CFO: George T Cornett

D-U-N-S 18-382-5553 IMP/EXP
■ **GTO ACCESS SYSTEMS LLC**
(Suby of NORTEK SECURITY & CONTROL LLC)
3121 Hartsfield Rd, Tallahassee, FL 32303-3149
Tel (850) 575-0176 Founded/Ownrshp 1987
Sales 24.9MM^E EMP 90
SIC 3699 Security control equipment & systems
Pr: Shaun Burke
Pr: Joseph A Kelley
*Pr: Douglas Waldal
VP: Brian Campbell
Manager: Pauline Haas
Sls Mgr: Mike Jessen

GTP
See GLOBAL TUNGSTEN & POWDERS CORP

D-U-N-S 62-180-0325
GTR ENTERPRISES INC
THOMASVILLE TOYOTA
14724 Us Highway 19 S, Thomasville, GA 31757-4817
Tel (229) 584-0865 Founded/Ownrshp 1991
Sales 27.2MM^E EMP 58
SIC 5511 Automobiles, new & used; Automobiles, new & used
Pr: Gregg Isaacs
VP: Travis Ostrom
Off Mgr: Sherri Tyson
Sls Mgr: Joe Scarbor
Sales Asso: Ray Flowers
Sales Asso: Brandon Mock

GTRI
See GLOBAL TECHNOLOGY RESOURCES INC

GTS
See GEORGE T SANDERS CO

GTS
See GAS TRANSMISSION SYSTEMS INC

GTS
See GLOBAL TRADING AND SOURCING CORP

GTS
See GROUP TRANSPORTATION SERVICES INC

D-U-N-S 09-856-0055
GTS DRYWALL SUPPLY CO
GTS INTERIOR SUPPLY
(Suby of G M S) ★
10819 120th Ave Ne, Kirkland, WA 98033-5024
Tel (425) 828-0608 Founded/Ownrshp 2000
Sales 84.5MM^E EMP 350
SIC 5032

D-U-N-S 80-442-7859
GTS HOLDINGS INC
EMPIRE CLS WORLDWIDE
225 Madowlands Pkwy Ste 1, Secaucus, NJ 07094
Tel (201) 784-1200 Founded/Ownrshp 2005
Sales 68.9MM^E EMP 561
SIC 4119 4111 Limousine rental, with driver; Airport limousine, scheduled service; Limousine rental, with driver; Airport limousine, scheduled service
Pr: David Seelinger
Pr: Abbie Kelly
*CFO: Nat Buonfiglio
VP: Jerry Dickson
VP: Marissa Natsikostas
VP: Joey Phelps
Dir Bus: Abbie Siek
Admn Mgr: Jerry De Armond
CIO: Alan Bourassa
CTO: Jeff Thorson
IT Man: James Gilbert

GTS INTERIOR SUPPLY
See GTS DRYWALL SUPPLY CO

GTS-WELCO
See PRAXAIR DISTRIBUTION MID-ATLANTIC LLC

D-U-N-S 79-077-6780
▲ **GTT COMMUNICATIONS INC**
7900 Tysons One Pl 1450, Mc Lean, VA 22102-5971
Tel (703) 442-5500 Founded/Ownrshp 2005
Sales 207.3MM EMP 294^E
Tkr Sym GTT Exch NYS
SIC 4813 ; ; ;
Pr: Richard D Calder Jr
Ch Bd: H Brian Thompson
CFO: Michael Sicoli
Chf Mktg O: Gina Nomellini
Ex VP: Chris McKee
Sr VP: John G Hendler
Sr VP: Brent McCutchin
VP: Peter Berg
VP: Jake Cummins
VP: Bernie McGroder
VP: Luca Smuraglia
Dir Risk M: Layne Levine
Board of Directors: S Joseph Bruno, Rhodric C Hackman, Howard E Janzen, Morgan E O'brien, Theodore B Smith III

D-U-N-S 78-508-6997
GTW CONSULTANTS & ASSOCIATES LLC
(Suby of CHENEGA CORP) ★
5726 W Hausman Rd Ste 100, San Antonio, TX 78249-1651
Tel (210) 424-2094 Founded/Ownrshp 2006
Sales 42.2MM EMP 1^E
Accts Mcgladrey Llp Frederick Mary
SIC 8742 Business planning & organizing services; Business planning & organizing services
Genl Mgr: Stephanie Hill

D-U-N-S 13-120-7271
GU MARKETS LLC
GRAND UNION FAMILY MARKETS
(Suby of C&S WHOLESALE GROCERS INC) ★
4350 Middle Settlement Rd, New Hartford, NY 13413-5345
Tel (315) 793-9226 Founded/Ownrshp 2001
Sales 92.2MM^E EMP 1,100
SIC 5411 Grocery stores; Grocery stores
Ch Bd: Richard B Cohen
*CFO: William Hamlin
*Ex VP: Scott Charlton

D-U-N-S 13-520-5966 IMP
GU-YOUNG TECH CO LTD
GUYOUNG TECH
(Suby of GUYOUNG TECH CO., LTD.)
26555 Evergreen Rd, Southfield, MI 48076-4206
Tel (248) 701-6663 Founded/Ownrshp 2003
Sales 86.8MM EMP 129
Accts Pnjk Partners Llp Park Ridge
SIC 5013 Automotive supplies & parts; Automotive supplies & parts
Pr: Mia Kuratko

D-U-N-S 07-459-5422
GUADALUPE COUNTY
211 W Court St, Seguin, TX 78155-2545
Tel (830) 303-4188 Founded/Ownrshp 1846
Sales NA EMP 550
Accts Armstrong Vaughn And Assoc
SIC 9111 Executive offices; ; Executive offices;
Ofcr: Bill Macallister
*Ex Dir: Mike Wiggins
Board of Directors: Shirley Hester, Wyatt Butch Kunde, Jim Wolverston

D-U-N-S 15-391-0898
GUADALUPE ECONOMIC SERVICES CORP
G E S C
1502 Erskine St, Lubbock, TX 79403-3214
Tel (806) 744-4416 Founded/Ownrshp 1983
Sales 199.5M EMP 500
SIC 8322 8732 Individual & family services; Economic research; Individual & family services; Economic research
Ex Dir: Diana Lopez
*Pr: Richard Lopez
*VP: Mario Heredia

D-U-N-S 00-895-2806 IMP
GUADALUPE LUMBER & SUPPLY CO INC (TX)
1547 S Zarzamora St, San Antonio, TX 78207-7212
Tel (210) 223-4263 Founded/Ownrshp 1933
Sales 30.9MM^E EMP 129
SIC 5211 Lumber & other building materials; Lumber products; Doors, storm: wood or metal; Cabinets, kitchen; Lumber & other building materials; Lumber products; Doors, storm: wood or metal; Cabinets, kitchen
Pr: Mark Grothues
*VP: Phil M Grothues

D-U-N-S 07-462-0170
GUADALUPE REGIONAL MEDICAL CENTER
1215 E Court St, Seguin, TX 78155-5129
Tel (830) 379-2411 Founded/Ownrshp 1961
Sales 84.9MM EMP 678
Accts Bkd Llp Houston Tx
SIC 8062 General medical & surgical hospitals; General medical & surgical hospitals
CEO: Robert Haynes
*Ch Bd: Robert Galloway
*CFO: Penny Wallace
VP: Sheri Williams
Dir Rx: Larry Hicks
Chf Nrs Of: Daphne Blake
Prac Mgr: Susie Prichard
CIO: Chuck McWhorter
Telecom Mg: Mark Williams
Mktg Dir: Amanda Davila
Psych: Leigh Falk

D-U-N-S 10-707-9717
GUADALUPE VALLEY COMMUNICATIONS SYSTEMS INC
GVTC
(Suby of GUADALUPE VALLEY TELEPHONE COOPERATIVE INC) ★
36101 Fm 3159, New Braunfels, TX 78132-5903
Tel (830) 885-4411 Founded/Ownrshp 1980
Sales 31.0MM EMP 20^E
SIC 4841 Cable television services; Cable television services
CEO: Ritchie Sorrells
*CFO: Mark Gitter
Sr Cor Off: Lee Eubanks
Sr Cor Off: Edward Gottfried
VP: Ray Bacon
*VP: Robert Hunt

D-U-N-S 00-793-0589
GUADALUPE VALLEY ELECTRIC COOPERATIVE INC (TX)
GVEC
825 N Sarah Dewitt Dr, Gonzales, TX 78629
Tel (830) 857-1200 Founded/Ownrshp 1938
Sales 133.1MM^E EMP 300
SIC 4911

D-U-N-S 00-480-2393
GUADALUPE VALLEY TELEPHONE COOPERATIVE INC (TX)
GVTC
36101 Fm 3159, New Braunfels, TX 78132-5900
Tel (830) 885-4411 Founded/Ownrshp 1951
Sales 63.4MM EMP 229
SIC 4813 Local telephone communications; Local telephone communications
Pr: Ritchie Sorrells
*CFO: Mark J Gitter
Bd of Dir: Kathy Adolphson
Bd of Dir: Brandi Quinn
Bd of Dir: Diane Sinclair
Bd of Dir: Rusty Surratt
Bd of Dir: Clint Swindall
Bd of Dir: John Turner
Bd of Dir: Scott Wiebensohn
Top Exec: Cleta Akins
*Sr VP: Robert Hunt
*VP: Robert Hun
*VP: George O'Neal
*VP: Josh Pettiette

D-U-N-S 05-631-1608
GUADALUPE-BLANCO RIVER AUTHORITY INDUSTRIAL DEVELOPMENT CORP
933 E Court St, Seguin, TX 78155-5872
Tel (361) 575-6366 Founded/Ownrshp 1935
Sales 84.6MM^E EMP 165
Accts Thompson Williams Biediger K
SIC 4911 4941 4952 Generation, electric power; Water supply; Sewerage systems; Generation, electric power; Water supply; Sewerage systems
Pr: James L Powers
Ofcr: Karl Allen
Ofcr: Robert Garcia
Ofcr: Jason Hamilton
Ofcr: Maribel Perkins
*VP: Tommy Mathews
VP: John P Schneider Jr
Div Mgr: Darel Ball
Div Mgr: Mike Urrutia
Genl Mgr: Myrne McLeroy
Genl Mgr: E West

D-U-N-S 83-544-8580
GUAJOME PARK ACADEMY INC
2000 N Santa Fe Ave, Vista, CA 92083-1534
Tel (760) 631-6177 Founded/Ownrshp 1993
Sales 10.6MM EMP 300
Accts Vavrinektrineday & Co Llp Ran
SIC 8211 Private elementary & secondary schools; Private elementary & secondary schools
Psych: Maureen Changnon

D-U-N-S 07-886-2388
■ **GUANTANAMO FACILITY SERVICES LLC**
(Suby of EMCOR GOVERNMENT SERVICES INC) ★
2800 Crystal Dr Ste 600, Arlington, VA 22202-3590
Tel (571) 403-8900 Founded/Ownrshp 2013
Sales 7.2MM^E EMP 399
SIC 1791 8748 8744 Structural steel erection; Business consulting; Facilities support services; Structural steel erection; Business consulting; Facilities support services

D-U-N-S 15-160-9203 IMP
GUARACHI WINE PARTNERS
TGIC WINE IMP & WHOLESALER
22837 Ventura Blvd # 300, Woodland Hills, CA 91364-1224
Tel (818) 225-5100 Founded/Ownrshp 1988
Sales 46.2MM^E EMP 80
SIC 5182 Wine; Wine
Prin: Alex Guarachi
VP: Joseph Granados
Mktg Mgr: Christian Dix

D-U-N-S 09-059-0282 IMP/EXP
GUARAGUAO TRUCK SALES INC
Km 5 Hm 1 Rr 174, Bayamon, PR 00959
Tel (787) 780-0090 Founded/Ownrshp 1977
Sales 29.1MM EMP 64
Accts Ricardo Blanco Vega Bayamon
SIC 5511 3713 7538 Trucks, tractors & trailers: new & used; Truck cabs for motor vehicles; Truck engine repair, except industrial; Trucks, tractors & trailers: new & used; Truck cabs for motor vehicles; Truck engine repair, except industrial
Pr: Javier Covas
*Sec: Sonia Covas
*VP: Oscar W Covas
Genl Mgr: Lorenzo Lopez
IT Man: Ronald Hernandez
IT Man: Roberto Rivera

D-U-N-S 00-890-8519
GUARANTEE ELECTRICAL CO
3405 Bent Ave, Saint Louis, MO 63116-2601
Tel (314) 772-5400 Founded/Ownrshp 1945
Sales 168.9MM EMP 700
Accts Uhy Llp St Louis Missouri
SIC 1731 Electrical work; Electrical work
CEO: Rick Oertli
Pr: Douglas Mertzlufft
CFO: Josh Voegtli
Ex VP: Roger Oertli
VP: Dave Gralike
VP: Nazeeh Kiblawi
VP: Mike Minor
VP: Donald Umphryes
Exec: Linda McGillis
VP Mktg: Steve Briesacher
Sls Dir: Rick Sandahl

D-U-N-S 04-234-7265
GUARANTEE ELECTRICAL CONSTRUCTION CO
(Suby of GUARANTEE ELECTRICAL CO) ★
3415 Bent Ave, Saint Louis, MO 63116-2601
Tel (314) 772-5400 Founded/Ownrshp 1998
Sales 40.8MM^E EMP 700
SIC 1731 Electrical work; Electrical work
Sr VP: David Gralike
*Pr: Douglas Mertzlufft
*CFO: Josh Voegtli

D-U-N-S 95-790-5136
GUARANTEE ELECTRICAL CONTRACTING LLC
(Suby of GUARANTEE ELECTRICAL CO) ★
21250 E 31st Cir, Aurora, CO 80011-8138
Tel (303) 373-2400 Founded/Ownrshp 2003
Sales 26.2MM EMP 175
SIC 1731 General electrical contractor; General electrical contractor
Pr: Douglas Mertzlufft
CFO: Josh Voegtli
Sr VP: Steve Juan
Sfty Mgr: Gary Swanstrom

D-U-N-S 14-318-0433
GUARANTEE INSURANCE CO
401 E Las Olas Blvd # 1540, Fort Lauderdale, FL 33301-2247
Tel (954) 670-2900 Founded/Ownrshp 2003
Sales 40.2MM^E EMP 250
SIC 8741 6411 Administrative management; Insurance agents, brokers & service; Administrative management; Insurance agents, brokers & service
CEO: Steven Mariano
Pr: Charles K Schuver
COO: Gary Roche
CFO: Michael Grandstaff
CFO: Michael Sluka
Ofcr: Kim Davis
Off Mgr: Debra Gorson
Dir IT: Jeff Moeller
Genl Couns: Eric Dawson

D-U-N-S 96-285-9778
GUARANTEE INSURANCE GROUP
401 E Las Olas Blvd # 1650, Fort Lauderdale, FL 33301-2210
Tel (954) 670-2900 Founded/Ownrshp 2010
Sales NA EMP 390^E
SIC 6411 6331 Insurance agents, brokers & service; Workers' compensation insurance; Insurance agents, brokers & service; Workers' compensation insurance
CEO: Steven M Mariano
Pr: Thomas McCarthy
*Pr: John Rearer
*Pr: Charles K Schuver
Pr: Jessica Werckman
*COO: Bob Peters
CFO: Michael Grandstaff
*Treas: Michael J Sluka
Rgnl VP: Colin B Williams

*Ex VP: Michael W Grandstaff
Ex VP: Paul Halter
Ex VP: Christopher Pesch
Sr VP: Frank Kushler
Sr VP: Christopher Pizzo
VP: Lisa Balmer
VP: John Brant
VP: Michael McFadden
VP: Timothy O'Malley
VP: Joyce Predmesky
VP: Edward Sharples
VP: Anat Veader
Board of Directors: John R Del Pizzo

D-U-N-S 80-895-7484
GUARANTEE INTERIORS INC
GI CONSTRUCTION
2914 Locust St, Saint Louis, MO 63103-1311
Tel (314) 881-3300 Founded/Ownrshp 1993
Sales 38.3MM^E EMP 75
SIC 1611 1799 General contractor, highway & street construction; Home/office interiors finishing, furnishing & remodeling
Pr: Robert Farrell Sr
*VP: Robert Farrell Jr
*VP: Steve Farrell
VP: Steve Stroup

GUARANTEE MORTGAGE
See FUGI FINANCE INC

D-U-N-S 13-228-3735
GUARANTEE MORTGAGE CORP
SECURITY FIRST LOAN
7250 Redwood Blvd Ste 109, Novato, CA 94945-3269
Tel (415) 925-8080 Founded/Ownrshp 2003
Sales NA EMP 225
SIC 6163 Mortgage brokers arranging for loans, using money of others; Mortgage brokers arranging for loans, using money of others
Pr: Robert Michael Siefert
Pt: Rick Cunniffe
*COO: Carole Lombard
*CFO: Bahar Tolu
Ofcr: Jake Siefert

GUARANTEE RECORDS MANAGEMENT
See GRM INFORMATION MANAGEMENT SERVICES INC

D-U-N-S 07-974-2060
GUARANTEE TRUST LIFE INSURANCE CO
1275 Milwaukee Ave # 100, Glenview, IL 60025-2489
Tel (847) 699-0600 Founded/Ownrshp 1957
Sales NA EMP 250
SIC 6321 6311 Accident insurance carriers; Health insurance carriers; Life insurance carriers; Accident insurance carriers; Health insurance carriers; Life insurance carriers
Pr: Richard S Holson III
COO: Jim Knutson
*Treas: Barbara Taube
*Sr VP: Mark Stevenson
*VP: Don Abbs
*VP: Richard Affenit
VP: Tim Barrett
VP: Joe Demonte
VP: Reed Gass
VP: Michael Haas
VP: Lesley Hanslope
VP: Rick Harman
VP: Richard M Herman
VP: Bobby Jann
VP: Edward Konar
VP: Carl Leader
VP: Demetri Simos
Exec: Nancy Carbone

GUARANTEED BANKING CALIFORNIA
See GBC INTERNATIONAL BANK

GUARANTEED BANKING CALIFORNIA
See G B C HOLDINGS INC

GUARANTEED RATE
See SUPERIOR MORTGAGE CORP

D-U-N-S 83-966-6919
GUARANTEED RATE INC
3940 N Ravenswood Ave, Chicago, IL 60613-2420
Tel (773) 290-0349 Founded/Ownrshp 1999
Sales NA EMP 2,158
SIC 6162 Mortgage bankers; Mortgage bankers
Pr: Victor Ciardelli III
Pr: Matthew Leahy
COO: Rob Sampson
*CFO: Ted Ahern
Ofcr: John Grad
Ex VP: Charles Bachtell
Ex VP: Adal Bisharat
Sr VP: Ricardo H Brasil
Sr VP: Juli Rennie
VP: Dirk Allman
VP: Frank Babb
VP: Allison Barker
VP: Bianca Barton
*VP: Anne Benoist
VP: Jeremy Bierlein
VP: Steven Bottone
VP: Joe Burke
VP: Joe Caltabiano
VP: Bob Carr
VP: Brandon Coll
VP: Anna Crossley

GUARANTEED RECYCLING XPERTS
See METECH RECYCLING INC

GUARANTEED RETURNS
See DEVOS LTD

GUARANTEED SAND & GRAVEL
See SOUTHERN MINNESOTA CONSTRUCTION CO INC

D-U-N-S 02-459-1059
GUARANTEED SUPPLY CO
1211 Rotherwood Rd, Greensboro, NC 27406-3825
Tel (336) 273-3491 Founded/Ownrshp 1965
Sales 178.2MM^E EMP 300
SIC 5032 Brick, stone & related material
Pr: Willie Goncharow

*Ch Bd: Kirby Ward
*Treas: Marie Grogan

D-U-N-S 07-242-8329
GUARANTY ABSTRACT CO (OK)
320 S Boulder Ave, Tulsa, OK 74103-3400
Tel (918) 587-6621 Founded/Ownrshp 1928
Sales 25.6MM^E EMP 140
SIC 6541 Title abstract offices
Pr: John C Kirkpatrick
*Treas: Ann Wallace
*Ex VP: Dale Astle
*Ex VP: Bonnie Hudson
Ex VP: Sherry McGann
*Sr VP: Larry Johnson
VP: Julie Lamprich

D-U-N-S 15-764-2823
▲ **GUARANTY BANCORP**
1331 17th St Ste 200, Denver, CO 80202-1566
Tel (303) 296-9600 Founded/Ownrshp 2004
Sales NA EMP 389^E
Accts Crowe Horwath Llp Oak Brook
Tkr Sym GBNK Exch NGS
SIC 6022 State commercial banks; State commercial banks
Pr: Paul W Taylor
*Ch Bd: Edward B Cordes
CFO: Christopher G Treece
Chf Cred: Cathy P Goss
Ofcr: Terry Justis
Ex VP: Zsolt K Bessk
Ex VP: James Simons
VP: Sean Larkin
VP: Amy Lovell
VP: Jody Soper
VP: Carolyn Tyrrell
VP: Jordan Walgreen
Exec: Steven Kitchen
Board of Directors: John M Eggemeyer, Keith R Finger, Stephen D Joyce, Gail H Klapper, Stephen G McConahey, W Kirk Wycoff, Albert C Yates

D-U-N-S 07-260-8185
GUARANTY BANCSHARES INC
100 W Arkansas St, Mount Pleasant, TX 75455-4420
Tel (903) 572-9881 Founded/Ownrshp 1979
Sales NA EMP 245
SIC 6022 State commercial banks; State commercial banks
Ch Bd: Art B Scharlach
*Pr: Tyson T Abston
*CFO: Clifton A Payne
Sr VP: Melissa Merchant
VP: Clifton Apayne
VP: Bond Bank
VP: Barry Jones
*VP: Kirk Lee
VP: Mary Munsinger
VP: Robin Sharp
IT Man: Craig Roberts

D-U-N-S 03-829-9640
■ **GUARANTY BANK**
(Suby of GUARANTY FEDERAL BANCSHARES INC) ★
1341 W Battlefield St # 100, Springfield, MO 65807-4101
Tel (417) 520-4333 Founded/Ownrshp 1997
Sales NA EMP 150
SIC 6036 Savings institutions, not federally chartered; Savings institutions, not federally chartered
Ex VP: William B Williams
Pr: Carter Peters
COO: Robin E Robeson
Treas: Derek Fraley
Ofcr: Carol Sparlin
Ex VP: Sheri Biser
Sr VP: Kenton Devries
Sr VP: Michael Frerking
Sr VP: Lyndall Magers
Sr VP: Mike McConnell
Sr VP: Lance Pearce
VP: Brad Farris
VP: Micah Scott

D-U-N-S 07-116-4388
GUARANTY BANK
(Suby of GUARANTY FINANCIAL MHC) ★
4000 W Brown Deer Rd, Milwaukee, WI 53209-1221
Tel (414) 362-4000 Founded/Ownrshp 2003
Sales NA EMP 958
SIC 6035 6029 Federal savings & loan associations; Commercial banks; Federal savings & loan associations; Commercial banks
Pr: Jill Belconis
*CEO: Doug Levy
*CFO: Richard Larson
*CFO: Randy Vandenhouten
Sr VP: Michael Spillane
Sr VP: Bill Verbos
VP: Dan Kindl
Exec: Lisa Decker
CTO: George Clark
IT Man: Claudia Reid
Sls Mgr: Chris Hogg

D-U-N-S 00-499-9157
GUARANTY BANK & TRUST NA
(Suby of GUARANTY BANCSHARES INC) ★
201 S Jefferson Ave, Mount Pleasant, TX 75455-4425
Tel (903) 572-9881 Founded/Ownrshp 1913
Sales NA EMP 245
SIC 6022 State commercial banks; State commercial banks
CEO: Tyson Abston
Pr: Chuck Allen
Pr: Theta Hicks
*Pr: Kirk Lee
*Pr: Clifton A Payne
Sr Cor Off: Kim Shumate
*Ex VP: Robin Sharp
Sr VP: Gene Erwin
Sr VP: David Hand
Sr VP: Melissa Merchant
Sr VP: Terry Todd
Sr VP: Mick Trusty
VP: Alisa Boatner
VP: Dureen Fuller
VP: Joey Hamm

VP: Andrew Hoeniges
VP: Terri Lee
VP: Mary Munsinger
VP: Suzanne Walker

D-U-N-S 00-691-5557
■ **GUARANTY BANK AND TRUST CO**
(Suby of GUARANTY BANCORP) ★
1331 17th St Lbby, Denver, CO 80202-5892
Tel (303) 298-6977 Founded/Ownrshp 2005
Sales NA EMP 365^E
SIC 6022 State commercial banks; State commercial banks
Ch Bd: Paul W Taylor
*Pr: Michael B Hobbs
Ex VP: Erik Hammer
Ex VP: Anthony Pizzichini
Ex VP: Mark Truitt
Ex VP: Robert Unger
Sr VP: Brian Brennan
Sr VP: Matthew Carrothers
Sr VP: Nancy Henry
*Sr VP: Amy Lovell
Sr VP: Jim Ocken
Sr VP: Jennifer Ostenson
VP: Clint Crews
VP: Sandra Crosthwaite
VP: Maren Eckert
VP: John Fiedler
*VP: Cathy Goss
VP: Michael A Justice
VP: Brian Kooienga
VP: Marilyn Mace
VP: Lee Maher

D-U-N-S 15-723-3727
GUARANTY BANK AND TRUST CO
210 N Hayden St, Belzoni, MS 39038-3636
Tel (662) 247-1454 Founded/Ownrshp 1981
Sales NA EMP 61
SIC 6022 State commercial banks; State commercial banks
CEO: Huey Townsend
Sr VP: Myra Dunlap
VP: Terry Burford
VP: Cousia Giglio
*VP: Jerry Gillespie
VP: Norma Quinn
VP: Anne Tirey
Brnch Mgr: Terisa Cochran
Dir IT: Monte Kramer

D-U-N-S 00-796-8845
GUARANTY CHEVROLET MOTORS INC (CA)
711 E 17th St, Santa Ana, CA 92701-2578
Tel (714) 953-6133 Founded/Ownrshp 1952, 1975
Sales 61.6MM^E EMP 105
Accts Parke Guptill & Co
SIC 5511 Automobiles, new & used; Automobiles, new & used
CEO: Bruce J Hamlin
*Treas: Evelyn Long
*VP: Bruce Hamlin
Exec: Nancy Reyes
Dept Mgr: Randy Boswell
Dept Mgr: Jim Debelak
Dept Mgr: Greg Mayfield
Dept Mgr: Jack Nesheiwat
Dept Mgr: Andy Pena
Sls Mgr: Michael Benning
Sls Mgr: Joe Renden

D-U-N-S 00-820-6963
GUARANTY CORP
929 Government St Ste 101, Baton Rouge, LA 70802-6034
Tel (225) 383-0355 Founded/Ownrshp 1926
Sales NA EMP 175
SIC 6311 Life insurance; Life insurance
Ch Bd: George A Foster Jr
*Pr: John Lancaster
*Treas: Forrest Mills Jr
*VP: George Foster III

D-U-N-S 09-509-3683
▲ **GUARANTY FEDERAL BANCSHARES INC**
1341 W Battlefield St, Springfield, MO 65807-4101
Tel (417) 520-4333 Founded/Ownrshp 1997
Sales NA EMP 167^E
Tkr Sym GFED Exch NGM
SIC 6022 State commercial banks
Pr: Shaun A Burke
*Ch Bd: Don M Gibson
CFO: Carter Peters
Ex VP: Robin E Robeson
Sr VP: Eric Leonard
VP: Paul Fry
CIO: Kenneth Johnston
IT Man: Chandler Johnston
Site Mgr: Jennifer Gunter
Site Mgr: Stacey Richardson
Snr Mgr: Kent Chambers

D-U-N-S 84-920-2932
GUARANTY FINANCIAL MHC
4000 W Brown Deer Rd, Milwaukee, WI 53209-1221
Tel (414) 362-4000 Founded/Ownrshp 1993
Sales NA EMP 1,933
SIC 6035 Federal savings & loan associations; Federal savings & loan associations
CEO: John T Stuart
COO: Kevin Hanigan
CFO: Althea Bickham
CFO: Ronald D Murff
Treas: Steven Rafael
Ex VP: Scott A Almy
Board of Directors: John S Ettenheim, Milton B Ettenheim Jr, Max Gendelman, Jack Recht, Samuel D Saffro, Abe A Tannenbaum

D-U-N-S 09-957-6662
GUARANTY INSURANCE SERVICES INC
(Suby of INSURICA INC) ★
3721 Executive Center Dr # 200, Austin, TX 78731-1645
Tel (512) 381-8350 Founded/Ownrshp 2011
Sales NA EMP 240
SIC 6411 Insurance agents; Insurance agents

Pr: Harold L Shults Jr
*VP: Von Breaux
VP: Devin Stewart

D-U-N-S 02-766-0588
GUARANTY RV INC
20 Highway 99 S, Junction City, OR 97448-9714
Tel (541) 998-2333 Founded/Ownrshp 1966
Sales 152.8MM^E EMP 425
SIC 5561 5511 Recreational vehicle dealers; Recreational vehicle parts & accessories; Automobiles, new & used; Recreational vehicle dealers; Recreational vehicle parts & accessories; Automobiles, new & used
Pr: Herbert N Nill
*COO: Shannon Nill
*CFO: Ed Morgan
Treas: Evelyn Long
Exec: Bruce Kremis
Ex Dir: Jolene Loudon
Genl Mgr: Derek Vonotterstedt
Dir IT: Terry Creighton
Sales Exec: Bret Frost
Sls Mgr: Doug Ebner
Sales Asso: Ken Cooper

D-U-N-S 17-002-4343
GUARANTY TITLE SERVICES INC
481 E Division St Ste 800, Fond Du Lac, WI 54935-3769
Tel (920) 921-1300 Founded/Ownrshp 1983
Sales NA EMP 100
SIC 6361 Real estate title insurance
CEO: Louis Andrew
*VP: Debra Walgenbach
Dir IT: James Ditter
IT Man: Lori Reeths

D-U-N-S 61-462-0664
GUARANTY TITLE SERVICES INC
151 N Main St, Juneau, WI 53039-1099
Tel (920) 386-2300 Founded/Ownrshp 1990
Sales NA EMP 120
SIC 6361 Title insurance
Pr: Louis Andrew
*VP: Diane Scherer

D-U-N-S 14-764-3753
GUARANTY TRUST CO
(Suby of VOLUNTEER STATE BANK) ★
316 Robert Rose Dr, Murfreesboro, TN 37129-6337
Tel (615) 895-5101 Founded/Ownrshp 1988
Sales NA EMP 41
Accts Crowe Horwath Llp Brentwood
SIC 6162 Mortgage bankers
Pr: Wendell O Mandrell
VP: Retta Gardner
Brnch Mgr: Kevin Blankenship

D-U-N-S 60-819-7182
GUARD FINANCIAL GROUP INC
16 S River St, Wilkes Barre, PA 18702-2406
Tel (570) 825-9900 Founded/Ownrshp 1982
Sales NA EMP 310
SIC 6331 8741 Fire, marine & casualty insurance: stock; Administrative management; Fire, marine & casualty insurance: stock; Administrative management
Ch Bd: Y Judd Shoval
Pr: Susan W Shoval
CFO: Jeffrey E Picker

D-U-N-S 60-805-5232
■ **GUARD INSURANCE GROUP INC**
WESTGUARD INSURANCE COMPANY
(Suby of BERKSHIRE HATHAWAY INC) ★
16 S River St, Wilkes Barre, PA 18702-2494
Tel (570) 825-9900 Founded/Ownrshp 2012
Sales NA EMP 275
SIC 6331

D-U-N-S 07-018-1826
GUARD MANAGEMENT INC
G M I
8001 Vickers St, San Diego, CA 92111-1917
Tel (858) 279-8282 Founded/Ownrshp 1992
Sales 12.6MM^E EMP 510
SIC 7381 Guard services; Guard services
Pr: Larry Abrams
CFO: Barry Williamson
Brnch Mgr: Thomas Redmann
Opers Mgr: Brianna Wiley

D-U-N-S 00-902-9893
GUARD PUBLISHING CO
REGISTER GUARD, THE
3500 Chad Dr, Eugene, OR 97408-7426
Tel (541) 485-1234 Founded/Ownrshp 1961
Sales 43.1MM^E EMP 275^E
SIC 2711 Newspapers, publishing & printing; Newspapers, publishing & printing
Pr: Alton F Baker III
*Ch Bd: Edwin M Baker
*Treas: Ann Baker Mack
*VP: R Fletcher Little
Dist Mgr: Jeff Lawton
Genl Mgr: Alan Beck
CTO: Chris McIntosh
Sfty Mgr: Lisa Hanson
Advt Mgr: Donovan Mack
Mktg Mgr: Sally Wickes
Assoc Ed: Paul Neville

D-U-N-S 04-921-4281 IMP
GUARD-LINE INC
215 S Louise St, Atlanta, TX 75551-2718
Tel (903) 796-4111 Founded/Ownrshp 1960
Sales 23.0MM^E EMP 220
SIC 3151 3842 2394 2381 2353 2326 Gloves, leather: work; Welders' gloves; Personal safety equipment; Clothing, fire resistant & protective; Gloves, safety; Canvas & related products; Fabric dress & work gloves; Hats, caps & millinery; Men's & boys' work clothing; Gloves, leather: work; Welders' gloves; Personal safety equipment; Clothing, fire resistant & protective; Gloves, safety; Canvas & related products; Fabric dress & work gloves; Hats, caps & millinery; Men's & boys' work clothing

Pr: Dennis J Stanley
**VP:* H Lee Stanley
Sls Mgr: C Sharpe

D-U-N-S 02-274-4093
GUARD-SYSTEMS INC
1190 Monterey Pass Rd, Monterey Park, CA 91754-3615
Tel (626) 443-0031 *Founded/Ownrshp* 1961
Sales 7.9MM *EMP* 1,150
Accts Lucashorsfall Murphy & Pindr
SIC 7381 Detective & armored car services; Guard services; Security guard service; Detective & armored car services; Guard services; Security guard service
Pr: Theodore Haas
**VP:* Leo Austin

GUARDIA NACIONAL DE PR
See NATIONAL GUARD PUERTO RICO

GUARDIAN, THE
See FOSTER KLIMA & CO LLC

D-U-N-S 07-559-8750
GUARDIAN AD LITEM
600 S Calhoun St Ste 274, Tallahassee, FL 32301-2009
Tel (850) 922-7213 *Founded/Ownrshp* 1990
Sales 43.0MM *EMP* 695
SIC 8322 Child related social services

D-U-N-S 83-275-5198 IMP
GUARDIAN AGRICULTURAL PLASTICS CORP
(*Suby of* MCNEEL CAPITAL) ★
5401 W Kennedy Blvd, Tampa, FL 33609-2428
Tel (813) 286-8680 *Founded/Ownrshp* 2007
Sales 1.3MM^E *EMP* 450^E
SIC 3081 Unsupported plastics film & sheet
Pr: Clayton W McNeel
**CFO:* Rene M Wood
**VP:* Ian E McNeel

D-U-N-S 05-769-8409
GUARDIAN ALARM CO OF MICH
20800 Southfield Rd, Southfield, MI 48075-4238
Tel (248) 423-1000 *Founded/Ownrshp* 1930
Sales 44.6MM^E *EMP* 500
SIC 7382 1731 Burglar alarm maintenance & monitoring; Protective devices, security; Fire detection & burglar alarm systems specialization; Burglar alarm maintenance & monitoring; Protective devices, security; Fire detection & burglar alarm systems specialization
Ch Bd: Milton Pierce
**Pr:* Douglas Pierce
**Sec:* Richard Pierce
Genl Mgr: Chris Heringer
Genl Mgr: Karen Majeske
Netwrk Mgr: Carl Zahrt
MIS Mgr: Harry Hayden
Opers Mgr: Julina Paprich
Sales Asso: Andrea Stone

D-U-N-S 79-253-5135
GUARDIAN ANALYTICS INC
2465 Latham St Ste 200, Mountain View, CA 94040-4792
Tel (650) 383-9200 *Founded/Ownrshp* 2005
Sales 25.5MM^E *EMP* 27
SIC 5045 Computer software
CEO: Greg Owens
Pr: Dennis Concannon
Pr: Steve Gibson
CFO: Leslie Lucas
VP: Steve Schramm
Dir IT: Lien McCarthy
Sftwr Eng: Devesh Singh
VP Mktg: Craig Priess
Mktg Dir: Eric Labadie
Mktg Dir: Alexa Sevilla
Sls Dir: Jim Cook

D-U-N-S 61-450-9474
GUARDIAN ANGELS HOMECARE LLC
405 Maple Ave Ste 1, Cheshire, CT 06410-2154
Tel (203) 439-7731 *Founded/Ownrshp* 2005
Sales 2.0MM *EMP* 350
SIC 8082 5999 Home health care services; Medical apparatus & supplies; Home health care services; Medical apparatus & supplies

GUARDIAN AUTO GLASS
See GUARDIAN GLASS CO

D-U-N-S 07-055-1937
GUARDIAN AUTO LEASING LLC
GRAFF CHEVROLET
1405 E Main St, Grand Prairie, TX 75050-5939
Tel (972) 264-0700 *Founded/Ownrshp* 1999
Sales 23.4MM^E *EMP* 150
SIC 5511 5521 Automobiles, new & used; Automobiles, used cars only; Automobiles, new & used; Automobiles, used cars only
Genl Mgr: Ron Harris

D-U-N-S 00-532-2052 IMP
GUARDIAN AUTOMOTIVE CORP (MI)
GUARDIAN AUTOMOTIVE TRIM
(*Suby of* SRG GLOBAL INC) ★
23751 Amber Ave, Warren, MI 48089-6000
Tel (586) 757-7800 *Founded/Ownrshp* 1949, 1996
Sales 275.0MM^E *EMP* 2,500
SIC 3089 3465 Extruded finished plastic products; Molding primary plastic; Moldings or trim, automobile: stamped metal; Extruded finished plastic products; Molding primary plastic; Moldings or trim, automobile: stamped metal
CEO: Daniel J Davis
**Sr VP:* Kevin Myers
**VP:* Joseph Abbruzzi
**VP:* Chuck Wilson
Plnt Mgr: David Serpa

GUARDIAN AUTOMOTIVE TRIM
See GUARDIAN AUTOMOTIVE CORP

D-U-N-S 00-700-1050
GUARDIAN AUTOMOTIVE TRIM INC (NV)
SRG GLOBAL EVANSVILLE
(*Suby of* SRG GLOBAL INC) ★
601 N Congress Ave, Evansville, IN 47715-2448
Tel (812) 473-6200 *Founded/Ownrshp* 1964, 1988
Sales 125.6MM^E *EMP* 790
SIC 3089 Injection molded finished plastic products; Injection molded finished plastic products
Pr: Kevin Baird
**Treas:* Doug Girdler
Exec: Kathleen Lapekas
Opers Mgr: Shelby Evans

GUARDIAN BONDED SECURITY
See GUARDIAN GUARD SERVICES INC

D-U-N-S 07-914-1333
GUARDIAN BUILDING PRODUCTS INC
(*Suby of* GUARDIAN INDUSTRIES CORP) ★
979 Batesville Rd Ste A, Greer, SC 29651-6819
Tel (800) 569-4262 *Founded/Ownrshp* 1990
Sales NA *EMP* 900
SIC 3296 2452 8741 Fiberglass insulation; Prefabricated wood buildings; Business management; Fiberglass insulation; Prefabricated wood buildings; Business management
Pr: Steven D Ziessler
Comm Man: Michelle Lock
Dir IT: Steve Lanzl
Natl Sales: Aaron Hock

D-U-N-S 82-598-5450 IMP
GUARDIAN BUILDING PRODUCTS INC
(*Suby of* GBP MANAGEMENT INC) ★
979 Batesville Rd Ste A, Greer, SC 29651-6819
Tel (864) 297-6101 *Founded/Ownrshp* 1991
Sales 733.8MM^E *EMP* 857^E
SIC 5031 5033 5051 5032 5039 5023 Lumber, plywood & millwork; Millwork; Skylights, all materials; Roofing, siding & insulation; Roofing, asphalt & sheet metal; Insulation materials; Siding, except wood; Metals service centers & offices; Iron & steel (ferrous) products; Brick, stone & related material; Stucco; Drywall materials; Ceiling systems & products; Fireplace equipment & accessories
CEO: Thomas Highley
**CFO:* Wayne Feasby
Prgrm Mgr: Darrin Neitzke
Brnch Mgr: Chad Mizell
IT Man: Brian Bradshaw
VP Opers: Bruce Schneider
Manager: Ron Thomas

D-U-N-S 07-881-7821
GUARDIAN COMMUNITY LIVING LLC (TN)
(*Suby of* D&S RESIDENTIAL SERVICES LP) ★
105 Westpark Dr Ste 100, Brentwood, TN 37027-5010
Tel (901) 682-1940 *Founded/Ownrshp* 2003, 2013
Sales 5.8MM^E *EMP* 650
SIC 8059 Home for the mentally retarded, exc. skilled or intermediate; Home for the mentally retarded, exc. skilled or intermediate
CEO: Joe A Owen
Treas: Donald Ireland

GUARDIAN COMPLIANCE
See SEALTECH INC

D-U-N-S 87-884-8779
GUARDIAN CONSOLIDATED TECHNOLOGIES INC
(*Suby of* KELCO INDUSTRIES INC)
1425 Lake Ave, Woodstock, IL 60098-7419
Tel (815) 337-0050 *Founded/Ownrshp* 1930
Sales 66.9MM^E *EMP* 842
SIC 3625 Relays & industrial controls
Ch: Michael J Kelly
**Pr:* Kevin Kelly

D-U-N-S 05-352-6539
GUARDIAN CORP
GUARDIAN FOOD SERVICE
3801 Sunset Ave Ste A, Rocky Mount, NC 27804-3126
Tel (252) 443-4101 *Founded/Ownrshp* 1981
Sales 44.0MM^E *EMP* 1,500
SIC 5812 Fast-food restaurant, chain; Fast-food restaurant, chain
Ch Bd: Leon A Dunn Jr
**Pr:* Vincent Andracchio
**CFO:* Debra W Williams
**VP:* Martha Bridges

D-U-N-S 11-921-0276 IMP
GUARDIAN DRUG CO INC
2 Charles Ct, Dayton, NJ 08810-1508
Tel (609) 860-2600 *Founded/Ownrshp* 1984
Sales 32.9MM^E *EMP* 90
SIC 2834 Drugs acting on the gastrointestinal or genitourinary system; Antacids; Drugs acting on the gastrointestinal or genitourinary system; Antacids
Pr: Arvind B Dhruv

D-U-N-S 12-837-8515
GUARDIAN EAGLE SECURITY INC
4311 Wilshire Blvd # 419, Los Angeles, CA 90010-3713
Tel (888) 990-0002 *Founded/Ownrshp* 2002
Sales 8.3MM^E *EMP* 500
SIC 7381 Security guard service; Security guard service
CEO: Hassan M Galal
**VP:* Fadwa Galal
Board of Directors: Hassan Galal

D-U-N-S 92-636-8523
GUARDIAN ELDER CARE
BRADYVIEW MANOR
8796 Route 219, Brockway, PA 15824-6010
Tel (814) 265-7806 *Founded/Ownrshp* 1995
Sales 91.0MM^E *EMP* 375
SIC 8741 Nursing & personal care facility management; Nursing & personal care facility management
Pr: Eddy Inzana
**Treas:* Steven R Verischetti
**VP:* Frank A Varischetti
Ex Dir: Krista Geer
Brnch Mgr: Lisa Richner

D-U-N-S 00-509-4180 IMP
GUARDIAN ELECTRIC MANUFACTURING CO
(*Suby of* GUARDIAN CONSOLIDATED TECHNOLOGIES INC) ★
1425 Lake Ave, Woodstock, IL 60098-7419
Tel (815) 334-3600 *Founded/Ownrshp* 1931, 1993
Sales 20.1MM^E *EMP* 80
SIC 3679 3625 Solenoids for electronic applications; Relays & industrial controls; Relays, electric power; Switches, electric power; Solenoid switches (industrial controls)
Ch: Michael Kelly
**Pr:* Kevin Kelly
IT Man: Cacilia Rakiewicz

D-U-N-S 02-018-2670
GUARDIAN ENERGY LLC
4745 380th Ave, Janesville, MN 56048-1932
Tel (507) 234-5003 *Founded/Ownrshp* 2009
Sales 23.3MM^E *EMP* 50
SIC 2869 High purity grade chemicals, organic; High purity grade chemicals, organic
CFO: Kavin Guse
Dir Lab: Lauren Alsager
IT Man: Jared Kahle
VP Opers: Tom Hanson

D-U-N-S 96-297-2899
GUARDIAN FABRICATION INC
(*Suby of* GUARDIAN INDUSTRIES CORP) ★
2300 Harmon Rd, Auburn Hills, MI 48326-1714
Tel (248) 340-1800 *Founded/Ownrshp* 1987
Sales 24.4MM^E *EMP* 625
SIC 3211 Flat glass; Flat glass
Pr: William Davidson

GUARDIAN FOOD SERVICE
See GUARDIAN CORP

D-U-N-S 00-552-9693
GUARDIAN FUELING TECHNOLOGIES INC
9452 Philips Hwy Ste 5, Jacksonville, FL 32256-1332
Tel (904) 680-0850 *Founded/Ownrshp* 2000
Sales 22.5MM^E *EMP* 117
Accts Howard & Company Cpas Pa
SIC 1799 Service station equipment installation & maintenance; Gasoline pump installation; Service station equipment installation, maintenance & repair; Service station equipment installation & maintenance; Gasoline pump installation; Service station equipment installation, maintenance & repair
Pr: Joey Batchelor
**CFO:* Patrick D Reese
VP: Jeff Strait
Exec: Steve Bender
Brnch Mgr: Patrick Eakins
Brnch Mgr: Roger Henson
IT Man: Joshua Ali
IT Man: Ken Weiss
Opers Mgr: Tony Almond
Sales Asso: Lonnie Campbell

D-U-N-S 05-904-7167 IMP
GUARDIAN GLASS CO
GUARDIAN AUTO GLASS
(*Suby of* GUARDIAN INDUSTRIES CORP) ★
2300 Harmon Rd, Auburn Hills, MI 48326-1714
Tel (248) 340-1800 *Founded/Ownrshp* 1972
Sales 26.3MM^E *EMP* 375
SIC 7536 Automotive glass replacement shops; Automotive glass replacement shops
CEO: William Davidson
**Sec:* Oscar H Feldman
Site Mgr: Jeremy Smith

D-U-N-S 08-430-0003
GUARDIAN GUARD SERVICES INC
GUARDIAN BONDED SECURITY
18000 W 8 Mile Rd, Southfield, MI 48075-4338
Tel (248) 423-1000 *Founded/Ownrshp* 2005
Sales 30.8MM^E *EMP* 1,500
SIC 7381 Security guard service; Security guard service
Pr: Douglas Pierce
**Treas:* Richard Pierce
Exec: Patrick Henry
Genl Mgr: Karen Majeske
Mtls Mgr: Robert Beyer
Opers Mgr: Tom Furlong
Natl Sales: Steve Anton

D-U-N-S 11-954-0602
■ **GUARDIAN HEALTH SERVICE LLC**
(*Suby of* TENET HEALTHCARE CORPORATION)
100 Main Ave Nw Ste 200, Hickory, NC 28601-6200
Tel (828) 324-3025 *Founded/Ownrshp* 2002
Sales 7.4MM^E *EMP* 300
SIC 8082 Home health care services; Home health care services

D-U-N-S 96-234-5158
GUARDIAN HEALTHCARE LLC
418c Centre St, Jamaica Plain, MA 02130-1869
Tel (617) 477-8290 *Founded/Ownrshp* 2008
Sales 6.7MM *EMP* 360
SIC 8082 Home health care services

D-U-N-S 94-915-8927
GUARDIAN HEALTHCARE PROVIDERS INC
105 Westpark Dr Ste 100, Brentwood, TN 37027-5010
Tel (615) 377-9140 *Founded/Ownrshp* 1991
Sales 36.4MM^E *EMP* 950
SIC 8082 Home health care services; Home health care services
Pr: Joe A Owen
CFO: Donald Ireland
**Treas:* Don Ireland
Dist Mgr: Billy Hunt
Dist Mgr: Ryan Tempel
Off Mgr: Zina Jackson
Off Mgr: Liz Rodriguez
Off Mgr: Joanne Smyth

D-U-N-S 88-438-5212 IMP
GUARDIAN IGNITION INTERLOCK MANUFACTURING INC
GUARDIAN MANUFACTURING
2971 Oxbow Cir Ste A, Cocoa, FL 32926-4500
Tel (321) 205-1730 *Founded/Ownrshp* 1991
Sales 22.7MM^E *EMP* 60
SIC 3674 Microprocessors
Pr: Charles E Smith
VP: Don Lueders
**VP:* Steve Smith
Genl Mgr: Randall Brown
Sftwr Eng: Brad Smith

GUARDIAN INDUSTRIES
See CONSOLIDATED GLASS & MIRROR CORP

D-U-N-S 05-467-1169 EXP
GUARDIAN INDUSTRIES CORP (DE)
2300 Harmon Rd, Auburn Hills, MI 48326-1714
Tel (248) 340-1800 *Founded/Ownrshp* 1968, 1989
Sales 5.1MMM^E *EMP* 19,000
SIC 3211 Flat glass; Flat glass
CEO: Ron Vaupel
Pt: Jerry Ray
Treas: Ann Waichunas
VP: Joseph Bruce
VP: Bruce H Cummings
VP: Richard Johnson
VP: Paul M Rappaport
VP: Lajos Sapi
VP: Marc Talbert
VP: Scott Thomsen
VP: Donald Trofholz
Exec: John Buckner
Board of Directors: Chuck Croskey, Russell J Ebeid, Michael Filipek, David Jaffe, Anna Kalil, Mark Lacasse, Jim Moore

D-U-N-S 18-833-3702
GUARDIAN INSURANCE & ANNUITY CO INC
(*Suby of* GUARDIAN LIFE INSURANCE CO OF AMERICA) ★
7 Hanover Sq, New York, NY 10004-2616
Tel (212) 598-8000 *Founded/Ownrshp* 1970
Sales NA *EMP* 1,500
SIC 6311 6371 Life insurance carriers; Pension, health & welfare funds; Life insurance carriers; Pension, health & welfare funds
Ch: Dennis Manning
Pr: John Jennings
Pr: Matthew Kelly
Pr: Deanna Mulligan
Ofcr: Linda Senker
Ofcr: Kevin Silvey
Ofcr: Ali Thornsberry
Ex VP: Marc Costantini
VP: Peter Cook
VP: Michael Hess
VP: Frank Loscalzo
VP: David Posluszny
VP: Jasonn D Potter
VP: Nicholas Volpe
Exec: Dean Rothman

GUARDIAN LIFE INSURANCE
See SIRAK FINANCIAL SERVICES

GUARDIAN LIFE INSURANCE THE
See MW FINANCIAL GROUP LTD

D-U-N-S 00-185-4256
GUARDIAN LIFE INSURANCE CO OF AMERICA
7 Hanover Sq Fl 14, New York, NY 10004-4025
Tel (212) 598-8000 *Founded/Ownrshp* 1860
Sales NA *EMP* 5,008
SIC 6311 6371 6324 6321 6722 6282 Life insurance carriers; Life reinsurance; Pensions; Group hospitalization plans; Dental insurance; Disability health insurance; Reinsurance carriers, accident & health; Mutual fund sales, on own account; Investment advice; Life insurance carriers; Life reinsurance; Pensions; Group hospitalization plans; Dental insurance; Disability health insurance; Reinsurance carriers, accident & health; Mutual fund sales, on own account; Investment advice
CEO: Deanna Mulligan
Pr: Deon Hall-Garriques
**Pr:* Deanna M Mulligan
**CFO:* Marc Costantini
Treas: Barry Belfer
Chf Mktg O: Maria Umbach
**Ofcr:* Anthony S Marino
Ex VP: Rone Baldwin
Ex VP: Armand M De Palo
Ex VP: Gary B Lenderink
Ex VP: John P McCarthy
**Ex VP:* Tracy Rich
**Ex VP:* Thomas G Sorell
Sr VP: David W Allen
**Sr VP:* Joseph A Caruso
**Sr VP:* Michael B Cefole
**Sr VP:* Dean Del Vecchio
Sr VP: John Flannigan
Sr VP: Dennis P Mosticchio
Sr VP: James D Ranton
Sr VP: Nancy F Rogers
Board of Directors: Leo R Futia, John J Brennan, Paul B Guenther, Lloyd E Campbell, James A Kennedy, John B Caswell, Joseph D Sargent, Richard E Cavanaugh, Eric K Shinseki, Kay Knight Clarke, John A Somers, Martin J Cleary, Donald C Waite III, Nancy E Cooper, James E Daley, Deborah L Duncan

GUARDIAN MANUFACTURING
See GUARDIAN IGNITION INTERLOCK MANUFACTURING INC

GUARDIAN MILLBURY
See CUSTOM GLASS SOLUTIONS MILLBURY CORP

D-U-N-S 04-582-5585
GUARDIAN OF GEORGIA INC
ACKERMAN SECURITY SYSTEMS
1346 Oakbrook Dr Ste 175, Norcross, GA 30093-2204
Tel (770) 552-1111 *Founded/Ownrshp* 2005

Sales 50.0MM *EMP* 300
SIC 7382

D-U-N-S 03-175-2897
■ GUARDIAN PIPELINE LLC
(*Suby of* ONEOK PARTNERS LP) ★
100 W 5th St, Tulsa, OK 74103-4279
Tel (918) 588-7000 *Founded/Ownrshp* 2002
Sales 12.5MM^E *EMP* 300
SIC 4922

D-U-N-S 01-496-3532
GUARDIAN PROTECTION SERVICES INC
HOME SECURITY
(*Suby of* ARMSTRONG HOLDINGS INC) ★
174 Thorn Hill Rd, Warrendale, PA 15086-7528
Tel (412) 788-2580 *Founded/Ownrshp* 1991
Sales 196.5MM^E *EMP* 1,000
SIC 1731 5999 7382 Safety & security specialization; Fire detection & burglar alarm systems specialization; Alarm signal systems; Security systems services; Safety & security specialization; Fire detection & burglar alarm systems specialization; Alarm signal systems; Security systems services
CEO: Russell L Cersosimo
**Pr:* Joseph Colosimo
**CFO:* Richard Yobbi
**Treas:* Kirby I Campbell
Ex VP: Lawrence Wargo
VP: Jim Breisinger
VP: Jim Greene
VP: Brian Helt
VP: Joe Lininger
VP: John Piroli
VP: Kevin Santelli
**VP:* Jay L Sedwick
VP: Jay Stuck
**VP:* Jeff Szajnecki

D-U-N-S 08-005-4331 IMP
GUARDIAN REAL ESTATE SERVICES LLC
The Crane Bldg 710, Portland, OR 97209
Tel (503) 802-3600 *Founded/Ownrshp* 2002
Sales 25.5MM^E *EMP* 490
SIC 6531 Management services; Real estate agents & managers; Real estate managers
Pr: Thomas B Brenneke
Pr: Bob Osbrink
**CFO:* Sandra Rankin
**VP:* Adrian Boly
VP: Bradley Bullock
**VP:* Karon Paul
VP: Daniel J Steffey
Rgnl Mgr: Tyler McKee

D-U-N-S 07-472-5128
GUARDIAN SAVINGS BANK
FEDERAL SAVINGS BANK
6100 W Chester Rd, West Chester, OH 45069-2943
Tel (513) 942-3535 *Founded/Ownrshp* 1992
Sales NA *EMP* 253
SIC 6163 6035 Loan brokers; Federal savings banks; Loan brokers; Federal savings banks
Ch Bd: Louis Beck
**Pr:* Richard L Burkhart
**CFO:* Kevin Motley
Ofcr: Chris Cullion
**Sr VP:* Paul Warner
VP: Eileen Cameron
VP: Barry Prince
**VP:* Yvonne Rich
VP: Bill Voorhees
VP: Darlene Waggoner
Brnch Mgr: Tam Yokeley

D-U-N-S 08-251-3151
GUARDIAN SECURITY SYSTEMS INC (WA)
1743 1st Ave S, Seattle, WA 98134-1432
Tel (206) 622-6545 *Founded/Ownrshp* 1976
Sales 30.9MM^E *EMP* 100
SIC 1731 Fire detection & burglar alarm systems specialization; Communications specialization
Pr: Frank A Close
IT Man: McElhany Chip
Sales Asso: Rich Carter

D-U-N-S 09-750-5754
GUARDIAN SERVICE INDUSTRIES INC
161 Ave Of The Amer, New York, NY 10013-1205
Tel (212) 645-9500 *Founded/Ownrshp* 1957
Sales 79.8MM^E *EMP* 1,500^E
SIC 7349

D-U-N-S 60-318-7332 IMP
GUARDIAN TECHNOLOGIES LLC
GERM GUARDIAN
26251 Bluestone Blvd # 7, Euclid, OH 44132-2826
Tel (216) 706-2250 *Founded/Ownrshp* 2003
Sales 25.8MM *EMP* 24
Accts Zion Synek & Associates Inde
SIC 3564 Air purification equipment
Sls Dir: Pat Sullivan

GUARDIAN TRAILER RENTALS
See HERB REDL PROPERTIES

D-U-N-S 36-066-1995
GUARDSMARK HOLDINGS INC
PEOPLEMARK, INC.
(*Suby of* GUARDSMARK LLC) ★
22 S 2nd St, Memphis, TN 38103-2695
Tel (901) 522-6000 *Founded/Ownrshp* 1985
Sales 30.6MM^E *EMP* 1,201
SIC 7363 Temporary help service
Ch Bd: Ira A Lipman
**VP:* Terri Duff
**VP:* Tommy Yarborough

D-U-N-S 00-705-5551
GUARDSMARK LLC
MARK LIPMAN DIV
(*Suby of* UNIVERSAL PROTECTION SERVICE LP) ★
10 Rockefeller Plz Fl 12, New York, NY 10020-1903
Tel (212) 603-3800 *Founded/Ownrshp* 2015
Sales 559.7MM^E *EMP* 8,000
SIC 7381 2721 8742 Security guard service; Private investigator; Periodicals: publishing only; Industry specialist consultants; Security guard service; Private investigator; Periodicals: publishing only; Industry specialist consultants
CEO: Ira A Lipman
Treas: Joshua Lipman
Ex VP: Gustave Lipman
Sr VP: Howard Spector
VP: John Clark
VP: Tammy Nixon
Brnch Mgr: Patricia Ballentine
CTO: Philip Lee
Plnt Mgr: Ronal Poll
Secur Mgr: Michael Dunn
Snr Mgr: David Dupre

D-U-N-S 10-269-2634
GUASTAVINOS INC
(*Suby of* CONRAN HOLDINGS LIMITED)
344 E 69th St, New York, NY 10022-1593
Tel (212) 980-2455 *Founded/Ownrshp* 1999
Sales 8.2MM^E *EMP* 320
SIC 5812 French restaurant; French restaurant
CFO: Peter Thyne
**Pr:* Joel Kissin
Ex Dir: John Rose
Sls Dir: Joseph Gabis

D-U-N-S 83-262-7421
GUAVUS INC
1820 Gateway Dr Ste 250, San Mateo, CA 94404-4032
Tel (650) 243-3400 *Founded/Ownrshp* 2006
Sales 80.9MM^E *EMP* 450
SIC 7372 Prepackaged software; Prepackaged software
CEO: Anukool Lakhina
**Ch Bd:* Mike Lajoie
Pr: Michael Crane
**COO:* Ty Nam
**CFO:* Mike Staiger
**Ofcr:* Anupam Rastogi
Sr VP: Louis Brun
Sr VP: Tim Dyer
**VP:* Eric Carr
VP: Rob Chimsky
VP: Swati Choksi
VP: Anita Gupta
VP: Rowan Scranage
VP: Sergey Sukov

D-U-N-S 04-278-6392 IMP
GUCCI AMERICA INC
685 5th Ave Fl 8, New York, NY 10022-4292
Tel (212) 750-5220 *Founded/Ownrshp* 1993
Sales 132.3MM^E *EMP* 1,000^E
SIC 5632 5948 5661 5611 5621 5137 Handbags; Apparel accessories; Luggage, except footlockers & trunks; Women's shoes; Men's shoes; Men's & boys' clothing stores; Ready-to-wear apparel, women's; Handbags; Handbags; Apparel accessories; Luggage, except footlockers & trunks; Women's shoes; Men's shoes; Men's & boys' clothing stores; Ready-to-wear apparel, women's; Handbags
Ch Bd: Christophe De Pous
CFO: Alexis Babeau
VP: Frida Giannini
VP: Doug McCullough
Exec: Sally Lu
Genl Mgr: Amy Figueroa
Genl Mgr: Israel Lugo
Genl Mgr: Michael Mathis
Genl Mgr: Aaron Roescher
Genl Mgr: Joe Sena
Store Mgr: Kimberly Eshelman

D-U-N-S 82-599-7315 IMP
GUCCI TIMEPIECES (AMERICA) INC
(*Suby of* GUCCIO GUCCI SPA)
50 Hartz Way, Secaucus, NJ 07094-2420
Tel (201) 867-8800 *Founded/Ownrshp* 2005
Sales 55.7MM^E *EMP* 800^E
SIC 5632 5948 5661 5611 5621 Handbags; Apparel accessories; Luggage, except footlockers & trunks; Women's shoes; Men's shoes; Men's & boys' clothing stores; Ready-to-wear apparel, women's; Handbags; Apparel accessories; Luggage, except footlockers & trunks; Women's shoes; Men's shoes; Men's & boys' clothing stores; Ready-to-wear apparel, women's
Pr: William Franz
**CEO:* Patrizio Di Marco

D-U-N-S 04-401-0270 IMP
GUCKENHEIMER ENTERPRISES INC
1850 Gateway Dr Ste 500, San Mateo, CA 94404-4064
Tel (650) 592-0460 *Founded/Ownrshp* 1963
Sales 149.4MM^E *EMP* 2,500
SIC 5812

D-U-N-S 00-228-1541 IMP
GUDEBROD INC (PA)
274 Shoemaker Rd, Pottstown, PA 19464-6434
Tel (610) 327-4050 *Founded/Ownrshp* 1897
Sales 59.9MM^E *EMP* 180
SIC 2824 2298 3843

D-U-N-S 09-453-6612 IMP
GUDEL INC
(*Suby of* GUDEL GROUP AG)
4881 Runway Blvd, Ann Arbor, MI 48108-9558
Tel (734) 214-0000 *Founded/Ownrshp* 1996
Sales 35.0MM^E *EMP* 78
SIC 3535 Conveyors & conveying equipment; Conveyors & conveying equipment
CEO: Stefan Nilsson
**VP:* Joe Campbell
Mng Dir: Mariano Garcia
IT Man: Ariel Sacerdoti
Mfg Dir: Tim Reynolds
Opers Mgr: Dave Root
Manager: Matt Berch
Snr Mgr: Shawn Lameau

D-U-N-S 08-130-8827
GUDENKAUF CORP (OH)
2679 Mckinley Ave, Columbus, OH 43204-3898
Tel (614) 488-1776 *Founded/Ownrshp* 1977
Sales 50.3MM^E *EMP* 140
Accts Winkel Green & Van Horn Llp C
SIC 1623 Telephone & communication line construction; Underground utilities contractor; Gas main construction; Telephone & communication line construction; Underground utilities contractor; Gas main construction
Pr: Jeffrey Gudenkauf
**Pr:* Sandy Potterton
Ex VP: Curt Nolan
**VP:* Susan Gudenkauf
**VP:* Sanford Potterton
**VP:* Dave Robinson
**VP:* Mark Rogers
Div Mgr: Josh Bowman
VP Opers: Vince Paxton
Mtls Mgr: Pat Casey
Mtls Mgr: Jim Spaulding

D-U-N-S 62-415-2021
GUELPH TOOL SALES INC
(*Suby of* GUELPH TOOL INC)
24150 Gibson Dr, Warren, MI 48089-4308
Tel (586) 755-3333 *Founded/Ownrshp* 1990
Sales 81.3MM^E *EMP* 900
SIC 3465 8744 Body parts, automobile: stamped metal; Facilities support services; Body parts, automobile: stamped metal; Facilities support services
Pr: Robert Ireland

D-U-N-S 01-750-9134
GUENTHER MECHANICAL INC
1248 Middle Rowsburg Rd, Ashland, OH 44805-2813
Tel (419) 289-6900 *Founded/Ownrshp* 1961
Sales 30.0MM^E *EMP* 120
SIC 1711 Mechanical contractor; Mechanical contractor
Pr: Herbert E Guenther
Treas: Andrews Isolde
**VP:* James B Andrews
**VP:* Jim Cutright
VP: Steve Harp

D-U-N-S 01-821-5124
GUERDON ENTERPRISES LLC
5556 S Federal Way, Boise, ID 83716-9617
Tel (208) 345-2838 *Founded/Ownrshp* 2001
Sales 71.8MM^E *EMP* 350
SIC 5211 5032 1522 Modular homes; Brick, stone & related material; Residential construction; Modular homes; Brick, stone & related material; Residential construction
Mng Pt: Lad Dawson
Prd Mgr: Joy Koelling
Manager: Randy Duggan
Snr Mgr: Curtis Fletcher
Snr Mgr: Mitch Hovaldt

D-U-N-S 04-840-5724 IMP/EXP
GUERLAIN INC
(*Suby of* GUERLAIN SOCIETE ANONYME)
19 E 57th St, New York, NY 10022-2506
Tel (212) 931-2400 *Founded/Ownrshp* 1926
Sales 28.8MM^E *EMP* 152
SIC 5122 Perfumes; Cosmetics; Perfumes; Cosmetics
Pr: Patrick Waterfield
VP: Beth A Catalano

D-U-N-S 18-000-4095
GUERNSEY HEALTH ENTERPRISES INC
(*Suby of* GUERNSEY HEALTH SYSTEMS INC) ★
1341 Clark St, Cambridge, OH 43725-9614
Tel (740) 439-3561 *Founded/Ownrshp* 1985
Sales 1.9MM^E *EMP* 700
Accts Ernst & Young
SIC 4119 8059 5912 Ambulance service; Rest home, with health care; Drug stores; Ambulance service; Rest home, with health care; Drug stores
Pr: Raymond Shorey

D-U-N-S 18-005-3795
GUERNSEY HEALTH SYSTEMS INC
1341 Clark St, Cambridge, OH 43725-9614
Tel (740) 439-3561 *Founded/Ownrshp* 1985
Sales 2.0MM *EMP* 735
Accts Tucker & Tucker Cpas Llc Camb
SIC 4119 8062 8052 Local passenger transportation; General medical & surgical hospitals; Intermediate care facilities; Local passenger transportation; General medical & surgical hospitals; Intermediate care facilities
CEO: Philip Hearing
**CFO:* Donald P Huelskamp
Board of Directors: Clarance Bell, J Bryan Fawcett, Dale Hileman, Bill Murray

D-U-N-S 05-518-3362
GUERNSEY INC
45070 Old Ox Rd Ste 100, Dulles, VA 20166-2343
Tel (703) 968-8200 *Founded/Ownrshp* 1971
Sales 36.4MM^E *EMP* 250
Accts Linda Etter Cpa
SIC 5943 5712 Office forms & supplies; Office furniture; Office forms & supplies; Office furniture
Pr: David Guernsey
CFO: Kenneth R Deckard
Treas: Douglas D Guernsey Jr
VP: Bonnie Fritz
VP: Gordon Thrall
Mktg Dir: Katie Burke
Mktg Dir: Kevin Hanlon

D-U-N-S 00-790-3826
GUERNSEY-MUSKINGUM ELECTRIC COOPERATIVE INC
17 S Liberty St, New Concord, OH 43762-1230
Tel (740) 826-7661 *Founded/Ownrshp* 1938
Sales 34.5MM *EMP* 44^E
SIC 4911 Distribution, electric power; Distribution, electric power
Pr: Shirley Stutz
Pr: Brian Hill
Sec: John Enos
Genl Mgr: Garry Mbiad
Genl Mgr: Kim Swinehart
IT Man: Andrew Bone
IT Man: John Sellers
Opers Mgr: Ed Wagner

GUERTIN BROS
See NORDT CO INC JOHN C

D-U-N-S 02-745-1731 IMP
▲ GUESS INC
1444 S Alameda St, Los Angeles, CA 90021-2433
Tel (213) 765-3100 *Founded/Ownrshp* 1981
Sales 2.4MMM *EMP* 14,600
Accts Ernst & Young Llp Los Angeles
Tkr Sym GES *Exch* NYS
SIC 2325 2339 5611 5621 5641 Men's & boys' jeans & dungarees; Women's & misses' outerwear; Clothing, sportswear, men's & boys'; Women's sportswear; Children's & infants' wear stores; Men's & boys' jeans & dungarees; Women's & misses' outerwear; Clothing, sportswear, men's & boys'; Women's sportswear; Children's & infants' wear stores
CEO: Paul Marciano
Pr: Nancy Shachtman
COO: Michael Relich
CFO: Megan Byars
CFO: Sandeep Reddy
CFO: Dennis R Seco
Bd of Dir: Carlos Alberini
Bd of Dir: Kay Leibowitz
Ofcr: Sharleen Ernster
Ex VP: Armand Marciano
Sr VP: Stephanie Labelle
Dir: Brent Viklund
Board of Directors: Anthony Chidoni, Joseph Gromek, Kay Isaacson-Leibowitz, Maurice Marciano, Alex Yemenidjian

GUESS WATCH
See CALLANEN INTERNATIONAL INC

GUESS WATCHES
See SEQUEL INTERNATIONAL INC

GUEST DIRECT
See CUSTOMER DIRECT LLC

D-U-N-S 00-177-3076
■ GUEST PACKAGING LLC
(*Suby of* GUEST SUPPLY SERVICES) ★
414 E Inman Ave, Rahway, NJ 07065-4705
Tel (732) 382-7270 *Founded/Ownrshp* 1985
Sales 30.1MM^E *EMP* 250
SIC 7389 Packaging & labeling services; Packaging & labeling services
Brnch Mgr: Charlie Deandrea
Ql Cn Mgr: Bob Glassman

D-U-N-S 00-691-9807
GUEST SERVICES INC (DC)
3055 Prosperity Ave, Fairfax, VA 22031-2290
Tel (703) 849-9300 *Founded/Ownrshp* 1917
Sales 375.2MM *EMP* 3,500
Accts Pricewaterhousecoopers Mclean
SIC 5148 8741 Fresh fruits & vegetables; Cafeteria; Souvenirs; Hotels; Management services; Fresh fruits & vegetables; Management services
CEO: Gerard T Gabrys
**Pr:* Jeffrey Marquis
**CFO:* Nico Fores
CFO: Jeffrey A Mrquis
Ch: Peter S Prichard
**VP:* Jerrold Chadwick
**VP:* Beverly Frazer
**VP:* John N Gates
**VP:* Richard Hirsch
VP: William J Hybl
**VP:* Barry Trice

GUEST SUPPLY SERVICES
See SYSCO GUEST SUPPLY LLC

D-U-N-S 79-396-2796
GUESTS INC
MCDONALD'S
521 W Washington St, Brainerd, MN 56401-2927
Tel (218) 829-9477 *Founded/Ownrshp* 1991
Sales 13.7MM^E *EMP* 400
SIC 5812 Fast-food restaurant, chain; Fast-food restaurant, chain
CEO: Glen Cook
Sys/Mgr: Teri Butler

D-U-N-S 80-033-6344
GUGGENHEIM CAPITAL LLC
227 W Monroe St Ste 4900, Chicago, IL 60606-4900
Tel (312) 827-0100 *Founded/Ownrshp* 2001
Sales 144.0MM^E *EMP* 540
SIC 6726 Investment offices; Investment offices
CEO: Mark R Walter

D-U-N-S 07-832-0748
GUGGENHEIM LIFE AND ANNUITY CO
(*Suby of* GUGGENHEIM PARTNERS LLC) ★
401 Penn Pkwy Ste 300, Indianapolis, IN 46280-1385
Tel (317) 574-6213 *Founded/Ownrshp* 2010
Sales NA *EMP* 499^E
SIC 6311 Life reinsurance
Pr: Jeffrey Lange

D-U-N-S 14-260-3567
GUGGENHEIM PARTNERS LLC
330 Madison Ave Rm 201, New York, NY 10017-5045
Tel (212) 739-0700 *Founded/Ownrshp* 2006
Sales 1.4MMM^E *EMP* 10,650
SIC 8742 Business consultant; Business consultant
CEO: Mark R Walter
Pr: Todd L Boehly
Ch: Alan Schwartz
Top Exec: Rick McCracken
Ex VP: Gene Borsattino
Sr VP: Kara Hansen
Mng Dir: Tony Butler
Mng Dir: Michael Dimaso
Mng Dir: Raul Elia
Mng Dir: Ron Iervolino
Mng Dir: Vinod Lala

D-U-N-S 08-984-9400 IMP
GUHRING INC (WI)
(*Suby of* GUHRING KG)
1445 Commerce Ave, Brookfield, WI 53045-5289
Tel (262) 784-6730 *Founded/Ownrshp* 1978
Sales 79.1MM^E *EMP* 400

SIC 3545 Drills (machine tool accessories); Drills (machine tool accessories)
Ch Bd: Jorg Guhring
**Pr:* Peter Haenle
**CFO:* Craig Rotta
**VP:* Don Jacquart
Rgnl Mgr: Jeffrey Brown
Rgnl Mgr: Todd Madaus
Rgnl Mgr: Tom Resler
Rgnl Mgr: Israel Roman
Div Mgr: Scott Salamonski
Sftwr Eng: Josh Hart
VP Opers: Craig Zacher
Board of Directors: Bob Hellinger

GUHSD
See GLENDALE UNION HIGH SCHOOL DISTRICT

D-U-N-S 01-872-8535
GUIDA-SEIBERT DAIRY CO
GUIDA'S MILK & ICE CREAM
433 Park St, New Britain, CT 06051-2700
Tel (860) 224-2404 *Founded/Ownrshp* 1932
Sales 77.6MM^E *EMP* 275
SIC 2026 2033 5143 5149 Milk processing (pasteurizing, homogenizing, bottling); Fruit juices: packaged in cans, jars, etc.; Dairy products, except dried or canned; Juices; Milk processing (pasteurizing, homogenizing, bottling); Fruit juices: packaged in cans, jars, etc.; Dairy products, except dried or canned; Juices
CEO: Pat Panko
**Pr:* Michael Young
**Treas:* Michael J A Guida
**VP:* Alex Bachelor
**VP:* Joel Clark
**VP:* James Guida
**VP:* David Meyer
QA Dir: Matthew Titterington
Dir IT: Joel Bartolome
Sales Exec: Mary Bowen
Cust Svc D: David Drezek
Board of Directors: Bernard Guida

D-U-N-S 08-547-1944
GUIDANCE CENTER
DOWN RIVER GUIDANCE CLINIC
13101 Allen Rd, Southgate, MI 48195-2216
Tel (734) 287-5197 *Founded/Ownrshp* 1958
Sales 41.6MM *EMP* 700
Accts Plante & Moran Pllc Southfie
SIC 8322 8093 Individual & family services; Mental health clinic, outpatient; Substance abuse clinics (outpatient); Individual & family services; Mental health clinic, outpatient; Substance abuse clinics (outpatient)
Pr: Kari D Walker
**COO:* Sarah Bannon
**CFO:* Gary Guetschow
CTO: Michael Lott
IT Man: Paul Frankel
Corp Couns: William Ullrich

GUIDANCE CHANNEL
See GLOBAL VIDEO LLC

D-U-N-S 01-381-4426
▲ GUIDANCE SOFTWARE INC
1055 E Colo Blvd Ste 400, Pasadena, CA 91106
Tel (626) 229-9191 *Founded/Ownrshp* 1997
Sales 108.6MM *EMP* 460
Accts Ernst & Young Llp Los Angele
Tkr Sym GUID *Exch* NGM
SIC 7372 3572 Prepackaged software; Prepackaged software; Computer storage devices
CEO: Barry Plaga
**Ch Bd:* Shawn McCreight
Ofcr: James Habben
Ofcr: Michael Harris
Sr VP: Ken Basore
Sr VP: Alfredo Gomez
Sr VP: Mark Harrington
Sr VP: Stephanie Urbach
VP: Linda Souza
Dir Risk M: Jay Ackerman
Dir Risk M: Daryk Rowland
Assoc Dir: Manoj Sharma
Board of Directors: Max Carbecchia, Christopher Poole, Stephen Richards, Robert G Van Schoonenberg

D-U-N-S 16-835-7601
GUIDANT FINANCIAL GROUP INC
1100 112th Ave Ne Ste 100, Bellevue, WA 98004-8577
Tel (425) 289-3200 *Founded/Ownrshp* 2003
Sales 40.3MM^E *EMP* 72
SIC 6282 Investment advice
CEO: Stephan Rochk
**Pr:* Jeremy Ames
Ex VP: Devin Miller
VP: Michelle Flandreau
**VP:* David Nelson
VP: Barry Schnell
VP Sls: Katie Burckhardt

D-U-N-S 62-162-8007
■ GUIDANT PUERTO RICO BV
(*Suby of* GUIDANT SALES LLC) ★
12 Carr 698 Ste 171, Dorado, PR 00646-3315
Tel (787) 796-2115 *Founded/Ownrshp* 1989
Sales 171.0MM^E *EMP* 815
SIC 3845 Pacemaker, cardiac; Pacemaker, cardiac; Defibrillator
Pr: A Jay Graf
**Treas:* Zulma Suarez
**VP:* Dale Devries
**VP:* Richard R Doyle
**VP:* Jeffrey Neuenfeldt
Genl Mgr: Heriberto Diaz
Snr Ntwrk: Luis Rivera

D-U-N-S 87-726-0471
■ GUIDANT SALES LLC
GUIDANT/C P I
(*Suby of* BOSTON SCIENTIFIC CORP) ★
4100 Hamline Ave N, Saint Paul, MN 55112-5700
Tel (800) 949-9459 *Founded/Ownrshp* 2006
Sales 1.0MMM^E *EMP* 12,000
SIC 3841 3845 5047 8733 Surgical & medical instruments; Catheters; Instruments, microsurgical: except electromedical; Retractors; Electromedical equipment; Pacemaker, cardiac; Defibrillator; Medical & hospital equipment; Medical equipment & supplies; Diagnostic equipment, medical; Medical research; Surgical & medical instruments; Catheters; Instruments, microsurgical: except electromedical; Retractors; Electromedical equipment; Pacemaker, cardiac; Defibrillator; Medical & hospital equipment; Medical equipment & supplies; Diagnostic equipment, medical; Medical research
CEO: J Raymond Elliott
Pr: Mark C Bartell
Pr: Daniel J Brennan
Pr: Kelly Phillips
Pr: Ann Wilcox
Ch: A Jay Graf
Ofcr: Michael B Gropp
Sr VP: Kathy Lundberg
VP: Douglas J Cronin
VP: Beverly H Lorell MD
VP: Timothy A Pratt

GUIDANT/C P I
See GUIDANT SALES LLC

GUIDA'S MILK & ICE CREAM
See GUIDA-SEIBERT DAIRY CO

D-U-N-S 08-244-7319
GUIDE DOGS FOR BLIND INC (CA)
G D B
350 Los Ranchitos Rd, San Rafael, CA 94903-3606
Tel (415) 499-4000 *Founded/Ownrshp* 1942
Sales 43.3MM *EMP* 265
Accts Crowe Howarth Llp Sacramento
SIC 0752 8299 Animal training services; Educational service, nondegree granting: continuing educ.; Animal training services; Educational service, nondegree granting: continuing educ.
CEO: Chris Benninger
**CFO:* Cathy Martin
**CFO:* Kenneth Stupi
Ofcr: Janet Benjamin
Ex Dir: Sigrid Button
Off Mgr: Debbie Hibbard
Nurse Mgr: Helen Brackley
Off Admin: Jennifer Seiler
Dir IT: Laura Peabody
Mktg Dir: Karen Woon

GUIDED ONLINE ACADEMIC
See GOAL ACADEMY

D-U-N-S 00-869-8862
GUIDENT TECHNOLOGIES INC (VA)
(*Suby of* CRGT INC) ★
198 Van Buren St Ste 120, Herndon, VA 20170-5338
Tel (703) 326-0888 *Founded/Ownrshp* 1997, 2013
Sales 20.1MM^E *EMP* 230
SIC 7379 8748 Computer related consulting services; Systems engineering consultant, ex. computer or professional; Computer related consulting services; Systems engineering consultant, ex. computer or professional
Pr: Boyd Harter
**Pr:* Thomas Ferrando
**Sr VP:* Ken Raffel
**VP:* Dan Ackerman
**VP:* Timothy Clements
**VP:* Federico Matheu
**VP:* David Pearson

D-U-N-S 06-848-8451
GUIDEONE AMERICA INSURANCE CO
GUIDEONE AMERICA MUTL INSUR CO
(*Suby of* GUIDEONE INC) ★
1111 Ashworth Rd, West Des Moines, IA 50265-3544
Tel (515) 267-5000 *Founded/Ownrshp* 1993
Sales NA *EMP* 750
SIC 6331 Fire, marine & casualty insurance & carriers; Fire, marine & casualty insurance & carriers
Pr: James Wallace

GUIDEONE AMERICA MUTL INSUR CO
See GUIDEONE AMERICA INSURANCE CO

D-U-N-S 10-395-0887
GUIDEONE INC
1111 Ashworth Rd, West Des Moines, IA 50265-3544
Tel (515) 267-5000 *Founded/Ownrshp* 1983
Sales NA *EMP* 800
SIC 6311 Mutual association life insurance; Life insurance carriers; Mutual association life insurance; Life insurance carriers
Pr: Jim Wallace
Genl Mgr: Joe Schnieders
Sls Dir: Terrence Bedford
Sls Dir: Doug Dickey

GUIDEONE INSURANCE
See GUIDEONE MUTUAL INSURANCE CO

D-U-N-S 16-145-4405
GUIDEONE MUTUAL INSURANCE CO
(*Suby of* GUIDEONE INC) ★
1111 Ashworth Rd, West Des Moines, IA 50265-3544
Tel (515) 267-5000 *Founded/Ownrshp* 1996
Sales NA *EMP* 60
SIC 6331 Fire, marine & casualty insurance & carriers; Fire, marine & casualty insurance & carriers
Pr: Jim Wallace
VP: Scott Redding

D-U-N-S 80-227-2307
GUIDEONE MUTUAL INSURANCE CO
GUIDEONE INSURANCE
1111 Ashworth Rd, West Des Moines, IA 50265-3544
Tel (515) 267-5000 *Founded/Ownrshp* 1947
Sales NA *EMP* 720
SIC 6411 Insurance agents, brokers & service; Insurance agents, brokers & service
CEO: Jim Wallace
**COO:* Scott Reddig
CFO: Mark Joos
Bd of Dir: Bernard Hengesbaugh
**Sr VP:* Doug Cretsinger
Sr VP: John Whalin
VP: Tim Anders
**VP:* Sarah Buckley
VP: Mike Faley
VP: Gilbert Korthals
VP: Dave Sours
Exec: Kelli Peters

D-U-N-S 01-332-2775
GUIDEPOINT GLOBAL LLC
730 3rd Ave Fl 11, New York, NY 10017-3216
Tel (212) 375-2980 *Founded/Ownrshp* 2003
Sales 34.5MM^E *EMP* 135
SIC 8732 Market analysis, business & economic research; Market analysis, business & economic research
CEO: Albert Sebag
Pr: Christopher Catania
Pr: Elizabeth Crouch
Pr: Richard Ginsberg
COO: John Polis
COO: Vince Tortorella
CFO: John Campanella
Chf Mktg O: Michael Fertman
Ofcr: Mario Pati
VP: Mundeep Basi
VP: Charles Devine
VP: Brendan Gaffney
VP: Brian Gallo
VP: Chris Gaudioso
VP: Leong Loh
VP: Timothy Wang
Dir Soc: Jessica Kagin

D-U-N-S 00-564-4870
GUIDEPOINT SECURITY LLC (VA)
2201 Coop Way Ste 225, Herndon, VA 20171
Tel (877) 889-0132 *Founded/Ownrshp* 2011
Sales 33.0MM^E *EMP* 113
SIC 7379 Computer related maintenance services; Computer related consulting services
Genl Pt: Scott Kasper
VP: Matt Keller
**VP:* Bryan Orme
Mktg Dir: Cristelle Michael
Sales Asso: Amanda Hooker

D-U-N-S 93-334-1562
GUIDESOFT INC
KNOWLEDGE SERVICES
5875 Castle Crk Pkwy N, Indianapolis, IN 46250-4331
Tel (317) 578-1700 *Founded/Ownrshp* 1994
Sales 50.8MM^E *EMP* 175^E
SIC 7379 Computer related consulting services; Computer related consulting services
Pr: Joseph A Bielawski
**CFO:* Julianna M Bielawski
Ex VP: Dan Nierste
**VP:* Bill Evans
**VP:* Damon Grothe
Prgrm Mgr: Samantha Alcocer
Prgrm Mgr: Andrea Connell
Prgrm Mgr: Nate Kresge
Genl Mgr: Cindy Becher

D-U-N-S 07-761-4154
GUIDESTONE FINANCIAL RESOURCES OF SOUTHERN BAPTIST CONVENTION
2401 Cedar Springs Rd, Dallas, TX 75201-1407
Tel (214) 720-0511 *Founded/Ownrshp* 1918
Sales NA *EMP* 400
SIC 6411 Insurance agents & brokers; Medical insurance claim processing, contract or fee basis; Insurance agents & brokers; Medical insurance claim processing, contract or fee basis
Pr: O S Hawkins
**COO:* John R Jones
**Ofcr:* Rodric E Cummins
Mktg Mgr: Wendy Ashley

GUIDEWELL SOURCE
See DIVERSIFIED SERVICE OPTIONS INC

D-U-N-S 11-436-5257
GUIDEWIRE INC
551 E Columbus Ave, Springfield, MA 01105-2556
Tel (413) 733-6100 *Founded/Ownrshp* 1982
Sales 16.0MM^E *EMP* 400
Accts Lester Halpern & Company Pc
SIC 8361 Residential care for the handicapped; Residential care for the handicapped
Pr: Linda S Sullivan
**CFO:* Catherine Parmentier
Sr VP: Stephanie Brown
Adm Dir: Colleen Adamski
Prgrm Mgr: Taryn Mancivalano
Prgrm Mgr: Patricia Wright
VP Opers: Peter Vangsness
Pgrm Dir: Tricia Beaudoin
Pgrm Dir: Andrea Rigali

D-U-N-S 12-662-5701
▲ GUIDEWIRE SOFTWARE INC
1001 E Hillsdale Blvd # 800, Foster City, CA 94404-1643
Tel (650) 357-9100 *Founded/Ownrshp* 2001
Sales 380.5MM *EMP* 1,341^E
Accts Kpmg Llp Santa Clara Califor
Tkr Sym GWRE *Exch* NYS
SIC 7372 Prepackaged software; Prepackaged software
Pr: Marcus S Ryu
**Ch Bd:* John Cavoores
CFO: Richard Hart
Ch: Priscilla Hung
Chf Mktg O: Brian Desmond
Ofcr: Mike Polelle
Sr VP: John True
VP: David Barter
VP: Judith Neumann
Snr Sftwr: Jerry Brenner
Snr Sftwr: Derek Faulkner
Board of Directors: Andrew Brown, Craig Conway, Guy Dubois, Peter Gassner, Clifton Thomas Weatherford

D-U-N-S 07-525-5232 IMP
GUIDING EYES FOR BLIND INC
611 Granite Springs Rd, Yorktown Heights, NY 10598-3499
Tel (914) 245-4024 *Founded/Ownrshp* 1954
Sales 33.7MM *EMP* 125
Accts Bdo Usa Llp New York Ny
SIC 8322 Social services for the handicapped
Pr: William D Badger
**VP:* Sue Dishart
Rgnl Mgr: Nicole Guite
Rgnl Mgr: Joy Hawksby
Rgnl Mgr: Maureen Hollis
Rgnl Mgr: Rachel Silverman
IT Man: Susan Ludwig
IT Man: Judi Mandile

D-U-N-S 01-266-3191
GUIDO & COMPANIES
8526 Vidor Ave, San Antonio, TX 78216-6045
Tel (210) 344-8321 *Founded/Ownrshp* 1947
Sales 31.5MM^E *EMP* 78^E
Accts The Hanke Group Pc San Ant
SIC 1542 5211 5031 Commercial & office building, new construction; Commercial & office buildings, renovation & repair; Lumber & other building materials; Lumber: rough, dressed & finished
Ch: Cosmo F Guido
CEO: Mary Ann Guido
Treas: Antoinette Browning
VP: Thomas L Guido
Off Mgr: Benny Rondrea
Off Mgr: Audrey Schneider

D-U-N-S 00-813-3092
GUIDO LUMBER CO INC
(*Suby of* GUIDO & COMPANIES) ★
8526 Vidor Ave, San Antonio, TX 78216-6045
Tel (210) 344-8321 *Founded/Ownrshp* 1946
Sales 22.4MM^E *EMP* 40
Accts Bkd Llp
SIC 5031 Millwork; Lumber: rough, dressed & finished
CEO: Maryanne A Guido
**Pr:* Thomas L Guido
**Ch:* Cosmo F Guido
**Treas:* Antoinette Browning

D-U-N-S 03-737-0061
GUIDOS QUALITY FRUIT AND PRODUCE INC
1020 South St, Pittsfield, MA 01201-8225
Tel (413) 442-9912 *Founded/Ownrshp* 1977
Sales 24.2MM^E *EMP* 150
SIC 5431 Fruit stands or markets; Vegetable stands or markets
Pr: Matthew G Masiero
**Treas:* Christopher P Masiero

D-U-N-S 02-056-8630
GUILD FOR EXCEPTIONAL CHILDREN INC
260 68th St, Brooklyn, NY 11220-5201
Tel (718) 833-6633 *Founded/Ownrshp* 1967
Sales 27.8MM *EMP* 550
Accts O Connor Davies Munns & Dobbin
SIC 8361 8052 8331 8322 Home for the mentally handicapped; Rehabilitation center, residential: health care incidental; Intermediate care facilities; Job training & vocational rehabilitation services; Individual & family services; Home for the mentally handicapped; Rehabilitation center, residential: health care incidental; Intermediate care facilities; Job training & vocational rehabilitation services; Individual & family services
Pr: Anthony Setta
**Pr:* Anthony Santoro
**CFO:* Annette Shoen
**VP:* Arlene Rutuelo
**VP:* Noreen Ryan
VP: Joanne Wall
Ex Dir: Paul Casson

GUILD HOME FOR AGED BLIND
See JGB HEALTH FACILITIES CORP

D-U-N-S 05-571-0354
GUILD MORTGAGE CO
COMSTOCK MORTGAGE
5898 Copley Dr Fl 4, San Diego, CA 92111-7916
Tel (800) 283-8823 *Founded/Ownrshp* 1960
Sales NA *EMP* 1,000
Accts Richey May & Co Englewood C
SIC 6162 6733 Mortgage bankers; Trusts, except educational, religious, charity: management; Mortgage bankers; Trusts, except educational, religious, charity: management
Pr: Mary Ann McGarry
Pr: Margie Orwig
**CFO:* Terry Schmidt
Ofcr: Sherrie Fico
Ofcr: Julia Hansen
Ofcr: Lori Hosac
Ofcr: Debbie McLaughlin
Ofcr: Oleg Tkach
Ofcr: Kristen Villanueva
Ex VP: Barry Horn
Ex VP: James Madsen
Ex VP: Aaron Nemec
Sr VP: Catherine Blocker
Sr VP: Michael Rish
Sr VP: Linda Scott
VP: Rhona Kaninau
Exec: Kristi Shanks

D-U-N-S 02-066-4595
GUILDERLAND CENTRAL SCHOOL DISTRICT (NY)
8 School Rd, Guilderland Center, NY 12085
Tel (518) 456-6200 *Founded/Ownrshp* 1950
Sales 94.2MM *EMP* 1,100
SIC 8211 Public elementary & secondary schools; High school, junior or senior; Public elementary & secondary schools; High school, junior or senior
**Treas:* John Rizzo

D-U-N-S 00-224-8834 IMP
GUILDMASTER INC (NC)
(*Suby of* SRC HOLDINGS CORP) ★
1938 E Phelps St, Springfield, MO 65802-2281
Tel (417) 447-1871 *Founded/Ownrshp* 2001
Sales 37.8MM^E *EMP* 554
SIC 2392 5023 Household furnishings; Decorative home furnishings & supplies; Household furnishings; Decorative home furnishings & supplies
Ch Bd: Stephen R Crowder
COO: Vikas V Karode
CFO: Daniel F Graham
Ex VP: James K Parsons
VP: J Michael Sandel
Telecom Ex: Zac Brewer
VP Sls: Buzz Leer
Board of Directors: Richard B Chalker, Steven W Fox, Caroline Hipple, Ronald L Jones

D-U-N-S 78-547-8152
GUILDNET INC
JGB
(*Suby of* JEWISH GUILD FOR BLIND) ★
15 W 65th St, New York, NY 10023-6601
Tel (212) 769-6200 *Founded/Ownrshp* 1996
Sales 672.8MM *EMP* 377^E
Accts Loeb & Troper Llp New York N
SIC 8011 Medical centers; Medical centers
CEO: Alan R Morse
**Ch:* James M Dubin
**Treas:* Lawrence E Goldschmidt
VP Admn: Larry Carr

D-U-N-S 78-368-3626 IMP/EXP
GUILFORD
141 Wideawake St, Pine Grove, PA 17963-1211
Tel (570) 345-2611 *Founded/Ownrshp* 1986
Sales NA *EMP* 575
SIC 2258

GUILFORD BUSINESS FORMS
See GBF INC

D-U-N-S 07-782-5941
GUILFORD CHILD DEVELOPMENT
1200 Arlington St, Greensboro, NC 27406-1421
Tel (336) 378-7700 *Founded/Ownrshp* 1998
Sales 17.8MM *EMP* 310
SIC 8351 8322 Child day care services; Individual & family services; Child day care services; Individual & family services
Ch: Laurence Aikens
**Treas:* Steve Elliott
**Ex Dir:* C Robin Britt

D-U-N-S 04-242-6064
GUILFORD COLLEGE
5800 W Friendly Ave, Greensboro, NC 27410-4173
Tel (336) 299-6908 *Founded/Ownrshp* 1837
Sales 52.0MM *EMP* 428
Accts Davenport Marvin Joyce & Co Ll
SIC 8221 College, except junior; College, except junior
Pr: Jane K Fernandes
VP: Greg Bursavich
VP: Randy Doss
VP: Kim Goodman
**VP:* Jimmy Wilson
Assoc Dir: Erin Kelly
Assoc Dir: Daniel Nonte
Assoc Dir: Teresa Sanford
Genl Mgr: Kate Schwab
Off Mgr: Patricia Daniel
Dir IT: Richard Schilhavy

D-U-N-S 05-469-9491
GUILFORD COUNTY SCHOOL SYSTEM
G C S
712 N Eugene St, Greensboro, NC 27401-1622
Tel (336) 370-8100 *Founded/Ownrshp* 1898
Sales 348.2MM^E *EMP* 8,000
SIC 8211 Public elementary & secondary schools; Public elementary & secondary schools
Ex Dir: Doris Brown
Prgrm Mgr: Mitzi Barber
CIO: Barbara Weaver
MIS Dir: Richard Sumner
Dir IT: Donna Yow
IT Man: Phillip Henry
Teacher Pr: Steve Foster
Teacher Pr: Alyson Yates
Pgrm Dir: Dennis Cole

D-U-N-S 11-247-4023
GUILFORD HEALTH CARE CENTER INC
2041 Willow Rd, Greensboro, NC 27406-3831
Tel (336) 272-9700 *Founded/Ownrshp* 1990
Sales 877.5MM *EMP* 125
SIC 8051 Skilled nursing care facilities; Skilled nursing care facilities
Exec: Jackie Gonzales

D-U-N-S 00-323-2428 IMP/EXP
■ **GUILFORD MILLS INC**
(*Suby of* LEAR CORP) ★
1001 Military Cutoff Rd # 300, Wilmington, NC 28405-4376
Tel (910) 794-5800 *Founded/Ownrshp* 1946, 2012
Sales 491.8MM^E *EMP* 2,600
SIC 2258 2399 Cloth, warp knit; Dyeing & finishing lace goods & warp knit fabric; Automotive covers, except seat & tire covers; Cloth, warp knit; Dyeing & finishing lace goods & warp knit fabric; Automotive covers, except seat & tire covers
Pr: Matt Simoncini
Pr: Chad Brooks
Pr: Shannon White
Bd of Dir: Terrence Geremski
Bd of Dir: Paul Gillease
Bd of Dir: Cheryl Jacobs
Bd of Dir: Grant Wilson
Ex VP: David Taylor
VP: Ron Houser
VP: Deborah Poole
Prgrm Mgr: John Rinere

D-U-N-S 00-797-1245
GUILFORD SAVINGS BANK (INC)
1 Park St, Guilford, CT 06437-2646
Tel (203) 453-2015 *Founded/Ownrshp* 1875
Sales NA *EMP* 105
SIC 6022 State commercial banks; State commercial banks
Pr: Chales O'Malley
**Sr VP:* Margaret Livingston
VP: Renee Pallenberg
VP: Janet Sandella
Dir Bus: Lisa Lemonte
Brnch Mgr: Keira Eule
IT Man: Lisa Kaye
Netwrk Mgr: Bryan Mierzejewski
Mktg Mgr: Mike Storiale
Snr Mgr: Heather Hackley

D-U-N-S 14-276-0342
GUION PARTNERS INC
590 Madison Ave, New York, NY 10022-2524
Tel (212) 851-3730 *Founded/Ownrshp* 2006
Sales 30.0MM *EMP* 12
SIC 8742 Management consulting services; Management consulting services
Prin: Lindsay Guion

D-U-N-S 03-198-2796
GUIRYS INC
620 Canosa Ct, Denver, CO 80204-4108
Tel (720) 360-4840 *Founded/Ownrshp* 1962
Sales 123.5MM^E *EMP* 105
SIC 5198 5231 5999 Paints; Wallcoverings; Paint; Wallpaper; Artists' supplies & materials; Paints; Wallcoverings; Paint; Wallpaper; Artists' supplies & materials
Pr: Richard L Guiry

D-U-N-S 80-805-4774
GUITAR CENTER HOLDINGS INC
5795 Lindero Canyon Rd, Westlake Village, CA 91362-4013
Tel (818) 735-8800 *Founded/Ownrshp* 2007
Sales 2.1MMM *EMP* 10,188
SIC 5736 Musical instrument stores; Drums & related percussion instruments; Keyboard instruments; Musical instrument stores; Drums & related percussion instruments; Keyboard instruments
CEO: Tim Martin
Ex VP: John Bagan
Ex VP: Frank Hamlin
Sr VP: Dennis Haffeman

D-U-N-S 09-147-8008 IMP
GUITAR CENTER INC
(*Suby of* GUITAR CENTER HOLDINGS INC) ★
5795 Lindero Canyon Rd, Westlake Village, CA 91362-4013
Tel (818) 735-8800 *Founded/Ownrshp* 2007
Sales 1.8MMM^E *EMP* 10,188
SIC 5736 Musical instrument stores; Drums & related percussion instruments; Keyboard instruments; Musical instrument stores; Drums & related percussion instruments; Keyboard instruments
CEO: Darrell Webb
**CFO:* Tim Martin
**Treas:* John Unger
Ex VP: Michael Amkreutz
**Ex VP:* Dennis Haffeman
Ex VP: Stephen Zapf
Admn Mgr: Ashley Depas
Dept Mgr: Jake Bodnar
Dept Mgr: Daniel Bogan
Dept Mgr: Amanda Burnisky
Dept Mgr: Mario Carter

D-U-N-S 18-065-3912 IMP
GUITAR CENTER STORES INC
MUSIC & ARTS CENTERS
(*Suby of* GUITAR CENTER INC) ★
5795 Lindero Canyon Rd, Westlake Village, CA 91362-4013
Tel (818) 735-8800 *Founded/Ownrshp* 2000
Sales 103.5MM^E *EMP* 835^E
SIC 5736 Musical instrument stores
Pr: Darrell Webb
**CFO:* Erick Mason
**Ex VP:* John Bagan
**Ex VP:* Dennis Haffeman
**Ex VP:* Tim Martin
**Sr VP:* Kevin Kazubowski

D-U-N-S 00-911-6286 IMP/EXP
GUITTARD CHOCOLATE CO
10 Guittard Rd, Burlingame, CA 94010-2203
Tel (650) 697-4427 *Founded/Ownrshp* 1868
Sales 85.0MM^E *EMP* 240
SIC 2066 2064 Chocolate; Cocoa & cocoa products; Candy & other confectionery products; Chocolate; Cocoa & cocoa products; Candy & other confectionery products
Pr: Gary W Guittard
VP Opers: Gerry Allen
Opers Mgr: Jerry Allen
Opers Mgr: Alvin Oey
Plnt Mgr: Eric Blickenstaff
Mktg Dir: Amy Guittard
Sls Dir: Rick Osteen
Manager: Vickie Raulino
Sales Asso: Gary Dinstuhl
Sales Asso: Allan White
Snr Mgr: Gerrit Dirkmaat

GULBRANDSEN CHEMICALS
See GULBRANDSEN TECHNOLOGIES INC

D-U-N-S 60-408-8849 IMP/EXP
GULBRANDSEN CHEMICALS INC
GULBRANDSEN MANUFACTURING
183 Gulbrandsen Rd, Orangeburg, SC 29115-8986
Tel (803) 531-2413 *Founded/Ownrshp* 1989
Sales 29.3MM^E *EMP* 100
SIC 2869 2819 Industrial organic chemicals; Industrial inorganic chemicals; Industrial organic chemicals; Industrial inorganic chemicals
CEO: Donald E Gulbrandsen
IT Man: Lewis Hughes

GULBRANDSEN MANUFACTURING
See GULBRANDSEN CHEMICALS INC

D-U-N-S 92-716-4749
GULBRANDSEN TECHNOLOGIES INC
GULBRANDSEN CHEMICALS
2 Main St, Clinton, NJ 08809-1328
Tel (908) 735-5458 *Founded/Ownrshp* 1982
Sales 21.5MM^E *EMP* 40^E
SIC 2899 Chemical preparations
Pr: Donald Gulbrandsen
VP: Dave Drolinger
**VP:* Fredrika Gulbrandsen
Exec: John Knychala

GULF
See SAVEWAY PETROLEUM INC

GULF
See SANTA PAULA OIL CORP

D-U-N-S 02-659-9084
GULF & BASCO CORP (TX)
2425 Broad St, Houston, TX 77087-1407
Tel (713) 645-6611 *Founded/Ownrshp* 1937
Sales 49.8MM^E *EMP* 220
SIC 5031 5064

D-U-N-S 78-721-7397
GULF & CARIBBEAN CARGO INC
(*Suby of* SHADRACK LLC)
6860 S Service Dr, Waterford, MI 48327-1652
Tel (248) 666-5910 *Founded/Ownrshp* 1991
Sales 63.7MM *EMP* 80
SIC 5541 Filling stations, gasoline; Filling stations, gasoline
CEO: Alan Ross
**Pr:* Michael N Church
**Treas:* Martha Wale
Ofcr: Tim Hunter
Ofcr: Ashton Kind

D-U-N-S 17-709-6013
GULF BEACH HOTEL INC
PERDIDO BEACH RESORT
27200 Perdido Beach Blvd, Orange Beach, AL 36561-3205
Tel (251) 981-9811 *Founded/Ownrshp* 1987
Sales 23.0MM^E *EMP* 300
SIC 7011 5812 5813 Resort hotel; Eating places; Cocktail lounge; Resort hotel; Eating places; Cocktail lounge
Pr: Nancy B Meadlock
Exec: John Hamme
Genl Mgr: Nancy Medlock
Genl Mgr: Leslie Murry
Manager: Lisa Grotefend

D-U-N-S 78-733-2998
GULF BUILDING LLC
633 S Federal Hwy Ste 500, Fort Lauderdale, FL 33301-3163
Tel (954) 492-9191 *Founded/Ownrshp* 2009
Sales 60.0MM *EMP* 140
SIC 1542 Commercial & office building contractors; Commercial & office buildings, renovation & repair
VP: Kevin Murphy
Pdt Mgr: George Chekuri

GULF CAOST STABILIZED MTLS
See CAMPBELL CONCRETE & MATERIALS LP

D-U-N-S 15-048-7924
GULF CARE INC
GULF COAST VILLAGE
1333 Santa Barbara Blvd, Cape Coral, FL 33991-2803
Tel (239) 772-1333 *Founded/Ownrshp* 1982
Sales 20.1MM *EMP* 300
Accts Bobbitt Pittenger & Company Pa
SIC 8051 8059 Skilled nursing care facilities; Nursing home, except skilled & intermediate care facility; Skilled nursing care facilities; Nursing home, except skilled & intermediate care facility
CEO: Richard Heath
Exec: Charles Gould
Exec: Norbert Mess
**Prin:* Thomas N Cash
**Prin:* Michael M Spilane

D-U-N-S 15-408-6581 IMP
GULF CHEMICAL AND METALLURGICAL CORP
(*Suby of* COMILOG US INC) ★
302 Midway Rd, Freeport, TX 77542
Tel (979) 415-1500 *Founded/Ownrshp* 1991
Sales 30.5MM^E *EMP* 120^E
SIC 3356 8748 4953 3341 Nonferrous rolling & drawing; Business consulting; Refuse systems; Secondary nonferrous metals; Nonferrous rolling & drawing; Business consulting; Refuse systems; Secondary nonferrous metals
Pr: William G Deering
**Treas:* Dave Arthur
**VP:* Zenon Llanos
VP: Allan Orr
Sfty Mgr: Ronnie Muller
Plnt Mgr: Patrick Blake

D-U-N-S 03-404-0089
GULF CITY BODY AND TRAILER WORKS INC (AL)
601 S Conception St Ste 3, Mobile, AL 36603-2101
Tel (251) 438-5521 *Founded/Ownrshp* 1945, 1967
Sales 60.0MM^E *EMP* 55
Accts Seibert Baxter & Company Pc
SIC 5511 3715 7539 5012 Trucks, tractors & trailers: new & used; Truck trailer chassis; Trailer repair; Trailers for trucks, new & used; Trucks, tractors & trailers: new & used; Truck trailer chassis; Trailer repair; Trailers for trucks, new & used
Pr: Hunter Lyons
**CEO:* Barry E Gritter
**VP:* Melissa G Fontenot
**VP:* Teresa G Weaver

GULF CLEANING & LAUNDRY SUPPLY
See FABRICLEAN SUPPLY INC

D-U-N-S 13-036-1702 EXP
GULF COAST AIR & HYDRAULICS INC
3415 Halls Mill Rd, Mobile, AL 36693-5601
Tel (251) 666-6683 *Founded/Ownrshp* 1985
Sales 32.0MM^E *EMP* 25
SIC 5084 7699 Hydraulic systems equipment & supplies; Hydraulic equipment repair
Pr: Charles Moorehead
**VP:* Karen Williamson
Off Mgr: Dawn Collins

D-U-N-S 92-679-9701
GULF COAST BANCSHARES
221 S State St, Abbeville, LA 70510-5917
Tel (337) 893-7733 *Founded/Ownrshp* 1983
Sales NA *EMP* 100
SIC 6022 State commercial banks; State commercial banks
Pr: Paul Patout

D-U-N-S 02-085-3677
GULF COAST BANK
(*Suby of* GULF COAST BANCSHARES) ★
221 S State St, Abbeville, LA 70510-5917
Tel (337) 893-7733 *Founded/Ownrshp* 1983
Sales NA *EMP* 99
SIC 6022 State commercial banks; State commercial banks
Ch Bd: Patrick Patout
**Pr:* Paul Patout
Ofcr: Murphy Guilbeaux Jr
Sr VP: Richard Billeaud
**Sr VP:* Lorraine Leblanc
VP: Chris Dardeau
VP: Errol Lebla
VP: Cathy Roy
VP: Roberta Trahan
Brnch Mgr: Kort Boring
IT Man: Scott Boudreaux
Board of Directors: Richard Dubois

D-U-N-S 61-362-1010
GULF COAST BANK AND TRUST CO
200 Saint Charles Ave, New Orleans, LA 70130-2903
Tel (504) 561-6100 *Founded/Ownrshp* 1990
Sales NA *EMP* 315
SIC 6022 State trust companies accepting deposits, commercial; State trust companies accepting deposits, commercial
Pr: Guy T Williams
**CFO:* Greg Hoilier
Ofcr: Scott Lagarde
Ofcr: Maggie Leblanc
Ofcr: Ana Perkins
Assoc VP: Joseph Spampneto
Sr VP: Susan Nye
VP: Herman Boudreaux
VP: T Caldwell
VP: Minaxi Chase
VP: Marcia Leone
VP: Patricia Levie
VP: Ronald Lopez
VP: Rance Mangipano
VP: Janell Nichols
VP: Diane Wahl

D-U-N-S 00-780-4149
GULF COAST BROADCASTING CO
KRIS TV CHANNEL SIX
(*Suby of* EPI GROUP LLC) ★
409 S Staples St, Corpus Christi, TX 78401-3330
Tel (361) 886-6100 *Founded/Ownrshp* 1935
Sales 46.4MM^E *EMP* 1,515
SIC 4833 5812 Television broadcasting stations; Eating places; Television broadcasting stations; Eating places
Pr: T Frank Smith Jr
**Treas:* Susan M Hines
**VP:* T Frank Smith IV
Pgrm Dir: Joyce Applebee

D-U-N-S 07-939-1082
GULF COAST CENTER
123 Rosenberg St Ste 600, Galveston, TX 77550-1454
Tel (281) 488-2839 *Founded/Ownrshp* 1965
Sales 27.5MM *EMP* 200
Accts Davis Kinard & Co Pc Abilene
SIC 8361 Home for the mentally handicapped; Home for the mentally retarded; Home for the mentally handicapped; Home for the mentally retarded
Ex Dir: G Michael Winburn
**COO:* Pat Wareing
**CFO:* Rick Elizondo
VP: James Webb
Exec: Jim Hall
Netwrk Mgr: Michael Coffey

GULF COAST CHEMICAL
See GULF COAST COMPANIES INC

GULF COAST COMMUNITY COLLEGE
See GULF COAST STATE COLLEGE

D-U-N-S 83-969-6739
GULF COAST COMMUNITY FOUNDATION
VENICE ENDOWMENT
601 Tamiami Trl S, Venice, FL 34285-3237
Tel (941) 486-4600 *Founded/Ownrshp* 1995
Sales 49.3MM *EMP* 18
SIC 8399 Community development groups; Community development groups
Pr: Mark Pritchett
CFO: Cory Reeves
Ofcr: Kirstin Fulkerson
Ofcr: Kelly Romanoff

D-U-N-S 07-842-3134
GULF COAST COMMUNITY SERVICES ASSOCIATION (TX)
9320 Kirby Dr, Houston, TX 77054-2515
Tel (713) 393-4700 *Founded/Ownrshp* 1965
Sales 20.3MM *EMP* 400
Accts Mcconnell & Jones Llp Houston
SIC 8351 Head start center, except in conjunction with school; Head start center, except in conjunction with school
CEO: Dr Jonita Wallace Reynolds
CFO: Julio Flores
CFO: Debra Rogers

*Ch: Kevin Owens
Exec: Patricia Roberts

D-U-N-S 01-712-3449 IMP
GULF COAST COMPANIES INC
GULF COAST CHEMICAL
220 Jacqulyn St, Abbeville, LA 70510-8408
Tel (337) 893-1563 Founded/Ownrshp 1981
Sales 38.6MM^E EMP 55
SIC 5169 Chemicals, industrial & heavy
Pr: Jimmy Lee Fusilier
Treas: Michael Nadin
*VP: Ruth Fusilier
Genl Mgr: Bayne Trahan
Opers Mgr: Blair Smith

D-U-N-S 18-335-0065
GULF COAST DODGE INC
CLEAR LAKE DODGE
15711 Gulf Fwy, Webster, TX 77598-3809
Tel (281) 481-1000 Founded/Ownrshp 2009
Sales 64.3MM^E EMP 200
SIC 5511 Automobiles, new & used; Pickups, new & used; Vans, new & used; Automobiles, new & used; Pickups, new & used; Vans, new & used
Pr: Charles Tubbs
*Treas: Harry W Buescher
*Ex VP: Robert Edinfield
*VP: Malcolm Garland
Genl Mgr: Jennifer Lazerus
Dir IT: Bill Belk
Sls Mgr: Jim Surber

D-U-N-S 04-796-6015
GULF COAST ELECTRIC COOPERATIVE INC
722 Highway 22, Wewahitchka, FL 32465-9504
Tel (850) 639-2216 Founded/Ownrshp 1946
Sales 46.7MM EMP 80
Accts He Allen Cpa Americus Ga
SIC 4911 Electric services; Electric services
CEO: Michael E White
Brnch Mgr: Roy Barnes
Dir IT: Carl Elmore
Opers Mgr: Eudon Baxley
Opers Mgr: Josh Pitts
Sls&Mrk Ex: Christine Bennett

D-U-N-S 18-481-3210
GULF COAST FORD INC
2440 Nw Us Highway 19, Crystal River, FL 34428-2967
Tel (352) 795-7371 Founded/Ownrshp 1988
Sales 29.4MM EMP 38
SIC 5511 Automobiles, new & used; Pickups, new & used; Automobiles, new & used; Pickups, new & used
Pr: Nick Nicholas
*Sec: Linda Nicholas
*VP: Shane Bryant

D-U-N-S 82-926-9435
GULF COAST FORD LTD
3100 N Highway 288, Angleton, TX 77515-7504
Tel (713) 422-7200 Founded/Ownrshp 2002
Sales 30.4MM^E EMP 130
SIC 5511 Automobiles, new & used; Automobiles, new & used
Pr: Robert Baldwin III

D-U-N-S 87-682-0981
GULF COAST HEALTH CARE LLC
40 Palafox Pl Ste 400, Pensacola, FL 32502-5699
Tel (800) 881-9907 Founded/Ownrshp 2008
Sales 87.9MM^E EMP 992^E
SIC 8051 Skilled nursing care facilities
Prin: Barry Williams
Ofcr: Cindy Ledford
CIO: Earl Page
Dir IT: Jon Dossey
Nrsg Dir: Sharyn Figgins
Nrsg Dir: Lisa Gahring
Nrsg Dir: Leanne Hyatt
Nrsg Dir: Christine Kimball
Nrsg Dir: Michael Militello
HC Dir: Deidra Melton
HC Dir: Diane Moses

GULF COAST HOSPITAL
See DOCTORS OSTEOPATHIC MEDICAL CENTER INC

GULF COAST IGNITION & CONTROLS
See LONGVIEW DISTRIBUTION I LLC

D-U-N-S 07-994-4479
GULF COAST II LITHOTRIPSY LP
9825 Spectrum Dr Bldg 3, Austin, TX 78717-4930
Tel (866) 598-2734 Founded/Ownrshp 2003, 2015
Sales 10.3MM^E EMP 457
SIC 3845 Electromedical apparatus
Prin: Russell Newman

D-U-N-S 15-080-2163
GULF COAST JEWISH FAMILY AND COMMUNITY SERVICES INC
14041 Icot Blvd, Clearwater, FL 33760-3702
Tel (727) 479-1800 Founded/Ownrshp 1945
Sales 32.3MM EMP 480
Accts Lewis Birch & Ricardo Llc Cle
SIC 8322 Individual & family services; Individual & family services
Ch Bd: Jay Miller
*Ch Bd: Barbara Sterensis
*Pr: Eric Feder
*Treas: David Pilkington
*VP: Julie Klavans
VP: Harvey Landress
*VP: Carla Washinko
Exec: Millie Wagner

D-U-N-S 06-728-1709
GULF COAST LIMESTONE INC
1402 3rd St, Seabrook, TX 77586-3519
Tel (281) 474-4124 Founded/Ownrshp 1966
Sales 50.4MM^E EMP 60
Accts Marty R Chenault Cpa Housto
SIC 1411 1422 1423 1481 1429 Dimension stone; Crushed & broken limestone; Crushed & broken granite; Nonmetallic mineral services; Igneous rock, crushed & broken-quarrying
Pr: Robert Robinson
VP: Kristi Fowler
*VP: Suzy Mayfield
*VP: Glenda Walker
Sales Exec: Harris Robert
Sls Mgr: Eddie Flores
Sls Mgr: Amy McCrory

D-U-N-S 00-690-1011
GULF COAST MARINE SUPPLY CO
501 Stimrad Rd, Mobile, AL 36610-4133
Tel (251) 452-8066 Founded/Ownrshp 1935
Sales 50.1MM^E EMP 85
SIC 5085 5088

GULF COAST MEDICAL CENTER
See BAY HOSPITAL INC

D-U-N-S 01-001-4519
■ **GULF COAST MEDICAL CENTER**
BAY HOSPITAL
(Suby of HCA-HOSPITAL CORP OF AMERICA) ★
449 W 23rd St, Panama City, FL 32405-4507
Tel (850) 769-8341 Founded/Ownrshp 1977
Sales 76.2MM^E EMP 850^E
SIC 8011 Medical centers; Medical centers
CEO: Carlton Ulmer
*Pr: Brian Baumgardner
*CFO: Don Murphy
VP: Loretta Flynn
Dir OR: Anita Jordan
Dir Risk M: Dave Coughlin
IT Man: Frank Dettloff
IT Man: Charlie Hicks
Psych: Irena Pankiewicz
HC Dir: Ruth Hicks
Snr Mgr: Charlie Hix

D-U-N-S 07-826-9646
GULF COAST MEDICAL CENTER
10141 Us 59 Hwy, Wharton, TX 77488-7224
Tel (979) 532-1908 Founded/Ownrshp 1998
Sales 46.9MM^E EMP 180
SIC 8062 General medical & surgical hospitals
CEO: Randy Slack
CFO: Barbara Starling
Dir OR: Lucy Buenger
Dir OR: Debbie Mahoney
Dir Inf Cn: Jennifer Monroe
Dir Rad: Melissa Kalina
Dir Rx: Janet Dusek
CIO: Teresa Mata
Sfty Dirs: Joy Janak
Mktg Dir: Carol Wootton
Ansthlgy: Arnold Wallace

D-U-N-S 96-865-9284
GULF COAST MEDICAL CENTRE LTD
13691 Metro Pkwy Ste 110, Fort Myers, FL 33912-4348
Tel (239) 343-1000 Founded/Ownrshp 1994
Sales 284.2MM EMP 268
SIC 8062 General medical & surgical hospitals; General medical & surgical hospitals
Prin: Jeffrey R Green

D-U-N-S 18-113-9353
GULF COAST MOTOR SALES INC
PALMER'S TOYOTA SUPERSTORE
470 Schillinger Rd S, Mobile, AL 36695-8950
Tel (800) 868-0801 Founded/Ownrshp 1994
Sales 41.3MM^E EMP 95
SIC 5511 Automobiles, new & used; Automobiles, new & used
Pr: Ernest Palmer
CFO: Leslie Freitas
*Treas: Keith Palmer

D-U-N-S 08-467-0793
GULF COAST OFFICE PRODUCTS INC
5801 River Oaks Rd S, New Orleans, LA 70123-2170
Tel (504) 733-3830 Founded/Ownrshp 1977
Sales 28.7MM^E EMP 80
SIC 5044 5065 Photocopy machines; Facsimile equipment
Pr: Robert D Walsh
*Ex VP: William Kenny

D-U-N-S 79-967-3074
GULF COAST OFFICE PRODUCTS INC OF NORTHWEST FLORIDA
6020 Enterprise Dr, Pensacola, FL 32505-1610
Tel (850) 434-5588 Founded/Ownrshp 1993
Sales 20.5MM EMP 75
SIC 5943 5021 5112 5712 Office forms & supplies; Office furniture; Stationery & office supplies; Office furniture; Office forms & supplies; Office furniture; Stationery & office supplies; Office furniture
Pr: Mark Wright
Pr: Lane V Harper
Treas: William Kenny
Treas: James D Wright
Genl Mgr: Mike Johnson
IT Man: Lauren Hawley
Web Prj Mg: Gregory Miller
Opers Mgr: Rich Gillen

D-U-N-S 01-079-5136 IMP
GULF COAST OIL & GAS INDUSTRIES LLC
CARBIDE FABRICATORS
1204 Hays St, Houston, TX 77009-6318
Tel (713) 236-1158 Founded/Ownrshp 1974
Sales 29.4MM^E EMP 85
SIC 3533 3494 Oil & gas field machinery; Valves & pipe fittings; Oil & gas field machinery; Valves & pipe fittings
Pr: Gaylon B Hale
*VP: John W Hale
Off Mgr: Denise Smith

D-U-N-S 02-717-9415
GULF COAST PAPER CO INC
3705 Houston Hwy, Victoria, TX 77901
Tel (361) 852-5252 Founded/Ownrshp 2013
Sales 231.9MM^E EMP 185
Accts Roloff Hnatek & Co Llp Vic
SIC 5113 5087 Industrial & personal service paper; Janitors' supplies; Industrial & personal service paper; Janitors' supplies
Ch Bd: Speed Bancroft
*Pr: F Speed Bancroft
*VP: Sonny Bratz
*VP: Clay Dibble
VP: John McQuillen
*VP: Joe Morris
*VP: Donald Wade
Brnch Mgr: Bruce Kotzur
Brnch Mgr: Mike Trevino
Genl Mgr: Nelda Laurel
IT Man: Donna Durbin

D-U-N-S 61-105-8330 IMP
GULF COAST PRE-STRESS INC
494 N Market St, Pass Christian, MS 39571-2712
Tel (228) 452-7270 Founded/Ownrshp 1967
Sales 23.4MM^E EMP 130^E
SIC 3272 Prestressed concrete products; Prestressed concrete products
Pr: Michael Spruill
*Treas: Peter Wareing
Exec: Nole Monaghan
Sfty Mgr: Derik Warfield
Snr Mgr: Pete Shoemaker

D-U-N-S 93-333-7875
GULF COAST PRODUCE DISTRIBUTORS INC
194 Bohn St, Biloxi, MS 39530-3812
Tel (228) 435-0005 Founded/Ownrshp 1994
Sales 44.2MM^E EMP 40
SIC 5148 Fresh fruits & vegetables
Pr: Christi Alise
*VP: Mike Alise
Genl Mgr: Steve Casselman
Sls Dir: Beau Blalock
Sls Mgr: Nicole Graham

D-U-N-S 08-509-4597
GULF COAST PROJECT SERVICES INC
5800 Lakewood Rnch Blvd N, Lakewood Ranch, FL 34240-8479
Tel (941) 921-6087 Founded/Ownrshp 1976
Sales 23.0MM^E EMP 93
SIC 1522 1542 Remodeling, multi-family dwellings; Commercial & office building, new construction
Ch: William R Dooley
*Pr: Kenneth D Smith
*CFO: Wendy L Mack
Ex VP: Tim Lynch
Sr VP: Charles Evans
VP: Patrick White
Dir Bus: Michael Korcheck
Dir Bus: Laura Orlando
Ex Dir: Peter Harris
Dir IT: Gordon Graham
Sfty Dirs: Joe Spoto

D-U-N-S 01-080-2080
GULF COAST REGIONAL BLOOD CENTER
BLOOD CENTER, THE
1400 La Concha Ln, Houston, TX 77054-1887
Tel (713) 790-1200 Founded/Ownrshp 1974
Sales 97.5MM EMP 634
Accts Ernst & Young Llp Houston Tx
SIC 8099 Blood bank; Blood bank
Pr: Brian G Gannon
COO: Caron Baker
*CFO: Melissa Fisher
*Ch: David M McClanahan
*Treas: Greg Bernica
*Chf Mktg O: Susan Rossmann
Dir Risk M: Connie Foland
Dir Rx: Eric Eaton
Rgnl Mgr: Clare Wong
QA Dir: Adan Rodriguez
VP Opers: Ian Stephens

D-U-N-S 96-650-1868
GULF COAST SHIPPERS LIMITED PARTNERSHIP
UNISHIPPERS
3337 N Hullen St Ste 300, Metairie, LA 70002-3455
Tel (504) 780-7000 Founded/Ownrshp 1990
Sales 24.8MM^E EMP 75
SIC 4731 Freight transportation arrangement; Freight transportation arrangement
Pt: Ed Copain
Pt: Janiane Ahlstedt
Pt: Southpoint Credit LLC
CFO: Dan Reese

D-U-N-S 83-117-8020 IMP
GULF COAST SHIPYARD GROUP INC
13085 Seaway Rd, Gulfport, MS 39503-4607
Tel (228) 276-1051 Founded/Ownrshp 2003
Sales 165.0MM EMP 932^E
SIC 3731 Shipbuilding & repairing; Shipbuilding & repairing
Pr: John Dane III
*COO: Marvin Serna
*CFO: Mitchell Skrmetta
Board of Directors: John Dane, Edmund Feeley, Michael Klein, Brian Michaud, William Smith

D-U-N-S 02-628-0982
GULF COAST STATE COLLEGE
GULF COAST COMMUNITY COLLEGE
5230 W Highway 98, Panama City, FL 32401-1041
Tel (850) 769-1551 Founded/Ownrshp 1956
Sales 1.4MM EMP 332
Accts David W Martin Cpa Tallahas
SIC 8222 Community college; Community college
Pr: Dr Jim Kerley
Off Mgr: Mark Lamberson
Ql Cn Mgr: Joan Hamm
Psych: Cindy Boshelle

D-U-N-S 00-864-4742 EXP
GULF COAST SUPPLY & MANUFACTURING LLC
14429 Sw 2nd Pl Ste 30, Newberry, FL 32669-6388
Tel (352) 498-0778 Founded/Ownrshp 1997
Sales 22.2MM^E EMP 52^E
SIC 5033 3448 Roofing, asphalt & sheet metal; Prefabricated metal buildings
Pr: Jonathan C Sherrill
Bd of Dir: David Morris
Genl Mgr: Jonathan Sherrill
Manager: Timothy Nordstrom
Mktg Dir: Mark Risley
Sls Mgr: Russell Bowen
Sales Asso: Tom O'Neal

D-U-N-S 13-121-9198
GULF COAST TEACHING FAMILY SERVICES INC
2400 Edenborn Ave Ste 299, Metairie, LA 70001-1817
Tel (504) 831-6561 Founded/Ownrshp 1983
Sales 23.9MM EMP 1,150
Accts Bernard & Franks Corp Of Cp
SIC 8322 Social service center; Social service center
CEO: Rick Hardie

GULF COAST THERMAL KING
See HUNT INC

D-U-N-S 07-417-6348
GULF COAST TRADES CENTER
143 Forest Service Rd 233, New Waverly, TX 77358
Tel (936) 344-6677 Founded/Ownrshp 1971
Sales 4.3MM EMP 300
Accts Gomez & Company Houston Tx
SIC 8361 8299 Rehabilitation center, residential: health care incidental; Vocational counseling; Rehabilitation center, residential: health care incidental; Vocational counseling
VP: Dale Underwood
CFO: Dianne Wood
Dir IT: Sandi Belcher
Dir IT: Cory Platt
IT Man: Joyce Pasket

D-U-N-S 78-753-7521
■ **GULF COAST TREATMENT CENTER INC**
(Suby of UNIVERSAL HEALTH SERVICES INC) ★
1015 Mar Walt Dr, Fort Walton Beach, FL 32547-6612
Tel (850) 863-4160 Founded/Ownrshp 2003
Sales 14.1MM^E EMP 290
SIC 8322 8361 8063 Drug abuse counselor, nontreatment; Juvenile correctional home; Psychiatric hospitals; Drug abuse counselor, nontreatment; Juvenile correctional home; Psychiatric hospitals
CEO: Jeanette Jackson
*CFO: Karen Jackson
VP: Dulce Mooney

D-U-N-S 03-402-5726
GULF COAST TRUCK & EQUIPMENT CO INC (AL)
2260 Halls Mill Rd, Mobile, AL 36606-4617
Tel (251) 476-2744 Founded/Ownrshp 1954
Sales 40.0MM EMP 95
SIC 5511 5012 Trucks, tractors & trailers: new & used; Trucks, commercial; Trucks, tractors & trailers: new & used; Trucks, commercial
Pr: John R Cross Jr
*CFO: Nancy Seibt
*VP: Chad Cross
VP: Mark Cross
Genl Mgr: Doug Bradford
Off Mgr: Bobbi Quina
Sales Asso: Travis Taylor

D-U-N-S 08-341-5062
GULF COAST UTILITY CONTRACTORS LLC
13938 Highway 77, Panama City, FL 32409-4688
Tel (850) 265-9166 Founded/Ownrshp 1999
Sales 28.9MM^E EMP 83
SIC 1623 Water & sewer line construction
*VP: Christopher Corbin

GULF COAST VILLAGE
See GULF CARE INC

D-U-N-S 07-390-3106
GULF COAST WASTE DISPOSAL AUTHORITY
910 Bay Area Blvd, Houston, TX 77058-2604
Tel (281) 488-4115 Founded/Ownrshp 1969
Sales 66.4MM EMP 154
Accts Whitley Penn Llp Houston Tex
SIC 4953 Refuse systems; Refuse systems
Genl Mgr: Charles Ganze
VP: Raj Bhattarai
Dir Lab: Diane Maloy
Genl Mgr: Dick Brown
CIO: Ken Tucker

D-U-N-S 09-194-7200
GULF COAST WATER AUTHORITY
GCWA
3630 Highway 1765, Texas City, TX 77591-4824
Tel (409) 935-2438 Founded/Ownrshp 1945
Sales 39.2MM EMP 50
Accts Sandersen Knox & Co Cpas Su
SIC 4941 Water supply; Water supply
Pr: James McWhorter
*Sec: R Sue Edrozo
*VP: Russell Jones

D-U-N-S 04-954-8803 EXP
GULF CONTROLS CO LLC (DE)
(Suby of EMPLOYEE OWNED HOLDINGS INC) ★
5201 Tampa West Blvd, Tampa, FL 33634-2498
Tel (813) 884-0471 Founded/Ownrshp 2001, 2013
Sales 51.7MM^E EMP 86
SIC 5084 7699 Hydraulic systems equipment & supplies; Hydraulic equipment repair; Hydraulic systems equipment & supplies; Hydraulic equipment repair
Pr: Andrew J Deboer
*Pr: John Flieman III
Chf Mktg O: Rod Longnecker
Ofcr: Rick Sawson
*VP: Cynthia Deboer
*VP: Jean M Lidinsky
*VP: Mark P Poljak
Exec: Barbara Palmer
Dist Mgr: Dustin Kerr
DP Dir: Jan Mertzman
Dir IT: Edwin Coelho

D-U-N-S 19-321-4822
GULF COUNTY SCHOOL DISTRICT
150 Middle School Dr, Port Saint Joe, FL 32456-2261
Tel (850) 229-8256 Founded/Ownrshp 1988
Sales 21.8MM^E EMP 537

SIC 8211 5541 Public combined elementary & secondary school; Filling stations, gasoline; Public combined elementary & secondary school; Filling stations, gasoline
Dir IT: Chuck Worley
Schl Brd P: Linda Wood
HC Dir: Martha Weimorts

D-U-N-S 05-101-5311 EXP
GULF CRANE SERVICES INC
73413 Bollfield Dr, Covington, LA 70435-5650
Tel (985) 892-0056 *Founded/Ownrshp* 1982
Sales 43.1MM^E *EMP* 150
Accts Kenneth J Hembel
SIC 1799 7699 5084 3536 Insulation of pipes & boilers; Engine repair & replacement, non-automotive; Industrial machinery & equipment repair; Hydraulic systems equipment & supplies; Cranes, industrial plant; Insulation of pipes & boilers; Engine repair & replacement, non-automotive; Industrial machinery & equipment repair; Hydraulic systems equipment & supplies; Cranes, industrial plant
CEO: Charles Bollinger Jr
**Pr:* Brandon Bollinger
CFO: Paul Harpham

D-U-N-S 06-673-5085 IMP
GULF DISTRIBUTING CO INC
3378 Moffett Rd, Mobile, AL 36607-1797
Tel (251) 476-9600 *Founded/Ownrshp* 1973
Sales 51.1MM^E *EMP* 130
SIC 5181 5182 Beer & other fermented malt liquors; Wine; Beer & other fermented malt liquors; Wine
Pr: Elliot B Maisel
**Pr:* Billy Dial
**CFO:* Tom Gangle
VP: David Gaines
**VP:* Jimmy Marston
Area Mgr: Ricky Bowen
Area Mgr: Shawn Dunn
Area Mgr: Morgan McAfoos
Genl Mgr: Taska Clayton
Sls Mgr: Kevin Thomas
Genl Couns: Rebecca Maisel

D-U-N-S 82-829-7189 IMP
GULF DISTRIBUTING CO OF MOBILE LLC
3378 Moffett Rd, Mobile, AL 36607-1797
Tel (251) 476-9600 *Founded/Ownrshp* 2000
Sales 22.1MM^E *EMP* 300
SIC 2086 Bottled & canned soft drinks; Bottled & canned soft drinks
Mktg Mgr: Andrea Bertagnolli

GULF EAGLE SUPPLY
See GULFSIDE SUPPLY INC

D-U-N-S 00-973-6588
GULF ELECTROQUIP MANAGEMENT LLC
425 N Wayside Dr, Houston, TX 77020-7516
Tel (713) 675-2525 *Founded/Ownrshp* 1960
Sales 26.9MM^E *EMP* 50
SIC 5063 6512 3621 3612 Motors, electric; Generators; Commercial & industrial building operation; Motors & generators; Transformers, except electric
COO: Bill Riggins
VP: Jeff Thrasher
IT Man: Philip Mohr
Info Man: James Peterson
Sales Asso: Sandy Jeane

D-U-N-S 00-799-4486 IMP
GULF ENGINEERING CO LLC
WATER MANAGEMENT/OMI EQP SLS
611 Hill St, Jefferson, LA 70121-1000
Tel (504) 733-4868 *Founded/Ownrshp* 1924
Sales 20.1MM^E *EMP* 75
SIC 1796 3443 3599 5169 5084 7389 Machinery dismantling; Machinery installation; Millwright; Power generating equipment installation; Fabricated plate work (boiler shop); Machine shop, jobbing & repair; Chemicals & allied products; Industrial machinery & equipment; Industrial & commercial equipment inspection service; Petroleum refinery inspection service; Pipeline & power line inspection service

GULF ENGINEERS AND CONSULTANTS
See E C G INC

D-U-N-S 18-766-4172
GULF EQUIPMENT CORP
5540 Business Park Way, Theodore, AL 36582-1616
Tel (251) 653-5075 *Founded/Ownrshp* 1984
Sales 51.6MM *EMP* 133
Accts Warren Averett Llc Foley Al
SIC 1542 1623 Commercial & office building, new construction; Transmitting tower (telecommunication) construction; Commercial & office building, new construction; Transmitting tower (telecommunication) construction
Pr: Lw Ramsay Jr
**CFO:* J Anthony Dees
**Treas:* Ashley Ramsay
VP: William M McGough Jr
VP: William McGough
**VP:* John C Ramsay
VP: Rhea Silvemail

GULF FIELD SERVICES
See GULF INTERSTATE ENGINEERING CO

GULF GREYHOUND PARK
See GULF GREYHOUND PARTNERS LTD

D-U-N-S 79-210-3590
GULF GREYHOUND PARTNERS LTD
GULF GREYHOUND PARK
1000 Fm 2004 Rd, La Marque, TX 77568-2478
Tel (409) 986-9500 *Founded/Ownrshp* 1989
Sales 11.0MM^E *EMP* 300
SIC 7948 Dog race track operation; Dog race track operation
Genl Mgr: Sally Griggs
Exec: Jackie Archie
CIO: Phil Pierce

D-U-N-S 07-262-2459
GULF HEALTH HOSPITALS INC
THOMAS HOSPITAL
(*Suby of* INFIRMARY HEALTH SYSTEM INC) ★
750 Morphy Ave, Fairhope, AL 36532-1812
Tel (251) 928-2375 *Founded/Ownrshp* 2005
Sales 10.4MM^E *EMP* 1,200
SIC 8062 8011 General medical & surgical hospitals; Offices & clinics of medical doctors; General medical & surgical hospitals; Offices & clinics of medical doctors
Chf Path: Lloyd L Gardner
Chf OB: Angela R McCool
Chf Rad: Michael J Quinn
**CFO:* Patrick Murphy
Treas: Charles Earle Jr
VP: Harry Brislin
VP: Carl Craddock
VP: Doug Garner
VP: Michael L McBrearty
VP: Eddy Stephens
Dir Inf Cn: Patti Thames
Dir Lab: Art Goodson
Dir Rad: Kathy Linam
Dir Rx: Lisa Stanley

D-U-N-S 05-090-8086
GULF INDUSTRIES INC
PAVEMENT MARKING CO
70393 Bravo St, Covington, LA 70433-8926
Tel (985) 892-6500 *Founded/Ownrshp* 1970
Sales 48.9MM^E *EMP* 169
SIC 8711 3661 2952 5088 Engineering services; Telephone sets, all types except cellular radio; Asphalt felts & coatings; Golf carts; Engineering services; Telephone sets, all types except cellular radio; Asphalt felts & coatings; Golf carts
Pr: Jack B Harper
**Pr:* Douglas A Brooks
COO: Wayne E Burgr
**Treas:* Sarah Frantovich
**Treas:* Monica B Hodges
**Sr VP:* Renee Cedotal
**VP:* Wayne E Burger
**VP:* Jeffrey R Diemont
Genl Mgr: Jeff Jones
CIO: Brain Chaisson

D-U-N-S 62-420-3824
GULF INTERNATIONAL CORP
(*Suby of* G.I. INTERNATIONAL HOLDING AMSTERDAM B.V.)
16010 Barkers Point Ln # 6, Houston, TX 77079-4024
Tel (713) 850-3400 *Founded/Ownrshp* 1989
Sales 251.8MM *EMP* 1,100
Accts Bdo Usa Llp Houston Tx
SIC 8711 Consulting engineer; Consulting engineer
Pr: H D Evans
**CFO:* John Thomas
**Treas:* N R Kurtis
Treas: N R Kutis
**Sec:* James J McMahon
**VP:* David Buza

D-U-N-S 00-485-2877
GULF INTERSTATE ENGINEERING CO
GULF FIELD SERVICES
(*Suby of* GULF INTERNATIONAL CORP) ★
16010 Barkers Point Ln # 600, Houston, TX 77079-9000
Tel (713) 850-3400 *Founded/Ownrshp* 1953
Sales 116.3MM^E *EMP* 350
SIC 8711 Petroleum, mining & chemical engineers; Consulting engineer; Petroleum, mining & chemical engineers; Consulting engineer
CEO: H Doug Evans
Pr: Bob Sprick
VP: Rick Barnard
Off Admin: Laura Steves
Ql Cn Mgr: Joseph Bohinsky
Ql Cn Mgr: Joshua Brannon
Snr Mgr: Zaheer Mohammed
Snr Mgr: Lance Thomas

D-U-N-S 83-023-1457
GULF INTRACOASTAL CONSTRUCTORS A JOINT VENTURE
6800 Bellaire Dr, New Orleans, LA 70124-1536
Tel (504) 681-5000 *Founded/Ownrshp* 2009
Sales 21.4MM^E *EMP* 331
SIC 1629 Levee construction; Levee construction
Prin: Bruce E Grewcock

D-U-N-S 13-924-0618
▲ GULF ISLAND FABRICATION INC
16225 Park Ten Pl Ste 280, Houston, TX 77084-5138
Tel (713) 714-6100 *Founded/Ownrshp* 1985
Sales 506.6MM *EMP* 1,700
Tkr Sym GIFI *Exch* NGS
SIC 3441 1389 Fabricated structural metal; Construction, repair & dismantling services; Oil field services; Fabricated structural metal; Construction, repair & dismantling services; Oil field services
Pr: Kirk J Meche
**Ch Bd:* John P Laborde
COO: Todd F Ladd
CFO: Jeffrey Favret
VP: William G Blanchard
VP: William J Fromenthal
VP: Edward J Herbert
Genl Mgr: Michael Bordelon
Genl Mgr: Barry Lebouef
Genl Mgr: Robert Shivers
Board of Directors: Murry W Burns, William E Chiles, Gregory J Cotter, Jerry D Dumas Sr, Michael A Flick, Christopher M Harding, Michael J Keeffe

D-U-N-S 62-156-0072 IMP
■ GULF ISLAND LLC
(*Suby of* GULF ISLAND FABRICATION INC) ★
583 Thompson Rd, Houma, LA 70363-7326
Tel (985) 872-2100 *Founded/Ownrshp* 1999
Sales 57.6MM^E *EMP* 674^E
SIC 1389 Construction, repair & dismantling services
CEO: Kirk J Meche
CEO: Debra Knoblock
VP: William Blanchard
VP: Jeffery Favret
VP: Roy P Francis
VP: Todd Ladd
VP: Robin Seibert
Opers Mgr: Cliff Long

D-U-N-S 96-583-9827 IMP
■ GULF ISLAND MARINE FABRICATORS LLC
(*Suby of* GULF ISLAND FABRICATION INC) ★
301 Gulf Island Rd, Houma, LA 70363
Tel (985) 872-2305 *Founded/Ownrshp* 2008
Sales 76.0MM^E *EMP* 99
SIC 3441 Fabricated structural metal; Fabricated structural metal
CEO: Edward Jhebert
CFO: Jeffery Favret
VP: Joseph Duke
VP: Joseph Gallagher
VP: Jay Hebert
VP Admn: Greg Risher
CIO: John Lirette
QA Dir: Toby Talbot
Dir IT: Paul Bourdeaux
IT Man: William Blanchard
IT Man: Francis Smith

D-U-N-S 60-482-1074
■ GULF MANAGEMENT INC
LEXUS OF TAMPA BAY
(*Suby of* AUTONATION INC) ★
5852 N Dale Mabry Hwy, Tampa, FL 33614-5606
Tel (813) 888-8221 *Founded/Ownrshp* 1989
Sales 64.1MM^E *EMP* 219
SIC 5511 7538 7515 New & used car dealers; General automotive repair shops; Passenger car leasing; New & used car dealers; General automotive repair shops; Passenger car leasing
Genl Mgr: Joe Petrillo
**Pr:* Ronald M Salhany
Exec: Joe Cutillo

D-U-N-S 03-440-0333 IMP/EXP
GULF MARINE - FAR EAST LLC
5501 Jefferson Hwy # 116, New Orleans, LA 70123-4229
Tel (504) 525-6252 *Founded/Ownrshp* 1964
Sales 52.5MM^E *EMP* 119
SIC 5088 5141 5182 5194 Marine supplies; Food brokers; Liquor; Cigarettes; Marine supplies; Food brokers; Liquor; Cigarettes
Pr: John Costoradis

D-U-N-S 18-571-3369 IMP
GULF MARINE REPAIR CORP
G M R
1800 Grant St, Tampa, FL 33605-6042
Tel (813) 247-3153 *Founded/Ownrshp* 1988
Sales 31.0MM^E *EMP* 200^E
SIC 3731 Shipbuilding & repairing; Shipbuilding & repairing
Pr: Aaron Hendry
**Treas:* Dennis E Manelli
VP: C R Watts Jr
**VP:* Claude R Watts
VP: Rick Watts
Off Mgr: Kim Williams

D-U-N-S 60-235-2577
GULF MEDICAL SERVICES INC
3103 N 12th Ave, Pensacola, FL 32503-4006
Tel (850) 438-3217 *Founded/Ownrshp* 1987
Sales 21.5MM^E *EMP* 64
SIC 5999 7699 Medical apparatus & supplies; Medical equipment repair, non-electric
Pr: Kenneth R Steber
**Pr:* Steber Kenneth R
**VP:* Richard A Roberts

D-U-N-S 14-703-7154 IMP
GULF OIL LIMITED PARTNERSHIP
GREAT ISLAND ENERGY
(*Suby of* CUMBERLAND FARMS INC) ★
100 Crossing Blvd, Framingham, MA 01702-5401
Tel (508) 270-8300 *Founded/Ownrshp* 1988
Sales 712.4MM^E *EMP* 334
SIC 5172 5171 Fuel oil; Gasoline; Petroleum bulk stations & terminals; Fuel oil; Gasoline; Petroleum bulk stations & terminals
CEO: Joe Petrowski
Pt: Jayne Fitzpatrick
Pt: Ronald R Sabia
Chf Mktg O: Richard Dery
Ofcr: Robert Far
VP: Stephanie Caldwell
VP: Michael Capparell
VP: Jeff Cutting
VP: Eileen Farrell
VP: Sorin Hilgen
VP: Paul Kelly
VP: Lawrence Kennedy
VP: Raymond Leather
VP: Maxine Mannino
VP: David Masuret
VP: Todd O'Malley
VP: Geraldine Otto
VP: Howard Rosenstein
VP: Meredith Sadlowski
VP: Gregory Scott
VP: Jeffrey Sweetman

D-U-N-S 02-690-8009 IMP/EXP
GULF PACIFIC INC
GULF PACIFIC RICE
12010 Taylor Rd, Houston, TX 77041-1239
Tel (713) 464-0606 *Founded/Ownrshp* 1994
Sales 69.0MM^E *EMP* 89
SIC 5153 0723 Rice, unpolished; Rice drying services; Rice, unpolished; Rice drying services
CEO: Christian Brenckmann
**Pr:* Friedrich Brenckmann
**CFO:* Patrick J Casserly
**VP:* Roger Gilmore
VP: John Poole
Opers Mgr: Jay Putt
Mktg Dir: Peter Reis

GULF PACIFIC RICE
See GULF PACIFIC INC

GULF PACKAGING
See GULF-GREAT LAKES PACKAGING CORP

GULF PACKAGING
See GULF SYSTEMS INC

D-U-N-S 00-692-3429 IMP
■ GULF POWER CO (FL)
(*Suby of* SOUTHERN CO) ★
1 Energy Pl, Pensacola, FL 32520-0001
Tel (850) 444-6111 *Founded/Ownrshp* 1925
Sales 1.5MMM *EMP* 1,410^E
Accts Deloitte & Touche Llp Atlanta
Tkr Sym GLFPO *Exch* OTC
SIC 4911 Generation, electric power; Transmission, electric power; Distribution, electric power; ; Generation, electric power; Transmission, electric power; Distribution, electric power;
Pr: S W Connally Jr
COO: Thomas Fanning
CFO: Richard S Teel
Ofcr: Michael L Burroughs
VP: Terry Bentina
VP: John Hodges
VP: Bentina C Terry
Sftwr Eng: Thomas Sapp
VP Opers: Adrianne Collins
Opers Mgr: Bill Aycock
Plnt Mgr: Keith Cuevas
Board of Directors: Allan G Bense, Deborah H Calder, William C Cramer Jr, Julian B Macqueen, J Mort O'sullivan III, Michael T Rehwinkel, Winston E Scott

D-U-N-S 00-815-4411
■ GULF PUBLISHING CO INC
SUN HERALD
(*Suby of* MCCLATCHY CO) ★
205 Debuys Rd, Gulfport, MS 39507-2838
Tel (228) 896-2100 *Founded/Ownrshp* 2006
Sales 44.0MM^E *EMP* 238
SIC 2711 2752 Newspapers, publishing & printing; Commercial printing, lithographic; Newspapers, publishing & printing; Commercial printing, lithographic
Pr: Ricky Mathews
CFO: Flora Point
Art Dir: Larry Wols

D-U-N-S 00-194-4719 IMP
GULF REDUCTION CORP
(*Suby of* US ZINC CORP) ★
6020 Esperson St, Houston, TX 77011-2330
Tel (713) 926-1705 *Founded/Ownrshp* 1949
Sales 25.8MM^E *EMP* 135
SIC 3341 2816 Zinc smelting & refining (secondary); Zinc pigments: zinc oxide, zinc sulfide; Zinc smelting & refining (secondary); Zinc pigments: zinc oxide, zinc sulfide
Pr: Shawn Bradley
**Pr:* Sean M Stack
**Treas:* Scott A McKinley
**Sec:* Christopher R Clegg
**VP:* Barry Hamilton

D-U-N-S 78-063-5988 IMP
GULF SHIP LLC
12351 Glascock Dr, Gulfport, MS 39503-4646
Tel (228) 897-9189 *Founded/Ownrshp* 2006
Sales 95.9MM^E *EMP* 400
SIC 3731 Military ships, building & repairing; Military ships, building & repairing
Sls Mgr: Tony Havard

D-U-N-S 80-032-6311 IMP
GULF SHORE ASSEMBLIES LLC
249a Clover Rd, Lincoln, AL 35096-5145
Tel (205) 355-8100 *Founded/Ownrshp* 2007
Sales 26.7MM^E *EMP* 50
SIC 3711 Automobile assembly, including specialty automobiles

GULF SHORES DIALYSIS CENTER
See RENAL TREATMENT CENTERS-SOUTHEAST LP

D-U-N-S 03-266-1126 IMP
■ GULF SOUTH MEDICAL SUPPLY INC
(*Suby of* PHYSICIAN SALES & SERVICE) ★
4345 Sthpint Blvd Ste 100, Jacksonville, FL 32216
Tel (904) 332-3000 *Founded/Ownrshp* 1998
Sales 255.1MM^E *EMP* 942
SIC 5047 Medical equipment & supplies; Surgical equipment & supplies; Incontinent care products & supplies; Instruments, surgical & medical; Medical equipment & supplies; Surgical equipment & supplies; Incontinent care products & supplies; Instruments, surgical & medical
Pr: Gary J Nutter
**VP:* David Bronson
VP: Billy Clemons
**VP:* Joshua Derienzis
VP: Jeff Glassick
**VP:* David Klarner
VP: John Piper Jr
VP: Kevin Seramur
VP: Billy Williams
**Prin:* Gary Corless
Ex Dir: Eric Lambert

D-U-N-S 07-844-4247 IMP
■ GULF SOUTH PIPELINE CO LP
(*Suby of* BOARDWALK PIPELINES LP) ★
9 Greenway Plz Ste 2800, Houston, TX 77046-0926
Tel (888) 315-5005 *Founded/Ownrshp* 1930
Sales 467.3MM *EMP* 260
Accts Deloitte & Touche Llp Houston
SIC 4923 Gas transmission & distribution; Gas transmission & distribution
Pr: Stan Horton
Sr VP: John Boone
VP: Jeff Bittel
VP: Kerry Comeaux
VP: John Early
VP: Stacy Franz
VP: Kimberly Tarr
Comm Dir: Liz Johnson
Sfty Dirs: Earl Lawson
Snr Mgr: Garry Dick
Snr Mgr: Al Jeansonne

D-U-N-S 00-954-4391
GULF SOUTH SERVICES INC
280 Ford Industrial Rd, Morgan City, LA 70380-6803
Tel (985) 876-8796 *Founded/Ownrshp* 2000
Sales 66.2MM^E *EMP* 300
SIC 1799 1389 Scaffolding construction; Oil field services; Scaffolding construction; Oil field services
Pr: Ryan Robichaux
**Sec:* Regan Robichaux
VP: James Dean
**Genl Mgr:* Jasone Stilley

D-U-N-S 14-049-4407 IMP
GULF SPECIAL SERVICES INC
(*Suby of* ESEASA CONSTRUCCIONES, S.A. DE C.V.)
7455 Cullen Blvd, Houston, TX 77051-1713
Tel (281) 853-6404 *Founded/Ownrshp* 1997
Sales 46.7MM^E *EMP* 70
SIC 5082 7353 7699 4731 General construction machinery & equipment; Heavy construction equipment rental; Construction equipment repair; Foreign freight forwarding; General construction machinery & equipment; Heavy construction equipment rental; Construction equipment repair; Foreign freight forwarding
Pr: Reynaldo Santos De La Cruz
**VP:* Reynaldo Santos Lara

D-U-N-S 05-884-6916
GULF STATES CANNERS INC
1006 Indl Pk Dr, Clinton, MS 39056
Tel (601) 924-0511 *Founded/Ownrshp* 1971
Sales 37.6MM^E *EMP* 75
SIC 2086 Carbonated beverages, nonalcoholic: bottled & canned
Pr: Albert C Clark
Treas: Frank McDermott
Treas: Stacey Pugh
**VP:* Hardy P Graham
**VP:* H L Williams Jr
**Genl Mgr:* Randy Lee

D-U-N-S 06-789-6324
GULF STATES FINANCIAL SERVICES INC (TX)
SERVCO LIFE INSURANCE CO
1375 Enclave Pkwy, Houston, TX 77077-2026
Tel (713) 580-3000 *Founded/Ownrshp* 1982
Sales NA *EMP* 300
SIC 6411 Advisory services, insurance; Advisory services, insurance
Pr: Stephen Amos
CFO: Dianna Dryer
VP: Robert Hehr
**VP:* F R Mason
Ex Dir: Andy Bush
Area Mgr: Ricky Patterson
Dist Mgr: Kurt Boutin
Dist Mgr: Justin Palmer
Dist Mgr: Scott Ray
Dir IT: Russell Ridley

D-U-N-S 12-874-5663
GULF STATES INC
G S I
(*Suby of* TIC - INDUSTRIAL CO) ★
6711 E Highway 332, Freeport, TX 77541-3016
Tel (979) 233-4461 *Founded/Ownrshp* 2003
Sales 179.6MM^E *EMP* 1,600
SIC 1541 1629 Industrial buildings & warehouses; Power plant construction; Industrial buildings & warehouses; Power plant construction
CEO: Gary B McKenzie
**Pr:* Richard Stoffel
**VP:* James B Heath

GULF STATES INTERMODAL
See BOASSO AMERICA CORP

D-U-N-S 07-929-8503
■ **GULF STATES MANUFACTURERS LLC**
(*Suby of* NUCOR CORP) ★
101 Airport Rd, Starkville, MS 39759-9682
Tel (662) 323-8021 *Founded/Ownrshp* 2007
Sales 39.0MM *EMP* 185
SIC 3448 Prefabricated metal buildings; Prefabricated metal buildings
Ch: Danny Coggins
Dist Mgr: Brad Cook
Dist Mgr: Johnny Jackson
Sfty Mgr: Rick McDaniel
Manager: Bill Holloway
Sls Mgr: Leonard Grabia
Sls Mgr: Hal Hill
Sls Mgr: Chris Holden
Sls Mgr: Dann Juntunen
Sls Mgr: Larry Lorton
Sls Mgr: Butch McKee

D-U-N-S 13-759-8561
GULF STATES PLUMBING & MECHANICAL INC
12340 Palmsprings Dr, Houston, TX 77034-3853
Tel (713) 943-1035 *Founded/Ownrshp* 1984
Sales 21.0MM *EMP* 120^E
SIC 1711 Plumbing contractors
Pr: Jerry Farmer
**VP:* John Belinowski

D-U-N-S 04-890-6713
GULF STATES TOYOTA INC (TX)
(*Suby of* AUTODIRECT SOLUTIONS) ★
1375 Enclave Pkwy, Houston, TX 77077-2026
Tel (713) 580-3300 *Founded/Ownrshp* 1969
Sales 331.3MM^E *EMP* 1,200
SIC 5012 5013 Automotive brokers; Trucks, commercial; Automotive supplies & parts; Automotive brokers; Trucks, commercial; Automotive supplies & parts
Ch Bd: Thomas H Friedkin
**Pr:* Toby N Hynes
CFO: Ed Dickinson
Ofcr: Bruce Stricklin
Sr VP: J C Faafino
VP: J C Fassino
VP: Jeff Parent
VP: Scott Russeau
VP: Laura Ryan
VP: J C Sassino
**Prin:* Jerry H Pyle

D-U-N-S 10-234-6764
GULF STREAM COACH INC
YELLOWSTONE RV
503 S Oakland Ave, Nappanee, IN 46550-2328
Tel (574) 773-7761 *Founded/Ownrshp* 1983
Sales 194.9MM^E *EMP* 1,200
SIC 3716 3792 3714 2451 Motor homes; Recreational van conversion (self-propelled), factory basis; Travel trailers & campers; House trailers, except as permanent dwellings; Motor vehicle parts & accessories; Mobile homes; Motor homes; Recreational van conversion (self-propelled), factory basis; Travel trailers & campers; House trailers, except as permanent dwellings; Motor vehicle parts & accessories; Mobile homes
Pr: Dan Shea
**Ch Bd:* James F Shea Jr
**Pr:* Brian Shea
CFO: Kevin Elliott
Ex VP: Philip Sarvari
**Ex VP:* Phil Savari
VP: Edward Ludwick
IT Man: Kim Miller
Sfty Mgr: Simon Timmons
Plnt Mgr: Tom McDaniel
Plnt Mgr: Bob Reyes
Board of Directors: Kelly Foreman

D-U-N-S 18-001-9259
GULF STREAM CONSTRUCTION CO INC
(*Suby of* BEACH CO) ★
3820 Faber Place Dr # 200, North Charleston, SC 29405-8548
Tel (843) 572-4363 *Founded/Ownrshp* 1966
Sales 50.8MM^E *EMP* 230
SIC 1794 Excavation work; Excavation work
Pr: Kenneth A Holseberg
**CFO:* Pete Shelley
**VP:* Matthew K Blackwood
**VP:* J Mark Hylton
Dir Bus: Claude Blanchard

GULF STREAM INTERNATIONAL ARLN
See SILVER AIRWAYS CORP

D-U-N-S 78-445-7624
GULF STREAM MARINE INC
10000 Manchester St Ste C, Houston, TX 77012-2412
Tel (713) 289-2102 *Founded/Ownrshp* 2012
Sales 87.3MM^E *EMP* 600
SIC 4491 Stevedoring; Marine terminals; Stevedoring; Marine terminals
Pr: Richard F Ragusan
Pr: Rick Ragusen
CEO: Kevin Bourbonnais
**VP:* Ken Jack
Genl Mgr: Jorge Laredo
Genl Mgr: Jorge Loredo
CIO: Herman Kroon
VP Opers: Mitch Heiserman
VP Opers: Mark Hoskins
Mtls Mgr: Richard Bourne
Opers Mgr: Tony Jaworski

D-U-N-S 11-261-3166
GULF SULPHUR SERVICES LTD LLP
SAVAGE SERVICES
4500 Old Port Indus Rd, Galveston, TX 77554-2892
Tel (409) 763-5374 *Founded/Ownrshp* 2002
Sales 22.6MM^E *EMP* 32
SIC 5131 Piece goods & notions
CEO: Allen Alexander
Pr: Jerry Arnold Rayburn
VP: John Samuel Coons
Tech Mgr: Bobby Wright

D-U-N-S 07-050-5888
GULF SUPPLY CO INC
1502 Telegraph Rd, Chickasaw, AL 36611-2212
Tel (251) 457-4591 *Founded/Ownrshp* 2012
Sales 21.2MM^E *EMP* 23
SIC 5084 Safety equipment
Pr: Colleen H Kennedy
**VP:* Clifford Butch Kennedy

D-U-N-S 08-835-8684 IMP/EXP
GULF SYSTEMS INC
GULF PACKAGING
7720 Fm 1960 Rd E, Humble, TX 77346-2256
Tel (281) 852-6700 *Founded/Ownrshp* 1977
Sales 67.5MM^E *EMP* 150
SIC 3565 2671 3497 Packaging machinery; Paper coated or laminated for packaging; Metal foil & leaf

D-U-N-S 07-965-7463
■ **GULF TANKS HOLDINGS INC**
(*Suby of* MOBILE MINI INC) ★
16441 Space Center Blvd, Houston, TX 77058-2015
Tel (281) 332-5170 *Founded/Ownrshp* 2014
Sales 38.8MM^E *EMP* 297
SIC 4226 1791 5084 6719 Liquid storage; Storage tanks, metal: erection; Pumps & pumping equipment; Personal holding companies, except banks; Liquid storage; Storage tanks, metal: erection; Pumps & pumping equipment; Personal holding companies, except banks
CEO: Guy Huelat

D-U-N-S 94-869-6679 IMP
GULF WINDS INTERNATIONAL INC
411 Brisbane St, Houston, TX 77061-5003
Tel (713) 747-4909 *Founded/Ownrshp* 1996
Sales 116.8MM *EMP* 71
SIC 4225 4731 General warehousing; Freight transportation arrangement; General warehousing; Freight transportation arrangement
Pr: Todd Stewart
**Ch Bd:* Tommy Stephen Stewart
CFO: Dustin Hebrank
VP: Arthur Flanagan
**VP:* Ron Messner
**VP:* Buddy Sexton
**VP:* BJ Tarver
Sfty Dirs: Orlando Mursuli
Trfc Dir: Maggie Gallegos
Trfc Dir: Rachel Zurita
Sls Mgr: Jared Couvillon

D-U-N-S 03-901-0194 IMP
GULF-GREAT LAKES PACKAGING CORP
GULF PACKAGING
756 N Main St Ste 3, Crown Point, IN 46307-3268
Tel (708) 849-8100 *Founded/Ownrshp* 1975
Sales 58.8MM^E *EMP* 52
SIC 5085 Hose, belting & packing; Adhesives, tape & plasters
CEO: Arman Sarkisian
**Pr:* Carl Fleck
Dir IT: Joseph Fleck
Sls Mgr: Steve Cummings

D-U-N-S 00-810-6569 IMP
GULFEX HOLDINGS LLC
401 State St, South Houston, TX 77587-3025
Tel (713) 946-6614 *Founded/Ownrshp* 1966
Sales 29.0MM^E *EMP* 55
SIC 3443 Housings, pressure
CEO: Greg Bregstone
Pt: W B Sheehy
Pr: Wb Sheehy
VP: Ron Adams
VP: Aubrey Davis

D-U-N-S 00-984-0240
GULFGATE CONSTRUCTION LLC
2644 Ambssdor Cffery Pkwy, Lafayette, LA 70506-5902
Tel (337) 981-4200 *Founded/Ownrshp* 1999
Sales 29.8MM^E *EMP* 120
SIC 1623 Telephone & communication line construction

D-U-N-S 11-380-2057
GULFGATE DODGE INC
(*Suby of* J DAVIS AUTOMOTIVE GROUP INC) ★
7250 Gulf Fwy, Houston, TX 77017-1528
Tel (281) 477-6767 *Founded/Ownrshp* 2000
Sales 22.5MM^E *EMP* 52
SIC 5511 Automobiles, new & used
Pr: Gerard P Quinn
**Sec:* Jean Logan
**Genl Mgr:* James H Davis Jr
Genl Mgr: Bill Sweat
Sales Asso: Andrew Cordova

D-U-N-S 14-586-7144
■ **GULFMARK AMERICAS INC**
(*Suby of* GULFMARK OFFSHORE INC) ★
842 W Sam Houston Pkwy S, Houston, TX 77042
Tel (713) 963-9522 *Founded/Ownrshp* 2008
Sales 29.2MM^E *EMP* 300
SIC 4491 Waterfront terminal operation; Waterfront terminal operation
CEO: Quintin V Kneen
**Ex VP:* John E Leech
**VP:* Samuel R Rubio
VP Admn: David Darling

D-U-N-S 61-505-6884
■ **GULFMARK ENERGY INC**
(*Suby of* ADAMS RESOURCES & ENERGY INC) ★
17 S Briar Hollow Ln # 400, Houston, TX 77027-3155
Tel (713) 881-3603 *Founded/Ownrshp* 1992
Sales 562.1MM^E *EMP* 165
SIC 5172 Crude oil; Crude oil
Pr: W Garney Griggs
**Pr:* Geoff Griffith
CFO: Richard Abshire
**Treas:* Richard B Abshire

D-U-N-S 04-056-5439
▲ **GULFMARK OFFSHORE INC**
842 W Sam Houston Pkwy N, Houston, TX 77024-4591
Tel (713) 963-9522 *Founded/Ownrshp* 1996
Sales 495.7MM *EMP* 2,000^E
Accts Kpmg Llp Houston Texas
Tkr Sym GLF *Exch* NYS
SIC 4412 Deep sea foreign transportation of freight; Deep sea foreign transportation of freight
Pr: Quintin V Kneen
**Ch Bd:* David J Butters
COO: Arlene Persad
COO: David B Rosenwasser
COO: Bruce Streeter
CFO: James M Mitchell
Ex VP: Gene Leech
Sr VP: David E Darling
Sr VP: Van Dewitt
Sr VP: Lee R Johnson
Sr VP: Samuel R Rubio
Sr VP: Richard M Safier
Dir Bus: David Rossenwasser
Board of Directors: Peter I Bijur, Brian R Ford, Sheldon S Gordon, Steven S Kohlhagen, William C Martin, Rex C Ross, Charles C Valutas

D-U-N-S 06-083-1500
GULFPORT CAPITAL LLC (MS)
CHAMPION CHRYSLER DODGE JEEP
435 E Pass Rd, Gulfport, MS 39507-3237
Tel (228) 896-1515 *Founded/Ownrshp* 1999
Sales 26.6MM^E *EMP* 86
SIC 5511

D-U-N-S 00-485-0660
▲ **GULFPORT ENERGY CORP**
14313 N May Ave Ste 100, Oklahoma City, OK 73134-5003
Tel (405) 848-8807 *Founded/Ownrshp* 1997
Sales 671.2MM *EMP* 203^E
Tkr Sym GPOR *Exch* NGS
SIC 1311 1382 Crude petroleum & natural gas production; Oil & gas exploration services; Crude petroleum & natural gas production; Oil & gas exploration services
Pr: Michael G Moore
COO: J Ross Kirtley
CFO: Aaron Gaydosik
VP: Steve R Baldwin
VP: Rob Jones
VP: Stuart A Maier
VP: Lester Zitkus
Board of Directors: Donald Dillingham, Craig Groeschel, David L Houston, C Doug Johnson, Ben T Morris, Scott E Streller

D-U-N-S 36-101-4082
GULFPORT MEMORIAL HOSPITAL EMR
4500 13th St, Gulfport, MS 39501-2515
Tel (228) 867-4000 *Founded/Ownrshp* 2005
Sales 45.0MM^E *EMP* 2,400
SIC 8062 General medical & surgical hospitals; General medical & surgical hospitals
CEO: Gary Marchand
Trst: Oney Raines

D-U-N-S 10-245-2281
GULFPORT SCHOOL DISTRICT
2001 Pass Rd, Gulfport, MS 39501-4902
Tel (228) 865-4600 *Founded/Ownrshp* 2008
Sales 57.9MM *EMP* 900
Accts Cunningham Cpas Pllc Fairhop
SIC 8211 Public elementary school; Public junior high school; Public senior high school; Public elementary school; Public junior high school; Public senior high school
**Pr:* David Mauffray
CFO: Tammy Smith
**VP:* Ruthy Dixon
Dir Soc: Beau Bradberry
Dir Soc: Venita Goins

D-U-N-S 13-270-4136
GULFQUEST LP
2900 North Loop W # 1300, Houston, TX 77092-8815
Tel (832) 553-3300 *Founded/Ownrshp* 2002
Sales 20.6MM^E *EMP* 250
SIC 8741 Management services; Management services
Genl Mgr: Scott Huebner
CFO: Kristinn Benton
VP: John Biggers
Sls Mgr: Elodia Gallo

GULFSIDE CASINO PARTNERSHIP
See GULFSIDE CASINOS INC

D-U-N-S 06-596-2024
GULFSIDE CASINO PARTNERSHIP
ISLAND VIEW CASINO RESORT
3300 W Beach Blvd, Gulfport, MS 39501-1800
Tel (228) 314-2100 *Founded/Ownrshp* 2006
Sales 31.7MM^E *EMP* 1,200
SIC 7011 Casino hotel; Casino hotel
Genl Pt: Joel R Carter Sr
Pt: Terry Green

D-U-N-S 05-796-1950
GULFSIDE CASINOS INC
GULFSIDE CASINO PARTNERSHIP
3300 W Beach Blvd, Gulfport, MS 39501-1800
Tel (228) 314-2175 *Founded/Ownrshp* 1998
Sales 18.3MM^E *EMP* 770
SIC 7999 Gambling establishment; Gambling establishment
Pr: Joel R Carter Sr
**VP:* Terry Green

D-U-N-S 15-080-8301
■ **GULFSIDE MECHANICAL INC**
(*Suby of* COMFORT SYSTEMS USA INC) ★
435 Corday St, Pensacola, FL 32503-2216
Tel (850) 484-4999 *Founded/Ownrshp* 2005
Sales 21.9MM^E *EMP* 300
SIC 1711 7623 Warm air heating & air conditioning contractor; Air conditioning repair; Warm air heating & air conditioning contractor; Air conditioning repair
Pr: Kim Anderson
**VP:* Trent McKenna
**VP:* William I George II

D-U-N-S 60-922-8184
GULFSIDE REGIONAL HOSPICE INC
2061 Collier Pkwy, Land O Lakes, FL 34639-5202
Tel (800) 561-4883 *Founded/Ownrshp* 1988
Sales 29.0MM *EMP* 280
Accts Cliftonlarsonallen Llp Orland
SIC 8082 Home health care services; Home health care services
Pr: Linda Word
**COO:* Cathy Postiglione
**CFO:* David C Brown
VP: Tara Scalise
Pr Dir: Ashley Juno

D-U-N-S 06-279-5893 EXP
GULFSIDE SUPPLY INC
GULF EAGLE SUPPLY
2900 E 7th Ave Ste 200, Tampa, FL 33605-4200
Tel (813) 636-9808 *Founded/Ownrshp* 1973
Sales 633.1MM^E *EMP* 850
SIC 5033 Roofing, asphalt & sheet metal; Roofing, asphalt & sheet metal
CEO: James S Resch
**Pr:* Bradley James Resch
CFO: Jim Barnish
**Sec:* Molly A Resch
Sr VP: Peter Nazaretian
**VP:* Jill Buehler
VP: Jill Buhler
**VP:* Stephanie Resch
Rgnl Mgr: Greg Stealey
Brnch Mgr: Corey Bryan
Brnch Mgr: Kevin Clinge
Board of Directors: Jill M Buhler, Stephanie Resch, Stephanie A Rich

D-U-N-S 00-253-6978 IMP
GULFSPAN INDUSTRIAL LLC
5990 Chance Dr, Beaumont, TX 77705
Tel (409) 842-8808 *Founded/Ownrshp* 2011
Sales 66.0MM^E *EMP* 62^E
SIC 5082 Oil field equipment
Pr: William E Harrington Jr
Ch: James Duplissey
Treas: Vincent G Duplissey
VP: Charles Courville

D-U-N-S 82-886-0150
GULFSTAR CORP
1712 Pioneer Ave Ste 751, Cheyenne, WY 82001-4406
Tel (307) 637-6932 *Founded/Ownrshp* 2007
Sales 25.0MM *EMP* 7
SIC 6719 Investment holding companies, except banks
Pr: Mark F Butler

D-U-N-S 61-179-2912 IMP
■ **GULFSTREAM AEROSPACE CORP**
(*Suby of* GENERAL DYNAMICS CORP) ★
500 Gulfstream Rd, Savannah, GA 31408-9643
Tel (912) 965-3000 *Founded/Ownrshp* 2001
Sales 2.1MMM^E *EMP* 8,068
SIC 3721 4581 Aircraft; Aircraft maintenance & repair services; Aircraft; Aircraft maintenance & repair services
Pr: Larry R Flynn
**Pr:* Larry Flynn
**CFO:* Dan Clare
CFO: Joseph Hartman
CFO: Michael McConnell
**Ex VP:* Joe Lombardo
**Sr VP:* Jason Aiken
**Sr VP:* Ira Berman
Sr VP: Leda Chong
Sr VP: Dan Nale
Sr VP: Helen Roche
**Sr VP:* Dennis Stuligross
VP: Mike Baker
VP: Steve Belko
VP: Stan Dixon
VP: McDonnell Douglas
VP: Richard Emery
**VP:* Preston Henne
VP: Peter Jacobi
VP: Jeff Kreide
**VP:* Jim Ross

D-U-N-S 08-893-5366
■ **GULFSTREAM AEROSPACE CORP (GEORGIA)**
(*Suby of* GULFSTREAM DELAWARE CORP) ★
500 Gulfstar Rd, Savannah, GA 31408-9643
Tel (912) 965-3000 *Founded/Ownrshp* 1990
Sales 1.3MMM^E *EMP* 6,800
SIC 3721 Airplanes, fixed or rotary wing; Airplanes, fixed or rotary wing
CEO: Larry R Flynn
**CFO:* Jason W Aiken
**Treas:* Bill Skinner
**Sr VP:* Preston Henne
VP: Vincent J Hrenak
VP: Daniel D Nale
**VP:* Mike West
**CIO:* Sheryl Bunton

D-U-N-S 11-946-3250
■ **GULFSTREAM ASSET MANAGEMENT**
(*Suby of* APOLLO GLOBAL MANAGEMENT LLC) ★
4201 Congress St Ste 475, Charlotte, NC 28209-4614
Tel (704) 552-7711 *Founded/Ownrshp* 2011
Sales 38.7MM^E *EMP* 21
SIC 6531 Real estate agents & managers

D-U-N-S 78-186-4579
GULFSTREAM BANCSHARES INC
2400 Se Monterey Rd # 100, Stuart, FL 34996-3351
Tel (772) 426-8100 *Founded/Ownrshp* 2007
Sales 35.4MM *EMP* 0^E
Accts Hacker Johnson & Smith Pa Cp
SIC 6719 Holding companies; Holding companies

D-U-N-S 02-399-1755
■ **GULFSTREAM DELAWARE CORP**
(*Suby of* GULFSTREAM AEROSPACE CORP) ★
500 Gulfstream Rd, Savannah, GA 31408-9643
Tel (912) 965-3000 *Founded/Ownrshp* 1990
Sales 1.4MMM^E *EMP* 7,400^E
SIC 3721 5088 Aircraft; Aircraft & space vehicle supplies & parts; Aircraft & parts; Aircraft equipment & supplies
Pr: Larry Flynn
Ofcr: Tom Huff
**Sr VP:* Jason Aiken
VP: Dick Johnson
**VP:* Joe Lombardo
Snr Mgr: Douglas Paul
Board of Directors: Brad Kraft

D-U-N-S 07-698-5928
GULFSTREAM GOODWILL INDUSTRIES INC
1715 E Tiffany Dr, West Palm Beach, FL 33407-3224
Tel (561) 848-7200 *Founded/Ownrshp* 1966
Sales 45.1MM *EMP* 1,000
SIC 8399 Fund raising organization, non-fee basis; Fund raising organization, non-fee basis
Pr: Marvin A Tanck
**CFO:* Sherry Steff
**VP:* Rhonda Counes
VP: Brian Edwards
Dist Mgr: Delores Rannie
Store Mgr: Tony Zamba
CTO: Michele Carter
Dir IT: Susan Bykofsky
IT Man: Karen Novak
Netwrk Eng: Jerome Robinson
VP Mktg: Cal Miller

GULFSTREAM INTERNATIONAL ARLN
See VPAA CO

D-U-N-S 03-283-6249 EXP
GULFSTREAM MOTORS INC
MERCEDES BENZ OF PALM BEACH
4000 Okeechobee Blvd, West Palm Beach, FL 33409-3202
Tel (561) 689-6363 *Founded/Ownrshp* 1959
Sales 47.4MM^E *EMP* 150
SIC 5511 Automobiles, new & used; Automobiles, new & used
Pr: Bryan Sattar
**Sec:* Mary Lee Bastin
**VP:* Brian Bastin
Sales Asso: Frederic Fischer

D-U-N-S 10-719-2122 IMP/EXP
GULFSTREAM SERVICES INC
GSI
103 Dickson Rd, Houma, LA 70363-7306
Tel (985) 868-0303 *Founded/Ownrshp* 2000
Sales 142.5MM^E *EMP* 140
SIC 1382 7359 Oil & gas exploration services; Equipment rental & leasing; Oil & gas exploration services; Equipment rental & leasing
Pr: Michael F Mire
**Sec:* Gina Mir
**Sec:* Regina Mire
VP: Mark Chauvin
Opers Mgr: Mark Charpentier
Sales Asso: Emeric Watson

D-U-N-S 92-671-3454
GULFSTREAM TLC INC
367 Eagle Dr, Jupiter, FL 33477-4065
Tel (561) 627-7458 *Founded/Ownrshp* 1995
Sales 45.0MM *EMP* 10
SIC 8741 Management services; Management services
Pr: John T Corcia
**CFO:* Joseph Hartman

D-U-N-S 80-900-0508
GULFSTREAM TOMATO PACKERS
21150 Sw 167th Ave, Miami, FL 33187-4302
Tel (305) 235-4161 *Founded/Ownrshp* 1989
Sales 11.4MM^E *EMP* 300
SIC 0723 0161 5148 Vegetable packing services; Tomato farm; Fresh fruits & vegetables; Vegetable packing services; Tomato farm; Fresh fruits & vegetables
Pt: Joseph E Hagan
Pt: Donald Hagen

D-U-N-S 11-470-5713 IMP
GULFTECH INTERNATIONAL INC
616 E Hyman Ave Ste 204, Aspen, CO 81611-1981
Tel (970) 925-2496 *Founded/Ownrshp* 1999
Sales 59.4MM^E *EMP* 285
SIC 3556 Food products machinery; Food products machinery
Ch Bd: Martin Flug
**Pr:* Jeremy Flug
**CFO:* Richard Boerner
**Treas:* Stephen Ferreall

D-U-N-S 18-045-8275
GULICK TRUCKING INC
5419 Ne 88th St Ste G, Vancouver, WA 98665-0994
Tel (360) 699-0999 *Founded/Ownrshp* 1973
Sales 32.5MM^E *EMP* 120^E
SIC 4213 4212 Contract haulers; Local trucking, without storage
Pr: Willard G Gulick
**Pr:* Bill Gulick Jr
**VP:* Charles Cunning

D-U-N-S 79-694-1151
GULL COMMUNICATIONS INC
RICHFIELD REAPER
(*Suby of* B C I) ★
65 W Center St, Richfield, UT 84701-2546
Tel (435) 896-5476 *Founded/Ownrshp* 1888
Sales 32.8MM^E *EMP* 731
SIC 2711 Newspapers; Newspapers
Prin: Mark Fuellenbach
**Pr:* W J Brehm Jr
**Treas:* Jeff Johnson
Assoc Ed: David Anderson

D-U-N-S 05-827-3673
GULLETT & ASSOCIATES INC
7705 South Loop E, Houston, TX 77012-4116
Tel (713) 454-0385 *Founded/Ownrshp* 1969
Sales 36.2MM *EMP* 194
SIC 8713 1623 Surveying services; Pipeline construction; Surveying services; Pipeline construction
CEO: Jerry Copeland
**Sec:* Jannie Johnson

D-U-N-S 01-037-5483
GULLEY ENTERPRISES INC
VILLAGE INN RESTAURANT
1001 S Douglas Hwy Ste B7, Gillette, WY 82716-4984
Tel (307) 682-4421 *Founded/Ownrshp* 1975
Sales 14.6MM^E *EMP* 350
SIC 5812 Restaurant, family: chain; Restaurant, family: chain
Pr: Paul J Gulley
**Sec:* Martha Gulley

D-U-N-S 07-601-1170 IMP/EXP
GULLIVER SCHOOLS INC
9350 S Dixie Hwy Ste 100, Miami, FL 33156-2994
Tel (305) 666-6333 *Founded/Ownrshp* 1926
Sales 67.5MM *EMP* 450
Accts Verdeja & De Armas Llp Miami
SIC 8211 Private elementary & secondary schools; Preparatory school; Private elementary & secondary schools; Preparatory school
Pr: Marian Krutulis
Ex Dir: Jim Santoro
Dir IT: George Philotas
Netwrk Eng: Charlie Garcia

GULLIVERS TRAVEL ASSOCIATES
See GTA AMERICAS LLC

GULLIVER'S TRAVEL ASSOCIATES
See GTA NORTH AMERICA INC

D-U-N-S 95-647-1908
GULLO CARS OF CONROE INC
GULLO FORD MERCURY OF CONROE
925 Interstate 45 S, Conroe, TX 77301-4274
Tel (936) 756-5500 *Founded/Ownrshp* 1996
Sales 71.5MM^E *EMP* 250
SIC 5511 Automobiles, new & used; Automobiles, new & used
Pr: Anthony Gullo Sr
CFO: Jason Shaw
**VP:* Sparky Gullo
CTO: Thorooa Echrock
CTO: Fred Watt

Dir IT: Daryl Nelson
Sls&Mrk Ex: Jeff Murray

GULLO FORD MERCURY OF CONROE
See GULLO CARS OF CONROE INC

GULLO TOYOTA CONROE
See TONY GULLO MOTORS I LP

D-U-N-S 00-281-4143
GULLY TRANSPORTATION INC (IL)
GULLY TRUCK LEASING
3820 Wisman Ln, Quincy, IL 62305-9550
Tel (217) 224-0770 *Founded/Ownrshp* 1961, 1973
Sales 45.7MM^E *EMP* 250
SIC 4213 4231 Trucking, except local; Trucking terminal facilities; Trucking, except local; Trucking terminal facilities
Pr: William Gully
**Treas:* Barbara Gully
**VP:* Michael Gully
IT Man: Steve Quach

GULLY TRUCK LEASING
See GULLY TRANSPORTATION INC

D-U-N-S 18-460-6184 IMP
GULSHAN ENTERPRISES INC
4415 Highway 6, Sugar Land, TX 77478-4476
Tel (281) 201-2700 *Founded/Ownrshp* 1987
Sales 30.4MM^E *EMP* 58
SIC 5541 5411 Gasoline service stations; Convenience stores, independent
Pr: Shoukat A Dhanani
**VP:* Mohammed A Dhanani

GUMBY'S CIGARETTE WORLD
See GUMBYS LLC

D-U-N-S 79-801-9790
GUMBYS LLC
GUMBY'S CIGARETTE WORLD
98 E Cove Ave Ste 1, Wheeling, WV 26003-5080
Tel (304) 242-0002 *Founded/Ownrshp* 1992
Sales 23.1MM^E *EMP* 115
SIC 5921 5993 Beer (packaged); Cigarette store

D-U-N-S 78-664-3395
GUMBYS PIZZA SYSTEMS INC
3911 W Newberry Rd Ste C, Gainesville, FL 32607-2354
Tel (352) 338-7775 *Founded/Ownrshp* 1985
Sales 15.0MM *EMP* 1,300
SIC 5812 Pizzeria, chain; Pizzeria, chain
Pr: Jeff O'Brian
COO: Joe Obrien

D-U-N-S 01-821-6804
GUMMER WHOLESALE INC
1945 James Pkwy, Heath, OH 43056-4000
Tel (740) 928-0415 *Founded/Ownrshp* 1953
Sales 53.2MM^E *EMP* 97
SIC 5194 5145 5199 5141 Tobacco & tobacco products; Candy; Novelties, paper; Groceries, general line; Tobacco & tobacco products; Candy; Novelties, paper; Groceries, general line
Pr: Chad Gummer
COO: Jeff Morrison
CFO: Lou Dellapina
**Sec:* Lillian Gummer
**VP:* Michael Gummer
VP Sls: Keith Myers

D-U-N-S 10-291-0023 IMP
GUMPS CORP
(*Suby of* GUMPS HOLDINGS LLC) ★
135 Post St, San Francisco, CA 94108-4701
Tel (415) 982-1616 *Founded/Ownrshp* 2005
Sales 27.4MM^E *EMP* 100
SIC 5947 Gifts & novelties
CEO: Claudia Hollingsworth
Pr: Jed Pogran
CFO: Polly Boe
VP: Susan Quintana
IT Man: Marilou Viray-Mosley
Sales Asso: Natutu Siregar

D-U-N-S 07-885-2505
GUMPS HOLDINGS LLC (NV)
135 Post St, San Francisco, CA 94108-4701
Tel (415) 982-1616 *Founded/Ownrshp* 2004
Sales 45.4MM^E *EMP* 250^E
SIC 5961 Mail order house; Catalog sales; Mail order house; Catalog sales

GUN LAKE FARMS
See MIEDEMA PRODUCE INC

D-U-N-S 00-121-3057 IMP
GUND
GUND INC
(*Suby of* ENESCO LLC) ★
1 Runyons Ln, Edison, NJ 08817-2277
Tel (732) 248-1500 *Founded/Ownrshp* 1898, 2008
Sales 26.6MM^E *EMP* 230
SIC 5092

D-U-N-S 05-494-2479 IMP
GUND CO INC (MO)
M M & M ELECTRICAL SUPPLY
2121 Walton Rd, Saint Louis, MO 63114-5807
Tel (314) 492-4826 *Founded/Ownrshp* 1951
Sales 70.0MM *EMP* 350
SIC 3644 Insulators & insulation materials, electrical; Insulators & insulation materials, electrical
Pr: Stephen Gund
**Pr:* Richard Gund
Pr: Mike Moran
VP: Joe Bradlo
VP: Michael Marcum
Exec: Art Davies
Exec: Anderson John
Exec: Joe Schomaker
Genl Mgr: Jay Bollman
Genl Mgr: Phillip Williford
IT Man: Tim Marien
Board of Directors: Richard Gund, Stephen Gund, Michelle Smith

GUND INC
See GUND

GUNDAKER REALTORS BETTER HOMES
See COLDWELL BANKER GUNDAKER REAL ESTATE SCHOOL

D-U-N-S 14-816-7414 IMP
GUNDER & ASSOCIATES INC
1215 W Crosby Rd Ste 200, Carrollton, TX 75006-6952
Tel (972) 620-2801 *Founded/Ownrshp* 1980
Sales 85.0MM *EMP* 19
SIC 5075 Air conditioning equipment, except room units; Warm air heating equipment & supplies; Air conditioning equipment, except room units; Warm air heating equipment & supplies
Pr: Marshall S Gunder
VP: Pat Gunder
Sales Asso: Bryan Moates

D-U-N-S 00-412-8856 EXP
GUNDERLIN LTD INC (FL)
3625 E 11th Ave, Hialeah, FL 33013-2929
Tel (305) 696-6071 *Founded/Ownrshp* 1954
Sales 44.5MM^E *EMP* 95
SIC 3534 Elevators & equipment; Elevators & equipment
Pr: Jay Bass
**Sec:* Lynn Kislack
**VP:* Russ Marot
**VP:* Charlie Sammarco
Exec: Charles Sammaplo

D-U-N-S 07-762-9830
GUNDERSEN CLINIC LTD
GUNDERSON LUTHERAN MEDICAL CEN
(*Suby of* GUNDERSEN HEALTH SYSTEM) ★
1836 South Ave, La Crosse, WI 54601-5494
Tel (608) 782-7300 *Founded/Ownrshp* 2010
Sales 193.7MM *EMP* 4,500
SIC 8011 Clinic, operated by physicians; Clinic, operated by physicians
CEO: Jeffrey E Thompson
**VP:* Julio Bird MD

D-U-N-S 83-015-1739
GUNDERSEN HEALTH SYSTEM
GUNDERSON LUTHERAN MEDICAL CTR
1900 South Ave, La Crosse, WI 54601-5467
Tel (608) 782-7300 *Founded/Ownrshp* 1996
Sales 1.2MMM^E *EMP* 6,000^E
SIC 8062 General medical & surgical hospitals; General medical & surgical hospitals
CEO: Jeffrey E Thompson
**Pr:* Daniel J Lilly
**CFO:* Michael Allen
Ofcr: Kari Adank
**VP:* Jan Dehaan
**VP:* Bryan Erdmann
VP: Cathy Fischer
VP: Sigurd Gudersen
VP: Melissa Kovacevich
**VP:* Deb Rislow
Dir Rad: Dave Clayton

D-U-N-S 13-746-4124
GUNDERSEN LUTHERAN ADMINISTRATIVE SERVICES INC
(*Suby of* GUNDERSEN HEALTH SYSTEM) ★
1900 South Ave, La Crosse, WI 54601-5467
Tel (608) 782-7300 *Founded/Ownrshp* 2010
Sales 652.4MM *EMP* 6,000
Accts Kpmg Llp Omaha Ne
SIC 8621 Health association; Health association
CEO: Jeff Thompson
**Treas:* Wendy Lommen
**VP:* Gregory Prairie
**VP:* Wendy Williams
IT Man: Liz Larsen
Prd Dir: Elaine Elliott

D-U-N-S 07-179-3673
■ **GUNDERSEN LUTHERAN MEDICAL CENTER INC**
LUTHERAN HOSPITAL - LA CROSSE
(*Suby of* GUNDERSEN HEALTH SYSTEM) ★
1900 South Ave, La Crosse, WI 54601-5467
Tel (608) 782-7300 *Founded/Ownrshp* 2010
Sales 349.7MM^E *EMP* 4,500
SIC 8062 5912 General medical & surgical hospitals; Drug stores & proprietary stores; General medical & surgical hospitals; Drug stores & proprietary stores
CEO: Jeffery Thompson MD
COO: Claudia Caine
CFO: Michael Allen
CFO: Daryl Applebury
Ofcr: Mary Jafari
Ofcr: Jean Krause
Ofcr: Mary Ellen McCartney
Ex VP: Julio J Bird
Sr VP: Kathy Klock
**VP:* Julio Bird
VP: Jan Dehaan
VP: Michael J Dolan
**VP:* S B Gundersen III
VP: Sigurd B Gundersen
VP: Mary Jo Klos
**VP:* Deb Rislow

D-U-N-S 13-666-6638
GUNDERSEN LUTHERAN MEDICAL FOUNDATION INC
1900 South Ave, La Crosse, WI 54601-5467
Tel (608) 775-6600 *Founded/Ownrshp* 1977
Sales 26.6MM *EMP* 55^E
SIC 8011 Primary care medical clinic; Primary care medical clinic
Ch: Mark Connelly
**CEO:* Jeffrey E Thompson
**CFO:* Gordon Edwards
Ofcr: Mary McCartney
**Ex VP:* Julio Bird
**VP:* Jerry Arndt
VP: Marilu Bintz
VP: Jan Dehaan
VP: Michael Dolan
**VP:* Bryan Erdmann
VP: Mary Gerke

VP: Gundersen Sigurd
VP: Barbara Skogen

GUNDERSON CLINIC
See GUNDERSON LUTHERAN INC

D-U-N-S 92-850-2848
GUNDERSON DETTMER STOUGH VILLENEUVE FRANKLIN & HACHIGIAN LLP
1200 Seaport Blvd, Redwood City, CA 94063-5537
Tel (650) 321-2400 *Founded/Ownrshp* 1995
Sales 32.2MM^E *EMP* 150
SIC 8111 General practice law office; General practice law office
Pt: Robert Gunderson
Pt: Darrin Brown
Pt: Colin Chapman
Pt: Dan O Connor
Pt: Joshua Cook
Pt: Scott Dettmer
Pt: Steve Franklin
Pt: Jay Hachigian
Pt: Michael Irvine
Pt: Jerry Ku
Pt: Shawn Lampton
Pt: Dan Niehans
Pt: David Sharrow
Pt: Brooks Stough
Pt: Thomas Villeneuve
Pt: Greg Volkmar
Pt: David Young
Pt: Celina Almondia
Pr: Edolia Blackmon
Pr: Joanne Hernandez
Pr: Alicia Keigan

D-U-N-S 13-197-4057 EXP
■ **GUNDERSON LLC**
(*Suby of* GREENBRIER COMPANIES INC) ★
4350 Nw Front Ave, Portland, OR 97210-1499
Tel (503) 972-5700 *Founded/Ownrshp* 1984
Sales 407.0MM^E *EMP* 1,300
SIC 3743 Railroad equipment; Railroad car rebuilding; Railroad equipment; Railroad car rebuilding
CEO: William A Furman
VP: Mark Rittenbaum
Off Mgr: Tita Lin
QA Dir: Oscar Carlson
VP Opers: Paul Wostmann
Sfty Mgr: Byron Johnson
Snr Mgr: Gregory Saxton

D-U-N-S 15-326-9386
GUNDERSON LUTHERAN INC
GUNDERSON CLINIC
1836 South Ave, La Crosse, WI 54601-5429
Tel (608) 782-7300 *Founded/Ownrshp* 1996
Sales 11.6MM *EMP* 5,000
SIC 8011 Pulmonary specialist, physician/surgeon; Pulmonary specialist, physician/surgeon
CEO: Jeffrey E Thompson
**CFO:* Michael Allen
Treas: Barb Mussman
Bd of Dir: Peg Myhre
**Ex VP:* Julio Bird
**Sr VP:* Kathy Klock
**Sr VP:* Mark Platt
VP: Marilu Blintz
VP: Sigurd B Gundersen
Ex Dir: Phil Schumacher
DP Dir: Tabitha Bruley

GUNDERSON LUTHERAN MEDICAL CEN
See GUNDERSEN CLINIC LTD

GUNDERSON LUTHERAN MEDICAL CTR
See GUNDERSEN HEALTH SYSTEM

GUNDERSON NISSAN
See EL MONTE IMPORTS INC

D-U-N-S 19-167-9393 IMP
■ **GUNDERSON RAIL SERVICES LLC**
YSD INDUSTRIES
(*Suby of* GUNDERSON LLC) ★
1 Centerpointe Dr Ste 200, Lake Oswego, OR 97035-8612
Tel (503) 802-5103 *Founded/Ownrshp* 1993
Sales 226.8MM^E *EMP* 1,200
SIC 3743 Railroad car rebuilding; Railroad car rebuilding
CEO: Bill Furman
**Pr:* William Glenn

D-U-N-S 79-487-1459
■ **GUNDERSON RAIL SERVICES LLC**
(*Suby of* GUNDERSON LLC) ★
101 Park St, Cleburne, TX 76031-4038
Tel (817) 556-9191 *Founded/Ownrshp* 1992
Sales 33.2MM^E *EMP* 275
SIC 3743 Railroad car rebuilding; Railroad car rebuilding
Pr: Tim Stucky
Off Mgr: Mike Roland
Ql Cn Mgr: Steve McIntyre

GUNDLACH
See ROTEX GLOBAL LCC

D-U-N-S 00-677-6397
GUNDLACH CHAMPION INC
(*Suby of* CHAMPION INC) ★
180 Traders Mine Rd, Iron Mountain, MI 49801-1447
Tel (906) 779-2303 *Founded/Ownrshp* 1898
Sales 37.8MM *EMP* 100
SIC 1541 8741 1542 Industrial buildings, new construction; Construction management; Commercial & office building, new construction; Industrial buildings, new construction; Construction management; Commercial & office building, new construction
Ch Bd: William C Verrette
**Ch Bd:* Gary Benjamin
**Pr:* James Ebli
**Sec:* Daniel Wentarmini
**VP:* Jon Zander
Board of Directors: Steve Alexa, Gary Benjamin, Jim Ebili, Paul Jurmu, Thomas Verrette, William Verrette, Daniel Wentarmini, Jon Zander

D-U-N-S 18-593-8524 IMP
■ **GUNDLACH EQUIPMENT CORP**
(*Suby of* HILLENBRAND INC) ★
1 Freedom Dr, Belleville, IL 62226-5104
Tel (618) 233-7208 *Founded/Ownrshp* 2006
Sales 20.9MM^E *EMP* 80
SIC 3532 Mining machinery; Mining machinery
Pr: Mark Kohler
VP: Mike Hamby
VP: Carrie Little
DP Exec: David McAlpin
Mfg Mgr: Todd Ruff

D-U-N-S 18-013-4355 IMP
GUNITE CORP
302 Peoples Ave, Rockford, IL 61104-7092
Tel (815) 964-3301 *Founded/Ownrshp* 2000
Sales 274.1MM^E *EMP* 1,010
SIC 3714 Motor vehicle brake systems & parts; Brake drums, motor vehicle; Wheels, motor vehicle; Motor vehicle brake systems & parts; Brake drums, motor vehicle; Wheels, motor vehicle
Pr: James Cirar
Pr: Richard Dauch
CFO: Jeff Elmer
VP: Omar Fakhoury
Software D: Kelly Bodway
VP Sls: Thomas Splinter

D-U-N-S 00-502-8105 EXP
GUNITE EMI CORP
EMI DIVISION
(*Suby of* GUNITE CORP) ★
302 Peoples Ave, Rockford, IL 61104-7035
Tel (815) 964-7124 *Founded/Ownrshp* 1880
Sales 26.7MM^E *EMP* 285
SIC 3321 3714 Ductile iron castings; Gray iron castings; Brake drums, motor vehicle; Motor vehicle wheels & parts; Ductile iron castings; Gray iron castings; Brake drums, motor vehicle; Motor vehicle wheels & parts
Pr: James Sirar

GUNK
See RADIATOR SPECIALTY CO INC

D-U-N-S 19-993-6550 IMP
■ **GUNLOCKE CO L L C**
(*Suby of* HNI CORP) ★
1 Gunlocke Dr, Wayland, NY 14572-9515
Tel (585) 728-5111 *Founded/Ownrshp* 1902
Sales 127.7MM^E *EMP* 800^E
SIC 2521 Wood office furniture; Wood office furniture
Treas: Clarence L Burkey
VP: Phil Gerlach
Div Mgr: Jodi Dykstra
VP Mktg: Kevin Gorman

GUNN AUTOMOTIVE GROUP
See CURTIS C GUNN INC

D-U-N-S 04-322-4062
GUNN CHEVROLET INC
(*Suby of* CURTIS C GUNN INC) ★
16550 Interstate 35 N, Selma, TX 78154-1460
Tel (210) 599-5000 *Founded/Ownrshp* 1980
Sales 51.8MM^E *EMP* 170
SIC 5511 Automobiles, new & used; Automobiles, new & used
Ch Bd: Curtis C Gunn Jr
**Pr:* Wesley Burk
Sls Mgr: Charlie Odaniel

GUNN HONDA
See GUNN IMPORTS INC

D-U-N-S 04-393-0247
GUNN IMPORTS INC
GUNN HONDA
(*Suby of* CURTIS C GUNN INC) ★
14610 W Interstate 10, San Antonio, TX 78249-3200
Tel (210) 680-3371 *Founded/Ownrshp* 1980
Sales 36.7MM^E *EMP* 100
SIC 5511 Automobiles, new & used; Automobiles, new & used
Ch: Curtis C Gunn Jr
**CFO:* Kelly Collins
**VP:* Paul Young
Exec: Tim Rivers
Sls Mgr: Jay Carver
Sales Asso: Terry Bartelli
Sales Asso: Garland Berry
Sales Asso: Daniel Tawney

D-U-N-S 18-745-9185
GUNNALLEN FINANCIAL INC
5002 W Waters Ave, Tampa, FL 33634-1313
Tel (800) 713-4046 *Founded/Ownrshp* 1986
Sales 129.1MM^E *EMP* 1,137
SIC 6211 Security brokers & dealers; Security brokers & dealers
CEO: Frederick O Kraus
Pr: Robert Alvarez
**Pr:* Donald Gunn
**CEO:* Richard Frueh
**COO:* Christopher Frankel
CFO: Declan Obeirne
**Chf Cred:* Andrew Butte
Sr VP: Kevin Daniels
Sr VP: James Dicesaro
VP: Frank S Dicicco
VP: Daclan O'Beirne
VP: David Ruhling

D-U-N-S 02-092-6432
GUNNISON VALLEY HOSPITAL
64 E 100 N, Gunnison, UT 84634
Tel (435) 528-7246 *Founded/Ownrshp* 1970
Sales 40.5MM^E *EMP* 200
Accts Hawkins Cloward & Simister Or
SIC 8062 General medical & surgical hospitals; General medical & surgical hospitals
**CFO:* Brian Murray
Dir OR: Cheryl Hansen
Mtls Mgr: Jeanette Andersen
Dir Health: Shelly Lemon

D-U-N-S 96-530-0499
GUNNISON VALLEY HOSPITAL
711 N Taylor St, Gunnison, CO 81230-2296
Tel (970) 641-1456 *Founded/Ownrshp* 2010
Sales 51.1MM^E *EMP* 250
SIC 8062 General medical & surgical hospitals; General medical & surgical hospitals
Ch: Ronda Connaway
**CEO:* Randall Phelps
CFO: James Barbuat
**CFO:* Tim Cashman
Trst: Martyn Cooper
Dir OR: Casey Pitt
Dir Lab: Tina Wilson
Dir Rad: Mark Swift
Dir Rx: Karen Gorman
Chf Nrs Of: Chris Evans
Ex Dir: Sarah Andrews

GUNSTERYOAKLEY
See GUNSTERYOAKLEY & STEWART PA

D-U-N-S 08-018-7313
GUNSTERYOAKLEY & STEWART PA (FL)
GUNSTERYOAKLEY
777 S Flagler Dr Ste 500e, West Palm Beach, FL 33401-6194
Tel (561) 655-1980 *Founded/Ownrshp* 1973
Sales 59.3MM^E *EMP* 400
SIC 8111 General practice law office; General practice law office
Pr: William Perry
V Ch: Lila Jaber
Pr: Carol Borden
Pr: Donna Gomersall
Pr: Marcelle Manship
Pr: Gail Robarge
Pr: Lesly Vanegas
**Ch:* George Lemieux
**Treas:* Michael Mitrione
**VP:* Lewis Crippen
Mktg Dir: Jenni Garrison

D-U-N-S 96-521-2178
GUNSTERYOAKLEY PA
777 S Flagler Dr Ste 500, West Palm Beach, FL 33401-6121
Tel (561) 650-0713 *Founded/Ownrshp* 1999
Sales 10.6MM^E *EMP* 400
SIC 8111 Legal services; Legal services
CEO: Donald J Beuttenmuller Jr

D-U-N-S 15-359-9030
GUNSTOCK AREA COMMISSION
719 Cherry Valley Rd Ofc, Gilford, NH 03249-7817
Tel (603) 293-4341 *Founded/Ownrshp* 1959
Sales 29.6MM^E *EMP* 800
Accts Vachon Clukay & Company Pc N
SIC 7999 7033 Recreation center; Aerial tramway or ski lift, amusement or scenic; Ski instruction; Ski rental concession; Campgrounds; Recreation center; Aerial tramway or ski lift, amusement or scenic; Ski instruction; Ski rental concession; Campgrounds
Genl Mgr: Gregory Goddard
IT Man: Cindy Balint
IT Man: Peg Purcell
Mktg Dir: Bill Quigley

D-U-N-S 05-727-4672
GUNTER CONSTRUCTION CO INC
455 Fredrix Aly, Lawrenceville, GA 30046-4668
Tel (770) 963-7760 *Founded/Ownrshp* 1972
Sales 28.5MM^E *EMP* 202
SIC 1623 Pipeline construction
Pr: Bryan Boyd
**VP:* Bill E Gunter

D-U-N-S 94-153-5122 IMP
GUNTERSVILLE BREATHABLES INC
FROGG TOGGS
131 Sundown Dr Nw, Arab, AL 35016-4494
Tel (256) 931-1580 *Founded/Ownrshp* 2009
Sales 22.1MM^E *EMP* 49
SIC 5136 5137 5611 5632 Sportswear, men's & boys'; Sportswear, women's & children's; Clothing, sportswear, men's & boys'; Women's accessory & specialty stores
Pr: Alan Campbell
**CEO:* Drake Maples
Natl Sales: Kevin Gentle

D-U-N-S 00-911-8191 IMP/EXP
GUNTERT & ZIMMERMAN CONST DIV INC (CA)
222 E 4th St, Ripon, CA 95366-2761
Tel (209) 599-0066 *Founded/Ownrshp* 1942
Sales 23.5MM^E *EMP* 50
SIC 3531 3599 Pavers; Machine & other job shop work
CEO: Ronald M Guntert Jr
Ex VP: Ron Meskis
**VP:* Gerald Dahlinger
**VP:* Denise Guntert
**VP:* Don Sheets

D-U-N-S 00-923-3370
GUNTERT SALES DIV INC
GUNTERT STEEL
222 E 4th St, Ripon, CA 95366-2761
Tel (209) 599-6131 *Founded/Ownrshp* 1945
Sales 64.3MM^E *EMP* 45
SIC 5051 Plates, metal; Bars, metal; Pipe & tubing, steel
CEO: Ronald M Guntert Jr
Pr: Gerald Dahlinger
**Pr:* Keith Kirschenman
**VP:* Ronald Ruffoni
**VP:* Deanna Tocco
Genl Mgr: Mike Williams
Dir IT: Jerry Dahlinger
Mfg Mgr: Alessandro Bernacchia

GUNTERT STEEL
See GUNTERT SALES DIV INC

GUNTHER MAZDA
See GUNTHER MOTOR CO OF GEORGIA INC

D-U-N-S 05-217-2632 EXP
GUNTHER MOTOR CO OF GEORGIA INC
GUNTHER MAZDA
3711 Buford Dr, Buford, GA 30519-4919
Tel (678) 745-9950 *Founded/Ownrshp* 1969
Sales 107.0MM^E *EMP* 330
SIC 5511 Automobiles, new & used; Automobiles, new & used
Pr: Joseph F Gunther Jr
**Treas:* Casey Gunther
**VP:* Richard Stoff
Genl Mgr: Oswald Ferrufino

D-U-N-S 03-104-2849 IMP/EXP
GUNTHER SALT CO
101 Buchanan St, Saint Louis, MO 63147-3537
Tel (314) 241-7075 *Founded/Ownrshp* 2007
Sales 25.0MM^E *EMP* 23
SIC 5169 Salts, industrial
Pr: John M Gunther
**VP:* Peter W Gunther
IT Man: Christa Cross
Plnt Mgr: Darrin Chapman
VP Sls: Dave Steidemann

D-U-N-S 05-742-8653 EXP
GUNTHER VOLKSWAGON OF COCONUT CREEK
4300 N State Road 7, Coral Springs, FL 33073-3817
Tel (954) 590-3750 *Founded/Ownrshp* 2001
Sales 52.8MM^E *EMP* 200
SIC 5511 Automobiles, new & used; Automobiles, new & used
Genl Mgr: Robert Klein
Dir Bus: Phil Elios
DP Exec: June Chase
Sls Mgr: Jeff Foreman
Sls Mgr: Ben James
Sls Mgr: Mike Zavell
Sales Asso: Michael Lair

D-U-N-S 05-999-3444 IMP/EXP
GUNTHER-NASH INC
RECON SOLUTIONS
(*Suby of* ALBERICI GROUP INC) ★
8800 Page Ave, Saint Louis, MO 63114-6106
Tel (314) 733-2000 *Founded/Ownrshp* 2001
Sales 29.2MM *EMP* 4
SIC 1629 1799 Dams, waterways, docks & other marine construction; Post-disaster renovations
Pr: James Frey
**VP:* Gregory Hesser

D-U-N-S 00-445-1183
GUNTON CORP
PELLA WINDOW & DOOR
26150 Richmond Rd, Cleveland, OH 44146-1438
Tel (216) 831-2420 *Founded/Ownrshp* 1954
Sales 101.2MM^E *EMP* 380
SIC 5031 Windows; Doors; Metal doors, sash & trim; Windows; Doors; Metal doors, sash & trim
Co-Ch Bd: Robert J Gunton
**Pr:* Mark Mead
COO: Bob Gunton
**Co-Ch Bd:* William E Gunton
**Treas:* Reggie Stacy
VP: Mike Slates
IT Man: Robert Wanamaker
Mktg Mgr: Rick Balabon
Sls Mgr: Darlene Hermann
Sales Asso: Michael Weisberg

D-U-N-S 19-505-5785 IMP
GUNZE ELECTRONICS USA CORP
ELTECH
(*Suby of* GUNZE LIMITED)
2113 Wells Branch Pkwy # 54, Austin, TX 78728-6970
Tel (512) 990-3400 *Founded/Ownrshp* 2007
Sales 228.8MM^E *EMP* 8,000
SIC 3577 Computer peripheral equipment; Computer peripheral equipment
Pr: Hisakazu Hiriawa
IT Man: Michael Merritt
Sls Mgr: Marshall Jackson

D-U-N-S 01-491-4493 IMP
GUPTA PERMOLD CORP
234 Lott Rd, Pittsburgh, PA 15235-4025
Tel (412) 793-3511 *Founded/Ownrshp* 1980
Sales 46.4MM^E *EMP* 180
SIC 3365 3621 3743 2448 3699 3369 Machinery castings, aluminum; Motors & generators; Interurban cars & car equipment; Wood pallets & skids; Electrical equipment & supplies; Nonferrous foundries; Machinery castings, aluminum; Motors & generators; Interurban cars & car equipment; Wood pallets & skids; Electrical equipment & supplies; Nonferrous foundries
Pr: Lakshmi P Gupta
Mktg Mgr: Anil Gupta

GURLEY LEEP AUTOMOTIVE GROUP
See GURLEY-LEEP AUTOMOTIVE MANAGEMENT CORP

GURLEY LEEP HYUNDAY
See GURLEY-LEEP BUICK-GMC TRUCK INC

D-U-N-S 03-574-3467
GURLEY MOTOR CO (NM)
FORD LINCOLN MERCURY
701 W Coal Ave, Gallup, NM 87301-6503
Tel (505) 722-6621 *Founded/Ownrshp* 1933
Sales 45.3MM^E *EMP* 115
Accts Newberry & Associates Ltd G
SIC 5511 Automobiles, new & used; Pickups, new & used; Automobiles, new & used; Pickups, new & used
Pr: Patrick J Gurley
Pr: Steve Gurley
**Pr:* Steven Gurley

D-U-N-S 80-956-7845
GURLEY PRECISION INSTRUMENTS INC
514 Fulton St, Troy, NY 12180-3315
Tel (518) 272-6300 *Founded/Ownrshp* 1993
Sales 30.0MM^E *EMP* 105

SIC 3827 3824 3829 3823 3674 3663 Optical instruments & lenses; Water meters; Physical property testing equipment; Industrial instrmnts msrmnt display/control process variable; Semiconductors & related devices; Radio & TV communications equipment; Optical instruments & lenses; Water meters; Physical property testing equipment; Industrial instrmnts msrmnt display/control process variable; Semiconductors & related devices; Radio &TV communications equipment
Ch Bd: O Patrick Brady
**CFO:* Ronald H Laberge
VP: Rick Evans
IT Man: Mike Turnbaugh
Mfg Dir: Yuiry Benderskiy
Sfty Mgr: Tom Reed
Plnt Mgr: Bruce Martin

D-U-N-S 92-709-7527
GURLEY-LEEP AUTOMOTIVE MANAGEMENT CORP
GURLEY LEEP AUTOMOTIVE GROUP
215 W Douglas Rd, Mishawaka, IN 46545-1241
Tel (574) 272-0990 *Founded/Ownrshp* 1974
Sales 78.9MM^E *EMP* 242
SIC 5531 7532 5521 5511 7538 Automotive parts; Body shop, automotive; Automobiles, used cars only; Automobiles, new & used; General automotive repair shops; Automotive parts; Body shop, automotive; Automobiles, used cars only; Automobiles, new & used; General automotive repair shops
Pr: Michael Leep
CFO: Clyde Wheeler
VP: James Leep
Genl Mgr: John Kabzinski
Genl Mgr: Jeff Lennex
Genl Mgr: Scott Pharr
Dir IT: Lynn Law
Prd Mgr: Greg Tomkiewicz
Sls Dir: Chip Snyder
Sls Mgr: Tim Chapman
Sls Mgr: Scott Cizewski

D-U-N-S 08-458-6635
GURLEY-LEEP BUICK-GMC TRUCK INC
GURLEY LEEP HYUNDAY
5302 Grape Rd, Mishawaka, IN 46545-1312
Tel (574) 258-7711 *Founded/Ownrshp* 1999
Sales 74.1MM^E *EMP* 197
SIC 5511 7549 Automobiles, new & used; Pickups, new & used; Automotive maintenance services; Automobiles, new & used; Pickups, new & used; Automotive maintenance services
Ch Bd: Michael Leep Jr
**Pr:* Michael Leep Sr

D-U-N-S 06-401-6561
GURNEE DODGE INC
7255 Grand Ave, Gurnee, IL 60031-5270
Tel (847) 623-3000 *Founded/Ownrshp* 1980
Sales 25.1MM^E *EMP* 60
SIC 5511 7538 Automobiles, new & used; General automotive repair shops; Automobiles, new & used; General automotive repair shops
Pr: Michael Fohrman
**CFO:* Fifi Bozonelos
**Treas:* Rose Fohrman
**VP:* Arnie Singer
Mktg Dir: Mark Ruffolo
Sls Mgr: Mitch Horwitz

D-U-N-S 07-016-3449
GURNEE SCHOOL DISTRICT 56
900 Kilbourne Rd, Gurnee, IL 60031-1947
Tel (847) 336-8997 *Founded/Ownrshp* 1870
Sales 25.5MM *EMP* 233
SIC 8211 Public elementary school; Public junior high school; School board; Public elementary school; Public junior high school; School board
Schl Brd P: Heidi May
Instr Medi: Kathy Kibitlewski

D-U-N-S 96-501-3290
GURNEE WATER PARK LLC
KEY LIME COVE WATER RESORT
1700 Nations Dr, Gurnee, IL 60031-9136
Tel (224) 656-8685 *Founded/Ownrshp* 2010
Sales 27.1MM^E *EMP* 560
SIC 7011 Resort hotel; Resort hotel
Genl Mgr: Dale McFarland
Sls Mgr: Nick Farrell

D-U-N-S 00-450-4122 IMP/EXP
GURRENTZ INTERNATIONAL CORP
1501 Ardmore Blvd Ste 400, Pittsburgh, PA 15221-4451
Tel (412) 351-3200 *Founded/Ownrshp* 1961
Sales 25.4MM^E *EMP* 20
SIC 5142 Meat, frozen: packaged
Pr: Roger Gurrentz
**Treas:* Patrick Gurrentz

D-U-N-S 00-555-3334
GURTZ ELECTRIC CO
GURTZ TECHNICAL SERVICES
77 W Seegers Rd, Arlington Heights, IL 60005-3916
Tel (847) 734-2400 *Founded/Ownrshp* 1958
Sales 87.2MM^E *EMP* 300
SIC 1731 Fiber optic cable installation; Voice, data & video wiring contractor; General electrical contractor; Fiber optic cable installation; Voice, data & video wiring contractor; General electrical contractor
CEO: Frank Gurtz
**COO:* Paul Laskowske
**CFO:* Thomas Maimonis
Ex VP: Bohdan Gnyra
**Ex VP:* Pat Thornton
Sfty Mgr: Luis Hernandez
Snr PM: Marek Bogdanowicz
Snr PM: Brian Karlow

GURTZ TECHNICAL SERVICES
See GURTZ ELECTRIC CO

D-U-N-S 12-820-2798 IMP
GURU DENIM INC
TRUE RELIGION BRAND JEANS
(*Suby of* TRUE RELIGION APPAREL INC) ★
1888 Rosecrans Ave, Manhattan Beach, CA 90266-3712
Tel (323) 266-3072 *Founded/Ownrshp* 2002
Sales 123.7MM^E *EMP* 809
SIC 5611 5137 Clothing accessories: men's & boys'; Women's & children's clothing; Clothing accessories: men's & boys'; Women's & children's clothing
CEO: John Ermatinger
**CFO:* Eric Bauer
Bd of Dir: Marcello Bottoli
Site Mgr: Ashton Aguilar
Site Mgr: Ashley Crow
Site Mgr: Melissa Moss
Site Mgr: Jaimi Smith
**Genl Couns:* Ilene Eskenazi

D-U-N-S 80-817-2865
GURU KNITS INC
225 W 38th St, Los Angeles, CA 90037-1405
Tel (323) 235-9424 *Founded/Ownrshp* 2007
Sales 35.2MM^E *EMP* 60
SIC 7389 ;
CEO: Kevin Port

GURVICH DETECTIVE AGENCY
See NEW ORLEANS PRIVATE PATROL SERVICE INC

GURWIN JEWISH NURSING
See ROSALIND AND JOSEPH GURWIN JEWISH GERIATRIC CENTER OF LONG ISLAND INC

D-U-N-S 88-487-5246 IMP
GURWITCH PRODUCTS LLC
(*Suby of* ALTICOR INC) ★
8 Greenway Plz Ste 700, Houston, TX 77046-0826
Tel (281) 275-7000 *Founded/Ownrshp* 2006
Sales 55.8MM^E *EMP* 350^E
SIC 2844 Cosmetic preparations; Cosmetic preparations
CEO: Claudia Poccia
Ex VP: John Tedeschi
VP: Robert E Hurtte
**VP:* Renee McBride
Sls Mgr: Mark Gearing

GUS JOHNSON FORD
See FORD MCCOLLUM SALES INC

D-U-N-S 05-302-7314 EXP
GUS MACHADO FORD INC
1200 W 49th St, Hialeah, FL 33012-3293
Tel (305) 822-3211 *Founded/Ownrshp* 1983
Sales 71.8MM^E *EMP* 139
SIC 5511 Automobiles, new & used; Trucks, tractors & trailers: new & used; Automobiles, new & used; Trucks, tractors & trailers: new & used
Pr: Gus Machado
CFO: Jorge Martinez
**VP:* Victor Benitez
Sls Mgr: Sean Pearson
Sales Asso: Alex Garrido
Sales Asso: Howard Wollaston

GUS PAULOS CHEVROLET
See PAULOS GUS CHEVROLET INC

D-U-N-S 00-147-9815 IMP
GUSMER ENTERPRISES INC
1165 Globe Ave, Mountainside, NJ 07092-2903
Tel (908) 301-1811 *Founded/Ownrshp* 1918
Sales 24.9MM^E *EMP* 160
SIC 3569 5085 5084 5159

GUSTAFSON FARM
See GUSTAFSONS FAMILY ENTERPRISES INC

D-U-N-S 00-406-1289
GUSTAFSONS FAMILY ENTERPRISES INC (FL)
GUSTAFSON FARM
4169 County Road 15a, Green Cove Springs, FL 32043-8132
Tel (904) 284-3750 *Founded/Ownrshp* 1992
Sales 18.0MM^E *EMP* 325
SIC 0241 Dairy farms; Dairy farms
Pr: Edwin S McBride
**Treas:* Gunnar J Gustafson
**VP:* Edwin S Gustafson Jr

D-U-N-S 00-177-8232
GUSTAVE A LARSON CO (WI)
JOHNSON CONTROLS
W233n2869 Roundy Cir W, Pewaukee, WI 53072-6285
Tel (262) 542-0200 *Founded/Ownrshp* 1936
Sales 210.0MM *EMP* 425
SIC 5075 5078 5084 5046

D-U-N-S 19-403-7206
GUSTAVO JIMENEZ INC
SOUTHWEST FREIGHTLINES
11931 Transpark Dr, El Paso, TX 79927-2352
Tel (915) 860-8592 *Founded/Ownrshp* 1986
Sales 73.1MM^E *EMP* 300
SIC 4213 Contract haulers; Contract haulers
Pr: Gustavo Jimenez
Exec: Nuco Gonzalez
Natl Sales: Greg Fuller

D-U-N-S 00-176-3531
GUSTAVO PRESTON CO INC (MA)
23 Industrial Ave, Chelmsford, MA 01824-3611
Tel (978) 250-3333 *Founded/Ownrshp* 1881, 1994
Sales 21.5MM^E *EMP* 50
SIC 5084 Pumps & pumping equipment
Pr: David Pellegrini
**COO:* Dom Sestito
**VP:* David Downey
Genl Mgr: Dominic Sestito
Sls Mgr: Susan Trudeau

D-U-N-S 00-622-1808
GUSTAVUS ADOLPHUS COLLEGE
800 W College Ave, Saint Peter, MN 56082-1498
Tel (507) 933-7508 *Founded/Ownrshp* 1862
Sales 133.2MM *EMP* 700
Accts Baker Tilly Virchow Krause Llp
SIC 8221 College, except junior; College, except junior
Pr: Rebecca Bergman
Mng Pt: George Hicks
Pr: Jackie Peterson
**Treas:* Ken Westpha
Bd of Dir: Anna Hulseberg
VP: Mark Anderson
VP: Eric Dugdale
VP: Chuck Niederriter
VP: Jones Vanhecke
Exec: Kirk Beyer
Dir IT: Bruce Aarsvold

D-U-N-S 02-327-9300
GUSTMAN CHEVROLET SALES INC
GUSTMAN PONTIAC
1450 Delanglade St, Kaukauna, WI 54130-4128
Tel (920) 766-3581 *Founded/Ownrshp* 1947
Sales 70.0MM *EMP* 75
SIC 5511 Automobiles, new & used; Automobiles, new & used
Pr: Thomas Gustman
**VP:* Jeffrey P Gustman
Exec: Keith Pingel
Ex Dir: Al Mengarelli

GUSTMAN PONTIAC
See GUSTMAN CHEVROLET SALES INC

D-U-N-S 03-524-5778 IMP
GUSTO DISTRIBUTING CO INC
BRUCE WATKINS DISTRIBUTING CO.
501 Crescent Cir, Great Falls, MT 59404-3275
Tel (406) 265-4369 *Founded/Ownrshp* 1965
Sales 37.2MM^E *EMP* 70
Accts Bloomgren Rivera & Co Pllc
SIC 5181 Beer & other fermented malt liquors; Beer & other fermented malt liquors
Pr: Ardelle C Watkins
**Pr:* Bruce L Watkins
**VP:* Agnes Mabe

GUSTO PACKING COMPANY
See BUTTERBALL LLC

GUSWEILER G M CENTER
See GUSWEILER JIM CHEVROLET OLDSMOBILE PONTIAC BUICK CADILLAC GEO INC

D-U-N-S 11-735-9943
GUSWEILER JIM CHEVROLET OLDSMOBILE PONTIAC BUICK CADILLAC GEO INC
GUSWEILER G M CENTER
1132 State Route 41 Sw, Wshngtn CT Hs, OH 43160-8784
Tel (740) 335-2200 *Founded/Ownrshp* 1984
Sales 22.0MM^E *EMP* 65
SIC 5511 5521 Automobiles, new & used; Used car dealers; Automobiles, new & used; Used car dealers
Pr: James J Gusweiler
Sales Asso: Jimmy Carter
Sales Asso: James Reese

D-U-N-S 00-222-8328
GUTCHESS LUMBER CO INC (NY)
890 Mclean Rd, Cortland, NY 13045-9393
Tel (607) 753-3393 *Founded/Ownrshp* 1904, 1978
Sales 74.6MM^E *EMP* 350
SIC 2421 2426 Building & structural materials, wood; Lumber, hardwood dimension; Building & structural materials, wood; Lumber, hardwood dimension
Ch Bd: Gary H Gutchess
**Treas:* Jeffrey D Breed
VP: HUD Caldwell
**VP:* Matthew F Gutchess

D-U-N-S 62-387-5890
GUTHRIE & HUEBNER CO INC
5797 Dietrich Rd, San Antonio, TX 78219-3599
Tel (210) 661-4251 *Founded/Ownrshp* 2003
Sales 538.2MM^E *EMP* 2,500
Accts Rinaldo J Gonzalez Pc San An
SIC 1541 1629 1542 Industrial buildings, new construction; Mine loading & discharging station construction; Commercial & office building, new construction; Industrial buildings, new construction; Mine loading & discharging station construction; Commercial & office building, new construction
Pr: Arthur D Huebner
**COO:* Timothy J Henning
CFO: Nita B Mc Bride
Board of Directors: Jack F Farris Chairman, Timothy S Geppert, Bruce A Jeffrey, Richard D Swartout, Robert L Urban

D-U-N-S 07-944-8475
GUTHRIE CLINIC
1 Guthrie Sq Ste B, Sayre, PA 18840-1699
Tel (570) 888-5858 *Founded/Ownrshp* 2000
Sales 663.6MM^E *EMP* 4,500^E
SIC 8011 8062 8082 Offices & clinics of medical doctors; Group health association; Health maintenance organization; Primary care medical clinic; General medical & surgical hospitals; Home health care services; Offices & clinics of medical doctors; Group health association; Health maintenance organization; Primary care medical clinic; General medical & surgical hospitals; Home health care services
Pr: Joseph Scopelliti MD
**Pr:* Francis Belardi MD Faafp
CEO: Donald Skerpon
**COO:* Staci Thompson Mha Cmpe
**COO:* Paul Vervalin MBA Facmpe
**CFO:* Richard I Bennett CPA
**Ex VP:* Paul Chacona
**Ex VP:* Marie T Droege Mha Fache
**Ex VP:* Frank Pinkosky
**Ex VP:* Michael Scalzone MD Mhcm Facog
Dir Risk M: Lynn Noone

GUTHRIE ENTERPRISES
See TWIN TIER MANAGEMENT CORP

D-U-N-S 07-528-7599
GUTHRIE HEALTHCARE SYSTEM
GUTHRIE ROBERT PACKER HOSPITAL
1 Guthrie Sq Ste B, Sayre, PA 18840-1625
Tel (570) 888-6666 *Founded/Ownrshp* 1982
Sales NA *EMP* 2,575
SIC 8011 7352 8741

D-U-N-S 06-959-8274
GUTHRIE MEDICAL GROUP PC
(*Suby of* GUTHRIE CLINIC) ★
1 Guthrie Sq Ste B, Sayre, PA 18840-1625
Tel (570) 888-5858 *Founded/Ownrshp* 1910
Sales 228.5MM *EMP* 4,500
SIC 8011 Group health association; Group health association
Pr: Joseph A Scopelliti
Chf Rad: David Channin
**COO:* Paul Chacona
COO: Dan Swingle
**Ex VP:* Michael Scalzone
**Ex VP:* Paul G Vervalin
VP: Minhphuong Dang
VP: Barb Pennypacker
**VP:* Frank Pinkosky
VP: Nate Shinagawa
VP: Michele Sisto
Dir Inf Cn: Andrew Klee

D-U-N-S 06-077-2753
GUTHRIE PUBLIC SCHOOLS
GUTHRIE SCHOOL DISTRICT
802 E Vilas Ave, Guthrie, OK 73044-5228
Tel (405) 282-8900 *Founded/Ownrshp* 1889
Sales 21.0MM^E *EMP* 411
SIC 8211 Public combined elementary & secondary school; School board; Public combined elementary & secondary school; School board
Treas: Donna Scheihing

GUTHRIE ROBERT PACKER HOSPITAL
See GUTHRIE HEALTHCARE SYSTEM

GUTHRIE SCHOOL DISTRICT
See GUTHRIE PUBLIC SCHOOLS

D-U-N-S 07-149-7945
GUTHRIE THEATER FOUNDATION
818 S 2nd St, Minneapolis, MN 55415-1252
Tel (612) 377-2224 *Founded/Ownrshp* 1963
Sales 44.6MM *EMP* 187
SIC 7922 Theatrical producers & services; Theatrical producers & services
Pr: Wendy Nelson
COO: Kay McGuire
**Treas:* Jay Kiedrowski
**Treas:* Steven C Webster
Prin: Jodeen Kozlak
Genl Mgr: Hillary Hart
Mktg Dir: Rachael Crew
Mktg Dir: Elizabeth Deacon

D-U-N-S 80-577-6783
GUTHY-RENKER FULFILLMENT SERVICES LLC
1845 Brevard Rd, Arden, NC 28704-9145
Tel (828) 684-4300 *Founded/Ownrshp* 2007
Sales 89.9MM^E *EMP* 600
SIC 7389 7374 Telemarketing services; Data processing service

D-U-N-S 60-831-5453 IMP
GUTHY-RENKER LLC
41550 Eclectic St Ste 200, Palm Desert, CA 92260-1967
Tel (760) 773-9022 *Founded/Ownrshp* 1988
Sales 389.5MM^E *EMP* 155
SIC 5099 7812 5999 7389 Tapes & cassettes, prerecorded; Commercials, television: tape or film; Cosmetics; Telemarketing services; Tapes & cassettes, prerecorded; Commercials, television: tape or film; Cosmetics; Telemarketing services
Pr: Greg Renker
Pr: Shelly Elkins
CFO: Carlye Duckworth
Ex VP: Kevin Knee
Sr VP: Kimber Maderazzo
VP: Natalie Dilallo
VP: Jeff Engler
**VP:* Bill Guthy
VP: Richard Herzog
VP: Margo Lane
VP: Keith Manning
Creative D: Lenny Lieberman
Board of Directors: Richard Woolsey

D-U-N-S 09-427-2234
GUTIERREZ CO
200 Wheeler Rd, Burlington, MA 01803-5501
Tel (781) 270-3212 *Founded/Ownrshp* 1978
Sales 26.8MM^E *EMP* 62
SIC 1542 1541 6531 6552 Commercial & office building, new construction; Institutional building construction; Industrial buildings & warehouses; Real estate managers; Land subdividers & developers, commercial
Pr: Arthur J Gutierrez
**Pr:* Arthur Gutierrez Jr
Ex VP: John Cataldo
**VP:* Douglas Fainelli
Corp Couns: Gloria Gutierrez

D-U-N-S 07-942-5989
GUTKNECHT CONSTRUCTION CO
2280 Citygate Dr, Columbus, OH 43219-3588
Tel (614) 532-5410 *Founded/Ownrshp* 1975
Sales 23.5MM^E *EMP* 44
SIC 1542 Commercial & office building, new construction; Commercial & office buildings, renovation & repair
Pr: Jeff Feinman
**CFO:* Mike Poyer
**VP:* Ben Lindsay
**VP:* Jamie Weisent
Snr Mgr: Craig Turner

D-U-N-S 05-285-7844
GUTRIDGE PLUMBING INC
88 S 2nd St, Newark, OH 43055-5417
Tel (740) 345-5760 *Founded/Ownrshp* 1970
Sales 27.0MM^E *EMP* 140^E
SIC 1711 Plumbing contractors; Fire sprinkler system installation; Plumbing contractors; Fire sprinkler system installation
Pr: Gilbert Gutridge
**Pr:* Rod Gutridge
**Pr:* Wayde Gutridge
Dept Mgr: Dennis Glaub
Off Mgr: Eric Morgan

D-U-N-S 01-140-6717
GUTTENPLANS FROZEN DOUGH INC
100 State Route 36 E, North Middletown, NJ 07748-5249
Tel (732) 495-9480 *Founded/Ownrshp* 1908, 1967
Sales 59.0MM *EMP* 100
Accts Eisneramper Llp Iselin New J
SIC 2041 Doughs, frozen or refrigerated; Doughs, frozen or refrigerated
Pr: Abe Littenberg
**VP:* Jack Guttenplan
Prd Mgr: Tony Lopez

GUTTER HELMET OF MICHIGAN
See INFINITY HOME IMPROVEMENT INC

GUTTERMANS SUPPLY
See GUTTERMANS SUPPLY CORP OF AMERICA

D-U-N-S 36-256-6671
GUTTERMANS SUPPLY CORP OF AMERICA
GUTTERMANS SUPPLY
1620 Ne Argyle Dr, Portland, OR 97211-1664
Tel (503) 285-2500 *Founded/Ownrshp* 1984
Sales 51.2MM^E *EMP* 64
SIC 5051 3444 Aluminum bars, rods, ingots, sheets, pipes, plates, etc.; Sheet metalwork; Aluminum bars, rods, ingots, sheets, pipes, plates, etc.; Sheet metalwork
Pr: Kenneth D Cripps Sr
**VP:* Kenneth A Cripps

D-U-N-S 08-846-4730
GUTTMACHER INSTITUTE INC (NY)
125 Maiden Ln Fl 7, New York, NY 10038-4723
Tel (212) 248-1111 *Founded/Ownrshp* 1964, 1968
Sales 22.2MM *EMP* 70
SIC 8732 Commercial nonphysical research
Pr: Sharon Camp
V Ch: Bob Diamond
V Ch: Cynthia Gomez
CFO: Kendell Burroughs
**Ch:* Melissa Gilliams
**Ex VP:* Cory Richards
VP: Patricia Donovan
**VP:* Susheela Singh
VP: Cynrthia Summers
Comm Dir: Gustavo Surez
Admn Mgr: Mercedes Pacrez

D-U-N-S 00-893-5009
GUTTMAN ENERGY INC
200 Speers Rd, Belle Vernon, PA 15012-1017
Tel (724) 489-5199 *Founded/Ownrshp* 1950
Sales 94.3MM^E *EMP* 280
SIC 8731 5172 Energy research; Lubricating oils & greases; Energy research; Lubricating oils & greases
CEO: Alan R Guttman
**Pr:* Richard Guttman
CFO: Scott Schaffner
**VP:* James L Guttman
Dir IT: Paul Schreck
IT Man: Lisa Dochinez
VP Mktg: Gary Smelko
S&M/VP: Larry Flannelly
Mktg Dir: Dave Robinson
Sls Mgr: George Rodgers
Sales Asso: Kristie Dejuliis

D-U-N-S 03-783-8844
GUY & ONEILL INC (WI)
617 Tower Dr, Fredonia, WI 53021-9323
Tel (262) 692-2469 *Founded/Ownrshp* 1980
Sales 35.0MM *EMP* 125^E
SIC 2834 Packaging & labeling services; Pharmaceutical preparations; Pressed fiber & molded pulp products except food products; Plastic processing; Pharmaceutical preparations
CEO: Ralph Patitucci
**COO:* Tom Misgen
CFO: Brian Delfield
**CFO:* Brian Glynn
VP Opers: Tom Misgin

D-U-N-S 03-299-1460
GUY BROWN MANAGEMENT LLC (TN)
320 Seven Springs Way # 450, Brentwood, TN 37027-4537
Tel (615) 777-1500 *Founded/Ownrshp* 1997
Sales 251.0MM *EMP* 82
SIC 5112 Office supplies; Office supplies
CEO: Maria Teresa Vasquez
CFO: Jay Chawan
Chf Mktg O: Philip Markuson
Sr VP: Steve Creed
VP: Dan Cappetto
VP: Barkey Clarke
VP: Mike Ducey
VP: Jack McGuire
VP: Bill Petrie
VP: Tera Vazquez
VP: CAM Willis

D-U-N-S 15-393-9491
GUY C LEE BUILDING MATERIALS LLC
235 E Market St, Smithfield, NC 27577-3917
Tel (919) 934-6195 *Founded/Ownrshp* 1985
Sales 39.5MM^E *EMP* 180
SIC 5211

D-U-N-S 06-988-5036
■ **GUY CARPENTER & CO INC OF PENNSYLVANIA**
(*Suby of* MARSH & MCLENNAN COMPANIES INC) ★
1717 Arch St Ste 800, Philadelphia, PA 19103-2795
Tel (215) 864-3600 *Founded/Ownrshp* 1938, 1950
Sales NA *EMP* 120
SIC 6411 Insurance information & consulting services
Sr VP: Mark Killingsworth
VP: Charles Klaniecki
VP: Paul Marino
VP: Richard Puchalski
Mng Dir: Guy Carpenter
IT Man: Steven Noone

D-U-N-S 07-100-6191
■ **GUY CARPENTER & CO LLC**
(*Suby of* MARSH & MCLENNAN COMPANIES INC) ★
1166 Ave Of The Americas, New York, NY 10036-2708
Tel (917) 937-3000 *Founded/Ownrshp* 1919
Sales NA *EMP* 2,000
SIC 6411 8742 8732 Insurance information & consulting services; Financial consultant; Market analysis, business & economic research; Insurance information & consulting services; Financial consultant; Market analysis, business & economic research
Pr: Alex Moczarski
**Ch Bd:* Britt Newhouse
**CEO:* Andrew Marcell
CEO: Chris McKeown
**CEO:* Alex Moczarski
CFO: Eunice Adler
CFO: Ajay Junarkar
CFO: Elizabeth A Keys
**CFO:* Robert Pietrucha
Ofcr: Iain Boyer
Ofcr: Charles Higham
Ofcr: Catherine Sacks
Ex VP: Brian Johnston
Ex VP: Michael D Schnur
Ex VP: Kevin Stokes
Sr VP: Carlos Abrantes
Sr VP: Debra Fox
**Sr VP:* Eric Johnson
Sr VP: Frank Johnson
Sr VP: Andy Justice
Sr VP: Daniel Meyer

D-U-N-S 07-413-8629
GUY CHADDOCK & CO
1100 La Avenida St, Mountain View, CA 94043-1452
Tel (408) 907-9200 *Founded/Ownrshp* 1953
Sales 21.9MM^E *EMP* 250
SIC 2512 2521 2511 Upholstered household furniture; Wood office furniture; Wood household furniture

D-U-N-S 04-599-8445
GUY F ATKINSON CONSTRUCTION LLC
(*Suby of* CLARK CONSTRUCTION GROUP LLC) ★
350 Indiana St Ste 600, Golden, CO 80401-5098
Tel (303) 985-1660 *Founded/Ownrshp* 1999, 2000
Sales 250.0MM *EMP* 600
SIC 1611 Highway & street construction; Highway & street construction
Pr: John O'Keefe
VP: Jan Bohn

D-U-N-S 11-742-6510
GUY HOPKINS CONSTRUCTION CO INC
SOUTH LOUISIANA MASONRY
13855 W Amber Ave, Baton Rouge, LA 70809-5440
Tel (225) 751-2158 *Founded/Ownrshp* 1984
Sales 22.8MM^E *EMP* 50
SIC 1542 1541 Nonresidential construction; Industrial buildings & warehouses
Pr: Henry Guy Hopkins III
**VP:* Dennis Gremillion
**VP:* M Collette Lambert
Exec: Colette Lambert

D-U-N-S 00-779-4167
GUY M TURNER INC (NC)
TURNER TRANSFER
4514 S Holden Rd, Greensboro, NC 27406-9510
Tel (336) 294-4660 *Founded/Ownrshp* 1924
Sales 71.4MM *EMP* 250
Accts Sharrard Mcgee & Co Pa Hig
SIC 4213 1796 7389 Heavy machinery transport; Installing building equipment; Machine moving & rigging; Crane & aerial lift service; Heavy machinery transport; Installing building equipment; Machine moving & rigging; Crane & aerial lift service
Pr: Jimmy D Clark
**CFO:* Jeanette A Landreth
**VP:* Robert T Grose
**VP:* Michael W Hoggard
**VP:* Donald W Morrison
**VP:* Joseph White
Genl Mgr: Kirk Patterson
Mtls Mgr: Roger Hixson
Sls Mgr: Robert Ontolchik

D-U-N-S 03-837-2660 IMP/EXP
GUY METALS INC
1890 Guy Metals Dr, Hammond, WI 54015-5089
Tel (715) 796-5858 *Founded/Ownrshp* 1980
Sales 54.8MM^E *EMP* 45
SIC 5051 Steel
Pr: Roger A Young III
**VP:* Guy Young
Rgnl Mgr: Tim McGladdery
Manager: Brady Donahue
Sales Asso: Justin Miller

D-U-N-S 10-378-4570 IMP
GUY POND INC
AIRMAX ECOSYSTEM
15425 Chets Way St, Armada, MI 48005-1160
Tel (586) 589-7663 *Founded/Ownrshp* 2000
Sales 23.7MM^E *EMP* 30
SIC 5191 5261 Garden supplies; Garden supplies & tools
Prin: Jason G Blake
VP Opers: Pond Guy
Sls Mgr: Cary Martin

D-U-N-S 17-325-6991
GUY YOCOM CONSTRUCTION INC
3299 Horseless Carriage R, Norco, CA 92860-3604
Tel (951) 284-3456 *Founded/Ownrshp* 1978
Sales 33.6MM *EMP* 600^E
SIC 1771 Concrete work; Concrete work
Pr: Guy Yocom
**CFO:* Greg Wilson
**Ex VP:* Richard Majestic
VP: John Hamilton
**VP:* Dave Kent
VP: Bill Taylor
Dir IT: Henry May

D-U-N-S 05-630-3894
GUYCO INC
175 Private Road 3020, Lampasas, TX 76550-1452
Tel (512) 556-5451 *Founded/Ownrshp* 1982
Sales 25.1MM *EMP* 45
Accts Angela M Pogue Pc Austin
SIC 1522 1542 Remodeling, multi-family dwellings; Commercial & office buildings, renovation & repair; Remodeling, multi-family dwellings; Commercial & office buildings, renovation & repair
Pr: William L Crawford
**Treas:* Karen Smith
**VP:* Steve Hudson

GUYOUNG TECH
See GU-YOUNG TECH CO LTD

D-U-N-S 61-756-0938 IMP
GUYOUNG TECH USA INC
(*Suby of* GUYOUNG TECH CO., LTD.)
4988 Highway 31, Evergreen, AL 36401-7653
Tel (251) 966-4880 *Founded/Ownrshp* 2004
Sales 13.1MM^E *EMP* 350
SIC 3465 Automotive stampings
Pr: Moo Chan Lee
Sls Mgr: Tay Jun

D-U-N-S 83-727-6179
GUYS FISH INC
5320 W 23rd St Ste 160, Minneapolis, MN 55416-1657
Tel (612) 339-7720 *Founded/Ownrshp* 1995
Sales 20.0MM^E *EMP* 35
SIC 5146 Fish & seafoods
Pr: Mike Hagens
**CFO:* Jim Kuehn

D-U-N-S 18-215-8840 IMP
GUYS NICEST AROUND INC
AUTOWORLD DODGE CHRYSLER JEEP
1370 Auto Center Dr, Petaluma, CA 94952-6507
Tel (707) 762-2712 *Founded/Ownrshp* 1987
Sales 31.3MM^E *EMP* 85
SIC 5511 Automobiles, new & used; Automobiles, new & used
Pr: Victor Gonella
**VP:* Bud Andrews

GUYTON PAINT
See ROLLIE WILLIAMS PAINT SPOT INC

D-U-N-S 03-749-1909
GUZZLER MANUFACTURING INC
1621 S Illinois St, Streator, IL 61364-3945
Tel (815) 672-3171 *Founded/Ownrshp* 1998
Sales 32.4MM^E *EMP* 170
SIC 3559 3561 Automotive related machinery; Industrial pumps & parts; Automotive related machinery; Industrial pumps & parts
Pr: Bill Gass
Exec: Mary Funke
Sls&Mrk Ex: Brian Halstead
Sls&Mrk Ex: Tracy Krebsbach
Sls&Mrk Ex: Steve Shafer
Sls Mgr: Michael Kohn
Sls Mgr: Joe Varca
Sls Mgr: Dan Zelaski

GV MOORE LUMBER CO
See MOORE FAMILY REALTY INC

GVEC
See GUADALUPE VALLEY ELECTRIC COOPERATIVE INC

GVFS
See GREEN VALLEY FARM SUPPLY INC

G.V.G
See GRENE VISION GROUP LLC

D-U-N-S 14-670-7026
GVH DISTRIBUTION LTD
2601 Se Loop 289 Lubbock, Lubbock, TX 79404
Tel (806) 687-5264 *Founded/Ownrshp* 2003
Sales 85.0MM *EMP* 60
SIC 5199 Packaging materials; Packaging materials
Pt: Joe Schmidt
Pt: Buddy Furgerson
Pt: Clay Robinett
Genl Mgr: John Loper

D-U-N-S 03-975-4619 IMP
GVM INC
224 E King St Ste 102, East Berlin, PA 17316-9512
Tel (717) 677-6197 *Founded/Ownrshp* 1977
Sales 25.3MM^E *EMP* 92
SIC 3523 3953 Farm machinery & equipment; Fertilizing machinery, farm; Marking devices; Farm machinery & equipment; Fertilizing machinery, farm; Marking devices
Pr: Mark Anderson
IT Man: Linda Brown
IT Man: Rod Grass
VP Mfg: Guy Muller
VP Mfg: Mark Spaseff
VP Opers: Jim Hansen
Mfg Mgr: Matt Sheaffer
Mktg Dir: Andrea Bell
Mktg Dir: Brett Schlottag
Sls Mgr: Rob Roben

GVS NORTH AMERICA
See MAINE MANUFACTURING LLC

GVTC
See GUADALUPE VALLEY TELEPHONE COOPERATIVE INC

GVTC
See GUADALUPE VALLEY COMMUNICATIONS SYSTEMS INC

D-U-N-S 00-311-2054 IMP
GVW GROUP LLC
GVW HOLDINGS
625 Roger Williams Ave, Highland Park, IL 60035-4807
Tel (847) 926-7697 *Founded/Ownrshp* 2005, 2006
Sales 152.9MM^E *EMP* 406
SIC 3713 Truck bodies (motor vehicles); Truck bodies (motor vehicles)
Ch: Andrew Taitz
CFO: Mark Lecher
**VP:* John Gruber
VP: Jim Sicking
Mng Dir: Eric Schwartz
Dir IT: Troy Henikoff
IT Man: Karen Ibele
Corp Couns: Lacey Cordero
Corp Couns: Katie Knapp

GVW HOLDINGS
See GVW GROUP LLC

D-U-N-S 60-504-7377
GW COMMUNICATIONS LLC
801 Hammond St Ste 375, Coppell, TX 75019-4498
Tel (972) 316-6360 *Founded/Ownrshp* 2005
Sales 26.4MM^E *EMP* 58
SIC 1623 1731 8711 Cable laying construction; Cable television line construction; Telephone & communication line construction; Cable television installation; Consulting engineer
CEO: Robert Kowalski
**COO:* Charlie Middleton
CFO: Gary Chatha
Prac Mgr: Jim McWhorter

D-U-N-S 14-336-7030
GW CONSULTING INC
GARDAWORLD
(*Suby of* CORPORATION DE SECURITE GARDA WORLD)
1101 Wilson Blvd Ste 1725, Arlington, VA 22209-2293
Tel (703) 253-8080 *Founded/Ownrshp* 2009
Sales 47.1MM^E *EMP* 2,500^E
SIC 7381 Detective services; Detective services
CEO: Oliver Westmacott
**Treas:* Deborah Ray
**Sec:* Brent Wegner
**Sr VP:* Peter Dordal Jr
VP: Nicole Watson

D-U-N-S 06-191-5534
GW HUNTER INC (FL)
HUNTER OIL
1130 W Us Highway 90, Lake City, FL 32055-3750
Tel (386) 758-7507 *Founded/Ownrshp* 1975, 1972
Sales 50.0MM *EMP* 7
SIC 5171 Petroleum bulk stations; Petroleum bulk stations
CEO: Terry L Hunter
**Sec:* John B Hunter
**VP:* George D Hunter

D-U-N-S 00-221-7834 IMP
GW LISK CO INC
2 South St, Clifton Springs, NY 14432-1118
Tel (315) 462-2611 *Founded/Ownrshp* 1953
Sales 113.1MM^E *EMP* 750
SIC 3679 4119 3492

D-U-N-S 79-261-7854 IMP
GW PLASTICS SAN ANTONIO INC
(*Suby of* G W PLASTICS INC) ★
901 Paulsun St, San Antonio, TX 78219-3125
Tel (210) 225-1516 *Founded/Ownrshp* 1992
Sales 60.2MM^E *EMP* 200
SIC 3089 Injection molding of plastics; Injection molding of plastics
Pr: Brenan Riehlk
**Treas:* Thomas Johansen
VP: Art Bennert
**VP:* Arthur Bennert
VP: Benjamin Bouchard
Sfty Mgr: Ed Immel
Opers Mgr: Karl Hellsten
Plnt Mgr: Rafael Sojo
Plnt Mgr: Javier Zamorano
Sls Mgr: Ed Oswald

D-U-N-S 07-047-2209 IMP
GW PLASTICS TUCSON INC
(*Suby of* G W PLASTICS INC) ★
2901 E Valencia Rd, Tucson, AZ 85706-5920
Tel (520) 294-9400 *Founded/Ownrshp* 1995
Sales 81.1MM^E *EMP* 230
SIC 3089 Injection molding of plastics
Pr: Benjamin Riehl
**CFO:* Thomas G Johansen
VP: Terrence Hamm
**VP:* Timothy Holmes
**VP:* Timothy Reis
Exec: Alan Gorman
Web Dev: Eleanor Carpenter
Prd Mgr: Joe Ruiz

D-U-N-S 07-953-1828
■ **GW&K INVESTMENT MANAGEMENT LLC**
(*Suby of* AFFILIATED MANAGERS GROUP INC) ★
222 Berkeley St Ste 1500, Boston, MA 02116-3761
Tel (617) 236-8900 *Founded/Ownrshp* 2008
Sales 25.6MM^E *EMP* 71
SIC 6282 Investment advisory service
CEO: Harold G Kotler
**Pr:* Thomas Fx Powers
Sr VP: Nancy G Anel
**Sr VP:* Nancy G Angel
Sr VP: Nancy G Angell
VP: Phillip Anspach
VP: Scott Baughman
VP: Cynthia Brown
VP: John M Castro
VP: John Castro
VP: Joseph Chimenti
VP: David Claus
VP: Charles Devens III

VP: Dino Difronzo
VP: Thomas Duff
VP: Eileen M Durey
VP: John Gaines
VP: Gabriela Greenman
VP: Mark R Gudaitis
VP: Taras Huzar
VP: Mary Kane

GWAEA
See GRANT WOOD AREA EDUCATION AGENCY

GWALTNEY OF SMITHFIELD
See SMITHFIELD PACKING CO INC

GWATNEY BUICK GMC
See NORTH LITTLE ROCK PONTIAC -BUICK-GMC INC

D-U-N-S 07-857-6352
GWATNEY CHEVROLET INC
GWATNEY ISUZU
2000 Covington Pike, Memphis, TN 38128-6982
Tel (901) 387-2000 *Founded/Ownrshp* 1988
Sales 22.9MM^E *EMP* 100
SIC 5511 Automobiles, new & used; Pickups, new & used; Automobiles, new & used; Pickups, new & used
Pr: J Russell Gwatney
**Treas:* Syble E Gwatney
**VP:* William A Gwatney
Sls Mgr: Zak Imam

GWATNEY CHEVROLET/GEO
See HAROLD GWATNEY CHEVROLET CO

GWATNEY ISUZU
See GWATNEY CHEVROLET INC

D-U-N-S 93-249-1798
GWC WARRANTY CORP
G W C
40 Coal St, Wilkes Barre, PA 18702-5236
Tel (570) 414-7777 *Founded/Ownrshp* 2013
Sales NA *EMP* 112
SIC 6399 Warranty insurance, automobile
Pr: Robert Glander
**CFO:* Paul Dreabit
VP: Mike Melby
Rgnl Mgr: Joe Kuhta
VP Opers: Joseph Brennan
VP Sls: Chris Barry
Mktg Dir: Kate Eltringham

D-U-N-S 00-726-2728
GWD LTD (NE)
GERKIN WINDOW & DOORS
5000 Rhino Rd, South Sioux City, NE 68776-3872
Tel (402) 494-6000 *Founded/Ownrshp* 1932, 1991
Sales 27.6MM *EMP* 150
Accts Henjesconner & Williams Pc
SIC 3442 Screen & storm doors & windows; Screen & storm doors & windows
Pr: Steve W Schneider
**Ch:* Otto Schneider
**Sec:* Paul W Schneider
VP Sls: Scott Gerkin

D-U-N-S 08-811-9149
GWF ENERGY LLC
14590 W Schulte Rd, Tracy, CA 95377
Tel (925) 766-7532 *Founded/Ownrshp* 2001
Sales 25.4MM^E *EMP* 33
SIC 4911 Generation, electric power
Pr: Malcolm Jacobson
**CFO:* Eric Miller

D-U-N-S 18-989-0705
GWFS EQUITIES INC
(*Suby of* GREAT WEST FINANCIAL) ★
8515 E Orchard Rd, Greenwood Village, CO 80111-5002
Tel (303) 737-3817 *Founded/Ownrshp* 1984
Sales 366.4MM *EMP* 16
Accts Deloitte & Touche Llp Denver
SIC 6211 Brokers, security; Dealers, security; Brokers, security; Dealers, security
Ch Bd: CP Nelson
Chf Cred: Ba Byrne
Ex VP: Rk Shaw
Sr VP: Ch Cumming
Sr VP: Ws Harmon
Sr VP: Rj Laeyendecker
Sr VP: GE Seller
VP: SA Bendrick
VP: C Bergeon
VP: SA Ghazaleh
VP: Judith G Gibbs
VP: SM Gile
VP: Brent Neese

D-U-N-S 01-299-2613
GWG HOLDINGS INC
220 S 6th St Ste 1200, Minneapolis, MN 55402-4512
Tel (877) 494-2388 *Founded/Ownrshp* 2008
Sales NA *EMP* 46
Accts Baker Tilly Virchow Krause Ll
Tkr Sym GWGH *Exch* NAS
SIC 6311 8748 Life insurance; Business consulting; Life insurance; Business consulting
CEO: Jon R Sabes
**Ch Bd:* Paul Siegert
**Pr:* Steve Sabes
**COO:* Jon Gangelhoff
**CFO:* William Acheson
Bd of Dir: Charles Maguire
**Chf Mktg O:* Chris Maddox
Sr VP: Jason Plucinak
Dir Bus: Tim Whitmore
IT Man: Dale Kalsow
Snr Mgr: Beau Mayfield

GWI
See WILLIAMSON GOFORTH INC

D-U-N-S 03-183-1977
GWINNER FARMERS ELEVATOR
108 1st St Nw, Gwinner, ND 58040-4015
Tel (701) 678-2468 *Founded/Ownrshp* 1914
Sales 75.4MM *EMP* 20
SIC 5153 5191 Grain elevators; Farm supplies; Feed; Seeds: field, garden & flower; Fertilizer & fertilizer materials; Grain elevators; Farm supplies; Feed; Seeds: field, garden & flower; Fertilizer & fertilizer materials
Pr: Dan Jacobson

D-U-N-S 80-861-7166
GWINNETT AUTO MALL LLC
AUTOMALL OF GEORGIA, THE
3505 Buford Dr, Buford, GA 30519-4907
Tel (678) 957-9161 *Founded/Ownrshp* 1999
Sales 58.6MM^E *EMP* 200^E
SIC 5511 Automobiles, new & used; Automobiles, new & used
Ch: John Williams
Exec: Russ Patrick
Off Mgr: Candyce Brown
Sls Mgr: Patrick Berwise
Sls Mgr: John Duran
Sls Mgr: Willie Littleton
Sls Mgr: Justin McCain
Sls Mgr: Harley Wyman
Sales Asso: Travis Covin

D-U-N-S 14-847-8753
GWINNETT AUTOMOTIVE SERVICE INC
GWINNETT PLACE HONDA
3325 Satellite Blvd, Duluth, GA 30096-4642
Tel (678) 957-5000 *Founded/Ownrshp* 1982
Sales 71.8MM^E *EMP* 200
SIC 5511 7538 Automobiles, new & used; General automotive repair shops; Automobiles, new & used; General automotive repair shops
Pr: J R Hendrick III
**Sec:* James F Huzl
VP: Randy Hughes
Exec: Danny Whang

D-U-N-S 08-697-3195
GWINNETT COUNTY BOARD OF EDUCATION
437 Old Peachtree Rd Nw, Suwanee, GA 30024-2978
Tel (678) 301-6000 *Founded/Ownrshp* 1890
Sales 639.2MM^E *EMP* 20,000
SIC 8211 Public elementary & secondary schools; Public elementary & secondary schools
Dir IT: Mark Walls
IT Man: Deana Triemer
HC Dir: David Johns

D-U-N-S 05-727-2734
GWINNETT COUNTY GOVERNMENT
GWINNETT JUSTICE AND ADM CTR
75 Langley Dr, Lawrenceville, GA 30046-6935
Tel (770) 822-8000 *Founded/Ownrshp* 1818
Sales NA *EMP* 4,000
Accts Mauldin & Jenkins Llc Atlant
SIC 9111 ;
Ofcr: David Bell
Ofcr: Julian Bruce
Ofcr: Maritza Felger
Ofcr: Kendrick Gregory
Ofcr: Tiffany Hall
Ofcr: Stanley Jones
Ofcr: Melinda Lahr
Ofcr: Amy Noggle
Ofcr: Rebecca Reivitis
Ofcr: Kimberly Scott
VP: Alice Johnson
Dir Risk M: Bill Swiger
Board of Directors: Charles Bannisster, Lorraine Treen-District On, Bert Nasuti-District Two, Mike Beaudreau-District th, Kevin Kenerly-District Fou

D-U-N-S 13-307-2165
GWINNETT COUNTY PUBLIC LIBRARY
1001 Lawrenceville Hwy, Lawrenceville, GA 30046-4707
Tel (770) 822-5336 *Founded/Ownrshp* 1937
Sales 14.1MM^E *EMP* 380
SIC 8231 General public libraries; General public libraries
Ofcr: Deidre Falcon
Ex Dir: Charles Pace
Brnch Mgr: Leslie Clark
Brnch Mgr: Gail Evans
Brnch Mgr: Kari Evans
Brnch Mgr: Leigh Skowronski
Dir IT: Michael Casey

D-U-N-S 07-951-6185
GWINNETT COUNTY PUBLIC SCHOOLS
437 Old Peachtree Rd Nw, Suwanee, GA 30024-2978
Tel (678) 301-6000 *Founded/Ownrshp* 2014
Sales 521.3MM^E *EMP* 20,000^E
SIC 8211 Public elementary & secondary schools; Public elementary & secondary schools
Dir: Greg Stanfield
Dir Sec: Wayne Rikard
CIO: Scot Futrell
CTO: Rick Overton
MIS Dir: Frank Elmore
Dir IT: Amanda Scott
Netwrk Eng: Donald Telander
Pr Dir: Laura Nurse
Teacher Pr: Sid Camp
Instr Medi: Mary Barbee
HC Dir: Kim M Smith

D-U-N-S 05-126-8193
GWINNETT COUNTY SCHOOL DST
ARCHER HIGH SCHOOL
(*Suby of* GWINNETT COUNTY BOARD OF EDUCATION) ★
2255 New Hope Rd, Lawrenceville, GA 30045-6560
Tel (678) 407-7700 *Founded/Ownrshp* 2010
Sales 52.7MM^E *EMP* 5,029^E
SIC 8211 Public junior high school
Prin: J Alvin Wilbanks

D-U-N-S 01-876-8684
GWINNETT HEALTH SYSTEM INC
1000 Medical Center Blvd, Lawrenceville, GA 30046-7694
Tel (678) 312-1000 *Founded/Ownrshp* 1993
Sales 642.2MM^E *EMP* 2,050^E
Accts Draffin & Tucker Llp Albany
SIC 8062 General medical & surgical hospitals; General medical & surgical hospitals
CEO: Philip R Wolfe
**Pr:* Franklin Rinker
**CFO:* Thomas Y McBride
Bd of Dir: Kelly Dunham
Ofcr: Carol Regan
VP: Michael Boblitz
VP: Wallace Brown
Dir Rx: Michael Naughton
Off Admin: Heather Boyce
Off Admin: Angela Hamlet
MIS Dir: Kevin Aureleo

D-U-N-S 07-587-7290
GWINNETT HOSPITAL SYSTEM INC
MEDCARE
(*Suby of* GWINNETT HEALTH SYSTEM INC) ★
1000 Medical Center Blvd, Lawrenceville, GA 30046-7694
Tel (678) 343-3428 *Founded/Ownrshp* 1956
Sales 642.1MM *EMP* 2,050
Accts Kpmg Llp Atlanta Georgia
SIC 8062 General medical & surgical hospitals; General medical & surgical hospitals
CEO: Philip R Wolfe
**Pr:* Lea Bay
**Pr:* Jason Chandler
**Pr:* Franklin M Rinker
**COO:* Jay Dennard
**COO:* Thomas Karr
COO: Jeff Nowlin
**CFO:* Thomas Y Mc Bride III
CFO: Tommy McBride III
Bd of Dir: Greg Shumate
Ofcr: Karen Walsh
**Ex VP:* Alan Bier
**Sr VP:* Ed Brown
**Sr VP:* Patty Lavely
**VP:* Georgia P Brogdon
Dir Risk M: Suzanne Compau
Dir Lab: Rhonda Hairston
Dir Lab: Pamela Henderson

D-U-N-S 16-331-9432 IMP
GWINNETT INTERNATIONAL FARMERS MARKET INC
3825 Shackleford Rd, Duluth, GA 30096-8269
Tel (770) 921-8288 *Founded/Ownrshp* 2004
Sales 38.0MM^E *EMP* 105^E
SIC 5141 Groceries, general line; Groceries, general line
CEO: Yong D Kim
Genl Mgr: Alice Kim

GWINNETT JUSTICE AND ADM CTR
See GWINNETT COUNTY GOVERNMENT

D-U-N-S 01-107-6900
GWINNETT MEDICAL SERVICES INC
GMSI
1000 Medical Center Blvd, Lawrenceville, GA 30046-7694
Tel (678) 312-4160 *Founded/Ownrshp* 1994
Sales 63.3MM *EMP* 18
Accts Draffin & Tucker Llp Albany
SIC 8062 General medical & surgical hospitals; General medical & surgical hospitals
CEO: Philip R Wolfe
**CFO:* Thomas Y McBride III
Surgeon: Nala D Avery

D-U-N-S 03-356-5029
GWINNETT PLACE CHEVROLET LLC
HENDRICKS CHEVROLET
3277 Satellite Blvd, Duluth, GA 30096-9094
Tel (678) 957-5400 *Founded/Ownrshp* 1957
Sales 30.6MM^E *EMP* 83
SIC 5511 Automobiles, new & used; Pickups, new & used; Automobiles, new & used; Pickups, new & used
Exec: Darla Leistiko
Exec: Joann Mathews
Exec: Billy Pickering
Sls Mgr: Eric King

GWINNETT PLACE FORD
See GAFVT MOTORS INC

GWINNETT PLACE HONDA
See GWINNETT AUTOMOTIVE SERVICE INC

GWINNETT PLACE NISSAN
See GANVT MOTORS INC

D-U-N-S 07-887-0125
GWINNETT TECHNICAL COLLEGE
5150 Sugarloaf Pkwy, Lawrenceville, GA 30043-5702
Tel (770) 962-7580 *Founded/Ownrshp* 2013
Sales 22.6MM^E *EMP* 210^E
SIC 8299 Educational services
Pr: Sharon Rigsby
Ex Dir: Richard Ludwig
CTO: Elzey Jeff
Dir IT: Skip Jordan
Pgrm Dir: Dennis Bowers

D-U-N-S 09-794-1785
GWINS TRAVEL PLANNERS INC
111 N Taylor Ave Stop 1, Kirkwood, MO 63122-4374
Tel (314) 822-1940 *Founded/Ownrshp* 1979
Sales 25.0MM *EMP* 40
SIC 4724 8741 Travel agencies; Management services; Travel agencies; Management services
CEO: Gig W Gwin
**Pr:* Jerry Kaminski
**Treas:* Teresa Gwin

D-U-N-S 14-569-4753
GWL&A FINANCIAL INC
GREAT WEST FINANCIAL
(*Suby of* GREAT-WEST LIFE ASSURANCE COMPANY, THE)
8515 E Orchard Rd Ste 2t3, Greenwood Village, CO 80111-5002
Tel (303) 737-3000 *Founded/Ownrshp* 2003
Sales 2.8MMM^E *EMP* 6,600
SIC 6211 6311 Investment holding companies, except banks; Investment firm, general brokerage; Life insurance
Ch Bd: Robert Gratton
Pr: Charles P Nelson
CEO: Robert L Reynolds
Ex VP: SM Corbett
Ex VP: Robert K Shaw
Sr VP: Miles R Edwards
Sr VP: Ernie P Friesen
Sr VP: David McLeod
Sr VP: RG Schultz
Sr VP: Jh Van Harmelen
VP: Rm Southall

D-U-N-S 96-513-2793
GWL&A INS CO EMPLOYEE WELFARE BENEFIT PLAN
8525 E Orchard Rd, Greenwood Village, CO 80111-5002
Tel (303) 737-3000 *Founded/Ownrshp* 2010
Sales NA *EMP* 2
SIC 6411 Insurance agents, brokers & service; Insurance agents, brokers & service
Prin: James L McCallen

D-U-N-S 94-050-5790 IMP
GWLA ACQUISITION CORP
8600 Rheem Ave, South Gate, CA 90280-3333
Tel (323) 789-7800 *Founded/Ownrshp* 2002
Sales 69.9MM^E *EMP* 400^E
SIC 3211 3231 6719 Tempered glass; Mirrored glass; Investment holding companies, except banks; Tempered glass; Mirrored glass; Investment holding companies, except banks
Pr: Randy Steinberg
CFO: Michael Torres

D-U-N-S 06-715-4682
GWP HOLDINGS LLC
WESTERN PETERBILT
3801 Airport Way S, Seattle, WA 98108-5213
Tel (206) 624-7383 *Founded/Ownrshp* 2014
Sales 116.7MM^E *EMP* 300
SIC 5511 7513 7538 5012 Trucks, tractors & trailers: new & used; Truck leasing, without drivers; General automotive repair shops; Automobiles & other motor vehicles; Trucks, tractors & trailers: new & used; Truck leasing, without drivers; General automotive repair shops; Automobiles & other motor vehicles
CEO: Frank Anglin
**CFO:* Bill Helenberg
Info Man: Roger Martindell

D-U-N-S 00-433-0098 IMP/EXP
GWP INDUSTRIES INC (DE)
822 Depot St, Parkersburg, WV 26101-5249
Tel (304) 422-3103 *Founded/Ownrshp* 2000
Sales NA *EMP* 325^E
SIC 7389 4783 4953 4225

D-U-N-S 83-081-5994
GWTM LLC
(*Suby of* GREATWIDE LOGISTICS SERVICES LLC) ★
12404 Park Central Dr 300s, Dallas, TX 75251-1800
Tel (972) 228-7344 *Founded/Ownrshp* 2008
Sales 39.5MM^E *EMP* 135
SIC 4213 Trucking, except local
CEO: Robert C Larose
**Sec:* John N Hove
**Sr VP:* Michael J Skipworth
**VP:* Edward A Barnes
**VP:* Jeff Lester
**VP:* Michael Skipworth
**VP:* Joseph Wojceichowski

GWU MEDICAL FACULTY ASSOCIATES
See MEDICAL FACULTY ASSOCIATES INC

D-U-N-S 96-324-4871
■ **GXS GROUP INC**
(*Suby of* OPEN TEXT CORPORATION)
9711 Washingtonian Blvd, Gaithersburg, MD 20878-7365
Tel (301) 340-4000 *Founded/Ownrshp* 2014
Sales 95.6MM^E *EMP* 3,000
SIC 7372 Prepackaged software; Prepackaged software
Pr: Mark J Barrenechea

D-U-N-S 03-530-2503
GXS HOLDINGS INC
100 Edison Park Dr, Gaithersburg, MD 20878-3209
Tel (301) 340-5370 *Founded/Ownrshp* 2010
Sales NA *EMP* 3,000
SIC 6719 Investment holding companies, except banks; Investment holding companies, except banks
CEO: Gary Greenfield
Pr: Michael Schwab
Ex VP: Hamid Mohyi
VP: Daniel Casco
VP: Gary Randolph
VP: George Schulze
Prgrm Mgr: Judy Lyons
Snr Sftwr: Steven Bixby
Snr Sftwr: Ray Chu
Snr Sftwr: Joe Dorman
Snr Sftwr: Rob Gillen

D-U-N-S 92-716-6082
■ **GXS INC**
GE GLOBAL EXCHANGE SERVICES
(*Suby of* OPEN TEXT CORPORATION)
9711 Washingtonian Blvd # 5, Gaithersburg, MD 20878-7365
Tel (301) 340-4000 *Founded/Ownrshp* 2014
Sales 349.4MM^E *EMP* 779^E
SIC 7374 Data processing & preparation
Pr: Mark J Barrenechea
COO: Tom Thomas
CFO: Jean Charhon
**CFO:* Gregg Clevenger
Chf Mktg O: Robert E Fair
**Ex VP:* Karl Salnoske
Ex VP: Steven Scala
Ex VP: David Swanlaw
Sr VP: Clara Bart
Sr VP: Chris Beall

VP: Swanlaw David
**VP:* David Goldberg
VP: Duncan Robb
VP: Pat Salmonese
VP: Karl D Salnoske
VP: Jeff Stewart
VP: Raymond Teh
Exec: Mark Shooman
Dir: Steven Hillon
Dir Bus: Lentz Robert

D-U-N-S 14-545-1253
■ GXS WORLDWIDE INC
OPENTEXT GXS
(*Suby of* OPEN TEXT CORPORATION)
9711 Washingtonian Blvd # 5, Gaithersburg, MD 20878-7365
Tel (301) 340-4000 *Founded/Ownrshp* 2014
Sales 68.3MM^E *EMP* 400^E
SIC 7373 7372 Computer integrated systems design; Prepackaged software; Computer integrated systems design; Prepackaged software
CEO: Robert Segert
COO: Corrie Jackson
Ex VP: Gregg Clevenger
VP: Terry Goodwin
VP: Edward Murphy
VP: Susan Popyer
VP: Gary Randolph
Exec: Nancy Stough
Dir IT: Deborah Berryman
Telecom Mg: Clara Bart
IT Man: Fernando Camp

D-U-N-S 18-930-4269
GYANSYS INC
702 Adams St, Carmel, IN 46032-7541
Tel (317) 580-4200 *Founded/Ownrshp* 2005
Sales 56.7MM^E *EMP* 400
SIC 7379 Computer related consulting services
Pr: Rajkishore Una
**COO:* Arun Kotagiri
**COO:* Chuck Stahl
**CFO:* Padmaja Una
**Ex VP:* Prem Desai
**VP:* Michael Van Der Breggan
VP: Neeraj Sahu
VP Sls: Arpit Bitta
Sls Dir: Satya Gandikota
Board of Directors: Adrian Jagow, Tom Martin

D-U-N-S 07-940-0116
GYM SOURCE USA LLC
40 E 52nd St Frnt B, New York, NY 10022-5911
Tel (212) 688-4222 *Founded/Ownrshp* 2013
Sales 24.6MM^E *EMP* 300
SIC 5941 Exercise equipment; Exercise equipment
Pr: Richard Miller
**CFO:* Richard Jannelli
**Sr VP:* William Kemnitzer
**VP:* Tom Staub
Store Mgr: Terry Klysz
Store Mgr: Otis Lester
Store Mgr: Mark Zaleski

D-U-N-S 03-885-5029 IMP
GYMBOREE CORP
(*Suby of* GIRAFFE HOLDING INC) ★
500 Howard St, San Francisco, CA 94105-3000
Tel (415) 278-7000 *Founded/Ownrshp* 2010
Sales 1.2MMM *EMP* 14,716
SIC 5641 Children's & infants' wear stores; Children's & infants' wear stores; Children's wear; Infants' wear
CEO: Mark Breitbard
COO: Joelle Maher
CFO: Blair Lambert
CFO: Andrew B North
Treas: F Mario Petrocco
Treas: Mario F Petrocco
Ofcr: Lisa Tam
Sr VP: Kenneth F Meyers
VP: Della Berger
VP: Troy Berry
VP: Joann H Davis
VP: Katherine Green
VP: Deborah Nash
VP: Susan Neal
VP: Victor Spina
VP: Laura Wilkin
VP: Laura Willensky
Board of Directors: Joshua Bekenstein, Yvonne Hao, Jordan Hitch, Marko Kivisto, Lewis Klessel

D-U-N-S 02-449-5447 IMP
GYMBOREE MANUFACTURING INC (CA)
(*Suby of* GYMBOREE CORP) ★
500 Howard St Fl 2, San Francisco, CA 94105-3027
Tel (415) 278-7000 *Founded/Ownrshp* 1994
Sales 51.7MM^E *EMP* 500
SIC 5641 Children's & infants' wear stores; Children's & infants' wear stores
CEO: Mark Breitbrad
**CFO:* Blair Lambert
**Prin:* Evan Price

D-U-N-S 19-602-5712
GYPSUM EXPRESS LTD
8280 Sixty Rd, Baldwinsville, NY 13027-1232
Tel (315) 638-2201 *Founded/Ownrshp* 1985
Sales 96.6MM^E *EMP* 650
SIC 4212 4213 Local trucking, without storage; Trucking, except local; Local trucking, without storage; Trucking, except local
Ch Bd: John Wight
COO: Jerry Harris
CFO: Janet Gmyr
**VP:* John Zink
IT Man: Jason Lamoureaux
Sfty Dirs: Dennis Plucinik
Trfc Dir: Joni Kern

D-U-N-S 06-273-3332 IMP
GYPSUM MANAGEMENT AND SUPPLY INC
G M S
100 Crescent Center Pkwy # 800, Tucker, GA 30084-7062
Tel (770) 939-1711 *Founded/Ownrshp* 1972
Sales 844.3MM^E *EMP* 3,000
SIC 5032 8742

D-U-N-S 09-780-3209
GYPSUM SUPPLY CO
ABBOTT ASSOCIATES
859 74th St Sw, Byron Center, MI 49315-8379
Tel (616) 583-9300 *Founded/Ownrshp* 1979
Sales 118.6MM^E *EMP* 183
SIC 5032 Brick, stone & related material; Drywall materials; Brick, stone & related material; Drywall materials
Pr: Todd Grasman
**Pr:* Roger Abbott
**Treas:* Don Offringa
**VP:* James Abbott
**VP:* Michael Holbrook
Corp Couns: Mary Osborn

D-U-N-S 09-530-1198
GYPSUM SUPPLY CO
1125 Harrison Ave, Rockford, IL 61104-7293
Tel (815) 397-5718 *Founded/Ownrshp* 1978
Sales 126.7MM^E *EMP* 150
SIC 5032 Plastering materials; Plastering materials; Drywall materials
Pr: James M Gabelbauer
**Sec:* Rich Taeglow
Brnch Mgr: Doug Davenport
IT Man: Jeff Jaeger
Opers Mgr: John Cummings
Opers Mgr: Angelo Flores
Opers Mgr: Kory Gehring
Opers Mgr: Brandon Greetham
Opers Mgr: Mario Hernandez
Opers Mgr: Bob Scott
Opers Mgr: Scott Small

D-U-N-S 07-160-6354
GYPSUM WHOLESALERS INC
3334 Walters Rd, Syracuse, NY 13209-9759
Tel (315) 451-5322 *Founded/Ownrshp* 1974
Sales 35.0MM^E *EMP* 50
SIC 5032 5033 5039 5031 5051 Drywall materials; Insulation materials; Ceiling systems & products; Millwork; Iron & steel (ferrous) products
Pr: John C Wight
Sales Exec: Brad Emmick
Snr Mgr: Michael Flynn

D-U-N-S 79-002-0460
GYRO LLC
HSR BUSINESS TO BUSINESS
7755 Montgomery Rd # 300, Cincinnati, OH 45236-4291
Tel (513) 671-3811 *Founded/Ownrshp* 1999
Sales 40.0MM *EMP* 138
SIC 7311 Advertising agencies; Advertising agencies
CEO: Richard A Segal Jr
**CFO:* Pam Brosch
**Chf Cred:* Tom Rentschler
**Ex VP:* Michael Hensley
Sr VP: John Dobbs
VP: Frannie J Danzinger
VP: Pattie Kushner
VP: Carolyn Ladd
Creative D: Barrett Condy
Creative D: Don Dunbar
Creative D: Greg Fioretti
Creative D: Carolyn Frank
Creative D: Devin Grimes
Creative D: Doug Kamp
Creative D: Sarah Lyons
Creative D: Jaime Schwarz
Creative D: Ted Wahlberg
Comm Man: Stephanie Mohorn

D-U-N-S 02-460-1718 IMP/EXP
GYRODATA INC (DE)
23000 Nw Lake Dr, Houston, TX 77095-5344
Tel (713) 461-3146 *Founded/Ownrshp* 1980
Sales 522.3MM^E *EMP* 300
SIC 1389 8713 Oil field services; Surveying services; Oil field services; Surveying services
CEO: Steve Klopp
Pr: Bob McMahan
COO: Angela Lunan
CFO: Robert B Trainer Jr
Treas: Robert Trainer Jr
VP: Rob Shoup
VP: Gary Uttecht
VP: Johnathan Wilcox
Area Mgr: Kris Earl
Dist Mgr: Donny Detliff
Dist Mgr: Dean Sheppard

GYRUS ACMI
See GYRUS MEDICAL INC

D-U-N-S 00-719-8742 IMP
GYRUS ACMI INC
A C M I
(*Suby of* OLYMPUS CORP OF AMERICAS) ★
136 Turnpike Rd Ste 300, Southborough, MA 01772-2118
Tel (508) 804-2600 *Founded/Ownrshp* 2007
Sales 200.2MM^E *EMP* 870
SIC 3841 5047 Surgical & medical instruments; Surgical & medical instruments; Medical equipment & supplies
CEO: Roy Davis
**CFO:* Simon Shaw
VP: Mark Jensen
CTO: James Frassica
MIS Dir: Mark Feldman
QA Dir: Vance Myers
Dir IT: Bill Forrestall
IT Man: Ketan Patel
Mfg Mgr: Domenick Di Preta
VP Sls: Nils Ericson
Sls Dir: Jason Bening

D-U-N-S 00-833-8030
GYRUS ACMI LP
(*Suby of* A C M I) ★
9600 Louisiana Ave N, Minneapolis, MN 55445-3280
Tel (763) 416-3000 *Founded/Ownrshp* 2007
Sales 101.3MM^E *EMP* 867
SIC 3841 Surgical & medical instruments; Surgical & medical instruments
Pr: Jim Hershner
VP: Laurence Hicks
VP: Albert M Juergens
VP: Gary Mell
Ql Cn Mgr: Joel Collins
Ql Cn Mgr: Brent Traynor

D-U-N-S 14-759-0566 IMP
GYRUS MEDICAL INC
GYRUS ACMI
(*Suby of* A C M I) ★
6655 Wedgwood Rd N # 160, Maple Grove, MN 55311-3601
Tel (763) 416-3000 *Founded/Ownrshp* 2001
Sales 44.2MM^E *EMP* 240
SIC 3845 Electromedical apparatus; Electromedical apparatus
Prin: Georg Schloer
VP: Steve Blakemore
IT Man: Chuck Vrchota
Mtls Mgr: Laurk Iverson

D-U-N-S 05-345-2827
GZA GEOENVIRONMENTAL INC
(*Suby of* GZA GEOENVIRONMENTAL TECHNOLOGIES INC) ★
249 Vanderbilt Ave, Norwood, MA 02062-5033
Tel (781) 278-3700 *Founded/Ownrshp* 1989
Sales 91.0MM^E *EMP* 380
SIC 8711 8734 Consulting engineer; Soil analysis; Consulting engineer; Soil analysis
Pr: William R Beloff
COO: Daniel Tilley
**CFO:* Joseph P Hehir
Exec: Andrew Pajak
Off Mgr: Kathleen Cyr
Dir IT: Mark Howlank
IT Man: Donna McLane
Sfty Mgr: Rick Eckard
Snr PM: Nathaniel Arai
Snr PM: John Colbert
Snr PM: Guy Dalton

D-U-N-S 60-266-5812
GZA GEOENVIRONMENTAL TECHNOLOGIES INC
249 Vanderbilt Ave Unit 2, Norwood, MA 02062-5033
Tel (781) 278-3700 *Founded/Ownrshp* 1964
Sales 91.0MM^E *EMP* 455
SIC 8711 8999 1799 8744 Pollution control engineering; Building construction consultant; Geological consultant; Boring for building construction; ; Pollution control engineering; Building construction consultant; Geological consultant; Boring for building construction;
CEO: Bill Beloff
CFO: Joseph Hehir
VP: David Hassrick

H

H & A
See HANTZ FINANCIAL SERVICES INC

H & B
See HUNT & BEHRENS INC

D-U-N-S 05-154-7419
H & C FOOD INC
1300 Metropolitan Ave, Brooklyn, NY 11237-1104
Tel (718) 821-9188 *Founded/Ownrshp* 2015
Sales 50.0MM *EMP* 60
SIC 5148 Fresh fruits & vegetables
Pr: Sailu Pan

D-U-N-S 62-551-1282 IMP
H & C HEADWEAR INC
KING'S CAPS
17145 Margay Ave, Carson, CA 90746-1209
Tel (310) 324-5263 *Founded/Ownrshp* 1991
Sales 41.9MM^E *EMP* 100^E
SIC 5136 6794 Caps, men's & boys'; Copyright buying & licensing
CEO: Shun On Ngan
**Pr:* John Lee
Exec: Chuck Schoonover
**Prin:* Ken Feldman
Mng Dir: Tracey Cloth
Dir IT: Buddy Chang
Mktg Dir: Dennis Avila

D-U-N-S 02-902-9626
H & D ELECTRIC
5237 Walnut Ave Ste 100, Sacramento, CA 95841-2694
Tel (916) 332-0794 *Founded/Ownrshp* 1957
Sales 40.6MM^E *EMP* 360
SIC 1731 General electrical contractor; General electrical contractor
Pr: Mark E Cooper

H & D STEEL SERVICE CENTER
See H & D STEEL SERVICE INC

D-U-N-S 06-408-6424 IMP
H & D STEEL SERVICE INC
H & D STEEL SERVICE CENTER
9960 York Alpha Dr, North Royalton, OH 44133-3588
Tel (440) 237-3390 *Founded/Ownrshp* 1972
Sales 56.8MM^E *EMP* 50
SIC 5051 Iron or steel flat products; Sheets, metal; Tubing, metal; Bars, metal; Home workshop machine tools, metalworking; Industrial tools
Ch Bd: Raymond Gary Schreiber
**Pr:* Joseph Bubba
**VP:* James P Schreiber
**Prin:* Joseph A Cachat
**Prin:* R M Jones
**Prin:* R G Schreiber
Sales Exec: Scott Sustar
Sls&Mrk Ex: John Gustafston

D-U-N-S 06-109-9669 IMP
H & F GULF INC
H&F TIRE SERVICE
1834 Lincoln Hwy E, Lancaster, PA 17602-3344
Tel (717) 392-6793 *Founded/Ownrshp* 1969
Sales 101.3MM^E *EMP* 70
SIC 5014 5531 Automobile tires & tubes; Automotive tires; Automobile tires & tubes; Automotive tires
Pr: Barry Lee Fitzgerald
**Sec:* Mary Ann Fitzgerald

D-U-N-S 08-977-6819
H & F MANUFACTURING CO INC
8949 Zachary Ln N, Maple Grove, MN 55369-4006
Tel (763) 493-5606 *Founded/Ownrshp* 1978
Sales 21.9MM^E *EMP* 75
SIC 3444 Sheet metalwork
Pr: Richard M Farniok Sr
**VP:* Steve Farniok
QA Dir: Ed Gallagher

D-U-N-S 02-978-6357
H & G SALES INC
SCHULTZ DOOR
11635 Lackland Rd, Saint Louis, MO 63146-3562
Tel (314) 432-8188 *Founded/Ownrshp* 1967
Sales 20.1MM^E *EMP* 72
SIC 5072 5031

D-U-N-S 19-217-2158
H & GL FUNDS OF NJ
700 Raymond Blvd, Newark, NJ 07105-2909
Tel (973) 589-5056 *Founded/Ownrshp* 2005
Sales 116.8MM *EMP* 13^E
SIC 8699 Charitable organization; Charitable organization
CFO: Hema Gandhi
Dir IT: Susie Lopes

D-U-N-S 02-075-1327
H & H AGENCY INC (CA)
20351 Sw Acacia St, Newport Beach, CA 92660-1703
Tel (949) 260-8840 *Founded/Ownrshp* 1969
Sales NA *EMP* 133^E
SIC 6331 Automobile insurance; Automobile insurance
CEO: Michael Weinstein
Genl Couns: Helen Hayden

H & H BUILDING
See HARRELL & HALL ENTERPRISES INC

D-U-N-S 04-903-2493
H & H CASTINGS INC
4300 Lincoln Hwy, York, PA 17406-8022
Tel (717) 751-0064 *Founded/Ownrshp* 1965
Sales 21.4MM^E *EMP* 75
SIC 3369 Nonferrous foundries
Pr: Kenneth Haugh
**VP:* Rodney E Haugh
VP: John Smeltzer
Genl Mgr: Michael Hoffmaster
Ql Cn Mgr: Jan Newcomer
Sls Mgr: Daniel Williams

D-U-N-S 18-069-5702
H & H CHARTERS INC
ACURA OF PORTLAND
12030 Se Stark St, Portland, OR 97216-3766
Tel (503) 252-2872 *Founded/Ownrshp* 1984
Sales 32.4MM^E *EMP* 100
SIC 5511 Automobiles, new & used; Automobiles, new & used
Pr: Richard Hannah
VP: Jason Hannah
VP: Jennifer Hannah
Exec: Amy Frost
Sales Asso: James Binder

D-U-N-S 03-512-0864
H & H CHEVROLET CO
4645 S 84th St, Omaha, NE 68127-1792
Tel (402) 596-2700 *Founded/Ownrshp* 1999
Sales 56.7MM^E *EMP* 140
SIC 5511 7532 Automobiles, new & used; Top & body repair & paint shops; Automobiles, new & used; Top & body repair & paint shops
Pr: Steve Hinchcliff
CFO: Gelaine Halverson
**Treas:* Teri Hurlbutt
**Sr VP:* Mike Kenefick
**VP:* Mark McDermott
Off Mgr: Amber Jones
Store Mgr: Troy Johnson
VP Mktg: John Costello
Sls Mgr: Matt Smock
Sls Mgr: Stanley Washington

D-U-N-S 01-457-7126
H & H CHEVROLET OLDSMOBILE & CADILLAC INC (PA)
H&H CHEVROLET - CADILLAC
730 E King St, Shippensburg, PA 17257-1510
Tel (717) 532-2121 *Founded/Ownrshp* 1932
Sales 23.2MM^E *EMP* 60
SIC 5511 7515 7513 5521 5012 Automobiles, new & used; Passenger car leasing; Truck rental & leasing, no drivers; Used car dealers; Automobiles & other motor vehicles; Automobiles, new & used; Passenger car leasing; Truck rental & leasing, no drivers; Used car dealers; Automobiles & other motor vehicles
Pr: W Mickey Nye
**VP:* Timothy M Nye

D-U-N-S 06-796-7422
H & H COLOR LAB INC
8906 E 67th St, Raytown, MO 64133-5638
Tel (816) 358-6677 *Founded/Ownrshp* 1970
Sales 35.5MM^E *EMP* 250
SIC 7384 Photographic services; Photographic services
Pr: Wayne Haub
Bd of Dir: Bentley Skeie
Ofcr: Bill Boda
VP: Victor Harsch
VP: Shirley Haub
Software D: Andrew Brower
Sftwr Eng: Desmond Todd
Snr Mgr: Tim Stanley
Snr Mgr: Bethany Still

H & H CONSTRUCTION
See H & H GENERAL EXCAVATING CO INC

D-U-N-S 94-607-5082
H & H CONSTRUCTION GROUP LLC
368 Highland Colony Pkwy, Ridgeland, MS 39157-6036
Tel (601) 206-7600 *Founded/Ownrshp* 1997
Sales 22.1MM^E *EMP* 162
Accts Horne Llp Ridgeland Mississi
SIC 1542 1541 Commercial & office building contractors; Industrial buildings & warehouses; Commercial & office building contractors; Industrial buildings & warehouses
VP: Tim J Fitzpatrick
VP: Don Parks
VP Sls: Tom Black
Snr PM: Dupree Petty

D-U-N-S 15-597-1786
H & H CONSTRUCTORS INC
H & H HOMES
2919 Breezewood Ave # 400, Fayetteville, NC 28303-5501
Tel (910) 486-4864 *Founded/Ownrshp* 1992
Sales 22.3MM^E *EMP* 60
SIC 1521 1522 Single-family housing construction; Multi-family dwellings, new construction
Pr: D Ralph Huff III
**COO:* Warren Tillman
CFO: David Vannoy
**Sec:* Linda B Huff
Sr VP: Kristie Meave
VP Opers: Maurice Wren
Snr Mgr: Jack Rostetter

D-U-N-S 02-557-4393
H & H CONTINENTAL MOTORS INC
CONTINENTAL NISSAN
5750 S La Grange Rd, Countryside, IL 60525-4062
Tel (708) 352-9200 *Founded/Ownrshp* 1963
Sales 37.9MM^E *EMP* 65
SIC 5511 Automobiles, new & used; Automobiles, new & used
Pr: John Weinberger
Pr: John Burke
Genl Mgr: Bill Milins
Dir IT: Mark Johnson
Info Man: Lois Daniels
Mktg Dir: Lois Cates
Mktg Dir: Joe Migoio
Sls Mgr: Tim Duda
Sls Mgr: Joe Miglio
Sales Asso: Peter Kashuba
Sales Asso: Matt Klein

H & H DISTRIBUTING
See HOCH INC

D-U-N-S 07-960-9151
H & H ELECTRIC INC
8369 Southpark Ln Ste A, Littleton, CO 80120-5671
Tel (303) 974-5273 *Founded/Ownrshp* 2014
Sales 40.0MM *EMP* 5
SIC 4911 4931 Electric services; Transmission, electric power; Electric & other services combined
CFO: Tryn Hendricks
**CFO:* Tyrn Hendricks

D-U-N-S 07-974-6836
H & H ENERGY SERVICES INC
3201 Latham Dr, Madison, WI 53713-4615
Tel (608) 273-4464 *Founded/Ownrshp* 2013
Sales 20.0MM^E *EMP* 121
SIC 4911
Prin: Kathy Dulaney

D-U-N-S 15-461-9886
H & H ENGINEERING CONSTRUCTION INC
212 Industrial Dr, Stockton, CA 95206-3905
Tel (209) 983-0708 *Founded/Ownrshp* 1985
Sales 29.0MM^E *EMP* 75
SIC 1629 Railroad & railway roadbed construction
CEO: Robert L Hallanger
VP: Lou Castaneda
**VP:* D Douglas Reynolds
Info Man: Kathy Obrien

D-U-N-S 05-165-7674
H & H GENERAL EXCAVATING CO INC
H & H CONSTRUCTION
660 Old Hanover Rd, Spring Grove, PA 17362-8914
Tel (717) 225-4669 *Founded/Ownrshp* 1967
Sales 60.7MM^E *EMP* 100^E
SIC 5193 1794 2421 Flowers & florists' supplies; Excavation & grading, building construction; Sawmills & planing mills, general; Flowers & florists' supplies; Excavation & grading, building construction; Sawmills & planing mills, general
Pr: Michael A Hartman
**VP:* Charles Hartman Jr

D-U-N-S 96-478-8926
H & H GROUP HOLDINGS INC
3201 Latham Dr, Madison, WI 53713-4615
Tel (608) 273-4464 *Founded/Ownrshp* 2009
Sales 21.1MM *EMP* 110
SIC 1731 1711 Electrical work; Solar energy contractor; Electrical work; Solar energy contractor
Pr: William T Howe
**VP:* Joshua Kaurich
Board of Directors: Jesse Defosse, Jeff Howe, Todd Pfeil

H & H HOMES
See H & H CONSTRUCTORS INC

D-U-N-S 07-384-6024 IMP
H & H INDUSTRIES INC
2801 Syene Rd, Madison, WI 53713-3203
Tel (608) 273-3434 *Founded/Ownrshp* 2011
Sales 35.7MM^E *EMP* 80
SIC 1711 Plumbing contractors
CEO: Paul Christensen
**Pr:* Michael Christensen
**Pr:* Brady Farrell
**Sec:* Martin Becker

D-U-N-S 17-509-5350 EXP
H & H TRADING INC
5400 Spotswood Trl, Penn Laird, VA 22846-9660
Tel (540) 574-3545 *Founded/Ownrshp* 2003
Sales 40.0MM *EMP* 5
SIC 5411 Co-operative food stores; Co-operative food stores
Pr: Bryant R Harper Jr
**VP:* Danny Hales
IT Man: Eric Regan

D-U-N-S 03-932-1588 IMP
H & H WHOLESALE SERVICES INC
1099 Rochester Rd, Troy, MI 48083-6026
Tel (248) 616-3030 *Founded/Ownrshp* 1996
Sales 24.5MM^E *EMP* 40
SIC 5149 Health foods
Pr: Howard Goldman

D-U-N-S 02-061-3063
H & H X-RAY SERVICES INC (LA)
MISSICIPPIE X RAY
104 Enterprise St, West Monroe, LA 71292-8012
Tel (318) 651-0216 *Founded/Ownrshp* 1975
Sales 22.3MM *EMP* 200
Accts Robinson Gardner Langston &
SIC 8734 Product testing laboratories; Product testing laboratories
Pr: Kenneth Y Head
**Sec:* Kenneth Y Head Jr
**Sec:* T G Head
**VP:* Roy D Head Jr

D-U-N-S 01-800-0406 IMP/EXP
H & K INTERNATIONAL INC
(*Suby of* H & K INTERNATIONAL INC) ★
2200 Skyline Dr, Mesquite, TX 75149
Tel (214) 818-3500 *Founded/Ownrshp* 1993
Sales 38.8MM^E *EMP* 200^E
SIC 3556 5087 3589 Food products machinery; Restaurant supplies; Cooking equipment, commercial; Food products machinery; Restaurant supplies; Cooking equipment, commercial
Ch: Brian Ranilow
**Pr:* Mike Azhadi
**Treas:* Guy Wade
**VP:* Mark Hogan
Sls Mgr: Mike Azahdi

D-U-N-S 92-692-4523 IMP/EXP
H & K INTERNATIONAL INC
2200 Skyline Dr, Mesquite, TX 75149
Tel (214) 818-3500 *Founded/Ownrshp* 1993
Sales 298.6MM^E *EMP* 825
SIC 5087 3589 Restaurant supplies; Cooking equipment, commercial; Restaurant supplies; Cooking equipment, commercial
CEO: David Bobbett
**Pr:* Brian Ranalow
COO: Guy Wade
Sr VP: Tim Honeck
VP: Barry Barnett
VP: Mark Hogan
Exec: Ramin Azhadi
Exec: Elsa Barnes
Exec: Rich Bolthouse
Exec: John Slovak
Dir Bus: Mike Azhadi

D-U-N-S 02-231-8401
H & K PARTNERS LLC
KFC
7840 W Hicks St Stop 1, Milwaukee, WI 53219-1158
Tel (414) 431-4532 *Founded/Ownrshp* 2000
Sales 23.0MM^E *EMP* 700
SIC 5812 Fast-food restaurant, chain; Fast-food restaurant, chain
Pr: Peter Helf

H & L
See H & L ELECTRIC INC

D-U-N-S 79-066-9956
H & L ELECTRIC INC
H & L
4111 28th St, Long Island City, NY 11101-3732
Tel (718) 361-6400 *Founded/Ownrshp* 1989
Sales 20.0MM^E *EMP* 200^E
SIC 8741 7699 1731 Construction management; Miscellaneous building item repair services; Electrical work; Construction management; Miscellaneous building item repair services; Electrical work
Ch Bd: Hal Sokoloff
**Ex VP:* Lloyd Sokoloff
VP: Michael Borman

D-U-N-S 04-192-5900
H & L MANUFACTURING CO
900 E Mn St, Middleville, MI 49333
Tel (269) 795-5000 *Founded/Ownrshp* 1964
Sales 32.6MM^E *EMP* 130
SIC 3714 3694 Motor vehicle parts & accessories; Engine electrical equipment; Motor vehicle parts & accessories; Engine electrical equipment
CEO: Steve Sawdy
VP: Matt Emery
Genl Mgr: Dale Wirkman

D-U-N-S 00-534-4635
■ **H & L TOOL CO INC**
(*Suby of* CHICAGO RIVET & MACHINE CO) ★
32701 Dequindre Rd, Madison Heights, MI 48071-1595
Tel (248) 585-7474 *Founded/Ownrshp* 1996
Sales 21.4MM^E *EMP* 100
SIC 3451 3452 3316 Screw machine products; Rivets, metal; Bolts, metal; Cold finishing of steel shapes
Pr: Michael Bourg
Genl Mgr: Charles Abbat
Ql Cn Mgr: Rich Duff

D-U-N-S 03-559-5925
H & M BAY INC
1800 Industrial Park Rd, Federalsburg, MD 21632-2690
Tel (410) 754-8001 *Founded/Ownrshp* 1982
Sales 126.3MM^E *EMP* 400
Accts Orth & Kowalick Pa Dover
SIC 4731 Transportation agents & brokers; Transportation agents & brokers
Ch Bd: Lawrence Hayman
**Pr:* Walter Messick
**COO:* Walter Messick III
COO: Mike Ryan
Dir Risk M: Dianna Whitby
Div Mgr: Bryan Towers

H & M COMPANY
See H AND M CONSTRUCTION CO INC

D-U-N-S 00-889-5567
H & M CONSTRUCTION CO LLC
5000 Hwy 156, Pennington, AL 36916
Tel (205) 654-3091 *Founded/Ownrshp* 1997
Sales 28.7MM^E *EMP* 60^E
SIC 1542 1541 Nonresidential construction; Industrial buildings & warehouses

H & M CONSTRUCTORS
See MB HAYNES CORP

D-U-N-S 09-395-6311 EXP
H & M HENNES & MAURITZ LP
H&M
(*Suby of* H & M HENNES & MAURITZ HOLDING B.V.)
110 5th Ave Fl 11, New York, NY 10011-5665
Tel (212) 564-9922 *Founded/Ownrshp* 2000
Sales 736.8MM^E *EMP* 7,500
SIC 5651 Family clothing stores; Family clothing stores
CFO: Peter Scaramelli
Mng Dir: Richard Din
Dist Mgr: Eric Manuzak
Genl Mgr: Dan Dent
Genl Mgr: Danielle Kulle
Genl Mgr: Sue McDonough
Dir IT: Harald Sperger
IT Man: Per Tunklint
Opers Mgr: Luis Macias
Prd Mgr: Maria Gao
Prd Mgr: Edgar Rivera

D-U-N-S 06-429-5934
H & M INTERNATIONAL TRANSPORTATION INC
485b Us Highway 1 S # 110, Iselin, NJ 08830-3068
Tel (732) 510-4640 *Founded/Ownrshp* 1968
Sales 180.8MM^E *EMP* 1,000
SIC 4731 8741 4225 Freight forwarding; Freight consolidation; Management services; General warehousing & storage; Freight forwarding; Freight consolidation; Management services; General warehousing & storage
Pr: Charles T Connors
**Pr:* Robert J Gildersleeve
Pr: Eric Witham
**CFO:* Leonard Fischetti
**Treas:* George Willmott
Ex VP: Mike Hosmer
VP: Ray Cznadel
Genl Mgr: Tom Curry
MIS Dir: Chris Walsh
IT Man: James Giaquinto

D-U-N-S 07-963-5061
■ **H & M MECHANICAL INC**
(*Suby of* COMFORT SYSTEMS USA INC) ★
3100 Richard Arrington, Birmingham, AL 35203-1313
Tel (205) 664-3300 *Founded/Ownrshp* 1998
Sales 46.2MM^E *EMP* 150
SIC 1711 Plumbing contractors; Plumbing contractors
Pr: Coy T Head
CFO: Fred Cook
**VP:* Thomas Lampkin

D-U-N-S 61-058-0201
H & M TRUCKING INC
2522 Edward Babe Gmez Ave, Omaha, NE 68107-4446
Tel (402) 431-9410 *Founded/Ownrshp* 1987
Sales 22.4MM^E *EMP* 53
SIC 4213 Trucking, except local
Pr: Randell Mueller
**VP:* Dale Cook
VP: Burt Geer
Opers Mgr: Chuck Radke

D-U-N-S 02-260-1835
H & M WAGNER & SONS INC
7204 May Wagner Ln, Glen Burnie, MD 21061-2859
Tel (410) 766-1150 *Founded/Ownrshp* 1964
Sales 59.1MM^E *EMP* 175
SIC 5046

D-U-N-S 02-233-6275
H & N CHEVROLET BUICK CO INC
713 Grand Ave, Spencer, IA 51301-3707
Tel (712) 262-3230 *Founded/Ownrshp* 1957
Sales 48.6MM *EMP* 36
SIC 5511 7515 Automobiles, new & used; Passenger car leasing; Automobiles, new & used; Passenger car leasing
Pr: John D Hart
**Sec:* Tom Howe

H & N FISH COMPANY
See H & N FOODS INTERNATIONAL INC

H & N FOODS INTERNATIONAL
See H & N GROUP INC

D-U-N-S 05-742-5746 IMP
H & N FOODS INTERNATIONAL INC
H & N FISH COMPANY
(*Suby of* H & N FOODS INTERNATIONAL) ★
5580 S Alameda St, Vernon, CA 90058-3426
Tel (323) 586-9300 *Founded/Ownrshp* 1981
Sales 109.8MM^E *EMP* 170
SIC 5146 Fish, fresh; Fish, frozen, unpackaged; Fish, fresh; Fish, frozen, unpackaged
CEO: Hua Thanh Ngo
**Ex VP:* Christine Ngo
IT Man: Anh Le
Board of Directors: Robert Bertholf

D-U-N-S 07-834-9547
H & N GROUP INC (CA)
H & N FOODS INTERNATIONAL
5580 S Alameda St, Vernon, CA 90058-3426
Tel (323) 586-9388 *Founded/Ownrshp* 2008
Sales 127.8MM^E *EMP* 194^E
SIC 5146 Fish & seafoods; Fish & seafoods
CEO: Hua T Ngo

D-U-N-S 08-208-5754
H & R ACCOUNTS INC
AVADYNE HEALTH
7017 John Deere Pkwy, Moline, IL 61265-8072
Tel (309) 736-2255 *Founded/Ownrshp* 2006
Sales 26.9MM^E *EMP* 360
SIC 7322 7371 8741 Collection agency, except real estate; Computer software development; Business management; Collection agency, except real estate; Computer software development; Business management
Pr: Moises Eilemberg
**COO:* Shaun Magill
**Ofcr:* David Sheil
**Sr VP:* Lincoln Fish
**Sr VP:* Olivier Witteveen
**Sr VP:* John York
**VP:* Thomas Conway
VP: Patti Schaeffer
VP: Melodi Williams
Off Mgr: Anna Acosta
Dir IT: David Parker

H & R AGRI-POWER
See AGRI-POWER INC

D-U-N-S 04-395-1235
▲ **H & R BLOCK INC** (MO)
1 H&R Block Way, Kansas City, MO 64105
Tel (816) 854-3000 *Founded/Ownrshp* 1955
Sales 3.0MMM *EMP* 98,600
Accts Deloitte & Touche Kansas City
Tkr Sym HRB *Exch* NYS
SIC 7291 6794 Tax return preparation services; Franchises, selling or licensing; Tax return preparation services; Franchises, selling or licensing
Pr: William C Cobb
**Ch Bd:* Robert A Gerard
CFO: Gregory J Macfarlane
Treas: Brian N Schell
Chf Cred: Brandon Lorey
Chf Mktg O: Kathy Collins
Chf Inves: Gretel Garcia
Ofcr: Bruce Daise
Ofcr: Bob Hewes
Ofcr: Brenda Rose
Ex VP: Jeffery W Yabuki
Sr VP: Marilyn Hersh
Sr VP: Stephanie R Otto
VP: Mark A Ciaramitaro
VP: Julie E Markey
Dir Risk M: Jeffrey T Brown
Board of Directors: Paul J Brown, David Baker Lewis, Victoria J Reich, Bruce C Rohde, Tom D Seip, James F Wright

D-U-N-S 16-688-4366
H & R INDUSTRIAL CONTRACTORS INC
21370 Us Highway 31, Vinemont, AL 35179-5969
Tel (256) 737-0132 *Founded/Ownrshp* 2004
Sales 35.0MM *EMP* 25
SIC 1541 Industrial buildings & warehouses; Industrial buildings & warehouses
Pr: Clark Rodgers
**Treas:* Herman Hinkle
**VP:* Heath Rogers

D-U-N-S 00-308-3607 IMP
H & S BAKERY INC (MD)
MIGHTY GOOD
600-619 S Bond St, Baltimore, MD 21231
Tel (410) 558-3050 *Founded/Ownrshp* 1948, 1953
Sales 289.1MM^E *EMP* 756
SIC 2051 Bread, all types (white, wheat, rye, etc): fresh or frozen; Rolls, bread type: fresh or frozen; Bread, all types (white, wheat, rye, etc): fresh or frozen; Rolls, bread type: fresh or frozen
Ch Bd: Harry Tsakalos
**Pr:* Bill Paterakis
**Treas:* Liberty Tsakalos
VP: Chuck Paterakis
Exec: Don Mann
**Prin:* John Paterakis
Opers Mgr: Christopher Tsakalos
Plnt Mgr: Jackie Eddis

D-U-N-S 04-402-9536
H & S CITRUS INC (FL)
1237 Grose Rd, Fort Pierce, FL 34982-6575
Tel (772) 461-1455 *Founded/Ownrshp* 1966
Sales 35.2MM^E *EMP* 100
SIC 5148 5499 Fruits, fresh; Juices, fruit or vegetable; Fruits, fresh; Juices, fruit or vegetable
Pr: John S Cemer
**Ch Bd:* Robert Deery
Bd of Dir: Connie Evans
**VP:* George Brown
Plng Mgr: Cindy Levengood

D-U-N-S 03-191-0607
H & S CONSTRUCTORS INC (TX)
1616 Corn Product Rd, Corpus Christi, TX 78409-3017
Tel (361) 668-8674 *Founded/Ownrshp* 1982
Sales 172.2MM^E *EMP* 750
SIC 1711 Mechanical contractor; Mechanical contractor
Pr: Patrick Horn
**VP:* Michael Scott
Exec: Brian Trawick
Off Mgr: Lea Colwell
IT Man: Rob Zarate
Mtls Mgr: Daniel Duncan
Mtls Mgr: Dan Jordan
Opers Mgr: Ricky Mata
Sls&Mrk Ex: Mark Garcia

D-U-N-S 05-364-2906
H & S DEVELOPERS INC
GROCERY STORE
12486 S Foothills Blvd, Yuma, AZ 85367-6099
Tel (928) 342-3344 *Founded/Ownrshp* 1959
Sales 26.2MM^E^ *EMP* 125
SIC 6552 5411 4941 7992 7538 7542

D-U-N-S 09-604-3195
H & S MACHINERY CORP
1941 Industrial Blvd, Harvey, LA 70058-2315
Tel (504) 347-5707 *Founded/Ownrshp* 1979
Sales 24.0MM *EMP* 10
SIC 5084 Machine tools & accessories
Pr: Hollis B Eddins
**Pr:* Scott Eddins
**Sec:* Sharon Eddins

D-U-N-S 04-314-0847 IMP/EXP
H & S MANUFACTURING CO INC (WI)
(*Suby of* HEIK HOLDING CO INC) ★
2608 S Hume Ave, Marshfield, WI 54449-5551
Tel (715) 387-3414 *Founded/Ownrshp* 1967, 1993
Sales 28.3MM^E^ *EMP* 203
SIC 3523 3531

D-U-N-S 03-605-6299
H & S OIL CO INC (SC)
308 Martin Luther King Dr, Andrews, SC 29510-2752
Tel (843) 264-3518 *Founded/Ownrshp* 1947, 1966
Sales 36.2MM *EMP* 56
Accts Harper Poston & Moree Cpas
SIC 5171 5411 5983 Petroleum bulk stations; Convenience stores, independent; Fuel oil dealers; Petroleum bulk stations; Convenience stores, independent; Fuel oil dealers
Pr: H Edsel Hemingway Sr
IT Man: Bill Hemingway

H & T
See HUNGERFORD & TERRY INC

D-U-N-S 00-116-4581 IMP
H & T BATTERY COMPONENTS USA INC (CT)
57 Callender Rd, Watertown, CT 06795-1627
Tel (860) 945-8324 *Founded/Ownrshp* 1963
Sales 32.7MM^E^ *EMP* 98
SIC 3469 Stamping metal for the trade; Stamping metal for the trade
Pr: Richard L Bouffard
**Ch:* William Shannon
**VP:* Grant Demerchant
**VP:* Mario Lambiase
**VP:* Daniel D Moffa

D-U-N-S 92-688-3505 IMP
H & T SEAFOOD INC
5598 Lindbergh Ln, Bell, CA 90201-6410
Tel (323) 526-0888 *Founded/Ownrshp* 1994
Sales 60.0MM^E^ *EMP* 41
SIC 5146 Fish & seafoods
Pr: Thong Lu

D-U-N-S 61-509-2426
H + M INDUSTRIAL SERVICES INC
121 Edwards Dr, Jackson, TN 38301-7716
Tel (731) 422-5211 *Founded/Ownrshp* 1989
Sales 22.8MM^E^ *EMP* 200
SIC 7699 1796 1731 7378 Photocopy machine repair; Millwright; Electrical work; Computer maintenance & repair; Photocopy machine repair; Millwright; Electrical work; Computer maintenance & repair
CEO: James E Campbell III
**Sec:* Mike Farris
**VP:* James Royer
Snr PM: Tommy McCalmon
Snr PM: Jessie Mitchell

D-U-N-S 00-691-2380 IMP
H - INVESTMENT CO
GOLDEN STATE FLOORING
6999 Southfront Rd, Livermore, CA 94551-8221
Tel (925) 245-4300 *Founded/Ownrshp* 1974
Sales 93.8MM^E^ *EMP* 240
SIC 5031 Hardboard; Lumber: rough, dressed & finished; Plywood; Doors & windows; Hardboard; Lumber: rough, dressed & finished; Plywood; Doors & windows
CEO: Harry S Anthony
**Pr:* Jonathan R Long
**CEO:* Matthew R Long
CFO: Fernanda Aguiar
CFO: Michael Flener
**CFO:* Larry W Knox
VP: Dana Brandt
VP: Matt Long
**VP:* Scott M Watson
Opers Mgr: Robin Salin
Plnt Mgr: Jim Bilinski
Board of Directors: T Nola

H 2 M
See H2M ARCHITECTS ENGINEERS LAND SURVEYING AND LANDSCAPE ARCHITECTURE DPC

H 2 S CONSULTANTS
See AMERICAN SAFETY SERVICES INC

H A A R T
See H I V/ A I D S ALLIANCE FOR REGION TWO INC

D-U-N-S 00-172-9375
H A BERKHEIMER INC (PA)
BERKHEIMER TAX ADMINISTRATOR
50 N 7th St, Bangor, PA 18013-1798
Tel (610) 588-0965 *Founded/Ownrshp* 1946, 1986
Sales 32.3MM^E^ *EMP* 250
SIC 7389 3281

D-U-N-S 00-882-3908
H A MAPES INC (ME)
152 Pleasant St, Springvale, ME 04083-1216
Tel (207) 324-0174 *Founded/Ownrshp* 1936, 1969
Sales 36.0MM^E^ *EMP* 20
SIC 5172 Gasoline
Pr: H Allen Mapes
**VP:* Jonathan Mapes
Dir IT: Christine Bangs

H A P
See HEALTHCARE ADMINISTRATIVE PARTNERS LLC

H A S C
See HEBREW ACADEMY FOR SPECIAL CHILDREN (INC)

D-U-N-S 04-522-9358
H AND H DRUG STORES INC
WESTERN DRUG
3604 San Fernando Rd, Glendale, CA 91204-2917
Tel (818) 956-6691 *Founded/Ownrshp* 1998
Sales 38.6MM^E^ *EMP* 152
SIC 5912 Drug stores; Drug stores
Ch Bd: Hagop Youredjian
**VP:* Zarig Youredjian
Dir IT: Chris Olson
Cert Phar: Christopher Cowland

H AND H ENTERPRISES
See TIMES UP

D-U-N-S 80-812-8743
H AND H MEDICAL SERVICES INC
4720 Crawford St Apt 1, Houston, TX 77004-5031
Tel (713) 738-1221 *Founded/Ownrshp* 1955
Sales 11.1MM^E^ *EMP* 332
Accts Patrick E Aneji Cpa Houston
SIC 8082 Home health care services; Home health care services
Pr: Charles H Hebert Jr

D-U-N-S 11-472-4789
H AND J CONTRACTING INC
3160 Fairlane Farms Rd, Wellington, FL 33414-8775
Tel (561) 791-1953 *Founded/Ownrshp* 1998
Sales 42.6MM^E^ *EMP* 200^E^
SIC 1799 Building site preparation; Building site preparation
Pr: Mary Lynn Rusbridge
**VP:* Dino G Marini
**VP:* Jeremy Rury

D-U-N-S 03-480-7313
H AND M CONSTRUCTION CO INC
H & M COMPANY
50 Security Dr, Jackson, TN 38305-3611
Tel (731) 664-6300 *Founded/Ownrshp* 1957
Sales 200.0MM^E^ *EMP* 300
Accts Crowe Horwath Llp Brentwood
SIC 1541 1542 Industrial buildings & warehouses; Factory construction; Warehouse construction; Nonresidential construction; School building construction; Industrial buildings & warehouses; Factory construction; Warehouse construction; Nonresidential construction; School building construction
CEO: James Campbell III
**Pr:* Chris Carroll
**Sec:* Michael Farris
**Sr VP:* Roger Cook
Genl Mgr: Michael Campbell
Snr PM: Barry Flynn
Snr PM: Jessie Mitchell

D-U-N-S 11-339-3839
H B BOYS LC
BURGER KING
2280 S Main St, Salt Lake City, UT 84115-2629
Tel (801) 486-6777 *Founded/Ownrshp* 1984
Sales 21.4MM^E^ *EMP* 416
SIC 5812 Fast-food restaurant, chain; Fast-food restaurant, chain
VP: Gary Moore
Off Mgr: Doree Cordeiro

H B C
See HIAWATHA BROADBAND COMMUNICATIONS INC

H B C
See JVC HENDRICKS BOX CO INC

D-U-N-S 06-434-4294
H B FRAZER CO-PENNSYLVANIA
514 Shoemaker Rd, King of Prussia, PA 19406-3522
Tel (610) 768-0400 *Founded/Ownrshp* 1970
Sales 52.1MM^E^ *EMP* 200
SIC 1731 Electrical work; Electrical work
Pr: Franklin P Holleran
**CFO:* Robert Cubberley
Bd of Dir: Ken Hull Jr
**VP:* Ed Gilmore
VP: Janice Moell
Genl Mgr: Edwin Anderson
Genl Mgr: Dick Brotzman
Genl Mgr: Dan Drake
Sfty Dirs: Christopher Bittner
Sls Mgr: Michael Helhowski

H B I
See HOLTGER BROS INC

H B I
See HOME BUILDERS INSTITUTE

H B L DEALERSHIP
See HBL HOLDINGS INC

D-U-N-S 06-809-3632
H B MAGRUDER MEMORIAL HOSPITAL
MAGRUDER HOSPITAL
615 Fulton St, Port Clinton, OH 43452-2001
Tel (419) 734-3131 *Founded/Ownrshp* 1940
Sales 49.6MM^E^ *EMP* 400
SIC 8062 General medical & surgical hospitals; General medical & surgical hospitals
Pr: J Todd Almendinger
Dir Recs: Shelly Stone
CFO: Todd Almendinger
Trst: Rick Comings
Sr VP: Karen Klaege
VP: Sue Johnson
VP: Jan Troeger
Dir Inf Cn: Melanie Hoover
Dir Rx: Nick Marisco
**Prin:* Michael Long
Dir IT: Jennifer Briede

D-U-N-S 08-486-8140
H B MCCLURE CO
600 S 17th St, Harrisburg, PA 17104-2259
Tel (717) 232-4328 *Founded/Ownrshp* 1980
Sales 64.5MM^E^ *EMP* 220^E^
SIC 1711 Plumbing contractors; Warm air heating & air conditioning contractor; Plumbing contractors; Warm air heating & air conditioning contractor
CEO: Robert F Whalen
**Pr:* Robert F McClure
**CFO:* Andy Henry
VP: Eric Crawford
**VP:* Jeri A Donadee
VP: Korey Kann
**VP:* Donald L Lay
Genl Mgr: Michael Snyder
IT Man: Kyle Seaman
IT Man: John Stover

H B O
See HOME BOX OFFICE INC

H B O
See HBO SERVICES INC

D-U-N-S 82-805-4960
H BANKCORP LLC
7151 Columbia Gateway Dr A, Columbia, MD 21046-2139
Tel (410) 536-7336 *Founded/Ownrshp* 2014
Sales NA *EMP* 368
SIC 6022 State commercial banks; State commercial banks
Ch Bd: Eric D Hovde
**Pr:* Joseph J Thomas
**CFO:* William Weller
**Ofcr:* Shawn Murphy

D-U-N-S 11-620-1468
H BECK INC
11140 Rockville Pike Fl 4, Rockville, MD 20852-3138
Tel (301) 468-0100 *Founded/Ownrshp* 1984
Sales 50.0MM *EMP* 55
SIC 6211 Brokers, security; Brokers, security
CEO: Eric Meyers
**Ch Bd:* Norman Kamerow
**Pr:* James H Dresselaers
COO: Scott C Thorson
Ofcr: Raymond Hessling
**Sr VP:* Gary Hurvitz
**Sr VP:* Steven R Porter
**Sr VP:* John Prokopchak
VP: Richard Merritt
Dir IT: Matthew Anderson

D-U-N-S 01-156-0919 IMP
H BETTI INDUSTRIES INC
BETSON ENTERPRISES DIVISION
303 Paterson Plank Rd, Carlstadt, NJ 07072-2307
Tel (201) 438-1300 *Founded/Ownrshp* 1934
Sales 134.0MM^E^ *EMP* 380
SIC 5046 5091 7699 Coin-operated equipment; Billiard equipment & supplies; Vending machine repair; Coin-operated equipment; Billiard equipment & supplies; Vending machine repair
CEO: Peter Betti
**Pr:* Robert Geschine
**Sec:* Steven Betti
Bd of Dir: Joe Kirby
**Ex VP:* Robert Betti
VP: Serge Ray
Exec: Paul Cardea
Genl Mgr: David Lerner
Dir IT: Debby Wilson
Dir IT: Rob Zigmont
IT Man: Joseph Fienberg

D-U-N-S 02-287-9696
H BROOKS AND CO LLC
600 Lakeview Point Dr, New Brighton, MN 55112-3494
Tel (651) 635-0126 *Founded/Ownrshp* 2000
Sales 62.0MM^E^ *EMP* 80^E^
SIC 5148 Fruits, fresh; Vegetables, fresh; Fruits, fresh; Vegetables, fresh
Pr: Phillip Brooks
**Sec:* Ray Ralston
Comm Man: Ray Larson
Opers Mgr: Al Blanton

D-U-N-S 07-468-3236
H BRUCE AND SONS INC
BRUCE & MERRILEES ELECTRIC CO
930 Cass St Ste 1, New Castle, PA 16101-5241
Tel (724) 652-5566 *Founded/Ownrshp* 1979
Sales 64.3MM^E^ *EMP* 300
Accts Carbis Walker Llp Cpa New
SIC 1731 5063 General electrical contractor; Electrical apparatus & equipment; Boxes & fittings, electrical; Circuit breakers; Wire & cable; General electrical contractor; Electrical apparatus & equipment; Boxes & fittings, electrical; Circuit breakers; Wire & cable
Pr: Jay H Bruce
CEO: Robert J Bruce
CFO: Debby Van Kirk
Treas: Gary Bruce
VP: Jonathan R Bruce
VP: Justin L Bruce

H C A HEALTHCARE
See NOTAMI LLC

D-U-N-S 96-824-1240
H C BOBS INC
160 Corporate Ct, Meriden, CT 06450-7177
Tel (203) 235-5775 *Founded/Ownrshp* 1990
Sales 85.7MM^E^ *EMP* 3,008^E^
SIC 5651 5611 5699 5621 5641 5661 Family clothing stores; Clothing accessories: men's & boys'; Clothing, sportswear, men's & boys'; Sports apparel; Women's clothing stores; Children's wear; Men's shoes; Women's shoes; Children's shoes
Pr: David Farrell

H C C
See HAGERSTOWN COMMUNITY COLLEGE

D-U-N-S 96-855-7442
■ **H C CROWN LLC**
(*Suby of* HALLMARK CARDS INC) ★
2501 Mcgee St, Kansas City, MO 64108-2615
Tel (818) 755-2400 *Founded/Ownrshp* 1999
Sales 415.6MM^E^ *EMP* 344^E^
SIC 4841 Cable & other pay television services; Cable & other pay television services
Pr: William J Abbott
CFO: Andrew Rooke

H C D
See HOME CARE DELIVERED INC

H C G
See HARRELL CONTRACTING GROUP LLC

H C I
See HCI INC

H C I
See HURON CASTING INC

H C I
See HUNT CONSOLIDATED INC

H C I SUPPLY
See JACKSON WHOLESALE HARDWARE CO

D-U-N-S 00-685-3576
H C OLSEN CONSTRUCTION CO INC (CA)
710 Los Angeles Ave, Monrovia, CA 91016-4250
Tel (626) 359-8900 *Founded/Ownrshp* 1946, 1989
Sales 24.7MM^E^ *EMP* 75
SIC 1541 Industrial buildings, new construction
CEO: Linda Jacqueline Pearson
**Sec:* Karl Pearson
CTO: Paul Inciti
Snr PM: Paul Hudson

H C P
See HENDRICKS COMMERCIAL PROPERTIES LLC

H C R
See L WOERNER INC

D-U-N-S 03-292-4094
H C RUSTIN CORP
RUSTIN CONCRETE
50 E Main St, Durant, OK 74701-5962
Tel (580) 924-3260 *Founded/Ownrshp* 1998
Sales 20.1MM^E^ *EMP* 77
SIC 3273 5211 Ready-mixed concrete; Concrete & cinder block
Pr: Philip Rustin
**VP:* Barton L Rustin
Off Mgr: Charla Rustin

D-U-N-S 04-790-6185
H C SCHAU & SON INC
(*Suby of* GREENCORE US HOLDINGS INC) ★
10350 Argonne Dr Ste 400, Woodridge, IL 60517-4999
Tel (630) 783-1000 *Founded/Ownrshp* 2012
Sales 130.8MM^E^ *EMP* 200
SIC 5147 2099 Meats, fresh; Food preparations; Meats, fresh; Food preparations
CEO: Charles H Schau
**VP:* Randall C Schau

D-U-N-S 06-009-1956 IMP
H C STARCK INC
(*Suby of* OPUS INVESTMENT SARL)
45 Industrial Pl, Newton, MA 02461-1951
Tel (617) 630-5800 *Founded/Ownrshp* 2007
Sales 141.5MM^E^ *EMP* 566
SIC 3339 3356 3313 Primary nonferrous metals; Nonferrous rolling & drawing; Electrometallurgical products; Primary nonferrous metals; Nonferrous rolling & drawing; Electrometallurgical products
Pr: Dmitry Shashkov
COO: Mark Confroy
CFO: Jan Loesch
CFO: Dirk Plaga
Treas: Richard E Howard
Ofcr: Melody Randolph
VP: Francois Dary
VP: Joe Hirt
VP: John Noteman
VP: Robert K Sarafian
Genl Mgr: Lynn Brooks
Board of Directors: Dr Andreas Meier

H CT
See HEALTH CARE TEMPORARIES INC

D-U-N-S 08-007-2507
■ **H CT INC**
HYATT REGENCY MISSION BAY SPA
(*Suby of* CHESAPEAKE LODGING TRUST) ★
1441 Quivira Rd, San Diego, CA 92109-7805
Tel (619) 224-1234 *Founded/Ownrshp* 2012
Sales 17.9MM^E^ *EMP* 300
SIC 7011 4491 5813 5812 Hotels & motels; Marine terminals; Piers, incl. buildings & facilities: operation & maintenance; Drinking places; Eating places; Hotels & motels; Marine terminals; Piers, incl. buildings & facilities: operation & maintenance; Drinking places; Eating places
Pr: Mohsen Kaleghi
**Pr:* Mark S Hoplamazian
Exec: Linda Villalobos
Genl Mgr: Mohsen Khaleghi

D-U-N-S 02-846-7876
H CALDWELL JACK & SONS INC
CHOICE PAK PRODUCTS
4035 E 52nd St, Maywood, CA 90270-2205
Tel (323) 589-4008 *Founded/Ownrshp* 2004
Sales 36.1MM^E^ *EMP* 60
SIC 5148 Vegetables, fresh; Vegetables, fresh
Pr: Harry Caldwell
**VP:* Duke Caldwell
Genl Mgr: Morie Thomas
Ql Cn Mgr: Luz Martinez
Mktg Dir: Ana Baldridge

H CARE
See HURLEY/BINSONS MEDICAL EQUIPMENT INC

D-U-N-S 00-680-7671 IMP
H CARR & SONS INC
100 Royal Little Dr, Providence, RI 02904-1859
Tel (401) 331-2277 Founded/Ownrshp 1919
Sales 60.4MM^E EMP 511
SIC 1742 1799 1542 Drywall; Acoustical & ceiling work; Plastering, plain or ornamental; Fireproofing buildings; Nonresidential construction; Drywall; Acoustical & ceiling work; Plastering, plain or ornamental; Fireproofing buildings; Nonresidential construction
Pr: James L Carr Jr
*CFO: Mary Anne Wood
*VP: Richard Elderkin
*VP: John Fitzgibbons
Rgnl Mgr: Tom Pucillo
Off Admin: Jackie Legnos

D-U-N-S 04-130-9154
H CLARK JAMES & SON INC
4100 S 663 W, Salt Lake City, UT 84123
Tel (801) 266-9322 Founded/Ownrshp 1994
Sales 22.6MM EMP 115
SIC 4213

D-U-N-S 01-741-7742 IMP
H COX & SON INC
1402 Sawyer Rd, Traverse City, MI 49685-9365
Tel (231) 943-4730 Founded/Ownrshp 1969
Sales 24.6MM^E EMP 65
SIC 5181 Beer & other fermented malt liquors; Beer & other fermented malt liquors
Pr: Mark L Ribel
*VP: Mark C Ribel

H D C
See HOMIER DISTRIBUTING CO INC

H D C
See HOOVEN - DAYTON CORP

D-U-N-S 02-726-0835 EXP
H D FOWLER CO INC
13440 Se 30th St, Bellevue, WA 98005-4439
Tel (425) 746-8400 Founded/Ownrshp 1947
Sales 401.7MM^E EMP 424
SIC 5084 5083 5085 3321 Industrial machinery & equipment; Landscaping equipment; Industrial supplies; Valves & fittings; Water pipe, cast iron; Industrial machinery & equipment; Landscaping equipment; Industrial supplies; Valves & fittings; Water pipe, cast iron
Pr: Harold D Fowler
COO: Brian Nelson
*Treas: James Fowler
*VP: David P Kirker
VP: Bob Koehler
Brnch Mgr: Darin Graves
Brnch Mgr: Jeff Ockerman
Brnch Mgr: Frankie Rickels
Genl Mgr: Kelly Allerdice
IT Man: Eric Poule
IT Man: Stacey Rushent

D-U-N-S 09-248-0722
H D H INSTRUMENTS CORP
3166 Hwy 359 N, Pattison, TX 77466
Tel (281) 375-6835 Founded/Ownrshp 1978
Sales 29.7MM^E EMP 130
SIC 3533 Drilling tools for gas, oil or water wells; Drilling tools for gas, oil or water wells
Pr: John Hovas
*Owner: Greg Hovas

H D I
See DIRECTDME INC

H D R
See HDR ENGINEERING INC

D-U-N-S 19-480-1106 IMP
H D R P INC
SUPERIOR RIGGING AND ERECTING
3250 Woodstock Rd Se, Atlanta, GA 30316-4552
Tel (404) 627-1335 Founded/Ownrshp 2002
Sales 22.2MM^E EMP 125
SIC 1791 7353 Structural steel erection; Cranes & aerial lift equipment, rental or leasing; Structural steel erection; Cranes & aerial lift equipment, rental or leasing
CEO: Patrick C Lewis
Sec: Mark Lynch
VP: Herschell Lynch

D-U-N-S 06-685-4894
H D S OF BEAVER FALLS INC
BRIGHTON HOT DOG SHOPPE
300 S Walnut Ln Ste 400, Beaver, PA 15009-1738
Tel (724) 775-9070 Founded/Ownrshp 1968
Sales 9.0MM^E EMP 325
SIC 5812 Hot dog stand; Coffee shop; Hot dog stand; Coffee shop
Pr: Frank G Papa

H D SEGUR
See HOLLIS D SEGUR INC

D-U-N-S 00-172-4400 IMP/EXP
H D SHELDON & CO INC (NY)
143 W 29th St Ste 12, New York, NY 10001-5103
Tel (212) 627-1759 Founded/Ownrshp 1943, 1979
Sales 41.4MM EMP 24
Accts O Connor Davies Llp Paramus
SIC 5078 5046 Refrigeration equipment & supplies; Cooking equipment, commercial; Refrigeration equipment & supplies; Cooking equipment, commercial
Ch Bd: Robert Metros
Sls Mgr: Kristopher Hassett
Sls Mgr: Hazel Magee

D-U-N-S 02-585-6899
H D SMITH LLC
SMITH MEDICAL PARTNERS DIV
3063 Fiat Ave, Springfield, IL 62703-5930
Tel (866) 232-1222 Founded/Ownrshp 1954
Sales 1.8MMM^E EMP 500
SIC 5122 8082 Drugs & drug proprietaries; Pharmaceuticals; Proprietary (patent) medicines; Druggists' sundries; Home health care services; Drugs & drug proprietaries; Pharmaceuticals; Proprietary (patent) medicines; Druggists' sundries; Home health care services
Ch: Henry Dale Smith
Pr: David Duross
*Pr: J Christopher Smith
*CEO: Henry Dale Smith Jr
COO: John Heller
COO: Christopher Smith
*CFO: Bill Williams
*Ex VP: Karen Callaway
*Ex VP: Tom Doyle
Sr VP: Joseph Conda
VP: Timothy Booth
VP: Kathleen Cross
VP: Mark De Bruin
VP: Robert Dynek
VP: Jeff Greer
VP: Chris Mirwald
VP: Chandra Prakash
VP Bus Dev: Bob Rash

D-U-N-S 13-003-4957
H D V C H FOUNDATION
DE VOST CHLDREN HOSP FUNDATION
(Suby of SPECTRUM HEALTH SYSTEM) ★
100 Michigan St Ne, Grand Rapids, MI 49503-2560
Tel (616) 391-2000 Founded/Ownrshp 2010
Sales 23.3MM EMP 31
Accts Crowe Horwath Llp Chicago Il
SIC 8399 Fund raising organization, non-fee basis; Fund raising organization, non-fee basis
Pr: Vicki Weaver
Doctor: Amy Neilson

H D VEST FINANCIAL SERVICES
See HD VEST INC

D-U-N-S 12-603-2747
■ **H D VEST INVESTMENT SECURITIES INC**
(Suby of H D VEST FINANCIAL SERVICES) ★
6333 N State Highway 161 # 400, Irving, TX 75038-2200
Tel (972) 870-6041 Founded/Ownrshp 1986
Sales 27.8MM^E EMP 325
SIC 6211 8721 Brokers, security; Dealers, security; Accounting, auditing & bookkeeping; Brokers, security; Dealers, security; Accounting, auditing & bookkeeping
Pr: Roger Ochs
*COO: Daniel Wright
*Treas: Joel Bennett

H D W
See HARDWARE DISTRIBUTION WAREHOUSES INC

H E
See HOUSEHOLD ESSENTIALS LLC

D-U-N-S 01-053-7306
H E BUTT FOUNDATION
719 Earl Garrett St, Kerrville, TX 78028-3324
Tel (830) 896-2505 Founded/Ownrshp 1933
Sales 20.8MM EMP 35
SIC 8661 Religious organizations; Religious organizations
Pr: Howard E Butt Jr
*VP: S Dwight Lacy
*VP: David M Rogers
Dir IT: Glenn Echols

D-U-N-S 00-792-4756 IMP
H E BUTT GROCERY CO (TX)
H-E-B FOOD/DRUG STORES
646 S Flores St, San Antonio, TX 78204
Tel (210) 938-8000 Founded/Ownrshp 1905
Sales 18.1MMM^E EMP 80,000
Accts Ernst & Young Llp
SIC 5411 Supermarkets, chain; Supermarkets, hypermarket; Supermarkets, 55,000-65,000 square feet (superstore); Supermarkets, 66,000-99,000 square feet; Supermarkets, chain; Co-operative food stores
Ch Bd: Charles C Butt
*Pr: Craig L Boyan
*Pr: Howard E Butt III
CFO: Larry Davis
*CFO: Martin H Otto
CFO: Martin Otto
Treas: Jeanine Merrill
Treas: Megan Rooney
Chf Mktg O: Rob Easley
Ex VP: Roxanne Orsak
*Ex VP: Todd A Piland
Ex VP: Todd Piland
*Sr VP: Stephen W Butt
VP: Bob McCullough
VP: Steve Mount
Exec: Lisa Smith
Dir Rx: Susan Masters
Board of Directors: Howard E Butt Jr, Eleanor Butt Crook

D-U-N-S 10-666-3727
H E G ENTERPRISES
FISHERMANS RESTAURANT
1301 Alaskan Way, Seattle, WA 98101-2013
Tel (206) 623-3500 Founded/Ownrshp 1983
Sales 9.2MM^E EMP 302
SIC 5812 5813 Seafood restaurants; Cocktail lounge; Seafood restaurants; Cocktail lounge
Pr: Harold Griffith

D-U-N-S 01-647-2680
H E MCGONIGAL INC
2828 E Markland Ave, Kokomo, IN 46901-6668
Tel (765) 454-5187 Founded/Ownrshp 1928, 1995
Sales 34.7MM^E EMP 80
SIC 5511 Automobiles, new & used; Pickups, new & used; Vans, new & used; Automobiles, new & used; Pickups, new & used; Vans, new & used
CEO: Ivan Gingerich
*Pr: Rex A Gingerich
*VP: Lisa A Birkhimer
DP Exec: Irene Brantley
Mktg Dir: Amanda L Jolliffe
Sales Asso: Matt Crummel
Sales Asso: Aaron Pitts

D-U-N-S 00-450-1722
H E NEUMANN CO
100 Middle Creek Rd, Triadelphia, WV 26059-1109
Tel (304) 232-3040 Founded/Ownrshp 1975
Sales 25.4MM EMP 100
SIC 1711 7692 3498 3443 Plumbing contractors; Warm air heating & air conditioning contractor; Welding repair; Fabricated pipe & fittings; Fabricated plate work (boiler shop); Plumbing contractors; Warm air heating & air conditioning contractor; Welding repair; Fabricated pipe & fittings; Fabricated plate work (boiler shop)
CEO: Scott Winters
Pr: Rodney Boniti
Treas: James C Cochran Jr
VP: Micheal A Carl
Trfc Dir: Hannah Baker
Trfc Dir: Janet Weese
Natl Sales: Dianna Kurr
Board of Directors: James Peyton, Gary West

D-U-N-S 93-974-3274
H E NUEMANN CO MECHANICAL CONTRACTORS
1100 Grafton Rd, Morgantown, WV 26508-4709
Tel (304) 292-5462 Founded/Ownrshp 2001
Sales 22.0MM EMP 20
Accts Wiseman Hutzell & Co Wheelin
SIC 1711 Warm air heating & air conditioning contractor; Ventilation & duct work contractor; Warm air heating & air conditioning contractor; Ventilation & duct work contractor
Pr: Rodney Bliniti
*Ch Bd: Don Wagenheim
*CEO: K Scott Winters
Trfc Dir: Jimmy Baller

D-U-N-S 01-303-5373
H E P MATERIALS CORP
H E P SALES
446 Waterloo Geneva Rd, Waterloo, NY 13165-1260
Tel (315) 789-4970 Founded/Ownrshp 1965
Sales 51.3MM^E EMP 200
Accts Davie Kaplan Cpa Pc Rochest
SIC 5999 5251 Plumbing & heating supplies; Hardware; Plumbing & heating supplies; Hardware
Pr: John J Krueger
*VP: John Wilson
Advt Mgr: Jonathan Cowles
Sls Mgr: Paul Barry

H E P SALES
See H E P MATERIALS CORP

D-U-N-S 04-388-1481
H E ROHRER INC
ROHRER BUS SERVICE
1515 State Rd, Duncannon, PA 17020-9535
Tel (717) 957-5114 Founded/Ownrshp 1982
Sales 20.3MM^E EMP 130^E
SIC 4142 4151 4141 Bus charter service, except local; School buses; Local bus charter service
Pr: John M Schrantz
*VP: Howard E Rohrer III
Sfty Dirs: John Allison

H E S
See HANCHETT ENTRY SYSTEMS INC

H. E. SARGENT
See SARGENT CORP

D-U-N-S 00-715-8363 IMP
H E WILLIAMS INC (MO)
831 W Fairview Ave, Carthage, MO 64836-3736
Tel (417) 358-4065 Founded/Ownrshp 1924
Sales 134.1MM^E EMP 350
SIC 3646 Fluorescent lighting fixtures, commercial; Fluorescent lighting fixtures, commercial
Pr: Mark Williams
*CFO: T Paul Eckels
*Ex VP: Danny Lambeth
Genl Mgr: Ronald Snyder
CIO: Kent Peterson
IT Man: Dean Vandergriff
Web Dev: Mark Shipley
Sftwr Eng: Robert Wallace
Plnt Mgr: Jason Proctor
Ql Cn Mgr: Todd King
Ql Cn Mgr: Greg Sanders

D-U-N-S 00-507-6690 IMP
H E WISDOM & SONS INC
WISDOM ADHESIVES
1575 Executive Dr, Elgin, IL 60123-9363
Tel (847) 841-7002 Founded/Ownrshp 1953
Sales 25.0MM^E EMP 41
SIC 2295 2891 Resin or plastic coated fabrics; Adhesives; Glue
Pr: Jeffry Wisdom
Chf Mktg O: Cathy Westhouse
*VP: Linda Preston
VP: Andrea Steiger
Ex Dir: Rose Reinert
Off Mgr: Wendy Thomas
Prd Mgr: Mario Delgado
Sales Exec: Paul Preston
Natl Sales: Peter Bushmaker
Sls Mgr: Tim Seeley

D-U-N-S 05-704-8092
H EIKENHOUT & SONS INC
346 Wealthy St Sw, Grand Rapids, MI 49503-4007
Tel (616) 459-4523 Founded/Ownrshp 1971
Sales 69.8MM EMP 45
Accts Monroe Sweeris & Tromp Plc
SIC 5033 5085 Roofing, asphalt & sheet metal; Siding, except wood; Tools; Roofing, asphalt & sheet metal; Siding, except wood; Tools
Pr: Greg Schierbeek
*Ch Bd: Henry Schierbeek
*Treas: Richard Sonneveldt
*VP: Erik Brooks
*VP: Mike Chase
*Prin: Robert Schierbeek

H. ENTERPRISES
See H ENTERPRISES INTERNATIONAL INC

D-U-N-S 18-965-4304 IMP/EXP
H ENTERPRISES INTERNATIONAL INC
H. ENTERPRISES
120 S 6th St Ste 2300, Minneapolis, MN 55402-5158
Tel (612) 343-8293 Founded/Ownrshp 1988
Sales 134.2MM^E EMP 429
SIC 5032 8611 5211 Brick, stone & related material; Concrete & cinder building products; Concrete building products; Masons' materials; Business associations; Lumber & other building materials; Brick, stone & related material; Concrete & cinder building products; Concrete building products; Masons' materials; Business associations; Lumber & other building materials
Pr: John E Byrne
*Ch Bd: Richard E O'Leary
*VP: Michael Gorman
*VP: Susan Lewis
VP: Mary Schelde

H F
See HAUSMAN FOODS LLC

D-U-N-S 06-667-0902
H F COX INC
COX PETROLEUM TRANSPORT
7641 Edison Hwy, Bakersfield, CA 93307-9011
Tel (661) 366-3236 Founded/Ownrshp 1993
Sales 971.0M EMP 350
Accts Nmil Er Plan Se Llp North Ho
SIC 4213 4212 Trucking, except local; Petroleum haulage, local; Trucking, except local; Petroleum haulage, local
Pr: Dainiel L Mairs
*Treas: Gwen Mairs
*VP: Bruce McKinnon
IT Man: David Greene
Snr Mgr: Cox-Chad Luton

H F F
See HOLLIDAY FENOGLIO FOWLER LP

H F I
See HUGHES FURNITURE INDUSTRIES INC

D-U-N-S 04-719-8304
H F LENZ CO
1407 Scalp Ave, Johnstown, PA 15904-3329
Tel (814) 269-3380 Founded/Ownrshp 1948
Sales 23.0MM EMP 172^E
Accts Wessel & Company Johnstown P
SIC 8711 Consulting engineer; Consulting engineer
CEO: Rick Madzar
*Pr: John R Boderocco
*CFO: Matthew Donatelli
*Treas: Robert F Stano
Bd of Dir: Ryan Buff
*VP: Steve J Gridley
CIO: Robert Shiery

H F M A
See HEALTHCARE FINANCIAL MANAGEMENT ASSOICATION

D-U-N-S 04-192-9115
H F Z CAPITAL GROUP LLC
600 Madison Ave Fl 1700, New York, NY 10022-1680
Tel (212) 300-8000 Founded/Ownrshp 1998
Sales 31.3MM^E EMP 30
SIC 6799 Investors
CFO: Harold Willig
Mng Dir: Andrew Posner
Mng Dir: John Shannon
Snr PM: Jason Persico
Snr PM: Steven Spektor
Snr Mgr: Laurie Golub

H G A
See HAMMEL GREEN AND ABRAHAMSON INC

H G C
See HGC CONSTRUCTION CO

H G R
See HGR INDUSTRIAL SURPLUS INC

H G R
See H G REYNOLDS CO INC

D-U-N-S 04-398-0879
H G REYNOLDS CO INC (SC)
H G R
113 Contract Dr, Aiken, SC 29801-7004
Tel (803) 641-1402 Founded/Ownrshp 1948
Sales 62.0MM^E EMP 125
SIC 1541 1542 8711 Industrial buildings & warehouses; Industrial buildings, new construction; Renovation, remodeling & repairs: industrial buildings; Nonresidential construction; Commercial & office building, new construction; Commercial & office buildings, renovation & repair; Institutional building construction; Engineering services; Industrial buildings & warehouses; Industrial buildings, new construction; Renovation, remodeling & repairs: industrial buildings; Nonresidential construction; Commercial & office building, new construction; Commercial & office buildings, renovation & repair; Institutional building construction; Engineering services
Pr: Jeffrey Reynolds
VP: Ken Long
*VP: Leland Reynolds
*Prin: Carl H Zipf III

D-U-N-S 18-046-1428
H G SCHLICKER & ASSOCIATES INC
607 Main St, Oregon City, OR 97045-1832
Tel (503) 655-8113 Founded/Ownrshp 1980
Sales 16.1MM^E EMP 344
SIC 8748 Environmental consultant; Environmental consultant
Pr: James Gless

H G TRANSPORT
See HARTLEY GRAIN CO INC

D-U-N-S 10-763-6946 IMP/EXP
H GROUP HOLDING INC
HAWTHORN SUITES
222 W Adams St Ste 250, Chicago, IL 60606-5308
Tel (312) 750-1234 *Founded/Ownrshp* 1982
Sales 811.7MM^E *EMP* 42,000
SIC 4512 7011 5812 5813 Air passenger carrier, scheduled; Hotel, franchised; Eating places; Drinking places; Air passenger carrier, scheduled; Hotel, franchised; Eating places; Drinking places
Pr: Jay A Pritzker
**Treas:* Kenneth R Posner
**VP:* Harold Handelsman
**VP:* Thomas Pritzker
VP: John Stellato

H H
See HOYT HAYNER CORP

D-U-N-S 01-721-2317
H H BARNUM CO
7915 Lochlin Dr, Brighton, MI 48116-8329
Tel (248) 437-6707 *Founded/Ownrshp* 1976
Sales 87.5MM^E *EMP* 70
SIC 5084 Controlling instruments & accessories; Controlling instruments & accessories
Pr: Kenneth M Koza Jr
**VP:* Edward M Koza
IT Man: Steve Myers
Mktg Mgr: Laura Sliwa
Sls Mgr: Mark Rossman
Sls Mgr: Ed Seguin
Sales Asso: Chris Brandt
Sales Asso: Tony Ford
Sales Asso: Ron Galard
Sales Asso: Zack Kotila
Sales Asso: Jody Robison

H. H. BROWN RETAIL, INC.
See MACRO RETAILING LLC

D-U-N-S 01-285-2257
H H DOBBINS INC
99 West Ave, Lyndonville, NY 14098-9744
Tel (585) 765-2271 *Founded/Ownrshp* 1996
Sales 20.8MM *EMP* 70
SIC 7389 Fruits; Warehousing, cold storage or refrigerated; Packaging & labeling services
Pr: Howard H Dobbins III
**VP:* James Kankoski

H H I
See HOLLOWAY-HOUSTON INC

D-U-N-S 01-406-8449
H H KNOEBEL SONS INC
KNOEBEL'S AMUSEMENT RESORT
391 Knoebels Blvd, Elysburg, PA 17824-7127
Tel (570) 672-2572 *Founded/Ownrshp* 1900
Sales 46.8MM *EMP* 160
SIC 7996 5031 5211

H H S
See HOSPITAL HOUSEKEEPING SYSTEMS LLC

H H S
See HHS HEALTH OPTIONS

D-U-N-S 00-544-7743 IMP
H HOFFMAN IDN INC
7330 W Montrose Ave, Norridge, IL 60706-1158
Tel (708) 456-9600 *Founded/Ownrshp* 1953
Sales 47.5MM^E *EMP* 65
SIC 5087 5046 5072 5063 Locksmith equipment & supplies; Signs, electrical; Hardware; Electrical apparatus & equipment
Pr: Karen Hoffman Kahl
CFO: Patatty Single
**Sec:* Laurie Larson
**VP:* Alvin Hoffman
Brnch Mgr: Mark Guetschow
Mktg Mgr: Kathleen Kempf
Sls Mgr: Dan Lamb

H I C
See HOP INDUSTRIES CORP

H I M S S
See HEALTHCARE INFORMATION AND MANAGEMENT SYSTEMS SOCIETY

H I M S S AUSTIN TEXAS CHAPTER
See HEALTH INFORMATION MANAGEMENT SYSTEM SOCIETY

D-U-N-S 12-162-1416
H I S
ST. JOHNS CONFERENCE CENTER
44045 Five Mile Rd, Plymouth, MI 48170-2555
Tel (734) 414-0600 *Founded/Ownrshp* 1999
Sales 5.7MM^E *EMP* 300
SIC 8322 Multi-service center; Multi-service center
Pr: Ronald Wilson
**VP:* Casey Baker

H I S D
See HOUSTON INDEPENDENT SCHOOL DISTRICT

D-U-N-S 96-775-4987
H I V/ A I D S ALLIANCE FOR REGION TWO INC
H A A R T
4550 North Blvd Ste 250, Baton Rouge, LA 70806-4013
Tel (225) 927-1269 *Founded/Ownrshp* 1995
Sales 28.4MM *EMP* 9
SIC 8322 Individual & family services; Individual & family services
Ex Dir: Timothy Young
VP: Charles Harvey
Snr Mgr: Nina Julien

D-U-N-S 00-698-0635 IMP/EXP
H J BAKER & BRO INC
2 Corporate Dr Ste 545, Shelton, CT 06484-6248
Tel (203) 682-9200 *Founded/Ownrshp* 1850, 1994
Sales 138.1MM^E *EMP* 195
SIC 2048 5191 5052 Poultry feeds; Feed; Fertilizer & fertilizer materials; Sulfur; Poultry feeds; Feed; Fertilizer & fertilizer materials; Sulfur
Ch Bd: Matthew M Smith
Pr: Ed Devylder
**Pr:* David Smith
**CEO:* Christopher V B Smith
**CFO:* Stuart Adendorff
**Ex VP:* Jack L Williams
VP: Edgar Devylder
VP: Steve Mansfield
VP: Ken Medlock
Dir Bus: Art Bentley
CIO: Louis Angerame

H J F
See HENRY M JACKSON FOUNDATION FOR ADVANCEMENT OF MILITARY MEDICINE INC

D-U-N-S 06-524-3581 IMP/EXP
■ **H J HEINZ CO LP**
HEINZ NORTH AMERICA
(*Suby of* HEINZ KRAFT FOODS CO) ★
357 6th Ave, Pittsburgh, PA 15222-2530
Tel (412) 237-5757 *Founded/Ownrshp* 2000
Sales 116.2MM^E *EMP* 225
SIC 2038 Frozen specialties; Frozen specialties
CEO: Robert James Meier
Pr: Jeffrey P Berger
Ex VP: Ted Bobby
Ex VP: Brendon Buckley
VP: Tammy Langford
VP: Tammy Lankford
Prgrm Mgr: Marja Lieman
Sales Exec: Dave Moran
Mktg Mgr: David Gecht
Mktg Mgr: Robert Hoover
Counsel: Laura Hillock

D-U-N-S 10-111-7310
■ **H J HEINZ FINANCE CO**
(*Suby of* HEINZ KRAFT FOODS CO) ★
1 Ppg Pl Ste 3100, Pittsburgh, PA 15222-5447
Tel (412) 456-5700 *Founded/Ownrshp* 2001
Sales NA *EMP* 565^E
SIC 6141 Consumer finance companies
Prin: Kathy Thomas
VP: John Kraus
VP: Daniel Shaw

D-U-N-S 00-512-8467
■ **H J M P CORP** (IL)
HOME JUICE CO OF MEMPHIS
(*Suby of* NATIONAL BEVERAGE CORP) ★
1930 George St Ste 2, Melrose Park, IL 60160-1501
Tel (708) 345-5370 *Founded/Ownrshp* 1946
Sales 538.1MM^E *EMP* 1,000
SIC 2033 5149 0174 2037 Fruit juices: packaged in cans, jars, etc.; Beverages, except coffee & tea; Juices; Orange grove; Frozen fruits & vegetables; Fruit juices: packaged in cans, jars, etc.; Beverages, except coffee & tea; Juices; Orange grove; Frozen fruits & vegetables
Pr: Stan Sheraton
Pr: Mike Hoeppel
**VP:* Allen Domzalski

D-U-N-S 00-388-2685
H J RUSSELL & CO (GA)
504 Fair St Sw, Atlanta, GA 30313-1206
Tel (404) 330-1000 *Founded/Ownrshp* 1959
Sales 377.9MM^E *EMP* 733
SIC 1542 8741 7389 8742 Commercial & office building, new construction; Personnel management; Brokers, contract services; Construction project management consultant; Commercial & office building, new construction; Personnel management; Brokers, contract services; Construction project management consultant
CEO: Michael B Russell
**Pr:* H Jerome Russell Jr
Pr: James Wille
**CFO:* Ed Bradford
**Ch:* Herman Russell
VP: Barry Compton
VP: Bruce Harris
VP: Eric Hilton
Exec: Ed Perry
Off Admin: Genethia Beasley
Sfty Mgr: Paul Kennedy

D-U-N-S 62-225-4506
H K GLOBAL TRADING LTD
HKG DUTY FREE
1 E Broward Blvd Ste 1605, Fort Lauderdale, FL 33301-1838
Tel (956) 728-5180 *Founded/Ownrshp* 1991
Sales 27.3MM^E *EMP* 135
SIC 8748 8742 Business consulting; Marketing consulting services; Business consulting; Marketing consulting services
**CFO:* Edward Beckelhymer
VP: Alan Huxtable
**VP:* Shahram Khalebi
VP Merchng: Marco Arilli

D-U-N-S 03-854-7576
H K RESEARCH CORP
908 Old Lenoir Rd, Hickory, NC 28601-3447
Tel (828) 328-1721 *Founded/Ownrshp* 1980
Sales 26.0MM *EMP* 49
SIC 2821 Polyesters
Pr: Richard Higgins
**Sec:* Jan Higgins
**VP:* David Higgins
CTO: Jerry Killian
Opers Mgr: Ted Hilton
Opers Mgr: Nathan Rivera
Opers Mgr: Tom Smith

D-U-N-S 82-618-3931
H K RETAIL CONCEPTS INC
41395 Carlotta Dr, Palm Desert, CA 92211-3265
Tel (760) 341-4223 *Founded/Ownrshp* 1991
Sales 25.2MM *EMP* 13
SIC 8742 Retail trade consultant; Retail trade consultant
Mng Pt: Robert Heggie

D-U-N-S 00-506-7772
H KRAMER & CO (IL)
1345 W 21st St, Chicago, IL 60608-3111
Tel (312) 226-6600 *Founded/Ownrshp* 1888
Sales 49.3MM^E *EMP* 150
SIC 3341 Brass smelting & refining (secondary); Brass smelting & refining (secondary)
Pr: Howard K Chapman Jr
CFO: Bill Obrien
**Ex VP:* Adam Chapman
**Ex VP:* William O'Brien
**Ex VP:* Brian Wagner
**Ex VP:* Randall K Weil
Sr VP: Fred Solymos
VP: Ryan Heller
Sfty Dirs: Tom Mavronicles
Plnt Mgr: Kalish Purohit
Trfc Mgr: Fulgencio Salgado

D-U-N-S 00-118-1775
H KREVIT AND CO INC
67 Welton St, New Haven, CT 06511
Tel (203) 772-3350 *Founded/Ownrshp* 1919
Sales 20.4MM^E *EMP* 44
SIC 2869 2819 3589 Industrial organic chemicals; Industrial inorganic chemicals; Water treatment equipment, industrial; Industrial organic chemicals; Industrial inorganic chemicals; Water treatment equipment, industrial
Pr: Thomas S Ross
Treas: Esther Krevit
Treas: Doug Ross
**VP:* Donald Dechello
Trfc Dir: Jim Chrismond

H L A
See HAROLD LEVINSON ASSOCIATES INC

D-U-N-S 05-042-0835
H L GAGE SALES INC (NY)
121 Washington Avenue Ext, Albany, NY 12205-5605
Tel (518) 456-8871 *Founded/Ownrshp* 1970, 1995
Sales 26.5MM^E *EMP* 59
SIC 5511 5531 7538 Trucks, tractors & trailers: new & used; Truck equipment & parts; General truck repair; Trucks, tractors & trailers: new & used; Truck equipment & parts; General truck repair
Pr: Gary Hans
**Treas:* Thomas Hans
**VP:* Theodore Hans Jr
Off Mgr: Sarah Vandewerker

H L I
See GENATT ASSOCIATES INC

D-U-N-S 00-969-7269
H L MOE CO INC
KEEFE PLUMBING SERVICES
526 Commercial St, Glendale, CA 91203-2861
Tel (818) 572-2100 *Founded/Ownrshp* 1964
Sales 44.0MM^E *EMP* 200
Accts Hutchinson Bloodgood
SIC 1711 Plumbing contractors; Plumbing contractors
CEO: Martha Tennyson
**Pr:* Michael C Davis
**VP:* Robert Francis
**VP:* Jeff Hachey
**VP:* Richard Herrea
VP: Ric Herrera
**VP:* Kenny Kang
**VP:* Paul Kanner
**Prin:* Jim Fox
Genl Mgr: Wayne Yamabe
Mktg Dir: Jaclyn Santiago

H L W
See HLW INTERNATIONAL LLP

D-U-N-S 18-857-7555
H L WIKER INC
709 Hartman Station Rd, Lancaster, PA 17601-5915
Tel (717) 509-4580 *Founded/Ownrshp* 1988
Sales 24.3MM^E *EMP* 130
SIC 1794 Excavation work; Excavation work
CEO: Harold L Wiker
**CFO:* Daniel H Roser
**VP:* Donna Shoff
Dir Bus: Brad Shulenberger

D-U-N-S 78-663-1044
H LYOH CO LLC
(*Suby of* DAY & ZIMMERMANN GROUP INC) ★
1500 Spring Garden St # 501, Philadelphia, PA 19130-4067
Tel (215) 656-2650 *Founded/Ownrshp* 1998
Sales 16.6MM^E *EMP* 525
SIC 7363 Help supply services; Help supply services
Pr: Anthony Bosco
VP: Scott Cook

D-U-N-S 08-412-2795 IMP
H LAMM INDUSTRIES INC
4425 Ne 6th Ter, Oakland Park, FL 33334-3253
Tel (954) 491-8929 *Founded/Ownrshp* 1974
Sales 23.7MM^E *EMP* 120
Accts William Webb & Associates Llc
SIC 1711 Ventilation & duct work contractor; Ventilation & duct work contractor
Pr: Helmut Lamm
**Sec:* Julie Lamm
**VP:* Jefery Hawk
VP: Robert Taleson
**VP:* Robert A Tolleson

D-U-N-S 02-511-6810
H LEE MOFFITT CANCER CENTER & RESEARCH INSTITUTE
12902 Usf Magnolia Dr, Tampa, FL 33612-9416
Tel (813) 745-4673 *Founded/Ownrshp* 1985
Sales 91.5MM *EMP* 100
SIC 8062 General medical & surgical hospitals; General medical & surgical hospitals
Prin: Beth A Houghton
CFO: Janene Culumber
Bd of Dir: Thomas Brandon
Ex VP: Thomas Sellers
VP: Lesley Harris
Assoc Dir: Cindy McGirk
Dir Rad: Martin Miller
Dir Rx: Viet Q Ho
IT Man: Dan Spinosa
Netwrk Eng: Saroney Guttoh
Surgeon: Surbhi Jain

D-U-N-S 13-930-1956
H LEE MOFFITT CANCER CENTER & RESEARCH INSTITUTE HOSPITAL INC
12902 Usf Magnolia Dr, Tampa, FL 33612-9416
Tel (813) 745-4673 *Founded/Ownrshp* 1984
Sales 951.0MM *EMP* 4,200
Accts Ernst & Young Llp
SIC 8733 Medical research; Medical research
CEO: Alan F List
**Pr:* Jack Kolosky
**CFO:* Yvette Tremonti
Ex VP: Nick Potter
**Ex VP:* Thomas Sellers

D-U-N-S 07-961-7417
H LEE MOFFITT CANCER CENTER AND RESEARCH INSTITUTE FOUNDATION INC
12902 Usf Magnolia Dr, Tampa, FL 33612-9416
Tel (888) 663-3488 *Founded/Ownrshp* 2014
Sales 59.6MM^E *EMP* 725^E
SIC 8733 Noncommercial research organizations
Owner: Darrin Beaupre
CIO: Mark Hulse
Snr Mgr: Mokenge Malafa

D-U-N-S 14-498-2241 EXP
H LEE MOFFITT CANCER CENTER AND RESEARCH INSTITUTE FOUNDATION INC
12902 Usf Magnolia Dr, Tampa, FL 33612-9416
Tel (813) 979-3822 *Founded/Ownrshp* 2004
Sales 24.7MM *EMP* 1
SIC 8069 Cancer hospital
CEO: William S Dalton
**COO:* John A Kolosky
**VP:* Susan Stern
Doctor: Barbara Centeno
Diag Rad: Jennifer Drukteinis

D-U-N-S 84-543-6294
H LEE MOFFITT CANCER CENTER AND RESEARCH INSTITUTE INC
12902 Usf Magnolia Dr, Tampa, FL 33612-9416
Tel (813) 745-4673 *Founded/Ownrshp* 1987
Sales NA *EMP* 3,000
SIC 8011

D-U-N-S 00-892-8244
H LEFF ELECTRIC CO
4700 Spring Rd, Cleveland, OH 44131-1027
Tel (216) 325-0941 *Founded/Ownrshp* 1921
Sales 128.6MM^E *EMP* 107
Accts Bober Markey Fedorovich Akron
SIC 5063 Electrical supplies; Electrical supplies
Pr: Bruce E Leff
CFO: Jules Altshuler
**Ex VP:* Sanford Leff Jr
VP: Debbie Leff
Brnch Mgr: Jim Anderson
Brnch Mgr: Randy Kellams
Dir IT: Dave Marcus
VP Sls: Bill Better
Sales Asso: Larry Aldridge
Sales Asso: Jason Cheetham
Snr PM: Shannon Skoda

H M
See HUDSON MERIDIAN CONSTRUCTION GROUP LLC

H M A
See PUNTA GORDA HMA INC

H M A A
See HAWAII WESTERN MANAGEMENT GROUP INC

D-U-N-S 78-848-8732
■ **H M A GAFFNEY INC**
HMA
(*Suby of* HEALTH MANAGEMENT ASSOCIATES INC) ★
1530 N Limestone St, Gaffney, SC 29340-4742
Tel (864) 487-4271 *Founded/Ownrshp* 1987
Sales 41.1MM *EMP* 400
SIC 8062 Hospital, AMA approved residency; Hospital, AMA approved residency
CEO: Brian Yates
Ex VP: Betty Dickson
Exec: Connie Gibson
Obsttrcn: Johnny L Neighbors
Doctor: John Conti
Doctor: Thomas Stern

D-U-N-S 14-436-1201
■ **H M A LOUISBURG INC**
(*Suby of* HEALTH MANAGEMENT ASSOCIATES INC) ★
100 Hospital Dr, Louisburg, NC 27549-2256
Tel (919) 496-5131 *Founded/Ownrshp* 1986
Sales 13.8MM^E *EMP* 350
SIC 8062 General medical & surgical hospitals; General medical & surgical hospitals
Ch Bd: William J Schoen
**Pr:* Joseph V Vumbacco
**CFO:* Robert Farnham
CFO: Thomas Whalen
**Sr VP:* Timothy R Parry

D-U-N-S 19-894-9935
H M BROWN AND ASSOCIATES INC
6532 S Revere Pkwy, Centennial, CO 80111-6418
Tel (303) 740-8065 *Founded/Ownrshp* 2011
Sales 35.6MM^E *EMP* 139^E
SIC 5511 5521 5012 New & used car dealers; Used car dealers; Automotive brokers
Pr: Harold M Brown
**VP:* Christopher Brown
VP: Colbert Harris
Sls Mgr: Jeff Strizich
Sls Mgr: Jay Titterington
Sales Asso: Mandy Archer
Sales Asso: Stan Ferrin
Sales Asso: Megi Scowcroft

H M C
See HUSSUNG MECHANICAL CONTRACTORS INC

H M C
See HEARTLAND MEAT CO INC

D-U-N-S 05-144-3919
H M CRAGG CO
7490 Bush Lake Rd, Edina, MN 55439-2801
Tel (952) 884-7775 *Founded/Ownrshp* 1988
Sales 36.0MM *EMP* 39
SIC 5063

D-U-N-S 07-316-2067 IMP
H M DUNN CO INC
HM DUNNAIR AEROSYSTEM
(*Suby of* HM DUNN AEROSYSTEMS INC) ★
3301 House Anderson Rd, Euless, TX 76040-2001
Tel (817) 283-3722 *Founded/Ownrshp* 2011
Sales 88.0MM^E *EMP* 440
SIC 3724 3599 Aircraft engines & engine parts; Machine & other job shop work; Machine shop, jobbing & repair; Aircraft engines & engine parts; Machine & other job shop work; Machine shop, jobbing & repair
CEO: Phil Milazzo
**COO:* Rick Rosenjack
**CFO:* Rebecca Tomlinson
Prgrm Mgr: Raffi Avakian
Prgrm Mgr: Earl Overcash
Prgrm Mgr: Franklin Stephanie
IT Man: Danny Grounds
IT Man: Cindy Winget
Prd Dir: Michael Webb
Mktg Dir: Willie Gandy
Snr Mgr: Ellis Jim

D-U-N-S 09-654-1669 IMP
H M DUNN CO INC
4201 S 119th St W, Wichita, KS 67215-9100
Tel (316) 522-5426 *Founded/Ownrshp* 1978
Sales 54.1MM^E *EMP* 191
SIC 3599 Machine shop, jobbing & repair; Machine shop, jobbing & repair
CEO: Phil Milazzo
**COO:* Rick Rosenjack
**CFO:* Rebecca Tomlinson
Prgrm Mgr: David McClure
Genl Mgr: Jake Byrne
QA Dir: Matt Hupp
Dir IT: Rick Gillespie
IT Man: Ken Veer
Mfg Mgr: Larry Ulin
Prd Mgr: James Bishop

H M E
See H M ELECTRONICS INC

D-U-N-S 06-311-5497 IMP
H M ELECTRONICS INC (CA)
H M E
14110 Stowe Dr, Poway, CA 92064-7147
Tel (858) 535-6000 *Founded/Ownrshp* 1971
Sales 162.8MM^E *EMP* 539
SIC 3669 Intercommunication systems, electric; Intercommunication systems, electric
Ch Bd: Harrison Y Miyahira
Recvr: Brandon Truby
**CEO:* Charles Miyahira
VP: Steven Anthony
VP: Paul Foley
VP: Scott Hoeptner
VP: Susan Penn
VP: Rick Sunamoto
VP: Scott Weldner
Prgrm Mgr: Lisa Jokinen
QA Dir: Rick Molina

H M G
See HOLSTON MEDICAL GROUP PC

H M T
See HOT MELT TECHNOLOGIES INC

D-U-N-S 12-811-2252
H M T TANK SERVICE INC
(*Suby of* HMT INC) ★
24 Waterway Ave Ste 400, The Woodlands, TX 77380-3197
Tel (281) 681-7000 *Founded/Ownrshp* 1978
Sales 77.1MM^E *EMP* 600
SIC 1799 Petroleum storage tanks, pumping & draining; Petroleum storage tanks, pumping & draining
Pr: Millard J Jones Jr
**VP:* Ruston P Chandler
**VP:* Lawrence W McAfee
**VP:* Scott D Spence
**VP:* Gary E Tesch
Corp Couns: Blair Bruce
Snr Mgr: James Long
Snr Mgr: Glenn Tate

H M WHITE
See HMW CONTRACTING LLC

D-U-N-S 01-879-4880 IMP
H MART BOSTON INC
3 Old Concord Rd, Burlington, MA 01803-5168
Tel (781) 221-4570 *Founded/Ownrshp* 2008
Sales 31.9MM *EMP* 3
Accts Choi Kim & Park Llp Irvine
SIC 5999 Miscellaneous retail stores; Miscellaneous retail stores
Prin: IL Y Kwon
Mktg Dir: Moonsoo Hwang

D-U-N-S 84-274-5775 IMP
H MART COMPANIES INC
SUPER H MART
(*Suby of* GRAND SUPERCENTER INC) ★
300 Chubb Ave, Lyndhurst, NJ 07071-3502
Tel (201) 507-9900 *Founded/Ownrshp* 2002
Sales 39.6MM^E *EMP* 182^E
SIC 5411 Grocery stores
Ch Bd: IL Yeon Kwon
CFO: William Choi
Sr VP: Edward Sohn
Genl Mgr: Charles Park
Genl Mgr: Adrian Won
IT Man: Jimmy Jim

D-U-N-S 83-251-6749
H MART FORT LEE LLC
112 Linwood Plz Ste 130, Fort Lee, NJ 07024-3701
Tel (201) 947-7800 *Founded/Ownrshp* 2009
Sales 25.6MM *EMP* 3
SIC 6512 Shopping center, community (100,000 - 300,000 sq ft); Shopping center, community (100,000 - 300,000 sq ft)

D-U-N-S 80-823-1166 IMP
H MART WEST INC
2825 S Diamond Bar Blvd, Diamond Bar, CA 91765-3414
Tel (909) 839-0300 *Founded/Ownrshp* 2006
Sales 24.6MM^E *EMP* 146^E
Accts Choi Kim & Park Llp Irvine
SIC 5411 Grocery stores
Pr: Ilyeon Kwon

H. MEYER DAIRY
See BORDEN DAIRY CO OF CINCINNATI LLC

D-U-N-S 00-896-6145 IMP/EXP
H MUEHLSTEIN & CO INC
MUEHLSTEIN COMPOUNDED PRODUCTS
10 Westport Rd Ste 200, Wilton, CT 06897-4548
Tel (203) 855-6000 *Founded/Ownrshp* 1996
Sales NA *EMP* 500
SIC 5162 5169 Plastics materials; Synthetic rubber

D-U-N-S 03-616-3461
H N AND FRANCES C BERGER FOUNDATION
42600 Cook St Ste 203, Palm Desert, CA 92211-5143
Tel (760) 341-5293 *Founded/Ownrshp* 2010
Sales 26.5MM *EMP* 21^E
SIC 8641 Civic social & fraternal associations; Civic social & fraternal associations
Prin: Ronald Auen

D-U-N-S 00-890-6455
■ **H N B BANK NA**
(*Suby of* MERCANTILE BANCORP INC) ★
100 N Main St, Hannibal, MO 63401-3537
Tel (573) 221-0050 *Founded/Ownrshp* 2007
Sales NA *EMP* 61
SIC 6021 National commercial banks; National commercial banks
Pr: Ronald Verdier
CFO: Linda Woodhurst
**VP:* Hal Benedict
IT Man: Janet Wells

D-U-N-S 17-623-3252
H NAGEL & SON CO
BRIGHTON MILLS
2428 Central Pkwy, Cincinnati, OH 45214-1804
Tel (513) 665-4550 *Founded/Ownrshp* 1970
Sales 30.0MM *EMP* 35
SIC 2041 Flour: blended, prepared or self-rising; Flour: blended, prepared or self-rising
Pr: William Nagel
**VP:* Michael Norris

D-U-N-S 00-143-0032
H O BOUCHARD INC (ME)
349 Coldbrook Rd, Hampden, ME 04444-1503
Tel (207) 862-4070 *Founded/Ownrshp* 1974
Sales 23.2MM^E *EMP* 110
SIC 4213 4212 Building materials transport; Lumber (log) trucking, local
Pr: Harold Bouchard
**VP:* Brian Bouchard
**Prin:* Robert Farrington

D-U-N-S 78-248-8902
H O C J INC
PREMIER TRANSPORTATION
323 Cash Memorial Blvd, Forest Park, GA 30297-2667
Tel (404) 675-1950 *Founded/Ownrshp* 1991
Sales 87.6MM^E *EMP* 173
SIC 4213 4731 Trucking, except local; Freight transportation arrangement; Trucking, except local; Freight transportation arrangement
CEO: Michael P Medici
**Pr:* Joseph T Hughes
CFO: Tom Rouce
**VP:* Greg Plese

H O K
See HELLMUTH OBATA & KASSABAUM INC

D-U-N-S 05-666-8577 EXP
H O PENN MACHINERY CO INC (NY)
122 Noxon Rd, Poughkeepsie, NY 12603-2940
Tel (845) 452-1200 *Founded/Ownrshp* 1923, 1965
Sales 285.5MM^E *EMP* 400
SIC 5082 5084 General construction machinery & equipment; Materials handling machinery; General construction machinery & equipment; Materials handling machinery
CEO: C E Thomas Cleveland
**Pr:* Robert W Cleveland
Ex VP: Jeff Mitchell
**Ex VP:* Jeffrey Mitchell
VP: John Bellardino
Genl Mgr: Anthony Bannister
Genl Mgr: Dennis Romanson
Dir IT: Walter Datto
Dir IT: Walter Dotto
VP Sls: Jim Rogan
Sls Dir: Joe Debuono
Board of Directors: Sue Steffanci

D-U-N-S 00-644-2610
H O WOLDING INC (WI)
9642 Western Way, Amherst, WI 54406-9026
Tel (715) 824-5513 *Founded/Ownrshp* 1935
Sales 91.1MM^E *EMP* 450
SIC 4213 Contract haulers; Contract haulers
Pr: Don Wolding
**VP:* Cathy Kirsling
**VP:* Marc Wolding
CIO: Kathy Kirsling
IT Man: Jeff Krutsa
Sls Dir: Mike Gross

H P FOOD STORE
See H P NEMENZ FOOD STORES INC

H P G
See HEALTHTRUST PURCHASING GROUP LP

D-U-N-S 15-134-0700
H P NEMENZ FOOD STORES INC
H P FOOD STORE
70 W Mckinley Way Ste 1, Youngstown, OH 44514-1967
Tel (330) 757-8940 *Founded/Ownrshp* 1985
Sales 58.9MM^E *EMP* 400
SIC 5411 Grocery stores, chain; Grocery stores, chain
Pr: Henry P Nemenz
**Sec:* Judy Gabriele
**Prin:* Donald P Herriott

D-U-N-S 00-220-5946 IMP
H P NEUN CO INC (NY)
100 Dunn Rd, Lyons, NY 14489-9767
Tel (585) 388-1360 *Founded/Ownrshp* 1880, 1981
Sales 40.8MM^E *EMP* 163
SIC 2653 2652 Boxes, corrugated: made from purchased materials; Setup paperboard boxes; Boxes, corrugated: made from purchased materials; Setup paperboard boxes
Ch Bd: Stephen M Bregande
**CFO:* Michael Schleahr
**VP:* Bruce Hilton
**VP:* Christopher Woods
Genl Mgr: Bruce Chilton
CIO: Ciaran Hanna
Opers Mgr: Matthew Dukat

D-U-N-S 01-641-1746 IMP
H P PRODUCTS CORP
CUSTODIAL TRUCKING COMPANY
(*Suby of* FERGUSON ENTERPRISES INC) ★
4220 Saguaro Trl, Indianapolis, IN 46268-2550
Tel (317) 298-9957 *Founded/Ownrshp* 2014
Sales 278.1MM^E *EMP* 400
SIC 5087 Janitors' supplies; Janitors' supplies
Pr: Bridget Shuel-Walker
**CFO:* Mark Willoughby
Ex VP: Allen Green
VP: Paul Hornsby
VP: Jim Krohn
VP: David Matasar
VP: Dale McGinty
VP: John Renard
VP: Mark Summers
Dir IT: James King
Dir IT: Tom Shock

D-U-N-S 00-412-8596
H P R MAZDA
CHAMPAIGN AUTO SUPERSTORE
1912 Moreland Blvd, Champaign, IL 61822-1241
Tel (217) 359-0036 *Founded/Ownrshp* 1995
Sales 41.3MM^E *EMP* 325
SIC 5511 Automobiles, new & used; Automobiles, new & used
Prin: William Ross

H P S
See HAYES PIPE SUPPLY INC

H P S C FINANCIAL SERVICES
See HPSC INC

D-U-N-S 62-162-5508
H P SERVICE INC
1890 S Bypass 35, Alvin, TX 77511-4606
Tel (281) 331-0669 *Founded/Ownrshp* 1990
Sales 8.1MM^E *EMP* 600
SIC 7361 0782 Labor contractors (employment agency); Mowing services, lawn; Labor contractors (employment agency); Mowing services, lawn
Pr: Gary D Pitts

D-U-N-S 78-206-3465
H P SKOLNICK INC
IMPERIAL FROZEN FOODS
99 Pacific St Ste 200b, Monterey, CA 93940-2493
Tel (831) 375-9866 *Founded/Ownrshp* 1991
Sales 40.7MM *EMP* 9
Accts Barry Dolowich Cpa Inc Mon
SIC 3556 Fruits, frozen; Bakery machinery
CEO: Henry Peter Skolnick
**VP:* Jon Waxman
**Prin:* Peter Skolnick

D-U-N-S 00-436-3875 IMP
H P W SPECIALTIES INC
ETOWAH CHEMICAL SALES & SVC
2618 Forrest Ave, Gadsden, AL 35904-1950
Tel (256) 547-7527 *Founded/Ownrshp* 1978
Sales 23.2MM^E *EMP* 55
SIC 5087 5169 7699 Cleaning & maintenance equipment & supplies; Janitors' supplies; Industrial chemicals; Detergents; Industrial machinery & equipment repair; Industrial equipment cleaning
Pr: Michael Turner
**VP:* Terry Murray

D-U-N-S 13-882-9796
H Q GLOBAL HOLDINGS INC
(*Suby of* REGUS H)
15305 Dallas Pkwy Ste 400, Addison, TX 75001-6922
Tel (972) 361-8100 *Founded/Ownrshp* 2004
Sales 12.7MM^E *EMP* 1,200
SIC 6519 7389 Sub-lessors of real estate; Office facilities & secretarial service rental; Sub-lessors of real estate; Office facilities & secretarial service rental
CEO: Peter H Harris
Ex VP: Kevin Naze
Ex VP: Kent Shoemaker
Ex VP: Brad Young
Prin: Regina Martin
Genl Mgr: Lavonia Brown
Genl Mgr: Rick Patterson
CIO: Gary Russell
MIS Dir: Gilbert Partida
IT Man: Arthur Pidgeon
MIS Mgr: Jennifer Kennedy

D-U-N-S 13-883-8904
H Q GLOBAL WORKPLACES LLC
(*Suby of* REGUS CORP) ★
15305 Dallas Pkwy Ste 400, Addison, TX 75001-6922
Tel (972) 361-8100 *Founded/Ownrshp* 2004
Sales 34.4MM^E *EMP* 1,190
SIC 6519 7389 Sub-lessors of real estate; Office facilities & secretarial service rental; Telephone answering service; Mailbox rental & related service; Sub-lessors of real estate; Office facilities & secretarial service rental; Telephone answering service; Mailbox rental & related service

H Q O
See HIGH QUALITY ORGANICS INC

H R 2
See HIGH REACH CO LLC

D-U-N-S 02-967-0734 IMP
H R BEELER TRACTOR AND EQUIPMENT INC
BEELER TRACTOR COMPANY
887 E Onstott Rd, Yuba City, CA 95991-3638
Tel (530) 673-3555 *Founded/Ownrshp* 1961
Sales 20.1MM *EMP* 28
Accts Matson And Isom Yuba City Ca
SIC 5999 5261 Farm equipment & supplies; Farm machinery; Lawn & garden equipment; Farm equipment & supplies; Farm machinery; Lawn & garden equipment
Pr: Michael Dihel
**Sec:* Cyndi Jayne
**VP:* Douglas Long

D-U-N-S 80-779-2072
H R HOUSTON
1818 East Rd, Houston, TX 77054-6012
Tel (713) 780-9960 *Founded/Ownrshp* 1943
Sales 1.5MM *EMP* 800
Accts Zientek & Co Pc Houston
SIC 8399 Fund raising organization, non-fee basis; Fund raising organization, non-fee basis
Pr: Judy Murphy
**Treas:* Rebecca Macleary
**Prin:* Ruth Eiler

D-U-N-S 87-622-3009
■ **H R I HOSPITAL INC**
ARBOUR-H R I HOSPITAL
(*Suby of* UNIVERSAL HEALTH SERVICES INC) ★
227 Babcock St, Brookline, MA 02446-6773
Tel (617) 731-3200 *Founded/Ownrshp* 1983
Sales 21.1MM^E *EMP* 160
SIC 8063 Psychiatric hospitals
CEO: Pat Moallemisn
**CEO:* Roy A Ettlinger
Dir IT: Bill Butler
Doctor: Raphael Weinstein
Dir Health: Ann Marie White
HC Dir: Shelly Baer

H R R V
See COVANTA HONOLULU RESOURCE RECOVERY VENTURE

D-U-N-S 05-742-5100 IMP
H R S FASTENER INC
716 Avenue H E, Arlington, TX 76011-3104
Tel (817) 640-9992 *Founded/Ownrshp* 1972
Sales 31.5MM *EMP* 28
SIC 5085 Industrial supplies; Fasteners & fastening equipment; Industrial supplies; Fasteners & fastening equipment
Pr: Ford Smith
**VP:* Aaron Ellis
**VP:* William Smith
IT Man: Keith Smith

D-U-N-S 02-758-9373
H R SPINNER CORP
115 S 1st Ave, Yakima, WA 98902-3400
Tel (509) 453-9111 *Founded/Ownrshp* 1916
Sales 22.2MM^E *EMP* 42
SIC 5085 5113 3554 Packing, industrial; Boxes, paperboard & disposable plastic; Box making machines, paper
Pr: Ed Jewett

D-U-N-S 05-225-4356
H RAUVEL INC (CA)
NOVA CONTAINER FREIGHT STATION
1710 E Sepulveda Blvd, Carson, CA 90745-6142
Tel (310) 604-0060 *Founded/Ownrshp* 1978
Sales 42.2MM^E *EMP* 300
SIC 4225 4731 General warehousing; Agents, shipping; Brokers, shipping; Freight consolidation; Railroad freight agency; General warehousing; Agents, shipping; Brokers, shipping; Freight consolidation; Railroad freight agency
Pr: Hector R Velasco
VP Opers: Chris Cash

D-U-N-S 78-794-8629
H ROSEN USA LLC
14120 Interdrive E, Houston, TX 77032-3324
Tel (281) 442-8282 *Founded/Ownrshp* 2007
Sales 21.1MM^E *EMP* 200
SIC 3999 5734 Atomizers, toiletry; Software, business & non-game
Pr: Hermann Rosen
Treas: Jan Frowijn
Sls Mgr: Bryce Brown

H S A
See HEALTH SERVICES DEPARTMENT

D-U-N-S 01-761-5381
H S B C OVERSEAS CORP (DE)
(*Suby of* HSBC USA INC) ★
300 Delaware Ave Ste 1400, Wilmington, DE 19801-1650
Tel (302) 657-8400 *Founded/Ownrshp* 1987
Sales 88.2MM *EMP* 17
SIC 6722 Mutual fund sales, on own account; Mutual fund sales, on own account
Pr: Richard Leigh

D-U-N-S 02-918-4616
H S C FOUNDATION INC
2013 H St Nw Ste 300, Washington, DC 20006-4203
Tel (202) 454-1220 Founded/Ownrshp 1984
Sales 14.0MM EMP 360
Accts Dixon Hughes Goodman Rockvill
SIC 8742 Hospital & health services consultant; Hospital & health services consultant
CEO: Thomas W Chapman
*Ex VP: John Mathewson
*VP: Lynne Hostetter
*VP: Jessie Mackinnon
*VP: Nancy J Southers

D-U-N-S 00-911-6518 IMP
H S CROCKER CO INC
12100 Smith Dr, Huntley, IL 60142-9618
Tel (847) 669-3600 Founded/Ownrshp 1998
Sales 20.5MM^E EMP 124
SIC 2671 2672 Packaging paper & plastics film, coated & laminated; Adhesive papers, labels or tapes: from purchased material; Packaging paper & plastics film, coated & laminated; Adhesive papers, labels or tapes: from purchased material
Pr: Ronald J Giordano
CFO: Tom Wilt
*VP: John C Dai
*VP: William Linehan
VP: Juan Spanolian
Genl Mgr: Dennis Anderson
Genl Mgr: John Narish
Genl Mgr: Lisa Sulma
DP Exec: Weizhen Tu
Plnt Mgr: John Rhodes
VP Sls: Norbert Suarez

D-U-N-S 05-094-7068 EXP
H S DIE & ENGINEERING INC
O-215 Lake Michigan Dr Nw, Grand Rapids, MI 49534-3397
Tel (616) 453-5451 Founded/Ownrshp 1969
Sales 76.9MM^E EMP 250^E
SIC 3544 Special dies, tools, jigs & fixtures; Special dies & tools; Aircraft parts & equipment; Special dies, tools, jigs & fixtures; Special dies & tools
CEO: Marcia Steele
*COO: Jeff Hearn
Genl Mgr: Dale Hermiller
Board of Directors: George Slykhouse

H S E
See HARTER SECREST & EMERY LLP

H S G
See HARSCO SERVICES GROUP LLC

H S G
See HARMON SOLUTIONS GROUP LLC

H S GUIDANCE OFFICE.
See WINNISQUAM REGIONAL SCHOOL DISTRICT

H S I
See HOUSTON SERVICE INDUSTRIES INC

H S I
See HEATER SPECIALISTS LLC

H S INDUSTRIES
See HUNTERS SPECIALTIES INC

D-U-N-S 85-978-0389
H S MORGAN LIMITED PARTNERSHIP
3158 Production Dr, Fairfield, OH 45014-4228
Tel (513) 870-4400 Founded/Ownrshp 1988
Sales 57.1MM^E EMP 250
SIC 2521 2522 Panel systems & partitions (free-standing), office: wood; Panel systems & partitions, office: except wood; Panel systems & partitions (free-standing), office: wood; Panel systems & partitions, office: except wood

D-U-N-S 02-382-4139
H SAVILLE AND SON INC
SAVILLE PRODUCE
(Suby of PRODUCE SOURCE PARTNERS INC) ★
3606 Acorn Ave, Newport News, VA 23607-3230
Tel (757) 244-0191 Founded/Ownrshp 2003
Sales 20.2MM^E EMP 90^E
SIC 5148 5147 5142 Fruits, fresh; Vegetables, fresh; Meats, fresh; Frozen vegetables & fruit products; Meat, frozen: packaged
Pr: Norman B Saville
Off Mgr: Nancy Johnson

D-U-N-S 15-999-8632
H SCHRIER & CO INC
4901 Glenwood Rd, Brooklyn, NY 11234-1131
Tel (718) 258-7500 Founded/Ownrshp 1986
Sales 116.7MM^E EMP 100
SIC 5141 Groceries, general line; Groceries, general line
Ch Bd: David Libertoff
*Sec: Jonathan Libertoff
Sales Exec: Mike Serotkin

D-U-N-S 00-697-3838 IMP
H SCHULTZ & SONS
777 Lehigh Ave, Union, NJ 07083-7626
Tel (212) 227-7325 Founded/Ownrshp 1921
Sales 59.1MM^E EMP 85
SIC 5064 5199 Electric household appliances; General merchandise, non-durable; Electric household appliances; General merchandise, non-durable
VP: David Schultz
Opers Mgr: Ran Lazarovitch

H T A
See HONDA TRADING AMERICA CORP

D-U-N-S 62-170-0939 IMP
■ H T A AEROSTRUCTURES INC
(Suby of GOODRICH AEROSTRUCTURES GROUP) ★
2005 Technology Way, San Marcos, TX 78666-8501
Tel (512) 754-3600 Founded/Ownrshp 1990
Sales 25.1MM^E EMP 200
SIC 3728 Aircraft parts & equipment; Aircraft parts & equipment
Genl Mgr: Bruce Tifft

Sr VP: Lawrence Chapman
Plnt Mgr: Bruce Tift

D-U-N-S 01-918-1759 IMP
H T BERRY CO INC
50 North St, Canton, MA 02021-3339
Tel (781) 828-6000 Founded/Ownrshp 1964
Sales 28.8MM EMP 52
Accts Croyle & Associates Pc Lynnf
SIC 5113 Industrial & personal service paper; Industrial & personal service paper
CEO: Henry T Berry
*Pr: Christopher D Nolan
*COO: Jane M Busconi
*VP: James R Berry
*VP: Paul W Maguire

D-U-N-S 82-952-0274
H T BOWLING INC
6629 Hickman Cemetery Rd, Fairlawn, VA 24141-5803
Tel (540) 639-9621 Founded/Ownrshp 1968
Sales 27.7MM^E EMP 113
SIC 1611 Highway & street construction
CEO: Harry T Bowling
*CEO: Linda Gordon
*CFO: Ola S Bowling
*Sec: Richard Gordon
*VP: Kenneth Bowling

H T C
See HORRY TELEPHONE COOPERATIVE INC

H T C
See HUMAN TECHNOLOGIES CORP

H T C
See HUTT TRUCKING CO INC

H T D
See HOOSIER TOOL & DIE CO INC

D-U-N-S 00-792-1356 IMP/EXP
H T HACKNEY CO (TN)
HACKNEY CASH & CARRY
502 S Gay St Ste 300, Knoxville, TN 37902-3607
Tel (865) 546-1291 Founded/Ownrshp 1891
Sales 22.3MM EMP 3,600
Accts Pugh & Company Pc Knoxville
SIC 5141 5172 2434 5084 Groceries, general line; Gasoline; Service station supplies, petroleum; Wood kitchen cabinets; Industrial machinery & equipment; Groceries, general line; Gasoline; Service station supplies, petroleum; Wood kitchen cabinets; Industrial machinery & equipment
Ch Bd: William B Sansom
*Pr: Charles Shue
*COO: Dean Ballinger
*CFO: Michael D Morton
Exec: Mike Delaguaro
Exec: Arlene Kitts
Exec: Linda Martin
*VP Admn: Leonard Robinette
Div Mgr: Scott Fitch
Genl Mgr: Jerry Friel
Genl Mgr: Mike Magill

D-U-N-S 06-403-5306
■ H T LYONS INC
(Suby of TALEN ENERGY SERVICES HOLDINGS LLC) ★
7165 Ambassador Dr, Allentown, PA 18106-9255
Tel (610) 530-2600 Founded/Ownrshp 1998
Sales 153.8MM^E EMP 350
SIC 1711 Mechanical contractor; Warm air heating & air conditioning contractor; Refrigeration contractor; Plumbing contractors; Mechanical contractor; Warm air heating & air conditioning contractor; Refrigeration contractor; Plumbing contractors
Pr: Rick Perosa
*VP: Chris Bernecker
*VP: Roeland F Hoeke
Genl Mgr: Buddy Kida
*Genl Mgr: K Scott Sine
IT Man: Jason Boehm
IT Man: Debbie Termini
Snr PM: Matthew Matsinko
Snr PM: Clinton Penkauskas

H T PUBLISHING CO
See ROMAN CATHOLIC CHURCH OF DIOCESE OF HOUMA THIBODAUX

H T S
See HEAT TRANSFER SOLUTIONS INC

D-U-N-S 00-251-3836
H T SWEENEY & SON INC (PA)
308 E Dutton Mill Rd # 1, Brookhaven, PA 19015-1197
Tel (610) 872-8896 Founded/Ownrshp 1947
Sales 30.2MM^E EMP 80
SIC 1794 1611 Excavation work; Highway & street paving contractor
Pr: Herbert T Sweeney III
*Treas: Brian Chidester
*VP: Richard Jenks
*VP: Glen S Sweeney
Mtls Mgr: Kevin Sauler

H U D
See UNITED STATES DEPT OF HOUSING AND URBAN DEVELOPMENT

D-U-N-S 15-520-7863
H V A C INC
HILL VENTILATING & AC
101 3rd St, Bristol, TN 37620-2335
Tel (423) 989-5000 Founded/Ownrshp 1986
Sales 41.4MM^E EMP 125
Accts James P Cline Cpa
SIC 1711 1731 1542 Plumbing contractors; Heating & air conditioning contractors; Electrical work; Commercial & office building contractors; Plumbing contractors; Heating & air conditioning contractors; Electrical work; Commercial & office building contractors
CEO: James E Hill
*Pr: B Keith Rhyner
Treas: Jennifer Bays
Genl Mgr: Priscilla Ward
IT Man: Keith Rhymer

H V L
See V L H INC

H V O
See HAYWOOD VOCATIONAL OPPORTUNITIES INC

D-U-N-S 00-921-2275
H V WELKER CO INC
WELKER BROS
970 S Milpitas Blvd, Milpitas, CA 95035-6323
Tel (408) 263-4400 Founded/Ownrshp 1954
Sales 33.8MM EMP 65
SIC 1752 Floor laying & floor work; Floor laying & floor work
Pr: Stuart Welker
*Ex VP: Jack Sanguinitti
*VP: Vincent A Grana
*VP: Timothy C Reynolds

H W
See HARVARD-WESTLAKE SCHOOL

D-U-N-S 00-315-9134
H W CULP LUMBER CO (NC)
491 Us Hwy 52 N, New London, NC 28127
Tel (704) 463-7311 Founded/Ownrshp 1924, 1950
Sales 61.6MM^E EMP 92
SIC 5031 Lumber, plywood & millwork; Lumber, plywood & millwork
Pr: H W Culp Jr
*Sec: Amy Shelton
*VP: H W Culp III
Plnt Mgr: David Richbourg

D-U-N-S 07-885-0876
H W FARREN LLC
(Suby of FARREN INTERNATIONAL LLC) ★
1578 Sussex Tpke Ste 510, Randolph, NJ 07869-1833
Tel (973) 927-2777 Founded/Ownrshp 2013
Sales 46.0MM EMP 130
SIC 4213 1796 Machine moving & rigging; Industrial trucks & tractors; Contract haulers; Machine moving & rigging
Pr: Philip Antonucci
COO: James Pascale
VP: Nick Mitchell

H W H
See HWH CORP

D-U-N-S 00-781-1144
H W HOUSTON CONSTRUCTION CO
210 S Victoria Ave, Pueblo, CO 81003-3435
Tel (719) 544-2791 Founded/Ownrshp 1972
Sales 49.3MM EMP 65
Accts Jerry W Brown Cpa Pc Pueblo
SIC 1542 1541 Commercial & office building, new construction; Commercial & office buildings, renovation & repair; Industrial buildings & warehouses; Renovation, remodeling & repairs: industrial buildings; Commercial & office building, new construction; Commercial & office buildings, renovation & repair; Industrial buildings & warehouses; Renovation, remodeling & repairs: industrial buildings
CEO: Paul Depatie
*Pr: Kenneth West
*CFO: Ernest Garcia
*Sr VP: Scott Robb
*VP: Richard Brake

D-U-N-S 02-837-0617
H W HUNTER INC
HUNTER DODGE CHRYSLER JEEP RAM
1130 Auto Mall Dr, Lancaster, CA 93534-6302
Tel (661) 948-8411 Founded/Ownrshp 1956
Sales 84.0MM EMP 100
SIC 5511 7538 Automobiles, new & used; Pickups, new & used; General automotive repair shops; Automobiles, new & used; Pickups, new & used; General automotive repair shops
CEO: Timothy H Fuller
Off Mgr: Jeanie Posan

D-U-N-S 03-477-2822 IMP
H W JENKINS CO
4155 Pidgeon Roost Rd, Memphis, TN 38118-6908
Tel (901) 363-7641 Founded/Ownrshp 1939
Sales 42.3MM^E EMP 60
SIC 5031 2452 2439 Lumber: rough, dressed & finished; Plywood; Millwork; Panels & sections, prefabricated, wood; Trusses, wooden roof
Pr: Harold W Jenkins
*Sec: Ernest M Bearden

D-U-N-S 07-423-6506
H W KAUFMAN FINANCIAL GROUP INC
(Suby of AJK ENTERPRISES INC) ★
30833 Northwestern Hwy, Farmington Hills, MI 48334-2551
Tel (248) 932-9000 Founded/Ownrshp 1996
Sales NA EMP 1,005
SIC 6141 6719 Installment sales finance, other than banks; Investment holding companies, except banks; Installment sales finance, other than banks; Investment holding companies, except banks
CEO: Alan Jay Kaufman
Ex VP: Daniel T Muldowney
Sr VP: Gary Batten
Sr VP: Donald Carson
Sr VP: Harvey Goldenberg
Sr VP: David Price
Sr VP: Christopher Zoidis
VP: Wayne Bates
VP: Michael Franzese
VP: Ken Laderoute
VP: Michael Maharaj
VP: Kermit Shaulis

D-U-N-S 02-520-8133
H W LOCHNER INC
225 W Washington St # 1200, Chicago, IL 60606-3100
Tel (312) 372-7346 Founded/Ownrshp 1940, 1944
Sales 113.8MM^E EMP 400
SIC 8711 8742 Consulting engineer; Planning consultant; Consulting engineer; Planning consultant
Ch: Hal Lochner
*Pr: Larry Thomas
*CEO: Jim Bishop

Sr VP: Jeanne Cormier
*VP: Paul Blachowicz
VP: Rick Bray
*VP: Roy Bruce
*VP: Chuck Craycraft
*VP: Denny Ingham
VP: Stephen Lewis
*VP: Tyler Robirds
VP: Carlye Sommers
VP: David Twiddy

D-U-N-S 09-915-2597
H W METAL PRODUCTS INC
19480 Sw 118th Ave Stop 2, Tualatin, OR 97062-7802
Tel (503) 692-1690 Founded/Ownrshp 1979
Sales 62.6MM^E EMP 75
SIC 5051 Sheets, metal; Sheets, metal
CEO: Howard H Wolfe
*Pr: Jack Suter
*VP: Brian Wolfe

D-U-N-S 96-824-5779 IMP
H W S CO INC
HICKORY WHITE COMPANY
(Suby of SHERRILL FURNITURE CO INC) ★
856 7th Ave Se, Hickory, NC 28602-3938
Tel (828) 322-8624 Founded/Ownrshp 1997
Sales 27.2MM^E EMP 315
SIC 2512 Couches, sofas & davenports: upholstered on wood frames; Chairs: upholstered on wood frames; Couches, sofas & davenports: upholstered on wood frames; Chairs: upholstered on wood frames
Pr: Harold W Sherrill
COO: Hall Dan
*VP: Robert L Choppa Jr
*VP: Thom Woller
Genl Mgr: Chris Canipe
Genl Mgr: Bryan Milleson
Plnt Mgr: Kim White

D-U-N-S 00-202-3307
H W WILSON CO INC
(Suby of EBSCO PUBLISHING INC) ★
950 University Ave, Bronx, NY 10452-4297
Tel (718) 588-8635 Founded/Ownrshp 2011
Sales 26.8MM^E EMP 450
SIC 2721 2731 Periodicals: publishing & printing; Books: publishing & printing; Periodicals: publishing & printing; Books: publishing & printing
Pr: F Dixon Brooke Jr
*Pr: J David Walker
*VP: Tim Collins

D-U-N-S 01-342-7992
H WEISS LLC
12 Labriola Ct Ste 1, Armonk, NY 10504-1342
Tel (914) 273-4400 Founded/Ownrshp 1919
Sales 31.1MM^E EMP 40
SIC 5023 5072 5046 5113 China; Cutlery; Commercial cooking & food service equipment; Industrial & personal service paper

D-U-N-S 08-422-0730
H WOLF EDWARD AND SONS INC
414 Kettle Moraine Dr S, Slinger, WI 53086-9550
Tel (262) 644-5030 Founded/Ownrshp 1976
Sales 281.7MM EMP 60
Accts Baker Tilly Virchow Krause Llp
SIC 5983 5171 Fuel oil dealers; Petroleum bulk stations; Fuel oil dealers; Petroleum bulk stations
Pr: Craig Wolf
*CFO: Steve Kreuser
*VP: Colette Troeller
Manager: Julie Brooks
Sls Mgr: Bob Hartwig
Sls Mgr: Toby Tyler
Sls Mgr: Jason Ventre

H WZ CONTRACTING-CINTI
See BH GROUP LLC

D-U-N-S 06-902-2119
H Y K CONSTRUCTION CO INC
430 Rahns Rd, Collegeville, PA 19426-1895
Tel (610) 489-2646 Founded/Ownrshp 1973
Sales 32.2MM^E EMP 162
SIC 3273 3272 Ready-mixed concrete; Prestressed concrete products; Ready-mixed concrete; Prestressed concrete products
Pr: Paul Yerk
*Sec: John R Kibblehouse
*VP: John B Haines IV
Genl Mgr: Dane Condiles

D-U-N-S 00-820-0016
▲ H&E EQUIPMENT SERVICES INC
7500 Pecue Ln, Baton Rouge, LA 70809-5107
Tel (225) 298-5200 Founded/Ownrshp 2002
Sales 1.0MMM EMP 1,900
Accts Bdo Usa Llp Dallas Texas
Tkr Sym HEES Exch NGS
SIC 7359 5082 Equipment rental & leasing; General construction machinery & equipment; Equipment rental & leasing; General construction machinery & equipment
CEO: John M Engquist
*Ch Bd: Gary W Bagley
Pr: Bradley W Barber
CFO: Leslie S Magee
VP: Ralf Vieten
Exec: Kurt Sorensen
Dir Risk M: Wade Gonzales
Brnch Mgr: Robert Ackman
Brnch Mgr: Mike Allen
Brnch Mgr: Paul Crawford
Brnch Mgr: Mike Criswell
Board of Directors: Paul N Arnold, Bruce C Bruckmann, Patrick L Edsell, Thomas J Galligan III, Lawrence C Karlson, John T Sawyer

H&F TIRE SERVICE
See H & F GULF INC

H&G SERVICES
See HERRMAN & GOETZ INC

D-U-N-S 12-653-5983
H&H CATERING LP
WOLFGANG PUCK CATERING
6801 Hollywood Blvd, Los Angeles, CA 90028-6136
Tel (323) 491-1250 *Founded/Ownrshp* 2002
Sales 14.0MM *EMP* 1,600E
SIC 5812 Caterers; Caterers
Pt: Carl Schuster
Pt: Wolfgang Puck

H&H CHEVROLET - CADILLAC
See H & H CHEVROLET OLDSMOBILE & CADILLAC INC

D-U-N-S 96-264-7033
H&H TRAILERS LLC
(*Suby of* LA EAST INC) ★
222 N 1st St, Clarinda, IA 51632-1907
Tel (712) 542-2618 *Founded/Ownrshp* 2009
Sales 42.0MM *EMP* 55
SIC 3715 Truck trailers
CFO: Lisa McGlashen
VP: Craig Hull
IT Man: Todd Reed
Sls&Mrk Ex: Wendy Trobst

H&K
See HARRINGTON & KING PERFORATING CO INC

H&M
See H & M HENNES & MAURITZ LP

D-U-N-S 02-610-9413
H&M WHOLESALE INC
4150 Highway 6 S, College Station, TX 77845-8964
Tel (979) 690-8925 *Founded/Ownrshp* 1980
Sales 46.1MM *EMP* 18
Accts Brewer Eyeington Patout & Co
SIC 5171 Petroleum bulk stations; Petroleum bulk stations
Pr: Mary Walker
**Sec:* Donna Watkins
**VP:* James Boedeker

D-U-N-S 01-689-6326
H&P TECHNOLOGIES INC
21251 Ryan Rd, Warren, MI 48091-4666
Tel (586) 758-0100 *Founded/Ownrshp* 1944
Sales 26.1MME *EMP* 62
SIC 5084 7699

D-U-N-S 80-685-8614
■ **H&R BLOCK BANK**
(*Suby of* BLOCK FINANCIAL CORP) ★
1 H And R Block Way, Kansas City, MO 64105-1905
Tel (888) 687-4722 *Founded/Ownrshp* 2006
Sales NA *EMP* 50
SIC 6035 Federal savings banks; Federal savings banks
Pr: Kathy Barney
Dir Risk M: James M Bedsole
Comm Dir: Janine Smiley

D-U-N-S 16-530-9159
■ **H&R BLOCK GROUP INC**
(*Suby of* H & R BLOCK INC) ★
4400 Main St, Kansas City, MO 64111-1812
Tel (816) 854-3000 *Founded/Ownrshp* 1993
Sales 554.8MME *EMP* 4,581
SIC 6211 8721 8742 Security brokers & dealers; Accounting, auditing & bookkeeping; Management consulting services
CEO: Mark A Ernst
Treas: Becky Shulman
Sr VP: Tammy Serati
Sr VP: Bernard Wilson
VP: Mike Elkins
VP: Kevin Mobley
Mng Dir: Linda Murphy
Brnch Mgr: Rose Altencaumer
Brnch Mgr: Susan Mitchell
Brnch Mgr: Patricia Noble
Brnch Mgr: Jeff Petty

D-U-N-S 10-126-5817 IMP/EXP
H&R CONSTRUCTION PARTS & EQUIPMENT INC
20 Milburn St, Buffalo, NY 14212-1709
Tel (716) 891-4311 *Founded/Ownrshp* 1983
Sales 25.1MME *EMP* 56
SIC 5082 General construction machinery & equipment
Pr: Larry Mohr
**Ch Bd:* Stephen Hansen
Opers Mgr: John Gaulin

D-U-N-S 80-056-2261 IMP
H&T WATERBURY INC
BOUFFARD METAL GOODS
984 Waterville St, Waterbury, CT 06710-1015
Tel (203) 574-2240 *Founded/Ownrshp* 2007
Sales 33.4MME *EMP* 150
SIC 3469 Metal stampings; Metal stampings
Ch: John Benaglio
**VP:* Daniel D Moffa
VP: Daniel Moffa
VP: William Shannon
**VP:* Ronald T Turmel
**Prin:* Christian Diemer
Genl Mgr: Reinhard Scholle
Genl Mgr: Ronald Turmel
Netwrk Mgr: Joerg Rafflenbeul
Plnt Mgr: Kevin Korn
Sls Mgr: Seth Greiner

D-U-N-S 05-286-9609 IMP
■ **H-C LIQUIDATING CORP**
HOMECREST CABINETRY
(*Suby of* OMEGA CABINETRY) ★
1002 Eisenhower Dr N, Goshen, IN 46526-5308
Tel (574) 535-9300 *Founded/Ownrshp* 1969
Sales 99.7MME *EMP* 1,025
SIC 2434 Wood kitchen cabinets; Vanities, bathroom: wood; Wood kitchen cabinets; Vanities, bathroom: wood
Pr: Warner R S
**Pr:* John Goebel
VP: Thomas Shmidt
CIO: Chris Eubank

D-U-N-S 61-993-6904
H-E PARTS INTERNATIONAL LLC
1117 Perimeter Ctr, Atlanta, GA 30338-5451
Tel (678) 443-2140 *Founded/Ownrshp* 2005
Sales 20.0MME *EMP* 50E
SIC 5082 General construction machinery & equipment
CEO: Jean Paul Richard
**Pr:* Steven R McBrayer
**COO:* Michael Coffey
**Mng Dir:* Ian Olivieri
Off Mgr: Maria Rangel

H-E-B FOOD/DRUG STORES
See H E BUTT GROCERY CO

H-G A C
See HOUSTON-GALVESTON AREA COUNCIL

D-U-N-S 05-771-1152
H-I-S PAINT MANUFACTURING CO INC
HIS COATINGS
1801 W Reno Ave, Oklahoma City, OK 73106-3248
Tel (405) 232-2077 *Founded/Ownrshp* 1972
Sales 22.8MM *EMP* 52
SIC 2851 Paints, waterproof; Paints: oil or alkyd vehicle or water thinned; Paints, waterproof; Paints: oil or alkyd vehicle or water thinned
CEO: Joe T Cox
**Sec:* Dorothy Cox
**VP:* Steve Bussjaeger
**VP:* J Kent Cox
**VP:* Kirk Cox
**VP:* Tony Cox
Dir Lab: Greg McCann
CIO: Sean Dupuis
IT Man: Richard Brown

D-U-N-S 04-422-0739
H-O-H WATER TECHNOLOGY INC
500 S Vermont St, Palatine, IL 60067-6948
Tel (847) 358-7400 *Founded/Ownrshp* 1979
Sales 29.5MME *EMP* 200
SIC 3589 2899 Water treatment equipment, industrial; Chemical preparations; Water treatment equipment, industrial; Chemical preparations
Pr: Thomas F Hutchison
VP: Henry Becker
VP: William Rutledge
Genl Mgr: Irene Ohlrich

D-U-N-S 00-446-9185 IMP/EXP
H-P PRODUCTS INC (OH)
512 W Gorgas St, Louisville, OH 44641-1305
Tel (330) 875-5556 *Founded/Ownrshp* 1948, 1976
Sales 54.3MME *EMP* 363
SIC 3498 3564 3494 3354 3317

D-U-N-S 06-449-9487 IMP
H2O INNOVATION USA INC
H2O INNOVATION
(*Suby of* H2O INNOVATION INC)
8900 109th Ave N Ste 1000, Champlin, MN 55316-3170
Tel (763) 566-8961 *Founded/Ownrshp* 2006
Sales 23.3MME *EMP* 100
SIC 3589 Water purification equipment, household type
Pr: Frederic Dugre

D-U-N-S 94-693-9832
H2C2 & ASSOCIATES INC
DEMO MASTERS
6925 San Leandro St, Oakland, CA 94621-3320
Tel (510) 562-6181 *Founded/Ownrshp* 1996
Sales 30.7MM *EMP* 50
SIC 1629 Subway construction; Subway construction
Pr: Mike Christie
**Treas:* Richard Cleveland
**VP:* Marvin Henderson

D-U-N-S 05-499-2334
H2M ARCHITECTS ENGINEERS LAND SURVEYING AND LANDSCAPE ARCHITECTURE DPC
H 2 M
538 Broad Hollo 4th Fl E # 4, Melville, NY 11747
Tel (631) 756-8000 *Founded/Ownrshp* 1956
Sales 29.2MM *EMP* 180E
Accts Albrecht Vggiano Zureck & Co
SIC 8711 Engineering services; Engineering services
Pr: Dennis Kelleher
**Ch Bd:* Richard W Humann
**Ch:* John J Molloy
Treas: Al Wallner
Sr VP: R M Scheiner
VP: Anthony Fisher
**VP:* Paul J Granger
VP: James Neri
VP: Guy Page
VP: Frank Russo
Dept Mgr: Bonnie Franson

H2O INNOVATION
See H2O INNOVATION USA INC

D-U-N-S 80-772-2947 IMP/EXP
H2O PLUS LLC
845 W Madison St, Chicago, IL 60607-2631
Tel (312) 377-2132 *Founded/Ownrshp* 1993
Sales 26.6MME *EMP* 150
SIC 2844 5999 5122 Toilet preparations; Cosmetics; Cosmetics; Toilet preparations; Cosmetics; Cosmetics
Pr: Joy Chen
**CEO:* Robert Seidl
Sls Mgr: Stephanie Sims

D-U-N-S 78-432-6808
H2O STEEL CONTRACTORS LLC
2000 Howard Rd, Waxahachie, TX 75165-9443
Tel (972) 938-2730 *Founded/Ownrshp* 2003
Sales 27.0MM *EMP* 22
SIC 1791 Structural steel erection; Structural steel erection

H2WR / EHS SERVICES
See TOTAL SAFETY US INC

HA ANDERSEN COMPANY
See ANDERSEN CONSTRUCTION CO

D-U-N-S 18-389-9587
HA AUTOMOTIVE INVESTMENTS LLC
RON CRTER CDILLAC HYUNDAI SAAB
18100 Gulf Fwy, Friendswood, TX 77546-2722
Tel (281) 283-7000 *Founded/Ownrshp* 2011
Sales 28.0MME *EMP* 160
SIC 5511 Automobiles, new & used
CFO: Don Snyder

D-U-N-S 00-237-3637
HA DEHART & SON INC (NJ)
311 Crown Point Rd, West Deptford, NJ 08086-6100
Tel (856) 845-2800 *Founded/Ownrshp* 1884, 1987
Sales 29.5MME *EMP* 55
SIC 5012 7538 5511 Commercial vehicles; Buses; Trailers for trucks, new & used; Truck bodies; General automotive repair shops; Trucks, tractors & trailers: new & used
Pr: Dennis Noon
Dir Bus: Brandon Lewis
Dir IT: Phillip Clifford
Opers Mgr: Rich Treharne

HA INTERNATIONAL, LCC
See HA-INTERNATIONAL LLC

D-U-N-S 11-073-9179
HA MOTORS LTD
ACURA OF ORANGE PARK
7200 Blanding Blvd, Jacksonville, FL 32244-4504
Tel (904) 777-5600 *Founded/Ownrshp* 1998
Sales 24.9MME *EMP* 74
SIC 5511 Automobiles, new & used; Automobiles, new & used
Pt: Jack Hanania
CFO: John Joyner

D-U-N-S 00-685-6702
HA SACK CO INC (GA)
SACK COMPANY, THE
3302 Zell Miller Pkwy, Statesboro, GA 30458-3219
Tel (912) 871-8771 *Founded/Ownrshp* 1945, 1957
Sales 51.8MME *EMP* 150
SIC 1731 1711 General electrical contractor; Mechanical contractor; General electrical contractor; Mechanical contractor
Ch Bd: Albert Roesel Sr
**Pr:* Paul Roesel
**CFO:* Don Salie
**VP:* Steve Deal
Dir IT: Brian Nutting
IT Man: Tonya Ivey
Pr Mgr: Brandon Russel

HA STORAGE SYSTEMS
See HIGH AVAILABILITY STORAGE SYSTEMS INC

HA&W INNOVATIVE TECHNOLOGIES
See HABIF AROGETI & WYNNE LLP

D-U-N-S 02-881-2845 IMP
HA-INTERNATIONAL LLC
HA INTERNATIONAL, LCC
630 Oakmont Ln, Westmont, IL 60559-5548
Tel (630) 575-5700 *Founded/Ownrshp* 2001
Sales 62.0MME *EMP* 180
SIC 2869 Industrial organic chemicals; Industrial organic chemicals
CEO: Keith McLean
CFO: Bill Sample
**CFO:* William Sample
**VP:* Michael Feehan
CIO: Donna Willoughby
Opers Mgr: Linda Hay
Plnt Mgr: Joe Ebens
Mktg Mgr: Lorena Oneill

HAAG & DECKER OIL
See HAAG OIL CO LLC

D-U-N-S 02-497-6045
HAAG FOOD SERVICE INC
HAAG FOODS AND POULTRY
300 N Haag St, Breese, IL 62230-1758
Tel (618) 526-7120 *Founded/Ownrshp* 1944
Sales 151.4MME *EMP* 90
SIC 5142 5144 5141 Packaged frozen goods; Meat, frozen: packaged; Fruits, frozen; Vegetables, frozen; Poultry products; Groceries, general line; Packaged frozen goods; Meat, frozen: packaged; Fruits, frozen; Vegetables, frozen; Poultry products; Groceries, general line
Pr: Jack E Garcia
**Sec:* Philip Garcia

HAAG FOODS AND POULTRY
See HAAG FOOD SERVICE INC

D-U-N-S 05-892-0869
HAAG INC
AAMCO TRANSMISSIONS
7233 Sw 85th St, Auburn, KS 66402-9732
Tel (785) 256-2311 *Founded/Ownrshp* 1970
Sales 20.0MM *EMP* 76
SIC 5541 Gasoline service stations; Gasoline service stations
Pr: Thomas Haag
**Sec:* Ida Haag
**VP:* Ernie Haag

D-U-N-S 03-140-5558
HAAG OIL CO LLC
HAAG & DECKER OIL
326 Se 15th St, Topeka, KS 66607-1204
Tel (785) 357-0270 *Founded/Ownrshp* 2000
Sales 21.7MME *EMP* 100
SIC 5171 Petroleum bulk stations; Petroleum bulk stations

D-U-N-S 87-881-9762
HAAG-STREIT USA INC
(*Suby of* HAAG-STREIT HOLDING US, INC)
3535 Kings Mills Rd, Mason, OH 45040-2303
Tel (513) 336-7255 *Founded/Ownrshp* 1998
Sales 37.3MME *EMP* 140
SIC 5047 5048 Surgical equipment & supplies; Ophthalmic goods; Surgical equipment & supplies; Ophthalmic goods
CEO: Ernest Cavin
**Pr:* Dominik Beck
**CFO:* David R Edenfield
**VP:* Steve Juenger
Exec: Sandra Mohring
Sls Dir: Brian Gallagher

HAAGEN-DAZS
See NESTLE DREYERS ICE CREAM CO

HAAKE COMPANIES
See CHAS G HAAKE & SONS INC

D-U-N-S 05-801-0349 EXP
HAAKER EQUIPMENT CO
TOTAL CLEAN
2070 N White Ave, La Verne, CA 91750-5679
Tel (909) 542-0800 *Founded/Ownrshp* 1972
Sales 52.6MM *EMP* 76
Accts Rogers Clem & Company Covina
SIC 5012 5087 5999 Ambulances; Cleaning & maintenance equipment & supplies; Cleaning equipment & supplies; Ambulances; Cleaning & maintenance equipment & supplies; Cleaning equipment & supplies
CEO: Edward R Blackman
**Pr:* Randy Blackman
**CFO:* Edward C Haaker
CFO: John Haaker
Area Mgr: Michael Harris

D-U-N-S 01-018-0267 IMP
HAAN CORP
1525 Oregon Pike Ste 602, Lancaster, PA 17601-4374
Tel (717) 209-7000 *Founded/Ownrshp* 2008
Sales 100.7MME *EMP* 380
SIC 5064 Vacuum cleaners, household; Vacuum cleaners, household
Pr: Romi Haan
IT Man: Thanh Tran

HAARTZ AUTO FABRIC
See HAARTZ CORP

D-U-N-S 00-102-3084 IMP
HAARTZ CORP (MA)
HAARTZ AUTO FABRIC
87 Hayward Rd, Acton, MA 01720-3000
Tel (978) 264-2600 *Founded/Ownrshp* 1922
Sales 109.8MME *EMP* 400
SIC 3069 2295 Rubberized fabrics; Resin or plastic coated fabrics; Rubberized fabrics; Resin or plastic coated fabrics
Pr: John Fox
CFO: Charles Quimby
Dir Bus: Craig Karamanian
Prgrm Mgr: Jill Perry
QA Dir: Gregg Kush
QA Dir: Dominique Throop
QA Dir: Mike Umbarger
IT Man: Laurie Favreau
Netwrk Mgr: Edward Doukszewicz
Sftwr Eng: Thomas Laford
Sls Mgr: Douglas Haartz

HAAS & WILKERSON INS AGENCY
See W RALPH WILKERSON JR INC

D-U-N-S 12-097-4571 IMP/EXP
HAAS AUTOMATION INC
2800 Sturgis Rd, Oxnard, CA 93030-8901
Tel (805) 278-1800 *Founded/Ownrshp* 1983
Sales 175.8MME *EMP* 1,400E
SIC 3541

D-U-N-S 00-637-3518 IMP
HAAS CABINET CO INC
625 W Utica St, Sellersburg, IN 47172-1197
Tel (812) 246-4431 *Founded/Ownrshp* 1939
Sales 40.5MME *EMP* 250
SIC 2434 4213 4225 2511 Wood kitchen cabinets; Vanities, bathroom: wood; Contract haulers; General warehousing; Wood household furniture; Wood kitchen cabinets; Vanities, bathroom: wood; Contract haulers; General warehousing; Wood household furniture
Ch: Don C Haas
**Pr:* Jeffrey Todd Haas
**VP:* Phillip Flora
**VP:* Bryant L Haas

D-U-N-S 94-132-3321
HAAS DOOR CO
320 Sycamore St, Wauseon, OH 43567-1100
Tel (419) 337-9900 *Founded/Ownrshp* 1971
Sales 24.3MME *EMP* 200
SIC 3442 Garage doors, overhead: metal; Garage doors, overhead: metal
Pr: Edward Nofziger
**Sec:* Carol Nofziger
Plnt Mgr: Tom Moyer

HAAS DOORS
See NOFZIGER DOOR SALES INC

D-U-N-S 01-843-3925
HAAS ENVIRONMENTAL INC
7 Red Lion Rd, Southampton, NJ 08088-8832
Tel (609) 859-3100 *Founded/Ownrshp* 1996
Sales 47.1MME *EMP* 180
SIC 3312 Blast furnaces & steel mills; Blast furnaces & steel mills
Pr: Gene Haas
**Pr:* Eugene Haas
**CFO:* Michael Hopkins
**Sr VP:* Wayne Muir
**VP:* Chris Hall

HAAS FACTORY OUTLET
See GEROTECH INC

D-U-N-S 02-164-0938
HAAS FACTORY OUTLET LLC
(*Suby of* GOSIGER INC) ★
580 Madrid Ave, Torrance, CA 90501-6231
Tel (310) 381-0750 *Founded/Ownrshp* 1997
Sales 21.7MME *EMP* 30

SIC 5084 Machine tools & accessories
VP: Haresh Shah
Dist Mgr: Glenn Cheshire
Dist Mgr: Patrick Ellison
Dist Mgr: Mike Steinbock
Sales Exec: Dan McCollum

D-U-N-S 83-863-7283
■ HAAS GROUP INC
(*Suby of* WESCO AIRCRAFT HOLDINGS INC) ★
1475 Phoenixville Pike, West Chester, PA 19380-1437
Tel (484) 564-4500 *Founded/Ownrshp* 2014
Sales 269.1MM^E *EMP* 1,300^E
SIC 8741 3369 Business management; Aerospace castings, nonferrous: except aluminum; Business management; Aerospace castings, nonferrous: except aluminum
CEO: Thaddeus J Fortin

D-U-N-S 00-227-5782
■ HAAS GROUP INTERNATIONAL LLC (PA)
(*Suby of* HAAS GROUP INC) ★
1475 Phoeni Pike Ste 101, West Chester, PA 19380
Tel (484) 564-4500 *Founded/Ownrshp* 1925
Sales 269.1MM^E *EMP* 786^E
SIC 8711 8741 8999 2899 Petroleum, mining & chemical engineers; Management services; Chemical consultant; Metal treating compounds; Water treating compounds; Petroleum, mining & chemical engineers; Management services; Chemical consultant; Metal treating compounds; Water treating compounds
Pr: Thomas Renehan
IT Man: Justin Jones
Sftwr Eng: Steve Buffum
Opers Mgr: Neil Hanson
Manager: Tulia Badillo
Counsel: Danielle Rodichok

HAAS HOP PRODUCTS
See JOHN I HAAS INC

HAAS, JEFF MAZDA
See JLH AUTOMOTIVE INC

D-U-N-S 87-296-5587
HAAS MANAGEMENT SERVICES INC
BURGER KING
2780 Waterfront Pkwy E Dr, Indianapolis, IN 46214-2044
Tel (317) 852-9889 *Founded/Ownrshp* 1987
Sales 10.8MM^E *EMP* 378
SIC 5812 Fast-food restaurant, chain; Fast-food restaurant, chain
Pr: Kathleen Haas
**VP:* Kathlene A Haas

HAAS METAL ENGINEERING
See M E H INC

D-U-N-S 15-359-5046 IMP
HAAS OUTDOORS INC
MOSSY OAK
1251 Highway 45 S Alts, West Point, MS 39773-9316
Tel (662) 494-8859 *Founded/Ownrshp* 1986
Sales 47.0MM^E *EMP* 125
SIC 5136 5961

D-U-N-S 06-641-2263
HAAS-ANDERSON CONSTRUCTION LTD
1402 Holly Rd, Corpus Christi, TX 78417-2008
Tel (361) 853-2535 *Founded/Ownrshp* 1973
Sales 63.7MM^E *EMP* 210
SIC 1629 1611 Land preparation construction; Highway & street paving contractor; Land preparation construction; Highway & street paving contractor
Mng Pt: Darryl O Haas
Pt: Jim Anderson
Pt: Edward D Haas
VP: Rob Dake
IT Man: Gary Traylelr

D-U-N-S 01-161-7891 EXP
■ HABAND CO LLC
(*Suby of* BEDFORD FAIR APPAREL) ★
1 International Blvd # 800, Mahwah, NJ 07495-0019
Tel (978) 998-3800 *Founded/Ownrshp* 2000, 2006
Sales 98.7MM^E *EMP* 349
SIC 5961 5611 5621 Clothing, mail order (except women's); Women's apparel, mail order; Men's & boys' clothing stores; Ready-to-wear apparel, women's; Clothing, mail order (except women's); Women's apparel, mail order; Men's & boys' clothing stores; Ready-to-wear apparel, women's
Pr: Duke Habernickel
Pr: Mary Kelly
Ex VP: Dean Perigard
VP: Richard Elia
VP: Peter Gilman
MIS Dir: Alex Belitsky
IT Man: George Kessler
Netwrk Mgr: Steve Helms
Info Man: Jason Bankston
Opers Mgr: Micheal Fleeming
Ql Cn Mgr: Patricia Chilek

D-U-N-S 60-888-0860 IMP
HABASIT ABT INC
(*Suby of* HABASIT AMERICA INC) ★
150 Industrial Park Rd, Middletown, CT 06457-1521
Tel (860) 632-2211 *Founded/Ownrshp* 1990
Sales 26.5MM^E *EMP* 140
SIC 3496 Conveyor belts; Conveyor belts
CEO: Harry Cardillo
Sls Mgr: Paul Stevens

D-U-N-S 04-287-6227 IMP/EXP
HABASIT AMERICA INC
(*Suby of* HABASIT HOLDING AG)
805 Satellite Blvd Nw, Suwanee, GA 30024-2879
Tel (678) 288-3600 *Founded/Ownrshp* 1967
Sales 123.4MM^E *EMP* 600
SIC 3566 Speed changers, drives & gears; Conveyors & conveying equipment; Plastic belting; Drives: belt, cable or rope; Speed changers, drives & gears
CFO: Victor D'Adamio
Pr: Chris Nigon
Sr VP: Maarten Aarts
VP: Bert Flieger
VP: Sam Johnson
Exec: Marc Knable
Dir Bus: Michael Peach
Rgnl Mgr: Kevin Dahill
Rgnl Mgr: Phil Resch
Area Mgr: Rick Borman
Dist Mgr: Steve Flaherty

D-U-N-S 01-761-7036 IMP
HABEGGER CORP
JOHNSON CONTROLS
4995 Winton Rd, Cincinnati, OH 45232-1504
Tel (513) 853-6644 *Founded/Ownrshp* 1952
Sales 116.5MM^E *EMP* 260
SIC 5075 Warm air heating equipment & supplies; Air conditioning & ventilation equipment & supplies; Warm air heating equipment & supplies; Air conditioning & ventilation equipment & supplies
Ch Bd: Fred Habegger III
**Pr:* John Dor
**CFO:* Suzanne Frey
Rgnl Mgr: Rick Travis
Brnch Mgr: Sean Kilbane
Div Mgr: Tom Lovich
Store Mgr: Bret Stephens
Netwrk Mgr: Mike Pope
Opers Mgr: Bill Engelland
Manager: Rob Weber
Sls Mgr: Jeff Clausen

D-U-N-S 03-104-3185
HABERBERGER INC MECHANICAL CONTRACTOR
9744 Pauline Pl, Saint Louis, MO 63123-4340
Tel (314) 631-3324 *Founded/Ownrshp* 1948
Sales 30.6MM *EMP* 140^E
Accts Uhy Llp St Louis Missouri
SIC 1711 8711 Warm air heating & air conditioning contractor; Process piping contractor; Mechanical engineering; Warm air heating & air conditioning contractor; Process piping contractor; Mechanical engineering
Ch: Mark Haberberger
**Pr:* Neil Haberberger
**CFO:* Greg Danker
**Treas:* Steve Haberberger
**VP:* Joe Wilhelm

D-U-N-S 13-076-0510 IMP/EXP
HABERLE STEEL INC
1946 E Cherry Ln Ste A, Souderton, PA 18964-1030
Tel (215) 723-8848 *Founded/Ownrshp* 2002
Sales 28.0MM^E *EMP* 85^E
Accts Scott A Miller & Co Cpa So
SIC 3441 Fabricated structural metal; Fabricated structural metal
Pr: Russell Haberle
Ofcr: Craig Haberle
**VP:* Bill Quade
IT Man: John Niziolek

D-U-N-S 02-637-1955
HABERSHAM COUNTY
HABERSHAM COUNTY COMMISSIONERS
555 Monroe St Ste 20, Clarkesville, GA 30523-7815
Tel (706) 754-3738 *Founded/Ownrshp* 1957
Sales NA *EMP* 310
SIC 9111 Executive offices; ; Executive offices;
Brnch Mgr: June Black
Dir IT: Jonathan Taylor
Snr Mgr: Jason Davey

D-U-N-S 04-068-9424
HABERSHAM COUNTY BOARD OF EDUCATION
HCBOE
132 Stanford Mill Rd, Clarkesville, GA 30523
Tel (706) 754-2110 *Founded/Ownrshp* 1901
Sales 62.0MM^E *EMP* 1,000
SIC 8211 Public elementary & secondary schools; School board
Ch Bd: Robert Barron
**CFO:* Staci Newsome
**Bd of Dir:* Gilbert Barrett
**Bd of Dir:* Don Corbett
Bd of Dir: Russ Nelson
**Bd of Dir:* Pat Taylor
Bd of Dir: Patsy Taylor
**Bd of Dir:* Rick Williams
VP: Shirley Dillard
Dir IT: Dennis Unbehant
HC Dir: Kathleen Clement

HABERSHAM COUNTY COMMISSIONERS
See HABERSHAM COUNTY

HABERSHAM COUNTY MEDICAL CTR
See HOSPITAL AUTHORITY OF HABERSHAM COUNTY

D-U-N-S 07-990-7637
HABERSHAM COUNTY SCHOOL DISTRICT
132 Stanford Mill Rd, Clarkesville, GA 30523
Tel (706) 754-2118 *Founded/Ownrshp* 2015
Sales 40.5MM^E *EMP* 1,068^E
SIC 8211 Public elementary & secondary schools
MIS Dir: Kathy Tart
Teacher Pr: Angela Robinson

D-U-N-S 00-797-6624
HABERSHAM ELECTRIC MEMBERSHIP CORP (GA)
6135 Highway 115, Clarkesville, GA 30523-6761
Tel (706) 754-2114 *Founded/Ownrshp* 1937, 1938
Sales 61.8MM *EMP* 107
SIC 4911 Distribution, electric power; Distribution, electric power
Pr: Todd Pealock
**Ch Bd:* Hugh Rucker
**Sec:* George Fry
IT Man: Rodney Pugh
Mktg Mgr: Kenneth McEntire
Board of Directors: Herman Barrett, Jeff Ferguson, George Fry, Ray Meaders, Hugh Rucker, Carl Tallent, Rick Wood

D-U-N-S 00-330-4284
HABERSHAM METAL PRODUCTS CO INC (GA)
264 Stapleton Rd, Cornelia, GA 30531-5643
Tel (706) 778-2212 *Founded/Ownrshp* 1954
Sales 52.9MM^E *EMP* 150
SIC 3442 Fire doors, metal; Fire doors, metal
Pr: James Stapleton Jr
**Pr:* James A Stapleton
COO: Keith Stapleton
**CFO:* Wes Dodd
**Ex VP:* Keith C Stapleton
Genl Mgr: James Bowman
Off Mgr: Stefanie Abbott
Plnt Mgr: Phillip Loggins
Ql Cn Mgr: Todd Dean
Snr Mgr: Dealease Carlan

D-U-N-S 03-713-5637
HABIB AMERICAN BANK
4 Wrld Fncl Ctr 250, New York, NY 10281-1023
Tel (718) 248-0152 *Founded/Ownrshp* 2011
Sales NA *EMP* 95^E
SIC 6099 Functions related to deposit banking
Prin: John Thain
V Ch: Samuel Chapin
Treas: Jan Johnson
Ofcr: Amanda Halliday
Ofcr: Araceli Hernandez
Ofcr: Jose Vazquez
Sr VP: Sophia Andonisio
Sr VP: Michael Boccio
Sr VP: Suzanne Dewitt-Shelley
Sr VP: Gregory Gonsalves
Sr VP: Gavin Jones
Sr VP: Peter Kurey
Sr VP: Matt Lazaro
Sr VP: Christopher Lia
Sr VP: James Morris
Sr VP: Alexander Rice
Sr VP: Harry Roberts
Sr VP: Frank Sutton
Sr VP: Alex Thomson
VP: Vincent Caruso
VP: Paul Grant II

D-U-N-S 12-156-1534
HABIB AMERICAN BANK
(*Suby of* MAHAM BETEILIGUNGSGESELLSCHAFT AG)
99 Madison Ave Frnt A, New York, NY 10016-7499
Tel (212) 532-4444 *Founded/Ownrshp* 1984
Sales NA *EMP* 120
SIC 6163 6022 Loan brokers; State commercial banks; Loan brokers; State commercial banks
Ch: A G Abbasi
**CEO:* Saleem Iqbal
**Ch:* Hyder M Habib
Ofcr: Irshad Noorani
Ofcr: Syed Rizvi
**Ex VP:* Ejaz M Hussain
Sr VP: Jerry Hurley
**Sr VP:* Javed Karim
Sr VP: George Markowsky
Sr VP: Joseph Powers
**Sr VP:* Rizwan Qureshi
Sr VP: Zilay Wahidy
VP: Albert Accatino
VP: Maureen Davison
**VP:* Abbas Somjee

D-U-N-S 07-936-7405
HABIF AROGETI & WYNNE LLP
HA&W INNOVATIVE TECHNOLOGIES
5 Concourse Pkwy Ste 1000, Atlanta, GA 30328-6132
Tel (404) 892-9651 *Founded/Ownrshp* 1954
Sales 68.6MM^E *EMP* 300^E
SIC 8721 Certified public accountant; Certified public accountant
Pt: Richard Kopelman
**Pt:* Robert Arogeti
**Pt:* Robert Casey
**Pt:* Ed Deck
**Pt:* Yelena Epova
**Pt:* Baron Frankel
**Pt:* Darrin Friedrich
**Pt:* Jeff Grosoff
**Pt:* Frank Gudger
**Pt:* Lisa Haynor
**Pt:* Jana Henderson
**Pt:* Marc L Kanne
**Pt:* Mitchell Kopelman
**Pt:* Jonathan L Miller
**Pt:* Richard A Rubin
**Pt:* Alan Vaughn
**Pt:* Merrill D Wynne
Mng Pt: Mark Murovitz
COO: Alan M Vaughn

D-U-N-S 13-153-5650
HABILITATIVE SERVICES INC
HSI
220 Milwaukee St Ste 2, Lakefield, MN 56150-9495
Tel (507) 662-5236 *Founded/Ownrshp* 1984
Sales 25.7MM^E *EMP* 930
SIC 8361 8742 Home for the mentally handicapped; Training & development consultant; Home for the mentally handicapped; Training & development consultant
Ch: Doug Teigen
**Pr:* Donaebill G Olson
**CFO:* Mark Lien
IT Man: Chad Wilkinson
Snr Mgr: Julie Bluhm

HABIT BURGER GRILL, THE
See HABIT RESTAURANTS LLC

D-U-N-S 02-374-3234
▲ HABIT RESTAURANTS LLC
HABIT BURGER GRILL, THE
17320 Red Hill Ave # 140, Irvine, CA 92614-5644
Tel (949) 851-8881 *Founded/Ownrshp* 2007
Sales 174.6MM *EMP* 800
Accts Moss Adams Llp Los Angeles C
Tkr Sym HABT *Exch* NGM
SIC 5812 Hamburger stand; Hamburger stand
CEO: Russell Bendel
COO: Tony Serritella
**CFO:* Ira Fils
Chf Mktg O: Matt Hood
Dist Mgr: Ron Obando
Off Admin: Katie Lawrence
VP Mktg: Mike Mirkil
Mktg Dir: Charlotte Lucich

D-U-N-S 06-620-2052
HABITAT CO LLC
HABITAT GROUP, THE
350 W Hubbard St Ste 500, Chicago, IL 60654-5739
Tel (312) 955-0413 *Founded/Ownrshp* 1971
Sales 59.4MM^E *EMP* 1,200
SIC 6531 Real estate managers; Real estate managers
Pr: Mark Segal
Dir Vol: Jill Cleveland
**CFO:* Barry Goldberg
Ofcr: Christine Manuel
**Ex VP:* Matthew Fiascone
Ex VP: Stephen Galler
Sr VP: Cindy Dietz
Sr VP: Patrick Phillips
VP: Maria Collins
VP: Tracy Cramer
VP: Jeff Head
VP: Marla Jackson
VP: Bob Walker
Exec: Sabrina Taylor

D-U-N-S 86-770-2029
HABITAT FOR HUMANITY INC OF COLLIER CO
640 N 9th St, Immokalee, FL 34142-2900
Tel (239) 657-4466 *Founded/Ownrshp* 1978
Sales 21.0MM *EMP* 8
Accts Rodgers Wood Hill Starman &
SIC 1521 Single-family home remodeling, additions & repairs; Single-family home remodeling, additions & repairs
Ex Dir: Suazanne Foster
**Pr:* Ed Sorenson
**Treas:* Peter Schwiers
**VP:* Charles Smith

D-U-N-S 09-584-9568
HABITAT FOR HUMANITY INTERNATIONAL INC
121 Habitat St, Americus, GA 31709-3498
Tel (800) 422-4828 *Founded/Ownrshp* 1989
Sales 268.2MM *EMP* 1,500
Accts Ernst & Young Llp Greenville
SIC 8399 8661 8322 1521 1531 Social change association; Religious organizations; Individual & family services; Single-family housing construction; Operative builders; Social change association; Religious organizations; Individual & family services; Single-family housing construction; Operative builders
Pr: Jonathan Reckford
CFO: Carolyn Jensen
CFO: Lyn Jensen
CFO: Ed Quibell
Treas: Jeff Livesay
Treas: Peter Luquer
Bd of Dir: Larry Erdhardt
Bd of Dir: Daniel Fuller
Bd of Dir: Daniel C Molhoek
Bd of Dir: Laura Young
Ofcr: Sharon Grant
Ofcr: Diana Juhlin
Ofcr: Zuzana Matusova
Ofcr: Wesley Nguyen
Ofcr: Stacy Summerset
Top Exec: Karen Lienau
Ex VP: Michael Carscaddon
Sr VP: Tony Dispigno
Sr VP: Larry Gluth
Sr VP: Robert Sayell
**VP:* Chris Clarke
Board of Directors: Ted Dosch, Jessica Jackley, Steven Preston, Chuck Thiemann, Nabil Abadir, Paul Ekelschot, Carol Johnson, Larry Prible, Justin Wall, Kathleen Bader, Cary Evert, Jamie Justice, Joe Price, Ed Schreyer Paula Whiting, Joe Blomeke, Chantal Hudicourt-Ewald, Mary Kazunga, Jonathan Reckford, Sue Wilhelm, Joe Burgess, Norris Friesen, Jack Kemp, Nic Retsinas, Bob Willumstead, Elizabeth Crossman, Adam Fusselman

D-U-N-S 08-067-6690
HABITAT FOR HUMANITY OF COLLIER COUNTY INC
11145 Tamiami Trl E, Naples, FL 34113-7753
Tel (239) 775-0036 *Founded/Ownrshp* 1978
Sales 21.0MM *EMP* 24
Accts Rogers Wood Hill Starman & Gus
SIC 1521 New construction, single-family houses; New construction, single-family houses
Pr: Sam Durso
**Treas:* John Cunningham
**VP:* Maryann Durso
VP: Damain Luizuga
Comm Dir: Kelly Ramsey
Store Mgr: Kayla Bratager

D-U-N-S 82-654-3472
HABITAT FOR HUMANITY OF GREATER LOS ANGELES
8739 Artesia Blvd, Bellflower, CA 90706-6330
Tel (310) 323-4663 *Founded/Ownrshp* 1990
Sales 33.2MM *EMP* 50
Accts Rossi Doskocil & Finkelstein
SIC 8399 Fund raising organization, non-fee basis; Fund raising organization, non-fee basis
Pr: Erin Garrity Rank
Dir Vol: Sasha Muraoka
**COO:* Mark Van Lue
**CFO:* Gia Stokes
**VP:* Veronica Garcia
**VP:* Alison Treleaven J
**VP:* Steve Sferrino
VP: Adam Sisson
Store Mgr: David Freeman
Off Admin: Sandy Keller
Pr Mgr: Chris Untiet

D-U-N-S 79-343-2498
HABITAT FOR HUMANITY OF NEWYORK STATE INC
106 Washington Ave Fl 2, Endicott, NY 13760-5307
Tel (607) 748-4138 *Founded/Ownrshp* 2006
Sales 28.4MM *EMP* 1
SIC 1521 Single-family housing construction
CEO: Karen Haycox
**Pr:* Judith Nelson
Off Mgr: Carrie Tocheny

HABITAT GROUP, THE
See HABITAT CO LLC

D-U-N-S 13-350-7959
HAC INC
HOMELAND
(*Suby of* ASSOCIATED GROCERS) ★
390 Ne 36th St, Oklahoma City, OK 73105-2508
Tel (405) 290-3000 *Founded/Ownrshp* 2011
Sales 612.9MM^E *EMP* 4,200
SIC 5411 Grocery stores; Grocery stores
CEO: Darryl Fitzgerald
**CFO:* Deborah A Brown
VP: Philip Payment
Dir Rx: Bob Pessel
VP Mktg: Phil Payment

HACAP
See HAWKEYE AREA COMMUNITY ACTION PROGRAM INC

HACC
See HARRISBURG AREA COMMUNITY COLLEGE FOUNDATION

D-U-N-S 00-528-6679 IMP/EXP
■ HACH CO
ELE INTERNATIONAL
(*Suby of* DANAHER CORP) ★
5600 Lindbergh Dr, Loveland, CO 80538-8842
Tel (970) 669-3050 *Founded/Ownrshp* 1999
Sales 248.0MM^E *EMP* 1,000
SIC 3826 3823 3231 2819 2869 Analytical instruments; Colorimeters (optical instruments); PH meters, except industrial process type; Turbidometers; Water quality monitoring & control systems; Medical & laboratory glassware: made from purchased glass; Chemicals, reagent grade: refined from technical grade; Laboratory chemicals, organic; Analytical instruments; Colorimeters (optical instruments); PH meters, except industrial process type; Turbidometers; Water quality monitoring & control systems; Medical & laboratory glassware: made from purchased glass; Chemicals, reagent grade: refined from technical grade; Laboratory chemicals, organic
Pr: Lance Reisman
Sr Cor Off: Glenn Ferguson
**VP:* Michael Strycker
VP: Derk Walker
Area Mgr: Molly Bing
Software D: Aaron Jarrette
VP Opers: Larry D Thompson
Opers Mgr: Leah Martinez
Mktg Mgr: Dan Thomas
Mktg Mgr: Eric Umbreit
Board of Directors: Chris Serafin

D-U-N-S 12-817-6885 IMP
HACHETTE BOOK GROUP INC
(*Suby of* HACHETTE LIVRE)
1290 Ave Of The Americas, New York, NY 10104-0101
Tel (212) 364-1200 *Founded/Ownrshp* 2006
Sales 283.7MM^E *EMP* 970
SIC 2731 5192 Books: publishing only; Books, periodicals & newspapers; Books: publishing only; Books, periodicals & newspapers
Ch Bd: David Young
COO: Joe Mangan
**COO:* Kenneth Michaels
**CFO:* Thomas A Maciag
CFO: Stephen Mubarek
Ex VP: Chris Barba
Ex VP: Carol Ross
Sr VP: Reagan Arthur
Sr VP: Tim Holman
Sr VP: Rolf Zettersten
VP: Craig Bauer
VP: Margaret Dunning
VP: Mitchell Kinzer
VP: Todd McGarity
**VP:* Stephen M Mubarek
VP: Megan Tingley
VP: Karen Torres
Exec: Andrea Shallcross
Dir Soc: Joanna Host
Creative D: Mario Pulice
Creative D: Jeffrey Shay
Board of Directors: Arnaud Nourry

D-U-N-S 62-246-0467
HACHETTE DISTRIBUTION INC
(*Suby of* LAGARDERE NORTH AMERICA INC) ★
60 E 42nd St Ste 1940, New York, NY 10165-6201
Tel (212) 477-7373 *Founded/Ownrshp* 2004
Sales 501.5MM^E *EMP* 5,160
SIC 5192 5994 5947 Magazines; Newsstand; Magazine stand; Gift shop; Novelties; Magazines; Newsstand; Magazine stand; Gift shop; Novelties
Pr: Gerry Savaria

D-U-N-S 06-325-9923
HACI MECHANICAL CONTRACTORS INC
2108 W Shangri La Rd, Phoenix, AZ 85029-4896
Tel (602) 944-1555 *Founded/Ownrshp* 1996
Sales 27.3MM *EMP* 100
SIC 1711 Mechanical contractor; Mechanical contractor
Pr: Timothy B King
VP: Mike McClanahan

HACIENDA FORD
See FORD YODER INC

D-U-N-S 09-415-4424
HACIENDA HOME CENTERS INC
DO IT BEST
2701 Arizona St Ne, Albuquerque, NM 87110-3330
Tel (505) 884-8811 *Founded/Ownrshp* 1975
Sales 23.5MM^E *EMP* 124
SIC 5211 Home centers; Home centers
Pr: Felix A Sanchez
**Sec:* Russell L Kauzlaric
**VP:* Leroy J Sanchez
Off Mgr: Elaine Valdez
Store Mgr: Ida Carrillo
Store Mgr: Mike Wilson

D-U-N-S 03-491-8516
HACIENDA HOTEL & CASINO
Us Hwy 93, Boulder City, NV 89005
Tel (702) 293-5000 *Founded/Ownrshp* 1982
Sales 10.1MM^E *EMP* 405
SIC 7993 7999 7011 5812 Gambling machines, coin-operated; Slot machines; Gambling establishment; Casino hotel; Eating places; Gambling machines, coin-operated; Slot machines; Gambling establishment; Casino hotel; Eating places
Genl Mgr: David Ensign

D-U-N-S 09-590-9701
HACIENDA INC (AZ)
(*Suby of* ARIZONA CHILDRENS HEALTH CARE CORP) ★
1402 E South Mountain Ave, Phoenix, AZ 85042-7925
Tel (602) 243-4231 *Founded/Ownrshp* 1967
Sales 20.7MM *EMP* 250
Accts Henry & Horne Llp Tempe Az
SIC 8059 8361 8051 Domiciliary care; Home for the mentally retarded, exc. skilled or intermediate; Residential care; Skilled nursing care facilities; Domiciliary care; Home for the mentally retarded, exc. skilled or intermediate; Residential care; Skilled nursing care facilities
CEO: William J Timmons
Board of Directors: Perry Petrilli, Leah Shaler

HACIENDA MEXICAN RESTAURANTS
See HMR ACQUISITION CO INC

D-U-N-S 82-704-3246
HACIENDA SURGERY CENTER LLC
4626 Willow Rd Ste 100, Pleasanton, CA 94588-8555
Tel (925) 734-6744 *Founded/Ownrshp* 2007
Sales 38.2MM^E *EMP* 765^E
SIC 8062 General medical & surgical hospitals

D-U-N-S 07-528-7854
HACIENDA-LA PUENTE UNIFIED SCHOOL DISTRICT
15959 Gale Ave, City of Industry, CA 91745-1604
Tel (626) 933-1000 *Founded/Ownrshp* 1970
Sales 120.1MM^E *EMP* 2,500
SIC 8211 Public elementary & secondary schools; Public elementary & secondary schools
Ofcr: Rene Mesta
Dir Sec: John Babbitt
Off Admin: Rosie Garcia
Off Admin: Elizabeth Hernandez
Off Admin: Dolores Torres
Site Mgr: Danny Salcido
Teacher Pr: Margaret Hesselgrave
Psych: Jamie Arneson
Psych: Rosanne Hoang
Psych: Jenny Tobias
Psych: Flora Yee

D-U-N-S 09-821-7052
HACKENSACK BOARD OF EDUCATION (INC)
191 2nd St, Hackensack, NJ 07601-5577
Tel (201) 646-1851 *Founded/Ownrshp* 1894
Sales 25.9MM^E *EMP* 650
SIC 8211 Public senior high school; Public junior high school; Public combined elementary & secondary school; Public senior high school; Public junior high school; Public combined elementary & secondary school
Pr: Joseph L Montesano
**VP:* John Bellocchio
**VP:* Daniel Kirsch
Snr Mgr: John Kahn

D-U-N-S 07-980-6917
HACKENSACK CITY SCHOOL DISTRICT
191 2nd St, Hackensack, NJ 07601-2417
Tel (201) 646-8000 *Founded/Ownrshp* 2015
Sales 4.8MM^E *EMP* 592^E
SIC 8211 Public elementary & secondary schools

D-U-N-S 07-991-4571
HACKENSACK UNIVERSITY HEALTH NETWORK INC
HACKENSACK UNIVERSITY MED CTR
30 Prospect Ave, Hackensack, NJ 07601-1915
Tel (551) 996-2000 *Founded/Ownrshp* 1888
Sales 72.9MM^E *EMP* 8,000
SIC 8062 General medical & surgical hospitals
Pr: Robert Charles Garrett

HACKENSACK UNIVERSITY MED CTR
See HACKENSACK UNIVERSITY HEALTH NETWORK INC

D-U-N-S 04-279-7571
HACKENSACK UNIVERSITY MEDICAL CENTER
30 Prospect Ave Ste 1, Hackensack, NJ 07601-1915
Tel (201) 996-2000 *Founded/Ownrshp* 1888
Sales 1.1MM^E *EMP* 7,175^E
SIC 8062 Hospital, medical school affiliation; Hospital, medical school affiliation
Pr: Robert Charles Garrett
**COO:* Ketul J Patel
**CFO:* Anthony Esposito
**CFO:* Harold P Hogstron
Ch: Joseph E Parrillo
Ofcr: Tom Flynn
Ex VP: Ihor S Sawczuk
**VP:* Dr William C Black
**VP:* Andre J Ferullo
**VP:* Antoinette Fiore
**VP:* Robert M Koller

HACKENSACKUMC AT PASCACK VLY
See PASCACK VALLEY HOSPITAL LLC

D-U-N-S 80-197-1511
HACKENSACKUMC MOUNTAINSIDE
MOUNTAINSIDE HOSPITAL
(*Suby of* LHP HOSPITAL GROUP INC) ★
1 Bay Ave, Montclair, NJ 07042-4837
Tel (973) 429-6000 *Founded/Ownrshp* 1891
Sales 210.6MM *EMP* 1,200
SIC 8249 8062 Vocational schools; General medical & surgical hospitals; Vocational schools; General medical & surgical hospitals
CEO: John Fromhold
Chf Rad: Richard Mattern
Chf Rad: Frank Yuppa
Pr: Marjory Langer
COO: Everett Devaney Fache
CFO: Al Aboud
Ch: Franklyn Jenifer
Treas: Mark Drzala
Trst: Kalavathy Balakumar
Trst: Romulo Baltazar
Trst: Madelyn Danoff
Trst: Jan Huston
Ofcr: Karen Palatella
Ofcr: Karen Patanella
Ex VP: Robert Silver
Sr VP: Joe Morris
VP: John Camus
VP: Dusan Knezevic
Dir Rad: Maloney Mha
Dir Rad: Colleen Smorra

D-U-N-S 16-150-7843
■ HACKER GROUP INC
(*Suby of* INTERPUBLIC GROUP OF COMPANIES INC) ★
1215 4th Ave Ste 2100, Seattle, WA 98161-1018
Tel (206) 805-1500 *Founded/Ownrshp* 1999
Sales 23.1MM^E *EMP* 95
SIC 7319 7331 Distribution of advertising material or sample services; Direct mail advertising services
Pr: Spyro Kourtis
Mng Pt: Claudia Schulte
**CFO:* Richard Jacroux
CFO: Dick Summerhaze
**Ex VP:* Gayl Curtiss
VP: Benjamin Dupont
VP: Haydn Sweterlitsch
Creative D: Paul Ford
Creative D: Abby Lisk
Dir Bus: Joe Ellis
Ex Dir: Nancy Bruner
Board of Directors: Steve Rosenblum

D-U-N-S 06-518-3097
▲ HACKETT GROUP INC
1001 Brickell Bay Dr # 3000, Miami, FL 33131-4905
Tel (305) 375-8005 *Founded/Ownrshp* 1997
Sales 236.7MM *EMP* 848,904^E
Tkr Sym HCKT *Exch* NGM
SIC 8742 Management consulting services; Management consulting services
Ch Bd: Ted A Fernandez
**V Ch:* David N Dungan
CFO: Robert A Ramirez
Ofcr: Ulysses S Knotts III
Ex VP: Michelle Ramirez
Sr VP: Robert C Greene
VP: Arthur Colombo
VP: Doug Hansen
CTO: Brad Frink
VP Mktg: Christina Perkins
Board of Directors: Richard N Hamlin, John R Harris, Edwin A Huston, Alan T G Wix

D-U-N-S 07-361-6930
HACKETTSTOWN COMMUNITY HOSPITAL (INC)
HACKETTSTOWN REGIONAL MED CTR
651 Willow Grove St Ste A, Hackettstown, NJ 07840-1798
Tel (908) 852-5100 *Founded/Ownrshp* 1973
Sales 88.8MM *EMP* 700^E
Accts Baker Tilly Virchow Krause Ll
SIC 8062 General medical & surgical hospitals; General medical & surgical hospitals
CEO: Joseph Atrunfio
Chf Rad: Albert Lo
**Pr:* Gene C Milton
**CEO:* Joseph A Trunfio
COO: Rick Armstrong
COO: Jason Coe
**COO:* Stella Visaggio
**CFO:* Robert Peterson
Chf Mktg O: Kenneth Janowski
Dir OR: Ron Wallman
Dir Rad: Frank Buonomo

HACKETTSTOWN REGIONAL MED CTR
See HACKETTSTOWN COMMUNITY HOSPITAL (INC)

D-U-N-S 15-193-3389
HACKLEY HEALTH SYSTEMS INC
1675 Leahy St Ste 101, Muskegon, MI 49442-5538
Tel (231) 728-4032 *Founded/Ownrshp* 1984
Sales 784.1M *EMP* 430
SIC 8741 6512 3812 Hospital management; Nursing & personal care facility management; Nonresidential building operators; Compasses & accessories; Hospital management; Nursing & personal care facility management; Nonresidential building operators; Compasses & accessories
Pr: Gordon A Mudler
**Ch Bd:* Richard C Lague
**Treas:* H Richard Morgenstern
**VP:* David Gingras
IT Man: Jeff Zack
Obsttrcn: Samir Hamati

D-U-N-S 05-585-7643 IMP
HACKLEY HOSPITAL
MERCY HEALTH PARTNERS
1700 Clinton St, Muskegon, MI 49442-5591
Tel (231) 728-4950 *Founded/Ownrshp* 1902
Sales 177.8MM *EMP* 1,500
SIC 8062 General medical & surgical hospitals; General medical & surgical hospitals
Ch Bd: Thomas E Stone
**Pr:* Gordon A Mudler
CFO: Gary Allore
**Treas:* William Eyke Jr
**V Ch Bd:* Richard Witham
Trst: Richard Wilcox
Sr VP: Shirley Lynch
VP: Jeff Alexander
Dir Rad: Steve Rop
Dir Rx: George Kuhnert
Chf Nrs Of: Scott Howard

D-U-N-S 04-482-9190
HACKLEY SCHOOL INC
293 Benedict Ave, Tarrytown, NY 10591-4395
Tel (914) 366-2600 *Founded/Ownrshp* 1899
Sales 30.3MM *EMP* 190
Accts Eisneramper Llp New York New
SIC 8211 Private elementary & secondary schools; Private elementary & secondary schools
**CFO:* Peter McAndrew
Bd of Dir: Mark R Gordon
Bd of Dir: Jonathan P Nelson
Top Exec: Adrianne E Pirc
HC Dir: Julie Core

HACKMANN LUMBER
See WETTERMAN INC

HACKNEY CASH & CARRY
See H T HACKNEY CO

D-U-N-S 96-355-0736 IMP
■ HACKNEY LADISH INC
(*Suby of* PCC) ★
708 S Elmira Ave, Russellville, AR 72802-9637
Tel (479) 968-7555 *Founded/Ownrshp* 1995
Sales 111.0MM^E *EMP* 330
SIC 3089 3463 Fittings for pipe, plastic; Flange, valve or pipe fitting forgings, nonferrous; Fittings for pipe, plastic; Flange, valve or pipe fitting forgings, nonferrous
CEO: Kenneth D Buck
**Pr:* Chris Forbis
**COO:* Brian Byrum
CFO: Ekua Ollennu
**VP:* Roger A Cooke
**VP:* Michael Maxwell
**VP:* Kirk Morgan
Dir IT: Michael Bodinger
IT Man: Larry Harmeyer
IT Man: Michel Lendish
Mtls Mgr: James Keene

HACKNEY'S ON HARMS DIV
See HACKNEYS ON LAKE INC

D-U-N-S 02-550-2352
HACKNEYS ON LAKE INC
HACKNEY'S ON HARMS DIV
1514 E Lake Ave, Glenview, IL 60025-2193
Tel (847) 724-7171 *Founded/Ownrshp* 1939
Sales 11.5MM^E *EMP* 380
SIC 5812 5813 American restaurant; Cocktail lounge; American restaurant; Cocktail lounge
Ex VP: James Hebson
Exec: Ed Masterson

HACLA
See HOUSING AUTHORITY OF CITY OF LOS ANGELES

D-U-N-S 11-895-3827 IMP
HACOR INC
(*Suby of* HANJIN HEAVY INDUSTRIES & CONSTRUCTION CO., LTD.)
8506 Osage Ave, Los Angeles, CA 90045-4421
Tel (310) 645-9011 *Founded/Ownrshp* 1983
Sales 34.4MM^E *EMP* 400
SIC 5812 Contract food services; Contract food services
Pr: Eyong Kim
**Pr:* N H Cho
**VP:* Doo Nam Lee
Genl Mgr: Yong Nam Park
Mktg Mgr: Francis Sengol

HACSB
See HOUSING AUTHORITY OF COUNTY OF SANTA BARBARA

D-U-N-S 06-747-8339
HADADY CORP
510 W 172nd St, South Holland, IL 60473-2717
Tel (219) 322-7417 *Founded/Ownrshp* 1973
Sales 28.8MM^E *EMP* 150
SIC 3499 3743 3452 Machine bases, metal; Locomotives & parts; Pins; Machine bases, metal; Locomotives & parts; Pins
Pr: Jane Sullivan
**CFO:* Roger Gordon
VP: Tom Casper
VP: Nick Eldridge
Mktg Dir: Mike Gilbert
Sales Asso: Kevin Barker

D-U-N-S 07-329-6535
HADASSAH MEDICAL RELIEF ASSOCIATION INC
40 Wall St, New York, NY 10005-1304
Tel (212) 355-7900 *Founded/Ownrshp* 1925
Sales 103.1MM *EMP* 330
Accts Kpmg Llp New York Ny
SIC 8322 First aid service; Temporary relief service; Refugee service; First aid service; Temporary relief service; Refugee service
Pr: Gary Slavin
**Treas:* Ruth B Hurwitz
**VP:* Sandra Alfonsi
**VP:* Sharon Jacobson
**VP:* Sandra King
**VP:* Susan Mark
**VP:* Renee Resnik
**VP:* Natalie Silverman
**VP:* Roselle Ungar
**VP:* Theda Zuckerman

D-U-N-S 06-823-6546
HADASSAH WOMENS ZIONIST ORGANIZATION OF AMERICA INC (NY)
40 Wall St, New York, NY 10005-1304
Tel (212) 355-7900 *Founded/Ownrshp* 1912

Sales 13.5MM *EMP* 330E
Accts Kpmg Llp New York Ny
SIC 8699 Charitable organization; Charitable organization
CEO: Janice Weinman
Pr: Pennie Branden
Pr: Kathy Hershfield
Pr: Carol Rosenthal
**Pr:* June Walker
COO: Larry Blum
**CFO:* Rick Annis
Treas: Ellyn Lyons
**Treas:* Marcie Natan
Ex VP: Jeffrey Richardson
VP: Sandra Alfonsi
VP: Joan Baron
VP: Eddyse Kessler
VP: Susan Mark
**VP:* Joyce Rabin
VP: Roni Schwartz
VP: Judy Shereck
VP: Aisha Stephen
VP: Laurie Werner

D-U-N-S 08-284-3954
HADCO CONSTRUCTION LLC
1450 W 1850 N, Lehi, UT 84043-5652
Tel (801) 766-7611 *Founded/Ownrshp* 1976
Sales 56.3MME *EMP* 320
SIC 1794 Excavation work; Excavation work
Mng Pt: Kendall Page

D-U-N-S 04-631-2559 IMP/EXP
■ HADCO CORP
(*Suby of* SANMINA CORP) ★
12a Manor Pkwy, Salem, NH 03079
Tel (603) 421-3400 *Founded/Ownrshp* 2000
Sales 423.2MME *EMP* 7,850
SIC 3672 Printed circuit boards; Printed circuit boards
Pr: Andrew E Lietz
**Ch Bd:* Horace H Irvine II
**CFO:* Timothy P Losik
Genl Mgr: Jose Carraquello

D-U-N-S 78-998-7620 IMP/EXP
HADCO METAL TRADING CO LLC
(*Suby of* SCOPE METALS GROUP LTD)
555 State Rd, Bensalem, PA 19020-7704
Tel (215) 695-2705 *Founded/Ownrshp* 2006
Sales 188.1MME *EMP* 160
SIC 5051 Aluminum bars, rods, ingots, sheets, pipes, plates, etc.; Aluminum bars, rods, ingots, sheets, pipes, plates, etc.
CEO: Gilad Fishman
CFO: Ayelet Shtaub
**Prin:* Ori Ben-Amotz
Genl Mgr: John Meany
CTO: Itay Shtaub
IT Man: Steven Autrey
Sls Mgr: Terry Miller
Sales Asso: Nicolo Biundo
Sales Asso: Jason Ganser

D-U-N-S 07-047-1875
■ HADCO SANTA CLARA INC
(*Suby of* SANMINA CORP) ★
500 El Camino Real, Santa Clara, CA 95050-4345
Tel (408) 241-9900 *Founded/Ownrshp* 2005
Sales 59.2MME *EMP* 2,000E
SIC 3672 3679 Printed circuit boards; Harness assemblies for electronic use: wire or cable; Printed circuit boards; Harness assemblies for electronic use: wire or cable
Sr VP: Chris Mastrogiacomo
VP: Jerry Bauer
Dir Sec: Jeff Patrignani

HADCO SUPPLY
See AIREFCO INC

D-U-N-S 78-366-0723 IMP
HADDAD APPAREL GROUP LTD
HADDAD BRANDS
(*Suby of* HADDAD ORGANIZATION LTD) ★
90 E 5th St Ste 1, Bayonne, NJ 07002-4272
Tel (201) 356-2000 *Founded/Ownrshp* 1990
Sales 128.2MME *EMP* 230
SIC 5137 Women's & children's clothing; Women's & children's clothing
Ch Bd: Edward Haddad
Ex VP: Richard Haddad
VP: Jessica Falco
**VP:* Charles S Haddad
VP: Marc Weintraub
Trfc Dir: Tom Bay
Mktg Dir: Fran Boller
Mktg Mgr: John Strashum

HADDAD BRANDS
See HADDAD APPAREL GROUP LTD

HADDAD DODGE
See BAKERSFIELD DODGE INC

D-U-N-S 13-796-8749
HADDAD MOTOR GROUP INC
HADDAD PONTIAC BUICK JEEP
130 Pittsfield Rd, Pittsfield, MA 01202
Tel (413) 445-4535 *Founded/Ownrshp* 1987
Sales 36.0MM *EMP* 65
SIC 5511 Automobiles, new & used; Automobiles, new & used
Pr: George L Haddad
**VP:* Elizabeth M Sheehan
Sales Asso: Dale Cease
Sales Asso: Steve Davis
Sales Asso: Bill Pikula

D-U-N-S 07-009-5237
HADDAD ORGANIZATION LTD
HADSON REALTY DIV
90 E 5th St Ste 1, Bayonne, NJ 07002-4272
Tel (201) 339-0665 *Founded/Ownrshp* 1902
Sales 128.2MME *EMP* 457
SIC 6531 Real estate agents & managers; Real estate agents & managers
Pr: Edward Haddad
**VP:* Marc Weintraub

HADDAD PONTIAC BUICK JEEP
See HADDAD MOTOR GROUP INC

D-U-N-S 03-481-6033
HADDADS DEPARTMENT STORE
69 Crigger St, Munford, TN 38058-6492
Tel (901) 837-8025 *Founded/Ownrshp* 1947
Sales 50.0MM *EMP* 11
SIC 5651 5251 5712 5722 5611 Family clothing stores; Hardware; Furniture stores; Household appliance stores; Clothing, sportswear, men's & boys'
Owner: David Haddad
**Ltd Pt:* Francis Haddad
Off Mgr: Lana Haddad

D-U-N-S 00-194-9916 IMP/EXP
HADDON HOUSE FOOD PRODUCTS INC
250 Old Marlton Pike, Medford, NJ 08055-8760
Tel (609) 654-7901 *Founded/Ownrshp* 1960
Sales 629.8MME *EMP* 700
SIC 5149 Spices & seasonings; Specialty food items; Spices & seasonings; Specialty food items
Pr: Harold T Anderson
Pr: John Loveys
**VP:* David H Anderson
VP: Mark Hackenberry
VP: Craig McClain
VP: Bill Schultz
CIO: Mike Fabrico
Dir IT: Craig McClane
IT Man: Tom Murray
Mktg Dir: Lee Rucker
Manager: Scott Mook

D-U-N-S 08-324-2537
HADDONFIELD BOARD OF EDUCATION
HADDONFIELD PUBLIC SCHOOLS
1 Lincoln Ave, Haddonfield, NJ 08033-1866
Tel (856) 429-7510 *Founded/Ownrshp* 1850
Sales 18.9MME *EMP* 300
SIC 8211 Public elementary & secondary schools; Public elementary & secondary schools

HADDONFIELD PUBLIC SCHOOLS
See HADDONFIELD BOARD OF EDUCATION

D-U-N-S 08-609-4232 IMP
HADDY J G SALES CO INC
3401 Etiwanda Ave, Mira Loma, CA 91752-1128
Tel (951) 681-0666 *Founded/Ownrshp* 1971
Sales 38.3MME *EMP* 121E
SIC 5199 4213 4212 Packaging materials; Trucking, except local; Local trucking, without storage; Packaging materials; Trucking, except local; Local trucking, without storage
Pr: Joseph G Haddy
**Sec:* William J Smerber
**VP:* James E Ford

D-U-N-S 00-643-3676 IMP
HADER INDUSTRIES INC (WI)
15600 W Lincoln Ave, New Berlin, WI 53151-2823
Tel (262) 641-6000 *Founded/Ownrshp* 1951, 1954
Sales 47.3MME *EMP* 175
SIC 3561 3441 3594 Industrial pumps & parts; Cylinders, pump; Fabricated structural metal; Fluid power pumps; Industrial pumps & parts; Cylinders, pump; Fabricated structural metal; Fluid power pumps
Pr: Wayne K Hader
VP: Randy Symes
Off Mgr: Cindy Alivo
Mktg Mgr: T J Hader
Sls Mgr: Kim Lovinus

HADLEY MEMORIAL HOSPITAL
See SPECIALTY HOSPITAL OF WASHINGTON-HADLEY LLC

D-U-N-S 11-552-1408 IMP
HADLEY PRODUCTS CORP
(*Suby of* HUMPHREY COMPANIES LLC) ★
2851 Prairie St Sw Ste A, Grandville, MI 49418-2179
Tel (616) 530-1717 *Founded/Ownrshp* 1996
Sales 33.4MME *EMP* 193
SIC 3714 Motor vehicle parts & accessories; Motor vehicle parts & accessories
Ch Bd: John W Humphrey
**Pr:* Robert Dubsky
**CEO:* James Humphrey
**VP:* James Green
Prgrm Mgr: Joe Rankin
IT Man: Scott Finkhouse
Ql Cn Mgr: Beth Hawkins
Mktg Dir: Bob Zirlin

HADLEY ROMA
See ROMA INDUSTRIES LLC

D-U-N-S 06-697-3637
HADLEY TOWN OF INC
239 River Dr, Hadley, MA 01035-9638
Tel (413) 586-6375 *Founded/Ownrshp* 1661
Sales NA *EMP* 378
SIC 9221 9224 9111 Municipal police; Fire protection; City & town managers' offices; ; Municipal police; Fire protection; City & town managers' offices;
**Prin:* Anthony J Waskiewicz

D-U-N-S 06-425-0533
HADLOCK PAINT CO INC
HADLOCK'S HOUSE OF PAINT
7273 State Route 96, Victor, NY 14564-8974
Tel (585) 924-8420 *Founded/Ownrshp* 1973
Sales 23.7MME *EMP* 25
SIC 5198 5231 Paints; Wallcoverings; Paint; Wallcoverings
CEO: Donald J Dacey
**Pr:* Terry Dacey
VP: Sean Dacey
IT Man: Chris Marshano

D-U-N-S 05-725-9855 IMP
■ HADLOCK PLASTICS LLC
(*Suby of* COMPOSITE GROUP) ★
110 N Eagle St, Geneva, OH 44041-1196
Tel (440) 466-4876 *Founded/Ownrshp* 2011
Sales 28.2MME *EMP* 107
SIC 3089 Injection molded finished plastic products
Pr: Terry Morgan
QA Dir: Tim Clark

HADLOCK'S HOUSE OF PAINT
See HADLOCK PAINT CO INC

HADSON REALTY DIV
See HADDAD ORGANIZATION LTD

D-U-N-S 06-700-1560
HADWIN-WHITE BUICK GMC INC
2325 E Highway 501, Conway, SC 29526-9599
Tel (843) 347-4633 *Founded/Ownrshp* 1986
Sales 27.5MME *EMP* 60
SIC 5511 Automobiles, new & used; Automobiles, new & used
Pr: Gary L Hadwin Sr
**Genl Mgr:* Giordan Hadwin
Genl Mgr: Jordan Hadwin
Store Mgr: Pat Black
Sls Mgr: Lee Windham

HAECO AMERICAS
See TIMCO AVIATION SERVICES INC

HAECO AMERICAS CABIN SOLUTIONS
See TIMCO AEROSYSTEMS LLC

D-U-N-S 09-639-4317
HAEGELIN CONSTRUCTION CO LTD
15311 Fm 1325, Austin, TX 78728-2800
Tel (512) 388-9900 *Founded/Ownrshp* 1979
Sales 20.1MM *EMP* 95
Accts Padgett Stratemann & Co Llp
SIC 1623 Water main construction; Sewer line construction; Water main construction; Sewer line construction
Pt: Albert L Haegelin
Genl Pt: Haegelin M LLC
IT Man: Brian Haegelin

D-U-N-S 00-521-2758 IMP
HAEGER INDUSTRIES INC (IL)
HAEGER POTTERIES DIV
7 Maiden Ln, East Dundee, IL 60118-2307
Tel (847) 426-3441 *Founded/Ownrshp* 1871
Sales 26.5MME *EMP* 185
SIC 3269 Pottery household articles, except kitchen articles; Pottery florists' articles; Pottery household articles, except kitchen articles; Pottery florists' articles
CEO: Alexandra Haeger Estes
**COO:* Craig S Zachrich
**CFO:* Robert B Snyder
VP Mfg: Terry Rosborough
S&M/VP: Gene McGahan

HAEGER POTTERIES DIV
See HAEGER INDUSTRIES INC

D-U-N-S 05-782-7420 IMP
▲ HAEMONETICS CORP
400 Wood Rd, Braintree, MA 02184-2486
Tel (781) 848-7100 *Founded/Ownrshp* 1971
Sales 910.3MM *EMP* 3,383
Accts Ernst & Young Llp Boston Mas
Tkr Sym HAE *Exch* NYS
SIC 3841 3845 Medical instruments & equipment, blood & bone work; Blood transfusion equipment; Electromedical equipment; Medical instruments & equipment, blood & bone work; Blood transfusion equipment; Electromedical equipment
CEO: Ronald Gelbman
**Ch Bd:* Richard J Meelia
COO: Kent Davies
Ofcr: Sandra Jesse
Ofcr: David Ryan
Ofcr: Jonathan White
Ex VP: Brian Burns
Ex VP: David Helsel
Ex VP: Christopher Lindop
VP: Jerome Baligod
VP: Walter Hauck
VP Bus Dev: George Russo
Board of Directors: Charles J Dockendorff, Susan Bartlett Foote, Pedro P Granadillo, Mark W Kroll, Ronald L Merriman, Ellen Zane

D-U-N-S 09-615-7375 IMP
HAFELE AMERICA CO (NC)
(*Suby of* HAFELE GMBH & CO KG)
3901 Cheyenne Dr, Archdale, NC 27263-3157
Tel (336) 434-2322 *Founded/Ownrshp* 1973
Sales 102.3MME *EMP* 350
SIC 5072 Hardware; Furniture hardware; Hardware; Furniture hardware
Pr: Paul K Smith
**CFO:* Gary A Crysel
**VP:* Ursula Hafele
Exec: Gary Davis
Rgnl Mgr: Ken Pratt
Genl Mgr: Brad Borne
Genl Mgr: Barry Piercy
Dir IT: Martin Miller
Tech Mgr: Michael Wood
Web Dev: David Durand
Opers Mgr: Tommy Hazelwood

HAFEN USA
See KRYSTAL LOGISTICS USA INC

D-U-N-S 16-801-1328
HAFEZ CORP
MCDONALD'S
30892 Jay Dr, Spanish Fort, AL 36527-5202
Tel (251) 625-1716 *Founded/Ownrshp* 1997
Sales 24.0MM *EMP* 220
SIC 5812 Fast-food restaurant, chain; Fast-food restaurant, chain
Pr: Ebrahim Maghsoud

HAFFNERS SERV STAS
See HAFFNERS SERVICE STATIONS INC

D-U-N-S 01-942-1304
HAFFNERS SERVICE STATIONS INC
HAFFNERS SERV STAS
2 International Way, Lawrence, MA 01843-1064
Tel (978) 683-2771 *Founded/Ownrshp* 1923
Sales 54.7MME *EMP* 200
SIC 5541 5983 5172 Filling stations, gasoline; Fuel oil dealers; Gasoline; Gases, liquefied petroleum (propane); Filling stations, gasoline; Fuel oil dealers; Gasoline; Gases, liquefied petroleum (propane)
Pr: E Haffner Fournier
**Treas:* David Fournier

HAFTR
See HEBREW ACADEMY OF FIVE TOWNS AND ROCKAWAY

D-U-N-S 00-390-1543
HAGADONE HOSPITALITY CO (ID)
COEUR D'ALENE RESORT
(*Suby of* HAGADONE INVESTMENT CO INC) ★
111 S 1st St, Coeur D Alene, ID 83814-2794
Tel (208) 765-4000 *Founded/Ownrshp* 1961, 1983
Sales 35.8MME *EMP* 600
SIC 7011 5812 5813 7992 4489 Hotels & motels; Resort hotel; Eating places; Cocktail lounge; Public golf courses; Sightseeing boats; Hotels & motels; Resort hotel; Eating places; Cocktail lounge; Public golf courses; Sightseeing boats
Ch Bd: Duane B Hagadone
**Pr:* Jerald Jaeger
**Treas:* Art Flagan
**VP:* Bradley Hagadone
Exec: Gene Tillman

D-U-N-S 04-148-8537
HAGADONE INVESTMENT CO INC
111 S 1st St, Coeur D Alene, ID 83814-2794
Tel (208) 667-3431 *Founded/Ownrshp* 1959
Sales 347.0MME *EMP* 2,250
SIC 2711 7011 Newspapers, publishing & printing; Motels; Hotels; Newspapers, publishing & printing; Motels; Hotels
Pr: Duane B Hagadone
**CFO:* Doug Magnuson
**Treas:* Art Flagan
**VP:* Brad Hagadone
**VP:* Leslie Ward

D-U-N-S 00-920-2839 IMP/EXP
HAGADONE PRINTING CO INC (HI)
(*Suby of* HAGADONE INVESTMENT CO INC) ★
274 Puuhale Rd, Honolulu, HI 96819-4998
Tel (808) 847-5310 *Founded/Ownrshp* 1995
Sales 29.3MME *EMP* 140
SIC 2752 7331 Commercial printing, lithographic; Mailing service; Commercial printing, lithographic; Mailing service
Pr: Clint Schroeder
**Pr:* Scrhoeder Clint
**Treas:* Arthur Flagon
**VP:* Ed Chung
**Prin:* Erwin Hudelist
Plnt Mgr: Donald Dimato
Sales Exec: Jan Mills
Sales Exec: Nicholas Riopelle
Sales Exec: Guy Watarai
Sls Mgr: Jeff Texeira

D-U-N-S 00-700-5473
HAGAN & STONE WHOLESALE INC (KY)
B G STEEL
1387 N Main St, Tompkinsville, KY 42167-9434
Tel (270) 487-6138 *Founded/Ownrshp* 1947
Sales 20.0MM *EMP* 33
Accts Campbell Myers & Rutledge Pl
SIC 5072 Builders' hardware; Builders' hardware
Pr: Gene R Hagan
Treas: Terry Wells
**VP:* Stephen R Hagan
Info Man: Roxanna Proffitt
Sls Mgr: Anthony Poland

D-U-N-S 78-251-3311
HAGAN BENEFITS INC
1741 S Cleveland Ave # 102, Sioux Falls, SD 57103-3295
Tel (605) 334-1030 *Founded/Ownrshp* 1988
Sales NA *EMP* 50
SIC 6371 Pension, health & welfare funds
Pr: Michael J Hagen Sr
Ex VP: Jeffrey Pederson
VP: Dana Hagen

D-U-N-S 62-424-9751
HAGAN HOLDING CO
HOWCO ENVIRONMENTAL SERVICES
3701 Central Ave, Saint Petersburg, FL 33713-8338
Tel (727) 327-8467 *Founded/Ownrshp* 1975
Sales 34.0MME *EMP* 51
SIC 4953 4959 Liquid waste, collection & disposal; Oil spill cleanup
Pr: A Timothy Hagan
Ofcr: Richard Dillen
Dir IT: Timothy Hagan
Sfty Mgr: David Roehm

D-U-N-S 96-721-7154
HAGAN SCHOLARSHIP FOUNDATION
3806 Frontenac Pl, Columbia, MO 65203-5807
Tel (573) 875-2020 *Founded/Ownrshp* 2011
Sales 39.1MM *EMP* 2
Accts William G Stockglausner Cpa Pc
SIC 8699 Charitable organization; Charitable organization
Prin: Dan Hagan

D-U-N-S 02-456-8404
HAGAN-KENNINGTON OIL CO INC (NC)
HK INDUSTRIES
1405 Industrial Pike Rd, Gastonia, NC 28052-8431
Tel (704) 865-9561 *Founded/Ownrshp* 1955
Sales 38.6MM *EMP* 45
Accts Mccannon Rogers Driscoll & A
SIC 5172 5983 Petroleum products; Lubricating oils & greases; Fuel oil dealers; Petroleum products; Lubricating oils & greases; Fuel oil dealers
Pr: Grady Kennington
**Sec:* Bill Toomey
**VP:* Cynthia S Wilson
Genl Mgr: Artie Newcombe
Genl Mgr: Dale Toomey
**VP Sls:* Artie Newcomb

HAGAN-SPACKENKILL SCHOOL
See SPACKENKILL UNION FREE SCHOOL DISTRICTS (INC)

D-U-N-S 07-997-7179 IMP
HAGAR RESTAURANT EQUIPMENT SERVICE INC
HAGAR RESTAURANT SERVICE
6200 Nw 2nd St, Oklahoma City, OK 73127-6520
Tel (405) 235-2184 *Founded/Ownrshp* 1956
Sales 29.5MM *EMP* 185E
SIC 5087 7699 Restaurant supplies; Restaurant equipment repair; Restaurant supplies; Restaurant equipment repair
CEO: Larry C Basden
**Pr:* Lorn Dale Hagar
Treas: Adele Hagar
**VP:* Billy Hagar
Brnch Mgr: Les Carlson
Off Mgr: Beverly Landin

HAGAR RESTAURANT SERVICE
See HAGAR RESTAURANT EQUIPMENT SERVICE INC

D-U-N-S 07-884-1833
HAGEL METAL FABRICATION INC
2001 E Washington St, East Peoria, IL 61611-2963
Tel (309) 694-1045 *Founded/Ownrshp* 2008
Sales 32.2MME *EMP* 87
SIC 3441 Fabricated structural metal
Pr: David R Wrigley
Plnt Mgr: Howard Miles
Plnt Mgr: Charles Rice
Ql Cn Mgr: Tim Keller
Ql Cn Mgr: Ryan Wrigley

D-U-N-S 13-013-0966
HAGELAND AVIATION SERVICES INC
RAVN CONNECT
(*Suby of* HOTH INC) ★
4700 Old Intl Airport Rd, Anchorage, AK 99502-1020
Tel (907) 266-8448 *Founded/Ownrshp* 2008
Sales 21.8MME *EMP* 270
SIC 4512 4522 Air transportation, scheduled; Air transportation, nonscheduled; Air cargo carrier, scheduled; Air cargo carriers, nonscheduled
CEO: Robert Hajdukovich
**Pr:* James Hickerson
**CFO:* Walter Dallis
IT Man: John Hajdukovich
Sfty Dirs: Ron Burkevich

HAGEMEYER NORTH AMERICA
See HAGEMEYER PPS LTD

D-U-N-S 13-222-8862
HAGEMEYER NORTH AMERICA HOLDINGS INC
(*Suby of* REXEL HOLDING NETHERLANDS B.V.)
11680 Great Oaks Way, Alpharetta, GA 30022-2457
Tel (843) 745-2400 *Founded/Ownrshp* 1999
Sales 221.8MME *EMP* 3,400
SIC 5085 Industrial supplies; Industrial supplies
CEO: David Gabriel
**CFO:* Andros Neocleous

D-U-N-S 78-280-7804 IMP/EXP
HAGEMEYER NORTH AMERICA INC
CAM BAR
(*Suby of* SONEPAR MANAGEMENT US INC) ★
1460 Tobias Gadson Blvd, Charleston, SC 29407-4793
Tel (843) 745-2400 *Founded/Ownrshp* 2008
Sales 5.4MMME *EMP* 5,978E
SIC 5063 Electrical supplies
Pr: Lisa Mitchell
**Sr VP:* Will Lutz
**Sr VP:* Pat McClure
Sr VP: Per Ohstrom
VP: Charmaine Black
**VP:* David Blackwood
VP: Lynne Blair
**VP:* David Bolt
VP: Scott Moore
VP: Brian Thompson
Exec: Bob Belfiglio
Exec: Bob Gray
Exec: Frank Handwerk
Exec: Matt Kiefer

D-U-N-S 80-640-5119
HAGEMEYER PPS LTD
HAGEMEYER NORTH AMERICA
(*Suby of* SONEPAR USA HOLDINGS INC) ★
1460 Tobias Gadson Blvd, Charleston, SC 29407-4793
Tel (843) 745-2400 *Founded/Ownrshp* 1999
Sales 221.8MME *EMP* 3,200
SIC 5063 Industrial machinery & equipment; Management services; Electrical apparatus & equipment
Pr: David Gabriel
**Sec:* Andros Neocleous

D-U-N-S 15-541-0426
HAGEN CONSTRUCTION INC
2207 State Rd, Bensalem, PA 19020-7253
Tel (215) 633-7540 *Founded/Ownrshp* 1987
Sales 30.0MM *EMP* 175
Accts Baratz & Associates Pa Mar
SIC 1742 1751 Carpentry work; Plastering, drywall & insulation; Plastering, drywall & insulation; Carpentry work
Pr: Alfred D Hagen
CFO: Elliot Miller
**VP:* Peter Altomari
**VP:* George W Jackson

D-U-N-S 01-673-3560
HAGEN FORD INC
3980 N Euclid Ave, Bay City, MI 48706-2029
Tel (989) 684-4600 *Founded/Ownrshp* 1961
Sales 23.0MME *EMP* 47
SIC 5511 5521 Automobiles, new & used; Pickups, new & used; Vans, new & used; Used car dealers; Automobiles, new & used; Pickups, new & used; Vans, new & used; Used car dealers
Pr: Thomas S Hagen
**Sec:* Robert G Hagen
Store Mgr: Kevin Burk
Sales Asso: Terry Snider

D-U-N-S 17-652-6317 IMP/EXP
HAGEN PET FOODS INC
(*Suby of* ROLF C. HAGEN INC)
702 Broad Street Ext, Waverly, NY 14892-9562
Tel (607) 565-3497 *Founded/Ownrshp* 1997
Sales 35.4MME *EMP* 65
SIC 5149 2047 Pet foods; Dog food
Ch Bd: Normand Viau
**Pr:* Rolf Hagen Jr
Ql Cn Mgr: Carl Williams

HAGER HINGE COMPANY
See C HAGER & SONS HINGE MANUFACTURING CO

D-U-N-S 03-164-4669
HAGER OIL CO INC (AL)
1002 Old Birmingham Hwy, Jasper, AL 35501-2301
Tel (205) 384-3422 *Founded/Ownrshp* 1954, 1974
Sales 38.1MME *EMP* 55
Accts Haynes Downard Llp Birmingham
SIC 5171 5541 Petroleum bulk stations & terminals; Filling stations, gasoline; Petroleum bulk stations & terminals; Filling stations, gasoline
Pr: Russell S Hager
Trfc Dir: Randy Aaron

D-U-N-S 00-693-7122
HAGERMAN CONSTRUCTION CORP
510 W Washington Blvd, Fort Wayne, IN 46802-2918
Tel (260) 424-1470 *Founded/Ownrshp* 1908, 1933
Sales 91.8MME *EMP* 150
Accts Baden Gage & Schroeder Llc Fo
SIC 1542 1541 Nonresidential construction; Industrial buildings, new construction; Nonresidential construction; Industrial buildings, new construction
CEO: Mark F Hagerman
**Pr:* Jeffrey Hagerman
CFO: Theresa Lanning
Ex VP: Bruce Molter
VP: Dave Hall
VP: Mike Holtkamp
Exec: Peggi Little
IT Man: Rich Superius
Info Man: Richard Sutorius
VP Opers: Nathan Fink
Sfty Dirs: Richard Hawkins

D-U-N-S 05-119-1914
HAGERMAN GROUP
GEUPEL DEMARS HAGERMAN, LLC
(*Suby of* HAGERMAN CONSTRUCTION CORP) ★
10315 Allisonville Rd, Fishers, IN 46038-2016
Tel (317) 713-0636 *Founded/Ownrshp* 1998
Sales 20.6MME *EMP* 100
SIC 1541 1542 Industrial buildings, new construction; Nonresidential construction; Industrial buildings, new construction; Nonresidential construction
Ex VP: Terry Greene
Ex VP: David A Hall
VP: Gary Smith
Area Mgr: John Meyer
Sales Exec: Bobbi Albert
Mktg Dir: Stacy Neill
Board of Directors: Richard B De Mars

D-U-N-S 84-702-5756
HAGERMAN INC
510 W Washington Blvd, Fort Wayne, IN 46802-2918
Tel (260) 424-1470 *Founded/Ownrshp* 1992
Sales 81.4MME *EMP* 150E
Accts Baden Gage & Schroeder Llc Fo
SIC 1542 1541 Nonresidential construction; Industrial buildings & warehouses; Nonresidential construction; Industrial buildings & warehouses
Ch Bd: Richard E Sutorius
**Ch Bd:* Jeffrey Hagerman
**Pr:* Scott Miller
**Pr:* Bruce Molter
**CEO:* Mark Hagerman
COO: Steve Becker
CFO: Randy Horstman
VP: Nate Fink
Sfty Dirs: Richard Hawkins
Snr PM: Jay Wilhelm

D-U-N-S 07-494-7128
HAGERSTOWN COMMUNITY COLLEGE
H C C
11400 Robinwood Dr, Hagerstown, MD 21742-6514
Tel (240) 500-2000 *Founded/Ownrshp* 1946
Sales 58.4MME *EMP* 300
SIC 8222 8221 Junior college; Colleges universities & professional schools; Junior college; Colleges universities & professional schools
Pr: Guy Altieri
VP: Anna Barker
Off Mgr: Daniel Dell
Off Admin: Sally Matthis
Sls&Mrk Ex: Beth Stull
Pr Dir: Heather Barnhart

HAGERSTOWN FORD
See KING HAGERSTOWN MOTORS LLC

D-U-N-S 03-033-6432
HAGERSTOWN GOODWILL INDUSTRIES INC
14515 Pennsylvania Ave, Hagerstown, MD 21742-1670
Tel (301) 733-7330 *Founded/Ownrshp* 1955
Sales 18.1MM *EMP* 430
Accts Smith Elliott & Kearns & Compa
SIC 8331 Job training & vocational rehabilitation services; Job training & vocational rehabilitation services
CEO: Craig Mac Lean
**Ch Bd:* Kirt Dwoney
COO: Maclean Craig
Dir IT: Cynthia Dixon
IT Man: Dan Hull

D-U-N-S 00-693-5308 IMP
HAGERTY BROTHERS CO
INDUSTRIAL PRODUCTS DIV
1506 W Detweiller Dr, Peoria, IL 61615-1601
Tel (309) 589-0200 *Founded/Ownrshp* 1860
Sales 114.6MME *EMP* 275
SIC 5072 Hardware; Saw blades; Bolts; Nuts (hardware); Hardware; Saw blades; Bolts; Nuts (hardware)
Pr: Randy Fellerhoff
**VP:* Tom Clark
Sls Mgr: Kris Ray

D-U-N-S 62-627-5465
HAGERTY INSURANCE AGENCY INC
141 Rvers Edge Dr Ste 200, Traverse City, MI 49684
Tel (231) 947-6868 *Founded/Ownrshp* 1992
Sales NA *EMP* 400
SIC 6411 Insurance agents, brokers & service; Insurance agents, brokers & service
Pr: McKeel Hagerty
**Pr:* Louise Hagerty
**Treas:* Fred Turcotte
Bd of Dir: Derek Prechtl
Chf Mktg O: Clinton Sly
VP: Bill Bayer
VP: Daniel Beutler
VP: Angie Gallo
VP: Joseph Niemer
VP: Eric Okerstrom
VP: Carmen Stevens

HAGGAR CLOTHING COMPANY
See HAGGAR CORP

D-U-N-S 00-792-6645 IMP
HAGGAR CLOTHING CO (NV)
(*Suby of* HAGGAR CLOTHING CO) ★
11511 Luna Rd, Dallas, TX 75234-6022
Tel (214) 352-8481 *Founded/Ownrshp* 1926
Sales 515.6MME *EMP* 2,200
SIC 2325 2311 2321 5611 5651 Men's & boys' trousers & slacks; Men's & boys' jeans & dungarees; Shorts (outerwear): men's, youths' & boys'; Slacks, dress: men's, youths' & boys'; Tailored suits & formal jackets; Suits, men's & boys': made from purchased materials; Tailored dress & sport coats: men's & boys'; Men's & boys' furnishings; Men's & boys' dress shirts; Sport shirts, men's & boys': from purchased materials; Flannel shirts, except work: men's, youths' & boys'; Men's & boys' clothing stores; Family clothing stores; Men's & boys' trousers & slacks; Men's & boys' jeans & dungarees; Shorts (outerwear): men's, youths' & boys'; Slacks, dress: men's, youths' & boys'; Tailored suits & formal jackets; Suits, men's & boys': made from purchased materials; Tailored dress & sport coats: men's & boys'; Men's & boys' furnishings; Men's & boys' dress shirts; Sport shirts, men's & boys': from purchased materials; Flannel shirts, except work: men's, youths' & boys'; Men's & boys' clothing stores; Family clothing stores
CEO: Michael B Stitt
Pr: David Yarbrough
**CFO:* Robert H Adamek
Treas: Robert Qualls
Bd of Dir: Melody Busby
Chf Mktg O: Edward M Jones III
Sr VP: Steve Bernier
Sr VP: Linda Harrell
Sr VP: Joseph Harris
Sr VP: Rich Honiball
Sr VP: Tad Parnell
Sr VP: Sandi Stevens
Sr VP: Nanditha Zuckerman
VP: Tony Anzovino
VP: Paul Cronin
VP: Nancy Dowling
VP: Rebecca Maticko
VP: Don Schneider
VP: Linda Shirley
Dir: Kevin Oneill

D-U-N-S 16-091-1657 IMP
HAGGAR CORP
HAGGAR CLOTHING COMPANY
(*Suby of* TEXAS CLOTHING HOLDING CORP) ★
11511 Luna Rd, Dallas, TX 75234-6022
Tel (214) 352-8481 *Founded/Ownrshp* 1926
Sales 515.6MME *EMP* 3,200
SIC 2325 2311 2321 5611 6794 Men's & boys' trousers & slacks; Slacks, dress: men's, youths' & boys'; Jeans: men's, youths' & boys'; Shorts (outerwear): men's, youths' & boys'; Tailored suits & formal jackets; Suits, men's & boys': made from purchased materials; Tailored dress & sport coats: men's & boys'; Men's & boys' furnishings; Men's & boys' dress shirts; Sport shirts, men's & boys': from purchased materials; Flannel shirts, except work: men's, youths' & boys'; Men's & boys' clothing stores; Copyright buying & licensing; Men's & boys' trousers & slacks; Slacks, dress: men's, youths' & boys'; Jeans: men's, youths' & boys'; Shorts (outerwear): men's, youths' & boys'; Tailored suits & formal jackets; Suits, men's & boys': made from purchased materials; Tailored dress & sport coats: men's & boys'; Men's & boys' furnishings; Men's & boys' dress shirts; Sport shirts, men's & boys': from purchased materials; Flannel shirts, except work: men's, youths' & boys'; Men's & boys' clothing stores; Copyright buying & licensing
CEO: Michael B Stitt
**Pr:* Tim Lyons
**CFO:* William Davenport
**CFO:* John W Feray
**Chf Mktg O:* Alan C Burks
**Chf Mktg O:* Steven Croncota
**Ex VP:* David G Roy
VP: Tony Anzovino
VP: Barbara Gardsbane
VP: Nanditha Zuckerman
Dir IT: Lance Arrington
Board of Directors: Rae F Evans, Donald E Godwin, Richard W Heath, Thomas G Kahn, J Neal Thomas, John C Tolleson

D-U-N-S 01-643-3484
HAGGARD & STOCKING ASSOCIATES INC
5318 Victory Dr, Indianapolis, IN 46203-5951
Tel (317) 788-4661 *Founded/Ownrshp* 1972
Sales 68.3MME *EMP* 76
SIC 5084 Metalworking tools (such as drills, taps, dies, files); Metalworking tools (such as drills, taps, dies, files)
Pr: Herbert Haggard
**Ex VP:* Kevin Burnett
**VP:* Ron Barnett
**VP:* Jeff Haggard
Dir IT: Jim Slaymon
Opers Mgr: Jack Russell
Sls Mgr: Jeffrey Haggard
Sls Mgr: Adam Jackson
Sls Mgr: David Keith
Sls Mgr: Ryan Torivo
Sales Asso: Jon Coles

D-U-N-S 07-982-3517
HAGGEN ACQUISITION LLC
(*Suby of* HAGGEN OPERATIONS HOLDINGS LLC) ★
2211 Rimland Dr Ste 300, Bellingham, WA 98226-5699
Tel (360) 733-8720 *Founded/Ownrshp* 2011
Sales 1.0MMME *EMP* 12,247E
SIC 8748 Business consulting
CFO: Blake Barnett

D-U-N-S 02-726-6733
HAGGEN INC
TOP FOOD & DRUGS
(*Suby of* HAGGEN ACQUISITION LLC) ★
2211 Rimland Dr Ste 300, Bellingham, WA 98226-5699
Tel (360) 733-8720 *Founded/Ownrshp* 1962
Sales 1.0MMME *EMP* 3,900
Accts Moss Adams Llp
SIC 5411 5912 Supermarkets, chain; Supermarkets, chain; Drug stores
Pr: Ron Stevens
Pr: Clement Stevens
Pr: John Turley
Co-Ch Bd: Donald Haggen
Sr VP: Chris Linskey
Sr VP: Dave Norton
Sr VP: Wendy Oliver
VP: Fred Byrum
VP: Glen Foresman
VP: Brad Haggen
VP: Lewis Harrison
VP: Harrison Lewis
VP: Jaime Praeger
Dir Soc: Sheena Dezarn
Dir Soc: Jessica Solbeck
Dir Rx: Nik Seifter

D-U-N-S 07-982-2034
HAGGEN OPERATIONS HOLDINGS LLC
2211 Rimland Dr Ste 300, Bellingham, WA 98226-5699
Tel (360) 733-8720 *Founded/Ownrshp* 2014
Sales 1.1MMME *EMP* 12,408E
SIC 8748 Business consulting

HAGGERTY PONTIAC GMC
See HAGGERTY PONTIAC INC

D-U-N-S 07-703-0476
HAGGERTY PONTIAC INC
HAGGERTY PONTIAC GMC
300 W Roosevelt Rd, Villa Park, IL 60181-3590
Tel (630) 279-2000 *Founded/Ownrshp* 1975
Sales 21.6MME *EMP* 53
SIC 5511 7538 Automobiles, new & used; General automotive repair shops; Automobiles, new & used; General automotive repair shops
Pr: Gerard J Haggerty Sr
**Sec:* Judith S Haggerty
**VP:* William G Haggerty

D-U-N-S 03-444-9277
HAGGIN MARKETING INC
STEREOMAX
100 Shoreline Hwy A200, Mill Valley, CA 94941-3650
Tel (415) 289-1110 *Founded/Ownrshp* 2001
Sales 15.6MME *EMP* 430
SIC 7311 Advertising consultant; Advertising consultant
Pr: Steve Freedman
**CFO:* Valter Calamita
**Ex VP:* Mike Wychcoki
Sr VP: Mike Lapchick
VP: Betsy Wetthorn

D-U-N-S 00-529-4947 IMP/EXP
HAGIE HOLDING CO (IA)
721 Central Ave W, Clarion, IA 50525-1335
Tel (515) 532-2861 *Founded/Ownrshp* 1947
Sales NA *EMP* 860
SIC 3523 Sprayers & spraying machines, agricultural; Planting, haying, harvesting & processing machinery; Sprayers & spraying machines, agricultural; Planting, haying, harvesting & processing machinery
CEO: Alan B Hagie
CFO: Melissa Hackley
Dir Soc: Carmen Rodriguez
Dept Mgr: Doug Johanns
Dept Mgr: Mike Prehn
MIS Dir: Wendy Brandt
IT Man: Lucas Boyken
Sfty Mgr: Dave Larson
Plnt Mgr: Jim Schaefer
Plnt Mgr: Mel Wilson
Prd Mgr: Nic Wycoff

HAGIN, KENNETH MINISTRIES
See RHEMA BIBLE CHURCH

D-U-N-S 08-905-7103
HAGLE LUMBER CO INC
3100 Somis Rd, Somis, CA 93066-9549
Tel (805) 987-3887 *Founded/Ownrshp* 1978
Sales 21.8MME *EMP* 30
SIC 5031 Lumber, plywood & millwork
CEO: Ralph Hagle
**Pr:* Rick Hagle
**VP:* Joe Ferreira
Sales Exec: Jim Bell

D-U-N-S 96-700-9887 IMP
HAGLER SYSTEMS INC
607 Sand Bar Ferry Rd, Augusta, GA 30901-1941
Tel (803) 278-2728 Founded/Ownrshp 1994
Sales 88.5MM^E EMP 80
SIC 5082 Mining machinery & equipment, except petroleum; Dredges & draglines, except ships; Mining machinery & equipment, except petroleum; Dredges & draglines, except ships
Pr: Robert Hagler
*Treas: David Hagler
*VP: Ben Hagler

D-U-N-S 18-673-3739
HAGUE EQUIPMENT CO OF MICHIGAN INC
GREAT LAKES HYDRAULICS
410 E Dresden St, Kalkaska, MI 49646-8795
Tel (231) 258-9886 Founded/Ownrshp 1987
Sales 25.0MM^E EMP 26
SIC 5084 Pumps & pumping equipment
Pr: Gerald Peal
*Sec: Ruth Peal

HAGUE QUALITY WATER INTL
See WILLIAM R HAGUE INC

D-U-N-S 80-119-4205 IMP
HAHL INC
126 Glassmaster Rd, Lexington, SC 29072-3710
Tel (803) 359-0706 Founded/Ownrshp 2011
Sales 21.4MM^E EMP 70
SIC 3089 Monofilaments, nontextile
CEO: Van Allen Kierzek
*CFO: Andrew Acciardo
Site Mgr: Steve Pruitt
Mfg Mgr: Luther Hicklin
Opers Mgr: Andy Accairdo
Ql Cn Mgr: Robert Worley

D-U-N-S 00-806-5252 IMP/EXP
HAHN & CLAY LTD
5100 Clinton Dr, Houston, TX 77020-7998
Tel (713) 980-1320 Founded/Ownrshp 1993
Sales 79.5MM^E EMP 200
SIC 3443 3599 7692 3444 Fabricated plate work (boiler shop); Machine shop, jobbing & repair; Welding repair; Sheet metalwork; Fabricated plate work (boiler shop); Machine shop, jobbing & repair; Welding repair; Sheet metalwork
Pr: Don B Sheffield
COO: Mike Escamilla
QA Dir: Alan Henrikson

D-U-N-S 01-310-9863
HAHN AUTOMOTIVE WAREHOUSE INC
ADVANTAGE AUTO STORES
(Suby of GLICK LLC) ★
415 W Main St, Rochester, NY 14608-1944
Tel (585) 235-1595 Founded/Ownrshp 2001
Sales 377.8MM^E EMP 1,000
SIC 5013 Automotive supplies & parts; Automotive supplies & parts
Ch Bd: Eli Futerman
*Pr: Daniel J Chessin
CFO: Mike Piccolo
VP: Michael Kasel
*VP: Timothy Vergo
Adm Dir: Michelle Verhay
Dist Mgr: Brian Aveyard
Genl Mgr: Keith Scott
Genl Mgr: Eddie Seagroves
Dir IT: Peter Ferrari
Dir IT: Steven Opladen

D-U-N-S 15-534-8907
HAHN HOLDING CO
90 W Main St, New Market, MD 21774-6290
Tel (301) 865-5467 Founded/Ownrshp 1986
Sales 20.5MM^E EMP 200
Accts Bauer & Borneman Cpa
SIC 4213 Contract haulers; Contract haulers
Pr: Robert S Windsor Jr
*Prin: Barbara Windsor

D-U-N-S 08-014-6947
HAHN LOESER & PARKS LLP
200 Public Sq Ste 2800, Cleveland, OH 44114-2303
Tel (216) 621-0150 Founded/Ownrshp 1960
Sales 30.1MM^E EMP 198
SIC 8111 General practice law office; General practice law office
CEO: Josh Knerly
Pt: S Josh Knerly
Pt: Stephen J Knerly Jr
Pt: N Herschel Koblenz
Pt: Lawrence Oscar
Pt: Jennifer Jefferson-Beard
COO: David Finch
Exec: Jenny Tyger
Off Admin: Julie Koenig-Hill
Dir IT: Dennis Rose
Info Man: Stephen Faulstich
Board of Directors: Stephen J Knerly

D-U-N-S 00-316-9174
HAHN-MASON AIR SYSTEMS INC (NC)
4901 Dwight Evans Rd, Charlotte, NC 28217-1445
Tel (704) 523-5000 Founded/Ownrshp 1952, 1968
Sales 24.2MM^E EMP 50
SIC 5075 Warm air heating & air conditioning
Pr: Richard Hahn
*Pr: Richard Hahn Jr
Brnch Mgr: Steve Cannon
IT Man: Charles Willingham
Sls Mgr: Randy Ballenger
Sls Mgr: Terri Clouatre
Sls Mgr: Brad Gross
Sales Asso: Jason Flowers
Sales Asso: Valerie Simmons

D-U-N-S 00-109-9159
HAHNEL BROS CO (ME)
BANGOR ROOFING & SHTMTL CO
46 Strawberry Ave, Lewiston, ME 04240-5942
Tel (207) 784-6477 Founded/Ownrshp 1916
Sales 23.7MM^E EMP 107
SIC 1761 3444 Roofing contractor; Sheet metalwork; Sheet metalwork; Roofing contractor; Sheet metalwork; Sheet metalwork
Pr: Alan R Hahnel
*Ex VP: William H Hunter
VP: William Hunter

HAHNEMANN UNIVERSITY HOSPITAL
See TENET HEALTHSYSTEM HAHNEMANN LLC

D-U-N-S 07-999-1721
HAIER AMERICA CO LLC
(Suby of HAIER GROUP CORPORATION)
1800 Valley Rd, Wayne, NJ 07470-2047
Tel (973) 617-1800 Founded/Ownrshp 2014
Sales 500.0MM EMP 356
SIC 5064 Electrical appliances, major; Ranges; Electric household appliances
CEO: Adrian Micu
CFO: Richard Cao

D-U-N-S 78-815-0790 IMP
HAIER AMERICA REFRIGERATORS CO LTD
(Suby of HAIER GROUP CORPORATION)
50 Haier Blvd, Camden, SC 29020-7640
Tel (803) 424-8424 Founded/Ownrshp 1999
Sales 27.3MM^E EMP 150
SIC 3632 Household refrigerators & freezers; Household refrigerators & freezers
Pr: Xioabin Lu
Ex VP: Bob Cunningham
VP: Jeffrey Armstrong
Sfty Dirs: Theresa Justice
Prd Mgr: Mark Benedict
Art Dir: Richard Edelman

D-U-N-S 04-581-5722 IMP/EXP
HAIER AMERICA TRADING L L C
(Suby of HAIER GROUP CORPORATION)
1800 Valley Rd, Wayne, NJ 07470-2047
Tel (973) 617-1800 Founded/Ownrshp 1999
Sales 209.7MM^E EMP 215^E
SIC 5064 Electrical appliances, major; Ranges; Electric household appliances; Electrical appliances, major; Ranges; Electric household appliances
CEO: Adrian Micu
*Pr: Shariff Kan
*COO: Kevin Dexter
CFO: Ike Jiang
*CFO: Grace Li
Sr VP: Rian Cain
*Sr VP: Lintau Lu
VP: Maryjane Fanizzi
VP: Dan Franklin
VP: Audrey Rohan
MIS Mgr: Michael Zammit

D-U-N-S 14-927-4073 IMP
HAIFA NORTH AMERICA INC
(Suby of HAIFA CHEMICALS LTD.)
307 Cranes Roost Blvd, Altamonte Springs, FL 32701-3441
Tel (407) 862-6400 Founded/Ownrshp 2003
Sales 21.6MM^E EMP 20
SIC 5191 5169 Fertilizer & fertilizer materials; Food additives & preservatives
CEO: Marc Lebl
*Ch: Natan Feldman
VP: Jeffrey Bourgeois
VP: Yoel Nitzani
Manager: Clarence Harvey

HAIGHT ASHBURY FREE CLINIC
See HEALTHRIGHT 360

D-U-N-S 06-090-0693
HAIGHT BROWN & BONESTEEL LLP
555 S Flower St Ste 4500, Los Angeles, CA 90071-2441
Tel (213) 542-8000 Founded/Ownrshp 1980
Sales 26.4MM^E EMP 130
SIC 8111 General practice law office; General practice law office
Mng Pt: S Christian Stouder
Sr Pt: Kenneth Anderson
Sr Pt: Michael Bonesteel
Pr: Roberta Williams
CFO: Carolyn Harper
IT Man: Marie Wolfe
Mktg Dir: Tiffany Truffo
Sls Mgr: William Baumgaertner
Counsel: Florence H Gerlitz
Counsel: Christopher Kendrick

D-U-N-S 04-896-6654 IMP
HAIGHTS CROSS COMMUNICATIONS INC
136 Madison Ave Fl 8, New York, NY 10016-6711
Tel (212) 209-0500 Founded/Ownrshp 1997
Sales 99.1MM^E EMP 542^E
SIC 2731 Book publishing; Book publishing
CEO: Rick Noble
Pr: Kevin R Brueggeman
Pr: Rich Freese
CFO: Scott August
CFO: Melissa L Linsky
Sr VP: Julie Latzer
VP: Diane Q Curtin
VP: Faiz Mohammed

D-U-N-S 79-827-4358
HAIGHTS CROSS OPERATING CO
(Suby of HAIGHTS CROSS COMMUNICATIONS INC) ★
10 New King St Ste 102, White Plains, NY 10604-1208
Tel (914) 289-9400 Founded/Ownrshp 1999
Sales 66.4MM^E EMP 568^E
SIC 2731 Book publishing
Ch Bd: Peter J Quandt
*CFO: Paul J Crecca
*Treas: Melissa L Linsky
*Ex VP: Linda Koons
*Ex VP: Kevin M Mc Aliley
Sr VP: Julie Latzer
*VP: Mark Kurtz
Sales Exec: Ginger Gardner

D-U-N-S 02-599-4468
HAIGOOD & CAMPBELL LLC (TX)
108 E Walnut St, Archer City, TX 76351
Tel (940) 574-4622 Founded/Ownrshp 1947, 2000
Sales 24.8MM EMP 23
SIC 5172 Petroleum brokers; Petroleum brokers
Sls Mgr: Brian Hallock

HAILEY ADVENT
See W L HAILEY & CO INC

D-U-N-S 17-639-0131
HAILEY DEVELOPMENT GROUP LLC
236 5th Ave Fl 11b, New York, NY 10001-7946
Tel (212) 847-7267 Founded/Ownrshp 2004
Sales 78.0MM EMP 156
SIC 8741 Business management
*CFO: Mary Filocamo
Exec: Midhat Serbagi

D-U-N-S 82-470-0850 EXP
▲ **HAIN CELESTIAL GROUP INC**
1111 Marcus Ave Ste 100, New Hyde Park, NY 11042-2033
Tel (516) 587-5000 Founded/Ownrshp 1993
Sales 2.6MMM EMP 6,307
Accts Ernst & Young Llp Jericho Ne
Tkr Sym HAIN Exch NGS
SIC 2023 2034 2096 2086 2844 Dried & powdered milk & milk products; Dried milk preparations; Dietary supplements, dairy & non-dairy based; Vegetable flour, meal & powder; Potato chips & similar snacks; Iced tea & fruit drinks, bottled & canned; Toilet preparations; Dried & powdered milk & milk products; Dried milk preparations; Dietary supplements, dairy & non-dairy based; Vegetable flour, meal & powder; Potato chips & similar snacks; Iced tea & fruit drinks, bottled & canned; Toilet preparations
Ch Bd: Irwin D Simon
Pr: Steven List
CEO: Phillippe Woitrin
COO: Jay Lieberman
CFO: Pasquale Conte
Chf Cred: Denise M Faltischek
Chf Mktg O: Emma Froelich-Shea
Ofcr: Adam Levit
Ex VP: Francis Daily
Sr VP: Ellen B Deutsch
VP: Gerry Amantea
VP: Ron Boser
VP: Anthony Leis
VP: Stephen Powhida
VP: Ross Weiner
Board of Directors: Richard C Berke, Andrew R Heyer, Raymond W Kelly, Roger Meltzer, Scott M O'neil, Adrianne Shapira, Lawrence S Zilavy

D-U-N-S 00-340-3409
■ **HAIN PURE PROTEIN CORP**
(Suby of HAIN CELESTIAL GROUP INC) ★
220 N Center St, Fredericksburg, PA 17026-9723
Tel (717) 865-2136 Founded/Ownrshp 1919, 2005
Sales 45.8MM^E EMP 200^E
SIC 2015 Poultry, slaughtered & dressed; Poultry, slaughtered & dressed
Pr: Joe Tepippo
Exec: Teresa Allwein
Sls Dir: Bill Rogers
Sales Asso: Shannon Hunsinger

D-U-N-S 96-336-8662
■ **HAIN REFRIGERATED FOODS INC**
GREEK GODS
(Suby of HAIN CELESTIAL GROUP INC) ★
21707 66th Ave W, Mountlake Terrace, WA 98043-2103
Tel (425) 485-2476 Founded/Ownrshp 2010
Sales 107.0MM EMP 18
SIC 2024 5143 Ice cream & ice milk; Yogurt; Ice cream & ice milk; Yogurt
CEO: Basel Nassar
*Pr: Irwin D Simon
*Prin: Stephanos Margaritis

D-U-N-S 00-446-4764 IMP
HAINES & CO INC (OH)
CRISS CROSS DIRECTORIES
8050 Freedom Ave Nw, North Canton, OH 44720-6985
Tel (330) 494-9111 Founded/Ownrshp 1932
Sales 38.4MM^E EMP 152
SIC 2741 7331 2752 2759 Directories: publishing & printing; Mailing list compilers; Commercial printing, lithographic; Commercial printing; Directories: publishing & printing; Mailing list compilers; Commercial printing, lithographic; Commercial printing
Ch Bd: William K Haines Jr
*Treas: Delores Ball
*Prin: Leonard W Haines
*Prin: Harriett E Jones
Prd Mgr: Lori Hohman
Mktg Mgr: Joni Nlwc
Snr Mgr: William Jansen

D-U-N-S 04-455-4731 IMP
HAINES AND KIBBLEHOUSE INC
LOCUST RIDGE QUARRY
2052 Lucon Rd, Skippack, PA 19474
Tel (610) 584-8500 Founded/Ownrshp 1967
Sales 103.3MM^E EMP 150
SIC 1794 1611 1422 2951 Excavation work; Surfacing & paving; Limestones, ground; Asphalt paving mixtures & blocks; Excavation work; Surfacing & paving; Limestones, ground; Asphalt paving mixtures & blocks
Ch Bd: Scott Haines
*Pr: John B Haines IV
*Sec: John R Kibblehouse
Bd of Dir: John P Sivick
Top Exec: Jeff Litweiler
Off Mgr: Jeremy Huiser
CIO: Jeff Litwiler
IT Man: Rodger Rickenbrode
Trfc Dir: Brian Hohenshilt
Sales Exec: David Potter

D-U-N-S 07-319-6867
■ **HAINES CITY HEALTH MANAGEMENT ASSOCIATION INC**
HMA
(Suby of HEALTH MANAGEMENT ASSOCIATES INC) ★
40100 Highway 27, Davenport, FL 33837-5906
Tel (863) 422-4971 Founded/Ownrshp 1993
Sales 108.5MM^E EMP 800
SIC 8062 General medical & surgical hospitals; General medical & surgical hospitals
CEO: Jay Finnegan
*COO: Brent Burish
*CFO: Tonja Mosley
*VP: Ann Barnheart
VP: Timothy R Parry
Dir Rad: Ronald Brinsko
Dir Rx: John Dougherty
Orthpdst: Paul Dowdy
Orthpdst: Ponnavolu Reddy
Nrsg Dir: Christine Kipt Rn

HAIR CLUB FOR MEN & WOMEN
See HC (USA) INC

D-U-N-S 07-863-4592
HAIR CLUB FOR MEN LLC
(Suby of HAIR CLUB FOR MEN & WOMEN) ★
1515 S Federal Hwy # 401, Boca Raton, FL 33432-7451
Tel (561) 367-7600 Founded/Ownrshp 2001
Sales 40.0MM EMP 625
SIC 5999 Hair care products; Hair care products
Pr: Fraser Clarke
Treas: Patty Bonderenko
Sr VP: Michael Brisson

D-U-N-S 04-347-7207 IMP
HAIR SYSTEMS INC
30 Park Ave, Englishtown, NJ 07726-1607
Tel (732) 446-2202 Founded/Ownrshp 1991
Sales 51.0MM^E EMP 160
SIC 2844 Bleaches, hair; Hair coloring preparations; Bleaches, hair; Hair coloring preparations
Ch: Marjorie M Covey
*Pr: William Covey Jr
*CFO: Bill Delpizzo
CFO: Tom McMann
IT Man: John Ruch
Mtls Mgr: James Hely
Mtls Mgr: Michael Pierro
Plnt Mgr: Sunny Shah
Plnt Mgr: Shah Sunny
Plnt Mgr: Sunny Sunnyshah
Plnt Mgr: Jeff Ylagan

HAIR U WEAR
See HAIRUWEAR INC

HAIR VANITIES
See P-1 ENTERPRISES INC

D-U-N-S 78-127-1655 EXP
HAIR ZONE INC
SENSATIONNEL
10 State St, Moonachie, NJ 07074-1405
Tel (201) 641-2223 Founded/Ownrshp 2012
Sales 26.1MM^E EMP 70
SIC 5087 7231 Beauty parlor equipment & supplies; Unisex hair salons
Pr: Steve Choi
*VP: Kay Choi
Exec: Hyun Sook
Sales Exec: Nancy Lee

D-U-N-S 79-369-2252
HAIRCUTTERS
14529 Ventura Blvd # 200, Sherman Oaks, CA 91403-3772
Tel (818) 716-5319 Founded/Ownrshp 1984
Sales 13.9MM^E EMP 450
SIC 7231 Beauty shops; Beauty shops
Pr: Daren Saville
*VP: Michael Saville

D-U-N-S 80-602-3990
HAIRSTYLISTS MANAGEMENT SYSTEMS INC
URBAN HAIR AND SPA
12700 Industrial Park Blv, Minneapolis, MN 55441-3947
Tel (763) 550-1332 Founded/Ownrshp 1993
Sales 15.6MM^E EMP 1,000
SIC 7231 Beauty shops; Beauty shops
Pr: Michael Kunin
*CEO: Elliot Cohen
*CFO: Michael Brooks
*Ch: Daniel Kunin

D-U-N-S 05-409-5096
HAIRUWEAR INC
HAIR U WEAR
(Suby of MRN ACQUISITION CORP)
14865 W 105th St, Lenexa, KS 66215-2007
Tel (816) 231-3700 Founded/Ownrshp 1996
Sales 24.7MM^E EMP 50
SIC 5199 Wigs
CEO: Norman L Levine
Pr: Michael Napolitano
VP: Jason Lumsden

D-U-N-S 80-962-4146 IMP/EXP
HAITAI INC
HAITAI USA
7227 Telegraph Rd, Montebello, CA 90640-6512
Tel (323) 890-0101 Founded/Ownrshp 2005
Sales 22.0MM^E EMP 40
SIC 5141 Groceries, general line
Pr: Taeki Min
CFO: Soon Cha
*Prin: Ryan OH
Sls Mgr: Jaeho Han

HAITAI USA
See HAITAI INC

D-U-N-S 10-672-4565
HAIVISION NETWORK VIDEO INC
13975 W Polo Trail Dr # 102, Lake Forest, IL 60045-5119
Tel (847) 362-6800 Founded/Ownrshp 2002
Sales 40.0MM EMP 170
SIC 7373 Computer integrated systems design
CEO: Miroslav Wicha
*CFO: Dan Rabinowitz
*Chf Mktg O: Peter Maag
*Ex VP: Mahmoud J Al-Daccak
Ex VP: Chance Mason
VP: Brian Zorc
Snr Sftwr: Benjamin Gagosian
Snr Sftwr: Rich Insley
QA Dir: Aruna Dutt

Software D: Fred Allen
Software D: Kyle Dassoff

D-U-N-S 00-941-7783 IMP
HAJ INC
CHRISTENSON OIL
3821 Nw Saint Helens Rd, Portland, OR 97210-1434
Tel (503) 478-9905 *Founded/Ownrshp* 1979
Sales 27.3MM^E *EMP* 38
SIC 5172 5169 2992 2899 Lubricating oils & greases; Chemicals & allied products; Alcohols & anti-freeze compounds; Lubricating oils & greases; Chemical preparations
CEO: John Holcomb
**Pr:* Larry Lesniak
**Sr VP:* Glen S Morrison

D-U-N-S 10-669-7274
HAJ SUPERMARKETS
JACK'S SUPER IGA
370 Bloomfield Ave, Caldwell, NJ 07006-4905
Tel (973) 226-2122 *Founded/Ownrshp* 1998
Sales 20.8MM^E *EMP* 50
SIC 5141 Groceries, general line
Pr: John Shakoor
**Treas:* Mary Ellen Shakoor

D-U-N-S 00-137-9429
HAJOCA CORP (ME)
WEINSTEIN SUPPLY
127 Coulter Ave, Ardmore, PA 19003-2473
Tel (610) 649-1430 *Founded/Ownrshp* 1981
Sales 3.8MMM^E *EMP* 3,500
SIC 5074 Plumbing fittings & supplies; Plumbing fittings & supplies
Pr: Rick Fantham
**Pr:* Richard J Klau
**Treas:* Christopher M Pappo
VP: David Beale
VP: Barbara Ryan
VP: Lee Tracy
Exec: Eileen Urso
Brnch Mgr: Rick Ashe
Brnch Mgr: Christopher Bounds
Brnch Mgr: Jack Hagan
Brnch Mgr: Stoneman Hodnett

D-U-N-S 11-502-7567
HAK INC
KEYES EUROPEAN
5400 Van Nuys Blvd, Sherman Oaks, CA 91401-5627
Tel (818) 461-3900 *Founded/Ownrshp* 1964
Sales 30.4MM^E *EMP* 86
SIC 5511 5521 Automobiles, new & used; Used car dealers; Automobiles, new & used; Used car dealers
Pr: Howard Keyes
**VP:* Lawrence Abramson
**VP:* Eddie Frank
Genl Mgr: Simon Sarriedine
**Genl Mgr:* Jim Sarvey
Sales Exec: Wael Khzam
Mktg Dir: Anoush Sadegh
Sls Mgr: Darren Arnaud
Sls Mgr: Ilia Shapiro
Sls Mgr: Wil Silva
Sls Mgr: Elan Yakovee

D-U-N-S 18-076-4677
HAKES SASH & DOOR INC
31945 Corydon St, Lake Elsinore, CA 92530-8524
Tel (951) 674-2414 *Founded/Ownrshp* 2005
Sales 23.1MM^E *EMP* 190
SIC 1751 3442 5211 Window & door installation & erection; Window & door frames; Sash, wood or metal; Window & door installation & erection; Window & door frames; Sash, wood or metal
Pr: Allen J Hakes
VP: Teo Villasenor
Off Mgr: Christina Rupp
Opers Mgr: Ricky Luper
Sls Mgr: Gaspar Santos

D-U-N-S 15-184-9051
HAKKASAN HOLDINGS LLC
ANGEL MANAGEMENT GROUP
6385 S Rainbow Blvd # 800, Las Vegas, NV 89118-3201
Tel (702) 212-8804 *Founded/Ownrshp* 2011
Sales 108.1MM^E *EMP* 564^E
SIC 8741 Hotel or motel management
Pr: Angela Lester
CFO: Jan Marks
VP: Jason Aranas
VP: Jerome Klint
CIO: Mike Novak
Dir IT: Dan Adams
Opers Mgr: Alexandra Ciobota
Mktg Dir: Nick Gold
Mktg Dir: Salvatore Wise
Mktg Mgr: Dimitrios Aletras
Mktg Mgr: Dana Boyce

D-U-N-S 80-228-3572
HAKS ENGINEERS ARCHITECTS AND LAND SURVEYORS PC
40 Wall St Fl 11, New York, NY 10005-1357
Tel (212) 747-1997 *Founded/Ownrshp* 1991
Sales 114.8MM *EMP* 595
SIC 8712 8711 8713

HAL BRANCH ACADEMY
See PARSONS VENTURES CORP

D-U-N-S 78-855-2032
HAL HAYS CONSTRUCTION INC
4181 Latham St, Riverside, CA 92501-1729
Tel (951) 369-1008 *Founded/Ownrshp* 1990
Sales 74.8MM *EMP* 127
SIC 1541 1542 1623 1629 1611 1771 Industrial buildings & warehouses; Commercial & office buildings, renovation & repair; Water, sewer & utility lines; Dams, waterways, docks & other marine construction; Highway & street paving contractor; Concrete work; Industrial buildings & warehouses; Commercial & office buildings, renovation & repair; Water, sewer & utility lines; Dams, waterways, docks & other marine construction; Highway & street paving contractor; Concrete work
Pr: Hal Hays
**CFO:* E Denise Hays
Opers Mgr: Allan Findley

D-U-N-S 04-816-9056 IMP/EXP
HAL LEONARD CORP
7777 W Bluemound Rd, Milwaukee, WI 53213-3400
Tel (414) 774-3630 *Founded/Ownrshp* 1947
Sales 81.7MM^E *EMP* 420
SIC 2741

D-U-N-S 02-940-8770
HAL MCBRIDE CAR SALES INC
HOME MOTORS
1313 E Main St, Santa Maria, CA 93454-4703
Tel (805) 928-7744 *Founded/Ownrshp* 1974
Sales 37.5MM^E *EMP* 100^E
SIC 5511 Automobiles, new & used; Automobiles, new & used
Pr: Charles R Hebard
**CEO:* Michael McNulty
**Sec:* Nancy Sewell
**VP:* William Byrd

D-U-N-S 79-559-6683
HAL SMITH MARKETING GROUP LLC
CHARLESTON'S
3101 W Tecumseh Rd # 200, Norman, OK 73072-1815
Tel (405) 321-2600 *Founded/Ownrshp* 1992
Sales 25.5MM^E *EMP* 525
SIC 5812 Eating places; Eating places
Pr: Hal Smith
**Sec:* David Brauckmann
VP Opers: Mike Rogers

D-U-N-S 18-748-0306 EXP
HAL STICKEL INC
STICKEL PACKAGING SUPPLY
1991 Rutgers Blvd, Lakewood, NJ 08701-4538
Tel (732) 905-2811 *Founded/Ownrshp* 1984
Sales 24.0MM^E *EMP* 33
SIC 5085 Packing, industrial
Pr: Hal Stickel
**Sr VP:* Christopher Borriello
**VP:* Peter Borriello
Dist Mgr: Robert Jakub
Dist Mgr: Ed Maley

D-U-N-S 00-922-1854
HALABI INC
DURACITE
2100 Huntington Dr, Fairfield, CA 94533-9731
Tel (707) 402-1600 *Founded/Ownrshp* 1995
Sales 112.2MM^E *EMP* 297
SIC 3281 1799 Cut stone & stone products; Counter top installation; Cut stone & stone products; Counter top installation
CEO: Delbert Boyle
**CFO:* George Marino
**Prin:* Fadi M Halabi

D-U-N-S 00-635-8386
HALBERT PIPE AND STEEL CO INC
400 N Olive St, North Little Rock, AR 72114-5424
Tel (501) 374-4865 *Founded/Ownrshp* 1954
Sales 22.7MM^E *EMP* 31
SIC 5051 Pipe & tubing, steel; Steel
CEO: Rick Halbert
**Pr:* Ricky L Halbert II
**Sec:* Deborah Halbert
**VP:* Jerry Cooper

D-U-N-S 04-966-8189
HALCO (MINING) INC
12 Federal St Ste 320, Pittsburgh, PA 15212-5700
Tel (412) 235-0265 *Founded/Ownrshp* 1953
Sales 292.9MM^E *EMP* 2,400^E
SIC 1099 Bauxite mining; Bauxite mining
Pr: Pat Fyore
**Treas:* Robert St Pierre

HALCO EXPRESS AUTO PARTS
See HALCO INDUSTRIES INC

D-U-N-S 06-259-2449 IMP/EXP
HALCO INDUSTRIES INC
HALCO EXPRESS AUTO PARTS
1015 Norcross Indus Ct, Norcross, GA 30071-2619
Tel (770) 840-3480 *Founded/Ownrshp* 1989
Sales 45.6MM^E *EMP* 53
SIC 5013 5172 2992 Automotive supplies & parts; Petroleum products; Lubricating oils & greases; Lubricating oils & greases
Pr: Alan Parker
**CFO:* Robert M McLean

D-U-N-S 19-497-9860
■ **HALCON HOLDINGS INC**
(*Suby of* HALCON RESOURCES CORP) ★
1000 La St Ste 6700, Houston, TX 77002
Tel (832) 538-0300 *Founded/Ownrshp* 1987
Sales 22.8MM^E *EMP* 188
SIC 6792 1311 Oil leases, buying & selling on own account; Crude petroleum production; Natural gas production; Oil leases, buying & selling on own account; Crude petroleum production; Natural gas production
CEO: Floyd C Wilson
**Pr:* Stephen Herod
**CFO:* Mark Mize
**Ex VP:* David S Elkouri
**VP:* Jason Brown
**VP:* Leah Kasparek
**VP:* Joseph Rinando
**VP:* Scott Zuehlke

D-U-N-S 79-093-5170
▲ **HALCON RESOURCES CORP**
1000 La St Ste 6700, Houston, TX 77002
Tel (832) 538-0300 *Founded/Ownrshp* 2012
Sales 1.1MMM *EMP* 419^E
Tkr Sym HK *Exch* NYS
SIC 1311 Crude petroleum & natural gas; Crude petroleum & natural gas
Ch Bd: Floyd C Wilson
Pr: Jason Brown
Pr: Stephen W Herod
COO: Charles E Cusack III
CFO: Mark J Mize
Ex VP: Robert J Anderson
Ex VP: David S Elkouri
Sr VP: Tina S Obut
VP: Mary E Brook
VP: Larry Helm
VP: Walter Mayer
VP: Joseph Rinando
VP: David W Tippett
VP: Scott Zuehlke
Dir Risk M: Tim McDonald
Board of Directors: Tucker S Bridwell, Thomas R Fuller, Kevin E Godwin, David S Hunt, David B Miller, Daniel A Rioux, Michael A Vlasic, Mark A Welsh IV, James W Christmas

D-U-N-S 82-928-3915
■ **HALCON RESOURCES OPERATING INC**
(*Suby of* HALCON RESOURCES CORP) ★
1000 La St Ste 6700, Houston, TX 77002
Tel (832) 538-0300 *Founded/Ownrshp* 2004
Sales 43.1MM^E *EMP* 188
SIC 1311

D-U-N-S 04-642-5435 EXP
HALCORE GROUP INC
HORTON EMERGENCY VEHICLES
(*Suby of* ALLIED SPECIALTY VEHICLES INC) ★
3800 Mcdowell Rd, Grove City, OH 43123-4022
Tel (614) 539-8181 *Founded/Ownrshp* 1997, 2010
Sales 74.0MM^E *EMP* 300^E
SIC 3713 Ambulance bodies; Ambulance bodies
Pr: John Slawson
VP: Greg Amato
VP: Bruce Temple
Exec: Brian Lehman
Prd Mgr: Dan Sisson
VP Sls: Bill Baer
VP Sls: David Cole
Manager: Dave Digangi

D-U-N-S 09-546-7353 IMP/EXP
HALCORE GROUP INC
AMERICAN EMERGENCY VEHICLES
165 American Way, Jefferson, NC 28640-9195
Tel (336) 982-9824 *Founded/Ownrshp* 1997
Sales 64.5MM^E *EMP* 366^E
SIC 3711 Ambulances (motor vehicles), assembly of; Ambulances (motor vehicles), assembly of
Pr: Mark Van Arnam
**Treas:* Chris Eppel
**Ex VP:* Randy Hanson
**VP:* Dino Cusumano
VP: Greg Warmuth

D-U-N-S 61-052-4576
HALCROW INC
(*Suby of* HALCROW HOLDINGS LIMITED)
22 Cortlandt St Fl 31, New York, NY 10007-3142
Tel (212) 608-3990 *Founded/Ownrshp* 2005
Sales 29.3MM^E *EMP* 600
SIC 8711 Consulting engineer; Consulting engineer
Pr: Michael Dellarocca
**CFO:* M Colleen Brennen
Treas: Jonathan Goldstick
**Sr VP:* Helga Junold
VP: Lawrence Cunningham
VP: Patrick King
**VP:* James T Lindner
Assoc Dir: Karen Macpherson
Assoc Dir: Peter Spencer

D-U-N-S 01-148-8483
HALCYON ASSET MANAGEMENT LLC
477 Madison Ave Fl 8, New York, NY 10022-5868
Tel (212) 303-9400 *Founded/Ownrshp* 1981
Sales 43.0MM^E *EMP* 125^E
SIC 6722 Management investment, open-end; Management investment, open-end
**V Ch:* Kevah Konner
**COO:* Thomas P Hirschfeld
**CFO:* Aaron Goldberg
**Ch:* John M Bader
Ofcr: Suzanne McDermott
Sr VP: Mason Christopher
Sr VP: Todd Solomon
VP: Ryan Bendixen
VP: Craig Dworkin
VP: Michael Rosner
Admn Mgr: James Coppola

D-U-N-S 04-223-0305
HALCYON ASSETS MANAGEMENT
HALCYON OFFSHORE ASSETS MGT
477 Madison Ave Fl 8, New York, NY 10022-5868
Tel (212) 303-9400 *Founded/Ownrshp* 1982
Sales 40.0MM *EMP* 79
SIC 6282 Investment advice; Investment advice
Off Mgr: Lauren Ross

HALCYON OFFSHORE ASSETS MGT
See HALCYON ASSETS MANAGEMENT

D-U-N-S 07-955-6714
HALCYON SUPPLY CHAIN SOLUTIONS LLC
3455 Millennium Ct, Columbus, OH 43219-5550
Tel (614) 563-6513 *Founded/Ownrshp* 2013
Sales 30.0MM *EMP* 5
SIC 4789 8742 Cargo loading & unloading services; Manufacturing management consultant; Cargo loading & unloading services; Manufacturing management consultant
Pr: Angela N Cauley
**VP:* Ian Blount
**VP:* Denis Bruncak
**VP:* Aaron Dryer

D-U-N-S 00-825-5937
HALDEMAN INC
2937 Tanager Ave, Commerce, CA 90040-2761
Tel (323) 726-7011 *Founded/Ownrshp* 1918
Sales 25.6MM^E *EMP* 55
SIC 5075 Warm air heating & air conditioning
CEO: Albert Thomas Haldeman
**Pr:* Tom Haldeman
**Treas:* Sue Haldeman

D-U-N-S 02-289-9975
HALDEMAN-HOMME INC
430 Industrial Blvd Ne, Minneapolis, MN 55413-2979
Tel (612) 331-4880 *Founded/Ownrshp* 1951
Sales 101.2MM^E *EMP* 140
SIC 5021 5211 5084 Office & public building furniture; Racks; Shelving; Flooring, wood; Materials handling machinery; Office & public building furniture; Racks; Shelving; Flooring, wood; Materials handling machinery
Ch Bd: Ernest Stalock
**Pr:* Mike Propp
**Treas:* K C Gunther
**Ex VP:* Paul Fedji
**VP:* Ron Johnson
Div Mgr: Rusty Flocken
Genl Mgr: Dan Moran
Genl Mgr: Kyle Saewert
IT Man: Dan Weinmeyer
Opers Mgr: Bob Anderson
Opers Mgr: Jared Judson

D-U-N-S 96-251-1601 IMP
HALDEX BRAKE CORP
(*Suby of* HALDEX BRAKE PRODUCTS CORP) ★
10930 N Pomona Ave, Kansas City, MO 64153-1256
Tel (816) 382-3785 *Founded/Ownrshp* 1999
Sales 58.0MM *EMP* 153
SIC 3714 Air brakes, motor vehicle; Air brakes, motor vehicle
Pr: Jay Longbottom
CFO: Stefan Johansson
IT Man: Mike McMaster
Opers Mgr: Doug Roof

D-U-N-S 10-651-3385 IMP
HALDEX BRAKE PRODUCTS CORP
(*Suby of* HALDEX INC) ★
10930 N Pomona Ave, Kansas City, MO 64153-1256
Tel (816) 891-2470 *Founded/Ownrshp* 1998
Sales 330.0MM *EMP* 500
SIC 3714 Air brakes, motor vehicle; Air brakes, motor vehicle
VP: Gary Boznik
Pr: Ulf Herlin
CFO: Stefan Johanon
Chf Mktg O: Mike Regan
Exec: Kim Garn
Mng Dir: Magnus Bergstr
Genl Mgr: Jim Muntean
Genl Mgr: Greg Vassmer
CTO: Jan Webber

D-U-N-S 02-144-0151 IMP
HALDEX INC
HALDEX PRODUCTS
(*Suby of* HALDEX AB)
10930 N Pomona Ave, Kansas City, MO 64153-1256
Tel (816) 891-2470 *Founded/Ownrshp* 1973
Sales 451.5MM^E *EMP* 3,715
SIC 3714 3594 Motor vehicle brake systems & parts; Fluid power pumps; Pumps, hydraulic power transfer; Motor vehicle brake systems & parts; Fluid power pumps; Pumps, hydraulic power transfer
Pr: Claes Warnander
VP: Dan Debord
**VP:* Lennard Hammargren
**VP:* Charles Kleinhagen
**VP:* John Pepe
Sls Mgr: Wayne Brown
Sls Mgr: Scott Crouch
Sls Mgr: Chris Gomez

HALDEX PRODUCTS
See HALDEX INC

D-U-N-S 07-787-4162 IMP/EXP
HALDOR TOPSOE INC
(*Suby of* HALDOR TOPSOE A/S)
17629 El Cam Ste 300, Houston, TX 77058
Tel (281) 228-5000 *Founded/Ownrshp* 1968
Sales 59.8MM^E *EMP* 262
SIC 2819 8711 Catalysts, chemical; Chemical engineering; Catalysts, chemical; Chemical engineering
Ch Bd: Haldor Topsoe
CEO: Bjerne S Clausen
CEO: Anders N Olsen
VP: Edward Andersson III
Tech Mgr: Klavs Beldring
Tech Mgr: Bent Dahlstron
Counsel: David Juist

D-U-N-S 00-368-3935
HALE & HEARTY SOUPS LLC
75 9th Ave Frnt 9, New York, NY 10011-7041
Tel (212) 255-2400 *Founded/Ownrshp* 1996
Sales 35.7MM^E *EMP* 200
SIC 5499

D-U-N-S 04-847-2682
HALE AREA SCHOOL DISTRICT
200 W Main St, Hale, MI 48739-9255
Tel (989) 728-7661 *Founded/Ownrshp* 1943
Sales 65.0MM *EMP* 100
Accts Weinlander Fitzhugh
SIC 8211 Public elementary & secondary schools; School board; Public elementary & secondary schools; School board
Prin: Rhonda A Provoast

D-U-N-S 03-481-1398
■ **HALE BROTHERS SUMMIT LLC**
PFG-HALE
(*Suby of* P F G) ★
5262 S Air Park Blvd, Morristown, TN 37813-4304
Tel (423) 318-8700 *Founded/Ownrshp* 1989
Sales 43.7MM^E *EMP* 167
SIC 5141 5142 5148 Groceries, general line; Packaged frozen goods; Fruits, fresh; Vegetables, fresh; Groceries, general line; Packaged frozen goods; Fruits, fresh; Vegetables, fresh

D-U-N-S 13-102-5223
HALE COUNTY BANCSHARES INC
201 W 6th St, Plainview, TX 79072-8005
Tel (806) 293-3635 *Founded/Ownrshp* 1978
Sales NA *EMP* 92

SIC 6022 State commercial banks; State commercial banks
Pr: Brian Pohlmeier
Board of Directors: John C Anderson, Richard Kimbrough, James E Laney, H L Maggard, Brian Pohlmeier

D-U-N-S 79-333-7676
HALE COUNTY BOARD OF EDUCATION
1115 Powers St, Greensboro, AL 36744-1205
Tel (334) 624-3051 *Founded/Ownrshp* 1920
Sales 19.8MM^{E} *EMP* 407
SIC 8211 Public elementary & secondary schools; Public elementary & secondary schools
**CFO:* Leslie Craig
HC Dir: Connie Avery

D-U-N-S 07-979-9762
HALE COUNTY SCHOOL DISTRICT
1115 Powers St, Greensboro, AL 36744-1219
Tel (334) 624-8836 *Founded/Ownrshp* 2015
Sales 4.1MM^{E} *EMP* 358^{E}
SIC 8211 Public elementary & secondary schools
MIS Dir: Marilyn Pickens
Teacher Pr: Evelyn Seale
HC Dir: Phyllis McCue

D-U-N-S 07-766-4142 IMP
HALE HOOLA HOU INC
KALIHI PALAMA HEALTH CENTER
915 N King St, Honolulu, HI 96817-4544
Tel (808) 848-1438 *Founded/Ownrshp* 1997
Sales 22.9MM^{E} *EMP* 220^{E}
Accts Bkd Llp Springfield Mo
SIC 8011 Primary care medical clinic; Primary care medical clinic
Ex Dir: May Akamine
Ofcr: John D Lowry
Doctor: Steven Nishi

HALE INDIAN RIVER GROVES
See SOUTHERN FULFILLMENT SERVICES LLC

HALE, LEALIS L MD
See WHITE WILLSON MED CLINIC PA

D-U-N-S 07-769-7993
HALE MAKUA HEALTH SERVICES
472 Kaulana St, Kahului, HI 96732-2099
Tel (808) 442-4551 *Founded/Ownrshp* 1946
Sales 32.9MM *EMP* 450
Accts Lester J Hee Cpa Honolulu Hi
SIC 8051 8082 Skilled nursing care facilities; Home health care services; Skilled nursing care facilities; Home health care services
CEO: Anthony J Krieg
**CFO:* Joyce Tamori
Sr VP: Ted Tucker
HC Dir: Margie Albete

D-U-N-S 01-600-3126 IMP
■ **HALE PRODUCTS INC**
CLASS 1
(*Suby of* HALE PRODUCTS INC) ★
607 Nw 27th Ave, Ocala, FL 34475-5623
Tel (352) 629-5020 *Founded/Ownrshp* 1991, 2001
Sales 32.4MM^{E} *EMP* 240
SIC 3625 3088 3714 3699 Electric controls & control accessories, industrial; Plastics plumbing fixtures; Motor vehicle parts & accessories; Electrical equipment & supplies; Electric controls & control accessories, industrial; Plastics plumbing fixtures; Motor vehicle parts & accessories; Electrical equipment & supplies
CEO: Bill Simmons
**Treas:* Keith Miller
**Treas:* Greg Thompson

D-U-N-S 05-900-4614
■ **HALE PRODUCTS INC**
(*Suby of* IDEX CORP) ★
607 Nw 27th Ave, Ocala, FL 34475-5623
Tel (610) 825-6300 *Founded/Ownrshp* 1994
Sales 71.2MM^{E} *EMP* 700
SIC 3569 3561 3594 Firefighting apparatus; Industrial pumps & parts; Fluid power pumps & motors; Firefighting apparatus; Industrial pumps & parts; Fluid power pumps & motors
VP: Bruce Lear
VP: Ken Bostwick
VP: David D Hart
VP: Dean Perry
VP: Mark Schaub
CIO: Divakar Kamath
Mktg Mgr: Linda Roothame

D-U-N-S 00-608-0071 IMP
HALE TJ CO (WI)
W139n9499 State Road 145, Menomonee Falls, WI 53051-1618
Tel (262) 509-5522 *Founded/Ownrshp* 1950
Sales 25.6MM^{E} *EMP* 110
SIC 2541 Store fixtures, wood
CEO: John R Hale
**Pr:* David Pape
**CFO:* Lynn Hawkins
Dir IT: Gary Lobermier
Mtls Mgr: Dave Nadolski

D-U-N-S 07-366-3247
HALE TRAILER BRAKE & WHEEL INC
Cooper Rd Rr 73, Voorhees, NJ 08043
Tel (856) 768-1330 *Founded/Ownrshp* 1999
Sales 126.6MM^{E} *EMP* 170
SIC 5511 7539 5531 Trucks, tractors & trailers: new & used; Trailer repair; Automobile & truck equipment & parts; Trucks, tractors & trailers: new & used; Trailer repair; Automobile & truck equipment & parts
Pr: Barry J Hale
VP: Ann Fletcher
Brnch Mgr: Ryan Emerick
Dir IT: Ray Mroczkowski
IT Man: Ira Eckstein
IT Man: Michael Sferrazza

D-U-N-S 01-711-7334
HALEKULANI CORP
(*Suby of* 1251 AMERICAS ASSOCIATES) ★
2222 Kalakaua Ave Ste 900, Honolulu, HI 96815-2524
Tel (808) 923-2311 *Founded/Ownrshp* 2005
Sales 21.0MM^{E} *EMP* 927^{E}
SIC 7011 5812 Resort hotel; Eating places
VP: Peter Shaindlin
COO: Nancy Azeri
CFO: Lawrence Chang
Ex VP: Yoshinori Maeda
**Sr VP:* Takashi Nakayama
VP: James F Pedone
Exec: Vikram Garg
Exec: Alexandre Trancher
Genl Mgr: Ulrich Krauer
Off Mgr: Wayne Takeshita
CIO: Rod Tateyama

D-U-N-S 10-866-9763
HALES MACHINE TOOL INC
2730 Niagara Ln N, Plymouth, MN 55447-4877
Tel (763) 553-1711 *Founded/Ownrshp* 1983
Sales 31.7MM *EMP* 21
Accts Olsen Thielen & Co Ltd Ede
SIC 5084 7699 Machine tools & accessories; Industrial machinery & equipment repair; Machine tools & accessories; Industrial machinery & equipment repair
Pr: Dan Hales
VP: Brad George
**VP:* Tim Hales

D-U-N-S 62-758-1630 IMP/EXP
HALEX CORP
4200 Santa Ana St Ste A, Ontario, CA 91761-1539
Tel (909) 629-6219 *Founded/Ownrshp* 2002
Sales 39.6MM^{E} *EMP* 260
SIC 3423 Carpet layers' hand tools; Carpet layers' hand tools
Pr: Mark Chichak
**Pr:* Craig Silvers
VP: Jim Barry
**VP:* Aiden Costello
VP: Tom Downey

D-U-N-S 04-706-7749
HALEY & ALDRICH INC
70 Blanchard Rd Ste 204, Burlington, MA 01803-5100
Tel (617) 886-7400 *Founded/Ownrshp* 1957
Sales 143.6MM^{E} *EMP* 504
Accts Dicicco Gulman & Company Llp
SIC 8748 8711 Environmental consultant; Consulting engineer; Environmental consultant; Consulting engineer
Pr: Lawrence Smith
**CFO:* Robert Gabel
Bd of Dir: Eric Isacoff
Chf Mktg O: Anne Nason
Ofcr: William Fisher
Sr VP: Anntonette Alberti
**Sr VP:* Mark X Haley
**Sr VP:* Steven R Kraemer
VP: Lisa Jn Bradley
VP: Joseph Savarese
VP: Diane Sullivan

HALEY BROS
See T M COBB CO

D-U-N-S 62-385-9365 IMP
HALEY BROS INC
(*Suby of* HALEY BROS) ★
6291 Orangethorpe Ave, Buena Park, CA 90620-1339
Tel (714) 670-2112 *Founded/Ownrshp* 1987
Sales 39.3MM^{E} *EMP* 200
SIC 2431 Doors, wood; Moldings, wood: unfinished & prefinished; Doors, wood; Moldings, wood: unfinished & prefinished
CEO: Thomas J Cobb
CIO: Doug Finch
Dir IT: Rick Boyle
IT Man: Rick Budz
Sls Mgr: Ronald Barry

HALEY BUICK GMC
See HALEY PONTIAC-GMC TRUCK INC

D-U-N-S 88-476-4556
HALEY BUILDERS INC
10102 Whitesel Rd, Ashland, VA 23005-3513
Tel (804) 798-3817 *Founded/Ownrshp* 1995
Sales 37.4MM^{E} *EMP* 50
Accts Barry Strickland & Company Ri
SIC 1542 1521 Commercial & office building, new construction; New construction, single-family houses
Pr: Gregory W Haley
**VP:* Steve Haley
**VP:* David Hanky
VP: John Murrell
VP: Chris Taylor

D-U-N-S 17-582-9498 IMP
HALEY CONSTRUCTION INC
900 Orange Ave, Daytona Beach, FL 32114-4764
Tel (386) 944-0470 *Founded/Ownrshp* 1986
Sales 49.3MM^{E} *EMP* 60
Accts Horne Holmes Crenshaw & Blak
SIC 1542 Commercial & office building, new construction; Commercial & office buildings, renovation & repair
Pr: Dan Haley
**VP:* Gordon Lloyd
**VP:* Stacy McRitchie
Off Mgr: Kimberly Reny
VP Opers: David Nutter

HALEY FORD
See HALEY SOUTH INC

D-U-N-S 05-713-0965 EXP
HALEY PAINT CO
FINNAREN & HALEY COMPANY
194 Greenfield Rd, Lancaster, PA 17601-5832
Tel (717) 299-6771 *Founded/Ownrshp* 1920
Sales 29.0MM^{E} *EMP* 160
SIC 5231 2851 Paint & painting supplies; Paints: oil or alkyd vehicle or water thinned; Paint & painting supplies; Paints: oil or alkyd vehicle or water thinned
CEO: Robert A Haley Jr
**Pr:* Joseph Giandonato
**Pr:* Regina Haley Pakradooni
**Treas:* Francis X Connell
VP: Fran Connell
VP: Francis Feeley
**VP:* Daniel McManus

D-U-N-S 02-390-5904
HALEY PONTIAC-GMC TRUCK INC
HALEY BUICK GMC
9831 Midlothian Tpke, North Chesterfield, VA 23235-4811
Tel (804) 320-9054 *Founded/Ownrshp* 1972
Sales 28.6MM^{E} *EMP* 73^{E}
SIC 5511

D-U-N-S 04-835-8969
HALEY SOUTH INC
HALEY FORD
10724 Jefferson Davis Hwy, North Chesterfield, VA 23237-4234
Tel (804) 748-2253 *Founded/Ownrshp* 1998
Sales 21.8MM^{E} *EMP* 45^{E}
SIC 5511 Automobiles, new & used
Genl Mgr: Brian Johnson
CFO: Paul Bischoff
**Prin:* Martin Mathias
Store Mgr: Wes Hanline
Sls Mgr: Corey Axel
Sls Mgr: George Mastermaker

D-U-N-S 09-544-9831
HALEY-GREER INC
2257c Lombardy Ln, Dallas, TX 75220
Tel (972) 556-1177 *Founded/Ownrshp* 1979
Sales 38.0MM^{E} *EMP* 150
SIC 1793 Glass & glazing work; Glass & glazing work
CEO: Don Haley
**Pr:* Letitia Haley Barker
**VP:* Jeff Benson
**VP:* Louie Duncan
**Prin:* Mike Harvey
**Prin:* Norbert Klotz
**Prin:* Chandra Stroope

D-U-N-S 05-519-1464
HALF HOLLOW HILLS CENTRAL SCHOOL DISTRICT
525 Half Hollow Rd, Dix Hills, NY 11746-5828
Tel (631) 592-3000 *Founded/Ownrshp* 1952
Sales 30.2MM^{E} *EMP* 376
SIC 8211 Public elementary school; Public junior high school; Public senior high school; School board; Public elementary school; Public junior high school; Public senior high school; School board
Dir Sec: David Spera
MIS Dir: Sunil John
Instr Medi: Phyllis Wenger
Board of Directors: Hal Austein, Vin Costello, Fran Greenspan, Ilene Herz, Vicki Leopold, Stuart Pastrich

HALF MOON BAY GOLF LINKS
See OCEAN COLONY PARTNERS LLC

D-U-N-S 02-720-1219 IMP
HALF PRICE BOOKS RECORDS MAGAZINES INC
TEXAS BOOKMAN, THE
5803 E Northwest Hwy, Dallas, TX 75231-6519
Tel (214) 379-8000 *Founded/Ownrshp* 1972
Sales 244.2MM^{E} *EMP* 1,740^{E}
SIC 5942 5192 Book stores; Books; Book stores; Books
Pr: Sharon Anderson Wright
CFO: Laura Beverly
**Treas:* Nando Arduini II
**Ex VP:* Jan Cornelius
**Ex VP:* Tim Jernigan
Ex VP: Ellen O'Neal
Ex VP: Alexandra Pennington
Ex VP: Kathy Thomas
VP: Bill Holland
VP: Eric James
**VP:* Charles Dee Mitchell
**VP:* Ellen O Neal
**VP:* Stephen Powers
**VP:* Kathy Doyle Thomas
**VP:* Robert Wilkie
Dir Risk M: Ken Wright

D-U-N-S 55-758-1779
HALFAKER AND ASSOCIATES LLC
2900 S Quincy St Ste 410, Arlington, VA 22206-2281
Tel (703) 434-3900 *Founded/Ownrshp* 2005
Sales 25.2MM *EMP* 100
SIC 7299 Information services, consumer; Information services, consumer
Pr: Dawn Halfaker
Ex VP: Phil Vincenzes
VP: Suzanne Paul
Mng Ofcr: Debbie Storey
Prgrm Mgr: Valerie Hoyle
Prgrm Mgr: Kindra Paravecchia
Snr Sftwr: Alan Tarica
CTO: Michael King
IT Man: Andrea Farris
Software D: Robert Milner
Opers Mgr: Kevin Moore

D-U-N-S 05-013-1655
HALFF ASSOCIATES INC
ALBERT H HALFF ASSOCIATES
1201 N Bowser Rd, Richardson, TX 75081-2262
Tel (214) 346-6200 *Founded/Ownrshp* 1953
Sales 101.0MM^{E} *EMP* 532
SIC 8711 8713

D-U-N-S 80-132-8808 IMP
HALIBURTON INTERNATIONAL FOODS INC
3855 Jurupa St, Ontario, CA 91761-1404
Tel (909) 428-8520 *Founded/Ownrshp* 1992
Sales 36.6MM^{E} *EMP* 150^{E}
SIC 2037 2038

D-U-N-S 04-135-3715
HALIFAX CORP OF VIRGINIA
100 Sterling Pkwy Ste 100, Mechanicsburg, PA 17050-2903
Tel (717) 610-3200 *Founded/Ownrshp* 2010
Sales NA *EMP* 331
SIC 7371 8744

D-U-N-S 10-007-9680
HALIFAX COUNTY PUBLIC SCHOOLS
1030 Mary Bethune St, Halifax, VA 24558-3213
Tel (434) 476-2171 *Founded/Ownrshp* 1900
Sales 82.4M *EMP* 1,100
SIC 8211 Public elementary & secondary schools; Public elementary & secondary schools
Bd of Dir: Walter Potts
MIS Dir: Jeannie Hawks

D-U-N-S 07-200-3817
HALIFAX COUNTY SCHOOL DISTRICT
9525 Us Highway 301, Halifax, NC 27839-9755
Tel (252) 583-5111 *Founded/Ownrshp* 1900
Sales 43.7MM^{E} *EMP* 951
SIC 8211 Public elementary & secondary schools; Public elementary & secondary schools
Ql Cn Mgr: Michelle Winstead

HALIFAX HEALTH
See HALIFAX HOME HEALTH

D-U-N-S 01-052-3041
HALIFAX HEALTH CARE SYSTEMS INC
303 N Clyde Morris Blvd, Daytona Beach, FL 32114-2709
Tel (386) 254-4000 *Founded/Ownrshp* 1928
Sales 292.2MM^{E} *EMP* 4,800
SIC 8062 8011 8063

D-U-N-S 79-830-0901
HALIFAX HOME HEALTH
HALIFAX HEALTH
3800 Woodbriar Trl, Port Orange, FL 32129-9626
Tel (386) 322-4700 *Founded/Ownrshp* 1987
Sales 464.9MM *EMP* 135
SIC 8082 7361 Home health care services; Nurses' registry; Home health care services; Nurses' registry

D-U-N-S 02-104-6429
■ **HALIFAX MEDIA GROUP LLC**
(*Suby of* NEW MEDIA INVESTMENT GROUP INC) ★
2339 Beville Rd, Daytona Beach, FL 32119-8720
Tel (386) 265-6700 *Founded/Ownrshp* 2015
Sales 225.0MM^{E} *EMP* 2,900
SIC 2711 Newspapers; Newspapers
CEO: Michael Redding
COO: Rick Martin
Sr VP: Bernie Szachara
Sls Dir: Mike Baskin
Sls Mgr: Ken Workowski

D-U-N-S 01-352-6929
HALIFAX MEDIA HOLDINGS LLC
901 6th St, Daytona Beach, FL 32117-3352
Tel (386) 681-2404 *Founded/Ownrshp* 2009
Sales 278.1MM^{E} *EMP* 2,144^{E}
SIC 2711 2791 Newspapers; Typesetting
CEO: Michael Redding

HALIFAX MEDICAL CTR ATL CAMPUS
See ATLANTIC MEDICAL CENTER

D-U-N-S 00-685-5431
HALIFAX PAVING INC (FL)
860 Hull Rd, Ormond Beach, FL 32174-8729
Tel (386) 676-0200 *Founded/Ownrshp* 1953, 1955
Sales 53.4MM^{E} *EMP* 130
SIC 1611 Highway & street paving contractor; Highway & street paving contractor
Pr: Thomas A Durrance
**Sec:* Leonard CMR Durrance
**VP:* Joseph Lmr Durrance
VP: Tommy Durrance

HALIFAX REGIONAL HEALTH SYSTEM
See HALIFAX REGIONAL HOSPITAL INC

D-U-N-S 06-539-9677
HALIFAX REGIONAL HOSPITAL INC
HALIFAX REGIONAL HEALTH SYSTEM
(*Suby of* SENTARA HEALTHCARE) ★
2204 Wilborn Ave, South Boston, VA 24592-1638
Tel (434) 515-3100 *Founded/Ownrshp* 2013
Sales 120.2MM *EMP* 590
SIC 8062 General medical & surgical hospitals; General medical & surgical hospitals
CEO: Chris A Lumsden
**Pr:* W Joseph Ferguson
Exec: Brian Worley
Ex Dir: Cecil Hazelwood
IT Man: Billy Anderson
Tech Mgr: John Buchinsky
Site Mgr: Charlotte Davis
Doctor: Grey Leighton
Nrsg Dir: Kathy Lynn
Nrsg Dir: Tamara Simmons
Dietician: Lisa Caudle
Board of Directors: J Logan Young

D-U-N-S 07-558-3393
HALIFAX REGIONAL MEDICAL CENTER INC
250 Smith Church Rd, Roanoke Rapids, NC 27870-4914
Tel (215) 994-4000 *Founded/Ownrshp* 1972
Sales 83.5MM *EMP* 830
SIC 8062 8011 General medical & surgical hospitals; Medical centers; General medical & surgical hospitals; Medical centers
Pr: Wil Mahone
CFO: Cindy Robinson
VP: Fache Bruce
VP: Karen Daniels
**VP:* Sherry Jensen
Dir Lab: Wanda Catts
Comm Dir: Elizabeth Huffman
Nurse Mgr: Rhonda Yarboro
MIS Dir: Robert Gordon
Netwrk Eng: Daniel Bennett
Netwrk Eng: Christian Chang

D-U-N-S 92-934-8258 IMP/EXP
HALIFAX SECURITY INC
NORTH AMERICAN VIDEO
301 Drum Point Rd, Brick, NJ 08723-6831
Tel (732) 477-0686 *Founded/Ownrshp* 2008
Sales 44.0MM^E *EMP* 125
SIC 1731 Safety & security specialization; Safety & security specialization
CEO: Jason Oakley
Pr: Robert Biscardi
* *CFO:* Peter Rode
Ofcr: Suzanne Thomas
VP: Steve Malia
Brnch Mgr: Ben Olson
Brnch Mgr: Robert West
Dir IT: John Phillips
VP Sls: Laurie Smock
Sls Mgr: Bill Stoetzel
Sales Asso: Jaime Boyarsky

D-U-N-S 96-656-8581
HALIFAX STAFFING INC
303 N Clyde Morris Blvd, Daytona Beach, FL 32114-2709
Tel (386) 226-4560 *Founded/Ownrshp* 2011
Sales 220.2MM *EMP* 2
SIC 7363 Help supply services; Help supply services
Prin: Betty Holness

D-U-N-S 12-149-0759
HALJOHN - SAN ANTONIO INC
MCDONALD'S
7300 Blanco Rd Ste 302, San Antonio, TX 78216-4939
Tel (210) 344-9707 *Founded/Ownrshp* 1982
Sales 29.1MM^E *EMP* 850
SIC 5812 Fast-food restaurant, chain; Fast-food restaurant, chain
Pr: John V Bohling
VP: Bohling Virginia

D-U-N-S 02-602-4273
HALJOHN INC
MCDONALD'S
704 E Wonsley Dr Ste 100, Austin, TX 78753-6562
Tel (512) 837-2551 *Founded/Ownrshp* 1962
Sales 18.5MM^E *EMP* 730
SIC 5812 Fast-food restaurant, chain; Fast-food restaurant, chain
Pr: Harold A Leverson
* *VP:* Frankie Leverson
Off Mgr: Connie Hamilton
Opers Mgr: Bryna Schulze

D-U-N-S 10-187-7884 IMP
■ **HALKEY-ROBERTS CORP**
(*Suby of* ATRION CORP) ★
2700 Halkey Roberts Pl N, Saint Petersburg, FL 33716-4103
Tel (727) 471-4200 *Founded/Ownrshp* 1996
Sales 96.6MM^E *EMP* 450
SIC 3842 Surgical appliances & supplies; Surgical appliances & supplies
Pr: David Battat
VP: Jim Bowling
* *VP:* Alan King
* *VP:* Lewis P Lecceardone
* *VP:* John H Lucius
VP: Jeffery Strickland
Plng Mgr: Hanna Jasiukiewicc
CTO: Thomas Frank
CTO: John Toomey
IT Man: Robert Kubas
IT Man: Timothy McCabe

HALL 2801 NETWORK ASSOC.
See HALL FINANCIAL GROUP LTD

D-U-N-S 06-379-8599
HALL AMBULANCE SERVICE INC
1001 21st St, Bakersfield, CA 93301-4792
Tel (661) 322-8741 *Founded/Ownrshp* 1971
Sales 43.4MM^E *EMP* 215
SIC 5999 Mobile telephones & equipment; Mobile telephones & equipment
Pr: Harvey L Hall
* *Sec:* Mary Kenny
IT Man: Adam Hirsch
Mktg Mgr: Mark Corum
Mktg Mgr: Steven Cowan

D-U-N-S 60-198-4842
HALL AUTO WORLD OF VIRGINIA INC
HALL AUTOMOTIVE-HONDA
441 Viking Dr, Virginia Beach, VA 23452-7309
Tel (757) 431-9930 *Founded/Ownrshp* 1986
Sales 21.9MM^E *EMP* 62
SIC 5511 5521 5012 Automobiles, new & used; Used car dealers; Automobiles & other motor vehicles; Automobiles, new & used; Used car dealers; Automobiles & other motor vehicles
Ch: Kenneth A Hall
* *Treas:* Thad Nowak
Genl Mgr: Mark Sands
Genl Mgr: Lee Shearin
IT Man: Meredith Barthelemy
Mktg Dir: Jean Mahon

HALL AUTOMOTIVE
See HALL CHEVROLET CO INC

D-U-N-S 06-599-7199
HALL AUTOMOTIVE LLC
441 Viking Dr, Virginia Beach, VA 23452-7309
Tel (757) 431-9944 *Founded/Ownrshp* 2006
Sales 380.5MM^E *EMP* 1,211
SIC 5511 Automobiles, new & used; Automobiles, new & used
* *Pr:* William R Baker
* *CEO:* Steven B Fader
CFO: William Baker
* *Sec:* Christine M Champigny
* *Ex VP:* Louis S Richards
* *Ex VP:* Lonnie L Swiger
Genl Mgr: Carl Litner
Dir IT: Nathan Warrior
Site Mgr: Bill Baker
Site Mgr: David Kauffman
Sales Asso: John Christian

HALL AUTOMOTIVE-HONDA
See HALL AUTO WORLD OF VIRGINIA INC

D-U-N-S 62-692-6331
HALL BOOTH SMITH PC
191 Peachtree St Ne # 2900, Atlanta, GA 30303-1740
Tel (404) 586-6605 *Founded/Ownrshp* 1989
Sales 31.3MM^E *EMP* 236
SIC 8111 General practice law office; General practice law office
CEO: Alex Booth
Pr: Lisa R Crosby
* *Pr:* John Hall
* *CFO:* Rush S Smith Jr
Exec: Heather McGrotty
Mng Dir: Rufus Montgomery
Counsel: Scott H Moulton

HALL BUICK GMC
See TYLER MOTOR CO INC

D-U-N-S 05-526-4162
HALL BUILDING CORP
33 Main St, Farmingdale, NJ 07727-1218
Tel (732) 938-3399 *Founded/Ownrshp* 1980
Sales 35.5MM *EMP* 40
SIC 1542 Institutional building construction; Institutional building construction
CEO: John R Hall
Sfty Mgr: Clint Hall

D-U-N-S 62-228-5153
HALL CAPITAL PARTNERS LLC
1 Maritime Plz Fl 5, San Francisco, CA 94111-3408
Tel (415) 288-0544 *Founded/Ownrshp* 1995
Sales 24.1MM^E *EMP* 90^E
SIC 6282 Investment counselors; Investment counselors
CEO: Kathryn A Hall
* *Pr:* John W Buoymaster
Pr: Brian Taylor
* *COO:* William Powers
Top Exec: Steve Sutherland
VP: Winnie L Chiang
Mng Dir: Eric Alt
Mktg Dir: Alison Diessner

D-U-N-S 36-205-8067
HALL CHEVROLET CO INC
HALL AUTOMOTIVE
11011 W North Ave, Milwaukee, WI 53226-2286
Tel (414) 778-1500 *Founded/Ownrshp* 1927
Sales 35.6MM^E *EMP* 135
SIC 5511 Automobiles, new & used; Automobiles, new & used
Pr: Andrew Hall
* *VP:* Robert Hall
* *Genl Mgr:* Charlie Hall
Sales Asso: Pat Vanselow

D-U-N-S 07-307-6957
HALL CHEVROLET LLC
(*Suby of* HALL AUTOMOTIVE LLC) ★
3412 Western Branch Blvd, Chesapeake, VA 23321-5108
Tel (757) 233-8120 *Founded/Ownrshp* 2006
Sales 24.0MM^E *EMP* 81
SIC 5511 Automobiles, new & used; Automobiles, new & used
Pr: William Baker
Genl Mgr: Evan Seltzer

D-U-N-S 00-679-8474
HALL CONSTRUCTION CO INC
149 Yellowbrook Rd # 200, Farmingdale, NJ 07727-3884
Tel (732) 681-2500 *Founded/Ownrshp* 1955
Sales 30.8MM^E *EMP* 100
SIC 1542 1541 Commercial & office building, new construction; Industrial buildings, new construction; Commercial & office building, new construction; Industrial buildings, new construction
Ch Bd: Conrad F Hall Sr
* *Pr:* Mark D Hall
* *Treas:* Margaret Mary Lefebvre
* *VP:* Scott V Hall
Snr PM: Robert Fucetola

D-U-N-S 00-701-4202
HALL CONTRACTING CORP
6415 Lakeview Rd, Charlotte, NC 28269-2602
Tel (704) 598-0818 *Founded/Ownrshp* 1954
Sales 31.7MM^E *EMP* 50
SIC 1623 Underground utilities contractor
Pr: Michael K Hall
* *VP:* Wayne E Helms
Prin: Jess Walters
Snr PM: William Lindsay
Snr Mgr: James Elder
Snr Mgr: Barron Thiessenn

D-U-N-S 01-024-1508
HALL CONTRACTING OF KENTUCKY INC (KY)
POWER-TEL ELECTRICAL
3800 Crittenden Dr, Louisville, KY 40209-1124
Tel (502) 367-6151 *Founded/Ownrshp* 1999
Sales 136.5MM^E *EMP* 220^E
SIC 1541 1623 1761 1731 Industrial buildings & warehouses; Underground utilities contractor; Roofing, siding & sheet metal work; Electrical work; Industrial buildings & warehouses; Underground utilities contractor; Roofing, siding & sheet metal work; Electrical work
CEO: Stephen M Priebe
CFO: Chris Allen
* *Sec:* Chris S Allen
* *VP:* Mike Chism
* *VP:* David Fischer
* *VP:* Forrest T Roberts
* *VP:* Tom Roberts Jr
* *VP:* Jim Scott
* *VP:* Anthony Shade
* *VP:* Richard Shutt
Mtls Mgr: Stephen Gerlach

D-U-N-S 06-919-0502
HALL COUNTY BOARD OF EDUCATION
711 Green St Nw Ste 100, Gainesville, GA 30501-3368
Tel (770) 534-1080 *Founded/Ownrshp* 1953
Sales 126.0MM^E *EMP* 3,600
Accts Russell W Hinton Cpa Cgfm
SIC 8211 Public elementary & secondary schools; School board
Ch: Nath Morris

HALL COUNTY GOVERNMENT
See HALL COUNTY OF GEORGIA

D-U-N-S 07-812-4617
HALL COUNTY OF GEORGIA
HALL COUNTY GOVERNMENT
2875 Browns Bridge Rd, Gainesville, GA 30504-5635
Tel (770) 535-8288 *Founded/Ownrshp* 1818
Sales NA *EMP* 1,600
Accts Bates Carter Co Llp Gaines
SIC 9111 ;
Ch: Richard Mecum
Ofcr: Katie Crumly
Dir: William Meyer
Opers Mgr: Brent Wine

D-U-N-S 07-847-3818
HALL COUNTY SCHOOL DISTRICT
711 Green St Nw Ste 100, Gainesville, GA 30501-3368
Tel (770) 534-1080 *Founded/Ownrshp* 2012
Sales 102.3MM^E *EMP* 2,773^E
SIC 8211 Public elementary & secondary schools
Bd of Dir: Sam Chapman
Bd of Dir: Todd Murrow
Bd of Dir: Brian Sloan
Adm Dir: Gary Stewart
Dir Sec: Earl Roach
Sls&Mrk Ex: Cindy Crow
Pr Dir: Gordon Higgins
Schl Brd P: Nath Morris
Teacher Pr: Brad Brown
Psych: Monie Shope
HC Dir: Mamie Coker

D-U-N-S 10-060-2622
HALL COUNTY SCHOOL DISTRICT 2
GRAND ISLAND PUBLIC SCHOOLS
123 S Webb Rd, Grand Island, NE 68803-5110
Tel (308) 385-5886 *Founded/Ownrshp* 1882
Sales 78.8MM^E *EMP* 1,700
Accts Almquist Maltzahn Galloway & L
SIC 8211 9411 Elementary & secondary schools; School board; Administration of educational programs; Elementary & secondary schools; School board; Administration of educational programs
Ofcr: Ben Arrants
Genl Mgr: James Duff
MIS Dir: Corey Earhart
IT Man: Lori Forsythe
IT Man: Julie Hehnke
IT Man: Rose Zlomke
Pr Dir: Jack Sheard
Sales Asso: Jeff Leep
Psych: Carrie Marx
Psych: Tara Retzlaff
Psych: Camie See

D-U-N-S 01-630-8868
HALL DRIVE-INS INC
HALL'S CATERING
216 State Road 930 W, New Haven, IN 46774-2148
Tel (260) 493-3522 *Founded/Ownrshp* 2002
Sales 18.9MM^E *EMP* 680
SIC 5812 7011 American restaurant; Hotels & motels; American restaurant; Hotels & motels
Pr: Donald Hall II
* *VP:* Samuel Hall

D-U-N-S 83-460-6543
HALL ENTERPRISES INC
LOGISTICS PLANNING SERVICES
731 Bielenberg Dr Ste 108, Woodbury, MN 55125-1701
Tel (651) 552-4905 *Founded/Ownrshp* 1987
Sales 85.4MM^E *EMP* 85
SIC 4731 Freight transportation arrangement
Ch Bd: Pamela I Hall
* *Ch Bd:* Larry Hall
* *Pr:* Justin Hall
* *CEO:* Kirsten Hall
* *VP:* Nathan Hall

HALL ESTILL
See HALL ESTILL HARDWICK GABLE GOLDEN & NELSON DC INC

D-U-N-S 08-594-8800
HALL ESTILL HARDWICK GABLE GOLDEN & NELSON DC INC
HALL ESTILL
320 S Boston Ave Ste 200, Tulsa, OK 74103-3705
Tel (918) 594-0400 *Founded/Ownrshp* 1967
Sales 28.5MM^E *EMP* 235
SIC 8111 General practice attorney, lawyer; General practice law office; General practice attorney, lawyer; General practice law office
Ch Bd: Michael D Cooke
Pr: Allison Astor
Pr: Renee Griffith
* *VP:* Mark K Blongewicz
* *VP:* J Patrick Cremin
* *VP:* James Hardwick
* *VP:* J Kevin Hayes
* *VP:* James D Satrom
* *VP:* Michael E Smith
* *Ex Dir:* Stephen H Neal
Dir IT: Jennifer Estes

D-U-N-S 12-359-0015
HALL FAMILY FOUNDATION
2501 Mcgee St, Kansas City, MO 64108-2615
Tel (816) 274-8516 *Founded/Ownrshp* 1943
Sales 38.1MM^E *EMP* 2
SIC 7389 Fund raising organizations; Fund raising organizations
Pr: William A Hall
Ofcr: Sally Groves
VP: Jeanne Bates

VP: John Macdonald
VP: Angela McClelland

D-U-N-S 00-195-0138 IMP
HALL FESSENDEN INC (NJ)
1050 Sherman Ave, Pennsauken, NJ 08110-2674
Tel (856) 665-2210 *Founded/Ownrshp* 1890, 1952
Sales 52.8MM^E *EMP* 150
SIC 5031 Lumber, plywood & millwork; Lumber, plywood & millwork
CFO: Raymond Jungclaus
CEO: Edward Birdsall
Ex Dir: Humbert Minella
Genl Mgr: Roeby Birdsall
Sls Mgr: Chris Kilbride

D-U-N-S 05-532-6110
HALL FINANCIAL GROUP LTD
HALL 2801 NETWORK ASSOC.
2323 Ross Ave Ste 200, Dallas, TX 75201-2723
Tel (972) 377-1100 *Founded/Ownrshp* 1997
Sales 92.0MM^E *EMP* 600
Accts Lane Gorman Trubitt Llp Dalla
SIC 6552 6531 Land subdividers & developers, commercial; Real estate managers; Land subdividers & developers, commercial; Real estate managers
Genl Pt: Donald Braun
Pt: Craig Hall
Sr VP: Patricia Meadows
Genl Mgr: Sherry Thweatt

D-U-N-S 04-128-5107
HALL FORD LLC (VA)
(*Suby of* HALL AUTOMOTIVE LLC) ★
12896 Jefferson Ave, Newport News, VA 23608-3031
Tel (757) 989-5700 *Founded/Ownrshp* 2006
Sales 22.1MM^E *EMP* 67
SIC 5511 Automobiles, new & used; Automobiles, new & used
Pr: William R Baker
VP: Daniel Nance
Genl Mgr: Mark Sands

D-U-N-S 06-910-0063
HALL HARPETH SCHOOL (TN)
3801 Hobbs Rd, Nashville, TN 37215-2233
Tel (615) 297-9543 *Founded/Ownrshp* 1951
Sales 24.9MM *EMP* 137
Accts Kraftcpas Pllc Nashville Tn
SIC 8211 Private junior high school; Private senior high school; Private junior high school; Private senior high school
Ex Dir: Jacquie Watlington
Store Mgr: Emily Runzo

HALL HONDA
See HALL OF VIRGINIA BEACH LLC

D-U-N-S 18-839-5859
HALL IMPORTS
(*Suby of* HALL AUTOMOTIVE) ★
19809 W Bluemound Rd, Brookfield, WI 53045-5951
Tel (262) 432-9053 *Founded/Ownrshp* 1986
Sales 20.6MM^E *EMP* 45
SIC 5511 Automobiles, new & used
Pr: Andrew Hall
* *VP:* Robert Hall
Sls Mgr: Doug Schultz

D-U-N-S 00-451-3081 IMP
HALL INDUSTRIES INC (PA)
514 Mecklem Ln, Ellwood City, PA 16117-3028
Tel (724) 752-2000 *Founded/Ownrshp* 1966
Sales 28.3MM^E *EMP* 116
SIC 3451 3494 3471 Screw machine products; Valves & pipe fittings; Plating & polishing; Screw machine products; Valves & pipe fittings; Plating & polishing
Pr: Jonathan C Hall
CFO: John Schlafhaufer
* *Treas:* John Schlafhauser
* *VP:* H Mark Hall
IT Man: Tony Kaper
VP Opers: Frank Schlafhaufer
Plnt Mgr: Joe Davis
Plnt Mgr: Ron Hyslop
Ql Cn Mgr: Bill Hanna
Sls Dir: Mark Hall

HALL, JON JEEP EAGLE
See JON HALL CHEVROLET INC

D-U-N-S 08-312-4789
HALL MANAGEMENT CORP
LAND & PERSONNEL MANAGEMENT
759 S Madera Ave, Kerman, CA 93630-1744
Tel (559) 846-7382 *Founded/Ownrshp* 2001
Sales 98.4MM^E *EMP* 2,000
Accts Gary C Simonian & Co Fresno
SIC 8741 Management services; Personnel management; Management services; Personnel management
Pr: Stacy Hampton
* *VP:* James Randles
Off Mgr: Louie Romero

D-U-N-S 78-679-6367 IMP
HALL MANUFACTURING LLC
BUSH-WHACKER
3706 E Washington Ave, North Little Rock, AR 72114-6436
Tel (501) 945-0048 *Founded/Ownrshp* 1991
Sales 27.8MM^E *EMP* 60
SIC 5083 3523 Farm equipment parts & supplies; Farm machinery & equipment
CFO: Walt Howard
Genl Mgr: Matt Baltz
Mktg Mgr: Andy Capel

D-U-N-S 78-181-5340
HALL MOTORS
LAWRENCE HALL LNCLN-MERC-MAZDA
1300 S Clack St, Abilene, TX 79605-4606
Tel (325) 695-8811 *Founded/Ownrshp* 2001
Sales 20.3MM *EMP* 35
SIC 5511 Automobiles, new & used; Automobiles, new & used
Prin: Larry Hall

D-U-N-S 08-479-7414
HALL NEIGHBORHOOD HOUSE INC
52 George E Pipkins Way, Bridgeport, CT 06608-2425
Tel (203) 345-2000 *Founded/Ownrshp* 1886
Sales 4.9MM *EMP* 290
Accts Hope & Hernandez Pc Bridgepor
SIC 8322 Individual & family services; Individual & family services
Pr: Reginald Walker
V Ch: David Daniels III
CFO: Jill Lamberti
**Ch:* Mark J Appleberg
**Ch:* Donald Goodson

D-U-N-S 78-967-9784
HALL OF VIRGINIA BEACH LLC
HALL HONDA
(*Suby of* HALL AUTOMOTIVE LLC) ★
3516 Virginia Beach Blvd, Virginia Beach, VA 23452-4422
Tel (757) 431-4300 *Founded/Ownrshp* 2006
Sales 23.3MM^E *EMP* 91
SIC 5511 Automobiles, new & used; Automobiles, new & used
Pr: William R Baker
Genl Mgr: Erin Bessey
Genl Mgr: Dennis Moore
Sales Exec: Al Stevens
Sls Mgr: Mike P Hill
Sales Asso: John Christian

D-U-N-S 11-215-3291
HALL RENDER KILLIAN HEATH & LYMAN PC
1 American Sq Ste 2000, Indianapolis, IN 46282-0004
Tel (317) 633-4884 *Founded/Ownrshp* 1966
Sales 37.1MM^E *EMP* 275
SIC 8111

HALL SADDLERY
See LAACKE & JOYS CO LLC

D-U-N-S 04-862-9760 IMP
HALL TECHNOLOGIES INC (DE)
(*Suby of* ENTRUST SERVICES LLC) ★
6300 Bartmer Indus Dr, Saint Louis, MO 63130-2625
Tel (314) 725-2600 *Founded/Ownrshp* 1938
Sales 33.4MM^E *EMP* 23
Accts Kirkland Russ Murphy & Tapp
SIC 5169 Industrial chemicals; Organic chemicals, synthetic
Pr: Jeff Laurant
**Pr:* H Jeff Laurent
MIS Dir: Ed Roesch
IT Man: Ray Lefler
IT Man: Shelley Oerding
Opers Mgr: Christina Lammert
Opers Mgr: Kim Oblein
Mktg Dir: Mark Loudenslager

D-U-N-S 02-065-6435
HALL VANDERHEYDEN INC (NY)
614 Cooper Hill Rd, Wynantskill, NY 12198-2906
Tel (518) 283-6500 *Founded/Ownrshp* 1890
Sales 17.4MM *EMP* 285
SIC 8361 Children's home; Home for destitute men & women; Halfway home for delinquents & offenders; Home for the physically handicapped; Children's home; Home for destitute men & women; Halfway home for delinquents & offenders; Home for the physically handicapped
Ch Bd: Patrick Hughes
**CEO:* Karen Carpenter Palumbo
**CFO:* Lori Eason

HALL VISION CLINIC
See THOMAS RONALD HALL OD

D-U-N-S 11-343-8563 IMP
HALL WINES LLC
401 Saint Helena Hwy S, Saint Helena, CA 94574-2200
Tel (707) 967-0700 *Founded/Ownrshp* 2003
Sales 27.9MM^E *EMP* 50
SIC 5182 0172 Wine; Grapes
Pr: Mike Reynolds
VP: Whitney Jacobson
Dir Soc: Myriah Mutrux
Opers Mgr: Gabriel Valenzuela
Natl Sales: Elise Faur
Mktg Dir: Bronwyn Ney
Pr Mgr: Lisa Heckaman
Mktg Mgr: Joe Reeder
Sls Mgr: Nicky Fox
Sls Mgr: Richard Reeves
Sls Mgr: Jeffrey Zappelli

HALL-DALE MANOR
See NORTH COUNTRY ASSOCIATES INC

HALL-HOUSTON EXPLORATION FUND
See HALL-HOUSTON EXPLORATION PARTNERS LLC

D-U-N-S 78-498-5603
HALL-HOUSTON EXPLORATION PARTNERS LLC
HALL-HOUSTON EXPLORATION FUND
4605 Post Oak Place Dr # 100, Houston, TX 77027-9729
Tel (713) 333-0930 *Founded/Ownrshp* 2005
Sales 50.0MM *EMP* 10
SIC 1382 Oil & gas exploration services; Oil & gas exploration services
CFO: Brad Bynum

HALL-IRWIN CONSTRUCTION DIV
See HALL-IRWIN CORP

D-U-N-S 03-208-4436
HALL-IRWIN CORP
HALL-IRWIN CONSTRUCTION DIV
301 Centennial Dr, Milliken, CO 80543-3222
Tel (970) 352-6057 *Founded/Ownrshp* 1963
Sales 28.2MM^E *EMP* 200
SIC 6531

D-U-N-S 10-180-4409
HALL-KIMBRELL ENVIRONMENTAL SERVICES INC
(*Suby of* PROFESSIONAL SERVICE INDUSTRIES INC) ★
1901 S Meyers Rd Ste 400, Oakbrook Terrace, IL 60181-5208
Tel (630) 691-1490 *Founded/Ownrshp* 1990
Sales 19.1MM^E *EMP* 500
SIC 8711 Engineering services; Consulting engineer; Engineering services; Consulting engineer
COO: Branum Howell
**CFO:* Murray Savage

D-U-N-S 80-957-3918
HALL-MARK FIRE APPARATUS INC
3431 Nw 27th Ave, Ocala, FL 34475-3307
Tel (352) 629-6305 *Founded/Ownrshp* 1993
Sales 31.1MM^E *EMP* 40
SIC 5511 7538 Pickups, new & used; General automotive repair shops
Pr: James W Hall
VP: Bill Alm
VP: William D Alm

D-U-N-S 03-600-2806
HALLADAY MOTORS INC
HALLADAY USED CAR & TRUCK CTR
2100 Westland Rd, Cheyenne, WY 82001-3328
Tel (307) 634-1511 *Founded/Ownrshp* 1944, 1993
Sales 41.1MM^E *EMP* 85
SIC 5511 Automobiles, new & used; Automobiles, new & used
Ch Bd: Carl Halladay Jr
**Pr:* Tim Joannides
**VP:* Chris Joannides
**VP:* Kathy Joannides
Genl Mgr: Jim Casey
IT Man: Rayna Hamilton
IT Man: Michelle Radford
Sls Mgr: Karena Adrian
Sales Asso: Pat Cohea
Sales Asso: Gabe Meza

HALLADAY USED CAR & TRUCK CTR
See HALLADAY MOTORS INC

D-U-N-S 08-265-3858
▲ HALLADOR ENERGY CO
1660 Lincoln St Ste 2700, Denver, CO 80264-2701
Tel (303) 839-5504 *Founded/Ownrshp* 1949
Sales 241.1MM *EMP* 370^E
Tkr Sym HNRG *Exch* NAS
SIC 1241 1311 1382 Coal mining services; Crude petroleum & natural gas production; Oil & gas exploration services; Coal mining services; Crude petroleum & natural gas production; Oil & gas exploration services
Pr: Brent K Bilsland
**Ch Bd:* Victor P Stabio
CFO: W Anderson Bishop
CFO: Lawrence D Martin
Board of Directors: David C Hardie, Steven Hardie, Bryan H Lawrence, Sheldon B Lubar, John Van Heuvelen

D-U-N-S 13-165-0277
HALLAM ASSOCIATES INC
HALLAM-ICS
38 Eastwood Dr Ste 200, South Burlington, VT 05403-4403
Tel (802) 658-4891 *Founded/Ownrshp* 1991
Sales 21.9MM *EMP* 75
Accts Gallagher Flynn & Company Ll
SIC 1731 8711 Electrical work; Mechanical engineering
Pr: Keith Flaherty
CFO: Brenda Matthews
VP: John R Butterfield
VP: Peter T Niarchos
VP: Bernard Tink Pelkey
VP: Jeffrey N Silcox
Rgnl Mgr: Lamonte Hugh
Sfty Mgr: Jennifer Barr
Snr PM: Bill Neuburger

HALLAM-ICS
See HALLAM ASSOCIATES INC

D-U-N-S 00-587-6636
HALLAMORE CORP (MA)
KENNEBEC CRANE
795 Plymouth St Ste 1, Holbrook, MA 02343-1936
Tel (781) 767-2000 *Founded/Ownrshp* 1895, 1955
Sales 27.0MM^E *EMP* 250
SIC 7353 4213 Cranes & aerial lift equipment, rental or leasing; Contract haulers; Cranes & aerial lift equipment, rental or leasing; Contract haulers
Ch: Joseph L Barry Jr
**Pr:* Dennis E Barry
Genl Mgr: Hallamore Spencer
Sales Exec: Christopher Barry

HALLE COMPANIES
See HALLE ENTERPRISES INC

D-U-N-S 07-011-3089
HALLE ENTERPRISES INC
HALLE COMPANIES
2900 Linden Ln Ste 300, Silver Spring, MD 20910-1299
Tel (301) 495-1520 *Founded/Ownrshp* 1972
Sales 31.0MM^E *EMP* 70
SIC 1542 8741 Commercial & office building contractors; Construction management
Pr: Warren E Halle
CFO: ADI Adair
**VP:* Stephen Fleischman
**VP:* Edwin Halle
**VP:* Martha D Halle
Off Mgr: Michelle Dunn

D-U-N-S 00-891-5944
HALLEN CONSTRUCTION CO INC
4270 Austin Blvd, Island Park, NY 11558-1626
Tel (516) 432-8300 *Founded/Ownrshp* 1952
Sales 171.7MM *EMP* 250
Accts Albrecht Viggiano Zureck & C
SIC 1623 Water, sewer & utility lines; Water, sewer & utility lines
Ch Bd: Thomas B Poole
Pr: Ken Biondi
**Pr:* Shepard T Poole
**CEO:* Robert L Meschi
**Treas:* Monika Franke
**Ex VP:* Eugene J Hickey

D-U-N-S 00-918-5810
HALLER ENTERPRISES INC
212 Bucky Dr, Lititz, PA 17543-7695
Tel (717) 733-0968 *Founded/Ownrshp* 1981
Sales 76.9MM^E *EMP* 290
SIC 1711 1731 Plumbing contractors; Warm air heating & air conditioning contractor; General electrical contractor; Plumbing contractors; Warm air heating & air conditioning contractor; General electrical contractor
CEO: J Richard Haller
**CFO:* Mark Weaver
Brnch Mgr: Leslie Cloonan
Brnch Mgr: Drew Fitzkee
Brnch Mgr: Ryan Hartsough
CIO: Steve Walter
DP Exec: Phil Weaver
Trfc Dir: Dan Landis
Trfc Dir: Eric Rittenhouse
Trfc Dir: Derrick Sites
Mtls Mgr: Austin Haller

HALLETT MATERIALS
See OMG MID WEST INC

D-U-N-S 07-918-1005 IMP
HALLIBURTON
10200 Bellaire Blvd, Houston, TX 77072-5232
Tel (281) 575-3000 *Founded/Ownrshp* 2013
Sales 33.9MM^E *EMP* 126^E
SIC 1731 Energy management controls
CEO: David J Lesar
**Ex VP:* Albert O Cornelison Jr
**Ex VP:* Mark A McCollum
**Ex VP:* Jeff Miller
Sr VP: Don Murphy
VP: Robert Moran
VP: Mark Niblett
VP: Donny Winslow
Dir Soc: Pam Mayes
Creative D: Barbara Moore
Comm Dir: John Touchet

D-U-N-S 96-440-9007 EXP
▲ HALLIBURTON CO
3000 N Sam Houston Pkwy E, Houston, TX 77032-3299
Tel (281) 871-2699 *Founded/Ownrshp* 1919
Sales 32.8MMM *EMP* 80,000
Tkr Sym HAL *Exch* NYS
SIC 1389 1382 1381 8711 Oil field services; Cementing oil & gas well casings; Well logging; Perforating well casings; Oil & gas exploration services; Drilling oil & gas wells; Petroleum, mining & chemical engineers; Oil field services; Cementing oil & gas well casings; Well logging; Perforating well casings; Oil & gas exploration services; Drilling oil & gas wells; Petroleum, mining & chemical engineers
Ch Bd: David J Lesar
**Pr:* Jeffrey A Miller
CFO: Christian A Garcia
Bd of Dir: James Jackson
Ofcr: Mark A McCollum
Ex VP: Lawrence J Pope
Ex VP: Robb L Voyles
Sr VP: Christian Garcia
Sr VP: James B Renfroe
VP: Charles E Geer Jr
Dir Risk M: Paul Credo
Dir Risk M: Jeffrey Cregg
Dir Risk M: Paul Heuermann
Creative D: Darrell Picha
Board of Directors: Alan M Bennett, James R Boyd, Milton Carroll, Murry S Gerber, Jose C Grubisich, Abdulaziz F Al Khayyal, Robert A Malone, J Landis Martin, Debra L Reed

D-U-N-S 96-464-5022 IMP
■ HALLIBURTON DELAWARE INC
(*Suby of* HALLIBURTON CO) ★
3000 Houston Ave, Houston, TX 77009-6735
Tel (713) 759-2600 *Founded/Ownrshp* 1996
Sales 2.9MMM^E *EMP* 57,300
SIC 1629 1611 1622 8711 1389 Power plant construction; Chemical plant & refinery construction; Oil refinery construction; Marine construction; Highway & street paving contractor; Bridge, tunnel & elevated highway; Bridge construction; Engineering services; Consulting engineer; Sanitary engineers; Pollution control engineering; Oil field services; Cementing oil & gas well casings; Well logging; Perforating well casings; Power plant construction; Chemical plant & refinery construction; Oil refinery construction; Marine construction; Highway & street paving contractor; Bridge, tunnel & elevated highway; Bridge construction; Engineering services; Consulting engineer; Sanitary engineers; Pollution control engineering; Oil field services; Cementing oil & gas well casings; Well logging; Perforating well casings
Pr: David J Lesar
**Pr:* Lester L Colma
**Pr:* Garry H Dlaurton
**Pr:* Robert F Heinemann
**Pr:* Susan S Keith
**Pr:* Gary T Marcus
**Pr:* Gary V Mars
**Pr:* Charles Muchmore Jr
Ex VP: Albert O Cornelison
Ex VP: Christopher Gaut
Ex VP: Andy Lane
Sr VP: James B Renfroe
VP: Lyn Beaty
VP: Margaret Carriere
VP: David King
VP: Kenneth King
VP: Paul Koeller
VP: Michele Mastrean
VP: Susan Ponce
VP: Jim Renfroe
VP: Bill Sanstrom

D-U-N-S 04-329-6920 IMP
■ HALLIBURTON ENERGY SERVICES INC
(*Suby of* HALLIBURTON CO) ★
10200 Bellaire Blvd, Houston, TX 77072-5232
Tel (713) 839-3950 *Founded/Ownrshp* 1919, 1996
Sales 17.9MMM^E *EMP* 50,000^E
SIC 1389 Oil field services; Cementing oil & gas well casings; Well logging; Perforating well casings; Oil field services; Cementing oil & gas well casings; Well logging; Perforating well casings
Ch Bd: David J Lesar
**Pr:* Jeffrey Allen Miller
**CFO:* C Christopher Gaut
**CFO:* Mark A McCollum
**Treas:* Christian A Garcia
**Ex VP:* John W Gibson
**Ex VP:* Lawrence J Pope
**Sr VP:* Evelyn M Angelle
**VP:* Albert O Cornelison Jr
IT Man: Steve Matthews
IT Man: Binh Nguyen

D-U-N-S 00-607-0239
HALLMAN/LINDSAY PAINTS INC (WI)
1717 N Bristol St, Sun Prairie, WI 53590-1287
Tel (608) 834-8844 *Founded/Ownrshp* 1956, 1983
Sales 27.2MM *EMP* 130
SIC 2851 5231 Paints & allied products; Paints & paint additives; Varnishes; Paint, glass & wallpaper; Paint; Paint brushes, rollers, sprayers & other supplies; Paints & allied products; Paints & paint additives; Varnishes; Paint, glass & wallpaper; Paint; Paint brushes, rollers, sprayers & other supplies
Pr: Timothy A Mielcarek
Exec: Mary Frieders
Dir Lab: Steve Olson
Dir Bus: John Heenan
Brnch Mgr: Eric Marsh
Genl Mgr: Tom Wiltzius
Dir IT: Jesse Breidenbach
Ql Cn Mgr: Jane Saliture

HALLMARK
See J & J CARDS INC

HALLMARK
See BANNER MANAGEMENT CO INC

D-U-N-S 88-309-0532
HALLMARK AVIATION SERVICES LP
(*Suby of* SWISSPORT INTERNATIONAL AG)
5757 W Century Blvd # 860, Los Angeles, CA 90045-6417
Tel (310) 215-7213 *Founded/Ownrshp* 1989
Sales 50.0MM *EMP* 1,400
SIC 7363 Help supply services; Help supply services
Pr: Philipp Huber
Rgnl Mgr: Adenilto Simoes
S&M/VP: Hosi Kapadia

D-U-N-S 82-677-8607
HALLMARK BUILDERS INC
520 S Main St, Middlebury, IN 46540-9701
Tel (574) 825-9850 *Founded/Ownrshp* 1992
Sales 190.0MM *EMP* 4
SIC 1521 Single-family housing construction; Single-family housing construction
Pr: Cliff Miller

D-U-N-S 07-384-3997
HALLMARK BUILDING SUPPLIES INC
2120 Pewaukee Rd Ste 100, Waukesha, WI 53188-2491
Tel (262) 408-4200 *Founded/Ownrshp* 1974
Sales 81.8MM^E *EMP* 69
SIC 5031 Lumber, plywood & millwork; Lumber, plywood & millwork
CEO: O Joseph Balthazor
Pr: Todd Lienke
**CFO:* Bonnie Caravella
**VP:* Lon Bahr
VP: Caravella Bonnie
**VP:* Louis J Paynter
**VP:* Roland Pfender
VP Opers: Kent Holtz
Mktg Mgr: Linda Heipp

D-U-N-S 13-920-6010
HALLMARK CAPITAL GROUP LLC
HALLMARK GROUP
14043 S Gessner Rd, Missouri City, TX 77489-1000
Tel (713) 270-1294 *Founded/Ownrshp* 2002
Sales 22.8MM^E *EMP* 290
Accts Durio & Company Pc Houston T
SIC 8744 8741 Facilities support services; Management services; Facilities support services; Management services
Pr: Monique D Freeman
Off Mgr: Dawn Powell
VP Opers: John Rodgers
VP Sls: Pamela Barber

D-U-N-S 00-713-1113 IMP/EXP
▲ HALLMARK CARDS INC (MO)
2501 Mcgee St, Kansas City, MO 64108-2600
Tel (816) 274-5111 *Founded/Ownrshp* 1910
Sales 5.1MMM^E *EMP* 16,200
SIC 2771

HALLMARK CHANNEL
See CROWN MEDIA UNITED STATES LLC

D-U-N-S 60-102-4003
▲ HALLMARK FINANCIAL SERVICES INC
777 Main St Ste 1000, Fort Worth, TX 76102-5314
Tel (817) 348-1600 *Founded/Ownrshp* 1990
Sales NA *EMP* 393^E
Tkr Sym HALL *Exch* NGM
SIC 6411 6311 Property & casualty insurance agent; Life insurance; Property & casualty insurance agent; Life insurance
Pr: Naveen Anand
**Ch Bd:* Mark E Schwarz
Pr: Michael P Binns
Pr: James A Damonte
Ex VP: Kevin T Kasitz
Sr VP: Jeffrey R Passmore
VP: Martha Bell
VP: Bill Doherty
VP: Wes Olfers

VP: William Tayler
VP: Billee Taylor
Board of Directors: Scott T Berlin, James H Graves, Jim W Henderson

D-U-N-S 17-030-8337
■ HALLMARK GLOBAL SERVICES LLC
(*Suby of* HALLMARK CARDS INC) ★
2501 Mcgee St, Kansas City, MO 64108-2615
Tel (816) 274-5111 *Founded/Ownrshp* 2011
Sales 38.0MM *EMP* 128
SIC 8741 Administrative management
Pr: Craig McMonigle
**Treas:* Jeff McMillen
**VP:* Tom Ferrell
**VP:* Brian Gardner
**VP:* Daniel Krouse
**VP:* Brian Kurtz
**VP:* Deanne Stedem

HALLMARK GROUP
See HALLMARK CAPITAL GROUP LLC

D-U-N-S 11-524-7496
HALLMARK HEALTH CORP
LAWRENCE MEMORIAL HOSPITAL
170 Governors Ave, Medford, MA 02155-1643
Tel (781) 306-6000 *Founded/Ownrshp* 1900
Sales 6.0MM *EMP* 2,700
Accts Hallmark Health System Inc Me
SIC 8741 7389 Hospital management; Nursing & personal care facility management; Fund raising organizations; Hospital management; Nursing & personal care facility management; Fund raising organizations
CEO: Michael V Sack
Chf Path: Dean Pappas
V Ch: Alan G Macdonald
V Ch: William F Rucci
V Ch: Donna West
**Pr:* Diane Farraher-Smith
COO: Robert Wasserman
CFO: Linda Pike
**Treas:* David Drain
**Treas:* John Keenan
**Treas:* James Nania
VP: Nancy Bittner
VP: Junior Briner
VP: Pam Duchene
**VP:* Sylena Keeping
Dir OR: Donna Begum
Dir Lab: Billie Chan

D-U-N-S 08-337-9198
HALLMARK HEALTH SYSTEM INC
(*Suby of* HALLMARK HEALTH CORP) ★
585 Lebanon St, Melrose, MA 02176-3225
Tel (781) 979-3000 *Founded/Ownrshp* 1921
Sales 270.9MM *EMP* 2,600
SIC 8062 General medical & surgical hospitals; General medical & surgical hospitals
Pr: Michael V Sack
**CFO:* James Nania
**Treas:* David Drain
Ex VP: Steven Kapfhammer
VP: Maureen Hurton
Dir Pat Ca: Laurie M Cadden
Dir Rad: Elaine Gale
Off Mgr: Margaret Malenchini
CIO: Carol Dreer
IT Man: Carol Dresser
Pharmcst: Shirin Atashband

D-U-N-S 06-230-9299
■ HALLMARK HEALY GROUP INC
LEACH GARNER - A BERKSHIRE
(*Suby of* LEACH GARNER - A BERKSHIRE HATHAWAY CO) ★
49 Pearl St, Attleboro, MA 02703-3940
Tel (508) 222-9234 *Founded/Ownrshp* 1965
Sales 20.6MM^E *EMP* 200
SIC 3915 5944 3911 Jewelers' findings & materials; Jewelry stores; Jewelry, precious metal; Jewelers' findings & materials; Jewelry stores; Jewelry, precious metal
Pr: Howard Kilguss
Sr VP: Fred Poluhovich
VP: James E Carr
VP: Mary Denham
VP: Roberta Shapiro
Netwrk Mgr: Gil Gomes
Sls&Mrk Ex: Mike Morolla
Board of Directors: Lawrence Demichele

D-U-N-S 03-078-7014
HALLMARK INNS & RESORTS INC
HALLMARK RESORT
15455 Hallmark Dr Ste 200, Lake Oswego, OR 97035-3476
Tel (503) 635-4555 *Founded/Ownrshp* 1984
Sales 18.5MM^E *EMP* 321
SIC 7011 Resort hotel; Resort hotel
Pr: William J Allred
**Ch Bd:* Georgianna Hay
CFO: Robert Thompson
Sls Mgr: Sunny Golden

D-U-N-S 60-710-1326
■ HALLMARK INSURANCE CO
PHOENIX INDEMNITY INSURANCE CO
(*Suby of* HALLMARK FINANCIAL SERVICES INC) ★
6500 Pinecrest Dr Ste 100, Plano, TX 75024-2945
Tel (972) 960-2277 *Founded/Ownrshp* 2003
Sales NA *EMP* 120
SIC 6411 Property & casualty insurance agent
Pr: Brookland Davis
VP: Greg Birdsall
VP: Robert Kuchta
VP: Charles McMillan
VP: Edward Stokes
QA Dir: Judy Phillips
IT Man: Nathan Meyer
Opers Mgr: Wendy Kaylor
Manager: Steven Lorenzen

D-U-N-S 04-674-8679 IMP/EXP
■ HALLMARK MARKETING CO LLC
(*Suby of* HALLMARK CARDS INC) ★
2501 Mcgee St, Kansas City, MO 64108-2615
Tel (816) 274-5111 *Founded/Ownrshp* 1971
Sales 3.4MMM^E *EMP* 16,200^E
SIC 5947 2542 7389 Greeting cards; Office & store showcases & display fixtures; Brokers, business: buying & selling business enterprises; Greeting cards; Office & store showcases & display fixtures; Brokers, business: buying & selling business enterprises
V Ch: Donald J Hall
Pr: Richard Chalker
CFO: Ronald Neiger
VP: Robert Kipp
Dir Risk M: Larry Hannah
Creative D: Jeff Shumway
Creative D: Peggy Wrightsman
Comm Dir: Dean Rodenbaugh
Brnch Mgr: Rick Byrd
CIO: Jason Elder
MIS Dir: Jenny Hawk

D-U-N-S 07-996-3470
HALLMARK PINE RIDGE LLC
125 Venus Dr, Port Saint Joe, FL 32456-5270
Tel (770) 984-2100 *Founded/Ownrshp* 2015
Sales 5.9MM^E *EMP* 280
SIC 6531 Real estate agents & managers

D-U-N-S 07-996-3486
HALLMARK PINE TERRACE III LLC
45177 Brown St, Callahan, FL 32011-7907
Tel (770) 984-2100 *Founded/Ownrshp* 2015
Sales 6.7MM^E *EMP* 280
SIC 6531 Real estate agents & managers

D-U-N-S 07-996-3508
HALLMARK POST OAK LLC
996 Citrona Dr Apt 2601, Fernandina Beach, FL 32034-4610
Tel (770) 984-2100 *Founded/Ownrshp* 2015
Sales 6.7MM^E *EMP* 280
SIC 6531 Real estate agents & managers

D-U-N-S 13-694-7459
HALLMARK REHABILITATION GP LLC
27442 Portola Pkwy # 200, El Toro, CA 92610-2822
Tel (949) 282-5900 *Founded/Ownrshp* 2003
Sales 27.0MM^E *EMP* 1,200
SIC 8322 Rehabilitation services; Rehabilitation services
VP: David Van Matre
Area Mgr: Merrisue Corris
Area Mgr: Brigid Dowd
Area Mgr: Marcie Tidd

HALLMARK RESORT
See HALLMARK INNS & RESORTS INC

D-U-N-S 02-303-2261 IMP/EXP
■ HALLMARK RETAIL LLC
(*Suby of* MIX HOLDINGS INC) ★
2440 Pershing Rd Ste 200, Kansas City, MO 64108-2501
Tel (816) 274-5878 *Founded/Ownrshp* 2015
Sales 328.7MM^E *EMP* 4,000
SIC 5947 Greeting cards; Gift shop; Greeting cards; Gift shop
Pr: John X Watson
QA Dir: John Boyd
IT Man: Ken Cameron
Snr Mgr: Tina Chapman

D-U-N-S 07-996-3587
HALLMARK RIDGECREST MANOR LLC
37 Ridgeview Dr, Debary, FL 32713-2342
Tel (770) 984-2100 *Founded/Ownrshp* 2015
Sales 7.4MM^E *EMP* 280
SIC 6531 Real estate agents & managers

D-U-N-S 07-996-3603
HALLMARK ROSEMONT MANOR LLC
1801 N County Road 19a, Eustis, FL 32726-1904
Tel (770) 984-2100 *Founded/Ownrshp* 2015
Sales 7.4MM^E *EMP* 280
SIC 6531 Real estate agents & managers

D-U-N-S 83-137-4959
HALLMARK SERVICES CORP
(*Suby of* BLUE CROSS AND BLUE SHIELD) ★
1000 E Warrenville Rd # 400, Naperville, IL 60563-2046
Tel (630) 328-4400 *Founded/Ownrshp* 2009
Sales NA *EMP* 1^E
SIC 6321 Accident & health insurance carriers
Pr: Colleen Reitan
Telecom Mg: Beth Meekma
VP Opers: Gerry Jacobus

D-U-N-S 04-291-5160 IMP
HALLMARK STONE CO ACQUISITION LLC
2200 Cassens Dr, Fenton, MO 63026-2521
Tel (636) 680-9431 *Founded/Ownrshp* 1998
Sales 21.8MM^E *EMP* 135
SIC 3281 Granite, cut & shaped; Granite, cut & shaped
Exec: Don Womack
Sls Mgr: Tony Russo

HALLMARK TOYOTA-BMW-KIA
See HERRIN-GEAR INC

D-U-N-S 07-996-3643
HALLMARK VILLAGE CHASE LLC
39216 Village Chase, Zephyrhills, FL 33542-8700
Tel (770) 984-2100 *Founded/Ownrshp* 2015
Sales 7.4MM^E *EMP* 280
SIC 6531 Real estate agents & managers

D-U-N-S 07-996-3987
HALLMARK VILLAGE WALK LLC (FL)
6012 Village Walk, Zephyrhills, FL 33542-2756
Tel (770) 984-2100 *Founded/Ownrshp* 2015
Sales 7.4MM^E *EMP* 280
SIC 6531 Real estate agents & managers

D-U-N-S 07-996-3990
HALLMARK WATER OAK LLC (FL)
315 Water Oak Cir, Orange City, FL 32763-7441
Tel (770) 984-2100 *Founded/Ownrshp* 2015
Sales 7.4MM^E *EMP* 280
SIC 6531 Real estate agents & managers

D-U-N-S 07-996-3993
HALLMARK WILDWOOD TERRACE LLC
500 Gilliam St, Wildwood, FL 34785-4600
Tel (770) 984-2100 *Founded/Ownrshp* 2015
Sales 6.7MM^E *EMP* 280
SIC 6531 Real estate agents & managers

D-U-N-S 07-996-4133
HALLMARK WOODLAND TERRACE LLC (FL)
4309 Nolte Rd, Saint Cloud, FL 34772-7159
Tel (770) 984-2100 *Founded/Ownrshp* 2015
Sales 7.4MM^E *EMP* 280
SIC 6531 Real estate agents & managers

D-U-N-S 12-663-5007 IMP
HALLMART COLLECTIBLES INC
7119 Fair Ave, North Hollywood, CA 91605-6304
Tel (818) 759-0770 *Founded/Ownrshp* 2000
Sales 44.0MM *EMP* 30
SIC 5021 Beds & bedding
Pr: Jesse Galili
**VP:* Joseph Babazadeh
Off Mgr: Mitchell Estrada
VP Opers: Jay Allen

D-U-N-S 02-802-4354
HALLOWELL CHEVROLET CO INC (CA)
HEDRICK'S HALLOWELL CHEVROLET
961 W Shaw Ave, Clovis, CA 93612-3295
Tel (559) 291-7711 *Founded/Ownrshp* 1944
Sales 45.3MM^E *EMP* 105
SIC 5511

HALL'S CATERING
See HALL DRIVE-INS INC

D-U-N-S 00-584-0921
HALLS FAST MOTOR FREIGHT INC
501 Kentile Rd, South Plainfield, NJ 07080-4800
Tel (908) 756-6242 *Founded/Ownrshp* 1922, 1965
Sales 20.3MM *EMP* 83
Accts Leaf Saltzman Manganelli Pfeil
SIC 4214 Local trucking with storage; Local trucking with storage
Ch Bd: William E Jayne
**Pr:* William E Jayne III
COO: Thomas Brennan
**CFO:* Warren Tamaroff
**Treas:* Dale R Jayne
**VP:* Bruce A Jayne
Sls Dir: Salvatore Labruno

D-U-N-S 14-353-4837
■ HALLS MERCHANDISING LLC
(*Suby of* HALLMARK CARDS INC) ★
2450 Grand Blvd Ste 333, Kansas City, MO 64108-2516
Tel (816) 531-4830 *Founded/Ownrshp* 2004
Sales 72.7MM^E *EMP* 500
SIC 5094 Jewelry; Jewelry

D-U-N-S 06-871-5416
HALLS WAREHOUSE CORP
501 Kentile Rd, South Plainfield, NJ 07080-4800
Tel (908) 756-6242 *Founded/Ownrshp* 1965
Sales 41.9MM *EMP* 285
Accts Leaf Saltzman Manganelli Te
SIC 4225 General warehousing; General warehousing
Pr: William Jayne III
**Pr:* Bruce A Jayne
**CFO:* Warren Tamaroff
**Treas:* Dale R Jayne
**Ex VP:* William E Jayne III
VP: Perry Myers
Admn Mgr: Pat Weiss
Opers Mgr: Kevin Schneider

D-U-N-S 06-318-4923
HALLSDALE-POWELL UTILITY DISTRICT (INC)
3745 Cunningham Rd, Knoxville, TN 37918-5304
Tel (865) 922-7547 *Founded/Ownrshp* 1954
Sales 78.8MM^E *EMP* 85
Accts Mitchell Emert & Hill Pc K
SIC 4941 4952 Water supply; Sewerage systems; Water supply; Sewerage systems
Ch Bd: Jimmie Hill
**Pr:* Darren Cardwell
CFO: James Smith
Genl Mgr: Sandra Liford
Plnt Mgr: Chad Scheidecker

D-U-N-S 18-390-0182 IMP
HALLSTAR CO
120 S Riverside Plz # 1620, Chicago, IL 60606-3911
Tel (312) 554-7400 *Founded/Ownrshp* 1986
Sales 60.6MM^E *EMP* 142^E
SIC 2869 5169 Plasticizers, organic: cyclic & acyclic; Industrial chemicals; Plasticizers, organic: cyclic & acyclic; Industrial chemicals
CEO: John J Paro
Ch Bd: George A Vincent
CFO: William J Holbrook
Sr VP: David Rosenberger
VP: Keith Carlson
VP: Gail A Gerono
VP: Jeff Jaworek
VP: Jim Savastano
VP: Gary Wentworth
Dir Bus: Varun Mathur
Dept Mgr: Rick Snyder
Board of Directors: James R Conaty, Robert B Covalt, James N Hallene

D-U-N-S 02-270-2070
HALLSVILLE INDEPENDENT SCHOOL DISTRICT (TX)
210 S Green St, Hallsville, TX 75650-6106
Tel (903) 668-5990 *Founded/Ownrshp* 1949
Sales 158.3M *EMP* 650
Accts Knuckols Duvall Hallum & Co
SIC 8211 Public elementary & secondary schools; Public elementary school; Public elementary & secondary schools; Public elementary school
Dir Vol: Angie Mauldin
Treas: Charles Thomson
VP: Rick Tryon
Pr Dir: Carol Greer
HC Dir: Kerri Brice
HC Dir: Paula Bure

D-U-N-S 06-327-8170
HALLUM INC
HALLUM OIL
707 E Mingus Ave Ste 501, Cottonwood, AZ 86326-6707
Tel (928) 526-3869 *Founded/Ownrshp* 1972
Sales 52.0MM *EMP* 60
SIC 5172 5541 5411 Petroleum products; Gasoline service stations; Convenience stores, independent; Petroleum products; Gasoline service stations; Convenience stores, independent
Pr: Dana Hallum
**VP:* David W Hallum

HALLUM OIL
See HALLUM INC

HALLWAY FEEDS
See FARMERS FEED MILL INC

D-U-N-S 83-052-8696
HALLWOOD FINANCIAL LIMITED
3710 Rawlins St Ste 1500, Dallas, TX 75219-4282
Tel (214) 523-1288 *Founded/Ownrshp* 2008
Sales 93.4MM^E *EMP* 479^E
SIC 6211 Security brokers & dealers; Security brokers & dealers
Ch Bd: Anthony J Gumbiner

D-U-N-S 07-163-0297 IMP
HALLWOOD GROUP INC
(*Suby of* HALLWOOD FINANCIAL LIMITED) ★
3710 Rawlins St Ste 1500, Dallas, TX 75219-4282
Tel (214) 528-5588 *Founded/Ownrshp* 2014
Sales 76.8MM^E *EMP* 439^E
SIC 2221 7389 Broadwoven fabric mills, manmade; Textile & apparel services; Broadwoven fabric mills, manmade; Textile & apparel services
Ch Bd: Anthony J Gumbiner
Pr: William L Guzzetti
CFO: Richard Kelley
Off Mgr: Andrea Rivera
IT Man: John Aplin
Snr Mgr: Melvin Melle
Board of Directors: Gert Lessing

D-U-N-S 11-622-7851 IMP/EXP
HALMA HOLDINGS INC
(*Suby of* HALMA INTERNATIONAL LIMITED) ★
11500 Northlake Dr # 306, Cincinnati, OH 45249-1658
Tel (513) 772-5501 *Founded/Ownrshp* 1979
Sales 522.0MM^E *EMP* 112
SIC 3826

D-U-N-S 60-417-5856
HALMAR INTERNATIONAL LLC
421 E Route 59, Nanuet, NY 10954-2908
Tel (845) 735-3511 *Founded/Ownrshp* 2005
Sales 73.4MM^E *EMP* 120
SIC 1622 1611 1629 Bridge, tunnel & elevated highway; Airport runway construction; Subway construction; Bridge, tunnel & elevated highway; Airport runway construction; Subway construction
Ql Cn Mgr: Ernie Morrissey

D-U-N-S 02-393-9119 IMP
HALMODE APPAREL INC
HALMODE PETITE DIV
(*Suby of* KELLWOOD CO LLC) ★
1400 Brdwy 11th & Fl 16, New York, NY 10018
Tel (212) 819-9114 *Founded/Ownrshp* 1994
Sales 40.2MM^E *EMP* 600
SIC 2339 2335 5137 Sportswear, women's; Uniforms, athletic: women's, misses' & juniors'; Maternity clothing; Women's, juniors' & misses' dresses; Women's & children's clothing; Sportswear, women's; Uniforms, athletic: women's, misses' & juniors'; Maternity clothing; Women's, juniors' & misses' dresses; Women's & children's clothing
CEO: Jay Diamond
CFO: John Winston
**Ex VP:* Bea Myerson
VP: Pam Powell
**VP:* Michael M Saunders

HALMODE PETITE DIV
See HALMODE APPAREL INC

D-U-N-S 12-510-2223 IMP/EXP
HALO BRANDED SOLUTIONS INC
HALO/LEE WAYNE
(*Suby of* HALO HOLDING CORP) ★
1980 Industrial Dr, Sterling, IL 61081-9064
Tel (815) 632-6988 *Founded/Ownrshp* 2003
Sales 616.3MM^E *EMP* 550
SIC 5199 Advertising specialties; Advertising specialties
Pr: Marc Simon
**CFO:* Linda Janczkowski
VP: Thomas Cohan
VP: Dennis Gerlich
VP: Phyllis Jones
VP: Anne Langone
VP: Dawn Olds
VP: Chris Piper
VP: Virginia Smith
VP: Paul Steinberg
VP: Doug Stotts

HALO CAPITAL
See HALO GROUP INC

D-U-N-S 01-812-7832
HALO ELECTRONICS INC
3005 E Post Rd, Las Vegas, NV 89120-5707
Tel (702) 898-8721 *Founded/Ownrshp* 1988
Sales 40.0MM *EMP* 3

SIC 3572 Magnetic storage devices, computer; Magnetic storage devices, computer
Pr: James Heaton
**VP:* Jeffery Heaton

D-U-N-S 82-474-0414
HALO GROUP INC
HALO CAPITAL
814 33rd St, Des Moines, IA 50312-3729
Tel (515) 974-6908 *Founded/Ownrshp* 2007
Sales NA *EMP* 12
SIC 6163 Mortgage brokers arranging for loans, using money of others; Mortgage brokers arranging for loans, using money of others
Pr: David Baker

D-U-N-S 05-403-3504
HALO GROUP REALTY LLC (TX)
825 Market St Ste 230, Allen, TX 75013-3790
Tel (214) 239-1889 *Founded/Ownrshp* 2012
Sales 25.0MM *EMP* 115
SIC 6531 8742 Real estate brokers & agents; Real estate consultant
Pr: Barrett A Morris

D-U-N-S 13-170-6397 IMP
HALO HOLDING CORP
(*Suby of* CANDLELIGHT INVESTMENT HOLDINGS INC) ★
1980 Industrial Dr, Sterling, IL 61081-9064
Tel (815) 632-6800 *Founded/Ownrshp* 2012
Sales 616.3MM^E *EMP* 550
SIC 5199 Advertising specialties; Advertising specialties
CEO: Marc Simon

D-U-N-S 82-525-5706 IMP
HALO INNOVATIONS INC
HALO SLEEP SYSTEMS
111 Cheshire Ln Ste 700, Minnetonka, MN 55305-2325
Tel (952) 259-1500 *Founded/Ownrshp* 1994
Sales 26.7MM *EMP* 21
Accts Grant Thornton Llp Minneapoli
SIC 2341 Women's & children's nightwear; Women's & children's nightwear
CEO: Charles Dorsey
**Ch Bd:* William Schmid
**CFO:* Bob Hiben
VP: Karen Casson

D-U-N-S 61-036-9311
HALO LLC
BASTIAN SOLUTIONS
10585 N Meridian St Fl 3, Indianapolis, IN 46290-1069
Tel (317) 575-9992 *Founded/Ownrshp* 2000
Sales 147.8MM *EMP* 320
SIC 8711 3535 Cement making machinery; Engineering services; Conveyors & conveying equipment
CEO: William A Bastian II
CFO: John Smith

D-U-N-S 82-960-9168 IMP
HALO PHARMACEUTICAL INC
30 N Jefferson Rd, Whippany, NJ 07981-1030
Tel (973) 428-4000 *Founded/Ownrshp* 2006
Sales 29.7MM^E *EMP* 100^E
SIC 2834 Pharmaceutical preparations; Pharmaceutical preparations
CEO: Lee Karras
**Pr:* Clive V Bennett
Pr: Michael Pelini
Pr: Indraneel Shah
**CFO:* Mohd Asif
**VP:* John Garvey
**VP:* Phyllis Lambridis
VP: Anthony Qu
**VP:* Al Rosenton
**VP:* Mark Stier
**Prin:* George Bobotas

D-U-N-S 07-701-0221
HALO SHEET METAL INC
140 Lehigh Ave, Lakewood, NJ 08701-4526
Tel (732) 901-0080 *Founded/Ownrshp* 1979
Sales 21.0MM^E *EMP* 170
SIC 1711 Solar energy contractor; Solar energy contractor
Pr: Patricia Pellegrino
**VP:* Art Burns
VP: Robert Gumnic
**VP:* Robert Gumnick

HALO SLEEP SYSTEMS
See HALO INNOVATIONS INC

D-U-N-S 03-024-3906
HALO TRUST USA INC
1730 Rhode Island Ave Nw # 403, Washington, DC 20036-3101
Tel (202) 331-1266 *Founded/Ownrshp* 2001
Sales 20.4MM *EMP* 2^E
Accts Kpmg Llp Washington Dc
SIC 8699 Charitable organization; Charitable organization
Ofcr: Luan Jaupi

HALO/LEE WAYNE
See HALO BRANDED SOLUTIONS INC

D-U-N-S 00-202-7514 IMP
HALOCARBON PRODUCTS CORP
887 Kinderkamack Rd Ste 2, River Edge, NJ 07661-2307
Tel (201) 262-8899 *Founded/Ownrshp* 1950
Sales 39.0MM^E *EMP* 168
SIC 2834 Pharmaceutical preparations; Ointments; Pharmaceutical preparations; Ointments
CEO: David Bacon
**Pr:* Emely Ehrenfeld
**CEO:* Peter Murin
**Chf Mktg O:* Ron Epstein
VP: Robert Ehrenfeld
**VP:* Barbara Gardner
Trfc Mgr: Leslie Hirsch

D-U-N-S 07-851-3978 IMP
HALOPOLYMER TRADING INC
2100 West Loop S Ste 900, Houston, TX 77027-3522
Tel (954) 304-3008 *Founded/Ownrshp* 2012
Sales 25.0MM *EMP* 2
SIC 5162 Plastics materials & basic shapes; Plastics materials & basic shapes
Pr: Igor M Khrapov

D-U-N-S 02-607-7359
▲ HALOZYME THERAPEUTICS INC
11388 Sorrento Valley Rd # 200, San Diego, CA 92121-1345
Tel (858) 794-8889 *Founded/Ownrshp* 1998
Sales 75.3MM *EMP* 170^E
Accts Ernst & Young Llp San Diego
Tkr Sym HALO *Exch* NGM
SIC 2834 2836 Pharmaceutical preparations; Biological products, except diagnostic; Pharmaceutical preparations; Biological products, except diagnostic
Pr: Helen I Torley
**Ch Bd:* Kathryn E Falberg
CFO: David A Ramsay
CFO: Laurie Stelzer
Chf Mktg O: Athena Countouriotis
Sr VP: Harry J Leonhardt
VP: Stephen Daly
VP: Sunil Joshi
Dir Sec: Michael J Labarre
Board of Directors: Jeffrey W Henderson, Kenneth J Kelley, Randal J Kirk, Connie L Matsui, John S Patton, Matthew I Posard

D-U-N-S 80-677-6274
HALPER I PAPER & SUPPLIES INC
51 Hook Rd, Bayonne, NJ 07002-5012
Tel (201) 339-2244 *Founded/Ownrshp* 1981
Sales 27.7MM^E *EMP* 30
SIC 5113 Paper tubes & cores
Pr: Irwin Halper
**VP:* Andrew Halper

HALPERNS PRVYORS STEAK SEAFOOD
See HALPERNS STEAK AND SEAFOOD CO LLC

D-U-N-S 55-608-4254 IMP/EXP
HALPERNS STEAK AND SEAFOOD CO LLC
HALPERNS PRVYORS STEAK SEAFOOD
(*Suby of* GORDON FOOD SERVICE INC) ★
4685 Welcome All Rd Sw, Atlanta, GA 30349-2541
Tel (404) 767-9229 *Founded/Ownrshp* 2015
Sales 589.6MM^E *EMP* 600^E
SIC 5147 Meats & meat products; Meats & meat products
CEO: Howard Halpern
**Pr:* Ray Hicks
**CFO:* Lawrence Bayer
**Ex VP:* Ray Farmer
**Ex VP:* Kirk Halpern
Dir IT: Brandon Ensley
Dir IT: Keith McBride

D-U-N-S 00-896-2078 IMP
HALQUIST STONE CO INC (WI)
N51w23563 Lisbon Rd N 51 W, Sussex, WI 53089-4405
Tel (262) 246-9000 *Founded/Ownrshp* 1929
Sales 36.2MM^E *EMP* 80^E
SIC 1422 1411 5032 3281 Limestones, ground; Limestone, dimension-quarrying; Building stone; Cut stone & stone products
Pr: Thomas Halquist
Sls&Mrk Ex: Angela Riemenschneide
Sls Mgr: Robert Madsen

D-U-N-S 05-949-7990
HALREC INC
STEVENS CREEK TOYOTA
4202 Stevens Creek Blvd, San Jose, CA 95129-1336
Tel (408) 984-1234 *Founded/Ownrshp* 1972
Sales 71.8MM^E *EMP* 250
SIC 5511 7539 7538 7532 Automobiles, new & used; Automotive repair shops; General automotive repair shops; Top & body repair & paint shops; Automobiles, new & used; Automotive repair shops; General automotive repair shops; Top & body repair & paint shops
Ch Bd: Harold Cornelius
**CFO:* Mark Feldman
**VP:* Stephen C Cornelius
Sls Mgr: Joseph WEI
Sales Asso: Francisco Madrid

D-U-N-S 07-834-5486
HALRES LLC
1000 La St Ste 6700, Houston, TX 77002
Tel (832) 538-0300 *Founded/Ownrshp* 2011
Sales 22.4MM^E *EMP* 206
SIC 1311 Crude petroleum & natural gas; Crude petroleum & natural gas
Ch: Floyd C Wilson
**Pr:* Stephen W Herod
**Ex VP:* Robert J Anderson
**Ex VP:* David S Elkouri
**Ex VP:* Mark J Mize
**VP:* Joseph S Rinando III

D-U-N-S 02-324-6994 EXP
HALRON LUBRICANTS INC
1618 State St, Green Bay, WI 54304-3539
Tel (920) 436-4000 *Founded/Ownrshp* 1927
Sales 34.6MM^E *EMP* 55
SIC 5172

HALSEY FOODSERVICE
See W L HALSEY GROCERY CO INC

D-U-N-S 02-691-8433
HALSEY MCCORMACK & HELMER INC
MANCINI DUFFY
275 7th Ave Fl 19, New York, NY 10001-6738
Tel (212) 213-4595 *Founded/Ownrshp* 1920
Sales 21.7MM^E *EMP* 100
SIC 8712 Architectural services; Architectural services
CEO: Anthony P Schirripa
**Pr:* Dina Frank
**CFO:* David Hannaford

Dir Bus: Christina Daly
Snr PM: Brian Guze

D-U-N-S 00-619-8683
HALSTAD ELEVATOR CO (INC) (MN)
Hwy 75 N, Halstad, MN 56548
Tel (218) 456-2135 *Founded/Ownrshp* 1899
Sales 30.0MM *EMP* 19
SIC 5153 5191 Grains; Fertilizer & fertilizer materials; Chemicals, agricultural; Feed; Grains; Fertilizer & fertilizer materials; Chemicals, agricultural; Feed
Pr: Curtis Sorenson
**Pr:* Rod Olson

D-U-N-S 15-728-0819 IMP/EXP
HALTEC CORP
32585 N Price Rd, Salem, OH 44460-9513
Tel (330) 222-1501 *Founded/Ownrshp* 1985
Sales 35.8MM *EMP* 70
Accts Mayer Hoffman Mccann Pc Akr
SIC 3714 Motor vehicle parts & accessories; Tire valve cores
Pr: Thomas Moyer
**CFO:* Frank Bezon
**Ch:* Edward Russell
VP: Brian Bostick
**VP:* David Caruso
**VP:* Judith Russell
**VP:* Mike Russell
IT Man: Michael Russell
Plnt Mgr: Shari Althouse

HALTERMAN AUTO RANCH
See JAMES W HALTERMAN INC

HALTERMANN SOLUTIONS
See JOHANN HALTERMANN LTD

HALTOM GLOBAL SERVICES
See HALTON GROUP AMERICAS INC

D-U-N-S 00-790-8692 IMP
HALTON CO (OR)
CATERPILLAR
4421 Ne Columbia Blvd, Portland, OR 97218-1338
Tel (503) 288-6411 *Founded/Ownrshp* 1943, 2007
Sales 38.6MM^E *EMP* 350
SIC 5082 5084 7699 General construction machinery & equipment; Logging equipment & supplies; Materials handling machinery; Engines & parts, diesel; Construction equipment repair; Industrial machinery & equipment repair; Engine repair & replacement, non-automotive; General construction machinery & equipment; Logging equipment & supplies; Materials handling machinery; Engines & parts, diesel; Construction equipment repair; Industrial machinery & equipment repair; Engine repair & replacement, non-automotive
Pr: E H Halton
**Treas:* Mark Fahey
VP: Sue Halton
VP: Susan Halton-Findlay
Mktg Mgr: Kathryn Rebagliati

D-U-N-S 79-065-6842 IMP
HALTON GROUP AMERICAS INC
HALTOM GLOBAL SERVICES
2413 Nashville Rd C4, Bowling Green, KY 42101-4101
Tel (270) 393-7214 *Founded/Ownrshp* 2005
Sales 46.4MM *EMP* 6^E
Accts Bkd Llp Bowling Green Ky
SIC 3564 Blowers & fans; Blowers & fans
CEO: Heikki Rinne
**Pr:* Rick A Bagwell
**Ch:* Mika Halttunen
Area Mgr: Robert Dzikowski
CTO: Andrey Livchak
Sls&Mrk Ex: Lee Ling
Sls Mgr: Onur Cakir
Sls Mgr: Mikko Liljeberg

D-U-N-S 05-449-6682
HALVOR LINES INC (MN)
217 Grand Ave, Superior, WI 54880-1241
Tel (715) 392-8161 *Founded/Ownrshp* 1968
Sales 73.3MM^E *EMP* 350^E
SIC 4213 Trucking, except local; Contract haulers; Trucking, except local; Contract haulers
Pr: Jon Vinje
CFO: Mark Illikainen
**VP:* Peter Haines
Dir Risk M: Terry Osvold
Genl Mgr: Cameron Fraley
Genl Mgr: Steve Pint
CIO: Bonnie Ramsay
Trfc Dir: Scott Amys
Opers Mgr: Buck Hammann

D-U-N-S 55-749-1128
HALYARD CAPITAL FUND LP
(*Suby of* BMO NESBITT BURNS INC)
250 Park Ave Ste 810, New York, NY 10177-0800
Tel (212) 554-2121 *Founded/Ownrshp* 2001
Sales NA *EMP* 498
SIC 6712 7311 8742 Bank holding companies; Advertising agencies; Management consulting services; Bank holding companies; Advertising agencies; Management consulting services
Mng Pt: Robert B Nolan Jr
**Mng Pt:* Bruce A Eatroff
CFO: Joseph Bondarenko
VP: Michael F Furey
VP: Richard V Reyea
Mng Dir: Kenneth J Hanau
Mng Dir: Peter A Hurwitz
Mng Dir: Christopher H Ruth

D-U-N-S 03-362-6867
HALYARD EDUCATION PARTNERS LLC
EDUCATIONDYNAMICS
(*Suby of* HALYARD CAPITAL FUND LP) ★
5 Marine View Plz, Hoboken, NJ 07030-5756
Tel (201) 377-3000 *Founded/Ownrshp* 2005
Sales 48.3MM^E *EMP* 180
SIC 8742 Marketing consulting services; Marketing consulting services
CEO: Tom Anderson
**Ch Bd:* Tom Reddin
**COO:* Richard Stalzer

**CFO:* Keith Hall
CFO: Greg Mazzenoble
Div Pres: Andrew Gansler
Div Pres: Peter Kraft
Div Pres: Robert Peyree
Div Pres: Marc Stormes
Bd of Dir: Tim Loomer
Ofcr: Aja Baxter
**Ofcr:* Bruce Douglas
**Ex VP:* Richard Capezzali
Ex VP: Howard Mandel
Sr VP: Carol Aslanian
Sr VP: Gloria Baldino
Sr VP: John Messina
VP: Patricia Franz
VP: Mitch Grady
VP: Brian Miller

D-U-N-S 07-937-5431
▲ HALYARD HEALTH INC
5405 Windward Pkwy, Alpharetta, GA 30004-3894
Tel (678) 425-9273 *Founded/Ownrshp* 2014
Sales 1.6MMM^E *EMP* 12,000^E
Tkr Sym HYH *Exch* NYS
SIC 3842 3841 3845 Surgical appliances & supplies; Surgical & medical instruments; Electromedical equipment; Ultrasonic scanning devices, medical; Surgical appliances & supplies; Surgical & medical instruments; Electromedical equipment; Ultrasonic scanning devices, medical
Ch Bd: Robert E Abernathy
COO: Christopher M Lowery
CFO: Steven E Voskuil
Ofcr: Rhonda D Gibby
Sr VP: Christopher G Isenberg
Sr VP: Warren J Machan
Sr VP: John W Wesley
Board of Directors: Gary D Blackford, John P Byrnes, Ronald W Dollens, Heidi K Fields, Patrick J O'leary, Maria Sainz, Julie Shimer

D-U-N-S 07-961-7666
■ HALYARD SALES LLC
(*Suby of* HALYARD HEALTH INC) ★
5405 Windward Pkwy # 100, Alpharetta, GA 30004-3894
Tel (678) 425-9273 *Founded/Ownrshp* 2014
Sales 228.8MM^E *EMP* 5,018^E
SIC 3845 3841 Electromedical equipment; Surgical & medical instruments
CEO: Robert E Abernathy
**CFO:* Steven E Voskuil
**Sec:* John W Wesley

D-U-N-S 04-723-1436
HAM HONEYBAKED CO
11935 Mason Montgomery Rd # 200, Cincinnati, OH 45249-3702
Tel (513) 583-9700 *Founded/Ownrshp* 1957
Sales 73.3MM^E *EMP* 400
SIC 5421 2099 2024 2013 Meat markets, including freezer provisioners; Food preparations; Ice cream & frozen desserts; Sausages & other prepared meats; Meat markets, including freezer provisioners; Food preparations; Ice cream & frozen desserts; Sausages & other prepared meats
CEO: Craig Kurz
**Ch Bd:* George S Kurz
**Pr:* George J Kurz
**COO:* Keith Kurz
Sls Dir: Mike Columbus

D-U-N-S 10-307-9174 IMP
HAM PRODUCE AND SEAFOOD INC
918 Bannister St, Honolulu, HI 96819-3335
Tel (808) 842-7171 *Founded/Ownrshp* 1977
Sales 27.8MM^E *EMP* 80^E
SIC 5148 5142 5144 Vegetables, fresh; Fruits, fresh; Fish, frozen: packaged; Meat, frozen: packaged; Poultry: live, dressed or frozen (unpackaged); Vegetables, fresh; Fruits, fresh; Fish, frozen: packaged; Meat, frozen: packaged; Poultry: live, dressed or frozen (unpackaged)
Pr: Nelli Hugh
**VP:* Sam Hugh
**VP:* Robert Phu

D-U-N-S 83-505-7035 IMP
HAM PRODUCE CO INC
963 Hwy 258 S, Snow Hill, NC 28580-8964
Tel (252) 747-8200 *Founded/Ownrshp* 1971
Sales 51.5MM^E *EMP* 65
SIC 5148 Fresh fruits & vegetables; Fresh fruits & vegetables
Pr: Bobby Ham
**VP:* Wood Ham Allen
**VP:* Stacy Ham Lane

D-U-N-S 03-110-0514
HAM STEVISON CO
TENNESSEE TRADITIONS
125 Stevison Ham Rd, Portland, TN 37148-2037
Tel (615) 325-4161 *Founded/Ownrshp* 1946
Sales 24.7MM^E *EMP* 100
SIC 2011 Pork products from pork slaughtered on site; Pork products from pork slaughtered on site
Pr: Mike Stevison
**VP:* Raymond A Stevison Jr
Genl Mgr: Lara Stevison
Plnt Mgr: Wanda Phye
VP Sls: Ron Long

D-U-N-S 01-583-4857
HAMA CORP
301 Pike St, Charlestown, IN 47111-8608
Tel (812) 256-3351 *Founded/Ownrshp* 1999
Sales 24.6MM^E *EMP* 350
SIC 8742 Manufacturing management consultant; Manufacturing management consultant
Pr: Kenji Kanii

D-U-N-S 08-906-9652 IMP
HAMALOT INC
ELECTROWIRE
933 Remington Rd, Schaumburg, IL 60173-4515
Tel (847) 944-1500 *Founded/Ownrshp* 1978
Sales 73.3MM^E *EMP* 160

SIC 5063 3496 3315 Wire & cable; Electronic wire & cable; Miscellaneous fabricated wire products; Steel wire & related products; Wire & cable; Electronic wire & cable; Miscellaneous fabricated wire products; Steel wire & related products
Pr: Mickey M Hamano
CFO: John Breslin
VP: Kurt King
**VP:* Kevin Mc Namara
VP: Kevin McNamara
Brnch Mgr: Doug Sedgwick
Dist Mgr: Bill Schoonmaker
Plnt Mgr: Jerry Kaminsky
Manager: Michael Melnick
Sls Mgr: Mike Cournoyer
Sales Asso: Luis Mandujano

D-U-N-S 06-869-1609 IMP
HAMAMATSU CORP
(*Suby of* PHOTONICS MANAGEMENT CORP) ★
360 Foothill Rd, Bridgewater, NJ 08807-2932
Tel (908) 231-0960 *Founded/Ownrshp* 1969
Sales 36.4MM^E *EMP* 251
SIC 3671 5065 3674 3641 Photomultiplier tubes; Electronic tubes: receiving & transmitting or industrial; Electronic parts; Semiconductors & related devices; Electric lamps; Photomultiplier tubes; Electronic tubes: receiving & transmitting or industrial; Electronic parts; Semiconductors & related devices; Electric lamps
Pr: Craig Walling
Pr: Eric Atanda
VP: Shoh Masafumi Asai
VP: Thomas Baker
VP: Mary Boyle
CIO: David Leinwand
IT Man: Norm Weiss
Sfty Mgr: Bob Sobel
Prd Mgr: Tom Baker
Ql Cn Mgr: Terri Carrol
VP Sls: Reji Samuel

D-U-N-S 03-607-4974
HAMASPIK OF ROCKLAND COUNTRY INC
58 Route 59 Ste 1, Monsey, NY 10952-3740
Tel (845) 356-8400 *Founded/Ownrshp* 1997
Sales 28.5MM *EMP* 48
SIC 8322 Individual & family services
Pr: Meyer Werthermer
Pgrm Dir: Esther Brach

D-U-N-S 12-864-1693
HAMBLEN COUNTY BOARD OF EDUCATION
210 E Morris Blvd, Morristown, TN 37813-2341
Tel (423) 586-7700 *Founded/Ownrshp* 1960
Sales 47.5MM^E *EMP* 1,275
SIC 8211 Public elementary & secondary schools; Public elementary & secondary schools
Board of Directors: Teresa Ayers, Charles Cross, Joe Gibson, Roger Greene, James Grigsby, Janice S Haun, Pamela Jones, Clyde Kinder, Teresa Templin

D-U-N-S 07-979-9729
HAMBLEN COUNTY SCHOOL DISTRICT
210 E Morris Blvd, Morristown, TN 37813-2341
Tel (423) 586-7700 *Founded/Ownrshp* 2015
Sales 11.3MM^E *EMP* 1,139^E
SIC 8211 Public elementary & secondary schools

D-U-N-S 09-422-9861
HAMBURG AREA SCHOOL DISTRICT
701 Windsor St, Hamburg, PA 19526-1347
Tel (610) 562-3861 *Founded/Ownrshp* 1966
Sales 21.1MM^E *EMP* 300
SIC 8211 Public elementary school; Public junior high school; Public senior high school; School board; Public elementary school; Public junior high school; Public senior high school; School board
Pr: Brooke Adams
Treas: Stuart Whitelether
Psych: Meredith Hollis
HC Dir: Barbara Long

D-U-N-S 07-402-1841
HAMBURG CENTRAL SCHOOL DISTRICT
5305 Abbott Rd, Hamburg, NY 14075-1699
Tel (716) 646-3222 *Founded/Ownrshp* 1950
Sales 93.4M *EMP* 705
Accts Lumsden & Mccormick Llp Cpa
SIC 8211 Public senior high school; Public junior high school; Public elementary school; Public senior high school; Public junior high school; Public elementary school
Treas: Diane Haight
Bd of Dir: Michelle Hill
Bd of Dir: Michelle Kujawa
Bd of Dir: Kelly Mulvey
Bd of Dir: Georgette Rush
Bd of Dir: Kristina Strauss
Dir Sec: James Martinez

D-U-N-S 08-566-6709 IMP
HAMBURG PLUMBING AND SUPPLY CO INC
180 State Rt 23 S, Hamburg, NJ 07419-1707
Tel (973) 827-2553 *Founded/Ownrshp* 1997
Sales 34.1MM^E *EMP* 43
SIC 5074 5999 5211 Plumbing & hydronic heating supplies; Plumbing & heating supplies; Cabinets, kitchen
Pr: James Roche
**VP:* Joseph D Roche

D-U-N-S 00-167-9760
HAMBURG SUD NORTH AMERICA INC
(*Suby of* HAMBURG SUDAMERIKANISCHE DAMPF-SCHIFFFAHRTS-GESELLSCHAFT KG)
465 South St Ste 3, Morristown, NJ 07960-6439
Tel (973) 775-5300 *Founded/Ownrshp* 1990
Sales 37.4MM^E *EMP* 130
SIC 4731 Agents, shipping; Agents, shipping
Ch Bd: Klaus Meves
**Pr:* Ottmar Gast
Sr VP: Matthias Dietrich
Sr VP: Poul Hestbaek
**VP:* Rainer Dehe
VP: Jeff Parker
VP: Tom Pirie
VP: Joerg Zimmermann
IT Man: Raymond Drogon
Opers Mgr: Russell Fox
Sls Mgr: Liliana Garzon

D-U-N-S 06-140-6765
HAMBY & ALOISIO INC (GA)
53 Perimeter Ctr E # 400, Atlanta, GA 30346-2204
Tel (770) 551-3270 *Founded/Ownrshp* 1972
Sales NA *EMP* 65
SIC 6411 Insurance agents & brokers; Insurance agents & brokers
Pr: Robert R Hamby Jr
**Treas:* Charles M Hamby
VP: Victor Hamby
Genl Mgr: John Aaron

D-U-N-S 19-198-8831
HAMCOR INC
DUBLIN TOYOTA
4321 Toyota Dr, Dublin, CA 94568-4600
Tel (925) 829-7700 *Founded/Ownrshp* 1986
Sales 70.2MM^E *EMP* 120
SIC 5511 Automobiles, new & used; Automobiles, new & used
Pr: Harold Cornelius
CIO: Chojiro Hirose
IT Man: Raoul Krakowski
Sls Mgr: Matt Lanning
Sls Mgr: Willey Mary

D-U-N-S 07-212-1304
HAMDEN TOWN OF (INC)
2750 Dixwell Ave Fl 2, Hamden, CT 06518-3320
Tel (203) 287-7100 *Founded/Ownrshp* 1786
Sales NA *EMP* 1,260
SIC 9111 ;
Ofcr: Holly Masi
Ofcr: Adam Zonas
Ex Dir: Frank Rizzuti
IT Man: Salvatore Decola

D-U-N-S 06-243-0330
HAMEL BUILDERS INC
5710 Furnace Ave Ste H, Elkridge, MD 21075-5102
Tel (202) 584-2100 *Founded/Ownrshp* 1988
Sales 97.3MM^E *EMP* 150
SIC 1542 Hospital construction; Hospital construction
Pr: Philip W Gibbs
**CFO:* Jane Radford
Ex VP: Tom Wahl
VP: Ken Maffey
Exec: Michael Mueller
Exec: Peter Saunder
IT Man: Jason Parks
Opers Mgr: Holly Wahl

HAMER MOTORS
See GL HMH LLC

D-U-N-S 82-525-1580
HAMERA CORP
FIRST CAPITAL
16780 Lark Ave Frnt, Los Gatos, CA 95032-7693
Tel (310) 458-0010 *Founded/Ownrshp* 2006
Sales NA *EMP* 150^E
SIC 6163 Mortgage brokers arranging for loans, using money of others; Mortgage brokers arranging for loans, using money of others
Pr: Jay Robertson
**CFO:* Richard Miyake
CFO: Richard Miyaki
Sr VP: Cort Wagner
VP: Colleen Williams
VP Sls: Tayt Ianni
Sls Mgr: Farmingale Ncgann

D-U-N-S 03-250-8608
HAMERSMITH INC
3330 Nw 125th St, Miami, FL 33167-2410
Tel (305) 685-7451 *Founded/Ownrshp* 1991
Sales 22.4MM^E *EMP* 36
SIC 4225 General warehousing & storage
Pr: Joyce Hamersmith
**Treas:* Minda Hamersmith
**Ex VP:* Steven Hamersmith
**VP:* Henry Hamersmith

HAMILTN-FLTON-MONTGOMERY BOCES
See HAMILTON-FULTON-MONTGOMERY BOCES

D-U-N-S 11-837-3562 IMP/EXP
■ **HAMILTON BEACH BRANDS INC**
(*Suby of* HB PS HOLDING CO INC) ★
4421 Waterfront Dr, Glen Allen, VA 23060-3375
Tel (804) 273-9777 *Founded/Ownrshp* 1990
Sales 547.7MM^E *EMP* 500
SIC 3634 Toasters, electric: household; Ovens, portable: household; Irons, electric: household; Coffee makers, electric: household; Toasters, electric: household; Ovens, portable: household; Irons, electric: household; Coffee makers, electric: household
Pr: Greg Trepp
Ch: Alfred M Rankin Jr
Treas: Denise Brown
Treas: James H Taylor
VP: Eric Beam
VP: Malcolm Bronson
VP: Keith Burns
VP: Kathleen Diller
VP: Judith B McBee
VP: Greg Salyers
VP: Jim Taylor
VP: Scott Tidey
Dir Bus: Erin Israel
Board of Directors: Alfred M Rankin, ian M Ro, Jennifer Dickerman, Robert M Gates, Leon J Hendrix Jr, Dennis W Labarre, Richard De J Osborne, Thomas T Rankin, Britton Taplin, David F Taplin, John F Turben

D-U-N-S 06-502-7252
HAMILTON BIG COUNTRY FORD INC
AUTO WORLD
2400 Mabry Dr, Clovis, NM 88101-8387
Tel (575) 762-4427 *Founded/Ownrshp* 1996
Sales 45.1MM *EMP* 85
SIC 5511 Automobiles, new & used; Pickups, new & used; Automobiles, new & used; Pickups, new & used
Pr: Gary Hamilton
**Treas:* Gary Westfall
IT Man: Gary Watkins
Sls Mgr: Sean Belden

D-U-N-S 07-203-1461
HAMILTON CENTER INC
AFFINITY STRESS CENTER
620 8th Ave, Terre Haute, IN 47804-2771
Tel (812) 231-8323 *Founded/Ownrshp* 1967
Sales 31.8MM^E *EMP* 652
Accts Blue & Co Llc Indianapolis I
SIC 8063 8093 Hospital for the mentally ill; Rehabilitation center, outpatient treatment; Hospital for the mentally ill; Rehabilitation center, outpatient treatment
CEO: Mel Burks
CFO: John Browning
**CFO:* Sue Thompson
Bd of Dir: Louise Anderson
Ofcr: Dana Guthrie
Dir Inf Cn: Stephanie Steele
**Ex Dir:* Galen Goode
CIO: Robin Cooprider
IT Man: Melanie Hurst
Mtls Dir: Bobby White
Pr Mgr: Margie Anshutz

D-U-N-S 07-490-9094
HAMILTON CHATTANOOGA COUNTY HOSPITAL AUTHORITY (TN)
ERLANGER HEALTH SYSTEM
975 E 3rd St, Chattanooga, TN 37403-2147
Tel (423) 778-7000 *Founded/Ownrshp* 1889
Sales 837.2MM^E *EMP* 4,700
SIC 8062 Hospital, AMA approved residency; Hospital, AMA approved residency
CEO: Kevin Spiegel
Pr: James Brexler
COO: Charlesetta Woodard-Thompson
Trst: Russell T King Jr
Ofcr: Gregg Gentry
Ofcr: Shelia Hall
Ofcr: Jan Keys
Ofcr: Kathy Powell
Ofcr: Kim Sexton
Sr VP: Lynn Whisman
VP: Joseph Fache
VP: Debra Poteet-Johnson
VP: Lorraine Vamprine
Dir Inf Cn: Susan Berry
Dir Rx: Jim Lowe

D-U-N-S 01-743-6569
HAMILTON CHEVROLET INC
5800 E 14 Mile Rd, Warren, MI 48092-3199
Tel (586) 838-1530 *Founded/Ownrshp* 1956
Sales 36.2MM^E *EMP* 75
SIC 5511 Automobiles, new & used; Automobiles, new & used
Pr: Donald Hamilton
**CFO:* Jake Post
**VP:* Mike Boguth
Sales Asso: Dave Asmar
Sales Asso: Jeanine Bellman
Sales Asso: Dan Dilay
Sales Asso: Debbie English
Sales Asso: Broo Jamieson
Sales Asso: Brad Querry
Sales Asso: Dave Stefaniak

D-U-N-S 10-761-2863
HAMILTON CITY SCHOOL DISTRICT
533 Dayton St, Hamilton, OH 45011-3455
Tel (513) 887-5000 *Founded/Ownrshp* 1900
Sales 61.2MM^E *EMP* 1,038
SIC 8211 Public senior high school; Public junior high school; Public elementary school; Public senior high school; Public junior high school; Public elementary school
Bd of Dir: Susan Cox
Ofcr: Melanie Yaden
Dir Lab: Helen Baker
Dir Lab: Kym Ware
Dir IT: Dan Molloy
IT Man: Michael Schlereth
Psych: Alexander Lopez
Psych: Patty Rodriguez
Psych: Erin Vincent

D-U-N-S 00-847-7820 IMP
HAMILTON CO
(*Suby of* HAMILTON BONADUZ AG)
4970 Energy Way, Reno, NV 89502-4123
Tel (775) 858-3000 *Founded/Ownrshp* 1950
Sales 74.9MM^E *EMP* 459^E
SIC 3826 Liquid testing apparatus; Liquid testing apparatus
Pr: Steven Hamilton
CFO: John Williams
Treas: Carla Dunham
**Treas:* Dan Hamilton
VP: Bobby Chavli
VP: Eric Riedi
VP: Bob West
Admn Mgr: Kelli Cavallaro
Snr Sftwr: Alan Alfers
Snr Sftwr: Doug Clemens
Snr Sftwr: David Myers

D-U-N-S 00-225-3540
HAMILTON COLLEGE
198 College Hill Rd, Clinton, NY 13323-1295
Tel (315) 859-4727 *Founded/Ownrshp* 1812
Sales 127.7MM *EMP* 650
Accts Kpmg Llp Albany Ny
SIC 8221 College, except junior; College, except junior
Pr: John H Stewart
**Owner:* Amy Clausen
Bd of Dir: Sarah Izzo
Trst: Susannah Morgan
Chf Inves: Peter Tonetti
Ofcr: Kathleen Wiese
VP: Steve Bellona
**VP:* Karen Leach
VP: Patrick D Reynolds
**VP:* Richard Tantillo
Assoc Dir: Claudet Ferrone
Assoc Dir: Amy Lindner
Assoc Dir: Laurie Russell
Assoc Dir: Maureen Scoones
Assoc Dir: Christina Willemsen

HAMILTON CONSTRUCTION
See HAMILTON HEALTHCARE CONSTRUCTION INC

D-U-N-S 00-585-3932
HAMILTON CONSTRUCTION CO
AMERICAN CONCRETE CUTTING
2213 S F St, Springfield, OR 97477-5207
Tel (541) 746-2426 *Founded/Ownrshp* 1995
Sales 85.8MM *EMP* 150
SIC 1622 3441

D-U-N-S 95-675-0921 EXP
HAMILTON CONSTRUCTION LLC
564 22nd Ave, Skagway, AK 99840
Tel (907) 983-2702 *Founded/Ownrshp* 1985
Sales 20.2MM^E *EMP* 35
SIC 1422 1542 Cement rock, crushed & broken-quarrying; Commercial & office building, new construction
Admn Mgr: Denise Sager

D-U-N-S 11-294-7341
HAMILTON COUNTY ECONOMIC DEVELOPMENT FOUNDATION INC
3074 Hickory Valley Rd, Chattanooga, TN 37421-1265
Tel (423) 209-8400 *Founded/Ownrshp* 1993
Sales NA *EMP* 6,137^E
SIC 9411 Administration of educational programs; ; Administration of educational programs;

D-U-N-S 09-394-8636
HAMILTON COUNTY EDUCATIONAL SERVICE CENTER
HCESC
11083 Hamilton Ave, Cincinnati, OH 45231-1409
Tel (513) 674-4200 *Founded/Ownrshp* 1927
Sales 75.0MM *EMP* 560
SIC 8211 Public elementary & secondary schools; Public elementary & secondary schools
**CFO:* Donald Rabe
Ofcr: Onnen Julie
**Prin:* Patrick Albrinck
**Prin:* Karen Austin
**Prin:* Sandra Bauman
IT Man: Shelley Mueller

D-U-N-S 96-272-4589
HAMILTON COUNTY PUBLIC HOSPITAL
HAMILTON HOMECARE
2350 Hospital Dr, Webster City, IA 50595-6600
Tel (515) 832-9400 *Founded/Ownrshp* 1930
Sales 25.0MM^E *EMP* 240^E
SIC 8062 General medical & surgical hospitals; General medical & surgical hospitals
Pr: Jo Abens
Chf Rad: Michael Baker
**CEO:* Lori Rathbun
COO: Janette Payne
**CFO:* Alice Heinrichs
**Sec:* Troy Hassebrock
**VP:* Phil Voge
Dir Rad: Matt McKinney
Dir Rx: Karen Johnson
Dir Rx: Mary Tasler
Sfty Mgr: Leigh Miller
Board of Directors: Jo Abens, Justin Deppe, Doug Follmann, Jack Foster, David Hagedorn, Robert Hudson, Sherri Lambi, Pat Powers, Pam Vanderlught

D-U-N-S 12-189-2491
HAMILTON COUNTY SCHOOL DISTRICT
5683 Us Highway 129 S # 1, Jasper, FL 32052-6794
Tel (386) 792-1228 *Founded/Ownrshp* 1845
Sales 25.3MM^E *EMP* 507
SIC 8211 Public elementary & secondary schools; Public elementary & secondary schools
VP: Maribeth Windham
Dir IT: Gene Milton
Dir IT: Adam Walker
Schl Brd P: Damon Deas

D-U-N-S 79-369-1135
HAMILTON COUNTY SCHOOL DISTRICT
3074 Hickory Valley Rd, Chattanooga, TN 37421-1265
Tel (423) 209-8400 *Founded/Ownrshp* 2007
Sales 36.9MM^E *EMP* 800
SIC 8211 Public elementary & secondary schools; Public elementary & secondary schools
**Prin:* Ann Bates
**Prin:* Carol McDowell
**Prin:* Dorothy A Morton
MIS Dir: Patty Kinsey
Teacher Pr: Sheryl Randolph
Teacher Pr: Ava Warren
Instr Medi: Becky Coleman
HC Dir: Sheryl Rogers

D-U-N-S 11-037-5800
HAMILTON COURT JUSTICE OFFICE
SHERIFFS DEPARTMENT
1000 Sycamore St Ste 110, Cincinnati, OH 45202-1336
Tel (513) 946-6400 *Founded/Ownrshp* 2015
Sales NA *EMP* 1,200
SIC 9229 Law enforcement statistics center, government

HAMILTON DISTRIBUTING
See HAMILTON EQUIPMENT INC

HAMILTON DRYWALL PRODUCTS
See HAMILTON MATERIALS WASHINGTON LLC

D-U-N-S 00-302-9451 IMP
HAMILTON EQUIPMENT INC (PA)
HAMILTON DISTRIBUTING
567 S Reading Rd, Ephrata, PA 17522-1835
Tel (717) 733-7951 *Founded/Ownrshp* 1938
Sales 31.7MM^E *EMP* 65
Accts Herben & Company Inc Readin

SIC 5198 5083 5084 Paints; Paint brushes, rollers, sprayers; Agricultural machinery; Lawn machinery & equipment; Garden machinery & equipment; Industrial machinery & equipment
Pr: Robert J Hamilton Jr
**Treas:* Aileen E Hamilton
MIS Mgr: Will Ginder
Sls Mgr: David Rupp

D-U-N-S 05-742-6603 EXP
HAMILTON FORM CO LTD
7009 Midway Rd, Richland Hills, TX 76118-7099
Tel (817) 590-2111 *Founded/Ownrshp* 1981
Sales 23.3MM^E *EMP* 80
SIC 3559 3443 Concrete products machinery; Fabricated plate work (boiler shop)
Pt: William F Daily
**Pt:* L Oliphant
**Pt:* B A Plotnicki
CFO: Dick L Oliphant
Treas: Dick Oliphant
Sls Mgr: Skip Plotnicki

D-U-N-S 02-813-3036
HAMILTON GROWERS INC
SOUTHERN VLY FRT & VEGETABLE
2775 Ellnton Norman Pk Rd, Norman Park, GA 31771-5036
Tel (229) 769-3676 *Founded/Ownrshp* 1995
Sales 37.6MM^E *EMP* 475
SIC 0161 0171 Vegetables & melons; Berry crops; Vegetables & melons; Berry crops
CEO: Kent Hamilton
**CFO:* Wanda Hamilton-Tyler

D-U-N-S 79-881-3432
HAMILTON HEALTH CARE SYSTEM INC
1200 Memorial Dr, Dalton, GA 30720-2529
Tel (706) 278-2105 *Founded/Ownrshp* 1983
Sales 22.3MM *EMP* 1,200^E
Accts Dixon Hughes Goodman Llp Ashe
SIC 8322 8062 Senior citizens' center or association; General medical & surgical hospitals; Senior citizens' center or association; General medical & surgical hospitals
Pr: John Bowling
**CFO:* Gary Howard
VP: Dee Burkett Jr
VP: Janice Keys

D-U-N-S 07-120-2485
HAMILTON HEALTH CENTER INC
CAPITAL HLTH SYSTM HAMILTON HL
110 S 17th St, Harrisburg, PA 17104-1123
Tel (717) 230-3909 *Founded/Ownrshp* 1969
Sales 20.9MM *EMP* 80
Accts Baker Tilly Virchow Krause Llp
SIC 8093 Specialty outpatient clinics
CEO: Janine Peterson
CFO: Alberk Bearbock
CFO: Kim Kurtz
**CFO:* Kimberly Kurtz
Dir IT: Eric Beamesider
Software D: Jane Witney
Podiatrist: Barbara Black
Pharmcst: Amanda Calhoun

D-U-N-S 92-729-7382
HAMILTON HEALTHCARE CONSTRUCTION INC
HAMILTON CONSTRUCTION
202 Mercury Cir, Pomona, CA 91768-3212
Tel (909) 594-7523 *Founded/Ownrshp* 1995
Sales 25.8MM *EMP* 30
Accts Eidi & Payne Llp Ontario Ca
SIC 1521 Single-family housing construction; Single-family housing construction
Pr: Bruce L Mills
Off Mgr: Peggy McCroskey

D-U-N-S 96-345-6137
HAMILTON HEIGHTS SCHOOL CORP
410 W Main St, Arcadia, IN 46030
Tel (317) 984-3538 *Founded/Ownrshp* 1964
Sales 19.4MM^E *EMP* 286
SIC 8211 Elementary & secondary schools; Elementary & secondary schools
**Treas:* Kristin McCarty
Treas: Cathy Pickett
Sfty Dirs: Rob Breeding

D-U-N-S 08-927-0003
HAMILTON HEIGHTS SCHOOL DISTRICT
(*Suby of* HAMILTON HEIGHTS SCHOOL CORP) ★
25350 State Road 19, Arcadia, IN 46030-9523
Tel (317) 984-1530 *Founded/Ownrshp* 1964
Sales 12.3MM^E *EMP* 280
SIC 8211 Private elementary school; Private junior high school; Private senior high school; School board; Private elementary school; Private junior high school; Private senior high school; School board
**Treas:* Pauleeta Browning
Dir IT: Dave Slabe
Dir IT: Matthew Wallace

HAMILTON HOMECARE
See HAMILTON COUNTY PUBLIC HOSPITAL

HAMILTON HONDA
See ALL STAR MOTORS LLC

D-U-N-S 07-973-3255
HAMILTON ITASCA ONE PIERCE OWNER LLC
300 Park Blvd Ste 500, Itasca, IL 60143-2635
Tel (630) 250-5966 *Founded/Ownrshp* 2011
Sales 4.2MM^E *EMP* 300
SIC 6512 Nonresidential building operators

D-U-N-S 02-884-4231 IMP
HAMILTON L FISHER L C
HAMILTON SCIENTIFIC
(*Suby of* OPENGATE CAPITAL LLC) ★
1716 Lawrence Dr Ste 1, De Pere, WI 54115-9108
Tel (920) 793-1121 *Founded/Ownrshp* 2012
Sales 320.8MM^E *EMP* 1,100
SIC 3821 Laboratory furniture; Laboratory equipment: fume hoods, distillation racks, etc.; Laboratory furniture; Laboratory equipment: fume hoods, distillation racks, etc.
Pr: Jack Roberts
**VP:* Rico Salazar
Dir Bus: Jose Leon
Rgnl Mgr: Tina Doise
Rgnl Mgr: James McDowall
Sftwr Eng: Kevin Crowley
Mtls Mgr: Angel Cortez
Ql Cn Mgr: Alejandro Gomez
**VP Sls:* Tim Cloutier

D-U-N-S 62-748-7333
HAMILTON LANE ADVISORS INC
1 Presidential Blvd Fl 4, Bala Cynwyd, PA 19004-1017
Tel (610) 934-2222 *Founded/Ownrshp* 1991
Sales 21.5MM^E *EMP* 50
SIC 8742 Management consulting services; Human resource consulting services
Ch Bd: Leslie Brun
**CEO:* Mario Giannini
Ofcr: Daniel Connaughton
VP: Greg Baty
VP: Janet Bauman
VP: Stephen Brennan
VP: Keith Brittain
VP: Elizabeth Foo
VP: Jenna Greer
VP: Olin Honore
VP: Richard Hope
VP: Mark Kashima
VP: Michael Koenig
VP: Lars Pace
VP: Grant Saul
VP: Daniel Schoneveld
VP: Kristin Williamson

D-U-N-S 09-989-7241 IMP/EXP
HAMILTON MARINE INC
HAMILTON MARINE PORTLAND
155 E Main St, Searsport, ME 04974-3322
Tel (207) 548-6302 *Founded/Ownrshp* 1985
Sales 43.1MM^E *EMP* 95
SIC 5551 5088 5961 Marine supplies; Marine supplies; Mail order house; Marine supplies; Marine supplies; Mail order house
Pr: Wayne C Hamilton
**VP:* Loraine Hamilton

HAMILTON MARINE PORTLAND
See HAMILTON MARINE INC

D-U-N-S 13-522-9651 IMP
HAMILTON MATERIALS WASHINGTON LLC
HAMILTON DRYWALL PRODUCTS
295 N Pekin Rd, Woodland, WA 98674-9586
Tel (360) 225-6888 *Founded/Ownrshp* 1997
Sales 68.6MM^E *EMP* 60^E
SIC 3259 Wall coping, clay
Plnt Mgr: Larry Lucas

D-U-N-S 10-926-7898
HAMILTON MEDICAL CENTER INC
1200 Memorial Dr, Dalton, GA 30720-2529
Tel (706) 272-6000 *Founded/Ownrshp* 1982
Sales 207.5MM *EMP* 1,446
SIC 8062

D-U-N-S 10-266-9116 IMP/EXP
HAMILTON METALS INC
818 Town And Country Blvd # 310, Houston, TX 77024-4577
Tel (713) 463-4700 *Founded/Ownrshp* 1981
Sales 71.3MM^E *EMP* 50
SIC 5051 Steel; Steel
Pr: James S Millman
**Pr:* John Gunn
CFO: Mary Gauss
**CFO:* Mary Goss
Sfty Mgr: Pat Fletcher
Ql Cn Mgr: Mel Burgos
Natl Sales: Gene Lockard
VP Sls: Drew Delaune
Sls Mgr: Jesslyn Ng
Sales Asso: Thomas Mitchell

D-U-N-S 00-699-9452
■ **HAMILTON MUTUAL INSURANCE CO** (IA)
(*Suby of* EMPLOYERS MUTUAL CASUALTY CO) ★
11311 Cornell Park Dr # 500, Blue Ash, OH 45242-1891
Tel (513) 221-6010 *Founded/Ownrshp* 2005
Sales NA *EMP* 2,338
SIC 6331 Fire, marine & casualty insurance: mutual; Fire, marine & casualty insurance: mutual
Ch Bd: Richard Felts
**Pr:* Jeffrey Felts
**Treas:* M Brent Rouse
**Prin:* Kent A Kochheiser
Admn Mgr: Donald Harmeyer
Board of Directors: George W Kochheinser, John M Lockhart, Phillip Van Ekeren

HAMILTON PACIFIC
See NISCAYAH INC

D-U-N-S 60-646-7413
HAMILTON PARK HEALTH CARE CENTER LTD
533 Monmouth St, Jersey City, NJ 07302-1527
Tel (201) 653-8800 *Founded/Ownrshp* 1989
Sales 17.5MM^E *EMP* 300
SIC 8051 Skilled nursing care facilities; Skilled nursing care facilities
Pr: Lorraine Mocco
**CFO:* Donald Wuertz
Info Man: Rafael Cabrera

D-U-N-S 17-481-6710
HAMILTON PARTNERS INC
300 Park Blvd Ste 201, Itasca, IL 60143-3106
Tel (630) 250-9700 *Founded/Ownrshp* 1987
Sales 95.8MM^E *EMP* 220
SIC 6552 6512 Land subdividers & developers, commercial; Commercial & industrial building operation; Land subdividers & developers, commercial; Commercial & industrial building operation
Pr: John Wauterlek
**CFO:* Laura Judd
**VP:* Ron Lunt
VP: Scott Schroeder

D-U-N-S 00-174-7104 IMP
HAMILTON PILCHER CORP
6845 Kingery Hwy, Willowbrook, IL 60527-5114
Tel (630) 655-8100 *Founded/Ownrshp* 1904
Sales 63.0MM^E *EMP* 102^E
SIC 5162 Plastics sheets & rods
Pr: John M Gaughan
Treas: Wayne Kancler
IT Man: Brian Jenkins

D-U-N-S 15-473-1566 IMP
HAMILTON PLASTICS INC
2641 Riverport Rd, Chattanooga, TN 37406-1723
Tel (423) 622-2200 *Founded/Ownrshp* 1986
Sales 42.3MM^E *EMP* 125
SIC 2671 2673 Plastic film, coated or laminated for packaging; Plastic bags: made from purchased materials; Plastic film, coated or laminated for packaging; Plastic bags: made from purchased materials
Pr: Hershad Shah
CFO: Shalin Tejani
Plnt Mgr: Tom Barringer

D-U-N-S 00-207-0191 IMP
HAMILTON PRINTING CO INC (NY)
22 Hamilton Way, Castleton On Hudson, NY 12033-1015
Tel (518) 732-2161 *Founded/Ownrshp* 1912, 1953
Sales 22.8MM^E *EMP* 140
SIC 2732 2789 Books: printing & binding; Binding only: books, pamphlets, magazines, etc.; Books: printing & binding; Binding only: books, pamphlets, magazines, etc.
CEO: John Paeglow
**VP:* William Greenawalt
**VP:* Brian F Payne
Plnt Mgr: Don Toniatti

D-U-N-S 07-831-1266 IMP
HAMILTON RELAY INC
(*Suby of* HAMILTON TELECOMMUNICATIONS) ★
1006 12th St, Aurora, NE 68818-2003
Tel (402) 694-5299 *Founded/Ownrshp* 2011
Sales 27.3MM^E *EMP* 800
SIC 4813 Telephone communication, except radio
Pr: John Nelson
VP: Dixie Ziegler

D-U-N-S 17-518-9257
HAMILTON RISK MANAGEMENT CO
(*Suby of* ACADIA ACQUISITION PARTNERS, L.P.)
3155 Nw 77th Ave, Miami, FL 33122-3700
Tel (305) 716-6000 *Founded/Ownrshp* 1992
Sales NA *EMP* 198^E
SIC 6331 7323 6141 6541 6411 Fire, marine & casualty insurance; Property damage insurance; Credit reporting services; Automobile loans, including insurance; Financing: automobiles, furniture, etc., not a deposit bank; Title search companies; Insurance agents, brokers & service
Pr: Roberto Espin Jr
COO: Alberto Naon
CFO: Kevin Walton

HAMILTON RYKER COMPANY
See HAMILTON-RYKER GROUP INC

D-U-N-S 02-046-9995
HAMILTON SCHOOL DISTRICT
W220n6151 Town Line Rd, Sussex, WI 53089-3923
Tel (262) 246-1973 *Founded/Ownrshp* 1959
Sales 34.8MM^E *EMP* 456
Accts Reilly Penner & Benton Llp
SIC 8211 Public elementary school; Public junior high school; Public senior high school; Public elementary school; Public junior high school; Public senior high school
**Pr:* Gabe Kolesari
**VP:* James E Long
Netwrk Eng: Ryan McMillan
Pr Dir: Denise Dorn-Lindberg

HAMILTON SCIENTIFIC
See HAMILTON L FISHER L C

HAMILTON SORTER
See WORKSTREAM INC

D-U-N-S 04-031-0856
HAMILTON SOUTHEASTERN SCHOOL DISTRICT
13485 Cumberland Rd, Fishers, IN 46038-3602
Tel (317) 594-4100 *Founded/Ownrshp* 1964
Sales 53.6MM^E *EMP* 800
SIC 8211 Public elementary & secondary schools; Public elementary & secondary schools
Treas: Jo Hildebrand
Off Admin: Judy Perryman
IT Man: J R Denney
Pr Dir: Marina Fleming
Pr Dir: Beverly Smith
Teacher Pr: Gary Zgunda
Psych: Carlabeth Mathias

D-U-N-S 79-205-7981
HAMILTON STATE BANK
1907 Highway 211 Nw, Hoschton, GA 30548-3525
Tel (678) 866-0500 *Founded/Ownrshp* 2004
Sales NA *EMP* 611
SIC 6022 State commercial banks; State commercial banks
CEO: Robert C Oliver
**CFO:* Jeff Powell
CFO: Mike Ricketson
Ofcr: Josh Higgins
Sr VP: Keith Hales
VP: Beau Sheppard
Brnch Mgr: Dodie Cason
Brnch Mgr: Shirley Iles
Brnch Mgr: Becky Richey
Brnch Mgr: Anderea Williams

D-U-N-S 07-176-7334 IMP/EXP
■ **HAMILTON SUNDSTRAND CORP**
(*Suby of* UNITED TECHNOLOGIES CORP) ★
1 Hamilton Rd, Windsor Locks, CT 06096-1000
Tel (860) 654-6000 *Founded/Ownrshp* 1999
Sales 2.6MMM^E *EMP* 16,000
SIC 3621 3594 3728 3625 3823 3822 Frequency converters (electric generators); Power generators; Fluid power pumps & motors; Gears, aircraft power transmission; Actuators, industrial; Turbine flow meters, industrial process type; Auto controls regulating residntl & coml environmt & applncs
CEO: Alain Bellemare
**Ch Bd:* Ronald Mc Kenna
Pr: David Gitlin
**Pr:* David P Hess
**Pr:* Curtis Reusser
Pr: Jeff Wiemelt
CFO: Marie Missen
CFO: David Nord
**Sr VP:* Dave Gitlin
VP: Steve Peery
**VP:* Thomas Rogan
Dir Bus: Martin Chell
Comm Man: Tom Callaghan
Comm Man: Susan Hacking

D-U-N-S 05-107-9937
HAMILTON SUNDSTRAND SERVICE CORP
1 Hamilton Rd, Windsor Locks, CT 06096-1000
Tel (860) 654-6000 *Founded/Ownrshp* 1999
Sales 406.7MM^E *EMP* 2,300^E
SIC 3324 Aircraft & heavy equipment repair services; Industrial instrmnts msrmnt display/control process variable; Aerospace investment castings, ferrous
CEO: Michael Robert Dumais
VP: James Peterson
Prgrm Mgr: Duane Teske
Genl Mgr: Philip Meseck
Sfty Mgr: Randy Maclin
Opers Mgr: Daniel Leider
Snr Mgr: Tom Lemaster

D-U-N-S 14-481-7934 IMP
HAMILTON SUNDSTRAND SPACE SYSTEMS INTERNATIONAL INC
1 Hamilton Rd, Windsor Locks, CT 06096-1000
Tel (860) 654-6000 *Founded/Ownrshp* 1994
Sales 196.5MM^E *EMP* 700
SIC 3841 3826 Diagnostic apparatus, medical; Thermal analysis instruments, laboratory type; Diagnostic apparatus, medical; Thermal analysis instruments, laboratory type
Pr: Edward Francis
Treas: Robert Deroy
**Treas:* Michael Randall
Prgrm Mgr: Brent Sherrill
**Genl Mgr:* Lawrence McNamara
**Oper/Dir:* Daneil Lee

HAMILTON TELECOMMUNICATIONS
See NEDELCO INC

D-U-N-S 00-682-1177 IMP
HAMILTON TELEPHONE CO
(*Suby of* HAMILTON TELECOMMUNICATIONS) ★
1001 12th St, Aurora, NE 68818-2004
Tel (402) 694-5101 *Founded/Ownrshp* 1963
Sales 24.1MM^E *EMP* 300
Accts Dohman Akerlund & Eddy Llc
SIC 4813 Local telephone communications; Local telephone communications
Pr: Phillip C Nelson
**Sec:* Betty Van Luchene
**Sr VP:* Gary Warren

D-U-N-S 07-550-1601
HAMILTON TOWNSHIP BOARD OF EDUCATION
90 Park Ave, Trenton, NJ 08690-2024
Tel (609) 631-4100 *Founded/Ownrshp* 1919
Sales 100.7MM^E *EMP* 1,500
SIC 8211 Public elementary & secondary schools; Management services; School board
Pr: Anthony Celentano

D-U-N-S 04-814-7300
HAMILTON TOWNSHIP SCHOOL DISTRICT
HAMILTON TWP SCHOOL DIST
1876 Dr Dennis Foreman Dr, Mays Landing, NJ 08330-2206
Tel (609) 476-6300 *Founded/Ownrshp* 1885
Sales 25.8MM^E *EMP* 500
Accts Hodulik & Morrison Pa Cpas
SIC 8211 Public elementary school; Public elementary school
Psych: Andrew Disque

D-U-N-S 96-264-0772
HAMILTON TOWNSHIP SCHOOL DISTRICT
90 Park Ave, Trenton, NJ 08690-2024
Tel (609) 631-4100 *Founded/Ownrshp* 2010
Sales 39.0MM^E *EMP* 1,613^E
SIC 8211 Public elementary & secondary schools
Teacher Pr: Joyce Palumbo

HAMILTON TWP SCHOOL DIST
See HAMILTON TOWNSHIP SCHOOL DISTRICT

D-U-N-S 09-938-0446
HAMILTON WHITE GROUP LLC
2411 E Highland St, Phoenix, AZ 85025
Tel (602) 644-7000 *Founded/Ownrshp* 2007
Sales 60.0MM *EMP* 400
SIC 8222 Junior college; Junior college
**CFO:* Debra Kotila

D-U-N-S 03-978-8534
HAMILTON-FULTON-MONTGOMERY BOCES
HAMILTN-FLTON-MONTGOMERY BOCES
2755 State Highway 67, Johnstown, NY 12095-3747
Tel (518) 736-4310 *Founded/Ownrshp* 1968
Sales 10.4MM^E *EMP* 315
SIC 8249 Trade school; Trade school
Pr Dir: Jennie Kerwood

D-U-N-S 01-789-5368 IMP
HAMILTON-PARKER CO (INC)
1865 Leonard Ave, Columbus, OH 43219-4500
Tel (614) 358-7800 *Founded/Ownrshp* 1934
Sales 25.9MM^E *EMP* 95^E
SIC 5211 5075 5032 5031 Lumber & other building materials; Brick; Tile, ceramic; Warm air heating & air conditioning; Brick, stone & related material; Lumber, plywood & millwork
Pr: Adam Lewin
**Treas:* Connie Tuckerman
IT Man: Adam Beckett
Trfc Mgr: Dave Blankenship
Sales Asso: Brent Jones
Sales Asso: Eric Schwenker

D-U-N-S 04-101-5780
HAMILTON-RYKER GROUP INC
HAMILTON RYKER COMPANY
947 Main St, Martin, TN 38237-2525
Tel (731) 587-3161 *Founded/Ownrshp* 2002
Sales 55.0MM *EMP* 150
SIC 7363 8748 Help supply services; Business consulting; Help supply services; Business consulting
CEO: Wayne McCreight
**Pr:* Kelly McCreight
**CFO:* Crawford Gallimore
CFO: Wayne Mc Creight
Brnch Mgr: Brittany Burcham
Brnch Mgr: William Rommell

D-U-N-S 07-656-8153
HAMILTON-WENHAM REGIONAL SCHOOL DISTRICT
HWRSD
5 School St, Wenham, MA 01984-1427
Tel (978) 626-0821 *Founded/Ownrshp* 1962
Sales 22.6MM^E *EMP* 400
SIC 8211 Public combined elementary & secondary school; Public combined elementary & secondary school
**Pr:* Sarah Gaylord
**VP:* Jim Cooper

D-U-N-S 12-628-5415
HAMISTER GROUP INC
10 Lafayette Sq Ste 1900, Buffalo, NY 14203-1801
Tel (716) 839-4000 *Founded/Ownrshp* 2001
Sales 160.2MM^E *EMP* 3,253
SIC 7011 8052 8741 Hotels & motels; Intermediate care facilities; Hotel or motel management; Hotels & motels; Intermediate care facilities; Hotel or motel management
CEO: Mark E Hamister
**CFO:* W Earl McCartney
Bd of Dir: Kelly Serventi
**Sr VP:* Cheryl Green
**Sr VP:* Daniel Hamister
Sr VP: David Paul
VP: Nektaria Hamister
Genl Mgr: Janis Moeller
Genl Mgr: Teagan Tilson
Dir IT: Joan Hudak
Sls Dir: Lisa Hurley

D-U-N-S 09-334-3135
■ **HAMLET HMA LLC**
HMA
(*Suby of* HEALTH MANAGEMENT ASSOCIATES INC) ★
1000 W Hamlet Ave, Hamlet, NC 28345-4522
Tel (910) 205-8000 *Founded/Ownrshp* 1987
Sales 45.5MM^E *EMP* 300
SIC 8062 General medical & surgical hospitals; General medical & surgical hospitals
CEO: Michael McNair
**CFO:* Lynn Rudisill
Dir Lab: David Park
Off Mgr: Denise Deese

D-U-N-S 80-476-2503
HAMLET HOLDING LLC
2 Manhattanville Rd, Purchase, NY 10577-2113
Tel (914) 694-8000 *Founded/Ownrshp* 2004
Sales 487.0MM^E *EMP* 87,000^E
SIC 7011 7999 Hotels & motels; Gambling establishment; Hotels & motels; Gambling establishment; Gambling machines, operation

D-U-N-S 00-607-9925 IMP
HAMLIN ELECTRONICS LIMITED PARTNERSHIP
(*Suby of* KEY ELECTRONICS OF NEVADA, INC)
612 E Lake St, Lake Mills, WI 53551-1798
Tel (920) 648-3000 *Founded/Ownrshp* 1998
Sales 75.6MM^E *EMP* 230
SIC 3625 3812 3674 3643 Switches, electronic applications; Relays, for electronic use; Search & navigation equipment; Semiconductors & related devices; Current-carrying wiring devices; Switches, electronic applications; Relays, for electronic use; Search & navigation equipment; Semiconductors & related devices; Current-carrying wiring devices
Pr: Antony Howell
Treas: Robert Saltarelli
QA Dir: Shirley Hofer
Plnt Mgr: Tom Lenz
Ql Cn Mgr: Herbert Gibson
Natl Sales: Paul Kerivan

D-U-N-S 05-701-5273
HAMLIN TOOL & MACHINE CO INC
1671 E Hamlin Rd, Rochester Hills, MI 48307-3624
Tel (248) 651-6302 *Founded/Ownrshp* 1972
Sales 21.8MM^E *EMP* 100
SIC 3714 3465 Motor vehicle parts & accessories; Automotive stampings; Motor vehicle parts & accessories; Automotive stampings
Pr: Patrick Pihjalic
Mng Dir: Patrick Pihajlic
Genl Mgr: Jim O'Connell
Genl Mgr: Chuminatto Thom
Opers Mgr: Terry Frisch
Sls Dir: Bob Siegwald

D-U-N-S 07-869-4155
HAMLINE UNIVERSITY
1536 Hewitt Ave, Saint Paul, MN 55104-1284
Tel (651) 523-2015 *Founded/Ownrshp* 1854
Sales 91.6MM *EMP* 563^E
Accts Clifton Larson Allen Llp Minn
SIC 8221 University; University
Pr: Linda N Hanson
CFO: Vicki Plaistow
Trst: Joe Graba
VP: Douglas P Anderson
VP: Pamela Johnson
VP: Mark Kondrak
Exec: Mona Freeberg
Exec: Jeanne Kosieradzki
Assoc Dir: Kitty Atkins
Assoc Dir: Carey Otto
Ex Dir: Angela McCaffrey

D-U-N-S 04-461-4204
■ **HAMM ENTERPRISES INC**
BERG MECHANICAL
(*Suby of* JOHNSON CONTROLS INC) ★
531 W 61st St, Shreveport, LA 71106-2512
Tel (318) 683-3884 *Founded/Ownrshp* 1929
Sales 19.5MM^E *EMP* 350
SIC 1711 1629

D-U-N-S 12-236-9411
HAMM INC
(*Suby of* SUMMIT MATERIALS CORPS I INC) ★
609 Perry Pl, Perry, KS 66073-4201
Tel (785) 597-5111 *Founded/Ownrshp* 2009
Sales 109.9MM^E *EMP* 350
SIC 1411 1771 1611 Limestone, dimension-quarrying; Blacktop (asphalt) work; Highway & street construction; Limestone, dimension-quarrying; Blacktop (asphalt) work; Highway & street construction
Pr: Gary Hamm
VP: Bradley T Hamm
Sls Mgr: Roe Timmons

D-U-N-S 03-964-4158 IMP/EXP
HAMMACHER SCHLEMMER & CO INC
FAIRFIELD WHOLESALE
9307 N Milwaukee Ave, Niles, IL 60714-1303
Tel (847) 581-8600 *Founded/Ownrshp* 1980
Sales 60.3MM^E *EMP* 200
SIC 5961 5331 General merchandise, mail order; Variety stores; General merchandise, mail order; Variety stores
Ch Bd: Richard W Tinberg
**Pr:* Fred H Berns
Bd of Dir: Joe Jamrosz
Exec: Kristine Nelson
Creative D: John Gagliardi
CTO: Annette Brown
Opers Mgr: Kerri Calderone
Mktg Dir: April Bern
Mktg Dir: Charlotte Carpenter
Mktg Dir: Lester Hsieh
Mktg Dir: Maggie Kessler
Board of Directors: John R Mac Arthur

HAMMAKER EAST
See RUSSELL STANDARD CORP

D-U-N-S 05-831-9922
HAMMEL GREEN AND ABRAHAMSON INC
H G A
420 N 5th St Ste 100, Minneapolis, MN 55401-2338
Tel (612) 758-4000 *Founded/Ownrshp* 1953
Sales 124.2MM *EMP* 600
Accts Boulay Pllp Cpas Minneapolis
SIC 8712 8711 Architectural services; Engineering services; Architectural services; Engineering services
CEO: Daniel Avchen
**COO:* Dan Rectenwald
COO: Roger Santelman
**CFO:* Kent S Mainquist
**Treas:* Carey Bonnabeau
Bd of Dir: Corey Powers
Assoc VP: Kelly Cardella
Assoc VP: Sean Collins
Assoc VP: Sean Cotton
Assoc VP: Jane Dedering
Assoc VP: John Ellingson
Assoc VP: Kevin Flynn
Assoc VP: Dave Janous
Assoc VP: Nick Koch
Assoc VP: Jeff Millmann
Assoc VP: Dennis Vonasek
VP: Debra Barnes
VP: Michael Bjornberg
VP: Rich Bonnin
VP: John Cook
VP: Steven Dwyer

D-U-N-S 17-534-4092 IMP
HAMMELMANN CORP
(*Suby of* INTERPUMP GROUP SPA)
436 Southpointe Dr, Miamisburg, OH 45342-6459
Tel (937) 859-8777 *Founded/Ownrshp* 2008
Sales 32.5MM^E *EMP* 17^E
SIC 5084 3443 Pumps & pumping equipment; Fabricated plate work (boiler shop)
VP: Gisela Hammelmann
Sec: Peter Englehardt
VP: Michael Goecke
VP: John Tsolis
Rgnl Mgr: Stephen Laviers
Genl Mgr: Kathy Miller
Sls Mgr: Denny Mesarvey

D-U-N-S 60-208-3354 IMP
HAMMER & STEEL INC
11912 Missouri Bottom Rd, Hazelwood, MO 63042-2312
Tel (314) 895-4600 *Founded/Ownrshp* 1989
Sales 33.1MM^E *EMP* 52
SIC 5082 7353 General construction machinery & equipment; Mining machinery & equipment, except petroleum; Heavy construction equipment rental
Pr: Joe Dittmeier
**VP:* Robert Laurence
Off Mgr: Debbie Blackmon
Trfc Mgr: Tammie Davis
Manager: Todd Maxa
Sls Mgr: Daraius Tata

D-U-N-S 96-903-8699 IMP
HAMMER & STEEL INC
11916 Missouri Bottom Rd, Hazelwood, MO 63042-2312
Tel (314) 895-4600 *Founded/Ownrshp* 1989
Sales 31.3MM^E *EMP* 52
SIC 5084 7353 Drilling equipment, excluding bits; Heavy construction equipment rental
Pr: Joe Bittmeier
**VP:* Robert Laurence

D-U-N-S 60-807-5644
HAMMER CONSTRUCTION INC
2424 Springer Dr Ste 200, Norman, OK 73069-3966
Tel (405) 310-3160 *Founded/Ownrshp* 1990
Sales 113.5MM^E *EMP* 120
SIC 1389 1794 Oil field services; Excavation & grading, building construction; Oil field services; Excavation & grading, building construction
Pr: Shirley Hammer
**VP:* Robby Moore
Ex Dir: Tamara Thomasson

D-U-N-S 02-321-6630 IMP
HAMMER HAAG STEEL INC
12707 Us Highway 19 N, Clearwater, FL 33764-7213
Tel (727) 216-6903 *Founded/Ownrshp* 2011
Sales 56.3MM^E *EMP* 52^E
SIC 5051 Steel
Pr: Constantine Haag
Snr Mgr: Zac Radandt

D-U-N-S 94-545-3058
HAMMER LGC INC
4 W English St, Samson, AL 36477-1152
Tel (334) 898-2700 *Founded/Ownrshp* 2002
Sales 26.8MM *EMP* 27
Accts Mcdaniel & Associates Pc Dot
SIC 1521 1795 1711 1623 1541 1771 Single-family housing construction; Wrecking & demolition work; Plumbing, heating, air-conditioning contractors; Water, sewer & utility lines; Industrial buildings & warehouses; Concrete work; Single-family housing construction; Wrecking & demolition work; Plumbing, heating, air-conditioning contractors; Water, sewer & utility lines; Industrial buildings & warehouses; Concrete work
CEO: George Hammer
**CFO:* Linda M Hammer
**Ex VP:* Michael Pascoe

D-U-N-S 00-221-3502 IMP
HAMMER PACKAGING CORP (NY)
200 Lucius Gordon Dr, West Henrietta, NY 14586-9685
Tel (585) 424-3880 *Founded/Ownrshp* 1912, 1980
Sales 119.2MM *EMP* 350
Accts Bonadio & Co Llp Pittsford
SIC 2759 Labels & seals: printing; Labels & seals: printing
Pr: James E Hammer
**CFO:* Christopher F Wieser
**VP:* Jason Hammer
**VP:* Marty Karpie
**VP:* Louis Lovoli
**VP:* Tom Mason
VP: Patrick Oliveto
Exec: Ann Graham
Exec: Edward Nugent
IT Man: Neil Kendrick
VP Opers: Martin Karpie

D-U-N-S 08-510-1392
HAMMER RESIDENCES INC
1909 Wayzata Blvd, Wayzata, MN 55391-2047
Tel (763) 473-1261 *Founded/Ownrshp* 1923
Sales 23.4MM *EMP* 250
Accts Larsonallen Llp Minneapolis
SIC 8361 Residential care for the handicapped; Home for the mentally handicapped; Home for the physically handicapped; Residential care for the handicapped; Home for the mentally handicapped; Home for the physically handicapped
CEO: Tim Nelson
Comm Dir: Tony Baisley
Prgrm Mgr: Mary Gaasch
Prgrm Mgr: Aaron Garcia
Prgrm Mgr: Dan Pysno
CTO: Terriann Matejcek
Pgrm Dir: Jay Butler

HAMMERHEAD TRENCHLESS EQP
See EARTH TOOL CO LLC

D-U-N-S 61-480-0589
HAMMERLUND CONSTRUCTION INC
7556 Reynolds Dr, Sedalia, CO 80135-8805
Tel (720) 457-2339 *Founded/Ownrshp* 1990
Sales 50.0MM *EMP* 545^E
SIC 1794 1623 1771 Excavation & grading, building construction; Water & sewer line construction; Concrete work; Excavation & grading, building construction; Water & sewer line construction; Concrete work
CEO: Thomas Hammerlund Sr
**Pr:* Thomas Hammerlund Jr
**CFO:* John Stene
**VP:* Todd Hammerlund

D-U-N-S 78-437-5599
HAMMERMAN & GAINER INTERNATIONAL INC
1010 Common St Ste 2600, New Orleans, LA 70112-2429
Tel (504) 681-6135 *Founded/Ownrshp* 1929
Sales 95.0MM *EMP* 250
SIC 8742 Management consulting services; Management consulting services
Ch Bd: Larry D Oney
CFO: Terry Hightower

D-U-N-S 80-241-2601
HAMMERS CONSTRUCTION INC
1411 Woolsey Hts, Colorado Springs, CO 80915-5400
Tel (719) 570-1599 *Founded/Ownrshp* 1986
Sales 64.2MM^E *EMP* 157
SIC 1542 Commercial & office building contractors; Commercial & office building contractors
Pr: Steven R Hammers
**Sec:* Kay Hammers

**VP:* David J Hammers
Off Admin: Lindsey Bickert
Snr PM: Jeremy Hammers

D-U-N-S 13-972-5725
HAMMERSMITH DATA MANAGEMENT INC
HAMMERSMITH MANAGEMENT
5619 Dtc Pkwy Ste 900, Greenwood Village, CO 80111-3096
Tel (303) 980-0700 *Founded/Ownrshp* 1981
Sales 44.8MM^E *EMP* 256
SIC 8741 Management services; Management services
CEO: John Hammersmith
**Pr:* Ann Williams
COO: Alicia Granados
CFO: Jeffrey D Brothers
**Treas:* Kim McMahon
Bd of Dir: Dan Krummick
**VP:* Michael Glade
**VP:* Kyle Heckman
**VP:* Terry Jarrett
**VP:* Tom Johnson
**VP:* Bob Jones

HAMMERSMITH MANAGEMENT
See HAMMERSMITH DATA MANAGEMENT INC

D-U-N-S 00-717-4212 EXP
HAMMERSMITH MFG & SALES INC (KS)
VAIL PRODUCTS
401 Central Ave, Horton, KS 66439-1739
Tel (785) 486-2121 *Founded/Ownrshp* 1964
Sales 21.5MM *EMP* 90
Accts Douthett & Co
SIC 3443 7692 Fabricated plate work (boiler shop); Welding repair; Fabricated plate work (boiler shop); Welding repair
Pr: Edward A Hammersmith
**CFO:* Van Norris
**Ch:* Dennis Hammersmith
Sys/Mgr: Mike Bayless
Plnt Mgr: Alan Ely

D-U-N-S 80-103-0719
HAMMES CO LLC
18000 W Sarah Ln Ste 250, Brookfield, WI 53045-5842
Tel (262) 792-5900 *Founded/Ownrshp* 1993
Sales 74.7MM^E *EMP* 452
SIC 8741 Hospital management; Hospital management
Pr: Richard Galling
Pt: Todd Kibler
VP: Nicholas Horsfield
VP: Steve Kucharczyk
VP: Mark Sherry
VP: Patrick Walters
Exec: Rodney Casey
Exec: Erika Gay
Exec: Ryan Labarbera
Exec: Rick Schroeder
Exec: Jay Wall

D-U-N-S 00-505-0919
HAMMILL MANUFACTURING CO (OH)
IMPACT CUTOFF DIV
360 Tomahawk Dr, Maumee, OH 43537-1612
Tel (419) 476-0789 *Founded/Ownrshp* 1955
Sales 30.1MM^E *EMP* 200
SIC 3842 3545 Implants, surgical; Chucks: drill, lathe or magnetic (machine tool accessories); Implants, surgical; Chucks: drill, lathe or magnetic (machine tool accessories)
Ch Bd: John Hammill
Pr: Bob Doubler
**Pr:* John E Hamill Jr
Ex VP: Brian Burns
**Ex VP:* Robert Doubler
**VP:* Carl Barnard
Genl Mgr: Brian Lewandowski
IT Man: Bryan Hunt
Opers Mgr: James Ardner
Plnt Mgr: Dean Johnson
Plnt Mgr: Jeff Mack

HAMMONASSET LINCOLN
See FORD HAMMONASSET INC

HAMMOND
See MILWAUKEE VALVE CO INC

HAMMOND ASSEMBLY SOLUTION
See HAMMOND ELECTRONICS INC

D-U-N-S 15-815-3338
■ **HAMMOND ASSOCIATES INSTITUTIONAL FUND CONSULTANTS INC**
(*Suby of* MERCER INVESTMENT CONSULTING INC) ★
701 Market St Ste 1100, Saint Louis, MO 63101-1867
Tel (800) 733-9802 *Founded/Ownrshp* 2011
Sales 25.5MM^E *EMP* 130
SIC 6282 Investment counselors; Investment counselors
CEO: Jeff Schutes
**Pr:* Russ Lamore
**CFO:* Rob Robinson
Ex Dir: David Hammond
**CIO:* Anthony Brown
Dir IT: Rex Rakow
Netwrk Mgr: Elvir Mandzukic
Mktg Dir: Claudette Hammond

D-U-N-S 06-619-4721
HAMMOND CLINIC LLC
FRANCISCAN HAMMOND
7905 Calumet Ave Ste 1, Munster, IN 46321-1298
Tel (219) 836-5800 *Founded/Ownrshp* 1957
Sales 31.3MM^E *EMP* 450
SIC 8011 Clinic, operated by physicians; Clinic, operated by physicians
VP: Tracey Franovich
**CEO:* Beverly Delao
CFO: Karen Wyre
Ex Dir: Rob Jensen
Opthamlgy: Alice G Karpik
Doctor: Michael Bommarito
Doctor: Therese E Fitzsimons
Doctor: James Kim MD
Doctor: Michael S Laron MD

Doctor: Edward Lee MD
Doctor: Wael Mc Tabi

D-U-N-S 07-068-0442
HAMMOND CLINIC SPECIALTY CENTER
7905 Calumet Ave Ste 1, Hammond, IN 46321-1298
Tel (219) 836-5800 *Founded/Ownrshp* 1976
Sales 2.9MM *EMP* 500
SIC 6512 Commercial & industrial building operation; Commercial & industrial building operation
Pt: Thomas Pacebich
Pt: Donald Stork
Pt: Robert Wadeo

D-U-N-S 06-173-3218
HAMMOND CONSTRUCTION INC (OH)
1278 Park Ave Sw, Canton, OH 44706-1599
Tel (330) 455-7039 *Founded/Ownrshp* 1973, 1996
Sales 34.3MM^E^ *EMP* 80
Accts Bruner-Cox Llp Canton Ohio
SIC 1542 1541 Commercial & office building contractors; Industrial buildings & warehouses
Pr: William A Schurman
CFO: Heather Davis
**Sec:* Victor Gramoy Jr
**Ex VP:* John Kirkpatrick
Off Mgr: Caron Packurdi
Snr Mgr: Robert McAuliffe

D-U-N-S 01-111-1879
HAMMOND CONTRACTING CO INC (NJ)
291 Route 22 E Ste 24, Lebanon, NJ 08833
Tel (908) 534-1110 *Founded/Ownrshp* 1916
Sales 23.0MM *EMP* 8
Accts Goldsmith & Platter Cpa S
SIC 1711 Heating & air conditioning contractors; Ventilation & duct work contractor; Heating & air conditioning contractors; Ventilation & duct work contractor
Pr: Paul Chew
Off Mgr: Georganna Thew

D-U-N-S 00-407-6030 IMP
HAMMOND ELECTRONICS INC (FL)
HAMMOND ASSEMBLY SOLUTION
1230 W Central Blvd, Orlando, FL 32805-1815
Tel (407) 849-6060 *Founded/Ownrshp* 1947
Sales 106.4MM^E^ *EMP* 195
SIC 5065 Intercommunication equipment, electronic; Connectors, electronic; Semiconductor devices; Intercommunication equipment, electronic; Connectors, electronic; Semiconductor devices
Pr: John T Hammond
**VP:* David T Klein
VP: Jim Quirk
Genl Mgr: George Borke
Genl Mgr: Bob Kenney
Genl Mgr: Randy Smith
CTO: Bob Segal
MIS Dir: Steven Falcone
MIS Dir: Wagner Roddy
Dir IT: Tom Arline
Info Man: Mark Fleck

D-U-N-S 00-522-6790 IMP/EXP
HAMMOND GROUP INC
1414 Field St Bldg B, Hammond, IN 46320-2678
Tel (219) 931-9360 *Founded/Ownrshp* 1930
Sales 48.0MM^E^ *EMP* 150
SIC 2819 Lead compounds or salts, inorganic, not used in pigments; Lead compounds or salts, inorganic, not used in pigments
Pr: Terrence H Murphy
Pr: Eric Holtan
**CFO:* Charles T Miller
**Treas:* Peter F Murphy III
**Bd of Dir:* Willard F Haas
**Bd of Dir:* Paul Melichar
VP: Walt Winginroth
MIS Dir: Gerry Kaoukis
Cust Svc D: Bonnie Mescal
Mktg Mgr: Mark Volkmann
Sls Mgr: Bruce Brackbill

D-U-N-S 00-171-2959
HAMMOND KENNEDY WHITNEY & CO INC (NY)
HKW
420 Lexington Ave Rm 402, New York, NY 10170-0499
Tel (212) 867-1010 *Founded/Ownrshp* 1903, 1965
Sales 81.9MM^E^ *EMP* 421
SIC 7389 Brokers, business: buying & selling business enterprises; Brokers, business: buying & selling business enterprises
Ch Bd: Jeffrey G Wood
**VP:* Forrest E Crisman Jr
**VP:* Glenn Scolnik

HAMMOND KINETICS
See KINETICS NOISE CONTROL INC

D-U-N-S 00-111-0360
HAMMOND LUMBER CO
2 Hammond D, Belgrade, ME 04917
Tel (207) 495-3303 *Founded/Ownrshp* 1953
Sales 95.1MM^E^ *EMP* 415
SIC 5211 2421 5031 Lumber & other building materials; Sawmills & planing mills, general; Lumber: rough, dressed & finished; Lumber & other building materials; Sawmills & planing mills, general; Lumber: rough, dressed & finished
Pr: Donald C Hammond
**VP:* Michael J Hammond
VP: Bob Thing
Exec: Rod Bockford
Store Mgr: Larry Demerchant
Store Mgr: Al Feather
Store Mgr: Bill Veilleux
IT Man: Mitchell Bickford
Sls&Mrk Ex: Rod Wells
Sls Mgr: Andrea Hodgdon
Sls Mgr: Bill Krause

D-U-N-S 00-611-3450 IMP
HAMMOND POWER SOLUTIONS INC
(*Suby of* HAMMOND POWER SOLUTIONS INC)
1100 Lake St, Baraboo, WI 53913-3000
Tel (608) 356-3921 *Founded/Ownrshp* 2001
Sales 99.9MM^E^ *EMP* 130
SIC 5084 Industrial machinery & equipment; Industrial machinery & equipment
Ch Bd: William G Hammond
**Pr:* Francis A Raftis
CFO: Chris Huether
**CFO:* Christopher R Huether

D-U-N-S 06-849-7189
HAMMOND PUBLIC SCHOOLS
41 Williams St, Hammond, IN 46320-1948
Tel (219) 933-2400 *Founded/Ownrshp* 1894
Sales 94.7MM^E^ *EMP* 1,800
SIC 8211 Public elementary & secondary schools; Public elementary & secondary schools
**VP:* Anna Mamala
Sys Mgr: Joseph Hardy
HC Dir: Sarah Ligon

D-U-N-S 10-573-5898
HAMMOND TRACTOR CO
JOHN DEERE
216 Center Rd, Fairfield, ME 04937-3316
Tel (207) 453-7131 *Founded/Ownrshp* 1983
Sales 32.0MM *EMP* 70
SIC 5083 Agricultural machinery; Agricultural machinery
Pr: Gary Hammond
Chf Mktg O: Ben Blackwell
**VP:* Dave Hammond
Genl Mgr: Dave Bryant

HAMMOND-HENRY HOSPITAL
See HENRY HOSPITAL DISTRICT

D-U-N-S 00-707-5740 IMP
HAMMONDS CANDIES SINCE 1920 II LLC
5735 Washington St, Denver, CO 80216-1321
Tel (303) 333-5588 *Founded/Ownrshp* 1920
Sales 31.0MM^E^ *EMP* 130
Accts Causey Demgen & Moore Inc De
SIC 2064 Candy & other confectionery products; Candy & other confectionery products
CEO: Andrew Schuman
**CFO:* Ralph Nafziger
Chf Mktg O: Lori Schuman
VP: Anna Abromovich
Genl Mgr: Melissa Joslin
Natl Sales: A Whisler
VP Mktg: Laurie Shuman

D-U-N-S 00-696-8879
HAMMONS INC (MO)
COURTYARD BY MRROTT SPRNGFIELD
300 S John Q Hammons Pkwy # 900, Springfield, MO 65806-2550
Tel (417) 864-4300 *Founded/Ownrshp* 1971
Sales NA *EMP* 4,835
SIC 7011 Hotels & motels

D-U-N-S 08-709-4629
HAMMONTON BOARD OF EDUCATION
HAMMONTON ELEMENTARY SCHOOL
566 Old Forks Rd, Hammonton, NJ 08037-2644
Tel (609) 567-7006 *Founded/Ownrshp* 1965
Sales 20.5MM^E^ *EMP* 332
Accts Board Secretary/ School Asdmin
SIC 8211 Public elementary & secondary schools; Public elementary & secondary schools
Board of Directors: Robert Capoferri, Rosemarie Jacobs

HAMMONTON CENTER FOR REHABILIT
See INNOVA ATLANTIC WHITE HORSE OPERATIONS LLC

HAMMONTON ELEMENTARY SCHOOL
See HAMMONTON BOARD OF EDUCATION

HAMMOUND ROTO-FINISH
See KALAMAZOO CO

D-U-N-S 04-005-2250
HAMNER INSTITUTES
6 Davis Dr, Durham, NC 27709-0003
Tel (919) 558-1200 *Founded/Ownrshp* 2005
Sales 25.0MM^E^ *EMP* 130
Accts Cherry Bekaert & Holland Ll
SIC 8733 Noncommercial research organizations; Scientific research agency; Noncommercial research organizations; Scientific research agency
Pr: William Greenlee
**V Ch:* Dr John A Moore
**Ch:* Eugene D Ervin
**Treas:* Raymond Mc Gowan
VP: Frederick J Miller
Assoc Dir: Cecilia Tan
Opers Mgr: Paul Ross

HAMON
See THERMAL TRANSFER CORP

D-U-N-S 61-531-9324
HAMON CONTRACTORS INC
5670 Franklin St, Denver, CO 80216-1518
Tel (303) 297-0340 *Founded/Ownrshp* 1990
Sales 33.6MM^E^ *EMP* 100
SIC 1611 1622 1741 Highway & street construction; Bridge construction; Foundation & retaining wall construction; Highway & street construction; Bridge construction; Foundation & retaining wall construction
CEO: Bruce Hamon
**Treas:* Michael D Walters
IT Man: Thomas Evered

D-U-N-S 15-428-0598 IMP
HAMON CORP
(*Suby of* HAMON & CIE (INTERNATIONAL) SA)
58 E Main St, Somerville, NJ 08876-2312
Tel (908) 685-4000 *Founded/Ownrshp* 1979
Sales 137.5MM^E^ *EMP* 340
SIC 1629 3564 3499 5084 Industrial plant construction; Blowers & fans; Friction material, made from powdered metal; Industrial machinery & equipment; Industrial plant construction; Blowers & fans; Friction material, made from powdered metal; Industrial machinery & equipment
CEO: William P Dillon
**COO:* Oliver Acheson
**Ex VP:* Don Kawecki
**Ex VP:* H James Peters
**Ex VP:* Robert Recio
VP: Neil Dahlberg
Genl Mgr: Jean-Claude Blanquet
Genl Mgr: Karl Wilber
Dir IT: Jay Demartino
QC Dir: Tom Pratt
Sls Mgr: Terry King

D-U-N-S 96-956-9982 IMP/EXP
HAMON DELTAK INC
(*Suby of* HAMON CORP) ★
13330 12th Ave N, Minneapolis, MN 55441-4510
Tel (763) 557-7440 *Founded/Ownrshp* 2011
Sales 64.7MM^E^ *EMP* 140
SIC 3511 Steam turbine generator set units, complete; Steam turbine generator set units, complete
Pr: Peter W Dawes
**CEO:* William Dillon
**VP:* Roger Sjoberg
VP Mfg: Steve Rice

D-U-N-S 07-877-7815 IMP
HAMON RESEARCH-COTTRELL INC
(*Suby of* HAMON CORP) ★
58 E Main St, Somerville, NJ 08876-2312
Tel (908) 333-2003 *Founded/Ownrshp* 1998
Sales 25.4MM^E^ *EMP* 40^E^
SIC 5075 Air pollution control equipment & supplies
CEO: William P Dillon
**Pr:* Bhushan Ranade
**CFO:* Oliver Acheson
Ex VP: Timothy Ottie
**VP:* Robert Recio
Opers Mgr: Jose Rodriguez
Sales Exec: Mark Manara
Sls Mgr: Barry Stolzman
Sales Asso: Traci Macilroy
Snr PM: John Kali
Snr PM: Michael Kelaher

D-U-N-S 10-630-7655
HAMOT HEALTH FOUNDATION
201 State St, Erie, PA 16550-0002
Tel (814) 877-7020 *Founded/Ownrshp* 1981
Sales 4.0MM *EMP* 2,032
Accts Parentebeard Llc Philadelphia
SIC 8741 8062 6514 Hospital management; Nursing & personal care facility management; General medical & surgical hospitals; Dwelling operators, except apartments; Hospital management; Nursing & personal care facility management; General medical & surgical hospitals; Dwelling operators, except apartments
Pr: John T Malone
Chf Rad: Richard Williams
**Pr:* V James Fiorenzo
COO: David Gibbons
**CFO:* Stephen Danch
**Ch:* B Scott Kern
Ex VP: Joseph Pepicello
**Sr VP:* Hershey Bell
**Sr VP:* Donald Inderlied
**Sr VP:* Rochelle Krowinski
**Sr VP:* Dr Joseph McClellan
**Sr VP:* Dr James Pepicello
**Sr VP:* Lee Van Voris
**VP:* Debbie A Burbules
VP: Joseph P Butler
**VP:* Stephen M Danch
VP: Raymond E Moluski
Exec: Sharie Argeny
Dir Rx: Thomas J Thompson

HAMOT MEDICAL CENTER
See UPMC HAMOT

D-U-N-S 79-059-5628
HAMPDEN BANCORP INC
19 Harrison Ave, Springfield, MA 01103-1618
Tel (413) 736-1812 *Founded/Ownrshp* 2007
Sales NA *EMP* 125^E^
SIC 6036 Savings institutions, not federally chartered

D-U-N-S 15-533-8528
HAMPDEN BANK
19 Harrison Ave, Springfield, MA 01103-1618
Tel (413) 736-1812 *Founded/Ownrshp* 1825
Sales NA *EMP* 105
SIC 6022 State commercial banks

D-U-N-S 00-111-7266
HAMPDEN ENGINEERING CORP (MA)
99 Shaker Rd, East Longmeadow, MA 01028-2762
Tel (413) 525-3981 *Founded/Ownrshp* 1954
Sales 21.0MM^E^ *EMP* 85
Accts Nolan Calcasola & Co Pc
SIC 3629 Electronic generation equipment
Pr: John M Flynn
**Treas:* Sheila R Flynn
VP: Stanley Bandoski
**VP:* John D Flynn
Sfty Mgr: Stanley Witcop
Plnt Mgr: Chuck Witkop
Manager: Ryan Szalankiewicz

D-U-N-S 00-111-5526 IMP
HAMPDEN PAPERS INC (MA)
100 Water St, Holyoke, MA 01040-6298
Tel (413) 536-1000 *Founded/Ownrshp* 1880
Sales 24.5MM^E^ *EMP* 105^E^
SIC 2671 2672 2631 Plastic film, coated or laminated for packaging; Coated & laminated paper; Coated paperboard; Plastic film, coated or laminated for packaging; Coated & laminated paper; Coated paperboard
CEO: Robert K Fowler
**Pr:* Richard J Wells
Treas: Timothy Fowler
**VP:* John W Phelps
IT Man: Harry Dumas
**VP Mfg:* Michael E Archambeault
Sls&Mrk Ex: James Kennedy
**VP Sls:* Robert H Adams
VP Sls: Robert Fitzgerald

D-U-N-S 05-212-5598
HAMPDEN-WILBRAHAM REG SCH DIST
621 Main St, Wilbraham, MA 01095-1603
Tel (413) 596-3884 *Founded/Ownrshp* 1956
Sales 35.0MM^E^ *EMP* 516
SIC 8211 Public combined elementary & secondary school; Public combined elementary & secondary school
MIS Dir: Georgina Trebbe
Schl Brd P: Marc Ducey

D-U-N-S 03-061-8623
HAMPEL OIL DISTRIBUTORS INC
3727 S West St, Wichita, KS 67217-3803
Tel (316) 529-1162 *Founded/Ownrshp* 1976
Sales 100.0MM^E^ *EMP* 180
SIC 5171 Petroleum bulk stations; Petroleum bulk stations
Pr: William Hampel
COO: Scott Hampel
**VP:* Ed Hampel
Brnch Mgr: Jon Hampel
IT Man: Bob Hampel
Opers Mgr: Dustin Ruth
Manager: Ricky Peel
Sls Mgr: Chip Emms
Sls Mgr: Brian Mackey
Sls Mgr: Ann Pardy

D-U-N-S 14-649-3312
HAMPSHIRE COMPANIES LLC
HAMPSHIRE RE COMPANIES
22 Maple Ave, Morristown, NJ 07960-5452
Tel (973) 292-9595 *Founded/Ownrshp* 2002
Sales 45.4MM^E^ *EMP* 50^E^
SIC 6531 6798 Real estate agents & managers; Real estate investment trusts
Ch: Jon F Hanson
**Pr:* James E Hanson II
**Ex VP:* Jeffrey B Hanson
**Ex VP:* Deborah H Imperatore
VP: John Durso
VP: Donald Engels
Opers Mgr: Cheryll McMurray

D-U-N-S 09-300-9884
HAMPSHIRE COUNTY BOARD OF EDUCATION
111 School St, Romney, WV 26757-1522
Tel (304) 822-3528 *Founded/Ownrshp* 1935
Sales 21.1MM^E^ *EMP* 550
SIC 8211 Public elementary & secondary schools; Public elementary & secondary schools
Psych: Edward Morgret

D-U-N-S 07-979-8891
HAMPSHIRE COUNTY SCHOOLS
111 School St, Romney, WV 26757-1522
Tel (304) 822-3528 *Founded/Ownrshp* 2015
Sales 15.7MM^E^ *EMP* 423^E^
SIC 8211 Public elementary & secondary schools
Teacher Pr: Terrie Deville

D-U-N-S 09-206-0292
HAMPSHIRE FIRE PROTECTION CO INC
8 N Wentworth Ave, Londonderry, NH 03053-7438
Tel (603) 432-8221 *Founded/Ownrshp* 1978
Sales 30.1MM^E^ *EMP* 110
SIC 1711 3999 Fire sprinkler system installation; Fire extinguishers, portable; Fire sprinkler system installation; Fire extinguishers, portable
Pr: Lawrence J Thibodeau

D-U-N-S 08-847-0802 IMP
▲ **HAMPSHIRE GROUP LIMITED**
114 W 41st St, New York, NY 10036-7315
Tel (864) 231-1200 *Founded/Ownrshp* 1917
Sales 91.4MM *EMP* 831^E^
Tkr Sym HAMP *Exch* OTO
SIC 2339 2329 2253 Women's & misses' outerwear; Women's & misses' athletic clothing & sportswear; Women's & misses' jackets & coats, except sportswear; Sweaters & sweater jackets: men's & boys'; Men's & boys' sportswear & athletic clothing; Knit outerwear mills; Women's & misses' outerwear; Women's & misses' athletic clothing & sportswear; Women's & misses' jackets & coats, except sportswear; Sweaters & sweater jackets: men's & boys'; Men's & boys' sportswear & athletic clothing; Knit outerwear mills
Ch Bd: Paul M Buxbaum
Pr: Eric Prengel
Pr: Robert Stec
Pr: Howard L Zwilling
COO: David Price
CFO: William Drozdowski
Ex VP: Mitchell Smiles
Sr VP: Susan Firavanti
Board of Directors: Thomas J Doyle Jr, Brett Fialkoff, Benjamin C Yogel

D-U-N-S 96-351-6468
HAMPSHIRE HEALTH CARE CENTER
Hc 74, Three Churches, WV 26757
Tel (304) 822-7527 *Founded/Ownrshp* 2010
Sales 570.5MM *EMP* 17^E^
SIC 8051 Skilled nursing care facilities; Skilled nursing care facilities
HC Dir: Janet Haines

D-U-N-S 07-856-7234
HAMPSHIRE HOUSE
CHEERS
440 Rutherford Ave # 300, Charlestown, MA 02129-1625
Tel (617) 242-4134 *Founded/Ownrshp* 2012
Sales 6.7MM^E^ *EMP* 400
SIC 5651 5812 Family clothing stores; Family restaurants; Family clothing stores; Family restaurants

D-U-N-S 07-829-7942
HAMPSHIRE MEMORIAL HOSPITAL INC
363 Sunrise Blvd, Romney, WV 26757-4607
Tel (304) 822-4561 *Founded/Ownrshp* 1982
Sales 21.9MM *EMP* 150
SIC 8051 8062 Skilled nursing care facilities; General medical & surgical hospitals

Pr: Neil McLaughlin
**VP:* Christine Lowman
Mktg Dir: Kittie Ault
Nrsg Dir: Cheryl Dent
Nrsg Dir: Julia Sites

D-U-N-S 78-221-5128
HAMPSHIRE PET PRODUCTS LLC
7502 E 26th St, Joplin, MO 64804-7967
Tel (417) 206-6137 *Founded/Ownrshp* 2000
Sales 41.5MM^E *EMP* 180
SIC 3999 2048 Pet supplies; Prepared feeds; Pet supplies; Prepared feeds
Pr: Julie Larson
CFO: Bob Weaver
VP: Earl Clements
VP: Curt Dudley
Ql Cn Mgr: Todd Dunlop
Ql Cn Mgr: Shelby Scott

HAMPSHIRE RE COMPANIES
See HAMPSHIRE COMPANIES LLC

HAMPSTEAD HOSPITAL
See HAMPSTEAD OUTLOOK INC

D-U-N-S 06-990-8093
HAMPSTEAD OUTLOOK INC
HAMPSTEAD HOSPITAL
218 East Rd, Hampstead, NH 03841-2305
Tel (603) 329-4640 *Founded/Ownrshp* 1973
Sales 29.2MM^E *EMP* 200
SIC 8063 8069 Psychiatric hospitals; Specialty hospitals, except psychiatric; Psychiatric hospitals; Specialty hospitals, except psychiatric
Prin: Henry Audesse
COO: Lisa Ryan
Chf Mktg O: John Monarca
Dir Inf Cn: Lisa Caron
Nrsg Dir: Patricia Shea
HC Dir: Janet Stammely

HAMPTON AFFILIATES
See HAMPTON INVESTMENT CO

D-U-N-S 02-853-0199
HAMPTON AUTOMOTIVE GROUP INC
HAMPTON MITSUBISHI
(*Suby of* HAMPTON PRODUCTS INTERNATIONAL CORP) ★
230 Hollywood Blvd Sw, Fort Walton Beach, FL 32548-4760
Tel (850) 244-8600 *Founded/Ownrshp* 1998
Sales 20.1MM^E *EMP* 50
SIC 5511 Automobiles, new & used
Pr: Mark A Hampton
Ex VP: Mary Sanders
Mktg Mgr: Caroline Gray

D-U-N-S 03-429-9669
HAMPTON AUTOMOTIVE INC
HAMPTON TOYOTA
6191 Johnston St, Lafayette, LA 70503-5618
Tel (337) 984-5010 *Founded/Ownrshp* 2001
Sales 34.2MM^E *EMP* 71
SIC 5511 Automobiles, new & used; Automobiles, new & used
Sls Mgr: Michael Alfano
Sls Mgr: Michael Green
Board of Directors: Zach Moore, Shawn Tucker

HAMPTON CHEVROLET JEEP-MAZDA
See HAMPTON MOTOR CORP

D-U-N-S 18-435-6012
HAMPTON CITY SCHOOL DISTRICT
1 Franklin St Fl 2, Hampton, VA 23669-3570
Tel (757) 727-2000 *Founded/Ownrshp* 1994
Sales 142.9MM^E *EMP* 3,000^E
SIC 8211 Public elementary & secondary schools; School board; Public elementary & secondary schools; School board
Ofcr: Aaron Webb
Ofcr: Ernest Williams
Dir IT: Rubenia Felton
IT Man: Patricia McFadden
IT Man: James Murray
Pr Dir: Diana Gulotta
HC Dir: Glory Gill
Snr Mgr: Carolyn Holmes
Snr Mgr: James Ruffin

D-U-N-S 01-319-9708
HAMPTON COUNTY NORTH SCHOOL DISTRICT 1
372 Pine St E, Varnville, SC 29944-9618
Tel (803) 943-4576 *Founded/Ownrshp* 1830
Sales 7.3MM^E *EMP* 396
Accts Dooley And Company Llp
SIC 8211 Public elementary & secondary schools; Public elementary & secondary schools

D-U-N-S 04-028-6701
HAMPTON CREEK INC
371 10th St, San Francisco, CA 94103-3832
Tel (844) 423-6637 *Founded/Ownrshp* 2011
Sales 128.6MM^E *EMP* 249
SIC 2035 2052 Mayonnaise; Cookies; Mayonnaise; Cookies
CEO: Joshua Tetrick
Comm Dir: Morgan Oliveira

D-U-N-S 93-842-7424 IMP
HAMPTON DIRECT INC
291 Hurricane Ln, Williston, VT 05495-2074
Tel (802) 876-1500 *Founded/Ownrshp* 1997
Sales 21.2MM^E *EMP* 50^E
SIC 5199 General merchandise, non-durable
CEO: Steve G Heroux
Ex VP: Stephanie Gillen
**VP:* Timothy A George
VP: Christy Shusda
VP: Pierre Timothy
VP Sls: Cheryl Coates
Sales Asso: Rincy Jacob
Snr Mgr: Tom Fron

D-U-N-S 02-772-7247 IMP/EXP
HAMPTON DISTRIBUTION COMPANIES
CALIFORNIA BUILDERS SUPPLY
(*Suby of* HAMPTON LUMBER SALES CO) ★
9600 Sw Barnes Rd, Portland, OR 97225-6665
Tel (503) 297-7691 *Founded/Ownrshp* 1984
Sales 27.2MM^E *EMP* 120
SIC 5031

HAMPTON FARM
See PORTALES SELECT PEANUT INC

HAMPTON FARMS
See MEHERRIN AGRICULTURAL & CHEMICAL CO

D-U-N-S 01-847-4667 IMP/EXP
HAMPTON FARMS INC
413 Main St, Severn, NC 27877
Tel (757) 654-1400 *Founded/Ownrshp* 2010
Sales 46.4MM^E *EMP* 150
SIC 0139 Peanut farm
Prin: Verdola Cook
Rgnl Mgr: Kevin Sterner
Opers Mgr: Royal Watson
Ql Cn Mgr: Goldie Potter
S&M/VP: Tom Nolan
Sls Mgr: Mary Orozco

D-U-N-S 07-809-2962
HAMPTON HYDRAULICS LLC
SEABEE
(*Suby of* LIGON INDUSTRIES LLC) ★
712 1st St Nw, Hampton, IA 50441-1304
Tel (641) 456-4871 *Founded/Ownrshp* 2001
Sales 53.3MM^E *EMP* 256
SIC 3593 3471 3325 Fluid power cylinders, hydraulic or pneumatic; Chromium plating of metals or formed products; Alloy steel castings, except investment; Fluid power cylinders, hydraulic or pneumatic; Chromium plating of metals or formed products; Alloy steel castings, except investment
Pr: George Winchester
Genl Mgr: Helm Hansen
Genl Mgr: John Lang
Plnt Mgr: Tery Bents
Ql Cn Mgr: Michael Barnes
Ql Cn Mgr: Lonnie Miller

HAMPTON INN
See HILTON WORLDWIDE INC

HAMPTON INN
See HOLLYWOOD GRILL RESTAURANT INC

HAMPTON INN
See ATLANTIC HOST LLC

HAMPTON INN
See INTERSTATE HOTELS & RESORTS INC

HAMPTON INN
See BENNETT ENTERPRISES INC

HAMPTON INN
See BLACK CANYON HOSPITALITY INC

HAMPTON INN
See HIGHPOINTE HOSPITABILITY INC

HAMPTON INN
See GRAND HERITAGE HOTEL PORTLAND

HAMPTON INN
See TRAMZ HOTELS LLC

HAMPTON INN
See DRURY SOUTHWEST INC

HAMPTON INN
See HIGH HOTELS LTD

HAMPTON INN
See SUMMIT GROUP INC

HAMPTON INN
See SUMMIT HOTEL PROPERTIES LLC

HAMPTON INN
See CROSSROADS HOSPITALITY CO LLC

HAMPTON INN
See SUNSTONE HOTEL PROPERTIES INC

HAMPTON INN DAYTONA SPEEDWAY
See PRINCE BUSH INVESTMENTS-DAYTONA

HAMPTON INSTITUE
See HAMPTON UNIVERSITY

D-U-N-S 10-406-5701 IMP/EXP
HAMPTON INVESTMENT CO
HAMPTON AFFILIATES
9600 Sw Barnes Rd Ste 200, Portland, OR 97225-6666
Tel (503) 297-7691 *Founded/Ownrshp* 1978
Sales 334.7MM^E *EMP* 1,300
SIC 5031 2436 2435 2426

D-U-N-S 05-221-7106 IMP/EXP
HAMPTON LUMBER MILLS INC
WILLAMINA LUMBER COMPANY
(*Suby of* HAMPTON RESOURCES INC) ★
9600 Sw Barnes Rd Ste 200, Portland, OR 97225-6666
Tel (503) 297-7691 *Founded/Ownrshp* 1983
Sales 64.6MM^E *EMP* 560
SIC 2421

D-U-N-S 79-990-8087 IMP/EXP
HAMPTON LUMBER SALES CO
(*Suby of* HAMPTON RESOURCES INC) ★
9600 Sw Barnes Rd Ste 200, Portland, OR 97225-6666
Tel (503) 297-7691 *Founded/Ownrshp* 2000
Sales 191.8MM^E *EMP* 130
SIC 5031 2421 7389 Lumber, plywood & millwork; Sawmills & planing mills, general; Log & lumber broker; Lumber, plywood & millwork; Sawmills & planing mills, general; Log & lumber broker
Pr: Mike Phillips
**CFO:* Steve Zika
Dir IT: Matt Fellows
Snr Mgr: Andy McNiece

HAMPTON MITSUBISHI
See HAMPTON AUTOMOTIVE GROUP INC

D-U-N-S 02-375-6000
HAMPTON MOTOR CORP
HAMPTON CHEVROLET JEEP-MAZDA
1073 W Mercury Blvd, Hampton, VA 23666-3308
Tel (757) 838-5450 *Founded/Ownrshp* 1980
Sales 35.8MM^E *EMP* 95
SIC 5511 5521 New & used car dealers; Automobiles, new & used; Used car dealers; Automobiles, new & used; Used car dealers
Pr: F Lewis Wood
**Sec:* Sandra Scott
**VP:* William Hobbs
**VP:* Ashton Lewis Jr
Sls Mgr: Dustin Edmonds

D-U-N-S 07-339-9362 IMP
HAMPTON PRODUCTS INTERNATIONAL CORP
50 Icon, Foothill Ranch, CA 92610-3000
Tel (949) 472-4256 *Founded/Ownrshp* 1990
Sales 191.7MM^E *EMP* 350
SIC 5072 Hardware; Padlocks; Hardware; Padlocks
Pr: Hayward K Kelley III
Pr: Jon Quan
COO: Chris Francis
COO: Richard Tysdal
Ex VP: Bob Hansen
Sr VP: Mike Kreeger
VP: Jim Bzovy
VP: Robert Gast
VP: Fred Holgate
MIS Dir: Howard Shen
IT Man: Bob Gast

D-U-N-S 06-932-9928
HAMPTON REGIONAL MEDICAL CENTER
595 W Carolina Ave, Varnville, SC 29944-4735
Tel (803) 943-1253 *Founded/Ownrshp* 1993
Sales 24.0MM *EMP* 225
SIC 8062 General medical & surgical hospitals; General medical & surgical hospitals
Pr: David Hamill
CFO: Julie Allen
Dir Inf Cn: Gwen Smith
Dir Lab: Alison Johnstone
Dir Rad: Dennis McElhone
Dir Rx: Krissy Brunson
Dir IT: Janine Terry
Mtls Mgr: Suesan Richardson
Mktg Dir: Nikki Troxclair
Mktg Mgr: Pete Tucker

D-U-N-S 11-267-7927 IMP/EXP
HAMPTON RESOURCES INC
(*Suby of* HAMPTON AFFILIATES) ★
9600 Sw Barnes Rd Ste 200, Portland, OR 97225-6666
Tel (503) 297-7691 *Founded/Ownrshp* 1983
Sales 311.4MM^E *EMP* 600
SIC 5031 2421 0811

D-U-N-S 96-791-9692
HAMPTON RIDGE HEALTHCARE & REHABILITATION LLC
94 Stevens Rd Ste 1, Toms River, NJ 08755-1490
Tel (732) 286-5005 *Founded/Ownrshp* 2010
Sales 20.3MM *EMP* 34^E
SIC 8051 Skilled nursing care facilities
Prin: Fred Jacobs

D-U-N-S 05-512-6341
▲ HAMPTON ROADS BANKSHARES INC
641 Lynnhaven Pkwy, Virginia Beach, VA 23452-7307
Tel (757) 217-1000 *Founded/Ownrshp* 2001
Sales NA *EMP* 536^E
Tkr Sym HMPR *Exch* NGS
SIC 6021 National commercial banks; National commercial banks
Ch Bd: Charles M Johnston
Pr: Chris Corchiani
Pr: Ronald A Day
Pr: J Lawrence Mansfield Jr
Pr: F Scot McAlexander
Pr: W Thomas Mears
Pr: Donna W Richards
Pr: David R Twiddy
COO: Glenn R Astolfi
CFO: Thomas B Dix III
Ofcr: Denise D Hinkle
Ex VP: John F Marshall Jr
Sr VP: Kevin J Chase
Sr VP: Kenneth K Donner
Sr VP: Daniel H Flye Jr
Sr VP: Lisa M Lentz
Sr VP: Myra Maglalang-Langston
Sr VP: Deborah B Mast
Sr VP: Rene R McKinney
Sr VP: John S Pearsall
Sr VP: John R Schroeder
Board of Directors: James F Burr, Patrick E Corbin, Henry P Custis Jr, Robert B Goldstein, Hal F Goltz, William A Paulette, John S Poelker, Billy G Roughton, W Lewis Witt

D-U-N-S 07-793-2770 IMP
HAMPTON ROADS SANITATION DISTRICT (INC)
HRSD
1434 Air Rail Ave, Virginia Beach, VA 23455-3002
Tel (757) 460-2261 *Founded/Ownrshp* 1946
Sales 225.5MM *EMP* 700
Accts Kpmg Llp Norfolk Va
SIC 4952 Sewerage systems
Exec: Kristin Bauer
Dir Lab: Paula Hogg
**CIO:* Don Corrado
CTO: Clay Wise
IT Man: Tim Marsh
IT Man: Jules Robichaud
Plnt Mgr: Brian McNamara
Mktg Dir: Jennifer Heilman
Snr Mgr: Richard Baumler
Snr Mgr: Gary Hart
Snr Mgr: Samuel Jones

HAMPTON ROADS TRANSIT
See TRANSPORTATION DIST COMMISION OF HAMPTON ROADS

D-U-N-S 09-959-1216
HAMPTON RUBBER CO
(*Suby of* SBP HOLDINGS) ★
1669 W Pembroke Ave, Hampton, VA 23661-1901
Tel (757) 722-9818 *Founded/Ownrshp* 1999
Sales 169.2MM^E *EMP* 286
SIC 5085 Rubber goods, mechanical; Gaskets; Hose, belting & packing; Bearings
Pr: Donald Fritzinger
**Treas:* George Dappert
**VP:* Otis A Dufrene
**VP:* Kenneth Ketterman
Off Mgr: Susan Paul
IT Man: Wayne Dunn

D-U-N-S 12-606-1936
HAMPTON SCHOOL DISTRICT 2
319 4th St E, Estill, SC 29918-4839
Tel (803) 625-5000 *Founded/Ownrshp* 1951
Sales 13.6MM^E *EMP* 362
Accts Payton W Warren Cpa Florence
SIC 8211 Public elementary & secondary schools; Public elementary & secondary schools
Pr: Myrtle Sumter
**CFO:* William J Diamond
Teacher Pr: Conchita Bostick

D-U-N-S 03-992-7066
HAMPTON TOWNSHIP SCHOOL DISTRICT
4591 School Dr, Allison Park, PA 15101-2516
Tel (724) 449-8888 *Founded/Ownrshp* 1960
Sales 42.7MM *EMP* 350
Accts Hosack Specht Muetzel & Wood
SIC 8211 Public elementary & secondary schools; Public elementary & secondary schools
MIS Dir: Ed McKaveney
Pr Dir: Shari Berg

HAMPTON TOYOTA
See HAMPTON AUTOMOTIVE INC

HAMPTON TREE FARMS, INC.
See HAMPTON TREE FARMS LLC

D-U-N-S 00-902-9919 IMP
HAMPTON TREE FARMS LLC
HAMPTON TREE FARMS, INC.
(*Suby of* HAMPTON RESOURCES INC) ★
9600 Sw Barnes Rd Ste 200, Portland, OR 97225-6666
Tel (503) 297-7691 *Founded/Ownrshp* 1983
Sales 77.9MM^E *EMP* 50
SIC 0811

D-U-N-S 00-313-5068
HAMPTON UNIVERSITY (VA)
HAMPTON INSTITUE
100 E Queen St, Hampton, VA 23668-0108
Tel (757) 727-5000 *Founded/Ownrshp* 1868
Sales 166.3MM^E *EMP* 1,050
Accts Dixon Hughes Goodman Llp Newp
SIC 8221 University; University
Pr: William R Harvey
Pr: Evelyn Oakley
Ex VP: Jo A Haysbert
VP: Jean Chouteau
VP: Laron J Clark Jr
Dir Lab: Cynthia Peterson
Prgrm Mgr: Gerald Swenson
Dir IT: Keith Perkins
Netwrk Eng: David Javier
Plnt Mgr: Sarita Scott
Sls&Mrk Ex: Arthur Holmes

D-U-N-S 60-738-2694
HAMPTON WOODS HEALTH & REHABILITATION CENTER
200 Hmpton Wods Cmplex Rd, Jackson, NC 27845-9503
Tel (252) 534-0131 *Founded/Ownrshp* 1990
Sales 435.3MM *EMP* 90
SIC 8051 8052 Skilled nursing care facilities; Intermediate care facilities; Skilled nursing care facilities; Intermediate care facilities
Nrsg Dir: Donna Tritt Rn

D-U-N-S 15-502-8541
HAMPTON-NEWPORT NEWS COMMUNITY SERVICES BOARD PROPERTY CO INC
300 Medical Dr, Hampton, VA 23666-1765
Tel (757) 788-0300 *Founded/Ownrshp* 1971
Sales NA *EMP* 792
Accts Dooley & Vicars Richmond Va
SIC 9431 Mental health agency administration, government; ; Mental health agency administration, government
Pr: Charles A Hall
**Ch:* Steven Brown
**Treas:* William Baker
**Sec:* Charles K Young
MIS Mgr: Lyle Zimpelman
Opers Supe: Karen Forde
Doctor: Baltej Gill

HAMPTONS CENTER FOR
See NORTH SEA ASSOCIATES LLC

D-U-N-S 62-611-7159
HAMRA MANAGEMENT CO LLC
1855 S Ingram Mill Rd, Springfield, MO 65804-2100
Tel (417) 886-8550 *Founded/Ownrshp* 2006
Sales 77.9MM^E *EMP* 48^E
SIC 8741 Management services

D-U-N-S 00-335-3448
HAMRICK MILLS INC (SC)
515 W Buford St, Gaffney, SC 29341-1703
Tel (864) 489-4731 *Founded/Ownrshp* 1900
Sales 82.7MM^E *EMP* 425
SIC 2211 2299 Sheets & sheetings, cotton; Yarns & thread, made from non-fabric materials; Sheets & sheetings, cotton; Yarns & thread, made from non-fabric materials
Pr: Carlisle Hamrick
**Ch Bd:* Wylie L Hamrick
**Sec:* Charles Hamrick
**VP:* Lyman Hamrick
IT Man: Scott Butterbaugh
Cust Svc D: Kelly Galloway

D-U-N-S 04-912-3995 IMP
HAMRICKS INC
L HAMRICK'S
742 Peachoid Rd, Gaffney, SC 29341-3499
Tel (864) 489-6095 *Founded/Ownrshp* 1945
Sales 273.6MM^E *EMP* 1,600
SIC 5651 2337 2331 2335 2339 5087

D-U-N-S 08-007-5179 IMP
HAMROCK INC (CA)
12521 Los Nietos Rd, Santa Fe Springs, CA 90670-2915
Tel (562) 944-0255 *Founded/Ownrshp* 1976
Sales 55.1MM^E *EMP* 250
SIC 3315 2542 3496 3317 Wire & fabricated wire products; Racks, merchandise display or storage: except wood; Miscellaneous fabricated wire products; Steel pipe & tubes; Wire & fabricated wire products; Racks, merchandise display or storage: except wood; Miscellaneous fabricated wire products; Steel pipe & tubes
CEO: Stephen Hamrock
**Treas:* Michael Hamrock
VP: Michael Meh
Dir IT: Israel Vela
Mktg Dir: Wayne Salvino

D-U-N-S 96-642-4947
HAMS RESTAURANTS INC
(*Suby of* CHELDA, INC)
3017 W Gate City Blvd # 2, Greensboro, NC 27403-3655
Tel (336) 851-4800 *Founded/Ownrshp* 1986
Sales 21.7MM^E *EMP* 1,100
SIC 5812 5813 American restaurant; Tavern (drinking places); American restaurant; Tavern (drinking places)
Pr: Charles Erwin
**Treas:* Robin Young
**VP:* Steve Stern

D-U-N-S 96-886-0929
HAMSARD USA INC
(*Suby of* HAMSARD 5037 LIMITED)
2330 S Nova Rd Ste A, Daytona Beach, FL 32119-2574
Tel (386) 761-1830 *Founded/Ownrshp* 2007
Sales 33.6MM^E *EMP* 175^E
SIC 3272 Bathtubs, concrete; Bathtubs, concrete
Pr: Iain Whyte

D-U-N-S 09-936-4408
HAMSHAW LUMBER INC
CHESHIRE HORSE
3 Bradco St, Keene, NH 03431-3900
Tel (603) 352-6506 *Founded/Ownrshp* 1980
Sales 28.4MM *EMP* 140
Accts Oster & Wheeler Pc Cpas Kee
SIC 5211 Lumber & other building materials; Lumber & other building materials
Pr: Douglas P Hamshaw
**VP:* Kenneth Hamshaw
Web Dev: Scott Hamshaw
Board of Directors: Mark Carrier

D-U-N-S 01-668-2700
HAMSTRA BUILDERS INC
HAMSTRA GROUP
12028 N 200 W, Wheatfield, IN 46392-9615
Tel (219) 956-3111 *Founded/Ownrshp* 1956
Sales 56.8MM^E *EMP* 90
SIC 1542 1541 6512 Commercial & office building, new construction; Industrial buildings, new construction; Nonresidential building operators; Commercial & office building, new construction; Industrial buildings, new construction; Nonresidential building operators
CEO: Wilbert Hamstra
**Pr:* Greg A Hamstra
**Ex VP:* Mitch Van Kley
**VP:* Robert I Przybylsk

HAMSTRA GROUP
See HAMSTRA BUILDERS INC

D-U-N-S 03-986-6801
HAMTRAMCK PUBLIC SCHOOLS
HPS
3201 Roosevelt St, Detroit, MI 48212-3753
Tel (313) 892-2013 *Founded/Ownrshp* 1909
Sales 22.0MM^E *EMP* 377
SIC 8211 Boarding school; Public elementary school; Public junior high school; Public senior high school; Boarding school; Public elementary school; Public junior high school; Public senior high school

HAN AH REUM
See HAR RIDGEFIELD CORP

HAN AH REUM SUPERMARKET
See MELROSE PARK HAR INC

D-U-N-S 82-486-2379 IMP/EXP
HAN FENG INC
HD FOOD SERVICES
6001 W Market St, Greensboro, NC 27409-2145
Tel (336) 268-2080 *Founded/Ownrshp* 1997
Sales 56.5MM^E *EMP* 60
SIC 5148 5146 5147 Fresh fruits & vegetables; Fish & seafoods; Meats & meat products
Pr: Chan Sin Wong
**VP:* Zhou Min Ni

D-U-N-S 60-476-0210
HAN NARA ENTERPRISES LP
ASHLEY FURNITURE HOMESTORE
5026 Frankford Ave, Lubbock, TX 79424-1131
Tel (806) 687-3000 *Founded/Ownrshp* 2005
Sales 51.4MM^E *EMP* 250
SIC 5712 Furniture stores; Furniture stores
Genl Pt: Aggie Choi

D-U-N-S 60-714-6735
HANA FINANCIAL INC
1000 Wilshire Blvd Fl 20, Los Angeles, CA 90017-5645
Tel (213) 240-1234 *Founded/Ownrshp* 1994
Sales 35.0MM^E *EMP* 130
SIC 7359 6153 6159 Factoring services; Equipment rental & leasing; Small business investment companies; Equipment rental & leasing; Factoring services; Small business investment companies
CEO: Sunnie S Kim
Ex VP: Louis Sulpizo
Sr VP: Charles Cho
Sr VP: Rosario Jauregui
Sr VP: Ken Lee
Sr VP: Susan Lee
Sr VP: Sung OH
**Sr VP:* Young Shim
Sr VP: Neil Sokoler
Sr VP: Kevin Thomas
VP: Irene Baca
VP: Charlotte Kwoun
Exec: Virginia Tatlonghi

D-U-N-S 10-310-8874 IMP
HANA SPORTS INC
13942 Orange Ave, Paramount, CA 90723-2029
Tel (562) 232-0020 *Founded/Ownrshp* 1981
Sales 26.1MM^E *EMP* 32
SIC 5139 Footwear, athletic
CEO: Sang Churl Chon
**VP:* Bruce Lee

D-U-N-S 14-318-0235
HANAHREUM CORP
8103 Lee Hwy, Falls Church, VA 22042-1111
Tel (703) 573-6300 *Founded/Ownrshp* 1997
Sales 22.7MM *EMP* 72
SIC 5411 Grocery stores; Grocery stores
Pr: Ilyeon Kewon
Exec: Young Kim

HANAHREUM GROUP
See GRAND SUPERCENTER INC

D-U-N-S 00-906-4242 IMP
HANAN ENTERPRISE SALES INC
10 Beena Way, Manalapan, NJ 07726-4330
Tel (732) 617-2269 *Founded/Ownrshp* 1991
Sales 25.0MM^E *EMP* 4
SIC 5122 Cosmetics, perfumes & hair products; Cosmetics, perfumes & hair products
Pr: Michael Barbanel

D-U-N-S 02-666-7451
HANBURY EVANS WRIGHT VLATTAS + CO
120 Atlantic St, Norfolk, VA 23510-1729
Tel (757) 321-9600 *Founded/Ownrshp* 1979
Sales 20.3MM *EMP* 80
SIC 8712 7389 Architectural services; Interior designer; Architectural services; Interior designer
Pr: Jane C Wright
**COO:* Nicholas E Vlattas
**VP:* S Michael Evans
Mng Dir: L Roberts
Mng Dir: David A Smith
CTO: Ron Agresta
Dir IT: David Turnbull

D-U-N-S 07-896-0788
HANCEVILLE NURSING HOME INC
420 Main St Ne, Hanceville, AL 35077-5455
Tel (256) 352-6481 *Founded/Ownrshp* 1996
Sales 23.6MM^E *EMP* 204
SIC 1752 Floor laying & floor work; Floor laying & floor work
Pr: Donna Guthrie
Off Mgr: Maxine Elliot

D-U-N-S 05-162-8675 IMP
HANCHETT ENTRY SYSTEMS INC
H E S
(*Suby of* ASSA ABLOY INC) ★
10027 S 51st St Ste 102, Phoenix, AZ 85044-5219
Tel (623) 582-4626 *Founded/Ownrshp* 1998
Sales 20.8MM^E *EMP* 85
SIC 3699 3429 Security control equipment & systems; Manufactured hardware (general)
Pr: Scott Baker
Pr: Michael A Webb
Treas: Deon Arnold
VP: Paul Hodges

D-U-N-S 00-543-5896
HANCHETT PAPER CO (IL)
SHORR PACKAGING
800 N Commerce St, Aurora, IL 60504-7931
Tel (630) 978-1000 *Founded/Ownrshp* 1945, 1953
Sales 228.5MM^E *EMP* 230
SIC 5084 5199 Packaging materials; Processing & packaging equipment; Packaging materials
Pr: Craig Funkhouser
CFO: Bert Dieter
**CFO:* Kevin Vrba
**Sec:* Leo A Dieter
Exec: Tim Ewalt
Brnch Mgr: Lila Fischer
Brnch Mgr: Tim Milet
Brnch Mgr: Kevin Mills
Brnch Mgr: Robert Taylor
Brnch Mgr: Mark Trainer
Dir IT: Bill Riley

D-U-N-S 02-967-7390 IMP
HANCOCK & MOORE INC
CABOT WRENN
166 Hancock & Moore Ln, Hickory, NC 28601
Tel (828) 495-8235 *Founded/Ownrshp* 1981
Sales 97.3MM^E *EMP* 500
SIC 2512 2522 Couches, sofas & davenports: upholstered on wood frames; Chairs: upholstered on wood frames; Chairs, office: padded or plain, except wood; Couches, sofas & davenports: upholstered on wood frames; Chairs: upholstered on wood frames; Chairs, office: padded or plain, except wood
CEO: Jack Glasheen
**Pr:* Tim Rogers
**Ex VP:* Jimmy L Moore
VP: Thomas O'Connell
IT Man: Chris Dale
Sfty Mgr: Tamalita Smith

D-U-N-S 60-303-8571 EXP
HANCOCK & MOORE INC
CABOT WRENN
405 Rink Dam Rd, Hickory, NC 28601
Tel (828) 495-4607 *Founded/Ownrshp* 1982
Sales 32.0MM^E *EMP* 400
SIC 2512 5712 2522 2521 2511 Upholstered household furniture; Furniture stores; Office furniture, except wood; Wood office furniture; Wood household furniture; Upholstered household furniture; Furniture stores; Office furniture, except wood; Wood office furniture; Wood household furniture
Pr: Ryan Stites
**CEO:* Jack Glachaen
VP: Bradley Killian
**VP:* Jimmy Moore
IT Man: Judy Caywood
Plnt Mgr: Bryan Craft
Plnt Mgr: Jim Scott

D-U-N-S 00-694-6404
■ **HANCOCK BANK OF LOUISIANA** (LA)
(*Suby of* HANCOCK HOLDING CO) ★
2600 Citiplace Ct Ste 125, Baton Rouge, LA 70808-2718
Tel (225) 248-7100 *Founded/Ownrshp* 1946
Sales NA *EMP* 834
SIC 6022 State trust companies accepting deposits, commercial; State trust companies accepting deposits, commercial
Pr: Hartie Spence
Ofcr: Tina Delvalle
Ofcr: Mary Pucheu
Sr VP: Sam Kendricks
VP: Gale Bonaventure
Exec: Robert Bluth
CTO: Don Castle
Dir IT: Ronald Milliet

D-U-N-S 00-618-4931
HANCOCK CONCRETE PRODUCTS LLC (MN)
17 Atlantic Ave, Hancock, MN 56244-9715
Tel (320) 392-5207 *Founded/Ownrshp* 1917
Sales 37.7MM^E *EMP* 240
SIC 3272 Culvert pipe, concrete; Sewer pipe, concrete; Manhole covers or frames, concrete; Culvert pipe, concrete; Sewer pipe, concrete; Manhole covers or frames, concrete
**VP:* David Schmidgall
Sfty Mgr: Cory Jones
Opers Mgr: Terry Nohl
Plnt Mgr: Todd Greig
Plnt Mgr: Doug Schmidgall
Plnt Mgr: John Tuttle
Sls Mgr: Scott Hofer

HANCOCK COUNTY
See COUNTY OF HANCOCK

D-U-N-S 06-343-3031
HANCOCK COUNTY BOARD OF EDUCATION
104 N Court, New Cumberland, WV 26047-9602
Tel (304) 564-3411 *Founded/Ownrshp* 1899
Sales 41.8MM *EMP* 807
Accts State Of West Virginia-Glen B
SIC 8211 Public elementary school; Public junior high school; Public senior high school; Public special education school; Public elementary school; Public junior high school; Public senior high school; Public special education school
Prin: Danny Kaser
VP: Betsy Martin

D-U-N-S 15-494-0860
HANCOCK COUNTY BOARD OF EDUCATION
HANCOCK COUNTY SCHOOLS
11311 Ga Highway 15, Sparta, GA 31087-4123
Tel (706) 444-5775 *Founded/Ownrshp* 1950
Sales 16.8MM^E *EMP* 300
SIC 8211 8748 7999 Public elementary & secondary schools; Business consulting; Recreation center; Public elementary & secondary schools; Business consulting; Recreation center

D-U-N-S 02-217-4163
HANCOCK COUNTY COOPERATIVE OIL ASSOCIATION
245 State St, Garner, IA 50438-1121
Tel (641) 923-2635 *Founded/Ownrshp* 1930
Sales 23.6MM *EMP* 66
SIC 5411 5171 5531 Convenience stores, independent; Petroleum bulk stations & terminals; Automotive tires; Convenience stores, independent; Petroleum bulk stations & terminals; Automotive tires
Pr: Dan Brozik
Brnch Mgr: Betty Davis
Genl Mgr: Brad Frein

D-U-N-S 08-141-8980
HANCOCK COUNTY SCHOOL DISTRICT
17304 Highway 603, Kiln, MS 39556-8210
Tel (228) 255-0376 *Founded/Ownrshp* 1955
Sales 29.0MM^E *EMP* 500
SIC 8211 9111 Public elementary & secondary schools; County supervisors' & executives' offices; Public elementary & secondary schools; County supervisors' & executives' offices
Schl Brd P: Jennifer Seal

HANCOCK COUNTY SCHOOLS
See HANCOCK COUNTY BOARD OF EDUCATION

D-U-N-S 07-979-8972
HANCOCK COUNTY SCHOOLS
104 N Court, New Cumberland, WV 26047-9602
Tel (304) 564-3411 *Founded/Ownrshp* 2015
Sales 6.2MM^E *EMP* 419^E
SIC 8211 Public elementary & secondary schools
HC Dir: Andrea Dulaney

D-U-N-S 03-345-2954 IMP
▲ **HANCOCK FABRICS INC**
1 Fashion Way, Baldwyn, MS 38824-8547
Tel (662) 365-6000 *Founded/Ownrshp* 1957
Sales 283.1MM *EMP* 3,100
Accts Burr Pilger Mayer Inc San F
Tkr Sym HKFI *Exch* OTO
SIC 5949 Sewing, needlework & piece goods; Fabric stores piece goods; Notions, including trim; Patterns: sewing, knitting & needlework; Sewing, needlework & piece goods; Fabric stores piece goods; Notions, including trim; Patterns: sewing, knitting & needlework
Pr: Steven R Morgan
COO: Gail Moore
CFO: James B Brown
Sr VP: Dean Abraham
Sr VP: Dennis Lyons
Sr VP: Bob Monroe
Sr VP: Susan Zewicke
VP: Sue Arlotta
VP: Joe Finley
VP: Tony Gillette
VP: Debby Hettinger
VP: Cheryl McDonald
VP: Linda G Moore
VP: Bill Sheffield
Exec: Linda Mangum
Creative D: Todd Knowlton
Comm Man: Stephanie Waits
Board of Directors: Sam P Cortez, Steven D Scheiwe, Neil S Subin

D-U-N-S 12-269-4490
▲ **HANCOCK HOLDING CO**
2510 14th St, Gulfport, MS 39501-1948
Tel (228) 868-4000 *Founded/Ownrshp* 1984
Sales NA *EMP* 3,794^E
Tkr Sym HBHC *Exch* NGS
SIC 6022 State commercial banks; State commercial banks
Pr: John M Hairston
**Ch Bd:* James B Estabrook Jr
Pr: Joseph S Exnicios
CFO: Michael M Achary
Chf Cred: Samuel B Kendricks
Chf Cred: Suzanne C Thomas
Ofcr: D Shane Loper
Ofcr: Roxanne Reynolds
Ex VP: Michael K Dickerson
Ex VP: Edward G Francis
Ex VP: Joy Lambert Phillips
Ex VP: Clifton J Saik
VP: Freida Dobson
VP: John Fox
VP: Emile Koury
VP: Kristy Oehms
VP: Thom Swanson
VP: Spencer Wiggins
Board of Directors: Robert W Roseberry, Frank E Bertucci, Anthony J Topazi, Hardy B Fowler, Terence E Hall, Randall W Hanna, James H Horne, Jerry L Levens, Eric J Nickelsen, Thomas H Olinde, Christine L Pickering

D-U-N-S 09-551-5466
HANCOCK LIFE INSURANCE CO (USA) JOHN
JOHN HANCOCK
(*Suby of* JOHN HANCOCK FINANCIAL SERVICES INC) ★
201 Townsend St Ste 900, Lansing, MI 48933-1529
Tel (248) 644-1444 *Founded/Ownrshp* 1982
Sales NA *EMP* 200
SIC 6311 Life insurance carriers; Life insurance carriers
Ch Bd: John Desprez III
**Treas:* Denis Turner

D-U-N-S 19-982-5662
HANCOCK LUMBER CO INC
4 Edes Falls Rd, Casco, ME 04015-3053
Tel (207) 627-4201 *Founded/Ownrshp* 1989
Sales 141.2MM^E *EMP* 550
SIC 5211 5031 Lumber & other building materials; Lumber, plywood & millwork; Lumber & other building materials; Lumber, plywood & millwork
Pr: Kevin Hancock
**CFO:* Glenn Alby
VP: Ronald Wormwood
Genl Mgr: Joe Koval
Genl Mgr: Cary Latham
Genl Mgr: Steve Rickert
Genl Mgr: Joshua Wiseman
Store Mgr: Matt Newcomb
IT Man: Kevin Murphy
Sfty Mgr: Gregg Speed
Opers Mgr: Jim Foster

D-U-N-S 92-931-6784
HANCOCK MEDICAL CENTER INC
149 Drinkwater Rd, Bay Saint Louis, MS 39520-1658
Tel (228) 467-8600 *Founded/Ownrshp* 1984
Sales 43.6MM *EMP* 200^E
SIC 8062 General medical & surgical hospitals; General medical & surgical hospitals
CEO: Hal Leftwich
Chf Path: Robert A Brierty
CFO: Brandon Slocum
Dir Risk M: Robin Barnett
Dir QC: Sydney Saucier

D-U-N-S 79-786-3255
HANCOCK NATURAL RESOURCE GROUP INC
JOHN HANCOCK
(*Suby of* JOHN HANCOCK LIFE INSURANCE CO (USA)) ★
99 High St Fl 26, Boston, MA 02110-2377
Tel (617) 747-1600 *Founded/Ownrshp* 2008
Sales NA *EMP* 150
SIC 6411 Insurance agents & brokers
CEO: Daniel Christensen
**Pr:* Celine Bernier
**Pr:* Bill Peressini
COO: Bruce McKnight
CFO: Charlie Amalfi
**CFO:* Mike Morgan
Ofcr: Daniel Lambert
**VP:* Carolyn Bailey
VP: Brett Macneil
**VP:* Suzanne Sturman

**VP:* Oliver Williams
VP: Joan Wilson

D-U-N-S 19-516-9461
HANCOCK PARK ASSOCIATES II LP
10350 Santa Monica Blvd # 295, Los Angeles, CA 90025-5074
Tel (310) 228-6900 *Founded/Ownrshp* 1986
Sales 118.1MM^E *EMP* 682
SIC 6552 Subdividers & developers; Subdividers & developers
Genl Pt: Michael J Fourticq
Pt: Ted Fourticq
Pt: Michael F Gooch
VP: Martin Irani
Dir IT: Ekta Chopra
Genl Couns: Eric Foker

D-U-N-S 07-204-2070
HANCOCK REGIONAL HOSPITAL
801 N State St, Greenfield, IN 46140-1270
Tel (317) 462-5544 *Founded/Ownrshp* 2010
Sales 193.9MM *EMP* 1,300
Accts Blue & Co Llc Indianapolis
SIC 8062 General medical & surgical hospitals; General medical & surgical hospitals
CEO: Robert C Keen
Chf OB: Thomas Jones
Chf Rad: Mary Wolfe
COO: Michael Fletcher
Treas: Rick Edwards
Treas: David Willis
VP: Bobbi Dunne
VP: Roberta Dunne
VP: Sherry Gehring
VP: Carolyn Konfirst
Dir Rx: Tim Livesay

D-U-N-S 00-779-2633
HANCOCK RURAL TELEPHONE CORP
HANCOCK TELECOM
2243 E Main St, Greenfield, IN 46140-8135
Tel (317) 326-3131 *Founded/Ownrshp* 1953
Sales 46.6MM *EMP* 50
SIC 4813 Local telephone communications
Ch Bd: Darrell Thomas
**Pr:* Tim Hills
VP: Mike Kindler
IT Man: Monica Sexton
Prd Mgr: John West
Sls Dir: Jill Snyder

HANCOCK TELECOM
See HANCOCK RURAL TELEPHONE CORP

HANCOCK, W S CONSTRUCTION CO
See W S RED HANCOCK INC

D-U-N-S 00-893-0463
HANCOCK-WOOD ELECTRIC COOPERATIVE INC
2451 Grant Rd, North Baltimore, OH 45872-9665
Tel (419) 257-3241 *Founded/Ownrshp* 1938
Sales 44.3MM *EMP* 45
SIC 4911 Electric services; Electric services
Pr: George Walton
VP: Marcia Jones
Opers Mgr: Bill Barnhart

D-U-N-S 14-748-8266 IMP/EXP
■ **HANCOR HOLDING CORP**
(*Suby of* ADVANCED DRAINAGE SYSTEMS INC) ★
401 Olive St, Findlay, OH 45840-5358
Tel (419) 422-6521 *Founded/Ownrshp* 2005
Sales 157.3MM^E *EMP* 1,095
SIC 3084 Plastics pipe; Plastics pipe
Pr: Steven Anderson
CFO: John Haughawout
CFO: John Maag
VP: Barbara Mewhorter

D-U-N-S 05-163-3139 IMP/EXP
■ **HANCOR INC**
(*Suby of* HANCOR HOLDING CORP) ★
4640 Trueman Blvd, Hilliard, OH 43026-2438
Tel (614) 658-0050 *Founded/Ownrshp* 1968
Sales 157.3MM^E *EMP* 1,000
SIC 3084 3088 3089 3083 Plastics pipe; Plastics plumbing fixtures; Septic tanks, plastic; Laminated plastics plate & sheet; Plastics pipe; Plastics plumbing fixtures; Septic tanks, plastic; Laminated plastics plate & sheet
Pr: Steven A Anderson
**CFO:* John Maag
**VP:* William E Altermatt
**VP:* Pat Ferren
**VP:* Derek Kamp
Dir IT: Tim Stuart
Opers Supe: Linda Morris
Plnt Mgr: Larry Dunson
Plnt Mgr: Lark Inniger

D-U-N-S 07-912-9334
HAND ARENDALL LLC (AL)
11 N Water St Ste 30200, Mobile, AL 36602-3809
Tel (251) 432-5511 *Founded/Ownrshp* 1900, 1940
Sales 20.9MM^E *EMP* 133
SIC 8111 General practice law office; General practice law office
Pr: Alesia Day
**CEO:* Treston Bolt
COO: Anne Burrows
Chf Mktg O: Dawn Pontious
IT Man: Semih Kangal

D-U-N-S 13-620-7516
HAND CONSTRUCTION CO
(*Suby of* NEVADA HAND INC) ★
295 E Warm Springs Rd, Las Vegas, NV 89119-4210
Tel (702) 410-2701 *Founded/Ownrshp* 1997
Sales 27.3MM *EMP* 11
SIC 1531 Operative builders; Operative builders
Pr: Michael Mullin
**CFO:* Margaret A Freman
Ex VP: Bob Feibleman
**Ex VP:* Robert D Feibleman
IT Man: Merida Contreras
Pr Mgr: Lee Caffrey

D-U-N-S 03-795-7446
HAND CONSTRUCTION LLC
9445 Stevens Rd Ste 200, Shreveport, LA 71106-7573
Tel (318) 686-4170 *Founded/Ownrshp* 1980
Sales 25.2MM^E *EMP* 38^E
SIC 1542 1522 1541 Commercial & office building contractors; Multi-family dwellings, new construction; Industrial buildings, new construction
CFO: Adam Hubble

D-U-N-S 12-067-3947 IMP
■ **HAND HELD PRODUCTS INC**
HONEYWELL IMAGING AND MOBILITY
(*Suby of* HONEYWELL INTERNATIONAL INC) ★
700 Visions Dr, Skaneateles Falls, NY 13153-5312
Tel (315) 554-6000 *Founded/Ownrshp* 1999
Sales 193.7MM^E *EMP* 770
SIC 3577 3571 3663 3578 Magnetic ink & optical scanning devices; Electronic computers; Radio & TV communications equipment; Calculating & accounting equipment; Magnetic ink & optical scanning devices; Electronic computers; Radio & TV communications equipment; Calculating & accounting equipment
Ch Bd: John F Waldron
**CEO:* Kevin Jost
**CFO:* Joseph Hennigan
**Ch:* Darius Adamczyk
VP: Michael A Ehrhart
**VP:* David Guido
VP: Kim Ingram
Ex Dir: Paul Dickau
Prgrm Mgr: Michael Pease
Software D: David Mangicaro
Mfg Mgr: Paul Puleo

D-U-N-S 04-029-3219
HAND SURGERY ASSOCIATES OF INDIANA INC
INDIANA HAND CENTER
8501 Harcourt Rd, Indianapolis, IN 46260-2046
Tel (317) 872-5101 *Founded/Ownrshp* 1973
Sales 22.7MM^E *EMP* 240
SIC 8011 Physicians' office, including specialists; Physicians' office, including specialists
Pr: William B Kleinman MD
Mng Pt: James Creighton
**Sr VP:* Hill Hastings II
VP: Robert M Baltera MD
**VP:* Alexander D Mih MD
Exec: Mary Miller
Off Mgr: Cindy Vocke
Surgeon: Jeffrey Greenberg
Doctor: Kurt Anderson
Doctor: Christopher Henley
Doctor: Larry Lett

D-U-N-S 11-835-5981
HANDBILL PRINTERS LP
820 E Parkridge Ave, Corona, CA 92879-6611
Tel (951) 547-5910 *Founded/Ownrshp* 1984
Sales 34.9MM^E *EMP* 45
SIC 2752 7336 Commercial printing, lithographic; Graphic arts & related design; Commercial printing, lithographic; Graphic arts & related design
Pr: Don J Messick
Pt: Dane Messick

HANDEE HUGO'S
See SAMPSON-BLADEN OIL CO INC

HANDEE HUGO'S
See UNITED ENERGY INC

HANDERA
See TRG PRODUCTS INC

D-U-N-S 62-300-0192
HANDEX CONSULTING AND REMEDIATION LLC
HCR
1350 Orange Ave Ste 101, Winter Park, FL 32789-4932
Tel (352) 735-1800 *Founded/Ownrshp* 2005
Sales 90.6MM^E *EMP* 140
SIC 4959 Toxic or hazardous waste cleanup; Toxic or hazardous waste cleanup
Ch: Brett Fadeley
Pr: Bruce Bosserman
CEO: Robert B Case
Genl Mgr: Robert Sevret
CIO: Richard Beard
IT Man: Rob Santana

D-U-N-S 02-592-0588 IMP/EXP
HANDGARDS INC
901 Hawkins Blvd, El Paso, TX 79915-1202
Tel (915) 779-6606 *Founded/Ownrshp* 1986
Sales 70.6MM^E *EMP* 300^E
SIC 3089 2673 3021 2385 3081 2326 Work gloves, plastic; Plastic containers, except foam; Plastic bags: made from purchased materials; Boots, plastic; Aprons, waterproof: made from purchased materials; Bibs, waterproof: made from purchased materials; Unsupported plastics film & sheet; Men's & boys' work clothing; Work gloves, plastic; Plastic containers, except foam; Plastic bags: made from purchased materials; Boots, plastic; Aprons, waterproof: made from purchased materials; Bibs, waterproof: made from purchased materials; Unsupported plastics film & sheet; Men's & boys' work clothing
CEO: Robert McLellan
Ex VP: Bob Hamilton
Ex VP: Robert Hamilton
VP: Mark Collier
VP: Brian Hughes
VP: Ana Ramos
Exec: Rebecca Trujillo
Dist Mgr: John Carpenter
IT Man: Thomson Jerry
Sfty Dirs: Alicia Duran
Opers Mgr: Sergio Vela

D-U-N-S 00-510-1126 IMP
HANDI PRODUCTS INC
HANDI-RAMP
510 North Ave, Libertyville, IL 60048-2025
Tel (847) 816-7525 *Founded/Ownrshp* 1958
Sales 21.3MM^E *EMP* 32
SIC 5084 3446 Metalworking machinery; Architectural metalwork
CEO: Thomas Disch
Off Mgr: Lee Teplitz
IT Man: Jaime Gibbs
Web Dev: Andon Mardov
Sls Mgr: Jeff Mann
Sls Mgr: Jim Shaw
Sales Asso: Alex Disch
Sales Asso: Christopher Diver
Snr Mgr: Paul Gerth

D-U-N-S 04-428-6263 IMP
HANDI QUILTER INC
501 N 400 W, North Salt Lake, UT 84054-2704
Tel (877) 697-8458 *Founded/Ownrshp* 2011
Sales 73.4MM^E *EMP* 100
SIC 5064 Sewing machines, household: electric
CEO: Darren Denning
**Pr:* Mark D Hyland
**VP:* Scott Heiner
**Prin:* Laurel Barrus
Board of Directors: Nate Arnesen, Brenda Groelz, Scott Heiner, Gary Konzak, Glen Salter, Shelly Withers

D-U-N-S 07-106-3796
HANDI SKILLS INC (NC)
GOODWILL INDUSTRIES
1616 Patton Ave, Asheville, NC 28806-1726
Tel (828) 771-2192 *Founded/Ownrshp* 1969
Sales 11.1MM^E *EMP* 400
SIC 8331 Job counseling; Vocational rehabilitation agency
Pr: Joshua Pierce

D-U-N-S 05-587-2634 IMP/EXP
HANDI-CRAFT CO
4433 Fyler Ave, Saint Louis, MO 63116-1803
Tel (314) 773-2979 *Founded/Ownrshp* 2005
Sales 45.0MM^E *EMP* 266
SIC 3944 4783 Games, toys & children's vehicles; Packing & crating; Games, toys & children's vehicles; Packing & crating
Pr: Carl Rhodes
**CFO:* Roger Patterson
**VP:* Charles Miller
Off Mgr: Donna Jackson
QA Dir: Kelly Kane
Mtls Mgr: Matthew Whaley
VP Sls: Dan Orsini
Mktg Dir: Jesse Lehnhoff
Mktg Mgr: Christy Pogorelac

D-U-N-S 11-538-1139 IMP
HANDI-FOIL CORP
135 E Hintz Rd, Wheeling, IL 60090-6059
Tel (847) 520-1000 *Founded/Ownrshp* 1984
Sales 87.0MM^E *EMP* 840
SIC 3497 Foil containers for bakery goods & frozen foods; Foil containers for bakery goods & frozen foods
Pr: Norton Sarnoff
**CFO:* Peter Perkins
**VP:* Brad Sarnoff
Plnt Mgr: Rich Kendzior
Snr Mgr: Kathy Buntrock

D-U-N-S 00-348-5158
HANDI-HOUSE MFG CO
741 Us Highway 1 S, Swainsboro, GA 30401-4983
Tel (478) 237-6708 *Founded/Ownrshp* 1979
Sales 22.1MM^E *EMP* 140
SIC 3448 Buildings, portable: prefabricated metal; Carports: prefabricated metal; Buildings, portable: prefabricated metal; Carports: prefabricated metal
Pr: Donald E Flanders
**Sec:* Lois Phillips
**VP:* Steelie Moore

HANDI-MART
See BP OIL PRODUCTS JOBBER/SANGAREE OIL CO

HANDI-RAMP
See HANDI PRODUCTS INC

D-U-N-S 06-961-8593
HANDICAP VILLAGE
OPPORTUNITY VILLAGE
1200 N 9th St W, Clear Lake, IA 50428-1100
Tel (641) 357-5277 *Founded/Ownrshp* 1971
Sales 26.4MM *EMP* 484
Accts Williams & Associates Plc Mas
SIC 8361 Home for the mentally handicapped; Home for the physically handicapped; Home for the mentally handicapped; Home for the physically handicapped
CEO: John Severtson
**CFO:* Greg Braun
**Treas:* Marcus Younge
VP: Todd Rognes
**VP:* Vickie Snyder
MIS Dir: Chancy Chipman
MIS Dir: Elda Stone

D-U-N-S 07-807-5868
HANDICAPPED DEVELOPMENT CENTER
3402 Hickory Grove Rd, Davenport, IA 52806-3312
Tel (563) 391-4834 *Founded/Ownrshp* 1969
Sales 17.5MM *EMP* 350
Accts Anderson Lower Whitlow Pc Bet
SIC 8331 6552 2396 Vocational rehabilitation agency; Subdividers & developers; Automotive & apparel trimmings; Vocational rehabilitation agency; Subdividers & developers; Automotive & apparel trimmings
Ex Dir: Michael F Mc Aleer
Treas: Ann Kautz

HANDIMART FOOD STORES
See NORDSTROM OIL CO

D-U-N-S 05-666-5417
HANDLER TEXTILE CORP
AALPHA DIE
60 Metro Way, Secaucus, NJ 07094-1913
Tel (201) 272-2000 *Founded/Ownrshp* 1980
Sales 63.7MM *EMP* 35
Accts Mahoney Cohen & Company Cpa Pc
SIC 5131 Piece goods & other fabrics; Textiles, woven; Piece goods & other fabrics; Textiles, woven
Pr: Ed Lemack
**CFO:* James Pope
**Ex VP:* Jay Waxer
**VP Sls:* Robert Peek

D-U-N-S 10-927-5818
HANDLERY HOTELS INC
180 Geary St Ste 700, San Francisco, CA 94108-5606
Tel (415) 781-4550 *Founded/Ownrshp* 1946
Sales 30.0MM^E *EMP* 400
SIC 7011 6512 5812 Hotels; Commercial & industrial building operation; Eating places; Hotels; Commercial & industrial building operation; Eating places
CEO: Arthur John Pekrul
**Pr:* Jon S Handlery
**Sr VP:* Michael K Handlery
**VP:* Sharon London

HANDMADE REAL FOODS
See HMR FOODS HOLDING LP

D-U-N-S 12-658-1326
HANDRAIL DESIGN INC
HDI RAILINGS
3905 Continental Dr, Columbia, PA 17512-9779
Tel (717) 285-4088 *Founded/Ownrshp* 2002
Sales 20.9MM^E *EMP* 91
SIC 3446 Railings, bannisters, guards, etc.: made from metal pipe
Pr: Kevin Downs
**Sec:* Tracy Downs
Ex Dir: Mary Phong

D-U-N-S 07-872-6728 IMP
HANDS USA CORP
(*Suby of* HANDS CORPORATION LTD.)
3000 Town Ctr Ste 407, Southfield, MI 48075-1172
Tel (248) 909-7830 *Founded/Ownrshp* 2009
Sales 35.0MM *EMP* 1
SIC 5051 Aluminum bars, rods, ingots, sheets, pipes, plates, etc.; Aluminum bars, rods, ingots, sheets, pipes, plates, etc.
Pr: Du Yoon

D-U-N-S 02-002-4217
HANDS-ON MOBILE AMERICAS INC (CA)
208 Utah St Ste 300, San Francisco, CA 94103-4890
Tel (415) 580-6400 *Founded/Ownrshp* 2001
Sales 35.2MM^E *EMP* 817
SIC 7373 Computer system selling services
CEO: Jonathan Sacks
**Ch Bd:* Dan Kranzler
Pr: Dave Arnold
**Pr:* Niccolo De Masi
Pr: Kevin Dent
Pr: John Rousseau
Pr: Dave Smiddy
COO: Scott Scherer
CFO: Addo Barrows
Ex VP: Robert Tercek
Sr VP: Matt Edelman
VP: David Saitta
Dir Surg: Todd Suchevits

HANDSTANDS
See AMERICAN COVERS INC

D-U-N-S 00-206-3915 IMP
HANDWEAR SALES INC (NY)
74 Bleecker St, Gloversville, NY 12078-2919
Tel (518) 725-8641 *Founded/Ownrshp* 1913
Sales 20.8MM^E *EMP* 1,200
SIC 3151 3949 2253 3021

HANDWORK CONTRACTORS
See GLEN BLOOMING CONTRACTORS INC

HANDY & HARMAN
See HANDYTUBE CORP

D-U-N-S 00-202-8876 IMP
■ **HANDY & HARMAN**
(*Suby of* HANDY & HARMAN GROUP LTD) ★
1133 Westchester Ave N-222, White Plains, NY 10604-3571
Tel (914) 461-1300 *Founded/Ownrshp* 2013
Sales 373.9MM^E *EMP* 1,621
SIC 3356 3399 3341 3317 3315 Precious metals; Gold & gold alloy: rolling, drawing or extruding; Silver & silver alloy: rolling, drawing or extruding; Gold & gold alloy bars, sheets, strip, etc.; Powder, metal; Flakes, metal; Silver powder; Secondary precious metals; Gold smelting & refining (secondary); Silver smelting & refining (secondary); Steel pipe & tubes; Tubing, mechanical or hypodermic sizes: cold drawn stainless; Wire products, ferrous/iron: made in wiredrawing plants; Cable, steel: insulated or armored; Precious metals; Gold & gold alloy: rolling, drawing or extruding; Silver & silver alloy: rolling, drawing or extruding; Gold & gold alloy bars, sheets, strip, etc.; Powder, metal; Flakes, metal; Silver powder; Secondary precious metals; Gold smelting & refining (secondary); Silver smelting & refining (secondary); Steel pipe & tubes; Tubing, mechanical or hypodermic sizes: cold drawn stainless; Wire products, ferrous/iron: made in wiredrawing plants; Cable, steel: insulated or armored
Pr: Jeffrey A Svoboda
**Sr VP:* Paul E Dixon
**Sr VP:* James McCabe
**VP:* Paul W Bucha
**VP:* Robert A Davidow
**VP:* Marvin L Olshan

D-U-N-S 96-792-6309
■ **HANDY & HARMAN GROUP LTD**
(*Suby of* HANDY & HARMAN LTD) ★
1133 Westchester Ave N-222, White Plains, NY 10604-3571
Tel (914) 461-1300 *Founded/Ownrshp* 2010
Sales 551.1MM^E *EMP* 1,925^E
SIC 3462 Turbine engine forgings, ferrous; Turbine engine forgings, ferrous
Ch: Warren G Lichtenstein
**CFO:* James F McCabe

D-U-N-S 84-938-2411 EXP
■ HANDY & HARMAN LTD
(Suby of SPH GROUP HOLDINGS LLC) ★
1133 Westchester Ave N-222, White Plains, NY 10604-3571
Tel (914) 461-1300 Founded/Ownrshp 1994
Sales 600.4MM EMP 1,925
Tkr Sym HNH Exch NAS
SIC 3339 3011 3312 Precious metals; Tire & inner tube materials & related products; Wire products, steel or iron; Precious metals; Tire & inner tube materials & related products; Wire products, steel or iron
V Ch: Jack L Howard
Ch Bd: Warren G Lichtenstein
V Ch: Glen M Kassan
CFO: Michael Held
CFO: James F McCabe Jr
Sr VP: Daniel P Murphy
Sr VP: Jeffrey A Svoboda
VP: James G Bradley
VP: Paul Dixon
VP: Eric Lussier
VP: Paul J Mooney
Board of Directors: Patrick A Demarco, Robert Frankfurt, John H McNamara Jr

D-U-N-S 00-233-5222 IMP/EXP
■ HANDY & HARMAN TUBE CO INC
CAMDEL METALS
(Suby of HANDY & HARMAN) ★
701 W Township Line Rd, Norristown, PA 19403
Tel (610) 539-3900 Founded/Ownrshp 1958
Sales 51.1MM^E EMP 303
SIC 3317 5051 Tubes, seamless steel; Metals service centers & offices
Ch Bd: Ronald La Bow
*Sr VP: Paul E Dixon
VP: Bill Spellane
MIS Dir: Larry Bonk
VP Mfg: Tom Curran

HANDY ANDY
See BEXAR COUNTY MARKETS INC

HANDY AUTO PARTS
See RJ INDUSTRIES INC

D-U-N-S 02-378-8839 EXP
HANDY CO N B
65 10th St, Lynchburg, VA 24504-1621
Tel (434) 847-4495 Founded/Ownrshp 1891
Sales 119.3MM^E EMP 330
SIC 5051 5074 5075

D-U-N-S 94-063-4512
HANDY HARDWARE LLC
8300 Tewantin Dr, Houston, TX 77061-4605
Tel (713) 644-1495 Founded/Ownrshp 2013
Sales 71.8MM^E EMP 230
SIC 5251 5072 Hardware; Hardware; Hardware; Hardware
CEO: Doug Miller
*Pr: Thomas Schifanella
*VP: John Gearing
*VP Mktg: Mickey Schulte
*VP Sls: Ken Harvey
Merch Mgr: Boyd White
Manager: Jamie Tucker

D-U-N-S 02-660-0569 IMP
■ HANDY HARDWARE WHOLESALE INC
(Suby of LITTLEJOHN & CO LLC) ★
8300 Tewantin Dr, Houston, TX 77061-4699
Tel (713) 644-1495 Founded/Ownrshp 1961
Sales 221.8MM^E EMP 410
SIC 5072 5074 5063 5031 5198 Hardware; Plumbing & hydronic heating supplies; Electrical apparatus & equipment; Lumber, plywood & millwork; Paints, varnishes & supplies; Hardware; Plumbing & hydronic heating supplies; Electrical apparatus & equipment; Lumber, plywood & millwork; Paints, varnishes & supplies
CEO: Doug Miller
*CFO: Thomas J Schifanella Jr
Ofcr: Lynn J Bradley
*Ex VP: Craig Cowart
*Sr VP: Micky Schulte
*VP: Ken Harvey
*VP: Dan King
Exec: Savanna Cashi
Dir IT: Chris Bennett
IT Man: Jon Vacek
VP Sls: Ken R Harvey

HANDY HOME
See BACKYARD PRODUCTS LLC

HANDY HOUSE CONVENIENCE STORES
See J M DAVIS INDUSTRIES INC

D-U-N-S 04-378-3679
HANDY PONTIAC CADILLAC BUICK G M C INC
405 Swanton Rd, Saint Albans, VT 05478-2611
Tel (802) 524-6531 Founded/Ownrshp 1953
Sales 120.0MM EMP 25
SIC 5511 Automobiles, new & used; Automobiles, new & used
Pr: Lawrence Handy
*Treas: Jeffrey Handy
*VP: David Handy
VP: F E Handy
Sales Asso: Korey Counos
Sales Asso: Dave Reszewski

HANDY SOLUTIONS CELLTECH
See NAVAJO MANUFACTURING CO

D-U-N-S 00-910-1569
HANDY TRUCK LINE INC
400 W 100 S, Paul, ID 83347-8634
Tel (208) 438-5071 Founded/Ownrshp 1947
Sales 28.7MM^E EMP 200
SIC 4214 7389 Local trucking with storage; ; Local trucking with storage;
Ch Bd: L Donald Handy
*Pr: Clay Handy
*Sec: Brice Morgan
*VP: Lyle Bair

HANDY TV APPLIANCE
See T V HANDY INC

HANDYMAN HARDWARE & TOOL SUP
See SERVICE TOOL CO LLC

D-U-N-S 79-677-4672 IMP
■ HANDYTUBE CORP
HANDY & HARMAN
(Suby of HANDY & HARMAN) ★
12244 Willow Grove Rd, Camden, DE 19934-2281
Tel (302) 697-9521 Founded/Ownrshp 1980
Sales 38.8MM^E EMP 220^E
SIC 3317 Steel pipe & tubes; Steel pipe & tubes
Pr: John Coates
QC Dir: Keia Bennett
Mktg Mgr: Julie Wyatt
Sls Mgr: Pam Zook

D-U-N-S 07-862-1551
HANERGY HOLDING (AMERICA) LLC
(Suby of HANERGY HOLDING GROUP LIMITED)
1350 Bayshore Hwy, Burlingame, CA 94010-1823
Tel (650) 288-3722 Founded/Ownrshp 2012
Sales 48.4MM^E EMP 400^E
SIC 3674 6719 Solar cells; Investment holding companies, except banks; Solar cells; Investment holding companies, except banks
CEO: Yi Wu
COO: Pyramythliu Liu
Dir Bus: Tony Forte
Admn Mgr: Julie Du
Counsel: Tina Hesby

D-U-N-S 07-151-8358
HANERGY HOLDING AMERICA INC
(Suby of HANERGY HOLDING GROUP LIMITED)
1350 Bayshore Hwy Ste 825, Burlingame, CA 94010-1848
Tel (650) 288-3722 Founded/Ownrshp 2011
Sales 303.3MM^E EMP 360
SIC 4911 6719 Generation, electric power; Investment holding companies, except banks; Generation, electric power; Investment holding companies, except banks
Ch Bd: Yi Wu
*Pr: Jeff Zhou
*COO: Richard Gaertner

D-U-N-S 13-936-2420 IMP
■ HANES COMPANIES INC
HANES INDUSTRIES
(Suby of LEGGETT & PLATT INC) ★
815 Buxton St, Winston Salem, NC 27101-1310
Tel (336) 747-1600 Founded/Ownrshp 1986
Sales 734.2MM^E EMP 805
SIC 5131 2261 2262 Piece goods & notions; Dyeing cotton broadwoven fabrics; Bleaching cotton broadwoven fabrics; Refinishing cotton broadwoven cloth for the trade; Dyeing: manmade fiber & silk broadwoven fabrics; Bleaching: manmade fiber & silk broadwoven fabrics; Refinishing: manmade fiber & silk broadwoven fabrics; Piece goods & notions; Dyeing cotton broadwoven fabrics; Bleaching cotton broadwoven fabrics; Refinishing cotton broadwoven cloth for the trade; Dyeing: manmade fiber & silk broadwoven fabrics; Bleaching: manmade fiber & silk broadwoven fabrics; Refinishing: manmade fiber & silk broadwoven fabrics
Pr: Jerry W Greene Jr
CFO: Kim Howard
CFO: Waller Kim Howard
Treas: J Richard Calhoun
Ex VP: Bruce Cloninger
*VP: Earnest Jett
*VP: Kenneth W Purser
VP: Tony Spencer
*VP: Michael S Walters
Exec: Ryan Day
Exec: Ian Geitner
Exec: Bill McCall
Exec: Patrick Steagall

HANES INDUSTRIES
See HANES COMPANIES INC

D-U-N-S 00-211-0492 IMP
HANES SUPPLY INC (NY)
55 James E Casey Dr, Buffalo, NY 14206-2361
Tel (716) 826-2636 Founded/Ownrshp 1930
Sales 98.5MM^E EMP 150
SIC 5085 5082 3496 1799 Contractors' materials; Industrial supplies; Cable splicing service; Miscellaneous fabricated wire products; Industrial supplies; Contractors' materials; Miscellaneous fabricated wire products; Cable splicing service
Pr: William Hanes
VP: David Learn
Dir Soc: Ted Hanes
Off Admin: Cheryl Edelman
IT Man: Amanda Maute
Sfty Mgr: Ken Jezuit
VP Mktg: Diane Morris
Sls Dir: Eric Kuras
Sls Mgr: Billy Hanes
Sls Mgr: Paul Piciulo
Sales Asso: Bob Delong

D-U-N-S 78-024-5564
■ HANESBRANDS DIRECT LLC
(Suby of HANESBRANDS INC) ★
450 W Hanes Mill Rd, Morganton, NC 28655
Tel (336) 519-8080 Founded/Ownrshp 2004
Sales 98.4MM^E EMP 10,001
SIC 8742 Business consultant; Business consultant
Prin: Catherine Long

D-U-N-S 62-145-4722 IMP/EXP
▲ HANESBRANDS INC
1000 E Hanes Mill Rd, Winston Salem, NC 27105-1383
Tel (336) 519-8080 Founded/Ownrshp 2005
Sales 5.3MMM EMP 59,825
Accts Pricewaterhousecoopers Llp Gr
Tkr Sym HBI Exch NYS
SIC 2253 2342 2341 2322 2252 2251 T-shirts & tops, knit; Bras, girdles & allied garments; Panties: women's, misses', children's & infants'; Underwear, men's & boys': made from purchased materials; Socks; Panty hose; T-shirts & tops, knit; Bras, girdles & allied garments; Panties: women's, misses', children's & infants'; Underwear, men's & boys': made from purchased materials; Socks; Panty hose
Ch Bd: Richard A Noll
COO: Gerald W Evans Jr
CFO: Richard D Moss
Bd of Dir: John Bradburn
Ofcr: Jeffrey Ritz
Ex VP: Kevin Hall
Exec: Elizabeth Burger
Creative D: Kevin Tapp
Dept Mgr: Rick Hill
Brnch Mgr: Vickie Trent
Genl Mgr: Nadine Hall
Board of Directors: Bobby J Griffin, James C Johnson, Jessica T Mathews, Robert Moran, J Patrick Mulcahy, Ronald L Nelson, Andrew J Schindler, David V Singer, Ann E Ziegler

D-U-N-S 00-279-7462
HANEY TRUCK LINE LLC (OR)
(Suby of HANEY TRUCKLINE) ★
3710 Gun Club Rd, Yakima, WA 98901-9531
Tel (509) 248-2996 Founded/Ownrshp 1924
Sales 63.3MM^E EMP 380
SIC 4731 Freight transportation arrangement; Freight transportation arrangement
Pr: Mike Richardson

HANEY TRUCKLINE
See QUALITY TRANSPORTATION SERVICES INC

D-U-N-S 04-182-2699
HANFORD COMMUNITY HOSPITAL
115 Mall Dr, Hanford, CA 93230-5786
Tel (559) 537-7300 Founded/Ownrshp 2011
Sales 222.6MM EMP 11^E
SIC 8062 General medical & surgical hospitals
Pr: Wayne A Ferch

D-U-N-S 07-185-8435
HANFORD COMMUNITY HOSPITAL
HANFORD COMMUNITY MEDICAL CTR
(Suby of ADVENTIST HEALTH SYSTEM/WEST) ★
450 Greenfield Ave, Hanford, CA 93230-3513
Tel (559) 582-9000 Founded/Ownrshp 1956
Sales 218.5MM^E EMP 700
SIC 8062 General medical & surgical hospitals; General medical & surgical hospitals
Ch: Scott Reiner
CFO: Eric Martinson
VP: Randal Fache
VP: Carrie Luyster
Dir OR: Lori Ruffner
Dir Rx: Deborah Camacho
Mktg Dir: K C Fowler
Pathlgst: Stephen M Avalos
Pathlgst: Reuben S Doggett
Obsttrcn: Richard Ellsworth

HANFORD COMMUNITY MEDICAL CTR
See HANFORD COMMUNITY HOSPITAL

D-U-N-S 10-064-4269
HANFORD ELEMENTARY SCHOOL DISTRICT
714 N White St, Hanford, CA 93230-4029
Tel (559) 585-3600 Founded/Ownrshp 1933
Sales 53.7MM EMP 700
Accts Vavrinek Trine Day & Co Ll
SIC 8211 Public elementary school; Public junior high school; Public elementary school; Public junior high school
IT Man: Karen Azevedo
Sls&Mrk Ex: Debbie Wilson

D-U-N-S 02-176-9922
HANFORD JOINT UNION HIGH SCHOOL DISTRICT
823 W Lacey Blvd, Hanford, CA 93230-4328
Tel (559) 583-5901 Founded/Ownrshp 1901
Sales 26.8MM^E EMP 400
Accts Borchardt Corona & Faeth Fre
SIC 8211 Public senior high school; Public adult education school; Public senior high school; Public adult education school
Prin: Marie Bancuelos
IT Man: Jill Shakespeare
Schl Brd P: Karol Anderson
HC Dir: Janice Ede
Pgrm Dir: Nancy Runyan

HANFORD PHARMACEUTICALS
See G C HANFORD MANUFACTURING CO

HANGER CLINIC
See HANGER INC

D-U-N-S 15-466-6218
▲ HANGER INC
HANGER CLINIC
10910 Domain Dr Ste 300, Austin, TX 78758-7807
Tel (512) 777-3800 Founded/Ownrshp 1861
Sales 941.7MM^E EMP 4,800
Tkr Sym HGR Exch NYS
SIC 8093 5047 3842 Specialty outpatient clinics; Artificial limbs; Orthopedic equipment & supplies; Prosthetic appliances; Braces, orthopedic; Abdominal supporters, braces & trusses; Specialty outpatient clinics; Artificial limbs; Orthopedic equipment & supplies; Prosthetic appliances; Braces, orthopedic; Abdominal supporters, braces & trusses
Pr: Samuel Liang
Pr: Rebecca J Hast
Pr: Kenneth W Wilson
CFO: Thomas E Kiraly
CFO: George McHenry
Treas: Russell G Allen
Ofcr: Caryn Meth-Gottfried
Ofcr: Keith Vinnecour
Ex VP: Richmond L Taylor
VP: Melissa A Debes
VP: Thomas E Hartman
Board of Directors: Christopher B Begley, Thomas P Cooper, Cynthia L Feldmann, Stephen E Hare, Cynthia L Lucchese, Richard R Pettingill, Kathryn Sullivan

D-U-N-S 00-324-3920
■ HANGER PROSTHETICS & ORTHOTICS INC (CA)
ORTHO MOLD
(Suby of HANGER CLINIC) ★
10910 Main Dr Ste 300, Austin, TX 78758
Tel (512) 777-3800 Founded/Ownrshp 1861, 1989
Sales 49.2MM^E EMP 200
SIC 3842 Limbs, artificial; Limbs, artificial
Pr: Tom Kirk
*Pr: Randy E Hosler
*CEO: Vinit Asar
CFO: George McHenry
*Ch: Ivan Sabel
Ex Dir: Mitchell Blutt

D-U-N-S 04-093-1126
HANGING ROCK LTC LLC
1435 Hwy 258 N, Kinston, NC 28504-7208
Tel (252) 523-9094 Founded/Ownrshp 2010
Sales 19.9MM^E EMP 413
SIC 1721 Wallcovering contractors; Wallcovering contractors

D-U-N-S 02-860-0133 IMP
HANGING ROOM ONLY INC
ANTHONY'S CUSTOM CLOSETS
22 Old Dock Rd Ste B, Yaphank, NY 11980-9760
Tel (631) 924-2200 Founded/Ownrshp 1992
Sales 30.9MM^E EMP 159
SIC 5211 Closets, interiors & accessories; Closets, interiors & accessories
Pr: Anthony Pergola
CFO: Antony Capcci

D-U-N-S 02-148-6814 IMP
HANIL E HWA INTERIOR SYSTEMS GEORGIA INC
(Suby of SEOYON CO., LTD.)
104 Wiley Rd, Lagrange, GA 30240-5811
Tel (706) 298-9701 Founded/Ownrshp 2010
Sales 89.1MM^E EMP 100
SIC 3089 Automotive parts, plastic
CEO: Tae Sik
*Pr: Kyung Nai Rau

D-U-N-S 61-037-1564 IMP
HANIL E-HWA INTERIOR SYSTEMS ALABAMA LLC
(Suby of SEOYON CO., LTD.)
200 Craig Industrial Park, Selma, AL 36701-8103
Tel (334) 410-7100 Founded/Ownrshp 1972
Sales 145.4MM EMP 1,350
Accts Choi Kim & Park Llp Montgom
SIC 3089 Automotive parts, plastic; Automotive parts, plastic
Pr: Jaewoong Jeon
Mtls Mgr: Sungrak Kim
Ql Cn Mgr: In Jang

D-U-N-S 10-231-3728
HANIL ELECTRONICS AMERICA
2155 Britannia Blvd Ste B, San Diego, CA 92154-8307
Tel (619) 268-3090 Founded/Ownrshp 1997
Sales 43.5MM EMP 5
Accts Kim & Yoo San Diego Californ
SIC 7359 Electronic equipment rental, except computers; Electronic equipment rental, except computers
CEO: Kim Yoon-Kyong
*CFO: Minsu Seo

HANJIN EXPRESS
See HANJIN INTERMODAL AMERICA INC

HANJIN GLOBAL LOGISTICS
See HANJIN TRANSPORTATION CO LIMITED

D-U-N-S 01-092-9029
HANJIN INTERMODAL AMERICA INC
HANJIN EXPRESS
(Suby of HANJIN TRANSPORTATION CO., LTD.)
1111 E Watson Center Rd, Carson, CA 90745-4217
Tel (310) 984-2127 Founded/Ownrshp 1996
Sales 38.5MM EMP 45
SIC 4731 Freight transportation arrangement
CEO: Ki Young Lee
*Pr: Jun B Park
IT Man: Sungjin Ahn
IT Man: Phillip Cho

D-U-N-S 07-844-8658
HANJIN SHIPPING AMERICA LLC
(Suby of EUSU HOLDINGS CO., LTD.)
80 E State Rt 4 Ste 490, Paramus, NJ 07652-2622
Tel (201) 291-4600 Founded/Ownrshp 2012
Sales 115.0MM^E EMP 600
SIC 4449 Transportation (freight) on bays & sounds of the ocean; Transportation (freight) on bays & sounds of the ocean
*CEO: Eun Young Choi

D-U-N-S 13-693-7658
HANJIN SHIPPING CO LTD
(Suby of EUSU HOLDINGS CO., LTD.)
80 E State Rt 4 Ste 490, Paramus, NJ 07652-2655
Tel (201) 291-4600 Founded/Ownrshp 1994
Sales 77.5MM^E EMP 691
SIC 4499 Steamship leasing; Steamship leasing
Ex Dir: Sung-Young Kim
VP: Christian Sur
Exec: Arif Ashfaq
Exec: Alaa Barakat
Exec: Juan Candelario
Exec: Alicia Cordova
Exec: Teresa Jimenez
Exec: Carlos Ocana
Exec: Andrea Pichardo
Exec: Erin Rogers
Exec: Balaam Valdez

D-U-N-S 16-884-9730
HANJIN TRANSPORTATION CO LIMITED
HANJIN GLOBAL LOGISTICS
(*Suby of* HANJIN CORPORATION CO., LTD)
1111 E Watson Center Rd C, Carson, CA 90745-4217
Tel (310) 522-5030 *Founded/Ownrshp* 1989
Sales 35.5MM^E *EMP* 90
SIC 4731 Transportation agents & brokers; Transportation agents & brokers
Pr: Bryce Dalziel

D-U-N-S 01-680-0955
HANK GRAFF CHEVROLET INC
800 N State Rd, Davison, MI 48423-1179
Tel (810) 653-4111 *Founded/Ownrshp* 1973
Sales 71.8MM^E *EMP* 150
SIC 5511

HANKE CONSTRUCTORS
See FACILITY DEFENSE CONSULTANTS INC

D-U-N-S 02-105-3210
HANKIN GROUP
707 Eagleview Blvd # 400, Exton, PA 19341-1159
Tel (610) 458-1900 *Founded/Ownrshp* 1958
Sales 48.2MM^E *EMP* 100
SIC 1531 6513 6512 Speculative builder, single-family houses; Apartment building operators; Commercial & industrial building operation; Speculative builder, single-family houses; Apartment building operators; Commercial & industrial building operation
Pr: Robert Hankin
CFO: R Robert McElwee

D-U-N-S 00-703-9878
HANKINS LUMBER SALES INC (MS)
496 Nat G Troutt Rd, Elliott, MS 38926
Tel (662) 226-2961 *Founded/Ownrshp* 1950
Sales 44.5MM^E *EMP* 117
SIC 5031 2421 Lumber: rough, dressed & finished; Lumber: rough, sawed or planed; Lumber: rough, dressed & finished; Lumber: rough, sawed or planed
Pr: Albert B Hankins Jr
**Sec:* Jerry A Pegg
**VP:* Lee J Hankins

D-U-N-S 11-910-8665
HANKINS SERVICES INC
6014 N State Route 9 D, Kansas City, MO 64152-3670
Tel (816) 600-5945 *Founded/Ownrshp* 2006
Sales 23.4MM^E *EMP* 100
SIC 3449 1761 Miscellaneous metalwork; Roofing contractor
Pr: Randall L Milbourn
**VP:* Paul A Coussens
VP: Paul Coussens
VP: Dan Hafley

D-U-N-S 83-229-2812
■ **HANKINSON RENEWABLE ENERGY LLC**
(*Suby of* MURPHY OIL USA INC) ★
9230 County Road 1, Hankinson, ND 58041-9484
Tel (701) 242-9420 *Founded/Ownrshp* 2009
Sales 340.0MM *EMP* 51
SIC 2869 Ethyl alcohol, ethanol; Ethyl alcohol, ethanol
Dir Lab: Shala Krump
**Genl Mgr:* Wes Plummer
Genl Mgr: Linda Schiltz

D-U-N-S 00-740-3280 IMP/EXP
HANKOOK TIRE AMERICA CORP
(*Suby of* HANKOOK TIRE WORLDWIDE CO., LTD.)
1450 Valley Rd, Wayne, NJ 07470-2039
Tel (973) 406-3500 *Founded/Ownrshp* 1981, 2003
Sales 44.4MM^E *EMP* 150
SIC 3011 Automobile tires, pneumatic; Automobile tires, pneumatic
Pr: Byeong Jin Lee
**Ex VP:* Ho Y Pae
Genl Mgr: Simon Lim
Opers Mgr: Philipp Rathgeb
Trfc Mgr: Tom Barnable
VP Sls: Dan Wheeler
Manager: Darrin King
Manager: Fabian Moran
Sls Mgr: Pablo Fabelo
Sls Mgr: Hankook-Bruce James

HANK'S DISCOUNT FINE FURNITURE
See HANKS FURNITURE INC

D-U-N-S 08-663-0373 IMP
HANKS FURNITURE INC
HANK'S DISCOUNT FINE FURNITURE
5708 Warden Rd, Sherwood, AR 72120-6070
Tel (501) 542-1000 *Founded/Ownrshp* 1981
Sales 68.4MM^E *EMP* 350
SIC 5712 Furniture stores; Furniture stores
Ch Bd: Henry C Browne
**Pr:* Mary A Browne
CFO: Scott Henderson
**VP:* Walt Davis
Dir IT: Kelly Sake
Mktg Dir: Cathy Browne

D-U-N-S 07-026-7067
HANKS SPECIALTIES INC
2050 Old Highway 8 Nw, New Brighton, MN 55112-2308
Tel (651) 633-5020 *Founded/Ownrshp* 1976
Sales 35.1MM^E *EMP* 80
SIC 5023 Floor coverings; Floor coverings
Pr: Randy Grachek
**Owner:* Bruce Grachek
Brnch Mgr: Christian Alley
Sfty Dirs: Marv Berg
Mktg Mgr: Scott Shikowsky

D-U-N-S 14-007-4189 IMP
HANKY PANKY LTD
373 Park Ave S Fl 12, New York, NY 10016-8805
Tel (212) 725-4996 *Founded/Ownrshp* 1977
Sales 86.2MM^E *EMP* 150
SIC 5137 Women's & children's lingerie & undergarments; Women's & children's lingerie & undergarments
CEO: Lida Orzeck
**Pr:* Gale Epstein
Plng Mgr: Hannah Kim
Dir IT: Chuck Lee
Prd Mgr: Rachel Stoll
Sls Dir: Ila Wood
Sls Mgr: Brenda Berger
Sls Mgr: Shannerri Dechalus

D-U-N-S 19-692-8600
HANKYU HANSHIN EXPRESS (USA) INC
(*Suby of* HANKYU HANSHIN EXPRESS CO.,LTD.)
909 W Irving Park Rd, Itasca, IL 60143-2023
Tel (630) 238-6070 *Founded/Ownrshp* 1986
Sales 61.3MM^E *EMP* 194
SIC 4731 Freight forwarding; Customhouse brokers; Freight forwarding
CEO: Seisaku Okafuji
**Pr:* Tamotsu Yamasaki
**Sec:* Tetsuya Ueno
**VP:* Naoki Kojima
**VP:* Kurt Moss

D-U-N-S 87-916-6809
HANLEES HILLTOP INC
HANLEES HILLTOP TOYOTA
3255 Auto Plz, Richmond, CA 94806-1931
Tel (510) 243-2020 *Founded/Ownrshp* 1995
Sales 27.7MM^E *EMP* 69
SIC 5511 Automobiles, new & used; Automobiles, new & used
Pr: Kyong Han
**VP:* Dong I Lee
Netwrk Mgr: Victor Cortes
Sls Mgr: David Ruiter

HANLEES HILLTOP TOYOTA
See HANLEES HILLTOP INC

HANMI
See WANG GLOBALNET

D-U-N-S 06-890-1164
■ **HANMI BANK**
(*Suby of* HANMI FINANCIAL CORP) ★
3660 Wilshire Blvd Ph A, Los Angeles, CA 90010-2387
Tel (213) 427-5757 *Founded/Ownrshp* 1981
Sales NA *EMP* 450^E
SIC 6022 State commercial banks; State commercial banks
Ch Bd: Joon H Lee
Pr: Susan Kim
Pr: Chong Guk Kum
Pr: Mohammad Tariq
COO: Bonita I Lee
CFO: Lonny D Robinson
CFO: Shick Yoon
Treas: Max Cucinella
Chf Cred: Randall G Ewig
Ofcr: Michael Adams
Ofcr: Anthony Kim
Ofcr: Greg Kim
Ofcr: Katie Kwon
Ofcr: Jean Lim
Ofcr: Sharon Min
Ofcr: Peter Yang
Ex VP: Anna Chung
Ex VP: David Yang
Sr VP: Chris Cho
Sr VP: Elaine Chung
Sr VP: Michael Gelormino
Board of Directors: George S Chey, John A Hall, Paul S Kim, Steve Y Oh, Joseph K Rho, William J Stolte

D-U-N-S 06-430-6132
▲ **HANMI FINANCIAL CORP**
3660 Wilshire Blvd Penths Ste A, Los Angeles, CA 90010
Tel (213) 382-2200 *Founded/Ownrshp* 2000
Sales NA *EMP* 499^E
Tkr Sym HAFC *Exch* NGS
SIC 6021 National commercial banks; National commercial banks
Pr: Chong Guk Kum
**Ch Bd:* Joseph K RHO
Pr: Sue Kim
COO: Bonita I Lee
CFO: Michael McCall
CFO: Michael W McCall
Ofcr: Randall G Ewig
Ofcr: Anthony Kim
Ofcr: Greg Kim
Ofcr: Sean Lee
Ofcr: Peter Yang
Ex VP: Greg D Kim
Ex VP: Min S Park
Sr VP: Juliet Stone
VP: Youn Park

D-U-N-S 09-635-6548
HANN & HANN INC (MD)
12307 Washington Ave, Rockville, MD 20852-1819
Tel (301) 468-3340 *Founded/Ownrshp* 1972
Sales 21.9MM^E *EMP* 67^E
SIC 1542 7349 Commercial & office building, new construction; Building maintenance services
Pr: Terry R Hann
**CFO:* Daniel S Wakefield
VP: Ray Feness
**VP:* Gary F Hann
VP: Andrew Martin
Dir Bus: Todd El-Taher
S&M/VP: George Duvall

HANNA
See JIM COLEMAN CO

D-U-N-S 12-164-4124 IMP
HANNA ANDERSSON LLC
(*Suby of* SUN CAPITAL PARTNERS INC) ★
608 Ne 19th Ave, Portland, OR 97232-2832
Tel (503) 242-0920 *Founded/Ownrshp* 2008
Sales 119.7MM^E *EMP* 400
SIC 5961 5641 Clothing, mail order (except women's); Children's wear; Clothing, mail order (except women's); Children's wear
Pr: Adam Stone
V Ch: Tom Wilscher
**COO:* Russ Bowers
CFO: Laura A McCue
VP: Phillip Bulebar
VP: Bonnie Choruby
VP: Julie Rood
VP: Lisa Strubel
Exec: Laura Mc Cue
Dir Soc: Cathy Hunter
Store Mgr: Angela Bergamy

D-U-N-S 07-463-4700
HANNA BOYS CENTER
17000 Arnold Dr, Sonoma, CA 95476-3242
Tel (707) 996-6767 *Founded/Ownrshp* 1946
Sales 21.8MM^E *EMP* 150
SIC 8211 Boarding school
CEO: Jack R Bertges
**CFO:* Monica Clark
CFO: Monica Clarke
**Ex Dir:* Brian Farragher
Snr Mgr: Kris Giesen

D-U-N-S 07-464-7462
HANNA BROPHY MAC LEAN MC ALEER & JENSEN LLP
555 12th St Ste 1450, Oakland, CA 94607-4085
Tel (510) 839-1180 *Founded/Ownrshp* 1943
Sales 32.9MM^E *EMP* 182
SIC 8111 General practice law office; General practice law office
Mng Pt: Leslie Tuxhorn
Pt: Joseph Nisim
Pt: Barbara Wood
Exec: Wendy Harnett
IT Man: Sean Kennedy
IT Man: Beatrice Yao

D-U-N-S 07-834-8895 IMP
HANNA CYLINDERS LLC
8901 102nd St, Pleasant Prairie, WI 53158-2212
Tel (262) 764-8300 *Founded/Ownrshp* 1986
Sales 31.9MM^E *EMP* 110
SIC 3593 3443 Fluid power cylinders & actuators; Cylinders, pressure: metal plate; Fluid power cylinders & actuators; Cylinders, pressure: metal plate
Pr: Kimball J Bradley
IT Man: Karla Gonzalez
Sls Mgr: Jorge Montemayor

D-U-N-S 07-496-0550
HANNA HOLDINGS INC
HOWARD HANNA REAL ESTATE
1090 Freeport Rd Ste 1a, Pittsburgh, PA 15238-3166
Tel (412) 967-9000 *Founded/Ownrshp* 1957
Sales 41.6MM^E *EMP* 633
SIC 6531 6162 6361 Real estate brokers & agents; Mortgage bankers & correspondents; Title insurance; Real estate brokers & agents; Mortgage bankers & correspondents; Title insurance
Ch Bd: Howard W Hanna Jr
**Pr:* Helen Hanna Casey
**Pr:* Howard W Hanna III
**CFO:* Tracy Rossettidelvaux
Ofcr: Susan Ostrowski
**Ex VP:* Annie E Hanna
**Sr VP:* Tom Ceponis
Exec: Cathy Winghart
Brnch Mgr: Linda Lafleur
Opers Mgr: Danielle Shearer
Pr Dir: Deborah Donahue

D-U-N-S 85-904-7318 IMP
HANNA INSTRUMENTS INC
584 Park East Dr, Woonsocket, RI 02895-6177
Tel (401) 765-7500 *Founded/Ownrshp* 1986
Sales 26.0MM^E *EMP* 59
SIC 3825 3845 3826 3823 2813 Electrical power measuring equipment; Electromedical equipment; Analytical instruments; Industrial instrmnts msrmnt display/control process variable; Industrial gases
Pr: Martino Nardo
**VP:* Anna Maria Nardo
Info Man: Tom Simbron
Sls Mgr: Jessica Hoagland
Sls Mgr: Mike Muzik
Board of Directors: Michelle Giguere

D-U-N-S 12-100-6415
HANNA PAPER RECYCLING INC
(*Suby of* HANNA PAPER FIBRES LIMITED)
31 Suffolk Rd, Mansfield, MA 02048-1815
Tel (508) 339-3210 *Founded/Ownrshp* 1977
Sales 29.6MM^E *EMP* 78
SIC 4953 Recycling, waste materials
Pr: George Millar Jr
**Treas:* James Millar
**VP:* Joseph Jelson

D-U-N-S 00-402-9294 IMP
HANNA STEEL CORP (AL)
4527 Southlake Pkwy, Hoover, AL 35244-3238
Tel (205) 820-5200 *Founded/Ownrshp* 1980
Sales 2.0MM *EMP* 363
SIC 3317 5051 3312 3441 Welded pipe & tubes; Metals service centers & offices; Coated or plated products; Fabricated structural metal; Welded pipe & tubes; Metals service centers & offices; Coated or plated products; Fabricated structural metal
CEO: Pete M Hanna
**Pr:* Dwarrensandra Bailey
**Ex VP:* Sam A Mango
VP: Jim Gustin
VP Opers: Roger Black
Sfty Dirs: Clark Wood
Plnt Mgr: Rick Daniel
Sales Asso: Curtis Armstrong
Sales Asso: Tony Byrd
Sales Asso: Darrell Graf
Sales Asso: Doug Green

D-U-N-S 06-569-5140
HANNABERY ELECTRIC INC
HANNABERY HVAC
200 Schantz Rd, Allentown, PA 18104-8600
Tel (610) 366-9400 *Founded/Ownrshp* 1984
Sales 29.1MM^E *EMP* 200
SIC 1711 Warm air heating & air conditioning contractor; Warm air heating & air conditioning contractor
Pr: Zach Nicolai
Treas: Richard A Lichtenwalner
Sls Mgr: Tom Bowen

HANNABERY HVAC
See HANNABERY ELECTRIC INC

D-U-N-S 00-694-9556 IMP
HANNAFORD BROS CO LLC (ME)
HANNAFORD SUPERMARKET
(*Suby of* DELHAIZE AMERICA LLC) ★
145 Pleasant Hill Rd, Scarborough, ME 04074-7118
Tel (207) 883-2911 *Founded/Ownrshp* 1883, 2000
Sales 3.8MMM^E *EMP* 26,000
SIC 5411 5912 Supermarkets; Drug stores; Supermarkets; Drug stores
CEO: Jim Moody
**Pr:* Hugh Farrington
**CFO:* Paul A Fritzson
Ex VP: Michelle Hayes
Ex VP: Ed Tag
**Sr VP:* Garrett Bowne
VP: Gary Browne
VP: David Criscione
**VP:* Emily Dickinson
VP: Emily D Dickinson
VP: Marty Greeley
VP: Charles R Hurdman
VP: Gregory Lucarelli
VP: Blythe Mc Garvie
VP: Brian Pike
VP: Tom Witwicki
VP: Brian Zappala
Exec: Karen Coughlin
Exec: Kathy Del Giacco
Exec: Gary Prairie

D-U-N-S 02-478-1213
HANNAFORD BROTHERS CO
(*Suby of* HANNAFORD BROS CO LLC) ★
145 Pleasant Hill Rd, Scarborough, ME 04074-9309
Tel (207) 883-2911 *Founded/Ownrshp* 2015
Sales 277.5MM^E *EMP* 2,700^E
SIC 5411 6519 Supermarkets, chain; Real property lessors; Supermarkets, chain; Real property lessors
Pr: Michael Vail
CFO: Paul Fritzson
Exec: Mike Fisher
Exec: Fern Pelkey
IT Man: Mary Doran

HANNAFORD SUPERMARKET
See HANNAFORD BROS CO LLC

HANNAH, DICK HONDA
See HANNAH MOTOR CO

D-U-N-S 02-756-3733
HANNAH MOTOR CO
HANNAH, DICK HONDA
3400 Ne Auto Mall Dr, Vancouver, WA 98662-7194
Tel (360) 944-3424 *Founded/Ownrshp* 1952
Sales 212.5MM^E *EMP* 625
SIC 5511 Automobiles, new & used; Automobiles, new & used
Pr: Richard Hannah
**VP:* Jason Hannah
Genl Mgr: Rachel Smith
Prd Mgr: John Curtis

D-U-N-S 03-018-8288
HANNAHVILLE INDIAN COMMUNITY
ISLAND RESORT AND CASINO
N14911 Hannahville Rd B 1, Wilson, MI 49896-9612
Tel (906) 466-2932 *Founded/Ownrshp* 1934
Sales NA *EMP* 1,000
SIC 9111 Executive offices; Executive offices
Ch Bd: Kenneth Meshigaud
**CFO:* Scott Herioux
Bd of Dir: Anna Larson
Prgrm Mgr: Stephanie Bliss
Prgrm Mgr: Robin Clark
Dir IT: Joe Stanchina
IT Man: Donald Kincheloe
Cert Phar: Jeanette Eno
Pgrm Dir: Carol Bergquist

HANNAM CHAIN SUPER 1 MARKET
See HANNAM CHAIN USA INC

D-U-N-S 18-819-1126 IMP
HANNAM CHAIN USA INC
HANNAM CHAIN SUPER 1 MARKET
2740 W Olympic Blvd, Los Angeles, CA 90006-2633
Tel (213) 382-2922 *Founded/Ownrshp* 1987
Sales 81.7MM^E *EMP* 324
SIC 5046 5411 Restaurant equipment & supplies; Supermarkets, independent; Restaurant equipment & supplies; Supermarkets, independent
CEO: Kee W Ha

D-U-N-S 05-759-2016
HANNAN SUPPLY CO
1565 N 8th St, Paducah, KY 42001-7406
Tel (270) 442-5456 *Founded/Ownrshp* 1971
Sales 21.3MM *EMP* 50
SIC 5063 5085 Electrical supplies; Industrial supplies; Electrical supplies; Industrial supplies
Pr: Bruce Brockenborough
COO: Greg Hunt
**CFO:* Katherine Zaninovich
Bd of Dir: Jim Pierce
**Ex VP:* Philip Haire
Brnch Mgr: Mack Scott
Sls Mgr: Rich Eggemeyer
Sales Asso: Brad Byers
Sales Asso: Cheryl Clary
Sales Asso: Gary Downs
Sales Asso: Gene Edwards

D-U-N-S 18-355-1662 IMP/EXP
HANNAS CANDLE CO
HCC BRANDS
2700 S Armstrong Ave, Fayetteville, AR 72701-7274
Tel (479) 443-5467 *Founded/Ownrshp* 1987
Sales 88.1MM^E *EMP* 500
SIC 3999 2844 5999 Potpourri; Candles; Toilet preparations; Candle shops; Potpourri; Candles; Toilet preparations; Candle shops
Pr: Burt Hanna
**VP:* Thad Hanna

**VP:* John Scott
**VP:* Joe Williams

D-U-N-S 00-207-4763 IMP/EXP
HANNAY REELS INC (NY)
553 State Route 143, Westerlo, NY 12193-2618
Tel (518) 797-3791 *Founded/Ownrshp* 1933
Sales 46.0MM^E *EMP* 147
SIC 3569 3499 Firehose equipment: driers, rack & reels; Reels, cable: metal; Firehose equipment: driers, rack & reels; Reels, cable: metal
Ch Bd: Roger A Hannay
**CEO:* Eric A Hannay
**VP:* Elaine Hannay Gruener
**VP:* David G Hannay
IT Man: Ron Schoof
IT Man: Ron Sholf
Sfty Dirs: Marcia Casuelu
Sfty Mgr: Mark Saker
Mktg Mgr: Jennifer Wing
Sales Asso: George Eignor
Sales Asso: Rob Motschmann

D-U-N-S 07-195-4853
HANNIBAL CLINIC OPERATIONS LLC
100 Medical Dr, Hannibal, MO 63401-6877
Tel (573) 221-5250 *Founded/Ownrshp* 1958
Sales 36.2MM^E *EMP* 333
SIC 8011 Clinic, operated by physicians; Clinic, operated by physicians
Pr: Michael Buckstein

D-U-N-S 14-718-1630 IMP/EXP
HANNIBAL INDUSTRIES INC
3851 S Santa Fe Ave, Vernon, CA 90058-1712
Tel (323) 513-1200 *Founded/Ownrshp* 2008
Sales 80.5MM^E *EMP* 297
SIC 3317 Tubes, seamless steel; Tubes, seamless steel
Pr: Blanton Bartlett
CFO: Heidy Moon
VP: Steve Rogers
QA Dir: Carlos Rosillo
VP Mfg: Don Kirk
Sls&Mrk Ex: Amanda Versulys
Sls Mgr: Terri W Felix

D-U-N-S 10-304-5696 EXP
HANNIBAL MATERIAL HANDLING
(*Suby of* HANNIBAL INDUSTRIES INC) ★
2230 E 38th St, Vernon, CA 90058-1629
Tel (323) 587-4060 *Founded/Ownrshp* 1997
Sales 47.4MM^E *EMP* 214
SIC 2542 Partitions & fixtures, except wood; Partitions & fixtures, except wood
Pr: Blanton Bartlett
**VP:* Heidy Moon
**VP:* Steve Roger
Exec: Patty Gotluzkyes
Opers Mgr: Don Kirk
Ql Cn Mgr: Jose Perez
VP Sls: Stephen Rogers

D-U-N-S 07-588-6341
HANNIBAL REGIONAL HOSPITAL FOUNDATION
175 Shinn Ln, Hannibal, MO 63401-6754
Tel (573) 629-3577 *Founded/Ownrshp* 1965
Sales 1.8MM *EMP* 850
Accts Wade Stables Pc Quincy Il
SIC 8062 General medical & surgical hospitals; General medical & surgical hospitals
Pr: Wendy Harrington
**CEO:* C Todd Ahrens
**CFO:* Roger Dix
**VP:* Jeff Evans
**VP:* Julie H Leverenz
**VP:* Doug Ruble

D-U-N-S 16-479-1902
HANNIBAL REGIONAL HOSPITAL INC
HANNIBAL REGIONAL HOSPITAL OFF
6000 Hospital Dr, Hannibal, MO 63401-6887
Tel (573) 248-1300 *Founded/Ownrshp* 1901
Sales 121.6MM *EMP* 850
SIC 8062 General medical & surgical hospitals; General medical & surgical hospitals
CEO: Lynn Olson
Bd of Dir: Arvin Abueg
VP: Jeff Evans
VP: Suzanne Koehler
VP: Julie Leverenz
Exec: Amanda Wosman
Dir OR: Lori Fohey
Dir Teleco: Jean Buffington
Dir Inf Cn: Keith Griffeth
Dir Rx: Kirstin Meyer
Dir Rx: Dawn Youngblood

HANNIBAL REGIONAL HOSPITAL OFF
See HANNIBAL REGIONAL HOSPITAL INC

D-U-N-S 12-056-5130
HANNIBAL SCHOOL DISTRICT
4650 Mcmasters Ave, Hannibal, MO 63401-2244
Tel (573) 221-1258 *Founded/Ownrshp* 1900
Sales 24.2MM^E *EMP* 500
SIC 8211 Public elementary & secondary schools; School board; Public elementary & secondary schools; School board
VP: Karen Sutor

D-U-N-S 07-875-4724
▲ HANNON ARMSTRONG SUSTAINABLE INFRASTRUCTURE CAPITAL INC
1906 Towne Centre Blvd, Annapolis, MD 21401-3676
Tel (410) 571-9860 *Founded/Ownrshp* 2000
Sales 28.6MM *EMP* 27^E
Tkr Sym HASI *Exch* NYS
SIC 6798 Real estate investment trusts
Ch Bd: Jeffrey W Eckel
COO: Nathaniel J Rose
CFO: J Brendan Herron
Ex VP: Steve L Chuslo
Ex VP: Brendan Herron
Ex VP: M Rhem Wooten Jr

D-U-N-S 00-446-3543
HANNON CO (OH)
CHARLES REWINDING DIV
1605 Waynesburg Dr Se, Canton, OH 44707-2137
Tel (330) 456-4728 *Founded/Ownrshp* 1926
Sales 27.7MM^E *EMP* 140
SIC 3621 3825 5084 3699 3612 3567 Motors, electric; Test equipment for electronic & electrical circuits; Transformers, portable: instrument; Industrial machinery & equipment; Electrical equipment & supplies; Transformers, except electric; Industrial furnaces & ovens; Motors, electric; Test equipment for electronic & electrical circuits; Transformers, portable: instrument; Industrial machinery & equipment; Electrical equipment & supplies; Transformers, except electric; Industrial furnaces & ovens
Ch Bd: Thomas W Hannon
**Pr:* Tom McAllister
**COO:* Steven R Harper
**Treas:* Patrick J Hoover
VP: John Haswell
**VP:* Merrill R Mossbarger
**Prin:* Gary Gonzalez
**Prin:* Carol Wood
IT Man: Ann Paris
**Plnt Mgr:* Mike McAllister
Sls Mgr: Steve Osborne

D-U-N-S 04-039-0163 IMP
HANNON HYDRAULICS INC
HANNON OFFSHORE DRILLING EQP
625 N Loop 12, Irving, TX 75061-8796
Tel (972) 438-2870 *Founded/Ownrshp* 1985
Sales 25.5MM *EMP* 88
Accts Teague Marquess & Associates
SIC 7699 3593 3594 Hydraulic equipment repair; Fluid power cylinders, hydraulic or pneumatic; Motors: hydraulic, fluid power or air
Pt: Wade Reed
**Pt:* Mark Klatt
**Pt:* Don Mullins
**Pt:* Clay Reed
Opers Mgr: J Mireles

HANNON OFFSHORE DRILLING EQP
See HANNON HYDRAULICS INC

D-U-N-S 79-181-1532
HANNONS FOOD SERVICE INC
361 Edgewood Terrace Dr, Jackson, MS 39206-6217
Tel (601) 982-2553 *Founded/Ownrshp* 1976
Sales 15.5MM *EMP* 450
SIC 5812 Fast-food restaurant, chain; Fast-food restaurant, chain
Pr: John L Hannon
**Sec:* Lolita Hannon

D-U-N-S 03-334-6669
HANNONS KENTUCKY FRIED CHICKEN OF JACKSON MISSISSIPPI
KFC
361 Edgewood Terrace Dr, Jackson, MS 39206-6217
Tel (601) 982-2552 *Founded/Ownrshp* 1962
Sales 8.2MM^E *EMP* 400
SIC 5812 Fast-food restaurant, chain; Fast-food restaurant, chain
Pr: John L Hannon
**Sec:* Lolita Hannon

D-U-N-S 09-743-9632
HANNOUSH JEWELERS INC
GOLDSTEIN, SWANK & GORDON
1655 Boston Rd Unit B7, Springfield, MA 01129-1155
Tel (413) 439-2830 *Founded/Ownrshp* 1980
Sales 83.5MM^E *EMP* 575
SIC 5944 Jewelry, precious stones & precious metals; Watches; Jewelry, precious stones & precious metals; Watches
Pr: Anthony A Hannoush
**Sec:* Norman Hannoush
**VP:* Camile A Hannoush
**VP:* George A Hannoush
**VP:* Nabil Hannoush
**VP:* Peter Hannoush
Brnch Mgr: Jean Courtney
Brnch Mgr: Dave Fields
Store Mgr: Peter Zografos
Dir IT: Andrea Maney
Sls Mgr: Richard McGarvey

D-U-N-S 03-173-2307
HANNOVER LIFE REASSURANCE CO OF AMERICA
1290 N Broadway Ste 1600, Denver, CO 80203-5605
Tel (303) 860-6011 *Founded/Ownrshp* 2010
Sales NA *EMP* 110
SIC 6321 Reinsurance carriers, accident & health
Pr: Peter Schaefer
VP: Steve Habegger

D-U-N-S 79-010-0911
HANNOVER LIFE REASSURANCE CO OF AMERICA
(*Suby of* HANNOVER RUCK SE)
200 S Orange Ave Ste 1900, Orlando, FL 32801-3440
Tel (407) 649-8411 *Founded/Ownrshp* 1991
Sales NA *EMP* 76^E
SIC 6311 6321 Life reinsurance; Reinsurance carriers, accident & health
Pr: Peter Schafer
Sec: Dennis Braziel
Sr VP: Steven Najjar
Sr VP: Kevin Oldani
VP: Gary Gray
VP: O Alex Kozij
VP: Anthony Laudato
VP: Cliff Titcomb
Genl Mgr: Claude Vercasson
Software D: Bibi Baldeo

D-U-N-S 01-439-0058
HANNUMS HARLEY DAVIDSON SALES INC
1011 W Baltimore Pike, Media, PA 19063-5101
Tel (610) 566-5562 *Founded/Ownrshp* 1954
Sales 20.6MM^E *EMP* 55
SIC 5571 7699 Motorcycle dealers; Motorcycle repair service
Pr: Thomas B Hannum Jr
Treas: Mary Hannum
**Sec:* Tonda Hannum Dipasqu
**VP:* Thomas B Hannum III
Dir IT: Paul Baum
Sls Mgr: John Reardon

D-U-N-S 07-881-5873
HANON SYSTEMS USA LLC
HVCC-USA
(*Suby of* HANON SYSTEMS)
1 Village Center Dr, Van Buren Twp, MI 48111-5711
Tel (734) 710-5000 *Founded/Ownrshp* 2012
Sales 275.4MM^E *EMP* 1,000^E
SIC 3714 3585 3699 Air conditioner parts, motor vehicle; Radiators & radiator shells & cores, motor vehicle; Heaters, motor vehicle; Compressors for refrigeration & air conditioning equipment; Heat emission operating apparatus; Air conditioner parts, motor vehicle; Radiators & radiator shells & cores, motor vehicle; Heaters, motor vehicle; Compressors for refrigeration & air conditioning equipment; Heat emission operating apparatus
Pr: Bob Hickson
**Mng Pt:* Robert Willing
**VP:* Kwangtaek Hong
**VP:* Jay Son
Snr Mgr: Dave Lumley

D-U-N-S 82-489-3549
HANOR CO OF WISCONSIN LLC
E4614 Us Hwy 14 And 60, Spring Green, WI 53588-9509
Tel (608) 588-9170 *Founded/Ownrshp* 1994
Sales 115.6MM^E *EMP* 670
SIC 0291 Animal specialty farm, general; Animal specialty farm, general
CEO: Myrl Mortenson
CFO: Carl Stoner
Sr VP: Baxter Gutknecht

HANORA SPINNING DIV
See FIRST REPUBLIC CORP OF AMERICA

D-U-N-S 80-459-7693
■ HANOVER AMERICAN INSURANCE CO
(*Suby of* HANOVER INSURANCE CO) ★
440 Lincoln St, Worcester, MA 01653-0002
Tel (508) 855-1000 *Founded/Ownrshp* 2008
Sales NA *EMP* 1^E
SIC 6331 Fire, marine & casualty insurance
CEO: Frederick H Eppinger

HANOVER ARCHITECTURA
See HANOVER PREST-PAVING CO

D-U-N-S 96-207-6837
■ HANOVER CAPITAL MORTGAGE HOLDINGS LP
(*Suby of* WALTER INVESTMENT MANAGEMENT CORP) ★
3000 Bayport Dr Ste 1100, Tampa, FL 33607-8405
Tel (813) 421-7600 *Founded/Ownrshp* 1997
Sales 10.3MM^E *EMP* 688^E
SIC 6798 Mortgage investment trusts
Prin: Paul Pedrotti

D-U-N-S 07-132-5393
HANOVER COLLEGE
484 Ball Dr, Hanover, IN 47243-9669
Tel (812) 866-7000 *Founded/Ownrshp* 1827, 1988
Sales 53.5MM *EMP* 300
Accts Bkd Llp Indianapolis In
SIC 8221 Colleges & universities; Colleges & universities
Pr: Sue Dewine
Trst: Charles Bowerman
Trst: Lawrence Goyd
Trst: Elizabeth Hammond
Trst: Suzanne Hazelett
Trst: Gerald R Johnson
Trst: Boyce E Martin
Trst: Robert F Muhlhauser
Trst: Michael S Needler
Trst: William Shrewsberry
Trst: Samuel Washburn
VP: Jane Jakoubek

HANOVER COLLEGE CENTER FOR CHI
See HANOVER COLLEGE INC

D-U-N-S 92-619-6866
HANOVER COLLEGE INC
HANOVER COLLEGE CENTER FOR CHI
348 File St, Hanover, IN 47243-9657
Tel (812) 866-5139 *Founded/Ownrshp* 1992
Sales 38.3MM *EMP* 5
SIC 8351 Child day care services; Child day care services

D-U-N-S 01-891-7310
HANOVER CONSUMER COOPERATIVE SOCIETY INC
COOP SERVICE CENTRE
45 S Park St, Hanover, NH 03755-2157
Tel (603) 643-2667 *Founded/Ownrshp* 1937
Sales 59.0MM^E *EMP* 400
SIC 5411 5541

D-U-N-S 01-328-1498
HANOVER COUNTY PUBLIC SCHOOLS
200 Berkley St, Ashland, VA 23005-1302
Tel (804) 365-4500 *Founded/Ownrshp* 1850
Sales 89.6MM^E *EMP* 2,100
SIC 8211 Public elementary & secondary schools; Public elementary & secondary schools
V Ch: Henry Lowry
Dir Sec: Sherol Sotherland
IT Man: Stephanie Koren
Pr Dir: Chris Whitley
Psych: Alison Adams
Psych: Megan Cox
Psych: Jessica Goldman
Psych: Dorothy Heimlich
Psych: Sarah Willson
HC Dir: Terry Woody

HANOVER DIRECT
See CO STORE INC

D-U-N-S 00-698-5352 IMP
HANOVER DIRECT INC
HANOVER DIRECT OPERATING GROUP
(*Suby of* CHELSEY DIRECT LLC) ★
1200 Harbor Blvd Fl 9, Weehawken, NJ 07086-6728
Tel (201) 863-7300 *Founded/Ownrshp* 2003
Sales 456.5MM^E *EMP* 1,975
SIC 5712 5961 7389 2211 2221 Bedding & bedsprings; Catalog & mail-order houses; Telemarketing services; Pillow tubing; Comforters & quilts, manmade fiber & silk; Bedding & bedsprings; Catalog & mail-order houses; Telemarketing services; Pillow tubing; Comforters & quilts, manmade fiber & silk
Pr: Don Kelley
Sr VP: Ralph J Bulle
VP: Farley Nachemin
VP: Hallie Sturgill
IT Man: Pete Van Donk
Ql Cn Mgr: Al Rapella
Mktg Mgr: Susan Tosches
Sales Asso: Reene Lynch

HANOVER DIRECT OPERATING GROUP
See HANOVER DIRECT INC

D-U-N-S 06-856-5456
HANOVER ENGINEERING ASSOCIATES INC
252 Brodhead Rd Ste 100, Bethlehem, PA 18017-8944
Tel (610) 691-5644 *Founded/Ownrshp* 1972
Sales 22.5MM *EMP* 120
Accts Joseph Szerencsits Jr Inc
SIC 8711 Civil engineering; Civil engineering
Pr: Charles H Unangst
**COO:* Jill Smith
**CFO:* Brien Kocher
**VP:* Scott J Brown
**VP:* Robert Lynn
**VP:* J Bradley Youst

D-U-N-S 00-300-4439 IMP/EXP
HANOVER FOODS CORP
1486 York St, Hanover, PA 17331-7956
Tel (717) 632-6000 *Founded/Ownrshp* 1924
Sales 651.4MM^E *EMP* 2,205
SIC 2033 2032 2037 2038 2099 Canned fruits & specialties; Vegetables: packaged in cans, jars, etc.; Canned specialties; Beans & bean sprouts, canned, jarred, etc.; Macaroni: packaged in cans, jars, etc.; Frozen fruits & vegetables; Vegetables, quick frozen & cold pack, excl. potato products; Frozen specialties; Dinners, frozen & packaged; Salads, fresh or refrigerated; Canned fruits & specialties; Vegetables: packaged in cans, jars, etc.; Canned specialties; Beans & bean sprouts, canned, jarred, etc.; Macaroni: packaged in cans, jars, etc.; Frozen fruits & vegetables; Vegetables, quick frozen & cold pack, excl. potato products; Frozen specialties; Dinners, frozen & packaged; Salads, fresh or refrigerated
Pr: John A Warehime
Treas: Steve Robertson
Treas: Steven E Robertson
Sr VP: Alan T Young
VP: Ken Bartosh
VP: Pietro D Giraffa Jr
VP: Daniel E Schuchart
Admn Mgr: Clair Mensinger
Genl Mgr: Bruce Dubuc
Genl Mgr: Joe Groves
Genl Mgr: Jim Kelly

D-U-N-S 92-636-9497 IMP/EXP
HANOVER HEALTH CORP INC
300 Highland Ave, Hanover, PA 17331-2297
Tel (717) 637-3711 *Founded/Ownrshp* 1926
Sales 107.5M *EMP* 1,000
SIC 8062 8011 5912 General medical & surgical hospitals; Surgeon; Drug stores; General medical & surgical hospitals; Surgeon; Drug stores
Ch Bd: Michael Rice
**Pr:* William R Wald
**V Ch Bd:* C Daniel Webber
Sr VP: Marilyn Hassel
Ex Dir: Margaret Mc Kinnish
CIO: Pamela Owens
MIS Dir: Harold Drumhuller
Dir IT: Greg Strevig
IT Man: Joe Zutell
Sls Mgr: Krista Hayward
Plas Surg: Zaher Srour

D-U-N-S 06-978-8644
HANOVER HOSPITAL INC
300 Highland Ave, Hanover, PA 17331-2297
Tel (717) 637-3711 *Founded/Ownrshp* 1924
Sales 141.0MM *EMP* 1,400
Accts Bdo Usa Llp Bethesda Md
SIC 8062 General medical & surgical hospitals; General medical & surgical hospitals
CEO: James E Wissler
V Ch: Steven G McKonly
**COO:* Michael Hockenberry
**CFO:* Michael Gaskins
Sr VP: Marilyn Hassle
Sr VP: William Tung
**VP:* Michael Ader
Exec: Michelle Lee
**Prin:* Patricia Saunders
Genl Mgr: Paul Speakman
Snr Ntwrk: Joseph Blucher

D-U-N-S 05-292-9759
■ HANOVER INSURANCE CO
(*Suby of* OPUS INVESTMENT MANAGEMENT INC) ★
440 Lincoln St, Worcester, MA 01653-0001
Tel (508) 853-7200 *Founded/Ownrshp* 1852, 1995
Sales NA *EMP* 2,500
SIC 6331 6351 Fire, marine & casualty insurance & carriers; Property damage insurance; Liability insurance; Fire, marine & casualty insurance & carriers; Property damage insurance; Liability insurance
Pr: Frederick Eppinger
Pr: Lee M Patkus
COO: Gregory D Tranter
CFO: Edward J Parry
Ex VP: Maribeth Bearfield
Ex VP: David Greenfield
Ex VP: Kendall Huber
VP: Scott Hallworth

VP: Sue King
VP: Joseph Rovito
Mktg Mgr: Carl Drennen

D-U-N-S 88-478-3739

▲ HANOVER INSURANCE GROUP INC
440 Lincoln St, Worcester, MA 01653-0001
Tel (508) 855-1000 *Founded/Ownrshp* 1852
Sales NA *EMP* 5,100[E]
Tkr Sym THG *Exch* NYS
SIC 6331 6311 Automobile insurance; Property damage insurance; Workers' compensation insurance; Life insurance; Automobile insurance; Property damage insurance; Workers' compensation insurance; Life insurance
Pr: Frederick H Eppinger
Pr: Karen Andrade
Pr: Mary Corcoran
Pr: Richard W Lavey
Pr: Greg Leffard
Pr: Eric Paynter
Pr: Allan Sague
Pr: Robert A Stuchbery
Pr: John Sullivan
Pr: Richard Tackett
CFO: David B Greenfield
Bd of Dir: Warren E Barnes
Chf Mktg O: Richard Lavey
Ofcr: Bruce B Bartell
Ofcr: Mark L Berthiaume
Ofcr: Christine Bilotti-Peterson
Ex VP: J Kendall Huber
Ex VP: Dennis Sproull
Sr VP: Ann K Tripp
VP: Charles F Cronin
VP: Kathleen Cunningham
Board of Directors: Harriett Taggart, Michael P Angelini, Richard H Booth, P Kevin Condron, Cynthia L Egan, Neal F Finnegan, Karen C Francis, Daniel T Henry, Wendell J Knox, Joseph R Ramrath

D-U-N-S 18-679-2693 IMP/EXP

HANOVER PREST-PAVING CO
HANOVER ARCHITECTURA
5000 Hanover Rd, Hanover, PA 17331-9077
Tel (717) 637-0500 *Founded/Ownrshp* 1987
Sales 21.1MM[E] *EMP* 50
SIC 3559 3272 3271 2951 Concrete products machinery; Concrete products; Concrete block & brick; Asphalt paving mixtures & blocks; Concrete products machinery; Concrete products; Concrete block & brick; Asphalt paving mixtures & blocks
Pr: John Repasky
**Sec:* Christine Repasky
Sales Exec: Daniel Utz
Sls Mgr: Andy Repasky
Sales Asso: Lee Fuhrman
Sales Asso: Beth Gallagher

D-U-N-S 07-838-8943

HANOVER PUBLIC SCHOOLS
SALMOND SCHOOL, THE
188 Broadway, Hanover, MA 02339-2312
Tel (781) 878-0786 *Founded/Ownrshp* 2012
Sales 15.2MM[E] *EMP* 311[E]
SIC 8211 Elementary & secondary schools
**Prin:* William Marriner

HANOVER REALTY SERVICES PARTNR
See HANOVER RS LIMITED PARTNERSHIP

D-U-N-S 86-116-4879

HANOVER RS LIMITED PARTNERSHIP
HANOVER REALTY SERVICES PARTNR
5847 San Felipe St, Houston, TX 77057-3000
Tel (713) 267-2100 *Founded/Ownrshp* 1993
Sales 49.0MM[E] *EMP* 340
Accts Deloitte & Touche Llp
SIC 6552 6531 1522 Subdividers & developers; Real estate managers; Multi-family dwellings, new construction; Subdividers & developers; Real estate managers; Multi-family dwellings, new construction
CEO: Murry Bowden
VP: Judy Hopper

HANOVER SHOE FARM
See STANDARDBRED HORSE SALES CO

D-U-N-S 09-926-3923 IMP

HANOVER WAREHOUSES INC
17 Cable Dr, Kearny, NJ 07032-6503
Tel (973) 589-2119 *Founded/Ownrshp* 1979
Sales 27.4MM[E] *EMP* 250
Accts Hendel & Hendel Cpa S Paramu
SIC 4225 General warehousing; General warehousing
Ch Bd: Dominick A Telesco
**Pr:* David Telesco
**VP:* James Marzano
**VP:* Joseph Rodriguez

D-U-N-S 07-961-8434

HANRAHANMEYERS ARCHITECTS LLP
6 Maiden Ln Rm 510, New York, NY 10038-5138
Tel (212) 989-6026 *Founded/Ownrshp* 2008
Sales 179.0MM *EMP* 2
SIC 8712 Architectural engineering; Architectural engineering
Pt: Victoria Meyer
Pt: Thomas Hanrahan

D-U-N-S 00-736-8517 IMP

HANS JOHNSEN CO (TX)
8901 Chancellor Row, Dallas, TX 75247-5363
Tel (214) 879-1550 *Founded/Ownrshp* 1901
Sales 21.9MM[E] *EMP* 42[E]
SIC 5087 5091 Locksmith equipment & supplies; Bicycles; Bicycle tires & tubes; Bicycle parts & accessories
CEO: Howard Johnsen
**Pr:* Lance Johnsen
**CEO:* Howard L Johnsen
**VP:* Reid Hill
**VP:* Anders J Johnsen
Exec: Johnsen Howard
Off Mgr: Jeff Donovan
Manager: Randy Davis
Sls Mgr: Scott Crawley

Sls Mgr: Sidney Monzingo
Sales Asso: Ian Watson

D-U-N-S 12-101-1126

HANS KISSLE CO LLC
9 Creek Brook Dr Hverhill Haverhill, Haverhill, MA 01830
Tel (978) 556-4500 *Founded/Ownrshp* 1984
Sales 40.1MM[E] *EMP* 140
SIC 2099 Salads, fresh or refrigerated; Salads, fresh or refrigerated
CFO: Charles O'Donnell
Treas: Robert Annand
Sfty Mgr: Chris Azzarito
Plnt Mgr: Chris Gelinas
Ql Cn Mgr: Dean Kenney
Ql Cn Mgr: Andrea Urel
Mktg Mgr: Joellen Gallant

D-U-N-S 08-230-2761

HANSCOM FEDERAL CREDIT UNION
1610 Eglin St, Bedford, MA 01731-2616
Tel (781) 274-6335 *Founded/Ownrshp* 1954
Sales NA *EMP* 70
SIC 6061 6062 Federal credit unions; State credit unions; Federal credit unions; State credit unions
Ch Bd: Paul Marotta
**Pr:* David P Sprague
CFO: Kimberly J Houle

D-U-N-S 94-681-5834

HANSEL DEALERSHIPS INC
HANSEL HONDA
1310 Auto Center Dr, Petaluma, CA 94952-6507
Tel (707) 769-4000 *Founded/Ownrshp* 1996
Sales 26.0MM[E] *EMP* 80
SIC 5511 Automobiles, new & used; Automobiles, new & used
Pr: Henry C Hansel
**CFO:* Dave Morris
**VP:* Stephen Hansel
Genl Mgr: Justin Hansel
Off Mgr: Linda Cella
IT Man: Dan Thompson
Netwrk Mgr: Ryan Seaman
Sls Mgr: Jeff Hendrickson
Sls Mgr: Jeff Visser
Sales Asso: Seth Allen
Sales Asso: Julie Dormire

D-U-N-S 02-942-6624

HANSEL FORD INC
(*Suby of* HANSEL ENTERPRISES, INC.)
3075 Corby Ave, Santa Rosa, CA 95407-7879
Tel (707) 543-7300 *Founded/Ownrshp* 1982
Sales 50.8MM[E] *EMP* 163[E]
SIC 5511

HANSEL HONDA
See HANSEL DEALERSHIPS INC

D-U-N-S 01-208-9447

HANSEL N GRETEL BRAND INC
7936 Cooper Ave, Glendale, NY 11385-7530
Tel (718) 326-0041 *Founded/Ownrshp* 1980
Sales 21.6MM[E] *EMP* 150
SIC 2013 2015 Prepared pork products from purchased pork; Prepared beef products from purchased beef; Turkey processing & slaughtering; Prepared pork products from purchased pork; Prepared beef products from purchased beef; Turkey processing & slaughtering
Pr: Milton Rattner
CFO: Linda Kazimiroff
**Ex VP:* Ruth Rattner

HANSEN & ADKINS
See HANSEN AUTO TRANSPORT INC

D-U-N-S 94-230-7109 IMP

HANSEN AUTO TRANSPORT INC
HANSEN & ADKINS
3552 Green Ave Ste 201, Los Alamitos, CA 90720-3250
Tel (562) 430-4100 *Founded/Ownrshp* 1994
Sales 158.1MM[E] *EMP* 511
SIC 4213 Automobiles, transport & delivery; Automobiles, transport & delivery
CEO: Louie R Adkins
**VP:* Steve Hansen
**VP:* Mark Rumfola
**VP:* Barry Williams
Rgnl Mgr: John Price
Area Mgr: Glenn Moore
Area Mgr: Tim Shorter
Off Admin: Rhonda Fortenberry
Dir IT: Gary Collier
Trfc Dir: Jeff Alexa
QC Dir: Rick Beroza

D-U-N-S 00-919-4838

HANSEN BROS ENTERPRISES
HBE RENTAL
11727 La Barr Meadows Rd, Grass Valley, CA 95949-7722
Tel (530) 273-3100 *Founded/Ownrshp* 1953
Sales 45.4MM[E] *EMP* 90
SIC 1442 3273 1794 7359 Gravel mining; Ready-mixed concrete; Excavation work; Equipment rental & leasing
Pr: Orson Hansen
**Treas:* Frank Bennallack
VP: Helen Hansen
**VP:* Sue Peterson
Opers Mgr: Mike Saulsman
Plnt Mgr: Dave Frye
Ql Cn Mgr: Dave Jedlicka

D-U-N-S 08-427-1220 IMP

HANSEN CORP
(*Suby of* ELECTROCRAFT INC) ★
901 S 1st St, Princeton, IN 47670-2369
Tel (812) 385-3000 *Founded/Ownrshp* 2014
Sales 61.0MM[E] *EMP* 300
SIC 3621 3873 3566 Motors, electric; Timing motors, synchronous, electric; Sliprings, for motors or generators; Frequency converters (electric generators); Watches, clocks, watchcases & parts; Speed changers, drives & gears; Motors, electric; Timing motors, synchronous, electric; Sliprings, for motors or generators; Frequency converters (electric generators); Watches, clocks, watchcases & parts; Speed changers, drives & gears
Pr: Mike Karsonovich
Sls Mgr: Vicky Cameron

HANSEN DISTRIBUTION GROUP
See HAWAIIAN HOUSEWARES LTD

D-U-N-S 02-758-5769

HANSEN FRUIT & COLD STORAGE CO
10 E Mead Ave, Yakima, WA 98903-3712
Tel (509) 457-4153 *Founded/Ownrshp* 1948
Sales 23.0MM[E] *EMP* 50
SIC 5148 Fruits, fresh
Pr: Gary Hansen

D-U-N-S 82-484-6596 IMP

HANSEN INTERNATIONAL INC
130 Zenker Rd, Lexington, SC 29072-8929
Tel (803) 695-1500 *Founded/Ownrshp* 1920
Sales 39.8MM[E] *EMP* 56
SIC 5013 3714 Motor vehicle supplies & new parts; Motor vehicle parts & accessories
Pr: John Seehof
Dir IT: Mary Parsons
IT Man: Robert Young

D-U-N-S 10-229-2745 EXP

HANSEN MANUFACTURING CORP
HI ROLLER CONVEYORS
(*Suby of* NORDSTRONG EQUIPMENT LIMITED)
4511 N Northview Ave, Sioux Falls, SD 57107-0833
Tel (605) 332-3200 *Founded/Ownrshp* 2007
Sales 30.8MM[E] *EMP* 58
SIC 3535 Belt conveyor systems, general industrial use
CEO: Phil Clark
**Pr:* Gary Anderson
**Pr:* John Nelson
**VP:* Paul Franzmann
Genl Mgr: Steve Tweet
CTO: Charles Lacy

D-U-N-S 02-838-8262

HANSEN MARKETING SERVICES INC
1000 Decker Rd, Walled Lake, MI 48390-3218
Tel (248) 669-2323 *Founded/Ownrshp* 1982
Sales 28.5MM[E] *EMP* 42
SIC 5031 5033 5039 Molding, all materials; Paneling, wood; Insulation materials; Ceiling systems & products
Pr: Jim Frensley
**Ch:* Marty Gillespie
Mktg Dir: Monica Doerr

D-U-N-S 05-680-1202

■ HANSEN MECHANICAL CONTRACTORS INC
(*Suby of* EMCOR GROUP INC) ★
4475 W Quail Ave, Las Vegas, NV 89118-3094
Tel (702) 361-5111 *Founded/Ownrshp* 1994
Sales 43.9MM[E] *EMP* 250
SIC 1711 Plumbing contractors; Warm air heating & air conditioning contractor; Plumbing contractors; Warm air heating & air conditioning contractor
Pr: Randy Lamb
**Ex VP:* Jeffrey M Levy
**VP:* Thomas G Lamb

HANSEN MUELLER TRUCKING
See HANSEN-MUELLER CO

D-U-N-S 06-981-0497

HANSEN OIL CO
411 E 2nd S, Soda Springs, ID 83276-1447
Tel (208) 547-3692 *Founded/Ownrshp* 1984
Sales 91.1MM *EMP* 17
Accts Austin L Moses Cpa Pc Soda
SIC 5171 Petroleum bulk stations; Petroleum bulk stations
Pr: Kirk Hansen

D-U-N-S 06-800-5818

HANSEN PLASTICS CORP
2758 Alft Ln, Elgin, IL 60124
Tel (847) 741-4510 *Founded/Ownrshp* 1971
Sales 31.6MM[E] *EMP* 65
SIC 3089 Injection molding of plastics
CEO: David Watermann
**Pr:* Roy D Lilly
CFO: Robert Ruehl
**CFO:* Mike Weeks
Ql Cn Mgr: Bob Acerrano
Sls Mgr: Steve Doty

D-U-N-S 09-685-5184

HANSEN PROPERTIES INC (PA)
1401 Morris Rd, Blue Bell, PA 19422-1424
Tel (215) 616-8200 *Founded/Ownrshp* 1967
Sales 22.8MM[E] *EMP* 100[E]
SIC 1629 6531 6512 Golf course construction; Real estate agents & managers; Nonresidential building operators
Pr: Elmer F Hansen Jr
**Sec:* E F Hansen III
**VP:* Dave Sherman
CTO: Alfredo Delapenna

D-U-N-S 80-541-2624

HANSEN RANCHES
7124 Whitley Ave, Corcoran, CA 93212-9669
Tel (559) 992-3111 *Founded/Ownrshp* 1987
Sales 20.6MM *EMP* 60
Accts Jorge & Yribarren Selma Ca
SIC 0191 General farms, primarily crop; General farms, primarily crop
Pt: James Hansen
CFO: Edward Halverstadt

D-U-N-S 09-839-2053 IMP

HANSEN-MUELLER CO
HANSEN MUELLER TRUCKING
12231 Emmet St Ste 1, Omaha, NE 68164-4191
Tel (402) 491-3385 *Founded/Ownrshp* 1979
Sales 68.1MM[E] *EMP* 130[E]
SIC 6221 Commodity brokers, contracts; Commodity brokers, contracts
Pr: Jack L Hansen
**CFO:* Ryan Torpy
**VP:* Josh R Hansen
Dir IT: Tracy Kempkes

D-U-N-S 06-087-4633

HANSEN-RICE INC
1717 E Chisholm Dr, Nampa, ID 83687-6846
Tel (208) 465-0200 *Founded/Ownrshp* 2001
Sales 94.1MM[E] *EMP* 200
SIC 1541 Industrial buildings & warehouses; Industrial buildings & warehouses
COO: Burke Hansen
Pr: Arron Mann
**CFO:* John Rice
Ex VP: Robert Cooper
Ex VP: Daniel Hansen
Dir Bus: Taylor Ebright
Dir Bus: Steve Wertz
Genl Mgr: Rick Daniel
Opers Mgr: Curt Madsen
Snr PM: Armijo Tony

D-U-N-S 00-195-8677 IMP

HANSER MUSIC GROUP INC
3015 Kustom Dr, Hebron, KY 41048-8164
Tel (859) 817-7100 *Founded/Ownrshp* 1924
Sales 30.1MM[E] *EMP* 92
SIC 5099 3931 Musical instruments; Musical instruments; Musical instruments; Musical instruments
Pr: John F Hanser III
**CFO:* David F Rasfeld
**Sec:* Timothy J Hanser
**VP:* Gary Hanser
Exec: Nancy Gillespie
IT Man: Derrick Cundiff

D-U-N-S 19-497-7179 IMP

■ HANSGROHE INC
(*Suby of* HANSGROHE SE)
1490 Bluegrass Lakes Pkwy, Alpharetta, GA 30004-7710
Tel (770) 360-9880 *Founded/Ownrshp* 1995
Sales 99.0MM[E] *EMP* 325
SIC 3432 5074 3431 Plumbing fixture fittings & trim; Plumbing fittings & supplies; Metal sanitary ware; Plumbing fixture fittings & trim; Plumbing fittings & supplies; Metal sanitary ware
CEO: Erik Christensen
**CFO:* Sibylle Mair
Top Exec: Joachim Huber
Exec: Beatrix Pfundstein
Mng Dir: K Lee
Area Mgr: Joby Hardman
Opers Mgr: Stefan Hammann
Opers Mgr: Roger Proffitt
Ql Cn Mgr: Erol Saracevic
Natl Sales: Russ Kinney
Natl Sales: Cindy Welsh

D-U-N-S 60-441-3984

HANSJOERG WYSS FOUNDATION
AO/ASIF CONTINUING EDUCATION
1690 Russell Rd, Paoli, PA 19301-1222
Tel (610) 647-9700 *Founded/Ownrshp* 2000
Sales 40.7MM *EMP* 4
SIC 8249 Medical training services; Medical training services
Prin: Joseph Fisher

D-U-N-S 78-023-3151 EXP

HANSOL AMERICA INC
(*Suby of* HANSOL HOLDINGS CO., LTD.)
400 Kelby St Ste 6, Fort Lee, NJ 07024-2938
Tel (201) 461-6661 *Founded/Ownrshp* 1991
Sales 159.0MM *EMP* 22
Accts Kpmg Llp New York Ny
SIC 5113 Industrial & personal service paper; Industrial & personal service paper
CEO: Seung R Choi
**Treas:* Sara Choi

D-U-N-S 12-824-4097

HANSON AGGREGATES EAST LLC
(*Suby of* HANSON LEHIGH INC) ★
2300 Gateway Centre Blvd, Morrisville, NC 27560-9669
Tel (919) 380-2500 *Founded/Ownrshp* 1998
Sales 680.2MM[E] *EMP* 10,600[E]
SIC 3531 5032 Asphalt plant, including gravel-mix type; Batching plants, for aggregate concrete & bulk cement; Aggregate; Asphalt plant, including gravel-mix type; Batching plants, for aggregate concrete & bulk cement; Aggregate
Pr: Jim Sprinkle
**Pr:* Dan Harrington
**Pr:* Howard Nye
CIO: Bob Dieter
IT Man: Richard Smith
Natl Sales: Don Kula
Mktg Mgr: Jeff Avant
Mktg Mgr: Rob Hatten
Mktg Mgr: Roger Hutchinson
Mktg Mgr: Raymond Liddick
Sls Mgr: Mark Odell

D-U-N-S 09-356-6040

HANSON AGGREGATES LLC
SOUTHERN STAR CONCRETE
(*Suby of* HANSON LEHIGH INC) ★
8505 Freeport Pkwy Ste 500, Irving, TX 75063
Tel (469) 417-1200 *Founded/Ownrshp* 1968
Sales 295.7MM[E] *EMP* 1,000
SIC 3273 2951 5032 Ready-mixed concrete; Asphalt paving mixtures & blocks; Gravel; Sand, construction; Ready-mixed concrete; Asphalt paving mixtures & blocks; Gravel; Sand, construction
CEO: Daniel Harrington
Pr: Martin Vogt
**CFO:* Seyda Pirinccioglu

VP: Tommy Abbott
**VP:* Michael Hyer
VP: Paul Schickler
Exec: Anna Allis
Exec: Charlotte Fitzgerald
Off Mgr: Mandy Burton
Off Mgr: Karen Holbrooks
Dir IT: Matthew Clay

D-U-N-S 00-694-5414
HANSON AGGREGATES MIDWEST LLC
(*Suby of* HANSON LEHIGH INC) ★
207 Old Harrods Creek Rd, Louisville, KY 40223-2553
Tel (502) 244-7550 *Founded/Ownrshp* 1928, 2011
Sales 1.4MMM^E *EMP* 1,000
SIC 1422 1611

D-U-N-S 00-791-2504
HANSON AGGREGATES PENNSYLVANIA LLC
LEHIGH MASONRY CEMENT
(*Suby of* HANSON LEHIGH INC) ★
7660 Imperial Way, Allentown, PA 18195-1016
Tel (800) 523-5488 *Founded/Ownrshp* 1900
Sales NA *EMP* 700
SIC 1422 1442 1429 2951 Limestones, ground; Common sand mining; Grits mining (crushed stone); Concrete, bituminous; Limestones, ground; Common sand mining; Grits mining (crushed stone); Concrete, bituminous
CEO: Daniel M Harrington
VP: Mark Kendrick
IT Man: Sterling Thomas

D-U-N-S 00-320-2272
HANSON AGGREGATES SOUTHEAST INC
(*Suby of* HANSON LEHIGH INC) ★
2310 Parklake Dr Ne # 550, Atlanta, GA 30345-2913
Tel (770) 491-2777 *Founded/Ownrshp* 1909, 2011
Sales 246.1MM^E *EMP* 860
SIC 1423 1442 Crushed & broken granite; Construction sand & gravel; Crushed & broken granite; Construction sand & gravel
VP: Justin Williams
Sls Mgr: Jeff Miller

D-U-N-S 04-132-2405 IMP
HANSON AGGRGTS PCFC STHWST INC
(*Suby of* HANSON LEHIGH INC) ★
9229 Harris Plant Rd, San Diego, CA 92145-0001
Tel (858) 715-5639 *Founded/Ownrshp* 1991
Sales 34.4MM^E *EMP* 360
SIC 2951 1623 1611 3272 2875 1442 Asphalt & asphaltic paving mixtures (not from refineries); Cable laying construction; Highway & street paving contractor; Concrete products; Fertilizers, mixing only; Construction sand & gravel; Asphalt & asphaltic paving mixtures (not from refineries); Cable laying construction; Highway & street paving contractor; Concrete products; Fertilizers, mixing only; Construction sand & gravel
Pr: Dave Hummel
Exec: Leslie Russell

D-U-N-S 06-186-0110 IMP
HANSON BRICK EAST LLC
3820 Serr Rd, Corunna, MI 48817-1146
Tel (989) 743-3444 *Founded/Ownrshp* 1990
Sales 134.7MM^E *EMP* 1,150
SIC 3251 Brick & structural clay tile; Brick & structural clay tile
Sfty Dirs: Carl Gewirtz
Plnt Mgr: Tom Carr

D-U-N-S 62-198-9367 IMP
HANSON BRICK EAST LLC
(*Suby of* HANSON AGGREGATES WRP, INC)
7400 Carmel Executive Par, Charlotte, NC 28226-6453
Tel (704) 752-4700 *Founded/Ownrshp* 2002
Sales 40.0MM^E *EMP* 230
SIC 3251 Structural brick & blocks; Structural brick & blocks
Pr: Michael J Donahue
**CFO:* Charlie Ward
Off Mgr: Veronica Sanchez
Sls&Mrk Ex: Cathy Jachym
Sls Mgr: Scott Geiger

D-U-N-S 06-245-6793
HANSON BRIDGETT LLP
425 Market St Fl 26, San Francisco, CA 94105-5401
Tel (415) 543-2055 *Founded/Ownrshp* 1958
Sales 48.9MM^E *EMP* 311
SIC 8111 General practice attorney, lawyer; General practice attorney, lawyer
Sr Pt: Alexander J Berline
Pt: Lawrence Cirelli
Pt: Frank Lopez
Pt: Mary McEachron
Pt: Teresa Pahl
Pr: Susan Finnegan
Pr: Dena Hong-Yee
CFO: Roger Robles
Bd of Dir: Stephen Cassidy
Adv Bd Mbr: Scott Smith
Ex Dir: James J Nichols

D-U-N-S 79-144-4867
HANSON BUILDING MATERIALS AMERICA LLC
HANSON NORTH AMERICA
300 E John Carpenter Fwy, Irving, TX 75062-2727
Tel (972) 653-5500 *Founded/Ownrshp* 2007
Sales 27.9MM^E *EMP* 119^E
SIC 5211 Lumber & other building materials
Pr: Alan J Murray
**Treas:* Seyda Pirinccioglu
**VP:* Jill M Blundon
**VP:* Daniel L Grant
**VP:* John M Hutchinson
**Prin:* James K Kitzmiller
**Prin:* Richard C Manning
Rgnl Mgr: Bill Wilkins

D-U-N-S 00-695-7203
HANSON COLD STORAGE CO (MI)
HANSON LOGISTICS
2900 S State St Ste 4e, Saint Joseph, MI 49085-2467
Tel (269) 982-1390 *Founded/Ownrshp* 1954, 1989
Sales 35.4MM^E *EMP* 155
SIC 4222 4225 2097 Storage, frozen or refrigerated goods; Warehousing, cold storage or refrigerated; General warehousing & storage; Manufactured ice; Storage, frozen or refrigerated goods; Warehousing, cold storage or refrigerated; General warehousing & storage; Manufactured ice
Pr: Gregory P Hanson
**Pr:* Andrew B Janson
**Pr:* Matt Luckas
**CFO:* James Reits
**CFO:* Jack White
Bd of Dir: Merlin Hanson
Ex VP: James Reitz
**VP:* Daniel Bernson
VP: Kris Craig
VP: Jeff Drach
**VP:* Blake Larkin

D-U-N-S 02-812-4535
HANSON DISTRIBUTING CO (CA)
975 W 8th St, Azusa, CA 91702-2246
Tel (626) 224-9800 *Founded/Ownrshp* 1954
Sales 52.7MM *EMP* 295
SIC 5013 Automotive supplies & parts; Automotive supplies & parts
CEO: Daniel L Hanson
**COO:* Steven A Cox
**VP:* Jake Boggs
**VP:* Daniel L Hanson II
**VP Sls:* Bill Copeland

D-U-N-S 01-802-9892
HANSON DISTRIBUTING CO INC
BEERCO DISTRIBUTING CO
(*Suby of* SUPERIOR DISTRIBUTING CO INC)
22116 Township Road 218, Fostoria, OH 44830-9612
Tel (419) 435-3214 *Founded/Ownrshp* 1958
Sales 25.0MM *EMP* 75
SIC 5181 Ale; Beer & other fermented malt liquors; Ale; Beer & other fermented malt liquors
Pr: Kent Allen Brodbeck
**Treas:* Mike Klepper
**VP:* Kris Klepper

D-U-N-S 04-472-4961
HANSON EQUIPMENT INC
HANSON INTERNATIONAL WSTN COLO
2332 I-70 Frontage Rd, Grand Junction, CO 81505-9601
Tel (970) 243-7771 *Founded/Ownrshp* 1968
Sales 25.5MM^E *EMP* 55
SIC 5511 Trucks, tractors & trailers: new & used; Trucks, tractors & trailers: new & used
Pr: Robert Hanson
**Treas:* Dale Rooks

D-U-N-S 83-266-0984
HANSON GROUP INC
1525 S 6th St, Springfield, IL 62703-2801
Tel (217) 788-2450 *Founded/Ownrshp* 1992
Sales 69.6MM *EMP* 420
Accts Pehlman & Dold Pc Springfi
SIC 8712 8711 Architectural services; Engineering services; Architectural services; Engineering services
Pr: Sergio A Pecori
VP: John Coombe
VP: Robert W Cusick
VP: Jo Ellen Kein

HANSON INTERNATIONAL WSTN COLO
See HANSON EQUIPMENT INC

D-U-N-S 96-734-2197 IMP/EXP
HANSON LEHIGH INC
(*Suby of* HEIDELBERGCEMENT AG)
300 E John Carpenter Fwy, Irving, TX 75062-2727
Tel (972) 653-5500 *Founded/Ownrshp* 1984
Sales 5.4MMM^E *EMP* 10,700
SIC 1442 1422 1423 3297 3273 3272 Sand mining; Gravel & pebble mining; Crushed & broken limestone; Crushed & broken granite; Cement refractories; Ready-mixed concrete; Concrete products used to facilitate drainage; Sand mining; Gravel & pebble mining; Crushed & broken limestone; Crushed & broken granite; Cement refractories; Ready-mixed concrete; Concrete products used to facilitate drainage
CEO: Daniel Harrington
**Pr:* James K Kitzmiller
Pr: Robert Pischke
**CEO:* Jon Morrish
**CFO:* Helmut Fischer
CFO: Simon Nicholls
CFO: Leslie Russell
**Treas:* John T Berry
Sr VP: Scott Szwejbka
**VP:* Henner Bttcher
VP: George Lefler
VP: Gerhard Muehlbeyer
**VP:* Robert L Ross
VP: David Stipe
Exec: Delia Kell
Comm Man: Jeff Sieg

HANSON LOGISTICS
See HANSON COLD STORAGE CO

HANSON MATERIAL SERVICE
See MATERIAL SERVICE CORP

D-U-N-S 06-955-2412
HANSON MOTORS INC
HANSON SUBARU
2300 Carriage Loop Sw, Olympia, WA 98502-1018
Tel (360) 943-2120 *Founded/Ownrshp* 1974
Sales 24.4MM^E *EMP* 58
SIC 5511 5531 Automobiles, new & used; Automotive parts; Automobiles, new & used; Automotive parts
Pr: Steven Hanson
Treas: Gail Hanson
**Sec:* Maryanne Hanson
**VP:* Vincent Hanson

HANSON NORTH AMERICA
See HANSON BUILDING MATERIALS AMERICA LLC

D-U-N-S 82-886-1430
HANSON PRESSURE PIPE INC
(*Suby of* FORTERRA PIPE & PRECAST LLC) ★
1003 Macarthur Blvd, Grand Prairie, TX 75050-7943
Tel (972) 262-3600 *Founded/Ownrshp* 2008
Sales 228.8MM^E *EMP* 1,559^E
SIC 3317 3272 3999 Steel pipe & tubes; Liquid catch basins, tanks & covers: concrete; Barber & beauty shop equipment
Pr: Clifford Hahne
Sr VP: Ken Primavera
Dir Soc: Tammie Jimenez
Prd Mgr: Charlie McAuley
VP Sls: Gord Gajich

D-U-N-S 04-422-9284
HANSON PROFESSIONAL SERVICES INC (DE)
(*Suby of* HANSON GROUP INC) ★
1525 S 6th St, Springfield, IL 62703-2801
Tel (217) 788-2450 *Founded/Ownrshp* 1954, 1992
Sales 69.6MM *EMP* 420
Accts Pehlman & Dold Pc Springfiel
SIC 8711 8712 Engineering services; Construction & civil engineering; Civil engineering; Building construction consultant; Architectural services; Architectural engineering; Engineering services; Construction & civil engineering; Civil engineering; Building construction consultant; Architectural services; Architectural engineering
Pr: Sergio A Pecori
CFO: Jo Ellen Keim
Ex VP: Jeff Ball
Ex VP: John P Coombe
Ex VP: Robert W Cusick
Sr VP: William C Bradford
Sr VP: Edward J Collora
Sr VP: Joan Freitag
Sr VP: James Messmore
Sr VP: Gary Potts
Sr VP: Charles H Snowten
Sr VP: Daniel J Whalen
VP: Dan Rayhill

D-U-N-S 02-179-5208 IMP
HANSON ROOF TILE INC
(*Suby of* HANSON LEHIGH INC) ★
10651 Elm Ave, Fontana, CA 92337-7324
Tel (888) 509-4787 *Founded/Ownrshp* 2001
Sales 27.7MM^E *EMP* 422
SIC 3272

HANSON STRUCTRUAL PRECAST INC
See HANSON STRUCTRUAL PRECAST LLC

D-U-N-S 05-831-9393
HANSON STRUCTRUAL PRECAST LLC
HANSON STRUCTRUAL PRECAST INC
(*Suby of* HANSON LEHIGH INC) ★
6087 W 5400 S, Salt Lake City, UT 84118-7680
Tel (801) 966-1060 *Founded/Ownrshp* 2012
Sales 27.5MM^E *EMP* 250^E
SIC 3272 Prestressed concrete products; Prestressed concrete products
CEO: Plamen Jordanoff
Pr: Richard Manning
CFO: Tom Kapalla
VP: Matthew Wesgaard

HANSON SUBARU
See HANSON MOTORS INC

D-U-N-S 13-192-7824
HANSON TRUSS INC
13950 Yorba Ave, Chino, CA 91710-5520
Tel (909) 591-9256 *Founded/Ownrshp* 1985
Sales 37.1MM^E *EMP* 300
SIC 2439 Trusses, wooden roof; Trusses, wooden roof
Pr: Donald R Hanson
**Sec:* Tom Hanson
VP: Donald Milkey
IT Man: Allen Cooksey
Sys/Mgr: Anna Reyes

D-U-N-S 06-469-4845
HANSON WORLDWIDE LLC
2425 E Magnesium Rd, Spokane, WA 99217-5122
Tel (509) 252-9290 *Founded/Ownrshp* 2010
Sales 23.4MM^E *EMP* 53
SIC 3532 3531 Mining machinery; Construction machinery
Pr: Christopher Wood

HANSON'S WINDOW & SIDING CO
See HANSONS WINDOW AND CONSTRUCTION INC

D-U-N-S 60-457-6751
HANSONS WINDOW AND CONSTRUCTION INC
HANSON'S WINDOW & SIDING CO
977 E 14 Mile Rd, Troy, MI 48083-4519
Tel (248) 581-3030 *Founded/Ownrshp* 1988
Sales 25.4MM^E *EMP* 200
SIC 1751 1761

D-U-N-S 15-180-9530 IMP
HANSSEM CORP
(*Suby of* HANSSEM CO., LTD.)
20 Kilmer Rd, Edison, NJ 08817-2422
Tel (908) 226-3470 *Founded/Ownrshp* 1985
Sales 20.8MM^E *EMP* 114
SIC 2599 Cabinets, factory; Cabinets, factory
Pr: Sin Hyun Yoon

D-U-N-S 02-984-2085 IMP/EXP
HANTOVER INC
5200 W 110th St Ste 200, Overland Park, KS 66211-1203
Tel (913) 214-4800 *Founded/Ownrshp* 1978
Sales 117.2MM^E *EMP* 160
SIC 5099 5084 Safety equipment & supplies; Food industry machinery; Materials handling machinery; Safety equipment & supplies; Food industry machinery; Materials handling machinery
Ch Bd: Bernard Huff
**Sec:* Karon Huff
Netwrk Mgr: Scott McIntosh
Opers Mgr: Jeff Miller
Natl Sales: Larry Smith
Sales Asso: Leonard Kowalski
Sales Asso: Sarah Miller
Sales Asso: Greg Parrish
Sales Asso: Bill Stuckey
Sales Asso: David Summerly

D-U-N-S 00-385-5355
HANTZ FINANCIAL SERVICES INC (MI)
H & A
(*Suby of* HANTZ GROUP INC) ★
26200 American Dr Ste 500, Southfield, MI 48034-6101
Tel (248) 304-2855 *Founded/Ownrshp* 1998
Sales 52.2MM^E *EMP* 250
SIC 6282 Investment advisory service; Investment advisory service
Pr: John Hantz
**VP:* Rex Foster
VP: William Korte
Sftwr Eng: Heather Drennan

D-U-N-S 36-172-6008
HANTZ GROUP INC
26200 American Dr Ste 500, Southfield, MI 48034-6101
Tel (248) 304-2855 *Founded/Ownrshp* 1997
Sales 96.7MM^E *EMP* 266^E
SIC 6282 Investment advice; Investment advice
Pr: John Hantz
Ofcr: Eric Vredeveld
VP: Adam Hollier
Snr Sftwr: Surabhi Sardesai

D-U-N-S 18-719-7611
HANUMAN BUSINESS INC
RAMOCO FUELS
5026 Wynnefield Ave, Philadelphia, PA 19131-2531
Tel (609) 929-5146 *Founded/Ownrshp* 1987
Sales 200.0MM *EMP* 12
SIC 5541 7538 Filling stations, gasoline; General automotive repair shops; Filling stations, gasoline; General automotive repair shops
Pr: Ratnkar Patlola

D-U-N-S 04-541-8811 IMP/EXP
HANWA AMERICAN CORP
(*Suby of* HANWA CO.,LTD.)
Parker Plz 12th Fl 400k, Fort Lee, NJ 07024
Tel (201) 363-4500 *Founded/Ownrshp* 1968
Sales 36.0MM^E *EMP* 50
Accts Kpmg Llp New York Ny
SIC 5051 5172 5031 5084 5146 Steel; Miscellaneous nonferrous products; Fuel oil; Lumber: rough, dressed & finished; Industrial machinery & equipment; Fish & seafoods
Pr: Kozo Yamabe
**Pr:* Yamabe Kozo
Snr Mgr: Jai Dave

D-U-N-S 19-927-2027 IMP
HANWHA ADVANCED MATERIALS AMERICA LLC
(*Suby of* HANWHA L & C HOLDINGS USA LLC) ★
4400 N Park Dr, Opelika, AL 36801-9685
Tel (334) 741-7725 *Founded/Ownrshp* 2011
Sales 92.4MM *EMP* 70
SIC 3714 Motor vehicle parts & accessories; Motor vehicle parts & accessories
Plnt Mgr: Chris Hickman

D-U-N-S 14-852-9159 IMP/EXP
HANWHA AZDEL INC
(*Suby of* HANWHA L & C HOLDINGS USA LLC) ★
2000 Enterprise Dr, Forest, VA 24551-2652
Tel (434) 385-6524 *Founded/Ownrshp* 2007
Sales 26.4MM^E *EMP* 200
SIC 3083

D-U-N-S 82-693-4106 IMP
HANWHA HOLDINGS (USA) INC
(*Suby of* HANWHA CORPORATION)
300 Frank W Burr Blvd # 52, Teaneck, NJ 07666-6703
Tel (609) 655-2500 *Founded/Ownrshp* 2007
Sales 440.4MM^E *EMP* 608
SIC 5169 5013 5084 Chemicals & allied products; Automotive supplies; Industrial machinery & equipment; Chemicals & allied products; Automotive supplies; Industrial machinery & equipment
Pr: Tom Kim
**Treas:* Wooseok Kim

D-U-N-S 06-595-1147 IMP/EXP
HANWHA INTERNATIONAL LLC
(*Suby of* HANWHA HOLDINGS (USA) INC) ★
300 Frank W Burr Blvd # 52, Teaneck, NJ 07666-6703
Tel (201) 347-3000 *Founded/Ownrshp* 2007
Sales 42.6MM^E *EMP* 30^E
SIC 5169 5013 5084 Chemicals & allied products; Automotive supplies; Industrial machinery & equipment
CEO: Simon Lee
**Pr:* Sang Mook Lee
Treas: Wooseok Kim
Ex VP: Jason Kim
Genl Mgr: Ken Lee
Off Mgr: Jamie Cho
Snr Mgr: Hoon Park

D-U-N-S 82-855-5073
HANWHA L & C HOLDINGS USA LLC
(*Suby of* HANWHA HOLDINGS (USA) INC) ★
4400 N Park Dr, Opelika, AL 36801-9685
Tel (334) 741-7725 *Founded/Ownrshp* 2008
Sales 118.8MM^E *EMP* 270^E
SIC 3083 3714 Thermoplastic laminates: rods, tubes, plates & sheet; Motor vehicle parts & accessories; Thermoplastic laminates: rods, tubes, plates & sheet; Motor vehicle parts & accessories

CEO: Hee Chung Kim

D-U-N-S 08-745-2496
HAP INC
322 Main St, Springfield, MA 01105-2403
Tel (413) 233-1500 *Founded/Ownrshp* 1972
Sales 61.7MM *EMP* 104
Accts Daniel Dennis & Company Llp D
SIC 5812 Eating places; Eating places
Pr: John Downs
**CFO:* Ellen Hatzakis
**Treas:* Leeann Pasquini
**Treas:* Charles Rucks
**VP:* Joanne Campbell
**VP:* Joseph Laplante
**VP:* Jim Sherbo
**VP:* Carlos Vega
**Assoc Dir:* Jim Reis
Comm Dir: Carol Walker
Ex Dir: Linda Ciarcia

D-U-N-S 05-831-2711
HAPAG-LLOYD (AMERICA) LLC
(*Suby of* HAPAG-LLOYD AG)
399 Hoes Ln Ste 101, Piscataway, NJ 08854-4162
Tel (732) 562-1800 *Founded/Ownrshp* 1978
Sales 7.3MM *EMP* 711
Accts Pricewaterhousecoopers Llp
SIC 4731 Agents, shipping; Agents, shipping
CEO: Wolfgang Freeser
**CFO:* Hercules Angelatos
**Treas:* Michael Stillitano
Sr VP: Helmut Bode
Sr VP: Cameron L Bowie
**Sr VP:* Peter Braedel
Sr VP: Timothy P Collins
Sr VP: Wolfgang Freese
Sr VP: M Sharan Jain
Sr VP: Sharan M Jain
Sr VP: John Nardi
**Sr VP:* Stuart Sandlin

D-U-N-S 15-984-8365
HAPAG-LLOYD USA LLC
(*Suby of* HAPAG-LLOYD AG)
399 Hoes Ln Ste 101, Piscataway, NJ 08854-4162
Tel (800) 834-6314 *Founded/Ownrshp* 2006
Sales 31.7MM^E *EMP* 276^E
SIC 4412 Deep sea foreign transportation of freight; Deep sea foreign transportation of freight
CEO: John Murray
**CFO:* J P Lacasse
**Treas:* Craig Thaxton
VP: Jim Brasier
**VP:* Jared Henry
**VP:* James Wachtel

D-U-N-S 83-322-9185 IMP
HAPCO AMERICAN FLAGPOLE INC
26252 Hillman Hwy, Abingdon, VA 24210-7616
Tel (276) 628-7171 *Founded/Ownrshp* 1962
Sales 28.2MM^E *EMP* 200
SIC 1799 Flag pole erection
Pr: David Oakley
**CFO:* Ron Thorne
**VP:* Bob Walls
Exec: Joyce Warner
Dir IT: Albert Lawson
Dir IT: B J McIntyre
Plnt Mgr: Don Stuck
S&M/VP: Derek Stafford
Mktg Mgr: Kalonn Roberts
Manager: Andrew Dyer
Sls Mgr: Britty Hunt

D-U-N-S 06-593-4192
HAPCO FARMS LLC
889 Harrison Ave Fl 4, Riverhead, NY 11901-2090
Tel (631) 369-7000 *Founded/Ownrshp* 1945
Sales 65.0MM *EMP* 140
SIC 5148 Potatoes, fresh; Fruits, fresh; Vegetables, fresh; Potatoes, fresh; Fruits, fresh; Vegetables, fresh
Pr: Andrew Pollak
CFO: Joe Leuci
VP Mktg: Paul Visentin

HAPI
See HEALTH ALLIANCE WITH PHYSICIAN

D-U-N-S 08-148-5195
HAPO COMMUNITY CREDIT UNION
601 Williams Blvd Ste 1b, Richland, WA 99354-3258
Tel (509) 943-5676 *Founded/Ownrshp* 1953
Sales NA *EMP* 102
SIC 6062 6163 6061 State credit unions; Loan brokers; Federal credit unions; State credit unions; Loan brokers; Federal credit unions
Pr: David Schulz
CFO: John Schnellbach
VP: Carolyn Oniel
Off Mgr: Sabrina Esparza
Mktg Dir: Bernadette Flynn

D-U-N-S 07-924-8632
HAPPIEST MINDS TECHNOLOGIES PRIVATE LIMITED
(*Suby of* HAPPIEST MINDS TECHNOLOGIES PRIVATE LIMITED)
2051 Junction Ave Ste 208, San Jose, CA 95131-2118
Tel (408) 961-7421 *Founded/Ownrshp* 2011
Sales 30.0MM *EMP* 6
SIC 7371 Computer software development; Computer software development
Pr: Joseph Anantharaju

D-U-N-S 06-300-1432 IMP
HAPPY BEES INC
HAPPY STEAK
2122 Patterson Rd, Riverbank, CA 95367-9504
Tel (209) 863-1002 *Founded/Ownrshp* 1965
Sales 12.3MM^E *EMP* 400
SIC 5812 Steak restaurant; Restaurant, family: chain; Steak restaurant; Restaurant, family: chain
Pr: Jeffrey E Burns
**VP:* Steve Burns

D-U-N-S 04-843-7396
HAPPY DAY CORP
TACO TIME
703 Main St, Lewiston, ID 83501-1835
Tel (208) 743-0583 *Founded/Ownrshp* 1969
Sales 15.5MM *EMP* 380
Accts Presnell Gage Pllc Lewiston
SIC 5812 Fast-food restaurant, chain; Fast-food restaurant, chain
Pr: Bruce Finch
**CFO:* Mike Cooper
**Sec:* Cherron Finch
Ex VP: Sam Worrell
Off Mgr: Roma Borders
Mktg Dir: Ken King

HAPPY DOUGHNUTS
See DOBAKE BAKERIES INC

HAPPY FAMILY BRANDS
See NURTURE INC

HAPPY FLOORS
See A B PROPERTY SERVICES INC

D-U-N-S 17-334-5588
HAPPY GUESTS INTERNATIONAL INC
SALTY'S AT REDONDO
1936 Harbor Ave Sw, Seattle, WA 98126-2031
Tel (206) 938-1858 *Founded/Ownrshp* 1974
Sales 58.4MM^E *EMP* 500
SIC 5813 5812 Cocktail lounge; American restaurant; Cocktail lounge; American restaurant
Pr: Gerald Kingen
CFO: Scott Switzer
**VP:* Kathy Kingen

D-U-N-S 01-104-2140 IMP
■ **HAPPY HARRYS INC**
(*Suby of* WALGREEN CO) ★
326 Ruthar Dr, Newark, DE 19711-8017
Tel (302) 366-0335 *Founded/Ownrshp* 1962, 2006
Sales 139.0MM^E *EMP* 2,000
SIC 5912 Drug stores; Drug stores
Pr: Alan Levin
**Sec:* Thomas Salvatore
VP: Lois Becker
VP: Ralph Larson

D-U-N-S 03-058-9356
HAPPY HOUSE LLC (AZ)
18823 N 92nd Way, Scottsdale, AZ 85255-9251
Tel (480) 854-0788 *Founded/Ownrshp* 2011
Sales 400.0MM *EMP* 4
SIC 1521 Single-family housing construction

HAPPY HYUNDAI
See OAK LAWN HYUNDAI INC

D-U-N-S 06-325-3645
HAPPY JOES PIZZA AND ICE CREAM PARLOR INC
2705 Happy Joe Dr Ste 1, Bettendorf, IA 52722-3297
Tel (563) 332-8811 *Founded/Ownrshp* 1972
Sales 12.5MM *EMP* 550
SIC 5812 6794 Pizzeria, chain; Franchises, selling or licensing; Pizzeria, chain; Franchises, selling or licensing
Ch: Lawrence J Whitty
Exec: Sarah Carroll
Genl Mgr: Richard Abel

D-U-N-S 19-535-5813
HAPPY KIDS INC
31 W 34th St Fl 7, New York, NY 10001-3031
Tel (212) 695-1151 *Founded/Ownrshp* 1999
Sales 23.9MM^E *EMP* 180
Accts Grant Thornton Llp
SIC 5137 Women's & children's clothing; Women's & children's clothing
Ch Bd: Jack Benun
**CFO:* Stuart Bender
**Ex VP:* Mark Benun
**Sr VP:* Isaac Levy

D-U-N-S 03-632-0992
HAPPY STATE BANK
FIRST NATIONAL BANK
(*Suby of* OLNEY BANCSHARES OF TEXAS INC) ★
701 S Taylor St Lb120, Amarillo, TX 79101-2405
Tel (806) 373-2265 *Founded/Ownrshp* 1970
Sales NA *EMP* 20
SIC 6022 National commercial banks; State commercial banks
CEO: J Pat Hickman
Pr: Kyle Fuston
Pr: Craig Wells
Ofcr: Elaine Lee
Sr VP: Kayla Carpenter
Sr VP: Beverly Gaines
Sr VP: Mark Hanbury
Sr VP: Mike Jackson
VP: Annette Anders
**VP:* Randy Crawford
VP: Kent David
VP: Ryan Evans
VP: Randy Morris
VP: Chancy Via
VP: Rosalinda Villalon

HAPPY STEAK
See HAPPY BEES INC

D-U-N-S 07-359-0452
HAPPY VALLEY CORP
FLATTOP GRILL
(*Suby of* FLAT OUT CRAZY LLC) ★
1200 Harger Rd Ste 421, Oak Brook, IL 60523-1818
Tel (708) 358-8200 *Founded/Ownrshp* 2009
Sales 26.3MM^E *EMP* 300
SIC 5813 Drinking places; Drinking places
CEO: Keene Addington III
**VP:* Robin Pearce
Genl Mgr: Juan Becerril
Genl Mgr: Tyesha Malone
VP Opers: Vincent Vella

D-U-N-S 02-141-5538
HAPPYS PIZZA CO
30201 Orchrd Lke Rd 200, Farmington Hills, MI 48334
Tel (248) 358-8888 *Founded/Ownrshp* 2005
Sales 73.0MM^E *EMP* 1,683^E
SIC 5812 Pizza restaurants
Prin: Feds Indict
VP: Christina Rice
**Prin:* Happy Asker

D-U-N-S 12-924-5804 IMP
HAR NORTHERN INC
15640 Northern Blvd, Flushing, NY 11354-5034
Tel (718) 888-0005 *Founded/Ownrshp* 2002
Sales 29.5MM *EMP* 3
SIC 5411 Supermarkets; Supermarkets
Pr: IL Yeon Kwon

D-U-N-S 94-445-9622
HAR RIDGEFIELD CORP
HAN AH REUM
321 Broad Ave Ste 118, Ridgefield, NJ 07657-2339
Tel (201) 943-9600 *Founded/Ownrshp* 1999
Sales 46.0MM *EMP* 87
SIC 5411 Grocery stores, independent; Grocery stores, independent
Pr: Ilyeon Kwon

D-U-N-S 06-383-7777
HAR-BRO INC
2750 Signal Pkwy, Signal Hill, CA 90755-2207
Tel (562) 528-8000 *Founded/Ownrshp* 1956
Sales 83.3MM^E *EMP* 175
SIC 1542 1521 1522

D-U-N-S 80-678-3382
HAR-CON MECHANICAL CONTRACTORS LLC
9009 W Little York Rd, Houston, TX 77040-4113
Tel (713) 869-8451 *Founded/Ownrshp* 2005
Sales 29.7MM^E *EMP* 100
SIC 1711 Warm air heating & air conditioning contractor
Pr: Charles D Newberry
**VP:* William M Reed

D-U-N-S 07-027-3594
HAR-MAR FOODS INC (MN)
HARDEE'S
200 S Oconnell St Ste 500, Marshall, MN 56258-3813
Tel (507) 532-2238 *Founded/Ownrshp* 1976
Sales 10.2MM^E *EMP* 350
SIC 5812 Fast-food restaurant, chain; Fast-food restaurant, chain
CEO: Lionel Bolden
**Treas:* Michael Boedigheimer

HARA SOFTWARE
See VERISAE INC

D-U-N-S 04-036-2055 IMP
HARALAMBOS BEVERAGE CO
2300 Pellissier Pl, City of Industry, CA 90601-1500
Tel (562) 347-4300 *Founded/Ownrshp* 1976
Sales 319.2MM^E *EMP* 300^E
SIC 5181 5149 Beer & other fermented malt liquors; Beverages, except coffee & tea; Beer & other fermented malt liquors; Beverages, except coffee & tea
CEO: H T Haralambos
**Pr:* Anthony Haralambos
CFO: Denise Conot
**VP:* Thomas Haralambos
VP: Marty Varela
Rgnl Mgr: Ford Poland
Dir IT: Charles Mavudzi
VP Sls: Steve Juarez
Manager: Fred Akroush
Manager: Rich Belliston
Manager: Greg Kovacic

D-U-N-S 07-591-8607
HARALSON COUNTY BOARD OF EDUCATION
299 Robertson Ave, Tallapoosa, GA 30176-1232
Tel (770) 574-2500 *Founded/Ownrshp* 1940
Sales 26.5MM^E *EMP* 575
Accts Department Of Audits And Accou
SIC 8211 Public elementary & secondary schools; Public elementary & secondary schools
CTO: Marty Bray

D-U-N-S 78-087-7031 IMP
HARBAR LLC
320 Turnpike St, Canton, MA 02021-2703
Tel (781) 828-0848 *Founded/Ownrshp* 2006
Sales 22.1MM^E *EMP* 60
SIC 2099 Tortillas, fresh or refrigerated
Pr: Jose Sanchez
VP: Thomas Stacey
Off Mgr: Richard Paterson
VP Opers: Luis Tueme
Ql Cn Mgr: Imelda Gutierrez
Sales Exec: Enrique Montemayor
Sls Mgr: Keith Brennan

D-U-N-S 18-577-2423
HARBEC INC
369 State Route 104, Ontario, NY 14519-8958
Tel (585) 265-0010 *Founded/Ownrshp* 1986
Sales 30.2MM^E *EMP* 100
SIC 3089 Injection molded finished plastic products
Pr: Robert Bechtold
Ex Dir: Bob Steinorth
DP Dir: Scott Owens
IT Man: Bob Bechtold
IT Man: Jim Crowley
Counsel: Gerald Wahl
Snr PM: Jerry Spronz

D-U-N-S 09-447-1430
HARBERT CORP
2100 3rd Ave N Ste 600, Birmingham, AL 35203-3416
Tel (205) 987-5500 *Founded/Ownrshp* 1977
Sales 91.5MM^E *EMP* 202^E
SIC 4911 6799 Electric services; Investors
Pr: Raymond J Harbert
**Pr:* Michael D Luce
COO: Mike Luce

CFO: David Batwell
**Ex VP:* David A Boutwell
**Ex VP:* Charles D Miller

D-U-N-S 87-840-3914
HARBERT MANAGEMENT CORP
2100 3rd Ave N Ste 600, Birmingham, AL 35203-3416
Tel (205) 987-5500 *Founded/Ownrshp* 1993
Sales 131.6MM^E *EMP* 225
SIC 6726 6799 Investment offices; Investors; Investment offices; Investors
Ch: Raymond J Harbert
**Pr:* Michael D Luce
**Ex VP:* David A Boutwell
**Ex VP:* William W Brooke
**Ex VP:* Charles D Miller
Sr VP: John McCullough
VP: Michael C Bauder
VP: James Flood
VP: Jeffrey Seidman
Ex Dir: John Floyd
Mng Dir: Richard F Brereton

D-U-N-S 04-605-8780
HARBILL INC
CREST CHEVROLET
909 W 21st St, San Bernardino, CA 92405-3201
Tel (909) 883-8833 *Founded/Ownrshp* 1958
Sales 70.6MM^E *EMP* 93
SIC 5511 5012 5531 5521 Automobiles & other motor vehicles; Automobiles, new & used; Top & body repair & paint shops; Automotive & home supply stores; Used car dealers; Automobiles, new & used; Automobiles & other motor vehicles; Automotive & home supply stores; Used car dealers
CEO: D William Bader
**Pr:* Robert Bader
**VP:* Douglas Bader

D-U-N-S 07-078-0317
HARBIN CLINIC LLC (GA)
221 Technology Pkwy Nw, Rome, GA 30165-1644
Tel (706) 295-5331 *Founded/Ownrshp* 1948
Sales 171.4MM^E *EMP* 1,200
SIC 8011 Clinic, operated by physicians; Clinic, operated by physicians
Pr: Ken Davis
COO: Kenna Stock
Exec: Kelly Barnett
Dept Mgr: Donna Whitmire
Off Mgr: Tonya West
Nurse Mgr: Bobbi Freeman
Telecom Ex: Tom Fricks
DP Exec: Michael Jones
Dir IT: David Marks
Sls&Mrk Ex: Natalie Simms
Mktg Dir: Brenda Bowen

HARBIN HOT SPRINGS
See HEART CONSCIOUSNESS CHURCH INC

D-U-N-S 03-375-8541
HARBIN LUMBER CO INC (GA)
DO IT BEST
560 Smith Rd, Lavonia, GA 30553-2918
Tel (706) 356-5041 *Founded/Ownrshp* 1917, 1982
Sales 27.9MM^E *EMP* 200
SIC 5211 Lumber & other building materials; Lumber & other building materials
Pr: Barron C Harbin
**CEO:* Chris Moon
**CFO:* Philip Hunt
Genl Mgr: Jody Page
Sls Mgr: Randy Wells
Sales Asso: Ricky Knowles
Sales Asso: Valerie Osborne
Sales Asso: Corey Smith
Sales Asso: Harbin Tillman

D-U-N-S 80-226-9246
HARBINGER CAPITAL PARTNERS GP LLC
450 Park Ave Fl 30, New York, NY 10022-2637
Tel (212) 339-5800 *Founded/Ownrshp* 2001
Sales 107.6MM^E *EMP* 239^E
SIC 6211 Investment firm, general brokerage
Prin: Mr Philip A Falcone
**CFO:* Mr Peter Jensen
Sr VP: Kathleen Murphy
**Prin:* Mr Omar Marwan Asali
Off Mgr: Rene Opinsky

D-U-N-S 96-805-3814
■ **HARBINGER OM LLC**
(*Suby of* HRG GROUP INC) ★
450 Park Ave Fl 27, New York, NY 10022-2605
Tel (212) 906-8555 *Founded/Ownrshp* 2010
Sales 255.6MM^E *EMP* 1,285^E
SIC 6726 Investment offices; Investment offices
Pr: Philip Falcone
**CFO:* Francis T McCarron

D-U-N-S 79-293-2287 IMP/EXP
HARBISON CORP
15450 South Outer 40 Rd # 120, Chesterfield, MO 63017-2062
Tel (314) 727-8200 *Founded/Ownrshp* 1992
Sales 195.7MM^E *EMP* 1,200
SIC 3089 Plastic containers, except foam; Plastic processing; Closures, plastic; Plastic containers, except foam; Plastic processing; Closures, plastic
Pr: Keith S Harbison
**CFO:* Bob Robison
VP: Dave Winslett
CTO: Daniel Charron
Plnt Mgr: Jeff Oathout

D-U-N-S 00-802-5959 IMP/EXP
■ **HARBISON-FISCHER INC**
HARBISON-FISCHER MANUFACTURING
(*Suby of* DOVER ARTIFICIAL LIFT INTERNATIONAL LLC) ★
901 N Crowley Rd, Crowley, TX 76036-3798
Tel (817) 297-2211 *Founded/Ownrshp* 1933, 2007
Sales 119.7MM^E *EMP* 450
SIC 3533 3443 Oil field machinery & equipment; Tanks, lined: metal plate; Oil field machinery & equipment; Tanks, lined: metal plate
Pr: David Martin
Pr: Benny Williams

*CFO: Jason Taylor
*VP: Darryl Polasek
*VP: Jason Thompson
Area Mgr: Mark Lee
Brnch Mgr: Tom Demos
Dist Mgr: Dennis Brown
Dist Mgr: Ian Rimmer
Off Mgr: Lorraine Fischer
Telecom Mg: Sandra Bitz

HARBISON-FISCHER MANUFACTURING
See HARBISON-FISCHER INC

D-U-N-S 94-950-1522 IMP/EXP
HARBISON-WALKER REFRACTORIES CO
(Suby of GLOBAL INDUSTRIAL TECHNOLOGIES INC) ★
1305 Cherrington Pkwy, Coraopolis, PA 15108-4355
Tel (412) 375-6600 Founded/Ownrshp 2013
Sales 98.9MM^E EMP 856^E
SIC 3255 3297 Clay refractories; Nonclay refractories
Pr: Jon A Allegretti
*CEO: Steven M Delo
*CFO: Frances Winfield
*Treas: Gabriel Faimann
Ofcr: Joe Schartner
*Sr VP: Douglas Hall
*Sr VP: Carol Jackson
Area Mgr: John Bortner
Area Mgr: Patrick Brittain
Sls Mgr: Bill Daman

D-U-N-S 78-418-7580 IMP/EXP
HARBISONWALKER INTERNATIONAL INC
AP GREEN REFRACTORIES
1305 Cherrington Pkwy # 100, Moon Township, PA 15108-4355
Tel (412) 375-6600 Founded/Ownrshp 2013
Sales 738.7MM^E EMP 1,500
SIC 3297 3272 1459 Commercial physical research; Nonclay refractories; Clay refractories; Magnesite mining; Power-driven handtools; Solid containing units, concrete; Nonclay refractories; Solid containing units, concrete; Magnesite mining
CEO: Steven M Delo
*CFO: Frances Winfield
*Sr VP: Douglas Hall
*Sr VP: Carol Jackson
Dir Risk M: Peggy Groover
Mng Dir: Carl Apel
Mng Dir: Kathleen Humiston
Mng Dir: Thomas Robich
Mng Dir: Rhonda Vete
Dist Mgr: Jack Bentley
Genl Mgr: David Bates

D-U-N-S 02-025-9495
HARBOR (OH)
4334 Secor Rd, Toledo, OH 43623-4234
Tel (419) 479-3233 Founded/Ownrshp 1941
Sales 40.2MM EMP 225
Accts Weber Obrien Ltd Sylvania O
SIC 8093 Mental health clinic, outpatient; Mental health clinic, outpatient
CEO: Dale Shreve
VP: Steve Benjamin
VP: Charles Stewart
VP: Cuneyd Tolek
Ex Dir: Rachel Smolinski

D-U-N-S 55-551-0221
HARBOR ATHLETIC CLUB INC
2529 Allen Blvd, Middleton, WI 53562-2211
Tel (608) 831-6500 Founded/Ownrshp 1985
Sales 9.7MM^E EMP 320
SIC 7991 7997 7999 Athletic club & gymnasiums, membership; Membership sports & recreation clubs; Racquetball club, non-membership; Athletic club & gymnasiums, membership; Membership sports & recreation clubs; Racquetball club, non-membership
Pr: Paul Ernst
*Sec: Francine Ernst
*VP: Mike Teff

D-U-N-S 84-743-1681
HARBOR BANKSHARES CORP
25 W Fayette St, Baltimore, MD 21201-3702
Tel (410) 528-1800 Founded/Ownrshp 1992
Sales NA EMP 80
Accts Stegman & Company Baltimore
SIC 6712 Bank holding companies; Bank holding companies
Pr: Joseph Haskins Jr
Treas: Teodoro J Hernandez
VP: Karl Malloy
VP: Christopher McFadden
VP: Deanna Pierce

D-U-N-S 16-801-8054 IMP
HARBOR BUNKERING CORP
404 Ave Fernandez Juncos, San Juan, PR 00901-3223
Tel (787) 723-1182 Founded/Ownrshp 2004
Sales 82.8MM^E EMP 43
SIC 5172 Diesel fuel
Pr: Alfredo Santaella
*Pr: Alfredo Santaella Suarez
*VP: Fernando Rivera
Opers Mgr: Eric Rivera

D-U-N-S 00-986-8233
HARBOR CHEVROLET CORP (CA)
HARBOR CHEVROLET SALES AND SVC
3770 Cherry Ave, Long Beach, CA 90807-4321
Tel (562) 426-3341 Founded/Ownrshp 1923, 1956
Sales 86.2MM EMP 90
SIC 5511

HARBOR CHEVROLET SALES AND SVC
See HARBOR CHEVROLET CORP

HARBOR CHILD CARE
See HARBOR DAY CARE CENTER INC

D-U-N-S 08-124-9070
HARBOR COMMUNITY BANK FSB
(Suby of HCBF HOLDING CO INC) ★
15588 Sw Warfield Blvd, Indiantown, FL 34956-3501
Tel (772) 597-2181 Founded/Ownrshp 1960
Sales NA EMP 13^E
SIC 6022 State commercial banks; State commercial banks
Ch Bd: Robert M Post
Pr: Edward C Appleton
Bd of Dir: Bobby Tucker
Ofcr: Maria Reyes
Ofcr: Amy Speak
Ex VP: Richard Meyers
VP: Nikki Beisler
VP: Mildred Chilson
VP: Brian Hartman
VP: Jill Knapp
VP: Michael Phillips
VP: Chuck Schad

D-U-N-S 83-388-2798
HARBOR CRUISES LLC
BOSTON HARBOR CRUISES
63 Long Wharf, Boston, MA 02110-3602
Tel (617) 227-4321 Founded/Ownrshp 1996
Sales 20.0MM^E EMP 230
SIC 4725 Sightseeing tour companies; Sightseeing tour companies
CTO: Laura Howes
Sales Exec: Rick Noland

D-U-N-S 07-580-2926
HARBOR DAY CARE CENTER INC
HARBOR CHILD CARE
121 Jackson Ave, Mineola, NY 11501-2709
Tel (516) 493-9830 Founded/Ownrshp 1973
Sales 7.1MM^E EMP 300
Accts Lehman Newman Flynn Vollaro Cp
SIC 8351 Group day care center; Group day care center
Bd of Dir: Mary Geary
*CFO: Nick Katos
*Ex Dir: Jill Rooney
Board of Directors: Mary Geary, Tom Harrington, John Kierman, Regina Spinazzola-Kinney, Kim Malerba, Gary O'connor, Sara Oommen, Stephan Parmett

D-U-N-S 08-837-1638
HARBOR DEVELOPMENTAL DISABILITIES FOUNDATION INC
HARBOR REGIONAL CENTER
21231 Hawthorne Blvd, Torrance, CA 90503-5501
Tel (310) 540-1711 Founded/Ownrshp 1977
Sales 152.2MM EMP 225
Accts Lautze & Lautze San Francisco
SIC 8399 Council for social agency; Council for social agency
CFO: Judy Wada
Ex Dir: Patricia Del Monico
Ex Dir: Patricia Monico
Prgrm Mgr: Liz Cohen-Zeboulon
Prgrm Mgr: Leslie Estrada
Prgrm Mgr: Mary Hernandez
Prgrm Mgr: Pablo Ibanez
Prgrm Mgr: Yolanda Lopez
Prgrm Mgr: Tonantzin Martinez
Prgrm Mgr: Patricia Piceno
Prgrm Mgr: Brandy Stewart

D-U-N-S 05-483-0187 IMP
HARBOR DIESEL AND EQUIPMENT INC
JOHN DEERE
537 W Anaheim St, Long Beach, CA 90813-2895
Tel (562) 591-5665 Founded/Ownrshp 1971
Sales 26.7MM EMP 51
SIC 5084 5531 7538 Engines & parts, diesel; Truck equipment & parts; Diesel engine repair: automotive; Engines & parts, diesel; Truck equipment & parts; Diesel engine repair: automotive
Ch Bd: James V Zupanovich
*Pr: Mike Zupanovich
CFO: David Hiveley
*VP: Thomas E Weersing
Opers Mgr: Brett Roa

D-U-N-S 02-803-4536 IMP
HARBOR DISTRIBUTING LLC
(Suby of REYES HOLDINGS LLC) ★
5901 Bolsa Ave, Huntington Beach, CA 92647-2053
Tel (714) 933-2400 Founded/Ownrshp 1989
Sales 124.7MM^E EMP 400
SIC 5181 Beer & other fermented malt liquors; Beer & other fermented malt liquors
Manager: Cantu Richard

D-U-N-S 61-690-8646
■ **HARBOR ELECTRIC ENERGY CO**
(Suby of EVERSOURCE ENERGY) ★
800 Boylston St, Boston, MA 02199-1900
Tel (617) 424-2000 Founded/Ownrshp 1989
Sales 291.7MM^E EMP 942^E
SIC 4911 Electric services
Ch Bd: Thomas J May
*Treas: James Judge
*Genl Couns: Doug Horan

D-U-N-S 05-047-9518 IMP/EXP
HARBOR FOOTWEAR GROUP LTD
55 Harbor Park Dr, Port Washington, NY 11050-4668
Tel (516) 621-8400 Founded/Ownrshp 1969
Sales 45.9MM^E EMP 110
SIC 5139 Footwear; Footwear
Ch Bd: Dennis S Lazar
COO: Jason Lazar
*CFO: Israel Weintraub
VP: Jim Tangeman
IT Man: John Lufrano
VP Mktg: Barry Specht

HARBOR FREIGHT TOOLS
See CENTRAL PURCHASING LLC

D-U-N-S 00-509-6875 IMP/EXP
HARBOR FREIGHT TOOLS USA INC
26541 Agoura Rd, Calabasas, CA 91302-2093
Tel (818) 836-5000 Founded/Ownrshp 1993
Sales 2.1MMM^E EMP 10,000
SIC 5251 Tools; Tools
Pr: Eric L Smidt
Pr: Trey Feiler
*COO: Robert Rene
CFO: Robert Glickman
Ofcr: Allan Mutchnik
VP: Kelly Brown
VP: Jerry Dammeir
VP: Jonathan Kendall
VP: Tony Laik
VP: Peter Racine
VP: Barry Richman
VP: Roger Sheaves

D-U-N-S 06-751-9728
HARBOR FREIGHT TRANSPORT CORP
301 Craneway St, Newark, NJ 07114-3104
Tel (973) 589-6700 Founded/Ownrshp 1947
Sales 25.3MM^E EMP 65
Accts Sga Group Cpas & Consultants
SIC 4731 4214 Freight consolidation; Local trucking with storage
Pr: Steve Liberti Sr
*VP: Steve Liberti Jr
Off Mgr: Danny Butler
Opers Supe: Robert Valentin

D-U-N-S 00-447-7563
HARBOR GROUP INC
INTERSTATES CONSTRUCTION SERVI
1520 N Main Ave, Sioux Center, IA 51250-2111
Tel (712) 722-1661 Founded/Ownrshp 1999
Sales 114.9MM EMP 550
Accts Nichols Rise & Company Llp
SIC 1731 General electrical contractor; General electrical contractor
CEO: Larry E Den Herder
*Pr: Scott R Peterson
IT Man: Tom Schulte
Opers Mgr: Eric Vandenberg

D-U-N-S 11-872-6595
HARBOR GROUP INC
1115 E Broadway Ave, Norton Shores, MI 49444-2333
Tel (231) 739-7152 Founded/Ownrshp 1983
Sales 80.1MM^E EMP 130
Accts Steensma Novotny Plc Muskegon
SIC 5051 Metals service centers & offices; Metals service centers & offices
Pr: David F Folkert
*CFO: Joseph Gerhardt

D-U-N-S 18-960-9373
HARBOR GROUP MANAGEMENT CO
999 Waterside Dr Ste 2300, Norfolk, VA 23510-3324
Tel (757) 640-0800 Founded/Ownrshp 1985
Sales 37.8MM^E EMP 200
SIC 6531 Real estate managers; Real estate managers
Pr: Friedman Robert S
Pr: Artie Schneider
*CFO: Brian Schaefgen
*Ch: Slone Jordan E
*Ch: Jordan Slone
*Sr VP: Michael Belka
VP: Michael Heinricher
VP: Jeremy Voigtmann
Mng Dir: Alan Dworetzky
Rgnl Mgr: Lindsay Seay
Rgnl Mgr: Faye Shaw

D-U-N-S 07-953-1729
HARBOR HEALTH SERVICES INC
1135 Morton St, Mattapan, MA 02126-2834
Tel (617) 533-2300 Founded/Ownrshp 1970
Sales 61.1MM EMP 450
Accts Alexander Aronson Finning & Co
SIC 8351 8093 8399 Child day care services; Specialty outpatient clinics; Health & welfare council; Child day care services; Specialty outpatient clinics; Health & welfare council
CEO: Daniel Driscoll
*CFO: Walter Keeley
*Treas: Susan Beagle
Obsttrcn: Thao Thieu
Nutrtnst: Laurie Bilyeu
Nutrtnst: Micheline Cabrol
Nutrtnst: Emily McPhee
Cert Phar: Kaitlin Burke

D-U-N-S 19-482-1674
HARBOR HEALTHCARE AND REHABILITATION CENTER INC
301 Ocean View Blvd, Lewes, DE 19958-1270
Tel (302) 644-2092 Founded/Ownrshp 1988
Sales 14.6MM EMP 300
SIC 8051 Skilled nursing care facilities; Skilled nursing care facilities
Pr: Ronald Schafer
*VP: Stephen Silver
Dir IT: Patti Moore

D-U-N-S 62-757-0877
HARBOR HEALTHCARE SYSTEM LP
3406 College St, Beaumont, TX 77701-4612
Tel (409) 813-2332 Founded/Ownrshp 2006
Sales 72.8MM^E EMP 500^E
SIC 8062 General medical & surgical hospitals; General medical & surgical hospitals
CEO: Qamar U Arfeen
*COO: Joe Chapman
*CFO: Rodney Smith
Genl Couns: Maggie Neusel
Genl Couns: Mary Parker

D-U-N-S 05-964-2196
HARBOR HOSPITAL
3001 S Hanover St, Baltimore, MD 21225-1290
Tel (410) 350-3200 Founded/Ownrshp 2010
Sales 65.7MM^E EMP 1,065^E
SIC 8062 General medical & surgical hospitals
Pr: Dennis W Pullin
V Ch: Kaiser Robertson
CFO: Rodney Smith
Ofcr: Joe Chapman
VP: Gaynell Murrell
Ansthlgy: Cedric Regelin

D-U-N-S 03-804-5063
HARBOR HOSPITAL CENTER INC
LABOUR DEPARTMENT
3001 S Hanover St, Baltimore, MD 21225-1290
Tel (410) 350-3200 Founded/Ownrshp 1903
Sales 209.0MM EMP 1,231
Accts Kpmg Llp Norfolk Va
SIC 8062 General medical & surgical hospitals; General medical & surgical hospitals
CEO: Joseph Oddis
Mtls Mgr: Nita Griffith

D-U-N-S 05-490-5930
HARBOR HOSPITAL FOUNDATION INC (MD)
(Suby of MEDSTAR HEALTH INC) ★
3001 S Hanover St, Baltimore, MD 21225-1233
Tel (410) 350-2563 Founded/Ownrshp 1903
Sales 64.5MM^E EMP 1,220
Accts Kpmg Llp Norfolk Va
SIC 8062 General medical & surgical hospitals; General medical & surgical hospitals
CEO: L Barney Johnson

D-U-N-S 15-171-1579 IMP
HARBOR HOUSE SEAFOOD INC
504 Bridgeville Hwy, Seaford, DE 19973-1522
Tel (302) 629-0444 Founded/Ownrshp 1985
Sales 60.6MM^E EMP 76
SIC 5146 Seafoods; Seafoods
Pr: Gary Colbourne
*VP: Mark Bryan

D-U-N-S 00-602-7536 IMP
HARBOR INDUSTRIES INC (MI)
14130 172nd Ave, Grand Haven, MI 49417-9446
Tel (616) 842-5330 Founded/Ownrshp 1950
Sales 165.0MM^E EMP 551
Accts Deloitte & Touche Llp
SIC 2541 3993 Display fixtures, wood; Signs & advertising specialties; Display fixtures, wood; Signs & advertising specialties
Pr: Henry T Parker Jr
Pr: Timothy Parker
VP: Michael Detenber
VP: Gregory Hankamp
VP: Thomas Nook
VP: Frank Tamburello
Creative D: Bill Emrich
Prin: Susan Wright
CTO: Rob Doremire
Prd Mgr: Eric Thompson
Natl Sales: Rich Draeger

D-U-N-S 08-078-0455 IMP/EXP
■ **HARBOR LINEN LLC**
LINEN HOLDINGS
(Suby of BED BATH & BEYOND INC) ★
2 Foster Ave, Gibbsboro, NJ 08026-1194
Tel (856) 545-9149 Founded/Ownrshp 1973, 2012
Sales 55.8MM^E EMP 110
SIC 5023 Linens & towels; Bedspreads; Draperies; Linens, table; Linens & towels; Bedspreads; Draperies; Linens, table
Ch Bd: Earl Waxman
*COO: Chris Nelson
Ofcr: Jonathan Kuhl
*VP: Ron Brozo
*VP: Gary Geiger
*VP: Lou Gostino
VP: Dan Harper
VP: Stephen O'Connell
*VP: Lamar Tomlin
*VP: Rob Will
Area Mgr: Donny Briggs

D-U-N-S 18-159-1306
HARBOR MEDICAL GROUP
(Suby of NORTH SHORE MEDICAL CENTER INC) ★
55 Highland Ave Ste 102, Salem, MA 01970-2100
Tel (978) 741-9500 Founded/Ownrshp 1996
Sales 31.6MM^E EMP 2,693^E
SIC 8011 Offices & clinics of medical doctors
Prin: North Shore Medical Center
Doctor: Gary Cohen
Doctor: Yurly Levin

D-U-N-S 08-286-7185
HARBOR MOTOR CO INC
HARBOR OLDSMOBILE GMC TRUCK
6100 Us Highway 6, Portage, IN 46368-5059
Tel (219) 763-2500 Founded/Ownrshp 1977, 1992
Sales 30.0MM EMP 44
SIC 5511 Automobiles, new & used; Automobiles, new & used
Pr: David A Lawson
COO: Dave Pennington
CFO: Serafin Garcia
CFO: Robert Kendall
Exec: Jeff Robinson

HARBOR NISSAN
See FREELAND MOORE INC

HARBOR OLDSMOBILE GMC TRUCK
See HARBOR MOTOR CO INC

D-U-N-S 07-857-1001
HARBOR PAPER LLC
801 23rd St, Hoquiam, WA 98550-5001
Tel (888) 676-6528 Founded/Ownrshp 2012
Sales 40.3MM^E EMP 170
SIC 2621 Paper mills; Uncoated paper; Paper mills; Uncoated paper
CEO: John Begley
CFO: Ernest Conrads

D-U-N-S 00-968-6593
HARBOR PIPE AND STEEL INC (CA)
JAMES METALS
1495 Columbia Ave Bldg 10, Riverside, CA 92507-2074
Tel (951) 369-3990 Founded/Ownrshp 1962
Sales 161.9MM^E EMP 150
SIC 5051 Steel; Steel
Pr: Joseph W Beattie
*Sec: Martha Fournier
*Prin: Tom Liljegren
*Prin: P Jay Peterson
*Prin: Jorge Robles
*Genl Mgr: Mike Stegman
Sales Asso: Leo Recinos
Sales Asso: Bradley Witt

D-U-N-S 92-958-4746
HARBOR RAIL SERVICES OF CALIFORNIA INC
1550 W Colorado Blvd, Pasadena, CA 91105-1415
Tel (626) 398-4065 *Founded/Ownrshp* 1995
Sales 53.8MM *EMP* 115
Accts Holthouse Carlin & Van Trigt L
SIC 4789 Railroad maintenance & repair services; Railroad maintenance & repair services
Pr: Mark Myronowicz
**CFO:* Joseph Mavilia
**Sec:* Ilona Chandler
Sls Dir: Vanessa Knapton

HARBOR REGIONAL CENTER
See HARBOR DEVELOPMENTAL DISABILITIES FOUNDATION INC

D-U-N-S 07-922-4753
■ **HARBOR RESORT HOTEL LLC** (FL)
SHERATON
(*Suby of* SHERATON CORP) ★
33 Tamiami Trl, Punta Gorda, FL 33950-3630
Tel (941) 637-6770 *Founded/Ownrshp* 2007
Sales 22.0MM^E *EMP* 28^E
SIC 7011 Hotels & motels
Exec: Doug Brown

D-U-N-S 12-586-3402
HARBOR RETIREMENT ASSOCIATES LLC
BALLMORAL
(*Suby of* SULLIVAN UNIVERSITY SYSTEM INC) ★
1440 Highway A1a, Vero Beach, FL 32963-2310
Tel (772) 492-5002 *Founded/Ownrshp* 2002
Sales 45.7MM^E *EMP* 800
SIC 8361 Residential care; Residential care
Pr: Tim Smick
**COO:* Sarabeth Hanson
**CFO:* Thomas Mitchell
**VP:* Michael Adamson
VP: Juan Gonzalez
VP: Becky Kees
VP Opers: Kim Lewis
S&M/VP: Dora Barber
Sls Dir: Sallie Adams

D-U-N-S 00-309-7177 IMP
HARBOR SALES CO (MD)
1000 Harbor Ct, Sudlersville, MD 21668-1818
Tel (410) 758-5461 *Founded/Ownrshp* 1931, 1963
Sales 34.3MM^E *EMP* 56
SIC 5031 2891 Plywood; Millwork; Adhesives; Adhesives, plastic
Ch Bd: Don K Covington Jr
Pr: Duncan S Covington
VP: Pamela Covington

HARBOR SCHOOL DST - NJROTC
See OAK HARBOR SCHOOL DISTRICT

D-U-N-S 07-861-2470 IMP/EXP
HARBOR SEAFOOD INC
969 Lakeville Rd, New Hyde Park, NY 11040-3000
Tel (800) 645-2211 *Founded/Ownrshp* 1975
Sales 47.4MM^E *EMP* 29
SIC 5146 Fish, frozen, unpackaged
Ch Bd: Peter V Cardone
QA Dir: Kim Lavelle
IT Man: Michael Lemmon
Sls Mgr: Joanne McKinnon

D-U-N-S 78-272-1856
HARBOR SOLUTIONS INC
HARBOR TECHNOLOGIES
9000 Commerce Pkwy Ste H, Mount Laurel, NJ 08054-2234
Tel (856) 222-0643 *Founded/Ownrshp* 2007
Sales 25.1MM^E *EMP* 55
Accts Harrison Mauro & Morgan Pa
SIC 5045 Computer peripheral equipment; Terminals, computer
Pr: Alan Lampe

D-U-N-S 05-101-4744
HARBOR SPECIALTY INSURANCE CO
(*Suby of* CLARENDON NATIONAL INSURANCE CO (MD CORP)) ★
1177 Ave Of The Americas, New York, NY 10036-2714
Tel (212) 805-9700 *Founded/Ownrshp* 1995
Sales NA *EMP* 80
SIC 6331 Fire, marine & casualty insurance & carriers
CEO: Dr Betlef Steiner
**CFO:* Anders Folke Larsson

D-U-N-S 04-140-5960
HARBOR STEEL AND SUPPLY CORP
(*Suby of* HARBOR GROUP INC) ★
1115 E Broadway Ave, Norton Shores, MI 49444-2333
Tel (231) 739-7152 *Founded/Ownrshp* 1985
Sales 80.0MM^E *EMP* 130
Accts Steensma Plamondon Novotny Plc
SIC 5051 Metals service centers & offices; Ferrous metals; Miscellaneous nonferrous products; Nonferrous metal sheets, bars, rods, etc.; Metals service centers & offices
CEO: David F Folkert
**Pr:* Stephen Heneveld
CFO: Joseph Gerhardt

HARBOR TECHNOLOGIES
See HARBOR SOLUTIONS INC

D-U-N-S 78-822-2297
HARBOR TRUCK BODIES INC
HARBOR TRUCK BODY
255 Voyager Ave, Brea, CA 92821-6223
Tel (714) 996-0411 *Founded/Ownrshp* 1992
Sales 22.8MM^E *EMP* 79
SIC 3713 7532 Truck & bus bodies; Body shop, automotive
Pr: Ken Lindt
Dir IT: Doug Anderson
Sls Dir: Warren Mason
Sls Mgr: Kimberly Bellamy
Sls Mgr: James Fulweber
Sales Asso: Tony Anderson
Sales Asso: Jeff Bonnett
Sales Asso: Stephanie Hugo
Sales Asso: Andre Robinson

HARBOR TRUCK BODY
See HARBOR TRUCK BODIES INC

D-U-N-S 16-156-0644
HARBOR TRUCK SALES AND SERVICE INC
BALTIMORE FREIGHTLINER
2723 Annapolis Rd, Baltimore, MD 21230-3513
Tel (410) 685-4474 *Founded/Ownrshp* 1986
Sales 30.7MM^E *EMP* 85
SIC 5012 5511 Trucks, commercial; Trucks, tractors & trailers: new & used; Trucks, commercial; Trucks, tractors & trailers: new & used
Pr: Edward S Dentz
**Sec:* Frank E Cook Jr
Off Mgr: Michelle Kahl
Store Mgr: Brian Prince
Dir IT: Tom Wollslager
Sls Mgr: John Coombe
Sls Mgr: John Kim

HARBOR UCLA MED FOUNDATION
See HARBOR-UCLA MEDICAL FOUNDATION INC

HARBOR VIEW HEALTH CARE CENTER
See JERNIGAN NURSING HOME SERVICES INC

D-U-N-S 79-210-2287
HARBOR VIEW HOLDINGS INC
433 California St Fl 7, San Francisco, CA 94104-2011
Tel (415) 982-7777 *Founded/Ownrshp* 1984
Sales 250.2MM^E *EMP* 3,500
SIC 1522 1521 6512 8741 Hotel/motel, new construction; Single-family housing construction; Nonresidential building operators; Hotel or motel management; Restaurant management; Hotel/motel, new construction; Single-family housing construction; Nonresidential building operators; Hotel or motel management; Restaurant management
Pr: Lawrence Lui
CFO: James E Evans
VP: Tamsen McCracken

D-U-N-S 02-724-8913
HARBOR WHOLESALE GROCERY INC
3901 Hogum Bay Rd Ne, Lacey, WA 98516-3136
Tel (360) 754-4484 *Founded/Ownrshp* 1970
Sales 137.9MM^E *EMP* 300
SIC 5141 5194 5142 5122

D-U-N-S 10-095-2667
HARBOR-UCLA MEDICAL CENTER
1000 W Carson St 2, Torrance, CA 90502-2059
Tel (310) 222-2345 *Founded/Ownrshp* 1989
Sales 184.0MM^E *EMP* 3,000
SIC 8062 General medical & surgical hospitals; General medical & surgical hospitals
CEO: Miguel Ortiz
Ansthlgy: Phil Tsai
Doctor: David Atkinson

D-U-N-S 60-370-5526
HARBOR-UCLA MEDICAL FOUNDATION INC
HARBOR UCLA MED FOUNDATION
21840 S Norm Ave Ste 100, Torrance, CA 90502
Tel (310) 222-5015 *Founded/Ownrshp* 1967
Sales 12.3MM *EMP* 400
Accts Deloitte Tax Llp Costa Mesa
SIC 8741 Hospital management; Hospital management
CEO: Chester Choi
Chf Nrs Of: Mary Davila
Surgeon: David Plurad

HARBORAGE, THE
See PALISADES GENERAL CARE

D-U-N-S 07-216-1102
HARBORCREEK SCHOOL DISTRICT INC
6375 Buffalo Rd, Harborcreek, PA 16421-1632
Tel (814) 897-2100 *Founded/Ownrshp* 1882
Sales 18.9MM^E *EMP* 350
Accts Gorzynski Felix & Gloekler P
SIC 8211 Elementary & secondary schools; Public elementary & secondary schools; Elementary & secondary schools; Public elementary & secondary schools
Schl Brd P: Tom Fortin
Board of Directors: John Hamilton, A Nine Member Board

D-U-N-S 84-807-4415
HARBORFIELDS CENTRAL SCHOOL DISTRICT
2 Oldfield Rd, Greenlawn, NY 11740-1235
Tel (631) 754-5300 *Founded/Ownrshp* 1956
Sales 26.5MM^E *EMP* 450
SIC 8211 Public elementary & secondary schools; Public elementary & secondary schools
Schl Brd P: Nicholas P Jiuliano
Psych: Lisa Drake

HARBORLITE
See IMERYS PERLITE USA INC

D-U-N-S 06-010-7240
HARBORONE BANK
770 Oak St, Brockton, MA 02301-1100
Tel (508) 895-1000 *Founded/Ownrshp* 1917
Sales NA *EMP* 373
SIC 6036 State savings banks, not federally chartered; State savings banks, not federally chartered
Pr: James W Blake
**Ch Bd:* David Frenette
Pr: Maureen Wilkinson
**CFO:* Joseph Casey
Bd of Dir: Adam Cupples
Chf Mktg O: Dave Tryder
Ofcr: Karla Dennison
Ofcr: James Hanlon
Ofcr: Dayna Holmes
Ofcr: Carol Martyn
**Sr VP:* Richard W Bastiansen
**Sr VP:* Marcia G Dmitruk
**Sr VP:* Leo Donahue
**Sr VP:* Christopher K Gibbons
**Sr VP:* Leo A Macneil
Sr VP: David Reilly
Sr VP: Scott Sanborn
**Sr VP:* Patricia M Williams
VP: Murray Charron
VP: Allen Cordeiro
VP: Shirley Donahue

D-U-N-S 07-442-0142
HARBORQUEST INC
14 E Jackson Blvd # 1210, Chicago, IL 60604-2233
Tel (312) 612-7600 *Founded/Ownrshp* 1970
Sales 4.3MM *EMP* 1,500
Accts Fgmk Llc Deerfield Il
SIC 7363 4119 7361 Temporary help service; Local passenger transportation; Employment agencies; Temporary help service; Local passenger transportation; Employment agencies
Pr: John J Plunkett
**Pr:* Robert E Wordlaw
**Sec:* Jane Davies
**VP:* Mark Mulroe
VP: Richard S Peabody Jr
**VP:* William A Schwarz
Ex Dir: Robert Wordlaw

HARBOR'S INSURANCE
See SHAW & PETERSEN INSURANCE INC

HARBORSIDE FINANCIAL CENTER
See IPC SYSTEMS HOLDINGS CORP

D-U-N-S 96-650-6821
HARBORSIDE HEALTHCARE ADVISORS LIMITED PARTNERSHIP
(*Suby of* KHI LLC)
101 Sun Ave Ne, Albuquerque, NM 87109-4373
Tel (505) 821-1216 *Founded/Ownrshp* 1987
Sales 28.2MM^E *EMP* 1,343^E
SIC 8051 Skilled nursing care facilities
Pr: William Mathies

D-U-N-S 02-024-8738
HARBORSTONE CREDIT UNION (WA)
6019 Lake Grove St Sw, Tacoma, WA 98499-2761
Tel (253) 584-2260 *Founded/Ownrshp* 1955
Sales NA *EMP* 180
SIC 6062 6163 State credit unions, not federally chartered; Loan brokers; State credit unions, not federally chartered; Loan brokers
Pr: Rich Schmidtke
**Pr:* Phil Jones
CFO: Bill Jones
**Treas:* Edward Seidenberg

HARBORTOUCH
See UNITED BANK CARD INC

D-U-N-S 15-293-9328 IMP
HARBORTOWN INDUSTRIES INC
28477 N Ballard Dr, Lake Forest, IL 60045-4510
Tel (847) 327-9900 *Founded/Ownrshp* 1997
Sales 92.0MM *EMP* 75
SIC 5023 Frames & framing, picture & mirror; Frames & framing, picture & mirror
Pr: Terry Rozdolsky
**Ex VP:* Dennis Regano
**VP:* Jack Smith

D-U-N-S 13-657-8817
HARBORVIEW MEDICAL CENTER
UNIVERSITY OF WASHINGTON
(*Suby of* UNIVERSITY OF WASHINGTON INC) ★
325 9th Ave, Seattle, WA 98104-2499
Tel (206) 731-3000 *Founded/Ownrshp* 1930
Sales 470.5MM^E *EMP* 4,000^E
SIC 8062 General medical & surgical hospitals; General medical & surgical hospitals
Ex Dir: Eileen Whalen
COO: Claudette Cooper
COO: Scott Davies
Off Mgr: Brenda Tillery
Off Mgr: Bahaa Wanly
Sftwr Eng: Lee Fouche
Opers Mgr: Ruchi Aggarwal
Pathlgst: Byung Kim
Obsttrcn: Susan D Reed
Plas Surg: Kimberly K Lu
Nutrtnst: Kathleen Givan

D-U-N-S 15-343-7058
HARBOUR CONTRACTORS INC
23830 W Main St, Plainfield, IL 60544-2120
Tel (815) 230-3674 *Founded/Ownrshp* 1959
Sales 23.0MM *EMP* 40
SIC 1542 8741 1611 Design & erection, combined: non-residential; Construction management; General contractor, highway & street construction; Design & erection, combined: non-residential; Construction management; General contractor, highway & street construction
Pr: Patrick C Harbour
**VP:* Chris Kozak
VP: George Macko
VP: Leonardo Pinto
VP: Steve Vitas
VP Bus Dev: Ron Mick
Dir Bus: Janet Scott
CTO: Roger Sprague
Snr PM: Ken Johnson
Snr Mgr: Lonnie Schultz

D-U-N-S 14-706-1592 IMP/EXP
HARBOUR GROUP LTD
7701 Forsyth Blvd Ste 600, Saint Louis, MO 63105-1802
Tel (314) 727-5550 *Founded/Ownrshp* 1980
Sales 1.3MMM^E *EMP* 5,200
SIC 3823 Boiler controls: industrial, power & marine type; Boiler controls: industrial, power & marine type
CEO: Jeff Fox
V Ch: Donald E Nicklson
Pr: Greg Fox
Pr: Samuel A Hamacher
Pr: James C Janning
CFO: Mike Santoni
Treas: Janelle Rickermann
V Ch Bd: Donald E Nickelson
V Ch Bd: William A Schmalz
VP: Audrey Chang
VP: Greg Meier
VP: Scott Nieberle
Board of Directors: Edward J Bock, Alfred Fleishman, Reuben Mark, John McGuckian, Julian Meyer, Stanley Rosenblum, Mahlon Rubin, Murray Weidenbaum

D-U-N-S 00-242-8894 IMP
■ **HARBOUR INDUSTRIES LLC**
(*Suby of* MARMON GROUP LLC) ★
4744 Shelburne Rd, Shelburne, VT 05482-6695
Tel (802) 985-3311 *Founded/Ownrshp* 1994
Sales 23.1MM^E *EMP* 120
SIC 3357 Nonferrous wiredrawing & insulating; Nonferrous wiredrawing & insulating
Pr: Dennis R Dodd
**VP:* Paul Horn
IT Man: Jeff Cofran
VP Opers: Joseph Hennessy
Plnt Mgr: Jim Tye
Ql Cn Mgr: Scott Debaise
Natl Sales: Trum Rittling
Mktg Dir: Michael Wells
Sls Mgr: Kristin Peet

D-U-N-S 15-040-5017
HARBOUR PETROLEUM CORP OF BREVARD INC
21 W Fee Ave Ste F, Melbourne, FL 32901-4478
Tel (321) 724-0641 *Founded/Ownrshp* 1984
Sales 114.4MM *EMP* 7
Accts Averett Warmus Durkee Orlando
SIC 5171 Petroleum bulk stations & terminals; Petroleum bulk stations & terminals
Pr: Sam Gornto
**CFO:* Mark Gornto

HARBOURVEST INTL PRIVATE
See HARBOURVEST PARTNERS LLC

D-U-N-S 03-806-8917
HARBOURVEST PARTNERS LLC
HARBOURVEST INTL PRIVATE
1 Financial Ctr Ste 4401, Boston, MA 02111-2650
Tel (617) 348-3707 *Founded/Ownrshp* 1996
Sales 35.4MM^E *EMP* 100
SIC 6282 6211 Investment advice; Security brokers & dealers; Investment advice; Security brokers & dealers
Pr: Paul Fiore
Treas: Mark Manfra
Treas: Sandra Pasquale
Sr VP: Diane Goodwin
VP: Francisco Arboleda
VP: Monique Austin
VP: Sebastiaan Berg
VP: Maggie Chan
VP: Tony Cobuzzi
VP: Cory Cook
VP: Nicholas Cros
VP: Tim Flower
VP: Danielle Green
VP: Edward Holdsworth
VP: Kapil Kirpalani
VP: Bert Kwan
VP: Craig Macdonald
VP: Nhora Otalora
VP: Amanda Outerbridge
VP: Danielle Perfetuo
VP: Corentin Roy

HARCO
See HARRINGTON CORP

D-U-N-S 04-562-9656
■ **HARCO INC**
(*Suby of* RITE AID CORP) ★
30 Hunter Ln, Camp Hill, PA 17011-2400
Tel (717) 761-2633 *Founded/Ownrshp* 1997
Sales 270.0MM^E *EMP* 2,600
Accts Arthur Andersen Llp Birmingha
SIC 5912 Drug stores
Pr: Kenneth C Black
**Treas:* Matthew Schroeder
**VP:* Gerald Cardinale
**VP:* Susan Lowell
**VP:* Michael A Podgurski

D-U-N-S 00-118-4076
■ **HARCO LLC** (CT)
(*Suby of* AEROCONTROLEX) ★
186 Cedar St, Branford, CT 06405-6011
Tel (203) 483-3700 *Founded/Ownrshp* 1951, 2012
Sales 59.2MM^E *EMP* 137
SIC 3829 Aircraft & motor vehicle measurement equipment; Aircraft & motor vehicle measurement equipment
CEO: Raymond Laubenthal
**Pr:* Michael Milardo
**Sec:* Gregory Rufus
VP: Jim Viglione

D-U-N-S 79-044-1682 IMP
HARCO MANUFACTURING GROUP LLC
3535 Kettering Blvd, Moraine, OH 45439-2014
Tel (937) 528-5000 *Founded/Ownrshp* 2006
Sales 40.9MM^E *EMP* 300
SIC 3714 Motor vehicle brake systems & parts; Motor vehicle brake systems & parts
Off Mgr: Kathy Weaver
IT Man: Dennis Piper
Sls Mgr: Dave Homan

D-U-N-S 08-422-3668
HARCO NATIONAL INSURANCE CO (IL)
(*Suby of* IAT REINSURANCE COMPANY LTD.)
1701 Golf Rd Ste 1-600, Rolling Meadows, IL 60008-4241
Tel (847) 321-4800 *Founded/Ownrshp* 1955, 2001
Sales NA *EMP* 85
SIC 6331 Fire, marine & casualty insurance; Fire, marine & casualty insurance
Pr: Stephen L Stephano
**Treas:* David Pirrung
**VP:* Albert J Birch
VP: Lynn Ford
VP: James Miller
Dir IT: Debbie Richardson
Manager: Bob Burd

D-U-N-S 96-711-9660
HARCO SERVICES LLC
3271 Old 41 Hwy Nw, Kennesaw, GA 30144-1127
Tel (770) 917-8846 *Founded/Ownrshp* 1996
Sales 26.2MME *EMP* 30
SIC 1542 Service station construction

D-U-N-S 78-166-3331
HARCON INC
1121 Alderman Dr Ste 101, Alpharetta, GA 30005-5470
Tel (770) 343-9998 *Founded/Ownrshp* 1989
Sales 72.2MME *EMP* 450
Accts Tarpley & Underwood Pc Atl
SIC 1771 Concrete work; Concrete work
Pr: Michael A Hardin
**CFO:* Melvin E Burges

D-U-N-S 10-355-9258
HARCOURT ASSESSMENT INC
CLINICAL ASSESSMENT
(*Suby of* PEARSON PLC)
19500 Bulverde Rd, San Antonio, TX 78259-3707
Tel (210) 339-5000 *Founded/Ownrshp* 2008
Sales 45.3MME *EMP* 1,000
SIC 8748 2741 Testing service, educational or personnel; Test development & evaluation service; Miscellaneous publishing; Testing service, educational or personnel; Test development & evaluation service; Miscellaneous publishing
Ch Bd: John R Dilworth
**Ch Bd:* Michael E Hansen
Pr: Josh Williams
**CEO:* Barry Topol
Treas: Kenneth E Fogarty
**VP:* Scott Barnes
VP: Charles P Fontaine
VP: Terry Turner
VP: Joe Wong
Dir Surg: Ray Christensen
CTO: Mickey Corona

D-U-N-S 19-412-8765 IMP/EXP
HARCROS CHEMICALS INC
5200 Speaker Rd, Kansas City, KS 66106-1048
Tel (913) 321-3131 *Founded/Ownrshp* 2001
Sales 919.0MME *EMP* 550
SIC 5169 2869 Industrial gases; Industrial organic chemicals; Industrial gases; Industrial organic chemicals
CEO: Kevin Mirner
**CFO:* Mark Loethen
VP: Nick Harden
VP: Daniel Larsen
**VP:* Martin Morgan
**VP:* Peter Radford
Dir Risk M: Clifton Wiksten
Rgnl Mgr: Wade Christensen
Dist Mgr: Brian Aaron
Dist Mgr: Doug Gwatney
Dist Mgr: Dennis Whipple

D-U-N-S 07-549-6240
HARCUM COLLEGE
750 Montgomery Ave, Bryn Mawr, PA 19010-3476
Tel (610) 525-4100 *Founded/Ownrshp* 1953
Sales 33.2MM *EMP* 125
SIC 8222

HARD CORE CORING & CON CUTNG
See NORMAN MECHANICAL INC

D-U-N-S 10-326-8710 IMP
HARD ROCK CAFE FOUNDATION INC
(*Suby of* SEMINOLE TRIBE OF FLORIDA T V INC) ★
6100 Old Park Ln Ste 100, Orlando, FL 32835-2499
Tel (407) 445-7625 *Founded/Ownrshp* 2006
Sales 158.8MME *EMP* 3,000E
SIC 5812 5813 7922 7011 6794 Eating places; Bar (drinking places); Theatrical producers & services; Hotels & motels; Franchises, selling or licensing; Eating places; Bar (drinking places); Theatrical producers & services; Hotels & motels; Franchises, selling or licensing
Pr: Hamish Dodds
**Treas:* Chris Knipfing
Ex VP: Jon Lucas
**VP:* Thomas Gispanski
VP: Marie Grimm
VP: Mike Kneidinger
VP: Michael Wozniak
Rgnl Mgr: Maria Nino
Admn Mgr: Jim McGonal
Genl Mgr: Jason Taflinger
Netwrk Mgr: Jeremiah Collins

D-U-N-S 96-175-6780
HARD ROCK CAFE INTERNATIONAL (ORLANDO) INC
(*Suby of* HARD ROCK CAFE FOUNDATION INC) ★
6050 Universal Blvd, Orlando, FL 32819-7611
Tel (407) 351-7625 *Founded/Ownrshp* 1988
Sales 13.9MME *EMP* 500
SIC 5812 5813 Eating places; Drinking places; Eating places; Drinking places
Pr: Hamish Dodds
**VP:* Gispanski Thomas
Dir Soc: Bonnie Ell
Genl Mgr: Nicos Charalamdous
Genl Mgr: Tray Moore

D-U-N-S 95-990-5399
HARD ROCK CAFE INTERNATIONAL (STP) INC
HARD ROCK CAFE INTL STP
(*Suby of* HARD ROCK CAFE FOUNDATION INC) ★
1501 Broadway, New York, NY 10036-5601
Tel (212) 343-3355 *Founded/Ownrshp* 1971
Sales 9.9MME *EMP* 325
SIC 5812 5813 5947 Eating places; Bar (drinking places); Gift, novelty & souvenir shop; Eating places; Bar (drinking places); Gift, novelty & souvenir shop
CEO: Pete Beaudralt
Ex VP: Michael Shindler
Dir Soc: Kristin Forkin
Genl Mgr: David Miller
Genl Mgr: Martin Perdich

D-U-N-S 80-978-9709
HARD ROCK CAFE INTERNATIONAL (USA) INC
ROCK SHOP
(*Suby of* SEMINOLE TRIBE OF FLORIDA INC) ★
6100 Old Park Ln Ste 100, Orlando, FL 32835-2499
Tel (407) 445-7625 *Founded/Ownrshp* 2007
Sales 71.3MME *EMP* 1,500
SIC 5812 Eating places; Eating places
Pr: Hamish Dodds
**COO:* Fred Thimm
Ex VP: Jon Lucas
Ex VP: Marco Roca
**VP:* Michael Beacham
**VP:* John Galloway
**VP:* Thomas Gispanski
VP: Patrick Manion
Dir Soc: Bonnie Brownell
MIS Dir: Ron Ward
Opers Mgr: Pablo Czarnik

HARD ROCK CAFE INTL STP
See HARD ROCK CAFE INTERNATIONAL (STP) INC

D-U-N-S 79-696-4955
HARD ROCK CONSTRUCTION CO
2305 L And A Rd, Metairie, LA 70001-5955
Tel (504) 835-1050 *Founded/Ownrshp* 1989
Sales 32.0MME *EMP* 80
SIC 1542 1611 Commercial & office building, new construction; Highway & street construction; Commercial & office building, new construction; Highway & street construction
Pr: Carl E Panebiango
**VP:* Chris Darkshanni
**VP:* Jeffrey D Young

HARD ROCK HOTEL
See T-12 THREE LLC

HARD ROCK HOTEL AND CASINO
See HRHH HOTEL/CASINO LLC

D-U-N-S 80-958-5974
HARD ROCK HOTEL HOLDINGS LLC
4455 Paradise Rd, Las Vegas, NV 89169-6598
Tel (702) 693-5000 *Founded/Ownrshp* 2011
Sales 28.6MME *EMP* 1,362E
SIC 7011 Hotels & motels; Casino hotel; Hotels & motels; Casino hotel
Pr: Fred J Kleisner
Sr VP: Matt Greene
**VP:* Richard Szymanski
Dir IT: Rob Kosier

D-U-N-S 10-298-7344
HARD ROCK HOTEL INC
HARD ROCK LAS VEGAS
4455 Paradise Rd, Las Vegas, NV 89169-6598
Tel (702) 693-5000 *Founded/Ownrshp* 1993
Sales 144.1MME *EMP* 1,362
SIC 7011 Casino hotel; Casino hotel
Pr: Richard Szymanski
**Ch Bd:* Peter A Morton
**CEO:* Jody Lake
**COO:* Kevin Kelley
**CFO:* Dean Boswell
**CFO:* James D Bowen
CFO: James Bowen
CFO: James E Conley
Bd of Dir: Gilbert B Friesen
Chf Mktg O: Jennifer Dunne
**Sr VP:* Brian D Ogaz
VP: Mark Kelly
VP: Javier De La Rosa
VP: Paul McGuire
Exec: Marcus O'Brien
Exec: Mark Sherline
Dir Soc: Candice Cordery

HARD ROCK LAS VEGAS
See HARD ROCK HOTEL INC

HARD TAIL
See RICHARD CANTRELL

HARD TIMES CAFE
See F&K MANAGEMENT INC

D-U-N-S 94-151-2824
HARDAGE HOTELS I LLC
CHASE SUITE HOTEL BY WOODFIN
12555 High Bluff Dr # 330, San Diego, CA 92130-3005
Tel (858) 314-7910 *Founded/Ownrshp* 1995
Sales 42.4MME *EMP* 700
SIC 7011 Hotels & motels; Hotels & motels
CFO: Rick Neza
Exec: Annette Hays
Exec: Keith Hindenlang
Exec: Jud Leibee
Exec: Colleen Manzer
Exec: Travis Wiederien
Dir IT: Martin Bustos
Dir IT: Bremner Jim
IT Man: Beth Chaney
Sales Exec: Mary Smith

HARDAWAY CNSTR CORP TENN
See HARDAWAY CONSTRUCTION CORP

D-U-N-S 06-074-7953
HARDAWAY CONSTRUCTION CORP (TN)
HARDAWAY CNSTR CORP TENN
(*Suby of* MAIN STREET OPERATING CO INC) ★
615 Main St, Nashville, TN 37206-3617
Tel (615) 254-5461 *Founded/Ownrshp* 1924
Sales 100.0MME *EMP* 225
SIC 1542 1541 1522 Commercial & office building, new construction; Industrial buildings, new construction; Multi-family dwelling construction; Commercial & office building, new construction; Industrial buildings, new construction; Multi-family dwelling construction
Pr: Stan H Hardaway
**CFO:* Kerry P Sloan
**Treas:* Catherine L Hardaway
**Ex VP:* John F Sloan
VP: Ed Bullington
VP: Gary W Chesley
VP: Linda Guinn CPA
VP: Bret Obrien
Snr PM: David Dierks
Board of Directors: Susan K Goodrum, Billy D Grover, Andy Higgins, Richard M Miller, Frank Woods

D-U-N-S 13-105-6467
HARDAWAY GROUP INC
615 Main St, Nashville, TN 37206-3603
Tel (615) 254-5461 *Founded/Ownrshp* 1986
Sales 108.7MME *EMP* 250
SIC 1542 1541 1522 6531 Commercial & office building, new construction; Industrial buildings, new construction; Apartment building construction; Real estate managers; Commercial & office building, new construction; Industrial buildings, new construction; Apartment building construction; Real estate managers
Ch Bd: Stan H Hardaway
VP: Linda Guinn CPA
**VP:* Kerry P Sloan

D-U-N-S 10-711-9158
HARDCASTLE CONSTRUCTION INC
26800 Oklahoma 74, Washington, OK 73093
Tel (405) 288-2311 *Founded/Ownrshp* 1988
Sales 22.3MME *EMP* 65
SIC 1542 Commercial & office buildings, new construction; Commercial & office buildings, renovation & repair
Pr: Bill Hardcastle
**VP:* Gene Hardcastle
**VP:* Jim Hardcastle

HARDCOVER RESTAURANT
See BARNSIDER MANAGEMENT CORP

HARDE' MARTS
See CENTRAL OIL & SUPPLY CORP

HARDEE COUNTY SCHOOL DISTRICT
See SCHOOL BOARD OF HARDEE COUNTY

HARDEE'S
See SANDYS ASSOCIATES INC

HARDEE'S
See DORO INC

HARDEE'S
See BODDIE-NOELL ENTERPRISES INC

HARDEE'S
See HAR-MAR FOODS INC

HARDEE'S
See WADE-CARY ENTERPRISES INC

HARDEE'S
See RESTAURANT MANAGEMENT CORP

HARDEE'S
See PONDER ENTERPRISES INC

HARDEE'S
See SIX-O-ONE INC

HARDEE'S
See CHESAPEAKE PRODUCTS & SERVICES INC

HARDEE'S
See OTAC INC

HARDEE'S
See CKE RESTAURANTS HOLDINGS INC

HARDEE'S
See DIAMOND HOSPITALITY ENTERPRISES

D-U-N-S 10-212-7735
HARDEES OF SHELBYVILLE
111 Midland Blvd, Shelbyville, KY 40065-9732
Tel (502) 633-5100 *Founded/Ownrshp* 1983
Sales 9.1MME *EMP* 346
SIC 5812 Fast-food restaurant, chain; Fast-food restaurant, chain
Sr Pt: John T McGinnis III
Off Mgr: Pat Marcum

D-U-N-S 79-696-2629
HARDEES OF SOUTHWEST MISSOURI INC
608 W Kathryn St, Nixa, MO 65714-8462
Tel (417) 724-0250 *Founded/Ownrshp* 1991
Sales 22.0MM *EMP* 750
SIC 5812 Fast-food restaurant, chain; Fast-food restaurant, chain
Pr: Michael Shay

D-U-N-S 00-320-2900
HARDEES RESTAURANTS LLC
(*Suby of* CKE RESTAURANTS HOLDINGS INC) ★
100 N Broadway Ste 1200, Saint Louis, MO 63102-2706
Tel (314) 259-6200 *Founded/Ownrshp* 1960
Sales 530.7MME *EMP* 16,680
SIC 5812 Fast-food restaurant, chain; Fast-food restaurant, chain
Pr: Andrew F Puzder
**CFO:* Theodore Abajian
Ex VP: Jeffrey Chasney
Ex VP: Michael E Murphy
Sr VP: Will Fisher
**Sr VP:* Bruce Frazer
Sr VP: James Speed
Off Mgr: Theresa Jones
Netwrk Mgr: Darry Dugger
Sales Exec: Phil Campbell
Sales Exec: Freda Davis

HARDEL BUILDERS CENTER
See HARDEL MUTUAL PLYWOOD CORP

D-U-N-S 00-926-2072
HARDEL MUTUAL PLYWOOD CORP
HARDEL BUILDERS CENTER
143 Maurin Rd, Chehalis, WA 98532-8716
Tel (360) 740-0232 *Founded/Ownrshp* 1955
Sales 33.6MME *EMP* 190
Accts Mcgladrey & Pullen Llp Olymp
SIC 2436 Plywood, softwood; Plywood, softwood
Pr: Tuan Vo
**Treas:* An Lee
Treas: William Pan
**VP:* Kha Phan
Sls Mgr: Tracy Trogden

D-U-N-S 09-379-3883
HARDEMAN COUNTY BOARD OF EDUCATION
10815 Old Highway 64, Bolivar, TN 38008-3599
Tel (731) 658-2510 *Founded/Ownrshp* 1800
Sales 32.2MME *EMP* 650
SIC 8211 School board; Public junior high school; Public senior high school; Public vocational/technical school; School board; Public junior high school; Public senior high school; Public vocational/technical school
IT Man: Michelle Johnson

D-U-N-S 07-979-9001
HARDEMAN COUNTY SCHOOLS
10815 Old Highway 64, Bolivar, TN 38008-3599
Tel (731) 658-2510 *Founded/Ownrshp* 2015
Sales 19.4MME *EMP* 543E
SIC 8211 Public elementary & secondary schools
Teacher Pr: Beth Waller
HC Dir: Vanessa Holmberg

D-U-N-S 03-379-2458
HARDEN & ASSOCIATES INC
501 Rverside Ave Ste 1000, Jacksonville, FL 32202
Tel (904) 355-1700 *Founded/Ownrshp* 1960
Sales NA *EMP* 120E
SIC 6411 Insurance agents; Insurance brokers
Pr: Marvin Harden III
CFO: Katie Longway
Treas: Barry Henry
**Treas:* Paul Lunetta
Ex VP: Richard Pierpont
Sr VP: Lawrence Giusti
VP: Justin Terry
Exec: Kelly Harden
Dir IT: Igor Skocic
Sls&Mrk Ex: Kurt Thoresen

D-U-N-S 80-360-4839
HARDEN HEALTHCARE SERVICES LLC
3350 Riverwood Pkwy Se # 1, Atlanta, GA 30339-6401
Tel (512) 634-4965 *Founded/Ownrshp* 2007
Sales 282.7MME *EMP* 32,000
SIC 8082 Home health care services; Home health care services
CEO: Lew Little Jr
Pr: Jay Koeper
**Pr:* Kim Layton
**Pr:* Chris Roussos
**Pr:* Steve Wood
**COO:* Mike McMaude
Ofcr: Maryann Choi
**Sr VP:* Ben Hanson
VP: Brianna Braden
VP: Joyce Goss
Exec: Ken Word

D-U-N-S 83-229-2754
HARDEN HEALTHCARE TEXAS LP
GRACYWOODS NURSING CENTER
(*Suby of* HARDEN HEALTHCARE SERVICES LLC) ★
8701 N Mopac Expy, Austin, TX 78759-8376
Tel (512) 615-4965 *Founded/Ownrshp* 2001
Sales 20.0MME *EMP* 1,800
SIC 8059 Nursing home, except skilled & intermediate care facility; Nursing home, except skilled & intermediate care facility
Pt: Lew Little
CFO: Steve Wood
Sr VP: Brianna Braden
Exec: Ken Word
Genl Couns: Benjamin Hanson

D-U-N-S 80-767-9829
HARDEN HOME HEALTH LLC
AUXI HEALTH
(*Suby of* HARDEN HEALTHCARE SERVICES LLC) ★
8701 N Mopac Expy, Austin, TX 78759-8376
Tel (512) 634-4909 *Founded/Ownrshp* 2007
Sales 6.0MME *EMP* 1,650E
SIC 8082 Home health care services
Prin: Lew Little Jr

D-U-N-S 07-945-1414
HARDENBERGH INSURANCE GROUP
8000 Sagemore Dr Ste 8101, Marlton, NJ 08053-3941
Tel (856) 489-9100 *Founded/Ownrshp* 2014
Sales NA *EMP* 63E
SIC 6411 Insurance agents & brokers
Pr: Richard J Hardenbergh
**VP:* John McCrudden

D-U-N-S 00-643-9186
HARDER CORP (WI)
7029 Raywood Rd, Monona, WI 53713-2271
Tel (608) 271-5127 *Founded/Ownrshp* 1947, 1989
Sales 21.1MME *EMP* 48
SIC 5113 5087 Industrial & personal service paper; Towels, paper; Napkins, paper; Shipping supplies; Janitors' supplies
Owner: Richard Zimmerman
**VP:* Suzanne Zimmerman
Sls Mgr: Chris Moser

D-U-N-S 04-248-3107
HARDER MECHANICAL CONTRACTORS INC
HMC
2148 Ne Mlk Blvd, Portland, OR 97212-3792
Tel (503) 281-1112 *Founded/Ownrshp* 1965
Sales 385.0MME *EMP* 650
SIC 1711 7389

D-U-N-S 05-455-2252
HARDESTY & HANOVER LLC
1501 Broadway Ste 310, New York, NY 10036-5587
Tel (212) 944-1150 *Founded/Ownrshp* 1887, 1945
Sales 57.3MME *EMP* 250
SIC 8711 Consulting engineer; Consulting engineer
Pt: Sean A Bluni
Pt: Charles J Gozdziewski
Pt: Timothy J Noles
Pt: Glen E Schetelich
Pt: Paul M Skelton

Pt: Anna Volynsky
Pt: Daniel Wan
Mng Pt: Andrew W Herrmann
COO: Ira Rosen
Brnch Mgr: Brian Hamill
IT Man: AMR Elkerdawy

D-U-N-S 07-241-8155
HARDESTY CO INC
(*Suby of* GRUPO CEMENTOS DE CHIHUAHUA, S.A.B. DE C.V.)
4141 N Memorial Dr, Tulsa, OK 74115-1400
Tel (918) 585-3100 *Founded/Ownrshp* 2006
Sales 64.0MM^E *EMP* 881
SIC 3273 6799 1542 1522 Ready-mixed concrete; Investors; Commercial & office building, new construction; Apartment building construction; Ready-mixed concrete; Investors; Commercial & office building, new construction; Apartment building construction
Pr: Floyd R Hardesty
**Sec:* Thomas L Parkinson
**Ex VP:* J Michael Hays
**VP:* Randall Edgar
Mktg Dir: Bonnie Giesken

D-U-N-S 00-400-1301
HARDIE-TYNES CO INC
800 28th St N, Birmingham, AL 35203-1221
Tel (205) 252-5191 *Founded/Ownrshp* 1997
Sales 26.0MM^E *EMP* 68
SIC 3563 3491 3511 3536 3443 3441 Air & gas compressors including vacuum pumps; Water works valves; Steam turbines; Hoists; Fabricated plate work (boiler shop); Fabricated structural metal
Pr: Earnest Wright
**Treas:* Bill Brock
**Ex VP:* Lynn Taylor
**Sr VP:* Wayne Jones
VP Sls: Charles Debardeleben

D-U-N-S 02-624-6959
HARDIES FRUIT AND VEGETABLE CO LP
1005 N Cockrell Hill Rd, Dallas, TX 75211-1318
Tel (214) 426-5666 *Founded/Ownrshp* 1943
Sales 104.6MM^E *EMP* 137^E
SIC 5148 Fresh fruits & vegetables; Fresh fruits & vegetables
CEO: David Hardie
**Genl Pt:* John D Hardie
**Pt:* Sandra Hardie
**Pr:* Mark Austin
**VP:* Dave Allen
Genl Mgr: Hank Weinstein
IT Man: Ray Hicks
Natl Sales: Alma Rincon
Mktg Mgr: Sherry Nielsen

D-U-N-S 78-100-7492
HARDIES FRUIT AND VEGETABLE CO-SOUTH LP
9715b Burnet Rd Ste 100, Austin, TX 78758-5589
Tel (512) 451-8757 *Founded/Ownrshp* 2006
Sales 27.7MM^E *EMP* 150
SIC 5148 Fresh fruits & vegetables; Fresh fruits & vegetables
Genl Pt: Greg Rowe

HARDIGG CASES
See HARDIGG INDUSTRIES INC

D-U-N-S 00-112-1912 IMP/EXP
HARDIGG INDUSTRIES INC
HARDIGG CASES
(*Suby of* PELICAN PRODUCTS INC) ★
147 N Main St, South Deerfield, MA 01373-1026
Tel (413) 665-2163 *Founded/Ownrshp* 2009
Sales 61.6MM^E *EMP* 450
SIC 3559 3089 3086 8711 8734 3412

D-U-N-S 02-783-0264
HARDIN AUTOMOTIVE (CA)
HARDIN BUICK PONTIAC GMC
1381 S Auto Center Dr, Anaheim, CA 92806-5612
Tel (714) 533-6200 *Founded/Ownrshp* 1957
Sales 97.2MM^E *EMP* 235
SIC 5511 General automotive repair shops; Automobiles, new & used; Automobiles, new & used
CEO: Dennis D Hardin
IT Man: Roger Gagnon
VP Mktg: Jared Hardin
Sls Dir: Odett Karam
Sls Mgr: Mark Johnson
Sls Mgr: Tony Kallah
Sls Mgr: Dennis Leatherman
Sls Mgr: Mike Lee

HARDIN BUICK PONTIAC GMC
See HARDIN AUTOMOTIVE

D-U-N-S 08-696-8344
HARDIN CONSTRUCTION CO LLC
HARDIN MANAGEMENT COMPANY
3301 Windy Ridge Pkwy Se # 400, Atlanta, GA 30339-8537
Tel (404) 264-0404 *Founded/Ownrshp* 2013
Sales NA *EMP* 600
SIC 8741 1542 1541 1522

HARDIN COUNTY AIRPORT
See COUNTY OF HARDIN

D-U-N-S 09-566-8513
HARDIN COUNTY BANK (TN)
(*Suby of* HARDIN COUNTY BANCSHARES INC)
235 Wayne Rd, Savannah, TN 38372-1941
Tel (731) 926-1200 *Founded/Ownrshp* 1973
Sales NA *EMP* 80
SIC 6022 State commercial banks; State commercial banks
Pr: Gordon Majors
CFO: Ashley Dennis
Chf Cred: Emily Gray
Sr VP: Larry Higgins
VP: Dan Adkisson
**VP:* Rex Daniel Adkisson
VP: Jeff Cummings
**VP:* Robert Jones

Ex Dir: Dr John Gallien
Sls&Mrk Ex: Ashley Winningham

D-U-N-S 04-042-6629
HARDIN COUNTY BOARD OF EDUCATION
65 W A Jenkins Rd, Elizabethtown, KY 42701-8452
Tel (270) 369-7370 *Founded/Ownrshp* 1908
Sales 135.9MM *EMP* 2,700
Accts Stiles Carter & Associates P
SIC 8211 Public elementary & secondary schools; Public elementary & secondary schools
Off Mgr: Gloria Manis
HC Dir: Janay Sutton

D-U-N-S 15-961-8610
HARDIN COUNTY BOARD OF EDUCATION
HARDIN COUNTY SCHOOL DISTRICT
155 Guinn St, Savannah, TN 38372-2025
Tel (731) 925-3943 *Founded/Ownrshp* 1840
Sales 21.1MM^E *EMP* 510
SIC 8211 Elementary & secondary schools; Elementary & secondary schools
Dir IT: Matt Colburn
Dir IT: Stephen Johnson

D-U-N-S 06-909-8705
HARDIN COUNTY GENERAL HOSPITAL (TN)
HARDIN MEDICAL CENTER
935 Wayne Rd, Savannah, TN 38372-1904
Tel (731) 926-8000 *Founded/Ownrshp* 1952
Sales 61.2MM^E *EMP* 300
Accts Lattimore Black Morgan & Cain
SIC 8062 General medical & surgical hospitals; General medical & surgical hospitals
Ofcr: Nick Lewis
**CEO:* Charlotte Burns
**CFO:* Mike Harbor
Dir OR: Cindy Coleman
Dir Lab: Jordan Gray
Dir Rad: Graham Sexton

D-U-N-S 96-953-6171
HARDIN COUNTY GENERAL HOSPITAL
HARDIN MEDICAL CENTER
935 Wayne Rd, Savannah, TN 38372-1904
Tel (731) 925-4954 *Founded/Ownrshp* 1952
Sales 37.2MM *EMP* 400
Accts Lattimore Black Morgan & Cain
SIC 8062 General medical & surgical hospitals; General medical & surgical hospitals
CEO: Charlotte C Burns
**CFO:* Mike Harbor

D-U-N-S 09-567-1384
HARDIN COUNTY NURSING HOME INC
HARDIN MEDICAL CENTER HEALTH A
935 Wayne Rd, Savannah, TN 38372-1904
Tel (731) 926-8132 *Founded/Ownrshp* 1974
Sales 37.2MM *EMP* 57
SIC 8052 8051 Intermediate care facilities; Skilled nursing care facilities; Intermediate care facilities; Skilled nursing care facilities

HARDIN COUNTY SCHOOL DISTRICT
See HARDIN COUNTY BOARD OF EDUCATION

D-U-N-S 07-979-8816
HARDIN COUNTY SCHOOLS
155 Guinn St, Savannah, TN 38372-2025
Tel (731) 925-3943 *Founded/Ownrshp* 2015
Sales 4.6MM^E *EMP* 298^E
SIC 8211 Public elementary & secondary schools

D-U-N-S 07-785-6268
HARDIN COUNTY WATER DISTRICT 2
360 Ring Rd, Elizabethtown, KY 42701-6777
Tel (270) 737-1056 *Founded/Ownrshp* 1969
Sales 21.2MM^E *EMP* 39
SIC 4941 Water supply
Genl Mgr: Barry De Witt
Dir Lab: Dwayne Barnes
Genl Mgr: Witt De
IT Man: Scott Clark
IT Man: Lea Sims

HARDIN MANAGEMENT COMPANY
See HARDIN CONSTRUCTION CO LLC

HARDIN MEDICAL CENTER
See HARDIN COUNTY GENERAL HOSPITAL

HARDIN MEDICAL CENTER
See HARDIN COUNTY GENERAL HOSPITAL

HARDIN MEDICAL CENTER HEALTH A
See HARDIN COUNTY NURSING HOME INC

D-U-N-S 05-872-2018
HARDIN MEMORIAL HOSPITAL
OHIOHEALTH
921 E Franklin St, Kenton, OH 43326-2099
Tel (419) 673-0761 *Founded/Ownrshp* 1943
Sales 22.5MM^E *EMP* 200^E
SIC 8062 General medical & surgical hospitals; General medical & surgical hospitals
CEO: David Blom
**Pr:* Mark Seckinger
**CFO:* Ron Snyder
**Ex VP:* Michael W Louge
Dir OR: Jeryl Kissling
Dir Rad: Laura Johnson
Dir Rx: Sue Bailey
CIO: Gloria Grappy
Mktg Dir: Chris Davis
Pharmcst: Merrilee Rogers
Phys Thrpy: Aaron Burkett

D-U-N-S 03-985-0045
HARDIN MEMORIAL HOSPITAL FOUNDATION INC (KY)
913 N Dixie Ave, Elizabethtown, KY 42701-2503
Tel (270) 737-1212 *Founded/Ownrshp* 1954
Sales 24.7M *EMP* 1,480
Accts Bkd Llp Firm S Pl Eliza
SIC 8062 General medical & surgical hospitals; General medical & surgical hospitals
Pr: Harry L Berry
Chf Path: Sidney Verble
Dir Recs: Ron Haulk

COO: Diane Logsdon
**CFO:* Elmer Cummings
Ofcr: Ronnie Hawks
VP: Elmer Cumming
**VP:* Dennis Johnson
Dir Lab: Terry Henry
Dir Sec: Roy Williams
Prac Mgr: Cindy Peters
Board of Directors: Bill Brandenburg, Bill Hay, Gary King

D-U-N-S 06-995-4568
HARDIN SCHIFF LLP
233 S Wacker Dr Ste 6600, Chicago, IL 60606-6307
Tel (312) 258-5500 *Founded/Ownrshp* 1962
Sales 113.0MM^E *EMP* 630
SIC 8111 General practice law office; General practice law office
Genl Pt: Ronald S Safer
Pt: Michael Burnstein
Pt: Gerald Carp
Pt: W Brinkley Dickerson Jr
Pt: Peter V Fazio Jr
Pt: Aaron J Kramer
Pt: Owen Macbride
Pt: Robert H Riley
Pt: Gary Rubin
Pt: Thomas P White
Pt: Christopher J Zinski
Pr: Maureen Carter
Pr: Maria Ceccacci
Pr: Sharon Harris
Pr: Leann Love
Pr: Mary Spengler
Board of Directors: Gary Eeves, Richard Krossee

D-U-N-S 00-447-9663
HARDIN TAYLOR SECURE MEDICAL FACILITY
(*Suby of* ALABAMA DEPT OF MENTAL HEALTH) ★
1301 Jack Warner Pkwy Ne, Tuscaloosa, AL 35404-1060
Tel (205) 556-7060 *Founded/Ownrshp* 1981
Sales NA *EMP* 1,000
SIC 9199 ;
Pr: Jim Reddick
Dir Sec: Robert Anderson
Sfty Dirs: Patricia Lyons
Nrsg Dir: Deborah Hunt

D-U-N-S 08-150-0233
HARDIN-JEFFERSON INDEPENDENT SCHOOL DISTRICT
520 W Herring St, Sour Lake, TX 77659-7801
Tel (409) 981-6400 *Founded/Ownrshp* 1960
Sales 21.4MM *EMP* 300^E
Accts West Davis & Company Llp Aus
SIC 8211 Public elementary school; Public junior high school; Public senior high school; Public elementary school; Public junior high school; Public senior high school
Bd of Dir: Mary Fontenot
Dir IT: Scott Hagedorn
Instr Medi: Cindy Gault

D-U-N-S 06-423-4628
HARDIN-SIMMONS UNIVERSITY
2200 Hickory St, Abilene, TX 79601-2345
Tel (325) 670-1000 *Founded/Ownrshp* 1891
Sales 67.3MM *EMP* 275
Accts Davis Kinard & Co Pc Abilene
SIC 8221 University; University
Pr: Craig Turner
**Pr:* Lanny Hall
Pr: Tina Sartor
VP: Dave Rozeboom
Off Mgr: Tabitha Pannell
Phys Thrpy: Renee Faulks

D-U-N-S 01-730-8107
HARDING & HILL INC (MI)
HARDING'S FRIENDLY MARKET
533 Allegan St, Plainwell, MI 49080-1297
Tel (269) 685-0992 *Founded/Ownrshp* 1948, 1975
Sales 52.0MM^E *EMP* 600
SIC 5411 5461 Supermarkets, chain; Bakeries; Supermarkets, chain; Bakeries
Pr: Martin Hill
VP: Garland Smith

D-U-N-S 09-379-2315
HARDING ACADEMY OF MEMPHIS INC
1100 Cherry Rd, Memphis, TN 38117-5421
Tel (901) 683-2440 *Founded/Ownrshp* 1952
Sales 13.4MM *EMP* 350
SIC 8211 Private combined elementary & secondary school; Private combined elementary & secondary school
Pr: Trent Williamson
**CFO:* Greg Howell
VP: Chris Dahlberg
Off Mgr: Brenda David
Snr Mgr: Phipps Janelle
Snr Mgr: Betsy Kolznak

D-U-N-S 18-385-5113
HARDING HOLDINGS INC
184 E 53rd Ave, Anchorage, AK 99518-1222
Tel (907) 344-1577 *Founded/Ownrshp* 1975
Sales 106.8MM *EMP* 350
SIC 1389 1542 Construction, repair & dismantling services; Commercial & office building, new construction; Commercial & office buildings, renovation & repair; Construction, repair & dismantling services; Commercial & office building, new construction; Commercial & office buildings, renovation & repair
Pr: James Gilbert
**CEO:* James Udelhoven
**VP:* Tim Jacques

D-U-N-S 16-179-6123
HARDING PUMP & SUPPLY INC
392 Johnston Rd, Gonzales, TX 78629-1007
Tel (830) 672-2889 *Founded/Ownrshp* 2010
Sales 25.0MM *EMP* 14
SIC 5084 7699 Oil well machinery, equipment & supplies; Pumps & pumping equipment repair

Pr: Darren D Harding
VP: Jack Vick

D-U-N-S 07-566-1892
HARDING UNIVERSITY INC
915 E Market Ave, Searcy, AR 72149-5615
Tel (501) 279-4000 *Founded/Ownrshp* 1924
Sales 116.7MM *EMP* 1,445
Accts Mallroy & Associates Little R
SIC 8221 University; University
Pr: Bruce McLarty
Pr: Nate Copeland
Ofcr: Ken Bissell
Ofcr: Phil Miller
VP: Keith Cronk
**VP:* Mel Sansom
Dir Rx: Landry Kamdem PHD
Dir Rx: Bobbi Krizan
Comm Man: Dan Tullos
Off Mgr: Sandra Ogburn
Cmptr Lab: Heather Vandiver

D-U-N-S 00-220-4063 IMP/EXP
▲ HARDINGE INC (NY)
1 Hardinge Dr, Elmira, NY 14902
Tel (607) 734-2281 *Founded/Ownrshp* 1890
Sales 311.6MM *EMP* 1,478^E
Accts Ernst & Young Llp Buffalo Ne
Tkr Sym HDNG *Exch* NGS
SIC 3541 3545 3553 3549 Machine tools, metal cutting type; Lathes; Grinding, polishing, buffing, lapping & honing machines; Collets (machine tool accessories); Lathes, wood turning: including accessories; Metalworking machinery; Machine tools, metal cutting type; Lathes; Grinding, polishing, buffing, lapping & honing machines; Collets (machine tool accessories); Lathes, wood turning: including accessories; Metalworking machinery
Ch Bd: Richard L Simons
Pr: J P Ervin
CFO: Douglas J Malone
Sr VP: Douglas C Tifft
VP: Edward J Gaio
VP: James P Langa
Opers Mgr: Thomas McKaig
Opers Mgr: Brian Straub
Opers Mgr: Michael Vitucci
Manager: Bradley Devon
Manager: Pete Leclair
Board of Directors: Douglas A Greenlee, Phillip Hunter, Robert J Lepofsky, John J Perrotti, Mitchell I Quain, R Tony Tripeny

D-U-N-S 05-909-1108
HARDINGER TRANSFER CO INC
TEAM HRDNGER TRNSP WRERHOUSING
1314 W 18th St, Erie, PA 16502-1517
Tel (814) 453-6587 *Founded/Ownrshp* 1969
Sales 48.6MM^E *EMP* 150
Accts Demarco Wachter & Co Erie P
SIC 4225 4212 4213 General warehousing; Local trucking, without storage; Trucking, except local
Owner: William Schaal Sr
**VP:* Samuel J Varo
**Prin:* H Bender

D-U-N-S 60-930-6154
HARDINGPOORMAN INC
FULL COURT PRESS
4923 W 78th St, Indianapolis, IN 46268-4170
Tel (317) 876-3355 *Founded/Ownrshp* 1967
Sales 48.1MM^E *EMP* 134
SIC 2752 Commercial printing, offset; Commercial printing, offset
Pr: David A Harding
**COO:* Steve Anzalone
**VP:* Bob Poorman
Prd Mgr: Mark Shirley

HARDING'S FRIENDLY MARKET
See HARDING & HILL INC

D-U-N-S 06-586-3078
HARDINGS GALESBURG MARKET INC
HARDING'S SUPERMARKET
8960 E De Ave, Richland, MI 49083-9639
Tel (269) 629-9638 *Founded/Ownrshp* 1974
Sales 27.2MM^E *EMP* 189
SIC 5411 5912 Grocery stores, independent; Drug stores & proprietary stores; Grocery stores, independent; Drug stores & proprietary stores
Pr: Thomas Harding
**Sec:* Carol Harding

D-U-N-S 18-136-1478
HARDINGS MARKET-WEST INC
211 E Bannister St Ste E, Plainwell, MI 49080-1372
Tel (269) 427-8003 *Founded/Ownrshp* 1987
Sales 109.6MM^E *EMP* 700
SIC 5411 Grocery stores, chain; Grocery stores, chain
Pr: Martin Hill
**VP:* Garland Smith
Store Mgr: Len Adams
CIO: Brian De Vries
Sls&Mrk Ex: Curt Devries

HARDING'S SUPERMARKET
See HARDINGS GALESBURG MARKET INC

D-U-N-S 15-095-4741
HARDISON/DOWNEY CONSTRUCTION INC
6150 N 16th St Ste A, Phoenix, AZ 85016-1777
Tel (602) 861-0044 *Founded/Ownrshp* 1985
Sales 47.5MM^E *EMP* 75
SIC 1542 Commercial & office building, new construction
Treas: James T Swanson
**Prin:* John Patrick Downey
Sfty Dirs: Susan Cruz
Sfty Dirs: Grace Miller
Snr PM: Brian Johnson
Snr PM: Jim Moon

D-U-N-S 09-295-5095
HARDMAN CONSTRUCTION INC (MI)
242 S Brye Rd, Ludington, MI 49431-9362
Tel (231) 845-1236 *Founded/Ownrshp* 1979
Sales 25.0MM^E *EMP* 75

SIC 1622 1794 1629 Excavation & grading, building construction; Pile driving contractor; Dams, waterways, docks & other marine construction; Bridge, tunnel & elevated highway; Bridge, tunnel & elevated highway; Excavation & grading, building construction; Pile driving contractor
CEO: Bruce Lowing
**Pr:* Todd Schrader

D-U-N-S 03-372-1184
HARDMAN JIM PONTIAC-BUICK-GMC TRUCK INC
JIM HARDMAN BUICK
1592 Browns Bridge Rd, Gainesville, GA 30501-4701
Tel (770) 718-3100 *Founded/Ownrshp* 1979
Sales 25.5MM^E *EMP* 90
SIC 5511 7532 7515 7513 5521 Automobiles, new & used; Pickups, new & used; Exterior repair services; Passenger car leasing; Truck rental & leasing, no drivers; Used car dealers; Automobiles, new & used; Pickups, new & used; Exterior repair services; Passenger car leasing; Truck rental & leasing, no drivers; Used car dealers
Pr: James D Hardman
**Sec:* Jennifer S Cole

D-U-N-S 00-619-6828
HARDRIVES INC
14475 Quiram Dr Ste 1, Rogers, MN 55374-9067
Tel (763) 428-8886 *Founded/Ownrshp* 1997
Sales 120.4MM^E *EMP* 315
SIC 1611 2951 Highway & street paving contractor; Resurfacing contractor; Asphalt paving mixtures & blocks; Highway & street paving contractor; Resurfacing contractor; Asphalt paving mixtures & blocks
Pr: Steven K Hall
Treas: Brad Mehlhaff
**VP:* Kevin Gannon
**VP:* Donald R Hall
**VP:* Sig Langerud
CTO: Sigmund Langrud
Sfty Dirs: Brian Knutson

D-U-N-S 06-566-2488
HARDRIVES OF DELRAY INC
2101 S Congress Ave, Delray Beach, FL 33445-7307
Tel (561) 278-0456 *Founded/Ownrshp* 1985
Sales 25.9MM^E *EMP* 130
SIC 1611 Resurfacing contractor; Resurfacing contractor
Pr: George T Elmore
**Sec:* Douglas Gordon
Ex VP: Allen Poston
**VP:* Craig K Elmore
**VP:* W Allen Poston

D-U-N-S 60-440-8831
HARDROCK CONCRETE PLACEMENT CO INC
4839 W Brill St, Phoenix, AZ 85043-1815
Tel (602) 233-3334 *Founded/Ownrshp* 1989
Sales 29.6MM *EMP* 300
Accts Barry & Moore Pc Phoenix
SIC 1771 Concrete work; Concrete work
Pr: Elias Lopez
**CFO:* Dean Abrahamson
**VP:* Cindy Kennemer
VP: Keith Shangler
IT Man: Gilbert Lopez
Opers Mgr: Claude Lopez
Opers Mgr: Terry White
Snr Mgr: Devia Murray

HARDROCK HOTEL & CASINO BILOXI
See PREMIER ENTERTAINMENT BILOXI LLC

D-U-N-S 87-319-6245 IMP
HARDSTONE CONSTRUCTION LLC
302 S Rampart Blvd, Las Vegas, NV 89145-5717
Tel (702) 947-2670 *Founded/Ownrshp* 2007
Sales 23.0MM *EMP* 35
SIC 1521 1542 Single-family housing construction; Commercial & office building, new construction; Single-family housing construction; Commercial & office building, new construction

HARDTNER MEDICAL CENTER
See HOSPITAL SERVICE DISTRICT NUMBER ONE OF PARISH OF LA SALLE

D-U-N-S 05-118-9322 IMP
HARDWARE DISTRIBUTION WAREHOUSES INC
H D W
6900 Woolworth Rd, Shreveport, LA 71129-9468
Tel (318) 686-8527 *Founded/Ownrshp* 1994
Sales 71.7MM *EMP* 175
Accts Smith Pugh & Seal Llp Shreve
SIC 5072 5063 5074 5085 Hardware; Electrical supplies; Plumbing fittings & supplies; Industrial supplies; Hardware; Electrical supplies; Plumbing fittings & supplies; Industrial supplies
Pr: Kenneth R Beauvais
Pr: Billy Stapleton
**CFO:* Wade Wilkerson
Ofcr: Bill Millerd
**VP:* James Coghlan
Exec: Judy Stubblefield
Genl Mgr: Mary Burton
Opers Mgr: Bill Burgan
Sls Dir: Barry Flint
Merch Mgr: Patrick Beauvais
Merch Mgr: Larry Jones
Board of Directors: Roy Hurley

D-U-N-S 03-321-8199
HARDWARE HAWAII KAILUA LTD
(*Suby of* HH HOLDINGS INC.)
30 Kihapai St, Kailua, HI 96734-2612
Tel (808) 266-1133 *Founded/Ownrshp* 1954
Sales 39.2MM^E *EMP* 240
SIC 5211

HARDWARE IMAGINATION TECH
See LARS LLC

D-U-N-S 94-478-2648 IMP
HARDWARE RESOURCES INC
(*Suby of* HARBOUR GROUP LTD) ★
4319 Marlena St, Bossier City, LA 71111-7503
Tel (318) 742-0660 *Founded/Ownrshp* 2010
Sales 79.7MM^E *EMP* 166
SIC 5072 2499 Furniture hardware; Kitchen, bathroom & household ware: wood; Woodenware, kitchen & household; Furniture hardware; Kitchen, bathroom & household ware: wood; Woodenware, kitchen & household
Pr: Gregory Gottlieb
CFO: Richard Yancey
Genl Mgr: Dan Young
CTO: Michael Wortel
Dir IT: Wendy Hanes
Sftwr Eng: Jim Hermann
Sfty Dirs: Bill Smith
Sfty Mgr: Randy Grace
Plnt Mgr: Christi Keenan
Mktg Mgr: Stephanie Lowe

D-U-N-S 02-726-8655 IMP/EXP
HARDWARE SALES INC
2034 James St, Bellingham, WA 98225-4298
Tel (360) 734-6140 *Founded/Ownrshp* 1962
Sales 31.0MM^E *EMP* 123
SIC 5251 5712 5072 7359

HARDWARE SPECIALIST
See DOORS INC

D-U-N-S 00-129-9650 IMP
HARDWARE SPECIALTY CO INC (NY)
4875 36th St, Long Island City, NY 11101-1994
Tel (718) 361-9320 *Founded/Ownrshp* 1932
Sales 95.0MM^E *EMP* 270
SIC 5063 5085 Electrical fittings & construction materials; Fasteners & fastening equipment; Electrical fittings & construction materials; Fasteners & fastening equipment
Pr: Edward Kaufman
CFO: Tom Moranzoni
**CFO:* Hyman Needleman
**Ex VP:* Jeffrey Kaufman
**VP:* Jeffrey Sands
Brnch Mgr: Freida Knick
Brnch Mgr: Jennifer Plower
Genl Mgr: Peter Foyto
Dir IT: Edwin Holmes
Info Man: John Roman
Sales Asso: Robert Quinn

HARDWARE TECHNOLOGIES
See HOPPE NORTH AMERICA INC

HARDWICK DRY KILNS
See CERSOSIMO LUMBER CO INC

D-U-N-S 03-921-4903 IMP
HARDWOOD INDUSTRIES INC
20548 Sw Wildrose Pl, Sherwood, OR 97140-8564
Tel (503) 692-6620 *Founded/Ownrshp* 1980
Sales 27.5MM^E *EMP* 50
SIC 5031 2426 2541 Lumber, plywood & millwork; Lumber, hardwood dimension; Wood partitions & fixtures
Pr: Jeffrey Wirkkala
Sales Exec: Paul Zech
**Sls Mgr:* Dough Wirkkala

D-U-N-S 14-382-8882 EXP
HARDWOOD LUMBER MANUFACTURING INC
567 N Charlotte Ave, Waynesboro, VA 22980-2856
Tel (540) 946-9150 *Founded/Ownrshp* 2002
Sales 96.2MM^E *EMP* 675
SIC 2426 Hardwood dimension & flooring mills; Hardwood dimension & flooring mills
Pr: Theodore P Rossi
CFO: Ralph Lamb
**VP:* Andrew E Becker

D-U-N-S 00-110-1419 IMP
HARDWOOD PRODUCTS CO LP
PURITAN MEDICAL PRODUCTS
31 School St, Guilford, ME 04443-6388
Tel (207) 876-3311 *Founded/Ownrshp* 1919
Sales 46.7MM *EMP* 382
Accts Macpage Llc South Portland M
SIC 3842 2499 Surgical appliances & supplies; Handles, poles, dowels & stakes: wood; Surgical appliances & supplies; Handles, poles, dowels & stakes: wood
Genl Mgr: Terry Young
CFO: Scott Wellman
Ex VP: Timothy Templet
VP: Lori Armstrong
VP: Heidi Corkery
VP: Mehdi Karamchi
VP: Elaine Maliff
VP: Ashley McKusick
VP: Melissa Schnoer
Dir IT: Heidi Thompson
VP Opers: James Cartwright

D-U-N-S 92-702-2822
HARDWOODS INC
HARDWOODS INC OF ATLANTA
5400 Riverview Rd Se, Mableton, GA 30126-2997
Tel (404) 792-0910 *Founded/Ownrshp* 1993
Sales 52.4MM^E *EMP* 68^E
SIC 5031 Lumber, plywood & millwork
Pr: James W Howard Jr
**CFO:* Paul Harris
**VP:* John Biedermann

HARDWOODS INC OF ATLANTA
See HARDWOODS INC

HARDWOODS OF MICHIGAN
See FORESTRY MANAGEMENT SERVICES INC

D-U-N-S 06-970-5408 IMP
HARDWOODS SPECIALTY PRODUCTS US LP
(*Suby of* HARDWOODS DISTRIBUTION INC)
2700 Lind Ave Sw Ste 100, Renton, WA 98057-3310
Tel (425) 251-1213 *Founded/Ownrshp* 2004
Sales 59.4MM^E *EMP* 150
SIC 5031 Lumber, plywood & millwork; Lumber, plywood & millwork
CEO: Lance Blanco
Pt: Daniel A Besen
Pt: Bryan R Hoyt
Pt: Garry W Warner
VP: Robert J Brown
VP Sls: Brian Graham

D-U-N-S 02-480-7992
HARDY BROTHERS INC
6406 Siloam Rd, Siloam, NC 27047-9145
Tel (336) 374-5050 *Founded/Ownrshp* 1963
Sales 29.1MM^E *EMP* 126
SIC 4213 4212 Trucking, except local; Local trucking, without storage; Trucking, except local; Local trucking, without storage
Pr: Eddie R Hardy
**Ch Bd:* Ralph J Hardy
**VP:* Lynne S Hardy
Genl Mgr: Marie Ramey
Sfty Dirs: Fay Hooker
Sfty Dirs: Joe Mone

HARDY CHEVROLET GEO
See HARDY CHEVROLET INC

D-U-N-S 03-372-6639
HARDY CHEVROLET INC
HARDY CHEVROLET GEO
2115 Browns Bridge Rd, Gainesville, GA 30501-4743
Tel (770) 532-4389 *Founded/Ownrshp* 1982
Sales 34.1MM^E *EMP* 90
SIC 5511 5012 Automobiles, new & used; Pickups, new & used; Trucks, tractors & trailers: new & used; Automobiles & other motor vehicles; Automobiles, new & used; Pickups, new & used; Trucks, tractors & trailers: new & used; Automobiles & other motor vehicles
Pr: Jeanette Hardy
Exec: Bob Bentley
Sls Mgr: A J Hardy

D-U-N-S 16-988-3303
HARDY CHEVROLET-PONTIAC-BUICK INC
1249 Charles Hardy Pkwy, Dallas, GA 30157-1181
Tel (770) 445-9411 *Founded/Ownrshp* 1978
Sales 48.4MM^E *EMP* 99
SIC 5511 Automobiles, new & used; Automobiles, new & used
Pr: Charles L Hardy
**Sec:* Renee Hardy Gordon
**VP:* John C Hardy
Sls&Mrk Ex: Jason Benson
Sls Mgr: Chuck Nunn
Sls Mgr: Brad Wilson
Sales Asso: Tom Busker
Sales Asso: Jeffrey Richter

D-U-N-S 00-682-9766
HARDY CONSTRUCTION CO (MT)
420 N 25th St, Billings, MT 59101-1346
Tel (406) 252-0510 *Founded/Ownrshp* 1953
Sales 23.4MM^E *EMP* 40
Accts Eidebailly Llp Billings Mont
SIC 1541 1542 Industrial buildings, new construction; Commercial & office building, new construction; Industrial buildings, new construction; Commercial & office building, new construction
Pr: Greg Hardy
**Sec:* Mary Patton
VP: Jay Dee Broadbent
**VP:* Leslie G Hardy Jr
**VP:* Cory Moore
**VP:* Larry Patterson

D-U-N-S 00-401-0245
HARDY CORP (AL)
HARDY SERVICES
350 Industrial Dr, Birmingham, AL 35211-4443
Tel (205) 252-7191 *Founded/Ownrshp* 1943, 1991
Sales 73.1MM^E *EMP* 300
Accts Carr Riggs Ingram Llc-Cpa
SIC 1711 Plumbing, heating, air-conditioning contractors; Mechanical contractor; Process piping contractor; Refrigeration contractor; Plumbing, heating, air-conditioning contractors; Mechanical contractor; Process piping contractor; Refrigeration contractor
Pr: Thomas N Cordell
**Treas:* Craig Westendorf
**VP:* Keith Marbury
VP: Bill Myers
VP: Harold Robertson
Exec: Wayne Mathews
Exec: Craig Westndorf
Dir IT: Ronnie Vines
Snr PM: Al Mauro

D-U-N-S 06-938-6746
HARDY COUNTY BOARD OF EDUCATION
MOOREFIELD HIGH SCHOOL
510 Ashby St, Moorefield, WV 26836-1001
Tel (304) 530-2348 *Founded/Ownrshp* 1930
Sales 13.3MM^E *EMP* 280
SIC 8211 Public elementary & secondary schools; High school, junior or senior; Public vocational/technical school; Public senior high school; Public elementary & secondary schools; High school, junior or senior; Public vocational/technical school; Public senior high school
HC Dir: Diane Tusing

D-U-N-S 03-998-1550 IMP/EXP
HARDY DIAGNOSTICS
1430 W Mccoy Ln, Santa Maria, CA 93455-1005
Tel (805) 346-2766 *Founded/Ownrshp* 1980
Sales 79.1MM^E *EMP* 168
SIC 5047 2836 Medical equipment & supplies; Agar culture media; Medical equipment & supplies; Agar culture media
Pr: Jay R Hardy
**CFO:* Nathaniel Graessle
Ex VP: Ralph Hardy
QA Dir: Jay Hamrick
Mfg Dir: Robert Volk
Sfty Mgr: Daniel Crawford
Ql Cn Mgr: Alistair Wood

Manager: Bill Carlson
Manager: Lloyd Christiansen
Manager: Cindy Green
Manager: David Roberts

D-U-N-S 04-461-8569
HARDY ENTERPRISES INC
598 W 2600 S, Bountiful, UT 84010-7798
Tel (801) 298-1180 *Founded/Ownrshp* 1966
Sales 56.4MM^E *EMP* 205
SIC 5541 5411 Filling stations, gasoline; Convenience stores, chain; Filling stations, gasoline; Convenience stores, chain
Pr: Bob N Hardy
**VP:* Shirley R Hardy

HARDY FAMILY FORD
See FAMILY FORD INC

D-U-N-S 05-427-2604
HARDY PROCESS SOLUTIONS (CA)
(*Suby of* DYNAMIC INSTRUMENTS INC) ★
9440 Carroll Park Dr # 150, San Diego, CA 92121-5201
Tel (858) 278-2900 *Founded/Ownrshp* 1980
Sales 21.2MM^E *EMP* 70
SIC 3823 3829 3596 Industrial instrmnts msrmnt display/control process variable; Measuring & controlling devices; Scales & balances, except laboratory
Pr: Eric Schellenberger
**CFO:* Steve Hanes
VP: David Cornwell
Dir Bus: Jim Ephraim
QA Dir: Debra Lawson
Opers Mgr: Fernando Soto
Mktg Mgr: Ted Kopczynski
Manager: Thomas Au
Manager: Scott Foster
Manager: Frank Wang

HARDY SERVICES
See HARDY CORP

D-U-N-S 04-001-0238
HARDY WINDOW CO
3425 E La Palma Ave, Anaheim, CA 92806-2021
Tel (714) 996-1807 *Founded/Ownrshp* 1998
Sales 20.1MM^E *EMP* 83^E
SIC 1751 Window & door installation & erection
Pr: Kimberly Hardy

HARE CHEVROLET
See W HARE & SON INC

D-U-N-S 07-200-6646
HARE PIPELINE CONSTRUCTION INC
2320 Ten Ten Rd, Apex, NC 27539-8117
Tel (919) 362-0001 *Founded/Ownrshp* 1975
Sales 22.0MM^E *EMP* 170
SIC 1623 Water main construction; Sewer line construction; Oil & gas pipeline construction; Water main construction; Sewer line construction; Oil & gas pipeline construction
Pr: W Nelson Hare
**VP:* David Hooks

D-U-N-S 00-885-8920
HAREN & LAUGHLIN CONSTRUCTION CO INC (KS)
HAREN LAUGHLIN CONSTRUCTION
8035 Nieman Rd, Shawnee Mission, KS 66214-1544
Tel (913) 495-9558 *Founded/Ownrshp* 1932
Sales 48.0MM^E *EMP* 45
SIC 1542 1541 6552 Nonresidential construction; Industrial buildings & warehouses; Subdividers & developers; Nonresidential construction; Industrial buildings & warehouses; Subdividers & developers
Pr: C Wells Haren III
Mng Pt: Charlie Penner
**Pr:* Wells Haren III
Opers Mgr: Jeff Wasinger
Snr PM: Mike Mannino

D-U-N-S 00-484-0740
HAREN CONSTRUCTION CO INC
1715 Highway 411 N, Etowah, TN 37331-5499
Tel (423) 263-5561 *Founded/Ownrshp* 1979
Sales 62.7MM^E *EMP* 130
SIC 1623 1541 Commercial & office building contractors; Industrial buildings & warehouses; Pumping station construction; Industrial buildings & warehouses
Ch Bd: Frank E Haren
**Pr:* Evan Haren
**Sec:* Andrew Haren
**VP:* David Berry
Mtls Mgr: Paul White

HAREN LAUGHLIN CONSTRUCTION
See HAREN & LAUGHLIN CONSTRUCTION CO INC

HARFORD CNTY GOVERNMENT TRSRY
See COUNTY OF HARFORD

D-U-N-S 07-492-4333
HARFORD COMMUNITY COLLEGE
401 Thomas Run Rd, Bel Air, MD 21015-1696
Tel (443) 412-2000 *Founded/Ownrshp* 1957
Sales 50.7MM^E *EMP* 775
SIC 8221 8222

D-U-N-S 06-940-2642
HARFORD COUNTY BOARD OF EDUCATION (INC)
102 S Hickory Ave, Bel Air, MD 21014-3731
Tel (410) 838-7300 *Founded/Ownrshp* 1869
Sales 522.8MM *EMP* 90^E
Accts Sb & Company Hunt Valley Mar
SIC 8211 Public elementary & secondary schools; School board
Pr: Nancy Reynolds
CFO: John Markowski
VP: Francis Grambo III
Cmptr Lab: Kelly Mangum
Snr Mgr: Wendy Holston

D-U-N-S 82-580-2986
HARFORD COUNTY PUBLIC SCHOOL DISTRICT
FOUNTAIN GREEN ELEM SCHOOL
102 S Hickory Ave, Bel Air, MD 21014-3731
Tel (410) 838-7300 *Founded/Ownrshp* 1993
Sales 150.1MM^E *EMP* 4,327
SIC 8211 Public elementary & secondary schools; Public elementary & secondary schools
Bd of Dir: Cassandra Beverley
Bd of Dir: Alysson Krchnavy
Ofcr: Jeff Laporta
Exec: Dave Betz
Dir Sec: Robert Benedetto
Genl Mgr: Gavin Zorbach
Off Mgr: Kim Holthaus
Netwrk Eng: Sarah Seidl
Instr Medi: Patricia O'Donnell
Psych: Elizabeth Grupp
Psych: Katie Jenkins

D-U-N-S 79-054-6675
HARFORD GROUP INC
FIRST LINE INSURANCE
(*Suby of* FIRSTLINE NATIONAL INSURANCE C) ★
200 N Main St, Bel Air, MD 21014-3554
Tel (410) 838-4000 *Founded/Ownrshp* 1988
Sales NA *EMP* 120^E
SIC 6411 Property & casualty insurance agent
Pr: Philip Raub
**Sr VP:* John Stielberger
VP: Frank Hiser
IT Man: Stephen Fabian
IT Man: Mike Winn

D-U-N-S 06-939-2991
HARFORD MEMORIAL HOSPITAL INC
(*Suby of* UPPER CHESAPEAKE HEALTH FOUNDATION INC) ★
501 S Union Ave, Havre De Grace, MD 21078-3493
Tel (443) 843-5000 *Founded/Ownrshp* 1984
Sales 83.0MM *EMP* 625
SIC 8062 General medical & surgical hospitals; General medical & surgical hospitals
Pr: Lyle E Sheldon
**CFO:* Joseph Hoffman
Dir Rad: Sherry Roberts
Dir Rx: Steve Low
CIO: Rick Casteeo
IT Man: Joan Horner
VP Opers: Eugene Currotto

D-U-N-S 80-380-2821
HARFORD MEMORIAL HOSPITAL INC
(*Suby of* UPPER CHESAPEAKE HEALTH FOUNDATION INC) ★
501 S Union Ave, Havre De Grace, MD 21078-3493
Tel (410) 939-2400 *Founded/Ownrshp* 1911
Sales 93.7MM *EMP* 800
Accts Grant Thornton Llp Philadelph
SIC 8062 General medical & surgical hospitals; General medical & surgical hospitals
Pr: Lyle E Sheldon
VP: Craig Willig
Dir: Joy D Hoover
Dir Rx: John Ness
Pharmcst: Ross Bouchard
HC Dir: Barb Baughman

D-U-N-S 00-695-0646
HARFORD MUTUAL INSURANCE CO (MD)
FIRSTLINE NATIONAL INSURANCE C
200 N Main St, Bel Air, MD 21014-3544
Tel (410) 879-2360 *Founded/Ownrshp* 1842
Sales NA *EMP* 122
SIC 6331 Fire, marine & casualty insurance & carriers; Fire, marine & casualty insurance & carriers
Pr: Steven D Linkous
CFO: Steve Linkous
**Treas:* June Poole
**Ex VP:* John Spielberger
VP: Jamie Elkins
VP: Frank Hiser
VP: Frank Keller
**VP:* Robert Ohler
**VP:* Ellen Truant
IT Man: Phillip Kerr
IT Man: Mike Winn

D-U-N-S 09-136-9306
HARGIS INDUSTRIES LP
SEALTITE BUILDING FASTENERS
6357 Reynolds Rd, Tyler, TX 75708-6016
Tel (903) 592-2826 *Founded/Ownrshp* 1992
Sales 41.0MM^E *EMP* 150
SIC 5085 5072 Fasteners, industrial: nuts, bolts, screws, etc.; Bolts, nuts & screws; Fasteners, industrial: nuts, bolts, screws, etc.; Bolts, nuts & screws
CEO: Joe A Hargis
Pt: Bruce Crouch
Rgnl Mgr: Randy Floyd
Off Mgr: Glenda Griffin

D-U-N-S 61-530-1694 IMP/EXP
HARGRAY COMMUNICATIONS GROUP INC
856 William Hilton Pkwy, Hilton Head Island, SC 29928-3423
Tel (843) 785-2166 *Founded/Ownrshp* 1986
Sales 196.9MM^E *EMP* 350
SIC 4813 Local telephone communications; Long distance telephone communications; Local telephone communications; Long distance telephone communications
Pr: Gloria Taggart
**Ex VP:* Leroy Harvey Jr
**VP:* Michael R Shepard
Prin: Mike Miscavage
Genl Couns: David Armistead

D-U-N-S 00-379-3122
HARGRAY TELEPHONE CO INC (SC)
(*Suby of* HARGRAY COMMUNICATIONS GROUP INC) ★
856 William Hilton Pkwy, Hilton Head Island, SC 29928-3423
Tel (843) 785-2166 *Founded/Ownrshp* 1953, 1985
Sales 25.4MM^E *EMP* 75
SIC 4813 Local telephone communications
CEO: Michael Gottdenker
**Pr:* Gloria Taggart
**CFO:* Peter Ley
**VP:* Leroy Harvey Jr
**VP:* Michael Shepard
Dir IT: Nathan Jellum

D-U-N-S 03-679-3149
HARGROVE AND ASSOCIATES INC
HARGROVE ENGINEERS & CONSTRS
20 S Royal St, Mobile, AL 36602-3202
Tel (251) 476-0605 *Founded/Ownrshp* 1997
Sales 216.0MM^E *EMP* 700
SIC 8711 Consulting engineer; Consulting engineer
Pr: Ralph A Hargrove
**COO:* Jim Backes
Ex VP: Durward Weeks
VP: Jim Backen
**VP:* Phil Hamilton
**VP:* Vicki M Studstill
**VP:* Dennis Watson
Sfty Mgr: Linda Robinson
Sfty Mgr: Sonney Weaks
Snr PM: Hannia Koolman
Snr PM: Gil Pierre

HARGROVE ENGINEERS & CONSTRS
See HARGROVE AND ASSOCIATES INC

D-U-N-S 02-261-7021
HARGROVE INC
1 Hargrove Dr, Lanham, MD 20706-1804
Tel (301) 306-9000 *Founded/Ownrshp* 1965
Sales 75.2MM *EMP* 185
Accts Regan Schickner Shah Harper Ll
SIC 7389 Trade show arrangement; Trade show arrangement
CEO: Timothy McGill
**Pr:* Carla McGill
VP: Heidi Le N
Prd Mgr: Bill Alexander
Prd Mgr: Kathryn Botsford
Mktg Dir: Robb Clawson

D-U-N-S 80-884-8337
HARI-WORLD TRAVELS INC
3 W 35th St Fl 5, New York, NY 10001-2204
Tel (212) 997-3300 *Founded/Ownrshp* 1978
Sales 40.0MM *EMP* 46
SIC 4724 Travel agencies; Travel agencies
CEO: Prem Cohly
**Pr:* Kamini Cohly

HARING'S PRIDE CATFISH
See WISNER MINNOW HATCHERY INC

D-U-N-S 07-912-5104
HARKAND GULF SERVICES LLC
1441 Park Ten Blvd, Houston, TX 77084-5028
Tel (713) 467-7799 *Founded/Ownrshp* 2013
Sales 24.0MM^E *EMP* 31^E
SIC 1389 Construction, repair & dismantling services
CEO: John Reed
**CFO:* Ben Gujral

D-U-N-S 12-585-1535
■ **HARKEMA SERVICES INC**
(*Suby of* UNIVERSAL CORP) ★
305 Albany Tpke, Canton, CT 06019-2528
Tel (860) 693-8378 *Founded/Ownrshp* 1946
Sales 1.5MM^E *EMP* 24,875^E
SIC 5159 Tobacco, leaf
Pr: E T Kelly
**Ch:* J Van Huystu

D-U-N-S 07-631-0226
HARKER SCHOOL (CA)
3800 Blackford Ave, San Jose, CA 95117-1928
Tel (408) 248-2510 *Founded/Ownrshp* 1893, 1973
Sales 30.1MM^E *EMP* 450
Accts Robert Lee & Associates Llp S
SIC 8211 Private combined elementary & secondary school; Boarding school; Private combined elementary & secondary school; Boarding school
Pr: Howard Nichols
Netwrk Mgr: Mark Locascio
Psych: Lori Kohan
Snr Mgr: Ali Bo
Snr Mgr: Liz Jorgensen

D-U-N-S 07-243-0515
HARKINS AMUSEMENT ENTERPRISES INC
HARKINS THEATRES
7511 E Mcdonald Dr, Scottsdale, AZ 85250-6085
Tel (480) 627-7777 *Founded/Ownrshp* 1974
Sales 14.0MM^E *EMP* 299
SIC 7832 7359 Motion picture theaters, except drive-in; Video cassette recorder & accessory rental; Motion picture theaters, except drive-in; Video cassette recorder & accessory rental
CEO: Daniel E Harkins
**Pr:* Michael L Bowers
**VP:* Tyler S Cooper
**VP:* Racheal R Wilson
Dist Mgr: Robert Bill

D-U-N-S 09-239-8189
HARKINS BUILDERS INC
2201 Warwick Way, Marriottsville, MD 21104-1600
Tel (410) 750-2600 *Founded/Ownrshp* 2002
Sales 93.0MM^E *EMP* 180
SIC 1522 1542

HARKINS THEATRES
See HARKINS AMUSEMENT ENTERPRISES INC

D-U-N-S 84-879-0275
HARKINS THEATRES INC
7511 E Mcdonald Dr, Scottsdale, AZ 85250-6085
Tel (480) 627-7777 *Founded/Ownrshp* 1990
Sales 54.8MM^E *EMP* 648^E
SIC 7832 Motion picture theaters, except drive-in
Pr: Daniel E Harkins
**Pr:* Michael L Bowers
**VP:* Tyler S Cooper
**VP:* Greta J Newell
**VP:* Racheal R Wilson
Snr Mgr: Earnest Coleman
Snr Mgr: Gabriela Torres

D-U-N-S 82-928-9813 IMP
HARLAN BAKERIES LLC
7597 E Us Highway 36, Avon, IN 46123-7171
Tel (317) 272-3600 *Founded/Ownrshp* 2007
Sales 1.5MMM^E *EMP* 1,500
SIC 5149 2051 2045 Bakery products; Bread, cake & related products; Prepared flour mixes & doughs; Bakery products; Bread, cake & related products; Prepared flour mixes & doughs
Pr: Hugh Harlan
**Ex VP:* Doug Harlan
Ex VP: Paul Hayden
Off Mgr: Carol Johnson
VP Sls: Joe Latouf
Sls Dir: Dan Spence
Sls Mgr: Gary Coyle

D-U-N-S 14-707-5170 IMP
HARLAN BAKERIES-AVON LLC
(*Suby of* HARLAN BAKERIES LLC) ★
7597 E Us Highway 36, Avon, IN 46123-7171
Tel (317) 272-3600 *Founded/Ownrshp* 1991
Sales 92.0MM^E *EMP* 375
SIC 5149 2051 2045 Bakery products; Bread, cake & related products; Prepared flour mixes & doughs; Bakery products; Bread, cake & related products; Prepared flour mixes & doughs
Pr: Hugh Harlan
**CFO:* John P Menne
**Ex VP:* Doug H Harlan
**Ex VP:* Paul G Hayden

D-U-N-S 18-361-6937
HARLAN CASTLE INC
150 E 58th St Fl 38, New York, NY 10155-0017
Tel (212) 644-8600 *Founded/Ownrshp* 1987
Sales NA *EMP* 13,450
SIC 6153 Short-term business credit; Short-term business credit
Ch Bd: John K Castle
Mng Pt: Josh Harlan
**Ch Bd:* Leonard M Harlan
V Ch: Gary Appel
**Co-Pr:* Howard Morgan
**Co-Pr:* Bill Pruellage
VP: Thomas M Hickey
VP: John E Morningstar
VP: Tariq Osman
VP: Heidi Petroff
VP: William M Purellage
VP: Sylvia Rosen

D-U-N-S 08-619-5443
HARLAN COUNTY PUBLIC SCHOOLS
HARLAN PUBLIC SCHOOLS
251 Ball Park Rd, Harlan, KY 40831-1753
Tel (606) 573-4330 *Founded/Ownrshp* 1915
Sales 48.8MM^E *EMP* 816
SIC 8211 Public elementary & secondary schools; Public elementary & secondary schools
**Treas:* Mark Howard

D-U-N-S 00-696-0876
■ **HARLAN ELECTRIC CO** (MI)
CYBER/SOURCE
(*Suby of* MYR GROUP INC) ★
2695 Crooks Rd, Rochester Hills, MI 48309-3658
Tel (248) 853-4601 *Founded/Ownrshp* 1940, 1995
Sales 55.0MM^E *EMP* 218
SIC 1623 Communication line & transmission tower construction; Cable laying construction; Telephone & communication line construction; Communication line & transmission tower construction; Cable laying construction; Telephone & communication line construction
Ch Bd: William A Koetner
**Treas:* Marco A Martinez
**Sr VP:* John A Fluss
**Sr VP:* William H Green
**VP:* Gerald B Engren Jr
Dist Mgr: Robert Kohl

HARLAN PUBLIC SCHOOLS
See HARLAN COUNTY PUBLIC SCHOOLS

D-U-N-S 02-042-8173
HARLAN-CUMBERLAND COAL CO LLC (KY)
29 Grays Branch Rd, Grays Knob, KY 40829
Tel (606) 573-2232 *Founded/Ownrshp* 1973
Sales 31.5MM^E *EMP* 182
SIC 1222 Bituminous coal-underground mining; Bituminous coal-underground mining

D-U-N-S 02-017-6969 IMP/EXP
HARLAND CLARKE CORP
(*Suby of* HARLAND CLARKE HOLDINGS CORP) ★
15955 La Cantera Pkwy, San Antonio, TX 78256-2589
Tel (830) 609-5500 *Founded/Ownrshp* 2007
Sales 439.3MM^E *EMP* 1,301
SIC 2782 2754 7389 Blankbooks & looseleaf binders; Bank checkbooks & passbooks; Commercial printing, gravure; Telemarketing services; Advertising, promotional & trade show services; Blankbooks & looseleaf binders; Bank checkbooks & passbooks; Commercial printing, gravure; Telemarketing services; Advertising, promotional & trade show services
Sr VP: Deborah Serot
VP: Matt Ames
VP: Kristi Lawton
VP: Rakesh Raju
Comm Dir: Heather Carleston
Ex Dir: Skip Wilks
Snr Sftwr: Stephen Hahn
QA Dir: Octavio Guerra
QA Dir: Jarvaun Lindsay
Sftwr Eng: Peter Lewis
Sftwr Eng: Grant Pimpler

D-U-N-S 09-721-6469
HARLAND CLARKE HOLDINGS CORP
(*Suby of* M & F WORLDWIDE CORP) ★
10931 Laureate Dr, San Antonio, TX 78249-3312
Tel (210) 697-8888 *Founded/Ownrshp* 2005
Sales 1.6MMM^E *EMP* 9,000^E
SIC 2782 2754 7389 Blankbooks & looseleaf binders; Bank checkbooks & passbooks; Commercial printing, gravure; Telemarketing services; Advertising, promotional & trade show services; Blankbooks & looseleaf binders; Bank checkbooks & passbooks; Commercial printing, gravure; Telemarketing services; Advertising, promotional & trade show services
Pr: Charles T Dawson
**Pr:* Dan Singleton
**CEO:* Chuck Dawson
**CFO:* Peter A Fera Jr
Sr VP: Andrew Bland
Sr VP: Larhesa Pollock
Sr VP: Joe Rawlins
Sr VP: Andrea Turk
VP: Shelley Christ-Pizana
VP: Wayne Hand
VP: Bob Madrid
VP: Terri Panhans
**VP:* Martin Wexler
VP: Bob White
Board of Directors: Paul G Savas, Barry F Schwartz

HARLAND FINANCIAL SOLUTIONS
See MERCK EMPLOYEES FEDERAL CREDIT UNION INC

D-U-N-S 02-846-3883 IMP/EXP
HARLAND M BRAUN & CO INC
BRAUN EXPORT
4010 Whiteside St, Los Angeles, CA 90063-1617
Tel (323) 263-9275 *Founded/Ownrshp* 1957
Sales 324.4MM *EMP* 30
Accts Brian Jung
SIC 5159 5199 Hides; Skins, raw; Leather & cut stock; Hides; Skins, raw; Leather & cut stock
Pr: Mike Hamilton
**VP:* Gene Beenders
**VP:* Di CK Veale
**Genl Mgr:* Roland Sebastian

D-U-N-S 03-092-0011
HARLANDALE INDEPENDENT SCHOOL DISTRICT PUBLIC FACILITIES CORP
102 Genevieve Dr, San Antonio, TX 78214-2902
Tel (210) 989-4340 *Founded/Ownrshp* 1924
Sales 170.6MM *EMP* 2,000
Accts Garza/Gonzalez & Associates S
SIC 8211 Public combined elementary & secondary school; Public combined elementary & secondary school
**Pr:* Joshua J Cerna
**CFO:* Ricardo Hernandez
**VP:* David Abundis
**VP:* Christine Carrillo
**Prin:* Oscar Perez
Schl Brd P: Velma Ybarra

D-U-N-S 07-861-3353
HARLEM CHILDRENS ZONE INC
35 E 125th St, New York, NY 10035-1816
Tel (212) 534-0700 *Founded/Ownrshp* 1974
Sales 82.7MM *EMP* 1,200
Accts Grant Thornton Llp New York
SIC 8299 Educational services; Educational services
Pr: Geoffrey Canada
COO: Anne Isom
CFO: Jim Hutter
Prgrm Mgr: Abishai Freeman
Off Mgr: Tracey Crowder
Off Admin: Angela Brown
CTO: Lekeisha Eubanks
Info Man: Ilone Barrett
Info Man: Shellina Shidnia
Info Man: Shawntae Walden
Pgrm Dir: Nia Dawson

D-U-N-S 07-771-8997
HARLEM EAST LIFE PLAN
2367 2nd Ave 69, New York, NY 10035-3108
Tel (212) 876-2300 *Founded/Ownrshp* 1972
Sales NA *EMP* 65
SIC 6324 Hospital & medical service plans
Ex Dir: Stewart Steiner
Ex Dir: Stewart Stiner

HARLEM FURNITURE
See TRP ACQUISITION INC

D-U-N-S 02-990-0599
HARLEM HOSPITAL CENTER
(*Suby of* NEW YORK CITY HEALTH AND HOSPITALS CORP) ★
506 Malcolm X Blvd, New York, NY 10037-1889
Tel (212) 939-1000 *Founded/Ownrshp* 2001
Sales 80.9MM^E *EMP* 46^E
SIC 8062 General medical & surgical hospitals
Prin: Stephen Shafer
Dir Risk M: Horace Felix
Dir Lab: Charles Morant
Dir Lab: Helen Richards
Dir Lab: Angus Sampath
Assoc Dir: Dilcia Ortega
Prgrm Mgr: Monique Hedmann
Off Mgr: Greta Hamer
Opers Supe: Balvant Kabrawala
Sfty Mgr: Kevin Shao
Psych: Renee Krinsky

D-U-N-S 09-177-6096
HARLEM SCHOOL DISTRICT 122
8605 N 2nd St, Machesney Park, IL 61115-2003
Tel (815) 654-4500 *Founded/Ownrshp* 1994
Sales 64.1MM^E *EMP* 1,000
Accts Bdo Seldman Llp Rockford Il
SIC 8211 8741 Public elementary school; Public junior high school; Public senior high school; Management services; Public elementary school; Public jupior high school; Public senior high school; Management services
**Pr:* Sandi Johnson
**Treas:* Joshua Aurand
Ofcr: Gail Lanigan
Ofcr: Catherene Martin
Ofcr: Jim Nordstrom

D-U-N-S 61-709-6862
HARLEM UNITED COMMUNITY AIDS CENTER INC
306 Malcolm X Blvd, New York, NY 10027-4465
Tel (212) 803-2850 *Founded/Ownrshp* 1990
Sales 24.4MM *EMP* 170
Accts Cohnreznick Llp New York Ny
SIC 8399 Health systems agency; Health systems agency
CEO: Steven C Bussey
**COO:* Stephane Howze
**CFO:* Neil Flynn
**Sr VP:* Sara Gillen
**Sr VP:* Kelsey Louis
Dir Surg: Kitty Chan
Pgrm Dir: Ronald Halem

HARLEQUIN BOOKS
See HARLEQUIN SALES CORP

D-U-N-S 13-863-7322
HARLEQUIN DISTRIBUTION CENTER
3010 Walden Ave, Depew, NY 14043-2696
Tel (716) 684-1800 *Founded/Ownrshp* 1947
Sales 83.8MM^E *EMP* 300
SIC 5192 Books; Books
Pr: Donna Hayes
Dir IT: Karl Shoop

D-U-N-S 96-381-1609
HARLEQUIN RETAIL INC
3010 Walden Ave, Depew, NY 14043-2696
Tel (716) 684-1800 *Founded/Ownrshp* 1979
Sales 44.1MM^E *EMP* 350
SIC 5192 Books; Books
Pr: Donna Hayes
**Genl Mgr:* John Randal

D-U-N-S 03-641-4001 IMP
■ **HARLEQUIN SALES CORP**
HARLEQUIN BOOKS
(*Suby of* HARLEQUIN ENTERPRISES LIMITED)
3010 Walden Ave, Depew, NY 14043-2696
Tel (716) 684-1800 *Founded/Ownrshp* 1971
Sales 153.1MM^E *EMP* 250
SIC 5192 Books; Books
Pr: Donna Hasyes
**VP:* Jim Robinson
Genl Mgr: John Reindl
Plnt Mgr: John Reindo

HARLER ON THE WAY STORES
See HARPER OIL CO

HARLEY ATTACHMENTS
See SWEEPSTER ATTACHMENTS LLC

D-U-N-S 05-503-7170 IMP
HARLEY DAVIDSON OF SALT LAKE CITY LC
HARLEY-DAVIDSON
2928 S State St, Salt Lake City, UT 84115-3811
Tel (801) 487-4647 *Founded/Ownrshp* 1984
Sales 21.0MM *EMP* 50^E
SIC 5571 Motorcycle dealers; Motorcycle dealers
COO: Wayne Bassham
Sls Mgr: John Tedrow

D-U-N-S 04-496-0581
HARLEY ELLIS DEVEREAUX CORP
26913 Nrthwstrn Hwy 200, Southfield, MI 48033
Tel (248) 262-1500 *Founded/Ownrshp* 1973
Sales 43.5MM *EMP* 225
Accts Plante & Moran Pllc Southfie
SIC 8712 Architectural engineering; Architectural engineering
Pr: J Peter Devereaux
**CFO:* Michael Maraone
**Ch:* Gary L Skog
Bd of Dir: Barbara McGee
VP: Ed Hayes
Board of Directors: Richard Hall

D-U-N-S 04-254-2345
HARLEY MARINE SERVICES INC
PACIFIC TERMINAL SERVICES
910 Sw Spokane St, Seattle, WA 98134-1125
Tel (206) 628-0051 *Founded/Ownrshp* 1998
Sales 128.7MM^E *EMP* 400
SIC 4449 4492 Transportation (freight) on bays & sounds of the ocean; Tugboat service; Transportation (freight) on bays & sounds of the ocean; Tugboat service
Pr: Harley V Franco
**CFO:* Todd Prophet
**Sr VP:* Rod Gullickson
**VP:* Deborah Franco
**VP:* Matt Godden
VP: Peter Hofmann
**VP:* Bo Jun
**VP:* Gregg Nelsen
Genl Mgr: Bill Taylor
CIO: Matt Garden
IT Man: Robin Houghton

HARLEY-DAVIDSON
See D W H LTD

HARLEY-DAVIDSON
See HARLEY DAVIDSON OF SALT LAKE CITY LC

HARLEY-DAVIDSON
See SETECH INC

HARLEY-DAVIDSON
See SMOKY MOUNTAIN HARLEY

HARLEY-DAVIDSON
See CIGAR CITY MOTORS INC

D-U-N-S 79-825-5923
■ **HARLEY-DAVIDSON CREDIT CORP**
(*Suby of* HARLEY-DAVIDSON FINANCIAL SERVICES INC) ★
4150 Technology Way, Carson City, NV 89706-2026
Tel (775) 886-3393 *Founded/Ownrshp* 1992
Sales 39.6MM^E *EMP* 250
SIC 5571 Motorcycle dealers; Motorcycle dealers
Pr: Lawrence G Hund
**Pr:* Donna F Zarcone
**Treas:* James D Thomas
**VP:* Donald Hummer Jr

D-U-N-S 79-825-5584
■ **HARLEY-DAVIDSON FINANCIAL SERVICES INC**
(*Suby of* HARLEY-DAVIDSON INC) ★
222 W Adams St Ste 2000, Chicago, IL 60606-5307
Tel (312) 368-9501 *Founded/Ownrshp* 1995
Sales NA *EMP* 650
SIC 6141 6411 Automobile loans, including insurance; Insurance agents, brokers & service; Automobile loans, including insurance; Insurance agents, brokers & service
Pr: Lawrence G Hund
**CFO:* Mike Sulentic
Prgrm Mgr: Suresh Upadhyayula
Rgnl Mgr: Brendan Liston

D-U-N-S 16-703-5380
■ **HARLEY-DAVIDSON FUNDING CORP**
(*Suby of* HARLEY-DAVIDSON FINANCIAL SERVICES INC) ★
3850 Arrowhead Dr, Carson City, NV 89706-2016
Tel (775) 885-1582 *Founded/Ownrshp* 1993
Sales NA *EMP* 30^E
SIC 6141 6411 7519 Automobile loans, including insurance; Insurance agents, brokers & service; Recreational vehicle rental
Pr: Lawrence G Hund
**Treas:* Perry A Glasgow

D-U-N-S 10-222-4623 IMP/EXP
▲ **HARLEY-DAVIDSON INC**
3700 W Juneau Ave, Milwaukee, WI 53208-2865
Tel (414) 342-4680 *Founded/Ownrshp* 1903
Sales 6.2MMM *EMP* 6,500
Tkr Sym HOG *Exch* NYS
SIC 3751 6153 6141 6411 6399 Motorcycles & related parts; Motorcycle accessories; Financing of dealers by motor vehicle manufacturers organ.; Financing: automobiles, furniture, etc., not a deposit bank; Property & casualty insurance agent; Warranty insurance, product; except automobile; Motorcycles & related parts; Motorcycle accessories; Financing of dealers by motor vehicle manufacturers organ.; Financing: automobiles, furniture, etc., not a deposit bank; Property & casualty insurance agent; Warranty insurance, product; except automobile
Pr: Matthew S Levatich
CFO: John A Olin
Chf Cred: Paul J Jones
VP: Joanne M Bischmann
VP: Sean J Cummings
VP: Mike Kennedy
VP: Rob Lindley
VP: Marc McAllister
CTO: Sean McCormack
Mktg Dir: Kimberly Cosby
Sls Mgr: Jackie Perevosnik
Board of Directors: R John Anderson, Richard I Beattie, Michael J Cave, George H Conrades, Donald A James, Sara L Levinson, N Thomas Linebarger, George L Miles Jr, James A Norling

D-U-N-S 00-608-0519 IMP/EXP
■ **HARLEY-DAVIDSON MOTOR CO INC** (WI)
(*Suby of* HARLEY-DAVIDSON INC) ★
3700 W Juneau Ave, Milwaukee, WI 53208-2865
Tel (414) 343-4056 *Founded/Ownrshp* 1903, 1981
Sales 784.7MM^E *EMP* 4,000
SIC 3751 Motorcycles, bicycles & parts; Motorcycles, bicycles & parts
Pr: Matthew S Levatich
CFO: John A Olin
Chf Cred: Paul J Jones
VP: Joanne M Bischmann
VP: Gail Lione
Board of Directors: R John Anderson, Richard I Beattie, Michael J Cave, George H Conrades, Donald A James, Sara L Levinson, N Thomas Linebarger, George L Miles Jr, James A Norling

D-U-N-S 10-144-8140
HARLEYSVILLE GROUP INC
(*Suby of* NATIONWIDE MUTUAL INSURANCE CO) ★
355 Maple Ave, Harleysville, PA 19438-2222
Tel (215) 256-9773 *Founded/Ownrshp* 2012
Sales NA *EMP* 1,706^E
SIC 6331 6411 Property damage insurance; Fire, marine & casualty insurance: mutual; Insurance agents, brokers & service; Property damage insurance; Fire, marine & casualty insurance: mutual; Insurance agents, brokers & service
Pr: Stephen R Smith
**Pr:* Michael L Browne
Pr: Kelly Dalmass
**CFO:* Arthur E Chandler
**Treas:* Mark R Cummins
Trst Ofcr: Gene Noce
**Sr VP:* Allan R Becker
**Sr VP:* Thomas E Clark
**Sr VP:* Robert A Kauffman
**Sr VP:* Theodore A Majewski
Sr VP: Debbie Neuscheler-Fritsch
**Sr VP:* Kevin M Toth
VP: Jonathan L Griggs
VP: Richard Schumacher
Exec: E Ratz

D-U-N-S 06-180-5396
HARLEYSVILLE LIFE INSURANCE CO (PA)
(*Suby of* HARLEYSVILLE MUTUAL INSURANCE CO) ★
355 Maple Ave, Harleysville, PA 19438-2222
Tel (215) 513-6400 *Founded/Ownrshp* 1960
Sales NA *EMP* 70^E
SIC 6411 Insurance agents, brokers & service
CEO: Michael Brown
**Pr:* Theldore A Majewski
**Treas:* Mark R Cummins
VP: Allan Becker

D-U-N-S 00-791-1159
HARLEYSVILLE MUTUAL INSURANCE CO (PA)
355 Maple Ave, Harleysville, PA 19438-2222
Tel (215) 256-5000 *Founded/Ownrshp* 1917
Sales NA *EMP* 1,898
SIC 6311 6331 Life insurance carriers; Property damage insurance; Fire, marine & casualty insurance & carriers; Life insurance carriers; Property damage insurance; Fire, marine & casualty insurance & carriers
CEO: Walter R Bateman II
Pr: Clinton Bothwell
Pr: Michael L Browne
Pr: William D Granato
Pr: Brandon J Hickey
Pr: Dennis J Otmaskin
CFO: Arthur Chandler
Treas: Mark Cummings
Bd of Dir: W Storts
Ofcr: David Galloway
Sr VP: Beth A Friel
Sr VP: Robert Kauffman
Sr VP: John B Keefe
Sr VP: Jenifer L Rinehart
VP: Roger Beekley
VP: John Mannato
VP: James C O Neill
Board of Directors: Ellen M Dunn

D-U-N-S 79-307-1036
HARLEYSVILLE PENNLAND INSURANCE CO
(*Suby of* HARLEYSVILLE MUTUAL INSURANCE CO) ★
355 Maple Ave, Harleysville, PA 19438-2222
Tel (215) 256-5000 *Founded/Ownrshp* 2003
Sales NA *EMP* 10
SIC 6321 Accident & health insurance carriers; Accident & health insurance carriers
Pr: Michael L Browne
Treas: Mark Cummins
Ex VP: Catherine Strauss
Sr VP: David Bond
Sr VP: Arthur Chandler
Sr VP: Thomas Clark
Sr VP: Robert Kauffman
Sr VP: Theodore Majewski
Sr VP: Tim O'Malley
Sr VP: Kevin Toth
Sr VP: Bob Whitlock

D-U-N-S 08-188-1781
▲ **HARLEYSVILLE SAVINGS FINANCIAL CORP**
271 Main St, Harleysville, PA 19438-2415
Tel (215) 256-8828 *Founded/Ownrshp* 1999
Sales NA *EMP* 128^E
Tkr Sym HARL *Exch* OTC
SIC 6021 National commercial banks; National commercial banks
CEO: Ronald B Geib
**Ch Bd:* Edward J Molnar
**Pr:* Brendan J McGill
CFO: M Shane Michalak
Sr VP: Adrian D Gordon
Sr VP: Sheri L Strouse
VP: Rodney Kipp
VP: Kim Licata
VP: Craig Munson
VP: Dean Shollenberger
VP: John Weierman
VP: Jean Wieder
Board of Directors: Sanford L Alderfer, Thomas D Clemens, Mark R Cummins, Charlotte A Hunsberger, George W Meschter, James L Rittenhouse

D-U-N-S 07-888-9411
HARLEYSVILLE WORCESTER INSURANCE CO (PA)
(*Suby of* HARLEYSVILLE GROUP INC) ★
355 Maple Ave, Harleysville, PA 19438-2222
Tel (215) 256-5000 *Founded/Ownrshp* 2013
Sales NA *EMP* 325^E
SIC 6331 Fire, marine & casualty insurance
Pr: David K Bond

D-U-N-S 06-946-3784
HARLINGEN CONSOLIDATED INDEPENDENT SCHOOL DISTRICT
407 N 77 Sunshinestrip, Harlingen, TX 78550-5820
Tel (956) 430-9500 *Founded/Ownrshp* 1900
Sales 88.6MM^E *EMP* 2,400
Accts Long Chilton Llp Harlingen
SIC 8211 Public elementary school; Public junior high school; Public senior high school; Public elementary school; Public junior high school; Public senior high school
MIS Dir: Olga Garcia
Pr Dir: Shane Strubhart
Teacher Pr: Melissa Nieto
Instr Medi: Mireya Galvin

D-U-N-S 79-691-9061
HARLINGEN MEDICAL CENTER LIMITED PARTNERSHIP
(*Suby of* PRIME HEALTHCARE SERVICES INC) ★
5501 S Expressway 77, Harlingen, TX 78550-3213
Tel (956) 365-3947 *Founded/Ownrshp* 2011
Sales 89.8MM^E *EMP* 528
SIC 8062 General medical & surgical hospitals; General medical & surgical hospitals
CEO: Brenda Ivory
**CFO:* David Glassburn
Pharmcst: Omar Sharif
Snr Mgr: Dan McLean

D-U-N-S 08-464-6079
HARLINGEN PHYSICIAN NETWO
2101 Pease St, Harlingen, TX 78550-8307
Tel (956) 698-5400 *Founded/Ownrshp* 2001
Sales 23.4MM *EMP* 4
Accts Bkd Llp Houston Tx
SIC 8011 General & family practice, physician/surgeon; General & family practice, physician/surgeon
Pr: William Adams

D-U-N-S 00-601-5770
HARLO CORP (MI)
4210 Ferry St Sw, Grandville, MI 49418-1573
Tel (616) 538-0550 *Founded/Ownrshp* 1938
Sales 29.0MM^E *EMP* 107
SIC 3537 3613 Lift trucks, industrial: fork, platform, straddle, etc.; Control panels, electric; Lift trucks, industrial: fork, platform, straddle, etc.; Control panels, electric
Ch: Craig Crooks
**CEO:* Mary Helen Crooks
VP: Michael Allen
**VP:* Richard G Crooks
VP Mktg: Doug Hardy
Sls Dir: Mike Frey

HARLOFF BMW
See HARLOFF ENTERPRISES INC

D-U-N-S 02-813-4328
HARLOFF ENTERPRISES INC
HARLOFF BMW
2146 Manchester Ave, Cardiff, CA 92007-1860
Tel (760) 335-6124 *Founded/Ownrshp* 1963
Sales 20.6MM^E *EMP* 94
SIC 5511 Automobiles, new & used; Pickups, new & used; Vans, new & used; Automobiles, new & used; Pickups, new & used; Vans, new & used
Pr: Edward J Harloff
**VP:* John Harloff
Genl Mgr: Ann Harloff

D-U-N-S 04-973-9428
HARLOW AEROSTRUCTURES LLC
1501 S Mclean Blvd, Wichita, KS 67213-4303
Tel (316) 265-5268 *Founded/Ownrshp* 1954
Sales 34.7MM^E *EMP* 97
SIC 3728 3452 Aircraft parts & equipment; Bolts, nuts, rivets & washers; Aircraft parts & equipment; Bolts, nuts, rivets & washers
CEO: Phillip C Friedman
**Pr:* Jim Barnes
**CFO:* Sid Sprunger

D-U-N-S 80-564-1698
HARLOW-HRK SALES & MARKETING INC
2501 Neff Rd, Dayton, OH 45414-5001
Tel (937) 274-1905 *Founded/Ownrshp* 2006
Sales 25.2MM^E *EMP* 95
SIC 5141 Food brokers; Food brokers
CFO: Pat Hobby
IT Man: Stephanie Lewis

D-U-N-S 02-157-5212
HARLOWS BUS SALES INC
3721 Highway 66, Rolette, ND 58366-9002
Tel (701) 246-3700 *Founded/Ownrshp* 1980
Sales 42.0MM^E *EMP* 130^E
SIC 5012 Buses; Buses
Pr: Harlow Hageness

HARLOW'S CASINO RESORT
See SW GAMING LLC

D-U-N-S 05-959-1339 IMP
HARMAC MEDICAL PRODUCTS INC
2201 Bailey Ave, Buffalo, NY 14211-1797
Tel (716) 897-4500 *Founded/Ownrshp* 1981
Sales 65.7MM^E *EMP* 400^E
SIC 3841 Surgical & medical instruments; Surgical & medical instruments
Pr: John F Somers
CFO: Ellen Burkhardt
Genl Mgr: Mick McEnroe
CTO: Cynthia Humphrey
QA Dir: Kris Bolt
QA Dir: Al Germann
QA Dir: William Turski
Plnt Mgr: Matt McBride
Ql Cn Mgr: John Aman
Ql Cn Mgr: Nathan Monin
Mktg Dir: Jim Laversa

D-U-N-S 01-925-5041 IMP/EXP
■ **HARMAN BECKER AUTOMOTIVE SYSTEMS INC**
HARMAN CONSUMER GROUP
(*Suby of* HARMAN INTERNATIONAL INDUSTRIES INC) ★
39001 W 12 Mile Rd, Farmington Hills, MI 48331-2912
Tel (248) 848-9972 *Founded/Ownrshp* 1981
Sales 702.2MM^E *EMP* 2,000
SIC 3931 3812 Autophones (organs with perforated music rolls); Navigational systems & instruments; Autophones (organs with perforated music rolls); Navigational systems & instruments
Pr: Klaus Blickle
**Ex VP:* Herbert K Parker
**Prin:* Dinesh C Paliwal
Off Mgr: Mary Simoneau
Snr Sftwr: William Day
Snr Sftwr: Dan Engel
Snr Sftwr: Dan Miller
Snr Sftwr: Craig Szymanski
Snr Sftwr: Sreenivasulu Vaka
Dir IT: Bernd Vogt
IT Man: Jason Easter

HARMAN CONSUMER GROUP
See HARMAN BECKER AUTOMOTIVE SYSTEMS INC

D-U-N-S 07-959-4682
HARMAN INTERNATIONAL
8799 W 12 Mile Rd, Farmington Hills, MI 48331
Tel (203) 328-3500 *Founded/Ownrshp* 2014
Sales 22.6MM^E *EMP* 35^E
SIC 5064 Electrical appliances, television & radio
VP: Jeff Poggi
Assoc Dir: Catherine Louchart
Sftwr Eng: Adam Eckhardt
Sftwr Eng: Lynn Galvin
Ql Cn Mgr: James Roberts
Mktg Mgr: Kishore Reddy
Snr Mgr: Robert Haase
Snr Mgr: Kent Handelsman
Snr Mgr: Eric Hochwald

D-U-N-S 04-765-3555 IMP/EXP
▲ HARMAN INTERNATIONAL INDUSTRIES INC
400 Atlantic St Ste 15, Stamford, CT 06901-3533
Tel (203) 328-3500 Founded/Ownrshp 1980
Sales 6.1MMM EMP 24,197E
Accts Kpmg Llp Stamford Connecticu
Tkr Sym HAR Exch NYS
SIC 3651 Household audio & video equipment; Household audio equipment; Audio electronic systems; Household video equipment; Household audio & video equipment; Household audio equipment; Audio electronic systems; Household video equipment
Ch Bd: Dinesh C Paliwal
Pr: Phillip Eyler
Pr: Michael Mauser
CFO: Sandra E Rowland
Chf Mktg O: Ralph Santana
Ofcr: John Stacey
Ex VP: Maria Methe
Ex VP: I P Park
Ex VP: Todd A Suko
VP: Yijing H Brentano
VP: Dennis Hamilton
VP: Raj Sharma
VP: Karney Yakmalian
Board of Directors: Adriane M Brown, John W Diercksen, Ann McLaughlin Korologos, Edward H Meyer, Rob Nail, Avi Reichental, Kenneth Reiss, Frank S Sklarsky, Gary G Steel

D-U-N-S 96-534-5940
HARMAN MEDIA LLC
WASHINGTON POST
1150 15th St Nw, Washington, DC 20071-0001
Tel (202) 334-6000 Founded/Ownrshp 2010
Sales 127.8MME EMP 776
SIC 2721 Magazines: publishing only, not printed on site; Magazines: publishing only, not printed on site
CEO: Sidney Harman PHD
Snr Ntwrk: Milo Milovanovic

D-U-N-S 19-627-3874 IMP/EXP
■ HARMAN PROFESSIONAL INC
(Suby of HARMAN INTERNATIONAL INDUSTRIES INC) ★
8500 Balboa Blvd, Northridge, CA 91329-0003
Tel (818) 894-8850 Founded/Ownrshp 2006
Sales 111.7MME EMP 500
SIC 3651 Household audio equipment; Household audio equipment
Pr: Blake Augsburger
VP: Dennis Berry
VP: Mark Ureda
Dir Bus: Susan Paley
Mktg Dir: Randy Patton
Mktg Dir: Steve Romeo
Mktg Mgr: Bose Denmark

D-U-N-S 02-092-4197 IMP
■ HARMAN PROFESSIONAL SIGNAL PROCESSING (DE)
DOD DIGITECH
(Suby of HARMAN INTERNATIONAL INDUSTRIES INC) ★
10653 S River Front Pkwy, South Jordan, UT 84095-3527
Tel (801) 566-8800 Founded/Ownrshp 1986
Sales 64.0MME EMP 360
SIC 3651 Household audio equipment; Sound reproducing equipment; Household audio equipment; Sound reproducing equipment
Pr: Rob Urry
Pr: John Hanson
Pr: James Pennock
Sr VP: Eliptha Votsis
Exec: Adam Holladay
IT Man: Delmar Reay
Netwrk Mgr: Adam Anderson
Sftwr Eng: John Lee
Sls Mgr: Dave Fata

HARMAN SPECIALTY GROUP
See LEXICON INC

D-U-N-S 04-978-4168
HARMAN-MANAGEMENT CORP
199 1st St Ste 212, Los Altos, CA 94022-2767
Tel (650) 941-5681 Founded/Ownrshp 1968
Sales 201.7MME EMP 7,000
SIC 8741 5812 5046 Restaurant management; Fast-food restaurant, chain; Restaurant equipment & supplies; Restaurant management; Fast-food restaurant, chain; Restaurant equipment & supplies
Pr: James Jackson
*COO: Mr Vern Wardle
Ex VP: Alexander James
Ex VP: Doone Ray
Admn Mgr: Dwane Hanson
Admn Mgr: Chad Nicol
Admn Mgr: Craig Roberson
Dir IT: Jonathan Packer
IT Man: Terri Mayoral

D-U-N-S 12-739-3978 IMP
HARMAR MOBILITY LLC
2075 47th St, Sarasota, FL 34234-3109
Tel (941) 351-2776 Founded/Ownrshp 2005
Sales 42.4MME EMP 80
SIC 3537 Lift trucks, industrial: fork, platform, straddle, etc.
VP: David Baxter
Off Mgr: Janet Swedo
Dir IT: Brad Westover
S&M/VP: Paul Johnson
Sls Dir: Todd Bick
Snr Mgr: Dan Toolan

D-U-N-S 09-434-2862
HARMELIN & ASSOCIATES INC (PA)
HARMELIN MEDIA
525 Righters Ferry Rd # 1, Bala Cynwyd, PA 19004-1315
Tel (610) 668-7900 Founded/Ownrshp 1978, 1982
Sales 46.7MME EMP 98
SIC 8748 Communications consulting
CEO: Joanne M Harmelin
*Ex VP: Scott Davis
*Ex VP: Lyn Strickler
VP: Tom Garrity
VP: Jennifer Harlacher
VP: Monica Olivio
Assoc Dir: Stephen Zartarian
MIS Dir: Rob Lubrano

HARMELIN MEDIA
See HARMELIN & ASSOCIATES INC

D-U-N-S 06-148-2758 IMP
HARMER STEEL PRODUCTS CO (OR)
9933 Nw 107th Ave, Portland, OR 97231-1052
Tel (559) 665-2050 Founded/Ownrshp 1928
Sales 69.1MME EMP 130E
SIC 5051 Rails & accessories
Pr: George B Webb
*VP: J David Lynn
Brnch Mgr: Lawrence Peterson
IT Man: Vivian Stafford

D-U-N-S 03-536-4249 IMP/EXP
HARMON CITY INC
HARMONS GROCERY
3540 S 4000 W, Salt Lake City, UT 84120-3260
Tel (801) 969-8261 Founded/Ownrshp 1932
Sales 390.2MME EMP 2,800
SIC 5411

D-U-N-S 17-536-0205
HARMON CONSTRUCTION INC
18989 W 158th St, Olathe, KS 66062-8014
Tel (913) 962-5888 Founded/Ownrshp 1987
Sales 23.0MM EMP 20
SIC 1542 Design & erection, combined: non-residential
Pr: Tim J Harmon
Pr: Sam Shelhorn
*Sec: Janet Harmon
VP: Sara Harmon
*VP: Todd Ramsey
Snr PM: Tony Papish
Snr Mgr: David Favero

HARMON DISCOUNT STORES
See HARMON OF YONKERS INC

D-U-N-S 01-097-0580
■ HARMON DISCOUNT STORES INC
(Suby of HARMON DISCOUNT STORES) ★
11 Paft Rd, Totowa, NJ 07512
Tel (973) 266-0989 Founded/Ownrshp 1974
Sales 50.7MME EMP 525
SIC 5999 Toiletries, cosmetics & perfumes; Toiletries, cosmetics & perfumes
Pr: Robert Germano
*Ch Bd: Newton Sheldon
*Ex VP: Scott Sheldon

D-U-N-S 02-069-0525
HARMON ELECTRIC INC
HARMON SOLAR
945 W Deer Valley Rd # 100, Phoenix, AZ 85027-2132
Tel (623) 879-0010 Founded/Ownrshp 2005
Sales 20.8MM EMP 71
Accts Pittman & Murdough Pllc Pho
SIC 1731 Electrical work; Electrical work
Pr: Julie King
*Sec: Dan King

D-U-N-S 04-121-4230
HARMON FOODS INC
1255 W Morton Ave, Jacksonville, IL 62650-2770
Tel (217) 243-8615 Founded/Ownrshp 1979
Sales 20.0MM EMP 300
SIC 5411 Grocery stores, independent; Grocery stores, independent
Pr: Thomas Harmon
Genl Mgr: Tom Glossop

D-U-N-S 02-764-7051 IMP
■ HARMON INC
HARMON SERVICE GLASS
(Suby of APOGEE ENTERPRISES INC) ★
7900 Xerxes Ave S # 1800, Bloomington, MN 55431-1105
Tel (952) 944-5700 Founded/Ownrshp 1949
Sales 211.4MME EMP 1,087
SIC 5039 Glass construction materials; Glass construction materials
VP: Dennis Pilkinton
*CEO: Russell Huffer
*CEO: Joseph F Puishys
Genl Mgr: Jim Bald
Genl Mgr: Jacob Johnson
Sfty Mgr: Steven Evans
Opers Mgr: Chad Hoffmann
Sales Exec: Bill Kruger
Sls Dir: Peter Koukos
Mktg Mgr: Thyra Nelson
Snr PM: Scott Macdonald

D-U-N-S 94-718-5021
HARMON LAW OFFICES PC
150 California St, Newton, MA 02458-1005
Tel (617) 558-0500 Founded/Ownrshp 1997
Sales 20.5MME EMP 135
SIC 8111 7322 Real estate law; Adjustment & collection services; Real estate law; Adjustment & collection services
Pr: Mark P Harmon
IT Man: Sean Barrett
IT Man: Drew Womack

D-U-N-S 07-272-6391 IMP
■ HARMON OF YONKERS INC
HARMON DISCOUNT STORES
(Suby of BED BATH & BEYOND INC) ★
650 Liberty Ave, Union, NJ 07083-8107
Tel (908) 688-0888 Founded/Ownrshp 1974
Sales 52.2MME EMP 595
SIC 5912

HARMON OIL & PROPANE CO
See HARMON OIL CO INC

D-U-N-S 02-108-9669
HARMON OIL CO INC (MI)
HARMON OIL & PROPANE CO
6696 Beech St, North Branch, MI 48461-6105
Tel (810) 688-3575 Founded/Ownrshp 1977
Sales 22.4MME EMP 30
SIC 5171 5172 Petroleum bulk stations; Gases, liquefied petroleum (propane)
Owner: Tom Harmon
*Pr: Claude Harmon
*Sec: Inez Harmon

HARMON SERVICE GLASS
See HARMON INC

HARMON SOLAR
See HARMON ELECTRIC INC

D-U-N-S 80-867-0983
HARMON SOLUTIONS GROUP LLC
H S G
404 S Barstow St Ste 1, Eau Claire, WI 54701-3679
Tel (715) 830-6000 Founded/Ownrshp 2004
Sales 35.6MM EMP 150
Accts Baker Tilly Virchow Krause Ll
SIC 8742 Administrative services consultant; Administrative services consultant
COO: Michael Anderson
VP: Jeff Holte
QA Dir: Sherry Bangsund
QA Dir: Patrick Davidson
S&M/VP: Gary Turner
Sls Dir: Courtney Coughlin

D-U-N-S 11-044-1925 IMP
HARMONI INTERNATIONAL SPICE INC CALIFORNIA
HARMONY GROUP
881 S Azusa Ave, City of Industry, CA 91748-1028
Tel (626) 330-1550 Founded/Ownrshp 1992
Sales 85.6MM EMP 23
SIC 5148 5149 Fresh fruits & vegetables; Spices & seasonings
CEO: Xiao Yang Zhou
*CFO: Rick Zhou
Admn Mgr: Jo Ann Shu
Genl Mgr: Yazhou Yan
Opers Mgr: Patrick Cruz
Opers Mgr: Betty Si
Sls Mgr: Catherine Chang

D-U-N-S 60-278-8580 IMP
▲ HARMONIC INC
4300 N 1st St, San Jose, CA 95134-1258
Tel (408) 542-2500 Founded/Ownrshp 1988
Sales 433.5MM EMP 1,028E
Tkr Sym HLIT Exch NGS
SIC 3663 3823 Television broadcasting & communications equipment; Industrial instrmnts msrmnt display/control process variable; Television broadcasting & communications equipment; Industrial instrmnts msrmnt display/control process variable
Pr: Patrick J Harshman
CFO: Harold Covert
Sr VP: Peter Alexander
Sr VP: Nimrod Ben-Natan
Sr VP: Charles J Bonasera
Sr VP: Bart Spriester
Sr VP: George Stromeyer
VP: Yaniv Ben-Shushan
VP: Dario Choi
VP: Alvaro Martin
Manager: Matt Dannehl
Board of Directors: Patrick Gallagher, E Floyd Kvamme, Mitzi Reaugh, William F Reddersen, Susan G Swenson, Nikos Theodosopoulos

D-U-N-S 10-086-6297
HARMONIUM INC
CITY ARTS ACADEMY
9245 Activity Rd Ste 200, San Diego, CA 92126-2383
Tel (858) 684-3080 Founded/Ownrshp 1975
Sales 9.3MM EMP 800
Accts Sonnenberg & Company Cpas Sa
SIC 8351 Child day care services; Child day care services
CEO: Rosa Ana Lozada
COO: Doug Reiss
*CFO: Melinda Mallie

D-U-N-S 96-222-2121
HARMONIX MUSIC SYSTEMS INC
(Suby of HARMONIX-SBE HOLDINGS LLC) ★
625 Mssachusetts Ave Fl 2, Cambridge, MA 02139
Tel (617) 491-6144 Founded/Ownrshp 2010
Sales 30.7MME EMP 220
SIC 5734 Software, computer games; Software, computer games
Pr: Alex Rigopulos
*COO: Florien Unzicker
Sftwr Eng: Michael Mandel

D-U-N-S 96-646-9673
HARMONIX-SBE HOLDINGS LLC
625 Msschusetts Ave Ste 2, Cambridge, MA 02139
Tel (617) 491-6144 Founded/Ownrshp 2010
Sales 36.2MME EMP 276E
SIC 6719 Personal holding companies, except banks; Personal holding companies, except banks

HARMONS GROCERY
See HARMON CITY INC

D-U-N-S 05-108-5348
HARMONY CENTER INC
2736 Florida Blvd, Baton Rouge, LA 70802-2719
Tel (225) 383-9139 Founded/Ownrshp 1978
Sales 14.8MME EMP 405
SIC 8361 Home for the mentally handicapped; Juvenile correctional home; Home for the mentally handicapped; Juvenile correctional home
Pr: Collis Temple Jr
*Sec: Saundra Temple

D-U-N-S 02-318-8337
HARMONY COUNTRY COOPERATIVES
702 S Division St, Colby, WI 54421-9689
Tel (715) 223-2306 Founded/Ownrshp 1915
Sales 54.0MM EMP 75
Accts Clifton Gunderson Llp Marshf
SIC 5191 5541 5153 Feed; Seeds: field, garden & flower; Fertilizer & fertilizer materials; Filling stations, gasoline; Grains; Feed; Seeds: field, garden & flower; Fertilizer & fertilizer materials; Filling stations, gasoline; Grains
Genl Mgr: Jim Hager

HARMONY ENGINEERING
See J & E MANUFACTURING CO

D-U-N-S 00-618-0467 IMP/EXP
HARMONY ENTERPRISES INC (MN)
704 Main Ave N, Harmony, MN 55939-8839
Tel (507) 886-6666 Founded/Ownrshp 1962
Sales 33.1MME EMP 55
SIC 3569 2394 Baling machines, for scrap metal, paper or similar material; Convertible tops, canvas or boat: from purchased materials; Awnings, fabric: made from purchased materials
Pr: Steven Cremer
Treas: Deb Skaalen
Opers Mgr: Jim Johnson
Opers Mgr: Mikel Smith
Mktg Dir: Chris Cremer
Manager: Dan Berg
Manager: Nick Roberts
Sls Mgr: Brent Christiansen

D-U-N-S 09-322-3865 IMP
HARMONY FOODS CORP
SANTA CRUZ NUTRITIONALS
2200 Delaware Ave, Santa Cruz, CA 95060-5707
Tel (831) 457-3200 Founded/Ownrshp 2013
Sales 213.3MME EMP 400
SIC 2834 2064 Vitamin, nutrient & hematinic preparations for human use; Candy & other confectionery products; Vitamin, nutrient & hematinic preparations for human use; Candy & other confectionery products
CEO: Michael Westhusing
*COO: Randy Bridges
VP: John Conrado
VP: Mark Wobken
QA Dir: Donna Drew
Dir IT: Merit Herman
IT Man: Anthony Romaine
QC Dir: Lindsey Nylander
Mfg Mgr: Tim Nash
Opers Mgr: Thomas Burge
Sls&Mrk Ex: Doug Hopkinson

HARMONY GROUP
See HARMONI INTERNATIONAL SPICE INC CALIFORNIA

HARMONY HEALTH PLAN ILLINOIS
See HARMONY HEALTH SYSTEMS INC

D-U-N-S 94-911-6495
■ HARMONY HEALTH SYSTEMS INC
HARMONY HEALTH PLAN ILLINOIS
(Suby of WELL CARE HMO INC)
200 W Adams St Ste 800, Chicago, IL 60606-5220
Tel (312) 372-3471 Founded/Ownrshp 2004
Sales NA EMP 125
SIC 6324 8011 Health maintenance organization (HMO), insurance only; Offices & clinics of medical doctors; Health maintenance organization (HMO), insurance only; Offices & clinics of medical doctors
Ch Bd: Christopher Adams
*Pr: John T Blank

HARMONY HOME HEALTH & HOSPICE
See HARMONY HOME HEALTH SERVICES LLC

D-U-N-S 11-098-6403
HARMONY HOME HEALTH SERVICES LLC
HARMONY HOME HEALTH & HOSPICE
5650 S Green St, Murray, UT 84123-5796
Tel (801) 264-8000 Founded/Ownrshp 1996
Sales 23.2MME EMP 478E
SIC 8082 Home health care services; Home health care services
Ofcr: Garrett Barnes
Ex Dir: Cindy Clark
IT Man: Kari Domm
Board of Directors: Garrett Barnes, Nathan Cogburn, Michael Garza, David Stong

D-U-N-S 03-157-5173
HARMONY INVESTMENTS INC
1300 Diamond Springs Rd # 204, Virginia Beach, VA 23455-3645
Tel (757) 363-9671 Founded/Ownrshp 1993
Sales 21.5MME EMP 610
SIC 7011 Hotels & motels; Hotels & motels
Pr: Mark F Garcea
*CFO: John Sarvella
*VP: Page S Johnson Jr
*VP: Harvey Moore
Dir IT: Dan Hampson

HARMONY KIDS
See NEWCO INTERNATIONAL INC

D-U-N-S 08-518-7438
HARMONY PUBLIC SCHOOLS
9321 W Sam Houston Pkwy S, Houston, TX 77099-5204
Tel (281) 888-9764 Founded/Ownrshp 1999
Sales 239.5MM EMP 3,262
Accts Gomez & Company Houston Tx
SIC 8211 Private elementary & secondary schools;
Pr: Oner Ulvi Celepcikay
*Treas: Mustafa Ata Atik
VP: Laurie Bricker
*VP: Cengizhan Keskin
*VP: Ellen A Macdonald
*Prin: Mehmet Basoglu
*Prin: Serkan Kilic
Ex Dir: David Dunn
Mng Dir: Deborah S Jones
Sls&Mrk Ex: Mark Namver
Pgrm Dir: Grace Cruz

D-U-N-S 87-444-8921 IMP
HARMONY SYSTEMS AND SERVICE INC
1711 Commerce Dr, Piqua, OH 45356-2601
Tel (937) 778-1082 *Founded/Ownrshp* 1994
Sales 22.6MM^E *EMP* 70
SIC 3089 Injection molding of plastics
CEO: Edward Adams
**Pr:* Nellie Adams
**Genl Couns:* Hugh Wall

HARMS EXCAVATING
See GEORGE HARMS CONSTRUCTION CO INC

D-U-N-S 06-048-4615
HARMS OIL CO
CENTRAL STATES PETROLEUM
337 22nd Ave S, Brookings, SD 57006-2828
Tel (605) 696-5000 *Founded/Ownrshp* 1976
Sales 105.9MM^E *EMP* 80
SIC 5172 Diesel fuel; Gasoline; Lubricating oils & greases; Diesel fuel; Gasoline; Lubricating oils & greases
Pr: Duane D Harms
**VP:* Jason Harms

HARNESS DICKEY
See HARNESS DICKEY & PIERCE PLC

D-U-N-S 07-634-8549
HARNESS DICKEY & PIERCE PLC
HARNESS DICKEY
5445 Corporate Dr Ste 200, Troy, MI 48098-2683
Tel (248) 641-1600 *Founded/Ownrshp* 1994
Sales 34.9MM^E *EMP* 290
SIC 8111 General practice attorney, lawyer; General practice attorney, lawyer
Dir IT: Mark Linsangan
IT Man: Jason Russo
MIS Mgr: Bev Norman
Counsel: Beverley Crump
Counsel: Derek Richmond
Counsel: Gregory Walters

D-U-N-S 14-364-7998
HARNESS ROOFING INC
415 S Main St, Harrison, AR 72601-5505
Tel (870) 741-0245 *Founded/Ownrshp* 1987
Sales 23.2MM *EMP* 130
SIC 1761 Roofing contractor; Sheet metalwork; Roofing contractor; Sheet metalwork
Pr: Roger L Harness
CFO: Donna Nichols
VP: Justin Harness
Brnch Mgr: Mike Dillard
Off Mgr: Rita Holland
Off Mgr: Jessica Moore
Off Mgr: Kim Williams
Off Mgr: Denise Wright
Off Mgr: Adrienne Yocham

D-U-N-S 10-371-5694
HARNETT COUNTY BOARD OF EDUCATION
HARNETT COUNTY SCHOOLS
1008 11th St, Lillington, NC 27546
Tel (910) 893-8151 *Founded/Ownrshp* 1905
Sales 161.1MM *EMP* 2,105
Accts Dixon Hughes Goodman Llp Pin
SIC 8211 Public elementary & secondary schools; Public elementary & secondary schools

D-U-N-S 09-156-5986
HARNETT COUNTY OF NORTH CAROLINA
102 E Front St, Lillington, NC 27546-6683
Tel (910) 893-7557 *Founded/Ownrshp* 1905
Sales NA *EMP* 937^E
SIC 9111 Executive offices; ; Executive offices;
Ofcr: Sylvia Blinson
Ofcr: Scott Guy
Plng Mgr: Landon Chandler
Sfty Mgr: Glenn McFadden

HARNETT COUNTY SCHOOLS
See HARNETT COUNTY BOARD OF EDUCATION

D-U-N-S 07-979-8915
HARNETT COUNTY SCHOOLS
1008 11th St, Lillington, NC 27546
Tel (910) 893-8151 *Founded/Ownrshp* 2015
Sales 55.4MM^E *EMP* 2,028^E
SIC 8211 Public elementary & secondary schools
Dir Sec: Deborah Kitchens
Pr Dir: Patricia Harmon-Lewis

D-U-N-S 07-202-3310
HARNETT HEALTH SYSTEM INC
BETSY JOHNSON REGIONAL HOSPITA
800 Tilghman Dr, Dunn, NC 28334-5510
Tel (910) 892-1000 *Founded/Ownrshp* 1935
Sales 70.9MM *EMP* 730^E
SIC 8062 General medical & surgical hospitals; General medical & surgical hospitals
Pr: Ken Bryan
Chf Rad: Demir E Bastug
Treas: Ernest Alphin
Trst: Mary Dafford
**VP:* Vicki Allen
**VP:* Sondra Davis
**VP:* Wallace J Horne
**VP:* Eric Young
Exec: Sandra Davis
Dir Rx: Alice Holmes
Off Mgr: Lauren Whittington

D-U-N-S 17-816-9645 IMP/EXP
HARNEY & SONS TEA CORP
5723 Route 22, Millerton, NY 12546-4521
Tel (518) 789-2100 *Founded/Ownrshp* 1983
Sales 58.4MM^E *EMP* 100
SIC 5149 5499 Tea; Tea
Pr: John Harney
**VP:* Michael Harney
Sls Mgr: Halil Agcayazi
Sales Asso: Chelsea Burns

D-U-N-S 94-461-4627
HARNEY COUNTY HEALTH DISTRICT
HARNEY DISTRICT HOSPITAL
557 W Washington St, Burns, OR 97720-1441
Tel (541) 573-7281 *Founded/Ownrshp* 1990
Sales 37.2MM^E *EMP* 130
Accts Oster Burns Oregon
SIC 8062 General medical & surgical hospitals
CEO: James Bishop
Treas: Ann Clark
Dir Lab: Miquel Angarita
Pharmcst: Kara Bowman

HARNEY DISTRICT HOSPITAL
See HARNEY COUNTY HEALTH DISTRICT

D-U-N-S 00-624-0634 IMP/EXP
HARNISH GROUP INC (WA)
17035 W Valley Hwy, Tukwila, WA 98188-5519
Tel (425) 251-9800 *Founded/Ownrshp* 1929
Sales 545.4MM^E *EMP* 1,000
SIC 5082 5013 5083 Construction & mining machinery; Tractors, construction; Front end loaders; Graders, motor; Automotive engines & engine parts; Agricultural machinery & equipment; Tractors, agricultural; Cultivating machinery & equipment; Planting machinery & equipment; Construction & mining machinery; Tractors, construction; Front end loaders; Graders, motor; Automotive engines & engine parts; Agricultural machinery & equipment; Tractors, agricultural; Cultivating machinery & equipment; Planting machinery & equipment
Pr: John J Harnish
**VP:* Don Linn
VP: Dave Thomas
VP: Tom Topel
Brnch Mgr: Justin Shearer
Sfty Dirs: Randy Pickett
Mktg Mgr: Scott Field

D-U-N-S 11-792-8155
HARO & HARO ENTERPRISES INC
115 W Walnut St Ste 4, Lodi, CA 95240-3541
Tel (209) 334-2035 *Founded/Ownrshp* 1997
Sales 12.6MM^E *EMP* 1,000
SIC 0761 Farm labor contractors; Farm labor contractors
Pr: Emelia Haro
**Prin:* Jose Haro

D-U-N-S 96-302-7862
HAROLD ALFOND FOUNDATION
2 Monument Sq, Portland, ME 04101-4093
Tel (207) 828-7999 *Founded/Ownrshp* 2010
Sales 30.4MM *EMP* 2
Accts Albin Randall & Bennett Portl
SIC 8699 Charitable organization
Ch: Gregory Powell

D-U-N-S 96-567-5536
HAROLD AND HELEN DERFNER FOUNDATION
245 E 80th St, New York, NY 10075-0506
Tel (212) 744-2727 *Founded/Ownrshp* 2010
Sales 74.5MM *EMP* 2
SIC 8699 Charitable organization
Prin: Harold Derfner

D-U-N-S 05-762-8851
HAROLD FRIEDMAN INC
FRIEDMAN'S SUPERMARKETS
530 Fairground Hill Rd, Butler, PA 16001-2634
Tel (724) 283-6030 *Founded/Ownrshp* 1900
Sales 29.8MM^E *EMP* 150
SIC 5411 Supermarkets, independent; Supermarkets, independent
Pr: Carole F Bitter
Genl Mgr: Don Eury

D-U-N-S 00-783-7446
HAROLD G BUTZER INC (MO)
721 Wicker Ln, Jefferson City, MO 65109-4720
Tel (573) 636-4115 *Founded/Ownrshp* 1926, 1949
Sales 21.7MM^E *EMP* 75^E
SIC 1711 Plumbing, heating, air-conditioning contractors
Pr: Jason E Thompson
**VP:* Larry J Hoffmann
**VP:* Dale R Knipp
**VP:* Mark A Reuter

D-U-N-S 78-954-0288
HAROLD GRINSPOON FOUNDATION
67 Hunt St Ste 100, Agawam, MA 01001-1913
Tel (413) 276-0700 *Founded/Ownrshp* 2006
Sales 37.8MM *EMP* 52^E
Accts Meyers Brothers Kalicka Pc
SIC 8641 Social club, membership; Social club, membership
Prin: Harold Grinspoon
CFO: Matthew Motyka
Ofcr: Jordanna Amsel
Ofcr: Dena Kaufman
Off Mgr: Sandy Gingras
Dir IT: Peter Wansick

D-U-N-S 03-552-8645
HAROLD GWATNEY CHEVROLET CO
GWATNEY CHEVROLET/GEO
1301 T P White Dr, Jacksonville, AR 72076-3261
Tel (501) 982-2102 *Founded/Ownrshp* 1957
Sales 53.3MM^E *EMP* 130
SIC 5511 Automobiles, new & used; Pickups, new & used; Automobiles, new & used; Pickups, new & used
Pr: Harold Gwatney
CFO: Harold Waldon
**VP:* Syble Gwatney
Off Mgr: Linda Casteel
Sls Mgr: Kevin Cascio
Sales Asso: Caleb Morris
Sales Asso: Marcus Stevenson

D-U-N-S 01-205-5331 IMP/EXP
HAROLD IMPORT CO INC
HAROLD'S KITCHEN
747 Vassar Ave, Lakewood, NJ 08701-6908
Tel (732) 367-2800 *Founded/Ownrshp* 1957
Sales 38.9MM^E *EMP* 99
SIC 5023 China; Kitchen tools & utensils; China; Kitchen tools & utensils
CEO: Mildred L Polansky
**Pr:* Robert Laub
**CFO:* John Mulligan
VP: Caroline Himmel
Off Mgr: Alicia Marotta
IT Man: Larry Ross
Mktg Dir: Nicole Herman
Sls Mgr: Allyn Teilborg

D-U-N-S 00-382-4661
■ **HAROLD LEMAY ENTERPRISES INC**
PIERCE COUNTY REFUSE
(*Suby of* WASTE CONNECTIONS INC) ★
4111 192nd St E, Tacoma, WA 98446-2745
Tel (253) 875-5053 *Founded/Ownrshp* 2008
Sales 31.4MM^E *EMP* 568
SIC 4212 Garbage collection & transport, no disposal; Garbage collection & transport, no disposal
Pr: Nancy Lemay
**VP:* Doug Lemay
Admn Mgr: Neil Pelligrini
IT Man: Kelli Barker
IT Man: Laura Kapusciniski

D-U-N-S 10-766-0912
HAROLD LEVINSON ASSOCIATES INC
H L A
21 Banfi Plz N, Farmingdale, NY 11735-1544
Tel (516) 852-7800 *Founded/Ownrshp* 1975
Sales 404.0MM^E *EMP* 400^E
SIC 5194 5145 Cigarettes; Smoking tobacco; Candy; Cigarettes; Smoking tobacco; Candy
CEO: Edward Berro
**CFO:* Andrew P Defrancesco
CFO: Andrew Defrancesco
Ex VP: Michael Berro
**VP:* Rita Berro
**VP:* Barry Feldman
**VP:* Marty Glick
VP: Ian Kessler
Rgnl Mgr: Paul Dwyer
CIO: Kate Kochanasaz
Dir IT: Brad Sauer

HAROLD PENER MENS WEAR
See DB PENER INC

HAROLD PRIMARY CARE
See CONSOLIDATED HEALTH SYSTEMS INC

D-U-N-S 60-092-3770
HAROLD SIMMONS FOUNDATION
5430 Lyndon B Johnson Fwy, Dallas, TX 75240-2601
Tel (972) 233-2134 *Founded/Ownrshp* 2005
Sales 31.4MM *EMP* 3
SIC 8641 Civic social & fraternal associations; Civic social & fraternal associations
Prin: Glen Simmons

HAROLD ZEIGLER AUTO GROUP
See HAROLD ZEIGLER KALAMAZOO INC

D-U-N-S 06-470-6955
HAROLD ZEIGLER FORD-ELKHART INC
2525 Bypass Rd, Elkhart, IN 46514-1519
Tel (574) 294-1563 *Founded/Ownrshp* 1995
Sales 34.5MM^E *EMP* 80
SIC 5511 Automobiles, new & used; Automobiles, new & used
Pr: Harold Zeigler
**Sec:* Kevin Killelea
**VP:* Robert Hayden
Sales Asso: Bill Cammett

D-U-N-S 09-780-6384
HAROLD ZEIGLER KALAMAZOO INC
HAROLD ZEIGLER AUTO GROUP
4201 Stadium Dr, Kalamazoo, MI 49008-1427
Tel (269) 375-4500 *Founded/Ownrshp* 1979
Sales 73.8MM^E *EMP* 140
SIC 5511

HAROLD'S CAVE CREEK CORRAL
See HAROLDS RESTAURANTS LLC

HAROLD'S KITCHEN
See HAROLD IMPORT CO INC

D-U-N-S 60-998-0958
HAROLDS RESTAURANTS LLC
HAROLD'S CAVE CREEK CORRAL
6895 E Cave Creek Rd, Cave Creek, AZ 85331-8614
Tel (480) 488-1906 *Founded/Ownrshp* 1988
Sales 34.0MM *EMP* 65
SIC 8641 Bars & restaurants, members only; Bars & restaurants, members only

D-U-N-S 05-842-4024
HARP BUSINESS SERVICES INC
HARP INK
2725 Northwoods Pkwy A2, Peachtree Corners, GA 30071-5707
Tel (678) 482-0675 *Founded/Ownrshp* 1998
Sales 127.0MM^E *EMP* 11
SIC 2759 4225 5699 Commercial printing; General warehousing & storage; Uniforms & work clothing; Commercial printing; General warehousing & storage; Uniforms & work clothing
CEO: Hy L Dorfman
**CFO:* Patti Dorfman
Mktg Dir: Lisa Rolince

HARP INK
See HARP BUSINESS SERVICES INC

D-U-N-S 96-877-0706 IMP
HARPAK-ULMA PACKAGING LLC
175 John Quincy Adams Rd, Taunton, MA 02780-1035
Tel (508) 884-2500 *Founded/Ownrshp* 2010
Sales 31.4MM^E *EMP* 75^E
SIC 5084 Packaging machinery & equipment
Pr: Jan Erik Kuhlmann
VP: Robert Hamilton
VP: Heidi Harlfinger
Manager: Conrad Carpenter
Manager: Carson Howard
Manager: Mark Hyde
Manager: Kevin Kennedy
Manager: Jerry Rundle
Manager: Steve Silva
Manager: Gilles Trudeau

D-U-N-S 03-198-4289
HARPEL OIL CO
5480 Brighton Blvd, Commerce City, CO 80022-3607
Tel (303) 294-0767 *Founded/Ownrshp* 1937
Sales 106.9MM *EMP* 16^E
Accts Eks&H Lllp Denver Colorado
SIC 5171 5983 5172 Petroleum bulk stations; Fuel oil dealers; Gasoline; Petroleum bulk stations; Fuel oil dealers; Gasoline
Pr: Doug Harpel
**VP:* Tammie Barr

D-U-N-S 00-285-3588
HARPER CO
W.L.HARPER CO., THE
1648 Petersburg Rd, Hebron, KY 41048-9669
Tel (859) 586-8890 *Founded/Ownrshp* 1937
Sales 31.4MM *EMP* 250
Accts Vonlehman And Company Cincinn
SIC 1611 1623 Airport runway construction; Concrete construction: roads, highways, sidewalks, etc.; Water main construction; Sewer line construction; Airport runway construction; Concrete construction: roads, highways, sidewalks, etc.; Water main construction; Sewer line construction
Ch Bd: Bruce Huff
**Pr:* Jim Thomas
**VP:* Shawn Green
**VP:* Lois Morgan

D-U-N-S 07-189-3840
HARPER COLLEGE
HARPER COMMUNITY COLLEGE
1200 W Algonquin Rd, Palatine, IL 60067-7373
Tel (847) 925-6707 *Founded/Ownrshp* 1965
Sales 153.7MM^E *EMP* 1,307
SIC 8221 Colleges universities & professional schools; Colleges universities & professional schools
Pr: Kenneth Ender
Comm Dir: Phil Burdick

HARPER COMMUNITY COLLEGE
See HARPER COLLEGE

D-U-N-S 14-740-3638
HARPER CONSTRUCTION CO INC
2241 Kettner Blvd Ste 300, San Diego, CA 92101-1769
Tel (619) 233-7900 *Founded/Ownrshp* 1974
Sales 258.0MM^E *EMP* 140
SIC 1542 1521 Commercial & office building contractors; Single-family housing construction; Commercial & office building contractors; Single-family housing construction
CEO: Jeffrey A Harper
CFO: Gary Fitzgerald
**Ch:* Ron Harper
Ofcr: Stephen Lee
Ofcr: Myrna Smith
Ofcr: Karianne Tyler
VP: Bernard Firenz
VP: David Gerke
VP: Paul Jimenez
VP: Stephen Marble
VP: Bernie Stertzer
VP: Brad Vanvick
VP: Les Willigar
Exec: Mark Hoffman

D-U-N-S 00-336-9121
HARPER CORP - GENERAL CONTRACTORS
35 W Court St Ste 400, Greenville, SC 29601-2875
Tel (864) 527-2500 *Founded/Ownrshp* 1950
Sales 53.9MM^E *EMP* 65
Accts Elliott Davis Llc Greenville
SIC 1542 1541 Commercial & office building, new construction; Industrial buildings & warehouses; Commercial & office building, new construction; Industrial buildings & warehouses
Ch Bd: Doug Harper
**Pr:* David Wise
**CFO:* Donald M Oates
**Ch:* John M Harper Jr
**VP:* Jenkins Richardson
VP: Rick Richardson
Dir Bus: Kyle Snipes
Snr PM: Mike Odom
Snr PM: Frank Tucker

D-U-N-S 08-589-8617
HARPER CREEK COMMUNITY SCHOOLS (MI)
7454 B Dr N, Battle Creek, MI 49014-8381
Tel (269) 441-6560 *Founded/Ownrshp* 1949
Sales 15.0MM^E *EMP* 350
Accts Rehmann Robson Cpa S
SIC 8211 Public elementary & secondary schools; High school, junior or senior; Public elementary & secondary schools; High school, junior or senior

D-U-N-S 83-261-7372
HARPER DIRECT LLC
5100 Schenley Pl, Greendale, IN 47025-2181
Tel (214) 245-5026 *Founded/Ownrshp* 2009
Sales 25.5MM^E *EMP* 300
SIC 2621 Catalog paper; Catalog paper
CEO: Eric Hanent
Genl Mgr: Susan Reding

HARPER GROUP
See CIRCLE INTERNATIONAL INC

HARPER HOUSE CONDOMINIUMS
See VILLAGE OF CROSS KEYS RECREATION ASSOCIATION INC

D-U-N-S 03-392-6572 IMP
HARPER INDUSTRIES INC
DEWEZE MANUFACTURING
151 E Us Highway 160, Harper, KS 67058-8201
Tel (620) 896-7381 *Founded/Ownrshp* 1998
Sales 33.9MM^E *EMP* 84

SIC 3523 3524 3594 Farm machinery & equipment; Haying machines: mowers, rakes, stackers, etc.; Grounds mowing equipment; Lawn & garden equipment; Fluid power pumps & motors
CEO: Tim Penner
**VP:* Rita Polsley
**VP:* Heber Ramer
Opers Mgr: Vic Thetge
Natl Sales: Dennis Roberts
Mktg Mgr: Angie Higgs

D-U-N-S 04-181-4534
HARPER INDUSTRIES INC (TN)
960 N Hc Mathis Dr, Paducah, KY 42001-1771
Tel (270) 442-2753 *Founded/Ownrshp* 1980
Sales 101.9MM^E *EMP* 250
SIC 3273 1711 1611 1542 Ready-mixed concrete; Mechanical contractor; General contractor, highway & street construction; Commercial & office building, new construction; Commercial & office buildings, renovation & repair; Ready-mixed concrete; Mechanical contractor; General contractor, highway & street construction; Commercial & office building, new construction; Commercial & office buildings, renovation & repair
Pr: Billy Harper
Treas: Doug Ford

D-U-N-S 00-210-9932 IMP/EXP
HARPER INTERNATIONAL CORP (NY)
4455 Genesee St Ste 123, Buffalo, NY 14225-1965
Tel (716) 684-7400 *Founded/Ownrshp* 1988, 1989
Sales 49.6MM^E *EMP* 100
SIC 3567 Industrial furnaces & ovens; Industrial furnaces & ovens
CEO: Wayne Robinson
Pr: Charles Miller
CFO: Thomas Kittell
CFO: Jeffrey A Leavoy
CFO: Jeffery Levoy
Ch: Waldron Bamford
Dir IT: Prasad Apte
Dir IT: Thomas Mroz
IT Man: Sandy McNerney
Opers Mgr: Arun Bodapati
Mktg Mgr: Diana Robbins
Board of Directors: W L Bamford, Reinhard Jabs

HARPER KIA
See HARVEY M HARPER CO

D-U-N-S 00-408-5635
HARPER LIMBACH LLC
(*Suby of* LIMBACH ENGRG & DESIGN SVCS) ★
5401 Benchmark Ln, Sanford, FL 32773-6433
Tel (407) 321-8100 *Founded/Ownrshp* 1911, 1983
Sales 22.5MM^E *EMP* 120
SIC 1711

D-U-N-S 04-663-1441
HARPER MANAGEMENT INC
MCDONALD'S
415 E Main St, Lancaster, OH 43130-3807
Tel (740) 653-3073 *Founded/Ownrshp* 1975
Sales 24.9MM^E *EMP* 200
SIC 6719 Personal holding companies, except banks; Personal holding companies, except banks
Pr: Paul Harper
**Sec:* Natalie Harper
**VP:* Matthew Harper

D-U-N-S 02-699-7696
HARPER MECHANICAL CONTRACTORS LLC
1011 Camino Del Rio S, San Diego, CA 92108-3531
Tel (619) 543-1296 *Founded/Ownrshp* 2007
Sales 38.0MM^E *EMP* 80
SIC 5046 1611 Commercial equipment; Grading; Commercial equipment; Grading

D-U-N-S 02-585-0207
HARPER OIL CO
HARLER ON THE WAY STORES
2301 W Jefferson St, Springfield, IL 62702-2274
Tel (217) 698-4088 *Founded/Ownrshp* 2004
Sales 60.8MM^E *EMP* 250
SIC 5541 5411 Filling stations, gasoline; Convenience stores, independent; Filling stations, gasoline; Convenience stores, independent
Pr: Mary K Sommer
**Treas:* Ken Sommer
**VP:* Scott Eggleston
VP: Bruce Sommer
**VP:* Christopher Sommer
**VP:* Bruce Sommers

D-U-N-S 07-470-9205
HARPER OIL PRODUCTS INC
7975 Kentucky Dr, Florence, KY 41042-2914
Tel (859) 283-1001 *Founded/Ownrshp* 1955
Sales 26.2MM^E *EMP* 28
SIC 5172 Petroleum products
Pr: B Stephen Harper
Ch Bd: Bobby L Harper
Treas: Kevin S Harper
VP: Larry D Harper
Dir Risk M: Ann Lightfoot
Genl Mgr: Tim Dupin

HARPER PORSCHE
See HYB INC

D-U-N-S 05-877-5842
HARPER SHIELDS & CO
4591 Pacheco Blvd, Martinez, CA 94553-4698
Tel (510) 653-9119 *Founded/Ownrshp* 1917
Sales 67.0MM^E *EMP* 66
SIC 5084 Petroleum industry machinery; Petroleum industry machinery
Ch Bd: Barton F Scowley
**Pr:* J David Sarginson
**CEO:* Barton A Scowley
CFO: Greg Brown
**VP:* James F Fuchs
Brnch Mgr: Mark Neal
Dist Mgr: Richard Iacovelli
Dist Mgr: Mike Wade
Div Mgr: Mark Sarginson
**Genl Mgr:* Doug De Long

D-U-N-S 00-724-3702 IMP
HARPER TRUCKS INC (KS)
1522 S Florence St, Wichita, KS 67209-2634
Tel (316) 942-1381 *Founded/Ownrshp* 1953
Sales 30.0MM *EMP* 130
SIC 3537 Industrial trucks & tractors; Industrial trucks & tractors
Ch Bd: Phillip G Ruffin
**VP:* Gary Leiker
IT Man: William Jarvis
Natl Sales: Darrell Neugebauer
Sls Mgr: David Rife

HARPER UNIVERSITY HOSPITAL
See VHS HARPER-HUTZEL HOSPITAL INC

D-U-N-S 16-177-9228
HARPER VEHICLES LLC
9901 Kingston Pike, Knoxville, TN 37922-3320
Tel (865) 691-0393 *Founded/Ownrshp* 1996
Sales 30.0MM^E *EMP* 35
SIC 5511 Automobiles, new & used; Automobiles, new & used

D-U-N-S 00-163-0169 IMP
■ **HARPERCOLLINS PUBLISHERS LLC**
WILLIAM MORROW PUBLISHING
(*Suby of* NEWS CORP) ★
195 Broadway Fl 2, New York, NY 10007-3132
Tel (212) 207-7000 *Founded/Ownrshp* 1817, 2013
Sales 216.8MM^E *EMP* 1,918
SIC 5942 2731 Book stores; Books: publishing only; Book stores; Books: publishing only
CEO: Brian Murray
Pr: David Steinberger
Ex VP: Lawrence Nevins
Sr VP: Mark Tauber
VP: Jonathan Burnham
VP: Hollis Heimbouch
VP: Doug Jones
VP: Stephen Koenig
VP: Len Marshall
VP: Michael McGinnis
VP: Joe Park
VP: Beth Silfin
VP: Liate Stehlik
Assoc Dir: Heather Drucker

D-U-N-S 01-453-4219
HARPETH FINANCIAL SERVICES LLC
ADVANCE FINANCIAL
100 Oceanside Dr, Nashville, TN 37204-2351
Tel (615) 341-5900 *Founded/Ownrshp* 2008
Sales NA *EMP* 1,182^E
SIC 6162 Mortgage bankers & correspondents
CEO: Tina Hodges
CFO: Patrick Conroy
Ch: Mike Hodges
VP: Cullen Earnest
CIO: Bryan Link

D-U-N-S 07-912-4426
HARPETH VALLEY UTILITIES DISTRICT OF DAVIDSON AND WILLIAMSON COUNTIES
HVUD
5910 River Rd, Nashville, TN 37209-5607
Tel (615) 352-7076 *Founded/Ownrshp* 1959
Sales 36.2MM^E *EMP* 75
SIC 4941 4952 Water supply; Sewerage systems; Water supply; Sewerage systems
Pr: Robert Wheaton
**VP:* Bernard Kwas

HARPO ENTERTAINMENT GROUP
See HARPO PRODUCTIONS INC

D-U-N-S 79-284-5901
HARPO PRODUCTIONS INC
HARPO ENTERTAINMENT GROUP
110 N Carpenter St, Chicago, IL 60607-2146
Tel (312) 633-1000 *Founded/Ownrshp* 1988
Sales 23.6MM^E *EMP* 200
SIC 7812 Television film production; Video tape production; Television film production; Video tape production
Ch Bd: Oprah Winfrey
**Pr:* Tim Bennett
**CFO:* Doug Pattison
Sr VP: Selena Saldana
**VP:* Bill Becker
Netwrk Mgr: Byron Ward
Opers Mgr: Katherine Kelly
VP Mktg: Peggy Panosh
Pgrm Dir: Laurie Cantillo
Snr Mgr: Amy Weinblum

D-U-N-S 14-854-4443
HARPOINT HOLDINGS INC
200 Front St, Millersburg, PA 17061-1324
Tel (717) 692-2113 *Founded/Ownrshp* 2003
Sales 21.8MM^E *EMP* 210
SIC 3545 Cutting tools for machine tools; Cutting tools for machine tools
Pr: William F Coyle Jr
**VP:* David R Pelizzon

D-U-N-S 00-889-1699
HARPOLE CONSTRUCTION INC
60 Road 3961, Farmington, NM 87401-1050
Tel (505) 325-1249 *Founded/Ownrshp* 2001
Sales 30.0MM *EMP* 150
SIC 1623 1381 Pipeline & power line inspection service; Drilling water intake wells; Water, sewer & utility lines; Water, sewer & utility lines; Pipeline construction; Directional drilling oil & gas wells
Pr: Jerry Harpole
**CFO:* Rusty Hunter
**Sec:* Deborah Harpole

D-U-N-S 79-066-0067
■ **HARPOON ACQUISITION CORP**
(*Suby of* FISERV INC) ★
455 Winding Brook Dr, Glastonbury, CT 06033-4315
Tel (860) 815-5736 *Founded/Ownrshp* 2013
Sales 213.4MM^E *EMP* 1,700^E
SIC 7372 7373 Business oriented computer software; Systems integration services; Business oriented computer software; Systems integration services
CEO: Louis Hernandez Jr

HARPOON BREWERY
See MASS BAY BREWING CO INC

D-U-N-S 04-266-4581
HARPS FOOD STORE
WALLACE
1003 N Douglass St, Malden, MO 63863-1515
Tel (573) 276-3353 *Founded/Ownrshp* 1949
Sales 29.2MM^E *EMP* 366
SIC 5411 Grocery stores, chain; Grocery stores, chain
Pr: Steve Wallace
**Sec:* Richard Wallace

HARPS FOOD STORES
See HARPS FOOD STORES INC

D-U-N-S 03-564-0630 IMP
HARPS FOOD STORES INC
HARPS FOOD STORES
918 S Gutensohn Rd, Springdale, AR 72762-5165
Tel (479) 751-7601 *Founded/Ownrshp* 1925
Sales 573.9MM^E *EMP* 3,000
SIC 5411 5122 Supermarkets, chain; Drugs, proprietaries & sundries; Supermarkets, chain; Drugs, proprietaries & sundries
CEO: Roger Collins
**Pr:* Kim Eskew
**CFO:* Jim Natz
VP: Frank Ray
Dist Mgr: Boyd Tillotson
IT Man: Jim Tackett
Pharmcst: Brandon Davis
Pharmcst: Todd Herriman
Pharmcst: Rhonda Schossow

D-U-N-S 82-519-8492
HARPURE ENTERPRISES INC
13560 Colombard Ct, Fontana, CA 92337-7702
Tel (951) 681-9697 *Founded/Ownrshp* 1992
Sales 41.9MM^E *EMP* 190
SIC 6719 Investment holding companies, except banks; Investment holding companies, except banks
CEO: Earl L Harper
**Pr:* Buck Long

HARR CHRYSLER JEEP-DODGE
See HARR- MOTOR CO

D-U-N-S 00-586-9177
HARR- MOTOR CO (MA)
HARR CHRYSLER JEEP-DODGE
100-110 Gold Star Blvd, Worcester, MA 01606
Tel (508) 471-2700 *Founded/Ownrshp* 1933
Sales 30.3MM^E *EMP* 60
SIC 5511

HARRAH'S
See CAESARS ENTERTAINMENT OPERATING CO INC

D-U-N-S 17-042-6217
■ **HARRAHS ATLANTIC CITY OPERATING CO LLC**
HARRAH'S RESORT
(*Suby of* CAESARS ENTERTAINMENT OPERATING CO INC) ★
777 Harrahs Blvd, Atlantic City, NJ 08401-1985
Tel (609) 441-5000 *Founded/Ownrshp* 1995
Sales 101.1MM^E *EMP* 3,570
SIC 7011 Casino hotel; Casino hotel
**CEO:* Gary W Loveman
**Ex VP:* Donald Colvin
Exec: Louis Heckel
Exec: Robert Schoell
Dir IT: Janet Miller
Netwrk Eng: David Pritchard
VP Opers: Elizabeth Cartlidge

HARRAHS ATLANTIC CY CASINO HT
See MARINA ASSOCIATES LTD

HARRAH'S CASINO
See JAZZ CASINO CO LL C

HARRAH'S CASINO AND HOTEL
See TRIBAL CASINO GAMING ENTERPRISES

HARRAH'S CHESTER CASINO
See CHESTER DOWNS AND MARINA LLC

HARRAHS CNCIL BLUFFS CASINO HT
See HARVEYS IOWA MANAGEMENT CO INC

HARRAHS GRAND
See BL DEVELOPMENT CORP

HARRAHS LAUGHLIN CASINO & HT
See HARRAHS LAUGHLIN LLC

D-U-N-S 19-588-3004
■ **HARRAHS LAUGHLIN LLC**
HARRAHS LAUGHLIN CASINO & HT
(*Suby of* CAESARS ENTERTAINMENT OPERATING CO INC) ★
2900 S Casino Dr, Laughlin, NV 89029-1521
Tel (702) 298-4600 *Founded/Ownrshp* 1989
Sales 55.4MM^E *EMP* 1,500
SIC 7011 5812 Casino hotel; Eating places; Casino hotel; Eating places
Pr: Philip G Satre

D-U-N-S 07-315-6234
■ **HARRAHS LOUISIANA DOWNS TRANSITORY SUB INC**
(*Suby of* CAESARS ENTERTAINMENT CORP) ★
8000 E Texas St, Bossier City, LA 71111-7016
Tel (318) 742-5555 *Founded/Ownrshp* 2002
Sales 13.5MM^E *EMP* 300
SIC 7948 7993 5812 Horse race track operation; Gambling establishments operating coin-operated machines; American restaurant; Horse race track operation; Gambling establishments operating coin-operated machines; American restaurant
Pr: Anthony Sanfilippo

D-U-N-S 95-955-5392
HARRAHS MARYLAND HEIGHTS OPERATING CO INC
HARRAH'S ST LOUIS
777 Casino Center Dr, Maryland Heights, MO 63043-4821
Tel (314) 770-8100 *Founded/Ownrshp* 2008
Sales NA *EMP* 2,200
SIC 7011 5813 5812 Casino hotel; Drinking places; Eating places

D-U-N-S 83-313-7610
■ **HARRAHS NORTH KANSAS CITY LLC**
(*Suby of* CAESARS ENTERTAINMENT CORP) ★
1 Riverboat Dr, North Kansas City, MO 64116-3267
Tel (816) 472-7777 *Founded/Ownrshp* 1999
Sales 30.7MM^E *EMP* 1,200
SIC 7999 Gambling establishment; Gambling establishment
Advt Mgr: Katie Knox

HARRAH'S RESORT
See HARRAHS ATLANTIC CITY OPERATING CO LLC

HARRAH'S ST LOUIS
See HARRAHS MARYLAND HEIGHTS OPERATING CO INC

HARREL
See DAVIS-STANDARD LLC

D-U-N-S 18-590-9157
HARRELL & HALL ENTERPRISES INC
H & H BUILDING
43 Airpark Ct, Alabaster, AL 35007-9505
Tel (205) 664-9191 *Founded/Ownrshp* 1987
Sales 50.1MM^E *EMP* 150
SIC 5013 5531 Truck parts & accessories; Automotive & home supply stores; Truck parts & accessories; Automotive & home supply stores
Pr: Wayne Hall
**Sec:* Danny Harrell

D-U-N-S 13-081-4460
HARRELL - FISH INC
HFI
2010 W Vernal Pike, Bloomington, IN 47404-2873
Tel (812) 339-2579 *Founded/Ownrshp* 1998
Sales 35.9MM^E *EMP* 95
SIC 1711 Mechanical contractor
Pr: Stephen R Dawson
**Treas:* Davis E Conner
VP: Teresa Boshears
VP: Brad Schlegel
Genl Mgr: Lisa Vandeventer
Off Mgr: Michelle Vincel
Trfc Dir: Randy Chambers

D-U-N-S 16-527-1276
■ **HARRELL CONTRACTING GROUP LLC**
H C G
(*Suby of* ANDERSON COMPANIES INC) ★
368 Highland Colony Pkwy, Ridgeland, MS 39157-6036
Tel (601) 206-7538 *Founded/Ownrshp* 2003
Sales 32.3MM^E *EMP* 150
Accts Horne Llp Ridgeland Mississi
SIC 1541 Industrial buildings, new construction; Industrial buildings, new construction
VP: Tom Black
VP: Darryl Lane
VP: Don Parks
Snr PM: Scott Trueblood

HARRELL NUT COMPANY
See GOLDEN PEANUT & TREE NUTS

D-U-N-S 03-241-8311 IMP/EXP
HARRELLS INC
720 Kraft Rd, Lakeland, FL 33815-3244
Tel (863) 687-2774 *Founded/Ownrshp* 2008
Sales 90.1MM^E *EMP* 213^E
SIC 2875 5191 Fertilizers, mixing only; Fertilizers & agricultural chemicals

D-U-N-S 80-588-0072 IMP/EXP
HARRELLS LLC
720 Kraft Rd, Lakeland, FL 33815-3244
Tel (863) 687-2774 *Founded/Ownrshp* 2007
Sales 78.1MM^E *EMP* 300^E
SIC 2875 5191 Fertilizers, mixing only; Fertilizers & agricultural chemicals; Fertilizers, mixing only; Fertilizers & agricultural chemicals
CEO: Jack Harrell
Pr: Rick Helpingstine
**Pr:* David Schermerhorn
COO: Matthew Shook
**CFO:* Carl McKenzie
**CFO:* Gary Rust
**VP:* Alex Barcia
VP: Jeff Higgins
Off Mgr: Robin Carter
IT Man: Brian Fischer
Opers Mgr: Brad Bolyard

HARRELSON TOYOTA
See LF HARRELSON INC

D-U-N-S 01-487-9720 IMP
HARRIET CARTER GIFTS INC
425 Stump Rd, Montgomeryville, PA 18936-9631
Tel (215) 361-5100 *Founded/Ownrshp* 1958
Sales 45.9MM^E *EMP* 250
SIC 5961 Novelty merchandise, mail order; Novelty merchandise, mail order
Pr: Ronald P Lassin
**Treas:* Bernie Smith
**VP:* William Garbose
**VP:* Harriet Lassin
VP: Michel Martinez
**VP:* Ralph B Smith
IT Man: Lowell Bergey
IT Man: Cecily Craig
VP Mktg: Bill Garbose
Mktg Mgr: Mary Norton

D-U-N-S 06-245-3105
HARRIGAN LUMBER CO INC (AL)
1033 Hornady Dr, Monroeville, AL 36460-6604
Tel (251) 575-4821 *Founded/Ownrshp* 1972
Sales 27.6MM *EMP* 103
Accts Lanigan & Associates Pc Tall
SIC 2421 Sawmills & planing mills, general; Sawmills & planing mills, general
Ch Bd: Chip Harrigan
**Pr:* Patrick Harrigan
**Treas:* David D Mims III

D-U-N-S 09-643-9240
HARRIMAN OIL CO LLC
804 Highway 321 N Ste 250, Lenoir City, TN 37771-6432
Tel (865) 986-4766 *Founded/Ownrshp* 1999
Sales 49.7MM *EMP* 13
Accts Averett Warmus Durkee Orlando
SIC 5541 Marine service station; Marine service station

D-U-N-S 00-792-1091
HARRIMAN UTILITY BOARD
CITY OF HARRIMAN UTILITIES
300 N Roane St, Harriman, TN 37748-2038
Tel (865) 882-3242 *Founded/Ownrshp* 1939
Sales 25.4MM *EMP* 90
SIC 4931 Electric & other services combined; Electric & other services combined
Genl Mgr: Chuck Flora
Sfty Mgr: Jeremy Gibson

D-U-N-S 00-909-3246 IMP
HARRINGTON & CO (UT)
760 W Layton Ave, Salt Lake City, UT 84104-1727
Tel (801) 972-3131 *Founded/Ownrshp* 1938
Sales 44.9MM^E *EMP* 70^E
SIC 5033 5072 Roofing, siding & insulation; Builders' hardware; Roofing, siding & insulation; Builders' hardware
Ch: Elden H Booth
**Pr:* Stephen Booth
**Sec:* Phillip Arnold
**VP:* Leora Booth
VP: Donald Lafay
Store Mgr: Scott Travis
Sls Mgr: Brian Booth
Sls Mgr: Craig Oby
Sls Mgr: Con Olsen
Sls Mgr: Gary Robison

D-U-N-S 00-512-1587
HARRINGTON & KING PERFORATING CO INC (IL)
H&K
5655 W Fillmore St, Chicago, IL 60644-5504
Tel (773) 626-1800 *Founded/Ownrshp* 1883
Sales 28.8MM^E *EMP* 155
SIC 3469 3089

D-U-N-S 00-623-0643
HARRINGTON CO (MT)
PEPSI-COLA
1740 Holmes Ave, Butte, MT 59701-3515
Tel (406) 494-3200 *Founded/Ownrshp* 1943
Sales 40.0MM^E *EMP* 170
SIC 2086 5046 Carbonated beverages, nonalcoholic: bottled & canned; Restaurant equipment & supplies; Carbonated beverages, nonalcoholic: bottled & canned; Restaurant equipment & supplies
VP: Mark Harrington
**CFO:* Ted Connors
**Sec:* Shirley Harrington
**VP:* Lynn Harrington

D-U-N-S 04-474-2567 IMP/EXP
HARRINGTON CORP
HARCO
3721 Cohen Pl, Lynchburg, VA 24501-5047
Tel (434) 845-7094 *Founded/Ownrshp* 1966
Sales 24.8MM^E *EMP* 103^E
SIC 3089 3498 Fittings for pipe, plastic; Fabricated pipe & fittings
Pr: Michael B Harrington
**VP:* Steve Baily
**VP:* Eichmann E C
**VP:* Steven C Harrington
**VP:* John Riordan
**Prin:* Douglas Harrington
Mtls Mgr: Cindy Grishaw
Prd Mgr: Dan Hicks
Natl Sales: Edward Eichmann
Sales Asso: Phil Busman

D-U-N-S 00-274-7876
■ **HARRINGTON HEALTH SERVICES INC**
FISERV HEALTH
(*Suby of* UMR INC) ★
780 Brooksedge Plaza Dr, Westerville, OH 43081-4914
Tel (614) 212-7000 *Founded/Ownrshp* 2000, 2008
Sales NA *EMP* 900
SIC 6411 Insurance claim processing, except medical; Insurance claim processing, except medical
Pr: Jeff Mills
**CFO:* Terry Moore
IT Man: Kathy Oyster

D-U-N-S 78-063-8979 IMP
HARRINGTON HOISTS INC
(*Suby of* KITO CORPORATION)
401 W End Ave, Manheim, PA 17545-1703
Tel (717) 665-2000 *Founded/Ownrshp* 1990
Sales 26.7MM^E *EMP* 150
SIC 3536 Hoists, cranes & monorails; Hoists, cranes & monorails
Pr: Edward W Hunter
CFO: Joseph Bidus
VP: Yoshio Morita
Exec: Lyn Geib
IT Man: Savi Porter
VP Opers: Scott Miller
Plnt Mgr: William Erkenbrack
Plnt Mgr: Guy Haney
S&M/VP: Carlo Lonardi
Board of Directors: Carlo Lonardi, Yoshio Merita, Scott Miller, Tom Suzuki

D-U-N-S 02-851-5344 IMP/EXP
HARRINGTON INDUSTRIAL PLASTICS LLC
(*Suby of* ALIAXIS PARTICIPATIONS)
14480 Yorba Ave, Chino, CA 91710-5766
Tel (909) 597-8641 *Founded/Ownrshp* 2002
Sales 212.5MM^E *EMP* 415
SIC 5074 Pipes & fittings, plastic; Plumbing & heating valves; Pipes & fittings, plastic; Plumbing & heating valves
Pr: Jim Reid
Area Mgr: Craig Giles
Brnch Mgr: David Wahrmund
Dir IT: David Arnold
Mtls Mgr: Kevin Uch
Opers Mgr: Bruce Moulton
Sales Asso: Barry Brakefield
Sales Asso: Tony Grganto
Sales Asso: Charles Matiyasic
Sales Asso: David McNutt
Sales Asso: Roscoe Moon

D-U-N-S 07-534-0877
HARRINGTON MEMORIAL HOSPITAL INC
100 South St Ste 1, Southbridge, MA 01550-4047
Tel (508) 765-9771 *Founded/Ownrshp* 1928
Sales 107.7MM *EMP* 1,100
SIC 8062 General medical & surgical hospitals; General medical & surgical hospitals
Pr: Edward Moore
**COO:* Douglas Crapser
VP: Donald Brechner
**VP:* Thomas Hijeck
VP: Charlene Richard
VP: Arthur Russo
VP: Peg Skowron
VP: Thomas Sullivan
Dir OR: Laura Fortin
Dir Lab: Kathryn Anestis
Dir Rad: Rola Shaheen
Dir Rx: Anthony Dubois

D-U-N-S 05-689-5258
HARRINGTON MORAN BARKSDALE INC
2000 E Lamar Blvd Ste 710, Arlington, TX 76006-7341
Tel (817) 299-9320 *Founded/Ownrshp* 1993
Sales 15.2MM^E *EMP* 300
SIC 6531 Real estate agent, commercial; Real estate agent, commercial
Pr: Alfred C Moran
**VP:* Maurice L Barksdale

D-U-N-S 94-976-8501
HARRINGTON RACEWAY INC
MIDWAY SLOTS & SIMULCAST
Rr 13, Harrington, DE 19952
Tel (302) 398-5346 *Founded/Ownrshp* 1996
Sales 13.9MM^E *EMP* 450
SIC 7999 7993 5813 5812 Gambling & lottery services; Gambling establishments operating coin-operated machines; Drinking places; Eating places; Gambling & lottery services; Gambling establishments operating coin-operated machines; Drinking places; Eating places
Genl Mgr: Bruce McKee

HARRINGTON RIGHTER & PARSONS
See HARRINGTON RIGHTER & PARSONS LP

D-U-N-S 07-524-0044
■ **HARRINGTON RIGHTER & PARSONS LP**
HARRINGTON RIGHTER & PARSONS
(*Suby of* COX ENTERPRISES INC) ★
805 3rd Ave Fl 24, New York, NY 10022-7541
Tel (212) 759-0191 *Founded/Ownrshp* 2011
Sales 81.6MM^E *EMP* 320
SIC 7313 Radio, television, publisher representatives; Radio, television, publisher representatives
Pr: Murray Berkowitz
Genl Pt: Cox HRP
Ltd Pt: Cox Enterprises
Pr: Kerry Boehme
Sr VP: Ray Karczewski
VP: Nan Diley
VP: Margaret Genter
VP: Charlie Lizzo
VP: Donald O'Toole
VP: Clark Spell
VP: Tracey Tynan
VP: Maury Wind

HARRIS & ASSOCIATES CNSTR MGT
See HARRIS & ASSOCIATES INC

D-U-N-S 07-393-0802
HARRIS & ASSOCIATES INC
HARRIS & ASSOCIATES CNSTR MGT
1401 Wllw Pca Rd 500, Concord, CA 94520
Tel (925) 827-4900 *Founded/Ownrshp* 1974
Sales 83.7MM^E *EMP* 300
Accts Campbell Benn & Taylor Sacra
SIC 8711 8712 Construction & civil engineering; Civil engineering; Sanitary engineers; Architectural engineering; Construction & civil engineering; Civil engineering; Sanitary engineers; Architectural engineering
CEO: Lisa Larrabee
**Ch Bd:* Carl Harris
**Pr:* Guy Erickson
Pr: Gary Yagade
COO: Ehab Gerges
CFO: Gary Wohl
Ofcr: Kyle Gisbrecht
Ex VP: Bob Guletz
**Sr VP:* Neil McCosker
Sr VP: James Parmley
**Sr VP:* Vernon Phillips
**Sr VP:* Byron Tobey Jr
VP: Keith Anderson
VP: Mike Cooper
VP: Isaac Dee
VP: Christopher Dunne
VP: Jules Feher
VP: Allyson Gipson
VP: Jim Guerrero
VP: Greg Ow
VP: Randall Raup

D-U-N-S 82-462-3003 IMP/EXP
HARRIS & FORD LLC
9307 E 56th St, Indianapolis, IN 46216-2068
Tel (317) 591-0000 *Founded/Ownrshp* 1994
Sales 221.0MM *EMP* 55
SIC 5169 5085 Chemicals & allied products; Industrial supplies; Chemicals & allied products; Industrial supplies
Pr: Timothy Harris II
**VP:* Joseph E Ford
Opers Mgr: Brad Harris
Sales Asso: Scott Paris

D-U-N-S 60-486-7523
HARRIS & HARRIS LTD
CHICAGO LAW GROUP
111 W Jackson Blvd # 400, Chicago, IL 60604-4135
Tel (312) 251-2300 *Founded/Ownrshp* 1977
Sales 47.5MM^E *EMP* 320
SIC 7322 8711 Adjustment & collection services; Electrical or electronic engineering; Adjustment & collection services; Electrical or electronic engineering
Pr: Arnold S Harris
**Ex VP:* David L Harris

D-U-N-S 78-827-4728
HARRIS & HART INC
1759 W 12th St, Ogden, UT 84404-5446
Tel (253) 735-3351 *Founded/Ownrshp* 1992
Sales 24.2MM^E *EMP* 125
SIC 1761 Sheet metalwork
Pr: Richard R Harris
**Ch Bd:* James F Hart
**Pr:* Steven F Harris
**Treas:* Nolan E Karras
**VP:* Bradley J Hart

D-U-N-S 13-838-0717
HARRIS ACQUISITION III LLC
SUPERIOR AIR HANDLING
200 E 700 S, Clearfield, UT 84015-1712
Tel (801) 776-1997 *Founded/Ownrshp* 2008
Sales 37.6MM^E *EMP* 65^E
SIC 5084 Materials handling machinery
**Pr:* Randy Richter
**Sec:* Sharon A Stewart
**VP:* Zach Sargent
**VP:* Addie Dawn Stewart
**Prin:* John Powell
Off Admin: Alexandria Dunn
Sls Mgr: Gene Bjorkland

HARRIS ASSEMBLY GROUP
See ARNOLD-DAVIS LLC

D-U-N-S 07-070-1008
HARRIS ASSOCIATES LP
(*Suby of* NATIXIS GLOBAL ASSET MANAGEMENT LP) ★
111 S Wacker Dr Ste 4600, Chicago, IL 60606-4319
Tel (312) 621-0600 *Founded/Ownrshp* 2000
Sales 64.5MM^E *EMP* 168^E
Accts Pricewaterhousecoopers Llp C
SIC 6282 Investment advisory service; Investment advisory service
Genl Pt: John R Raitt
Pt: Robert M Levy
Pr: Kristi Rowsell
COO: John N Desmond
Ofcr: Richard Gorman
Ofcr: Colin McFarland
Ofcr: T J Newberg
Ofcr: Dawn Reeves
Ofcr: Bob Reey
Sr VP: Sharon Pitera
VP: Suzanne Mueller
VP: Paula Theodore

HARRIS BAKING COMPANY
See OZARK EMPIRE DISTRIBUTORS INC

D-U-N-S 00-693-6371
HARRIS BANK
(*Suby of* BMO BANKCORP INC) ★
520 Green Bay Rd, Winnetka, IL 60093-2552
Tel (847) 441-4444 *Founded/Ownrshp* 1909
Sales NA *EMP* 50
SIC 6021 6022 National commercial banks; State commercial banks; National commercial banks; State commercial banks
Pr: Wade Bundi
Sr VP: Bill McKinley
Sr VP: Steven Neudecker
VP: Randi Blume
VP: Robert Burchmore
VP: D Magers
VP: Eric Robison
VP: Bill Thanoukos
Exec: Steven Zandpour
Reg Pr: Chris Michalski
Board of Directors: R G Durham, F F Fowle, H H Howard, L Howe, B A Warnes

D-U-N-S 07-443-9092
HARRIS BANK HINSDALE NA
HARRIS BANKS
(*Suby of* BMO BANKCORP INC) ★
50 S Lincoln St, Hinsdale, IL 60521-4065
Tel (630) 920-7000 *Founded/Ownrshp* 1985
Sales NA *EMP* 107
SIC 6021 National commercial banks; National commercial banks
Pr: Mary Alingenburger
**Ch Bd:* James R Mansell
Pr: Jamie Maravich
Pr: Sunday P Perry
Sr VP: David Beery
Sr VP: Peter O'Connor
Sr VP: Roy Thygesen
Sr VP: Kristin Warren
VP: Dawn Barnhart
VP: Mark Dahm
VP: Francesca Tenuta
Board of Directors: Kenneth H Beard, Michael Godwin, Richard K Green, Constance T Keller, Paul Maca, Sally Porter

HARRIS BANKS
See HARRIS BANK HINSDALE NA

D-U-N-S 07-369-8607
HARRIS BEACH PLLC
99 Garnsey Rd Ste 1, Pittsford, NY 14534-4596
Tel (585) 419-8800 *Founded/Ownrshp* 1995
Sales 73.0MM^E *EMP* 450
SIC 8111 General practice law office; General practice law office
CEO: James A Spitz Jr
Mng Pt: David Capriotti
Mng Pt: Steven Rice
COO: William H Kedley
COO: Gregory McDonald
CFO: Thomas S Abbott
Bd of Dir: Donald J Martin
Exec: Kevin Ryan
Admn Mgr: Tim Corcoran
Off Mgr: Stacey Juhl
Dir IT: Samir Christensen

D-U-N-S 00-693-0416 IMP
HARRIS BMO BANK NATIONAL ASSOCIATION
(*Suby of* BMO BANKCORP INC) ★
111 W Monroe St Ste 1200, Chicago, IL 60603-4014
Tel (312) 461-2323 *Founded/Ownrshp* 1882
Sales NA *EMP* 4,319
SIC 6021 National commercial banks; National commercial banks
V Ch Bd: Edward Lyman Jr
Pr: Ed Guske
Pr: John Renzelmann
Pr: Todd Senger
Pr: Steven Zandpour
**CEO:* Allan Castilo
COO: Mark Trembacki
Bd of Dir: Matthew Barrett
Bd of Dir: Haven Cockerham
Ofcr: Dora Araiza
Ofcr: Joan Devereaux
Ofcr: Edwin Marquez
Assoc VP: Eric Lempke
**Ex VP:* Yasmin T Bates
Ex VP: Joe Calabrese
**Ex VP:* Timothy Crane
Ex VP: Debra Delaney
Ex VP: Timothy Finnerty
Ex VP: Christopher McComish
**Ex VP:* Peter McNitt
**Ex VP:* Charles R Tonge

HARRIS BRIAN PONTIAC BUICK GMC
See BRIAN HARRIS

HARRIS BROADCAST
See IMAGINE COMMUNICATIONS CORP

HARRIS CALORIFIC
See HARRIS PRODUCTS GROUP

HARRIS CAPROCK
See CAPROCK GOVERNMENT SOLUTIONS INC

D-U-N-S 02-592-7625 IMP/EXP
■ **HARRIS CAPROCK COMMUNICATIONS INC** (TX)
(*Suby of* HARRIS CORPORATION)
4400 S Sam Houston Pkwy E, Houston, TX 77048-5902
Tel (888) 482-0289 *Founded/Ownrshp* 1981, 2010
Sales 81.1MM^E *EMP* 230
SIC 4813 Telephone communication, except radio; Telephone communication, except radio
CEO: Peter Shaper
**Pr:* Tracey Haslam
Pr: Pal Jensen
Pr: Keith Johnson
**COO:* Douglas Tutt
Sr Cor Off: Jere Thompson
**Ex VP:* David Myers
**VP:* Alan Aronowitz
VP: Britt Carina Horncastle
VP: J J Thakkar
Exec: Jill M Pavlas

D-U-N-S 16-178-8955
HARRIS CHEVROLET II LLC
BRIAN HARRIS AUTO PLEX
15015 Florida Blvd, Baton Rouge, LA 70819-2602
Tel (225) 272-6500 *Founded/Ownrshp* 1987
Sales 63.4MM^E *EMP* 165
SIC 5511 Automobiles, new & used; Automobiles, new & used
Pr: Brian P Harris
**Sec:* Mildred R Harris
Genl Mgr: Mike Venable
Sls Mgr: Marcus Magee

D-U-N-S 04-317-8961
HARRIS CONNECT LLC
(*Suby of* WICKS COMMUNICATIONS & MEDIA PARTNERS III LP) ★
1400 Crossways Blvd Ste A, Chesapeake, VA 23320-0207
Tel (757) 965-8000 *Founded/Ownrshp* 1963, 2008
Sales 61.0MM^E *EMP* 900
SIC 7389 7374 Fund raising organizations; Data processing service; Fund raising organizations; Data processing service
CEO: Robert Gluck
CFO: Ruth Brophy
CFO: John Harris
Sr VP: Susan D'Agostino
Sr VP: Susan Dagostino
Sr VP: Kurt Worrell
VP: Beth Dembitz
VP: Nancy Liguori
Snr Sftwr: Charles Hacker
Snr Sftwr: Jackie MA
Snr Sftwr: Liang Zhang

D-U-N-S 00-796-4158 IMP
HARRIS CONSTRUCTION CO INC (CA)
5286 E Home Ave, Fresno, CA 93727-2103
Tel (559) 251-0301 *Founded/Ownrshp* 1914, 1986
Sales 83.3MM^E *EMP* 150

SIC 1542 1541 Hospital construction; Commercial & office building, new construction; Food products manufacturing or packing plant construction; Hospital construction; Commercial & office building, new construction; Food products manufacturing or packing plant construction
CEO: David P Parkes
**Pr:* Timothy Marsh
COO: Robert Willis
**Ch:* Richard F Spencer
**VP:* Doug Reitz
**VP:* Mike Spencer
Exec: Greg Bacchetti
Sfty Mgr: Jeff Gross
Sfty Mgr: Aaron Sherfield
Mktg Mgr: Diane Tjerrild

D-U-N-S 10-866-4368
HARRIS CONTRACTING CO
RM THORNTON
909 Montreal Cir, Saint Paul, MN 55102-4296
Tel (651) 602-6500 *Founded/Ownrshp* 1983
Sales 256.1MM^E *EMP* 1,100
SIC 1711 Plumbing contractors; Mechanical contractor; Plumbing contractors; Mechanical contractor
CEO: Greg Hosch
**Ch Bd:* Robert F Hosch
**CFO:* Tom Depauw
Genl Mgr: Tom Danley
Genl Mgr: Vinnie Figlioli

D-U-N-S 00-329-6977
HARRIS COUNTY APPRAISAL DISTRICT
13013 Nw Fwy, Houston, TX 77040-6305
Tel (713) 812-5800 *Founded/Ownrshp* 1980
Sales 60.2MM *EMP* 527
Accts Belt Harris Pechacek Llip
SIC 7389 Appraisers, except real estate; Appraisers, except real estate
CIO: Al Garcia
Snr Mgr: Guy Griscom

HARRIS COUNTY BOARD EDUCATION
See HARRIS COUNTY SCHOOL DISTRICT

D-U-N-S 18-832-6151
HARRIS COUNTY DEPARTMENT OF EDUCATION PUBLIC FACILITY CORP
6300 Irvington Blvd, Houston, TX 77022-5618
Tel (713) 694-6300 *Founded/Ownrshp* 1889
Sales 36.2MM^E *EMP* 1,278
SIC 8299 Educational services; Educational services
**Pr:* Angela Chesnut
**CFO:* Jesus Amezqua
Bd of Dir: Ann Petty
Ofcr: John Weber
Exec: Carlota Rodriguez
Dir Sec: John Wilson
Prgrm Mgr: Shaheen Farishta
Prgrm Mgr: Martin Loa
Prgrm Mgr: Kay Vacarro
IT Man: Dwayne Brooms
IT Man: Rosa Torres

D-U-N-S 96-876-0772
HARRIS COUNTY EMERGENCY CORPS
2800 Aldine Bender Rd, Houston, TX 77032-3502
Tel (281) 449-3131 *Founded/Ownrshp* 2011
Sales 39.7MM *EMP* 35
SIC 4119 Ambulance service; Ambulance service
Pr: Jeremy Hyde
VP: Janice Metzger
Comm Dir: Martin Douglas
Dir IT: Michael Newman
VP Opers: Heath White
Mktg Dir: Abbey Lee
Mktg Mgr: Misty Worrell

D-U-N-S 17-407-9756
HARRIS COUNTY FLOOD CONTROL DISTRICT
9900 Northwest Fwy, Houston, TX 77092-8601
Tel (713) 684-4000 *Founded/Ownrshp* 1937
Sales NA *EMP* 331
SIC 9512 Land conservation agencies; Land conservation agencies
Ofcr: Richard McCullough
Comm Dir: Fred Garcia
IT Man: Anthony Bacarisse
IT Man: Curtis Lampley
Software D: Haiyan Kong
Opers Mgr: Joe Medina
Prd Mgr: Natalia Reynolds
Snr Mgr: Mark McGarity
Snr Mgr: Denise Wade

D-U-N-S 10-001-3846
HARRIS COUNTY SCHOOL DISTRICT
HARRIS COUNTY BOARD EDUCATION
132 Barnes Mill Rd, Hamilton, GA 31811-5418
Tel (706) 628-4206 *Founded/Ownrshp* 1836
Sales 48.3MM^E *EMP* 562
SIC 8211 Public elementary & secondary schools; Public elementary & secondary schools
Ch Bd: Karen Hopkins
Bd of Dir: Will Cliatt
Bd of Dir: Steve Goodnoe
Bd of Dir: Charles Ragsdale

D-U-N-S 07-966-6230
HARRIS DENISE ANN TRUST
DENISE ANN HARRIS ESTATE
301 W Bay St Ste 14117, Jacksonville, FL 32202-5184
Tel (888) 504-0994 *Founded/Ownrshp* 2014
Sales 150.0MM *EMP* 1
SIC 6733 Private estate, personal investment & vacation fund trusts
Trst: Denise Cross

D-U-N-S 00-949-6027
HARRIS ELECTRIC INC
4020 23rd Ave W, Seattle, WA 98199-1274
Tel (206) 282-8080 *Founded/Ownrshp* 1959
Sales 22.0MM^E *EMP* 75
SIC 1731 General electrical contractor; Communications specialization; General electrical contractor; Communications specialization
Pr: John Jackson
**Pr:* Richard Sundholm
VP: David Gleaves
**VP:* William Morgan
Genl Mgr: Chris Bretthauer
Genl Mgr: Todd King
Genl Mgr: Gary Taylor
Dir IT: Robert Bright

D-U-N-S 00-177-0262
HARRIS ENVIRONMENTAL SYSTEMS INC (MA)
11 Connector Rd, Andover, MA 01810-5926
Tel (978) 470-8600 *Founded/Ownrshp* 1940
Sales 27.5MM^E *EMP* 90
SIC 3585 Heating & air conditioning combination units; Heating & air conditioning combination units
Pr: Alexander Murray
**CFO:* Charles A Rohrbach
**Treas:* Mary Lawnicki
**VP:* Arthur P Champagne
**VP:* Alexander J Murray
Genl Mgr: Justine Becotte
CIO: Philip Hunt
Opers Mgr: Yury Langer

D-U-N-S 05-322-7708
HARRIS FARMS INC
HARRIS RANCH BEEF CO
29475 Fresno Coalinga Rd, Coalinga, CA 93210-9699
Tel (559) 884-2435 *Founded/Ownrshp* 1977
Sales 5.6MM^E *EMP* 1,300
SIC 0191 0211 2011 7011 5812 5541

D-U-N-S 04-433-8429 IMP/EXP
HARRIS FREEMAN & CO INC
HARRIS TEA COMPANY
3110 E Miraloma Ave, Anaheim, CA 92806-1906
Tel (714) 765-1190 *Founded/Ownrshp* 1981
Sales 284.3MM^E *EMP* 560
SIC 5149 2099 Coffee & tea; Spices, including grinding; Coffee & tea; Spices, including grinding
CFO: Anil J Shah
**Pr:* Kevin Shah
**Treas:* Meena Shah
VP: Ray Borooah
VP: Sonal Shah
QA Dir: Matthew Moreno
Plnt Mgr: Sunil Vayes
Plnt Mgr: Sunil Vyas

HARRIS, GENE PROPANE
See GENE HARRIS PETROLEUM INC

D-U-N-S 07-926-6433
HARRIS GROUP INC
300 Elliott Ave W Ste 500, Seattle, WA 98119-4114
Tel (206) 494-9400 *Founded/Ownrshp* 1975
Sales 81.9MM^E *EMP* 370
SIC 8711 Engineering services; Engineering services
CEO: John Marrow
Pr: James Gabriel
CFO: Ron Rodli
Sr VP: John Logsdon
Sr VP: Ed Portaro
VP: Doug Dugeon
VP: Juergen Miller
VP: Ernie Moffet
VP: Cary Redmond
Mng Dir: Gennady Berestetsky

D-U-N-S 08-697-6214 IMP
HARRIS HEALTH SYSTEM
SMITH CLINIC
2525 Holly Hall St, Houston, TX 77054-4124
Tel (713) 566-6400 *Founded/Ownrshp* 1965
Sales 324.9MM^E *EMP* 5,532
SIC 8062 8011 Hospital, affiliated with AMA residency; Clinic, operated by physicians; Hospital, affiliated with AMA residency; Clinic, operated by physicians
Pr: John Guest
Dir Vol: Elizabeth Tise
Ch Bd: J Evans Attwell
CFO: Liz Alhand
CFO: Clifford Bottom
Ch: Stephen H Doncarlos
Ofcr: Vince Temples
Ex VP: Michael Norby
Sr VP: Alicia Reyes
VP: King Hillier
VP: Victoria Nikitin
VP: Christopher Okezie
Dir Lab: Nabaska Richardson
Dir Rad: Cleveland Black
Dir Rx: Shahana Quadri
Board of Directors: Elvin Franklin Jr, Danny F Jackson, Jim Lemond, Mary C Spinks, E Dale Wortham

D-U-N-S 78-900-9719
HARRIS HILL NURSING FACILITY
2699 Wehrle Dr, Williamsville, NY 14221-7332
Tel (716) 632-3700 *Founded/Ownrshp* 1992
Sales 20.3MM *EMP* 200
SIC 8051 Skilled nursing care facilities; Skilled nursing care facilities
Pt: Francis J McGuire
Pt: Donald J Smith
Nrsg Dir: Sherry Trinkwalder

HARRIS INTERACTIVE
See NIELSEN CONSUMER INSIGHTS INC

HARRIS INVESTMENT MANAGEMENT,
See BMO ASSET MANAGEMENT CORP

HARRIS ISUZU
See HARRIS-FORD INC

D-U-N-S 60-293-8771
■ **HARRIS IT SERVICES CORP**
(*Suby of* HARRIS CORPORATION)
2235 Monroe St, Herndon, VA 20171-2824
Tel (703) 673-1400 *Founded/Ownrshp* 2008
Sales 215.9MM^E *EMP* 3,000
SIC 8711 3663 3674 Engineering services; Radio & TV communications equipment; Semiconductors & related devices; Engineering services; Radio & TV communications equipment; Semiconductors & related devices
Pr: Wayne Lucernoni
**Treas:* Charles J Greene
VP: Tony Azar
**VP:* John L Draheim
**VP:* Scott T Mikuen
**VP:* Lewis A Schwartz

D-U-N-S 94-866-9783
HARRIS JOINT VENTURE
MCDONALD'S
115 N Jackson St, Albany, GA 31701-2516
Tel (229) 431-2090 *Founded/Ownrshp* 2001
Sales 12.0MM *EMP* 400
SIC 5812 Fast-food restaurant, chain; Fast-food restaurant, chain
Pt: Michael Harris

D-U-N-S 94-330-2653
HARRIS MACKESSY & BRENNAN INC
HMB INFORMATION SYS DEVELOPERS
570 Polaris Pkwy Ste 125, Westerville, OH 43082-7924
Tel (614) 794-0294 *Founded/Ownrshp* 1994
Sales 33.6MM^E *EMP* 150
SIC 8742 3577 Management consulting services; Decoders, computer peripheral equipment; Management consulting services; Decoders, computer peripheral equipment
Prin: Thomas Harris
**Pr:* Tom Harris
**VP:* Mark Buchy
Snr Ntwrk: Jarrod Jenkins
IT Man: Dan Whetstone
Software D: James Caple
Software D: Andrew Leininger
Netwrk Eng: Joshua Irish

D-U-N-S 01-114-4073 IMP
HARRIS MATERIAL EXCHANGE INC
590 W 500 S, Berne, IN 46711-9707
Tel (260) 589-8965 *Founded/Ownrshp* 1995
Sales 26.1MM^E *EMP* 55
SIC 5093 Plastics scrap
Pr: Doug Harris
**Sec:* Connie Sprunger
Sr Cor Off: Douglas Harris
**VP:* Dan Frank

HARRIS MEDICAL LABORATORY
See TEXAS HEALTH HARRIS METHODIST HOSPITAL FORT WORTH

D-U-N-S 14-480-1425
HARRIS MYCFO INC
2200 Geng Rd Ste 100, Palo Alto, CA 94303-3358
Tel (650) 210-5000 *Founded/Ownrshp* 2003
Sales 20.0MM^E *EMP* 130
SIC 8742 Financial consultant
Pr: Joe Calabrese
Pr: John Benevides
Pr: Craig Rawlins
Ex Dir: Harvey Armstrong
Dir IT: Radhika RAO

D-U-N-S 96-248-9899
HARRIS PREFERRED CAPITAL CORP
111 W Monroe St Fl 20, Chicago, IL 60603-4020
Tel (312) 461-2220 *Founded/Ownrshp* 2010
Sales 21.1MM *EMP* 2
Accts Kpmg Llp Chicago Illinois
SIC 6799 Investors; Investors
Prin: Pamela Piarowski

HARRIS PRODUCTS GROUP, THE
See J W HARRIS CO INC

D-U-N-S 11-946-9927 IMP
■ **HARRIS PRODUCTS GROUP**
HARRIS CALORIFIC
(*Suby of* LINCOLN ELECTRIC CO) ★
2345 Murphy Blvd, Gainesville, GA 30504-6001
Tel (770) 536-8801 *Founded/Ownrshp* 2006
Sales 31.5MM^E *EMP* 150
SIC 3548 Welding & cutting apparatus & accessories; Welding & cutting apparatus & accessories
Pr: David J Nangle
**CFO:* Vincent Petrella
VP: Cathey Sexton
Dir IT: Julia Kreisher
Sales Exec: Ann Elliott
Mktg Dir: Ira Bennett
Sls Mgr: Jeff Szymik

D-U-N-S 08-573-5454 IMP/EXP
HARRIS PUBLICATIONS INC
1115 Broadway Fl 8, New York, NY 10010-3455
Tel (212) 807-7100 *Founded/Ownrshp* 1977
Sales 45.5MM^E *EMP* 125
SIC 2721 Magazines: publishing only, not printed on site; Magazines: publishing only, not printed on site
Pr: Stanley Harris
**CFO:* Warren Sherman
VP: Eileen Cassidy
Exec: Elizabeth Lurie
Exec: Bosaz Nino
Exec: Dave Schwartz
Web Dev: Carlos Bonilla
Mktg Mgr: Ricardo Gonzalez
Art Dir: James Allocca
Art Dir: Tracy Burg
Art Dir: Socrates Gomez

HARRIS RANCH BEEF CO
See HARRIS FARMS INC

D-U-N-S 84-707-3202 IMP
■ **HARRIS REBAR NORTHERN CALIFORNIA INC**
(*Suby of* HARRIS STEEL ULC)
355 S Vasco Rd, Livermore, CA 94550-5300
Tel (925) 373-0733 *Founded/Ownrshp* 1985
Sales 47.3MM^E *EMP* 250
SIC 3449 Bars, concrete reinforcing: fabricated steel; Bars, concrete reinforcing: fabricated steel
Pr: Tyler Keith
**CFO:* Connie Caisse
**VP:* Ed Mize
**VP:* Lyle Sieg
Exec: Thomas Coler
Rgnl Mgr: Jeff Albert
Area Supr: Manfred Gruening
Genl Mgr: Bill Olmo
Off Admin: Kris Glassner
Off Admin: Jodi Kramer
Software D: Treva Thrush

D-U-N-S 36-115-6370
HARRIS REBAR NUFAB LLC
1342 S Grandstaff Dr, Auburn, IN 46706-2661
Tel (260) 925-5440 *Founded/Ownrshp* 2004
Sales 61.1MM^E *EMP* 177^E
SIC 3441 Fabricated structural metal
**Treas:* Dave Worthington

D-U-N-S 62-489-0984 IMP/EXP
HARRIS REBAR SOUTH PACIFIC INC
91-178 Kalaeloa Blvd B, Kapolei, HI 96707-1845
Tel (808) 682-4766 *Founded/Ownrshp* 1990
Sales 20.9MM^E *EMP* 150
SIC 1791 Structural steel erection; Structural steel erection
CEO: Les Sherrill
CFO: Alan Kunihisa
Brnch Mgr: Doug Ewart

D-U-N-S 08-611-7223
HARRIS RESEARCH INC
CHEM-DRY
(*Suby of* BAIRD CAPITAL PARTNERS MANAGEMENT CO III LLC) ★
1530 N 1000 W, Logan, UT 84321-1966
Tel (435) 755-7038 *Founded/Ownrshp* 2011
Sales 23.0MM^E *EMP* 70
SIC 6794 5087 2842 2841 Franchises, selling or licensing; Carpet & rug cleaning equipment & supplies, commercial; Specialty cleaning, polishes & sanitation goods; Soap & other detergents
Pr: Dan Tarantin
**Pr:* Craig L Donaldson
**CFO:* Grant Mortensen
Exec: Dermot Morris
Sales Exec: Erickson Charlie
Sales Exec: Charlie Erickson

HARRIS RIVER BEND FARMS
See BOB HARRIS OIL CO

HARRIS, ROBERT T MD
See RALEIGH MEDICAL GROUP PA

D-U-N-S 06-783-8060
■ **HARRIS SANITATION INC** (FL)
(*Suby of* WASTE MANAGEMENT INC OF FLORIDA) ★
7382 Talona Dr, Melbourne, FL 32904-1695
Tel (321) 723-4455 *Founded/Ownrshp* 1968, 1971
Sales 24.7MM^E *EMP* 191
SIC 4953 4212 Refuse systems; Rubbish collection & disposal; Local trucking, without storage; Refuse systems; Rubbish collection & disposal; Local trucking, without storage
Pr: James E O'Connor
**Treas:* Steve Ferguson
**VP:* Harold L Jorski

D-U-N-S 13-197-2051
HARRIS SOUP CO
HARRY'S FRESH FOODS
(*Suby of* JGC FOOD CO LLC) ★
17711 Ne Riverside Pkwy, Portland, OR 97230-7370
Tel (503) 445-9234 *Founded/Ownrshp* 2013
Sales 92.0MM^E *EMP* 200
SIC 2092 2099 Fresh or frozen fish or seafood chowders, soups & stews; Food preparations; Fresh or frozen fish or seafood chowders, soups & stews; Food preparations
CEO: Stan McCammon
**Pr:* Anthony Muscato
**CFO:* Claudia Pieropan
**VP:* Brian Meiners
Admn Mgr: Megan Lammers
Opers Mgr: Dick Hughes
Sls&Mrk Ex: Maureen Hotchkiss
**VP Sls:* Debra Onken
Manager: Ed Montoya
Manager: Laura Smith
Sls Mgr: Ed Brand

D-U-N-S 00-542-0906
HARRIS STEEL CO (IL)
1223 S 55th Ct, Cicero, IL 60804-1297
Tel (708) 656-5500 *Founded/Ownrshp* 1950
Sales 28.2MM^E *EMP* 70
SIC 5051 3316 3312 Metals service centers & offices; Cold finishing of steel shapes; Blast furnaces & steel mills; Metals service centers & offices; Cold finishing of steel shapes; Blast furnaces & steel mills
Ch: Jack Harris Jr
**Pr:* Thomas Eliasek
CFO: Bernie McCudden
Exec: Brian Eliasek
IT Man: Bill Gurin
Plnt Mgr: Scott Decker
Sls Mgr: Bill Gerlesits
Sls Mgr: Philip Wendell

HARRIS TEA COMPANY
See HARRIS FREEMAN & CO INC

D-U-N-S 96-889-1499
■ **HARRIS TECHNICAL SERVICES CORP**
(*Suby of* HARRIS CORPORATION)
21000 Atl Blvd Ste 300, Dulles, VA 20166
Tel (703) 610-4200 *Founded/Ownrshp* 1987
Sales 60.1MM^E *EMP* 2,000
SIC 7371 7379 8711 3577 Computer software development; Computer related consulting services; Engineering services; Computer peripheral equipment; Computer software development; Computer related consulting services; Engineering services; Computer peripheral equipment
VP: Cavallucci E S
**Treas:* Greene C J
VP: David Cain
**VP:* McArthur Gary
Prgrm Mgr: Matthew Braud
Prgrm Mgr: Joe Marcinek
Off Mgr: Anneke Chy
Dir IT: Dave Jensen
IT Man: Glenn Gram
Mktg Mgr: Sandy Moore
Mktg Mgr: Lisa Sullivan

D-U-N-S 04-846-3103 IMP
■ HARRIS TEETER LLC
(*Suby of* HARRIS TEETER SUPERMARKETS INC) ★
701 Crestdale Rd, Matthews, NC 28105-1744
Tel (704) 844-3100 *Founded/Ownrshp* 2013
Sales 3.5MMME *EMP* 18,000
SIC 5411 Supermarkets, chain; Supermarkets, chain
Pr: Fred J Morganthall II
Treas: Douglas Stephenson
Sr VP: Daniel J Bruni
Sr VP: Karen Stout
**VP:* Rod Antolock
VP: George R Faulk Jr
VP: Mark G Hilton
VP: James M Hunter
VP: John G Hutchens Jr
VP: Luke Laperriere
VP: Jerry E Leclair
VP: Rory Mecham
VP: Dwight Moore
VP: Scott K Nations
VP: Theresa D Priore
VP: Chris Sprull
VP: Scott Wippel
Dir Risk M: Bill Richardson

D-U-N-S 04-727-9351 IMP/EXP
■ HARRIS TEETER SUPERMARKETS INC
(*Suby of* KROGER CO) ★
701 Crestdale Rd, Matthews, NC 28105-1744
Tel (704) 844-3100 *Founded/Ownrshp* 2014
Sales 3.6MMME *EMP* 25,800
SIC 5411 Supermarkets, chain; Supermarkets, chain
CEO: W Rodney McMullen
**Pr:* Rod Antolock
Pr: John Rohr
Treas: Doug Stephenson
Ex VP: Dawn Schomette
Sr VP: Jerry Clontz
Sr VP: Jeff Sherman
Sr VP: Craig Stover
VP: Charles Corbeil
VP: Bradley Graham
VP: John Hutchens
Exec: Vernan Moore
Dir Rx: Kevin Pultorak

D-U-N-S 09-914-8363 IMP
HARRIS THERMAL TRANSFER PRODUCTS INC
615 S Springbrook Rd, Newberg, OR 97132-7077
Tel (503) 538-1260 *Founded/Ownrshp* 1992
Sales 27.8MME *EMP* 86
SIC 3443 Heat exchangers, condensers & components
Pr: Arnold Fuchs
**VP:* Leonard Thompson
Exec: Wendy Bowman
IT Man: Don Mitchel
Opers Mgr: Tom Fields

D-U-N-S 05-016-5919 IMP
HARRIS TIRE AND RUBBER CO INC
HARRIS TIRE COMPANY
1100 S Brundidge St, Troy, AL 36081-3123
Tel (334) 670-6226 *Founded/Ownrshp* 1982
Sales 45.9MME *EMP* 77
SIC 5014 Automobile tires & tubes; Automobile tires & tubes
CFO: Jason Berry
**Genl Mgr:* Ace B Coley Jr

HARRIS TIRE COMPANY
See HARRIS TIRE AND RUBBER CO INC

D-U-N-S 80-586-6878
HARRIS TRANSPORTATION CO LLC
HTC
3077 Nw Saint Helens Rd, Portland, OR 97210-2043
Tel (503) 552-5800 *Founded/Ownrshp* 1928
Sales 24.8MME *EMP* 190
SIC 4212 4213 Liquid transfer services; Liquid petroleum transport, non-local; Liquid transfer services; Liquid petroleum transport, non-local
CFO: Jan Frost
Sec: Alice Evans
Top Exec: Kathi Gibson
VP: Cornel Notenboom
Brnch Mgr: Bruce Callan
CTO: Jim Aronhalt

D-U-N-S 61-757-5436 IMP
HARRIS WASTE MANAGEMENT GROUP INC
(*Suby of* AVIS INDUSTRIAL CORP) ★
315 W 12th Ave, Cordele, GA 31015-2333
Tel (229) 273-2500 *Founded/Ownrshp* 2014
Sales 59.3MME *EMP* 225
SIC 3569 Baling machines, for scrap metal, paper or similar material; Baling machines, for scrap metal, paper or similar material
Pr: Ken Galason
Treas: William Harris
VP: Christopher S Bryan
VP: Javier Herrera
VP: Jim Jagou
VP: Mike Lee
VP: Douglas Sebastian
Sales Exec: Eric Farmer
S&M/VP: Bob Pfeffer
Manager: Scott Holder
Manager: Ken Ventullo

D-U-N-S 08-586-1151
HARRIS WEBBER LTD
34121 N Us Highway 45 # 208, Grayslake, IL 60030-1774
Tel (847) 996-0600 *Founded/Ownrshp* 1976
Sales 23.3MME *EMP* 154
SIC 6552 6531 Subdividers & developers; Real estate managers
Pr: Kyle Stiverson

D-U-N-S 11-379-3996 IMP
HARRIS WILLIAM & CO INC
WILLIAM HARRIS INVESTORS
191 N Wacker Dr Ste 1500, Chicago, IL 60606-1899
Tel (312) 621-0590 *Founded/Ownrshp* 1966
Sales 116.1MME *EMP* 320
SIC 6799 3317 Investment clubs; Steel pipe & tubes; Investment clubs; Steel pipe & tubes
CEO: Jack R Polsky
**Ch Bd:* Irving B Harris
**COO:* Adam Langsam
Treas: Ann Wolf
Admn Mgr: James Orth
Dir IT: Duane Dibble
Genl Couns: David Novick

D-U-N-S 86-799-2240
■ HARRIS WILLIAMS & CO
(*Suby of* PNC FINANCIAL SERVICES GROUP INC) ★
1001 Haxall Point Fl 9, Richmond, VA 23219-3944
Tel (804) 648-0072 *Founded/Ownrshp* 2005
Sales 60.1MME *EMP* 200
SIC 6211 Investment bankers; Investment bankers
Pr: H Hiter Harris III
Bd of Dir: Jim Reinhart
Ofcr: Andrew Tino
**VP:* David Allebach
VP: Corey Benjamin
VP: John D Beverige
VP: Chris Burnham
VP: Matt Conaty
VP: Joseph Conner
VP: William Kayser
VP: Doug Kinard
VP: Carl Kirkeby
VP: Paul Meyer
VP: Brad Morrison
VP: Cheairs Porter
VP: Luke Semple

D-U-N-S 05-731-4031
HARRIS-FORD INC
HARRIS ISUZU
20006 64th Ave W, Lynnwood, WA 98036-5906
Tel (425) 678-0391 *Founded/Ownrshp* 1956
Sales 46.1MME *EMP* 139
SIC 5511 5012 7532 7515 5521 3714 Automobiles, new & used; Pickups, new & used; Automobiles & other motor vehicles; Top & body repair & paint shops; Passenger car leasing; Used car dealers; Motor vehicle parts & accessories; Automobiles, new & used; Pickups, new & used; Automobiles & other motor vehicles; Top & body repair & paint shops; Passenger car leasing; Used car dealers; Motor vehicle parts & accessories
Pr: Beckey Stupey
**Pr:* James P Pierre
**VP:* Rebecca Bright
**VP:* Michael Shane Pierre
Sls Mgr: Rikk Holguin

D-U-N-S 00-779-8192
HARRIS-MCBURNEY CO
2120 N Us Highway 301, Tampa, FL 33619-2654
Tel (813) 626-7171 *Founded/Ownrshp* 2007
Sales 21.0MME *EMP* 120
SIC 1731 8711 Telephone & telephone equipment installation; Engineering services
CEO: Linda Gilbert
**Pr:* Gerry Gilbert
**CFO:* Terry Moats
Sfty Dirs: Tom Newton

D-U-N-S 03-735-3935
HARRIS-STOWE STATE UNIVERSITY ALUMNI ASSOCIATION INC
3026 Laclede Ave, Saint Louis, MO 63103-2136
Tel (314) 340-3366 *Founded/Ownrshp* 1857
Sales 33.9MME *EMP* 300
SIC 8221 College, except junior; College, except junior
Pr: Henry Givens Jr
**VP:* Constance Gully

D-U-N-S 06-977-4214
HARRISBURG AREA COMMUNITY COLLEGE FOUNDATION
HACC
1 Hacc Dr, Harrisburg, PA 17110-2903
Tel (717) 780-2300 *Founded/Ownrshp* 1964
Sales 7.9MM *EMP* 1,520
Accts Lb Smith Elliott Kearns & Comp
SIC 8222 Community college; Community college
Pr: John Sygielski
Sr VP: Lori Amspacker
CIO: Robert Messner
DP Exec: Raymond Matzelle
Sls&Mrk Ex: Raymond Antonelli
Snr Mgr: Tamara Gillis
Board of Directors: Daniel Jusco, Sue Morris, Jennifer Thompson

D-U-N-S 07-120-4937
HARRISBURG AREA YMCA (PA)
NORTHERN DAUPHIN CNTY BR YMCA
123 Forster St Ste 2, Harrisburg, PA 17102-3409
Tel (717) 232-2068 *Founded/Ownrshp* 1854
Sales 12.4MM *EMP* 600
Accts Sf & Company Harrisburg Penn
SIC 8641 7991 8351 7032 8322 Youth organizations; Physical fitness facilities; Child day care services; Youth camps; Individual & family services; Youth organizations; Physical fitness facilities; Child day care services; Youth camps; Individual & family services
Pr: Richard A Curl
CFO: John Monsted
**Ch:* Robert Lyon
**Treas:* Robert Jones
**Treas:* Beth A Peiffer
**VP:* Mark Caldwell
**VP:* Thomas Kirchhoff
**Prin:* Beth Peiffer
Mktg Dir: Rosie Turner

HARRISBURG AUTHORITY, THE
See CITY OF HARRISBURG

HARRISBURG AUTO AUCTION
See AMERICAS AUTO AUCTION HARRISBURG INC

D-U-N-S 00-893-6114
HARRISBURG DAIRIES INC (PA)
2001 Herr St, Harrisburg, PA 17103-1624
Tel (717) 233-8701 *Founded/Ownrshp* 1946
Sales 28.7MME *EMP* 105
SIC 2026 5149 Milk processing (pasteurizing, homogenizing, bottling); Juices; Mineral or spring water bottling; Milk processing (pasteurizing, homogenizing, bottling); Juices; Mineral or spring water bottling
Ch: Frederick B Dewey Sr
**Pr:* Frederick B Dewey Jr
Off Mgr: Janis Brown
Plnt Mgr: Ross Thoman
Ql Cn Mgr: Rob Madigan
Sls Dir: Jim Okum
Mktg Mgr: Chrissie Dewey

HARRISBURG HAULING
See ADVANCED DISPOSAL SERVICES SHIPPENSBURG LLC

D-U-N-S 61-421-7883
HARRISBURG HOTEL ASSOCIATES LP
HILTON
1 N 2nd St, Harrisburg, PA 17101-1601
Tel (717) 233-6000 *Founded/Ownrshp* 1988
Sales 9.8MM *EMP* 300
SIC 7011 Hotels & motels; Hotels & motels
Pr: William D Kohl
VP: Jeffrey Edelson
Genl Mgr: Laura Goyette
Genl Mgr: Curt Maceachern
IT Man: Robert Shank
Sls Dir: Brenda Keller
Sls Mgr: Kim Deline
Sls Mgr: Tracy Derk
Sls Mgr: Carolyn Workinger

D-U-N-S 01-742-3315
HARRISBURG HOTEL CORP (PA)
11 N 3rd St Ste 100, Harrisburg, PA 17101-1733
Tel (717) 236-3399 *Founded/Ownrshp* 1988
Sales 23.2MM *EMP* 396
Accts Parente Beard Llc Harrisburg
SIC 6531 8741 Real estate agents & managers; Management services; Real estate agents & managers; Management services
Pr: William Kohl
**CFO:* Andy McCliff
**Ch:* Russel C Ford
**Treas:* Jeff Edelson

HARRISBURG INTERNATIONAL ARPRT
See SUSQUEHANNA AREA REGIONAL AIRPORT AUTHORITY

D-U-N-S 07-712-2141
HARRISBURG MEDICAL CENTER INC
100 Dr Warren Tuttle Dr, Harrisburg, IL 62946-2718
Tel (618) 253-7671 *Founded/Ownrshp* 1975
Sales 47.0MM *EMP* 600
Accts Kerber Eck & Braeckel Llp C
SIC 8062 8063 General medical & surgical hospitals; Psychiatric hospitals; General medical & surgical hospitals; Psychiatric hospitals
CEO: Rodney Smith
**CFO:* June Hayes
VP: Danny Kutzner
VP: Danny Lampley
Dir OR: Paul Woolard
Sls Dir: Ludene Treat
Psych: Susan Allen
Pharmcst: Brian Smith

D-U-N-S 01-418-2471
HARRISBURG NEWS CO
CEDAR BOOK & CARD SHOP
980 Briarsdale Rd, Harrisburg, PA 17109-6253
Tel (717) 561-8377 *Founded/Ownrshp* 1975
Sales 119.1MME *EMP* 460
SIC 5192

D-U-N-S 01-058-1601
HARRISBURG SCHOOL DISTRICT INC
1601 State St, Harrisburg, PA 17103-1466
Tel (717) 703-4000 *Founded/Ownrshp* 1843
Sales 82.4MME *EMP* 1,200
SIC 8211 Public elementary & secondary schools; Public elementary & secondary schools
Ofcr: Regis Barwin
**Ofcr:* Audrey Utley
MIS Dir: Robert Hilinski
Dir IT: Craig Glass
IT Man: Jodi Davis
IT Man: Bilal Hasan
IT Man: Kayla Orange
Netwrk Mgr: Greg Pankake
Psych: Katie Neitheimer
Snr Mgr: Maria McGlosson

D-U-N-S 17-511-6748
■ HARRISON & STAR LLC
(*Suby of* OMNICOM GROUP INC) ★
75 Varick St Fl 6, New York, NY 10013-1946
Tel (212) 727-1330 *Founded/Ownrshp* 1993
Sales 34.7MME *EMP* 124E
SIC 7311 Advertising agencies
CEO: Ty Curran
**COO:* Charles Doomany
Sr VP: Stella Daily
Sr VP: Daniel Daley
Sr VP: Larry Fiori
Sr VP: Kirsten Hanton
Sr VP: Kathy Magnuson
Sr VP: Bill Major
Sr VP: Mario Muredda
Sr VP: Michael Norkin
Sr VP: Michael Patterson
Sr VP: Stephanie Schulman
Sr VP: Eva Tolk
VP: Andrea Armusewicz
VP: Joseph Bailey
VP: Michael Banke
VP: Candace Barbato
VP: Ashley Bond
VP: Karin Cook
VP: James Ferber
VP: Maria Fermin

D-U-N-S 04-566-5817
HARRISON CENTRAL SCHOOL DISTRICT
50 Union Ave, Harrison, NY 10528-2008
Tel (914) 835-3300 *Founded/Ownrshp* 1898
Sales 31.8MME *EMP* 500
Accts O Connor Davies Munns & Dobbin
SIC 8211 Public elementary & secondary schools; Public elementary & secondary schools
Treas: Margaret Modugno
Ofcr: Richie Abbate
Ofcr: Dominick Gentile
Prin: Bruce D Downer
Off Admin: Geraldine Barbagallo
Off Admin: David Johnson
Dir IT: Brian Seligman
Info Man: Dan Welsh

D-U-N-S 03-449-4823
HARRISON CO LLC
4801 Viking Dr, Bossier City, LA 71111-7423
Tel (318) 747-0700 *Founded/Ownrshp* 1986
Sales 102.4MME *EMP* 150E
SIC 5194 5145 5141 Cigarettes; Cigars; Chewing tobacco; Candy; Groceries, general line; Cigarettes; Cigars; Chewing tobacco; Candy; Groceries, general line
Ex VP: Don W Bellah Jr
**Prin:* Wayne M Baquet Jr
**Prin:* John D Georges
**Prin:* Wgilbert Stroud Jr

HARRISON COLLEGE
See EDUCATIONAL MANAGEMENT CORP

HARRISON CONSTRUCTION CO.
See APAC-ATLANTIC INC

HARRISON COUNTY
See COUNTY OF HARRISON

HARRISON COUNTY BD SUPERVISORS
See COUNTY OF HARRISON

D-U-N-S 07-945-7526
HARRISON COUNTY COAL CO
46226 National Rd W, Saint Clairsville, OH 43950-8742
Tel (740) 338-3100 *Founded/Ownrshp* 2014
Sales 37.0MME *EMP* 60E
SIC 1241 Coal mining services

D-U-N-S 96-549-4656
HARRISON COUNTY COMMUNITY HOSPITAL DISTRICT
2600 Miller St, Bethany, MO 64424-2701
Tel (660) 425-2211 *Founded/Ownrshp* 1955
Sales 26.5MME *EMP* 235
Accts Wendling Noe Nelson & Johnson
SIC 8062 General medical & surgical hospitals; General medical & surgical hospitals
CEO: Kelly Dpottorff
**CFO:* Lee Ann Miles
Dir OR: Crystal Hicks
Dir Inf Cn: Vicky Still
Dir Sec: Erica Babinski
Off Mgr: Cindy Lee
Snr Mgr: Kim Strain

D-U-N-S 06-974-7293
HARRISON COUNTY HOSPITAL ASSOCIATION
MARSHALL REGIONAL MEDICAL CTR
811 S Washington Ave, Marshall, TX 75670-5336
Tel (903) 927-6000 *Founded/Ownrshp* 1911
Sales 62.7MM *EMP* 600
SIC 8062 General medical & surgical hospitals; General medical & surgical hospitals
Pr: Russell J Collier
**COO:* James F Hodges
Dir Lab: Roy Terhune
Off Mgr: Mary B Reeves
Dir Health: Linda Hickering

D-U-N-S 96-938-3921
HARRISON COUNTY HOSPITAL ASSOCIATION GOOD SHEPHERD MEDICAL CENTER-MARSHALL
811 S Washington Ave, Marshall, TX 75670-5336
Tel (903) 927-6703 *Founded/Ownrshp* 2011
Sales 111.6MM *EMP* 10E
Accts Bkd Llp Houston Tx
SIC 8062 General medical & surgical hospitals; General medical & surgical hospitals
Prin: Walter Grimes

D-U-N-S 00-679-9092
HARRISON COUNTY RURAL ELECTRIC MEMBERSHIP CORP
HARRISON REMC
1165 Old Forest Rd Nw, Corydon, IN 47112-1910
Tel (812) 738-4115 *Founded/Ownrshp* 1939
Sales 57.9MM *EMP* 51
Accts Monroe Shine & Co Inc Cpa S
SIC 4911 Distribution, electric power; Distribution, electric power
Pr: Maynard Lambertus
**CEO:* Paul D Beckort
CFO: Virginia Taylor
**Sec:* C Daniel Boone
Off Mgr: Steve Moore
Sfty Mgr: John Wernert
Opers Mgr: Randy Matthews

D-U-N-S 10-065-3518
HARRISON COUNTY SCHOOL DISTRICT
11072 Highway 49, Gulfport, MS 39503-4110
Tel (228) 539-5956 *Founded/Ownrshp* 1958
Sales 119.3MME *EMP* 1,800
Accts Wright Ward Hatten & Guel P
SIC 8211 Public elementary & secondary schools; Public elementary & secondary schools
Dir IT: Amy Dupree
Schl Brd P: David Latner

D-U-N-S 09-951-4275
HARRISON COUNTY SCHOOL DISTRICT
408 E B Saunders Way, Clarksburg, WV 26301-3712
Tel (304) 326-7300 *Founded/Ownrshp* 1932
Sales 64.0MME *EMP* 1,400

SIC 8211 9111 Public elementary & secondary schools; County supervisors' & executives' offices; Public elementary & secondary schools; County supervisors' & executives' offices
*Treas: Sharon Haddix
IT Man: Bobbye Geopi
IT Man: Marianne Martin
Netwrk Eng: Tom Fishbaugh

D-U-N-S 06-093-0468
HARRISON COUNTY SCHOOLS
308 Webster Ave, Cynthiana, KY 41031-1647
Tel (859) 234-7110 Founded/Ownrshp 1900
Sales 18.5MM^E EMP 450
SIC 8211 Public combined elementary & secondary school; Public combined elementary & secondary school
Teacher Pr: Tammy Klaphke

D-U-N-S 11-741-6263
HARRISON COUNTY UTILITY AUTHORITY
10271 Express Dr, Gulfport, MS 39503-4676
Tel (228) 868-8752 Founded/Ownrshp 1982
Sales 25.0MM EMP 8
SIC 4952 Sewerage systems; Sewerage systems

HARRISON, DWIGHT VOLKSWAGEN
See STONE MOUNTAIN VOLKSWAGON INC

D-U-N-S 12-858-7685
HARRISON ELECTRICAL WORKERS TRUSTS
1220 Sw Morrison St # 300, Portland, OR 97205-2235
Tel (503) 224-0048 Founded/Ownrshp 1954
Sales 94.4MM EMP 2
SIC 6733 Trusts; Trusts
Ch: Tim Gauthier

D-U-N-S 05-990-8702
HARRISON FRENCH & ASSOCIATES LTD
HFA
1705 S Walton Blvd Ste 3, Bentonville, AR 72712-7113
Tel (479) 273-7780 Founded/Ownrshp 1990
Sales 20.5MM^E EMP 111
SIC 8712 8711 Architectural engineering; Professional engineer; Architectural engineering; Professional engineer
CEO: Harrison French
*Pr: Larry Lott
*CFO: Chris Horton
Prgrm Mgr: Don Cronk
Prgrm Mgr: Branson Hall
Prgrm Mgr: Bobby Morrison
Prgrm Mgr: Tim Perrien
Prgrm Mgr: Chet Savage
Prgrm Mgr: Ernest Yonkers
Off Admin: Jennifer Brown
IT Man: Brian Owens

D-U-N-S 07-880-1210
HARRISON GLOBAL LLC
224 Calvary St, Waltham, MA 02453-8366
Tel (781) 863-2626 Founded/Ownrshp 2012
Sales 71.4MM^E EMP 1,500
SIC 4789 Cargo loading & unloading services
Genl Mgr: Brad Jackson

D-U-N-S 00-746-6626 IMP
HARRISON GYPSUM LLC (OK)
ALLIED CUSTOM GYPSUM
1550 Double C Dr, Norman, OK 73069-8288
Tel (405) 366-9500 Founded/Ownrshp 1978
Sales 237.6MM^E EMP 150
SIC 1499 4213 Gypsum mining; Trucking, except local; Gypsum mining; Trucking, except local
CEO: C W Russ Harrison Jr
CFO: E R Shily
Sr VP: Dan Northewitt
*VP: Nathan Shirley
Dir IT: Michael White
Tech Mgr: Jacob De Souza
VP Opers: Kris Kinder
Opers Mgr: Keela Hamilton
VP Sls: Jim Hill
Sls Mgr: Gina Russell

HARRISON HEALTH OF CHRISTIANA
See SALISBURY RETIREMENT CENTER INC

D-U-N-S 12-072-5601
HARRISON HILLS CITY SCH DIST
730 Peppard Ave, Cadiz, OH 43907-1067
Tel (740) 942-7800 Founded/Ownrshp 1971
Sales 18.1MM^E EMP 412^E
SIC 8211 Public elementary & secondary schools; School board; Public elementary & secondary schools; School board
Prin: Jim Dresler
Pr: Tim Kenny
*CEO: Dana Snider
*Treas: Roxane Harding
Board of Directors: Deborah Kenny Judy Crawsha

D-U-N-S 61-903-2886
HARRISON HOLDINGS CORP
300 Strode Ave, Coatesville, PA 19320-2874
Tel (610) 383-4225 Founded/Ownrshp 2004
Sales 32.3MM^E EMP 200^E
SIC 8361 Home for the aged; Home for the aged
Pr: Chris Richetti

D-U-N-S 09-542-2895
HARRISON INN-BOARDWALK INC
QUALITY INN
106 N Baltimore Ave, Ocean City, MD 21842-4019
Tel (410) 289-4444 Founded/Ownrshp 1953
Sales 6.0MM^E EMP 300
SIC 7011 5812 5331 Hotels & motels; American restaurant; Variety stores; Hotels & motels; American restaurant; Variety stores
Pt: John H Harrison

HARRISON MARINE CENTER
See MARINE SPORTS LLC

HARRISON MEDICAL CENTER
See HARRISON MEMORIAL HOSPITAL INC

D-U-N-S 06-714-5052
HARRISON MEDICAL CENTER
GENERAL MEDICAL SURGICAL
2520 Cherry Ave, Bremerton, WA 98310-4229
Tel (360) 744-6510 Founded/Ownrshp 1943
Sales 351.1MM EMP 2,400^E
SIC 8062 General medical & surgical hospitals; General medical & surgical hospitals
Pr: Scott Bosch
Chf Rad: Ruben Krishnananthan
Bd of Dir: Ruth Hansten
Chf Mktg O: Elizabeth Hyde
*Ex VP: Adar Palis
*Sr VP: Patty Cochrell
*Sr VP: Forrest G Ehlinger
*Sr VP: Mariel S Kagan
Dir OR: Donna Sulier
Dir Inf Cn: Cathy M Donald
Dir Inf Cn: Cathy McDonald
Dir Rx: Charles Ho
Dir Rx: Larry Pelham

D-U-N-S 07-184-4583
HARRISON MEMORIAL HOSPITAL INC
HARRISON MEDICAL CENTER
2520 Cherry Ave, Bremerton, WA 98310-4229
Tel (360) 377-3911 Founded/Ownrshp 1943
Sales NA EMP 1,725
SIC 8062 Hospital, AMA approved residency

D-U-N-S 08-159-5035
HARRISON MEMORIAL HOSPITAL INC (KY)
1210 Ky Highway 36 E # 1, Cynthiana, KY 41031-7498
Tel (859) 234-2300 Founded/Ownrshp 1907, 1920
Sales 34.0MM EMP 300
Accts Dean Dorton Allen Ford Pllc L
SIC 8062 General medical & surgical hospitals; General medical & surgical hospitals
CEO: Sheila Currans
*Ch Bd: Brian Mulberry
*CFO: David Mellett
*CFO: Jim Spears
Ofcr: Patty Insko
Dir Pat Ca: Wendy Reeder
Dir Rad: Pam Bowles
Nurse Mgr: Alan Teegarden
CIO: Martha Sullivan
Mktg Dir: Mollie Smith
HC Dir: Diana Monroe

D-U-N-S 00-329-2281 EXP
HARRISON POULTRY INC (GA)
HARRISON PROPANE GAS CO
107 Star St W, Bethlehem, GA 30620-2119
Tel (770) 867-9105 Founded/Ownrshp 1958, 1959
Sales 164.6MM^E EMP 835
SIC 0254 2015 5984 2013 2011 Chicken hatchery; Poultry slaughtering & processing; Liquefied petroleum gas, delivered to customers' premises; Sausages & other prepared meats; Meat packing plants; Chicken hatchery; Poultry slaughtering & processing; Liquefied petroleum gas, delivered to customers' premises; Sausages & other prepared meats; Meat packing plants
CEO: Sam Sloan
*Pr: Michael Welch
*CFO: Greg Finch
*CFO: Jeff Megahee
CFO: Kurt Pruett
VP Opers: David Bleth
Plnt Mgr: Andy Harris
Plnt Mgr: Nick Strange
Plnt Mgr: Bobby Wiley
Plnt Mgr: Devin Wood
Mktg Mgr: Larry Guest

HARRISON PROPANE GAS CO
See HARRISON POULTRY INC

HARRISON REMC
See HARRISON COUNTY RURAL ELECTRIC MEMBERSHIP CORP

D-U-N-S 07-920-5367
HARRISON SCHOOL DISTRICT NO 1
110 S Cherry St, Harrison, AR 72601-5024
Tel (870) 741-7600 Founded/Ownrshp 2013
Sales 5.0MM^E EMP 362^E
SIC 8299 Schools & educational service

D-U-N-S 09-191-1826
HARRISON SCHOOL DISTRICT TWO
1060 Harrison Rd, Colorado Springs, CO 80905-3586
Tel (719) 579-2000 Founded/Ownrshp 1874
Sales 90.5MM EMP 1,700^E
Accts Hoelting & Company Inc Color
SIC 8211 Public elementary school; Public junior high school; Public senior high school; Public elementary school; Public junior high school; Public senior high school
Dir IT: Stacy Aldridge
IT Man: Alan Smith
Schl Brd P: Victor Torres
Psych: Sirena Carnell

D-U-N-S 00-517-3471 IMP
HARRISON STEEL CASTINGS CO
900 S Mound St, Attica, IN 47918-1632
Tel (765) 762-2481 Founded/Ownrshp 1906
Sales 149.9MM^E EMP 850
SIC 3325 Steel foundries; Alloy steel castings, except investment; Steel foundries; Alloy steel castings, except investment
Pr: Wade C Harrison II
*Ch Bd: Edward G Curtis
*Treas: Robert S Harrison
*VP: Geoffrey H Curtis
*VP: Trevor H Curtis
*VP: Wade C Harrison III
CIO: Pam Lich
Netwrk Mgr: Shane Rogers
Sfty Dirs: James Murphy

D-U-N-S 61-648-0997
HARRISON STREET REAL ESTATE CAPITAL LLC
71 S Wacker Dr Ste 3575, Chicago, IL 60606-4610
Tel (312) 920-0500 Founded/Ownrshp 2005
Sales 21.5MM^E EMP 52^E
SIC 6531 Real estate agents & managers
Sr VP: Andrew Denekas
Sr VP: Mike Gershowitz
Sr VP: Joey Lansing
Sr VP: James McNamara
Sr VP: Ben Mohns
Sr VP: Tonia Nelson
Sr VP: Brian Thompson
Sr VP: Chris Zollo
VP: Jill Brosig
VP: Tom Erath
VP: Josh Miller

D-U-N-S 09-363-8729
HARRISON TRUCK CENTERS INC
101 Plaza Dr, Elk Run Heights, IA 50707-2086
Tel (319) 234-4453 Founded/Ownrshp 1997
Sales 91.3MM EMP 160
SIC 5511 7538 Trucks, tractors & trailers: new & used; General truck repair; Trucks, tractors & trailers: new & used; General truck repair
Pr: Brian Harrison
Genl Mgr: Mike Wester

D-U-N-S 00-721-6211
HARRISON-ORR AIR CONDITIONING LLC (OK)
4100 N Walnut Ave, Oklahoma City, OK 73105-3751
Tel (405) 528-3333 Founded/Ownrshp 1960
Sales 31.0MM EMP 125^E
Accts Engelbach Roberts & Co Pllc
SIC 1711 Heating systems repair & maintenance; Heating & air conditioning contractors; Warm air heating & air conditioning contractor; Heating systems repair & maintenance; Heating & air conditioning contractors; Warm air heating & air conditioning contractor
VP: Gale Harms
VP: Timothy McCoy
VP: John Montin
CIO: Brian Youngblood

D-U-N-S 10-007-9706
HARRISONBURG CITY PUBLIC SCHOOLS
1 Court Sq Ste 2, Harrisonburg, VA 22802-3725
Tel (540) 434-9916 Founded/Ownrshp 1849
Sales 29.4MM^E EMP 672
SIC 8211 Public elementary & secondary schools; School board; Public elementary & secondary schools; School board
MIS Dir: Mike Cox
IT Man: Peggy McIntyre

HARRISONBURG HONDA
See F I N INC

HARRISONVILLE PUBLIC SCHOOLS
See HARRISONVILLE SCHOOLS

D-U-N-S 08-212-8083
HARRISONVILLE SCHOOLS
HARRISONVILLE PUBLIC SCHOOLS
503 S Lexington St, Harrisonville, MO 64701-2415
Tel (816) 380-2727 Founded/Ownrshp 1900
Sales 17.8MM^E EMP 300
SIC 8211 Public elementary & secondary schools; Public elementary & secondary schools
*Prin: Craig Eaton
IT Man: Susan Brooker
Instr Medi: Jeannie Frazier

D-U-N-S 00-693-6256
HARRISONVILLE TELEPHONE CO
(Suby of HTC HOLDING CO) ★
213 S Main St, Waterloo, IL 62298-1325
Tel (618) 939-6112 Founded/Ownrshp 1896
Sales 23.6MM^E EMP 92
SIC 4813 Telephone communication, except radio; Telephone communication, except radio
Pr: H R Gentsch
Pr: Maurice Koesterer
*Ex VP: Karen G Bergman
*VP: Craig A Hern
*VP: Lee H Whitcher
Advt Mgr: Val Chism

D-U-N-S 00-323-2881 EXP
HARRISS & COVINGTON HOSIERY MILLS INC
1250 Hickory Chapel Rd, High Point, NC 27260-7187
Tel (336) 882-6811 Founded/Ownrshp 1920
Sales 55.9MM^E EMP 240
SIC 2252 Socks; Socks
Pr: Edward H Covington
*VP: Danny McNair

D-U-N-S 07-120-6999
HARRISTOWN DEVELOPMENT CORP
11 N 3rd St Ste 100, Harrisburg, PA 17101-1733
Tel (717) 236-5061 Founded/Ownrshp 1974
Sales 25.8MM EMP 31
Accts Reinsel Kuntz Lesher Llp Lanc
SIC 6552 Subdividers & developers; Subdividers & developers
Pr: Russel C Ford
*CFO: Andrew McCleaf
*Sr VP: William Kohl
*Sr VP: Neal West
*VP: Sharon Hassinger
*VP: Bradley Jones
*VP: Carole Rossi

HARRODSBURG HEALTH & REHAB CTR
See LP HARRODSBURG LLC

D-U-N-S 78-034-5448
HARROGATE INC
400 Locust St Ste 1, Lakewood, NJ 08701-7408
Tel (732) 905-4626 Founded/Ownrshp 1999
Sales 20.3MM EMP 32^E
SIC 6513 8051 Retirement hotel operation; Skilled nursing care facilities
Pr: Edwin J O'Malley Jr
Dir Recs: Rachel Brown
*Ex VP: William J Slivka
Assoc Dir: Lnha Sutton
Dir Soc: Pat Richards
*Prin: Lisa Olsen

*Ex Dir: Donald A Johansen
*Ex Dir: Clyde C Sutton

HARROLD FORD
See ELLSWORTH HARROLD CO

D-U-N-S 82-633-9611
HARRON COMMUNICATIONS LP
70 E Lancaster Ave, Malvern, PA 19355-2150
Tel (610) 993-1111 Founded/Ownrshp 1964
Sales 237.7MM^E EMP 394^E
SIC 4841 Cable & other pay television services
CEO: James J Bruder Jr
CFO: Thomas Marturano
Ofcr: Constance Prince
Ex VP: Ryan Pearson
VP: Emily Pollack
VP: Linda Stuchell
VP: Andrew Walton
Manager: Steve Inzaina
Snr PM: Angela Cockerham

D-U-N-S 13-060-6051 IMP
HARROW SPORTS INC
600 W Bayaud Ave, Denver, CO 80223-1802
Tel (303) 295-1657 Founded/Ownrshp 2000
Sales 24.9MM^E EMP 75^E
SIC 5091 Athletic goods
Pr: Mark Hayden
Comm Man: Courtney Tavener
Dir IT: Michael Moseley
Site Mgr: Jeremy Gurley
Site Mgr: Jeremy Niedermaier
Prd Mgr: Lance Vitt
Sls Dir: Keith Krasney
Mktg Mgr: Amanda Mastera
Sls Mgr: Bruce Garber
Sales Asso: Kelsey Aburn
Sales Asso: Mikael Chullen

D-U-N-S 14-953-1084 IMP/EXP
■ **HARRY & DAVID HOLDINGS INC**
(Suby of 1-800-FLOWERS.COM INC) ★
2500 S Pacific Hwy, Medford, OR 97501-8724
Tel (541) 864-2362 Founded/Ownrshp 2014
Sales 251.0MM^E EMP 1,026
Tkr Sym HARR Exch OTO
SIC 5961 1541 Catalog & mail-order houses; Food products manufacturing or packing plant construction; Catalog & mail-order houses; Food products manufacturing or packing plant construction
Pr: Craig J Johnson
Sr VP: Jackie Ardrey
Sr VP: Joseph Foley

D-U-N-S 05-352-4877 IMP
■ **HARRY AND DAVID LLC**
(Suby of HARRY & DAVID HOLDINGS INC) ★
2500 S Pacific Hwy, Medford, OR 97501-8724
Tel (541) 864-2500 Founded/Ownrshp 2004
Sales 229.0MM^E EMP 1,000
SIC 5961 5947 Fruit, mail order; Gift, novelty & souvenir shop; Fruit, mail order; Gift, novelty & souvenir shop
Pr: Barbara Hurd
CFO: Jason Phillipson
Sr VP: Jackie Ardrey
Sr VP: John Bancroft
Sr VP: Tom Forsythe
VP: Mona Cato
VP: David Fairbanks
VP: Tony Huckabee
VP: Mark Oedekoven
Creative D: Troy Forrest
Genl Mgr: Tom Ward

D-U-N-S 00-170-7876
HARRY BRAINUM JR INC
360 Mcguinness Blvd Ste 1, Brooklyn, NY 11222-1291
Tel (718) 389-4080 Founded/Ownrshp 1993
Sales 22.1MM^E EMP 20
SIC 5051 Sheets, galvanized or other coated
Pr: Gail Brainum
VP: Richard Cooper
Genl Mgr: Jarett Siegel
Opers Mgr: Zeni Rukaj
Sls Mgr: Buddy Townsend

HARRY BROWNS FAMILY AUTOMOTIVE
See HARRY BROWNS INC

D-U-N-S 06-819-6641
HARRY BROWNS INC (MN)
HARRY BROWNS FAMILY AUTOMOTIVE
1747 Grant St Nw, Faribault, MN 55021-4826
Tel (507) 332-7441 Founded/Ownrshp 1966
Sales 35.0MM^E EMP 85
SIC 5511 5521 New & used car dealers; Used car dealers; New & used car dealers; Used car dealers
Pr: Mike Brown
*VP: Steve Brown
Sls Mgr: Dave Wolf

HARRY C TREXLER TRUST
See TREXLER TRUST

D-U-N-S 87-767-2196
HARRY CHAPIN FOOD BANK OF SOUTHWEST FLORIDA INC
3760 Fowler St Ste B, Fort Myers, FL 33901-0930
Tel (239) 334-7007 Founded/Ownrshp 1983
Sales 32.3MM EMP 52
Accts Myers Brettholtz & Company Pa
SIC 8699 8322 Charitable organization; Individual & family services; Charitable organization; Individual & family services
Ex Dir: Alan Brislain
Bd of Dir: Rabbi Jeremy Barras
Bd of Dir: Noelle Melanson
Bd of Dir: Alex Robinson
Bd of Dir: Ed Ryan
VP: Jo Anna Bradshaw
Pr Mgr: Marta Hodson
Pgrm Dir: Kari Lefort

D-U-N-S 00-696-8853
HARRY COOPER SUPPLY CO (MO)
(Suby of C B MANAGEMENT CO INC) ★
605 N Sherman Pkwy, Springfield, MO 65802-3656
Tel (417) 865-8392 Founded/Ownrshp 1895

Sales 71.3MME *EMP* 200
SIC 5074 5063 5051

HARRY COOPERS SUPPLY CO
See C B MANAGEMENT CO INC

D-U-N-S 02-756-3063
HARRY E FERRYMAN
FERRYMAN ENTERPRISES
9110 Ne Highway 99 Ste A, Vancouver, WA 98665-8978
Tel (360) 574-0911 *Founded/Ownrshp* 1963
Sales 5.1MME *EMP* 300
SIC 7011 1531 Hotels & motels; Speculative builder, single-family houses; Hotels & motels; Speculative builder, single-family houses
Owner: Harry E Ferryman

D-U-N-S 01-603-8655
HARRY GREEN CHEVROLET INC
HARRY GREEN NISSAN
1858 E Pike St, Clarksburg, WV 26301-9263
Tel (304) 624-6304 *Founded/Ownrshp* 1959
Sales 40.3MME *EMP* 100
SIC 5511 Automobiles, new & used; Pickups, new & used; Vans, new & used; Automobiles, new & used; Pickups, new & used; Vans, new & used
Pr: Harry L Green III
**Pr:* Harry L Green Jr
Genl Mgr: Frank Smith
Sales Asso: Ross Frame
Sales Asso: Mike Hawkinberry
Sales Asso: Patrick Moore
Sales Asso: Eddie West

HARRY GREEN NISSAN
See HARRY GREEN CHEVROLET INC

D-U-N-S 00-583-9170
HARRY GRODSKY & CO INC (MA)
33 Shaws Ln, Springfield, MA 01104-3019
Tel (413) 785-1947 *Founded/Ownrshp* 1918
Sales 80.8MME *EMP* 300
Accts Aaron Smith Pc
SIC 1711 Plumbing contractors; Heating & air conditioning contractors; Process piping contractor; Plumbing contractors; Heating & air conditioning contractors; Process piping contractor
Pr: Ronald Grodsky
CFO: Scott Grodsky
Ex VP: Jeffrey Grodsky
Ex VP: Allen Sawyer
VP: Rivers Christine
VP: Richard Kelly
VP: Thomas Mahan
VP: Robert Ranahan
VP: David Streeter
VP: Brian Toomey
VP: Anthony Victor
Board of Directors: Robert G Agnoli

D-U-N-S 05-056-3741
HARRY HOLLAND & SON INC (IL)
HOLLAND APPLIED TECHNOLOGIES
7050 High Grove Blvd, Burr Ridge, IL 60527-7597
Tel (630) 325-5130 *Founded/Ownrshp* 1927, 1980
Sales 48.4MME *EMP* 51
SIC 5084 5169 Industrial machinery & equipment; Industrial chemicals
Pr: Tim Racke
**Treas:* Robert Soukup
**VP:* Ray Vwiedel
**Prin:* David S Cheney

D-U-N-S 08-293-0645
HARRY J KLOEPPEL & ASSOCIATES INC
246 E Janata Blvd Ste 300, Lombard, IL 60148-5383
Tel (630) 206-5810 *Founded/Ownrshp* 1977
Sales 90.0MM *EMP* 12E
SIC 5049 Laboratory equipment, except medical or dental; Laboratory equipment, except medical or dental
Pr: Harry J Kloeppel
**Pr:* Tom Keaveney
Off Mgr: Cindy Detlof
Off Mgr: Cindy Detlos

D-U-N-S 03-902-5986
HARRY J LAWALL & SON INC (PA)
8028 Frankford Ave, Philadelphia, PA 19136-2697
Tel (215) 338-6611 *Founded/Ownrshp* 1979, 2007
Sales 21.2MME *EMP* 120
SIC 3842 Limbs, artificial; Orthopedic appliances; Limbs, artificial; Orthopedic appliances
VP: Edward Moran
Off Admin: Kristy Gangloff
Web Dev: Lori Morrison

D-U-N-S 00-128-5683 IMP
HARRY J RASHTI & CO INC (NY)
RASHTI & RASHTI BABI GIFT CO
875 Avnue Of The Americas, New York, NY 10001-3507
Tel (212) 594-3733 *Founded/Ownrshp* 1937
Sales 21.4MME *EMP* 45
SIC 5137 Children's goods
Ch Bd: Michael Rashti
**Pr:* Charlotte Rashti
**CFO:* Ken Rugg
VP: Andrew Freed
VP: Dana Weissman
Creative D: Pamela Sayles
Prd Mgr: Anna Okiebisu
VP Mktg: Christine Lanigan
Sls Dir: Cliff Lesser
Sls Mgr: Kevin Woodward

D-U-N-S 01-523-0449 IMP/EXP
HARRY KRANTZ CO LLC
50 Heartland Blvd, Edgewood, NY 11717-8365
Tel (516) 742-6300 *Founded/Ownrshp* 1997
Sales 47.3MME *EMP* 37
SIC 5065 Electronic parts; Electronic parts
CEO: David Friede
**COO:* Anne Poncheri
Ofcr: Kerri Beimann
Ofcr: Barbara Rein
VP: Barbara Mandello
Dir Bus: Bill Kaspar
QA Dir: John Cochran
IT Man: Dennis Esnes
QC Dir: Camie Genna
QI Cn Mgr: Bogdan Modzolewski

D-U-N-S 03-469-0537
HARRY LANE CHRYSLER-PLYMOUTH INC
1660 Botsford Dr, Knoxville, TN 37922-8048
Tel (865) 531-4000 *Founded/Ownrshp* 1981
Sales 20.5MME *EMP* 85
SIC 5511 5521 Automobiles, new & used; Vans, new & used; Used car dealers; Automobiles, new & used; Vans, new & used; Used car dealers
Pr: Harry Lane
**VP:* Kenny Lane
**VP:* Mary Lane
IT Man: Judy Rice

HARRY LONDON CHOCOLATES
See LONDON HARRY CANDIES INC

D-U-N-S 04-681-8712
■ **HARRY M STEVENS INC OF NEW JERSEY**
(*Suby of* ARAMARK SERVICES INC) ★
1101 Market St, Philadelphia, PA 19107-2934
Tel (215) 238-3000 *Founded/Ownrshp* 1994
Sales 60.2MME *EMP* 5,000
SIC 5812 Concessionaire; Concessionaire
Pr: Charles Gillespie
**Treas:* Melvin Mahoney

D-U-N-S 00-537-1877
HARRY MAJOR MACHINE & TOOL CO
24801 Capital Blvd, Clinton Township, MI 48036-1347
Tel (586) 783-7030 *Founded/Ownrshp* 1962
Sales 22.4MME *EMP* 75
SIC 3535 Conveyors & conveying equipment
Pr: H Curtis Major

D-U-N-S 08-114-0642
HARRY MEYERING CENTER INC
109 Homestead Rd, Mankato, MN 56001-5741
Tel (507) 387-8281 *Founded/Ownrshp* 1974
Sales 8.5MM *EMP* 285
Accts Abdo Eick & Meyers Llp Mankat
SIC 8052 8082 8361 Home for the mentally retarded, with health care; Home health care services; Residential care; Home for the mentally retarded, with health care; Home health care services; Residential care
Ex Dir: Carol Lee
IT Man: James Kline
Pgrm Dir: Joey Freyberg

D-U-N-S 00-135-6971 IMP
HARRY N ABRAMS INC (NY)
STEWART TOBORI & CHANG DIV
(*Suby of* LA MARTINIERE GROUPE)
115 W 18th St Fl 6, New York, NY 10011-4113
Tel (212) 206-7715 *Founded/Ownrshp* 1949
Sales 32.0MME *EMP* 94
SIC 2731 Books: publishing only; Books: publishing only
Ch Bd: Herve De La Martiniere
**Ch Bd:* Michael Jacobs
CFO: Thomas Moloney
Sr VP: Leslie Stoker
VP: Sam Antupit
VP: Pamela Harwood
VP: Margaret Kaplan
**VP:* Tom Moloni
VP: Howard Reeves
Ex Dir: Larry Goldberg
Admn Mgr: Arthur Dorros

HARRY NORMAN REALTORS
See HN REAL ESTATE GROUP LLC

D-U-N-S 06-110-2281 IMP
HARRY O HAHN SEAFOOD INC
ADELPHIA SEAFOOD
3024 Penn Ave Ste 2, Reading, PA 19609-1445
Tel (610) 670-2500 *Founded/Ownrshp* 2007
Sales 41.0MME *EMP* 90
SIC 5146 5421 Seafoods; Seafood markets; Seafoods; Seafood markets
Pr: Jason Hurleman
**CFO:* Edward J Kuhn
IT Man: Bill Vogel
Prd Mgr: Chuck Grimm
Prd Mgr: Mike Martino

D-U-N-S 00-982-1422 EXP
■ **HARRY PEPPER & ASSOCIATES INC**
(*Suby of* EMCOR GOVERNMENT SERVICES INC) ★
9000 Regency Square Blvd # 1, Jacksonville, FL 32211-8102
Tel (904) 721-3300 *Founded/Ownrshp* 2010
Sales 28.4MME *EMP* 80
SIC 1629 1711 8711 Industrial plant construction; Mechanical contractor; Construction & civil engineering
Pr: David Pepper
**Ex VP:* Willie Doves
IT Man: Paul Safirulla
IT Man: Balamurugan Somasundaram
Sfty Dirs: Joe Whitfield

D-U-N-S 04-430-6538
HARRY PRODUCTS INC (PA)
TRADER HORN
495 Pittsburgh Rd, Butler, PA 16002-7691
Tel (724) 586-9411 *Founded/Ownrshp* 1967
Sales 45.1MME *EMP* 400
SIC 5331

D-U-N-S 02-763-9251
HARRY RITCHIE JEWELER INC
DON'S JEWELERS
956 Willamette St, Eugene, OR 97401-3134
Tel (541) 686-1787 *Founded/Ownrshp* 1956
Sales 29.7MME *EMP* 250
SIC 5944

D-U-N-S 07-264-9601 IMP
HARRY S EKLOF JR & ASSOCIATES INC
3401 Pennsy Dr, Landover, MD 20785-1608
Tel (301) 772-1700 *Founded/Ownrshp* 1968
Sales 47.0MM *EMP* 60
SIC 5074 Plumbing & hydronic heating supplies; Plumbing & hydronic heating supplies
Pr: Harry S Eklof Jr
**Sec:* Jennifer Eklof
**VP:* John R Coster
**VP:* Gary Eklof
**VP:* R Steven Price
VP: Steven Price
**VP:* Jack Schulz
Sales Asso: Jayne Angles

D-U-N-S 00-135-9983 IMP
HARRY WINSTON INC
(*Suby of* THE SWATCH GROUP AG)
1330 Avenue Of The Americ, New York, NY 10019-5408
Tel (212) 315-7900 *Founded/Ownrshp* 1932, 2013
Sales 36.6MME *EMP* 200
SIC 3911 5944 Jewelry, precious metal; Jewelry, precious stones & precious metals; Jewelry, precious metal; Jewelry, precious stones & precious metals
Ch Bd: Ronald Winston
CEO: Frederic De Narp
CFO: Robert Scott
VP: Nancy Murray

D-U-N-S 07-877-5950
HARRY WINSTON INC (NY)
718 5th Ave, New York, NY 10019-4195
Tel (212) 245-2000 *Founded/Ownrshp* 1932
Sales 33.6MME *EMP* 77E
SIC 5094 Diamonds (gems); Jewelers' findings
CEO: Nayla Hayek
CFO: Robert Scott
Ofcr: Susan Korb
Mng Dir: Jennifer Liu
Genl Mgr: Michael Moser
Opers Mgr: Pia Dahlsten
Sales Exec: Alix Alexander
Sales Exec: Mark Briggs
Sales Exec: Rozalyn Columbo
Sales Exec: William Frishkorn
Sales Exec: Debra Levasseur

D-U-N-S 02-699-2180
HARRYS BUILDING MATERIALS INC
361 W 6th St, Rusk, TX 75785-1189
Tel (903) 683-4618 *Founded/Ownrshp* 1974
Sales 25.7MME *EMP* 115
SIC 5211 Lumber & other building materials
Pr: Harry Robert Tosh
**Sec:* Magoline Tosh
**VP:* Harvey Merrill
**VP:* Johnny R Sanders
**VP:* David Slaton
**VP:* Robby Tosh

HARRY'S FRESH FOODS
See HARRIS SOUP CO

D-U-N-S 55-644-2556
HARRYS OF AMERICA LLC
HARRY'S SEAFOOD BAR AND GRILLE
9995 Gate Pkwy N Ste 400b, Jacksonville, FL 32246-1897
Tel (904) 642-2165 *Founded/Ownrshp* 1987
Sales 17.6MME *EMP* 500
SIC 5812 Seafood restaurants; Oyster bar; Seafood shack
VP: Jesse Jabot

HARRY'S SEAFOOD BAR AND GRILLE
See HARRYS OF AMERICA LLC

HARRY'S SHOES
See JERR SHOES INC

D-U-N-S 02-772-7684
HARSCH INVESTMENT REALTY LLC
1121 Sw Salmon St Ste 500, Portland, OR 97205-2092
Tel (503) 242-2900 *Founded/Ownrshp* 2005
Sales 16.2MME *EMP* 801
SIC 6513 7011 6512 7521

D-U-N-S 00-300-2268
▲ **HARSCO CORP** (DE)
350 Poplar Church Rd, Camp Hill, PA 17011-2599
Tel (717) 763-7064 *Founded/Ownrshp* 1853
Sales 2.0MMM *EMP* 12,200
Accts Pricewaterhousecoopers Llp Ph
Tkr Sym HSC *Exch* NYS
SIC 7359 7353 5082 3443 3585 4789 Equipment rental & leasing; Heavy construction equipment rental; Construction & mining machinery; Scaffolding; Fuel tanks (oil, gas, etc.): metal plate; Cryogenic tanks, for liquids & gases; Cylinders, pressure: metal plate; Heat exchangers: coolers (after, inter), condensers, etc.; Evaporative condensers, heat transfer equipment; Railroad maintenance & repair services; Equipment rental & leasing; Heavy construction equipment rental; Construction & mining machinery; Scaffolding; Fuel tanks (oil, gas, etc.): metal plate; Cryogenic tanks, for liquids & gases; Cylinders, pressure: metal plate; Heat exchangers: coolers (after, inter), condensers, etc.; Evaporative condensers, heat transfer equipment; Railroad maintenance & repair services
Pr: F Nicholas Grasberger
Pr: James E Cline
Pr: James M Demitrieus
Pr: William R Jacob
Pr: Richard E Lundgren
Pr: Daniel S McAtee
Pr: Eric A Reisner
COO: Gene A Iannazzo
CFO: Peter Minan
CFO: Peter F Minan
Ofcr: Nicholas Grasberger
Ex VP: Robert Safier
Sr VP: Tony Degregorio
VP: William Alexander
VP: Francis Ezeuzoh
VP: Scott H Gerson
VP: Scott W Jacoby
VP: Krysten Powers
VP: Linda Toth
VP: Jeremy Zahn
Board of Directors: James F Earl, Kathy G Eddy, David C Everitt, Stuart E Graham, Terry D Growcock, Henry W Knueppel, Elaine La Roche, James M Loree, Phillip C Widman

D-U-N-S 07-880-3741
■ **HARSCO SERVICES GROUP LLC**
H S G
(*Suby of* HARSCO CORP) ★
5730 Fm 646 Rd E, Dickinson, TX 77539-2417
Tel (281) 860-1900 *Founded/Ownrshp* 2013
Sales 33.1MME *EMP* 160
SIC 1629 Industrial plant construction; Industrial plant construction
Genl Mgr: Ken Chevis

D-U-N-S 00-707-5294
HARSH INTERNATIONAL INC
600 Oak Ave, Eaton, CO 80615-3404
Tel (970) 454-2291 *Founded/Ownrshp* 1948
Sales 27.2MM *EMP* 150
SIC 3523

D-U-N-S 07-080-8746
HARSHAW SERVICE INC
HARSHAW TRANE SERVICE
12700 Plantside Dr, Louisville, KY 40299-6387
Tel (502) 499-7000 *Founded/Ownrshp* 1976
Sales 88.1MME *EMP* 156
SIC 5075 1711 5074 Air conditioning equipment, except room units; Electrical heating equipment; Warm air heating & air conditioning contractor; Plumbing & hydronic heating supplies; Air conditioning equipment, except room units; Electrical heating equipment; Warm air heating & air conditioning contractor; Plumbing & hydronic heating supplies
Pr: W Frank Harshaw
**COO:* Doug Michael
**Prin:* Kurt Barrett

HARSHAW TRANE
See W FRANK HARSHAW AND ASSOCIATES INC

HARSHAW TRANE SERVICE
See HARSHAW SERVICE INC

D-U-N-S 18-214-0293 IMP
■ **HART & COOLEY INC**
(*Suby of* AIR DISTRIBUTION TECHNOLOGIES INC) ★
5030 Corp Exch Blvd Se, Grand Rapids, MI 49512
Tel (616) 656-8200 *Founded/Ownrshp* 2014
Sales 641.8MME *EMP* 1,700
SIC 3822 3446 3564 Blowers & fans; Auto controls regulating residntl & coml environmt & applncs; Registers (air), metal; Grillwork, ornamental metal; Auto controls regulating residntl & coml environmt & applncs; Registers (air), metal; Blowers & fans
Pr: Michael Winn
VP: Daniel J Disser
VP: Mark Walraven
IT Man: Gonzalez Carlos
Mtls Mgr: Hector Perez
Mtls Mgr: Debbie Sneed
Plnt Mgr: Dave Seiler
VP Mktg: Christopher J Pfaus
Manager: Tom Bauer
Sls Mgr: David Littlefield
Sls Mgr: Jon Mathison

D-U-N-S 07-169-3741 IMP/EXP
HART CHEMICALS INC (CA)
PACIFIC COAST CHEMICALS CO.
2424 4th St, Berkeley, CA 94710-2404
Tel (510) 549-3535 *Founded/Ownrshp* 1958, 1970
Sales 93.4MME *EMP* 75
SIC 5191 5169 Farm supplies; Chemicals & allied products; Farm supplies; Chemicals & allied products
CEO: Aaron K Stull
**CFO:* Don Stull
Sls Mgr: Jim Collins
Sls Mgr: Mike Harris
Sls Mgr: Steve Shaffer

D-U-N-S 10-002-7366
HART CO SCHOOL DISTRICT
511 W Union St, Munfordville, KY 42765-8909
Tel (270) 524-9161 *Founded/Ownrshp* 1940
Sales 26.6MME *EMP* 1,012
SIC 8211 Public elementary & secondary schools; Public elementary & secondary schools
**Treas:* Judy Lawler

D-U-N-S 19-152-3104 IMP
HART CONSTRUCTION LLC
1560 W Beebe Capps Expy, Searcy, AR 72143-5169
Tel (501) 279-2493 *Founded/Ownrshp* 2009
Sales 31.4MME *EMP* 113E
SIC 1542 Commercial & office building contractors
Prin: Adam Hart
Off Mgr: Cindy Hearnsberger

D-U-N-S 17-523-3071
HART COUNTY BOARD OF EDUCATION
284 Campbell Dr, Hartwell, GA 30643-2223
Tel (706) 376-5141 *Founded/Ownrshp* 1871
Sales 25.4MME *EMP* 488
Accts Russell W Hinton Atlanta Ge
SIC 8211 School board; School board

D-U-N-S 07-979-8876
HART COUNTY CHARTER SYSTEM
284 Campbell Dr, Hartwell, GA 30643-2223
Tel (706) 376-5141 *Founded/Ownrshp* 2015
Sales 7.4MME *EMP* 490E
SIC 8211 Public elementary & secondary schools
Prin: Kay Adams
HC Dir: Pam Gordon

D-U-N-S 07-982-7285
HART COUNTY SCHOOLS
25 Quality St, Munfordville, KY 42765-9476
Tel (270) 524-2631 *Founded/Ownrshp* 2015
Sales 11.8MME *EMP* 335E
SIC 8211 Public elementary & secondary schools

D-U-N-S 07-183-7470
HART CROWSER INC
3131 Elliott Ave Ste 600, Seattle, WA 98121-1047
Tel (206) 324-9530 *Founded/Ownrshp* 1974
Sales 21.0MM^E *EMP* 110
SIC 8748 1081 1241 1481 Environmental consultant; Metal mining services; Metal mining exploration & development services; Mine development, metal; Coal mining services; Mine preparation services; Anthracite mining services, contract basis; Mine & quarry services, nonmetallic minerals
CEO: Mike Bailey
**CFO:* Robert Jenson
**VP:* Daivd G Winter
Snr PM: Steven Hoffman

D-U-N-S 00-797-7044
HART ELECTRIC MEMBERSHIP CORP (GA)
1071 Elberton Hwy, Hartwell, GA 30643-4572
Tel (706) 376-4714 *Founded/Ownrshp* 1937
Sales 70.4MM *EMP* 132
Accts Mcnair Mclemore Middlebrooks
SIC 4911 Distribution, electric power; Distribution, electric power
Pr: Jeffrey W Murphy
V Ch Bd: Guerry Hall
Dir IT: Bryan Zabella
Counsel: Walter Gordon

D-U-N-S 06-731-7073
HART ENERGY PUBLISHING LLLP
1616 S Voss Rd Ste 1000, Houston, TX 77057-2641
Tel (713) 993-9320 *Founded/Ownrshp* 2004
Sales 60.2MM^E *EMP* 180
SIC 2721 8748 2741 8742 Magazines: publishing only, not printed on site; Business consulting; Directories: publishing only, not printed on site; Newsletter publishing; Business planning & organizing services; Magazines: publishing only, not printed on site; Business consulting; Directories: publishing only, not printed on site; Newsletter publishing; Business planning & organizing services
CEO: Richard Eichler
**Pr:* Kevin Higgins
Ex VP: John Paisie
**Sr VP:* Tammy Klein
**VP:* Shelley Lamb
Mng Dir: Michael Silber
CTO: Mark Chiles
IT Man: Kyle Munz
Web Dev: Hai Nguyen
Mktg Dir: Kim V Blarcom
Mktg Mgr: Eduardo Hernandez

D-U-N-S 16-132-5931
HART ENGINEERING CORP
800 Scenic View Dr, Cumberland, RI 02864-8706
Tel (401) 658-4600 *Founded/Ownrshp* 1984
Sales 77.1MM^E *EMP* 250
SIC 1711 Mechanical contractor; Mechanical contractor
Ch Bd: C Frank Rampone
**Pr:* David F Rampone
**CFO:* Frank Carnevale
**VP:* Robert Cole
**VP:* Michael Dellefave
**VP:* Paul S Rampone
MIS Dir: Jim Reffelt
Snr Mgr: Richard Jope

D-U-N-S 13-168-5422
HART HOTELS INC
617 Dingens St Ste 4, Buffalo, NY 14206-2474
Tel (716) 893-6551 *Founded/Ownrshp* 1999
Sales 72.0MM^E *EMP* 1,100
SIC 7011 Hotels & motels; Hotels & motels
Ch Bd: David P Hart
**Sec:* William P Hart
VP: Judith Glatzhofer
Exec: Anthony Sole
Admn Mgr: Richard Likus
Brnch Mgr: Karen Piazza
Genl Mgr: Carol Bonner
Genl Mgr: Harry Falk
Genl Mgr: Sonny Karimi
Genl Mgr: Christopher Scott
Genl Mgr: Heather Strauss

HART INDUSTRIAL PRODUCTS DIV
See HART INDUSTRIES INC

D-U-N-S 01-819-0926 IMP
HART INDUSTRIES INC (OH)
HART INDUSTRIAL PRODUCTS DIV
931 Jeanette St, Middletown, OH 45044-5701
Tel (513) 541-4278 *Founded/Ownrshp* 1966
Sales 36.3MM^E *EMP* 76
SIC 5085 Industrial supplies; Rubber goods, mechanical; Industrial supplies; Rubber goods, mechanical
CEO: Herman E Hart
**Pr:* Roger Hart
**Treas:* Christopher Hart

D-U-N-S 01-129-5821
HART INTERCIVIC INC
(*Suby of* C AG ACQUISITIONS INC)
15500 Wells Port Dr, Austin, TX 78728-4573
Tel (512) 252-6400 *Founded/Ownrshp* 1999
Sales 39.4MM^E *EMP* 58^E
SIC 5087 Voting machines
Prin: Gregg Burt
Pr: Phillip Braithwaite
Pr: Derek Hutson
CFO: Julie Mathis
CFO: Edward P Simmonds
VP: Jim Canter
VP: Ron Clevenger
VP: Chuck Girard
VP: Pete Lichtenheld
VP: Matt Walker
Genl Mgr: David Ashworth

D-U-N-S 55-721-4343
HART JEFFREY GROUP INC
4400 N Federal Hwy, Boca Raton, FL 33431-5187
Tel (561) 997-2238 *Founded/Ownrshp* 1991
Sales 110.0MM *EMP* 14
SIC 8732 6799 Merger, acquisition & reorganization research; Investors; Merger, acquisition & reorganization research; Investors
Pr: Jeffrey S Obligen

D-U-N-S 07-827-2216
HART LYMAN COMPANIES LLC
7085 Manlius Center Rd, East Syracuse, NY 13057-2607
Tel (315) 503-3109 *Founded/Ownrshp* 2009
Sales 56.1MM *EMP* 16
SIC 6552 Subdividers & developers; Subdividers & developers
CFO: Ron Mucci

D-U-N-S 02-395-2187
HART MOTOR CO INC
SATURN
1341 E Main St, Salem, VA 24153-4413
Tel (540) 444-4444 *Founded/Ownrshp* 1954
Sales 39.2MM^E *EMP* 100
SIC 5511 5531 7532 7538 Automobiles, new & used; Automotive parts; Body shop, automotive; General automotive repair shops; Automobiles, new & used; Automotive parts; Body shop, automotive; General automotive repair shops
Pr: Carlos B Hart
**Treas:* Patricia Hart
**VP:* Daniel L Hart
**VP:* Gregory S Hart

D-U-N-S 13-880-2249
HART RESTAURANT MANAGEMENT INC
BURGER KING
108 N Mesquite St, Corpus Christi, TX 78401-2823
Tel (361) 882-4100 *Founded/Ownrshp* 2000
Sales 44.0MM^E *EMP* 1,000
SIC 5812 Fast-food restaurant, chain; Fast-food restaurant, chain
Pr: Robert G Hart III

D-U-N-S 02-152-9771 IMP
HART SPECIALTIES INC
NEW YORK EYE
5000 New Horizons Blvd, Amityville, NY 11701-1143
Tel (631) 226-5600 *Founded/Ownrshp* 1980
Sales 21.6MM *EMP* 70
Accts Weiser Mazars Llp Woodbury N
SIC 3827 5995 Optical goods; Optical instruments & apparatus; Optical goods stores
Ch Bd: Arthur Jankolovits
**VP:* Shannon Johnson
**VP:* Lucy Korn
**VP:* Jan Phillips
Exec: Stella Rossman

D-U-N-S 01-921-4857 IMP
HART SUPPLY CO INC
50 Pond Park Rd, Hingham, MA 02043-4300
Tel (781) 749-4000 *Founded/Ownrshp* 1946
Sales 40.6MM^E *EMP* 56
SIC 5046 5198 5162 Signmaker equipment & supplies; Paints, varnishes & supplies; Plastics products
Pr: Dennis Ryan
**Treas:* Bruce Ryan
**VP:* Thomas Ryan

D-U-N-S 78-909-7003
■ **HARTE HANKS DIRECT INC**
(*Suby of* HARTE HANKS INC) ★
777 Township Ste 300, Yardley, PA 19067
Tel (215) 750-6600 *Founded/Ownrshp* 1996
Sales 40.4MM^E *EMP* 200
SIC 7311 Advertising agencies; Advertising agencies
Pr: Jennine Falcone
IT Exec: Robb Didio
Art Dir: Sean Murphy

D-U-N-S 04-701-1085
▲ **HARTE HANKS INC**
9601 Mcallister Fwy # 610, San Antonio, TX 78216-4632
Tel (210) 829-9000 *Founded/Ownrshp* 1997
Sales 553.6MM *EMP* 5,423
Tkr Sym HHS *Exch* NYS
SIC 7331 7372 Direct mail advertising services; Prepackaged software; Direct mail advertising services; Prepackaged software
Pr: Karen Puckett
**Ch Bd:* Christopher M Harte
COO: Jonathan Bevan
CFO: Kim Shipman
Ofcr: Frank Grillo
Ofcr: Gavin Pommernelle
Ex VP: Tony Paul
Sr VP: Rick Carbone
Sr VP: Craig Combest
Sr VP: Don Crews
Sr VP: James S Davis
Sr VP: Charles H Everill
Sr VP: Herbert Hill
Sr VP: Jacques Kerrest
Sr VP: Robert L R Munden
Sr VP: Joseph Voica
VP: Amy Bybee
VP: Johnny Castaneda
VP: Carolyn Deluca
VP: Andrew Harrison
VP: Federico Ortiz

D-U-N-S 78-366-4790
HARTE INFINITI INC
HARTE INFINITY BODY SHOP
150 Weston St, Hartford, CT 06120-1512
Tel (860) 524-1993 *Founded/Ownrshp* 1991
Sales 68.4MM^E *EMP* 200
SIC 5511 Automobiles, new & used; Automobiles, new & used
Pr: George C Harte Jr
**VP:* Gregory Harte
Genl Mgr: Bruce Levey
Sls Mgr: Kelvin Davis

HARTE INFINITY BODY SHOP
See HARTE INFINITI INC

D-U-N-S 10-895-2441
HARTE NISSAN INC
165 W Service Rd, Hartford, CT 06120-1543
Tel (860) 549-2800 *Founded/Ownrshp* 1983
Sales 30.6MM^E *EMP* 69
SIC 5511 Automobiles, new & used; Automobiles, new & used
Pr: George C Harte Jr
CFO: Candace Platt
Genl Mgr: Amardeep Kumar
Sls Mgr: Michael Veprinsky
Sls Mgr: Joshua Wagner
Sls Mgr: Jeff Whitman

HARTE-HANKS CRM
See SELECT MARKETING INC

D-U-N-S 09-488-4798
■ **HARTE-HANKS DIRECT MARKETING**
(*Suby of* HARTE HANKS INC) ★
4545 Annapolis Rd, Baltimore, MD 21227-4898
Tel (410) 636-6660 *Founded/Ownrshp* 1978
Sales 18.7MM^E *EMP* 400
SIC 7331 7374 7319 Direct mail advertising services; Computer processing services; Circular & handbill distribution; Direct mail advertising services; Computer processing services; Circular & handbill distribution
CEO: Stephen Carley
**Pr:* Micheal Castaldi
**Pr:* David L Copeland
Exec: Anne George
Opers Mgr: Mike Levin

D-U-N-S 09-650-5557
■ **HARTE-HANKS DIRECT MARKETING/CINCINNATI INC**
(*Suby of* HARTE HANKS INC) ★
2750 114th St Ste 100, Grand Prairie, TX 75050-8737
Tel (513) 458-7600 *Founded/Ownrshp* 1993
Sales 19.1MM^E *EMP* 300
SIC 7374 7331 Data processing service; Direct mail advertising services; Mailing list compilers; Mailing service; Data processing service; Direct mail advertising services; Mailing list compilers; Mailing service
Pr: Dan Reising
**Prin:* B I White
**Prin:* P E Fay
**Prin:* V L Turk

D-U-N-S 16-199-4587
■ **HARTE-HANKS LOGISTICS LLC**
(*Suby of* HARTE HANKS INC) ★
1525 Nw 3rd St Ste 21, Deerfield Beach, FL 33442-1696
Tel (954) 429-3771 *Founded/Ownrshp* 1978
Sales 59.4MM^E *EMP* 178
SIC 4213 4212 Trucking, except local; Local trucking, without storage; Trucking, except local; Local trucking, without storage
Pr: Robert A Paul
**Treas:* Federico Ortiz
VP: Peter Gorman
**VP:* Houston H Harte
**VP:* Richard Ritchie

D-U-N-S 88-453-5964
HARTE-HANKS MARKET INTELLIGENCE
ABERDEEN GROUP, THE
9980 Huennekens St, San Diego, CA 92121-2900
Tel (858) 450-1667 *Founded/Ownrshp* 2015
Sales 29.7MM^E *EMP* 350
SIC 7374 Data processing & preparation; Data processing & preparation
Pr: Robert G Brown
Ex VP: Randall W Wussler
Sls&Mrk Ex: Lisa Torres
VP Mktg: Tim Savitt
VP Sls: Robert Mackey

D-U-N-S 01-190-8688
■ **HARTE-HANKS RESPONSE MANAGEMENT/BOSTON INC**
(*Suby of* HARTE HANKS INC) ★
600 N Bedford St Ste 1, East Bridgewater, MA 02333-3117
Tel (508) 894-1500 *Founded/Ownrshp* 1980
Sales 30.9MM^E *EMP* 224
SIC 7331 Direct mail advertising services; Direct mail advertising services
Pr: Matthew Pollock
**Treas:* Federico Ortiz
**VP:* Gary J Skidmore
Telecom Ex: Joe Ricketts

D-U-N-S 88-499-6620
HARTEC INC
(*Suby of* SEWS) ★
1018 Ashley St, Bowling Green, KY 42103-2499
Tel (270) 782-7397 *Founded/Ownrshp* 1998
Sales 27.3MM^E *EMP* 871
SIC 4225 General warehousing & storage; General warehousing & storage
Pr: Yoshio Ebihara
**CFO:* Frances Smith

D-U-N-S 00-971-2506
HARTER EQUIPMENT INC (NJ)
KUBOTA
615 State Route 33, Millstone Township, NJ 08535-8105
Tel (732) 446-7600 *Founded/Ownrshp* 1967
Sales 20.1MM^E *EMP* 33
SIC 5082 General construction machinery & equipment
Pr: Susan G Harter
**VP:* Victor Riga

D-U-N-S 07-369-7930
HARTER SECREST & EMERY LLP
H S E
1600 Bausch And Lomb Pl, Rochester, NY 14604-2711
Tel (585) 232-6500 *Founded/Ownrshp* 1893
Sales 35.2MM^E *EMP* 255
SIC 8111 General practice law office; General practice law office
Mng Pt: Michael R McEvoy
Pt: William L Kreienberg
**CFO:* David A Higgins
CFO: David Higgins
Tech Mgr: Beth Larocca
Netwrk Eng: Gary Pifer
Genl Couns: Kimberly Shimomura
Counsel: Andrew Anderson
Counsel: Paul Berndt
Counsel: A Britton
Counsel: Paul Britton

D-U-N-S 07-149-9115 IMP
HARTFIEL AUTOMATION INC
6533 Flying Cloud Dr # 100, Eden Prairie, MN 55344-3333
Tel (952) 974-2500 *Founded/Ownrshp* 2000
Sales 55.3MM^E *EMP* 93
SIC 5084 Industrial machinery & equipment; Hydraulic systems equipment & supplies; Power plant machinery; Industrial machinery & equipment; Hydraulic systems equipment & supplies; Power plant machinery
Ch Bd: Myron Moser
**Pr:* Patrick L Schusted
CFO: Bill Hartfiel
**CFO:* Jeff Murphy
VP: Mary Duerr
VP: David Hendrickson
**VP:* Gary Simonson
Telecom Mg: Karie Fox
Telecom Mg: Jane Plas
Ql Cn Mgr: David Preston
S&M/VP: Craig Ohlson

D-U-N-S 00-691-7173
■ **HARTFORD ACCIDENT & INDEMNITY CO**
(*Suby of* HARTFORD FIRE INSURANCE CO (INC)) ★
1 Hartford Plz, Hartford, CT 06155-0001
Tel (860) 547-5000 *Founded/Ownrshp* 1913
Sales NA *EMP* 3,500
SIC 6411 Insurance agents, brokers & service; Insurance agents, brokers & service
CEO: Liam E McGee
**Pr:* Beth Bombara
CFO: Carol Acunto
**Ex VP:* Martha Gervasi
**Ex VP:* Alan J Kreczko
Ex VP: Alpa Patel
**Ex VP:* Robert Rupp
Ex VP: Jack Stoddard
Sr VP: Lois Grady
VP: John Diehl
VP: Kate Jorens
VP: Colleen Mastroianni
Exec: Donald Aderhold
Dir: Louise Durej

D-U-N-S 00-700-5564
HARTFORD BAKERY INC
(*Suby of* LEWIS BROTHERS BAKERIES INC) ★
500 N Fulton Ave, Evansville, IN 47710-1571
Tel (812) 425-4642 *Founded/Ownrshp* 1963
Sales 55.0MM *EMP* 475
SIC 2051 Bread, all types (white, wheat, rye, etc): fresh or frozen; Rolls, bread type: fresh or frozen; Cakes, bakery: except frozen; Bread, all types (white, wheat, rye, etc): fresh or frozen; Rolls, bread type: fresh or frozen; Cakes, bakery: except frozen
Pr: R Jack Lewis Jr
**Treas:* Rodger L Lesh
Exec: Paul Alexander
IT Man: Kyle Kinder
Plnt Mgr: Nathan Ponder

D-U-N-S 00-691-7058
■ **HARTFORD CASUALTY INSURANCE CO**
(*Suby of* HARTFORD FIRE INSURANCE CO (INC)) ★
690 Asylum Ave, Hartford, CT 06155-0002
Tel (860) 547-5000 *Founded/Ownrshp* 1929
Sales NA *EMP* 635
SIC 6411 6331 Insurance agents, brokers & service; Fire, marine & casualty insurance: mutual; Insurance agents, brokers & service; Fire, marine & casualty insurance: mutual
Pr: Andre A Napoli
Pr: Michael Byam
**Treas:* Robert W Paiano
Sr VP: Peggy Anson
Sr VP: Jonathan Bennett
VP: Philip Bossy
VP: Ernest McNeill
VP: Michael Wilder
CIO: Christina Divigard
CIO: Dana Drago
CIO: Michael Green

D-U-N-S 06-926-2962
HARTFORD CATHOLIC DEVELOPMENT CORP (CT)
ARCHDIOCESE OF HARTFORD, THE
134 Farmington Ave, Hartford, CT 06105-3723
Tel (860) 541-6491 *Founded/Ownrshp* 1837
Sales 60.3MM^E *EMP* 2,000
SIC 8661 Religious organizations; Religious organizations
Treas: Rev Charles Daly
**Pr:* Henry J Mansell
**Pr:* Archb Henry Manselo
**Sec:* John J McCarthy
**VP:* Christie A Macaluso
Ex Dir: Cori Thibodeau

HARTFORD CITY HALL
See CITY OF HARTFORD

HARTFORD COLLEGE FOR WOMEN
See UNIVERSITY OF HARTFORD

D-U-N-S 00-115-0747
■ **HARTFORD COURANT CO LLC** (CT)
(*Suby of* TRIBUNE MEDIA CO) ★
285 Broad St, Hartford, CT 06115-3785
Tel (860) 241-6200 *Founded/Ownrshp* 1764, 2000
Sales 192.2MM^E *EMP* 750
SIC 2711 Newspapers: publishing only, not printed on site; Newspapers: publishing only, not printed on site
CEO: Rick Daniels
CFO: Richard Feeney

**Treas:* Thomas Brown
**VP:* Mary Lou Stoneburner
Dir IT: Bob Fancher
Dir IT: David Holub
Dir IT: Diana Perkins
Prd Dir: Andrea Pape
Sfty Mgr: Hans Keck
S&M/VP: Michael Vanacore
Advt Mgr: Michele Tingley

D-U-N-S 01-864-9608
HARTFORD DISTRIBUTORS INC
FRANKLIN FINE BEERS
131 Chapel Rd, Manchester, CT 06042-1633
Tel (860) 643-2337 *Founded/Ownrshp* 1963
Sales 110.2MM *EMP* 170^E^
SIC 5181

D-U-N-S 00-144-8042
HARTFORD ELECTRIC SUPPLY CO INC (CT)
HESCO
30 Inwood Rd Ste 1, Rocky Hill, CT 06067-3437
Tel (860) 236-6363 *Founded/Ownrshp* 1925
Sales 31.9MM^E^ *EMP* 57^E^
Accts Miller Moriarty & Company Ll
SIC 5063 Electrical apparatus & equipment; Wiring devices; Electrical construction materials
CEO: B Patrick Depasquale
Genl Mgr: Todd Depasquale
Opers Mgr: Ed Crowe
VP Sls: James Gottschalk
VP Sls: Gregg Williams
Sls Mgr: Brad Richardson
Sales Asso: Angela Kress
Sales Asso: Dave Pero

D-U-N-S 11-836-5931
■ **HARTFORD EQUITY SALES CO INC**
HESCO
(*Suby of* HARTFORD LIFE INC) ★
200 Hopmeadow St, Weatogue, CT 06089-9793
Tel (860) 843-8213 *Founded/Ownrshp* 2008
Sales 160.9MM^E^ *EMP* 2,000
SIC 6211 Brokers, security; Brokers, security
Pr: Lowndes A Smith
Treas: J Richard Garrett
**Sr VP:* John P Ginnetti
**Sr VP:* David J McDonald
VP: Paul S Bosnyak
VP: Charles A Clinton
VP: Donald J Znamierowski
Board of Directors: Howard A York

D-U-N-S 78-708-5893
▲ **HARTFORD FINANCIAL SERVICES GROUP INC**
1 Hartford Plz, Hartford, CT 06155-0001
Tel (860) 547-5000 *Founded/Ownrshp* 1810
Sales NA *EMP* 17,500
Tkr Sym HIG *Exch* NYS
SIC 6331 6311 6351 6321 Fire, marine & casualty insurance; Property damage insurance; Automobile insurance; Workers' compensation insurance; Life insurance; Life insurance carriers; Life reinsurance; Surety insurance; Liability insurance; Accident & health insurance; Accident insurance carriers; Health insurance carriers; Fire, marine & casualty insurance; Property damage insurance; Automobile insurance; Workers' compensation insurance; Life insurance; Life insurance carriers; Life reinsurance; Surety insurance; Liability insurance; Accident & health insurance; Accident insurance carriers; Health insurance carriers
Ch Bd: Christopher J Swift
Pr: James E Davey
Pr: Douglas Elliot
Pr: Michele Frost
Pr: Debra Hampson
Pr: Brion Johnson
Pr: Kevin Yorgensen
Pr: Kenneth Zygiel
CFO: Beth A Bombara
Bd of Dir: Marc Sacher
Chf Mktg O: Stephanie Pritchett
Ex VP: William A Bloom
Ex VP: Martha Gervasi
Ex VP: Alan J Kreczko
Ex VP: Robert Rupp
Ex VP: Raymond J Sprague
Sr VP: Scott R Lewis
Comm Man: Jamie Theroux
Board of Directors: H Patrick Swygert, Robert B Allardice III, Trevor Fetter, Kathryn A Mikells, Michael G Morris, Thomas A Renyi, Julie G Richardson, Teresa Wynn Roseborough, Virginia P Ruesterholz, Charles B Strauss

HARTFORD FINANCIAL SVCS GROUP
See HARTFORD INSURANCE CO OF ILLINOIS

D-U-N-S 00-691-7181
■ **HARTFORD FIRE INSURANCE CO (INC)**
(*Suby of* HARTFORD FINANCIAL SERVICES GROUP INC) ★
1 Hartford Plz, Hartford, CT 06115-1703
Tel (860) 547-5000 *Founded/Ownrshp* 1810
Sales NA *EMP* 18,800
SIC 6411 6311 6351 7373 Insurance agents, brokers & service; Life insurance; Surety insurance; Fidelity insurance; Systems integration services; Insurance agents, brokers & service; Life insurance; Surety insurance; Fidelity insurance; Systems integration services
CEO: Liam E McGee
Pr: Jaci Coleman
Treas: James R Garrett
Ofcr: Timothy Carling
Ex VP: Brad Burdick
Ex VP: Srini Krishnamurthy
Sr VP: Peggy Anson
Sr VP: Jack T Crawford
Sr VP: Scott Lewis
Sr VP: Michael O'Halleran
Sr VP: Michael Ohalleran
Sr VP: Paul Schwartzott
VP: Christopher Abreu
VP: Patrick Greiten
VP: Othia Horn
VP: Tom Jones
VP: Shannon Lapierre
VP: Wade Seward
Exec: Stephanie Dimasso
Exec: Laurie Scotti

D-U-N-S 62-458-5576
HARTFORD FOUNDATION FOR PUBLIC GIVING
10 Columbus Blvd Fl 8, Hartford, CT 06106-1976
Tel (860) 548-1888 *Founded/Ownrshp* 1925
Sales 113.4MM *EMP* 40
Accts Blum Shapiro & Company Pc
SIC 6732 8733 Charitable trust management; Noncommercial research organizations; Charitable trust management; Noncommercial research organizations
Pr: Linda J Kelly
CFO: Virgil Blondet
Ofcr: Yvette Bello
Ofcr: Carol Buckheit
Ofcr: George Chappell
Ofcr: Wanda Correa
Ofcr: Gretchen Fountain
Ofcr: Dawn Grant
Ofcr: Jennyfer Holmes
Ofcr: Mary Macdonald
Ofcr: Judy McBride
Ofcr: Deborah Rothstein
Ofcr: Doug Shipman
Ofcr: Sally Weisman
Ofcr: Maggie Willard
Ofcr: Tom Zeleznock
Sr Inv Off: Alison Granger
VP: Christopher H All
VP: Nancy Benben
VP: Cyrus Driver
Exec: Louise Galvin

D-U-N-S 18-688-5687
HARTFORD HEALTHCARE CORP
1 State St Fl 19, Hartford, CT 06103-3102
Tel (860) 545-5000 *Founded/Ownrshp* 1985
Sales 2.1MMM *EMP* 5,100
Accts Ernst & Young Llp Hartford
SIC 8059 Personal care home, with health care; Personal care home, with health care
Ch Bd: Andrew Salner MD
Pt: James Fantus
**Pr:* Elliot Joseph
**CFO:* Jeffrey A Flaks
CFO: Thomas J Marchozzi
**CFO:* Thomas Marcozzi
**Treas:* Raymond Kowalski
Ofcr: Jim Bowman
Ex VP: James P Cardon
Ex VP: Patricia Walden
Sr VP: James M Blazar
Sr VP: Rocco Orlando III
Sr VP: Richard Stys
Sr VP: Luis E Taveras
VP: Chris Carlin
VP: Tricia Hasselman
Exec: Tracy Church

D-U-N-S 14-457-7959
■ **HARTFORD HOLDINGS INC**
(*Suby of* HARTFORD FINANCIAL SERVICES GROUP INC) ★
200 Hopmeadow St, Simsbury, CT 06070
Tel (860) 547-5000 *Founded/Ownrshp* 2002
Sales NA *EMP* 7,501
SIC 6311 Life insurance; Life insurance
Pr: Thomas M Marra
**Ch Bd:* Ramani Ayer

D-U-N-S 06-553-3796
HARTFORD HOSPITAL
80 Seymour St, Hartford, CT 06102-8000
Tel (860) 545-5555 *Founded/Ownrshp* 1986
Sales 986.6MM *EMP* 7,500
SIC 8062 General medical & surgical hospitals; General medical & surgical hospitals
Pr: Jeffrey A Flaks
COO: Janice Giuca
CFO: Tom Marchozzi
Sr VP: James Blazar
Sr VP: Luis Tavares
VP: Gerry J Boisvert
VP: Laurine Bow
VP: Chris Carlin
Assoc Dir: Marcin R Dada
Assoc Dir: John Mah
Assoc Dir: Mickey Orkin
Assoc Dir: Steven Zweibel
Dir Bus: Peter Kowalski
Mng Ofcr: Rocco Orlando

D-U-N-S 96-493-6272
HARTFORD HOSPITAL REHABILITATION NETWORK
181 Patricia M Genova Dr # 5, Newington, CT 06111-1500
Tel (860) 696-2500 *Founded/Ownrshp* 1995
Sales 16.8MM^E^ *EMP* 400
SIC 8049 Physical therapist; Physical therapist
CFO: Catherine Anderson

D-U-N-S 78-695-4776
■ **HARTFORD INSURANCE CO OF ILLINOIS**
HARTFORD FINANCIAL SVCS GROUP
(*Suby of* HARTFORD FIRE INSURANCE CO (INC)) ★
690 Asylum Ave, Hartford, CT 06105-3845
Tel (860) 547-5000 *Founded/Ownrshp* 1979
Sales NA *EMP* 5,001
SIC 6411 Insurance agents, brokers & service; Insurance agents, brokers & service
Pr: David K Zwiener
Pr: Jim Daley
Pr: Betsy Enloe
**Pr:* David K Zwiener
**CFO:* Michael J Dury
CFO: Rick Fergeson
CFO: Raymond Godin
CFO: John Hess
CFO: Thomas Johnston
CFO: Christopher Swift
CFO: Marilyn Wyman
Assoc VP: Patrick Brown
Ex VP: David M Johnson
Ex VP: Alan Kreczko
Ex VP: Judith Patterson
Ex VP: Illene Whelley
Sr VP: Brenda J Furlong
Sr VP: Randall I Kiviat
Sr VP: Christine H Repasy
Sr VP: William J Smith
VP: Andrea Gardner
Board of Directors: Timothy Galvin III, David P Halper, Donald J Lavalley, Debora G Westcott, Richard S Wilcox

D-U-N-S 78-695-6227
■ **HARTFORD INVESTMENT MANAGEMENT CO**
HIMCO
(*Suby of* HARTFORD FINANCIAL SERVICES GROUP INC) ★
1 Hartford Plz, Hartford, CT 06155-0001
Tel (860) 297-6700 *Founded/Ownrshp* 2008
Sales 234.0MM^E^ *EMP* 220
SIC 6282 Investment advice; Investment advice
Pr: Brion Johnson
Pr: Curtis Koppang
Ofcr: Robert Lewton
Ex VP: Joseph Darcy
Ex VP: Erica Evans
Ex VP: Christopher Hanlon
Ex VP: Bill Holm
Ex VP: Richard Van Steenbergen
Ex VP: Mark Waterhouse
Sr VP: Ryan Bloom
Sr VP: Paul Bukowski
Sr VP: Adriane Collimore
Sr VP: Jim Comnofly
Sr VP: Eric Fay
Sr VP: Jun Han
Sr VP: William Holm
Sr VP: Gregory Kuhl
Sr VP: Michael Mondo
Sr VP: Kevin Nolin
Sr VP: Harry Norman
Sr VP: Chris Paolino

D-U-N-S 15-118-0270
■ **HARTFORD LIFE AND ACCIDENT INSURANCE CO INC**
(*Suby of* HARTFORD LIFE INC) ★
200 Hopmeadow St, Weatogue, CT 06089-9793
Tel (860) 547-5000 *Founded/Ownrshp* 1993
Sales NA *EMP* 5,000
SIC 6311 Life insurance; Life insurance
CEO: Liam E McGee
**Pr:* Thomas M Marra
Ex VP: Sharon Ritchey
Ex VP: Robert Rupp
Sr VP: Robert Arena
Sr VP: Peter Sannizzaro
VP: Gregory A Boyko
**VP:* Thomas A Campbell
VP: Stuart Carlisle
VP: Mary Jane Fortin
VP: James Jflynn
VP: Peg Lesiak
VP: Ernest McNeill
**VP:* Christine H Repsy
VP: Diane Tatelman
Exec: Richard Costello

D-U-N-S 07-478-1253
■ **HARTFORD LIFE AND ANNUITY INSURANCE CO**
(*Suby of* HARTFORD LIFE INC) ★
200 Hopmeadow St, Weatogue, CT 06089-9793
Tel (860) 547-5000 *Founded/Ownrshp* 2008
Sales NA *EMP* 15
SIC 6311 6321 Life insurance carriers; Accident insurance carriers; Health insurance carriers
Ex VP: Thomas Marra
Pr: Ramani Ayer
Treas: Gregory Boyko
Off Mgr: Don Lavalley

D-U-N-S 01-720-6447
■ **HARTFORD LIFE INC**
(*Suby of* HARTFORD HOLDINGS INC) ★
200 Hopmeadow St, Simsbury, CT 06070
Tel (860) 547-5000 *Founded/Ownrshp* 1997
Sales NA *EMP* 7,500
SIC 6311 Life insurance; Life insurance
Ch Bd: Ramani Ayer
Pr: John Enos
**CFO:* Glenn Lammey
CFO: Lizabeth Zlatkus
**Ex VP:* Gregory Boyko
**Ex VP:* Michael Kalen
Ex VP: Sharon A Ritchey
**Sr VP:* Terry Walker
Sr VP: Raymond P Welnicki
VP: Shelia Hagan
VP: Mark Socha
Dir Bus: Karen Cramer

D-U-N-S 04-303-1459
■ **HARTFORD LIFE INSURANCE CO**
(*Suby of* HARTFORD LIFE INC) ★
200 Hopmeadow St, Weatogue, CT 06089-9793
Tel (860) 547-5000 *Founded/Ownrshp* 1902
Sales NA *EMP* 3^E^
Accts Deloitte & Touche Llp Hartfor
SIC 6411 Insurance agents, brokers & service; Insurance agents, brokers & service
Pr: Brion S Johnson
Pr: Jeff Zyonse
CFO: Elisabeth Zlatkus
Ex VP: Lizabeth Zlatkus
Sr VP: David Bowen
**Sr VP:* Mark Niland
Sr VP: Peter F Sannizzaro
VP: Gregory Boyko
VP: Michael Casey
VP: Donna Jarvis
Prgrm Mgr: Terri Lindahl

D-U-N-S 80-884-5382
HARTFORD LIFE PRIVATE PLACEMENT LLC
(*Suby of* PHILADELPHIA FINANCIAL GROUP INC) ★
100 Campus Dr Ste 250, Florham Park, NJ 07932-1023
Tel (973) 966-5522 *Founded/Ownrshp* 2012
Sales NA *EMP* 120^E^
SIC 6411 8742 Insurance agents, brokers & service; Management consulting services
Pr: Joseph Mahoney
CFO: James Van Etten
Ex VP: David Bedard
VP: Neil Chaffee
VP: Keven Cruz
VP: James Hedreen
VP: Michael Jandoli
VP: Gerard Martin
VP: Paul Reiss
Exec: Natalie Fazendeiro

D-U-N-S 05-779-9637
HARTFORD PROVISION CO
HPC FOODSERVICE
625 Nutmeg Rd N, South Windsor, CT 06074-2440
Tel (860) 583-3908 *Founded/Ownrshp* 1908
Sales 172.2MM^E^ *EMP* 130
SIC 5141 Groceries, general line; Groceries, general line
Pr: Barry Pearson
**Treas:* Jeff Lotstein
**VP:* Michael Faeth
**VP:* Bob Lopena
**VP:* Richard Lotstein

HARTFORD PUBLIC SCHOOLS
See HARTFORD SCHOOL DISTRICT

HARTFORD RETIREMENT SVCS LLC
See MASSMUTUAL RETIREMENT SERVICES LLC

D-U-N-S 04-171-3541
HARTFORD SCHOOL DISTRICT
HARTFORD PUBLIC SCHOOLS
960 Main St Fl 9, Hartford, CT 06103-1218
Tel (860) 695-8400 *Founded/Ownrshp* 2002
Sales 139.2MM^E^ *EMP* 2,797^E^
SIC 8211 Public elementary & secondary schools; Public elementary & secondary schools
**Ch:* Matthew K Poland
Exec: Guillermo Garcia
Exec: Nancy Santiago
Exec: Paul Stringer
Dir Sec: Joseph Sikora
CIO: Sabina Sitaru
IT Man: Madeline Vasquez
Pr Dir: David Medina
Pr Dir: Kelvin Roldan
Schl Brd P: Richard Wareing
HC Dir: Deborah Chameides

D-U-N-S 10-060-7258
HARTFORD SCHOOL DISTRICT
1 Gifford Rd, White River Junction, VT 05001-8021
Tel (802) 295-8600 *Founded/Ownrshp* 2010
Sales 32.4MM *EMP* 500
Accts Pace & Hawle Llc Montpelier
SIC 8211 Public senior high school; Public senior high school
Treas: Derry Goodwin
Teacher Pr: Byron Baribeau

D-U-N-S 15-262-3195
HARTFORD SOUTH LLC
7326 S Orange Ave, Orlando, FL 32809-6055
Tel (407) 438-9773 *Founded/Ownrshp* 1986
Sales 24.9MM^E^ *EMP* 120
SIC 1761 Roofing contractor; Roofing contractor
Pr: Jay A Rintelmann
Treas: Danyel Sullivan-Marrero
Snr PM: Donny Cammenga

D-U-N-S 11-836-9214
■ **HARTFORD SPECIALTY CO**
(*Suby of* HARTFORD ACCIDENT & INDEMNITY CO) ★
Hartford Plz, Hartford, CT 06115
Tel (860) 547-4202 *Founded/Ownrshp* 1981
Sales NA *EMP* 450
SIC 6331 Fire, marine & casualty insurance; Property damage insurance; Fire, marine & casualty insurance; Property damage insurance
Pr: David R Bradley
Sr VP: Richard Collier
VP: Gregory Boyko
VP: Brian D First
VP: Craig Quinility

HARTFORD STEAM
See TEN COMPANIES LLC

D-U-N-S 00-691-7223
HARTFORD STEAM BOILER INSPECTION AND INSURANCE CO
HSBIIC
(*Suby of* MUNICH-AMERICAN HOLDING CORP) ★
1 State St Fl 5-12, Hartford, CT 06103-3102
Tel (860) 722-1866 *Founded/Ownrshp* 1866
Sales NA *EMP* 1,216^E^
SIC 6331 8711 7373 8742 Boiler insurance; Consulting engineer; Systems software development services; Maintenance management consultant; Boiler insurance; Consulting engineer; Systems software development services; Maintenance management consultant
Pr: Gregg Barats
Pr: Edward Condon
CFO: Normand Mercier
**CFO:* Peter Richter
**Treas:* Ted Kmiascik
Ex VP: Anthony Trivella
Sr VP: Loren Shoemaker
Sr VP: Tony Trivella
VP: Joseph Conklin
**VP:* Roberta A O'Brien
VP: Denis O'Shea
VP: J A Smith
VP: Nancy Teed
Exec: Peter Tingus

D-U-N-S 94-224-9368
HARTFORD STEAM BOILER INSPECTION AND INSURANCE CO OF CONNECTICUT
HSBCT
(*Suby of* GLOBAL STANDARDS, LLC)
1 State St Fl 5-12, Hartford, CT 06103-3102
Tel (860) 722-5057 *Founded/Ownrshp* 2009
Sales 33.1MM[E] *EMP* 515
SIC 7389 8711 6311 Industrial & commercial equipment inspection service; Engineering services; Life reinsurance; Industrial & commercial equipment inspection service; Engineering services; Life reinsurance
Pr: Fred Bull
Sr VP: Loren Shoemaker
**VP:* Jean Cohn
VP: Joseph Conklin
VP: Douglas Marshall
Mng Dir: Catherine Coseno
Netwrk Mgr: Larry Pisani

D-U-N-S 06-925-0967
HARTFORD STEAM CO (CT)
(*Suby of* HARTFORD STEAM) ★
60 Columbus Blvd, Hartford, CT 06103-2805
Tel (860) 548-7350 *Founded/Ownrshp* 1962, 1982
Sales 26.8MM[E] *EMP* 30
SIC 4961 Steam heating systems (suppliers of heat); Air conditioning supply services; Steam heating systems (suppliers of heat); Air conditioning supply services
Ch: Arthur Marquardt
**Pr:* James Laurito
**Pr:* Derek H Rudd
**CFO:* Frank E Dicola
**Treas:* Curtis I Call
**Treas:* Andy Johnson
**Sr VP:* Anthony Mirabella
**VP:* Timothy Canavan
**VP:* Michael Jingoli
**VP:* David Robbins Jr
Genl Mgr: Jeffrey Lindberg

HARTFORD TOYOTA SUPERSTORE
See MAC MOTORS INC

D-U-N-S 02-720-3967
HARTFORD UNION HIGH SCHOOL DISTRICT
805 Cedar St, Hartford, WI 53027-2303
Tel (262) 670-3200 *Founded/Ownrshp* 2006
Sales 21.0MM[E] *EMP* 202
Accts Hawkins Ash Baptie & Company
SIC 8211 Public elementary & secondary schools; Public elementary & secondary schools
Ex Dir: Michael Kremer
Ofcr: Eric Rasmussen
MIS Dir: Chad Behnke

D-U-N-S 00-586-9193
HARTIG DRUG CO (IA)
HARTIG USA DRUG
703 Main St, Dubuque, IA 52001-6814
Tel (563) 588-8700 *Founded/Ownrshp* 1904
Sales 65.5MM[E] *EMP* 300
SIC 5912 Drug stores; Drug stores
CEO: D Ick Hartig
**Pr:* Keith J Bibelhausen
**CEO:* Dick Hartig
**Sec:* Marilyn A Kammiller
VP: John Meyer
Dir IT: John Klein
Mktg Dir: Jennifer Quick
Pharmcst: Emily Vyverberg

HARTIG USA DRUG
See HARTIG DRUG CO

D-U-N-S 18-460-7174 IMP
HARTING INC OF NORTH AMERICA
(*Suby of* HARTING KGAA)
1370 Bowes Rd, Elgin, IL 60123-5556
Tel (847) 741-1500 *Founded/Ownrshp* 2012
Sales 45.9MM[E] *EMP* 100
SIC 5065 3678 Connectors, electronic; Electronic connectors; Connectors, electronic; Electronic connectors
Ch Bd: Dietmar Harting
Sr VP: Margrit Harting
Sr VP: Maresa Harting-Hertz
Sr VP: Michael Putz
Mng Dir: Ellen McMillan
Mng Dir: Soeren Montag
Rgnl Mgr: Peter Addison
Rgnl Mgr: Mike Brookes
Area Mgr: Dale Adamski
Area Mgr: Jeremy Bechtol
Area Mgr: Drew Carstens

D-U-N-S 09-301-6012
HARTJE LUMBER INC
HARTJE TRASPORT
E4525a Schuette Rd, La Valle, WI 53941-9210
Tel (608) 985-7207 *Founded/Ownrshp* 1969
Sales 30.5MM *EMP* 50
Accts Engelson & Associates Ltd L
SIC 5211 5031 Lumber & other building materials; Lumber: rough, dressed & finished; Lumber & other building materials; Lumber: rough, dressed & finished
Pr: Virgil Hartje
**Treas:* Mary Neary
**VP:* Michael Hartje

HARTJE TRASPORT
See HARTJE LUMBER INC

D-U-N-S 04-057-8718
HARTLAND CONSOLIDATED SCHOOLS
9525 E Highland Rd, Howell, MI 48843-9098
Tel (810) 626-2100 *Founded/Ownrshp* 2005
Sales 33.7MM[E] *EMP* 650
SIC 8211 Public elementary & secondary schools; Public elementary & secondary schools
**Pr:* Kevin Kaszyca
**Treas:* Charlie Aberasturi
**VP:* Thom Dumond
Dir IT: Scott Usher

D-U-N-S 83-921-6785
HARTLAND FUEL PRODUCTS LLC
920 10th Ave N, Onalaska, WI 54650-2166
Tel (715) 842-3863 *Founded/Ownrshp* 1995
Sales 82.9MM[E] *EMP* 35
SIC 5172 Petroleum products
VP: Jeff Mackeben
IT Man: Heather Murphy

D-U-N-S 85-976-8244
HARTLAND INSURANCE GROUP INC
691 N Squirrel Rd Ste 190, Auburn Hills, MI 48326-2863
Tel (248) 377-9600 *Founded/Ownrshp* 1998
Sales NA *EMP* 160
SIC 6411 Insurance agents & brokers; Insurance agents & brokers
Pr: Raymond Elliott
VP: Peter Elliott

D-U-N-S 00-281-3202 IMP
HARTLEY & PARKER LIMITED INC (CT)
100 Browning St, Stratford, CT 06615-7170
Tel (203) 375-5671 *Founded/Ownrshp* 1941
Sales 115.0MM[E] *EMP* 150
SIC 5182 Liquor; Wine; Liquor; Wine
Pr: Julius Rosenberg
Chf Mktg O: David Nathanson
**VP:* David Rosenberg
**VP:* Jerry Rosenberg
Dept Mgr: Gary Wilhelm
Dist Mgr: Tramazzo Blaise
Dist Mgr: Drew Hoyle
Dist Mgr: Earl Parent
IT Man: Terry Wilhelm
Sls Mgr: Frank Latorra
Sls Mgr: Scott Randall

D-U-N-S 01-756-6035
HARTLEY CO
FLEMINGS-DIV
319 Wheeling Ave, Cambridge, OH 43725-2245
Tel (740) 432-2328 *Founded/Ownrshp* 1957
Sales 174.2MM *EMP* 125
Accts Rea & Associates Inc Cambri
SIC 5541 5172 Filling stations, gasoline; Petroleum products; Filling stations, gasoline; Petroleum products
Ch: William H Hartley
**Pr:* Thomas C Hartley
Sr VP: Eric Johnson
**VP:* Joan Gross
**VP:* William H Hartley III

D-U-N-S 06-555-6607
HARTLEY GRAIN CO INC
H G TRANSPORT
100 S Cob St, Elwood, IN 46036-8419
Tel (765) 552-7311 *Founded/Ownrshp* 1973
Sales 32.9MM *EMP* 8
Accts Somerset Cpa S Pc Indianapol
SIC 5153 5191 Grain elevators; Fertilizer & fertilizer materials; Chemicals, agricultural; Grain elevators; Fertilizer & fertilizer materials; Chemicals, agricultural
Pr: Bruce D Hartley

D-U-N-S 84-703-5144
HARTLINE DACUS BARGER DREYER LLP
8750 N Cntl Expy Ste 1600, Dallas, TX 75231
Tel (214) 369-2100 *Founded/Ownrshp* 1994
Sales 23.0MM[E] *EMP* 105[E]
SIC 8111 Patent, trademark & copyright law; General practice law office
Pt: Richard W Crews
Pt: Darrell Barger
Pt: John C Dacus
Pt: Kyle Dreyer
Pt: Scott Edwards
Pt: Larry Grayson
Pt: Vermon Hartline
Pt: Jeffrey Patterson
Mng Pt: Thomas Fitzsimmons
Pr: Cindy Parnell
Pr: Kim Tucker
VP: Bellanne Toren

D-U-N-S 09-332-7260
HARTMAN & HARTMAN INC
67 Seal Rd, Eighty Four, PA 15330-1828
Tel (724) 239-6002 *Founded/Ownrshp* 1989
Sales 61.8MM[E] *EMP* 100
SIC 1541 1711 1731

D-U-N-S 07-840-2948
HARTMAN AND TYNER INC (MI)
GEORGIAN MANOR APTS
24700 W 12 Mile Rd, Southfield, MI 48034-1218
Tel (248) 352-2010 *Founded/Ownrshp* 1933, 1953
Sales 33.5MM[E] *EMP* 1,000
SIC 6513 6531 Apartment building operators; Real estate agents & managers; Apartment building operators; Real estate agents & managers
Pr: Herbert Tyner
**Treas:* Ala Julie
**VP:* Daniel Adkins
Dir Risk M: Joy Frederick
Dir IT: Paul Gorman

HARTMAN DISTRIBUTING CO
See FALSTAFF SALES CO OF VICTORIA INC

D-U-N-S 08-773-2194
HARTMAN NEWSPAPERS LP
1914 4th St, Rosenberg, TX 77471-5140
Tel (281) 342-8691 *Founded/Ownrshp* 1974
Sales 35.6MM[E] *EMP* 200
SIC 2711 Newspapers, publishing & printing; Newspapers, publishing & printing
Pt: J W Hartman
Pt: Fred B Hartman

D-U-N-S 08-584-9412
HARTMANN STUDIOS INC
IMPACT LIGHTING & PRODUCTION
70 W Ohio Ave Ste H, Richmond, CA 94804-2033
Tel (510) 232-5060 *Founded/Ownrshp* 1988
Sales 26.3MM[E] *EMP* 150
SIC 7389 Convention & show services; Convention & show services
Pr: Matt Guelfi
**VP:* Matthew Guelfi
VP: Scott Lowry
Genl Mgr: Wright Summers
Off Mgr: Jessica Titshaw
IT Man: Dan Paladini
Opers Mgr: Errol Stewart
Prd Mgr: Jeff Bogan
Sales Asso: Toni Hill
Sales Asso: Melanie Leinweber
Sales Asso: Nikki Rege

D-U-N-S 01-013-7511 IMP
HARTMANN USA INC
(*Suby of* PAUL HARTMANN AG)
481 Lakeshore Pkwy, Rock Hill, SC 29730-4205
Tel (803) 325-7600 *Founded/Ownrshp* 2001
Sales 44.7MM[E] *EMP* 198
SIC 3842 Bandages & dressings; Gauze, surgical; Splints, pneumatic & wood; Bandages & dressings; Gauze, surgical; Splints, pneumatic & wood
Pr: John Gilbert
CFO: Bryan Sherrel
**CFO:* James W Worthy
Exec: Ernie Goulet
Rgnl Mgr: Stephanie Klevorn
IT Man: Josh Dixon
VP Opers: Steve Gusse
Plnt Mgr: Marty Rawls
Sales Exec: Jeff Chamberlain
Natl Sales: Bobbie Camp
VP Sls: Kevin Rooney

D-U-N-S 08-701-6606
HARTNELL COLLEGE
411 Central Ave, Salinas, CA 93901-1688
Tel (831) 755-6700 *Founded/Ownrshp* 1920
Sales 24.4MM[E] *EMP* 500
SIC 8222 8221 Community college; Colleges universities & professional schools; Community college; Colleges universities & professional schools
Pr: Willard Clark Lewallen
**Pr:* Phoebe Helm
CFO: Gemma Uribe
VP: Suzanne Flannigan
VP: Lori Kildal
VP: Stephanie Low
VP: Steve McShane
Comm Dir: Esmeralda Montenegro-Owen
MIS Dir: William Pertle
Psych: Mitzi Nohr
Psych: Martha Pantoja

D-U-N-S 07-804-9640
■ **HARTNESS HOLDINGS INC** (SC)
(*Suby of* ILLINOIS TOOL WORKS INC) ★
500 Hartness Dr, Greenville, SC 29615-7502
Tel (864) 297-1200 *Founded/Ownrshp* 1973, 2009
Sales 8.0M *EMP* 420
SIC 6719 Packaging machinery; Industrial machinery & equipment; Investment holding companies, except banks
CEO: Thomas Heartness
**Owner:* Pat Hartness
**Pr:* Thomas P Hartness
**CFO:* Lamar Jordan
**Treas:* Robert G Hartness
**VP:* Scott Smith

D-U-N-S 06-641-0457
■ **HARTON JOHN W REGIONAL MEDICAL CENTER INC**
HARTON REGIONAL MEDICAL CENTER
(*Suby of* HEALTH MANAGEMENT ASSOCIATES INC) ★
1801 N Jackson St, Tullahoma, TN 37388-8259
Tel (931) 393-3000 *Founded/Ownrshp* 2003
Sales 81.5MM[E] *EMP* 500
SIC 8062 General medical & surgical hospitals; General medical & surgical hospitals
CEO: Russ Spray
**COO:* Larry Leter
**COO:* Steven Sayler
**CFO:* Shaun Adams
VP: Edna High
Dir Rad: Ginger Baker
Ansthlgy: Charles Padget
Diag Rad: Joel Birdwell
Diag Rad: Grant Ordiway

HARTON REGIONAL MEDICAL CENTER
See HARTON JOHN W REGIONAL MEDICAL CENTER INC

D-U-N-S 01-595-6162 IMP
HARTREE PARTNERS LP
HETCO
1185 Ave Of The Americas, New York, NY 10036-2601
Tel (212) 536-8915 *Founded/Ownrshp* 1997, 2014
Sales 719.9MM[E] *EMP* 200[E]
SIC 1382 6221 Petroleum refining; Commodity contracts brokers, dealers; Aerial geophysical exploration oil & gas; Commodity contracts brokers, dealers
Pt: Toby Davies
Pt: Hugh Edmondson
Pt: Stephen M Hendel
Pt: Jason Lemme
Pt: Guy Merison
VP: Lewis Chan
Mng Dir: Stephen Semlitz

D-U-N-S 10-000-0488
HARTSELLE CITY BOARD OF EDUCATION
HARTSELLE CITY SCHOOLS
305 College St Ne, Hartselle, AL 35640-1938
Tel (256) 773-5419 *Founded/Ownrshp* 1975
Sales 24.1MM[E] *EMP* 380
SIC 8211 Public combined elementary & secondary school; School board; Public combined elementary & secondary school; School board
**Prin:* Robin Varwig
Teacher Pr: Jan Bird

HARTSELLE CITY SCHOOLS
See HARTSELLE CITY BOARD OF EDUCATION

D-U-N-S 07-989-3938
HARTSELLE CITY SCHOOLS
305 College St Ne, Hartselle, AL 35640-1938
Tel (256) 773-5419 *Founded/Ownrshp* 2015
Sales 3.0MM[E] *EMP* 354[E]
SIC 8211 Public elementary & secondary schools

D-U-N-S 16-138-5018
HARTSELLE UTILITIES
1010 Sparkman St Nw, Hartselle, AL 35640-4530
Tel (256) 773-3340 *Founded/Ownrshp* 1989
Sales 34.1MM[E] *EMP* 53[E]
SIC 4941 4952 4932 1623 Water supply; Sewerage systems; Gas & other services combined; Water, sewer & utility lines
Ch Bd: Mark Gunter
**Sec:* Terry Phililips
Sfty Mgr: Greg Sandlin

HARTSFIELD-JACKSON ATLNTA INT'
See CITY OF ATLANTA DEPARTMENT OF AVIATION

D-U-N-S 00-653-7690
HARTSIG SUPPLY CO INC (MI)
3885 Auburn Rd, Auburn Hills, MI 48326-3325
Tel (248) 852-3900 *Founded/Ownrshp* 1963
Sales 23.8MM[E] *EMP* 25
SIC 5082 5074 Wellpoints (drilling equipment); Heating equipment (hydronic)
Pr: Donald R Landerschier
**Prin:* Keith Bull
**Prin:* Dave Landerschier
**Prin:* Don Landerschier Sr
**Prin:* Scott Landerschier

D-U-N-S 00-605-4779
HARTSON-KENNEDY CABINET TOP CO INC
522 W 22nd St, Marion, IN 46953-2926
Tel (765) 673-0451 *Founded/Ownrshp* 1948
Sales 90.8MM[E] *EMP* 563
SIC 3083 Plastic finished products, laminated; Plastic finished products, laminated
Pr: William Kennedy
**VP:* Christopher L Kennedy
Off Mgr: Mark Nelson
IT Man: Jennifer Fettig
Sales Exec: Glen Divit
Natl Sales: Doug Burkhardt

D-U-N-S 07-372-2498
HARTSVILLE LLC
CAROLINA PNES REGIONAL MED CTR
(*Suby of* CAPELLA HEALTHCARE INC) ★
1304 W Bobo Newsom Hwy, Hartsville, SC 29550-4710
Tel (843) 339-2100 *Founded/Ownrshp* 2014
Sales 94.6MM *EMP* 625
SIC 8011 General medical & surgical hospitals; Medical centers
CEO: Timothy Browne
**CFO:* Anthony J Seminaro
Dir Risk M: Candace Morton
Dir Rad: Steven Rogers
Surgeon: Jacqueline Mixon
Doctor: Sally Regan
Pgrm Dir: Abraham Areephanthu
Snr Mgr: Naomi Holley

D-U-N-S 06-184-7612
HARTT TRANSPORTATION SYSTEMS INC (ME)
262 Bomarc Rd, Bangor, ME 04401-2655
Tel (207) 947-1106 *Founded/Ownrshp* 1972
Sales 129.0MM *EMP* 562[E]
SIC 4213

D-U-N-S 06-043-8439
HARTUNG BROTHERS INC
708 Heartland Trl # 2000, Madison, WI 53717-2172
Tel (608) 829-6000 *Founded/Ownrshp* 1975
Sales 120.0MM *EMP* 500
Accts Smith & Gesteland Llp Madiso
SIC 0161 0115 8748 Vegetables & melons; Corn; Business consulting; Vegetables & melons; Corn; Business consulting
Pr: Dan Hartung
**VP:* Donald Hartung
**VP:* James Noltner
Genl Mgr: Don Bennett
Board of Directors: Galen Hartung, James Hartung, John Hartung, Randy Hartung, Robert Hartung, Tara Mc Donald, Gayle Noltner

D-U-N-S 00-948-2753 IMP
HARTUNG GLASS INDUSTRIES INC
17830 W Valley Hwy, Tukwila, WA 98188-5532
Tel (425) 656-2626 *Founded/Ownrshp* 2004
Sales 160.3MM[E] *EMP* 402
SIC 5023 3211 Glassware; Flat glass; Glassware; Flat glass
Pr: Nick Sciola
**CFO:* Richard Jamieson
Dir IT: Carrie Dick
MIS Mgr: Carey Dyck
Software D: Riley Dyck
Opers Mgr: Bob Miller
Plnt Mgr: Mark Etscheid
Prd Mgr: Ken Nordyke
Manager: Sue Morton
Sls Mgr: Bob Morse
Sls Mgr: Jason Walsh

D-U-N-S 14-125-3679
HARTVILLE GROUP INC
1210 Massillon Rd, Akron, OH 44306-3327
Tel (330) 484-8166 *Founded/Ownrshp* 2000
Sales NA *EMP* 67[E]
SIC 6399 Health insurance for pets
Pr: Dennis C Rushovich
Ch Bd: Nicholas J Leighton
Pr: Chris Chaney
CFO: Christopher R Sachs
Chf Mktg O: Christopher Edgar
Chf Mktg O: Christopher Edgar
Ex VP: Hirsch C Ribakow
VP: Mary Leininger
VP: Lynn Thompson
VP Bus Dev: Rob Hall
Comm Man: Lisa Hockensmith

Board of Directors: Michel Amsalem, Lawrence Geneen, Alan J Kaufman

D-U-N-S 10-545-3794 IMP
HARTVILLE HARDWARE INC
JOHN DEERE
(*Suby of* HRM ENTERPRISES INC) ★
1315 Edison St Nw, Hartville, OH 44632-9046
Tel (330) 877-4690 *Founded/Ownrshp* 1972
Sales 71.8MM^E *EMP* 210
SIC 5251 Hardware; Hardware
Pr: Howard Miller Jr
**VP:* Wayne Miller
Dept Mgr: Mary Smith
Dir IT: Micale Scott
Opers Mgr: Dan Wolf
Sls&Mrk Ex: Christa Domer
Sales Asso: Matt Maranville
Sales Asso: Bill Melvin

HARTWELL APPAREL
See HARTWELL INDUSTRIES INC

D-U-N-S 00-828-6536 IMP
■ HARTWELL CORP
HASCO
(*Suby of* MCKECHNIE AEROSPACE INVESTMENTS, INC.)
900 Richfield Rd, Placentia, CA 92870-6788
Tel (714) 993-2752 *Founded/Ownrshp* 2012
Sales 152.5MM^E *EMP* 1,000
SIC 3429 Aircraft hardware; Aircraft hardware
CEO: Joel Reiss
Pr: Chris Cummings
**Pr:* John Leary
**CFO:* Vicki Saugstad
VP: J Chambers
VP: Simon Elliot
VP: Jim Swanke
Genl Mgr: George Postlethwait
Dir IT: David Gwilt
Dir IT: Cinda Singer
IT Man: Suzanne Baeza

D-U-N-S 03-198-6651 IMP
HARTWELL INDUSTRIES INC
HARTWELL APPAREL
(*Suby of* PATRIARCH PARTNERS LLC) ★
97 Winfield Cir, Hartwell, GA 30643-1954
Tel (706) 856-4900 *Founded/Ownrshp* 2005
Sales 34.8MM^E *EMP* 45
SIC 5137 5136 Women's & children's clothing; Men's & boys' clothing
CEO: Bob Shell
**CFO:* Jason Burr
VP: Angela Church
VP: Julius Ill
IT Man: Russell Reed
VP Sls: Bert Severns
S&M/VP: Doug Ball
Manager: John Ronan

D-U-N-S 02-067-2374
HARTWICK COLLEGE
1 Hartwick Dr, Oneonta, NY 13820-4000
Tel (607) 431-4000 *Founded/Ownrshp* 1797
Sales 81.8MM *EMP* 475^E
SIC 8221 Colleges & universities; Colleges & universities
Pr: Margaret L Drugovich
**Pr:* Richard Detweiler
Treas: Connie Anderson
VP: Jim Broschart
VP: Ellen Falduto
VP: Meg Nowak
VP: Michael Tannenbaum
Ex Dir: Mary Vanderlaan
Off Admin: Jillian Malnati
Off Admin: Bernadette Roberts
CTO: Peter Fiduccia

HARTWIG BROTHERS
See HARTWIG TRANSIT INC

D-U-N-S 03-104-5131 IMP
HARTWIG INC
10617 Trenton Ave, Saint Louis, MO 63132-1208
Tel (816) 231-1850 *Founded/Ownrshp* 1960
Sales 60.8MM^E *EMP* 145
SIC 5084 Metalworking machinery; Metalworking machinery
Ch Bd: Gary R Hartwig
**Pr:* Geoff Hartwig
Brnch Mgr: Heather Johnson
Brnch Mgr: Brittney Rhude
Off Mgr: Gittemeier Bev
Off Mgr: Manuel Schafer
IT Man: Tim Francis
IT Man: Randy Jokerst
IT Man: Sander Liebert
IT Man: Todd Schutte
Opers Mgr: Jay Seigel

D-U-N-S 02-540-4930
HARTWIG TRANSIT INC
HARTWIG BROTHERS
3833 Industrial Ave, Rolling Meadows, IL 60008-1038
Tel (847) 749-1101 *Founded/Ownrshp* 1966
Sales 37.8MM^E *EMP* 230
SIC 4212 4213 Mail carriers, contract; Trucking, except local; Mail carriers, contract; Trucking, except local
CEO: Wayne Wickwire
**VP:* Gerald R Hartwig

D-U-N-S 18-328-3035
HARTWYCK AT OAKTREE INC
JFK MEDICAL CENTER
(*Suby of* JFK HEALTH SYSTEM INC) ★
2048 OakTree Rd, Edison, NJ 08820-2012
Tel (732) 906-2100 *Founded/Ownrshp* 1985
Sales 40.7MM *EMP* 600
SIC 8051 Skilled nursing care facilities; Skilled nursing care facilities
Pr: John P Mc Gee
COO: Raymond Fredericks

D-U-N-S 96-447-3727
HARTWYCK AT OAKTREE INC
JFK HARTWYCK AT OAKTREE INC
(*Suby of* HARTWYCK AT OAKTREE INC) ★
98 James St Ste 400, Edison, NJ 08820-3902
Tel (732) 549-7000 *Founded/Ownrshp* 2010
Sales 38.2MM^E *EMP* 2
Accts Eisneramper Llp Edison Nj
SIC 6513 Apartment building operators; Apartment building operators
Prin: John M Gee

HARTY INTEGRATED SOLUTIONS
See HARTY PRESS INC

D-U-N-S 01-875-3434
HARTY PRESS INC
HARTY INTEGRATED SOLUTIONS
25 James St, New Haven, CT 06513-4218
Tel (203) 562-5112 *Founded/Ownrshp* 1957
Sales 34.1MM^E *EMP* 86
SIC 2752 Commercial printing, lithographic
Pr: George Platt
**Sec:* Michael Platt
**VP:* Bill Nims
**VP:* Kevin Platt
Sales Asso: John Kortekaas
Snr Mgr: Eric Nims

D-U-N-S 78-566-6330 IMP
HARTZ BROADWAY INC
101 Hartz Blvd, Broadway, VA 22815-9476
Tel (540) 896-2200 *Founded/Ownrshp* 2007
Sales 21.7MM^E *EMP* 550
SIC 2253 2311 Pants, slacks or trousers, knit; Men's & boys' suits & coats; Pants, slacks or trousers, knit; Men's & boys' suits & coats
Pr: Stanley Hartz
**Pr:* Abraham Cohen
VP: Gilbert Benjamin J

D-U-N-S 02-515-3081
HARTZ CONSTRUCTION CO INC
9026 Heritage Pkwy, Woodridge, IL 60517-4939
Tel (630) 228-3711 *Founded/Ownrshp* 1960
Sales 28.6MM *EMP* 30
SIC 1521 Single-family housing construction; Single-family housing construction
Pr: Donald L Hartz
**VP:* Edward P Kennedy Jr
**VP:* Robert Topor

D-U-N-S 12-214-7820
HARTZ GROUP INC
(*Suby of* HARTZ MOUNTAIN INDUSTRIES INC) ★
667 Madison Ave Fl 24, New York, NY 10065-8099
Tel (212) 308-3336 *Founded/Ownrshp* 1984
Sales 125.7MM^E *EMP* 400
SIC 6512 6552 6531 6159 Commercial & industrial building operation; Land subdividers & developers, commercial; Land subdividers & developers, residential; Real estate agent, commercial; Real estate agent, residential; Small business investment companies; Commercial & industrial building operation; Land subdividers & developers, commercial; Land subdividers & developers, residential; Real estate agent, commercial; Real estate agent, residential; Small business investment companies
CEO: Leonard Stern
**Pr:* Edward Stern
**V Ch Bd:* Curtis B Schwartz
Ex VP: Lawrence Garb

D-U-N-S 05-810-9158 IMP/EXP
HARTZ MOUNTAIN CORP (NJ)
(*Suby of* UNICHARM CORPORATION)
400 Plaza Dr Ste 400, Secaucus, NJ 07094-3688
Tel (201) 271-4800 *Founded/Ownrshp* 1971, 2011
Sales 632.9MM^E *EMP* 1,200
SIC 5199 3999 Pet supplies; Pet supplies; Pet supplies; Pet supplies
Pr: Gumpei Futagami
Pr: Josephm Aronds
Pr: Frank Cangelosi
Pr: Padilla Cesar
Pr: Dan Detrolio
Ex VP: Peter Michelis
Ex VP: Gus Milano
Ex VP: Walter Smith
VP: Vincent Antonacci
VP: Anita Digiulio
VP: Marta Draper
VP: Glenn Frankel
VP: Al Gunneson
VP: Joseph Hradil
VP: Mark Killough
VP: John Kubilus
VP: Allen Magrini
VP: Max Marx
VP: Richard Milder
VP: Vince Nolan
VP: Frank Roscitt

D-U-N-S 06-427-8278
HARTZ MOUNTAIN INDUSTRIES INC
HARTZ NORTH BERGEN
400 Plaza Dr Ste 400, Secaucus, NJ 07094-3688
Tel (201) 348-1200 *Founded/Ownrshp* 1986
Sales 151.5MM^E *EMP* 428
SIC 6531 Real estate agent, commercial; Real estate agent, commercial
Ch Bd: Leonard Stern
**Pr:* Emanuel Stern
CFO: Peter Pankiw
**Ex VP:* Irwin Horowitz
**Ex VP:* Phillip Patton
Exec: Stephen Cox
IT Man: Jeremy Kohn
Opers Mgr: Ray Muniz
Sales Exec: Bobby Clark

HARTZ NORTH BERGEN
See HARTZ MOUNTAIN INDUSTRIES INC

HARTZELL AEROSPACE
See INDUSTRIAL TUBE CO LLC

HARTZELL AEROSPACE
See ELECTROFILM MANUFACTURING CO LLC

D-U-N-S 96-502-0048 IMP
HARTZELL ENGINE TECHNOLOGIES LLC
JANAERO
(*Suby of* TAILWIND TECHNOLOGIES INC) ★
2900 Selma Hwy, Montgomery, AL 36108-5038
Tel (334) 386-5400 *Founded/Ownrshp* 1987
Sales 26.8MM^E *EMP* 120
SIC 3724 4581 Engine heaters, aircraft; Aircraft maintenance & repair services; Aircraft servicing & repairing; Engine heaters, aircraft; Aircraft maintenance & repair services; Aircraft servicing & repairing
Pr: Mike Disbrow
Pr: Rick Quave
VP: Pete Schreiner
Off Mgr: Carole Nettles
VP Opers: Rose Foster
Ql Cn Mgr: Mike Strickland
Sls Mgr: John Popel

D-U-N-S 05-655-1039 EXP
HARTZELL FAN INC
910 S Downing St, Piqua, OH 45356-3824
Tel (937) 773-7411 *Founded/Ownrshp* 1927
Sales 47.7MM^E *EMP* 185
SIC 3564 3433 Blowers & fans; Ventilating fans: industrial or commercial; Heating equipment, except electric; Blowers & fans; Ventilating fans: industrial or commercial; Heating equipment, except electric
Ch Bd: James Robert Hartzell
Pr: George Atkinson
CEO: Jeff Bannister Hartzell
CFO: Michael Bardo
Treas: Randi Pearson
VP: Thomas Gustafson
VP: Ric Wallace
Ql Cn Mgr: Marc Height
Sales Asso: Greg Vangorden

D-U-N-S 19-900-8186 EXP
HARTZELL HARDWOODS INC
1025 S Roosevelt Ave, Piqua, OH 45356-3713
Tel (937) 773-7054 *Founded/Ownrshp* 1988
Sales 34.6MM^E *EMP* 90
SIC 5031 2421 2426 Lumber: rough, dressed & finished; Sawmills & planing mills, general; Hardwood dimension & flooring mills
Ch Bd: James Robert Hartzell
CEO: Jeffery Bannister
VP: Brad Bishop

D-U-N-S 83-680-3049
HARTZELL PFO INC
CHUCK & DON'S PETFOOD OUTLET
756 Stillwater Rd, Mahtomedi, MN 55115-2060
Tel (651) 747-8704 *Founded/Ownrshp* 1990
Sales 30.4MM^E *EMP* 350
SIC 5999 Pets & pet supplies
Pr: Bob Hartzell
**CFO:* Thomas Murphy
**Sec:* Charles Anderson

D-U-N-S 15-068-1294 IMP/EXP
HARTZELL PROPELLER INC
(*Suby of* TAILWIND TECHNOLOGIES INC) ★
1 Propeller Pl, Piqua, OH 45356-2656
Tel (937) 778-4200 *Founded/Ownrshp* 1988
Sales 62.8MM^E *EMP* 285
SIC 3728 Aircraft propellers & associated equipment; Aircraft propellers & associated equipment
Pr: Joseph W Brown
**Ex VP:* Jj Frigge
**VP:* Robert G Allenbaugh
VP: Frank Barhorst
VP: Connie Brown
**VP:* Bruce C Hanke
VP: Charles Hawes
**VP:* Burt Mattice
VP: Jerry Seay
**Prin:* James Brown III
CIO: Will Adams

D-U-N-S 04-831-3902
HARTZLER EQUIPMENT CO INC (MO)
30211 Se Outer Rd, Harrisonville, MO 64701-6307
Tel (816) 884-2551 *Founded/Ownrshp* 1977
Sales 24.0MM^E *EMP* 45
SIC 5083 7353 Farm implements; Heavy construction equipment rental; Farm implements; Heavy construction equipment rental
Ch Bd: Jay Hartzler
**Pr:* Lowell Hartzler
Sls Mgr: Randy Henry

D-U-N-S 03-386-9673 IMP
■ HARVARD APPARATUS INC (MA)
HBIO
(*Suby of* HARVARD BIOSCIENCE INC) ★
84 October Hill Rd Ste 10, Holliston, MA 01746-1388
Tel (508) 893-8999 *Founded/Ownrshp* 1996
Sales 38.6MM^E *EMP* 80
SIC 5049 3841 3561 Scientific instruments; Surgical & medical instruments; Pumps & pumping equipment; Scientific instruments; Surgical & medical instruments; Pumps & pumping equipment
Pr: David Green
**Treas:* Chane Graziano
Exec: Wendy Palmer
IT Man: Christina Connolly
IT Man: Lisa Outchcunis
IT Man: Mark Pasternak
Web Dev: Andrew Zaluski
Mfg Dir: Robin Butler
VP Sls: John Christensen
VP Sls: Alberto Correia
Mktg Mgr: Ron Sostek

D-U-N-S 94-540-5116
▲ HARVARD BIOSCIENCE INC
84 October Hill Rd Ste 10, Holliston, MA 01746-1371
Tel (508) 893-8999 *Founded/Ownrshp* 1901
Sales 108.6MM *EMP* 447^E
Tkr Sym HBIO *Exch* NGM
SIC 3821 Laboratory apparatus & furniture; Laboratory apparatus & furniture
Pr: Jeffrey A Duchemin
**Ch Bd:* Earl R Lewis
CFO: Robert E Gagnon
Bd of Dir: Neal Harte
VP: Frank Aubuchon
VP: Yoav Sibony
VP: Yong Sun
CIO: Joshua Jones
Mktg Dir: Mara Potter
Board of Directors: David Green, James Green, Neal J Harte, John F Kennedy, Bertrand Loy, George Uveges

HARVARD BUSINESS REVIEW
See HARVARD BUSINESS SCHOOL PUBLISHING CORP

D-U-N-S 96-271-4973
HARVARD BUSINESS SCHOOL INTERACTIVE INC
Soldiers Field Rd, Boston, MA 02163
Tel (617) 495-6000 *Founded/Ownrshp* 1997
Sales 31.2MM *EMP* 16^E
SIC 8211 Elementary & secondary schools; Elementary & secondary schools
Pr: Nancy Dellarocco
COO: Barbara McGill
**Treas:* Richard Melnick
Snr Sftwr: Ravi Mynampaty

D-U-N-S 82-773-1829 IMP
HARVARD BUSINESS SCHOOL PUBLISHING CORP
HARVARD BUSINESS REVIEW
(*Suby of* HARVARD UNIVERSITY) ★
300 North Beacon St, Watertown, MA 02472-5750
Tel (617) 783-7400 *Founded/Ownrshp* 1994
Sales 84.7MM^E *EMP* 390^E
Accts Pricewaterhousecoopers Llp Bo
SIC 2721 2731 2741 Periodicals: publishing only; Books: publishing only; Newsletter publishing; Periodicals: publishing only; Books: publishing only; Newsletter publishing
Pr: David Wan
V Ch: Ronald Walton
**Pr:* Linda S Doyle
Pr: Patrick McManus
**COO:* Raymond Carvey
**Treas:* Dwight B Crane
Assoc Dir: Jennifer Mucciarone
Ex Dir: John Korn
Mng Dir: Josh Macht
Dir Sec: Arthur McKenzie
Sftwr Eng: Rebecca Searls

D-U-N-S 79-692-6546
HARVARD BUSINESS SCHOOL STUDENT ASSOCIATION INC
HBSP
Soldiers Fld, Boston, MA 02163
Tel (617) 495-6000 *Founded/Ownrshp* 1972
Sales 105.4MM^E *EMP* 1,200
SIC 8221 University; University
Pr: Ifunanya Maduka
Mng Pt: Bob Higgins
Pr: Peter Hantman
**COO:* Liz Kolshak
**CFO:* Omar Muakkassa
CFO: Brenda Newkirk
Treas: Mark Young
Bd of Dir: Paul Marshall
Chf Mktg O: Mark Addicks
Chf Mktg O: Brian S Kenny
Ofcr: Lisa Smith
VP: Sanjay Banker
VP: Shari Eberts
VP: Mike Ghaffary
VP: Barry Rudolph
Assoc Dir: Ted Adams
Assoc Dir: Chris Brazda
Assoc Dir: Eileen Chang
Assoc Dir: Paul Craig
Assoc Dir: Maria Curcio
Assoc Dir: Chris Darwall

HARVARD CARD SYSTEMS
See HARVARD LABEL INC

D-U-N-S 01-857-1088
HARVARD CLINICAL RESEARCH INSTITUTE INC
HCRI
930 Commonwealth Ave, Boston, MA 02215-1274
Tel (617) 307-5200 *Founded/Ownrshp* 2000
Sales 36.7MM *EMP* 190
Accts Alexander Aronson Finning & Co
SIC 8731 Medical research, commercial; Medical research, commercial
Pr: Spencer Goldsmith
**CFO:* Bob Loeb
CFO: Jean Moses
Treas: Richard Gelber
Bd of Dir: Anne-Marie Mercando
Chf Inves: Robert Atchinson
Dir IT: Leonardo Escarfullery
IT Man: Gene Lichtman
Counsel: Ben Harrower

D-U-N-S 07-281-1995
HARVARD CLUB OF NEW YORK CITY
35 W 44th St, New York, NY 10036-6613
Tel (212) 840-6600 *Founded/Ownrshp* 1887
Sales 33.2MM *EMP* 250
SIC 8641 Alumni association; Alumni association
Pr: Nicole M Parent
CFO: Scott Gronick
Treas: Laurin Blum
**Treas:* Thomas Mattos
Ofcr: Seth Cunniff
**VP:* Andreas Beroutsos
**VP:* Kennth Powell
VP: Josselyn G Simpson
Dir Soc: Brianna Scanlon
Comm Dir: Chad Belisario
Dir Sec: Thomas Hovagim

D-U-N-S 04-703-6462
HARVARD COMMUNITY UNIT SCHOOL DISTRICT 50
401 N Division St, Harvard, IL 60033-3031
Tel (815) 943-4022 *Founded/Ownrshp* 1954
Sales 21.4MM^E *EMP* 269
Accts Knutte & Associates Inc Dar

SIC 8211 Public junior high school; Public senior high school; Public junior high school; Public senior high school
Bd of Dir: Diana Bird
Bd of Dir: Richard Stoxen
Prin: Jeanne Kearby
**Prin:* Lauri Tobias

D-U-N-S 00-695-3764
HARVARD COOPERATIVE SOCIETY INC
COOP, THE
1400 Massachusetts Ave, Cambridge, MA 02138-3833
Tel (617) 499-2000 *Founded/Ownrshp* 2000
Sales 42.8MM *EMP* 11
SIC 5311 Department stores, non-discount; Department stores, non-discount
Ch Bd: Allan Bufferd
**Pr:* Jeremiah Murphy Jr
**V Ch Bd:* Michael Shinagel

D-U-N-S 19-142-7277 EXP
■ HARVARD DRUG GROUP L L C
MAJOR PHARMACEUTICALS
(*Suby of* CARDINAL HEALTH INC) ★
31778 Enterprise Dr, Livonia, MI 48150-1960
Tel (734) 525-8700 *Founded/Ownrshp* 2015
Sales 313.0MM^E *EMP* 450
SIC 5122 5047 8734 Pharmaceuticals; Medical & hospital equipment; Testing laboratories; Pharmaceuticals; Medical & hospital equipment; Testing laboratories
CEO: Kurt Hilzinger
Pr: David Presper
COO: Doug Bowman
Treas: Karen Boik
Ofcr: Steve Bencetic
Sr Ex VP: Gregory Lake
Sr VP: Larry Kramer
Sr VP: Greg Lake
VP: Chris Diton
VP: Paul Eichholz
VP: Mike Hall
VP: Dana Lilly
VP: Bob Lindberg
VP: Kerry Porter
VP: Samir Shah
VP: Wyn Tindall
VP: Todd Way
VP: Jarret Zerbe

D-U-N-S 00-100-8424 IMP/EXP
HARVARD FOLDING BOX CO INC (MA)
IDEAL BOX COMPANY
15 Union St Ste 555, Lawrence, MA 01840-1823
Tel (978) 683-2802 *Founded/Ownrshp* 1951
Sales 21.9MM^E *EMP* 150
SIC 2657 Folding paperboard boxes; Folding paperboard boxes
CEO: David Simkins
**Pr:* Leon J Simkins
**Treas:* Barbara Camera
Plnt Mgr: Charles Peterson

D-U-N-S 78-009-9008
HARVARD INTERNATIONAL RELATIONS COUNCIL INC
HARVARD MODEL UNITED NATIONS
59 Shepard St, Cambridge, MA 02138-1558
Tel (617) 398-0772 *Founded/Ownrshp* 1974
Sales 749.0M *EMP* 400
SIC 5192 Magazines; Magazines
Pr: Courtney Blair
**Treas:* Weiyi Guo
**VP:* Anthony Carlson
**VP:* Joseph Kerns
**VP:* Sameer Lakha
**VP:* Victoria Phan

D-U-N-S 00-366-0248 IMP
HARVARD LABEL INC (CA)
HARVARD CARD SYSTEMS
111 Baldwin Park Blvd, City of Industry, CA 91746-1402
Tel (626) 333-8881 *Founded/Ownrshp* 1996
Sales 37.7MM^E *EMP* 115
SIC 2752 Business form & card printing, lithographic; Business form & card printing, lithographic
Pr: Mike Tan
**Pr:* David Banducci
Pr: Roby Sanchez
Sls Mgr: Sandy Babila

D-U-N-S 07-329-0728
HARVARD MAINTENANCE INC
2 S Biscayne Blvd # 3650, Miami, FL 33131-1806
Tel (305) 351-7300 *Founded/Ownrshp* 1977
Sales 217.3MM^E *EMP* 4,300
SIC 7349 Building maintenance services; Building maintenance services
Pr: Stanley K Doobin
CFO: Joanne C Plemenos
Bd of Dir: Nathalie Doobin
Ex VP: Dan Duffy
Sr VP: John Ravaris
VP: Catherine Coleman
VP: Robert Conforti
VP: Paul Crepaldi
VP: Kiplyn Duffy
VP: Pat Mullin
VP: Keith Prewitt
Dir Bus: Brenda Koon
Dir Bus: Angela McAvoy

D-U-N-S 05-190-9448
HARVARD MANAGEMENT CO INC
(*Suby of* HARVARD UNIVERSITY) ★
600 Atlantic Ave Ste 15, Boston, MA 02210-2203
Tel (617) 720-6526 *Founded/Ownrshp* 1974
Sales 31.0MM^E *EMP* 179
Accts Pricewaterhousecoopers Llp Bo
SIC 8741 6722 Financial management for business; Management investment, open-end; Financial management for business; Management investment, open-end
Pr: Stephen Blyth
**COO:* Robert A Ettl
CFO: Kevin Shannon
Ofcr: Molly Lanzarotta
Ofcr: Angelica Natera
Ex VP: Carol Covell
Sr VP: Francis Corbett
Sr VP: Michael Fisher
Sr VP: Alec Polnarev
VP: Eric Mazur
VP: Stewart Porter
VP: Marc Seidner
Exec: Jennifer Goldstein
Exec: Patricia Sylvia
Dir Risk M: Neil Mason

D-U-N-S 78-132-8513
HARVARD MEDICAL FACULTY PHYSICIANS AT BETH ISRAEL DEACONESS MEDICAL CENTER INC
HMFP
(*Suby of* BETH ISRAEL DEACONESS MEDICAL CENTER INC) ★
375 Longwood Ave Ste 3, Boston, MA 02215-5395
Tel (617) 632-9755 *Founded/Ownrshp* 1998
Sales 68.9MM^E *EMP* 800
SIC 8621 Medical field-related associations; Medical field-related associations
CEO: Stuart A Rosenberg
Ofcr: Scott Bradner
**VP:* Edward L Grab

D-U-N-S 60-357-2731
HARVARD MEDICAL SCHOOL
(*Suby of* HARVARD UNIVERSITY) ★
25 Shattuck St, Boston, MA 02115-6092
Tel (617) 432-1000 *Founded/Ownrshp* 1639
Sales 57.9MM^E *EMP* 479
SIC 8221 Colleges universities & professional schools; Colleges universities & professional schools
Ch: Senator William H
**Pr:* Drew Faust
Ofcr: Colleen Cody
Ofcr: Melissa Maher
Ofcr: Michelle Schatz
Exec: Allison Ackerman
Exec: Julie Stanley
Dir Lab: Danijela Dukovski
Dir Lab: Shawn Fields-Berry
Dir Lab: Seth Maleri
Assoc Dir: Deborah Good
Assoc Dir: Colleen Graham
Assoc Dir: Alexa McCray
Assoc Dir: Henry Warren
Dir Bus: Michal Preminger

D-U-N-S 01-022-6280
HARVARD MEMORIAL HOSPITAL INC
MERCY HARVARD HOSPITAL
901 Grant St, Harvard, IL 60033-1821
Tel (815) 943-5431 *Founded/Ownrshp* 1953
Sales 25.3MM *EMP* 187
Accts Baker Tilly Virchow Krause Llp
SIC 8062 8052 General medical & surgical hospitals; Intermediate care facilities; General medical & surgical hospitals; Intermediate care facilities
Pr: Javon Bea
**COO:* Sue Ripch
**CFO:* Jan Brenner
Sr VP: Dan Colby

HARVARD MODEL UNITED NATIONS
See HARVARD INTERNATIONAL RELATIONS COUNCIL INC

D-U-N-S 07-172-1088
HARVARD PILGRIM HEALTH CARE INC
93 Worcester St, Wellesley, MA 02481-3609
Tel (781) 263-6000 *Founded/Ownrshp* 1968
Sales NA *EMP* 1,300
Accts Pricewaterhousecoopers Llp Bo
SIC 6324 Health maintenance organization (HMO), insurance only; Health maintenance organization (HMO), insurance only
Pr: Charles Baker
**COO:* Roberta Herman
Treas: Steven Flood
**Ofcr:* Jack Lane
**Ofcr:* Laura Peabody
Sr VP: Geoffrey J Coffman
VP: Roberta Bartholdson
VP: Robert Forrester
VP: Barbara Stern
VP: John Whisnant
Exec: Lane Jack
Assoc Dir: Joel Rubinstein
Board of Directors: Alan R Morse Jr, Gilbert L Shapiro MD

D-U-N-S 96-399-5675
HARVARD PROPERTY TRUST LLC
15601 Dallas Pkwy Ste 600, Addison, TX 75001-6026
Tel (214) 655-1600 *Founded/Ownrshp* 2001
Sales 69.5MM^E *EMP* 600
SIC 6798 Real estate investment trusts; Real estate investment trusts
Pr: Robert S Aisner
**COO:* Jason Mattox
**CFO:* Gary S Bresky
**Ex VP:* Robert J Chapman
**Ex VP:* Michael D Cohen
Sr VP: Margaret M Daly
VP: Gerald J Reihsen III

HARVARD S G
See HARVARD SERVICES GROUP INC

D-U-N-S 84-837-0743
HARVARD SERVICES GROUP INC
HARVARD S G
33 Wood Ave S Ste 600, Iselin, NJ 08830-2717
Tel (973) 515-9302 *Founded/Ownrshp* 1986
Sales 21.0MM^E *EMP* 450
SIC 7349 Janitorial service, contract basis; Janitorial service, contract basis
Pr: Nathalie Doobin
Ex VP: Stanley Doobin
Area Mgr: Robert Wojcik
VP Opers: Thomas E Smiley
Opers Mgr: Jorge Ferraz

D-U-N-S 01-929-8389
HARVARD STUDENT AGENCIES INC
67 Mount Auburn St, Cambridge, MA 02138-4961
Tel (617) 495-3030 *Founded/Ownrshp* 1957
Sales 1.7MM *EMP* 1,000
SIC 7361 Employment agencies; Employment agencies
Mng Pt: Michael Cronin
Bd of Dir: Priscilla Claman
Bd of Dir: Ellen Hoffman
Bd of Dir: Das Narayandas
VP: Joe Molimock
Dir IT: Robert Bedetti
Dir IT: WEI-Te Ting
Dir IT: Calvin Tonini
Dir IT: Lukas Toth
Opers Mgr: Jullian Duran
Mktg Mgr: Lorraine Facella

HARVARD UNIVERSITY
See PRESIDENT AND FELLOWS OF HARVARD COLLEGE

HARVARD UNIVERSITY
See PRESIDENT AND FELLOWS OF HARVARD COLLEGE

D-U-N-S 02-745-2776
HARVARD UNIVERSITY HARVARD CYCLING TEAM ON EARLY MORNING PRACTICE RUN
1060 Holyoke Ctr, Cambridge, MA 02138-3846
Tel (617) 495-1588 *Founded/Ownrshp* 2011
Sales 18.5MM^E *EMP* 284^E
SIC 8221 University
Prin: Harvard Univ
VP: Hannah Phillips
Ex Dir: Aviva Argote
Mng Dir: Samantha Earp
Genl Mgr: Lance Davidow
Doctor: John O'Donnell
Snr Mgr: Benoit Gaucherin
Snr Mgr: Donald Oppenheimer

HARVARD VANGUARD MED ASSOC INC
See ATRIUS HEALTH INC

D-U-N-S 07-620-9758
HARVARD-WESTLAKE SCHOOL
H W
3700 Coldwater Canyon Ave, North Hollywood, CA 91604-2301
Tel (818) 980-6692 *Founded/Ownrshp* 1900
Sales 80.3MM *EMP* 300
Accts Armanino Mckenna Llp San Ramo
SIC 8211 Preparatory school; Preparatory school
CEO: Richard B Commons
**Ch Bd:* Christine Hazy
**Pr:* Thomas C Hudnut
**CFO:* Robert Levin
Ofcr: Katrina Sprague
Store Mgr: Melissa Ouellet
Snr Sftwr: Alan Homan
Sftwr Eng: Joey Navarro
Plnt Mgr: Felipe Anguiano
Plnt Mgr: Felipe Westlake

D-U-N-S 04-361-6366
HARVE BENARD LTD
HB-GM ACQUISTION
125 Delawanna Ave, Clifton, NJ 07014-1529
Tel (973) 249-1230 *Founded/Ownrshp* 1967
Sales 38.5MM^E *EMP* 400
SIC 2331 2325 2311 2339 2337 Blouses, women's & juniors': made from purchased material; Slacks, dress: men's, youths' & boys'; Suits, men's & boys': made from purchased materials; Women's & misses' jackets & coats, except sportswear; Suits: women's, misses' & juniors'; Blouses, women's & juniors': made from purchased material; Slacks, dress: men's, youths' & boys'; Suits, men's & boys': made from purchased materials; Women's & misses' jackets & coats, except sportswear; Suits: women's, misses' & juniors'
Pr: Bernard Holtzman
**CFO:* Harvey J Schutzbank
**VP:* Morton Holtzman

D-U-N-S 92-794-0564
■ HARVEST CAPITAL STRATEGIES LL
(*Suby of* JMP GROUP INC) ★
600 Montgomery St # 1100, San Francisco, CA 94111-2702
Tel (415) 835-3967 *Founded/Ownrshp* 1999
Sales 33.0MM *EMP* 20^E
SIC 6211 Investment bankers; Brokers, security; Securities flotation companies; Investment bankers; Brokers, security; Securities flotation companies
Pr: Joe Jolson
Ex VP: Raymond Jackson
VP: John Hecht
VP: Carlos Herrera
VP: Michael Moscuzza
VP: Andrew Palmer
Mng Dir: Donald Destino
Mng Dir: Laura Hegarty
Mng Dir: Ray Jackson
Mng Dir: Thomas Kilian
Mng Dir: Daniel Mazur

D-U-N-S 07-094-1562
HARVEST CHRISTIAN FELLOWSHIP INC
HARVEST PRODUCTIONS
6115 Arlington Ave, Riverside, CA 92504-1999
Tel (951) 687-6902 *Founded/Ownrshp* 1972
Sales 32.9MM^E *EMP* 282
Accts Capin Crouse Llp Brea Ca
SIC 8211 8661 5942 Private elementary school; Christian & Reformed Church; Books, religious; Private elementary school; Christian & Reformed Church; Books, religious
CEO: Greg Laurie
COO: John Collins
**Treas:* Dennis Davenport

D-U-N-S 04-964-2416 IMP
HARVEST CONSUMER PRODUCTS LLC
(*Suby of* HARVEST POWER INC) ★
215 Overhill Dr 200, Mooresville, NC 28117-7036
Tel (980) 444-2000 *Founded/Ownrshp* 2011
Sales 80.0MM *EMP* 150
Accts Ernst & Young Llp Boston Ma
SIC 2499 Mulch, wood & bark; Mulch, wood & bark
Sr VP: David Hitchcock
**CFO:* Christian G Kasper
**Sr VP:* Brian Kura
Mktg Dir: Dave Devine

HARVEST DIRECT TV
See HARVEST TRADING GROUP INC

D-U-N-S 87-792-8903
HARVEST DISTRIBUTION INC
4360 Buckingham Dr # 200, Colorado Springs, CO 80907-3738
Tel (719) 599-7661 *Founded/Ownrshp* 1994
Sales 21.0MM *EMP* 23
SIC 5149 Specialty food items
Pr: Richard Holland
**VP:* Fred Burgess

D-U-N-S 17-487-9759
■ HARVEST FACILITY HOLDINGS LP
(*Suby of* FORTRESS INVESTMENT GROUP LLC) ★
5885 Meadows Rd Ste 500, Lake Oswego, OR 97035-8646
Tel (503) 370-7070 *Founded/Ownrshp* 2007
Sales 15.0MM^E *EMP* 750
SIC 6513 Retirement hotel operation; Retirement hotel operation
Genl Pt: Mark Burnham
Pt: Sheryl Bauer
Pt: Scott S Berger
Pt: Don Harris
Pt: Rick Orizotti

D-U-N-S 14-182-6011
HARVEST FAMILY ENTERTAINMENT LLC
HAWAIIAN FALLS GARLAND
4400 Paige Rd, The Colony, TX 75056-2534
Tel (972) 675-8888 *Founded/Ownrshp* 2004
Sales 22.8MM^E *EMP* 400
SIC 7996 Amusement parks; Amusement parks
Pr: David Busch
Sls Mgr: Jana McClinton

HARVEST FARM
See DENVER RESCUE MISSION

D-U-N-S 12-096-6296 IMP
HARVEST FARMS INC
(*Suby of* GOOD SOURCE SOLUTIONS INC) ★
45000 Yucca Ave, Lancaster, CA 93534-2526
Tel (661) 945-3636 *Founded/Ownrshp* 2003
Sales 32.7MM^E *EMP* 100
SIC 2038 5144 Lunches, frozen & packaged; Poultry & poultry products; Lunches, frozen & packaged; Poultry & poultry products
CEO: Craig Shugert
**CFO:* Eric Shiring
Genl Mgr: Joe Hughes
CTO: Scott Nelson

D-U-N-S 13-421-4415 IMP
HARVEST FOOD GROUP INC
30w260 Butterfield Rd 201b, Warrenville, IL 60555-1569
Tel (630) 821-4000 *Founded/Ownrshp* 1999
Sales 45.7MM^E *EMP* 50
SIC 5141 5142 Groceries, general line; Packaged frozen goods
Pr: Jason Eckert

D-U-N-S 05-463-2492 IMP
HARVEST FOOD PRODUCTS CO INC (CA)
710 Sandoval Way, Hayward, CA 94544-7111
Tel (510) 675-0383 *Founded/Ownrshp* 1981, 1982
Sales 20.4MM^E *EMP* 100
SIC 2038 5812 2099 Frozen specialties; Ethnic foods, frozen; Eating places; Food preparations; Frozen specialties; Ethnic foods, frozen; Eating places; Food preparations
Pr: Danny Kha

D-U-N-S 96-433-6502
HARVEST FOUNDATION OF PIEDMONT
1 Ellsworth St, Martinsville, VA 24112-2845
Tel (276) 632-3329 *Founded/Ownrshp* 2010
Sales 25.4MM *EMP* 3
SIC 8641 Civic social & fraternal associations; Civic social & fraternal associations
Prin: E Larry Ryder

D-U-N-S 07-947-7130
HARVEST HILL BEVERAGE CO
1 High Ridge Park Fl 2, Stamford, CT 06905-1322
Tel (203) 914-1620 *Founded/Ownrshp* 2014
Sales 310.9MM^E *EMP* 565^E
SIC 5149 Groceries & related products
Pr: Salvatore Deprima
**CFO:* James Sheppard
**Chf Mktg O:* Ilene Bergenfeld
Sr VP: David Champlin
Sr VP: Richard Hubli

D-U-N-S 12-357-6811
HARVEST HOPE FOOD BANK
2220 Shop Rd, Columbia, SC 29201-5162
Tel (803) 254-4432 *Founded/Ownrshp* 1981
Sales 45.9MM *EMP* 85
Accts Elliott Davis Llc Columbia
SIC 8322 Emergency social services; Meal delivery program; Emergency social services; Meal delivery program
Ex Dir: Denise Holland
Dir Vol: Sara Bouknight
Dir Vol: Faith Brown
**Ch Bd:* Mark Zion
V Ch: Denise Whittington
COO: Bobbi Bouknight
Bd of Dir: Charles Duvall
Bd of Dir: Ritchie McQueenie
Bd of Dir: Fred Miller

Bd of Dir: Michele Studer
Comm Dir: Marsha Thompson

D-U-N-S 00-798-6821
HARVEST LAND CO-OP INC
1435 Nw 5th St, Richmond, IN 47374-1841
Tel (765) 962-1527 *Founded/Ownrshp* 1927
Sales 324.8MM^E *EMP* 200
Accts Blue & Co Llc Seymour In
SIC 5191 5153 Fertilizers & agricultural chemicals; Grain elevators; Fertilizers & agricultural chemicals; Feed; Seeds: field, garden & flower; Grain elevators
Pr: Marlin Larson
**Ch:* Myron Moyer
**Treas:* Lloyd Lee
Mktg Dir: Ben Cramer
Snr Mgr: Randy Ludwig

D-U-N-S 02-296-3755
HARVEST LAND COOPERATIVE
AG QUEST
711 Front St, Morgan, MN 56266
Tel (507) 249-3196 *Founded/Ownrshp* 1904
Sales 225.8MM *EMP* 150
Accts Carlson Highland & Co Llp N
SIC 5153 5191 0253 Grains; Feed; Seeds: field, garden & flower; Chemicals, agricultural; Turkeys & turkey eggs; Grains; Feed; Seeds: field, garden & flower; Chemicals, agricultural; Turkeys & turkey eggs
CEO: Dave Stock
**Treas:* Tim Sullivan
**Genl Mgr:* Dennis Schreier
Genl Mgr: Mike Weelborg
CIO: Randy Ludwig

D-U-N-S 05-490-1912
HARVEST MANAGEMENT SUB LLC
HOLIDAY RETIREMENT
5885 Meadows Rd Ste 500, Lake Oswego, OR 97035-8646
Tel (503) 370-7070 *Founded/Ownrshp* 2008
Sales 437.6MM^E *EMP* 13,000
SIC 8361 Geriatric residential care; Geriatric residential care
CEO: Edward F Lange Jr
**Pr:* Kai Hsiao
**COO:* Harvey Brownlee
**CFO:* Scott Shanaberger
**Ex VP:* Shamim Wu
Snr Mgr: Nicholas Hibbs
Snr Mgr: John Lee

D-U-N-S 03-093-2084
HARVEST MANAGING MEMBER I LLC
5885 Meadows Rd Ste 500, Lake Oswego, OR 97035-8646
Tel (503) 370-7070 *Founded/Ownrshp* 2012
Sales 23.4MM^E *EMP* 107^E
SIC 8741 Management services

HARVEST MARKET
See CYPRESS HOLDING INC

HARVEST MASTER
See JUNIPER SYSTEMS INC

D-U-N-S 87-836-0049 IMP/EXP
HARVEST MEAT CO INC
(*Suby of* SAND DOLLAR HOLDINGS INC) ★
1022 Bay Marina Dr # 106, National City, CA 91950-6327
Tel (619) 477-0185 *Founded/Ownrshp* 1998
Sales 235.7MM^E *EMP* 200
SIC 5147 Meats & meat products; Meats & meat products
CEO: John J Leavy
Pr: Kevin Leavy
CFO: Eric Doan
CFO: Greg Johnson
VP: Dennis Leavy
Prin: Dennis Kevin
Brnch Mgr: Darla Houston
Genl Mgr: Tim Gaskin
Genl Mgr: Mike Leavy
Genl Mgr: Maury Leff
Genl Mgr: Matt Ryan

D-U-N-S 36-067-2851 EXP
HARVEST NATURAL RESOURCES INC
1177 Enclave Pkwy Ste 300, Houston, TX 77077-1885
Tel (281) 899-5700 *Founded/Ownrshp* 1988
Sales 58.3MM^E *EMP* 30
Tkr Sym HNR *Exch* NYS
SIC 1382 1311 Oil & gas exploration services; Crude petroleum & natural gas production
Pr: James A Edmiston
V Ch: Tom Sellers
CFO: Stephen C Haynes
Sr VP: Byron A Dunn
Sr VP: Robert Speirs
VP: Keith L Head

HARVEST OF THE SEA
See ORE-CAL CORP

D-U-N-S 82-969-9292
HARVEST POWER INC
221 Crescent St Ste 402, Waltham, MA 02453-3425
Tel (781) 314-9500 *Founded/Ownrshp* 2008
Sales 245.8MM^E *EMP* 350
SIC 4953 Recycling, waste materials; Recycling, waste materials
CEO: Christian G Kasper
Ch Bd: Paul Sellew
Pr: Christopher Peters
CFO: Brian Sheehan
Sr VP: John Eustermann
Sr VP: David Hitchcock
Sr VP: Jeff Knapp
Sr VP: Brian Kura
Sr VP: Steve Liffers
Sr VP: Sam Monaco
VP: Wayne Davis
VP: Kieran Furlong
VP: Thomas Kraemer
VP: Matt Mitchell
Board of Directors: Bob Simpson

HARVEST PRIDE
See KENT CORP

HARVEST PRODUCTIONS
See HARVEST CHRISTIAN FELLOWSHIP INC

HARVEST PUBLICATIONS DIV
See BAPTIST GENERAL CONFERENCE INC

HARVEST RANCH MARKET
See DALLO & CO INC

HARVEST SELECT CATFISH
See ALABAMA CATFISH INC

D-U-N-S 83-046-0221 IMP
HARVEST SENSATIONS LLC
3030 E Washington Blvd, Los Angeles, CA 90023-4220
Tel (213) 895-6968 *Founded/Ownrshp* 2001
Sales 75.0MM *EMP* 110^E
SIC 5148 Fresh fruits & vegetables; Fresh fruits & vegetables
Pr: Chris Coffman
**Ch Bd:* Charles Gilbert
**CFO:* Bob Kiehnle
Mktg Dir: Guen Gulliksen

D-U-N-S 07-541-5971
HARVEST SPORTING GROUP INC
SPORTSMAN'S SUPPLY
2219 Hitzert Ct, Fenton, MO 63026-2562
Tel (314) 378-8905 *Founded/Ownrshp* 2001
Sales 112.9MM^E *EMP* 60
SIC 5091 Sporting & recreation goods
Pr: Tom Siegmund
Pr: Greg Glickfeld
**COO:* Eugene Horwitz
IT Man: Brad Bishop
IT Man: Eric Kauss

D-U-N-S 04-029-4787
HARVEST SUPERMARKETS INC
TOPS HARDWARE
915 Jackson St, Anderson, IN 46016-1494
Tel (765) 643-6415 *Founded/Ownrshp* 1976
Sales 47.0MM^E *EMP* 290
SIC 5411 5251 Supermarkets, chain; Hardware
CEO: Roy R Kipp
**Pr:* Jeffrey Huffman
**VP:* Steve Hudelson
**VP:* Allison K Vores

D-U-N-S 61-320-3728 IMP
HARVEST TRADING GROUP INC
HARVEST DIRECTTV
61 Accord Park Dr, Norwell, MA 02061-1614
Tel (781) 982-7330 *Founded/Ownrshp* 1990
Sales 27.0MM *EMP* 21
SIC 5141 Food brokers
Pr: James P Lewis
Treas: John T Lewis Jr

D-U-N-S 16-704-6432
HARVESTERS - COMMUNITY FOOD NETWORK
3801 Topping Ave, Kansas City, MO 64129-1744
Tel (816) 231-3173 *Founded/Ownrshp* 1979
Sales 85.0MM^E *EMP* 55
Accts Cbiz Mhm Llc Leawood Ks
SIC 8322 Individual & family services; Individual & family services
Ch: Dan Weaver
**CEO:* Karen T Haren
Dir Soc: Libby Coulter
Comm Dir: Ellen Feldhausen
**Prin:* Valerie Nicholson-Watson
Prgrm Mgr: Angela Jeppesen
QA Dir: Noreen Zahner
Dir IT: Matt Quinn
IT Man: Robin Potts
Opers Mgr: Jeff Gartin

D-U-N-S 08-722-0893
HARVEY & MADDING INC (CA)
DUBLIN HONDA
6300 Dublin Blvd, Dublin, CA 94568-7657
Tel (925) 828-8030 *Founded/Ownrshp* 1977
Sales 89.1MM^E *EMP* 82
SIC 5511 7538 5015 5013 Automobiles, new & used; General automotive repair shops; Motor vehicle parts, used; Motor vehicle supplies & new parts; Automobiles, new & used; General automotive repair shops; Motor vehicle parts, used; Motor vehicle supplies & new parts
CEO: Kenneth C Harvey
**VP:* Brenda S Harvey
Sls Mgr: Steve Bado
Sales Asso: Wais Azizi
Sales Asso: Shah Delery
Sales Asso: Marcos Varela

HARVEY BUILDING PRODUCTS
See HARVEY INDUSTRIES INC

D-U-N-S 01-635-8285
HARVEY CONSTRUCTION CO INC
9125 E 146th St, Noblesville, IN 46060-4310
Tel (317) 773-7302 *Founded/Ownrshp* 1960
Sales 24.5MM^E *EMP* 150
SIC 1623 1629 Water, sewer & utility lines; Water main construction; Earthmoving contractor; Water, sewer & utility lines; Water main construction; Earthmoving contractor
Pr: Harold Harvey

D-U-N-S 80-764-4372 EXP
HARVEY CONSTRUCTION CORP
10 Harvey Rd, Bedford, NH 03110-6805
Tel (603) 624-4600 *Founded/Ownrshp* 2010
Sales 44.1MM^E *EMP* 85
SIC 1542 1541 Commercial & office building contractors; Commercial & office buildings, renovation & repair; Commercial & office building, new construction; Industrial buildings, new construction; Renovation, remodeling & repairs: industrial buildings; Commercial & office building contractors; Commercial & office buildings, renovation & repair; Commercial & office building, new construction; Industrial buildings, new construction; Renovation, remodeling & repairs: industrial buildings
Pr: William Stevens
**CFO:* Kevin McIntyre
**VP:* Rob Tiunier
IT Man: Gerry Sherman

HARVEY EXPORT
See EL HARVEY & SONS INC

D-U-N-S 16-663-8569
HARVEY FERTILIZER AND GAS CO
HARVEY GIN & COTTON
303 Bohannon Rd, Kinston, NC 28501-7434
Tel (252) 526-4150 *Founded/Ownrshp* 1871
Sales 413.8MM^E *EMP* 244
SIC 5191 2873 2875 Farm supplies; Nitrogenous fertilizers; Fertilizers, mixing only; Farm supplies; Chemicals, agricultural; Fertilizer & fertilizer materials; Nitrogenous fertilizers; Fertilizers, mixing only
Pr: Herbert Rouse
**CFO:* Frankie Hill
**Sec:* Llyod E Cooper
Ex VP: Gary Floyd
VP: Paul Bridgers
IT Man: Maryanne Craft
Sfty Dirs: Linda Huggins

HARVEY GENERAL CONTRACTING
See HARVEY INC

HARVEY GIN & COTTON
See HARVEY FERTILIZER AND GAS CO

D-U-N-S 04-342-8135 IMP
HARVEY GULF INTERNATIONAL MARINE LLC (LA)
701 Poydras St Ste 3700, New Orleans, LA 70139-7704
Tel (504) 348-2466 *Founded/Ownrshp* 1960, 2008
Sales 56.5MM^E *EMP* 235
SIC 4731 Brokers, shipping; Brokers, shipping
Ex VP: Frank Annerino
Ex VP: Dudley Plaisance
**Ex VP:* Lance Reynolds
VP: Andrew Adgate
VP: Kevin Hopel
VP: Wade Pitre
VP: Jake Stahl
Snr Ntwrk: Kermit Ortolano
Snr Ntwrk: Joey Siamwiza
IT Man: Andy Edgate
Genl Couns: Robert Vosbein

HARVEY HONDA
See BURLINGAME AUTOMOTIVE MANAGEMENT INC

D-U-N-S 11-816-0597 IMP
■ **HARVEY HUBBELL CARIBE INC**
HUBELL CARIBE LIMITED
(*Suby of* HUBBELL INC) ★
Km 17 Hm 3 Rr 686, Vega Baja, PR 00693
Tel (787) 855-1075 *Founded/Ownrshp* 1984
Sales 211.6MM^E *EMP* 900
SIC 3643 Connectors & terminals for electrical devices; Plugs, electric; Connectors & terminals for electrical devices; Plugs, electric
Pr: George Ruiz
Sfty Dirs: Mirian Candelaria

D-U-N-S 96-833-8280
HARVEY INC
HARVEY GENERAL CONTRACTING
9455 Ridgehaven Ct # 200, San Diego, CA 92123-1649
Tel (858) 769-4000 *Founded/Ownrshp* 2005
Sales 30.9MM^E *EMP* 125
SIC 1542 Commercial & office building contractors
CEO: Stephen Harvey
**CFO:* Debra Gillespie
**VP:* Paul J Pietsch

D-U-N-S 00-141-3764 IMP
HARVEY INDUSTRIES INC
HARVEY BUILDING PRODUCTS
1400 Main St Fl 3, Waltham, MA 02451-1689
Tel (781) 899-3500 *Founded/Ownrshp* 1961
Sales 1.4MMM^E *EMP* 1,610
SIC 5031 5033 3442 2431 Roofing, asphalt & sheet metal; Siding, except wood; Windows; Storm doors or windows, metal; Windows, wood; Windows; Roofing, asphalt & sheet metal; Storm doors or windows, metal; Windows, wood
CEO: Thomas Bigony
**Pr:* James M Barreira
**CFO:* Scott Lassonde
**Ch:* Erik Jarnryd
Sr VP: Steve Berberian
**Sr VP:* Thomas Russell
**Sr VP:* Vincent Walsh
VP: James Barreira
VP: Randy Cail
VP: Jeffrey Ribeiro
Brnch Mgr: Rich Rose

D-U-N-S 80-260-6330 IMP
HARVEY INDUSTRIES LLC
3837 Mill St, Wabash, IN 46992-7838
Tel (260) 563-8371 *Founded/Ownrshp* 2007
Sales 105.3MM^E *EMP* 350
SIC 3463 3365 Aluminum forgings; Aluminum foundries

D-U-N-S 02-814-5852
HARVEY M HARPER CO
HARPER KIA
4800 N Us Highway 101, Eureka, CA 95503-9401
Tel (707) 443-7311 *Founded/Ownrshp* 1912
Sales 29.4MM^E *EMP* 80^E
SIC 5511 New & used car dealers; New & used car dealers
Pr: Harvey G Harper
**Sec:* Elizabeth Harper
**VP:* Dan Harper
Sls Mgr: Chris Arnold

D-U-N-S 01-677-3822
HARVEY MILLING CO INC
HARVEY'S LAWN & GARDEN CENTER
9650 Roosevelt Rd, Carson City, MI 48811-9609
Tel (989) 584-3466 *Founded/Ownrshp* 1964
Sales 36.3MM^E *EMP* 50
SIC 5191 Farm supplies
CEO: Michael Mc Crackin
**Pr:* Jim Sheppard
Mktg Mgr: Jamie Ward

D-U-N-S 06-669-1130
HARVEY MUDD COLLEGE
HMC BUSINESS AFFAIRS DEPT
301 Platt Blvd, Claremont, CA 91711-5901
Tel (909) 621-8000 *Founded/Ownrshp* 1955
Sales 98.3MM *EMP* 250^E
Accts Moss Adams Llp Los Angeles C
SIC 8221 College, except junior; College, except junior
Pr: Maria Klawe
Pr: Janel Hastings
Pr: Timothy Hussey
Pr: Scott Martin
CFO: Robin Aspinall
**CFO:* Andrew Dorantes
Assoc VP: Matt Leroux
VP: Jeff Groves
VP: Francis E Su
VP: Jacky Wright
Assoc Dir: Raissa Diamante
Assoc Dir: Kristina Sanchez
Assoc Dir: Falone Serna

D-U-N-S 86-149-9697
HARVEY OF BOSSIER CITY INC
JOHN HARVEY TOYOTA
2901 Benton Rd, Bossier City, LA 71111-2313
Tel (318) 741-1578 *Founded/Ownrshp* 1994
Sales 42.1MM^E *EMP* 100
SIC 5511 Automobiles, new & used; Automobiles, new & used
Pr: John L Harvey
**Treas:* Laura P Harvey
**VP:* John T Harvey
IT Man: Stephen Haltom
Sls Mgr: Jeff Kupers
Sls Mgr: John Leger
Sls Mgr: Greg Powell

HARVEY PUBLIC SCHOOLS DST 152
See COOK COUNTY SCHOOL DISTRICT NO 152

D-U-N-S 07-741-0389
HARVEY SALT CO
1325 Mohrs Ln, Baltimore, MD 21220-1488
Tel (410) 391-9100 *Founded/Ownrshp* 1961
Sales 49.0MM^E *EMP* 62^E
SIC 5169 Salts, industrial
Pr: Louis W Hammen
**Treas:* Michael Di Dominicus
**VP:* Sharon Davis

D-U-N-S 00-616-0097
HARVEY VOGEL MANUFACTURING CO (MN)
425 Weir Dr, Woodbury, MN 55125-1200
Tel (651) 714-2362 *Founded/Ownrshp* 1942
Sales 31.5MM^E *EMP* 158^E
SIC 3469 Stamping metal for the trade; Stamping metal for the trade
CEO: Harvey C Vogel Jr
**Pr:* Robert W Verhey
IT Man: Brent Baxter
Sfty Dirs: Donna Winter
Plnt Mgr: Gary Banaszewski
Ql Cn Mgr: John Nosbusch

D-U-N-S 00-323-8011
HARVEY W HOTTEL INC (DE)
18900 Woodfield Rd Ste A, Gaithersburg, MD 20879-6704
Tel (301) 921-9599 *Founded/Ownrshp* 1945, 1963
Sales 31.6MM^E *EMP* 130^E
SIC 1711 Plumbing, heating, air-conditioning contractors; Refrigeration contractor; Plumbing, heating, air-conditioning contractors; Refrigeration contractor
CEO: Richard W Hottel
**Pr:* Jeffrey F Hottel
COO: Leslie Titcomb
CFO: Stacy Argyros
CFO: Rich Harrington
Snr Mgr: Troy Luskey

HARVEYS CASINO HOTEL
See HARVEYS CASINO RESORTS

D-U-N-S 00-923-8965
■ **HARVEYS CASINO RESORTS**
HARVEYS CASINO HOTEL
(*Suby of* CAESARS ENTERTAINMENT OPERATING CO INC) ★
Hwy 50 & Stateline Ave, Stateline, NV 89449
Tel (775) 588-2411 *Founded/Ownrshp* 2001
Sales 96.7MM^E *EMP* 4,090^E
SIC 7011 Casino hotel; Casino hotel
Ch: Phillip Satre
**CEO:* Gary Loveman
**CFO:* Charles Atwood
IT Man: Sam Khalifa

D-U-N-S 13-449-6160 IMP
HARVEYS INDUSTRIES INC
ORIGINAL SEATBELTBAG , THE
1918 E Glenwood Pl, Santa Ana, CA 92705-5108
Tel (714) 277-4700 *Founded/Ownrshp* 1997
Sales 27.2MM^E *EMP* 55
SIC 5137 5632 Handbags; Women's accessory & specialty stores
CEO: Dana Harvey

D-U-N-S 94-771-0141
■ **HARVEYS IOWA MANAGEMENT CO INC**
HARRAHS CNCIL BLUFFS CASINO HT
(*Suby of* HARVEYS CASINO HOTEL) ★
1 Harrahs Blvd, Council Bluffs, IA 51501-5680
Tel (712) 329-6000 *Founded/Ownrshp* 1996
Sales 32.4MM^E *EMP* 1,306
SIC 7011 Casino hotel; Casino hotel
Pr: Gary Loveman
**CEO:* Gaye Gullo
**Sr VP:* Peter J Weien

HARVEY'S LAWN & GARDEN CENTER
See HARVEY MILLING CO INC

HARVEY'S SUPERMARKETS
See JH HARVEY CO LLC

HARVEY'S TIRE EXCHANGE
See A & E TIRE INC

D-U-N-S 11-601-2840 IMP/EXP
HARVIC INTERNATIONAL LTD
10 W 33rd St Rm 508, New York, NY 10001-3306
Tel (212) 967-6666 *Founded/Ownrshp* 1983
Sales 33.0MM *EMP* 21
SIC 5136 5137 Men's & boys' clothing; Women's & children's clothing
Pr: Henry Abadi
**VP:* Maurice Abadi

D-U-N-S 01-125-3874 IMP
HARVILL INDUSTRIES LTD
2021 Postal Way, Dallas, TX 75212-6319
Tel (214) 905-9668 *Founded/Ownrshp* 2001
Sales 21.6MM^E *EMP* 20
SIC 5084 Industrial machinery & equipment
Pr: Bill Harvill
**COO:* Dwane Laufer

D-U-N-S 05-724-7793 IMP/EXP
HARWICK STANDARD DISTRIBUTION CORP
60 S Seiberling St, Akron, OH 44305-4217
Tel (330) 798-9300 *Founded/Ownrshp* 1971
Sales 81.7MM^E *EMP* 70
SIC 5169 Chemicals, industrial & heavy; Chemicals, industrial & heavy
Prin: Daniel G Laporte
**Pr:* Jeffrey J Buda
CFO: Mark Cohn
CFO: Jim Houston
VP: Dan Davis
VP: D R Hardesty
**VP:* Ernest E Pouttu
**VP:* David Sultz
Creative D: Bryan Shields
**Prin:* Richard A Chenoweth
**Prin:* Mary Ann Osley

HARWOOD, EMMA L MD
See EUGENIA CHANG MD

D-U-N-S 60-906-4605
HARWOOD PLACE INC
HARWOOD PLACE RETIREMENT CTR
(*Suby of* LUTHERAN HOME INC) ★
8220 Harwood Ave Apt 19, Milwaukee, WI 53213-2577
Tel (414) 256-6800 *Founded/Ownrshp* 1989
Sales 7.3MM *EMP* 515
Accts Bdo Usa Llp Milwaukee Wi
SIC 6513 8052 Apartment building operators; Intermediate care facilities; Apartment building operators; Intermediate care facilities
Pr: Robert Pieters

HARWOOD PLACE RETIREMENT CTR
See HARWOOD PLACE INC

D-U-N-S 10-067-3508
HARWOOD UNION HS DIST 19
WASHINGTON WEST SUPERVISORY UN
1673a Main St Ste A, Waitsfield, VT 05673-8002
Tel (802) 496-2272 *Founded/Ownrshp* 1960
Sales NA *EMP* 350
SIC 9411 ;

D-U-N-S 82-611-3193
HAS SUPPLY INC
A H I
2800 N Gordon St, Alvin, TX 77511-9581
Tel (281) 331-0088 *Founded/Ownrshp* 1994
Sales 63.6MM^E *EMP* 160
SIC 5032 3241 3441 3271 Brick, stone & related material; Building stone; Masonry cement; Fabricated structural metal; Architectural concrete: block, split, fluted, screen, etc.; Brick, stone & related material; Building stone; Masonry cement; Fabricated structural metal; Architectural concrete: block, split, fluted, screen, etc.
Ch Bd: Robert N Allen
**Pr:* William M Hill
**VP:* Christopher Sellers

D-U-N-S 00-965-6075
HASA INC
23119 Drayton St, Saugus, CA 91350-2547
Tel (661) 259-5848 *Founded/Ownrshp* 1964
Sales 33.7MM^E *EMP* 175
SIC 2812

HASBRO CHILDREN'S HOSPITAL
See RHODE ISLAND HOSPITAL

D-U-N-S 00-120-0443 IMP
▲ **HASBRO INC** (RI)
1027 Newport Ave, Pawtucket, RI 02861-2500
Tel (401) 431-8697 *Founded/Ownrshp* 1926
Sales 4.2MMM *EMP* 5,000
Tkr Sym HAS *Exch* NGS
SIC 3944 3942 3069 Games, toys & children's vehicles; Board games, children's & adults'; Board games, puzzles & models, except electronic; Electronic games & toys; Stuffed toys, including animals; Dolls, except stuffed toy animals; Teething rings, rubber; Baby pacifiers, rubber; Games, toys & children's vehicles; Board games, children's & adults'; Board games, puzzles & models, except electronic; Electronic games & toys; Stuffed toys, including animals; Dolls, except stuffed toy animals; Teething rings, rubber; Baby pacifiers, rubber
Pr: Brian Goldner
**Ch Bd:* Alfred J Verrecchia
Pr: John Frascotti
Pr: Kenneth Romanzi
COO: Peter Ferraro
CFO: Deborah Thomas
Treas: Martin R Trueb
Ofcr: Stephen J Davis
Ofcr: Barbara Finigan
Ofcr: Christine Meehan
Ex VP: Duncan J Billing
Ex VP: David D R Hargreaves
Sr VP: Finn Arnesen
Sr VP: Mark Blecher
Sr VP: Donna Ebbs
Sr VP: Mike Eisner
Sr VP: Brooke Goldstein
Sr VP: Ira Hernowitz
Sr VP: Jerry Perez
Sr VP: Simon Waters
VP: Dan Ratigan
Board of Directors: Tracy A Leinbach, Basil L Anderson, Michael W O Garrett, Alan R Batkin, Edward M Philip, Frank J Biondi Jr, Richard S Stoddart, Kenneth A Bronfin, Linda Zecher, Michael Burns, John M Connors Jr, Lisa Gersh, Jack M Greenberg, Alan G Hassenfeld

D-U-N-S 60-677-5153
■ **HASBRO INTERNATIONAL INC**
(*Suby of* HASBRO INC) ★
1027 Newport Ave, Pawtucket, RI 02861-2500
Tel (401) 431-8697 *Founded/Ownrshp* 1974
Sales 309.8MM^E *EMP* 4,180
SIC 3944 Games, toys & children's vehicles; Games, toys & children's vehicles
Pr: Brian Coldner
CFO: David D Hargreaves
Sr VP: Wayne S Charness
Sr VP: Jackie Daya
Sr VP: Barry Nagler
VP: Paul J Alexander
VP: Kurt R Benson
VP: Nelson R Chaffee Corp
VP: Joanne Haworth
VP: Mark Monday
**VP:* Judis A Smith
VP: Sibley Tarrant

D-U-N-S 84-808-1951
■ **HASBRO MANAGERIAL SERVICES INC**
(*Suby of* HASBRO INC) ★
1027 Newport Ave, Pawtucket, RI 02861-2500
Tel (401) 431-8697 *Founded/Ownrshp* 1923
Sales 97.2MM^E *EMP* 5,000
SIC 8741 Management services; Management services
VP: Barry Nagler

D-U-N-S 96-591-0974
HASC CENTER INC
5601 1st Ave, Brooklyn, NY 11220-2517
Tel (718) 745-7575 *Founded/Ownrshp* 2010
Sales 35.4MM *EMP* 2
Accts J Gliksman Cpa Pc Brooklyn
SIC 8331 Job training & vocational rehabilitation services; Job training & vocational rehabilitation services
Prin: Lilan Lieberman
Prac Mgr: Shaina Rosenfeld

D-U-N-S 07-257-8958
HASCALL STEEL CO
4165 Spartan Indus Dr Sw, Grandville, MI 49418-2553
Tel (616) 531-8600 *Founded/Ownrshp* 1971
Sales 78.9MM^E *EMP* 165
SIC 5051

HASCO
See HARTWELL CORP

D-U-N-S 01-886-5124
▲ **HASCO HOLDINGS LLC**
14809 Hampton Ct, Dallas, TX 75254-7681
Tel (972) 931-1911 *Founded/Ownrshp* 2008
Sales 91.0MM^E *EMP* 262^E
SIC 8082 Home health care services; Home health care services
Prin: Harold F Compton Sr

D-U-N-S 01-762-9549
■ **HASCO MEDICAL INC** (FL)
(*Suby of* HASCO HOLDINGS LLC) ★
16800 Dallas Pkwy Ste 200, Dallas, TX 75248-1961
Tel (214) 302-0930 *Founded/Ownrshp* 2009
Sales 91.0MM *EMP* 262^E
Accts Weaver And Tidwell Llp Da
Tkr Sym HASC *Exch* OTO
SIC 5999 8082 Home health care services; Wheelchair lifts; Home health care services
Pr: Hal Compton Jr
**Ch Bd:* Harold F Compton Sr
COO: Alfredo Olivierre III
COO: Alfredo Ollivierre
CFO: Shane Jorgenson
VP: Mike Dumais
VP: John Hill
Snr Mgr: Robyn Priest

D-U-N-S 06-627-3004
HASEKO (HAWAII) INC
HASEKO HAWAII INC
(*Suby of* HASEKO AMERICA INC) ★
91-1001 Kaimalie St 205, Ewa Beach, HI 96706-6247
Tel (808) 689-7772 *Founded/Ownrshp* 2001
Sales 51.4MM^E *EMP* 60
SIC 6552 6531 Land subdividers & developers, commercial; Land subdividers & developers, residential; Real estate agents & managers
Ch Bd: Koji Kato
Pr: Toru Nagayama
Treas: Makoto Murakami
Ex VP: Richard Dunn
Ex VP: Raymond S Kanna
Ex VP: Nancy Maeda
VP: Dan Wiley

D-U-N-S 04-962-9798
HASEKO AMERICA INC
(*Suby of* HASEKO CORPORATION)
91-1001 Kmlie St Apt 205a, Ewa Beach, HI 96706
Tel (808) 689-7772 *Founded/Ownrshp* 2001
Sales 51.5MM^E *EMP* 75
SIC 6552 Land subdividers & developers, commercial
Ch Bd: Koji Kato
**Pr:* Toru Nagayama
**Treas:* Makoto Murakami

HASEKO HAWAII INC
See HASEKO (HAWAII) INC

D-U-N-S 10-849-1325
HASELDEN CONSTRUCTION LLC
6950 S Potomac St Ste 100, Centennial, CO 80112-4039
Tel (303) 751-1478 *Founded/Ownrshp* 1983
Sales 198.4MM^E *EMP* 279^E
Accts Martin Vejvoda And Associates
SIC 1542 Commercial & office building, new construction; Hospital construction; School building construction; Commercial & office building, new construction; Hospital construction; School building construction
CEO: Ed J Haselden
**Pr:* Byron Haselden
**COO:* Mike Haselden
**CFO:* Troy Schroeder
**Ex VP:* Dave Lueders
**VP:* Greg Conger
**VP:* James Michael Haselden
Board of Directors: Byron Haselden

D-U-N-S 02-727-4976
HASELWOOD BUICK-PONTIAC CO
HASELWOOD CHEVROLET BUICK GMC
501 W Hills Blvd, Bremerton, WA 98312-4390
Tel (360) 479-4910 *Founded/Ownrshp* 1956
Sales 25.2MM^E *EMP* 55
SIC 5511 7538

HASELWOOD CHEVROLET BUICK GMC
See HASELWOOD BUICK-PONTIAC CO

D-U-N-S 18-056-9485 IMP
HASKEL INTERNATIONAL LLC
(*Suby of* ACCUDYNE INDUSTRIES LLC) ★
100 E Graham Pl, Burbank, CA 91502-2076
Tel (818) 843-4000 *Founded/Ownrshp* 2013
Sales 94.3MM^E *EMP* 335
SIC 3561 3594 5084 5085 3699 Pumps & pumping equipment; Fluid power pumps; Hydraulic systems equipment & supplies; Hose, belting & packing; Valves, pistons & fittings; Electrical equipment & supplies; Pumps & pumping equipment; Fluid power pumps; Hydraulic systems equipment & supplies; Hose, belting & packing; Valves, pistons & fittings; Electrical equipment & supplies
CEO: Chris Krieps
VP Opers: Cliff KAO
S&M/VP: Peter Duffy
Snr Mgr: Juan Zarta

D-U-N-S 80-884-4278 IMP
HASKEL TRADING INC
245 Route 109, West Babylon, NY 11704-6216
Tel (631) 270-3600 *Founded/Ownrshp* 1989
Sales 29.8MM^E *EMP* 40
Accts Cywiak & Company
SIC 5149 Groceries & related products; Groceries & related products
Pr: Ely Baum
CFO: Cheski Baum

D-U-N-S 10-695-6824 EXP
HASKELL CO
111 Riverside Ave, Jacksonville, FL 32202-4950
Tel (904) 791-4500 *Founded/Ownrshp* 1999
Sales 978.9MM^E *EMP* 1,110
SIC 1541 1542 1522 1623 8712 3272

D-U-N-S 03-238-9942
HASKELL CO INC
JAX UTILITIES & WATERPROOFING
(*Suby of* HASKELL CO) ★
111 Riverside Ave, Jacksonville, FL 32202-4950
Tel (904) 791-4500 *Founded/Ownrshp* 1965
Sales 148.6MM^E *EMP* 550
SIC 1541 1542 1522 1623 8712 3272 Industrial buildings, new construction; Commercial & office building, new construction; Multi-family dwelling construction; Underground utilities contractor; Sewer line construction; Architectural engineering; Prestressed concrete products; Industrial buildings, new construction; Commercial & office building, new construction; Multi-family dwelling construction; Underground utilities contractor; Sewer line construction; Architectural engineering; Prestressed concrete products
CEO: Preston H Haskell
Pr: Steven T Halverson
CFO: Haas G Tanzler
Sr VP: John Cobb
**Sr VP:* Greg Ferrell
Sr VP: James A Gray
Sr VP: John H Patten
Sr VP: Robert Soulby
**Sr VP:* C Edward Vandergriff
Sys/Mgr: Clark Tucker

D-U-N-S 00-794-2147
HASKELL CORP (WA)
1001 Meador Ave, Bellingham, WA 98229-5808
Tel (360) 734-1200 *Founded/Ownrshp* 1890
Sales 146.9MM^E *EMP* 300
SIC 1542 Nonresidential construction; Nonresidential construction
Pr: Fred Haskell
**CFO:* Jeff Jenkins
**VP:* Terrance Corrigan

HASKELL COUNTY COMMUNITY HOSP
See CAH ACQUISITION CO 16 LLC

D-U-N-S 00-128-3431 IMP
HASKELL JEWELS LLC
MIRIAM HASKILL
390 5th Ave Fl 2, New York, NY 10018-8162
Tel (201) 330-9205 *Founded/Ownrshp* 1926
Sales 55.4MM^E *EMP* 200
SIC 5094 3961 Jewelry & precious stones; Costume jewelry, ex. precious metal & semiprecious stones; Jewelry & precious stones; Costume jewelry, ex. precious metal & semiprecious stones
CEO: Frank Fialkoff
COO: Gabrielle Fialkoff
Ex VP: Beverly Eichel
VP: Jacqueline Canzone
VP: Neville Ward
Exec: Steve Johns
Dir: Rebecca Michaelson
Creative D: Roni Lifshitz
Mng Dir: Brett Fialkoff
Off Mgr: Ilene Florin
Sales Exec: Julie Rossing

D-U-N-S 12-259-2439
HASKELL LEMON CONSTRUCTION CO
3800 Sw 10th St, Oklahoma City, OK 73108-2047
Tel (405) 947-6069 *Founded/Ownrshp* 1985
Sales 94.6MM^E *EMP* 150
SIC 5032 1611 3272 2951 Paving materials; Highway & street paving contractor; Concrete products; Asphalt paving mixtures & blocks; Paving materials; Highway & street paving contractor; Concrete products; Asphalt paving mixtures & blocks
Pr: Kent Wert
**Sec:* Larry Lemon
Ofcr: Gayle Ballard
VP: Linuel Graddy
**VP:* Bob Lemon
Sfty Mgr: Craig Riley
Plnt Mgr: Brian Wolf
Sls Dir: Chuck West

D-U-N-S 05-273-8325
HASKELLS INC (MN)
81 S 9th St Ste 130, Minneapolis, MN 55402-3224
Tel (612) 342-2437 *Founded/Ownrshp* 1934, 1970
Sales 40.0MM *EMP* 170
SIC 5921 5813 Liquor stores; Bar (drinking places)
CEO: John F Farrell
**Pr:* Brian Farrell
**COO:* Daniel A Manning
**VP:* Theodore Farrell
**VP:* David Johantgen

D-U-N-S 62-251-9718 IMP
HASKINS ELECTRIC LLC
1414 N 25th Ave, Phoenix, AZ 85009-3614
Tel (623) 937-3999 *Founded/Ownrshp* 1990
Sales 24.0MM^E *EMP* 120
SIC 1731 General electrical contractor; General electrical contractor
Pr: Charles B Haskins Jr
CFO: Bryan Cameron
Sec: Katrina Haskins
VP: Jeff Johnson
Exec: Marysue Periera

D-U-N-S 00-906-3512
■ **HASKINS STEEL CO INC**
(*Suby of* AMERICAN METALS CORP) ★
3613 E Main Ave, Spokane, WA 99202-4732
Tel (509) 252-9724 *Founded/Ownrshp* 2013
Sales 110.2MM^E *EMP* 95
SIC 5051 Steel; Steel
Pr: Sterling Haskins
Treas: Scott A Hskins
**Sec:* Scott A Haskins
**VP:* Craig Diaz
VP: Caron Munsen
Sfty Mgr: Dave Kruger
Sls Mgr: Rick Pickel
Sales Asso: Cathy Niblock
Sales Asso: Dan Skinner
Sales Asso: Dave Wright

D-U-N-S 00-183-8861 IMP
HASLER INC (DE)
478 Wheelers Farms Rd, Milford, CT 06461-9105
Tel (203) 301-3400 *Founded/Ownrshp* 1969
Sales NA *EMP* 381
SIC 5044 3565 3596 8741

D-U-N-S 01-620-6765
HASLER OIL CO INC
NAPA AUTO PARTS
45 E Mechanic St, Bloomfield, IN 47424-1431
Tel (812) 384-8063 *Founded/Ownrshp* 1956
Sales 33.1MM *EMP* 90
SIC 5531 5171 5541 5983 Automobile & truck equipment & parts; Automotive parts; Petroleum bulk stations & terminals; Gasoline service stations; Fuel oil dealers; Automobile & truck equipment & parts; Automotive parts; Petroleum bulk stations & terminals; Gasoline service stations; Fuel oil dealers
Pr: Joe Chipman

D-U-N-S 07-635-7805
HASLETT PUBLIC SCHOOL DISTRICT
5593 Franklin St, Haslett, MI 48840-5000
Tel (517) 339-8242 *Founded/Ownrshp* 1900
Sales 16.4MM^E *EMP* 350
Accts Maner Costerisan Lansing Mi
SIC 8211 Public elementary & secondary schools; Public elementary & secondary schools

D-U-N-S 14-936-6119
HASSAN & SONS INC
HASSAN AND SONS
2860 N Santiago Blvd # 200, Orange, CA 92867-1722
Tel (714) 761-5426 *Founded/Ownrshp* 1996
Sales 22.9MM^E *EMP* 400
SIC 5541 5411 Filling stations, gasoline; Convenience stores
CEO: Salaheddin Fawzi Hassan

HASSAN AND SONS
See HASSAN & SONS INC

D-U-N-S 00-285-0253
HASSE CONSTRUCTION CO INC (IL)
10 Lincoln Ave, Calumet City, IL 60409-2606
Tel (708) 862-2450 *Founded/Ownrshp* 1956
Sales 22.5MM^E *EMP* 50^E
SIC 1541 1623 Industrial buildings & warehouses; Sewer line construction
Pr: William A Hasse Jr
VP: Ed Hewitt

HASSEL BMW
See HASSEL MOTORS INC

D-U-N-S 05-059-3433 IMP
HASSEL MOTORS INC
HASSEL BMW
291 W Sunrise Hwy, Freeport, NY 11520-3227
Tel (516) 223-6160 *Founded/Ownrshp* 1984
Sales 32.7MM^E *EMP* 84
SIC 5511 Automobiles, new & used; Automobiles, new & used
Ch Bd: Frank Dellaquila
Genl Mgr: Diane Smith
Sls Mgr: Steve Mahoney

D-U-N-S 00-404-1901
HASSELL & HUGHES LUMBER CO INC (TN)
GREENWAY PRMIUM WD FUEL PLLETS
608 Highway 13 S, Collinwood, TN 38450-4693
Tel (931) 724-9191 *Founded/Ownrshp* 1929
Sales 31.0MM^E *EMP* 210
SIC 2421 Sawmills & planing mills, general; Sawmills & planing mills, general
Pr: Ralph M Hughes Jr

D-U-N-S 04-032-4980
HASSELL CONSTRUCTION CO INC
16111 Hollister St, Houston, TX 77066-1409
Tel (281) 893-2570 *Founded/Ownrshp* 1975
Sales 31.3MM^E *EMP* 150
SIC 1623 1611 Underground utilities contractor; General contractor, highway & street construction; Underground utilities contractor; General contractor, highway & street construction
CEO: J Phillip Hassell
**Pr:* Phillip Hassell
**CEO:* J Phillip Hasselll
**Sec:* Shawn Potts
**Ex VP:* Joe Rebecek
**VP:* Michael L Hassell

HASSETT AIR EXPRESS, INC.
See HASSETT EXPRESS LLC

D-U-N-S 07-914-3261
HASSETT EXPRESS HOLDINGS LLC
877 S Il Route 83, Elmhurst, IL 60126-4740
Tel (630) 530-6515 *Founded/Ownrshp* 2013
Sales 76.1MM^E *EMP* 301^E
SIC 4731 Freight transportation arrangement; Freight transportation arrangement
Pr: Michelle Halkerston
Ex VP: Mike Stone
Sr VP: Francis Stone
VP: Frank Borta
VP: Don Prentice
IT Man: Steven Nickerson
VP Opers: Dennis Cartwright
Opers Supe: Mike Terracciano

D-U-N-S 06-621-6698
HASSETT EXPRESS LLC
HASSETT AIR EXPRESS, INC.
(*Suby of* HASSETT EXPRESS HOLDINGS LLC) ★
877 S Il Route 83, Elmhurst, IL 60126-4740
Tel (630) 530-6515 *Founded/Ownrshp* 2013
Sales 76.1MM^E *EMP* 226
SIC 4512 4213 Air cargo carrier, scheduled; Trucking, except local; Household goods transport; Air cargo carrier, scheduled; Trucking, except local; Household goods transport
Pr: Michelle Halkerston
**Ex VP:* Mike Stone
**VP:* Frank Borta
**VP:* Dennis Cartwright
**VP:* Don Prentice

D-U-N-S 04-044-6163
HASSETT LINCOLN-MERCURY SALES INC
3530 Sunrise Hwy, Wantagh, NY 11793-4061
Tel (516) 785-7800 *Founded/Ownrshp* 1981
Sales 31.3MM^E *EMP* 70^E
SIC 5511 Automobiles, new & used; Automobiles, new & used
Pr: Donald V Zergebel
Treas: Joyce Green
Sls Mgr: Sal Rivela
Sales Asso: Ron Borgese
Sales Asso: Phil Deitch
Sales Asso: John Descul
Sales Asso: John Hodgetts
Sales Asso: Alex Micic
Sales Asso: Fred Pusterla
Sales Asso: Michael N Scannello
Sales Asso: Bill Walsh

D-U-N-S 02-703-1814
HASSLOCHER ENTERPRISES INC
FRONTIER MEAT & SUPPLY
8520 Crownhill Blvd, San Antonio, TX 78209-1119
Tel (210) 828-1493 *Founded/Ownrshp* 1946
Sales 48.3MM^E *EMP* 1,300
SIC 5812 5142 6552 Coffee shop; Meat, frozen: packaged; Subdividers & developers; Coffee shop; Meat, frozen: packaged; Subdividers & developers
Ch: Germano Hasslocher
**Ch Bd:* Veva Hasslocher
**Pr:* Robert C Hasslocher
COO: Patrick Richardson
CFO: Ron Riemenschneider
Treas: Susan Hasslocher
VP: Jim Green
**VP:* James C Hasslocher

D-U-N-S 05-182-2989
HASTING S FORD INC
3013 E 10th St, Greenville, NC 27858-4119
Tel (252) 215-5263 *Founded/Ownrshp* 1970
Sales 27.9MM^E *EMP* 70
SIC 5511 7538 5521 Automobiles, new & used; Trucks, tractors & trailers: new & used; General automotive repair shops; Used car dealers; Automobiles, new & used; Trucks, tractors & trailers: new & used; General automotive repair shops; Used car dealers
Pr: Sherry Woolard
**VP:* William A Mc Clung
Off Mgr: Michelle Page
IT Man: David Carraway

D-U-N-S 08-036-6818
HASTINGS AREA SCHOOL SYSTEM
232 W Grand St, Hastings, MI 49058-2225
Tel (269) 948-0894 *Founded/Ownrshp* 1935
Sales 23.1MM^E *EMP* 415
Accts Norman & Paulisen Pc Cpa
SIC 8211 Public elementary & secondary schools; High school, junior or senior; Public elementary & secondary schools; High school, junior or senior
**Prin:* Maragrie Haas
**Prin:* Tim Johnston
**Prin:* Micheal Karasinski
**Prin:* Susan Linacre
**Prin:* Amy Tebo
IT Man: Brian Osteirink
Schl Brd P: Jon Hart
Teacher Pr: Elizabeth Rowse
Pgrm Dir: Mary Robinson

HASTINGS BOOKS, MUSIC & VIDEO
See HASTINGS ENTERTAINMENT INC

D-U-N-S 05-430-3912
HASTINGS COLLEGE (NE)
710 N Turner Ave, Hastings, NE 68901-7696
Tel (402) 463-2402 *Founded/Ownrshp* 1882
Sales 49.2MM *EMP* 250
Accts Kpmg Llp Omaha Ne
SIC 8221 College, except junior; College, except junior
Pr: Don Jackson
**Treas:* Garry Freeman
**VP:* Dennis Krienert
Assoc Dir: Austin McDonald
CTO: Dan Glomski
Sls Mgr: Deb Bunde

D-U-N-S 00-616-3992
HASTINGS COOPERATIVE CREAMERY CO (MN)
1701 Vermillion St, Hastings, MN 55033-3164
Tel (651) 437-9414 *Founded/Ownrshp* 1914
Sales 65.6MM *EMP* 38
Accts Carlson Highland Cpas Amery
SIC 2026 5451 Fluid milk; Dairy products stores; Fluid milk; Milk processing (pasteurizing, homogenizing, bottling); Dairy products stores
Pr: Ray Deutsch
Genl Mgr: David Bwert
Genl Mgr: David Zwart
Sls Mgr: Greg Nelson

D-U-N-S 04-813-3417 IMP
HASTINGS ENTERTAINMENT INC
HASTINGS BOOKS, MUSIC & VIDEO
(*Suby of* DRAW ANOTHER CIRCLE LLC) ★
3601 Plains Blvd, Amarillo, TX 79102-1098
Tel (806) 351-2300 *Founded/Ownrshp* 2014
Sales 814.3MM^E *EMP* 4,738
SIC 5735 5942 7841 Video discs & tapes, prerecorded; Records, audio discs & tapes; Book stores; Video disk/tape rental to the general public; Video discs & tapes, prerecorded; Records, audio discs & tapes; Book stores; Video disk/tape rental to the general public
CEO: Joel Weinshanker
**Pr:* Alan Van Ongevalle
**CFO:* Dan Crow
VP: Victor D Fuentes
**VP:* Phil McConnell
VP: Scott Voth
IT Man: Christy Hall
Snr Mgr: Joseph Young

D-U-N-S 00-601-9582 IMP/EXP
HASTINGS FIBER GLASS PRODUCTS INC (MI)
770 Cook Rd, Hastings, MI 49058-9616
Tel (269) 945-9541 *Founded/Ownrshp* 1959
Sales 28.1MM^E *EMP* 93
SIC 3423 Hand & edge tools
CEO: Larry Baum
**Ch Bd:* Earl L Mc Mullin
**Pr:* David Baum
**Sec:* Earlene Baum
Sales Exec: Kirk Mulder

D-U-N-S 94-571-1869
■ **HASTINGS FILTERS INC**
(*Suby of* CLARCOR INC) ★
4400 Highway 30 E, Kearney, NE 68847-9797
Tel (308) 233-9499 *Founded/Ownrshp* 1995
Sales 54.5MM^E *EMP* 217
SIC 3714 Filters: oil, fuel & air, motor vehicle; Filters: oil, fuel & air, motor vehicle
Pr: Sam Ferrise
**VP:* Hans Alpsteg
**VP:* Kevin Jenn
Rgnl Mgr: Terry Makinster

D-U-N-S 80-037-4212 EXP
HASTINGS FOODS LLC
JUST FOODS
3321 Island Cir, Grand Island, NE 68803-5275
Tel (308) 384-6623 *Founded/Ownrshp* 1991
Sales 23.1MM^E *EMP* 80
SIC 5147 Meats & meat products; Meats & meat products

D-U-N-S 61-163-3363
HASTINGS HEALTH SYSTEMS INC
241 North Rd, Poughkeepsie, NY 12601-1154
Tel (845) 471-2000 *Founded/Ownrshp* 1987
Sales 35.2MM^E *EMP* 1,950
SIC 8741 8062 Hospital management; General medical & surgical hospitals; Hospital management; General medical & surgical hospitals
Pr: Robert Savage
**Pr:* Sister M Ann Elizabeth
**CFO:* Marianne Muise
**CFO:* Robert Patrick
**Ex VP:* Donald Murphy

D-U-N-S 02-157-4850
HASTINGS INDEPENDENT SCHOOL DISTRICT 200
1000 11th St W, Hastings, MN 55033-3717
Tel (651) 480-7000 *Founded/Ownrshp* 1897
Sales 58.0MM *EMP* 625
Accts Malloy Montague Karnowski R
SIC 8211 Public senior high school; Public junior high school; Public elementary school; School board; Public senior high school; Public junior high school; Public elementary school; School board
V Ch: Angie McGinnis
Ofcr: Wayne Hicks
Ofcr: Tammy Loberg
Ofcr: Craig Puch
Ofcr: Linde Raway
Exec: Robert Majeski
IT Man: Kelly Hagen
Schl Brd P: Ann Skogland
Psych: Kirk Johnson
Psych: Naomi Marietta
HC Dir: Anne Conklin

D-U-N-S 00-726-9418 EXP
HASTINGS IRRIGATION PIPE CO
1801 E South St, Hastings, NE 68901-6481
Tel (402) 463-6633 *Founded/Ownrshp* 1949
Sales 35.0MM *EMP* 90
SIC 3354 3443 Aluminum pipe & tube; Fabricated plate work (boiler shop); Aluminum pipe & tube; Fabricated plate work (boiler shop)
Pr: Gale Beirow
**Treas:* Nancy Pavelka
Sales Exec: Gail Jones

D-U-N-S 00-695-9688
HASTINGS MUTUAL INSURANCE CO
404 E Woodlawn Ave, Hastings, MI 49058-1091
Tel (800) 442-8277 *Founded/Ownrshp* 1885
Sales NA *EMP* 432
SIC 6411 Insurance agents & brokers; Insurance agents & brokers
Treas: Joseph J Babiak Jr
Sr Pt: Christopher Fluke
CFO: Michael T Kinnary
Ofcr: Jane Hapway
VP: Christo N Ballantyne
VP: Timothy Bremer
VP: Robert J Eshelbrenner
VP: Bill Gregor
VP: Daniel G Hill
VP: Keith E Jandahl
VP: Darrell L Oldham
**VP:* Michael W Puerner
VP: Dana A Walters
Exec: Carl Surma
Board of Directors: Christopher J Fluke, Frederic L Halbert, Mark A Kolanowski, Bruce J Osterink, James R Toburen, John L Ward

D-U-N-S 13-241-8039
HASTINGS PUBLIC SCHOOLS
1924 W A St, Hastings, NE 68901-5650
Tel (402) 461-7500 *Founded/Ownrshp* 1906
Sales 12.1MM^E *EMP* 566
SIC 8211 Public elementary & secondary schools; School board
Bd of Dir: Jackie Maynard
IT Man: Connie Niles
Schl Brd P: Jim Heyen
Psych: Kylee Greisen

D-U-N-S 01-022-9904
■ **HASTINGS WALGREEN CO** (NE)
WALGREENS
(*Suby of* WALGREEN CO) ★
200 Wilmot Rd, Deerfield, IL 60015-4620
Tel (847) 940-2500 *Founded/Ownrshp* 1968
Sales 46.2MM^E *EMP* 568
SIC 5912 Drug stores; Drug stores
Pr: Mark A Wagner
**Treas:* Jason M Dubinsky

HASTINGS YOUTH ACADEMY
See G4S YOUTH SERVICES LLC

D-U-N-S 79-350-9241
HAT BRANDS HOLDING CORP
601 Marion Dr, Garland, TX 75042-7930
Tel (972) 494-7133 *Founded/Ownrshp* 1992
Sales 130.4MM^E *EMP* 1,700
SIC 2353 3914 3144 3143 Caps: cloth, straw & felt; Hats: cloth, straw & felt; Silversmithing; Women's footwear, except athletic; Men's footwear, except athletic; Caps: cloth, straw & felt; Hats: cloth, straw & felt; Silversmithing; Women's footwear, except athletic; Men's footwear, except athletic
Pr: John R Tillotson
**Ch Bd:* John R Muse
CFO: Thomas A Hough

D-U-N-S 07-150-1977
HAT LIMITED PARTNERSHIP
MANPOWER
1155 W 4th St Ste 223, Reno, NV 89503-5149
Tel (775) 328-6020 *Founded/Ownrshp* 1979
Sales 32.6MM^E *EMP* 1,500
Accts Cupit Milligan Ogden & Willi
SIC 7363 Manpower pools; Manpower pools
Pt: Gary Harrigan
Pt: Harrigan Enterprises
Admn Mgr: Kim Hill
Genl Mgr: Mike Harrigan
IT Man: Pat Harrigan

D-U-N-S 06-988-0040
HAT WHITE MANAGEMENT LLC
LIFE SKILLS CENTER
121 S Main St Ste 200, Akron, OH 44308-1426
Tel (330) 535-6868 *Founded/Ownrshp* 1998
Sales 36.7MM^E *EMP* 116
SIC 4142 8741 Bus charter service, except local; Business management
VP: Rodd Coker
VP: Robert L Fox
VP: Kerry Jupina
VP: Wendy Rydarowicz
Mktg Dir: Lori Zoss-Kraska
Board of Directors: Tom Probert

D-U-N-S 04-033-4588 IMP
■ **HAT WORLD INC**
LIDS SPORTS GROUP
(*Suby of* GENESCO INC) ★
5304 W 74th St, Indianapolis, IN 46268-4179
Tel (317) 871-4390 *Founded/Ownrshp* 1995
Sales 52.7MM^E *EMP* 267
SIC 5611 Men's & boys' clothing stores; Men's & boys' clothing stores
CEO: Ken Kocher
CFO: Richard Cramer
**VP:* Rick Cramer
VP: John Dewaal
VP: Lawrence Havlik
VP: David Seifert
Dist Mgr: Keith O'Neill
Dist Mgr: Tom Quinn
CIO: Dick Proffit
Dir IT: Tony Harte
IT Man: Tom Clements

D-U-N-S 07-548-6316
HATBORO-HORSHAM SCHOOL DISTRICT
HH
229 Meetinghouse Rd, Horsham, PA 19044-2192
Tel (215) 420-5000 *Founded/Ownrshp* 1966
Sales 49.0MM^E *EMP* 765
SIC 8211 8748 Public elementary & secondary schools; Business consulting; Public elementary & secondary schools; Business consulting
**Pr:* Dr Russel S Bleile
**Treas:* Marian McCouch
**VP:* Louis A Polaneczky
Prin: Karen Davis
Prin: Eleanor Seif
Prin: Leta Thompson
IT Man: Travis Pillen
IT Man: Marianne Ruby
Pr Dir: Nancey Delucia
Teacher Pr: Linda Gloner
Instr Medi: Bob Anderson

D-U-N-S 06-364-8802
HATCH ASSOCIATES CONSULTANTS INC
(*Suby of* HATCH LTD)
1600 W Carson St Ste 1, Pittsburgh, PA 15219-1031
Tel (412) 471-3090 *Founded/Ownrshp* 1975
Sales 32.6MM^E *EMP* 221
SIC 8711 8742 Consulting engineer; General management consultant; Consulting engineer; General management consultant
Ch Bd: Kurt Stobele
**Treas:* Irving Langill
Board of Directors: Ronald Nolan, Bert Wasmund

D-U-N-S 84-017-5046
HATCH CHILE CO LLC
2005 S Commercial Dr, Brunswick, GA 31525-1144
Tel (912) 267-9906 *Founded/Ownrshp* 2010
Sales 23.0MM *EMP* 12
SIC 5141 Groceries, general line
Pr: Steve Dawson
CFO: Mike Gleaton
VP Sls: Jim Garcia

D-U-N-S 10-789-2473
HATCH INC
HATCH TECHNOLOGY & TOYS
(*Suby of* DEMCO INC) ★
301 N Main St Ste 102, Winston Salem, NC 27101-3819
Tel (336) 744-7280 *Founded/Ownrshp* 2007
Sales 37.8MM^E *EMP* 140
SIC 7373 Computer integrated systems design; Computer integrated systems design
Pr: Ginny Norton
**CFO:* Stacy Stout
**VP:* Ty Brown
VP: Beverly Griffin
**VP:* Susan Gunnewig
**VP:* Dana Love
**VP:* John Yazumbek
Dir IT: Katie Ford
IT Man: Ginisa Ebert

D-U-N-S 15-675-7200
HATCH MOTT MACDONALD FLORIDA LLC
(*Suby of* HATCH MOTT MACDONALD GROUP INC) ★
220 W Garden St Ste 700, Pensacola, FL 32502-5745
Tel (850) 484-6011 *Founded/Ownrshp* 2003
Sales 24.7MM^E *EMP* 300
SIC 8711 Engineering services; Engineering services

D-U-N-S 14-162-9753
HATCH MOTT MACDONALD GROUP INC
111 Wood Ave S Ste 5, Iselin, NJ 08830-2700
Tel (973) 379-3400 *Founded/Ownrshp* 2001
Sales 507.4MM *EMP* 2,500
Accts Bdo Usa Llp Woodbridge Nj
SIC 8711 Engineering services; Engineering services
Pr: Nicholas Denichilo
**Ch Bd:* Kurt Strobele
CFO: Margaret McGrath
**Treas:* Jeff Hilla
VP: Michael Altland
VP: James Forster
VP: John Hawley
Snr PM: Dirk De Bruyn
Snr PM: Doug Hinton

Snr PM: Anthony Soccodato
Snr PM: Lisa Taylor

D-U-N-S 15-037-9618
HATCH MOTT MACDONALD I&E LLC
(*Suby of* HATCH MOTT MACDONALD GROUP INC) ★
111 Wood Ave S Ste 410, Iselin, NJ 08830-2700
Tel (973) 379-3400 *Founded/Ownrshp* 2001
Sales 37.7MM^E *EMP* 500
SIC 8711 8712 8741 1541 Engineering services; Architectural services; Construction management; Industrial buildings & warehouses; Engineering services; Architectural services; Construction management; Industrial buildings & warehouses
VP: Richard Steinhart
Snr PM: Mark Stirrup
Snr PM: Andy Thompson

D-U-N-S 93-793-9171
HATCH MOTT MACDONALD LLC
(*Suby of* HATCH MOTT MACDONALD GROUP INC) ★
4301 Hacienda Dr Ste 300, Pleasanton, CA 94588-2724
Tel (925) 469-8010 *Founded/Ownrshp* 2001
Sales 47.2MM^E *EMP* 500
SIC 8711 Consulting engineer; Consulting engineer
CEO: Nicholas Denichilo

D-U-N-S 04-037-9301
HATCH REALTY GROUP INC
1611 Lodi Ave, San Mateo, CA 94401-3644
Tel (650) 438-2444 *Founded/Ownrshp* 2013
Sales 300.0MM *EMP* 5
SIC 6531 Real estate brokers & agents; Real estate brokers & agents
Pr: Monica Sagullo
**Prin:* Benedict Paras

D-U-N-S 00-533-8603 EXP
HATCH STAMPING CO LLC
(*Suby of* PROPHET EQUITY LP) ★
635 E Industrial Dr, Chelsea, MI 48118-1599
Tel (734) 475-8628 *Founded/Ownrshp* 1965
Sales 6.3MM *EMP* 650
SIC 3465 3544 Automotive stampings; Special dies & tools; Automotive stampings; Special dies & tools
Pr: Dan Craig
Ch Bd: Ronald Hatch
CFO: Christopher A Parrott
Ofcr: Steve Rauscher
VP: Todd Fyall
Prgrm Mgr: Ryan Bucher
Prgrm Mgr: Jason Burton
Dir IT: Steve Rocher
Sys Mgr: Kevin Fenn
Opers Mgr: Valerie Houle
Opers Mgr: Terri Kesling

HATCH TECHNOLOGY & TOYS
See HATCH INC

D-U-N-S 04-461-2361
HATCHBEAUTY PRODUCTS LLC
10951 W Pico Blvd Ste 300, Los Angeles, CA 90064-2182
Tel (310) 396-7070 *Founded/Ownrshp* 2010
Sales 120.0MM *EMP* 84
SIC 5122 Cosmetics, perfumes & hair products; Cosmetics, perfumes & hair products
Mng Pt: Ben Bennett
**Pt:* Benjamin Bennett
**Mng Pt:* Tracy Holland
Off Mgr: Erika Beckles

HATCI
See HYUNDAI AMERICA TECHNICAL CENTER INC

D-U-N-S 00-610-6884 IMP
HATCO CORP (WI)
635 S 28th St, Milwaukee, WI 53215-1298
Tel (414) 671-6350 *Founded/Ownrshp* 1950, 2007
Sales 86.4MM^E *EMP* 360
SIC 3589 Commercial cooking & foodwarming equipment; Food warming equipment, commercial; Commercial cooking & foodwarming equipment; Food warming equipment, commercial
Pr: David C Rolston
**VP:* Randall M Baumgart
**VP:* Joseph Hatchell
**VP:* Michael L Whiteley
Off Admin: Anne Kuhnz
Manager: Joe Cash
Snr Mgr: Scott Patza

D-U-N-S 02-660-1583
HATFIELD AND CO INC
JOHNSON CONTROLS
2475 Discovery Blvd, Rockwall, TX 75032-6200
Tel (972) 288-7625 *Founded/Ownrshp* 1959
Sales 130.4MM *EMP* 102
Accts Lloyd Hughes Cpa Dallas Tex
SIC 5084 3677 5074 Industrial machinery & equipment; Filtration devices, electronic; Plumbing & heating valves; Industrial machinery & equipment; Filtration devices, electronic; Plumbing & heating valves
CEO: George Hatfield
**Pr:* Greg Hatfield
**CFO:* George Boles
Brnch Mgr: Steve Schroder
Off Mgr: Jane Warner
CIO: Harvey Sparhawk
VP Sls: Scott Beeman
Sls Mgr: Janey Evans
Sls Mgr: Shawn Guidry
Sls Mgr: Tommy Johnson
Sls Mgr: Matt Keenan

HATFIELD ELECTRIC INDUSTRIAL
See HECO INC

D-U-N-S 80-265-8799
HATFIELD JEEP EAGLE INC
JEEP EAGLE WEST VOLKSWAGEN W
1495 Auto Mall Dr, Columbus, OH 43228-3658
Tel (614) 870-5425 *Founded/Ownrshp* 1989
Sales 47.1MM *EMP* 44
Accts Dan Newman Cpa Pittsburgh P
SIC 5511 Automobiles, new & used; Automobiles, new & used
Pr: Dan Hatfield
Treas: L Diane Honigford
Off Mgr: Darlene Henson

D-U-N-S 07-980-3276
HATHAWAY BROWN SCHOOL
19600 N Park Blvd, Shaker Heights, OH 44122-1899
Tel (216) 932-4214 *Founded/Ownrshp* 1876
Sales 28.1MM *EMP* 200
Accts Maloney Novotny Llc Cleveland
SIC 8211 Preparatory school; Preparatory school
Comm Dir: Terry Dubow
Ex Dir: Natalie Celeste
Dir IT: Tara Anderson
Mktg Dir: Vanessa Butler

D-U-N-S 96-195-3056
HATHAWAY DINWIDDIE CONSTRUCTION CO
(*Suby of* HATHAWAY DINWIDDIE CONSTRUCTION GROUP) ★
275 Battery St Ste 300, San Francisco, CA 94111-3378
Tel (415) 986-2718 *Founded/Ownrshp* 1996
Sales 158.5MM^E *EMP* 400
SIC 1542 Commercial & office building, new construction; Commercial & office buildings, renovation & repair; Commercial & office building, new construction; Commercial & office buildings, renovation & repair
CEO: Greg Cosko
**Pr:* Paul Gregory Cosko
**Ex VP:* Stephen W McCoid
**Sr VP:* Gordon D Smith
VP: Greg Burg
**VP:* Ed Conlon

D-U-N-S 96-259-9221
HATHAWAY DINWIDDIE CONSTRUCTION GROUP
275 Battery St Ste 300, San Francisco, CA 94111-3378
Tel (415) 352-1501 *Founded/Ownrshp* 1996
Sales 178.9MM^E *EMP* 400
SIC 1542 Commercial & office building contractors; Commercial & office building contractors
CEO: Greg Cosko
**CFO:* David Miller
**Sr VP:* Stephen E Smith
**VP:* Stephen W McCoid
VP: Ronald Velo

D-U-N-S 08-377-6674
HATHAWAY-SYCAMORES CHILD AND FAMILY SERVICES
210 S De Lacey Ave # 110, Pasadena, CA 91105-2048
Tel (626) 844-1677 *Founded/Ownrshp* 1920
Sales 51.8MM *EMP* 670
Accts Green Hasson & Janks Llp Los
SIC 8361 8093 Home for the emotionally disturbed; Mental health clinic, outpatient; Home for the emotionally disturbed; Mental health clinic, outpatient
Ch Bd: Michael Galper
**Pr:* William Martone
Ex VP: Samuel Heinrichs
Ex VP: Tonya Nowakowski
Ex VP: Steven Shaw
VP: Charles Buchanan
Ex Dir: Joan Cochran
IT Man: Robert Myers
Opers Supe: Lindsey Bogan
Opers Supe: Nancy Sheppard
Psych: Sharon Chan

D-U-N-S 09-100-5686 IMP
HATILLO CASH & CARRY INC
Km 87 Hm 1 Rr 2, Hatillo, PR 00659
Tel (787) 898-5840 *Founded/Ownrshp* 1978
Sales 34.8MM^E *EMP* 151
SIC 5141 5411 Groceries, general line; Grocery stores, independent; Groceries, general line; Grocery stores, independent
Pr: Isidoro Rosa
**Pr:* Isidoro Rosa Herrera
**VP:* Isidoro Rossa

D-U-N-S 80-273-6251
▲ HATTERAS FINANCIAL CORP
751 W 4th St Ste 400, Winston Salem, NC 27101-2795
Tel (336) 760-9347 *Founded/Ownrshp* 2007
Sales 355.7MM *EMP* 30^E
Tkr Sym HTS *Exch* NYS
SIC 6798 Real estate investment trusts; Real estate investment trusts
CEO: Michael R Hough
Pr: Benjamin M Hough
CFO: Kenneth A Steele
Ofcr: John J Dalena
Ex VP: Frederick J Boos II
Mng Dir: Michael Buttner

HATTERAS FUNDS
See HATTERAS INVESTMENT PARTNERS LLC

D-U-N-S 96-227-8078
■ HATTERAS INVESTMENT PARTNERS LLC
HATTERAS FUNDS
(*Suby of* RCS CAPITAL CORP) ★
6601 Six Forks Rd, Raleigh, NC 27615-6589
Tel (919) 846-2324 *Founded/Ownrshp* 2014
Sales 20.4MM^E *EMP* 208^E
SIC 6282 Investment advice
CEO: David B Perkins
Pr: Robert L Worthington
COO: J Michael Fields
CFO: Lance Baker
Ofcr: Andrew P Chica

D-U-N-S 13-166-2371
HATTERAS PRESS INC
56 Park Rd, Tinton Falls, NJ 07724-9715
Tel (732) 935-9800 *Founded/Ownrshp* 1983
Sales 90.8MM^E *EMP* 260
SIC 2752 2796 Commercial printing, offset; Platemaking services; Commercial printing, lithographic; Platemaking services
Pr: Charles F Duerr
Pr: Scott Duerr
**Pr:* William Duerr
CFO: Stan Cryla
Sr VP: Richard McKenna
VP: Thomas Ayala
VP: August Bartolone
Genl Mgr: Richard Lanza
CIO: Brent McNally
VP Opers: Sean Scanlon
Sfty Mgr: Scott Manson

HATTERAS YACHTS
See HATTERAS/CABO YACHTS LLC

D-U-N-S 09-757-1140 IMP/EXP
HATTERAS YACHTS INC
110 N Glenburnie Rd, New Bern, NC 28560-2703
Tel (252) 633-3101 *Founded/Ownrshp* 2013
Sales NA *EMP* 1,320
SIC 3732

D-U-N-S 07-913-9368
HATTERAS/CABO YACHTS LLC
HATTERAS YACHTS
110 N Glenburnie Rd, New Bern, NC 28560-2703
Tel (252) 633-3101 *Founded/Ownrshp* 2013
Sales 39.2MM^E *EMP* 145^E
SIC 3732 Yachts, building & repairing
IT Man: Michelle Martines

D-U-N-S 07-674-4655
HATTIE LARLHAM CENTER FOR CHILDREN WITH DISABILITIES
9772 Diagonal Rd, Mantua, OH 44255-9160
Tel (330) 274-2272 *Founded/Ownrshp* 1963
Sales 18.9MM *EMP* 368
Accts Howard Weshbale & Co Clevela
SIC 8361 8322 8052 Home for the mentally retarded; Individual & family services; Intermediate care facilities; Home for the mentally retarded; Individual & family services; Intermediate care facilities
CEO: Dennis Allen
**COO:* Darryl E Mast
Ofcr: Jennie Dawes
**VP:* Michelle Anderson
**VP:* Dotty Grexa
**VP:* Sandy Neal

D-U-N-S 08-764-9349
HATTIESBURG CITY SCHOOL BOARD INC (MS)
301 Mamie St, Hattiesburg, MS 39401-4200
Tel (601) 584-6283 *Founded/Ownrshp* 1898
Sales 10.7MM^E *EMP* 750
SIC 8211 Public elementary school; Public junior high school; Public senior high school; Public elementary school; Public junior high school; Public senior high school
**Prin:* Jimmy Hopkins

D-U-N-S 07-790-1908
HATTIESBURG CLINIC PROFESSIONAL ASSOCIATION
415 S 28th Ave, Hattiesburg, MS 39401-7283
Tel (601) 579-5444 *Founded/Ownrshp* 1998
Sales 149.5MM^E *EMP* 1,693
SIC 8011 Clinic, operated by physicians; Clinic, operated by physicians
CEO: Tommy G Thornton
**Pr:* John M Fitzpatrick
**CFO:* Alex Agnew
**Sec:* Petra Schneider-Redden
**VP:* Steven W Stogner MD
Off Mgr: Jeananne Potin
Orthpdst: Brian Humpherys
Doctor: Bryan N Batso

D-U-N-S 18-449-8256 IMP
HATTIESBURG PAPER CO LLC
(*Suby of* SELECT PRODUCT GROUP LP) ★
1085 Parkview Rd, Green Bay, WI 54304-5616
Tel (920) 498-5100 *Founded/Ownrshp* 2007
Sales 38.9MM^E *EMP* 180^E
SIC 2679 Paper products, converted; Paper products, converted
Pr: Gregory Paul Santaga
Exec: Jim Peppich

D-U-N-S 61-172-0079
HATTIESBURG PUBLIC SCHOOL DISTRICT
HPSD
301 Mamie St, Hattiesburg, MS 39401-4200
Tel (601) 582-5078 *Founded/Ownrshp* 1898
Sales 30.8MM^E *EMP* 500
SIC 8211 Public elementary & secondary schools; Public elementary & secondary schools
Pr: Marcus Cathey
Dir Sec: Tony Davis
MIS Dir: Jackie Walley
Dir IT: Dane Conrad
Dir IT: Ross Randall
Psych: Della Watson

D-U-N-S 00-698-5121
HATZEL & BUEHLER INC
(*Suby of* CONSTRUCTION MANAGEMENT SERVICES INC) ★
3600 Silverside Rd Ste A, Wilmington, DE 19810-5116
Tel (302) 478-4200 *Founded/Ownrshp* 1884
Sales 242.6MM *EMP* 700
Accts Horty & Horty Pa Wilmington
SIC 1731 General electrical contractor; General electrical contractor
Pr: William A Goeller
Treas: Gerard J Herr
VP: Michael C Goeller
VP Admn: Regina Camponelli

D-U-N-S 14-847-3168 EXP
HAU-ENYING LLC
Y & W ENTERPRISES
12550 Whittier Blvd, Whittier, CA 90602-1042
Tel (562) 698-2400 *Founded/Ownrshp* 1973
Sales 23.1MM^E *EMP* 200
SIC 5661 5999 Shoe stores; Pet supplies; Shoe stores; Pet supplies

D-U-N-S 00-121-3420 IMP
HAUCK MANUFACTURING CO
HAUCK MFG KROMSCHRODER CONTRLS
(*Suby of* ELSTER GMBH)
100 N Harris St, Cleona, PA 17042-3100
Tel (717) 272-3051 *Founded/Ownrshp* 2007
Sales 21.8MM^E *EMP* 100^E
SIC 3564 3433 Blowers & fans; Oil burners, domestic or industrial; Blowers & fans; Oil burners, domestic or industrial
Pr: Michael Shay
**VP:* Jim Feese
Mng Dir: Ng Fan
MIS Dir: Richard Carpenter

HAUCK MFG KROMSCHRODER CONTRLS
See HAUCK MANUFACTURING CO

D-U-N-S 06-144-4642
HAUG ENTERPRISES INC
CUB FOODS OF MINNETONKA
4801 County Road 101, Minnetonka, MN 55345-2636
Tel (952) 938-1404 *Founded/Ownrshp* 1972
Sales 30.5MM^E *EMP* 220
SIC 5411 5992 5912 5461 Supermarkets, chain; Florists; Drug stores & proprietary stores; Bakeries; Supermarkets, chain; Florists; Drug stores & proprietary stores; Bakeries
Pr: Douglas Winsor
**Treas:* Arnette Lindeen
**VP:* Marion Strand

D-U-N-S 36-102-1231
HAULERS INSURANCE CO INC
(*Suby of* SHELTER INSURANCE) ★
1101 New Highway 7, Columbia, TN 38401-6664
Tel (931) 381-5406 *Founded/Ownrshp* 2009
Sales NA *EMP* 52
Accts Faulker Mackie & Cochran Pc
SIC 6331 Automobile insurance; Automobile insurance
CEO: Ricky Means
**Treas:* Stephen Daniel Clapp
**VP:* Henry Lloyd Montgomery
**Genl Mgr:* John Stephen Wilkinson
Sls Dir: Tom Wilson

D-U-N-S 00-521-4796
HAUMILLER ENGINEERING CO (IL)
445 Renner Dr, Elgin, IL 60123-6991
Tel (847) 695-9111 *Founded/Ownrshp* 1953
Sales 24.7MM^E *EMP* 105
SIC 3599 Custom machinery; Custom machinery
Pr: Russ Holmer
**CFO:* Rick Cremerius
Off Mgr: Meg Cerda
Dir IT: William Stangler
Sls Dir: Paul Mierzwa

HAUN COMPANIES
See HAUN WELDING SUPPLY INC

D-U-N-S 00-225-7939
HAUN WELDING SUPPLY INC (NY)
HAUN COMPANIES
5921 Court Street Rd, Syracuse, NY 13206-1742
Tel (315) 463-5241 *Founded/Ownrshp* 1958
Sales 58.8MM^E *EMP* 135
SIC 5085 Welding supplies; Welding supplies
Ch Bd: Mark C Haun
Ofcr: Eric Mark
VP: Wayne Brownson
VP: Gary Craft
**VP:* Janine Haun
Brnch Mgr: Rob Johnson
Brnch Mgr: Warren Kelly
Sfty Dirs: Stephen Rake
Sls Mgr: Greg Storie

HAUNDAI
See GARVEY VOLKSWAGEN INC

D-U-N-S 04-362-2711 IMP
HAUNI RICHMOND INC
(*Suby of* HAUNI MASCHINENBAU AG)
2800 Charles City Rd, Richmond, VA 23231-4500
Tel (804) 222-5259 *Founded/Ownrshp* 1995
Sales 36.0MM^E *EMP* 120
SIC 3559 5084 3565 Tobacco products machinery; Industrial machinery & equipment; Bread wrapping machinery; Tobacco products machinery; Industrial machinery & equipment; Bread wrapping machinery
Pr: John L Miller
CFO: Jerry Chrzaszcz
**Ch:* Christopher Somm
**VP:* Peter Moderegger
**VP:* James K Shannon
**Prin:* Dr Martin Herman
**Prin:* Jrgen Spykman
Tech Mgr: Chuck Schultz
Sls Mgr: Darrell Basinger
Sls Mgr: Sergio Coronado
Sls Mgr: Steve McClenny

D-U-N-S 87-826-3664 IMP
▲ HAUPPAUGE DIGITAL INC
91 Cabot Ct, Hauppauge, NY 11788-3717
Tel (631) 434-1600 *Founded/Ownrshp* 1994
Sales 34.0MM *EMP* 99^E
Tkr Sym HAUP *Exch* OTC
SIC 3577 Computer peripheral equipment; Computer peripheral equipment
Ch Bd: Kenneth Plotkin
CFO: Gerald Tucciarone
VP: John Casey
Snr Sftwr: Richard Vollkommer
IT Man: Al Venterino
VP Sls: Ron Petralia
S&M/VP: Yehia Oweiss
Board of Directors: Adam M Zeitsiff

D-U-N-S 06-596-5907
HAUPPAUGE UNION FREE SCHOOL DISTRICT
495 Hoffman Ln, Hauppauge, NY 11788-3102
Tel (631) 265-3630 *Founded/Ownrshp* 1943
Sales 52.2MM^E *EMP* 1,151
Accts R.s Abrams & Co Llp Ronkonk

SIC 8211 Public elementary & secondary schools; Public elementary & secondary schools
Schl Brd P: David Barshay

D-U-N-S 18-345-1426
HAUSBECK BROTHERS INC
HAUSBECK DAVE TRUCKING
2695 W Vassar Rd, Reese, MI 48757-9352
Tel (989) 759-2010 *Founded/Ownrshp* 1983
Sales 27.9MM^E *EMP* 100
SIC 4212 4213 Local trucking, without storage; Trucking, except local
Pr: Dave Hausbeck
**VP:* Richard Harrison
**VP:* Kristin Titsworth
**VP:* John Yardley

HAUSBECK DAVE TRUCKING
See HAUSBECK BROTHERS INC

HAUSER GROUP, THE
See ART HAUSER INSURANCE INC

D-U-N-S 02-616-9359 IMP
HAUSMAN FOODS LLC
H F
4261 Beacon St, Corpus Christi, TX 78405-3326
Tel (361) 883-5521 *Founded/Ownrshp* 1939
Sales 46.0MM^E *EMP* 104
SIC 5147

D-U-N-S 00-189-2660 IMP/EXP
HAUSMANN INDUSTRIES INC (NJ)
130 Union St, Northvale, NJ 07647-2290
Tel (201) 767-0255 *Founded/Ownrshp* 1955
Sales 22.5MM^E *EMP* 95
SIC 2599 2531 Hospital furniture, except beds; Public building & related furniture
CEO: David H Hausmann
**Pr:* Werner Hausmann

D-U-N-S 09-855-0775
HAUSMANN JOHNSON INSURANCE INC
700 Regent St Ste 100, Madison, WI 53715-2634
Tel (608) 257-3795 *Founded/Ownrshp* 1946
Sales NA *EMP* 60
SIC 6411 6331 6321 6311 Insurance agents; Fire, marine & casualty insurance; Accident & health insurance; Life insurance
Pr: Tim Hasmann
Pt: Melody Hope
**Pr:* Tim Hausmann
**COO:* Jeffrey Hausmann
**Treas:* Sandra Hasz
**VP:* Steve Squires
Admn Mgr: Traci Stanek
Off Mgr: Suzanne Templin

D-U-N-S 10-457-4319
HAUSTEN LLC
IKEA SAN DIEGO
(*Suby of* IKEA NORTH AMERICA SERVICES LLC) ★
2149 Fenton Pkwy, San Diego, CA 92108-4739
Tel (619) 283-6166 *Founded/Ownrshp* 2008
Sales 25.3MM^E *EMP* 300
SIC 5712 Furniture stores; Furniture stores

D-U-N-S 01-501-9871
HAUTE HIPPIE ENTERPRISES LLC
336 W 37th St Rm 1430, New York, NY 10018-4763
Tel (212) 239-6825 *Founded/Ownrshp* 2007
Sales 22.8MM^E *EMP* 50^E
SIC 5137 Women's & children's clothing
COO: Jason Epstein
VP: Jennifer Giffen
Pr Mgr: Elise Draude

D-U-N-S 03-104-5404
HAUTLY CHEESE CO INC
251 Axminister Dr, Fenton, MO 63026-2938
Tel (636) 533-4400 *Founded/Ownrshp* 1934
Sales 20.9MM *EMP* 17^E
SIC 5143 Cheese
Pr: Alan C Hautly
Opers Mgr: Dan Kastner

HAVANA AUTO PARTS & MACHINE
See HAVANA AUTO PARTS INC

D-U-N-S 04-072-3637
HAVANA AUTO PARTS INC
HAVANA AUTO PARTS & MACHINE
901 S Havana St, Aurora, CO 80012-3003
Tel (303) 341-2611 *Founded/Ownrshp* 1976
Sales 22.2MM^E *EMP* 150
SIC 5013 5531 Automotive supplies & parts; Automotive parts; Automotive supplies & parts; Automotive parts
Pr: Frank Welsh
**VP:* Kate Welsh

HAVANA MEDICAL ASSOCIATES
See MASON DISTRICT HOSPITAL

D-U-N-S 12-436-7413
HAVAS EDGE LLC
2386 Faraday Ave Ste 200, Carlsbad, CA 92008-7223
Tel (760) 929-1357 *Founded/Ownrshp* 2001
Sales 25.0MM^E *EMP* 115^E
SIC 7311 Advertising agencies; Advertising agencies
Pr: Dan Alderman
**Pr:* Greg Johnson
**Ex VP:* Abed Abusaleh
**Ex VP:* Shannon Ellis
Sr VP: Gary Epstein
**Sr VP:* George Sylva
VP: Jay Dobson
VP: Sean Kalub
VP: Michael Lodge
VP: Ben McEachen
VP: Jennifer Peabody
VP: Taft W Zitoun
Creative D: Jason Campos
Creative D: Steve Reepmeyer

D-U-N-S 94-659-0395
HAVAS FORMULA LLC
FORMULA PR INC.
(*Suby of* HAVAS)
1215 Cushman Ave, San Diego, CA 92110-3904
Tel (619) 234-0345 *Founded/Ownrshp* 2014
Sales 21.4MM^E *EMP* 100
SIC 8743 Public relations services
Pr: Michael A Olguin
Pr: David Heimlich
**Sr VP:* Alexis McCance
VP: Kelly Baker
Rgnl Mgr: Marissa Marquez
Snr Mgr: Jaymie Martinez

D-U-N-S 05-026-8234
HAVAS HEALTH INC (NY)
HEALTH4BRANDS CATAPULT
(*Suby of* HAVAS NORTH AMERICA INC) ★
200 Madison Ave Fl 7, New York, NY 10016-3907
Tel (212) 532-1000 *Founded/Ownrshp* 1980, 1989
Sales 75.6MM^E *EMP* 250
SIC 7311 Advertising agencies; Advertising agencies
Ex VP: Anthony Tramontana
Sr VP: Meredith L Bernstein
Sr VP: Barry Goldberg
Sr VP: Jess Seilheimer
VP: Sandra Nevistich
Mng Dir: Christina Dappolonia
**Brnch Mgr:* Doug Burcin
Art Dir: Eleanor Wong

D-U-N-S 78-206-0057
HAVAS NORTH AMERICA INC
(*Suby of* HAVAS)
200 Hudson St, New York, NY 10013-1807
Tel (212) 886-2000 *Founded/Ownrshp* 2001
Sales 362.2MM^E *EMP* 10,500
SIC 7311 5963 Advertising agencies; Direct sales, telemarketing; Advertising agencies; Direct sales, telemarketing
Ch Bd: David Jones
Pr: Andrew Benett
Treas: Elizabeth Matrisciano
**Treas:* Liz Matrisciano
**Ofcr:* Darren Moran
**VP:* Colleen Sayther
Creative D: Giselle Sols
Mng Dir: Katerina Wheeler
CIO: Jeff Marshall

D-U-N-S 07-935-3134
HAVAS WORLDWIDE LLC
200 Hudson St Fl 4, New York, NY 10013-1807
Tel (212) 886-2000 *Founded/Ownrshp* 1991
Sales 65.8MM^E *EMP* 800^E
SIC 7311 Advertising agencies; Advertising agencies
Pr: Lee Noonan
CFO: Elba Arroyo
CFO: Frank Mangano
Ex VP: Jacques Dillies
Sr VP: Chris Jarrin
Sr VP: Matt Silver
VP: Robert Cronin
VP: Alec Tallman
Creative D: Marc Blanchard
Creative D: Katie Connolly
Creative D: Joseph Delhommer
Creative D: Josh Greenspan
Creative D: Ralph Hollingsworth
Creative D: Jim Hord
Creative D: Andrew Jeske
Creative D: Kevin Kelly
Creative D: David Leinwohl
Creative D: Chris Pacetti
Creative D: Rocky Pina
Creative D: Evan Sharenow
Creative D: Phil Silvestri

D-U-N-S 04-202-9116
HAVAS WORLDWIDE NEW YORK INC
(*Suby of* HAVAS NORTH AMERICA INC) ★
200 Hudson St, New York, NY 10013-1807
Tel (212) 886-2000 *Founded/Ownrshp* 1973
Sales 69.8MM^E *EMP* 475^E
SIC 7311 Advertising agencies; Advertising agencies
CEO: Yannick Bollor
Pr: Andrew Benett
Pr: Ron Bess
CEO: Chris Hirst
CEO: David Jones
COO: Larry Dexhammer
COO: Levent Guenes
CFO: Jean-Marc Antoni
CFO: Elba Arroyo
CFO: Jacques Dillies
CFO: Frank Mangano
Chf Mktg O: Cyril Lemaire
Ofcr: Vin Farrell
Ofcr: Barbara Jewell
Ofcr: Tim Maleeny
Ofcr: Tom Morton
Assoc VP: Charlstie Laytin
VP: Heather Breslow
VP: Allison Ceraso
VP: Jeffrey Goldberg
VP: Jay Hartmann

HAVASU REGIONAL MEDICAL CENTER
See PHC-LAKE HAVASU INC

D-U-N-S 08-938-2873 IMP
HAVCO WOOD PRODUCTS LLC
3200 E Outer Rd, Scott City, MO 63780-9794
Tel (573) 334-0611 *Founded/Ownrshp* 2012
Sales 102.9MM^E *EMP* 460
SIC 2426 Flooring, hardwood; Furniture dimension stock, hardwood; Flooring, hardwood; Furniture dimension stock, hardwood
Off Mgr: Mike David
VP Opers: Chuck Bradford
Sfty Dirs: Dean Walker
Plnt Mgr: Doug McDaniel

D-U-N-S 04-639-9333
HAVEL BROS INC
HAVEL BROTHERS
7525 Disalle Blvd, Fort Wayne, IN 46825-3372
Tel (260) 487-7900 *Founded/Ownrshp* 1957
Sales 20.9MM^E *EMP* 120
SIC 1796 5075 Installing building equipment; Warm air heating equipment & supplies; Air conditioning equipment, except room units; Installing building equipment; Warm air heating equipment & supplies; Air conditioning equipment, except room units
Pr: Jim Witzenman
**Treas:* Frank Feichter

HAVEL BROTHERS
See HAVEL BROS INC

HAVELOCK NEWS, THE
See FREEDOM EASTERN NORTH CAROLINA COMMUNICATIONS INC

D-U-N-S 78-725-1532
HAVEN BEHAVIORAL HEALTHCARE INC
3102 West End Ave # 1000, Nashville, TN 37203-1324
Tel (615) 393-8800 *Founded/Ownrshp* 2006
Sales 96.9MM^E *EMP* 1,000^E
SIC 8011 Psychiatrist; Psychiatrist
CEO: Michael Lindley
**Pr:* Vernon Westrich
**COO:* Al Smith
**CFO:* Rodney Cawood
**CFO:* Ken Miles
**Ofcr:* Page Barnes
**Sr VP:* Kirk McConnell
**VP:* Brian Beutin
VP: Melissa Duffy
VP: Jackie Pawlikowski
VP: Michelle Spurlock
Dir Soc: Doree Baker

D-U-N-S 07-887-7598
HAVEN HEALTH GROUP LLC
450 S 400 E Ste 100, Bountiful, UT 84010-5091
Tel (801) 296-5100 *Founded/Ownrshp* 2012
Sales 43.8MM^E *EMP* 550
SIC 8059 Nursing home, except skilled & intermediate care facility; Nursing home, except skilled & intermediate care facility
Pr: Brett Robertson
**Ch Bd:* Robert Samuelian
**COO:* Spencer Samuelian

D-U-N-S 07-919-7010
HAVEN OF CAMP VERDE LLC (AZ)
(*Suby of* HAVEN HEALTH GROUP LLC) ★
86 W Salt Mine Rd, Camp Verde, AZ 86322-7013
Tel (928) 567-5253 *Founded/Ownrshp* 2012
Sales 11.3MM^E *EMP* 512
SIC 8059 Convalescent home; Convalescent home
Prin: Brett Robertson

D-U-N-S 07-919-7012
HAVEN OF COTTONWOOD LLC
(*Suby of* HAVEN HEALTH GROUP LLC) ★
197 S Willard St, Cottonwood, AZ 86326-4123
Tel (928) 634-5548 *Founded/Ownrshp* 2012
Sales 10.8MM^E *EMP* 512
SIC 8059 Convalescent home; Convalescent home

D-U-N-S 07-919-6913
HAVEN OF FLAGSTAFF LLC
(*Suby of* HAVEN HEALTH GROUP LLC) ★
800 W University Ave, Flagstaff, AZ 86001-7103
Tel (928) 779-6931 *Founded/Ownrshp* 2012
Sales 16.4MM^E *EMP* 512
SIC 8059 Convalescent home; Convalescent home
Off Mgr: Cladette Charles
QC Dir: Edward Le
Nrsg Dir: Mattie Elliott

D-U-N-S 07-919-6897
HAVEN OF SHOW LOW LLC (AZ)
2401 E Hunt Dr, Show Low, AZ 85901-7920
Tel (928) 537-5333 *Founded/Ownrshp* 2012
Sales 10.3MM^E *EMP* 512
SIC 8059 Convalescent home; Convalescent home

D-U-N-S 06-582-3494
HAVEN SAVINGS BANK
(*Suby of* HAVEN BANCORP, INC.)
621 Washington St, Hoboken, NJ 07030-4907
Tel (201) 659-3600 *Founded/Ownrshp* 1938
Sales NA *EMP* 75
SIC 6036 State savings banks, not federally chartered; State savings banks, not federally chartered
Pr: John H Wessling
Ch Bd: John H Wessling Jr
Treas: Kevin P O'Connell
Ofcr: Lisa M Franconeri
Ofcr: Stephen J Lynch
Sr VP: John Wessling III
VP: Paul A Deponte
Brnch Mgr: Manny Alers
Brnch Mgr: Marybeth Perry
Snr Mgr: Bryan Houston

D-U-N-S 04-910-3906 EXP
HAVEN STEEL PRODUCTS INC
13206 S Willison Rd, Haven, KS 67543-8580
Tel (620) 465-2573 *Founded/Ownrshp* 1968
Sales 58.1MM^E *EMP* 85
Accts Cahn & Cahn Ltd Chicago
SIC 3493 Steel springs, except wire; Steel springs, except wire
Pr: Marlon Cohn
**Treas:* Steve Oker
Exec: Peggy Wiard
Genl Mgr: Barney Kassman
Genl Mgr: Tom Oxkley
Sales Exec: Kevin Popp

HAVENWOOD HERITAGE HEIGHTS
See UNITED CHURCH OF CHRIST RETIREMENT COMMUNITY INC

D-U-N-S 10-154-8691
HAVENWYCK HOSPITAL INC
HSA HAVENWYCK HOSPITAL
1525 University Dr, Auburn Hills, MI 48326-2675
Tel (248) 373-9200 *Founded/Ownrshp* 1998
Sales 39.9MM^E *EMP* 350
SIC 8063 Psychiatric hospitals; Psychiatric hospitals
CFO: Mirhee Chun
CFO: David Kunkle
Mktg Dir: Julie Szyska

HAVERFIELD AVIATION
See HAVERFIELD INTERNATIONAL INC

D-U-N-S 13-202-0384
HAVERFIELD INTERNATIONAL INC
HAVERFIELD AVIATION
1750 Emmitsburg Rd, Gettysburg, PA 17325-7109
Tel (717) 334-1826 *Founded/Ownrshp* 2007
Sales 27.1MM^E *EMP* 130
SIC 4785 Inspection & fixed facilities
CEO: Darryl K Ed
**CFO:* Christine N Cassell
VP: Scott Cook
**VP:* Brian D Parker
IT Man: Rachel Palmer
Prd Mgr: Stanton Braun
Snr Mgr: Gene Dickerson

D-U-N-S 07-947-9077
HAVERFORD SCHOOL (PA)
450 Lancaster Ave, Haverford, PA 19041-1397
Tel (610) 642-3020 *Founded/Ownrshp* 1884
Sales 38.5MM *EMP* 200
Accts Parentebeard Llc Wilmington
SIC 8211 Private combined elementary & secondary school; Private combined elementary & secondary school
Ch: John F Stoviak
**Prin:* William C Yoh
Off Mgr: Kerry Cassell
Dir IT: Heayung Cho
Mktg Dir: Timothy Stay

D-U-N-S 03-028-9755
HAVERFORD TOWNSHIP SCHOOL DISTRICT
50 E Eagle Rd, Havertown, PA 19083-1532
Tel (610) 853-5900 *Founded/Ownrshp* 1800
Sales 98.5MM *EMP* 1,000
Accts Maillie Llp Oaks Pennsylvan
SIC 8211 Public elementary & secondary schools; High school, junior or senior; Public elementary & secondary schools; High school, junior or senior
Dir IT: Lillian Finley
IT Man: Blu Taylor
Pr Dir: Fred Brown
Psych: Colleen Malczynski
Psych: Colleen Pelton

D-U-N-S 61-691-2705
HAVERFORD TRUST CO
3 Radnor Corp Ctr Ste 450, Radnor, PA 19087-4580
Tel (610) 995-8700 *Founded/Ownrshp* 1992
Sales 30.4MM *EMP* 60
SIC 6282 Investment advisory service; Investment counselors; Investment advisory service; Investment counselors
Ch Bd: Joseph J McLaughlin Jr
Pt: Harrison Segal
V Ch: Wilson McElhinny
Pr: Paul Isenberg
Pr: Binney Wietlisbach
Treas: Paul S Rovner
**V Ch Bd:* George W Connell
Ofcr: Jeanne Pattalino
Sr Inv Off: Derick Colonello
Sr Inv Off: Kim Southmayd
Sr Tst Off: Jackie Meehan
Trst Ofcr: Melissa Bruner
Sr VP: Charles Ingersoll
VP: Jeffrey Bagley
VP: John Blair
VP: John Derderian
VP: John H Donaldson
VP: Eric Drossner
VP: Marianne G Famous
VP: Frank Files
VP: Thomas Hipp
Board of Directors: Diego F Calderin

D-U-N-S 07-827-0541 EXP
HAVERHILL CHEMICALS LLC
450 Gears Rd Ste 510, Houston, TX 77067-4513
Tel (281) 885-8900 *Founded/Ownrshp* 2011
Sales 228.8MM^E *EMP* 178
SIC 2899 Chemical preparations; Chemical preparations
CEO: Alberto Spera
**CFO:* Elizabeth Labarbara
Off Admin: Laurie Mullis
IT Man: Aaron Fry
Sfty Dirs: Dave Kinker
Prd Mgr: Mark Tipton
Snr Mgr: Todd Bahner
Snr Mgr: David Brown

D-U-N-S 15-377-9538 IMP
■ **HAVERHILL COKE CO LLC**
SUN COKE ENERGY
(*Suby of* SUNCOKE ENERGY PARTNERS LP) ★
2446 Gallia Pike, Franklin Furnace, OH 45629-8837
Tel (740) 355-9800 *Founded/Ownrshp* 2014
Sales 68.2MM^E *EMP* 65
SIC 5051 Steel; Steel
VP: Steve Baker
Opers Mgr: Chris Collier

D-U-N-S 62-726-2421
HAVERHILL PUBLIC SCHOOLS
4 Summer St Ste 104, Haverhill, MA 01830-5843
Tel (978) 374-3400 *Founded/Ownrshp* 2014
Sales 18.3MM^E *EMP* 983^E
SIC 8211 Public elementary & secondary schools
Schl Brd P: Paul Magliocchetti
Psych: Frank Viscuse

HAVERLING CENTRAL SCHOOL
See BATH CENTRAL SCHOOL DISTRICT

D-U-N-S 87-971-7882
■ **HAVERSTICK CONSULTING INC**
(*Suby of* KRATOS DEFENSE & ROCKET SUPPORT SERVICES INC) ★
8770 Guion Rd Ste A, Indianapolis, IN 46268-3017
Tel (317) 218-1700 *Founded/Ownrshp* 2007
Sales 63.3MM^E *EMP* 1,420
SIC 7371 7373 Computer software development & applications; Systems integration services; Computer software development & applications; Systems integration services

Pr: Eric M Demarco
COO: Dave Carter
CFO: Deanna H Lund
Treas: Laura Siegal
VP: Phil Carrai
VP: David Carter
VP: Michael W Fink
VP: Bruce Rankin
VP Opers: Edward M Lake

D-U-N-S 01-471-3697
HAVERSTICK-BORTHWICK CO
400 Stenton Ave Ste 5, Plymouth Meeting, PA 19462-1251
Tel (610) 825-9300 *Founded/Ownrshp* 1922
Sales 25.6MM *EMP* 50
Accts Morison Cogen Llp Bala Cynwyd
SIC 1541 1542 Renovation, remodeling & repairs: industrial buildings; Commercial & office buildings, renovation & repair; Renovation, remodeling & repairs: industrial buildings; Commercial & office buildings, renovation & repair
CEO: William A Cobb Jr
**VP:* Arthur Cobb

D-U-N-S 08-189-2911
HAVERSTRAW STONY POINT CENTRAL SCHOOL DISTRICT INC
NORTH ROCKLAND CENTL SCHL DST
65 Chapel St, Garnerville, NY 10923-1238
Tel (845) 942-3053 *Founded/Ownrshp* 1957
Sales 61.5MM^E *EMP* 1,400
SIC 8211 Public elementary & secondary schools; Public elementary & secondary schools
Bd of Dir: James Kraus
Psych: Robert Canna
Psych: Greta Toledo

D-U-N-S 00-692-5036 IMP/EXP
▲ HAVERTY FURNITURE COMPANIES INC
HAVERTYS
780 Johnson Ferry Rd, Atlanta, GA 30342-1434
Tel (404) 443-2900 *Founded/Ownrshp* 1885
Sales 768.4MM *EMP* 3,388^E
Accts Ernst & Young Llp Atlanta Ge
Tkr Sym HVT *Exch* NYS
SIC 5712 5722 5713 5021 Furniture stores; Bedding & bedsprings; Household appliance stores; Floor covering stores; Furniture stores; Bedding & bedsprings; Household appliance stores; Floor covering stores; Mattresses
Ch Bd: Clarence H Smith
CFO: Dennis L Fink
Treas: Jenny Hill Parker
Ex VP: Steven Burdette
Ex VP: Ed Clary
Sr VP: Richard D Gallagher
**Sr VP:* Rawson Haverty Jr
Sr VP: Janet E Taylor
VP: Matt C Scalf
Brnch Mgr: Sondra Sheltra
CIO: Clary Edward
Board of Directors: John T Glover, L Phillip Humann, Frank S McGaughey III, Terence F McGuirk, Vicki R Palmer, Fred L Schuermann, Al Trujillo

HAVERTYS
See HAVERTY FURNITURE COMPANIES INC

D-U-N-S 78-998-6499
■ HAVERTYS CREDIT SERVICES INC
(*Suby of* HAVERTY FURNITURE COMPANIES INC) ★
1501 Riverside Dr Ste 117, Chattanooga, TN 37406-4332
Tel (423) 624-1969 *Founded/Ownrshp* 2006
Sales NA *EMP* 1^E
SIC 6162 Mortgage bankers & correspondents
Prin: Ben Koonce

D-U-N-S 86-726-9172
HAVI GLOBAL SOLUTIONS LLC
MCDONALD'S
(*Suby of* HAVI GROUP LIMITED PARTNERSHIP) ★
3500 Lacey Rd Ste 600, Downers Grove, IL 60515-5440
Tel (630) 493-7400 *Founded/Ownrshp* 1994
Sales 220.2MM^E *EMP* 500
SIC 8748 Business consulting; Business consulting
Pr: Daniel Musachia
COO: Daniel Musachia
**CFO:* Carol Cienkus
**Ex VP:* Michael Hickey
Ex VP: Richard Watson
**Ex VP:* James Woods
Ex VP: Jim Woods
Sr VP: Carmeli Eli
**Sr VP:* David Ficken
VP: Shane Bertsch
VP: Maria Conroy
VP: Alicia Flores
VP: Patricia Sullivan
Dir Bus: Mark Rafferty

D-U-N-S 60-896-8525
HAVI GROUP LIMITED PARTNERSHIP
PERSECO COMPANY DIV
3500 Lacey Rd Ste 600, Downers Grove, IL 60515-5440
Tel (630) 353-4200 *Founded/Ownrshp* 1988
Sales 4.2MMM^E *EMP* 1,000
SIC 5113 5142 5199 Disposable plates, cups, napkins & eating utensils; Napkins, paper; Packaged frozen goods; Advertising specialties; Disposable plates, cups, napkins & eating utensils; Napkins, paper; Packaged frozen goods; Advertising specialties
CEO: Russ Smyth
COO: Dan Musachia
CFO: Russell Doll
Ch: Theodore F Perlman
VP: Y S Kong

D-U-N-S 18-724-6475 IMP
HAVILAND CONSUMER PRODUCTS INC
HAVILAND POOL & SPA PRODUCTS
(*Suby of* HAVILAND ENTERPRISES INC) ★
421 Ann St Nw, Grand Rapids, MI 49504-2019
Tel (616) 361-6691 *Founded/Ownrshp* 1991
Sales 60.0MM *EMP* 90
SIC 5169 5085 Swimming pool & spa chemicals; Hose, belting & packing; Swimming pool & spa chemicals; Hose, belting & packing
Pr: E Bernard Haviland
Manager: Galen Hostutler
Board of Directors: H Richard Garner, Marie Haviland James

D-U-N-S 00-504-1827
HAVILAND DRAINAGE PRODUCTS CO (OH)
100 W Main St, Haviland, OH 45851
Tel (419) 622-4611 *Founded/Ownrshp* 1924, 1946
Sales 52.4MM^E *EMP* 26
SIC 3259 Drain tile, clay
Pr: Russell Stoller
**Sec:* Todd Stoller

D-U-N-S 06-017-4364 IMP
HAVILAND ENTERPRISES INC
421 Ann St Nw, Grand Rapids, MI 49504-2019
Tel (616) 361-6691 *Founded/Ownrshp* 1936
Sales 180.0MM^E *EMP* 225
Accts Crowe Horwath Llp Grand Rapid
SIC 5169 Chemicals, industrial & heavy; Specialty cleaning & sanitation preparations; Salts, industrial; Swimming pool & spa chemicals; Chemicals, industrial & heavy; Specialty cleaning & sanitation preparations; Salts, industrial; Swimming pool & spa chemicals
Prin: H Richard Garner
**CFO:* Terrence J Schoen
**VP:* Arthur F Harre
**VP:* Michael J Marmo
Exec: Cindy Vand
MIS Dir: Bruce Wiersman
Opers Mgr: Ken Daly
Plnt Mgr: Tom Dyke
Sls&Mrk Ex: Mark Sigerett

HAVILAND POOL & SPA PRODUCTS
See HAVILAND CONSUMER PRODUCTS INC

D-U-N-S 00-602-8492 IMP
HAVILAND PRODUCTS CO
(*Suby of* HAVILAND ENTERPRISES INC) ★
421 Ann St Nw, Grand Rapids, MI 49504-2075
Tel (616) 361-6691 *Founded/Ownrshp* 1979
Sales 120.0MM *EMP* 220
SIC 5169 2819 Chemicals, industrial & heavy; Industrial inorganic chemicals; Chemicals, industrial & heavy; Industrial inorganic chemicals
Pr: E Bernard Haviland
CFO: Jerry Schoen
CFO: Thomas Simmons
Dir Lab: Paul Nederveld
Ex Dir: Richard Nielsen
Genl Mgr: Mark Petzold
Dir IT: Eddy Merral
Opers Mgr: Thomas Dyke
Opers Mgr: Robert Pike
Opers Mgr: Brian Schoen
Trfc Mgr: Kurt Bunce

D-U-N-S 02-323-2705
HAVILL-SPOERL FORD LINCOLN MERCURY INC
1642 Janesville Ave, Fort Atkinson, WI 53538-2726
Tel (920) 568-4444 *Founded/Ownrshp* 1989
Sales 21.0MM *EMP* 63
SIC 5511 Automobiles, new & used; Automobiles, new & used
Pr: Daryl Spoerl
**VP:* Marv Havill

D-U-N-S 00-292-0551 IMP
HAVIS INC
75 Jacksonville Rd, Warminster, PA 18974-4803
Tel (215) 957-0720 *Founded/Ownrshp* 1927
Sales 63.6MM^E *EMP* 170
SIC 5049 3711 3647 3648 3641

HAVRE PUBLIC SCHOOLS
See HAVRE SCHOOL DISTRICT 16-A

D-U-N-S 10-004-3488
HAVRE SCHOOL DISTRICT 16-A
HAVRE PUBLIC SCHOOLS
425 6th St, Havre, MT 59501-4032
Tel (406) 265-4356 *Founded/Ownrshp* 1890
Sales 34.6MM^E *EMP* 1,000
SIC 8211 Public combined elementary & secondary school; Public combined elementary & secondary school
IT Man: Alita Newton
Schl Brd P: Karla Wohlwend
Teacher Pr: Craig Muller
HC Dir: Jeri Erickson

D-U-N-S 13-025-3388
HAVTECH INC
9505 Berger Rd, Columbia, MD 21046-1514
Tel (301) 206-9225 *Founded/Ownrshp* 1983
Sales 33.2MM^E *EMP* 150
SIC 5075

D-U-N-S 18-953-5107
HAWAI I PACIFIC HEALTH
55 Merchant St Ste 2500, Honolulu, HI 96813-4306
Tel (808) 535-7350 *Founded/Ownrshp* 1986
Sales 145.8MM *EMP* 5,400
Accts Ernst & Young Us Llp San Diego
SIC 8062 8011 General medical & surgical hospitals; Clinic, operated by physicians; General medical & surgical hospitals; Clinic, operated by physicians
CEO: Raymond Vara
Pr: Timothy Olderr
CFO: David Okabe
Ofcr: David Fox
Ofcr: Teresa Pytel
Ex VP: Gail Lerch
VP: Paula Dias
VP: Maureen Flannery
VP: Delia Knudsen
VP: Kenneth B Robbins
VP Bus Dev: Bob Ching
Assoc Dir: Jessica Sphar

D-U-N-S 07-249-8132
HAWAI I PACIFIC UNIVERSITY
1164 Bishop St Ste 800, Honolulu, HI 96813-2817
Tel (808) 544-0200 *Founded/Ownrshp* 1965
Sales 107.4MM *EMP* 1,300
Accts Ernst & Young Us Llp Honolulu
SIC 8221 University; University
Pr: Geoffrey Bannister
V Ch: Justin Brown
CFO: Bruce Edwards
CFO: William Kline
Ch: Joachim Cox
Treas: Ajello James
Ofcr: Robert Cyboron
Ex VP: Janet S Kloenhamer
VP: Sharon Blanton
VP: Cassie Carter
VP: Kathleen Clark
VP: Bryan Cole
VP: Scott Stensrud
Assoc Dir: Adrienne Lampitelli

D-U-N-S 79-040-4255 IMP
HAWAII BUSINESS EQUIPMENT INC
(*Suby of* TOSHIBA AMERICA BUSINESS SOLUTIONS INC) ★
2 Musick, Irvine, CA 92618-1631
Tel (949) 462-6000 *Founded/Ownrshp* 2011
Sales 159.0MM^E *EMP* 2,700^E
SIC 5999 7629 5044 Business machine repair, electric; Office equipment; Business machines & equipment; Business machines & equipment; Business machine repair, electric; Office equipment
CEO: Masahiro Yamada
**Pr:* Renee Gomes
**Pr:* Mark Mathews
**VP:* Lester Higa
**VP:* Leighann Iha
**VP:* Gregory Valen

D-U-N-S 11-322-6005
HAWAII CARE AND CLEANING INC
4374 Kukui Grove St # 101, Lihue, HI 96766-2007
Tel (808) 245-6514 *Founded/Ownrshp* 1983
Sales 30.0MM *EMP* 12
SIC 7349 Janitorial service, contract basis; Window cleaning; Janitorial service, contract basis; Window cleaning
Pr: William Allen
COO: Steve Aheong
**Sec:* Colette Buis

D-U-N-S 96-591-3309
HAWAII CARPENTERS HEALTH AND WELFARE FUND
200 N Vineyard Blvd # 100, Honolulu, HI 96817-3950
Tel (808) 841-7575 *Founded/Ownrshp* 2010
Sales NA *EMP* 3
Accts James P Hasselman Cpa Llc Hon
SIC 6371 Pension, health & welfare funds; Pension, health & welfare funds
Prin: James Ramirez

D-U-N-S 07-594-4418
HAWAII CARPENTERS UNION
CARPENTERS UNION LOCAL 745
1311 Houghtailing St # 201, Honolulu, HI 96817-2799
Tel (808) 848-0794 *Founded/Ownrshp* 2001
Sales 44.0MM *EMP* 15
SIC 8631 Trade union; Trade union

HAWAII COFFEE CO
See PARADISE BEVERAGE INC

D-U-N-S 60-963-2534
HAWAII COMMUNITY FOUNDATION
827 Fort Street Mall, Honolulu, HI 96813-4317
Tel (808) 537-6333 *Founded/Ownrshp* 1987
Sales 55.1MM *EMP* 50^E
Accts Oshima Company Cpa Honolulu
SIC 6732 Charitable trust management; Charitable trust management
CEO: Kelvin Taketa
V Ch: Gary Caulfield
Ofcr: Jeanne Hamilton

D-U-N-S 07-251-9671
HAWAII DENTAL SERVICE
HDS
700 Bishop St Ste 700, Honolulu, HI 96813-4196
Tel (808) 521-1431 *Founded/Ownrshp* 1962
Sales NA *EMP* 90
SIC 6324 Dental insurance; Dental insurance
Pr: Faye Kurren
**Treas:* Kelvin N Asahina
**VP:* Kathy Fay
**VP:* Cheryl Takitani
MIS Dir: Tom Delaney
MIS Dir: Harlan Mattos

D-U-N-S 80-993-5216
HAWAII DEPARTMENT OF ACCOUNTING AND GENERAL SERVICES
(*Suby of* EXECUTIVE OFFICE OF STATE OF HAWAII) ★
1151 Punchbowl St Rm 412, Honolulu, HI 96813-3047
Tel (808) 586-0400 *Founded/Ownrshp* 1959
Sales NA *EMP* 900
SIC 9199 General government administration; ; General government administration;

D-U-N-S 80-993-5331
HAWAII DEPARTMENT OF BUDGET & FINANCE
(*Suby of* EXECUTIVE OFFICE OF STATE OF HAWAII) ★
250 S Hotel St Ste 305, Honolulu, HI 96813-2831
Tel (808) 586-1518 *Founded/Ownrshp* 1963
Sales NA *EMP* 290
SIC 9311 Finance, taxation & monetary policy; ; Finance, taxation & monetary policy;

D-U-N-S 80-993-5406
HAWAII DEPARTMENT OF COMMERCE AND CONSUMER AFFAIRS
COMMERCE & CONSMR AFFAIRS DEPT
(*Suby of* EXECUTIVE OFFICE OF STATE OF HAWAII) ★
335 Merchant St, Honolulu, HI 96813-2945
Tel (808) 586-2850 *Founded/Ownrshp* 1982
Sales NA *EMP* 371
SIC 9611 Administration of general economic programs; Consumer protection office, government; ; Administration of general economic programs; Consumer protection office, government;
IT Man: Kay Okimoto

D-U-N-S 80-993-5505
HAWAII DEPARTMENT OF DEFENSE
OFFICE OF ADJUTANT GENERAL
(*Suby of* EXECUTIVE OFFICE OF STATE OF HAWAII) ★
3949 Diamond Head Rd, Honolulu, HI 96816-4413
Tel (808) 733-4246 *Founded/Ownrshp* 1959
Sales NA *EMP* 977
SIC 9711 National security; ; National security;
Genl Mgr: Robert Lee

D-U-N-S 82-467-1218
HAWAII DEPARTMENT OF HUMAN RESOURCES DEVELOPMENT
(*Suby of* EXECUTIVE OFFICE OF STATE OF HAWAII) ★
235 S Beretania St # 1400, Honolulu, HI 96813-2406
Tel (808) 587-1100 *Founded/Ownrshp* 1959
Sales NA *EMP* 14,254
SIC 9199 General government administration;

D-U-N-S 82-467-1176
HAWAII DEPARTMENT OF HUMAN SERVICES
(*Suby of* EXECUTIVE OFFICE OF STATE OF HAWAII) ★
1390 Miller St Ste 209, Honolulu, HI 96813-2403
Tel (808) 586-4997 *Founded/Ownrshp* 1987
Sales NA *EMP* 1,800^E
Accts N & K Cpas Inc Honolulu Ha
SIC 9441 Administration of social & manpower programs; ; Administration of social & manpower programs;
Ofcr: Edwin Igrashi
Ofcr: Susan Kawamoto
IT Man: Ryan Shimamuro
IT Man: David Won

D-U-N-S 82-467-1192
HAWAII DEPARTMENT OF LABOR AND INDUSTRIAL RELATIONS
(*Suby of* EXECUTIVE OFFICE OF STATE OF HAWAII) ★
830 Punchbowl St Rm 321, Honolulu, HI 96813-5095
Tel (808) 586-8842 *Founded/Ownrshp* 1939
Sales NA *EMP* 343
SIC 9651 Labor regulatory agency; ; Labor regulatory agency;
IT Man: Norman Ahu

D-U-N-S 82-467-1168
HAWAII DEPARTMENT OF PUBLIC SAFETY
(*Suby of* EXECUTIVE OFFICE OF STATE OF HAWAII) ★
919 Ala Moana Blvd # 407, Honolulu, HI 96814-4920
Tel (808) 587-1288 *Founded/Ownrshp* 1990
Sales NA *EMP* 2,100
SIC 9221 9229 State police; ; Public order & safety statistics centers; ; State police; ; Public order & safety statistics centers;
Ofcr: Clifford Asato

D-U-N-S 82-467-1457
HAWAII DEPARTMENT OF TAXATION
(*Suby of* EXECUTIVE OFFICE OF STATE OF HAWAII) ★
830 Punchbowl St Ste 126, Honolulu, HI 96813-5094
Tel (808) 587-1510 *Founded/Ownrshp* 1960
Sales NA *EMP* 400
SIC 9311 Taxation department, government; ; Taxation department, government;

D-U-N-S 82-467-1465
HAWAII DEPARTMENT OF TRANSPORTATION
EXECUTIVE OFFICE OF THE
(*Suby of* EXECUTIVE OFFICE OF STATE OF HAWAII) ★
869 Punchbowl St Rm 509, Honolulu, HI 96813-5003
Tel (808) 587-1830 *Founded/Ownrshp* 1959
Sales NA *EMP* 2,215^E
Accts Kobayashi Kanetoku Doi Lum
SIC 9621 Regulation, administration of transportation; ; Regulation, administration of transportation;
Brnch Mgr: Reynaldo Domingo
Brnch Mgr: Ken Tatsuguchi

D-U-N-S 82-467-1200
HAWAII DEPT OF LAND AND NATURAL RESOURCES
(*Suby of* EXECUTIVE OFFICE OF STATE OF HAWAII) ★
1151 Punchbowl St Rm 110, Honolulu, HI 96813-3047
Tel (808) 587-0344 *Founded/Ownrshp* 1959
Sales NA *EMP* 800^E
Accts Ohata Chun Yuen Llp Honolulu
SIC 9512 Land, mineral & wildlife conservation; ; Land, mineral & wildlife conservation;
Ch Bd: Suzanne Case
**Ch:* Peter Young
Ofcr: Juliet Kazanjian

D-U-N-S 05-199-2592 IMP
■ HAWAII ELECTRIC LIGHT CO INC
(*Suby of* HAWAIIAN ELECTRIC CO INC) ★
54 Halekauila St, Hilo, HI 96720-4511
Tel (808) 935-1171 *Founded/Ownrshp* 1970
Sales 329.7MM^E *EMP* 310
SIC 4911 Electric services; Electric services
Pr: Jay M ignacio

CFO: Paul Fujioka
Ofcr: George Iuta
**VP:* Darcy L Endo-Omoto
**VP:* Susan A Li
**VP:* Patsy H Nanbu
**VP:* Tayne S Y Sekimura
CTO: Chuck Strain
IT Man: David Nakamura

D-U-N-S 96-676-8835
HAWAII ELECTRICIANS HEALTH AND WELFARE FUND
1935 Hau St Ste 300, Honolulu, HI 96819-5003
Tel (808) 841-6169 *Founded/Ownrshp* 2011
Sales 23.9MM *EMP* 2E
SIC 8099 Health & allied services; Health & allied services

D-U-N-S 79-954-1909
HAWAII EMPLOYERS MUTUAL INSURANCE CO
1100 Alakea St Ste 1400, Honolulu, HI 96813-2834
Tel (808) 524-3642 *Founded/Ownrshp* 1997
Sales NA *EMP* 70
SIC 6411 6331 Insurance agents, brokers & service; Workers' compensation insurance
CEO: Martin J Welch
Treas: Richard Alexander MA
Sr VP: Michael Redman
Sr VP: Jason Tatsuo Yoshimi
VP: Faye Michiko Bueno
VP: Carlton Wah Tim Chun
VP: Constance Lou Faria
VP: Joe Hee
VP: Stacy Miller
VP: Michael Dennis Redma
VP: Tammy Teixeira
Board of Directors: David Rietow, Dwayne Betsill, Jack Schneider, Pamela Burns, Barbara Tomber, Michael Chinaka, Robert Dove, Alan Gottlieb, Roland Higashi, Charles Ota,kathryn Inkine, Thomas Johnson, Richard Okazaki

D-U-N-S 07-768-5147
HAWAII ENERGY RESOURCES INC
733 Bishop St Fl 28, Honolulu, HI 96813-4022
Tel (808) 547-3111 *Founded/Ownrshp* 1992
Sales 99.8MME *EMP* 740
SIC 5172 2911 5171 Crude oil; Petroleum refining; Petroleum bulk stations; Crude oil; Petroleum refining; Petroleum bulk stations
Pr: Henry G Neal
**Pr:* Faye Kurren
**VP:* Eric Lee
**VP:* Andy Nomura
**VP:* George Putman

D-U-N-S 10-390-1799
HAWAII FOODBANK INC
2611 Kilihau St, Honolulu, HI 96819-2021
Tel (808) 836-3600 *Founded/Ownrshp* 1982
Sales 31.0MM *EMP* 27
Accts Accuity Llp Cpas Honolulu H
SIC 8399 Advocacy group; Advocacy group
CEO: Linda Chu Takayama
**Pr:* Dick Grimm

D-U-N-S 03-202-8321
HAWAII FOODSERVICE ALLIANCE LLC
2720 Waiwai Loop, Honolulu, HI 96819-1940
Tel (808) 839-2004 *Founded/Ownrshp* 1997
Sales 88.7MME *EMP* 83E
SIC 5141 5812 Food brokers; Eating places; Food brokers; Eating places; Food services, direct sales

HAWAII GAS
See GAS CO LLC

D-U-N-S 07-848-9360
HAWAII HEALTH CONNECTOR
201 Merchant St Ste 1810, Honolulu, HI 96813-2963
Tel (808) 321-0105 *Founded/Ownrshp* 2011
Sales NA *EMP* 13
SIC 6321 Health insurance carriers; Health insurance carriers
Ex Dir: Coral Andrews
COO: Kevin Hause
IT Man: Diane Reich
Snr Mgr: Anjali Kataria

D-U-N-S 78-765-0790
HAWAII HEALTH SYSTEMS CORP
HHSC
3675 Kilauea Ave, Honolulu, HI 96816-2333
Tel (808) 733-4020 *Founded/Ownrshp* 1996
Sales 105.5MME *EMP* 1,097
Accts Plante & Moran Pllc Grand Ra
SIC 8082 Home health care services; Home health care services
CEO: Alice Hall
V Ch: William F Mielcke
CEO: Derek Akiyoshi
CFO: Edward N Chu
Treas: Pedro Giron
Dir Lab: Yuanan Lu
CIO: Alan Ito
Netwrk Eng: Zena Elliott
HC Dir: Lula Smith
Snr Mgr: Jay Kreuzer

HAWAII HOTEL & RESTAURANT SUP
See ALAKAI MECHANICAL CORP

HAWAII HVAC
See HEIDE & COOK LLC

D-U-N-S 04-740-2961 IMP
■ **HAWAII INDEPENDENT ENERGY LLC**
(*Suby of* HAWAII PACIFIC ENERGY, LLC)
800 Gessner Rd Ste 875, Houston, TX 77024-4498
Tel (281) 899-4829 *Founded/Ownrshp* 2013
Sales 210.1MME *EMP* 420
SIC 5541 2911 Gasoline service stations; Petroleum refining; Gasoline service stations; Petroleum refining
Pr: Bruce Smith
**Pr:* Goff Greg J
**COO:* William J Finnerty
**CFO:* Gregory A Wright
**Treas:* Jackson Tracy D
**VP:* Grimmer Ralph J
VP: Andrew Nomura
VP: Scott Rammell
VP: Milton Tengan
Genl Mgr: Eric Lee

D-U-N-S 96-620-0573
HAWAII IRON WORKERS HEALTH AND WELFARE PLAN
94-497 Ukee St, Waipahu, HI 96797-4243
Tel (808) 671-8225 *Founded/Ownrshp* 2011
Sales 58.3MM *EMP* 3E
Accts Lemke Chinen & Tanaka Cpa Inc
SIC 8631 Labor unions & similar labor organizations; Labor unions & similar labor organizations

D-U-N-S 03-930-2229
HAWAII ISLAND AIR INC
550 Paiea St Ste 236, Honolulu, HI 96819-1837
Tel (808) 840-2400 *Founded/Ownrshp* 1996
Sales 42.0MME *EMP* 250
SIC 4512 Air passenger carrier, scheduled; Air passenger carrier, scheduled
CEO: Paul Casey
CEO: David Pflieger
COO: Tim Rainey
CFO: Ed Davidson
CFO: Lesley Kaneshiro
CFO: Glenn Yee
VP: Joe Edwards
VP: George Tanoue

D-U-N-S 84-065-3331
HAWAII MANAGEMENT ALLIANCE ASSOCIATION
HAWAII MEDICAL ASSURANCE ASSN
737 Bishop St Ste 1200, Honolulu, HI 96813-3205
Tel (808) 591-0088 *Founded/Ownrshp* 1990
Sales NA *EMP* 95E
SIC 6321 Health insurance carriers
CEO: Marc Baptiste
**Pr:* Arnie Baptiste
CFO: Rodney Park
Sr VP: Grace Joyce
VP: Denise Dias

HAWAII MEDICAL ASSURANCE ASSN
See HAWAII MANAGEMENT ALLIANCE ASSOCIATION

D-U-N-S 80-999-7203
HAWAII MEDICAL CENTER
2230 Liliha St Ste 227, Honolulu, HI 96817-1646
Tel (808) 547-6881 *Founded/Ownrshp* 2007
Sales 80.4MME *EMP* 1,501
SIC 8062 General medical & surgical hospitals; General medical & surgical hospitals
CEO: Danelo Canete MD
COO: Catherine Tanaka
Prgrm Mgr: Julie Jennings-Park
Site Mgr: Neill Segawa
Doctor: Antonio Cordero
Doctor: Kent Davenport
Doctor: Jeffery Harpstrite
Doctor: Elizabeth Ignacio
Doctor: John Kristofich
Doctor: Clifford Lau
Doctor: Jeffrey Lee

HAWAII MEDICAL CENTER W PHRM
See HAWAII MEDICAL CENTER WEST LLC

D-U-N-S 61-030-0071 IMP
HAWAII MEDICAL CENTER WEST LLC
HAWAII MEDICAL CENTER W PHRM
(*Suby of* HAWAII MEDICAL CENTER) ★
91-2141 Fort Weaver Rd, Ewa Beach, HI 96706-1993
Tel (808) 678-7000 *Founded/Ownrshp* 2007
Sales 172.5M *EMP* 1,250
SIC 8062 General medical & surgical hospitals; General medical & surgical hospitals
CFO: Rose Choy

D-U-N-S 06-290-9809
HAWAII MEDICAL SERVICE ASSOCIATION
HMSA
818 Keeaumoku St Ste 200, Honolulu, HI 96814-2393
Tel (808) 948-6111 *Founded/Ownrshp* 2004
Sales NA *EMP* 1,500
SIC 6321 6324 Accident & health insurance; Hospital & medical service plans; Accident & health insurance; Hospital & medical service plans
Pr: Michael Gold
**COO:* Mike Gold
COO: Dale Moyen
Sr Cor Off: Fumie Lum
**Ex VP:* Gwen S Miyasato
**Sr VP:* Michael J Cheng
**Sr VP:* Michel Danon
VP: Garet H Azama
VP: David Butterworth
VP: Joan M Millar
VP: George Yamada

D-U-N-S 15-650-7956
HAWAII NATIONAL BANCSHARES INC
45 N King St, Honolulu, HI 96817-5649
Tel (808) 528-7711 *Founded/Ownrshp* 1986
Sales NA *EMP* 235
SIC 6021 National commercial banks; National commercial banks
Ch Bd: Warren Luke
CFO: Ernest T Muraa
CFO: Ernest T Murata

D-U-N-S 00-692-6893
HAWAII NATIONAL BANK
(*Suby of* HAWAII NATIONAL BANCSHARES INC) ★
45 N King St, Honolulu, HI 96817-5182
Tel (808) 528-7711 *Founded/Ownrshp* 1960
Sales NA *EMP* 202
SIC 6021 National commercial banks; National commercial banks
CEO: Warren K K Luke
**CFO:* Ricky Ching
**CFO:* Robert K Nobriga
Sr Cor Off: Robert Reich
Bd of Dir: Arthur Tokin
Top Exec: Leslie Menor
**Ex VP:* Bryan K K Luke
VP: Kurt Kunihiro
VP: Michael Toyota
VP: Dennis Wong
VP: Grant Yoshikami
Board of Directors: William S Chee, Arthur S K Fong, Tan Tek Lum, Arthur Tokin

D-U-N-S 94-150-4599
HAWAII NISSAN INC
NEW CITY NISSAN
2295 N King St, Honolulu, HI 96819-4505
Tel (808) 524-2111 *Founded/Ownrshp* 1995
Sales 35.6MME *EMP* 84
SIC 5511 7538 Automobiles, new & used; General automotive repair shops; Automobiles, new & used; General automotive repair shops
Pr: John Uekawa
**Ch Bd:* Frank Kudo
IT Man: Rickie Manuel

D-U-N-S 07-911-8281
HAWAII PARENT CORP
600 Montgomery St Fl 32, San Francisco, CA 94111-2807
Tel (415) 263-3660 *Founded/Ownrshp* 2013
Sales 124.1MME *EMP* 495E
SIC 6726 Investment offices; Investment offices
Pt: Orlando Bravo

D-U-N-S 07-766-9570
HAWAII PERMANENTE MEDICAL GROUP INC
KAISER PERMANENTE
3288 Moanalua Rd, Honolulu, HI 96819-1469
Tel (808) 432-0000 *Founded/Ownrshp* 1972
Sales 39.1MME *EMP* 302
SIC 8011 Offices & clinics of medical doctors; Offices & clinics of medical doctors
Pr: Michael Chaffin
**Treas:* Susan Stewart
**VP:* Geoffrey Galbraith MD
**VP:* Stephen Miller MD
**VP:* Karl Pregitzer MD
Dir Lab: Karen Higa
Dir Lab: Lucio Kang
Dir Lab: Lorena Shimizu
Dir Lab: Rodney Shinen
Comm Dir: Jan Kagehiro
Dir Rx: Lyell Hirashiki
Dir Rx: Marc Takemoto

D-U-N-S 05-678-9415
HAWAII PIZZA HUT INC
(*Suby of* TD FOOD GROUP INC) ★
828 Fort Street Mall # 130, Honolulu, HI 96813-4314
Tel (808) 566-3200 *Founded/Ownrshp* 1984
Sales 36.1MME *EMP* 1,800
SIC 5812 Pizzeria, chain; Pizzeria, chain
Pr: Henry Katsuda
**CFO:* Kevin Kurihara
**VP:* Rahul Agtarwal
**VP:* Anthony Choe
Pgrm Dir: Tom Matsuda

D-U-N-S 00-922-7901 IMP/EXP
HAWAII PLANING MILL LTD (HI)
HPM BUILDING SUPPLY
16-166 Melekahiwa St, Keaau, HI 96749-8016
Tel (808) 966-5466 *Founded/Ownrshp* 1921
Sales 32.6M *EMP* 409
SIC 5031 5211 3444 2439 Building materials, interior; Building materials, exterior; Lumber & other building materials; Building materials, interior; Building materials, exterior; Lumber & other building materials; Metal roofing & roof drainage equipment; Structural wood members
Ch Bd: Robert M Fujimoto
**Pr:* Michael Fujimoto
**Ex VP:* Thuy N Fujimoto
VP: Glen Shigehara
Genl Mgr: Patrick Batchelder
Genl Mgr: Eric Scicchitano
CTO: Dawn Pacheco
Opers Mgr: Tracie White
Mktg Dir: Lee Wilson
Sales Asso: John Heideman

D-U-N-S 06-627-1289
HAWAII PREPARATORY ACADEMY
65-1692 Kohala Mtn Rd, Kamuela, HI 96743-8476
Tel (808) 885-7321 *Founded/Ownrshp* 1949
Sales 26.3MM *EMP* 135
SIC 8211 Preparatory school; Preparatory school
CFO: Robert McKendry
VP: Richard Kaneen

HAWAII PRINCE GOLF CLUB
See HAWAII PRINCE HOTEL WAIKIKI LLC

D-U-N-S 78-690-5935
HAWAII PRINCE HOTEL WAIKIKI LLC
HAWAII PRINCE GOLF CLUB
100 Holomoana St, Honolulu, HI 96815-1436
Tel (808) 956-1111 *Founded/Ownrshp* 1990
Sales 31.0MME *EMP* 400
SIC 7011 7992 Resort hotel; Public golf courses; Resort hotel; Public golf courses
VP: Koryu Nakamura
Off Mgr: Kent Horiuchi
IT Man: Chuck Davis
Sls Mgr: Yoonjun Lee
Sls Mgr: Joann Machiguchi
Sls Mgr: Susan Uyetake

D-U-N-S 07-252-3913
HAWAII PROTECTIVE ASSOCIATION LTD
1290 Maunakea St Ste A, Honolulu, HI 96817-4195
Tel (808) 537-5938 *Founded/Ownrshp* 1962
Sales 6.6MME *EMP* 300
SIC 7381 Security guard service; Security guard service
Pr: Larry Mehau
**VP:* Michael Mehau

D-U-N-S 02-310-6529
HAWAII REAL ESTATE PROFESSIONALS
98-211 Pali Momi St # 610, Aiea, HI 96701-4301
Tel (808) 487-9925 *Founded/Ownrshp* 1989
Sales 26.0MM *EMP* 16
SIC 6531 6163 Real estate agents & managers; Loan brokers; Real estate agents & managers; Loan brokers
Pr: Albert Joy
**VP:* Marion Joy

D-U-N-S 10-988-1664
HAWAII RESIDENCY PROGRAMS INC
1356 Lusitana St Ste 510, Honolulu, HI 96813-2409
Tel (808) 586-2890 *Founded/Ownrshp* 1982
Sales 19.0MM *EMP* 300
Accts Kmh Llp Honolulu Hi
SIC 8299 Educational services; Educational services
IT Man: Gary Belcher

D-U-N-S 80-993-5513
HAWAII STATE DEPARTMENT OF EDUCATION
EDUCATION BOARD
(*Suby of* EXECUTIVE OFFICE OF STATE OF HAWAII) ★
1390 Miller St Rm 305309, Honolulu, HI 96813-2493
Tel (808) 586-3310 *Founded/Ownrshp* 1959
Sales NA *EMP* 20,000
Accts Kpmg Llp Honolulu Hi
SIC 9411 Administration of educational programs; ; Administration of educational programs;
CEO: Donald G Horner
**VP:* Brian J De Lima
MIS Dir: Richard Asato
MIS Dir: Susan Chandler
Dir IT: Allan Stone
Psych: David Randall

D-U-N-S 07-767-8118
HAWAII STATE FEDERAL CREDIT UNION
560 Halekauwila St Fl 5, Honolulu, HI 96813-5085
Tel (808) 587-2700 *Founded/Ownrshp* 1936
Sales NA *EMP* 520
SIC 6061 Federal credit unions; Federal credit unions
Pr: Andrew Rosen
**Pr:* Elliot Hatico
**Pr:* Deborah Kim
CFO: Edmond Pang
CFO: Rachael Sasaki
Ofcr: Gordon Caluya
Ofcr: Kevin Higa
Ofcr: Allen Murayama
VP: Cindy Ching
VP: Joan Kaneshiro
VP: Patrick Langille

D-U-N-S 96-952-7451
HAWAII TEAMSTERS HEALTH & WELFARE TRUST
560 N Nimitz Hwy Ste 209, Honolulu, HI 96817-5328
Tel (808) 523-0199 *Founded/Ownrshp* 2011
Sales 35.8MM *EMP* 3
Accts Lemke Chinen & Tanaka Cpa Inc
SIC 8631 Labor unions & similar labor organizations; Labor unions & similar labor organizations

D-U-N-S 06-627-7302
HAWAII VISITORS & CONVENTION BUREAU (HI)
2270 Kalakaua Ave Ste 801, Honolulu, HI 96815-2568
Tel (808) 923-1811 *Founded/Ownrshp* 1903
Sales 34.2MM *EMP* 79
Accts Kpmg Llp Honolulu Hi
SIC 7389 Convention & show services; Tourist information bureau
CEO: John Monahan
**COO:* Wayne Arita
CFO: Terry Hee
Dir IT: Paul Lawler
VP Mktg: Jay Talwar
Mktg Dir: Maile Brown
Sls Dir: Lisa Nakamasu

HAWAII WATER
See MENEHUNE WATER CO INC

D-U-N-S 87-841-4051
HAWAII WESTERN MANAGEMENT GROUP INC
H M A A
737 Bishop St Ste 1200, Honolulu, HI 96813-3205
Tel (808) 591-0088 *Founded/Ownrshp* 1994
Sales NA *EMP* 86
SIC 6411 Insurance brokers; Insurance brokers
Pr: Arnold M Baptiste
Pr: Mary Lorenzo

D-U-N-S 00-692-6901
■ **HAWAIIAN AIRLINES INC**
(*Suby of* HAWAIIAN HOLDINGS INC) ★
3375 Koapaka St Ste G350, Honolulu, HI 96819-1804
Tel (808) 835-3700 *Founded/Ownrshp* 2002
Sales 2.7MM *EMP* 3,039
Accts Ernst & Young Llp San Diego
SIC 4512 Air passenger carrier, scheduled; Air cargo carrier, scheduled; Air passenger carrier, scheduled; Air cargo carrier, scheduled
Pr: Mark Dunkerley
**CFO:* Peter R Ingram
**CFO:* Shannon Okinaka
**Treas:* Karen A Berry
Ofcr: John Garibaldi
Ex VP: Russell G Chew
Sr VP: Barbara Falvey
Sr VP: AVI Mannis
**VP:* Sayle Hirashima
VP: Jim Landers
VP: Donald Sealey
VP: Brian Worth
Dir Surg: Richard Petersen
Comm Dir: Alison Croye
Board of Directors: William M Weisfield, Gregory S Anderson, Todd G Cole, Robert G Coo, Joseph P Hoar, Reno F Morella, Samson Poomaihealani, Edward Z Safady, Sharon L Soper, Thomas J Trzanowski

HAWAIIAN BUILDING MAINTAINCE
See HBM ACQUISITIONS LLC

D-U-N-S 02-625-1010 IMP
■ HAWAIIAN COMMERCIAL & SUGAR CO
(*Suby of* ALEXANDER & BALDWIN LLC) ★
1 Hansen St, Puunene, HI 96784-2001
Tel (808) 877-0081 *Founded/Ownrshp* 2010
Sales 184.2MM^E *EMP* 708
SIC 2061 Raw cane sugar
Genl Mgr: Rick W Volner Jr
**Sr VP:* Anna M Skrobecki
VP: Keith Goto
VP: Felix Hubinger
VP: Douglas Jones
Genl Mgr: Christopher Benjamin
Mtls Mgr: Mike Jensen

D-U-N-S 07-924-1293
HAWAIIAN DEVELOPMENT USA LLC
4464 Lawai Rd, Koloa, HI 96756-9608
Tel (808) 212-1016 *Founded/Ownrshp* 2013
Sales 45.0MM *EMP* 28
SIC 6552 Subdividers & developers; Subdividers & developers

D-U-N-S 12-262-7289 IMP
HAWAIIAN DREDGING CONSTRUCTION CO INC
(*Suby of* KAJIMA INTERNATIONAL INC) ★
201 Merchant St Ste 900, Honolulu, HI 96813-2999
Tel (808) 735-3211 *Founded/Ownrshp* 1992
Sales 227.2MM^E *EMP* 500^E
Accts Deloitte Touche Llp Honolulu
SIC 1542 1611 1522 1521 Nonresidential construction; General contractor, highway & street construction; Hotel/motel, new construction; Multi-family dwellings, new construction; New construction, single-family houses; Nonresidential construction; General contractor, highway & street construction; Hotel/motel, new construction; Multi-family dwellings, new construction; New construction, single-family houses
Pr: William J Wilson
**VP:* Leonard Dempsey
**VP:* Eric Hashizume
**VP:* Cedric Ota
**VP:* Paul Silen
IT Man: Barrett Hara
IT Man: Joseph Majkut
IT Man: Michael Tsue
IT Man: Miles K Yamada
Ql Cn Mgr: Wayne Castro
Ql Cn Mgr: Justin Ohara

D-U-N-S 00-692-6927 IMP
■ HAWAIIAN ELECTRIC CO INC
(*Suby of* HAWAIIAN ELECTRIC INDUSTRIES INC) ★
900 Richards St, Honolulu, HI 96813-2956
Tel (808) 543-7771 *Founded/Ownrshp* 1983
Sales 2.9MMM *EMP* 2,759
Accts Pricewaterhousecoopers Llp Lo
SIC 4911 Generation, electric power; Transmission, electric power; Distribution, electric power; Generation, electric power; Transmission, electric power; Distribution, electric power
Pr: Alan M Oshima
**Ch Bd:* Constance H Lau
CFO: Tayne S Y Sekimura
VP: Richard Houck
VP: Lynne Unemori
Dir IT: Irene Harada
IT Man: Camille Au
IT Man: Dora Nakamaru
IT Man: Mark Sora
Snr Mgr: Steve McMenamin
Board of Directors: Don E Carroll, Thomas B Fargo, Peggy Y Fowler, Timothy E Johns, Micah A Kane, Bert A Kobayashi Jr, Kelvin H Taketa

D-U-N-S 10-390-1773 IMP
▲ HAWAIIAN ELECTRIC INDUSTRIES INC
1001 Bishop St Ste 2900, Honolulu, HI 96813-3480
Tel (808) 543-5662 *Founded/Ownrshp* 1981
Sales 3.2MMM *EMP* 3,966^E
Accts Pricewaterhousecoopers Llp L
Tkr Sym HE *Exch* NYS
SIC 4911 6035 Generation, electric power; Transmission, electric power; Distribution, electric power; Federal savings banks; Generation, electric power; Transmission, electric power; Distribution, electric power; Federal savings banks
Pr: Constance H Lau
**Ch Bd:* Jeffrey N Watanabe
CFO: James A Ajello
Treas: Robert Mougeot
Ofcr: Chester A Richardson
Ex VP: Bill Bonnet
Ex VP: Thomas A Bowers
Sr VP: Dan Giovanni
Sr VP: Stephen M McMenamin
CIO: Steve McMenami
Counsel: Julie Smolinski
Board of Directors: Thomas B Fargo, Peggy Y Fowler, A Maurice Myers, Keith P Russell, James K Scott, Kelvin H Taketa, Barry K Taniguchi

HAWAIIAN FALLS GARLAND
See HARVEST FAMILY ENTERTAINMENT LLC

D-U-N-S 00-717-4191 IMP
HAWAIIAN GARDENS CASINO
21520 Pioneer Blvd # 305, Hawaiian Gardens, CA 90716-2602
Tel (562) 860-8890 *Founded/Ownrshp* 1998
Sales 60.5MM^E *EMP* 1,000^E
SIC 7999 Card & game services; Card & game services
CEO: David Moskowitz
**Pr:* Irving Moskowitz
CFO: Jennifer Wright
VP: Sergio Cuevas

D-U-N-S 12-941-3436
▲ HAWAIIAN HOLDINGS INC
3375 Koapaka St Ste G350, Honolulu, HI 96819-1804
Tel (808) 835-3700 *Founded/Ownrshp* 1929
Sales 2.3MMM *EMP* 5,249^E
Tkr Sym HA *Exch* NGS
SIC 4512 Air transportation, scheduled; Air transportation, scheduled
Pr: Mark B Dunkerley
**Ch Bd:* Lawrence S Hershfield
COO: Sean E Menke
CFO: Shannon Okinaka
Ex VP: Ron Anderson-Lehman
Ex VP: Peter R Ingram
Sr VP: AVI A Mannis
Sr VP: Theo Panagiotoulias
VP: Philip Moore
VP: Brent Overbeek
Board of Directors: Gregory S Anderson, Randall L Jenson, Bert T Kobayashi Jr, Samson Poomaihealani, Crystal K Rose, William S Swelbar, Duane E Woerth, Richard N Zwern

D-U-N-S 00-917-4020 IMP/EXP
HAWAIIAN HOST INC
500 Alakawa St Rm 111, Honolulu, HI 96817-4576
Tel (808) 848-0500 *Founded/Ownrshp* 1965
Sales 55.1MM^E *EMP* 450
SIC 2066 Chocolate candy, solid; Chocolate candy, solid
Pr: Keith Sakamoto
CFO: Mark Yamada
Exec: Ahmad Yu
Genl Mgr: Alan Yamaguchi
Plnt Mgr: Joselito Aquiat
Mktg Mgr: Diane Bruce
Sls Mgr: Howard Higa

D-U-N-S 00-923-1671 IMP
HAWAIIAN HOUSEWARES LTD
HANSEN DISTRIBUTION GROUP
96-1282 Waihona St, Pearl City, HI 96782-1968
Tel (808) 453-8000 *Founded/Ownrshp* 1956
Sales 153.6MM^E *EMP* 175
SIC 5199 5194 5141 5145 General merchandise, non-durable; Tobacco & tobacco products; Groceries, general line; Candy; General merchandise, non-durable; Tobacco & tobacco products; Groceries, general line; Candy
Ch Bd: Diana Allen
**Pr:* Joe Heidelmaier
**COO:* Bob Piccinino
VP: John Howard
**VP:* Vanoush Petrossian
Opers Mgr: Kalipo Bowen

D-U-N-S 93-225-1655
HAWAIIAN ISLES KONA COFFEE CO LTD
(*Suby of* HIE HOLDINGS INC) ★
2839 Mokumoa St, Honolulu, HI 96819-4402
Tel (808) 839-3255 *Founded/Ownrshp* 1994
Sales 57.9MM^E *EMP* 150
SIC 5149 2095 Coffee, green or roasted; Roasted coffee; Coffee, green or roasted; Roasted coffee
CEO: Michael Boulware
**COO:* Glenn Boulware
**Treas:* Karen Erwin
**Sr VP:* Steven Boulware
Sls Dir: Darryl Hara
Mktg Mgr: Sean Gano

HAWAIIAN ISLES WATER CO
See ROYAL HAWAIIAN WATER CO LTD

D-U-N-S 80-637-3754
HAWAIIAN NATIVE CORP
900 Fort Street Mall # 1850, Honolulu, HI 96813-3721
Tel (808) 536-5500 *Founded/Ownrshp* 2004
Sales 416.8MM^E *EMP* 25^E
SIC 8699 Charitable organization
Pr: Christopher M Dawson
Ex Dir: Lulani Arquette

D-U-N-S 78-496-5399
■ HAWAIIAN TELCOM COMMUNICATIONS INC
(*Suby of* HAWAIIAN TELCOM HOLDCO INC) ★
1177 Bishop St, Honolulu, HI 96813-2808
Tel (808) 546-4511 *Founded/Ownrshp* 2005
Sales 547.8MM^E *EMP* 1,400^E
SIC 4813 4812 Telephone communication, except radio; Local & long distance telephone communications; ; Cellular telephone services; Telephone communication, except radio; Local & long distance telephone communications; ; Cellular telephone services
Pr: Eric K Yeaman
V Ch: James A Attwood
**COO:* Kurt Hoffmann
**CFO:* Robert F Reich
Sr VP: Michael Edl
Sr VP: Craig T Inouye
Sr VP: John T Komeiji
VP: Steven P Golden
VP: Francis Mukai
IT Man: Marc Hemingway
Sales Asso: Jaylene Pilgrim
Board of Directors: James A Attwood Jr, Matthew P Boyer, Walter A Dods Jr, Stephen C Gray, William E Kennard, Raymond A Ranelli

D-U-N-S 78-496-4426
▲ HAWAIIAN TELCOM HOLDCO INC
1177 Bishop St, Honolulu, HI 96813-2837
Tel (808) 546-4511 *Founded/Ownrshp* 1883
Sales 390.7MM *EMP* 1,400^E
Tkr Sym HCOM *Exch* NGS
SIC 4813 Telephone communication, except radio; Telephone communication, except radio
Pr: Eric K Yeaman
V Ch: Stephen C Gray
COO: Scott K Barber
CFO: Dan T Bessey
CFO: Robert F Reich
Sr VP: Craig T Inouye
Sr VP: John T Komeiji
Sr VP: Kevin T Paul
VP: Paul G Krueger
VP: Matthew Riley
Prgrm Mgr: Arthur Garbiso
Board of Directors: Kurt M Cellar, Walter A Dods Jr, Warren H Haruki, Richard A Jalkut, Steven C Oldham, Bernard R Phillips III

D-U-N-S 00-692-6943 IMP
■ HAWAIIAN TELCOM INC (HI)
(*Suby of* HAWAIIAN TELCOM COMMUNICATIONS INC) ★
1177 Bishop St, Honolulu, HI 96813-2837
Tel (808) 643-3456 *Founded/Ownrshp* 1883, 2005
Sales 542.8MM^E *EMP* 1,920
SIC 4813 5065 7629 Local & long distance telephone communications; Local telephone communications; Telephone equipment; Telecommunication equipment repair (except telephones); Local & long distance telephone communications; Local telephone communications; Telephone equipment; Telecommunication equipment repair (except telephones)
Pr: Eric K Yeaman
**COO:* Scott K Barber
**COO:* Kevin Nystrom
**CFO:* Dan T Bessey
Sr VP: Meredith J Ching
**Sr VP:* Michael Czerwinski
**Sr VP:* John T Komeiji
**VP:* William Chung
**VP:* John Duncan
**VP:* Michael Edl
**VP:* Steven Golden
**VP:* Galen Haneda
**VP:* Jeffrey Hoffman
**VP:* Rose Houser
**VP:* Craig Inouye
VP: Paul Krueger
**VP:* James Laclair
**VP:* Geoffrey Loui
**VP:* Francis Makai
Dir Bus: John Chun
Adv Bd Mbr: June Maekawa

D-U-N-S 08-889-2455
■ HAWAIIAN TROPIC EUROPE INC
(*Suby of* PLAYTEX PRODUCTS LLC) ★
1190 N Us Highway 1, Ormond Beach, FL 32174-8733
Tel (386) 677-9559 *Founded/Ownrshp* 2007
Sales NA *EMP* 501
SIC 6719 Investment holding companies, except banks; Investment holding companies, except banks
Pr: Neil P Defeo
**Treas:* William Jennings
**Ex VP:* Bill Jennings
**VP:* Larry L Adams
**VP:* Jack E Surrette

HAWE HYDRAULICS
See HAWE NORTH AMERICA INC

D-U-N-S 03-650-8802 IMP
HAWE NORTH AMERICA INC (NC)
HAWE HYDRAULICS
(*Suby of* HAWE HYDRAULIK SE)
9009 Perimeter Woods Dr K, Charlotte, NC 28216-1871
Tel (704) 509-1599 *Founded/Ownrshp* 1997
Sales 38.1MM^E *EMP* 77^E
SIC 5085 Pistons & valves; Pistons & valves
CEO: Karl Haeusgen
**Pr:* Carl Haeusgen
**VP:* Charles Houghton
Rgnl Mgr: John Rusling
Dir IT: Bob Pettit
IT Man: Jean McAllister
Opers Mgr: Scott Dodson
Manager: John Corona
Manager: Edmund Konsen
Manager: Tim Multerer
Manager: Andy Robertson

HAWK FABRICATION
See HAWK INSTALLATION AND CONSTRUCTION INC

HAWK FORD OF OAK LAWN
See INCIPE LLC

D-U-N-S 06-865-9191
HAWK HOLLOW PROPERTIES INC
EAGLE EYE GOLF COURSE
15500 Chandler Rd, Bath, MI 48808-9611
Tel (517) 641-4570 *Founded/Ownrshp* 2011
Sales 714.4M^E *EMP* 300
SIC 7997 7999 Golf club, membership; Golf services & professionals
Pr: Alex Coss

D-U-N-S 14-523-2906
HAWK INSTALLATION AND CONSTRUCTION INC
HAWK FABRICATION
315 N Main St, Bogata, TX 75417-2405
Tel (903) 632-4464 *Founded/Ownrshp* 1989
Sales 25.1MM^E *EMP* 120
SIC 1796

D-U-N-S 88-387-7888
HAWK JIM GROUP INC
3119 S 9th St, Council Bluffs, IA 51501-7664
Tel (712) 366-2241 *Founded/Ownrshp* 1993
Sales 145.9MM^E *EMP* 275
SIC 5012 7539 Trailers for trucks, new & used; Trailer repair; Trailers for trucks, new & used; Trailer repair
Pr: James V Hawk
**Sec:* Lanny Goetzinger
**VP:* Charles O'Hollearn
Genl Mgr: Richard Dunaway

HAWK PERFORMANCE
See FRICTION PRODUCTS CO

D-U-N-S 15-971-4567
HAWK RIDGE SYSTEMS LLC
4 Orinda Way Ste 100b, Orinda, CA 94563-2507
Tel (510) 482-6110 *Founded/Ownrshp* 2000
Sales 20.2MM^E *EMP* 100
SIC 5734 7371 Computer & software stores; Custom computer programming services
CEO: Steve Wilcox
Off Admin: Melissa Rodrigues
IT Man: Lorenzo Baldoria
Mktg Dir: Kimberly Enright
Sls Mgr: David Hallmark
Sls Mgr: Gabriel Rapisardo
Sls Mgr: Bryan Wakehouse
Sales Asso: Larry Freeman
Sales Asso: Marlon Gillies

D-U-N-S 06-664-9005
HAWK STEEL INDUSTRIES INC
4010 S Eden Rd, Kennedale, TX 76060-7412
Tel (817) 483-7511 *Founded/Ownrshp* 1983
Sales 22.3MM^E *EMP* 65
SIC 5051 5093 4953 3341

D-U-N-S 07-775-6484
HAWKEN SCHOOL
12465 County Line Rd, Gates Mills, OH 44040
Tel (440) 423-4446 *Founded/Ownrshp* 1915
Sales 40.9MM *EMP* 200
Accts Maloney Novotny Llc Cleveland
SIC 8211 Private combined elementary & secondary school; Private combined elementary & secondary school
**CFO:* Donna M Pacchioni
Assoc Dir: Doug Smith
Dir: Peter Anagnostos
Dir IT: Ryan Wooley
Info Man: Robin Baringer

D-U-N-S 00-724-7315 IMP
■ HAWKER BEECHCRAFT GLOBAL CUSTOMER SUPPORT LLC
(*Suby of* BEECHCRAFT CORP) ★
10511 E Central Ave, Wichita, KS 67206-2557
Tel (316) 676-7111 *Founded/Ownrshp* 1995
Sales 67.3MM^E *EMP* 1,300
SIC 7699 Aircraft & heavy equipment repair services; Aircraft & heavy equipment repair services
VP: Ted Farid
**CFO:* Sidney E Anderson
**Treas:* George M Sellew
**VP:* James E Knight
IT Man: Brandy Herrman

D-U-N-S 61-523-5454
HAWKER PACIFIC AEROSPACE
(*Suby of* LUFTHANSA TECHNIK AG)
11240 Sherman Way, Sun Valley, CA 91352-4942
Tel (818) 765-6201 *Founded/Ownrshp* 2002
Sales 60.7MM^E *EMP* 355
SIC 7699 5088 3728 Hydraulic equipment repair; Aircraft & parts; Aircraft parts & equipment; Hydraulic equipment repair; Aircraft & parts; Aircraft parts & equipment
CEO: Bernd Riggers
**CFO:* Troy Trower
Ex VP: Blas Maidagan
**VP:* Brian Carr
Mng Dir: Valerie Fortner
Opers Mgr: Martin Martinez
Plnt Mgr: Pete Masson
Ql Cn Mgr: James Meszaro
Ql Cn Mgr: Jim Meszaros
Sales Exec: Carmen Schmeltzer
Board of Directors: Andreas Tielman, Klaus Wachholz

D-U-N-S 61-145-4380 IMP/EXP
■ HAWKER POWERSOURCE INC
(*Suby of* ENERSYS) ★
9404 Ooltewah Indus Blvd, Ooltewah, TN 37363-8700
Tel (423) 238-5700 *Founded/Ownrshp* 2002
Sales 94.5MM^E *EMP* 174
SIC 5063 Batteries; Batteries
Prin: Bob Aaron
**VP:* Waseem Ahmad
Plnt Mgr: Dave Colwell
Prd Mgr: Kelly Hogan

D-U-N-S 07-809-2350
HAWKEYE AREA COMMUNITY ACTION PROGRAM INC
HACAP
1515 Hawkeye Dr, Hiawatha, IA 52233-1102
Tel (319) 393-7811 *Founded/Ownrshp* 1965
Sales 28.3MM *EMP* 350
SIC 8399 Community action agency; Community action agency
CEO: Jane Drapeaux
CFO: Carrie Johnson
VP: Tammy Wetjen
IT Man: Mitch Finn
Nutrtnst: Debby Hildebrand

D-U-N-S 05-786-7228
HAWKEYE BUILDING DISTRIBUTORS LIMITED
7922 42nd St W, Rock Island, IL 61201-7321
Tel (309) 787-0714 *Founded/Ownrshp* 1981
Sales 29.9MM *EMP* 64
Accts Mcgladrey Llp Davenport Iowa
SIC 5031 Building materials, exterior; Building materials, interior; Doors & windows; Building materials, exterior; Building materials, interior; Doors & windows
Pr: Donald De Wulf
**VP:* Carl R Stahler
Off Mgr: Susie Oberhaus

D-U-N-S 79-468-4720
HAWKEYE COMMUNICATIONS OF CLINTON
2205 Ingersoll Ave, Des Moines, IA 50312-5229
Tel (515) 246-1890 *Founded/Ownrshp* 2000
Sales 21.6MM^E *EMP* 191
SIC 4841 Cable television services; Cable television services
Pr: Dan Summers

D-U-N-S 07-348-5716
HAWKEYE COMMUNITY COLLEGE
1501 E Orange Rd, Waterloo, IA 50701-9014
Tel (319) 296-4201 *Founded/Ownrshp* 1966
Sales 27.6MM *EMP* 1,112
Accts Williams & Company Pc Spenc
SIC 8222 Community college; Technical institute; Community college; Technical institute
Pr: Linda Allen
Pr: Donna McNulty
**Treas:* Denise Bouska
**VP:* Jane Bradley
**VP:* Kathy Flynn

*VP: Daniel Gillen
VP: Pat Stanley
Assoc Dir: Holly Grimm-See
*Prin: Casey P McLaughlin
CIO: Brian McCormick
IT Man: Marilyn Dolph

D-U-N-S 00-515-9314 IMP/EXP
HAWKEYE CONCRETE PRODUCTS CO
HAWKEYE PEDERSHAAB CONCRETE
506 Wapello St S, Mediapolis, IA 52637-7876
Tel (319) 394-3197 Founded/Ownrshp 1958
Sales 47.5MM^E EMP 125
SIC 3559 Concrete products machinery; Concrete products machinery
Ch Bd: H Henry Schmidgall
Treas: Steve Laird
VP: Darrell Harr
*VP: Jon Schmidgall
IT Man: Benjamin Nahorny
VP Mfg: Aaron Schmidgall
Mtls Mgr: Mark Schmidgall
Plnt Mgr: Tony Thomas
VP Sls: Darrell Haar
VP Sls: Jorn Hoffmann
VP Sls: Brad Schmidgall

HAWKEYE CONVENIENCE STORES
See HAWKEYE OIL CO INC

D-U-N-S 10-735-8103
HAWKEYE ELECTRICAL CONTRACTORS OF CEDAR RAPIDS LTD
1711 Hawkeye Dr, Hiawatha, IA 52233-4703
Tel (319) 743-9891 Founded/Ownrshp 1986
Sales 22.0MM EMP 60
SIC 1731 General electrical contractor; General electrical contractor
Pr: Tim Wilson
*VP: Linda Wilson

HAWKEYE INTERNATIONAL TRUCKS
See THOMPSON TRUCK & TRAILER INC

D-U-N-S 06-413-3648
HAWKEYE INTERNATIONAL TRUCKS INC
HAWKEYE TRUCK LEASING
2740 6th St Sw, Cedar Rapids, IA 52404-4002
Tel (319) 364-2491 Founded/Ownrshp 1982
Sales 23.5MM^E EMP 300
SIC 5012 7538 5013 Trucks, commercial; General truck repair; Truck parts & accessories; Trucks, commercial; General truck repair; Truck parts & accessories
Pr: Dennis Thompson

D-U-N-S 02-205-0421
HAWKEYE OIL CO INC
HAWKEYE CONVENIENCE STORES
572 10th St Sw, Cedar Rapids, IA 52404-1838
Tel (319) 364-7146 Founded/Ownrshp 1945
Sales 21.9MM^E EMP 100
SIC 5541 5172 Filling stations, gasoline; Gasoline; Filling stations, gasoline; Gasoline
Pr: Don A Petersen
*VP: Marshall Petersen

HAWKEYE PEDERSHAAB CONCRETE
See HAWKEYE CONCRETE PRODUCTS CO

D-U-N-S 96-315-8105
HAWKEYE PRIDE EGG FARMS LLP
4135 Garfield Ave, Sioux Center, IA 51250-7429
Tel (712) 722-0132 Founded/Ownrshp 2008
Sales 59.4MM EMP 25
SIC 0252 Chicken eggs; Chicken eggs
Pt: James R Dean
CFO: Randy Geyerman
Off Mgr: Mona Bode

HAWKEYE REC
See HAWKEYE TRI COUNTY ELECTRIC COOPERATIVE

D-U-N-S 09-802-1207 IMP/EXP
HAWKEYE STEEL PRODUCTS INC
PRIDE OF THE FARM
609 Main St, Houghton, IA 52631
Tel (319) 469-4141 Founded/Ownrshp 1920
Sales 25.3MM^E EMP 100^E
SIC 3523 3556 Farm machinery & equipment; Hog feeding, handling & watering equipment; Water troughs; Poultry brooders, feeders & waterers; Poultry processing machinery; Farm machinery & equipment; Hog feeding, handling & watering equipment; Water troughs; Poultry brooders, feeders & waterers; Poultry processing machinery
Pr: Thomas W Wenstrand
Dept Mgr: Bonnie Menke
Sys/Dir: Jaci Peterson
Manager: Rod Schamle

D-U-N-S 00-694-0720
HAWKEYE TRI COUNTY ELECTRIC COOPERATIVE
HAWKEYE REC
24049 Highway 9, Cresco, IA 52136-8500
Tel (563) 547-3801 Founded/Ownrshp 1936
Sales 24.0MM EMP 36
Accts Eide Bailly Llp Sioux Falls
SIC 4911 Electric services; Electric services
CEO: Brian Krambeer
*CFO: Peggy Berg

HAWKEYE TRUCK LEASING
See HAWKEYE INTERNATIONAL TRUCKS INC

D-U-N-S 10-855-6333
HAWKINS ASSOCIATES INC
HAWKINS PERSONNEL GROUP
909 Ne Loop 410 Ste 104, San Antonio, TX 78209-1315
Tel (210) 349-9911 Founded/Ownrshp 1977
Sales 16.0MM EMP 4,000
SIC 7363 7361 Temporary help service; Placement agencies; Temporary help service; Placement agencies
Pr: Sally Hawkins
*VP: Jennifer Hawkins
*VP: William P Hawkins
*VP Sls: Liz Hawkins

D-U-N-S 08-283-9358
HAWKINS COMPANIES LLC
855 W Broad St Ste 300, Boise, ID 83702-7154
Tel (208) 376-8521 Founded/Ownrshp 1978
Sales 27.6MM EMP 58
SIC 6512 Nonresidential building operators; Nonresidential building operators
CEO: Gary Hawkins
*Owner: Gail Hawkins
*Pr: Rob Phillips
*COO: Jeffery L Hess
*CFO: Kelly Grange
MIS Dir: Allan Whitehead
Mktg Dir: Patricia Wennstrom
Genl Couns: Brett Hamm
Corp Couns: Rob Dickinson

D-U-N-S 00-287-3693
HAWKINS CONSTRUCTION CO
2516 Deer Park Blvd, Omaha, NE 68105-3771
Tel (402) 342-4455 Founded/Ownrshp 1960
Sales 187.0MM EMP 400
SIC 1542 1611 1541 Farm building construction; Resurfacing contractor; Industrial buildings, new construction; Farm building construction; Resurfacing contractor; Industrial buildings, new construction
CEO: Fred Hawkins Jr
*Pr: Kim Hawkins
*COO: Chris Hawkins
*Ex VP: James Gregory
*Ex VP: Matt Miller
*Ex VP: Dudley Rinaker
*VP: Robert A Bloechle
VP: Ted Butler
*VP: Tom Crockett
*VP: Jeff Fuqua
*VP: Chris Grojean
*VP: Chris Harnly
*VP: David Langenberg
*VP: Kurt Peyton

D-U-N-S 07-759-5924
HAWKINS CONSTRUCTION INC
1430 L And R Indus Blvd, Tarpon Springs, FL 34689-6807
Tel (727) 937-2690 Founded/Ownrshp 2007
Sales 85.2MM^E EMP 110^E
Accts Gregory Sharer & Stuart Pa
SIC 1542 Commercial & office building, new construction; Commercial & office building, new construction
Pr: John McCaugherty
*CFO: David Frazier
CFO: Jean Snyder
*Ex VP: Mike Beausir
*Ex VP: Earle Cooper
Ex VP: John McCaughtery
*Ex VP: Don Ondrejcak
VP: Miguel Leyva
*VP: Todd Mullins
*VP: Dave Sicca
Dir Bus: R J Walker

D-U-N-S 10-007-2925
HAWKINS COUNTY SCHOOL DISTRICT
200 N Depot St, Rogersville, TN 37857-2639
Tel (423) 272-7629 Founded/Ownrshp 2010
Sales 33.3MM^E EMP 890^E
SIC 8211 Elementary & secondary schools
IT Man: Leslie Jones

D-U-N-S 07-887-9350
HAWKINS DELAFIELD & WOOD LLP
28 Liberty St Fl 42, New York, NY 10005-1448
Tel (212) 509-1612 Founded/Ownrshp 1945
Sales 26.8MM^E EMP 158
SIC 8111 General practice law office; General practice law office
Mng Pt: Eric S Petersen
*Pt: John V Connorton Jr
*Pt: Martin Geiger
*Pt: Samuel Hellman
*Pt: Joseph J Rogers Jr
*Pt: Howard Zucker
Off Mgr: Joseph Annicelli

D-U-N-S 04-119-9639 IMP
▲ HAWKINS INC
2381 Rosegate, Roseville, MN 55113-2625
Tel (612) 331-6910 Founded/Ownrshp 1938
Sales 364.0MM EMP 419
Accts Kpmg Llp Minneapolis Minneso
Tkr Sym HWKN Exch NGS
SIC 5169 5074 2899 Chemicals & allied products; Swimming pool & spa chemicals; Industrial chemicals; Water purification equipment; Chemical preparations; Chemicals & allied products; Swimming pool & spa chemicals; Industrial chemicals; Water purification equipment; Chemical preparations
Pr: Patrick H Hawkins
*Ch Bd: John S McKeon
CFO: Kathleen P Pepski
Treas: Jason Wilm
VP: Richard G Erstad
VP: Thomas J Keller
VP: Steve Matthews
VP: Steven D Matthews II
VP: Theresa R Moran
VP: John R Sevenich
Dir Lab: Sue Niemela
Board of Directors: James A Faulconbridge, Duane M Jergenson, Mary J Schumacher, Daryl I Skaar, James T Thompson, Jeffrey L Wright

D-U-N-S 10-362-9135
HAWKINS LEASE SERVICE INC
3205 Fm 2403 Rd, Alvin, TX 77511-1448
Tel (281) 331-2739 Founded/Ownrshp 1981
Sales 40.6MM^E EMP 70^E
SIC 1389 Oil field services
Pr: Richard J Hawkins
Genl Mgr: Will Hawkins

D-U-N-S 08-752-1530
HAWKINS PARNELL THACKSTON & YOUNG LLP
303 Peachtree St Ne, Atlanta, GA 30308-3201
Tel (404) 614-7400 Founded/Ownrshp 1963
Sales 32.6MM^E EMP 238
SIC 8111

HAWKINS PERSONNEL GROUP
See HAWKINS ASSOCIATES INC

HAWKS CAY RESORT
See CWI KEYS HOTEL LLC

HAWKS CAY RESORT
See KEYS HOTEL OPERATOR INC

D-U-N-S 07-942-6956
HAWKWOOD ENERGY LLC
4582 S Ulster St Ste 500, Denver, CO 80237-2642
Tel (303) 823-4175 Founded/Ownrshp 2012
Sales 35.0MM EMP 20^E
SIC 1382 Oil & gas exploration services; Oil & gas exploration services
CEO: Patrick R Oenbring
Pr: Leonard Gurule
CFO: Matt O'Neill

D-U-N-S 13-145-3250 IMP
HAWLEY LLC
(Suby of CYCLES LAMBERT INC)
1181 S Lake Dr, Lexington, SC 29073-7744
Tel (803) 359-3492 Founded/Ownrshp 2011
Sales 36.8MM EMP 90
Accts Moore Beauston Woodham Columb
SIC 5091 Bicycle parts & accessories; Bicycle parts & accessories
Pr: Steve Hawley
VP: W R Haley
Dir IT: Dave Carson
Sls Dir: Ian Cross

D-U-N-S 07-298-9635
HAWLEY TROXELL ENNIS & HAWLEY LLP
877 W Main St Ste 1000, Boise, ID 83702-5884
Tel (208) 344-6000 Founded/Ownrshp 1964
Sales 20.2MM^E EMP 103
SIC 8111 General practice law office
Pt: John T Hawley
Pt: Gary Babbitt
Pt: Brian Ballard
Pt: Phil Barber
Pt: Albert P Barker
Pt: Steven W Berenter
Pt: Rita Berry
Pt: Harold D Burnett
Pt: Ronald E Bush
Pt: Tom Chandler
Pt: Merlyn Clark
Pt: Patrick Collins
Pt: Robert S Erickson
Pt: Carl Harder
Pt: Jess B Hawley Jr
Pt: John T Jack Hawley
Pt: Ken Howell
Pt: Donald Knickrehm
Pt: John F Kurtz Jr
Pt: Joseph Langfield
Pt: Edward Lawson

D-U-N-S 07-245-2204 IMP
HAWORTH CORP
1110 E Missouri Ave # 200, Phoenix, AZ 85014-2754
Tel (602) 861-1080 Founded/Ownrshp 1972
Sales 25.3MM EMP 34
Accts Henry & Horn Llp Tempe Ariz
SIC 1542 8741 Nonresidential construction; Construction management; Nonresidential construction; Construction management
Pr: Daniel M Haworth
*VP: Lisa A Bruno
*VP: Brian Ciha
*VP: Michael E Eggen
VP: Barr Haworth
*VP: William David Barr Haworth
Dir Bus: Jill Stewart
Manager: Stefan Kuemmel

D-U-N-S 07-259-5457 IMP/EXP
HAWORTH INC
(Suby of HAWORTH INTERNATIONAL LTD) ★
1 Haworth Ctr, Holland, MI 49423-8820
Tel (616) 393-3000 Founded/Ownrshp 1948
Sales 963.3MM^E EMP 5,950
SIC 2522 2521 Office furniture, except wood; Wood office furniture; Office furniture, except wood; Wood office furniture
Ch Bd: Matthew Haworth
*Pr: Franco Bianchi
CFO: Rick Perkins
VP: Jos Amaral
VP: Pamela W Armstrong
VP: Mabel Casey
VP: Todd James
VP: Michael Moon Sr
*VP: John K Mooney
VP: Paul K Smith
Exec: Deb Roh
Board of Directors: Richard G Haworth

D-U-N-S 07-928-2059 IMP
HAWORTH INTERNATIONAL LTD (MI)
1 Haworth Ctr, Holland, MI 49423-8820
Tel (616) 393-3000 Founded/Ownrshp 1948, 1975
Sales 1.2MMM^E EMP 5,950
SIC 2522 2521 Office furniture, except wood; Wood office furniture; Office furniture, except wood; Wood office furniture
Ch Bd: Matthew Haworth
*Pr: Frankco Bianchi
Treas: Daniel Zona
VP: John K Mooney

D-U-N-S 07-650-7045
HAWORTH MARKETING & MEDIA CO
45 S 7th St Ste 2400, Minneapolis, MN 55402-1624
Tel (612) 677-8900 Founded/Ownrshp 1995
Sales 21.4MM^E EMP 108
SIC 7319 8732

D-U-N-S 00-912-4785 IMP/EXP
HAWS CORP (NV)
1455 Kleppe Ln, Sparks, NV 89431-6467
Tel (775) 359-4712 Founded/Ownrshp 1906, 1953
Sales 52.2MM^E EMP 150
SIC 5074 5078 5099 3432 3431

D-U-N-S 80-695-0507
▲ HAWTHORN BANCSHARES INC
132 E High St, Jefferson City, MO 65101-2960
Tel (573) 761-6179 Founded/Ownrshp 1992
Sales NA EMP 358^E
Tkr Sym HWBK Exch NGS
SIC 6021 National commercial banks; National commercial banks
Ch Bd: David T Turner
CFO: W Bruce Phelps
Sr VP: Kathleen L Bruegenhemke
Sr VP: Kathleen Bruegenhemke

D-U-N-S 03-631-5075
■ HAWTHORN BANK
(Suby of UNION STATE BANCSHARES INC) ★
132 E High St, Jefferson City, MO 65101-2960
Tel (573) 761-6100 Founded/Ownrshp 1932
Sales NA EMP 105
SIC 6022 State commercial banks; State commercial banks
CEO: James E Smith
Pr: Scott Franklin
COO: Shirley Wilson
Sr VP: Gary Collins
Sr VP: Gene Henry
Sr VP: Becky Lea
Sr VP: Duane Muck
Sr VP: Ernie Spaasheim
VP: Darrell Hockenberry
VP: Joshua Houtz
VP: Robert Kreisler
VP: Susan Mosley
VP: Helena Strope
Exec: Betty Beach

D-U-N-S 06-417-9856
HAWTHORN CC SCHOOL DIST 73
841 W End Ct, Vernon Hills, IL 60061-1376
Tel (847) 990-4200 Founded/Ownrshp 1926
Sales 24.8MM^E EMP 475
Accts Eder Casella & Co Mchenry
SIC 8211 Public elementary school; Public elementary school
Teacher Pr: Lynn Barkley
HC Dir: Renee Ullburg

D-U-N-S 10-001-7649
HAWTHORN COMMUNITY CONSOLIDATED SCHOOL DISTRICT 73
841 W End Ct, Vernon Hills, IL 60061-1376
Tel (847) 367-3226 Founded/Ownrshp 1923
Sales 13.1MM^E EMP 500^E
SIC 8211 Public elementary & secondary schools; Public elementary school; Public elementary & secondary schools; Public elementary school

D-U-N-S 79-787-1493
HAWTHORN COMMUNITY CONSTRUCTION SCHOOL DISTRICT 73
841 W End Ct, Vernon Hills, IL 60061-1376
Tel (847) 990-4200 Founded/Ownrshp 2007
Sales 6.8MM^E EMP 450
SIC 8211 Elementary & secondary schools; Elementary & secondary schools
*Treas: Allan Hahn

D-U-N-S 03-300-6016
HAWTHORN GROUP LTD
HAWTHORN INDUSTRIAL
605 N Main St, Cape Girardeau, MO 63701-7211
Tel (573) 335-4257 Founded/Ownrshp 1980
Sales 21.0MM^E EMP 95
SIC 5112 7374 5085 Business forms; Data processing service; Industrial supplies
Pt: Cordell Dombrowski
VP: Ellen Scotti-Belli
Off Mgr: Lori Cook

HAWTHORN INDUSTRIAL
See HAWTHORN GROUP LTD

D-U-N-S 07-569-7359 IMP
HAWTHORN MEDICAL ASSOCIATES LLC
535 Faunce Corner Rd, Dartmouth, MA 02747-1242
Tel (508) 996-3991 Founded/Ownrshp 1970
Sales 41.8MM^E EMP 275
SIC 8011 Offices & clinics of medical doctors; Offices & clinics of medical doctors
Pr: James Tracey
CEO: James Gularek
Brnch Mgr: Robert Nixon
Surgeon: Steven Andelman
Surgeon: Edward Klein
Surgeon: Roger Rosen
Surgeon: Harmandeep Singh
Obsttrcn: Susan Vogler
Doctor: Robert Browne
Doctor: Debra Hussey MD
Doctor: Richard Reimer

HAWTHORN SUITES
See H GROUP HOLDING INC

D-U-N-S 01-131-1933
HAWTHORNE AUTOMOBILE SALES CO (INC) (NJ)
HAWTHORNE CHEVROLET
1180 Goffle Rd, Hawthorne, NJ 07506-2024
Tel (973) 427-1560 Founded/Ownrshp 1927
Sales 40.6MM^E EMP 85
SIC 5511 7513 7514 7538 5521 Automobiles, new & used; Truck rental & leasing, no drivers; Passenger car rental; General automotive repair shops; Used car dealers; Automobiles, new & used; Truck rental & leasing, no drivers; Passenger car rental; General automotive repair shops; Used car dealers
Pr: Steven L Barna
*Treas: Eugene C Meyers
*VP: Mark Meyers
*Genl Mgr: Tom Pasquazi

IT Man: Miguel Morel
Sls Mgr: Bert Kurmonov
Sales Asso: Larry Aliberto
Sales Asso: Tom Brown
Sales Asso: Dennis Johnson
Sales Asso: Bobby Madden
Sales Asso: Lou Tripodi

HAWTHORNE CHEVROLET
See HAWTHORNE AUTOMOBILE SALES CO (INC)

D-U-N-S 04-132-2710
HAWTHORNE MACHINERY CO
CATERPILLAR
16945 Camino San Bernardo, San Diego, CA 92127-2499
Tel (858) 674-7000 *Founded/Ownrshp* 1941
Sales 157.3MM^E *EMP* 1,000
SIC 7353 7699 5082 7359 Heavy construction equipment rental; Construction equipment repair; Construction & mining machinery; Equipment rental & leasing; Heavy construction equipment rental; Construction equipment repair; Construction & mining machinery; Equipment rental & leasing
Pr: Tee K Ness
COO: David Ness
VP: Howard Blair
Netwrk Mgr: Troy Lowe
Sfty Mgr: Steve Hollingsworth
Mktg Dir: Wes Campbell

D-U-N-S 79-767-4397 EXP
HAWTHORNE PACIFIC CORP
CATERPILLAR
(*Suby of* CATERPILLAR) ★
94-025 Farrington Hwy, Waipahu, HI 96797-2201
Tel (808) 676-0227 *Founded/Ownrshp* 2004
Sales 92.8MM^E *EMP* 243
SIC 5084 7353 Industrial machinery & equipment; Heavy construction equipment rental; Industrial machinery & equipment; Heavy construction equipment rental
Pr: Tee K Ness
**Pr:* Stephen E Wittman
**Treas:* Richard J Moss
**VP:* Mike Johnson
VP: Verna Martin
VP: Kevin Tam
MIS Mgr: Roger Staehle

D-U-N-S 08-837-7684 EXP
HAWTHORNE SCHOOL DISTRICT
14120 Hawthorne Blvd, Hawthorne, CA 90250-7006
Tel (310) 676-2276 *Founded/Ownrshp* 1907
Sales 52.9MM^E *EMP* 836
SIC 8211 Public elementary & secondary schools; Public elementary & secondary schools
Ofcr: Brenda Muse
Dir Risk M: David Jefferson
Prgrm Mgr: Suzanne Hill
Netwrk Mgr: Reggie Cancel
Psych: Marta Avila
Psych: Linda Lopez

D-U-N-S 15-750-3871
HAWTHORNE SERVICES INC
(*Suby of* LOUIS BERGER SERVICES INC) ★
6543 Fain St, North Charleston, SC 29406-4909
Tel (843) 797-8484 *Founded/Ownrshp* 2013
Sales 33.5MM^E *EMP* 375
SIC 4581 8744 Airports, flying fields & services; Facilities support services; Airports, flying fields & services; Facilities support services
VP: Daniel M Stoddard
Pr: Bruce Stoehr
Ex VP: Sue Johnson
VP: Dave Bush

D-U-N-S 04-567-1419
HAWTHORNE-CEDAR KNOLLS UNION FREE SCHOOL DISTRICT
226 Linda Ave, Hawthorne, NY 10532-2018
Tel (914) 749-2903 *Founded/Ownrshp* 1939
Sales 13.9MM^E *EMP* 300
Accts Bennett Kielson Storch Yablon
SIC 8211 Public elementary & secondary schools; Public elementary & secondary schools
**Pr:* Lois Bauman
Prin: Stephen Gornstein
Prin: John Sasso
Prin: Stephanie Wise
IT Man: Jane Laforge
IT Man: Linda Luca
Board of Directors: A Four Other Board Members

HAY ACQUISITION COMPANY I INC
See HAY GROUP HOLDINGS INC

D-U-N-S 62-317-7987
HAY GROUP HOLDINGS INC
HAY ACQUISITION COMPANY I INC
(*Suby of* HAY GROUP INVESTMENT HOLDING B.V.)
1650 Arch St Ste 2300, Philadelphia, PA 19103-2001
Tel (215) 861-2000 *Founded/Ownrshp* 1990
Sales 47.5M^E *EMP* 2,110
SIC 8742 8249 8733 Management consulting services; Human resource consulting services; Business training services; Educational research agency
Ch Bd: Chris Matthews
**CEO:* Stephen Kaye
**CFO:* Jesse Deutsch

D-U-N-S 07-548-0350
HAY GROUP INC
1650 Arch St Ste 2300, Philadelphia, PA 19103-2001
Tel (215) 861-2000 *Founded/Ownrshp* 1990
Sales 133.0MM^E *EMP* 432
SIC 8742

D-U-N-S 14-437-6639 IMP
HAY HOUSE INC
2776 Loker Ave W, Carlsbad, CA 92010-6611
Tel (760) 431-7695 *Founded/Ownrshp* 1978
Sales 61.6MM^E *EMP* 92
SIC 5192 5099 5942 5735 Books;Tapes & cassettes, prerecorded; Book stores; Audio tapes, prerecorded; Books;Tapes & cassettes, prerecorded; Book stores; Audio tapes, prerecorded
Ch Bd: Louise L Hay
**Pr:* Reid Tracy

D-U-N-S 96-354-5694 IMP/EXP
HAY ISLAND HOLDING CORP
20 Thorndal Cir, Darien, CT 06820-5421
Tel (203) 656-8000 *Founded/Ownrshp* 1995
Sales 598.7MM^E *EMP* 1,600
SIC 5194 2131 Tobacco & tobacco products; Chewing tobacco; Snuff; Tobacco & tobacco products; Chewing tobacco; Snuff
Pr: William T Ziegler
VP: Helen Z Benjamin
**VP:* Cynthia Brighton
**VP:* Peter Ziegler

D-U-N-S 14-424-2955 IMP/EXP
HAYASHI TELEMPU NORTH AMERICA CORP
HTNA
(*Suby of* HAYASHI TELEMPU CO.,LTD.)
14328 Genoa Ct, Plymouth, MI 48170-2457
Tel (734) 456-5221 *Founded/Ownrshp* 1983
Sales 61.9MM^E *EMP* 400
SIC 2396

D-U-N-S 04-522-8087
HAYCOCK PETROLEUM CO
JARDINE PETROLEUM
(*Suby of* THOMAS PETROLEUM LLC) ★
4825 N Sloan Ln, Las Vegas, NV 89115-1924
Tel (702) 382-1620 *Founded/Ownrshp* 2009
Sales 38.0MM^E *EMP* 130
SIC 5171 Petroleum bulk stations; Petroleum bulk stations
Ch Bd: Sterling J Jardine

D-U-N-S 09-351-9023
HAYDAY INC (TX)
CTWP COMPUTERLAND
3730 Franklin Ave, Waco, TX 76710-7330
Tel (504) 458-0380 *Founded/Ownrshp* 1978
Sales 33.7MM^E *EMP* 103
SIC 5044 5045 7629 7378 Office equipment; Computers, peripherals & software; Business machine repair, electric; Computer maintenance & repair
Pr: David Willie
**VP:* Dudley Jones
Brnch Mgr: Greg Bridgeman
Brnch Mgr: Trey Dendy
Off Mgr: Kelli Stevens
IT Man: Jones Dudley

HAYDEN BEVERAGE CO
See BOISE SALES CO

D-U-N-S 12-227-7536
HAYDEN BUILDING MAINTENANCE CORP
169 Western Hwy, West Nyack, NY 10994-2637
Tel (845) 353-3400 *Founded/Ownrshp* 1982
Sales 22.2MM^E *EMP* 80
Accts Goldstein Karlewicz & Goldste
SIC 1761 1799 Roof repair; Waterproofing
Pr: Gregory P Hayden
**VP:* Robert Hayden
**VP:* Anthony Squilla
**VP:* Bruce J Terwilliger

D-U-N-S 01-136-7468 IMP
HAYDEN CALEEL LLC
GLOPROFESSIONAL
600 W Bayaud Ave, Denver, CO 80223-1802
Tel (800) 903-4321 *Founded/Ownrshp* 2013
Sales 81.3MM^E *EMP* 115
SIC 5122 Cosmetics; Cosmetics
VP: Velma Sauer
Rgnl Mgr: Audra Ryan
Dir IT: Laura Marzari
IT Man: Mike Moseley
VP Opers: Jeremy Gurley
VP Mktg: Robin Olson
Manager: Julie Anselmo
Manager: Paige Powell
Manager: Tasha Shuman
Sls Mgr: Tonja Marusic
Sales Asso: Jenna Beetstra

HAYDEN ELECTRIC
See GEORGE J HAYDEN INC

HAYDEN INDUSTRIAL PRODUCTS
See HAYDEN PRODUCTS LLC

D-U-N-S 01-685-9071 IMP
HAYDEN PRODUCTS LLC
HAYDEN INDUSTRIAL PRODUCTS
1393 E San Bernardino Ave, San Bernardino, CA 92408-2964
Tel (951) 736-2600 *Founded/Ownrshp* 2001
Sales 32.6MM^E *EMP* 80
SIC 3443 Heat exchangers, condensers & components
Co-Ownr: Peter Camenzind
Pr: James Neitz
IT Man: Loper Greg
Sls Mgr: Dave Cole
Sales Asso: Sue Misenhelter

D-U-N-S 55-594-0832 IMP
HAYDEN VALLEY FOODS INC
TROPICAL NUT & FRUIT
3150 Urbancrest Indus Dr, Urbancrest, OH 43123-1767
Tel (614) 539-7233 *Founded/Ownrshp* 1984
Sales 43.8MM^E *EMP* 73^E
SIC 5145 5149 2068 2064 2034 2032

D-U-N-S 00-621-1213 IMP
HAYDEN-MURPHY EQUIPMENT CO
9301 E Bloomington Fwy, Minneapolis, MN 55420-3498
Tel (952) 884-2301 *Founded/Ownrshp* 1977
Sales 26.7MM^E *EMP* 43
SIC 5082 7699 General construction machinery & equipment; Construction equipment repair
Pr: Len Kirk
CFO: Donald Knackstedt
IT Man: Mary Zegelin

VP Sls: Kenneth Boehm
VP Sls: Greg Steege
Board of Directors: James Lupient, Don Pederson, Richard Schradel

D-U-N-S 03-591-0202
HAYDON BUILDING CORP
4640 E Cotton Gin Loop, Phoenix, AZ 85040-4819
Tel (602) 296-1496 *Founded/Ownrshp* 1995
Sales 162.6MM *EMP* 250
Accts Weintraub & Schanck Pc Pho
SIC 1541 1542 Industrial buildings & warehouses; Commercial & office building, new construction; Industrial buildings & warehouses; Commercial & office building, new construction
Pr: Gary T Haydon
**CFO:* Cynthia Lee
**VP:* Mark D Eklund
**VP:* Leslie H Keeble
**VP:* James A Pulice Jr

D-U-N-S 18-860-6693 IMP
HAYDON CORP
415 Hamburg Tpke Ste 1, Wayne, NJ 07470-2164
Tel (973) 904-0800 *Founded/Ownrshp* 1993
Sales 31.2MM^E *EMP* 90
SIC 3449 3634 3567 Miscellaneous metalwork; Heating units, electric (radiant heat): baseboard or wall; Industrial furnaces & ovens; Miscellaneous metalwork; Heating units, electric (radiant heat): baseboard or wall; Industrial furnaces & ovens
Pr: Doug H Hillman

D-U-N-S 00-700-2306
HAYDON HOLDINGS LLC
40 Lucknow Ct, Bardstown, KY 40004-2113
Tel (502) 348-3926 *Founded/Ownrshp* 1953
Sales 49.5MM^E *EMP* 165
SIC 3412 1422 1611 Metal barrels, drums & pails; Limestones, ground; Resurfacing contractor; Metal barrels, drums & pails; Limestones, ground; Resurfacing contractor
Genl Mgr: Bill McCreary

D-U-N-S 00-259-0008
■ **HAYDON KERK MOTION SOLUTIONS INC**
(*Suby of* AMETEK INC) ★
1500 Meriden Rd, Waterbury, CT 06705-3982
Tel (203) 756-7441 *Founded/Ownrshp* 1963, 2010
Sales 39.8MM^E *EMP* 140
SIC 3823 Industrial instrmnts msrmnt display/control process variable; Industrial instrmnts msrmnt display/control process variable
Pr: John P Norris
CFO: John Frank
**Treas:* William J Burke
**VP:* Robert S Feit
Genl Mgr: Frank Morton
MIS Dir: Kathy Mehmet
MIS Dir: Kathy Mehrnet
IT Man: Stewart Arnold
VP Sls: Lisa Kochersperger

D-U-N-S 08-340-1695
HAYDON KERK MOTION SOLUTIONS INC
KERK MOTION PRODUCTS
56 Meadowbrook Dr, Milford, NH 03055
Tel (603) 465-7227 *Founded/Ownrshp* 2009
Sales 20.6MM^E *EMP* 80
SIC 3452 Screws, metal
CEO: John Norris
**Pr:* Keith W Erikson
QA Dir: Richard Blais
QC Dir: Steve Brady

HAYDON MOTION EUROPE
See TRITEX CORP

HAYES & LUNSFORD ELEC CONTRS
See PRESLEY GROUP LTD

D-U-N-S 00-801-1520
HAYES & STOLZ INDUSTRIAL MANUFACTURING CO LLC
3521 Hemphill St, Fort Worth, TX 76110-5212
Tel (817) 926-3391 *Founded/Ownrshp* 1992
Sales 23.5MM^E *EMP* 50
SIC 3523 3559 3556 Feed grinders, crushers & mixers; Elevators, farm; Plastics working machinery; Food products machinery
Pr: B J Masters
Info Man: Marrion Fuller
**VP Sls:* Mark Hayes
Sls Mgr: Steve Ray
Snr Mgr: Marko Calaunan

D-U-N-S 05-786-3953 IMP
HAYES BEER DISTRIBUTING CO INC (IL)
12160 S Central Ave, Alsip, IL 60803-3406
Tel (708) 389-8200 *Founded/Ownrshp* 1954
Sales 54.8MM^E *EMP* 150
SIC 5181 5182 Beer & other fermented malt liquors; Wine; Beer & other fermented malt liquors; Wine
Pr: James D Hayes Sr
**Pr:* John J Hayes Jr
CFO: Tina Schuur
CTO: Dawn Jett
Mktg Mgr: Chris Denzer
Sls Mgr: Don Bollman
Sls Mgr: Dale Brumm
Sls Mgr: Dean Marinucci

HAYES BRAKE
See HB PERFORMANCE SYSTEMS INC

D-U-N-S 61-651-9401 IMP
HAYES BUSINESS GROUP LLC
ALLAN INDUSTRIAL COATINGS
22191 Highway 3, Allison, IA 50602-9345
Tel (319) 267-2292 *Founded/Ownrshp* 2007
Sales 23.0MM^E *EMP* 143
SIC 1799 Coating, caulking & weather, water & fireproofing
CEO: John Cork
VP: Monte Allan
Sls Mgr: Don Scroggin

HAYES CHRYSLER DODGE
See HAYES CHRYSLER-DODGE-JEEP INC

D-U-N-S 05-101-1476
HAYES CHRYSLER-DODGE-JEEP INC
HAYES CHRYSLER DODGE
719 Duluth Hwy, Lawrenceville, GA 30046-4305
Tel (770) 963-5251 *Founded/Ownrshp* 1971
Sales 133.5MM^E *EMP* 380
SIC 5511 Automobiles, new & used; Automobiles, new & used
Pr: Albert David Hayes
**Sec:* Tim Hayes
**VP:* Donald E Hayes
Exec: Travis Dixon
Exec: John Nelson
Web Prj Mg: Chris Terry
Sales Exec: Stacy Kelley
Sls Mgr: Chipper Jones
Sls Mgr: Jack Webb

D-U-N-S 09-653-0936 IMP
HAYES CO LLC
HAYES FENCE
567 W Douglas Ave, Wichita, KS 67213-4701
Tel (316) 838-8000 *Founded/Ownrshp* 2009
Sales 42.2MM^E *EMP* 225
SIC 3446 Ornamental metalwork; Ornamental metalwork
CFO: Dean Coleman

HAYES COMPUTER SYSTEMS
See HAYES E-GOVERNMENT RESOURCES INC

D-U-N-S 11-074-8543
HAYES E-GOVERNMENT RESOURCES INC
HAYES COMPUTER SYSTEMS
2551 Welaunee Blvd, Tallahassee, FL 32308-4500
Tel (850) 297-0551 *Founded/Ownrshp* 2000
Sales 23.0MM^E *EMP* 62
SIC 7373 Computer integrated systems design
Pr: Karen S Hayes
COO: Marsha Pittman
VP: Danny Hayes
IT Man: Joseph Cornelius

HAYES FENCE
See HAYES CO LLC

HAYES GREEN BEACH HOSPITAL
See HAYES GREEN BEACH MEMORIAL HOSPITAL

D-U-N-S 08-034-2207
HAYES GREEN BEACH MEMORIAL HOSPITAL
HAYES GREEN BEACH HOSPITAL
321 E Harris St, Charlotte, MI 48813-1629
Tel (517) 543-1050 *Founded/Ownrshp* 1972
Sales 48.9MM *EMP* 290
SIC 8062 General medical & surgical hospitals; General medical & surgical hospitals
V Ch: Frederick Darin
**CEO:* Matthew Rush
**CFO:* Kim Capp
**Treas:* Denise Wheaton
Ex VP: Patrick Salow
Dir OR: Karen Wilson
Dir Rad: Greg Bradford
Chf Nrs Of: Maureen Hillary
Ex Dir: Susan Allen
Ex Dir: Kim Dickinson
Dir IT: David Sebnick

D-U-N-S 80-132-1332 EXP
HAYES HOLDINGS INC
14030 Florence Rd Ste E, Sugar Land, TX 77498-3356
Tel (281) 565-8111 *Founded/Ownrshp* 1992
Sales 20.6MM^E *EMP* 125
SIC 3089 Plastic processing; Injection molding of plastics; Plastic processing; Injection molding of plastics
Pr: Norris O Hayes
**VP:* Bobby Field

HAYES LEMMERZ INTERNATIONAL
See MAXION WHEELS

D-U-N-S 08-764-5206
HAYES MANUFACTURING CO INC
106 Pelican Dr, Pineville, LA 71360-5372
Tel (318) 487-0100 *Founded/Ownrshp* 1955
Sales 24.1MM *EMP* 95
SIC 1791 7692

D-U-N-S 02-515-3826
HAYES MECHANICAL LLC
5959 S Harlem Ave, Chicago, IL 60638-3131
Tel (773) 784-0000 *Founded/Ownrshp* 1935
Sales 100.0MM^E *EMP* 250^E
SIC 1711 Mechanical contractor; Heating & air conditioning contractors; Ventilation & duct work contractor; Plumbing contractors; Mechanical contractor; Heating & air conditioning contractors; Ventilation & duct work contractor; Plumbing contractors
Ch: Richard J Mooney
Pr: Terry W Ancel
Pr: Larry Klein
CFO: Mark Tibbetts
Sr VP: Bob Gabrysiak
Sr VP: Eric Heuser
VP: George Englebrecht
VP: J D Mooney
Div Mgr: Vicky Saltz
IT Man: Derick Fields
IT Man: Derrick Moore

D-U-N-S 07-545-1674
HAYES PIPE SUPPLY INC
H P S
950 Fiber Glass Rd, Nashville, TN 37210-4633
Tel (615) 255-4040 *Founded/Ownrshp* 1973
Sales 71.8MM^E *EMP* 100
SIC 5032 Sewer pipe, clay; Sewer pipe, clay
Pr: William J Hayes
Exec: Walt Sommer
Brnch Mgr: Steve Barnett
Brnch Mgr: David Lenoir
Brnch Mgr: Trey Peterson
Brnch Mgr: Justin Scott
Brnch Mgr: Gary Yarbrough

Opers Mgr: Josh Hart
Opers Mgr: Robbie Helmly
Opers Mgr: Eddie Muldrow
Sales Asso: Tracie Basham

D-U-N-S 00-142-0629
HAYES PUMP INC (MA)
66 Old Powder Mill Rd I, Concord, MA 01742-4696
Tel (978) 369-8800 *Founded/Ownrshp* 1898
Sales 96.4MME *EMP* 80
SIC 5084 3561 Pumps & pumping equipment; Pumps & pumping equipment; Pumps & pumping equipment; Pumps & pumping equipment
Pr: Eric W Zadravec
**Ch Bd:* Patrick Furnari
Pr: Bob Simonds
**CFO:* Scott Putman
Ex VP: Joseph Larkin
**Sr VP:* Robert L Simonds
VP: Craig Huff
IT Man: Elvis Cabral
**VP Sls:* J Craig Huff III
S&M/VP: Walter A Barron
Sales Asso: Lino Dimichino

D-U-N-S 04-697-9027
■ **HAYES SEAY MATTERN & MATTERN INC**
(*Suby of* AECOM) ★
10 S Jefferson St # 1600, Roanoke, VA 24011-1331
Tel (540) 857-3100 *Founded/Ownrshp* 2007
Sales 22.8MME *EMP* 660
SIC 8711 8712 Engineering services; Civil engineering; Architectural services; Engineering services; Civil engineering; Architectural services
Pr: Cecil G Doyle
**COO:* Steve Clinton
CFO: Roger Herald
Sr VP: Charles S Garrett
Sr VP: Glen W Pickelsimer
VP: Michael Brennan
VP: Robert Canova
VP: Edward Janney
VP: Randolph Leech
VP: James Lowe
VP: Robert J Smith

D-U-N-S 94-150-0126
HAYES-PMC LLC
POWER MAINTENANCE CONSTRUCTORS
201 Tower Plz, Belleville, IL 62220-3466
Tel (618) 277-1245 *Founded/Ownrshp* 1995
Sales 50.4MME *EMP* 350
SIC 1711 Boiler maintenance contractor; Boiler maintenance contractor
Pr: Alan R Howkins
Dir Bus: Jim Zwick
**Mng Dir:* Jeremy McKinney
Off Mgr: Deneen Helfrich
Snr Mgr: Brad Jones

D-U-N-S 00-616-3653
HAYFIELD WINDOW & DOOR CO INC (MN)
107 9th St Se, Hayfield, MN 55940-8917
Tel (507) 477-3224 *Founded/Ownrshp* 1950, 1977
Sales 21.7MM *EMP* 90
SIC 3089 3442 Window frames & sash, plastic; Windows, plastic; Sash, door or window: metal; Metal doors; Window frames & sash, plastic; Windows, plastic; Sash, door or window: metal; Metal doors
Pr: Richard Rouhoff
**CFO:* Greg McGohan
**Treas:* Linda Rouhoff
**VP:* Brian Rouhoff
**Prin:* Len Oelkers
MIS Dir: Jennifer Fish
Plnt Mgr: Trent Wolter

D-U-N-S 01-077-9262
HAYLOR FREYER & COON INC
JAMES HOWARD WAYNE ASSOCIATION
231 Salina Meadows Pkwy # 200, Syracuse, NY 13212-4524
Tel (315) 451-1500 *Founded/Ownrshp* 1963
Sales NA *EMP* 200
SIC 6411 Insurance agents; Insurance agents
Ch Bd: James A Stoddard Sr
**Pr:* Victor Diserio
**CEO:* James D Freyer Jr
**COO:* Richard Howland
**CFO:* Mark Mc Ananey
**Ex VP:* C Bruce Wichmann
Sr VP: Robert Rayo
VP: Sean Dalton
VP: Linda Dardaris
**VP:* Michael Dribnak
VP: Chuck Lacomb
VP: Tim Nolan
VP: Doreen Riccinto
VP: Alan Spoto
**VP:* James Stoddard Jr
Exec: Tom Sharkey
Dir Bus: Jon Houppert

HAYM SALOMON HOME FOR THE AGED
See HAYM SOLOMON HOME FOR AGED LLC

D-U-N-S 04-006-8587
HAYM SOLOMON HOME FOR AGED LLC
HAYM SALOMON HOME FOR THE AGED
2340 Cropsey Ave, Brooklyn, NY 11214-5706
Tel (718) 373-1700 *Founded/Ownrshp* 2011
Sales 21.6MME *EMP* 240
SIC 8051 Skilled nursing care facilities; Skilled nursing care facilities
Mng Pt: Olga Lipschitz
**Pt:* Anna Paneth
**Pt:* Tzipporah Paneth
**Pt:* Adolph Weider
Exec: Isaac Markovitz

D-U-N-S 07-635-2855
HAYMAN CO
29100 Northwstn Hwy 410, Southfield, MI 48034
Tel (248) 879-7777 *Founded/Ownrshp* 1970
Sales 29.6MME *EMP* 600
SIC 6531 Real estate managers; Rental agent, real estate; Real estate managers; Rental agent, real estate
Pr: Stephen P Hayman

COO: Cheryl Buol
CFO: Karen Gerstenberger
CFO: Karen Roe
Sec: Alan J Hayman
Ex VP: Thomas T Schoenberger
Sr VP: John Cohen
Sr VP: Maurice Miller
Sr VP: Jerry Tonn
VP: Bill Basirico
VP: John Pitrone
VP: Jeffrey Raitt
VP: Lawrence Randazzo
VP: Dan Reese
VP: Michael Rice
VP: Robert Schrader
VP: Valerie H Sklar
VP: Steven Wohlman
Dir Risk M: Greg Peek

D-U-N-S 02-858-6258 IMP
HAYMARKET MEDIA INC
PRWEEK/PRESCRIBING REFERENCE
(*Suby of* HAYMARKET WORLDWIDE LIMITED)
114 W 26th St Fl 4, New York, NY 10001-6812
Tel (646) 638-6000 *Founded/Ownrshp* 1984
Sales 63.7MME *EMP* 250
SIC 2721 Magazines: publishing only, not printed on site; Magazines: publishing only, not printed on site
CEO: Kevin Costello
**CFO:* Michael Kriak
**Ch:* Rupert Heseltine
Bd of Dir: Robert M Guthrie
Bd of Dir: Sergio Pinon
Sr VP: Tammy Chernin
**VP:* Marck Bugni
VP: Cy Caine
VP: Lynne Callea
VP: Trevor Deal
**VP:* Lisa Kirk
**VP:* Lee Maniscalco
**VP:* Louis Morrin
Creative D: Paul Harpin

D-U-N-S 00-165-8520 IMP/EXP
HAYNEEDLE INC
9394 W Dodge Rd Ste 300, Omaha, NE 68114-3319
Tel (402) 715-3000 *Founded/Ownrshp* 2002
Sales 146.0MME *EMP* 355
SIC 5719 5943 5945 5947 Kitchenware; Lighting, lamps & accessories; Bath accessories; Stationery stores; Hobby, toy & game shops; Gift, novelty & souvenir shop; Kitchenware; Lighting, lamps & accessories; Bath accessories; Stationery stores; Hobby, toy & game shops; Gift, novelty & souvenir shop
Pr: Jon Barker
**Ch Bd:* Douglas S Nielsen
Pr: Dawn Block
**CFO:* Donn Raymond
Treas: Randy Houck
**Sec:* Mark Hasebroock
**Chf Mktg O:* Ash Eldifrawi
**VP:* Dana Coonce
VP: Greg Hand
Prgrm Mgr: Tara Nordquist
Genl Mgr: Kim Sindelar
Board of Directors: Ken Goldman, James Goodwin, Jeff Gordman

D-U-N-S 09-570-4987
HAYNES AMBULANCE OF ALABAMA INC (AL)
2530 E 5th St, Montgomery, AL 36107-3126
Tel (334) 265-1208 *Founded/Ownrshp* 1972, 1987
Sales 26.2MME *EMP* 180
SIC 4119 Ambulance service
Pr: Tony A Haynes
**CFO:* Scott Haynes
CFO: Patricia Lanier
VP: W A Haynes Jr
VP: Daniel W Martin
Sls Mgr: Brandee Haynes

D-U-N-S 08-514-8146
HAYNES AND BOONE LLP
2323 Victory Ave Ste 700, Dallas, TX 75219-7673
Tel (214) 651-5000 *Founded/Ownrshp* 2008
Sales 154.8MME *EMP* 1,026
SIC 8111

D-U-N-S 03-481-7726
HAYNES BROS LUMBER CO LP (TN)
739 Nw Broad St, Murfreesboro, TN 37129-2930
Tel (615) 893-1515 *Founded/Ownrshp* 1945
Sales 36.9MM *EMP* 59
Accts Grannis & Associates Pc Cpas
SIC 5211 Lumber & other building materials; Lumber & other building materials
Genl Pt: Terry G Haynes
**Owner:* Grady Hayne
CTO: Ross Dewberry
Sls Mgr: Emily Dutton

D-U-N-S 84-042-2906
HAYNES ELECTRIC UTILITY CORP
(*Suby of* H & M CONSTRUCTORS) ★
187 Deaverview Rd, Asheville, NC 28806-1707
Tel (828) 254-6141 *Founded/Ownrshp* 1987
Sales 22.8MME *EMP* 130
SIC 1623 Electric power line construction; Electric power line construction
Pr: Tony Gentry
**Pr:* Larry Hayes
**CFO:* Faison Sester
**Ch:* Nathaniel E Kennedy III
**Treas:* N E Cannady Jr

D-U-N-S 13-099-4150
HAYNES EQUIPMENT CO LLC
117 Nw 132nd St, Oklahoma City, OK 73114-2398
Tel (405) 755-1357 *Founded/Ownrshp* 1999
Sales 20.2MME *EMP* 18
SIC 5074 Water purification equipment
Sls Mgr: Joe Mossauer

D-U-N-S 00-895-6096 IMP
HAYNES FURNITURE CO INC
DUMP, THE
5324 Virginia Beach Blvd, Virginia Beach, VA 23462-1898
Tel (804) 276-1060 *Founded/Ownrshp* 1949
Sales 176.4MME *EMP* 700
SIC 5713 5712 Carpets; Furniture stores; Carpets; Furniture stores
Pr: Ellis Strelitz
COO: Naveen Pinglay
CFO: William Hutchinson
**Sr VP:* Bruce Breedlove
Sr VP: Joshua Mallenbaum
**Sr VP:* Kurt M Rosenbach
VP: Robert Glick
VP: Wanda Solomon
VP: David Weinstein
Adm Dir: Randi Strelitz
CIO: Rich Boettcher

D-U-N-S 01-879-2101
HAYNES GROUP INC
30d Progress Ave, Seymour, CT 06483-3921
Tel (203) 888-8133 *Founded/Ownrshp* 1988
Sales 31.6MM *EMP* 150
SIC 1542 Commercial & office building, new construction; Commercial & office buildings, renovation & repair; Institutional building construction; Commercial & office building, new construction; Commercial & office buildings, renovation & repair; Institutional building construction
Pr: Thomas R Haynes
**VP:* Paul J Haynes

D-U-N-S 00-697-9509
HAYNES INC (MD)
3701 Pender Dr Ste 250, Fairfax, VA 22030-7471
Tel (703) 273-2354 *Founded/Ownrshp* 2007
Sales 34.7MM *EMP* 200
SIC 8721 Accounting, auditing & bookkeeping; Accounting, auditing & bookkeeping
CEO: Aggrey R Haynes
**CFO:* Robert Reiley

D-U-N-S 16-117-8660 IMP
▲ **HAYNES INTERNATIONAL INC**
1020 W Park Ave, Kokomo, IN 46901-6330
Tel (765) 456-6000 *Founded/Ownrshp* 1912
Sales 487.6MM *EMP* 1,053
Tkr Sym HAYN *Exch* NGS
SIC 3356 Nickel; Titanium; Nickel; Titanium
Pr: Mark M Comerford
**Ch Bd:* John C Corey
CFO: Daniel W Maudlin
VP: Janice W Gunst
VP: Jean Nell
VP: Jeffrey L Young
Exec: Keith Kruger
Dir Lab: Brian Carver
Dir Lab: Kevin Fuller
Dir Lab: Annette Oconnell
Off Mgr: Kim Miller
Board of Directors: Donald C Campion, Ronald H Getz, Timothy J McCarthy, Michael L Shor, William P Wall

D-U-N-S 19-117-3728
HAYNES MATERIALS CO
30d Progress Ave, Seymour, CT 06483-3921
Tel (203) 888-8177 *Founded/Ownrshp* 1961
Sales 71.2MME *EMP* 200E
SIC 5083 Farm & garden machinery; Farm & garden machinery
Pr: Thomas Haynes
**CFO:* Michael Welch
**VP:* Paul Haynes
Board of Directors: Maria Roy

D-U-N-S 07-645-0287
HAYNES MECHANICAL SYSTEMS INC
5654 Greenwood Plaza Blvd, Greenwood Village, CO 80111-2310
Tel (303) 779-0787 *Founded/Ownrshp* 1995
Sales 64.3MME *EMP* 115
SIC 5075 7623 Warm air heating & air conditioning; Air conditioning repair; Warm air heating & air conditioning; Air conditioning repair
Pr: Kraig Haynes
**CEO:* Fred Haynes
COO: Jerry Hegge
**VP:* Roxann J Haynes
**VP:* Terry Koneig
Genl Mgr: Nicholas Lafortuna
IT Man: Carrie Stolarz
Trfc Dir: Anna Hernandez
VP Mktg: Carrie Eggers
Sales Asso: Russ Barber
Sales Asso: James Long

HAYNES WIRE ROPE
See HWC WIRE & CABLE CO

D-U-N-S 08-223-4113
HAYNSWORTH SINKLER BOYD PA
134 Meeting St Fl 3, Charleston, SC 29401-2224
Tel (843) 722-3366 *Founded/Ownrshp* 2001
Sales 46.9MM *EMP* 260
Accts Elliott Davis Llc Columbia
SIC 8111 General practice attorney, lawyer; General practice attorney, lawyer
Pr: Boyd B Nicholson
COO: Larry Mack
COO: Jean Pinckney
Bd of Dir: Tara Nauful
Chf Mktg O: Samuel W Hoell
VP: Chris Cumalander
Dir Risk M: Brenda Snyder
Mng Dir: Joseph Blake
IT Man: Mark Baxa
Genl Couns: Stephen Darling
Counsel: Carol Clark

D-U-N-S 10-724-6225
HAYS & SONS CONSTRUCTION INC
HAYS SONS COMPLETE RESTORATION
757 E Murry St, Indianapolis, IN 46227-1139
Tel (317) 788-0911 *Founded/Ownrshp* 1989
Sales 30.8MME *EMP* 120
Accts Somerset Cpas Pc Indianapol
SIC 1521 Single-family home remodeling, additions & repairs; Single-family home remodeling, additions & repairs
Pr: Mark Hays
**CFO:* Robert Johnson
**VP:* Brian R Hays
Genl Mgr: Brian Bell

HAYS 1
See HAYS FOOD TOWN INC

D-U-N-S 03-952-7841
HAYS AND SON OIL CO INC
302 Broadway Dr Sw, Cullman, AL 35055-5312
Tel (256) 734-1525 *Founded/Ownrshp* 1945
Sales 45.1MME *EMP* 77
Accts Gaylon W Drake
SIC 5172 Crude oil; Crude oil
Pr: J E Hays Jr
**Sec:* Terry Hays

D-U-N-S 02-807-3142
HAYS AUTOMOTIVE SUPERVISION INC
6015 Preston Hwy, Louisville, KY 40219-1317
Tel (502) 736-7160 *Founded/Ownrshp* 2009
Sales 24.4MME *EMP* 82E
SIC 7538 General automotive repair shops
Prin: Justin E Hays

D-U-N-S 16-669-8274
HAYS CHRYSLER-PLYMOUTH-DODGE INC
3115 Frontage Rd, Gainesville, GA 30504-8210
Tel (770) 535-2835 *Founded/Ownrshp* 1984
Sales 42.1MME *EMP* 120
SIC 5511 Automobiles, new & used; Automobiles, new & used
Pr: Albert David Hayes
**Sec:* Tim Hayes
**VP:* Donald E Hayes

HAYS CISD
See HAYS CONSOLIDATED I S D

D-U-N-S 04-322-6729
HAYS CITY CORP (TX)
KWIK MART
4906 Burleson Rd, Austin, TX 78744-1212
Tel (512) 444-0451 *Founded/Ownrshp* 1939
Sales 53.2MME *EMP* 56
SIC 5172 Petroleum products; Petroleum products
Pr: Clayton B Johnson
**Sec:* Jeanette S Ramsey
**VP:* Robert T Ramsey
**VP:* Sue Ramsey
**Prin:* Tim Ramsey
Sls Mgr: Brian Rogers

HAYS COMPANIES
See HAYS GROUP INC

D-U-N-S 10-067-2930
HAYS CONSOLIDATED I S D
HAYS CISD
21003 Interstate 35, Kyle, TX 78640-4745
Tel (512) 268-8442 *Founded/Ownrshp* 1967
Sales 155.8M *EMP* 3,000
Accts Linda Teneyuque Ito Cpa Ve Ky
SIC 8211 Public elementary & secondary schools; Public elementary & secondary schools
COO: Marty Marinez
COO: Ebell Steven
CFO: David Anderson
Trst: Marty Kanetzky
Trst: Patti Woods
VP: Mark Jones
VP: Willie Tenorio
Exec: Michelle Barrera
Exec: Marcia McClendon
Assoc Dir: Christian Huston
Assoc Dir: Anthony P Leflet

HAYS DIV
See ROMAC INDUSTRIES INC

D-U-N-S 14-160-3709 IMP
HAYS ENERGY LLC
1601 Frances Harris Ln, San Marcos, TX 78666-8967
Tel (512) 805-7200 *Founded/Ownrshp* 1998
Sales 27.1MME *EMP* 38
SIC 4911 Distribution, electric power; Generation, electric power; Transmission, electric power;
Pr: Herman Schopman

D-U-N-S 03-566-7294
HAYS FOOD TOWN INC
HAYS 1
1876 Falls Blvd N, Wynne, AR 72396-4026
Tel (870) 238-2656 *Founded/Ownrshp* 1977
Sales 75.7MM *EMP* 471
Accts Meyer & Ward Cpa Pa Wynne
SIC 5411 Grocery stores, chain; Grocery stores, chain
Pr: Michael J King
**VP:* David Allen King

D-U-N-S 86-702-3475
HAYS GROUP INC
HAYS COMPANIES
80 S 8th St Ste 700, Minneapolis, MN 55402-2105
Tel (612) 347-8377 *Founded/Ownrshp* 1994
Sales NA *EMP* 650
SIC 6411 Insurance agents & brokers; Insurance agents & brokers
Pr: James Hays
Mng Pt: Bill Mershon
Pr: Jack Diehl
Pr: John Ramonas
**CFO:* Stephen Lerum
CFO: Steve Lerum
Ex VP: Russell Berman
Ex VP: David Britt
Ex VP: Claude Campbell
Ex VP: Rose Huff
Ex VP: Doug Livingston
**Ex VP:* William Mershon
Ex VP: Dan Robinson
Ex VP: Kevin Schaffer
Ex VP: Gerald Schwalbach
Ex VP: Steve Verbeski
Ex VP: Kevin Wiskus

Ex VP: Leslie Young
Sr VP: Sean Dugan
**Sr VP:* Michael Egan
Sr VP: Lynne Little

D-U-N-S 07-330-4214
HAYS MEDICAL CENTER INC
HAYSMED
2220 Canterbury Dr, Hays, KS 67601-2370
Tel (785) 623-5000 *Founded/Ownrshp* 1942
Sales 201.5MM *EMP* 1,178
Accts Wendling Noe Nelson Johnson Ll
SIC 8062 8051 General medical & surgical hospitals; Skilled nursing care facilities; General medical & surgical hospitals; Skilled nursing care facilities
Pr: John H Jeter MD
Pr: Steve Balthazor
**COO:* Bryce A Young
**CFO:* George Harms
**CFO:* William Overbey
Treas: Kenneth Beran
Sr Cor Off: Charlene Koochel
Ofcr: Joannah Applequist
VP: Christy Stahl
Exec: Roseanne Dreiling
Dir Lab: Chardell Parke
Dir Rad: Lisa Dinkel

HAYS SONS COMPLETE RESTORATION
See HAYS & SONS CONSTRUCTION INC

D-U-N-S 12-526-2105
HAYS UNIFIED SCHOOL DISTRICT 489
323 W 12th St, Hays, KS 67601-3812
Tel (785) 623-2400 *Founded/Ownrshp* 1965
Sales 18.1MM^E *EMP* 310
SIC 8211 9411 Public combined elementary & secondary school; Administration of educational programs; Public combined elementary & secondary school; Administration of educational programs
Bd of Dir: Lori Vitztum
IT Man: Melea Kraemer
Schl Brd P: Sharon Befort
HC Dir: Mary Shorman

D-U-N-S 06-212-3179
HAYS UTILITY SERVICE CORP
2200 Sciaaca Rd, Spring, TX 77373-6107
Tel (281) 353-9809 *Founded/Ownrshp* 1970
Sales 26.7MM^E *EMP* 92
SIC 4941 Water supply; Water supply
Pr: Donald J Hays
**Sec:* Ann Hays
Sr VP: Howard Wilhite
VP: Leesa Palmer
**VP:* H Danny Wright
Opers Mgr: Robert Byerly

D-U-N-S 07-944-5272
HAYSITE REINFORCED PLASTICS LLC
5599 Perry Hwy, Erie, PA 16509-3562
Tel (814) 868-3691 *Founded/Ownrshp* 2014
Sales 30.3MM^E *EMP* 75
SIC 3083 Laminated plastics plate & sheet
Pr: Mark Anderson
VP: Scott Besco
Exec: John Steimer
S&M/VP: Tom Gardner
Sls Mgr: Timothy Bates

HAYSMED
See HAYS MEDICAL CENTER INC

D-U-N-S 00-607-4876 IMP
HAYSSEN INC (MO)
HAYSSEN PACKAGING TECHNOLOGIES
(*Suby of* BARRY-WEHMILLER COMPANIES INC) ★
225 Spartangreen Blvd, Duncan, SC 29334-9400
Tel (864) 486-4000 *Founded/Ownrshp* 1910, 1997
Sales 72.1MM^E *EMP* 280
Accts Ernst & Young Llp St Louis
SIC 3565 Packaging machinery; Packaging machinery
CEO: Bob Chapman
**Pr:* Dan Jones
**CFO:* Adam Thompson
**VP:* David M Gianini
VP: Jack Johnson
VP: Bill Stabler
VP: David Thompson
Sfty Dirs: Ken Deyoung
Sales Exec: Carson Wheeler
VP Sls: Lynn Damske
Snr Mgr: Mark Hoosier

HAYSSEN PACKAGING TECHNOLOGIES
See HAYSSEN INC

D-U-N-S 02-629-5970
HAYSTAX TECHNOLOGY INC
8251 Greensboro Dr # 1111, Mc Lean, VA 22102-4938
Tel (571) 297-3800 *Founded/Ownrshp* 2012
Sales 32.4MM^E *EMP* 339^E
SIC 7374 7379 Data processing service; Data processing service;
CEO: William B Van Vleet III
**Ch Bd:* Peter Pace
**CFO:* James E Doyle
VP: Chriss Knisley
**VP:* Thomas F Safir
**CTO:* Bryan Ware

HAYWARD AREA MEMORIAL HOSPITAL
See MEDICAL SERVICES INC

D-U-N-S 04-676-6895 IMP/EXP
HAYWARD BAKER INC
(*Suby of* KELLER FOUNDATION) ★
7550 Teague Rd Ste 300, Hanover, MD 21076-1807
Tel (410) 551-8200 *Founded/Ownrshp* 1990
Sales 416.1MM^E *EMP* 1,200
Accts Kmpg Llp Baltimore Md
SIC 1799 Building site preparation; Building site preparation
Pr: Eric R Drooff
Pr: John Rush
CFO: Phillip Tannery
CFO: Richard N Yale
Treas: Art D Pengelly
VP: Andy Anderson
VP: Daniel E Jordan
VP: Arthur Pengelly
VP: Alan Ringen
VP: John P Rubright
VP: Steve Scherer

D-U-N-S 02-446-5163
HAYWARD COMMUNITY SCHOOL DISTRICT
10665 Main St, Hayward, WI 54843-6595
Tel (715) 634-2619 *Founded/Ownrshp* 1890
Sales 20.7MM *EMP* 211
Accts Anderson Hager & Moe Hayward
SIC 8211 2711 Public elementary & secondary schools; Newspapers; Public elementary & secondary schools; Newspapers
Treas: Don Semler
Ofcr: Dan Glaze
VP: Lynell Swenson
Cmptr Lab: Dawn Cox

D-U-N-S 00-448-7617
HAYWARD DISTRIBUTING CO
4061 Perimeter Dr, Columbus, OH 43228-1048
Tel (614) 272-5953 *Founded/Ownrshp* 1990
Sales 35.2MM *EMP* 46
Accts Mcgladrey Llp Columbus Ohio
SIC 5083 5023 Lawn machinery & equipment; Garden machinery & equipment; Grills, barbecue; Lawn machinery & equipment; Garden machinery & equipment; Grills, barbecue
Ch Bd: John M Budde
**Pr:* Ronald L Monroe
Opers Mgr: Mark Roberts
Sls Mgr: Michael Fink
Sls Mgr: Mark Koenig

HAYWARD FLOW CONTROL
See HAYWARD POOL PRODUCTS INC

D-U-N-S 78-713-7694
HAYWARD FORD INC
1111 Marina Blvd, San Leandro, CA 94577-3364
Tel (510) 352-2000 *Founded/Ownrshp* 1991
Sales 36.3MM^E *EMP* 135
SIC 5511 7538 7515 7513 5531 5013 Automobiles, new & used; Pickups, new & used; Vans, new & used; General automotive repair shops; Passenger car leasing; Truck rental & leasing, no drivers; Automotive & home supply stores; Motor vehicle supplies & new parts; Automobiles, new & used; Pickups, new & used; Vans, new & used; General automotive repair shops; Passenger car leasing; Truck rental & leasing, no drivers; Automotive & home supply stores; Motor vehicle supplies & new parts
Pr: Robert Knezevich
**Sec:* James Blakely
MIS Dir: Bill Piercell
MIS Dir: Milo Roche
MIS Dir: Arnold Russ

D-U-N-S 05-487-0225 IMP/EXP
HAYWARD INDUSTRIAL PRODUCTS INC
HAYWARD PLASTIC PRODUCTS DIV
(*Suby of* HAYWARD INDUSTRIES INC) ★
620 Division St, Elizabeth, NJ 07201-2004
Tel (908) 351-5400 *Founded/Ownrshp* 1980
Sales 72.3MM^E *EMP* 500
SIC 3089 3492 3491 3494 3949 3564 Plastic hardware & building products; Control valves, fluid power: hydraulic & pneumatic; Pressure valves & regulators, industrial; Line strainers, for use in piping systems; Sporting & athletic goods; Blowers & fans; Plastic hardware & building products; Control valves, fluid power: hydraulic & pneumatic; Pressure valves & regulators, industrial; Line strainers, for use in piping systems; Sporting & athletic goods; Blowers & fans
CEO: Robert Davis
CIO: Donald Tresslar

D-U-N-S 00-245-3041 IMP/EXP
HAYWARD INDUSTRIES INC
HAYWOOD POOL PRODUCTS
620 Division St, Elizabeth, NJ 07201-2004
Tel (908) 351-5400 *Founded/Ownrshp* 1924
Sales 682.2MM^E *EMP* 1,600
SIC 3589 3561 3423 3494 3569 3089 Swimming pool filter & water conditioning systems; Pumps & pumping equipment; Pumps, domestic: water or sump; Leaf skimmers or swimming pool rakes; Valves & pipe fittings; Filters & strainers, pipeline; Plastic hardware & building products; Fittings for pipe, plastic; Swimming pool filter & water conditioning systems; Pumps & pumping equipment; Pumps, domestic: water or sump; Leaf skimmers or swimming pool rakes; Valves & pipe fittings; Filters & strainers, pipeline; Plastic hardware & building products; Fittings for pipe, plastic
Pr: Robert Davis
Ch Bd: Oscar Davis
**Pr:* Clark Hale
COO: Larry Silber
CFO: Andrew Diamond
Treas: Len Brooks
Bd of Dir: Martin Krugman
Comm Man: Bruce Porter
Dir IT: Dave Caldwell
Dir IT: Dean Deptula
IT Man: Dustin Leonard

D-U-N-S 80-019-5513 IMP
HAYWARD LABORATORIES INC
(*Suby of* ET BROWNE DRUG CO INC) ★
1921 Paradise Trl, East Stroudsburg, PA 18301-9197
Tel (570) 424-9512 *Founded/Ownrshp* 1992
Sales 38.3MM^E *EMP* 180
SIC 2844 Toilet preparations; Toilet preparations
Pr: Robert Neis

HAYWARD PLASTIC PRODUCTS DIV
See HAYWARD INDUSTRIAL PRODUCTS INC

D-U-N-S 05-486-9789 IMP
HAYWARD POOL PRODUCTS INC
HAYWARD FLOW CONTROL
(*Suby of* HAYWARD INDUSTRIES INC) ★
620 Division St, Elizabeth, NJ 07201-2004
Tel (888) 429-4635 *Founded/Ownrshp* 1980
Sales 346.9MM^E *EMP* 900
SIC 5091 3569 Swimming pool filter & water conditioning systems; Heaters, swimming pool: electric; Swimming pools, equipment & supplies; Heaters, swimming pool: electric
Ch Bd: Oscar Davis
**CFO:* Andrew Diamond
VP: Curtis Carleton
VP: Tracy Hall
VP: Frank Harvey
**VP:* George Metkovich
VP: Jim Ow
VP: Kim Rogers
Dir IT: George Sbordone
IT Man: Glenn Levine
Opers Mgr: Frank Crippen

HAYWARD QUARTZ MACHINING CO
See HAYWARD QUARTZ TECHNOLOGY INC

D-U-N-S 16-541-1554 IMP
HAYWARD QUARTZ TECHNOLOGY INC
HAYWARD QUARTZ MACHINING CO
1700 Corporate Way, Fremont, CA 94539-6107
Tel (510) 657-9605 *Founded/Ownrshp* 1989
Sales 55.4MM^E *EMP* 250
SIC 3674 Semiconductor circuit networks; Semiconductor circuit networks
CEO: Nhe Thi Le
**Pr:* Ha Vinh Ly
CFO: Quang Le
VP: Nhe Le
Plnt Mgr: Jimmy Phan
Plnt Mgr: Mark Rodriquez
Mktg Mgr: Hanh Lang
Sls Mgr: Dean Gehrman

D-U-N-S 07-654-1515
HAYWARD SISTERS HOSPITAL
ST ROSE HOSPITAL
(*Suby of* ALECTO HEALTHCARE SERVICES LLC) ★
27200 Calaroga Ave, Hayward, CA 94545-4339
Tel (510) 264-4000 *Founded/Ownrshp* 2013
Sales 123.9MM *EMP* 850
Accts Tca Partners Llp Fresno Ca
SIC 8062 General medical & surgical hospitals; General medical & surgical hospitals
Pr: Michael Mahoney
VP: Mariellen Faria
VP: Kinzi Richholt
Dir Rad: Lucina Mallavarapu
Dir Rx: Joy Lai
Ex Dir: Antoinette Yelek
Opers Mgr: Margaret Cormier
Mktg Dir: Mike Cobb
Nrsg Dir: Sylvia Ventura
Pharmcst: Sara Jacobs
Pharmcst: Juliana Murdasanu

D-U-N-S 08-007-6870
HAYWARD TILTON & ROLAPP INSURANCE ASSOCIATES INC
888 S Disneyland Dr # 400, Anaheim, CA 92802-1846
Tel (714) 637-0312 *Founded/Ownrshp* 1978
Sales NA *EMP* 63
SIC 6411 Insurance brokers
Pr: Roger Whitmore Rolapp
**COO:* Joan Kay Kolbe
**Treas:* Tom Tilton
**Sr VP:* Stephen Moriyana
VP: Murray Sportsman
**VP:* R Murray Sportsman

HAYWARD TOYOTA
See AUTO MISSION LTD

D-U-N-S 07-655-7883
HAYWARD UNIFIED SCHOOL DISTRICT
24411 Amador St, Hayward, CA 94544-1301
Tel (510) 784-2600 *Founded/Ownrshp* 1983
Sales 112.9MM^E *EMP* 2,400
SIC 8211 Public elementary & secondary schools; Public elementary school; Public junior high school; Public senior high school; Public elementary & secondary schools; Public elementary school; Public junior high school; Public senior high school
CEO: Stan Data Dobbs
Bd of Dir: Lisa Brunner
VP: Annette Walker
**Prin:* Donald Evans
Ex Dir: Leticia Salinas
Dir Sec: Lynn Bravewomon
Off Mgr: Marla Sather
Off Admin: Natalie Key
IT Man: Patrick Simon
Netwrk Mgr: Saleem Mahmood
Opers Supe: Mary Kerr

D-U-N-S 07-452-5007
HAYWOOD COMMUNITY COLLEGE
(*Suby of* NORTH CAROLINA COMMUNITY COLLEGE SYSTEM) ★
185 Freedlander Dr, Clyde, NC 28721-9432
Tel (828) 627-2821 *Founded/Ownrshp* 1965
Sales 15.1MM^E *EMP* 353
SIC 8222 9199 Community college; ; Community college;
Int Pr: Bill Aiken
**Pr:* Rose Johnson
VP: Buddy Tignor
Store Mgr: Gail McElroy
Dir IT: Annmarie Timmerman

HAYWOOD COUNTY ALTERNATIVE
See HAYWOOD COUNTY SCHOOL DISTRICT

D-U-N-S 05-513-4423
HAYWOOD COUNTY PUBLIC SCHOOLS INC
1230 N Main St, Waynesville, NC 28786-3310
Tel (828) 456-2400 *Founded/Ownrshp* 1970
Sales 76.8MM *EMP* 1,280
SIC 8211 Public elementary & secondary schools; Public elementary & secondary schools
Adm Dir: Rick Stiles
Ex Dir: Jenny Wood
Dir Sec: Mark Sheppard
IT Man: Bob Phillips
Info Man: Brooke King
Info Man: Darlene Silver
Info Man: M Swanger
Schl Brd P: Chuck Francis
Teacher Pr: Jason Heinz
Snr Mgr: Ryan Gibson

D-U-N-S 10-007-2933
HAYWOOD COUNTY SCHOOL DISTRICT
HAYWOOD COUNTY ALTERNATIVE
900 E Main St, Brownsville, TN 38012-2647
Tel (731) 772-9613 *Founded/Ownrshp* 1823
Sales 26.6MM^E *EMP* 500
SIC 8211 Public elementary & secondary schools; Public elementary & secondary schools
Ch: Harold Garrett
**Pr:* Robbie Jarrett-King

D-U-N-S 02-485-1867
HAYWOOD OIL CO INC
GAS N GROCERIES
2707 Asheville Rd, Waynesville, NC 28786-2723
Tel (828) 456-9035 *Founded/Ownrshp* 1973
Sales 54.7MM^E *EMP* 150
Accts Crisp Hughes Evans Llp Ashevi
SIC 5541 5411 Gasoline service stations; Convenience stores; Gasoline service stations; Convenience stores
CEO: David C Blevins
**Pr:* David Todd Blevins

HAYWOOD POOL PRODUCTS
See HAYWARD INDUSTRIES INC

D-U-N-S 07-450-6759
HAYWOOD REGIONAL MEDICAL CENTER
MIDWEST HAYWOOD
262 Leroy George Dr, Clyde, NC 28721-7430
Tel (828) 456-7311 *Founded/Ownrshp* 1927
Sales 101.2MM *EMP* 1,000
SIC 8062 General medical & surgical hospitals; General medical & surgical hospitals
CEO: Steve Heatherly
Dir Recs: Joyce Adkinson
Dir Recs: Beth Rathbone
**Pr:* Mike Poore
**COO:* Teresa Reynolds
**CFO:* Mike McKnight
**CFO:* Gene Winters
Treas: Glenn White
Ex VP: Dale Chernich
**VP:* Patricia Ward
Dir Lab: Terry Barnett
Dir Lab: Creig Toliver

D-U-N-S 13-070-3267
HAYWOOD VOCATIONAL OPPORTUNITIES INC
H V O
172 Riverbend St, Waynesville, NC 28786-1969
Tel (828) 454-9682 *Founded/Ownrshp* 1972
Sales 31.1MM *EMP* 328
Accts Ray Bumgarner Kingshill & As
SIC 8331 Sheltered workshop; Sheltered workshop
Pr: George Marshall
VP: Phyllis Brooks
VP Sls: John Duckett

D-U-N-S 55-627-1468
HAZ-MAT RESPONSE INC
1203 S Parker St Ste C, Olathe, KS 66061-4291
Tel (913) 782-5151 *Founded/Ownrshp* 1990
Sales 61.6MM^E *EMP* 78
SIC 4959 Environmental cleanup services
Pr: Luke Stockdale
**Pr:* Jack Stockdale
**Sec:* Jo Wilhite
**VP:* Robert McRae
**VP:* John Negrete

D-U-N-S 00-691-1382
HAZARD CONSTRUCTION CO (CA)
6465 Marindustry Dr, San Diego, CA 92121-2536
Tel (858) 587-3600 *Founded/Ownrshp* 1926
Sales 45.9MM^E *EMP* 100
SIC 1611 1622 Highway & street construction; Grading; Surfacing & paving; Guardrail construction, highways; Bridge construction; Highway & street construction; Grading; Surfacing & paving; Guardrail construction, highways; Bridge construction
VP: Klaus Guttau
Treas: Noly Gavino
Trfc Dir: David Prescott
Sls&Mrk Ex: Jason Mraz
Snr PM: Gordon Cloes

HAZEKAMPS WHOLESALE MEAT CO
See BERT HAZEKAMP & SON INC

HAZEL CREEK ASSISTED LIVING
See SUMMERVILLE AT HAZEL CREEK LLC

HAZEL HAWKINS MEMORIAL HOSP
See SAN BENITO HEALTH CARE DISTRICT

D-U-N-S 04-135-5157
HAZEL INC WILLIAM A
4305 Hazel Park Ct, Chantilly, VA 20151-2925
Tel (703) 378-8300 *Founded/Ownrshp* 1964
Sales 120.1MM^E *EMP* 530
SIC 1623 1794

D-U-N-S 03-986-6926
HAZEL PARK PUBLIC SCHOOL DISTRICT
HAZEL PARK SCHOOLS
1620 E Elza Ave, Hazel Park, MI 48030-2358
Tel (248) 658-5280 *Founded/Ownrshp* 1883
Sales 42.9MM^E *EMP* 1,000
SIC 8211 Public combined elementary & secondary school; Public combined elementary & secondary school; Public senior high school; Vocational high school
**Pr:* Clinton Adkins

*Treas: Tom Pollard
Trst: Sherrie Polowski
*VP: Monica Crawford

HAZEL PARK SCHOOLS
See HAZEL PARK PUBLIC SCHOOL DISTRICT

D-U-N-S 07-134-0467
HAZELDEN BETTY FORD FOUNDATION
HAZELDEN PUBG & EDUCTL SVCS
15251 Pleasant Valley Rd, Center City, MN 55012-9640
Tel (651) 213-4000 Founded/Ownrshp 1949
Sales 153.9MM EMP 651
SIC 8361 2731

HAZELDEN PUBG & EDUCTL SVCS
See HAZELDEN BETTY FORD FOUNDATION

D-U-N-S 11-875-2971 EXP
HAZELNUT GROWERS OF OREGON INC
OREGON ORCHARD
401 N 26th Ave, Cornelius, OR 97113-8510
Tel (503) 648-4176 Founded/Ownrshp 1983
Sales 25.0MMᴱ EMP 60
SIC 2068 Nuts: dried, dehydrated, salted or roasted
Pr: Jeff Fox
*Ch Bd: Jeff Koenig
*Pr: Compton Chase Lansdale
*Sec: Garry Rodakowski
QA Dir: Keily Kooken
Opers Mgr: Renee Lopez
Prd Mgr: Steve Schussman

D-U-N-S 78-554-7928
HAZELTINE NURSERIES INC
2401 N River Rd, Venice, FL 34292-4102
Tel (941) 485-1272 Founded/Ownrshp 1994
Sales 23.0MMᴱ EMP 120
SIC 0781 Landscape services
Pr: Stephen L Hazeltine
COO: Joe Ferretti
*Treas: Thomas Truesdale
Ofcr: Michael Hazeltine
*VP: Kirk Brummett
*VP: Richard A Harrison
Admn Mgr: Carla Hoffnann
Sls Dir: Taren Sufferling

D-U-N-S 09-591-9429 IMP
HAZELWOOD ENTERPRISES INC
HAZELWOOD'S GIFTS
402 N 32nd St, Phoenix, AZ 85008-6205
Tel (702) 860-3873 Founded/Ownrshp 1977
Sales 21.4MMᴱ EMP 200
SIC 5947 5611 5621 Gift shop; Men's & boys' clothing stores; Women's specialty clothing stores; Gift shop; Men's & boys' clothing stores; Women's specialty clothing stores
CEO: Richard L Hazelwood
*Pr: John Felix
VP: Craig Allen

D-U-N-S 07-195-4176
HAZELWOOD SCHOOL DISTRICT
GARRETT ELEMENTARY SCHOOL
15955 New Halls Ferry Rd, Florissant, MO 63031-1298
Tel (314) 953-5000 Founded/Ownrshp 1951
Sales 101.4MMᴱ EMP 2,031
SIC 8211 Public elementary & secondary schools; Public elementary & secondary schools
Ofcr: Beverly Richards
Dir Sec: Vershaun Howze
Dir IT: David McCorkle

HAZELWOOD'S GIFTS
See HAZELWOOD ENTERPRISES INC

D-U-N-S 06-496-6138
HAZEN AND SAWYER DPC
498 Fashion Ave Fl 11, New York, NY 10018-6710
Tel (212) 539-7000 Founded/Ownrshp 1977
Sales 212.3MMᴱ EMP 775
SIC 8711 Consulting engineer; Designing: ship, boat, machine & product; Pollution control engineering; Consulting engineer; Designing: ship, boat, machine & product; Pollution control engineering
Pr: Charles Hocking
CFO: Bill Crown
VP: Michael Broder
*VP: Patrick A Davis
*VP: Robert D Fiore
*VP: Sandeep Mehrotra
*VP: Richard Peters
*VP: Robert Taylor
*VP: Ronald Taylor
*VP: Peter Young
Prin: Tom McGarry

D-U-N-S 00-111-7597 IMP
HAZEN PAPER CO (MA)
240 S Water St, Holyoke, MA 01040-5979
Tel (413) 538-8204 Founded/Ownrshp 1925
Sales 77.0MMᴱ EMP 210
SIC 2672 3497 Coated paper, except photographic, carbon or abrasive; Foil, laminated to paper or other materials; Coated paper, except photographic, carbon or abrasive; Foil, laminated to paper or other materials
Pr: John H Hazen
*CFO: Robert M Sylvester
Sr VP: Stephen Smith

D-U-N-S 04-874-2175
HAZEN RESEARCH INC
4601 Indiana St, Golden, CO 80403-1895
Tel (303) 279-4501 Founded/Ownrshp 1985
Sales 41.1MMᴱ EMP 200ᴱ
SIC 8731 Commercial physical research; Commercial physical research
Pr: Nick Hazen
*Sec: Robert S Rochat
Sr VP: Dennis Gertenbach
VP: Joy Cheney
VP: Charles W Kenney
VP: Bob Rochat
Exec: Maureen Dignum
Mng Dir: Kaye Obry
VP Mfg: Bill Youngclaus

D-U-N-S 12-829-1536
HAZENS INVESTMENT LLC
SHERATON
6101 W Century Blvd, Los Angeles, CA 90045-5310
Tel (310) 642-1111 Founded/Ownrshp 2002
Sales 31.2MMᴱ EMP 395
SIC 7011 Hotels & motels; Hotels & motels
Exec: Orazio Parisi
Dir Soc: Pamela Pasley
Genl Mgr: Alberto Andrade
Genl Mgr: Phyllis McCall
Genl Mgr: Michael Miner
Prd Mgr: Mary Banzon
Natl Sales: Thomas Shaw
VP Sls: Gayle Santos
Sls Dir: Monica Bledsoe
Sls Dir: Dan Sparacino
Mktg Mgr: Billy Cubillas

D-U-N-S 08-563-7650
HAZLET TOWNSHIP BOARD OF EDUCATION
421 Middle Rd, Hazlet, NJ 07730-2428
Tel (732) 264-8404 Founded/Ownrshp 1920
Sales 15.8MMᴱ EMP 400
SIC 8211 Public elementary & secondary schools; Public elementary & secondary schools

D-U-N-S 07-980-6947
HAZLET TOWNSHIP PUBLIC SCHOOLS
421 Middle Rd, Hazlet, NJ 07730-2428
Tel (732) 264-8401 Founded/Ownrshp 2015
Sales 5.8MMᴱ EMP 470ᴱ
SIC 8211 Public elementary & secondary schools

D-U-N-S 09-874-1283
HAZLETON AREA SCHOOL DISTRICT
1515 W 23rd St, Hazle Township, PA 18202-1647
Tel (570) 459-3111 Founded/Ownrshp 1966
Sales 123.9MM EMP 1,400
Accts Dennis R Moore & Associates
SIC 8211 Public elementary school; Public junior high school; Public senior high school; Public vocational/technical school; Public elementary school; Public junior high school; Public senior high school; Public vocational/technical school
VP: Anthony Bonomo

HAZLETON PUMPS
See WEIR HAZLETON INC

D-U-N-S 10-861-1682
HAZMAT ENVIRONMENTAL GROUP INC
60 Commerce Dr, Buffalo, NY 14218-1040
Tel (716) 827-8265 Founded/Ownrshp 1984
Sales 37.4MM EMP 175
Accts Lumsden Mccormick Llp Buffalo
SIC 4213 8742 Trucking, except local; Industrial consultant; Trucking, except local; Industrial consultant
Pr: Dennis Dintino
COO: Brian Reid
COO: Jennifer Weremblewski
*CFO: Eric C Hoxsie
VP: John Stewart
Sys/Mgr: Craig Herron
Sls Mgr: Ron McGrath

D-U-N-S 55-599-6578 IMP/EXP
HAZMATPAC INC
7905 Blankenship Dr, Houston, TX 77055-1005
Tel (713) 923-2222 Founded/Ownrshp 1991
Sales 24.2MMᴱ EMP 50
SIC 5113 Corrugated & solid fiber boxes
Pr: Donald H Hausmann

HB
See HOHMANN & BARNARD INC

D-U-N-S 00-339-7734 IMP
HB & G BUILDING PRODUCTS INC
(Suby of GRAHAM PARTNERS INC) ★
1015 S Brundidge Blvd, Troy, AL 36081-3109
Tel (334) 566-5000 Founded/Ownrshp 2003
Sales 155.9MMᴱ EMP 830
SIC 2431 2421 2821 Millwork; Sawmills & planing mills, general; Plastics materials & resins; Millwork; Sawmills & planing mills, general; Plastics materials & resins
CEO: Lance Servais
COO: Brian Murray
Treas: Scott Stevenson
VP: Paul Deal
VP: Mike Gibbons
Dir IT: Barbara Sitler
Mktg Mgr: Tim Bobo

D-U-N-S 08-996-1304
HB CARBIDE CO (MI)
(Suby of STAR CUTTER CO) ★
4210 Doyle, Lewiston, MI 49756-9083
Tel (989) 786-4223 Founded/Ownrshp 1978
Sales 42.1MMᴱ EMP 100
SIC 3545 Cutting tools for machine tools
Pr: Norman B Lawton
*VP: Bradley L Lawton
*VP: Richard Mc Leod
*VP: Boyd E Moilanen
*VP: Martin Woodhouse
IT Man: Jeffrey Lawton
Plnt Mgr: Jeff Kleven

D-U-N-S 01-874-5430
HB COMMUNICATIONS INC (CT)
60 Dodge Ave, North Haven, CT 06473-1124
Tel (203) 747-7174 Founded/Ownrshp 1961
Sales 135.2MMᴱ EMP 420
SIC 5064 5065 5731

HB DENTAL
See ASPEN DENTAL MANAGEMENT INC

D-U-N-S 07-195-9147 IMP/EXP
■ **HB FULLER ADHESIVES LLC**
(Suby of HB FULLER CO) ★
1200 Willow Lake Blvd, Saint Paul, MN 55110-5101
Tel (651) 236-5823 Founded/Ownrshp 2012
Sales 61.6MMᴱ EMP 320
SIC 2891 Adhesives; Adhesives
CEO: Jim Owens
*CFO: James Giertz
*Sr VP: Traci Jensen
*Sr VP: Steven Kenny
*Sr VP: Pat Trippel
Board of Directors: John Carley, Daniel Keist, Michael Riva, Randy Siewert

D-U-N-S 00-615-9776 IMP
▲ **HB FULLER CO** (MN)
1200 Willow Lake Blvd, Saint Paul, MN 55110-5101
Tel (651) 236-5900 Founded/Ownrshp 1887
Sales 2.1MMM EMP 3,700ᴱ
Tkr Sym FUL Exch NYS
SIC 2891 2899 Adhesives & sealants; Adhesives; Adhesives, paste; Adhesives, plastic; Chemical preparations; Adhesives & sealants; Adhesives; Adhesives, paste; Adhesives, plastic; Chemical preparations
Pr: James J Owens
Pr: Michele Volpi
CFO: James R Giertz
Ofcr: Patrick L Jones
Sr VP: Traci L Jensen
Sr VP: Steven Kenny
VP: Elin E Gabriel
VP: Elin Gabriel
VP: Timothy J Keenan
VP: Antonio Lobo
VP: James C Mreary
VP: Gerald J Rudolph
Board of Directors: Thomas W Handley, Maria Teresa Hilado, J Michael Losh, Lee R Mitau, Dante C Parrini, Ann W H Simonds, John C Van Roden Jr, R William Van Sant

H.B. FULLER CONSTRUCTION PDTS
See HB FULLER CONSTRUCTION PRODUCTS INC

D-U-N-S 60-258-2504 IMP/EXP
■ **HB FULLER CONSTRUCTION PRODUCTS INC**
H.B. FULLER CONSTRUCTION PDTS
(Suby of HB FULLER CO) ★
1105 S Frontenac St, Aurora, IL 60504-6451
Tel (630) 978-7766 Founded/Ownrshp 1988
Sales 50.4MMᴱ EMP 180
SIC 2891 Adhesives; Adhesives
CEO: Rose Mary Clyburn

D-U-N-S 16-275-3920
HB MANAGEMENT GROUP INC
7100 Broadway Ste 6l, Denver, CO 80221-2925
Tel (303) 539-0150 Founded/Ownrshp 2003
Sales 34.3MMᴱ EMP 950ᴱ
SIC 8082 Home health care services; Home health care services
Ch Bd: Kathy Hughes
*Pr: Brad Brandt
*COO: Patrick Hughes
*CFO: Rick Leforce

D-U-N-S 13-020-5441
HB PARKCO CONSTRUCTION INC
3190 Arprt Loop Dr Ste F, Costa Mesa, CA 92626
Tel (714) 444-1441 Founded/Ownrshp 2002
Sales 36.1MMᴱ EMP 400
SIC 1771 Parking lot construction; Parking lot construction
CEO: Brett D Behrns
*Pr: W Adrian Hoyle
*CFO: Micheal Barry

D-U-N-S 10-672-9627 IMP
HB PERFORMANCE SYSTEMS INC
HAYES BRAKE
5800 W Donges Bay Rd, Mequon, WI 53092-4429
Tel (262) 242-4300 Founded/Ownrshp 1998
Sales 62.6MMᴱ EMP 400
SIC 3714 3751

HB PLASTICS
See HBP INC

D-U-N-S 78-318-0961
■ **HB PS HOLDING CO INC**
(Suby of NACCO INDUSTRIES INC) ★
4421 Waterfront Dr, Glen Allen, VA 23060-3375
Tel (804) 273-9777 Founded/Ownrshp 2011
Sales 547.7MMᴱ EMP 492ᴱ
SIC 5722 Household appliance stores; Household appliance stores
Pr: Alfred M Rankin Jr
*Treas: J C Butler
VP: Dave Mitchell

D-U-N-S 01-284-5053 IMP/EXP
■ **HB RENTALS LLC**
(Suby of SESI LLC) ★
5813 Highway 90 E, Broussard, LA 70518-5914
Tel (337) 839-1641 Founded/Ownrshp 1995
Sales 61.0MMᴱ EMP 350
SIC 7353 6531 Oil equipment rental services; Oil field equipment, rental or leasing; Oil well drilling equipment, rental or leasing; Real estate leasing & rentals; Oil equipment rental services; Oil field equipment, rental or leasing; Oil well drilling equipment, rental or leasing; Real estate leasing & rentals
Pr: Peter Armstrong
VP: David Caillier
VP: John Nagel
Exec: Heddi Frederick
Dist Mgr: Todd Cox
Genl Mgr: Andy Davidson
Genl Mgr: Tony Delarosa
S&M/VP: Glenn Aguilar
Manager: Stan Dombroski
Sls Mgr: Jill Adams
Sls Mgr: Sean Corkran
Board of Directors: Tasha Castille

D-U-N-S 06-467-4229 IMP/EXP
HB SEALING PRODUCTS INC
BULLDOG HYDRAULICS & GASKETS
(Suby of DIPLOMA HOLDINGS INC) ★
1016 N Belcher Rd, Clearwater, FL 33765-2100
Tel (727) 796-1300 Founded/Ownrshp 1999
Sales 45.6MMᴱ EMP 200
SIC 2869 5085 Hydraulic fluids, synthetic base; Acetates: amyl, butyl & ethyl; Seals, industrial; Pistons & valves; Hydraulic fluids, synthetic base; Acetates: amyl, butyl & ethyl; Seals, industrial; Pistons & valves
Pr: Russell Brown
*CFO: Shawn O'Hara
*Sec: Brian Collins
VP: Ron Garcia
VP: Sonny Goldsmith
VP: Ian Henderson
Genl Mgr: Russ Petrie
IT Man: John Deal
IT Man: Tim Eichholtz
IT Man: David Miller
Sfty Mgr: Bill Taylor

HB SPECIALTY FOODS
See HYDROBLEND INC

D-U-N-S 00-793-6974 IMP
HB ZACHRY CO (TX)
(Suby of ZACHRY INDUSTRIAL INC) ★
527 Logwood Ave, San Antonio, TX 78221-1738
Tel (210) 475-8000 Founded/Ownrshp 1924, 2008
Sales 201.9MMᴱ EMP 1,000
Accts Ernst & Young Llp San Antonio
SIC 1611 1622 1623 1629 General contractor, highway & street construction; Highway & street paving contractor; Bridge construction; Pipeline construction; Dam construction; General contractor, highway & street construction; Highway & street paving contractor; Bridge construction; Pipeline construction; Dam construction
Ch Bd: Henry B Zachry Jr
*Treas: Gonzalo Ornelas
*Ex VP: Charles Ebrom
*VP: Stephen L Hoech
*VP: Murray L Johnston Jr
*VP: Joe J Lozano
*VP: D Kirk McDonald

HB-GM ACQUISTION
See HARVE BENARD LTD

D-U-N-S 07-727-5485 IMP
HBA CORP
5310 Nw 33rd Ave Ste 211, Fort Lauderdale, FL 33309-6319
Tel (954) 731-3350 Founded/Ownrshp 1974
Sales 34.5MMᴱ EMP 1,014
SIC 8051 Convalescent home with continuous nursing care; Convalescent home with continuous nursing care
Pr: Barton D Weisman
*Sec: Howard Lipschutz
*VP: Dr Arthur Krosneck

HBA INTERNATIONAL
See HIRSCH/BEDNER INTERNATIONAL INC

D-U-N-S 17-523-8075
HBC ADJUSTING INC
3070 Lakecrest Cir, Lexington, KY 40513-1937
Tel (888) 962-9222 Founded/Ownrshp 2004
Sales NA EMP 280
SIC 6411 Insurance claim adjusters, not employed by insurance company; Insurance claim adjusters, not employed by insurance company
Pr: John Glukowsky
*VP: John Beaton

D-U-N-S 07-872-9713
HBC HOLDINGS LLC
324a Half Acre Rd, Cranbury, NJ 08512-3254
Tel (609) 860-9990 Founded/Ownrshp 2012
Sales 240.6MMᴱ EMP 180
SIC 5072 5087 5074 Hardware; Janitors' supplies; Plumbing & hydronic heating supplies; Hardware; Shelf or light hardware; Security devices, locks; Janitors' supplies; Plumbing & hydronic heating supplies
CEO: James Brower
VP: Jack Imszennik

D-U-N-S 78-763-6948 IMP
HBC SERVICE CO
601 Meadowlands Blvd, Washington, PA 15301-8934
Tel (724) 873-5100 Founded/Ownrshp 1996
Sales 24.4MMᴱ EMP 27ᴱ
SIC 5141 Groceries, general line
Prin: Walt Durr

D-U-N-S 07-876-6887
HBC SOLUTIONS HOLDINGS LLC
10877 Wilshire Blvd Fl 18, Los Angeles, CA 90024-4373
Tel (321) 727-9100 Founded/Ownrshp 2013
Sales 61.0MMᴱ EMP 1,002
SIC 3663 Radio broadcasting & communications equipment; Television broadcasting & communications equipment; Radio broadcasting & communications equipment; Television broadcasting & communications equipment

HBCS
See HOSPITAL BILLING & COLLECTION SERVICE LTD

D-U-N-S 04-536-4270
HBD CONSTRUCTION INC
5517 Manchester Ave, Saint Louis, MO 63110-1918
Tel (314) 781-8000 Founded/Ownrshp 2004
Sales 70.7MM EMP 75
SIC 1542 Commercial & office building contractors; Commercial & office building contractors
Pr: Mike Perry
*COO: Brian M Kowert
*Sec: Paul Kowert
*VP: Brian C Kowert

D-U-N-S 18-480-8053 IMP/EXP
HBD INDUSTRIES INC
5200 Upper Ste 110, Dublin, OH 43017
Tel (614) 526-7000 Founded/Ownrshp 1987
Sales 255.0MM EMP 1,534
SIC 3052 3621 3566 3564 3812

D-U-N-S 82-629-3651 EXP
HBD/THERMOID INC
(Suby of HBD INDUSTRIES INC) ★
1301 W Sandusky Ave, Bellefontaine, OH 43311-1082
Tel (937) 593-5010 Founded/Ownrshp 2003
Sales 51.6MM^E EMP 250
SIC 3429 3052 Manufactured hardware (general); Rubber & plastics hose & beltings; Manufactured hardware (general); Rubber & plastics hose & beltings
Genl Mgr: Randy Lady
Dist Mgr: Chris Rapp
Plnt Mgr: Ken Harriger
Sales Asso: Thomas Pastuszek

D-U-N-S 05-694-8383
HBE CORP
HOSPITAL BUILDING & EQP CO
11330 Olive Blvd, Saint Louis, MO 63141-7149
Tel (314) 567-9000 Founded/Ownrshp 1960
Sales 755.0MM^E EMP 2,907
Accts Rubinbrown Llp Cpa Saint Lou
SIC 1542 8742 Nonresidential construction; Specialized public building contractors; Bank building construction; Hospital construction; Marketing consulting services; Financial consultant; Nonresidential construction; Specialized public building contractors; Bank building construction; Hospital construction; Marketing consulting services; Financial consultant
Pr: Joseph Lehrer
COO: Matthew Nail
CFO: Doug Adrian
*V Ch Bd: June Kummer
Sr VP: Richard Abel
Sr VP: Joe Arnold
Sr VP: Matthew T Baldy
VP: Howard Ackerman
VP: Brett Goodman
VP: Gene Kemp
VP: James Moore
VP: Tim Rand
Creative D: Steve O'Rourke

HBE RENTAL
See HANSEN BROS ENTERPRISES

D-U-N-S 05-608-7398
HBE TRAILER CORP
ADAM'S MARK HOTEL
(Suby of CHARTRES LODGING GROUP LLC) ★
315 Chestnut St, Saint Louis, MO 63102-1813
Tel (314) 241-7400 Founded/Ownrshp 2008
Sales 7.0MM^E EMP 552
SIC 7011 7991 7359 5812 Hotels; Physical fitness facilities; Equipment rental & leasing; Eating places; Hotels; Physical fitness facilities; Equipment rental & leasing; Eating places
Pr: Fred S Kummer

D-U-N-S 13-935-0169 IMP
HBF INTERNATIONAL LLC
310 Ne Kirby St, McMinnville, OR 97128-4301
Tel (503) 843-6304 Founded/Ownrshp 1992
Sales 70.2MM EMP 20
SIC 0723 4731 0171

HBF TEXTILES
See HICKORY BUSINESS FURNITURE LLC

D-U-N-S 18-705-7732 IMP
HBH ENTERPRISES
HBH PET PRODUCTS
1060 Spring Creek Pl, Springville, UT 84663-3037
Tel (801) 489-3815 Founded/Ownrshp 1985
Sales 20.0MM^E EMP 50
SIC 2048 Fish food
Pr: Frank W Ballard
*VP: Carey A Carter
VP: Scott Lawson

HBH PET PRODUCTS
See HBH ENTERPRISES

HBIO
See HARVARD APPARATUS INC

D-U-N-S 83-555-5897
HBK INVESTMENTS LP
2101 Cedar Ste 700, Dallas, TX 75201
Tel (214) 758-6100 Founded/Ownrshp 1991
Sales 56.3MM^E EMP 250^E
SIC 6799 Investors; Investors
Pr: David Costen Haley
COO: Kevin Alan O'Neal
CFO: John Baker Gentry
Exec: Hallett Ben

D-U-N-S 04-398-7361
■ **HBL HOLDINGS INC**
H B L DEALERSHIP
(Suby of PENSKE AUTOMOTIVE GROUP INC) ★
8545 Leesburg Pike # 600, Vienna, VA 22182-2283
Tel (703) 442-8200 Founded/Ownrshp 2001
Sales 31.5MM^E EMP 125^E
SIC 5511 5013 Automobiles, new & used; Automotive supplies & parts; Automobiles, new & used; Automotive supplies & parts
Ch Bd: Roger S Penske Jr
*Pr: Robert F Farrell
*Sec: Thomas E Schmitt
*Sr VP: Samuel X Difeo
*VP: Whitfield Ramonat
*VP: Robert K Wilshaw

D-U-N-S 60-085-7200
■ **HBL LLC**
MERCEDES-BENZ OF TYSONS CORNER
(Suby of H B L DEALERSHIP) ★
8545 Leesburg Pike # 600, Vienna, VA 22182-2283
Tel (703) 442-8200 Founded/Ownrshp 2001
Sales 31.5MM^E EMP 97^E
SIC 5511 New & used car dealers
Ch Bd: Roger S Penske Jr
Genl Mgr: Robert Farrell
CTO: Kay Kim
Sales Asso: Charles Roeder
Sales Asso: Mike Sarwar

D-U-N-S 82-536-0246
HBM ACQUISITIONS LLC
HAWAIIAN BUILDING MAINTAINCE
1001 Bishop St Ste 955, Honolulu, HI 96813-3491
Tel (808) 537-4561 Founded/Ownrshp 2006
Sales 39.9MM^E EMP 700
SIC 7299 Facility rental & party planning services; Facility rental & party planning services
Pr: Craig Peterson
VP: Maximo Cristobal

D-U-N-S 16-336-5609
HBM HOLDINGS CO
3870 S Lindbergh Blvd # 160, Saint Louis, MO 63127-1393
Tel (314) 543-6300 Founded/Ownrshp 2012
Sales 38.3MM^E EMP 252^E
SIC 3599 3714 Flexible metal hose, tubing & bellows; Hose, flexible metallic; Motor vehicle parts & accessories
CEO: Michael A Decola

HBO LATIN AMERICA GROUP
See OLE HBO PARTNERS

D-U-N-S 82-564-3380
■ **HBO SERVICES INC**
H B O
(Suby of TIME WARNER CABLE ENTERPRISES LLC) ★
1100 Ave Of The Am Frnt 3, New York, NY 10036
Tel (212) 512-1000 Founded/Ownrshp 2003
Sales 27.7MM^E EMP 2,050
SIC 7822 Distribution, exclusive of production: motion picture; Distribution, exclusive of production: motion picture
CEO: Jeffrey L Bewkes

D-U-N-S 04-981-4783 IMP
HBP INC
HB PLASTICS
107 N Henderson Rd, Freeport, IL 61032-3335
Tel (815) 235-3000 Founded/Ownrshp 2000
Sales 21.8MM^E EMP 100
SIC 3089 Molding primary plastic; Thermoformed finished plastic products
Pr: William R Bailey
Genl Mgr: Ted Neels
Ql Cn Mgr: Lori Reed

HBP PIPE & PRECAST LLC
See FORTERRA PIPE & PRECAST LLC

D-U-N-S 96-890-6714
HBR CONSULTING INC
440 S La Salle St # 2200, Chicago, IL 60605-1028
Tel (312) 201-8400 Founded/Ownrshp 2011
Sales 20.8MM^E EMP 100
SIC 7373 Computer integrated systems design
CEO: Chris Petrini-Poli
COO: James Rojas
Mng Dir: Bobbi Basile
Mng Dir: Kevin Clem
Mng Dir: Kevin McClean
Dir IT: Jason Conley
Mktg Mgr: Laura Stanner
Snr Mgr: Mike Baer
Snr Mgr: Ryan Mittman

D-U-N-S 96-610-3595
HBR KENTUCKY LLC
(Suby of HARBORSIDE HEALTHCARE LIMITED PARTNERSHIP)
101 Sun Ave Ne, Albuquerque, NM 87109-4373
Tel (505) 821-3355 Founded/Ownrshp 2010
Sales 9.1MM^E EMP 2,990^E
SIC 8051 Skilled nursing care facilities
Prin: John Bickel

D-U-N-S 03-939-7356
HBS INC
HUDSON SERVICES
314 N Jefferson Ave, Saint Louis, MO 63103-1527
Tel (314) 621-3440 Founded/Ownrshp 2001
Sales 7.7MM^E EMP 400
SIC 7381 7217 Security guard service; Carpet & upholstery cleaning; Security guard service; Carpet & upholstery cleaning
Pr: William Hudson

HBSP
See HARVARD BUSINESS SCHOOL STUDENT ASSOCIATION INC

HBW GROUP
See HBW PROPERTIES INC

D-U-N-S 15-997-7693
HBW INSURANCE SERVICES LLC
(Suby of 2-10 HOME BUYERS WARRANTY) ★
4501 Circ 75 Pkwy Sef6200, Atlanta, GA 30339
Tel (678) 742-6300 Founded/Ownrshp 1999
Sales NA EMP 75
SIC 6411 Insurance agents, brokers & service; Insurance agents, brokers & service

D-U-N-S 07-483-3336
HBW PROPERTIES INC
HBW GROUP
1055 1st St Ste 200, Rockville, MD 20850-8400
Tel (301) 424-2900 Founded/Ownrshp 1969
Sales 80.8MM EMP 85
SIC 1542 6512 6531

D-U-N-S 08-258-6983
HC (USA) INC
HAIR CLUB FOR MEN & WOMEN
(Suby of ADERANS COMPANY LIMITED)
1515 S Federal Hwy # 401, Boca Raton, FL 33432-7450
Tel (561) 883-7665 Founded/Ownrshp 2013
Sales 51.8MM^E EMP 920
SIC 7299 6794 Hair weaving or replacement; Franchises, selling or licensing; Hair weaving or replacement; Franchises, selling or licensing
VP: Frank De Carlo
*Pr: Rick Narcisi
Pr: Mike Nassar
*Pr: David O'Toole
COO: Susan Fox
*COO: Steven Hudson
*CFO: Richard Smith
*Sr VP: Michael Brisson
VP: Carlo De
*VP: Carlos Sariol
VP: Steve Stickney
VP: Luba Zeldis

D-U-N-S 79-139-6257
HC CAPITAL GROUP INC
4214 Plnfeld Ave Ne Ste B, Grand Rapids, MI 49503
Tel (616) 361-7044 Founded/Ownrshp 2005
Sales 30.0MM EMP 250^E
SIC 7389 Fund raising organizations; Fund raising organizations
Pr: Jeremy J Overweg
CFO: Fred Persch

D-U-N-S 07-969-9597
HC COMPANIES INC
(Suby of WINGATE PARTNERS V LP) ★
2450 Edison Blvd Ste 3, Twinsburg, OH 44087-4335
Tel (440) 632-3333 Founded/Ownrshp 2015
Sales NA EMP 570
SIC 2821 Plastics materials & resins
Pr: Chris Koscho
*CFO: John Landefeld

D-U-N-S 13-097-9037 EXP
HC COMPOSITES LLC
POWERCAT GROUP
1090 W Saint James St, Tarboro, NC 27886-4822
Tel (252) 641-8000 Founded/Ownrshp 2002
Sales 23.8MM^E EMP 70
SIC 3732 Boat building & repairing
Pr: Andrew V Brown
*CFO: Bruce Mygatt
VP: Greg McLogan
VP: Herman Watson
Genl Mgr: Phyllis Manning
CTO: Christopher Brockway
Plnt Mgr: Kenneth Brown
VP Mktg: Dave Tuchler
Sales Asso: Christina Harris
Snr Mgr: Vicky Pittman

D-U-N-S 86-725-4336
HC CONTRACTORS INC
1296 Old Richardson Hwy, North Pole, AK 99705
Tel (907) 488-5983 Founded/Ownrshp 1993
Sales 40.7MM^E EMP 270
Accts Rjg Fairbanks Alaska
SIC 1629 Earthmoving contractor; Earthmoving contractor
Pr: William Hoople
IT Man: Sally Zundell

D-U-N-S 00-526-7893 IMP/EXP
HC DUKE & SON LLC
ELECTRO FREEZE
(Suby of ALI SPA)
2116 8th Ave, East Moline, IL 61244-1800
Tel (309) 755-4553 Founded/Ownrshp 2004
Sales 52.5MM^E EMP 150
SIC 3556 Ice cream manufacturing machinery; Ice cream manufacturing machinery
Sr VP: Penny Klingler
VP: Jim Duke
Div Mgr: Mark Holden
Genl Mgr: Dorothy Ball
VP Sls: Penny Klinger
Sls Mgr: Joe Sacco
Sales Asso: Valerie Swanson

D-U-N-S 78-418-7499
HC INNOVATIONS INC
10 Progress Dr 200, Shelton, CT 06484-6216
Tel (203) 925-9600 Founded/Ownrshp 2006
Sales 27.8MM EMP 2
SIC 3714 Motor vehicle parts & accessories; Motor vehicle parts & accessories
Ofcr: R Scott Walker
Div Pres: Salvatore V Bastardi
Ex VP: Tina Bartelmay

D-U-N-S 02-160-2750
HC PHARMACY CENTRAL INC
3175 E Carson St, Pittsburgh, PA 15203-2130
Tel (412) 647-2240 Founded/Ownrshp 1978
Sales 42.0MM^E EMP 41
SIC 5122 Pharmaceuticals
VP: Dr Mary Beth Lang
*Pr: Deborah Redmond
*Treas: Paul Castillo

D-U-N-S 03-564-1661
HC SCHMIEDING PRODUCE CO LLC
(Suby of WOERNER HOLDINGS LP) ★
2330 N Thompson St, Springdale, AR 72764-1709
Tel (479) 751-4517 Founded/Ownrshp 2015
Sales 86.8MM^E EMP 35
SIC 5148 Fresh fruits & vegetables; Fresh fruits & vegetables
Ch Bd: Lester J Woerner
CFO: Chris Gryskiewicz
IT Man: Nelva House
S&M/VP: Gary Owens

D-U-N-S 92-979-2240
HC STARCK (OHIO) INC
21801 Tungsten Rd, Cleveland, OH 44117-1117
Tel (216) 692-3990 Founded/Ownrshp 2000
Sales 37.7MM^E EMP 500
SIC 3341 Secondary nonferrous metals
CEO: Larry McHugh
*COO: Joel Hoffman
*Sr VP: Pete Calfo
*Sr VP: John Durham
Opers Mgr: Dave Schwartz

D-U-N-S 87-432-3868
▲ **HC2 HOLDINGS INC**
505 Huntmar Park Dr # 325, Herndon, VA 20170-5155
Tel (703) 456-4100 Founded/Ownrshp 1994
Sales 543.2MM EMP 1,886
Tkr Sym HCHC Exch ASE
SIC 4813 3325 8731 ;Telephone/video communications; Steel foundries; Biological research; ;Telephone/video communications; Steel foundries; Biological research
Ch Bd: Philip A Falcone
COO: Keith M Hladek
CFO: Mesfin Demise
CFO: Ken Schwarz
*Ex VP: Robert Pons
Sr VP: Peter Aquino
VP: William Carter
VP: John F Depodesta
VP: Jim Erickson
VP: Mary Horne
VP: Hilton Reading
VP: Scott Reskey
VP: Jay Rosenblatt
VP: Tom Scott
Board of Directors: Wayne Barr Jr, Robert V Leffler, Daniel Tseung

D-U-N-S 79-491-9675
HC2 INC
HIRE COUNCIL
360 Lexington Ave Rm 1100, New York, NY 10017-6556
Tel (646) 356-0595 Founded/Ownrshp 2003
Sales 16.5MM^E EMP 350
SIC 7361 Employment agencies; Employment agencies
Pr: Lynn Mestel
*COO: Willa Fawler
*CFO: Mary Wenze

D-U-N-S 02-710-3187
■ **HCA - INFORMATION TECHNOLOGY & SERVICES INC**
(Suby of HCA INC) ★
1 Park Plz Bldg 32, Nashville, TN 37203-6527
Tel (615) 344-9551 Founded/Ownrshp 1986
Sales 20.5MM^E EMP 30^E
SIC 7379
Pr: Noel Brown Williams
VP: Mark Penkhus

D-U-N-S 07-581-7015
HCA GENESIS INC
MERCY OF NORTHERN NEW YORK
218 Stone St, Watertown, NY 13601-3211
Tel (315) 782-7400 Founded/Ownrshp 2011
Sales 8.4MM^E EMP 563
SIC 8059 8082 8071 8092 8093 Rest home, with health care; Nursing home, except skilled & intermediate care facility; Home health care services; Medical laboratories; Kidney dialysis centers; Rehabilitation center, outpatient treatment; Rest home, with health care; Nursing home, except skilled & intermediate care facility; Home health care services; Medical laboratories; Kidney dialysis centers; Rehabilitation center, outpatient treatment
COO: Randy Gerlack
Dir Recs: Mary Christy
Sec: Susan Renshaw
Sr Cor Off: Anthony Salerno
Dir Soc: Blair Bertrain
Off Mgr: Rae Ann La Fave
Nrsg Dir: Elaine O'Brien
Phys Thrpy: Kelly Spies
HC Dir: Dawn Johnson

HCA GREEN OAKS
See GREEN OAKS BEHAVIORAL HEALTHCARE SERVICES

D-U-N-S 07-321-6582
■ **HCA HEALTH SERVICES OF FLORIDA INC**
COLUMBIA HCA
(Suby of HCA INC) ★
1 Park Plz, Nashville, TN 37203-6527
Tel (615) 344-9551 Founded/Ownrshp 1968
Sales 259.6MM^E EMP 5,100
SIC 8062 8093 General medical & surgical hospitals; Specialty outpatient clinics; General medical & surgical hospitals; Specialty outpatient clinics
Ch: Richard M Bracken
*Pr: Richard Bracke
*CEO: R Milton Johnson
*Sr VP: David G Anderson
*Sr VP: Victor L Campbell
*Sr VP: Jana J Davis
*Sr VP: John M Steele

D-U-N-S 92-647-4768
■ **HCA HEALTH SERVICES OF FLORIDA INC**
COLUMBIA HCA
(Suby of HCA INC) ★
14000 Fivay Rd, Hudson, FL 34667-7103
Tel (727) 819-2929 Founded/Ownrshp 2007
Sales 37.4MM^E EMP 1,000
SIC 4789 Cargo loading & unloading services; Cargo loading & unloading services
CEO: David Williams
Dir Risk M: Cheere Manulak
Dir Rad: Ralph Uzzi

D-U-N-S 94-913-9521
■ **HCA HEALTH SERVICES OF GEORGIA INC**
COLUMBIA HCA
(Suby of HCA INC) ★
1 Park Plz, Nashville, TN 37203-6527
Tel (615) 344-9551 Founded/Ownrshp 1981
Sales 28.0MM^E EMP 515
SIC 8062 General medical & surgical hospitals; General medical & surgical hospitals
Pr: Thomas Frist
VP: Caroline Kirkman
CIO: Ron Brannan

D-U-N-S 07-398-1417
■ **HCA HEALTH SERVICES OF NEW HAMPSHIRE INC**
COLUMBIA HCA
(Suby of HCA INC) ★
333 Borthwick Ave, Portsmouth, NH 03801-7128
Tel (603) 436-0600 Founded/Ownrshp 1994
Sales 174.0MM^E EMP 1,551

SIC 8062 8063 General medical & surgical hospitals; Psychiatric hospitals; General medical & surgical hospitals; Psychiatric hospitals
Pr: William J Schuler
**CFO:* Richard Senger
VP: Jackie Brighton
Dir Rx: Jeffrey Newberg
Dir Bus: Jeff Newberg
Dir Sec: Bill Duffy
QA Dir: Donna Fitts
Dir IT: Jane McNamara
Info Man: Robert Young
Software D: Donna Lewallen
Mktg Dir: Donavon Albertson

D-U-N-S 79-769-6528
■ HCA HEALTH SERVICES OF OKLAHOMA INC
OU MEDICAL CENTER
(*Suby of* HCA INC) ★
700 Ne 13th St, Oklahoma City, OK 73104-5004
Tel (405) 271-6035 *Founded/Ownrshp* 1980
Sales 319.4MM^E *EMP* 2,900
SIC 8062 General medical & surgical hospitals; General medical & surgical hospitals
CEO: Charles L Spicer Jr
**CEO:* Cole Eslyn
COO: Donald Whitehead
**CFO:* Watson Jim
**CFO:* James Watson
**VP:* Daniel Pryor
VP: Lance Torcom
Dir Sec: Ed Welch
Off Mgr: Susan Cloer
Telecom Ex: Craig Amburn
Dir IT: Jeff Wilkins

D-U-N-S 83-192-2039
■ HCA HEALTH SERVICES OF OKLAHOMA INC
CHILDRENS HOSPITAL INSPTN STN
(*Suby of* HCA HEALTH SERVICES OF OKLAHOMA INC) ★
940 Ne 13th St Grrson Twr, Oklahoma City, OK 73104
Tel (405) 271-3325 *Founded/Ownrshp* 2009
Sales 203.1M^E *EMP* 881^E
SIC 8062 General medical & surgical hospitals
Prin: Jerry Maier

D-U-N-S 10-177-0519
■ HCA HEALTH SERVICES OF TENNESSEE INC
COLUMBIA HCA
(*Suby of* HCA INC) ★
1 Park Plz, Nashville, TN 37203-6527
Tel (615) 344-9551 *Founded/Ownrshp* 2007
Sales 255.0MM^E *EMP* 1,550
SIC 8062 General medical & surgical hospitals; General medical & surgical hospitals
Pr: Jack Bouender
**VP:* Bettye Daugherty

D-U-N-S 17-883-6750
■ HCA HEALTH SERVICES OF TENNESSEE INC
TRISTAR SOUTHERN HILLS MED CTR
(*Suby of* COLUMBIA HCA) ★
391 Wallace Rd, Nashville, TN 37211-4851
Tel (615) 781-4000 *Founded/Ownrshp* 1978
Sales 88.5MM^E *EMP* 650
SIC 8011 8062 Offices & clinics of medical doctors; General medical & surgical hospitals; Offices & clinics of medical doctors; General medical & surgical hospitals
CEO: R Milton Johnson
VP: Jeff Whitehorn
Dir QC: Paulette Cole
Doctor: Gina Hamrang
Snr Mgr: Robert Ripley
Snr Mgr: Mary Sharp

D-U-N-S 96-413-8275
■ HCA HEALTH SERVICES OF TENNESSEE INC
SUMMIT MEDICAL CENTER
(*Suby of* COLUMBIA HCA) ★
5655 Frist Blvd, Hermitage, TN 37076-2053
Tel (615) 316-3000 *Founded/Ownrshp* 1995
Sales 166.5MM *EMP* 1,150
SIC 8062 General medical & surgical hospitals; General medical & surgical hospitals
CEO: Jeff Whitehorn
COO: Kelly Curry
Dir Lab: Lawanda Davis
Ex Dir: Barbara Willoughby
DP Dir: Rachel Tucker
QA Dir: Colleen Patterson
Dir IT: Joel Bain
Phys Thrpy: Holly Hill

D-U-N-S 78-763-3478
■ HCA HEALTH SERVICES OF TEXAS INC
TRISTAR HEALTH SYSTEMS
(*Suby of* HCA INC) ★
1 Park Plz, Nashville, TN 37203-6527
Tel (615) 344-9551 *Founded/Ownrshp* 1968
Sales 317.9MM^E *EMP* 4,000
SIC 8062 General medical & surgical hospitals; General medical & surgical hospitals
CEO: Richard M Bracken
**Sr VP:* David G Anderson
**Sr VP:* Jana J Davis
**VP:* Michael Bray
CIO: Christopher A Young

D-U-N-S 07-792-2409
■ HCA HEALTH SERVICES OF VIRGINIA INC
HCA VIRGINIA
(*Suby of* HCA INC) ★
1602 Skipwith Rd, Richmond, VA 23229-5205
Tel (804) 289-4500 *Founded/Ownrshp* 1994
Sales 166.1MM^E *EMP* 1,500
SIC 8062 8093 General medical & surgical hospitals; Mental health clinic, outpatient; General medical & surgical hospitals; Mental health clinic, outpatient
Pr: Samuel N Hazen

**Treas:* David C Anderson
**Sr VP:* Donald W Stinnett
**VP:* Natalie H Cline
**VP:* John M Franck II
Dir Rad: James D Wasworth
Dir Rx: Kim B Hayes
Chf Nrs Of: Sue Johnson
Dir Sec: Buddy Blanton
MIS Dir: Daniel Patton
Phys Thrpy: Tony Santowasso

HCA HEALTHCARE
See OKEECHOBEE HOSPITAL INC

HCA HEALTHCARE
See WHMC INC

HCA THE HEALTHCARE COMPANY
See HOSPITAL CORP OF AMERICA

D-U-N-S 96-769-7686
▲ HCA HOLDINGS INC
1 Park Plz, Nashville, TN 37203-6527
Tel (615) 344-9551 *Founded/Ownrshp* 1990
Sales 36.9MMM *EMP* 225,000^E
Tkr Sym HCA *Exch* NYS
SIC 8062 General medical & surgical hospitals; General medical & surgical hospitals
Ch Bd: R Milton Johnson
Chf Path: Stephanie Hanson
Pr: Joseph Cazayoux
Pr: Paul Currie
Pr: Rob Dibernardo
Pr: Kristin Gence
Pr: Suzanne Griffith
Pr: Kimberly Hatchel
Pr: Thomas Hinton
Pr: Rebeca McDade
Pr: Janet Meyers
Pr: Tom Morris
Pr: Martin Plevak
COO: Samuel N Hazen
CFO: William B Rutherford
Sr VP: Victor L Campbell
Sr VP: Jana J Davis
Sr VP: Donald W Stinnett
Sr VP: Robert A Waterman
VP: Sheryle D'Amico
VP: Mary-Beth Fisk

D-U-N-S 05-810-4613
■ HCA HOSPITAL SERVICES OF SAN DIEGO
COLUMBIA HCA
(*Suby of* HCA INC) ★
550 N Hillside St, Wichita, KS 67214-4910
Tel (316) 962-2000 *Founded/Ownrshp* 1994
Sales 107.0MM^E *EMP* 3,080
SIC 8062 Hospital, medical school affiliated with residency; Hospital, medical school affiliated with residency
CEO: David S Nevill
CFO: David Busatti
Dir Rx: Jack Bond
Dir IT: Jeff Schauf
HC Dir: Deb Miller

D-U-N-S 19-430-3616
■ HCA INC
HOSPITAL COPORATION OF AMERICA
(*Suby of* HCA HOLDINGS INC) ★
1 Park Plz, Nashville, TN 37203-6527
Tel (615) 344-9551 *Founded/Ownrshp* 2006
Sales 26.7MMM^E *EMP* 190,000
SIC 8063 8062 8069 8093 Psychiatric hospitals; General medical & surgical hospitals; Specialty hospitals, except psychiatric; Specialty outpatient clinics; Psychiatric hospitals; General medical & surgical hospitals; Specialty hospitals, except psychiatric; Specialty outpatient clinics
Ch Bd: Richard M Bracken
Chf Path: Dan Pankowski
Pr: Kevin Hicks
**Pr:* R Milton Johnson
Pr: Margaret G Lewis
COO: Rebecca Benoit
COO: Mathew Davis
COO: Nancy Dodson
COO: Lori Rakes Fache
COO: Troy Wood Fache
**COO:* Sam Hazen
COO: Susan Hicks
COO: Michele Meyer
COO: Patti Monczewski
COO: Matthew Sogard
CFO: Alissa Bert
CFO: Amy Chaffin
CFO: Brian Maccolley
Chf Mktg O: Jonathan Perlin
Ofcr: Sue Rachuig
Ofcr: Donald Stewart
Board of Directors: Stephen G Pagliuca, Christopher J Birosak, Nathan C Thorne, John P Connaughton, James D Forbes, Kenneth W Freeman, Thomas F Frist III, William R Frist, Christopher R Gordon, Michael W Michelson, James C Momtazee

D-U-N-S 61-344-1609
HCA INFORMATION SERVICES INC
2555 Park Plz, Nashville, TN 37203-1512
Tel (615) 344-9551 *Founded/Ownrshp* 1987
Sales 73.8MM^E *EMP* 1,100
SIC 7374 Data processing & preparation; Data processing & preparation
Pr: Noel Brown Williams

HCA MIDWEST
See BAPTIST-LUTHERAN MEDICAL CENTER

HCA MIDWEST
See MIDWEST DIVISION - LSH LLC

HCA MIDWEST CENTER
See LAFAYETTE REGIONAL HEALTH CENTER AUXILIARY INC

D-U-N-S 36-166-5719
HCA NORTH FLORIDA SUPPLY CHAIN SERVICES
8501 Westside Indus Dr, Jacksonville, FL 32219-3275
Tel (904) 378-7000 *Founded/Ownrshp* 2003
Sales 35.1MM^E *EMP* 176
SIC 5047 Medical equipment & supplies; Medical equipment & supplies
Ofcr: Pete Lowhorne
CFO: Cheryl Andrews

HCA PHYSICIAN SERVICES
See TENNESSEE HEALTHCARE MANAGEMENT INC

D-U-N-S 06-435-6538
■ HCA PSYCHIATRIC CO
(*Suby of* HCA INC) ★
1 Park Plz, Nashville, TN 37203-6527
Tel (615) 344-2390 *Founded/Ownrshp* 1997
Sales 48.4MM^E *EMP* 5,500
SIC 8063 8011 Hospital for the mentally ill; Psychiatrists & psychoanalysts; Hospital for the mentally ill; Psychiatrists & psychoanalysts
Ch: Thomas Frish Jr
**Pr:* Jack Bovender

HCA VIRGINIA
See HCA HEALTH SERVICES OF VIRGINIA INC

D-U-N-S 95-997-0971
■ HCA-HEALTHONE LLC
PRESBYTERIAN ST LUKES MED CTR
(*Suby of* HCA INC) ★
4900 S Monaco St Ste 380, Denver, CO 80237-3487
Tel (303) 788-2500 *Founded/Ownrshp* 1999
Sales 727.5MM^E *EMP* 4,500^E
SIC 8062 General medical & surgical hospitals; General medical & surgical hospitals
COO: Lynn Cook
Dir Recs: Colleen Simianer
CFO: Greg D'Argonne
CFO: David Housand
Bd of Dir: David Boyles
Sr VP: Leonard Kalm
VP: Kathy Ashenfelter
VP: Matthew English
VP: Linda Kanamine
VP: J D Michael
VP: David Roy
Comm Dir: Leslie Horna
Dir Rx: Steve Porter

D-U-N-S 36-257-8999
■ HCA-HOSPITAL CORP OF AMERICA
(*Suby of* HCA INC) ★
1 Park Plz, Nashville, TN 37203-6527
Tel (615) 344-9551 *Founded/Ownrshp* 1994
Sales 5.9MMM^E *EMP* 134,000
SIC 8062 8063 General medical & surgical hospitals; Psychiatric hospitals; General medical & surgical hospitals; Psychiatric hospitals
Ch Bd: Thomas F Frist Jr
Board of Directors: Robert J Dennis, John W Rowe

HCAP
See HONOLULU COMMUNITY ACTION PROGRAM INC

D-U-N-S 01-852-0303
HCBF HOLDING CO INC
311 S 2nd St, Fort Pierce, FL 34950-1556
Tel (772) 489-3113 *Founded/Ownrshp* 2010
Sales NA *EMP* 241^E
SIC 6712 Bank holding companies
CEO: Michael J Brown
**Pr:* Hal Roberts

D-U-N-S 07-981-9721
HCBF HOLDING CO INC
200 S Indian River Dr, Fort Pierce, FL 34950-4387
Tel (772) 403-0275 *Founded/Ownrshp* 2010
Sales NA *EMP* 300
SIC 6022 State trust companies accepting deposits, commercial
CEO: Michael J Brown

HCBOE
See HOUSTON COUNTY BOARD OF EDUCATION

HCBOE
See HABERSHAM COUNTY BOARD OF EDUCATION

HCC
See HIGHLAND COMMUNITY COLLEGE

D-U-N-S 18-176-4192
■ HCC AEGIS INC
(*Suby of* HCC INDUSTRIES INC) ★
50 Welby Rd, New Bedford, MA 02745-1100
Tel (508) 998-3141 *Founded/Ownrshp* 2004
Sales 54.1MM^E *EMP* 325^E
SIC 3674 Microcircuits, integrated (semiconductor); Microcircuits, integrated (semiconductor)
Pr: Timothy N Jones
**Treas:* William J Burke
VP: Manuella Calderon
**VP:* Gregory Myers
VP: Kevin Oconnors
**Prin:* Janet M Pierpont
**Prin:* Steve Struck
Mng Dir: Claude Abeyewardena
Web Prj Mg: Charles Strader

D-U-N-S 78-544-5990
■ HCC AVIATION INSURANCE GROUP INC
(*Suby of* HCC INSURANCE HOLDINGS INC) ★
16415 Addison Rd Ste 900, Dallas, TX 75248
Tel (972) 447-2000 *Founded/Ownrshp* 1997
Sales NA *EMP* 105
SIC 6411 Insurance brokers; Insurance brokers
VP: Michael Donovan
**COO:* Antony Bacewicz

HCC BRANDS
See HANNAS CANDLE CO

D-U-N-S 17-353-4744 IMP/EXP
HCC INC
1501 1st Ave, Mendota, IL 61342-1385
Tel (815) 539-9371 *Founded/Ownrshp* 1987
Sales 62.5MM^E *EMP* 200
SIC 3523 Farm machinery & equipment; Combines (harvester-threshers); Farm machinery & equipment; Combines (harvester-threshers)
Ch Bd: Donald Bickel
**Pr:* Bryan Nelson
COO: Don Bickel
**CFO:* Dave Van Den Bussche
Bd of Dir: Cindy Saylor
**Bd of Dir:* Carter Sorenson
VP: Jim Register
Dir Bus: Mark Lamboley
Mtls Mgr: Robert Glessner
Mfg Mgr: Rick Edwards
Opers Mgr: Jef Fields

D-U-N-S 05-644-4060
■ HCC INDUSTRIES INC
(*Suby of* AMETEK INC) ★
4232 Temple City Blvd, Rosemead, CA 91770-1552
Tel (626) 443-8933 *Founded/Ownrshp* 2005
Sales 152.5MM^E *EMP* 800
SIC 3679 Hermetic seals for electronic equipment; Hermetic seals for electronic equipment
Pr: Richard Ferraid

D-U-N-S 78-112-0100
▲ HCC INSURANCE HOLDINGS INC
13403 Northwest Fwy, Houston, TX 77040-6006
Tel (713) 690-7300 *Founded/Ownrshp* 1974
Sales NA *EMP* 2,472^E
Tkr Sym HCC *Exch* NYS
SIC 6311 6321 6331 Life insurance; Accident & health insurance; Fire, marine & casualty insurance; Life insurance; Accident & health insurance; Fire, marine & casualty insurance
CEO: Christopher J B Williams
**Pr:* William N Burke Jr
Pr: Nathan Harris
**CFO:* Brad T Irick
Treas: Frank J Bramanti
Treas: Jonathan Lee
Treas: Susan Nicosia
Bd of Dir: Lydia Beebe
Ex VP: Mark Callahan
Ex VP: Pamela J Penny
Ex VP: Peter Smith
Ex VP: Robert Thomas
Sr VP: Randy D Rinicella
Sr VP: Larry Stewart
VP: Mark Buechler
VP: Doug Busker
VP: Leigh Farley
VP: Pam Gruidl
VP: Robert Haire
VP: Phil Joschko
VP: Christopher Lewis
Board of Directors: Ian Brimecome, Akira Harashima, Ichiro Ishii

D-U-N-S 17-812-0689
■ HCC LIFE INSURANCE CO
(*Suby of* HCC INSURANCE HOLDINGS INC) ★
225 Townpark Dr Nw # 350, Kennesaw, GA 30144-3710
Tel (770) 973-9851 *Founded/Ownrshp* 1987
Sales NA *EMP* 278
SIC 6411 Insurance brokers; Insurance brokers
Pr: Craig J Kelbel Jr
**COO:* Daniel Strusz
**CFO:* Mark Sanderford
Bd of Dir: Mark Carney
Ex VP: Andrew Bard
**Sr VP:* David Grider
**Sr VP:* Larry Stewart
VP: Edward H Ellis Jr
VP: Jeannie Lee
VP: Tom Matchinsky
VP: Jay Ritchie

HCC SERVICE
See HOUSTON CASUALTY CO

HCC SURETY GROUP
See AMERICAN CONTRACTORS INDEMNITY CO

HCCAA
See HILL COUNTRY COMMUNITY ACTION ASSOCIATION INC

HCCAO
See HIGHLAND COUNTY COMMUNITY ACTION ORGANIZATION INC

HCDS
See HOMER CENTRAL SCHOOL DISTRICT

D-U-N-S 02-857-8390
HCENTIVE INC
(*Suby of* HCENTIVE TECHNOLOGY INDIA PRIVATE LIMITED)
12355 Sunrise Valley Dr # 310, Reston, VA 20191-3497
Tel (800) 984-7952 *Founded/Ownrshp* 2009
Sales 35.0MM *EMP* 133
SIC 4813
CEO: Sanjay Singh
**Pr:* Manoj Agarwala
Sr VP: Vj Bala
Sr VP: Maydad Cohen
Sr VP: Mary Good

HCESC
See HAMILTON COUNTY EDUCATIONAL SERVICE CENTER

D-U-N-S 07-756-1538
HCF MANAGEMENT INC
HEALTH CARE FACILITIES
1100 Shawnee Rd, Lima, OH 45805-3583
Tel (419) 999-2010 *Founded/Ownrshp* 1968
Sales 149.9MM^E *EMP* 3,100
SIC 8051 6513 Skilled nursing care facilities; Apartment building operators; Skilled nursing care facilities; Apartment building operators
Pr: Jim Unverferth
**CEO:* Robert Wilson
VP: Gabrielle Fardwell
VP: Steve Fischbach
VP: Michael Hohl
**VP:* Robert Noft
**VP:* Fred J Rinehart
VP: David Seitz

VP: Richard Unverferth
VP: Steve Wilder
*VP: Michalynn Wilson

HCGH HOWARD COUNTY GEN HOSP
See HOWARD COUNTY GENERAL HOSPITAL INC

D-U-N-S 04-104-0528
HCH ADMINISTRATION INC
(Suby of HEALTH ALLIANCE MEDICAL PLANS INC) ★
301 S Vine St, Urbana, IL 61801-3347
Tel (800) 322-1516 Founded/Ownrshp 2008
Sales NA EMP 150
SIC 6411 Insurance agents, brokers & service
Pr: James Stevenson

D-U-N-S 07-151-9601
■ **HCHC ACQUISITION INC**
(Suby of LADENBURG THALMANN FINANCIAL SERVICES INC) ★
4400 Biscayne Blvd, Miami, FL 33137-3212
Tel (305) 572-4100 Founded/Ownrshp 2014
Sales 112.0MM^E EMP 191^E
SIC 6211 Investment firm, general brokerage
Pr: Richard J Lampen
CFO: Brett H Kaufman

HCI
See HUGHES CIRCUITS INC

HCI
See HEALTH COALITION INC

HCI EQUITY PARTNERS
See EQUITY HCI PARTNERS L P

D-U-N-S 01-022-1574
▲ **HCI GROUP INC** (FL)
5300 W Cypress St Ste 100, Tampa, FL 33607-1712
Tel (813) 849-9500 Founded/Ownrshp 2006
Sales NA EMP 280
Accts Dixon Hughes Hughes Llp Cle
Tkr Sym HCI Exch NYS
SIC 6411 Property & casualty insurance agent; Property & casualty insurance agent
Ch Bd: Paresh Patel
CFO: Richard R Allen
VP: Andrew L Graham
*VP: Sanjay Madhu
VP: Gregory Nelsen
IT Man: Tom Mitchell
Sls Mgr: Darienne Zamot
Board of Directors: George Apostolou, Wayne Burks, James Macchiarola, Gregory Politis, Anthony Saravanos, Martin A Traber

D-U-N-S 05-374-0353 EXP
HCI INC (CA)
H C I
(Suby of LOMBARDY HOLDINGS INC) ★
3166 Hrseless Carriage Rd, Norco, CA 92860-3612
Tel (951) 520-4202 Founded/Ownrshp 1981
Sales 85.0MM^E EMP 400
SIC 1623 Communication line & transmission tower construction; Communication line & transmission tower construction
Pr: Steven G Silagi
CFO: Stephen Young
Bd of Dir: Rakesh Garach
VP: Brian Clarke

HCI INTEGRATED SOLUTIONS
See HURRICANE CONSULTING INC

D-U-N-S 01-500-6068
HCI SYSTEMS INC (CA)
HCIS
1354 S Parkside Pl, Ontario, CA 91761-4555
Tel (909) 628-7773 Founded/Ownrshp 2008
Sales 23.0MM^E EMP 50^E
SIC 1731 General electrical contractor
Pr: Hany Dimitry
Pr: Michael Peters
VP: Daniel Downs
VP: Jeff Kresge
*VP: Curtis Vance
Div Mgr: Kevin Gray
Genl Mgr: Vince Defriese
Off Mgr: Sean Defriese
Off Mgr: Maria Espinoza
Opers Mgr: Jason Hughes

HCIS
See HCI SYSTEMS INC

HCL
See HIGH COUNTRY LUMBER INC

D-U-N-S 19-729-8524
HCL AMERICA INC
(Suby of HCL TECHNOLOGIES LIMITED)
330 Potrero Ave, Sunnyvale, CA 94085-4194
Tel (408) 733-0480 Founded/Ownrshp 1995
Sales 2.3MMM EMP 7,000
Accts Sr Batliboi & Co Llp Cpas
SIC 7371 8741 Computer software development; Management services; Computer software development; Management services
Ch: Shiv Nadar
Pr: Saurav Adhikari
*CEO: Roshni Nadar Malhotra
CFO: Pawan K Danwar
Chf Mktg O: Sundararajan M Sundar
Assoc VP: Srinivas Ajjarapu
Assoc VP: Ravi Bhatheja
Assoc VP: Saket Bhatnagar
Assoc VP: Eduardo Diezel
Assoc VP: Todd Johnson
Assoc VP: Murali Krishnamurthy
Assoc VP: Eswar Subramanian
Assoc VP: Paul Van Deventer
Assoc VP: Anil Verma
Ex VP: Darren Oberst
Ex VP: Matt Preschern
Sr VP: Andrew Jornod
VP: Richard Mizuno
VP: Richard Seel
VP: Jay Srinivasan
Exec: Ashu Rampal
Board of Directors: Amal Ganguli

HCL AXON
See AXON SOLUTIONS INC

D-U-N-S 36-299-7889
HCL GLOBAL SYSTEMS INC
24543 Indoplex Cir # 220, Farmington Hills, MI 48335-2529
Tel (248) 473-0720 Founded/Ownrshp 2005
Sales 78.7MM EMP 11,000
SIC 7379 7371 Computer related consulting services; Software programming applications; Computer related consulting services; Software programming applications
Pr: Durga Prassad Gadde

D-U-N-S 11-342-4154 IMP
HCL LIQUIDATION LTD
HUSSEY FABRICATED PRODUCTS
100 Washington St, Leetsdale, PA 15056-1000
Tel (724) 251-4200 Founded/Ownrshp 1984
Sales 111.5MM^E EMP 697
SIC 3351 Rails, copper & copper alloy; Rails, copper & copper alloy
CFO: Brian Benjamin
CFO: Joseph Criptko
VP: R L Peterson
CIO: Jim Bish
MIS Dir: James Zanotti
Tech Mgr: Jeff Kirk
VP Mktg: R A Stragand
Mktg Dir: Amy Miller
Sls Dir: Mary Graff
Sls Dir: Richard Kyle
Mktg Mgr: Dan Borkowski

D-U-N-S 07-993-3535
HCL MECHANICAL SERVICES LLC
(Suby of HUMPHREY CO LTD) ★
6877 Wynnwood Ln, Houston, TX 77008-5023
Tel (713) 586-8141 Founded/Ownrshp 2015
Sales 25.0MM EMP 150
SIC 1711 Plumbing, heating, air-conditioning contractors
Pr: Christopher D Humphrey

D-U-N-S 80-642-4839
HCL OF NORTH CAROLINA LLC
LIFECARE HEALTH PARTNERS
(Suby of LIFECARE FAMILY OF HOSPITALS) ★
1051 Noell Ln, Rocky Mount, NC 27804-1761
Tel (252) 451-2300 Founded/Ownrshp 2002
Sales 20.6MM EMP 160
SIC 8052 8062 Intermediate care facilities; General medical & surgical hospitals; Intermediate care facilities; General medical & surgical hospitals
CEO: Kevin S Cooper
Dir Rx: Nesheka Jessup
Off Mgr: Pam Bloodworth
Sls&Mrk Ex: Lora Mangum
Phys Thrpy: Cathy Bass

D-U-N-S 01-006-7015
HCM-MTE ASSOCIATES INC
CARTER MYERS AUTOMOTIVE
(Suby of CARTER MYERS AUTOMOTIVE) ★
100 Myers Dr, Charlottesville, VA 22901-1166
Tel (434) 978-3711 Founded/Ownrshp 1986
Sales 61.5MM EMP 90
Accts Mitchell Wiggins & Company Llp
SIC 5511 Automobiles, new & used; Automobiles, new & used
Pr: Hamilton C Myers III
*Pr: H Carter Myers III
*Treas: Diane Lawson
VP: Pete Borches
*VP: Carolyn K Kyger
Genl Mgr: Warren Polson

HCNA
See HEALTHCARE NETWORK ASSOCIATIION

D-U-N-S 05-801-2022 IMP/EXP
HCO HOLDING I CORP
(Suby of HNC PARENT INC) ★
999 N Sepulveda Blvd, El Segundo, CA 90245-2714
Tel (323) 583-5000 Founded/Ownrshp 2012
Sales 214.0MM^E EMP 560
SIC 6719 Investment holding companies, except banks; Investment holding companies, except banks
CEO: Mike Kenny
*CEO: Brian C Strauss
CFO: Jason Peel
*CFO: Dori M Reap
*Sr VP: Robert D Armstrong
*Sr VP: James F Barry
*Sr VP: Christopher J Brink
*Sr VP: Alan K Davenport
Sr VP: Estevan Fairfax
*Sr VP: Kirk R Kandler
VP: Mark Adams
VP: Mark R Adams
VP: Bob Armstrong
VP: Inigo Bang
VP: Craig T Carter
VP: Alok Gupta
VP: Donald Lenaker
VP: Ariel Lender
VP: Eric Velander

D-U-N-S 07-853-3727
HCO HOLDING II CORP
(Suby of HCO HOLDING I CORP) ★
999 N Sepulveda Blvd, El Segundo, CA 90245-2714
Tel (310) 955-9200 Founded/Ownrshp 2005
Sales 207.6MM^E EMP 560
SIC 2952 2821 2891 Roof cement: asphalt, fibrous or plastic; Polyurethane resins; Sealants; Roof cement: asphalt, fibrous or plastic; Polyurethane resins; Sealants
Pr: Brian C Strauss

D-U-N-S 78-407-7781
HCP GROSVENOR ORLANDO OWNER LLC
WYNDHAM LK BUENA VISTA RESORT
1850 Hotel Plaza Blvd, Lake Buena Vista, FL 32830-8406
Tel (407) 828-4444 Founded/Ownrshp 2006
Sales 14.7MM^E EMP 334
SIC 7011 5812 5947 Hotels; Eating places; Gift, novelty & souvenir shop; Hotels; Eating places; Gift, novelty & souvenir shop
CTO: Isaac Martinez
IT Man: Andrew Phoenix
Sls Mgr: David Gans

D-U-N-S 14-745-2494
▲ **HCP INC**
1920 Main St Ste 1200, Irvine, CA 92614-7230
Tel (949) 407-0700 Founded/Ownrshp 1985
Sales 2.2MMM EMP 170^E
Accts Deloitte & Touche Llp Los Ang
Tkr Sym HCP Exch NYS
SIC 6798 Real estate investment trusts; Real estate investment trusts
Pr: Lauralee E Martin
CFO: Susan Cullen
CFO: Timothy M Schoen
Ofcr: James W Mercer
Ex VP: Jonathan Bergschneider
Ex VP: Paul F Gallagher
Ex VP: Paul Gallagher
Ex VP: Thomas M Klaritch
Ex VP: Thomas Klaritch
Ex VP: Susan M Tate
Sr VP: Scott A Anderson
Sr VP: Michael A Congdon
Sr VP: Timothy Hall
Sr VP: Darren Kowalske
Sr VP: Stephen Robie
Sr VP: Patrick Strangle
VP: Matthew A Brill
VP: Matthew Brill
VP: William J Budzinski
VP: Michael Congdon
VP: Sean Conlon
Board of Directors: Brian G Cartwright, Christine N Garvey, David B Henry, James Hoffmann, Michael D McKee, Peter L Rhein, Joseph P Sullivan

D-U-N-S 14-729-1996
HCP PACKAGING USA INC
1 Waterview Dr Ste 102, Shelton, CT 06484-4368
Tel (203) 924-2408 Founded/Ownrshp 2003
Sales 20.4MM^E EMP 250
SIC 7336 Package design; Package design
CEO: Jeff Chen
*Pr: Al Lustrino
*Pr: Eddy Wu
Sr VP: Tom Holloway

D-U-N-S 01-936-9425
HCPRO INC
GREELEY COMPANY
(Suby of HALYARD CAPITAL FUND LP) ★
75 Sylvan St Ste A101, Danvers, MA 01923-2772
Tel (781) 639-1872 Founded/Ownrshp 2008
Sales 39.5MM^E EMP 265
SIC 2741 8742 8331 2721 Newsletter publishing; Shopping news: publishing only, not printed on site; Management consulting services; Job training & vocational rehabilitation services; Newsletter publishing; Shopping news: publishing only, not printed on site; Management consulting services; Job training & vocational rehabilitation services; Periodicals: publishing only; Magazines: publishing only, not printed on site
Pr: James Malkin
*COO: Rob Stuart
Ex VP: Henry Boye
*Ex VP: Augustus Crocker
*Sr VP: Monique Fayad
Sr VP: Bruce Guzowski
*Sr VP: Amy Murphy
*VP: Henry J Boye
VP: Sam Julier
VP: Bernard Rotundo
VP: Leslie Zacks
Exec: Jennifer Cofer

HCPSS
See HOWARD COUNTY PUBLIC SCHOOL SYSTEM

HCR
See HOME CARE RESEARCH OF ROCHESTER INC

HCR
See HANDEX CONSULTING AND REMEDIATION LLC

D-U-N-S 82-981-3398
■ **HCR III HEALTHCARE LLC**
(Suby of MANOR CARE INC) ★
333 N Summit St Ste 103, Toledo, OH 43604-2617
Tel (419) 252-5500 Founded/Ownrshp 2007
Sales 59.5MM^E EMP 185
SIC 8051 Skilled nursing care facilities; Skilled nursing care facilities

D-U-N-S 83-172-6547
■ **HCR IV HEALTHCARE LLC**
(Suby of MANOR CARE INC) ★
333 N Summit St, Toledo, OH 43604-1531
Tel (419) 252-5500 Founded/Ownrshp 2010
Sales 127.4MM^E EMP 43^E
SIC 8051 Skilled nursing care facilities

HCR MANOR CARE
See LEADER NURSING & REHABILITATION CENTER OF SCOTT TOWNSHIP INC

D-U-N-S 07-932-0794
■ **HCR MANOR CARE INC**
(Suby of MANOR CARE INC) ★
333 N Summit St Ste 100, Toledo, OH 43604-2617
Tel (419) 252-5743 Founded/Ownrshp 2005
Sales 478.8MM^E EMP 55,765^E
SIC 8051 Skilled nursing care facilities
Prin: David Lanning
Dir Bus: Tony Marquez
Genl Mgr: Pete Allegretti
QA Dir: Devra Hall
Dir IT: Gary Mierzwiak
IT Man: Jim Sabovik
Mktg Dir: Ken Connelly
Mktg Dir: Theresa Delaine
Mktg Dir: Rebekah Wilson
HC Dir: Dionne Blassingame
Counsel: Rebecca Nowak

D-U-N-S 04-831-4108
■ **HCR MANORCARE MEDICAL SERVICES OF FLORIDA LLC**
MANOR CARE
(Suby of MANOR CARE OF AMERICA INC) ★
333 N Summit St Ste 100, Toledo, OH 43604-2617
Tel (419) 252-5500 Founded/Ownrshp 1981
Sales 80.4MM^E EMP 520
SIC 8051 Convalescent home with continuous nursing care; Convalescent home with continuous nursing care
Ch Bd: Paul Ormond
COO: Stephen L Guillard
*COO: Keith Weikel
CFO: Steven M Cardnavgn
*CFO: Steve Cavannough
*Treas: Douglas G Haag
*VP: R Jeffrey Bixler
Off Mgr: Alice Brandon
Mktg Dir: Traci Roberts

HCRI
See HARVARD CLINICAL RESEARCH INSTITUTE INC

HCRS
See HEALTHCARE RESOLUTION SERVICES INC

HCS
See HOLLISTER CONSTRUCTION SERVICES LLC

D-U-N-S 07-962-2871
HCSB GROUP INC
1250 S Miami Ave Apt 1404, Miami, FL 33130-4107
Tel (305) 600-7540 Founded/Ownrshp 2014
Sales 50.0MM EMP 200
SIC 2389 Cummerbunds; Cummerbunds
Pr: Yoel Bouza

HCSB NOMCO
See CENTENNIAL BANK

HCSC
See HEALTH CARE SERVICE CORP ILLINOIS STATE PAC NFP

D-U-N-S 07-366-5432
HCSC BLOOD CENTER
MILLER-KEYSTONE BLOOD CENTER
2171 28th St Sw, Allentown, PA 18103-7073
Tel (610) 791-2222 Founded/Ownrshp 1969
Sales 35.2MM EMP 195
SIC 8099 Blood donor station; Blood donor station
Pr: J Michael Lee
*CFO: Thomas D Fenstermacher
VP: David Goodson
*VP: Joseph Yelo

D-U-N-S 14-438-5346
HCSC INSURANCE SERVICES CO
(Suby of BLUE CROSS AND BLUE SHIELD) ★
300 E Randolph St, Chicago, IL 60601-5014
Tel (312) 653-6000 Founded/Ownrshp 2005
Sales NA EMP 1^E
SIC 6311 Life insurance
Pr: Raymond F McCaskey
Ex VP: Martin G Foster
Sr VP: Deborah D Rodriguez
CIO: Maria Suarez
Mktg Dir: Cynthia Jania
Mktg Dir: William Jeffries
Mktg Dir: Jen Kruse
Mktg Dir: Phil Pitt
Snr Mgr: Heath Port

HCSC-LAUNDRY
See HOSPITAL CENTRAL SERVICES COOPERATIVE INC

HCSG
See HOIST & CRANE SERVICE GROUP INC

D-U-N-S 19-807-1529
■ **HCSG SUPPLY INC**
(Suby of HEALTHCARE SERVICES GROUP INC) ★
45 Runway Dr Ste H, Levittown, PA 19057-4737
Tel (215) 269-0988 Founded/Ownrshp 2005
Sales 116.7MM^E EMP 3,309^E
SIC 5099 Durable goods
Prin: Daniel Mc Cartney

HCSS
See HEAVY CONSTRUCTION SYSTEMS SPECIALISTS INC

D-U-N-S 00-805-0911 IMP
HCT PACKAGING INC
721 Us Highway 202/206 # 300, Bridgewater, NJ 08807-1760
Tel (908) 203-8610 Founded/Ownrshp 1996
Sales 23.1MM^E EMP 50
SIC 5199 7336 Packaging materials; Package design
Pr: Chris Thorpe
COO: Robert Tognetti
VP: Erwan Depays
VP: Cindy Lim
VP Sls: Nick Gardner
Sls Dir: Jackie Paterno
Mktg Mgr: Brianne Baker
Snr PM: Cat Kong
Snr PM: Lisa Sheldon

HCTC
See HILL COUNTRY TELEPHONE COOPERATIVE INC

D-U-N-S 02-857-8187
HCTEC PARTNERS LLC
7105 S Springs Dr Ste 208, Franklin, TN 37067-1712
Tel (615) 577-4030 Founded/Ownrshp 2010
Sales 120.0MM EMP 110
SIC 8741 Management services
CEO: William Bartholomew
*COO: Steve Schott
*CFO: Lance Fusacchia
*Ch: Campbell Langdon
*VP: Ben Bernecker
*VP: Ryan Roth
Dir IT: Bob Craig
Dir IT: Frank Hood

D-U-N-S 05-045-8975 EXP
HD AMERICAN ROAD LLC
ORLANDO HARLEY DAVIDSON
3770 37th St, Orlando, FL 32805-6617
Tel (407) 423-0346 *Founded/Ownrshp* 2000
Sales 88.8MM^E *EMP* 250
SIC 5571 Motorcycle dealers; Motorcycles; Motorcycle dealers; Motorcycles
CFO: Rob Ferrentino
IT Man: Scott Buxton
Mktg Mgr: Amanda Duitsman
Sls Mgr: Chris Skinner

D-U-N-S 79-317-2250 IMP
■ **HD BUILDER SOLUTIONS GROUP LLC**
(*Suby of* HD SUPPLY HOLDINGS LLC) ★
2455 Paces Ferry Rd Se C9, Atlanta, GA 30339-1834
Tel (770) 443-8211 *Founded/Ownrshp* 2007
Sales 500.0MM^E *EMP* 1,631^E
SIC 5023 1752 1799 Floor coverings; Floor laying & floor work; Drapery track installation; Floor coverings; Floor laying & floor work; Drapery track installation
Pr: Tom Lazzaro

HD BUTTERCUP
See HD BUTTERCUP LP

D-U-N-S 16-698-2947 IMP
HD BUTTERCUP LP
HD BUTTERCUP
3225 Helms Ave, Los Angeles, CA 90034-3209
Tel (310) 558-8900 *Founded/Ownrshp* 2004
Sales 35.2MM *EMP* 150
SIC 5963 5713 5719 Furnishings, including furniture, house-to-house; Rugs; Housewares
Pt: Evan Cole
Pr: Frank Seddigh
Ex Dir: Karen Michail
Rgnl Mgr: Carly Young
Genl Mgr: Kathleen Lawler
Store Mgr: Sheldon Matthews
Manager: Julian Chan
Mktg Dir: Nichole Williams
Sls Mgr: Jay Krich

HD FOOD SERVICES
See HAN FENG INC

D-U-N-S 00-509-3463 IMP
HD HUDSON MANUFACTURING CO (MN)
500 N Michigan Ave Fl 23, Chicago, IL 60611-3766
Tel (312) 644-2830 *Founded/Ownrshp* 1929
Sales 65.0MM *EMP* 300
SIC 3523 Sprayers & spraying machines, agricultural; Dusters, mechanical: agricultural; Sprayers & spraying machines, agricultural; Dusters, mechanical: agricultural
Pr: R C Hudson III
**Ch Bd:* Robert C Hudson Jr
**Pr:* W A Hudson
Plnt Mgr: Mike Olson

HD MICROSYSTEMS
See HITACHI CHEMICAL DUPONT MICROSYSTEMS LLC

D-U-N-S 78-099-1233 IMP
■ **HD SUPPLY CONSTRUCTION SUPPLY GROUP INC**
(*Suby of* HD SUPPLY HOLDINGS LLC) ★
501 W Church St, Orlando, FL 32805-2247
Tel (407) 841-4755 *Founded/Ownrshp* 1996
Sales 2.5MMM^E *EMP* 3,740^E
SIC 5072 5039 5031 Hardware; Air ducts, sheet metal; Joists; Soil erosion control fabrics; Lumber, plywood & millwork; Hardware; Air ducts, sheet metal; Joists; Soil erosion control fabrics; Lumber, plywood & millwork
CEO: Joseph J Deangelo

D-U-N-S 19-251-0290 IMP/EXP
■ **HD SUPPLY CONSTRUCTION SUPPLY LTD**
(*Suby of* HD SUPPLY CONSTRUCTION SUPPLY GROUP INC) ★
3100 Cumberland Blvd Se # 1700, Atlanta, GA 30339-5939
Tel (770) 852-9000 *Founded/Ownrshp* 2005
Sales 1.6MMM^E *EMP* 3,740^E
SIC 5031 5039 5072 Lumber, plywood & millwork; Air ducts, sheet metal; Joists; Soil erosion control fabrics; Hardware; Lumber, plywood & millwork; Air ducts, sheet metal; Joists; Soil erosion control fabrics; Hardware
CEO: Joseph J Deangelo
Pr: John Stegeman
VP: Ricardo Numez
Brnch Mgr: Chris Holden

D-U-N-S 78-444-9485 IMP/EXP
HD SUPPLY DISTRIBUTION SERVICES LLC
CROWN BOLT
26940 Aliso Viejo Pkwy, Aliso Viejo, CA 92656-2622
Tel (949) 643-4700 *Founded/Ownrshp* 2005
Sales NA *EMP* 1,078
SIC 5072 Screws; Bolts; Nuts (hardware); Miscellaneous fasteners

D-U-N-S 79-146-4022
■ **HD SUPPLY FACILITIES MAINTENANCE GROUP INC**
(*Suby of* HD SUPPLY HOLDINGS LLC) ★
3100 Cumberland Blvd Se, Atlanta, GA 30339-5940
Tel (770) 852-9000 *Founded/Ownrshp* 2007
Sales 3.8MMM^E *EMP* 3,976^E
SIC 5087 Cleaning & maintenance equipment & supplies
Pr: Joseph J Deangelo

D-U-N-S 17-121-8949 IMP
■ **HD SUPPLY FACILITIES MAINTENANCE LTD**
USABLUEBOOK
(*Suby of* HD SUPPLY FACILITIES MAINTENANCE GROUP INC) ★
10641 Scripps Summit Ct, San Diego, CA 92131-3961
Tel (858) 831-2000 *Founded/Ownrshp* 2004
Sales 3.8MMM^E *EMP* 3,967^E
SIC 5087 Cleaning & maintenance equipment & supplies; Cleaning & maintenance equipment & supplies
Pr: Joseph J Deangelo
**CFO:* Evan Levitt
CFO: Ronald F Turk
VP: Kevin Peters
Exec: Iain Docherty
Exec: Kevin Olsen
Comm Man: Chris Alvarez
Area Mgr: Michael Beierschmitt
Area Mgr: Steve Deyoung
Area Mgr: John Hill
Brnch Mgr: James Andrade

HD SUPPLY GLOBAL SUPPORT CENTER
See HD SUPPLY INC

D-U-N-S 82-584-0593
▲ **HD SUPPLY HOLDINGS INC**
3100 Cumberland Blvd Se # 1700, Atlanta, GA 30339-5939
Tel (770) 852-9000 *Founded/Ownrshp* 2007
Sales 8.8MMM *EMP* 15,000^E
Tkr Sym HDS *Exch* NGS
SIC 5087 5072 5085 Cleaning & maintenance equipment & supplies; Hardware; Industrial supplies; Cleaning & maintenance equipment & supplies; Hardware; Industrial supplies
Pr: Joseph J Deangelo
**Ch Bd:* James G Berges
**CFO:* Evan Levitt
CFO: Evan J Levitt
**Ex VP:* John Stegeman
**Sr VP:* Ronald J Domanico
**Sr VP:* Margaret Newman
**Sr VP:* Ricardo J Nunez
VP: Jim Maddox
CIO: Brad Cowles
VP Sls: Lester Jenkins

D-U-N-S 61-357-1038
■ **HD SUPPLY HOLDINGS LLC**
(*Suby of* HD SUPPLY GLOBAL SUPPORT CENTER) ★
3100 Cumberland Blvd Se # 1700, Atlanta, GA 30339-5939
Tel (770) 852-9000 *Founded/Ownrshp* 2004
Sales 10.3MMM^E *EMP* 14,999
SIC 5051 5074 5084 5099 Cast iron pipe; Pipes & fittings, plastic; Meters, consumption registering; Safety equipment & supplies; Cast iron pipe; Pipes & fittings, plastic; Plumbing & heating valves; Meters, consumption registering; Safety equipment & supplies
Pr: Anesa Chaibi
Pr: Rich Feichter
Pr: Frank Garcia
Pr: Tom Lazzaro
COO: Steve Leclair
CFO: Mark T Jamieson
Sr VP: Vidya Chauhan
Sr VP: Paul Iaderosa

HD SUPPLY HOME IMPRV SOLUTIONS
See HD SUPPLY REPAIR & REMODEL LLC

D-U-N-S 02-912-7586 IMP
■ **HD SUPPLY INC**
HD SUPPLY GLOBAL SUPPORT CENTER
(*Suby of* HDS HOLDING CORP) ★
3100 Cumberland Blvd Se # 1700, Atlanta, GA 30339-5939
Tel (770) 852-9000 *Founded/Ownrshp* 2007
Sales 8.8MMM *EMP* 15,000
SIC 5031 5033 Building materials, exterior; Building materials, interior; Doors & windows; Roofing, siding & insulation; Building materials, exterior; Building materials, interior; Doors & windows; Roofing, siding & insulation
Pr: Joseph J Deangelo
**Ch Bd:* James G Berges
Pr: Mark Foster
CFO: Evan J Levitt
Sr VP: Margaret Newman
Sr VP: Ricardo Nunez
Creative D: Catherin Stevenson
Rgnl Mgr: Glenn Gaudet
Area Mgr: Alan Baker
Area Mgr: Cliff Kemp
Area Mgr: Brian Ouellette
Board of Directors: Brian A Bernasek, Paul B Edgerley, Mitchell Jacobson, Lew Klessel, Nathan K Sleeper, Stephen M Zide

HD SUPPLY INTERIOR SOLUTIONS
See CREATIVETOUCH INTERIORS INC

D-U-N-S 79-146-5086 EXP
HD SUPPLY PLUMBING/HVAC GROUP INC
3300 Brecknrdg Blvd, Duluth, GA 30096-8983
Tel (407) 841-4755 *Founded/Ownrshp* 2011
Sales NA *EMP* 550^E
SIC 5074 5085 Plumbing & hydronic heating supplies; Pipeline wrappings, anti-corrosive

D-U-N-S 79-204-7545
■ **HD SUPPLY POWER SOLUTIONS GROUP INC**
(*Suby of* HD SUPPLY HOLDINGS LLC) ★
501 W Church St Ste 100, Orlando, FL 32805-2270
Tel (407) 841-4755 *Founded/Ownrshp* 2004
Sales 364.7MM^E *EMP* 847
SIC 5063 Electrical apparatus & equipment; Electrical apparatus & equipment
Pr: Joseph J Deangelo
**VP:* Marc Gonzalez
VP: Jason Herin
**VP:* Evan Levitt
**VP:* Ricardo Nunez

D-U-N-S 60-301-3256 IMP
■ **HD SUPPLY REPAIR & REMODEL LLC**
HD SUPPLY HOME IMPRV SOLUTIONS
(*Suby of* HD SUPPLY GP & MANAGEMENT, INC.)
1695 Eureka Rd, Roseville, CA 95661-3027
Tel (916) 751-2300 *Founded/Ownrshp* 2007
Sales 156.3MM^E *EMP* 800
SIC 5211 Home centers; Home centers
Pr: Rich Fiechter
CFO: Jody Porter

D-U-N-S 00-331-5934 IMP
■ **HD SUPPLY WATERWORKS GROUP INC**
(*Suby of* HD SUPPLY HOLDINGS LLC) ★
501 W Church St Ste 100, Orlando, FL 32805-2270
Tel (407) 841-4755 *Founded/Ownrshp* 2004
Sales 2.8MMM^E *EMP* 2,966^E
SIC 5051 5074 5084 5099 Cast iron pipe; Pipes & fittings, plastic; Plumbing & heating valves; Meters, consumption registering; Safety equipment & supplies; Cast iron pipe; Pipes & fittings, plastic; Plumbing & heating valves; Meters, consumption registering; Safety equipment & supplies
CEO: Joseph J Deangelo
**Pr:* Anesa Chaibi
**Pr:* Rich Fiechter
**Pr:* Frank Garcia
**Pr:* Tom Lazzaro
**Pr:* Steve Margolius
**Pr:* Rick McClure
**Pr:* Mike Stanwood
**Pr:* Jerry Webb
**COO:* Steve Leclair
**CFO:* Mark T Jamieson
**Sr VP:* Vidya Chauhan
**Sr VP:* Paul Iaderosa
**Sr VP:* Michele Markham
**Sr VP:* Meg Newman
**Sr VP:* Ricardo Nunez

D-U-N-S 62-756-4029 EXP
■ **HD SUPPLY WATERWORKS LTD**
(*Suby of* HD SUPPLY WATERWORKS GROUP INC) ★
3100 Cumberland Blvd Se, Atlanta, GA 30339-5940
Tel (770) 852-9000 *Founded/Ownrshp* 2004
Sales 1.5MMM^E *EMP* 2,600
SIC 5074 Plumbing & hydronic heating supplies; Plumbing & hydronic heating supplies
Pr: Jerry Webb
CFO: Don Clayton
Dir IT: Neil Brinson
Dir IT: Paul Conry
Dir IT: Kay Kirkland
Sys Mgr: Chuck Hooper
Software D: Terry Pettijohn
Netwrk Eng: Joe Balchunas
VP Opers: Paul Iaderosa
Opers Mgr: Craig Christensen
Sales Asso: Kenneth Jensen

D-U-N-S 18-318-2138
■ **HD VEST INC**
H D VEST FINANCIAL SERVICES
(*Suby of* WELLS FARGO & CO) ★
6333 N State Highway 161, Irving, TX 75038-2200
Tel (972) 870-6000 *Founded/Ownrshp* 2011
Sales 137.9MM^E *EMP* 340
SIC 6282 Investment advisory service; Investment advisory service
Pr: Roger C Ochs
**CFO:* Ted Sinclair
Ofcr: Casey Griffin
VP: Steven Brewer
Dir Risk M: Tony Rogers
Off Mgr: Dona Currie
QA Dir: Brad Harris
QA Dir: Thomas Kendall
IT Man: Marc Brasher
Web Dev: Erich Davis
Web Dev: Jeremy Elkins

D-U-N-S 80-450-9115 IMP
HD WINDOW FASHIONS INC
M & B WINDOW FASHIONS
(*Suby of* HUNTER DOUGLAS INC) ★
1818 Oak St, Los Angeles, CA 90015-3302
Tel (213) 749-6333 *Founded/Ownrshp* 1975
Sales 50.2MM^E *EMP* 800
SIC 2591 Mini blinds; Venetian blinds; Window shades; Blinds vertical; Mini blinds; Venetian blinds; Window shades; Blinds vertical
Pr: Wayne Gourlay
CFO: Greg Buscher
**Genl Mgr:* Dominique Au Yeung

HDA
See HUMAN DEVELOPMENT ASSOCIATION INC

D-U-N-S 05-977-3861
HDA MOTORS INC
CONTINENTAL HONDA
5901 S La Grange Rd, Countryside, IL 60525-4067
Tel (708) 352-6000 *Founded/Ownrshp* 1979
Sales 39.7MM^E *EMP* 90
SIC 5511 Automobiles, new & used; Automobiles, new & used
Pr: John J Weinberger
CFO: John P Stanley
Exec: Mark Brescia
Sls Mgr: Mike Bromer
Sales Asso: Rudy Lika

D-U-N-S 02-353-0080 IMP
HDC DISTRIBUTING LTD
7100 High Life Dr, Houston, TX 77066-3713
Tel (281) 880-2730 *Founded/Ownrshp* 2009
Sales 203.7MM *EMP* 2
Accts Tiller & Company Baytown Tex
SIC 5199 Nondurable goods; Nondurable goods

D-U-N-S 92-616-5606
HDG MANSUR INVESTMENT SERVICES INC
10 W Market St Ste 1200, Indianapolis, IN 46204-2854
Tel (317) 655-7700 *Founded/Ownrshp* 1994
Sales 21.7MM^E *EMP* 83
SIC 6799 Real estate investors, except property operators

CEO: Harold D Garrison
**Pr:* W Robert Echols
**Ex VP:* John A Crawford
**Ex VP:* Thomas T Kmiecik

D-U-N-S 60-316-5569
HDH LLC
HILTON ST LOUIS AT BALLPARK
1 S Broadway, Saint Louis, MO 63102-1703
Tel (314) 421-1776 *Founded/Ownrshp* 2005
Sales 15.5MM^E *EMP* 300
SIC 7011 Hotels & motels; Hotels & motels
Genl Mgr: Jayson Pollard
Exec: John Surtin
Dir Sec: Brian Conway

HDI
See HYDRAQUIP INC

HDI
See HORIZON DISTRIBUTION INC

D-U-N-S 96-212-1914
HDI LANDING GEAR USA INC
(*Suby of* HEROUX-DEVTEK INC)
663 Montgomery Ave, Springfield, OH 45506-1847
Tel (513) 619-1203 *Founded/Ownrshp* 2008
Sales 28.8MM^E *EMP* 150
SIC 3728 Alighting (landing gear) assemblies, aircraft
Pr: Michael Meshay
Treas: William Michalski
IT Man: Donna Harvanec
IT Man: Kevin Lewis

HDI RAILINGS
See HANDRAIL DESIGN INC

HDIS
See HOME DELIVERY INCONTINENT SUPPLIES CO

D-U-N-S 80-882-8503
HDL CONSTRUCTION INC
4393 Kelson Ave, Marianna, FL 32446-3044
Tel (850) 526-2035 *Founded/Ownrshp* 1993
Sales 20.1MM *EMP* 40
Accts Millward & Co Cpas Fort Laud
SIC 1522 Condominium construction; Condominium construction
CEO: Dwight E Dykes
**Pr:* Marc Weiss
**Sec:* Linda Messina
**VP:* Jeff Knox

D-U-N-S 61-108-9376 IMP
HDM HYDRAULICS LLC
(*Suby of* LIGON INDUSTRIES LLC) ★
125 Fire Tower Dr, Tonawanda, NY 14150-5880
Tel (716) 694-8004 *Founded/Ownrshp* 1979
Sales 30.5MM^E *EMP* 100
SIC 3511 Hydraulic turbine generator set units, complete; Hydraulic turbine generator set units, complete
Pr: William Anderson
CTO: Heckman Barry

D-U-N-S 02-317-4023
HDOS ACQUISITION LLC
HOT DOG ON A STICK
(*Suby of* GLOBAL FRANCHISE GROUP LLC) ★
1902 Wright Pl Ste 200, Carlsbad, CA 92008-6583
Tel (800) 321-8400 *Founded/Ownrshp* 2014
Sales 23.5MM^E *EMP* 700^E
SIC 5812 Hot dog stand; Hot dog stand
Genl Mgr: Daniel Smith

D-U-N-S 82-826-3686
HDP ENTERPRISES INC
MIKE HUDSON DISTRIBUTING
2237 S Mcdowell Blvd Ext, Petaluma, CA 94954-5661
Tel (707) 763-7388 *Founded/Ownrshp* 2000
Sales 48.8MM^E *EMP* 55
SIC 5143 5147 5113 Cheese; Meats, cured or smoked; Disposable plates, cups, napkins & eating utensils
CEO: George R Parisi
**Ex VP:* Frank Haynes
**VP:* James Davis
Rgnl Mgr: Ed Colombo
Area Mgr: Paul De Marco
Area Mgr: John Elu
Area Mgr: Paul Marco
Mktg Mgr: Diane Moore
Sales Asso: Brandee Corda

D-U-N-S 03-512-2456
HDR ARCHITECTURE INC
(*Suby of* HDR INC) ★
8404 Indian Hills Dr, Omaha, NE 68114-4098
Tel (402) 399-1000 *Founded/Ownrshp* 1996
Sales 237.3MM *EMP* 1,426
Accts Ernst & Young Llp Omaha Ne
SIC 8711 Designing: ship, boat, machine & product; Designing: ship, boat, machine & product
CEO: George A Little
**Pr:* Eric L Keen
**Pr:* Douglas Wignall
**CFO:* Terence C Cox
**Treas:* Chad Hartnett
VP: Scott Nelson
Dir: Jeffrey Johnson

D-U-N-S 18-729-4624
HDR ENGINEERING INC
H D R
(*Suby of* HDR INC) ★
8404 Indian Hills Dr, Omaha, NE 68114-4098
Tel (402) 399-1000 *Founded/Ownrshp* 1996
Sales 1.1MMM *EMP* 6,111
Accts Ernst & Young Llp Omaha Ne
SIC 8742 8711 Management consulting services; Engineering services; Management consulting services; Engineering services
CEO: George A Little
Pr: Eric L Keen
COO: George Little
CFO: Terence C Cox
Treas: Chad M Hartnett
Ex VP: Terry Cox
VP: Laurence D Bory

VP: Phil Curry
VP: Ptoe Sharp
Tech Mgr: Doug Wilson
Secur Mgr: Matt Hrynkow

D-U-N-S 61-162-3646
HDR ENGINEERING INC OF CAROLINAS
(*Suby of* H D R) ★
440 S Church St Ste 1000, Charlotte, NC 28202-2075
Tel (704) 338-6700 *Founded/Ownrshp* 1948
Sales 22.0MM *EMP* 139
SIC 8711 Engineering services; Engineering services
VP: Matt Ryan

D-U-N-S 78-591-8954
HDR ENVIRONMENTAL OPERATIONS AND CONSTRUCTION INC
(*Suby of* HDR INC) ★
9781 S Meridian Blvd # 400, Englewood, CO 80112-5934
Tel (303) 754-4200 *Founded/Ownrshp* 2010
Sales 56.3MM *EMP* 393
Accts Ernst & Young Llp Omaha Ne
SIC 8748 Environmental consultant; Environmental consultant
Pr: Donald Curtis
**Ex VP:* Douglas McAneny
**Sr VP:* Glen R Turney
VP: Daniel Graber
**VP:* Russell J Schwehr
Exec: Henry Benjes Jr

D-U-N-S 04-823-5774
HDR ICA
ICA ENGINEERING, INC.
(*Suby of* I C A) ★
2550 Irvin Cobb Dr, Paducah, KY 42003-0131
Tel (270) 444-9691 *Founded/Ownrshp* 2010
Sales 33.3MM^E *EMP* 300
SIC 8711 Consulting engineer; Consulting engineer
Pr: Mark Acuff
**CEO:* Rob Echols
**COO:* Shawn Washer
**CFO:* Suzanne Sanders
**Ch:* Ben Glunt
**Ex VP:* David Beaty
**Ex VP:* Roger Colburn
**Ex VP:* Robert Echols Jr
**Ex VP:* Keith Franklin
**Ex VP:* Stan King
**Ex VP:* Warren Lamb
Ex VP: Harris Scott III
**VP:* Bob Evers

D-U-N-S 06-866-8805
HDR INC
8404 Indian Hills Dr, Omaha, NE 68114-4098
Tel (402) 399-1000 *Founded/Ownrshp* 1996
Sales 1.4MMM *EMP* 9,200
Accts Ernst & Young Llp Omaha Ne
SIC 8712 8711 8742 8748 4789 Architectural services; Engineering services; Management consulting services; Industry specialist consultants; Systems analysis & engineering consulting services; Passenger train services; Architectural services; Engineering services; Management consulting services; Industry specialist consultants; Systems analysis & engineering consulting services; Passenger train services
Ch Bd: George A Little
V Ch: Ronald L Harrisformer
Pr: Eric L Keen
CFO: Terence C Cox
CFO: Terrence C Cox
CFO: Terry Cox
Treas: Wendy L Lacey
Treas: Bahram Seifipour
Bd of Dir: Eddie Bumbaugh
Assoc VP: Michael Allwright
Assoc VP: Scott Davis
Assoc VP: Karen Freund
Assoc VP: Steven Friedman
Assoc VP: Kevin Lloyd
Assoc VP: Tom Pullukat
Ex VP: Gary L Bleeker
Ex VP: Craig Close
Ex VP: Elwin Larson
Ex VP: Charles O'Reilly
Sr VP: Shannon D'Agostino
Sr VP: Rex Fisher
Board of Directors: Richard R Bell

D-U-N-S 07-932-4218
HDR INTERNATIONAL INC (NE)
8404 Indian Hills Dr, Omaha, NE 68114-4098
Tel (402) 399-1000 *Founded/Ownrshp* 1994
Sales 14.4MM^E *EMP* 600^E
SIC 8712 8711 8742 8748 Architectural services; Engineering services; Management consulting services; Industry specialist consultants; Systems analysis & engineering consulting services; Architectural services; Engineering services; Management consulting services; Industry specialist consultants; Systems analysis & engineering consulting services
Ch Bd: George A Little
**CFO:* Terrence C Cox
**Treas:* Wendy L Lacey
**VP:* Louis Pachman

D-U-N-S 78-286-6110
HDR/ J&S SEATTLE JOINT VENTURE
500 108th Ave Ne Ste 1200, Bellevue, WA 98004-5549
Tel (425) 450-6200 *Founded/Ownrshp* 2006
Sales 10.1MM^E *EMP* 400
SIC 8711 8712 Engineering services; Architectural services; Engineering services; Architectural services
Pt: John Cowdery
Pt: William Raleigh

HDS
See HAWAII DENTAL SERVICE

D-U-N-S 82-587-9104
■ **HDS HOLDING CORP**
(*Suby of* HD SUPPLY HOLDINGS INC) ★
3100 Cumberland Blvd Se, Atlanta, GA 30339-5940
Tel (770) 852-9000 *Founded/Ownrshp* 2007
Sales 8.8MMM^E *EMP* 15,000^E
SIC 5087 5072 5085 Cleaning & maintenance equipment & supplies; Hardware; Industrial supplies
CEO: Joseph J Deangelo
Corp Couns: Jim Brumsey

D-U-N-S 18-443-0627 IMP
HDS RETAIL NORTH AMERICA LP
LS TRAVEL RETAIL NORTH AMERICA
(*Suby of* HACHETTE DISTRIBUTION INC) ★
60 E 42nd St Rm 3410, New York, NY 10165-3410
Tel (212) 477-7373 *Founded/Ownrshp* 1988
Sales 500.0MM^E *EMP* 4,506^E
SIC 5994 News dealers & newsstands; News dealers & newsstands
Pt: Gerry Savaria
Pt: Craig Liden
Pt: Vadim Motlik
VP: Karen Hardy

D-U-N-S 60-361-1133 IMP/EXP
HDS TRADING CORP
1305 Jersey Ave, North Brunswick, NJ 08902-1621
Tel (732) 418-0418 *Founded/Ownrshp* 2002
Sales 30.0MM *EMP* 40
SIC 5719 Housewares; Housewares
Pr: Victor H Guindi
**VP:* Fred Guindi

HDT ENGINEERED TECHNOLOGIES
See HUNTER DEFENSE TECHNOLOGIES INC

D-U-N-S 15-077-7738 IMP
HDT EXPEDITIONARY SYSTEMS INC
(*Suby of* HDT ENGINEERED TECHNOLOGIES) ★
30500 Aurora Rd Ste 100, Solon, OH 44139-2776
Tel (540) 887-4778 *Founded/Ownrshp* 2005
Sales 40.9MM^E *EMP* 132^E
SIC 2393 2394 Canvas bags; Canvas & related products; Tents: made from purchased materials
Pr: James Maurer
**VP:* Brian Dearing
Board of Directors: Deborah Tucker

D-U-N-S 80-060-7454
HDT GLOBAL INC
30500 Aurora Rd Ste 100, Solon, OH 44139-2776
Tel (216) 438-6111 *Founded/Ownrshp* 2014
Sales 319.1MM^E *EMP* 650
SIC 8711 Engineering services; Engineering services
Pr: R Andrew Hove
**COO:* Tom Van Doren PHD
**CFO:* Anthony Dilucente
CFO: Flavia Pachi
VP: Rob Hodges Jr
VP: Greg Miller
VP: Rita Thomas
VP: Philip Won
Creative D: James Willard
Dir Bus: Dean Jorgensen
Prgrm Mgr: John Creed

HEA
See HOMER ELECTRIC ASSOCIATION INC

D-U-N-S 04-033-3155
HEA CLINIC PA
HOUSTON EYE ASSOCIATES
2855 Gramercy St, Houston, TX 77025-1756
Tel (713) 668-6828 *Founded/Ownrshp* 1962
Sales 26.8MM^E *EMP* 200
SIC 8011 Ophthalmologist; Ophthalmologist
Pr: Jeffrey Lanier
COO: Sam Tishler
Bd of Dir: Lanier Whilden
Trst: Richard Ou
**VP:* Paul C Salmonsen
Dir IT: Damon Brownd
Doctor: Jeffrey Arnoult
Doctor: William H Quayle
Doctor: Louis Verstringhe MD

D-U-N-S 11-259-3223
HEAD INC
4477 E 5th Ave, Columbus, OH 43219-1817
Tel (614) 338-8501 *Founded/Ownrshp* 1927
Sales 21.4MM^E *EMP* 50
SIC 1541 1542 Industrial buildings, new construction; Institutional building construction
Ch Bd: Middleton E Head Jr
**Pr:* James M Head
**VP:* Paul Ondera
IT Man: Glen Williams

D-U-N-S 79-881-3572
HEAD INJURY ASSOCIATION INC
300 Kennedy Dr, Hauppauge, NY 11788-4013
Tel (631) 231-1672 *Founded/Ownrshp* 1988
Sales 12.9MM *EMP* 325
Accts Bdo Usa Llp New York Ny
SIC 8322 8093 Rehabilitation services; Rehabilitation center, outpatient treatment; Rehabilitation services; Rehabilitation center, outpatient treatment
CEO: Liz Giordano
**Pr:* Stuart Gleiber

HEAD INJURY ASSOCIATION IND
See BRAIN INJURY ASSOCIATION OF INDIANA

HEAD PENN RACQUET SPORTS
See HEAD USA INC

HEAD START
See SELF-HELP INC

HEAD START
See OPTIONS FOR LEARNING

HEAD START
See FAMILY DEVELOPMENT SERVICES INC

D-U-N-S 13-036-5851
■ **HEAD START FAMILY HAIR SALON INC**
(*Suby of* REGIS CORP) ★
7201 Metro Blvd, Minneapolis, MN 55439-2131
Tel (952) 947-7777 *Founded/Ownrshp* 1983
Sales 3.9MM^E *EMP* 330
Accts Conrad Burnett & Co Pc
SIC 7231 Beauty shops; Beauty shops
Pr: Charlie Bruno
**VP:* Laura Bruno

HEAD START OF EL PASO COUNTY
See COMMUNITY PARTNERSHIP FOR CHILD DEVELOPMENT INC

D-U-N-S 60-661-8650
HEAD START OF GREATER DALLAS INC
3954 Gannon Ln, Dallas, TX 75237-2919
Tel (972) 296-8941 *Founded/Ownrshp* 1988
Sales 37.1MM *EMP* 740
SIC 8351 8322 Head start center, except in conjunction with school; Child guidance agency; Head start center, except in conjunction with school; Child guidance agency
CEO: Kenneth Gilbert
**CFO:* Joan A Cox
Dir IT: Lisa White
Site Mgr: Elsa Ibarra
Site Mgr: Dwuna Richards
Site Mgr: Lisa Tarrant

HEAD START SCHOOL
See MISSISSIPPI ACTION FOR PROGRESS INC

HEAD TYROLIA WINTER SPORTS
See HTM USA HOLDINGS INC

D-U-N-S 15-466-6341 IMP
HEAD USA INC
HEAD PENN RACQUET SPORTS
(*Suby of* HEAD TYROLIA WINTER SPORTS) ★
3125 Sterling Cir Ste 101, Boulder, CO 80301-2394
Tel (800) 874-3235 *Founded/Ownrshp* 1996
Sales 100.0MM *EMP* 109
SIC 5091 Diving equipment & supplies; Skiing equipment; Racquet sports equipment & supplies
Ch Bd: Johan Eliasch
**CEO:* Kevin Kempin
**COO:* Rose Mary Traynor
**Treas:* Gunter Hagspiel
Comm Man: Allison Barnett

HEAD WEST
See HEADWEST INC

D-U-N-S 07-394-6121
HEAD-ROYCE SCHOOL
4315 Lincoln Ave, Oakland, CA 94602-2528
Tel (510) 531-1300 *Founded/Ownrshp* 1957
Sales 27.7MM *EMP* 140
Accts Lautze & Lautze San Francisco
SIC 8211 Preparatory school; Private combined elementary & secondary school; Preparatory school; Private combined elementary & secondary school
Ch: Charles N Freiberg
V Ch: Lori Fogarty
Comm Dir: Elizabeth Owen
**Prin:* Robert A Lake
Dir IT: Samantha Hall

D-U-N-S 00-176-2137
HEADCO INDUSTRIES INC (IL)
BEARING HEADQUARTERS CO
2601 Parkes Dr, Broadview, IL 60155-4517
Tel (708) 681-4400 *Founded/Ownrshp* 1939, 1968
Sales 131.4MM^E *EMP* 275
SIC 5085 3599 5084

HEADINGTON COMPANIES
See HEADINGTON OIL LIMITED 1993 LP

D-U-N-S 08-139-8828
HEADINGTON OIL LIMITED 1993 LP
HEADINGTON COMPANIES
2711 N Haskell Ave # 2800, Dallas, TX 75204-2940
Tel (214) 696-0606 *Founded/Ownrshp* 1994
Sales 31.0MM^E *EMP* 65
SIC 1311 Crude petroleum production; Natural gas production; Crude petroleum production; Natural gas production
Genl Pt: Tim Headington
Pt: Brooks Purnell
Pt: Pat Smith
CFO: Michael E Tregoning
Treas: R Keith Bunch
Off Mgr: Rose Holman
Off Mgr: Ingrid Wonder

D-U-N-S 00-506-6816
HEADLY MANUFACTURING CO (IL)
2700 23rd St, Broadview, IL 60155-4512
Tel (708) 338-0800 *Founded/Ownrshp* 1921
Sales 26.0MM^E *EMP* 133^E
SIC 3469 3544 Machine parts, stamped or pressed metal; Special dies, tools, jigs & fixtures; Machine parts, stamped or pressed metal; Special dies, tools, jigs & fixtures
Pr: Albert Giusfredi
Genl Mgr: Jim Oles

HEADQUARTER HONDA
See HEADQUARTER ORLANDO LLC

D-U-N-S 96-210-7558
HEADQUARTER ORLANDO LLC
HEADQUARTER HONDA
17700 State Road 50, Clermont, FL 34711-7130
Tel (407) 395-7500 *Founded/Ownrshp* 2010
Sales 25.1MM^E *EMP* 52
SIC 5511 Automobiles, new & used
Genl Mgr: Jero Esteve
Pr Dir: Rudy Martinez
Sls Dir: Chris Cutting
Sls Mgr: John Bannon
Sales Asso: Royal De Jong
Sales Asso: T J Nevins
Sales Asso: Paul Rienzi
Sales Asso: Ed Rivera
Sales Asso: Chris Taylor

HEADQUARTERS
See LHOIST NORTH AMERICA OF ARIZONA INC

HEADQUARTERS
See NATIONWIDE LEGAL LLC

D-U-N-S 12-462-6276
HEADQUARTERS WEST LTD
8700 E Pinnacle Peak Rd, Scottsdale, AZ 85255-3540
Tel (602) 258-1647 *Founded/Ownrshp* 2012
Sales 21.0MM *EMP* 12
SIC 6531 Real estate brokers & agents; Appraiser, real estate; Real estate brokers & agents; Appraiser, real estate
Pr: Sam Hubbell
**Sec:* Walter Lane
**VP:* Con Englehorn
**VP:* Andy Groseta

D-U-N-S 07-758-0335 EXP
HEADS & THREADS INTL LLC
1212 Dolton Dr Ste 302, Dallas, TX 75207-2114
Tel (630) 868-2300 *Founded/Ownrshp* 2005
Sales 21.3MM^E *EMP* 175
SIC 5085 Fasteners & fastening equipment; Fasteners & fastening equipment
CEO: Bill Marthens
Pr: Michael Wrenn
CFO: Fred Webber
VP: Richard Megliola

HEADSTART
See COMMUNITY ACTION PARTNERSHIP OF RAMSEY AND WASHINGTON COUNTIES

D-U-N-S 03-989-1197 IMP
HEADSTART NURSERY INC
4860 Monterey Rd, Gilroy, CA 95020-9511
Tel (408) 842-3030 *Founded/Ownrshp* 1977
Sales 64.9MM^E *EMP* 190
SIC 5193 5261 Plants, potted; Nursery stock; Nurseries & garden centers; Plants, potted; Nursery stock; Nurseries & garden centers
Pr: Steven H Costa
**VP:* Don Christopher
**VP:* Randy Costa
Genl Mgr: Doug Iten
Genl Mgr: Chris Peck
Prd Mgr: Mike Bushman
Prd Mgr: Grant Cornia
Prd Mgr: Cole Iten
Sls Mgr: Lisa Branco
Sls Mgr: Michael Trebino

D-U-N-S 11-203-6939
HEADSTRONG CORP
(*Suby of* GENPACT LLC) ★
11921 Freedom Dr Ste 550, Reston, VA 20190-5635
Tel (703) 272-6761 *Founded/Ownrshp* 2011
Sales 114.3MM^E *EMP* 2,300
SIC 7379 8999 Computer related consulting services; Communication services; Computer related consulting services; Communication services
Pr: Sandeep Sahai
CFO: Peter Cowern
**CFO:* Adarsh Mehra
VP: Sandeep Kumar
VP: Ben Levy
VP: Madhan Velumani
Exec: Sameer Srivastava
Prgrm Mgr: Harish Velaga
Snr Sftwr: Indu Bisht
Snr Sftwr: Vikas Shukla
Snr Sftwr: Dhivya Thiruvengadam

D-U-N-S 11-263-0504
HEADSTRONG INC
(*Suby of* HEADSTRONG CORP) ★
11921 Freedom Dr Ste 550, Reston, VA 20190-5635
Tel (703) 272-6700 *Founded/Ownrshp* 2000
Sales 27.7MM^E *EMP* 400
Accts Deloitte & Touche Llp
SIC 7373 Systems engineering, computer related; Systems engineering, computer related
CEO: Arjun Malhotra
CFO: Adarsh Mehra

D-U-N-S 80-441-1093
HEADSTRONG SERVICES LLC
(*Suby of* HEADSTRONG CORP) ★
11921 Freedom Dr Ste 550, Reston, VA 20190-5635
Tel (703) 272-6700 *Founded/Ownrshp* 1998
Sales 27.1MM^E *EMP* 260
SIC 7379 Computer related consulting services; Computer related consulting services
Pr: Sandeep Sahai
Sr VP: Sudhir Singh
Sr VP: Knk Venkataraman
Board of Directors: Alphonse Valbrune

HEADWATERS BD
See HEADWATERS MB L L C

D-U-N-S 00-734-1720
■ **HEADWATERS CONSTRUCTION MATERIALS LLC** (TX)
PALESTINE CONCRETE TILE CO
(*Suby of* HEADWATERS INC) ★
2500 W Reagan St, Palestine, TX 75801-2201
Tel (903) 729-2217 *Founded/Ownrshp* 1946
Sales 22.1MM^E *EMP* 70
SIC 3271 Blocks, concrete or cinder: standard
Pr: Bobby L Whishant
**CFO:* Donald P Newman
**Treas:* Scott Jackson
**VP:* Harlan M Hatfield
Opers Mgr: Kevin Skloss

D-U-N-S 82-975-7595
■ **HEADWATERS CONSTRUCTION MATERIALS LLC**
SOUTHWEST CONCRETE PRODUCTS
(*Suby of* HEADWATERS INC) ★
2088 Fm 949, Alleyton, TX 78935-2124
Tel (713) 393-3300 *Founded/Ownrshp* 2006
Sales 79.0MM^E *EMP* 250
SIC 3271 Concrete block & brick
CEO: Kirk A Benson
**Pr:* Bobby L Whishant
**CFO:* Donald P Newman
**Treas:* Scott Jackson
**VP:* Harlan M Hatfield
VP: John Lents
Prd Mgr: Bart Jackson

HEADWATERS CONSTRUCTION MTLS
See SOUTHWEST CONCRETE PRODUCTS CO

D-U-N-S 78-619-5701 IMP/EXP
▲ HEADWATERS INC
10701 S River Front Pkwy # 300, South Jordan, UT 84095-3524
Tel (801) 984-9400 *Founded/Ownrshp* 1995
Sales 895.3MM *EMP* 2,831
Accts Bdo Usa Llp Costa Mesa Cali
Tkr Sym HW *Exch* NYS
SIC 3272 3271 2999 Concrete products; Siding, precast stone; Concrete block & brick; Fuel briquettes & waxes; Concrete products; Siding, precast stone; Concrete block & brick; Fuel briquettes & waxes
Ch Bd: Kirk A Benson
Pr: Brent Spann
CFO: Donald P Newman
**V Ch Bd:* James A Herickhoff
V P: Blake Asel
VP: Gary England
VP: Harlan M Hatfield
VP: David Marshall
VP: Bing Zhou
VP Sls: John Ward
Board of Directors: Thomas N Chieffe, R Sam Christensen, Blake O Fisher Jr, Sylvia Summers

D-U-N-S 07-293-9346
HEADWATERS MB L L C
HEADWATERS BD
1225 17th St Frnt, Denver, CO 80202-2033
Tel (303) 572-6000 *Founded/Ownrshp* 2001
Sales 20.9MM^E *EMP* 110^E
SIC 6211 Investment bankers; Investment bankers
Bd of Dir: Marcus Peperzak
Bd of Dir: G J Tankersley Jr
Bd of Dir: William Thorndike
Sr VP: Bill Casey
VP: Brendan Burke
VP: Rachel Candler
VP: Chad Gardiner
VP: Matt Huebner
VP: Brian Krehbiel
VP: Ryan McCarthy
Mng Dir: Sakis Asteriadis
Board of Directors: Lawrence R Buchalter, Marcus B Peperzak

D-U-N-S 03-089-0953 IMP/EXP
■ HEADWATERS RESOURCES INC
ISG RESOURCES
(*Suby of* HEADWATERS INC) ★
10701 S River Front Pkwy # 300, South Jordan, UT 84095-3524
Tel (801) 984-9400 *Founded/Ownrshp* 2002
Sales 316.2MM^E *EMP* 1,000
SIC 5032 4953 8711 Cement; Masons' materials; Refuse systems; Engineering services; Cement; Masons' materials; Refuse systems; Engineering services
Pr: William H Gehrmann
**Pr:* Kurt Benson
**CFO:* Don Newman
**Treas:* Scott Jackson
**Treas:* Steven G Stewart
**VP:* Harlan M Hatfield
Sls&Mrk Ex: John Ward

D-U-N-S 08-865-3576
HEADWAY TECHNOLOGIES INC
(*Suby of* TDK CORPORATION)
682 S Hillview Dr, Milpitas, CA 95035-5457
Tel (408) 942-1941 *Founded/Ownrshp* 1994
Sales 131.3MM^E *EMP* 650
SIC 3572 Magnetic storage devices, computer; Magnetic storage devices, computer
Pr: Mao-Min Chen
CFO: Thomas Surran
VP: Moris Dovek
**VP:* Gary Pester
Snr Ntwrk: David Stoeckle
CTO: Jinsong Wang
Snr Mgr: Yuhui Tang

D-U-N-S 10-651-9424 IMP
HEADWEST INC
HEAD WEST
15650 S Avalon Blvd, Compton, CA 90220-3207
Tel (310) 527-3767 *Founded/Ownrshp* 1977
Sales 24.9MM^E *EMP* 114^E
SIC 3231 2759 2396 Mirrored glass; Screen printing; Automotive & apparel trimmings
CEO: Louis E Fideler
**Pr:* Harold Kline
VP: Kevin Farr
VP Opers: Michael Fideler
Opers Mgr: Andy Wong
Sls Mgr: Scott Irvine

D-U-N-S 00-353-3069
HEADWORKS INC (TX)
LANOUE CONSULTING
11000 Brittmoore Park Dr # 100, Houston, TX 77041-6939
Tel (713) 647-6667 *Founded/Ownrshp* 1993
Sales 29.9MM^E *EMP* 27
SIC 5084 Industrial machinery & equipment
CEO: Michele Lanoue
**Sr VP:* Jack Gardiner
**Sr VP:* Gerald Seidl
VP: Afnan Din
CIO: Wayne McCauley
Manager: Ranjit Nair

D-U-N-S 03-324-0797
HEAFNER MOTORS INC (MS)
935 Highway 6 W, Batesville, MS 38606-8900
Tel (662) 563-7631 *Founded/Ownrshp* 1959
Sales 21.5MM^E *EMP* 48
SIC 5511 Automobiles, new & used; Pickups, new & used
Pr: Henry E Heafner
**Treas:* Samuel K Heafner
**VP:* Mark Heafner

D-U-N-S 83-352-6473
HEAFNER TIRE GROUP INC EMPLOYEE WELFARE BENEFIT PLAN
12200 Herbert Wayne Ct, Huntersville, NC 28078-6335
Tel (704) 992-2000 *Founded/Ownrshp* 2010
Sales 23.6MM *EMP* 2
Accts Bdo Usa Llp Atlanta Ga
SIC 5531 Automotive tires; Automotive tires
Mktg Mgr: William Berry
Sr VP: Jim Williams

D-U-N-S 07-186-8988
HEALD COLLEGE LLC
(*Suby of* HEALD CAPITAL, LLC)
124 Washington St Ste 101, Foxboro, MA 02035-1368
Tel (415) 808-1400 *Founded/Ownrshp* 2007
Sales 57.4MM^E *EMP* 800
SIC 8221 8222 Colleges universities & professional schools; Junior colleges & technical institutes; Colleges universities & professional schools; Junior colleges & technical institutes
Pr: Nolan Miura
COO: Seyed Amiry
**CFO:* Eeva Deshon
Trst: Fran A Streets
Trst: James P Ware
Ex VP: Lisa Ratto
Ex Dir: Bob Nodolf
Ex Dir: Jason Smith
Netwrk Eng: Stoddard Cris
Sales Exec: Ezra Salas
HC Dir: Edward Lubin

HEALDSBURG DISTRICT HOSPITAL
See NORTH SONOMA COUNTY HOSPITAL DISTRICT

D-U-N-S 19-007-7219
HEALDSBURG DISTRICT HOSPITAL REHABILITATION SERVICES
1540 Healdsburg Ave, Healdsburg, CA 95448-3253
Tel (707) 433-9150 *Founded/Ownrshp* 2005
Sales NA *EMP* 100
SIC 6324 Hospital & medical service plans

D-U-N-S 02-943-7373
HEALDSBURG LUMBER CO INC
HLC
359 Hudson St, Healdsburg, CA 95448-4415
Tel (707) 431-9663 *Founded/Ownrshp* 1973
Sales 23.6MM *EMP* 90
SIC 5251 5211 2431 Hardware; Lumber & other building materials; Millwork; Hardware; Lumber & other building materials; Millwork
CEO: Eric A Ziedrich
**Sec:* Janet Ziedrich
Opers Mgr: Neal Geils
Mktg Mgr: Matt McPherson
Sales Asso: Mike Yaeger

D-U-N-S 09-564-7921
HEALDSBURG UNIFIED SCHOOL DISTRICT
1028 Prince Ave, Healdsburg, CA 95448-3596
Tel (707) 431-3488 *Founded/Ownrshp* 1998
Sales 18.7MM^E *EMP* 345
SIC 8211 Public elementary & secondary schools; Public elementary & secondary schools
Dir IT: Rich Easterday
Dir IT: Laurel Krsek
Dir IT: Christopher Moghtaderi
Teacher Pr: Francesca Whitcomb

HEALEY BROTHERS
See WS HEALEY CHEVROLET-BUICK INC

D-U-N-S 96-562-9868
HEALEY CHRYSLER PLYMOUTH DODGE JEEP EAGLE LLC
557 Route 52, Beacon, NY 12508-1212
Tel (845) 831-1148 *Founded/Ownrshp* 1997
Sales 31.0MM *EMP* 41
SIC 5511 Automobiles, new & used; Automobiles, new & used
Prin: Paul J Healey
Sls Mgr: Michael Ciardullo
Sales Asso: John Martorano
Sales Asso: Anthony Minervini
Sales Asso: Manny Robalo
Sales Asso: Timothy Warren

D-U-N-S 00-386-2778
HEALEY RR CORP
1900 Mt Hermon Rd, Midlothian, VA 23112-5702
Tel (804) 379-3904 *Founded/Ownrshp* 1949
Sales 184.0MM^E *EMP* 150
SIC 1629 Railroad & railway roadbed construction; Railroad & railway roadbed construction
Pr: Glenn V Healey
**CFO:* David Lambertson
Sfty Dirs: Joe Sweeney

D-U-N-S 86-130-5415
HEALICS INC
8919 W Heather Ave, Milwaukee, WI 53224-2417
Tel (414) 375-1600 *Founded/Ownrshp* 1995
Sales NA *EMP* 55
SIC 6321 Assessment associations, accident & health insurance
Pr: Pathi Plough
**Owner:* Michael Naparalla
Pr: Debbie Wissbeck

D-U-N-S 83-048-4437
HEALING CHURCH OF CHRIST
1750 East West Hwy, Hyattsville, MD 20783-3034
Tel (202) 374-0558 *Founded/Ownrshp* 2009
Sales 16.1MM^E *EMP* 500
SIC 6732 Trusts: educational, religious, etc.; Trusts: educational, religious, etc.

D-U-N-S 03-436-6358
HEALIX INC (TX)
14140 Southwest Fwy # 400, Sugar Land, TX 77478-3759
Tel (281) 295-4000 *Founded/Ownrshp* 2008
Sales 16.6MM^E *EMP* 450
SIC 8093 5122 Specialty outpatient clinics; Drugs, proprietaries & sundries
Ch: Mort Baharloo
**Pr:* Alan B Chaveleh
VP: Frank Chaveleh
VP: Earl Silverstein
VP: Noemi Sirisaengtaksin
VP: Lucinda Van Anglen
Dir Risk M: Scott Wise
Dir Rx: Reza Kamali
Div Mgr: Marla Boswell
Div Mgr: Ryan Wendt
Opers Supe: Laura Guerin

D-U-N-S 60-690-4266
HEALIX INFUSION THERAPY INC
14140 Se Fwy Ste 400, Sugar Land, TX 77478
Tel (281) 295-4000 *Founded/Ownrshp* 2000
Sales 44.5MM^E *EMP* 469
SIC 8093 5122 Specialty outpatient clinics; Drugs, proprietaries & sundries; Specialty outpatient clinics; Drugs, proprietaries & sundries
CEO: Alan Chaveleh
**COO:* Mark Winters
**CFO:* Joe Gallegos
**Ch:* Mort Baharloo
**Sr VP:* Noemi Sirisaengtaksin
VP: Lucinda Anglen
Div Mgr: Will Guzman
IT Man: Craig Hunter
Opers Supe: Laura Guerin

D-U-N-S 07-951-5003
HEALTH & EDUCATION SERVICES INC
199 Rosewood Dr Ste 250, Danvers, MA 01923-1388
Tel (978) 921-1293 *Founded/Ownrshp* 1971
Sales 28.2MM^E *EMP* 1,000
Accts Deloitte Taxllp Boston Ma
SIC 8093 Mental health clinic, outpatient; Mental health clinic, outpatient
Pr: Paul O'Shea
**Ch:* Michael Shea
**Treas:* Janice Preston
**Prin:* Kevin Norton

D-U-N-S 92-704-9767
HEALTH & FAMILY SERVICES KENTUCKY CABINET FOR
(*Suby of* EXECUTIVE OFFICE OF COMMONWEALTH OF KENTUCKY) ★
275 E Main St B, Frankfort, KY 40601-2321
Tel (502) 564-5497 *Founded/Ownrshp* 1996
Sales NA *EMP* 8,300
SIC 9431 Administration of public health programs; ; Administration of public health programs;
Prin: Mark D Birdwhistell
Ofcr: Audrey Haynes
Brnch Mgr: Rickd Johnson
CIO: Laurie Robinson
IT Man: Donna Temple
Pharmcst: Trista Chapman

D-U-N-S 05-295-2058
HEALTH & HOSPITAL CORP OF MARION COUNTY
DIVISION OF PUBLIC HEALTH
3838 N Rural St Fl 8, Indianapolis, IN 46205-2930
Tel (317) 221-2000 *Founded/Ownrshp* 1951
Sales 521.7MM^E *EMP* 3,982
SIC 8062 General medical & surgical hospitals; General medical & surgical hospitals
Pr: Mack Gutwein
CFO: Marjorie Olaughlin
CFO: Dan Seller
Treas: Marjorie Laughlin
**Treas:* Daniel Sellers
**VP:* Greg Porter
Comm Dir: Kate McGaffery
Ex Dir: Michael Hurst
Ex Dir: Catherine Parker
Brnch Mgr: Michael Brune
Brnch Mgr: Davod Jackson

HEALTH ACCESS NETWORK
See CROZER-KEYSTONE HEALTH NETWORK

D-U-N-S 07-578-7333
HEALTH ACQUISITION CORP
ALLEN HEALTH CARE SERVICES
(*Suby of* NATIONAL HOME HEALTH CARE CORP) ★
7000 Austin St Ste 2, Forest Hills, NY 11375-4739
Tel (718) 657-2966 *Founded/Ownrshp* 1987
Sales 16.4MM^E *EMP* 1,500
SIC 8082 Home health care services; Home health care services
Pr: Ian Rowe
**CFO:* Robert P Heller

D-U-N-S 13-913-3180
■ HEALTH ADVOCATE INC
(*Suby of* WEST CORP) ★
3043 Walton Rd Ste 150, Plymouth Meeting, PA 19462-2389
Tel (610) 825-1222 *Founded/Ownrshp* 2014
Sales 51.0MM^E *EMP* 304
SIC 8399 Advocacy group; Advocacy group
Pr: Mike J Cardillo
Pr: Kathy Adler
Pr: Wendy Wright
CFO: Thomas A Masci Jr CPA
Chf Mktg O: Arthur N Leibowitz MD
Chf Mktg O: Martin B Rosen
Chf Mktg O: Martin Rosen
Ex VP: Daniel S Messina
Ex VP: David S Rocchino
VP: Norbert Alicea
VP: Kevin Astrup
VP: Kate Begley
VP: Norbert Bert
VP: Patricia Imken
VP: Francine Miller
VP: Esther Nash
VP: Marcia Otto
VP: Kurt Schaum
VP: Suzanne Starker
VP: Wendi Thomas
VP: Eric Weaver

D-U-N-S 02-119-1014
HEALTH ADVOCATES LLC
14721 Califa St, Van Nuys, CA 91411-3107
Tel (818) 995-9500 *Founded/Ownrshp* 2009
Sales 23.8MM^E *EMP* 371
SIC 8399 Advocacy group; Advocacy group
COO: Steve Levine
IT Man: AVI Leibovic
Snr Mgr: Tallien Perry

HEALTH AFFILIATED SERVICES
See HENDRICK SOUTHWESTERN HEALTH DEVELOPMENT CORP

D-U-N-S 14-869-4581
HEALTH AID OF OHIO INC
5230 Hauserman Rd, Parma, OH 44130-1224
Tel (216) 252-3900 *Founded/Ownrshp* 1983
Sales 23.8MM^E *EMP* 75
SIC 5999 Medical apparatus & supplies
Pr: Carol Gilligan
Ofcr: Laura Carver
VP: Cortney Baird
**VP:* Cortney B McDowell

D-U-N-S 83-169-8431
HEALTH ALLIANCE INC
HEALTHALLIANCE OF HUDSON VLY
741 Grant Ave, Lake Katrine, NY 12449-5350
Tel (845) 334-3151 *Founded/Ownrshp* 2007
Sales 3.8MM *EMP* 2,100^E
Accts Charles A Barragato & Co Llp
SIC 8062 General medical & surgical hospitals; General medical & surgical hospitals
Pr: David Scarpino
CFO: Steven Haas
Sr VP: Margo McGilvrey
Chf Nrs Of: Kathy Luney
QA Dir: Joseph Marsciovete
IT Man: Leslie Dawson

D-U-N-S 17-482-2775
HEALTH ALLIANCE MEDICAL PLANS INC
(*Suby of* CARLE HOLDING CO INC) ★
301 S Vine St, Urbana, IL 61801-7429
Tel (217) 337-8000 *Founded/Ownrshp* 1989
Sales NA *EMP* 540^E
Accts Kpmg Llp Chicago Illinois
SIC 6321 6324 Accident & health insurance; Health maintenance organization (HMO), insurance only; Accident & health insurance; Health maintenance organization (HMO), insurance only
CEO: Jeff Ingrum
COO: Rick Born
COO: Robin Winskas
**CFO:* Gordon W Salm
Ofcr: Wyatt Scheiding
VP: Melissa Buhrmester
VP: Kristie Burke
VP: Theresa Radosevich
VP: Patti Thornton
Comm Dir: Dana Meek
Dir Rx: Jen Pharmd
Comm Man: Laura Mabry

D-U-N-S 06-054-8005
HEALTH ALLIANCE OF HUDSON VALLEY BROADWAY CAMPUS
HEALTHALLIANCE HOSPITAL
(*Suby of* HEALTH ALLIANCE INC) ★
396 Broadway, Kingston, NY 12401-4626
Tel (845) 331-3131 *Founded/Ownrshp* 2004
Sales 108.9MM *EMP* 800
Accts Pricewaterhousecoopers Llp Al
SIC 8062 General medical & surgical hospitals; General medical & surgical hospitals
Pr: David Buchmueller
Chf Rad: Bruce Moor
Dir Vol: Amy McAden
Pr: Pat Husted
**Treas:* Linda Tucker
Sr VP: Sandra Horan
VP: Joseph Bailey
VP: Frank Ehrlich
VP: Carolyn Hoffman
VP: Kathy Lunney
VP: Joseph Marsicovete
VP: Margo McGilvrey
VP: Dennis Pignato
Dir Risk M: Sherie Ashdawn
Dir Lab: Kahaih Khan
Dir Rx: Priti Shah

D-U-N-S 09-382-3185
HEALTH ALLIANCE PLAN OF MICHIGAN
(*Suby of* HENRY FORD HEALTH SYSTEM) ★
2850 W Grand Blvd, Detroit, MI 48202-2692
Tel (313) 872-8100 *Founded/Ownrshp* 1973
Sales NA *EMP* 774
Accts Mcgladrey Llp Chicago Il
SIC 6324 8011 8099 Hospital & medical service plans; Health maintenance organization; Group health association; Medical services organization; Hospital & medical service plans; Health maintenance organization; Group health association; Medical services organization
Ex Dir: William Alvin
Pr: Timothy Sullivan
COO: Matthew Walsh
CFO: Ronald Berry
Ofcr: Dawn Geisert
Assoc VP: Christopher Johnston
Assoc VP: Marc Vanderburg
Ex VP: Dianna Ronan
Sr VP: Maurice McMurray
Sr VP: Naim Munir
VP: Derick W Adams
VP: Deandre Lipscomb
VP: Annette Marcath
VP: Mary Ann Tournoux
VP: Jennifer Zbytowski
Assoc Dir: Brian Jones

D-U-N-S 11-338-0849
HEALTH ALLIANCE WITH PHYSICIAN
HAPI
60 Hospital Rd, Leominster, MA 01453-2205
Tel (978) 466-2000 *Founded/Ownrshp* 1997
Sales NA *EMP* 25
SIC 6411 Medical insurance claim processing, contract or fee basis
Ex Dir: John Minizhiello

D-U-N-S 00-822-3596
HEALTH ALLIANCE-MIDWEST INC
(*Suby of* HEALTH ALLIANCE MEDICAL PLANS INC) ★
102 E Main St Ste 400, Urbana, IL 61801-2734
Tel (217) 337-8010 *Founded/Ownrshp* 1996

Sales NA *EMP* 150
SIC 6324 6321 Health maintenance organization (HMO), insurance only; Accident & health insurance; Health maintenance organization (HMO), insurance only; Accident & health insurance
CEO: Jeff Ingrum
VP: Lori Cowdrey

HEALTH AND DENTAL PLAN
See W W GRAINGER INC GROUP BENEFIT TRUST I

HEALTH AND PALLIATIVE SERVICES
See HOSPICE OF TREASURE COAST INC

D-U-N-S 78-746-3082
HEALTH AND PALLIATIVE SERVICES OF TREASURE COAST INC
TREASURE COAST HOSPICES
1201 Se Indian St, Stuart, FL 34997-5688
Tel (772) 403-4500 *Founded/Ownrshp* 1981
Sales 17.2MM *EMP* 400
Accts Crowe Horwath Llp Fort Lauder
SIC 8082 Home health care services; Home health care services
CEO: Luis Benson
Doctor: Robert Anderson
Doctor: A Buttles

HEALTH AND WELFARE DEPT OF THE
See LABORERS PENSION & WELFARE FUNDS

D-U-N-S 96-729-2962
HEALTH AND WELFARE FUND PHILADELPHIA FEDERATION OF TEACHERS INC
1816 Chestnut St, Philadelphia, PA 19103-4902
Tel (215) 561-2722 *Founded/Ownrshp* 1972
Sales 33.7MM *EMP* 40
SIC 8631 Labor unions & similar labor organizations; Labor unions & similar labor organizations
Pr: Ted Kirsch
**Treas:* Jack Steinberg
**VP:* Jerry Jordan

D-U-N-S 61-285-6831
HEALTH ANSWERS EDUCATION LLC
SOUTHERN HENNESSEY
(*Suby of* SUDLER & HENNESSEY LLC) ★
700 Dresher Rd, Horsham, PA 19044-2206
Tel (215) 442-9010 *Founded/Ownrshp* 2003
Sales 15.8MM^E *EMP* 465
SIC 8742 Training & development consultant; Training & development consultant
Pr: Mark Samuel
**CFO:* Tom Dougherty
VP: Dale Edwards
VP: David Saddock
IT Man: Nicholas Galiatsatos

D-U-N-S 96-236-8841
■ **HEALTH BUSINESS SYSTEMS INC**
COMMUNICATION SERVICE CO DIV
(*Suby of* CATAMARAN CORP) ★
738 Louis Dr, Warminster, PA 18974-2829
Tel (215) 442-9300 *Founded/Ownrshp* 2010
Sales 33.1MM^E *EMP* 85^E
Accts Wouch Maloney Miller
SIC 5045 Computers, peripherals & software; Computers, peripherals & software
Pr: Mark Thierer
**Pr:* Louis Greenberg
**Ex VP:* Bruce Share
Sr VP: Mike Shapiro
VP: Kelly Makay
QA Dir: Lauren Bain

D-U-N-S 09-551-1010
HEALTH CARE & REHAB SERVICES OF SOUTHEASTERN VERMONT INC
390 River St, North Springfield, VT 05150
Tel (802) 886-4500 *Founded/Ownrshp* 1975
Sales 46.8MM *EMP* 500
Accts Kittell Branagan & Sargent Cp
SIC 8093 Mental health clinic, outpatient; Mental health clinic, outpatient
CEO: Judith Hayward
COO: George Karabakakis
**CFO:* Edmund Moore
**VP:* David Mulholland
Exec: Lesa Hinkley
IT Man: Warren Sergeant
Psych: Ingrid Sell

D-U-N-S 03-093-3667
HEALTH CARE ADMINISTRATION CO
SKYVIEW LIVING CENTERS
845 Proton Rd, San Antonio, TX 78258-4203
Tel (210) 340-7155 *Founded/Ownrshp* 1991
Sales 19.3MM^E *EMP* 900
SIC 8059 Nursing home, except skilled & intermediate care facility; Home for the mentally retarded, exc. skilled or intermediate; Nursing home, except skilled & intermediate care facility; Home for the mentally retarded, exc. skilled or intermediate
Ch Bd: Robert L Bowers
**Pr:* Gary Bowers
**VP:* Henry Bowers
Dir IT: Tony Spearing

HEALTH CARE ADVERTISING
See AMERICAN DENTAL CENTERS DR SAM JAFFE & ASSOCIATES INC

D-U-N-S 00-790-3347
■ **HEALTH CARE AND RETIREMENT CORP OF AMERICA**
(*Suby of* MANOR CARE INC) ★
333 N Summit St Ste 103, Toledo, OH 43604-2617
Tel (419) 252-5500 *Founded/Ownrshp* 1991
Sales 32.8MM^E *EMP* 572
SIC 8051 Convalescent home with continuous nursing care; Convalescent home with continuous nursing care
Ch Bd: Paul A Ormond
**CFO:* Steven Cavanaugh
**Treas:* Matt Kang
**Sr VP:* Stephen Guillard
**VP:* Spence C Moler
**VP:* Richard Parr

D-U-N-S 07-546-3034
HEALTH CARE AUTHORITY OF CITY OF ENTERPRISE INC
ENTERPRISE HEALTH AND REHABILI
300 Plaza Dr, Enterprise, AL 36330-3311
Tel (334) 347-9541 *Founded/Ownrshp* 1961
Sales 15.8MM *EMP* 325
SIC 8051 Skilled nursing care facilities; Skilled nursing care facilities
Ex Dir: Barbara Stinson

D-U-N-S 07-912-4053
HEALTH CARE AUTHORITY OF CITY OF HUNTSVILLE
HUNTSVILLE HOSP WOMEN CHILDREN
101 Sivley Rd Sw, Huntsville, AL 35801-4421
Tel (256) 265-1000 *Founded/Ownrshp* 1986
Sales 5.4MM^E *EMP* 7,800
SIC 8062 8011 General medical & surgical hospitals; Offices & clinics of medical doctors; General medical & surgical hospitals; Offices & clinics of medical doctors
CEO: David Spillers
Chf Rad: Timothy Baker
**CFO:* Lonnie Younger
VP: Michael W D
Pharmcst: Melissa O'Neill

D-U-N-S 60-288-7726
HEALTH CARE AUTHORITY OF CULLMAN COUNTY
CULLMAN EMERGENCY MEDICAL SERV
1912 Al Highway 157, Cullman, AL 35058-0609
Tel (256) 737-2000 *Founded/Ownrshp* 1984
Sales 96.5MM *EMP* 1,000^E
Accts Draffin & Tucker Llp Albany
SIC 8062 General medical & surgical hospitals; General medical & surgical hospitals
CEO: James D Weidner
**COO:* Jete Edmisson
**Treas:* Debbie Mickle

D-U-N-S 07-545-7283
HEALTH CARE AUTHORITY OF LAUDERDALE COUNTY AND CITY OF FLORENCE
COFFEE HEALTH GROUP
205 Marengo St, Florence, AL 35630-6033
Tel (256) 768-9191 *Founded/Ownrshp* 1943
Sales 67.0MM^E *EMP* 1,475^E
SIC 8051 8062 Skilled nursing care facilities; General medical & surgical hospitals; Skilled nursing care facilities; General medical & surgical hospitals
Pr: Carl Bailey
Dir Case M: Neida Fuqua
Dir Rx: Jarod Ott
Comm Man: Kelli Frederick
Chf Nrs Of: Barbara Murphy
Dir Pat Ac: Dave Davis
Telecom Ex: Doug Kirkland
Psych: Connie Fleming
Doctor: Brian Cole
Nrsg Dir: Tiffany Keys
Pharmcst: Mark Donaldson

D-U-N-S 07-898-3939
HEALTH CARE AUTHORITY OF MORGAN COUNTY - CITY OF DECATUR
DECATUR MORGAN HOSPITAL
1201 7th St Se, Decatur, AL 35601-3337
Tel (256) 355-0370 *Founded/Ownrshp* 1915
Sales 169.8MM^E *EMP* 1,500
SIC 8062 Hospital, AMA approved residency; Hospital, AMA approved residency
Pr: Nat Richardson
**CFO:* Danny Crowe
**VP:* Trudy Grisham
**VP:* Jason Lockette
VP: Allen Tsai
Chf Nrs Of: Anita Walden
Sfty Mgr: Phyllis West
Cert Phar: Mac Hazel
Cert Phar: Sharmalita Hines
Cert Phar: Heather Stewart

D-U-N-S 96-793-6860
HEALTH CARE BEN PL TR AGREEM OF WAKE FOREST UNIV SCHOOL OF MEDICINE
Medical Center Blvd, Winston Salem, NC 27157-0001
Tel (336) 716-4445 *Founded/Ownrshp* 2011
Sales 47.8MM *EMP* 2
SIC 8099 Health & allied services; Health & allied services

HEALTH CARE CAPITAL CNSLD
See HEALTH CARE CAPITAL INC

D-U-N-S 80-831-5725
HEALTH CARE CAPITAL INC
HEALTH CARE CAPITAL CNSLD
2 Ravinia Dr Ste 1350, Atlanta, GA 30346-2116
Tel (770) 393-3355 *Founded/Ownrshp* 1993
Sales NA *EMP* 1,532
Accts Deloitte & Touche Llp
SIC 6162 8051 8741 Mortgage bankers & correspondents; Skilled nursing care facilities; Management services; Mortgage bankers & correspondents; Skilled nursing care facilities; Management services
Pr: Michael S Brown
**COO:* Richard Greer
**CFO:* Bryan F Sodel
**Treas:* Wayne Moorhead
**VP:* Bill Nida
**VP:* Matt Robinson

HEALTH CARE CENTER
See ST JAMES PLACE OF BATON ROUGE

D-U-N-S 07-148-9553
HEALTH CARE CENTER
THE NILE HEALTH CARE CENTER
3720 23rd Ave S, Minneapolis, MN 55407-3010
Tel (612) 724-5495 *Founded/Ownrshp* 1999
Sales 3.9MM^E *EMP* 300
SIC 8051 Skilled nursing care facilities; Skilled nursing care facilities
VP: Delys Golberish
Dir IT: Jack Nugent
Doctor: Lisa Utphall

D-U-N-S 02-768-3799
HEALTH CARE CONNECTIONS INC
2401 W University Ave, Muncie, IN 47303-3428
Tel (765) 747-3111 *Founded/Ownrshp* 2008
Sales 39.5MM *EMP* 3
SIC 8099 Health & allied services
Prin: Carol E Seals

D-U-N-S 79-637-1151
HEALTH CARE CORP
216 E Henry St, Spartanburg, SC 29306-3248
Tel (864) 582-8983 *Founded/Ownrshp* 1991
Sales 14.8MM^E *EMP* 400
SIC 8051 8062 Skilled nursing care facilities; General medical & surgical hospitals; Skilled nursing care facilities; General medical & surgical hospitals
Pr: David W Cecil II
**VP:* CAM Cecil
**VP:* Miriam Polladora

D-U-N-S 80-534-6798 IMP/EXP
HEALTH CARE COST CONTAINMENT SYSTEM ARIZONA
AHCCCS
(*Suby of* EXECUTIVE OFFICE OF STATE OF ARIZONA) ★
801 E Jefferson St Md5700, Phoenix, AZ 85034-2217
Tel (602) 417-4000 *Founded/Ownrshp* 1992
Sales NA *EMP* 990
Accts Mayer Hoffman Mccann Pc Pho
SIC 9431 Administration of public health programs; ; Administration of public health programs;
Ofcr: Steve Leibensperger III
IT Man: Eric Royce
Netwrk Mgr: Ben Hall
Sls&Mrk Ex: Dara Johnson

D-U-N-S 13-666-8972
HEALTH CARE DISTRICT OF PALM BEACH COUNTY
2601 10th Ave N Ste 100, Palm Springs, FL 33461-3133
Tel (561) 659-1270 *Founded/Ownrshp* 1988
Sales 68.7MM^E *EMP* 300^E
SIC 8748 Urban planning & consulting services; Urban planning & consulting services
CEO: Ronald J Weiwora
CFO: Darcy Davis
**Ch:* Benjamin Frank
Ofcr: Nicholas Romanello
CIO: Tracy Legenos
IT Man: Katherine Wilburn
Pharmcst: Jonathan Bostic
Pharmcst: Marid Gomez
Pharmcst: Karamchand Oodal
Pharmcst: Luis Rodriguez

HEALTH CARE FACILITIES
See HCF MANAGEMENT INC

D-U-N-S 15-116-5297
HEALTH CARE FOR MID-COLUMBIA REGION
MID COLUMBIA MEDICAL CENTER
1700 E 19th St, The Dalles, OR 97058-3317
Tel (541) 296-1111 *Founded/Ownrshp* 1983
Sales 1.6MM *EMP* 500
SIC 8062 8721 5999 7352 6514 8011 General medical & surgical hospitals; Billing & bookkeeping service; Hospital equipment & supplies; Invalid supplies rental; Residential building, four or fewer units: operation; Offices & clinics of medical doctors; General medical & surgical hospitals; Billing & bookkeeping service; Hospital equipment & supplies; Invalid supplies rental; Residential building, four or fewer units: operation; Offices & clinics of medical doctors
CEO: Duane Francis
**CFO:* Donald Arbon

D-U-N-S 19-985-5151
HEALTH CARE FOUNDATION OF GREATER KANSAS CITY
2700 E 18th St Ste 220, Kansas City, MO 64127-2653
Tel (816) 241-7006 *Founded/Ownrshp* 2005
Sales 23.6MM *EMP* 12
Accts House Park & Dobratz Pc Ka
SIC 6733 Trusts, except educational, religious, charity: management; Trusts, except educational, religious, charity: management
V Ch: Larry Blankinship
Bd of Dir: Christina Esteban
Bd of Dir: Susan Wilson
VP: Rhonda Holman
Prin: Dan Couch

D-U-N-S 06-266-9478
HEALTH CARE FOUNDATION OF WILSON
WILSON MEDICAL CENTER
1705 Tarboro St Sw, Wilson, NC 27893-3428
Tel (252) 399-8040 *Founded/Ownrshp* 1988
Sales 117.2MM *EMP* 1,100
SIC 8062 General medical & surgical hospitals; General medical & surgical hospitals
CEO: William E Caldwell
COO: Bert Beard
CFO: Melissa Packer
VP: Rick Guarino
VP: Denise O'Hara

HEALTH CARE GROUP
See HEALTH CARE INDUSTRIES CORP

D-U-N-S 14-747-4886
HEALTH CARE INC
PROMISE REGIONAL MEDICAL CTR
1701 E 23rd Ave, Hutchinson, KS 67502-1105
Tel (620) 665-2000 *Founded/Ownrshp* 1983
Sales 130.9MM *EMP* 1,300
Accts Bkd Llp Wichita Ks
SIC 8062 7352 6512 General medical & surgical hospitals; Medical equipment rental; Nonresidential building operators; General medical & surgical hospitals; Medical equipment rental; Nonresidential building operators
Pr: Kevin Miller
COO: James McComes
**CFO:* David Busatti
CFO: Ken Johnson
Ofcr: Linnell Maier
VP: Tom Borrego
VP: Kevin Chiles
VP: Thomas Smith
VP: Dan Stafford
VP: Julie Ward
Dir OR: Jenny Schulte
Dir Lab: Lori Christensen
Dir Lab: Jeff Paulsen
Dir Rad: Jeremy Taylor
Dir Rx: Nicolette Lindstrom
Dir Rx: Patrick Mowder

D-U-N-S 96-214-2977
HEALTH CARE INDEMNITY INC
1 Park Plz, Nashville, TN 37203-6527
Tel (615) 344-5864 *Founded/Ownrshp* 1994
Sales NA *EMP* 60
SIC 6331 Fire, marine & casualty insurance
Pr: James D Hinton
COO: Janene Madden
**VP:* Shirley Fuller Cooper
**VP:* Joseph S Haase

D-U-N-S 04-432-5272
HEALTH CARE INDUSTRIES CORP (OH)
HEALTH CARE GROUP
4195 Sugarcreek Dr, Bellbrook, OH 45305-1328
Tel (937) 848-2973 *Founded/Ownrshp* 1980
Sales 46.0MM^E *EMP* 1,025
SIC 8051 8052 Skilled nursing care facilities; Intermediate care facilities; Skilled nursing care facilities; Intermediate care facilities
Pr: Rosalyn B Semelsburger

D-U-N-S 78-935-7308
HEALTH CARE INNOVATIONS INC
2155 Pless Dr Ste C, Brighton, MI 48114-5306
Tel (810) 227-7544 *Founded/Ownrshp* 1991
Sales 10.1MM^E *EMP* 400^E
SIC 7363 7361 Temporary help service; Nurses' registry; Temporary help service; Nurses' registry
CEO: Rick Creyts

D-U-N-S 01-996-2302
HEALTH CARE INNOVATIONS PRIVATE SERVICES INC
4300 Highline Blvd F200, Oklahoma City, OK 73108-1889
Tel (405) 943-0094 *Founded/Ownrshp* 1996
Sales 22.4MM^E *EMP* 800
SIC 8082 8322 Home health care services; Individual & family services; Home health care services; Individual & family services
**Pr:* Brian Wilson
**CFO:* Francis Brewer
VP: Lola Edwards
**VP:* George Schluterman
Snr Mgr: Eric Valkenberg

D-U-N-S 06-001-6433
HEALTH CARE INSURANCE CO (NJ)
746 Alexander Rd, Princeton, NJ 08540-6305
Tel (609) 452-9404 *Founded/Ownrshp* 1976
Sales NA *EMP* 350
SIC 6324 6331 Hospital & medical service plans; Fire, marine & casualty insurance; Hospital & medical service plans; Fire, marine & casualty insurance
Ch Bd: Barry Brown
**Pr:* Donald E Smith
**Treas:* Richard Schaub

D-U-N-S 09-215-9383 IMP
HEALTH CARE LOGISTICS INC (OH)
450 Town St, Circleville, OH 43113-2244
Tel (740) 477-1686 *Founded/Ownrshp* 1985
Sales 51.7MM^E *EMP* 150
SIC 5047

D-U-N-S 17-709-0248
HEALTH CARE MANAGEMENT ADMINISTRATORS INC
HEALTHCARE MGT ADMINISTRATORS
(*Suby of* REGENCE BLUESHIELD) ★
220 120th Ave Ne, Bellevue, WA 98005-3040
Tel (425) 462-1000 *Founded/Ownrshp* 1986
Sales NA *EMP* 121^E
SIC 6411 Insurance claim adjusters, not employed by insurance company
CEO: David Snodgrass
**VP:* Clay Ellis

HEALTH CARE MGT COUNSELORS
See KURT SALMON US INC

HEALTH CARE PERSONNEL
See PRN NURSE INC

D-U-N-S 08-033-9401
HEALTH CARE PLAN INC
UNIVERA HEALTHCARE
205 Park Club Ln, Buffalo, NY 14221-5239
Tel (716) 847-1480 *Founded/Ownrshp* 1976
Sales 60.0MM^E *EMP* 562
Accts Deloitte & Touche Llp
SIC 8011 Health maintenance organization; Health maintenance organization
Pr: Dr Arthur Goshin
**Ch Bd:* Frederick F Yanni Jr
Pr: Jeffrey K Lowry
Pr: Jeffrey A Spencer
**Treas:* James P Nolan MD
Chf Mktg O: Richard Vienne
Ofcr: Susan Emhof
Sr VP: Paul H Huefner
Sr VP: Donna McDonald
VP: Carrie Frank
VP: Jeff Lowry
VP: Pete Rushefsky

VP: Jason Smith
Dir Teleco: Jerilynn Fiorella

D-U-N-S 09-640-5246
HEALTH CARE PROFESSIONALS INC
FREMONT AREA MEDICAL CTR
450 E 23rd St, Fremont, NE 68025-2303
Tel (402) 727-3722 *Founded/Ownrshp* 1988
Sales 5.7MM *EMP* 898
SIC 8011 Clinic, operated by physicians; Clinic, operated by physicians
Pr: D Michael Leibert
**Sec:* David Hanen
**VP:* Peg Kennedy
Dir Rad: Mark Svoboda
Dir Rx: Nick Hummel
Off Mgr: Jeni Archer
CIO: Richard Beran
Software D: Mark Adkins
Sfty Dirs: Deb Jerina
Mtls Mgr: Cory Moss
Sfty Mgr: Linda Bontrager

HEALTH CARE PROVIDER
See CHAPTERS HEALTH SYSTEM INC

D-U-N-S 07-756-4482
▲ HEALTH CARE REIT INC
4500 Dorr St, Toledo, OH 43615-4040
Tel (419) 247-2800 *Founded/Ownrshp* 1970
Sales 3.3MMM *EMP* 438ᴱ
Tkr Sym HCN *Exch* NYS
SIC 6798 Real estate investment trusts; Real estate investment trusts
CEO: Thomas J Derosa
Pr: Charles J Herman Jr
**COO:* Jeffrey H Miller
**CFO:* Scott A Estes
**Treas:* Michael A Crabtree
Chf Inves: Scott M Brinker
**Ex VP:* Erin C Ibele
Sr VP: Stephen Buckeridge
Sr VP: Christy Contardi
Sr VP: Michael A Healy
VP: Eric Benington
VP: Crispen Carey
VP: Michael Garst
VP: Richard Hansen
VP: David Horwitz
VP: Brent Mussery
VP: Greg Schonert
VP: Marcus Stallings
VP: Christian Sweetser
Board of Directors: Jeffrey H Donahue, Fred S Klipsch, Geoffrey G Meyers, Timothy J Naughton, Sharon M Oster, Judith C Pelham, Sergio D Rivera, R Scott Trumbull

D-U-N-S 18-350-9066
■ HEALTH CARE RETIREMENT CORP
(*Suby of* HEALTH CARE AND RETIREMENT CORP OF AMERICA) ★
333 N Summit St Ste 100, Toledo, OH 43604-2615
Tel (419) 252-5500 *Founded/Ownrshp* 1985
Sales 17.6MMᴱ *EMP* 500
SIC 8051 Skilled nursing care facilities; Skilled nursing care facilities
Pr: Paul A Ormond
**Treas:* Spencer Molen
**VP:* Michael Keith Weikel

HEALTH CARE SERVICE
See DENTAL NETWORK OF AMERICA LLC

D-U-N-S 07-860-4947
HEALTH CARE SERVICE CORP ILLINOIS STATE PAC NFP
HCSC
300 E Randolph St Fl 4, Chicago, IL 60601-7302
Tel (312) 653-6000 *Founded/Ownrshp* 2002
Sales NA *EMP* 338ᴱ
SIC 6321 Accident & health insurance
VP: John Gatto
VP: Vijay Murugappan
VP: Britt Olander
VP: Jeff Welch
Dir IT: Vincent Carter
IT Man: Harry Preste

D-U-N-S 85-880-7852
HEALTH CARE SOLUTIONS INC
HOME RESPITORY & INFUSION SVCS
3741 Plaza Dr Ste 1a, Ann Arbor, MI 48108-1880
Tel (734) 327-6588 *Founded/Ownrshp* 1989
Sales 13.5MMᴱ *EMP* 750
SIC 8082 5912 Home health care services; Drug stores; Home health care services; Drug stores
Pr: Timothy Patton
**COO:* Steve Clark
CFO: Mike Cantwell

HEALTH CARE SRVC CORP
See ACADEMIC HEALTHPLANS INC

D-U-N-S 01-428-7171
HEALTH CARE TEMPORARIES INC
H C T
8926 Sherbourne St Ste D, Houston, TX 77016-4900
Tel (713) 631-7106 *Founded/Ownrshp* 1980
Sales 14.6MMᴱ *EMP* 1,100
SIC 8082 1542 1522 1081 5082 Home health care services; Commercial & office building contractors; Remodeling, multi-family dwellings; Metal mining services; General construction machinery & equipment; Home health care services; Commercial & office building contractors; Remodeling, multi-family dwellings; Metal mining services; General construction machinery & equipment
Pr: Arthur Woods
**Sec:* D'Anne Woods
**VP:* Bonita Woods

D-U-N-S 62-099-9706
HEALTH CARE UNLIMITED INC
CENTURY MEDICAL
1100 E Laurel Ave, McAllen, TX 78501-5722
Tel (956) 994-9911 *Founded/Ownrshp* 1990
Sales 80.0MMᴱ *EMP* 500
SIC 5047 8082 Medical equipment & supplies; Home health care services; Medical equipment & supplies; Home health care services
Pr: Joseph Ramon III
Ex VP: Ana Solis
Exec: Karla Puente
IT Man: Joseph Raman
Sales Exec: Steve Tyler
Mktg Mgr: Joe Ramirez

D-U-N-S 09-161-6214
HEALTH CARECHAIN INC
MD IT TRANSCRIPTION SERVICES
4940 Pearl East Cir # 100, Boulder, CO 80301-2442
Tel (720) 932-6262 *Founded/Ownrshp* 2000
Sales 30.6MMᴱ *EMP* 650
SIC 8621 Medical field-related associations; Medical field-related associations
Pr: Thomas Carson
VP: Michael Murphy
Mng Dir: Gary Hutchings
Mng Dir: Karen Kasper
Dir IT: Martin Harris

HEALTH CATALYST
See HQC HOLDINGS INC

HEALTH CENRAL
See WEST ORANGE HEALTHCARE DISTRICT INC

HEALTH CENTER AT RENAISSANCE
See OLMSTED HEALTH AND SERVICE CORP

HEALTH CENTER AT RICHLAND PL
See RICHLAND HEALTH CENTER INC

D-U-N-S 17-253-5197
HEALTH CENTER COMMISSION FOR COUNTY OF CHESTERFIELD VIRGINIA
LUCY CORR VILLAGE
506 Water Pointe Ln, Midlothian, VA 23112-2274
Tel (804) 748-1511 *Founded/Ownrshp* 1970
Sales 22.5MMᴱ *EMP* 300ᴱ
Accts Kpmg Llp Richmond Va
SIC 8051 Convalescent home with continuous nursing care; Convalescent home with continuous nursing care
CEO: James R Musgrave
Ofcr: Charlie Phillips
DP Exec: Kurt Holstrom
MIS Mgr: Kurt Holmstrom
Nrsg Dir: Frances Robinson
HC Dir: Susan Harlow

D-U-N-S 05-066-7083
HEALTH CENTER OF MERRITT ISLAND (FL)
500 Crockett Blvd, Merritt Island, FL 32953-5034
Tel (321) 454-4035 *Founded/Ownrshp* 1990
Sales 19.2MMᴱ *EMP* 300
SIC 8051 Convalescent home with continuous nursing care; Convalescent home with continuous nursing care
Pr: Leslie Williams
Dir Pat Ac: Alaine Fink
Sls&Mrk Ex: Sandy Lengyel

HEALTH CENTRAL
See WEST ORANGE MEMORIAL HOSPITAL TAX DISTRICT

D-U-N-S 03-602-4428
HEALTH CENTRAL PARK
411 N Dillard St, Winter Garden, FL 34787-2816
Tel (407) 296-1600 *Founded/Ownrshp* 2013
Sales 21.1MM *EMP* 43ᴱ
SIC 8099 Health & allied services
Prin: Betsy Ann Harth
Ofcr: Lori Jowett
Off Mgr: Kimberly Dobard
HC Dir: Peggy Samaroo-Sirju

D-U-N-S 07-261-9542
HEALTH CHOICE ARIZONA INC
(*Suby of* IASIS INVESTMENT LLC) ★
410 N 44th St Ste 900, Phoenix, AZ 85008-6522
Tel (480) 968-6866 *Founded/Ownrshp* 1990
Sales NA *EMP* 200
SIC 6321 6411 Accident & health insurance; Insurance agents, brokers & service; Accident & health insurance; Insurance agents, brokers & service
Pr: Carolyn Rose
Dir IT: Melissa Small
Netwrk Mgr: Forad Matti

D-U-N-S 87-762-3926
HEALTH CHOICE NETWORK OF FLORIDA INC
9064 Nw 13th Ter, Doral, FL 33172-2907
Tel (305) 599-1015 *Founded/Ownrshp* 1994
Sales 41.6MM *EMP* 150
SIC 8742 Hospital & health services consultant; Hospital & health services consultant
CEO: Kevin Kearns
Sr VP: Sornia Joseph
Sr VP: Kevin S Kearns
Manager: Tia Harris
Manager: Frank Lillo

D-U-N-S 19-854-7192
HEALTH COALITION INC
HCI
8320 Nw 30th Ter, Doral, FL 33122-1915
Tel (305) 662-2988 *Founded/Ownrshp* 1988
Sales 21.9MMᴱ *EMP* 24
SIC 5122 Blood plasma
Pr: Walter R Shikany Jr
VP: Mark Price
Opers Mgr: Giovanna Flores

D-U-N-S 94-187-6419
HEALTH COMP ADMINISTRATORS INC
621 Santa Fe Ave, Fresno, CA 93721-2724
Tel (559) 499-2450 *Founded/Ownrshp* 1995
Sales NA *EMP* 185
SIC 6411 Medical insurance claim processing, contract or fee basis; Medical insurance claim processing, contract or fee basis
Pr: Phillip Musson
**VP:* Mike Bouskos
VP: Kelly Springsted
VP Admn: Kelly Ferreira
IT Man: Scott Olds

HEALTH CONNECTION, THE
See REVIEW AND HERALD PUBLISHING ASSOCIATION

HEALTH CTR AT HRRISON MEM HOSP
See TRILOGY REHAB SERVICES LLC

D-U-N-S 07-425-7932
HEALTH DELIVERY INC
BAYSIDE HEALTH CENTER
501 Lapeer Ave, Saginaw, MI 48607-1255
Tel (989) 759-6400 *Founded/Ownrshp* 1968
Sales 30.3MM *EMP* 345
Accts Quast Janke And Company Pc
SIC 8011 8021 Medical centers; Dental clinic; Medical centers; Dental clinic
Pr: Santiago Peregrino
**Ch Bd:* Saleem Mannan
**Pr:* Brenda Coughlin
**Pr:* David R Gamez
**Treas:* Albert Martenis III
**Treas:* Timothy Zlomak
Pr Mgr: Monica Woods
Psych: Taylor Flynn

HEALTH DEPARTMENT
See NORTH DAKOTA DEPARTMENT OF HEALTH

HEALTH, DEPARTMENT OF
See SALUD DEPARTAMENTO DE

D-U-N-S 11-125-3712
HEALTH DEPARTMENT OKLAHOMA STATE
(*Suby of* EXECUTIVE OFFICE OF STATE OF OKLAHOMA) ★
1000 Ne 10th St, Oklahoma City, OK 73117-1207
Tel (405) 271-5600 *Founded/Ownrshp* 1970
Sales NA *EMP* 2,200ᴱ
SIC 9431 Administration of public health programs; ; Administration of public health programs;
Ofcr: Jeremie Fisher
Ofcr: Dick Gunn
Ofcr: Phillip Lindsey
Comm Dir: Leslea Bennett-Webb
IT Man: Grace Brown
IT Man: Patsy Leisering
IT Man: Michael Truitt
Doctor: Jana Winfree
Genl Couns: Jimmy Givens
Genl Couns: Don Maisch
Pgrm Dir: Janet Love

D-U-N-S 61-347-8098
HEALTH DESIGN PLUS INC
1755 Georgetown Rd, Hudson, OH 44236-4057
Tel (330) 656-1072 *Founded/Ownrshp* 1988
Sales NA *EMP* 92
SIC 6411 Medical insurance claim processing, contract or fee basis
CEO: Ruth Coleman
**Pr:* William Coleman
CFO: Louis Castellano
Bd of Dir: Frederick Kinsler
Chf Mktg O: Britt Hayes
VP: Roberta Kordish
VP: Noreen Sussman
CIO: John Strickland
Software D: Brandon Mercer
Opers Mgr: Maureen Campbell
QI Cn Mgr: Pat Laird

D-U-N-S 01-455-2258
HEALTH DIAGNOSTIC LABORATORY INC
INNOVATIVE DIAGNOSTIC LAB
(*Suby of* TRUE HEALTH DIAGNOSTICS LLC) ★
737 N 5th St Ste 103, Richmond, VA 23219-1441
Tel (804) 343-2718 *Founded/Ownrshp* 2015
Sales 314.0MM *EMP* 511ᴱ
SIC 8734 Testing laboratories; Testing laboratories
CEO: Joseph McConnell
Chf Mktg O: Tara Dall
Ex VP: Anna McKean
Ex VP: Douglas L Sbertoli
Sr VP: Dan Dunham
Sr VP: Mark A Herzog
Sr VP: Leslie Strickler
Sr VP: Cheryl Wiltshire
VP: Scott Blackwell
VP: Connie Chao-Shern
VP: Maciek Sasinowski
Dir Lab: Daniel Hoefner

D-U-N-S 82-813-6064
HEALTH DIAGNOSTICS LLC
HEALTH DIAGNOSTICS OF MIAMI
8 Corporate Center Dr # 105, Melville, NY 11747-3193
Tel (631) 420-3701 *Founded/Ownrshp* 2008
Sales 33.4MMᴱ *EMP* 500ᴱ
Accts Marcum & Kliegman Llp New Yo
SIC 8011 Offices & clinics of medical doctors; Offices & clinics of medical doctors
Pr: Brad Peters
**Sr Pt:* John Ross
COO: Timothy Damadian
Sr VP: Ronald Lehman
**VP:* Jim Persoons
Pr Mgr: Debbie Llanes

HEALTH DIAGNOSTICS OF MIAMI
See HEALTH DIAGNOSTICS LLC

D-U-N-S 93-394-9158
■ HEALTH DIALOG SERVICES CORP
(*Suby of* RITE AID CORP) ★
100 Summer St Ste 1400, Boston, MA 02110-2134
Tel (617) 406-5200 *Founded/Ownrshp* 2014
Sales 35.8MMᴱ *EMP* 300
SIC 8082 Home health care services; Home health care services
CFO: Web Golinkin
**COO:* Karen Staniforth
CFO: Gregg Spiro
**Treas:* Greg Spiro
Sr Cor Off: Ray Caron
Sr Cor Off: Don Hawley
Sr Cor Off: Patrick Martingly
Ofcr: Kate Bolland
**Ofcr:* Peter Goldbach
Sr VP: David Barlow
Sr VP: Barry Dyer
VP: Greg Cornellier
VP: Elise Gemeinhardt-Burns
VP: Rochelle Porper
VP: Matthew Siegel
Exec: Mary Bresnahan

D-U-N-S 13-754-4552
HEALTH E SYSTEMS LLC
HEALTHESYSTEMS
5100 W Lemon St Ste 311, Tampa, FL 33609-1129
Tel (813) 463-1235 *Founded/Ownrshp* 2002
Sales NA *EMP* 412
SIC 6411 Insurance information & consulting services; Insurance information & consulting services
Ofcr: Terry Ridenour
Assoc VP: David Gray
Sr VP: Robert Goldberg
Dir Rx: Ralph Kendall
Off Mgr: Stephanie Narvades
Snr Sftwr: Michael Gibaldi
QA Dir: Elizabeth Acosta
QA Dir: Ramadevi Devulapalli
QA Dir: Joleen Jones
QA Dir: Prasanth Nair
Dir IT: Craig Hoss

HEALTH EAST WOODWINDS
See WOODWINDS HEALTH CAMPUS

D-U-N-S 12-316-0629
HEALTH ENTERPRISES LIFE LONG PLAN INC
HEALTH ENTPS LIFE-LONG PLANS
5805 Sepulveda Blvd, Van Nuys, CA 91411-2546
Tel (818) 654-0330 *Founded/Ownrshp* 1999
Sales 6.7MMᴱ *EMP* 500
SIC 8082 Home health care services; Home health care services
Pr: Johnathan Istrin

HEALTH ENTPS LIFE-LONG PLANS
See HEALTH ENTERPRISES LIFE LONG PLAN INC

D-U-N-S 80-587-4018
HEALTH EVOLUTION PARTNERS
555 Mission St Ste 2300, San Francisco, CA 94105-0925
Tel (415) 362-5800 *Founded/Ownrshp* 2007
Sales 24.8MMᴱ *EMP* 290ᴱ
SIC 8741 Management services; Management services
Pr: David J Brailer
Pt: Ned Brown
Pt: David A Smith
Pt: Kay Yun
CFO: Nina Labatt
VP: Thomas P Chung
VP: Kevin Tseng

D-U-N-S 86-741-0003
HEALTH EXCHANGE OF ARIZONA INC
1540 E Maryland Ave # 100, Phoenix, AZ 85014-1448
Tel (602) 265-9606 *Founded/Ownrshp* 1992
Sales 5.9MMᴱ *EMP* 300
SIC 7361 Nurses' registry; Nurses' registry
CEO: Richard Bloome
**Pr:* Tom Ramsberger

HEALTH EXTRAS CATALYST RX
See CATALYST RX INC

D-U-N-S 36-293-5173
HEALTH FACILITIES MANAGEMENT CORP
(*Suby of* CIRCLE B ENTERPRISES HOLDING CO INC) ★
731 N Main St, Sikeston, MO 63801-2151
Tel (573) 471-1276 *Founded/Ownrshp* 1984
Sales 36.0MMᴱ *EMP* 2,800
SIC 6531 Real estate managers; Real estate managers
Pr: Don C Bedell
**Treas:* Lonnie Hasty
**VP:* William C Mitchell

D-U-N-S 03-944-8006
HEALTH FACILITY STAFFING INC
8630 Delmar Blvd Ste 201, Saint Louis, MO 63124-2208
Tel (314) 991-3166 *Founded/Ownrshp* 1998
Sales 9.8MMᴱ *EMP* 600
SIC 7361 8082 Nurses' registry; Home health care services; Nurses' registry; Home health care services
Pr: William Mahon
**VP:* Theodore J Mahon

HEALTH FIRST
See SENIOR HEALTH PARTNERS INC

HEALTH FIRST
See HF MANAGEMENT SERVICES LLC

HEALTH FIRST HEALTH PLANS
See CAPE CANAVERAL HOSPITAL INC

HEALTH FIRST HEALTH PLANS
See HOLMES REGIONAL MEDICAL CENTER INC

HEALTH FIRST HEALTH PLANS
See HEALTH FIRST INC

D-U-N-S 94-718-7423
HEALTH FIRST HEALTH PLANS INC
(*Suby of* HEALTH FIRST HEALTH PLANS) ★
6450 Us Highway 1, Rockledge, FL 32955-5747
Tel (321) 434-5600 *Founded/Ownrshp* 1997
Sales NA *EMP* 155
Accts Ernst & Young Orlando Fl
SIC 6324 Health maintenance organization (HMO), insurance only; Health maintenance organization (HMO), insurance only
Pr: Jerry Senne
**Ch Bd:* William Brennan
**Treas:* Robert Galloway
**VP:* Larry Garrison

D-U-N-S 80-704-9655
HEALTH FIRST INC
HEALTH FIRST HEALTH PLANS
6450 Us Highway 1, Rockledge, FL 32955-5747
Tel (321) 434-4300 *Founded/Ownrshp* 1995
Sales 1.1MMM *EMP* 6,900
Accts Ernst & Young Llp Orlando Fl
SIC 8062 8011 8082 8069 7991 6324 General medical & surgical hospitals; Medical centers; Home health care services; Chronic disease hospital; Health club; Health maintenance organization (HMO), insurance only; General medical & surgical hospitals; Medical centers; Home health care services; Chronic disease hospital; Health club; Health maintenance organization (HMO), insurance only
Pr: Steve Johnson
Ch Bd: James Shaw
V Ch: Albert Francis
Pr: Christine Rushnell
COO: Larry F Garrison
COO: Jo Powell
CFO: Robert C Galloway
V Ch Bd: Russell E Fischer
Ofcr: Ed Hannah
Ex VP: Stuart Mitchell
Sr VP: Lori Delone
VP: Sally Forsberg
VP: Roberta B Stoner
Exec: Paula Just
Exec: Robert Suttles
Exec: Dan Tesenair
Dir Rx: Katherine Goldman

D-U-N-S 07-833-0206
HEALTH FIRST MEDICAL GROUP LLC
MIMA SERVICES, INC.
(*Suby of* HEALTH FIRST HEALTH PLANS) ★
6450 Us Highway 1, Rockledge, FL 32955-5747
Tel (321) 434-4300 *Founded/Ownrshp* 2013
Sales 33.6MM^E *EMP* 750
SIC 8011 Internal medicine, physician/surgeon; Internal medicine, physician/surgeon
CEO: Jeffrey S Stalnaker MD
**Pr:* Travis Douglas
**Sec:* Joseph G Felkner
VP: Terri Keith
VP: Drew A Rector
Obsttrcn: Danielle Boucher
Doctor: Victor Benezra
Doctor: John Campbell
Doctor: Leonard Grecul
Doctor: Nelson Sang MD
Doctor: Lee Scheinbart

HEALTH FIRST SERVICE
See COCOA BEACH AREA HEALTH SERVICE INC

D-U-N-S 18-319-6138
HEALTH FITNESS CORP
(*Suby of* TRUSTMARK COMPANIES) ★
1700 W 82nd St Ste 200, Minneapolis, MN 55431-1465
Tel (800) 639-7913 *Founded/Ownrshp* 2010
Sales 132.1MM^E *EMP* 3,472^E
SIC 7991 8099 Physical fitness facilities; Health screening service; Physical fitness facilities; Health screening service
Pr: Paul Lotharius
**COO:* Brian Gagne
**CFO:* Karen Preusker
**Chf Mktg O:* James O Reynolds MD
**Chf Mktg O:* Dennis Richling
**Ofcr:* Tatiana Shnaiden
Sr VP: Kathy Machak
Sr VP: J Mark McConnell
Sr VP: Sean McManamy
VP: Edward Framer
VP: Greg Siedschlag
VP Bus Dev: Nancy Cashon
VP Bus Dev: Scott Kinzer
Assoc Dir: Sandy Reimer
Board of Directors: David F Durenberger, K James Ehlen MD, Wendy D Lynch, Robert J Marzec, John C Penn, Curtis M Selquist, Mark W Sheffert, Linda Hall Whitman, Rodney A Young

D-U-N-S 03-312-4793
■ **HEALTH FOOD ASSOCIATES INC** (OK)
AKINS NATURAL FOODS MARKET
(*Suby of* AMCON DISTRIBUTING CO INC) ★
7807 E 51st St, Tulsa, OK 74145-7847
Tel (918) 663-4137 *Founded/Ownrshp* 1961, 1999
Sales 39.3MM^E *EMP* 262
SIC 5499 5999 Health & dietetic food stores; Cosmetics; Health & dietetic food stores; Cosmetics
Pr: Eric Hinkefent
Bd of Dir: Mary A O Dell
VP: R P Mannshreck

D-U-N-S 11-228-1998
HEALTH FORUM LLC
(*Suby of* AHA) ★
155 N Wacker Dr Ste 400, Chicago, IL 60606-1719
Tel (312) 893-6800 *Founded/Ownrshp* 1999
Sales 15.0MM^E *EMP* 450
SIC 8082 Home health care services; Home health care services
Bd of Dir: David L Bernd
Bd of Dir: Joan Elcock
Ex Dir: Michaeleen Hogan
Ex Dir: J J Rorie
Ex Dir: Elizabeth Summy
Ex Dir: Laura Woodburn
Sls Mgr: Mark Harju
Doctor: Edward Miller
Art Dir: Cheri Kusek

D-U-N-S 07-288-5312
HEALTH FOUNDATION OF CLINTON COUNTY
610 W Mn St, Wilmington, OH 45177
Tel (937) 382-6611 *Founded/Ownrshp* 1951
Sales 73.5MM^E *EMP* 760
SIC 8062 General medical & surgical hospitals; General medical & surgical hospitals
Pr: Mark Dooley
**COO:* Bradley Mabry
**CFO:* Bradley Boggus
Exec: Gene Hook
Pgrm Dir: Rhonda Dick

D-U-N-S 05-433-3521
HEALTH FUTURE LLC (OR)
916 Town Centre Dr, Medford, OR 97504-6100
Tel (541) 772-3062 *Founded/Ownrshp* 1979
Sales NA *EMP* 60
SIC 6324 8742 6321 Hospital & medical service plans; Management consulting services; Accident & health insurance
VP: Denise Ernst
Rgnl Mgr: Leslie Flick

D-U-N-S 05-226-6181
HEALTH IN COMPASS INC
318 Maxwell Rd Ste 500, Alpharetta, GA 30009-2064
Tel (770) 274-0482 *Founded/Ownrshp* 2000
Sales 35.9MM^E *EMP* 250
SIC 8742 Hospital & health services consultant; Hospital & health services consultant
Pr: Dan A Fuller
Pr: Don Smith
**CEO:* Robert Holloway
VP: Caryn Bremer
VP: Damian Grzywacz
VP: Tom Smith
VP: Gavin Warner
Dir Bus: Matt Clough

D-U-N-S 07-924-6934
HEALTH INFORMATION MANAGEMENT SYSTEM SOCIETY
H I M S S AUSTIN TEXAS CHAPTER
(*Suby of* H I M S S) ★
P.O. Box 6011 (78762-6011)
Tel (512) 785-2227 *Founded/Ownrshp* 2004
Sales 20.0M *EMP* 500
SIC 8621 Health association; Health association
Pr: Emma Cartmell

HEALTH INSUR PLAN ADMNSTRATORS
See HIP ADMINISTRATORS OF FLORIDA INC

D-U-N-S 01-679-6499
▲ **HEALTH INSURANCE INNOVATIONS INC**
15438 N Florida Ave # 201, Tampa, FL 33613-1256
Tel (877) 376-5831 *Founded/Ownrshp* 2008
Sales NA *EMP* 285^E
Accts Grant Thornton Llp Tampa Flo
Tkr Sym HIIQ *Exch* NGM
SIC 6411 Insurance agents, brokers & service; Insurance agents, brokers & service
Ch Bd: Michael W Kosloske
Pr: Patrick McNamee
COO: Bruce A Telkamp
Ex VP: Michael A Petrizzo Jr
Sr VP: Michael Hershberger
**CTO:* Sheldon Wang

D-U-N-S 02-091-8533
HEALTH INTEGRATED INC
10008 N Dale Mabry Hwy, Tampa, FL 33618-4424
Tel (813) 264-7577 *Founded/Ownrshp* 2003
Sales 51.2MM^E *EMP* 200
SIC 8011 8322 Health maintenance organization; Individual & family services; Health maintenance organization; Individual & family services
CEO: Shan S Padda
Pr: Dave Beery
Pr: Trish Dare
Pr: Heidi Howard
Pr: Steven Wigginton
COO: H Bradley Weaver
COO: Craig S Wigginton
CFO: Thomas M Bendoraitis
Treas: Sam D Toney
Bd of Dir: Brad Fluegel
Ex VP: Zachary Fritz
Ex VP: Tracy Korman
Ex VP: Tracy Weil Korman
Sr VP: Victor R Dragon
Sr VP: Tom Joyer
Sr VP: Angie Merkel
Sr VP: Francisco Perin
Sr VP: G Francisco Perin
Sr VP: Daniel Prewitt
Sr VP: Jane Scott
Sr VP: Bradley Weaver
Board of Directors: Tom Craren, Brad Fluegel, Charlene Frizzera

D-U-N-S 19-014-6923
HEALTH INTEGRITY LLC
(*Suby of* QUALITY HEALTH STRATEGIES INC) ★
28464 Marlboro Ave, Easton, MD 21601-2732
Tel (410) 822-0697 *Founded/Ownrshp* 2005
Sales 46.1MM *EMP* 196
Accts Mcgladrey Llp Baltimore Mary
SIC 8099 Hospital & health services consultant; Medical services organization
Pr: Sandy Love
**CFO:* Rebecca Combs
**Sr VP:* Jaysen Eisengrein
Genl Mgr: Helen Orme

D-U-N-S 13-311-9359
HEALTH INVENTURES LLC
(*Suby of* SURGICAL CARE AFFILIATES LLC) ★
1070 W Century Dr Ste 202, Louisville, CO 80027-1657
Tel (720) 304-8940 *Founded/Ownrshp* 2013
Sales 30.2MM^E *EMP* 450
SIC 8062 General medical & surgical hospitals; General medical & surgical hospitals
CEO: Dick Hanley
Pr: Christian D Ellison
Assoc VP: Susan Armbruster
Sr VP: Dennis Martin
VP: Sherry Goldstein
VP: Dan Hamilton
VP: Wayne Lee
VP: Suzanne Rogers
VP: Glen Weaver
VP: Bradley Welling
Software D: Lori Vernon

HEALTH KEEPERZ
See HEALTHKEEPERZ INC

D-U-N-S 03-409-5229
HEALTH LANGUAGE INC (DE)
(*Suby of* WOLTERS KLUWER HEALTH INC) ★
4600 S Syracuse St # 1200, Denver, CO 80237-2743
Tel (303) 307-4400 *Founded/Ownrshp* 2001, 2013
Sales 26.8MM^E *EMP* 80
SIC 5045 Computer software
Pr: George Schwend
**CFO:* Brian McDonald
**Sr VP:* Dr Brian Levy
**VP:* Marc Horowitz
VP: April Yoder
VP: Harlan Zeinstra
Dir Bus: Benton Barney
Snr Sftwr: Pedro Barrios
Snr Sftwr: Jeremy Kasmann
**CTO:* Oswaldo H Leon
Software D: Joe Mielke

D-U-N-S 05-501-9997
HEALTH LEADS INC
2 Oliver St Ste 10e, Boston, MA 02109-4926
Tel (617) 391-3633 *Founded/Ownrshp* 2003
Sales 25.1MM *EMP* 25
SIC 8099 Health & allied services
CEO: Rebecca Onie
Pr: Brian Hermanspan
COO: Sarah Troia
Sr VP: Sue Dalelio
Sr VP: Kelly Hall
VP: Karen Tirozzi
Dir Bus: Bill Gleason
Ex Dir: Adam Shyevitch
Prgrm Mgr: Debbie Appel
Prgrm Mgr: Katrina Cosner
Prgrm Mgr: Sarah Hewes

HEALTH LINE CLINICAL LAB
See TAURUS WEST INC

D-U-N-S 08-619-0493
■ **HEALTH MANAGEMENT ASSOCIATES INC**
HMA
(*Suby of* COMMUNITY HEALTH SYSTEMS INC) ★
5811 Pelican Bay Blvd # 500, Naples, FL 34108-2711
Tel (239) 598-3131 *Founded/Ownrshp* 2014
Sales 5.1MMM^E *EMP* 40,400
SIC 8062 General medical & surgical hospitals; General medical & surgical hospitals
Pr: John M Starcher Jr
Chf Rad: Jim Barnes
**Ch Bd:* William J Schoen
COO: Cindi Butcher
COO: Daniel J Knell
COO: Harlo McCall
COO: Phil Minden
COO: Christopher Rakunas
COO: Joshua Self
COO: Christian Stroucken
COO: Patrice Tavernier
COO: Joseph Webb
CFO: Cassie Ball
CFO: Thomas Brook
**CFO:* Kelly E Curry
CFO: Bob Farnham
CFO: Kyle Johnson
CFO: Arthur Koszalinski
CFO: Gregory Pearson
**Ex VP:* Kerrin E Gillespie
**Sr VP:* Steven E Clifton

D-U-N-S 17-492-4845
HEALTH MANAGEMENT ASSOCIATES INC
HMA
120 N Washington Sq # 705, Lansing, MI 48933-1618
Tel (517) 482-9236 *Founded/Ownrshp* 1985
Sales 30.2MM^E *EMP* 85
SIC 8748 8742 Business consulting; Management consulting services
CEO: Marilynn Y Evert
**Pr:* Jay Rosen
**COO:* Kelly Johnson
**CFO:* Bruce Gould
**VP:* Vernon Smith
VP: Elliot Wicks
Dir Risk M: Vicki Skinner
Comm Dir: Kelly Niebel
Ex Dir: Linda Hamacher
Mng Dir: James Epolito
Admn Mgr: Terrence Conway

D-U-N-S 13-140-5318
■ **HEALTH MANAGEMENT CORP**
(*Suby of* ANTHEM INC) ★
2015 Staples Mill Rd, Richmond, VA 23230-3108
Tel (804) 662-6800 *Founded/Ownrshp* 2009
Sales NA *EMP* 39^E
SIC 6324 Group hospitalization plans
Pr: Joan Kennedy
**CFO:* Mike Modiz
VP: Samuel Cramer
VP: Jim Hinkle
VP: Paul Martino
Exec: Cary Boehnlein

D-U-N-S 78-646-5070
HEALTH MANAGEMENT OF KANSAS INC
WINDSOR PLACE
104 W 8th St, Coffeyville, KS 67337-5806
Tel (620) 251-6545 *Founded/Ownrshp* 1992
Sales 14.1MM^E *EMP* 319
SIC 8741 Nursing & personal care facility management; Nursing & personal care facility management
Pr: Charles W Wurth

D-U-N-S 07-526-6346
■ **HEALTH MANAGEMENT SYSTEMS INC**
HMS BUSINESS SERVICES
(*Suby of* HMS HOLDINGS CORP) ★
5615 High Point Dr # 100, Irving, TX 75038-2434
Tel (214) 453-3000 *Founded/Ownrshp* 1974
Sales 164.3MM^E *EMP* 1,125
SIC 7374 7372 Data processing & preparation; Application computer software; Business oriented computer software; Data processing & preparation; Application computer software; Business oriented computer software
Pr: William C Lucia
Pr: Carrie Cunningham
Pr: Christopher Frey
Pr: Arika Pierce
CFO: Pam Baffoni
**CFO:* Walter Hosp
CFO: Jeffrey Sherman
Ofcr: Alexandra Holt
Sr VP: Kimberly Glenn
Sr VP: Joe Joy
**Sr VP:* Joseph Joy
Sr VP: Dennis Oakes
**Sr VP:* Donna Price
**Sr VP:* Stephen Vaccaro
**VP:* Thomas A Baggett Jr
VP: Peter Demy
VP: Peter Fleischman
VP: Lawrence Friedman
**VP:* Michael Hostetler
VP: Mark Olson
VP: Dave Viestenz

D-U-N-S 00-462-3992
HEALTH MARKET SCIENCE INC
(*Suby of* LEXISNEXIS RISK SOLUTIONS INC) ★
2700 Horizon Dr Ste 300, King of Prussia, PA 19406-2677
Tel (610) 940-4002 *Founded/Ownrshp* 2015
Sales 54.4MM^E *EMP* 200
SIC 7371 7372 Computer software development; Prepackaged software; Computer software development; Prepackaged software
CEO: Matt Reichert
**Pr:* Jeff Klein
**CFO:* Jeffrey Weiss
Sr VP: Craig Ford
Sr VP: Zack Henderson
VP: Don Destefano
VP: Stacey Levas
Dir Bus: John Hopkins
**Dir Sec:* F Thomas Balzer
Snr Sftwr: Alan Horton
CIO: Tony Chough

HEALTH MART
See GRANDVIEW PHARMACY INC

HEALTH MART
See PVP OF MONROE INC

HEALTH MART
See BONDS DRUG STORE INC

HEALTH MART
See KAUP PHARMACY INC

D-U-N-S 80-939-9892
HEALTH MISSISSIPPI ORGANIZATION INC
FINANCE AND ACCOUNTS
(*Suby of* EXECUTIVE OFFICE OF STATE OF MISSISSIPPI) ★
570 E Woodrow Wilson Ave, Jackson, MS 39216-4538
Tel (601) 576-7400 *Founded/Ownrshp* 1877
Sales 108.5MM^E *EMP* 2,000
SIC 8099 Administration of public health programs; ; Physical examination service, insurance
**Ch Bd:* Lucius Lampton
Ofcr: Mitchell Adcock
Ofcr: Paul Byers
Ofcr: Scottie Martin
Ofcr: Dena Pope IV
VP: Steve Beckham
Dir Lab: Wanda Ingersoll
Dir Lab: Sammie Malone
Dir Lab: Daphne Ware
Comm Dir: Liz Sharlot
Prgrm Mgr: Steven Quilter

HEALTH MOR AT HOME CBP
See HMI INDUSTRIES INC

HEALTH NATURAL SYSTEMS
See HYPER NETWORK SOLUTIONS LLC

D-U-N-S 84-800-3661
■ **HEALTH NET FEDERAL SERVICES LLC**
(*Suby of* HEALTH NET INC) ★
2025 Aerojet Rd, Rancho Cordova, CA 95742-6418
Tel (916) 935-5000 *Founded/Ownrshp* 1997
Sales NA *EMP* 1,000
SIC 6324 Hospital & medical service plans; Hospital & medical service plans
Pr: Thomas F Carrato
Chf Mktg O: Jay L Siverstein
Prgrm Mgr: Hariharan Sundararajan
CTO: Thomas Carrato
Snr Mgr: Patrick Kurlej

D-U-N-S 09-848-9776
■ **HEALTH NET HEALTH PLAN OF OREGON INC**
(*Suby of* HEALTH NET INC) ★
13221 Sw 68th Pkwy Ste 20, Tigard, OR 97223-8328
Tel (503) 213-5000 *Founded/Ownrshp* 1997
Sales NA *EMP* 250
SIC 6324 8011 Hospital & medical service plans; Offices & clinics of medical doctors; Hospital & medical service plans; Offices & clinics of medical doctors
Ch Bd: C E Skeeters MD
**Pr:* Chris Ellertson
**CEO:* Martin A Preizler
**CFO:* Pat Isaac
**Ofcr:* Brenda Bruns
VP: Ted Falk
VP: Kevin McCartin
VP: Ron Morgan
VP: Louise Walczak
Ex Dir: Judy Irving

D-U-N-S 11-520-5437
■ **HEALTH NET INC**
(*Suby of* HEALTH NET INC) ★
21281 Burbank Blvd Fl 4, Woodland Hills, CA 91367-7073
Tel (818) 676-6775 *Founded/Ownrshp* 1997
Sales NA *EMP* 1,075

SIC 6324 8062 6311 6321 6331 5912 Hospital & medical service plans; General medical & surgical hospitals; Life insurance carriers; Disability health insurance; Accident & health insurance carriers; Workers' compensation insurance; Drug stores & proprietary stores; Hospital & medical service plans; General medical & surgical hospitals; Life insurance carriers; Disability health insurance; Accident & health insurance carriers; Workers' compensation insurance; Drug stores & proprietary stores
Ch Bd: Jay Gellert
CFO: Owen Block
Chf Cred: Patricia Clarey
Bd of Dir: Bruce Willison
Ex VP: Joseph Capezza
VP: Angelee F Bouchard
VP: Martin Esquivel
VP: David Haddad
VP: Sharon Lewis
VP: Dorothy Lucas
VP: Adrienne Morrell
Exec: Barbara Armstrong
Exec: Donna Hoffmeier

D-U-N-S 79-833-0908
▲ HEALTH NET INC
21650 Oxnard St Fl 25, Woodland Hills, CA 91367-7829
Tel (818) 676-6000 *Founded/Ownrshp* 1997
Sales NA *EMP* 8,014
Tkr Sym HNT *Exch* NYS
SIC 6324 Hospital & medical service plans; Hospital & medical service plans
Pr: Jay M Gellert
Pr: Thomas F Carrato
Pr: Steven H Nelson
COO: James E Woys
Chf Mktg O: Dan Lieberman
Ofcr: Rich Hall
Ofcr: Juanell Hefner
Ex VP: Marvin Rich
Ex VP: Gary Smith
Sr VP: Angelee F Bouchard
Sr VP: Gerald V Coil
Sr VP: Karin D Mayhew
VP: Peter Oneill
Creative D: Lisa Eisen
Dir Rx: Scott Wert
Board of Directors: Mary Anne Citrino, Theodore F Craver Jr, Vicki B Escarra, Gale S Fitzgerald, Roger F Greaves, Douglas M Mancino, George Miller, Bruce G Willison, Frederick C Yeager

D-U-N-S 79-633-2844
■ HEALTH NET LIFE INSURANCE CO
(*Suby of* HEALTH NET INC) ★
21281 Burbank Blvd, Woodland Hills, CA 91367-7073
Tel (800) 865-6288 *Founded/Ownrshp* 2007
Sales NA *EMP* 242ᴱ
SIC 6324 Hospital & medical service plans
Prin: James Edwin Woys

D-U-N-S 80-984-5167
■ HEALTH NET OF ARIZONA INC
(*Suby of* HEALTH NET INC) ★
1230 W Washington St # 401, Tempe, AZ 85281-1250
Tel (602) 286-9242 *Founded/Ownrshp* 1997
Sales NA *EMP* 700
SIC 6324 Hospital & medical service plans; Hospital & medical service plans
Pr: Rose Megian
Ofcr: Sharon Bottrill
VP: Chad Niles

D-U-N-S 05-864-8838
HEALTH NETWORK LABORATORIES LIMITED PARTNERSHIP
794 Roble Rd, Allentown, PA 18109-9110
Tel (610) 402-8170 *Founded/Ownrshp* 1998
Sales 31.1MMᴱ *EMP* 676ᴱ
SIC 8071 8721 Pathological laboratory; Accounting, auditing & bookkeeping; Pathological laboratory; Accounting, auditing & bookkeeping
CEO: Peter E Fisher MD
**COO:* Beth A Rokus
**CFO:* John P Hoch
**Ch:* Daniel F Brown
**VP:* Lisa Anthony
**CIO:* Jane Erdman

D-U-N-S 15-242-7324
HEALTH NEW ENGLAND INC
BAYSTATE HEALTH SYS HLTH SVCS
(*Suby of* BAYSTATE HEALTH SYSTEM HEALTH SERVICES INC) ★
1 Monarch Pl Ste 1500, Springfield, MA 01144-1500
Tel (413) 787-4000 *Founded/Ownrshp* 1985
Sales NA *EMP* 222
SIC 6324 Health maintenance organization (HMO), insurance only; Health maintenance organization (HMO), insurance only
Ch: Michael J Daly
**Pr:* Peter Straley
**CEO:* Maura McCaffrey
CFO: Robert Kosior
**Treas:* Dennis Chalke
**Chf Mktg O:* Laurie E Gianturco
Ofcr: Patrick O'Shea
**VP:* David Boss
**VP:* James M Kessler
**VP:* Philip M Lacombe
**VP:* Bruce M Ruder

HEALTH ONE
See ROSE MEDICAL GROUP

D-U-N-S 13-931-2565
HEALTH OPTIONS INC
FLORIDA BLUE HMO
4800 Deerwood Campus Pkwy, Jacksonville, FL 32246-6498
Tel (904) 564-5700 *Founded/Ownrshp* 1984
Sales NA *EMP* 450
Accts Price Waterhouse Coopers Llp
SIC 6324 Group hospitalization plans; Health maintenance organization (HMO), insurance only
Pr: Joyce Kramzer
CFO: Robert Chris
**Treas:* William Coats
**VP:* Charles Richards
**Prin:* Robert Lufrano

HEALTH PARTNERS
See TENNESSEE WEST HEALTHCARE INC

D-U-N-S 55-688-1464
HEALTH PARTNERS INC
17515 W 9 Mile Rd # 1185, Southfield, MI 48075-4403
Tel (248) 423-3466 *Founded/Ownrshp* 1990
Sales 21.3MM *EMP* 304
Accts Derderian Kann Seyferth & Salu
SIC 8082 7363 Home health care services; Medical help service; Home health care services; Medical help service
Pr: Michael R Gillet
**Sr VP:* Richard Brown
VP: John Prosser
VP Opers: Peggy Clink

D-U-N-S 94-822-2021
HEALTH PARTNERS INC
HEALTH PARTNERS ORGANIZATION
8170 33rd Ave S, Minneapolis, MN 55425-1614
Tel (952) 883-6000 *Founded/Ownrshp* 1984
Sales 206.1MMᴱ *EMP* 9,000
SIC 8062 General medical & surgical hospitals; General medical & surgical hospitals
Pr: Mary Brainerd
Mng Pt: Bradley E Cooper
V Ch: Margaret A Lund
Pr: Laura Oberst
Sr VP: Cathy Holmes
Sr VP: Doug Smith
VP: Donna Zimmerman
Ex Dir: Eliot Seide
CIO: Alan Abramson
DP Exec: Leroy Guba
Dir IT: Craig Taylor

HEALTH PARTNERS ORGANIZATION
See HEALTH PARTNERS INC

D-U-N-S 18-696-0332
HEALTH PARTNERS PLANS INC
901 Market St Ste 500, Philadelphia, PA 19107-4496
Tel (215) 849-9606 *Founded/Ownrshp* 1985
Sales 910.1MM *EMP* 620ᴱ
Accts Kpmg Llp Philadelphia Penns
SIC 8011 Health maintenance organization; Health maintenance organization
Pr: William S George
**COO:* Elaine Markezin
**CFO:* Martin J Brill
**Treas:* Karen Armtrong
**Sr VP:* Don Daddario
Sr VP: Lovell Harmon
**Sr VP:* Judy B Harrington
**Sr VP:* Debra Kircher
**Sr VP:* Vicki Sessoms
Sr VP: Steven E Szebenyi
VP: Johnna Baker
VP: Rebecca Kohl
VP: Douglas Roberts
VP: Caroline Russell
VP: Tal Zarom

HEALTH PDTS DIV
See TEFRON USA INC

D-U-N-S 10-572-2623
■ HEALTH PLAN OF NEVADA INC
(*Suby of* SIERRA HEALTH SERVICES INC) ★
2720 N Tenaya Way, Las Vegas, NV 89128-0424
Tel (702) 242-7300 *Founded/Ownrshp* 1981
Sales 1.3MMM *EMP* 250
SIC 8011 Health maintenance organization; Health maintenance organization
Pr: Jon Bunker
Chf Mktg O: Steven Evans
Sr VP: A P Smith Jr

D-U-N-S 92-983-9777
HEALTH PLAN OF SAN JOAQUIN
7751 S Manthey Rd, French Camp, CA 95231-9802
Tel (209) 942-6300 *Founded/Ownrshp* 1994
Sales NA *EMP* 120
Accts Deloitte & Touche Llp
SIC 6324 Health maintenance organization (HMO), insurance only; Health maintenance organization (HMO), insurance only
CEO: Amy Shinn
CFO: Paul Antitua
Chf Mktg O: Lakshmi Dhanvanthari
CIO: Sanjay Vail
Dir IT: Katherine Kutz
Info Man: Jerry Sonderman
Pharmcst: Johnathan Yeh

HEALTH PLAN OF SAN MATEO
See SAN MATEO HEALTH COMMISSION

D-U-N-S 09-420-8816
HEALTH PLAN OF UPPER OHIO VALLEY INC (WV)
52160 National Rd E, Saint Clairsville, OH 43950-9306
Tel (740) 695-3585 *Founded/Ownrshp* 1979
Sales NA *EMP* 400
Accts Ernst & Young Us Llp Indianap
SIC 6324 8082 Health maintenance organization (HMO), insurance only; Home health care services; Health maintenance organization (HMO), insurance only; Home health care services
Pr: Phillip D Wright
**Ch Bd:* James Newton
CFO: Jeff Knight
**CFO:* John J Yeager
VP: Patti Fass
CIO: Robert Roset
MIS Dir: Bob Roset
Mktg Dir: Patti Fast
Cert Phar: Cortney Bostic

D-U-N-S 00-514-6840
HEALTH PLANS INC
(*Suby of* HARVARD PILGRIM HEALTH CARE INC) ★
1500 W Park Dr Ste 330, Westborough, MA 01581-3912
Tel (508) 752-2480 *Founded/Ownrshp* 2005
Sales NA *EMP* 222
SIC 6411 Insurance agents, brokers & service; Insurance agents, brokers & service
Pr: William R Breidenbach
**VP:* Deborah Hodges
Manager: John Webber

D-U-N-S 07-748-4280
■ HEALTH PLUS PREPAID HEALTH SERVICES PLAN INC
(*Suby of* AMERIGROUP CORP) ★
9 Pine St Fl 14, New York, NY 10005-4702
Tel (718) 532-1011 *Founded/Ownrshp* 2011
Sales NA *EMP* 800
SIC 6321 6324 8741 Accident & health insurance; Hospital & medical service plans; Management services; Accident & health insurance; Hospital & medical service plans; Management services
CEO: Thomas Early
Ex Dir: Berry Volin

D-U-N-S 06-870-8999
HEALTH PRODUCTS RESEARCH INC
ADVANCE INSIGHTS
(*Suby of* INVENTIV HEALTH INC) ★
500 Atrium Dr Ste 100, Somerset, NJ 08873-4161
Tel (908) 534-4148 *Founded/Ownrshp* 1999
Sales 98.4MMᴱ *EMP* 2,810
SIC 8742 8732 Marketing consulting services; Sales (including sales management) consultant; Commercial nonphysical research; Marketing consulting services; Sales (including sales management) consultant; Commercial nonphysical research
Pr: Norman Stalsberg
VP: Diana Dobrovolny
VP: Ashish Kathuria
Mng Dir: Charles Schneider
IT Man: Eric Langman

D-U-N-S 13-789-9022
HEALTH PROFESSIONS EDUCATION FOUNDATION
400 R St Ste 460, Sacramento, CA 95811-6213
Tel (916) 326-3640 *Founded/Ownrshp* 2007
Sales NA *EMP* 13
Accts Gilbert Associates Inc Sacr
SIC 6111 Student Loan Marketing Association; Student Loan Marketing Association
Ex Dir: Lupe Alonzo-Diaz

HEALTH PROVIDENCE SERVICES
See PROVIDENCE REAL ESTATE AND CONSTRUCTION

D-U-N-S 61-929-1052
HEALTH QUEST
FOUNDATION FOR VBMC, THE
(*Suby of* HEALTH QUEST SYSTEMS INC) ★
45 Reade Pl, Poughkeepsie, NY 12601-3947
Tel (845) 454-8500 *Founded/Ownrshp* 2006
Sales 151.2MM *EMP* 11
Accts Pricewaterhousecoopers Llp N
SIC 8099 Medical services organization; Medical services organization
CEO: Adil Ameer
Dir Vol: Michelle Piazza
**CFO:* Donna M McGregor
Ofcr: Florie Munroe
Sr VP: Robert Diamond
VP: Disanto Benjamin
VP: Patricia Caragine
VP: Mark Kochanowski
VP: David Ping
Exec: Ronald Tatelbaum
Exec: Rosemary Wieting
Assoc Dir: Thomas Diaz
Dir Rx: William Silta

D-U-N-S 07-850-6618
HEALTH QUEST MEDICAL PRACTICE PC
1351 Route 55 Ste 200, Lagrangeville, NY 12540-5144
Tel (845) 475-9757 *Founded/Ownrshp* 2012
Sales 68.4MM *EMP* 3
Accts Pricewaterhousecoopers Llp N
SIC 8099 Health & allied services
CEO: Michael T Weber

D-U-N-S 61-716-3977
HEALTH QUEST SYSTEMS INC
1351 Route 55 Ste 200, Lagrangeville, NY 12540-5144
Tel (845) 475-9500 *Founded/Ownrshp* 1985
Sales 796.7MM *EMP* 2,000
Accts Pricewaterhousecoopers Llp Ne
SIC 8741 Hospital management; Hospital management
CEO: Denise George
CFO: Joseph Hart
**CFO:* Yann Kepple
Bd of Dir: Drayton Grant
Ex VP: Robert Friedberg
**Sr VP:* Ann Armater
Sr VP: Michael Holzhueter
**Sr VP:* David Ping
**Sr VP:* Ron Tatelbaumm
**VP:* Mary Ann Keppel
VP: Ann McMackin

D-U-N-S 00-243-6061
HEALTH RESEARCH INC (NY)
FOOD LBS/SFETY INSPTN DVSN-GMT
150 Broadway Ste 560, Menands, NY 12204-2726
Tel (518) 431-1200 *Founded/Ownrshp* 1953
Sales 677.8MM *EMP* 1,400
Accts Bonadio & Co Llp Albany Ne
SIC 8733 Noncommercial research organizations; Noncommercial research organizations
Ex Dir: Barbara Ryan
**Ex Dir:* Cheryl Mattox

D-U-N-S 04-400-7990
■ HEALTH RESOURCES & SERVICES ADMINISTRATION
HRSA
(*Suby of* UNITED STATES DEPARTMENT OF HEALTH & HUMAN SERVICES) ★
5600 Fishers Ln, Rockville, MD 20852-1750
Tel (301) 443-5460 *Founded/Ownrshp* 1997
Sales NA *EMP* 1,860
SIC 9431 Administration of public health programs; ; Administration of public health programs;
Ofcr: Zandra White
Ofcr: Tigisty Zerislassie
IT Man: Cathie Alderks
IT Man: Marcia Horton
Snr Mgr: Walter Harris
Snr Mgr: Melinda Leighton
Snr Mgr: Iran Naqvi
Snr Mgr: Judy Rodgers

D-U-N-S 10-312-1034
■ HEALTH RESOURCES CORP OF AMERICA-CALIFORNIA
COASTAL COMMUNITY HOSPITAL
(*Suby of* KPC HEALTHCARE INC) ★
2701 S Bristol St, Santa Ana, CA 92704-6201
Tel (714) 754-5454 *Founded/Ownrshp* 1984
Sales 12.0MMᴱ *EMP* 400
SIC 8062 General medical & surgical hospitals; General medical & surgical hospitals
Pr: Trevor Fetter

D-U-N-S 92-928-0782
HEALTH RESOURCES GROUP
HERITAGE PHYSICIAN GROUP
1 Mercy Ln Ste 201, Hot Springs, AR 71913-6457
Tel (501) 609-2229 *Founded/Ownrshp* 1995
Sales 9.5MMᴱ *EMP* 276
SIC 8011 Clinic, operated by physicians; Clinic, operated by physicians
Ch: Robert W Aspell MD
**Pr:* Terry Brown
Surgeon: Alberta Gibbs
Surgeon: Joe Howe
Surgeon: Kimberly Jackman
Surgeon: Ron Kaler
Surgeon: John Webb

D-U-N-S 18-177-1536
HEALTH RESOURCES INC
5010 Carriage Dr, Evansville, IN 47715-2570
Tel (812) 424-1444 *Founded/Ownrshp* 1986
Sales NA *EMP* 40
SIC 6324 Dental insurance; Dental insurance
Pr: Allan L Reid

D-U-N-S 06-757-1174
HEALTH SCHOLARSHIPS INC
1005 Boulder Dr, Gray, GA 31032-6141
Tel (478) 742-6569 *Founded/Ownrshp* 1988
Sales 189.1MM *EMP* 1
Accts Mcnair Mclemore Middlebrooks
SIC 6732 Trusts: educational, religious, etc.; Trusts: educational, religious, etc.
Pr: Joe Wall

D-U-N-S 16-727-5382
HEALTH SCIENCE CENTER AT BROOKLYN FOUNDATION INC
HSBC FOUNDATION
450 Clarkson Ave 1219, Brooklyn, NY 11203-2012
Tel (718) 270-3045 *Founded/Ownrshp* 1976
Sales 66.6MM *EMP* 2
SIC 6732 Trusts: educational, religious, etc.; Trusts: educational, religious, etc.
Pr: Alan Dzija
**VP:* John C Larosa

HEALTH SCIENCES CENTER
See TTU HSC RESEARCH & GRADUATE SCHOOL

D-U-N-S 60-271-2630
HEALTH SCIENCES CONSTRUCTION GROUP LTD
HSC BUILDERS & CNSTR MANAGERS
304 New Mill Ln, Exton, PA 19341-2522
Tel (610) 280-7793 *Founded/Ownrshp* 1987
Sales 44.6MMᴱ *EMP* 90
SIC 1541 Pharmaceutical manufacturing plant construction; Pharmaceutical manufacturing plant construction
Pr: Mark Heim
**Treas:* Jay E Heim III
**VP:* Jim Viner
Dir IT: Kim Campbell
Mktg Mgr: Valerie Powers
Mktg Mgr: Wendy Wark
Snr PM: Jeffrey Graef
Snr PM: Gerry Myers
Snr PM: Vincent Oddo

HEALTH SCIENCES DIVISION
See TRUSTEES OF COLUMBIA UNIVERSITY IN CITY OF NEW YORK

D-U-N-S 10-902-9991
HEALTH SCIENCES FOUNDATION INC
SEAHEC
2511 Delaney Ave, Wilmington, NC 28403-6003
Tel (910) 343-0161 *Founded/Ownrshp* 1972
Sales 25.3MM *EMP* 154ᴱ
Accts Earney & Company Llp Wilmingt
SIC 8299 Educational service, nondegree granting: continuing educ.; Educational service, nondegree granting: continuing educ.
CEO: Joseph Pino
**CFO:* James Shaw
**Treas:* William McMillan
Off Mgr: Kim Shepard
IT Man: Avery Cloud
Pgrm Dir: Kimberly Thrasher
Board of Directors: Fred Michael

D-U-N-S 01-970-4037
HEALTH SCIENCES SOUTH CAROLINA (SC)
1320 Main St Ste 625, Columbia, SC 29201-3286
Tel (803) 544-4772 *Founded/Ownrshp* 2004
Sales 69.8MM *EMP* 10
Accts Bdo Usa Llp Atlanta Ga
SIC 8731 Biological research; Biological research
Pr: Helga Rippen
VP: Michelle Dodenhoff
Snr Mgr: Mike Randall

HEALTH SEMINARS
See EPI PRINTERS INC

HEALTH SERVICE/ HUMAN SERVICES
See LUTHERAN FAMILY SERVICES OF VIRGINIA INC

D-U-N-S 83-862-0888
HEALTH SERVICES & BENEFIT ADMINISTRATORS INC
HSBA
4160 Dublin Blvd Ste 400, Dublin, CA 94568-7756
Tel (925) 833-7300 *Founded/Ownrshp* 1989
Sales NA *EMP* 80^E
SIC 6371 Union welfare, benefit & health funds
Pr: Stanley R Fisher
**COO:* Angela Rampone
**CFO:* David Haumesser
**Sr VP:* Michael Taime
**VP:* Mary Callahan
IT Man: Michael Haley

D-U-N-S 04-066-4161
HEALTH SERVICES (INC)
LISTER HILL
1845 Cherry St, Montgomery, AL 36107-2613
Tel (334) 420-5001 *Founded/Ownrshp* 1968
Sales 21.3MM *EMP* 215
SIC 8011 8021 5912 Medical centers; Offices & clinics of dentists; Drug stores & proprietary stores; Medical centers; Offices & clinics of dentists; Drug stores & proprietary stores
CEO: C Bernell Mapp
**CFO:* George R Waldrop
Dir Lab: Michael Randall
Surgeon: Jacob Griffin
Surgeon: Catherine Key
Surgeon: Harry Ohme
Obsttrcn: Eugene Evans
Podiatrist: Anglin Ace

D-U-N-S 11-444-3260
HEALTH SERVICES ADVISORY GROUP INC
(*Suby of* HEALTH SERVICES HOLDINGS INC) ★
3133 E Cmlback Rs Ste 100, Phoenix, AZ 85016
Tel (602) 264-6382 *Founded/Ownrshp* 1982
Sales 41.0MM^E *EMP* 200
SIC 8099

D-U-N-S 80-518-2839
HEALTH SERVICES ADVISORY GROUP OF FLORIDA INC
FMQAI
(*Suby of* HEALTH SERVICES ADVISORY GROUP INC) ★
3000 Bayport Dr Ste 300, Tampa, FL 33607-8415
Tel (813) 354-9111 *Founded/Ownrshp* 1993
Sales 41.0MM *EMP* 211
SIC 8742 8099 Management consulting services; Physical examination service, insurance; Management consulting services; Physical examination service, insurance
Pr: Mary Ellen Dalton
**CFO:* Joellen Tenison
IT Man: Zak Henshaw
Web Dev: John Jennings

D-U-N-S 80-474-5420
HEALTH SERVICES DEPARTMENT
H S A
(*Suby of* EXECUTIVE OFFICE OF STATE OF ARIZONA) ★
150 N 18th Ave Ste 163, Phoenix, AZ 85007-3237
Tel (602) 542-1025 *Founded/Ownrshp* 1912
Sales NA *EMP* 3,486
SIC 9431 Administration of public health programs; ; Administration of public health programs;
CFO: David Reese
Ofcr: Margaret Lindsay
Ofcr: Kathy McCanna
Ofcr: Ruth Penn
Ofcr: Patricia Tarango
Ofcr: Wayne Tormala
Ofcr: Richard Young
Comm Dir: Laura Adhs
Comm Dir: Laura Oxley
Prgrm Mgr: Hong Chartrand
Prgrm Mgr: Laura Erhart
Board of Directors: Catherine Eden

D-U-N-S 87-642-4854
HEALTH SERVICES FOR CHILDREN WITH SPECIAL NEEDS INC
1101 Vermont Ave Nw # 1002, Washington, DC 20005-3560
Tel (202) 467-2737 *Founded/Ownrshp* 1994
Sales 155.1MM *EMP* 100
Accts Cohen Rutherford Knight Pc Be
SIC 8322 Social services for the handicapped
CEO: Thomas Chapman
**COO:* Bruce Goldman
Off Mgr: Phyllis Montgomery

D-U-N-S 93-799-5553
HEALTH SERVICES GROUP INC
601 Sw 2nd Ave Ste 1940, Portland, OR 97204-3176
Tel (503) 228-6554 *Founded/Ownrshp* 1991
Sales NA *EMP* 700
SIC 6719 Investment holding companies, except banks; Investment holding companies, except banks
Pr: Robert Gootee

D-U-N-S 19-657-8053
HEALTH SERVICES HOLDINGS INC
3133 E Camelback Rd # 300, Phoenix, AZ 85016-4544
Tel (602) 264-6382 *Founded/Ownrshp* 2004
Sales 41.8MM^E *EMP* 280^E
Accts Mayer Hoffman Mccann Pc Pho
SIC 8099 Medical services organization; Medical services organization
Pr: Lawrence Shapiro
CFO: Kerri Sanchez
CFO: Andrea Silvey
**VP:* Mary Ellen Dalton
**VP:* Henry Kaldenbaugh
**VP:* Joellen Tenison
Ex Dir: Thomas Jackson

D-U-N-S 02-804-4481
HEALTH SERVICES MANAGEMENT INC
206 Fortress Blvd, Murfreesboro, TN 37128-5269
Tel (615) 896-1191 *Founded/Ownrshp* 2009
Sales 156.1MM *EMP* 3
Accts Randall Matlock & Associates P
SIC 8741 Hospital management; Nursing & personal care facility management; Hospital management; Nursing & personal care facility management
Prin: Preston Sweeney

D-U-N-S 12-092-2815
HEALTH SERVICES MANAGEMENT OF TEXAS
13415 Med Cmplex Dr Ofc, Tomball, TX 77375-6441
Tel (832) 843-5038 *Founded/Ownrshp* 2003
Sales 20.9MM^E *EMP* 640
SIC 8051 Skilled nursing care facilities; Skilled nursing care facilities
Prin: Preston Sweeny

D-U-N-S 79-103-3702
HEALTH SERVICES OF CENTRAL GEORGIA INC
691 Cherry St Fl 4, Macon, GA 31201-7341
Tel (478) 633-6713 *Founded/Ownrshp* 2007
Sales 49.8MM *EMP* 2^E
Accts Draffin & Tucker Llp Atlanta
SIC 8099 Business services; Health & allied services
Prin: Louis W Goolsby

D-U-N-S 79-660-9857
HEALTH SERVICES OF FOX CHASE CANCER CENTER
(*Suby of* FOX CHASE CANCER CENTER FOUNDATION) ★
333 Cottman Ave, Philadelphia, PA 19111-2434
Tel (215) 728-6900 *Founded/Ownrshp* 1985
Sales 228.3M *EMP* 1,800
SIC 8011 8062 8733 Offices & clinics of medical doctors; General medical & surgical hospitals; Medical research; Offices & clinics of medical doctors; General medical & surgical hospitals; Medical research
Pr: Robert C Young MD
**COO:* R Donald Leedy
**CFO:* Tresa Laribee
**Treas:* Joseph Hediger

D-U-N-S 17-285-3558
HEALTH SERVICES OF NORTHERN NEW YORK INC
MEDLINK OF NEW YORK
(*Suby of* HAMISTER GROUP INC) ★
56 Market St, Potsdam, NY 13676-1942
Tel (716) 839-4000 *Founded/Ownrshp* 1985
Sales 4.8MM^E *EMP* 302
SIC 8082 Home health care services; Home health care services
Pr: Mark E Hamister
**Pr:* Jack Turesky
Board of Directors: Lisa Clark Driscoll

D-U-N-S 08-890-7514
HEALTH SERVICES OF VIRGINIAS INC
500 Cherry St, Bluefield, WV 24701-3306
Tel (304) 327-1100 *Founded/Ownrshp* 1976
Sales 317.4M *EMP* 1,040^E
Accts Brown Edwards & Company Ll
SIC 8062 General medical & surgical hospitals; General medical & surgical hospitals
Pr: Robert Perkinson
CFO: Richard Cox
**CFO:* Patti Gusler
**Ch:* Chandler Wote
**Sec:* Bill Albert
Ofcr: Leland Farnell
**VP:* Jack Brewster
Dir Lab: Mary Boysaw
Dir Lab: Vicki Cunningham
Dir Rad: Kay Cooper
Dir Rx: Alok Gupta

D-U-N-S 03-293-6281
HEALTH SHARE OF OREGON
2121 Sw Broadway Ste 200, Portland, OR 97201-3181
Tel (503) 416-2172 *Founded/Ownrshp* 2013
Sales 663.2MM^E *EMP* 3
Accts Moss Adams Llp Portland Or
SIC 8099 Health & allied services
COO: Susan Kirchoff
CFO: Lee Hullinger
Assoc Dir: Alyssa Craigie
Comm Man: Beth Sorensen
QA Dir: Mike Holmes
Snr PM: Paul Bollinger
Snr PM: Sandra Clark

D-U-N-S 04-071-6516
HEALTH SOLUTIONS
1026 W Abriendo Ave, Pueblo, CO 81004-1128
Tel (719) 545-2746 *Founded/Ownrshp* 1962
Sales 22.1MM *EMP* 217
Accts Bain And Jones Cpas Louisvill
SIC 8093 8361 Alcohol clinic, outpatient; Mental health clinic, outpatient; Residential care; Alcohol clinic, outpatient; Mental health clinic, outpatient; Residential care
Pr: Dorothy Perry
COO: Dennis Carter
**CFO:* Paige Burkes
Bd of Dir: Ann Genova
Ofcr: Barbara Mettler
VP: Barbara Archuleta
IT Man: Dana Brown
IT Man: Mark Miller
IT Man: Richard Veatch
Opers Mgr: Rob Kepplinger
Pgrm Dir: Danielle Kolakowski

D-U-N-S 62-433-0759
■ **HEALTH SOUTH REHABILITATION HOSPITAL OF MEMPHIS**
(*Suby of* HEALTHSOUTH CORP) ★
1282 Union Ave, Memphis, TN 38104-3414
Tel (901) 722-2000 *Founded/Ownrshp* 1986
Sales 18.0MM^E *EMP* 300
SIC 8093 Rehabilitation center, outpatient treatment; Rehabilitation center, outpatient treatment
CEO: Michael Pierce
CFO: Valerie Jones
Pr Dir: Ginger Stafford
Pharmcst: Thomas King

D-U-N-S 96-197-0725
HEALTH SYSTEMS COOPERATIVE LAU
725 E Minnehahaave, Saint Paul, MN 55106
Tel (651) 774-8620 *Founded/Ownrshp* 2010
Sales 20.6MM *EMP* 13^E
Accts Mcgladrey Llp Minneapolis Mi
SIC 7215 Coin-operated laundries & cleaning
Prin: Larry Hilton

D-U-N-S 02-305-3713
HEALTH SYSTEMS COOPERATIVE LAUNDRIES
55 5th St E Ste 960, Saint Paul, MN 55101-1717
Tel (651) 774-8620 *Founded/Ownrshp* 1996
Sales 21.6MM *EMP* 250
Accts Mcgladrey Llp Minneapolis Mi
SIC 7219 Laundry, except power & coin-operated; Laundry, except power & coin-operated
Pr: Brian Knapp
**CFO:* Kyle Roberts

D-U-N-S 96-489-6968
HEALTH SYSTEMS FACILITIES INC
1005 Boulder Dr, Gray, GA 31032-6141
Tel (478) 621-2100 *Founded/Ownrshp* 2010
Sales 116.5MM *EMP* 1
Accts Mcnair Mclemore Middlebrooks
SIC 7389 Business services; Business services
CEO: Kay F Gray

D-U-N-S 02-329-7240
HEALTH SYSTEMS INC
1220 N Main St, Sikeston, MO 63801-4827
Tel (573) 481-9625 *Founded/Ownrshp* 1998
Sales NA *EMP* 948
SIC 6321 8011 8322 Health insurance carriers; Internal medicine, physician/surgeon; Referral service for personal & social problems; Health insurance carriers; Internal medicine, physician/surgeon; Referral service for personal & social problems
Pr: Jim Lincoln
VP: Tara Smith
**Prin:* Marty Beuke
**Prin:* Tracey Smith

HEALTH SYSTEMS MINNESOTA
See PARK NICOLLET HEALTH SERVICES

D-U-N-S 17-432-2818
HEALTH TECH AFFILIATES INC
(*Suby of* BAPTIST MEMORIAL HEALTH CARE CORP) ★
350 N Humphreys Blvd, Memphis, TN 38120-2177
Tel (901) 227-2926 *Founded/Ownrshp* 1986
Sales 9.1MM^E *EMP* 382
SIC 8011 5999 8071 7361 7352 Offices & clinics of medical doctors; Hospital equipment & supplies; Technical aids for the handicapped; Orthopedic & prosthesis applications; Convalescent equipment & supplies; Pathological laboratory; Nurses' registry; Medical equipment rental; Offices & clinics of medical doctors; Hospital equipment & supplies; Technical aids for the handicapped; Orthopedic & prosthesis applications; Convalescent equipment & supplies; Pathological laboratory; Nurses' registry; Medical equipment rental
Ex VP: Donald Pounds

D-U-N-S 87-674-4009
HEALTH TEXAS MEDICAL GROUP
2961 Mossrock, San Antonio, TX 78230-5119
Tel (210) 731-4800 *Founded/Ownrshp* 2009
Sales 28.1MM^E *EMP* 37^E
SIC 4953 Recycling, waste materials
Pr: Christopher Caulfield
VP: Jack Keller
VP: Jeannine Ruffner
QA Dir: Diana Leza
Dir IT: Gregory Gleason
Mktg Dir: Jeff Hunsaker

HEALTH TEXAS PROVIDE NETWORK
See FAMILY MEDICAL CENTER AT ROCKWALL

D-U-N-S 07-723-6651 IMP
■ **HEALTH VALLEY FOODS INC**
(*Suby of* HAIN CELESTIAL GROUP INC) ★
16007 Cmino De La Cantera, Irwindale, CA 91702
Tel (626) 334-3241 *Founded/Ownrshp* 1999
Sales 18.1MM^E *EMP* 300
SIC 5149 Health foods; Natural & organic foods; Health foods; Natural & organic foods
Pr: Irwin Simon

D-U-N-S 01-207-3040
HEALTH WATCH INC
(*Suby of* QUALITY HEALTH STRATEGIES INC) ★
28464 Marlboro Ave, Easton, MD 21601-2732
Tel (410) 822-0697 *Founded/Ownrshp* 1991
Sales 711.0M^E *EMP* 450
SIC 8099 Medical services organization
Pr: Ronald G Forsythe
CEO: Fredia Wadley
COO: Ron Forsythe
CFO: Rebecca Combs

D-U-N-S 94-048-7051
HEALTH WATCH OF VISITING NURSE INC
JEWISH HOSPITAL
101 W Chestnut St, Louisville, KY 40202-3836
Tel (502) 587-4252 *Founded/Ownrshp* 1996
Sales 61.2MM *EMP* 8
SIC 8082 Home health care services; Home health care services
Prac Mgr: Pamela Kelly
Psych: Lisa Jones

D-U-N-S 83-776-1808 IMP
HEALTH WRIGHT PRODUCTS INC
12482 Se Capps Rd, Clackamas, OR 97015-9093
Tel (503) 722-4344 *Founded/Ownrshp* 1995
Sales 26.4MM^E *EMP* 49
SIC 5149 Health foods
Pr: Mark Wright

HEALTH4BRANDS CATAPULT
See HAVAS HEALTH INC

HEALTHALLIANCE HOSPITAL
See HEALTH ALLIANCE OF HUDSON VALLEY BROADWAY CAMPUS

D-U-N-S 06-052-8064
HEALTHALLIANCE HOSPITAL MARYS AVENUE CAMPUS
(*Suby of* HEALTH ALLIANCE INC) ★
105 Marys Ave, Kingston, NY 12401-5848
Tel (845) 338-2500 *Founded/Ownrshp* 1903
Sales 113.5MM^E *EMP* 2,100
SIC 8062 8051

D-U-N-S 06-992-0916
HEALTHALLIANCE HOSPITALS INC
60 Hospital Rd, Leominster, MA 01453-2205
Tel (978) 466-2000 *Founded/Ownrshp* 1993
Sales 180.2MM^E *EMP* 1,350
SIC 8062 Hospital, affiliated with AMA residency; Hospital, affiliated with AMA residency
Pr: Deborah Weymouth
Dir Recs: Debbie Borkowski
**CFO:* Michael Cofone
Obsttrcn: Bettyann Cirillo
Ansthlgy: Louise Lu

HEALTHALLIANCE OF HUDSON VLY
See HEALTH ALLIANCE INC

D-U-N-S 00-215-7407
HEALTHBACK HOLDINGS LLC (OK)
HEALTHBACK OF OKC
16211 N May Ave, Edmond, OK 73013-8871
Tel (405) 842-1700 *Founded/Ownrshp* 2000
Sales 19.0MM^E *EMP* 400
SIC 8082 Home health care services; Home health care services
CFO: Michael Curtis
IT Man: Wathena Branham

HEALTHBACK OF OKC
See HEALTHBACK HOLDINGS LLC

D-U-N-S 14-685-6849
HEALTHBRIDGE CHILDRENS HOSPITAL - HOUSTON LTD
(*Suby of* NEXUS HEALTH SYSTEMS INC) ★
2929 Woodland Park Dr, Houston, TX 77082-2687
Tel (281) 293-7774 *Founded/Ownrshp* 2003
Sales 21.4MM^E *EMP* 160
SIC 8062 General medical & surgical hospitals
CEO: John W Cassidy
Dir Rx: Evelyn Perridon
QA Dir: Tiffany Todd
Nrsg Dir: Anna Morris
HC Dir: Kimberly Dunbar
HC Dir: Monica Garcia

D-U-N-S 96-910-7143
HEALTHCARE ADMINISTRATIVE PARTNERS LLC
H A P
112 Chesley Dr Ste 200, Media, PA 19063-1762
Tel (610) 892-8889 *Founded/Ownrshp* 1997
Sales 28.0MM^E *EMP* 200
SIC 8741 Hospital management; Nursing & personal care facility management; Hospital management; Nursing & personal care facility management
Pr: Brian Effron
**VP:* Carin Carlson
**VP:* Joanne Dougherty
**VP:* Jane Knox
Dir Bus: George Soulard
Opers Mgr: Kimberly Smith

D-U-N-S 02-057-9967 IMP
HEALTHCARE ASSOCIATES IN MEDICINE PC (NY)
ORTHOPEDIC ASSOCIATES OF NY
2535 Arthur Kill Rd, Staten Island, NY 10309-1207
Tel (718) 448-3210 *Founded/Ownrshp* 1970, 1997
Sales 24.0MM *EMP* 282
Accts Smith & Associates Cpa S Pa
SIC 8011 Orthopedic physician; Surgeon; Offices & clinics of medical doctors
CEO: Steve Pego
**CEO:* Paul Burkley
VP: Lenny Lagana
Doctor: Pat Honig

D-U-N-S 78-411-0082
HEALTHCARE ASSOCIATES OF IRVING LLP
1110 Cottonwood Ln L100, Irving, TX 75038-6117
Tel (972) 258-7499 *Founded/Ownrshp* 2007
Sales 23.7MM^E *EMP* 100
SIC 8011 General & family practice, physician/surgeon
Bd of Dir: Raymond Damadian
Surgeon: David Drucker
Surgeon: Joseph Giovinazzo
Surgeon: John Reilly
Doctor: Dianne Cook
Doctor: Connie Schwoeppe

HEALTHCARE AUTH FOR BPTST HLTH
See BAPTIST HEALTH

D-U-N-S 14-457-9646
HEALTHCARE AUTHORITY FOR BAPTIST HEALTH AND AFFILIATE OF UAB HEALTH SYSTEM
BAPTIST MEDICAL CENTER SOUTH
2105 E South Blvd, Montgomery, AL 36116-2409
Tel (334) 286-2987 *Founded/Ownrshp* 1963
Sales 543.8MM *EMP* 1,500^E
SIC 8062 General medical & surgical hospitals; General medical & surgical hospitals
CEO: Russell Tyner
**COO:* Robin Barca
**CFO:* Katrina Belt
CFO: Guy Laprad
VP: Cynthia Barginere

*VP: Ben F Kelley Jr
Dir Rad: Jackie Davis
Dir Rad: Jeffrey Hicks
Dir Rx: Clint Peevy
Chf Nrs Of: Lisa Person
Nurse Mgr: Tammy Cousins
Board of Directors: Ben Kelly

D-U-N-S 62-246-5474
HEALTHCARE BUSINESS RESOURCES INC
5959 Shallowford Rd # 575, Chattanooga, TN 37421-2240
Tel (423) 499-0652 Founded/Ownrshp 2002
Sales 9.2MM^E EMP 360
SIC 8099 7322 Blood related health services; Collection agency, except real estate; Blood related health services; Collection agency, except real estate
Pr: Ed Suggs
*CFO: Allen Smith
*Ch: Steven Scott
*Ex VP: Victor Sarkissian
*Sr VP: Ed Gaines

D-U-N-S 07-831-4688
HEALTHCARE CENTER OF DOWNEY LLC
LAKEWOOD HEALTHCARE CENTER
12023 Lakewood Blvd, Downey, CA 90242-2635
Tel (562) 869-0978 Founded/Ownrshp 2011
Sales 23.2MM^E EMP 250
SIC 8051 Mental retardation hospital
CEO: Vince Hambright

D-U-N-S 03-216-4674
■ **HEALTHCARE CORP OF AMERICA**
(Suby of HEALTHCARE CORP OF AMERICA) ★
66 Ford Rd, Denville, NJ 07834-1379
Tel (973) 983-6300 Founded/Ownrshp 2013
Sales 50.0MM EMP 50
SIC 8099 Medical services organization; Medical services organization
CEO: Natasha Giordano
*Ch Bd: Yaron Eitan
*VP: Joseph Drucker

D-U-N-S 96-870-7625
▲ **HEALTHCARE CORP OF AMERICA**
66 Ford Rd, Denville, NJ 07834-1379
Tel (646) 421-6666 Founded/Ownrshp 2011
Sales 58.0MM EMP 59^E
Accts Bdo Usa Llp Woodbridge Nj
Tkr Sym HCCA Exch OTO
SIC 6799 Investors; Investors
Pr: Gary J Sekulski
*Treas: Scott Weeber
*Sec: Ann F Saskowitz
VP: John M Phelps
VP Admn: Ruth Ackerman

D-U-N-S 11-623-6910
HEALTHCARE FACILITY MANAGEMENT LLC
LLC, RESIDENT CARE CONSULTING
4700 Ashwood Dr, Blue Ash, OH 45241-2465
Tel (513) 530-1654 Founded/Ownrshp 1984
Sales 41.0MM^E EMP 450
SIC 8741 Hospital management; Nursing & personal care facility management; Hospital management; Nursing & personal care facility management
Pr: Stephen L Rosedale
*VP: Beatrice Rosedale

D-U-N-S 06-860-0683
HEALTHCARE FINANCIAL MANAGEMENT ASSOICATION
H F M A
3 Westb Corpo Cente Ste 6, Westchester, IL 60154
Tel (708) 531-9600 Founded/Ownrshp 1956
Sales 24.8MM EMP 81
SIC 8621 Medical field-related associations; Medical field-related associations
Ch Bd: Mary Beth Briscoe
Pr: Joseph J Fifer
CEO: Rijoseph J Fifer
Sec: Kari S Cornicelli
Sr VP: Edwin P Czopek
VP: Susan Brenku
VP: Richard L Gundling
VP: Diane Simmons
Sls&Mrk Ex: Gina Cavelle

D-U-N-S 80-907-9064 IMP
HEALTHCARE INFORMATION AND MANAGEMENT SYSTEMS SOCIETY
H I M S S
33 W Monroe St Ste 1700, Chicago, IL 60603-5616
Tel (312) 664-4467 Founded/Ownrshp 1993
Sales 81.7MM EMP 500^E
SIC 8099 Blood related health services; Blood related health services
Ch Bd: Scott Maclean
*Pr: H Stephen Lieber
*COO: J Norris Orms
COO: R N Orms
*CFO: Dennis R James
Bd of Dir: Steven J Fox
Bd of Dir: John Hansmann
Bd of Dir: Anna M Harris
Bd of Dir: Daniel Herman
Bd of Dir: Joy Keeler
Bd of Dir: Sunny Sanyal
Bd of Dir: Tricia Spellman
*Ex VP: Jeremy Bonfini
*Ex VP: John Hoyt
Ex VP: John P Hoyt
Ex VP: R Orms
*Ex VP: Steve Rosenfield
VP: Rosemary Brandt
VP: Susan Farrell
VP: John Hoyt
VP: Liz Johnson

D-U-N-S 11-158-5170
HEALTHCARE INNOVATIONS HOLDINGS LLC
213 48th Ave Nw, Norman, OK 73072-4443
Tel (405) 447-8700 Founded/Ownrshp 1996
Sales 5.4MM^E EMP 340
SIC 8082 Home health care services; Home health care services
Off Mgr: Tammy Keller

D-U-N-S 06-845-3422
HEALTHCARE LAUNDRY SYSTEMS LLC
CROTHALL LAUNDRY SERVICE
(Suby of CROTHALL HEALTHCARE INC) ★
45 W Hintz Rd, Wheeling, IL 60090-6073
Tel (847) 941-7000 Founded/Ownrshp 2006
Sales 23.4MM^E EMP 530
SIC 7218 Industrial launderers; Industrial launderers
Pr: Chuck Rossmiller
*CFO: Gina Cocking
Mtls Mgr: Dean Leensvaart

D-U-N-S 94-900-1606
HEALTHCARE MANAGEMENT ASSOCIATES LLC
1401 S Brentwood Blvd # 170, Saint Louis, MO 63144-1416
Tel (314) 963-7570 Founded/Ownrshp 1996
Sales 22.6MM^E EMP 495
SIC 8741 Hospital management; Nursing & personal care facility management; Hospital management; Nursing & personal care facility management

D-U-N-S 12-714-9784
HEALTHCARE MANAGEMENT SOLUTIONS LLC
1000 Tech Dr Ste 1310, Fairmont, WV 26554
Tel (304) 368-0288 Founded/Ownrshp 2002
Sales 21.6MM EMP 176
Accts Dixon Hughes Goodman Llp Cha
SIC 8742 Hospital & health services consultant; Hospital & health services consultant
VP: Lynne Moore
Snr Sftwr: Chris Wright
Sftwr Eng: Aaron Ely
Sftwr Eng: Hani Saad

HEALTHCARE MGT ADMINISTRATORS
See HEALTH CARE MANAGEMENT ADMINISTRATORS INC

D-U-N-S 94-349-1795
HEALTHCARE NETWORK ASSOCIATIION
HCNA
701 N 1st St, Springfield, IL 62781-0001
Tel (217) 757-7491 Founded/Ownrshp 1992
Sales 22.0MM EMP 9
Accts Ernst & Young Llp Saint Louis
SIC 8011 8741 8062 Medical centers; Management services; General medical & surgical hospitals; Medical centers; Management services; General medical & surgical hospitals
Pr: J Travis Dowl
*VP: Travis Dowell

HEALTHCARE NETWORK OF SW FL
See COLLIER HEALTH SERVICES INC

D-U-N-S 07-431-9237
HEALTHCARE OF IOWA INC
4080 1st Ave Ne Ste 103, Cedar Rapids, IA 52402-3160
Tel (319) 362-8916 Founded/Ownrshp 1973
Sales 21.7MM^E EMP 529
SIC 8052 Personal care facility; Personal care facility
Pr: Donald Chensvold
VP: Amy Tressel
VP: Thomas Wagg

D-U-N-S 55-736-2618
HEALTHCARE PARTNERS INVESTMENTS LLC
HPI
14024 Quail Pointe Dr, Oklahoma City, OK 73134-1006
Tel (405) 424-6677 Founded/Ownrshp 2004
Sales 54.3MM^E EMP 1,000
SIC 8093 Specialty outpatient clinics; Specialty outpatient clinics
CEO: Ed Gray
*Ch Bd: C Robert Steves
*CFO: Carl Mikesh
VP: Thomas Fondren
VP: Donald Grunden
CIO: Steven Clark
CTO: Kevin Marshall
VP Mktg: Ken Talton

D-U-N-S 94-497-5622
■ **HEALTHCARE PARTNERS LLC**
HEALTHCARE PARTNERS MED GROUP
(Suby of DAVITA HEALTHCARE PARTNERS INC) ★
19191 S Vermont Ave, Torrance, CA 90502-1018
Tel (310) 354-4200 Founded/Ownrshp 2012
Sales 363.8MM^E EMP 3,700
SIC 8011 Group health association; Group health association
CEO: Robert J Margolis
Pr: Marianne Garrity
COO: Dennis L Kogod
CFO: Ted Halkias
Bd of Dir: Gary Standke
Ofcr: Chan Chuang
Ofcr: Hugo Ruiz
Ofcr: Melayne Yokum
*Ex VP: Matthew Mazdyasni
Sr VP: Mary Evans
VP: Merlin Aalborg
Dir Rad: Ravi Sookdeo

HEALTHCARE PARTNERS MED GROUP
See HEALTHCARE PARTNERS LLC

D-U-N-S 02-763-2659
HEALTHCARE PARTNERS NEVADA LLC
700 E Warm Springs Rd # 230, Las Vegas, NV 89119-4311
Tel (702) 932-8500 Founded/Ownrshp 2009
Sales 94.0MM^E EMP 1,000^E
SIC 8011 Medical centers; Medical centers
Pr: Sherif Abdou
Sr VP: Bard Coats
Sr VP: Todd Lefkowitz
VP: Phil Fegan
Prac Mgr: Candace Fisher
Prac Mgr: Kimberly McDonald
Dir IT: Chavis Martin
Opers Mgr: Peter Manterola

D-U-N-S 13-593-8640
HEALTHCARE PROVIDERS INSURANCE CO
116 Woodgreen Crossing, Madison, MS 39110-4522
Tel (601) 362-6722 Founded/Ownrshp 2003
Sales NA EMP 17
SIC 6324 Workers' compensation insurance; Hospital & medical service plans
Pr: Alasdair Roe

D-U-N-S 80-872-0007
HEALTHCARE REALTY TRUST INC
3310 West End Ave Ste 700, Nashville, TN 37203-1097
Tel (615) 269-8175 Founded/Ownrshp 1992
Sales 370.8MM EMP 239^E
SIC 6798 Real estate investment trusts; Real estate investment trusts
Ch Bd: David R Emery
COO: JD Steele
CFO: Scott W Holmes
Assoc VP: Jessica King
Assoc VP: Kimberly Sullivan
Ex VP: John M Bryant Jr
Ex VP: Todd J Meredith
Ex VP: B Douglas Whitman II
Sr VP: Richard Langreck
Sr VP: Julie Wilson
VP: Amanda Callaway
VP: Stephen Cox
VP: Ryan Crowley
VP: Robert Dillard
VP: Julie Ferrell
VP: Rob Hull
VP: Revell Lester
VP: Andrew Loope
VP: Revell Michael
VP: Rebecca Oberlander
VP: Sushil Puria
Board of Directors: Errol L Biggs, Charles Raymond Fernandez, Edwin B Morris III, John Knox Singleton, Bruce D Sullivan, Roger O West, Dan S Wilford

D-U-N-S 08-168-8934
HEALTHCARE RESOLUTION SERVICES INC
HCRS
14504 Greenview Dr # 300, Laurel, MD 20708-4237
Tel (410) 792-7760 Founded/Ownrshp 1998
Sales 22.5MM^E EMP 325
SIC 8741 8742 Hospital management; Hospital & health services consultant; Hospital management; Hospital & health services consultant
CEO: Jarvis Doles
*Pr: Brenda Doles
Prgrm Mgr: Mia Alderete

D-U-N-S 94-195-2657
HEALTHCARE RESOURCE GROUP INC
12610 E Mirabeau Pkwy # 900, Spokane Valley, WA 99216-1534
Tel (509) 209-2000 Founded/Ownrshp 1994
Sales NA EMP 208
SIC 6411 7322 8742 8721 Medical insurance claim processing, contract or fee basis; Adjustment & collection services; Management consulting services; Accounting, auditing & bookkeeping; Medical insurance claim processing, contract or fee basis; Adjustment & collection services; Management consulting services; Accounting, auditing & bookkeeping
CEO: Steven McCoy
*COO: Gregory West
*CFO: Kristina English
*VP: Richard Lewis
Ex Dir: Jason Coffin
Rgnl Mgr: Nash Castle

D-U-N-S 15-331-5429
HEALTHCARE RESOURCES CORP
HOMESTEAD NURSING HOME
(Suby of GENESIS HEALTHCARE CORP) ★
1113 Easton Rd, Willow Grove, PA 19090-1901
Tel (215) 659-3060 Founded/Ownrshp 1982
Sales 1.5MMM EMP 240
SIC 8059 8361 Nursing home, except skilled & intermediate care facility; Rehabilitation center, residential: health care incidental; Nursing home, except skilled & intermediate care facility; Rehabilitation center, residential: health care incidental
Ch Bd: Michael Walker
*Pr: David C Barr
CFO: George V Hager Jr
Treas: Barbara J Hauswald
Sr VP: James Wankmiller
Off Mgr: Sharon Adams
Nrsg Dir: Charles Hall
HC Dir: Jennifer Romain
Board of Directors: Richard R Howard

D-U-N-S 03-089-0891
HEALTHCARE SERVICE CORP
BLUE CROSS AND BLUE SHIELD
300 E Randolph St, Chicago, IL 60601-5014
Tel (312) 653-6000 Founded/Ownrshp 1936
Sales NA EMP 14,264
Accts Ernst & Young Llp Chicago Il
SIC 6324 6321 6411 Hospital & medical service plans; Dental insurance; Health maintenance organization (HMO), insurance only; Health insurance carriers; Medical insurance claim processing, contract or fee basis; Hospital & medical service plans; Dental insurance; Health maintenance organization (HMO), insurance only; Health insurance carriers; Medical insurance claim processing, contract or fee basis
CEO: Patricia Hemingway Hall
*Pr: Karen Atwood
*Pr: M Ted Haynes
*Pr: Bert Marshall
*Pr: Mark Owen
*Pr: Kurt Shipley
*Pr: Jeffery Tikkanen
COO: Colleen F Reitan
COO: Patricia Williams
*CFO: Kenneth Avner
CFO: Denise A Bujck
*Treas: Gerard Mallen
Chf Mktg O: Theresa Arias
Ofcr: Linda Seman
*Ex VP: John Cannon
*Ex VP: Martin Foster
Ex VP: Tara D Gurber
*Ex VP: Colleen Reitan
*Ex VP: Paula Steiner
*Sr VP: Gary Brantz
*Sr VP: Carolyn Clift
Board of Directors: Marlin Ray Perryman, Timothy Burke, Waneta Tuttle, Milton Carroll, Robert Clarke, Michelle Collins, James Corrigan, Dennis Gannon, Dianne Gasbarra, Patricia Heminway Hall, Thomas Hix

HEALTHCARE SERVICES
See SAN JOAQUIN HOSPITAL

D-U-N-S 08-419-2111
▲ **HEALTHCARE SERVICES GROUP INC** (PA)
3220 Tillman Dr Ste 300, Bensalem, PA 19020-2028
Tel (215) 639-4274 Founded/Ownrshp 1976
Sales 1.2MMM EMP 45,700
Tkr Sym HCSG Exch NGS
SIC 8059 7349 8049 Cleaning service, industrial or commercial; Building maintenance, except repairs; Hospital housekeeping; Industrial launderers; Linen supply; Nursing home, except skilled & intermediate care facility; Hospital housekeeping; Dietician
Pr: Theodore Wahl
*Ch Bd: Daniel P McCartney
CFO: John Griffin
CFO: John C Shea
Chf Cred: Jason J Bundick
*Ex VP: Michael E McBryan
Ex VP: Bryan D McCartney
VP: John Bullock
VP: Josh Dubler
VP: Stephen Foresman
VP: Tim Hubka
VP: Jim Keeley
VP: Jason Lecroy
VP: Kevin McCartney
VP: Brian Mejia
VP: James O'Toole
VP: Patrick Orr
VP: James Pliego
VP: Nicholas Rucker
VP: David Smigel
VP: Ryan Viets
Board of Directors: John M Briggs, Diane S Casey, Robert L Frome, John J McFadden, Robert J Moss, Dino D Ottaviano, Jude Visconto

D-U-N-S 60-310-0988
HEALTHCARE SERVICES MANAGEMENT INC
1 Batterymarch Park # 311, Quincy, MA 02169-7454
Tel (617) 745-0003 Founded/Ownrshp 2005
Sales 30.0MM EMP 150
SIC 8741 Management services; Management services
CEO: David Devine
VP: Chris Clark

D-U-N-S 08-489-1985
HEALTHCARE SERVICES OF OZARKS INC (MO)
OXFORD HEALTHCARE
3660 S National Ave, Springfield, MO 65807-7311
Tel (417) 882-4170 Founded/Ownrshp 1974
Sales 22.3MM EMP 1,400
Accts Bkd Llp Springfield Mo
SIC 7363 Temporary help service; Medical help service; Temporary help service; Medical help service
Pr: Karen R Thomas
CFO: Rick McGge
*VP: Bob Bezamsom
Dir IT: Phil Dasal
IT Man: Lauren Murphy
Sls&Mrk Ex: Becky Graf
Sls&Mrk Ex: Rick McGee

D-U-N-S 96-216-0839
■ **HEALTHCARE SOLUTIONS INC**
(Suby of CATAMARAN CORP) ★
2736 Meadow Church Rd # 300, Duluth, GA 30097-5236
Tel (866) 810-4332 Founded/Ownrshp 2015
Sales 116.5MM^E EMP 400^E
SIC 8742 Compensation & benefits planning consultant; Compensation & benefits planning consultant
Pr: Joe Boures
Pr: Brian Keeton
CFO: Tom Oram
Ex VP: Jim Andrews
Ex VP: Joe Favazzo
Ex VP: Joe Pagano
Ex VP: Eileen Ramallo
Ex VP: Dennis Sponer
Sr VP: Brian Carpenter
Sr VP: Arlene Fricke
Sr VP: Nancy Hamlet
Sr VP: Elaine Vega
Sr VP: Lon Waterman
Sr VP: Chris Wicker
VP: Dean Castaldo
VP: Matthew Depew
VP: Pamela Johnson
VP: Matt Pitts
VP: Tamara Webb

D-U-N-S 07-932-2834
HEALTHCARE STAFFING SERVICES LLC
6399 S Fiddlers Green Cir # 100, Greenwood Village, CO 80111-4974
Tel (800) 736-8773 Founded/Ownrshp 2014
Sales 26.6MM^E EMP 205^E
SIC 7361 Nurses' registry
CEO: Allison Beer

D-U-N-S 11-916-1784
HEALTHCARE STRATEGIES INC
9841 Broken Land Pkwy # 315, Columbia, MD 21046-1169
Tel (410) 381-9682 Founded/Ownrshp 1984
Sales NA EMP 85
SIC 6371 Pension, health & welfare funds
Sr VP: Thomas Dolsak
*Pr: Janice K Albert
*CFO: Harold Stephens
*VP: Henry Detitta

*VP: Kathy Hilton
*VP: William Keenan
*VP: Del Lockett
VP: Judith Mueller

HEALTHCARE STRGC INITIATIVES
See NEXTGEN RCM SERVICES LLC

HEALTHCARE SYETMS
See SOUTH COUNTY HOSPITAL HEALTHCARE SYSTEM ENDOWMENT AND AFFILIATES

HEALTHCARE SYTEMS
See SOUTH COUNTY HOSPITAL HEALTHCARE SYSTEM

D-U-N-S 82-737-1928
■ **HEALTHCARE TECHNOLOGY INTERMEDIATE HOLDINGS INC**
(Suby of HEALTHCARE TECHNOLOGY INTERMEDIATE INC) ★
301 Commerce St Ste 3300, Fort Worth, TX 76102-4133
Tel (817) 871-4000 Founded/Ownrshp 2009
Sales 2.6MMM^E EMP 7,300^E
SIC 8732 Market analysis or research; Business research service; Market analysis or research; Business research service

D-U-N-S 07-944-6230
■ **HEALTHCARE TECHNOLOGY INTERMEDIATE INC**
(Suby of IMS HEALTH HOLDINGS INC) ★
83 Wooster Hts, Danbury, CT 06810-7548
Tel (203) 448-4600 Founded/Ownrshp 2010
Sales 2.6MMM^E EMP 7,300^E
SIC 8742 8732 Business consultant; Market analysis or research; Business research service

D-U-N-S 83-017-0010
HEALTHCARE TRUST OF AMERICA INC
16435 N Scottsdale Rd, Scottsdale, AZ 85254-1533
Tel (480) 998-3478 Founded/Ownrshp 2006
Sales 371.5MM EMP 170^E
SIC 6798 Real estate investment trusts; Real estate investment trusts
Ch Bd: Scott D Peters
CFO: Robert A Milligan
Ex VP: Kristen Armstrong
Ex VP: Mark D Engstrom
Ex VP: Amanda L Houghton
VP: Dawna Powell
VP Opers: Judy Klein
Board of Directors: W Bradley Blair II, Maurice J Dewald, Warren D Fix, Peter N Foss, Larry L Mathis, Steve W Patterson, Gary T Wescombe

D-U-N-S 55-697-7564
HEALTHCARE UNIFORM CO INC
LIFE UNIFORM
(Suby of LIFE UNIFORM) ★
2132 Kratky Rd, Saint Louis, MO 63114-1704
Tel (314) 824-2900 Founded/Ownrshp 2013
Sales 22.1MM^E EMP 180
SIC 5661 5699 Shoe stores; Uniforms & work clothing
Pr: Bob Buzzell
VP: Bryan Graiff
VP: Andrew Riley

D-U-N-S 61-668-5848
HEALTHCARESOURCE HR INC
100 Sylvan Rd Ste 100, Woburn, MA 01801-2083
Tel (781) 368-1033 Founded/Ownrshp 2015
Sales 24.6MM^E EMP 98^E
SIC 8741 Management services
Pr: Peter Segall
Pr: Steve Mahoney
COO: Gary Burmylo
CFO: Bryce Chicoyne
Sr VP: Gene Gainey
Sr VP: Jonathan Russell
VP: Michael Dipietro
QA Dir: Yujia An
QA Dir: Chris Glynn
IT Man: Pat Brennen
IT Man: Christina Williams

HEALTHCHECK360
See BUTLER HEALTHCORP INC

HEALTHCHOICE
See EMPLOYEES GROUP INSURANCE DIVISION

D-U-N-S 95-942-3021
HEALTHCOMP
HEALTHCOMP ADMINISTRATORS
621 Santa Fe Ave, Fresno, CA 93721-2724
Tel (559) 499-2450 Founded/Ownrshp 1994
Sales NA EMP 260
SIC 6411 Medical insurance claim processing, contract or fee basis; Medical insurance claim processing, contract or fee basis
CEO: Phillip Musson
*CFO: Michael Bouskos
*VP: Monique Bouskos
*VP: Kelly Ferreira
VP: Kelly Ferriera
*VP: Charles Johnson
MIS Dir: Alan Backer
Sls Mgr: Diana Button

HEALTHCOMP ADMINISTRATORS
See HEALTHCOMP

D-U-N-S 79-053-4341
HEALTHEAST CARE INC
HEALTHEAST CARE SYSTEMS
(Suby of HEALTHEAST CARE SYSTEM) ★
559 Capitol Blvd, Saint Paul, MN 55103-2101
Tel (651) 232-2300 Founded/Ownrshp 1990
Sales 69.2MM^E EMP 1,000
SIC 8741 8721 Hospital management; Accounting, auditing & bookkeeping; Hospital management; Accounting, auditing & bookkeeping
CEO: Timothy Hanson
*COO: Ann Schrader
*CFO: Bob Gill
VP: Steve Kolar
Dir IT: Darlene Mc Donough
Trfc Dir: Joe Max
Opers Mgr: Chris Schultz
Mktg Dir: Lia Christiansen
Doctor: Kendall Price
Pharmcst: Christina Glasgow
Pharmcst: Erin Gulbransen

D-U-N-S 04-372-6900
HEALTHEAST CARE SYSTEM (MN)
(Suby of HEALTHEAST COMPANIES INC) ★
559 Capitol Blvd, Saint Paul, MN 55103-2101
Tel (651) 232-2300 Founded/Ownrshp 1980
Sales 23.9MM^E EMP 100^E
SIC 8011 6512 8082 8062 Clinic, operated by physicians; Nonresidential building operators; Home health care services; General medical & surgical hospitals
Pr: Tim Hanson
*Pr: Scott North
CFO: Doug Davenport
Bd of Dir: Andrew Hanson
Bd of Dir: Leonard Randolph Jr
Chf Mktg O: Bob Gill
Ofcr: Kris Hoefs
Ofcr: Craig Svendsen
VP: Kevin Garrett
VP: Randolph Leonard
Exec: Chris Keane
Exec: John Piatkowski

D-U-N-S 17-439-7265
HEALTHEAST CARE SYSTEM
HEALTHEAST CORPORATE
1700 University Ave W # 5, Saint Paul, MN 55104-3727
Tel (651) 232-5353 Founded/Ownrshp 1986
Sales 943.5MM EMP 5,500
SIC 8741 8062 7389 Hospital management; General medical & surgical hospitals; Document storage service; Hospital management; General medical & surgical hospitals; Document storage service
Pr: Timothy H Hanson
*Pr: Kathryn Correia
COO: Anne Schrader
Sr VP: Paul Torgerson
*VP: Dr Robert Beck
*VP: Gary French
*VP: Roger Green
VP: Steve Kolar
VP: Martin Paul
VP: William Scandrett
*VP: Ann Schrader
*VP: Steven Sprint
VP: Ginny Sullivan
Dir Rx: Risa Eckardt
Dir Bus: Len Kaiser
Board of Directors: Tim Marx

HEALTHEAST CARE SYSTEMS
See HEALTHEAST CARE INC

D-U-N-S 04-355-0037
HEALTHEAST COMPANIES INC
(Suby of HEALTHEAST CARE SYSTEM) ★
1700 University Ave W, Saint Paul, MN 55104-3727
Tel (651) 232-2300 Founded/Ownrshp 1980
Sales 35.8MM^E EMP 1,508
SIC 8082 8051 8011 Home health care services; Skilled nursing care facilities; Offices & clinics of medical doctors; Home health care services; Skilled nursing care facilities; Offices & clinics of medical doctors
Pr: Timothy H Hanson
*VP: Roger Green

HEALTHEAST CORPORATE
See HEALTHEAST ST JOHNS HOSPITAL

HEALTHEAST CORPORATE
See HEALTHEAST CARE SYSTEM

D-U-N-S 14-850-7254
HEALTHEAST HOME CARE INC
(Suby of HEALTHEAST COMPANIES INC) ★
1700 University Ave W, Saint Paul, MN 55104-3727
Tel (651) 232-2800 Founded/Ownrshp 1985
Sales 12.7MM EMP 450
SIC 8082 Home health care services; Home health care services

D-U-N-S 15-758-0002
HEALTHEAST ST JOHNS HOSPITAL
HEALTHEAST CORPORATE
(Suby of HEALTHEAST CARE SYSTEM) ★
1575 Beam Ave, Saint Paul, MN 55109-1126
Tel (651) 232-7000 Founded/Ownrshp 2001
Sales 127.0MM^E EMP 713
SIC 8062 General medical & surgical hospitals; General medical & surgical hospitals
Pr: Kathryn Correia
COO: Lee Miller
Exec: Jill Gillispie
Pharmcst: Cori Amesbury

D-U-N-S 78-451-2527
HEALTHEAST ST JOSEPHS HOSPITAL
ST. JOSEPH'S HOSPITAL
69 Exchange St W, Saint Paul, MN 55102-1004
Tel (651) 232-3000 Founded/Ownrshp 1987
Sales 270.4MM EMP 1,164
SIC 8062 General medical & surgical hospitals; General medical & surgical hospitals
Pr: Timothy Hanson
Doctor: Karen McConville

D-U-N-S 19-385-7914
HEALTHEDGE SOFTWARE INC
30 Corporate Dr Ste 150, Burlington, MA 01803-4257
Tel (781) 285-1300 Founded/Ownrshp 2004
Sales 40.5MM^E EMP 100^E
SIC 7372 Prepackaged software; Prepackaged software
Pr: Rob Gillette
COO: Steve Sharp
CFO: Matt Hughes
Ex VP: Chris Conte
Ex VP: Ray Desrochers
Ex VP: Dan Welch
VP: Arik Hill
CTO: Matt Kuntz

D-U-N-S 79-350-6390
▲ **HEALTHEQUITY INC**
15 W Scenic Pointe Dr # 100, Draper, UT 84020-6120
Tel (801) 727-1000 Founded/Ownrshp 2002
Sales 87.8MM EMP 455^E
Tkr Sym HQY Exch NGS
SIC 8399 6371 6036 6321 6282 Health systems agency; Pension, health & welfare funds; Savings institutions, not federally chartered; Accident & health insurance; Investment advice; Health systems agency; Pension, health & welfare funds; Savings institutions, not federally chartered; Accident & health insurance; Investment advice
Pr: Jon Kessler
CFO: Darcy Mott
*V Ch Bd: Stephen D Neeleman
Ex VP: Ashley Dreier
Ex VP: Frode Jensen
Ex VP: Jon Soldan
Ex VP: Matthew Sydney
VP: Stephen Burns
VP: Angelique Hill
VP Mktg: John Sweeney
Board of Directors: Frank A Corvino, Evelyn Dilsaver, Michael O Leavitt, Frank T Medici, Manu Rana, Ian Sacks, Robert W Selander

HEALTHESYSTEMS
See HEALTH E SYSTEMS LLC

D-U-N-S 80-809-8094
HEALTHFIRST HEALTH PLAN OF NEW JERSEY INC
25 Broadway Fl 9, New York, NY 10004-1058
Tel (212) 801-6000 Founded/Ownrshp 2007
Sales NA EMP 1
SIC 6321 Health insurance carriers; Health insurance carriers
Pr: Paul Dickstein

D-U-N-S 80-948-8588
HEALTHFIRST INC
100 Church St Fl 17, New York, NY 10007-2607
Tel (212) 801-6000 Founded/Ownrshp 1993
Sales 32.7MM EMP 12^E
Accts Ernst & Young Llp New York N
SIC 8011 Health maintenance organization
Pr: Pat Wang
COO: Larry Garrison
COO: Gregory Kaladjian
CFO: Maria Escurra
CFO: Doug Johnston
CFO: Mary Keegan
CFO: Thomas McFarland
Bd of Dir: Tom Tyree
Ofcr: Sonya L Henderson
Ex VP: George Frawley
*Ex VP: Daniel McCarthy
*Sr VP: Arun Bhatia
Sr VP: Keith Gordon
Sr VP: Gil Marchany
*Sr VP: Elizabeth St Clair
*Sr VP: Marybeth Tita
VP: Scott Greene
VP: Kimberly Noel
Exec: Linda Kirkland
Exec: Heather Lloyd
Exec: Tamara Megue

D-U-N-S 80-809-7021
HEALTHFIRST PHSP INC
(Suby of HEALTHFIRST INC) ★
100 Church St Fl 17, New York, NY 10007-2607
Tel (212) 801-6000 Founded/Ownrshp 1994
Sales NA EMP 11
SIC 6321 Health insurance carriers; Health insurance carriers
Pr: Pat Wang

D-U-N-S 83-453-6612
HEALTHFIRST TPA INC
(Suby of EAST TEXAS MEDICAL CENTER REGIONAL HEALTHCARE SYST) ★
821 E Se Loop 323 Ste 200, Tyler, TX 75701-9666
Tel (903) 581-2600 Founded/Ownrshp 1997
Sales NA EMP 213
SIC 6411 Medical insurance claim processing, contract or fee basis; Medical insurance claim processing, contract or fee basis
CEO: Tom Slack
*COO: Larea Albert
*CFO: Doug Johnston
*Treas: Byron Hale
CIO: Paula Anthony
Dir IT: Tony Jones

D-U-N-S 04-710-4870
HEALTHGRADES OPERATING CO INC
CPM HEALTHGRADES
999 18th St Ste 600, Denver, CO 80202-2422
Tel (303) 716-0041 Founded/Ownrshp 2001
Sales 54.6MM^E EMP 320^E
SIC 8062 General medical & surgical hospitals; General medical & surgical hospitals
CEO: Roger C Holstein
*Pr: Jeff Surges
*Chf Mktg O: Keith Nyhouse
*Sr Ex VP: Robert Draughon
Ex VP: John Neal
Ex VP: Andrea Pearson
Sr VP: Tod Baker
Sr VP: Mark Bartling
Sr VP: Christopher Catallo
Sr VP: Mayur Gupya
Sr VP: Josh Schwartz
Sr VP: Mike Shanks
Sr VP: Doug Sundlof
VP: Brian Irby
Creative D: Melissa Grow-Cusumano

D-U-N-S 85-849-1046
HEALTHGRAM INC
1515 Mockingbird Ln, Charlotte, NC 28209-3236
Tel (704) 523-2758 Founded/Ownrshp 1977
Sales NA EMP 105
SIC 6411 Medical insurance claim processing, contract or fee basis
CEO: David R Tate
*Pr: Paul R Tate
Ofcr: Sally McElwee
*Ex VP: Robert Salton
VP: Michael Hughes
VP: Shira Wilensky
Dir IT: John Jamison
Mktg Dir: David McCachern

HEALTHHELP HOLDINGS
See HEALTHHELP LLC

D-U-N-S 95-665-9411
HEALTHHELP LLC
HEALTHHELP HOLDINGS
(Suby of MTS HEALTH INVESTORS LLC) ★
16945 Northchase Dr # 1300, Houston, TX 77060-2133
Tel (281) 447-7000 Founded/Ownrshp 2008
Sales NA EMP 300
SIC 6411 Insurance agents, brokers & service; Insurance agents, brokers & service
Pr: Cherrill Farnsworth
*Pr: Donna Baker-Miller
Ex VP: Randall Lindner
*VP: John Golden
VP: Gerald Kiplinger
Ex Dir: Chris Sullivan
Prgrm Mgr: Kiersten Williams-Bolton
*CIO: Steve Spar
QA Dir: Jenifer Deuel
Dir IT: Kathleen Inglet-Spar
Dir IT: Kathleen Spar

D-U-N-S 62-391-3001
■ **HEALTHKEEPERS INC**
(Suby of ANTHEM SOUTHEAST INC) ★
2220 Edward Holland Dr, Richmond, VA 23230-2519
Tel (800) 421-1880 Founded/Ownrshp 1985
Sales NA EMP 105
SIC 6324 Health maintenance organization (HMO), insurance only
Pr: Thomas Snead
*VP: Bob Watson

D-U-N-S 17-857-6609
HEALTHKEEPERZ INC
HEALTH KEEPERZ
509 W 3rd St, Pembroke, NC 28372-9546
Tel (910) 522-0001 Founded/Ownrshp 1997
Sales 16.4MM^E EMP 450^E
SIC 8082 7361 Home health care services; Nurses' registry; Home health care services; Nurses' registry
Ch: Howard Brooks

D-U-N-S 06-690-5357
HEALTHLAND INC
RYCAN
1600 Utica Ave S Ste 300, Minneapolis, MN 55416-1468
Tel (612) 787-3120 Founded/Ownrshp 1980
Sales 68.8MM^E EMP 488^E
SIC 7373 5045 Turnkey vendors, computer systems; Computers; Turnkey vendors, computer systems; Computers
CEO: Chris Bauleke
Pr: Angie Franks
CFO: Todd Laddusaw
CFO: Patrick Spangler
Ex VP: Julie Weber-Kramer
Ex VP: Thomas Ziel
Sr VP: James D Anderson
Sr VP: Mark Middendorf
VP: Julie Kramer
Software D: Christina Finazzo
Sftwr Eng: Karen Johnson
Board of Directors: Jack A Kane, Carl Witonsky

D-U-N-S 07-862-8739
HEALTHLAND INC
625 S Lakeshore Dr, Glenwood, MN 56334-1549
Tel (320) 634-5331 Founded/Ownrshp 2004
Sales 23.7MM^E EMP 100
SIC 7373 5045 Computer integrated systems design; Computers, peripherals & software; Computer integrated systems design; Computers, peripherals & software
CEO: Christopher Bauleke
*CEO: Angela Franks
*CFO: Patrick Spangler
*Sr VP: James D Anderson
*Sr VP: Michael Karaman

HEALTHLINK
See LRGHEALTHCARE

D-U-N-S 05-768-0480 IMP
HEALTHMARK INDUSTRIES CO INC
33671 Doreka, Fraser, MI 48026-1610
Tel (586) 774-7600 Founded/Ownrshp 1969
Sales 43.6MM^E EMP 69^E
SIC 5047 Medical & hospital equipment; Hospital equipment & supplies; Medical equipment & supplies; Industrial safety devices: first aid kits & masks
Pr: Mark Basile
*VP: Ralph J Basile
*VP: Suzanne Basile
IT Man: Vicky Oland
*VP Sls: Steven J Basile
Sales Asso: Van Horn

D-U-N-S 96-813-8420
HEALTHMARK PARTNERS INC
8 Cadillac Dr Ste 200, Brentwood, TN 37027-5316
Tel (615) 329-9000 Founded/Ownrshp 1996
Sales 12.1MM^E EMP 300
SIC 8741 Hospital management; Nursing & personal care facility management; Hospital management; Nursing & personal care facility management
Ch Bd: Andrew Miller

HEALTHMARK/ATG
See FCB WORLDWIDE INC

D-U-N-S 13-955-2087
HEALTHMARKETS INC
9151 Boulevard 26, North Richland Hills, TX 76180-5600
Tel (817) 255-5200 Founded/Ownrshp 1984
Sales NA EMP 1,340
Accts Kpmg Llp Dallas Texas
SIC 6311 6321 Life insurance; Health insurance carriers; Life insurance; Health insurance carriers
Pr: Kenneth J Fasola
*COO: Derrick A Duke
*CFO: R Scott Donovan
Chf Mktg O: Tim Roach
*Ex VP: Richard Fiedotin
*Ex VP: Brian Poger
*Ex VP: Mark H Smith
Sr VP: Susan E Dew
Sr VP: Susan Dew
VP: Denise Cotter
VP: Peter Daggett
VP: Consuelo Palacios
VP: Alan Tracy

D-U-N-S 96-311-5857
HEALTHMARKETS LLC
(Suby of HEALTHMARKETS INC) ★
9151 Boulevard 26, North Richland Hills, TX 76180-5600
Tel (817) 255-3100 Founded/Ownrshp 2006
Sales NA EMP 700E
SIC 6311 6321 Life insurance; Health insurance carriers; Life insurance; Health insurance carriers
CFO: Donna Bruskie
Dir IT: Philip Bardowell

D-U-N-S 07-857-7642
HEALTHMEDX LLC
5100 N Towne Centre Dr, Ozark, MO 65721-7479
Tel (417) 582-1816 Founded/Ownrshp 2011
Sales 26.8MME EMP 180
SIC 7371 7372 8748 Computer software systems analysis & design, custom; Prepackaged software; Business consulting; Computer software systems analysis & design, custom; Prepackaged software; Business consulting
CEO: Pamela J Pure
*Pr: Charlie Daniels
CFO: Vince Estrada
*VP: Mary E Beach
VP: Chris Bingham
*VP: Craig Lund
CTO: Dan Cobb
QA Dir: Jason Buchek
QA Dir: Lorrie Eury
QA Dir: Debbie Hoffmeister
QA Dir: Erin Pering

D-U-N-S 95-846-5007
HEALTHNET AEROMEDICAL SERVICES INC
110 Wyoming St Ste 101, Charleston, WV 25302-2340
Tel (304) 340-8000 Founded/Ownrshp 1987
Sales NA EMP 140
Accts Arnett Foster Toothman Pllc C
SIC 6324 Hospital & medical service plans; Hospital & medical service plans
Pr: Clinton Burley
*Ch Bd: David Ramsey
*CFO: Brian Doughty
*V Ch Bd: Albert Wright

D-U-N-S 15-065-9126
HEALTHNET INC
3403 E Raymond St, Indianapolis, IN 46203-4744
Tel (317) 788-9769 Founded/Ownrshp 1983
Sales 20.0MME EMP 250
Accts Blue & Co Llc Indianapolis I
SIC 8052 Intermediate care facilities; Intermediate care facilities
Pr: Mary Moore
COO: Rick Diaz
*Prin: Larry Forck
Doctor: Arundathi Prasad

D-U-N-S 61-385-0593
HEALTHNET PHO INC
320 Pomfret St, Putnam, CT 06260-1836
Tel (860) 774-3366 Founded/Ownrshp 1982
Sales 17.9MME EMP 846
SIC 8741 8062 Hospital management; General medical & surgical hospitals; Hospital management; General medical & surgical hospitals
Ex Dir: Charles Schneider

D-U-N-S 01-347-0133
HEALTHNOW NEW YORK INC
BLUE CROSS BLUE SHIELD WSTN NY
257 W Genesee St, Buffalo, NY 14202-2657
Tel (716) 887-6900 Founded/Ownrshp 1940
Sales NA EMP 2,200
SIC 6324 6411 Group hospitalization plans; Insurance agents, brokers & service; Group hospitalization plans; Insurance agents, brokers & service
Ex VP: Cheryl Howe
CEO: Alphonso O'Neil-White
COO: Bob Hoover
CFO: Christopher Leardini
CFO: Stephen Swift
Bd of Dir: Dena Owens
Ofcr: Nancy Schoellkopf
Sr VP: Christopher Leardini
VP: Gloria Beczkowski
VP: Pauline E Cataldi
VP: Gretchen Fierle
VP: Jay Gandhi
VP: Jared Gross
VP: Gary Kerl
VP: Bruce Morlock
VP: Raghu Ram
VP: Melissa Tucker

D-U-N-S 02-778-1348
HEALTHONE LLC
COLUMBIA AURORA MIDWIVES
1501 S Potomac St, Aurora, CO 80012-5411
Tel (303) 695-2600 Founded/Ownrshp 1960
Sales 118.6MME EMP 1,500E
SIC 8062 General medical & surgical hospitals; General medical & surgical hospitals
CEO: Dan Miller
COO: Ryan Simpson
CFO: Bill Voloch
Ofcr: Richard Hemmett
Ofcr: John Sanchez
VP: Kathy Yeager
Dir Risk M: Jillian Eldridge
Dir Lab: Lucy Tyler
Dir Rad: Terry Hurlbert
Dir IT: Lea Kurlinski
Mktg Dir: Bailey Hulslander

D-U-N-S 04-470-4052
HEALTHPARTNERS
9200 Nicollet Ave S, Minneapolis, MN 55420-3714
Tel (952) 883-5200 Founded/Ownrshp 2011
Sales NA EMP 33E
SIC 6321 Health insurance carriers
Owner: Mary Brainerd

D-U-N-S 79-705-3212
HEALTHPARTNERS INC
8170 33rd Ave S, Bloomington, MN 55425-4516
Tel (952) 883-6000 Founded/Ownrshp 1984
Sales 1.1MMME EMP 9,000
Accts Kpmg Llp Minneapolis Mn
SIC 8011 Health maintenance organization (HMO), insurance only; Offices & clinics of medical doctors
Pr: Mary Brainerd
*Pr: Ann Gjelten
*COO: Craig Amundson DDS
*CFO: Kathleen M Cooney
Bd of Dir: John E Gherty
Bd of Dir: Alejandro Maldonado
Bd of Dir: Eliot A Seide
*Ex VP: Kirby Erickson
*Sr VP: Andrea Walsh
*Sr VP: Ted Wise
VP: David Bergh
*VP: Tony Bongiovanni
VP: Don Daddario
VP: Tammie Lindquist
VP: Nicolaas P Pronk
VP: Vicki Sessoms
VP: Mary Stom
VP: Barbara Tretheway
*VP: Valerie Welch

D-U-N-S 02-919-1355
HEALTHPARTNERS INSTITUTE
(Suby of HEALTHPARTNERS INC) ★
3311 E Old Shakopee Rd, Bloomington, MN 55425-1361
Tel (952) 967-5001 Founded/Ownrshp 1989
Sales 20.0MME EMP 112
Accts Kpmg Llp Minneapolis Mn
SIC 8231 8299 8733 Medical library; Educational services; Educational service, nondegree granting: continuing educ.; Research institute; Medical library; Educational services; Educational service, nondegree granting: continuing educ.; Research institute
Pr: Steve Connelly
Ex Dir: Carl Patow

D-U-N-S 02-894-8573
HEALTHPLAN HOLDINGS INC
(Suby of WATER STREET HEALTHCARE PARTNERS LLC) ★
3501 E Frontage Rd, Tampa, FL 33607-1704
Tel (813) 289-1000 Founded/Ownrshp 2008
Sales NA EMP 1,051
Accts Pricewaterhousecoopers Llp Ta
SIC 6399 Deposit insurance; Deposit insurance
Pr: Jeff W Bak
CEO: Art Schultz
*CFO: Stephen M Saft
Ofcr: Joy Easterwood
*Sr VP: George Durot
*Sr VP: Karen W Mulroe
VP: Delana Anderson
VP: Dan Currie
VP: Susan Murray
VP: Kim Warner
Snr Ntwrk: Yury Shmerlis

D-U-N-S 18-822-7268
HEALTHPLAN SERVICES INC
(Suby of HEALTHPLAN HOLDINGS INC) ★
3501 E Frontage Rd # 125, Tampa, FL 33607-1704
Tel (813) 289-1000 Founded/Ownrshp 2001
Sales 300.0MM EMP 1,051
SIC 8741 Hospital management; Nursing & personal care facility management; Hospital management; Nursing & personal care facility management
Pr: Jeffery W Bak
COO: Kristin Baca
CFO: Thomas Chadwick
CFO: Stephen M Saft
Ofcr: Michael Buda
Ex VP: Arthur T Schultz
Sr VP: Mark Andrews
Sr VP: Todd Cowan
Sr VP: Gregory C Fisher
Sr VP: Jay McLauchlin
Sr VP: Dennis Prysner
VP: Gregory T Fisher
VP: Lori Gonzalez
VP: David Holton
VP: Pat Keplinger
VP: Trent King
VP: Barbara Mathey
VP: Karen Mulroe
VP: Steven Strobl
VP: Delana Traugott
VP: Ronald Walters

D-U-N-S 13-089-6392
HEALTHPLEX INC
333 Earle Ovington Blvd # 300, Uniondale, NY 11553-3608
Tel (516) 542-2200 Founded/Ownrshp 1984
Sales NA EMP 620
SIC 6324 Dental insurance; Dental insurance
Ch Bd: Stephen J Cuchel
Pr: Sharon Zelkind
COO: Christopher Schmidt
CFO: Vignola Valerie
CFO: Valerie Vignola
Treas: George Kane
Ex VP: Martin Kane
VP: Valerie Foster
VP: Joni Howe
VP: Philip J Rizzuto
Comm Dir: Mariann Raab

D-U-N-S 96-333-2312
HEALTHPLUS INSURANCE CO
2050 S Linden Rd, Flint, MI 48532-4159
Tel (810) 230-2000 Founded/Ownrshp 2010
Sales NA EMP 2
SIC 6321 Health insurance carriers; Health insurance carriers
Prin: Bea Raymond

D-U-N-S 09-540-0909
HEALTHPLUS OF MICHIGAN INC
HEALTHPLUS PARTNERS
2050 S Linden Rd, Flint, MI 48532-4159
Tel (810) 230-2000 Founded/Ownrshp 1979
Sales NA EMP 400
SIC 6324 Health maintenance organization (HMO), insurance only; Health maintenance organization (HMO), insurance only
Pr: Michael Genord MD
*CFO: Keith Collin CPA
VP: Antoinette Geyer
VP: Erik Helms
Prgrm Mgr: Nancy Davis
Dir IT: John Hicks
Dir IT: Bridget Hollingsworth
Dir IT: Cheryl Wagner
IT Man: Shelley Indlekofer
IT Man: Steve Krizan
Mktg Dir: Raj Baj

HEALTHPLUS PARTNERS
See HEALTHPLUS OF MICHIGAN INC

D-U-N-S 07-950-1356
■ HEALTHPOCKET INC
(Suby of HEALTH INSURANCE INNOVATIONS INC) ★
444 Castro St Ste 710, Mountain View, CA 94041-2080
Tel (800) 606-7317 Founded/Ownrshp 2014
Sales NA EMP 142E
SIC 6321 Health insurance carriers
CEO: Bruce Telkamp
*Pr: Sheldon Wang

D-U-N-S 18-112-3050
HEALTHPOINT
955 Powell Ave Sw Ste A, Renton, WA 98057-2908
Tel (425) 235-5755 Founded/Ownrshp 1971
Sales 69.3MM EMP 305
Accts Cliftonlarsonallen Llp Bellev
SIC 8011 Offices & clinics of medical doctors; Offices & clinics of medical doctors
CEO: Thomas Trompeter
*COO: Debbie Wilkinson
*CFO: Jody Putman
VP: Marcus Girolamo
*VP: Vicki Hammond
Dir Rx: David Rose
Doctor: Sara Thompson
Snr Mgr: Lisa Yohalem

D-U-N-S 13-462-6220
HEALTHPOINT CAPITAL LLC
505 Park Ave Fl 12, New York, NY 10022-9318
Tel (212) 935-7780 Founded/Ownrshp 2002
Sales 26.4MME EMP 195
SIC 8733 Medical research; Medical research
CFO: Joseph Fitzpatrick
Bd of Dir: Lisa Ferrara
Ex VP: William T White III
VP: Steven Reinecke
Mng Dir: Laing Rikkers
Dir IT: Matt Jaffe

D-U-N-S 96-563-4504
HEALTHPOINT LTD
CORIA PHARMACEUTICALS
3909 Hulen St, Fort Worth, TX 76107-7253
Tel (817) 900-4000 Founded/Ownrshp 2012
Sales 70.6MME EMP 220
SIC 2834 Pharmaceutical preparations; Pharmaceutical preparations
Pr: Travis E Baugh
Pr: Michael E Steadman
Sr Cor Off: John Foster
Sr VP: Robert Bancroft
Sr VP: Sue Kraueter
VP: Johnny Cantu
VP: Paul H Duesterhoft
VP: F B Fitzgerald
VP: Mark A Mitchell
VP: Jeff Williams
Assoc Dir: Tommy Lee

D-U-N-S 15-255-3228
HEALTHPORT INC
925 North Point Pkwy # 350, Alpharetta, GA 30005-5214
Tel (770) 360-1700 Founded/Ownrshp 2008
Sales NA EMP 3,875
SIC 6324 7373 7374 Hospital & medical service plans; Turnkey vendors, computer systems; Data processing & preparation; Hospital & medical service plans; Turnkey vendors, computer systems; Data processing & preparation
Pr: Michael J Labedz
*COO: Steve Roberts
*CFO: Brian M Grazzini
*Ch: Pat Haynes
Ofcr: Rita K Bowen
*Sr VP: Jonathan Arkin
Sr VP: Kerry De Vallette
Sr VP: Bill Garvis
*Sr VP: Bill Matitts
VP: Rasheed Allen
VP: Larry Arnold
VP: Bryan Gery
VP: Paul Gue
VP: Warren Hooten
VP: Jan Kelley
VP: Craig F Klein
*VP: Deryl Metze
VP: Patrick Nord
*VP: Matt Rohs
VP: Catherine Valyi

D-U-N-S 02-107-4307
HEALTHPORT TECHNOLOGIES LLC
(Suby of CT TECHNOLOGIES HOLDINGS INC) ★
925 North Point Pkwy # 350, Alpharetta, GA 30005-5210
Tel (770) 360-1700 Founded/Ownrshp 1976
Sales 517.5MME EMP 4,000
SIC 7375 7371 Information retrieval services; Custom computer programming services; Information retrieval services; Custom computer programming services
CEO: Mike Labetz
*CFO: Brian Grazzini
Sr VP: Terry Cameron
VP: Tim Engelbracht
VP Opers: Clorie Robinson
Manager: Nickole Naumann
Counsel: Jennifer Napier

D-U-N-S 60-686-0542
HEALTHPRIME INC
925 North Point Pkwy # 440, Alpharetta, GA 30005-5210
Tel (770) 619-0866 Founded/Ownrshp 1989
Sales 30.2MME EMP 520E
SIC 8741

HEALTHRIDER
See ICON HEALTH & FITNESS INC

D-U-N-S 06-014-2130
HEALTHRIGHT 360
HAIGHT ASHBURY FREE CLINIC
1735 Mission St Ste 2001, San Francisco, CA 94103-2417
Tel (415) 762-3700 Founded/Ownrshp 1966
Sales 40.7MME EMP 450
Accts Armanino Llp San Ramon Ca
SIC 8093 8011 Detoxification center, outpatient; Clinic, operated by physicians; Psychiatric clinic; Detoxification center, outpatient; Clinic, operated by physicians; Psychiatric clinic
CEO: Vitka Eisen
V Ch: Maria Mangini
*COO: Warren Lyons
CFO: Pamela Banks
*CFO: David Crawford
CFO: Carl Gill
*VP: Wayne Garcia
*VP: Mardell Gavriel
CIO: Jegan Anandasakaran
IT Man: Denise Williams

D-U-N-S 94-555-7239
HEALTHSCOPE BENEFITS INC
27 Corporate Hill Dr, Little Rock, AR 72205-4537
Tel (501) 225-1551 Founded/Ownrshp 2008
Sales 52.5MME EMP 302
SIC 8741 8742 Hospital management; Administrative services consultant; Hospital management; Administrative services consultant
CEO: Joe K Edwards
*Pr: Mary C Person
*COO: Matt Gray
*VP: Cathleen Armstrong
*VP: Scott Barnes
*VP: Robert Bracy
*VP: Mike Castleberry
VP: Richard Cole
*VP: Brett Edwards
VP: Carol Gaines
VP: Tom Gildea
VP: Jim Johnson
VP: Todd Johnson
VP: Wesley Jones
VP: Rebecca McSwain
VP: Paula Thompson

D-U-N-S 15-193-5749
HEALTHSHARE INC
CHILD DEVELOPMENT CENTER
416 Connable Ave, Petoskey, MI 49770-2212
Tel (231) 487-4803 Founded/Ownrshp 1982
Sales 226.9MM EMP 150E
Accts Ernst & Young Llp Grand Rapid
SIC 8741 8062 Hospital management; Nursing & personal care facility management; General medical & surgical hospitals; Hospital management; Nursing & personal care facility management; General medical & surgical hospitals
Pr: Jeffrey Wendling
*Ch Bd: Lawrence D Buhl
*Treas: Richard Lent
*V Ch Bd: Thomas N Fairbairn

D-U-N-S 11-787-2643
HEALTHSMART HOLDINGS INC
222 Las Colinas Blvd W, Irving, TX 75039-5421
Tel (214) 574-3546 Founded/Ownrshp 2003
Sales 28.4MME EMP 100E
SIC 8399 Health systems agency
Pr: Daniel D Crowley
*Pr: James M Pennington
*CFO: William Dembereckyj
*Ex VP: Mark Stadler
*VP: Bill Dembereckyj
VP: Michele Wilfer

D-U-N-S 06-382-8842
HEALTHSMART PACIFIC INC
LONG BEACH PAIN CENTER
20377 Sw Acacia St # 110, Newport Beach, CA 92660-0781
Tel (562) 595-1911 Founded/Ownrshp 1997
Sales 102.0MME EMP 1,200
Accts Statewide Health Planning & De
SIC 8062 General medical & surgical hospitals; General medical & surgical hospitals
CEO: Michael Ddrobot
*CEO: Michael D Drobot
CFO: Jim Canedo
Dir Case M: Patricia Bussey
Dir Sec: Robert Vance
CTO: Javier Chavez
Pathlgst: Luke Watson
Pharmcst: Arleioh Williams
Phys Thrpy: Heidi Endert
Board of Directors: Randolph Taylor

D-U-N-S 95-744-6289
HEALTHSMART PREFERRED CARE II LP
2002 W Loop 289 Ste 103, Lubbock, TX 79407-7701
Tel (806) 473-2500 *Founded/Ownrshp* 1994
Sales NA *EMP* 314
SIC 6324 Hospital & medical service plans; Hospital & medical service plans
Ch Bd: Ted L Parker
**Pr:* David Adams
Treas: Mike Hedlund
**VP:* Jane Williamson Rn
VP Mktg: Lynda Woods

D-U-N-S 03-545-2221
■ **HEALTHSOUND CARDINAL HILL REHABILTIATION HOSPITAL LLC**
CARDINAL HL RHABILITATION HOSP
(*Suby of* HEALTHSOUTH CORP) ★
2050 Versailles Rd, Lexington, KY 40504-1405
Tel (859) 254-5701 *Founded/Ownrshp* 2001
Sales 72.5MM^E *EMP* 650
SIC 8062 General & family practice, physician/surgeon; General medical & surgical hospitals
Pr: Jay Grinney
COO: Mark Tarr
CFO: Douglas Coltharp

D-U-N-S 14-732-4128 EXP
HEALTHSOURCE DISTRIBUTORS LLC
7200 Rutherford Rd # 150, Baltimore, MD 21244-2717
Tel (410) 653-1113 *Founded/Ownrshp* 2003
Sales 187.5MM *EMP* 20
Accts Weil Akman Baylin & Coleman
SIC 5122 Pharmaceuticals; Pharmaceuticals
Pr: Jerry Wolasky

D-U-N-S 14-426-1724
■ **HEALTHSOURCE INC**
(*Suby of* CIGNA HEALTH CORP) ★
2 College Park Dr, Hooksett, NH 03106-1636
Tel (603) 268-7000 *Founded/Ownrshp* 1997
Sales NA *EMP* 4,100
SIC 6324 8741 8011 Hospital & medical service plans; Administrative management; Health maintenance organization; Hospital & medical service plans; Administrative management; Health maintenance organization
Pr: H Edward Hanway
CFO: Robert C Williams
Treas: Bach MAI Tai
VP: Ann Duscoll
Mktg Mgr: Jenn Work
Surg Cl Rc: Glenn Osgoodby

D-U-N-S 09-394-2175 IMP
HEALTHSOURCE OF OHIO INC (OH)
PEEBLES FAMILY HLTH & DNTL CTR
5400 Dupont Cir Ste A, Milford, OH 45150-2770
Tel (513) 576-7700 *Founded/Ownrshp* 1976
Sales 36.5MM *EMP* 325
SIC 8093

D-U-N-S 06-983-5544
HEALTHSOURCE SAGINAW INC
WHITE PINE PSYCHIATRIC CENTER
3340 Hospital Rd, Saginaw, MI 48603-9622
Tel (989) 790-7837 *Founded/Ownrshp* 1928
Sales 39.4MM *EMP* 425^E
SIC 8062 General medical & surgical hospitals; General medical & surgical hospitals
Acting CEO: Lisa Lapham
**CFO:* Glen Chipman
CFO: Jeff Engelsman
Off Mgr: Joan Duran
Nurse Mgr: Janice Maciejewski
CIO: Randall Sanborn
QA Dir: Susan Graham
Opers Mgr: Nita McKenzie
Mktg Dir: Dave Koepplinger
Mktg Dir: Lynne Price
Nrsg Dir: Karleen Latty

HEALTHSOUTH
See FAIRLAWN FOUNDATION INC

HEALTHSOUTH
See LAKESHORE SYSTEM SERVICES INC

HEALTHSOUTH
See TYLER REHAB ASSOCIATES LP

D-U-N-S 16-138-0696
■ **HEALTHSOUTH - MONTGOMERY INC**
(*Suby of* HEALTHSOUTH CORP) ★
4465 Narrow Lane Rd, Montgomery, AL 36116-2953
Tel (334) 284-7700 *Founded/Ownrshp* 1994
Sales 24.2MM^E *EMP* 300
SIC 8069 Specialty hospitals, except psychiatric; Specialty hospitals, except psychiatric
CEO: Linda Wade
Chf Nrs Of: Dan Hall

D-U-N-S 11-430-2219 IMP
▲ **HEALTHSOUTH CORP**
3660 Grandview Pkwy # 200, Birmingham, AL 35243-3332
Tel (205) 967-7116 *Founded/Ownrshp* 1984
Sales 2.3MMM *EMP* 29,000
Tkr Sym HLS *Exch* NYS
SIC 8069 8051 Specialty hospitals, except psychiatric; Extended care facility; Specialty hospitals, except psychiatric; Extended care facility
Pr: Jay Grinney
COO: Mark J Tarr
CFO: Douglas E Coltharp
Ex VP: John P Whittington
VP: Rob McCallum
VP: Liz Ross
VP: Robert Wisner
Dir Rx: Rosemary Baumgardner
Dir Rx: Sara Gibbons
Dir Sec: Kenneth Lavergne
Genl Couns: Sandy Murvin
Board of Directors: John W Chidsey, Donald L Correll, Yvonne M Curl, Charles M Elson, Joan E Herman, Leo I Higdon Jr, John E Maupin Jr, L Edward Shaw Jr

D-U-N-S 06-874-7690
■ **HEALTHSOUTH HARMARVILLE REHABILITATION HOSPITAL**
(*Suby of* HEALTHSOUTH CORP) ★
320 Guys Run Rd, Pittsburgh, PA 15238
Tel (412) 828-1300 *Founded/Ownrshp* 1996
Sales 29.5MM^E *EMP* 795
SIC 8361 Rehabilitation center, residential: health care incidental; Rehabilitation center, residential: health care incidental
Prin: Ken Anthony
Prin: Helen Todd
QA Dir: Nancy Simons
Phys Thrpy: Mark Vanvolkenburg
HC Dir: Laura Glesk

D-U-N-S 07-967-9121
■ **HEALTHSOUTH HOME HEALTH CORP**
(*Suby of* HEALTHSOUTH HOME HEALTH HOLDINGS INC) ★
3660 Grandview Pkwy, Birmingham, AL 35243-3330
Tel (205) 967-7116 *Founded/Ownrshp* 2014
Sales 1.6MM^E *EMP* 3,800^E
SIC 8082 8099 Home health care services; Medical services organization
Pr: Jay Grinney

D-U-N-S 07-967-9204
■ **HEALTHSOUTH HOME HEALTH HOLDINGS INC**
(*Suby of* HEALTHSOUTH CORP) ★
3660 Grandview Pkwy, Birmingham, AL 35243-3330
Tel (205) 967-7116 *Founded/Ownrshp* 2014
Sales 1.6MM^E *EMP* 3,800^E
SIC 8099 8082 6719 Medical services organization; Home health care services; Personal holding companies, except banks
Pr: Jay Grinney

D-U-N-S 07-211-0869
■ **HEALTHSOUTH METRO WEST HOSPITAL INC**
(*Suby of* HEALTHSOUTH CORP) ★
3660 Grandview Pkwy, Birmingham, AL 35243-3330
Tel (205) 967-7116 *Founded/Ownrshp* 2003
Sales 10.3MM^E *EMP* 470
SIC 8062 8011 General medical & surgical hospitals; Offices & clinics of medical doctors; General medical & surgical hospitals; Offices & clinics of medical doctors
Dir IT: Robbie Bruce
VP Mktg: Ginger Smith

D-U-N-S 14-731-3423
■ **HEALTHSOUTH OF ALTOONA INC**
(*Suby of* HEALTHSOUTH CORP) ★
2005 Valley View Blvd, Altoona, PA 16602-4548
Tel (814) 944-3535 *Founded/Ownrshp* 1994
Sales 15.7MM^E *EMP* 350
SIC 8093 8062 Rehabilitation center, outpatient treatment; General medical & surgical hospitals; Rehabilitation center, outpatient treatment; General medical & surgical hospitals
Ex Dir: Scott Filler
Dir Inf Cn: Pam Beeler
Dir Inf Cn: Theresa Friedenberger
Dir Soc: Darla Summerville
CTO: Chris Ganley

D-U-N-S 61-195-2193
■ **HEALTHSOUTH OF AUSTIN INC**
(*Suby of* HEALTHSOUTH CORP) ★
1215 Red River St, Austin, TX 78701-1921
Tel (512) 474-5700 *Founded/Ownrshp* 1993
Sales 28.5MM^E *EMP* 337
SIC 8069 Specialty hospitals, except psychiatric; Specialty hospitals, except psychiatric
Prin: Cathy Snyder

D-U-N-S 08-621-2511
■ **HEALTHSOUTH OF ERIE INC**
(*Suby of* HEALTHSOUTH CORP) ★
143 E 2nd St, Erie, PA 16507-1501
Tel (814) 878-1200 *Founded/Ownrshp* 1994
Sales 29.5MM^E *EMP* 400
SIC 8069 8361 8093 Specialty hospitals, except psychiatric; Residential care; Specialty outpatient clinics; Specialty hospitals, except psychiatric; Residential care; Specialty outpatient clinics
CEO: John Ferritto
Dir Inf Cn: Janet Rossi
Opers Mgr: William Chiaramonte

D-U-N-S 87-759-5827
■ **HEALTHSOUTH OF HOUSTON INC**
(*Suby of* HEALTHSOUTH CORP) ★
18550 Interstate 45 S, Shenandoah, TX 77384-4119
Tel (281) 364-2000 *Founded/Ownrshp* 1994
Sales 21.9MM *EMP* 300^E
SIC 8069 Specialty hospitals, except psychiatric; Specialty hospitals, except psychiatric
Pr: J Grenny
VP: Chris Lasserre
Chf Nrs Of: Renne Hastings
Pharmcst: Charles Nguyen

D-U-N-S 87-710-8514
■ **HEALTHSOUTH OF MISSOURI INC**
(*Suby of* HEALTHSOUTH CORP) ★
1 Healthsouth Pkwy S, Birmingham, AL 35243-2358
Tel (205) 968-4456 *Founded/Ownrshp* 1988
Sales 8.8MM^E *EMP* 650
SIC 8069 Specialty hospitals, except psychiatric; Specialty hospitals, except psychiatric
CEO: Jay Grinney

D-U-N-S 87-715-3619
■ **HEALTHSOUTH OF NEW MEXICO INC**
(*Suby of* HEALTHSOUTH CORP) ★
7000 Jefferson St Ne, Albuquerque, NM 87109-4357
Tel (505) 344-9478 *Founded/Ownrshp* 1985
Sales 23.9MM^E *EMP* 294
SIC 8069 Specialty hospitals, except psychiatric; Specialty hospitals, except psychiatric
Nrsg Dir: Veronica Gadonski
Nrsg Dir: Gretchen Martinez
HC Dir: Bob Scanlon

D-U-N-S 18-904-8242
■ **HEALTHSOUTH OF SAN ANTONIO INC**
(*Suby of* HEALTHSOUTH CORP) ★
9119 Cinnamon Hl, San Antonio, TX 78240-5401
Tel (210) 691-0737 *Founded/Ownrshp* 1994
Sales 30.7MM^E *EMP* 288
SIC 8069 Specialty hospitals, except psychiatric; Specialty hospitals, except psychiatric
CEO: Diane Lampe
Ofcr: Scott Butcher
Off Mgr: Fran Flores
Dietician: Julie Poidevin

D-U-N-S 87-716-2818
■ **HEALTHSOUTH OF SEA PINES LIMITED PARTNERSHIP**
(*Suby of* HEALTHSOUTH CORP) ★
101 E Florida Ave, Melbourne, FL 32901-8301
Tel (321) 984-4600 *Founded/Ownrshp* 2005
Sales 18.0MM *EMP* 340
SIC 8069 Specialty hospitals, except psychiatric; Specialty hospitals, except psychiatric
Genl Pt: Healthsouth Rehabilitation Cor
VP: Barbara Rhoden
Pathlgst: Debra Grayson
Nutrtnst: Sandra Jones
Doctor: Robert Byrum
Resp Thrpy: Caren Meyers

D-U-N-S 78-494-5040
■ **HEALTHSOUTH OF TEXARKANA INC**
(*Suby of* HEALTHSOUTH CORP) ★
515 W 12th St, Texarkana, TX 75501-4416
Tel (903) 793-0088 *Founded/Ownrshp* 1994
Sales 20.9MM^E *EMP* 250
SIC 8069 8741 Specialty hospitals, except psychiatric; Management services; Specialty hospitals, except psychiatric; Management services
CEO: Jerry Jasper
CFO: Mike Treadway
VP: Janan Quinn
Exec: Ann Clapp
Dir Inf Cn: Vornetta Compton
Doctor: Gail Spicer
Nrsg Dir: Cassie Turner
Pharmcst: David Stewart
Phys Thrpy: Todd Wallace
HC Dir: Greg Burt

D-U-N-S 15-260-8584
■ **HEALTHSOUTH OF TREASURE COAST INC**
(*Suby of* HEALTHSOUTH CORP) ★
1600 37th St, Vero Beach, FL 32960-4863
Tel (772) 778-2100 *Founded/Ownrshp* 1993
Sales 27.1MM^E *EMP* 350
SIC 8069 Specialty hospitals, except psychiatric; Specialty hospitals, except psychiatric

D-U-N-S 78-808-2022 IMP
■ **HEALTHSOUTH OF YORK INC**
(*Suby of* HEALTHSOUTH CORP) ★
1850 Normandie Dr, York, PA 17408-1534
Tel (717) 767-6941 *Founded/Ownrshp* 1994
Sales 17.4MM^E *EMP* 342
SIC 8069 Specialty hospitals, except psychiatric; Specialty hospitals, except psychiatric
CEO: Mark Freeburn

D-U-N-S 00-461-2462
HEALTHSOUTH PLANO REHAB HOSP
2800 W 15th St, Plano, TX 75075-7526
Tel (972) 612-9000 *Founded/Ownrshp* 2009
Sales 27.6MM *EMP* 51^E
SIC 8049 Physical therapist
Prin: Shane Everett
Ofcr: Jennifer Brewer
Dir Rx: Thanh Nguyen

D-U-N-S 60-487-1038
■ **HEALTHSOUTH REHABILITATION HOSPITAL OF CYPRESS LLC**
(*Suby of* HEALTHSOUTH CORP) ★
3660 Grandview Pkwy, Birmingham, AL 35243-3330
Tel (205) 967-7116 *Founded/Ownrshp* 1998
Sales 29.0MM^E *EMP* 1,000
SIC 8093 Specialty outpatient clinics; Specialty outpatient clinics
Ch Bd: Richard Scrushy

D-U-N-S 87-715-1233
■ **HEALTHSOUTH REHABILITATION HOSPITAL OF LARGO**
(*Suby of* HEALTHSOUTH CORP) ★
901 Clearwater Largo Rd N, Largo, FL 33770-4126
Tel (727) 586-2999 *Founded/Ownrshp* 1989
Sales 20.2MM *EMP* 250
SIC 8099 8069 Medical services organization; Specialty hospitals, except psychiatric; Medical services organization; Specialty hospitals, except psychiatric
Dir Rx: Edward G Sojak
QA Dir: Mary Heger

D-U-N-S 07-825-5619 IMP
■ **HEALTHSOUTH REHABILITATION HOSPITAL OF NEW JERSEY (INC)**
(*Suby of* HEALTHSOUTH CORP) ★
14 Hospital Dr, Toms River, NJ 08755-6402
Tel (732) 244-3100 *Founded/Ownrshp* 1994
Sales 21.8MM^E *EMP* 430
SIC 8069 Specialty hospitals, except psychiatric; Specialty hospitals, except psychiatric
COO: Patricia Ostaszewski
Dir Recs: Marilyn Mc Guire
**CFO:* David Totaro
Dir Rx: Brian Furbush
Pharmcst: Ankit Mehta
Cert Phar: Arlene Klett

D-U-N-S 15-047-2231
■ **HEALTHSOUTH REHABILITATION HOSPITAL OF SARASOTA**
(*Suby of* HEALTHSOUTH CORP) ★
6400 Edgelake Dr, Sarasota, FL 34240-8813
Tel (941) 921-8600 *Founded/Ownrshp* 1994
Sales 29.3MM^E *EMP* 250
SIC 8069 8093 Specialty hospitals, except psychiatric; Rehabilitation center, outpatient treatment; Specialty hospitals, except psychiatric; Rehabilitation center, outpatient treatment
Pr: Dan Epply
Dir Rx: Kathleen Hnat

D-U-N-S 87-716-0275
■ **HEALTHSOUTH SUB-ACUTE CENTER OF MECHANICSBURG INC**
(*Suby of* HEALTHSOUTH CORP) ★
175 Lancaster Blvd, Mechanicsburg, PA 17055-3562
Tel (717) 691-3700 *Founded/Ownrshp* 1993
Sales 14.8MM^E *EMP* 650
SIC 8093 Rehabilitation center, outpatient treatment; Rehabilitation center, outpatient treatment
Pr: Richard M Scrushy
Dir Recs: Teresa Spickler
**Treas:* Aaron J Beam

D-U-N-S 13-178-7707
■ **HEALTHSOUTH SUNRISE REHABILITATION HOSPITAL**
(*Suby of* HEALTHSOUTH CORP) ★
4399 N Nob Hill Rd, Sunrise, FL 33351-5813
Tel (954) 749-0300 *Founded/Ownrshp* 1994
Sales 46.0MM *EMP* 411
SIC 8069 Specialty hospitals, except psychiatric; Specialty hospitals, except psychiatric
COO: Jay Delos Reyes
COO: Jay De Los Reyes
VP: Kevin Conn
Dir Inf Cn: Jeannette Callaway
HC Dir: Joyce Ayala

D-U-N-S 15-532-9006
■ **HEALTHSOUTH/MAINE MEDICAL CENTER LLC**
(*Suby of* HEALTHSOUTH CORP) ★
335 Brighton Ave Ste 201, Portland, ME 04102-2361
Tel (207) 775-4000 *Founded/Ownrshp* 1996
Sales 14.7MM^E *EMP* 314
SIC 8069 8093 Specialty hospitals, except psychiatric; Rehabilitation center, outpatient treatment; Specialty hospitals, except psychiatric; Rehabilitation center, outpatient treatment
Dir Rx: Stephen Moulton
Phys Thrpy: Sharon Hartl

D-U-N-S 80-882-2894
HEALTHSPAN INC
225 Pictoria Dr Ste 320, Cincinnati, OH 45246-1616
Tel (513) 551-1400 *Founded/Ownrshp* 1991
Sales NA *EMP* 25^E
SIC 6324 Health maintenance organization (HMO), insurance only
Pr: Kenneth Page

D-U-N-S 14-719-9533
HEALTHSPAN INTEGRATED CARE
(*Suby of* MERCY HEALTH) ★
1001 Lakeside Ave E # 1200, Cleveland, OH 44114-1172
Tel (216) 621-5600 *Founded/Ownrshp* 2013
Sales 497.9MM *EMP* 1,240
SIC 8011 Health maintenance organization; Health maintenance organization
CEO: Kenneth Page
**Pr:* Patricia D Kennedy-Scott
**CEO:* George Halverson
**CFO:* Thomas Revis
Sls Mgr: Mark Scheuer
Counsel: Paula Ohliger

D-U-N-S 08-831-8618
■ **HEALTHSPRING INC**
(*Suby of* CIGNA) ★
530 Great Circle Rd, Nashville, TN 37228-1309
Tel (615) 291-7000 *Founded/Ownrshp* 2012
Sales NA *EMP* 3,200^E
SIC 6324 Hospital & medical service plans; Group hospitalization plans; Health maintenance organization (HMO), insurance only; Hospital & medical service plans; Group hospitalization plans; Health maintenance organization (HMO), insurance only
CEO: Herbert A Fritch
**Pr:* Michael G Mirt
Pr: Allen Perez
**COO:* Mark A Tulloch
CFO: Thomas McCarthy
**CFO:* Karey L Witty
Ch: Gerald Coil
Ex VP: Lisa Bacus
**Ex VP:* Sharad Mansukani
**Sr VP:* J Gentry Barden
Sr VP: Dirk Wales
VP: Jeff Brown
VP: Paul Erickson
VP: Peter Gardner
VP: Louise McCagg
VP: Ron Minson
Comm Dir: Desiree Dankowski
Dir Rx: Mark Belcher

D-U-N-S 83-632-4681
■ **HEALTHSPRING MANAGEMENT INC**
(*Suby of* NEWQUEST LLC) ★
530 Great Circle Rd, Nashville, TN 37228-1309
Tel (615) 291-7000 *Founded/Ownrshp* 2006
Sales 22.8MM^E *EMP* 549
SIC 7389 8011 Financial services; Health maintenance organization; Financial services; Health maintenance organization
CEO: Herb Fritch
**Pr:* David K Ellwanger
CFO: James Lordeman
**VP:* Wendy Bottomley
VP: Jon Buss
VP: Cheryl Debold
**Med Dir:* Dr James Geraughty

D-U-N-S 16-120-6644
■ **HEALTHSPRING OF ALABAMA INC**
(*Suby of* NEWQUEST LLC) ★
2 Perimeter Park S 300w, Birmingham, AL 35243-2329
Tel (205) 968-1000 *Founded/Ownrshp* 2012
Sales NA *EMP* 171
Accts Kpmg Llp
SIC 6324 Health maintenance organization (HMO), insurance only; Health maintenance organization (HMO), insurance only
Pr: Renet Moret
**CFO:* David Buchane
VP: David L Terry
VP: David Terry

D-U-N-S 83-789-3064
HEALTHSPRING OF ALABAMA INC
(*Suby of* BAPTIST HEALTH SYSTEM INC) ★
2 Chase Corporate Dr # 300, Hoover, AL 35244-1016
Tel (205) 423-1000 *Founded/Ownrshp* 1997
Sales NA *EMP* 104
SIC 6324 Health maintenance organization (HMO), insurance only
Pr: Robin McElsaterick
**VP:* Kathy Deya
VP: Mark Garnett
**VP:* Sandra Lutz
Opers Mgr: Megan Schrimsher

D-U-N-S 01-230-3297
■ **HEALTHSPRING USA LLC**
(*Suby of* HEALTHSPRING INC) ★
44 Vantage Way Ste 300, Nashville, TN 37228-1550
Tel (615) 291-7000 *Founded/Ownrshp* 2006
Sales NA *EMP* 42^E
SIC 6324 Hospital & medical service plans; Group hospitalization plans; Health maintenance organization (HMO), insurance only; Hospital & medical service plans; Group hospitalization plans; Health maintenance organization (HMO), insurance only
Pr: Shawn Morris
Pr: Kyle Duke
Pr: Scott Jacobson
Pr: Victor Wesolowski
COO: Greg Allen
CFO: Cynthia Williams
Sr VP: Gentry Barden
Sr VP: Lyle Hill
Sr VP: Teresa Jordan
VP: Heather Peterson
VP: David Wesch
VP: Wendy Wetzel

D-U-N-S 18-170-2804
HEALTHSTAR COMMUNICATIONS INC
1000 Wyckoff Ave, Mahwah, NJ 07430-3164
Tel (201) 560-5370 *Founded/Ownrshp* 1987
Sales 111.3MM^E *EMP* 620
SIC 7372 7311 6719 Prepackaged software; Advertising agencies; Personal holding companies, except banks; Prepackaged software; Advertising agencies; Personal holding companies, except banks
CEO: Jerry Brager
**Pr:* John Corcoran
**Pr:* Myron Holubiak
COO: Leigh Paeschke
CFO: Joseph Leoce
**CFO:* Jim Sivori
**Ex VP:* Peter Cossman
Ex VP: Ray Fortune
Ex VP: Joseph Mastracchio
Ex VP: Bob Muratore
Ex VP: Donna Weber
**Sr VP:* Patricia Brock
Sr VP: Brian Curcura
Sr VP: Mike McCauley
VP: Eric Broadway
VP: Lewis Campanaro
VP: Patty Kearnan
VP: Larry Keary
VP: Jim King
VP: Jeanine Kober
VP: Lisa Miccinilli

D-U-N-S 96-313-1461
HEALTHSTAR NETWORK INC
STELLARIS HEALTH NETWORK
135 Bedford Rd, Armonk, NY 10504-1945
Tel (914) 273-5454 *Founded/Ownrshp* 1996
Sales 30.7MM *EMP* 1^E
Accts Deloitte Tax Llp Jericho Ny
SIC 8099 Blood related health services; Blood related health services
Pr: Arthur Nizza
COO: Edward Leonard
**CFO:* Sharon Lucian
VP: Lisa Hanrahan
VP: Nancy Laemle
VP: Matthew Shafiroff
Dir Rad: Raymond Farquharson
Dir Pat Ac: Fran Gardner
CIO: Sue Prince
Telecom Mg: Brian Chiodo

D-U-N-S 17-971-2302
HEALTHSTAR PHYSICIANS PC
420 W Morris Blvd 400a, Morristown, TN 37813-2283
Tel (423) 581-5925 *Founded/Ownrshp* 1995
Sales 31.4MM^E *EMP* 250
SIC 8011 Pediatrician; Pediatrician
CEO: Don Lee
**Treas:* Derek Cooze
**Treas:* Peter Sutherland
Brnch Mgr: Vince Trull
Off Mgr: Ida Carpenter
Nurse Mgr: Jennifer Davis
Sfty Mgr: Terry Moore
Sls&Mrk Ex: Trish Hatfield
Surgeon: William Cummins

HEALTHSTH MNTNVW REGNL REHAB
See WEST VIRGINIA REHABILITATION HOSPITAL INC

D-U-N-S 62-588-8748
▲ **HEALTHSTREAM INC**
209 10th Ave S Ste 450, Nashville, TN 37203-0788
Tel (615) 301-3100 *Founded/Ownrshp* 1999
Sales 170.6MM *EMP* 787^E
Tkr Sym HSTM *Exch* NGS
SIC 7372 7371 Prepackaged software; Custom computer programming services; Prepackaged software; Custom computer programming services
Ch Bd: Robert A Frist Jr
COO: J Edward Pearson
CFO: Gerard M Hayden Jr
Ofcr: Stephen Brunton
Assoc VP: Mollie Condra
Ex VP: Arthur E Newman
Sr VP: Jeffrey S Doster
Sr VP: Thomas Schultz
Sr VP: Michael Sousa
VP: Stephen Clemens
VP: Albert Dan
VP: Tom Dugger
VP: Robert H Laird Jr
VP: Jim Reeves
VP: Alex Scott
Board of Directors: Thompson S Dent, Frank Gordon, C Martin Harris, Jeffrey L McLaren, Dale Polley, Linda Rebrovick, Michael Shmerling, William W Stead, Deborah Taylor Tate

D-U-N-S 79-115-4961
HEALTHSUN HEALTH PLANS INC
3250 Mary St Ste 400, Miami, FL 33133-5232
Tel (305) 448-8100 *Founded/Ownrshp* 2004
Sales NA *EMP* 25^E
SIC 6321 Health insurance carriers
CEO: Alexander Fuster
**COO:* Gale Lam
**CFO:* Robert Armstrong
**Treas:* Ramon Corona
Ofcr: Mari Delallama
Ofcr: Marianela De La Llama
Ofcr: Marianela La Llama
Ofcr: Mari Llama
Sr VP: Scott Griesemer
Sr VP: Stan Sanchez
VP: Inez Abreu
**VP:* Claudio Alvarez
VP: Juan Mora
VP: Sergio Rumie

D-U-N-S 96-159-2222
HEALTHTECH HOLDINGS INC
3102 West End Ave Ste 400, Nashville, TN 37203-1623
Tel (615) 383-7300 *Founded/Ownrshp* 2009
Sales 117.8MM^E *EMP* 419^E
SIC 7372 Prepackaged software; Prepackaged software
CEO: Thomas M Stephenson
VP: Eric Anderton
VP: Stan Gilbreath
**CIO:* Geoff Roten
**CTO:* Alan Maclamroc
VP Mktg: Tom Mitchell

D-U-N-S 96-554-3080
HEALTHTECH LLC
5110 Maryland Way Ste 200, Brentwood, TN 37027-2307
Tel (615) 309-6053 *Founded/Ownrshp* 2010
Sales 27.8MM^E *EMP* 30^E
SIC 8741 Hospital management
CEO: Derek Morkel

D-U-N-S 80-434-3960
HEALTHTECH MANAGEMENT SERVICES INC
(*Suby of* HEALTHTECH LLC) ★
5110 Maryland Way Ste 200, Brentwood, TN 37027-2307
Tel (615) 309-6053 *Founded/Ownrshp* 2010
Sales 24.9MM^E *EMP* 367^E
SIC 8741 Hospital management
Pr: Dave Woodland
CFO: Lynn Lambert
Treas: Richard D Gore
Sr VP: A E Brim
CTO: Robert Reinhardt Jr
Mktg Mgr: Frank Boggio

D-U-N-S 83-695-4099
HEALTHTEXAS PROVIDER NETWORK
(*Suby of* BAYLOR HEALTH CARE SYSTEM) ★
8080 N Cntrl Expy Ste 600, Dallas, TX 75206-3794
Tel (972) 860-8600 *Founded/Ownrshp* 1994
Sales 206.8MM *EMP* 350
SIC 8011 Offices & clinics of medical doctors; Offices & clinics of medical doctors
Pr: Gary Brock
**Pr:* William Roberts
**Treas:* Sarah Gahm

D-U-N-S 16-198-6757
HEALTHTRAX INC
WORK FIT
2345 Main St, Glastonbury, CT 06033-2211
Tel (860) 633-5572 *Founded/Ownrshp* 1986
Sales 49.4MM^E *EMP* 1,000
SIC 7991 7997 Health club; Racquetball club, membership; Health club; Racquetball club, membership
Pr: Kenneth F Navarro
**COO:* Robert E Stauble Jr
**CFO:* Pat Donnelly
Ofcr: Patsy Eagleson
Prgrm Mgr: Joshua Gallimore
VP Opers: Michael Vanamberg
Snr Mgr: Bill White

D-U-N-S 80-862-3636
HEALTHTRAX INTERNATIONAL INC
2345 Main St, Glastonbury, CT 06033-2211
Tel (860) 633-5572 *Founded/Ownrshp* 1984
Sales 8.1MM *EMP* 1,400
SIC 7991 Physical fitness facilities; Physical fitness facilities
Prin: Robert E Stauble Jr

D-U-N-S 95-908-1746 IMP
■ **HEALTHTRONICS INC**
(*Suby of* ENDO HEALTH SOLUTIONS INC) ★
9825 Spectrum Dr Bldg 3, Austin, TX 78717-4930
Tel (512) 328-2892 *Founded/Ownrshp* 2015
Sales 97.7MM^E *EMP* 430^E
SIC 3845 Lithotripters; Lithotripters
CEO: Richard Rusk
VP: Scott Eden
**VP:* Gary Kozen
VP: Scott Macpherson
VP: James Maguire
VP: Mark Rooney
VP Opers: Gary J Kozen
Snr Mgr: Alan Terry

D-U-N-S 02-214-7063
HEALTHTRONICS SERVICE CENTER LLC
9825 Spectrum Dr Bldg 3, Austin, TX 78717-4930
Tel (512) 328-2892 *Founded/Ownrshp* 1992
Sales 165.9MM *EMP* 400
SIC 1389 Construction, repair & dismantling services; Construction, repair & dismantling services

D-U-N-S 00-772-8459
HEALTHTRUST INC
25 Triangle Park Dr, Concord, NH 03301-5799
Tel (603) 226-2861 *Founded/Ownrshp* 2003
Sales NA *EMP* 100
SIC 6371 Pension, health & welfare funds
Pr: John Andrews

D-U-N-S 06-840-6763
HEALTHTRUST PURCHASING GROUP LP
H P G
155 Franklin Rd Ste 400, Brentwood, TN 37027-4693
Tel (615) 377-1294 *Founded/Ownrshp* 2002
Sales 92.6MM^E *EMP* 200^E
SIC 7389 Purchasing service; Purchasing service
CEO: Ed Jones
Pr: Mike Bishop
Pr: Netta Collins
Pr: Fred Keller
Pr: Belinda Vanatta
CFO: John Paul
Treas: Samuel Howard
Ex VP: Michael Berryhill
VP: Bill Francis
VP: Melanie McMeekan
VP: Scott Miller
VP: Doug Swanson
VP: Shelly Workman
VP: Allen Wright

HEALTHWAY
See MAKERS OF KAL INC

D-U-N-S 94-833-4714
■ **HEALTHWAYS HEALTH SUPPORT LLC**
(*Suby of* HEALTHWAYS INC) ★
701 Cool Springs Blvd, Franklin, TN 37067-2697
Tel (615) 614-4929 *Founded/Ownrshp* 1981
Sales NA *EMP* 1^E
SIC 6371 6321 Pension, health & welfare funds; Accident & health insurance
CEO: Donato Tramuto
**CEO:* Ben R Leedle

D-U-N-S 05-995-1988
▲ **HEALTHWAYS INC**
701 Cool Springs Blvd, Franklin, TN 37067-2697
Tel (615) 614-4929 *Founded/Ownrshp* 1981
Sales 742.1MM *EMP* 2,700
Tkr Sym HWAY *Exch* NGS
SIC 8082 8099 Home health care services; Health screening service; Home health care services; Health screening service
CEO: Alfred Lumsdaine
**Ch Bd:* Donato Tramuto
Pr: Peter Choueiri
COO: Matthew Michela
COO: Linda Morrison
Bd of Dir: Cris Bisgard
Bd of Dir: Mary England
Ofcr: Chris Dancy
Ofcr: Michael Farris
Ofcr: James E Pope
Ex VP: Ben R Leedle
Ex VP: Don Taylor
Sr VP: Nicholas A Balog
Sr VP: Janet S Calhoun
Sr VP: William Gold
Sr VP: Matthew A Michela
VP: Katrina Melton
Board of Directors: Lee A Shapiro, Mary Jane England, Kevin G Wills, Robert J Greczyn Jr, Robert J Greczyn Jr, Bradley S Karro, Paul H Keckley, Conan J Laughlin, William Novelli, Alison Taunton-Rigby, Lee A Shapiro

HEALTHWISE
See NUTRITIONAL RESOURCES INC

D-U-N-S 08-283-9515
HEALTHWISE INC (ID)
2601 N Bogus Basin Rd, Boise, ID 83702-0909
Tel (208) 345-1161 *Founded/Ownrshp* 1975
Sales 34.1MM *EMP* 230
Accts Hooper Cornell Pllc Bois
SIC 8399 Community development groups; Community development groups
Ch Bd: Donald W Kemper
Pr: Jim Giuffre
Chf Mktg O: Martin J Gabica
Admn Mgr: Vicki Mentink
Software D: Matt Berther
Art Dir: Annette Bush

HEALTHWORKS
See LUTHER HOSPITAL

D-U-N-S 95-721-5445
HEALTHWORKS HOME MEDICAL INC
HEALTHWORKS PCA
114 5th St Se, Minneapolis, MN 55414-1145
Tel (612) 617-9562 *Founded/Ownrshp* 1996
Sales 8.7MM^E *EMP* 450
SIC 8082 5999 Home health care services; Medical apparatus & supplies; Home health care services; Medical apparatus & supplies
Pr: Chad Jellum
**Treas:* Ruth Jellum
**VP:* Bob Jellum

HEALTHWORKS PCA
See HEALTHWORKS HOME MEDICAL INC

D-U-N-S 94-898-9793
HEALTHWORKS REHAB SERVICES
(*Suby of* LEHIGH VALLEY HEALTH NETWORK) ★
2545 Schoenersville Rd, Bethlehem, PA 18017-7300
Tel (484) 884-2249 *Founded/Ownrshp* 1996
Sales 20.3MM^E *EMP* 748^E
SIC 8093 Rehabilitation center, outpatient treatment
Pr: Elliot Sussman
**Ex Dir:* Paul Patalis

HEALTHWRKS WELLNESS FITNES CTR
See CORNING HOSPITAL

HEALTHY ADVICE NETWORKS
See PATIENTPOINT NETWORK SOLUTIONS LLC

D-U-N-S 80-999-5152 IMP
HEALTHY BACK STORE LLC
HEALTHY BACK STORES
10300 Southard Dr, Beltsville, MD 20705-2107
Tel (888) 469-2225 *Founded/Ownrshp* 2001
Sales 59.1MM^E *EMP* 150
SIC 5712 Furniture stores; Furniture stores
Creative D: Karl Feldman
Genl Mgr: Peter Dassira
Genl Mgr: Aimee Debrandt
Genl Mgr: Joseph Lilli

HEALTHY BACK STORES
See HEALTHY BACK STORE LLC

D-U-N-S 18-447-4315 IMP
HEALTHY BRAND OIL CORP
5215 11th St Ste 3, Long Island City, NY 11101-5830
Tel (718) 937-0806 *Founded/Ownrshp* 2004
Sales 75.6MM^E *EMP* 20^E
SIC 2079 Cooking oils, except corn: vegetable refined
Ch: Bradly Green
**VP:* Jason Thomas
Off Mgr: Kim Goockner

D-U-N-S 15-026-1183
HEALTHY DIRECTIONS LLC
DOCTORS PREFERRED
(*Suby of* HELEN OF TROY LP) ★
6710 Rockledge Dr Ste 500, Bethesda, MD 20817-1864
Tel (301) 340-2100 *Founded/Ownrshp* 2014
Sales 46.2MM^E *EMP* 215^E
SIC 5499 Vitamin food stores; Vitamin food stores
CEO: Connie Hallquist
**COO:* Roger Difato
**CFO:* Tawney Laurie
CFO: Ben Teicher
**Chf Mktg O:* Colleen Sugarman
VP: Manuel A Ajuria
VP: Jeanne Chatfield
VP: Rich Pompilio
VP: Michelle Riley
Creative D: Dann Hall
Genl Mgr: Jim Dean

D-U-N-S 80-016-2633 IMP
HEALTHY FOOD BRANDS LLC
992 Bedford Ave, Brooklyn, NY 11205-4502
Tel (212) 444-9909 *Founded/Ownrshp* 2007
Sales 30.6MM^E *EMP* 30
SIC 5145 Candy
Manager: Rob Kowitt

D-U-N-S 04-770-3803
HEALTHY FOOD CONCEPTS LLC
2595 Lk Ridge Shores Cir, Reno, NV 89519
Tel (775) 762-2334 *Founded/Ownrshp* 2010
Sales 18.3MM^E *EMP* 600^E
SIC 5812 Eating places; Eating places
Prin: Linda Addi

D-U-N-S 79-301-4333 IMP
HEALTHY FOOD INGREDIENTS LLC
SK FOOD INTERNATIONAL
4666 Amber Valley Pkwy S, Fargo, ND 58104-8612
Tel (701) 356-4106 *Founded/Ownrshp* 2013
Sales 22.8MM^E *EMP* 30
SIC 5149 Groceries & related products
CEO: Brad Hover
CFO: Steve Rhodes
Off Mgr: Melodie Lane

HEALTHY KIDS INITIATIVES
See UNITED WAY OF METROPOLITAN DALLAS INC

D-U-N-S 17-335-1826 IMP
HEALTHY PET LP
(*Suby of* J. RETTENMAIER & SOHNE GMBH + CO. KG)
6960 Salashan Pkwy, Ferndale, WA 98248-8314
Tel (360) 734-7415 *Founded/Ownrshp* 2013
Sales 26.7MM^E *EMP* 130
SIC 3999 2899 Pet supplies; Oil absorption equipment; Pet supplies; Oil absorption equipment
CEO: Ted Mischaikov
CFO: Dave Thompson
Dir IT: Mike Sumpter
Opers Mgr: Todd Caty
Opers Mgr: Walt Kulpa
Prd Mgr: Nancey Daniels
Prd Mgr: Tim Etringer
Manager: Chuck Kohrer
Sls Mgr: Judy Kurscheidt

D-U-N-S 02-475-8743
HEALTHY START COALITION OF PALM BEACH COUNTY IN
1919 N Flagler Dr, West Palm Beach, FL 33407-9803
Tel (561) 740-7000 *Founded/Ownrshp* 2009
Sales 87.8MM *EMP* 2
Accts Keefe Mccullough & Co Ft L
SIC 8351 Child day care services; Child day care services
Prin: Triste Brooks

D-U-N-S 07-947-5774
HEALTHY START MOMCARE NETWORK INC (FL)
1311 N Paul Russell Rd D2, Tallahassee, FL 32301-4880
Tel (850) 999-6200 *Founded/Ownrshp* 2012
Sales 41.0MM *EMP* 3
SIC 8082 Home health care services

Pr: Martha Zimmerman
**Pr:* Dawn Clarke
**Treas:* Dixie Morgese
**VP:* Jennifer Floyd

D-U-N-S 06-064-8110
HEALTHYS INC
DOWN TO EARTH NATURAL FOODS
2515 S King St, Honolulu, HI 96826-3101
Tel (808) 947-7678 *Founded/Ownrshp* 1977
Sales 26.3MM^E *EMP* 205
SIC 5499 Health foods; Health foods
CEO: Mark Fergusson
Genl Mgr: Clifford Hillier
Genl Mgr: Carmela Wolf
IT Man: David Moore

D-U-N-S 04-464-9119 IMP
HEALY TIBBITTS BUILDERS INC
(*Suby of* WEEKS MARINE INC) ★
99-994 Iwaena St Ste A, Aiea, HI 96701-5607
Tel (808) 487-3664 *Founded/Ownrshp* 1955, 1989
Sales 24.5MM^E *EMP* 120^E
SIC 1629 Marine construction; Marine construction
Pr: Richard A Heltzel
**VP:* Lou Cannizzo
Genl Mgr: Roberta Griffith

D-U-N-S 02-455-5211 IMP
HEALY WHOLESALE CO INC
4021 Distribution Dr, Fayetteville, NC 28311-2853
Tel (910) 822-3827 *Founded/Ownrshp* 1978
Sales 26.3MM^E *EMP* 110
SIC 5181 5182 Beer & other fermented malt liquors; Wine; Beer & other fermented malt liquors; Wine
Pr: John M Healy
Treas: Edna Sullivan
**VP:* Frederick A Healy

D-U-N-S 06-170-7899
HEAPY ENGINEERING INC (OH)
1400 W Dorothy Ln, Dayton, OH 45409-1310
Tel (937) 224-0861 *Founded/Ownrshp* 1945, 2005
Sales 26.3MM^E *EMP* 170
SIC 8711

HEAR MORE
See MAXI AIDS INC

D-U-N-S 07-591-9837
HEARD COUNTY BOARD OF EDUCATION
HEARD COUNTY SCHOOL SYSTEM
131 E Court Sq, Franklin, GA 30217-8019
Tel (706) 675-3320 *Founded/Ownrshp* 1900
Sales 16.5MM^E *EMP* 311
Accts Russell W Hinton Cpa Cgfm
SIC 8211 Public elementary & secondary schools; Public elementary & secondary schools

HEARD COUNTY SCHOOL SYSTEM
See HEARD COUNTY BOARD OF EDUCATION

D-U-N-S 07-920-5366
HEARD COUNTY SCHOOL SYSTEM
131 E Court Sq, Franklin, GA 30217-8019
Tel (706) 675-3320 *Founded/Ownrshp* 2013
Sales 11.7MM^E *EMP* 291^E
SIC 8211 Public elementary & secondary schools

D-U-N-S 11-644-1338
HEARD LINEBARGER GRAHAM GOGGAN BLAIR PENA & SAMPSON
711 Navarro St Ste 300, San Antonio, TX 78205-1749
Tel (210) 225-6763 *Founded/Ownrshp* 1964
Sales 14.9MM^E *EMP* 319
SIC 8111 Specialized law offices, attorneys; Criminal law; Labor & employment law; Taxation law; Specialized law offices, attorneys; Criminal law; Labor & employment law; Taxation law
Pt: Thomas Goggan
Pt: Jim Blair
Mng Pt: Clif Douglass
Mng Pt: Cristina Gonzalez

D-U-N-S 82-769-3503 IMP/EXP
HEARING LAB TECHNOLOGY LLC
GSM - WALKER PRODUCTS
3385 Roy Orr Blvd, Grand Prairie, TX 75050-4208
Tel (469) 586-0448 *Founded/Ownrshp* 2007
Sales 49.3MM^E *EMP* 475
SIC 8742 Management consulting services; Management consulting services
CEO: Timothy D Schnell
**Treas:* Tim Mele
**Sr VP:* Henry C Smith
**VP:* Brian Gilbreath
**VP:* Hanna Tong

HEARN-KIRKWOOD
See GILBERT FOODS LLC

D-U-N-S 07-839-5421
HEARSAY SOCIAL INC
185 Berry St Ste 3800, San Francisco, CA 94107-1725
Tel (888) 990-3777 *Founded/Ownrshp* 2009
Sales 21.1MM^E *EMP* 60^E
SIC 7372 Publishers' computer software
CEO: Clara Shih
**Pr:* Michael H Lock
**CFO:* William Salisbury
**VP:* Mark Gilbert
**VP:* Caitlin Haberberger
**VP:* Gary Liu
**VP:* Yasmin Zarabi
Web Dev: Mark Fleschler
Sftwr Eng: Daniel Boeve
Sftwr Eng: Daniel Cash
Sftwr Eng: Nag Chunduru

D-U-N-S 02-906-2072
HEARST BUSINESS MEDIA CORP
(*Suby of* HEARST CORP) ★
2620 Barrett Rd, Gainesville, GA 30507-7901
Tel (770) 532-4111 *Founded/Ownrshp* 1980
Sales 85.8MM^E *EMP* 75
SIC 2721 Magazines: publishing only, not printed on site; Magazines: publishing only, not printed on site
Pr: Richard P Malloch
**Treas:* Robert D Wilbanks
**VP:* Thomas D Cross
**VP:* Peter Rowlinson
VP: Martin Silver
Snr Sftwr: Charles Henry

D-U-N-S 11-750-4282
HEARST BUSINESS PUBLISHING INC
DIVERSION MAGAZINE DIV
(*Suby of* HEARST BUSINESS MEDIA CORP) ★
214 N Tryon St Fl 33, Charlotte, NC 28202-1078
Tel (704) 348-8614 *Founded/Ownrshp* 1992
Sales 48.0MM *EMP* 75
SIC 6794 2731 Periodicals; Book publishing; Copyright buying & licensing; Book publishing
Pr: Richard Malloch
**Treas:* Robert D Wilbanks
**VP:* Kathryn M Chacana
**VP:* Peter Rowlinson

D-U-N-S 00-920-4371 IMP
HEARST COMMUNICATIONS INC
SAN FRANCISCO CHRONICLE
901 Mission St, San Francisco, CA 94103-3052
Tel (415) 777-1111 *Founded/Ownrshp* 1865
Sales 438.6MM^E *EMP* 1,700
SIC 2711 Newspapers, publishing & printing; Newspapers, publishing & printing
Pr: Frank J Vega
CFO: Jerretta Avery
CFO: Elizabeth Cain
CFO: Joe Podulka
Bd of Dir: John Nejedly
Ex VP: Gary Anderson
VP: James Artz
VP: Fred Broi
VP: Peter Negulescu
VP: Hernan Ponce
VP: Michele Slack
Exec: Darien Dumanis
Exec: Barbara Wright
Board of Directors: Carlos Gutierrez

D-U-N-S 00-152-7241 IMP
HEARST CORP
HEARST MAGAZINES
300 W 57th St Fl 42, New York, NY 10019-3790
Tel (212) 649-2000 *Founded/Ownrshp* 1887
Sales 6.2MMM^E *EMP* 20,589
SIC 2721 2731 2711 4832 4833 7383 Magazines: publishing only, not printed on site; Books: publishing only; Newspapers, publishing & printing; Newspapers: publishing only, not printed on site; Radio broadcasting stations; Television broadcasting stations; News feature syndicate; Magazines: publishing only, not printed on site; Books: publishing only; Newspapers, publishing & printing; Newspapers: publishing only, not printed on site; Radio broadcasting stations; Television broadcasting stations; News feature syndicate
Pr: Steven R Swartz
**Pr:* Mark E Aldam
Pr: Nick Brien
Pr: David A Schirmer
**Ch:* William R Hearst III
**Treas:* Carlton J Charles
Chf Mktg O: Bob Brown
Chf Inves: Roger P Paschke
**Ofcr:* Neeraj Khemlani
Ex VP: Michael C Labonia
**Ex VP:* Lincoln Millstein
**Sr VP:* James M Asher
**Sr VP:* Eve Burton
**VP:* Gerardo Delia
VP: Mike Deluca
VP: Denielle Dewynter
VP: George J Green
**VP:* Mary Hayes
VP: Joel Laffer
**VP:* Cynthia Lewis
**VP:* Stephen Rodgers
Board of Directors: Mark E Aldam, Eve Burton, Mitchell I Scherzer, Christian A Tarafa, Jordan Wertlieb

D-U-N-S 15-138-1548
HEARST ENTERTAINMENT INC
(*Suby of* HEARST CORP) ★
888 7th Ave, New York, NY 10106-0001
Tel (212) 649-2000 *Founded/Ownrshp* 1980
Sales 12.8MM^E *EMP* 500
SIC 7812 Cartoon motion picture production; Cartoon production, television; Cartoon motion picture production; Cartoon production, television
Ch Bd: Scott M Sassa
**Pr:* William Miller
**Treas:* Bill Waller
**VP Sls:* William Kunkel

D-U-N-S 14-463-6370
HEARST FOUNDATION INC
300 W 57th St Fl 26, New York, NY 10019-3741
Tel (212) 586-5404 *Founded/Ownrshp* 1945
Sales 31.8MM *EMP* 16^E
SIC 8699 Charitable organization; Charitable organization
Pr: George Hearst Jr
Treas: Mary Fisher
Ofcr: Alison Yu
Ex Dir: Robert M Frehse

D-U-N-S 13-592-8922 IMP
HEARST HOLDINGS INC
(*Suby of* HEARST CORP) ★
300 W 57th St, New York, NY 10019-3741
Tel (212) 649-2000 *Founded/Ownrshp* 1996
Sales 590.9MM^E *EMP* 15,000
SIC 2721 4841 Magazines: publishing only, not printed on site; Cable television services; Magazines: publishing only, not printed on site; Cable television services
Ch Bd: George R Hearst Jr
**CFO:* Ronald J Doerfler
Treas: Jon D Smith Jr
**Ofcr:* James M Asher
**Sr VP:* Cathleen P Black
**Sr VP:* John G Conomikes
**Sr VP:* George B Irish
**Sr VP:* Raymond E Joslin
Art Dir: Ron Gabriel

HEARST MAGAZINES
See HEARST CORP

D-U-N-S 02-959-5878
HEARST NEWSPAPERS LLC
HOUSTON CHRONICLE
801 Texas St, Houston, TX 77002-2904
Tel (713) 220-7171 *Founded/Ownrshp* 2007
Sales 284.0MM^E *EMP* 1,320^E
SIC 2711 Newspapers; Newspapers
Ch: Jack Sweeney
**Pr:* John T O'Loughlin
CFO: Elizabeth Scott
Treas: James Smith
**Ex VP:* Jeff Cohen
Ex VP: Robert D Cravaritis
VP: Mario Barson
VP: Linda Schaible
Exec: Fonnie Ray Davis
Ex Dir: Sam Brown
IT Man: David Brister

D-U-N-S 93-364-9824
HEARST STATIONS INC
KITV-TV
(*Suby of* HEARST TELEVISION INC) ★
801 S King St, Honolulu, HI 96813-3008
Tel (808) 535-0400 *Founded/Ownrshp* 2013
Sales 26.7MM^E *EMP* 180^E
SIC 4833 Television broadcasting stations
Pr: Michael Rosenberg
Sls Mgr: William Gaeth

D-U-N-S 87-774-9861
HEARST TELEVISION INC
(*Suby of* HEARST CORP) ★
300 W 57th St, New York, NY 10019-3741
Tel (212) 887-6800 *Founded/Ownrshp* 2013
Sales 487.6MM^E *EMP* 3,324
SIC 4833 Television broadcasting stations; Television broadcasting stations
Ch Bd: David J Barrett
Ch Bd: Frank A Bennack Jr
Pr: Glenn Haygood
Pr: Jordan Wertlieb
Ex VP: Terry Mackin
Ex VP: Anthony J Vinciquerra
Sr VP: Frank C Biancuzzo
Sr VP: Roger Keating
Sr VP: Philip M Stolz
VP: Caroline Scollard-Taplett
Genl Mgr: Samantha Irwin
Board of Directors: John G Conomikes, Ken J Elkins, George R Hearst Jr, William R Hearst III, Bob Marbut, Gilbert C Maurer, David Pulver, Caroline L Williams

D-U-N-S 04-007-9022
HEARST WILLIAM RANDOLPH FOUNDATION
300 W 57th St Fl 26, New York, NY 10019-3741
Tel (212) 586-5404 *Founded/Ownrshp* 1947
Sales 60.7MM^E *EMP* 32
SIC 8699 Charitable organization; Charitable organization
Ex Dir: P Dinovitz
**VP:* Paul Dinovitz
**VP:* George Irish
**Prin:* Mason Granger
Rgnl Mgr: Mayra Cedeno
Pgrm Dir: Jan C Watten

HEART & FITNESS CENTER
See GENERAL HEALTH SYSTEM

D-U-N-S 84-946-3216
HEART & VASCULAR CENTER OF WEST TENNESSEE
(*Suby of* DELTA CLINICS CARDIOVASCULAR) ★
17 Centre Plaza Dr, Jackson, TN 38305-2862
Tel (731) 512-0104 *Founded/Ownrshp* 2003
Sales 27.5MM^E *EMP* 504^E
SIC 8011 Cardiologist & cardio-vascular specialist
Prin: Shan Wilks

D-U-N-S 03-064-0228
HEART 2 HEART
1151 Harbor Bay Pkwy, Alameda, CA 94502-6540
Tel (510) 769-5914 *Founded/Ownrshp* 2010
Sales 23.4MM^E *EMP* 3^E
SIC 8099 Health & allied services; Health & allied services
Prin: Angie Toussaint

HEART 2 HEART HOME CARE
See MEDICAL STAFFING ASSOCIATES INC

HEART AMERICA MEDICAL CENTER
See GOOD SAMARITAN HOSPITAL ASSOCIATION

D-U-N-S 02-117-6292
HEART CONSCIOUSNESS CHURCH INC (CA)
HARBIN HOT SPRINGS
18424 Harbin Springs Rd, Middletown, CA 95461-9687
Tel (707) 987-2477 *Founded/Ownrshp* 1975
Sales 23.7MM *EMP* 230
SIC 7041 Membership-basis organization hotels; Membership-basis organization hotels
Pr: Robert F Hartley
CFO: Sajjad Mohoud
**Treas:* Suzie Lecavalier
**VP:* Julie Adams
**VP:* Sajjad Mahmud
Board of Directors: Julie Adams, Luc Allard, Will Erme, Steve Foster, Andrew Hunt

D-U-N-S 03-003-2887
HEART EMPLOYEE LEASING INC (TX)
9442 N Capital Of Texas H, Austin, TX 78759-7257
Tel (512) 266-8304 *Founded/Ownrshp* 1997
Sales 11.4MM^E *EMP* 600
SIC 7363 Employee leasing service; Employee leasing service
Pr: Don Hansen

D-U-N-S 02-547-0300
HEART HOSPITAL AT DEACONESS GA
4007 Gateway Blvd, Newburgh, IN 47630-8947
Tel (812) 842-4508 *Founded/Ownrshp* 2008
Sales 53.1MM *EMP* 38^E
SIC 8062 General medical & surgical hospitals; General medical & surgical hospitals
Prin: Rebecca Malotte

D-U-N-S 19-087-2593
HEART HOSPITAL BAYLOR DENTON
2801 S Mayhill Rd, Denton, TX 76208-5910
Tel (940) 220-0600 *Founded/Ownrshp* 2013
Sales 21.0MM^E *EMP* 150
SIC 8062 8069 General medical & surgical hospitals; Specialty hospitals, except psychiatric
Pt: Barry Smith
Pt: Sandra Harlan
CFO: Sandra Sam
Off Mgr: Jack Peterson
IT Man: Al Bhakta
IT Man: Mike Sullivan
Pgrm Dir: Kathie Roberts

D-U-N-S 00-935-7391
HEART HOSPITAL IV LP
HEART HOSPITAL OF AUSTIN
(*Suby of* COLUMBIA ST DAVIDS DIV OFF) ★
3801 N Lamar Blvd, Austin, TX 78756-4080
Tel (512) 458-1006 *Founded/Ownrshp* 2010
Sales 98.4MM^E *EMP* 400
SIC 8062 General medical & surgical hospitals; General medical & surgical hospitals
Pt: David Laird
CFO: Mike Norby
Dir OR: Tim Simcek
Dir Lab: Denise Cushing
Dir Rx: Michael Matthews
Nurse Mgr: Jennifer Chu
QA Dir: Sandra Young
Mktg Dir: Richard Woehl
Mktg Mgr: Richard Wall
Doctor: Sam Narra
Nrsg Dir: Candice Fonke

HEART HOSPITAL OF AUSTIN
See HEART HOSPITAL IV LP

D-U-N-S 04-342-1598
HEART HOSPITAL OF DTO LLC
DAYTON HEART & VASCULAR HOSP
(*Suby of* MEDCATH INC) ★
2222 Philadelphia Dr, Dayton, OH 45406-1813
Tel (937) 734-8000 *Founded/Ownrshp* 1999
Sales 7.5MM^E *EMP* 300
SIC 8062 8069 General medical & surgical hospitals; Specialty hospitals, except psychiatric; General medical & surgical hospitals; Specialty hospitals, except psychiatric

D-U-N-S 79-093-8786
HEART HOSPITAL OF LAFAYETTE
(*Suby of* MEDCATH CORP) ★
1105 Kaliste Saloom Rd, Lafayette, LA 70508-5705
Tel (337) 521-1000 *Founded/Ownrshp* 2008
Sales 38.6MM^E *EMP* 224
SIC 8069 Specialty hospitals, except psychiatric; Specialty hospitals, except psychiatric
Pr: Karen Wyble
**COO:* Christy Hockaday
CFO: Jerry Pickett
VP: Monique Gary
Pharmcst: Lisa Goforth

D-U-N-S 87-629-1175
HEART HOSPITAL OF SOUTH DAKOTA LLC
AVERA HEART HOPSITAL SD
4500 W 69th St, Sioux Falls, SD 57108-8148
Tel (605) 977-7000 *Founded/Ownrshp* 1999
Sales 52.4MM^E *EMP* 400
SIC 8062 3842 General medical & surgical hospitals; Sterilizers, hospital & surgical; General medical & surgical hospitals; Sterilizers, hospital & surgical
CEO: Jon Soderholm
**CFO:* Jean White
VP: Becky Smith
Exec: Vicki Tencate
Dir Lab: David Ohrt
Dir IT: Dan Marnach

HEART LNCSTER REGIONAL MED CTR
See LANCASTER HMA INC

HEART N SOUL
See BIG STRIKE LLC

D-U-N-S 15-103-8544
HEART OF AMERICA MANAGEMENT LLC
1501 River Dr, Moline, IL 61265-1315
Tel (309) 797-9300 *Founded/Ownrshp* 1978
Sales 85.3MM^E *EMP* 1,500
SIC 8741 5812 7011 Business management; Eating places; Hotels & motels; Business management; Eating places; Hotels & motels
CEO: Mike Whalen
Ex VP: Kim Whalen
Sr VP: Damen Trebilcock
VP: Melinda Kuehne
VP: John Schulz
Genl Mgr: Cathy Lenzi
Genl Mgr: Brian Roberts
Genl Mgr: Brian Tyler
Snr Mgr: Kris Milligan
Snr Mgr: Terry Waite

D-U-N-S 15-584-9487
HEART OF COMPASSION FOOD DISTR
600 S Maple Ave, Montebello, CA 90640-5406
Tel (323) 727-7997 *Founded/Ownrshp* 2004
Sales 36.0MM *EMP* 1
Accts Davidson Deily & Company Ana
SIC 8661 Pentecostal Church; Pentecostal Church
Prin: Eric Tietzes

D-U-N-S 08-891-3392
HEART OF DIXIE INC
1103 County Road 1194, Vinemont, AL 35179-8668
Tel (256) 737-1712 *Founded/Ownrshp* 1991
Sales 63.0MM^E *EMP* 110

SIC 4731 Brokers, shipping; Brokers, shipping
Pr: Wyles Griffith
**CFO:* Shane McMinn
**Sec:* Jerry Lovell
**VP:* Donavon Lovell

D-U-N-S 13-547-2194
HEART OF TEXAS COMMUNITY HEALTH CENTER INC
FAMILY PRACTICE CENTER
1600 Providence Dr, Waco, TX 76707-2261
Tel (254) 750-8200 *Founded/Ownrshp* 1998
Sales 38.6MM *EMP* 300
SIC 8011 Medical centers; Medical centers
CEO: Allen Patterson
Dir Lab: Lisa Brenson
Dir Lab: Angie Jobe
Pgrm Dir: John H Gill

D-U-N-S 00-750-9698
HEART OF TEXAS ELECTRIC COOPERATIVE INC
1111 Johnson Dr, Mc Gregor, TX 76657-1917
Tel (254) 840-2871 *Founded/Ownrshp* 1937
Sales 39.8MM *EMP* 58
Accts Briscoe Burke & Grigsby Llp
SIC 4911 Electric services; Distribution, electric power
CEO: Rick Haile
**Pr:* Garland Cook
**VP:* Larry Stock
Board of Directors: Garland Cook, Dewayne Draeger, Kermit Dreyer, Paul Edge, Dan Foster, Kenneth Hollas, Bobby Nawara, Allen Shows, Larry Stock

D-U-N-S 07-838-1878
HEART OF TEXAS GOODWILL INDUSTRIES
1700 S New Rd, Waco, TX 76711-1749
Tel (254) 753-7337 *Founded/Ownrshp* 1955
Sales 13.2MM *EMP* 350
Accts Pattillo Brown & Hill Llp W
SIC 5932 8331 Used merchandise stores; Community service employment training program; Used merchandise stores; Community service employment training program
Ch: D Ick Dwinell
**Pr:* Daniel Nisley
COO: Charlsey Nisley
**Treas:* Aubrey Brickhouse
Mktg Dir: Kirby Killough

D-U-N-S 01-047-0870
HEART OF TEXAS REGION MENTAL HEALTH & MENTAL RETARDATION CENTER
110 S 12th St, Waco, TX 76701-1810
Tel (254) 752-3451 *Founded/Ownrshp* 1970
Sales 23.2MM^E *EMP* 345
SIC 8093 Specialty outpatient clinics; Mental health clinic, outpatient; Specialty outpatient clinics; Mental health clinic, outpatient
Pr: Barbra Tate
**Ch Bd:* Peter Kulgen
QA Dir: Jeanette Howell
IT Man: Colette Sulak
Opers Supe: Tiffany Owens
Psych: John Turnage
Doctor: Shamji Badhiwala
Doctor: Sue Cutbirth

HEART OF THE ROCKIES REGIONAL
See SALIDA HOSPITAL DISTRICT

HEART OF THE VALLEY HOSPICE
See ELDERCARE HOME HEALTH & HOSPICE

D-U-N-S 80-977-8566
HEART TO HEART INTERNATIONAL INC
13250 W 98th St, Lenexa, KS 66215-1359
Tel (913) 764-5200 *Founded/Ownrshp* 1992
Sales 99.5MM *EMP* 30
Accts Keller & Owens Llc Overland
SIC 8399 Health systems agency; Health systems agency
Pr: Gary Morsch
**Ch Bd:* Jim Kerr
**CEO:* Jim Mitchum
CFO: Curtis Aubrey
**CFO:* Bud Jeffress
VP: Pete Brumbaugh
Assoc Dir: Brian McDonell

D-U-N-S 00-537-2990
HEART TRUSS & ENGINEERING CORP (MI)
1830 N Grand River Ave, Lansing, MI 48906-3905
Tel (517) 372-0850 *Founded/Ownrshp* 1963
Sales 26.3MM^E *EMP* 100
SIC 2439 Trusses, wooden roof
Pr: Curtis Schaberg
**VP:* Joe Butcher
IT Man: Chris Zimmerman

D-U-N-S 12-167-9273
HEARTCARE HEALTH SYSTEM
415 W Columbia St, Evansville, IN 47710-1656
Tel (812) 492-5344 *Founded/Ownrshp* 1998
Sales 46.8MM *EMP* 10
SIC 8062 General medical & surgical hospitals; General medical & surgical hospitals
Ex Dir: Becky Malotte

D-U-N-S 80-441-1283
HEARTFLOW INC
1400 Seaport Blvd Bldg B, Redwood City, CA 94063-5594
Tel (650) 241-1221 *Founded/Ownrshp* 2007
Sales 20.5MM^E *EMP* 73^E
SIC 7373 Systems software development services
CEO: John Stevens
**Pr:* Yoshikl Kawabata
**CFO:* Baird Radford
**Chf Cred:* Brent Ness
**Chf Mktg O:* Campbell Rogers
Sr VP: Phil Mui
**VP:* Heather A Brown
VP: Nathalie D'Amours
**VP:* Leo Grady
**VP:* Dustin Michaels
VP: Paul Temple
**VP:* Christopher K Zarins
Board of Directors: Kent Walker, William C Weldon

D-U-N-S 96-283-1095 IMP
■ **HEARTH & HOME TECHNOLOGIES LLC**
HEATILATOR
(*Suby of* HNI CORP) ★
7571 215th St W, Lakeville, MN 55044-9887
Tel (952) 985-6000 *Founded/Ownrshp* 1981
Sales 442.1MM^E *EMP* 2,800
SIC 3429 4925 Fireplace equipment, hardware: andirons, grates, screens; Gas production and/or distribution; Fireplace equipment, hardware: andirons, grates, screens; Gas production and/or distribution
Pr: Brad D Determan
Pr: Bob Hawkinson
VP: Peter Dircks
VP: Linda Lonson
**VP:* Michael Ramsay
VP: Ed Ray
VP: Jacob Sill
VP: Rich Wilson
VP Bus Dev: Tim Rethlake
Rgnl Mgr: Ed Ricklick
Store Mgr: Faye Schimke

D-U-N-S 96-868-2526 IMP
■ **HEARTHMARK LLC**
JARDEN BRANDS CONSUMABLES
(*Suby of* JARDEN CORP) ★
9999 E 121st St, Fishers, IN 46037-9727
Tel (765) 557-3000 *Founded/Ownrshp* 2003
Sales 351.5MM^E *EMP* 1,400
SIC 3221 Food containers, glass; Food containers, glass
Pr: Chris Scherzinger
**Treas:* Ian G H Ashken
VP: Mike Servie
**VP:* Robert P Totte
Area Mgr: A H Ngai
Opers Mgr: Ryan Chalupsky
Opers Mgr: Zach Ebeling
Plnt Mgr: Mary Andrae
Plnt Mgr: Tim McKinnon
Plnt Mgr: Roy Stanley
Ql Cn Mgr: Michael Walters

D-U-N-S 83-035-3103 EXP
HEARTHSIDE FOOD SOLUTIONS LLC
3250 Lacey Rd Ste 200, Downers Grove, IL 60515-8384
Tel (630) 967-3600 *Founded/Ownrshp* 2009
Sales 2.2MMM^E *EMP* 7,500
SIC 2043 2038 Cereal breakfast foods; Snacks, including onion rings, cheese sticks, etc.; Cereal breakfast foods; Snacks, including onion rings, cheese sticks, etc.
CEO: Richard Sealise
CFO: Scott Edgcomb
CFO: James Jorasky
**CFO:* James Wojciechowski
Sr VP: Ronald Hink
VP: Matthew Sagendorf
VP: John Weller
Area Supr: Diane Phipps
QA Dir: Jason Eastman
QA Dir: Donna Eversole
VP Opers: Rick Mortenson

HEARTHSONG
See PLOW & HEARTH LLC

HEARTHSTONE
See YORK GENERAL HOSPITAL INC

D-U-N-S 80-343-2038
HEARTHSTONE
24151 Ventura Blvd, Calabasas, CA 91302-1449
Tel (415) 257-3600 *Founded/Ownrshp* 1992
Sales 21.2MM^E *EMP* 70
SIC 6722 6552 8742 Management investment, open-end; Land subdividers & developers, residential; Real estate consultant
Pr: Charles Schetter
**CFO:* Mark Porath
VP: Tony Igisky

D-U-N-S 16-405-0028 IMP
HEARTHWARE INC
IBC-HEARTHWARE
1795 N Butterfield Rd, Libertyville, IL 60048-1212
Tel (847) 775-8123 *Founded/Ownrshp* 2004
Sales 21.0MM^E *EMP* 82^E
SIC 5719 Kitchenware
Pr: Jung S Moon
Sr VP: Gene Kim
VP: Steven Jeon
Genl Couns: Lewis T Steadman

HEARTLAND AEA
See AREA EDUCATION AGENCY 11 (INC)

D-U-N-S 11-868-8662
HEARTLAND AG INC
3836 W Us Highway 30, Grand Island, NE 68803-5037
Tel (308) 384-1102 *Founded/Ownrshp* 1983
Sales 27.2MM^E *EMP* 33
SIC 5083 Agricultural machinery & equipment; Farm equipment parts & supplies
Pr: Bill Oltean
**Sec:* Matthew Dan Halferty
**Sec:* Timothy D White

D-U-N-S 17-353-7390
HEARTLAND AG INC
407 Depot Rd, Farmer City, IL 61842-8048
Tel (309) 928-9491 *Founded/Ownrshp* 1975
Sales 31.7MM^E *EMP* 24
SIC 5191 Chemicals, agricultural
Pr: Brad Reed
Sec: Todd Reed
VP: Brian Reed
Genl Mgr: Doug Bobb
Opers Mgr: Scott Kelley

HEARTLAND AMERICA
See IMPORT SPECIALTIES INC

D-U-N-S 18-617-3860 IMP
HEARTLAND AUTOMOTIVE INC
300 S Warren Dr, Greencastle, IN 46135-7573
Tel (765) 653-4263 *Founded/Ownrshp* 1997
Sales 228.8MM^E *EMP* 600
SIC 3714 Motor vehicle parts & accessories; Motor vehicle parts & accessories
Pr: Steven Maxey
Sr VP: Yoshio Otaki
Exec: Beth Gregory
Dist Mgr: Todd Anderson
Dist Mgr: Ryan Findlay
Dist Mgr: Brian Santangelo
Dist Mgr: Robert Yancey
Genl Mgr: Nobuhide Takasugi
QC Dir: Patrick Garrison
QC Dir: Dan George
Opers Mgr: Frank Maggio

D-U-N-S 06-816-0548
HEARTLAND AUTOMOTIVE LLC
GATEWAY COLLISION CENTER
501 38th St S, Fargo, ND 58103-1114
Tel (701) 282-5522 *Founded/Ownrshp* 2000
Sales 79.9MM^E *EMP* 200
SIC 5511 7538 5521 7532 7515 Automobiles, new & used; Pickups, new & used; General automotive repair shops; Used car dealers; Top & body repair & paint shops; Passenger car leasing; Automobiles, new & used; Pickups, new & used; General automotive repair shops; Used car dealers; Top & body repair & paint shops; Passenger car leasing
COO: George Miller
Sls Mgr: John Cole
Sls Mgr: Todd Thompson
Sls Mgr: Todd Trauman

D-U-N-S 83-487-2400
HEARTLAND AUTOMOTIVE SERVICES INC
JIFFY LUBE
(*Suby of* HAS HOLDINGS, INC.)
105 Decker Ct Ste 900, Irving, TX 75062-2227
Tel (972) 812-7900 *Founded/Ownrshp* 1995
Sales 74.9MM^E *EMP* 450
SIC 7549 Lubrication service, automotive; Lubrication service, automotive
CEO: Jim Marcum
**Pr:* Brett Ponton
**Sr VP:* Steve Isom
**VP:* Brian Clark
Dist Mgr: Tim Sophy

D-U-N-S 01-976-7292
HEARTLAND BANK (OH)
850 N Hamilton Rd, Gahanna, OH 43230-1757
Tel (614) 337-4600 *Founded/Ownrshp* 1988, 2015
Sales NA *EMP* 140
SIC 6022 State commercial banks; State commercial banks
Pr: Tiney M Mc Comb
Ch Bd: G Scott McComb
COO: Steve Hines
V Ch Bd: Jay Eggspuehler
Sr VP: Herbert Thomas
VP: Bob Crow
VP: Bill Daily
VP: Laurie Pfeiffer
VP: Marc Ridgway
VP: Ashley Trout
Board of Directors: William J Schottenstein

D-U-N-S 05-494-2297
HEARTLAND BANK
(*Suby of* MIDLAND STATES BANCORP INC) ★
212 S Central Ave Ste 200, Saint Louis, MO 63105-3500
Tel (314) 512-8500 *Founded/Ownrshp* 1887, 2014
Sales NA *EMP* 303
SIC 6035 Federal savings banks; Federal savings banks
Pr: David P Minton
Pr: Herb Roach
Chf Cred: Tracy Beckette
Ofcr: Timothy Feller
Ofcr: Dawn Knudtson
Ofcr: Leslie Kollar
Ofcr: Michelle Page
Ex VP: E Tracy Beckette
Ex VP: Lisa G Frederick
Ex VP: William I Peters
Sr VP: Jerry Lee
Sr VP: Patricia Tocco
VP: Connie Boyer
VP: Glen Calvin
VP: Gloria Clement
VP: Lisa Jones
VP: Kent Kelso
VP: Mark Lafata
VP: Brian Lingle
VP: Donna Pequignot
VP: Lynda Prebil

D-U-N-S 08-209-5761
HEARTLAND BANK AND TRUST
(*Suby of* HEARTLAND BANCORP INC)
401 N Hershey Rd, Bloomington, IL 61704-3742
Tel (309) 662-4444 *Founded/Ownrshp* 1971
Sales NA *EMP* 125
SIC 6022 State commercial banks; State commercial banks
CEO: Fred L Drake
**Pr:* Patrick F Busch
COO: Martin Dudley
**CFO:* Matt Doherty
Trst Ofcr: Brian Massey
**Ex VP:* Lance Carter
**Ex VP:* Diane Lanier

D-U-N-S 19-667-7561
HEARTLAND BANK CORP
2365 Old Stringtown Rd, Grove City, OH 43123-3921
Tel (614) 875-1884 *Founded/Ownrshp* 1988
Sales NA *EMP* 150
SIC 6022 State commercial banks; State commercial banks
Pr: Tiney M McComb

D-U-N-S 02-162-1516
HEARTLAND BEEF INC
ARBY'S
1703 N College Ave, Bloomington, IN 47404-2420
Tel (812) 332-4838 *Founded/Ownrshp* 1999
Sales 24.0MM *EMP* 340
SIC 5812 Fast-food restaurant, chain; Fast-food restaurant, chain
Pr: Thomas R Browne
VP: Jill Garner

D-U-N-S 03-924-9672
HEARTLAND BEHAVIORAL HEALTHCARE
3000 Erie St S, Massillon, OH 44646-7976
Tel (330) 833-3135 *Founded/Ownrshp* 1989
Sales 22.0MM^E *EMP* 320
SIC 8063 Psychiatric hospitals; Psychiatric hospitals
CEO: Helen Stevens
CFO: Pat Henderschot
Dir Rx: Michael Rynearson
Ex Dir: Matthew Herttna
Doctor: Steven Thomson

HEARTLAND BEHAVORIAL HLTH SVCS
See GREAT PLAINS HOSPITAL INC

HEARTLAND BLOOD CENTERS
See AURORA AREA BLOOD BANK

D-U-N-S 82-676-9382
HEARTLAND BUILDING CO INC
119 William St, Middlesex, NJ 08846-2542
Tel (732) 302-9277 *Founded/Ownrshp* 1993
Sales 38.0MM *EMP* 146
SIC 1542 Nonresidential construction; Nonresidential construction
CEO: Warren Evanko
**Pr:* Arthur Mackey
**COO:* Michael Mackey
**CFO:* James Mackey

HEARTLAND BUSINESS SYSTEMS
See HEARTLAND LABEL PRINTERS LLC

D-U-N-S 96-651-1250
HEARTLAND CARES FOUNDATION
1 Heartland Way, Jeffersonville, IN 47130-5870
Tel (812) 280-8222 *Founded/Ownrshp* 2005
Sales 207.0M *EMP* 800
SIC 8641 Civic social & fraternal associations; Civic social & fraternal associations
Pr: Anne Gordon

D-U-N-S 92-929-2712
HEARTLAND CATFISH CO INC
55001 Highway 82 W, Itta Bena, MS 38941-9613
Tel (662) 254-7100 *Founded/Ownrshp* 1995
Sales 78.9MM^E *EMP* 415
SIC 2092 Fresh or frozen packaged fish; Fresh or frozen packaged fish
CEO: Danny Walker
**Pr:* William Tackett
**Pr:* Joseph A Walker
**Sec:* Brian L Crawford
**VP:* Jimmy Killies Tackett
Rgnl Mgr: Johnny Jarrell
QA Dir: Rodger Chisholm
VP Opers: Tim Millwood
Mktg Dir: Dan Sawin
Manager: Malone Kimbrell

HEARTLAND CHEVROLET
See INVESTORS IN HEARTLAND INC

D-U-N-S 00-798-7563
HEARTLAND CO-OP
2829 Westown Pkwy Ste 350, West Des Moines, IA 50266-1340
Tel (515) 225-1334 *Founded/Ownrshp* 1907
Sales 823.8MM *EMP* 678
Accts Bergan Paulsen & Company Pc
SIC 5153 0762 2048 Grains; Farm management services; Livestock feeds; Grains; Farm management services; Livestock feeds
Pr: Arthur L Churchill
VP: Clair Rew
IT Man: Kami Snider
IT Man: Mike Thronson

D-U-N-S 14-780-6574
HEARTLAND COMMUNICATIONS GROUP INC
1003 Central Ave Ste 100, Fort Dodge, IA 50501-4042
Tel (515) 955-1600 *Founded/Ownrshp* 1986
Sales 34.3MM^E *EMP* 201
SIC 2721 7389 6512 Trade journals: publishing & printing; Telemarketing services; Commercial & industrial building operation; Trade journals: publishing & printing; Telemarketing services; Commercial & industrial building operation
Ch Bd: Joseph Peed
**Pr:* Gale McKinney
Dir Bus: Pat Sharkey
**Prin:* Gale W McKinney
Web Dev: Fred Tyre
Art Dir: Jeff Hanson

D-U-N-S 78-128-3338
HEARTLAND COMMUNITY COLLEGE FOUNDATION
1500 W Raab Rd, Normal, IL 61761-9446
Tel (309) 268-8000 *Founded/Ownrshp* 1992
Sales 12.8MM *EMP* 653
Accts Cliftonlarsonallen Llp Peori
SIC 8222 Community college; Community college
Pr: Robert D Widmer
**VP:* Rick Pearce
**VP:* Marybeth Trakinat
Exec: Robert Dennison
CIO: Scott Bross
CTO: Jill Voyles
Mktg Dir: Amy Humphreys
Mktg Dir: Alexandria Stanton

D-U-N-S 80-317-9571
HEARTLAND COMPUTERS INC
1000 Ridgeview Dr, McHenry, IL 60050-7009
Tel (815) 271-9400 *Founded/Ownrshp* 2010
Sales 28.6MM^E *EMP* 40

SIC 5045 Computers, peripherals & software
CEO: Jerry P Greenwald
*VP: Patricia Greenwald
*Genl Mgr: Todd Greenwald

D-U-N-S 07-291-1878
HEARTLAND CONSUMERS POWER DISTRICT
432 Se 12th St, Madison, SD 57042-3500
Tel (605) 256-6536 Founded/Ownrshp 1969
Sales 82.0MM EMP 10
Accts Bkd Llp Lincoln Nebraska
SIC 4911 Generation, electric power; Transmission, electric power; ; Generation, electric power; Transmission, electric power;
Pr: Dan O'Connor
*Treas: Ron Anderson
*VP: Mike McDowell
*VP: Merlin Vanwalleghen

D-U-N-S 02-320-5503
HEARTLAND COOPERATIVE SERVICES (WI)
100 Parkside Dr, Dorchester, WI 54425-9708
Tel (715) 654-5134 Founded/Ownrshp 1998
Sales 34.0MM^E EMP 130
Accts Clifton Gunderson Llp Marshfi
SIC 5999 5984 5251 Farm equipment & supplies; Liquefied petroleum gas dealers; Hardware
CEO: Dennis Schultz

D-U-N-S 04-525-1183
HEARTLAND COUNTRY CO-OP
405 South Mnr, Westby, WI 54667
Tel (608) 634-3184 Founded/Ownrshp 1998
Sales 26.3MM^E EMP 58
SIC 5171 5191 5541 Petroleum bulk stations; Feed; Filling stations, gasoline; Petroleum bulk stations; Feed; Filling stations, gasoline
Genl Mgr: Randy Dahlen

D-U-N-S 00-133-3645
HEARTLAND CROP INSURANCE INC (KS)
(Suby of EVEREST REINSURANCE HOLDINGS INC) ★
120 Se 6th Ave Ste 210, Topeka, KS 66603-3515
Tel (785) 235-5566 Founded/Ownrshp 2000, 2011
Sales NA EMP 32
SIC 6331 Agricultural insurance
Pr: Michael Miller
*CFO: James Eastburn
*Treas: Wade Shuler
*VP: Travis Gedlatly
CIO: Mike Hartquist
IT Man: Trent Nauholz

D-U-N-S 07-997-1647
■ **HEARTLAND EMPLOYMENT SERVICES LLC**
(Suby of HCR MANOR CARE INC) ★
333 N Summit St, Toledo, OH 43604-1531
Tel (419) 252-5743 Founded/Ownrshp 2004
Sales 98.4MM^E EMP 55,000
SIC 7361 Nurses' registry

D-U-N-S 09-568-1342
■ **HEARTLAND EXPRESS** (TN)
(Suby of HEARTLAND EXPRESS INC) ★
840 Eastern Star Road Ext, Kingsport, TN 37663-3296
Tel (423) 349-6664 Founded/Ownrshp 1978, 1997
Sales 14.0MM^E EMP 277
SIC 4213 Contract haulers; Contract haulers

D-U-N-S 15-512-1668
▲ **HEARTLAND EXPRESS INC**
901 N Kansas Ave, North Liberty, IA 52317-4726
Tel (319) 626-3600 Founded/Ownrshp 1978
Sales 871.3MM EMP 4,500^E
Tkr Sym HTLD Exch NGS
SIC 4213 Trucking, except local; Contract haulers; Trucking, except local; Contract haulers
Ch Bd: Michael Gerdin
CFO: John P Cosaert
Ex VP: Richard Meehan
VP: Thomas Hill
VP: Todd Trimble
CTO: Larry Byrd
VP Sls: Lynsey Rain
VP Sls: Lindsey Rains
Board of Directors: Benjamin J Allen, Lawrence D Crouse, Larry D Gordon, James G Pratt

D-U-N-S 00-986-5684
■ **HEARTLAND EXPRESS INC OF IOWA**
(Suby of HEARTLAND EXPRESS INC) ★
901 N Kansas Ave, North Liberty, IA 52317-4726
Tel (319) 626-3600 Founded/Ownrshp 1978
Sales 528.6MM EMP 2,862
SIC 4213 Contract haulers; Contract haulers
Pr: Michael Gerdin
*CFO: John Cosaert
*Ex VP: Rich Meehan
*VP: Todd Trimble
*VP: Dennis Wilkinson

D-U-N-S 05-073-3083
HEARTLAND FAMILY DENTAL CARE
1200 Network Centre Dr # 2, Effingham, IL 62401-4637
Tel (217) 540-5000 Founded/Ownrshp 2001
Sales 18.1MM^E EMP 331
SIC 8021 Dental clinics & offices; Dental clinics & offices
*Pr: Rick Workman DDS

D-U-N-S 02-017-8331
HEARTLAND FAMILY SERVICE
2101 S 42nd St, Omaha, NE 68105-2909
Tel (402) 553-3000 Founded/Ownrshp 1875
Sales 26.8MM EMP 350
SIC 8322 Individual & family services; Child related social services; Substance abuse counseling; Individual & family services; Child related social services; Substance abuse counseling
Ch Bd: Christine Wendlandt
*Pr: John F Herzog
*CEO: John Jeanetta
*CFO: Kristine Hull
VP: Ann O'Connor

Dir IT: Craig Wolf
Opers Supe: Tanya Gorman
Pgrm Dir: Teffany Heywood
Pgrm Dir: Jenny Schulte
Pgrm Dir: Andrea Wright

HEARTLAND FARMS
See SBM DAIRIES INC

D-U-N-S 80-230-5334
HEARTLAND FARMS INC
907 3rd Ave, Hancock, WI 54943-9533
Tel (715) 249-5555 Founded/Ownrshp 1990
Sales 24.1MM^E EMP 130^E
SIC 0134 0161 Irish potatoes; Vegetables & melons; Pea & bean farms; Corn farm, sweet
Pr: Richard Pavelski
*VP: David Knights
MIS Dir: Marc Bouwer
VP Opers: T J Kennedy

D-U-N-S 80-784-4170
▲ **HEARTLAND FINANCIAL USA INC**
1398 Central Ave, Dubuque, IA 52001-5021
Tel (563) 589-2100 Founded/Ownrshp 1981
Sales NA EMP 1,631^E
Tkr Sym HTLF Exch NGS
SIC 6022 State commercial banks; State commercial banks
Ch Bd: Lynn B Fuller
Pr: Bruce K Lee
COO: Bruce J Rehmke
CFO: Bryan R McKeag
*V Ch Bd: Mark C Falb
Chf Cred: Kenneth J Erickson
Ex VP: Michael J Coyle
Ex VP: Brian J Fox
Ex VP: Douglas J Horstmann
Ex VP: Mark G Murtha
Ex VP: Rodney L Sloan
Ex VP: Frank E Walter
Sr VP: Brian McCarthy
VP: Veronica Nichols
VP: Coleen North
VP: Shelley Phillips
VP: Leila Shanoff
VP: Troy Steger
VP: Bret Tuley
VP: Marti Vandemore
VP: Cheri Wheelan
Board of Directors: James F Conlan, John W Cox Jr, Thomas L Flynn, R Michael McCoy, Kurt M Saylor, John K Schmidt, Duane E White

D-U-N-S 14-579-1625
HEARTLAND FOOD LLC
BURGER KING
1400 Opus Pl Ste 900, Downers Grove, IL 60515-5762
Tel (630) 598-3300 Founded/Ownrshp 2007
Sales 171.6MM^E EMP 4,000
SIC 5812 8741 Fast-food restaurant, chain; Restaurant management; Fast-food restaurant, chain; Restaurant management
Pr: Christopher J Ondrula
*CEO: Todd Bartmess
*CFO: Joel Aaseby
Chf Mktg O: Dave Dixon
*VP: Bryan Anderson
*VP: John Schank
*VP: Pam Smith
Exec: Jeff Macdonald
Mktg Dir: Vicky Weshal

D-U-N-S 61-506-4669 EXP
HEARTLAND FOOD PRODUCTS GROUP LLC
14300 Clay Terrace Blvd, Carmel, IN 46032-3629
Tel (317) 566-9750 Founded/Ownrshp 2004
Sales 168.7MM^E EMP 475^E
SIC 2099 Sorghum syrups: for sweetening; Sorghum syrups: for sweetening
CEO: Teodor Gelov
Dir IT: Marc Yoder
VP Sls: Peter Zarse
S&M/VP: Eddie Pellegrino

D-U-N-S 78-432-3227
HEARTLAND FOR CHILDREN INC
1239 E Main St, Bartow, FL 33830-5058
Tel (863) 519-8900 Founded/Ownrshp 2006
Sales 43.0MM EMP 2
SIC 8322 Child related social services; Child related social services
CEO: Teri Saunders
*Prin: Timothy Brooks Chair
*Prin: Mary Lee Hollis
*Prin: Kevin Roberts
*Prin: Michael J Self
*Prin: Cherie Simmers
*Prin: Mischelle Anderson V-Chair

D-U-N-S 18-120-1773
HEARTLAND HEALTH
5325 Faraon St, Saint Joseph, MO 64506-3488
Tel (816) 271-6000 Founded/Ownrshp 1984
Sales 577.8MM EMP 32,000
Accts Bkd Llp Kansas City Missouri
SIC 8062 7322 8721 General medical & surgical hospitals; Adjustment & collection services; Billing & bookkeeping service; General medical & surgical hospitals; Adjustment & collection services; Billing & bookkeeping service
CEO: Mark Laney MD
V Ch: Carol Roever
V Ch: Sheri Spader
*Pr: Lowell Kruse
Pr: Christine Rattin
*COO: Cut Kretzinger
COO: Kur Krezinger
COO: Amy Royle
CFO: David Warmerdam
*CFO: John Wilson
*Ch: Alfred L Purcell
*Ch: David Solanski
Bd of Dir: Becky Davison
Bd of Dir: Nancy Donahue
*Chf Mktg O: Robert Permet
Ofcr: Chuck Tozer
VP: James Direnna
VP: Charles Mullican

Exec: Jim Lloyd
Dir Rx: Barbara Bilek

HEARTLAND HEALTH CARE CENTER-CANTON #625
See HEARTLAND OF CANTON MI LLC

D-U-N-S 96-752-6141
HEARTLAND HEALTH CARE PLAN TRUST FUND
5325 Faraon St, Saint Joseph, MO 64506-3488
Tel (816) 271-6000 Founded/Ownrshp 2011
Sales 33.3MM EMP 2^E
Accts Bkd Llp Kansas City Mo
SIC 8099 Health & allied services; Health & allied services
Prin: John P Wilson

D-U-N-S 86-098-1695
HEARTLAND HEALTH OUTREACH INC
TRAVELERS
(Suby of TRAVELERS & IMMIGRANTS AIDS HEARTLAND ALLIANCE FOR HUMAN NEEDS & HUMAN RIGHTS) ★
208 S Lasalle St Ste 1300, Chicago, IL 60604
Tel (312) 751-4104 Founded/Ownrshp 1991
Sales 23.7MM EMP 265
Accts Mcgladrey Llp Chicago Il
SIC 8011 Offices & clinics of medical doctors; Primary care medical clinic; Offices & clinics of medical doctors; Primary care medical clinic
Pr: Sid Mohn
*Ex Dir: Karen Batia
IT Man: Rory Osgood
QC Dir: Kelli Spencer
VP Mktg: Bonnifer Ballard

D-U-N-S 07-198-6277
HEARTLAND HEALTH SYSTEM INC
FAYETTE COUNTY HOSPITAL DST
650 W Taylor St, Vandalia, IL 62471-1227
Tel (618) 283-1231 Founded/Ownrshp 2005
Sales 44.3MM^E EMP 246
SIC 8062 8051 General medical & surgical hospitals; Skilled nursing care facilities; General medical & surgical hospitals; Skilled nursing care facilities
Pr: Gregory Starnes
Dir OR: Melissa Willms
Dir Rad: John Provinzano
Dir Rx: J Carroll
Dir QC: Amy Schaal
Psych: Dan Gantz
HC Dir: Debby McCormick
Snr Mgr: Marci Barth

D-U-N-S 83-443-6875
■ **HEARTLAND HEALTHCARE SERVICES LLC**
(Suby of OMNICARE INC) ★
4755 South Ave, Toledo, OH 43615-6422
Tel (419) 535-8435 Founded/Ownrshp 1994
Sales 204.4MM EMP 200
Accts Ernst & Young Llp Toledo Oh
SIC 8011 Offices & clinics of medical doctors; Offices & clinics of medical doctors
CFO: Jeffrey Cremean
Exec: Jodi Lenic
Genl Mgr: Jerry Krbec
Sfty Dirs: Cheryl Paxton
Opers Mgr: Paula Johnson
Pharmcst: Stacy Arnett
Pharmcst: Daniel Feyes Jr
Pharmcst: Mary Garcia
Pharmcst: Charvette Mars
Pharmcst: Joseph McKown
Pharmcst: Dan Ngur

HEARTLAND HM HALTHCARE HOSPICE
See IN HOME HEALTH LLC

D-U-N-S 94-639-0614
■ **HEARTLAND HOSPICE SERVICES LLC**
(Suby of MANOR CARE INC) ★
333 N Summit St, Toledo, OH 43604-1531
Tel (419) 252-5500 Founded/Ownrshp 1994
Sales 12.2MM^E EMP 307
SIC 8082 Home health care services; Home health care services

D-U-N-S 62-079-7944
HEARTLAND HOTEL CORP
HEARTLAND SERVICES
4403 1st Ave Se Ste 114, Cedar Rapids, IA 52402-3255
Tel (319) 363-8613 Founded/Ownrshp 1990
Sales 27.6MM^E EMP 750
SIC 7011 6519 8741 Hotels; Real property lessors; Industrial management; Hotels; Real property lessors; Industrial management
Pr: Derick Rackham
*VP: James R Smith

D-U-N-S 14-958-4877
HEARTLAND HUMAN CARE SERVICES INC
208 S La Salle St # 1300, Chicago, IL 60604-1286
Tel (312) 660-1300 Founded/Ownrshp 1995
Sales 49.0MM EMP 500
Accts Mcgladrey Llp Chicago Il
SIC 8322 Individual & family services; Social service center; Individual & family services; Social service center
VP: Joseph Antolin
Treas: Jean Brophy
VP: Michael Goldberg
Exec: Sabrina Robinson
Assoc Dir: Michael Talbot
Ex Dir: Gwenn Rausch
*Ex Dir: David Sinski
Snr Mgr: Abayomi Ibrahim

D-U-N-S 78-739-5151
HEARTLAND IMAGING COMPANIES INC
LAWRENCE PHOTO-GRAPHIC
1211 W Cambridge Cir Dr, Kansas City, KS 66103-1313
Tel (913) 621-1211 Founded/Ownrshp 1981
Sales 141.0MM EMP 373
Accts Baird Kurtz & Dobson

SIC 5043 Photographic equipment & supplies; Printing apparatus, photographic; Photographic equipment & supplies; Printing apparatus, photographic
Ch: Robert J Gourley
*Treas: Thomas M Prater
VP: Walter Stolarski
*VP: Vernon Vogel
Brnch Mgr: Tom Kelly
Genl Mgr: Ty Roth

D-U-N-S 07-208-8201
▲ **HEARTLAND INC**
1005 N 19th St, Middlesboro, KY 40965-1805
Tel (606) 248-7323 Founded/Ownrshp 2003
Sales 42.1MM^E EMP 230^E
Tkr Sym HTLJ Exch OTO
SIC 3412 3441 Metal barrels, drums & pails; Fabricated structural metal; Metal barrels, drums & pails; Fabricated structural metal
Ch Bd: Terry L Lee
CFO: Mitchell L Cox
*Sec: Thomas C Miller
Bus Dev Di: Ross Huagen

HEARTLAND INDUSTRIES
See BACKYARD STORAGE SOLUTIONS LLC

D-U-N-S 60-440-2750
HEARTLAND INNS OF AMERICA LLC
HEARTLAND MIDWEST MANAGEMENT
1027 Peoples Sq, Waterloo, IA 50702-5740
Tel (319) 235-1025 Founded/Ownrshp 1984
Sales 11.7MM^E EMP 425
SIC 7011 8741 Hotels & motels; Motels; Hotels; Inns; Hotel or motel management; Hotels & motels; Motels; Hotels; Inns; Hotel or motel management

D-U-N-S 61-502-9352 EXP
HEARTLAND LABEL PRINTERS LLC
HEARTLAND BUSINESS SYSTEMS
1700 Stephen St, Little Chute, WI 54140-2550
Tel (920) 788-7720 Founded/Ownrshp 1994
Sales 253.4MM^E EMP 130
Accts Erickson & Associates Sc A
SIC 5065 2672 Modems, computer; Adhesive papers, labels or tapes: from purchased material; Modems, computer; Adhesive papers, labels or tapes: from purchased material
CEO: Peter Helander
Pr: Steve Wilhelms
VP: Bud Nackers
Mng Dir: Ben Turner
Snr Ntwrk: Paul Fandrey
Snr Ntwrk: Matthew Villemure
IT Man: Renee Miller
Opers Mgr: Lori Adamski
Plnt Mgr: Paul Duran
Mktg Mgr: Jim Check
Mktg Mgr: Randy Themar

D-U-N-S 04-777-1530
HEARTLAND MEAT CO INC
H M C
3461 Main St, Chula Vista, CA 91911-5828
Tel (619) 407-3668 Founded/Ownrshp 1971
Sales 42.6MM^E EMP 70
SIC 5147 2013 Meats & meat products; Sausages & other prepared meats; Meats & meat products; Sausages & other prepared meats
CEO: Joseph E Stidman
*Sec: Stephanie Stidman
*VP: James Methey
Genl Mgr: Brandon Marvin
Mktg Dir: Christina Stidman

D-U-N-S 14-875-8175
HEARTLAND MIDWEST LLC
15795 S Mahaffie St # 100, Olathe, KS 66062-4002
Tel (913) 397-9911 Founded/Ownrshp 2001
Sales 29.8MM^E EMP 185
SIC 4939 Combination utilities; Combination utilities
Genl Mgr: Don Guthrie
Dir IT: Terrie Gustafson
Sfty Mgr: Travis Clark
Sfty Mgr: Joe Steineger

HEARTLAND MIDWEST MANAGEMENT
See HEARTLAND INNS OF AMERICA LLC

D-U-N-S 82-560-9001
HEARTLAND MOTOR CO
HEARTLAND TOYOTA
901 W Hills Blvd, Bremerton, WA 98312
Tel (360) 377-1200 Founded/Ownrshp 1992
Sales 20.9MM^E EMP 60
SIC 5511 Automobiles, new & used; Automobiles, new & used
Pr: Rick Wiler
*Sec: Eric Wiler

D-U-N-S 60-226-8489
■ **HEARTLAND OF CANTON MI LLC**
HEARTLAND HEALTH CARE CENTER-CANTON #625
(Suby of MANOR CARE INC) ★
7025 N Lilley Rd, Canton, MI 48187-3533
Tel (734) 394-3100 Founded/Ownrshp 2005
Sales 22.5MM EMP 1^E
SIC 8351 Child day care services

HEARTLAND PAPER
See CHRIS CAM CORP

D-U-N-S 07-946-7480
■ **HEARTLAND PAYMENT SOLUTIONS INC**
(Suby of HEARTLAND PAYMENT SYSTEMS INC) ★
90 Nassau St Fl 2, Princeton, NJ 08542-4529
Tel (609) 683-3831 Founded/Ownrshp 2013
Sales 34.6MM^E EMP 171^E
SIC 7389 8721 Credit card service; Payroll accounting service
CEO: Robert O Carr

D-U-N-S 01-083-9657
▲ **HEARTLAND PAYMENT SYSTEMS INC**
90 Nassau St, Princeton, NJ 08542-4529
Tel (609) 683-3831 Founded/Ownrshp 2000
Sales 2.3MMM EMP 3,734^E
Accts Deloitte & Touche Llp Philade
Tkr Sym HPY Exch NYS

SIC 7389 8721 Credit card service; Payroll accounting service; Credit card service; Payroll accounting service
Ch Bd: Robert O Carr
V Ch: Robert H B Baldwin Jr
COO: Robert Sherby
CFO: Samir M Zabaneh
Ofcr: Tony Capucille
Ofcr: Charles H N Kallenbach
Exec: Bob Clark
Exec: Steven Gamary
Adm Dir: Dan Corle
Area Mgr: Jack Hatfield
Div Mgr: Bill Bernicker
Board of Directors: Maureen Breakiron-Evans, Mitchell L Hollin, Robert H Niehaus, Marc J Ostro, Jonathan J Palmer, Richard W Vague

D-U-N-S 07-953-9855
■ HEARTLAND PET FOODS MANUFACTURING INC
(*Suby of* BLUE BUFFALO CO LTD) ★
8101 E 32nd St, Joplin, MO 64804-7966
Tel (417) 952-1400 *Founded/Ownrshp* 2012
Sales 200.0MM *EMP* 150
SIC 2048 Dry pet food (except dog & cat); Dry pet food (except dog & cat)
Pr: William Bishop Jr
**Sec:* Christopher Bishop

D-U-N-S 13-943-5296
HEARTLAND PETROLEUM LLC
4001 E 5th Ave, Columbus, OH 43219-1812
Tel (614) 441-4001 *Founded/Ownrshp* 2003
Sales 25.7MM^E^ *EMP* 49
SIC 5172 Petroleum brokers
CEO: William C Snedegar
Ofcr: Michael Kopf
VP: Robert Snedegar
Genl Mgr: Donna Weeda
VP Sls: Rex Snedegar
Manager: Roxy Tiller

D-U-N-S 82-829-9318
HEARTLAND PRECISION LLC
2100 15th St N, Wahpeton, ND 58075-3148
Tel (701) 671-6200 *Founded/Ownrshp* 2008
Sales 20.7MM^E^ *EMP* 150
SIC 3443 Pipe, large diameter: metal plate; Pipe, large diameter: metal plate

D-U-N-S 60-720-9855
HEARTLAND PRODUCE CO
4550 70th Ave, Kenosha, WI 53144-1798
Tel (262) 653-0410 *Founded/Ownrshp* 1989
Sales 74.0MM^E^ *EMP* 110
SIC 5148 Fresh fruits & vegetables; Fresh fruits & vegetables
Pr: William Dietz Jr

D-U-N-S 61-007-6572
HEARTLAND PROPERTIES INC
535 W Broadway Ste 100, Council Bluffs, IA 51503-0831
Tel (712) 325-0445 *Founded/Ownrshp* 1988
Sales 33.0MM *EMP* 68
SIC 6531 Real estate brokers & agents; Real estate brokers & agents
Pr: John H Jerkovich
VP: Dan Fosdick
**Genl Mgr:* Randy Carroll
Sales Asso: Brian Shepard

D-U-N-S 93-297-7879 IMP
HEARTLAND PUMP RENTAL AND SALES INC
1800 Supply Rd A, Carterville, IL 62918-3395
Tel (618) 985-5297 *Founded/Ownrshp* 1995
Sales 33.1MM^E^ *EMP* 85
SIC 5084 7359 Industrial machinery & equipment; Equipment rental & leasing; Industrial machinery & equipment; Equipment rental & leasing
Pr: Mae Payne
**Pr:* Grant Salstrom
**Sec:* J Neil Martin
**VP:* John Payne
IT Man: Jennifer Gerlock
Sales Asso: Joe Chotner

HEARTLAND READY MIX
See GARCIA CONSTRUCTION GROUP INC

D-U-N-S 14-333-8056
■ HEARTLAND RECREATIONAL VEHICLES LLC
HEARTLAND RV
(*Suby of* THOR INDUSTRIES INC) ★
2831 Dexter Dr, Elkhart, IN 46514-8225
Tel (574) 266-8726 *Founded/Ownrshp* 2010
Sales 204.1MM^E^ *EMP* 700^E^
SIC 3799 Recreational vehicles; Recreational vehicles
CEO: Timothy M Hoffman
Genl Mgr: Jim Hickey
Mktg Dir: Steve Liddy
Mktg Mgr: Damon Miles
Manager: Joel Eberlein
Manager: John Leonard
Manager: Matt Olds

D-U-N-S 01-064-5919
HEARTLAND REGIONAL MEDICAL CENTER
(*Suby of* HEARTLAND HEALTH) ★
5325 Faraon St, Saint Joseph, MO 64506-3488
Tel (816) 271-6000 *Founded/Ownrshp* 1898
Sales 563.1MM *EMP* 2,600
Accts Bkd Llp Kansas City Mo
SIC 8062 General medical & surgical hospitals; General medical & surgical hospitals
Ch: Alfred L Purcell
**CEO:* Mark Laney
CFO: Spencer Klaasen
Bd of Dir: David Berger
VP: Rattin Christine
Dir Risk M: Becky Kanjirathinkou
Dir Case M: Linda Bahrke
Cmptr Lab: Cheryl Morrow
QA Dir: Stacey Counts
IT Man: Kevin Wells
Pathlgst: David Halbach

HEARTLAND REGIONAL MEDICAL CTR
See MARION HOSPITAL CORP

D-U-N-S 14-719-6174
■ HEARTLAND REHABILITATION SERVICES INC
(*Suby of* MANOR CARE INC) ★
3425 Executive Pkwy # 128, Toledo, OH 43606-1326
Tel (419) 537-0764 *Founded/Ownrshp* 1992
Sales 13.2MM^E^ *EMP* 400
SIC 8093 Rehabilitation center, outpatient treatment; Rehabilitation center, outpatient treatment
Prin: Pat Smith
Ex Dir: Jon Turner
Mktg Mgr: Todd Hanneman

D-U-N-S 14-522-6150
HEARTLAND RETAIL CONSTRUCTION INC
4956 Memco Ln Ste A, Racine, WI 53404-1160
Tel (262) 681-8200 *Founded/Ownrshp* 2004
Sales 29.5MM^E^ *EMP* 46
SIC 1542 Commercial & office buildings, renovation & repair
VP: Douglas M Campese
**VP:* James H Brown Jr

D-U-N-S 96-644-3970
HEARTLAND RURAL ELECTRIC COOPERATIVE INC
110 Enterprise St, Girard, KS 66743-2058
Tel (620) 724-8251 *Founded/Ownrshp* 1997
Sales 25.4MM *EMP* 41
Accts Dreyer & Kelso Pc Pa Girard
SIC 4911 Electric services; Electric services
CEO: Dale Coomes
**Pr:* Robert Stainbrook
**Sec:* Donald Davied
**VP:* Harry Oehlert
Comm Man: Ron Graber
Off Mgr: Janet Ashbacher
IT Man: Leon Forsythe

HEARTLAND RV
See HEARTLAND RECREATIONAL VEHICLES LLC

HEARTLAND SERVICES
See HEARTLAND HOTEL CORP

HEARTLAND SIDING
See PROVIA PRODUCTS LLC

D-U-N-S 15-423-7002
HEARTLAND SUPPLY CO INC
1248 E Pump Station Rd, Fayetteville, AR 72701-7273
Tel (479) 444-0970 *Founded/Ownrshp* 1987
Sales 60.0MM^E^ *EMP* 9
SIC 5169 Food additives & preservatives; Food additives & preservatives
Pr: Patricia Pummill
**Treas:* Tom Suchecki
**VP:* Jim Morris

D-U-N-S 85-946-8647 IMP
HEARTLAND TANNING INC
4251 Ne Port Dr, Lees Summit, MO 64064-1773
Tel (816) 795-1414 *Founded/Ownrshp* 1967
Sales 39.3MM^E^ *EMP* 140
SIC 5099 2599 7299 3949 Tanning salon equipment & supplies; Beds, not household use; Tanning salon; Sporting & athletic goods; Tanning salon equipment & supplies; Beds, not household use; Tanning salon; Sporting & athletic goods
CEO: Greg Henson
**Sec:* Holly Henson
**Ex VP:* Brad Henson
VP: Bill Straka
Dir IT: Ilya Sedykh
VP Mfg: Tom Feekin
Sls Dir: Bill Mandry
Sales Asso: Cindy Dimitras-Feist
Sales Asso: Kacee Gibson
Art Dir: Craig Simpson

D-U-N-S 04-964-3195
■ HEARTLAND TELECOMMUNICATIONS CO OF IOWA
CONSOLIDATED COMMUNICATIONS
(*Suby of* ENVENTIS CORP) ★
221 E Hickory St, Mankato, MN 56001-3610
Tel (507) 387-1151 *Founded/Ownrshp* 1995
Sales 217.7M^E^ *EMP* 489
SIC 4813 Telephone/video communications
Pr: Robert Udell Jr
**Ofcr:* Carol Wirsbinski
IT Man: Mike Olsen
Board of Directors: Robert Currey, Steven Shirar, Matthew Smith

HEARTLAND TOYOTA
See HEARTLAND MOTOR CO

D-U-N-S 93-394-0991
HEARTLAND TRADING INC
120 N Hickory, Roff, OK 74865-9001
Tel (580) 456-7142 *Founded/Ownrshp* 1996
Sales 24.0MM^E^ *EMP* 32^E^
SIC 6221 Commodity brokers, contracts; Commodity traders, contracts
Pr: Gene Garrett
CFO: Chad King
**VP:* Roger Callison

D-U-N-S 96-776-9118
HEARTLAND VIDEO SYSTEMS INC
1311 Pilgrim Rd, Plymouth, WI 53073-4969
Tel (319) 294-1360 *Founded/Ownrshp* 1997
Sales 28.0MM *EMP* 27
SIC 5065 Communication equipment
Pr: Dennis Klas
**Sec:* Jody Klas
**VP:* Bill Tessman

D-U-N-S 96-352-5493
■ HEARTLAND-WASHINGTON MANOR OF KENOSHA WI LLC
MANORCARE HLTH SRVCES- KENOSHA
(*Suby of* HCR MANOR CARE INC) ★
3100 Washington Rd, Kenosha, WI 53144-1604
Tel (262) 658-4622 *Founded/Ownrshp* 1985
Sales 341.0MM *EMP* 1^E^
SIC 8051 Skilled nursing care facilities; Skilled nursing care facilities

HEARTPLACE
See DALLAS CARDIOLOGY ASSOCIATES P A

D-U-N-S 09-484-8587 IMP
HEARTS ON FIRE CO LLC
99 Summer St Ste 400, Boston, MA 02110-1200
Tel (617) 523-5588 *Founded/Ownrshp* 1978
Sales 33.0MM^E^ *EMP* 100^E^
SIC 5094 Diamonds (gems)
Pr: Caryl Capeci
COO: Tom Carlo
COO: Richard Fields
CFO: William Anderson
CFO: Bob Gorton
Ex VP: Ellen Maloney
Ex VP: Peter Smith
VP: Tish Berard
VP: Jacqueline Raffi
Dir Risk M: Michael Quinn
Dir IT: Maureen Haley

HEARTSHARE HUMAN SERVICES NY
See HEARTSHARE HUMAN SERVICES OF NY ROMAN CATHOLIC DIOCESE OF BROOKLYN

D-U-N-S 80-186-2772
HEARTSHARE HUMAN SERVICES OF NY ROMAN CATHOLIC DIOCESE OF BROOKLYN
HEARTSHARE HUMAN SERVICES NY
12 Metrotech Ctr Fl 29, Brooklyn, NY 11201-3858
Tel (718) 422-4200 *Founded/Ownrshp* 1914
Sales 72.4MM^E^ *EMP* 1,200^E^
Accts Loeb & Troper Llp New York N
SIC 8322 Individual & family services; Individual & family services
Pr: William R Guarinello
**Treas:* Michael Abatemarco
**Ex VP:* Mia Higgins
**Ex VP:* Linda Tempel
**Sr VP:* Evelyn Alvarez
**Sr VP:* Anthony F Bianca
**Sr VP:* George Cincotta Jr
**Sr VP:* Carol Smith-Njiiri
VP: Ken Callahan
**VP:* Robert C Golden
**VP:* John T Sharkey
**VP:* Ralph A Subbiondo

D-U-N-S 04-191-3047
HEARTSPRING INC
8700 E 29th St N, Wichita, KS 67226-2169
Tel (316) 634-8700 *Founded/Ownrshp* 1934
Sales 15.9MM *EMP* 320
Accts Bkd Llp Wichita Ks
SIC 8211 8093 8049 School for physically handicapped; Specialty outpatient clinics; Audiologist; School for physically handicapped; Specialty outpatient clinics; Audiologist
Pr: Gary Singleton
**CFO:* David Dorf
**VP:* Paul Faber
Mktg Dir: Dusty Buell
Psych: Bruce Hauser

D-U-N-S 14-605-4536
HEARTWARE INC
(*Suby of* HEARTWARE PTY LIMITED)
14400 Nw 60th Ave, Miami Lakes, FL 33014-2807
Tel (305) 818-4100 *Founded/Ownrshp* 1998
Sales 29.5MM^E^ *EMP* 120
SIC 3841 Medical instruments & equipment, blood & bone work; Medical instruments & equipment, blood & bone work
Pr: Douglas Godshall
**CFO:* David McIntyre
**Ex VP:* Jeff Larose
**Sr VP:* Larry Knopf
**Sr VP:* Peter McAree
**Sr VP:* Jim Schuermann
**VP:* Lauren Farrell
VP: James Schuermann
Rgnl Mgr: Gregory Balme
QA Dir: Carolina Castro
QA Dir: Joseph Diaz

D-U-N-S 83-043-5702
▲ HEARTWARE INTERNATIONAL INC
500 Old Connecticut Path, Framingham, MA 01701-4574
Tel (508) 739-0950 *Founded/Ownrshp* 2008
Sales 278.4MM *EMP* 585^E^
Accts Grant Thornton Llp Fort Laude
Tkr Sym HTWR *Exch* NGS
SIC 3841 Surgical & medical instruments; Surgical & medical instruments
Pr: Douglas Godshall
**Ch Bd:* C Raymond Larkin Jr
CFO: Peter F McAree
Chf Mktg O: Katrin Leadley
Ex VP: Jeffrey Larose
Sr VP: Larry Knopf
Board of Directors: Timothy Barberich, Cynthia Feldman, Seth Harrison, Robert Stockman, Robert Thomas, Denis Wade

D-U-N-S 19-896-0734
HEARTWAY CORP
215 Se 4th St, Evansville, IN 47713-1201
Tel (812) 422-7774 *Founded/Ownrshp* 1987
Sales 10.3MM^E^ *EMP* 538
SIC 8051 Skilled nursing care facilities; Skilled nursing care facilities
Pr: Rob Dewald

D-U-N-S 80-978-8359
HEARTY FRESH INC
HEARTY FRESH PRODUCE
1260 100th St Sw, Byron Center, MI 49315-9342
Tel (616) 878-4100 *Founded/Ownrshp* 1993
Sales 44.5MM^E^ *EMP* 80
SIC 5148 Fresh fruits & vegetables; Fresh fruits & vegetables
Pr: Randall D Huizinga

HEARTY FRESH PRODUCE
See HEARTY FRESH INC

HEARUSA
See AUDIOLOGY DISTRIBUTION LLC

D-U-N-S 00-911-8407 IMP/EXP
HEAT AND CONTROL INC (CA)
21121 Cabot Blvd, Hayward, CA 94545-1132
Tel (510) 259-0500 *Founded/Ownrshp* 1950
Sales 222.6MM^E^ *EMP* 1,200
SIC 3556 7699

D-U-N-S 02-039-6122
HEAT AND WARMTH FUND
535 Griswold St Ste 200, Detroit, MI 48226-3612
Tel (313) 226-9465 *Founded/Ownrshp* 1985
Sales 32.4MM *EMP* 14
Accts Doeren Mayhew Troy Mi
SIC 8322 Family service agency; Family service agency
CEO: Saunteel A Jenkins
**CFO:* Deborah Diviny
Mktg Dir: Jill Brunett
Mktg Mgr: Kate Heil

D-U-N-S 13-172-9691
HEAT SEAL LLC
AMPAK
4580 E 71st St, Cleveland, OH 44125-1018
Tel (216) 341-2022 *Founded/Ownrshp* 1956
Sales 30.2MM^E^ *EMP* 110
SIC 3565 2542 Packaging machinery; Wrapping machines; Bag opening, filling & closing machines; Vacuum packaging machinery; Fixtures, store: except wood; Packaging machinery; Wrapping machines; Bag opening, filling & closing machines; Vacuum packaging machinery; Fixtures, store: except wood
Sls Mgr: Tom Birkel
Sls Mgr: Ozzie Oswald
Sls Mgr: Bryan Rakovec

D-U-N-S 86-705-4462
HEAT SOFTWARE USA INC
(*Suby of* FRONTRANGE SOLUTIONS INC) ★
490 N Mccarthy Blvd, Milpitas, CA 95035-5118
Tel (719) 531-5007 *Founded/Ownrshp* 1994
Sales 43.0MM^E^ *EMP* 271
SIC 7372 Prepackaged software; Prepackaged software
VP: Kevin J Smith
Pr: Frank Huang
**CEO:* Jonathan Temple
**CFO:* Cary Baker
Ex VP: Natalie Burdick
Ex VP: Carrie Cornella
Ex VP: Tony Delollis
Ex VP: Prajval Parthasarathy
VP: Keith Barr
VP: Andy Burton
VP: David Smith
VP: Stephane Zadri
Dir Surg: Patrice Tollenaere

HEAT TRANSFER PRODUCTS
See HTP INC

D-U-N-S 13-700-6933 EXP
HEAT TRANSFER PRODUCTS GROUP LLC
WITT HEAT TRANSFER PRODUCTS
(*Suby of* RHEEM MANUFACTURING CO INC) ★
201 Thomas French Dr, Scottsboro, AL 35769-7405
Tel (256) 259-7400 *Founded/Ownrshp* 2013
Sales 221.8MM^E^ *EMP* 200
SIC 5084 Heat exchange equipment, industrial; Heat exchange equipment, industrial
CFO: Joseph Sklencar
Ex VP: Tommy Gaubatz
Ex VP: Dick Torpey
IT Man: Ruben Reyes
VP Opers: Paul Andrzejewski
Opers Mgr: Mark Humphrey
QI Cn Mgr: William Salomon

D-U-N-S 96-339-7133
HEAT TRANSFER PRODUCTS GROUP LLC
HTPG
(*Suby of* AMERICAN REFRIGERATION INC) ★
8101 E Kaiser Blvd # 110, Anaheim, CA 92808-2661
Tel (714) 529-1935 *Founded/Ownrshp* 2010
Sales 49.4MM^E^ *EMP* 330
SIC 3585 Refrigeration equipment, complete; Refrigeration equipment, complete

D-U-N-S 01-116-8775
HEAT TRANSFER SOLUTIONS INC
H T S
(*Suby of* HTS ENGINEERING LTD)
3350 Yale St, Houston, TX 77018-7741
Tel (832) 328-1010 *Founded/Ownrshp* 2000
Sales 113.7MM^E^ *EMP* 100
SIC 5075 Air conditioning & ventilation equipment & supplies; Air conditioning & ventilation equipment & supplies
Pr: Derek Gordon
**CFO:* David Kvirling
VP: David Warner
**Prin:* Mike Donovan
**Prin:* Grant Yaney
Off Mgr: Melinda Barry
IT Man: Jeff Mamaux
Opers Mgr: Maurice Mullins
Mktg Dir: Ashley Heisler
Sales Asso: Brock Hutchison

HEAT TREAT
See AXLETECH INTERNATIONAL

D-U-N-S 06-728-5072
HEAT TREATING SERVICES CORP OF AMERICA
217 Central Ave, Pontiac, MI 48341-2924
Tel (248) 858-2230 Founded/Ownrshp 1978
Sales 21.5MM^E EMP 114
Accts Jenkins Magnus Volk & Carroll
SIC 3398 Metal heat treating; Metal heat treating
Pr: Stephen R Hynes
*Sec: Tara Kranz
*VP: Brad Hynes
Genl Mgr: Sueneal Jain
Plnt Mgr: Tim Anderson
Plnt Mgr: Tony Patterson
Plnt Mgr: Pat Vanderworp
Ql Cn Mgr: Franklin Shepard
Ql Cn Mgr: Joann Zavicar
VP Sls: John Lund
Board of Directors: Dawn Whaley

HEATCON COMPOSITE SYSTEMS
See HEATCON INC

D-U-N-S 08-993-8500
HEATCON INC (WA)
HEATCON COMPOSITE SYSTEMS
600 Andover Park E, Tukwila, WA 98188-7610
Tel (206) 575-0815 Founded/Ownrshp 1978
Sales 35.4MM^E EMP 72
SIC 5075 3625 4581 Electrical heating equipment; Thermostats; Control equipment, electric; Aircraft maintenance & repair services; Electrical heating equipment; Thermostats; Control equipment, electric; Aircraft maintenance & repair services
Pr: Eric Casterline
CFO: Diana Bendickson
Mng Dir: Thomas Lane
IT Man: Chris Smith
Mktg Mgr: Nicole Rodriguez

D-U-N-S 14-540-4112 IMP
■ **HEATCRAFT REFRIGERATION PRODUCTS LLC**
HEATCRAFT WORLDWIDE RFRGN PDTS
(Suby of LENNOX INTERNATIONAL INC) ★
2175 W Park Place Blvd, Stone Mountain, GA 30087-3535
Tel (770) 465-5600 Founded/Ownrshp 2000
Sales 291.9MM^E EMP 1,100
SIC 3585 Refrigeration equipment, complete; Refrigeration equipment, complete
VP Opers: Michael Vincent
Natl Sales: Les Kahrnoff
Bus Dev Di: Kevin Chunn

HEATCRAFT WORLDWIDE RFRGN PDTS
See HEATCRAFT REFRIGERATION PRODUCTS LLC

D-U-N-S 08-119-4250 EXP
■ **HEATEC INC**
(Suby of ASTEC INDUSTRIES INC) ★
5200 Wilson Rd, Chattanooga, TN 37410-2149
Tel (423) 821-5200 Founded/Ownrshp 1977
Sales 34.1MM^E EMP 148^E
SIC 3567 Heating units & devices, industrial: electric; Heating units & devices, industrial: electric
Pr: Richard J Dorris
*Pr: Robert Wilfong
*Pr: Tom Wilkey
Manager: Scott Moore

D-U-N-S 19-557-7440
HEATER SPECIALISTS LLC
H S I
(Suby of ENERGY PROCESS TECHNOLOGIES INC) ★
3171 N Toledo Ave, Tulsa, OK 74115-1804
Tel (918) 835-3126 Founded/Ownrshp 1988
Sales 53.7MM^E EMP 100
SIC 3255 3443 Cement, clay refractory; Industrial vessels, tanks & containers; Cement, clay refractory; Industrial vessels, tanks & containers
CFO: Randy Light
Ql Cn Mgr: Howard Thompson

D-U-N-S 00-106-0656 IMP
HEATH CONSULTANTS INC
TEX SOL
9030 W Monroe Rd, Houston, TX 77061-5212
Tel (713) 844-1300 Founded/Ownrshp 1933
Sales 128.9MM^E EMP 460
SIC 8711 3826 3812 Engineering services; Consulting engineer; Analytical instruments; Water testing apparatus; Gas analyzing equipment; Environmental testing equipment; Search & navigation equipment; Engineering services; Consulting engineer; Analytical instruments; Water testing apparatus; Gas analyzing equipment; Environmental testing equipment; Search & navigation equipment
Ch Bd: Milton W Heath Jr
*Pr: Carolyn Heath Haag
Sr VP: Paul Wehnert
*Prin: Graham G Midgley
Sfty Dirs: Brandy Duncan
Mfg Mgr: Bill Leslie

D-U-N-S 05-482-7472
HEATH OIL INC (PA)
5821 Us Rte 322 Vctr Hts, Franklin, PA 16323
Tel (814) 437-7802 Founded/Ownrshp 1977
Sales 23.6MM^E EMP 35
SIC 5171 5983 Petroleum bulk stations; Fuel oil dealers
Pr: Daniel L Heath
*VP: Richard Fisher

D-U-N-S 15-037-8748
HEATH TECNA INC
ZODIAC ARLN CABIN & INTR WASH
(Suby of ZODIAC AEROSPACE CS20001)
3225 Woburn St, Bellingham, WA 98226-5656
Tel (360) 738-2005 Founded/Ownrshp 2011
Sales 135.4MM^E EMP 660^E
SIC 3728 5088 Aircraft parts & equipment; Aircraft & space vehicle supplies & parts; Aircraft parts & equipment; Aircraft & space vehicle supplies & parts
Pr: Rich Ballantyne
*CFO: Bob Ihlenfeldt
VP: Robert Beale
VP: Brian Berg
VP: Lynn Bottoms
VP: Gary Chris
VP: David Flemming
VP: Derick Neumann
VP: Cindy Schiller
Prgrm Mgr: Alok Innani
Prgrm Mgr: Lance Turk

D-U-N-S 05-928-8449
HEATH VILLAGE
HEATH VILLAGE RETIREMENT CMNTY
430 Schooleys Mountain Rd # 1, Hackettstown, NJ 07840-4066
Tel (908) 852-4801 Founded/Ownrshp 1962
Sales 23.1MM EMP 250^E
Accts Parentebeard Llc Philadelphia
SIC 8051 Skilled nursing care facilities; Skilled nursing care facilities
Pr: Patrick Brady
COO: Mary A Bove
Genl Mgr: Jim Irding
Nrsg Dir: Marilyn Gibbs
HC Dir: Jill Mutek

HEATH VILLAGE RETIREMENT CMNTY
See HEATH VILLAGE

HEATH ZENITH
See HEATHCO LLC

D-U-N-S 80-626-3310 IMP
HEATHCO LLC
HEATH ZENITH
(Suby of DUCHOSSOIS GROUP INC) ★
2445 Nashville Rd, Bowling Green, KY 42101-4030
Tel (270) 846-8400 Founded/Ownrshp 2007
Sales 42.6MM^E EMP 200^E
SIC 3699 Household electrical equipment; Household electrical equipment
Opers Mgr: Tamara Canterbury
Opers Mgr: Mike Minton
Opers Mgr: Gary Scott
Opers Mgr: Carol Switzer
Mktg Mgr: Eric Booth
Sls Mgr: Bob Hohman

HEATHER HL REHABILITATION HOSP
See UNIVERSITY HOSPITALS HEALTH SYSTEM-HEATHER HILL INC

HEATILATOR
See HEARTH & HOME TECHNOLOGIES LLC

D-U-N-S 02-911-7066
■ **HEATING & COOLING SUPPLY LLC**
(Suby of WATSCO INC) ★
1669 Brandywine Ave Ste A, Chula Vista, CA 91911-6073
Tel (619) 591-4615 Founded/Ownrshp 1960
Sales 74.4MM^E EMP 275
SIC 5075 Warm air heating & air conditioning; Warm air heating & air conditioning
Sr VP: Jack Sinkler
Dir Bus: James Gooch
Sales Exec: Hendrich Jerry
Manager: Ron Vetsch
Sls Mgr: Kimball Webb

D-U-N-S 02-236-3014
HEATING AND COOLING SUPPLY CO
105 Broadway St, Waterloo, IA 50703-5800
Tel (319) 233-5206 Founded/Ownrshp 1983
Sales 21.4MM^E EMP 34
SIC 5075 Warm air heating & air conditioning
Pr: Robert Thompson
*VP: Steven Roe
Opers Mgr: Jim Vondran
Sls Mgr: Criag Hein
Sls Mgr: Phillip Keys
Sls Mgr: Colton Sankey
Sls Mgr: David Schnathorst

D-U-N-S 00-882-5267
HEATING AND PLUMBING ENGINEERS INC
HPE
407 Fillmore Pl, Colorado Springs, CO 80907-6049
Tel (719) 633-5571 Founded/Ownrshp 1985
Sales 105.9MM^E EMP 400
SIC 1711 Mechanical contractor; Mechanical contractor
Pr: William Eustace
COO: Kelly Eustace
VP: Douglas Geist
Dir Risk M: Gary Leak
Assoc Dir: John Thompson
Div Mgr: Dennis Schroeder
IT Man: Draschil Dave
IT Man: Dani Howling
IT Man: Jenny Kiggins
IT Man: Sean Lauck
IT Man: Lauck Sean

D-U-N-S 61-867-2760 IMP
HEATMAX INC
HOT HANDS
(Suby of KOBAYASHI PHARMACEUTICAL CO., LTD.)
245 Kraft Dr, Dalton, GA 30721-1502
Tel (706) 226-1800 Founded/Ownrshp 1990
Sales 28.2MM^E EMP 142
SIC 3999 Heating pads, nonelectric; Heating pads, nonelectric
CEO: Daniel Yim
COO: Danny Garvey
CFO: John Weathers
Sls Mgr: Jeff Manning

D-U-N-S 01-270-2320 IMP
HEATRON INC (MO)
3000 Wilson Ave, Leavenworth, KS 66048-4637
Tel (913) 651-4420 Founded/Ownrshp 1976, 1987
Sales 133.1MM^E EMP 275
SIC 3567 3634 Heating units & devices, industrial: electric; Electric housewares & fans; Heating units & devices, industrial: electric; Electric housewares & fans
CEO: Michael Keenan
*Pr: H B Turner
*Bd of Dir: Norman Beal
*Bd of Dir: Pat McKinzie
*VP: Laurie Harrod Boyd
VP: Marc Conway
*VP: Robert H Martter
*VP: Bernard Rogers
QC Dir: Brian Stewart
Sfty Mgr: John Burch
Ql Cn Mgr: Randy Meador

D-U-N-S 00-637-1272 IMP/EXP
HEAVEN HILL DISTILLERIES INC (KY)
1064 Loretto Rd, Bardstown, KY 40004-2229
Tel (502) 348-3921 Founded/Ownrshp 1935, 1942
Sales 176.7MM^E EMP 505
SIC 2085 Bourbon whiskey; Bourbon whiskey
Pr: Max L Shapira
CFO: Kelvin Haynes
*Ex VP: Harry J Shapira
*VP: Craig Beam
VP: Parker Bean
VP: Steve Feller
*VP: Joseph L Fraser
*VP: Debbie Morris
*VP: H Mark Pulliam
Rgnl Mgr: Bruce Jacobson
Sfty Mgr: Liz Ashby

HEAVENER NURSING CENTER
See K & C LLC

D-U-N-S 06-080-1529
HEAVY & GENERAL CONSTRUCTION LABORERS UNION LOCAL NO 472
LABORS LOCAL NO 472
700 Raymond Blvd, Newark, NJ 07105-2909
Tel (973) 589-5050 Founded/Ownrshp 1946
Sales 116.8MM EMP 14
Accts Hulse & Associates Pc Fairfie
SIC 8631 Labor union
Pr: John Hibbs
*Prin: Eugene Grambo

D-U-N-S 02-488-1091
HEAVY & GENERAL LABORERS LOCAL 472 & 172 FUNDS OF NJ
604 Us Highway 206, Trenton, NJ 08610-4314
Tel (609) 291-9197 Founded/Ownrshp 2001
Sales 105.2MM EMP 4
Accts Schultheis & Panettieri Llp H
SIC 8631 Labor unions & similar labor organizations; Labor unions & similar labor organizations

D-U-N-S 61-202-3598
HEAVY CONSTRUCTION SYSTEMS SPECIALISTS INC
HCSS
13151 W Airport Blvd, Sugar Land, TX 77478-6161
Tel (713) 270-4000 Founded/Ownrshp 1986
Sales 33.8MM EMP 184
Accts Rick Roome Pc Stafford Texas
SIC 7371 Computer software development; Software programming applications; Computer software development; Software programming applications
CEO: Mike Rydin
*Pr: Steve McGough
Sr VP: John Lassig
*VP: Dan Briscoe
*VP: John Davis
*VP: Sophie Rydin
VP: Tom Webb
Off Mgr: Chelsea Worrell
Snr Sftwr: Dov Kivlovitz
QA Dir: Tiffany Murphree
QA Dir: Addison Smith

D-U-N-S 12-210-0555
HEAVY CONSTRUCTORS INC
EXCAVATING SPECIALISTS
4101 Deadwood Ave, Rapid City, SD 57702-9692
Tel (605) 342-3144 Founded/Ownrshp 1983
Sales 83.7MM^E EMP 300
SIC 1542 1794 1623 1611 Commercial & office building, new construction; Excavation & grading, building construction; Underground utilities contractor; Highway & street construction; Commercial & office building, new construction; Excavation & grading, building construction; Underground utilities contractor; Highway & street construction
Pr: David Gustafson
*Treas: Wayne D Gustafson
*VP: Terry Larson

D-U-N-S 06-065-8137
HEAVY EQUIPMENT MOVERS & INSTALLATION LLC
HEMI SYSTEMS
366 Industrial Park Way, Commerce, GA 30529-1317
Tel (706) 423-9595 Founded/Ownrshp 2009
Sales 23.8MM^E EMP 80
SIC 1796 Millwright
Opers Mgr: Skip Greene

D-U-N-S 04-843-6377
HEAVY HIGHWAY HEALTH & WELFARE FUND
665 N Broad St, Philadelphia, PA 19123-2418
Tel (215) 765-4633 Founded/Ownrshp 2001
Sales 24.7MM EMP 20
SIC 8631 Labor unions & similar labor organizations; Labor unions & similar labor organizations

D-U-N-S 05-569-2321 IMP
HEAVY MACHINES INC
HMI ELECTRIC DIVISION
3926 E Raines Rd, Memphis, TN 38118-6936
Tel (901) 260-2200 Founded/Ownrshp 1971
Sales 65.9MM^E EMP 141
SIC 5082 7699 7353 3531 5063 Construction & mining machinery; Mining machinery & equipment, except petroleum; Cranes, construction; Forestry equipment; Industrial machinery & equipment repair; Heavy construction equipment rental; Forestry related equipment; Motors, electric; Construction & mining machinery; Mining machinery & equipment, except petroleum; Cranes, construction; Forestry equipment; Industrial machinery & equipment repair; Heavy construction equipment rental; Forestry related equipment; Motors, electric
Pr: Richard O Wilson Jr
*CFO: Ted Bailey
VP: James A Nelson
VP: Steve Northcross
Exec: Michael Moseley
Sales Exec: Phillip Burton
Sls Mgr: Jim McNeil

HEAVY STRUCTURES
See BLUESCOPE CONSTRUCTION INC

D-U-N-S 80-990-1036
HEAVY VEHICLE ELECTRONIC LICENSE PLATE INC
101 N 1st Ave Ste 2275, Phoenix, AZ 85003-1906
Tel (602) 412-2240 Founded/Ownrshp 1993
Sales 79.2MM EMP 5
Accts Mcgladrey Llp Phoenix Az
SIC 7538 Motor vehicle supplies & new parts; General automotive repair shops
Pr: Karen Rasmussen
IT Man: Peter Monn

HEAVYQUIP
See ITR AMERICA LLC

HEAVYQUIP
See ITR NORTH AMERICA LLC

HEB GROCERY
See HEB MANUFACTURING

D-U-N-S 80-864-8245 IMP
HEB GROCERY CO LP
(Suby of H E BUTT GROCERY CO) ★
646 S Flores St, San Antonio, TX 78204-1219
Tel (210) 938-8000 Founded/Ownrshp 2001
Sales 89.2MM^E EMP 451^E
SIC 5411 Supermarkets, chain
CEO: Charles Butt
CFO: Martin Otto
VP: Winell Herron
VP: Robert Loeffler
Ex Dir: John Archer
Ex Dir: Max Campbell
Ex Dir: Gus Kroos
Store Dir: Ryan Wilson
Admn Mgr: Felix Perez
Dir IT: Ray Fevold
IT Man: Mark Webb

HEB ISD
See HURST-EULESS-BEDFORD INDEPENDENT SCHOOL DISTRICT

D-U-N-S 55-710-3335 IMP
HEB MANUFACTURING
HEB GROCERY
4710 N Interstate 35, San Antonio, TX 78218-5430
Tel (210) 938-5432 Founded/Ownrshp 1984
Sales 33.4MM^E EMP 120^E
SIC 5411 Grocery stores; Supermarkets; Supermarkets, chain
Prin: Charles Butt
Treas: Jenine Merrill
Opers Mgr: Kristopher Ward

D-U-N-S 01-997-7664
HEBCO PETROLEUM DISTRIBUTORS INC (TX)
(Suby of H E BUTT GROCERY CO) ★
646 S Main Ave, San Antonio, TX 78204-1210
Tel (210) 938-8419 Founded/Ownrshp 1998
Sales 76.4MM^E EMP 80
SIC 5172 Petroleum products; Petroleum products
Pr: Charles C Butt

D-U-N-S 14-863-2904
HEBCO PRODUCTS INC
(Suby of QUALITOR INC) ★
1232 Whetstone St, Bucyrus, OH 44820-3539
Tel (419) 562-7987 Founded/Ownrshp 1984
Sales 80.6MM^E EMP 862
SIC 3714 3451 3429 5013 Motor vehicle brake systems & parts; Screw machine products; Manufactured hardware (general); Automotive supplies & parts; Motor vehicle brake systems & parts; Screw machine products; Manufactured hardware (general); Automotive supplies & parts
Pr: Andrew Ason
*VP: Ralph Reins
Plnt Mgr: Bruce Newman

D-U-N-S 01-373-0403 IMP
HEBELER CORP
2000 Military Rd, Tonawanda, NY 14150-6704
Tel (716) 873-9300 Founded/Ownrshp 1929, 2001
Sales 37.3MM^E EMP 140^E
SIC 3599 Custom machinery; Custom machinery
Ch: John Coleman
*Pr: Ken Snyder
IT Man: Lisa Calkins
Plnt Mgr: Harry Monin
Prd Mgr: Charlie Snyder

D-U-N-S 08-983-5086 EXP
HEBERT STEEL CO INC
39179 Highway 74, Gonzales, LA 70737-6404
Tel (225) 343-9036 Founded/Ownrshp 1978
Sales 28.7MM^E EMP 72
SIC 1542 Nonresidential construction
Pr: Sterling Hebert
*Sec: Gary L Hebert
*VP: Ronald Phebert Sr
*VP: Ronnie Hebert

D-U-N-S 80-760-8385
HEBREW ACADEMY FOR SPECIAL CHILDREN (INC)
HASC
5902 14th Ave Ste A, Brooklyn, NY 11219-5039
Tel (718) 686-5900 *Founded/Ownrshp* 1933
Sales 36.5MM *EMP* 400E
Accts Independent
SIC 8211 Private elementary & secondary schools; Private elementary & secondary schools
*Ex Dir: Soloman Stern
QA Dir: Barbara Kerman
IT Man: Eric Rogers
Pgrm Dir: Lois Hofflin

D-U-N-S 02-955-1850
HEBREW ACADEMY OF FIVE TOWNS AND ROCKAWAY (NY)
HAFTR
389 Central Ave, Lawrence, NY 11559-1607
Tel (516) 569-3370 *Founded/Ownrshp* 1956
Sales 19.4MME *EMP* 350
SIC 8211 Private combined elementary & secondary school; Private combined elementary & secondary school
Ex Dir: Reuben Maron
Exec: Eileen Silverman
Prin: Yotav Eliach
Prin: Ruth Katz
Prin: David Leibtag
Board of Directors: Teddy Selinger, Ira Sturm, Lee Wallach

D-U-N-S 06-925-0710
HEBREW HOME AND HOSPITAL INC (CT)
1 Abrahms Blvd, West Hartford, CT 06117-1525
Tel (860) 523-3974 *Founded/Ownrshp* 1904
Sales 44.3MM *EMP* 800
SIC 8051 8069 Skilled nursing care facilities; Chronic disease hospital; Skilled nursing care facilities; Chronic disease hospital
Pr: Bonnie B Gauthier
V Ch: David Rosenthal
*Pr: David A Houle
Pr: Fred Schnider
*VP: Renata Ogrodnik
*VP: Henry Schneiderman
*VP: Jonas Steiner
Dir: Susan Moatz
Off Mgr: Terry Fagan
Nurse Mgr: Emmanuel Enokpa
Nurse Mgr: Genevieve Tipson

D-U-N-S 07-325-7008
HEBREW HOME FOR AGED AT RIVERDALE
5901 Palisade Ave, Bronx, NY 10471-1205
Tel (718) 581-1000 *Founded/Ownrshp* 1917
Sales 72.6MM *EMP* 1,200
Accts Loeb & Troper Llp New York N
SIC 8059 Rest home, with health care; Rest home, with health care
Pr: Daniel A Reingold
CFO: Fred German
*CFO: Luz Liebeskind
*Ch: Jeffrey S Maurer
*Treas: Joseph Wygoda
*Ex VP: Daniel Reingold
CIO: David Finkelstein
Mktg Mgr: David Pomeranz
Doctor: Ernesto Espana
Doctor: George Gancsos
Doctor: Roupa Sadana

D-U-N-S 02-000-4693
HEBREW HOME FOR AGED DISABLED (CA)
JEWISH HOME FOR THE AGED
302 Silver Ave, San Francisco, CA 94112-1510
Tel (415) 334-2500 *Founded/Ownrshp* 1889
Sales 46.4MM *EMP* 600
Accts Seiler Llp Redwood City Ca
SIC 8051 Skilled nursing care facilities; Skilled nursing care facilities
Pr: Daniel Ruth
CFO: Vic Meinke
*CFO: Kevin T Potter
Ofcr: Ellen Berger
Ofcr: Sharon Fried
Ofcr: Ilana Glaun
Assoc Dir: Barbara Newman
Off Mgr: Janet Garcia
CIO: Kathy Burkle
IT Man: David Robertson
Doctor: Yelena Zalkina MD

D-U-N-S 07-091-4155
HEBREW HOME OF GREATER WASHINGTON (MD)
CHARLES EAST LIFE COMMUNITY
6121 Montrose Rd, Rockville, MD 20852-4803
Tel (301) 881-0300 *Founded/Ownrshp* 1910
Sales 70.1MM *EMP* 1,000
Accts Schiavi Wallace & Rowe Pc L
SIC 8051 Skilled nursing care facilities; Skilled nursing care facilities
CEO: Warren R Slavin
*Ch: Marc F Solomon
*Treas: Harry A Harrison
*Sr VP: Pat Carter
*Sr VP: Karen Rosenthal
Sr VP: Terri Tanner-Hill
*VP: Stephanie Baker
VP: Edward Coutren
VP: Beth Delucenay
VP: Barry Eisenberg
*VP: Tom Keefe
*VP: Nicholas Simmonds
*VP: Edward Van Coutren
*VP: Carol Cohen Wolfe
Exec: Gale Deitch

D-U-N-S 07-326-3238
HEBREW HOSPITAL HOME INC
HHH HOME CARE
2100 Bartow Ave Ste 310, Bronx, NY 10475-4614
Tel (718) 678-1500 *Founded/Ownrshp* 1928
Sales 34.0MME *EMP* 525E
SIC 8051 Skilled nursing care facilities; Skilled nursing care facilities
CEO: Mary Frances Barrett
*CFO: Brian Perino
Sr VP: Maura Bordas
VP: Cheryl McAndrew

D-U-N-S 96-632-0926
HEBREW REHAB CENTER
1200 Centre St, Boston, MA 02131-1011
Tel (617) 363-8000 *Founded/Ownrshp* 2011
Sales 115.3MM *EMP* 1
Accts Ernst & Young Us Llp Greenvil
SIC 8742 Hospital & health services consultant; Hospital & health services consultant
Prin: Len Fishman
COO: Denise McQuaide
COO: Mary Moscato
CFO: Jim Hart
CFO: Fred Leathers
VP: Margaret Corbett
VP: Lewis Lipsitz
VP: Katelyn Quynn
VP: Mindy Spitz
VP: Rachel J Whitehouse
Ex Dir: Steve Colwell

D-U-N-S 03-083-2075
HEBREW REHABILITATION CENTER
HEBREW SENIOR LIFE
1200 Centre St, Boston, MA 02131-1011
Tel (617) 363-8000 *Founded/Ownrshp* 1903
Sales 111.7MM *EMP* 1,500E
SIC 8069 Chronic disease hospital; Chronic disease hospital
Pr: Louis J Woolf
Dir Vol: Sara Smolover
Ch Bd: Andrew I Glincher
CFO: James D Hart
CFO: James Hart
CFO: Allan Satterwhite
Treas: Leo R Breitman
Bd of Dir: Howard Cohen
Ofcr: Joan Berns
Ofcr: Marsha Slotnick
VP: Kimberly Brooks
VP: Bill Hughes
VP: Alan Jones
VP: Lewis Lipsitz
VP: Lewis A Lipsitz MD
VP: Joe Martini
VP: John Matulis
VP: Bob Shuman
VP: Mindy Spitz
Dir Lab: Lisa Cashman
Dir Bus: Dana Kern

HEBREW SENIOR LIFE
See HEBREW REHABILITATION CENTER

HEBREW SENIORLISE HM HLTH CARE
See ORCHARD COVE INC

D-U-N-S 07-288-2749
HEBREW UNION COLLEGE-JEWISH INSTITUTE OF RELIGION
3101 Clifton Ave, Cincinnati, OH 45220-2488
Tel (513) 221-1875 *Founded/Ownrshp* 1875
Sales 47.6MM *EMP* 250
SIC 8221

D-U-N-S 03-181-8750
HEBRON BRICK SUPPLY CO (ND)
(*Suby of* DACCO INC) ★
2300 Main Ave, Fargo, ND 58103-1340
Tel (701) 232-0781 *Founded/Ownrshp* 1975, 1986
Sales 24.6MME *EMP* 50
SIC 5032 5074 Brick, except refractory; Building blocks; Masons' materials; Fireplaces, prefabricated
Pr: Rodney Paseka
*VP: Corey Schultz
VP: Gene Thurston
Store Mgr: Dan Berglind
Mktg Dir: Bill Aker

D-U-N-S 03-582-3418
HEBRON SAVINGS BANK (MD)
(*Suby of* HSB BANCORP, INC.)
101 Main St, Hebron, MD 21830
Tel (410) 749-1185 *Founded/Ownrshp* 1910
Sales NA *EMP* 95
SIC 6022 State commercial banks; State commercial banks
Pr: Gregory Johnson
Pr: Jenny Bailey
Pr: John Murray
Pr: Richard Vangelder
CFO: Donna Adams
Bd of Dir: Katherine E Dryden
Ex VP: Donna Defino
Sr VP: Craig McConnell
VP: Amy Hayden
VP: Wanda Henderson
VP: Mark Sewell

D-U-N-S 00-424-3465 IMP
HEC INVESTMENTS INC
4800 Wadsworth Rd, Dayton, OH 45414-4224
Tel (937) 278-9123 *Founded/Ownrshp* 1975, 1978
Sales 24.8MME *EMP* 144
SIC 3291 Abrasive products; Abrasive products
Pr: Lynne Henson
*Ex VP: Shane Miller
VP: Christie Hinshaw
IT Man: Mark Cook
Plnt Mgr: Rich Smith
Prd Mgr: Delma Overman

D-U-N-S 83-613-4163 IMP
HECKETHORN MANUFACTURING CO INC
2005 Forrest St, Dyersburg, TN 38024-3683
Tel (731) 285-3310 *Founded/Ownrshp* 2006
Sales 63.9MME *EMP* 160
SIC 3714 Exhaust systems & parts, motor vehicle; Exhaust systems & parts, motor vehicle
Pr: Jon Walter
V Ch: Danny Whittle
CFO: Doug Grace
*Treas: Bruce Kerr
VP: Garry McArthur
*VP: Tim McKinney
*VP: Philip Morris
*VP: Gary Whittle
MIS Dir: Jeffery Moore
Dir IT: Shannon Hill
Dir IT: Mary Myers

D-U-N-S 18-876-9058
■ **HECKMANN WATER RESOURCES (CVR) INC**
COMPLETE VACUUM AND RENTAL
(*Suby of* NUVERRA ENVIRONMENTAL SOLUTIONS INC) ★
24900 Pitkin Rd Ste 310, Spring, TX 77386-1806
Tel (281) 203-3434 *Founded/Ownrshp* 2010
Sales 51.8MME *EMP* 250
SIC 1389 Removal of condensate gasoline from field (gathering) lines; Removal of condensate gasoline from field (gathering) lines
CEO: Mark Jonhfrud
*VP: Brian R Anderson
*VP: W Christopher Chisholm
*VP: Billy G Clark
*VP: Damian C Georgino
*VP: Sean D Hawkins
*VP: Beth Huddleston
*VP: John Lucey
*VP: Michael Welch

D-U-N-S 87-840-8520
HECKSCHER FOUNDATION
123 E 70th St, New York, NY 10021-5006
Tel (212) 744-0190 *Founded/Ownrshp* 2007
Sales 34.4MM *EMP* 8
SIC 8699 Charitable organization
Pr: Virginia Sloane
Ofcr: Shelby Marzouk
Ofcr: Heather Sutton

D-U-N-S 13-411-9358 IMP
■ **HECLA GREENS CREEK MINING CO**
(*Suby of* HECLA MINING CO) ★
13401 Glacier Hwy, Juneau, AK 99801-8402
Tel (907) 789-8100 *Founded/Ownrshp* 2008
Sales 57.6MME *EMP* 345
SIC 1031 1041 1044 Lead & zinc ores; Gold ores; Silver ores; Lead & zinc ores; Gold ores; Silver ores
Pr: Hartman Scott
*Treas: Sabala James
*VP: McDonald Dean W A
*VP: Radford Lawrence P

D-U-N-S 00-692-7610 IMP
▲ **HECLA MINING CO**
6500 N Mineral Dr Ste 200, Coeur D Alene, ID 83815-9408
Tel (208) 769-4100 *Founded/Ownrshp* 1891
Sales 500.7MM *EMP* 1,312
Accts Bdo Usa Llp Spokane Washing
Tkr Sym HL *Exch* NYS
SIC 1041 1044 1031 1081 Gold ores; Silver ores; Lead & zinc ores; Exploration, metal mining; Gold ores; Silver ores; Lead & zinc ores; Exploration, metal mining
Pr: Phillips S Baker Jr
*Ch Bd: Ted Crumley
CFO: James A Sabala
Sr VP: Lawrence P Radford
VP: Clayr Alexander
VP: Mark Board
VP: Paul Glader
VP: John Jordan
VP: Don Poirier
VP: David C Sienko
VP: George Sturgis
Board of Directors: George R Nethercutt Jr, Terry V Rogers, Charles B Stanley, Anthony P Taylor

D-U-N-S 87-816-8459
HECNY TRANSPORTATION INC
1416 Francisco St, Torrance, CA 90501
Tel (310) 347-3400 *Founded/Ownrshp* 1995
Sales 100.0MM *EMP* 20
SIC 4731 Freight transportation arrangement; Freight transportation arrangement
Pr: Tony Lee

D-U-N-S 01-717-1737
HECO INC (MI)
HATFIELD ELECTRIC INDUSTRIAL
3509 S Burdick St, Kalamazoo, MI 49001-4835
Tel (269) 381-7200 *Founded/Ownrshp* 1959
Sales 50.3MME *EMP* 55
SIC 5063 7694 3699 3677 3621 3596 Motors, electric; Armature rewinding shops; Electric motor repair; Electrical equipment & supplies; Electronic coils, transformers & other inductors; Motors & generators; Scales & balances, except laboratory
Pr: Mark S Hatfield
*Ch Bd: Terrell Lee Hatfield
COO: Tom Baney
*VP: Brad S Hatfield
*VP: Todd A Hatfield
*Prin: Joyce Hatfield
IT Man: John Jones
Manager: Bob Bolhuis

D-U-N-S 80-780-6021
HECTOR INC
8686 Kirby Dr, Houston, TX 77054-2804
Tel (713) 748-3221 *Founded/Ownrshp* 1992
Sales 3.2MME *EMP* 450
SIC 7011 5812 5813 Hotels; Ethnic food restaurants; Bar (drinking places); Hotels; Ethnic food restaurants; Bar (drinking places)
Pr: Robert G Harter

HECTOR TURF
See TESCO SOUTH INC

D-U-N-S 04-747-5835 IMP/EXP
HECTOR TURF INC
1301 Nw 3rd St, Deerfield Beach, FL 33442-1697
Tel (954) 428-1229 *Founded/Ownrshp* 1983
Sales 44.7MME *EMP* 58
SIC 5083 Lawn machinery & equipment; Irrigation equipment; Garden machinery & equipment
Pr: Jim Mantey
*Ex VP: Sandra Mantey
*VP: John Goetz
Mktg Dir: Chris Fordney

D-U-N-S 10-587-1339
HED INC
(*Suby of* HARDEES RESTAURANTS LLC) ★
321 Jeffreys Rd, Rocky Mount, NC 27804-6623
Tel (314) 259-6100 *Founded/Ownrshp* 1996
Sales 20.2MME *EMP* 45
SIC 5046 Restaurant equipment & supplies
CEO: Andy Puzder

D-U-N-S 78-278-8798
HED LAND ENTERPRISES INC
FREEDOM FORD
2828 W Us Highway 50, Pueblo, CO 81008-1627
Tel (719) 545-3673 *Founded/Ownrshp* 1989
Sales 21.4MME *EMP* 100
SIC 5511 Automobiles, new & used; Automobiles, new & used
Pr: Charles Hedrick
*Treas: Ronald Schill
*VP: Reginald Landrum

D-U-N-S 00-886-8721
HEDAHLS INC (ND)
BENCO EQUIPMENT
100 E Broadway Ave, Bismarck, ND 58501-3839
Tel (701) 223-8393 *Founded/Ownrshp* 1916, 1930
Sales 43.7MME *EMP* 165
Accts Eide Bailly Llp Bismarck Nor
SIC 5013 Automotive supplies & parts; Automotive supplies & parts
Pr: Richard Hedahl
*CFO: Harold Larson
*VP: Jane Schrech
IT Man: Pom Barth
Mktg Mgr: Dale Helfrich

D-U-N-S 16-196-2485
HEDBERG AGGREGATES INC
HEDBERG LANDSCAPE SUPPLIES
1205 Nathan Ln N, Minneapolis, MN 55441-5040
Tel (763) 545-4400 *Founded/Ownrshp* 1987
Sales 24.1MME *EMP* 60
SIC 5032 5083 5999 Brick, stone & related material; Aggregate; Stucco; Landscaping equipment; Aquarium supplies
Pr: Stephen Hedberg
*Treas: George Simons
VP Admn: Robert Evidon
Off Mgr: Tammy Bader
Sfty Mgr: Kevin Willenbring

HEDBERG LANDSCAPE SUPPLIES
See HEDBERG AGGREGATES INC

D-U-N-S 04-786-2936
■ **HEDGEMETRIX LLC**
(*Suby of* SS&C TECHNOLOGIES HOLDINGS INC) ★
201 E John Carpenter Fwy # 6, Irving, TX 75062-2707
Tel (469) 522-7901 *Founded/Ownrshp* 2012
Sales 115.8MME *EMP* 705E
SIC 7372 7371 Prepackaged software; Custom computer programming services

D-U-N-S 09-138-8090
HEDGES ASSOCIATES INC
COLDWELL BANKER
5408 Blairs Forest Way Ne, Cedar Rapids, IA 52402-8802
Tel (319) 378-8760 *Founded/Ownrshp* 1950
Sales 235.0MM *EMP* 80
SIC 6531 Real estate agent, residential; Real estate agent, residential
Pr: Carl Esker
*Sec: Carol Esker
Sr VP: Ron Baty
Sls&Mrk Ex: Ben Wheeler
Sales Asso: Akwi Nji
Doctor: Wieslaw Machnowski

D-U-N-S 02-152-9399
HEDGESERV CORP
1271 Avenue Of The Americ, New York, NY 10020-1309
Tel (212) 920-3520 *Founded/Ownrshp* 2008
Sales 27.3MME *EMP* 93E
SIC 7379
Pr: Justin Nadler
*Ch Bd: James P Kelly
V Ch: Robert Aaron
*Pr: Justin Natler
*CEO: Gene Mannella
COO: Keith Waller
CFO: Laurie Fredericks
Mng Dir: Pracheer Bansal
Mng Dir: Kelly Ireland
Mng Dir: Jeff Pannullo
Mng Dir: Scott Rhodes

D-U-N-S 60-364-4006
HEDRICH NORTH AMERICA LLC
18627 Northline Dr Ste G, Cornelius, NC 28031-9344
Tel (704) 895-9723 *Founded/Ownrshp* 1997
Sales 30.0MM *EMP* 7
SIC 5084 Processing & packaging equipment; Processing & packaging equipment
Prin: Wilhelm Hedrich

D-U-N-S 08-166-2769
HEDRICK BROTHERS CONSTRUCTION CO INC
2200 Centre Park West Dr # 100, West Palm Beach, FL 33409-6473
Tel (561) 689-8880 *Founded/Ownrshp* 1979
Sales 65.3MM *EMP* 100
Accts Templeton & Company Llp West
SIC 1542 Commercial & office building, new construction; Commercial & office buildings, renovation & repair; Commercial & office building, new construction; Commercial & office buildings, renovation & repair
Pr: Dale Hedrick
*CFO: Eric Engstrom
*Ex VP: Gene Parker
VP: Donald Jones
Dir Bus: Ryan Bridger

Off Mgr: Christine Corrigan
Off Mgr: Diane Harper
**Genl Couns:* Patrick Painter
Snr PM: Brian French
Snr PM: Robin Lunsford

HEDRICK MEDICAL CENTER
See SAINT LUKES HOSPITAL OF CHILLICOTHE

HEDRICK'S HALLOWELL CHEVROLET
See HALLOWELL CHEVROLET CO INC

HEDSTROM FITNESS
See BALL BOUNCE AND SPORT INC

D-U-N-S 00-306-0340 IMP
HEDWIN CORP (MD)
1600 Roland Heights Ave, Baltimore, MD 21211-1299
Tel (410) 467-8209 *Founded/Ownrshp* 2004
Sales NA *EMP* 300
SIC 3089 Plastic containers, except foam

HEEIA ELEMENTARY SCHOOL
See WINDWARD OAHU SCHOOL DISTRICT

D-U-N-S 03-353-2094 EXP
HEELY-BROWN CO
1280 Chattahoochee Ave Nw, Atlanta, GA 30318-3683
Tel (404) 352-0022 *Founded/Ownrshp* 1947
Sales 103.4MM^E *EMP* 92
SIC 5033 Roofing & siding materials; Roofing & siding materials
CFO: John Comiskey
**Pr:* William H Brown
**Treas:* Mike Spencer
Off Mgr: Greg Crosby
MIS Dir: Jeffrey Karl
Board of Directors: Mary M Brown, Jeffrey Karl

D-U-N-S 01-708-5929
HEEREN BROS INC
RIDGE KING APPLE PACKAGING
1060 Hall St Sw, Grand Rapids, MI 49503-4864
Tel (616) 452-8641 *Founded/Ownrshp* 1962
Sales 72.5MM^E *EMP* 150
Accts Hungerford Aldrin Nichols &
SIC 5148 Fruits, fresh; Vegetables, fresh; Fruits, fresh; Vegetables, fresh
CEO: Hal Roy
**Pr:* James C Heeren
**Treas:* Mark E Heeren
**VP:* Bruce Heeren

D-U-N-S 04-581-1809
HEERY INTERNATIONAL INC
(*Suby of* BALFOUR BEATTY LLC) ★
999 Peachtree St Ne # 300, Atlanta, GA 30309-4426
Tel (404) 881-9880 *Founded/Ownrshp* 1986
Sales 72.9MM^E *EMP* 700
Accts Deloitte & Touche Llp New Yo
SIC 8712 8711 8742 Architectural services; Engineering services; Management consulting services; Architectural services; Engineering services; Management consulting services
Pr: Richard B Driggs
**COO:* Theodore E Sak
Sr VP: Mark Chen
Sr VP: Rich Driggs
Sr VP: John M Furman
Sr VP: James T Isaf
**Sr VP:* Glenn Jardine
Sr VP: Glenn M Jardine
**Sr VP:* Richard N Kahn
Sr VP: Gregory H Peirce
VP: Douglas Graham
VP: Robert Power
Dir Bus: Ray Hollifield

D-U-N-S 00-649-0254
HEETCO INC
520 N 30th St Ste 40, Quincy, IL 62301-3618
Tel (217) 223-2461 *Founded/Ownrshp* 1961
Sales 22.1MM^E *EMP* 80
SIC 5172 Gases, liquefied petroleum (propane); Gases, liquefied petroleum (propane)
Pr: Joe Murfin
**Treas:* Dean Phillips
**VP:* Diane Tieman

HEETER DIRECT
See HEETER PRINTING CO INC

D-U-N-S 00-432-3689
HEETER PRINTING CO INC
HEETER DIRECT
441 Technology Dr, Canonsburg, PA 15317-9583
Tel (724) 746-8900 *Founded/Ownrshp* 1971
Sales 33.2MM^E *EMP* 90
SIC 2752 Commercial printing, lithographic
Pr: Scott Heeter
Pr: Stephen Cousins
**VP:* Timothy Thomas
IT Man: Alfred Russo
VP Opers: Kirk Schlecker
Sales Exec: Brian Mathews
VP Sls: Chris Connors
VP Sls: Brian Reddecliff

D-U-N-S 04-001-9770
HEFFERNAN INSURANCE BROKERS
1350 Carlback Ave, Walnut Creek, CA 94596-7299
Tel (925) 934-8500 *Founded/Ownrshp* 1988
Sales NA *EMP* 430
SIC 6411

D-U-N-S 03-800-8561
HEFFLER RADETICH & SAITTA LLP
1515 Market St Ste 1700, Philadelphia, PA 19102-1926
Tel (215) 972-5045 *Founded/Ownrshp* 1941
Sales 23.0MM^E *EMP* 85
SIC 8721 Certified public accountant
Pt: Edward Radetich
Pt: George Saitta
Genl Mgr: Cathy Miller
Mktg Dir: Colleen Staub
Snr Mgr: Alexander Hoinsky
Snr Mgr: Matthew Pierce

D-U-N-S 00-979-1260
HEFFRON CO INC
4940 Nicholson Ct Ste 100, Kensington, MD 20895-1054
Tel (301) 816-2088 *Founded/Ownrshp* 1946
Sales 41.8MM^E *EMP* 100
SIC 1542 1711 Commercial & office building contractors; Mechanical contractor; Commercial & office building contractors; Mechanical contractor
CEO: George R Dunn Jr
**Ex VP:* Frank Weis
VP: Fred Goldsmith

D-U-N-S 01-027-3936
HEFTER INDUSTRIES INC
55 E Jackson Blvd Ste 600, Chicago, IL 60604-4402
Tel (312) 346-8131 *Founded/Ownrshp* 1959
Sales 24.7MM^E *EMP* 160^E
SIC 8711 8712 8742 Engineering services; Architectural engineering; Construction project management consultant; Engineering services; Architectural engineering; Construction project management consultant
Pr: Harry O Hefter
**CFO:* Tom Kutas

HEFTY SEED CO
See AGRONOMY SCIENCES LLC

D-U-N-S 18-566-0560
HEGEDORNS INC
(*Suby of* BILL GRAYS INC) ★
964 Ridge Rd, Webster, NY 14580-2555
Tel (585) 671-4450 *Founded/Ownrshp* 1952
Sales 25.2MM^E *EMP* 200^E
SIC 5411 Supermarkets, 66,000-99,000 square feet; Supermarkets, 66,000-99,000 square feet
Pr: Bruce Hegedorn
**Treas:* Mary Hegedorn
**VP:* John Gonzalez
Genl Mgr: Noreen Roesser

D-U-N-S 16-786-4979 IMP
HEGELE LOGISTIC LLC
855 N Wood Dale Rd Unit A, Wood Dale, IL 60191-1138
Tel (847) 690-0430 *Founded/Ownrshp* 2004
Sales 23.7MM^E *EMP* 70
Accts Source By Fax On August 7 200
SIC 5047 Medical & hospital equipment
VP: Nicola Rackebrandt
Dir IT: Andrew Pech
Snr Mgr: Daniel Rosu

D-U-N-S 03-198-5054
HEGGEM-LUNDQUIST PAINT CO
1391 S Cherokee St, Denver, CO 80223-3208
Tel (303) 778-1373 *Founded/Ownrshp* 1949
Sales 28.2MM^E *EMP* 250
Accts Jones Ponto & Co Centennial
SIC 1721 1742 Commercial painting; Drywall; Commercial painting; Drywall
CEO: Ron Lundquist
**COO:* Ruthanne Zueger
**Treas:* Beth Lundquist
**VP:* Kirk Lundquist
Exec: Susan Lundquist
Opers Mgr: Milo Fritts

D-U-N-S 02-348-9628
HEHLI-VOLD CORP
VALUE IMPLEMENT
50971 10th St, Osseo, WI 54758-7608
Tel (715) 597-3173 *Founded/Ownrshp* 1992
Sales 31.8MM^E *EMP* 90
SIC 5083 Farm implements; Farm implements
Pr: David L Hehli DDS

D-U-N-S 00-829-4332 IMP
HEHR INTERNATIONAL INC
HEHR INTERNATIONAL POLYMERS
3333 Casitas Ave, Los Angeles, CA 90039-2207
Tel (323) 663-1261 *Founded/Ownrshp* 1945
Sales 167.7MM^E *EMP* 750
SIC 3442 Window & door frames; Window & door frames
CEO: Mary G Utick
Ex VP: Tad Lindquist
Genl Mgr: Beth Utick
Manager: Jeff Christensen
Board of Directors: Warren Jones

HEHR INTERNATIONAL POLYMERS
See HEHR INTERNATIONAL INC

HEI
See HIGHLAND ENGINEERING INC

D-U-N-S 60-866-3688
■ **HEI DIVERSIFIED INC**
(*Suby of* HAWAIIAN ELECTRIC INDUSTRIES INC) ★
900 Richards St, Honolulu, HI 96813-2919
Tel (808) 543-5861 *Founded/Ownrshp* 1988
Sales NA *EMP* 400
SIC 6712 Bank holding companies; Bank holding companies
Pr: Robert F Clarke
Treas: Robert F Mougeot

D-U-N-S 83-035-3962
■ **HEI HOLDING CO ONE INC**
(*Suby of* CAESARS ENTERTAINMENT CORP) ★
1 Caesars Palace Dr, Las Vegas, NV 89109-8969
Tel (702) 407-6000 *Founded/Ownrshp* 2006
Sales 15.4MM^E *EMP* 2,758^E
SIC 7999 Gambling establishment
Prin: Gary W Loveman
Sr VP: Richard Appel
VP: Frank Muscolina
IT Man: Lanette Myers

D-U-N-S 13-333-8256
HEI HOSPITALITY LLC
HEI HOTELS & RESORTS
101 Merritt 7 Corp, Norwalk, CT 06851
Tel (203) 849-8844 *Founded/Ownrshp* 2002
Sales 267.7MM^E *EMP* 3,250
SIC 7011 Hotels & motels; Hotels & motels
CEO: Anthony Rutledge
Ch Bd: Gary Mendell
CEO: Ted Darnall
CEO: Anthony R Rutledge
CFO: Clark W Hanrattie
Ex VP: Tory Waterman
VP: Stephen L Chan
VP: Charles Colletta
VP: W J Maciver
VP: Brian Mayer
VP: Marygrace McCaffrey
VP: Dave Nussear
VP: George Rendell
VP: Brian Russo
VP: Mark Shuda
VP: Dan Walworth

HEI HOTELS & RESORTS
See HEI HOSPITALITY LLC

D-U-N-S 04-539-7270 IMP
▲ **HEI INC**
1495 Steiger Lake Ln, Victoria, MN 55386-9537
Tel (952) 443-2500 *Founded/Ownrshp* 1968
Sales 48.4MM^E *EMP* 250
Tkr Sym HEII *Exch* OTC
SIC 3674 Hybrid integrated circuits; Light sensitive devices; Hybrid integrated circuits; Light sensitive devices
CEO: Mark Thomas
**Pr:* Mark B Thomas
Top Exec: Christopher Bohne
Top Exec: Markus Spreng
VP: Tim Hammers
VP: Micheal Horton
VP Sls: Brian Bender
Sls Mgr: Marc Schnippering
Sls Mgr: David Taj

D-U-N-S 07-853-6785
HEI/GC HOLLYWOOD & VINE LLC
(*Suby of* HEI HOSPITALITY LLC) ★
6250 Hollywood Blvd, Los Angeles, CA 90028-5325
Tel (323) 798-1300 *Founded/Ownrshp* 2007
Sales 67.1MM *EMP* 6
SIC 6798 Real estate investment trusts; Real estate investment trusts
Pr: Anthony Rutledge
CFO: Clark Hanrattie

D-U-N-S 04-411-7455 IMP
■ **HEICO AEROSPACE CORP**
(*Suby of* HEICO AEROSPACE HOLDINGS CORP) ★
3000 Taft St, Hollywood, FL 33021-4441
Tel (954) 987-6101 *Founded/Ownrshp* 1993
Sales 141.5MM^E *EMP* 311
SIC 3724 3812 Aircraft engines & engine parts; Search & navigation equipment; Aircraft engines & engine parts; Search & navigation equipment
Pr: Luis J Morell
**CEO:* Eric A Mendelson
**Treas:* Thomas S Irwin
**Treas:* Carlos L Macau
Sr VP: Mike Siegel
VP: Marc Alter
VP: Vladimir Cervera
Dir Lab: Jay Bankemper

D-U-N-S 02-795-3590 IMP
■ **HEICO AEROSPACE HOLDINGS CORP**
(*Suby of* HEICO CORP) ★
3000 Taft St, Hollywood, FL 33021-4441
Tel (954) 987-6101 *Founded/Ownrshp* 1997
Sales 300.8MM^E *EMP* 1,011
SIC 3724 Aircraft engines & engine parts; Aircraft engines & engine parts
Ch Bd: Laurans Mendelson
**CEO:* Eric Mendelson
**Treas:* Thomas S Irwin
**Ex VP:* James R Reum
VP: Pat Markham

D-U-N-S 14-297-9728
■ **HEICO AEROSPACE PARTS CORP**
FLIGHT SPECIALTIES COMPONENTS
(*Suby of* HEICO AEROSPACE CORP) ★
375 Alpha Park, Highland Heights, OH 44143-2237
Tel (954) 987-6101 *Founded/Ownrshp* 2001
Sales 23.1MM^E *EMP* 300
SIC 3728 Aircraft parts & equipment
Pr: Luis J Morell
**Treas:* Carlos L Macau
Genl Mgr: Jeff Williams

HEICO COMPANY
See LEADER TECH INC

D-U-N-S 78-653-3117 IMP
HEICO COMPANIES L L C
5600 Three 1st Natl Plz St, Chicago, IL 60602
Tel (312) 419-8220 *Founded/Ownrshp* 1988
Sales 1.6MMM^E *EMP* 2,300
SIC 3315 3589 3448 3531 1731 3663 Wire, ferrous/iron; Wire products, ferrous/iron: made in wiredrawing plants; Sewage & water treatment equipment; Sewer cleaning equipment, power; Shredders, industrial & commercial; Prefabricated metal buildings; Prefabricated metal buildings; Construction machinery; Cranes; Logging equipment; Cranes, locomotive; Electrical work; Radio & television switching equipment; Wire, ferrous/iron; Wire products, ferrous/iron: made in wiredrawing plants; Sewage & water treatment equipment; Sewer cleaning equipment, power; Shredders, industrial & commercial; Prefabricated metal buildings; Prefabricated metal buildings; Construction machinery; Cranes; Logging equipment; Cranes, locomotive; Electrical work; Radio & television switching equipment
Ch: Emily Heisley Stoeckel
**Pr:* E A Roskovensky
CFO: Terence R Rogers
**CFO:* L G Wolski

D-U-N-S 80-957-0781 IMP
▲ **HEICO CORP**
3000 Taft St, Hollywood, FL 33021-4441
Tel (954) 987-4000 *Founded/Ownrshp* 1993
Sales 1.1MMM *EMP* 3,500^E
Accts Deloitte & Touche Llp Miami
Tkr Sym HEI *Exch* NYS
SIC 3724 3728 7699 Aircraft engines & engine parts; Aircraft training equipment; Aircraft & heavy equipment repair services; Aircraft flight instrument repair; Aircraft engines & engine parts; Aircraft training equipment; Aircraft & heavy equipment repair services; Aircraft flight instrument repair
CEO: Laurans A Mendelson
Pr: Eric A Mendelson
CFO: Carlos L Macau Jr
Sr Ex VP: Thomas S Irwin
Sr VP: Tom Moorefield
VP: Adam Bentkover
VP: Mike Garcia
VP: William Harlow
VP: Pat Markham
VP: Val Shelley
QA Dir: Tamyka Campbell
Board of Directors: Thomas M Culligan, Adolfo Henriques, Samuel L Higginbottom, Mark H Hildebrandt, Wolfgang Mayrhuber, Julie Neitzel, Alan Schriesheim, Frank J Schwitter

D-U-N-S 07-104-1797
■ **HEICO ELECTRONIC TECHNOLOGIES CORP**
(*Suby of* HEICO CORP) ★
3000 Taft St, Hollywood, FL 33021-4441
Tel (954) 987-6101 *Founded/Ownrshp* 1996
Sales 113.6MM^E *EMP* 1,340
SIC 3728 Aircraft parts & equipment; Aircraft parts & equipment
Pr: Laurans Mendelson
**Prin:* Thomas Irwin

D-U-N-S 01-396-7015
■ **HEICO FLIGHT SUPPORT CORP**
(*Suby of* HEICO CORP) ★
3000 Taft St, Hollywood, FL 33021-4441
Tel (954) 987-4000 *Founded/Ownrshp* 2012
Sales 30.7MM^E *EMP* 25^E
SIC 4581 Aircraft maintenance & repair services
Pr: Eric Mendelson
**Treas:* Carlos Macau
Prd Mgr: Scott Carrie

D-U-N-S 00-514-6592
HEICO HOLDING INC
27501 Bella Vista Pkwy, Warrenville, IL 60555-1609
Tel (630) 353-5000 *Founded/Ownrshp* 2000
Sales 1.3MMM^E *EMP* 6,800
SIC 6719 Investment holding companies, except banks; Investment holding companies, except banks
Pr: Michael E Heisley
**Ex VP:* E A Roskovensky
Board of Directors: Michael E Heisley Jr, Emily Heisley Stoeckel

D-U-N-S 06-247-8268 IMP
HEICO OHMITE LLC
OHMITE MANUFACTURING
(*Suby of* HEICO COMPANIES L L C) ★
27501 Bella Vista Pkwy, Warrenville, IL 60555-1609
Tel (847) 258-0300 *Founded/Ownrshp* 1988
Sales 74.1MM^E *EMP* 423
SIC 3625 5065 Resistors & resistor units; Rheostats; Industrial electrical relays & switches; Resistors, electronic; Electronic parts; Resistors & resistor units; Rheostats; Industrial electrical relays & switches; Resistors, electronic; Electronic parts
Pr: Greg Pace

HEICO PARTS GROUP
See JET AVION CORP

HEICO REPAIR GROUP
See NORTHWINGS ACCESSORIES CORP

D-U-N-S 07-846-7629
HEIDE & COOK LLC
HAWAII HVAC
1714 Kanakanui St, Honolulu, HI 96819-3299
Tel (808) 841-6161 *Founded/Ownrshp* 2012
Sales 20.4MM^E *EMP* 2
SIC 1711 Plumbing, heating, air-conditioning contractors; Plumbing, heating, air-conditioning contractors
Pr: Earle Matsuda
**Pr:* Gabe Kompkoff
**CFO:* Rebecca Myren
**VP:* Angela Astle
VP: Patrick Miura

HEIDEBREICHT CHEVROLET
See HEIDEBREICHT INC

D-U-N-S 01-670-4843
HEIDEBREICHT INC
HEIDEBREICHT CHEVROLET
64200 Van Dyke Rd, Washington, MI 48095-2577
Tel (586) 752-5900 *Founded/Ownrshp* 1971
Sales 26.2MM^E *EMP* 53
SIC 5511 Automobiles, new & used; Automobiles, new & used
Pr: William Heidebreicht
**Sec:* Kurt W Heidebreicht
**Genl Mgr:* John Boyce
Store Mgr: Matt Walmfley
Sls Mgr: Lara Couwlier
Sls Mgr: Ashley Kiper
Sls Mgr: John Sabol
Sls Mgr: Eric Smith

D-U-N-S 80-472-7568 IMP/EXP
HEIDELBERG AMERICAS INC
(*Suby of* HEIDELBERGER DRUCKMASCHINEN AG)
1000 Gutenberg Dr Nw, Kennesaw, GA 30144-7028
Tel (770) 419-6500 *Founded/Ownrshp* 1983
Sales 434.6MM^E *EMP* 3,000
SIC 5084 Printing trades machinery, equipment & supplies; Printing trades machinery, equipment & supplies
Pr: James P Dunn

HEIDELBERG DISTRIBUTING DIV
See DAYTON HEIDELBERG DISTRIBUTING CO

D-U-N-S 95-927-1537 IMP
■ HEIDELBERG ENGINEERING INC
(*Suby of* HEIDELBERG ENGINEERING GMBH)
1808 Aston Ave Ste 130, Carlsbad, CA 92008-7367
Tel (760) 598-3770 *Founded/Ownrshp* 1994
Sales 35.9MM^E *EMP* 72
SIC 5047 Diagnostic equipment, medical
VP: Cheryl Shramm
Exec: Tom Rouse
IT Man: Regina Green
Sls Dir: Armond Dantino

D-U-N-S 07-777-3497
HEIDELBERG UNIVERSITY (OH)
HEIDELBERG UNIVERSITY
310 E Market St, Tiffin, OH 44883-2434
Tel (419) 448-2000 *Founded/Ownrshp* 1850
Sales 51.7MM *EMP* 226
Accts Bkd Llp Fort Wayne In
SIC 8221 College, except junior; College, except junior
Pr: Robert Huntington
Treas: Ralph Talmage
Ofcr: Ronda Winkler
VP: Doug Kellar
VP: James Troha
Dir IT: Nancy King
Mktg Mgr: Daniel Higgins
Snr Mgr: Erica Figley

D-U-N-S 05-317-1617 IMP/EXP
HEIDELBERG USA INC (DE)
(*Suby of* HEIDELBERG AMERICAS INC) ★
1000 Gutenberg Dr Nw, Kennesaw, GA 30144-7028
Tel (770) 419-6500 *Founded/Ownrshp* 1970, 1993
Sales 408.4MM^E *EMP* 1,000
SIC 5084 3555 Printing trades machinery, equipment & supplies; Printing trades machinery; Printing trades machinery, equipment & supplies; Printing trades machinery
Pr: Harald Weimer
CFO: Thomas Topp
Sr VP: Ulrich Koehler
Sr VP: Susan P Nofi
VP: Brian Chapin
VP: Ralph Pasquariello
Mng Dir: Andy V Jensen
Genl Mgr: Guenther Keppler
Genl Mgr: Jason Ong
Dir IT: Marc Herbig
Mktg Mgr: Jarmil Kralicek

D-U-N-S 02-515-4527
HEIDENHAIN CORP
(*Suby of* HEIDENHAIN HOLDING INC) ★
333 E State Pkwy, Schaumburg, IL 60173-5337
Tel (847) 490-1191 *Founded/Ownrshp* 1991
Sales 40.0MM^E *EMP* 75
SIC 5084 3825 Measuring & testing equipment, electrical; Instruments to measure electricity; Measuring & testing equipment, electrical; Instruments to measure electricity
Pr: Rick J Korte
Ch Bd: Ludwig Wagatha
Exec: Linda Castro
Rgnl Mgr: Scott Warner
Area Mgr: Randy Booth
Area Mgr: Robert Gee
Dir IT: Roscoe Dechalus
Dir IT: Mark Shafer
Sftwr Eng: Sean Dorval
Opers Mgr: Sharon Bahumes
Natl Sales: John Thormodsgard

D-U-N-S 78-280-8091 IMP
HEIDENHAIN HOLDING INC
(*Suby of* DR. JOHANNES HEIDENHAIN GESELLSCHAFT MIT BESCHRANKTER HAFTUNG)
333 E State Pkwy, Schaumburg, IL 60173-5337
Tel (716) 661-1700 *Founded/Ownrshp* 1889
Sales 66.0MM^E *EMP* 470
SIC 3545 5084 Machine tool accessories; Measuring & testing equipment, electrical; Machine tool accessories; Measuring & testing equipment, electrical
Ch Bd: Rainer Burkhard

D-U-N-S 01-793-9083
HEIDMAN INC
MCDONALD'S
500 Grant St, Akron, OH 44311-1121
Tel (330) 535-8400 *Founded/Ownrshp* 1959
Sales 29.9MM^E *EMP* 1,000
SIC 5812 Fast-food restaurant, chain; Fast-food restaurant, chain
Pr: John Blickle
**Prin:* Charles Booth

D-U-N-S 83-026-3427
HEIDMAR INC
20 Glover Ave Ste 14, Norwalk, CT 06850-1236
Tel (203) 662-2600 *Founded/Ownrshp* 2000
Sales 111.2MM^E *EMP* 154^E
SIC 1389 Oil field services
CEO: Hans Van Der Zijde
**Pr:* Olaf Halvorssen
**COO:* Ben Ognibene
**CFO:* Kathleen Haines
**Treas:* Charles N Tammara
**Ex VP:* Per Heilmann
Mng Dir: Jim Hurley
Mng Dir: Tasos Pantelias
Dir IT: Johan Wenman

D-U-N-S 00-552-5159
▲ HEIDRICK & STRUGGLES INTERNATIONAL INC (DE)
233 S Wacker Dr Ste 4900, Chicago, IL 60606-6372
Tel (312) 496-1200 *Founded/Ownrshp* 1953
Sales 513.2MM *EMP* 1,483^E
Accts Kpmg Llp Chicago Illinois
Tkr Sym HSII *Exch* NGS
SIC 7361 Employment agencies; Executive placement; Employment agencies; Executive placement
Pr: Tracy R Wolstencroft
Pt: Lori Perella
Pt: Chris Pierce-Cooke
Pt: Guy Sava
Pt: Bill Trau
Mng Pt: Robbie Knight
Ch Bd: Richard I Beattie
V Ch: Nathaniel Sutton
CEO: Anne Lim O'Brien
COO: Anna Pearson
CFO: Richard W Pehlke
Ofcr: Richard W Greene
Ex VP: Stephen W Beard
Ex VP: Colin Price
Board of Directors: Lyle Logan

HEIDTMAN STEEL PRODUCTS
See CENTAUR INC

D-U-N-S 19-097-2260
HEIDTMAN STEEL PRODUCTS
2401 Front St, Toledo, OH 43605-1199
Tel (419) 691-4646 *Founded/Ownrshp* 1954
Sales 53.4MM^E *EMP* 800
SIC 5051 Iron & steel (ferrous) products
Pr: Tim Berra

D-U-N-S 00-292-9610 IMP
HEIDTMAN STEEL PRODUCTS INC (OH)
(*Suby of* CENTAUR INC) ★
2401 Front St, Toledo, OH 43605-1199
Tel (419) 691-4646 *Founded/Ownrshp* 1962, 1984
Sales 180.5MM^E *EMP* 1,000
SIC 3316 3312 Strip steel, cold-rolled: from purchased hot-rolled; Sheet or strip, steel, hot-rolled; Strip steel, cold-rolled: from purchased hot-rolled; Sheet or strip, steel, hot-rolled
Ch Bd: John C Bates
Pr: Tim Berra
CFO: Mark Ridenour
Prin: F Wm Heidtman
Prin: Margery Heidtman
MIS Dir: Jim Hill

HEIFER INTERNATIONAL
See HEIFER PROJECT INTERNATIONAL INC

D-U-N-S 07-739-9780
HEIFER PROJECT INTERNATIONAL INC
HEIFER INTERNATIONAL
1 World Ave, Little Rock, AR 72202-3825
Tel (501) 907-2600 *Founded/Ownrshp* 1989
Sales 125.2MM *EMP* 304
Accts Deloitte & Touche Llp Little
SIC 8399 6732 9532 Social change association; Trusts: educational, religious, etc.; Community & rural development; Social change association; Trusts: educational, religious, etc.; Community & rural development
CEO: Pierre Ferrari
**COO:* Steve Denne
**CFO:* Robert Bob Bloom
CFO: Ken Harrison
CFO: Mickie Marter
Ofcr: Rebecca Alderfer
Ofcr: Lárissa Barry
Ofcr: Dilip Bhandari
Ofcr: Elizabeth Elango
Ofcr: Maria Schrader
VP: Sahr Lebbie
VP: Christopher Lu
Board of Directors: Charles Stewart

D-U-N-S 11-457-1862
HEIGHTS FINANCE CORP
7707 N Knoxville Ave # 201, Peoria, IL 61614-2014
Tel (309) 693-6688 *Founded/Ownrshp* 1992
Sales NA *EMP* 470
SIC 6141 6163 Consumer finance companies; Loan brokers; Consumer finance companies; Loan brokers
Pr: Timothy L Stanley
Pr: Paul Worachek
**Treas:* Pamela Johnson
**Treas:* Delores Metzger
**Sr VP:* David W Harrison
Brnch Mgr: Helen Goodman
Brnch Mgr: Carl Gretenhardt
Brnch Mgr: Dean Manley
Brnch Mgr: Tyler Swanson
Brnch Mgr: Todd Vain
Dir IT: John Stewart

D-U-N-S 82-597-8281 IMP
HEIK HOLDING CO INC
2608 S Hume Ave, Marshfield, WI 54449-5551
Tel (715) 387-3414 *Founded/Ownrshp* 1993
Sales 28.3MM^E *EMP* 205
Accts Wipfli Ullrich Bertelson Mars
SIC 3523 Farm machinery & equipment; Farm machinery & equipment
Pr: Lauri Heikenen
**VP:* Chris Heikenen
**VP:* Gary Heikenen
Board of Directors: Fay Heinkenen

D-U-N-S 01-681-9427
HEIL BUILDERS INC
100
1200 E Patapsco Ave, Baltimore, MD 21225-2233
Tel (410) 355-1014 *Founded/Ownrshp* 1986
Sales 22.0MM *EMP* 85
SIC 1751 3448 2439 2452 2436 Framing contractor; Trusses & framing: prefabricated metal; Trusses, wooden roof; Panels & sections, prefabricated, wood; Panels, softwood plywood; Framing contractor; Trusses & framing: prefabricated metal; Trusses, wooden roof; Panels & sections, prefabricated, wood; Panels, softwood plywood
CEO: Edwin Heil
**Pr:* Scott Stevens
**VP:* Richard Hughes
**VP:* Robert Strenge
IT Man: Matt Carson

D-U-N-S 00-609-7398 IMP
■ HEIL CO
HEIL ENVIRONMENTAL
(*Suby of* DOVER ENGINEERED SYSTEMS INC) ★
2030 Hamilton Place Blvd # 200, Chattanooga, TN 37421-6040
Tel (423) 899-9100 *Founded/Ownrshp* 1901, 2011
Sales 478.1MM^E *EMP* 2,000
SIC 3713 3715 Dump truck bodies; Trailer bodies; Dump truck bodies; Trailer bodies
Pr: Pat Carroll
**CFO:* Darren Bird
VP: Ken Chandler
VP: Jim McKee
VP: Yassir Shanghai
**VP:* Tom Vatter
VP: Alex Waddell
Dir IT: Sean Neimarlija
Tech Mgr: David McGee
Plnt Mgr: John Kalson
Ql Cn Mgr: Randell Morris

HEIL ENVIRONMENTAL
See HEIL CO

HEIL OF TEXAS
See TEXAN WASTE EQUIPMENT INC

HEIL TRAILER INTERNATIONAL CO
See HEIL TRAILER INTERNATIONAL LLC

D-U-N-S 78-672-8092 IMP/EXP
HEIL TRAILER INTERNATIONAL LLC
HEIL TRAILER INTERNATIONAL CO
(*Suby of* AMERICAN INDUSTRIAL PARTNERS CAPITAL FUND IV (PARALLEL) LP) ★
1850 Executive Park Nw, Cleveland, TN 37312-2700
Tel (800) 400-6913 *Founded/Ownrshp* 2011
Sales 355.8MM^E *EMP* 1,000^E
SIC 3715 Truck trailers; Truck trailers
CEO: Randall Swift
**CFO:* Tim Davis
CFO: Ricardo Iglesias
VP: Saowanee Sajjaboontawee
**VP:* Jim Sanko
Prgrm Mgr: Kevin Tumlin
IT Man: Jessica Mahan
Sales Exec: Zack Coley
Sls&Mrk Ex: Amanda Boren
S&M/VP: Greg Heyer
Manager: Lester Evans

HEILDELBERG UNIVERSITY
See HEIDELBERG UNIVERSITY

D-U-N-S 06-661-2698 IMP
HEILIND ELECTRONICS INC
MAVERICK ELECTRONICS
58 Jonspin Rd, Wilmington, MA 01887-1068
Tel (978) 658-7000 *Founded/Ownrshp* 1974
Sales 787.7MM^E *EMP* 705
SIC 5065 3679 5063 Electronic parts & equipment; Harness assemblies for electronic use: wire or cable; Hanging & fastening devices, electrical; Electronic parts & equipment; Harness assemblies for electronic use: wire or cable; Hanging & fastening devices, electrical
CEO: Robert W Clapp
Rgnl Mgr: Brandon Clountz
Brnch Mgr: Bret Schwartzkopf
Sales Exec: Sharon Benjamin
Sales Asso: Erin Sanders
Sales Asso: Doreen Valdez

D-U-N-S 07-871-1754 IMP
HEILINDMIL - AERO LLC
INTERSTATE CNNCTING COMPONENTS
(*Suby of* HEILIND ELECTRONICS INC) ★
120 Mount Holly Byp, Lumberton, NJ 08048
Tel (856) 722-5535 *Founded/Ownrshp* 2012
Sales 38.3MM^E *EMP* 130
SIC 3678 Electronic connectors
Pr: Robert Clapp
Exec: Kellie Dibiase
Genl Mgr: Michael Wetzel
Off Mgr: Lauren Dorn
Off Admin: Tierney Thomas
QA Dir: Jeff Retallick
Dir IT: Brian King
Dir IT: Jason Rosario
IT Man: Allen King
VP Opers: Paul Ahlers
Prd Mgr: Roger Barnes

HEIM COMPANY
See EDWIN L HEIM CO

D-U-N-S 08-876-5177
HEIMAN MILLER INC
10509 Prof Cir Ste 100, Reno, NV 89521
Tel (303) 572-7075 *Founded/Ownrshp* 2013
Sales 45.8MM^E *EMP* 310
SIC 8742

HEIMARK DISTRIBUTING
See TRIANGLE DISTRIBUTING CO

D-U-N-S 83-266-3335
HEIMES CORP
9144 S 147th St, Omaha, NE 68138-3671
Tel (402) 894-1000 *Founded/Ownrshp* 1998
Sales 23.3MM^E *EMP* 90
SIC 1542 Commercial & office building, new construction; Commercial & office building, new construction
Pr: Raymond G Heimes
**Pr:* Thomas F Heimes
Sales Exec: Jeff Jenkins
VP Sls: Brenda Koster

D-U-N-S 02-169-7024
HEIN + ASSOCIATES LLP
1999 Broadway Ste 4000, Denver, CO 80202-5703
Tel (303) 298-9600 *Founded/Ownrshp* 1977
Sales 23.9MM^E *EMP* 96
SIC 8721 Accounting services, except auditing
Mng Pt: Clarence D Hein
Pt: James Brendel
Pt: Dennis K Brown
Pt: Vance Bryson
Pt: Greg A Dickey
Pt: Richard Domercq
Pt: Audra Evans
Pt: Mira J Fine
Pt: Rob Friedman
Pt: Kenneth Grace
Pt: Wayne R Gray
Pt: Brian Mandell-Rice
Pt: John Nobel
Pt: Allan Richards
Pt: John K Steinbeck
Pt: Keith Tunnell
Pt: Larry Unruh
Pt: William L Yeates
CFO: Tom McEntire
CFO: James Winton
Ofcr: Joan Solano

D-U-N-S 02-339-3721
HEIN ELECTRIC SUPPLY CO
12745 W Townsend St, Brookfield, WI 53005-3153
Tel (262) 790-8400 *Founded/Ownrshp* 1946
Sales 70.9MM^E *EMP* 60
SIC 5063 Electrical supplies
Ch: Sidney Kohlenberg
**Pr:* Ronald Kohlenberg
**CFO:* Bob Bartzen
**VP:* Chris Storning
Brnch Mgr: Fred Grabow
Opers Mgr: Kevin Calverley
Mktg Mgr: Laura Longston

D-U-N-S 18-713-1990 IMP/EXP
HEINAMAN CONTRACT GLAZING INC
26981 Vista Ter Ste E, Lake Forest, CA 92630-8127
Tel (949) 525-4555 *Founded/Ownrshp* 1988
Sales 26.1MM^E *EMP* 100
SIC 1799 1793 Window treatment installation; Glass & glazing work
Pr: John L Heinaman
**Treas:* Gaye Howhannesian
**Ex VP:* Angela Heinaman
**VP:* Mark Heinaman

D-U-N-S 00-892-1215 IMP
HEINEKEN USA INC
(*Suby of* HEINEKEN BROUWERIJEN B.V.)
360 Hamilton Ave Ste 1103, White Plains, NY 10601-1882
Tel (914) 681-4100 *Founded/Ownrshp* 1991
Sales 282.7MM^E *EMP* 400
SIC 5181 Beer & other fermented malt liquors; Beer & other fermented malt liquors
Ch Bd: Rudolf Gs Van Den Brink
**Pr:* Frans Van Der Minne
**CFO:* Gabriele Giudici
**CFO:* Dan Sullivan
Chf Mktg O: Lesya Lysyj
Ofcr: Raymond Faust
**Sr VP:* Scott Blazek
**Sr VP:* Dirk De Vos
VP: Jeffrey Colbert
VP: Peter Hall
**VP:* Julie Kinch
**VP:* Amy Nenner
**VP:* T Daniel Tearno
**VP:* Daniel Walsh
Comm Dir: Tamara M Moore
Dir Bus: Eric Mullen

D-U-N-S 07-182-2633
HEINENS FINE FOODS
4540 Richmond Rd, Cleveland, OH 44128-5757
Tel (216) 475-2300 *Founded/Ownrshp* 2011
Sales 24.9MM^E *EMP* 96^E
SIC 5411 Supermarkets
CFO: Dan Musio

D-U-N-S 00-699-8611 IMP
HEINENS INC
4540 Richmond Rd, Warrensville Heights, OH 44128-5757
Tel (216) 475-2300 *Founded/Ownrshp* 1929
Sales 335.0MM^E *EMP* 2,350
Accts Hill & Stonestreet
SIC 5411 Supermarkets, hypermarket; Supermarkets, hypermarket
CEO: J Jeffrey Heinen
**Pr:* Thomas J Heinen
**CFO:* Maryanne Correnti
Dir Risk M: Jennifer Artino
Store Dir: Tom Rudar
Genl Mgr: Sharri Pieczynski
Tech Mgr: Patrick Fratantonio

D-U-N-S 04-409-8622
HEINKE TECHNOLOGY INC
HTI PLASTICS
(*Suby of* IT WATCHDOGS) ★
5120 Nw 38th St, Lincoln, NE 68524-1822
Tel (402) 470-2600 *Founded/Ownrshp* 1995
Sales 24.0MM^E *EMP* 130
SIC 3089 Plastic processing; Plastic processing
Pr: Sam Featherstone
**Pr:* Paul Almburg
CFO: Shelly Carpenter
VP: Lari Rabe
IT Man: Will Kerns
QC Dir: Barb Schmidt
Opers Mgr: Scott Scheffert
Prd Mgr: Nate Whitmore
Ql Cn Mgr: Rob White
Natl Sales: Jodi Dobbs
Snr Mgr: Kyle Heerspink

D-U-N-S 02-995-0458
HEINRICH BAUER VERLAG BETEILIGUNGS GMBH
WOMAN'S WORLD MAGAZINE
(*Suby of* HEINRICH BAUER VERLAG BETEILIGUNGS GMBH)
270 Sylvan Ave Ste 210, Englewood Cliffs, NJ 07632-2523
Tel (201) 569-0006 *Founded/Ownrshp* 2006
Sales 36.5MM^E *EMP* 300^E
SIC 2721 Magazines: publishing only, not printed on site; Magazines: publishing only, not printed on site
Pr: Hubert Boehle
Sec: Richard Teehan
Ex VP: Sebastian Raatz
Sr VP: Richard Buchert
Sr VP: Dennis Cohen
Sr VP: Richard Parker

D-U-N-S 01-283-9700
HEINRICH CHEVROLET CORP (NY)
5775 S Transit Rd, Lockport, NY 14094-5811
Tel (716) 434-6681 *Founded/Ownrshp* 1965
Sales 34.4MM^E *EMP* 90

SIC 5511 Automobiles, new & used; Pickups, new & used; Automobiles, new & used; Pickups, new & used
Pr: David A Heinrich
**VP:* Charles Heinrich
Sls Mgr: Brian Hy

D-U-N-S 00-625-0617
HEINRICH ENVELOPE CORP (MN)
(*Suby of* COMMERCIAL PRINT GROUP INC) ★
925 Zane Ave N, Minneapolis, MN 55422-4692
Tel (763) 544-3571 *Founded/Ownrshp* 1898
Sales 30.9MM^E *EMP* 85
SIC 2677 Envelopes
CEO: William Cahill
Mng Dir: Kathy Rock
**Genl Mgr:* Wesley Clerc

D-U-N-S 08-967-2463
HEINZ ENDOWMENTS (PA)
625 Liberty Ave Fl 30, Pittsburgh, PA 15222-3110
Tel (412) 281-5777 *Founded/Ownrshp* 1995
Sales 120.5MM *EMP* 32
SIC 6732 Charitable trust management; Educational trust management
Pr: Grant Oliphant
**CFO:* Jack Kim
Ofcr: Megan Andros
Ofcr: Melanie R Brown
Ofcr: Ellen Dorsey
Ofcr: Carmen Lee
Ofcr: Kerry Spindler
Ofcr: Suzanne Walsh
Ofcr: Stephanie Wilson
Ex VP: Mallory Walker
Dir Surg: John M Ellis

D-U-N-S 04-526-3092 EXP
■ **HEINZ FROZEN FOOD CO**
(*Suby of* HEINZ KRAFT FOODS CO) ★
357 6th Ave, Pittsburgh, PA 15222-2539
Tel (412) 237-5700 *Founded/Ownrshp* 1993
Sales 228.8MM^E *EMP* 2,602
SIC 2038 2037 8741 Frozen specialties; Potato products, quick frozen & cold pack; Vegetables, quick frozen & cold pack, excl. potato products; Management services; Frozen specialties; Potato products, quick frozen & cold pack; Vegetables, quick frozen & cold pack, excl. potato products; Management services
CEO: William R Johnson
**Pr:* Neil Harrison
CFO: Art Winkleblack
**Treas:* John C Crowe
Chf Mktg O: Brian Hansberry
VP: Brendan Foley
**VP:* Charles C White
Plnt Mgr: Jim Kirton

HEINZ FROZEN FOODS
See HJ HEINZ CO LP

D-U-N-S 07-867-6229
HEINZ INC
370 W Anchor Dr Ste 210, Dakota Dunes, SD 57049-5153
Tel (605) 232-6031 *Founded/Ownrshp* 2010
Sales 22.0MM^E *EMP* 127
SIC 5541 Filling stations, gasoline
CEO: Tom Heinz

D-U-N-S 60-977-6877
HEINZ JOHN INSTITUTE OF REHABILITATION MEDICINE
ALLIED SVCS JOHN HEINZ INST
150 Mundy St Ste 1, Wilkes Barre, PA 18702-6830
Tel (570) 826-3800 *Founded/Ownrshp* 1989
Sales 13.0MM^E *EMP* 495
Accts Parente Randolph Llc Wilkes-
SIC 8361 8093 Rehabilitation center, residential: health care incidental; Rehabilitation center, outpatient treatment; Rehabilitation center, residential: health care incidental; Rehabilitation center, outpatient treatment
Pr: James Brady
CFO: Michael Avvinato
**Treas:* Michael J Aronica
VP: Thomas E De Pugh
**VP:* Thomas E Pugh
Phys Thrpy: Michelle Babcock
Board of Directors: Alan Graf, Marcie Jones, Ralph Lomma, Andrew McGowan

D-U-N-S 07-932-0220
■ **HEINZ KRAFT CO**
(*Suby of* BERKSHIRE HATHAWAY INC) ★
1 Ppg Pl, Pittsburgh, PA 15222-5415
Tel (412) 456-5700 *Founded/Ownrshp* 2015
Sales 26.3MMM^E *EMP* 24,500^E
Tkr Sym KHC *Exch* NGS
SIC 2033 2038 2032 2098 Tomato sauce: packaged in cans, jars, etc.; Frozen specialties; Baby foods, including meats: packaged in cans, jars, etc.; Bean sprouts: packaged in cans, jars, etc.; Soups, except seafood: packaged in cans, jars, etc.; Macaroni & spaghetti
CEO: Bernardo Hees
**Ch Bd:* Alexandre Behring
COO: Georges El-Zoghbi
CFO: Paulo Basilio
**V Ch Bd:* John T Cahill
Ex VP: Eduardo Pelleissone
Sr VP: Nina Barton
Sr VP: James Savina
VP: Christopher R Skinger
Board of Directors: Gregory Abel, Warren E Buffett, Tracy Britt Cool, L Kevin Cox, Jeanne P Jackson, Jorge Paulo Lemann, Mackey J McDonald, John C Pope, Marcel Herrmann Telles

D-U-N-S 00-431-8846 IMP/EXP
■ **HEINZ KRAFT FOODS CO**
(*Suby of* HEINZ KRAFT CO) ★
1 Ppg Pl Ste 3200, Pittsburgh, PA 15222-5415
Tel (412) 456-5700 *Founded/Ownrshp* 2013
Sales 11.5MMM *EMP* 24,000
SIC 2033 2038 2032 2098 Tomato sauce: packaged in cans, jars, etc.; Frozen specialties; Baby foods, including meats: packaged in cans, jars, etc.; Bean sprouts: packaged in cans, jars, etc.; Soups, except seafood: packaged in cans, jars, etc.; Macaroni & spaghetti; Tomato sauce: packaged in cans, jars, etc.; Frozen specialties; Baby foods, including meats: packaged in cans, jars, etc.; Bean sprouts: packaged in cans, jars, etc.; Soups, except seafood: packaged in cans, jars, etc.; Macaroni & spaghetti
CEO: Bernardo Hees
Pr: Brendan Foley
Pr: Matt Hill
Pr: Emin Mammadov
Pr: Jane S Miller
Pr: Michael D Milone
Pr: Dave Moran
Pr: Scott Ohara
COO: Mike Nolan
CFO: Paulo Basilio
CFO: Arthur Winkelblack
Ofcr: Stephen S Clark
Ofcr: Edward Smyth
Ex VP: Theodore N Bobby
Ex VP: Joe Jiminez
Ex VP: David Moran
Ex VP: Eduardo Pelleissone
Ex VP: Malcolm Ritchie
Ex VP: Stacie Stratthaus
Ex VP: Dave Woodward
Sr VP: Edward J McMenamin
Board of Directors: Thomas J Usher, Charles E Bunch, Michael F Weinstein, Leonard S Coleman Jr, John G Drosdick, Edith E Holiday, Candace Kendle, Dean R O'Hare, Nelson Peltz, Dennis H Reilley, Lynn C Swann

HEINZ NORTH AMERICA
See H J HEINZ CO LP

D-U-N-S 84-207-8750 EXP
HEINZEL IMPORT & EXPORT INC
(*Suby of* WILFRIED HEINZEL AKTIENGE-SELLSCHAFT)
220 E 42nd St Rm 3010, New York, NY 10017-5816
Tel (212) 953-3200 *Founded/Ownrshp* 1980
Sales 221.0MM^E *EMP* 10
Accts Mcgladrey Llp New York New Y
SIC 5111 Printing & writing paper; Printing & writing paper
Pr: Andrew Paul
**COO:* Moncef Reisner
**CFO:* Dietmar Geigl
**Ex VP:* Claire Fraser

D-U-N-S 12-516-6660
HEINZEN MANUFACTURING INC
HEINZEN MANUFACTURING INTL
405 Mayock Rd, Gilroy, CA 95020-7040
Tel (408) 842-7233 *Founded/Ownrshp* 1978
Sales 20.0MM *EMP* 97
SIC 3556

HEINZEN MANUFACTURING INTL
See HEINZEN MANUFACTURING INC

D-U-N-S 08-274-1547
HEINZERLING FOUNDATION
HEINZERLING MEM FOUNDATION
1800 Heinzerling Dr, Columbus, OH 43223-3642
Tel (614) 272-8888 *Founded/Ownrshp* 1959
Sales 24.8MM *EMP* 550
Accts Plante & Moran Pllc Columbus
SIC 8059 8052 Home for the mentally retarded, exc. skilled or intermediate; Intermediate care facilities; Home for the mentally retarded, exc. skilled or intermediate; Intermediate care facilities
Ex Dir: Robert Heninzerli
Ex Dir: Robert Heinzerling
Board of Directors: William Brown, M Joann Buya, Judith A Clarkson, J Paul Cooper, Hugh Higgins

HEINZERLING MEM FOUNDATION
See HEINZERLING FOUNDATION

HEIRLOOM
See COVINGTON FABRIC & DESIGN LLC

HEIRLOOM DISTRIBUTORS
See ROGERS JEWELRY CO

D-U-N-S 61-225-1413
HEISER CHEVROLET INC
10200 W Arthur Ave, Milwaukee, WI 53227-2005
Tel (414) 327-2300 *Founded/Ownrshp* 1990
Sales 25.7MM^E *EMP* 70
SIC 5511 5531 7538 Automobiles, new & used; Automotive parts; General automotive repair shops; Automobiles, new & used; Automotive parts; General automotive repair shops
Pr: Steve Sadek
**Ch Bd:* Sam Scaffidi
**VP:* Larry Freschl
Exec: Scott Stewart
Genl Mgr: Walter Heiser
Plnt Mgr: Mark Au
Sls Mgr: Mark Borcowitz
Sls Mgr: Rich Brusky
Sls Mgr: Melvin Coulter
Sls Mgr: Jean Ross
Sales Asso: Jason Clark

D-U-N-S 06-351-8815
HEISER FORD INC
LINCOLN MERCURY
1700 W Silver Spring Dr, Milwaukee, WI 53209-4421
Tel (414) 228-5700 *Founded/Ownrshp* 1973
Sales 34.2MM^E *EMP* 70
SIC 5511 5521 7538 Automobiles, new & used; Used car dealers; General automotive repair shops; Automobiles, new & used; Used car dealers; General automotive repair shops
Pr: Stephen Sadek
**VP:* Larry Freschl
Sls Mgr: Barbara Gomez

D-U-N-S 09-179-1798
HEISER LINCOLN MERCURY INC
1700 W Silver Spring Dr, Milwaukee, WI 53209-4421
Tel (414) 577-1630 *Founded/Ownrshp* 1977
Sales 21.1MM^E *EMP* 80^E
SIC 5511 5521 Automobiles, new & used; Used car dealers; Automobiles, new & used; Used car dealers
Pr: Steven Sadek
CFO: Mark Borkowicz
**VP:* Larry Freschl
VP Opers: Joseph St Marie
Plnt Mgr: Mark Au
Sales Exec: Gerry Arnholt

D-U-N-S 01-733-0492
HEISNER ENTERPRISES PARTNERSHIP
MCDONALD'S
14007 S Bell Rd Ste 314, Homer Glen, IL 60491-8463
Tel (815) 603-9721 *Founded/Ownrshp* 2010
Sales 9.0MM^E *EMP* 365
SIC 5812 Fast-food restaurant, chain; Fast-food restaurant, chain
Pt: Michele Heisner
Off Mgr: Laura Ambrose

D-U-N-S 08-419-2558
HEIST THOMAS H INSURANCE AGENCY INC
700 West Ave, Ocean City, NJ 08226-3717
Tel (609) 736-7226 *Founded/Ownrshp* 1987
Sales NA *EMP* 51^E
SIC 6411 Insurance agents; Insurance brokers
Pr: Thomas H Heist IV
**VP:* Blancha Adams
VP: Delores Schroyer

D-U-N-S 11-975-6240
HEITECH SERVICES INC
8400 Corporate Dr Ste 500, Landover, MD 20785-2294
Tel (301) 918-9500 *Founded/Ownrshp* 1999
Sales 46.8MM^E *EMP* 400
SIC 7379 Computer related consulting services; Computer related consulting services
Pr: Heidi Gerding
**Ex VP:* James Clement

D-U-N-S 08-500-4430 IMP
HEITKAMP INC
(*Suby of* SEKISUI AMERICA CORP) ★
99 Callender Rd, Watertown, CT 06795-1627
Tel (860) 274-5468 *Founded/Ownrshp* 1982
Sales 62.2MM^E *EMP* 130
SIC 1629 Waste water & sewage treatment plant construction; Waste water & sewage treatment plant construction
Pr: Benedict Ebner
CFO: Joseph McCann
**Treas:* Sandy Hutchison
**VP:* John Hohider
Rgnl Mgr: Robertewright Wright
Off Mgr: Lisa Ballou
Off Mgr: Jan Macri
Sfty Dirs: Gordon Baldwin

D-U-N-S 13-087-0132
HEITMAN LLC
191 N Wacker Dr Ste 2500, Chicago, IL 60606-1885
Tel (312) 855-5700 *Founded/Ownrshp* 1998
Sales 33.2MM^E *EMP* 320
SIC 6531 Real estate managers; Real estate managers
Pr: Maury Tognarelli
Pr: Michael Schick
COO: Richard Kateley
**CFO:* Roger E Smith
**Ch:* Jerry Claeys III
Ofcr: Randy Ramey
Ex VP: James Bachner
Ex VP: John Clement
Ex VP: Howard Edelman
Ex VP: Pete Fawcett
Ex VP: Lewis Ingall
Sr VP: James Proud
Sr VP: John Bonino
Sr VP: Julie Feller
Sr VP: Brian Pieracci
Sr VP: Christina Polito
Sr VP: Jenna Sheehan
Sr VP: Steven Warsaw
VP: Lauren Hogan
VP: Katherine Sandstrom
VP: Jeff Shillington

HEITMEYER GROUP
See ATRIUM PERSONNEL & CONSULTING SERVICES LLC

D-U-N-S 95-968-0810 IMP
HEIZER AEROSPACE INC
8750 Pevely Industrial Dr, Pevely, MO 63070-1919
Tel (636) 475-9104 *Founded/Ownrshp* 1996
Sales 20.3MM^E *EMP* 100
SIC 3728 3769 Aircraft parts & equipment; Guided missile & space vehicle parts & auxiliary equipment
Pr: Charles K Heizer
COO: Hedy Gahn
**Sr VP:* Thomas Heizer
Sr VP: Tom Heizer
**VP:* Hedy Jane Heizer-Gahn
QA Dir: Jared Campbell
Opers Mgr: Rodney Mullins
Plnt Mgr: John Schiavi

D-U-N-S 02-339-6723
HEJDI INC
ALLIED HEALTH SERVICES
2421 W Holcombe Blvd, Houston, TX 77030-1901
Tel (713) 524-4422 *Founded/Ownrshp* 1998
Sales 5.5MM *EMP* 300
SIC 8049 Nurses & other medical assistants; Nurses & other medical assistants
Pr: Helen J Dichoso

D-U-N-S 06-862-5136
HEKTOEN INSTITUTE FOR MEDICAL RESEARCH
2240 W Ogden Ave Ste 2, Chicago, IL 60612-4882
Tel (312) 768-6000 *Founded/Ownrshp* 1943
Sales 31.9MM *EMP* 375^E
SIC 6732 8733 Trusts: educational, religious, etc.; Medical research; Trusts: educational, religious, etc.; Medical research
Pr: George Dunea
**Ch Bd:* Patrick Guinan
VP: Thomas Livingston

D-U-N-S 01-451-4869
HEKTOEN INSTITUTE OF MEDICINE
2240 W Ogden Ave Ste 2, Chicago, IL 60612-4882
Tel (312) 864-0540 *Founded/Ownrshp* 2009
Sales 32.1MM *EMP* 28^E
Accts Plante & Moran Pllc Chicago
SIC 8099 Health & allied services

D-U-N-S 02-972-0018 IMP
HELAC CORP
225 Battersby Ave, Enumclaw, WA 98022-8204
Tel (360) 802-1039 *Founded/Ownrshp* 1968
Sales 57.6MM^E *EMP* 250^E
SIC 3593 Fluid power actuators, hydraulic or pneumatic; Fluid power actuators, hydraulic or pneumatic
CEO: Dean Weyer
**Pr:* Bill Power
**Sr VP:* Tom Bundy
VP: Randy Arlt
VP: Doug Baldwin
**VP:* Greg Whitney
CTO: Richard Maxey
Mfg Dir: Chris Folk
Sls Dir: Marty Koval
Sls Dir: Dan Morgado
Sls Mgr: Gail Keates

D-U-N-S 84-881-1964
HELADOS LA TAPATIA INC
4495 W Shaw Ave, Fresno, CA 93722-6206
Tel (559) 441-1105 *Founded/Ownrshp* 1995
Sales 28.1MM^E *EMP* 40
SIC 5143 Ice cream & ices
Pr: Emilio Sandoval
**CFO:* Sergio Sandoval

HELBY IMPORT COMPANY
See M & Y TRADING CORP

D-U-N-S 92-957-7450
HELDENFELS ENTERPRISES INC
5700 S Ih 35, San Marcos, TX 78666-9505
Tel (512) 396-2376 *Founded/Ownrshp* 1995
Sales 37.4MM^E *EMP* 200
SIC 3241 Portland cement; Portland cement
Pr: Fred W Heldenfels III
CFO: Ron Reich
**VP:* Ronald G Reich
**VP:* Kurt R Schriefer
VP: Dan Visel
**VP:* Blaine R Withers
VP: Blaine Withers
Sls Mgr: Chris Leonard

D-U-N-S 08-033-8213
HELDS JANITORIAL SERVICE INC
1 Hsbc Ctr Ste 1, Buffalo, NY 14203-2842
Tel (716) 854-1408 *Founded/Ownrshp* 1971
Sales 10.0MM^E *EMP* 367
SIC 7349 Janitorial service, contract basis; Janitorial service, contract basis
Pr: William Held Jr
**VP:* Carolyn Held
**VP:* Michael Held

D-U-N-S 82-900-3839
HELEN BADER FOUNDATION INC
233 N Water St Fl 4, Milwaukee, WI 53202-5729
Tel (414) 224-6464 *Founded/Ownrshp* 1991
Sales 20.6MM^E *EMP* 11
Accts Foley & Lardner Llp Milwaukee
SIC 6732 Trusts: educational, religious, etc.; Trusts: educational, religious, etc.
Pr: Daniel Bader
COO: Linda Rucker
Bd of Dir: Michelle Bader
Bd of Dir: Maria Vento
Ofcr: Reuben Harpole
Ofcr: Jerry Roberts
VP Admn: Lisa Hiller
Off Mgr: Sheri Jackson

HELEN ELLIS MEMORIAL HOSPITAL
See TARPON SPRINGS HOSPITAL FOUNDATION INC

D-U-N-S 10-590-1540 IMP
HELEN FARABEE CENTERS
1000 Brook Ave, Wichita Falls, TX 76301-5007
Tel (940) 397-3300 *Founded/Ownrshp* 1969
Sales 16.5MM^E *EMP* 400
Accts Scott Singleton Fincher And
SIC 8093 Mental health clinic, outpatient; Mental health clinic, outpatient
Ex Dir: Raymond Atkins

D-U-N-S 05-030-2801
HELEN GORDON INTERESTS LTD
GREENSHEET
2601 Main St, Houston, TX 77002-9201
Tel (713) 371-3500 *Founded/Ownrshp* 1993
Sales 74.8MM^E *EMP* 325
SIC 2711 Newspapers: publishing only, not printed on site; Newspapers: publishing only, not printed on site
CEO: Kathy Douglass
Pt: Leo Kissner
CFO: Bill Chaney
VP: Steven Peisner
Exec: Rita Davis
Creative D: Jeff Walker
CIO: Mike Patterson
Netwrk Eng: Juan Valle
VP Sls: Maria Dent
S&M/VP: Ted Stiles
Sls Dir: Tom Waters

HELEN KELLER HOSPITAL
See COLBERT COUNTY-NORTHWEST ALABAMA HEALTH CARE AUTHORITY

D-U-N-S 03-779-9178
HELEN KELLER INTERNATIONAL
352 Park Ave S Fl 12, New York, NY 10010-1723
Tel (212) 532-0544 *Founded/Ownrshp* 1919
Sales 58.4MM *EMP* 600
Accts Tait Weller & Baker Llp Phil
SIC 8322 Association for the handicapped; Association for the handicapped
Pr: Kathy Spahn
CFO: Michael Kazim
**CFO:* Elspeth Taylor
Ex VP: Robert Ritch
**Sr VP:* Victoria Quinn
VP: Amanda Melton
VP: Lisa Tapert
Mktg Dir: Mary L Burton

D-U-N-S 09-561-0648
HELEN KELLER SERVICES FOR BLIND INC
57 Willoughby St Fl 6, Brooklyn, NY 11201-5290
Tel (718) 522-2122 *Founded/Ownrshp* 1977
Sales 25.0MM *EMP* 335
Accts Bdo Usa Llp New York Ny
SIC 8322 Social services for the handicapped; Social services for the handicapped
CEO: Thomas J Edwards
CFO: Marc Feldman
**CFO:* Mark Feltman
Treas: John Caughey
VP: Fred McPhilliamy
Ex Dir: John Lynch
Mng Dir: Frank Primeggia
IT Man: Garth White

D-U-N-S 07-477-9455
HELEN NEWBERRY JOY HOSPITAL & HEALTHCARE CENTER
GIBSON FAMILY HEALTH CENTER
502 W Harrie St, Newberry, MI 49868-1209
Tel (906) 293-9200 *Founded/Ownrshp* 1931
Sales 33.1MM *EMP* 205ᴱ
SIC 8062 8051 General medical & surgical hospitals; Skilled nursing care facilities; General medical & surgical hospitals; Skilled nursing care facilities
**CFO:* Scott Pillion
VP: Sundae Garrod
Dir Rx: Mark Fischer
Mng Dir: James Christensen
Dir IT: Howard Bliss
IT Man: Natasha King
Nutrtnst: Toby Smithson
Doctor: Bettie Myers
Nrsg Dir: Sue Forrester
HC Dir: Tina Brown

D-U-N-S 94-950-0292 IMP
HELEN OF TROY LP
(*Suby of* HELEN OF TROY TEXAS CORP) ★
1 Helen Of Troy Plz, El Paso, TX 79912-1150
Tel (915) 225-4845 *Founded/Ownrshp* 1996
Sales 120.1MMᴱ *EMP* 500ᴱ
SIC 3634 3999 Personal electrical appliances; Hair dryers, electric; Curling irons, electric; Razors, electric; Hair & hair-based products; Combs, except hard rubber; Hair, dressing of, for the trade; Personal electrical appliances; Hair dryers, electric; Curling irons, electric; Razors, electric; Hair & hair-based products; Combs, except hard rubber; Hair, dressing of, for the trade
CEO: Julien Mininberg
Pr: Michael Cafaro
Pr: Pedro Contreras
**CFO:* Thomas J Benson
Treas: Andre Miranda
Ofcr: Vincent Arson
Sr VP: Alan Ames
Sr VP: Thomas Benson
**VP:* Vincent D Carson
VP: Rodney Feltner
VP: Scott Hagstrom
VP: William Levy
VP: Alfredo Mayne-Nicholls
VP: Joann Parker

D-U-N-S 04-612-0994 IMP/EXP
HELEN OF TROY TEXAS CORP
(*Suby of* HELEN OF TROY LIMITED)
1 Helen Of Troy Plz, El Paso, TX 79912-1148
Tel (915) 225-8000 *Founded/Ownrshp* 1994
Sales 202.0MMᴱ *EMP* 815ᴱ
SIC 3999 Hair driers, designed for beauty parlors
CEO: Julien Mininberg
**CFO:* Thomas J Benson
**Treas:* Deanna Nasser
**Ex VP:* Arthur August
**Ex VP:* Michael Cafaro
**Sr VP:* Robert D Spear
Dir IT: Frank Gonzalez

D-U-N-S 07-153-5470
HELEN ROSS MCNABB CENTER INC
201 W Springdale Ave, Knoxville, TN 37917-5158
Tel (865) 637-9711 *Founded/Ownrshp* 1948
Sales 54.6MM *EMP* 519
SIC 8093 Mental health clinic, outpatient; Alcohol clinic, outpatient; Drug clinic, outpatient; Mental health clinic, outpatient; Alcohol clinic, outpatient; Drug clinic, outpatient
CEO: Jerry Vagnier
**Ch:* Ted Flickinger

HELENA CHEMICAL CO
See FOWLER ELEVATOR INC

D-U-N-S 00-703-6759 IMP
HELENA CHEMICAL CO
(*Suby of* MARUBENI AMERICA CORP) ★
225 Schilling Blvd # 300, Collierville, TN 38017-7177
Tel (901) 761-0050 *Founded/Ownrshp* 1957
Sales 3.8MMMᴱ *EMP* 4,000
Accts Ernst & Young Llp
SIC 5191 2819 Fertilizers & agricultural chemicals; Seeds & bulbs; Chemicals, high purity: refined from technical grade; Fertilizers & agricultural chemicals; Seeds & bulbs; Chemicals, high purity: refined from technical grade
CEO: Mike McCarty
Pr: Yasuo Yagi
CFO: Troy D Traxler Jr
Treas: Roger Lewis
VP: Steve Alexander
VP: Milton Allen
VP: Dave Thomas
Dir IT: Vickie Smith
Software D: Ying Zhang
Opers Mgr: Gary Bueche
Opers Mgr: Mike Joseph

D-U-N-S 02-762-4808 EXP
HELENA CHEMICAL CO
ROUND BUTTE SEED
505 C St, Culver, OR 97734-1574
Tel (541) 546-5222 *Founded/Ownrshp* 1961
Sales 24.2MM *EMP* 50
Accts Akt Llp Salem Oregon
SIC 5191 Nursery stock, seeds & bulbs; Fertilizer; Lawn & garden supplies; Seed cleaning; Vegetable drying services; Seeds: field, garden & flower; Fertilizer & fertilizer materials; Chemicals, agricultural; Fertilizers & agricultural chemicals; Animal feeds
Pr: Mike McCarty
**Pr:* Jim Carlson
**VP:* Britt Spaulding
Board of Directors: Diane Amstead, Dwight E Macy

D-U-N-S 61-193-0418
HELENA INDUSTRIES INC
(*Suby of* HELENA CHEMICAL CO) ★
225 Schilling Blvd # 200, Collierville, TN 38017-7177
Tel (901) 820-5700 *Founded/Ownrshp* 2005
Sales 92.1MMᴱ *EMP* 300
Accts Cannon & Company Memphis Ten
SIC 2819 Chemicals, high purity: refined from technical grade; Chemicals, high purity: refined from technical grade
Pr: Phil Hollis
**Sec:* Byron Phillips
Area Mgr: Beau Kelch
Opers Mgr: Josh Branch

D-U-N-S 07-939-6131 IMP
HELENA LABORATORIES CORP
1530 Lindbergh Dr, Beaumont, TX 77707-4131
Tel (409) 842-3714 *Founded/Ownrshp* 1966
Sales 208.2MMᴱ *EMP* 1,000
SIC 3841 3826 Medical instruments & equipment, blood & bone work; Electrophoresis equipment; Medical instruments & equipment, blood & bone work; Electrophoresis equipment
Ch: Tipton L Golias
Treas: Ann Golias
Chf Mktg O: Joe Golias
VP: Noel Bartlett
VP: David Mayes
VP: Ovay H Mayes
VP: John O'Keefe
VP: Eric Petersen
Dept Mgr: Alf Flowers
CTO: Anthony Weber
Software D: Curt Smith

D-U-N-S 00-582-3695
HELENA SAND & GRAVEL INC (MT)
2209 Airport Rd, Helena, MT 59601-1208
Tel (406) 442-1185 *Founded/Ownrshp* 1910
Sales 61.9MMᴱ *EMP* 250
SIC 1611 5032 1771 General contractor, highway & street construction; Sand, construction; Gravel; Asphalt mixture; Concrete mixtures; Concrete work; General contractor, highway & street construction; Sand, construction; Gravel; Asphalt mixture; Concrete mixtures; Concrete work
Pr: Scott Olsen

D-U-N-S 08-114-6102
HELENA SCHOOL DISTRICT NO 1 INC
55 S Rodney St, Helena, MT 59601-5763
Tel (406) 324-2000 *Founded/Ownrshp* 1867
Sales 50.8MMᴱ *EMP* 824
Accts Galusha Higgins & Galusha
SIC 8211 Public elementary & secondary schools; Public elementary school; Public junior high school; Public senior high school; Public elementary & secondary schools; Public elementary school; Public junior high school; Public senior high school
Dir IT: Marc Best
Schl Brd P: Julie Mitchell
Psych: Tami Darlow
Psych: Susan Dotter

D-U-N-S 09-917-8998
HELENA-WEST HELENA PUBLIC SCHOOLS
305 Valley Dr, Helena, AR 72342-1505
Tel (870) 338-4425 *Founded/Ownrshp* 1947
Sales 20.4MMᴱ *EMP* 500
SIC 8211 Public elementary & secondary schools; Public elementary & secondary schools
**Prin:* Willie Easter

HELFMAN DODGE CHRYSLER GJEEP
See HELFMAN DODGE INC

D-U-N-S 16-745-0357
HELFMAN DODGE INC
HELFMAN DODGE CHRYSLER GJEEP
7720 Katy Fwy, Houston, TX 77024-2004
Tel (713) 533-6100 *Founded/Ownrshp* 2002
Sales 68.3MMᴱ *EMP* 150
SIC 5511 Automobiles, new & used; Automobiles, new & used
Pr: Jack Helfman
**Pr:* Alan B Helfman
**CFO:* Mike Gross
**VP:* Steven Wolf
Store Mgr: Greg Luther
Sls Mgr: Jason Debner
Sls Mgr: Jesse Dotson

D-U-N-S 08-422-8915 IMP/EXP
HELGESEN INDUSTRIES INC
7261 State Road 60, Hartford, WI 53027-9222
Tel (262) 709-4444 *Founded/Ownrshp* 1977
Sales 110.2MMᴱ *EMP* 400
SIC 3443 Tanks, standard or custom fabricated: metal plate; Weldments; Tanks, standard or custom fabricated: metal plate; Weldments
Pr: Ronald S Marshall
**VP:* Thomas C Marshall
VP: Paul Vanderkin
IT Man: Terry Schneider
IT Man: David Urbaniak
**VP Mfg:* Nathaniel L Marshall
VP Sls: Edgar Riteris
Snr Mgr: Ron Firari
Snr Mgr: Kyle Johnson
Snr Mgr: Kirk Koch

D-U-N-S 10-909-6339
HELGET GAS PRODUCTS INC
4150 S 87th St, Omaha, NE 68127-1602
Tel (402) 339-1063 *Founded/Ownrshp* 1974
Sales 27.0MMᴱ *EMP* 50
SIC 5169 Gases, compressed & liquefied
Pr: James F Helget
**Sec:* Kathleen A Helget
Brnch Mgr: Dale Mitchell
Off Mgr: Heidi Mognesen
Opers Mgr: Steve Blassingame
Opers Mgr: Mark Boyd
Opers Mgr: Christopher Cox
Opers Mgr: Wayne Kreutzer
Sls Dir: Nate Lane

D-U-N-S 07-963-1651 IMP
HELI-MART INC
3184 Airway Ave Ste E, Costa Mesa, CA 92626-4619
Tel (714) 755-2999 *Founded/Ownrshp* 1973
Sales 44.0MMᴱ *EMP* 18
SIC 5088 Helicopter parts; Helicopter parts
CEO: Ed Brown
Mktg Mgr: Kyle Brown

D-U-N-S 03-367-0594
HELIAE DEVELOPMENT LLC
578 E Germann Rd, Gilbert, AZ 85297-2907
Tel (480) 424-2875 *Founded/Ownrshp* 2008
Sales 34.9MMᴱ *EMP* 105
SIC 2911 Oils, fuel; Oils, fuel
Ch Bd: Frank Mars
**Pr:* Daniel Simon
**COO:* Adrian Galvez
**CFO:* J Craig Johnson
**VP:* Len Smith
VP: Anna Lee Tonkovich
Off Mgr: Stacy Ronniger
IT Man: Justin Hall
Snr PM: John Cefola

D-U-N-S 04-443-7655
HELICAL PRODUCTS CO INC
(*Suby of* MATTHEW WARREN INC) ★
901 W Mccoy Ln, Santa Maria, CA 93455-1196
Tel (805) 928-3851 *Founded/Ownrshp* 2015
Sales 31.1MMᴱ *EMP* 120
SIC 3568 3495 3493 Couplings, shaft: rigid, flexible, universal joint, etc.; Instrument springs, precision; Steel springs, except wire; Couplings, shaft: rigid, flexible, universal joint, etc.; Instrument springs, precision; Steel springs, except wire
CEO: H L Merrell
Pr: Brent Darwin
COO: Dave Hastings
CFO: Alan Stringfellow
VP: A P Ater
VP: Michael Schick
DP Exec: David Palmerston
Sfty Dirs: Michael Johnson

D-U-N-S 61-452-7919
■ **HELICOPTER CONSULTANTS OF MAUI LLC**
BLUE HAWAIIAN HELICOPTERS
(*Suby of* AIR METHODS CORP) ★
105 Kahului Heliport, Kahului, HI 96732
Tel (808) 871-8844 *Founded/Ownrshp* 2013
Sales 21.5MMᴱ *EMP* 170
SIC 4522

D-U-N-S 14-492-1343 IMP/EXP
■ **HELICOPTER SUPPORT INC**
SIKORSKY COMMERCIAL
(*Suby of* SIKORSKY AIRCRAFT CORP) ★
124 Quarry Rd, Trumbull, CT 06611-4816
Tel (203) 416-4000 *Founded/Ownrshp* 1998
Sales 183.4MMᴱ *EMP* 270
SIC 5088 4581 3728 Helicopter parts; Aircraft maintenance & repair services; Aircraft parts & equipment; Aircraft body & wing assemblies & parts; Helicopter parts; Aircraft maintenance & repair services; Aircraft parts & equipment; Aircraft body & wing assemblies & parts
Pr: David Adler
**Treas:* Rajeev Bhalla
**Treas:* Richard S Caswell
**Ex VP:* John Chimini
**VP:* Christopher Bogan
VP: Peter Boss
VP: Daryl Charton
Mng Dir: Paul Robinson
Prgrm Mgr: Donn Cornell
Prgrm Mgr: Paul Golia
IT Man: Kayle Frost

D-U-N-S 01-248-9340
HELICOPTERS INC
5000 Omega Dr, Cahokia, IL 62206-1469
Tel (618) 337-2903 *Founded/Ownrshp* 1981
Sales 29.5MMᴱ *EMP* 140
SIC 4512 Helicopter carrier, scheduled; Air passenger carrier, scheduled; Helicopter carrier, scheduled; Air passenger carrier, scheduled
Pr: Stephen C Lieber
Genl Mgr: Jeff Lieber

D-U-N-S 07-858-6145
HELIGEAR ACQUISITION CO
NORTHSTAR AEROSPACE CHICAGO
6006 W 73rd St, Bedford Park, IL 60638-6106
Tel (708) 728-2000 *Founded/Ownrshp* 2012
Sales 267.3MMᴱ *EMP* 780ᴱ
SIC 3724 Aircraft engines & engine parts; Aircraft engines & engine parts
CEO: David McConnaughey
CFO: R Burkhardt
**CFO:* Robert Burkhardt
VP: John Giudici
Prgrm Mgr: Bill Kaml
QI Cn Mgr: Clay Culver
Snr Mgr: Kristina Gillespie

D-U-N-S 07-858-6148
HELIGEAR ACQUISITION CO
NORTHSTAR AEROSPACE PHOENIX
401 S 36th St, Phoenix, AZ 85034-2812
Tel (602) 275-4406 *Founded/Ownrshp* 2012
Sales 34.5MMᴱ *EMP* 99
SIC 3728 7699 3769 Aircraft power transmission equipment; Aircraft & heavy equipment repair services; Airframe assemblies, guided missiles
CEO: David McConnaughey
**CFO:* Robert Burkhardt
**VP:* Gregory Gleason
**VP:* Ian Kirson
**VP:* Terry Theodore
Admn Mgr: Tom Smith
Sls Mgr: Cheri Tamplin

D-U-N-S 04-168-2753
HELIMEDS INC
2245 E 3rd St, Tucson, AZ 85719-5108
Tel (520) 326-2794 *Founded/Ownrshp* 1984
Sales 50.0MM *EMP* 80
SIC 7359 8299 Aircraft rental; Airline training; Aircraft rental; Airline training
Pr: David Kubista

D-U-N-S 10-217-1238 IMP
HELIO PRECISION PRODUCTS INC
HN PRECISION
601 N Skokie Hwy Ste B, Lake Bluff, IL 60044-1500
Tel (847) 473-1300 *Founded/Ownrshp* 1983
Sales 28.3MMᴱ *EMP* 160ᴱ
SIC 3592 Valves, engine; Valves, engine
Pr: Daniel Nash
CFO: Paul Ainsworth
QI Cn Mgr: Ed Mellinger
Board of Directors: Robin Kimmel

D-U-N-S 80-441-8338
HELIOPOWER INC
25747 Jefferson Ave, Murrieta, CA 92562-6903
Tel (951) 677-7755 *Founded/Ownrshp* 2001
Sales 30.1MMᴱ *EMP* 80ᴱ
SIC 1711 Solar energy contractor
Ch Bd: Ian Rogoff
**Pr:* Roy Douglas
**CEO:* Scott Gordon
**COO:* MO Rousso
**Treas:* Vicki Zelfer
**VP:* Steve Huang
VP: Jonah Liebes
VP: Tom Millhoff
Prgrm Mgr: Mike Murray
Dir IT: John Montgomery
VP Mktg: Glenna Wiseman

D-U-N-S 18-385-0031
HELIOS
(*Suby of* PROGRESSIVE ENTERPRISES HOLDINGS INC) ★
250 Progressive Way, Westerville, OH 43082-9615
Tel (614) 794-3300 *Founded/Ownrshp* 2010
Sales NA *EMP* 530ᴱ
SIC 6411

D-U-N-S 62-127-9061
HELIOS EDUCATION FOUNDATION
2415 E Camelback Rd # 500, Phoenix, AZ 85016-9289
Tel (602) 381-2260 *Founded/Ownrshp* 1982
Sales 116.8MM *EMP* 37ᴱ
SIC 8299 Arts & crafts schools
CEO: Paul J Luna
Ch: Vince Roig
Prgrm Mgr: Lindsay Thomas
Board of Directors: Vada O Manager

D-U-N-S 13-235-5210
HELIOS HEALTHCARE LLC
IDYLWOOD CARE CENTER
520 Capitol Mall Ste 800, Sacramento, CA 95814-4716
Tel (916) 471-2241 *Founded/Ownrshp* 2003
Sales 22.7MM *EMP* 264
Accts Moss Adams Llp Stockton Cali
SIC 8051 Skilled nursing care facilities; Skilled nursing care facilities
Genl Mgr: Margarita Rosero

D-U-N-S 96-701-9550
HELIS FOUNDATION
228 Saint Charles Ave # 902, New Orleans, LA 70130-2609
Tel (504) 523-1831 *Founded/Ownrshp* 2011
Sales 35.3MM *EMP* 2
SIC 8699 Charitable organization
Prin: David A Kerstein

D-U-N-S 05-711-9869
HELIS OIL & GAS CO LLC
228 Saint Charles Ave # 912, New Orleans, LA 70130-2601
Tel (504) 523-1831 *Founded/Ownrshp* 1983
Sales 49.8MMᴱ *EMP* 53
SIC 1382 1311 Oil & gas exploration services; Crude petroleum & natural gas production
Prin: David A Kerstein
**CFO:* Michael F Schott

HELITECH CONCRETE & STRL REPR
See SLAB MASTERS INC

D-U-N-S 92-956-2502 IMP
HELITEK CO LTD
(*Suby of* WAFER WORKS CORPORATION)
47338 Fremont Blvd, Fremont, CA 94538-6501
Tel (510) 933-7688 *Founded/Ownrshp* 1994
Sales 33.0MM *EMP* 15
SIC 5065 Semiconductor devices; Semiconductor devices
Pr: Ping-Hai Chiao

D-U-N-S 79-975-5439
HELIX EDUCATION INC
175 Suth W Temple Ste 700, Salt Lake City, UT 84101
Tel (801) 886-2002 *Founded/Ownrshp* 1989
Sales 47.5MME *EMP* 175
SIC 7331 Direct mail advertising services; Direct mail advertising services
Ch Bd: Tom Dearden
Pr: Jeff Adams
**CEO:* Matthew Schnittman
**CFO:* Eric W Muhlheim
CFO: Reid Simpson
**Sr VP:* Rick Bentz
**VP:* Scott Lomas
VP: Sherrie Martin
VP: Deborah Richman
**VP:* Brenda Robertson
**VP:* Pankaj Sharma
Creative D: Kim Carter
Creative D: Ed Richards

D-U-N-S 14-854-9512
HELIX ELECTRIC INC
6795 Flanders Dr, San Diego, CA 92121-2903
Tel (858) 535-0505 *Founded/Ownrshp* 1985
Sales 267.0MME *EMP* 1,500
SIC 1731

D-U-N-S 11-166-1893
HELIX ELECTRIC OF NEVADA LLC
(*Suby of* HELIX ELECTRIC INC) ★
3078 E Sunset Rd Ste 9, Las Vegas, NV 89120-2794
Tel (702) 732-1188 *Founded/Ownrshp* 2002
Sales 84.5MME *EMP* 300
SIC 1731 Electrical work; Electrical work
Pr: Victor Fuchs
VP: Darren Vanderford
Opers Mgr: Michael Vita

D-U-N-S 09-838-5404 IMP/EXP
▲ **HELIX ENERGY SOLUTIONS GROUP INC**
3505 W Sam Houston Pkwy N, Houston, TX 77043-1252
Tel (281) 618-0400 *Founded/Ownrshp* 1979
Sales 1.1MMM *EMP* 1,800
Accts Ernst & Young Llp Houston Te
Tkr Sym HLX *Exch* NYS
SIC 1629 1389 1311 Marine construction; Well logging; Crude petroleum production; Natural gas production; Marine construction; Well logging; Crude petroleum production; Natural gas production
Pr: Owen Kratz
Mng Pt: Keith Sparks
COO: Clifford V Chamblee
COO: Eric Vazquez
CFO: Anthony Tripodo
Treas: Clifford H Buster
Ofcr: Dennis Bartenbach
Ofcr: Mark Riepen
Ex VP: Johnny Edwards
Ex VP: Alisa B Johnson
Sr VP: Michael V Ambrose
Sr VP: James Lewis Connor III
VP: Hin Chiu
VP: Ian A Collie
VP: Jim Haag
VP: Wallace Hilliard
VP: Connor James
VP: Charles McGregor
Board of Directors: John V Lovoi, T William Porter, Nancy K Quinn, Jan Rask, William L Transier, James A Watt

D-U-N-S 17-530-6013
HELIX HEALTHCARE INC
ALVARADO PARKWAY INSTITUTE
7050 Parkway Dr, La Mesa, CA 91942-1535
Tel (619) 465-4411 *Founded/Ownrshp* 2003
Sales 54.9MME *EMP* 310
SIC 8063 Psychiatric hospitals; Psychiatric hospitals
CEO: Roy Rodriguez
COO: Megan Monrgomery -West
CFO: Chad Engbrecht
**VP:* Mohammed Bari
Genl Mgr: Patric Ziemer
CIO: Chung Wong
Mktg Dir: Eyra Leeper
Occ Thrpy: Mary Castle
Dir Health: Johnnie Munkres
HC Dir: Leslie Sanders

HELIX MEDICAL
See FREUDENBERG MEDICAL LLC

D-U-N-S 04-365-3518
HELIX WATER DISTRICT
7811 University Ave, La Mesa, CA 91942-0427
Tel (619) 443-1031 *Founded/Ownrshp* 1913
Sales 74.6MM *EMP* 126
Accts Rogers Anderson Malody & Sco
SIC 4941 Water supply; Water supply
Pr: Deana R Verbeke
CFO: Richard Stevenson
Treas: Lisa Irvine
Treas: Mark Weston
Bd of Dir: James Lewanski
**VP:* John Linden

D-U-N-S 09-375-9298 IMP/EXP
HELLA CORPORATE CENTER USA INC
(*Suby of* HELLA HOLDING INTERNATIONAL GMBH)
43811 Plymouth Oaks Blvd, Plymouth, MI 48170-2539
Tel (586) 232-4788 *Founded/Ownrshp* 1978
Sales 180.1MME *EMP* 680
Accts Gray Hunter Stenn Llp
SIC 3625 5013 5088 3822 3585 3429 Industrial electrical relays & switches; Automotive supplies & parts; Marine supplies; Auto controls regulating residntl & coml environmt & applncs; Refrigeration & heating equipment; Manufactured hardware (general); Industrial electrical relays & switches; Automotive supplies & parts; Marine supplies; Auto controls regulating residntl & coml environmt & applncs; Refrigeration & heating equipment; Manufactured hardware (general)
CEO: Joseph V Borruso
**Pr:* Steve Lietaert
**CFO:* Edward L Macek
**Treas:* C Elaine Wylie
CIO: Luis Gomezdelcampo
VP Sls: Richard Bloomfield
S&M/VP: Julie Martin
Sls Mgr: Marcel Gersting

D-U-N-S 11-904-5300 IMP
HELLA ELECTRONICS CORP
(*Suby of* HELLA CORPORATE CENTER USA INC) ★
43811 Plymouth Oaks Blvd, Plymouth, MI 48170-2539
Tel (734) 414-0900 *Founded/Ownrshp* 1983
Sales 141.3MME *EMP* 640
SIC 3625 3714 Industrial electrical relays & switches; Motor vehicle parts & accessories; Industrial electrical relays & switches; Motor vehicle parts & accessories
CEO: Joseph V Borruso
Pr: Steve Hubble
CEO: Marc Rosenmayr
CFO: Peter Martin
Treas: Kye Hemphill
Treas: Frank Mueller
Ex VP: Steve Profeta
VP: Mark Brainard
Mng Dir: Ramashankar Pandey
Prgrm Mgr: Kirk Hinkins
Prgrm Mgr: Nicholas Jordan

D-U-N-S 10-624-3991 IMP
HELLA INC
(*Suby of* HELLA CORPORATE CENTER USA INC) ★
201 Kelly Dr, Peachtree City, GA 30269-1924
Tel (770) 486-3427 *Founded/Ownrshp* 1990
Sales 28.5MME *EMP* 82
Accts Gray Hunter Stenn Llp
SIC 5013 5088 Motor vehicle supplies & new parts; Marine supplies
Pr: Carl Brown
Mng Pt: Jargen Behrend
CFO: Stephen Profeta
Ofcr: Vikas Gupta
Ofcr: Bu Sim
VP: Gary Hawkins
VP: Angie Head
Exec: Heiko Berk
Mng Dir: Wolfgang Ollig
Mng Dir: Kimmo Suupohja
Prgrm Mgr: Simon Bach

D-U-N-S 14-601-8887 IMP
HELLAS CONSTRUCTION INC
12710 Res Blvd Ste 240, Austin, TX 78759
Tel (512) 250-2910 *Founded/Ownrshp* 2003
Sales 126.7MM *EMP* 320
Accts Ha&W Llp Atlanta Georgia
SIC 1629 Athletic & recreation facilities construction; Athletic field construction; Golf course construction; Tennis court construction; Athletic & recreation facilities construction; Athletic field construction; Golf course construction; Tennis court construction
CEO: Reed J Seaton
CFO: Frank Petrini
VP: Robert G Allison
VP: Matt Schnitzler
Mktg Mgr: Michelle McDaniel
Board of Directors: Dan Schlopakohl

D-U-N-S 84-392-7513 IMP/EXP
HELLER CF DISTRIBUTING LLC
5151 Bannock St Ste 4, Denver, CO 80216-1846
Tel (303) 321-2369 *Founded/Ownrshp* 2000
Sales 73.2MME *EMP* 250E
SIC 5143 5142 Ice cream & ices; Dinners, frozen; Ice cream & ices; Dinners, frozen

D-U-N-S 09-797-1808 IMP
HELLER DISTRIBUTING CO INC
4920 Wilshire Ave Ne, Albuquerque, NM 87113-1957
Tel (505) 797-1600 *Founded/Ownrshp* 1977, 1991
Sales 66.5MME *EMP* 90
SIC 5142 Packaged frozen goods; Packaged frozen goods
Pr: Dave Roberts

D-U-N-S 02-424-4915
HELLER ELECTRIC CO INC (DC)
14218 Brandywine Rd, Brandywine, MD 20613-3100
Tel (301) 372-6816 *Founded/Ownrshp* 1963
Sales 20.4MME *EMP* 120
SIC 1731 General electrical contractor; General electrical contractor
Pr: William Heller
**Pr:* Michael J Ritchey
Ex VP: Brian Heller
**VP:* Jason M Clurman
**VP:* Brian J Heller
VP: Scott Heller

HELLER FORD-MERCURY
See FORD HELLER SALES INC

D-U-N-S 00-214-6892 IMP
HELLER INDUSTRIES INC
4 Vreeland Rd Ste 1, Florham Park, NJ 07932-1593
Tel (973) 377-6800 *Founded/Ownrshp* 1960, 1995
Sales 22.1MME *EMP* 82
SIC 3569 Assembly machines, non-metalworking
Pr: David Heller
Pr: Marc Peo
CFO: Sibyl Alleyne
VP: Chris Chang
VP: Wai Lee
Prgrm Mgr: David Wright
Tech Mgr: Jeff Brewen
Trfc Mgr: Aubrey Ward
Sls&Mrk Ex: Mike Hassell
Sls&Mrk Ex: Mike Shearer
Sls&Mrk Ex: Annen Steven

D-U-N-S 06-459-0557 IMP
HELLER MACHINE TOOLS LP
1225 Equity Dr, Troy, MI 48084-7107
Tel (248) 288-5000 *Founded/Ownrshp* 1986
Sales 38.4MME *EMP* 97
SIC 8711 5084

D-U-N-S 60-979-3356
HELLER MOTORS LLP
MERCEDES BENZ OF BOERNE
31445 Interstate 10 W, Boerne, TX 78006-9281
Tel (830) 981-6000 *Founded/Ownrshp* 2004
Sales 24.1MME *EMP* 60
SIC 5511 Automobiles, new & used
Pt: Bill Bird
Pt: Ron Heller

D-U-N-S 03-090-5808
HELLER-BIRD MOTORS LTD
MERCEDES BENZ OF SAN JUAN
400 W Expressway 83, San Juan, TX 78589-3637
Tel (956) 787-4400 *Founded/Ownrshp* 2009
Sales 32.1MME *EMP* 47E
SIC 5511 Automobiles, new & used
Pr: Alfonso Cavazos
Admn Mgr: Hector Morales
Sales Asso: Ricardo Gonzalez
Sales Asso: Modesto Montemayor
Sales Asso: Marco Salas

D-U-N-S 05-716-4014
HELLERMANNTYTON CORP
(*Suby of* HELLERMANNTYTON BETA SARL)
7930 N Faulkner Rd, Milwaukee, WI 53224-3423
Tel (414) 355-1130 *Founded/Ownrshp* 2006
Sales 77.1MME *EMP* 320
SIC 3089 2891 Injection molded finished plastic products; Extruded finished plastic products; Adhesives; Injection molded finished plastic products; Extruded finished plastic products; Adhesives
Pr: James R Campion
**Sec:* Peter D Jonas
VP: Mike Kennard
**VP:* Terry Turtle
Area Mgr: Terry Moore
Dist Mgr: Karen Spathias
Dir IT: Eric Schilder
Sales Exec: Thomas Jacomet

HELLGATE INTERMEDIATE SCH
See HELLGATE SCHOOL DISTRICT 4

D-U-N-S 80-048-0563
HELLGATE SCHOOL DISTRICT 4
HELLGATE INTERMEDIATE SCH
2385 Flynn Ln, Missoula, MT 59808-5608
Tel (406) 728-5626 *Founded/Ownrshp* 2007
Sales 8.4MM *EMP* 301
SIC 8211 Public elementary & secondary schools; Public elementary & secondary schools
IT Man: Carole Monlux
IT Man: Michele Nokelby
HC Dir: Lisa Flanagan

HELLIER
See ACUREN INSPECTION INC

D-U-N-S 88-368-9051
HELLMAN & FRIEDMAN LLC
1 Maritime Plz Fl 12, San Francisco, CA 94111-3502
Tel (415) 788-5111 *Founded/Ownrshp* 1993
Sales 2.2MMME *EMP* 8,703
SIC 6726 Investment offices; Investment offices
Sls&Mrk Ex: Philip Hammarskjold
Ofcr: Debra Dockery
VP: Kristen Garlinghouse
Mng Dir: Andy Ballard
Mng Dir: Lee Georgia
Mng Dir: Jeffrey Goldstein
Mng Dir: Brad Henske
Mng Dir: Goldstein Jeffrey
Mng Dir: David McVeigh
Mng Dir: Anupam Mishra
Mng Dir: Thomas Steyer

D-U-N-S 08-972-8273
HELLMAN ELECTRIC CORP (NY)
855 Brush Ave, Bronx, NY 10465-1880
Tel (347) 810-5401 *Founded/Ownrshp* 1978
Sales 53.4MME *EMP* 120
SIC 1731 General electrical contractor; General electrical contractor
Pr: Steven Lazzaro
**CFO:* John Eremita
**Ex VP:* Allen Cavalluzzi
**Sr VP:* Michael Dantone
**Sr VP:* Stephen Hendrickson
IT Man: Stan Plonchak
IT Man: Anthony Tassone
Trfc Dir: Nick Aromando
Sales Asso: James Cardillo
Snr PM: John Brescia

D-U-N-S 18-307-7684
HELLMANN WORLDWIDE LOGISTICS INC
(*Suby of* HELLMANN WORLDWIDE LOGISTICS GMBH & CO. KG)
10450 Nw 41st St, Doral, FL 33178-2372
Tel (305) 406-4500 *Founded/Ownrshp* 1997
Sales 226.0MME *EMP* 700
SIC 4731 Freight forwarding; Freight forwarding
CEO: Roger Haeussler
**Pr:* Christopher Dale
**COO:* Arnold Goldstein
CFO: Carsten Fuhlendorf
**CFO:* Julian Riches
Ofcr: Laisu Yon
Sr VP: Anthony Colucci
VP: Ian Beckman
VP: Joseph Goldman
VP: Ronald Hough
**VP:* Chris Sims
Dir Bus: Alexandra Arroyave
Dir Bus: James Cassidy
Dir Bus: Mari Dominguez
Dir Bus: Colby Gardner
Dir Bus: Ijlal Torres

D-U-N-S 80-634-5203
HELLMUTH OBATA & KASSABAUM INC
H O K
(*Suby of* HOK INC) ★
1 Bush St Ste 200, San Francisco, CA 94104-4404
Tel (415) 243-0555 *Founded/Ownrshp* 1995
Sales 30.9MME *EMP* 1,808
SIC 8712 8711 8742 7389 0781 Architectural services; Engineering services; Management consulting services; Interior design services; Landscape architects
CEO: Patrick Macleamy
**Pr:* William Hellmuth
**Treas:* Lisa Green
**Ofcr:* Thomas Robson
Sr VP: Dave Troup
VP: Crystal Barriscale
VP: Yan Chan
VP: Tom Fortier
VP: Matt Needham
VP: Mary Perkowski
VP: Mike Retford
VP: Yann Weymouth

D-U-N-S 05-561-0389
HELLMUTH OBATA AND KASSABAUM INC
(*Suby of* H O K) ★
211 N Broadway Ste 600, Saint Louis, MO 63102-2749
Tel (314) 421-2000 *Founded/Ownrshp* 2011
Sales 4.8MME *EMP* 831E
SIC 8712 Architectural services; Architectural engineering
Prin: Angelo Arzano
VP: Corinne Drobot
VP: Dennis Gillespie
VP: Peter Grandine
VP: Don Lemondsaia
VP: William Wahle
Off Mgr: Yolanda Van Hecke
IT Man: Greg Sledge

HELLO WORLD
See HELLOWORLD INC

HELLOFRESH
See GROCERY DELIVERY E-SERVICES USA INC

D-U-N-S 07-862-0153
HELLOWORLD INC
HELLO WORLD
(*Suby of* ENGAGEMENT HOLDINGS INC) ★
3000 Town Ctr Ste 2120, Southfield, MI 48075-1300
Tel (248) 543-6800 *Founded/Ownrshp* 2012
Sales 68.0MME *EMP* 351E
SIC 7313 7371 7336 Electronic media advertising representatives; Computer software systems analysis & design, custom; Creative services to advertisers, except writers; Electronic media advertising representatives; Computer software systems analysis & design, custom; Creative services to advertisers, except writers
Pr: Joshua Linkner
Pr: Jayne Aussavadegool
CFO: Chris Locke
Sr VP: Kim Smith
VP: Aaron Clark
VP: Deana Derocha
VP: Sara Kowal
Dir Risk M: Eric Larson
Prin: Robert Lippitt
IT Man: Dushan Shimko

D-U-N-S 10-168-9693 IMP/EXP
HELM AMERICA CORP
(*Suby of* HELM AG)
1110 Centennial Ave Ste 2, Piscataway, NJ 08854-4169
Tel (732) 981-1160 *Founded/Ownrshp* 1982
Sales 1.0MMME *EMP* 100
SIC 5169 5122 5191 4231 4226 Chemicals & allied products; Pharmaceuticals; Fertilizer & fertilizer materials; Trucking terminal facilities; Special warehousing & storage; Chemicals & allied products; Pharmaceuticals; Fertilizer & fertilizer materials; Trucking terminal facilities; Special warehousing & storage
Pr: Andreas Weimann
**Treas:* William Vanfossen
Bd of Dir: Hans-Christian Sievers
Mng Dir: Rahul Sonawane
Opers Mgr: Kimberly Richardson

D-U-N-S 10-195-2075
HELM BANK USA
999 Brickell Ave Ste 100, Miami, FL 33131-3217
Tel (305) 379-4356 *Founded/Ownrshp* 1989
Sales NA *EMP* 46
SIC 6022 State commercial banks; State commercial banks
Pr: Fernando R Munera
Ofcr: Ulises Garcia
Ex VP: Andres Restrepo
Sr VP: Maria E Ortiz
VP: Guillermo Cobos

D-U-N-S 14-841-7348 IMP
HELM FERTILIZER CORP (FLORIDA)
(*Suby of* HELM AMERICA CORP) ★
4042 Park Oaks Blvd # 330, Tampa, FL 33610-9539
Tel (813) 621-8846 *Founded/Ownrshp* 1986
Sales 947.4MME *EMP* 14
Accts Israeloff Trattner & Co Pc
SIC 5191 6221 Fertilizer & fertilizer materials; Commodity traders, contracts; Fertilizer & fertilizer materials; Commodity traders, contracts
Pr: Dale Miller
**Treas:* Mike Mohatt
VP: Michael Peyton

HELM GROUP, THE
See MECHANICAL INC

D-U-N-S 02-143-1333
HELM GROUP INC
2283 Route 20 E, Freeport, IL 61032-9643
Tel (815) 235-0990 *Founded/Ownrshp* 1979
Sales 146.8MME *EMP* 200
SIC 1611 1622 1629

D-U-N-S 15-218-6979
HELM HOLDING CO
14310 Hamilton Ave, Detroit, MI 48203-3792
Tel (313) 865-5000 *Founded/Ownrshp* 1943
Sales 58.8MME *EMP* 360
SIC 7389 5199 Packaging & labeling services; Advertising specialties; Packaging & labeling services; Advertising specialties
Pr: Dennis J Gusick

Pr: Janet Smith
COO: Justin Gusick
CFO: Robert Babcock
Treas: Martha Wenderlich
**VP:* Robert Malkiewicz
**VP:* Charles Stocks
Merch Mgr: Jason Dickman

D-U-N-S 00-531-8530 IMP
HELM INC
(*Suby of* HELM HOLDING CO) ★
47911 Halyard Dr, Plymouth, MI 48170-2461
Tel (734) 468-3700 *Founded/Ownrshp* 2014
Sales 44.5MM^E *EMP* 100^E
SIC 7389 5199 2741 Packaging & labeling services; Advertising specialties; Technical manual & paper publishing; Packaging & labeling services; Advertising specialties; Technical manual & paper publishing
CEO: Justin Gusick
CFO: Lorne Dubrowsky
Sr VP: Bob Malkiewicz
CIO: Michael Wacht
Netwrk Eng: Steve Bostedor
Opers Mgr: Mark Cortese
Sales Exec: Zina Taylor
Sls&Mrk Ex: Wendie Booker
VP Mktg: Garry Cole
S&M/VP: Don Laws
Merch Mgr: Jason Dickman

D-U-N-S 09-928-5504 IMP/EXP
HELM US CORP
(*Suby of* HELM AMERICA CORP) ★
1110 Centennial Ave Ste 2, Piscataway, NJ 08854-4169
Tel (732) 981-1116 *Founded/Ownrshp* 1984
Sales 66.6MM^E *EMP* 20
SIC 5169 Chemicals, industrial & heavy
VP: Soeren Beck
**CFO:* William V Fossen
VP: Robert Schiesser IV
VP: Christian Wulf
Sls Mgr: Robert Medlock

HELMAN HUR CHAR PEA ARCH INC
See HHCP DESIGN INTERNATIONAL INC

D-U-N-S 08-668-5682
HELMER INC
HELMER SCIENTIFIC
14400 Bergen Blvd, Noblesville, IN 46060-3307
Tel (317) 773-9073 *Founded/Ownrshp* 1993
Sales 50.7MM^E *EMP* 170
SIC 3841 3821 Blood transfusion equipment; Autoclaves, laboratory
Owner: David Helmer
VP: Jeff Conway
VP: Lori Gabrek
IT Man: Susan Bohr
Software D: Kyle Stout
Sls Dir: Scott Sargent
Sls Mgr: Laura Devault
Sls Mgr: Richard Forero
Snr Mgr: Thomas Larkner

HELMER SCIENTIFIC
See HELMER INC

D-U-N-S 00-520-8020
■ **HELMERICH & PAYNE (ARGENTINA) DRILLING CO**
(*Suby of* HELMERICH & PAYNE INTERNATIONAL DRILLING CO INC) ★
1437 S Boulder Ave # 1400, Tulsa, OK 74119-3623
Tel (918) 742-5531 *Founded/Ownrshp* 1973
Sales 13.5MM^E *EMP* 400
SIC 1381 Drilling oil & gas wells; Drilling oil & gas wells
Ch: Walter H Helmerich III
**Pr:* George S Dotson
**COO:* Hans Helmerich

D-U-N-S 78-606-1648
■ **HELMERICH & PAYNE C A**
(*Suby of* HELMERICH & PAYNE INTERNATIONAL DRILLING CO INC) ★
1437 S Boulder Ave # 1400, Tulsa, OK 74119-3623
Tel (918) 742-5531 *Founded/Ownrshp* 1958
Sales 16.7MM^E *EMP* 350
SIC 1381 Drilling oil & gas wells; Drilling oil & gas wells
CEO: Hans C Helmerich
**Pr:* George Dotson
VP: Lisa Gilley
**VP:* Clint Wisenhunt

D-U-N-S 00-722-3100 IMP/EXP
▲ **HELMERICH & PAYNE INC**
1437 S Boulder Ave # 1400, Tulsa, OK 74119-3623
Tel (918) 742-5531 *Founded/Ownrshp* 1920
Sales 3.1MMM *EMP* 6,738
Accts Ernst & Young Llp Tulsa Okla
Tkr Sym HP *Exch* NYS
SIC 1381 1389 6512 Drilling oil & gas wells; Gas field services; Nonresidential building operators; Commercial & industrial building operation; Shopping center, property operation only; Drilling oil & gas wells; Gas field services; Nonresidential building operators; Commercial & industrial building operation; Shopping center, property operation only
CEO: John W Lindsay
**Ch Bd:* Hans Helmerich
CFO: Juan Pablo Tardio
Ex VP: Steven R Mackey
VP: Ron Fullerton
VP: Lisa Gilley
VP: Gordon Helm
VP: Shane Marchand
VP: Steve Sparks
VP: Rob Stauder
VP: Andy Wingert
Board of Directors: William L Armstrong, Randy A Foutch, Paula Marshall, Thomas A Petrie, Donald F Robillard Jr, Francis Rooney, Edward B Rust Jr, John D Zeglis

D-U-N-S 04-150-0018 IMP
■ **HELMERICH & PAYNE INTERNATIONAL DRILLING CO INC**
(*Suby of* HELMERICH & PAYNE INC) ★
1437 S Boulder Ave # 1400, Tulsa, OK 74119-3623
Tel (918) 742-5531 *Founded/Ownrshp* 1967
Sales 3.0MMM^E *EMP* 6,574
Accts Ernst & Young Llp Tulsa Okla
SIC 1381 Drilling oil & gas wells; Directional drilling oil & gas wells; Drilling oil & gas wells; Directional drilling oil & gas wells
CEO: Hans Helmerich
**Pr:* Rob Stauder
**Ex VP:* John Lindsay
VP: James W Bishop
VP: Jeffrey L Flaherty
VP: Ronald D Fullerton
VP: Warren G Hubler
VP: David W Moyer
VP: Robert L Stauder
VP: Clint Whisenhunt
Exec: M A Orr

D-U-N-S 00-612-9472
■ **HELMERICH & PAYNE RASCO INC**
(*Suby of* HELMERICH & PAYNE INTERNATIONAL DRILLING CO INC) ★
1437 S Boulder Ave # 1400, Tulsa, OK 74119-3623
Tel (918) 742-5531 *Founded/Ownrshp* 1973
Sales 31.4MM^E *EMP* 200^E
SIC 1381 Drilling oil & gas wells; Drilling oil & gas wells
Pr: Hans Helmerich

D-U-N-S 62-709-2968
■ **HELMERICH & PAYNE TRINIDAD DRILLING INC**
HELMERICH/PAYNE INTRNTNL DRLL
(*Suby of* HELMERICH & PAYNE INTERNATIONAL DRILLING CO INC) ★
1579 E 21st St, Tulsa, OK 74114
Tel (918) 742-5531 *Founded/Ownrshp* 1973
Sales 20.7MM^E *EMP* 260
SIC 1381 Drilling oil & gas wells; Drilling oil & gas wells
Pr: Hans Helmerich
**Ch Bd:* Walter H Helmerich III
**Pr:* George S Dotson
CFO: Douglas E Fears
**Treas:* Robert G Gambrell
Telecom Mg: Chuck Clark

HELMERICH/PAYNE INTRNTNL DRLL
See HELMERICH & PAYNE TRINIDAD DRILLING INC

D-U-N-S 05-149-0530 IMP
■ **HELMET HOUSE INC**
TOUR MASTER
(*Suby of* CATERPILLAR INC) ★
26855 Malibu Hills Rd, Calabasas Hills, CA 91301-5100
Tel (800) 421-7247 *Founded/Ownrshp* 1969
Sales 73.6MM *EMP* 130^E
SIC 5136 3949 Men's & boys' clothing; Helmets, athletic; Men's & boys' clothing; Helmets, athletic
Pr: Robert M Niller
**CFO:* Randy Hutchings
**VP:* Philip Bellomy
Mng Dir: Gary Ramlow
Genl Mgr: Dennis Yohman
Dir IT: Bill Watson
Natl Sales: Rene Monestime
Mktg Mgr: Zane Steele
Manager: Rob Zampelli
Sales Asso: Paula Pope-Doyle
Sales Asso: Trish Thompson

D-U-N-S 96-962-5003
HELMKAMP CONSTRUCTION CO
707 Berkshire Blvd, East Alton, IL 62024-1326
Tel (314) 355-2808 *Founded/Ownrshp* 1996
Sales 35.0MM *EMP* 150
Accts Maher & Co St Louis Missou
SIC 1541 1542 Industrial buildings & warehouses; Commercial & office building contractors; Industrial buildings & warehouses; Commercial & office building contractors
CEO: Brad Farrell
Mng Pt: Ron Kinzinger
Pr: Rob Johnes
VP: Gary Bradstreet
VP: Robert Kohlburn
VP: Ted Mettler

D-U-N-S 01-237-2801
HELMS BROS INC (NY)
20824 Northern Blvd, Bayside, NY 11361-3103
Tel (718) 631-8181 *Founded/Ownrshp* 1935, 1977
Sales 40.9MM^E *EMP* 90^E
SIC 5511 7538 7515 5531 5521 Automobiles, new & used; General automotive repair shops; Passenger car leasing; Automotive & home supply stores; Used car dealers; Automobiles, new & used; General automotive repair shops; Passenger car leasing; Automotive & home supply stores; Used car dealers
Pr: Douglas Callahan
CIO: Richard Johnson
Sales Exec: Jennifer Lang
Sls Mgr: Walter Blum
Sls Mgr: Greg Cadwallader
Sls Mgr: Andrea Kass
Sales Asso: Kathleen Baade
Sales Asso: Ronald Dent
Sales Asso: Ricardo Faria
Sales Asso: Jeffrey Stampler

HELMS, EDD ELECTRIC
See EDD HELMS ELECTRIC LLC

D-U-N-S 05-829-2699
HELMSLEY ENTERPRISES INC
HELMSLEY ORGANIZATION
230 Park Ave Rm 659, New York, NY 10169-0698
Tel (212) 679-3600 *Founded/Ownrshp* 1970
Sales 231.5MM^E *EMP* 2,500
SIC 6513 8742 1522 Residential hotel operation; Apartment hotel operation; Real estate consultant; Residential construction; Residential hotel operation; Apartment hotel operation; Real estate consultant; Residential construction
Ch Bd: John Codey
**CFO:* Abe Wolf
VP: Harold Meriam
Exec: John Caracciola
Genl Mgr: Mark Briskin
Genl Mgr: Joseph Rene
Dir IT: Patrick Ward

HELMSLEY ORGANIZATION
See HELMSLEY ENTERPRISES INC

D-U-N-S 04-415-5869
HELMSLEY-NOYES CO LLC (NY)
(*Suby of* HELMSLEY ENTERPRISES INC) ★
230 Park Ave Rm 659, New York, NY 10169-0698
Tel (212) 679-6772 *Founded/Ownrshp* 1898
Sales 216.6MM *EMP* 10
SIC 6531 Real estate brokers & agents; Real estate managers; Real estate brokers & agents; Real estate managers
CFO: Martin Lloziski

D-U-N-S 16-184-4378
HELMSMAN MANAGEMENT SERVICES LLC
LIBERTY MUTUAL
(*Suby of* LIBERTY MUTUAL INSURANCE CO) ★
175 Berkeley St, Boston, MA 02116-5066
Tel (857) 224-1970 *Founded/Ownrshp* 1983
Sales NA *EMP* 400
SIC 6331 Fire, marine & casualty insurance; Fire, marine & casualty insurance
Pr: Douglas Nelson
Treas: Larry Yahia
**VP:* Peter Clas
IT Man: Darren Young

D-U-N-S 60-229-9794
HELP AT HOME INC
OXFORD HEALTHCARE
1 N State St Ste 800, Chicago, IL 60602-3312
Tel (312) 762-9999 *Founded/Ownrshp* 1975
Sales 35.0MM^E *EMP* 1,000
SIC 8082 Home health care services; Home health care services
CEO: Ron Ford
**COO:* Joel Davis
Dir Risk M: Michelle Wersching
Brnch Mgr: Jane Keim
Brnch Mgr: Todd Patterson
Brnch Mgr: Tess Zayyad
Off Admin: Amy Nelson
CTO: Shirley Driscoll
QA Dir: Jason Ford
Dir IT: Alan Bunag
Board of Directors: Joel Davis, Ron Ford

HELP CARD
See DENT-A-MED INC

D-U-N-S 82-511-8441
HELP CHILDREN WORLD FOUNDATION
INTERNATIONAL CHILDREN'S CHARI
26500 Agoura Rd Ste 657, Calabasas, CA 91302-1952
Tel (818) 706-9848 *Founded/Ownrshp* 1991
Sales 387.0M *EMP* 300
SIC 8322 Children's aid society; Children's aid society
Pr: Lev M Leznik
**VP:* Andrew Grey

D-U-N-S 78-477-9527
HELP GROUP CHILD AND FAMILY CENTER
13130 Burbank Blvd, Sherman Oaks, CA 91401-6000
Tel (818) 781-0360 *Founded/Ownrshp* 1941
Sales 20.4MM *EMP* 1^E
Accts Singerlewak Llp Los Angeles
SIC 8093 Speech defect clinic; Specialty outpatient clinics
Pr: Barbara Firestone

D-U-N-S 06-573-9187
HELP GROUP WEST
13130 Burbank Blvd, Sherman Oaks, CA 91401-6000
Tel (818) 781-0360 *Founded/Ownrshp* 1999
Sales 3.2MM *EMP* 400
Accts Singerlewak Llp Los Angeles
SIC 8093 Speech defect clinic; Speech defect clinic
Pr: Barbara Firestone
**CFO:* Michael Love
**Ex VP:* Susan Berman PH

D-U-N-S 60-937-1943
HELP HOMELESS SERVICE CORP
5 Hanover Sq Fl 17, New York, NY 10004-2682
Tel (212) 779-3350 *Founded/Ownrshp* 1986
Sales 22.8MM^E *EMP* 800
Accts Deloitte & Touche Llp
SIC 8399 Community development groups; Community development groups
Ch: Maria Cuomo Cole
**Pr:* Gary Heiserman
**CFO:* Joseph Gallo
Treas: Dan Labrecque
**Sr VP:* Thomas Mauro

D-U-N-S 02-020-6207
HELP HOSPITALIZED VETERANS II (CA)
36585 Penfield Ln, Winchester, CA 92596-9672
Tel (951) 926-4500 *Founded/Ownrshp* 1971
Sales 31.0MM *EMP* 65
SIC 8322 Individual & family services; Individual & family services
Ex Dir: Mike Lynch

D-U-N-S 96-571-1968
HELP HOSPITALIZED VETERANS INC
36585 Penfield Ln, Winchester, CA 92596-9672
Tel (951) 926-4500 *Founded/Ownrshp* 1971
Sales 31.0MM *EMP* 3^E
Accts Frank & Company Pc Mclean
SIC 8641 Veterans' organization; Veterans' organization
CEO: Joe McClain
**Prin:* Roger Chapin
Ex Dir: Michael Lynch
Netwrk Mgr: Al Horn

HELP PERSONNEL DIVISION
See HELP PERSONNEL INC

D-U-N-S 84-551-1096
HELP PERSONNEL INC
HELP PERSONNEL DIVISION
611 N Wymore Rd Ste 220, Winter Park, FL 32789-2843
Tel (407) 629-6888 *Founded/Ownrshp* 1992
Sales 6.3MM^E *EMP* 400
SIC 7363 Temporary help service; Temporary help service
Pr: Jeri Spriggs

HELP THE CHILDREN
See CHILDRENS NETWORK INTERNATIONAL INC

HELP UNLIMITED HOME CARE
See HELP UNLIMITED PERSONNEL SERVICE INC

D-U-N-S 79-174-8098
HELP UNLIMITED PERSONNEL SERVICE INC
HELP UNLIMITED HOME CARE
1767 Goodyear Ave Ste 104, Ventura, CA 93003-7769
Tel (805) 654-6990 *Founded/Ownrshp* 1975
Sales 23.3MM^E *EMP* 700
SIC 8082 7363 Home health care services; Medical help service; Home health care services; Medical help service
Pr: Gayle Bertsch
**Pr:* Jack Bertsch
**Treas:* Ariel Birch

D-U-N-S 82-723-3685
HELP USA INC
5 Hanover Sq Fl 17, New York, NY 10004-2682
Tel (212) 400-7000 *Founded/Ownrshp* 1986
Sales 109.7MM^E *EMP* 800
SIC 6513 8322 Apartment building operators; Individual & family services; Apartment building operators; Individual & family services
Pr: Tom Hameline
**Pr:* Laurence Belinsky
CFO: Joseph A Gallo
Sr VP: Thomas Hameline
VP: David Cleghor
VP: Pedro Fragoso
VP: James Lee
VP: Robert Platt
VP: Ronnie Silverman
Ex Dir: Craig Galati

D-U-N-S 14-884-2284
HELP-EQUITY HOMES INC
5 Hanover Sq Fl 17, New York, NY 10004-2682
Tel (212) 400-7020 *Founded/Ownrshp* 1996
Sales 9.9MM^E *EMP* 800
SIC 6531 Real estate agents & managers; Real estate agents & managers
Pr: Larry Belinsky
**CFO:* Joseph Gallo
**Sr VP:* Tom Hameline
**Sr VP:* Tom Mauro

HELP.COM
See CBS INTERACTIVE INC

HELP/PSI COBRA
See HELP/PSI INC

D-U-N-S 62-608-0055
HELP/PSI INC
HELP/PSI COBRA
248 W 35th St Fl 8, New York, NY 10001-2505
Tel (718) 681-6030 *Founded/Ownrshp* 1988
Sales 27.4MM *EMP* 250
Accts Loeb & Troper Llp New York N
SIC 8052 Intermediate care facilities; Intermediate care facilities
Ch: Richard Pruss
CFO: Neil Latman
CFO: Alan Zuckerman
**Treas:* Marshall Goldberg
VP: Randye Goldstein
**VP:* Nunzio Signorella
Adm Dir: Antonia Deleonardis
IT Man: Wanda Mitchell

D-U-N-S 17-221-0007
HELP/SYSTEMS LLC
6455 City West Pkwy, Eden Prairie, MN 55344-3246
Tel (952) 933-0609 *Founded/Ownrshp* 2015
Sales 100.0MM^E *EMP* 275
SIC 7372 Business oriented computer software; Business oriented computer software
CEO: Chris Heim
Pr: Jim Cassens
COO: Mark Ties
CFO: Dan Mayleben
VP: Tom Huntington
Snr Sftwr: Steve Ferrell
Snr Sftwr: Hamid Noorbakhsh
Snr Sftwr: Ronak Patel
Snr Sftwr: Nathan Ramaker
IT Man: Steven Smith
Tech Mgr: Jill Martin

D-U-N-S 03-535-5524
HELPING AGING NEEDY AND DISABLED INC
1640 E 2nd St B, Austin, TX 78702-4400
Tel (512) 477-2557 *Founded/Ownrshp* 1976
Sales 2.7MM *EMP* 285
Accts Faske Lay & Co Llp Austin
SIC 8322 Individual & family services; Individual & family services
Ex Dir: Amy Temperley

D-U-N-S 78-581-7896
HELPING HAND FOR RELIEF AND DEVELOPMENT INC
HELPING HAND USA
12541 Mcdougall St, Detroit, MI 48212-2262
Tel (313) 279-5378 *Founded/Ownrshp* 2005

Sales 28.7MM EMP 10E
Accts Alan C Young & Associates Pc
SIC 8322 Temporary relief service; Temporary relief service
Ex Dir: Shahid Hayat
*Ch: Raza Farrukh
VP: Anwar Chaudhry
Ex Dir: Farrukh Raza

D-U-N-S 87-462-1295
HELPING HAND NURSING SERVICE INC
8305 S Saginaw St Ste 4, Grand Blanc, MI 48439-1894
Tel (810) 606-8400 Founded/Ownrshp 1973
Sales 8.2MM EMP 450E
SIC 7361 8082 Nurses' registry; Home health care services; Nurses' registry; Home health care services
Pr: Jim Spangler
*Pr: James Spangler
*VP: Patricia Spangler
Brnch Mgr: Andrea Bowen

HELPING HAND USA
See HELPING HAND FOR RELIEF AND DEVELOPMENT INC

D-U-N-S 05-432-7254
HELPS INTERNATIONAL INC (TX)
15301 Dallas Pkwy Ste 200, Addison, TX 75001-4668
Tel (972) 386-5172 Founded/Ownrshp 1983
Sales 20.7MM EMP 40
Accts Sibley & Company Pc Dallas T
SIC 8322 Self-help organization; Self-help organization
Pr: Steve Miller
*VP: Donal O'Neill

D-U-N-S 02-084-4064
HELPSOURCE INC
CHILD & FAMILY SERVICES HURON
3879 Packard St, Ann Arbor, MI 48108-2011
Tel (734) 973-2408 Founded/Ownrshp 1969
Sales 2.8MM EMP 350
Accts Wright Griffin Davis & Co
SIC 8322 8361 Child related social services; Children's home; Group foster home; Home for the emotionally disturbed; Child related social services; Children's home; Group foster home; Home for the emotionally disturbed
Pr: Susan Wiant Crabb
Board of Directors: David Lutton, Clark Richardson

D-U-N-S 00-543-5987
HELSEL-JEPPERSON ELECTRICAL INC (IL)
103 N Halsted St, Chicago Heights, IL 60411-1283
Tel (708) 756-5600 Founded/Ownrshp 1946, 1983
Sales 42.1MME EMP 37
SIC 5063 Electrical supplies
Pr: Delores Helsel
*VP: Joseph Helsel

D-U-N-S 07-185-5787
HELSELL FETTERMAN LLP
1001 4th Ave Ste 4200, Seattle, WA 98154-1154
Tel (206) 292-1144 Founded/Ownrshp 1952
Sales 24.3MME EMP 155
SIC 8111 General practice law office; General practice law office
Mng Pt: Scott Collins
Pt: Bradley H Bagshaw
Pt: David Gross
Pt: Andrew J Kinstler
Pt: Gary F Linden
Pt: Phillip Noble
Pt: Llewelyn Prichard
Pt: Mark Rising
Pt: Paulene Smetka
Pt: Aimee Muul
Counsel: Polly Becker-Johnson

D-U-N-S 02-715-2271 IMP/EXP
HELSER INDUSTRIES INC
10750 Sw Tualatin Rd, Tualatin, OR 97062-8042
Tel (503) 692-6909 Founded/Ownrshp 1983
Sales 30.0MME EMP 100
SIC 3443 3564 3441 3272 Fabricated plate work (boiler shop); Dust or fume collecting equipment, industrial; Fabricated structural metal; Concrete products; Fabricated plate work (boiler shop); Dust or fume collecting equipment, industrial; Fabricated structural metal; Concrete products
Pr: Max R Helser
CIO: Roger White
Sales Exec: Dwight Nelson
Sls Mgr: Rick Thomsen

D-U-N-S 00-343-4522 IMP
HELUKABEL USA INC (IL)
(Suby of HELU KABEL GMBH)
1490 Crispin Dr, Elgin, IL 60123-5533
Tel (847) 930-5118 Founded/Ownrshp 2007
Sales 26.3MME EMP 25
SIC 5063 Wire & cable; Wire & cable
Pr: Marc Luksch
VP: Hartnut Kellner
Natl Sales: Nick Riemer
Manager: Lonnie Felder
Sls Mgr: Holger Weeber

HELVETIA CONTAINER LINE
See FRACHT FWO INC

D-U-N-S 04-632-1048 IMP/EXP
HELVOET PHARMA REALTY CO INC
DATWYLER PHARMA PACKAGING USA
(Suby of DATWYLER HOLDING AG)
9012 Pennsauken Hwy, Pennsauken, NJ 08110-1204
Tel (856) 663-2202 Founded/Ownrshp 1981
Sales 102.8MME EMP 350
SIC 5047 3841

D-U-N-S 00-610-6603 IMP/EXP
HELWIG CARBON PRODUCTS INC (WI)
8900 W Tower Ave, Milwaukee, WI 53224-2849
Tel (414) 354-0749 Founded/Ownrshp 1928
Sales 37.4MME EMP 250E
SIC 3624 Brushes & brush stock contacts, electric; Carbon specialties for electrical use; Brushes & brush stock contacts, electric; Carbon specialties for electrical use
Pr: Jay Koenitzer
CFO: Mark Umhoefer
VP: Helwig Carbon
Genl Mgr: Paul Casper
Opers Supe: Robert Brown
Ql Cn Mgr: Lee Ahern
Ql Cn Mgr: Kris Volgmann
Sales Asso: Andi Buckingham
Sales Asso: Sue Doetsch

HELZBERG DIAMONDS
See HELZBERGS DIAMOND SHOPS INC

D-U-N-S 00-696-5735
■ **HELZBERGS DIAMOND SHOPS INC**
HELZBERG DIAMONDS
(Suby of BERKSHIRE HATHAWAY INC) ★
1825 Swift Ave, Kansas City, MO 64116-3644
Tel (816) 842-7780 Founded/Ownrshp 1995
Sales 332.8MME EMP 2,500
SIC 5944 Jewelry stores; Jewelry stores
CEO: Beryl Raff
Chf Mktg O: Becky Higgins
Sr VP: Pat Duncan
Sr VP: Peggy Keller
Sr VP: Mitch Maggart
VP: Todd Chandler
VP: Nate Frazier
VP: Butch Jagoda
VP: Daniel Lindboe
VP: Jeff Rohr
VP: Jan Steck
VP: Randall Swain
VP: Randy Swain
VP: Michele Swarts
Exec: Kevin Fitzpatrick

D-U-N-S 62-247-4567
HEMA FOOD SERVICES
25324 Frampton Ave, Harbor City, CA 90710-2903
Tel (310) 534-3545 Founded/Ownrshp 1989
Sales 6.7MME EMP 300
SIC 5812 Contract food services; Contract food services
Pr: Siu Henry Ll

D-U-N-S 00-904-6405 IMP
HEMASOURCE INC
4158 W Nike Dr Ste B, West Jordan, UT 84088-5959
Tel (801) 280-5151 Founded/Ownrshp 2008
Sales 20.4MME EMP 28
Accts Wisan Smith Racker & Prescot
SIC 5047 Medical & hospital equipment
CEO: Todd H Tracey
*CFO: Matt Johnson
Sr Cor Off: Douglas McKay
*Ex VP: James J Sielatycki
*Sr VP: Kent F Janes
VP: Kent Janes
Off Mgr: Trisha Morrill

D-U-N-S 10-131-7097
HEMATOLOGY-ONCOLOGY ASSOCIATES OF CENTRAL NEW YORK PC
5008 Brittonfd Pkwy 700, East Syracuse, NY 13057
Tel (315) 472-7504 Founded/Ownrshp 1982
Sales 33.0MME EMP 230
Accts Dannible & Mckee Llp
SIC 8011 Oncologist; Hematologist; Oncologist; Hematologist
Ch Bd: John J Gullo MD
*Treas: Dr Jeffrey Kirshner
*VP: Dr Santo M Di Fino
Cert Phar: Brittany Murphy

HEMBREE BUICK CHEVROLET
See BOB HEMBREE MOTOR CO INC

D-U-N-S 03-950-3776
HEMET UNIFIED SCHOOL DISTRICT
HEMETUSD
1791 W Acacia Ave, Hemet, CA 92545-3797
Tel (951) 765-5100 Founded/Ownrshp 1964
Sales 3,9MM EMP 1,346
Accts Vavrinek Trine Day & Co Ll
SIC 8211 Public elementary & secondary schools; Elementary school; Public adult education school; Public elementary & secondary schools; Elementary school; Public adult education school
*Prin: Dr Lafaye Platter
Dir Sec: Lucy Dressel
CIO: Jeanne Clark
Dir IT: Emil Desilio
Opers Mgr: Sharon Peterson
Pr Dir: Alexandrea Cass
Schl Brd P: Paul Bakkurn
Psych: Terri Foster

HEMET VALLEY MEDICAL CENTER
See PHYSICIANS FOR HEALTHY HOSPITALS INC

D-U-N-S 07-249-6912
HEMET VALLEY MEDICAL CENTER-EDUCATION
1117 E Devonshire Ave, Hemet, CA 92543-3083
Tel (951) 652-2811 Founded/Ownrshp 2009
Sales 90.9MME EMP 1,200
SIC 8062 General medical & surgical hospitals; General medical & surgical hospitals
CEO: Kali Chaudhuri
Chf Path: Mildred Ramos
Chf OB: Syed Rizvi
Chf Rad: Frederick E Whit
COO: Joel Bergenfeld
CFO: Kathy Cain
Treas: Lorraine Augustine
Dir Rx: Steve Kelso
*Prin: Girdhari Purohit
Dir Sec: Kathy Spoon
CIO: Mike Dozier

HEMETUSD
See HEMET UNIFIED SCHOOL DISTRICT

HEMI SYSTEMS
See HEAVY EQUIPMENT MOVERS & INSTALLATION LLC

D-U-N-S 07-881-4566
▲ **HEMISPHERE MEDIA GROUP INC**
2000 Ponce De Leon Blvd Ph, Coral Gables, FL 33134-4439
Tel (305) 421-6364 Founded/Ownrshp 2013
Sales 111.9MM EMP 293E
Tkr Sym HMTV Exch NGM
SIC 4841 Cable & other pay television services; Cable & other pay television services
Pr: Alan J Sokol
*Ch Bd: Peter M Kern
CFO: Craig D Fischer
*V Ch Bd: James M McNamara

D-U-N-S 09-539-5216 IMP
HEMLOCK SEMICONDUCTOR CORP
HEMLOCK SEMICONDUCTOR GROUP
(Suby of DOW CORNING CORP) ★
12334 Geddes Rd, Hemlock, MI 48626-9409
Tel (989) 642-5201 Founded/Ownrshp 1959
Sales 207.9MME EMP 400
SIC 3295 Silicon, ultra high purity: treated; Silicon, ultra high purity: treated
Pr: Richard Doorndos
VP: Marie N Eckstein
VP: James Stutelberg
VP Mfg: Gregory Skufca
Snr Mgr: Mark Stachowiak

HEMLOCK SEMICONDUCTOR GROUP
See HEMLOCK SEMICONDUCTOR CORP

D-U-N-S 14-263-5676
HEMMA CONCRETE INC
819 Pickens Industrial Dr # 3, Marietta, GA 30062-3159
Tel (770) 612-8231 Founded/Ownrshp 2003
Sales 39.4MM EMP 120
Accts Hlb Gross Collins Pc Atlanta
SIC 1771 Concrete work
CEO: Reg Cook
*CFO: Andrew Noble
*Prin: Travis L Roberts
Off Mgr: Ashley Ginther
Off Mgr: Joseph J Pettit
Snr PM: Steve Matheson

HEMOCUE AMERICA
See HEMOCUE INC

D-U-N-S 12-956-5235
HEMOCUE INC
HEMOCUE AMERICA
(Suby of RADIOMETER MEDICAL APS)
250 S Kraemer Blvd # 250, Brea, CA 92821-6232
Tel (800) 881-1611 Founded/Ownrshp 2013
Sales 44.1MM EMP 82
SIC 5999 5047 Medical apparatus & supplies; Diagnostic equipment, medical; Medical apparatus & supplies; Diagnostic equipment, medical
Sls Mgr: Chip Neff

D-U-N-S 04-650-1206
HEMOPHILIA CENTER OF WESTERN PENNSYLVANIA
3636 Blvd Of The Allies, Pittsburgh, PA 15213-4306
Tel (412) 209-7280 Founded/Ownrshp 1974
Sales 37.6MM EMP 16
Accts Alpern Rosenthal Pittsburgh
SIC 8099 Blood donor station; Blood donor station
Pr: Margaret Ragni
Snr Mgr: Chris Osman

D-U-N-S 61-791-6481
■ **HEMOPHILIA HEALTH SERVICES INC**
(Suby of ACCREDO HEALTH INC) ★
6820 Charlotte Pike, Nashville, TN 37209-4260
Tel (615) 352-2500 Founded/Ownrshp 1997
Sales 54.5MME EMP 260E
SIC 5122 Pharmaceuticals; Pharmaceuticals
Pr: Kyle Callahan
VP: Vic Fisher
Ex Dir: Dena Shepard
Pharmcst: Melinda Mathews

D-U-N-S 00-128-3944 IMP
HEMPEL (USA) INC (TX)
(Suby of HEMPEL A/S)
600 Conroe Park North Dr, Conroe, TX 77303-2207
Tel (936) 523-6000 Founded/Ownrshp 1950
Sales 104.0MME EMP 295
SIC 2851 Marine paints; Paints & paint additives; Lacquers, varnishes, enamels & other coatings; Marine paints; Paints & paint additives; Lacquers, varnishes, enamels & other coatings
Pr: Lars Johansen
*CFO: Michael Reese
Ex VP: Kim Andersen
VP: Jesper Boedtkjer
*VP: Pierre Jullien
IT Man: Kasper Lydolph
IT Man: Marek Wrzosek
Sfty Mgr: Charles Zogg
Opers Mgr: David Sivek
*Sls&Mrk Ex: Malcolm Kerr

D-U-N-S 07-215-0394
HEMPFIELD AREA SCHOOL DISTRICT
4347 State Route 136, Greensburg, PA 15601-6411
Tel (724) 834-2590 Founded/Ownrshp 1960
Sales 87.0MM EMP 845
SIC 8211 Public elementary & secondary schools; High school, junior or senior; Public elementary & secondary schools; High school, junior or senior
Pr: Sonya Brajdic
*Pr: John Henry
*VP: Diane Caibattoni
Teacher Pr: Robert Reger
Teacher Pr: Patricia Strickengloss

D-U-N-S 09-715-4280
HEMPFIELD SCHOOL DISTRICT
200 Church St, Landisville, PA 17538-1300
Tel (717) 898-5564 Founded/Ownrshp 1958
Sales 62.3MME EMP 800
SIC 8211 Public elementary & secondary schools; Public elementary school; Public junior high school; Public senior high school; Public elementary & secondary schools; Public elementary school; Public junior high school; Public senior high school
Pr Dir: Shannon Zimmerman
HC Dir: Susan Horan
HC Dir: Jab Musser

D-U-N-S 04-775-4098
HEMPHILL CONSTRUCTION CO INC
1858 Highway 49 S, Florence, MS 39073-9427
Tel (601) 932-2060 Founded/Ownrshp 1963
Sales 118.2MME EMP 285
SIC 1623 1542 Water & sewer line construction; Commercial & office building, new construction; Water & sewer line construction; Commercial & office building, new construction
CEO: Richard Rula
*CFO: Diarin Granthan
*Ex VP: Lynn Guthrie
VP: Vic Borromeo
VP: Ricky Eiland
VP: Tim Temple
IT Man: David Jackson
Sfty Dirs: Dwayne Toombs

HEMPSTEAD AUTO SALES
See MILLENIUM HONDA

HEMPSTEAD LINCOLN MERCURY
See GARDEN CITY SAAB MOTORS CORP

D-U-N-S 07-626-7574
HEMPSTEAD PARK NURSING HOME
800 Front St, Hempstead, NY 11550-4600
Tel (516) 705-9700 Founded/Ownrshp 1967
Sales 10.5MME EMP 300
SIC 8051 Convalescent home with continuous nursing care; Convalescent home with continuous nursing care
Pt: Milton Stapen MD

D-U-N-S 04-559-0809
HEMPSTEAD UNION FREE SCHOOL DISTRICT
185 Peninsula Blvd, Hempstead, NY 11550-4900
Tel (516) 292-7001 Founded/Ownrshp 1847
Sales 188.2MM EMP 1,200
Accts Nawrocki Smith Llp Melville
SIC 8211 Public elementary & secondary schools; Public elementary & secondary schools
Bd of Dir: Dianne Hamilton
Dir Sec: Andrew Hardwick
MIS Dir: Daniel Espina
IT Man: David Lasker
Sls&Mrk Ex: Gene Levenstien

D-U-N-S 00-302-5285
HEMPT BROS INC (PA)
205 Creek Rd, Camp Hill, PA 17011-7499
Tel (717) 774-2911 Founded/Ownrshp 1925, 1969
Sales 107.5MME EMP 250
SIC 1611 3273 2951 1442 0212 General contractor, highway & street construction; Paving mixtures; Ready-mixed concrete; Construction sand mining; Gravel mining; Beef cattle except feedlots; General contractor, highway & street construction; Ready-mixed concrete; Paving mixtures; Construction sand mining; Gravel mining; Beef cattle except feedlots
Pr: Max J Hempt
*Treas: Joseph L Theurer
*Sec: Gerald L Hempt
*VP: Joseph R Nokovich
VP: Albert Tompkins
Dir IT: Christine Murphy
Sfty Dirs: Tyler Boudreau
Mtls Mgr: Lance Leber
Sls Mgr: Michael Snoke
Sls Mgr: Jeff Yost

HEMSI
See HUNTSVILLE EMERGENCY MEDICAL SERVICES INC

D-U-N-S 10-918-9035
HENCH ENTERPRISES INC
RAYS SUPERMARKETS
317 W Main Cross St, Findlay, OH 45840-3314
Tel (419) 782-0950 Founded/Ownrshp 1984
Sales 24.7MME EMP 200
SIC 5411 Grocery stores, independent; Grocery stores, independent
Pr: Eric C Hench

D-U-N-S 60-815-7046
HENDERSON & PHILLIPS INC
USI INSURANCE SERVICES
(Suby of USI HOLDINGS CORP) ★
101 W Main St Ste 900, Norfolk, VA 23510-1653
Tel (757) 625-1800 Founded/Ownrshp 1996
Sales NA EMP 125
SIC 6411 Insurance agents, brokers & service; Insurance brokers
CEO: Dudley Fulton
Pr: Jeff Snyder
CEO: Steve Deal
CFO: Robert Schneider
Treas: Dave Hess
Exec: Elizabeth Alley

D-U-N-S 04-810-6272
HENDERSON BEHAVIORAL HEALTH INC
4740 N State Road 7 # 201, Lauderdale Lakes, FL 33319-5839
Tel (954) 486-4005 Founded/Ownrshp 1953
Sales 36.3MM EMP 600
Accts Keefe Mccullough & Co Llp Cpa
SIC 8093 Mental health clinic, outpatient; Mental health clinic, outpatient
CEO: Dr Steven Ronik
*Pr: Richard F Kinzer
*COO: Pamala Galan
*CFO: Erika Ricketts
Ch: Marvin Chaney
*VP: Kanner R Kristin
Off Mgr: Satia Horn

QC Dir: Lee Wein
Doctor: Jorge Jorrido

D-U-N-S 08-551-9387
HENDERSON BROTHERS INC
KEMPER INSURANCE
920 Fort Duquesne Blvd, Pittsburgh, PA 15222-3620
Tel (412) 261-1842 *Founded/Ownrshp* 1893
Sales NA *EMP* 104
SIC 6411

D-U-N-S 03-472-5523
HENDERSON CHESTER FARMERS CO-OP
16219 Highway 22 N, Lexington, TN 38351-6574
Tel (731) 968-2087 *Founded/Ownrshp* 1935
Sales 25.5MM^E *EMP* 64
SIC 5191 5999 Farm supplies; Animal feeds; Farm equipment & supplies; Feed & farm supply; Farm supplies; Animal feeds; Farm equipment & supplies; Feed & farm supply
Opers Mgr: Mark Montgomery

D-U-N-S 88-495-4512
HENDERSON CHEVROLET CO
240 N Gibson Rd, Henderson, NV 89014-6700
Tel (702) 558-2438 *Founded/Ownrshp* 1993
Sales 55.1MM^E *EMP* 150
SIC 5511 7538 7532 5012 Automobiles, new & used; General automotive repair shops; Top & body repair & paint shops; Automobiles & other motor vehicles; Automobiles, new & used; General automotive repair shops; Top & body repair & paint shops; Automobiles & other motor vehicles
Pr: Greg Heinrich
Store Mgr: Jeremy Gresko
DP Exec: Dale Olsen

HENDERSON CHRYSLER JEEP
See HENDERSON-SAIA INC

D-U-N-S 62-099-0726
HENDERSON COLD STORAGE INC
(*Suby of* VERSACOLD US INC) ★
830 E Horizon Dr, Henderson, NV 89015-8458
Tel (702) 566-5810 *Founded/Ownrshp* 2006
Sales 14.8MM^E *EMP* 574^E
SIC 4222 Warehousing, cold storage or refrigerated
Prin: Ross Smith
Opers Mgr: Debbie Gadue

HENDERSON COUNTY BOARD EDUCATN
See HENDERSON COUNTY SCHOOL DISTRICT

D-U-N-S 87-646-0726
HENDERSON COUNTY BOARD OF EDUCATION
35 E Wilson St Ste B, Lexington, TN 38351-1863
Tel (731) 968-3661 *Founded/Ownrshp* 1920
Sales NA *EMP* 450
SIC 9411 ;

D-U-N-S 12-462-9528
HENDERSON COUNTY BOARD OF PUBLIC EDUCATION
HENDERSON COUNTY PUB SCHOOLS
414 4th Ave W, Hendersonville, NC 28739-4325
Tel (828) 698-4510 *Founded/Ownrshp* 1840
Sales 82.1MM^E *EMP* 1,850
SIC 8211 Public elementary & secondary schools; Public elementary & secondary schools
**CFO:* Kerry Shannon
Exec: Chad Auten
Dir IT: Jarod Pace
Pr Dir: Patrisha Allen
Teacher Pr: John Bryant

HENDERSON COUNTY CMNTY HOSP
See LEXINGTON HOSPITAL CORP

HENDERSON COUNTY GOVERNMENT
See COUNTY OF HENDERSON

D-U-N-S 07-451-2559
HENDERSON COUNTY HOSPITAL CORP (NC)
MARGARET R PARDEE MEMORIAL HOS
800 N Justice St, Hendersonville, NC 28791-3410
Tel (828) 698-7191 *Founded/Ownrshp* 1953
Sales 144.8MM *EMP* 1,300
SIC 8062 8051 8082 General medical & surgical hospitals; Skilled nursing care facilities; Home health care services; General medical & surgical hospitals; Skilled nursing care facilities; Home health care services
CEO: Robert P Goodwin
**CEO:* James Kirby
**CFO:* Pamela Booher
Sr VP: Karla Reese
VP: Denise Lucas
CIO: Barbara Shock
QA Dir: Suzan Stewart
Dir IT: Kelly Ogden
Dir IT: Freida Wade
Obsttrcn: David Beaty
Doctor: Nathaniel Jablecki

HENDERSON COUNTY PUB SCHOOLS
See HENDERSON COUNTY BOARD OF PUBLIC EDUCATION

D-U-N-S 07-979-9761
HENDERSON COUNTY SCHOOL DISTRICT
35 E Wilson St, Lexington, TN 38351-1862
Tel (731) 968-3661 *Founded/Ownrshp* 2015
Sales 4.4MM^E *EMP* 406^E
SIC 8211 Public elementary & secondary schools

D-U-N-S 92-799-0879
HENDERSON COUNTY SCHOOL DISTRICT
HENDERSON COUNTY BOARD EDUCATN
1805 2nd St, Henderson, KY 42420-3367
Tel (270) 831-5000 *Founded/Ownrshp* 1976
Sales 56.1MM^E *EMP* 1,130
Accts Crafton & Wilson & Co
SIC 8211 Public elementary & secondary schools; Public elementary & secondary schools
**CFO:* Walt Spencer
Pr Dir: Jeff Coursey

Pr Dir: Julie Wischer
Teacher Pr: Adrienne Cruse

D-U-N-S 07-979-8806
HENDERSON COUNTY SCHOOLS
414 4th Ave W, Hendersonville, NC 28739-4254
Tel (828) 697-4733
Sales 14.0MM^E *EMP* 1,831^E
SIC 8211 Public elementary & secondary schools
Exec: Molly Gorsuch

D-U-N-S 06-449-4966
HENDERSON ELECTRIC CO INC
5375 Oakbrook Pkwy, Norcross, GA 30093-2275
Tel (770) 279-2272 *Founded/Ownrshp* 1955
Sales 29.5MM^E *EMP* 200
SIC 1731 General electrical contractor; General electrical contractor
Pr: Harold L Machen
**VP:* Andrew L Shadrick
**VP:* Lawton Wimberly

D-U-N-S 08-878-8112
HENDERSON ELECTRIC INC
648 Anchors St Nw Unit 3a, Fort Walton Beach, FL 32548-3889
Tel (850) 243-2223 *Founded/Ownrshp* 1956
Sales 24.3MM^E *EMP* 50
SIC 1731 General electrical contractor
Pr: Douglas E Henderson
**VP:* Gloria Henderson
Off Mgr: Virginia Hodges

D-U-N-S 78-393-3336
HENDERSON ENGINEERS INC
8345 Lenexa Dr Ste 300, Lenexa, KS 66214-1777
Tel (913) 742-5000 *Founded/Ownrshp* 1989
Sales 63.3MM^E *EMP* 430
SIC 8711 Professional engineer; Electrical or electronic engineering; Professional engineer; Electrical or electronic engineering
CEO: Duane Henderson
**Pr:* Richard Smith
**COO:* David Haake
**CFO:* Richard Lahn
Chf Mktg O: Robin Broder
Ex VP: Gail Ensz
**Sr VP:* Dana Kettle
Sr VP: Mike McCluskey
Sr VP: Paul Mejia
**Sr VP:* Phil Miller
Sr VP: Drew Rimmer
VP: Cindy Carlson
VP: Christopher Culp
VP: Marc Feyh
VP: Mary Holy
VP: Elise Kirchhofer
VP: Craig Lanham
VP: Jeff Leathers
VP: Kevin Lewis
VP: Shane Lutz
VP: Patrick Mills

D-U-N-S 96-597-0549
■ **HENDERSON ENTERPRISES GROUP INC**
(*Suby of* DOUGLAS DYNAMICS INC) ★
1085 S 3rd St, Manchester, IA 52057-2003
Tel (563) 927-2828 *Founded/Ownrshp* 2014
Sales 75.5MM^E *EMP* 250^E
SIC 3715 Truck trailers; Truck trailers
Pr: Mart Ward
CFO: Steve Hoeger

HENDERSON FORD
See WEBSTER FORD INC

HENDERSON GENERAL CONTRACTORS
See HENDERSON INC

D-U-N-S 14-982-3739
HENDERSON HYUNDAI SUPERSTORE INC
460 N Boulder Hwy, Henderson, NV 89015-5310
Tel (702) 565-1500 *Founded/Ownrshp* 2002
Sales 42.6MM^E *EMP* 95
SIC 5511 7549 Automobiles, new & used; Automotive maintenance services; Automobiles, new & used; Automotive maintenance services
Pr: Frank Maione
CFO: Christina Ribaudo

D-U-N-S 03-452-8497
HENDERSON IMPLEMENT & MARINE LLC
TK PIZZA
211 W Service Rd, Welsh, LA 70591-3009
Tel (337) 734-2166 *Founded/Ownrshp* 1966
Sales 39.6MM *EMP* 70
SIC 5149 5083 Pizza supplies; Agricultural machinery & equipment; Pizza supplies; Agricultural machinery & equipment
Pr: Charles Henderson Jr

D-U-N-S 09-844-6818
HENDERSON INC
HENDERSON GENERAL CONTRACTORS
5806 Mooretown Rd, Williamsburg, VA 23188-1712
Tel (757) 565-1090 *Founded/Ownrshp* 1958
Sales 70.3MM^E *EMP* 100
SIC 1542 1611 1541 Commercial & office building, new construction; General contractor, highway & street construction; Industrial buildings, new construction; Commercial & office building, new construction; General contractor, highway & street construction; Industrial buildings, new construction
Pr: Peter V Henderson
**Pr:* Bill Strack
**CFO:* Jacob Liebler
**VP:* James M Neilson
**VP:* Leslie H Schultz
IT Man: Jennifer Stewart
Sales Exec: Mark Harvey

D-U-N-S 07-837-1051
HENDERSON INDEPENDENT SCHOOL DISTRICT
200 N High St, Henderson, TX 75652-3103
Tel (903) 655-5000 *Founded/Ownrshp* 1911
Sales 25.0MM^E *EMP* 580
Accts Richard P Loughlin Henderson

SIC 8211 Public elementary & secondary schools; Public elementary & secondary schools
Pr Dir: Stacy Johnson
Psych: Lori Vinson
HC Dir: Joy Pipes

HENDERSON MANUFACTURING
See HENDERSON PRODUCTS INC

D-U-N-S 07-138-5157
HENDERSON MEMORIAL HOSPITAL FOUNDATION (TX)
ETMC-HENDERSON HOSPITAL
300 Wilson St, Henderson, TX 75652-5956
Tel (903) 657-7541 *Founded/Ownrshp* 1928
Sales 19.6MM *EMP* 300^E
SIC 8062 General medical & surgical hospitals; General medical & surgical hospitals
CEO: Mark Leitner
CFO: Kevin Storey
Dir OR: Jeannette Belatin
Dir Rad: Sherry Harris
CIO: Kelley Fredrickson
Mktg Dir: Rebecca Kitchens
Mktg Dir: Debbie Roosth

D-U-N-S 02-044-3933
HENDERSON MUNICIPAL POWER & LIGHT (INC)
CITY UTILITY COMMISSION
100 5th St, Henderson, KY 42420-2911
Tel (270) 826-2726 *Founded/Ownrshp* 1896
Sales 37.3MM^E *EMP* 60
SIC 4911 ; Generation, electric power; Distribution, electric power
Pr: Jeff Garner

D-U-N-S 05-516-1616
HENDERSON OIL CO INC
745 Ashe St, Hendersonville, NC 28792-2612
Tel (828) 693-3487 *Founded/Ownrshp* 1971
Sales 33.3MM^E *EMP* 80
SIC 5541 5983 5411 5172 Filling stations, gasoline; Fuel oil dealers; Convenience stores, independent; Petroleum products
Pr: William D McKibbin
Pr: Barry Edwards
**CFO:* Paul E Jordan
**VP:* Margaret D McKibbin
Genl Mgr: C Barry Edwards

HENDERSON PARTS PRO'S
See HENDERSON WHEEL & WAREHOUSE SUPPLY INC

D-U-N-S 06-840-7266
■ **HENDERSON PRODUCTS INC**
HENDERSON MANUFACTURING
(*Suby of* HENDERSON ENTERPRISES GROUP INC) ★
1085 S 3rd St, Manchester, IA 52057-2003
Tel (563) 927-2828 *Founded/Ownrshp* 2009
Sales 75.5MM^E *EMP* 250
SIC 3537 Industrial trucks & tractors; Industrial trucks & tractors
Pr: Mart E Ward
**CFO:* Steve Hoeger
VP: Glennt Beck
VP: Jeff Coldert
VP: Robert McKinley
VP: Bruce Scott
Exec: Clayton Holden
Dir IT: Michael Bany
Plnt Mgr: Jeff Colbert
Manager: Doug Frauenholtz
Manager: Todd Stritzel

D-U-N-S 10-269-0380
HENDERSON SERVICES LLC
4502 Poplar Level Rd, Louisville, KY 40213-2124
Tel (502) 452-6327 *Founded/Ownrshp* 2001
Sales 35.7MM^E *EMP* 170
SIC 1731 General electrical contractor; General electrical contractor
Pr: Bruce M Henderson
CFO: Julie A Dean
VP: David W Gross
VP: Mickey Masterson

D-U-N-S 06-766-7196
HENDERSON STATE UNIVERSITY
1100 Henderson St, Arkadelphia, AR 71999-0001
Tel (870) 230-5000 *Founded/Ownrshp* 1929
Sales 77.7MM^E *EMP* 709^E
SIC 8221 University; University
Pr: Glendell Jones
**VP:* Bobby Jones
CTO: Rebecce Langley
Pr Dir: Penny Murphy

D-U-N-S 15-520-0140
HENDERSON STEEL CORP
4528 Marion Dr, Meridian, MS 39303
Tel (601) 484-3000 *Founded/Ownrshp* 1986
Sales 27.4MM^E *EMP* 27
SIC 5051 Structural shapes, iron or steel
Pr: Roger Henderson
**Sec:* Billy S Oubre

D-U-N-S 14-844-4875
HENDERSON WESSENDORFF FOUNDATION
611 Morton St, Richmond, TX 77469-3083
Tel (281) 342-2044 *Founded/Ownrshp* 2004
Sales 97.1MM *EMP* 1
Accts Barbara Nowotny Llc Bellaire
SIC 8699 Charitable organization; Charitable organization
Pr: Louise H Wessendorff
Ofcr: Joe Robinson

D-U-N-S 03-536-4777
HENDERSON WHEEL & WAREHOUSE SUPPLY INC
HENDERSON PARTS PRO'S
1845 S 300 W, Salt Lake City, UT 84115-1804
Tel (801) 486-2073 *Founded/Ownrshp* 1930
Sales 39.5MM^E *EMP* 165

SIC 5013 3714 Automotive supplies & parts; Axles, motor vehicle; Automotive supplies & parts; Axles, motor vehicle
Pr: John Henderson
**Treas:* Susan Castillo
**Treas:* Paul Henderson

D-U-N-S 80-012-2764
HENDERSON-SAIA INC
HENDERSON CHRYSLER JEEP
11955 Airline Hwy, Baton Rouge, LA 70817-4406
Tel (225) 753-2000 *Founded/Ownrshp* 1989
Sales 22.1MM^E *EMP* 55
SIC 5511 Automobiles, new & used
Pr: Jess Henderson

D-U-N-S 07-557-2016
■ **HENDERSON/VANCE HEALTHCARE INC**
MARIA PARHAM HOSPITAL
(*Suby of* DLP HEALTHCARE LLC) ★
566 Ruin Creek Rd, Henderson, NC 27536-2927
Tel (252) 438-4143 *Founded/Ownrshp* 2011
Sales 3.3MM^E *EMP* 850
Accts Dixon Hughes Goodman Llp Ashe
SIC 8062 General medical & surgical hospitals; General medical & surgical hospitals
CEO: Brian Sinotte
COO: Tim Harclerode
CFO: John Carpenter
CFO: Jim Chapman
CFO: Jim Chatman
Chf Mktg O: Ronald Stahl MD
VP: Edmond Raymond
Exec: Jay Kennedy
Dir Case M: Linda Overby
Dir Rx: John Cole
Ex Dir: Bob Richardson

HENDERSONS CONTRACTOR SUPPLY
See CITY CONSTRUCTION CO INC

D-U-N-S 94-841-3612
HENDRENS INC
JOHN DEERE
2100 Earlywood Dr, Franklin, IN 46131-8870
Tel (317) 887-1920 *Founded/Ownrshp* 1995
Sales 20.9MM *EMP* 63
SIC 5083 7699 Farm implements; Farm machinery repair; Farm implements; Farm machinery repair
Pr: Rich Hendren
**Sec:* Joni Hendren

HENDRICK
See LEWISVILLE VOLKSWAGEN LLC

D-U-N-S 17-355-5988 EXP
HENDRICK AUTOMOTIVE GROUP
6000 Monroe Rd Ste 100, Charlotte, NC 28212-6178
Tel (704) 568-5550 *Founded/Ownrshp* 1986
Sales 2.0MM^E *EMP* 5,000
SIC 5511

D-U-N-S 96-723-4332
HENDRICK AUTOMOTIVE GROUP EMPLOYEE BENEFIT TRUST
(*Suby of* HENDRICK AUTOMOTIVE GROUP) ★
6000 Monroe Rd Ste 100, Charlotte, NC 28212-6178
Tel (704) 568-5550 *Founded/Ownrshp* 2011
Sales 53.7MM *EMP* 2
Accts Dixon Hughes Pllc Raleigh Nc
SIC 7538 General automotive repair shops; General automotive repair shops

HENDRICK BMW
See IMPORTS AUTOMOTIVE CO

D-U-N-S 03-133-8437
HENDRICK CHEVROLET AUTOMOTIVE CO
8300 Shawnee Mission Pkwy, Shawnee Mission, KS 66202-2947
Tel (913) 384-1550 *Founded/Ownrshp* 1994
Sales 62.3MM^E *EMP* 200^E
SIC 5511 Automobiles, new & used; Pickups, new & used; Vans, new & used; Automobiles, new & used; Pickups, new & used; Vans, new & used
CEO: Rick Hendrick
Sales Exec: Phillip Miller

D-U-N-S 12-256-1587 IMP/EXP
HENDRICK CONSTRUCTION INC
9144 Arrowpoint Blvd # 150, Charlotte, NC 28273-8133
Tel (704) 887-0280 *Founded/Ownrshp* 2002
Sales 28.4MM *EMP* 30
SIC 1542 Nonresidential construction; Nonresidential construction
Pr: Roger Hendrick
COO: Nick Koulpasis
Snr PM: Scottie Richardson

HENDRICK DODGE
See CARY AUTOMOTIVE CO

HENDRICK HONDA
See HENDRICK MANAGEMENT LLC

HENDRICK HONDA
See SOUTH BOULEVARD AUTO INVESTORS CO LIMITED PARTNERSHIP

HENDRICK HONDA HICKORY
See JLH HICKORY LIMITED PARTNERSHIP

D-U-N-S 08-190-7032
HENDRICK HUDSON CENTRAL SCHOOL DISTRICT
61 Trolley Rd, Montrose, NY 10548-1121
Tel (914) 257-5100 *Founded/Ownrshp* 1926
Sales 52.8MM *EMP* 500
Accts Bennett Kielson Storch Desanti
SIC 8211 Public combined elementary & secondary school; Public elementary school; Public junior high school; Public senior high school; Public combined elementary & secondary school; Public elementary school; Public junior high school; Public senior high school
Schl Brd P: Mary-Pat Briggi

D-U-N-S 13-185-4841
HENDRICK MANAGEMENT LLC
HENDRICK HONDA
8901 South Blvd, Charlotte, NC 28273-6933
Tel (704) 552-2090 *Founded/Ownrshp* 1986
Sales 67.0MM^E *EMP* 216
SIC 5511 Management services; Automobiles, new & used
Pr: James F Huzl
CFO: Mathew Ricks
**VP:* Thomas A Blocker
**VP:* Kirk R Heppler
**VP:* Veronica A Zayatz

D-U-N-S 00-303-3636 IMP
HENDRICK MANUFACTURING CO (PA)
17th Ave, Carbondale, PA 18407
Tel (570) 282-1010 *Founded/Ownrshp* 1876
Sales 34.0MM^E *EMP* 200
SIC 3469 3496 3444 Perforated metal, stamped; Screening, woven wire: made from purchased wire; Sheet metalwork; Perforated metal, stamped; Screening, woven wire: made from purchased wire; Sheet metalwork
CEO: Michael D Drake
**CFO:* Darin Drake
VP: Dan Faramelli
VP: Michael Isbill
**VP:* Alicia McHale
Genl Mgr: Malcolm Sheppard
IT Man: Mel Malay
IT Man: Ramal Malay
Plnt Mgr: Jonathan Watt
Natl Sales: Darran Zimmermann
Manager: Tim Fitzgerald

D-U-N-S 06-838-2050
HENDRICK MEDICAL CENTER
1900 Pine St, Abilene, TX 79601-2432
Tel (325) 670-2000 *Founded/Ownrshp* 1923
Sales 394.2MM *EMP* 2,900
Accts Condley And Company Llp Abil
SIC 8062 General medical & surgical hospitals; General medical & surgical hospitals
CEO: Tim Lancaster
COO: Suzanne Starr
**CFO:* Jeremy Walker
**Sr VP:* Joe Pearson
**VP:* Norm Archibald
**VP:* Stephen T Faehnle
VP: Susan Wade
Exec: Terri Bloodgood
Dir Risk M: Carol Kramer
Prac Mgr: Marjohn Riney
Off Mgr: David Allen

HENDRICK MOTORS OF CHARLOTTE
See HMC LLC

D-U-N-S 13-190-1183
HENDRICK MOTORSPORTS LLC
(*Suby of* J.R. HENDRICK III MOTOR SPORTS TRUST)
4400 Papa Joe Hendrick, Charlotte, NC 28262-5703
Tel (704) 455-3400 *Founded/Ownrshp* 1986
Sales 43.3MM^E *EMP* 500
SIC 7948 Stock car racing; Stock car racing
Pt: Rick Hendrick
**Pt:* Hendrick M Corp
Ofcr: Scott Lampe
Genl Mgr: Jeff Turner
Dir IT: Chris Newsome
Netwrk Mgr: Matt Cochran
Plnt Mgr: Larry Zentmeyer
VP Mktg: Pat Perkins
Mktg Mgr: Chris Haid
Sales Asso: Laura Scott
Snr Mgr: Steve Letarte

HENDRICK, RICK IMPORTS
See CHARLESTON AUTOMOTIVE CO

D-U-N-S 02-559-6651
HENDRICK SOUTHWESTERN HEALTH DEVELOPMENT CORP
HEALTH AFFILIATED SERVICES
(*Suby of* HENDRICK MEDICAL DEVELOPMENT CORPORATION)
1900 Pine St, Abilene, TX 79601-2432
Tel (325) 695-4583 *Founded/Ownrshp* 1977
Sales 25.3MM^E *EMP* 66
SIC 6512 7389 8099 7352 5999 5047 Commercial & industrial building operation; Purchasing service; Physical examination & testing services; Medical equipment rental; Hospital equipment & supplies; Hospital equipment & supplies
Pr: Tim Lancaster
**CFO:* Stephen Kimmel
Ofcr: Bob Prewit
**Sr VP:* Jeremy Walker
**VP:* Norm Archibald
VP: Lisa Harp
Nurse Mgr: Dan Curl
CTO: Robert Lawson
Sftwr Eng: Jim Kirkland
Opers Mgr: Luke Martin
Mktg Dir: Leigh Black

HENDRICKS CHEVROLET
See GWINNETT PLACE CHEVROLET LLC

D-U-N-S 82-712-3394
HENDRICKS COMMERCIAL PROPERTIES LLC
H C P
525 3rd St Ste 300, Beloit, WI 53511-6211
Tel (608) 362-8981 *Founded/Ownrshp* 2000
Sales 27.1MM^E *EMP* 30^E
SIC 6531 6512 Real estate managers; Commercial & industrial building operation
CEO: Rob Gerbitz
**CFO:* Mark Koziol
Sr VP: Les Birbaum
**Sr VP:* Larry Evinger
**Sr VP:* Kevin Rogers
**Sr VP:* Jacquie Seymour
VP: Daniel Barkes
VP: Steve Eaheart

HENDRICKS COUNTY AUDITORS OFF
See COUNTY OF HENDRICKS

D-U-N-S 13-449-4108
HENDRICKS COUNTY R E M C
86 N County Rd, Danville, IN 46122
Tel (317) 745-5473 *Founded/Ownrshp* 2003
Sales 78.0MM *EMP* 3^E
SIC 4813 ;
Prin: Matt Hession

D-U-N-S 00-693-6702
HENDRICKS COUNTY RURAL ELECTRIC MEMBERSHIP CORP
HENDRICKS POWER COOPERATIVE
86 N County Road 500 E, Avon, IN 46123-9481
Tel (317) 745-5473 *Founded/Ownrshp* 1936
Sales 86.3MM *EMP* 75
SIC 4911 Distribution, electric power; Distribution, electric power
CEO: Donnis Mizelle
Pr: Matthew Hession

D-U-N-S 02-462-2532 IMP
HENDRICKS FURNITURE GROUP LLC
BOYLES FURNITURE
1123 4th St Sw, Conover, NC 28613-9627
Tel (828) 345-5200 *Founded/Ownrshp* 1950
Sales 82.8MM^E *EMP* 600
SIC 5712

D-U-N-S 60-195-1218
HENDRICKS HOLDING CO INC
690 3rd St Ste 300, Beloit, WI 53511-6214
Tel (608) 362-8981 *Founded/Ownrshp* 2000
Sales 124.2MM^E *EMP* 512
SIC 6726 Investment offices; Management investment funds, closed-end; Investment offices; Management investment funds, closed-end
CEO: Brent Fox
**Pr:* Rob Gerbitz
**CFO:* Mark Koziol
Treas: Carla Swain
**Sr VP:* Larry Evinger
**Sr VP:* Kevin Rogers
**Sr VP:* Jacquie Seymour
VP: Karl Leo
Mng Dir: Jon Coulter
Mng Dir: Ned Moser

HENDRICKS POWER COOPERATIVE
See HENDRICKS COUNTY RURAL ELECTRIC MEMBERSHIP CORP

D-U-N-S 15-060-8644 IMP
HENDRICKS REGIONAL HEALTH GUILD INC
1000 E Mn St, Danville, IN 46122
Tel (317) 745-4451 *Founded/Ownrshp* 1962
Sales 129.0M *EMP* 1,600^E
SIC 8062 General medical & surgical hospitals; General medical & surgical hospitals
CEO: Kevin Speer
Chf Rad: Joseph Hunt
**Pr:* Bonnie Walton
**Treas:* Mary Kay Hood
Ofcr: Tammy Vukusich
VP: Gary Everling
VP: John Sparzo
Exec: Gordon Reed
Dir OR: Don Stewart
Dir Rad: Stan Metzger
Dir Rad: Stan Metzger

D-U-N-S 62-279-1689 IMP/EXP
HENDRICKSON INTERNATIONAL CORP
(*Suby of* BOLER CO) ★
500 Park Blvd Ste 450, Itasca, IL 60143-3153
Tel (630) 773-9111 *Founded/Ownrshp* 1967
Sales 77.6MM^E *EMP* 500
SIC 7513 Truck rental & leasing, no drivers; Truck rental & leasing, no drivers
Pr: Gary Gerstenslager
**Prin:* John M Boler

HENDRICKSON STAMP DIV
See BOLER CO

HENDRICKSON TRUCK SUSPENSION
See HENDRICKSON USA LLC

D-U-N-S 78-312-8465
HENDRICKSON TRUCKING INC
7080 Florin Perkins Rd, Sacramento, CA 95828-2609
Tel (916) 387-9614 *Founded/Ownrshp* 1977
Sales 85.7MM^E *EMP* 280
SIC 4213 Trucking, except local; Trucking, except local
CEO: William Hendrickson
**Pr:* Ward Hendrickson
CFO: Alban Lang
Sfty Dirs: Candice Masters
Opers Mgr: Kenneth Williams

D-U-N-S 78-707-2151
HENDRICKSON USA LLC
(*Suby of* BOLER CO) ★
500 Park Blvd Ste 450, Itasca, IL 60143-3153
Tel (630) 874-9700 *Founded/Ownrshp* 2005
Sales 89.8MM^E *EMP* 344^E
SIC 3537 Industrial trucks & tractors
Sls Mgr: Jim Schnurr

D-U-N-S 79-012-6143 IMP
HENDRICKSON USA LLC
HENDRICKSON TRUCK SUSPENSION
(*Suby of* BOLER CO) ★
800 S Frontage Rd, Woodridge, IL 60517-4900
Tel (630) 910-2800 *Founded/Ownrshp* 2004
Sales 585.3MM^E *EMP* 2,400^E
SIC 3469 Metal stampings; Metal stampings
Mtls Mgr: Tim Bentz
Sales Asso: Mark Martella

D-U-N-S 00-321-9201 IMP
HENDRIX BATTING CO (NC)
2310 Surrett Dr, High Point, NC 27263-8509
Tel (336) 431-1181 *Founded/Ownrshp* 1960
Sales 33.5MM^E *EMP* 150
SIC 2299 2297 Batting, wadding, padding & fillings; Nonwoven fabrics; Batting, wadding, padding & fillings; Nonwoven fabrics

Pr: Kenneth Hendrix Jr
**Treas:* Angela Hendrix Bennett

D-U-N-S 07-563-5094
HENDRIX COLLEGE (AR)
1600 Washington Ave, Conway, AR 72032-3080
Tel (501) 329-6811 *Founded/Ownrshp* 1884
Sales 80.7MM *EMP* 336
SIC 8221 University; University
Pr: William Tsutsui
Trst: Johnnie Amonette
Trst: Joseph Bates
Trst: Frank Cox
Trst: David Knight
VP: Kevin Braswell
VP: Pamela Owen
VP: Robert G Young
**Prin:* J Timmothy Cloyd
Dir IT: Jerry Blackburn
S&M/VP: Robert G Young
Board of Directors: Lydia McDonald

D-U-N-S 10-001-2848
HENDRY COUNTY SCHOOL DISTRICT
DISTRICT SCHOOL BOARD OF HENDR
25 E Hickpochee Ave, Labelle, FL 33935-5015
Tel (863) 674-4642 *Founded/Ownrshp* 1925
Sales 53.3MM^E *EMP* 1,000
SIC 8211 Public elementary & secondary schools; Public elementary & secondary schools
**Ch Bd:* Ray Clinard
Schl Brd P: Patrick Langford
HC Dir: Jeff Caulkins
HC Dir: Lucinda Kelley

D-U-N-S 01-205-9465
HENEGAN CONSTRUCTION CO INC
250 W 30th St Lbby 1, New York, NY 10001-4900
Tel (212) 947-6441 *Founded/Ownrshp* 1959
Sales 57.4MM^E *EMP* 95
SIC 1542 8741 Commercial & office buildings, renovation & repair; Construction management; Commercial & office buildings, renovation & repair; Construction management
CEO: Maureen A Henegan
Pr: Paul J Bryce
CFO: Steven P Schertz
Sr VP: Tom Mangan
VP: Dave Mullen
VP: Mary Raftery
VP: Henry Romer
Tech Mgr: Dan Lemetti
Snr PM: Robert Fitzpatrick

D-U-N-S 18-723-4179
HENGST OF NORTH AMERICA INC
(*Suby of* HENGST SE & CO. KG)
29 Hengst Blvd, Camden, SC 29020-7796
Tel (803) 432-5992 *Founded/Ownrshp* 2005
Sales 96.0MM *EMP* 270
Accts Bauknight Pietras Stormer Pa
SIC 3714 Filters: oil, fuel & air, motor vehicle; Filters: oil, fuel & air, motor vehicle
Pr: Robert Junker
**Sec:* Ingo Van De Kamp
**VP:* Carsten Schnese
Genl Mgr: Martin Wachenfeld

D-U-N-S 12-940-9996 IMP
HENGST USA INC
(*Suby of* HENGST SE & CO. KG)
29 Hengst Blvd, Camden, SC 29020-7796
Tel (803) 432-5992 *Founded/Ownrshp* 2004
Sales 164.0MM *EMP* 239
SIC 3714 Filters: oil, fuel & air, motor vehicle; Filters: oil, fuel & air, motor vehicle
Pr: Jens Roettgering
CFO: Hans Gruenhag
Genl Mgr: Martin Wachenfeld
Off Mgr: Iris Mante
Ql Cn Mgr: Jorg Hemsing
Ql Cn Mgr: James Houser
Snr Mgr: Hayk Gasparyan
Snr Mgr: Montrell Pressley

D-U-N-S 06-929-9381
HENIFF TRANSPORTATION SYSTEMS LLC
2015 Spring Rd Ste 780, Oak Brook, IL 60523-3941
Tel (630) 230-2100 *Founded/Ownrshp* 2007
Sales 95.9MM^E *EMP* 450
SIC 4213 Trucking, except local; Trucking, except local
Pr: Robert J Heniff
**VP:* Scott Templeman

D-U-N-S 01-431-7614 IMP
HENISE TIRE SERVICE INC
558 E Penn Ave, Cleona, PA 17042-2539
Tel (717) 272-2051 *Founded/Ownrshp* 1982
Sales 63.5MM^E *EMP* 72
SIC 5014 5531 7534 Automobile tires & tubes; Truck tires & tubes; Automotive tires; Rebuilding & retreading tires; Automobile tires & tubes; Truck tires & tubes; Automotive tires; Rebuilding & retreading tires
Pr: David Henise
**VP:* Joan G Henise
Store Mgr: Todd Griffiths
Store Mgr: Jon Hinkel
Sls Mgr: Norm Card
Sls Mgr: Dave Lineaweaver
Sales Asso: Nathan Eisenhower
Sales Asso: Jason Krall

D-U-N-S 80-703-7452
■ **HENKE MANUFACTURING CORP**
(*Suby of* ALAMO GROUP INC) ★
3070 Wilson Ave, Leavenworth, KS 66048-4637
Tel (913) 682-9000 *Founded/Ownrshp* 1993
Sales 24.4MM^E *EMP* 90
SIC 3711 Snow plows (motor vehicles), assembly of
Pr: Douglas Metcalf
Pr: Randal Wolf
Sls Mgr: Bob Lacy

D-U-N-S 01-672-6572
HENKEL CHRYSLER JEEP INC
1275 W Dickman Rd, Springfield, MI 49037-4841
Tel (269) 441-8100 *Founded/Ownrshp* 1993
Sales 20.7MM^E *EMP* 46
SIC 5511 Automobiles, new & used

Pr: Eric Henkel

D-U-N-S 00-530-4753
HENKEL CONSTRUCTION CO INC (IA)
208 E State St, Mason City, IA 50401-3406
Tel (641) 423-5674 *Founded/Ownrshp* 1892, 1989
Sales 41.8MM *EMP* 80
Accts Benes & Krueger Sc Waukesh
SIC 1541 1542 1611 Industrial buildings, new construction; Commercial & office building, new construction; General contractor, highway & street construction; Industrial buildings, new construction; Commercial & office building, new construction; General contractor, highway & street construction
Pr: Gary J Schmit
**CFO:* Timothy Sautter
**Treas:* Steve Watson
**VP:* Kent Brcka
Dir IT: Carolyn Kilborn

D-U-N-S 00-588-4449 IMP/EXP
HENKEL CONSUMER GOODS INC
(*Suby of* HENKEL CORP) ★
7201 E Henkel Way, Scottsdale, AZ 85255-9678
Tel (860) 571-5100 *Founded/Ownrshp* 2004
Sales 775.1MM^E *EMP* 2,900
SIC 2841 Soap & other detergents; Soap & other detergents
Pr: Norbert Koll
Treas: Todd Gatzulis
**Treas:* Raphaela Lessmann
**VP:* Brad A Gazaway
VP: Bill Tyree
Creative D: George Polowyk
Dir Bus: Cheryl Wilson
Prgrm Mgr: Matt Taha
Prgrm Mgr: Shane Turner
Prgrm Mgr: Michael Vanhaerents
Prgrm Mgr: Tony West

D-U-N-S 05-144-1731 IMP
HENKEL CORP
SCHWARZOPF
(*Suby of* HENKEL OF AMERICA INC) ★
1 Henkel Way, Rocky Hill, CT 06067-3581
Tel (860) 571-5100 *Founded/Ownrshp* 1970
Sales 1.7MMM^E *EMP* 4,542
SIC 2843 2821 2833 2899 2891 Surface active agents; Plastics materials & resins; Thermoplastic materials; Medicinals & botanicals; Vitamins, natural or synthetic: bulk, uncompounded; Chemical preparations; Adhesives; Surface active agents; Plastics materials & resins; Thermoplastic materials; Medicinals & botanicals; Vitamins, natural or synthetic: bulk, uncompounded; Chemical preparations; Adhesives
CEO: Kasper Rorsted
Ch Bd: Dr Jochen Krautter
Pr: Chris Hallsey
Pr: Jeffrey C Piccolomini
CFO: Michael Desalvio
CFO: Michael Grimaud
Treas: Raphaela Dohm
Ex VP: Carsten Knobel
VP: Renata Casaro
VP: Gregory Gaglione
VP: Andy N Garcia
VP: Brad Gazaway
VP: John Schofield
VP: Marco Swoboda
Dir Soc: Lindsey Ossim
Dir: Michael Gansow
Dir Rx: Yuan K Lai
Dir Bus: Cynthia Ll
Comm Man: Bettina Fischer

D-U-N-S 00-113-9617 IMP
HENKEL LOCTITE CORP (DE)
1 Henkel Way, Rocky Hill, CT 06067-3581
Tel (860) 571-5100 *Founded/Ownrshp* 2008
Sales NA *EMP* 400^E
SIC 2891 3677 8731 8711 Adhesives; Sealants; Inductors, electronic; Commercial physical research; Engineering services

D-U-N-S 05-474-4784 IMP
HENKEL OF AMERICA INC
(*Suby of* HENKEL AG & CO. KGAA)
1 Henkel Way, Rocky Hill, CT 06067-3581
Tel (860) 571-5100 *Founded/Ownrshp* 1979
Sales 1.7MMM^E *EMP* 5,342
SIC 2869 2843 2821 2833 2899 2891 Industrial organic chemicals; Fatty acid esters, aminos, etc.; Surface active agents; Plastics materials & resins; Thermoplastic materials; Medicinals & botanicals; Vitamins, natural or synthetic: bulk, uncompounded; Chemical preparations; Adhesives; Industrial organic chemicals; Fatty acid esters, aminos, etc.; Surface active agents; Plastics materials & resins; Thermoplastic materials; Medicinals & botanicals; Vitamins, natural or synthetic: bulk, uncompounded; Chemical preparations; Adhesives
Pr: Jeffrey C Piccolomini
**Ch Bd:* Dr Lothar Steinebach
**Treas:* Raphaela Dohm
**Sr VP:* William B Read III
VP: Frederic Chupin
**VP:* Raphaela Lessmann
VP: Scot Miller
VP: Dan Wohletz
VP Sls: Bobby Santulli

D-U-N-S 09-050-6239 IMP/EXP
HENKEL PUERTO RICO INC
(*Suby of* HENKEL CORP) ★
9 Ave Vicente Quilinchini, Sabana Grande, PR 00637-1997
Tel (787) 873-6500 *Founded/Ownrshp* 1965, 2008
Sales 37.8MM^E *EMP* 225^E
SIC 2891 Adhesives & sealants
Pr: Peter J Dowling
**Treas:* Raphaela Dohm
**VP:* James R Polifka

D-U-N-S 00-307-9902 IMP
HENKEL-HARRIS LLC (VA)
2983 S Pleasant Valley Rd, Winchester, VA 22601-4240
Tel (540) 667-4900 *Founded/Ownrshp* 1946, 2013

Sales 38.0MM[E] *EMP* 325
SIC 2511 2521 Wood bedroom furniture; Dining room furniture: wood; Wood office furniture; Wood bedroom furniture; Dining room furniture: wood; Wood office furniture
VP: William F Edmonson
MIS Dir: Charlie Murphy

D-U-N-S 00-893-7815 IMP
HENKELS & MCCOY INC (PA)
985 Jolly Rd, Blue Bell, PA 19422-1958
Tel (215) 283-7600 *Founded/Ownrshp* 1923
Sales 1.1MMM *EMP* 5,000
SIC 1623

D-U-N-S 00-325-9801
HENLEY CONSTRUCTION CO INC (MD)
ROBERT J HENLEY CNSTR CO
7940 Queenair Dr, Gaithersburg, MD 20879-4138
Tel (301) 519-3703 *Founded/Ownrshp* 1964
Sales 75.4MM *EMP* 46
Accts E Cohen And Company Cpas Ro
SIC 1542 School building construction; Religious building construction; Commercial & office building contractors; School building construction; Religious building construction; Commercial & office building contractors
CEO: Robert J Henley
**Pr:* Robert C Henley
**Treas:* Robyn Bloodgood
VP: Buddy Henley
**VP:* David Riffle
Genl Mgr: Suleika Wiles
Mktg Dir: Jennifer Schrider

D-U-N-S 03-717-6518
HENLEY MANAGEMENT CO
555 Skokie Blvd Ste 555, Northbrook, IL 60062-2854
Tel (847) 480-4690 *Founded/Ownrshp* 1979
Sales 92.7MM[E] *EMP* 584[E]
SIC 6719 Investment holding companies, except banks
Pr: Richard W Colburn

D-U-N-S 04-610-7330 IMP
HENMAN ENGINEERING AND MACHINE INC
3301 W Mt Pleasant Blvd, Muncie, IN 47302-9103
Tel (765) 288-8098 *Founded/Ownrshp* 1978
Sales 28.2MM *EMP* 62
SIC 3714 Transmission housings or parts, motor vehicle; Transmission housings or parts, motor vehicle
Pr: Thomas Henman Sr
**Sec:* Dixie Henman
**VP:* Thomas Henman Jr
Dir IT: Tom Rootz
Sfty Mgr: Scott Coffman
Ql Cn Mgr: Ralph Mills
Ql Cn Mgr: Gary Oliver

D-U-N-S 02-601-9638
HENNA CHEVROLET LP (TX)
8805 N Ih 35, Austin, TX 78753-4875
Tel (512) 832-1888 *Founded/Ownrshp* 1936
Sales 61.7MM[E] *EMP* 170
SIC 5511

D-U-N-S 82-961-8755 IMP
HENNECKE INC
HENNECKE USA
(*Suby of* HENNECKE GROUP GMBH)
55 Park Dr, Lawrence, PA 15055
Tel (724) 271-3603 *Founded/Ownrshp* 2007
Sales 23.0MM[E] *EMP* 83[E]
SIC 3569 Assembly machines, non-metalworking
Pr: Alois Schmid
S&M/Mgr: Lutz Heidrich

HENNECKE USA
See HENNECKE INC

D-U-N-S 00-423-2062
■ **HENNEGAN CO** (OH)
(*Suby of* CONSOLIDATED GRAPHICS INC) ★
7455 Empire Dr, Florence, KY 41042-2923
Tel (859) 282-3600 *Founded/Ownrshp* 1886, 2007
Sales 78.5MM[E] *EMP* 370
SIC 2752 2789 Commercial printing, lithographic; Color lithography; Bookbinding & related work; Commercial printing, lithographic; Color lithography; Bookbinding & related work
Pr: Gary Greis
Pr: Robert B Ott Jr
Treas: Donald C Fleck
Treas: Alex McDermott
VP: Jeff Beiting
VP: Michael D Butler
VP: Michael Fleury
VP: Roger Helms
VP: Dennis J Purcell
VP: Greg Trachsel
VP: Mike Vandenburg

D-U-N-S 11-782-3612
HENNELLY TIRE & AUTO INC
TIRE CHOICE
2400 E Coml Blvd Ste 1050, Fort Lauderdale, FL 33308
Tel (954) 491-5724 *Founded/Ownrshp* 2002
Sales 52.3MM[E] *EMP* 121
SIC 5531 7538 5014 Automotive tires; General automotive repair shops; Tires & tubes
CEO: Daniel W Hennelly
**CFO:* Diane C Hennelly

D-U-N-S 04-504-9939
HENNEMAN ENGINEERING INC
1605 S State St Ste 101, Champaign, IL 61820-7264
Tel (217) 359-1514 *Founded/Ownrshp* 1976
Sales 29.8MM[E] *EMP* 145
SIC 8711 8712 Consulting engineer; Civil engineering; Mechanical engineering; Electrical or electronic engineering; Architectural engineering; Consulting engineer; Civil engineering; Mechanical engineering; Electrical or electronic engineering; Architectural engineering
Pr: Elizabeth Douglas
**Ch Bd:* Ralph J Henneman
**Pr:* Michael Henneman
Pr: Thomas Sutton
**Ex VP:* Al Raufeisen
Sr VP: Joseph Summers
Dir IT: Bob Boice
Opers Mgr: James Slack

D-U-N-S 06-815-8369
HENNEPIN COUNTY
300 S 6th St, Minneapolis, MN 55487-0999
Tel (612) 348-3000 *Founded/Ownrshp* 1852
Sales NA *EMP* 10,246
SIC 9111 County supervisors' & executives' offices; County supervisors' & executives' offices
Bd of Dir: Saundra Dawson
Bd of Dir: Pam Flenniken
Bd of Dir: Lorraine Lutgen
Ofcr: Roy Artis
Ofcr: Derrick Carter
Ofcr: Michael Desmarais
Ofcr: Angela Kaiser
Ofcr: Kristi Lahti-Johnson
Ofcr: Todd Miller
Ofcr: Sarah Nordby
Ofcr: Shirley Qual
Ofcr: Roxanne Radeck
Ofcr: John Vogelpohl
Ofcr: John Zanmiller
Ofcr: Claire Zindler
Comm Man: Michael Freeman
Board of Directors: Gail Dorfman, Randy Johnson, Linda Koblick, Peter McLaughlin, Mike Opat, Penny Steele, Mark Stenglein

D-U-N-S 12-038-0894
HENNEPIN COUNTY LIBRARY-MINNEAPOLIS CENTRAL
(*Suby of* CITY OF MINNEAPOLIS) ★
300 Nicollet Mall, Minneapolis, MN 55401-1925
Tel (612) 543-8000 *Founded/Ownrshp* 1885
Sales 11.7MM[E] *EMP* 557
SIC 8231 Public library; Public library
Ex Dir: Brian Herstig

HENNEPIN COUNTY MEDICAL CENTER
See HENNEPIN HEALTHCARE SYSTEM INC

D-U-N-S 12-118-8106
HENNEPIN FACULTY ASSOCIATES INC
120 S 6th St Ste 155, Minneapolis, MN 55402-1816
Tel (612) 347-7226 *Founded/Ownrshp* 1984
Sales 34.6MM[E] *EMP* 922[E]
SIC 8011 8733 Physicians' office, including specialists; Medical research; Physicians' office, including specialists; Medical research
Ch: Dr Donald M Jacobs
**Pr:* Lawrence R Fosbury

D-U-N-S 12-001-9070
HENNEPIN HEALTHCARE SYSTEM INC
HENNEPIN COUNTY MEDICAL CENTER
(*Suby of* HENNEPIN COUNTY) ★
701 Park Ave, Minneapolis, MN 55415-1623
Tel (612) 873-3000 *Founded/Ownrshp* 2007
Sales 789.2MM *EMP* 5,000
SIC 8062 5912 General medical & surgical hospitals; Drug stores & proprietary stores; General medical & surgical hospitals; Drug stores & proprietary stores
CEO: Jon Pryor
IT Man: Jen Muehlhausen
IT Man: Carol Wise
Secur Mgr: Michael Cole
Psych: Amber Ehrlich
Psych: Jennifer Rademacher
Psych: Matthew Syzdek
Surgeon: Mark Hill
Surgeon: Nancy Luger
Surgeon: Ashley Marek
Surgeon: Chad Richardson

D-U-N-S 83-151-9181
HENNEPIN THEATRE TRUST
615 Hennepin Ave Ste 140, Minneapolis, MN 55403-1818
Tel (612) 455-9500 *Founded/Ownrshp* 2000
Sales 30.6MM *EMP* 12[E]
Accts Silverman And Associates Cpas
SIC 7922 Theatrical producers & services; Theatrical producers & services
Pr: Thomas Hoch
Dir Vol: Gale Peterson
VP: Jim Sheeley

HENNESSEY CAPITAL
See HITACHI CAPITAL AMERICA CORP

D-U-N-S 02-320-4795 IMP
HENNESSEY IMPLEMENT INC
1414 State Road 23, Dodgeville, WI 53533-2119
Tel (608) 935-3326 *Founded/Ownrshp* 1961
Sales 40.0MM *EMP* 19
SIC 5999 Farm equipment & supplies; Farm equipment & supplies
Pr: William Hennessey

D-U-N-S 09-250-7144
HENNESSEYS TAVERN INC
LIGHTHOUSE CAFE
1845 S Elena Ave Ste 300, Redondo Beach, CA 90277-5708
Tel (310) 540-2274 *Founded/Ownrshp* 1976
Sales 35.0MM *EMP* 800
SIC 5813 5812 Bar (drinking places); American restaurant; Bar (drinking places); American restaurant
Pr: Paul Hennessey
CFO: Jim Cram
CFO: Nicole Fay
Rgnl Mgr: Matt Gilmore

D-U-N-S 80-733-2838
▲ **HENNESSY ADVISORS INC**
7250 Redwood Blvd Ste 200, Novato, CA 94945-3272
Tel (415) 899-1555 *Founded/Ownrshp* 1989
Sales 44.7MM *EMP* 21[E]
Accts Marcum Llp San Francisco Cal
Tkr Sym HNNA *Exch* NAS
SIC 6282 Investment advice; Investment advice
Ch Bd: Neil J Hennessy
Pr: Kevin A Rowell
**COO:* Teresa M Nilsen
Bd of Dir: Rodger Offenbach
**Ex VP:* Daniel B Steadman
VP Opers: Ana Miner

D-U-N-S 03-353-2326
HENNESSY CADILLAC INC
LANDROVER NORTHPOINT
3040 Piedmont Rd Ne, Atlanta, GA 30305-2636
Tel (404) 261-5700 *Founded/Ownrshp* 1986
Sales 121.4MM[E] *EMP* 325
SIC 5511 Automobiles, new & used; Automobiles, new & used
CEO: Mark W Hennessy
**Sec:* Devers Hayes
**VP:* Steve Hennessy
Genl Mgr: Brad Selz
Store Mgr: Tony Hendrix
Sls Mgr: Mike Johnson
Sales Asso: John Allen
Sales Asso: Larry Bass
Sales Asso: Bob Beers
Sales Asso: Steven Crawford
Sales Asso: Brenda Davis

HENNESSY HONDA OF WOODSTOCK
See VALLEY PARTNERS INC

D-U-N-S 00-554-9159 IMP/EXP
■ **HENNESSY INDUSTRIES INC** (DE)
(*Suby of* DANAHER CORP) ★
1601 Jp Hennessy Dr, La Vergne, TN 37086-3524
Tel (615) 641-7533 *Founded/Ownrshp* 1961, 1986
Sales 97.1MM[E] *EMP* 438
SIC 3714 Motor vehicle parts & accessories; Motor vehicle parts & accessories
Pr: Sanjay Chowbey
VP: Roger Peniche
Ql Cn Mgr: Phil Bourassa
Mktg Dir: Doug Fox
Sls Mgr: Chris Cherryholmes

HENNESSY LEXUS
See TUXEDO-PARTNERS INC

D-U-N-S 08-204-2342 IMP
HENNIG INC
(*Suby of* ADVANCED MACHINE AND ENGRG) ★
9900 N Alpine Rd, Machesney Park, IL 61115-8211
Tel (815) 636-9900 *Founded/Ownrshp* 1999
Sales 20.9MM[E] *EMP* 115
SIC 3444 Machine guards, sheet metal
Pr: Dietmar Goellner
**Ch Bd:* Willy Goellner
**Pr:* Dietmer Goellner
**CFO:* David Leezer
**Sec:* Marika Mertz
**VP:* Greg Champion
**VP:* Robin Moore
Sfty Dirs: Varlene Weed
Plnt Mgr: Bruce Beaver
Manager: Larry Carver
Manager: Ken Davis

D-U-N-S 80-913-3775
HENNIGES AUTOMOTIVE HOLDINGS INC
2750 High Meadow Cir, Auburn Hills, MI 48326-2796
Tel (248) 340-4100 *Founded/Ownrshp* 2007
Sales 621.4MM[E] *EMP* 7,000
SIC 3069 2891 3714 Rubber automotive products; Adhesives & sealants; Motor vehicle electrical equipment; Rubber automotive products; Adhesives & sealants; Motor vehicle electrical equipment
CEO: Douglas Delgrosso
CFO: Larry Williams
VP: Ann Budin
VP: Geri Gasperut
VP: Boris Gavric
VP: Larry Rollins
VP: Peter Soto
Mtls Mgr: Daniel Flores

D-U-N-S 00-997-1289
HENNIGES AUTOMOTIVE IOWA INC
(*Suby of* SCHLEGEL CORP) ★
3200 Main St, Keokuk, IA 52632-2259
Tel (319) 524-4560 *Founded/Ownrshp* 1951
Sales 131.9MM[E] *EMP* 500
SIC 3069 3714 3442 3429 2295 Rubber automotive products; Motor vehicle parts & accessories; Metal doors, sash & trim; Manufactured hardware (general); Sealing or insulating tape for pipe: coated fiberglass; Rubber automotive products; Motor vehicle parts & accessories; Metal doors, sash & trim; Manufactured hardware (general); Sealing or insulating tape for pipe: coated fiberglass
Pr: Greg Finch
**Treas:* Alan Flavell

D-U-N-S 08-674-6310 IMP
HENNIGES AUTOMOTIVE NORTH AMERICA INC
(*Suby of* AVIATION INDUSTRY CORPORATION OF CHINA BEIJING CHANGCHENG METERING TESTING TECHN OLOGY RES)
2750 High Meadow Cir, Auburn Hills, MI 48326-2796
Tel (248) 340-4100 *Founded/Ownrshp* 2015
Sales 102.8MM[E] *EMP* 195[E]
SIC 5013 3053 Automotive supplies & parts; Automotive trim; Gaskets, packing & sealing devices
CEO: Douglas Delgrosso
Pr: Thomas Wolanzyk
CFO: Larry Williams
Ex VP: Margaret Sheng
VP: Ann Budin
VP: Geri Gasperut
VP: Boris Gavric
VP: Larry Rollins
VP: Peter Seto

D-U-N-S 86-900-0067 IMP
HENNIGES AUTOMOTIVE NORTH AMERICA INC
(*Suby of* SCHLEGEL CORP) ★
226 Watlington Indus Dr, Reidsville, NC 27320-8147
Tel (336) 342-9300 *Founded/Ownrshp* 2001
Sales 66.4MM[E] *EMP* 375
SIC 3053 Gaskets & sealing devices; Gaskets & sealing devices
Pr: Mark Drumheller
**VP:* Larry Williams
Plnt Mgr: James Mackin

D-U-N-S 09-614-1098 IMP
HENNIGES AUTOMOTIVE OKLAHOMA INC
(*Suby of* SCHLEGEL CORP) ★
1801 Flying Fortress, Frederick, OK 73542-7000
Tel (580) 335-5503 *Founded/Ownrshp* 2001
Sales 3.7MM[E] *EMP* 400
SIC 3069 3999

D-U-N-S 17-678-4585 IMP/EXP
HENNIGES AUTOMOTIVE SEALING SYSTEMS NORTH AMERICA INC
METZELER AUTO PROFILE SYSTEMS
(*Suby of* HENNIGES AUTOMOTIVE HOLDINGS INC) ★
2750 High Meadow Cir, Auburn Hills, MI 48326-2796
Tel (248) 553-5300 *Founded/Ownrshp* 2008
Sales 141.9MM[E] *EMP* 735
SIC 3053 2891 3714 Gaskets, packing & sealing devices; Adhesives & sealants; Motor vehicle parts & accessories; Gaskets, packing & sealing devices; Adhesives & sealants; Motor vehicle parts & accessories
CEO: Rob Depierre
**CFO:* Larry Williams

D-U-N-S 00-681-9841
HENNING CONSTRUCTION CO LLC (IA)
5800 Merle Hay Rd Ste 14, Johnston, IA 50131-1217
Tel (515) 253-0943 *Founded/Ownrshp* 1924, 1971
Sales 91.6MM *EMP* 145
Accts Mcgladrey Llp Des Moines Iow
SIC 1521 1542 1541 Single-family housing construction; Agricultural building contractors; Commercial & office building contractors; Industrial buildings & warehouses; Single-family housing construction; Agricultural building contractors; Commercial & office building contractors; Industrial buildings & warehouses
Ch Bd: Jeff Henning
**Pr:* Al Koch
**CFO:* Jeff Charlson
**Ex VP:* Heather Henning
**Sr VP:* Darrell Reeves
**Sr VP:* William Schreck
**VP:* David Dirks
**VP:* Del Farrer

D-U-N-S 00-787-3243
HENNINGSEN COLD STORAGE CO (OR)
21435 Nw Cherry Ln, Hillsboro, OR 97124-6630
Tel (503) 531-5400 *Founded/Ownrshp* 1923
Sales 87.7MM[E] *EMP* 300
SIC 4222 6512 Warehousing, cold storage or refrigerated; Commercial & industrial building operation; Warehousing, cold storage or refrigerated; Commercial & industrial building operation
Pr: Michael E Henningsen
Pr: Michael Henningsen Jr
COO: Harry Drajpuch
CFO: Eric Mauss
Ex VP: Anthony Lucarelli
Ex VP: Tony Lucarelli
VP: Christopher R Henningsen
Genl Mgr: Jim Bell
Genl Mgr: Kevin Cummings
MIS Dir: Gerald Smith
Opers Mgr: Eli Williams

D-U-N-S 00-132-6545 EXP
HENNINGSEN FOODS INC (NY)
(*Suby of* KIFUKI USA CO INC) ★
14334 Industrial Rd, Omaha, NE 68144-3398
Tel (402) 330-2500 *Founded/Ownrshp* 1889, 1990
Sales 49.5MM[E] *EMP* 190
Accts Ernst & Young Llp New York N
SIC 2015 2013 Poultry slaughtering & processing; Sausages & other prepared meats; Poultry slaughtering & processing; Sausages & other prepared meats
Pr: Jeff Walker
CFO: James Harshman
**VP:* Darrell Kahler
Dir IT: Dave Slaughter
Opers Mgr: Gina Blankenau
Plnt Mgr: Mike Behrendt

D-U-N-S 60-687-0764
HENNION & WALSH INC
2001 Rte 46 Waterview Plz, Parsippany, NJ 07054
Tel (973) 541-4822 *Founded/Ownrshp* 1990
Sales 27.7MM[E] *EMP* 117[E]
SIC 6211 Security brokers & dealers; Security brokers & dealers
Pr: Bill Walsh
Pr: Ronald Farrise
**CFO:* Debbie Williams
Chf Cred: Al Vermitsky
Sr VP: William Hennion
VP: Ted Breen
VP: Michael De Luz
VP: Gregg Heller
**VP:* Richard Hennion
VP: Nathan Ibarra
VP: John McLoughlin
VP: Brian Rieman
VP: Joseph Rodriguez
VP: Patrick Walsh

D-U-N-S 00-425-6814 IMP/EXP
HENNY PENNY CORP
1219 Us Route 35, Eaton, OH 45320-8621
Tel (937) 456-8400 *Founded/Ownrshp* 1986
Sales 158.4MM[E] *EMP* 631
SIC 3589 Cooking equipment, commercial; Food warming equipment, commercial; Cooking equipment, commercial; Food warming equipment, commercial
CEO: Steve Cobb
Pr: Rob Connelly
CFO: Brian Brooks
CFO: Art Harlan
Off Mgr: Judy Phillips

Dir IT: Sam Stewart
Opers Mgr: John Olsen

HENNY PENNY EGGS
See MCANALLY ENTERPRISES INC

D-U-N-S 04-252-6749 EXP
HENRICKSEN & CO INC
1101 W Thorndale Ave, Itasca, IL 60143-1366
Tel (630) 250-9090 *Founded/Ownrshp* 1968
Sales 152.4MM *EMP* 210
Accts Sikich Llp Naperville Illino
SIC 5021 7389 Office furniture; Interior designer; Office furniture; Interior designer
Pr: Michael D Assell
**CFO:* Tim Osborn
**Ch:* Stephen E McPartlin
**Ex VP:* Russell Frees
**VP:* Dick Nash
Sls&Mrk Ex: Mark Jezior
Mktg Dir: Renee Bouchez
Mktg Dir: John Comeaux
Snr PM: Sheila Reinhart
Snr PM: Dominick Sanginito

D-U-N-S 08-812-1421
HENRICO COUNTY SCHOOL DISTRICT
3820 Nine Mile Rd Ste A, Richmond, VA 23223-4831
Tel (804) 652-3717 *Founded/Ownrshp* 1960
Sales 171.8MM^E *EMP* 5,600^E
SIC 8211 Public elementary & secondary schools; Public elementary & secondary schools
Ch Bd: Beverly L Cocke
Psych: Elizabeth Alvarez
Psych: Christina Conlon
Psych: Teresa Crenshaw
Psych: Cheryl Eslinger
Psych: John Markey
Psych: Jessica Murray
Psych: Shavon Peacock
Psych: Shepard Stephenson

HENRICO COUNTY, VIRGINIA
See COUNTY OF HENRICO

D-U-N-S 11-283-2865
HENRICO DOCTORS HOSPITAL
1602 Skipwith Rd, Richmond, VA 23229-5298
Tel (804) 289-4500 *Founded/Ownrshp* 2002
Sales 428.3MM *EMP* 63^E
SIC 8069 Cancer hospital; Cancer hospital
CFO: Chris Benton
VP: Richard Stauffer
**Prin:* Patrick Farell
Pathlgst: Linda Magovern
Doctor: Stephen W Cross MD

D-U-N-S 06-790-6941
HENRIETTA BUILDING SUPPLIES INC
ENERGY INSULATION SYSTEMS
1 Riverton Way, West Henrietta, NY 14586-9754
Tel (585) 334-2365 *Founded/Ownrshp* 1974
Sales 78.0MM^E *EMP* 100
SIC 5031 Building materials, exterior; Building materials, exterior
Ch: Richard Szustakowski
CFO: Ronald Cedruly

D-U-N-S 07-174-1995
HENRIETTA D GOODALL HOSPITAL INC
25 June St, Sanford, ME 04073-2621
Tel (207) 324-4310 *Founded/Ownrshp* 1928
Sales 91.6MM *EMP* 1,016
SIC 8062

D-U-N-S 03-778-5326 IMP
HENRIKSEN-BUTLER DESIGN GROUP LLC
249 S 400 E, Salt Lake City, UT 84111-2631
Tel (801) 363-5881 *Founded/Ownrshp* 1998
Sales 63.4MM^E *EMP* 100
Accts Mayer Hoffman Mccann Pc Sal
SIC 5021 7389 Office & public building furniture; Interior designer; Office & public building furniture; Interior designer
CEO: Dave Colling
**Pr:* Ian Anderson
**CFO:* Mike Taylor
**Sr VP:* Dennis Hobb
**Sr VP:* Paige Wright

D-U-N-S 07-447-1509 IMP
HENRY & HORNE LLP
2055 E Warner Rd Ste 101, Tempe, AZ 85284-3487
Tel (480) 483-1170 *Founded/Ownrshp* 1998
Sales 23.1MM^E *EMP* 150
SIC 8721 Certified public accountant; Certified public accountant
Mng Pt: Mark Eberle
Pt: James E Barrington
Pt: Debra Callicutt
Pt: James L Crampton
Pt: Gary Fleming
Pt: Charles Goodmiller
Pt: Kathy Hosletler
Pt: Charles Inderieden
Pt: Wendell E Jones
Pt: Donald Kretschmar
Pt: Wendell Peters

D-U-N-S 01-708-2413 IMP
HENRY A FOX SALES CO
HENRY A FOX SALES CO INC
(*Suby of* FOX FINANCIAL CORP) ★
4494 36th St Se, Grand Rapids, MI 49512-1917
Tel (616) 949-1210 *Founded/Ownrshp* 1970
Sales 31.1MM^E *EMP* 90
SIC 5182 5181 5149 Wine; Beer & other fermented malt liquors; Beverages, except coffee & tea; Wine; Beer & other fermented malt liquors; Beverages, except coffee & tea
Ch: Henry A Fox Jr
V Ch: Patrick Fox
Pr: Richard Drieborg
Treas: Joanne Fiedler
VP: Brien Fox
Mng Dir: Robert Horsford
Dist Mgr: Phil Wittkowski
IT Man: Lesa Porter
IT Man: Lisa Porter

Opers Mgr: Kyle Seeley
Sales Asso: Shea Nowlan

HENRY A FOX SALES CO INC
See HENRY A FOX SALES CO

D-U-N-S 00-694-6131
HENRY A PETTER SUPPLY CO LLC
5110 Charter Oak Dr, Paducah, KY 42001-5209
Tel (270) 575-6922 *Founded/Ownrshp* 1890
Sales 145.0MM^E *EMP* 209
SIC 5085 Industrial supplies; Industrial supplies
**Pr:* Bruce Austin
Pr: Rick Farlee
**Pr:* John Sircy
**Ch:* Bob Petter
Ex VP: Crystal Renauldo
VP: Jim Ferguson
Exec: Patsy Hayden
Brnch Mgr: Ronnie Austin
Brnch Mgr: Matthew Kelley
IT Man: Ron Overton
IT Man: Bruce Wilcox

D-U-N-S 02-814-0234 IMP
HENRY AVOCADO CORP
2355 E Lincoln Ave, Escondido, CA 92027-1298
Tel (760) 745-6632 *Founded/Ownrshp* 1924
Sales 169.1MM *EMP* 88
Accts White Nelson Diehl Evans Llp
SIC 0179 4213 Avocado orchard; Trucking, except local; Avocado orchard; Trucking, except local
Pr: Philip Henry
CFO: Jerry Miller
VP: Betty Guerrero
VP: Rick Opel
Off Mgr: Lori Deaver
Sfty Mgr: Elizabeth Ramirez
Opers Mgr: Uziel Gonzales
VP Sls: Don Hoey
Sls Mgr: Chris Varvel

D-U-N-S 00-597-5669
HENRY BROS CO (IL)
9821 S 78th Ave, Oak Lawn, IL 60457-2324
Tel (708) 430-5400 *Founded/Ownrshp* 1921
Sales 20.2MM^E *EMP* 50
SIC 1542 1541 Institutional building construction; Industrial buildings, new construction; Renovation, remodeling & repairs: industrial buildings
Pr: George W Ferrell
**CFO:* Sandy Austin
**Sr VP:* David Binkley
VP: Michael Concannon
**VP:* Stanley Jagielski
Art Dir: Melissa Mickey
Snr Mgr: Mike Kruse

D-U-N-S 10-572-0437
■ **HENRY BROS ELECTRONICS INC**
NATIONAL SAFE
(*Suby of* HENRY BROS ELECTRONICS INC) ★
1511 E Orangethorpe Ave A, Fullerton, CA 92831-5204
Tel (714) 525-4350 *Founded/Ownrshp* 2002
Sales 22.4MM^E *EMP* 200
SIC 7373 7382 5063 Computer integrated systems design; Security systems services; Burglar alarm systems; Computer integrated systems design; Security systems services; Burglar alarm systems
Pr: Eric Demarco
**CEO:* Deanna Lund
**Treas:* Laura Siegal
**VP:* Michael Fink
VP: Andy Koller
VP: Gary Marcinkowski
IT Man: Linda Stangel
**VP Opers:* Ben Goodwin

D-U-N-S 12-293-6607
■ **HENRY BROS ELECTRONICS INC**
(*Suby of* KRATOS DEFENSE & SECURITY SOLUTIONS INC) ★
17-01 Pollitt Dr Ste 5, Fair Lawn, NJ 07410-2808
Tel (201) 794-6500 *Founded/Ownrshp* 2010
Sales 42.7MM^E *EMP* 205
SIC 7373 3699 Computer integrated systems design; Electrical equipment & supplies; Security control equipment & systems; Computer integrated systems design; Electrical equipment & supplies; Security control equipment & systems
CEO: James Henry
**Pr:* Ben Goodwin
**Pr:* Jim Henry
COO: Carl Erickson
COO: Ken Noe
COO: Brian Smith
**Ex VP:* Fred Thomas
**Sr VP:* Jim Cotter
**Sr VP:* Chris Peckham
VP: Michael Fink
VP: Ted Gjini

D-U-N-S 06-669-5800
HENRY BUILDING INC
2450 N Interstate 35 E, Lancaster, TX 75134-2110
Tel (972) 224-8291 *Founded/Ownrshp* 1971
Sales 26.0MM *EMP* 85
SIC 1542 1541 1522 Commercial & office buildings, renovation & repair; Industrial buildings, new construction; Renovation, remodeling & repairs: industrial buildings; Apartment building construction; Condominium construction; Commercial & office building contractors; Commercial & office buildings, renovation & repair; Industrial buildings, new construction; Renovation, remodeling & repairs: industrial buildings; Apartment building construction; Condominium construction
Ch Bd: A E Henry
**Pr:* Jack C Henry
**Sec:* Marie Davidson
**VP:* Shirley Ann Henry

D-U-N-S 02-891-2640
HENRY C HANSEL INC
HENRY CURTIS FORD
(*Suby of* HANSEL ENTERPRISES, INC.)
1120 Auto Center Dr, Petaluma, CA 94952-1100
Tel (707) 769-2300 *Founded/Ownrshp* 1979
Sales 24.8MM^E *EMP* 70^E
SIC 5511

D-U-N-S 00-894-2013
HENRY CARLSON CO
1205 W Russell St, Sioux Falls, SD 57104-1324
Tel (605) 336-2410 *Founded/Ownrshp* 1919
Sales 34.4MM^E *EMP* 99
SIC 1542 1611 Commercial & office building, new construction; Surfacing & paving; Commercial & office building, new construction; Surfacing & paving
Pr: Henry Carlson III
**Treas:* Sue Harms
**VP:* Meredith Larson
Snr PM: Chad Nelson

D-U-N-S 15-281-7714
HENRY CO HOMES INC
4229 Highway 90, Pace, FL 32571-5000
Tel (850) 994-0984 *Founded/Ownrshp* 1983
Sales 31.6MM *EMP* 30^E
SIC 1531 Speculative builder, single-family houses; Speculative builder, single-family houses
Pr: Edwin Henry
Opers Mgr: Justin Davis

D-U-N-S 07-853-3815
HENRY CO LLC
(*Suby of* HCO HOLDING II CORP) ★
999 N Sepulveda Blvd, El Segundo, CA 90245-2714
Tel (310) 955-9200 *Founded/Ownrshp* 2010
Sales 224.4MM^E *EMP* 560
SIC 2952 2821 2891 Roof cement: asphalt, fibrous or plastic; Polyurethane resins; Sealants; Roof cement: asphalt, fibrous or plastic; Polyurethane resins; Sealants
CEO: Frank Ready
**CFO:* Jason Peel
**CFO:* Dori M Reap
**Sr VP:* Mark R Adams
**Sr VP:* James F Barry
**Sr VP:* Christopher J Brink
Sr VP: Alan K Davenport
**Sr VP:* Kirk R Kandler
Sls Mgr: Roger Bender

D-U-N-S 84-891-5302
HENRY COUNTY BANCSHARES INC
4806 N Henry Blvd, Stockbridge, GA 30281-3522
Tel (770) 474-7293 *Founded/Ownrshp* 1982
Sales NA *EMP* 139
SIC 6022 State commercial banks; State commercial banks
Pr: David H Gill
CFO: Charles W Blair Jr
Sec: Florence Fitzenrieter
Ofcr: Rhonda Cantrell
Ofcr: Kimberly Dagger
Ofcr: Jordan Gill
Ofcr: Thomas Gunnels
Ofcr: Debra Lindsey
Ofcr: Rhonda McIntyre
Ofcr: Paula Shockley
VP: Bonnie Lecroy
VP: Kimberly Lee
Board of Directors: Paul J Cates Jr, Phillip H Cook, H K Elliott Jr, G R Foster III, Edwin C Kelley Jr, Mary Lynn E Lambert, Ronald M Turpin, James C Waggoner

D-U-N-S 08-602-3454
HENRY COUNTY BOARD OF EDUCATION
217 Grove Blvd, Paris, TN 38242-4711
Tel (731) 642-9733 *Founded/Ownrshp* 1900
Sales 23.0MM *EMP* 450
SIC 8211 Boarding school; Elementary school; High school, junior or senior; Boarding school; Elementary school; High school, junior or senior

D-U-N-S 10-000-0496
HENRY COUNTY BOARD OF EDUCATION
300 N Trawick St, Abbeville, AL 36310
Tel (334) 585-2206 *Founded/Ownrshp* 1918
Sales 26.0MM *EMP* 200
Accts Ronald L Jones Chief Examine
SIC 8211 Public elementary & secondary schools; Public elementary & secondary schools
Prin: Dennis Coe

D-U-N-S 10-001-3879
HENRY COUNTY BOARD OF EDUCATION
HENRY COUNTY SCHOOL
33 N Zack Hinton Pkwy, McDonough, GA 30253-2344
Tel (770) 957-6601 *Founded/Ownrshp* 1935
Sales 290.0MM^E *EMP* 5,200
SIC 8211 Public elementary & secondary schools; Public elementary & secondary schools
Ofcr: Joseph Chambers
Ofcr: Earl Parker
IT Man: Stephen Thompson
Pr Dir: John D Hardin
Psych: Monica Militello

D-U-N-S 09-725-9253
HENRY COUNTY BOARD OF EDUCATION
HENRY COUNTY SCHOOL DISTRICT
326 S Main St, New Castle, KY 40050-2573
Tel (502) 845-8600 *Founded/Ownrshp* 1925
Sales 16.6MM^E *EMP* 400
Accts Charles T Mitchelle Co Fran
SIC 8211 Public elementary & secondary schools; Public elementary & secondary schools

HENRY COUNTY CLERK
See COUNTY OF HENRY

HENRY COUNTY HEALTH CENTER
See HENRY COUNTY SOLDIERS AND SAILORS MEMORIAL HOSPITAL

HENRY COUNTY HOSPITAL
See HENRY COUNTY MEMORIAL HOSPITAL

D-U-N-S 06-371-9207
HENRY COUNTY HOSPITAL INC
1600 E Riverview Ave Frnt, Napoleon, OH 43545-9399
Tel (419) 592-4015 *Founded/Ownrshp* 1958
Sales 25.2MM *EMP* 308
Accts Blue & Co Llc Columbus Oh
SIC 8062 General medical & surgical hospitals; General medical & surgical hospitals
CEO: Kim Bordenkircher
**COO:* Michelle Rychener
Dir Rx: Cindy Latta
Mktg Dir: Karlee Badenhop
Doctor: Stephen Knipe MD
Doctor: Ed Ledden

D-U-N-S 07-976-1320
HENRY COUNTY HOSPITAL INC
11600 County Road 424, Napoleon, OH 43545
Tel (419) 591-3837 *Founded/Ownrshp* 2015
Sales 26.7MM *EMP* 10^E
SIC 8062 General medical & surgical hospitals

HENRY COUNTY LANDFILL
See COUNTY OF HENRY

D-U-N-S 06-771-7165
HENRY COUNTY MEDICAL CENTER EMS INC (TN)
301 Tyson Ave, Paris, TN 38242-4544
Tel (731) 644-8578 *Founded/Ownrshp* 1953
Sales 1.8MM *EMP* 795
SIC 8062 8051 General medical & surgical hospitals; Skilled nursing care facilities; General medical & surgical hospitals; Skilled nursing care facilities
CEO: Thomas H Gee
**CFO:* Lisa Casteel
Ofcr: Janice Stanton

D-U-N-S 07-203-3061
HENRY COUNTY MEMORIAL HOSPITAL
HENRY COUNTY HOSPITAL
1000 N 16th St, New Castle, IN 47362-4395
Tel (765) 521-0890 *Founded/Ownrshp* 1930
Sales 69.8MM *EMP* 787
SIC 8062 General medical & surgical hospitals; General medical & surgical hospitals
CFO: Paul F Janssen
Dir Vol: Ruth Ann Miers
**Ch Bd:* John Pidgeon
**Pr:* Blake Dye
CFO: Darren Brown
**V Ch Bd:* Sheldon Dynes
Dir Lab: Cindy Kissick
Dir Lab: Steve Myers
Dir Rad: Todd Wright
Dir Rx: Kevin Thomas
CIO: Michael Spencer

HENRY COUNTY PUBLIC SCHOOLS
See HENRY COUNTY SCHOOL DISTRICT

HENRY COUNTY R E M C
See HENRY COUNTY RURAL ELECTRIC MEMBERSHIP CORP

D-U-N-S 00-693-9474
HENRY COUNTY RURAL ELECTRIC MEMBERSHIP CORP (IN)
HENRY COUNTY R E M C
201 N 6th St, New Castle, IN 47362-4825
Tel (765) 529-1212 *Founded/Ownrshp* 1935
Sales 20.3MM *EMP* 35
SIC 4911 Distribution, electric power; Distribution, electric power
Pr: Don Cross
**Treas:* Jake Martin
**Genl Mgr:* Steve Wolfron
IT Man: Joshua Gideon
Board of Directors: Herman Boque, Donald Cross, Jake Martin, William E Ricks, J Frank Smith, William Snodgrass, George Sweigart, William Webb, D Gene Whisler

HENRY COUNTY SCHOOL
See HENRY COUNTY BOARD OF EDUCATION

HENRY COUNTY SCHOOL DISTRICT
See HENRY COUNTY BOARD OF EDUCATION

D-U-N-S 19-352-6209
HENRY COUNTY SCHOOL DISTRICT
HENRY COUNTY PUBLIC SCHOOLS
3300 Kings Mountain Rd, Collinsville, VA 24078
Tel (276) 634-4700 *Founded/Ownrshp* 1995
Sales 48.9MM^E *EMP* 1,200
SIC 8211 Public elementary & secondary schools; Public elementary & secondary schools
MIS Dir: Teh-Way Lee
Pr Dir: Monica Hatchett
Psych: David Kirk

HENRY COUNTY SCHOOL SYSTEM
See COUNTY OF HENRY

D-U-N-S 07-979-9709
HENRY COUNTY SCHOOL SYSTEM
217 Grove Blvd, Paris, TN 38242-4711
Tel (731) 642-9733 *Founded/Ownrshp* 2015
Sales 3.9MM^E *EMP* 308^E
SIC 8211 Public elementary & secondary schools
MIS Dir: Denton Jordan
HC Dir: Stephanie Winders

D-U-N-S 07-989-4371
HENRY COUNTY SCHOOLS
33 N Zack Hinton Pkwy, McDonough, GA 30253-2344
Tel (770) 957-6601 *Founded/Ownrshp* 2015
Sales 163.7MM^E *EMP* 4,503^E
SIC 8211 Public elementary & secondary schools

D-U-N-S 78-478-7939
HENRY COUNTY SOLDIERS AND SAILORS MEMORIAL HOSPITAL
HENRY COUNTY HEALTH CENTER
407 S White St, Mount Pleasant, IA 52641-2263
Tel (319) 385-3141 *Founded/Ownrshp* 1919
Sales 31.2MM^E *EMP* 300
Accts Seim Johnson Llp Omaha Nebr

SIC 8062 8052 General medical & surgical hospitals; Intermediate care facilities; General medical & surgical hospitals; Intermediate care facilities
CEO: Rob Gardner
CFO: Dave Muhs
**CFO:* David Muhs
Dir Lab: Brian Bockting
Off Mgr: Lori Bolin
Off Admin: Susan Brecht
Obsttrcn: Robert Smith
Nrsg Dir: Jodi Geerts
Pharmcst: Michele Birdsell
Phys Thrpy: Andy Youngquist
HC Dir: Judy Sammons
Board of Directors: Shelley Doak, Deb Leichty

D-U-N-S 07-439-4263 IMP
HENRY CROWN AND CO
CC INDUSTRIES
222 N La Salle St # 2000, Chicago, IL 60601-1120
Tel (312) 236-6300 *Founded/Ownrshp* 1973
Sales 1.2MMM^E *EMP* 1,483
SIC 2514 Lawn furniture: metal; Lawn furniture: metal
Pr: James S Crown
Genl Pt: Richard Goodman
Treas: Michael Podgorski
VP: Sonya Anderson

HENRY CURTIS FORD
See HENRY C HANSEL INC

HENRY, DAN DISTRIBUTING
See CAPITOL BEVERAGE CO INC

D-U-N-S 87-760-9388
HENRY DAY FORD INC
4091 W 3500 S, West Valley City, UT 84120-3201
Tel (801) 973-7030 *Founded/Ownrshp* 1954
Sales 42.3MM^E *EMP* 100
SIC 5511 5531 Automobiles, new & used; Automotive parts; Automobiles, new & used; Automotive parts
Prin: Michael H Day
Sales Asso: Roy Galbraith
Sales Asso: Scott McAtee
Sales Asso: Michael Midgley
Sales Asso: Randall Miller
Sales Asso: Henri Schrecengost
Sales Asso: Don Werber

HENRY DOORLY ZOO
See OMAHA ZOOLOGICAL SOCIETY

D-U-N-S 96-952-7600
HENRY E HUNTINGTON LIBRARY AND ART GALLERY
1151 Oxford Rd, San Marino, CA 91108-1218
Tel (626) 405-2100 *Founded/Ownrshp* 2011
Sales 90.0MM *EMP* 3
Accts Singerlewak Llp Los Angeles
SIC 8231 Libraries; Libraries

D-U-N-S 00-251-5088
HENRY F MICHELL CO
225 W Church Rd, King of Prussia, PA 19406-3231
Tel (610) 265-4200 *Founded/Ownrshp* 1890
Sales 34.3MM^E *EMP* 75
SIC 5191 5193 Seeds: field, garden & flower; Nursery stock; Seeds: field, garden & flower; Nursery stock
CEO: Henry F Michell III
**Pr:* Frank B Michell Jr
**Treas:* Henry F Michell IV
**Prin:* Rick Michell
Mktg Mgr: Bob Steinlage

D-U-N-S 01-392-6779 IMP
HENRY F TEICHMANN INC
HFT
3009 Washington Rd, Mc Murray, PA 15317-3202
Tel (724) 941-9550 *Founded/Ownrshp* 1947
Sales 183.3MM^E *EMP* 400
SIC 1541 8711 8742 Industrial buildings, new construction; Industrial buildings, new construction; Engineering services; Construction project management consultant
Pr: Archie L McIntyre
**Ch Bd:* Newton N Teichmann Sr
Pr: Daniel Chen
**VP:* Kenneth E Lemasters Jr
VP Opers: Gordon Jungquist
VP Opers: Mark Piedmonte

D-U-N-S 05-015-7627
HENRY FARM CENTER INC
CCS TECHNOLOGY CENTERS
809 Columbia Rd, Abbeville, AL 36310-2741
Tel (334) 585-5525 *Founded/Ownrshp* 1969
Sales 80.0MM *EMP* 98
Accts Mcclintock Nelson & Associate
SIC 5734 4212 3523 Computer & software stores; Local trucking, without storage; Farm machinery & equipment; Computer & software stores; Local trucking, without storage; Farm machinery & equipment
Pr: Lester Howard Killebrew
**Ex VP:* John W Blankenship
Mktg Dir: Kenneth Lott
Sls Mgr: Mike Bailey
Sls Mgr: Michael Hubbard
Sls Mgr: Gary Lowe

D-U-N-S 02-363-8039
HENRY FORD ACADEMY
20900 Oakwood Blvd, Dearborn, MI 48124-5029
Tel (313) 271-1570 *Founded/Ownrshp* 1996
Sales 53.0MM *EMP* 27^E
SIC 8211 Private elementary & secondary schools
Pr: Denise Thal
CFO: James Connelly
**Ch:* Janet Lawson
**Treas:* Mike Schmidt
Comm Man: Andrew Johnson
Dir IT: Michael Butman
Pr Dir: Wendy Metros

D-U-N-S 08-277-0264
HENRY FORD CONTINUING CARE CORP
(*Suby of* HENRY FORD HEALTH SYSTEM) ★
19840 Harper Ave, Harper Woods, MI 48225-1804
Tel (313) 881-9556 *Founded/Ownrshp* 1982
Sales 15.5MM^E *EMP* 430
Accts Deloitte & Touche Llp
SIC 8051 Skilled nursing care facilities; Skilled nursing care facilities
Pr: Ann Kochanski
HC Dir: Theresa Dean

D-U-N-S 07-313-4603 IMP
HENRY FORD HEALTH SYSTEM
HENRY FORD HOSPITAL
1 Ford Pl, Detroit, MI 48202-3450
Tel (313) 916-2600 *Founded/Ownrshp* 1989
Sales 4.5MMM *EMP* 23,000
Accts Deloitte & Touche Llp Detroit
SIC 8062 General medical & surgical hospitals; General medical & surgical hospitals
CEO: Nancy Schlichting
Dir Recs: Karen Schmidt
**Pr:* Gail L Warden
COO: Gary Beaulac
COO: Thomas S Nantais
**COO:* Robert Riney
CFO: Edward G Chadwick
**CFO:* James M Connelly
Treas: Brian Gamble
Treas: David Mazurkiewicz
Trst: Marwan S Abouljoud
Trst: Lynn F Alandt
Trst: Manuel L Brown
Trst: Allan D Gilmour
Trst: Steven D Harrington
Trst: David M Hempstead
Trst: Joseph R Jordan
Trst: Alan M Kiriluk
Trst: David B Lewis
Trst: John C Plant
Chf Mktg O: Allen White

D-U-N-S 96-459-0777
HENRY FORD HEALTH SYSTEM
HENRY FORD HOSPITAL
(*Suby of* HENRY FORD HEALTH SYSTEM) ★
1 Ford Pl 5f, Detroit, MI 48202-3450
Tel (313) 876-1031 *Founded/Ownrshp* 2010
Sales 2.3MMM *EMP* 185^E
SIC 8699 Charitable organization

HENRY FORD HOSPITAL
See HENRY FORD HEALTH SYSTEM

HENRY FORD HOSPITAL
See HENRY FORD HEALTH SYSTEM

D-U-N-S 07-839-6058
HENRY FORD MACOMB HOSPITAL CORP
ST JOSEPH MERCY OF MACOMB
(*Suby of* HENRY FORD HEALTH SYSTEM) ★
15855 19 Mile Rd, Clinton Township, MI 48038-3504
Tel (586) 263-2300 *Founded/Ownrshp* 1990
Sales 21.0MM^E *EMP* 3,400
SIC 8062 General medical & surgical hospitals; General medical & surgical hospitals
CEO: Barbara Rossmann
CFO: Terry Goodbailian
Chf Mktg O: Joseph Naoum
**Ex VP:* Gary Beaulac
Sr VP: Barbara Rossman
VP: Terry Goodbalian
**VP:* Michael Markel Jr
VP: Debora Murray
VP: Karen Standfest
Dir Case M: Judy Rivard
Dir Rad: Deep G Bai
Dir Rad: Joseph Blechinger
Dir Rx: Richard Jennings

D-U-N-S 00-547-0750
HENRY FORD MACOMB HOSPITALS
(*Suby of* HENRY FORD HEALTH SYSTEM) ★
215 North Ave, Mount Clemens, MI 48043-1716
Tel (586) 466-9310 *Founded/Ownrshp* 2008
Sales 55.2MM^E *EMP* 608^E
SIC 8062 General medical & surgical hospitals
Pr: Stephen J Hathaway
Ex Dir: Sheila Sperti
HC Dir: Susanne Gleason

D-U-N-S 01-891-8894
HENRY FORD MEDICAL CENTER
(*Suby of* HENRY FORD HEALTH SYSTEM) ★
39450 W 12 Mile Rd, Novi, MI 48377-3600
Tel (248) 661-7393 *Founded/Ownrshp* 2009
Sales 39.7MM^E *EMP* 1,294^E
SIC 8011 Offices & clinics of medical doctors
Prin: Daniel Kus
Mktg Mgr: Jody Bott

HENRY FORD MUSEUM
See EDISON INSTITUTE

D-U-N-S 80-173-7388
HENRY FORD VILLAGE INC
15101 Ford Rd, Dearborn, MI 48126-4611
Tel (313) 584-1000 *Founded/Ownrshp* 1992
Sales 34.7MM *EMP* 300
Accts Bdo Usa Llp Grand Rapids Mi
SIC 8361 Geriatric residential care; Geriatric residential care
Ex Dir: Darrel Jensen
**Pr:* Larry Vidovic
**Ex Dir:* Bruce Blalock
Ex Dir: Lawrence Vidovic
Snr Mgr: Jeff Jacobs

D-U-N-S 06-098-3871 IMP
HENRY FORD WYANDOTTE HOSPITAL
(*Suby of* HENRY FORD HEALTH SYSTEM) ★
2333 Biddle Ave, Wyandotte, MI 48192-4668
Tel (734) 246-6000 *Founded/Ownrshp* 1999
Sales 259.0MM *EMP* 1,600
SIC 8062 General medical & surgical hospitals; General medical & surgical hospitals
CEO: Denise Brooks-Williams
**Pr:* Annette S Phillips
**CEO:* Nancy M Schlichting
VP: Dennis Lemanski
Exec: Sharon Maloney
Dir Rad: Jay Pockyarath
Dir Rx: Steve Corden
Off Mgr: Jane Cain
Sfty Dirs: Kevin Malane
Surgeon: Shawn Dowling
Obsttrcn: Michael Bork

D-U-N-S 00-249-7204 IMP
HENRY FRANCIS DUPONT WINTERTHUR MUSEUM INC
WINTERTHUR MUSEUM AND COUNTRY
5105 Kennett Pike, Winterthur, DE 19735-1819
Tel (302) 888-4852 *Founded/Ownrshp* 1930
Sales 25.4MM *EMP* 160
Accts Cover & Rossiter Pa Wilmingto
SIC 8412 Museum; Museum
Ex Dir: Sarah Willoughby
Snr Mgr: Kris Demesse

D-U-N-S 09-842-7123 EXP
HENRY GROUP INC
3734 Hwy 34 S, Greenville, TX 75402-5133
Tel (903) 883-2002 *Founded/Ownrshp* 1994
Sales 20.3MM *EMP* 96
SIC 3556 1796

D-U-N-S 00-342-1625
HENRY H LEWIS CONTRACTORS LLC (MD)
(*Suby of* POOLE CONSTRUCTION) ★
55 Gwynns Mill Ct, Owings Mills, MD 21117-3562
Tel (410) 654-7599 *Founded/Ownrshp* 1966
Sales 21.1MM^E *EMP* 55
SIC 1542 Commercial & office building, new construction; Commercial & office buildings, renovation & repair
CEO: Rich D Poole
Dir Bus: Ellington Churchill

D-U-N-S 07-534-2279
HENRY HEYWOOD MEMORIAL HOSPITAL
HEYWOOD HOSPITAL
(*Suby of* HEYWOOD HEALTHCARE INC) ★
242 Green St, Gardner, MA 01440-1336
Tel (978) 632-3420 *Founded/Ownrshp* 1907
Sales 95.0MM *EMP* 850
SIC 8062

D-U-N-S 05-580-0353
HENRY HOSPITAL DISTRICT (IL)
HAMMOND-HENRY HOSPITAL
600 N College Ave Ofc, Geneseo, IL 61254-1092
Tel (309) 944-6431 *Founded/Ownrshp* 1950
Sales 36.0MM *EMP* 360
SIC 8062

D-U-N-S 15-796-2820
HENRY HOWARD SERVICES LLC
1800 Saint James Pl # 207, Houston, TX 77056-4181
Tel (713) 781-7300 *Founded/Ownrshp* 2007
Sales 41.0MM *EMP* 104
SIC 4212 Heavy machinery transport, local

D-U-N-S 60-356-8528 IMP
HENRY II CO
2911 E Slauson Ave, Huntington Park, CA 90255-3135
Tel (323) 583-5000 *Founded/Ownrshp* 1989
Sales 44.1MM^E *EMP* 140
SIC 5182 6719 Wine coolers, alcoholic; Personal holding companies, except banks; Wine coolers, alcoholic; Personal holding companies, except banks
**Ch Bd:* William Baribault
**CFO:* Jeffrey A Wahba
**Treas:* Verne Thibodeaux

D-U-N-S 07-631-9870
HENRY J KAISER FAMILY FOUNDATION
2400 Sand Hill Rd Ste 200, Menlo Park, CA 94025-6910
Tel (650) 854-9400 *Founded/Ownrshp* 1948
Sales 33.8MM *EMP* 135^E
Accts Deloitte & Touche Llp San Fra
SIC 6732 Trusts: educational, religious, etc.; Trusts: educational, religious, etc.
Pr: Drew Altman
Trst: Charles J Ogletree
**Sr VP:* Koonal Gandhi
VP: Marla Bolotsky
**VP:* Timothy Ortez
Assoc Dir: Evonne Young
Pgrm Dir: Cara James

D-U-N-S 03-608-3582
HENRY J LEE DISTRIBUTORS LLC
(*Suby of* REYES HOLDINGS LLC) ★
315 Marymeade Dr, Summerville, SC 29483-5244
Tel (843) 554-0268 *Founded/Ownrshp* 1987
Sales 54.1MM^E *EMP* 160
SIC 5181 Beer & other fermented malt liquors; Beer & other fermented malt liquors
Pr: Dennis J Lee
**VP:* James L Wicks

HENRY J. SEAGROATT CO
See SEAGROATT FLORAL CO INC

D-U-N-S 14-467-6566
HENRY M JACKSON FOUNDATION FOR ADVANCEMENT OF MILITARY MEDICINE INC
H J F
6720a Rockledge Dr # 100, Bethesda, MD 20817-1888
Tel (240) 694-2000 *Founded/Ownrshp* 1983
Sales 414.2MM *EMP* 2,200
Accts Grant Thornton Llp Mclean Va
SIC 8099 Medical services organization; Medical services organization
Pr: John W Lowe
**CFO:* Craig Anderson
**VP:* Elizabeth Folk
**VP:* Arthur W Hapner
**VP:* Craig D Lebo
Prgrm Mgr: Chris Bayer
Prgrm Mgr: Wen Nie
Dir IT: P J Clark
IT Man: Richard Burris
Counsel: Aida Lebbos

D-U-N-S 96-687-8006
HENRY M ROWAN FAMILY FOUNDATION INC
P.O. Box 157 (08073-0157)
Tel (609) 267-9000 *Founded/Ownrshp* 2011
Sales 34.0MM *EMP* 2^E
SIC 8699 Charitable organization; Charitable organization

D-U-N-S 08-540-5439
HENRY MAYO NEWHALL HOSPITAL
23845 Mcbean Pkwy, Valencia, CA 91355-2083
Tel (661) 253-8000 *Founded/Ownrshp* 1972
Sales 249.7MM *EMP* 1,600^E
Accts Bdo Usa Llp Costa Mesa Ca
SIC 8062 General medical & surgical hospitals; General medical & surgical hospitals
Pr: Roger E Seaver
Ch Bd: Elizabeth Hopp
CFO: Cathy Richardson
Treas: James Hickens
Ofcr: Kelly Wildhaber
Sr VP: C R Hudson
VP: Richard Frankenstein
VP: Jonathan Miller
VP: John Schleif
VP: Fredy Shen
Dir Risk M: Katie Brown
Dir Lab: Cindy Martin
Dir Lab: Rashida Soni

D-U-N-S 87-436-1608
HENRY MAYO NEWHALL MEMORIAL HEALTH FOUNDATION INC
HENRYMAYO NEWHALL MEM HOSP
23845 Mcbean Pkwy, Valencia, CA 91355-2001
Tel (661) 253-8000 *Founded/Ownrshp* 1972
Sales 251.8MM *EMP* 1,500
SIC 8062 General medical & surgical hospitals; General medical & surgical hospitals
Pr: Roger Seaver
CIO: Cindy Petersen
Obsttrcn: Nicholas J Tuso
Pharmcst: Dele Akao
Pgrm Dir: Glenn Dabatos

D-U-N-S 03-610-4799
HENRY MAYO NEWHALL MEMORIAL HOSPITAL
23845 Mcbean Pkwy, Valencia, CA 91355-2001
Tel (661) 253-8112 *Founded/Ownrshp* 2013
Sales 245.5MM *EMP* 94^E
SIC 8011 General & family practice, physician/surgeon; General & family practice, physician/surgeon
Prin: Roger Charles Wallace

D-U-N-S 00-891-9961 IMP
HENRY MODELL & CO INC
MODELL'S SPORTING GOODS
498 7th Ave Fl 20, New York, NY 10018-6704
Tel (212) 822-1000 *Founded/Ownrshp* 1946
Sales 604.7MM *EMP* 5,430
Accts Bdo Usa Llp New York Ny
SIC 5941 5661 5611 5621 5641 5961 Sporting goods & bicycle shops; Footwear, athletic; Clothing, sportswear, men's & boys'; Women's sportswear; Children's & infants' wear stores; Catalog & mail-order houses; Sporting goods & bicycle shops; Footwear, athletic; Clothing, sportswear, men's & boys'; Women's sportswear; Children's & infants' wear stores; Catalog & mail-order houses
Ch Bd: Mitchell B Modell
Pr: Joe Paltenstein
Ex VP: Holly Bann
Ex VP: Lawrence Brustein
Ex VP: Cary Deleo
Sr VP: Bill Barrett
Sr VP: Lynn Larocca
Sr VP: Mark Oliver
VP: James Buoni
VP: Joseph Conley
VP: Willy Kaplan
VP: Jim McDonald
VP: Justin Miller
Exec: John Olguin

D-U-N-S 03-164-4750
HENRY OIL CO INC
DON'S
2621 Whitehouse Rd, Jasper, AL 35501-6420
Tel (205) 777-0080 *Founded/Ownrshp* 1966
Sales 23.0MM^E *EMP* 40
SIC 5171 5411 Petroleum bulk stations; Convenience stores, independent
Pr: Donald C Henry Sr
**Sec:* Morris Knott
**VP:* Donald C Henry Jr

D-U-N-S 00-634-1277
HENRY PARSONS CROWELL AND SUSAN COLEMAN
1880 Office Club Pt # 2200, Colorado Springs, CO 80920-5008
Tel (719) 272-8300 *Founded/Ownrshp* 2010
Sales 20.9MM *EMP* 2
SIC 6722 Management investment, open-end
Prin: Henry Parsons Crowell

D-U-N-S 09-261-5640 IMP
HENRY PLASTIC MOLDING INC
HPMI
41703 Albrae St, Fremont, CA 94538-3120
Tel (510) 490-7991 *Founded/Ownrshp* 1978
Sales 39.5MM^E *EMP* 165
SIC 3089 Plastic processing; Plastic processing
CEO: Edwin Henry
**Sec:* Helen Henry
**VP:* Linda Henry
Genl Mgr: Nathan Chambler
QC Dir: Dennis Bush
Opers Mgr: Don Hoverter

D-U-N-S 60-416-7338 IMP
■ **HENRY PRATT CO LLC**
(*Suby of* MUELLER CO LLC) ★
401 S Highland Ave, Aurora, IL 60506-5580
Tel (630) 844-4000 *Founded/Ownrshp* 1901
Sales 74.8MM^E *EMP* 420
SIC 3491 Industrial valves; Water works valves; Valves, nuclear; Industrial valves; Water works valves; Valves, nuclear
Pr: Dale B Smith
**CFO:* Darrell Jean
**VP:* Randy Berger
**VP:* Steve Sharp
MIS Dir: Sarada Mohapatra
Sfty Mgr: Ryan Kline
Opers Mgr: John Howard
VP Sls: Bernard Haviland

D-U-N-S 00-280-9077
HENRY PRODUCTION INC (NM)
PUMPS & SERVICE DIV
3440 Morning Star Dr, Farmington, NM 87401-8814
Tel (505) 327-0422 *Founded/Ownrshp* 1962
Sales 43.8MM^E *EMP* 108
SIC 5084 7353 Oil well machinery, equipment & supplies; Oil field equipment, rental or leasing; Oil well machinery, equipment & supplies; Oil field equipment, rental or leasing
Ch: Harvey H Henry
**Pr:* Samuel H Henry
**VP:* Tony Henry
Sales Asso: Hop Lee

D-U-N-S 14-837-1651 IMP
HENRY PRODUCTS INC
H.P.I.
302 S 23rd Ave, Phoenix, AZ 85009-5228
Tel (602) 253-3191 *Founded/Ownrshp* 2013
Sales 24.5MM^E *EMP* 82
SIC 5033 5032 Insulation materials; Plastering materials; Insulation materials; Plastering materials
Pr: James Owen
**VP:* Sylvie S Owen
**Genl Mgr:* Mark Norgaard
Plnt Mgr: George Reichling

D-U-N-S 01-262-3799
HENRY QUENTZEL PLUMBING SUPPLY CO INC
379 Throop Ave, Brooklyn, NY 11221-1312
Tel (718) 455-6600 *Founded/Ownrshp* 1959
Sales 21.8MM^E *EMP* 40
SIC 5074 Plumbing fittings & supplies; Heating equipment (hydronic)
Ch Bd: Ann Quentzel
**Sec:* Andrew Quentzel
**VP:* Arnold Greenwald

D-U-N-S 00-737-0521
HENRY S MILLER CO REALTORS
5001 Spring Valley Rd 1100w, Dallas, TX 75244-3950
Tel (972) 419-4000 *Founded/Ownrshp* 1991
Sales 50.0MM *EMP* 15
SIC 6531 Real estate brokers & agents; Real estate managers; Real estate brokers & agents; Real estate managers
Pr: Virginia Cook
**Ch Bd:* Vance C Miller
CFO: Stephen Harris
Sec: Robert Dubois
Ex VP: David R Dunn
Ex VP: Greg Trout
Sr VP: Elton Harwell
VP: Max Lindsay
VP: Ross J Love

HENRY SCHEIN ANIMAL HEALTH
See BUTLER ANIMAL HEALTH SUPPLY LLC

D-U-N-S 88-366-0144 IMP
■ **HENRY SCHEIN EUROPE INC**
(*Suby of* HENRY SCHEIN INC) ★
135 Duryea Rd, Melville, NY 11747-3834
Tel (631) 843-5500 *Founded/Ownrshp* 1990
Sales 59.9MM^E *EMP* 420^E
SIC 5047 Dental equipment & supplies; Dental equipment & supplies
Ch Bd: Stanley M Bergman
**CFO:* Steven Paladino
**Ex VP:* James P Breslawski
VP: Robert Minowitz
**VP:* Michael Zack

D-U-N-S 01-243-0880 IMP
▲ **HENRY SCHEIN INC**
135 Duryea Rd, Melville, NY 11747-3834
Tel (631) 843-5500 *Founded/Ownrshp* 1932
Sales 10.3MMM *EMP* 16,000
Accts Bdo Usa Llp New York Ny
Tkr Sym HSIC *Exch* NGS
SIC 5047 5122 7372 Dental equipment & supplies; Medical equipment & supplies; Veterinarians' equipment & supplies; Pharmaceuticals; Business oriented computer software; Dental equipment & supplies; Medical equipment & supplies; Veterinarians' equipment & supplies; Pharmaceuticals; Business oriented computer software
Ch Bd: Stanley M Bergman
**Pr:* James P Breslawski
Pr: Peter McCarthy
Pr: Lonnie Shoff
COO: Leonard David
CFO: Michael Lugassy
**CFO:* Steven Paladino
Treas: Joel Geliebter
Chf Mktg O: Kevin Bunker
**Ofcr:* Gerald A Benjamin
**Ex VP:* Mark E Mlotek
Sr VP: Walter Siegel
Dir Bus: Feng Han
Dir Bus: Rodi Rozin
Board of Directors: Louis W Sullivan, Barry J Alperin, Lawrence S Bacow, Paul Brons, Donald J Kabat, Philip A Laskawy, Norman S Matthews, Carol Raphael, E Dianne Rekow, Bradley T Sheares

D-U-N-S 94-777-0058
■ **HENRY SCHEIN PRACTICE SOLUTIONS INC**
(*Suby of* HENRY SCHEIN INC) ★
1220 S 630 E 100, American Fork, UT 84003-3680
Tel (801) 847-7000 *Founded/Ownrshp* 1985
Sales 49.0MM^E *EMP* 360
SIC 8011 General & family practice, physician/surgeon; General & family practice, physician/surgeon
Prin: Stanley Bergman
Pr: Kevin Bunker
VP: Jim Hughes
VP: Brian Peterson
Snr Sftwr: Bryan Campbell
Snr Sftwr: Rich Dahl
QA Dir: Bridger Henriksen
QA Dir: Jeremie Roberts
Sys Mgr: Rob Gray
Software D: Claire Chenn
Software D: John Stephens

D-U-N-S 07-526-6619 IMP
HENRY STREET SETTLEMENT
265 Henry St, New York, NY 10002-4808
Tel (212) 766-9200 *Founded/Ownrshp* 1893
Sales 33.9MM *EMP* 850
Accts Loeb & Troper Llp New York N
SIC 8322 Community center; Community center
Ch Bd: Audrey Rosenman
**Pr:* Scott L Swid
**CFO:* Josephine C Lume
**Ch:* Philip T Ruegger III
**Treas:* Walter Maynard Jr
**V Ch Bd:* John C Nelson
Ofcr: Larraine Ahto
Ofcr: Jeremy Reiss
**VP:* Anne Abrons
**VP:* Dale Burch
**VP:* Frederic S Papert
**VP:* Stephanie Wise
Exec: Saba Hocek
Dir Bus: Jeanie Tung

HENRY TECH INC INTL SLS CO
See HENRY TECHNOLOGIES INC

D-U-N-S 00-507-1741
HENRY TECHNOLOGIES INC (IL)
HENRY TECH INC INTL SLS CO
(*Suby of* HENDRICKS HOLDING CO INC) ★
701 S Main St, Chatham, IL 62629-1655
Tel (217) 483-2406 *Founded/Ownrshp* 1914
Sales 74.1MM^E *EMP* 500
SIC 3491 3585 3567 3564 3545 3494 Gas valves & parts, industrial; Automatic regulating & control valves; Regulators (steam fittings); Refrigeration equipment, complete; Evaporative condensers, heat transfer equipment; Industrial furnaces & ovens; Blowers & fans; Machine tool accessories; Valves & pipe fittings; Gas valves & parts, industrial; Automatic regulating & control valves; Regulators (steam fittings); Refrigeration equipment, complete; Evaporative condensers, heat transfer equipment; Industrial furnaces & ovens; Blowers & fans; Machine tool accessories; Valves & pipe fittings
Pr: Michael Giordano
Genl Mgr: Sandy Macdonald
Opers Mgr: Tony Grissom
Manager: Bill Mezin
Sls Mgr: Ron Ceminsky
Sls Mgr: Jim Funk
Sls Mgr: Kenny Price

D-U-N-S 00-226-7920 IMP
HENRY TROEMNER LLC
201 Wolf Dr, West Deptford, NJ 08086-2245
Tel (856) 686-1600 *Founded/Ownrshp* 1840
Sales 41.3MM^E *EMP* 150
SIC 3821 Laboratory apparatus & furniture; Laboratory apparatus & furniture

HENRY VISCARDI SCHOOL
See ABILITIES INC

HENRY WINE GROUP, THE
See CENTRAL COAST WINE CO

D-U-N-S 10-990-9858 IMP
HENRY WINE GROUP LLC
HENRY WINE GROUP OF C.A., THE
4301 Industrial Way, Benicia, CA 94510-1227
Tel (707) 745-8500 *Founded/Ownrshp* 2003
Sales 102.1MM^E *EMP* 315
SIC 5182 Wine; Wine
**VP:* Chris Choate

HENRY WINE GROUP OF C.A., THE
See HENRY WINE GROUP LLC

D-U-N-S 80-025-6534
HENRY WISCONSIN LLC
107 W Coleman St, Rice Lake, WI 54868-2452
Tel (715) 736-3030 *Founded/Ownrshp* 2006
Sales 22.0MM^E *EMP* 100
SIC 3489 3429 Guns or gun parts, over 30 mm.; Manufactured hardware (general)
Genl Mgr: Andy Wickstrom

D-U-N-S 00-714-8042
HENRY WURST INC (MO)
NORTH KANSAS CITY
1331 Saline St, North Kansas City, MO 64116-4400
Tel (816) 701-0825 *Founded/Ownrshp* 1937
Sales 119.2MM^E *EMP* 320
SIC 2752 7331 Commercial printing, lithographic; Commercial printing, lithographic; Mailing service
Ch: John C Wurst
**Pr:* Mark Hanf
**CEO:* Michael S Wurst
**CFO:* Kate Stewart
Plnt Mgr: Randy Radosevich
Plnt Mgr: Howard Stamper
Prd Mgr: Edwina Cook
Prd Mgr: Sherri Meyer
Sales Exec: Mark Gearon

HENRYMAYO NEWHALL MEM HOSP
See HENRY MAYO NEWHALL MEMORIAL HEALTH FOUNDATION INC

D-U-N-S 02-296-4340
HENRYS FOODS INC
234 Mckay Ave N, Alexandria, MN 56308-8550
Tel (320) 763-3194 *Founded/Ownrshp* 1929
Sales 155.1MM^E *EMP* 150
SIC 5194 5145 5111 5113 5141 Tobacco & tobacco products; Confectionery; Printing & writing paper; Industrial & personal service paper; Groceries, general line; Tobacco & tobacco products; Confectionery; Printing & writing paper; Industrial & personal service paper; Groceries, general line
CEO: H Thomas Eidsvold
**VP:* Jim Eidsvold
Dir Bus: Leann Anderson
Off Mgr: Karren Janachovsky
IT Man: Meduna Daniel
IT Man: Daniel Meduna
Opers Mgr: Scott Hokanson

D-U-N-S 04-389-1159
HENRYS SEAFOOD INC
FISH MARKET, THE
5865 Lincoln Hwy, York, PA 17406-8903
Tel (717) 252-1112 *Founded/Ownrshp* 1987
Sales 25.0MM *EMP* 15
SIC 5146 Fish & seafoods; Fish & seafoods
Co-Pr: Jeffrey S Geisel
**Co-Pr:* Scott Morrison
Exec: Russ Nave

D-U-N-S 04-438-0350 EXP
HENRYS TACKLE LLC
(*Suby of* BIG ROCK SPORTS LLC) ★
158 Little Nine Rd, Morehead City, NC 28557-8482
Tel (252) 726-6186 *Founded/Ownrshp* 1996
Sales 128.5MM^E *EMP* 350
SIC 5091 Sporting & recreation goods; Fishing tackle; Sporting & recreation goods; Fishing tackle

D-U-N-S 06-332-2085 IMP/EXP
HENSEL PHELPS CONSTRUCTION CO
420 6th Ave, Greeley, CO 80631-2332
Tel (970) 352-6565 *Founded/Ownrshp* 1960
Sales 2.5MMM *EMP* 2,000
Accts Kpmg Llp Denver Co
SIC 1542 1521 1771 1522 1541 1622 Nonresidential construction; Single-family housing construction; Concrete work; Residential construction; Industrial buildings & warehouses; Bridge, tunnel & elevated highway; Nonresidential construction; Single-family housing construction; Concrete work; Residential construction; Industrial buildings & warehouses; Bridge, tunnel & elevated highway
Pr: Jeffrey Wenaas
CFO: Stephen J Carrico
Ex VP: Jon W Ball
Ex VP: Michael J Choutka
Ex VP: Wayne S Lindholm
Ex VP: Richard G Tucker
VP: Leonard J Arnold
VP: Allan J Bliesmer
VP: Rashad Friday
VP: Steve M Grauer
VP: Kirk J Hazen
VP: Bradley A Jeanneret
VP: Robert P Majerus
VP: Cuyler R McGinley
VP: James R Pappas Jr
VP: Daniel Sherard
VP: William A Thompson
VP: Eric L Wilson
VP: Brad D Winans
Exec: Darin Stephens

D-U-N-S 83-565-6518
HENSEL PHELPS CONSTRUCTION CO
(*Suby of* HENSEL PHELPS CONSTRUCTION CO) ★
4129 E Van Buren St # 100, Phoenix, AZ 85008-6940
Tel (480) 383-8480 *Founded/Ownrshp* 1982
Sales 30.2MM^E *EMP* 294
SIC 1542 Commercial & office building contractors
VP: Steve Grauer
**VP:* Allan Bliesmer
**VP:* William Thompson III
**VP:* Brad Winans

D-U-N-S 96-779-4533
HENSEL PHELPS GRANITE HANGAR JOINT VENTURE
18850 Von Kamon 100, Irvine, CA 92612
Tel (949) 852-0111 *Founded/Ownrshp* 2011
Sales 300.0MM *EMP* 200
SIC 1542 1629 Nonresidential construction; Heavy construction; Nonresidential construction; Heavy construction
VP: Cuyler R McGinley
VP: John A Franich

D-U-N-S 83-261-3918
HENSEL PHELPS GRANITE TRAYLOR PACIFIC JV
420 6th Ave, Greeley, CO 80631-2332
Tel (970) 352-6565 *Founded/Ownrshp* 2009
Sales 200.0MM *EMP* 100
SIC 1541 1522 1542 1629 1611 1521 Industrial buildings & warehouses; Residential construction; Nonresidential construction; Heavy construction; Highway & street construction; Single-family housing construction; Industrial buildings & warehouses; Residential construction; Nonresidential construction; Heavy construction; Highway & street construction; Single-family housing construction
VP: Jon W Ball
Pr: William G Dorey

D-U-N-S 07-847-5336
HENSEL PHELPS SERVICES LLC
(*Suby of* HENSEL PHELPS CONSTRUCTION CO) ★
4437 Brookfield Corp 20 Ste 207, Chantilly, VA 20151
Tel (703) 828-3200 *Founded/Ownrshp* 2012
Sales 250.0MM *EMP* 5
SIC 1522 8744 1521 1541 1623 1611 Residential construction; Facilities support services; Single-family housing construction; Industrial buildings & warehouses; Water, sewer & utility lines; Highway & street construction; Residential construction; Facilities support services; Single-family housing construction; Industrial buildings & warehouses; Water, sewer & utility lines; Highway & street construction
Ex VP: Michael J Choutka
Pr: Edwin Glenn Miller

D-U-N-S 83-162-9238
HENSEL PHELPS SOLTEK JV
(*Suby of* HENSEL PHELPS CONSTRUCTION CO) ★
420 6th Ave, Greeley, CO 80631-2332
Tel (970) 352-6565 *Founded/Ownrshp* 2009
Sales 100.0MM *EMP* 4^E
SIC 1542 1541 Nonresidential construction; Industrial buildings & warehouses; Nonresidential construction; Industrial buildings & warehouses
Mng Pt: Edwin Calhoun

D-U-N-S 96-181-4295
HENSEL PHELPS-GRANITE JV
420 6th Ave, Greeley, CO 80631-2332
Tel (970) 352-6565 *Founded/Ownrshp* 2010
Sales 100.0MM *EMP* 40
SIC 1541 1542 1629 1611 Industrial buildings & warehouses; Nonresidential construction; Heavy construction; Highway & street construction; Industrial buildings & warehouses; Nonresidential construction; Heavy construction; Highway & street construction
VP: Jon Ball
Pr: William G Dorey

D-U-N-S 96-184-0829
HENSEL PHELPS/KSC A JOINT VENTURE
4437 Brkfeld Corp Dr 20, Chantilly, VA 20151
Tel (703) 828-3200 *Founded/Ownrshp* 2010
Sales 50.0MM *EMP* 150
SIC 1541 1542 1611 1622 Industrial buildings & warehouses; Nonresidential construction; Highway & street construction; Bridge, tunnel & elevated highway; Industrial buildings & warehouses; Nonresidential construction; Highway & street construction; Bridge, tunnel & elevated highway
Ex VP: Mark Baugh
Pr: Paul Carter
Ex VP: Van Groves
VP: Timothy J Cleary
VP: Steven Speer

D-U-N-S 09-365-1768 IMP
HENSLEY & CO
HENSLEY BEVERAGE COMPANY
4201 N 45th Ave, Phoenix, AZ 85031-2109
Tel (602) 264-1635 *Founded/Ownrshp* 1970
Sales 52.7MM^E *EMP* 75^E
SIC 5181 Beer & other fermented malt liquors; Beer & other fermented malt liquors
CEO: Robert M Delgado
Pr: James W Hensley
Ch: Cindy McCain

D-U-N-S 03-590-6171 IMP
HENSLEY AND CO WHOLESALE
HENSLEY BEVERAGE COMPANY
4201 N 45th Ave, Phoenix, AZ 85031-2109
Tel (602) 264-1635 *Founded/Ownrshp* 1955
Sales NA *EMP* 630
SIC 5181

HENSLEY BEVERAGE COMPANY
See HENSLEY AND CO WHOLESALE

HENSLEY BEVERAGE COMPANY
See HENSLEY & CO

D-U-N-S 06-288-7237 IMP/EXP
HENSLEY INDUSTRIES INC
(*Suby of* KOMATSU AMERICA CORP) ★
2108 Joe Field Rd, Dallas, TX 75229-3255
Tel (972) 241-2321 *Founded/Ownrshp* 1980
Sales 115.7MM^E *EMP* 500
SIC 3325 Alloy steel castings, except investment; Alloy steel castings, except investment
Pr: Hidekichi Kuribayashi
**CFO:* John Fielder
**VP:* Ralph Huebner
VP: Laura Merry
**VP:* K Tatsumikawa
Netwrk Eng: Blake Curry

D-U-N-S 01-544-2309
HENSON LUMBER LTD (TX)
11900 County Road 917, Cresson, TX 76035-4504
Tel (817) 396-4321 *Founded/Ownrshp* 2000
Sales 24.0MM *EMP* 60
Accts Robert T Warren Pc Plano Te
SIC 5211 4225 Lumber & other building materials; General warehousing & storage; Lumber & other building materials; General warehousing & storage
Pr: Betty Henson
Pt: Casey Wallace
Pt: Glenn R Wilson
Ex VP: Todd Garner
Div Mgr: Ronnie Hassell

D-U-N-S 84-962-1446
HENSON MOTOR CO INC
MULE BARN
105 S May St, Madisonville, TX 77864-2051
Tel (936) 348-3618 *Founded/Ownrshp* 1993
Sales 29.0MM^E *EMP* 65
SIC 5511 5531 Automobiles, new & used; Automotive tires; Automobiles, new & used; Automotive tires
Pr: Fred Henson
**Sec:* Liz Henson
**VP:* Arthur Henson
CTO: Lesa Hill

D-U-N-S 00-593-5747
HENSON ROBINSON CO
3550 Great Northern, Springfield, IL 62711-9403
Tel (217) 544-8451 *Founded/Ownrshp* 1861, 2010
Sales 45.5MM^E *EMP* 150

SIC 1711 1761 Warm air heating & air conditioning contractor; Roofing contractor; Warm air heating & air conditioning contractor; Roofing contractor
Pr: Daniel Hoselton
**Sec:* Steve Etheridge
Ofcr: Debbie Piehler
VP: Bill Hoselton
Sls Mgr: Mark Patrick

D-U-N-S 02-339-4158 IMP/EXP
HENTZEN COATINGS INC
6937 W Mill Rd, Milwaukee, WI 53218-1225
Tel (414) 353-4200 *Founded/Ownrshp* 1923
Sales 57.6MM^E *EMP* 278
SIC 2851

HEOTACORE
See HEPTACORE INC

HEPACO
See IMS ENVIRONMENTAL SERVICES INC

D-U-N-S 11-599-3297
HEPACO LLC
2711 Burch Dr, Charlotte, NC 28269-4476
Tel (704) 598-9782 *Founded/Ownrshp* 1984
Sales 297.8MM^E *EMP* 550
SIC 4959 Oil spill cleanup; Oil spill cleanup
Pr: Ron L Horton Jr
**Pr:* Ronald L Horton Sr
**CFO:* Ron Dwyer
**Treas:* Richard G Horton
Ex VP: Richard Lutz
Ex VP: Rhonda Pope
**VP:* Neville W Anderson
**VP:* Ronald L Horton Jr
Exec: Mark Boland
Exec: Chris Carmichael
Exec: Pat Lazaroski
Dir Bus: Joe Opatkiewicz

D-U-N-S 61-823-1281
HEPHAESTUS HOLDINGS INC
(*Suby of* KPS CAPITAL PARTNERS LP) ★
39475 W 13 Mile Rd # 105, Novi, MI 48377-2359
Tel (248) 479-2700 *Founded/Ownrshp* 2005
Sales 171.0MM^E *EMP* 1,000
SIC 3462 3463 Iron & steel forgings; Nonferrous forgings; Iron & steel forgings; Nonferrous forgings
CEO: George Thanopolous

D-U-N-S 84-986-3626
HEPHAISTOS BUILDING SUPPLIES INC
INTERNATIONAL GEOTECHNICAL
2402 37th Ave, Astoria, NY 11101-2121
Tel (718) 726-2226 *Founded/Ownrshp* 1994
Sales 23.7MM^E *EMP* 15
SIC 5031 5211 Building materials, exterior; Building materials, interior; Lumber & other building materials
Ch Bd: Michael Karantinidis

D-U-N-S 09-900-3816
HEPPNER HARDWOODS INC
555 W Danlee St, Azusa, CA 91702-2342
Tel (626) 969-7983 *Founded/Ownrshp* 1972
Sales 37.2MM^E *EMP* 60
SIC 5031 Lumber: rough, dressed & finished
Pr: Lorraine Heppner
COO: Brent Heppner
CFO: Jack Bogle
Sales Asso: Sean Haarberg

D-U-N-S 79-466-3179
HEPTACORE INC
HEOTACORE
12211 State Route Y # 200, Bloomsdale, MO 63627-9043
Tel (573) 483-2323 *Founded/Ownrshp* 1992
Sales 27.0MM^E *EMP* 92
SIC 1794 1623 Excavation & grading, building construction; Water & sewer line construction
Pr: Wayne P Drury

D-U-N-S 07-943-3553
HER INC
4261 Morse Rd, Columbus, OH 43230-1522
Tel (614) 221-7400 *Founded/Ownrshp* 1956
Sales 12.9MM^E *EMP* 300
SIC 6531 Real estate agent, residential; Real estate agent, residential
CEO: George W Smith
**Ch Bd:* Harley E Rouda Sr
**Pr:* Harley E Rouda Jr
**Sr VP:* Geri Van Lent
**Sr VP:* Robert E Zellar

HERAEUS EELCTRO
See HERAEUS ELECTRO-NITE CO LLC

D-U-N-S 15-728-8721 IMP
HERAEUS ELECTRO-NITE CO LLC
HERAEUS EELCTRO
(*Suby of* HERAEUS INC) ★
1 Summit Square Ctr Fl 1, Langhorne, PA 19047-1091
Tel (215) 944-9000 *Founded/Ownrshp* 1988
Sales 106.3MM^E *EMP* 401
SIC 3812 3825 3823 Instruments to measure electricity; Primary elements for process flow measurement; Thermal conductivity instruments, industrial process type; Search & navigation equipment; Search & navigation equipment; Instruments to measure electricity; Primary elements for process flow measurement
Pr: Michael G Midash
Exec: Helen Kettell
Brnch Mgr: Tony Eliott
Div Mgr: Anke Janning
Genl Mgr: Alex Lee
MIS Mgr: Mike Saracino
Mfg Dir: Shaun Bell
Opers Supe: Amy Burnham
Ql Cn Mgr: Juan Bermudez
Ql Cn Mgr: Wiebke Kuharic
Ql Cn Mgr: James Ledama

D-U-N-S 00-126-4563 IMP
HERAEUS INC
HERAEUS PRECIOUS METALS MGT
(*Suby of* HERAEUS HOLDING GESELLSCHAFT MIT BESCHRANKTER HAFTUNG)
540 Madison Ave Fl 16, New York, NY 10022-3249
Tel (212) 752-2180 *Founded/Ownrshp* 1978
Sales 441.9MM^E *EMP* 1,981
SIC 3399 3823 3339 3469 Paste, metal; Temperature measurement instruments, industrial; Precious metals; Machine parts, stamped or pressed metal; Paste, metal; Temperature measurement instruments, industrial; Precious metals; Machine parts, stamped or pressed metal
Pr: Maike Schuh Klaeren
**Treas:* Thomas Lyons
Off Mgr: Angrina Sthely
Off Mgr: Mary Yerkes

D-U-N-S 15-086-5459
HERAEUS KULZER LLC (MITSUI CHEMICALS GROUP)
(*Suby of* MITSUI CHEMICALS,INC.)
300 Heraeus Dr, South Bend, IN 46614-2557
Tel (574) 299-5466 *Founded/Ownrshp* 2013
Sales 73.4MM *EMP* 135
SIC 3843 Dental equipment & supplies; Dental equipment & supplies
IT Man: James Williams
Pr Mgr: Nina Mautner
Sls Mgr: Jeremy Franklin
Sls Mgr: Austin Furlong

D-U-N-S 86-830-3074
HERAEUS MEDICAL COMPONENTS INC
(*Suby of* HERAEUS KULZER LLC (MITSUI CHEMICALS GROUP)) ★
5030 Centerville Rd, Saint Paul, MN 55127-2203
Tel (651) 792-8500 *Founded/Ownrshp* 2004
Sales 133.1MM^E *EMP* 245
SIC 3493 Steel springs, except wire; Steel springs, except wire
Pr: Mark Kempf
**Ch Bd:* Frank Heinricht
Area Mgr: Alistair Campbell
Dist Mgr: Paul Frey
Opers Mgr: Franklin Soto
Plnt Mgr: Ralph Hall
Prd Mgr: Jeff Lewis
Ql Cn Mgr: Arthur Schultz
Snr Mgr: Patrick Griffin

D-U-N-S 00-244-9262 IMP/EXP
HERAEUS METALS NEW YORK LLC
(*Suby of* HERAEUS INC) ★
540 Madison Ave, New York, NY 10022-3213
Tel (212) 752-2181 *Founded/Ownrshp* 1927, 1989
Sales 195.4MM^E *EMP* 1,800
SIC 5094 Precious metals; Precious metals
**VP:* Artin Janian
Genl Mgr: Gerry Dawson

D-U-N-S 11-620-9354 IMP
HERAEUS NOBLELIGHT AMERICA LLC
FUSION UV SYSTEMS
(*Suby of* HERAEUS NOBLELIGHT GMBH)
910 Clopper Rd Ste 102n, Gaithersburg, MD 20878-1357
Tel (301) 527-2660 *Founded/Ownrshp* 2013
Sales 60.0MM *EMP* 180
SIC 5047 Electrical equipment & supplies; Medical equipment & supplies
Pr: Stan Shalk
**CFO:* Kochn Marmann
**CTO:* P K Swain
IT Man: Ed Bogen
Tech Mgr: Jeff Bragg
Netwrk Eng: Rusel Reyes
VP Opers: Jim Elliott
Sfty Mgr: Rick Brady
Plnt Mgr: Travis Steinmetz
Prd Mgr: John R Brady
Mktg Mgr: Gina Gonzalez

HERAEUS PRECIOUS METALS MGT
See HERAEUS INC

D-U-N-S 04-859-0046 IMP/EXP
HERAEUS PRECIOUS METALS NORTH AMERICA CONSHOHOCKEN LLC
(*Suby of* HERAEUS INC) ★
24 Union Hill Rd, Conshohocken, PA 19428-2719
Tel (610) 825-6050 *Founded/Ownrshp* 1980
Sales 32.5MM^E *EMP* 150
SIC 3399 Metal powders, pastes & flakes; Metal powders, pastes & flakes
Genl Mgr: Robert Housman

D-U-N-S 05-667-7503 IMP
HERAEUS PRECIOUS METALS NORTH AMERICA LLC
(*Suby of* HERAEUS DEUTSCHLAND GMBH & CO. KG)
15524 Carmenita Rd, Santa Fe Springs, CA 90670-5610
Tel (562) 921-7464 *Founded/Ownrshp* 2000
Sales 81.2MM^E *EMP* 414
SIC 3341 2899 Gold smelting & refining (secondary); Silver smelting & refining (secondary); Platinum group metals, smelting & refining (secondary); Chemical preparations; Salt; Gold smelting & refining (secondary); Silver smelting & refining (secondary); Platinum group metals, smelting & refining (secondary); Chemical preparations; Salt
Tech Mgr: Jeff Vandillen
Prd Mgr: Gustavo Covarrubias

HERALD
See EAST COAST NEWSPAPERS INC

HERALD & NEWS
See KLAMATH PUBLISHING CO

D-U-N-S 18-500-7440
■ **HERALD BRADENTON INC**
(*Suby of* MCCLATCHY CO) ★
1111 3rd Ave W Ste 100, Bradenton, FL 34205-8894
Tel (941) 748-0411 *Founded/Ownrshp* 2006
Sales 45.3MM^E *EMP* 245
SIC 2711 Newspapers, publishing & printing; Newspapers, publishing & printing
Pr: Mac Tully
VP: Darren Haimer
VP: Jim Lamb
**VP:* Robert G Turner
Sales Asso: Steve Mansfield

HERALD JOURNAL, THE
See HERALD NEWSPAPERS CO INC

D-U-N-S 83-443-9010
HERALD MEDIA HOLDINGS INC
70 Fargo St Ste 600, Boston, MA 02210-2131
Tel (617) 423-4545 *Founded/Ownrshp* 1994
Sales 112.1MM^E *EMP* 1,800
SIC 2711 Commercial printing & newspaper publishing combined; Commercial printing & newspaper publishing combined
Pr: Patrick J Purcell

D-U-N-S 00-223-6636
HERALD NEWSPAPERS CO INC
HERALD JOURNAL, THE
(*Suby of* ADVANCE PUBLICATIONS INC) ★
1 Clinton Sq, Syracuse, NY 13202
Tel (315) 470-0011 *Founded/Ownrshp* 1960
Sales 300.2MM^E *EMP* 3,496
SIC 2711 Newspapers, publishing & printing; Newspapers, publishing & printing
Ch: Stephen A Rogers
**Pr:* Tim Kennedy
**Treas:* Donald E Newhouse
Prd Dir: Patricia McAluney
Sales Exec: Patrice David
Advt Dir: Bill Allison

HERALD OFFICE SOLUTIONS
See HERALD OFFICE SUPPLY INC

D-U-N-S 03-613-2710
HERALD OFFICE SUPPLY INC
HERALD OFFICE SOLUTIONS
110 E Roosevelt St, Dillon, SC 29536-2440
Tel (843) 774-5155 *Founded/Ownrshp* 1984
Sales 29.0MM *EMP* 126
Accts Munn & Associates Pc Florenc
SIC 5943 2522 Office forms & supplies; Office furniture, except wood; Office forms & supplies; Office furniture, except wood
CEO: Arthur B Jordan III
**Pr:* Ronny Lee
**Sec:* Thomas Jordan
**VP:* L Cooper Jordan
IT Man: Mary Gaddy
Netwrk Mgr: Richard Tefertiller

D-U-N-S 08-350-9294
HERALD SPARTANBURG AND JOURNAL INC
(*Suby of* HALIFAX MEDIA HOLDINGS LLC) ★
189 W Main St, Spartanburg, SC 29306-2334
Tel (864) 582-4511 *Founded/Ownrshp* 1843, 2012
Sales 28.3MM^E *EMP* 250
SIC 2711 2791 Newspapers; Typesetting; Newspapers; Typesetting
Bd of Dir: William Porter
Board of Directors: Kathy Powell

HERALD TIMES
See HOOSIER TIMES INC

HERB ADCOX BODY SHOP
See HERB ADCOX CHEVROLET CO

D-U-N-S 03-456-6380
HERB ADCOX CHEVROLET CO
HERB ADCOX BODY SHOP
5721 Lee Hwy, Chattanooga, TN 37421-3542
Tel (423) 892-8310 *Founded/Ownrshp* 1959
Sales 20.2MM^E *EMP* 65
SIC 5511 5521 7538 5531 Automobiles, new & used; Used car dealers; General automotive repair shops; Automotive & home supply stores; Automobiles, new & used; Used car dealers; General automotive repair shops; Automotive & home supply stores
Pr: Herbert Adcox
**VP:* Dana G Robinette
Exec: Martin Baker

D-U-N-S 07-739-4950
HERB CHAMBERS 1168 INC
HERB CHAMBERS TOYOTA OF BOSTON
32 Brighton Ave, Allston, MA 02134-2310
Tel (617) 787-1700 *Founded/Ownrshp* 1999
Sales 34.7MM^E *EMP* 100
SIC 5511 Automobiles, new & used; Automobiles, new & used
Pr: Herb Chambers
Genl Mgr: Maz Abdel-Hafiz
Sls Mgr: Harry Maragianis
Sales Asso: Joshua Peled

D-U-N-S 12-979-2185 EXP
HERB CHAMBERS 1172 INC
HERB CHAMBERS BMW
1168 Commonwealth Ave, Boston, MA 02134-4618
Tel (617) 731-1700 *Founded/Ownrshp* 1991
Sales 63.9MM^E *EMP* 225
SIC 5511 Automobiles, new & used; Automobiles, new & used
Pr: Herbert Chambers
**VP:* Bruce Spatz
Sls Mgr: Neil Ferreira
Sls Mgr: Errol Gaudette
Sls Mgr: Kate George
Sales Asso: Rob Williams

HERB CHAMBERS BMW
See HERB CHAMBERS 1172 INC

HERB CHAMBERS CHRYSLER JEEP
See HERB CHAMBERS I 95 INC

D-U-N-S 14-024-1907
HERB CHAMBERS FORD OF WESTBOROUGH
310 Turnpike Rd, Westborough, MA 01581-2899
Tel (774) 760-0500 *Founded/Ownrshp* 2003
Sales 23.0MM^E *EMP* 60
SIC 5511 Automobiles, new & used; Automobiles, new & used
Pr: Herb Chambers
CFO: David G Massad Sr
**VP:* Bruce Spatz
**Genl Mgr:* Tom Quirk
Genl Mgr: Kevin Yarborough
Sales Asso: Jonathan Belez

HERB CHAMBERS HONDA
See CHAMBERS HERB 1186 INC

D-U-N-S 80-109-4640
HERB CHAMBERS HONDA OF SEEKONK
185 Taunton Ave, Seekonk, MA 02771-5320
Tel (508) 336-7100 *Founded/Ownrshp* 1985
Sales 22.0MM^E *EMP* 60
SIC 5511 Automobiles, new & used; Automobiles, new & used
Pr: Herb Chambers
**VP:* Bruce Spatz
Genl Mgr: Al Martin
Sales Asso: David High

D-U-N-S 04-943-9912
HERB CHAMBERS I 95 INC
HERB CHAMBERS CHRYSLER JEEP
(*Suby of* CHAMBERS MOTOR CARS OF BOSTON) ★
107 Andover St, Danvers, MA 01923-1414
Tel (978) 774-8840 *Founded/Ownrshp* 1978
Sales 26.1MM^E *EMP* 65
SIC 5511 Automobiles, new & used; Vans, new & used; Pickups, new & used; Automobiles, new & used; Vans, new & used; Pickups, new & used
Pr: Herb Chambers
Genl Mgr: Jim Klimas
Sls Mgr: Bill Lee
Sales Asso: John Pullio

D-U-N-S 05-347-4896
HERB CHAMBERS I-93 INC
CHAMBERS MOTOR CARS OF BOSTON
259 Mcgrath Hwy, Somerville, MA 02143-3417
Tel (617) 666-4100 *Founded/Ownrshp* 1992
Sales 495.1MM^E *EMP* 1,800
SIC 5511 Automobiles, new & used; Automobiles, new & used
Pr: Herb Chambers
CFO: James Duchesneau
**CFO:* Bruce H Spatz
**Treas:* Herbert G Chambers
VP: Mark Norman
**VP:* James L Xaros
VP: Jim Xaros
Genl Mgr: Scott Birtles
Genl Mgr: Bernie Moreno
Genl Mgr: Kosta Pappas
Off Admin: Dawn Bergstrom

D-U-N-S 62-278-1490
HERB CHAMBERS ROUTE 1 INC
LEXUS OF NORWOOD
25 Providence Hwy, Sharon, MA 02067-1651
Tel (508) 850-7513 *Founded/Ownrshp* 1991
Sales 23.1MM^E *EMP* 54
SIC 5511 Automobiles, new & used; Automobiles, new & used
Pr: Herbert G Chambers
**Pr:* Bruce Spatz
Sls Mgr: Don Smith
Sales Asso: David Hoppe
Sales Asso: William Noonan

HERB CHAMBERS TOYOTA OF BOSTON
See HERB CHAMBERS 1168 INC

HERB CONNOLLY CHEVROLET
See CONNOLLY BUICK CO INC

HERB DENMARK
See MERCHANT SERVICES INTL INC

D-U-N-S 00-803-8028
HERB EASLEY MOTORS INC
1125 Central Fwy, Wichita Falls, TX 76306-5944
Tel (940) 228-4402 *Founded/Ownrshp* 1960
Sales 37.7MM^E *EMP* 110
SIC 5511 5531 7538 Automobiles, new & used; Automotive parts; General automotive repair shops; Automobiles, new & used; Automotive parts; General automotive repair shops
Pr: J Herbert Easley
**Pr:* Pete Mankins
CFO: Jean Seabourn
Sls&Mrk Ex: Brad Lawson

D-U-N-S 03-495-6128
HERB HALLMAN CHEVROLET INC
CHAMPION CHEVROLET
800 Kietzke Ln, Reno, NV 89502-2016
Tel (775) 786-3111 *Founded/Ownrshp* 1988
Sales 77.9MM^E *EMP* 251
SIC 5511 7532 7538 5531 7513 5521 Body shop, automotive; Body shop, trucks; Automobiles, new & used; Pickups, new & used; Vans, new & used; General automotive repair shops; Automotive parts; Automotive accessories; Truck rental & leasing, no drivers; Used car dealers; New & used car dealers; Body shop, automotive; General automotive repair shops; Automotive parts; Truck rental & leasing, no drivers; Used car dealers
Pr: Jack Stanko Sr
**Sec:* Stanley F Bondick
**VP:* John P Stanko Jr
Sls Mgr: Jim Bayus

D-U-N-S 01-315-7623
HERB PHILIPSONS ARMY AND NAVY STORES INC
1899 Black River Blvd N, Rome, NY 13440-2427
Tel (315) 336-1302 *Founded/Ownrshp* 1951
Sales 21.2MM *EMP* 250
Accts Fitzgerald Depietro & Wojnas

SIC 5651 5661 5941 Family clothing stores; Jeans stores; Shoe stores; Footwear, athletic; Children's shoes; Sporting goods & bicycle shops; Hunting equipment; Fishing equipment; Camping equipment; Family clothing stores; Jeans stores; Shoe stores; Footwear, athletic; Children's shoes; Sporting goods & bicycle shops; Hunting equipment; Fishing equipment; Camping equipment
Ch Bd: Gary Philipson
CFO: Mike Palmer
Sr VP: Dave Sawdy
*VP: Aviva Philipson

D-U-N-S 00-498-6675
HERB REDL PROPERTIES
GUARDIAN TRAILER RENTALS
80 Washington St Ste 100, Poughkeepsie, NY 12601-2316
Tel (845) 471-6000 Founded/Ownrshp 1949
Sales 620.6M EMP 385
SIC 4225 6515 6512 General warehousing & storage; Warehousing, self-storage; Mobile home site operators; Nonresidential building operators; Property operation, retail establishment; General warehousing & storage; Warehousing, self-storage; Mobile home site operators; Nonresidential building operators; Property operation, retail establishment
Pt: Kari Redl Daniels
Owner: Herbert H Redl
Mng Pt: Kelley Hardisty
Mng Pt: Kari Redl-Daniels

D-U-N-S 00-654-6394
HERB RITSEMA CO
RITSEMA ASSOCIATES
(Suby of RDR PROPERTIES INC) ★
3000 Dormax St Sw, Grandville, MI 49418-1168
Tel (616) 538-0120 Founded/Ownrshp 1955
Sales 29.1MM^E EMP 167^E
SIC 1742 1752 Plastering, plain or ornamental; Acoustical & ceiling work; Drywall; Floor laying & floor work; Carpet laying
Pr: William Ritsema
*Sr VP: Michael Feichtenbiner
*VP: Wayne Monson
*Prin: Herbert Ritsema

D-U-N-S 01-762-5900
HERB THYME FARMS INC
8600 S Wilkinson Way G, Perrysburg, OH 43551-2598
Tel (866) 386-0854 Founded/Ownrshp 2000
Sales 13.4MM^E EMP 500
SIC 0191 General farms, primarily crop; General farms, primarily crop
Pr: Howard Roeder

D-U-N-S 07-928-9271 IMP
HERB-PHARM LLC
20260 Williams Hwy, Williams, OR 97544-9738
Tel (541) 846-6262 Founded/Ownrshp 2011
Sales 20.1MM^E EMP 100
SIC 2834 Vitamin, nutrient & hematinic preparations for human use; Vitamin, nutrient & hematinic preparations for human use
Sls Dir: Melodi Watson
Sls Mgr: Melissa Leffingwell
Sales Asso: Margie Durham

D-U-N-S 82-944-6108 IMP/EXP
HERBALIFE INTERNATIONAL INC
(Suby of HERBALIFE LTD INC) ★
990 W 190th St, Torrance, CA 90502-1014
Tel (310) 410-9600 Founded/Ownrshp 2010
Sales 277.8MM^E EMP 149^E
SIC 5122 Drugs, proprietaries & sundries
Pr: Michael O Johnson
Sr VP: Vasilios Frankos
VP: Andrew Shao
Snr Mgr: Kristy Appelhans

D-U-N-S 87-303-5968 IMP
HERBALIFE INTERNATIONAL OF AMERICA INC
(Suby of HERBALIFE LTD INC) ★
800 W Olympic Blvd # 406, Los Angeles, CA 90015-1360
Tel (310) 410-9600 Founded/Ownrshp 1984
Sales 1.1MMM^E EMP 2,000
SIC 5122 Vitamins & minerals; Vitamins & minerals
CEO: Michael O Johnson
*Pr: Des Walsh
*COO: Rich Goudis
*CFO: John De Simone
*Treas: Richard Yamashita
Sr VP: Eric Zepeda
VP: Mark Schissel
IT Man: Dan Moran
IT Man: Georgio Sorani

D-U-N-S 03-702-7554 IMP/EXP
HERBALIFE LTD INC
(Suby of WH INTERMEDIATE HOLDINGS LTD)
800 W Olympic Blvd # 406, Los Angeles, CA 90015-1360
Tel (310) 410-9600 Founded/Ownrshp 2002
Sales 1.5MMM^E EMP 3,000
SIC 2833 Chemicals & allied products; Medicinals & botanicals
Ch Bd: Michael O Johnson
Pr: Carol Hannah
Pr: Gregory Probert
CFO: John Desimone
Treas: William D Lowe
Bd of Dir: Ken Diekroeger
Ofcr: Anne Wong
Ex VP: Alan L Hoffman
Ex VP: Des Walsh
Sr VP: Stacy Brovitz
Sr VP: Amy Greene
Sr VP: Pamela Jones Harbour
Sr VP: William M Rahn
Sr VP: Henry Wang
VP: Angela Arboleda
VP: David Bartlett
VP: Julian Cacchioli
VP: Jean Marie Cacciatore
VP: Richard Caloca
VP: Michele Crocker
VP: Steven Dentali
Board of Directors: Carole Black, Lawrence Higby, Michael J Levitt

D-U-N-S 07-985-2200
HERBALIFE MANUFACTURING LLC
(Suby of HERBALIFE LTD INC) ★
3200 Temple School Rd, Winston Salem, NC 27107-3628
Tel (336) 970-6400 Founded/Ownrshp 2015
Sales 50.4MM^E EMP 350
SIC 5169 Chemicals & allied products

D-U-N-S 83-172-6935 IMP/EXP
HERBALIFE MANUFACTURING LLC
(Suby of HERBALIFE LTD INC) ★
20481 Crescent Bay Dr, Lake Forest, CA 92630-8817
Tel (949) 951-5150 Founded/Ownrshp 2009
Sales 29.3MM^E EMP 75
SIC 2087 2023 Beverage bases, concentrates, syrups, powders & mixes; Dietary supplements, dairy & non-dairy based; Beverage bases, concentrates, syrups, powders & mixes; Dietary supplements, dairy & non-dairy based
Sr VP: Gerry Holly
Sr VP: David Pezzullo
Ql Cn Mgr: Michelle Lane

D-U-N-S 87-425-7462
HERBCO INTERNATIONAL CORP
SNOQUALMIE RIVER RANCH HERBS
16661 W Sonqualmie Riv, Duvall, WA 98019-9202
Tel (425) 788-7903 Founded/Ownrshp 1993
Sales 52.0MM EMP 481
SIC 0182 Food crops grown under cover; Food crops grown under cover
Pr: Ted Andrews
*VP: Dave Lykins
Genl Mgr: Debbie Howard

D-U-N-S 05-689-4769
HERBERT E ORR CO INC
335 W Wall St, Paulding, OH 45879-1163
Tel (419) 399-4866 Founded/Ownrshp 1993
Sales 46.6MM^E EMP 125
SIC 5013 3479 Wheels, motor vehicle; Painting of metal products; Wheels, motor vehicle; Painting of metal products
Pr: Greg Johnson
*Treas: Donna Garman

D-U-N-S 80-101-5806
HERBERT G BIRCH
104 W 29th St Fl 3, New York, NY 10001-5310
Tel (212) 645-9971 Founded/Ownrshp 2007
Sales 54.6MM EMP 2
SIC 8351 Child day care services; Child day care services
Prin: Herbert Birch
COO: Susan Miller

D-U-N-S 96-452-8900
HERBERT H LEHMAN COLLEGE
AFFIRMATIVE ACTION/EEO DEPARTM
(Suby of AFFIRMATIVE ACTION/EEO DEPT) ★
250 Bedford Park Blvd W, Bronx, NY 10468-1527
Tel (718) 960-8261 Founded/Ownrshp 2010
Sales 1.3MM EMP 1,000
Accts Deans Archer & Co Cpa S Vall
SIC 8221 Colleges universities & professional schools; Colleges universities & professional schools
Pr: Ricardo R Fernandez

D-U-N-S 06-825-3939
HERBERT L JAMISON & CO LLC
(Suby of ASSUREDPARTNERS INC) ★
20 Commerce Dr Bsmt 2, Cranford, NJ 07016-3617
Tel (973) 731-0806 Founded/Ownrshp 2011
Sales NA EMP 70
SIC 6411 Insurance agents, brokers & service
Pr: Thomas Savvides
Ex VP: Joseph Caruso
Sr VP: Patricia Roberto
VP: Michelle Coleman
VP: Theresa Vines

D-U-N-S 00-961-6780 IMP
HERBERT MALARKEY ROOFING CO
MALARKEY ROOFING PRODUCTS
3131 N Columbia Blvd, Portland, OR 97217-7472
Tel (503) 283-1191 Founded/Ownrshp 1956
Sales 159.4MM^E EMP 380
SIC 2952 Roofing materials; Roofing materials
Pr: Michael O Malarkey
CFO: Bart Walker
*Treas: Mary Jane Murray
VP: John Cruba
*VP: Gregory B Malarkey
Exec: Ric Robbins
CTO: Jesse Nelson
QA Dir: Shawn Collins
Dir IT: John Kouba
IT Man: Gary Collins
Sfty Mgr: Michael Tuel

D-U-N-S 09-874-3057
HERBERT ROWLAND & GRUBIC INC
369 E Park Dr, Harrisburg, PA 17111-2730
Tel (717) 564-1122 Founded/Ownrshp 1962
Sales 34.4MM^E EMP 193
SIC 8711 Consulting engineer; Construction & civil engineering; Consulting engineer; Construction & civil engineering
Pr: Robert C Grubic
CFO: Bruce Yerger
*VP: Brian D Emberg
*VP: Andrew Kenworthy
VP: Michael Kreiger
Off Mgr: Daniel Santoro
Off Mgr: Tim Schram
Dir IT: Keith Persing
Mktg Dir: Denise Spong
Snr PM: John Klein
Board of Directors: Brian Emberg, Jason Fralick, Robert Grubic, Stanley Rapp, Bruce Yerger

D-U-N-S 07-258-6043
HERBRUCK POULTRY RANCH INC
6425 Grand River Ave, Saranac, MI 48881-9669
Tel (616) 642-9421 Founded/Ownrshp 1958
Sales 105.7MM^E EMP 400
SIC 0252 Chicken eggs; Chicken eggs
Pr: Stephen Herbruck
*Ch Bd: Marilyn Herbruck
*VP: Gregory Herbruck
*VP: Terry Herbruck
IT Man: Chris Clos
VP Prd: Mohamed Mousa
Snr Mgr: Mark Cebula

D-U-N-S 62-310-1664 IMP
HERBS GAIA INC
101 Gaia Herbs Rd, Brevard, NC 28712-8930
Tel (828) 884-4242 Founded/Ownrshp 1992
Sales 26.1MM^E EMP 90
SIC 2079 8011 2833 Edible oil products, except corn oil; Offices & clinics of medical doctors; Medicinals & botanicals
Pr: Ric Scalzo
*CFO: Etson Brandenburg
VP: Todd King
VP: Angela McElwee
VP: Jim Moore
Exec: Karen Domanski
Creative D: Matt Palomares
Creative D: David Terry
Plnt Mgr: Jamie Brandenburg
Plnt Mgr: Nathan Johnson
Plnt Mgr: Bryan Reece

D-U-N-S 62-020-6482 IMP
HERBS UNLIMITED INC
ROCK GARDEN SOUTH
2950 Nw 74th Ave, Miami, FL 33122-1426
Tel (305) 477-8833 Founded/Ownrshp 1989
Sales 37.4MM^E EMP 90
SIC 5149 5148 Spices & seasonings; Vegetables, fresh; Spices & seasonings; Vegetables, fresh
Pr: Charles Coiner
*Pr: Daniel F Coosemans
*VP: Jeff Bruff
Off Mgr: Manny Lepe
Prd Mgr: Enrique Guerrero

D-U-N-S 04-418-0867
HERC-U-LIFT INC
STORAGE CONCEPTS COMPANY DIVIS
5655 Highway 12, Maple Plain, MN 55359-9425
Tel (763) 479-2501 Founded/Ownrshp 1968
Sales 73.7MM^E EMP 128
SIC 5084 Lift trucks & parts; Materials handling machinery; Lift trucks & parts; Materials handling machinery
CEO: Lester Nielsen
Pr: Tom Showalter
Genl Mgr: Dan Showalter
Telecom Ex: Ann Bodin
Dir IT: Bill Swing
MIS Mgr: Bruce Whitehead
Sls&Mrk Ex: Mike Benauer
VP Sls: Jack Piche
Mktg Mgr: Mark Larson
Mktg Mgr: Duane Oestreich
Sls Mgr: Scott Barnard

HERCARE AT AMARILLO
See AMARILLO DIAGNOSTIC CLINIC PA

HERCULES
See UNIVERSAL METAL PRODUCTS INC

D-U-N-S 09-692-5508 IMP
HERCULES ADIRONDACK TIRE CORP
198 Morris Rd Ste 1, Schenectady, NY 12303-3414
Tel (518) 370-4175 Founded/Ownrshp 1979
Sales 24.7MM^E EMP 60
SIC 5014 5531 Automobile tires & tubes; Truck tires & tubes; Automotive tires
CEO: Lawrence O'Shea

HERCULES BAGS
See HERCULES POLY INC

D-U-N-S 04-420-2687 IMP/EXP
HERCULES CEMENT CO LP
(Suby of BUZZI UNICEM USA) ★
501 Hercules Dr, Stockertown, PA 18083-7009
Tel (610) 759-6300 Founded/Ownrshp 2003
Sales 30.9MM^E EMP 134
SIC 3241 Portland cement; Portland cement
CEO: Massimo Toso
*CFO: William S Collumbien
*VP: Thomas Hood

HERCULES DEADLINE ANCHOR CO
See QUADCO INC

D-U-N-S 00-504-4227 IMP
HERCULES DRAWN STEEL CORP (MI)
38901 Amrhein Rd, Livonia, MI 48150-1042
Tel (734) 464-4454 Founded/Ownrshp 1957
Sales 21.7MM^E EMP 100
SIC 3316 Bars, steel, cold finished, from purchased hot-rolled; Bars, steel, cold finished, from purchased hot-rolled
Pr: Mark Goodman
*Owner: Jeff Goodman
*VP: Gary Goodman
*VP: Glenn Huber
QC Dir: Joseph Okonowski
Prd Mgr: Patrick Greener

D-U-N-S 14-341-4188
■ **HERCULES DRILLING LLC**
HERCULES INTERNATIONAL DRLG
(Suby of HERCULES OFFSHORE INC) ★
9 Greenway Plz Ste 2200, Houston, TX 77046-0931
Tel (713) 350-5100 Founded/Ownrshp 2004
Sales 98.4MM^E EMP 1,800
SIC 8741 Management services; Management services
CEO: John T Rynd
*Ex VP: Stephen M Butz
*Ex VP: James W Noe
*Sr VP: Terry L Carr
*Sr VP: Troy L Carson
Sr VP: T O'Keefe
*VP: Richard E McClaine
*VP: Craig M Muirhead
IT Man: Robert Aultman
VP Opers: Mike Kelley

D-U-N-S 12-133-7757 IMP
HERCULES ENTERPRISES LLC
321 Valley Rd, Hillsborough, NJ 08844-4056
Tel (908) 369-0000 Founded/Ownrshp 2002
Sales 30.8MM^E EMP 100
SIC 3715 Truck trailers; Truck trailers
*Pr: Karl Massaro
Sales Exec: Frank Massaro

D-U-N-S 04-333-9548 IMP
HERCULES FENCE CO INC (NC)
1526 Early St, Norfolk, VA 23502-1604
Tel (757) 321-6700 Founded/Ownrshp 1958, 1985
Sales 31.9MM^E EMP 135
SIC 1799 5039 5211

D-U-N-S 07-978-5688
HERCULES FILMS LLC
12600 Cardinal Mdw, Sugar Land, TX 77478-6195
Tel (920) 284-0796 Founded/Ownrshp 2014
Sales 110.0MM^E EMP 25
SIC 3081 5199 Unsupported plastics film & sheet; Packaging materials

D-U-N-S 62-222-0580
HERCULES FORWARDING INC
(Suby of HERCULES FORWARDING INC)
7701 W 95th St, Hickory Hills, IL 60457-2204
Tel (323) 263-6100 Founded/Ownrshp 1990
Sales 23.5MM^E EMP 80
SIC 4212 4213 Local trucking, without storage; Trucking, except local
Pr: Ellen K Burnham
*VP: Martin Burnham
VP Opers: John Tofanelli
Sales Exec: Holly Storz

D-U-N-S 78-866-1358
HERCULES HOLDING II LLC
1 Park Plz, Nashville, TN 37203-6527
Tel (615) 344-9551 Founded/Ownrshp 2013
Sales 2.2MMM^E EMP 199,000
SIC 8062 8063 8069 8093 General medical & surgical hospitals; Psychiatric hospitals; Specialty hospitals, except psychiatric; Specialty outpatient clinics; General medical & surgical hospitals; Psychiatric hospitals; Specialty hospitals, except psychiatric; Specialty outpatient clinics
Prin: Jack Bovender

D-U-N-S 00-131-5647 IMP/EXP
■ **HERCULES INC**
(Suby of ASHLAND INC) ★
500 Hercules Rd, Wilmington, DE 19808-1513
Tel (302) 594-5000 Founded/Ownrshp 1912, 2008
Sales 2.0MMM^E EMP 4,660
SIC 2869 2891 Olefins; Adhesives; Olefins; Adhesives
CEO: Allen A Spizzo
*Treas: Stuart C Shears
Treas: Stuart Shears
Bd of Dir: Thomas Bates
Bd of Dir: Allan Cohen
Ex VP: David Hausrath
VP: Ray Fisher
VP: Scott Gregg
VP: Dale Macdonald
VP: Karen Murphy
VP: Paul C Raymond
VP: Vincent M Romano
VP: John T Rynd
VP: Anne Schumann
Board of Directors: Allan H Cohen

D-U-N-S 03-198-5484
HERCULES INDUSTRIES INC
1310 W Evans Ave, Denver, CO 80223-4027
Tel (303) 937-1000 Founded/Ownrshp 1962
Sales 71.4MM^E EMP 315
SIC 3498 5075

HERCULES INTERNATIONAL DRLG
See HERCULES DRILLING LLC

D-U-N-S 00-598-3879 IMP
HERCULES MACHINERY CORP
HMC FOUNDATION EQUIPMENT
5025 New Haven Ave, Fort Wayne, IN 46803-3022
Tel (260) 424-0405 Founded/Ownrshp 1964
Sales 24.9MM^E EMP 27
SIC 5082 7353 General construction machinery & equipment; Heavy construction equipment rental
Pr: John Jinnings
*VP: Justin D Reed
Sfty Mgr: John Moore
VP Sls: Tom Dame
Sls Mgr: Bryan Daniel

D-U-N-S 00-638-1891
HERCULES MANUFACTURING CO (KY)
800 Bob Posey St, Henderson, KY 42420-5617
Tel (270) 826-9501 Founded/Ownrshp 1902, 1959
Sales 35.5MM^E EMP 121^E
SIC 3713 3715 Truck bodies (motor vehicles); Trailer bodies
Pr: Joe Banna
*CEO: Jeffrey A Caddick
*Ch: George L Caddick
Opers Mgr: Ellen Redding
Sales Asso: Ryan Warren

D-U-N-S 60-540-2887 IMP/EXP
▲ **HERCULES OFFSHORE INC**
9 Greenway Plz Ste 2200, Houston, TX 77046-0931
Tel (713) 350-5100 Founded/Ownrshp 2004
Sales 900.2MM EMP 1,800^E
Tkr Sym HERO Exch NGS
SIC 1381 1389 Drilling oil & gas wells; Construction, repair & dismantling services; Derrick building, repairing & dismantling; Drilling oil & gas wells; Construction, repair & dismantling services; Derrick building, repairing & dismantling

Pr: John T Rynd
**Ch Bd:* Thomas R Bates Jr
Pr: Cecil Bowden
Pr: Claus E Feyling
CFO: Troy L Carson
Sr VP: Terrell L Carr
Sr VP: Todd A Pellegrin
Sr VP: Beau M Thompson
VP: John F Wasmuth
Exec: Jennifer Guidry
Genl Couns: William Gordon
Board of Directors: Thomas N Amonett, Thomas M Hamilton, Thomas J Madonna, F Gardner Parker, Thierry Pilenko, Steven A Webster

D-U-N-S 80-771-6303 IMP
HERCULES POLY INC
HERCULES BAGS
315 Main St, Eclectic, AL 36024-6216
Tel (334) 541-3525 *Founded/Ownrshp* 1993
Sales 23.1MM^E *EMP* 35
SIC 5162 5113 3081 2673 Plastics materials; Industrial & personal service paper; Unsupported plastics film & sheet; Bags: plastic, laminated & coated
Pr: Robert Price
**VP:* Bennet Price
Natl Sales: Scott Hauk
Manager: Dwayne Schaefer
Sls Mgr: Pam Booth

D-U-N-S 83-807-1207
HERCULES REAL ESTATE SERVICES INC
168 Business Park Dr # 103, Virginia Beach, VA 23462-6532
Tel (757) 473-3701 *Founded/Ownrshp* 1995
Sales 51.3MM^E *EMP* 260
SIC 6531 Real estate agents & managers; Real estate agents & managers
CEO: Todd Copeland
**Pr:* Diane Maddox
**Sec:* Robert Copeland
**Ex VP:* Jason Loftis
**VP:* M Scott Copeland

D-U-N-S 14-353-3532
▲ HERCULES TECHNOLOGY GROWTH CAPITAL INC
400 Hamilton Ave Ste 310, Palo Alto, CA 94301-1805
Tel (650) 289-3060 *Founded/Ownrshp* 2004
Sales 143.6MM *EMP* 38^E
Accts Pricewaterhousecoopers Llp Sa
Tkr Sym HTGC *Exch* NYS
SIC 6799 Venture capital companies; Venture capital companies
Ch Bd: Manuel A Henriquez
CFO: Jessica Baron
CFO: Mark R Harris
Chf Cred: Robert Lake
Chf Cred: Michael Penney
Ofcr: Michael Butler
VP: Michael Simms
Mng Dir: Anup Arora
Mng Dir: Kathy Conte
Mng Dir: Paul Edwards
Mng Dir: Daniel Holman
Board of Directors: Robert P Badavas, Thomas Fallon, Rodney A Ferguson, Allyn C Woodward Jr

D-U-N-S 00-117-8318 IMP/EXP
HERCULES TIRE & RUBBER CO (CT)
TIRE DEALERS WAREHOUSE
(*Suby of* AMERICAN TIRE DISTRIBUTORS INC) ★
16380 E Us Route 224 # 200, Findlay, OH 45840-1699
Tel (419) 425-6400 *Founded/Ownrshp* 1950, 2014
Sales 28.0MM^E *EMP* 65
SIC 5014

D-U-N-S 08-058-5110 IMP
HERCULES TIRE SALES INC (OK)
10130 E 51st St, Tulsa, OK 74146-5754
Tel (918) 357-3517 *Founded/Ownrshp* 1977
Sales 25.1MM^E *EMP* 60
SIC 5014 5531 Automobile tires & tubes; Tires, used; Truck tires & tubes; Automotive tires
Pr: Gary Sicka
**Sec:* Barbara Sicka
**Prin:* Stephen Welch

D-U-N-S 15-039-6950
HERCULES TRANSPORT INC
3452 Highway 145, Choudrant, LA 71227-3033
Tel (318) 768-2534 *Founded/Ownrshp* 1952
Sales 25.4MM^E *EMP* 90
SIC 4213 Liquid petroleum transport, non-local
Ch Bd: Tom M O'Neal
CFO: Billy Cox
Sls Mgr: Bill Green

HERCULITE PRODUCTS
See ABERDEEN ROAD CO

D-U-N-S 07-388-9842
HERD ENTERPRISES INC
BROWARD FACTORY SERVICE
3500 N 28th Ter, Hollywood, FL 33020-1104
Tel (954) 920-9774 *Founded/Ownrshp* 1973
Sales NA *EMP* 186
SIC 6351 Warranty insurance, home; Warranty insurance, home
Pr: Crockett Herd
**VP:* Christine Walton
Brnch Mgr: Rusty Herd
Board of Directors: Judith Herd

D-U-N-S 05-847-8751
HERDRICH PETROLEUM CORP
210 E Us Highway 52 Ste E, Rushville, IN 46173-8002
Tel (765) 932-3264 *Founded/Ownrshp* 1949, 1971
Sales 64.8MM^E *EMP* 185
SIC 5541 5172 Filling stations, gasoline; Gasoline; Fuel oil; Filling stations, gasoline; Gasoline; Fuel oil
Pr: William J Herdrich
**Treas:* Jeffery Herdrich
**VP:* Robert F Herdrich
Brnch Mgr: Debbie Lothamer

D-U-N-S 18-852-7162
HERE HOLDING CORP
(*Suby of* NOKIA OYJ)
425 W Randolph St, Chicago, IL 60606-1530
Tel (312) 894-7000 *Founded/Ownrshp* 2008
Sales 506.7MM^E *EMP* 3,364
SIC 7379 Computer software development; Disk & diskette conversion service
Pr: Denise Doyle
V Ch: Judson C Green
Pr: Amir Rakha
CFO: Steve Collins
**Treas:* Robert Burns
Bd of Dir: Andrew Green
Ex VP: Denise Doyle
Ex VP: John K Macleod
Ex VP: Jeffrey L Mize
Ex VP: Amreesh Modi
Sr VP: Winston V Guillory
VP: Lonnie Arima
VP: Mary Hardwick
Dir Bus: Koon Ng

D-U-N-S 83-069-8291
▲ HERE MEDIA INC
10990 Wilshire Blvd Fl 18, Los Angeles, CA 90024-3927
Tel (310) 943-5858 *Founded/Ownrshp* 2005
Sales 28.1MM^E *EMP* 66^E
Tkr Sym HRDI *Exch* OTO
SIC 4813 2721 ; Periodicals: publishing only; Magazines: publishing only, not printed on site
CEO: Paul Colichman
**CFO:* Tony Shyngle
**Ch:* Stephen Jarchow
Ex VP: Joe Landry

D-U-N-S 14-822-7317
HERE NORTH AMERICA LLC
(*Suby of* HERE HOLDING CORP) ★
425 W Randolph St, Chicago, IL 60606-1530
Tel (312) 894-7000 *Founded/Ownrshp* 1987
Sales 98.4MM^E *EMP* 850
SIC 7371 Computer software development; Computer software development
CEO: Sean Fernback
Pt: Marc Naddell
VP: Clifford I Fox
VP: Richard E Shuman

D-U-N-S 09-706-0511
HEREFORD INDEPENDENT SCHOOL DISTRICT
601 N 25 Mile Ave, Hereford, TX 79045-3024
Tel (806) 364-0606 *Founded/Ownrshp* 1907
Sales 38.6MM *EMP* 650
Accts Brown Graham & Company Amari
SIC 8211 Public elementary school; School board; Public elementary school; School board
Prin: Stacey Bixler
Prin: David Fanning
Prin: Sharon Hodges
Prin: Linda Lowe
Prin: Sandra Maldonado
Prin: Susan Robbins
Dir IT: Michelle Delozier
HC Dir: D'Ann Blair
Board of Directors: Keith Bridwell, Debbie Gallman, Jerry O Rear, Amy Schueler, Shannon Wallace, Luis Zamora

HERITAGE ADMINISTRATION SVCS
See HERITAGE WARRANTY INSURANCE RRG INC

HERITAGE AIR & HEAT
See BUILDER SERVICES NJ LLC

HERITAGE APPAREL
See TSG SKI & GOLF LLC

HERITAGE AUCTION GALLERIES
See HERITAGE CAPITAL CORP

D-U-N-S 60-315-5383
HERITAGE AUTO PLAZA INC
1800 Old Richmond Hwy, Alexandria, VA 22303-1858
Tel (703) 329-1300 *Founded/Ownrshp* 2000
Sales 30.1MM^E *EMP* 110^E
Accts Bourne & Painter Pc
SIC 5511 Automobiles, new & used; Automobiles, new & used
Pr: John P Collins
**Sec:* Michael P Ross
**VP:* Ann Collins

D-U-N-S 14-451-7505
HERITAGE AUTOMOBILE SALES INC
HERITAGE FORD
1620 Shelburne Rd, South Burlington, VT 05403-7703
Tel (802) 865-8200 *Founded/Ownrshp* 1982
Sales 36.9MM^E *EMP* 150
SIC 5511 5521 Automobiles, new & used; Pickups, new & used; Used car dealers; Automobiles, new & used; Pickups, new & used; Used car dealers
Pr: David Machavern
CFO: David Havern
Sls Mgr: Helen Wait

D-U-N-S 16-093-0558
HERITAGE AUTOMOTIVE CENTER INC
2122 N Locust Ave, Lawrenceburg, TN 38464-4401
Tel (931) 762-2299 *Founded/Ownrshp* 1993
Sales 23.1MM^E *EMP* 58
SIC 5511 7515 7513 Automobiles, new & used; Pickups, new & used; Passenger car leasing; Truck rental & leasing, no drivers; Automobiles, new & used; Pickups, new & used; Passenger car leasing; Truck rental & leasing, no drivers
Pr: James R Story III
**Genl Mgr:* Bill Gobble
Sales Exec: Brent Lewis

D-U-N-S 10-418-2485
HERITAGE AVIATION LTD
HERITAGE AVIATION SERVICES
419 Duncan Perry Rd # 109, Arlington, TX 76011-5438
Tel (972) 988-8000 *Founded/Ownrshp* 2001
Sales 20.7MM^E *EMP* 140
SIC 4581 Aircraft maintenance & repair services; Aircraft maintenance & repair services
Genl Mgr: Everet Horst
Pt: Don Salsbury
Genl Mgr: Everett Horst
Snr Mgr: Roger Hulsey

HERITAGE AVIATION SERVICES
See HERITAGE AVIATION LTD

D-U-N-S 06-412-0017 IMP
HERITAGE BAG CO
501 Gateway Pkwy, Roanoke, TX 76262-3481
Tel (972) 241-5525 *Founded/Ownrshp* 1973
Sales 105.1MM^E *EMP* 650
SIC 2673

D-U-N-S 60-176-4884
HERITAGE BANCORP
1401 S Virginia St, Reno, NV 89502-2805
Tel (775) 348-1000 *Founded/Ownrshp* 2005
Sales NA *EMP* 67^E
SIC 6022 State commercial banks
Prin: Stanley Wilmoth

D-U-N-S 79-107-9481
HERITAGE BANCSHARES GROUP INC
310 1st St S, Willmar, MN 56201-3304
Tel (320) 235-5720 *Founded/Ownrshp* 2007
Sales NA *EMP* 123^E
SIC 6712 Bank holding companies; Bank holding companies
Prin: Gary Geiger

HERITAGE BANK
See HERITAGE GROUP INC

D-U-N-S 01-576-8443
HERITAGE BANK
(*Suby of* HERITAGE BANK) ★
110 E 9th St, Wood River, NE 68883-2133
Tel (308) 398-4000 *Founded/Ownrshp* 2007
Sales NA *EMP* 50
SIC 6022 State commercial banks; State commercial banks
Pr: Sam Moyer
COO: Kevin Henderson
CFO: Bob Moyer
CIO: Jim Rennau
Opers Mgr: Casandra Athey
Opers Mgr: Jerry McMahan

D-U-N-S 03-633-7657
HERITAGE BANK (GA)
HERITAGE GROUP
(*Suby of* LIBERTY SHARES INC) ★
300 S Main St, Hinesville, GA 31313-3222
Tel (912) 408-6521 *Founded/Ownrshp* 1911
Sales NA *EMP* 300
SIC 6021 National commercial banks; National commercial banks
Pr: Brian Smith
COO: Ann Fish
CFO: Philip F Resch
Bd of Dir: Brook Allen
Ofcr: Catlin Jarriel
Ex VP: Leonard Moreland
VP: Gail Evans
VP: Barbara Smith
CIO: Lisa Welander

D-U-N-S 06-690-3097
■ HERITAGE BANK
(*Suby of* HOPFED BANCORP INC) ★
2700 Fort Campbell Blvd, Hopkinsville, KY 42240-4941
Tel (270) 885-1171 *Founded/Ownrshp* 1879
Sales NA *EMP* 200
SIC 6035 Federal savings & loan associations; Federal savings & loan associations
Pr: John E Peck
Pt: Jim Wiseman
COO: Michael L Woolfolk
CFO: Billy C Duvall
CFO: Billy Duvall
VP: Rebecca Cansler
VP: Penny Cayce
VP: Boyd Clark
VP: Charyl Knote
VP: Linda Vier
VP: Ty Watts
Board of Directors: D B Bostick Jr, C G Boyd, C Cochran, D Embry, W G Ezell, J N Hall Jr, W D Kelley, J B Todd

D-U-N-S 07-663-1209
■ HERITAGE BANK
(*Suby of* HERITAGE FINANCIAL CORP) ★
201 5th Ave Sw Ste 101, Olympia, WA 98501-1063
Tel (360) 943-1500 *Founded/Ownrshp* 1993
Sales NA *EMP* 242
SIC 6022 State commercial banks; State commercial banks
Pr: Jeffrey J Deuel
CFO: Ed Cameron
Ch: Donald V Rhodes
Treas: Don Hinson
Ofcr: Susan Derenzo
Ofcr: Amanda Kinder
Ofcr: Angela Martin
Ex VP: Donald J Hinson
Ex VP: Bryan McDonald
Ex VP: Greg Patjens
Sr VP: Clark Burkheimer
Sr VP: Lynn Eerkes
Sr VP: Ed Fischer
Sr VP: Charles M Folsom
Sr VP: Gary Gahan
Sr VP: James Hastings
Sr VP: Jim Liming
Sr VP: Beth Meidinger
Sr VP: John Parry
Sr VP: Lauren Pool
Sr VP: Lisa Welander

D-U-N-S 08-051-1520
HERITAGE BANK & TRUST (INC)
(*Suby of* JOHNSON BANK) ★
4001 N Main St, Racine, WI 53402-3104
Tel (262) 619-2700 *Founded/Ownrshp* 1979
Sales NA *EMP* 450
SIC 6022 State trust companies accepting deposits, commercial; State trust companies accepting deposits, commercial
Pr: Russell Weyers
Ch Bd: Samuel C Johnson
Sr VP: Barb Ingram
Sr VP: Frank Vidian
VP: Victor Opitz
VP: John Topczewski
Netwrk Eng: Matt Coss

D-U-N-S 61-783-0997
HERITAGE BANK INC
456 Commonwealth Ave, Erlanger, KY 41018-1426
Tel (859) 342-0920 *Founded/Ownrshp* 1990
Sales NA *EMP* 50
SIC 6022 State commercial banks; State commercial banks
Pr: Hollice Gritton
**Ch Bd:* Arnold Caddell
**Ex VP:* Harold Campbell
**VP:* Lee Scheben

D-U-N-S 84-065-9106
■ HERITAGE BANK OF COMMERCE
HERRITAGE BANK OF COMMERCE
(*Suby of* HERITAGE COMMERCE CORP) ★
150 Almaden Blvd Lbby, San Jose, CA 95113-2010
Tel (408) 947-6900 *Founded/Ownrshp* 1993
Sales NA *EMP* 188
SIC 6022 State commercial banks; State commercial banks
CEO: Walter Kaczmarek
Pr: Hank Bataille
COO: Richard Conniff
**COO:* Keith Wilton
**CFO:* Lawrence D McGovern
**Chf Cred:* Michael Ong
**Ofcr:* John Angelesco
Ofcr: Sandi Caporale
**Ex VP:* Michael Benito
**Ex VP:* William Del Biaggio Jr
Ex VP: Robert Gionfriddo
**Ex VP:* Raymond Parker
**Sr VP:* Ruth Brown
Sr VP: Toby Cordone
Sr VP: Christopher Gust
Sr VP: Andrea Head
Sr VP: Brian Kehoe
Sr VP: Gloria McLoughlin
Sr VP: Janice Mizota
**Sr VP:* Christine Moss
Sr VP: Chris Plummer
Board of Directors: Lon Normandin, Frank G Bisceglia, Jack L Peckham, Arthur C Carmichael Jr, Robert W Peters, James D'amico, Laura Roden, William Dallas, Kenneth Rodrigues, William Del Biaggio III, Kirk Rossmann, John Eggemeyer, W Kirk Wycoff, Tracey A Enfantino, Glenn A George, Robert T Moles

D-U-N-S 03-818-8475
HERITAGE BANK USA INC
4155 Lafayette Rd, Hopkinsville, KY 42240-5366
Tel (270) 885-1171 *Founded/Ownrshp* 1877
Sales NA *EMP* 264
SIC 6035 Savings institutions, federally chartered; Savings institutions, federally chartered
Pr: John Peck
COO: Mike Woolfolk
Ofcr: Sam Bancroft
Sr VP: Austin Stewart
VP: Pam Phillips
Mng Ofcr: Jim Lokesak
Off Mgr: Dan Dickerson
Off Mgr: Julie Parks
Dir IT: Hugh Roberts
Mktg Dir: Marlene Dade

D-U-N-S 08-001-2236
HERITAGE BIOLOGICS INC
255 Nw Victoria Dr, Lees Summit, MO 64086-4709
Tel (816) 875-5101 *Founded/Ownrshp* 2014
Sales 21.0MM *EMP* 35^E
SIC 5122 Animal medicines
CEO: Thomas O'Neil
**Pr:* Christopher Quesenberry

HERITAGE BRANDS
See INSIGHT PHARMACEUTICALS CORP

D-U-N-S 10-156-1371
HERITAGE BROADCASTING GROUP INC
(*Suby of* MICI INC) ★
22320 130th Ave, Cadillac, MI 49601
Tel (231) 775-3478 *Founded/Ownrshp* 1983
Sales 23.3MM^E *EMP* 100
SIC 4833 Television broadcasting stations
Pr: Mario F Iacobelli
**Treas:* William Kring

D-U-N-S 17-782-2087
HERITAGE BUSINESS SYSTEMS INC
2955 20th St, Vero Beach, FL 32960-3097
Tel (772) 299-5178 *Founded/Ownrshp* 1986
Sales 20.1MM^E *EMP* 45
SIC 5044 5065 Copying equipment; Facsimile equipment
Pr: Thomas Lizzio

D-U-N-S 02-515-6258
HERITAGE CADILLAC INC (IL)
303 W Roosevelt Rd, Lombard, IL 60148-4211
Tel (630) 629-3300 *Founded/Ownrshp* 1949
Sales 33.4MM^E *EMP* 75
SIC 5511 Automobiles, new & used; Automobiles, new & used
Pr: William E Hartigan
**VP:* Thomas J Hartigan
Sls Mgr: Michael Demarco
Sales Asso: Dave Fansher
Sales Asso: Charles Hughes
Snr PM: Wayne Balogh

D-U-N-S 78-514-9527
HERITAGE CADILLAC INC
HERITAGE CADILLAC SAAB
7134 Jonesboro Rd, Morrow, GA 30260-2907
Tel (770) 960-0060 *Founded/Ownrshp* 1994
Sales 33.8MM^E *EMP* 75
SIC 5511 Automobiles, new & used; Automobiles, new & used
CEO: Ernest M Hodge
CFO: Sabrina Crawford
Off Mgr: Sylvia Hughes
Mktg Mgr: Ingy Knourshed
Sales Asso: Sara Ali
Sales Asso: Frankie Walker

HERITAGE CADILLAC SAAB
See HERITAGE CADILLAC INC

HERITAGE CALIFORNIA ACO
See REGAL MEDICAL GROUP INC

D-U-N-S 05-312-6322 IMP
HERITAGE CAPITAL CORP (TX)
HERITAGE AUCTION GALLERIES
3500 Maple Ave Ste 1700, Dallas, TX 75219-3941
Tel (214) 528-3500 *Founded/Ownrshp* 1972
Sales 144.8MM^E *EMP* 300^E
SIC 5094 Coins; Coins
Pr: Greg Rohan
**Ch Bd:* R Steve Ivy
**Pr:* Todd Imhof
**COO:* Paul Minshull
**CFO:* Michael Haynes
**Co-Ch Bd:* James L Halperin
Sr VP: Michael Moline
VP: Jeff Greer
Assoc Dir: Poppy Davis
Genl Mgr: Hayley Brigham
Genl Mgr: Hayley Minshull

D-U-N-S 12-129-7944
HERITAGE CARE CENTERS INC
BOUNTIFUL HLTH CARE REHAB CTR
255 E 400 S Ste 200, Salt Lake City, UT 84111-2868
Tel (801) 596-8844 *Founded/Ownrshp* 1988
Sales 13.5MM^E *EMP* 450
SIC 8051 Skilled nursing care facilities; Skilled nursing care facilities
Ch: Charles Kirton
**CFO:* Corey Bell
**VP:* Robert Pommerville

HERITAGE CENTER
See HOLIDAY HOME HEALTH CARE CORP OF EVANSVILLE

HERITAGE CENTERS
See ERIE COUNTY CHAPTER NYSARC

D-U-N-S 00-799-9600
HERITAGE CHEVROLET INC
350 W Dickman Rd, Battle Creek, MI 49037-8497
Tel (269) 964-9431 *Founded/Ownrshp* 1926
Sales 27.8MM^E *EMP* 65
SIC 5511 Automobiles, new & used; Pickups, new & used; Vans, new & used; Automobiles, new & used; Pickups, new & used; Vans, new & used
Pr: Timothy J Kool
**Sec:* Allan Kinney
**VP:* Thomas Harris
Store Mgr: Joanne James
Sales Asso: Ron Boyd
Sales Asso: Rob Cape
Sales Asso: Jason Fields
Sales Asso: Dave Haughey
Sales Asso: Cameron Phillips

D-U-N-S 02-264-5485
HERITAGE CHEVROLET INC
(*Suby of* ATLANTIC AUTOMOTIVE CORP) ★
11234 Reisterstown Rd, Owings Mills, MD 21117-1908
Tel (410) 356-2200 *Founded/Ownrshp* 1983
Sales 22.2MM^E *EMP* 85
SIC 5511 Automobiles, new & used; Pickups, new & used; Automobiles, new & used; Pickups, new & used
Pr: Jerome H Fader
**VP:* Brian Fader
Board of Directors: Steven B Fader

D-U-N-S 05-566-4213
HERITAGE CHEVROLET INC (VA)
CARTER MYERS AUTOMOTIVE
(*Suby of* CARTER MYERS AUTOMOTIVE) ★
12420 Jefferson Davis Hwy, Chester, VA 23831-2319
Tel (804) 318-5269 *Founded/Ownrshp* 1938, 1981
Sales 45.0MM *EMP* 65^E
Accts Mitchell Wiggins & Company L
SIC 5511 5521 5012 Automobiles, new & used; Pickups, new & used; Used car dealers; Automobiles & other motor vehicles; Automobiles, new & used; Pickups, new & used; Used car dealers; Automobiles & other motor vehicles
Ch Bd: H Carter Myers III
**Pr:* John E Burchell Jr
**VP:* Robert Owen III
Sls Mgr: Josh Friedman
Sls Mgr: Mike Toohey
Sales Asso: Wayne Harris
Sales Asso: Wayne Jones
Sales Asso: Alexander Perry

D-U-N-S 11-418-4336 IMP
HERITAGE CHRISTIAN SERVICES INC
349 W Coml St Ste 2795, East Rochester, NY 14445
Tel (585) 340-2000 *Founded/Ownrshp* 1980
Sales 61.7MM *EMP* 500
Accts Bonadio & Co Llp Pittsford N
SIC 8059 Home for the mentally retarded, exc. skilled or intermediate; Home for the mentally retarded, exc. skilled or intermediate
Pr: Robert Pieters
Dir Vol: Kim Kennedy
Dir Vol: Kelly Nash
CFO: Ron Little
Bd of Dir: Paul Desarra
VP: Ben Levan
Exec: Bruce Davie
Assoc Dir: Lauri Bonnell
IT Man: Mark Zawacki
VP Opers: Drew Bielemeier
Pr Dir: Nancy Dwyer

D-U-N-S 00-635-4500
HERITAGE CO INC (AR)
HERITAGE TELEMARKETING
2402 Wildwood Ave Ste 500, North Little Rock, AR 72120-5094
Tel (501) 835-9111 *Founded/Ownrshp* 1958
Sales 41.9MM^E *EMP* 1,000
SIC 7389 2721 Telemarketing services; Periodicals: publishing only; Telemarketing services; Periodicals: publishing only
Pr: John C Braune
**Pr:* John Braune
**Pr:* Marilyn Michie Zornik
**CEO:* Sandra Franecke
**COO:* Mike Land
**CFO:* Glenda Keenihan
**Ex VP:* Chip Miller
VP: Kathy Kumpe
VP: Terry Mitchell
VP: Clarence Young
VP Sls: Rhonda Ward

HERITAGE COLLEGE
See WESTON EDUCATIONAL INC

D-U-N-S 04-234-2076
▲ HERITAGE COMMERCE CORP
150 Almaden Blvd Lbby, San Jose, CA 95113-2019
Tel (408) 947-6900 *Founded/Ownrshp* 1997
Sales NA *EMP* 193^E
Accts Crowe Horwath Llp Sacramento
Tkr Sym HTBK *Exch* NGS
SIC 6022 State commercial banks; State commercial banks
Pr: Walter T Kaczmarek
**Ch Bd:* Jack W Conner
COO: Keith A Wilton
CFO: Lawrence D McGovern
Chf Cred: Margaret Incandela Evp
Ofcr: Trisha Parnell
Ofcr: David E Porter
Ofcr: Serena Ruan
Ex VP: Michael E Benito
Ex VP: Deborah K Reuter
Sr VP: Bill Davis
Sr VP: John O Fox
Sr VP: Michael Hansen
Sr VP: Janice Miyatake
Sr VP: Jeffrey Perkins
Sr VP: Roxanne S Vane
VP: Celine Benzon
VP: Geri Cookson
VP: Shirlene Kaneda
VP: Nancy Landy
VP Bus Dev: David Beronio
Board of Directors: Frank G Bisceglia, John M Eggemeyer, Steven L Hallgrimson, Robert T Moles, Humphrey P Polanen, Laura Roden, Charles J Toeniskoetter, W Kirk Wycoff

HERITAGE CONCRETE
See PENNSY SUPPLY INC

D-U-N-S 83-180-5143
HERITAGE COOPERATIVE INC
11177 Township Road 133, West Mansfield, OH 43358-9709
Tel (419) 294-2371 *Founded/Ownrshp* 2009
Sales 693.0MM^E *EMP* 270^E
SIC 5153 5261 4925 4932 Grains; Fertilizer; Liquefied petroleum gas, distribution through mains; Gas & other services combined; Grains; Fertilizer; Liquefied petroleum gas, distribution through mains; Gas & other services combined
CEO: Eric N Parthemore
**COO:* John T Dunbar
**CFO:* Lyle Gottfried
VP: Terry House
VP: Ed Nienaber
Store Mgr: Jennifer Davenport
Sales Asso: Lee Orians

HERITAGE DEVELOPMENT
See BREEZY POINT LIMITED PARTNERSHIP

D-U-N-S 00-481-7193
HERITAGE ENCON GROUP INC (NC)
228 Westinghouse Blvd # 103, Charlotte, NC 28273-6230
Tel (704) 399-1369 *Founded/Ownrshp* 1982
Sales 64.1MM^E *EMP* 125^E
SIC 1742 Insulation, buildings
Pr: R L Huggins
**CFO:* R L Stewart

D-U-N-S 05-994-6756
HERITAGE ENTERPRISES INC
HERITAGE HEALTH
115 W Jefferson St # 401, Bloomington, IL 61701-3937
Tel (309) 828-4361 *Founded/Ownrshp* 1990
Sales 160.5MM^E *EMP* 2,500
SIC 8051 Skilled nursing care facilities; Skilled nursing care facilities
Pr: Steve Wannemacher
CFO: Craig Ater
Sec: Craig Hart
Ex VP: Benjamin Hart
Ex VP: Cheryl Lowney
Sr VP: Connie Hoselton
Sr VP: David Underwood
Plnt Mgr: Steve Luttrell

D-U-N-S 07-837-4967
HERITAGE ENVIRONMENTAL SERVICES INC
7901 W Morris St, Indianapolis, IN 46231-3301
Tel (317) 243-0811 *Founded/Ownrshp* 1970
Sales 327.2MM^E *EMP* 590
SIC 5093 4213 8731 7389 1799 8711 Oil, waste; Contract haulers; Commercial physical research; Brokers' services; Exterior cleaning, including sandblasting; Engineering services; Oil, waste; Contract haulers; Commercial physical research; Brokers' services; Exterior cleaning, including sandblasting; Engineering services
CEO: Kenneth S Price
**Treas:* John P Vercruysse
VP: Jim Copien
CIO: Jim Coplen
MIS Dir: Krisann Wampler
Dir IT: Bryan Bailey
Dir IT: Brad Hudson
S&M/VP: John Renkes

D-U-N-S 13-081-4528 IMP
HERITAGE ENVIRONMENTAL SERVICES LLC
SOLID OAK
(*Suby of* HERITAGE ENVIRONMENTAL SERVICES INC) ★
7901 W Morris St, Indianapolis, IN 46231-1366
Tel (317) 243-0811 *Founded/Ownrshp* 1989
Sales 327.2MM^E *EMP* 590
SIC 5093 4213 8731 7389 1799 8711 Oil, waste; Contract haulers; Commercial physical research; Brokers' services; Exterior cleaning, including sandblasting; Engineering services; Oil, waste; Contract haulers; Commercial physical research; Brokers' services; Exterior cleaning, including sandblasting; Engineering services
CFO: Jeff Baetzel
Ofcr: Gregory Busch
VP: Darci Ackerman
VP: Winde Hammerick
Prgrm Mgr: Rachel Marcum
Dir IT: Bryan Bailey
Dir IT: Jim Coplen
Telecom Mg: Jim Wampler
Opers Mgr: Tanya Cotten
Plnt Mgr: John Dillow

D-U-N-S 04-017-8126
HERITAGE EQUIPMENT INC
HERITAGE WESTERN STAR
322 Dry Hill Rd, Beckley, WV 25801-2602
Tel (304) 254-7827 *Founded/Ownrshp* 1998
Sales 52.8MM^E *EMP* 200
SIC 5012 Automobiles & other motor vehicles; Automobiles & other motor vehicles
Pr: Gary Kale
**VP:* Carl Hubbard
VP: Dave Petry
IT Man: Donna Johnson

HERITAGE FAMILY CREDIT UNION
See HERITAGE FAMILY FEDERAL CREDIT UNION

D-U-N-S 10-661-9943
HERITAGE FAMILY FEDERAL CREDIT UNION
HERITAGE FAMILY CREDIT UNION
30 Allen St, Rutland, VT 05701-4536
Tel (888) 252-8932 *Founded/Ownrshp* 1956
Sales NA *EMP* 140
SIC 6062 6163 State credit unions, not federally chartered; Loan brokers; State credit unions, not federally chartered; Loan brokers
Pr: Ronald Hance
**Ex VP:* Matthew Levandowski
**Ex VP:* Randy Martelle
VP: Michael McCloaud
Sls Mgr: Nan Kirbach

D-U-N-S 82-482-8966
▲ HERITAGE FINANCIAL CORP
201 5th Ave Sw, Olympia, WA 98501-1063
Tel (360) 943-1500 *Founded/Ownrshp* 1997
Sales NA *EMP* 748^E
Tkr Sym HFWA *Exch* NGS
SIC 6036 Savings institutions, not federally chartered; Savings & loan associations, not federally chartered; Savings institutions, not federally chartered; Savings & loan associations, not federally chartered
Pr: Brian L Vance
**Ch Bd:* Anthony B Pickering
CFO: Donald J Hinson
**V Ch Bd:* Brian S Charneski
Chf Cred: David A Spurling
Ex VP: Jeffrey J Deuel
VP: Charles M Folsom
VP: Mark Furman
VP: Patrice Hernandez
VP Opers: Soozie Heath
Board of Directors: Ann Watson, Rhoda L Altom, David H Brown, Gary B Christensen, John A Clees, Mark D Crawford, Kimberly T Ellwanger, Deborah J Gavin, Jeffrey S Lyon, Robert T Severns

D-U-N-S 18-130-9381
HERITAGE FINANCIAL GROUP INC
721 N Westover Blvd, Albany, GA 31707-1401
Tel (229) 420-0000 *Founded/Ownrshp* 2010
Sales NA *EMP* 426^E
SIC 6035 Savings institutions, federally chartered; Federal savings & loan associations; Federal savings banks

D-U-N-S 60-612-1184
HERITAGE FINANCIAL GROUP INC
120 W Lexington Ave # 200, Elkhart, IN 46516-3117
Tel (574) 522-8000 *Founded/Ownrshp* 1980
Sales 12.9MM^E *EMP* 400^E
SIC 6531 6141 5521 2451 6515 8742 Real estate managers; Consumer finance companies; Financing: automobiles, furniture, etc., not a deposit bank; Used car dealers; Mobile homes; Mobile home site operators; Financial consultant; Real estate managers; Consumer finance companies; Financing: automobiles, furniture, etc., not a deposit bank; Used car dealers; Mobile homes; Mobile home site operators; Financial consultant
Ch Bd: L Craig Fulmer
**Sec:* Sharon Martin
**Co-CEO:* Dan A Morrison
**Co-CEO:* Brian J Smith
VP: Kris Brinker
VP: Diane Price

D-U-N-S 18-548-1751 IMP/EXP
HERITAGE FOOD SERVICE GROUP INC
5130 Executive Blvd, Fort Wayne, IN 46808-1149
Tel (260) 482-1444 *Founded/Ownrshp* 2011
Sales 100.0MM^E *EMP* 233^E
SIC 5087 Restaurant supplies; Restaurant supplies
Pr: John McDonough
**CEO:* R Bruce Dye
COO: Michelle Miller
**Treas:* Peter Suffredini
**VP:* Michael Denvir
Sls Mgr: Linda Maynard

HERITAGE FORD
See MUIRFIELD INC

HERITAGE FORD
See HERITAGE MOTORS INC

HERITAGE FORD
See HERITAGE AUTOMOBILE SALES INC

D-U-N-S 10-293-0310
HERITAGE FORD INC
2100 Sisk Rd, Modesto, CA 95350-1753
Tel (209) 529-5110 *Founded/Ownrshp* 1979
Sales 34.5MM *EMP* 72^E
SIC 5511 Automobiles, new & used; Pickups, new & used; Automobiles, new & used; Pickups, new & used
Pr: Brett P Smart
**VP:* Pete Smart

D-U-N-S 07-484-2063
HERITAGE FOUNDATION
214 Msschstts Ave Ne Bsmt, Washington, DC 20002
Tel (202) 546-4400 *Founded/Ownrshp* 1973
Sales 112.6MM *EMP* 270
SIC 8733 Noncommercial research organizations; Noncommercial research organizations
Pr: Edwin J Feulner
Treas: John Vonkannon
Ofcr: Sarah Mills
**Ex VP:* Phillip N Truluck
VP: David Addington
**VP:* Stuart M Butler
VP: Ed Corrigan
VP: Becky N Dulop
**VP:* Becky Norton Dunlop
**VP:* John P Fogarty
**VP:* Michael G Franc
**VP:* Michael M Gonzalez
**VP:* Kim Holmes
VP: John Kannon
VP: Geoffrey Lysaught
**VP:* Edwin Meese III
VP: Derrick Morgan
**VP:* Ted E Schelenski
VP: Ted Schelenski
**VP:* Michael A Spiller
**VP:* John Von Kannon

D-U-N-S 79-313-3067
HERITAGE FS INC
F S
1381 S Crescent St, Gilman, IL 60938-6128
Tel (815) 265-4751 *Founded/Ownrshp* 1992
Sales 22.7MM *EMP* 79
SIC 0721 Crop planting & protection; Crop planting & protection
Genl Mgr: Mark Weildacher
Pr: Gary Boehrnsen
Treas: Richard Nelson
VP: Ron Bork
Genl Mgr: Gary Knauer
Genl Mgr: Shawn Oseman
Genl Mgr: Dana Robinson
Genl Mgr: Scott Sharp

D-U-N-S 16-854-9413 IMP
HERITAGE GEMS LLC
608 5th Ave Ste 701, New York, NY 10020-2303
Tel (212) 245-5533 *Founded/Ownrshp* 2000
Sales 30.0MM *EMP* 5
SIC 5999 Gems & precious stones; Gems & precious stones

D-U-N-S 07-939-3103
HERITAGE GLASS LLC (TN)
1450 Lincoln St, Kingsport, TN 37660-5194
Tel (423) 502-5827 *Founded/Ownrshp* 2014
Sales 50.0MM *EMP* 99
SIC 3211 Flat glass; Flat glass

D-U-N-S 12-568-5771 IMP
HERITAGE GOLF GROUP INC
(*Suby of* GTCR GOLDER RAUNER LLC) ★
12750 High Bluff Dr # 400, San Diego, CA 92130-3099
Tel (858) 720-0694 *Founded/Ownrshp* 1999
Sales 82.6MM^E *EMP* 1,200
SIC 7992 Public golf courses; Public golf courses
CEO: James A Husband
COO: John Hungerford
**CFO:* Angela Kasten
**Ex VP:* Gary L Dee
Ex VP: Gary Dee
Exec: Robin Irwin
Mng Dir: Donald Rhodes
Genl Mgr: Brady Boyd
Genl Mgr: Ryan Whitney
CIO: Rich Canale
Dir IT: Mike Jardines

D-U-N-S 02-537-9769
HERITAGE GRAIN COOPERATIVE (IL)
200 W Main St, Dalton City, IL 61925
Tel (217) 874-2392 *Founded/Ownrshp* 1908
Sales 54.0MM *EMP* 13
Accts D Piraino & Associates Pc
SIC 5153 Grain elevators; Grain elevators
CEO: Jerome Rowe
Pr: Dennis Smith
VP: Robert Rutherford
VP: Richard Tilton

HERITAGE GROUP
See HERITAGE BANK

D-U-N-S 96-396-7828
HERITAGE GROUP EMPLOYEE BENEFIT TRUST
10151 Hague Rd, Indianapolis, IN 46256-3312
Tel (317) 872-6010 *Founded/Ownrshp* 2010
Sales NA *EMP* 2^E

Accts R J Pile Llc Indianapolis I
SIC 6411 Insurance agents, brokers & service; Insurance agents, brokers & service

D-U-N-S 13-104-9459
HERITAGE GROUP INC
5400 W 86th St, Indianapolis, IN 46268-1502
Tel (317) 872-6010 *Founded/Ownrshp* 1976
Sales 22.4MM^E *EMP* 89^E
SIC 8731 Environmental research
Pr: Arthur A Angotti
CFO: John Vercruysse
VP: Jim Coplan
Netwrk Mgr: Jim Wampler

D-U-N-S 61-630-9279
HERITAGE GROUP INC
HERITAGE BANK
1101 12th St, Aurora, NE 68818-2005
Tel (402) 694-3136 *Founded/Ownrshp* 2000
Sales NA *EMP* 149
SIC 6029 Commercial banks; Commercial banks
VP: Kevin Henderson
Pr: Jim Coplen
Opers Mgr: Robert Morris
Mktg Dir: Katie Leff

HERITAGE HEALTH
See HERITAGE ENTERPRISES INC

D-U-N-S 82-537-3855
HERITAGE HEALTH AND HOUSING INC
416 W 127th St, New York, NY 10027-2516
Tel (212) 866-2600 *Founded/Ownrshp* 1969
Sales 21.2MM *EMP* 220
SIC 8322 Individual & family services; Individual & family services
CEO: Bonnick Lewis
Dir IT: Arthur Smith

HERITAGE HEALTH CARE
See HIGH DESERT MEDICAL CORP A MEDICAL GROUP

D-U-N-S 11-142-2275
HERITAGE HEALTH CARE SERVICES INC
1625 Indian Wood Cir, Maumee, OH 43537-4003
Tel (419) 867-2002 *Founded/Ownrshp* 1994
Sales 7.9MM^E *EMP* 300
SIC 8082 Home health care services; Home health care services
Pr: Rich Adams

D-U-N-S 62-640-0899
HERITAGE HEALTH CARE SERVICES INC
HERITAGE HEALTHCARE SERVICES
1009 Reservoir Ave, Cranston, RI 02910-5134
Tel (401) 946-6021 *Founded/Ownrshp* 1989
Sales 12.7MM^E *EMP* 315
SIC 7218 7349 Industrial launderers; Hospital housekeeping; Industrial launderers; Hospital housekeeping
CEO: Gerard Hainse
Pr: John Sepe
VP Mktg: Brian Hainse

D-U-N-S 36-247-4533
HERITAGE HEALTH SOLUTIONS LP
300 Parker Sq Ste 210, Flower Mound, TX 75028-7424
Tel (469) 293-1806 *Founded/Ownrshp* 2005
Sales NA *EMP* 50^E
SIC 6324 Hospital & medical service plans
Ch Bd: James L Rosengren
Pr: Tonya Clark
Ex VP: Allen Walker
Sr VP: Scott Steinfeldt
Genl Mgr: Adrienne Wheatley
Off Mgr: Diane Pierce
IT Man: Dan Riser
Mktg Dir: Patti McCoy

HERITAGE HEALTHCARE SERVICES
See HERITAGE HEALTH CARE SERVICES INC

HERITAGE HNDA PNTIAC BUICK GMC
See RHC (GA) INC

D-U-N-S 07-921-5662
HERITAGE HOME GROUP LLC
THOMASVILLE FURNITURE
401 E Main St, Thomasville, NC 27360-4152
Tel (314) 863-1100 *Founded/Ownrshp* 2013
Sales 1.7MMM^E *EMP* 4,324
SIC 2511 2512 2515 Wood bedroom furniture; Kitchen & dining room furniture; Dining room furniture: wood; Desks, household: wood; Wood upholstered chairs & couches; Chairs: upholstered on wood frames; Couches, sofas & davenports: upholstered on wood frames; Recliners: upholstered on wood frames; Sofa beds (convertible sofas); Wood bedroom furniture; Kitchen & dining room furniture; Dining room furniture: wood; Desks, household: wood; Wood upholstered chairs & couches; Chairs: upholstered on wood frames; Couches, sofas & davenports: upholstered on wood frames; Recliners: upholstered on wood frames; Sofa beds (convertible sofas)
CEO: Richard Lozyniak
CFO: A Jeffrey Zappone
Chf Mktg O: Roxanne Bernstein
Sr VP: Raymond Johnson
Sr VP: Lynda Scott
VP: Larry Ferguson
VP: David Grubbs
VP: Richard Isaak
VP: David Whittington
Rgnl Mgr: Paul Held
CTO: Tod Phelps

D-U-N-S 60-665-0401
HERITAGE HOME HEALTHCARE SERVICES INC
3721 Rutledge Rd Ne, Albuquerque, NM 87109-5567
Tel (505) 232-3311 *Founded/Ownrshp* 1999
Sales 22.9MM^E *EMP* 600^E
SIC 8082 Home health care services; Home health care services
Pr: Leonard Trainor III
**VP:* Elizabeth Trainor

IT Man: Sandra Barry
Nrsg Dir: Cheryl Reese

HERITAGE HONDA OF PARKVILLE
See HERITAGE OF TOWSON INC

D-U-N-S 82-573-4817
HERITAGE HOSPITAL INC
VIDANT EDGECOMBE HOSPITAL
(*Suby of* PITT COUNTY MEMORIAL HOSPITAL INC) ★
111 Hospital Dr Rm 301, Tarboro, NC 27886-2039
Tel (252) 641-7700 *Founded/Ownrshp* 1999
Sales 80.0MM *EMP* 709
SIC 8062 General medical & surgical hospitals; General medical & surgical hospitals
CEO: Wendel Becker
**CFO:* Charles Alford
**VP:* David Hughes
IT Man: Kimberly Whitehurst
Mktg Dir: Teresa Hyman
Surgeon: Charles Middleton

D-U-N-S 00-630-1732
HERITAGE HOSPITALITY MANAGEMENT INC (VA)
2815 N Augusta St Ste B, Staunton, VA 24401-2567
Tel (540) 886-0113 *Founded/Ownrshp* 2006
Sales 11.7MM^E *EMP* 300
SIC 8741 Management services
Pr: Scott Goldenberg
VP: Thomas Dahl

HERITAGE HOUSE
See WESLEYLIFE

D-U-N-S 80-312-2576
HERITAGE HOUSE NURSING CENTER
3103 Wisconsin Ave, Vicksburg, MS 39180-4825
Tel (601) 883-9911 *Founded/Ownrshp* 2007
Sales 318.8MM *EMP* 2^E
SIC 8049 Nurses, registered & practical; Nurses, registered & practical
Exec: Robert Greer

HERITAGE HOUSE NURSING HOME
See WEXNER HERITAGE VILLAGE

D-U-N-S 14-845-7575
HERITAGE IMPORTS
LARRY H MILLER HONDA
5808 S State St, Salt Lake City, UT 84107-6135
Tel (801) 262-3331 *Founded/Ownrshp* 1992
Sales 35.5MM^E *EMP* 100
SIC 5511 5531 7538 7515 5521 Automobiles, new & used; Automotive parts; General automotive repair shops; Passenger car leasing; Used car dealers; Automobiles, new & used; Automotive parts; General automotive repair shops; Passenger car leasing; Used car dealers
Pr: Jeff J Wilkinson
**Sec:* Larry H Miller
**VP:* Jeffery Gorringe
**VP:* Wendy W Gorringe
**VP:* Lynlee Wilkinson
**VP:* Mathew B Wilkinson
Genl Couns: Scott Bates

D-U-N-S 10-147-3825
HERITAGE IMPORTS INC
HERITAGE VOLKSWAGEN
(*Suby of* ATLANTIC AUTOMOTIVE CORP) ★
1 Olympic Pl Ste 700, Towson, MD 21204-4112
Tel (410) 363-8300 *Founded/Ownrshp* 1984
Sales 23.5MM^E *EMP* 75
SIC 5511 Automobiles, new & used; Automobiles, new & used
CEO: Steve Fader
**Pr:* Brian Fader
Sls Mgr: Greg Jacobson
Sls Mgr: Jeff Zeigler
Board of Directors: Steven B Fader

D-U-N-S 07-940-4956
▲ HERITAGE INSURANCE HOLDINGS INC
2600 Mccormick Dr Ste 300, Clearwater, FL 33759-1071
Tel (727) 362-7200 *Founded/Ownrshp* 2012
Sales NA *EMP* 90^E
Tkr Sym HRTG *Exch* NYS
SIC 6331 Fire, marine & casualty insurance; Fire, marine & casualty insurance
Ch Bd: Bruce Lucas
**Pr:* Richard Widdicombe
COO: Ernie Garateix
CFO: Stephen Rohde
Ex VP: Sharon Binnun
Ex VP: Melvin Russell
VP: Paul Neilson
VP: Joseph Peiso

D-U-N-S 62-667-4001
HERITAGE INTERACTIVE SERVICES LLC
3719 W 96th St, Indianapolis, IN 46268-3100
Tel (317) 334-2300 *Founded/Ownrshp* 2001
Sales 60.1MM^E *EMP* 107
SIC 5093 Scrap & waste materials; Scrap & waste materials
Pr: Bill McDaniel
VP: Jane Hicks
VP: Yanet Montanez
Prgrm Mgr: Chris Ash
Prgrm Mgr: Steve Barber
Prgrm Mgr: Joshua Barrick
Prgrm Mgr: Alli Benshoof
Prgrm Mgr: Ben Bitner
Prgrm Mgr: Bob Brown
Prgrm Mgr: Cage Cowan
Prgrm Mgr: Casey Diercks

D-U-N-S 07-915-2214
HERITAGE INTERESTS LLC
4300 Jetway Ct, North Highlands, CA 95660-5702
Tel (916) 481-5030 *Founded/Ownrshp* 2011
Sales 89.5MM^E *EMP* 252
SIC 1751 5031 2431 Cabinet & finish carpentry; Finish & trim carpentry; Lumber, plywood & millwork; Windows & window parts & trim, wood; Louver windows, glass, wood frame

Pr: Edward Zuckerman
CFO: Dennis Gardemeyer
VP: Charlie Gardemeyer

D-U-N-S 09-452-7173
HERITAGE INTERIORS ISI LLC
2501 W Phelps Rd, Phoenix, AZ 85023-3208
Tel (602) 943-8599 *Founded/Ownrshp* 1979
Sales 27.9MM^E *EMP* 125
SIC 5713 Floor covering stores
CEO: James Whitney

D-U-N-S 96-574-3326
HERITAGE INTERNATIONAL TRUCKS INC
322 Dry Hill Rd, Beckley, WV 25801-2602
Tel (304) 254-7827 *Founded/Ownrshp* 2009
Sales 48.7MM^E *EMP* 250
SIC 5013 Truck parts & accessories; Truck parts & accessories
Pr: Gary Kale
**Sec:* Richard Otten
**VP:* Carl Hubbard

HERITAGE INTL MINISTRIES
See MORNINGSTAR FELLOWSHIP CHURCH

D-U-N-S 96-157-6139
HERITAGE MANAGEMENT GROUP INC
(*Suby of* ASPHALT MATERIALS INC) ★
2384 Glebe St, Carmel, IN 46032-7272
Tel (317) 569-0877 *Founded/Ownrshp* 1993
Sales 176.8MM^E *EMP* 241
SIC 7389 Fund raising organizations; Fund raising organizations
Pr: Charles S Frick
Sec: Nancy Frick

HERITAGE MANOR NURSING HOME
See PLANTATION MANAGEMENT CO LLC

HERITAGE MAZDA
See I HERITAGE INC

HERITAGE MEDICAL CENTER
See SHELBYVILLE HOSPITAL CORP

D-U-N-S 94-307-0656
HERITAGE MEDICAL GROUP
BAKERSFIELD FAMILY MEDICAL CTR
4580 California Ave, Bakersfield, CA 93309-1104
Tel (661) 327-4411 *Founded/Ownrshp* 1984
Sales 23.8MM^E *EMP* 300^E
SIC 8011 Offices & clinics of medical doctors; Offices & clinics of medical doctors
CEO: Stanley Wohl
**Owner:* Richard Merkin

D-U-N-S 04-624-1836
HERITAGE MINISTRIES
4600 Route 60, Gerry, NY 14740-9562
Tel (716) 487-6800 *Founded/Ownrshp* 2011
Sales 2.0MM^E *EMP* 800^E
SIC 8661 Religious organizations
Ex Dir: David Smeltzer

D-U-N-S 09-140-7549
HERITAGE MORTGAGE CO INC
175 Derby St Ste 36, Hingham, MA 02043-4058
Tel (781) 740-5500 *Founded/Ownrshp* 1998
Sales NA *EMP* 8
SIC 6163 Mortgage brokers arranging for loans, using money of others; Mortgage brokers arranging for loans, using money of others
Pr: Judy McConell
**VP:* John Trotman

D-U-N-S 05-186-4122
HERITAGE MOTORS INC
HERITAGE FORD
1600 Shelburne Rd, South Burlington, VT 05403-7703
Tel (802) 865-8100 *Founded/Ownrshp* 1982
Sales 36.7MM^E *EMP* 95
SIC 5511 Automobiles, new & used; Pickups, new & used; Automobiles, new & used; Pickups, new & used
Pr: David Machavern
Sales Exec: John Elliott

D-U-N-S 94-271-2969
HERITAGE NEW YORK MEDICAL GROUP
1225 Franklin Ave Ste 100, Garden City, NY 11530-1659
Tel (516) 746-2200 *Founded/Ownrshp* 1995
Sales NA *EMP* 80
SIC 6324 Hospital & medical service plans
Pr: Richard Merkin
**VP:* Cindy Lighthill

HERITAGE NISSAN
See RNMC INC

D-U-N-S 10-306-5686
▲ HERITAGE OAKS BANCORP
1222 Vine St, Paso Robles, CA 93446-2268
Tel (805) 369-5200 *Founded/Ownrshp* 1994
Sales NA *EMP* 234^E
Tkr Sym HEOP *Exch* NAS
SIC 6022 State commercial banks; State commercial banks
Pr: Simone Lagomarsino
**Ch Bd:* Michael J Morris
V Ch: Donald Campbell
**Pr:* Simone F Lagomarsino
CFO: Jason Castle
Ofcr: Mark Holbrook
Ofcr: William A Schack
Ofcr: T Joseph Stronks
Ex VP: Karen Dally
Ex VP: Mark D Holbrook
Ex VP: Rob Osterbauer
Ex VP: Lonny Robinson
Ex VP: William Schack
Sr VP: Bill Filippin
VP: Scott Laycock
VP: Austin Petty
Board of Directors: Michael J Behrman, Mark C Fugate, Howard N Gould, Dolores T Lacey, James J Lynch, Daniel J O'hare, Michael E Pfau, Alexander F Simas, Stephen P Yost

D-U-N-S 60-599-5518
■ HERITAGE OAKS BANK
(*Suby of* HERITAGE OAKS BANCORP) ★
1222 Vine St, Paso Robles, CA 93446-2268
Tel (805) 239-5200 *Founded/Ownrshp* 1983
Sales NA *EMP* 220
SIC 6022 State commercial banks; State commercial banks
CEO: Simone Lagomarsino
Pr: Rick C Arredondo
Pr: Ronald Oliveira
CFO: Mark K Olson
Chf Cred: William Shack
Sr VP: Gloria Brady
Sr VP: Donna Breuer
Board of Directors: James J Lynch

HERITAGE OF GERING
See VETTER HEALTH SERVICES INC

D-U-N-S 09-012-2891
HERITAGE OF TOWSON INC (MD)
HERITAGE HONDA OF PARKVILLE
9213 Harford Rd, Parkville, MD 21234-3102
Tel (410) 882-3000 *Founded/Ownrshp* 1999
Sales 24.7MM^E *EMP* 100
SIC 5511 Automobiles, new & used; Automobiles, new & used
Pr: Jerry Fader
Creative D: Lena Karalnik
Genl Mgr: Gary Dove
Genl Mgr: John Rooney
Genl Mgr: Doug Smith
Genl Mgr: Bill Starr
CTO: David Aldrich
Telecom Mg: Deborah Meyers
Mktg Mgr: John Starchok
Sls Mgr: Jim Abbott
Sls Mgr: Saundra Bamberger

D-U-N-S 03-126-3767
HERITAGE ON LANIER INC
CARRIAGE NISSAN
2400 Browns Bridge Rd, Gainesville, GA 30504-6027
Tel (770) 532-6335 *Founded/Ownrshp* 1990
Sales 63.7MM *EMP* 68
SIC 5511 7532 Automobiles, new & used; Collision shops, automotive; Automobiles, new & used; Collision shops, automotive
Pr: David P Basha
CFO: Anwar Saad
Opers Mgr: Chris Ellison
Mktg Dir: Amanda Minish
Sls Mgr: Carl Eunice

D-U-N-S 07-840-1203
HERITAGE ONE CARPENTRY INC
(*Suby of* HERITAGE INTERESTS LLC) ★
2107 Forest Ave Ste 100, Chico, CA 95928-7696
Tel (530) 345-6622 *Founded/Ownrshp* 2012
Sales 33.9MM^E *EMP* 162
SIC 5031 1751 Lumber, plywood & millwork; Cabinet & finish carpentry
Pr: Charles Gardemeyer
**COO:* Stephen Beckham
**CFO:* Geoffrey Hughes
VP: Tyler Randolph

D-U-N-S 07-839-7493
HERITAGE ONE DOOR AND BUILDING SOLUTIONS LLC
(*Suby of* HERITAGE INTERESTS LLC) ★
4300 Jetway Ct, North Highlands, CA 95660-5702
Tel (916) 481-5030 *Founded/Ownrshp* 2011
Sales 31.6MM *EMP* 86
SIC 5031 2431 Doors & windows; Windows & window parts & trim, wood
**COO:* Stephen Beckham
**CFO:* Geoff Hughes
Area Mgr: Hector Franco
**Sls Mgr:* John Ballou

D-U-N-S 01-641-6815
HERITAGE ONE REALTORS
1711 N Hritg Pkwy Ste 100, Sherman, TX 75092
Tel (972) 658-5878 *Founded/Ownrshp* 1999
Sales 35.0MM *EMP* 5
SIC 6531 Real estate brokers & agents; Real estate brokers & agents
Owner: Kimberly Shivers

D-U-N-S 07-840-1771
HERITAGE ONE WINDOW AND BUILDING SOLUTIONS LLC
(*Suby of* HERITAGE INTERESTS LLC) ★
4300 Jetway Ct, North Highlands, CA 95660-5702
Tel (916) 481-5030 *Founded/Ownrshp* 2012
Sales 24.0MM^E *EMP* 4
SIC 5031 Doors & windows
COO: Stephen Beckham
CFO: Geoff Hughes
Sls Mgr: John Ballou

D-U-N-S 01-571-1591
■ HERITAGE OPERATING LP
HERITAGE PROPANE
(*Suby of* AMERIGAS PARTNERS LP) ★
754 River Rock Dr, Helena, MT 59602-0240
Tel (406) 442-9759 *Founded/Ownrshp* 2012
Sales 322.3MM^E *EMP* 2,521
SIC 5984 5172 Propane gas, bottled; Petroleum products; Propane gas, bottled; Petroleum products
Pr: James E Bertelsmeyer
**Pt:* Michael Krimbill
**Pr:* Robert Paul Grady
VP: C S Sheffield
Genl Mgr: Lacy Silvan

HERITAGE PAPER CO
See BAYCORR PACKAGING INC

D-U-N-S 08-658-7755 IMP
HERITAGE PAPER CO
(*Suby of* PIONEER PACKING INC) ★
2400 S Grand Ave, Santa Ana, CA 92705-5211
Tel (714) 540-9737 *Founded/Ownrshp* 1978
Sales 25.2MM^E *EMP* 80

SIC 2653 5199 Corrugated & solid fiber boxes; Packaging materials; Corrugated & solid fiber boxes; Packaging materials
CEO: Ron Scagliotti
**CFO:* Lenet Derksen
Exec: Bill Bumstead
Ql Cn Mgr: Terry Schnabel
Sls Mgr: Dan Feehan

D-U-N-S 60-693-2890
HERITAGE PARK SURGICAL HOSPITAL
3603 N Calais St, Sherman, TX 75090-1785
Tel (903) 813-3700 *Founded/Ownrshp* 2005
Sales 31.3MM *EMP* 180
SIC 8011 Ambulatory surgical center
CEO: Ray Ford
Mtls Mgr: Michael Norris

D-U-N-S 08-430-4419
HERITAGE PETROLEUM LLC
(*Suby of* WANNEMUEHLER OIL CO)
516 N 7th Ave, Evansville, IN 47710-1420
Tel (812) 422-3251 *Founded/Ownrshp* 1976
Sales 64.2MM[E] *EMP* 49
SIC 5172 Gasoline; Diesel fuel; Gasoline; Diesel fuel
CFO: Randy Brack
IT Man: John Clark
IT Man: Joe Kratochvil
IT Man: Bryan Smith
Sfty Dirs: Rodney Hunter
Sls Mgr: Chris Stratman
Genl Couns: Brian Townsend

D-U-N-S 07-875-8396
HERITAGE PHARMA HOLDINGS INC
12 Christopher Way # 300, Eatontown, NJ 07724-3330
Tel (732) 429-1000 *Founded/Ownrshp* 2011
Sales 25.7MM[E] *EMP* 162
SIC 6719 Investment holding companies, except banks; Investment holding companies, except banks
CEO: Jeffery Galzer

D-U-N-S 18-963-0168
HERITAGE PHARMA LABS INC
(*Suby of* HERITAGE PHARMA HOLDINGS INC) ★
21 Cotters Ln Ste B, East Brunswick, NJ 08816-2050
Tel (732) 238-7880 *Founded/Ownrshp* 2014
Sales 34.5MM[E] *EMP* 150
SIC 8731 2834 Commercial physical research; Pharmaceutical preparations; Commercial physical research; Pharmaceutical preparations
CEO: Jeffery Glazer
VP: Pankaj Dave
VP: Ashish Patel

HERITAGE PHYSICIAN GROUP
See HEALTH RESOURCES GROUP

D-U-N-S 18-717-5773 EXP
HERITAGE PLASTICS INC
1002 Hunt St, Picayune, MS 39466-5200
Tel (404) 425-1905 *Founded/Ownrshp* 1982
Sales 62.3MM[E] *EMP* 150
SIC 3087 Custom compound purchased resins; Custom compound purchased resins
Ch Bd: Carl F Allen
**Pr:* Paul Lewis
**CFO:* Michael J Dvornak
**VP:* William A Swope
Exec: Becky Winchester
Plnt Mgr: Craig Moore
Trfc Mgr: Tina Bourlet
Sls&Mrk Ex: Kathy D Tourne
VP Sls: Larry Bisio
Sls Dir: Sandy Wiedebusch

D-U-N-S 79-336-9042 EXP
HERITAGE PLASTICS LIQUIDATION INC
(*Suby of* ATKORE INTERNATIONAL INC) ★
861 N Lisbon St, Carrollton, OH 44615-9401
Tel (330) 627-8002 *Founded/Ownrshp* 2013
Sales 41.5MM[E] *EMP* 70
SIC 3084 Plastics pipe
Pr: John P Williamson
**CFO:* James A Mallak
VP: Holly Hansen
Plnt Mgr: Jack Hunt
Plnt Mgr: Dave Mott
Plnt Mgr: Wayne Pegram
Prd Mgr: Keith Dinkheller
VP Sls: Ron Pritchett
Sls Mgr: Sandra Gamble
Sls Mgr: Debbie Murray

HERITAGE POINTE
See UNITED METHODIST MEMORIAL HOME

D-U-N-S 19-644-7353 IMP
HERITAGE PRODUCTS INC
(*Suby of* HIRUTA KOGYO CO.,LTD.)
2000 Smith Ave, Crawfordsville, IN 47933-1055
Tel (765) 364-9002 *Founded/Ownrshp* 1988
Sales 113.0MM[E] *EMP* 216
SIC 3465 Automotive stampings; Automotive stampings
Pr: Kiichiro Yamamuro
**Treas:* Ryohei Kazahaya
Info Man: Takaya Yunoki
Ql Cn Mgr: Ron Willis

HERITAGE PROPANE
See HERITAGE OPERATING LP

HERITAGE PROPANE
See TITAN PROPANE LLC

D-U-N-S 16-444-0765
HERITAGE PROVIDER NETWORK INC
8510 Balboa Blvd Ste 285, Northridge, CA 91325-5804
Tel (818) 654-3461 *Founded/Ownrshp* 1996
Sales 44.1MM[E] *EMP* 714
SIC 8621 Medical field-related associations; Medical field-related associations
Pr: Richard N Merkin
Pt: Kevin J Conroy
COO: A D Villani
VP: Mercedes Haefs
VP: Rick Martin

D-U-N-S 07-931-9953
HERITAGE RESTAURANT GROUP OF TOTOWA INC
FIREHOUSE SUBS
2105 Us Hwy 46 W, Totowa, NJ 07512
Tel (973) 237-1320 *Founded/Ownrshp* 2013
Sales 825.0M *EMP* 500
SIC 5812 Sandwiches & submarines shop; Restaurant, lunch counter; Caterers; Sandwiches & submarines shop; Restaurant, lunch counter; Caterers
Pr: Ever Santana
**CFO:* Vincent Burchianti
**Prin:* Chris Sorensen

HERITAGE RESTORATIONS
See HOMESTEAD CRAFTSMEN ASSOCIATION

HERITAGE RSIDENTIAL TRTMNT CTR
See HERITAGE SCHOOLS FOUNDATION INC

D-U-N-S 79-387-0742
HERITAGE SATURN INC
(*Suby of* ATLANTIC AUTOMOTIVE CORP) ★
11234 Reisterstown Rd, Owings Mills, MD 21117-1908
Tel (410) 356-6900 *Founded/Ownrshp* 1989
Sales 36.4MM[E] *EMP* 222
SIC 5511 Automobiles, new & used; Automobiles, new & used
Pr: Jerome Fader

D-U-N-S 16-128-3288
HERITAGE SCHOOLS FOUNDATION INC
HERITAGE RSIDENTIAL TRTMNT CTR
5600 Heritage School Dr, Provo, UT 84604-7701
Tel (801) 226-4600 *Founded/Ownrshp* 1984
Sales 14.7MM *EMP* 325
SIC 8063 Psychiatric hospitals; Psychiatric hospitals
CEO: Jerry Spanos
**COO:* Glen Zaugg
CFO: Jeremy Brown
Ofcr: Jennifer Sommers
**Ex Dir:* Anneta Foote
**Ex Dir:* Vicky Geilman
**Ex Dir:* Betty McElroy

HERITAGE SECURITY SERVICES
See RICHMAN MANAGEMENT CORP

HERITAGE SHOPS
See MATUS ENTERPRISES INC

D-U-N-S 10-568-7859
HERITAGE SPORTSWEAR INC
VIRGINIA T'S
102 Reliance Dr, Hebron, OH 43025-9204
Tel (740) 928-7771 *Founded/Ownrshp* 1986
Sales 205.1MM[E] *EMP* 75[E]
SIC 5136 5137 Sportswear, men's & boys'; Sportswear, women's & children's; Sportswear, men's & boys'; Sportswear, women's & children's
Pr: Gerald T Jurden
Sls Mgr: Raeshawn Gorius
Sales Asso: Kristin Egan

D-U-N-S 04-970-7115 IMP
HERITAGE TECHNOLOGIES LLC
MICRONUTRIENTS DIVISION
1550 Research Way, Indianapolis, IN 46231-3350
Tel (317) 486-5880 *Founded/Ownrshp* 1995
Sales 21.4MM[E] *EMP* 60
SIC 2048 Feed supplements; Feed supplements
Chf Mktg O: Fred Steward
CFO: Thomas De Felice
**VP:* Jeff Cohen
VP: Ted Moore
Dir Bus: Kevin Perryman
Plnt Mgr: Rick Bowman

HERITAGE TELEMARKETING
See HERITAGE CO INC

HERITAGE THERMAL SERVICES
See HERITAGE-WTI INC

HERITAGE TITLE COMPANY
See HERITAGE TITLE CO OF AUSTIN INC

D-U-N-S 15-747-0949
HERITAGE TITLE CO OF AUSTIN INC
HERITAGE TITLE COMPANY
401 Congress Ave Ste 1500, Austin, TX 78701-3797
Tel (512) 505-5000 *Founded/Ownrshp* 1986
Sales NA *EMP* 80
SIC 6361 Title insurance
Pr: Gary S Farmer
Ex VP: Laura A Beuerlein
**VP:* Laura Beuerlein
VP: Mary Metz
VP: Melissa Morillo

D-U-N-S 00-827-8256 IMP
HERITAGE TRACTOR INC
JOHN DEERE
915 Industrial Park Rd, Baldwin City, KS 66006
Tel (785) 594-6486 *Founded/Ownrshp* 1997
Sales 58.5MM[E] *EMP* 202[E]
SIC 5083 Farm & garden machinery; Farm & garden machinery
CEO: Ken Wagner
**Treas:* Derek Dummermuth
Off Mgr: Tennille Wagner

D-U-N-S 10-724-3362
HERITAGE TRANSPORT LLC
7901 W Morris St, Indianapolis, IN 46231-1366
Tel (317) 243-0811 *Founded/Ownrshp* 1983
Sales 25.8MM[E] *EMP* 100
SIC 4213 Liquid petroleum transport, non-local
Telecom Mg: Jim Wampler

D-U-N-S 04-726-1557 IMP/EXP
HERITAGE TRAVELWARE LTD
650 E Algonquin Rd # 300, Schaumburg, IL 60173-3853
Tel (630) 614-7070 *Founded/Ownrshp* 1978
Sales 29.8MM[E] *EMP* 60
SIC 5099 Luggage
Pr: Scott Booth
**COO:* David Schreiber
**Ex VP:* Rick Kozlow
MIS Mgr: Karen Saccente

D-U-N-S 12-357-7538
HERITAGE UNIVERSITY
3240 Fort Rd, Toppenish, WA 98948-9562
Tel (509) 865-8500 *Founded/Ownrshp* 1982
Sales 32.8MM *EMP* 255
Accts Moss Adams Llp Yakima Wa
SIC 8221 College, except junior; College, except junior
Pr: Kathleen Ross
Pr: Bertha Ortega
Pr: Richard Sippola
COO: Terry Mullen
Ofcr: Bonnie Hughes
VP: Curt Guaglianone
VP: Michael Moore
VP: Michael O'Brien
VP: Sneh Veena
VP: Harold Wingood
VP: David Wise
Exec: Richard Swearingen
Assoc Dir: Dina Blum

D-U-N-S 12-168-6976
HERITAGE VALLEY HEALTH SYSTEM INC
SEWICKLEY VALLEY HOSPITAL
(*Suby of* SEWICKLEY VALLEY HOSPITAL) ★
1000 Dutch Ridge Rd, Beaver, PA 15009-9727
Tel (724) 728-7000 *Founded/Ownrshp* 1983
Sales 5.1MM *EMP* 4,291
Accts Carbis Walker Llp Pittsburgh
SIC 8741 8062 Management services; General medical & surgical hospitals; Management services; General medical & surgical hospitals
Pr: Norman F Mitry
Chf Path: Tae Min
**Ch Bd:* Timothy Merrill
V Ch: Laura A Vassamillet
**COO:* Rose Mary Nalan
Treas: Frank Papa
Ofcr: Victoria Alberti
Ofcr: Linda F Homyk
Ofcr: Rosemary Nolan
VP: Rick Beaver
**VP:* Daniel Brooks
**VP:* David Carleton
**VP:* John T Cinicola
**VP:* Bruce Edwards
VP: Anne Hitchak
VP: Laura Wagner
Exec: John Graziano
Dir Lab: Sue Bitcko
Dir Lab: Darlene Marion
Dir Rx: Bridget Walker

HERITAGE VILLAGE
See GERRY HOMES INC

HERITAGE VOLKSWAGEN
See HERITAGE IMPORTS INC

D-U-N-S 00-342-2412
HERITAGE WARRANTY INSURANCE RRG INC (NE)
HERITAGE ADMINISTRATION SVCS
400 Metro Pl N Ste 300, Dublin, OH 43017-3377
Tel (800) 753-5236 *Founded/Ownrshp* 1998, 2004
Sales NA *EMP* 73
SIC 6399 Warranty insurance, automobile
Pr: Larry S Roseberry
**CEO:* Haytham H Elzayn
**CFO:* Ronald L Uhing
**VP:* Stephen E Goodrich

HERITAGE WESTERN STAR
See HERITAGE EQUIPMENT INC

HERITAGE WHOLESALERS
See LANGFIELD GROUP INC

D-U-N-S 93-229-1974
HERITAGE WIRE HARNESS LIMITED LIABILITY CO
1500 Airport Rd W, Fort Payne, AL 35968-3305
Tel (256) 845-1321 *Founded/Ownrshp* 2008
Sales 23.9MM[E] *EMP* 80
SIC 3679 Harness assemblies for electronic use: wire or cable

D-U-N-S 02-853-4659
HERITAGE YMCA GROUP
NAPERVILLE YMCA
34 S Washington St, Naperville, IL 60540-5331
Tel (630) 420-6270 *Founded/Ownrshp* 1909
Sales 10.5MM *EMP* 585
SIC 8641 7991 8351 7032 8322 Youth organizations; Physical fitness facilities; Child day care services; Youth camps; Individual & family services; Youth organizations; Physical fitness facilities; Child day care services; Youth camps; Individual & family services
Pr: Tom Berntsen
**CFO:* Ginny Maloney
VP: R J Bartels

D-U-N-S 82-591-0420
▲ **HERITAGE-CRYSTAL CLEAN INC**
2175 Point Blvd Ste 375, Elgin, IL 60123-9211
Tel (847) 836-5670 *Founded/Ownrshp* 1980
Sales 339.0MM *EMP* 958
Tkr Sym HCCI *Exch* NGM
SIC 7699 8734 Waste cleaning services; Hazardous waste testing; Waste cleaning services; Hazardous waste testing
Pr: Joseph Chalhoub
COO: Gregory Ray
CFO: Mark Devita
Treas: Scott Peters
Sr VP: John Lucks
VP: Ellie Bruce
VP: Tom Hillstrom
Rgnl Mgr: Mike McGinn
Rgnl Mgr: Jim Tefft
Brnch Mgr: Gregory Comperchio
Brnch Mgr: John Essary

D-U-N-S 00-999-0065 IMP
■ **HERITAGE-CRYSTAL CLEAN LLC**
(*Suby of* HERITAGE-CRYSTAL CLEAN INC) ★
2175 Point Blvd Ste 375, Elgin, IL 60123-9211
Tel (847) 836-5670 *Founded/Ownrshp* 1999
Sales 337.1MM[E] *EMP* 540
SIC 4953 Hazardous waste collection & disposal; Hazardous waste collection & disposal

D-U-N-S 96-542-7263 IMP/EXP
HERITAGE-WTI INC
HERITAGE THERMAL SERVICES
1250 Saint George St # 1, East Liverpool, OH 43920-3461
Tel (330) 385-7337 *Founded/Ownrshp* 2008
Sales 98.9MM[E] *EMP* 184[E]
SIC 4953 Hazardous waste collection & disposal; Hazardous waste collection & disposal
Pr: Wendy Hamrick
**Pr:* John Peterka
**VP:* John Avdellas
**VP:* Stewart Fletcher
**VP:* Frank Murray
Sfty Mgr: Rob Blackburn
Opers Mgr: Robert Buchheit
Plnt Mgr: Mike Nicholson
Board of Directors: Gary F Lindgren, Dr Ken Price, Rudolf Zaengerle

D-U-N-S 01-273-2475
HERITAGENERGY (NY) INC (NY)
625 Sawkill Rd, Kingston, NY 12401-7157
Tel (845) 336-2000 *Founded/Ownrshp* 1921, 1958
Sales 56.7MM[E] *EMP* 90
Accts Paul J Mula Cpa Kingston N
SIC 5983 5984 5541 Fuel oil dealers; Liquefied petroleum gas, delivered to customers' premises; Gasoline service stations; Fuel oil dealers; Liquefied petroleum gas, delivered to customers' premises; Gasoline service stations
Pr: Abel Garraghan
**VP:* William Davenport

D-U-N-S 00-607-9560
HERKER INDUSTRIES INC
N57w13760 Carmen Ave, Menomonee Falls, WI 53051-6144
Tel (262) 781-8270 *Founded/Ownrshp* 1952
Sales 40.1MM[E] *EMP* 180
SIC 3451 3599 Screw machine products; Machine shop, jobbing & repair; Screw machine products; Machine shop, jobbing & repair
CEO: Edward Nunemaker
Pr: David Barta
**Pr:* Mickey Fancher
**Pr:* Robert Fancher
CFO: Richard Merten
Plnt Mgr: Joe Hamilton
Ql Cn Mgr: Bob Ertl

D-U-N-S 01-075-6773
HERKIMER COUNTY COMMUNITY COLLEGE
(*Suby of* STATE UNIVERSITY OF NEW YORK) ★
100 Reservoir Rd, Herkimer, NY 13350-1598
Tel (315) 866-0300 *Founded/Ownrshp* 1966
Sales 39.7MM[E] *EMP* 200
SIC 8222 9411 Community college; Administration of educational programs; ; Community college; Administration of educational programs;
Pr: Ronolds Williams
**Pr:* Ann Marie Murray
Pr: Daniel Sargent
Trst: Theodore Wind
Ofcr: Timothy Leonard
Ofcr: Jason McMahon
**VP:* Nicholas F Laino
VP: Todd Stoller
VP Admn: Nicholas Laino
Genl Mgr: Michael Giudice
Off Admin: Lori Dolly

D-U-N-S 00-241-7004
HERLEY INDUSTRIES INC
ULTRA ELECTRONICS HERLEY
(*Suby of* ULTRA ELECTRONICS DEFENSE INC) ★
3061 Industry Dr Ste 200, Lancaster, PA 17603-4092
Tel (717) 397-2777 *Founded/Ownrshp* 1965, 2015
Sales 151.1MM[E] *EMP* 1,022[E]
SIC 7382 Search & navigation equipment; Microwave components; Electronic connectors; Semiconductors & related devices; Radio & TV communications equipment; Power transmission equipment; Security systems services
CEO: Rakesh Sharma
COO: Carlos Santiago
CFO: Anello Garefino
Genl Mgr: Ed Weatherwax
CIO: Bob Brownell

D-U-N-S 07-117-9246
HERLEY-CTI INC (DE)
(*Suby of* HERLEY INDUSTRIES INC) ★
9 Whippany Rd, Whippany, NJ 07981-1540
Tel (973) 884-2580 *Founded/Ownrshp* 1973, 2004
Sales 81.3MM[E] *EMP* 900
SIC 3679 Microwave components; Oscillators; Microwave components; Oscillators
Pr: Eric Demarco
**CEO:* Deanna Lund
**Treas:* Laura Siegal
VP: Dottie Day
**VP:* Michael Fink
VP: Charles L Pourciau Jr
Div Mgr: Terence Ede
Genl Mgr: Edward Weatherwax
MIS Dir: Alan Kobb
QA Dir: Alexander Art
QC Dir: Arthur Alexander

D-U-N-S 00-380-1362
HERLIHY MID-CONTINENT CO (IL)
1306 Marquette Dr, Romeoville, IL 60446-1026
Tel (630) 378-1000 *Founded/Ownrshp* 1929, 1968
Sales 40.0MM[E] *EMP* 120

SIC 1622 1771 Bridge construction; Viaduct construction; Concrete work; Bridge construction; Viaduct construction; Concrete work
CEO: Donald R Schultz
**Pr:* Douglas D Schultz
MIS Dir: Art Ggerty
IT Man: John Obrien

D-U-N-S 00-457-4109
HERMAN ELECTRONICS INC (FL)
10110 Usa Today Way, Miramar, FL 33025-3903
Tel (305) 477-0063 *Founded/Ownrshp* 1963
Sales 43.2MMᴱ *EMP* 86
SIC 5065 5999 Electronic parts; Electronic parts & equipment; Electronic parts; Electronic parts & equipment
CEO: Arnold Wolf
**Pr:* David Wolf
**VP:* Jeffrey Wolf
Natl Sales: Joseph Steinberg
Manager: Luis Alix

D-U-N-S 00-893-7765
HERMAN GOLDNER CO INC
GOLDNER, HERMAN COMPANY
7777 Brewster Ave, Philadelphia, PA 19153-3298
Tel (215) 365-5400 *Founded/Ownrshp* 1887
Sales 97.0MM *EMP* 275
Accts Kreischer Miller Horsham Pen
SIC 1711 7699 Mechanical contractor; Plumbing contractors; Warm air heating & air conditioning contractor; Boiler & heating repair services; Mechanical contractor; Plumbing contractors; Warm air heating & air conditioning contractor; Boiler & heating repair services
Ch Bd: Gerard C Goldner
Pr: Stephen Williams
CEO: Herman W Goldner
CFO: John D Goldner
Ex VP: Thomas H Graziano
VP: Len Ditullio
VP: Steve Leonardo
DP Exec: Miriam Demattei
Opers Mgr: James Brunetto
Sales Exec: Rob Scanlan
Snr PM: Steve Dunn

D-U-N-S 04-774-9957 EXP
HERMAN GRANT CO INC
1100 Ashmore Ave, Chattanooga, TN 37415-6638
Tel (423) 266-6138 *Founded/Ownrshp* 1981
Sales 29.4MMᴱ *EMP* 40
SIC 5082 Excavating machinery & equipment
Pr: Paula G Shuford
**VP:* Jodie Martin
**Genl Mgr:* David Shuford

D-U-N-S 03-006-7805
HERMAN INVESTMENT CO INC (PA)
PRC COMMERCIAL
3700 S Water St Ste 100, Pittsburgh, PA 15203-2366
Tel (412) 261-6500 *Founded/Ownrshp* 1922
Sales 30.0MM *EMP* 30
SIC 6513 6531 Apartment building operators; Real estate agents & managers; Apartment building operators; Real estate agents & managers
Pr: Howard L Engelberg
**Treas:* Scott Engelberg
**VP:* Peter Hein

HERMAN KAY
See MYSTIC INC

D-U-N-S 07-713-8998
HERMAN L LOEB LLC
LOEB OIL
600 Country Club Rd, Lawrenceville, IL 62439-3369
Tel (618) 943-2227 *Founded/Ownrshp* 1946
Sales 50.0MM *EMP* 50
SIC 1311 Crude petroleum production; Crude petroleum production
CFO: David Lebovitz

D-U-N-S 07-957-5897
■ **HERMAN MILLER CONSUMER HOLDINGS INC**
(*Suby of* HERMAN MILLER INC) ★
711 Canal St Ste 3, Stamford, CT 06902-6094
Tel (203) 614-0600 *Founded/Ownrshp* 2014
Sales 17.5MMᴱ *EMP* 450
SIC 5021 3646 5063 5023 5712 Office & public building furniture; Office furniture; Commercial indusl & institutional electric lighting fixtures; Lighting fixtures; Floor coverings; Furniture stores; Office & public building furniture; Office furniture; Commercial indusl & institutional electric lighting fixtures; Lighting fixtures; Floor coverings; Furniture stores
CEO: Brian C Walker
**CFO:* Gregory J Bylsma

D-U-N-S 00-601-2801 IMP/EXP
▲ **HERMAN MILLER INC** (MI)
855 E Main Ave, Zeeland, MI 49464-1372
Tel (616) 654-3000 *Founded/Ownrshp* 1905
Sales 2.1MMM *EMP* 7,510ᴱ
Accts Ernst & Young Llp Grand Rapid
Tkr Sym MLHR *Exch* NGS
SIC 2521 2522 2541 2542 2531 Wood office furniture; Office furniture, except wood; Wood partitions & fixtures; Partitions & fixtures, except wood; Public building & related furniture; Wood office furniture; Office furniture, except wood; Wood partitions & fixtures; Partitions & fixtures, except wood; Public building & related furniture
Pr: Brian C Walker
**Ch Bd:* Michael A Volkema
Pr: Steven C Gane
Pr: Louise McDonald
Pr: John McPhee
CEO: John Edelman
CFO: Jeffrey M Stutz
Treas: Kevin Veltman
Ex VP: Gregory J Bylsma
Ex VP: Donald D Goeman
Ex VP: Andrew J Lock
Sr VP: Malisa Bryant
Sr VP: H Timothy Lopez
Sr VP: Michael F Ramirez
VP: Jeffrey L Kurburski
Board of Directors: Mary Vermeer Andringa, David A Brandon, Douglas D French, J Barry Griswell, John R Hoke III, Lisa A Kro, Heidi Manheimer, Dorothy A Terrell, David O Ulrich

D-U-N-S 00-340-2138
HERMAN R EWELL INC (PA)
H.R. EWELL
4635 Division Hwy, East Earl, PA 17519-9245
Tel (717) 354-4556 *Founded/Ownrshp* 1939
Sales 40.0MM *EMP* 200
SIC 4213

D-U-N-S 00-547-3681
HERMAN SEEKAMP INC (IL)
CLYDE'S DELICIOUS DOUGHNUTS
1120 W Fullerton Ave, Addison, IL 60101-4304
Tel (630) 628-6555 *Founded/Ownrshp* 1920
Sales 40.4MMᴱ *EMP* 115
SIC 2051 2052 2053 2099 2038 Bread, cake & related products; Doughnuts, except frozen; Pastries, e.g. danish: except frozen; Croissants, except frozen; Cookies; Doughnuts, frozen; Food preparations; Frozen specialties; Bread, cake & related products; Doughnuts, except frozen; Pastries, e.g. danish: except frozen; Croissants, except frozen; Cookies; Doughnuts, frozen; Food preparations; Frozen specialties
Ch: Willard Bickford
**Pr:* Kent W Bickford
**VP:* Kim D Bickford
Sfty Mgr: Marion Baranski
Natl Sales: David Bennett

D-U-N-S 00-895-9587 EXP
HERMAN STRAUSS INC
35th & Mccolloch St, Wheeling, WV 26003
Tel (304) 232-8770 *Founded/Ownrshp* 1982
Sales 23.4MMᴱ *EMP* 70
SIC 5093 4953 3341 3312 Nonferrous metals scrap; Ferrous metal scrap & waste; Refuse systems; Secondary nonferrous metals; Blast furnaces & steel mills
Pr: Carter Strauss
**COO:* Kenneth W Burns
**CFO:* John McDonald

D-U-N-S 04-440-5686
HERMAN WEISSKER INC (CA)
(*Suby of* MERUELO ENTERPRISES INC) ★
1645 Brown Ave, Riverside, CA 92509-1859
Tel (951) 826-8800 *Founded/Ownrshp* 1959, 1999
Sales 118.0MMᴱ *EMP* 500ᴱ
SIC 1623 8711 1731 Water, sewer & utility lines; Engineering services; Electrical work; Water, sewer & utility lines; Engineering services; Electrical work
CEO: Luis Alberto Armona
Pr: Roger Ashford
**Pr:* Ron Politte
**CFO:* Marty Mayeda
VP: Herman Weissker
Exec: Rowena Hernandez
Off Mgr: Kieth Nelson
DP Exec: Rick Astin
Sfty Mgr: Norm Hollinsworth

D-U-N-S 62-023-5911
HERMAN-STEWART CONSTRUCTION AND DEVELOPMENT INC
4550 Forbes Blvd Ste 200, Lanham, MD 20706-6306
Tel (301) 731-5555 *Founded/Ownrshp* 1990
Sales 73.3MMᴱ *EMP* 100
SIC 1542 1522 Commercial & office building, new construction; Restaurant construction; Shopping center construction; Hotel/motel, new construction; Commercial & office building, new construction; Restaurant construction; Shopping center construction; Hotel/motel, new construction
Pr: Ray Herman
**VP:* Michael Dennis
**VP:* Mike Durrwachter
**VP:* Terry L Varner
**VP:* Matt Whitney

D-U-N-S 04-350-1196 IMP/EXP
HERMANN COMPANIES INC (MO)
7701 Forsyth Blvd # 1000, Saint Louis, MO 63105-1818
Tel (314) 863-9200 *Founded/Ownrshp* 1956
Sales 181.1MMᴱ *EMP* 600
SIC 3086 Packaging & shipping materials, foamed plastic; Packaging & shipping materials, foamed plastic
Ch Bd: Robert R Hermann
**Pr:* Dolores M Frank

D-U-N-S 15-055-5027
HERMANN FORWARDING CO INC
HERMANN TRANSPORTATION
(*Suby of* HERMANN SERVICES INC) ★
83 Stults Rd, Dayton, NJ 08810-3001
Tel (609) 860-5810 *Founded/Ownrshp* 1933
Sales 28.0MMᴱ *EMP* 110
SIC 4213 6512 Trucking, except local; Commercial & industrial building operation
Pr: Dennis W Hermann
**Sec:* Richard J Hermann

D-U-N-S 06-314-1121 EXP
HERMANN SERVICES INC
83 Stults Rd Ste 1, Dayton, NJ 08810-3001
Tel (732) 297-4400 *Founded/Ownrshp* 1979
Sales 40.2MMᴱ *EMP* 200
SIC 7513 4213 4212 4225 Truck leasing, without drivers; Trucking, except local; Truck rental with drivers; General warehousing; Truck leasing, without drivers; Trucking, except local; Truck rental with drivers; General warehousing
Pr: Richard J Hermann
**Sec:* Dennis W Hermann
VP Sls: Rich Clonan
Mktg Mgr: Leena Vangeepuram

HERMANN SONS OF TEXAS
See GRAND LODGE OF ORDER OF SONS OF HERMANN

HERMANN TRANSPORTATION
See HERMANN FORWARDING CO INC

D-U-N-S 04-364-7254
HERMANOS LOPEZ INC
LA BODEGA WHOLESALE
388 W Calle Primera, San Ysidro, CA 92173-2803
Tel (619) 662-3032 *Founded/Ownrshp* 1968
Sales 72.5MMᴱ *EMP* 125
SIC 5141 5411 5921 Groceries, general line; Grocery stores, independent; Wine & beer; Groceries, general line; Grocery stores, independent; Wine & beer; Hard liquor
Pr: Roberto Lopez
**Treas:* Elena Trujillo
**VP:* Rodolpho Lopez
Off Mgr: Gloria Lopez

D-U-N-S 11-815-8914 IMP
HERMANOS SANTIAGO CASH & CARRY INC
Urb Industrial Reparada, Ponce, PR 00716
Tel (787) 842-4060 *Founded/Ownrshp* 1985
Sales 34.1MMᴱ *EMP* 127
SIC 5141 5149 Groceries, general line; Groceries & related products; Groceries, general line; Groceries & related products
Pr: Jose Santiago

HERMANS-PEAR'S COFFEE
See MARATHON VENTURES INC

D-U-N-S 02-747-6506
HERMANSON CO LLP (WA)
1221 2nd Ave N, Kent, WA 98032-2945
Tel (206) 575-9700 *Founded/Ownrshp* 1979
Sales 116.7MMᴱ *EMP* 270
Accts Berntson Porter & Co Bellevu
SIC 1711 Heating & air conditioning contractors; Ventilation & duct work contractor; Heating & air conditioning contractors; Ventilation & duct work contractor
Pr: Rick Hermanson
Pr: James Macdonald
COO: Dan Brock
Genl Mgr: Gerald D Hermanson
CIO: Bill Weinhagen
Dir IT: Jason Milliren
IT Man: Joe Carchi
Sfty Dirs: Brian Sorensen
VP Sls: Dan Lykken
Sls Mgr: David Gibson
Snr PM: Sean Bakey

HERMANTOWN COMMUNITY SCHOOLS
See HERMANTOWN INDEPENDENT SCHOOL DISTRICT 700

D-U-N-S 06-048-9291
HERMANTOWN INDEPENDENT SCHOOL DISTRICT 700
HERMANTOWN COMMUNITY SCHOOLS
4307 Ugstad Rd, Hermantown, MN 55811-1335
Tel (218) 729-9313 *Founded/Ownrshp* 1900
Sales 15.5MMᴱ *EMP* 280
SIC 8211 Public elementary school; Public junior high school; Public senior high school; Public elementary school; Public junior high school; Public senior high school
Ex Dir: Molly Johnson
IT Man: Clyde Cornelius
Schl Brd P: Gery Carlson

HERMEL CANDY COMPANY
See A H HERMEL CANDY & TOBACCO CO

D-U-N-S 09-844-6933 IMP/EXP
HERMES ABRASIVES LTD A LIMITED PARTNERSHIP
524 Viking Dr, Virginia Beach, VA 23452-7316
Tel (757) 431-6623 *Founded/Ownrshp* 1997
Sales 45.5MMᴱ *EMP* 220
SIC 3291 Coated abrasive products; Coated abrasive products
CEO: Jan Cord Becker
Pt: Ken Lamay
Pt: G Randall Stickley
Pt: Jerry Will
CFO: Johann Unterwieser
VP Mfg: Gary Predki
Natl Sales: Mike Harder
Manager: Frank Pipes
Manager: Mike Saben

D-U-N-S 05-790-3502
HERMES CO INC
HERMEY LANDSCAPING
13030 W 87th Street Pkwy # 100, Lenexa, KS 66215-4508
Tel (913) 888-2413 *Founded/Ownrshp* 1965
Sales 39.8MMᴱ *EMP* 150ᴱ
SIC 0782 1711 0181 Landscape contractors; Lawn services; Irrigation sprinkler system installation; Nursery stock, growing of
Pr: Dalton Hermes

D-U-N-S 05-812-9099 IMP
HERMES CONSOLIDATED LLC
WYOMING REFINING COMPANY
(*Suby of* BLACK ELK REFINING LLC) ★
1600 Broadway Ste 1550, Denver, CO 80202-4900
Tel (303) 894-9966 *Founded/Ownrshp* 2012
Sales 29.8MMᴱ *EMP* 120
SIC 2911 4612 Petroleum refining; Crude petroleum pipelines; Petroleum refining; Crude petroleum pipelines
CEO: Anthony Lewis
**Pr:* James Runyan
**CFO:* Terry Perardi
VP Sls: John Raber

D-U-N-S 78-250-8899 IMP
HERMES HOLDING U S INC
HERMES OF PARIS
(*Suby of* HERMES INTERNATIONAL)
55 E 59th St Frnt 2, New York, NY 10022-1197
Tel (212) 759-7585 *Founded/Ownrshp* 1990
Sales 72.2MMᴱ *EMP* 430
SIC 5611 5621 5136 5137 Clothing accessories: men's & boys'; Ready-to-wear apparel, women's; Men's & boys' clothing; Women's & children's clothing; Clothing accessories: men's & boys'; Ready-to-wear apparel, women's; Men's & boys' clothing; Women's & children's clothing
Treas: Grace Liu
VP Mktg: Mineaki Saito

D-U-N-S 78-372-2895
HERMES LANDSCAPING INC
(*Suby of* HERMES CO INC) ★
12421 Santa Fe Trail Dr, Shawnee Mission, KS 66215-3597
Tel (913) 888-2400 *Founded/Ownrshp* 1965
Sales 32.5MMᴱ *EMP* 100
SIC 0782

HERMES MUSIC DISTRIBUTING CO
See HERMES TRADING CO INC

HERMES OF PARIS
See HERMES HOLDING U S INC

D-U-N-S 05-880-1382
HERMES TRADING CO INC
HERMES MUSIC DISTRIBUTING CO
830 N Cage St Blvd, Pharr, TX 78577
Tel (956) 781-8472 *Founded/Ownrshp* 1983
Sales 21.6MMᴱ *EMP* 50
SIC 5099 5736 Musical instruments; Musical instruments parts & accessories; Musical instrument stores
CEO: Alberto Kreimerman
**Pr:* Jorge Saavedra
VP: Billy R Gaza
**VP:* Greg Morrison
Admn Mgr: Noe Billareal

D-U-N-S 61-759-7216
HERMETIC RUSH SERVICES INC
38 Old Highway 49 S, Flowood, MS 39232-4316
Tel (601) 932-7874 *Founded/Ownrshp* 1989
Sales 22.1MMᴱ *EMP* 70
SIC 1711 5078 Plumbing, heating, air-conditioning contractors; Commercial refrigeration equipment
Pr: Jimmy Jones
**Treas:* Lemuel Carpenter
**VP:* Charles W Rush
IT Man: Paula Hulsebosch
Sales Exec: David Paterson

D-U-N-S 03-718-5279
■ **HERMETIC SEAL CORP**
AMETEK HCC
(*Suby of* HCC INDUSTRIES INC) ★
4232 Temple City Blvd, Rosemead, CA 91770-1592
Tel (626) 443-8931 *Founded/Ownrshp* 1989
Sales 60.5MMᴱ *EMP* 548
SIC 3679 3469 Hermetic seals for electronic equipment; Metal stampings; Hermetic seals for electronic equipment; Metal stampings
Pr: Andrew Goldfarb
VP: Ronda Ross
CTO: Steve Horwitz
QA Dir: Alfred Enu-Kwesi
Ql Cn Mgr: Monica Gonzales
Sls Mgr: George McCormack

D-U-N-S 04-437-8263 EXP
HERMETIC SWITCH INC
HSI SENSING
3100 S Norge Rd, Chickasha, OK 73018-6169
Tel (405) 224-4046 *Founded/Ownrshp* 1968
Sales 52.1MMᴱ *EMP* 330ᴱ
SIC 3679 3823 3613 Switchgear & switchboard apparatus; Electronic switches; Industrial instrmnts msrmnt display/control process variable; Electronic switches; Industrial instrmnts msrmnt display/control process variable; Switchgear & switchboard apparatus
CEO: David Posey
**VP:* Ryan Posey
MIS Dir: Darrell White
Prd Mgr: Barbara Mandrell
Sls Mgr: Henry Dumas
Sls Mgr: Travis Graham

HERMEY LANDSCAPING
See HERMES CO INC

D-U-N-S 60-645-8479 IMP
HERMISTON FOODS INC
(*Suby of* NORPAC FOODS INC) ★
2250 S Highway 395, Hermiston, OR 97838-9466
Tel (541) 567-8448 *Founded/Ownrshp* 1988
Sales 228.8MMᴱ *EMP* 4,000
SIC 2037 Frozen fruits & vegetables; Vegetables, quick frozen & cold pack, excl. potato products; Potato products, quick frozen & cold pack; Frozen fruits & vegetables; Vegetables, quick frozen & cold pack, excl. potato products; Potato products, quick frozen & cold pack
Pr: Erik Jacobson
**VP:* George Smith
Ql Cn Mgr: Manuel Aviles

D-U-N-S 60-425-3356
HERMISTON GENERATING CO LP
(*Suby of* PERENNIAL HGC INC)
78145 Westland Rd, Hermiston, OR 97838-9520
Tel (541) 564-8320 *Founded/Ownrshp* 2004
Sales 22.5MMᴱ *EMP* 26
SIC 4911 Generation, electric power

D-U-N-S 15-935-8688
HERMISTON SCHOOL DISTRICT
305 Sw 11th St, Hermiston, OR 97838-1890
Tel (541) 667-6000 *Founded/Ownrshp* 1902
Sales 32.7MMᴱ *EMP* 487ᴱ
Accts Dickey And Temper Llp Pendle

SIC 8211 Public elementary school; Public junior high school; Public senior high school; Public elementary school; Public junior high school; Public senior high school
**Ch Bd:* Karen Sherman
Bd of Dir: Jason Middleton
Bd of Dir: Don Rankin
Bd of Dir: Dave Smith
**Prin:* Greg Harris
**Prin:* Ginny Holthus
Adm Dir: Sheri Marlow

HERMITAGE AT CEDAR FIELD
See VIRGINIA UNITED METHODIST HOMES INC

D-U-N-S 94-309-5687
HERMOSA BEACH CITY SCHOOL DISTRICT
1645 Valley Dr, Hermosa Beach, CA 90254-2921
Tel (310) 937-5877 *Founded/Ownrshp* 1950
Sales 12.1MM *EMP* 420
SIC 8211 Public elementary & secondary schools; Public elementary & secondary schools
**Pr:* Cathy McCurdy
Dir IT: Teri Tsosie

D-U-N-S 05-098-8013
HERNANDEZ BEEF & PROVISIONS INC
635 Henry St, Elizabeth, NJ 07201-2015
Tel (908) 352-8300 *Founded/Ownrshp* 1996
Sales 38.0MM *EMP* 18
SIC 5142 Meat, frozen: packaged; Poultry, frozen: packaged; Meat, frozen: packaged; Poultry, frozen: packaged
Pr: Oscar Hernandez

D-U-N-S 02-562-4321
■ HERNANDO HEALTHCARE INC (FL)
BROOKSVILLE REGIONAL HOSPITAL
(*Suby of* HEALTH MANAGEMENT ASSOCIATES INC) ★
17240 Cortez Blvd, Brooksville, FL 34601-8921
Tel (352) 796-5111 *Founded/Ownrshp* 1982
Sales 145.5MM *EMP* 131
SIC 8062 General medical & surgical hospitals; General medical & surgical hospitals
CEO: Kathy Burke
Chf OB: Imad Jandali
Chf Rad: Lana Bellon
Dir Recs: Linda Sanchez
Dir Inf Cn: Debbie Sonnier
Dir Lab: Asghar Shaikh
Dir Rad: Sheryl Clemente
Dir Rad: Amy Moore
CIO: Lee Burch
Ansthlgy: Christopher J Lombardi

D-U-N-S 03-645-0521
■ HERNANDO HMA INC
(*Suby of* HEALTH MANAGEMENT ASSOCIATES INC) ★
17240 Cortez Blvd, Brooksville, FL 34601-8921
Tel (352) 796-5111 *Founded/Ownrshp* 2005
Sales 161.1MM *EMP* 600
SIC 8062 General medical & surgical hospitals; General medical & surgical hospitals
CEO: Ken Wicker
**COO:* Bayode Omosaiye
**CFO:* Matthew Seagroves
Dir Rad: Amy Moore
**Ex Dir:* Thomas D Barb
Pathlgst: Loretta Augustine
Pathlgst: Meenakshi Malhotra
Doctor: Mowaffak Atfeh
Doctor: Adel Eldin
Doctor: Rajiva Goyal
Doctor: Jared Salinsky

D-U-N-S 18-965-2688
HERNANDO-PASCO HOSPICE INC
HPH HOSPICE
12107 Majestic Blvd, Port Richey, FL 34667-2455
Tel (727) 863-7971 *Founded/Ownrshp* 1982
Sales 44.3MM *EMP* 826
Accts Moore Stephens Lovelace Pa Cl
SIC 8082 Home health care services; Home health care services
Ex Dir: Rod Taylor
MIS Dir: Sissy Passarella
Mktg Mgr: Robin Kocher
Board of Directors: David McGrew

D-U-N-S 08-009-7712
HERNDON AEROSPACE & DEFENSE LLC
3801 Lloyd King Dr, O Fallon, MO 63368-2224
Tel (314) 739-7400 *Founded/Ownrshp* 2015
Sales 93.7MM^E *EMP* 145
SIC 5088 Aircraft & parts
Pr: Scott Herndon

D-U-N-S 05-950-9132
HERNDON CAPITAL MANAGEMENT LLC
191 Peachtree St Ne # 2500, Atlanta, GA 30303-1769
Tel (404) 582-9226 *Founded/Ownrshp* 2010
Sales 34.6MM *EMP* 36
Accts Dixon Hughes Goodman Llp Atl
SIC 6211 Security brokers & dealers; Security brokers & dealers
Pr: Drake Craig
Ofcr: Todd Campbell
Ofcr: Matthew Carney
Ofcr: Annette Marshall
Sr VP: Marc Sydnor
VP: Antoinette Scroggins
**Prin:* Randell A Cain Jr
**Prin:* Kenneth Holley
Netwrk Mgr: Shawn Ayton

D-U-N-S 04-564-1495
HERNDON CHEVROLET INC
5617 Sunset Blvd, Lexington, SC 29072-2727
Tel (803) 359-2504 *Founded/Ownrshp* 1968
Sales 51.6MM^E *EMP* 92
SIC 5511 Automobiles, new & used; Pickups, new & used; Automobiles, new & used; Pickups, new & used
Pr: David L Herndon
**Sec:* Carol H Perrin
Div Mgr: Larry King

Telecom Ex: Tripp Leonard
Sls Mgr: Larry Kalin

D-U-N-S 02-376-7312
HERNDON MOTOR CO INC
KOONS STERLING FORD
(*Suby of* JIM KOONS MANAGEMENT CO) ★
46869 Harry Byrd Hwy, Sterling, VA 20164-2250
Tel (800) 913-8648 *Founded/Ownrshp* 1986
Sales 40.0MM^E *EMP* 100
SIC 5511 Automobiles, new & used; Automobiles, new & used
Pr: James E Koons Jr
**Sec:* Cecilia Koons
Sls Mgr: James Morris

D-U-N-S 13-434-5169 IMP
HERNDON PRODUCTS LLC
HPI
(*Suby of* HERNDON AEROSPACE & DEFENSE LLC) ★
3801 Lloyd King Dr, O Fallon, MO 63368-2224
Tel (314) 739-7400 *Founded/Ownrshp* 2015
Sales 76.0MM *EMP* 120
SIC 5088 Aircraft & parts; Aircraft & parts
Pr: Scott Herndon
COO: Daniel Rodrigues
CFO: Gerry Modglin
Ex VP: Egon Poisl
Prgrm Mgr: Rachel Herndon
Prgrm Mgr: Paul Rice
CIO: Amy Sawvell
IT Man: Michelle Schilly
Opers Mgr: Rodney Vardiman
Ql Cn Mgr: Jeff Park

D-U-N-S 96-056-3489
HERO MEDIA LLC
343 S River St, Hackensack, NJ 07601-6838
Tel (201) 880-6435 *Founded/Ownrshp* 2008
Sales 28.0MM *EMP* 28
SIC 7311 7313 Advertising consultant; Electronic media advertising representatives
CEO: John Spitaletta
Creative D: Rafael Soberal

HERO NUTRITIONAL PRODUCTS
See HERO NUTRITIONALS LLC

D-U-N-S 94-770-4870
HERO NUTRITIONALS LLC
HERO NUTRITIONAL PRODUCTS
1900 Carnegie Ave Ste A, Santa Ana, CA 92705-5557
Tel (949) 498-2131 *Founded/Ownrshp* 1995
Sales 26.8MM^E *EMP* 40
SIC 5122 Vitamins & minerals
CEO: Jennifer Hodges
QA Dir: Ali Yazdchi
Natl Sales: Claire Polson
Sls Mgr: Jennifer Stone

D-U-N-S 03-983-4031
HEROES INC
UNITED VENDING & FOOD SERVICES
509 River Dr, North Sioux City, SD 57049-3008
Tel (402) 494-4166 *Founded/Ownrshp* 2001
Sales 50.2MM^E *EMP* 450
SIC 5962 5812 Food vending machines; Cafeteria; Food vending machines; Cafeteria
Pr: Cal Cathol
**Treas:* Joe Richter
**VP:* Scott Wilcox

D-U-N-S 96-818-9910
HEROLD PRECISION METALS LLC
1370 Hammond Rd, White Bear Township, MN 55110-5865
Tel (651) 490-5550 *Founded/Ownrshp* 1997
Sales 28.1MM^E *EMP* 73
SIC 3444 Sheet metalwork
Pr: Timothy Herold
CEO: Michael J Herold
CFO: Jayme Reinisch
VP: Robert Guertin
Opers Mgr: Nic Gianino
VP Sls: Larry A Freedmn

D-U-N-S 16-046-4017
HERON LAKE BIOENERGY LLC
(*Suby of* PROJECT VIKING LLC) ★
91246 390th Ave, Heron Lake, MN 56137-3175
Tel (507) 793-0077 *Founded/Ownrshp* 2013
Sales 149.4MM *EMP* 37
Accts Boulay Pllp Minneapolis Minn
SIC 1321 2869 Ethane (natural) production; Ethyl alcohol, ethanol
CEO: Steve Christensen
**Ch Bd:* Paul Enstad
CFO: Stacie Schuler
**V Ch Bd:* Rodney R Wilkison
Plnt Mgr: Brodie McKeown
Advt Mgr: Kim Henrickson
Board of Directors: Leslie Bergquist, Dean Buesing, Robert Ferguson, Kenton Johnson, Michael Kunerth, Milton McKeown, Doug Schmitz, Marty Seifert, David Woestehoff

D-U-N-S 10-209-9843
▲ HERON THERAPEUTICS INC
123 Saginaw Dr, Redwood City, CA 94063-4717
Tel (650) 366-2626 *Founded/Ownrshp* 2001
Sales 24.0MM^E *EMP* 59
Tkr Sym HRTX *Exch* NAS
SIC 2834 Pharmaceutical preparations
CEO: Barry D Quart
**Ch Bd:* Kevin C Tang
**Pr:* Robert H Rosen
CFO: Brian G Drazba
Ofcr: Neil J Clendeninn
Sr VP: Paul H Barone
VP: Yvette Payne
VP: Anastassios D Retzios
VP: Esme C Smith
VP Bus Dev: Jayne M Lange
VP Bus: Thomas Pitler
Board of Directors: Stephen R Davis, Craig A Johnson, Kimberly J Manhard, John W Poyhonen

D-U-N-S 01-429-1009
HERR & SACCO INC
1831 Auction Rd, Manheim, PA 17545-9165
Tel (717) 898-0111 *Founded/Ownrshp* 1986
Sales 34.6MM^E *EMP* 105
SIC 1711 3443

HERR ADULT MEDICAL DAY CENTER
See DAUGHTERS OF ISRAEL GERIATRICS CENTER (INC)

D-U-N-S 00-237-8784 EXP
HERR FOODS INC (PA)
20 Herr Dr, Nottingham, PA 19362-9788
Tel (610) 932-9330 *Founded/Ownrshp* 1946
Sales 507.1MM^E *EMP* 1,500
SIC 2096 Potato chips & similar snacks; Potato chips & other potato-based snacks; Potato chips & similar snacks; Potato chips & other potato-based snacks
Ch Bd: James M Herr
**Pr:* Edwin Herr
**CFO:* Gerry Kluis
Sr VP: Randy Longo
VP: Rick Dolan
VP: Jim Rock
Brnch Mgr: Jeff Dietz
Brnch Mgr: Patrick Sifer
Dir IT: Steve Eldreth
Netwrk Mgr: Kelli Strohmaier
Prd Mgr: Mark Broomell

D-U-N-S 78-808-4973
HERR HOLDINGS - CFI INC
COUNTRY FRESH
15479 Pin Oak Dr, Conroe, TX 77384-3549
Tel (281) 443-8300 *Founded/Ownrshp* 1999
Sales 25.0MM *EMP* 200
SIC 6799 Investors; Investors
Pr: Bryan Herr
Off Mgr: Laura Cardenas
Sales Exec: Bob Hill
VP Mktg: Robert Burris

D-U-N-S 07-913-6883
HERR PETROLEUM CORP (IL)
1693 State Highway 164, Galesburg, IL 61401-8548
Tel (309) 245-2586 *Founded/Ownrshp* 1964
Sales 34.4MM^E *EMP* 100
SIC 5172 5411 5541

D-U-N-S 02-290-2647 IMP
HERREGAN DISTRIBUTORS INC
3695 Kennebec Dr, Saint Paul, MN 55122-1002
Tel (651) 452-7200 *Founded/Ownrshp* 1966
Sales 47.8MM^E *EMP* 150
SIC 5023 Floor coverings; Carpets; Resilient floor coverings: tile or sheet; Floor coverings; Carpets; Resilient floor coverings: tile or sheet
CEO: Kenneth L Herriges
**Pr:* Robert Link
**VP:* Thomas Splinter
IT Man: Jim Burns
VP Sls: Pat Theis
Sls Mgr: Dave Artz
Sls Mgr: Pat Hill
Sls Mgr: Dave Keeley
Sls Mgr: Jeff Peters
Sls Mgr: Rick Theilig

D-U-N-S 15-462-7434
HERRERA ENVIRONMENTAL CONSULTANTS INC
2200 6th Ave Ste 1100, Seattle, WA 98121-1867
Tel (206) 441-9080 *Founded/Ownrshp* 1986
Sales 20.7MM^E *EMP* 90
SIC 8711 8748 Consulting engineer; Environmental consultant
Pr: Michael Spillane
**CFO:* Theresa Wood
**Treas:* Carlos Herrera
**VP:* Carol Slaughterbeck

D-U-N-S 79-150-5253
HERRERA PETROLEUM CORP
5209 Nw 74th Ave Ste 279, Miami, FL 33166-4800
Tel (786) 267-5467 *Founded/Ownrshp* 2006
Sales 71.8MM^E *EMP* 3,000
SIC 5983 Fuel oil dealers; Fuel oil dealers
Pr: Raul Herrera
**CEO:* Rafael Herrera
**Ofcr:* Edwin Cardona
**VP:* Victor Nasim

D-U-N-S 02-919-8025 IMP
HERRERO BUILDERS INC
2100 Oakdale Ave, San Francisco, CA 94124-1516
Tel (415) 824-7675 *Founded/Ownrshp* 1955
Sales 76.4MM^E *EMP* 130
SIC 1541 Industrial buildings, new construction; Industrial buildings, new construction
Ch Bd: Mark D Herrero
**Pr:* Rick Herrero
CFO: James Totoritis
Ofcr: Stephanie Roberson
Exec: Frank Luttringer
IT Man: John Garcia
Opers Mgr: Kathleen Carroll
Opers Mgr: Robert Purcell
Sales Exec: Sonia Menjivar
Snr Mgr: Alyce AP

D-U-N-S 00-913-7126 IMP
HERRICK CORP
STOCKTON STEEL DIVISION
3003 E Hammer Ln, Stockton, CA 95212-2801
Tel (209) 956-4751 *Founded/Ownrshp* 1988
Sales 311.1MM^E *EMP* 900
SIC 3441 Fabricated structural metal; Fabricated structural metal
CEO: David H Dornsife
**Pr:* Doug Griffin
**CFO:* Peter Abila
VP: Robert Hazleton
QA Dir: Jose Garcia
IT Man: Patrick Lynch
Snr PM: Lee Becker
Snr Mgr: Jim Dayton

D-U-N-S 07-526-4895
HERRICK FEINSTEIN LLP
2 Park Ave Fl 20, New York, NY 10016-9302
Tel (212) 592-1400 *Founded/Ownrshp* 1928
Sales 47.0MM^E *EMP* 329^E
SIC 8111 General practice attorney, lawyer; General practice attorney, lawyer
Pt: George J Wolf Jr
Pt: Harvey Feuerstein
Pt: David L Fox
Pt: Lawrence Kaye
Pt: Irwin Kishner
Pt: Mark Manewitz
Pt: Christoper Sullivan
Pt: Dan Swick
Bd of Dir: Chad Perlov
Mng Dir: George Wolf
Genl Mgr: Andrew Hecker

HERRICK MEDICAL CENTER
See HERRICK MEMORIAL HOSPITAL INC

D-U-N-S 80-305-6571
HERRICK MEMORIAL HOSPITAL INC
HERRICK MEDICAL CENTER
(*Suby of* PROMEDICA NORTH REGION INC) ★
500 E Pottawatamie St, Tecumseh, MI 49286-2018
Tel (517) 424-3000 *Founded/Ownrshp* 1992
Sales 35.2MM *EMP* 403
Accts Deloitte Tax Llp Indianapolis
SIC 8062 General medical & surgical hospitals; General medical & surgical hospitals
Pr: Greg Corbett
Chf Path: Morhinder Chadha
Ofcr: Pamela Piper
Assoc VP: Matt Hammond
VP: Kathy Greenlee
VP: Ricardo King
Dir Lab: Joan Summers
Dir Lab: Mary Wortman
Dir Rad: Tom Zelenak
Dir Rx: Jean Osborn
Dir Rx: Jean Osbourn

HERRICKS PUBLIC SCHOOLS
See HERRICKS UNION FREE SCHOOL DISTRICT

D-U-N-S 03-815-9836
HERRICKS UNION FREE SCHOOL DISTRICT
HERRICKS PUBLIC SCHOOLS
999 Herricks Rd Ste B, New Hyde Park, NY 11040-1353
Tel (516) 305-8903 *Founded/Ownrshp* 1898
Sales 138.7M^E *EMP* 373
SIC 8211 Public elementary & secondary schools; Public elementary & secondary schools
VP: Christine Turner

HERRIN-GEAR BMW
See HERRIN-GEAR CHEVROLET CO INC

D-U-N-S 04-575-1674
HERRIN-GEAR CHEVROLET CO INC
HERRIN-GEAR BMW
1685 High St, Jackson, MS 39202-3522
Tel (601) 354-2269 *Founded/Ownrshp* 1968
Sales 59.8MM^E *EMP* 150
SIC 5511 Automobiles, new & used; Automobiles, new & used
Pr: Jack T Herrin
**Sec:* Clifford C Davis III
**VP:* Dorothy Gear
**VP:* Nancy Herrin
**VP:* Holley H Noblitt
Sls Mgr: Adrian Blackwell
Sls Mgr: Larry Kemp

D-U-N-S 08-982-9600
HERRIN-GEAR INC
HALLMARK TOYOTA-BMW-KIA
6100 I 55 N, Jackson, MS 39211-2642
Tel (601) 956-9696 *Founded/Ownrshp* 2001
Sales 38.2MM^E *EMP* 105
SIC 5511 7538 5521 Automobiles, new & used; General automotive repair shops; Used car dealers; Automobiles, new & used; General automotive repair shops; Used car dealers
Pr: Carl Herrin
Sec: Cliff Davis
VP: Jack Herrin
Off Mgr: Neese Mona

D-U-N-S 78-582-9271
HERRING BANCORP
2201 Civic Cir Ste 1001, Amarillo, TX 79109-1853
Tel (806) 355-0153 *Founded/Ownrshp* 2006
Sales NA *EMP* 184^E
SIC 6029 Commercial banks
Prin: Jane Burgess

D-U-N-S 00-793-7634
HERRING BANK
(*Suby of* HERRING BANCORP) ★
2201 Civic Cir, Amarillo, TX 79109-1817
Tel (806) 677-7000 *Founded/Ownrshp* 1899
Sales NA *EMP* 150
SIC 6021 National commercial banks; National commercial banks
CEO: C Cmpbell Burgess
**Pr:* Bobby Crews
COO: John Cerny
Ex VP: Dave Riggs
Sr VP: Mark Arnold
**VP:* Rick Graf
VP: Carol Montgomery
IT Man: Aaron Baldauf
Snr Mgr: Shawndra Rutledge

D-U-N-S 00-885-2691
HERRING GAS CO INC OF LOUISIANA (MS)
33 Main St E, Meadville, MS 39653-9294
Tel (601) 384-5833 *Founded/Ownrshp* 1946
Sales 40.0MM *EMP* 175
Accts Breazeale Saunders & O Neil
SIC 5984 Propane gas, bottled; Propane gas, bottled
Ch Bd: Edward G Herring
**Pr:* Joseph E Herring
**CEO:* Robert Kimbrough
**Sec:* Dennis Walker
VP: Tommy Smallwood

HERRINGTON'S
See ED HERRINGTON INC

HERITAGE BANK OF COMMERCE
See HERITAGE BANK OF COMMERCE

D-U-N-S 05-121-5879
HERRMAN & GOETZ INC
H&G SERVICES
225 S Lafayette Blvd, South Bend, IN 46601-2109
Tel (574) 282-2596 *Founded/Ownrshp* 1968
Sales 71.9MM^E *EMP* 350
SIC 1711 1731 1623 7623 7629 Mechanical contractor; Warm air heating & air conditioning contractor; Plumbing contractors; Refrigeration contractor; General electrical contractor; Electronic controls installation; Computer installation; Communications specialization; Water, sewer & utility lines; Underground utilities contractor; Refrigeration service & repair; Generator repair; Mechanical contractor; Warm air heating & air conditioning contractor; Plumbing contractors; Refrigeration contractor; General electrical contractor; Electronic controls installation; Computer installation; Communications specialization; Water, sewer & utility lines; Underground utilities contractor; Refrigeration service & repair; Generator repair
Pr: Thomas J Herrman
VP: Kathy Herrman
Genl Mgr: Randy Ciesiolka
Off Mgr: Jennifer Williamson
CIO: Chris Long
IT Man: Harold Addington

D-U-N-S 18-370-5599
HERRMAN LUMBER CO INC
1917 S State Highway Mm, Springfield, MO 65802-7789
Tel (417) 862-3737 *Founded/Ownrshp* 1917
Sales 34.9MM^E *EMP* 215
SIC 5211

D-U-N-S 08-206-9170 IMP
HERRSCHNERS INC
2800 Hoover Rd, Stevens Point, WI 54481-7103
Tel (715) 342-0741 *Founded/Ownrshp* 1993
Sales 33.0MM^E *EMP* 250
SIC 5949 5961 Sewing, needlework & piece goods; Mail order house; Sewing, needlework & piece goods; Mail order house
Pr: Theodore Hesemann
**VP:* John Gritzmacher
VP: Maureen Ruth
VP: David Verhage
Exec: Jeff Wenndorf
Merch Mgr: Shannon Piotrowski

D-U-N-S 00-118-4613
HERSAM PUBLISHING CO
DARIEN TIMES
42 Vitti St, New Canaan, CT 06840-4823
Tel (203) 966-9541 *Founded/Ownrshp* 1986
Sales 11.0MM^E *EMP* 300
SIC 2711 2741 Newspapers, publishing & printing; Miscellaneous publishing; Newspapers, publishing & printing; Miscellaneous publishing
CEO: Martin Hersam
**Pr:* Donald V Hersam Jr

D-U-N-S 02-970-0283
HERSCHEND ENTERTAINMENT CO LLC
SILVER DOLLAR CITY
5445 Triangle Pkwy # 200, Norcross, GA 30092-2584
Tel (770) 441-1940 *Founded/Ownrshp* 1950
Sales 194.4MM^E *EMP* 2,500
Accts Bkd Llp Springfield Mo
SIC 7999 5947 5812 Tourist attraction, commercial; Cave operation; Gift shop; Novelties; Eating places; Tourist attraction, commercial; Cave operation; Gift shop; Novelties; Eating places
Pr: Joel Manby
V Ch: Chris Herschend
**CFO:* Andrew Wexler
**Ch:* Jack Herschend
VP: Gayle Barkley
VP: John Carson
VP: Anthony Esparza
VP: Jonathan Karron
VP: Kevin Keppel
VP: Ned Stancliff
VP: Brad Thomas
VP: Sara Vanpelt
Exec: Angie Parker
Dir: Eric Lent

D-U-N-S 61-222-4795
HERSCHEND FAMILY ENTERTAINMENT CORP
(*Suby of* HERSCHEND ENTERTAINMENT CO LLC) ★
399 Silver Dollar Cy Pkwy, Branson, MO 65616-6151
Tel (417) 336-5400?

Tel (770) 441-1940 *Founded/Ownrshp* 1962
Sales 95.2MM^E *EMP* 2,500
SIC 7996 Amusement parks; Amusement parks
Pr: Pete Herschend
Bd of Dir: Sandy Wilkinson
**VP:* Jack Herschend
IT Man: Danny Callison
Opers Mgr: Jon Williams
Merch Mgr: Jamie Maloney

D-U-N-S 07-914-2646
HERSCHER COMMUNITY UNIT SCHOOL
501 N Main St, Herscher, IL 60941-9595
Tel (815) 426-2162 *Founded/Ownrshp* 2013
Sales 8.1MM^E *EMP* 400
SIC 8211 Elementary & secondary schools
Bd of Dir: David Emling

D-U-N-S 07-143-7560
HERSCHER SCHOOL DISTRICT 2
501 N Main St, Herscher, IL 60941-9595
Tel (815) 426-2162 *Founded/Ownrshp* 1949
Sales 37.5MM^E *EMP* 1,020
SIC 8211 Public elementary school; Public junior high school; Public senior high school; School board; Public elementary school; Public junior high school; Public senior high school; School board
Pr: Marcie Kolberg

D-U-N-S 09-225-8099
HERSHA HOSPITALITY MANAGEMENT LP
44 Hersha Dr, Harrisburg, PA 17102-2241
Tel (717) 236-4400 *Founded/Ownrshp* 1998
Sales 181.9MM^E *EMP* 1,600
SIC 7011 Hotels & motels; Hotels & motels
Pt: Jay H Shah
Pt: David Desfor
Pt: Kanti D Patel
Pt: Thomas D Reese
Pt: Hasu Shah
COO: Michael Murray
COO: Neil H Shah
CFO: Ashish Parikh
Ex VP: Gregory Ade
Ex VP: Sal Shahriar
Sr VP: Simon J Little
Sr VP: Simon Little
VP: Foiz Ahmed
VP: Stephanie Esposito
VP: Robert C Hazard III

D-U-N-S 02-382-8945
HERSHA HOSPITALITY TRUST
44 Hersha Dr, Harrisburg, PA 17102-2241
Tel (717) 236-4400 *Founded/Ownrshp* 1998
Sales 417.4MM *EMP* 48^E
Accts Kpmg Llp Philadelphia Penns
SIC 6798 Real estate investment trusts; Real estate investment trusts
CEO: Jay H Shah
**Ch Bd:* Hasu P Shah
Pr: Neil H Shah
CFO: Ashish R Paikh
CFO: Ashish R Parikh
CFO: Ashish Parikh
Treas: David L Desfor
Trst: Michael Leven
Trst: John Sabin
Ex VP: Naveen Kakarla
Sr VP: Dani Elhachem
Sr VP: Dianna F Morgan
VP: Wayne Carney
VP: Christopher Doyle
VP: Kimberly Furlong
VP: Jay Linsey
VP: Bennett Thomas
VP: William J Walsh
Board of Directors: Thomas J Hutchison III, Donald J Landry, Michael A Leven, Dianna F Morgan, John M Sabin

D-U-N-S 00-300-2052 EXP
▲ HERSHEY CO
100 Crystal A Dr, Hershey, PA 17033-9524
Tel (717) 534-4200 *Founded/Ownrshp* 1894
Sales 7.4MMM *EMP* 22,450
Accts Kpmg Llp New York New York
Tkr Sym HSY *Exch* NYS
SIC 2066 2064 2099 Chocolate & cocoa products; Chocolate bars, solid; Chocolate candy, solid; Chocolate coatings & syrup; Candy & other confectionery products; Candy bars, including chocolate covered bars; Chocolate candy, except solid chocolate; Licorice candy; Baking powder & soda, yeast & other leavening agents; Dessert mixes & fillings; Chocolate & cocoa products; Chocolate bars, solid; Chocolate candy, solid; Chocolate coatings & syrup; Candy & other confectionery products; Candy bars, including chocolate covered bars; Chocolate candy, except solid chocolate; Licorice candy; Baking powder & soda, yeast & other leavening agents; Dessert mixes & fillings
Ch Bd: John P Bilbrey
Pr: Humberto P Alfonso
Pr: Chris Baldwin
Pr: Ted Jastrzebski
**CFO:* Patricia A Little
CFO: Robert J Mazzoni
Treas: Frank Cerminara
Sr Cor Off: Robert Steinberg
Ex VP: C Anderson
Ex VP: Bryan Crittenden
Ex VP: James Edris
Ex VP: Michael Pasquale
Sr VP: Raymond Brace
Sr VP: Michele G Buck
Sr VP: Michele Buck
Sr VP: Thomas Hernquist
Sr VP: Javier H Idrovo
**Sr VP:* Terence L O'Day
**Sr VP:* Leslie M Turner
**Sr VP:* D Michael Wege
Exec: Kathy Gibson
Board of Directors: David L Shedlarz, Pamela M Arway, Robert F Cavanaugh, Charles A Davis, Mary Kay Haben, Robert M Malcolm, James M Mead, James Nevels, Anthony J Palmer, Thomas J Ridge

D-U-N-S 00-301-0022
HERSHEY CREAMERY CO
HERSHEY'S ICE CREAM
301 S Cameron St, Harrisburg, PA 17101-2815
Tel (717) 238-8134 *Founded/Ownrshp* 1894, 1927
Sales 162.3MM^E *EMP* 450
SIC 2024 Ice cream & ice milk; Sherbets, dairy based; Ice cream & ice milk; Sherbets, dairy based
Pr: George H Holder
**Treas:* Thomas Holder
VP: Joe Gostomski
**VP:* Walter Holder
VP: Neil Patrick
**VP:* Thomas J Ryan III
Area Mgr: Eric Chamberlain
Area Mgr: Jim McElheny
Area Mgr: Kevin Mullen
Brnch Mgr: Chuck McStay
Brnch Mgr: David Tracy

D-U-N-S 00-791-1571
HERSHEY ENTERTAINMENT & RESORTS CO (PA)
HERSHEY LODGE & CONVENTION CTR
100 Hotel Rd, Hershey, PA 17033-9507
Tel (717) 534-3131 *Founded/Ownrshp* 1893, 1927
Sales 503.0MM^E *EMP* 7,100
SIC 7011 7996 Hotels; Amusement parks; Hotels; Amusement parks
Pr: W R Simpson
**Treas:* Wendy L McClintock
**VP:* Nate Douty
**VP:* David P Lavery
VP: John Lawn
**VP:* Franklin A Miles Jr
**VP:* James Miles
**VP:* Kimberly Schaller
**VP:* William F Simpson Jr
Exec: Ken Gladysz
Dir Risk M: Kim Zeiders

D-U-N-S 05-050-9603 IMP
HERSHEY EQUIPMENT CO INC
255 Plane Tree Dr, Lancaster, PA 17603-4085
Tel (717) 393-5807 *Founded/Ownrshp* 1974
Sales 70.3MM^E *EMP* 100
SIC 5083 5191 Poultry equipment; Livestock equipment; Farm supplies; Poultry equipment; Livestock equipment; Farm supplies
Pr: Donald C Hershey
**Treas:* Michael Dickson
**VP:* Doreen Dickson
VP: Christopher Hann

HERSHEY LODGE & CONVENTION CTR
See HERSHEY ENTERTAINMENT & RESORTS CO

HERSHEY'S ICE CREAM
See HERSHEY CREAMERY CO

D-U-N-S 01-570-5564
HERSHMAN CAPITAL CORP
45 Ne Industrial Rd, Branford, CT 06405-6801
Tel (203) 315-3100 *Founded/Ownrshp* 1986
Sales 121.0MM *EMP* 10^E
Accts Dworken Hillman Lamorth & St
SIC 5093 5113 Waste paper; Cardboard & products; Waste paper; Cardboard & products
Pr: Ethan J Hershman
**CFO:* Todd R Laggis
**VP:* David Ward

D-U-N-S 00-302-7844
HERSHOCKS INC (PA)
3501 N 6th St, Harrisburg, PA 17110-1425
Tel (717) 238-7331 *Founded/Ownrshp* 1935
Sales 43.6MM^E *EMP* 150
SIC 1793 5039 1751 Glass & glazing work; Store fixture installation; Window & door (prefabricated) installation; Glass construction materials; Glass & glazing work; Glass construction materials; Store fixture installation; Window & door (prefabricated) installation
Pr: Barry Deaven
**Treas:* Dwayne D Weaver
**VP:* Ronald L Candioto Jr
VP: Timothy Emig
Sls Mgr: Tom Bowman

HERSON'S HONDA
See HERSONS INC

D-U-N-S 02-424-5300
HERSONS INC (MD)
HERSON'S HONDA
15525 Frederick Rd, Rockville, MD 20855-2110
Tel (855) 513-2909 *Founded/Ownrshp* 1945, 1952
Sales 43.6MM^E *EMP* 125
SIC 5511 7538 7532 Automobiles, new & used; General automotive repair shops; Top & body repair & paint shops; Automobiles, new & used; General automotive repair shops; Top & body repair & paint shops
Pr: Gerald Herson
Pr: Vicki Poponi
**Sec:* Lorita Mendelson
Ex VP: John Mendel
**VP:* Lewis B Cohn
Sls Mgr: C J Tashman

D-U-N-S 55-707-2824
HERTCO INC
HERTRICH NISSAN-JEEP-EAGLE
1378 S Dupont Hwy, Dover, DE 19901-4404
Tel (302) 678-4553 *Founded/Ownrshp* 1990
Sales 20.8MM^E *EMP* 50
SIC 5511 Automobiles, new & used
Pr: Frederick Hertrich III
Genl Mgr: Len Simon
Off Mgr: Debbie Quinn

HERTFORD COUNTY INDUS DEV COMM
See COUNTY OF HERTFORD

HERTRICH NISSAN-JEEP-EAGLE
See HERTCO INC

HERTZ
See CARCO CARRIAGE CORP

HERTZ
See OVERLAND WEST INC

D-U-N-S 10-113-8733
■ HERTZ CLAIM MANAGEMENT CORP
(*Suby of* HERTZ CORP) ★
225 Brae Blvd, Park Ridge, NJ 07656-1870
Tel (201) 307-2000 *Founded/Ownrshp* 1981
Sales 18.0MM^E *EMP* 300
SIC 7514 Rent-a-car service; Rent-a-car service
VP: Vincent Moffa
Ex VP: Howard Rezak
VP: William Gavin
VP: Thomas A Sabella
MIS Dir: Larry Jorden
Board of Directors: Leo Massad Jr, Paul Tschirhart

D-U-N-S 00-698-5196 EXP
■ HERTZ CORP
(*Suby of* HERTZ INVESTORS INC) ★
8501 Williams Rd, Estero, FL 33928-3325
Tel (239) 301-7000 *Founded/Ownrshp* 1918, 2005
Sales 11.0MMM *EMP* 33,000
SIC 7514 7515 7513 7359 5521 6794 Rent-a-car service; Passenger car leasing; Truck rental, without drivers; Truck leasing, without drivers; Equipment rental & leasing; Automobiles, used cars only; Trucks, tractors & trailers: used; Franchises, selling or licensing; Rent-a-car service; Passenger car leasing; Truck rental, without drivers; Truck leasing, without drivers; Equipment rental & leasing; Automobiles, used cars only; Trucks, tractors & trailers: used; Franchises, selling or licensing
Pr: John P Tague
CFO: Elyse B Douglas
CFO: Thomas C Kennedy
Ofcr: Heather Hartman
Ofcr: Annette Mailhiot
Ofcr: Ryan McNichol
Ofcr: Priscilla Wood
Ex VP: Tyler A Best
Ex VP: John A Thomas
Sr VP: Robert J Bailey
Sr VP: Robin C Kramer
Sr VP: Dave Myrick
Sr VP: Harold E Rolfe
Sr VP: Donald F Steele
VP: Tony Bedalov
VP: Stuart Benzal
VP: Frank E Camacho
Exec: Jeffrey T Foland
Exec: Thomas Sabatino
Board of Directors: Carl T Berquist, Michael J Durham, Carolyn Everson, Vincent J Intrieri, Henry R Keizer, Michael F Koehler, Linda Fayne Levinson, Samuel Merksamer, Daniel A Ninivaggi

HERTZ ENTERTAINMENT SERVICES
See 24/7 STUDIO EQUIPMENT INC

D-U-N-S 00-556-9314 EXP
■ HERTZ EQUIPMENT RENTAL CORP
(*Suby of* HERTZ CORP) ★
27500 Rverview Ctr Bldg 7, Bonita Springs, FL 34134
Tel (239) 301-1001 *Founded/Ownrshp* 2011
Sales 1.0MMM^E *EMP* 6,166
SIC 7514 7515 7359 6794 Rent-a-car service; Passenger car leasing; Equipment rental & leasing; Patent owners & lessors; Rent-a-car service; Passenger car leasing; Equipment rental & leasing; Patent owners & lessors
Pr: Lawrence H Silber
**COO:* Bruce Dressel
CFO: Bob Goffredo
**CFO:* Paul J Siracusa
Ex VP: Brian Kennedy
VP: Carlo Cavecchi
VP: Andrew Lacko
Brnch Mgr: Jon Fisher
Brnch Mgr: Barry Roth
Genl Mgr: Don Yeoman
**CIO:* Richard Marani

D-U-N-S 02-805-3858
■ HERTZ EQUIPMENT RENTAL CORP
(*Suby of* HERTZ CORP) ★
5500 Commerce Blvd, Rohnert Park, CA 94928-1607
Tel (707) 586-4444 *Founded/Ownrshp* 1998
Sales 33.3MM^E *EMP* 550
SIC 7514 7359 Rent-a-car service; Stores & yards equipment rental; Tool rental; Party supplies rental services; Rent-a-car service; Stores & yards equipment rental; Tool rental; Party supplies rental services
Rgnl Mgr: Mark Hobson
Genl Mgr: Michael Tischbern
Sls Mgr: Ron Neuerburg

D-U-N-S 06-520-6930
HERTZ FARM MANAGEMENT INC
415 S 11th St, Nevada, IA 50201-3004
Tel (515) 382-1500 *Founded/Ownrshp* 1946
Sales 28.0MM^E *EMP* 112
SIC 0762 6531 Farm management services; Real estate brokers & agents
Pr: Loyd Brown
**Ch:* Joel R Hertz
**Treas:* Thomas A Hertz
**VP:* Randall V Hertz
**VP:* William J Holstine
**VP:* David R Jacobsen
**VP:* Sterling C Young

D-U-N-S 04-157-2553 EXP
HERTZ FURNITURE SYSTEMS LLC
170 Williams Dr, Ramsey, NJ 07446-2907
Tel (201) 529-2100 *Founded/Ownrshp* 2001
Sales 40.0MM *EMP* 10
SIC 5021

D-U-N-S 61-488-6062
▲ HERTZ GLOBAL HOLDINGS INC
999 Vanderbilt Beach Rd # 3, Naples, FL 34108-3508
Tel (239) 552-5800 *Founded/Ownrshp* 1918
Sales 11.0MMM *EMP* 33,000
Tkr Sym HTZ *Exch* NYS
SIC 7514 7515 7513 7359 5521 6794 Rent-a-car service; Passenger car leasing; Truck rental, without drivers; Truck leasing, without drivers; Equipment rental & leasing; Automobiles, used cars only; Trucks, tractors & trailers: used; Franchises, selling or licensing; Rent-a-car service; Passenger car leasing; Truck rental, without drivers; Truck leasing, without drivers; Equipment rental & leasing; Automobiles, used cars only; Trucks, tractors & trailers: used; Franchises, selling or licensing
Pr: John P Tague
CFO: Barbara Brasier
CFO: Thomas C Kennedy
Ofcr: Jeffrey Foland
Ex VP: Tyler A Best
Ex VP: Elyse Douglas
Ex VP: Bill Louttit
Ex VP: Alexandria Marren
Ex VP: Alexandria P Marren
Ex VP: Todd Poste
Ex VP: Robert J Stuart
Ex VP: Eliana Zem
Sr VP: Daniel Flynn
Sr VP: Thomas Frese
Sr VP: Dewayne Kirkham
Sr VP: Robin C Kramer
Sr VP: Lois I Boyd

Sr VP: Jim Mueller
Sr VP: Charles L Shafer
Sr VP: Maryann Waryjas
VP: Robert W Davis

D-U-N-S 00-698-5188 IMP
■ HERTZ INTERNATIONAL LTD
(*Suby of* HERTZ CORP) ★
225 Brae Blvd, Park Ridge, NJ 07656-1870
Tel (201) 307-2000 *Founded/Ownrshp* 1957, 1987
Sales 372.3MM^E *EMP* 5,470
SIC 7514 7515 7513 Rent-a-car service; Passenger car leasing; Truck rental, without drivers; Truck leasing, without drivers; Rent-a-car service; Passenger car leasing; Truck rental, without drivers; Truck leasing, without drivers
CEO: John Pague
**Pr:* Craig Kroch
**Treas:* Robert Rillings
**VP:* William Sider
Area Mgr: Roger Columbo
Area Mgr: Jordan Echard
Area Mgr: Chand Soni
Brnch Mgr: Carrie Barber
Brnch Mgr: Bert Bertrand
Brnch Mgr: Roxanne Brown
Brnch Mgr: Ceven Goodman

D-U-N-S 78-319-3639
■ HERTZ INVESTORS INC
(*Suby of* HERTZ GLOBAL HOLDINGS INC) ★
225 Brae Blvd, Park Ridge, NJ 07656-1870
Tel (201) 307-2000 *Founded/Ownrshp* 2005
Sales NA *EMP* 33,000
SIC 7514 7515 7513 7359 5521 6794 Rent-a-car service; Passenger car leasing; Truck rental, without drivers; Truck leasing, without drivers; Equipment rental & leasing; Automobiles, used cars only; Trucks, tractors & trailers: used; Franchises, selling or licensing; Rent-a-car service; Passenger car leasing; Truck rental, without drivers; Truck leasing, without drivers; Equipment rental & leasing; Automobiles, used cars only; Trucks, tractors & trailers: used; Franchises, selling or licensing
Prin: George Tamke

D-U-N-S 17-602-2929
■ HERTZ LOCAL EDITION CORP
(*Suby of* HERTZ CORP) ★
225 Brae Blvd, Park Ridge, NJ 07656-1870
Tel (201) 307-2000 *Founded/Ownrshp* 1980
Sales 147.9MM^E *EMP* 2,744^E
SIC 7514 Rent-a-car service
Prin: Kherri Gomez
Area Mgr: Carrie Tavares
Brnch Mgr: Maritza Guerra

D-U-N-S 78-157-7028 IMP
■ HERTZ TECHNOLOGIES INC
WARR ACRES
(*Suby of* HERTZ CORP) ★
5601 Nw Expressway, Warr Acres, OK 73132-5232
Tel (405) 721-6440 *Founded/Ownrshp* 1991
Sales 87.0MM^E *EMP* 1,009
SIC 7514 Rent-a-car service; Rent-a-car service
Pr: Gary Orrell
Treas: Robert H Rillings
Ex VP: Mark Holzwart
Netwrk Eng: Patrick Woidke
Opers Mgr: Lance Highfill

D-U-N-S 00-522-8721
HERTZBERG-NEW METHOD INC (IL)
PERMA-BOUND
617 E Vandalia Rd, South Jacksonville, IL 62650-3544
Tel (217) 243-5451 *Founded/Ownrshp* 1954
Sales 288.6MM^E *EMP* 600
SIC 5192 Books; Books
Pr: James Q Orr
**Sec:* Todd Young
CIO: Steve Henson
Natl Sales: Dan Coakley
Mktg Dir: Brett Hoffman
Manager: David Bannister
Sls Mgr: Ken Moldow
Sls Mgr: William White
Sales Asso: Kathy Pratt

D-U-N-S 07-521-1300
HERZFELD & RUBIN P C
125 Broad St Fl 12, New York, NY 10004-2423
Tel (212) 471-8500 *Founded/Ownrshp* 1971
Sales 22.9MM^E *EMP* 200
SIC 8111

D-U-N-S 02-338-2260
HERZING UNIVERSITY LTD
AKRON INSTITUTE HERZING UNIV
W140n8917 Lilly Rd, Menomonee Falls, WI 53051-2325
Tel (414) 271-8103 *Founded/Ownrshp* 1965
Sales 65.9MM^E *EMP* 475
SIC 8221 Colleges & universities; Colleges & universities
**Pr:* Renee Herzing
Pr: Susan Kalmuck
VP: Rene Burkard
VP: Frank Cianciaruso
VP: Elainna Guerrette
CIO: Mladen Grgic
Dir IT: Justin Shagam
IT Man: Jeffrey Grieger
HC Dir: Anissa Elder
HC Dir: Maribeth Graham
Board of Directors: Lynn Bardele, Alex Bell, Joseph Frohelich, William L Rootham, Walt Winding, Ava Harth Youngblood

D-U-N-S 04-674-1187 IMP/EXP
HERZOG CONTRACTING CORP
600 S Riverside Rd, Saint Joseph, MO 64507-9775
Tel (816) 233-9001 *Founded/Ownrshp* 1969
Sales 413.5MM^E *EMP* 950
SIC 1629 1611 4953

D-U-N-S 02-760-4115
HERZOG MOTORS INC
4275 Sw 139th Way, Beaverton, OR 97005-2389
Tel (503) 644-9121 *Founded/Ownrshp* 2002
Sales 31.9MM^E *EMP* 125
SIC 5511 Automobiles, new & used; Automobiles, new & used
Pr: Robert A Herzog
**Treas:* Michael J Herzog
Telecom Ex: Tom Herzog
Sls&Mrk Ex: Chris Meier

D-U-N-S 83-312-2356
HERZOG RAILROAD SERVICES INC
700 S Riverside Rd, Saint Joseph, MO 64507-2504
Tel (816) 233-9002 *Founded/Ownrshp* 2009
Sales 61.5MM^E *EMP* 275
SIC 4789 Cargo loading & unloading services; Cargo loading & unloading services
Pr: Rob Crawford
CFO: Phil Schieber
Ofcr: Max Lafferty
**VP:* Tim Francis
**VP:* George Williams
Sftwr Eng: Derek Spalding
Ql Cn Mgr: Scott Gillespie

D-U-N-S 78-673-2867
HERZOG SERVICES INC
(*Suby of* HERZOG CONTRACTING CORP) ★
700 S Riverside Rd, Saint Joseph, MO 64507-2504
Tel (816) 364-3000 *Founded/Ownrshp* 1992
Sales 40.4MM^E *EMP* 110
SIC 1629

D-U-N-S 00-891-6041
HERZOG SUPPLY CO INC
TRUE VALUE
151 Plaza Rd, Kingston, NY 12401-2972
Tel (845) 338-6300 *Founded/Ownrshp* 1909
Sales 39.4MM^E *EMP* 150
SIC 5231 5251 5999 5719 5211 5198 Paint; Hardware; Plumbing & heating supplies; Housewares; Millwork & lumber; Paints, varnishes & supplies; Paint; Hardware; Plumbing & heating supplies; Housewares; Millwork & lumber; Paints, varnishes & supplies
Pr: Bradley W Jordan
**Treas:* Todd Jordan
**Ex VP:* Paul H Jordan Jr
**VP:* Susan H Jordan
**Prin:* Nancy Evans
Genl Mgr: Fred Seeger
S&M/VP: Jackie Hintz

D-U-N-S 80-964-6052
HERZOG TRANSIT SERVICES INC
(*Suby of* HERZOG CONTRACTING CORP) ★
600 S Riverside Rd, Saint Joseph, MO 64507-9775
Tel (816) 233-9001 *Founded/Ownrshp* 1993
Sales 59.9MM^E *EMP* 390
SIC 4111 Commuter rail passenger operation; Commuter rail passenger operation
Pr: Stanley Herzog
**VP:* Norman J Jester
Genl Mgr: Douglas Honn
Sfty Mgr: Mike Maguire

HERZOG-MEIER AUTO CENTER
See JIM MEIER INC

D-U-N-S 96-376-6472
HES CONVENTION GROUP INC
HES CONVENTION SERVICES
7345 W Sand Lake Rd # 204, Orlando, FL 32819-5280
Tel (407) 472-4676 *Founded/Ownrshp* 1996
Sales 7.9MM^E *EMP* 410
SIC 7363 Help supply services; Help supply services
Pr: David Lehman
Sls Dir: Kim Moody

HES CONVENTION SERVICES
See HES CONVENTION GROUP INC

D-U-N-S 13-745-8076
HESCHEL JOSHUA ABRAHAM SCH
30 W End Ave, New York, NY 10023-7809
Tel (718) 549-3639 *Founded/Ownrshp* 2003
Sales 36.7MM *EMP* 7
Accts Eisneramper Llp New York Ny
SIC 8211 Elementary & secondary schools; Elementary & secondary schools
Prin: Ahuva Helberstan
Dir IT: John Hutzler

HESCO
See HARTFORD ELECTRIC SUPPLY CO INC

HESCO
See HARTFORD EQUITY SALES CO INC

D-U-N-S 00-175-2120 IMP
HESCO INC (IL)
6633 N Milwaukee Ave, Niles, IL 60714-4483
Tel (800) 822-7467 *Founded/Ownrshp* 1955, 1970
Sales 22.9MM^E *EMP* 80
SIC 5087 5064 Janitors' supplies; Vacuum cleaners, household; Vacuum cleaners
Ch Bd: Irwin B Gurson
**Pr:* Rory Gurson
VP: Albert Kendrick
VP: Ron Swiss
Brnch Mgr: Dixie Shreiner
Sys/Mgr: Heather Neander

D-U-N-S 60-363-1326 IMP
▲ HESKA CORP
3760 Rocky Mountain Ave, Loveland, CO 80538-7084
Tel (970) 493-7272 *Founded/Ownrshp* 1988
Sales 89.8MM *EMP* 301^E
Tkr Sym HSKA *Exch* NAS
SIC 2834 5122 Veterinary pharmaceutical preparations; Animal medicines; Veterinary pharmaceutical preparations; Animal medicines
Pr: Kevin S Wilson
**Ch Bd:* Sharon L Riley
Pr: Michael J McGinley
COO: Jason A Napolitano
Ex VP: Steven M Eyl

Ex VP: Rodney A Lippincott
Ex VP: Nancy Wisnewski
Genl Mgr: Laurie Peterson
IT Man: Mike Lyborg
Sales Exec: Aperfine Joe
Mktg Dir: Rose McConathy
Board of Directors: William A Aylesworth, G Irwin Gordon, David E Sveen, Bonnie J Trowbridge, Carol A Wrenn

D-U-N-S 08-444-6202
HESPERIA UNIFIED SCHOOL DISTRICT
15576 Main St, Hesperia, CA 92345-3482
Tel (760) 244-4411 *Founded/Ownrshp* 1880
Sales 125.0MM^E *EMP* 2,500
Accts Nigro Nigro & White
SIC 8211 Public combined elementary & secondary school; Public combined elementary & secondary school
Dir Sec: Debra Quinones
IT Man: Patty Torres
Schl Brd P: Niccole Childs
HC Dir: Matt Fedders
Counsel: Dennis Wagner

D-U-N-S 00-340-6196
HESS BROSFRUIT CO
500 Becker Rd, Leola, PA 17540-9775
Tel (717) 656-2631 *Founded/Ownrshp* 1957, 1975
Sales 38.2MM *EMP* 48
Accts Rottmund Cheek & Co Inc La
SIC 0723 Fruit (fresh) packing services; Fruit (fresh) packing services
Pr: Frederick Hess

D-U-N-S 03-879-0952
HESS CONSTRUCTION + ENGINEERING SERVICES INC (MD)
804 W Diamond Ave Ste 300, Gaithersburg, MD 20878-1411
Tel (301) 670-9000 *Founded/Ownrshp* 1978
Sales 53.5MM^E *EMP* 100^E
Accts Dixon Hughes Goodman Llp Roc
SIC 1542 Commercial & office buildings, new construction; Commercial & office buildings, renovation & repair; Commercial & office building, new construction; Commercial & office buildings, renovation & repair
CEO: Charles F Hess
Pr: Andrew D Hess
CFO: Christopher Carpenito
CFO: James Kyne
Sr VP: Ben McDonald
Sr VP: Todd Ward
Exec: Gary Baker
Exec: Jim Gladhill
Comm Dir: Joyce Donohue
QA Dir: Fred Cooper
IT Man: Sureet Sandhu

D-U-N-S 00-697-9785 IMP
▲ HESS CORP
1185 Ave Of The Americas, New York, NY 10036-2601
Tel (212) 997-8500 *Founded/Ownrshp* 1920
Sales 11.4MMM *EMP* 3,045
Accts Ernst & Young Llp New York N
Tkr Sym HES *Exch* NYS
SIC 1311 2911 5171 5541 4911 Crude petroleum production; Natural gas production; Petroleum refining; Petroleum bulk stations; Petroleum terminals; Filling stations, gasoline; Transmission, electric power; Crude petroleum production; Natural gas production; Petroleum refining; Petroleum bulk stations; Petroleum terminals; Filling stations, gasoline; Transmission, electric power
CEO: John B Hess
Pr: Gerald A Jamin
COO: Gregory P Hill
CFO: John P Rielly
Treas: Robert M Biglin
Treas: Erin Macher
Ofcr: Jonathan Stein
Ex VP: Curtis Carpenter
Ex VP: David Chaimengyew
Ex VP: Kim Nickles
Ex VP: Abhay Shah
Ex VP: Mark Steidl
Sr VP: Christopher Baldwin
Sr VP: A A Bernstein
Sr VP: Gary Boubel
Sr VP: William Drennen
Sr VP: John A Gartman
Sr VP: Zhanna Golodryga
Sr VP: Timothy B Goodell
Sr VP: Lawrence H Ornstein
Sr VP: John J Scelfo
Board of Directors: William G Schrader, Rodney F Chase, Mark R Williams, Terrence J Checki, Robert N Wilson, Harvey Golub, Edith E Holiday, David McManus, Kevin O Meyers, John H Mullin III, James H Quigley, Fredric G Reynolds

D-U-N-S 04-579-8840
■ HESS MECHANICAL CORP
(*Suby of* COMFORT SYSTEMS USA INC) ★
9600 Fallard Ct, Upper Marlboro, MD 20772-6718
Tel (301) 856-4700 *Founded/Ownrshp* 1998
Sales 33.0MM^E *EMP* 150
SIC 1711 Mechanical contractor; Plumbing contractors; Warm air heating & air conditioning contractor; Ventilation & duct work contractor; Mechanical contractor; Plumbing contractors; Warm air heating & air conditioning contractor; Ventilation & duct work contractor
CEO: Katharine Hess Teitel
**Pr:* Michael Smearman
**CFO:* Cordell A Black Sr
Ofcr: Michelle Baxter
VP: Montero Jose

D-U-N-S 07-384-5240
HESS MEMORIAL HOSPITAL INC
MILE BLUFF MEDICAL CENTER
1050 Division St, Mauston, WI 53948-1997
Tel (608) 847-6161 *Founded/Ownrshp* 1910
Sales 76.6MM *EMP* 642
Accts Eide Bailly Llp Dubuque Ia

SIC 8062 8051 General medical & surgical hospitals; Skilled nursing care facilities; General medical & surgical hospitals; Skilled nursing care facilities
CEO: James M O'Keefe
Treas: Peggy Saylor
VP: Julie Lynch
VP: Jean Surguy
Brnch Mgr: Jennifer Brandau
Off Mgr: Janie Jones
MIS Dir: Pat Stubbs
Surgeon: Rodney Malinowski
Surgeon: William Marculis
Nutrtnst: Shannon Moore
Doctor: David M Hoffmann MD

D-U-N-S 07-885-2704
■ HESS OIL VIRGIN ISLAND CORP
(*Suby of* HESS CORP) ★
1185 Ave Of The Amer 39, New York, NY 10036-2603
Tel (212) 997-8500 *Founded/Ownrshp* 1973
Sales 197.4MM^E *EMP* 3,000
SIC 2911 Petroleum refining; Petroleum refining
Ch Bd: John Hess
Sls Mgr: Mike King
Sls Mgr: Thomas P Petrella
Snr Mgr: Tom Duffy

HESS PRINT SOLUTIONS - OH
See PRESS OF OHIO INC

D-U-N-S 82-633-8238
HESS SERVICES INC
2670 E 9th St, Hays, KS 67601
Tel (785) 625-9295 *Founded/Ownrshp* 1994
Sales 39.6MM^E *EMP* 60
SIC 3443 Industrial vessels, tanks & containers
Pr: Dan Hess
**VP:* Lisa Hess
**Prin:* Allyssa Weigel

D-U-N-S 07-870-2574 IMP
HESS TRADING CORP
1501 Mckinney St, Houston, TX 77010-4010
Tel (713) 496-4000 *Founded/Ownrshp* 2012
Sales 148.6MM^E *EMP* 155^E
SIC 5199 Art goods & supplies
CEO: John B Hess
**Pr:* Gregory P Hill
CFO: Joe Wilders
**Sr VP:* Gary Boubel
**Sr VP:* Zhanna Golodryga
**Sr VP:* Richard Lynch
Sr VP: Bob Strode
VP: Barry Anderson
Exec: Chase Sobelman
Plng Mgr: Mariano Gurfinkel
IT Man: Robert Frow

D-U-N-S 06-752-4397
HESSE INDUSTRIAL SALES INC
VANEC
3370 N Benzing Rd, Orchard Park, NY 14127-1591
Tel (716) 827-4951 *Founded/Ownrshp* 1963
Sales 32.8MM^E *EMP* 75
SIC 5084 3443 Industrial machinery & equipment; Heat exchangers, condensers & components; Vessels, process or storage (from boiler shops): metal plate; Industrial machinery & equipment; Heat exchangers, condensers & components; Vessels, process or storage (from boiler shops): metal plate
Pr: Robert T Hesse
**Treas:* John J Breen
**VP:* Robert Keenehan
**VP:* Randy Streetman
Sales Asso: Gail Gram

D-U-N-S 02-087-1356
HESSEL HOLDING CO INC
WHITTON SUPPLY
1419 W Reno Ave, Oklahoma City, OK 73106-3209
Tel (405) 236-5561 *Founded/Ownrshp* 1981
Sales 27.5MM^E *EMP* 75^E
SIC 5084 5085 5072 7359 Industrial machinery & equipment; Industrial supplies; Hardware; Equipment rental & leasing; Industrial machinery & equipment; Industrial supplies; Hardware; Equipment rental & leasing
Pr: John Hessel
**Sec:* Dee Hessel
**VP:* Dave Hessel
**Prin:* Mary A Brown
**Prin:* Sally Oldham
**Prin:* Fran Wilkinson
IT Man: Christy Clark

D-U-N-S 04-450-8190 IMP
HESSELBEIN TIRE CO INC (MS)
GATEWAY TIRES
3004 J R Lynch St, Jackson, MS 39209-7396
Tel (601) 352-3611 *Founded/Ownrshp* 1967
Sales 52.5MM^E *EMP* 80
SIC 5014 5531 Automobile tires & tubes; Truck tires & tubes; Automotive tires; Automobile tires & tubes; Truck tires & tubes; Automotive tires
Pr: W D King
**Treas:* Brent Nickle
**VP:* Joseph A Dunlap
**VP:* M E Dunlap
**VP:* Robert H Dunlap
VP: John L King Jr

D-U-N-S 18-200-4374 IMP
HESSELBEIN TIRE SOUTHWEST INC
4823 Corner Pkwy, San Antonio, TX 78219-1893
Tel (210) 646-8448 *Founded/Ownrshp* 1987
Sales 53.0MM^E *EMP* 50
SIC 5014 Automobile tires & tubes; Motorcycle tires & tubes; Truck tires & tubes
Pr: Walter D King
**Treas:* Roderick V Draper
**VP:* Robert H Dunlap
IT Man: Jackelyn Desharnais

D-U-N-S 60-338-4843
HESSIAN CO LTD
FADDIS CONCRETE PRODUCTS
2206 Horseshoe Pike, Honey Brook, PA 19344-8657
Tel (610) 269-4685 *Founded/Ownrshp* 1989
Sales 25.2MM^E *EMP* 100

SIC 3272 Lintels, concrete
Pr: Donald M Cooper
Opers Mgr: Kevin Iddings
Sls Mgr: Robert Hess

HETCO
See HARTREE PARTNERS LP

D-U-N-S 08-507-9069 IMP
HETTICH AMERICA LP
(*Suby of* HETTICH MARKETING- UND VERTRIEBS GMBH)
4295 Hamilton Mill Rd # 400, Buford, GA 30518-3603
Tel (678) 835-0427 *Founded/Ownrshp* 1977
Sales 46.2MM^E *EMP* 90
SIC 5072 Furniture hardware; Furniture hardware
Pt: Thomas Ginschel
**Pt:* Wayne M Brunson
**Pt:* Anton Hettich
Prd Mgr: Jorg Dorp
Sls Mgr: Mike Brown

D-U-N-S 04-238-5146
HEUBEL MATERIAL HANDLING INC
(*Suby of* RAYMOND CORP) ★
6311 Equitable Rd, Kansas City, MO 64120-2155
Tel (816) 231-6900 *Founded/Ownrshp* 2007
Sales 78.0MM *EMP* 140
Accts Mize Houser & Company
SIC 5084 Lift trucks & parts; Lift trucks & parts
Pr: Chris Cella
**CFO:* Margaret Lee
**VP:* James Malvaso
**VP:* Brian Richardson
Genl Mgr: Nancy Streeter
IT Man: James Coonce
VP Sls: Steve Pocock
Sls Mgr: Dennis Melanson

D-U-N-S 05-337-0128
HEUBERGER MOTORS INC
HEUBERGER VOLKSWAGEN-SUBARU
1080 Motor City Dr, Colorado Springs, CO 80905-7311
Tel (719) 475-1920 *Founded/Ownrshp* 1970
Sales 40.7MM^E *EMP* 98
SIC 5511 Automobiles, new & used; Automobiles, new & used
CEO: Peet Heuberger
**Pr:* Gunnar Heuberger
**VP:* Carolyn Heuberger
Off Mgr: Regina Vigil
Sls Mgr: Robert Ieans
Snr Mgr: Yvonne Rimbert

HEUBERGER VOLKSWAGEN-SUBARU
See HEUBERGER MOTORS INC

D-U-N-S 00-906-3884
HEWES MARINE CO INC
HEWESCRAFT
2600 North Highway, Colville, WA 99114-8554
Tel (509) 684-5235 *Founded/Ownrshp* 1948
Sales 24.4MM^E *EMP* 92
Accts Maruji & Raines Ps Chewela
SIC 3732 Motorboats, inboard or outboard: building & repairing; Motorboats, inboard or outboard: building & repairing
Pr: David Ralph Hewes
**Sec:* Bill Hewes
**VP:* Launa Hewes

HEWESCRAFT
See HEWES MARINE CO INC

D-U-N-S 15-235-3632
HEWITT ASSOCIATES LLC
HEWITT RELOCATION
(*Suby of* AON HEWITT LLC) ★
100 Half Day Rd, Lincolnshire, IL 60069-3242
Tel (847) 295-5000 *Founded/Ownrshp* 1994
Sales NA *EMP* 15
SIC 6411 8742 Pension & retirement plan consultants; Management consulting services
CEO: Mr Russell P Fradin
COO: Daniel Holland
CFO: Dan Decanniere
Treas: Dalip Puri
VP: Steven J Kyono
VP: Matthew C Levin
VP: Kristi Savacool
VP: Barbara Williams
Dir Bus: Lydia Leon
Dir Bus: Jim Sawma
**Prin:* Ms Ilene Grant

HEWITT RELOCATION
See HEWITT ASSOCIATES LLC

D-U-N-S 07-860-3594
HEWITT SCHOOL (INC)
45 E 75th St, New York, NY 10021-2789
Tel (212) 288-1919 *Founded/Ownrshp* 1920
Sales 27.4MM *EMP* 73
Accts Eisneramper Llp New York Ny
SIC 8211 Private combined elementary & secondary school; Private combined elementary & secondary school
CEO: Linda Macmurray Gibbs
**Pr:* Juan Sabater
**Treas:* David Pearson
Bd of Dir: Linda Jackson
**VP:* Colin Knudsen
VP: Samantha Yanks
**Prin:* Mary Jane Yurchak
CIO: Andrew Monachelli

HEWITT USA
See G T SALES & MANUFACTURING INC

D-U-N-S 14-165-5931
HEWITT YOUNG ELECTRIC LLC
645 Maple St, Rochester, NY 14611-1721
Tel (585) 288-4480 *Founded/Ownrshp* 2003
Sales 21.7MM *EMP* 50
Accts Bonadio & Co Llp Pittsford
SIC 1731 Electrical work; Electrical work
Sales Asso: Michael Ferrara

HEWLETT PACKARD
See INDIGO AMERICA INC

D-U-N-S 07-874-3996
HEWLETT PACKARD
3000 Hanover St, Palo Alto, CA 94304-1185
Tel (650) 857-1501 *Founded/Ownrshp* 2013
Sales 98.4MM^E *EMP* 1,835^E
SIC 7371

D-U-N-S 07-983-4910
▲ HEWLETT PACKARD ENTERPRISE CO
3000 Hanover St, Palo Alto, CA 94304-1185
Tel (650) 857-1501 *Founded/Ownrshp* 2015
Sales 52.1MMM *EMP* 252,000^E
Tkr Sym HPE *Exch* NYS
SIC 7372 7379 3572 Prepackaged software; Computer related maintenance services; Computer storage devices
Pr: Margaret C Whitman
**Ch Bd:* Patricia F Russo
COO: Christopher P Hsu
CFO: Timothy C Stonesifer
Ex VP: Martin Fink
Ex VP: John F Schultz
Sr VP: Jeff T Ricci

D-U-N-S 00-155-9876
■ HEWLETT-PACKARD CREDIT CORP
HP
(*Suby of* HP INC) ★
3000 Hanover St, Palo Alto, CA 94304-1185
Tel (650) 857-1501 *Founded/Ownrshp* 1999
Sales 81.2MM^E *EMP* 1,000
SIC 3571 Personal computers (microcomputers); Minicomputers; Personal computers (microcomputers); Minicomputers
Sr VP: Ann O Baskins

D-U-N-S 83-127-6311 IMP
HEWLETT-PACKARD ENTERPRISES LLC
3000 Hanover St, Palo Alto, CA 94304-1185
Tel (650) 857-1501 *Founded/Ownrshp* 2012
Sales 270.1MM^E *EMP* 342^E
SIC 3571 Electronic computers
Sftwr Eng: Abraham Lui

D-U-N-S 09-075-4292
■ HEWLETT-PACKARD FINANCIAL SERVICES CO
(*Suby of* HP INC) ★
200 Connell Dr Ste 5000, Berkeley Heights, NJ 07922-2816
Tel (908) 898-4000 *Founded/Ownrshp* 2002
Sales NA *EMP* 1,800
SIC 6159 7519 7377 Equipment & vehicle finance leasing companies; Utility trailer rental; Computer rental & leasing; Equipment & vehicle finance leasing companies; Utility trailer rental; Computer rental & leasing
CEO: Irv Rothman
VP: G D McCarthy
CTO: Gary Thome
Dir IT: Bryan Holmes

D-U-N-S 02-020-8893
■ HEWLETT-PACKARD STATE & LOCAL ENTERPRISE SERVICES INC
STATE LCAL GVERNMENT DIV - EDS
(*Suby of* ELECTRONIC DATA SYSTEMS) ★
1115 Se 164th Ave Ste 210, Vancouver, WA 98683-8556
Tel (360) 516-7122 *Founded/Ownrshp* 1997, 2007
Sales 58.5MM^E *EMP* 600
SIC 7373 Computer integrated systems design; Computer integrated systems design
Pr: Paul Porrini
**Pr:* Rishi Varma
**CFO:* Shron Kease
**VP:* Frank Chechile
IT Man: Bonnie L Moore

HEWLETT-WOODMERE PUB SCHOOLS
See HEWLETT-WOODMERE UNION FREE SCHOOL DISTRICT

D-U-N-S 06-592-8426
HEWLETT-WOODMERE UNION FREE SCHOOL DISTRICT
HEWLETT-WOODMERE PUB SCHOOLS
1 Johnson Pl, Woodmere, NY 11598-1312
Tel (516) 374-8100 *Founded/Ownrshp* 1898
Sales 39.8MM^E *EMP* 630
SIC 8211 Public elementary school; Public junior high school; Public senior high school; Public elementary school; Public junior high school; Public senior high school
Ofcr: Barbara Giese
Schl Brd P: Scott McInnes
Nrsg Dir: Bonnie Rashbaum

HEX ARMOR
See PERFORMANCE FABRICS INC

D-U-N-S 01-520-2638
■ HEXACOMB CORP (IL)
(*Suby of* BOISE WHITE PAPER LLC) ★
1296 Barclay Blvd, Buffalo Grove, IL 60089-4500
Tel (847) 955-7984 *Founded/Ownrshp* 1988, 2011
Sales 66.5MM^E *EMP* 450
SIC 2671 2499 Paper coated or laminated for packaging; Decorative wood & woodwork; Paper coated or laminated for packaging; Decorative wood & woodwork
Pr: Alexander Toeldte

D-U-N-S 07-839-5354
■ HEXACOMB CORP
(*Suby of* BOISE INC) ★
1111 W Jefferson St, Boise, ID 83702-5383
Tel (208) 384-7000 *Founded/Ownrshp* 2012
Sales 62.7MM^E *EMP* 334^E
SIC 2671 Paper coated or laminated for packaging
Pr: Scott Daniel

D-U-N-S 14-493-6437 IMP
HEXAGON HOLDINGS INC
(*Suby of* HEXAGON AB)
250 Circuit Dr, North Kingstown, RI 02852-7441
Tel (401) 471-6900 *Founded/Ownrshp* 2001
Sales 326.2MM^E *EMP* 1,900
SIC 3823 3545 Industrial instrmnts msrmnt display/control process variable; Machine tool accessories; Industrial instrmnts msrmnt display/control process variable; Machine tool accessories
Pr: William Gruber
**Pr:* Norbert Hanke
**CFO:* Mark Delaney
**Treas:* Donna Cournoel

D-U-N-S 02-614-6535 IMP
HEXAGON METROLOGY INC
ADVANCED METROLOGY SOLUTIONS
(*Suby of* HEXAGON HOLDINGS INC) ★
250 Circuit Dr, North Kingstown, RI 02852-7441
Tel (401) 886-2000 *Founded/Ownrshp* 2001
Sales 326.2MM^E *EMP* 1,900
SIC 3823 3545 Industrial instrmnts msrmnt display/control process variable; Precision measuring tools; Industrial instrmnts msrmnt display/control process variable; Precision measuring tools
Pr: Norbert Hanke
V Ch: Robert Chisholm
**Pr:* Angus Taylor
**CFO:* Mark Delaney
VP: Mark Dellaney
VP: Bernard Haeberlin
IT Man: Kerry Fournier
Sls Mgr: Stu Reardon

D-U-N-S 82-836-9678
HEXAWARE TECHNOLOGIES INC
CALIBER POINT
(*Suby of* HEXAWARE TECHNOLOGIES LIMITED)
1095 Cranbury S Rvr Rd St, Jamesburg, NJ 08831-3411
Tel (609) 409-6950 *Founded/Ownrshp* 2001
Sales 231.8MM *EMP* 700
Accts Deloitte Haskins & Sells Llp
SIC 7379 Computer related consulting services; Computer related consulting services
CEO: P R Chandrasekar
**Pr:* Rajiv Pant
COO: Manab Sen
CFO: Rajesh Ghonasgi
Bd of Dir: Mark F Dzialga
Ofcr: Deependra Chumble
Ofcr: Eric Meerschaert
Assoc VP: Bennet Kumar
Assoc VP: Nitin Sawant
Assoc VP: Indira Viswanathan
Ex VP: Moorthi Chokkanathan
Sr VP: Yogendra Shah
VP: Rohit Arde
VP: Jeetendra Gupta
VP: Dhruv Patel
VP: Michael Rennell
Exec: Bhaskar Chatterjee
Exec: Sudha Iyer
Exec: Hanumant Karangutkar
Exec: Amit Kathare
Exec: Pradeep Katkade

D-U-N-S 00-911-8563 EXP
▲ HEXCEL CORP
281 Tresser Blvd Ste 1503, Stamford, CT 06901-3261
Tel (203) 969-0666 *Founded/Ownrshp* 1946
Sales 1.8MMM *EMP* 5,663
Accts Pricewaterhousecoopers Llp St
Tkr Sym HXL *Exch* NYS
SIC 2821 3728 3089 3624 2891 3469 Plastics materials & resins; Epoxy resins; Polyurethane resins; Elastomers, nonvulcanizable (plastics); Aircraft parts & equipment; Fiberglass doors; Fibers, carbon & graphite; Adhesives; Epoxy adhesives; Sealants; Honeycombed metal; Plastics materials & resins; Epoxy resins; Polyurethane resins; Elastomers, nonvulcanizable (plastics); Aircraft parts & equipment; Fiberglass doors; Fibers, carbon & graphite; Adhesives; Epoxy adhesives; Sealants; Honeycombed metal
Ch Bd: Nick L Stanage
CFO: Michael Bacal
CFO: Wayne C Pensky
Ofcr: Gary Jones
Sr VP: Robert G Hennemuth
Sr VP: Ira J Krakower
VP: Kimberly Hendricks
VP: Mark Seymour
VP Bus Dev: Timothy Swords
Mng Dir: Donald Cross
Genl Mgr: John Muller

D-U-N-S 96-446-7591
■ HEXCEL POTTSVILLE CORP
(*Suby of* HEXCEL CORP) ★
172 Industrial Park Rd, Saint Clair, PA 17970
Tel (570) 429-1741 *Founded/Ownrshp* 1995
Sales 27.3MM^E *EMP* 159
SIC 8742 Marketing consulting services; Marketing consulting services
Pr: Larry Flick
**VP:* Wayne C Pensky
Mktg Dir: Derek Patton

D-U-N-S 00-146-8214 IMP
■ HEXCEL REINFORCEMENTS CORP
(*Suby of* HEXCEL CORP) ★
1913 N King St, Seguin, TX 78155-2115
Tel (830) 379-1580 *Founded/Ownrshp* 2001
Sales 49.9MM^E *EMP* 224^E
SIC 2221 Fiberglass fabrics; Manmade & synthetic broadwoven fabrics; Fiberglass fabrics; Manmade & synthetic broadwoven fabrics
Pr: David E Berges
**Pr:* Joseph H Shaulson
**VP:* Rodney P Jenks Jr
**VP:* Ira J Krakower
**VP:* Wayne C Pensky
Sfty Dirs: Sylvia Guerrero
Mfg Mgr: Jennifer Zumwalt
Prd Mgr: Don Taylor

D-U-N-S 08-592-2466 IMP/EXP
HEXCO INTERNATIONAL
CRYOGENIC INDUSTRIES
25720 Jefferson Ave, Murrieta, CA 92562-6929
Tel (951) 677-2081 *Founded/Ownrshp* 1974, 1991
Sales 45.0MM^E *EMP* 117
SIC 3559 3561 3443 Cryogenic machinery, industrial; Pumps & pumping equipment; Fabricated plate work (boiler shop); Cryogenic machinery, industrial; Pumps & pumping equipment; Fabricated plate work (boiler shop)
CEO: Ross M Brown
**Pr:* William Hallinan

D-U-N-S 00-133-8797
HEXION INC
(*Suby of* HEXION LLC) ★
180 E Broad St Fl 26, Columbus, OH 43215-3707
Tel (614) 225-4000 *Founded/Ownrshp* 1899
Sales 5.1MMM *EMP* 5,200^E
SIC 2821 Thermosetting materials; Acrylic resins; Epoxy resins; Melamine resins, melamine-formaldehyde; Thermosetting materials; Acrylic resins; Epoxy resins; Melamine resins, melamine-formaldehyde
Ch Bd: Craig O Morrison
**CFO:* William H Carter
Treas: George F Knight
Ex VP: Marcello Boldrini
Ex VP: Julia Harp
Ex VP: Douglas A Johns
Ex VP: Judith A Sonnett
VP: Bill Hoffman
CTO: Rich Thompson

D-U-N-S 09-100-9787
HEXION INC
(*Suby of* HEXION INC) ★
Km 1 Cnr Rd 865 Rr 866, TOA Baja, PR 00949
Tel (787) 251-0060
Sales NA *EMP* 4,680^E
SIC 2869 Industrial organic chemicals
Prin: Ariosto Espino

D-U-N-S 16-649-5924 IMP/EXP
HEXION LLC
(*Suby of* MOMENTIVE PERFORMANCE MATERIALS HOLDINGS LLC) ★
180 E Broad St Fl 26, Columbus, OH 43215-3707
Tel (614) 225-4000 *Founded/Ownrshp* 2010
Sales NA *EMP* 6,210
SIC 2821 2899 Thermosetting materials; Chemical preparations; Thermosetting materials; Chemical preparations
CEO: Craig O Morrison
Pr: Dennis Ryan
**Ex VP:* William H Carter
**Sr VP:* George Knight
Snr Mgr: Joshua Johnson

D-U-N-S 15-322-1663
HEXPOL COMPOUNDING LLC
HEXPOL POLYMERS
(*Suby of* HEXPOL AB)
280 Crawford Rd, Statesville, NC 28625-8541
Tel (704) 872-1585 *Founded/Ownrshp* 2010
Sales 320.7MM^E *EMP* 800
SIC 3087 2821 Custom compound purchased resins; Thermoplastic materials; Custom compound purchased resins; Thermoplastic materials
CEO: Tracy Garrison
CFO: Eric Kiel
VP: Rakshit Lamba
VP: Leonard McClean
VP: Marc Pignataro
Genl Mgr: Stephen W Chase
Genl Mgr: Peter Mollett
Genl Mgr: Glenn Thurman
CIO: Steven Lubowicz
IT Man: Scott Bleistein
Mtls Mgr: Don Rogers

D-U-N-S 15-292-1862 IMP/EXP
HEXPOL COMPOUNDING NC INC
(*Suby of* HEXPOL AB)
280 Crawford Rd, Statesville, NC 28625-8541
Tel (704) 872-1585 *Founded/Ownrshp* 2004
Sales 228.8MM^E *EMP* 3,100
SIC 3069 3087 2891 Rubber automotive products; Custom compound purchased resins; Adhesives & sealants; Rubber automotive products; Custom compound purchased resins; Adhesives & sealants
Pr: Georg Brunstam
**Pr:* Shannon Smith
**CFO:* Urban Ottosson
Ex Dir: Angela Bailey

HEXPOL POLYMERS
See HEXPOL COMPOUNDING LLC

D-U-N-S 93-282-2943
HEXTER-FAIR TITLE CO
8333 Douglas Ave Ste 130, Dallas, TX 75225-5811
Tel (214) 373-9999 *Founded/Ownrshp* 1995
Sales 37.2MM^E *EMP* 210
SIC 6541 Title abstract offices; Title abstract offices
Ch Bd: David L Fair
**Sec:* Win Myers
Ex VP: Robert Blanshard
Sr VP: Tracey McCann
**VP:* Brian Watts
Mng Dir: Karen Mitzner
Mng Dir: Betty Peacock

D-U-N-S 00-218-5007 IMP
HEYCO INC
HEYCO PRODUCTS
1800 Industrial Way, Toms River, NJ 08755-4809
Tel (732) 286-4336 *Founded/Ownrshp* 1926
Sales 134.3MM^E *EMP* 200
SIC 3351 3469 3089 Rolled or drawn shapes: copper & copper alloy; Brass rolling & drawing; Bronze rolling & drawing; Stamping metal for the trade; Injection molding of plastics; Extruded finished plastic products; Rolled or drawn shapes: copper & copper alloy; Brass rolling & drawing; Bronze rolling & drawing; Stamping metal for the trade; Injection molding of plastics; Extruded finished plastic products
Ch Bd: Michael H Jemison
COO: Robert Weiss
**CFO:* Richard Cardone
**Treas:* Robert Lyons
**VP:* William D Jemison
VP: Mario Pieroni
Genl Mgr: Tony Lopez

CIO: Jerry Polce
Dir IT: Gerry Polec
Natl Sales: Patrick Carlin

HEYCO PRODUCTS
See HEYCO INC

D-U-N-S 96-281-6836
HEYCO PRODUCTS INC
(*Suby of* HEYCO INC) ★
1800 Industrial Way, Toms River, NJ 08755-4809
Tel (732) 286-4336 *Founded/Ownrshp* 1986
Sales 100.0MM^E *EMP* 200
SIC 3351 3679 Copper rolling & drawing; Commutators, electronic; Copper rolling & drawing; Commutators, electronic
Treas: Richard Cardone

D-U-N-S 80-382-9597
HEYDE COMPANIES INC
HEYDE HEALTH SYSTEMS
31 E Columbia St, Chippewa Falls, WI 54729-2522
Tel (715) 726-9094 *Founded/Ownrshp* 1975
Sales 26.5MM^E *EMP* 163
SIC 5047 5113 Medical & hospital equipment; Industrial & personal service paper; Medical & hospital equipment; Industrial & personal service paper
Pr: Dennis L Heyde
Ex VP: Martin Matten
Dir IT: Christopher Wensink

D-U-N-S 15-345-2404
HEYDE HEALTH SYSTEM INC
FAMILY HERITAGE
31 E Columbia St, Chippewa Falls, WI 54729-2522
Tel (715) 726-9094 *Founded/Ownrshp* 1986
Sales 11.1MM^E *EMP* 307
SIC 8051 8059 Skilled nursing care facilities; Rest home, with health care; Skilled nursing care facilities; Rest home, with health care
Pr: Dennis L Heyde
**Ex VP:* Marty Metten

HEYDE HEALTH SYSTEMS
See HEYDE COMPANIES INC

D-U-N-S 00-432-9595
HEYL & PATTERSON INC (PA)
400 Lydia St, Carnegie, PA 15106-2720
Tel (412) 788-9810 *Founded/Ownrshp* 1887
Sales 23.1MM^E *EMP* 50
SIC 8711

HEYL ROYSTER
See HEYL ROYSTER VOELKER & ALLEN - PROFESSIONAL CORP

D-U-N-S 03-054-7954
HEYL ROYSTER VOELKER & ALLEN - PROFESSIONAL CORP
HEYL ROYSTER
300 Hamilton Blvd Ste 100, Peoria, IL 61602-1234
Tel (309) 676-0400 *Founded/Ownrshp* 1956
Sales 30.3MM^E *EMP* 275
SIC 8111 General practice law office; General practice law office
Pr: Timothy L Bertschy
Mng Pt: Edward Wagner
Ex Dir: Debra Adams
Counsel: Steve Ayres
Counsel: Scott Salemi

D-U-N-S 00-748-9099
HEYL TRUCK LINES INC
220 Norka Dr, Akron, IA 51001-7733
Tel (712) 568-2451 *Founded/Ownrshp* 1955
Sales 89.5MM *EMP* 400
Accts East Vander Woude Grant & Co
SIC 4212 4213 Local trucking, without storage; Trucking, except local; Refrigerated products transport; Local trucking, without storage; Trucking, except local; Refrigerated products transport
Ch Bd: Don Heyl
**Pr:* Alan Heyl
**Treas:* Scott Heyl
**Sec:* David Heyl
**VP:* Roger Heyl

D-U-N-S 62-253-5979
HEYWOOD HEALTHCARE INC
242 Green St, Gardner, MA 01440-1336
Tel (978) 632-3420 *Founded/Ownrshp* 1986
Sales 319.2M *EMP* 2,500^E
Accts Kpmg Peat Marwick Llp
SIC 8741 Hospital management
Pr: Winfield Brown
**Ch Bd:* Kenneth Pierce
Netwrk Eng: Bob Bronson
Netwrk Eng: John Demalia

HEYWOOD HOSPITAL
See HENRY HEYWOOD MEMORIAL HOSPITAL

HF
See HOWARD FINISHING LLC

D-U-N-S 80-541-5205
▲ HF FINANCIAL CORP
225 S Main Ave, Sioux Falls, SD 57104-6309
Tel (605) 333-7556 *Founded/Ownrshp* 1991
Sales NA *EMP* 299^E
Accts Eide Bailly Llp Sioux Falls
Tkr Sym HFFC *Exch* NGM
SIC 6035 Savings institutions, federally chartered; Federal savings & loan associations; Savings institutions, federally chartered; Federal savings & loan associations
Pr: Stephen M Bianchi
CFO: Brent R Olthoff
VP: Jon Gadberry
VP: Michael Westberg

D-U-N-S 62-737-4452
HF GROUP LLC
8844 Mayfield Rd, Chesterland, OH 44026-2632
Tel (440) 729-2445 *Founded/Ownrshp* 2006
Sales 28.0MM *EMP* 1,516
SIC 2732 Books: printing & binding; Books: printing & binding

COO: Paul Parisi
VP: Jim Bratton
VP: Mark Melahn
Genl Mgr: Lori Johnson
CIO: Barb Jones
CTO: Dennis Schwab
Plnt Mgr: Tim Baker

D-U-N-S 78-489-2742
HF HOLDINGS INC
(*Suby of* BAIN CAPITAL LLC) ★
1500 S 1000 W, Logan, UT 84321-8206
Tel (435) 750-5000 *Founded/Ownrshp* 1999
Sales 94.9MM^E *EMP* 3,263
SIC 3949 3088 Treadmills; Exercising cycles; Gymnasium equipment; Trampolines & equipment; Hot tubs, plastic or fiberglass; Treadmills; Exercising cycles; Gymnasium equipment; Trampolines & equipment; Hot tubs, plastic or fiberglass
CEO: Robert C Gay
Sr VP: Jon White

D-U-N-S 12-650-7073
HF MANAGEMENT SERVICES LLC
HEALTH FIRST
100 Church St Fl 17, New York, NY 10007-2607
Tel (212) 801-6000 *Founded/Ownrshp* 1999
Sales 815.3MM^E *EMP* 1,850
Accts Ernst & Young Llp New York
SIC 8741 Management services; Management services
CEO: Daniel McCarthy
COO: Jim Boothe
COO: James Both
COO: Mary Hood
CFO: Dan Phillips
**CFO:* Steve Sakovits
**CFO:* Marybeth Tita
**Treas:* David Falk
**Chf Mktg O:* Jay Schectman
**Sr VP:* Keith Y Gordon
**Sr VP:* Michael Honig
**Sr VP:* Elizabeth St Clair
VP: Robert Allen
VP: Christie Bowes
VP: Robert Branchini
**VP:* Andrea Forino
VP: Sharon Gardner
VP: Dave Gutwald
VP: Stewart Hamilton
**VP:* Christine Helzner
VP: George Hulse

D-U-N-S 00-714-8406 IMP
HF RUBBER MACHINERY INC
(*Suby of* HARBURG-FREUDENBERGER MASCHINENBAU GMBH)
1701 Nw Topeka Blvd, Topeka, KS 66608-1822
Tel (785) 235-2336 *Founded/Ownrshp* 2005
Sales 25.0MM^E *EMP* 65
SIC 3542 Machine tools, metal forming type; Extruding machines (machine tools), metal; Machine tools, metal forming type; Extruding machines (machine tools), metal
Pr: Andreas Limper
VP: Ernie Els
VP Opers: Austin Rash
Sls Mgr: Jon Hanft

HFA
See HARRISON FRENCH & ASSOCIATES LTD

D-U-N-S 79-662-1449 IMP/EXP
HFA INC
135 E Hintz Rd, Wheeling, IL 60090-6035
Tel (847) 520-1000 *Founded/Ownrshp* 1991
Sales 228.8MM^E *EMP* 700
SIC 3497 Foil containers for bakery goods & frozen foods; Foil containers for bakery goods & frozen foods
Pr: Norton Sarnoff
**CFO:* Peter Perkins
**VP:* Brad Sarnoff
**VP:* David Sarnoff

D-U-N-S 79-937-6348
HFB FINANCIAL CORP
1602 Cumberland Ave, Middlesboro, KY 40965-1225
Tel (606) 248-1095 *Founded/Ownrshp* 1992
Sales NA *EMP* 51
Accts Bkd Llp Evansville Indiana
SIC 6035 Savings institutions, federally chartered; Savings institutions, federally chartered
Pr: David B Cook
Ch Bd: Robert Costanzo
COO: Alex Cook
CFO: Stanley Alexander Jr
Treas: John Moore
VP: Melissa McGill
Board of Directors: Earl Burchfield, E W Nagle, Francis Coffey Rasnic, Rober Roper

HFBE
See STOUT RISIUS ROSS INC

HFC
See HOUSEHOLD FINANCE CORP

HFD
See HOSPITALITY FURNISHINGS AND DESIGN INC

D-U-N-S 82-955-5361
HFE VALDOSTA LLC
WILD ADVENTURES
(*Suby of* HERSCHEND ENTERTAINMENT CO LLC) ★
3766 Old Clyattville Rd, Valdosta, GA 31601-1704
Tel (229) 219-7080 *Founded/Ownrshp* 2007
Sales 8.4MM^E *EMP* 500
SIC 7996 Theme park, amusement; Theme park, amusement
Exec: Jimmy Holmes

D-U-N-S 78-656-5544
HFF HOLDINGS LLC
HOLIDAY FENOGLIO FOWLER
1 Oxford Ctr, Pittsburgh, PA 15219-1400
Tel (412) 281-8714 *Founded/Ownrshp* 2003
Sales NA *EMP* 3

SIC 6162 Mortgage bankers & correspondents; Loan correspondents; Bond & mortgage companies; Mortgage bankers & correspondents; Loan correspondents; Bond & mortgage companies
CEO: John H Pelusi Jr
**CFO:* Gregory Conley
Off Mgr: Carol Colby

D-U-N-S 79-880-0749
▲ HFF INC
301 Grant St Ste 1100, Pittsburgh, PA 15219-1419
Tel (412) 281-8714 *Founded/Ownrshp* 1982
Sales NA *EMP* 721
Tkr Sym HF *Exch* NYS
SIC 6162 Mortgage bankers & correspondents; Loan correspondents; Mortgage bankers & correspondents; Loan correspondents
CEO: Mark D Gibson
**V Ch:* Joe B Thornton Jr
COO: Nancy O Goodson
CFO: Gregory R Conley
Assoc Dir: Becky Wisdom
Mktg Dir: Heather Pushinsky

D-U-N-S 80-672-4118
HFG ENGINEERING US INC
ALBERT-GRUDY CNSLTING ENGNEERS
3500 N Causeway Blvd # 600, Metairie, LA 70002-3527
Tel (504) 828-8839 *Founded/Ownrshp* 2006
Sales 14.0MM^E *EMP* 325
SIC 8711 Consulting engineer; Consulting engineer
Pr: Glenn Garaudy
**VP:* Garth Albert
**VP:* Keith Cruthirds
**VP:* Nick Routledge
VP Bus Dev: Bert Van Dijk
VP Sls: Peter Self

HFI
See HARRELL - FISH INC

D-U-N-S 10-692-7585
HFI ENTERPRISES INC
HINTZSCHE OIL
2s181 County Line Rd, Maple Park, IL 60151-8815
Tel (630) 557-2406 *Founded/Ownrshp* 1962
Sales 127.0MM^E *EMP* 125
SIC 5172 5191 Diesel fuel; Gasoline; Fuel oil; Chemicals, agricultural; Fertilizer & fertilizer materials; Feed; Diesel fuel; Gasoline; Fuel oil; Chemicals, agricultural; Fertilizer & fertilizer materials; Feed
Pr: David Hintzsche
CFO: Matthew Croll
**Treas:* Matt Gadow
**VP:* Ronald Hintzsche
Opers Mgr: Gerry Hinkston

D-U-N-S 00-429-3478 IMP/EXP
HFI LLC
59 Gender Rd, Canal Winchester, OH 43110-9733
Tel (614) 491-0700 *Founded/Ownrshp* 1969, 1993
Sales 149.5MM^E *EMP* 450
SIC 2396 2821 3714 3429 3086 Automotive trimmings, fabric; Polyurethane resins; Motor vehicle parts & accessories; Manufactured hardware (general); Plastics foam products; Automotive trimmings, fabric; Polyurethane resins; Motor vehicle parts & accessories; Manufactured hardware (general); Plastics foam products
COO: Larry Barth
**CFO:* Neil Fillman
VP: Robert S Chapell
Genl Mgr: Brad Myers
Dir IT: Karen Hartley
Mtls Mgr: Greg Galloway
Mtls Mgr: Jorge Martinez
Mfg Mgr: Thad Barker
Plnt Mgr: Derrice Alexander
Plnt Mgr: Rafael Pena
Ql Cn Mgr: Clarice Smith

D-U-N-S 08-507-4052 IMP
HFI WIND DOWN INC
DREXEL HERITAGE FURNITURE
1925 Eastchester Dr, High Point, NC 27265-1404
Tel (336) 888-4800 *Founded/Ownrshp* 2001
Sales 615.5MM^E *EMP* 3,300
SIC 2511 2512 Wood bedroom furniture; Dining room furniture: wood; Couches, sofas & davenports: upholstered on wood frames; Chairs: upholstered on wood frames; Wood bedroom furniture; Dining room furniture: wood; Couches, sofas & davenports: upholstered on wood frames; Chairs: upholstered on wood frames
Pr: Dan Bradley
**Pr:* Lenwood Rich
CFO: Chris Carril
**Sec:* Jon Botsford
VP: Carl Bundy
Mktg Mgr: Helen Campbell
Sls Mgr: Phil Miller

D-U-N-S 05-239-7106
HFOTCO LLC
HOUSTON FUEL OIL TERMINAL CO
(*Suby of* ALINDA CAPITAL PARTNERS LLC) ★
1201 S Sheldon Rd, Houston, TX 77015-6649
Tel (281) 864-9219 *Founded/Ownrshp* 2011
Sales 33.9MM^E *EMP* 70
SIC 4226 Oil & gasoline storage caverns for hire
CEO: Shaun M Revere
**Pr:* Willis Rossler
**CFO:* Steve Douglas
**Sr VP:* Robert Riemer
**VP:* Jim Bailey
**VP:* Tom Butler
**VP:* Clarence Jean
**VP:* John Lorren
**VP:* Mike Mangan
**VP:* Lex Moyers
**VP:* Blake Trahan

D-U-N-S 02-678-4732
HFPG INC
10 Columbus Blvd Ste 2n, Hartford, CT 06106-1976
Tel (860) 725-6830 *Founded/Ownrshp* 2009
Sales 62.0MM *EMP* 1
SIC 8748 Business consulting; Business consulting

Prin: Linda J Kelly

D-U-N-S 04-399-8798
HFRM II INC
2051 Hilltop Dr Ste A18, Redding, CA 96002-0234
Tel (530) 242-2010 *Founded/Ownrshp* 2008
Sales 6.9MM^E *EMP* 300
SIC 6512 Hotels & motels; Nonresidential building operators
CEO: Herbert F R Meyer Jr
**CFO:* Dara O'Farrell

HFS
See HOLSTEIN-FRIESIAN SERVICES INC

D-U-N-S 10-677-7667
HFS HOLDING CORP
HOSPITAL FORMS & SYSTEMS
8900 Ambassador Row, Dallas, TX 75247-4510
Tel (214) 634-8600 *Founded/Ownrshp* 1982
Sales 114.5MM^E *EMP* 550
SIC 2679 5112 2675 Labels, paper: made from purchased material; Business forms; Die-cut paper & board; Labels, paper: made from purchased material; Business forms; Die-cut paper & board
Pr: Peter A Pyhrr
VP Mfg: Tom Helenbrook
Manager: Melissa Whitehead

HFT
See HENRY FTEICHMANN INC

HG BUYING
See HOMEGOODS INC

D-U-N-S 07-968-2842
HG GLOBAL LLC (NV)
6750 Daniel Burnham Dr, Portage, IN 46368-1694
Tel (708) 323-2000 *Founded/Ownrshp* 2015
Sales 25.0MM^E *EMP* 20
SIC 5023 Home furnishings
Ch Bd: Piush Kumar
**CFO:* Pankaj Dave

H.G. HILL FOOD STORES
See S & C FOODS INC

D-U-N-S 00-922-8586 IMP
HG MAKELIM.CO
219 Shaw Rd, South San Francisco, CA 94080-6685
Tel (650) 827-7546 *Founded/Ownrshp* 1922
Sales 30.9MM^E *EMP* 30
SIC 5084 Engines & transportation equipment; Engines & parts, diesel
CEO: James Hess
**CFO:* Paul Hoffman
**VP:* Charles R Hess

D-U-N-S 00-243-0379
HG PAGE & SONS INC (NY)
(*Suby of* PAGE BROS ENTERPRISES LTD) ★
360 Manchester Rd, Poughkeepsie, NY 12603-2589
Tel (845) 452-7130 *Founded/Ownrshp* 1924
Sales 21.3MM^E *EMP* 58
SIC 5211 Home centers; Millwork & lumber
Pr: John J Page
**Sec:* William H Page
**VP:* Henry G Page Jr
Manager: James Fanelli

HG RHODES
See RHODES AUTO SALES INC

HG SOLTNS DIA-MO CLEAN TOP
See HUGHES GROUP LLC

HGA
See HUNT GUILLOT & ASSOCIATES LLC

HGA QUEST
See GERSTMAN LLC

D-U-N-S 11-624-1399
HGC CONSTRUCTION CO
H G C
2814 Stanton Ave, Cincinnati, OH 45206-1123
Tel (513) 861-8866 *Founded/Ownrshp* 1984
Sales 29.5MM^E *EMP* 106^E
SIC 1751 1796 Carpentry work; Millwright
Pr: Mike Huseman
Pr: Michael Breetz
COO: Steven Shipp
Genl Mgr: John Zembrodt
Mktg Dir: Pam Roebel
Snr PM: Tony Akers

D-U-N-S 07-986-1433
■ HGGC CITADEL PLASTICS HOLDINGS INC
(*Suby of* A SCHULMAN INC) ★
15000 Highway 41 N, Evansville, IN 47725-9360
Tel (812) 421-3600 *Founded/Ownrshp* 2015
Sales 193.1MM^E *EMP* 433^E
SIC 2821 Plastics materials & resins
CEO: Mike Huff
Pr: Kevin Andrews
CFO: Dennis Loughran
VP: Jason Jimerson
VP: Amy Rodgers
VP: Mario Sandoval

D-U-N-S 01-179-3958
HGGC LLC
1950 University Ave # 350, East Palo Alto, CA 94303-2286
Tel (650) 321-4910 *Founded/Ownrshp* 2007
Sales 293.4MM^E *EMP* 553
SIC 6799 Investors; Investors
CEO: Rich Lawson
Mng Pt: Gregory Benson
Mng Pt: Gary Crittenden
Mng Pt: James Learner
Pr: Jay Tabu
**CFO:* Les Brown
CFO: Lance Taylor
Ex VP: Rick Redle
VP: Paul C Huntsman
VP: Farouk Hussein
VP: Steven Leistner
VP: Steve Smith
VP: Steven P Smith

VP: Ryan Stratton
VP: Jay J Tabu
VP: Neil H White
Exec: Kurt Krieger

HGI
See HUCK GROUP INC

D-U-N-S 96-502-3281 IMP/EXP
HGI HOLDINGS INC
EDGEPARK MEDICAL SUPPLIES
1810 Summit Commerce Park, Twinsburg, OH 44087-2300
Tel (330) 963-6996 *Founded/Ownrshp* 2005
Sales NA *EMP* 950E
SIC 3841

D-U-N-S 14-857-0844
HGR CONSTRUCTION INC
1801 Lee Rd Ste 301, Winter Park, FL 32789-2101
Tel (407) 645-4447 *Founded/Ownrshp* 2003
Sales 32.6MME *EMP* 32
Accts Chesser & Company Pa Orlan
SIC 1542 Commercial & office building, new construction
CEO: Darrin Griffin
**Pr:* Richard Heinkel
**Sr VP:* Carson Brownell
**VP:* M Louie Akel
**VP:* Jim Rufrano

D-U-N-S 02-448-8343
HGR INDUSTRIAL SURPLUS INC (OH)
H G R
20001 Euclid Ave, Euclid, OH 44117-1480
Tel (216) 486-4567 *Founded/Ownrshp* 1998
Sales 32.2MME *EMP* 47E
SIC 5084 Industrial machinery & equipment
CEO: Brian Krueger
**Pr:* Paul Betori
**Prin:* Jeff McLain
Sls Mgr: Ron Tiedman
Sales Asso: Jon Frischkorn

D-U-N-S 06-742-1347
HGS (USA) LLC
(*Suby of* HINDUJA VENTURES LIMITED)
1901 E War Memorial Dr, Peoria, IL 61614-7807
Tel (309) 679-4261 *Founded/Ownrshp* 2004
Sales 176.2MME *EMP* 2,500
SIC 7389 ;
Pr: Kathy Hamburger
Pr: Bill Cook
CFO: Steve Czirjack
Bd of Dir: Jennifer Dorothy
Ex VP: Anthony Joseph
Ex VP: Sanjay Sinha
VP: Tom Asp
VP: Jack Biersdorfer
VP: Greg Johnson
**VP:* Lester Hnelson III
**VP:* Jaime Nunez
VP: Sreepathy Viswanathan
VP: Mary Wasner

D-U-N-S 94-429-2247
HGS LLC
ANGLER ENVIRONMENTAL
5367 Telephone Rd, Warrenton, VA 20187-9364
Tel (540) 216-3420 *Founded/Ownrshp* 1999
Sales 21.7MME *EMP* 60E
SIC 8748 Environmental consultant
Mktg Dir: Don Seaborn

D-U-N-S 12-609-6838 IMP
■ **HGST INC**
(*Suby of* WESTERN DIGITAL TECHNOLOGIES INC) ★
3403 Yerba Buena Rd, San Jose, CA 95135-1500
Tel (800) 801-4618 *Founded/Ownrshp* 2002
Sales 788.1MME *EMP* 2,303E
SIC 3572 Computer storage devices; Computer storage devices
CEO: John Coyne
**Pr:* Stephen Milligan
**COO:* Douglas A Gross
CFO: Tom Constantino
**CFO:* Michael A Murray
Sr VP: Dennis Brown
Sr VP: Mark Grace
VP: George Horvath
Dir Bus: Felipe Rodriguez
Genl Mgr: Fumio Kugiya
**CIO:* Craig Haught

HGT
See HUB GROUP TRUCKING INC

HGTV
See SCRIPPS NETWORKS LLC

HH
See HATBORO-HORSHAM SCHOOL DISTRICT

D-U-N-S 00-166-3962
HH BENFIELD ELECTRIC SUPPLY CO INC
25 Lafayette Ave, White Plains, NY 10603-1613
Tel (914) 948-6660 *Founded/Ownrshp* 1951
Sales 255.8MME *EMP* 200
Accts O Conner Davies Munns & Dobbin
SIC 5063 Electrical apparatus & equipment; Electrical supplies; Electrical apparatus & equipment; Electrical supplies
Ch Bd: Dan McLaughlin
**Pr:* Daniel J McLaughin
**CFO:* William G Roloff
VP: Joe Mauriello
Sls Mgr: Adam Kohli

D-U-N-S 00-112-7976 IMP
■ **HH BROWN SHOE CO INC**
COVE SHOE COMPANY DIVISION
(*Suby of* B H SHOE HOLDINGS INC) ★
124 W Putnam Ave Ste 1a, Greenwich, CT 06830-5317
Tel (203) 661-2424 *Founded/Ownrshp* 1992
Sales 188.3MME *EMP* 1,200
SIC 3143 3144 Work shoes, men's; Boots, dress or casual: men's; Women's footwear, except athletic; Work shoes, men's; Boots, dress or casual: men's; Women's footwear, except athletic

Ch Bd: Francis C Rooney Jr
Pr: James Issler
CEO: J E Issler
Ex VP: J Scott Bohling
VP: Philip Alsop
VP: Bud Clapsaddle
VP: Greg Goodreau
VP: John Heron
VP: Jon Lebo
VP: Mark McGranahan
VP: Tim Oconnor
VP: Jason Reed
VP: Robert Skorvanek
VP: John Sweeny
VP: Tony Tumio
VP: Stephen Whitney
Board of Directors: Warren E Buffett

D-U-N-S 96-167-9904
HH DISTRIBUTION INC
NEW ENGLAND BUILDING SUPPLY
174 Hampden St, Boston, MA 02119-2836
Tel (617) 445-5900 *Founded/Ownrshp* 2009
Sales 35.6MME *EMP* 48
SIC 5031 Building materials, exterior; Building materials, interior
Pr: Russell J Smith

D-U-N-S 01-976-7645
HH GLOBAL USA INC
(*Suby of* HH GLOBAL LIMITED)
175 E Hawthorn Pkwy # 325, Vernon Hills, IL 60061-1463
Tel (847) 816-6303 *Founded/Ownrshp* 2011
Sales 200.0MM *EMP* 90
SIC 8742 Marketing consulting services
CEO: Robert Macmillan
**Ch Bd:* Stuart Wallis
**CFO:* Andrew Lipinski
**CFO:* Edward Parsons

H.H. GREGG
See GREGG APPLIANCES INC

D-U-N-S 08-007-7510
HH HEALTH SYSTEM - SHOALS LLC (AL)
1300 S Mongomery Ave, Sheffield, AL 35660
Tel (256) 386-4673 *Founded/Ownrshp* 2014
Sales 2.2MME *EMP* 1,500
SIC 8062 General medical & surgical hospitals

D-U-N-S 00-563-2385
HH HOLDINGS INC
HUDDLE HOUSE
2969 E Ponce De Leon Ave, Decatur, GA 30030-2215
Tel (404) 377-5700 *Founded/Ownrshp* 1985
Sales 17.5MME *EMP* 750
SIC 5812 6794 5046 Fast-food restaurant, chain; Franchises, selling or licensing; Restaurant equipment & supplies; Fast-food restaurant, chain; Franchises, selling or licensing; Restaurant equipment & supplies
Pr: Philip M Greifeld
IT Man: Kenneth Grim

D-U-N-S 02-669-1444
HH LIQUIDATING CORP
ZINC CORPORATION AMERICA DIV
110 E 59th St Fl 34, New York, NY 10022-1308
Tel (646) 282-2500 *Founded/Ownrshp* 1981
Sales 86.0MME *EMP* 843
SIC 3624 2999 3356 3339 Carbon & graphite products; Electrodes, thermal & electrolytic uses: carbon, graphite; Carbon specialties for electrical use; Coke, calcined petroleum: made from purchased materials; Coke (not from refineries), petroleum; Lead & zinc; Zinc refining (primary), including slabs & dust; Carbon & graphite products; Electrodes, thermal & electrolytic uses: carbon, graphite; Carbon specialties for electrical use; Coke, calcined petroleum: made from purchased materials; Coke (not from refineries), petroleum; Lead & zinc; Zinc refining (primary), including slabs & dust
Ch Bd: William E Flaherty

D-U-N-S 96-939-5982
HH MEDSTAR HEALTH INC
5565 Sterrett Pl Ste 500, Columbia, MD 21044-2679
Tel (410) 772-6500 *Founded/Ownrshp* 2011
Sales 282.3MM *EMP* 8E
Accts Kpmg Llp Mc Lean Va
SIC 8082 Home health care services; Home health care services
Pr: Kenneth A Samet

HH RIGS AND SERVICES
See HONGHUA AMERICA LLC

D-U-N-S 01-509-8147
HH VENTURES LLC
READY WIRELESS
955 Kacena Rd Ste A, Hiawatha, IA 52233-1327
Tel (319) 294-6080 *Founded/Ownrshp* 2008
Sales 32.6MME *EMP* 80
SIC 7389 Telephone services; Telephone services
CFO: James Balvanz
Board of Directors: Stephen C Gray

HH&HC
See HOME HEALTH AND HOSPICE CARE INC

HHA SERVICES, INC.
See ABM HEALTHCARE SUPPORT SERVICES INC

HHC
See HOUSING AND HEALTHCARE FINANCE LLC

D-U-N-S 01-183-8619
HHC FOUNDATION OF NEW YORK CITY INC
160 Water St Fl 10, New York, NY 10038-5037
Tel (646) 458-2810 *Founded/Ownrshp* 2008
Sales NA *EMP* 35,000
Accts Kpmg Llp New York Ny
SIC 6321 Fraternal accident & health insurance organizations
Ch Bd: Michael Stocker

D-U-N-S 07-489-2076
■ **HHC INC**
(*Suby of* HOUSECALL HOME HEALTH) ★
6501 Deane Hill Dr, Knoxville, TN 37919-6006
Tel (865) 292-6000 *Founded/Ownrshp* 1994
Sales 25.0MME *EMP* 2,000
SIC 8082 Home health care services; Home health care services
Pr: Ladonna Dolomantino
**Pr:* Greg Davis

D-U-N-S 01-798-6595
HHC PHYSICIANSCARE INC
85 Seymour St Ste 425, Hartford, CT 06106-5523
Tel (860) 240-7099 *Founded/Ownrshp* 2012
Sales 78.2MME *EMP* 4E
SIC 8011 Cardiologist & cardio-vascular specialist
Ch: James P Cardon
**Treas:* Thomas Marchozzi

D-U-N-S 95-683-0095
HHCP DESIGN INTERNATIONAL INC
HELMAN HUR CHAR PEA ARCH INC
(*Suby of* H H C P INC)
120 N Orange Ave, Orlando, FL 32801-2309
Tel (407) 644-2656 *Founded/Ownrshp* 1991
Sales 27.0MM *EMP* 70
SIC 8712 Architectural services; Architectural services
Pr: Lawrence W Ziebarth
**CEO:* Dill Charvat
**Treas:* William C Charvat
Ex VP: William Charvat
**Sr VP:* Charles S Braun
**Sr VP:* Michael Chatham
**Sr VP:* Gregory Dungan
**Sr VP:* Mark R Gustetter
**Sr VP:* Alan C Helman
**Sr VP:* Richard D Houston
**Sr VP:* John H Jordan
**Sr VP:* Christopher F Obrien
**Sr VP:* Maureen A Walker
**VP:* John T Diflumeri
**VP:* Raymond Hsu
VP: John Newlin
VP: Joan Thyer
VP: James Warring
Board of Directors: Charles S Braun, William C Charval, Alan C Helman

D-U-N-S 07-841-7838
■ **HHG DISTRIBUTING LLC** (IN)
(*Suby of* GREGG APPLIANCES INC) ★
4151 E 96th St, Indianapolis, IN 46240-1442
Tel (317) 848-8710 *Founded/Ownrshp* 2004, 2014
Sales 94.5ME *EMP* 1,160E
SIC 8742 Distribution channels consultant
CEO: Dennis L May

D-U-N-S 80-691-9515
▲ **HHGREGG INC**
4151 E 96th St, Indianapolis, IN 46240-1414
Tel (317) 848-8710 *Founded/Ownrshp* 1955
Sales 2.1MMM *EMP* 5,400
Tkr Sym HGG *Exch* NYS
SIC 5731 5722 5712 Radio, television & electronic stores; Household appliance stores; Furniture stores; Radio, television & electronic stores; Household appliance stores; Furniture stores
Pr: Dennis L May
**Ch Bd:* Michael L Smith
CFO: Robert J Riesbeck
Chf Mktg O: Keith M Zimmerman
Ofcr: Charles B Young
VP: Donna Desilets
VP: Steve Piegza
VP: James W Witcher
Rgnl Mgr: Joey Elkins
Rgnl Mgr: Curtis Etheridge
Rgnl Mgr: Mike Hood
Board of Directors: Gregory M Bettinelli, Lawrence P Castellani, Benjamin D Geiger, Catherine A Langham, John M Roth, Peter M Starrett, Kathleen C Tierney

D-U-N-S 96-594-6671
HHH CHOICES HEALTH PLAN LLC
(*Suby of* HEBREW HOSPITAL HOME INC) ★
2100 Bartow Ave Unit 18, Bronx, NY 10475-4614
Tel (718) 678-6000 *Founded/Ownrshp* 2006
Sales 34.0MM *EMP* 59
SIC 8082 8361 8741 Home health care services; Rehabilitation center, residential: health care incidental; Nursing & personal care facility management; Home health care services; Rehabilitation center, residential: health care incidental; Nursing & personal care facility management
CFO: Brian Perino

HHH HOME CARE
See HEBREW HOSPITAL HOME INC

D-U-N-S 84-404-0746
HHH HOME CARE INC
61 Grasslands Rd, Valhalla, NY 10595-1543
Tel (914) 681-8666 *Founded/Ownrshp* 2008
Sales 47.0MM *EMP* 12E
Accts Abbate Demarinis Llp Garden C
SIC 8082 Home health care services; Home health care services
Ex Dir: Peter Sanna
Dir QC: Lauren Huber
Sls Mgr: Jose Lozano

HHH METRODOME
See METROPOLITAN SPORTS FACILITIES COMMISSION FOUNDATION INC

D-U-N-S 01-004-4865
HHHUNT CORP (VA)
800 Hethwood Blvd, Blacksburg, VA 24060-4207
Tel (540) 552-3515 *Founded/Ownrshp* 1972
Sales 52.6MME *EMP* 1,500
SIC 6513 Apartment building operators; Apartment building operators
CEO: Harry Hunt IV
**Ch Bd:* Harry H Hunt III
Pr: James Nicholson
COO: Daniel Schmitt

Ex VP: David Crowder
VP: James R King
VP: David E Tuggle
Exec: Pam Gibson
S&M/VP: Larry Mills

D-U-N-S 15-449-7523
HHHUNT PROPERTY MANAGEMENT INC
800 Hethwood Blvd, Blacksburg, VA 24060-4207
Tel (540) 552-3515 *Founded/Ownrshp* 1983
Sales 24.5MME *EMP* 1,000
SIC 6513 Apartment building operators; Apartment building operators
Pr: David E Reem Snyder
**Ch:* Harry H Hunt III
**VP:* Jim King
**VP:* Janet Riddlebarger
**VP:* David Tuggle
VP Bus: James Nicholson

D-U-N-S 07-867-1135
■ **HHI FORGING LLC**
(*Suby of* HHI GROUP HOLDINGS LLC) ★
2727 W 14 Mile Rd, Royal Oak, MI 48073-1712
Tel (248) 284-2900 *Founded/Ownrshp* 2005
Sales 110.0MME *EMP* 500E
SIC 3462 Automotive forgings, ferrous: crankshaft, engine, axle, etc.; Automotive forgings, ferrous: crankshaft, engine, axle, etc.

D-U-N-S 19-045-4988 IMP
HHI FORMTECH INDUSTRIES LLC
2727 W 14 Mile Rd, Royal Oak, MI 48073-1712
Tel (248) 597-3800 *Founded/Ownrshp* 2006
Sales 166.2MME *EMP* 600
SIC 3463 Automotive forgings, nonferrous; Automotive forgings, nonferrous
Ex VP: Richard J Larkin
**COO:* R Harris
**CFO:* Charles Moore
CFO: Chip Moore
Ofcr: Chris Jones
VP: Paul Barlow
Admn Mgr: Tim Welbaum
Plnt Mgr: Terry Cornell
Ql Cn Mgr: Kris Ianitelli
Ql Cn Mgr: Anna Pachut
Mktg Mgr: Harding Fears

D-U-N-S 96-219-6577
■ **HHI GROUP HOLDINGS LLC**
(*Suby of* METALDYNE PERFORMANCE GROUP INC) ★
2727 W 14 Mile Rd, Royal Oak, MI 48073-1712
Tel (248) 597-3800 *Founded/Ownrshp* 2012
Sales 108.5MME *EMP* 500E
SIC 7549 Automotive maintenance services; Automotive maintenance services
CEO: George Thanopoulos
VP: Dennis Cutright

D-U-N-S 60-856-6717
HHJ HOLDINGS LIMITED
830 Kirts Blvd, Troy, MI 48084-4892
Tel (248) 652-9716 *Founded/Ownrshp* 1998
Sales 124.8MME *EMP* 950
SIC 1611 2951 Highway & street paving contractor; Asphalt & asphaltic paving mixtures (not from refineries); Highway & street paving contractor; Asphalt & asphaltic paving mixtures (not from refineries)

D-U-N-S 07-916-8672
HHL HOLDINGS INC
HONOLULU HOMELOANS
745 Fort Street Mall # 1001, Honolulu, HI 96813-3800
Tel (808) 681-7500 *Founded/Ownrshp* 2011
Sales 35.5MME *EMP* 154E
SIC 6719 Investment holding companies, except banks
CEO: Thomas Zimmerman
**Pr:* Chason Ishii
CFO: Wendy Odo
Bd of Dir: Chad Okumura
Ofcr: Kelli Ishii
Ofcr: Caprice Itagaki
Ofcr: Scott Lee
Ex VP: Paul Andes
Ex VP: Earl Ching
Ex VP: Sharon Miyazaki
Ex VP: Wendy Zane
Sr VP: Tana Feeley
Sr VP: Paulette Suzuki
VP: Ryan Nakagawa
VP: Darnell Souza

HHM
See 44 NEW ENGLAND MANAGEMENT CO

D-U-N-S 60-550-6005
HHS HEALTH OPTIONS
H H S
2100 Raybrook St Se # 203, Grand Rapids, MI 49546-7759
Tel (616) 956-9440 *Founded/Ownrshp* 1980
Sales 21.6MM *EMP* 58
SIC 8742 Hospital & health services consultant; Hospital & health services consultant
Pr: Denise Zoeterman
Exec: Doug Himmelein

D-U-N-S 14-304-5115
HHSA LP
6700 W Interstate 10, San Antonio, TX 78201-2009
Tel (210) 736-6700 *Founded/Ownrshp* 2004
Sales 28.4MME *EMP* 283
SIC 8062 General medical & surgical hospitals; General medical & surgical hospitals
Pt: Craig Desmond
Pt: Dina Gonzalez
Pt: Cindy Y Henning
CFO: Dianh Gonzales
VP: Michael Allen
VP: Douglas Watkins
Exec: Miriam Babiak
Dir Lab: Barbara Pavey
Dir QC: Sandy Diaz
Psych: Hector Escamilla
Psych: Jude Espinoza

HHSC
See HAWAII HEALTH SYSTEMS CORP

HHSC
See TEXAS HEALTH AND HUMAN SERVICES COMMISSION

D-U-N-S 01-748-7443
HI -TECH TESTING SERVICES INC
35 Frj Dr, Longview, TX 75602-4703
Tel (903) 753-1412 Founded/Ownrshp 1996
Sales 36.3MM^E EMP 220^E
SIC 7389 Inspection & testing services; Inspection & testing services
Pr: Jamie Davis
*COO: Richard Bundrick
*CFO: Marshall Hammack
Ofcr: Eddie Gentry
*VP: Scott Lohr
*VP: Larry Richardson
Brnch Mgr: Matt Barefield
Brnch Mgr: Chris Davis
Opers Mgr: Chase Kindle

D-U-N-S 07-917-2266
■ HI CRUSH AUGUSTA LLC
(Suby of HI-CRUSH PARTNERS LP) ★
11011 S County Rd M, Augusta, WI 54722
Tel (715) 286-2079 Founded/Ownrshp 2012
Sales 14.8MM^E EMP 276^E
SIC 4731 Freight forwarding
Pr: Ray Hargrove

D-U-N-S 05-128-6706
HI DEVELOPMENT CORP
111 W Fortune St, Tampa, FL 33602-3206
Tel (813) 229-6686 Founded/Ownrshp 1959
Sales 60.5MM^E EMP 1,000
SIC 8741 Hotels & motels; Hotel or motel management
Pr: Andre Callen
*VP: Claire Callen
*VP: David H Callen
*VP: Robinson Callen
*Pr: Tarquin Callen
VP: David Clement
Off Mgr: Victoria Schrock

D-U-N-S 03-418-1495
HI NABOR SUPER MARKET INC
7201 Winbourne Ave, Baton Rouge, LA 70805-5593
Tel (225) 357-1448 Founded/Ownrshp 1963
Sales 27.3MM^E EMP 235
SIC 5411 2051 Supermarkets, independent; Bread, cake & related products; Supermarkets, independent; Bread, cake & related products
Pr: Samuel J Crifasi
*Treas: Jan Crifasi
*VP: Jim Crifasi

D-U-N-S 00-678-2122
HI PLAINS COOPERATIVE ASSOCIATION (KS)
HI-PLAINS CO-OP
405 E 4th St, Colby, KS 67701-2526
Tel (785) 462-3351 Founded/Ownrshp 1949
Sales 49.2MM^E EMP 65
SIC 5153 5191 Grain elevators; Feed; Fertilizer & fertilizer materials; Chemicals, agricultural; Grain elevators; Feed; Fertilizer & fertilizer materials; Chemicals, agricultural
Pr: John Strecker
Off Mgr: Dennis E Applegate

D-U-N-S 07-797-3824
HI REL CONNECTORS INC
HIREL CONNECTORS
760 Wharton Dr, Claremont, CA 91711-4800
Tel (909) 626-1820 Founded/Ownrshp 1967
Sales 62.9MM^E EMP 300
SIC 3643 3678 Connectors & terminals for electrical devices; Electronic connectors; Connectors & terminals for electrical devices; Electronic connectors
Pr: Fred Baumann
*Pr: Frederick Bb Baumann
Mng Ofcr: Rod Booty
CTO: Robert Reynozo
Ql Cn Mgr: Rod Ordonez
Sales Asso: Cristina Lafon

HI ROLLER CONVEYORS
See HANSEN MANUFACTURING CORP

HI TECH CONSULTANTS
See HTC GLOBAL SERVICES INC

D-U-N-S 60-927-8775
HI TECH HONEYCOMB INC
9355 Ruffin Ct, San Diego, CA 92123-5304
Tel (858) 974-1600 Founded/Ownrshp 1989
Sales 35.4MM^E EMP 136
SIC 3469 Honeycombed metal; Honeycombed metal
CEO: Joao J Costa
*Pr: Selma Costa
*CEO: John J Costa
*VP: John Costa
QA Dir: Stephen Eggleston
Ql Cn Mgr: Sergio Enriquez

D-U-N-S 00-418-6516
HI TECMETAL GROUP INC (OH)
HYDRO-VAC
1101 E 55th St, Cleveland, OH 44103-1026
Tel (216) 881-8100 Founded/Ownrshp 1943
Sales 20.6MM^E EMP 90
SIC 3398 7692 Brazing (hardening) of metal; Annealing of metal; Tempering of metal; Welding repair
Pr: Terence C Profughi
*VP: Cole Coe
*VP: Gregory Hercil
*Prin: Harold M Baron
*Prin: Mary C Finley
*Prin: N M Salkover

D-U-N-S 83-716-5021 IMP
▲ HI-CRUSH PARTNERS LP
3 Riverway Ste 1550, Houston, TX 77056-1916
Tel (713) 960-4777 Founded/Ownrshp 2012
Sales 386.5MM EMP 342^E
Tkr Sym HCLP Exch NYS
SIC 1442 1481 Sand mining; Mine & quarry services, nonmetallic minerals; Mine exploration, nonmetallic minerals; Sand mining; Mine & quarry services, nonmetallic minerals; Mine exploration, nonmetallic minerals
Co-CEO: Robert E Rasmus
Genl Pt: Hi-Crush GP LLC
COO: Jefferies V Alston III
Co-CEO: James M Whipkey
VP: Chad McEver
Natl Sales: Tony Curcio

HI-DESERT MEDICAL CENTER
See HI-DESERT MEMORIAL HEALTH CARE DISTRICT

D-U-N-S 07-252-2295
HI-DESERT MEMORIAL HEALTH CARE DISTRICT
HI-DESERT MEDICAL CENTER
6601 White Feather Rd, Joshua Tree, CA 92252-6607
Tel (760) 366-3711 Founded/Ownrshp 1964
Sales 81.7MM^E EMP 535
SIC 8062 Hospital, affiliated with AMA residency; Hospital, affiliated with AMA residency
CEO: Keith Mesmer
Dir Recs: Sharon Kulch
*CFO: Thoma Duda
Dir Rx: Herman Galicia
Nrsg Dir: Teresa Turbysill
Pharmcst: Al Wray

D-U-N-S 06-325-8826
HI-HEALTH SUPERMART CORP
7428 E Karen Dr Ste 200, Scottsdale, AZ 85260-2479
Tel (480) 951-9000 Founded/Ownrshp 1972
Sales 36.0MM^E EMP 200
SIC 5499 5961 Health foods; Food, mail order; Health foods; Food, mail order
CEO: Mitchell A Chalpin
COO: Jay Chopra
CFO: Lee Biberdorf
VP: Sunil Vulli
Prgrm Mgr: Christine Pembleton
Dist Mgr: Kim Fotiades
Dist Mgr: Jeff Hanks
Genl Mgr: Michael Slover
Dir IT: Brent Riggs

D-U-N-S 02-089-0059 IMP
HI-LEX AMERICA INC
(Suby of TSK OF AMERICA INC) ★
5200 Wayne Rd, Battle Creek, MI 49037-7392
Tel (269) 968-0781 Founded/Ownrshp 1975
Sales 118.3MM^E EMP 1,100
SIC 3496 3357 Cable, uninsulated wire: made from purchased wire; Nonferrous wiredrawing & insulating; Cable, uninsulated wire: made from purchased wire; Nonferrous wiredrawing & insulating
Ch Bd: Katsuaki Shima
*Pr: Tom Strictland
Sr VP: Ernest Waterhouse
VP: William Freeman
Exec: Annette Fredrick
Dir IT: Lee Lantz
IT Man: Dave Cubic
IT Man: Chris Cullingford
VP Opers: Toshio Fujimoto
Sfty Mgr: Kadena Warren
Opers Mgr: Tom Strickland
Board of Directors: K Tokuhiro, Thomas G Welsh

D-U-N-S 60-607-5836 IMP
HI-LEX CONTROLS INC
(Suby of TSK OF AMERICA INC) ★
152 Simpson Dr, Litchfield, MI 49252-9601
Tel (517) 542-2955 Founded/Ownrshp 1989
Sales 42.1MM^E EMP 177
SIC 3714 Motor vehicle parts & accessories; Motor vehicle electrical equipment; Motor vehicle parts & accessories; Motor vehicle electrical equipment
Pr: Tom Strickland
*COO: Tomoharu Otane
Snr Sftwr: Jeff Bliss
Snr Sftwr: June Rook
IT Man: Katsuaki Tokuhrio
Ql Cn Mgr: Bruce Krol
Ql Cn Mgr: William Scott
Ql Cn Mgr: Patti West

D-U-N-S 03-501-6328
HI-LINE COOPERATIVE INC
203 S Perkins Ave, Elsie, NE 69134-2028
Tel (308) 228-2291 Founded/Ownrshp 1963
Sales 71.8MM EMP 51
Accts Horst & Associates Pc Gran
SIC 5172 5191 Gasoline; Diesel fuel; Lubricating oils & greases; Fertilizer & fertilizer materials; Gasoline; Diesel fuel; Lubricating oils & greases; Fertilizer & fertilizer materials
Pr: Roy Evans

D-U-N-S 00-499-9561
HI-LINE ELECTRIC CO
2121 Valley View Ln, Dallas, TX 75234-8912
Tel (972) 247-6200 Founded/Ownrshp 1959
Sales 24.5MM^E EMP 170
SIC 5065 5731 5063 Connectors, electronic; Consumer electronic equipment; Electrical apparatus & equipment; Wire & cable; Connectors, electronic; Consumer electronic equipment; Electrical apparatus & equipment; Wire & cable
Pr: Mike Sheaffer
*Treas: Brian Grzymkowski
VP: Mark Boutwell
VP: Chris Cunningham
VP: Steve Duncan
VP: Jason Greenwald
VP: Felix Heimberg
VP: Pete Murdock
*VP: Kyle Schlabach
IT Man: Scott Ainsworth
IT Man: John Mixtacki

D-U-N-S 07-926-2248
HI-LITE AIRFIELD SERVICES LLC
18249 Hi Lite Dr, Adams Center, NY 13606
Tel (315) 583-6111 Founded/Ownrshp 2014
Sales 32.0MM EMP 150
SIC 4959 Road, airport & parking lot maintenance services
CFO: Theodore Misiewicz

D-U-N-S 86-696-5841
HI-LO MANAGEMENT CO
8601 Tabner, Houston, TX 77075
Tel (713) 991-6052 Founded/Ownrshp 2009
Sales 12.6MM^E EMP 300
SIC 5531 Automotive parts; Automotive accessories; Automotive parts; Automotive accessories
Pr: T Young
*Sr VP: Dirk A Hoyt
*VP: K Grant Hutchins

HI-PLAINS CO-OP
See HI PLAINS COOPERATIVE ASSOCIATION

HI-PLAS
See HIGHLAND PLASTICS INC

HI-PRO ANIMAL HEALTH
See FRIONA INDUSTRIES LP

D-U-N-S 02-115-8892
HI-PRO FEEDS INC
(Suby of HI-PRO FEEDS LP)
1201 E 11th St, Friona, TX 79035-1410
Tel (806) 250-2791 Founded/Ownrshp 2006, 2012
Sales 126.1MM^E EMP 425^E
SIC 2048 Prepared feeds; Prepared feeds
CEO: Dean Prevost
*Sr VP: Daren Kennett
VP: Mark Knief
Plnt Mgr: Tony Hiscock
Plnt Mgr: Lonnie Holland
Plnt Mgr: Gavin Keylock
Plnt Mgr: Robert Kruger
Plnt Mgr: Mark Osborne
Sales Asso: Kody Kimbrough
Sales Asso: Donald Schulze
Snr Mgr: David Smiddy

HI-SCHOOL PHARMACY HARDWARE &
See HI-SCHOOL PHARMACY INC

D-U-N-S 08-662-2487 IMP
HI-SCHOOL PHARMACY INC
HI-SCHOOL PHARMACY HARDWARE &
916 W Evergreen Blvd, Vancouver, WA 98660-3035
Tel (360) 693-5879 Founded/Ownrshp 1967
Sales 60.2MM^E EMP 300
SIC 5912 5251 5331 Drug stores; Builders' hardware; Variety stores; Drug stores; Builders' hardware; Variety stores
Pr: Steven J Oliva
*Treas: Janice Oliva
VP: Steve Oliva

D-U-N-S 00-828-8938 IMP
HI-SHEAR CORP
(Suby of LISI AEROSPACE)
2600 Skypark Dr, Torrance, CA 90505-5373
Tel (310) 784-4025 Founded/Ownrshp 1996
Sales 209.6MM^E EMP 1,070
SIC 3452 3429 Bolts, nuts, rivets & washers; Aircraft hardware; Bolts, nuts, rivets & washers; Aircraft hardware
CEO: Christian Darville
CFO: Jean S Micheletti
VP: Edmond Balassanian
VP: Jack Smith
CTO: Paul Maddox
IT Man: Christine Schreiber

D-U-N-S 15-087-5169
HI-TEC BUILDING SERVICES INC
6578 Roger Dr Ste A, Jenison, MI 49428-7303
Tel (616) 662-1623 Founded/Ownrshp 1991
Sales 7.8MM EMP 475^E
SIC 7349 Janitorial service, contract basis; Janitorial service, contract basis
Ch: Steven Lemmon
*Pr: Brain Hogan
CFO: Jennifer Ruff
*VP: Ryan Rinvelt
Dir Bus: Misty Yohannan
Off Mgr: Marilyn Walker
Opers Mgr: Stephen King

D-U-N-S 03-732-4928 IMP
HI-TEC SPORTS USA INC (CA)
(Suby of HI-TEC SPORTS PUBLIC LIMITED COMPANY)
4801 Stoddard Rd, Modesto, CA 95356-9318
Tel (209) 545-1111 Founded/Ownrshp 1978
Sales 35.2MM^E EMP 80
Accts Atherton & Associates Llp Mo
SIC 5139 Footwear, athletic; Boots; Footwear, athletic; Boots
CEO: Simon Bonham
CEO: Ed Van Wezel
CFO: William Berta
Ch: Frank Van Wezel
Prin: Brad Gebhard
Genl Mgr: Bill Delaplane
Mktg Dir: Trace Metcalf
Pr Mgr: Dayna Pierce
Mktg Mgr: Darin Jesberg
Sls Mgr: Scott Chantos
Sls Mgr: Giuseppe Ciminaghi

D-U-N-S 92-882-5876
HI-TEC SYSTEMS INC
6727 Delilah Rd, Egg Harbor Township, NJ 08234-9798
Tel (609) 272-1515 Founded/Ownrshp 1995
Sales 23.5MM^E EMP 120
SIC 8711 7371 Engineering services; Computer software development & applications; Engineering services; Computer software development & applications
Pr: Trib Singh
VP: Barry Rich
VP: Mark Rodgers
Genl Mgr: Kalpana Jain
Dir IT: Bill Stevens

HI-TECH BUILDING AUTOMATION
See ANDY J EGAN CO INC

HI-TECH COLOR
See CREPS UNITED PUBLICATIONS INC

HI-TECH DURAVENT
See FLEXIBLE TECHNOLOGIES INC

D-U-N-S 13-039-1998
HI-TECH ELECTRIC INC
HTE CONTRACTORS
11116 W Little York Rd # 8, Houston, TX 77041-5024
Tel (832) 243-0345 Founded/Ownrshp 1984
Sales 82.3MM EMP 300
Accts Sutton Frost Cary Llp
SIC 1731 Electrical work; Electrical work
Ch Bd: William Chase Canfield III
*Pr: Clarke Battle
*Sec: Patrick G McConn
*VP: Rick Booms
*VP: Troy Drouant
*VP: Mike Hanley
VP: Wendell Hill
*VP: Pat Russo
*VP: Ken Sauer
Board of Directors: Clarke Battle, William Chase Canfield III, Mike Hodge, Pat McConn, Charles Nettles, Pat Russo

D-U-N-S 01-390-0217
HI-TECH ELECTRONIC MANUFACTURING CORP
HITEM
7420 Carroll Rd, San Diego, CA 92121-2304
Tel (858) 657-0908 Founded/Ownrshp 1997
Sales 24.7MM^E EMP 80
SIC 3672 Circuit boards, television & radio printed
Pr: Vinh Lam
Prgrm Mgr: Sherry Nguyen
QA Dir: Kevin Pham
VP Sls: Dan Shepard
Mktg Dir: Nan Truong

D-U-N-S 11-918-7789 IMP
HI-TECH FABRICATION INC
8900 Midway West Rd, Raleigh, NC 27617-4604
Tel (919) 781-6150 Founded/Ownrshp 1984
Sales 29.6MM^E EMP 145
SIC 3469 3444 3479 3471 Stamping metal for the trade; Sheet metalwork; Painting of metal products; Chromium plating of metals or formed products
Pr: Joseph W Barbee
VP: Ralph Sandle
*VP: Kevin Sook
*VP: A Toney
*VP: Tyler Toney
VP Mfg: George Toney
Ql Cn Mgr: Thomas Talley

D-U-N-S 18-538-8980
HI-TECH FASTENERS INC
4940 Winchester Blvd, Frederick, MD 21703-7400
Tel (301) 874-3160 Founded/Ownrshp 1994
Sales 22.4MM EMP 46
Accts Cohn Reznick Llp Bethesda M
SIC 5085 Fasteners, industrial: nuts, bolts, screws, etc.; Fasteners, industrial: nuts, bolts, screws, etc.
Ch Bd: Thomas Waller Jr
*VP: Wayne A Conners
Genl Mgr: Mark Mertz
Genl Mgr: Edward Soorikian
Sales Exec: Daniel Amell
Sls Mgr: Ed Holland
Sales Asso: Amelia Bednarczyk
Sales Asso: Ashley Conners
Sales Asso: Michael Dafonseca
Sales Asso: Sherry Fisher
Sales Asso: Michael Kaiser

D-U-N-S 96-160-3805
HI-TECH MANUFACTURING LLC
9815 Leland Ave, Schiller Park, IL 60176-1328
Tel (847) 678-1616 Founded/Ownrshp 2012
Sales 33.2MM^E EMP 130^E
SIC 3541 Machine tools, metal cutting: exotic (explosive, etc.); Machine tools, metal cutting: exotic (explosive, etc.)
Pr: Aldo Eagle
Pr: Simon Sorsher
VP: Gregory Goldfarb
IT Man: Neoma Arcari
Plnt Mgr: Michael Netiuk

D-U-N-S 18-113-5807 IMP
HI-TECH MOLD & ENGINEERING INC
2775 Commerce Dr, Rochester Hills, MI 48309-3815
Tel (248) 852-6600 Founded/Ownrshp 1982
Sales 58.8MM^E EMP 175
SIC 3544 Forms (molds), for foundry & plastics working machinery; Dies, plastics forming; Forms (molds), for foundry & plastics working machinery; Dies, plastics forming
Ch: Siegfried Schulte
*Pr: Robert Schulte
*CFO: Shaun D Karn
Off Mgr: Mike Coussens
QC Dir: Matthew Perry
Mfg Mgr: Mike Olbrys
Sls Dir: Tom Liberati

HI-TECH PHARMACAL - AN AKORN
See HI-TECH PHARMACAL CO INC

D-U-N-S 10-119-6749 IMP
■ HI-TECH PHARMACAL CO INC
HI-TECH PHARMACAL - AN AKORN
(Suby of AKORN INC) ★
369 Bayview Ave, Amityville, NY 11701-2801
Tel (631) 789-8228 Founded/Ownrshp 2014
Sales 96.1MM^E EMP 448^E
SIC 2834 Pharmaceutical preparations; Pharmaceutical preparations
Pr: David S Seltzer
Pr: Gary M April
CFO: William Peters
Ex VP: Elan Barr
Ex VP: Kamel Egbaria
VP: Gary April
VP: Poli Dondeti
VP: Jesse Kirsh
VP: Tom Kronvich

VP: Chris Losardo
VP: Joseph Mataty
VP: Bill Peters
VP: Margaret Santorufo
Exec: Colleen Cooke
Dir Lab: Malini Batheja
Assoc Dir: Lana Vostrova

D-U-N-S 05-372-9492 IMP/EXP
HI-TECH PHARMACEUTICALS INC
6015 Unity Dr Ste B, Norcross, GA 30071-3575
Tel (770) 797-9959 *Founded/Ownrshp* 2009
Sales 51.4MM^E *EMP* 60^E
SIC 5122 Vitamins & minerals
Pr: Jared Wheat
VP: Stephen Smith

D-U-N-S 07-981-2559
HI-TECH WELD OVERLAY GROUP LLC
1695 Se Decker St, Lees Summit, MO 64081-3112
Tel (816) 524-9010 *Founded/Ownrshp* 2013
Sales 25.0MM *EMP* 25
SIC 3548 3589 Resistance welders, electric; Commercial cooking & foodwarming equipment
Pr: Paul O'Donald
CFO: Dennis Henderson
VP: Kent Lamfer

D-U-N-S 09-901-8236
HI-TEK MANUFACTURING INC
6050 Hi Tek Ct, Mason, OH 45040-2602
Tel (513) 459-1094 *Founded/Ownrshp* 1979
Sales 65.9MM^E *EMP* 180
SIC 3599 7692 3724 3714 3544 Machine shop, jobbing & repair; Welding repair; Aircraft engines & engine parts; Motor vehicle parts & accessories; Special dies, tools, jigs & fixtures; Machine shop, jobbing & repair; Welding repair; Aircraft engines & engine parts; Motor vehicle parts & accessories; Special dies, tools, jigs & fixtures
Pr: Cletis Jackson
QA Dir: Craig Enderle
Plnt Mgr: Scott Stang
Ql Cn Mgr: George Carrington
Sls Mgr: Brad Gundbrun

D-U-N-S 15-180-3988
HI-TEK PROFESSIONALS INC
850 Chester Pike, Prospect Park, PA 19076-2412
Tel (610) 534-8701 *Founded/Ownrshp* 1986
Sales 32.9MM *EMP* 160
SIC 7363 Temporary help service; Temporary help service
Pr: Joseph Parcell
**Sec:* Gregory S Ambrose
**VP:* Philip A Validi

D-U-N-S 19-853-9041 IMP/EXP
HI-TEK RATIONS INC
2002 Waldrep Indus Blvd, Dublin, GA 31021-2630
Tel (478) 272-8826 *Founded/Ownrshp* 1988
Sales 35.0MM *EMP* 120
SIC 2047 2048 Dog & cat food; Prepared feeds; Dog & cat food; Prepared feeds
Pr: Leonard Powell
Ofcr: Phillip Scott
**VP:* Sue Powell

D-U-N-S 07-228-0423 IMP
HI-TEMP INSULATION INC
4700 Calle Alto, Camarillo, CA 93012-8489
Tel (805) 484-2774 *Founded/Ownrshp* 1980
Sales 80.1MM *EMP* 410
Accts Bpe & H An Accountancy Corpor
SIC 3296 3469 Mineral wool; Fiberglass insulation; Acoustical board & tile, mineral wool; Spinning metal for the trade; Mineral wool; Fiberglass insulation; Acoustical board & tile, mineral wool; Spinning metal for the trade
CEO: Sieg Borck
Exec: Donna Porter
Genl Mgr: Elenita Aquino
IT Man: Kathleen Creamer
Mfg Dir: Mike Sieger
Mtls Mgr: Tracy Couldy
Mtls Mgr: Tracy Gouldy
Prd Mgr: Jay Wood
Ql Cn Mgr: Nathan Nunag
Ql Cn Mgr: Rick Spires
Sls Mgr: Jim Roth

D-U-N-S 06-778-3399 IMP
HI-TEMP METALS INC
HIGH TEMP METALS
12500 Foothill Blvd, Sylmar, CA 91342-6038
Tel (800) 500-2141 *Founded/Ownrshp* 1972
Sales 35.5MM *EMP* 19
SIC 5051

D-U-N-S 14-592-0760
HI-TOUCH IMAGING TECHNOLOGIES INC
(*Suby of* HITI DIGITAL, INC.)
727 Brea Canyon Rd Ste 2, Walnut, CA 91789-3014
Tel (909) 974-0099 *Founded/Ownrshp* 2002
Sales 80.0MM *EMP* 14
SIC 5045 5734 Printers, computer; Printers & plotters: computers; Printers, computer; Printers & plotters: computers
Pr: Wen Cheng Lee
**Genl Mgr:* Kerwin Yen

D-U-N-S 18-329-2643
HI-VOL PRODUCTS LLC
12955 Inkster Rd, Livonia, MI 48150-2212
Tel (734) 266-6900 *Founded/Ownrshp* 2011
Sales 41.8MM^E *EMP* 68
Accts Mcgladrey Llp Chicago Illino
SIC 5084 3399 Fuel injection systems; Metal fasteners; Fuel injection systems; Metal fasteners
Pr: Eli Crotzer
VP: Randy Hinz

D-U-N-S 08-233-8310 IMP
HI-WAY DISTRIBUTING CORP OF AMERICA
3716 E State St, Barberton, OH 44203-4548
Tel (330) 645-6633 *Founded/Ownrshp* 1975
Sales 33.8MM^E *EMP* 60
SIC 5199 5731 General merchandise, non-durable; Sound equipment, automotive
Pr: Jeff Hornak
VP: Spencer Falvo
**Prin:* J L Miller
**Prin:* Joseph P Mueller
**Prin:* Dominic A Musitano Jr
Manager: Eric Emerson
Sls Mgr: Mike Bennett
Sls Mgr: Jason Hile
Sls Mgr: Terry Johnson

D-U-N-S 06-598-9253
HI-WAY PAVING INC
4343 Weaver Ct N, Hilliard, OH 43026-1193
Tel (614) 876-1700 *Founded/Ownrshp* 1995
Sales 45.5MM^E *EMP* 100
SIC 1611 Concrete construction: roads, highways, sidewalks, etc.; Surfacing & paving; Airport runway construction; Concrete construction: roads, highways, sidewalks, etc.; Surfacing & paving; Airport runway construction
CEO: Charles L Keith
**Pr:* James Taylor
**CFO:* Mark Lamonte
Treas: Wils Vandam
**Ex VP:* Brad Allison
VP: Dustin Keith
**Prin:* Gail E Griffith

D-U-N-S 01-745-0180
HIA INC
1105 W 122nd Ave, Denver, CO 80234-3419
Tel (303) 394-6040 *Founded/Ownrshp* 1974
Sales 73.2MM^E *EMP* 92
Accts Hein & Associates Llp Denver
SIC 5083 5084 Irrigation equipment; Pumps & pumping equipment; Irrigation equipment; Pumps & pumping equipment
Pr: Alan Bergold

D-U-N-S 00-233-6600 IMP/EXP
HIAB USA INC
(*Suby of* CARGOTEC OYJ)
12233 Williams Rd, Perrysburg, OH 43551-6802
Tel (419) 482-6000 *Founded/Ownrshp* 1991
Sales 91.7MM^E *EMP* 140
SIC 5084 3536 Cranes, industrial; Hoists; Cranes, industrial plant; Hoists; Cranes, industrial; Hoists; Cranes, industrial plant; Hoists
Pr: Roland Sunden
**Pr:* Lennart Brelin
CFO: Howard Case
VP: June Aiello
Area Mgr: Kim Osborn
IT Man: Mary Gallagher
Sls&Mrk Ex: Katherine Warner
Advt Dir: Jeff Rosenberg
Sls Mgr: Mike Gonzalez

HIALEAH HOSPITAL
See TENET HIALEAH HEALTHSYSTEM INC

D-U-N-S 07-773-7989
HIAS INC
333 7th Ave Rm 1600, New York, NY 10001-5019
Tel (212) 967-4100 *Founded/Ownrshp* 1954
Sales 31.2MM *EMP* 70
Accts Loeb & Troper Llp New York N
SIC 8322 Refugee service
CEO: Mark Hetfield
CFO: Farhan Irshad
Bd of Dir: Bobbie Abrams
Ex VP: Jamie Metzl
Sr VP: Sussan Khozouri
VP: Melanie Nezer
Prin: Francine Stein
Snr Mgr: Elissa Mittman

HIATUS
See CREW KNITWEAR LLC

D-U-N-S 01-744-2653
HIAWATHA BROADBAND COMMUNICATIONS INC
H B C
58 Johnson St, Winona, MN 55987-3420
Tel (507) 474-4000 *Founded/Ownrshp* 1997
Sales 30.0MM^E *EMP* 90^E
Accts Wolter & Raak Ltd Rochester
SIC 4899 4841 4813 7375 Data communication services; Cable television services; ; Information retrieval services
Ch Bd: Robert Kierlin
**Pr:* Gary Evans
**Pr:* Dan Pecarina
**CFO:* Manuel Deangel
**Treas:* Pete Woodworth
Creative D: Lucia Kinghorn
Genl Mgr: Dean Otomo
CIO: Bechly Rita
CTO: Todd Schaefer
Netwrk Mgr: Pete Scherbring
VP Mktg: Brian Robertson

D-U-N-S 06-504-1386
HIBBARD NURSING HOME INC
1037 W Main St, Dover Foxcroft, ME 04426-3752
Tel (207) 564-8129 *Founded/Ownrshp* 1964
Sales 627.5MM *EMP* 135
SIC 8052 8051 Intermediate care facilities; Skilled nursing care facilities; Intermediate care facilities; Skilled nursing care facilities
Pr: Jane Hibbard-Merrill
Nrsg Dir: Melissa Phillips
HC Dir: Suzanne Reed

D-U-N-S 01-910-6277
HIBBERT & MCGEE WHOLESALERS INC
10 Pleasant St, East Barre, VT 05649
Tel (802) 476-5750 *Founded/Ownrshp* 1956
Sales 25.5MM *EMP* 25
SIC 5141

D-U-N-S 00-236-7761
HIBBERT CO
400 Pennington Ave, Trenton, NJ 08618-3105
Tel (609) 392-0478 *Founded/Ownrshp* 1933
Sales 84.8MM^E *EMP* 446
SIC 7331 7389 Direct mail advertising services; Printers' services: folding, collating; Direct mail advertising services; Printers' services: folding, collating
CEO: Timothy J Moonan
**Ch Bd:* Joan Moonan
COO: Brad Byrnes
**Sr VP:* Ron Arellano
**Sr VP:* Mario Devincenzi
**Sr VP:* Rosemary M Hober
Sr VP: Michael Phillips
**Sr VP:* Kenneth J Swiatkowski
**Sr VP:* Paul Zukowski
VP: Michael Cofone
VP: Mario De Vincenzi
VP: George Dowbnia
Exec: Judy Keepers

D-U-N-S 79-741-1964 IMP
■ **HIBBETT SPORTING GOODS INC**
HIBBETT SPORTS
(*Suby of* HIBBETT SPORTS INC) ★
2700 Milan Ct, Birmingham, AL 35211-6919
Tel (205) 942-4292 *Founded/Ownrshp* 1992
Sales 529.9MM^E *EMP* 5,200
SIC 5941 5661 5699 Sporting goods & bicycle shops; Team sports equipment; Footwear, athletic; Sports apparel; Sporting goods & bicycle shops; Team sports equipment; Footwear, athletic; Sports apparel
CEO: Michael J Newsome
**Pr:* Jeffrey O Rosenthal
**CFO:* Gary A Smith
Sr VP: Scott Bowman
VP: Mark Dobbins
VP: Jeff Gray
VP: Rob Irwin
VP: Chuck Mallett
**VP:* Cathy E Pryor
Exec: Joy McCord
Genl Mgr: Rob Watson

HIBBETT SPORTS
See HIBBETT SPORTING GOODS INC

D-U-N-S 79-273-9000 IMP
▲ **HIBBETT SPORTS INC**
2700 Milan Ct, Birmingham, AL 35211-6919
Tel (205) 942-4292 *Founded/Ownrshp* 1945
Sales 913.4MM *EMP* 8,700^E
Tkr Sym HIBB *Exch* NGS
SIC 5941 5661 5699 Sporting goods & bicycle shops; Team sports equipment; Footwear, athletic; Sports apparel; Sporting goods & bicycle shops; Team sports equipment; Footwear, athletic; Sports apparel
Pr: Jeffry O Rosenthal
CFO: Scott J Bowman
Sr VP: Jared S Briskin
Sr VP: Cathy E Pryor
Board of Directors: Jane F Aggers, Anthony F Crudele, Terrance G Finley, Albert C Johnson, Carl Kirkland, Michael J Newsome, Ralph T Parks, Thomas A Saunders III, Alton E Yother

D-U-N-S 05-031-3799 EXP
■ **HIBBING TACONITE CO**
(*Suby of* CLIFFS NATURAL RESOURCES INC) ★
4950 Highway 5, Hibbing, MN 55746-8409
Tel (218) 262-5950 *Founded/Ownrshp* 1994
Sales 23.0MM^E *EMP* 51^E
SIC 3339 Primary nonferrous metals
Prin: Jack Tuomi
Area Mgr: Jack Croswell

D-U-N-S 06-654-2952 IMP
HIBBING TACONITE CO (A JOINT VENTURE)
200 Public Sq Ste 3300, Cleveland, OH 44114-2315
Tel (216) 694-5700 *Founded/Ownrshp* 1973
Sales 1.1MMM^E *EMP* 1,560
SIC 1011 Iron ore mining; Iron ore pelletizing; Iron ore beneficiating; Iron ore mining; Iron ore pelletizing; Iron ore beneficiating
CEO: Joseph A Carrabba
Ex VP: Laurie Brlas
Ex VP: Donald Gallagher

D-U-N-S 05-086-0071
HIBBS-HALLMARK & CO
CLAIMS ADMINISTRATIVE SERVICE
501 Shelley Dr Ste 200, Tyler, TX 75701-9553
Tel (903) 561-8484 *Founded/Ownrshp* 1964
Sales NA *EMP* 69
SIC 6411 Insurance agents; Advisory services, insurance
Pr: Gary Howell
**CFO:* Karlista Patterson
**Ex VP:* Mark Blackbourn
**Ex VP:* Robert P Monaghan
Sr VP: Darin Cowart
**Sr VP:* David Dover
**Sr VP:* Brenda Thomas
VP: Gerald Barker
**VP:* Pam Golsan

D-U-N-S 61-164-5420
HIBERNATION HOLDING CO INC
VERMONT TEDDY BEAR COMPANY
6655 Shelburne Rd, Shelburne, VT 05482-6500
Tel (802) 985-3001 *Founded/Ownrshp* 2005
Sales 19.8MM^E *EMP* 290
SIC 3942 5961 Stuffed toys, including animals; Toys & games (including dolls & models), mail order; Stuffed toys, including animals; Toys & games (including dolls & models), mail order
Pr: John Gilbert
Mktg Mgr: Christian Manley

D-U-N-S 01-217-8831 IMP
HIBU INC
(*Suby of* HIBU PLC)
210 Rxr Plz, Uniondale, NY 11556-3814
Tel (516) 730-1900 *Founded/Ownrshp* 1930, 2001
Sales 1.1MMM^E *EMP* 7,000
SIC 2741 Directories: publishing & printing; Directories: publishing & printing
CEO: Mike Pocock
Genl Pt: Mark Boudreau
**Ch Bd:* John Condron
Pr: Chaffan Flynn
**Pr:* Joseph Walsh
**COO:* Mark Payne
**CFO:* Tony Bates
**CFO:* Jim Haddad
**Ch:* Bob Wigley
Sr Cor Off: Stephen Wolf
Ofcr: Patrick J Marshall
Ex VP: Jerry Kingkade
Sr VP: Victoria Sharrar
VP: Kevin Ashcroft
VP: Thomas Cody
VP: John Davis
VP: Kevin Jasper
VP: Jeff Lulenski
VP: Lisa Mueller
VP: Greg Sirianni
VP: Kathleen Tupker

D-U-N-S 03-540-4672
HICKEL INVESTMENT CO
HOTEL CAPTAIN COOK, THE
939 W 5th Ave, Anchorage, AK 99501-2049
Tel (907) 276-6000 *Founded/Ownrshp* 1948
Sales 26.2MM^E *EMP* 415
SIC 7011 6512 5812 5813 7991 5087 Hotels; Commercial & industrial building operation; Family restaurants; Cocktail lounge; Athletic club & gymnasiums, membership; Service establishment equipment; Hotels; Commercial & industrial building operation; Family restaurants; Cocktail lounge; Athletic club & gymnasiums, membership; Service establishment equipment
Pr: Robert Hickel
**CFO:* Matthew Thiel
**VP:* Walter J Hickel Jr
Sls Mgr: Alex Wong

D-U-N-S 09-915-5632
HICKEY AND EASTON LTD
MEDICAL STAFFING SERVICES
1834 Sw 58th Ave Ste 103, Portland, OR 97221-1455
Tel (503) 292-2735 *Founded/Ownrshp* 1979
Sales 11.1MM^E *EMP* 300
SIC 7363 7361 Temporary help service; Employment agencies; Temporary help service; Employment agencies
Pr: R Michael Hickey
**CEO:* Patrick Easton

HICKMAN COUNTY FINANCE OFFICE
See COUNTY OF HICKMAN

D-U-N-S 07-979-8811
HICKMAN COUNTY SCHOOLS
115 Murphree Ave, Centerville, TN 37033-1443
Tel (931) 729-3391 *Founded/Ownrshp* 2015
Sales 5.3MM^E *EMP* 444^E
SIC 8211 Public elementary & secondary schools
Bd of Dir: Jim Hudgins

HICKMAN FAMILY FARMS
See HICKMANS EGG RANCH INC

D-U-N-S 06-794-7507
HICKMAN MILLS C-1 SCHOOL DISTRICT
9000 Old Santa Fe Rd, Kansas City, MO 64138-3913
Tel (816) 316-7000 *Founded/Ownrshp* 1902
Sales 73.5MM^E *EMP* 1,500
SIC 8211 Public elementary & secondary schools; School board; Public elementary & secondary schools; School board
HC Dir: Yolanda Cargile

D-U-N-S 00-699-9460 IMP
HICKMAN WILLIAMS & CO
250 E 5th St Ste 300, Cincinnati, OH 45202-4198
Tel (513) 621-1946 *Founded/Ownrshp* 1890, 1922
Sales 247.2MM *EMP* 92
Accts Grant Thornton Llp Cincinnat
SIC 5051 5052 5169 5085 5084 Metals service centers & offices; Ferroalloys; Pig iron; Coal & other minerals & ores; Coke; Coal; Chemicals & allied products; Abrasives; Industrial machinery & equipment; Metals service centers & offices; Ferroalloys; Pig iron; Coal & other minerals & ores; Coke; Coal; Chemicals & allied products; Abrasives; Industrial machinery & equipment
Pr: David H Gelwicks
**Treas:* Pamela J Evans
**Treas:* Terry L Meadors
**VP:* Robert E Davis
VP: Terry Meadors
**VP:* Steven W Stark

D-U-N-S 03-586-4263 IMP
HICKMANS EGG RANCH INC
HICKMAN FAMILY FARMS
6515 S Jackrabbit Trl, Buckeye, AZ 85326-5641
Tel (623) 872-1120 *Founded/Ownrshp* 1944
Sales 44.1MM^E *EMP* 100^E
SIC 0252 5191 5499 7389 Chicken eggs; Feed; Eggs & poultry;
Pr: Glen Mitchell Hickman
COO: Lori Hickman
**Sec:* Gertrude Hickman
**VP:* Billy Grey Hickman
IT Man: David Davenport
Mtls Mgr: David Goss
Opers Mgr: Michael Kibbey
Plnt Mgr: Cheryl Gardner

D-U-N-S 08-910-7932
HICKOK & BOARDMAN INC
KEMPER INSURANCE
346 Shelburne Rd Ste 3a, Burlington, VT 05401-4938
Tel (802) 658-3500 *Founded/Ownrshp* 1821
Sales NA *EMP* 55
SIC 6411 Insurance agents
Pr: Scott Boardman
**Treas:* Mary Ann Dion
Sr VP: Michael Boardman Jr
**Sr VP:* Paul E Plunkett
VP: Brian Aitchison
**VP:* I Munn Boardman III
**VP:* Mary Ann Bradanese
**VP:* Steven K J Gentile

Genl Mgr: Brenda Schill
Dir IT: Shannon King
VP Mktg: Sybil Chicoine

D-U-N-S 82-541-4055
HICKORY AUTOMALL CHRYSLER PLYMOUTH INC
HICKORY R V CENTER
3300 Centennial Blvd, Claremont, NC 28610-9697
Tel (828) 459-9790 *Founded/Ownrshp* 1990
Sales 28.2MM^E *EMP* 92
SIC 5511 Automobiles, new & used; Automobiles, new & used
Pr: John Cathey
**VP:* Jerry Kahill
Sls Mgr: Jeff Schollnick

HICKORY BAR & GRILL
See SPRINGFIELD RESTAURANT GROUP INC

D-U-N-S 12-804-5148 IMP
■ HICKORY BUSINESS FURNITURE LLC
HBF TEXTILES
(*Suby of* HNI CORP) ★
900 12th Street Dr Nw, Hickory, NC 28601-4763
Tel (828) 322-1169 *Founded/Ownrshp* 1979
Sales 74.2MM^E *EMP* 650
SIC 2521 2299 Wood office furniture; Batting, wadding, padding & fillings; Wood office furniture; Batting, wadding, padding & fillings
Pr: Stan A Askren
**CFO:* Kurt A Tjaden
CFO: Karen Wilson
**Ex VP:* Don Mead
**VP:* Steven M Bradford
VP: Jill Vandersleet-Scott
Exec: Steve Taranto
Sales Asso: Alison Dimola

HICKORY CITY SCHOOLS
See HICKORY PUBLIC SCHOOLS

D-U-N-S 00-347-0788
HICKORY CONSTRUCTION CO (NC)
1728 9th Ave Nw, Hickory, NC 28601-3367
Tel (828) 322-9234 *Founded/Ownrshp* 1941
Sales 38.8MM^E *EMP* 98
SIC 1542 1541 1623

D-U-N-S 09-504-7247 IMP
HICKORY CONSTRUCTION INC
124 Kent Pl, Alcoa, TN 37701-1947
Tel (865) 983-7856 *Founded/Ownrshp* 1977
Sales 38.7MM *EMP* 48
SIC 1542 1521

D-U-N-S 08-021-0573
HICKORY CREEK HEALTHCARE FOUNDATION INC
5555 Glenridge Connector # 650, Atlanta, GA 30342-4761
Tel (678) 990-7262 *Founded/Ownrshp* 1999
Sales 36.1MM *EMP* 450
Accts Bradley & Associates Inc Indi
SIC 8051 Skilled nursing care facilities
Pr: Francis J Crosby
**CFO:* John Stoddard

D-U-N-S 05-107-3898 IMP
HICKORY CREEK NURSERY INC
20601 S La Grange Rd, Frankfort, IL 60423-1390
Tel (815) 469-1044 *Founded/Ownrshp* 1969
Sales 42.6MM^E *EMP* 175
SIC 5261 5251 Nurseries & garden centers; Hardware; Nurseries & garden centers; Hardware
Pr: David Christakes
**Pr:* William Christakes
**VP:* Chris Shepard
Off Mgr: Steffani Harm

D-U-N-S 17-520-7489 IMP
HICKORY FARMS INC
(*Suby of* SUN CAPITAL PARTNERS INC) ★
811 Madison Ave Fl 5, Toledo, OH 43604-5616
Tel (419) 893-7611 *Founded/Ownrshp* 2007
Sales 28.5MM^E *EMP* 95
SIC 5499 5961 5149 Gourmet food stores; Food, mail order; Specialty food items; Food gift baskets
Pr: Mark S Rodriguez
**CFO:* Joe Herman
**Chf Mktg O:* Michael Holton
**VP:* Ty Hanline
**VP:* Joe Loch
VP: James O Neill
Prd Mgr: Bryan Bouley
Prd Mgr: Arin Mosburger

D-U-N-S 14-644-6856
HICKORY FOODS INC
BUBBA BURGER
4339 Roosevelt Blvd # 400, Jacksonville, FL 32210-2004
Tel (904) 482-1900 *Founded/Ownrshp* 1995
Sales 23.6MM^E *EMP* 30^E
SIC 5147 2011 Meats & meat products; Meat packing plants
Pr: William Morris
**CFO:* Clark Schaffer

D-U-N-S 07-062-9001
HICKORY GROVE BAPTIST CHURCH CHARLOTTE NORTH CAROLINA INC
HICKORY GROVE BOOKSTORE
6050 Hickory Grove Rd, Charlotte, NC 28215-4197
Tel (704) 531-4000 *Founded/Ownrshp* 1955
Sales 23.0MM *EMP* 601
Accts Cherry Bekaert & Holland Ll
SIC 8661 Baptist Church; Baptist Church
IT Man: David A Romn

HICKORY GROVE BOOKSTORE
See HICKORY GROVE BAPTIST CHURCH CHARLOTTE NORTH CAROLINA INC

D-U-N-S 09-875-1514
■ HICKORY POINT BANK & TRUST
(*Suby of* ARCHER-DANIELS-MIDLAND CO) ★
225 N Water St Ste 102, Decatur, IL 62523-2377
Tel (217) 875-3131 *Founded/Ownrshp* 1986
Sales NA *EMP* 200
SIC 6021 6022 National commercial banks; State commercial banks; National commercial banks; State commercial banks
Pr: Anthony Mestler
**VP:* Peggy Myers

D-U-N-S 96-376-3672
■ HICKORY PRINTING SOLUTIONS LLC
(*Suby of* CONSOLIDATED GRAPHICS INC) ★
725 Reese Dr Sw, Conover, NC 28613-2935
Tel (828) 465-3431 *Founded/Ownrshp* 2010
Sales 24.9MM^E *EMP* 97^E
SIC 2752 2759 2791 2789 Color lithography; Labels & seals: printing; Typesetting; Bookbinding & related work
Pr: Stephen Patton
Plnt Mgr: David Londree

D-U-N-S 10-005-8619
HICKORY PUBLIC SCHOOLS
HICKORY CITY SCHOOLS
432 4th Ave Sw, Hickory, NC 28602-2805
Tel (828) 322-2855 *Founded/Ownrshp* 1903
Sales 40.1MM *EMP* 565
Accts Anderson Smith & Wike Pllc S
SIC 8211 Public elementary & secondary schools; Public elementary & secondary schools
VP: Rae Perez

HICKORY R V CENTER
See HICKORY AUTOMALL CHRYSLER PLYMOUTH INC

D-U-N-S 00-321-6850 IMP/EXP
HICKORY SPRINGS MANUFACTURING CO (NC)
HSM SOLUTIONS
235 2nd Ave Nw, Hickory, NC 28601-4950
Tel (828) 328-2201 *Founded/Ownrshp* 1944
Sales 426.9MM^E *EMP* 2,500
SIC 3069 3495 2514 5072 2399

D-U-N-S 14-852-2436 IMP
HICKORY SPRINGS OF CALIFORNIA INC
(*Suby of* HICKORY SPRINGS MANUFACTURING CO) ★
235 2nd Ave Nw, Hickory, NC 28601-4950
Tel (828) 328-2201 *Founded/Ownrshp* 1985
Sales 53.6MM^E *EMP* 607
SIC 3429 3086 Furniture hardware; Plastics foam products; Furniture hardware; Plastics foam products
Ch: David Underdown
**Ch Bd:* Parks C Underdown Jr
**Pr:* J Donald Coleman
**Sr VP:* Lee Lunsford

HICKORY WHITE COMPANY
See H W S CO INC

D-U-N-S 00-106-3130
HICKS BILL & CO LTD (MN)
15155 23rd Ave N, Minneapolis, MN 55447-4740
Tel (763) 476-6200 *Founded/Ownrshp* 1975
Sales 63.9MM^E *EMP* 90
SIC 5091 Hunting equipment & supplies
CEO: William W Hicks
**Pr:* Shelly Binstock
Sls Mgr: Beth Olson
Sales Asso: John Giebenhain

HICKS, ED NISSAN/MERCEDES/BENZ
See EDWARD S HICKS SR

D-U-N-S 62-279-0405
HICKS HOLDINGS LLC
2200 Ross Ave Ste 5000, Dallas, TX 75201-7902
Tel (214) 615-2300 *Founded/Ownrshp* 2004
Sales 157.2MM^E *EMP* 2,033
SIC 3679 Liquid crystal displays (LCD); Liquid crystal displays (LCD)
V Ch: Paul Savoldelli
COO: Joseph Armes
COO: Casey Shilts
VP: Curt Crofford
Exec: Mack Hicks
Mng Dir: Rick Neuman
Secur Mgr: Clark Emmert

D-U-N-S 00-402-9674 IMP
HICKS INC (AL)
95 W 3rd St, Luverne, AL 36049-1349
Tel (334) 335-3311 *Founded/Ownrshp* 1895
Sales 36.2MM^E *EMP* 70
SIC 5091 Fishing equipment & supplies; Hunting equipment & supplies
Pr: John M Wise Jr
**Ch Bd:* John M Wise Sr
**Sec:* Lilellen H Wise
VP: Mark Vandagriff
Sls Mgr: Scott Siefert
Sls Mgr: Mike Sullivan

D-U-N-S 00-693-5530
■ HICKS OILS & HICKSGAS INC
PROPANE CENTRAL
(*Suby of* NGL ENERGY PARTNERS LP) ★
204 N State Routes 54, Roberts, IL 60962
Tel (217) 895-2281 *Founded/Ownrshp* 2010
Sales 33.4MM^E *EMP* 35
SIC 5171 5984

D-U-N-S 19-698-0288
HICKS PLASTICS CO INC
51308 Industrial Dr, Macomb, MI 48042-4025
Tel (586) 786-5640 *Founded/Ownrshp* 1988
Sales 42.4MM^E *EMP* 115
SIC 3089 Injection molding of plastics; Injection molding of plastics
Pr: Carl E Hicks
**Ex VP:* Gail P Hicks
Genl Mgr: Tim Hicks
Genl Mgr: Eric Lavine

Off Mgr: Karen Haase
Plnt Mgr: Jeff Ward
Ql Cn Mgr: Sherry McCleary
Sls Mgr: Eric Raynsford

D-U-N-S 84-028-8919
HICKS SPORTS GROUP HOLDINGS LLC
100 Crescent Ct Ste 1200, Dallas, TX 75201-7860
Tel (214) 615-2300 *Founded/Ownrshp* 1999
Sales 9.4MM^E *EMP* 370
SIC 8741 Business management; Business management
CFO: Joseph B Armes

D-U-N-S 01-807-6380
HICKSVILLE GRAIN CO
259 E High St, Hicksville, OH 43526-1108
Tel (419) 542-6287 *Founded/Ownrshp* 1914
Sales 25.8MM *EMP* 29
SIC 5153 Grain elevators; Grain elevators
Pr: Tim Miller
**Pr:* Ben Shuman

HICKSVILLE MARATHON
See SLATTERY OIL CO INC

D-U-N-S 03-705-6413
HICKSVILLE UNION FREE SCHOOL DISTRICT (INC)
200 Division Ave, Hicksville, NY 11801-4827
Tel (516) 733-6600 *Founded/Ownrshp* 1901
Sales 104.3MM *EMP* 590
SIC 8211 Public elementary school; Public junior high school; Public senior high school; Public elementary school; Public junior high school; Public senior high school
**Treas:* Sharon Denueo
Schl Brd P: Phil Heckler

D-U-N-S 55-628-8280 IMP
HID GLOBAL CORP
(*Suby of* ASSA ABLOY INC) ★
611 Center Ridge Dr, Austin, TX 78753-1013
Tel (800) 237-7769 *Founded/Ownrshp* 2000
Sales 275.2MM^E *EMP* 961
SIC 3825 1731 8741 Radio frequency measuring equipment; Access control systems specialization; Management services; Radio frequency measuring equipment; Access control systems specialization; Management services
Pr: Denis Hebert
Sr VP: Rodney Glass
Sr VP: Tam Hulusi
VP: Marc Bielmann
VP: Bridget Burke
VP: Rob Haslam
VP: Mary Procyk
VP: Mary Procykv
VP: Debra Spitler
Snr Sftwr: Don McCoy
IT Man: Steven Roman

D-U-N-S 06-240-3597
HIDALGO COUNTY HEADSTART PROGRAM INC
1901 W State Highway 107, McAllen, TX 78504-9552
Tel (956) 383-0706 *Founded/Ownrshp* 1982
Sales 15.6MM^E *EMP* 600
SIC 8351 Head start center, except in conjunction with school; Head start center, except in conjunction with school
IT Man: Nora Muniz
Board of Directors: Robert Garate, Ramiro Guerra, Luciano Ozuna Jr

HIDALGO COUNTY WELFARE DEPT
See COUNTY OF HIDALGO

D-U-N-S 02-355-7663
HIDALGO INDEPENDENT SCHOOL DISTRICT SCHOLARSHIP FOUNDATION
324 Flora Ave, Hidalgo, TX 78557-4001
Tel (956) 843-3100 *Founded/Ownrshp* 1965
Sales 25.8MM^E *EMP* 500
Accts Pattillo Brown & Hill Llp Br
SIC 8211 Public elementary & secondary schools; High school, junior or senior; Public elementary & secondary schools; High school, junior or senior
Pr: Jose Rodriguez
**Treas:* Yesenia Ayala
**VP:* Carlos Cardoza Sr
Prin: Trine Barron
**Prin:* Blanca Lara
Instr Medi: Jennifer Bieillareal
HC Dir: Velma Molano

D-U-N-S 96-249-3730
HIDALGO INDUSTRIAL SERVICES INC
2535 Brennan Ave, Fort Worth, TX 76106-8408
Tel (817) 625-8222 *Founded/Ownrshp* 1992
Sales 75.1MM^E *EMP* 300^E
SIC 1711 Plumbing, heating, air-conditioning contractors; Plumbing, heating, air-conditioning contractors
CEO: Lanny Mooney
**Ex VP:* Jim Schneider
Sls&Mrk Ex: Pat Teagarden

HIDDEN CREEK COUNTRY CLUB
See FORE GOLF SERVICES LP

D-U-N-S 85-846-0509
HIDDEN EYES LLC
ENVERA SYSTEMS
4171 W Hillsboro Blvd # 2, Coconut Creek, FL 33073-2154
Tel (561) 910-5826 *Founded/Ownrshp* 2007
Sales 24.0MM^E *EMP* 45^E
SIC 5065 Security control equipment & systems
IT Man: Jeffrey Goodall

HIDDEN MEADOWS SHELL PLAZA
See LONESTAR PETROLEUM LP

D-U-N-S 96-224-2751
HIDDEN VALLEY COMPANIES INC
HV
1218 Pacific Oaks Pl, Escondido, CA 92029-2900
Tel (760) 466-7100 *Founded/Ownrshp* 2007
Sales NA *EMP* 300
Accts Akt Llp Escondido California
SIC 4731 Freight transportation arrangement; Freight transportation arrangement
CEO: Robert L Berti

D-U-N-S 18-329-6581
HIDDEN VALLEY INVESTMENTS INC
QUALITY CHEVROLET
1550 Auto Park Way, Escondido, CA 92029-2059
Tel (760) 745-7221 *Founded/Ownrshp* 1985
Sales 41.3MM^E *EMP* 90
SIC 5511 Automobiles, new & used; Automobiles, new & used
Pr: Joe Herold
**Sec:* Judy Repp
**VP:* Charles R Hebard
Genl Mgr: Lewis Singleterry
IT Man: Tom Rupert
Sls Mgr: Junior Bernal

D-U-N-S 02-813-8543
HIDDEN VALLEY MOVING AND STORAGE INC
1218 Pacific Oaks Pl, Escondido, CA 92029-2900
Tel (602) 252-7800 *Founded/Ownrshp* 1976
Sales 21.5MM^E *EMP* 120
SIC 4214 4213 Local trucking with storage; Contract haulers
CEO: Robert L Berti
**CFO:* David Boeller
Genl Mgr: Steve Gibson
IT Man: Quirk Tim

HIDDEN VILLA RANCH
See LUBERSKI INC

HIDDEN VILLA RANCH
See LUBERSKI INC

HIDY HONDA
See HIDY MOTORS INC

D-U-N-S 06-396-3136
HIDY MOTORS INC
HIDY HONDA
2300 Hller Drv Bevr Crk Beaver Creek, Dayton, OH 45434
Tel (937) 426-9564 *Founded/Ownrshp* 1980
Sales 35.1MM^E *EMP* 120
SIC 5511 5012 7515 Automobiles, new & used; Pickups, new & used; Vans, new & used; Automobiles & other motor vehicles; Passenger car leasing; Automobiles, new & used; Pickups, new & used; Vans, new & used; Automobiles & other motor vehicles; Passenger car leasing
Pr: David Hidy
**CFO:* Rita Mayes
Off Mgr: Rita Mays

D-U-N-S 94-140-1192
HIE HOLDINGS INC
2839 Mokumoa St, Honolulu, HI 96819-4402
Tel (808) 833-2244 *Founded/Ownrshp* 1981
Sales 101.8MM^E *EMP* 514^E
SIC 2095 7993 Roasted coffee; Coin-operated amusement devices
Pr: Michael Boulware
**Treas:* Karen Erwin
**Sr VP:* Steven Boulware
VP: Sidney Bouleware
**VP:* Glenn Boulware
Sls&Mrk Ex: Eloise Kim

HIENS
See GREENSPOINT PLAZA LTD PARTNERSHIP

D-U-N-S 11-820-3710
HIFFMAN SHAFFER ASSOCIATES INC
NAI-HIFFMAN
1 Oakbrook Ter Ste 600, Oakbrook Terrace, IL 60181-4485
Tel (630) 932-1234 *Founded/Ownrshp* 1986
Sales 41.7MM^E *EMP* 208
SIC 6531 6552 Real estate brokers & agents; Real estate managers; Subdividers & developers; Real estate brokers & agents; Real estate managers; Subdividers & developers
CEO: Dennis J Hiffman
COO: David Petersen
CTO: Douglas Mueller
Ofcr: Michael Flynn
Ex VP: James Adler
Ex VP: Duke Botthof Jr
Ex VP: John Cash
Ex VP: Joseph Geisel
VP: Brian Edgerton

D-U-N-S 04-077-6611
HIG
300 Corporate Center Dr, Camp Hill, PA 17011-1760
Tel (717) 302-5108 *Founded/Ownrshp* 2010
Sales 8.7MM^E *EMP* 361^E
SIC 8211 Elementary & secondary schools
Prin: Suzanne Andrews

D-U-N-S 96-302-6575
HIG ALL AMERICAN LLC
1450 Brickell Ave # 3100, Miami, FL 33131-3444
Tel (305) 379-2322 *Founded/Ownrshp* 1998
Sales 71.8MM^E *EMP* 612^E
SIC 6211 Investment firm, general brokerage; Investment firm, general brokerage
Pr: Richard M Lavers
IT Man: Richard Braman
IT Man: Yolanda Descartin

HIG CAPITAL
See HIG CAPITAL PARTNERS III LP

HIG CAPITAL
See ASHTON-POTTER USA LTD

D-U-N-S 14-845-7620
▲ HIG CAPITAL INC
1450 Brickell Ave # 3100, Miami, FL 33131-3460
Tel (305) 379-2322 *Founded/Ownrshp* 1998
Sales 204.9MM^E *EMP* 519

SIC 8742 6211 Management consulting services; Investment firm, general brokerage; Management consulting services; Investment firm, general brokerage
Pr: Sami Mnaymneh
**Pr:* Anthony Tamer
CFO: Bret Wiener
VP: David Correa
VP: Mike Gallagher
VP: Wang Hai
VP: Robert Jang
VP: Enoch Kariuki
VP: Arjun Mohan
VP: Joseph Pagliuca
VP: Chris Paldino
VP: Zaid Pardesi
VP: Matthew Robinson
VP: Praneeth Wanigasekera

D-U-N-S 13-462-2534 IMP
HIG CAPITAL LLC
1450 Brickell Ave Fl 31, Miami, FL 33131-3460
Tel (305) 379-2322 *Founded/Ownrshp* 1998
Sales 2.1MMM^E *EMP* 6,046^E
SIC 6211 Investment firm, general brokerage; Investment firm, general brokerage

D-U-N-S 82-489-1477
HIG CAPITAL MANAGEMENT INC
1450 Brickell Ave Fl 31, Miami, FL 33131-3460
Tel (305) 379-2322 *Founded/Ownrshp* 1993
Sales 5.0MMM^E *EMP* 17,010
SIC 6211 Investment firm, general brokerage; Investment firm, general brokerage
Pr: Sami Mnaymneh
Ofcr: David Dungan
VP: Blair Holert
VP: Paul Phillips
**VP:* Anthony Tamer
Prin: J Rn-Marc Vogler
Mng Dir: Jens Alsleben
**Mng Dir:* Doug Berman
**Mng Dir:* John Black
**Mng Dir:* John Bolduc
Mng Dir: Olivier Boyadjian

D-U-N-S 15-322-5631
HIG CAPITAL PARTNERS III LP
HIG CAPITAL
(*Suby of* HIG CAPITAL MANAGEMENT INC) ★
1450 Brickell Ave # 3100, Miami, FL 33131-3444
Tel (305) 379-2322 *Founded/Ownrshp* 2002
Sales 87.8MM^E *EMP* 530
SIC 6211 5084 7352 7699 8748 3842 Security brokers & dealers; Safety equipment; Medical equipment rental; Medical equipment repair, non-electric; Safety training service; Surgical appliances & supplies; Security brokers & dealers; Safety equipment; Medical equipment rental; Medical equipment repair, non-electric; Safety training service; Surgical appliances & supplies
Mng Pt: Sami Mnaymneh
Mng Dir: Doug Berman

D-U-N-S 07-858-8116 IMP
HIG MIDDLE MARKET LLC
1 Market Spear Tower 18f, San Francisco, CA 94105
Tel (415) 439-5500 *Founded/Ownrshp* 2008
Sales 126.7MM^E *EMP* 1,800^E
SIC 8021 Dentists' office; Dentists' office
Co-CEO: Sami Mnaymneh
Co-CEO: Tony Tamer

D-U-N-S 82-527-8968
HIG TRANSPORT HOLDINGS INC
(*Suby of* HIG CAPITAL LLC) ★
1450 Brickell Ave Fl 31, Miami, FL 33131-3460
Tel (305) 379-2322 *Founded/Ownrshp* 2007
Sales 23.1MM^E *EMP* 1,258
SIC 8742 Management consulting services; Management consulting services
Pr: Anthony Tamer

HIGA FOOD SERVICE
See HIGA MEAT AND PORK MARKET LIMITED

D-U-N-S 03-318-7360 IMP
HIGA MEAT AND PORK MARKET LIMITED
HIGA FOOD SERVICE
225 N Nimitz Hwy Unit 2, Honolulu, HI 96817-5349
Tel (808) 531-3591 *Founded/Ownrshp* 1945
Sales 21.0MM^E *EMP* 35
SIC 5147 5421 Meats, fresh; Meat markets, including freezer provisioners; Meats, fresh; Meat markets, including freezer provisioners
Pr: Sheldon Wright
**VP:* Jerry Higa

D-U-N-S 02-260-3901
HIGDON CONSTRUCTION INC
G & H CONSTRUCTION
28471 Robinson Rd, Conroe, TX 77385-7533
Tel (281) 465-4117 *Founded/Ownrshp* 1999
Sales 26.0MM *EMP* 120^E
SIC 1542 Commercial & office building contractors
Pr: Johnny W Higdon

D-U-N-S 00-978-2111
HIGGERSON-BUCHANAN INC
5300 Bainbridge Blvd, Chesapeake, VA 23320-6712
Tel (757) 545-4665 *Founded/Ownrshp* 1946
Sales 33.1MM^E *EMP* 122
SIC 1629 1611 1542

HIGGINBOTHAM BARTLETT
See HIGGINBOTHAM HOLDINGS LTD

D-U-N-S 00-792-4707
HIGGINBOTHAM HOLDINGS LTD (TX)
HIGGINBOTHAM BARTLETT
202 W Central Ave, Comanche, TX 76442-2702
Tel (325) 356-3456 *Founded/Ownrshp* 1901, 1999
Sales 76.0MM *EMP* 321
SIC 5211 5251 Home centers; Builders' hardware; Home centers; Millwork & lumber; Builders' hardware
CEO: Rufus H Duncan Jr
**COO:* Corby Biddle
**CFO:* Donald Smith

D-U-N-S 83-986-9435
HIGGINBOTHAM INSURANCE AGENCY INC
500 W 13th St Ste 200, Fort Worth, TX 76102-4659
Tel (817) 334-3200 *Founded/Ownrshp* 1948
Sales NA *EMP* 90^E
SIC 6411 Insurance agents; Insurance agents
CEO: Rusty Reid
**CFO:* James Krause
Ex VP: Douglas Dickerson
Mng Dir: William Blanchard
Mng Dir: John Huggins
Mng Dir: Rob Marsh
Mng Dir: Brian Penny
Mng Dir: Mark Vann
Mng Dir: David Weeks
Mktg Dir: Chris Rocker
Mktg Dir: Laurel Wilson

D-U-N-S 02-032-2418
HIGGINBOTHAM INSURANCE AGENCY MCKINNEY INC
500 W 13th St Ste 200, Fort Worth, TX 76102-4659
Tel (817) 336-2377 *Founded/Ownrshp* 1989
Sales NA *EMP* 240
SIC 6411 Insurance agents & brokers; Insurance agents & brokers
Pr: James R Reid
**CFO:* James Krause
VP: Paul Harrison
**VP:* James Hubbard
**VP:* R Morgan Woodruff

D-U-N-S 12-512-7618
HIGGINBOTHAM INSURANCE GROUP INC
500 W 13th St Ste 200, Fort Worth, TX 76102-4659
Tel (800) 728-2374 *Founded/Ownrshp* 2004
Sales NA *EMP* 234^E
SIC 6411 Insurance agents, brokers & service
Pr: Rusty Reid
**CFO:* Jim Krause
Ex VP: Matt Heinzelmann
Ex VP: Dana Jones
Ex VP: Jason Littlejohn
Sr VP: Michael Hermes
VP: Keith Dixon
VP: Stephen Hoffman
VP: Parker Holt
VP: Trey Lowack
VP: Beverly Saunders
VP: Andrea Silva
Dir Risk M: Kevin Springer

D-U-N-S 03-157-4866
HIGGINS ELECTRIC INC OF DOTHAN
1350 Columbia Hwy, Dothan, AL 36301-1828
Tel (334) 793-4859 *Founded/Ownrshp* 1988
Sales 38.7MM^E *EMP* 60
SIC 5065 7694 Electronic parts & equipment; Armature rewinding shops
Pr: Jim C Knighton
**Sec:* John H Watson
Tech Mgr: Keith Crews
Sls Mgr: Gary Grainger

D-U-N-S 07-338-0909
HIGGS FLETCHER & MACK LLP
401 W A St Ste 2600, San Diego, CA 92101-7913
Tel (619) 236-1551 *Founded/Ownrshp* 1939
Sales 24.3MM^E *EMP* 150
SIC 8111 General practice attorney, lawyer; General practice attorney, lawyer
Genl Pt: John Morrell
Pt: Anna F Roppo
Pt: Phillip C Samouis
Pt: Therese Ketteringham
Dir IT: Justin Greer
Genl Couns: Marco Garavaglia
Genl Couns: Timothy Waters
Counsel: Alexis Gutierrez
Counsel: Margaret Payne

D-U-N-S 60-200-6673
HIGGY INC
6520 State Route 96, Victor, NY 14564-1405
Tel (585) 742-8000 *Founded/Ownrshp* 2004
Sales 43.7MM^E *EMP* 500
SIC 7389 Auction, appraisal & exchange services; Auction, appraisal & exchange services
CEO: John Iannone
Exec: Lori Giordano
Genl Mgr: Andy Antonucci
Genl Mgr: Tom Rosati
Off Mgr: Pam Harris
Off Mgr: Melissa Turner
Dir IT: Adam Grossman
Ql Cn Mgr: Jay Meyer
Sls Mgr: Kevin Caruso
Sls Mgr: Herb Kimball
Sls Mgr: Gary Post

HIGH 5 GAMES
See PTT LLC

D-U-N-S 87-701-1721
HIGH AVAILABILITY STORAGE SYSTEMS INC
HA STORAGE SYSTEMS
7965 Stone Creek Dr # 120, Chanhassen, MN 55317-4627
Tel (952) 974-8056 *Founded/Ownrshp* 2000
Sales 43.0MM *EMP* 29
Accts Abdo Eick & Meyers Llp Minne
SIC 5999 Electronic parts & equipment; Electronic parts & equipment
Pr: Gregory Robertson
**VP:* Randy Kirsch
Snr PM: Michael Worth

HIGH BOARD OF EDUCATION
See HIGHLAND LOCAL SCHOOLS DISTRICT

HIGH CALIBER LINE
See CALIBRE INTERNATIONAL LLC

D-U-N-S 17-072-9896 IMP
HIGH CONCRETE GROUP LLC
HIGH CONCRETE STRUCTURES
(*Suby of* HIGH INDUSTRIES INC) ★
125 Denver Rd, Denver, PA 17517-9315
Tel (717) 336-9300 *Founded/Ownrshp* 2006
Sales 116.8MM^E *EMP* 900
Accts Kpmg Llp Harrisburg Pa
SIC 1791 3272 Precast concrete structural framing or panels, placing of; Prestressed concrete products; Precast concrete structural framing or panels, placing of; Prestressed concrete products
CEO: Michael F Shirk
**Pr:* John J Seroky
**COO:* Jeffrey L Sterner
**CFO:* Michael W Van Belle
**Treas:* Terrence A Warco
Ex VP: Lance Lorah
Ex VP: Ned Schneider
VP: Dave Carr
**VP:* Dean M Glick
**VP:* Daniel R Pietropola
**VP:* David B Schneider
VP: Chuck Weyland

HIGH CONCRETE STRUCTURES
See HIGH CONCRETE GROUP LLC

D-U-N-S 12-081-2800
HIGH CONSTRUCTION CO
(*Suby of* HIGH FAMILY PARTNERSHIP I LP) ★
1853 William Penn Way, Lancaster, PA 17601-6713
Tel (717) 291-2276 *Founded/Ownrshp* 1978
Sales 28.2MM^E *EMP* 75
Accts Parentebeard Llc York Pa
SIC 1541 1542 Industrial buildings, new construction; Nonresidential construction
Pr: Richard L Stoudt
**CEO:* Michael F Shirk
CFO: Jim Balsley
**CFO:* Michael W Van Belle
**Treas:* Terry A Warco
**VP:* Michel L Gibeault
VP: Jeffrey L Sterner
**VP:* Robert P Walsh
Sales Exec: Machel Gibeault

D-U-N-S 03-208-5508 IMP
HIGH COUNTRY BEVERAGE CORP
5706 Wright Dr, Loveland, CO 80538-8840
Tel (970) 622-8444 *Founded/Ownrshp* 1995
Sales 37.7MM^E *EMP* 80
SIC 5181 Beer & other fermented malt liquors; Beer & other fermented malt liquors
Pr: David Nichols
**Pr:* Steve Nichols
Sls Mgr: Cody Carlson

D-U-N-S 05-873-1720 IMP
HIGH COUNTRY CONTAINER INC
DELINE BOX CO
3700 Lima St, Denver, CO 80239-3309
Tel (303) 373-1430 *Founded/Ownrshp* 1971
Sales 53.1MM^E *EMP* 115
SIC 2653 Boxes, corrugated: made from purchased materials; Pallets, corrugated: made from purchased materials; Boxes, corrugated: made from purchased materials; Pallets, corrugated: made from purchased materials
CEO: Dave Deline
**VP:* James M Davis
Sfty Mgr: Steve Broich
Opers Mgr: Jessica Cress
Plnt Mgr: Ricardo Alvarez
Plnt Mgr: David Paul
Sales Exec: Jeff Putt
Sls Mgr: Cera Austin
Sls Mgr: Roger Plank

D-U-N-S 84-865-6567 IMP
HIGH COUNTRY FUSION CO INC
20 N Poly Fusion Pl, Fairfield, ID 83327
Tel (208) 764-2000 *Founded/Ownrshp* 1994
Sales 39.5MM *EMP* 54
Accts Eide Bailly Llp Boise Idaho
SIC 3498 7359 Fabricated pipe & fittings; Equipment rental & leasing; Fabricated pipe & fittings; Equipment rental & leasing
CEO: Steven J Wilson
**Pr:* David Hanks
**VP:* Todd Claiborn
Mng Dir: Dermot O'Dwyer
Off Mgr: Rose O'Dwyer

D-U-N-S 87-763-7231
HIGH COUNTRY INVESTOR INC
HILLTOP STEAKHOUSE MARKETPLACE
38 Main St Ste 2, Saugus, MA 01906-2356
Tel (781) 233-4422 *Founded/Ownrshp* 1994
Sales 16.8MM^E *EMP* 600
SIC 5812 5421 Steak & barbecue restaurants; Meat & fish markets; Steak & barbecue restaurants; Meat & fish markets
Pr: Richard Monfort
**Treas:* Dennis P January
**VP:* John Caccavaro
**VP:* Leonard De Rosa

D-U-N-S 05-102-1806
HIGH COUNTRY LUMBER INC
HCL
444 S Main St, Bishop, CA 93514-3421
Tel (760) 873-5874 *Founded/Ownrshp* 2000
Sales 24.3MM^E *EMP* 50
SIC 5031 5211 Lumber, plywood & millwork; Lumber & other building materials
Pr: Steven Joseph
Sec: Scott Piercey

D-U-N-S 06-097-3666
HIGH COUNTRY TRANSPORTATION INC (UT)
6560 Cr 24 3, Cortez, CO 81321
Tel (469) 759-2266 *Founded/Ownrshp* 1985
Sales 47.5MM *EMP* 130
Accts Dalby Wendland & Co Pc G
SIC 4213 4731 Contract haulers; Freight transportation arrangement; Contract haulers; Freight transportation arrangement
Pr: Don Crowley
**Sec:* Scott Knuckles
**VP:* Kirk Crowley

D-U-N-S 96-368-7293
HIGH DESERT & INLAND EMPLOYEE
18484 Us Highway 18, Apple Valley, CA 92307-2375
Tel (760) 242-3393 *Founded/Ownrshp* 2010
Sales 68.4MM *EMP* 1
Accts John W Hulterstorm Cpa Apple
SIC 7389 ;
Prin: Rick Aguayo

D-U-N-S 96-656-3319
HIGH DESERT AND INLAND EMPLOYEE EMPLOYER TRUST
18484 Us Highway 18 # 165, Apple Valley, CA 92307-2375
Tel (760) 242-3393 *Founded/Ownrshp* 2011
Sales 77.8MM *EMP* 3^E
Accts John W Hulterstorm Cpa Apple
SIC 7361 Employment agencies; Employment agencies

D-U-N-S 15-132-7483
HIGH DESERT MEDICAL CORP A MEDICAL GROUP
HERITAGE HEALTH CARE
43839 15th St W, Lancaster, CA 93534-4756
Tel (661) 945-5984 *Founded/Ownrshp* 1984
Sales 21.8MM^E *EMP* 200
SIC 8011 Clinic, operated by physicians; Clinic, operated by physicians
CEO: Richard N Merkin
Dir Case M: Susan Duncan
Off Mgr: Brenda Alexander
QA Dir: Jeanine Straight
Doctor: Tin Aung
Doctor: Charlene Chao MD
Doctor: Anthony Dulgeroff
Doctor: Davy Figueroa
Doctor: Miranda Gaw
Doctor: Jim Hammonds MD
Doctor: Richard Krajewski

D-U-N-S 78-062-7290 IMP
HIGH DESERT MILK INC
1033 Idaho St, Burley, ID 83318-4923
Tel (208) 878-6455 *Founded/Ownrshp* 2001
Sales 31.3MM^E *EMP* 150^E
SIC 2026 2023 Fluid milk; Powdered milk; Fluid milk; Powdered milk
CEO: Randy Robinson
**COO:* Derik Robinson
Bd of Dir: Brent Funk
VP: Dave Funk
Brnch Mgr: Dan Ward
Plnt Mgr: Shawn Burton
Plnt Mgr: Ralph Hansen
Prd Mgr: Phil RE

D-U-N-S 03-614-5113
HIGH DESERT PARTNERSHIP IN ACADEMIC EXCELLENCE FOUNDATION INC
LEWIS CENTER FOR EDUCTL RES
17500 Mana Rd, Apple Valley, CA 92307-2181
Tel (760) 946-5414 *Founded/Ownrshp* 1992
Sales NA *EMP* 350
Accts Nigro & Nigro Pc Murrieta C
SIC 9411 8732 Private elementary & secondary schools; State education department; Educational research
CEO: Gordon Soholt
Dir Vol: Laura Unferdorfer
**CEO:* Rick Piercy
COO: Patricia Holman
CFO: Larri Curtis
Ofcr: Jim Butcher
Ofcr: Judith Chabrowski
**VP:* Tim Baggerly
Exec: Deanna Grandy
Exec: Linda Locke
Exec: Maryann Tabush
Board of Directors: D K Porter

HIGH END SYSTEMS
See BARCO LIGHTING SYSTEMS INC

D-U-N-S 19-442-5336 IMP
HIGH FALLS BREWING CO LLC
NORTH AMERICAS BREWERIES
(*Suby of* NORTH AMERICAN BREWERIES INC) ★
445 Saint Paul St, Rochester, NY 14605-1726
Tel (585) 546-1030 *Founded/Ownrshp* 2009
Sales 72.9MM^E *EMP* 400^E
SIC 2082 Beer (alcoholic beverage); Ale (alcoholic beverage); Beer (alcoholic beverage); Ale (alcoholic beverage)
Treas: Andrew Yeager
VP: Michael Gaesser
IT Man: Jessica Chatterton

D-U-N-S 82-973-7415
HIGH FALLS OPERATING CO LLC
(*Suby of* NORTH AMERICAN BREWERIES INC) ★
445 Saint Paul St, Rochester, NY 14605-1726
Tel (585) 546-1030 *Founded/Ownrshp* 2009
Sales 121.1MM^E *EMP* 800
SIC 2082 Malt beverage products; Malt beverage products
COO: Kenneth Yartz

D-U-N-S 05-590-9208
HIGH FAMILY PARTNERSHIP I LP
(*Suby of* HIGH REAL ESTATE GROUP LLC) ★
1853 William Penn Way, Lancaster, PA 17601-6713
Tel (717) 293-4444 *Founded/Ownrshp* 2007
Sales 35.5MM^E *EMP* 240^E
SIC 6512 Nonresidential building operators; Nonresidential building operators
CEO: Michael F Shirk
CFO: Michael W Van Belle
Ch: S Dale High
Treas: Terry A Warco
Ex VP: Mark C Fitzgerald
VP: Thomas Dsmithgall
VP: Dean M Glick

HIGH FOCUS
See PYRAMID HEALTHCARE INC

D-U-N-S 00-253-4568 IMP
HIGH GRADE BEVERAGE
891 Georges Rd, Monmouth Junction, NJ 08852-3057
Tel (732) 821-7600 *Founded/Ownrshp* 1935
Sales 105.0MM^E *EMP* 300
SIC 5181 Beer & other fermented malt liquors; Beer & other fermented malt liquors
Ch Bd: Joseph De Marco
**Pr:* Anthony De Marco
**Sec:* Elizabeth De Marco
**Ex VP:* George Policastro
**VP:* Herbert Schloss
Dir IT: Guy Battaglia

D-U-N-S 04-248-9351
HIGH GRADE MATERIALS CO
9266 Snows Lake Rd, Greenville, MI 48838-8753
Tel (616) 754-5545 *Founded/Ownrshp* 1975
Sales 25.2MM^E *EMP* 95
SIC 3273 3272 1442 Ready-mixed concrete; Concrete products; Construction sand & gravel; Ready-mixed concrete; Concrete products; Construction sand & gravel
Pr: James Sturrus

D-U-N-S 19-724-0104
HIGH HOTELS LTD
HAMPTON INN
1853 William Penn Way, Lancaster, PA 17601-6713
Tel (717) 293-4446 *Founded/Ownrshp* 1988
Sales 39.1MM^E *EMP* 486
SIC 7011 Hotels & motels; Hotels & motels
CEO: Michael F Shirk
COO: Mark C Fitzgerald
CFO: Michael W Van Belle
Treas: Terry Warco
VP: Mark Aho
VP: Dean Glick
VP: Stephanie G Reese
Genl Mgr: Jay Bausher
Genl Mgr: Chris Shellhammer
Sls Dir: Susan Weisberger

D-U-N-S 60-504-9118 IMP/EXP
HIGH IMPACT TECHNOLOGY LLC
9900 Sw Tigard St, Tigard, OR 97223-5244
Tel (503) 639-0044 *Founded/Ownrshp* 2003
Sales 30.8MM^E *EMP* 51^E
SIC 5099 8742 Safety equipment & supplies; Management consulting services
Prgrm Mgr: Kathy Breakfield

D-U-N-S 08-487-7505
HIGH INDUSTRIES INC
1853 William Penn Way, Lancaster, PA 17601-6713
Tel (717) 293-4444 *Founded/Ownrshp* 2006
Sales 431.8MM^E *EMP* 2,107
Accts Kpmg Llp Harrisburg Pa
SIC 1791 3272 5051 3441 Structural steel erection; Prestressed concrete products; Steel; Fabricated structural metal; Structural steel erection; Prestressed concrete products; Steel; Fabricated structural metal
CEO: Michael F Shirk
**Ch Bd:* S Dale High
Pr: Jeffrey L Sterner
COO: Jeffrey Smith
CFO: Michael W Van Belle
CFO: Mike Vanbelle
Treas: James Tritch
Treas: Terrence A Warco
Treas: Terrence Warco
Bd of Dir: Michael Shirk
Sr VP: Darryl Gordon
Sr VP: Bob Shannon
VP: Michael Belle
VP: Karen A Biondolillo
VP: Thomas R Esposito
VP: Lisa Fulginiti
VP: Tina Ginnis
VP: Dean M Glick
VP: Michael Klatt
VP: Constantinos Kondos
VP: Bernd Laudorn
Board of Directors: Paula R Crowley, Gregory A High, Steven D High, W Thomas Kennedy III, Richard G King, Daniel R Langdon, Scott Newkam

D-U-N-S 62-619-6773 IMP
HIGH LIFE LLC
31 W 34th St Fl 6, New York, NY 10001-3032
Tel (212) 290-8455 *Founded/Ownrshp* 2005
Sales 23.2MM^E *EMP* 92
SIC 5136 5137 Men's & boys' clothing; Women's & children's clothing; Men's & boys' clothing; Women's & children's clothing
Pr: Isaac Levy
CFO: Joel Weisinger
Natl Sales: Joey Levy

D-U-N-S 02-993-4577 IMP
HIGH LIFE SALES CO
CENTRAL STATES BEVERAGE CO
14220 Wyandotte St, Kansas City, MO 64145-1526
Tel (816) 941-3300 *Founded/Ownrshp* 1960
Sales 40.6MM^E *EMP* 75
SIC 5181 Beer & other fermented malt liquors; Beer & other fermented malt liquors
Ch Bd: Gerard J Mos Jr
**Pr:* Gerard J Mos III
**CFO:* Kris Patton
**Sec:* R H Mos Jr
**VP:* John R Kane III
VP: Jeff Michael
Mktg Dir: Jon Poteet

D-U-N-S 96-799-7180 IMP
HIGH LIFTER PRODUCTS INC
780 Professional Dr N, Shreveport, LA 71105-5600
Tel (318) 213-6052 *Founded/Ownrshp* 1996
Sales 24.4MM^E *EMP* 40
SIC 5012 5571 Recreation vehicles, all-terrain; All-terrain vehicles
Pr: Scott Edward Smith
Genl Mgr: James Cassell
Mktg Mgr: Jamie Wilhelm
Sls Mgr: Jeff Newman

D-U-N-S 01-722-9842
HIGH LINE RANCH LLC
8526 N New Braunfels Ave, San Antonio, TX 78217-6304
Tel (830) 875-5386 *Founded/Ownrshp* 2008
Sales 45.5MM^E *EMP* 70
Accts Padgett Stratement & Co Ll
SIC 1311 Crude petroleum & natural gas; Crude petroleum & natural gas
Pr: Travis Davis
**CFO:* Wayne Schroeder
**VP:* Ryan Acker

HIGH LINER FOODS
See APS LLC

D-U-N-S 00-111-0055 IMP/EXP
HIGH LINER FOODS (USA) INC
(*Suby of* HIGH LINER FOODS INCORPORATED)
1 Highliner Ave, Portsmouth, NH 03801-7140
Tel (603) 431-6865 *Founded/Ownrshp* 1957
Sales 657.0MM^E *EMP* 1,100^E
SIC 2092 Seafoods, frozen: prepared; Seafoods, frozen: prepared
CEO: Henry Demone
**Pr:* Keith Decker
**Treas:* Kelvin Nelson
Sr VP: Chris Mulder
VP: Jeff Donde

D-U-N-S 83-213-3388
HIGH PERFORMANCE INDUSTRIES HOLDINGS INC
HOLLEY
1801 Russellville Rd, Bowling Green, KY 42101-3542
Tel (270) 782-2900 *Founded/Ownrshp* 2011
Sales 73.2MM^E *EMP* 605
SIC 3592 3714 Carburetors; Fuel pumps, motor vehicle; Carburetors; Fuel pumps, motor vehicle
Pr: Tom Tomlinson
VP: Terrill M Rutledge
VP: Stephen Trussell
VP: Trevor Wiggins

D-U-N-S 78-436-6544
■ **HIGH PERFORMANCE TECHNOLOGIES INNOVATIONS LLC**
(*Suby of* DYNAMICS RESEARCH CORP) ★
1320 Braddock Pl, Alexandria, VA 22314-1692
Tel (571) 226-8789 *Founded/Ownrshp* 2011
Sales 35.9MM^E *EMP* 450
SIC 7373 3721 8711 8742 8748 Systems integration services; Research & development on aircraft by the manufacturer; Consulting engineer; Business consultant; Systems engineering consultant, ex. computer or professional; Systems integration services; Research & development on aircraft by the manufacturer; Consulting engineer; Business consultant; Systems engineering consultant, ex. computer or professional
CEO: James P Regan
**CFO:* David Keleher
Grp VP: Curtis M Bedke
**Sr VP:* Thomas Connell
**Sr VP:* Peter Gaaserud
**Sr VP:* Jeanne Lefevre
**Sr VP:* Lawrence H O'Brien
**Sr VP:* Steven P Wentzell
VP: Maggie Bauer
VP: Michael Mikuta
VP: Joseph E Parker
Board of Directors: John S Anderegg Jr, George T Babbitt Jr, Charles P McCausland, Nickolas Stavropoulos, Richard G Tennant, W Scott Thompson

D-U-N-S 82-597-5048
HIGH PLAINS BAPTIST HOSPITAL
WARE MEMORIAL CARE CENTER
400 Sw 14th Ave, Amarillo, TX 79101-4140
Tel (806) 337-4000 *Founded/Ownrshp* 1983
Sales 5.6MM^E *EMP* 300
SIC 8059 8051 Nursing home, except skilled & intermediate care facility; Personal care home, with health care; Skilled nursing care facilities; Nursing home, except skilled & intermediate care facility; Personal care home, with health care; Skilled nursing care facilities
Ex Dir: Gary Hollinger

D-U-N-S 05-223-0406
HIGH PLAINS BAPTIST HOSPITAL INC
1600 Wallace Blvd, Amarillo, TX 79106-1789
Tel (806) 358-5800 *Founded/Ownrshp* 1995
Sales 37.3MM^E *EMP* 2,000
SIC 8062 6513 8051 General medical & surgical hospitals; Retirement hotel operation; Skilled nursing care facilities; General medical & surgical hospitals; Retirement hotel operation; Skilled nursing care facilities
CEO: John Hicks
**COO:* David Kilarski
**CFO:* Phyllis Cowling

D-U-N-S 96-791-8942
HIGH PLAINS CHRISTIAN MINISTRIES FDN
701 Park Place Ave Fl 2, Amarillo, TX 79101-4064
Tel (806) 337-5292 *Founded/Ownrshp* 2011
Sales 200.8MM *EMP* 2
Accts Connor Mcmillon Mitchell & She
SIC 8699 Membership organizations
Pr: T H Holloway

D-U-N-S 03-533-5200
HIGH PLAINS LIBRARY DISTRICT
2650 W 29th St, Greeley, CO 80631-8504
Tel (970) 506-8563 *Founded/Ownrshp* 2010
Sales 23.2MM *EMP* 2^E
Accts Anderson & Whitney Pc Gree
SIC 7389 Personal service agents, brokers & bureaus
Ex Dir: Janine Reid

D-U-N-S 03-131-9973
HIGH PLAINS PIZZA INC
PIZZA HUT
7 W Parkway Blvd, Liberal, KS 67901-2081
Tel (620) 624-5638 *Founded/Ownrshp* 1965
Sales 44.2MM^E *EMP* 1,100
SIC 5812 Pizzeria, chain; Pizzeria, chain
Pr: William K Colvin
**Sec:* Virginia Colvin
**VP:* Kent Colvin

D-U-N-S 01-427-1543
HIGH PLAINS POWER INC
1775 E Monroe, Riverton, WY 82501
Tel (800) 826-3446 *Founded/Ownrshp* 1997
Sales 95.8MM *EMP* 53
SIC 4911 Transmission, electric power; Transmission, electric power
Genl Mgr: Jeffrey Hohn
**Pr:* Robert Cardwell
**Treas:* Jim Miller
**Sec:* Hearley Dockham
**VP:* Matt Brown
Off Mgr: Ozzie Smith

D-U-N-S 06-909-1127
HIGH PLANES EDUCATION COOPERATIVE
621 E Oklahoma Ave, Ulysses, KS 67880-2897
Tel (620) 356-5577 *Founded/Ownrshp* 2002
Sales 8.5MM^E *EMP* 375
SIC 8211 8351 Specialty education; Child day care services; Specialty education; Child day care services
**Treas:* Chrissie Mangels

D-U-N-S 00-699-6896
HIGH POINT BANK AND TRUST CO (NC)
(*Suby of* HIGH POINT BANK CORP) ★
300 N Main St Ste 312, High Point, NC 27260-5056
Tel (336) 889-8733 *Founded/Ownrshp* 1905
Sales NA *EMP* 225
SIC 6022 6163 State commercial banks; Loan brokers; State commercial banks; Loan brokers
CEO: Charles L Myers
**CFO:* Thomas L Eller
**Sr VP:* David Black
VP: Lori Labor
CTO: John Swanner
Dir IT: Robert Rogers
S&M/Dir: Jane Blackwell

D-U-N-S 78-216-6235
HIGH POINT BANK CORP
300 N Main St Ste 401, High Point, NC 27260-5056
Tel (336) 881-3600 *Founded/Ownrshp* 1990
Sales NA *EMP* 225
Accts Dixon Hughes Goodman Llp Char
SIC 6022 State commercial banks; State commercial banks
CEO: Charles L Myers
CFO: Thomas Eller
Trst Ofcr: Elizabeth Terrell
Ex VP: Steven Hall
Ex VP: Tim Smyth
Sr VP: Carollynn Hufford
Sr VP: William Laney
VP: Chris Bettis
VP: Martha Brown
VP: Bill Daniel
VP: Rick Gabriel
VP: Steve Guy
VP: Matt McInnis
VP: Rhonda Peeden
VP: Robert Reagan
VP: Nichelle Rizk
Exec: Jessica Brewer

D-U-N-S 17-636-4289
HIGH POINT CONSTRUCTION GROUP LLC
643 Route 20 South Rd, Buckhannon, WV 26201-4047
Tel (304) 472-5595 *Founded/Ownrshp* 1997
Sales 25.1MM^E *EMP* 55
SIC 1542 Commercial & office buildings, renovation & repair

D-U-N-S 00-321-5811
HIGH POINT ENTERPRISE INC (NC)
THOMASVILLE TIMES
213 Woodbine St, High Point, NC 27260-8339
Tel (336) 888-3500 *Founded/Ownrshp* 1884
Sales 32.2MM^E *EMP* 200
SIC 2711 Commercial printing & newspaper publishing combined; Commercial printing & newspaper publishing combined
Pr: Fred Paxton
**Sec:* David Paxton
**Sr VP:* Nick Maheras

D-U-N-S 00-322-5620 IMP
HIGH POINT FURNITURE INDUSTRIES INC (NC)
HPFI
1104 Bedford St, High Point, NC 27263-1604
Tel (336) 431-7101 *Founded/Ownrshp* 1958
Sales 27.1MM^E *EMP* 200
SIC 2521 Wood office furniture; Chairs, office: padded, upholstered or plain: wood; Wood office furniture; Chairs, office: padded, upholstered or plain: wood
Pr: Spencer O'Meara
**Ch Bd:* Harry Samet
**Treas:* Jon Goskolka
Ex VP: Vince Cvijanovic
Mktg Mgr: Mike Wissman
Board of Directors: Joan K Samet

D-U-N-S 07-784-7952
HIGH POINT REGIONAL HEALTH
RADIATION THERAPY
(*Suby of* UNC HOSPITALS) ★
601 N Elm St, High Point, NC 27262-4331
Tel (336) 878-6000 *Founded/Ownrshp* 2013
Sales 254.0MM^E *EMP* 2,338
SIC 8062 General medical & surgical hospitals; General medical & surgical hospitals
Pr: Ernie Bovio
Dir Vol: Bobbi Watkins
COO: Greg Taylor
CFO: Kimberly Crews
Chf Mktg O: Dale Williams
Ofcr: Tammi-Erving Mengel
VP: Katherine Burns
VP: Denise Potter
Exec: Angela Culler
Dir Lab: Sherrie Livecchi
Dir Rad: Tara Eisenberg
Dir Rx: Mark Haltom

D-U-N-S 14-287-7179
HIGH POINT SAFETY AND INSURANCE MANAGEMENT CORP
(*Suby of* PALISADES SAFETY INSURANCE AGENCY INC) ★
331 Newman Springs Rd # 304, Red Bank, NJ 07701-5692
Tel (732) 978-6000 *Founded/Ownrshp* 2003
Sales NA *EMP* 585
SIC 6411 Insurance agents, brokers & service; Insurance agents, brokers & service
Pr: James A Tignanelli
V Ch: Gerry Wilson
**Prin:* Linda Schwabenbauer

HIGH POINT SCHOOL
See WASHTENAW INTERMEDIATE SCHOOL DISTRICT

D-U-N-S 95-844-1594
HIGH POINT SOLUTIONS INC
5 Gail Ct, Sparta, NJ 07871-3438
Tel (973) 940-0040 *Founded/Ownrshp* 1996
Sales 216.9MM *EMP* 75^E
SIC 5045 7373 Computers, peripherals & software; Computer integrated systems design; Computers, peripherals & software; Computer integrated systems design
Pr: Michael Mendiburu
**CFO:* Sandra Curran
**VP:* Tim Hennessey
**VP:* Tom Mendiburu
**VP:* Kurt Vandermark
Snr Ntwrk: Rick Bauer
Snr Ntwrk: Yiqiang Wang
Dir IT: Harry Jarvis
Natl Sales: Richard Kraszewski
VP Sls: Andrea Gasior
VP Sls: Mike Liebson

D-U-N-S 04-226-5087
HIGH POINT TREATMENT CENTER INC
98 N Front St Fl 3, New Bedford, MA 02740-7327
Tel (508) 997-0475 *Founded/Ownrshp* 1996
Sales 47.6MM *EMP* 520
SIC 8093 Detoxification center, outpatient; Detoxification center, outpatient
Pr: Daniel Mumbauer
**CFO:* James Hatch
VP: Millie Scott

D-U-N-S 06-743-9976
HIGH POINT UNIVERSITY
833 Montlieu Ave, High Point, NC 27268-4260
Tel (336) 841-9000 *Founded/Ownrshp* 1924
Sales 161.6MM *EMP* 680
Accts Smith Leonard Pllc High Point
SIC 8221 Colleges & universities; Colleges & universities
Pr: Dr Nido R Qubein
CFO: Deborah Butt
CIO: Wellington Desouza
IT Man: Matthew Brown
Netwrk Mgr: Phillip Chadwell
Pr Mgr: Natalie Haire

D-U-N-S 11-720-1868
HIGH POWER TECHNICAL SERVICES INC
2230 Ampere Dr, Louisville, KY 40299-3890
Tel (502) 254-0768 *Founded/Ownrshp* 1999
Sales 71.1MM^E *EMP* 325
SIC 4841 Satellite master antenna systems services (SMATV); Satellite master antenna systems services (SMATV)
Pr: Scott A Weis
**CFO:* Richard L Waddle

D-U-N-S 00-502-9640
■ **HIGH PRESSURE EQUIPMENT CO INC** (PA)
(*Suby of* GRACO INC) ★
2955 W 17th St, Erie, PA 16505-3928
Tel (814) 835-1800 *Founded/Ownrshp* 1954, 2015
Sales 23.4MM^E *EMP* 70
SIC 3498 Fabricated pipe & fittings
Pr: Lawrence Loper
Treas: J Douglas James
VP: Lawrence R Sorafin
CIO: Terry Unseld
IT Man: Kirk Julio
VP Mktg: Larry Fletcher
Mktg Mgr: Tony Pepicello

D-U-N-S 83-265-6263 IMP/EXP
HIGH QUALITY ORGANICS INC
H Q O
12101 Moya Blvd, Reno, NV 89506-2600
Tel (775) 971-8550 *Founded/Ownrshp* 2009
Sales 37.4MM^E *EMP* 51^E
SIC 5149 Natural & organic foods
Pr: Boligala Raju
Ch Bd: Jay Fishman
CFO: Rick May
VP: Fred Alejo
VP: Toby Eck

D-U-N-S 14-075-7654 IMP/EXP
HIGH REACH CO LLC
H R 2
615 Hickman Cir, Sanford, FL 32771-6937
Tel (321) 275-2100 *Founded/Ownrshp* 2003
Sales 61.4MM^E *EMP* 130
SIC 5084 7353 Industrial machinery & equipment; Cranes & aerial lift equipment, rental or leasing; Industrial machinery & equipment; Cranes & aerial lift equipment, rental or leasing
Genl Mgr: Lance Renzulli
Brnch Mgr: Pete Ginn
Brnch Mgr: Billy Pirollo
IT Man: Lorrie Huthmacher
IT Man: Mike Lyon
Sales Asso: Joel Sanders
Sales Asso: Joe Waller

D-U-N-S 80-625-5704
HIGH REAL ESTATE GROUP LLC
1853 William Penn Way, Lancaster, PA 17601-6713
Tel (800) 638-4414 Founded/Ownrshp 2006
Sales 45.2MM^E EMP 715
SIC 7041 6512 6513 6514 6531 Membership-basis organization hotels; Commercial & industrial building operation; Apartment building operators; Dwelling operators, except apartments; Real estate agents & managers; Membership-basis organization hotels; Commercial & industrial building operation; Apartment building operators; Dwelling operators, except apartments; Real estate agents & managers
CEO: Michael F Shirk
*Ch Bd: S Dale High
*Pr: Mark C Fitzgerald
*CFO: Michael W Van Belle
*Treas: Terrence A Warco
*Sr VP: Michael W Fruin
*Sr VP: Darryl P Gordon
*Sr VP: Matthew D Twomey
*VP: Dean M Glick
*VP: Elizabeth A Valen
Board of Directors: Paula R Crowley, Gregory A High, Steven D High, W Thomas Kennedy III, Richard G King, Daniel R Langdon, W Kirk Liddell, Scott Newkam, Michael F Shirk

D-U-N-S 96-578-1714
HIGH RIDGE BRANDS CO
(Suby of BRYNWOOD PARTNERS VII LP) ★
5 High Ridge Park Ste 100, Stamford, CT 06905-1329
Tel (203) 674-8080 Founded/Ownrshp 2008
Sales 22.7MM^E EMP 25
SIC 2844 Toilet preparations
COO: Richard S Kirk Jr
*Pr: James Daniels
Sls Dir: Mike Milano
Mktg Mgr: Milda Leonard

D-U-N-S 07-928-7175
HIGH RIDGE WIND LLC
15445 Innovation Dr, San Diego, CA 92128-3432
Tel (888) 903-6926 Founded/Ownrshp 2013
Sales 258.5MM^E EMP 826
SIC 4911 Electric services; Electric services
Pr: Tristan Grimbert
Sec: Robert Miller
VP: Ryan Pfaff

D-U-N-S 08-583-8345
HIGH RISE GOODIES RESTAURANT GROUP INC
TRIMANA
1875 Century Park E Ste A, Los Angeles, CA 90067-2535
Tel (310) 772-0726 Founded/Ownrshp 1996
Sales 23.5MM^E EMP 200
SIC 6794 Franchises, selling or licensing; Franchises, selling or licensing
Pr: Bijan Yadegar

D-U-N-S 86-761-0805
HIGH ROAD CAPITAL PARTNERS LLC
1251 Avenue Of The Americ, New York, NY 10020-1105
Tel (212) 554-3265 Founded/Ownrshp 2007
Sales 48.1MM^E EMP 35^E
SIC 7389 6726 Financial services; Investment offices

D-U-N-S 96-244-0108
HIGH SIERRA CRUDE OIL & MARKETING LLC
3773 Cherry Cree Ste 1000, Denver, CO 80209
Tel (303) 815-1010 Founded/Ownrshp 2004
Sales 35.2MM^E EMP 17^E
SIC 5172 Petroleum products
Pr: James Burke
*VP: Jack Eberhardt

D-U-N-S 61-533-2280
■ **HIGH SIERRA ENERGY LP**
(Suby of NGL ENERGY PARTNERS LP) ★
3773 Cherry Creek N Dr St, Denver, CO 80209-3804
Tel (303) 815-1010 Founded/Ownrshp 2012
Sales 135.8MM^E EMP 130
SIC 5172 Petroleum products; Petroleum products
Pt: James Burke
Pt: Nicholas Aretakis
Pt: Stephen Creamer
Pt: Marjorie A Hargrove
Pt: David Kehoe
Sr VP: Jack Eberhardt
Sr VP: Bill Laughlin
VP: Jonathan Cox
VP: Gene McDougald
VP: Kent Mundon
VP: Doran Oancia
VP: Wes Pearson
VP: Johan Van Themaat
VP: Douglas White
VP: Jim Winter

D-U-N-S 18-527-6917
■ **HIGH SIERRA OPERATING CO LLC**
(Suby of HIGH SIERRA ENERGY LP) ★
3773 E Cherry Creek N Dr, Denver, CO 80209-3804
Tel (303) 232-7751 Founded/Ownrshp 2004
Sales 20.5MM^E EMP 125
SIC 5172 Gases; Gases

D-U-N-S 05-166-1622
HIGH SIERRA POOLS INC
2704 Columbia Pike, Arlington, VA 22204-4440
Tel (703) 920-1750 Founded/Ownrshp 2001
Sales 94.7MM^E EMP 1,250
Accts Michael Meyer And Associates
SIC 8741 7389 Business management; Swimming pool & hot tub service & maintenance; Business management; Swimming pool & hot tub service & maintenance
Pr: Stephen Lavery
*VP: Radoslaw Kaczor
*VP: Viktor Nekoranec
Div Mgr: Karin Whitehead
Sfty Mgr: Dobrina Lyanguzova
Sales Exec: Radek Kaczor

HIGH STANDARD AVIATION
See AMETEK HSA INC

D-U-N-S 80-625-4012
HIGH STEEL SERVICE CENTER LLC
(Suby of HIGH INDUSTRIES INC) ★
400 Steel Way, Lancaster, PA 17601-3136
Tel (717) 299-8989 Founded/Ownrshp 2006
Sales 39.4MM^E EMP 60
Accts Kpmg Llp Harrisburg Pa
SIC 5051 Metals service centers & offices
CEO: Michael F Shirk
*Pr: Richard W Bennett
*COO: Jeffrey L Sterner
*CFO: Michael W Van Belle
Treas: John Vozzella
*Treas: Terrence A Warco
*VP: James F Cunningham
*VP: Dean M Glick
CIO: Tom Ruth
IT Man: Bob Wetisen
Sls Mgr: Michael Brenneman

D-U-N-S 80-621-7910
HIGH STEEL STRUCTURES LLC
(Suby of HIGH INDUSTRIES INC) ★
1915 Old Philadelphia Pike, Lancaster, PA 17602-3410
Tel (717) 299-5211 Founded/Ownrshp 1970
Sales 166.2MM EMP 600
Accts Kpmg Llp Harrisburg Pa
SIC 1541 Steel building construction; Steel building construction
CEO: Michael F Shirk
*Pr: Brian Laborde
*CFO: Michael W Van Belle
*Treas: Terrence A Warco
*Sr VP: Steven M Bussanmas
*VP: Dean M Glick
*VP: Paul A Lipinsky
*VP: Ronald D Medlock
*VP: Craig D Thompson
Sls Mgr: Rich Truxel

D-U-N-S 11-348-6393
HIGH TECH CONSTRUCTION & PROPERTIES INC
1201 4th Ave N, Billings, MT 59101-1514
Tel (406) 248-3700 Founded/Ownrshp 1984
Sales 42.9MM EMP 68
Accts Anderson Zurmuehlen & Co P
SIC 1542 1541 Commercial & office building, new construction; Commercial & office buildings, renovation & repair; Industrial buildings, new construction; Renovation, remodeling & repairs: industrial buildings; Commercial & office building, new construction; Commercial & office buildings, renovation & repair; Industrial buildings, new construction; Renovation, remodeling & repairs: industrial buildings
Pr: James F Haar
*VP: Scott Chartier

D-U-N-S 87-839-1478
HIGH TECH HIGH
(Suby of HTH LEARNING) ★
2861 Womble Rd, San Diego, CA 92106-6025
Tel (619) 243-5000 Founded/Ownrshp 2000
Sales 41.6MM EMP 265
Accts Christy White Associates San
SIC 8211 Public junior high school; Public senior high school; Public junior high school; Public senior high school
CEO: Larry Rosenstock
*COO: Judd Wallace
*CFO: Arnold Doolittle
*CFO: Kay McElrath
Web Dev: Patrick Hayman
Site Mgr: Naomi Craft
Pr Dir: Cheyenne Manske
Snr Mgr: Juliet Mohnkern

D-U-N-S 83-021-5435
HIGH TECH HIGH FOUNDATION
2861 Womble Rd, San Diego, CA 92106-6025
Tel (619) 398-8652 Founded/Ownrshp 2009
Sales 31.1MM EMP 4
Accts Christy White Accountancy Corp
SIC 8299 Schools & educational service
Pr: Larry Rosenstock

D-U-N-S 60-205-2896 IMP
HIGH TECH LANDSCAPES INC
10 Culnen Dr, Branchburg, NJ 08876-5400
Tel (908) 393-8334 Founded/Ownrshp 1989
Sales 22.4MM^E EMP 250
SIC 0782 Lawn & garden services; Lawn & garden services
Pr: Paul Cernuto
Ofcr: Theresa Hoffman
Brnch Mgr: Justin Reilly
Genl Mgr: Ginger Goddiess
Opers Mgr: Mark Inzano

HIGH TECH PERFORMANCE TRAILERS
See R C TWAY CO

HIGH TEMP METALS
See HI-TEMP METALS INC

D-U-N-S 10-408-4181
HIGH TOUCH INC
HIGH TOUCH TECH SOLUTIONS
110 S Main St Ste 600, Wichita, KS 67202-3746
Tel (316) 832-1611 Founded/Ownrshp 1984
Sales 51.9MM^E EMP 185
SIC 7373 Value-added resellers, computer systems; Value-added resellers, computer systems
Pr: Wayne Chambers
Pr: Russ Fahey
*COO: David Oles
*CFO: Vernon Dolezal
*VP: Dave Glover
*VP: Jason Mock
CIO: Kevin Colborn
Natl Sales: Jason Smith
Mktg Dir: Cyndra Perez
Mktg Mgr: Benita Duckett
Mktg Mgr: Tracy Lucas

HIGH TOUCH TECH SOLUTIONS
See HIGH TOUCH INC

D-U-N-S 86-146-7793
HIGH VOLTAGE SOFTWARE INC
2345 Pembroke Ave, Hoffman Estates, IL 60169-2009
Tel (847) 490-8982 Founded/Ownrshp 1992
Sales 23.7MM^E EMP 160
SIC 7371 Computer software development; Computer software development
CEO: Kerry J Ganofsky
Prgrm Mgr: Anthony Glueck
DP Dir: Bay Sonthipanya
QA Dir: Ashley Miller
Sftwr Eng: Jon Carr
Sftwr Eng: Abhinav Choudhary
Sftwr Eng: Justin Gantenberg
Sftwr Eng: Aaron Molina
Sftwr Eng: Jon Parson
Sftwr Eng: Jason Petersohn
Sftwr Eng: Tyler Trussell

D-U-N-S 00-794-8227
HIGH WEST ENERGY INC
6270 Rd 212, Pine Bluffs, WY 82082
Tel (307) 245-3261 Founded/Ownrshp 1939
Sales 33.0MM EMP 44
Accts Bolinger Segars Gilbert And Mo
SIC 4911 Distribution, electric power; Distribution, electric power
Genl Mgr: Brian Heithoff
IT Man: David Crouse
Opers Mgr: Jeff Bruckner
Opers Mgr: Tom Romig
Pr Mgr: Lorrell Walter

D-U-N-S 83-546-4264
HIGH-TEC INDUSTRIAL SERVICES INC
15 Industry Park Ct, Tipp City, OH 45371-3060
Tel (937) 667-1772 Founded/Ownrshp 1995
Sales 22.2MM^E EMP 139
SIC 3589 7349 Commercial cooking & foodwarming equipment; Building & office cleaning services; Commercial cooking & foodwarming equipment; Building & office cleaning services
Pr: William E Oldham
*VP: Christopher Taylor

D-U-N-S 06-431-9838
HIGH-TECH INSTITUTE HOLDINGS INC
ANTHEM EDUCATION GROUP
(Suby of EDUCATION TRAINING CORP) ★
3383 N State Road 7, Lauderdale Lakes, FL 33319-5617
Tel (602) 328-2800 Founded/Ownrshp 2012
Sales 146.3MM^E EMP 1,000^E
SIC 6719 Personal holding companies, except banks; Personal holding companies, except banks
CEO: David Knobel
*CFO: Jeffrey Pierne
Sls Mgr: Pat Delucia

D-U-N-S 02-165-7622
HIGH-TECH INSTITUTE INC
BRYMAN SCHOOL
(Suby of ANTHEM EDUCATION GROUP) ★
2250 W Peoria Ave A100, Phoenix, AZ 85029-4923
Tel (602) 274-4300 Founded/Ownrshp 1982
Sales 61.2MM^E EMP 1,000
SIC 8221 Colleges universities & professional schools; Colleges universities & professional schools
Ch: David Knobel
Pr: Jennifer Detto
*Pr: Jeffrey Pierne
Pr: Steven M Temple
Treas: Richard P Johnson
Sr VP: Tony Mediate
*VP: Neal Yawn
Sales Exec: Kim Galetti

D-U-N-S 87-672-9146
HIGHBRIDGE ADVISORY COUNCIL FAMILY SERVICES INC
880 River Ave Frnt 2, Bronx, NY 10452-9440
Tel (718) 992-1321 Founded/Ownrshp 1970
Sales 13.8MM EMP 300
SIC 8351 8322 Child day care services; Adult day care center; Child day care services; Adult day care center
CEO: James Nathaniel
CFO: Gana Sekarkan

D-U-N-S 55-711-1093 IMP
■ **HIGHBRIDGE CAPITAL MANAGEMENT LLC**
(Suby of J P MORGAN ASSET MANAGEMENT INC) ★
40 W 57th St Fl 33, New York, NY 10019-4001
Tel (212) 287-5496 Founded/Ownrshp 1989
Sales 83.5MM^E EMP 135^E
SIC 6211 Brokers, security; Brokers, security
Mng Pt: Scott Kapnick
Mng Pt: Martin Astengo
Mng Pt: Glenn Dubin
Pr: Todd Builione
COO: Todd C Builione
Sr VP: Christopher Berg
Sr VP: Eric Colandrea
Sr VP: Malda Hibri
Sr VP: Daniel Jackson
Sr VP: Michael Korby
Sr VP: Irina Mirkin
Sr VP: Maston O'Neal
Sr VP: Blair Salveson
Sr VP: Susan Soh
Sr VP: Ryan Spayde
VP: Eiler Andrew
VP: Alexander Artemenko
VP: Michael Brams
VP: Alex Chudner
VP: Jamie Donsky
VP: Prem Itharat

D-U-N-S 07-991-0728
HIGHCHEM AMERICA INC
(Suby of HIGHCHEM CO.,LTD.)
3300 Holcomb Bridge Rd # 270, Norcross, GA 30092-3238
Tel (470) 395-2912 Founded/Ownrshp 2013
Sales 24.3MM^E EMP 450
SIC 2899 5169 2851 Chemical preparations; Industrial chemicals; Paints & allied products
CEO: Zhenyu Li
Pr: Taka Ushio
CFO: Zailong Bai
Admn Mgr: Ken Lee

D-U-N-S 17-935-3370
HIGHCREST INVESTORS LLC
(Suby of BUFFALO INVESTORS CORP) ★
Icahn Associates Corp 767, New York, NY 10153
Tel (212) 702-4323 Founded/Ownrshp 1993
Sales 1.2MMM^E EMP 3,750
SIC 3743 4741 4789 4813 Freight cars & equipment; Rental of railroad cars; Railroad car repair; Local telephone communications; Long distance telephone communications; ; Freight cars & equipment; Rental of railroad cars; Railroad car repair; Local telephone communications; Long distance telephone communications;
Ch Bd: Carl C Icahn

D-U-N-S 07-886-1169
HIGHER EDUCATION
Ok State Univ 201 Advance, Stillwater, OK 74078-0001
Tel (405) 744-5140 Founded/Ownrshp 2013
Sales 6.0MM^E EMP 5,000
SIC 8221 University; University
Prin: Burns Hargis

D-U-N-S 83-501-0034
HIGHER EDUCATION COORDINATING BOARD TEXAS
(Suby of EXECUTIVE OFFICE OF STATE OF TEXAS) ★
1200 E Anderson Ln, Austin, TX 78752-1706
Tel (512) 427-6100 Founded/Ownrshp 1965
Sales NA EMP 290
SIC 9411 Administration of educational programs; ; Administration of educational programs;
Pr: Raymund Paredes
Bd of Dir: Linda Winder
Ofcr: Lamar Ford
Adm Dir: James Beck
Adm Dir: John Monk
Brnch Mgr: Susan Combs
Brnch Mgr: Waldo Morgan
Brnch Mgr: Todd Staples
IT Man: Dora Balladares

D-U-N-S 96-234-2254
▲ **HIGHER ONE HOLDINGS INC**
115 Munson St, New Haven, CT 06511-3540
Tel (203) 776-7776 Founded/Ownrshp 2000
Sales 220.1MM EMP 1,300^E
Tkr Sym ONE Exch NYS
SIC 7379 7389 ; Financial services; ; Financial services
Pr: Marc Sheinbaum
*Ch Bd: Miles Lasater
Pr: Whitney Stewart
COO: Casey McGuane
CFO: Christopher Wolf
Chf Mktg O: Lutz Braum
Ofcr: Richard Howells
Ofcr: Robert Reach
Sr VP: Andrew Crawford
VP: Catherine Eklund
VP: Jennifer Sanders
VP: Sean Townsend
VP: Donna Verdisco
VP: Coz Wilson
VP: Edward Worrilow
Dir Risk M: Mark Archer
Assoc Dir: Nicole Martin
Board of Directors: Thomas N Anderson, Samara Braunstein, Michael E Collins, David Cromwell, Sheldon Goldfarb, Robert Hartheimer, Lowell Robinson, Marc Volchek

D-U-N-S 86-757-9752
■ **HIGHER ONE INC**
(Suby of HIGHER ONE HOLDINGS INC) ★
115 Munson St, New Haven, CT 06511-3540
Tel (203) 776-7776 Founded/Ownrshp 2000
Sales 94.3MM^E EMP 450^E
SIC 7389 Financial services; Financial services
Ex VP: Miles Lasater
*COO: Casey McGuane
*CFO: Christopher Wolf
*Chf Cred: Richard J Howells
Bd of Dir: John Bado
Bd of Dir: Paul Biddelman
*Ofcr: Mark Archer
*Ofcr: Suzanne Cafferty Ross
*Sr VP: Rob Reach
Sr VP: Eric Reich
*VP: Tom Anderson
VP: David Bernier
VP: Wayne Christian
VP: Jack Debaar
VP: Paul Dickson
VP: Matt Dorf
VP: Doug Fraser
VP: Nora Lee
VP: Kelcey Reed
VP: Sebastian Rossi
VP: Whitney Stewart
Board of Directors: Robert Hartheimer

D-U-N-S 36-116-2956
HIGHERSCHOOL PUBLISHING CO
HIGHERSCHOOL TUTORING
1997 Annapolis Exch Pkwy, Annapolis, MD 21401-3271
Tel (410) 626-0076 Founded/Ownrshp 2002
Sales 4.5MM^E EMP 319
SIC 8299 Educational services; Tutoring school; Educational services; Tutoring school
CEO: David Irving

*Pr: Ricardo Burns
*CFO: Tove M Irving

HIGHERSCHOOL TUTORING
See HIGHERSCHOOL PUBLISHING CO

HIGHFIELD GARDENS CARE
See WEDGEWOOD CARE CENTER INC

HIGHGATE HOLDINGS
See HIGHGATE HOTELS INC

D-U-N-S 19-520-3922
HIGHGATE HOTELS INC
HIGHGATE HOLDINGS
545 E J Carpentr Fwy 14, Irving, TX 75062
Tel (972) 444-9700 Founded/Ownrshp 1976
Sales 131.9MM[E] EMP 968
SIC 8741 Hotel or motel management; Hotel or motel management
Pr: Mahmood Khimji
CFO: Paul Womble
*Treas: Mehdi Khimji
Ex VP: Karyn Marasco
Ex VP: Brian Winston
Sr VP: Kurien Jacob
Sr VP: John McMullen
Sr VP: David Snell
Sr VP: Rick Whitworth
VP: Keith Beck
VP: Andre De Araujo
*VP: Jaffer Khimji
VP: Paul McElroy
VP: Ankur Randev
VP: Jason Vlacich
VP: Geri Williams-Fitts

D-U-N-S 10-224-9158
HIGHJUMP SOFTWARE INC
(Suby of ACCELLOS INC) ★
5600 W 83rd St Ste 600, Minneapolis, MN 55437-1065
Tel (952) 947-4088 Founded/Ownrshp 2014
Sales 121.0MM[E] EMP 771
SIC 7371 Computer software development & applications; Computer software development & applications
CEO: Michael Cornell
CFO: Flint Seaton
Chf Mktg O: Chad Collins
Ex VP: Ross Elliott
Sr VP: Joe Couto
Sr VP: David Grosvenor
VP: David Houser
VP: Ole Pederson
VP: Amy Stelling
VP: Amy Stelling-Kahler
Genl Mgr: Bill Ashburn

D-U-N-S 07-951-9386
HIGHLAND AVENUE LLC (SC)
201 Caulder Ave, Spartanburg, SC 29306-5604
Tel (240) 382-2002 Founded/Ownrshp 2014
Sales 3.5MM[E] EMP 300
SIC 6513 Apartment building operators; Apartment building operators
Pr: Janaka Casper
Treas: Jeffrey Reed
Ex VP: Orlando Artz

D-U-N-S 15-209-4850
HIGHLAND BAKING CO INC
2301 Shermer Rd, Northbrook, IL 60062-6721
Tel (847) 677-2789 Founded/Ownrshp 1983
Sales 125.0MM[E] EMP 635
SIC 5149 2051 Bakery products; Bread, cake & related products; Bakery products; Bread, cake & related products
Pr: James Rosen
Ex VP: Ira Keeshin
QA Dir: Gaby Leal
IT Man: Liana Fishel
Sfty Mgr: Danny Cintron
Plnt Mgr: Michael Galenson
Plnt Mgr: Bill McKinsey
Prd Mgr: Bruce Forman
VP Sls: John Updegraff
Sls Dir: Ron Katarzynski

D-U-N-S 83-874-1585
HIGHLAND BANKSHARES INC
8140 26th Ave S Ste 160, Minneapolis, MN 55425
Tel (952) 854-2474 Founded/Ownrshp 1995
Sales NA EMP 170
SIC 6022 State commercial banks; State commercial banks
Pr: Fred L Wall III
VP: Kimberly Storey
Brnch Mgr: Alison Ford

D-U-N-S 96-930-0920
HIGHLAND BUILDERS INC
2342 Fabens Rd Ste 100, Dallas, TX 75229-7803
Tel (972) 501-0330 Founded/Ownrshp 1996
Sales 21.6MM[E] EMP 28
SIC 1542 Nonresidential construction; Nonresidential construction
Pr: Steve Westbrook
VP: Shane Cloud
VP: Dan Kubie
Genl Mgr: Marty Gunderson

D-U-N-S 01-023-7977
■ **HIGHLAND CAPITAL BROKERAGE INC**
(Suby of HCHC ACQUISITION INC) ★
3535 Grandview Pkwy Ste 6, Birmingham, AL 35243-1945
Tel (205) 263-4400 Founded/Ownrshp 2000, 2014
Sales NA EMP 267
SIC 6411 Insurance agents, brokers & service; Insurance agents, brokers & service
CEO: Jim Gelder
*CFO: Drew Lawrence
Sr VP: Mike McGlothlin
*VP: Keith A Miller
Prin: Paul M Harrington
VP Sls: Steve Enoch
VP Sls: Gerald Kleis

D-U-N-S 06-252-3548
HIGHLAND CAPITAL HOLDING CORP
(Suby of NFP ADVISORS) ★
3535 Grandview Pkwy # 600, Birmingham, AL 35243-1945
Tel (205) 263-4400 Founded/Ownrshp 2005
Sales NA EMP 550
SIC 6411 Insurance agents, brokers & service; Insurance agents, brokers & service
CEO: John L Robinson Jr
*COO: J Forrest Collier
*CFO: Keith D Duke
*Ex VP: W Todd Carlisle
*VP: Rhonda Padgett
Prin: Richard F Biborosch
Prin: Paul M Pistilli
Prin: Kenneth D Savino
VP Mktg: Tony Catrini
VP Mktg: Tracy McGrath
VP Sls: Kevin Donnelly

D-U-N-S 05-832-9769
HIGHLAND CAPITAL MANAGEMENT LP
300 Crescent Ct Ste 700, Dallas, TX 75201-7849
Tel (972) 628-4100 Founded/Ownrshp 1993
Sales 783.4MM[E] EMP 4,787
SIC 8741 Financial management for business; Financial management for business
Pr: James Dondero
Pt: James D Dondero
*Pt: Mark Okada
Pt: Jack Yang
Mng Pt: Gustavo Prilick
Pr: Terry Jones
Pr: Lisa Stuart
VP: Anthony Hazen
Assoc Dir: Candice Griffith
Dir Bus: Nikki Gill
Mng Dir: Michael Gregory

D-U-N-S 14-414-1967
HIGHLAND CARE CENTER INC
9131 175th St, Jamaica, NY 11432-5517
Tel (718) 883-7800 Founded/Ownrshp 1989
Sales 38.5MM EMP 245
SIC 8051 Skilled nursing care facilities; Skilled nursing care facilities
Pr: Chaim Kaminetzky
Nrsg Dir: Diana Brown

D-U-N-S 07-199-8876
HIGHLAND CITY OF INC
1115 Broadway, Highland, IL 62249-1902
Tel (618) 654-9891 Founded/Ownrshp 1884
Sales NA EMP 300
Accts Scheffel & Company Pc Cpas
SIC 9111 City & town managers' offices; ; City & town managers' offices;
MIS Mgr: Tracy Robinson

D-U-N-S 06-703-0841
HIGHLAND CLINIC A PROFESSIONAL MEDICAL CORP
1455 E Bert Koun Loop, Shreveport, LA 71105-5634
Tel (318) 798-4691 Founded/Ownrshp 2002
Sales 60.9MM[E] EMP 325
SIC 8011 Physicians' office, including specialists; Clinic, operated by physicians; Physicians' office, including specialists; Clinic, operated by physicians
Pr: Gordon M Mead MD
CFO: Michael Gustavson
*VP: Dr Carl G Goodman
Off Mgr: Lillie Smith
Dir IT: Chris Nash
Dir IT: Joey Prewett
IT Man: Jay Bond
VP Mktg: Leeann Tuminello
Surgeon: Edward Anglin
Surgeon: Brian Dockendorf
Surgeon: Stephen White

D-U-N-S 08-409-8136
HIGHLAND COMMUNITY COLLEGE
HCC
606 W Main St, Highland, KS 66035-4165
Tel (785) 442-6000 Founded/Ownrshp 1858
Sales 15.9MM[E] EMP 500[E]
Accts Berberich Trahan & Co Topeka
SIC 8222 Community college; Community college
Pr: David Reist
*VP: Cynthia Haggard
VP: Michael Parker
Exec: Rose Ferguson
Admn Mgr: David Braun

D-U-N-S 01-021-6521
HIGHLAND COMMUNITY COLLEGE FOUNDATION (IL)
COMMUNITY COLLEGE DST 519
(Suby of ILLINOIS COMMUNITY COLLEGE BD) ★
2998 W Pearl City Rd, Freeport, IL 61032-9338
Tel (815) 235-6121 Founded/Ownrshp 1962
Sales 9.7MM EMP 337
Accts Wipfli Llp Freeport Illinois
SIC 8222 9199 Community college; ; Community college;
Pr: Joe Karosky

D-U-N-S 10-655-9867
HIGHLAND COMMUNITY UNIT SCHOOL DISTRICT 5
400 Broadway, Highland, IL 62249-2024
Tel (618) 654-2106 Founded/Ownrshp 1950
Sales 21.4MM[E] EMP 300
SIC 8211 6531 Public elementary & secondary schools; Real estate agents & managers; Public elementary & secondary schools; Real estate agents & managers
VP: Cathy Orseske
*Prin: Lynne Newton
Psych: Jen Harsy
HC Dir: Jae Kuberski

D-U-N-S 09-791-7801
HIGHLAND COMPUTER FORMS INC
1025 W Main St, Hillsboro, OH 45133-8219
Tel (937) 393-4215 Founded/Ownrshp 1979
Sales 34.1MM[E] EMP 130
SIC 2761 Computer forms, manifold or continuous; Computer forms, manifold or continuous
Pr: Robert D Wilson
*Ch: Philip D Wilson
Sales Asso: Ashley Watson

D-U-N-S 78-741-1255
HIGHLAND CONTAINERS INC
(Suby of ADVANCE DESIGN & PACKAGING) ★
3520 Dillon Rd, Jamestown, NC 27282-9802
Tel (336) 887-5400 Founded/Ownrshp 1992
Sales 108.5MM[E] EMP 450
SIC 2653 Boxes, corrugated: made from purchased materials; Boxes, corrugated: made from purchased materials
Pr: Doug Johnston
Genl Mgr: Rodney Benson
Sls Mgr: Frank Autry

D-U-N-S 09-281-4201
HIGHLAND COUNTY COMMUNITY ACTION ORGANIZATION INC
HCCAO
1487 N High St Ste 500, Hillsboro, OH 45133-6812
Tel (937) 393-3060 Founded/Ownrshp 1965
Sales 5.3MM EMP 1,381
SIC 8322 Individual & family services; Individual & family services
Pr: Fred Berry
*Sec: Richard Graves
*VP: Greg Barr
Ex Dir: Douglas Powers
*Ex Dir: Julia Wise
Ex Dir: Julie Wise

D-U-N-S 07-679-7182
HIGHLAND COUNTY JOINT TOWNSHIP DISTRICT HOSPITAL
HIGHLAND DISTRICT HOSPITAL
1275 N High St, Hillsboro, OH 45133-8273
Tel (937) 393-6100 Founded/Ownrshp 1914
Sales 22.7MM[E] EMP 400
Accts Blue & Co Llc Columbus Oh
SIC 8062 General medical & surgical hospitals; General medical & surgical hospitals
CEO: Jim Baer
*CFO: Randy Lennartz
Exec: Bonnie Britton
Dir Lab: Earl Gross
Dir Rx: Melanie Parry
*Prin: Thomas Degen
*Prin: Paula Detterman
Mktg Dir: Kathy Jones
Mktg Dir: Melanie Phillips
Mktg Mgr: Cathy Jones
Pathlgst: Scott Arnold

HIGHLAND DISTRICT HOSPITAL
See HIGHLAND COUNTY JOINT TOWNSHIP DISTRICT HOSPITAL

D-U-N-S 15-387-9903 EXP
HIGHLAND ENGINEERING INC
HEI
1153 Grand Oaks Dr, Howell, MI 48843-8511
Tel (517) 548-4372 Founded/Ownrshp 1981
Sales 24.7MM[E] EMP 45
Accts Plante & Moran Pllc Flint M
SIC 3535 3599 3441 3469 3544 3443 Conveyors & conveying equipment; Machine shop, jobbing & repair; Fabricated structural metal; Stamping metal for the trade; Special dies, tools, jigs & fixtures; Fabricated plate work (boiler shop); Conveyors & conveying equipment; Machine shop, jobbing & repair; Fabricated structural metal; Stamping metal for the trade; Special dies, tools, jigs & fixtures; Fabricated plate work (boiler shop)
Pr: Ralph S Beebe
*CFO: Raymond A Beebe Jr
*VP: Stephanie Rife
VP: Disa Snider

D-U-N-S 04-482-5941
HIGHLAND FALLS FORT MONTGOMERY SCHOOL DISTRICT
TOWN OF HIGHLANDS BD EDCUATION
21 Morgan Rd, Fort Montgomery, NY 10922
Tel (845) 446-9575 Founded/Ownrshp 1960
Sales 24.0MM EMP 200
SIC 8211 Public elementary & secondary schools; School board; Public elementary & secondary schools; School board
VP: Ned Kopald
Schl Brd P: Patrick Kelly

D-U-N-S 96-471-7248
HIGHLAND FALLS PRESERVATION LP
WEYANT GREEN
40 W Point Hwy, Highland Falls, NY 10928-2317
Tel (845) 446-4966 Founded/Ownrshp 2010
Sales 22.6MM[E] EMP 1,828
SIC 6531 Real estate agents & managers; Real estate agents & managers
Pt: Larry Lipton

HIGHLAND HILLS MOTEL
See P & P ENTERPRISES INC

D-U-N-S 15-153-3726
HIGHLAND HOMES LTD
HIGHLAND HOMES OF DALLAS
5601 Democracy Dr Ste 300, Plano, TX 75024-3674
Tel (972) 789-3500 Founded/Ownrshp 1985
Sales 235.8MM[E] EMP 400
SIC 1521 1531 New construction, single-family houses; Speculative builder, single-family houses; New construction, single-family houses; Speculative builder, single-family houses
Pt: Rodger Sanders
Pt: Jean Ann Brock
VP: Gonzolo Romero
Div Mgr: Garon Bruce
Mktg Mgr: Erin Barton
Sls Mgr: Jason Walker
Sales Asso: Kelley Porter
Genl Couns: Brad Gahm
Snr PM: Fred Leal

HIGHLAND HOMES OF DALLAS
See HIGHLAND HOMES LTD

HIGHLAND HOSP HGHLAND WELLNESS
See ALAMEDA HEALTH SYSTEM

D-U-N-S 96-803-3220
HIGHLAND HOSPITAL
1000 South Ave, Rochester, NY 14620-2782
Tel (585) 341-6702 Founded/Ownrshp 2011
Sales 21.0MM[E] EMP 64[E]
SIC 8062 General medical & surgical hospitals
Prin: Tommye Hinton
VP: Anil Sharma
Dir Case M: Michael Sullivan
Dir Lab: Rosemary Ziemba-Ball
Dir Sec: Joseph Coon
Off Mgr: Christine Gray
QA Dir: Sharon Johnson
Dir IT: James Arenea
Dir IT: Mike Deroo
Dir IT: Jerry Powell
Opers Mgr: Ben McCormick

D-U-N-S 05-364-9430
HIGHLAND HOSPITAL OF ROCHESTER
(Suby of UNIVERSITY OF ROCHESTER) ★
1000 South Ave, Rochester, NY 14620-2782
Tel (585) 473-2200 Founded/Ownrshp 1889
Sales 302.9MM EMP 2,500
SIC 8062 General medical & surgical hospitals; General medical & surgical hospitals
Pr: Steven I Goldstein
*CFO: Adam Anolik
*CFO: Leonard J Shute
*VP: Kathy Parrinello R N
Assoc Dir: Sharon Martinez
Mtls Mgr: Eric Grayeski
Mktg Dir: Kristin Olaughlin
Pr Dir: Barb Ficarra
Doctor: Sidney S Weinstein MD
Pharmcst: Jeff Huntress
Pharmcst: Ryan Lamay

D-U-N-S 18-568-1329 IMP
HIGHLAND INDUSTRIES INC
(Suby of TAKATA) ★
1350 Bridgeport Dr Ste 1, Kernersville, NC 27284-3794
Tel (336) 992-7500 Founded/Ownrshp 1987
Sales 218.4MM[E] EMP 590
SIC 2221 Automotive fabrics, manmade fiber; Automotive fabrics, manmade fiber
Pr: David Jackson
Treas: Shunkichi Shimizu
*VP: Todd McCurry
VP: Bruce Thames
Exec: Jenny Fisher

D-U-N-S 08-921-2591
HIGHLAND LAKES COUNTRY CLUB & COMMUNITY ASSOCIATION
2240 Lakeside Dr W, Highland Lakes, NJ 07422-1857
Tel (973) 764-4366 Founded/Ownrshp 1936
Sales 2.7MM EMP 2,000
SIC 7997 Country club, membership; Country club, membership
Pr: Steve Hastie
*Treas: Jeanne Jameson

D-U-N-S 04-412-7520
HIGHLAND LIGHT STEAM LAUNDRY INC
WHITE PLAINS LINEN
4 John Walsh Blvd, Peekskill, NY 10566-5323
Tel (914) 737-2532 Founded/Ownrshp 1978
Sales 22.6MM[E] EMP 520
SIC 7211 2389 Power laundries, family & commercial; Uniforms & vestments; Power laundries, family & commercial; Uniforms & vestments
Pr: Bruce Botchman
*VP: Len Labonia
*VP: Daniel Ottaviano
VP Opers: Jhonathan Diaz
*VP Sls: Thomas Moscati
Sls Dir: Anthony Sciulio

D-U-N-S 09-450-2796
HIGHLAND LOCAL SCHOOLS DISTRICT
HIGH BOARD OF EDUCATION
3880 Ridge Rd, Medina, OH 44256-7920
Tel (330) 239-1901 Founded/Ownrshp 1955
Sales 31.6MM EMP 400
SIC 8211 Public elementary school; Public junior high school; Public senior high school; Public elementary school; Public junior high school; Public senior high school
Cmptr Lab: Beverly Ewing
Pr Dir: Dawn Marzano

D-U-N-S 62-485-5417 IMP
HIGHLAND LUMBER SALES INC
300 E Santa Ana St, Anaheim, CA 92805-3953
Tel (714) 778-2293 Founded/Ownrshp 1991
Sales 24.2MM[E] EMP 60
SIC 5031 2493 2431 5211 Lumber: rough, dressed & finished; Reconstituted wood products; Millwork; Lumber products
Pr: Ken Lobue
*Pr: Richard Phillips
*CEO: Richard J Phillips
Sys Mgr: Dan Lobue

HIGHLAND MANOR OF ELKO
See DESERT CARE FACILITIES

D-U-N-S 11-103-2178
■ **HIGHLAND MINING CO LLC**
(Suby of PATRIOT COAL CORP) ★
530 French Rd, Waverly, KY 42462-4992
Tel (270) 389-2332 Founded/Ownrshp 2007
Sales 58.9MM[E] EMP 500
SIC 1241 Coal mining services; Coal mining services
VP: Joseph W Bean
*Genl Mgr: Robert Bosch
Opers Mgr: Matt Haaga

HIGHLAND MINT
See BULLION INTERNATIONAL INC

D-U-N-S 00-996-9056
HIGHLAND PACKAGING SOLUTIONS INC
1420 Gordon Food Svc Dr, Plant City, FL 33563-7000
Tel (863) 425-5757 *Founded/Ownrshp* 1997
Sales 25.9MM^E *EMP* 150
SIC 7389 3089 2671 2672 Packaging & labeling services; Plastic containers, except foam; Packaging paper & plastics film, coated & laminated; Plastic film, coated or laminated for packaging; Adhesive papers, labels or tapes: from purchased material; Packaging & labeling services; Plastic containers, except foam; Packaging paper & plastics film, coated & laminated; Plastic film, coated or laminated for packaging; Adhesive papers, labels or tapes: from purchased material
CEO: Steven Maxwell
**CFO:* John Baird
Treas: Julianne Fore
**Sr VP:* Bill Clark
**VP:* John Durham
VP: Claudia Fuentes
**VP:* Scott Lindley
CTO: Robert Fore

D-U-N-S 03-720-3775
HIGHLAND PARK BOARD OF EDUCATION
435 Mansfield St, Highland Park, NJ 08904-2653
Tel (732) 572-6990 *Founded/Ownrshp* 1905
Sales 23.2MM^E *EMP* 325
SIC 8211 Public elementary & secondary schools; Public elementary & secondary schools
Prin: Vincent Occhino
Board of Directors: Michael Buchman, Will Calahan III, Elaine Paker-Herzog, Stephanie McIntyre, Elizabeth Raspa, Joy Schulman, Vickie White

D-U-N-S 05-359-3182
HIGHLAND PARK FORD SALES INC
1333 Park Ave W, Highland Park, IL 60035-2281
Tel (847) 433-7200 *Founded/Ownrshp* 1980
Sales 23.2MM^E *EMP* 75
SIC 5511 5521 Automobiles, new & used; Used car dealers; Automobiles, new & used; Used car dealers
Pr: Carl Statham
**Sec:* Don Raimondi

D-U-N-S 07-673-4920
HIGHLAND PARK INDEPENDENT SCHOOL DISTRICT
7015 Westchester Dr, Dallas, TX 75205-1061
Tel (214) 780-3000 *Founded/Ownrshp* 1914
Sales 144.0MM *EMP* 700
Accts Weaver & Tidwell Llp Dallas
SIC 8211 Public elementary & secondary schools; High school, junior or senior; Public elementary & secondary schools; High school, junior or senior
Bd of Dir: Jenny Castellaw
Trst: Kelly Walker
Comm Dir: Helen Williams
MIS Dir: Charlie Jackson

D-U-N-S 05-783-8294
HIGHLAND PARK MOTORS INC
MULLER HONDA
550 Skokie Valley Rd, Highland Park, IL 60035-4412
Tel (847) 831-4200 *Founded/Ownrshp* 1972
Sales 32.0MM^E *EMP* 75
SIC 5511 7532 Automobiles, new & used; Top & body repair & paint shops; Automobiles, new & used; Top & body repair & paint shops
Pr: Michael Muller
VP: Muller Honda
Genl Mgr: Jeff Harris
Sls Mgr: Harry Kim

HIGHLAND PARK SCHOOL DISTRICT
See SCHOOL DISTRICT OF CITY OF HIGHLAND PARK

D-U-N-S 07-979-9137
HIGHLAND PARK SCHOOL DISTRICT
435 Mansfield St, Highland Park, NJ 08904-2653
Tel (732) 572-6990 *Founded/Ownrshp* 2015
Sales 5.1MM^E *EMP* 380^E
SIC 8211 Public elementary & secondary schools

D-U-N-S 14-333-1317
HIGHLAND PAVING CO LLC
2031 Middle Rd, Eastover, NC 28312-9752
Tel (910) 482-0080 *Founded/Ownrshp* 2003
Sales 23.7MM^E *EMP* 95
SIC 1611 2951 Highway & street paving contractor; Asphalt & asphaltic paving mixtures (not from refineries); Highway & street paving contractor; Asphalt & asphaltic paving mixtures (not from refineries)

D-U-N-S 00-828-1321 IMP/EXP
HIGHLAND PLASTICS INC
HI-PLAS
3650 Dulles Dr, Mira Loma, CA 91752-3260
Tel (951) 360-9587 *Founded/Ownrshp* 1974
Sales 38.4MM^E *EMP* 130
SIC 3089 Injection molding of plastics
Pr: James L Nelson
**CFO:* William B Warren

HIGHLAND REGIONAL MEDICAL CTR
See SEBRING HOSPITAL MANAGEMENT ASSOCIATES LLC

D-U-N-S 07-937-3383
HIGHLAND RIDGE RV INC
OPEN RANGE RV
(*Suby of* BOTTOM LINE RV) ★
3195 N State Road 5, Shipshewana, IN 46565-9313
Tel (260) 768-7771 *Founded/Ownrshp* 2014
Sales 71.8MM^E *EMP* 330
SIC 5561 3799 3792 Recreational vehicle dealers; Recreational vehicles; Camping trailers & chassis; Recreational vehicle dealers; Recreational vehicles; Camping trailers & chassis
Pr: Randall Graber
**CFO:* Chris Good
Genl Mgr: Bill Flint
Prd Mgr: Jason Martin
Sls&Mrk Ex: Andrew Holland
Sls Mgr: Bob Cira

HIGHLAND RIVERS CENTER
See HIGHLAND RIVERS COMMUNITY SERVICE BOARD

D-U-N-S 10-853-8971
HIGHLAND RIVERS COMMUNITY SERVICE BOARD
HIGHLAND RIVERS CENTER
1401 Applewood Dr, Dalton, GA 30720-2699
Tel (706) 270-5000 *Founded/Ownrshp* 2002
Sales 950.0M *EMP* 474
SIC 8322 Family counseling services; Family counseling services
CEO: Ann Davies
Prin: Georgia Bennett

D-U-N-S 19-796-8803
HIGHLAND SOM DEVELOPMENT
GEIS COMPANY
10020 Aurora Hudson Rd, Streetsboro, OH 44241-1621
Tel (330) 528-3500 *Founded/Ownrshp* 1979
Sales 22.3MM^E *EMP* 33
SIC 6552 Land subdividers & developers, commercial
Pt: Erwin Geis
CFO: Joseph Schapel
Dir IT: Michael Demitrieff

D-U-N-S 00-627-8501
HIGHLAND SUPPLY CORP (IL)
1111 6th St, Highland, IL 62249-1408
Tel (618) 654-2161 *Founded/Ownrshp* 1937
Sales 66.4MM^E *EMP* 400
SIC 3497 2672 3081 2891 2673 Metal foil & leaf; Coated & laminated paper; Unsupported plastics film & sheet; Adhesives & sealants; Bags: plastic, laminated & coated; Metal foil & leaf; Coated & laminated paper; Unsupported plastics film & sheet; Adhesives & sealants; Bags: plastic, laminated & coated
Ch Bd: Donald Weder
**Treas:* Joe Burris
IT Man: Kyle Denny
Opers Mgr: Erwin Weder
VP Sls: Ken Kirschner

HIGHLAND TANK
See BIGBEE STEEL AND TANK CO INC

D-U-N-S 00-432-5924 EXP
HIGHLAND TANK AND MANUFACTURING CO (PA)
1 Highland Rd, Stoystown, PA 15563-6456
Tel (814) 893-5701 *Founded/Ownrshp* 1946
Sales 32.3MM^E *EMP* 140
SIC 3443 Tanks, standard or custom fabricated: metal plate; Tanks, standard or custom fabricated: metal plate
Pr: Michael Van Lenten
**Treas:* Charles A Frey
**Treas:* Robert E Jacob
**VP:* John W Jacob

D-U-N-S 84-985-3585
HIGHLAND TANK OF NORTH CAROLINA INC
2700 Patterson St, Greensboro, NC 27407-2317
Tel (336) 218-0801 *Founded/Ownrshp* 1994
Sales 29.3MM^E *EMP* 140
SIC 3443 Tanks, standard or custom fabricated: metal plate; Tanks, standard or custom fabricated: metal plate
CEO: Michael Vanlenten
**Pr:* John Jacob
**VP:* Charles A Frey

D-U-N-S 07-921-3260 EXP
HIGHLAND TRACTOR CO
JOHN DEERE
7398 Nw 44th Ave, Ocala, FL 34482-2202
Tel (321) 254-5111 *Founded/Ownrshp* 1975
Sales 27.8MM^E *EMP* 120
SIC 5999 5082 7699 Farm equipment & supplies; General construction machinery & equipment; Logging & forestry machinery & equipment; Industrial machinery & equipment repair
Pr: Sidney Varner
**Treas:* Gary L Coffman
**VP:* Joe A Varner

D-U-N-S 06-984-9235 EXP
HIGHLAND WHOLESALE FOODS INC
1604 Tillie Lewis Dr, Stockton, CA 95206-1170
Tel (209) 933-0580 *Founded/Ownrshp* 1999
Sales 60.7MM^E *EMP* 49
SIC 5148 Fresh fruits & vegetables
Pr: T Gregory Stagnitto
**COO:* Bill Burch
**Sr VP:* Tommy Sodaro

D-U-N-S 12-422-3491
HIGHLANDER MOTOR SALES INC
CHEROKEE COUNTY TOYOTA
301 Liberty Blvd, Canton, GA 30114-2851
Tel (770) 704-9525 *Founded/Ownrshp* 2000
Sales 29.8MM^E *EMP* 80
SIC 5511 Automobiles, new & used
CEO: Michael A Perrin
CFO: Barbara W Evans
Exec: Jim Pyron
Sales Exec: Paul Melda
Sls Mgr: Fernando Gordinho
Sls Mgr: Joey Roby

D-U-N-S 16-607-9249
HIGHLANDER PARTNERS LP
300 Crescent Ct Ste 550, Dallas, TX 75201-1817
Tel (214) 245-5000 *Founded/Ownrshp* 2004
Sales NA *EMP* 643
SIC 6159 Small business investment companies; Small business investment companies
Mng Pt: Jeff L Hull
Genl Pt: Highlander P GP
Pt: Alex L Guiva
Pt: Robert A Sussman
Pr: Michael R Nicolais
VP: Charles Thomas
Off Mgr: Rachael Giloini

D-U-N-S 18-657-9439
HIGHLANDS AT WYOMISSING
2000 Cambridge Ave, Reading, PA 19610-2714
Tel (610) 775-2300 *Founded/Ownrshp* 1987
Sales 27.1MM *EMP* 350
Accts Rice Cpa Reading Pa
SIC 6513 8059 8052 8051 Retirement hotel operation; Nursing home, except skilled & intermediate care facility; Intermediate care facilities; Skilled nursing care facilities; Retirement hotel operation; Nursing home, except skilled & intermediate care facility; Intermediate care facilities; Skilled nursing care facilities
Pr: Kevin P Deacosta
**Treas:* Michael A Hajost
Dir Soc: Donna Kuhn
IT Man: Kim Youse
Nrsg Dir: Rebecca Kesselring
HC Dir: Wendy Dyanzio

D-U-N-S 04-934-2293
▲ **HIGHLANDS BANKSHARES INC**
340 W Main St, Abingdon, VA 24210-2624
Tel (276) 628-9181 *Founded/Ownrshp* 1995
Sales NA *EMP* 222
Accts Brown Edwards & Company Llp
Tkr Sym HBKA *Exch* OTO
SIC 6022 State commercial banks; State commercial banks
CEO: Samuel L Neese
**Ch Bd:* James D Moore Jr
**Pr:* Charles P Olinger
CFO: Robert M Little Jr
Ofcr: R Bryan T Booher
Sr VP: C Wayne Perry
VP: James R Edmondson

D-U-N-S 15-653-1295
▲ **HIGHLANDS BANKSHARES INC**
GRANT COUNTY BANK, THE
3 N Main St, Petersburg, WV 26847-1517
Tel (304) 257-4111 *Founded/Ownrshp* 1985
Sales NA *EMP* 125
Tkr Sym HBSI *Exch* OTO
SIC 6022 State commercial banks; State commercial banks
CEO: John G Van Meter
CFO: Jeffrey B Reedy
**Treas:* Alan L Brill
Ofcr: Mike Cosner
VP: D Richardson
VP: Dempsey Richardson
Dir IT: Dan Fabbri
Sls&Mrk Ex: Barry Lupton

HIGHLANDS CNTY HUMN RESOURCES
See COUNTY OF HIGHLANDS

D-U-N-S 17-065-3372
HIGHLANDS COMMUNITY SERVICES BOARD
610 Campus Dr Ste 200, Abingdon, VA 24210-2589
Tel (276) 525-1550 *Founded/Ownrshp* 1975
Sales 20.9MM^E *EMP* 260
Accts Hicok Fern Brown & Garcia Cpas
SIC 8093 Specialty outpatient clinics; Specialty outpatient clinics
**CFO:* Kathryne Simpson
Comm Man: Danielle Lamson

D-U-N-S 07-979-8986
HIGHLANDS COUNTY SCHOOLS
426 School St, Sebring, FL 33870-4048
Tel (863) 471-5564 *Founded/Ownrshp* 2015
Sales 14.9MM^E *EMP* 1,728^E
SIC 8211 Public elementary & secondary schools

D-U-N-S 87-841-4333 IMP
HIGHLANDS DIVERSIFIED SERVICES INC
250 Westinghouse Dr, London, KY 40741-2700
Tel (606) 878-1856 *Founded/Ownrshp* 1994
Sales 62.0MM *EMP* 250
SIC 3469 Electrical equipment & supplies; Metal stampings; Metal stampings
Pr: James M Hurley
CFO: Janet French
**Treas:* Daryl Weaver
**VP:* Gerald Hockenderry
Dir IT: Barry Hickey
Mtls Mgr: Rick Centers
Opers Mgr: Shirley Culton
Plnt Mgr: Mike Wilson
Ql Cn Mgr: Claude Chumley
Ql Cn Mgr: Michelle Hamm

D-U-N-S 01-901-0529 IMP
HIGHLANDS FUEL DELIVERY LLC (ME)
IRVING ENERGY DIST & MKTG
(*Suby of* OCEAN INVESTMENTS CORP) ★
190 Commerce Way, Portsmouth, NH 03801-3242
Tel (603) 559-8739 *Founded/Ownrshp* 1986
Sales 881.6MM^E *EMP* 900
SIC 5172 5541 1389 Gasoline; Filling stations, gasoline; Construction, repair & dismantling services; Gasoline; Filling stations, gasoline; Construction, repair & dismantling services
Pr: Darren Gillis
**Treas:* James Sepanski
Ex Dir: Stephanie Pines
Area Mgr: Matthew Roach
Manager: Dennis Dillon
Snr Mgr: Jessica Diffin
Snr Mgr: Steve McLaughlin

D-U-N-S 11-911-7281
HIGHLANDS HOSPITAL
401 E Murphy Ave, Connellsville, PA 15425-2700
Tel (724) 628-1500 *Founded/Ownrshp* 1985
Sales 27.8MM *EMP* 350^E
Accts Arnett Carbis Tooth Man Lp Pi
SIC 8062 General medical & surgical hospitals; General medical & surgical hospitals
CEO: Michelle P Cunningham
**CFO:* John S Andursky
Exec: Jane Krosoff
Dir OR: Jennifer Boone
Dir Lab: Erin Fronczek
Mktg Dir: Cindy Murphy
Psych: Sue Mongell

D-U-N-S 06-813-5516
HIGHLANDS HOSPITAL CORP
HIGHLANDS REGIONAL MEDICAL CTR
(*Suby of* CONSOLIDATED HEALTH SYSTEMS INC) ★
5000 Ky Route 321, Prestonsburg, KY 41653-9113
Tel (606) 886-8511 *Founded/Ownrshp* 1986
Sales 66.6MM *EMP* 440
SIC 8062 8011 General medical & surgical hospitals; Offices & clinics of medical doctors; General medical & surgical hospitals; Offices & clinics of medical doctors
Pr: Harold Warman
**COO:* Chris Hoffman
**CFO:* Jack Blackbell
**Ch:* Dewey L Bocook Jr
**Ch:* Edward R Nairn
**Treas:* Paul D Nunn
Treas: Paul Nunn
VP: Susan Ellis
**VP:* Burl W Spurlock
Dir Inf Cn: Teresa Back
Dir Rx: Vylinda Howard

D-U-N-S 05-719-1967
HIGHLANDS INSURANCE CO
(*Suby of* HIGHLANDS INSURANCE GROUP INC) ★
275 Phillips Blvd Ste 2, Trenton, NJ 08618-1452
Tel (609) 895-3124 *Founded/Ownrshp* 1963
Sales NA *EMP* 270
SIC 6331 6351 Workers' compensation insurance; Fire, marine & casualty insurance & carriers; Assessment associations: fire, marine & casualty insurance; Surety insurance; Workers' compensation insurance; Fire, marine & casualty insurance & carriers; Assessment associations: fire, marine & casualty insurance; Surety insurance
Prin: Craig Koenig

D-U-N-S 80-670-0266
HIGHLANDS INSURANCE GROUP INC
10370 Richmond Ave, Houston, TX 77042-4141
Tel (713) 952-0665 *Founded/Ownrshp* 1990
Sales NA *EMP* 629
SIC 6331 6351 Fire, marine & casualty insurance; Workers' compensation insurance; Fire, marine & casualty insurance & carriers; Assessment associations: fire, marine & casualty insurance; Surety insurance; Fire, marine & casualty insurance; Workers' compensation insurance; Fire, marine & casualty insurance & carriers; Assessment associations: fire, marine & casualty insurance; Surety insurance
Pr: John W Cowley
CFO: Albert J Marino
**Sec:* Stephen L Kibblehouse

D-U-N-S 94-431-6934
HIGHLANDS ONCOLOGY GROUP PA
HOG
3232 N Northhills Blvd, Fayetteville, AR 72703-4005
Tel (479) 936-9900 *Founded/Ownrshp* 1996
Sales 32.3MM^E *EMP* 225
SIC 8011 Oncologist; Hematologist; Oncologist; Hematologist
Pr: Malcolm Hayward
**VP:* Dan Bradford
Off Mgr: Candy Hebar
Off Mgr: Sara Scott
Cmptr Lab: Barbara Sterling
Doctor: Patrick Travis MD
Board of Directors: J T Beck M D, Daniel Bradford M D, Hershel Garner M D, Gregory Oakhill M D, Stephen Rosenfeld M D, Joseph Ross M D, Eric Schaefer M D, Arnold Smith M D, Pat Travis M D

D-U-N-S 18-484-9800
HIGHLANDS RANCH COMMUNITY ASSOCIATION INC
HRCA
9568 S University Blvd, Highlands Ranch, CO 80126-2912
Tel (303) 791-2500 *Founded/Ownrshp* 1981
Sales 24.0MM *EMP* 703
Accts Eide Bailly Llp Golden Color
SIC 8641 Homeowners' association; Homeowners' association
CEO: Jerry Flannery
COO: Lori Lewis
Ex VP: Linda Techentien
Ql Cn Mgr: Demi Anderson

D-U-N-S 07-322-9213
■ **HIGHLANDS REGIONAL MEDICAL CENTER AUXILIARY INC**
HMA
(*Suby of* HEALTH MANAGEMENT ASSOCIATES INC) ★
3600 S Highlands Ave, Sebring, FL 33870-5416
Tel (863) 385-6101 *Founded/Ownrshp* 1984
Sales 62.4MM *EMP* 220^E
SIC 8062 General medical & surgical hospitals; General medical & surgical hospitals
CEO: Brian Hess
**COO:* Robert Palussek
**CFO:* Vicki Derenzis
Dir OR: Mary Ferguson
Dir Sec: Mike Taggert
QA Dir: Jennifer Forde
Pharmcst: Bob Brooks

HIGHLANDS REGIONAL MEDICAL CTR
See HIGHLANDS HOSPITAL CORP

HIGHLANDS RESOURCES INTL
See BRODAMS HOLDINGS INTERNATIONAL LLC

D-U-N-S 00-807-7182
HIGHLANDS SCHOOL DISTRICT
1500 Pacific Ave, Natrona Heights, PA 15065-2099
Tel (724) 226-2400 *Founded/Ownrshp* 1967
Sales 43.7MM^E *EMP* 500

SIC 8211 Public senior high school; Public elementary school; Public senior high school; Public elementary school
Dir IT: Doug Costa
Schl Brd P: Carrie Fox

HIGHLANDS TIRE SERVICE
See ZANE R HIGHLANDS INC

D-U-N-S 15-179-3189
■ HIGHLANDS UNION BANK
(*Suby of* HIGHLANDS BANKSHARES INC) ★
340 W Main St, Abingdon, VA 24210-2624
Tel (276) 628-9181 *Founded/Ownrshp* 1995
Sales NA *EMP* 200
SIC 6022 State commercial banks; State commercial banks
Ch Bd: J D Morefield
**Pr:* James Moore
**CEO:* Sam Neese
**CFO:* James R Edmondson
Sr VP: William Hutton
**VP:* Robert M Little Jr

D-U-N-S 01-689-1608
HIGHLANDS-CASHIERS HOSPITAL FOUNDATION INC
190 Hospital Dr, Highlands, NC 28741-7600
Tel (828) 526-1200 *Founded/Ownrshp* 1952
Sales 3.7MM *EMP* 415ᴱ
SIC 8062

D-U-N-S 10-674-9906
HIGHLIGHT INDUSTRIES INC
2694 Prairie St Sw, Grand Rapids, MI 49519-2461
Tel (616) 531-2464 *Founded/Ownrshp* 1981
Sales 21.3MMᴱ *EMP* 69
SIC 3565 Wrapping machines; Wrapping machines
Pr: Kurt Riemenschneider
**CFO:* Joseph Parnell
**VP:* Karen Riemenschneider
Dir Bus: Christina Agema
Comm Man: Cecil Rhoads
Plnt Mgr: Randy Himstra

D-U-N-S 02-233-0581
HIGHLIGHT REALTY CORP
HIGHLIGHT REALTY NETWORK
5323 Lake Worth Rd, Greenacres, FL 33463-3353
Tel (561) 641-6787 *Founded/Ownrshp* 2006
Sales 10.6MMᴱ *EMP* 450
SIC 6531 6519 Real estate agents & managers; Real property lessors; Real estate agents & managers; Real property lessors
Pr: John Sanchez

HIGHLIGHT REALTY NETWORK
See HIGHLIGHT REALTY CORP

D-U-N-S 00-449-5115 IMP
HIGHLIGHTS FOR CHILDREN INC (OH)
ESSENTIAL LEARNING PRODUCTS
1800 Watermark Dr, Columbus, OH 43215-1035
Tel (614) 486-0631 *Founded/Ownrshp* 1946
Sales 147.8MMᴱ *EMP* 737
SIC 2721

D-U-N-S 04-460-5715
HIGHLINE COMMUNITY COLLEGE
2400 S 240th St, Des Moines, WA 98198-2714
Tel (206) 878-3710 *Founded/Ownrshp* 1961
Sales 1.2MM *EMP* 781
Accts Ryan Jorgenson & Limoli Ps Gi
SIC 8221 Colleges universities & professional schools; Colleges universities & professional schools
Pr: Jack Bermingham
Assoc Dir: Monica Luce
Brnch Mgr: Mark Rasmussen

D-U-N-S 18-912-3318
HIGHLINE COMMUNITY COLLEGE FOUNDATION
2400 S 240th St, Des Moines, WA 98198-2714
Tel (206) 878-3710 *Founded/Ownrshp* 1972
Sales 969.0M *EMP* 400
SIC 8222 Community college; Community college

D-U-N-S 00-279-3107
HIGHLINE ELECTRIC ASSOCIATION
1300 S Interocean Ave, Holyoke, CO 80734-2100
Tel (970) 854-2236 *Founded/Ownrshp* 1938
Sales 56.5MM *EMP* 53
SIC 4911 Distribution, electric power; Distribution, electric power
Genl Mgr: Mark Farnsworth
**Pr:* Michael Bennett
**Pr:* Leo Brekel
**CEO:* Mark R Johnson
**Treas:* Merl Miller
Ex Dir: Nancy Berges

D-U-N-S 07-927-2761
HIGHLINE MEDICAL CENTER
HIGHLINE SPECIALTY CENTER
16251 Sylvester Rd Sw, Burien, WA 98166-3017
Tel (206) 244-9970 *Founded/Ownrshp* 1958
Sales 161.6MM *EMP* 1,253
SIC 8062 8051 General medical & surgical hospitals; Skilled nursing care facilities; General medical & surgical hospitals; Skilled nursing care facilities
Ch: Chris Henshaw
Chf Rad: William Grabowski
**Pr:* Sue O'Brien
COO: Karen Lautermilch
CFO: Henry Kotula
**CFO:* Lloyd Musselman
**Treas:* Mark Benedum
Trst: Uli CHI
Trst: Harry Pierce
Chf Mktg O: James Andrew
VP: Jeff Frankel
VP: Byron Kaersner
Exec: Beth Bautista
Dir Rad: Christa Christensen
Dir Rx: Thuy Vo
Board of Directors: Lori Anderson, Michael Dehaan, Scott Enck, Byron Kaersner, Steve Odachowski, Buddy Orr, Earl Wiitala

D-U-N-S 18-930-1518
HIGHLINE MEDICAL SERVICES INC
16255 Sylvester Rd Sw # 202, Burien, WA 98166-3017
Tel (206) 431-5304 *Founded/Ownrshp* 1985
Sales 102.6MM *EMP* 6
SIC 8011 Dispensery, operated by physicians; Dispensery, operated by physicians

D-U-N-S 07-821-4947
HIGHLINE PUBLIC SCHOOLS
15675 Ambaum Blvd Sw, Burien, WA 98166-2523
Tel (206) 433-2208 *Founded/Ownrshp* 1941
Sales 221.9MM *EMP* 2,000ᴱ
Accts Troy Kelley King County Wash
SIC 8211 Public elementary school; Public junior high school; Public senior high school; Public vocational/technical school; Public elementary school; Public junior high school; Public senior high school; Public vocational/technical school
Pr: Julie Burr- Spani
Prin: Tom Symons
Dir Sec: Dennis Decotcau
Dir Sec: Tony Zeman
Off Mgr: Gail Korakis
Pr Dir: Catherine C Carbone-Rogers
Teacher Pr: Steve Grubb
Teacher Pr: Don Waring
Psych: Connie Purdy
HC Dir: Aimee Denver
Snr PM: Barbara Martinez

HIGHLINE SPECIALTY CENTER
See HIGHLINE MEDICAL CENTER

HIGHMARK BLUE CROSS BLUE SHELD
See HIGHMARKS INC

D-U-N-S 07-217-9633
HIGHMARK BLUE CROSS BLUE SHIELD WEST VIRGINIA
HIGHMARK INC., PITTSBURGH, PA
(*Suby of* HIGHMARK BLUE CRSS-BLUE SHIELD) ★
614 Market St, Parkersburg, WV 26101-5146
Tel (304) 424-7700 *Founded/Ownrshp* 1937
Sales NA *EMP* 560
Accts Pricewaterhousecoopers Llp Ph
SIC 6321 Accident & health insurance carriers; Accident & health insurance carriers
Pr: J Fred Earley
CFO: J Sengewaltt
**Treas:* Karen Hanlon
Sr VP: Mark Sengewaltt
VP: Tom Alderson
VP: Cindy Ayers
VP: Steven Hunt
VP: James Miller
Comm Man: Catherine McAlister
Brnch Mgr: Kelly Schultz
Dir IT: Rich Bird

HIGHMARK BLUE CRSS-BLUE SHIELD
See HIGHMARK INC

D-U-N-S 78-657-3803
HIGHMARK CASUALTY INSURANCE CO
(*Suby of* HM INSURANCE GROUP INC) ★
120 5th Ave Ste 924, Pittsburgh, PA 15222-3024
Tel (412) 544-1000 *Founded/Ownrshp* 2006
Sales NA *EMP* 1ᴱ
SIC 6411 Insurance agents, brokers & service
Prin: Dan Lebish
CIO: Matthew Piroch

D-U-N-S 07-126-0375
HIGHMARK HEALTH
AHN - ALLEGHENY HEALTH NETWORK
120 5th Ave Ste 924, Pittsburgh, PA 15222-3024
Tel (412) 544-7226 *Founded/Ownrshp* 2013
Sales 44.7MMMᴱ *EMP* 35,000ᴱ
SIC 8099 6321 Organ bank; Health insurance carriers
Pr: David L Holmberg
**CFO:* Karen Hanlon
**Treas:* Nanette P Deturk
Ex VP: Melissa Anderson
Sr VP: David Carter

D-U-N-S 06-709-6644
HIGHMARK INC
HIGHMARK BLUE CRSS-BLUE SHIELD
(*Suby of* AHN - ALLEGHENY HEALTH NETWORK) ★
120 5th Ave Ste 924, Pittsburgh, PA 15222-3024
Tel (412) 544-7000 *Founded/Ownrshp* 1965
Sales NA *EMP* 35,000
SIC 6321 6324 6411 6512 Accident & health insurance; Group hospitalization plans; Dental insurance; Health maintenance organization (HMO), insurance only; Medical insurance claim processing, contract or fee basis; Nonresidential building operators; Accident & health insurance; Group hospitalization plans; Dental insurance; Health maintenance organization (HMO), insurance only; Medical insurance claim processing, contract or fee basis; Nonresidential building operators
Ch: J Robert Baum
**Pr:* William Winkenwerder
**CEO:* John S Brouse
CFO: Nanette P Nan Deturk
CFO: Domenic Palmieri
**Treas:* Nanette P Deturk
Treas: Karen Hanlon
Ofcr: James E Bylotas
**Ofcr:* Jayanth Godla
Ofcr: Maryann Neely
Ofcr: Lidia Wielechowski
Ex VP: Tyrone S Alexander
Ex VP: Virginia Calega
Ex VP: Daniel Lebish
Ex VP: David O'Brien
Ex VP: Jeff Smith
Sr VP: Evan Frazier
Sr VP: Gary R Truitt
VP: Melissa Anderson
VP: Wayne Berger
VP: Matthew Childs
Board of Directors: Terrence W Cavanaugh, Louis Civitarese

HIGHMARK INC., PITTSBURGH, PA
See HIGHMARK BLUE CROSS BLUE SHIELD WEST VIRGINIA

D-U-N-S 00-248-8542
HIGHMARKS INC
HIGHMARK BLUE CROSS BLUE SHELD
800 Delaware Ave Ste 900, Wilmington, DE 19801-1368
Tel (302) 421-3000 *Founded/Ownrshp* 1935
Sales NA *EMP* 650
Accts Ernst & Young Llp Baltimore
SIC 6321 Health insurance carriers; Health insurance carriers
Pr: Timothy J Constantine
CFO: Mark G Chaney
CFO: James Hynek
Chf Mktg O: Jay Reed
**Assoc VP:* Phillip A Carter
Ex VP: Thomas Boyd
VP: William Breskin
VP: Paul Brown
VP: Kalpesh Doshi
VP: Peg Eitl
VP: Jena Estes
Exec: Sandi Boyer
Comm Man: Mary Allen
Board of Directors: Thomas Arichie, Max S Bell Jr, Bernard Daney, Garrett B Lyons, Robert F Rider, Frances West

D-U-N-S 80-626-3633
HIGHMOUNT EXPLORATION & PRODUCTION LLC
(*Suby of* ENERVEST LTD) ★
1001 Fannin St Ste 800, Houston, TX 77002-6707
Tel (281) 873-1500 *Founded/Ownrshp* 2014
Sales 223.0MMᴱ *EMP* 300
SIC 1382 Oil & gas exploration services; Oil & gas exploration services
CEO: Steven B Hinchman
Pr: Malcolm Johns
**CFO:* Dennis G Millet

D-U-N-S 80-835-2202
HIGHPOINT GLOBAL LLC
300 N Meridian St Ste 190, Indianapolis, IN 46204-1779
Tel (317) 576-4500 *Founded/Ownrshp* 2006
Sales 95.0MM *EMP* 192
SIC 8742 Management consulting services; Management consulting services
CEO: Benjamin Lanius
**Pr:* Rachel Lanius
CFO: Stephen Niemeier
VP: Tom Miller

D-U-N-S 78-627-5813
HIGHPOINT SOLUTIONS LLC
301 E Germantown Pike # 1, East Norriton, PA 19401-6517
Tel (610) 233-2700 *Founded/Ownrshp* 2006
Sales 132.6MMᴱ *EMP* 475
Accts Grant Thornton Philadelphia
SIC 7371 Computer software systems analysis & design, custom; Computer software systems analysis & design, custom
CEO: John P Seitz
**Pr:* Thomas Clancy
**CFO:* James Dandy
Bd of Dir: Steve Brock
Sr VP: Jeff Dibartolomeo
Sr VP: James Sublowski
VP: Chris Colapietro
VP: Mike Germain
VP: Ralph Lynn
VP: Bret Piano
VP: Sam Schmitt
VP: Ray Schweighofer
Assoc Dir: Jack Adlevankin
Assoc Dir: Mayank Srivastava
Dir Bus: Ryan Davies
Board of Directors: Kayne Anderson

D-U-N-S 10-798-6622
HIGHPOINTE HOSPITABILITY INC
HAMPTON INN
311 Gulf Breeze Pkwy, Gulf Breeze, FL 32561-4463
Tel (850) 932-9314 *Founded/Ownrshp* 1982
Sales 45.5MMᴱ *EMP* 450
SIC 6552 8742 Land subdividers & developers, commercial; Management consulting services; Land subdividers & developers, commercial; Management consulting services
Pr: Darryl G Lapointe
Sr VP: Dave Cleveland
**Sr VP:* David Cleveland
Dir IT: Gregory Weekley
IT Man: Greg Weekly
Sls Dir: Sandrine Biavant

D-U-N-S 82-908-9932
HIGHRIDGE COSTA INVESTORS LLC
MACFARLANE CSTA HSING PARTNERS
330 W Victoria St, Gardena, CA 90248-3527
Tel (424) 258-2800 *Founded/Ownrshp* 2007
Sales 30.5MMᴱ *EMP* 104
SIC 1521 Single-family housing construction
Pr: Michael Costa
**CFO:* Robert Tetraul
Sr VP: Thomas Erickson
VP: Alison Abrams
VP: Pete Harispu
VP: Kevin Horner

HIGH'S
See NEW RIDGE ASSOCIATES INC

D-U-N-S 07-850-0953
HIGHS OF BALTIMORE LLC (MD)
2700 Loch Raven Rd, Baltimore, MD 21218-4729
Tel (410) 261-5460 *Founded/Ownrshp* 2012, 2015
Sales 44.6MMᴱ *EMP* 435ᴱ
SIC 5411 Convenience stores, chain
Pr: John Phelps
VP: Benjamin Jatlow

D-U-N-S 05-352-4306
HIGHSTREET IT SOLUTIONS LLC
8480 E Orchard Rd # 6200, Greenwood Village, CO 80111-5029
Tel (303) 802-5200 *Founded/Ownrshp* 2012
Sales 29.7MMᴱ *EMP* 105ᴱ
SIC 7371 7379 Computer software development & applications; Computer related consulting services; Computer software development & applications; Computer related consulting services
Pr: Mac Slingerlend
**Sr VP:* Russ Wheeler
VP: Shane Hackney

D-U-N-S 03-190-3941
HIGHT ENTERPRISES LTD
MCGUCKIN HARDWARE
2525 Arapahoe Ave Unit D1, Boulder, CO 80302-6725
Tel (303) 443-1822 *Founded/Ownrshp* 1960
Sales 27.8MM *EMP* 265
Accts R Waidler & Associates Pc B
SIC 5251 5941 Hardware; Sporting goods & bicycle shops; Hardware; Sporting goods & bicycle shops
CEO: David Keith Hight
**Pr:* Barry L Hight
**CFO:* Paul Gomez
Mktg Mgr: Louise Garrels

D-U-N-S 00-216-7100
HIGHTAIL INC
1919 S Bascom Ave, Campbell, CA 95008-2220
Tel (408) 879-9118 *Founded/Ownrshp* 2005
Sales 47.0MMᴱ *EMP* 100ᴱ
SIC 4813
Ch Bd: Brad Garlinghouse
Pr: Stephen Brady
**Pr:* Irwin Koon
**CFO:* Renee Budig
**CFO:* Ned Sizer
**Chf Mktg O:* Sandra Vaughan
VP: Brian Curry
VP: Viral Kadakia
Dir Bus: David Anderson
Dir Bus: Dennis Ferrell
Dir Bus: Fiaz Mohamed
Comm Man: Robyn Hannah
Board of Directors: Bruce Felt, Doug Hickey

D-U-N-S 94-811-6566
HIGHTOWER ADVISORS LLC
200 W Madison St Ste 2500, Chicago, IL 60606-3497
Tel (312) 962-3800 *Founded/Ownrshp* 2002
Sales 29.8MMᴱ *EMP* 261ᴱ
SIC 8742 Financial consultant; Financial consultant
CEO: Elliot Weissbluth
**Pr:* Michael Lamena
**CFO:* Larry Koehler
Ex VP: Chris Curtis
Dir Rx: Candice Kakar
Dir Bus: Ed Friedman
Mng Dir: Jason Ezzell
Mng Dir: Evan Nowack
Mng Dir: Mingdong Tan
Opers Mgr: Maureen Carney
Mktg Mgr: Kathleen Anderson

D-U-N-S 01-604-9700
HIGHTOWER HOLDINGS LLC
200 W Madison St Ste 2500, Chicago, IL 60606-3497
Tel (312) 962-3811 *Founded/Ownrshp* 2003
Sales 46.9MMᴱ *EMP* 300
SIC 7389 Financial services; Financial services
Mng Dir: Moss Crosby
Mng Dir: Jason Ezzell
Mng Dir: Lars Knudsen
Mng Dir: Francis Masse
Mng Dir: Roger Shaffer
Mng Dir: Dan Stober
Web Dev: Daryl Cheung
Board of Directors: Andrew Morse, Richard Saperstein

D-U-N-S 19-722-8737
HIGHTOWERS PETROLEUM CO INC
3577 Commerce Dr, Middletown, OH 45005-5232
Tel (513) 423-4272 *Founded/Ownrshp* 1985
Sales 308.0MM *EMP* 50
SIC 5172 Diesel fuel; Gasoline; Diesel fuel; Gasoline
CEO: Steve Hightower Sr
**CFO:* Gary Visher
**VP:* Yudell Hightower
Genl Mgr: Thomas Hoover
Genl Mgr: Randy Long
IT Man: Jason Hightower
Pr Mgr: Tracey Bunch

D-U-N-S 87-275-9803
HIGHWATER ETHANOL LLC
24500 Us Highway 14, Lamberton, MN 56152-1179
Tel (507) 752-6160 *Founded/Ownrshp* 2009
Sales 139.6MM *EMP* 40
Accts Mcgladrey Llp Sioux Falls So
SIC 2869 Ethyl alcohol, ethanol; Ethyl alcohol, ethanol
CEO: Brian Kletscher
**Ch Bd:* David G Moldan
CFO: Lucas Schneider
**Treas:* Luke Spalj
**V Ch Bd:* Timothy J Vanderwal
Dir Lab: Lisa Landkammer
Dir IT: George Goblish
Opers Mgr: Chad Altermatt
Opers Mgr: Scott Brittenham
Opers Mgr: Matt Lenning
Plnt Mgr: Greg Bergeron
Board of Directors: Russell J Derickson, William Garth, George M Goblish, Ronald E Jorgenson, Michael Landuyt

D-U-N-S 96-722-3459 EXP
HIGHWATER MARINE LLC
GODFREY MARINE
333 W Wacker Dr Ste 600, Chicago, IL 60606-1284
Tel (574) 522-8381 *Founded/Ownrshp* 2005
Sales 36.9MMᴱ *EMP* 99ᴱ
SIC 3732 Boat building & repairing; Boat building & repairing
CFO: Troy Randolph
Treas: Darin Schaeffer

Bd of Dir: Terry Carlson
Ofcr: Richard V Gasaway
Sr VP: John Forbes
Exec: Carol Evans
Exec: Erick Evans
Exec: Ed Robbins
Exec: Maggie Weaver
Off Mgr: Janae Richardson
Dir IT: Christopher Laware

D-U-N-S 96-611-0855
HIGHWATER SYSTEMS LLC
2020 Howell Mill Rd Nw, Atlanta, GA 30318-1732
Tel (404) 655-9788 *Founded/Ownrshp* 2010
Sales 22.8MM *EMP* 15
SIC 7373 8748 Systems engineering, computer related; Turnkey vendors, computer systems; Value-added resellers, computer systems; Systems engineering consultant, ex. computer or professional; Systems engineering, computer related; Turnkey vendors, computer systems; Value-added resellers, computer systems; Systems engineering consultant, ex. computer or professional

HIGHWAY AG SVC & CONVIENCE STR
See HWY AG SERVICES

HIGHWAY DEPARTMENT
See TOWN OF LORRAINE

D-U-N-S 01-418-2968 EXP
HIGHWAY EQUIPMENT & SUPPLY CO (PA)
4500 Paxton St, Harrisburg, PA 17111-2549
Tel (717) 564-3031 *Founded/Ownrshp* 1951
Sales 27.4MM^E *EMP* 72
SIC 5082

D-U-N-S 00-528-1001 IMP
HIGHWAY EQUIPMENT CO (IA)
NEW LEADER
1330 76th Ave Sw, Cedar Rapids, IA 52404-7038
Tel (319) 363-8281 *Founded/Ownrshp* 1978, 1997
Sales 43.7MM^E *EMP* 150
SIC 3523 3531 Spreaders, fertilizer; Road construction & maintenance machinery; Spreaders, fertilizer; Road construction & maintenance machinery
Pr: R R Shepard
Pr: Mike Podoll
CFO: Randal Willey
**VP:* Martin Richards
Telecom Ex: Larry Nelson
IT Man: John Wilke
Mtls Mgr: Clint Gibson
Plnt Mgr: Brad Wiedenhoff
Mktg Dir: Marty Wolske
Manager: Dave Baker
Manager: Larry Curry

D-U-N-S 02-376-3758
HIGHWAY MOTORS INC
5307 Peters Creek Rd Nw, Roanoke, VA 24019-3849
Tel (540) 434-6716 *Founded/Ownrshp* 1985
Sales 48.7MM^E *EMP* 106
SIC 5511 Trucks, tractors & trailers: new & used; Trucks, tractors & trailers: new & used
Pr: Thomas W Mohr
**Sec:* John Allen Spell

HIGHWAY OIL
See HY-WAY INC

HIGHWAY PARTOL
See TENNESSEE DEPARTMENT OF SAFETY

HIGHWAY PATROL
See OKLAHOMA DEPT OF PUBLIC SAFETY

D-U-N-S 87-888-3107
HIGHWAY PATROL CALIFORNIA
(*Suby of* BUSINESS TRANSPORTATION & HOUSING AGENCY STATE OF CALIFORNIA) ★
601 N 7th St, Sacramento, CA 95811-0208
Tel (916) 376-3256 *Founded/Ownrshp* 1947
Sales NA *EMP* 7,541^E
SIC 9221 State highway patrol; ; State highway patrol;
Ofcr: Robert Bond
Ofcr: Gary Britton
Ofcr: Jeff Closson
Ofcr: Paul Dahlen
Ofcr: Dennis Davidson
Ofcr: Don Donovan
Ofcr: Dave Duenas
Ofcr: James Dunn
Ofcr: Donald Feil
Ofcr: Scott Fischer
Ofcr: Pat Gomez
Ofcr: Hector Gutierrez
Ofcr: John Harris
Ofcr: Carter Howell
Ofcr: Ed Lewis
Ofcr: Mark Locey
Ofcr: Ron Lum
Ofcr: Matt Lyman
Ofcr: David Russell
Ofcr: Xavier Spencer
Ofcr: Ron Swenson

HIGHWAY PIZZA
See DANTES RESTAURANT INC

D-U-N-S 00-114-8428 EXP
HIGHWAY SAFETY CORP
CONNECTICUT GALVANIZING
239 Commerce St Ste C, Glastonbury, CT 06033-2448
Tel (860) 659-4330 *Founded/Ownrshp* 1980
Sales 51.7MM *EMP* 115
Accts Cohnreznick Llp Glastonbury
SIC 3444 3479 Guard rails, highway: sheet metal; Galvanizing of iron, steel or end-formed products; Guard rails, highway: sheet metal; Galvanizing of iron, steel or end-formed products
CEO: W Patric Gregory
Pr: Frank Luszcz
CFO: Robert West
VP: John Roy
VP: Randy Wingate
S&M/VP: Roy Riedl

D-U-N-S 78-533-3873
HIGHWAY SAFETY DEVICES INC
6480 Harney Rd, Tampa, FL 33610-9592
Tel (813) 759-1559 *Founded/Ownrshp* 1989
Sales 35.4MM^E *EMP* 100^E
SIC 1611 1799 Highway signs & guardrails; Guardrail construction, highways; Highway & street sign installation; Sign installation & maintenance; Highway signs & guardrails; Guardrail construction, highways; Highway & street sign installation; Sign installation & maintenance
Ch: Larry C Morgan
**Pr:* Gordon Johnson
Ex VP: Luis Pe
**VP:* Luis Buenaventura
**Prin:* Marian Price

D-U-N-S 14-420-5010
HIGHWAY SERVICE VENTURES INC
FLYING J
100 Arbor Oak Dr Ste 305, Ashland, VA 23005-2266
Tel (804) 752-4966 *Founded/Ownrshp* 1984
Sales 100.0MM^E *EMP* 450
Accts Kpmg Llp East Cary Street Ri
SIC 5541 5411 5812 Truck stops; Convenience stores; Restaurant, family: chain; Truck stops; Convenience stores; Restaurant, family: chain
Pr: Roger Cole
**CFO:* William Carter Dages
IT Man: Wes Moore
Counsel: Albert Lilly

HIGHWAY TECHNOLOGIES GROUP
See HTS ACQUISITION INC

D-U-N-S 60-698-2049
HIGHWAY TECHNOLOGIES INC
6811 Dixie Dr, Houston, TX 77087-5134
Tel (713) 845-1800 *Founded/Ownrshp* 2007
Sales NA *EMP* 1,000
SIC 1622 7359

D-U-N-S 00-717-1221
HIGHWAY TO HEALTH INC
HTH WORLDWIDE
100 Matsonford Rd Ste 1, Radnor, PA 19087-4565
Tel (610) 254-8700 *Founded/Ownrshp* 1997
Sales NA *EMP* 59^E
SIC 6321 Health insurance carriers
CEO: Angelo Masciantonio
Pt: Stephen M Goodman
**COO:* Andrew G Conn
**CFO:* Donald D Joseph
Dir: Michael Hartung
IT Man: James Greeley
Software D: Brian McGinley

D-U-N-S 82-716-0479
HIGHWAY TRANSPORT CHEMICAL LLC
1500 Amherst Rd, Knoxville, TN 37909-1203
Tel (865) 584-8631 *Founded/Ownrshp* 2008
Sales 22.7MM^E *EMP* 300
SIC 4789 Cargo loading & unloading services; Cargo loading & unloading services
Dir IT: Paul Noe

D-U-N-S 03-455-3610
HIGHWAYS INC
PAVING DIVISION
1623 Galleria Blvd, Brentwood, TN 37027-2926
Tel (615) 373-5445 *Founded/Ownrshp* 1981
Sales 89.6MM^E *EMP* 250
SIC 1611 Highway & street paving contractor; Highway & street paving contractor
Pr: Allen Linder
**Sec:* Linda Vaughn
**VP:* Mark Odom

HIGHWAYS MAGAZINE
See TL ENTERPRISES LLC

D-U-N-S 78-501-0872
HIGHWINDS NETWORK GROUP INC
807 W Morse Blvd Ste 101, Winter Park, FL 32789-3726
Tel (407) 215-2400 *Founded/Ownrshp* 2002
Sales 31.5MM^E *EMP* 177
SIC 7379 ;
CEO: Steve Miller
**Pr:* Chance Brannen
Pr: Steve Liddell
**CEO:* Thomas S Miller
COO: Van Macatee
COO: Scott Munger
**CFO:* Gabe Miller
Sr VP: Mike Padula Jr
VP: George Antoniou
VP: David Barmann
VP: Brad Beard
VP: Bob Bosco

HIGHWOODS PROPERTIES
See HIGHWOODS REALTY LIMITED PARTNERSHIP

D-U-N-S 09-512-1760
▲ **HIGHWOODS PROPERTIES INC**
3100 Smoketree Ct Ste 600, Raleigh, NC 27604-1050
Tel (919) 872-4924 *Founded/Ownrshp* 1978
Sales 608.4MM *EMP* 426
Accts Deloitte & Touche Llp Raleigh
Tkr Sym HIW *Exch* NYS
SIC 6798 Real estate investment trusts; Real estate investment trusts
Pr: Edward J Fritsch
**Ch Bd:* O Temple Sloan Jr
COO: Michael E Harris
CFO: Mark F Mulhern
Treas: Carman Liuzzo
Ofcr: Terry Steven
Sr VP: Barrett Brady
Sr VP: Theodore Klinck
Sr VP: Jeffrey D Miller
Sr VP: Kevin E Penn
VP: Rick Dehnert III
VP: David Doubman
VP: Kim Farr
VP: Steven J Garrity
VP: Thomas Hill
VP: Marcus H Jackson
VP: Julie Kelly
VP: Walton Makepeace
VP: Geoffrey Penn
VP: Mack D Pridgen III
VP: Hazel Ray
Board of Directors: Charles A Anderson, Gene H Anderson, Carlos E Evans, David J Hartzell, Sherry A Kellett, L Glenn Orr Jr

D-U-N-S 80-826-4290
■ **HIGHWOODS REALTY LIMITED PARTNERSHIP**
HIGHWOODS PROPERTIES
(*Suby of* HIGHWOODS PROPERTIES INC) ★
3100 Smoketree Ct Ste 600, Raleigh, NC 27604-1050
Tel (919) 872-4924 *Founded/Ownrshp* 1994
Sales 608.4MM *EMP* 432^E
Accts Deloitte & Touche Llp Raleigh
SIC 6519 6531 6798 Real property lessors; Real estate managers; Real estate investment trusts; Real property lessors; Real estate managers; Real estate investment trusts
Pr: Edward J Fritsch
Genl Pt: Highwoods Properties
CFO: Mark F Mulhern

HIGLEY ELEMENTARY SCHOOL
See HIGLEY UNIFIED SCHOOL DISTRICT

D-U-N-S 10-000-1544
HIGLEY UNIFIED SCHOOL DISTRICT
HIGLEY ELEMENTARY SCHOOL
2935 S Recker Rd, Gilbert, AZ 85295-7846
Tel (480) 279-7000 *Founded/Ownrshp* 1813
Sales 48.7MM^E *EMP* 600
SIC 8211 Public elementary & secondary schools; Public elementary school; High school, junior or senior; Public elementary & secondary schools; Public elementary school; High school, junior or senior
Pr: Greg Land
**VP:* Paul Howell
Exec: Meghann Sherman
Ex Dir: Tony Malaj
Dir IT: Sylvia Zapata
IT Man: Shauna Miller
Netwrk Eng: Lucas Rangel
Teacher Pr: Sheila Sorenson

D-U-N-S 18-063-1616
HIGMAN MARINE INC
1980 Post Oak Blvd # 1101, Houston, TX 77056-3877
Tel (713) 552-1101 *Founded/Ownrshp* 1982
Sales 34.9MM^E *EMP* 250
SIC 4492 Towing & tugboat service; Towing & tugboat service
Pr: George H Thomas
COO: Mark Flynn
**VP:* John T Mc Mahan
VP: John McMahan

HIGNELL COMPANIES, THE
See HIGNELL INC

D-U-N-S 07-612-0930
HIGNELL INC
HIGNELL COMPANIES, THE
1750 Humboldt Rd, Chico, CA 95928-8104
Tel (530) 894-0404 *Founded/Ownrshp* 2003
Sales 41.1MM^E *EMP* 153
SIC 6552 6531 Land subdividers & developers, commercial; Land subdividers & developers, residential; Real estate brokers & agents; Real estate managers
CEO: Philip Larios
**Ch Bd:* Douglas Hignell
CFO: Vito Mule
**CFO:* Mike Rossman
**VP:* Jeff Stiemsma
**VP:* Greg Wietbrock

HIGUCHI INTERNATIONAL
See HIGUCHI MANUFACTURING AMERICA LLC

D-U-N-S 02-242-1694 IMP
HIGUCHI INTERNATIONAL CORP
(*Suby of* HIGUCHI MANUFACTURING CO.,LTD.)
14901 Southton Rd, Elmendorf, TX 78112-9699
Tel (210) 633-2877 *Founded/Ownrshp* 2006
Sales 33.9MM^E *EMP* 162^E
SIC 3829 Automatic turnstiles & related apparatus
Pr: Nariie Higuchi

D-U-N-S 80-805-6118 IMP
HIGUCHI MANUFACTURING AMERICA LLC
HIGUCHI INTERNATIONAL
(*Suby of* HIGUCHI INTERNATIONAL CORP) ★
14901 Southton Rd, San Antonio, TX 78223
Tel (210) 633-2877 *Founded/Ownrshp* 1937
Sales 34.0MM^E *EMP* 130
SIC 3829 Measuring & controlling devices
Pr: Nariie Higuchi

D-U-N-S 60-911-6348 IMP
HII-FINANCE CORP
1600 Tysons Blvd Fl 6, Mc Lean, VA 22102-4865
Tel (703) 442-8668 *Founded/Ownrshp* 1989
Sales 23.3MM^E *EMP* 107
SIC 2311 5621 5611 8741 7373 8243 Men's & boys' suits & coats; Women's clothing stores; Men's & boys' clothing stores; Administrative management; Local area network (LAN) systems integrator; Software training, computer
Pr: Samia Farouki
**VP:* Hassan S Judeh
**Mng Dir:* David N Braus
Genl Mgr: Al Jayyousi

HIIG
See HOUSTON INTERNATIONAL INSURANCE GROUP LTD

HIIG-ELITE UNDERWRITING SVC
See ELITE BROKERAGE SERVICES INC

D-U-N-S 13-177-9717 IMP
HIJET BIT LLC
PDC LOGIC
2601 Venture Dr, Norman, OK 73069-8203
Tel (405) 321-8850 *Founded/Ownrshp* 2002
Sales 23.2MM^E *EMP* 45
SIC 5084 Drilling bits

D-U-N-S 36-144-4334 IMP
HIKAM AMERICA INC
(*Suby of* HIRAKAWA HEWTECH CORP.)
3521 Main St Ste 501, Chula Vista, CA 91911-0802
Tel (619) 420-0376 *Founded/Ownrshp* 1988
Sales 19.0MM^E *EMP* 300
SIC 3679 5063

D-U-N-S 00-779-9154
HIKVISION USA INC
(*Suby of* HANGZHOU HIKVISION DIGITAL TECHNOLOGY CO., LTD.)
908 Canada Ct, City of Industry, CA 91748-1136
Tel (909) 895-0400 *Founded/Ownrshp* 2007
Sales 75.0MM *EMP* 190
SIC 7382 Confinement surveillance systems maintenance & monitoring
CEO: Jeffrey He
VP: Polo Cai
VP: Oliver Zhang
Dir Bus: Vince Lupe
Mktg Dir: Alex Asnovich
Manager: Greg Kaplar
Manager: Steve Kennedy
Manager: Scott Lutke
Manager: Phil Smith
Manager: Qin Wang
Sls Mgr: Peng Guo

HILAND DAIRY FOOD
See ROBERTS DAIRY CO LLC

D-U-N-S 03-113-7391
HILAND DAIRY FOODS CO LLC
1133 E Kearney St, Springfield, MO 65803-3435
Tel (417) 862-9311 *Founded/Ownrshp* 1979
Sales 895.4MM *EMP* 1,350
Accts Bkd Llp Springfield Mo
SIC 2026 2037 2024 5143 Fluid milk; Cream, sour; Dips, sour cream based; Cottage cheese; Fruit juices; Ice cream & frozen desserts; Dairy products, except dried or canned; Fluid milk; Cream, sour; Dips, sour cream based; Cottage cheese; Fruit juices; Ice cream & frozen desserts; Dairy products, except dried or canned
VP: Marc Mullins
Brnch Mgr: Gabe Andes
Brnch Mgr: Sean Dudley
Brnch Mgr: Darren Johnson
Genl Mgr: Mike Flagg
Genl Mgr: Randy Richison
Genl Mgr: Catherine Vanness
QA Dir: Tracy Haverland
IT Man: Lynn Wall
Sfty Mgr: Karl Farris
Plnt Mgr: Cherb Coleman

D-U-N-S 07-871-9042
HILB GROUP LLC
8720 Stony Point Pkwy # 125, Richmond, VA 23235-1990
Tel (804) 414-6504 *Founded/Ownrshp* 2009
Sales NA *EMP* 188^E
SIC 6411 Insurance agents, brokers & service
CEO: Robert J Hilb
Pr: David Hobbs
CFO: Bill Widhelm
Chf Mktg O: Jason Angus
Sr VP: Robert Blanton
VP: Will Tucker

HILBERS CONTRACTORS & ENGRG
See HILBERS INC

D-U-N-S 07-155-7813
HILBERS INC
HILBERS CONTRACTORS & ENGRG
1210 Stabler Ln, Yuba City, CA 95993-2620
Tel (530) 673-2947 *Founded/Ownrshp* 1988
Sales 81.4MM *EMP* 75
Accts Kcoe Isom Llp Yuba City Cal
SIC 1542 1541 Commercial & office building contractors; Industrial buildings, new construction; Commercial & office building contractors; Industrial buildings, new construction
Pr: Kurt G Hilbers
**Treas:* Glenn Hilbers
VP: Susan P Growney
**VP:* Larry E Hilbers
**VP:* Tom Jones
Board of Directors: Mike Cagley

D-U-N-S 61-900-8683
HILBILT SALES CORP - ARKANSAS
20036 Interstate 30 N, Benton, AR 72019-8045
Tel (501) 316-2500 *Founded/Ownrshp* 1986
Sales 24.0MM^E *EMP* 70
SIC 5511 Trucks, tractors & trailers: new & used; Trucks, tractors & trailers: new & used
Pr: Vance Hill
CFO: Dennis Edwards
**Sec:* Mary Ruth Hill

HILBISH FORD MERCURY LINCOLN
See HILBISH MOTOR CO INC

D-U-N-S 02-465-1507
HILBISH MOTOR CO INC (NC)
HILBISH FORD MERCURY LINCOLN
2600 S Cannon Blvd, Kannapolis, NC 28083-6914
Tel (704) 938-3121 *Founded/Ownrshp* 1954
Sales 32.3MM^E *EMP* 68
SIC 5511 5521 5012 Automobiles, new & used; Pickups, new & used; Trucks, tractors & trailers: new & used; Used car dealers; Automobiles & other motor vehicles; Automobiles, new & used; Pickups, new & used; Trucks, tractors & trailers: new & used; Used car dealers; Automobiles & other motor vehicles
Pr: Frederick G Hilbish
**Genl Mgr:* Tim Vaughn
Store Mgr: Scott Williams
Store Mgr: Ray Zickafoose
Sls Mgr: Jeff Beam
Sls Mgr: Charles Brown
Sls Mgr: Rick Guido

D-U-N-S 15-510-9101
HILBY-YATES INC
282 Brokaw Rd, Santa Clara, CA 95050-4336
Tel (408) 988-0700 *Founded/Ownrshp* 1985
Sales 44.3MM^E *EMP* 250
SIC 5065 3577 3672 Electronic parts & equipment; Computer peripheral equipment; Printed circuit boards; Electronic parts & equipment; Computer peripheral equipment; Printed circuit boards
Pr: Ben H Yates
**VP:* Joanna Yates

D-U-N-S 00-895-0545
HILCO ELECTRIC COOPERATIVE INC (TX)
115 E Main St, Itasca, TX 76055-2118
Tel (800) 338-6425 *Founded/Ownrshp* 1937
Sales 57.9MM *EMP* 82
SIC 4911 Distribution, electric power; Corporation organizing; Distribution, electric power
Pr: George Thiess
**Sec:* Janet Smith
**VP:* Joseph Tedesco
Board of Directors: Margaret Hill, Leroy Huff, Ronald Roberts

D-U-N-S 79-308-2660
HILCO INC
HILCO TRADING
5 Revere Dr Ste 430, Northbrook, IL 60062-1583
Tel (847) 714-1288 *Founded/Ownrshp* 1990
Sales 86.3MM^E *EMP* 500
SIC 7389 6531 Merchandise liquidators; Real estate brokers & agents; Merchandise liquidators; Real estate brokers & agents
CEO: Neil R Aaronson
**Pr:* Gregory S Apter
**Pr:* Jeffrey B Hecktman
**Pr:* Michael Keefe
COO: Jeffrey Paronto
**CFO:* John P Chen
CFO: Mark Smiley
Ex VP: Cory Lipoff
Ex VP: Joseph Malfitano
**Ex VP:* Benjamin L Nortman
**Ex VP:* Edwared J Siskin
Sr VP: Len Berliner
Sr VP: Ed Cervac
Sr VP: Andrew Chused
Sr VP: Tom Davidson
**Sr VP:* David Kirshenbaum
Sr VP: Mike Mahler
**Sr VP:* Navin Nagrani
Sr VP: Michael Tsandilas
Sr VP: Matthew Wood
**VP:* Ross Block

D-U-N-S 14-061-6462
HILCO RECEIVABLES LLC
(*Suby of* HILCO INC) ★
5 Revere Dr Ste 510, Northbrook, IL 60062-8007
Tel (847) 509-1100 *Founded/Ownrshp* 2000
Sales NA *EMP* 220
SIC 6153 Purchasers of accounts receivable & commercial paper; Purchasers of accounts receivable & commercial paper
Sr VP: Bill Schmiederer
VP: Jason Frank
CIO: Steve Thorne

HILCO TRADING
See HILCO INC

D-U-N-S 83-157-2040
HILCO TRADING LLC
5 Revere Dr Ste 320, Northbrook, IL 60062-1569
Tel (847) 509-1100 *Founded/Ownrshp* 2006
Sales 65.0MM^E *EMP* 359^E
SIC 8741 Business management
CEO: Jeffrey B Hecktman
Mng Pt: Robert Levy
Mng Pt: Steve Wolf
**Pr:* Michael Keefe
**COO:* John P Chen
CFO: David Zwick
**Chf Mktg O:* Gary C Epstein
**Ex VP:* Eric W Kaup
**Ex VP:* Richard L Kaye
Ex VP: Cory Lipoff
**Ex VP:* Joseph A Malfitano
Ex VP: Joseph Malfitano
Ex VP: Benjamin L Nortman
**Ex VP:* Edward J Siskin
Sr VP: Len Berliner
Sr VP: Larry Foster
**VP:* Ian S Fredericks

D-U-N-S 18-841-2530
HILCO TRANSPORT INC
7700 Kenmont Rd, Greensboro, NC 27409-9012
Tel (336) 273-9441 *Founded/Ownrshp* 1987
Sales 42.4MM^E *EMP* 210
SIC 4213 5261 5032 4212 Liquid petroleum transport, non-local; Top soil; Stone, crushed or broken; Dump truck haulage; Liquid petroleum transport, non-local; Top soil; Stone, crushed or broken; Dump truck haulage
Pr: J Gurney Long
CFO: Bruce Quigley
CFO: Joe Wright
**VP:* Larry Clark
**VP:* Gary King
**VP:* W H Long
VP: Lynn Unsworth
VP: Richard Wohlford
Sls Dir: Jamie Lockhart
Mktg Mgr: Jaime Alberti

D-U-N-S 04-240-6205
HILCORP
1201 La St Ste 1400, Houston, TX 77002
Tel (337) 276-7676 *Founded/Ownrshp* 2010
Sales 29.5MM^E *EMP* 71^E
SIC 1389 Oil & gas field services
Prin: Kuntal Hazari

D-U-N-S 07-840-0654
HILCORP ALASKA LLC
3800 Centerpoint Dr, Anchorage, AK 99503-5825
Tel (907) 777-8300 *Founded/Ownrshp* 2011
Sales 78.4MM^E *EMP* 87^E
SIC 1382 Aerial geophysical exploration oil & gas

D-U-N-S 60-641-0538 IMP
HILCORP ENERGY CO
1201 La St Ste 1400, Houston, TX 77002
Tel (713) 209-2400 *Founded/Ownrshp* 1988
Sales 55.7MM^E *EMP* 20
SIC 1311 1382 Crude petroleum production; Oil & gas exploration services
CEO: Jeffrey D Hildebrand
**Pr:* Greg R Lalicker
Treas: Melinda Weilenger
VP: Mike Brezina
VP: Kimberly Doupe
VP: Bill Schroeter
Dir IT: Stefano Giani
Dir IT: Sandy Higgins
Dir IT: David Horn
Dir IT: Rene Lorenzo
Dir IT: Jim Noot

HILER INDUSTRIES
See ACCURATE CASTINGS INC

D-U-N-S 14-161-1496 IMP
HILEX POLY CO LLC
NOVOLEX
(*Suby of* NOVOLEX HOLDINGS INC) ★
101 E Carolina Ave, Hartsville, SC 29550-4213
Tel (800) 845-6051 *Founded/Ownrshp* 2003
Sales 1.5MMM^E *EMP* 4,200
SIC 2673 2674 Plastic bags: made from purchased materials; Paper bags: made from purchased materials; Plastic bags: made from purchased materials; Paper bags: made from purchased materials
CEO: Stanley B Bikulege
COO: David Bocher
CFO: Marv Liebman
Ex VP: Paul Ebbert
VP: Mark Daniels
VP: Grant Gamble
VP: Mike McGuiness
Exec: Mike Cole
Off Mgr: Justin Chapman
VP Opers: Vernon Fuller
VP Opers: Jim Lassiter

HILEY MAZDA
See ARLINGTON DEALERSHIP ACQUISITION LP

D-U-N-S 17-410-8092
HILITE INDUSTRIES INC
(*Suby of* HILITE INTERNATIONAL INC) ★
1671 S Broadway St, Carrollton, TX 75006-7496
Tel (972) 242-2116 *Founded/Ownrshp* 2002
Sales 126.9MM^E *EMP* 1,000
SIC 6719 Investment holding companies, except banks; Investment holding companies, except banks
CEO: Karl Hammer
**COO:* Jrg Feuring
**CFO:* Stefan Eck
**CFO:* Michael T Kestner
**Ch:* Craig Stinson
**Treas:* Ronald G Campbell
VP: Tim Bowes
VP: Art Johnson
VP: Richard Smith
Ql Cn Mgr: Paul Llamas
S&M/VP: William Person

D-U-N-S 11-829-1009 IMP
HILITE INTERNATIONAL INC
1671 S Broadway St, Carrollton, TX 75006-7496
Tel (972) 242-2116 *Founded/Ownrshp* 1999
Sales 396.3MM^E *EMP* 1,000
SIC 5531 Automotive parts; Automotive parts
Pr: Karl Hammer
**COO:* Joerge Feuring
COO: Jorg Feuring
**CFO:* Stefan Eck
CTO: Jason Chester
Ql Cn Mgr: Steven Livingston

D-U-N-S 60-795-6216
HILL & COX CORP
1820 Higdon Ferry Rd A, Hot Springs, AR 71913-6296
Tel (501) 525-8273 *Founded/Ownrshp* 1989
Sales 20.5MM *EMP* 20
SIC 1541 1542 Industrial buildings, new construction; Commercial & office building contractors; Industrial buildings, new construction; Commercial & office building contractors
Pr: Brian Hill
**Treas:* Nelta Hill
**VP:* Robert Cox

D-U-N-S 01-361-6594
HILL & MARKES INC (NY)
1997 State Highway 5s, Amsterdam, NY 12010-8177
Tel (518) 842-2410 *Founded/Ownrshp* 1906, 1937
Sales 116.9MM^E *EMP* 141
SIC 5087 5113 Restaurant supplies; Janitors' supplies; Industrial & personal service paper; Restaurant supplies; Janitors' supplies; Industrial & personal service paper
Pr: Jeffrey Finkle
**CEO:* Neal Packer
Ex VP: Jim Izzano
VP: Kristeen Jaracz
VP: Richard Michaud
**VP:* Andrea Packer
**VP:* Kelvin W Scharf
Opers Mgr: Keith Lamphere
Sls Mgr: Jason Packer
Sls Mgr: Barrett Quinn
Sls Mgr: Michael Shoemaker

D-U-N-S 04-971-2862 IMP/EXP
■ **HILL & SONS LLC**
HILL PARTS
(*Suby of* MEYN LLC) ★
211 Hogan Pond Ln, Ball Ground, GA 30107-4380
Tel (770) 735-4221 *Founded/Ownrshp* 1994
Sales 38.4MM^E *EMP* 256^E
SIC 3556 Poultry processing machinery
CFO: Alan Harris

D-U-N-S 04-268-6048
HILL & WILKINSON CONSTRUCTION GROUP LTD
HILL & WILKINSON GEN CONTRS
2703 Telecom Pkwy Ste 120, Richardson, TX 75082-3555
Tel (214) 299-4300 *Founded/Ownrshp* 1968
Sales 450.0MM *EMP* 240
SIC 1541 1542

HILL & WILKINSON GEN CONTRS
See HILL & WILKINSON CONSTRUCTION GROUP LTD

D-U-N-S 04-123-7058
HILL AND KNOWLTON STRATEGIES LLC
(*Suby of* WPP GROUP USA INC) ★
825 3rd Ave Fl 24, New York, NY 10022-9510
Tel (212) 885-0300 *Founded/Ownrshp* 2012
Sales 159.0MM^E *EMP* 2,400
SIC 8743 Public relations & publicity; Public relations & publicity
Ch Bd: Jack Martin
V Ch: Thomas Hoog
Pr: Alfonso Cuellar
**COO:* Ken Luce
**COO:* Mark Thorne
Bd of Dir: Elaine Cruikshanks
Ofcr: Mark Bunker
**Ex VP:* Ian W Bailey
Ex VP: Bill Coletti
Ex VP: Chris Gidez
Ex VP: Lindsay Hutter
**Ex VP:* Claire A Koeneman
Ex VP: Joshua Reynolds
**Sr VP:* Ryan J Barr
Sr VP: Bill Bennett
Sr VP: Brendan Hodgson
Sr VP: Claudia Husemann
Sr VP: Joshua Lamel
**Sr VP:* Michael J Moore
Sr VP: Peggy O'Neill
**Sr VP:* Charles B Sewell

D-U-N-S 83-262-6498
HILL ARIZONA GROCERY CO INC
RIDGWAY MOUNTAIN MARKET
490 Sherman St, Ridgway, CO 81432-9429
Tel (970) 626-5811 *Founded/Ownrshp* 2009
Sales 20.0MM^E *EMP* 150
SIC 5411 Grocery stores
Pr: Darin Hill

D-U-N-S 07-674-8938
HILL BARTH & KING LLC
6603 Summit Dr, Canfield, OH 44406-9509
Tel (330) 758-8613 *Founded/Ownrshp* 1949
Sales 45.7MM^E *EMP* 280
SIC 8721 Certified public accountant; Certified public accountant
CEO: Christopher M Allegretti
CFO: Leannah Hostetler
CFO: Leannah Hostetoler
**CFO:* Doug Stahl
CIO: Rob Garland
IT Man: Amy Arquilla
Mktg Dir: Michael Gallagher
Snr Mgr: Frank Balog

D-U-N-S 05-659-9178 IMP
HILL BROTHERS CHEMICAL CO
1675 N Main St, Orange, CA 92867-3499
Tel (714) 998-8800 *Founded/Ownrshp* 1923
Sales 101.8MM^E *EMP* 155^E
Accts Mcgladrey & Pullen
SIC 5169 2819 Acids; Calcium chloride & hypochlorite; Magnesium compounds or salts, inorganic; Acids; Calcium chloride & hypochlorite; Magnesium compounds or salts, inorganic
Pr: Ronald R Hill
**CFO:* Thomas F James
**Sec:* Kathryn J Waters
Ofcr: Shane Burkhart
**Ex VP:* Matthew Thorne
Opers Mgr: Terry Milligan
Opers Mgr: Nate Waters
VP Mktg: Rusty Mosher
VP Mktg: John Padilla Jr
S&M/VP: Andy Hill

D-U-N-S 08-954-3797
HILL BROTHERS CONSTRUCTION CO INC
20831 Highway 15, Falkner, MS 38629-9123
Tel (662) 837-3041 *Founded/Ownrshp* 1978
Sales 92.0MM^E *EMP* 500^E
SIC 1611 1622 1541 1542 General contractor, highway & street construction; Bridge, tunnel & elevated highway; Bridge construction; Highway construction, elevated; Tunnel construction; Industrial buildings & warehouses; Nonresidential construction; General contractor, highway & street construction; Bridge, tunnel & elevated highway; Bridge construction; Highway construction, elevated; Tunnel construction; Industrial buildings & warehouses; Nonresidential construction
CEO: Kenneth W Hill Jr
**Pr:* Gerald C Hill
**Treas:* Kenneth W Drewery
**VP:* Sterling Akers
**VP:* Clyde R Robertson
Mktg Mgr: Becky Lindsey

D-U-N-S 01-959-1564
HILL BROTHERS INC
7850 I St, Omaha, NE 68127-1830
Tel (402) 331-2503 *Founded/Ownrshp* 1985
Sales 40.9MM^E *EMP* 250
SIC 4213 Trucking, except local; Trucking, except local
Pr: Albert M Hill
**VP:* James R Hill

D-U-N-S 14-714-5098
HILL BROTHERS TRANSPORTATION INC
7850 I St, Omaha, NE 68127-1830
Tel (402) 331-2503 *Founded/Ownrshp* 1986
Sales 35.3MM^E *EMP* 300
SIC 4213 Trucking, except local; Trucking, except local
Pr: Albert M Hill
**Treas:* Peter J Hill
VP: Scott Brockett
**VP:* James R Hill
VP: Jolene Jankowski
Opers Mgr: Jason Long
Opers Mgr: Ashley Turner

D-U-N-S 03-346-3134
HILL CITY OIL CO INC OF MISSISSIPPI
EXXON OIL CO JOBBER
1409 Dunn St, Houma, LA 70360-6443
Tel (985) 873-4000 *Founded/Ownrshp* 1980
Sales 45.8MM^E *EMP* 150
Accts Sagona Bourg Lee Matthew &
SIC 5541 5411 5172 Filling stations, gasoline; Convenience stores, chain; Diesel fuel; Gasoline; Lubricating oils & greases; Filling stations, gasoline; Convenience stores, chain; Diesel fuel; Gasoline; Lubricating oils & greases
Pr: H E Stathes

D-U-N-S 09-046-8422 IMP
HILL CONSTRUCTION CORP
9410 Ave Los Romeros # 201, San Juan, PR 00926-7007
Tel (787) 287-3200 *Founded/Ownrshp* 1975
Sales 33.6MM^E *EMP* 700
SIC 1522 Multi-family dwellings, new construction; Multi-family dwellings, new construction
CEO: Thomas H Hill Sr
**Pr:* Thomas H Hill Jr
CFO: Walter Renaud
**Sec:* Dorothy Hill
**VP:* Manuel Rincon

D-U-N-S 08-457-9031 IMP
HILL CORP
5065 E Hunter Ave, Anaheim, CA 92807-6001
Tel (800) 328-7107 *Founded/Ownrshp* 1972
Sales 33.7MM^E *EMP* 250^E
SIC 5961 Catalog & mail-order houses; Catalog & mail-order houses
CEO: Brian Hill
**Pr:* Rhonda Hill Tolar
Genl Mgr: Carlos Manlapaz

D-U-N-S 02-642-7935
HILL COUNTRY BAKERY LLC
122 Stribling, San Antonio, TX 78204-1915
Tel (210) 475-9981 *Founded/Ownrshp* 1998
Sales 71.8MM^E *EMP* 600
SIC 5461 5149 Bakeries; Bakery products; Bakeries; Bakery products
**Mng Pt:* Steve O'Donnell
**CFO:* Phil J Butrum
Ex Dir: Henry Egeolu
QA Dir: Marce Hernandez
Mfg Dir: Juan Ancira
Sfty Mgr: Brandon Beck

D-U-N-S 09-705-2021
HILL COUNTRY COMMUNITY ACTION ASSOCIATION INC
HCCAA
2905 W Wallace St, San Saba, TX 76877-3840
Tel (325) 372-5167 *Founded/Ownrshp* 1966
Sales 16.5MM^E *EMP* 349
SIC 8399 8322 Community action agency; Individual & family services; Community action agency; Individual & family services
CEO: Tama Shaw
**Pr:* John Fisher
**Treas:* John E Firth
**VP:* Dale Jaecks
VP: Mary Sealy
Opers Mgr: Cynthia Jimenez

D-U-N-S 01-505-0839
HILL COUNTRY COMMUNITY MHMR CENTER
KENDALL COUNTY MENTAL HEALTH
819 Water St Ste 300, Kerrville, TX 78028-5330
Tel (830) 792-3300 *Founded/Ownrshp* 1997
Sales 30.9MM^E *EMP* 564
Accts Scott Singleton Fincher And
SIC 8093 8052 8322 Mental health clinic, outpatient; Home for the mentally retarded, with health care; Crisis intervention center; Mental health clinic, outpatient; Home for the mentally retarded, with health care; Crisis intervention center
Ex Dir: Linda J Werlein
**CFO:* Scott Arrington
**Ch:* John Kight

D-U-N-S 07-462-0261
HILL COUNTRY DAIRIES INC
912 Kramer Ln, Austin, TX 78758-4305
Tel (512) 836-6123 *Founded/Ownrshp* 1990
Sales 26.6MM^E *EMP* 70
SIC 5143

D-U-N-S 02-885-7147 IMP
■ **HILL COUNTRY ELECTRIC SUPPLY LP**
(*Suby of* WESCO DISTRIBUTION INC) ★
4801 Freidrich Ln Ste 200, Austin, TX 78744-2701
Tel (512) 428-9300 *Founded/Ownrshp* 2015
Sales 183.4MM^E *EMP* 110
SIC 5063 Electrical apparatus & equipment; Electrical apparatus & equipment
Pt: Scott Schieffer
Pt: Wayne Blasingame
Pt: David Inman
Rgnl Mgr: Joe Conaway
IT Man: Ryan Frisbie
IT Man: Darrell Jones
Opers Mgr: David Stockton
Sales Asso: Chris Aguilar
Sales Asso: Greg Ganem
Sales Asso: Abe Rhodes
Snr Mgr: David Hall

D-U-N-S 12-337-4352
HILL COUNTRY FURNITURE PARTNERS LTD
ASHLEY FURNITURE HOMESTORE
1431 Fm 1101, New Braunfels, TX 78130-2622
Tel (830) 515-1400 *Founded/Ownrshp* 2002

Sales 102.5MM[E] *EMP* 400
SIC 5712 Furniture stores; Furniture stores
Pt: Gary Seals
CFO: Travis Williams
Off Mgr: Alicia Joshlin
Store Mgr: John Malkey
Store Mgr: Theresa Mireles
Store Mgr: Eddie Noschese
Dir IT: Sylvia Fowler
Opers Mgr: Patrick Houman
Mktg Dir: Carolina Chavez

D-U-N-S 02-575-2961
HILL COUNTRY HOLDINGS LLC
1431 Fm 1101, New Braunfels, TX 78130-2622
Tel (830) 515-1400 *Founded/Ownrshp* 2008
Sales 77.3MM[E] *EMP* 256[E]
SIC 6719 Investment holding companies, except banks
VP: Shawn Seals

D-U-N-S 84-962-3368
HILL COUNTRY IMPORTS LTD
CLASSIC HONDA
2301 N Interstate 35, Round Rock, TX 78664-2011
Tel (512) 244-9000 *Founded/Ownrshp* 1989
Sales 53.7MM[E] *EMP* 250
SIC 5511 Automobiles, new & used; Automobiles, new & used
Pt: Don Tamburro
**Pt:* Guy Burrous
**Pt:* Charles King
Sls Mgr: David Carruthers
Sales Asso: Derek Adams
Sales Asso: Ron Baldwin
Sales Asso: Christine Bennett
Sales Asso: Johnnie Cazalas
Sales Asso: Lee Hunt
Sales Asso: Paul Koehler
Sales Asso: Olga Morquecho

HILL COUNTRY MEMORIAL HLTH SYS
See HILL COUNTRY MEMORIAL HOSPITAL

D-U-N-S 07-693-2250
HILL COUNTRY MEMORIAL HOSPITAL
HILL COUNTRY MEMORIAL HLTH SYS
1020 S State Highway 16, Fredericksburg, TX 78624-4471
Tel (830) 997-4353 *Founded/Ownrshp* 2008
Sales 65.0MM *EMP* 626[E]
Accts Bkd Llp Dallas Texas
SIC 8062 8011 General medical & surgical hospitals; Primary care medical clinic; General medical & surgical hospitals; Primary care medical clinic
CEO: Steve Kading
**CFO:* Mark Jones
CFO: Bob Smelserb
VP: Maria Foschi
Dir Lab: Jim Stacey
Dir Lab: Karla Taylor
Dir Sec: Frank Stead
CIO: Holly Schmidt
QA Dir: Debbye Wallace
Mktg Mgr: Barry Cheshire
Pathlgst: Cliff Richmond

D-U-N-S 11-891-6618
HILL COUNTRY RESTAURANTS INC
CLEAR SPRINGS RESTAURANT
1692 S State Highway 46, New Braunfels, TX 78130-1929
Tel (830) 629-3775 *Founded/Ownrshp* 1984
Sales 14.5MM[E] *EMP* 500
SIC 5812 Seafood restaurants; Seafood restaurants
Pr: Richard Dewitt Jr
**VP:* Barbra Dewitt

D-U-N-S 00-682-4007
HILL COUNTRY TELEPHONE COOPERATIVE INC
HCTC
220 Carolyn St, Ingram, TX 78025-3193
Tel (830) 367-5333 *Founded/Ownrshp* 1951
Sales 31.8MM[E] *EMP* 101
SIC 4813 Telephone communication, except radio; Telephone communication, except radio
Pr: James W Haynie
**Treas:* Randy Bass
**Treas:* Rocky Rocchio
**VP:* Kathy Bohn
**VP:* Billy R Chisum
IT Man: Phillip Rice
Plnt Mgr: Alan Link
Board of Directors: James Haynie

D-U-N-S 60-345-3556 EXP
HILL CRAFT FURNITURE CO
101 Industrial Dr, New Albany, MS 38652-3016
Tel (662) 534-7426 *Founded/Ownrshp* 1989
Sales 26.7MM[E] *EMP* 370
Accts Easton Balb & Smiths New Alb
SIC 2512 Living room furniture: upholstered on wood frames; Living room furniture: upholstered on wood frames
Pr: Barry Weeden
**VP:* Kereth Weeden

D-U-N-S 19-293-8871
■ **HILL CREST BEHAVIORAL HEALTH SERVICES**
(*Suby of* PSYCHIATRIC SOLUTIONS INC) ★
6869 5th Ave S, Birmingham, AL 35212-1866
Tel (205) 833-9000 *Founded/Ownrshp* 2005
Sales 19.8MM[E] *EMP* 350
SIC 8063 Psychiatric hospitals; Psychiatric hospitals
CEO: Steve McCabe
COO: Matt Hutcheson

D-U-N-S 02-170-1081
HILL ENTERPRISES INC
HILL PETROLEUM
6301 Ralston Rd, Arvada, CO 80002-2745
Tel (303) 424-6262 *Founded/Ownrshp* 1946, 1982
Sales 23.3MM[E] *EMP* 80[E]
SIC 5984

HILL GROUP, THE
See HILL MECHANICAL CORP

HILL HAVEN NURSING HOME
See ROCHESTER GENERAL LONG TERM CARE INC

HILL HEALTH CENTER
See CORNELL SCOTT-HILL HEALTH CORP

HILL HOLLIDAY
See INDEPENDENT ADVERTISING INC

D-U-N-S 08-080-4701
▲ **HILL INTERNATIONAL INC**
2005 Market St Fl 17, Philadelphia, PA 19103-7042
Tel (215) 309-7700 *Founded/Ownrshp* 2006
Sales 640.2MM *EMP* 4,558
Accts Eisneramper Llp Iselin New J
Tkr Sym HIL *Exch* NYS
SIC 8742 8741 Construction project management consultant; Construction management; Construction project management consultant; Construction management
Pr: David L Richter
**Ch Bd:* Irvin E Richter
Pr: Samuel O Atolaiye
Pr: Mohammed Rais
COO: Raouf S Ghali
CFO: John Fanelli III
Bd of Dir: Steven Kramer
Ofcr: William Bastidas
Ex VP: Richard Lamb
Sr VP: Osama A Abusitta
Sr VP: John A Arnold
Sr VP: Ken Baker
Sr VP: Jose Manuel Albaladejo Canedo-
Sr VP: William H Dengler Jr
Sr VP: Tracy M Doyle
Sr VP: Catherine H Emma
Sr VP: Ronald F Emma
Sr VP: Robert Ferguson
Sr VP: Dominick Fickeria
Sr VP: Vincent D Gallagher
Sr VP: Vincent Gallagher
Board of Directors: Camille S Andrews, Brian W Clymer, Steven R Curts, Alan S Fellheimer, Steven M Kramer, Gary F Mazzucco

D-U-N-S 01-800-3806 EXP
HILL INTERNATIONAL TRUCKS NA LLC (OH)
47866 Y And O Rd, East Liverpool, OH 43920-8724
Tel (330) 386-6440 *Founded/Ownrshp* 1890
Sales 95.7MM[E] *EMP* 195
SIC 5511 5531 7538 Trucks, tractors & trailers: new & used; Truck equipment & parts; General automotive repair shops; Trucks, tractors & trailers: new & used; Truck equipment & parts; General automotive repair shops
MIS Dir: Jim Wood
VP Opers: Michael Barber
VP Sls: Jeff Mundy
Mktg Mgr: Travis Biscella
Sales Asso: Mike Counahan

D-U-N-S 00-904-1823
HILL MEAT CO
1503 Nw 50th St, Pendleton, OR 97801-4513
Tel (541) 276-7621 *Founded/Ownrshp* 2001
Sales 20.7MM[E] *EMP* 65
SIC 2011 Meat packing plants
Pr: James Cheney
**Sec:* Billie Cheney
**VP:* David Farstod
**VP:* Nicole Sorensen
Off Mgr: David Frostad

D-U-N-S 04-999-3207
HILL MECHANICAL CORP
HILL GROUP, THE
11045 Gage Ave, Franklin Park, IL 60131-1437
Tel (847) 451-5000 *Founded/Ownrshp* 1936
Sales 125.1MM[E] *EMP* 500
SIC 1711

D-U-N-S 94-046-4055
HILL MECHANICAL LOGISTICS LLC
(*Suby of* HILL GROUP) ★
11045 Gage Ave, Franklin Park, IL 60131-1437
Tel (847) 451-5000 *Founded/Ownrshp* 2008
Sales 13.2MM[E] *EMP* 280[E]
SIC 4789 Transportation services
Prin: Emmanuel Lacson

HILL OIL
See JAMES P HILL DISTRIBUTOR INC

HILL PARTS
See HILL & SONS LLC

HILL PETROLEUM
See HILL ENTERPRISES INC

D-U-N-S 88-335-7436 IMP/EXP
■ **HILL PHOENIX INC**
(*Suby of* DOVER REFRIGERATION & FOOD EQUIPMENT INC) ★
2016 Gees Mill Rd Ne, Conyers, GA 30013-1301
Tel (770) 285-3100 *Founded/Ownrshp* 1996
Sales 904.8MM[E] *EMP* 3,500
SIC 3632 Household refrigerators & freezers; Household refrigerators & freezers
Pr: Bill Johnson
**CFO:* Al Alden
VP: Lynn Brenton
VP: Thomas Marcy
VP: Keith Wennik

D-U-N-S 60-563-8378
HILL PHYSICIANS MEDICAL GROUP INC
2409 Camino Ramon, San Ramon, CA 94583-4285
Tel (925) 820-8300 *Founded/Ownrshp* 1984
Sales 38.6MM[E] *EMP* 488
SIC 8011 8031 General & family practice, physician/surgeon; Offices & clinics of osteopathic physicians; General & family practice, physician/surgeon; Offices & clinics of osteopathic physicians
Pr: Steve McDermott
Treas: Robert C Feldman
CIO: Stephan Hookano
QA Dir: Fredrick Casey
QA Dir: Anupama Ramachandran
Dir IT: Jacqui Magee
Dir IT: Alvin Sockolov

Software D: Jeff Gustafson
Software D: Garrett Johnson
Software D: Sanjeev Kanajanavar
Sls&Mrk Ex: Dawn Bell

HILL REGIONAL HOSPITAL
See NHCI OF HILLSBORO INC

D-U-N-S 07-373-2554
HILL SCHOOL
717 E High St, Pottstown, PA 19464-5791
Tel (610) 326-1000 *Founded/Ownrshp* 1851
Sales 48.8MM *EMP* 212
Accts Tait Weller & Baker Llp Phil
SIC 8211 Boarding school; Boarding school
Ch: Thomas MCN Millhiser
**Pr:* David Dougherty
**CFO:* Donald Silverson
Assoc Dir: Christina Cerenzia
Assoc Dir: Virginia Yinger

D-U-N-S 03-477-0099
HILL SERVICES INC
HILL SERVICES, PLUMBING & HVAC
4940 Covington Way, Memphis, TN 38128-6938
Tel (901) 388-7500 *Founded/Ownrshp* 1923
Sales 22.0MM[E] *EMP* 75
SIC 1711 Plumbing, heating, air-conditioning contractors; Plumbing contractors; Warm air heating & air conditioning contractor
Ch Bd: Thomas T Hill Jr
**Pr:* David Hill
Sfty Dirs: Mike Richardson
Opers Mgr: Marcus Waldon

HILL SERVICES, PLUMBING & HVAC
See HILL SERVICES INC

D-U-N-S 08-009-2372 IMP
HILL TIRE CO
100 Hill Industrial Blvd, Forest Park, GA 30297-1734
Tel (404) 361-6337 *Founded/Ownrshp* 1976
Sales 54.3MM[E] *EMP* 100
SIC 5531 7534 Automotive tires; Tire retreading & repair shops
CEO: Fred E Hill
CFO: Allen F Hill

D-U-N-S 05-909-5877
HILL TOP RESEARCH INC
(*Suby of* CLIANTHA RESEARCH LIMITED)
4711 34th St N Unit 1, Saint Petersburg, FL 33714-3015
Tel (727) 344-7602 *Founded/Ownrshp* 2010
Sales 20.0MM[E] *EMP* 175
SIC 8734 Product testing laboratory, safety or performance; Product testing laboratory, safety or performance
Pr: Dr Gualberto Perez

HILL VENTILATING & AC
See H V A C INC

D-U-N-S 15-756-2984
HILL WARD & HENDERSON PROFESSIONAL ASSOCIATION
101 E Kennedy Blvd # 3700, Tampa, FL 33602-5195
Tel (813) 221-3900 *Founded/Ownrshp* 1986
Sales 57.0MM[E] *EMP* 320
SIC 8111 6733 General practice attorney, lawyer; Trusts; General practice attorney, lawyer; Trusts
Pr: Benjamin H Hill III
Ch Bd: Al Ward
Pr: Sharon Donofrio
**COO:* Christopher McDonald
CFO: Ming Jung
CFO: Christopher McDonnell
**Treas:* Dennis P Waggoner
**VP:* Thomas N Henderson
**VP:* David R Tyrell
Exec: Jeanie Poley
Ex Dir: Erik Abrahamson

D-U-N-S 80-598-3194
HILL YORK SERVICE CORP
2125 S Andrews Ave, Fort Lauderdale, FL 33316-3490
Tel (954) 525-4200 *Founded/Ownrshp* 1947
Sales 21.8MM[E] *EMP* 150
SIC 7623 1711 Air conditioning repair; Warm air heating & air conditioning contractor; Air conditioning repair; Warm air heating & air conditioning contractor
Ch Bd: Robert S Lafferty
**Pr:* Mark Kerney
**CEO:* Robert W Lafferty
**CFO:* Elden Bagley
Sr Cor Off: Herbert Dell
Sales Exec: Larry Clark
Mktg Mgr: Marie Papa

HILL-KELLY DDG CHRSLR JEEP RM
See HILL-KELLY DODGE INC

D-U-N-S 03-265-3800
HILL-KELLY DODGE INC
HILL-KELLY DDG CHRSLR JEEP RM
6171 Pensacola Blvd, Pensacola, FL 32505-2297
Tel (850) 476-9078 *Founded/Ownrshp* 1951
Sales 30.4MM[E] *EMP* 77[E]
SIC 5511 5521 Automobiles, new & used; Used car dealers; Automobiles, new & used; Used car dealers
Pr: Malinda L Fiveash
**Sec:* Jack Fiveash Jr
Genl Mgr: Thomas Reed
Sls Mgr: Rusty Hill
Sls Mgr: Cindy McCraney

D-U-N-S 80-968-8885
■ **HILL-ROM CO INC**
(*Suby of* HILL-ROM INC) ★
1069 State Road 46 E, Batesville, IN 47006-9167
Tel (812) 934-7777 *Founded/Ownrshp* 2008
Sales 99.5MM[E] *EMP* 910
SIC 7352 Medical equipment rental; Medical equipment rental
Pr: John J Greisch
**CFO:* Mark Guinan
**Sr VP:* Andreas G Frank
**Sr VP:* Scott Jeffers

VP: Mark Baron
VP: Bertha Hazelwood
**VP:* Richard G Keller
VP: Daniel Longoria
VP: Perry Stuckey
VP: Greg Tucholski
Snr Sftwr: James Allen

D-U-N-S 05-065-6982 IMP/EXP
▲ **HILL-ROM HOLDINGS INC**
2 Prudential Plz Ste 4100, Chicago, IL 60601
Tel (312) 819-7200 *Founded/Ownrshp* 1969
Sales 1.9MMM *EMP* 10,000
Accts Pricewaterhousecoopers Llp In
Tkr Sym HRC *Exch* NYS
SIC 3841 7352 Surgical & medical instruments; Medical equipment rental; Surgical & medical instruments; Medical equipment rental
Pr: John J Greisch
Pr: Jeff KAO
Pr: Greg Tucholski
COO: Carlyn D Solomon
CFO: Steven J Strobel
Ofcr: Kenneth Meyers
VP: Richard G Keller
VP: Andy Rieth
VP: Greg Zenko
CTO: Ben Marshall
Board of Directors: Rolf A Classon, William G Dempsey, James R Giertz, Charles E Golden, William H Kucheman, Ronald A Malone, Eduardo R Menasce, Stacy Enxing Seng

D-U-N-S 00-424-5668 IMP/EXP
■ **HILL-ROM INC**
QUERIES MARKET RESEARCH
(*Suby of* HILL-ROM HOLDINGS INC) ★
1069 State Route 46 E, Batesville, IN 47006-9167
Tel (812) 934-7777 *Founded/Ownrshp* 1969
Sales 569.7MM[E] *EMP* 6,000
SIC 7352 2599

D-U-N-S 78-593-8226
HILLANDALE FARMS CORP
1330 Austin Ave, Akron, OH 44306-3106
Tel (330) 724-3199 *Founded/Ownrshp* 1980
Sales 33.6MM[E] *EMP* 45
SIC 5144 5143 5147 5141 Eggs; Butter; Cheese; Meats & meat products; Groceries, general line
Pr: Orland Bethel
**Sec:* Gary Bethel

D-U-N-S 83-762-6894 EXP
HILLANDALE FARMS EAST INC
NEARBY EGGS
2862 Daron Rd, Spring Grove, PA 17362-7900
Tel (717) 229-0601 *Founded/Ownrshp* 1995
Sales 43.5MM[E] *EMP* 95
SIC 5144 Eggs; Eggs: cleaning, oil treating, packing & grading; Eggs; Eggs: cleaning, oil treating, packing & grading
CEO: Orland Bethel
**Pr:* Gary Bethel
**VP:* James Minkin

D-U-N-S 01-404-3897 EXP
HILLANDALE FARMS OF PA INC
4001 Crooked Run Rd Ste 2, North Versailles, PA 15137-2392
Tel (412) 672-9685 *Founded/Ownrshp* 1963
Sales 72.2MM[E] *EMP* 108
SIC 5143 5144 Dairy products, except dried or canned; Eggs; Dairy products, except dried or canned; Eggs
Pr: Orland R Bethel

D-U-N-S 08-671-5984
HILLANDALE FARMS OF PA INC
GARDENVIEW EGGS
(*Suby of* HILLANDALE FARMS OF PA INC) ★
319 Duke St, Reedsville, PA 17084-8948
Tel (717) 667-2711 *Founded/Ownrshp* 1977
Sales 26.3MM[E] *EMP* 108
SIC 5144 5143 Eggs; Butter; Cheese; Eggs; Butter; Cheese
Pr: Jerry Zeiders
**Sec:* James E Zeiders

D-U-N-S 09-270-8254
■ **HILLANDALE LLC**
(*Suby of* CAL-MAINE FOODS INC) ★
247 Nw Hillandale Gln, Lake City, FL 32055-5492
Tel (386) 397-1300 *Founded/Ownrshp* 2005
Sales 29.6MM *EMP* 200
SIC 0252 Chicken eggs; Chicken eggs
CFO: Jo N Ward
VP: Bob Scott

D-U-N-S 78-732-6073
HILLANDALE-GETTYSBURG LP
3910 Oxford Rd, Gettysburg, PA 17325-8367
Tel (717) 334-1973 *Founded/Ownrshp* 1999
Sales 26.9MM[E] *EMP* 190
SIC 0252 2015 Chicken eggs; Poultry slaughtering & processing; Chicken eggs; Poultry slaughtering & processing

D-U-N-S 16-169-7743
HILLARD DEVELOPMENT CORP
PROVIDENT NURSING HOME
4800 N Nob Hill Rd, Sunrise, FL 33351-4722
Tel (954) 748-3400 *Founded/Ownrshp* 1983
Sales 4.4MM[E] *EMP* 310
SIC 8059 Nursing home, except skilled & intermediate care facility; Nursing home, except skilled & intermediate care facility
CEO: Richard W Wolfe

HILLCO
See DISCOVERY INSURANCE CO INC

D-U-N-S 07-201-8278
HILLCO LTD
ROBERT HILL CONSTRUCTION CO
1435 Hwy 258 N, Kinston, NC 28504-7208
Tel (252) 523-9094 *Founded/Ownrshp* 1952
Sales 173.0MM[E] *EMP* 7,000

SIC 8051 8059 5047 5122 Skilled nursing care facilities; Rest home, with health care; Medical equipment & supplies; Pharmaceuticals; Skilled nursing care facilities; Rest home, with health care; Medical equipment & supplies; Pharmaceuticals
Pr: Steven Hill
Treas: Pete Eimen
**Sec:* Lucy Hill
VP: Catherine Emma
**VP:* Greg Hill
**VP:* Robert Hill Jr
Dir IT: Aaron Frizzell

D-U-N-S 92-641-8799
HILLCREST BANCSHARES INC
HILLCREST BANK
11111 W 95th St, Shawnee Mission, KS 66214-1824
Tel (913) 492-7500 *Founded/Ownrshp* 1975
Sales NA *EMP* 200
SIC 6022 State commercial banks; State commercial banks
Pr: Tom Davies
COO: Lucy Jones
CFO: Dick Degen
Ex VP: Kevin Kramer
Sr VP: Michael Balsbaugh
Sr VP: Tracy Pancost
VP: Nicole Davis
VP: Lois Stewart

HILLCREST BANK
See HILLCREST BANCSHARES INC

D-U-N-S 07-511-9024
HILLCREST BAPTIST MEDICAL CENTER (TX)
BRAZOS VALLEY HEALTH NETWORK
3000 Herring Ave, Waco, TX 76708-3239
Tel (254) 202-8675 *Founded/Ownrshp* 1920
Sales 221.2MM^E *EMP* 2,200
Accts Bkd Llp Houston Tx
SIC 8062 Hospital, medical school affiliated with nursing & residency; Hospital, medical school affiliated with nursing & residency
Pr: Glenn A Robinson
**CFO:* Richard W Perkins
Treas: Peter Eimen
Ex VP: Richard Perkins
Dir Lab: Kele Crouch
Off Mgr: Debbie Muerer
CIO: James Gillian
CIO: Richard Warren
MIS Dir: Gina Roberts
Dir IT: Darlene Gorham
Telecom Mg: Ray Bell

HILLCREST CENTER
See CRESTVIEW CONVALESCENT HOME INC

HILLCREST COMMONS
See HILLCREST EXTENDED CARE SERVICES INC

D-U-N-S 07-201-4160
HILLCREST CONVALESCENT CENTER INC
1417 W Pettigrew St, Durham, NC 27705-4898
Tel (919) 286-7705 *Founded/Ownrshp* 1957
Sales 1.1MMM *EMP* 162
SIC 8052 8051 Intermediate care facilities; Convalescent home with continuous nursing care; Intermediate care facilities; Convalescent home with continuous nursing care
Pr: Lenwood P Smith
**Treas:* Ted Smith
Exec: William Hoover

D-U-N-S 02-851-9163
HILLCREST COUNTRY CLUB
10000 W Pico Blvd, Los Angeles, CA 90064-3400
Tel (310) 553-8911 *Founded/Ownrshp* 1920
Sales 20.9MM *EMP* 180
Accts Hutchinson And Bloodgood Llp
SIC 7997 Country club, membership; Country club, membership
Pr: John Jameson
**CEO:* John Goldsmith
**CFO:* Tom Driefus
**Prin:* Chester Firestien
**Prin:* Leonard Fisher
**Prin:* Richard Powell

D-U-N-S 14-704-0414
HILLCREST EDUCATIONAL CENTERS INC
BROOKSIDE SCHOOL
788 South St, Pittsfield, MA 01201-8237
Tel (413) 499-7924 *Founded/Ownrshp* 1984
Sales 27.4MM *EMP* 460
SIC 8211

D-U-N-S 06-888-2091
HILLCREST EGG & CHEESE CO
HILLCREST FOOD SERVICE
2735 E 40th St, Cleveland, OH 44115-3510
Tel (216) 361-4625 *Founded/Ownrshp* 1974
Sales 136.0MM^E *EMP* 105
SIC 5143 5142 5147 5144 5149 5148 Dairy products, except dried or canned; Packaged frozen goods; Meats, fresh; Eggs; Canned goods: fruit, vegetables, seafood, meats, etc.; Fruits, fresh; Vegetables, fresh; Dairy products, except dried or canned; Packaged frozen goods; Meats, fresh; Eggs; Canned goods: fruit, vegetables, seafood, meats, etc.; Fruits, fresh; Vegetables, fresh
Pr: Armin Abraham
**Treas:* Galina Yakobovitch
**VP:* David Abraham
VP: Bret Roth
IT Man: Lloyd Langham
VP Sls: John Talbott

D-U-N-S 06-270-2720
HILLCREST EXTENDED CARE SERVICES INC
HILLCREST COMMONS
169 Valentine Rd, Pittsfield, MA 01201-3042
Tel (413) 445-2300 *Founded/Ownrshp* 2001
Sales 22.8MM *EMP* 25^E
SIC 8051 Skilled nursing care facilities; Skilled nursing care facilities

Pr: David E Phelps
**Pr:* William Jones

D-U-N-S 08-029-3467
HILLCREST FAMILY SERVICES
2005 Asbury Rd, Dubuque, IA 52001-3042
Tel (563) 583-7357 *Founded/Ownrshp* 1924
Sales 21.8MM *EMP* 250
Accts Eidebailly Llp Dubuque Iowa
SIC 8322 Family service agency; Family service agency
Ex Dir: Gary Gansemer
CFO: Michael Luedtke
VP: Carrie Bleile
VP: Deb Lang
VP: Francie Tuescher
VP: Julie Vyverberg
Exec: Cindy Hess
Prgrm Mgr: Julie Gabriel
Prgrm Mgr: Christan Reed
Off Admin: Sondra Bennett
Off Admin: Jennifer Reschly

HILLCREST FOOD SERVICE
See HILLCREST EGG & CHEESE CO

D-U-N-S 05-421-5546 IMP
HILLCREST FOODS INC
WAFFLE HOUSE
50 Satellit Blvd Nw Ste G, Suwanee, GA 30024-2400
Tel (770) 932-1137 *Founded/Ownrshp* 1967
Sales 28.0MM^E *EMP* 800
SIC 5812 Restaurant, family: chain; Restaurant, family: chain
Pr: Gilbert Miller
**Sec:* Robert O'Rear
**VP:* Todd Miller

D-U-N-S 94-779-2842
HILLCREST FORD LINCOLN-MERCURY INC
HYUNDAI
737 Interstate 45 S, Huntsville, TX 77340-6444
Tel (936) 295-3784 *Founded/Ownrshp* 1996
Sales 28.0MM^E *EMP* 93
SIC 5511 Automobiles, new & used; Automobiles, new & used
Pr: Tom Broadway
Sales Asso: David Larkins

HILLCREST HEALTHCARE
See HILLCREST MEDICAL NURSING INSTITUTE INC

D-U-N-S 10-986-6012
HILLCREST HEALTHCARE SYSTEM AN OKLAHOMA CORP
1120 S Utica Ave, Tulsa, OK 74104-4012
Tel (918) 579-1000 *Founded/Ownrshp* 1973
Sales 54.5MM^E *EMP* 456^E
SIC 8031 Offices & clinics of osteopathic physicians; Offices & clinics of osteopathic physicians
Pr: David Krug
CFO: James Washecka
Ofcr: Michael Blades
Ofcr: William Peterson
Comm Dir: Lee Gould
Chf Nrs Of: Abigail Kendall
Off Mgr: Carrie Bowen
Opers Mgr: Shelley Ohair
Surgeon: Charles Howard
Doctor: Supriya Koya
Pharmcst: Melissa Gaither

D-U-N-S 06-052-3693
HILLCREST HOSPITAL
165 Tor Ct, Pittsfield, MA 01201-3001
Tel (413) 443-4761 *Founded/Ownrshp* 1908
Sales 17.5MM^E *EMP* 500
SIC 8062 General medical & surgical hospitals; General medical & surgical hospitals
Pr: Eugene A Dellea
**CFO:* Anthony Rinaldi

HILLCREST HOSPITAL CLAREMORE
See CLAREMORE REGIONAL HOSPITAL LLC

HILLCREST HOSPITAL CLAREMORE
See AHS CLAREMORE REGIONAL HOSPITAL LLC

HILLCREST HOSPITAL CUSHING
See AHS CUSHING HOSPITAL LLC

D-U-N-S 07-152-6487
HILLCREST MEDICAL NURSING INSTITUTE INC (TN)
HILLCREST HEALTHCARE
5321 Beverly Park Cir, Knoxville, TN 37918-9253
Tel (865) 687-1321 *Founded/Ownrshp* 1960
Sales 35.2MM *EMP* 650
Accts Lattimore Black Morgan & Cain
SIC 8052 Intermediate care facilities; Intermediate care facilities
CEO: Carolyn Pointer
Exec: Kim Brach
CTO: Chase Conyers

HILLCREST REHAB HLTH CARE CTR
See BEVERLY ENTERPRISES - MINNESOTA LLC

D-U-N-S 00-684-8568 IMP/EXP
HILLDRUP COMPANIES INC
HILLDRUP MOVING & STORAGE
4022 Jefferson Davis Hwy, Stafford, VA 22554-4827
Tel (703) 221-7155 *Founded/Ownrshp* 1976
Sales 90.7MM *EMP* 450
SIC 4212

HILLDRUP MOVING & STORAGE
See HILLDRUP COMPANIES INC

D-U-N-S 03-075-8882
HILLEL COMMUNITY DAY SCHOOL INC
SAMUEL SCHECK HILLEL DAY SCHL
19000 Ne 25th Ave, Miami, FL 33180-3209
Tel (305) 931-2831 *Founded/Ownrshp* 1970
Sales 25.1MM *EMP* 250
Accts Morrison Brown Argiz & Farra L
SIC 8211 8351 Private elementary & secondary schools; Child day care services; Private elementary & secondary schools; Child day care services

COO: Leonard Traub
COO: Rafael Quintero

D-U-N-S 07-278-8482
HILLEL DAY SCHOOL OF METROPOLITAN DETROIT INC
PARENT CO: IN NY, NY
32200 Middlebelt Rd, Farmington Hills, MI 48334-1715
Tel (248) 626-3267 *Founded/Ownrshp* 1958
Sales 26.0MM *EMP* 140
Accts Frank Hirsch Subelsky & Freedm
SIC 8211 Private elementary school; Private junior high school
CEO: Mark Smiley

D-U-N-S 01-170-0817
HILLEL FOUNDATION FOR JEWISH CAMPUS LIFE
800 8th St Nw, Washington, DC 20001-3724
Tel (202) 216-9535 *Founded/Ownrshp* 1923
Sales 26.1MM *EMP* 65
Accts Dixon Hughes Goodman Llp Rock
SIC 8661 Religious organizations; Religious organizations
Pr: Wayne Firestone
Pr: Tracy Turoff
**CFO:* Aryeh Furst
**Ch:* Randall R Kaplan
Ofcr: David Eden
Ex Dir: Beth Gansky

D-U-N-S 82-516-5132
▲ **HILLENBRAND INC**
1 Batesville Blvd, Batesville, IN 47006-7756
Tel (812) 934-7500 *Founded/Ownrshp* 2007
Sales 1.6MMM *EMP* 6,000^E
Accts Pricewaterhousecoopers Llp In
Tkr Sym HI *Exch* NYS
SIC 3535 3995 Conveyors & conveying equipment; Bulk handling conveyor systems; Burial caskets; Burial vaults, fiberglass; Conveyors & conveying equipment; Bulk handling conveyor systems; Burial caskets; Burial vaults, fiberglass
Pr: Joe A Raver
**Ch Bd:* F Joseph Loughrey
Pr: Kim Ryan
Pr: Chris Trainor
CFO: Cynthia L Lucchese
Ofcr: Paul Douglas Wilson
Sr VP: Scott P George
Sr VP: John R Zerkle
VP: Elizabeth E Dreyer
VP: Darryl M Maslar
Board of Directors: Edward B Cloues II, Gary L Collar, Helen W Cornell, Mark C Deluzio, Joy M Greenway, Thomas H Johnson, Eduardo R Menasce, Neil S Novich, Stuart A Taylor II

D-U-N-S 00-799-2449
HILLENMEYER NURSERIES INC (KY)
2337 Sandersville Rd, Lexington, KY 40511-1039
Tel (859) 255-1091 *Founded/Ownrshp* 1841, 1984
Sales 23.2MM^E *EMP* 105^E
SIC 5261 0782 Nursery stock, seeds & bulbs; Landscape contractors
Pr: Stephen Hillenmeyer

D-U-N-S 03-440-2966 IMP
HILLER COMPANIES INC
(*Suby of* PON NORTH AMERICA INC) ★
3751 Joy Springs Dr, Mobile, AL 36693-5134
Tel (251) 661-1275 *Founded/Ownrshp* 1983
Sales 143.2MM^E *EMP* 604
SIC 1731 5084 5088 Fire detection & burglar alarm systems specialization; Safety equipment; Marine supplies; Fire detection & burglar alarm systems specialization; Safety equipment; Marine supplies
CEO: Patrick Lynch
CFO: James T Garner
CFO: Eric Savadra
**CFO:* Claude Warren
VP: Johnny Williams
Exec: Laurie Craver
Board of Directors: L Duncan Greenwood

D-U-N-S 03-512-2720
HILLER ELECTRIC CO
5404 Dayton St, Omaha, NE 68117-1343
Tel (402) 339-0524 *Founded/Ownrshp* 1978
Sales 20.5MM^E *EMP* 110
Accts Deboer & Associates Pc Omaha
SIC 1731 General electrical contractor
Pr: John F Hiller
**Sec:* Susan T Jack
**VP:* Raymond Jack
Opers Mgr: Dan Jack

D-U-N-S 01-739-5211
HILLER INC
SHOPPING CENTER MARKETS
24359 N Wstn Hwy Ste 150, Southfield, MI 48075
Tel (248) 355-2122 *Founded/Ownrshp* 1943
Sales 97.4MM^E *EMP* 600
SIC 5411 5921 Supermarkets, independent; Beer (packaged); Wine; Supermarkets, independent; Beer (packaged); Wine
Pr: James A Hiller
COO: Victor Iagnemma
CFO: Eva Shapiro

D-U-N-S 83-061-6967
HILLER LLC
915 Murfreesboro Pike, Nashville, TN 37217-1501
Tel (615) 292-6110 *Founded/Ownrshp* 1990
Sales 51.5MM^E *EMP* 160^E
Accts Cpa Consulting Group Pllc Na
SIC 1711 Plumbing contractors; Plumbing contractors
Pr: James Hiller
Brnch Mgr: Mike Scott
Brnch Mgr: Brian Wait
Opers Mgr: Steve Bourdon
Opers Mgr: Toby Hensley
Mktg Mgr: Lisa Cronin

D-U-N-S 00-637-5505 IMP/EXP
HILLERICH & BRADSBY CO
LOUISVILLE SLUGGER
800 W Main St, Louisville, KY 40202-2637
Tel (502) 585-5226 *Founded/Ownrshp* 1856
Sales 65.8MM^E *EMP* 317
SIC 3949 5091

D-U-N-S 10-647-2418
HILLIARD CITY SCHOOL DISTRICT
2140 Atlas St, Columbus, OH 43228-9647
Tel (614) 921-7000 *Founded/Ownrshp* 1887
Sales 212.3MM *EMP* 1,700
Accts Dave Yost Columbus Ohio
SIC 8211 Public elementary & secondary schools; School board; Public elementary & secondary schools; School board
**Treas:* Brian W Wilson
Ofcr: Eamfiyn Flowers
**Prin:* Dale A McVey
IT Man: Jana Blamble
HC Dir: Vicky Clark

D-U-N-S 00-220-6530 IMP
HILLIARD CORP (NY)
100 W 4th St, Elmira, NY 14901-2190
Tel (607) 733-7121 *Founded/Ownrshp* 1905
Sales 106.5MM *EMP* 610^E
Accts Mengel Metzer Barr & Co Llp
SIC 3564 3569 3823 Purification & dust collection equipment; Filters; Industrial instrmnts msrmnt display/control process variable; Purification & dust collection equipment; Filters; Industrial instrmnts msrmnt display/control process variable
Ch Bd: Arie J Van Den Blink
**Pr:* Gene A Ebbrecht
CFO: Lark Hilliard
**CFO:* Gordon J Webster
**Ex VP:* Steven J Chesebro
VP: Lindsey Canfield
**VP:* Michael V Cantando
**VP:* David Ochab
**VP:* Juan G Parra
**VP:* Jon L Williams
Mfg Dir: Doug Henry

HILLIARD LYONS
See J J B HILLIARD W L LYONS LLC

HILLIARD LYONS
See JJB HILLIARD WLLYONS LLC

D-U-N-S 05-533-5517
HILLIARD RANCHES INC
217 N 12th St, Temple, TX 76501-4358
Tel (254) 778-2748 *Founded/Ownrshp* 1948
Sales 23.0MM^E *EMP* 80
SIC 5181 Beer & ale; Beer & other fermented malt liquors; Beer & ale; Beer & other fermented malt liquors
Pr: Jack Hilliard Jr

HILLIARD'S CAREY RESTAURANT
See CAREY HILLIARDS DRIVE-IN RESTAURANT INC

D-U-N-S 19-960-4851
HILLIS-CARNES ENGINEERING ASSOCIATES INC
HILLIS-CARNES ENGRG ASSOC
10975 Guilford Rd Ste A, Annapolis Junction, MD 20701-1125
Tel (301) 470-4239 *Founded/Ownrshp* 1989
Sales 57.9MM^E *EMP* 250
SIC 8711 Consulting engineer; Consulting engineer
Pr: Richard M Hillis
**VP:* William M Carnes
VP: Nicole Wienecke
IT Man: Robert Skepton
Mktg Dir: Jody Bopst

HILLIS-CARNES ENGRG ASSOC
See HILLIS-CARNES ENGINEERING ASSOCIATES INC

D-U-N-S 04-126-2908 IMP/EXP
HILLMAN CO
330 Garnet Way 1900, Pittsburgh, PA 15224-2006
Tel (412) 281-2620 *Founded/Ownrshp* 1948
Sales 57.0MM^E *EMP* 60
SIC 5085 5084 Industrial supplies; Hydraulic systems equipment & supplies
Pr: Joseph C Manzinger
**Treas:* Ed Colano
**Treas:* Eric C Johnson
**Treas:* Edward F Kolano
Trst: Bruce Crocker
**Sr VP:* Timothy O Fisher
**VP:* John W Hall
**VP:* Mark M Poljak
VP: Mark Poljak
Mng Dir: Thomas Goff
Mng Dir: Bill Hallett
Board of Directors: Elsie Hilliard Hillman, Juliet Lea Hillman Simonds

D-U-N-S 16-094-6992 IMP/EXP
HILLMAN COMPANIES INC
(*Suby of* HMAN INTERMEDIATE II HOLDINGS CORP) ★
10590 Hamilton Ave, Cincinnati, OH 45231-1764
Tel (513) 851-4900 *Founded/Ownrshp* 2010
Sales 1.0MMM^E *EMP* 2,605
SIC 5072 7699 Hardware; Miscellaneous fasteners; Bolts, nuts & screws; Key duplicating shop; Hardware; Miscellaneous fasteners; Bolts, nuts & screws; Key duplicating shop
Ch Bd: Douglas J Cahill
CFO: Jeffrey S Leonard
CFO: Anthony A Vasconcellos
Ex VP: Robert Lackman
Sr VP: Terry R Owe
Sr VP: Todd Spangler
VP: Rick Buller
VP: Jim Gamble
VP: Rob Gruber
VP: Betty Hillman
VP: Bill Moreland

D-U-N-S 08-064-4248
HILLMAN FAMILY FOUNDATION INC
330 Garnet Way Ste 2000, Pittsburgh, PA 15224-2006
Tel (412) 338-3466 *Founded/Ownrshp* 1951
Sales 49.3MM *EMP* 4
SIC 6732 Charitable trust management
Pr: David K Roger
Treas: Lisa R Johns
* *Treas:* Mary Wagner
Ofcr: Lauri Fink
Exec: Carol Long

D-U-N-S 08-289-7922 IMP
HILLMAN GROUP INC
(*Suby of* HILLMAN COMPANIES INC) ★
10590 Hamilton Ave, Cincinnati, OH 45231-1764
Tel (513) 851-4900 *Founded/Ownrshp* 1998
Sales 221.8MM^E *EMP* 1,900
SIC 5072 Hardware; Hardware
Ch: Douglas J Cahill
* *CEO:* James P Waters
* *CFO:* Jeffrey S Leonard
CFO: Mike Schaeper
CFO: Anthony Vasconcellos
Sr VP: Ali Fartaj
Sr VP: John Glass
* *Sr VP:* Todd Spangler
VP: Gary L Seeds
Sfty Mgr: Rogar Peters
Mktg Dir: Bob Lyons

D-U-N-S 15-426-3644 IMP
HILLMAN GROUP INC
(*Suby of* HILLMAN COMPANIES INC) ★
8990 S Kyrene Rd, Tempe, AZ 85284-2907
Tel (800) 800-4900 *Founded/Ownrshp* 2000
Sales 200.3MM^E *EMP* 1,700
SIC 3429 5162 3599 Keys & key blanks; Plastics materials; Custom machinery; Keys & key blanks; Plastics materials; Custom machinery
CEO: Max W Hillman
* *Pr:* Richard P Hillman
* *Pr:* Stephen W Miller
* *VP:* George Heredia
* *VP:* Michael Mueller
* *VP:* David M Richards
IT Man: Dan Henderson
* *VP Mfg:* Mark Yeary
Mktg Mgr: Jim Hetterich
Sls Mgr: Matt Intrieri

D-U-N-S 03-891-0662
HILLMAN HOLDINGS LLC
116 W Cedar Ave, Tulare, CA 93274-5348
Tel (559) 685-6100 *Founded/Ownrshp* 2000
Sales 36.7MM^E *EMP* 446
SIC 0723 Feed milling custom services; Feed milling custom services

HILLMAN OYSTER COMPANY
See HILLMAN SHRIMP AND OYSTER CO

D-U-N-S 09-482-6856
HILLMAN SHRIMP & OYSTER CO
10700 Hillman Dr, Dickinson, TX 77539-3058
Tel (281) 339-1506 *Founded/Ownrshp* 1974
Sales 30.8MM^E *EMP* 300
Accts Joel J Marin Alvin Tx
SIC 2092 5146 Shellfish, frozen: prepared; Seafoods, frozen: prepared; Seafoods; Shellfish, frozen: prepared; Seafoods, frozen: prepared; Seafoods
Pr: Clifford Hillman
* *Sec:* Darla Hillman
* *VP:* Stephen Hillman

D-U-N-S 78-794-8962 EXP
HILLMAN SHRIMP AND OYSTER CO
HILLMAN OYSTER COMPANY
10700 Hillman Dr, Dickinson, TX 77539-3058
Tel (281) 339-1506 *Founded/Ownrshp* 1978
Sales 14.8MM *EMP* 290
SIC 2092 5146 Shellfish, frozen: prepared; Seafoods; Shellfish, frozen: prepared; Seafoods
Pr: Clifford Hillman
* *Sec:* Darla Hillman
* *VP:* Stephen Hillman

HILL'S ACE HARDWARE
See HILLS SUPPLY CO

D-U-N-S 07-841-7607
HILLS AND DALES GENERAL HOSPITAL
4675 Hill St, Cass City, MI 48726-1099
Tel (989) 872-2121 *Founded/Ownrshp* 1960
Sales 25.2MM *EMP* 250
Accts Plante & Moran Pllc East Lan
SIC 8062 General medical & surgical hospitals; General medical & surgical hospitals
Ch: Orvil Beecher
Chf Rad: Vikram RAO
* *Sec:* Pat Curtis
Dir Inf Cn: Faith Fahrner
* *Prin:* Danny Haag
Dir IT: Justin Nickrand
IT Man: Kathy Dropeski
Doctor: David L Carter MD
Snr Mgr: Jeanie Boyes

D-U-N-S 10-737-1494
▲ **HILLS BANCORPORATION**
131 Main St, Hills, IA 52235-7777
Tel (319) 679-2291 *Founded/Ownrshp* 1982
Sales NA *EMP* 421
Tkr Sym HBIA *Exch* OTO
SIC 6022 State commercial banks; State commercial banks
Pr: Dwight O Seegmilleer
COO: Keith Jones
CFO: Shari J Demaris
Trst Ofcr: Brian Globokar
Trst Ofcr: Aaron Schaefer
* *VP:* Theodore H Pacha
VP: Peter Sorensen
VP: Tracy Stotler
Board of Directors: Michael S Donovan, Thomas J Gill, Michael E Hodge, Emily A Hughes, James A Nowak, John W Phelan, Ann Marie Rhodes, Thomas R Wiele, Sheldon E Yoder

D-U-N-S 00-531-3846
■ **HILLS BANK AND TRUST CO** (IA)
(*Suby of* HILLS BANCORPORATION) ★
131 Main St, Hills, IA 52235-7777
Tel (319) 679-2291 *Founded/Ownrshp* 1904
Sales NA *EMP* 250
SIC 6022 State commercial banks; State commercial banks
Pr: Dwight Seegmiller
Ofcr: Jace Bailey
Ofcr: Shaun Barry
Ofcr: Molly Brown
Ofcr: Sarah Gould
Ofcr: Angela Hagedorn
Ofcr: Kenzie Hein
Ofcr: Holly Huggins
Ofcr: Peggy Keele
Ofcr: Brandon Keese
Ofcr: Bob Lamkins
Ofcr: Terry McAllister
Ofcr: Ryan Murphy
Ofcr: Todd Nelson
Ofcr: Matthew Olson
Ofcr: Holly Randall
Ofcr: Jane Rigby
Ofcr: Kim Snyder
Ofcr: Teresa Walker
Trst Ofcr: Dale Farland
Trst Ofcr: Erin Grabe

D-U-N-S 02-826-5528
HILLS FLAT LUMBER CO
380 Railroad Ave, Grass Valley, CA 95945-5909
Tel (530) 273-6171 *Founded/Ownrshp* 1950
Sales 26.3MM^E *EMP* 130
SIC 1731 5031 5193 5999 5199 7359 Electrical work; Doors & windows; Nursery stock; Plumbing & heating supplies; General merchandise, non-durable; Equipment rental & leasing; Electrical work; Doors & windows; Nursery stock; Plumbing & heating supplies; General merchandise, non-durable; Equipment rental & leasing
CEO: Jeffrey Edward Pardini
* *VP:* Jason Pardini
* *VP:* Kennan Pardini
* *VP:* Sandra Pardini
* *Prin:* Edward J Pardini Jr
Store Mgr: Daryl Davis

D-U-N-S 03-964-3759
HILLS MATERIALS CO
(*Suby of* OLDCASTLE INC) ★
3975 Sturgis Rd, Rapid City, SD 57702-0307
Tel (605) 394-3300 *Founded/Ownrshp* 1925
Sales 65.1MM^E *EMP* 250
SIC 1611 1422 1442 3273 2951 2491 Highway & street paving contractor; Limestones, ground; Gravel mining; Ready-mixed concrete; Asphalt paving mixtures & blocks; Wood preserving; Highway & street paving contractor; Limestones, ground; Gravel mining; Ready-mixed concrete; Asphalt paving mixtures & blocks; Wood preserving
Pr: Lynn Kading
* *VP:* William J Keller

D-U-N-S 06-877-5311 IMP/EXP
■ **HILLS PET NUTRITION INC**
(*Suby of* COLGATE-PALMOLIVE CO) ★
400 Sw 8th Ave Ste 101, Topeka, KS 66603-3925
Tel (785) 354-8523 *Founded/Ownrshp* 1987
Sales 1.9MMM^E *EMP* 2,700
SIC 5149 2048 2047 Pet foods; Prepared feeds; Dog & cat food; Pet foods; Prepared feeds; Dog & cat food
CEO: Neil Thompson
Bd of Dir: Brady Sisk
VP: Richard Hawkins
VP: Paul Houghton
Exec: Blake Hawley
Exec: Hein Meyer
Assoc Dir: Amanda Jay
Assoc Dir: Marjorie Lathrop-Allen
Assoc Dir: Jim Walsh
Comm Dir: Patricia Evans
Opers Mgr: Bart Fisher

D-U-N-S 05-333-1521 IMP/EXP
■ **HILLS PET NUTRITION SALES INC**
(*Suby of* HILLS PET NUTRITION INC) ★
400 Sw 8th Ave Ste 101, Topeka, KS 66603-3925
Tel (785) 354-8523 *Founded/Ownrshp* 1998
Sales 54.7MM^E *EMP* 700
SIC 5149 Pet foods; Pet foods
CEO: Robert Wheeler
* *Pr:* Justin Skala
* *CEO:* Neil Thomson

D-U-N-S 03-395-9215
HILLS PET PRODUCTS INC
400 Sw 8th Ave Ste 101, Topeka, KS 66603-3945
Tel (785) 354-8523 *Founded/Ownrshp* 2015
Sales 33.2MM^E *EMP* 750
SIC 5999 Pets
Pr: Peter Brons-Poulsen

D-U-N-S 03-392-6965
HILLS SUPPLY CO
HILL'S ACE HARDWARE
186 W Athens St, Winder, GA 30680-1783
Tel (770) 867-3925 *Founded/Ownrshp* 1947
Sales 22.9MM *EMP* 95
Accts Smith Adcock And Company Llp
SIC 5251 5211 5231 Hardware; Lumber & other building materials; Paint & painting supplies; Hardware; Lumber & other building materials; Paint & painting supplies
Pr: Alex R Hill
* *CFO:* Gwenith G Hill
* *VP:* Robert G Hill
IT Man: Brian Fisk

D-U-N-S 01-429-0639
HILLSBORO AVIATION INC (OR)
AIRMAN'S PROFICIENCY CENTER
3950 Ne 30th Ave, Hillsboro, OR 97124-4707
Tel (503) 648-2831 *Founded/Ownrshp* 1980, 1992
Sales 32.2MM^E *EMP* 70
SIC 4522 5599 4581 8249 Air transportation, nonscheduled; Flying charter service; Helicopter carriers, nonscheduled; Aircraft dealers; Aircraft, self-propelled; Aircraft instruments, equipment or parts; Aircraft maintenance & repair services; Aviation school; Air transportation, nonscheduled; Flying charter service; Helicopter carriers, nonscheduled; Aircraft dealers; Aircraft, self-propelled; Aircraft instruments, equipment or parts; Aircraft maintenance & repair services; Aviation school
Pr: Max Lyons
Genl Mgr: Jon Hay

HILLSBORO CITY SCHOOL DISTRICT
See HILLSBORO CITY SCHOOLS

D-U-N-S 03-872-1346
HILLSBORO CITY SCHOOLS
HILLSBORO CITY SCHOOL DISTRICT
39 Willetsville Pike, Hillsboro, OH 45133-8277
Tel (937) 393-4354 *Founded/Ownrshp* 1908
Sales 22.0MM *EMP* 318
SIC 8211 Public elementary & secondary schools; Public senior high school; Elementary school; Kindergarten; Public elementary & secondary schools; Public senior high school; Elementary school; Kindergarten
* *Treas:* Deborah Lawwell
Treas: Adam Zink
VP: Beverly Rhoads
Dir IT: Kevin Black
Schl Brd P: Terry Briton
Teacher Pr: Diane Michael

D-U-N-S 02-326-4492
HILLSBORO FARMERS COOPERATIVE WAREHOUSE INC
UNITED COOP
140 E Mill St, Hillsboro, WI 54634-4500
Tel (608) 489-2231 *Founded/Ownrshp* 1920
Sales 65.1MM^E *EMP* 120^E
Accts Clifton Gunderson Llp Tomah
SIC 5191 5171 5541 Feed; Seeds: field, garden & flower; Fertilizer & fertilizer materials; Chemicals, agricultural; Petroleum bulk stations; Gasoline service stations; Feed; Seeds: field, garden & flower; Fertilizer & fertilizer materials; Chemicals, agricultural; Petroleum bulk stations; Gasoline service stations
Genl Mgr: Norbert Schleicher
* *Genl Mgr:* Ed Gunderson

D-U-N-S 02-472-1227
HILLSBORO INDEPENDENT SCHOOL DISTRICT
121 E Franklin St, Hillsboro, TX 76645-2137
Tel (254) 582-8585 *Founded/Ownrshp* 1853
Sales 16.6MM^E *EMP* 308
Accts James E Rodgers And Company
SIC 8211 Public elementary & secondary schools; Public elementary & secondary schools
Pr: Chris Teague
* *VP:* Guadalupe Lupe Mancha
Dir IT: Donald Gordon
Dir IT: Jan Russell

D-U-N-S 04-291-9795
HILLSBORO R-3 SCHOOL DISTRICT (MO)
20 Hawk Dr, Hillsboro, MO 63050-5080
Tel (636) 789-0040 *Founded/Ownrshp* 1939
Sales 23.6MM^E *EMP* 400
SIC 8211 Public elementary & secondary schools; High school, junior or senior; Public elementary school; Public elementary & secondary schools; High school, junior or senior; Public elementary school

HILLSBORO REHABILITATI
See MIDAMERICA CARE FOUNDATION INC

D-U-N-S 03-078-5760
HILLSBORO SCHOOL DISTRICT 1J
3083 Ne 49th Pl, Hillsboro, OR 97124-6006
Tel (503) 640-8403 *Founded/Ownrshp* 1914
Sales 170.1MM^E *EMP* 3,500
Accts Pauly Rogers And Co PcT
SIC 8211 Public senior high school; Public junior high school; Public senior high school; Public junior high school
CFO: Diane Blaricom
VP: Walt Hellman
Off Mgr: Linda Cady
Pr Dir: Beth Graser
Pr Dir: Nicole Kaufman
Snr Mgr: Yvain McDaniel

D-U-N-S 18-389-8386
HILLSBOROUGH CITY SCHOOL DISTRICT
300 El Cerrito Ave, Hillsborough, CA 94010-6818
Tel (650) 342-5193 *Founded/Ownrshp* 1915
Sales 26.2MM *EMP* 172
Accts Vavrinek Trine Day & Co Ll
SIC 8211 Public elementary & secondary schools; Public elementary & secondary schools

D-U-N-S 06-591-5209
HILLSBOROUGH COMMUNITY COLLEGE INC
DISTRICT BRD TRUSTEES HILLSBOR
39 Columbia Dr, Tampa, FL 33606-3584
Tel (813) 253-7000 *Founded/Ownrshp* 1968
Sales 72.1MM^E *EMP* 1,311
SIC 8222 Community college; Community college
Pr: Ken Atwater
Pr: Pat Dix
Pr: Paul Nagy
* *Pr:* Gwen Stephenson
* *CFO:* Barbara Larson
Exec: Kimberly Mathew
Nrsg Dir: Alma I Vega

D-U-N-S 00-411-5754
HILLSBOROUGH COUNTY AVIATION AUTHORITY
TAMPA INTERNATIONAL AIRPORT
4100 Georg J Bn Pkwy 3311, Tampa, FL 33607
Tel (813) 870-8700 *Founded/Ownrshp* 1945
Sales 55.9MM^E *EMP* 600
SIC 4581 Airport; Airport
CEO: Joe Lopano
* *Ch:* Al Austin
* *Treas:* Ken Hagan
Bd of Dir: Lourdes Swope
Ofcr: James Basnight
Ofcr: Cameron Beall
Ofcr: Jimmie Bizzle
Ofcr: Kevin Durkin
Ofcr: Matthew Ewing
Ofcr: Mike Ferguson
Ofcr: Lane Gove
Ofcr: Daniel Jones
Ofcr: Gina Maggiacomo
Ofcr: Matthew Martinez
Ofcr: Duy Tran
* *Sr VP:* Ann Davis
VP: John Tiliacos
Dir Soc: Maria Cook
Comm Man: Emily Nipps

D-U-N-S 07-979-9075
HILLSBOROUGH COUNTY PUBLIC SCHOOLS
901 E Kennedy Blvd, Tampa, FL 33602-3502
Tel (813) 272-4050 *Founded/Ownrshp* 2015
Sales 3.0MMM *EMP* 26,000^E
SIC 8211 Public elementary & secondary schools

D-U-N-S 04-247-1060
HILLSBOROUGH COUNTY SCHOOL DISTRICT
MIDDLE SCHOOLS EDUCATION OFF
901 E Kennedy Blvd, Tampa, FL 33602-3502
Tel (813) 272-4000 *Founded/Ownrshp* 1934
Sales 1.9MMM *EMP* 25,000
Accts Kpmg Llp Tampa Fl
SIC 8211 Public elementary & secondary schools; Public elementary & secondary schools
CFO: Ed Nicholson
Bd of Dir: Francine Lawson
VP: Melanie Flowers
Dir Risk M: Xiomara Fuentes
Dir Risk M: Holly Sloop
Comm Man: Paula Romano
Dir Sec: John R Newman
CIO: Barrington Williamson
Prd Mgr: Denise Castillo
Teacher Pr: Dena Collins
Teacher Pr: James Goode

D-U-N-S 83-035-8060
HILLSBOROUGH COUNTY SCHOOL READINESS COALITION INC
EARLY LEARNING COALITION OF HI
6800 N Dale Mabry Hwy # 158, Tampa, FL 33614-3997
Tel (813) 515-2340 *Founded/Ownrshp* 2000
Sales 73.6MM *EMP* 29
Accts Ellen Fontana Cpa Llc Clearwa
SIC 8351 Child day care services; Child day care services
Ex Dir: David McGerald
CFO: Steve Costner
VP: Jean Flick
Ex Dir: Luanne Panacek
VP Opers: Marci Delaney

D-U-N-S 05-466-0617
HILLSBOROUGH KIDS INC
101 S Franklin St Ste 201, Tampa, FL 33602-5350
Tel (813) 225-1105 *Founded/Ownrshp* 2010
Sales 69.3MM *EMP* 2
Accts Rivero Gordimer & Company Pa
SIC 8699 Charitable organization; Charitable organization
CEO: Chris Card

D-U-N-S 05-238-9244
HILLSBOROUGH TOWNSHIP BOARD OF EDUCATION
379 S Branch Rd, Hillsborough, NJ 08844-4489
Tel (908) 369-0030 *Founded/Ownrshp* 2004
Sales 35.1MM^E *EMP* 1,200
Accts Timothy M Vrabel/Chris W Hwa
SIC 8211 Public elementary & secondary schools; Public senior high school; Public junior high school; Public elementary school; Public elementary & secondary schools; Public senior high school; Public junior high school; Public elementary school
Schl Brd P: Edward Plaskon
HC Dir: Lorraine Borek

D-U-N-S 79-119-0395
HILLSBOROUGH TOWNSHIP SCHOOL DISTRICT
HILLSBRUGH TWNSHIP PUB SCHOOLS
379 S Branch Rd, Hillsborough, NJ 08844-4489
Tel (908) 431-6600 *Founded/Ownrshp* 2007
Sales 22.0MM^E *EMP* 912^E
SIC 8211 Public elementary & secondary schools
Pr: Anthony Periera
Treas: Thomas Bittle
MIS Dir: Joel Handler
Pr Dir: Kia Berman

D-U-N-S 02-171-6816
HILLSBOROUGH TRANSIT AUTHORITY
HILLSBRUGH AREA REGIONAL TRNST
1201 E 7th Ave, Tampa, FL 33605-3502
Tel (813) 623-5835 *Founded/Ownrshp* 1979
Sales 17.3MM *EMP* 739
Accts Cliftonlarsonallen Llp Tampa
SIC 4131 4111 Intercity bus line; Local & suburban transit; Intercity bus line; Local & suburban transit
CEO: Katharine Eagan
CFO: Jeffrey Seward
Dir Risk M: Rickey Kendall
Genl Mgr: Steve Roberts
Off Mgr: Lena Petit
Sfty Dirs: David Kelsey
Mktg Mgr: Steve Rosenstock
Snr Mgr: Ruthie Burckard
Snr Mgr: Al Burns

HILLSBRUGH AREA REGIONAL TRNST
See HILLSBOROUGH TRANSIT AUTHORITY

HILLSBRUGH TWNSHIP PUB SCHOOLS
See HILLSBOROUGH TOWNSHIP SCHOOL DISTRICT

D-U-N-S 04-878-1561
HILLSDALE COLLEGE
HILLSDALE COLLEGE BOOK STORE
33 E College St, Hillsdale, MI 49242-1298
Tel (517) 437-7341 *Founded/Ownrshp* 2000
Sales 198.9MM *EMP* 504
Accts Plante & Moran Pllc Portage
SIC 8221 8211 College, except junior; Academy; Private elementary school; Private senior high school; College, except junior; Academy; Private elementary school; Private senior high school
Pr: Larry P Arnn
COO: Stacy Vondra
VP: Jack Oxenrider
Exec: Stephanie Maxwell
Off Admin: Emma Curtis
Doctor: Rein Zeller

HILLSDALE COLLEGE BOOK STORE
See HILLSDALE COLLEGE

D-U-N-S 04-524-5479
HILLSDALE COMMUNITY HEALTH CENTER
168 S Howell St, Hillsdale, MI 49242-2040
Tel (517) 437-4451 *Founded/Ownrshp* 1939
Sales 60.9MM *EMP* 420
Accts Plante & Moran Pllc Grand Ra
SIC 8062 8051 General medical & surgical hospitals; Skilled nursing care facilities; General medical & surgical hospitals; Skilled nursing care facilities
Ex Dir: Duke Anderson
**CFO:* Valerie Fetters
Dir OR: Bill Minion
Dir Lab: Marylee Playford
Dir Rx: Craig Merrill
Off Mgr: Lori Vogt
CIO: Jim Christy
Dir IT: Sheila Puffenberger
Mktg Dir: Judy Gabriele
Nrsg Dir: Julie Walters
Pharmcst: Tom Altenberger

D-U-N-S 01-976-3580
HILLSDALE COUNTY NATIONAL BANK
1 S Howell St, Hillsdale, MI 49242-1811
Tel (517) 437-3371 *Founded/Ownrshp* 1920
Sales NA *EMP* 149
SIC 6021 National commercial banks; National commercial banks
Pr: Craig Connor
Ofcr: Michelle Graber

D-U-N-S 87-724-9888 IMP/EXP
HILLSDALE FURNITURE LLC
3901 Bishop Ln, Louisville, KY 40218-2907
Tel (502) 562-0000 *Founded/Ownrshp* 2013
Sales 50.6MM^E^ *EMP* 128^E^
SIC 5021 Furniture; Furniture
CEO: Uri Glattstein
**COO:* David Brill
**CFO:* Jim Theilmann
**Ex VP:* Danny Glick
Exec: Michelle Eiden
VP Mktg: Jim Hembree
VP Sls: Bill Howard
VP Sls: Keith Meriwether

D-U-N-S 08-244-3813
HILLSDALE GROUP L P
1199 Howard Ave Ste 200, Burlingame, CA 94010-4273
Tel (650) 348-6783 *Founded/Ownrshp* 1981
Sales 13.5MM^E^ *EMP* 773
SIC 8059 Nursing home, except skilled & intermediate care facility; Convalescent home; Nursing home, except skilled & intermediate care facility; Convalescent home
Pr: Richard Stein
**CEO:* Andrew V Bradley
**CFO:* Gary Homan
VP: Jacob Friedman

D-U-N-S 00-521-3962 IMP/EXP
■ **HILLSHIRE BRANDS CO**
SARA LEE FOOD & BEVERAGE
(*Suby of* TYSON FOODS INC) ★
400 S Jefferson St Fl 1, Chicago, IL 60607-3812
Tel (312) 614-6000 *Founded/Ownrshp* 1942, 2014
Sales 2.7MMM^E^ *EMP* 9,100^E^
SIC 2013 2051 2053 Sausages & other prepared meats; Sausages from purchased meat; Frankfurters from purchased meat; Prepared pork products from purchased pork; Breads, rolls & buns; Frozen bakery products, except bread; Pastries (danish): frozen; Pies, bakery: frozen; Cakes, bakery: frozen; Sausages & other prepared meats; Breads, rolls & buns; Frozen bakery products, except bread
Pr: Sean M Connolly
**CFO:* Maria Henry
CFO: Dennis Leatherby
Sr Cor Off: Thao Dekool
Ofcr: Jon Harris
Ofcr: Tony Reece
Ofcr: Philip Usherwood
**Ex VP:* Andrew P Callahan
**Ex VP:* Kent B Magill
Ex VP: Judith Sprieser
Ex VP: David L Van Bebber
Sr VP: Brian Davison
Sr VP: James G Ruehlmann
VP: Sara Bakery
VP: Rick Elmore
VP: Ernie Hanington
Comm Dir: Walter Gilgert

D-U-N-S 08-298-4295
HILLSIDE BOARD OF EDUCATION INC (NJ)
195 Virginia St, Hillside, NJ 07205-2742
Tel (908) 352-7664 *Founded/Ownrshp* 1912
Sales 21.3MM^E^ *EMP* 589
SIC 8211 9111 Public elementary school; Public senior high school; School board; Mayors' offices; Public elementary school; Public senior high school; School board; Mayors' offices

D-U-N-S 05-743-0605 EXP
HILLSIDE CYCLE INC
HILLSIDE HONDA
13907 Hillside Ave, Jamaica, NY 11435-3228
Tel (718) 657-7810 *Founded/Ownrshp* 1972
Sales 34.1MM^E^ *EMP* 94
SIC 5511 5521 Automobiles, new & used; Used car dealers; Automobiles, new & used; Used car dealers
Pr: Steve Finochio
**Sec:* Rod Robitaille
Genl Mgr: Peter Petito
Sls Mgr: John Marino
Sls Mgr: Harry Potamianos
Sales Asso: Peter Mills

HILLSIDE ENTERPRISES
See ASSOCIATION FOR RETARDED CITIZENS-LONG BEACH INC

D-U-N-S 07-970-0878
HILLSIDE FAMILY OF AGENCIES
1183 Monroe Ave, Rochester, NY 14620-1662
Tel (585) 256-7500 *Founded/Ownrshp* 1837
Sales 113.0MM *EMP* 2,300
Accts Dopkins & Company Llp Buffal
SIC 8361 8093 8322 Children's home; Specialty outpatient clinics; Individual & family services; Children's home; Specialty outpatient clinics; Individual & family services
Pr: Dennis Richardson
COO: Clyde Comstock
CFO: Diana Nole
**CFO:* Paul Perrotto
Treas: Eileen Semmler
Chf Mktg O: John Barr
Ofcr: Kimberly Benson
Ex Dir: Cecilia Golden
Ex Dir: Wayne O'Connor
Prgrm Mgr: Jean Burdick
Prgrm Mgr: Alice McAdam

D-U-N-S 10-515-3584
HILLSIDE FAMILY OF AGENCIES
4887 State Route 96a, Romulus, NY 14541-9767
Tel (315) 585-3000 *Founded/Ownrshp* 2004
Sales 4.8MM^E^ *EMP* 315
SIC 8361 Residential care; Residential care

D-U-N-S 62-053-0147
HILLSIDE FAMILY OF AGENCIES
(*Suby of* HILLSIDE FAMILY OF AGENCIES) ★
1183 Monroe Ave, Rochester, NY 14620-1662
Tel (585) 256-7500 *Founded/Ownrshp* 1995
Sales 100.1MM *EMP* 1^E^
SIC 8322 Family service agency; Family service agency
Pr: Dennis Richardson

HILLSIDE HONDA
See HILLSIDE CYCLE INC

HILLSIDE HOSPITAL
See SAN MIGUEL HOSPITAL ASSOCIATION

D-U-N-S 88-392-9069
■ **HILLSIDE HOSPITAL LLC**
(*Suby of* HISTORIC LIFEPOINT HOSPITALS INC) ★
1265 E College St, Pulaski, TN 38478-4548
Tel (931) 363-7531 *Founded/Ownrshp* 2002
Sales 26.2MM *EMP* 180
SIC 8062 General medical & surgical hospitals; General medical & surgical hospitals
CEO: Jim Edmondson
Chf Rad: Richard Stults
Pr: Douglas Pearce
CFO: Donald Gabin
Ex VP: Shane Robinson
VP: Stephen Savage
Dir Lab: Regina Fitzgerald
Dir Lab: Nancy Rousseau
Psych: Gail Edmundson
HC Dir: Kerry White

HILLSIDE MANOR
See BEAVER DAM COMMUNITY HOSPITALS INC

D-U-N-S 07-853-1084
HILLSIDE MANOR REHABILITATION & EXTENDED CARE CENTER
18215 Hillside Ave, Jamaica, NY 11432-4853
Tel (718) 291-8200 *Founded/Ownrshp* 1975
Sales 21.0MM^E^ *EMP* 480
SIC 8051 Skilled nursing care facilities; Skilled nursing care facilities
Ex Dir: Stan Dicker
Nrsg Dir: Margaret Murphy
HC Dir: Rose Dennen
HC Dir: Carmen Hollingworth

D-U-N-S 15-970-9674
HILLSIDE PLASTICS CORP
125 Long Ave, Hillside, NJ 07205-2350
Tel (973) 923-2700 *Founded/Ownrshp* 1994
Sales 25.3MM^E^ *EMP* 60
SIC 3081 Plastic film & sheet
Pr: Harold Kaufman
Off Mgr: Ira Sussman

D-U-N-S 06-699-7511
HILLSIDE PLASTICS INC
SUGARHILL CONTAINERS
(*Suby of* CARR MANAGEMENT INC) ★
262 Millers Falls Rd, Turners Falls, MA 01376-1613
Tel (413) 863-2222 *Founded/Ownrshp* 2015
Sales 27.2MM^E^ *EMP* 120
SIC 3085 Plastics bottles; Plastics bottles
Pr: Peter M Haas
Treas: Kathryn L Colby

D-U-N-S 07-979-9146
HILLSIDE PUBLIC SCHOOLS
195 Virginia St, Hillside, NJ 07205-2742
Tel (908) 352-7664 *Founded/Ownrshp* 2015
Sales 5.2MM^E^ *EMP* 347^E^
SIC 8211 Public elementary & secondary schools
Teacher Pr: Patricia Zuber

HILLSIDE REHABILITATION HOSP
See FORUM HEALTH REHABILITATIVE SERVICES CO

D-U-N-S 07-412-5733
HILLSIDES (CA)
940 Avenue 64, Pasadena, CA 91105-2711
Tel (323) 254-2274 *Founded/Ownrshp* 1913
Sales 32.7MM *EMP* 460
Accts Harrington Group Cpas Llp P
SIC 8361 Home for the emotionally disturbed; Home for the emotionally disturbed
CEO: Joseph M Costa
COO: Carmela Bozulich
**CFO:* Ryan Herren
Bd of Dir: Margaret Campbell
Assoc Dir: Susanne Crummey
Comm Dir: Marisol Barrios
Ex Dir: John Hitchock
Prgrm Mgr: Ritch Greene
Prgrm Mgr: Cheryl Valladares
Info Man: Teressa Jackson
Psych: Amy Cousineau

D-U-N-S 10-542-3599
HILLSIDES CHILDRENS CENTER
HILLSIDE'S COMMUNITY SERVICE P
24 Liberty St, Bath, NY 14810-1507
Tel (607) 776-7480 *Founded/Ownrshp* 2002
Sales 100.0MM *EMP* 2
SIC 8322 Social service center
Prin: Dennis M Richardson

HILLSIDE'S COMMUNITY SERVICE P
See HILLSIDES CHILDRENS CENTER

D-U-N-S 08-351-3960
HILLSTONE RESTAURANT GROUP INC
BANDERA
147 S Beverly Dr, Beverly Hills, CA 90212-3002
Tel (310) 385-7343 *Founded/Ownrshp* 1977
Sales 150.0MM^E^ *EMP* 4,500
SIC 5812 5813 Restaurant, family: chain; Cocktail lounge; Restaurant, family: chain; Cocktail lounge
Pr: George W Biel
**COO:* James V Branstetter
**CFO:* Scott Ashby
Genl Mgr: Tim Landrey

D-U-N-S 00-424-5353
HILLTOP BASIC RESOURCES INC
HILLTOP CONCRETE
1 W 4th St Ste 1100, Cincinnati, OH 45202-3610
Tel (513) 684-8247 *Founded/Ownrshp* 1930
Sales 111.5MM^E^ *EMP* 190
SIC 1442 3273 Construction sand mining; Gravel mining; Ready-mixed concrete; Construction sand mining; Gravel mining; Ready-mixed concrete
CEO: John F Steele Jr
**Pr:* Kevin M Sheehan
**CFO:* Paul Hennekes
**VP:* Brad Slabaugh
Genl Mgr: Mike Marchioni
MIS Dir: Sabriana Ferree
Opers Mgr: Roger Thayer
S&M/Asst: Philis Wait

HILLTOP CHRYSLER PLYMOUTH
See MICHAEL STEADS AUTO DEPOT INC

HILLTOP COMMUNITY RESOURCES
See HILLTOP HEALTH SERVICES CORP

HILLTOP CONCRETE
See HILLTOP BASIC RESOURCES INC

D-U-N-S 15-197-0860
HILLTOP ENERGY INC
(*Suby of* D W DICKEY AND SON INC) ★
7896 Dickey Dr, Lisbon, OH 44432-9391
Tel (330) 424-1441 *Founded/Ownrshp* 1985
Sales 26.6MM^E^ *EMP* 70
Accts Packer Thomas Youngstown Ohi
SIC 5169 Explosives; Explosives
Pr: Tom Young
Treas: Dave Dickey
VP: Tim Dickey

HILLTOP GROUP HOME
See KREIDER SERVICES INC

D-U-N-S 13-950-4641
HILLTOP HEALTH SERVICES CORP
HILLTOP COMMUNITY RESOURCES
1331 Hermosa Ave, Grand Junction, CO 81506-4099
Tel (970) 242-4400 *Founded/Ownrshp* 1984
Sales 32.2MM *EMP* 650^E^
Accts Chadwickstkirchnerdavis & Co P
SIC 8361 Residential care; Residential care
CEO: James Michael Stahl
Ofcr: Mary Schaefer
**Prin:* Mike Stahl
Ex Dir: Cathy Story

D-U-N-S 04-837-0071
▲ **HILLTOP HOLDINGS INC**
200 Crescent Ct Ste 1330, Dallas, TX 75201-6920
Tel (214) 855-2177 *Founded/Ownrshp* 2007
Sales NA *EMP* 5,300
Tkr Sym HTH *Exch* NYS
SIC 6712 Bank holding companies; Bank holding companies
Pr: Jeremy B Ford
**Ch Bd:* Gerald J Ford
Ofcr: Darren E Parmenter
Ex VP: Corey G Prestidge
Sr VP: Keith Bornemann

HILLTOP LANDSCAPE ARCHITECTS
See HILLTOP TREE SERVICE

HILLTOP LDSCP ARCHTECTS CONTRS
See JAMAR INDUSTRIES INC

D-U-N-S 03-635-9529
HILLTOP NATIONAL BANK
(*Suby of* MIDLAND FINANCIAL CORPORATION)
300 Country Club Rd # 100, Casper, WY 82609-2113
Tel (307) 265-2740 *Founded/Ownrshp* 1964
Sales NA *EMP* 155
SIC 6021 6163 National trust companies with deposits, commercial; Loan brokers; National trust companies with deposits, commercial; Loan brokers
Pr: Robert Sutter
**Ch Bd:* Van Maren Jr
CFO: Wil Durham
Treas: Neville Tuft
Ofcr: Mike Terriere
**Sr VP:* John Jorgensen
**Sr VP:* Barton Neville
VP: Sharon Darr
VP: Leslie Demple
VP: Carol Wilson
VP: Lesli Wright

D-U-N-S 12-080-7011 EXP
HILLTOP RANCH INC
13890 Looney Rd, Ballico, CA 95303-9710
Tel (209) 874-1875 *Founded/Ownrshp* 1980
Sales 53.5MM^E^ *EMP* 175
SIC 0723 Almond hulling & shelling services; Almond hulling & shelling services
CEO: David Harrison Long
**CFO:* Brad Filbrun
**VP:* Christine Long
**VP:* Dave Long Jr
**VP:* Dexter Long
Exec: Julie Dorrepaal
IT Man: Genevieve Bardini-Davis

D-U-N-S 07-967-9560
■ **HILLTOP SECURITIES HOLDINGS LLC**
PERUNA LLC
(*Suby of* HILLTOP HOLDINGS INC) ★
200 Crescent Ct Ste 1330, Dallas, TX 75201-6920
Tel (214) 855-2177 *Founded/Ownrshp* 2014
Sales 165.6MM^E^ *EMP* 892^E^
SIC 6211 Brokers, security
Pr: Jeremy B Ford
CFO: Darren E Parmenter

HILLTOP STEAKHOUSE MARKETPLACE
See HIGH COUNTRY INVESTOR INC

D-U-N-S 04-849-0945
HILLTOP TREE SERVICE
HILLTOP LANDSCAPE ARCHITECTS
7909 Edith Blvd Ne, Albuquerque, NM 87113-1407
Tel (505) 898-9690 *Founded/Ownrshp* 2001
Sales 9.4MM^E^ *EMP* 400
SIC 0783 0782 Ornamental shrub & tree services; Lawn & garden services; Ornamental shrub & tree services; Lawn & garden services
Owner: James De Flon

D-U-N-S 80-163-9647
HILLTOPPER HOLDING CORP
303 Perimeter Ctr N # 500, Atlanta, GA 30346-3401
Tel (770) 698-9040 *Founded/Ownrshp* 2000
Sales 213.2MM^E^ *EMP* 10,000
SIC 8051 8741 Skilled nursing care facilities; Management services; Skilled nursing care facilities; Management services
CEO: Kent Fosha

D-U-N-S 18-504-4351 EXP
HILLTOWN PACKING CO INC
9 Harris Pl A, Salinas, CA 93901-4586
Tel (831) 784-1931 *Founded/Ownrshp* 1987
Sales 30.6MM^E^ *EMP* 300
SIC 0723 Vegetable packing services; Vegetable packing services
Pr: Chris Huntington
**Treas:* Louis Huntington Jr

D-U-N-S 01-415-8257
HILLVIEW MOTORS INC
5309 State Route 30, Greensburg, PA 15601-3573
Tel (724) 834-8440 *Founded/Ownrshp* 1961
Sales 23.0MM^E^ *EMP* 47
SIC 5511 Automobiles, new & used
Pr: Paul Schimizzi
**Treas:* Frank Schimizzi
**VP:* Robert Schimizzi

D-U-N-S 19-681-8488
HILLWOOD DEVELOPMENT CORP
3090 Olive St Ste 300, Dallas, TX 75219-7640
Tel (214) 303-5535 *Founded/Ownrshp* 1985
Sales 124.3MM^E^ *EMP* 150
SIC 6552 6531 Subdividers & developers; Real estate agent, commercial
Pr: David A Newsom
**Ch Bd:* H Ross Perot Jr
**CFO:* James C Swaim
**Treas:* M Thomas Mason
**Treas:* Tom Mason
Ex VP: Robert Vicente
VP: Chris Brown
VP: Timothy Kinnear
VP: Dan Kotch
**VP:* Todd L Platt
VP: Perry Wallace

D-U-N-S 02-187-5547
HILLWOOD MUSEUM & GARDENS FOUNDATION (DC)
M M POST FOUNDATION
4155 Linnean Ave Nw, Washington, DC 20008-3806
Tel (202) 686-5807 *Founded/Ownrshp* 1955
Sales 45.1MM *EMP* 100
SIC 8699 8412 8422 Charitable organization; Museum; Arboreta & botanical or zoological gardens
Ex Dir: Frederick Fisher
**COO:* Angie Dodson
Dir Soc: Adrienne Starr
**Ex Dir:* Kate Markert
Dir IT: Ed Vreeland
Sls Mgr: Amy Knox

D-U-N-S 02-997-9804
HILLYARD ENTERPRISES INC
302 N 4th St, Saint Joseph, MO 64501-1720
Tel (816) 233-1321 *Founded/Ownrshp* 1907
Sales 74.0MM^E^ *EMP* 165^E^
SIC 2842 Cleaning or polishing preparations; Floor waxes; Cleaning or polishing preparations; Floor waxes
Pr: James Carolus

*VP: M Scott Hillyard
*VP: James Roth
*VP: Robert W Roth

D-U-N-S 00-696-6865
HILLYARD INC
302 N 4th St, Saint Joseph, MO 64501-1720
Tel (816) 233-1321 Founded/Ownrshp 1907
Sales 387.2MM^E EMP 800
SIC 5169 5087 Industrial chemicals; Cleaning & maintenance equipment & supplies; Industrial chemicals; Cleaning & maintenance equipment & supplies
Pr: Robert Roth
CFO: Lance Woodall
Top Exec: Joe Kauth
*Ex VP: Scott Hillyard
Ex VP: Jim Roth
VP: Marc George
VP: Doug Holland
VP: Jon Martin
VP: Steven Stumpf
Exec: Matthew Gerstner
Brnch Mgr: Darin Miller

D-U-N-S 00-713-6096 IMP
HILLYARD INDUSTRIES INC
(Suby of HILLYARD ENTERPRISES INC) ★
302 N 4th St, Saint Joseph, MO 64501-1720
Tel (816) 233-1321 Founded/Ownrshp 1964
Sales 72.0MM^E EMP 150
SIC 2842 5087 Specialty cleaning preparations; Floor waxes; Cleaning or polishing preparations; Cleaning & maintenance equipment & supplies; Specialty cleaning preparations; Floor waxes; Cleaning or polishing preparations; Cleaning & maintenance equipment & supplies
Ch Bd: Jim Carolus
*Treas: Neal Ambrose
*VP: Mark W Hampton
*VP: M Scott Hillyard
*VP: James Roth
*VP: Robert W Roth
*VP: John Smith
Dir Lab: Mark Algaier

D-U-N-S 13-160-2112 IMP/EXP
HILMAR CHEESE CO INC
HILMAR INGREDIENTS
8901 Lander Ave, Hilmar, CA 95324-9327
Tel (209) 667-6076 Founded/Ownrshp 1984
Sales 190.0MM^E EMP 600^E
SIC 2022 Natural cheese; Natural cheese
Pr: John J Jeter
COO: Ted Dykzeul
CFO: Donald Jay Hicks
VP: Kyle Jensen
VP: Deborah Johnson
VP: Bethanie Lucas
VP: Tedd Struckmeyer
QA Dir: Taylor Genzoli
QA Dir: Hiram Roman
Tech Mgr: Jacob Heick
VP Opers: Rick Kaepernick

HILMAR INGREDIENTS
See HILMAR CHEESE CO INC

D-U-N-S 05-421-3413
HILMAR WHEY PROTEIN INC
9001 Lander Ave, Hilmar, CA 95320-8320
Tel (209) 667-6076 Founded/Ownrshp 1991
Sales 36.4MM^E EMP 400^E
SIC 2023 Concentrated whey; Concentrated whey
Pr: John J Jeter
Brnch Mgr: Dave Hudson

D-U-N-S 36-291-8034
HILMOT LLC
11925 W Carmen Ave, Milwaukee, WI 53225-2113
Tel (262) 544-9960 Founded/Ownrshp 2005
Sales 21.0MM EMP 105^E
SIC 3535 Belt conveyor systems, general industrial use
VP: Jeff Berken

HILO HATTIE
See POMARE LTD

D-U-N-S 09-145-7689
HILO MAINTENANCE SYSTEMS INC
HILO MATERIAL HANDLING GROUP
345 Oser Ave, Hauppauge, NY 11788-3607
Tel (631) 253-2600 Founded/Ownrshp 1977
Sales 57.9MM^E EMP 80
SIC 5084 7699 7359 Engines & transportation equipment; Industrial equipment services; Equipment rental & leasing; Engines & transportation equipment; Industrial equipment services; Equipment rental & leasing
CEO: Les Gobler
*Pr: Steven Lopiccolo
*CFO: Gail Gobler
*Sec: Laura Lopiccolo
Area Mgr: Michael Gisonna
Div Mgr: Rich Whitehill

HILO MATERIAL HANDLING GROUP
See HILO MAINTENANCE SYSTEMS INC

D-U-N-S 05-964-0362
HILO MEDICAL CENTER
1190 Waianuenue Ave, Hilo, HI 96720-2094
Tel (808) 932-3000 Founded/Ownrshp 2008
Sales 179.3MM^E EMP 1,310
SIC 8011 Medical centers; Medical centers
CEO: Dan Brinkman
Chf Rad: Ming Peng
*CFO: Money Atwal
Ansthlgy: Julie Soong

D-U-N-S 09-180-5077
HILO MEDICAL INVESTORS LTD
LIFE CARE CENTER OF HILO
(Suby of LIFE CARE CENTERS OF AMERICA INC) ★
944 W Kawailani St, Hilo, HI 96720-3218
Tel (808) 959-9151 Founded/Ownrshp 1977
Sales 27.2MM EMP 225
SIC 8059 Nursing home, except skilled & intermediate care facility; Nursing home, except skilled & intermediate care facility
Genl Pt: Fred Horwitz
Pt: Sam Kellett
Pt: Stiles Kellett
Off Mgr: Kandis Chadwick
Nrsg Dir: Allyson A Nelson
HC Dir: Margie Kanahele
HC Dir: Christine Kanemitsu

D-U-N-S 00-446-4392
HILSCHER-CLARKE ELECTRIC CO
519 4th St Nw, Canton, OH 44703-2699
Tel (330) 452-9806 Founded/Ownrshp 1946
Sales 48.7MM^E EMP 200
SIC 1731 General electrical contractor; General electrical contractor
Genl Mgr: John T Adkins
*Pr: Scott A Goodspeed
*CEO: Ronald D Becker
*CFO: Barb Zwick
VP: John Fether
VP: Ted Foster
*VP: Ronald Radcliff
Div Mgr: Mike Davis
Off Admin: Kristi Jordan
IT Man: John Weston
Sfty Dirs: Troy Manion

D-U-N-S 00-117-3525 IMP/EXP
HILTI INC
(Suby of HILTI OF AMERICA INC) ★
7250 Dallas Pkwy Ste 1000, Plano, TX 75024-4998
Tel (800) 879-8000 Founded/Ownrshp 1981
Sales 356.4MM^E EMP 800
SIC 5072 Hand tools; Hand tools
Pr: Cary Evert
*CFO: Eugene Hodel
Sr VP: Teresita Jimenez
*VP: Kelly Beaver
Comm Man: Dena Wind
Rgnl Mgr: Kent Cook
Rgnl Mgr: Earl Ducharme
Rgnl Mgr: Jason Flam
Rgnl Mgr: Matthew Merrill
Rgnl Mgr: Todd Palmquist
Dist Mgr: Tom Egan

D-U-N-S 03-278-1460
HILTI NORTH AMERICA LTD
(Suby of HILTI OF AMERICA INC) ★
5400 S 122nd East Ave, Tulsa, OK 74146-6099
Tel (918) 252-6000 Founded/Ownrshp 1980
Sales 51.9MM^E EMP 318
SIC 3546 5072 2821 7699 Power-driven handtools; Hand tools; Plastics materials & resins; Industrial equipment services; Power-driven handtools; Hand tools; Plastics materials & resins; Industrial equipment services
Pr: Cary Evert
*VP: John W Shearing
Prin: Lillian Martindale
Netwrk Mgr: Clint Holler
Manager: John Moodie

D-U-N-S 13-105-8364 IMP/EXP
HILTI OF AMERICA INC
(Suby of HILTI AKTIENGESELLSCHAFT)
7250 Dallas Pkwy Ste 1000, Plano, TX 75024-4998
Tel (800) 879-8000 Founded/Ownrshp 1981
Sales 443.3MM^E EMP 800^E
SIC 5084 3546 3825 Drilling equipment, excluding bits; Drills & drilling tools; Standards & calibration equipment for electrical measuring; Drilling equipment, excluding bits; Drills & drilling tools; Standards & calibration equipment for electrical measuring
Pr: Cary Evert

HILTON
See NICOTRA HOTEL I LLC

HILTON
See RED LION HOTEL AT PARK

HILTON
See DEZURIK INC

HILTON
See DAVIDSON HOTEL CO

HILTON
See HARRISBURG HOTEL ASSOCIATES LP

HILTON
See BAY ROSIE HOTEL LLP

HILTON
See TANNEX DEVELOPMENT CORP

HILTON ALEXANDRIA MARK CENTER
See SEMINARY ROAD HOTEL ASSOCIATES LLC

HILTON AMERICAS-HOUSTON
See HOUSTON FIRST CORP

HILTON ANCHORAGE
See CP ANCHORAGE HOTEL 2 LLC

HILTON ATLANTA
See ACC HOSPITALITY LESSEE INC

HILTON BALTIMORE BWI AIRPORT
See BPG HOTEL PARTNERS XI LLC

D-U-N-S 09-166-3229
HILTON CENTRAL SCHOOL DISTRICT
225 West Ave, Hilton, NY 14468-1253
Tel (585) 392-1000 Founded/Ownrshp 1949
Sales 76.0MM EMP 900
Accts Raymond F Wager Cpa Pc H
SIC 8211 Public elementary school; Public junior high school; Public senior high school; Public elementary school; Public junior high school; Public senior high school
VP: Matt D'Augustine

D-U-N-S 96-007-8314
HILTON CHICAGO INDIAN LAKES RESORT
(Suby of FIRST HOSPITALITY GROUP INC) ★
250 W Schick Rd Ofc 1, Bloomingdale, IL 60108-1290
Tel (630) 529-0200 Founded/Ownrshp 1987
Sales 27.8MM^E EMP 460
SIC 7011 Hotels & motels; Hotels & motels
Genl Mgr: Michael Hooper
*Pr: Steve Schwartz
Exec: Walt Hajduk
*Prin: Kristina Cooper
Mng Dir: John Callan
Mng Dir: Dan Smith
Web Prj Mg: Chris Washington
Sales Exec: Bob Oconnor

HILTON DAYTONA BCH
See GEPA HOTEL OPERATOR DAYTONA BEACH LLC

D-U-N-S 06-931-9333 IMP
HILTON DISPLAYS INC
125 Hillside Dr, Greenville, SC 29607-1856
Tel (864) 233-0401 Founded/Ownrshp 1981
Sales 26.2MM^E EMP 150
SIC 7389 3993 Sign painting & lettering shop; Electric signs
Pr: Stephen H Hilton
Plnt Mgr: Charlie Blakely
Natl Sales: Barry Robarge

D-U-N-S 18-995-1247
■ **HILTON GRAND VACATIONS CO LLC**
(Suby of HILTON WORLDWIDE INC) ★
5323 Millenia Lakes Blvd # 400, Orlando, FL 32839-3395
Tel (407) 722-3100 Founded/Ownrshp 2001
Sales 199.6MM^E EMP 611
SIC 6552 Subdividers & developers; Subdividers & developers
Treas: Stuart Zais
Ex VP: Sarah Kramer
Ex VP: Michael Shader
*Sr VP: Johann Murray
*Sr VP: Mark Wang
VP: David Desforges
VP: David Epstein
VP: Dave Hager
VP: Barbara Hollkamp
VP: Anthony Picciano
VP: Gus Riera
VP: Marie Sarno
*VP: Rebecca Sloan
VP: Casa Ybel

D-U-N-S 07-922-6805
■ **HILTON HAWAII CORP**
HILTON WORLDWIDE HOLDINGS
(Suby of HILTON WORLDWIDE HOLDINGS INC) ★
7930 Jones Branch Dr, Mc Lean, VA 22102-3388
Tel (703) 883-1000 Founded/Ownrshp 2013
Sales 9.4MM^E EMP 5,010^E
SIC 7011 Hotels & motels
Prin: Hilda Hilton
Sls&Mrk Ex: Julie Brandon

D-U-N-S 00-787-3268
■ **HILTON HAWAIIAN VILLAGE LLC** (HI)
(Suby of HILTON WORLDWIDE INC) ★
2005 Kalia Rd, Honolulu, HI 96815-1917
Tel (808) 949-4321 Founded/Ownrshp 1961, 1998
Sales 92.2MM^E EMP 1,725
SIC 7011 5812 5813

D-U-N-S 04-942-0862 EXP
HILTON HEAD AUTOMOTIVE LLC
1090 Fording Island Rd, Bluffton, SC 29910-6560
Tel (843) 815-1500 Founded/Ownrshp 2000
Sales 27.5MM^E EMP 70
SIC 5511 Automobiles, new & used; Automobiles, new & used
Top Exec: Jill Brenner
Top Exec: Keith Phares
*Exec: Martha Hartley
Genl Mgr: Tom Ditzig
Mktg Dir: Frank Bernardini
Sls Mgr: Rudy Rudisill
Sales Asso: Dan McGinnis
Sales Asso: Denny Weaver
Sales Asso: Jeff Weber

D-U-N-S 06-932-4689
■ **HILTON HEAD HEALTH SYSTEM LP**
HILTON HEAD HOSPITAL & CLINICS
(Suby of TENET HEALTHCARE CORPORATION)
25 Hospital Cntr Blvrd, Hilton Head Island, SC 29926
Tel (843) 681-6122 Founded/Ownrshp 1994
Sales 58.4MM^E EMP 425
SIC 8062 General medical & surgical hospitals; General medical & surgical hospitals
Genl Pt: Tenet Health System
COO: Brad Moore
COO: Tom Neal
Trfc Mgr: Fred Larsen

HILTON HEAD HOSPITAL & CLINICS
See HILTON HEAD HEALTH SYSTEM LP

D-U-N-S 86-140-6163
HILTON HEAD HOSPITAL REHAB
35 Bill Fries Dr Bldg D, Hilton Head Island, SC 29926-2731
Tel (843) 681-4088 Founded/Ownrshp 1994
Sales 94.3MM EMP 2
SIC 8049 Occupational therapist; Occupational therapist
Owner: R S Jones

HILTON HEAD ISLAND HONDA
See MODERN CLASSIC MOTORS INC

HILTON HEAD LEXUS
See CHATHAM MOTOR SALES INC

D-U-N-S 12-614-0776
■ **HILTON HONORS WORLDWIDE LLC**
(Suby of HILTON WORLDWIDE INC) ★
755 Crossover Ln, Memphis, TN 38117-4906
Tel (901) 374-5000 Founded/Ownrshp 1997
Sales 30.9MM^E EMP 500
SIC 7389 Personal service agents, brokers & bureaus; Personal service agents, brokers & bureaus
Sr VP: Russ Olivier
Admn Mgr: Robert York
Software D: Kevin Starling
Opers Mgr: Debbie Goodnight

D-U-N-S 07-910-5355
HILTON HOTELS CORP
9336 Civic Center Dr, Beverly Hills, CA 90210-3604
Tel (703) 883-1000 Founded/Ownrshp 2011, 2007
Sales 57.6MM^E EMP 252^E
SIC 7011 Hotels & motels
CEO: Christopher J Nassetta
COO: John Durr
Dir Bus: Guilherme Castro
Genl Mgr: Shahid Ali
Genl Mgr: James Lalanne
Genl Mgr: Tami Long
Sls Dir: Christina Anderson
Sls Mgr: Wan Yi
Sales Asso: Adriana Campos
Counsel: Glenna Shen

D-U-N-S 80-816-2098
HILTON HOTELS HOLDINGS CORP
345 Park Ave, New York, NY 10154-0004
Tel (212) 583-5000 Founded/Ownrshp 2007
Sales NA EMP 7,140
SIC 7011 6794

D-U-N-S 96-557-7872
■ **HILTON HOTELS HOLDINGS LLC**
(Suby of HILTON WORLDWIDE HOLDINGS INC) ★
7930 Jones Branch Dr, Mc Lean, VA 22102-3388
Tel (703) 883-1000 Founded/Ownrshp 2010
Sales 185.8MM^E EMP 7,150^E
SIC 7011 Hotels & motels; Hotels & motels

HILTON HOUSTON POST OAK
See POST OAK TX LLC

D-U-N-S 07-922-5234
■ **HILTON ILLINOIS HOLDINGS LLC**
(Suby of HILTON WORLDWIDE HOLDINGS INC) ★
7930 Jones Branch Dr, Mc Lean, VA 22102-3388
Tel (703) 883-1000 Founded/Ownrshp 2013
Sales 5.9MM^E EMP 5,005^E
SIC 7011 Hotels & motels

D-U-N-S 01-059-5163
HILTON INC
4116 N Highway 231, Panama City, FL 32404-9235
Tel (850) 769-9414 Founded/Ownrshp 1975
Sales 27.1MM^E EMP 378
SIC 7011 Hotels & motels; Hotel, franchised; Hotels & motels; Hotel, franchised
Pr: Lela G Hilton
Pr: Jesper Engman
*Sec: Julie K Hilton
*Sec: Nick Humble
*VP: Cody Khan

D-U-N-S 07-530-2570
■ **HILTON INNS INC**
(Suby of HILTON WORLDWIDE INC) ★
9336 Civic Center Dr, Beverly Hills, CA 90210-3604
Tel (310) 278-4321 Founded/Ownrshp 1965
Sales 232.5MM^E EMP 3,479^E
SIC 7011 Hotels & motels; Hotels & motels
Ch Bd: Stephen F Bollenbach
*Pr: Dieter H Huckestein
*CFO: Matthew J Hart
Ofcr: Spacey Shearouse
Ex VP: Lisa Blake
*Ex VP: Thomas L Keltner
Sr VP: Patrick B Terwilliger
VP: Craig Armstrong
VP: Damien Dean
VP: David Thompson
Exec: Jason Pena
Dir Bus: Hilton Doha
Dir Bus: David Wells

D-U-N-S 01-206-2642
HILTON INTERNATIONAL CO (INC) (DEL)
(Suby of HILTON INTERNATIONAL HOTELS (UK) LIMITED)
5201 Blue Lagoon Dr # 600, Miami, FL 33126-2075
Tel (305) 444-3444 Founded/Ownrshp 1987
Sales 381.1MM^E EMP 49,690
SIC 7011 5812 Hotels & motels; Eating places; Hotels & motels; Eating places
Prin: Christopher J Nassetta
*Pr: Joe Berger
*VP: Jeff Diskin
*VP: William G Margaritis
VP: Chris Marshall
*VP: Matthew W Schuyler

D-U-N-S 78-411-2864 IMP
HILTON INTERNATIONAL OF PUERTO RICO INC
CARIBE HILTON HOTEL
(Suby of HILTON INTERNATIONAL CO (INC) (DEL)) ★
Los Rosales St, San Juan, PR 00901
Tel (787) 721-0303 Founded/Ownrshp 1981
Sales 19.5MM^E EMP 608
SIC 7011 Hotels & motels; Hotels & motels
Genl Mgr: Jose Campo
Sls Dir: Madeline Nadal
Sls Mgr: Ingrid Navarro

HILTON JACKSON
See JACKSON AWH-BP HOTEL LLC

D-U-N-S 13-959-1643
HILTON LOS ANGELES UNIVERSAL CITY
555 Unversal Hollywood Dr, Universal City, CA 91608-1001
Tel (818) 506-2500 Founded/Ownrshp 2003
Sales 16.7MM^E EMP 380
SIC 7011 Hotels; Hotels
Genl Mgr: Juan Aquinde

HILTON LOS ANGLS/NVERSAL CY HT
See SUN HILL PROPERTIES INC

HILTON MANHATTAN EAST
See PNY III LLC

D-U-N-S 17-337-5775
■ HILTON MCLEAN LLC
HILTON MCLEAN TYSONS CORNER
(*Suby of* HILTON WORLDWIDE INC) ★
7920 Jones Branch Dr, Mc Lean, VA 22102-3302
Tel (703) 847-5000 *Founded/Ownrshp* 1998
Sales 26.4MM^E *EMP* 270
SIC 7011 5813 5812 Hotels; Drinking places; Eating places; Hotels; Drinking places; Eating places
Genl Mgr: Brian Kelleher
Bd of Dir: Antoinette M Aulay
Bd of Dir: Bari R Levingston
Bd of Dir: Donald Maclean
Board of Directors: Stephanie Snapkoski

HILTON MCLEAN TYSONS CORNER
See HILTON MCLEAN LLC

D-U-N-S 79-869-2539
■ HILTON NEW YORK
HILTON NEW YORK AND TOWERS
(*Suby of* HILTON WORLDWIDE INC) ★
1335 Ave Of The Americas, New York, NY 10019-6012
Tel (212) 586-7000 *Founded/Ownrshp* 2001
Sales 54.5MM^E *EMP* 1,400
SIC 6512 Commercial & industrial building operation; Commercial & industrial building operation
Genl Mgr: Mark Lauer
Bd of Dir: Conrad Wangeman
MIS Dir: Israel Deleon

HILTON NEW YORK AND TOWERS
See HILTON NEW YORK

HILTON ORLANDO
See A-R HHC ORLANDO CONVENTION HOTEL LLC

HILTON PHILADELPHIA CITY AVE
See STOUT ROAD ASSOCIATES INC

HILTON PHOENIX AIRPORT
See MASSACHUSETTS MUTUAL LIFE INSURANCE CO

D-U-N-S 03-167-6307
■ HILTON RESERVATIONS WORLDWIDE LLC
(*Suby of* HILTON WORLDWIDE INC) ★
2050 Chenault Dr, Carrollton, TX 75006-5096
Tel (972) 770-6100 *Founded/Ownrshp* 1997
Sales 97.8MM^E *EMP* 2,000
SIC 7011 Hotels & motels; Hotels & motels
CEO: Christopher J Nassetta
**Pr:* Joe Berger
**Ex VP:* Kathryn Beiser
**Ex VP:* Kristin Campbell
**Ex VP:* Jeff Diskin
Sr VP: Jim Astroff
IT Man: Jessica Hirsch
IT Man: Doug Weidler

HILTON SNTA FE BUFFALO THUNDER
See BUFFALO THUNDER INC

HILTON ST LOUIS AT BALLPARK
See HDH LLC

D-U-N-S 36-076-1951
■ HILTON SUITES INC
(*Suby of* HILTON WORLDWIDE INC) ★
7930 Jones Branch Dr, Mc Lean, VA 22102-3388
Tel (703) 883-1000 *Founded/Ownrshp* 1987
Sales 20.6MM^E *EMP* 450^E
SIC 7011 Hotels & motels; Hotels & motels
CEO: Christopher J Nassetta
**Pr:* Joseph Berger
**Ex VP:* Kathryn Beiser
**Ex VP:* Kristin Campbell
**Ex VP:* Kevin Jacobs
Mktg Dir: Barbara Schmaelzle

D-U-N-S 04-442-8506 IMP
■ HILTON SUPPLY MANAGEMENT INC
(*Suby of* HILTON WORLDWIDE INC) ★
7930 Jones Branch Dr, Mc Lean, VA 22102-3388
Tel (703) 883-1000 *Founded/Ownrshp* 1967
Sales 245.2MM^E *EMP* 330
SIC 5046 5021 Hotel equipment & supplies; Furniture; Hotel equipment & supplies; Furniture
Pr: Chris Nassetta
IT Man: Victoria Graham

HILTON TUCSON
See ECTENANT CORP

HILTON VRGINIA BCH OCEAN FRONT
See THIRTY FIRST STREET LLC

HILTON WOODCLIFF LAKE
See MASSACHUSETTS MUTUAL LIFE INSURANCE CO

HILTON WORLDWIDE
See BH HOTELS HOLDCO LLC

HILTON WORLDWIDE HOLDINGS
See HILTON HAWAII CORP

D-U-N-S 07-913-2993
▲ HILTON WORLDWIDE HOLDINGS INC
7930 Jones Branch Dr # 100, Mc Lean, VA 22102-3389
Tel (703) 883-1000 *Founded/Ownrshp* 2010
Sales 10.5MMM *EMP* 155,000
Accts Ernst & Young Llp Mcleanvirg
Tkr Sym HLT *Exch* NYS
SIC 7011 6794 Hotels & motels; Resort hotel; Franchises, selling or licensing; Hotels & motels; Resort hotel; Franchises, selling or licensing
Pr: Christopher J Nassetta
**Ch Bd:* Jonathan D Gray
CFO: Kevin J Jacobs
Ofcr: Matthew W Schuyler
Ex VP: Kristin A Campbell
Ex VP: Jeffrey A Diskin
Sr VP: Chris Silcock
Genl Mgr: Bryan Cable
Off Mgr: Osvaldo Hernandez
Board of Directors: Michael S Chae, Tyler S Henritze, Judith A McHale, John G Schreiber, Elizabeth A Smith, Douglas M Steenland, William J Stein

D-U-N-S 00-521-9816
■ HILTON WORLDWIDE INC
HAMPTON INN
(*Suby of* HILTON WORLDWIDE INC) ★
755 Crossover Ln, Memphis, TN 38117-4906
Tel (901) 374-5000 *Founded/Ownrshp* 1984, 1999
Sales 46.3MM^E *EMP* 250
SIC 7011 Hotels & motels; Hotels & motels
Pr: Thomas Keltner
Exec: David Brannigan
Genl Mgr: Kristynne Byers
Genl Mgr: Jimmy Chan
Genl Mgr: Ruth Lambo
Genl Mgr: Ali Meghji
Genl Mgr: Shannon Moore
Genl Mgr: Margaret Morley
Genl Mgr: Tammy Piker
Genl Mgr: Jessica Piotrowski
Genl Mgr: Matt Seamons

D-U-N-S 00-693-0531 IMP/EXP
■ HILTON WORLDWIDE INC
(*Suby of* HILTON WORLDWIDE HOLDINGS INC) ★
7930 Jones Branch Dr # 700, Mc Lean, VA 22102-3392
Tel (703) 883-1000 *Founded/Ownrshp* 1946
Sales 1.8MMM^E *EMP* 7,140
SIC 7011 6794 Hotels & motels; Franchises, selling or licensing; Hotels & motels; Franchises, selling or licensing
Pr: Christopher J Nassetta
Pr: Ian Carter
Pr: Martin Rinck
Pr: Mark Wang
CFO: Phillip Gaye
CFO: Thomas C Kennedy
CFO: William Samenos
Ch: Edmond Ip
Treas: Sean Dell'orto
Bd of Dir: Tiffany Floyd
Bd of Dir: Susan Heinis
Bd of Dir: Pierre Middleton-Baez
Bd of Dir: Brenda Morgan-Davis
Ex VP: Kathryn Beiser
Ex VP: Madeleine A Kleiner
Ex VP: Richard Lucas
Ex VP: Matthew W Schuyler
Sr VP: Paul Ades
Sr VP: J David Greydanus
Sr VP: Kevin Jacobs
Sr VP: Kevin J Jacobs

HIMA SAN PABLO HOSPITAL
See GRUPO HIMA-SAN PABLO INC

D-U-N-S 83-194-9545
HIMAGINE SOLUTIONS INC
600 Emerson Rd Ste 225, Saint Louis, MO 63141-6725
Tel (314) 627-5135 *Founded/Ownrshp* 2014
Sales 100.0MM *EMP* 1,000
SIC 8741 7361 Hospital management; Nursing & personal care facility management; Employment agencies
Pr: Peggy Pricher
**CEO:* Michael Dimarto
**COO:* Sam Farrell
**CFO:* Mark D Rowland
Sec: Paul Finney
**VP:* Amy Simpson
Dir IT: Don Sloan
Sls&Mrk Ex: Michelle Martin

D-U-N-S 03-311-4526 IMP
HIMATSINGKA AMERICA INC (NY)
(*Suby of* HIMATSINGKA HOLDINGS NA INC) ★
261 5th Ave Rm 1400, New York, NY 10016-7707
Tel (212) 545-8929 *Founded/Ownrshp* 2000, 2007
Sales 42.1MM^E *EMP* 150
SIC 2392 Bedspreads & bed sets: made from purchased materials; Bedspreads & bed sets: made from purchased materials
Ch: Dilip J Thakkar
**Pr:* Steve Zaffos
**CFO:* Ashutosh Halbe
VP Mfg: Denis Jackson

D-U-N-S 80-674-9276
HIMATSINGKA HOLDINGS NA INC
(*Suby of* HIMATSINGKA SEIDE LIMITED)
261 5th Ave Rm 1400, New York, NY 10016-7707
Tel (212) 545-8929 *Founded/Ownrshp* 2004
Sales 42.1MM^E *EMP* 208
SIC 2221 Silk broadwoven fabrics; Silk broadwoven fabrics
Ch Bd: Amitabh Himatsingka
**Pr:* Shrikant Himatsingka
**Ch:* Rajiv Khaitan
**Prin:* Ajoy Kumar Himatsingka
**Ex Dir:* Aditya Himatsingka

HIMCO
See HARTFORD INVESTMENT MANAGEMENT CO

D-U-N-S 18-329-0469
HIMEC INC
HIMEC MECHANICAL
1400 7th St Nw, Rochester, MN 55901-1703
Tel (507) 288-7713 *Founded/Ownrshp* 1976
Sales 41.6MM^E *EMP* 210
SIC 1711 3444 Plumbing contractors; Heating & air conditioning contractors; Sheet metalwork; Plumbing contractors; Heating & air conditioning contractors; Sheet metalwork
CEO: Greg Hosch
**Sr VP:* Joe Beckel
**Prin:* Greg Donley
MIS Dir: Charles Hiley
VP Opers: Dave Schultz

HIMEC MECHANICAL
See HIMEC INC

D-U-N-S 17-407-2413
HIMMELS ARCHITECTURAL DOOR AND HARDWARE INC
16491 Airline Hwy, Prairieville, LA 70769-3430
Tel (225) 673-8777 *Founded/Ownrshp* 1983
Sales 24.9MM^E *EMP* 67^E
SIC 5072 2542 3442 5251 5039 7699 Bolts, nuts & screws; Cabinets: show, display or storage: except wood; Window & door frames; Tools; Prefabricated structures; Locksmith shop; Bolts, nuts & screws; Cabinets: show, display or storage: except wood; Window & door frames; Tools; Prefabricated structures; Locksmith shop
Pr: Max Himmel
IT Man: Tara Carrier
IT Man: Himmel Chad

D-U-N-S 10-417-9440 IMP
HIMOINSA POWER SYSTEMS INC
HIMOINSA USA
(*Suby of* HIMOINSA SL)
16002 W 110th St, Lenexa, KS 66219-1328
Tel (913) 495-5557 *Founded/Ownrshp* 2008
Sales 35.0MM *EMP* 70
SIC 5063 Generators; Generators
Pr: Rafael R Acosta
**COO:* Samuel Silva
Admn Mgr: Dana Baker
Sls Dir: Stephen Sutton

HIMOINSA USA
See HIMOINSA POWER SYSTEMS INC

D-U-N-S 03-493-7810
HIMS CONSULTING GROUP INC
2155 Resort Dr Ste 220, Steamboat Springs, CO 80487-8842
Tel (970) 761-7000 *Founded/Ownrshp* 2004
Sales 22.0MM *EMP* 140
SIC 7361 Employment agencies; Employment agencies
CEO: Brian Parnell
COO: Joe Mendonca
CFO: Andrew C Brown
VP: Erich Strotbeck

D-U-N-S 10-752-1189 IMP
HINCKLEY & SCHMITT INC
HINCKLEY SPRINGS
(*Suby of* SUNTORY INTERNATIONAL CORP) ★
6055 S Harlem Ave, Chicago, IL 60638-3985
Tel (773) 586-8600 *Founded/Ownrshp* 1996
Sales 217.4MM^E *EMP* 2,190
SIC 2086 5149 7359 Water, pasteurized: packaged in cans, bottles, etc.; Water, distilled; Mineral or spring water bottling; Equipment rental & leasing; Water, pasteurized: packaged in cans, bottles, etc.; Water, distilled; Mineral or spring water bottling; Equipment rental & leasing
Pr: David A Krishcok

HINCKLEY ALLEN
See HINCKLEY ALLEN & SNYDER LLP

D-U-N-S 06-985-6680
HINCKLEY ALLEN & SNYDER LLP
HINCKLEY ALLEN
100 Westminster St # 1500, Providence, RI 02903-2395
Tel (401) 274-2000 *Founded/Ownrshp* 1906
Sales 51.2MM^E *EMP* 350^E
SIC 8111 General practice law office; General practice law office
Mng Pt: Marc A Crisafulli
Mng Pt: Kevin Cuvallo
Mng Pt: Michael Defanti
Pr: Jackie Carvalho
Pr: Eleanor Figueiredo
Pr: Linda Guastello
Pr: Pamela Ware
CFO: Kevin Curvello
CTO: Rachel Sanita
Mktg Dir: Gina Fajardo
Counsel: Charlie Allott

HINCKLEY COMPANY, THE
See TALARIA CO LLC

HINCKLEY SPRINGS
See HINCKLEY & SCHMITT INC

D-U-N-S 04-981-6382
HINDA INC
HINDA INCENTIVES
(*Suby of* THARPE CO INC) ★
2440 W 34th St, Chicago, IL 60608-5127
Tel (773) 843-3436 *Founded/Ownrshp* 2012
Sales 25.6MM^E *EMP* 85
SIC 8748 Business consulting
Pr: Dave Peer
VP: Bill Termini
Prgrm Mgr: Tashika White
QA Dir: Anthony Ditola
Netwrk Eng: Steve Handy
Sls&Mrk Ex: Kate Henehan
Mktg Dir: Larry Nowlin
Mktg Dir: Chuck Schwartz
Snr Mgr: Harry Adams
Snr Mgr: Fernando Gonzalez

HINDA INCENTIVES
See HINDA INC

D-U-N-S 12-673-4172
HINDLE POWER INC
1075 Saint John St, Easton, PA 18042-6661
Tel (610) 330-9000 *Founded/Ownrshp* 2001
Sales 24.1MM^E *EMP* 60
SIC 3612 Transformers, except electric
Pr: William A Hindle
Pr: William Bennett
**VP:* John Hindle
VP: Sutcliffe Jennings
MIS Dir: Carlos Infante
Sftwr Eng: David Skok
Prd Mgr: Ron Dempsey
Sls&Mrk Ex: Deborah Behler
Advt Dir: Gary Guagliardi

D-U-N-S 00-118-8911 IMP
HINDLEY MANUFACTURING CO INC (RI)
9 Havens St, Cumberland, RI 02864-8200
Tel (401) 722-2550 *Founded/Ownrshp* 1897
Sales 24.9MM^E *EMP* 80
SIC 3452 3496 3429 Bolts, nuts, rivets & washers; Screw eyes & hooks; Gate hooks; Cotter pins, metal; Miscellaneous fabricated wire products; Manufactured hardware (general); Bolts, nuts, rivets & washers; Screw eyes & hooks; Gate hooks; Cotter pins, metal; Miscellaneous fabricated wire products; Manufactured hardware (general)
Pr: Charles J Hindley
**CFO:* Roy A Medeiros
**VP:* Scott A Hindley
MIS Dir: Mark Shultise
Dir IT: Mark Schultheiss
Sfty Dirs: Jack Silva
Site Mgr: Mike Ricciardi

HINDS CNTY BD SUPERVISOR DST 2
See COUNTY OF HINDS

D-U-N-S 07-507-1399
HINDS COMMUNITY COLLEGE DISTRICT PUBLIC IMPROVEMENT CORP
501 E Main St, Raymond, MS 39154-9700
Tel (601) 857-5261 *Founded/Ownrshp* 1916
Sales 24.3MM^E *EMP* 1,000
SIC 8222 8221 Community college; Colleges universities & professional schools; Community college; Junior college; Colleges universities & professional schools
CEO: Robert Smith
**Pr:* Clayde Muse

HINDS COUNTY HEAD START PROGRA
See HINDS COUNTY HUMAN RESOURCE AGENCY

D-U-N-S 16-879-9203
HINDS COUNTY HUMAN RESOURCE AGENCY
HINDS COUNTY HEAD START PROGRA
258 Maddox Rd, Jackson, MS 39212-2312
Tel (601) 923-3940 *Founded/Ownrshp* 1993
Sales 18.8MM *EMP* 420^E
Accts Watkins Ward And Stafford Pllc
SIC 8322 Individual & family services; Individual & family services
Pr: Kenn Cockrell
CFO: Alfred R Junior
VP: Ruby Blake

D-U-N-S 10-003-9775
HINDS COUNTY SCHOOL DISTRICT
13192 Highway 18, Raymond, MS 39154-8936
Tel (601) 857-5222 *Founded/Ownrshp* 1953
Sales 43.4MM^E *EMP* 650
SIC 8211 Public elementary school; Public senior high school; Vocational high school; Public elementary school; Public senior high school; Vocational high school
**CFO:* Earl Burke
Schl Brd P: Ivan Smith
Teacher Pr: Sharon Harris

D-U-N-S 62-162-2653
HINES & ASSOCIATES INC
115 E Highland Ave, Elgin, IL 60120-5506
Tel (847) 741-1291 *Founded/Ownrshp* 1987
Sales NA *EMP* 105
SIC 6411 8011 Advisory services, insurance; Offices & clinics of medical doctors
Pr: Judith Hines
Ex VP: Lynn Breitbach
Ex Dir: Susette Stanton
Dir IT: Derek Christopher
IT Man: Mary Carpenter
IT Man: Mark Rundle
Manager: Jacob Breitbach
Manager: Sandy Schubert

D-U-N-S 19-732-9089 IMP
HINES CORP
1218 E Pontaluna Rd Ste B, Norton Shores, MI 49456-9634
Tel (231) 799-6240 *Founded/Ownrshp* 1987
Sales 223.0MM^E *EMP* 650
SIC 3443 3823 3589 3531 3535 5082 Boilers: industrial, power, or marine; Fluidic devices, circuits & systems for process control; Floor washing & polishing machines, commercial; Construction machinery; Roofing equipment; Conveyors & conveying equipment; General construction machinery & equipment; Boilers: industrial, power, or marine; Fluidic devices, circuits & systems for process control; Floor washing & polishing machines, commercial; Construction machinery; Roofing equipment; Conveyors & conveying equipment; General construction machinery & equipment
Pr: Larry Hines
CFO: Greg Longcore
VP: Michele Buckley
VP: Mark Hefty
VP: Jeffrey McCauley
VP: Tom Thompson
Software D: Ginger Smith

D-U-N-S 79-658-7918
HINES GB HOLDINGS LLC
2800 Post Oak Blvd # 4800, Houston, TX 77056-6100
Tel (713) 621-8000 *Founded/Ownrshp* 2007
Sales 13.2MM^E *EMP* 800^E
SIC 6531 Real estate managers; Real estate managers
CFO: Lars Huber
Sr VP: Tommy Craig
VP: Palmer Letzerich

D-U-N-S 83-147-5285
HINES GLOBAL REIT INC
2800 Post Oak Blvd # 5000, Houston, TX 77056-6100
Tel (888) 220-6121 *Founded/Ownrshp* 2008
Sales 456.2MM *EMP* 27^E
SIC 6798 Real estate investment trusts; Real estate investment trusts
CEO: Sherri Shugart
**CFO:* Ryan T Sims
**Treas:* J Shea Morgenroth
**Chf Inves:* Edmund A Donaldson

D-U-N-S 96-992-7375 IMP
HINES GROUP INC
5680 Old Highway 54, Philpot, KY 42366-9645
Tel (270) 729-4242 Founded/Ownrshp 1999
Sales 185.5MM^E EMP 1,283
SIC 3621 3469 3444 Motors & generators; Electric motor & generator parts; Metal stampings; Sheet metalwork; Motors & generators; Electric motor & generator parts; Metal stampings; Sheet metalwork
CEO: Ronald J Bamerger
*Pr: Kevin Booth
CFO: Bill Young
*VP: Joseph Acquisto
VP: Mark Osborne
*VP: Steven Shultz
Info Man: Henry Waldschmidt
VP Mfg: Ray Goodman
Opers Mgr: David Parsley
Mktg Dir: Allen Mills

D-U-N-S 61-925-0665 IMP
HINES HORTICULTURE INC
HINES NURSERIES
12621 Jeffrey Rd, Irvine, CA 92620
Tel (949) 559-4444 Founded/Ownrshp 2008
Sales 2.0MMM^E EMP 2,100
SIC 0181 5261

D-U-N-S 00-793-1645 IMP
HINES INTERESTS LIMITED PARTNERSHIP
2800 Post Oak Blvd # 4800, Houston, TX 77056-6118
Tel (713) 621-8000 Founded/Ownrshp 1957
Sales 991.5MM^E EMP 3,200
Accts Ernst & Young Llp Houston Tx
SIC 6552 Land subdividers & developers, commercial; Land subdividers & developers, commercial
Pt: Gerald D Hines
Pt: Jeffrey C Hines
Ofcr: Richard Treglown
Ex VP: Hasty Johnson
Sr VP: Daniel Rashin
VP: Eduardo Litterio
VP: Craig McKenzie
VP: Andrew Montgomery
VP: John Mooz
VP: Bill Olson
VP: Bart Swenson
VP: Rick Vance
VP: Chrissy Wilson
VP: Jon Wood

HINES NURSERIES
See HINES HORTICULTURE INC

D-U-N-S 00-198-9912 IMP/EXP
HINES NUT CO LTD (TX)
990 S Saint Paul St, Dallas, TX 75201-6120
Tel (214) 939-0253 Founded/Ownrshp 1925
Sales 51.9MM^E EMP 60
SIC 5159 5149 Nuts & nut by-products; Peanuts (bulk), unroasted; Fruits, dried
Pr: Chris Hines
Opers Mgr: Rod Gutierrez
Plnt Mgr: Mike Rodreick
Trfc Mgr: Mitch Melton

D-U-N-S 94-357-1992
HINES PARK FORD INC
56558 Pontiac Trl, New Hudson, MI 48165-9728
Tel (248) 437-6700 Founded/Ownrshp 1995
Sales 24.5MM^E EMP 75^E
SIC 5511 Automobiles, new & used; Trucks, tractors & trailers: new & used; Vans, new & used; Automobiles, new & used; Trucks, tractors & trailers: new & used; Vans, new & used
Pr: David Kolb
*VP: Michael Kolb
*Genl Mgr: Adam Kolb
Sls Mgr: Rebecca Donehue

D-U-N-S 05-204-7719
HINES PARK LINCOLN INC
40601 Ann Arbor Rd E, Plymouth, MI 48170-4448
Tel (734) 453-2424 Founded/Ownrshp 1997
Sales 51.7MM^E EMP 130
SIC 5511 7538 7532 5531 Automobiles, new & used; Vans, new & used; General automotive repair shops; Top & body repair & paint shops; Automotive & home supply stores; Automobiles, new & used; Vans, new & used; General automotive repair shops; Top & body repair & paint shops; Automotive & home supply stores
Pr: Michael Kolb
*VP: David Kolb
Genl Mgr: Adam Kolb
*Genl Mgr: Rhonda Sabatini
Sls Mgr: Tim Worthington
Sales Asso: Kris Bonnell
Sales Asso: Dennis Garrett
Sales Asso: Bill Guran
Sales Asso: Allen Oxley

D-U-N-S 82-603-4717
HINES REAL ESTATE INVESTMENT TRUST INC
2800 Post Oak Blvd # 4700, Houston, TX 77056-6100
Tel (713) 621-8000 Founded/Ownrshp 2004
Sales 236.0MM EMP 5^E
Accts Deloitte & Touche Llp Houston
SIC 6798 Real estate investment trusts; Real estate investment trusts
Prin: Jeffrey Hines

D-U-N-S 79-274-5122
HINES WARNER CENTER LP
5700 Canoga Ave Ste 140, Woodland Hills, CA 91367-6596
Tel (818) 887-3300 Founded/Ownrshp 2006
Sales 26.0MM EMP 11
SIC 8741 Management services; Management services
Genl Pt: Hines Warner Center GP LLC

HINGE INC
See HODGES INTERNATIONAL GROUP INC

D-U-N-S 00-695-4598
HINGHAM INSTITUTION FOR SAVINGS
55 Main St, Hingham, MA 02043-2590
Tel (781) 749-5877 Founded/Ownrshp 1834
Sales NA EMP 110
Accts Molf & Company Pc Boston
SIC 6036 State savings banks, not federally chartered; State savings banks, not federally chartered
Ch Bd: Robert H Gaughen Jr
Pr: Suzanne Brightbill
Pr: Kelly Kreinest
*Treas: Rober Bogart
VP: Paul Barry
VP: Mark Constable
VP: Joan Reydel
VP: Michael Sinclair
VP: Peter Smollett
VP: Edward Zec
VP Admn: William M Donovan

D-U-N-S 00-142-6162
HINGHAM MUTUAL FIRE INSURANCE CO
DANBURY INSURANCE COMPANY
230 Beal St, Hingham, MA 02043-1554
Tel (781) 749-0841 Founded/Ownrshp 1826
Sales NA EMP 56
SIC 6331 Fire, marine & casualty insurance & carriers; Fire, marine & casualty insurance & carriers
Pr: Brian R Wilkin
Pr: Chris Hunter
*Treas: George A Cole III
*VP: Bruce M Arnold
*VP: Cheryl Wigmore

D-U-N-S 10-003-1814
HINGHAM PUBLIC SCHOOL DISTRICT
220 Central St, Hingham, MA 02043-2745
Tel (781) 741-1500 Founded/Ownrshp 1990
Sales 32.6MM^E EMP 496
SIC 8211 Public elementary & secondary schools; School board; Public elementary & secondary schools; School board
Treas: Mary O'Donnell
Ofcr: Thomas Ford
Ofcr: Robert Ramsey
HC Dir: Deborah Whiting

D-U-N-S 07-470-6896
HINKLE CONTRACTING CORP
(Suby of SUMMIT MATERIALS LLC) ★
395 N Middletown Rd, Paris, KY 40361-2138
Tel (859) 987-3670 Founded/Ownrshp 2010
Sales 244.1MM^E EMP 850
SIC 1611 1422 3273 3272 3271 2951 Highway & street paving contractor; Grading; Crushed & broken limestone; Ready-mixed concrete; Concrete products; Concrete block & brick; Asphalt paving mixtures & blocks; Highway & street paving contractor; Grading; Crushed & broken limestone; Ready-mixed concrete; Concrete products; Concrete block & brick; Asphalt paving mixtures & blocks
CEO: Thomas Hinkle
*Pr: Henry Hinkle
CFO: Steve Hullett
*Treas: Thomas M Brannock
Ex VP: Bill Cress
*Ex VP: William Cress
VP: Willie Griffith
VP: Chris Keller
VP: Jeff Mingus
*VP: Gordon Wilson
Dir Bus: Greg Hensley

D-U-N-S 61-491-8316
HINKLE CONTRACTING CORP
100 Farmers Bank Sq # 400, Georgetown, KY 40324-8712
Tel (502) 868-0231 Founded/Ownrshp 1990
Sales 22.0MM EMP 30^E
SIC 1611 2951 Highway & street construction; Asphalt & asphaltic paving mixtures (not from refineries); Highway & street construction; Asphalt & asphaltic paving mixtures (not from refineries)
Pr: Frank Hamilton Jr
VP: Richard Hamilton

D-U-N-S 00-505-0505
HINKLE MANUFACTURING INC (OH)
348 5th St, Perrysburg, OH 43551-4922
Tel (419) 666-5550 Founded/Ownrshp 1963
Sales 40.2MM EMP 96
Accts Mosley Pfundt & Glick Inc
SIC 3086 2653 Packaging & shipping materials, foamed plastic; Corrugated boxes, partitions, display items, sheets & pad; Packaging & shipping materials, foamed plastic; Corrugated boxes, partitions, display items, sheets & pad
CEO: Taber H Hinkle
COO: Robert Hinkle
*CFO: Jeffrey M Wolens
Ofcr: Kirt Lembke
*VP: Burt Jamieson
Dir IT: Jason Cronan
VP Opers: Ted Banagis
Board of Directors: Robert L Hinkle, Taber H Hinkle

D-U-N-S 03-748-2742
HINKLE METALS & SUPPLY CO INC
3300 11th Ave N, Birmingham, AL 35234-2332
Tel (205) 326-3300 Founded/Ownrshp 1980
Sales 37.7MM^E EMP 107
SIC 5051 5033 5075

D-U-N-S 88-490-4624
HINO MOTORS MANUFACTURING USA INC
(Suby of HINO MOTORS, LTD.)
37777 Interchange Dr, Farmington Hills, MI 48335-1030
Tel (248) 442-9077 Founded/Ownrshp 1994
Sales 96.2MM^E EMP 64
SIC 5013 Truck parts & accessories
Pr: Hideyuki Omata
*CEO: Kazuhiro Somiya
*VP: Hiroyuri Kobayashi
VP: Yukitake Kudo
Admn Mgr: Lora Sorek
Prd Mgr: Thomas Alexander
Natl Sales: Lori Lambert
Sales Asso: Kim Shaieb
Corp Couns: Greg Champion
Counsel: Matthew Kulick
Snr Mgr: Jennifer Presher

D-U-N-S 15-054-9673 IMP/EXP
HINO MOTORS SALES USA INC
HINO TRUCKS
41180 Bridge St, Novi, MI 48375-1300
Tel (248) 699-9300 Founded/Ownrshp 1984
Sales 69.4MM^E EMP 120
SIC 5012 5013 Trucks, commercial; Truck parts & accessories; Trucks, commercial; Truck parts & accessories
CEO: Sumio Fukaya
*Pr: Yoshinori Noguchi
Sr VP: Robert McDowell
*Sr VP: Ayumi Oishi
*Sr VP: Hiroshi Oshima
Rgnl Mgr: Tom Hoffman
IT Man: Brad Czischke
Tech Mgr: Rob White
Opers Mgr: Dave Kubeshesky
Natl Sales: Tim Wenger
Sls Mgr: Paul Bien

HINO TRUCKS
See HINO MOTORS SALES USA INC

HINODE
See SUNFOODS LLC

D-U-N-S 12-199-9895
HINRICHS GROUP INC
IMPACT STRATEGIES, INC.
340 Office Ct Ste A, Fairview Heights, IL 62208-2059
Tel (618) 394-8400 Founded/Ownrshp 2002
Sales 26.1MM^E EMP 11
SIC 1542 6719 Commercial & office building, new construction; Personal holding companies, except banks; Commercial & office building, new construction; Personal holding companies, except banks
Pr: Mark Hinrichs
*VP: Michael Crist
Off Mgr: Kate Bonn

HINRICHS TRADING COMPANY
See HINRICHS TRADING LLC

D-U-N-S 95-915-6951 IMP/EXP
HINRICHS TRADING LLC
HINRICHS TRADING COMPANY
155 Se Kamiaken St, Pullman, WA 99163-2614
Tel (509) 332-8888 Founded/Ownrshp 1996
Sales 30.0MM EMP 35^E
SIC 5153 Grain & field beans; Grain & field beans
*COO: John Friel
*CFO: Sharae Garro
Off Mgr: Nikki Siebler

D-U-N-S 96-643-1629
■ **HINSDALE BANK & TRUST CO**
(Suby of WINTRUST FINANCIAL CORP) ★
25 E 1st St, Hinsdale, IL 60521-4119
Tel (630) 323-4404 Founded/Ownrshp 1993
Sales NA EMP 160
SIC 6022 Federal savings banks; State commercial banks; State trust companies accepting deposits, commercial
CEO: Dennis J Jones
*Pr: Richard A Eck
*COO: Timothy Murphy
*CFO: Michelle A Kennedy
Ofcr: Charlotte Hunt
Ofcr: Michael Kierys
Ofcr: Rhonda Mullen
Ofcr: Karen Novak
Ofcr: Betsy Russo
Ofcr: Monica Smuda
Ex VP: Mark Garrigus
Sr VP: Jeff Teague
VP: Dean Baseleon
VP: Mark Connelly
VP: Nancy Moskus
VP: Scott Muyskens
VP: Lori Ritzert

D-U-N-S 04-661-6348
HINSDALE COMMUNITY CONSOLIDATED SCHOOL DISTRICT NO 181
5905 S County Line Rd, Hinsdale, IL 60521-5099
Tel (630) 887-1070 Founded/Ownrshp 1940
Sales 18.4MM^E EMP 382
SIC 8211 Public elementary school; Public junior high school; Public elementary school; Public junior high school
Bd of Dir: Tracy Hauenstein
Bd of Dir: Donna Vorreyer

D-U-N-S 62-160-6060
HINSDALE HEALTH SYSTEM (INC)
120 N Oak St, Hinsdale, IL 60521-3829
Tel (630) 856-9000 Founded/Ownrshp 1989
Sales 23.1MM^E EMP 650
SIC 8741 Management services; Management services
VP: Thomas J Williams
*Pr: Robert Sackett
*CFO: Ronald L Rowe
Pathlgst: Raphael Borok
Pathlgst: Anthony Dombrowski
Ansthlgy: Durga Kanuri

D-U-N-S 08-755-0380
HINSDALE TOWNSHIP HIGH SCHOOL DISTRICT 86
5500 S Grant St, Hinsdale, IL 60521-4578
Tel (630) 655-6100 Founded/Ownrshp 1913
Sales 43.2MM^E EMP 600
SIC 8741 Public senior high school; Management services; Management services
Teacher Pr: Domenico Maniscalco

D-U-N-S 06-947-8352
HINSHAW & CULBERTSON LLP
222 N La Salle St Ste 300, Chicago, IL 60601-1081
Tel (312) 704-3000 Founded/Ownrshp 1934
Sales 200.0MM EMP 1,010
SIC 8111 General practice law office; General practice law office
Mng Pt: J William Roberts
Pt: Bruce W Bennett
Pt: Kevin Joseph Burke
Pt: Terese A Drew
Pt: Peter R Jarvis
Pt: Ronald L Kammer
Pt: Patrick F Koenen
Pt: Hal R Lieberman
Pt: Michael P Malone
Pt: Renee J Mortimer
Pt: Donald L Mrozek
Pt: David R Mylrea
COO: Evan Brown
CFO: Robert P Johnson
CFO: Ed Oconnell
VP: Theresa L Concepcion
VP: Jennifer Friedman
Exec: Steven Bonanno
Exec: Terry Wand

HINSHAW'S HONDA
See HINSHAWS INC

D-U-N-S 02-730-5572
HINSHAWS INC
HINSHAW'S HONDA
2605 Auburn Way N, Auburn, WA 98002-2446
Tel (253) 924-0550 Founded/Ownrshp 1950
Sales 29.7MM^E EMP 95
SIC 5511 5571 Automobiles, new & used; Motorcycles; Automobiles, new & used; Motorcycles
Prin: Hooman Bodaghi
Sls&Mrk Ex: Tim Lasso
Sls Mgr: Monte McCain
Board of Directors: Paul Hinshaw

D-U-N-S 04-797-0413
HINSON OIL CO
2040 Martin Luther King, Quincy, FL 32351-4701
Tel (850) 627-2940 Founded/Ownrshp 1968
Sales 61.2MM EMP 8
SIC 5171 Petroleum bulk stations; Petroleum bulk stations
Pr: E Wilson Hinson Jr
*Sec: Marion Hinson
*VP: E Wilson Hinson III

D-U-N-S 06-369-2263
HINTON LUMBER PRODUCTS INC
COTTONDALE WOOD PRODUCTS
1616 44th Ave, Tuscaloosa, AL 35401-2502
Tel (205) 758-2761 Founded/Ownrshp 1973
Sales 63.3MM^E EMP 295
SIC 2449 Wood containers; Wood containers
Owner: Mary George Howell
*Pr: Hinton Howell
*Pr: Larry Howell

HINTZSCHE OIL
See HFI ENTERPRISES INC

HINZE OIL
See RED EAGLE OIL INC

D-U-N-S 79-608-3090
HIOSSEN INC
OSSTEM
(Suby of OSSTEM IMPLANT CO.,LTD.)
85 Ben Fairless Dr, Fairless Hills, PA 19030-5012
Tel (267) 759-7002 Founded/Ownrshp 2007
Sales 34.2MM^E EMP 200
SIC 3843 Dental equipment; Dental equipment
CEO: Kyoo OK Choi
*Treas: Robert Lee
*Treas: Seung W Song

D-U-N-S 03-841-4004
HIP ADMINISTRATORS OF FLORIDA INC
HEALTH INSUR PLAN ADMNSTRATORS
(Suby of EMBLEMHEALTH INC) ★
3251 Hollywood Blvd 401, Hollywood, FL 33021
Tel (954) 893-6400 Founded/Ownrshp 1994
Sales NA EMP 500
SIC 6324 Hospital & medical service plans; Hospital & medical service plans
CEO: Anthony Watson
*VP: James Grenidge

D-U-N-S 05-503-1892
HIP ENTERPRISES
344 N Main St Rear, Layton, UT 84041-7104
Tel (801) 546-2488 Founded/Ownrshp 1971
Sales 19.1MM^E EMP 900
SIC 5812 American restaurant; American restaurant
Owner: Hersh Ipaktchian

HIP HEALTH PLAN OF NEWYORK
See HIP HEALTH PLANS INC

D-U-N-S 82-854-0315
HIP HEALTH PLANS INC
HIP HEALTH PLAN OF NEWYORK
(Suby of EMBLEMHEALTH INC) ★
55 Water St Ste Conc1, New York, NY 10041-8190
Tel (646) 428-3690 Founded/Ownrshp 1999
Sales NA EMP 45^E
SIC 6324 Hospital & medical service plans
CEO: Anthony L Watson
IT Man: Carlo Cabalbag
IT Man: Harry Son
Netwrk Eng: Curtis Vislocky

HIP IOWA
See IOWA COMPREHENSIVE HEALTH ASSOCIATION

D-U-N-S 01-641-0784
HIPCRICKET INC
401 Congress Ave Ste 2650, Austin, TX 78701-3708
Tel (425) 452-1111 Founded/Ownrshp 2000
Sales 26.6MM EMP 120^E
Tkr Sym HIPP Exch OTC
SIC 7372 7812 7311 Business oriented computer software; Audio-visual program production; Advertising agencies; Business oriented computer software; Audio-visual program production; Advertising agencies
Ch Bd: Todd E Wilson

Pr: Douglas Stovall
VP: Gay Gabrilska
VP: Erin Hunt
VP Bus Dev: Kelli Brooks
Prgrm Mgr: Wanda Chung
Snr Sftwr: Aaron Sprague
Sftwr Eng: Ryan Knopp
Sftwr Eng: Nicholas Lindsley
VP Sls: Kim Donaldson
Mktg Dir: Andrea Mocherman

D-U-N-S 00-940-0262
HIPEROS LLC
(*Suby of* OPUS GLOBAL HOLDINGS LLC) ★
176 E Main St Ste 8, Westborough, MA 01581-1763
Tel (908) 981-0080 *Founded/Ownrshp* 2014
Sales 22.9MM^E *EMP* 115
SIC 7373 Systems software development services
CEO: Greg Dickinson
Ofcr: Janet Coddington
VP: Sandeep Bhide
VP: Mark Deluca
VP: Eliot Madow
VP: Doug Udoff
Off Mgr: Kristy Kiely
CTO: John Abbatico

D-U-N-S 01-468-4206
HIPMUNK INC
434 Brannan St Ste 1, San Francisco, CA 94107-1714
Tel (201) 306-2253 *Founded/Ownrshp* 2010
Sales 23.3MM^E *EMP* 50
SIC 4724 Travel agencies
CEO: Adam Goldstein
Chf Mktg O: Susan Doherty
**VP:* Nancy Hang
**VP:* Seth Sakamoto
Off Mgr: Brit Malinauskus
**CTO:* Filip Mertens
Sftwr Eng: Niranjan Ramadas
Sls Mgr: Trevor Fox
Snr Mgr: Joe Gambescia

D-U-N-S 00-201-5030 IMP/EXP
■ **HIPOTRONICS INC**
(*Suby of* HUBBELL INC) ★
1650 Route 22, Brewster, NY 10509-4013
Tel (845) 279-8091 *Founded/Ownrshp* 1962
Sales 26.1MM^E *EMP* 225
SIC 3825 3679 3829 3677 3675 3674 Instruments to measure electricity; Test equipment for electronic & electric measurement; Power supplies, all types: static; Measuring & controlling devices; Electronic coils, transformers & other inductors; Electronic capacitors; Semiconductors & related devices; Instruments to measure electricity; Test equipment for electronic & electric measurement; Power supplies, all types: static; Measuring & controlling devices; Electronic coils, transformers & other inductors; Electronic capacitors; Semiconductors & related devices
Pr: Richard Davies
**CEO:* Timothy H Powers
Ofcr: Michael Hargrave
**VP:* Jeff Brown
VP: Reinold Grob
Opers Mgr: Charles Consalvo
Mktg Dir: Melissa Fiorello
Manager: Matt Waltz

D-U-N-S 83-065-9665
HIPPO ROOFING LLC
1555 N Harbor City Blvd, Melbourne, FL 32935-6568
Tel (321) 951-2500 *Founded/Ownrshp* 2008
Sales 24.0MM *EMP* 25
SIC 1761 Architectural sheet metal work
Sls Mgr: Brian Hippo

D-U-N-S 07-966-1552
HIRAIN TECHNOLOGIES USA INC
24100 Sthfeld Rd Ste 320h, Southfield, MI 48075
Tel (339) 206-3060 *Founded/Ownrshp* 2009
Sales 100.0MM *EMP* 6
SIC 5013 8711 Automotive supplies & parts; Engineering services; Automotive supplies & parts; Engineering services
CEO: Yong Deng

D-U-N-S 07-778-0377
HIRAM COLLEGE
11715 State Route 700, Hiram, OH 44234-9539
Tel (330) 569-5209 *Founded/Ownrshp* 1850
Sales 54.6MM^E *EMP* 512
SIC 8221 College, except junior; College, except junior
Pr: Thomas V Chema
**VP:* Stephen Jones

HIRE COUNCIL
See HC2 INC

D-U-N-S 10-673-8339
HIRE THINKING INC
ADVANTAGE XPO
(*Suby of* ADVANTAGE RESOURCING AMERICA INC) ★
220 Norwood Park S Ste 1, Norwood, MA 02062-4690
Tel (781) 251-8000 *Founded/Ownrshp* 2004
Sales 27.8MM^E *EMP* 1,250
SIC 7363 Temporary help service; Temporary help service
Pr: Karen Browne
**Treas:* Daniel A Lasman
Brnch Mgr: David Hannon
Brnch Mgr: Les Whelchel
VP Sls: Matt Stager

HIRECHECK
See FIRST ADVANTAGE BACKGROUND SERVICES CORP

D-U-N-S 17-551-3274
HIRED BY MATRIX INC
266 Harristown Rd Ste 202, Glen Rock, NJ 07452-3321
Tel (201) 587-0777 *Founded/Ownrshp* 1987
Sales 27.8MM^E *EMP* 240
SIC 7379 8742 Computer related consulting services; Management consulting services; Computer related consulting services; Management consulting services

Pr: Sharon Olzerowicz
**COO:* Frank Scarnicola
VP: Julie Daly
VP: Marty McDermott
VP: Robert B Randt
**Prin:* Alan Friedman
**Prin:* Peter Olzerowicz
Mng Dir: Todd Baker
IT Man: Christopher Kosar
Mktg Dir: Jennifer Cantanese

HIREL CONNECTORS
See HI REL CONNECTORS INC

D-U-N-S 79-234-8021
HIRERIGHT INC
(*Suby of* CORPORATE RISK HOLDINGS LLC) ★
3349 Michelson Dr Ste 150, Irvine, CA 92612-8881
Tel (949) 428-5800 *Founded/Ownrshp* 2013
Sales 282.6MM^E *EMP* 407^E
SIC 7375 7374 Data base information retrieval; Data base information retrieval; Data verification service
CEO: John Fennelly
COO: Brian Pierson
CFO: Richard Little
CFO: Thomas Spaeth
VP: Catherine Aldrich
VP: Gregg Freeman
VP: Susan Kirton
VP: Mary O'Loughlin
VP: Steven Spencer
Exec: Michele Dominguez
Mng Dir: Alexandra Kelly

D-U-N-S 15-080-2515
HIRERIGHT SOLUTIONS INC
AN ALTEGRITY COMPANY
(*Suby of* HIRERIGHT INC) ★
14002 E 21st St Ste 1200, Tulsa, OK 74134-1409
Tel (800) 331-9175 *Founded/Ownrshp* 2006
Sales 30.9MM^E *EMP* 400^E
SIC 7375 Information retrieval services; Information retrieval services
Pr: Michael Petrullo
**VP:* Richard L Harris
VP: Mark Rapp

HIRESTRATEGY
See ADDISON PROFESSIONAL FINANCIAL SEARCH LLC

D-U-N-S 15-977-5469
HIRING PARTNERS INC
2505 S Church St, Paris, TX 75460-7660
Tel (903) 785-1100 *Founded/Ownrshp* 1996
Sales 14.2MM^E *EMP* 450
SIC 7363 7361 Help supply services; Employment agencies; Help supply services; Employment agencies
Pr: Lisa Jones
Rgnl Mgr: Hunter Jones
Brnch Mgr: Ben Caffee
Opers Mgr: Shelby McDaniel
Opers Mgr: Amber Pitcock

HIRNING CADILLAC
See HIRNING PONTIAC CADILLAC GMC INC

D-U-N-S 03-399-2538
HIRNING PONTIAC CADILLAC GMC INC
HIRNING CADILLAC
509 Yellowstone Ave, Pocatello, ID 83201-4533
Tel (208) 232-8900 *Founded/Ownrshp* 1981
Sales 28.0MM^E *EMP* 68
SIC 5511 Automobiles, new & used; Automobiles, new & used
Pr: Arthur J Hirning
**Sec:* Claira Hirning
Exec: Doug Briggs
Genl Mgr: Kelly Hirning
Sls Mgr: Clay Bailey
Sales Asso: Dino Bushati
Sales Asso: Peyton Hatch
Sales Asso: Taylor Nettik

D-U-N-S 01-669-4218
HIROSE ELECTRIC (USA) INC
(*Suby of* HIROSE ELECTRIC CO., LTD.)
580 Waters Edge Ste 205, Lombard, IL 60148-6432
Tel (805) 522-7958 *Founded/Ownrshp* 1980
Sales 30.7MM^E *EMP* 75
SIC 5065 3678 Electronic parts & equipment; Electronic connectors
CEO: Yasushi Nakamura
**Ch:* Mitsugu Sugino
**Ex VP:* Naoki Shukuya
Rgnl Mgr: Jeff Christ
Genl Mgr: Nick Shuikuia
Opers Mgr: Javier Nunez
S&M/VP: Rick Van Weezel

D-U-N-S 36-072-9693 IMP/EXP
HIROTEC AMERICA INC
(*Suby of* HIROTEC CORPORATION)
3000 High Meadow Cir, Auburn Hills, MI 48326-2837
Tel (248) 836-5100 *Founded/Ownrshp* 1988
Sales 88.2MM^E *EMP* 300^E
Accts Plante & Moran Pllc Auburn H
SIC 3569 Assembly machines, non-metalworking; Assembly machines, non-metalworking
CEO: Katsutoshi Uno
**Pr:* Jim Toeniskoetter
**CFO:* Brian McGinnity
**Ex VP:* Paul Demarco
**VP:* Sharon Beetham
**VP:* Brian Hopkins
**VP:* Gary Krus

D-U-N-S 08-376-9752
HIRSCH DIDI PSYCHIATRIC SERVICE (CA)
DIDI HIRSCH COMMUNITY MENTAL H
4760 Sepulveda Blvd, Culver City, CA 90230-4820
Tel (310) 390-6612 *Founded/Ownrshp* 1944
Sales 44.4MM *EMP* 350
Accts Harrington Group Pasadena Ca
SIC 8322 8093 Individual & family services; Mental health clinic, outpatient; Individual & family services; Mental health clinic, outpatient
Ch: Michael Wierwille
**Pr:* Kita S Curry

**Treas:* Martin Frank
Ofcr: Janine Perron
VP: Peter Golio
Doctor: Nick Gutierrez

D-U-N-S 03-342-1731
HIRSCH ELECTRIC LLC
603 Dundalk Ave, Baltimore, MD 21224-2932
Tel (410) 246-3500 *Founded/Ownrshp* 1975
Sales 23.9MM^E *EMP* 130
SIC 1731 General electrical contractor; General electrical contractor
Pr: Thomas M Hirsch
VP: Joseph J Hirsch

D-U-N-S 00-626-4923
■ **HIRSCH ELECTRONICS LLC**
(*Suby of* IDENTIV INC) ★
1900 Carnegie Ave Ste B, Santa Ana, CA 92705-5557
Tel (949) 250-8888 *Founded/Ownrshp* 2009
Sales 22.4MM^E *EMP* 85
SIC 5065 Security control equipment & systems; Security control equipment & systems
Ex VP: Stephen Healy
VP: Mark Allen
Rgnl Mgr: Randy Lehman
Dir IT: Kurt Kohlhase
IT Man: Diana Midland
Sftwr Eng: Jeff Ogborn
Sales Asso: Angel Gutierrez

D-U-N-S 07-853-5184 IMP
HIRSCH INTERNATIONAL CORP
(*Suby of* HIRSCH INTERNATIONAL HOLDINGS) ★
490 Wheeler Rd Ste 285, Hauppauge, NY 11788-4367
Tel (631) 436-7100 *Founded/Ownrshp* 2009
Sales 36.6MM^E *EMP* 65^E
SIC 5084 Textile machinery & equipment
CEO: Paul Gallagher
**Pr:* Kristof Janowski
**CFO:* Brian Rees
**Ex VP:* Beverly Eichel
**VP:* Nicholas Paccione
IT Man: Rich Fleming
Opers Mgr: Steve Powers
Sls Dir: Rob Girardot
Sls Dir: Eric Quinn
Board of Directors: Henry Arnberg, Marvin Broitman, Christopher J Davino, Mary Ann Domuracki

D-U-N-S 83-261-0245
HIRSCH INTERNATIONAL HOLDINGS
490 Wheeler Rd Ste 285, Hauppauge, NY 11788-4367
Tel (631) 436-7100 *Founded/Ownrshp* 2009
Sales 36.6MM^E *EMP* 138^E
SIC 5084 Textile machinery & equipment; Textile machinery & equipment
CEO: Paul Gallagher

D-U-N-S 00-796-5460 EXP
HIRSCH PIPE & SUPPLY CO INC (CA)
15025 Oxnard St Ste 100, Van Nuys, CA 91411-2640
Tel (818) 756-0900 *Founded/Ownrshp* 1934, 1978
Sales 187.7MM^E *EMP* 265
SIC 5074 Plumbing & hydronic heating supplies; Plumbing & hydronic heating supplies
Pr: William D Glockner Jr
**Ch Bd:* Daniel J Mariscal
CFO: Bradley A Enstein
**CFO:* Joseph R King
**Treas:* Greg Mariscal
Brnch Mgr: Gonzalo Chanto
Brnch Mgr: Nery Iraheta
Brnch Mgr: Oscar Menendez
Brnch Mgr: Erick Pineda
IT Man: Bill Glockner
IT Man: Jeremiah Owen

D-U-N-S 02-792-5585
HIRSCH/BEDNER INTERNATIONAL INC
HBA INTERNATIONAL
3216 Nebraska Ave, Santa Monica, CA 90404-4214
Tel (310) 829-9087 *Founded/Ownrshp* 1964
Sales 30.8MM^E *EMP* 350
SIC 7389 Interior designer; Interior design services; Interior designer; Interior design services
CEO: Rene G Kaerskov
**Ch Bd:* Michael J Bedner
**Pr:* Howard Pharr
**Ex VP:* Bruce Jones

D-U-N-S 00-729-7955
HIRSCHBACH & SON INC
GROJEAN TRANSPORTATION
18355 Us Highway 20 W, East Dubuque, IL 61025-8514
Tel (815) 747-3850 *Founded/Ownrshp* 1956
Sales 42.9MM^E *EMP* 150
SIC 7513 Truck leasing, without drivers
Ch Bd: Thomas Grojean Sr
**Pr:* Brad Pinchuk
**CEO:* Thomas Grojean Jr
CFO: John Paresky
VP: Jim Coffren
VP: Terry Leahy
VP Opers: Dan Wallace
Opers Mgr: John Kalb
Opers Mgr: Manuel Mier

D-U-N-S 00-483-7662
HIRSCHBACH MOTOR LINES INC (NE)
(*Suby of* GROJEAN TRANSPORTATION) ★
18355 Us Highway 20 W, East Dubuque, IL 61025-8514
Tel (815) 747-3850 *Founded/Ownrshp* 1935, 1997
Sales 42.9MM^E *EMP* 130
SIC 4119 Local rental transportation
CEO: Thomas Grojean Jr
**Pr:* Brad Pinchuk
**Ch:* Thomas Grojean Sr
Ex VP: A J Tucker

D-U-N-S 00-166-6627
HIRSCHBERG SCHUTZ & CO INC
(*Suby of* HORIZON GROUP USA INC) ★
45 Technology Dr, Warren, NJ 07059-5184
Tel (908) 810-1111 *Founded/Ownrshp* 1912, 1987
Sales 25.7MM^E *EMP* 225^E

SIC 5092 Toys & hobby goods & supplies; Toys & hobby goods & supplies
Pr: Roshan Wijerama
**CFO:* Holli Gabler
VP: Laura Crlencic

D-U-N-S 82-843-5870 EXP
HIRSCHFELD HOLDINGS LP
HIRSCHFELD INDUSTRIES
112 W 29th St, San Angelo, TX 76903-2553
Tel (325) 486-4201 *Founded/Ownrshp* 2006
Sales 176.3MM^E *EMP* 800^E
SIC 1622 3441 Fabricated structural metal; Bridge construction; Bridge construction; Fabricated structural metal
Pt: Dennis Hirschfeld
**CFO:* Rodney L Goodwill
CFO: Brandon Moore
**Ex VP:* John O Quinn
**Sr VP:* Jacob Balderas
VP: Doug Ames
VP: Wendall Hirschfeld
VP: Gary Scherf
Trfc Dir: Rick Healey
Sfty Mgr: Kim Coats
Sfty Mgr: Brandon Lock

HIRSCHFELD INDUSTRIES
See HIRSCHFELD STEEL GROUP LP

HIRSCHFELD INDUSTRIES
See HIRSCHFELD HOLDINGS LP

D-U-N-S 83-511-8043
HIRSCHFELD INDUSTRIES BRIDGE LLC (FORMERLY CAROLINA STEEL GROUP LLC)
HIRSCHFELD INDUSTRIES-BRIDGE
(*Suby of* HIRSCHFELD HOLDINGS LP) ★
101 Centreport Dr Ste 400, Greensboro, NC 27409-9422
Tel (336) 275-9711 *Founded/Ownrshp* 2006
Sales 89.7MM^E *EMP* 723^E
SIC 1622 Bridge construction
Ex VP: John O'Quinn
**CFO:* Rodney L Goodwill
Sfty Mgr: Randy Bayliff

HIRSCHFELD INDUSTRIES-BRIDGE
See HIRSCHFELD INDUSTRIES BRIDGE LLC (FORMERLY CAROLINA STEEL GROUP LLC)

D-U-N-S 17-684-8893
HIRSCHFELD OF NEVADA INC
(*Suby of* HIRSCHFELD INDUSTRIES) ★
112 W 29th St, San Angelo, TX 76903-2553
Tel (325) 486-4201 *Founded/Ownrshp* 1979
Sales 32.5MM^E *EMP* 400
SIC 3441 Fabricated structural metal; Fabricated structural metal
Pr: Dennis C Hirschfeld

D-U-N-S 10-729-9851
HIRSCHFELD STEEL GROUP LP
HIRSCHFELD INDUSTRIES
(*Suby of* INSIGHT EQUITY LP) ★
112 W 29th St, San Angelo, TX 76903-2553
Tel (325) 486-4201 *Founded/Ownrshp* 2006
Sales 82.1MM^E *EMP* 400
SIC 3441 Fabricated structural metal; Fabricated structural metal
CEO: Dennis Hirschfeld
Pr: Richard W Phillips
CFO: Mide Depopus
CFO: Rodney L Goodwill
Ofcr: Jeff Jost

D-U-N-S 96-211-1527
HIRSCHI MASONRY LLC
4120 Losee Rd, North Las Vegas, NV 89030-3302
Tel (702) 633-7700 *Founded/Ownrshp* 2009
Sales 21.2MM^E *EMP* 79^E
SIC 1741 Masonry & other stonework
VP Opers: Brandon Marchant

D-U-N-S 36-205-3092 IMP/EXP
HIRSCHVOGEL INC
(*Suby of* HIRSCHVOGEL HOLDING GMBH)
2230 S 3rd St, Columbus, OH 43207-2431
Tel (614) 340-5657 *Founded/Ownrshp* 1988
Sales 47.7MM^E *EMP* 150
SIC 3714 Motor vehicle parts & accessories; Motor vehicle parts & accessories
Pr: Felix Schmieder
**CFO:* Charles Bentz
**VP:* Robert Hartwell
IT Man: John Lorenz
**VP Sls:* Mark Hoosier

D-U-N-S 00-528-0078 IMP
HIRSH INDUSTRIES INC (IA)
3636 Westown Pkwy Ste 100, West Des Moines, IA 50266-6713
Tel (515) 299-3200 *Founded/Ownrshp* 1986
Sales 171.4MM^E *EMP* 620
SIC 2522 2541 Filing boxes, cabinets & cases: except wood; Wood partitions & fixtures; Filing boxes, cabinets & cases: except wood; Wood partitions & fixtures
Pr: G Wayne Stewart
**Sec:* Howard Cook
DP Exec: Joe Antonelli
VP Opers: Joe Smith
Natl Sales: Roger Pettit
VP Mktg: Meagan Patterson
VP Sls: Dave Jensen
VP Sls: Dave Jenson
VP Sls: Jeff Stanton

D-U-N-S 00-622-2186
HIRSHFIELDS INC
LATHROP PAINT
725 2nd Ave N Ste 1, Minneapolis, MN 55405-1600
Tel (612) 377-3910 *Founded/Ownrshp* 1967
Sales 210.1MM^E *EMP* 305

SIC 5198 5231 2851 Wallcoverings; Paints; Varnishes; Paint brushes, rollers, sprayers; Wallpaper; Paint; Paint brushes, rollers, sprayers & other supplies; Paints & paint additives; Wallcoverings; Paints; Varnishes; Paint brushes, rollers, sprayers; Wallpaper; Paint; Paint brushes, rollers, sprayers & other supplies; Paints & paint additives
CEO: Frank Hirshfield
VP: Charles Gimon
Dist Mgr: Mary Angell
Dist Mgr: Jiai Hagen
Store Mgr: Ron Clarin
Store Mgr: Calvin Hendricks
Mktg Dir: Jeff Lein

D-U-N-S 62-300-8026
HIRTLE CALLAGHAN & CO LLC
300 Barr Harbor Dr # 400, Conshohocken, PA 19428-2998
Tel (610) 828-7200 *Founded/Ownrshp* 1988
Sales 22.2MM^E *EMP* 82^E
SIC 6282 Investment advisory service; Investment advisory service
COO: Bob Zion
**COO:* Robert Zion
Ofcr: Rhonda Fell
VP: Erik Almquist
VP: William Curran
VP: Paul Dokas
VP: Christine McGovern
VP: Douglas Monty
**VP:* Amy Schondra
VP: Patrick South
VP: Thomas Welsh

D-U-N-S 00-504-2346 IMP
HIRZEL CANNING CO (OH)
DEI FRATELLI
411 Lemoyne Rd, Northwood, OH 43619-1699
Tel (419) 693-0531 *Founded/Ownrshp* 1947, 1923
Sales 22.9MM^E *EMP* 100
SIC 2033 8611 2034 Tomato products: packaged in cans, jars, etc.; Tomato juice: packaged in cans, jars, etc.; Tomato paste: packaged in cans, jars, etc.; Tomato purees: packaged in cans, jars, etc.; Business associations; Dehydrated fruits, vegetables, soups; Tomato products: packaged in cans, jars, etc.; Tomato juice: packaged in cans, jars, etc.; Tomato paste: packaged in cans, jars, etc.; Tomato purees: packaged in cans, jars, etc.; Business associations; Dehydrated fruits, vegetables, soups
Pr: Karl A Hirzel Jr
**Treas:* William J Hirzel
QA Dir: Emily Neuenschwander
IT Man: Heidi Bandrowski
IT Man: Heidi Kopeck
Sls Mgr: Steve Hirzel

D-U-N-S 05-248-4961 IMP/EXP
HIS CO INC
HISCO
6650 Concord Park Dr, Houston, TX 77040-4098
Tel (713) 934-1700 *Founded/Ownrshp* 1940
Sales 221.1MM^E *EMP* 288^E
SIC 5065 5063 Electronic parts & equipment; Electronic wire & cable; Insulators, electrical; Electronic parts & equipment; Electronic wire & cable; Insulators, electrical
Pr: Robert Dill
COO: Edward Murphy
CFO: Mark Linville
**Ex VP:* Paul Gill
Sr VP: Tom McElroy
**VP:* Jim Caprile
**VP:* Bill Doshier
**VP:* Mark Joslyn
VP: Brian Murphy
VP: Gary Niemand
**VP:* Tommy O'Connor
VP: Nelson Picard
**VP:* Paul Seaback
**VP:* Thor Skonnord
**VP:* Scott Stover
**VP:* Merle O'Tanner

HIS COATINGS
See H-I-S PAINT MANUFACTURING CO INC

D-U-N-S 96-966-9811
HIS CONSTRUCTORS INC
HIS TRANSPORT
5150 E 65th St Ste B, Indianapolis, IN 46220-4995
Tel (317) 284-1195 *Founded/Ownrshp* 1997
Sales 28.6MM^E *EMP* 100
SIC 1799 4959 1622 8744 Decontamination services; Environmental cleanup services; Bridge construction;
Pr: Jim Nance
**Sr VP:* Steve Ahlersmeyer
**Sr VP:* Neil Comstock
VP: Ahlersmeyer Steve
Genl Mgr: Amy Kelly

D-U-N-S 80-373-8236 IMP/EXP
HIS INTERNATIONAL CORP
NO KIDDING
34 W 33rd St Fl 2, New York, NY 10001-3304
Tel (212) 594-4250 *Founded/Ownrshp* 1993
Sales 102.2MM *EMP* 40
SIC 5137 Infants' wear; Infants' wear
Pr: Stephen Rahmey
**CFO:* Eli Hamui
Ex VP: Ralph Zirdok

D-U-N-S 96-576-8075 IMP
HIS INTERNATIONAL GROUP LLC
(*Suby of* BENTEX GROUP INC) ★
34 W 33rd St Fl 2, New York, NY 10001-3304
Tel (212) 594-4250 *Founded/Ownrshp* 2009
Sales 100.0MM *EMP* 30
SIC 5136 Men's & boys' clothing; Men's & boys' clothing

D-U-N-S 78-526-5216
HIS INTERNATIONAL TOURS NY INC
(*Suby of* HIS USA INC) ★
420 E 3rd St Ste 608, Los Angeles, CA 90013-1645
Tel (213) 624-0777 *Founded/Ownrshp* 1988
Sales 73.0MM *EMP* 150
SIC 4725 Sightseeing tour companies
Pr: Mafuaki Kipaya
**Treas:* Hideo Sawda

D-U-N-S 01-728-0693
HIS PIPELINE LLC
7055 Monroe Highway Ball, Ball, LA 71405
Tel (318) 704-6085 *Founded/Ownrshp* 2004
Sales 27.0MM^E *EMP* 150
SIC 1623 Oil & gas pipeline construction; Oil & gas pipeline construction

HIS STAMPING DIVISION
See AMERICAN ENGINEERED COMPONENTS INC

HIS TRANSPORT
See HIS CONSTRUCTORS INC

D-U-N-S 83-039-3448
HIS USA INC
(*Suby of* H.I.S. CO., LTD.)
489 5th Ave Fl 20, New York, NY 10017-6125
Tel (212) 231-3282 *Founded/Ownrshp* 2010
Sales 90.0MM^E *EMP* 199^E
SIC 4724 Travel agencies
Pr: Mafuaki Kipaya

D-U-N-S 11-201-2323 IMP
HISADA AMERICA INC
(*Suby of* HISADA CO.,LTD.)
1191 S Walnut St Ste 102, Edinburgh, IN 46124-9053
Tel (812) 526-0756 *Founded/Ownrshp* 1997
Sales 24.5MM^E *EMP* 90
SIC 3714 Motor vehicle parts & accessories
Pr: Akio Saito
**Pr:* Makoto Fukui
**VP:* Toro Mituhara
VP: Ronald R Stevens
Ql Cn Mgr: Terry Rudinsky

HISAL
See HITACHI SOLUTIONS AMERICA LTD

D-U-N-S 01-320-0824
HISAMITSU PHARMACEUTICAL CO INC
(*Suby of* HISAMITSU PHARMACEUTICAL CO., INC.)
2730 Loker Ave W, Carlsbad, CA 92010-6603
Tel (760) 931-1756 *Founded/Ownrshp* 1998
Sales 153.1MM^E *EMP* 626
SIC 8733 Medical research; Medical research
CEO: Nakatomi Hirotaka

D-U-N-S 17-708-5789
HISCALL INC
1001 Gentry Cir, Dickson, TN 37055-3024
Tel (615) 740-7771 *Founded/Ownrshp* 2004
Sales 27.3MM^E *EMP* 115^E
SIC 8999 Communication services
Pr: Gary Luffman
CTO: Rich Clark
Trfc Dir: Jennifer Garton
Sales Asso: Angela Hill
Sales Asso: Kevin McCann

HISCO
See HIS CO INC

D-U-N-S 09-557-4620
HISCOCK & BARCLAY LLP
BARCLAY DAMON
1 Park Rd, Syracuse, NY 13212-3541
Tel (315) 425-2700 *Founded/Ownrshp* 1956
Sales 27.2MM^E *EMP* 280
SIC 8111 General practice law office; General practice law office
Mng Pt: John P Langan
Pt: H Douglas Barclay
Pt: Robert A Barrer
Pt: Christopher J Bonner
Pt: James J Canfield
Pt: J Eric Charlton
Pt: George S Deptula
Pt: Michael E Ferdman
Pt: Florine R Gingerich
Pt: Steven C Haas
Pt: John E Haslinger
Pt: Albert Hessberg III
Pt: Richard K Hughes
Pt: David B Liddell
Pt: Charles C Martorana
Pt: Frederick S Marty
Pt: Mark R McNamara
Pt: John C Merkel
Pt: Sandra S O'Loughlin
Pt: Taylor H Obold
Pt: Frederick F Shantz

D-U-N-S 79-047-0392
HISCOX INC
(*Suby of* HISCOX LTD)
520 Madison Ave Rm 3200, New York, NY 10022-4324
Tel (914) 273-7400 *Founded/Ownrshp* 2005
Sales NA *EMP* 150^E
SIC 6411 Fire insurance underwriters' laboratories; Insurance agents & brokers
Pr: Ben Walter
**Ch Bd:* Robert S Childs
**COO:* Eric Pruss
**CFO:* Gavin Watson
Sr VP: Neil Lipuma
Sr VP: Karen Neri
Sr VP: John O'Neil
VP: Brigitte Anninos
VP: Irma Edel
VP: Kevin Henry
VP: Doug Karpp
VP: Mark Lees
VP: Eric Micheals
VP: Brian Price
VP: Jennifer Rubin
VP: Daniel Sock

D-U-N-S 01-676-3662 IMP/EXP
HISENSE USA CORP
(*Suby of* HISENSE GROUP CO., LTD.)
7310 Mcginnis Ferry Rd # 100, Suwanee, GA 30024-0016
Tel (678) 318-9060 *Founded/Ownrshp* 2007
Sales 398.2MM^E *EMP* 50
SIC 7622 Household audio & video equipment; Radio & television repair; Television repair shop
CEO: Lawrence Lin
**CFO:* Sophie Chen
VP: Peter Erdman
VP: Arthur Hays
VP: Zhan Jiajin
VP: Lin Lan
VP: John Riddle
VP: Matthew Sekelick
VP Opers: Yunfang Feng
VP Mktg: Steven Cohen
VP Mktg: Jonathan Frank

D-U-N-S 18-503-2547
HISHMEH ENTERPRISES INC
DOMINO'S PIZZA
1811 Knoll Dr Ste A, Ventura, CA 93003-7321
Tel (805) 650-9946 *Founded/Ownrshp* 1990
Sales 13.0MM *EMP* 350
SIC 5812 Pizzeria, chain; Pizzeria, chain
CEO: Husam Hishmeh
**Ch Bd:* Nicola Hishmeh
**Pr:* Essem Hishmeh
**VP:* Wael Hishmeh
Snr Mgr: Tareq Hishmeh

D-U-N-S 01-700-6847
HISPANIC EXPRESS INC
1900 S Main St, Los Angeles, CA 90007-1418
Tel (213) 763-4949 *Founded/Ownrshp* 2001
Sales 57.2MM^E *EMP* 275
SIC 6211 4724 Security brokers & dealers; Travel agencies; Security brokers & dealers; Travel agencies
CEO: Gary Cypres

D-U-N-S 13-023-0746
HISPANIC FOODS INC
FIESTA FOODS
115 S 10th Ave, Pasco, WA 99301-6806
Tel (509) 545-0596 *Founded/Ownrshp* 2003
Sales 34.1MM^E *EMP* 169
SIC 5411 Grocery stores; Grocery stores
Pr: Craig Gaylord
Genl Mgr: Ted Owens

D-U-N-S 19-927-2613
HISPANIC GROUP CORP
8181 Nw 14th St Ste 250, Doral, FL 33126-1618
Tel (305) 477-5483 *Founded/Ownrshp* 2002
Sales 48.0MM *EMP* 35
SIC 7311 Advertising agencies; Advertising agencies
Pr: Jose L Valdarrama
**CFO:* Ricardo Samanez
**VP:* Kurt Pflucker
Creative D: Cesar Bettocchi
Dir IT: Charles Forrette

D-U-N-S 09-717-0872
HISPANIC HOUSING DEVELOPMENT CORP
325 N Wells St Fl 8, Chicago, IL 60654-8159
Tel (312) 602-6500 *Founded/Ownrshp* 1975
Sales 30.1MM *EMP* 208
Accts Plante & Moran Pllc Chicago
SIC 6513 Apartment hotel operation; Apartment hotel operation
Pr: Hipolito Roldan
**COO:* Laura Selby
Mktg Dir: Ramonita Ruiz

HISPANIC OUTREACH SERVICES
See ROMAN CATHOLIC DIOCESE OF ALBANY INC

HISSHO SUSHI
See LWIN FAMILY CO

D-U-N-S 09-328-1947
HISSONG GROUP INC
2820 Brecksville Rd, Richfield, OH 44286-9740
Tel (330) 659-3770 *Founded/Ownrshp* 1978
Sales 47.4MM^E *EMP* 115
SIC 5511 7538 Trucks, tractors & trailers: new & used; General truck repair; Trucks, tractors & trailers: new & used; General truck repair
Ch: Robert E Hissong
**Pr:* Darren Hissong
**CFO:* Alan J Murrow
Admn Mgr: Mike Grau

D-U-N-S 01-843-4084
HISSONG-KENWORTH INC (OH)
KENWORTH OF RITCHFIELD
(*Suby of* HISSONG GROUP INC) ★
2890 Brecksville Rd, Richfield, OH 44286-9740
Tel (330) 659-4123 *Founded/Ownrshp* 1961
Sales 20.7MM^E *EMP* 60
SIC 5511 5531 Trucks, tractors & trailers: new & used; Truck equipment & parts; Trucks, tractors & trailers: new & used; Truck equipment & parts
Pr: Darren Hissong
**CFO:* Alan Murrow
**Treas:* Robert E Hissong
Store Mgr: Todd Petrowski

HISTORIC AND DISTINCTIVE HOMES
See ROBERT N HOFF II

D-U-N-S 14-722-1006 IMP/EXP
■ **HISTORIC AOL LLC**
(*Suby of* AOL INC) ★
22000 Aol Way, Dulles, VA 20166-9302
Tel (703) 265-1000 *Founded/Ownrshp* 2001
Sales 867.1MM^E *EMP* 4,450
SIC 4813 7299 ; Information services, consumer; ; Information services, consumer
CEO: Timothy M Armstrong
**Ch Bd:* J Michael Kelly
V Ch: K J Nova
Pr: Brad Garlinghouse
**Pr:* Ron Grant
**Pr:* Lisa Hook
Pr: Jeff Levick
**Pr:* Joe Redling
**Pr:* Joanna Shields
**Pr:* Neil Smit
**CFO:* Arthur Minson
**V Ch Bd:* Ted Leonsis
**V Ch Bd:* Joseph A Ripp
**Chf Mktg O:* John Burbank
Top Exec: Bob Venezia
Ex VP: Peter Ashkin
Ex VP: Randall Boe
Ex VP: Ted Cahall
Ex VP: Joel Davidson
Ex VP: Chuck Gafvert
Ex VP: Dave Harmon

D-U-N-S 13-929-6776
HISTORIC HOTELS OF RICHMOND LLC
JEFFERSON HOTEL
101 W Franklin St, Richmond, VA 23220-5009
Tel (804) 788-8000 *Founded/Ownrshp* 1991
Sales 32.7MM^E *EMP* 375
SIC 7011 5812 5947 Hotels; Eating places; Caterers; Gift, novelty & souvenir shop; Hotels; Eating places; Caterers; Gift, novelty & souvenir shop
Exec: Walter Bundy
Genl Mgr: Robin West
Off Mgr: David Glover
Sls Mgr: Betsy Bagnell
Sls Mgr: Trisha Brinkley

D-U-N-S 05-310-8895
■ **HISTORIC LIFEPOINT HOSPITALS INC**
(*Suby of* LIFEPOINT HEALTH INC) ★
330 Seven Springs Way, Brentwood, TN 37027-5098
Tel (615) 372-8500 *Founded/Ownrshp* 1999, 2005
Sales 1.0MMM^E *EMP* 9,900
SIC 8062 General medical & surgical hospitals; General medical & surgical hospitals
CEO: William F Carpenter III
**COO:* William M Gracey
**CFO:* Leif M Murphy
**Sr VP:* Neil D Hemphill
Dir Rx: Ron Tucker
IT Man: David Wright
VP Mktg: Mary Shipp

D-U-N-S 80-354-7728
HISTORIC MISSION INN CORP
MISSION INN HOTEL AND SPA, THE
(*Suby of* ENTREPRENEURIAL CAPITAL CORP) ★
3649 Mission Inn Ave, Riverside, CA 92501-3364
Tel (951) 784-0300 *Founded/Ownrshp* 1992
Sales 55.4MM^E *EMP* 460
SIC 5813 5812 7011 8412 Drinking places; Eating places; Hotels; Museums & art galleries; Drinking places; Eating places; Hotels; Museums & art galleries
Pr: Duane R Roberts
**CFO:* Cliff Day
Bd of Dir: Kathy Wright
**VP:* Diana Rosure
Exec: Loren Lawe
Off Mgr: Ingrid Morgan
Dir IT: Robert Galvin
Sls Dir: Janice Hollis
Sls Mgr: Anderson Ewing
Sls Mgr: Kristina Porter
Sls Mgr: Opal Strong

D-U-N-S 16-200-0293
HISTORIC PRESERVATION AGENCY
1 Old State Capitol Plz, Springfield, IL 62701-1512
Tel (217) 782-4836 *Founded/Ownrshp* 1985
Sales 3.2MM^E *EMP* 350
SIC 8399 Council for social agency; Council for social agency

D-U-N-S 06-462-5205
HISTORIC RESTORATION INC
812 Gravier St Apt 200, New Orleans, LA 70112-1467
Tel (504) 493-6129 *Founded/Ownrshp* 1982
Sales 168.8MM^E *EMP* 530
SIC 6552 Land subdividers & developers, residential; Land subdividers & developers, commercial; Land subdividers & developers, residential; Land subdividers & developers, commercial
CFO: Ray Stadafora
**Sec:* Ray T Spadafora
VP: Sidney Barthelemy
VP: Josh Collen
VP: Hal Fairbanks
VP: Mark Maher
VP: Steven Nance
VP: Ron Pilgrim
Genl Mgr: Norman Hebert
Off Admin: Robin Cancienne
CTO: David Arthur

D-U-N-S 60-366-6488
HISTORIC TOURS OF AMERICA INC
201 Front St Ste 107, Key West, FL 33040-8346
Tel (305) 292-8909 *Founded/Ownrshp* 1984
Sales 51.8MM^E *EMP* 850
Accts Appelrouth O Farah & Co Cor
SIC 7999 4725 4141 5947 8422 Tour & guide services; Sightseeing tour companies; Local bus charter service; Gift shop; Aquariums & zoological gardens; Tour & guide services; Sightseeing tour companies; Local bus charter service; Gift shop; Aquariums & zoological gardens
Pr: Edwin O Swift III
**Treas:* Ben McPherson
**VP:* Gerald Mosher
Ex Dir: Beth Morrison
Genl Mgr: Dave Chatterton
Off Mgr: Leah Benner
IT Man: George Arnold
Natl Sales: Bob Bernreuter
Mktg Dir: Piper Smith

D-U-N-S 95-846-6278 IMP
■ **HISTORIC TW INC**
(*Suby of* TIME WARNER INC) ★
75 Rockefeller Plz, New York, NY 10019-6908
Tel (212) 484-8000 *Founded/Ownrshp* 1996
Sales 2.0MMM^E *EMP* 9,840^E

SIC 3652 6794 2741 7812 4841 2721 Compact laser discs, prerecorded; Magnetic tape (audio): prerecorded; Music licensing to radio stations; Performance rights, publishing & licensing; Music royalties, sheet & record; Music, sheet: publishing only, not printed on site; Music books: publishing only, not printed on site; Motion picture production & distribution; Television film production; Motion picture production & distribution, television; Video tape production; Cable television services; Magazines: publishing only, not printed on site
V Ch Bd: RE Turner
**Pr:* Richard D Parsons
**CFO:* Joseph Ripp
**Ex VP:* Christopher P Bogart
**VP:* Carl F Dill Jr
**CTO:* Michael Dunn

D-U-N-S 09-972-4275
HISTORICAL COMMISSION TEXAS
(*Suby of* EXECUTIVE OFFICE OF STATE OF TEXAS) ★
1511 Colorado St, Austin, TX 78701-1664
Tel (512) 463-6100 *Founded/Ownrshp* 2005
Sales NA *EMP* 299[E]
SIC 9199 General government administration; ; General government administration;
Ofcr: Carlos Castro
Ofcr: Bill Martin
Off Mgr: Ana Clark
Off Mgr: Donna McCarver
Off Mgr: Virginia Owens
Off Mgr: Mae Perkins
IT Man: Andrew Campbell
Site Mgr: Kaitlin Ammon
Site Mgr: Mitch Baird
Site Mgr: Ashley Carter
Site Mgr: Georgia Davis

D-U-N-S 84-570-7173
HISTORICAL SOCIETY OF CENTINELA VALLEY
7634 Midfield Ave, Los Angeles, CA 90045-3234
Tel (310) 649-6272 *Founded/Ownrshp* 1960
Sales 12.4MM[E] *EMP* 300
SIC 8412 Historical society; Historical society
Pr: Leonard Utter
**VP:* Claydine Burt

D-U-N-S 06-362-1981
HIT INC
1007 18th St Nw, Mandan, ND 58554-1639
Tel (701) 663-0376 *Founded/Ownrshp* 1979
Sales 26.6MM *EMP* 250
Accts Eide Bailly Llp Bismarck Nd
SIC 8399 8331 8322 8641 Community development groups; Vocational training agency; Child guidance agency; Civic social & fraternal associations; Community development groups; Vocational training agency; Child guidance agency; Civic social & fraternal associations
Ex Dir: Mike Rembold
**VP:* Kirk Greff
Snr Mgr: Christina Tosseth

D-U-N-S 10-184-7804 IMP/EXP
HIT PROMOTIONAL PRODUCTS INC
7150 Bryan Dairy Rd, Largo, FL 33777-1501
Tel (727) 541-5561 *Founded/Ownrshp* 1981
Sales 228.8MM[E] *EMP* 525
SIC 2759 3993 Promotional printing; Signs & advertising specialties; Promotional printing; Signs & advertising specialties
Pr: Arthur W Schmidt
**CFO:* Gary D Meadows
Chf Mktg O: Stacy Zumwalt
**VP:* Christopher J Schmidt
Exec: James Walsh
**Prin:* Elizabeth Schmidt
Rgnl Mgr: Tom Levin
MIS Dir: Anne Maass
Plnt Mgr: Mike Bingham
VP Mktg: Jennifer Grigorian
Mktg Dir: Frank Capolongo

D-U-N-S 05-156-2908 IMP/EXP
HITACHI AMERICA LTD
(*Suby of* HITACHI, LTD.)
50 Prospect Ave, Tarrytown, NY 10591-4698
Tel (914) 332-5800 *Founded/Ownrshp* 1959
Sales 2.1MMM[E] *EMP* 15,537
SIC 5084 5065 3577 5063 5045 3651

D-U-N-S 96-780-7111
HITACHI AMERICA LTD HEALTH &WELFARE PLAN
50 Prospect Ave, Tarrytown, NY 10591-4698
Tel (914) 332-5800 *Founded/Ownrshp* 2011
Sales 47.3MM *EMP* 2
Accts Eos Accountants Llp Teaneck
SIC 8099 Health & allied services; Health & allied services
Prin: G Takiguchi

HITACHI AUTOMOTIVE PRODUCTS
See HITACHI AUTOMOTIVE SYSTEMS AMERICAS INC

D-U-N-S 13-035-8682 IMP/EXP
HITACHI AUTOMOTIVE SYSTEMS AMERICAS INC
HITACHI AUTOMOTIVE PRODUCTS
(*Suby of* HITACHI AMERICA LTD) ★
955 Warwick Rd, Harrodsburg, KY 40330-1067
Tel (859) 734-9451 *Founded/Ownrshp* 1985
Sales 667.8MM[E] *EMP* 3,000
SIC 3694 3714 3699 3625 Alternators, automotive; Ignition systems, high frequency; Motor vehicle parts & accessories; Electrical equipment & supplies; Relays & industrial controls; Alternators, automotive; Ignition systems, high frequency; Motor vehicle parts & accessories; Electrical equipment & supplies; Relays & industrial controls
Pr: Masaaki Fujisawa
**COO:* Shigetoshi Nashimoto
**CFO:* Hiroyuki Okada
**Treas:* H Utsunomiya
Ex VP: Rex L Carter
VP: Lee Aho
**VP:* Scott McBroom
VP: William Mills
Prgrm Mgr: Ed Abernethy
Prgrm Mgr: Ed Brambs
Prgrm Mgr: Tim Granchi

D-U-N-S 15-400-8312 IMP
HITACHI CABLE AMERICA INC
(*Suby of* HITACHI METALS, LTD.)
2 Manhattanville Rd # 301, Purchase, NY 10577-2118
Tel (914) 694-9200 *Founded/Ownrshp* 1981
Sales 128.6MM[E] *EMP* 613
SIC 3052 Rubber & plastics hose & beltings; Rubber & plastics hose & beltings
CEO: Toro Aoki
CFO: David Zinsner
Sec: Tatsuo Kinoshita
Sr VP: John Gibson
Sr VP: Masaaki Tomiyama
VP: Katsura Ishikawa
QA Dir: Amor Fuentecilla
Netwrk Mgr: Jumpei Watanabe
Netwrk Eng: Kazutoshi Kariya
Mktg Dir: Makoto Matsuzaki
Sls Dir: Yuichi Kubota

D-U-N-S 19-267-1931
HITACHI CAPITAL AMERICA CORP
HENNESSEY CAPITAL
(*Suby of* HITACHI CAPITAL CORPORATION)
800 Connecticut Ave 4n01, Norwalk, CT 06854-1738
Tel (203) 956-3000 *Founded/Ownrshp* 1989
Sales NA *EMP* 102[E]
SIC 6159 Loan institutions, general & industrial; Loan institutions, general & industrial
CEO: Yoshiyuke Kume
**Pr:* William H Besgen
**CFO:* Terry Hatfield
**Sec:* Satoshi Tashiro
**Chf Cred:* Ryan Collison
**Sr VP:* Yoshi Kobayashi
VP: Junichi Akiyama
VP: Ryan Col
VP: Mark Duncan
**VP:* James M Giaimo
VP: Chris Petersen

D-U-N-S 02-126-4114 IMP
HITACHI CHEMICAL CO AMERICA LTD
(*Suby of* HITACHI CHEMICAL COMPANY, LTD.)
2150 N 1st St 350, San Jose, CA 95131-2020
Tel (408) 873-2200 *Founded/Ownrshp* 1975
Sales 23.0MM[E] *EMP* 50
Accts Armanino Mckenna Llp Cpas Sa
SIC 5169 5063 Industrial chemicals; Insulators, electrical
Pr: Toshinari Itakura
Treas: Hiroyuki Nii
VP: Terry Fischer
VP: Hiroyuki Takei
Sls Mgr: Bill Graves

D-U-N-S 10-211-3867
HITACHI CHEMICAL DIAGNOSTICS INC
(*Suby of* HITACHI CHEMICAL COMPANY, LTD.)
630 Clyde Ct, Mountain View, CA 94043-2239
Tel (650) 961-5501 *Founded/Ownrshp* 1982
Sales 36.5MM[E] *EMP* 190
SIC 3821 2835 8071 Laboratory measuring apparatus; In vitro diagnostics; Medical laboratories; Laboratory measuring apparatus; In vitro diagnostics; Medical laboratories
CEO: Takashi Miyamoto
Pr: Hideki Itaya
**Pr:* Kazuyoshi Tsunoda
CFO: John Billings
**CFO:* Keiichi Takeda
VP: Kiioshi Yasue
Ex Dir: Rob Stephens
Opers Mgr: Sharon Miyahara
Prd Mgr: Paul Magginetti
Ql Cn Mgr: Donald Postel
Sls Mgr: Dwight Smith

D-U-N-S 00-231-7506 IMP
HITACHI CHEMICAL DUPONT MICROSYSTEMS LLC
HD MICROSYSTEMS
250 Cheesequake Rd, Parlin, NJ 08859-1080
Tel (732) 613-2404 *Founded/Ownrshp* 1997
Sales 35.2MM[E] *EMP* 100[E]
SIC 2821 Polyimides (skybond, kaplon); Polyimides (skybond, kaplon)
Pr: Toichi Hamajima

D-U-N-S 60-289-8603 IMP
HITACHI COMPUTER PRODUCTS (AMERICA) INC
(*Suby of* HITACHI DATA SYSTEMS CORP) ★
1800 E Imhoff Rd, Norman, OK 73071-1200
Tel (405) 360-5500 *Founded/Ownrshp* 1986
Sales 97.1MM[E] *EMP* 600
SIC 3577 3572 7379 Computer peripheral equipment; Computer storage devices; Computer related consulting services; Computer peripheral equipment; Computer storage devices; Computer related consulting services
Pr: George Wilson
**Treas:* Randy Reynolds
Ex VP: Michiharu Nakamura
Sr VP: Stephen Gomersall
Sr VP: Kazumasa Kozawa
Sr VP: Kazuaki Masamoto
Sr VP: Takuo Nakashima
Dept Mgr: Shaun McGinnis
IT Man: Michelle Mertens
Mgr Info S: Robin Woodard
Opers Mgr: Melissa Ashley

D-U-N-S 00-459-5661 IMP
HITACHI CONSULTING CORP
(*Suby of* HITACHI, LTD.)
14643 Dallas Pkwy Ste 800, Dallas, TX 75254-8870
Tel (214) 665-7000 *Founded/Ownrshp* 2000
Sales 515.1MM[E] *EMP* 4,500
SIC 7379 7374 ; Data processing & preparation; ; Data processing & preparation
Pr: Philip R Parr
CFO: Bruce V Ballengee
**CFO:* Barry Honea
Ex VP: Stephen Brant
Ex VP: Larry Deboever
Ex VP: Sanjay Jesrani
Ex VP: Patrik Sj Stedt
Sr VP: Feroze Mohammed
VP: John Allen
VP: William Boucher
VP: Gary Brown
VP: Chris Buri
VP: Greg Carter
VP: Steve Crosnoe
VP: Bob Davis
VP: Ellen Dowd
VP: Stephen Engel
VP: Rob Farris
VP: Dan Gardner
VP: Willi Graef
VP: Randy Green

D-U-N-S 62-182-4911
HITACHI CONSULTING SOFTWARE SERVICES INC
(*Suby of* HITACHI CONSULTING CORP) ★
8000 Jarvis Ave 130, Newark, CA 94560-1154
Tel (510) 742-4100 *Founded/Ownrshp* 2011
Sales 26.2MM[E] *EMP* 2,000
SIC 7299 7371 Information services, consumer; Computer software development; Information services, consumer; Computer software development
CEO: Philip R Parr
**CFO:* Robert Hersh
**Ex VP:* Douglas Allen
**Ex VP:* Ismael Fernandez De La Mata
**Ex VP:* GK Murthy
**Ex VP:* John O'Brien
Sr VP: Allen Deary
VP: Suresh Babuween
VP: Phil Hodsdon
VP: Gopala Krishna
VP: Sudheer Reddy
VP: Nick Simanteris
VP: Xiaomin Zheng
Exec: Feroze Mohammad

D-U-N-S 09-853-3599 EXP
HITACHI DATA SYSTEMS CORP
(*Suby of* HITACHI DATA SYSTEMS HOLDING CORP) ★
2845 Lafayette St, Santa Clara, CA 95050-2642
Tel (408) 970-1000 *Founded/Ownrshp* 1979, 1989
Sales 1.6MMM[E] *EMP* 3,287
SIC 5045 7378 7379 5734 4225 3571 Computers; Computer & data processing equipment repair/maintenance; Computer related maintenance services; Computer & software stores; Modems, monitors, terminals & disk drives: computers; General warehousing & storage; Mainframe computers; Computers; Computer & data processing equipment repair/maintenance; Computer related maintenance services; Computer & software stores; Modems, monitors, terminals & disk drives: computers; General warehousing & storage; Mainframe computers
Pr: Jack Domme
Ch Bd: Minoru Kosuge
CFO: Susan Lynch
CFO: Rick Martig
Bd of Dir: Paul Brisson
Ex VP: Rex L Carter
Ex VP: Greg Coplans
Ex VP: Randy Demont
Ex VP: Brian Householder
Ex VP: Nancy Long
Ex VP: Mark Mickelson
Ex VP: Frans Van Rijn
Ex VP: Michael Vath
Ex VP: Marlene Woodworth
Sr VP: Rex Carter
Exec: Tamsin Coates
Exec: Kiyoshi Hojo
Exec: Mike Stasko

D-U-N-S 07-875-6944
HITACHI DATA SYSTEMS FEDERAL CORP
(*Suby of* HITACHI DATA SYSTEMS CORP) ★
11921 Freedom Dr Ste 900, Reston, VA 20190-5636
Tel (703) 787-2901 *Founded/Ownrshp* 2012
Sales 35.0MM *EMP* 15[E]
SIC 3571 3572 5045 7372 7378 Electronic computers; Computer storage devices; Computers, peripherals & software; Prepackaged software; Computer maintenance & repair; Electronic computers; Computer storage devices; Computers, peripherals & software; Prepackaged software; Computer maintenance & repair
Pr: Michael Tanner
VP: Luis Castillo

D-U-N-S 06-599-9646
HITACHI DATA SYSTEMS HOLDING CORP
(*Suby of* HITACHI, LTD.)
2845 Lafayette St, Santa Clara, CA 95050-2642
Tel (408) 970-1000 *Founded/Ownrshp* 1989
Sales 1.6MMM[E] *EMP* 3,600
SIC 7299 Personal item care & storage services; Personal item care & storage services
CEO: Jack Domme
**CFO:* Susan Lynch
Ofcr: Cheryl Davenport
VP: Keigo Iechika
VP: Atsushi Ugajin
Snr Mgr: Cathy Lott

D-U-N-S 10-565-0860 IMP
HITACHI HIGH TECHNOLOGIES AMERICA INC
(*Suby of* HITACHI HIGH-TECHNOLOGIES CORPORATION)
10 N Martingale Rd # 500, Schaumburg, IL 60173-2099
Tel (847) 273-4141 *Founded/Ownrshp* 2002
Sales 148.0MM[E] *EMP* 500
SIC 5065 Semiconductor test equipment; Semiconductor manufacturing machinery; Electronic parts & equipment
Pr: Masao Hisada
CFO: Shunichi Uno
Ex Ofcr: Junichi Hashimoto
Ex Ofcr: Joji Honda
Ex Ofcr: Toshiyuki Ikeda
Ex Ofcr: Ryuichi Nakashima
Ex Ofcr: Hirohide Omoto
Ex Ofcr: Hiroshi Tajima
Chf Mktg O: Toshio Kajimoto
Ofcr: Gunnar Nilsson
Ex VP: Ray Mizutani
Sr VP: Andrew Gelb
Sr VP: Norio Kobayashi
Sr VP: Takashi Matsuzaka
Sr VP: Naoki Mitarai
Sr VP: Masahiro Miyazaki
VP: Sarah Johnson
VP: Katsutaka Kimura
VP: Mike Levans
VP: Hidenori Nagao
VP: Morihiro Nishida

D-U-N-S 03-970-0430
HITACHI HOME ELECTRONICS (AMERICA) INC
(*Suby of* HITACHI AMERICA LTD) ★
2420 Fenton St 200, Chula Vista, CA 91914-3516
Tel (619) 591-5200 *Founded/Ownrshp* 1987
Sales 46.3MM[E] *EMP* 676
SIC 3651 Television receiving sets; Tape recorders: cassette, cartridge or reel: household use; Video cassette recorders/players & accessories; Television receiving sets; Tape recorders: cassette, cartridge or reel: household use; Video cassette recorders/players & accessories
CEO: Kenji Nakamura
**Pr:* Tomomi ITOH
CFO: Takashi Tsujiura
**Treas:* Tsuneo Yuki
**Ex VP:* Gary Bennett
Ex VP: Mike Cordano
Ex VP: Michiro Funatsu
**Ex VP:* Tatsou Hagiwara
VP: Carl Hamilton
**Prin:* Takehiko Kataoka
CTO: Adrienne Grady

D-U-N-S 09-286-2713 IMP
HITACHI HVB INC
(*Suby of* HITACHI, LTD.)
7250 Mcginnis Ferry Rd, Suwanee, GA 30024-1245
Tel (770) 495-1755 *Founded/Ownrshp* 1982
Sales 55.4MM[E] *EMP* 100
Accts Smith & Howard Atlanta Ga
SIC 3613 Power circuit breakers; Power circuit breakers
CEO: Norm Sone
V Ch: Kumio Katada
**CEO:* Geoff Bryant
**CFO:* Dennis McNulty
Sr VP: Clark Nishida
Sr VP: Terri Ono
VP: Gerard Corbett
Exec: Xi Zhu
CTO: Wess Wadsworth
QA Dir: Cecilia Jung
Opers Mgr: Tim Wideman

D-U-N-S 01-361-7840 IMP
HITACHI KOKI USA LTD
HITACHI POWER TOOL USA
(*Suby of* HITACHI KOKI CO., LTD.)
1111 Broadway Ave, Braselton, GA 30517-2900
Tel (770) 925-1774 *Founded/Ownrshp* 1995
Sales 86.9MM[E] *EMP* 175
SIC 5084 Industrial machinery & equipment; Industrial machinery & equipment
CEO: Shoji Matsushima
Sr VP: Karl Miyamoto
VP: Harry Baldwin
VP: Steve Karaga
VP: Hiro Yumoto
Genl Mgr: Benjie Hopkins
CIO: Jason Saur
Natl Sales: Bruce Weyhe
VP Sls: Joe Leffler
Sls Dir: Chanda Tacto
Sls Dir: Jason Trucchi

D-U-N-S 06-194-0441 IMP/EXP
HITACHI KOKUSAI ELECTRIC AMERICA LTD
(*Suby of* HITACHI KOKUSAI ELECTRIC INC.)
150 Crossways Park Dr, Woodbury, NY 11797-2028
Tel (516) 921-7200 *Founded/Ownrshp* 1963
Sales 24.8MM[E] *EMP* 28
Accts Ernst & Young Llp New York N
SIC 5043 3651 5065 3663 5084 Photographic cameras, projectors, equipment & supplies; Household audio & video equipment; Video equipment, electronic; Radio & TV communications equipment; Instruments & control equipment; Photographic cameras, projectors, equipment & supplies; Household audio & video equipment; Video equipment, electronic; Radio & TV communications equipment; Instruments & control equipment
Pr: Yuchi Otsuka
VP: Jack Breitenbucher
**VP:* Robert Johnston
Mktg Mgr: Toni Martin

D-U-N-S 19-690-3496 IMP
HITACHI MAXCO LTD
HITACHI MX
(*Suby of* HITACHI METALS TECHNO, LTD.)
1630 Cobb Intl Blvd Nw, Kennesaw, GA 30152-4353
Tel (678) 403-1387 *Founded/Ownrshp* 1987
Sales 37.7MM[E] *EMP* 90
SIC 5085 3568 1629 Industrial supplies; Chain, power transmission; Waste water & sewage treatment plant construction; Industrial supplies; Chain, power transmission; Waste water & sewage treatment plant construction
CEO: Mark Yamamoto
**CFO:* Douglas A Roberts
VP: Egbert David
**VP:* David Egbert
Sales Exec: Tracy Walker
Sls Mgr: Steven Egbert

D-U-N-S 60-315-6043 IMP
HITACHI MEDICAL SYSTEMS AMERICA INC
(*Suby of* HITACHI MEDICAL CORPORATION)
1959 Summit Commerce Park, Twinsburg, OH 44087-2371
Tel (330) 425-1313 *Founded/Ownrshp* 1989
Sales 221.8MM[E] *EMP* 370
SIC 5047 Diagnostic equipment, medical; Diagnostic equipment, medical
Pr: Donald Broomfield
COO: Steve Stofiel
**Treas:* Richard Kurz
**VP:* William Bishop
**VP:* James Confer
**VP:* Richard Katz
**VP:* Robert McCarthy
**VP:* Sheldon Schaffer
IT Man: Michelle Mertens
Opers Supe: Tony Radtke
VP Sls: Rechard Miller

D-U-N-S 07-057-2482 IMP/EXP
HITACHI METALS AMERICA LLC
HITACHI METALS AMERICA, LTD.
(*Suby of* HITACHI METALS, LTD.)
2 Manhattanville Rd # 301, Purchase, NY 10577-2103
Tel (914) 694-9200 *Founded/Ownrshp* 1965
Sales NA *EMP* 2,479
SIC 3264 3577 3365 5051 3321 3559 Magnets, permanent: ceramic or ferrite; Computer peripheral equipment; Aluminum & aluminum-based alloy castings; Steel; Castings, rough: iron or steel; Ductile iron castings; Gray iron castings; Automotive related machinery; Magnets, permanent: ceramic or ferrite; Computer peripheral equipment; Aluminum & aluminum-based alloy castings; Steel; Castings, rough: iron or steel; Ductile iron castings; Gray iron castings; Automotive related machinery
CEO: Hideaki Takahashi
**Ch Bd:* Tomoyasu Kubota
**Pr:* Tomoyuki Hatano
**Pr:* Hiroaki Nakanishi
**CFO:* Toshiki Aoki

HITACHI METALS AMERICA, LTD.
See HITACHI METALS AMERICA LLC

D-U-N-S 05-939-2535 IMP
HITACHI METALS AUTOMOTIVE COMPONENTS USA LLC
HMAC
(*Suby of* HITACHI METALS AMERICA LLC) ★
18986 Route 287, Tioga, PA 16946-8815
Tel (217) 347-0600 *Founded/Ownrshp* 1999
Sales 81.4MM[E] *EMP* 531
SIC 3465 3321 3559 Body parts, automobile: stamped metal; Ductile iron castings; Automotive related machinery; Body parts, automobile: stamped metal; Ductile iron castings; Automotive related machinery
**CFO:* John Sprangler

D-U-N-S 62-547-5900 IMP
HITACHI METALS NORTH CAROLINA LTD
(*Suby of* HITACHI METALS AMERICA LLC) ★
1 Hitachi Metals Dr, China Grove, NC 28023-9461
Tel (704) 855-2800 *Founded/Ownrshp* 1994
Sales 45.6MM[E] *EMP* 150
SIC 3264 Magnets, permanent: ceramic or ferrite; Magnets, permanent: ceramic or ferrite
Pr: Pat Barton
**Sec:* Mark Stockwell

HITACHI MX
See HITACHI MAXCO LTD

D-U-N-S 18-554-4889 IMP
HITACHI POWDERED METALS (USA) INC
1024 Barachel Ln, Greensburg, IN 47240-1277
Tel (812) 663-5058 *Founded/Ownrshp* 1987
Sales 23.6MM[E] *EMP* 250[E]
SIC 3714 Motor vehicle parts & accessories; Motor vehicle parts & accessories
Ch Bd: Jun Sakai
**VP:* Greg Owens
Mtls Mgr: John Zola
Sls Mgr: Makoto Osawa

HITACHI POWER TOOL USA
See HITACHI KOKI USA LTD

D-U-N-S 79-347-1509 IMP
HITACHI SOLUTIONS AMERICA LTD
HISAL
(*Suby of* HITACHI SOLUTIONS, LTD.)
851 Traeger Ave Ste 200, San Bruno, CA 94066-3037
Tel (650) 615-7600 *Founded/Ownrshp* 1990
Sales 98.6MM[E] *EMP* 300
SIC 5045 7372 7373 Computer software; Prepackaged software; Computer integrated systems design
Pr: Keiho Akiyama
Sr VP: Scott Millwood
CIO: Mark Veronda
Mktg Dir: Tamara Schoder
Mktg Mgr: Kacee Roberts
Snr Mgr: Tom Galambos

D-U-N-S 19-450-6200 IMP
HITACHI TRANSPORT SYSTEM (AMERICA) LTD
21061 S Wstn Ave Ste 300, Torrance, CA 90501
Tel (310) 787-3420 *Founded/Ownrshp* 1988
Sales NA *EMP* 283
SIC 4731 Freight forwarding; Customhouse brokers; Transportation agents & brokers

D-U-N-S 09-955-0352
HITCH ENTERPRISES INC
309 Northridge Cir, Guymon, OK 73942-2735
Tel (580) 338-8575 *Founded/Ownrshp* 1946
Sales 53.9MM[E] *EMP* 300[E]
SIC 0191 0211 0212 5154 6221 0741 General farms, primarily crop; Beef cattle feedlots; Beef cattle except feedlots; Cattle; Commodity brokers, contracts; Veterinary services for livestock; General farms, primarily crop; Beef cattle feedlots; Beef cattle except feedlots; Cattle; Commodity brokers, contracts; Veterinary services for livestock
Pr: Paul H Hitch
Dir IT: Mike Yates

D-U-N-S 00-626-0525 IMP
HITCHCOCK INDUSTRIES INC
8701 Harriet Ave S, Minneapolis, MN 55420-2787
Tel (952) 881-1000 *Founded/Ownrshp* 1917
Sales 57.2MM[E] *EMP* 375
SIC 3365 3364 3544 3369 Aluminum & aluminum-based alloy castings; Magnesium & magnesium-base alloy die-castings; Special dies, tools, jigs & fixtures; Nonferrous foundries; Aluminum & aluminum-based alloy castings; Magnesium & magnesium-base alloy die-castings; Special dies, tools, jigs & fixtures; Nonferrous foundries
Ch Bd: Gregory T Hitchcock
VP Opers: Michael McLaughlin
S&M/Mgr: Daniel Steele

D-U-N-S 07-143-8154
HITCHCOCK SCRAP YARD INC
Rr 78 Box S, Canton, IL 61520
Tel (309) 668-3217 *Founded/Ownrshp* 1972
Sales 23.7MM *EMP* 55
SIC 5093

D-U-N-S 05-261-4026
HITCHIN POST STEAK CO
1101 S 5th St, Kansas City, KS 66105-2100
Tel (913) 647-0543 *Founded/Ownrshp* 1999
Sales 25.4MM[E] *EMP* 100
SIC 2015 Chicken slaughtering & processing; Chicken slaughtering & processing
Pr: Kim Cunningham
**VP:* Jason Cunningham
VP Opers: Nick Shepard

D-U-N-S 00-107-8682 IMP
HITCHINER MANUFACTURING CO INC
594 Elm St, Milford, NH 03055-4306
Tel (603) 673-1100 *Founded/Ownrshp* 1949
Sales 215.3MM *EMP* 1,580
Accts Grant Thornton Llp Boston Ma
SIC 3324 Steel investment foundries; Steel investment foundries
Ch: John H Morison III
**Pr:* Michael Hanrahan
**VP:* Scott Biederman
**VP:* Michael Brisebois
**VP:* Jorge Campillo
**VP:* Randal J Donovan
**VP:* Ken Miller
VP: Tim Sullivan
**VP:* Timothy Sullivan
Exec: Dave Cashon
Genl Mgr: Jason Mays

D-U-N-S 05-143-5071
HITCHING POST INC
HITCHING POST MOTOR SPORTS
350 17th Ave N, Hopkins, MN 55343-7343
Tel (952) 933-9649 *Founded/Ownrshp* 1970
Sales 24.1MM[E] *EMP* 70
SIC 5571 5531 5599 5551 Motorcycles; Motorcycle parts & accessories; All-terrain vehicles; Trailer hitches, automotive; Snowmobiles; Jet skis
Pr: Sherry Rosoff
**VP:* James Furseth
Genl Mgr: Bob Harris
Genl Mgr: John Mulligan

HITCHING POST MOTOR SPORTS
See HITCHING POST INC

D-U-N-S 11-878-8368
HITCHINS REFRACTORIES LLC
U S REFRACTORIES
4500 Louisville Ave, Louisville, KY 40209-1410
Tel (502) 367-8705 *Founded/Ownrshp* 1988
Sales 28.4MM[E] *EMP* 9
SIC 5085 Refractory material

HITCHLAND GRAIN CO
See ATTEBURY GRAIN LLC

D-U-N-S 00-828-7518 IMP/EXP
HITCO CARBON COMPOSITES INC
(*Suby of* SGL CARBON LLC) ★
1600 W 135th St, Gardena, CA 90249-2506
Tel (310) 527-0700 *Founded/Ownrshp* 1997
Sales 2.4MM[E] *EMP* 549
SIC 3769 3728 2295 Guided missile & space vehicle parts & auxiliary equipment; Brakes, aircraft; Coated fabrics, not rubberized; Guided missile & space vehicle parts & auxiliary equipment; Brakes, aircraft; Coated fabrics, not rubberized
Pr: Anthony Lawson
CFO: Steven Bower
Sr VP: Mark Kokosinski
Sr VP: John Saliture
VP: Gerald Taccini

D-U-N-S 00-450-8750
HITE CO (PA)
3101 Beale Ave, Altoona, PA 16601-1509
Tel (814) 944-6121 *Founded/Ownrshp* 1949
Sales 126.7MM[E] *EMP* 230
SIC 5063 Electrical fittings & construction materials; Electrical fittings & construction materials
CEO: R Lee Hite
**Pr:* T Scott Lawhead
**COO:* Ronald R Eberhart
**CFO:* Ronald Muffie
VP: Katie Brouse
VP: John Hatch
VP: Paul Shields
Store Mgr: Mike Belmont
MIS Dir: Debbie Claar
Opers Mgr: Jim Leonard
VP Mktg: John E Hatch

HITEM
See HI-TECH ELECTRONIC MANUFACTURING CORP

D-U-N-S 96-240-4849 EXP
HITOUCH BUSINESS SERVICES LLC
74 Kenny Pl, Saddle Brook, NJ 07663-5916
Tel (201) 636-9900 *Founded/Ownrshp* 2010
Sales 591.2MM[E] *EMP* 379[E]
SIC 5112 5021 5149 Stationery & office supplies; Computer & photocopying supplies; Office & public building furniture; Groceries & related products; Stationery & office supplies; Computer & photocopying supplies; Office & public building furniture; Groceries & related products
Pr: Michael Brown
**CEO:* Howard L Brown
**COO:* Michael J Palmer
**CFO:* Anthony Cavalieri

D-U-N-S 00-238-7132 IMP
HITRAN CORP (NJ)
362 State Route 31, Flemington, NJ 08822-5741
Tel (908) 782-5525 *Founded/Ownrshp* 1944, 1975
Sales 61.3MM[E] *EMP* 150
SIC 3612 Power transformers, electric; Line voltage regulators; Power transformers, electric; Line voltage regulators
Ch Bd: John Hindle Jr
**Pr:* John C Hindle III
**Treas:* William Hindle
**VP:* James S Hindle
S&M/VP: Chris Hughes

D-U-N-S 00-325-8746 IMP
HITT CONTRACTING INC (VA)
2900 Fairview Park Dr # 300, Falls Church, VA 22042-4513
Tel (703) 846-9000 *Founded/Ownrshp* 1943
Sales 921.2MM *EMP* 720
Accts Deloitte & Touche Llp Mclean
SIC 1542 Commercial & office buildings, renovation & repair; Commercial & office buildings, renovation & repair
Ch Bd: Russell A Hitt
**CFO:* Michael McGrae
**Co-Pr:* Brett Hitt
**Co-Pr:* James E Millar
Ex VP: Thomas Boogher
**Ex VP:* John M Britt
Sr VP: Joseph P Lafonte Jr
Sr VP: David R Michaelson
Sr VP: Kevin L Ott
Sr VP: John Planz
Sr VP: Nick D Raico
VP: Sue Alexander
**VP:* Jeremy S Bardin
VP: Michael Bellusci
VP: Ruth Bodnar
VP: Ron Cayton
VP: Roger H Delaney
VP: Michael J Filipowicz
VP: James Landefeld
VP: Drew M Mucci
VP: Patrick A Thomas

D-U-N-S 13-166-9293
■ **HITTITE MICROWAVE LLC**
(*Suby of* ANALOG DEVICES INC) ★
2 Elizabeth Dr, Chelmsford, MA 01824-4112
Tel (978) 250-3343 *Founded/Ownrshp* 2014
Sales 145.1MM[E] *EMP* 506[E]
SIC 3674 Integrated circuits, semiconductor networks, etc.; Modules, solid state; Integrated circuits, semiconductor networks, etc.; Modules, solid state
Pr: Rick D Hess
CFO: William W Boecke
VP: Everett N Cole III
VP: Susan J Dicecco
VP: William D Hannabach
VP: Mike McCullar
VP: Larry W Ward

D-U-N-S 02-640-4333
HITTITE STEEL INC
5814 Washington Blvd, Arlington, VA 22205-2906
Tel (703) 625-2909 *Founded/Ownrshp* 2009
Sales 25.6MM[E] *EMP* 40
SIC 5051 Steel
Pr: Ertugrul Duzkale

D-U-N-S 07-175-8999
HIWAY FEDERAL CREDIT UNION
111 Empire Dr, Saint Paul, MN 55103-1860
Tel (651) 291-1515 *Founded/Ownrshp* 1931
Sales NA *EMP* 165[E]
SIC 6061 Federal credit unions; Federal credit unions
Pr: Jeff Schwalen
CFO: Aaron Kastner
Ofcr: Chris Ernster
Ofcr: Cami Horan
Ofcr: Sharron Howe
Ofcr: Sharon Kluegel
VP: Glenn Durbahn
**VP:* Dale Hovind
VP: Chris Olsen
CIO: Cara Pingle
IT Man: White Brian

D-U-N-S 79-819-6218 IMP
HIWIN CORP
(*Suby of* HIWIN TECHNOLOGIES CORP.)
1400 Madeline Ln, Elgin, IL 60124-7829
Tel (847) 827-2270 *Founded/Ownrshp* 1992
Sales 22.6MM[E] *EMP* 51
SIC 5084

HIXSON ARCHTCTS/NGNRS/NTERIORS
See HIXSON INC

D-U-N-S 79-825-7945
HIXSON AUTOPLEX ALEXANDRIA LLC
HIXSON FORD ALEXANDRIA
2506 S Macarthur Dr, Alexandria, LA 71301-2917
Tel (318) 448-0871 *Founded/Ownrshp* 1992
Sales 48.9MM[E] *EMP* 110
SIC 5511 7532 Automobiles, new & used; Top & body repair & paint shops; Automobiles, new & used; Top & body repair & paint shops
CFO: David Moore
Genl Mgr: Frank Diaz
Genl Mgr: Dallas Hixson
Sls Mgr: Alfonso Augustine
Sls Mgr: Billy Caldwell
Sales Asso: Curtis King

D-U-N-S 03-434-6882
HIXSON AUTOPLEX OF MONROE LLC
FORD
1201 Louisville Ave, Monroe, LA 71201-6019
Tel (318) 388-3300 *Founded/Ownrshp* 1997
Sales 37.9MM[E] *EMP* 100
SIC 5511 7538 7532 7515 7513 5521 Automobiles, new & used; General automotive repair shops; Top & body repair & paint shops; Passenger car leasing; Truck rental & leasing, no drivers; Used car dealers; Automobiles, new & used; General automotive repair shops; Top & body repair & paint shops; Passenger car leasing; Truck rental & leasing, no drivers; Used car dealers
Prin: Dallas L Hixson
CFO: David Moore
**Prin:* Clinton E Hixson
Genl Mgr: Dewayne Pybus
CIO: Mary Body
Sls Mgr: Brady Bowen

HIXSON FORD ALEXANDRIA
See HIXSON AUTOPLEX ALEXANDRIA LLC

D-U-N-S 05-066-3970
HIXSON INC (OH)
HIXSON ARCHTCTS/NGNRS/NTERIORS
659 Van Meter St Ste 300, Cincinnati, OH 45202-1568
Tel (513) 241-1230 *Founded/Ownrshp* 1948, 1983
Sales 29.0MM[E] *EMP* 125
SIC 8712 Architectural engineering; Architectural engineering
Pr: J Wickliffe Ach
**Treas:* Thomas J Benkert
Sr VP: Rick Hampton
**Sr VP:* Bruce Mirrielees
Sr VP: Bill Sander
**Sr VP:* William H Sander
VP: Thomas Ala
VP: Mark Frey
**VP:* William H Wiseman
Exec: Julie Beatty
Exec: Chet Stewart

D-U-N-S 03-561-7679 IMP
HIXSON LUMBER SALES INC
310 S Tennessee St, Pine Bluff, AR 71601-4453
Tel (870) 535-1436 *Founded/Ownrshp* 1959
Sales 200.0MM *EMP* 275
SIC 2421 5031

D-U-N-S 02-322-3803
HIXTON-FAIRCHILD FARMERS CO-OP
233 N Front St, Fairchild, WI 54741-8276
Tel (715) 334-2137 *Founded/Ownrshp* 2007
Sales 23.5MM[E] *EMP* 75
Accts Clifton Gunderson Llp Tomah
SIC 5191 5171 5172 5013 Farm supplies; Feed; Seeds: field, garden & flower; Fertilizer & fertilizer materials; Petroleum bulk stations; Gases, liquefied petroleum (propane); Automotive hardware; Farm supplies; Feed; Seeds: field, garden & flower; Fertilizer & fertilizer materials; Petroleum bulk stations; Gases, liquefied petroleum (propane); Automotive hardware
Genl Mgr: Rob Larson

D-U-N-S 00-225-1437
HJ BRANDELES CORP (NY)
300 Lafayette St, Utica, NY 13502-4215
Tel (315) 733-7565 *Founded/Ownrshp* 1897
Sales 22.5MM *EMP* 50
Accts Barone Howard & Co Cpas P
SIC 1711 Mechanical contractor; Mechanical contractor
Pr: Richard Falvo
**Ch Bd:* Louis A Falvo III
**Treas:* Mary Russo
**Prin:* Louis A Falvo Jr
Off Mgr: Louise Cronian

D-U-N-S 19-697-8167 IMP
HJ FOUNDATION CO
(*Suby of* KELLER FOUNDATION) ★
8275 Nw 80th St, Miami, FL 33166-2160
Tel (305) 592-8181 *Founded/Ownrshp* 2007
Sales 39.3MM[E] *EMP* 240
SIC 1741 Foundation building; Foundation building
Pr: Frank J Fonseca
**CFO:* Vincent S Palazzolo
VP: Jose Martinez
Exec: Frank Fonseca
Opers Mgr: Waylon Gillis
Opers Mgr: John Quini

D-U-N-S 10-657-2964 IMP
■ **HJ HEINZ CO LP**
HEINZ FROZEN FOODS
(*Suby of* HEINZ KRAFT FOODS CO) ★
1301 Oberlin Ave Sw, Massillon, OH 44647-7669
Tel (330) 837-8331 *Founded/Ownrshp* 2000
Sales 75.7MM[E] *EMP* 600
SIC 2037 Frozen fruits & vegetables; Frozen fruits & vegetables
Mng Pt: Allan Briggs
VP: John Crowe
Opers Mgr: Jim Astemborski

D-U-N-S 01-530-7754
HJC HOME HEALTH CARE SERVICES INC
ANTHONY'S HOME HEALTH CARE
709 E Esperanza Ave Ste A, McAllen, TX 78501-1408
Tel (956) 627-2610 *Founded/Ownrshp* 2010
Sales 8.2MM[E] *EMP* 600
SIC 8082 Home health care services; Home health care services
Pr: Frank A Mora

D-U-N-S 80-672-3441 IMP
HJD CAPITAL ELECTRIC INC
5424 W Us Highway 90, San Antonio, TX 78227-4219
Tel (210) 681-0954 Founded/Ownrshp 1993
Sales 25.3MM^E EMP 80
Accts Rodriguez Holland & Co Pc
SIC 1731 General electrical contractor; General electrical contractor
Pr: Henry Davila
*CFO: Maureen Seigler

D-U-N-S 96-231-8650
HJF MEDICAL RESEARCH INTERNATIONAL INC
6720a Rockledge Dr # 100, Bethesda, MD 20817-1888
Tel (240) 694-2000 Founded/Ownrshp 2010
Sales 32.5MM EMP 99
SIC 8099 Health & allied services; Health & allied services
Prgrm Mgr: Kenneth Crook

D-U-N-S 07-987-6875
HK DESIGNS
MY DIAMOND STORY
15 W 47th St Ste 303, New York, NY 10036-5703
Tel (212) 944-0518 Founded/Ownrshp 2003
Sales 85.0MM EMP 20
SIC 3911 Jewelry, precious metal
Pr: Hasmukh Dholakia
*CFO: David Narker

HK INDUSTRIES
See HAGAN-KENNINGTON OIL CO INC

HK MARKET
See GALLERIA MARKET LP

D-U-N-S 08-109-1126 IMP
HKF INC
THERM PACIFIC
5983 Smithway St, Commerce, CA 90040-1607
Tel (323) 225-1318 Founded/Ownrshp 1990
Sales 92.9MM^E EMP 450
SIC 5075 3873 5064 3567 3643 Warm air heating & air conditioning; Watches, clocks, watchcases & parts; Electrical appliances, television & radio; Industrial furnaces & ovens; Current-carrying wiring devices; Warm air heating & air conditioning; Watches, clocks, watchcases & parts; Electrical appliances, television & radio; Industrial furnaces & ovens; Current-carrying wiring devices
Pr: James P Hartfield

HKG DUTY FREE
See H K GLOBAL TRADING LTD

D-U-N-S 96-964-0791
HKI SUPPORT INC
352 Park Ave S, New York, NY 10010-1709
Tel (212) 532-0544 Founded/Ownrshp 2011
Sales 188.2MM EMP 2^E
SIC 8699 Charitable organization

HKP POWERSPORTS
See HOOKSETT KAWASAKI INC

HKS ARCHITECTS
See HKS INC

D-U-N-S 05-084-7490
HKS INC
HKS ARCHITECTS
350 N Saint Paul St # 100, Dallas, TX 75201-4200
Tel (214) 969-5599 Founded/Ownrshp 1980
Sales 293.0MM^E EMP 1,416
SIC 8712 Architectural engineering; Architectural engineering
Pr: Dan Noble
*Pr: H Ralph Hawkins
COO: J Mark Jones
COO: Gerry Klee
COO: Mark J Ones
CFO: Larry D Lemaster
Ex VP: Craig Beale
Ex VP: Nunzio M Desantis
Ex VP: Robert Marlineck
Ex VP: Robert Piatek
Ex VP: Jeff Stouffer
Ex VP: Mark Voorl
Ex VP: Laurie Waggener
Sr VP: Noel Barrick
Sr VP: Joseph Buskuhl
Sr VP: Lorenzo Castillo
Sr VP: Davis E Chauvir
Sr VP: Jesse R Corigan Jr
Sr VP: Ernest W Hanchey Jr
Sr VP: Thomas E Harvy
Sr VP: Richard Johnston

HKT BIG SKY MOTORS
See INDUSTRIAL ENGINE SERVICE CO

HKW
See HAMMOND KENNEDY WHITNEY & CO INC

D-U-N-S 01-727-3375
HL FINANCIAL SERVICES LLC
500 W Jefferson St, Louisville, KY 40202-2823
Tel (502) 588-8400 Founded/Ownrshp 2008
Sales 281.2MM^E EMP 1,155^E
SIC 7389 Financial services; Financial services

D-U-N-S 80-483-1311
HL INSURANCE SERVICES
(Suby of HILLIARD LYONS) ★
Hilliard Lyons Ctr, Louisville, KY 40202
Tel (502) 588-8400 Founded/Ownrshp 2000
Sales 39.8MM^E EMP 800
SIC 6211 6411 Security brokers & dealers; Insurance brokers; Security brokers & dealers; Insurance brokers
CEO: James Allen

D-U-N-S 19-670-4092 IMP
HL-A CO INC
HONDA LOCK OF AMERICA
(Suby of HONDA MOTOR CO., LTD.)
101 Thomas B Mur Ind Blvd, Bremen, GA 30110
Tel (678) 309-2000 Founded/Ownrshp 1988
Sales 114.6MM^E EMP 504^E
Accts Ernst & Young Llp
SIC 3429 3714 Locks or lock sets; Keys & key blanks; Motor vehicle body components & frame; Locks or lock sets; Keys & key blanks; Motor vehicle body components & frame
CEO: Tsugiaki Umeda
VP: Tim Keesee
VP: Roger Tinsley
VP: Sandra Wilkinson
MIS Dir: Ben Tolbert
QA Dir: Hiroyuki Watanabe
Plnt Mgr: Greg Phillips
Ql Cn Mgr: Billy Baker

D-U-N-S 19-220-5508
HLAVINKA EQUIPMENT CO
17405 Us 90a Hwy, East Bernard, TX 77435-8267
Tel (979) 335-7528 Founded/Ownrshp 1982
Sales 40.0MM EMP 125
SIC 5999 7699

HLC
See HEALDSBURG LUMBER CO INC

D-U-N-S 07-699-2734
HLC HOTELS INC
7080 Abercorn St, Savannah, GA 31406-2404
Tel (912) 355-7384 Founded/Ownrshp 1976
Sales 27.7MM^E EMP 500
SIC 8741 Hotel or motel management; Hotel or motel management
Pr: J Roger Hammond
*VP: Charles M Aimone

HLI ENERGY SERVICES
See HLI RESOURCES LLC

D-U-N-S 78-375-5254
HLI RESOURCES LLC
HLI ENERGY SERVICES
3600 W Highway 67, Cleburne, TX 76033-8523
Tel (817) 558-1018 Founded/Ownrshp 2006
Sales 45.0MM^E EMP 250
SIC 1382 Oil & gas exploration services; Oil & gas exploration services
CEO: Ross Gatlin
*Pr: John R Hardee
*CFO: Don Heierman
*Sr VP: Trevor Cohen

HLK
See HUGHESLEAHYKARLOVIC INC

D-U-N-S 17-778-3156
HLK AUTO GROUP INC
MEADOR CHRYSLER JEEP DODGE RAM
9501 South Fwy, Fort Worth, TX 76140-4923
Tel (817) 535-0535 Founded/Ownrshp 2009
Sales 39.2MM^E EMP 150
SIC 5511 7538 5531 5521 Automobiles, new & used; General automotive repair shops; Automotive parts; Automobiles, used cars only

D-U-N-S 13-590-6258
HLM HOLDINGS INC
50 Division St Ste 401, Somerville, NJ 08876-2943
Tel (908) 218-7900 Founded/Ownrshp 1989
Sales 41.5MM EMP 50
Accts Withumsmith&Brown Pc Somer
SIC 8741 Financial management for business; Financial management for business
Pr: David Loevner
*CFO: Rob Hillas

D-U-N-S 07-791-2512
HLS ENTERPRISES OF TEXAS INC
4600 Wright Rd, Stafford, TX 77477-4103
Tel (281) 494-1818 Founded/Ownrshp 1996
Sales 25.9MM^E EMP 150
SIC 1541 Industrial buildings & warehouses; Industrial buildings & warehouses
Pr: Stephanie Christison
*VP: Jacquelyn Christison

HLS EXPRESS LUBE
See FOUR SS INC

D-U-N-S 02-290-5992
HLS PHARMACIES INC
420 Nw 5th St Ste 1a, Evansville, IN 47708-1322
Tel (812) 759-6164 Founded/Ownrshp 1995
Sales 33.3MM^E EMP 99
SIC 5912 Drug stores & proprietary stores
Prin: Rick W Stradtner
Genl Mgr: Dean Blessinger

D-U-N-S 96-857-8000
HLSS MANAGEMENT LLC
(Suby of HLSS HOLDINGS, LLC)
2002 Summit Blvd Fl 6, Brookhaven, GA 30319-1560
Tel (561) 682-7561 Founded/Ownrshp 2011
Sales NA EMP 1
SIC 6162 Mortgage bankers; Mortgage bankers
CFO: James Lauter
VP: Bryon Stevens

D-U-N-S 07-922-8005
■ **HLT ESP INTERNATIONAL FRANCHISE LLC**
(Suby of HILTON WORLDWIDE HOLDINGS INC) ★
7930 Jones Branch Dr, Mc Lean, VA 22102-3388
Tel (703) 883-1000 Founded/Ownrshp 2013
Sales 2.8MM^E EMP 4,088^E
SIC 7011 Hotels & motels

D-U-N-S 09-945-3131
HLTC INC
REGENCY PARK HEALTH CARE CTR
1212 Broadrick Dr, Dalton, GA 30720-2503
Tel (706) 278-4043 Founded/Ownrshp 1997
Sales 27.5MM EMP 132
Accts Dixon Hughes Goodman Llp Ashe
SIC 8051 8099 Skilled nursing care facilities; Health screening service; Skilled nursing care facilities; Health screening service
Pr: Steve Fromm
Exec: June Burtt
HC Dir: Janice Lewis

D-U-N-S 06-821-7595
HLW INTERNATIONAL LLP
H L W
115 5th Ave Fl 5, New York, NY 10003-1004
Tel (212) 353-4600 Founded/Ownrshp 1985
Sales 57.3MM^E EMP 300
SIC 7389 8711 8712 Interior designer; Engineering services; Architectural services; Interior designer; Engineering services; Architectural services
Sr Pt: Theodore Hammer
*Pt: Richard Bernnan
*Pt: Susan Boyle
V Ch: Theodore Faia
COO: Scott Herrick
Comm Dir: Meredith Lovejoy
Dir Bus: Clayton Morrell
Mng Dir: Christopher Choa
Mng Dir: Rhonda Curliss
Mng Dir: Andrew Talbot
Mng Dir: Bronte Turner

D-U-N-S 80-944-6557
HM CENTERED HEALTH INC
ALLONE HEALTH MGT SOLUTIONS
(Suby of HIGHMARK BLUE CRSS-BLUE SHIELD) ★
19 N Main St, Wilkes Barre, PA 18711-0300
Tel (570) 200-2800 Founded/Ownrshp 2015
Sales NA EMP 27^E
SIC 6321 Accident & health insurance carriers
Pr: Denise S Cesare
Treas: Bruce E Sickel
VP: William I Farrell
Prin: Paul Gilpin
Sls&Mrk Ex: Mark Destefano
Pr Mgr: Anthony Matrisciano
Snr Mgr: Kelly Benn

D-U-N-S 07-940-4329
HM DUNN AEROSYSTEMS INC
3301 House Anderson Rd, Euless, TX 76040-2001
Tel (817) 283-3722 Founded/Ownrshp 2013
Sales 124.0MM EMP 620
SIC 3724 Aircraft engines & engine parts; Aircraft engines & engine parts
CEO: Philip Milazzo
*COO: Richard Rosenjack
*CFO: Rebecca Tomlinson
Genl Mgr: Chris Dunn
VP Sls: Tim Roussin

HM DUNNAIR AEROSYSTEM
See H M DUNN CO INC

D-U-N-S 04-902-6008
HM GRAPHICS INC
7840 W Hicks St Stop 2, Milwaukee, WI 53219-1158
Tel (414) 321-6600 Founded/Ownrshp 1969
Sales 25.0MM EMP 180
SIC 2752 2759 Commercial printing, offset; Letterpress printing; Commercial printing, offset; Letterpress printing
Ch Bd: James S Sandstrom
*CFO: Greg Dooley
*Treas: John J Sandstrom
*Ex VP: Kevin J Sandstrom
VP: Mary Polonske
*VP: David Sandstrom
*VP: Mary Sandstrom-Plonske
S&M/VP: Mark Mane

D-U-N-S 78-816-4358
HM INSURANCE GROUP INC
(Suby of HIGHMARK BLUE CRSS-BLUE SHIELD) ★
120 5th Ave, Pittsburgh, PA 15222-3000
Tel (412) 544-1000 Founded/Ownrshp 1990
Sales NA EMP 750
Accts Pricewaterhousecoopers Llp Ph
SIC 6311 6371 Life insurance; Pension, health & welfare funds; Life insurance; Pension, health & welfare funds
CEO: Michael W Sullivan
*Pr: Matt Rhenish
*Treas: Daniel I Wright
*Sr VP: Cathy Blanchard
Sr VP: Tony Lopez
Sr VP: Mark Nave
Sr VP: Steve Reeves
*Sr VP: Gene Susi
VP: Pamela Brown
VP: Mary Butler-Everson
VP: Dan Cloyd
VP: David Daley
VP: William Miller
VP: Steve Tyler
Exec: Pamela Morgan
Board of Directors: Jim Burgess

D-U-N-S 07-765-4424 IMP/EXP
HM OPERATING INC
7155 State Highway 13, Haleyville, AL 35565-3028
Tel (205) 486-7872 Founded/Ownrshp 1974
Sales 63.8MM^E EMP 675
SIC 2511 2431

D-U-N-S 60-274-3150 IMP
HM PUBLISHING CORP
(Suby of HOUGHTON MIFFLIN HOLDINGS INC) ★
222 Berkeley St, Boston, MA 02116-3748
Tel (617) 251-5000 Founded/Ownrshp 2003
Sales 126.4MM^E EMP 3,546^E
SIC 2731 Book publishing; Textbooks: publishing only, not printed on site
Ex VP: Stephen Richards
Sr VP: Gerald Hughes
Sr VP: Paul Weaver
Board of Directors: Michael Ward, David Blitzer, Charlese Brizius, Robert Friedman, Steve Gandy, Seth Lawry, James Levy, Mark Nunnelly, Michael Perik, Scott Sperling

D-U-N-S 17-679-7918 IMP/EXP
HM RICHARDS INC
414 County Road 2790, Guntown, MS 38849-6712
Tel (662) 365-9485 Founded/Ownrshp 1997
Sales 117.5MM EMP 838
SIC 2512 Living room furniture: upholstered on wood frames; Living room furniture: upholstered on wood frames
CEO: William A Quirk
CFO: Michael McCaulla
*Ch: Jeffrey Seaman
VP: Joe Tarrant
*VP: Joey Torrent
*VP Mfg: Thomas Wells

D-U-N-S 00-697-4877 IMP
HM ROYAL INC (NJ)
689 Pennington Ave, Trenton, NJ 08618-3098
Tel (609) 396-9176 Founded/Ownrshp 1925
Sales 34.8MM^E EMP 36
SIC 5169 Chemicals & allied products
Pr: Jos E Royal
*CFO: Henry W Royal
*Ch: H L Boyer Royal
*VP: Llew Royal

HMA
See POPLAR BLUFF REGIONAL MEDICAL CENTER

HMA
See HAINES CITY HEALTH MANAGEMENT ASSOCIATION INC

HMA
See HIGHLANDS REGIONAL MEDICAL CENTER AUXILIARY INC

HMA
See NEWPORT MEDICAL CENTER

HMA
See LAFOLLETTE MEDICAL CENTER INC

HMA
See HEALTH MANAGEMENT ASSOCIATES INC

HMA
See PEACE RIVER REGIONAL MEDICAL CENTER

HMA
See EAST POINTE HOSPITAL INC

HMA
See HAMLET HMA LLC

HMA
See MERIT HEALTH NACHEZ COMMUNITY CAMPUS

HMA
See HEALTH MANAGEMENT ASSOCIATES INC

HMA
See RIVER OAKS HOSPITAL LLC

HMA
See ST CLOUD REGIONAL MEDICAL CENTER

HMA
See LOWER KEYS MEDICAL CENTER

HMA
See SUMMIT MEDICAL CENTER

HMA
See H M A GAFFNEY INC

HMA
See SEBASTIAN RIVER MEDICAL CENTER

HMA
See HONDA MANUFACTURING OF ALABAMA LLC

HMA FENTRESS CNTY GEN HOSP INC
See HMA FENTRESS COUNTY GENERAL HOSPITAL LLC

D-U-N-S 96-911-5948
■ **HMA FENTRESS COUNTY GENERAL HOSPITAL LLC**
HMA FENTRESS CNTY GEN HOSP INC
(Suby of HEALTH MANAGEMENT ASSOCIATES INC) ★
436 Central Ave W, Jamestown, TN 38556-3031
Tel (931) 879-8171 Founded/Ownrshp 2002
Sales 89.3MM^E EMP 150
SIC 8062 General medical & surgical hospitals; General medical & surgical hospitals
CEO: Lynette Pritchett
Chf Rad: Keith Kimbrell
Chf Nrs Of: Amy Reagan
*Prin: John Lee

D-U-N-S 87-425-9781
HMA HOLDINGS INC
425 Lewis Hargett Cir, Lexington, KY 40503-3590
Tel (859) 219-3939 Founded/Ownrshp 1993
Sales 32.3MM EMP 750
Accts Deandorton & Fordcpa
SIC 8082 Home health care services; Home health care services
Pr: Zaheer Sardar
*VP: John Coan
Ansthlgy: Richard L Bennett
Ansthlgy: Jake De Maio
Ansthlgy: Florence A Melio
Ansthlgy: Stephanie A Shumate
Ansthlgy: William D White

D-U-N-S 10-734-6934
HMA INC
HOLMES MURPHY
3001 Westown Pkwy Stop 1, West Des Moines, IA 50266-1328
Tel (515) 223-6800 Founded/Ownrshp 1984
Sales NA EMP 344
SIC 6411 6321 8742 Insurance agents; Health insurance carriers; Disability health insurance; Reinsurance carriers, accident & health; Management consulting services; Insurance agents; Health insurance carriers; Disability health insurance; Reinsurance carriers, accident & health; Management consulting services
Ch Bd: J Douglas Reichardt
Pr: Nickolas J Henderson
Sr VP: Steve Flood
VP: James S Swift
Netwrk Mgr: Gentry Cairo

HMAC
See HITACHI METALS AUTOMOTIVE COMPONENTS USA LLC

D-U-N-S 07-947-8958
HMAN GROUP HOLDINGS INC
245 Park Ave Fl 16, New York, NY 10167-2402
Tel (212) 600-9600 Founded/Ownrshp 2014
Sales 372.7MM^E EMP 2,605^E
SIC 6719 5072 7699 Investment holding companies, except banks; Hardware; Key duplicating shop; Investment holding companies, except banks; Hardware; Miscellaneous fasteners; Bolts, nuts & screws; Key duplicating shop
Prin: Steve Murray

D-U-N-S 07-947-8956
HMAN INTERMEDIATE HOLDINGS CORP
(Suby of HMAN GROUP HOLDINGS INC) ★
245 Park Ave Fl 16, New York, NY 10167-2402
Tel (212) 600-9600 Founded/Ownrshp 2014
Sales 209.2MM^E EMP 2,605^E
SIC 6719 5072 7699 Investment holding companies, except banks; Hardware; Miscellaneous fasteners; Bolts, nuts & screws; Key duplicating shop; Investment holding companies, except banks; Hardware; Miscellaneous fasteners; Bolts, nuts & screws; Key duplicating shop
Prin: Steve Murray

D-U-N-S 07-936-4173
HMAN INTERMEDIATE II HOLDINGS CORP
(Suby of HMAN INTERMEDIATE HOLDINGS CORP) ★
10590 Hamilton Ave, Cincinnati, OH 45231-1764
Tel (513) 851-4900 Founded/Ownrshp 2014
Sales 1.0MMM^E EMP 2,605^E
SIC 5072 7699 Hardware; Miscellaneous fasteners; Bolts, nuts & screws; Key duplicating shop; Hardware; Miscellaneous fasteners; Bolts, nuts & screws; Key duplicating shop
CEO: James P Waters

HMB INFORMATION SYS DEVELOPERS
See HARRIS MACKESSY & BRENNAN INC

HMC
See HARDER MECHANICAL CONTRACTORS INC

HMC ARCHITECTS
See HMC GROUP

HMC BUSINESS AFFAIRS DEPT
See HARVEY MUDD COLLEGE

HMC FOUNDATION EQUIPMENT
See HERCULES MACHINERY CORP

D-U-N-S 06-449-0808
HMC GROUP
HMC ARCHITECTS
3546 Concours, Ontario, CA 91764-5583
Tel (909) 989-9979 Founded/Ownrshp 2011
Sales 67.3MM^E EMP 410
SIC 8712 Architectural services; Architectural services
CEO: Brian Staton
*Pr: Randal Peterson
*Pr: Beverly Prior
*Ch: Robert J Kain
Mng Dir: Meng Ho
Admn Mgr: Chin Lee
Admn Mgr: Ken Salyer
Pgrm Dir: Lydia Dahl
Snr Mgr: Simon Solis
Snr Mgr: Jeremiah Sugarman

D-U-N-S 94-887-9593
HMC LLC
HENDRICK MOTORS OF CHARLOTTE
5141 E Independence Blvd, Charlotte, NC 28212-6168
Tel (704) 535-6400 Founded/Ownrshp 2009
Sales 21.5MM^E EMP 100
SIC 5571 All-terrain vehicles

D-U-N-S 82-896-3475 IMP
HMC WADESBORO INC
2732 Us Highway 74 W, Wadesboro, NC 28170-7558
Tel (704) 694-6213 Founded/Ownrshp 2008
Sales NA EMP 330
SIC 5023 5032

D-U-N-S 00-390-7187
HMC/CAH CONSOLIDATED INC
1100 Main St Ste 2350, Kansas City, MO 64105-5186
Tel (816) 474-7800 Founded/Ownrshp 2007
Sales 25.5MM^E EMP 100^E
SIC 8062 8748 General medical & surgical hospitals; Business consulting
CEO: Larry Arthur
*COO: Gordon Docking
Ofcr: Al Arrowood
Sr VP: Val Schott
Snr Mgr: Dennis Davis
Snr Mgr: Dan Hiben
Snr Mgr: Scott Tongate

D-U-N-S 00-690-9634 IMP/EXP
HMCLAUSE INC (CA)
(Suby of GROUPE LIMAGRAIN HOLDING)
555 Codoni Ave, Modesto, CA 95357-0507
Tel (209) 579-7333 Founded/Ownrshp 1856, 1969
Sales 59.5MM^E EMP 300
SIC 0181 Seeds, vegetable: growing of; Seeds, vegetable: growing of
Pr: Matthew M Johnston
VP: Andr Cariou
*VP: Andre Cariou
Dir IT: Gerry Hawkins

D-U-N-S 12-508-0390
HME INC
HME SILVERFOX
(Suby of VALLEY TRUCK PARTS INC) ★
1950 Byron Center Ave Sw, Wyoming, MI 49519-1223
Tel (616) 534-1463 Founded/Ownrshp 1985
Sales 71.3MM^E EMP 120
SIC 3713 3546 3537 3536 3711 Truck & bus bodies; Power-driven handtools; Industrial trucks & tractors; Hoists, cranes & monorails; Motor vehicles & car bodies; Truck & bus bodies; Power-driven handtools; Industrial trucks & tractors; Hoists, cranes & monorails; Motor vehicles & car bodies
Pr: Ken Lenz
CFO: Todd M Grasman
*VP: Rod McNeil
*Prin: Rex Troost
S&M/VP: Russ Ford

HME SILVERFOX
See HME INC

HMEA
See HORACE MANN EDUCATIONAL ASSOCIATES INC

HMFP
See HARVARD MEDICAL FACULTY PHYSICIANS AT BETH ISRAEL DEACONESS MEDICAL CENTER INC

D-U-N-S 01-106-5469
HMH PHYSICIAN ORGANIZATION (TX)
(Suby of HUNTSVILLE MEMORIAL HOSPITAL AUXILIARY) ★
116c Medical Park Ln, Huntsville, TX 77340-4978
Tel (936) 439-1400 Founded/Ownrshp 2010
Sales 4.6MM EMP 418^E
Accts Carr Riggs & Ingram Llc Houst
SIC 8011 General & family practice, physician/surgeon
Prin: Walter Toronjo

D-U-N-S 07-848-0903
■ **HMH PUBLISHERS LLC**
HMRH ACQUISITION CO
(Suby of HOUGHTON MIFFLIN HARCOURT PUBLISHERS INC) ★
222 Berkeley St, Boston, MA 02116-3748
Tel (617) 351-5000 Founded/Ownrshp 2012
Sales 12.7MM^E EMP 3,296^E
SIC 2731 Book publishing
Pr: Linda Zecher
*CFO: Eric Shuman
*Treas: Joseph Flaherty
*Ex VP: William Bayers
*Sr VP: Michael Dolan

D-U-N-S 80-923-0303
HMHTTC RESPONSE INC
400 Valley Rd Ste 303, Mount Arlington, NJ 07856-2316
Tel (973) 770-6900 Founded/Ownrshp 1993
Sales 14.9MM^E EMP 300
SIC 1799 Athletic & recreation facilities construction; Athletic & recreation facilities construction
Pr: Scott Turner
*Treas: Carmen Turner

HMI ELECTRIC DIVISION
See HEAVY MACHINES INC

D-U-N-S 00-514-6535 IMP/EXP
HMI INDUSTRIES INC
HEALTH MOR AT HOME CBP
13325 Darice Pkwy Unit A, Strongsville, OH 44149-3819
Tel (440) 846-7800 Founded/Ownrshp 1928
Sales 27.6MM^E EMP 112
SIC 3634 Air purifiers, portable; Air purifiers, portable
CEO: Kirk Foley
*Pr: John Pryor
CFO: Julie A McGraw
VP: Daniel J Duggan
VP: Julie A Merkle
VP: Joseph Najm
VP: Ken Skoczen
VP: Darrell Weeter
Mktg Dir: Jill Lemieux
Mktg Dir: Carol Palichleb

HMI METAL POWDERS
See HOMOGENEOUS METALS INC

D-U-N-S 10-385-4279
HMK ENTERPRISES INC
SPECTRUM MANAGEMENT
750 Marrett Rd Ste 401, Lexington, MA 02421-7309
Tel (781) 891-6660 Founded/Ownrshp 1981
Sales 44.8MM^E EMP 750
SIC 5712 3325 6411 Office furniture; Steel foundries; Insurance agents, brokers & service; Office furniture; Steel foundries; Insurance agents, brokers & service
Ch Bd: Steven Karol
Prin: Jane Karol

HMMA
See HYUNDAI MOTOR MANUFACTURING ALABAMA LLC

D-U-N-S 87-298-7409
▲ **HMN FINANCIAL INC**
1016 Civic Center Dr Nw, Rochester, MN 55901-1881
Tel (507) 535-1200 Founded/Ownrshp 1994
Sales NA EMP 195^E
Accts Cliftonlarsonallen Llp Minnea
Tkr Sym HMNF Exch NGM
SIC 6035 Federal savings & loan associations; Federal savings & loan associations
Pr: Bradley C Krehbiel
CFO: Jon J Eberle
Sr VP: Dwain C Jorgensen
Sr VP: Susan K Kolling

D-U-N-S 83-487-0156
HMN INC
865 Bud Blvd, Fremont, NE 68025-6270
Tel (402) 721-3020 Founded/Ownrshp 1994
Sales 74.9MM^E EMP 320
SIC 4213 4731 Contract haulers; Truck transportation brokers; Contract haulers; Truck transportation brokers
Pr: Michael F Herre

HMO BLUE
See HORIZON HEALTHCARE PLAN HOLDING

D-U-N-S 07-272-6581
HMO MINNESOTA (MN)
BLUE PLUS
3535 Blue Cross Rd, Saint Paul, MN 55122-1154
Tel (952) 456-8434 Founded/Ownrshp 1974
Sales 1.0MMM EMP 40
SIC 8011 Health maintenance organization; Health maintenance organization
CEO: Andrew Czajkowski
*Ch Bd: Jonathon Killmer
*CFO: Tim Peterson
Board of Directors: Gerald Etesse, Lonnie Nichols, Patricia Riley

D-U-N-S 96-003-9022
HMO OF LOUISIANA INC
(Suby of BLUE CROSS) ★
5525 Reitz Ave, Baton Rouge, LA 70809-3802
Tel (225) 295-3307 Founded/Ownrshp 1985
Sales NA EMP 10
SIC 6324 Health maintenance organization (HMO), insurance only; Health maintenance organization (HMO), insurance only
Pr: Gery Barry
CFO: Carl Kennedy
DP Exec: Brian Lawrence

D-U-N-S 16-099-7037
HMO OF NORTHEASTERN PENNSYLVANIA INC
FIRST PRIORITY HEALTH
19 N Main St, Wilkes Barre, PA 18711-0302
Tel (570) 200-4300 Founded/Ownrshp 2015
Sales NA EMP 148
Accts Pricewaterhousecoopers Llp Ph
SIC 6324 Group hospitalization plans; Group hospitalization plans
Pr: Denise Cesare
COO: William Reed

D-U-N-S 00-516-3456 IMP/EXP
HMP SERVICES HOLDING INC
721 Union Blvd, Totowa, NJ 07512-2207
Tel (973) 812-0400 Founded/Ownrshp 1906, 2009
Sales 93.1MM^E EMP 550
SIC 5084 5199

HMR
See DHS OF MARYLAND INC

D-U-N-S 19-467-7423
HMR ACQUISITION CO INC
HACIENDA MEXICAN RESTAURANTS
1501 N Ironwood Dr, South Bend, IN 46635-1841
Tel (574) 272-5922 Founded/Ownrshp 1996
Sales 50.0MM EMP 13,000
SIC 5812 5813 Mexican restaurant; Cocktail lounge; Mexican restaurant; Cocktail lounge
Pr: Vicki Farmwald
*Pr: Dean Goodwin
*CEO: Robert Kill
*CFO: Tammy Boetsma
Genl Mgr: Gloria Marietta
Mktg Mgr: Jonathan Fizer

D-U-N-S 80-719-7454
HMR ADVANTAGE HEALTH SYSTEMS INC
101 Grace Dr, Easley, SC 29640-9088
Tel (864) 269-3725 Founded/Ownrshp 1993
Sales 1.3MMM^E EMP 253
SIC 8741 Nursing & personal care facility management; Nursing & personal care facility management
Pr: Michael H Mc Bride
*Pr: Michael H McBride
*Sec: John O'Brien
Ex Dir: Wayne Adams
Ex Dir: Todd Griggs
IT Man: Jeff Vassay
Nrsg Dir: Julius Shayo
HC Dir: Karey Kelley

D-U-N-S 08-006-7170
HMR FOODS HOLDING LP
HANDMADE REAL FOODS
2080 E 49th St, Vernon, CA 90058-2802
Tel (323) 923-2900 Founded/Ownrshp 2012
Sales 120.0MM EMP 1,000
SIC 2099 Food preparations; Ready-to-eat meals, salads & sandwiches
CEO: Lewis Macleod
CFO: Perry Morgan

D-U-N-S 07-961-4274
■ **HMR WEIGHT MANAGEMENT SERVICES CORP**
(Suby of MERCK & CO INC) ★
99 Summer St Ste 1200, Boston, MA 02110-1248
Tel (617) 357-9876 Founded/Ownrshp 2013
Sales 31.0MM EMP 130
SIC 8093 Weight loss clinic, with medical staff; Weight loss clinic, with medical staff
Pr: Leonard Tacconi

HMRH ACQUISITION CO
See HMH PUBLISHERS LLC

HMRH ACQUISITION CO
See FOUNDATION FOR MARINE ANIMAL HUSBANDRY INC

HMS BUSINESS SERVICES
See HEALTH MANAGEMENT SYSTEMS INC

D-U-N-S 03-045-0907
HMS CONSTRUCTION INC
2885 Scott St, Vista, CA 92081-8547
Tel (760) 727-9808 Founded/Ownrshp 1999
Sales 32.3MM^E EMP 100
SIC 1781 8711 Geothermal drilling; Engineering services; Geothermal drilling; Engineering services
Pr: Michael High
*VP: Ian High

D-U-N-S 05-274-5382
HMS GLOBAL MARITIME INC
115 E Market St, New Albany, IN 47150-3409
Tel (812) 941-9990 Founded/Ownrshp 1986, 2002
Sales 60.5MM^E EMP 374
Accts Harding Shymanski & Company
SIC 4482 4499 8742 Ferries; Boat & ship rental & leasing, except pleasure; Transportation consultant; Ferries; Boat & ship rental & leasing, except pleasure; Transportation consultant
Pr: John W Waggoner
CFO: Brian Seale
*VP: Gregory A Dronkert
*VP: John M Keever
VP: Matthew Miller
*VP: Gary W Seabrook
Genl Mgr: Fred Berley
Genl Mgr: Kevin Delanoy
Genl Mgr: Timothy Loesch
Off Mgr: Allison Nance
Snr Mgr: Stephen Picken

D-U-N-S 15-825-9239
■ **HMS HEALTHCARE INC**
(Suby of AETNA HEALTH HOLDINGS LLC) ★
6501 S Fiddlers Green Cir # 300, Greenwood Village, CO 80111-4931
Tel (303) 504-5701 Founded/Ownrshp 2005
Sales NA EMP 340
SIC 6324 6411 6321 Hospital & medical service plans; Insurance agents, brokers & service; Accident & health insurance; Hospital & medical service plans; Insurance agents, brokers & service; Accident & health insurance
CEO: Blair Tikker

D-U-N-S 12-907-7280
▲ **HMS HOLDINGS CORP**
5615 High Point Dr # 100, Irving, TX 75038-2434
Tel (214) 453-3000 Founded/Ownrshp 2003
Sales 443.2MM EMP 2,296^E
Tkr Sym HMSY Exch NGS
SIC 7322 Collection agency, except real estate; Collection agency, except real estate
Ch Bd: William C Lucia
Pr: Joel Portice
Pr: Douglas M Williams
CFO: Jeffrey S Sherman
Ofcr: Cynthia Nustad
Ofcr: Scott Pettigrew
Ex VP: Gene Defelice
Ex VP: Semone Wagner
Sr VP: Greg G Aunan
VP: Gil Marques
VP: Justin Ricketts
VP: John Williams
VP: Anthony Wong
Board of Directors: Craig R Callen, Daniel N Mendelson, William F Miller III, Ellen A Rudnick, Bart M Schwartz, Richard H Stowe, Cora M Tellez

HMS HOST INTERNATIONAL
See GIFT COLLECTION INC

D-U-N-S 03-000-7801
HMS HOST INTERNATIONAL INC
SPIRIT OF THE RED HORSE
(Suby of HMSHOST CORP) ★
7630 Excelsior Blvd, Minneapolis, MN 55426-4518
Tel (240) 694-4100 Founded/Ownrshp 1975, 2007
Sales 20.5MM^E EMP 215
SIC 5947 Gift shop; Gift shop
Pr: Elie Malouf

D-U-N-S 79-179-6642
HMS INSURANCE ASSOCIATES INC
KEMPER INSURANCE
20 Wight Ave Ste 300, Hunt Valley, MD 21030-2003
Tel (410) 337-9755 Founded/Ownrshp 1992
Sales NA EMP 75^E
SIC 6411 Insurance agents
Pr: Gary L Berger
CFO: Brian Cox
*Sec: Brian Wilcox
Ex VP: Tim Connelly
*Ex VP: Gary Pyne
*VP: Craig Bancroft
VP: Victor J Lizana
VP: Gavin Moag
VP: Scott R Reber
*VP: Eileen Wilcox
IT Man: Terrance Finnegan

D-U-N-S 01-805-2576 IMP
HMS MFG CO (MI)
1230 E Big Beaver Rd, Troy, MI 48083-1904
Tel (248) 689-3232 Founded/Ownrshp 1987
Sales 75.0MM EMP 70^E
SIC 3089 Injection molded finished plastic products
Pr: Janet Sofy
*Sec: David Sofy
*VP: Nancy Negohosian
Sls&Mrk Ex: Larry Schlaf

D-U-N-S 14-463-4565 IMP
HMS PRODUCTIONS INC
SPENCER JEREMY
250 W 39th St Fl 12, New York, NY 10018-8215
Tel (212) 719-9190 Founded/Ownrshp 1986
Sales 23.9MM^E EMP 85
SIC 2339 Sportswear, women's
Pr: Spenser Alpern
*Ch: Hal Alpern
CTO: Peter Goldberger
Prd Dir: Dusha Tomic

D-U-N-S 14-596-5872
HMS TECHNOLOGIES INC
1 Discovery Rd, Martinsburg, WV 25403-1844
Tel (304) 596-5583 Founded/Ownrshp 2003
Sales 32.4MM^E EMP 116
SIC 7373 Systems integration services; Systems integration services
Pr: Harry M Siegel
*CFO: Elizabeth M Andrews
*Sec: Wendy Siegel
*VP: Carter Craft
*VP: Roy Jones Jr
*VP: William Kirkpatrick

HMSA
See HAWAII MEDICAL SERVICE ASSOCIATION

D-U-N-S 83-922-3898 IMP
HMSHOST CORP
(*Suby of* AUTOGRILL SPA)
6905 Rockledge Dr Fl 1, Bethesda, MD 20817-7826
Tel (240) 694-4100 *Founded/Ownrshp* 1999
Sales 1.1MMM^E *EMP* 27,900
SIC 5812 5813 5994 5947 Grills (eating places); Concessionaire; Cocktail lounge; Newsstand; Gift shop; Grills (eating places); Concessionaire; Cocktail lounge; Newsstand; Gift shop
Pr: Steve Johnson
Treas: Joy Butler
**Treas:* Mark T. Ratych
Sr VP: Mike Hasenzahl
VP: Kevin Erickson
Prgrm Mgr: Michaela Lamarchesino
Genl Mgr: Asghar Pourhadi
Dir IT: Michele Adkins
MIS Mgr: Oakley Bright
Mktg Dir: Kerri Classen
Pgrm Dir: Cynthia Jones

D-U-N-S 78-652-0549
HMSHOST INTERNATIONAL INC
(*Suby of* HMSHOST CORP) ★
6905 Rockledge Dr, Bethesda, MD 20817-1828
Tel (240) 694-4100 *Founded/Ownrshp* 2006
Sales 28.5MM^E *EMP* 129^E
SIC 5963 5499 Food services, direct sales; Beverage stores
CEO: Steve Johnson
Pr: Anthony Alessi
Pr: Amy Dunne
**Pr:* Tom Fricke
CFO: Danielle Wise
Ex VP: Mall Maalouf
Ex VP: Chuck Powers
Sr VP: Pat Banducci
Sr VP: Martyn Holland
VP: Patrick Carroll
VP: Linda Dunn
**VP:* Paul Mamalian

HMSO
See LOURDES MEDICAL ASSOCIATES PA

D-U-N-S 08-583-3275
HMT HOLDINGS INC
HUNTER MARINE TRANSPORT
6615 Robertson Ave, Nashville, TN 37209-1689
Tel (615) 352-6935 *Founded/Ownrshp* 1976
Sales 24.5MM^E *EMP* 120
SIC 4492

D-U-N-S 09-599-5429 IMP/EXP
HMT INC
24 Waterway Ave Ste 400, The Woodlands, TX 77380-3197
Tel (281) 681-7000 *Founded/Ownrshp* 1978
Sales 119.1MM^E *EMP* 600
SIC 7699 3443 7389 1791 Tank repair; Fuel tanks (oil, gas, etc.): metal plate; Industrial & commercial equipment inspection service; Storage tanks, metal: erection; Tank repair; Fuel tanks (oil, gas, etc.): metal plate; Industrial & commercial equipment inspection service; Storage tanks, metal: erection
CEO: Millard H Jones
**Pr:* Gary E Tesch
**CEO:* S Kent Rockwell
**Treas:* J Wayne Jean
Treas: Nichole Wheeler
Ex VP: Tom Hoyer
**VP:* Scott D Spence
Dir Risk M: Kathy Adams
Area Mgr: Art Velasco
Area Mgr: Allen Wiltz
Genl Mgr: John Carnew

D-U-N-S 94-151-5442
HMW CONTRACTING LLC
H M WHITE
12855 Burt Rd, Detroit, MI 48223-3316
Tel (313) 531-8477 *Founded/Ownrshp* 2009
Sales 39.6MM *EMP* 150
Accts Iannuzzi Manetta & Company P
SIC 3444 Metal ventilating equipment; Metal ventilating equipment
Pr: Christopher Hulbert
Sec: Domenico Colone
VP: Jonathan Ricker
Dir IT: William White
Site Mgr: Mark Kohsmann
Snr PM: Dan Westen

D-U-N-S 18-640-6059
HMWALLACE INC
NATIONAL BUILDERS SUPPLY
210 The Blfs Ste A, Austell, GA 30168-7883
Tel (404) 941-8285 *Founded/Ownrshp* 2004
Sales 48.7MM^E *EMP* 45
SIC 5063 Lighting fixtures, commercial & industrial
CEO: Marcus V Morgan
CFO: Marcus Morgan
**Chf Mktg O:* Heath Hymeman
Chf Mktg O: Heath Hyneman
VP Opers: Thomas Snowden

D-U-N-S 83-122-9492
HMX LLC
HMX OPERATING CO
125 Park Ave Fl 7, New York, NY 10017-5627
Tel (212) 682-9073 *Founded/Ownrshp* 2009
Sales 199.4MM^E *EMP* 870^E
SIC 2211 Apparel & outerwear fabrics, cotton; Apparel & outerwear fabrics, cotton

HMX OPERATING CO
See HMX LLC

D-U-N-S 11-888-5057 IMP
HN INTERNATIONAL GROUP INC
20a Commerce Dr, Somerset, NJ 08873
Tel (732) 649-3610 *Founded/Ownrshp* 1999
Sales 35.0MM^E *EMP* 62
SIC 5023 Sheets, textile; Sheets, textile
Pr: Nagesh Malik

HN PRECISION
See HELIO PRECISION PRODUCTS INC

HN PRECISION-NY
See NATIONWIDE PRECISION PRODUCTS CORP

D-U-N-S 78-794-0261
■ **HN REAL ESTATE GROUP LLC**
HARRY NORMAN REALTORS
(*Suby of* HOMESERVICES OF AMERICA INC) ★
532 E Paces Fry Nw 300, Atlanta, GA 30305
Tel (404) 504-7300 *Founded/Ownrshp* 2006
Sales 15.4MM^E *EMP* 300
SIC 6531 Real estate brokers & agents; Real estate brokers & agents
CEO: Dan Parmer
**CFO:* William R Minick
VP: Hil Harper
Off Mgr: Mark Bracken
Off Mgr: Shanna Bryington
Off Mgr: Nicole Griffin
Off Mgr: Jodi Johnston
Off Mgr: Jenny Webster
Art Dir: Melissa Gailey

D-U-N-S 96-986-9072
HNA HUDSON VALLEY RESORT AND TRAINING CENTER LLC
MINNEWASKA HOSPITALITY CORP
400 Granite Rd, Kerhonkson, NY 12446-3557
Tel (888) 948-3766 *Founded/Ownrshp* 2015
Sales 7.3MM^E *EMP* 300
SIC 7011 Hotels & motels; Hotels & motels
Pr: Jeffrey Huang
VP: Joseph Huang
Genl Mgr: Orest Fedash

D-U-N-S 79-142-8170
HNB CORP
(*Suby of* BMO BANKCORP INC) ★
111 W Monroe St, Chicago, IL 60603-4096
Tel (312) 461-2121 *Founded/Ownrshp* 1981
Sales NA *EMP* 166
SIC 6022 State commercial banks; State trust companies accepting deposits, commercial; State commercial banks; State trust companies accepting deposits, commercial
CEO: Frank Teacher

D-U-N-S 07-853-4945
HNC PARENT INC
999 N Sepulveda Blvd, El Segundo, CA 90245-2714
Tel (310) 955-9200 *Founded/Ownrshp* 2012
Sales 214.0MM^E *EMP* 560
SIC 2952 2821 2891 Roof cement: asphalt, fibrous or plastic; Polyurethane resins; Sealants; Roof cement: asphalt, fibrous or plastic; Polyurethane resins; Sealants
Prin: Rob Newbold

D-U-N-S 00-526-9709 EXP
▲ **HNI CORP** (IA)
408 E 2nd St, Muscatine, IA 52761-4140
Tel (563) 272-7400 *Founded/Ownrshp* 1944
Sales 2.2MMM *EMP* 11,000
Accts Pricewaterhousecoopers Llp Ch
Tkr Sym HNI *Exch* NYS
SIC 2522 2542 2521 2541 3433 3429 Office furniture, except wood; Filing boxes, cabinets & cases: except wood; Desks, office: except wood; Chairs, office: padded or plain, except wood; Partitions for floor attachment, prefabricated: except wood; Wood office furniture; Filing cabinets (boxes), office: wood; Desks, office: wood; Chairs, office: padded, upholstered or plain: wood; Partitions for floor attachment, prefabricated: wood; Room heaters, except electric; Stoves, wood & coal burning; Manufactured hardware (general); Office furniture, except wood; Filing boxes, cabinets & cases: except wood; Desks, office: except wood; Chairs, office: padded or plain, except wood; Partitions for floor attachment, prefabricated: except wood; Wood office furniture; Filing cabinets (boxes), office: wood; Desks, office: wood; Chairs, office: padded, upholstered or plain: wood; Partitions for floor attachment, prefabricated: wood; Room heaters, except electric; Stoves, wood & coal burning; Manufactured hardware (general)
Ch Bd: Stan A Askren
Pr: Jerry Dittmer
Pr: Jeff Lorenger
CFO: Kurt A Tjaden
Treas: Ellsworth Mc
Treas: William F Snydacker
Ex VP: Bradley D Determan
Ex VP: Eric K Jungbluth
Ex VP: Phillip M Martineau
VP: Steven M Bradford
VP: Tom Eberhard
VP: Donna D Meade
VP: Bob Nichols
VP: Greg Radtke
VP: Chen Tim
Board of Directors: Mary H Bell, Miguel M Calado, Cheryl A Francis, James R Jenkins, Dennis J Martin, Larry B Porcellato, Abbie J Smith, Brian E Stern, Ronald V Waters III

D-U-N-S 06-687-6657
HNI INC (WI)
16805 W Cleveland Ave, New Berlin, WI 53151-3532
Tel (262) 782-3940 *Founded/Ownrshp* 1968
Sales NA *EMP* 70^E
SIC 6411 Insurance agents
Pr: Michael Natalizio
Mng Pt: Shawn Spencer
**CFO:* James Natalizio
Assoc VP: Jill Witting
Exec: Carolyn Wergin
Off Admin: Sara Hames
Sls Mgr: Tom Precia

D-U-N-S 05-561-6156
HNI RISK SERVICES INC
16805 W Cleveland Ave, New Berlin, WI 53151-3532
Tel (262) 782-3940 *Founded/Ownrshp* 2010
Sales NA *EMP* 15
SIC 6411 Insurance agents & brokers
CEO: Mike Natalizio
**CFO:* Jim Natalizio
**Ex Dir:* Anthony Fioretti

D-U-N-S 05-041-2157
HNI RISK SERVICES OF MINNESOTA LLC
(*Suby of* HNI RISK SERVICES INC) ★
6750 France Ave S Ste 275, Minneapolis, MN 55435-1967
Tel (952) 831-0607 *Founded/Ownrshp* 2012
Sales NA *EMP* 3
SIC 6411 Insurance agents & brokers; Insurance agents & brokers

HNMC
See HOUSTON NORTHWEST MEDICAL CENTER INC

D-U-N-S 03-623-7571
HNRC DISSOLUTION CO
AEI RESOURCES HOLDING
201 E Main St 100, Lexington, KY 40507-2003
Tel (606) 327-5450 *Founded/Ownrshp* 2007
Sales 405.9MM^E *EMP* 3,991
SIC 1222 Bituminous coal-underground mining; Bituminous coal-underground mining
Acting CEO: Scott M Tepper
**COO:* James Campbell
**Ch:* John J Delucca
**Ex VP:* Lance Sogan
**Sr VP:* Marc Merritt
**VP:* Richard Boone
**VP:* Keith Sieber

D-U-N-S 09-810-6495
HNS MANAGEMENT CO INC
CONNECTICUT TRANSIT
100 Leibert Rd, Hartford, CT 06120-1617
Tel (860) 522-8101 *Founded/Ownrshp* 1976
Sales 35.6MM *EMP* 915
Accts Marcum Llp Hartford Ct
SIC 4131 Intercity & rural bus transportation; Intercity & rural bus transportation
Pr: Richard Dunning
Comm Man: Jody Santoro
**Genl Mgr:* David Lee
Plng Mgr: Phillip Fry
MIS Dir: Richard Paterson

D-U-N-S 04-160-1790
HNTB CORP
(*Suby of* HNTB HOLDINGS LTD) ★
715 Kirk Dr, Kansas City, MO 64105-1310
Tel (816) 472-1201 *Founded/Ownrshp* 2003
Sales 900.0MM *EMP* 98
SIC 8711 8712 Consulting engineer; Architectural services
Pr: Robert Slimp
Pr: Dan Papiernik
COO: Jim Anglin
CFO: Brad Guilmino
Ch: Harvey Hammond
Ch: Michael Wright
Ch: Paul Yarossi
Treas: Terry Campbell
Bd of Dir: Charles Faggard
Assoc VP: Douglas Champlin
Assoc VP: Christine Hoagland
Assoc VP: Antonio Lagala
Assoc VP: Beth Larkin
Assoc VP: John Myers
Assoc VP: Joseph Pizzurro
Assoc VP: Raymond Sandiford
Assoc VP: Wendy Taylor
Assoc VP: Narayana Velaga
Assoc VP: Joseph Walshe
Assoc VP: Cyrill Weems
Assoc VP: Shelly A Wolff

D-U-N-S 16-787-6478
HNTB HOLDINGS LTD
715 Kirk Dr, Kansas City, MO 64105-1310
Tel (816) 472-1201 *Founded/Ownrshp* 2003
Sales 907.4MM^E *EMP* 3,125
SIC 8712 8711 Consulting engineer; Architectural services; Architectural services; Consulting engineer
Ch: Harvey Hammond
**Pr:* Paul A Yarossi
Assoc VP: Laurie Cullen
Assoc VP: Michael Inabinet
Assoc VP: Lawrence Meeker
**Ex VP:* Kenneth Graham
Ex VP: Joel Sorenson
**Ex VP:* Edward Spedon
VP: Charles Dulic
VP: James D Fisher
VP: Roland A Lavallee
VP: Scott M Smith
Exec: Deborah Caponetto
Exec: Jason Tindle
Dir Bus: Mary A Simons

D-U-N-S 60-955-8721 IMP
HO INC
LEXUS OF BELLEVUE
101 116th Ave Se, Bellevue, WA 98004-6408
Tel (425) 455-9995 *Founded/Ownrshp* 1989
Sales 85.3MM^E *EMP* 250
SIC 5511 Automobiles, new & used; Automobiles, new & used
CEO: Charles C Haselwood
**Pr:* Michael O'Brien
**VP:* Chantal O Brien
Sls Mgr: Kevin Burton
Sales Asso: Tim Forbes
Sales Asso: David Hara
Sales Asso: Ken Larsen
Sales Asso: Pat McFaul
Sales Asso: Michele Thoreson
Sales Asso: Andrew Timm
Sales Asso: Lynn Webb

HO-CHUNK CASINO
See HO-CHUNK NATION

D-U-N-S 88-455-5756
HO-CHUNK INC
(*Suby of* WINNEBAGO TRIBE OF NEBRASKA) ★
1 Mission Dr, Winnebago, NE 68071-4900
Tel (402) 878-4135 *Founded/Ownrshp* 1995
Sales 174.9MM^E *EMP* 310
Accts Mcgladrey & Pullen Llp Omaha
SIC 5172 Petroleum products; Petroleum products
CEO: Lance Morgan
**CFO:* Dennis Johnson
**VP:* Annette Hamilton
Prgrm Mgr: Brian Peeler
Dir IT: Joe Stoos
Board of Directors: Lauren Buchanan, Ann Downes, Kenny Mallory

D-U-N-S 11-842-8267
HO-CHUNK NATION
HO-CHUNK CASINO
W9814 Airport Rd, Black River Falls, WI 54615-5406
Tel (800) 280-2843 *Founded/Ownrshp* 1963
Sales NA *EMP* 3,300
SIC 9131 Indian reservation; Indian reservation
Pr: Wilfrid Cleveland
**Pr:* Wade Blackdeer
Treas: Sandra Gleason
Ofcr: Anthony Cooper
VP: Dan Brown
Exec: Anne Thundercloud
Ex Dir: Tracy Thundercloud
Prgrm Mgr: Lynette Bird
Genl Mgr: Casey Fitzpatrick
Genl Mgr: Jones Funmaker
Off Mgr: Caralee Murphy

D-U-N-S 62-618-3953
HOAG FAMILY CANCER INSTITUTE
1 Hoag Dr Bldg 41, Newport Beach, CA 92663-4162
Tel (949) 722-6237 *Founded/Ownrshp* 2006
Sales 37.6MM^E *EMP* 1,079^E
SIC 8062 General medical & surgical hospitals
Chf Rad: Mike Roossin
Ofcr: Robert Braithwaite
Dir Risk M: Lisa Bynum
Opers Mgr: Jennifer Rayner
Ansthlgy: Benjamin Conrad
Ansthlgy: Leighton Smith
Doctor: Craig Cox
Pharmcst: Peter Vanderplas

D-U-N-S 06-011-1226
HOAG FOLEY LLP
155 Seaport Blvd Ste 1600, Boston, MA 02210-2600
Tel (617) 832-1000 *Founded/Ownrshp* 1943
Sales 65.4MM^E *EMP* 439
SIC 8111 General practice law office; General practice law office
Mng Pt: Adam P Kahn
Pt: Tom Block
Pt: Kenneth S Leonetti
Pt: Peter M Rosenblum
Pt: Andrew Z Schwartz
Mng Pt: Mark Clark
Mng Pt: William R Kolb
Mng Pt: Michele A Whithm
COO: Thomas Block
CFO: Jeff Lerer
Dir IT: Frank G Bayley

D-U-N-S 82-588-8311
HOAG MEMORIAL HOSPITAL PRESBYTERIAN
1 Hoag Dr, Newport Beach, CA 92663-4162
Tel (949) 764-4624 *Founded/Ownrshp* 1944
Sales 784.5MM *EMP* 3,800
SIC 8062 General medical & surgical hospitals; General medical & surgical hospitals
CEO: Robert Braithwaite
Chf Rad: William Vandalsem
Dir Vol: Sherry Sumner
CFO: Rajesh Banker
CFO: Tim Paulson
Sr VP: Flynn A Andrizzi
VP: Bret Kelsey
VP: Timothy C Moore
Dir OR: Carole Metcalf
Dir Inf Cn: Rosalie Desantis
Dir Lab: Sue Beaty
Dir Lab: Sarina Rodriques
Dir Rad: Robert Marko
Dir Rx: Patrick Mok

D-U-N-S 02-858-0143
HOAG ORTHOPEDIC INSTITUTE LLC (CA)
16250 Sand Canyon Ave, Irvine, CA 92618-3714
Tel (855) 999-4641 *Founded/Ownrshp* 2008
Sales 91.2MM *EMP* 42^E
SIC 8011 Orthopedic physician; Orthopedic physician
CEO: Robert T Braithwaite
**Pr:* Flynn A Andrizzi
**Sr VP:* Jan L Blue
Sr VP: Dereesa Reid
**VP:* Bruce N Davidson

D-U-N-S 08-762-3633
HOAGLAND LONGO MORAN DUNST & DOUKAS LLP
40 Paterson St, New Brunswick, NJ 08901-1205
Tel (732) 545-4570 *Founded/Ownrshp* 1974
Sales 21.0MM^E *EMP* 140^E
SIC 8111 General practice law office; General practice law office
Pt: Kenneth J Doukas Jr
Pt: Alan I Dunst
Pt: Michael Baker
Pt: Karen Buerle
Pt: Andrew Carlowicz
Pt: Donald D Davidson
Pt: Michael Dolan
Pt: Douglas Fasciale
Pt: Mark Gaffrey
Pt: Robert Helwig
Pt: Gary Hoagland
Pt: Thaddeus J Hubert III
Pt: Jeff Intravatola
Pt: Robert Kenny
Pt: Bartholomew Longo
Pt: Patrick McDonald
Pt: James B Moran
Pt: John Simons
Pt: Michael John Stone
Pt: Thomas Walsh
Pt: Joan Weisblatt

D-U-N-S 78-956-1342
HOAK MEDIA LLC
3963 Maple Ave Ste 450, Dallas, TX 75219-3236
Tel (972) 960-4840 *Founded/Ownrshp* 2003
Sales 117.5MM^E *EMP* 580

SIC 4833 Television broadcasting stations; Television broadcasting stations
Pr: Eric D Van Den Branden
**Ch:* Jim Hoak
**Ex VP:* Rich Adams
**VP:* Jeff Rutan

D-U-N-S 36-168-9664
HOALOHA NA EHA LTD
OLD LAHAINA LUAU
1022 Front St, Lahaina, HI 96761-1613
Tel (808) 661-3322 *Founded/Ownrshp* 1987
Sales 12.6MM^E *EMP* 300
SIC 5812 7922 Eating places; Caterers; Theatrical companies; Eating places; Caterers; Theatrical companies
Pr: Michael Moore
**Sec:* Timothy Moore
**VP:* Robert Aguiar
Genl Mgr: Kawika Freitas
Dir IT: Hoaloha Eha

D-U-N-S 19-432-5056
HOAR CONSTRUCTION LLC
2 Metroplex Dr Ste 400, Birmingham, AL 35209-6877
Tel (205) 803-2121 *Founded/Ownrshp* 1972
Sales 442.0MM *EMP* 600
SIC 1541

HOARDS DAIRYMAN
See W D HOARD & SONS CO

D-U-N-S 79-607-8426
■ **HOB ENTERTAINMENT LLC**
HOUSE OF BLUES
(*Suby of* LIVE NATION WORLDWIDE INC) ★
7060 Hollywood Blvd, Los Angeles, CA 90028-6014
Tel (323) 769-4600 *Founded/Ownrshp* 2006
Sales 78.6MM^E *EMP* 3,000
SIC 7929 Entertainers & entertainment groups; Entertainers & entertainment groups
CEO: Michael Rapino
**Pr:* Joseph C Kaczorowski
Ex VP: Dave Fortin
**Sr VP:* Peter Cyffka
Sr VP: Paul Sewell
VP: Joseph Marcus
Dir Soc: Emmy Paulo
Netwrk Mgr: Adrian Black
Prd Mgr: Pierre Rochman
Sls Mgr: Heather Renkar
Counsel: Nancy Lee

D-U-N-S 83-553-9248 IMP
HOB-LOB LTD
HOBBY LOBBY CREATIVE CENTERS
7707 Sw 44th St, Oklahoma City, OK 73179-4808
Tel (405) 745-1100 *Founded/Ownrshp* 1994
Sales 71.8MM^E *EMP* 13,000
SIC 5945 5999 5949 5947 Arts & crafts supplies; Hobbies; Picture frames, ready made; Sewing & needlework; Gift, novelty & souvenir shop; Arts & crafts supplies; Hobbies; Picture frames, ready made; Sewing & needlework; Gift, novelty & souvenir shop
Pr: David Green
CFO: Jon Cargil
CFO: John Cargill
Ex VP: Steve Green
VP: John Bieri
VP: Brian Jones
VP: Steve Seay
Exec: Don Winslow
IT Man: Bill Adkerson
Site Mgr: Jimmy Overton
Opers Mgr: Richard Price

D-U-N-S 78-745-3828
HOBAN & ASSOCIATES INC
COAST REAL ESTATE SERVICES
2829 Rucker Ave, Everett, WA 98201-3456
Tel (425) 339-3638 *Founded/Ownrshp* 1990
Sales 17.0MM^E *EMP* 325
SIC 6531 Real estate managers; Real estate managers
Ch: Thomas P Hoban Jr
**Pr:* Shawn Hoban
**CFO:* Tom Hoban
VP: Carlton Brett
**VP:* Brett Carlton
**VP:* Craig Goldsmith
VP: Josh Jansen

D-U-N-S 07-968-0203
HOBART AND WILLIAM SMITH COLLEGES
300 Pulteney St, Geneva, NY 14456-3304
Tel (315) 781-3337 *Founded/Ownrshp* 1822
Sales 107.5MM *EMP* 337^E
SIC 8221 College, except junior; College, except junior
Pr: Mark D Gearan
Ofcr: William Hanvey
Ofcr: Emily Kane
VP: Robb Flowers
VP: Bob Murphy
VP: Jeff Vanlone
Exec: Elaine Ferrara
Dir Lab: William Zuk
Assoc Dir: Caitlin Connelly
Comm Dir: Cathy Williams
Off Mgr: Terri Travis

D-U-N-S 96-968-1654
HOBART AND WILLIAM SMITH COLLEGES
327 Pulteney St, Geneva, NY 14456-3301
Tel (315) 781-3337 *Founded/Ownrshp* 2011
Sales 161.7MM *EMP* 140
Accts Pricewaterhousecoopers Llp
SIC 8221 Colleges universities & professional schools

D-U-N-S 00-427-9337 IMP/EXP
■ **HOBART BROTHERS CO** (OH)
ITW HOBART BROTHERS
(*Suby of* ILLINOIS TOOL WORKS INC) ★
101 Trade Sq E, Troy, OH 45373-2488
Tel (937) 332-5439 *Founded/Ownrshp* 1917, 1996
Sales 283.2MM^E *EMP* 1,447
SIC 3548 3537 Welding apparatus; Industrial trucks & tractors; Welding apparatus; Industrial trucks & tractors
VP: Sundaram Nagarajan
CFO: Scott Koizumi
**VP:* Grant Harvey
VP: Jennifer Monnin
VP: S Nagarajan
VP: Andre Odrmatt
VP: Sarah Puls
VP: Ron Scott
Exec: Scott Santi
**Prin:* W H Hobart Et Al
**Prin:* S E Hobart

D-U-N-S 62-343-7951 IMP
■ **HOBART CORP**
(*Suby of* ILLINOIS TOOL WORKS INC) ★
701 S Ridge Ave, Troy, OH 45374-0005
Tel (937) 332-3000 *Founded/Ownrshp* 1981
Sales 202.2MM^E *EMP* 2,700
SIC 3589 3556 3596 3585 3321

D-U-N-S 13-963-7987
■ **HOBART INTERNATIONAL HOLDINGS INC**
(*Suby of* ILLINOIS TOOL WORKS INC) ★
701 S Ridge Ave, Troy, OH 45373-3000
Tel (937) 332-3000 *Founded/Ownrshp* 1981
Sales 36.9MM^E *EMP* 250
SIC 3556 Food products machinery; Food products machinery
VP: Thomas H Rodgers
**Pr:* Richard Gleitsmann
Mktg Mgr: Sue Flora

D-U-N-S 06-877-8646
HOBART OIL CO LLC
112 Dixon Ave, Molalla, OR 97038-9355
Tel (503) 829-2122 *Founded/Ownrshp* 1972
Sales 22.0MM *EMP* 4
SIC 5171 5983 Petroleum bulk stations; Fuel oil dealers; Petroleum bulk stations; Fuel oil dealers

D-U-N-S 09-045-0909 IMP
■ **HOBART SALES AND SERVICE INC**
HOBART SERVICES
(*Suby of* HOBART INTERNATIONAL HOLDINGS INC) ★
701 S Ridge Ave, Troy, OH 45373-3000
Tel (937) 332-3000 *Founded/Ownrshp* 1981
Sales 36.9MM^E *EMP* 151
SIC 5084 Food product manufacturing machinery; Food product manufacturing machinery
Pr: John McDonugh
Exec: Ian Clelland
Ex Dir: Shari Jarett-Horton
Brnch Mgr: Daniel Qualter
Info Man: Stephen Lawrence
Sftwr Eng: Larry Dickey
Sftwr Eng: Jeff Garrett
Trfc Mgr: Michelle Williams
Natl Sales: Kyle Graalum
Natl Sales: Garrett Redd
VP Sls: Tom Szafranski

HOBART SERVICE
See ITW FOOD EQUIPMENT GROUP LLC

HOBART SERVICES
See HOBART SALES AND SERVICE INC

D-U-N-S 15-467-8189 IMP
HOBAS PIPE USA LP
(*Suby of* HOBAS AG)
1413 E Richey Rd, Houston, TX 77073-3508
Tel (281) 821-2200 *Founded/Ownrshp* 2012
Sales 57.6MM^E *EMP* 110
SIC 3084 Plastics pipe; Plastics pipe
CEO: Ed Kocurek
Pt: Peter Schetty
Pt: Marcus Vajdos
VP: Larry W Johnson
VP: Kimberly Paggioli
VP: Richard C Turkopp
Exec: Ron Gibbons
Mng Dir: Doris Strohmaier
Dir IT: Vu Tran

D-U-N-S 06-233-1244 IMP/EXP
HOBBICO INC (IL)
GREAT PLANES MODEL DISTRS
1608 Interstate Dr, Champaign, IL 61822-1000
Tel (217) 398-3630 *Founded/Ownrshp* 1971, 2005
Sales 129.8MM^E *EMP* 700
SIC 5092 5961

D-U-N-S 14-821-4349
HOBBS & ASSOCIATES INC
4850 Brookside Ct Ste 100, Norfolk, VA 23502-2052
Tel (757) 468-8800 *Founded/Ownrshp* 1985
Sales 50.7MM^E *EMP* 50
SIC 5075 6512 Warm air heating equipment & supplies; Ventilating equipment & supplies; Air conditioning equipment, except room units; Nonresidential building operators
Pr: Hobbs C Bradford
Mng Pt: Mark Murray
**Prin:* John T Hobbs
Sls Mgr: Tom Ippolito

D-U-N-S 10-204-3320
HOBBS & CURRY FAMILY LIMITED PARTNERSHIP LLLP
4119 Massard Rd, Fort Smith, AR 72903-6223
Tel (479) 785-0844 *Founded/Ownrshp* 1995
Sales 109.0MM^E *EMP* 570
SIC 1542 Commercial & office building contractors; Commercial & office building contractors
Genl Pt: C David Curry
Pt: Janice Hobbs Powell

D-U-N-S 00-801-0761 IMP/EXP
HOBBS BONDED FIBERS INC
200 Commerce Dr, Waco, TX 76710-6975
Tel (254) 741-0040 *Founded/Ownrshp* 1968
Sales 122.0MM^E *EMP* 440
SIC 2297 2299 Bonded-fiber fabrics, except felt; Apparel filling: cotton waste, kapok & related material; Batts & batting: cotton mill waste & related material; Bonded-fiber fabrics, except felt; Apparel filling: cotton waste, kapok & related material; Batts & batting: cotton mill waste & related material
Pr: Carey Hobbs
**Pr:* Larry Hobbs
CFO: Brad Self
Ex VP: Bill Neal
VP Admn: Norman Brings
VP Admn: Norman Conner
Mtls Mgr: Roy Crossland
Manager: Steve Watson
Trfc Mgr: Odis Webster
Sales Exec: Andy Hobbs

D-U-N-S 07-379-8308
HOBBS BROOK MANAGEMENT LLC
(*Suby of* AFFILIATED FM INSURANCE CO) ★
1125 Bston Providence Hwy, Norwood, MA 02062-5001
Tel (781) 890-9300 *Founded/Ownrshp* 1998
Sales NA *EMP* 83
SIC 6331 Fire, marine & casualty insurance; Fire, marine & casualty insurance
CEO: Thomas Dusel
VP: Antony Mistretta
**VP:* Donald Oldemixon

D-U-N-S 03-574-9761
HOBBS IRON & METAL CO INC
STEEL DEPOT
920 S Grimes St, Hobbs, NM 88240-7831
Tel (575) 393-1726 *Founded/Ownrshp* 1978
Sales 43.1MM^E *EMP* 60
Accts Robinson Johnston & Patton Llp
SIC 5084 5051 Recycling machinery & equipment; Steel
Owner: Gene Day
Genl Mgr: Warner Key

D-U-N-S 06-897-3627
HOBBS MUNICIPAL SCHOOLS
1515 E Sanger St, Hobbs, NM 88240-4713
Tel (575) 433-0100 *Founded/Ownrshp* 1918
Sales 65.5MM^E *EMP* 1,050
Accts Accounting & Consulting Group
SIC 8211 Public elementary & secondary schools; Public elementary & secondary schools
VP: Joe Calderon
Ex Dir: James Johns
Schl Brd P: Lance Wiseman
Instr Medi: Starla Jones
HC Dir: Tamara James

HOBBY LOBBY CREATIVE CENTERS
See HOB-LOB LTD

D-U-N-S 06-103-8741 IMP
HOBBY LOBBY STORES INC
7707 Sw 44th St, Oklahoma City, OK 73179-4899
Tel (405) 745-1100 *Founded/Ownrshp* 1977
Sales 364.1MM^E *EMP* 1,260^E
SIC 5945 Franchises, selling or licensing; Piece goods & notions; Piece goods & other fabrics; Sewing supplies & notions; Art goods & supplies; Gifts & novelties; Fabrics, yarns & knit goods; Toys & hobby goods & supplies; Hobby supplies; Toys & games; Arts & crafts equipment & supplies; Hobby & craft supplies
CEO: David Green
**Pr:* John D Hastie
Pr: Bob Mackey
CFO: Jon Cargill
**Sec:* Mart Green
**Sr VP:* Ken Haywood
VP: Bill Darrow
VP: Peter Dobelbower
VP: Steve Seay
Admn Mgr: David Myers
Brnch Mgr: Michael King

D-U-N-S 60-864-1262 IMP
HOBBY PRODUCTS INTERNATIONAL INC
HPI RACING
70 Icon, Foothill Ranch, CA 92610-3000
Tel (949) 753-1099 *Founded/Ownrshp* 1994
Sales 24.0MM^E *EMP* 68^E
SIC 5092 3944 Toys & hobby goods & supplies; Electronic toys
CEO: Tatsuro Watanabe
**Pr:* Shawn Ireland

D-U-N-S 05-927-7632 IMP
HOBBY SHACK
GLOBAL HOBBY DISTRIBUTORS
18480 Bandilier Cir, Fountain Valley, CA 92708-7011
Tel (714) 964-0827 *Founded/Ownrshp* 1972
Sales 40.3MM^E *EMP* 200
SIC 5092 Toys & hobby goods & supplies; Toys & hobby goods & supplies
CEO: Paul Bender
**Pr:* Matt Fales
**CFO:* Gary Bender
**Sec:* Sally Bender

HOBEE'S CALIFORNIA RESTAURANT
See TABER FOOD SERVICES INC

D-U-N-S 04-269-0420 IMP
■ **HOBET MINING LLC**
DAL-TEX DIVISION HOBET MINING
(*Suby of* PATRIOT COAL CORP) ★
63 Corporate Center Dr, Scott Depot, WV 25560-7841
Tel (304) 369-6780 *Founded/Ownrshp* 2005
Sales 53.2MM^E *EMP* 600
SIC 1221 Bituminous coal surface mining; Bituminous coal surface mining
VP: Joseph W Bean

D-U-N-S 79-900-4536 IMP
HOBI INTERNATIONAL INC
1202 Nagel Blvd, Batavia, IL 60510-1451
Tel (630) 761-0500 *Founded/Ownrshp* 1992
Sales 28.3MM^E *EMP* 50
SIC 5045 5065 Computer peripheral equipment; Telephone equipment
CEO: Cathy Hill
**Pr:* Craig Boswell
Exec: Bill Boswell
Dir IT: Steve Wilson
Opers Mgr: Mike Shuck
Prd Mgr: Lance Davis
Sls Mgr: Joseph Hall

D-U-N-S 04-434-6260 IMP/EXP
HOBIE CAT CO
4925 Oceanside Blvd, Oceanside, CA 92056-3099
Tel (760) 758-9100 *Founded/Ownrshp* 1995
Sales 35.6MM^E *EMP* 150
SIC 3732 Sailboats, building & repairing; Sailboats, building & repairing
CEO: Richard Rogers
Pr: Greg Ketterman
**Pr:* Doug Skidmore
COO: Rich Gleason
**CFO:* Bill Baldwin
Plnt Mgr: Hugh Greenwald
Ql Cn Mgr: Graeme Wicks
Mktg Dir: Dan Mangus
Mktg Mgr: Matt Miller
Mktg Mgr: Morgan Promnitz

HOBO
See ONSET COMPUTER CORP

HOBO PANTRY FOOD STORES
See HOME OIL CO INC

D-U-N-S 19-602-2859
HOBOKEN BOARD OF EDUCATION INC
158 4th St 1, Hoboken, NJ 07030-3834
Tel (201) 356-3632 *Founded/Ownrshp* 1996
Sales 24.8MM^E *EMP* 448
SIC 8211 Public elementary & secondary schools; Public elementary & secondary schools
Pr: David Bailey

D-U-N-S 07-987-3842
HOBOKEN UNIVERSITY MEDICAL CENTER
(*Suby of* CAREPOINT HEALTH MANAGEMENT ASSOCIATES LLC) ★
308 Willow Ave, Hoboken, NJ 07030-3808
Tel (201) 418-1000 *Founded/Ownrshp* 2015
Sales 179.5MM *EMP* 37^E
SIC 8062 General medical & surgical hospitals

HOBOKEN UNIVERSITY MEDICAL CTR
See HUDSON HEALTHCARE INC

D-U-N-S 00-117-7609
HOBSON AND MOTZER INC (CT)
30 Airline Rd, Durham, CT 06422-1000
Tel (860) 349-1756 *Founded/Ownrshp* 1912, 1985
Sales 44.9MM^E *EMP* 150
SIC 3469 3544 Stamping metal for the trade; Special dies & tools; Stamping metal for the trade; Special dies & tools
Pr: Frank W Dworak
**VP:* James O'Brien
**VP:* Donald Zak
VP Opers: Jim Obrien

D-U-N-S 00-781-7125 IMP
HOBSON FABRICATING CORP
6428 S Business Way, Boise, ID 83716-5550
Tel (208) 343-5423 *Founded/Ownrshp* 1985
Sales 28.6MM *EMP* 160
SIC 1711 1761 Ventilation & duct work contractor; Warm air heating & air conditioning contractor; Sheet metalwork; Ventilation & duct work contractor; Warm air heating & air conditioning contractor; Sheet metalwork
Pr: Randy Frisbee
CFO: Brad Coe
**Sec:* Ted Frisbee Sr
Sls Mgr: Steve Wright

D-U-N-S 82-641-3924
HOBSONS INC
(*Suby of* DAILY MAIL AND GENERAL TRUST P L C)
50 E Business Way Ste 300, Cincinnati, OH 45241-2398
Tel (513) 891-5444 *Founded/Ownrshp* 1993
Sales 89.3MM^E *EMP* 550
SIC 8741 Administrative management; Administrative management
Pr: Craig Heldman
Pr: Todd Jibby
**Pr:* Stephen Smith
**CFO:* Adam Webster
**CFO:* Bobby Wilson
VP: Kathy Ovans
**VP:* Kathy Ovens
**VP:* Scot Winhusen
Mktg Dir: Nahid Sabti
Sales Asso: Heather Taylor

D-U-N-S 02-341-3444
HOC HOLDINGS INC
7310 Pacific Ave, Pleasant Grove, CA 95668-9708
Tel (916) 921-8950 *Founded/Ownrshp* 2008
Sales 384.9MM^E *EMP* 697^E
SIC 5082 5084 5083 7359 Construction & mining machinery; Tractors, construction; Materials handling machinery; Agricultural machinery; Equipment rental & leasing
Pr: Kenneth Monroe

D-U-N-S 03-144-1173 IMP
HOC INDUSTRIES INC
3511 N Ohio St, Wichita, KS 67219-3721
Tel (316) 838-4663 *Founded/Ownrshp* 1977
Sales 64.5MM^E *EMP* 28
SIC 5171 Petroleum bulk stations & terminals
Pr: William R Nath
**CFO:* Tharen Spahr
**Ex VP:* Tom Olsen
Trfc Mgr: Russ Kessler
Snr Mgr: Don Poschen

D-U-N-S 07-801-6490
HOCH INC
H & H DISTRIBUTING
4221 Gergan Rd, Grand Island, NE 68803
Tel (308) 384-2121 *Founded/Ownrshp* 1975

Sales 30.9MM^E *EMP* 70
SIC 5181 Beer & other fermented malt liquors; Beer & other fermented malt liquors
Pr: Harry Hoch Jr
**Sec:* Audrey Hoch
**VP:* Martin Hoch

D-U-N-S 93-236-7543
HOCHHEIM PRAIRIE CASUALTY INSURANCE CO
PIERCE INS CO
810 W 5th St, Yorktown, TX 78164-5022
Tel (361) 564-2234 *Founded/Ownrshp* 1981
Sales NA *EMP* 2
SIC 6411 Insurance agents, brokers & service; Insurance agents, brokers & service
Owner: Renae Pierce

HOCHHEIM PRAIRIE CSLTY INSUR
See HOCHHEIM PRAIRIE FARM MUTUAL INSURANCE ASSOCIATION

D-U-N-S 06-943-2466
HOCHHEIM PRAIRIE FARM MUTUAL INSURANCE ASSOCIATION
HOCHHEIM PRAIRIE CSLTY INSUR
500 Us Highway 77a S, Yoakum, TX 77995-1318
Tel (361) 293-5201 *Founded/Ownrshp* 1892
Sales NA *EMP* 92
SIC 6331 Fire, marine & casualty insurance: mutual; Fire, marine & casualty insurance: mutual; Property damage insurance; Automobile insurance
Pr: Linda Schmidt
**Sec:* Timothy McCoy

D-U-N-S 18-781-4348
HOCHHEIM PRAIRIE INSURANCE
(*Suby of* HOCHHEIM PRAIRIE CSLTY INSUR) ★
500 Us Highway 77a S, Yoakum, TX 77995-1399
Tel (361) 293-5201 *Founded/Ownrshp* 1979
Sales NA *EMP* 65
SIC 6331 Fire, marine & casualty insurance: mutual; Automobile insurance; Property damage insurance; Fire, marine & casualty insurance: mutual; Automobile insurance; Property damage insurance
Pr: John Trott Jr
CFO: Linda Schmidt
CIO: Mark Kimball
Mktg Mgr: Jim Brbozowski
Sls Mgr: Leigh Ferguson

D-U-N-S 05-732-3586 IMP
HOCHIKI AMERICA CORP
(*Suby of* HOCHIKI CORPORATION)
7051 Village Dr Ste 100, Buena Park, CA 90621-2268
Tel (714) 522-2246 *Founded/Ownrshp* 1918
Sales 34.9MM^E *EMP* 104
SIC 3669 5063 Fire detection systems, electric; Fire alarm systems; Fire detection systems, electric; Fire alarm systems
CEO: Hisham Harake
**CFO:* Hiroshi Kamei
**VP:* Sunichi Shoji
Rgnl Mgr: Jim Ross
Genl Mgr: Alfredo Aguillon
Genl Mgr: Mike Baca
Mfg Mgr: Tuan Bui
Manager: Rick Boisclair

D-U-N-S 12-860-4506 IMP
HOCHTIEF USA INC
(*Suby of* HOCHTIEF AMERICAS GMBH)
375 Hudson St Fl 6, New York, NY 10014-7462
Tel (212) 229-6000 *Founded/Ownrshp* 1996
Sales 10.6MMM^E *EMP* 6,000
SIC 1542 1541 1522 8741 8742 6799 Nonresidential construction; Commercial & office building, new construction; Design & erection, combined: non-residential; Specialized public building contractors; Industrial buildings & warehouses; Industrial buildings, new construction; Factory construction; Hotel/motel, new construction; Condominium construction; Construction management; Construction project management consultant; Real estate investors, except property operators; Nonresidential construction; Commercial & office building, new construction; Design & erection, combined: non-residential; Specialized public building contractors; Industrial buildings & warehouses; Industrial buildings, new construction; Factory construction; Hotel/motel, new construction; Condominium construction; Construction management; Construction project management consultant; Real estate investors, except property operators
Prin: Marcelino Fernndez Verdes
Genl Couns: Hartmut Paulsen

D-U-N-S 07-933-4900
HOCKADAY SCHOOL (TX)
11600 Welch Rd, Dallas, TX 75229-2999
Tel (214) 363-6311 *Founded/Ownrshp* 1913
Sales 47.1MM *EMP* 220
Accts Grant Thornton Llp Dallas Tx
SIC 8211 Private elementary school; Private junior high school; Private senior high school; Private elementary school; Private junior high school; Private senior high school
**Pr:* Maria Martineau Plankinton
**Treas:* Bethany Elliott Holloway
Ofcr: ABI Clark
Exec: David Haemisegger
Exec: Judy Mortenson
Comm Man: Jeanette Khan
Off Mgr: Jennifer Knott
IT Man: Thomas Johnson
HC Dir: Cyndi Lewis

D-U-N-S 10-759-8344 IMP
HOCKENBERGS EQUIPMENT AND SUPPLY CO INC
CHEF'S WAREHOUSE
7002 F St, Omaha, NE 68117-1013
Tel (402) 339-8900 *Founded/Ownrshp* 1985
Sales 142.2MM^E *EMP* 213
SIC 5046 Restaurant equipment & supplies; Restaurant equipment & supplies
Pr: Thomas D Schrack Jr
**Ch Bd:* Tom Schrack Sr
IT Man: Cathy Nixon
Mtls Mgr: Chris Thackray
Sales Asso: Ray Cutchall
Sales Asso: Bryce Gillett

D-U-N-S 03-111-6403
HOCKER OIL CO (MO)
505 N Mcarthur St, Salem, MO 65560-1229
Tel (573) 729-6651 *Founded/Ownrshp* 1960
Sales 58.4MM *EMP* 175
Accts Layman And Mitchell Certified
SIC 5541 Gasoline service stations; Gasoline service stations
Pr: James E Hocker
**VP:* Phyllis Hocker
**VP:* Jacques Sachs

HOCKING COLLEGE
See HOCKING TECHNICAL COLLEGE

D-U-N-S 07-164-8950
HOCKING TECHNICAL COLLEGE
HOCKING COLLEGE
3301 Hocking Pkwy, Nelsonville, OH 45764-9588
Tel (740) 753-3591 *Founded/Ownrshp* 1966
Sales 29.3MM *EMP* 1,021
Accts Millhuff-Stang Cpa Inc Por
SIC 8222 8249 8221 Technical institute; Vocational schools; Colleges universities & professional schools; Technical institute; Vocational schools; Colleges universities & professional schools
Pr: Ron Erickson
**CFO:* John Light PHD
**Treas:* J William Hill
Bd of Dir: Mike Brooks
Bd of Dir: Gary Edwards
Bd of Dir: Andrew Stone
Bd of Dir: Robert Troxel
Ex Dir: Libby Villavicencio

D-U-N-S 07-942-2077
HOCKING VALLEY COMMUNITY HOSPITAL MEMORIAL FUND INC
601 State Route 664 N, Logan, OH 43138-8541
Tel (740) 380-8000 *Founded/Ownrshp* 1966
Sales 33.8MM *EMP* 380^E
SIC 8062 General medical & surgical hospitals; General medical & surgical hospitals
CEO: Julie Stuck
**Pr:* Leeann Helber
CFO: Steve Berkhouse
Ofcr: Stacey Gabriel
Dir OR: Tara Lutz
Dir Case M: Gina Smalley
Dir Lab: Amy Scarberry
IT Man: John Burgess
QC Dir: Janelle Wallace
Nrsg Dir: Dawna Evans
Pharmcst: Cathy Brown

D-U-N-S 12-842-3118
HOCKOMOCK AREA Y M C A
300 Elmwood St, North Attleboro, MA 02760-1304
Tel (508) 695-7001 *Founded/Ownrshp* 1972
Sales 16.3MM *EMP* 600
Accts Kahn Litwin Renza & Co Ltd
SIC 7997 8351 Membership sports & recreation clubs; Group day care center; Nursery school; Membership sports & recreation clubs; Group day care center; Nursery school
Pr: Edwin H Hurley
CFO: Greg Meinertz
**Ch:* Jeffrey Dufficy
**Ch:* Gregory Spier
**Treas:* Paul Lenahan
Exec: Sandra Boyden

D-U-N-S 12-180-0122 IMP
HODELL-NATCO INDUSTRIES INC
LOCKTOOTH DIVISION
7825 Hub Pkwy, Cleveland, OH 44125-5710
Tel (773) 472-2305 *Founded/Ownrshp* 1993
Sales 31.9MM^E *EMP* 83
SIC 5072 Bolts; Nuts (hardware); Screws; Bolts; Nuts (hardware); Screws
CEO: Otto Reidl
**Pr:* Kevin Reidl
Treas: William Rex
VP: Floyd Lesti
**VP:* Brandon Liebhard
**VP:* Paul Starr
Admn Mgr: Mark Betts
Genl Mgr: Ken Lyman
Dir IT: Joseph Vislocky
Dir IT: Keith Wynn
IT Man: Ed Jacob

HODES LIVER & PANCREAS CENTER
See LIVER AND PANCREAS CENTER UNIVERSITY OF MARYLAND ST JOSEPH MEDICAL CENTER

D-U-N-S 19-557-9693 IMP
HODGDON YACHTS INC
14 School St, East Boothbay, ME 04544
Tel (207) 737-2802 *Founded/Ownrshp* 1816
Sales 30.3MM^E *EMP* 157^E
SIC 3732 Fishing boats: lobster, crab, oyster, etc.: small; Rowboats, building & repairing; Sailboats, building & repairing; Yachts, building & repairing; Fishing boats: lobster, crab, oyster, etc.: small; Rowboats, building & repairing; Sailboats, building & repairing; Yachts, building & repairing
Pr: Timothy S Hodgdon
**COO:* Andrew Wright
**CFO:* Don O Grady
Off Mgr: Christina Flood
IT Man: Don O'Grady
Mktg Mgr: Holly Paterson

D-U-N-S 00-986-1576 IMP
HODGE CO
HODGE MATERIAL HANDLING
7465 Chavenelle Rd, Dubuque, IA 52002-9664
Tel (563) 583-9781 *Founded/Ownrshp* 1960
Sales 75.4MM^E *EMP* 200
SIC 5084 4225 Materials handling machinery; General warehousing; Materials handling machinery; General warehousing
Pr: Timothy W Hodge
**Treas:* Michael R Hodge
**VP:* Andy Daughetee
Off Mgr: Andy Daughe

D-U-N-S 14-131-6468
HODGE FOUNDRY INC
(*Suby of* ELYRIA FOUNDRY CO LLC) ★
42 Leech Rd, Greenville, PA 16125-9724
Tel (724) 588-4100 *Founded/Ownrshp* 2014
Sales 39.7MM^E *EMP* 130
SIC 3321 Gray & ductile iron foundries
CEO: Bruce Smith
Pr: Joseph Simco
CFO: Timothy Dolan
VP: Michael Forsha
Exec: Melissa Clyde
IT Man: Ed Gearhart
Ql Cn Mgr: Frank Przywarty

HODGE MATERIAL HANDLING
See HODGE CO

D-U-N-S 07-924-8657
HODGES INTERNATIONAL GROUP INC (NY)
HINGE INC
250 Park Ave Fl 7, New York, NY 10177-0799
Tel (212) 602-1202 *Founded/Ownrshp* 2013
Sales 26.0MM *EMP* 25
SIC 6798 Real estate investment trusts; Real estate investment trusts
CEO: Jennifer Feigendaum
**Ch Bd:* Robert Hodges

D-U-N-S 96-045-9159
HODGES MACE BENEFITS GROUP INC
5775 Glenridge Dr A175, Atlanta, GA 30328-5380
Tel (404) 943-0535 *Founded/Ownrshp* 2007
Sales NA *EMP* 77^E
SIC 6411 Insurance agents, brokers & service
Prin: Peter Mace
CFO: Ron Shah
Ex VP: Jeff Graves
Opers Mgr: Susan Pitts

D-U-N-S 09-796-4936
HODGES OIL CO INC
201 W Reinken Ave, Belen, NM 87002-4241
Tel (505) 864-8611 *Founded/Ownrshp* 1979
Sales 30.0MM *EMP* 9
SIC 5171 Petroleum bulk stations
Pr: Benny Hodges
Sec: Mary Ellen Hodges
VP: Alexandra Hodges

D-U-N-S 09-690-8843 IMP
HODGES TRANSPORTATION INC
NEVADA AUTOMOTIVE TEST CENTER
605 Fort Churchill Rd, Silver Springs, NV 89429-8002
Tel (775) 629-2000 *Founded/Ownrshp* 1957
Sales 60.5MM^E *EMP* 160^E
SIC 8711 8734 Designing: ship, boat, machine & product; Automobile proving & testing ground; Designing: ship, boat, machine & product; Automobile proving & testing ground
Pr: Henry C Hodges Jr
Prgrm Mgr: Brett Horachek
Prgrm Mgr: Muluneh Sime
Sftwr Eng: Errol Burrow
Mktg Mgr: Kate Pope

D-U-N-S 00-288-8675
HODGES TRUCKING CO LLC
(*Suby of* AVEDA TRNSP & ENRGY SVCS) ★
4050 W I40, Oklahoma City, OK 73108
Tel (405) 947-7764 *Founded/Ownrshp* 2015
Sales 43.7MM^E *EMP* 350^E
SIC 4213 Heavy machinery transport; Heavy machinery transport
CEO: Kevin Roycraft
CFO: Bharat Mahajan
VP: Darwin Hartley

D-U-N-S 95-695-5520
HODGES UNIVERSITY INC
2655 Northbrooke Dr, Naples, FL 34119-7932
Tel (239) 513-1122 *Founded/Ownrshp* 1990
Sales 33.2MM *EMP* 500
Accts Cliftonlarsonallen Llp Naple
SIC 8221 College, except junior; College, except junior
Pr: Jeanette Brock
Ofcr: Erlis Abazi
Ex VP: John White
**VP:* Wendy Gehring
VP: Joseph Gilchrist
VP: Carol Morrison
Snr Mgr: Joe Turner

D-U-N-S 95-916-7883
HODGMAN ENTERPRISES INC
1 Branch St Ste 2, Methuen, MA 01844-1923
Tel (978) 682-8500 *Founded/Ownrshp* 1995
Sales 25.0MM *EMP* 8
SIC 7371 Computer software development; Computer software development
Pr: Philip W Hodgman
**Pr:* Philip Hodgman

D-U-N-S 05-998-6299
HODGSON MILL INC
1100 Stevens Ave, Effingham, IL 62401-4265
Tel (217) 347-0105 *Founded/Ownrshp* 2006
Sales 21.6MM^E *EMP* 94^E
SIC 2041 2045 5141 Flour & other grain mill products; Pancake mixes, prepared: from purchased flour; Groceries, general line; Flour & other grain mill products; Pancake mixes, prepared: from purchased flour; Groceries, general line
Pr: Robert J Goldstein
**Ch:* Cathy Goldstein
Treas: Regina Shafer
Ql Cn Mgr: Hope Adams-Yingst
Manager: Chuck Bath
Manager: Mike Zeccola

D-U-N-S 03-020-6502
HODGSON RUSS LLP
140 Pearl St Ste 100, Buffalo, NY 14202-4040
Tel (716) 856-4000 *Founded/Ownrshp* 1850
Sales 65.5MM^E *EMP* 473
SIC 8111 General practice law office; General practice law office
Pt: John Amershadian
Pt: Robert Conklin
Pt: Eileen Crotty
Pt: Paul Hartigan
Pt: Susie Kim
Pt: James M Wadsworth
Dir IT: Carol Baccoli
Dir IT: Kathy Krieger
IT Man: Donna Toepfer
Mktg Dir: Linda Schineller
Counsel: Wendy Fechter

D-U-N-S 00-151-9107 IMP/EXP
HOEGANAES CORP
(*Suby of* GKN NORTH AMERICA SERVICES INC) ★
1001 Taylors Ln, Cinnaminson, NJ 08077-2034
Tel (856) 303-0366 *Founded/Ownrshp* 1950, 2002
Sales 119.3MM^E *EMP* 523^E
SIC 3312 3399 Blast furnaces & steel mills; Metal powders, pastes & flakes
VP: Kalathur Narasimhan
COO: Tom Witherford
VP: Dennis Jackson
VP: William Michael
**VP:* Peter Saitis
VP: Jeffery Wilson
IT Man: Steven Lauria
Netwrk Mgr: Scott Riether
S&M/VP: Greg Wilkerson
Mktg Mgr: John Blauser

D-U-N-S 92-822-4898
HOEHN CO INC
HOEHN HONDA
5454 Paseo Del Norte, Carlsbad, CA 92008-4426
Tel (760) 438-1818 *Founded/Ownrshp* 1993
Sales 29.0MM *EMP* 80
SIC 5511 Automobiles, new & used; Automobiles, new & used
Pr: Robert A Hoehn
**Sec:* Gloria Rediker
**VP:* T William Hoehn III
Sls Mgr: Kevin O'Neill
Sls Mgr: Matt Seamark
Sales Asso: Brian Despirito

HOEHN HONDA
See HOEHN CO INC

D-U-N-S 07-335-7527
HOEHN MOTORS INC
HOEHN PORSCHE-MERCEDES-AUDI
5475 Car Country Dr, Carlsbad, CA 92008-4311
Tel (760) 438-4454 *Founded/Ownrshp* 1974
Sales 100.0MM^E *EMP* 200
SIC 5511 Automobiles, new & used; Automobiles, new & used
Pr: Theodore Hoehn III
**VP:* Robert Hoehn
Genl Mgr: Vas Chohan
Genl Mgr: Charles Eder
Genl Mgr: Kris Truman
Sls Mgr: Josh Beesemyer
Sls Mgr: Kevin Carnegie
Sls Mgr: Ron Edwards
Sales Asso: Liz Flower
Sales Asso: Willie Moreno
Sales Asso: Heick Moussavian

HOEHN PORSCHE-MERCEDES-AUDI
See HOEHN MOTORS INC

D-U-N-S 11-126-3054
HOEKSTRA TRANSPORTATION INC
3741 R B Chaffee Mem Dr, Grand Rapids, MI 49548
Tel (616) 245-7440 *Founded/Ownrshp* 1996
Sales 30.0MM *EMP* 40
SIC 5012 Buses; Buses
Pr: John Hoekstra
**Treas:* Mark Babiarz

D-U-N-S 11-666-3464 IMP
HOERBIGER AUTOMOTIVE COMFORT SYSTEMS INC
284 Enterprise Dr, Auburn, AL 36830-0503
Tel (334) 321-4785 *Founded/Ownrshp* 2001
Sales 32.7MM^E *EMP* 100
SIC 3511 3714 Hydraulic turbine generator set units, complete; Motor vehicle engines & parts; Hydraulic turbine generator set units, complete; Motor vehicle engines & parts
Pr: Gerhard Schoell
**Treas:* Helmut Kleiber
Ql Cn Mgr: Carmen Jordan
Ql Cn Mgr: Kenneth Pylant
Sls Mgr: Josh Colistra

D-U-N-S 14-464-6569 IMP
HOERBIGER COMPRESSION TECHNOLOGY AMERICA HOLDING
(*Suby of* HOERBIGER HOLDING AG)
3350 Gateway Dr, Pompano Beach, FL 33069-4841
Tel (954) 974-5700 *Founded/Ownrshp* 1999
Sales 169.3MM^E *EMP* 591
SIC 3494 7699 Valves & pipe fittings; Valve repair, industrial; Valves & pipe fittings; Valve repair, industrial
Pr: Franz Gruber
**Sec:* Peter Laube

D-U-N-S 00-179-4049 IMP
HOERBIGER CORP OF AMERICA INC (FL)
(*Suby of* HOERBIGER COMPRESSION TECHNOLOGY AMERICA HOLDING) ★
3350 Gateway Dr, Pompano Beach, FL 33069-4841
Tel (713) 224-9015 *Founded/Ownrshp* 1963
Sales 88.2MM^E *EMP* 350
Accts Deloitte Tax Llp Miami Flori
SIC 3491 Industrial valves; Industrial valves
Pr: Don York
Treas: Heather Henderson
**Sec:* Thomas Rabil
Ofcr: Dinesh Mathew

*Ex VP: Hannes Hunschosky
Sr VP: Josef Leitner
VP: Ben Boutin
VP: Tim Bremner
*VP: Bruce Driggett
*VP: Christean Kapp
*VP: Donald York

D-U-N-S 10-306-4788
HOERBIGER SERVICE INC
(Suby of HOERBIGER COMPRESSION TECHNOLOGY AMERICA HOLDING) ★
7042 S Revere Pkwy # 400, Centennial, CO 80112-6776
Tel (720) 588-4220 Founded/Ownrshp 2001
Sales 81.0MM^E EMP 200
SIC 5085 7699 Valves & fittings; Valve repair, industrial; Valves & fittings; Valve repair, industrial
Pr: Franz Ottitsch
*Sec: Peter Laube
*VP: Steve Jackson
Sftwr Eng: Jared Morell
Opers Mgr: James Chenevert

D-U-N-S 07-296-1329 EXP
HOFF COMPANIES INC
WESTERN WINDOWS
1840 N Lakes Pl, Meridian, ID 83646-1921
Tel (208) 884-2002 Founded/Ownrshp 1910
Sales 32.4MM^E EMP 150
SIC 5211 6552 Bathroom fixtures, equipment & supplies; Land subdividers & developers, commercial; Bathroom fixtures, equipment & supplies; Land subdividers & developers, commercial
Ch Bd: Harvey B Hoff
*CEO: Brian Hoff

D-U-N-S 10-850-1107 IMP
HOFFCO INC
7050 N 97th Plaza Cir, Omaha, NE 68122
Tel (402) 573-9244 Founded/Ownrshp 2004
Sales 31.9MM^E EMP 190
SIC 2434

D-U-N-S 04-751-0342
HOFFER FLOW CONTROLS INC
107 Kitty Hawk Ln, Elizabeth City, NC 27909-6756
Tel (252) 331-1997 Founded/Ownrshp 1969
Sales 20.1MM^E EMP 80
SIC 3823 Flow instruments, industrial process type
CEO: Kenneth Hoffer
*Pr: Bob Carrell
*VP: Sandee Kelly
Sftwr Eng: Mike Raines

D-U-N-S 00-521-6221 IMP/EXP
HOFFER PLASTICS CORP (DE)
500 N Collins St, South Elgin, IL 60177-1195
Tel (847) 741-5740 Founded/Ownrshp 1953
Sales 145.5MM^E EMP 375
SIC 3089 Injection molding of plastics; Injection molding of plastics
Pr: William A Hoffer
*Treas: Mary Eagin
*VP: Jack Shedd
QA Dir: Melanie Nelson
QC Dir: Jim Stoffel
Plnt Mgr: Fred Aguinia
Plnt Mgr: Bob Fowler
Plnt Mgr: Matt Olsen
VP Sls: Alex Hoffer
S&M/VP: William Hoffer
Mktg Dir: Charlotte Canning

D-U-N-S 00-193-4876 IMP
HOFFINGER INDUSTRIES INC
DOUGHBOY RECREATIONAL
315 N Sebastian, West Helena, AR 72390-2417
Tel (870) 572-3466 Founded/Ownrshp 1945
Sales 22.3MM^E EMP 128
SIC 3949 3589 7359 Swimming pools, plastic; Swimming pool filter & water conditioning systems; Home entertainment equipment rental; Swimming pools, plastic; Swimming pool filter & water conditioning systems; Home entertainment equipment rental
Pr: Doug Hollowell
Dir IT: Jim Larry
Dir IT: Jim Robb
Sls Dir: Melody Flowers
Mktg Mgr: Robin Bobo

D-U-N-S 07-156-8745
HOFFMAN & HOFFMAN INC (NC)
HOFFMAN BUILDING TECHNOLOGIES
3816 Patterson St, Greensboro, NC 27407-3238
Tel (336) 292-8777 Founded/Ownrshp 1947
Sales 77.3MM^E EMP 225
SIC 5075

D-U-N-S 03-115-6375
HOFFMAN AND REED INC
915 Shanklin St, Trenton, MO 64683-2532
Tel (660) 359-2258 Founded/Ownrshp 1949
Sales 41.6MM EMP 35
Accts Lockridge Constant & Conrad
SIC 5153 5191 Grains; Feed; Seeds: field, garden & flower; Fertilizer & fertilizer materials; Chemicals, agricultural; Grains; Feed; Seeds: field, garden & flower; Fertilizer & fertilizer materials; Chemicals, agricultural
Pr: Christopher B Hoffman

D-U-N-S 00-895-6104
HOFFMAN BEVERAGE CO INC
(Suby of ATLANTIC DOMINION DISTRIBUTORS) ★
5464 Greenwich Rd, Virginia Beach, VA 23462-6512
Tel (757) 499-1234 Founded/Ownrshp 1983
Sales 48.1MM^E EMP 195
SIC 5181

D-U-N-S 01-662-6657
HOFFMAN BROS AUTO ELECTRIC INC
HOFFMAN BROS AUTO PARTS
24355 Edison Rd, South Bend, IN 46628-4949
Tel (574) 239-1030 Founded/Ownrshp 1949
Sales 29.4MM^E EMP 85
SIC 5013 5531 Automotive supplies & parts; Automotive parts
Pr: James T Walsh Jr
*VP: Robert Walsh

HOFFMAN BROS AUTO PARTS
See HOFFMAN BROS AUTO ELECTRIC INC

D-U-N-S 06-585-3830
HOFFMAN BROS INC
8574 Verona Rd, Battle Creek, MI 49014-8404
Tel (269) 965-1207 Founded/Ownrshp 1999
Sales 36.6MM EMP 100
Accts Plante & Moran Pllc Portage
SIC 1611 Highway & street construction; Highway & street construction
Pr: Brian Hoffman
*Treas: Dan Eriksson
Trst: Richard Theirjung
Mtls Mgr: Todd Cole

HOFFMAN BUILDING TECHNOLOGIES
See HOFFMAN & HOFFMAN INC

D-U-N-S 02-260-6156
HOFFMAN CHEVROLET INC
HOFFMAN CHVRLT-CDLLC-LDSMOBILE
101 S Edgewood Dr, Hagerstown, MD 21740-6687
Tel (301) 733-5000 Founded/Ownrshp 1959
Sales 38.7MM^E EMP 100
SIC 5511 Automobiles, new & used; Automobiles, new & used
Pr: Charles W Hoffman
VP: Edison R Zayas
Exec: Jackie Weller
Genl Mgr: Julie Harbaugh

HOFFMAN CHVRLT-CDLLC-LDSMOBILE
See HOFFMAN CHEVROLET INC

D-U-N-S 00-895-9819
HOFFMAN CONSTRUCTION CO
123 Cth A, Black River Falls, WI 54615
Tel (715) 284-2512 Founded/Ownrshp 1910
Sales 58.3MM^E EMP 240
SIC 1611 1542

D-U-N-S 19-466-7945
HOFFMAN CONSTRUCTION CO OF OREGON
805 Sw Broadway Ste 2100, Portland, OR 97205-3361
Tel (503) 221-8811 Founded/Ownrshp 1994
Sales 69.7MM^E EMP 104
SIC 1629 Waste water & sewage treatment plant construction; Waste water & sewage treatment plant construction
Pr: Wayne Drinkward
Ofcr: Jessica Peterson
Ex VP: Bart Eberwein
VP: Dan D Harmon
VP: Gregory Johnston
VP: Tom Stein
Genl Mgr: Tim Fornadley
IT Man: Anne Belle
Sales Asso: Jeff Cook

D-U-N-S 11-267-7810
HOFFMAN CORP
805 Sw Broadway Ste 2100, Portland, OR 97205-3561
Tel (503) 221-8811 Founded/Ownrshp 1983
Sales 116.0MM^E EMP 750
Accts Kpmg Llp Portland Or
SIC 8741 1541 1542 1623 1629 Management services; Industrial buildings, new construction; Renovation, remodeling & repairs: industrial buildings; Commercial & office building, new construction; Water main construction; Waste water & sewage treatment plant construction; Management services; Industrial buildings, new construction; Renovation, remodeling & repairs: industrial buildings; Commercial & office building, new construction; Water main construction; Waste water & sewage treatment plant construction
Pr: Wayne A Drinkward
*CFO: Mario Nudo
*Ex VP: Richard L Silliman
Genl Mgr: Murl Ferguson
Genl Mgr: Ryan Thrush
IT Man: Anne Belle
MIS Mgr: Pat Gorrell
VP Opers: Bill Forsythe
Sfty Mgr: Paula Vandehay

D-U-N-S 13-073-2274 IMP
HOFFMAN ENCLOSURES INC
PENTAIR TECHNICAL PRODUCTS
(Suby of PENTAIR PUBLIC LIMITED COMPANY)
2100 Hoffman Way, Anoka, MN 55303-1745
Tel (763) 421-2240 Founded/Ownrshp 1988
Sales 1.2MMM^E EMP 1,500
SIC 3444 3699 3613 3469 3053 Housings for business machines, sheet metal; Electrical equipment & supplies; Switchgear & switchboard apparatus; Metal stampings; Gaskets, packing & sealing devices; Housings for business machines, sheet metal; Electrical equipment & supplies; Switchgear & switchboard apparatus; Metal stampings; Gaskets, packing & sealing devices
Pr: Alok Maskara
Treas: Mark Borin
Prgrm Mgr: Abby Hackbarth
Area Mgr: Dan Jasek
Natl Sales: Broc Krekelberg

D-U-N-S 00-145-2580
HOFFMAN ENGINEERING LLC (CT)
(PARENT IS AERONAUTICAL & GI HOLDINGS LIMITED)
(Suby of AERONAUTICAL & GI HOLDINGS LIMITED)
8 Riverbend Dr, Stamford, CT 06907-2629
Tel (203) 425-8900 Founded/Ownrshp 1987
Sales 21.2MM^E EMP 65
SIC 8734 3647 3826 3825 3674 3571 Testing laboratories; Aircraft lighting fixtures; Photometers; Instruments to measure electricity; Semiconductors & related devices; Electronic computers
Pr: Andrew Sadlon
VP: Pat Warner
IT Man: Chris Moher
Mtls Mgr: Ron Curtin
Ql Cn Mgr: Jim Stofko

HOFFMAN ENTERPRISES
See JETOBRA INC

HOFFMAN EQUIPMENT
See HOFFMAN INTERNATIONAL INC

D-U-N-S 07-705-1951
HOFFMAN ESTATES PARK DISTRICT INC
1685 W Higgins Rd Ste 100, Hoffman Estates, IL 60169-6998
Tel (847) 885-7500 Founded/Ownrshp 1964
Sales 19.4MM EMP 525
Accts Sikich Llp Naperville Illino
SIC 7999 Recreation services; Recreation services
Ex Dir: Dean Bostrom
V Ch: Lili Kilbridge
COO: Jeff Doschadis
Treas: Kathleen Musial
VP: Kaz Mohan
Prgrm Mgr: Jody Dodson
Prgrm Mgr: Jessica Senne
IT Man: John Agudelo

HOFFMAN FORDLAND
See FORD HOFFMAN SALES INC

D-U-N-S 18-069-1578
■ **HOFFMAN FUEL CO OF BRIDGEPORT**
(Suby of CHAMPION ENERGY CORP) ★
56 Quarry Rd Ste 2, Trumbull, CT 06611-4876
Tel (203) 373-5999 Founded/Ownrshp 1986
Sales 24.6MM^E EMP 105
SIC 5983 Fuel oil dealers; Fuel oil dealers
Ch: Peter Carini
*Pr: Anthony Silecchia
*VP: A J Bianco

D-U-N-S 00-177-6129 EXP
HOFFMAN INTERNATIONAL INC
HOFFMAN EQUIPMENT
300 S Randolphville Rd, Piscataway, NJ 08854-4110
Tel (732) 752-3600 Founded/Ownrshp 1922, 2002
Sales 36.8MM^E EMP 67
SIC 5082 7353 7699 Construction & mining machinery; Excavating machinery & equipment; Front end loaders; Pavers; Earth moving equipment, rental or leasing; Cranes & aerial lift equipment, rental or leasing; Construction equipment repair; Construction & mining machinery; Excavating machinery & equipment; Front end loaders; Pavers; Earth moving equipment, rental or leasing; Cranes & aerial lift equipment, rental or leasing; Construction equipment repair
Pr: Timothy J Watters
*CFO: Eric Shumaker
*VP: Michael Anderson
Sls Mgr: Steve Izzi

D-U-N-S 96-196-2482
HOFFMAN OF EAST HARTFORD INC
(Suby of HOFFMAN ENTERPRISES) ★
650 Connecticut Blvd, East Hartford, CT 06108-3287
Tel (888) 446-9258 Founded/Ownrshp 2007
Sales 20.0MM^E EMP 123^E
SIC 5511 New & used car dealers
Pr: Jeffrey S Hoffman
*VP: Bradley Hoffman

D-U-N-S 01-864-9723
HOFFMAN OLDSMOBILE INC
700 Connecticut Blvd, East Hartford, CT 06108-3263
Tel (860) 528-4811 Founded/Ownrshp 1931
Sales 23.2MM^E EMP 100
SIC 5511 7538 7532 5521 Automobiles, new & used; General automotive repair shops; Top & body repair & paint shops; Used car dealers; Automobiles, new & used; General automotive repair shops; Top & body repair & paint shops; Used car dealers
Pt: Bradley Hoffman
*Ch Bd: Burton Hoffman
Genl Mgr: Andrea Ballou

D-U-N-S 05-388-6479
HOFFMAN PLASTIC COMPOUNDS INC
16616 Garfield Ave, Paramount, CA 90723-5305
Tel (323) 636-3346 Founded/Ownrshp 1971
Sales 24.8MM^E EMP 66
SIC 2821 3087 Polyvinyl chloride resins (PVC); Custom compound purchased resins
Pr: Ronald P Hoffman
*Sec: Susan Hoffman
Sls Mgr: James Price

HOFFMAN PRODUCTS
See TPC WIRE & CABLE CORP

D-U-N-S 06-618-2957
HOFFMAN SOUTHWEST CORP
PRO PIPE
23311 Madero, Mission Viejo, CA 92691-2730
Tel (949) 495-1616 Founded/Ownrshp 2015
Sales 59.4MM^E EMP 535
SIC 7699 1711 Sewer cleaning & rodding; Plumbing contractors; Sewer cleaning & rodding; Plumbing contractors
VP Opers: Mark Metcalfe
Brnch Mgr: Ken Bunes
Brnch Mgr: Nick Lanoue
Brnch Mgr: Steve Powers
Brnch Mgr: Thomas Romero
Brnch Mgr: Parrish Topps
Div Mgr: Dean Monk
IT Man: Sandy Darone

D-U-N-S 16-150-0830
HOFFMAN STRUCTURES INC
(Suby of HOFFMAN CORP) ★
12130 Ne Ainsworth Cir # 225, Portland, OR 97220-9061
Tel (503) 548-2981 Founded/Ownrshp 1985
Sales 25.8MM^E EMP 486
Accts Kpmg Llp Portland Oregon
SIC 1771 Concrete work; Concrete work
Pr: Kevin L Joeckel
*CFO: Scott Fredricks
*Treas: Mario L Nudo
*VP: Blair Bubenik

D-U-N-S 17-082-6085
HOFFMAN TRANSPORT INC
485 Mason Dixon Rd, Greencastle, PA 17225-9639
Tel (717) 597-7117 Founded/Ownrshp 1981
Sales 28.4MM^E EMP 100^E
SIC 4213

D-U-N-S 00-643-9236
HOFFMAN YORK INC
HY CONNECT
(Suby of MYELIN COMMUNICATIONS) ★
1000 N Water St Ste 1600, Milwaukee, WI 53202-6667
Tel (414) 289-9700 Founded/Ownrshp 2015
Sales 76.6MM^E EMP 152
SIC 7311 7374 8742 8743 Advertising agencies; Public relations & publicity; Communications consulting; Marketing consulting services; Computer graphics service; Advertising agencies; Computer graphics service; Marketing consulting services; Public relations & publicity
Pr: Dave Sheehan
*Pr: Terry Jackson
Bd of Dir: Shradha Agarwal
Sr VP: Elissa Polston
Sr VP: Carol Rockow
Sr VP: Tom Watson
VP: Kathy Eurich
VP: Ken Lolli
Creative D: Stefanie Lyons
Creative D: Michael Matykiewicz
Prd Mgr: Dan Boehne

D-U-N-S 00-219-1211 IMP
■ **HOFFMANN-LA ROCHE INC** (NJ)
(Suby of ROCHE HOLDINGS INC) ★
340 Kingsland St, Nutley, NJ 07110-1199
Tel (973) 235-5000 Founded/Ownrshp 1905
Sales 949.8MM^E EMP 5,027
SIC 2834 8733 Pharmaceutical preparations; Medical research; Pharmaceutical preparations; Medical research
Pr: George B Abercrombie
Pr: Kurt Seiler
*CFO: Ivor Macleod
Treas: William L Hennrich
Bd of Dir: Lance Willsey
Sr VP: Alain Gscheidle
Sr VP: Maryjo Zaborowski
VP: Carl J Accettura
*VP: Frederick C Kentz III
*VP: Tom Lyon
VP: Steven C Sembler
VP: Barbara Senich
Exec: Peter Borgulya
Exec: Susan Gabra
Exec: Maria Rivas
Assoc Dir: Hans Bitter
Comm Dir: Odeta Rimkeviciute
Dir Bus: Guido Kaiser

D-U-N-S 04-314-7412 IMP/EXP
HOFFMASTER GROUP INC (DE)
2920 N Main St, Oshkosh, WI 54901-1221
Tel (920) 235-9330 Founded/Ownrshp 2005
Sales 488.1MM^E EMP 1,400
SIC 2676 Towels, napkins & tissue paper products; Napkins, paper: made from purchased paper; Towels, napkins & tissue paper products; Napkins, paper: made from purchased paper
CEO: Rory Leyden
Pr: Mike Marquardt
*Pr: William Mullenix
Pr: Mike Narquardt
*Pr: Russsell Snow
*CFO: David L Walkowski
VP: Jeff Cunningham
VP: Susan Dollinger
Exec: Fabricio Biscardi
Area Mgr: Chris Thake
Area Mgr: Dirk Vondeylen

D-U-N-S 06-311-6156 IMP
HOFFMEYER CO INC
1600 Factor Ave, San Leandro, CA 94577-5618
Tel (209) 576-0810 Founded/Ownrshp 1991
Sales 26.2MM^E EMP 46
SIC 5085 Hose, belting & packing; Rubber goods, mechanical
Ch Bd: Frederick J Oshay
*Pr: Rob Yob

HOFFPAUIR OUTDOOR SUPERSTORE
See JIM HOFFPAUIR INC

HOFFY
See SQUARE H BRANDS INC

D-U-N-S 00-125-3830 IMP/EXP
HOFMANN & LEAVY INC (NY)
TASSEL DEPOT
3251 Sw 13th Dr Ste 3, Deerfield Beach, FL 33442-8166
Tel (954) 698-0000 Founded/Ownrshp 1864, 1979
Sales 23.2MM^E EMP 200
SIC 2298 5085 2396 2782 Wire rope centers; Rope, cord & thread; Apparel findings & trimmings; Furniture trimmings, fabric; Sample books; Wire rope centers; Rope, cord & thread; Apparel findings & trimmings; Furniture trimmings, fabric; Sample books
Pr: Roger S Leavy
*VP: April Leavy

D-U-N-S 00-227-0304
HOFMANN INDUSTRIES INC
3145 Shillington Rd, Reading, PA 19608-1606
Tel (610) 678-8051 Founded/Ownrshp 1952
Sales 69.2MM^E EMP 275
SIC 3317 3498 3471 3479 Tubes, wrought: welded or lock joint; Fabricated pipe & fittings; Plating & polishing; Coating of metals & formed products; Tubes, wrought: welded or lock joint; Fabricated pipe & fittings; Plating & polishing; Coating of metals & formed products
Ch Bd: Bernard M Hofmann
*Pr: Stephen P Owens

*Treas: Robert E Hess
*VP: Jeffrey C Hills
*VP: John J Masley
*VP: J P Owens
Prd Mgr: Tom Ramsey

HOFS HUT LCLLES SMOKEHOUSE BBQ
See HOFS HUT RESTAURANT INC

D-U-N-S 05-291-5580
HOFS HUT RESTAURANT INC
HOFS HUT LCLLES SMOKEHOUSE BBQ
2601 E Willow St, Signal Hill, CA 90755-2214
Tel (310) 406-6340 Founded/Ownrshp 2010
Sales 142.0MM EMP 2,986E
SIC 5812 Barbecue restaurant; American restaurant
Pr: Craig Hofman
VP: Paul Williamson
Exec: Chris Ferrell
Genl Mgr: Allen Cameron
Opers Supe: Jorge Angulo
Opers Supe: Chris Gorman
Opers Supe: Brad Hoffman

HOF'S HUT RESTAURANTS AND BKY
See HOFS HUT RESTAURANTS INC

D-U-N-S 02-841-6196
HOFS HUT RESTAURANTS INC
HOF'S HUT RESTAURANTS AND BKY
2601 E Willow St, Signal Hill, CA 90755-2214
Tel (562) 596-0200 Founded/Ownrshp 1951
Sales 62.7MME EMP 1,345
SIC 5812 Restaurant, family: chain; Restaurant, family: chain
Pr: Craig Hoffman
*Pr: Paul Bowman
CFO: Dennis Jones
Genl Mgr: Carl Tierney
Dir IT: Dana Gonzalez

D-U-N-S 06-593-1800
HOFSTRA UNIVERSITY
100 Hofstra University, Hempstead, NY 11549-4000
Tel (516) 463-6600 Founded/Ownrshp 1935
Sales 397.4MM EMP 2,000
Accts Kpmg Llp New York Ny
SIC 8221 University; University
Pr: Stuart Rabinowitz
CFO: Joshua Robinson
Sr VP: Patricia Adamski
Sr VP: Herman A Berliner
VP: Melissa Cefalu
VP: Lindsay Dwyer
VP: Michael Hershfield
VP: Sandra S Johnson
VP: Robert W Juckiewicz
VP: Alan J Kelly
Mktg Mgr: Zhao Fang

HOG
See HIGHLANDS ONCOLOGY GROUP PA

D-U-N-S 06-854-7702
HOG INC
Rr 2 Box 8, Greenfield, IL 62044-9603
Tel (217) 368-2888 Founded/Ownrshp 1962
Sales 71.8MM EMP 26
Accts Scheffel Boyle Alton Illinoi
SIC 5191 5083 Feed; Farm & garden machinery; Feed; Farm & garden machinery
Pr: Randy Palan
Genl Mgr: Steve Ring

D-U-N-S 05-441-5021 IMP/EXP
HOG SLAT INC
206 Fayetteville St, Newton Grove, NC 28366-9071
Tel (866) 464-7528 Founded/Ownrshp 1970
Sales 598.1MME EMP 600
SIC 1542 3272 3523 0213 Farm building construction; Floor slabs & tiles, precast concrete; Hog feeding, handling & watering equipment; Hogs; Farm building construction; Floor slabs & tiles, precast concrete; Hog feeding, handling & watering equipment; Hogs
Ch Bd: William T Herring Sr
*Pr: William T Herring Jr
*Sec: Magalene Herring
*VP: David D Herring
Exec: Tommy Herring
Mng Dir: Cosmin Pomoje
Mng Dir: Claudiu Vida
Store Mgr: Lance Heuser
CTO: Denise Holland
Opers Mgr: Steve Smith
Ql Cn Mgr: Keith Riley

D-U-N-S 95-747-2996
HOGAN & ASSOCIATES CONSTRUCTION INC
940 N 1250 W, Centerville, UT 84014-1356
Tel (801) 951-7000 Founded/Ownrshp 1995
Sales 65.8MME EMP 130
SIC 1542 1541 1522

HOGAN ADMINISTRATIVE CENTER
See SCHOOL DISTRICT OF LACROSSE

HOGAN CARL CHVRLT-TOYOTA-MAZDA
See CARL HOGAN AUTOMOTIVE INC

D-U-N-S 03-317-3613
HOGAN CONSTRUCTION GROUP LLC (GA)
5075 Avalon Ridge Pkwy, Peachtree Corners, GA 30071-4738
Tel (770) 242-8588 Founded/Ownrshp 1998
Sales 53.8MME EMP 91
SIC 1541 Industrial buildings & warehouses
Pr: Paul Hogan

D-U-N-S 07-265-9238
HOGAN LOVELLS US LLP
555 13th St Nw, Washington, DC 20004-1109
Tel (202) 637-5600 Founded/Ownrshp 1994
Sales 435.5MME EMP 2,500
SIC 8111 Corporate, partnership & business law; Patent, trademark & copyright law; Securities law; Corporate, partnership & business law; Patent, trademark & copyright law; Securities law
Mng Pt: Emily Yinger
Pt: Jeanne S Archibald
Pt: Barton S Aronson
Pt: A C Arumi
Pt: Raymond J Batla
Pt: David H Ben-Meir
Pt: Barbara Bennett
Pt: Christopher D Berry
Pt: Dirk Besse
Pt: Arlene L Chow
Pt: Alexander D Cobey
Pt: Colin W Craik
Pt: Celine J Crowson
Pt: Alice V Curran
Pt: Daniel M Davidson
Pt: Agnes P Dover
Pt: Alexander E Dreier
Pt: David R Dunn
Pt: Prentiss E Feagles
Pt: Adam S Feuerstein
Pt: Amy B Freed

D-U-N-S 00-917-1992
HOGAN MFG INC (CA)
19527 Mchenry Ave, Escalon, CA 95320-9613
Tel (209) 838-7323 Founded/Ownrshp 1944, 1986
Sales 37.7MME EMP 275
SIC 3999 3441 3443 1791 Wheelchair lifts; Fabricated structural metal; Fabricated plate work (boiler shop); Structural steel erection; Wheelchair lifts; Fabricated structural metal; Fabricated plate work (boiler shop); Structural steel erection
Pr: Mark Hogan
*VP: Jeff Hogan
*VP: Paul Reichmuth
Genl Mgr: David Boyd
IT Man: Tyler Lucas
Sfty Mgr: Donny Sanderson
Plnt Mgr: Zach Hogan
Plnt Mgr: Jim Silveira
Sls Mgr: John Fusco

D-U-N-S 19-585-2686
HOGAN TRANSPORTS INC
2150 Schuetz Rd Ste 210, Saint Louis, MO 63146-3517
Tel (314) 421-6000 Founded/Ownrshp 1982
Sales 23.7MME EMP 50
SIC 4213 Trucking, except local
Pr: David Hogan
*VP: Steve Spiess

D-U-N-S 03-104-7913
HOGAN TRUCK LEASING INC
2150 Schuetz Rd Ste 210, Saint Louis, MO 63146-3517
Tel (314) 421-6000 Founded/Ownrshp 1918
Sales 32.5MME EMP 150
SIC 7513 Truck rental, without drivers; Truck rental, without drivers
Pr: Brian J Hogan
CFO: Geri Zinn
*VP: Carl G Hogan Jr
Area Mgr: Ralph Samples
Dir IT: Glen Jansen
VP Sls: Craig Thoelke

D-U-N-S 07-053-2945
HOGG ROBINSON USA LLC
HRG NORTHAMERICA
(Suby of HOGG ROBINSON GROUP PLC)
16 E 34th St Fl 3, New York, NY 10016-4371
Tel (212) 404-8800 Founded/Ownrshp 1999, 2005
Sales 48.8MME EMP 500
SIC 4724 Travel agencies; Travel agencies
COO: Brenda Reid
Ex VP: Chuck Wunz
VP: Rober Baker
VP: Kevin Brown
VP: Linda Garcia
Dir Bus: Tim Bachmann
Genl Mgr: Nizamuddin Ahmed
Genl Mgr: Rob De Laet
IT Man: Anke Korves
VP Opers: Ted Brooks
VP Opers: Michael Lelah

D-U-N-S 05-872-7645
HOGLE TRUCKLINES INC
7450 Cleveland Rd, Middleton, MI 48856-5111
Tel (989) 236-7225 Founded/Ownrshp 1982
Sales 23.0MME EMP 7
Accts Roslund Prestage & Company P
SIC 6221 4731 Commodity contracts brokers, dealers; Freight transportation arrangement; Commodity contracts brokers, dealers; Freight transportation arrangement
Pr: Robert Hogle
*Sec: Vanessa Colley
*Trst: Mike Hogle
*VP: Vicki Hogle

D-U-N-S 07-465-6653
HOGUE & ASSOCIATES INC
250 Montgomery St # 1500, San Francisco, CA 94104-3409
Tel (415) 788-4888 Founded/Ownrshp 1974
Sales 35.0MME EMP 39
SIC 5021 8741 Office furniture; Management services; Office furniture; Management services
Pr: Jonathan Gaber
*CFO: David D Boggs
Off Mgr: Catherine Ingber
IT Man: Kenneth Herdrick
Snr PM: Lauren Allen
Snr PM: Amanda Ghourdjian
Snr PM: Suzanne Haines

D-U-N-S 01-373-1815 IMP
HOHL INDUSTRIAL SERVICES INC
770 Riverview Blvd Ste 1, Tonawanda, NY 14150-7880
Tel (716) 332-0466 Founded/Ownrshp 1999
Sales 73.8MME EMP 120
SIC 1541 Industrial buildings & warehouses; Industrial buildings & warehouses
CEO: David Hohl
Off Mgr: Lisa Suggs

D-U-N-S 00-137-5443 IMP/EXP
■ **HOHMANN & BARNARD INC**
HB
(Suby of MITEK INDUSTRIES INC) ★
30 Rasons Ct, Hauppauge, NY 11788-4206
Tel (631) 234-0600 Founded/Ownrshp 2008
Sales 35.9MME EMP 160
SIC 3496 3462 3315 Clips & fasteners, made from purchased wire; Iron & steel forgings; Steel wire & related products; Clips & fasteners, made from purchased wire; Iron & steel forgings; Steel wire & related products
Ch Bd: Ronald P Hohmann
*Treas: Christopher Hohmann
VP: Bob Hohmann
Plnt Mgr: Winfred Freeman
VP Sls: Saverio Minucci
Manager: Victoria Minucci
Sales Asso: Michelle Nigro
Sales Asso: Kim Scaduto

D-U-N-S 00-697-7615 IMP
HOHNER INC
SONAR
(Suby of MATTH. HOHNER GMBH)
1000 Technology Park Dr, Glen Allen, VA 23059-4500
Tel (804) 515-1900 Founded/Ownrshp 1982
Sales 21.8MME EMP 50
Accts Keiter Stephens Hurst Gary
SIC 5099 Musical instruments
Pr: Clayman B Edwards
*CFO: Eg Martin
*Treas: Timothy Henry
*VP: Alan Scott Edwards
Sls Dir: B Green
Sls Mgr: Bill Greenhalgh
Sls Mgr: Scott Hile
Sls Mgr: David Watkinson
Sales Asso: Holt Nicholas
Sales Asso: Jimmy Zednik

HOIST & CRANE COMPANY
See GARRISON SERVICE CO

D-U-N-S 10-245-7207
HOIST & CRANE SERVICE GROUP INC
HCSG
4920 Jefferson Hwy, Jefferson, LA 70121-3101
Tel (504) 733-5881 Founded/Ownrshp 1983
Sales 76.3MME EMP 175
SIC 7389 Aircraft & heavy equipment repair services; Crane & aerial lift service
Pr: Terry Ross
*Treas: Rickey R Reynolds
*VP: David Cunningham

D-U-N-S 87-819-6922 IMP/EXP
HOIST LIFTRUCK MFG INC
6499 W 65th St, Bedford Park, IL 60638-5118
Tel (708) 458-2200 Founded/Ownrshp 1994
Sales 76.3MME EMP 120
SIC 3537 5084 Forklift trucks; Trucks, industrial; Forklift trucks; Trucks, industrial
CEO: Marty Flaska
*VP: Bob Fennewald
*VP: Michael Swieter
Ql Cn Mgr: Erik Purkey

HOISTING PORTABLE & SHOVEL ENG
See INTERNATIONAL UNION OF OPERATING ENGINEERS LOCAL 150

D-U-N-S 03-536-5386
HOJ ENGINEERING & SALES CO INC (UT)
MONARCH DOOR
3960 S 500 W, Salt Lake City, UT 84123-1360
Tel (801) 266-8881 Founded/Ownrshp 1963, 1964
Sales 44.6MME EMP 120
SIC 5084 5031

D-U-N-S 00-633-5251
HOK GROUP INC (GA)
10 S Broadway Ste 200, Saint Louis, MO 63102-1729
Tel (314) 421-2000 Founded/Ownrshp 1955, 1992
Sales 316.1MME EMP 1,839
SIC 8711 8712 8742 Planning consultant; Engineering services; Architectural services; Engineering services; Architectural services; Planning consultant
CEO: Patrick Macleamy
*Pr: William Hellmuth
*Treas: James Beittenmiller
Sr VP: Jim Fair
Sr VP: Bill O'Dell
VP: Javier Espinosa
VP: Todd Osborne
VP: Andy Singletary
IT Man: Donny Russell
Mktg Mgr: Kathie Dunn
Board of Directors: Carl Galioto, William Hellmuth, Patrick Macleamy, Richard Mascia, Thomas Robson

D-U-N-S 96-987-1560
HOK INC
(Suby of HOK GROUP INC) ★
10 S Broadway Ste 200, Saint Louis, MO 63102-1729
Tel (314) 421-2000 Founded/Ownrshp 1999
Sales 66.1MME EMP 1,808
SIC 0781 8712 8711 Landscape planning services; Architectural services; Engineering services
Pr: William Hellmuth
VP: Joseph Berra
VP: Chari Jalali
VP: Russell Lewis
VP: Michael Nolan
VP: Joseph Ostafi
VP: Misty Yanko
Dir Bus: Kristen Harrison
Off Mgr: Janet Song
Snr PM: Aaron Altman
Snr PM: Frank Ragland
Board of Directors: Daniel Hajjar, Sandra Paret, James Beittenmiller, Nancy Hamilton, Tom Polucci, Duncan Broyd, Jan Harmon, Thomas Robson, Robert Chicas, William Hellmuth, Paul Strohm, Ernest Cirangle, Susan Williams Klumpp, Jay Tatum, Kenneth Drucker, Richard Macia, Paul Woolford, Chris Fannin, Patrick Macleamy, Carl Galioto, Lawrence Malcic, Jeff Goodale, Rebecca Nolan, Lisa Green, William O'dell

D-U-N-S 10-005-8635
HOKE COUNTY BOARD OF EDUCATION
HOKE COUNTY SCHOOL DISTRICT
310 Wooley St, Raeford, NC 28376-3237
Tel (910) 875-4106 Founded/Ownrshp 1911
Sales 13.2M EMP 800
Accts Amyd Bullock Cpa Raeford Nc
SIC 8211 Public elementary & secondary schools; Public elementary school; Public junior high school; Public senior high school; Public elementary & secondary schools; Public elementary school; Public junior high school; Public senior high school
*CFO: Wannaa Chavis
*Ch: Irish Pickett
Ofcr: Willena Richardson
MIS Dir: Dawn Ramseur

HOKE COUNTY SCHOOL DISTRICT
See HOKE COUNTY BOARD OF EDUCATION

D-U-N-S 07-979-8916
HOKE COUNTY SCHOOLS
310 Wooley St, Raeford, NC 28376-3237
Tel (910) 875-4106 Founded/Ownrshp 2015
Sales 28.8MME EMP 781E
SIC 8211 Public elementary & secondary schools

HOKE GYROLOK
See CIRCOR INSTRUMENTATION TECHNOLOGIES INC

D-U-N-S 78-215-9321
HOL-DAV INC
JOHNSON LEXUS OF RALEIGH
5839 Capital Blvd, Raleigh, NC 27616-2937
Tel (919) 877-1800 Founded/Ownrshp 1990
Sales 95.1MME EMP 220
SIC 5511 5012 Automobiles, new & used; Automobiles & other motor vehicles; Automobiles, new & used; Automobiles & other motor vehicles
Pr: C David Johnson Jr
Sr VP: Charlie Bratton
Exec: Bonnie Clark
Dir Bus: Bishop Byerly
CTO: Bob Humphrey
Mktg Mgr: Leigh Fox
Sls Mgr: Brad Hodgeman
Sls Mgr: Stan Muecke
Sls Mgr: Jay Tetreault
Sales Asso: Sean Alazraki
Sales Asso: Larry Howell

D-U-N-S 06-366-6481 IMP
HOL-MAC CORP
2730 Highway 15, Bay Springs, MS 39422-7430
Tel (601) 764-4121 Founded/Ownrshp 1972
Sales 75.2MME EMP 265
SIC 3593 3523 3531 3559 Fluid power cylinders, hydraulic or pneumatic; Farm machinery & equipment; Construction machinery; Automotive related machinery; Fluid power cylinders, hydraulic or pneumatic; Farm machinery & equipment; Construction machinery; Automotive related machinery
Ch: Charles B Holder
*Pr: Jamie V Holder
*Treas: Joyce Holder
*Sec: Jeffrey D Holder
Plnt Mgr: Jerry Bennett
Plnt Mgr: Jeff Sumrall
Plnt Mgr: Trace Thurston
Prd Mgr: Jonathon Little
Sls Mgr: Chris Carpenter
Sls Mgr: Gary McLaughlin

D-U-N-S 04-424-3707
HOLABIRD & ROOT LLC (IL)
140 S Dearborn St Ste 500, Chicago, IL 60603-5205
Tel (312) 357-1771 Founded/Ownrshp 1880, 1980
Sales 21.6MME EMP 110
SIC 8712 8711 7389 8721 Architectural engineering; Civil engineering; Mechanical engineering; Electrical or electronic engineering; Structural engineering; Interior design services; Accounting, auditing & bookkeeping; Architectural engineering; Civil engineering; Mechanical engineering; Electrical or electronic engineering; Structural engineering; Interior design services; Accounting, auditing & bookkeeping
Mktg Mgr: Bridget Whitehouse

D-U-N-S 06-653-9743
HOLADAY CIRCUITS INC
11126 Bren Rd W, Minnetonka, MN 55343-9074
Tel (952) 988-8071 Founded/Ownrshp 1976
Sales 35.9MME EMP 155
SIC 3672 Printed circuit boards; Printed circuit boards
Pr: Marshall Lewis
*VP: John Erickson
*Exec: Dennis Pulanco

D-U-N-S 00-283-7508
HOLADAY-PARKS-FABRICATORS INC
4600 S 134th Pl, Tukwila, WA 98168-3241
Tel (206) 248-9700 Founded/Ownrshp 1952
Sales 84.0MM EMP 350
SIC 1711 Mechanical contractor; Sheet metalwork; Mechanical contractor
Co-Pr: Dave Beck
Co-Pr: Dan Connell
Co-Pr: Bijit Giri
VP: Jerry Freel
VP: June Nailon
VP: Grace Pizzey
VP: Eric Veen
Exec: Margaret Brown
Dir IT: Eric Der Veen
IT Man: Engwin Chang
IT Man: Erin Villeneuve

D-U-N-S 01-723-3789
HOLBROOK CO INC
3430 High Prairie Rd, Grand Prairie, TX 75050-4225
Tel (972) 465-3900 Founded/Ownrshp 2000
Sales 28.9MM EMP 130
Accts Perryman Chaney Russell Llp
SIC 1794 Excavation work; Excavation work
Pr: John G Holbrook
*VP: Sherri R Holbrook

Exec: Beth Wells
Mtls Mgr: John Mobley
Sls Mgr: Bill Flynn
Snr PM: Guadalupe Arciniega
Snr PM: Lupe Arciniega

D-U-N-S 08-558-1358
HOLCIM (TEXAS) LIMITED PARTNERSHIP
1800 Dove Ln, Midlothian, TX 76065-4435
Tel (972) 923-5800 *Founded/Ownrshp* 1984
Sales 29.4MM^E *EMP* 160
SIC 2891 Cement, except linoleum & tile; Cement, except linoleum & tile
Pr: Patrick Dolberg
Sfty Mgr: Falon Petty
Prd Mgr: Victor Cifuentes

D-U-N-S 60-896-3674 IMP
HOLCIM (US) INC
HOLCIM USA
(*Suby of* LAFARGEHOLCIM LTD)
6211 N Ann Arbor Rd, Dundee, MI 48131-9527
Tel (734) 529-4278 *Founded/Ownrshp* 1981
Sales 688.5MM^E *EMP* 1,800
SIC 3241 3272 Portland cement; Concrete products; Portland cement; Concrete products
Pr: Filiberto Ruiz
Sr VP: GA Tan Jacques
**Sr VP:* Norman L Jagger
**Sr VP:* Alyse Martinelli
**Sr VP:* Jeff Ouhl
VP: John Eichbauer
**VP:* David Loomes
VP: Rick Reinhart
VP: Chrysanth Silva
Exec: Dave Zenns
Prgrm Mgr: Jodie Earle

D-U-N-S 03-766-2025 IMP
HOLCIM TECHNOLOGY INC
(*Suby of* LAFARGEHOLCIM LTD)
5200 Blue Lagoon Dr # 790, Miami, FL 33126-7006
Tel (305) 728-1700 *Founded/Ownrshp* 2001
Sales 38.2MM^E *EMP* 20
SIC 5084 Cement making machinery
Pr: Carlos Moreno
**Treas:* Nilton Garcia
**Treas:* Ronald Jose Hernandez
Sr VP: Baudouin Nizet
VP: John Eichbauer
Genl Mgr: Rick Lewis
Off Admin: Donna Holcim
IT Man: Eric Lefevre
IT Man: Allen Schank
Sfty Mgr: Cecil Slattery
Prd Mgr: Mike Mullaney

HOLCIM USA
See HOLCIM (US) INC

D-U-N-S 00-291-5643
HOLCOMB ASSOCIATES INC (PA)
HOLCOMB BEHAVIORAL HEALTH SYST
467 Creamery Way, Exton, PA 19341-2508
Tel (610) 363-1488 *Founded/Ownrshp* 1979
Sales 23.3MM *EMP* 400
Accts Gorfine Schiller & Gardyn Pa
SIC 8093 Mental health clinic, outpatient; Mental health clinic, outpatient
Pr: Martin S Lampner
**COO:* William Difabio
**CFO:* Wendy Wait
**Treas:* Stewart C Lee
Ofcr: Susan H Berryman
**VP:* Robert R Ruth
Exec: Janice Potts
Rgnl Mgr: Denise Knuckles
IT Man: Richard Cossaboon
Snr Mgr: Roger Osmun

HOLCOMB BEHAVIORAL HEALTH SYST
See HOLCOMB ASSOCIATES INC

D-U-N-S 04-463-3142
■ **HOLDCO LLC**
(*Suby of* TIME WARNER CABLE ENTERPRISES LLC)
★
13820 Sunrise Valley Dr, Herndon, VA 20171-4659
Tel (703) 345-2400 *Founded/Ownrshp* 2001
Sales 103.8MM^E *EMP* 480
SIC 4813 ;
VP: Clay Carney
VP: Raj Kumar
VP Mktg: Chip Snyder
Mktg Dir: Margie Locke
Mktg Dir: Wendy Wilson

D-U-N-S 16-708-0667 IMP/EXP
HOLDEN INDUSTRIES INC
500 Lake Cook Rd Ste 400, Deerfield, IL 60015-5269
Tel (847) 940-1500 *Founded/Ownrshp* 2004
Sales 294.9MM^E *EMP* 1,091
SIC 2752 2672 3545 3589 3541 3441 Commercial printing, lithographic; Adhesive papers, labels or tapes: from purchased material; Machine tool accessories; Sewage & water treatment equipment; Sewer cleaning equipment, power; Machine tools, metal cutting type; Fabricated structural metal; Commercial printing, lithographic; Adhesive papers, labels or tapes: from purchased material; Machine tool accessories; Sewage & water treatment equipment; Sewer cleaning equipment, power; Machine tools, metal cutting type; Fabricated structural metal
Ch Bd: Joseph S Haas
**CFO:* Gregory R Hamilton
CFO: Donald Hotz
Ofcr: Joe Walsh
**Ex VP:* Arthur R Miller

D-U-N-S 07-534-0570
HOLDEN NURSING HOME INC
32 Mayo Dr, Holden, MA 01520-1597
Tel (508) 829-4327 *Founded/Ownrshp* 1964
Sales 12.3MM^E *EMP* 320
SIC 8051 Skilled nursing care facilities; Extended care facility; Skilled nursing care facilities; Extended care facility
Pr: Robert Oriol
Dir Recs: Sandy Trzpit
**VP:* David H Oriol
Dir Soc: Elaine Wilson
Nrsg Dir: Dawn Auger
Nrsg Dir: Terry T Kiredge
HC Dir: Ursala Hanus
HC Dir: Sandra Trzpit

D-U-N-S 01-956-0358
HOLDEN OIL INC
91 Lynnfield St, Peabody, MA 01960-5232
Tel (978) 531-2984 *Founded/Ownrshp* 1924
Sales 24.2MM^E *EMP* 50
Accts Gray Gray & Gray Llp Westwo
SIC 5983 5541 Fuel oil dealers; Gasoline service stations; Fuel oil dealers; Gasoline service stations
Pr: Charles E Holden
VP: Arthur Holden

D-U-N-S 07-427-1941
HOLDENVILLE GENERAL HOSPITAL SCHOLARSHIP FUND INC
100 Mcdougal Dr, Holdenville, OK 74848-2822
Tel (405) 379-4201 *Founded/Ownrshp* 1972
Sales 24.1MM^E *EMP* 142
SIC 8062 General medical & surgical hospitals
Prin: Jerry Hulin
**Pr:* Kathi Mask
CFO: Bob Tyk
**VP:* Sue Wood
**Prin:* Roberta Jeffrey

D-U-N-S 82-833-8488
HOLDER CONSTRUCTION CO
3333 Riverwood Pkwy Se # 400, Atlanta, GA 30339-3304
Tel (770) 988-3000 *Founded/Ownrshp* 1997
Sales 607.0MM^E *EMP* 734^E
SIC 1542 Commercial & office building, new construction
CEO: Thomas M Holder
**CFO:* Dave O'Haren
Ex VP: D Johnston
Ex VP: Lee Johnston
VP: Michael Kenig
VP: Tom Shumaker
CIO: Henry Petree
Software D: Jarin Whigham

D-U-N-S 11-029-2471 IMP
HOLDER CONSTRUCTION GROUP LLC
3333 Riverwood Pkwy Se # 400, Atlanta, GA 30339-3304
Tel (770) 988-3000 *Founded/Ownrshp* 2011
Sales 158.5MM^E *EMP* 450
SIC 1542 Commercial & office building, new construction; Commercial & office building, new construction
Pr: Dave W Miller
Pr: John Redmond
Pr: Thomas Shumaker
Pr: Drew Yantis
VP: John Thomas

D-U-N-S 00-332-0850
HOLDER CORP
3300 Cumberland Blvd Se # 200, Atlanta, GA 30339-3100
Tel (404) 503-9999 *Founded/Ownrshp* 1984
Sales 83.9MM^E *EMP* 470
SIC 6552 1542 Subdividers & developers; Commercial & office building, new construction; Subdividers & developers; Commercial & office building, new construction
Ch Bd: John Holder
V Ch: Michael E Kenig
**CFO:* Lori Pisarcik
**V Ch Bd:* Thomas M Holder
**Ex VP:* J C Pendrey Jr
Sr VP: Lee Johnston
**Sr VP:* Jeff Mixson
Sr VP: Rick Morgan
**Sr VP:* Chris Smith
**VP:* Henry Petree
Site Mgr: Jason Rollins

D-U-N-S 04-494-3801
HOLDER ELECTRIC SUPPLY INC (SC)
GALLERY OF LIGHTING, THE
431 N Pleasantburg Dr, Greenville, SC 29607-2127
Tel (864) 271-7111 *Founded/Ownrshp* 1968, 1996
Sales 29.7MM^E *EMP* 49
SIC 5063 5719

D-U-N-S 03-492-2641
HOLDER GROUP ELKO LLC
COMMERCIAL CASINO AND HOTEL
340 Commercial St, Elko, NV 89801-3666
Tel (775) 738-3181 *Founded/Ownrshp* 2005
Sales 9.3MM^E *EMP* 600
SIC 7999 5812 5813 7011 Gambling establishment; Eating places; Bar (drinking places); Casino hotel; Gambling establishment; Eating places; Bar (drinking places); Casino hotel
Treas: Marci Simon
CIO: Courtney Welch

D-U-N-S 11-405-6208
HOLDER/HARDIN CONSTRUCTION
3333 Riverwood Pkwy Se # 400, Atlanta, GA 30339-3304
Tel (770) 988-3000 *Founded/Ownrshp* 2002
Sales 48.0MM^E *EMP* 200
SIC 1521 Single-family housing construction; Single-family housing construction
Prin: Julie Noelle

D-U-N-S 83-550-5132
HOLDERNESS BUILDING MATERIALS INC
HOLDERNESS SUPPLIES
450 E Irvington Rd, Tucson, AZ 85714-2823
Tel (520) 889-1300 *Founded/Ownrshp* 1995
Sales 20.8MM^E *EMP* 45
SIC 5031 2439 Lumber, plywood & millwork; Trusses, wooden roof
Pr: Jim Hatfield
**Pr:* Howard L Hatfield Jr
**Sec:* Pat Carrico
**VP:* Richard Alejos
**VP:* Delcia Harvey
**VP:* Andy Huggins
**VP:* John McKethen
Sls Mgr: Ernie Perry

HOLDERNESS SUPPLIES
See HOLDERNESS BUILDING MATERIALS INC

D-U-N-S 79-668-2859
HOLDING CO OF VILLAGES INC
VILLAGES, THE
1000 Lake Sumter Lndg, The Villages, FL 32162-2693
Tel (352) 753-2270 *Founded/Ownrshp* 1959
Sales 265.7MM^E *EMP* 2,000^E
SIC 6531 Real estate agent, commercial; Real estate agent, commercial
CEO: H Gary Morse
**Pr:* Mark Morse
**Treas:* W Thomas Brooks
VP: Tracy Mathews
**VP:* Gary L Moyer
VP: John Parker
VP: Jennifer Parr
**VP:* John F Wife
Genl Mgr: Ingo Fockler
Genl Mgr: Greg Hightman
Genl Mgr: Chad Strausbaugh

D-U-N-S 07-279-8911
HOLDING GREENWICH HOUSE INC
27 Barrow St Fl 2, New York, NY 10014-3823
Tel (212) 242-4140 *Founded/Ownrshp* 1902
Sales 10.2MM^E *EMP* 300
SIC 8399 Fund raising organization, non-fee basis; Fund raising organization, non-fee basis
Pr: Steven Smith

HOLDRITE
See SECURUS INC

D-U-N-S 13-196-1161
HOLIDAY BUILDERS INC
2293 W Eau Gallie Blvd, Melbourne, FL 32935-3184
Tel (321) 610-5156 *Founded/Ownrshp* 1983
Sales 76.5MM^E *EMP* 101
Accts Berman Hopkins Wright & Laham
SIC 1521 New construction, single-family houses
CEO: Bruce Assam
Pr: Michelle Smallwood
**CFO:* Richard Fadil
Dir IT: Marc Littleton
Dir IT: Rich Pilock
Sales Asso: John Goetz

D-U-N-S 80-778-2750
HOLIDAY COMPANIES
4567 American Blvd W, Bloomington, MN 55437-1123
Tel (952) 830-8700 *Founded/Ownrshp* 1992
Sales 1.0MMM^E *EMP* 4,500
SIC 5541 5411 5172

D-U-N-S 62-623-2730
HOLIDAY DIVERSIFIED SERVICES INC
4567 W 80th St, Minneapolis, MN 55437
Tel (952) 830-8700 *Founded/Ownrshp* 1989
Sales 27.8MM^E *EMP* 400
Accts Arthur Andersen Llp Minneapol
SIC 6794 Franchises, selling or licensing; Franchises, selling or licensing
Pr: Brian A Erickson
**Treas:* C Eric Pihl
VP Mktg: Judson Reis

HOLIDAY FENOGLIO FOWLER
See HFF HOLDINGS LLC

D-U-N-S 01-735-1412
HOLIDAY FOOD CENTER INC
HOLIDAY MARKET
1203 S Main St, Royal Oak, MI 48067-3244
Tel (248) 541-1414 *Founded/Ownrshp* 1954
Sales 21.7MM^E *EMP* 160
SIC 5411 Grocery stores, independent; Grocery stores, independent
Pr: Tom Violante
Exec: Gina Violante
Brnch Mgr: Jon Mansoor
IT Man: Robert Marzak

D-U-N-S 05-183-6898
HOLIDAY FOODS & GROCERIES INC
12 N Kringle Pl Ste A, Santa Claus, IN 47579-6378
Tel (812) 937-4428 *Founded/Ownrshp* 1969
Sales 30.7MM *EMP* 337
Accts Melvin E Held Cpa Llc Sant
SIC 5411 5541 Supermarkets; Grocery stores, independent; Filling stations, gasoline; Supermarkets; Grocery stores, independent; Filling stations, gasoline
Pr: Russell Winkler
**VP:* Lloyd W Winkler

HOLIDAY FUN BOXES
See POWERHOUSE PRODUCE LLC

HOLIDAY HILL MINIATURE GOLF
See DRIVE-O-RAMA INC

D-U-N-S 07-785-9288
HOLIDAY HOME HEALTH CARE CORP OF EVANSVILLE
HERITAGE CENTER
1201 W Buena Vista Rd, Evansville, IN 47710-3336
Tel (812) 429-0700 *Founded/Ownrshp* 1971
Sales 19.2MM^E *EMP* 290
SIC 8052 8051 8059 Intermediate care facilities; Skilled nursing care facilities; Rest home, with health care; Intermediate care facilities; Skilled nursing care facilities; Rest home, with health care
CEO: Derek Dunigan
**Pr:* Don Hester
**CFO:* Mark Ambrose
Off Mgr: Sharon Harris
Nrsg Dir: Kim Gibson

D-U-N-S 06-832-0712
HOLIDAY HOUSE OF MANITOWOC COUNTY INC (WI)
2818 Meadow Ln, Manitowoc, WI 54220-3739
Tel (920) 682-4663 *Founded/Ownrshp* 1957
Sales 4.1MM *EMP* 290
Accts Hawkins Ash Baptie & Compan
SIC 8331 5199 Vocational rehabilitation agency; Gifts & novelties; Vocational rehabilitation agency; Gifts & novelties
Ex Dir: Thomas E Keil

HOLIDAY INN
See GREEN TOWNSHIP HOSPITALITY LLC

HOLIDAY INN
See CASPER R CALLEN TRUST

HOLIDAY INN
See WINGATE INNS INTERNATIONAL INC

HOLIDAY INN
See COURTYARD MARRIOTT

HOLIDAY INN
See MCKIBBON BROTHERS INC

HOLIDAY INN
See MIDAMERICA HOTELS CORP

HOLIDAY INN
See ERIN INC

HOLIDAY INN
See MURPHCO OF FLORIDA INC

HOLIDAY INN
See SERVUS HOTEL GROUP INC

HOLIDAY INN
See MM LOUISIANA INC

HOLIDAY INN
See SAFARI HOSPITALITY INC

HOLIDAY INN
See FEDERAL CENTER HOTEL ASSOCIATES LLC

HOLIDAY INN
See W P H AIRPORT ASSOCIATES

HOLIDAY INN
See SCHAHET COMPANIES INC

HOLIDAY INN
See TODAYS HOTEL CORP

HOLIDAY INN
See HOUSTON AIRPORT HOSPITALITY LP

HOLIDAY INN
See ATRIUM HOTELS INC

HOLIDAY INN
See ROSSLYN SYNDICATE LC

HOLIDAY INN
See WILSON HOTEL MANAGEMENT CO INC

HOLIDAY INN BAYSIDE
See BARTELL HOTELS

HOLIDAY INN BILLINGS
See HOTEL WEST II LP

HOLIDAY INN DUBLIN
See TREVI PARTNERS A CALIF LP

HOLIDAY INN SAN PADRE ISLAND
See POSADAS USA INC

HOLIDAY ISLE BCH RSORTS MARINA
See HOLIDAY ISLE RESORT & MARINA INC

D-U-N-S 09-852-7542
HOLIDAY ISLE RESORT & MARINA INC
HOLIDAY ISLE BCH RSORTS MARINA
84001 Overseas Hwy, Islamorada, FL 33036-3408
Tel (305) 664-2321 *Founded/Ownrshp* 1980, 1983
Sales 10.5MM^E *EMP* 280
SIC 7011 4493 6512 Resort hotel; Marinas; Nonresidential building operators; Resort hotel; Marinas; Nonresidential building operators
Pr: Mary Celentano
**Sec:* Richard A Loricco
Genl Mgr: Jeanne Deuel
CTO: Pam Flesch

HOLIDAY KITCHEN DIV
See MASTERCRAFT INDUSTRIES INC

HOLIDAY MANOR CARE CENTER
See SELA HEALTHCARE INC

HOLIDAY MARKET
See HOLIDAY FOOD CENTER INC

HOLIDAY MAZDA
See MIKE SHANNON AUTOMOTIVE INC

D-U-N-S 05-238-9491
HOLIDAY MEAT & PROVISION CORP
405 Centinela Ave, Inglewood, CA 90302-3294
Tel (310) 674-0541 *Founded/Ownrshp* 1965
Sales 60.0MM *EMP* 200
SIC 5147 5144 5146 Meats, fresh; Poultry products; Seafoods; Meats, fresh; Poultry products; Seafoods
Pr: Nat Rocker
Genl Mgr: David Rocker
Off Mgr: Pat Bryant

D-U-N-S 08-531-7741
HOLIDAY OIL CO
3115 W 2100 S, Salt Lake City, UT 84119-1211
Tel (801) 973-7002 *Founded/Ownrshp* 1964
Sales 67.6MM^E *EMP* 349
SIC 5541 5411 Filling stations, gasoline; Convenience stores, independent; Filling stations, gasoline; Convenience stores, independent
CEO: Jerald Wagstaff
**Sec:* Enid Deming

D-U-N-S 92-946-9104
HOLIDAY ORGANIZATION INC
255 Executive Dr Ste 408, Plainview, NY 11803-1707
Tel (516) 576-0444 *Founded/Ownrshp* 1984

Sales 22.5MM^E *EMP* 300
SIC 8742 Management consulting services; Management consulting services
Pr: Gerald Monter
CFO: Joseph Chase

HOLIDAY QUALITY FOODS
See NORTH STATE GROCERY INC

HOLIDAY RETIREMENT
See HARVEST MANAGEMENT SUB LLC

HOLIDAY RETIREMENT
See WICHITA RETIREMENT RESIDENCE LLC

HOLIDAY SHOP N BAG
See HOLIDAY SUPERMARKETS INC

HOLIDAY STATION STORES
See LYNDALE TERMINAL CO

D-U-N-S 04-596-5258
HOLIDAY STATIONSTORES INC
(*Suby of* HOLIDAY COMPANIES) ★
4567 American Blvd W, Bloomington, MN 55437-1123
Tel (952) 830-8700 *Founded/Ownrshp* 1964
Sales 951.9MM^E *EMP* 3,993
SIC 5541 5411

D-U-N-S 05-897-4841
HOLIDAY SUPERMARKETS INC
HOLIDAY SHOP N BAG
6499 Sackett St, Philadelphia, PA 19149-3118
Tel (215) 335-9474 *Founded/Ownrshp* 1970
Sales 44.5MM^E *EMP* 300
SIC 5411 Supermarkets; Supermarkets
Pr: Harry B Gilbert

D-U-N-S 93-895-8667
HOLIDAY SYSTEMS INTERNATIONAL OF NEVADA
7690 W Cheyenne Ave # 200, Las Vegas, NV 89129-6763
Tel (702) 254-3100 *Founded/Ownrshp* 1993
Sales 21.5MM *EMP* 205^E
SIC 4724 Tourist agency arranging transport, lodging & car rental; Tourist agency arranging transport, lodging & car rental
Pr: Craig A Morganson
Opers Mgr: Joseph Roller
Opers Mgr: Neil Snyder

D-U-N-S 01-416-5786
HOLIDAY TOURS INC
10367 Randleman Rd, Randleman, NC 27317-8076
Tel (336) 274-5749 *Founded/Ownrshp* 1996
Sales 48.6MM^E *EMP* 145
SIC 4724 Travel agencies
Pr: David Brown
**VP:* Gary Moody

D-U-N-S 05-222-2262 EXP
HOLIDAY TREE FARMS INC (OR)
SCHUDEL ENTERPRISES
800 Nw Cornell Ave, Corvallis, OR 97330-4579
Tel (541) 753-3236 *Founded/Ownrshp* 1957
Sales 44.4MM^E *EMP* 100
SIC 5199

HOLIDAY VALLEY RESORT
See WIN-SUM SKI CORP

D-U-N-S 80-997-2557
■ HOLIDAY VILLAGE OF SANDPIPER INC
(*Suby of* CLUB MED SALES INC) ★
3500 Se Morningside Blvd, Port Saint Lucie, FL 34952-6116
Tel (772) 398-5100 *Founded/Ownrshp* 1993
Sales 8.9MM^E *EMP* 300
SIC 7011 Resort hotel; Resort hotel
Ch: Henri Giscard Estaing
Board of Directors: Gilbert Trigano

D-U-N-S 02-361-4100 IMP
HOLIDAY WHOLESALE INC
225 Pioneer Dr, Wisconsin Dells, WI 53965-8397
Tel (608) 253-0404 *Founded/Ownrshp* 1951
Sales 188.4MM^E *EMP* 250
SIC 5194 5145 5113 5199 Tobacco & tobacco products; Candy; Industrial & personal service paper; General merchandise, non-durable; Tobacco & tobacco products; Candy; Industrial & personal service paper; General merchandise, non-durable
Pr: Joseph B Gussel
**Pr:* Bernard Gussel Jr
**Treas:* Angela Myer
Chf Mktg O: Dixie Marquardt
**VP:* Patrick Jagoe
VP: Mike Weaver
IT Man: Rist Ben
IT Man: Ben Wrist
Sls Mgr: Edward Wojnicz

D-U-N-S 96-634-6223
HOLIDAY WORLD OF HOUSTON LP
28909 Katy Fwy, Katy, TX 77494-1000
Tel (281) 371-7200 *Founded/Ownrshp* 1996
Sales 62.3MM^E *EMP* 150
SIC 5561 Recreational vehicle dealers
Pr: Michael Peay
Pt: Tom Daulton
Pt: Lenny Martynowicz
VP: Manny Carlson
Admn Mgr: Douglas Kacsir
Sales Exec: Nancy Hiller
Sales Exec: Kevin Hoffpauir
Sls Mgr: Mike Apel
Sales Asso: Steve Lankford

D-U-N-S 80-915-7175
HOLIEN INC
ANZA
312 9th Ave Se Ste B, Watertown, SD 57201-4853
Tel (605) 886-3889 *Founded/Ownrshp* 1993
Sales 183.0MM^E *EMP* 2,300^E
SIC 3612 3672 3993 Specialty transformers; Circuit boards, television & radio printed; Electric signs; Signs, not made in custom sign painting shops; Specialty transformers; Circuit boards, television & radio printed; Electric signs; Signs, not made in custom sign painting shops
Pr: Dennis D Holien
CFO: Greg Kulefa
CFO: Greg Kulesa

D-U-N-S 04-320-0344
HOLLADAY CORP
3400 Idaho Ave Nw Ste 400, Washington, DC 20016-3050
Tel (202) 362-2400 *Founded/Ownrshp* 1952
Sales 262.2MM^E *EMP* 770
SIC 1522 6531 Apartment building construction; Real estate managers; Apartment building construction; Real estate managers
Pr: Wallace F Holladay
**Sec:* Helga Carter
**VP:* John T Phair

D-U-N-S 80-701-9724
HOLLADAY GROUP
ONE MICHIANA SQUARE
227 S Main St Ste 300, South Bend, IN 46601-2124
Tel (574) 234-4381 *Founded/Ownrshp* 1986
Sales 12.4MM^E *EMP* 300
SIC 6512 Commercial & industrial building operation; Commercial & industrial building operation
Pt: One Michiana Investors
CFO: James Laskowski

D-U-N-S 01-062-0755
HOLLAND & HART LLP
555 17th St Ste 3200, Denver, CO 80202-3921
Tel (303) 295-8000 *Founded/Ownrshp* 1947
Sales 193.4MM^E *EMP* 904
SIC 8111 General practice law office; General practice law office
Mng Pt: Thomas O'Donnell
**Pt:* John Husband
Pt: Ronald Martin
Mng Pt: Edward Flitton
Mng Pt: Lawrence J Wolfe
Pr: Christine Broome
Pr: Colleen Jasper
Pr: Judy A Johnson
Pr: Cheryl Newmark
Pr: Brooke Nicholson
Pr: Wendy Shanks
Pr: Julie J Winkler
Chf Mktg O: Paul Ward
VP: Carolyn Gilroy

D-U-N-S 07-758-3318
HOLLAND & KNIGHT LLP
524 Grand Regency Blvd, Brandon, FL 33510-3931
Tel (813) 901-4200 *Founded/Ownrshp* 1968
Sales 363.3MM^E *EMP* 2,500
SIC 8111 General practice law office; General practice law office
Mng Pt: Steven Sonberg
Pt: Alfred B Adams
Pt: Jim Davis
Pt: Ralph T Lepore
Pt: Howell W Melton
Pt: George Mencio
Pt: Michael D Rechtin
CFO: Michael Marget
CTO: Elizabeth Crispino
Dir IT: Rob Hohenstein
Dir IT: Janis Surovell

D-U-N-S 05-995-0485
HOLLAND & SONS INC
JOHN DEERE
1701 S 13th Ave, Mendota, IL 61342-9738
Tel (815) 539-8029 *Founded/Ownrshp* 1985
Sales 30.3MM^E *EMP* 115
SIC 5083 Farm equipment parts & supplies; Farm equipment parts & supplies
Ch Bd: Gary Holland
**Pr:* Todd Holland
**VP:* Dale Goodrich
**VP:* Roger Goodrich
**VP:* Tyrone Holland

HOLLAND AMERCN LINES-WESTOURS
See HOLLAND AMERICA LINE INC

D-U-N-S 10-133-5172 IMP/EXP
■ HOLLAND AMERICA LINE INC
HOLLAND AMERCN LINES-WESTOURS
(*Suby of* CARNIVAL CORP) ★
300 Elliott Ave W Ste 100, Seattle, WA 98119-4122
Tel (206) 281-3535 *Founded/Ownrshp* 1989
Sales 233.3MM^E *EMP* 1,410
SIC 4725 Tour operators; Tour operators
CEO: Stein Kruse
Treas: Todd Kimmel
Ex VP: Charlie Ball
Ex VP: David Giersdorf
Ex VP: Tim Howie
Sr VP: Dan Grausz
Sr VP: Richard D Meadows
VP: Larry Calkins
VP: Steve Leonard
VP: Ares M Michaelides
VP: William J Morani
VP: Brendan Vierra

D-U-N-S 07-998-0401
HOLLAND AMERICA LINE NV DBA HOLLAND AMERICA LINE NV LLC
300 Elliott Ave W Ste 100, Seattle, WA 98119-4122
Tel (206) 281-3535 *Founded/Ownrshp* 1996
Sales 165.6MM^E *EMP* 1,500
SIC 4489 Excursion boat operators

HOLLAND APPLIED TECHNOLOGIES
See HARRY HOLLAND & SON INC

D-U-N-S 04-981-7588
HOLLAND APPLIED TECHNOLOGIES INC
(*Suby of* HARRY HOLLAND & SON INC) ★
7050 High Grove Blvd, Burr Ridge, IL 60527-7595
Tel (630) 325-5130 *Founded/Ownrshp* 1959
Sales 48.4MM^E *EMP* 50
SIC 5084 5169 3537 Industrial machinery & equipment; Industrial chemicals; Skids, metal
Pr: David Chaney
VP: Toby Hobick
**VP:* Robert Soukup
Mfg Mgr: John Pisors

D-U-N-S 00-601-2991 IMP
HOLLAND AWNING CO
BIG RED RESOURCES
10875 Chicago Dr, Zeeland, MI 49464-8126
Tel (616) 772-2052 *Founded/Ownrshp* 1946, 1978
Sales 59.9MM^E *EMP* 250^E
SIC 2394 Canvas & related products; Tents: made from purchased materials; Canvas & related products; Tents: made from purchased materials
CEO: Steven Schaftenaar
**Pr:* Doug Buma
**VP:* Scott Smith
**VP:* Todd Stockdale

D-U-N-S 15-343-7264 IMP
HOLLAND COLOURS AMERICAS INC
(*Suby of* HOLLAND COLOURS N.V.)
1501 Progress Dr, Richmond, IN 47374-1486
Tel (765) 935-4257 *Founded/Ownrshp* 1985
Sales 35.3MM^E *EMP* 85
SIC 2865 Color pigments, organic; Color pigments, organic
Tech Mgr: Rob Leversedge
Plnt Mgr: Dick Hetisimer
Prd Mgr: Craig Hopkins

D-U-N-S 07-257-7877
HOLLAND COMMUNITY HOSPITAL AUXILIARY INC (MI)
HOLLAND HOSPITAL
602 Michigan Ave, Holland, MI 49423-4918
Tel (616) 748-9346 *Founded/Ownrshp* 1917
Sales 220.2MM *EMP* 1,500
Accts Plante & Moran Pllc Portage
SIC 8062 General medical & surgical hospitals; General medical & surgical hospitals
Pr: Dale Sowders
Dir Recs: William Vliet
**VP:* Chuck Kohlruss
**VP:* Michael Matthews
**VP:* Mark Pawlak
**VP:* Patti Vandort
VP: Cynthia Visscher
Dir Rad: Erik Badgero
Ex Dir: Judy Rozendal
Opthamlgy: Thomas Cowden

D-U-N-S 04-475-0032
HOLLAND CONTRACTING CORP
ADVANCED DOOR SYSTEMS
1400 S 4th St, Forest City, IA 50436-2158
Tel (641) 585-2231 *Founded/Ownrshp* 1964
Sales 22.1MM^E *EMP* 65
Accts Bergan Paulsen & Company Pc
SIC 1542 1623 1771 Commercial & office building, new construction; Commercial & office buildings, renovation & repair; Sewer line construction; Water main construction; Concrete work; Commercial & office building, new construction; Commercial & office buildings, renovation & repair; Sewer line construction; Water main construction; Concrete work
Ch Bd: Charles S Holland
**Pr:* Jeff Holland
**Treas:* Tim Frederickson
**VP:* Brad Mary
**VP:* Brett West

D-U-N-S 84-142-0602
HOLLAND ENERGY LLC
Rr 2 Box 270, Beecher City, IL 62414-9802
Tel (618) 487-9140 *Founded/Ownrshp* 1999
Sales 43.1MM^E *EMP* 56^E
SIC 4911 Distribution, electric power
Genl Mgr: Barry Hatfield
**Sec:* Robert Hochstetler
Opers Mgr: Kent Schmohe

D-U-N-S 79-624-7484
HOLLAND ENTERPRISES INC
500 Carl Olsen St, Mapleton, ND 58059-4054
Tel (701) 280-2634 *Founded/Ownrshp* 1990
Sales 50.5MM^E *EMP* 230
Accts Roger D Nelson Fargo North
SIC 4213 Trucking, except local; Trucking, except local
Pr: Chris Holland

D-U-N-S 12-088-2493
HOLLAND FLOWER MARKET INC
755 Wall St Ste 7g, Los Angeles, CA 90014-2315
Tel (213) 627-9900 *Founded/Ownrshp* 1984
Sales 23.6MM^E *EMP* 59
SIC 5193 Flowers, fresh
Pr: Jaap Haverkate
Treas: Steve Yuge

D-U-N-S 07-242-2736
HOLLAND HALL (OK)
5666 E 81st St, Tulsa, OK 74137-2001
Tel (918) 481-1111 *Founded/Ownrshp* 1922
Sales 23.8MM *EMP* 220
Accts Hogan Taylor Llp Tulsa Ok
SIC 8211 Private combined elementary & secondary school; Private combined elementary & secondary school
Top Exec: Sarah Cox
Comm Dir: Elizabeth Anderson
Psych: Kathy Housh

D-U-N-S 06-020-1696
HOLLAND HOME (MI)
FULTON MANOR
2100 Raybrook St Se # 300, Grand Rapids, MI 49546-5783
Tel (616) 235-5000 *Founded/Ownrshp* 1892
Sales 62.4MM *EMP* 1,300
Accts Plante & Moran Pllc Grand Ra
SIC 8361 8051 Home for the aged; Skilled nursing care facilities; Home for the aged; Skilled nursing care facilities
CEO: H David Claus
Ex Dir: Steve Velzen
Nurse Mgr: Jessica Troyer
CTO: Paula Delorm
VP Mktg: Chris Micely
Snr Mgr: Karla Sorensen

HOLLAND HOSPITAL
See HOLLAND COMMUNITY HOSPITAL AUXILIARY INC

D-U-N-S 02-756-4012
HOLLAND INC
BURGERVILLE USA
109 W 17th St, Vancouver, WA 98660-2932
Tel (360) 694-1521 *Founded/Ownrshp* 1992
Sales 123.9MM^E *EMP* 1,600
SIC 8741 Restaurant management; Restaurant management
CEO: Jeff Harvey
COO: Janice Williams
Ex VP: Jack Graves
**VP:* Beth Brewer
Genl Mgr: John Crutchfield
Genl Mgr: Lance Hill
Genl Mgr: Tim Morgan
Genl Mgr: Michael Truesdell
Dir IT: Michelle Wong
Sales Exec: Tisa Rae
Mktg Dir: Cathy Miller

HOLLAND LITHO PRINTING SERVICE
See HOLLAND LITHO SERVICE INC

D-U-N-S 07-259-5010
HOLLAND LITHO SERVICE INC
HOLLAND LITHO PRINTING SERVICE
10972 Chicago Dr, Zeeland, MI 49464-8100
Tel (616) 392-4644 *Founded/Ownrshp* 1957
Sales 23.5MM^E *EMP* 100
SIC 2759 Commercial printing
Pr: Jerry Baarman
**Ex VP:* Brian Baarman
**Sr VP:* Tamas Baarman
**VP:* Rick Baarman
Sls Mgr: Doug Palmer

D-U-N-S 04-422-3139 IMP
HOLLAND LP
LEWIS RAIL SERVICE COMPANY
(*Suby of* CURRAN GROUP INC) ★
1000 Holland Dr, Crete, IL 60417-2120
Tel (708) 672-2300 *Founded/Ownrshp* 1974
Sales 198.9MM^E *EMP* 820
SIC 1799 3743 Welding on site; Railroad equipment; Welding on site; Railroad equipment
Pr: Philip C Moeller
Treas: Frank J Francis
VP: Kevin Flaherty
Genl Mgr: Kris Koski
Genl Mgr: Robert Norby
QA Dir: Jyll Boudreau
QA Dir: David Cooper
Dir IT: Lynne Sabuco
Dir IT: James Tieri
Software D: Wayne Dodgen
Software D: Andrea Ellis

D-U-N-S 02-063-8417
HOLLAND MANAGEMENT INC
1383 Sharon Copley Rd, Sharon Center, OH 44274
Tel (330) 239-4474 *Founded/Ownrshp* 1958
Sales 15.8MM^E *EMP* 300
SIC 6513 6512 Apartment building operators; Nonresidential building operators; Apartment building operators; Nonresidential building operators
Pr: John E Holland Jr

D-U-N-S 00-215-9317
HOLLAND MANUFACTURING CO INC
15 Main St, Succasunna, NJ 07876-1747
Tel (973) 584-8141 *Founded/Ownrshp* 1940
Sales 50.8MM^E *EMP* 150
SIC 2672 2621 2671 Gummed tape, cloth or paper base: from purchased materials; Gummed paper: made from purchased materials; Coated paper, except photographic, carbon or abrasive; Specialty or chemically treated papers; Building paper & felts; Packaging paper & plastics film, coated & laminated; Gummed tape, cloth or paper base: from purchased materials; Gummed paper: made from purchased materials; Coated paper, except photographic, carbon or abrasive; Specialty or chemically treated papers; Building paper & felts; Packaging paper & plastics film, coated & laminated
CEO: Jack Holland
VP: Steve Holland
**VP:* Michael Pallante
Opers Mgr: Brian Allanson
Plnt Mgr: Tom Dickinson
S&M/VP: Ray Hajek

D-U-N-S 06-331-4367
HOLLAND MOTOR HOMES
251 Travelers Way, San Marcos, CA 92069-2797
Tel (760) 798-8300 *Founded/Ownrshp* 1991
Sales 20.2MM^E *EMP* 46
SIC 5511 New & used car dealers; New & used car dealers
Pr: Michael Dykstra

D-U-N-S 05-248-9507
HOLLAND MOTOR HOMES & BUS CO
EMERGENCY VEHICLES PLUS
670 E 16th St, Holland, MI 49423-3792
Tel (616) 396-1461 *Founded/Ownrshp* 1970
Sales 23.1MM^E *EMP* 50
SIC 5561 7699 Motor homes; Mobile home repair
Pr: John M Dykstra
**Prin:* Brad Borr

D-U-N-S 83-318-4083
HOLLAND MPG PROPERTY LLC
(*Suby of* MORRIS PUBLISHING GROUP LLC) ★
725 Broad St, Augusta, GA 30901-1336
Tel (706) 724-0851 *Founded/Ownrshp* 2010
Sales 90.2M^E *EMP* 394^E
SIC 2711 Newspapers; Newspapers, publishing & printing

D-U-N-S 01-747-9825
HOLLAND OIL CO
1485 Marion Ave, Akron, OH 44313-7625
Tel (330) 835-1815 *Founded/Ownrshp* 1954
Sales 179.2MM *EMP* 625
Accts Bober Markey Fedorovich & Co
SIC 5541 5172 5411 Gasoline service stations; Gasoline; Service station supplies, petroleum; Convenience stores; Gasoline service stations; Gasoline; Service station supplies, petroleum; Convenience stores
Pr: Lisa M Holland-Toth
**Ex VP:* Lynn Gorman
**Sr VP:* Michael J Toth
MIS Dir: Joe Ryan
**VP Opers:* Carl Hummel
**VP Merchng:* John Ballard

HOLLAND PARTNERS GROUP
See HOLLAND PARTNERS ROCK CREEK LANDING LLC

D-U-N-S 13-203-1035
HOLLAND PARTNERS ROCK CREEK LANDING LLC
HOLLAND PARTNERS GROUP
1111 Main St Ste 700, Vancouver, WA 98660-2970
Tel (360) 694-7888 *Founded/Ownrshp* 2003
Sales 99.7MM^E *EMP* 752
SIC 6531 Real estate agents & managers; Real estate agents & managers
CEO: Clyde P Holland Jr
Pr: Jeff Dickerson
Pr: Thomas B Parsons
COO: Bob Coppess
COO: Robbie Dodd
COO: Eli Hanacek
VP: Julie Schuh
VP: Lydia Thompson
VP: Michael Voorhees

D-U-N-S 01-077-5211
HOLLAND PATENT CENTRAL SCHOOL DISTRICT
9601 Main St, Holland Patent, NY 13354-4618
Tel (315) 865-8152 *Founded/Ownrshp* 1934
Sales 29.1MM *EMP* 265
Accts Moore & Hart Utica New York
SIC 8211 Public elementary & secondary schools; High school, junior or senior; School board; Public elementary & secondary schools; High school, junior or senior; School board
Cmptr Lab: Nedra Isenburg
IT Man: Pam Backman

D-U-N-S 03-188-1956
HOLLAND PUBLIC SCHOOL DISTRICT
320 W 24th St, Holland, MI 49423-3267
Tel (616) 494-2000 *Founded/Ownrshp* 1884, 1984
Sales 54.6MM *EMP* 669
Accts Bdo Usa Llp Grand Rapids Mi
SIC 8211 Public elementary & secondary schools; Public elementary & secondary schools
Bd of Dir: Susan Dejong
Bd of Dir: Edward Walters
Dir IT: Rex Thelen
IT Man: Christy Durham
Site Mgr: Jennifer Jones
Pr Dir: Tom Page
Teacher Pr: Rich Zuker
Psych: Robyn Emde

D-U-N-S 07-979-9512
HOLLAND PUBLIC SCHOOLS
320 Brookfield Rd, Fiskdale, MA 01518-1017
Tel (508) 347-3077 *Founded/Ownrshp* 2015
Sales 3.9MM^E *EMP* 362^E
SIC 8211 Public elementary & secondary schools

D-U-N-S 09-284-1931 IMP
HOLLAND PUMP CO
7312 Westport Pl, West Palm Beach, FL 33413-1661
Tel (561) 697-3333 *Founded/Ownrshp* 1978
Sales 22.9MM^E *EMP* 90
SIC 3561 7359 Pumps & pumping equipment; Equipment rental & leasing; Pumps & pumping equipment; Equipment rental & leasing
VP: William W Blodgett
**CFO:* Patrick J Sweeney
**Ch:* Bill Blodgett
**VP:* Eugene Lant
Brnch Mgr: Brian Kieley
Opers Mgr: Dennis Olsen

D-U-N-S 16-745-9580
HOLLAND RESIDENTIAL LLC
(*Suby of* HOLLAND PARTNERS GROUP) ★
1111 Main St Ste 700, Vancouver, WA 98660-2970
Tel (360) 694-7888 *Founded/Ownrshp* 2003
Sales 93.8MM^E *EMP* 500^E
SIC 6513 8741 Real estate investors, except property operators; Apartment building operators; Management services
Pr: Joan Bougetz
**CFO:* Robbie Dodd
VP: Jeff Pedigo
Rgnl Mgr: Dee Cole

D-U-N-S 15-197-8129 IMP
HOLLAND ROOFING INC
7450 Industrial Rd, Florence, KY 41042-2916
Tel (859) 525-0887 *Founded/Ownrshp* 1986
Sales 42.4MM^E *EMP* 100
SIC 1761 Roofing contractor; Sheet metalwork
Pr: Hans Philippo
**Sec:* Donna Thornton
VP: Ken Hunt
**VP:* Paul Klensch
VP: Johnny Philippo
Genl Mgr: Martin Davin
Genl Mgr: Tony Kabel
Genl Mgr: Mike Spach
Off Mgr: Emily Lindsey
Dir IT: Nael Mabjish
Sls Mgr: Adam Bultman

HOLLAND SPECIAL DELIVERY
See HSD HOLDING CO

D-U-N-S 96-540-4473
HOLLAND SQUARE GROUP LLC
840 Crescent Centre Dr # 540, Franklin, TN 37067-6455
Tel (615) 829-8270 *Founded/Ownrshp* 2010
Sales 21.3MM^E *EMP* 180
SIC 7371 Custom computer programming services; Custom computer programming services

D-U-N-S 10-992-8841
HOLLAND VENTURES INC
J. P. MCGILLS HOTEL & CASINO
232 Bennett Dr, Cripple Creek, CO 80813
Tel (719) 689-2446 *Founded/Ownrshp* 1997
Sales 13.0MM^E *EMP* 500
SIC 7011 Casino hotel; Casino hotel
Pr: Rick Holland

D-U-N-S 07-889-0564
HOLLANDER HOME FASHIONS HOLDINGS LLC
6501 Congress Ave Ste 300, Boca Raton, FL 33487-2840
Tel (561) 997-6900 *Founded/Ownrshp* 1953
Sales 163.0MM^E *EMP* 924^E
SIC 2392 Cushions & pillows

D-U-N-S 15-372-5312
HOLLANDER INVESTMENTS INC
BEST WESTERN
119 N Coml St Ste 165, Bellingham, WA 98225
Tel (360) 647-1916 *Founded/Ownrshp* 1984
Sales 25.9MM^E *EMP* 400
SIC 7011 Hotels & motels; Hotels & motels
Ch: Mike Hollander
**Pr:* Mark Hollander
IT Man: Heather Ouilette

D-U-N-S 00-215-2817 IMP/EXP
HOLLANDER SLEEP PRODUCTS LLC
(*Suby of* HOLLANDER HOME FASHIONS HOLDINGS LLC) ★
6501 Congress Ave Ste 300, Boca Raton, FL 33487-2840
Tel (561) 997-6900 *Founded/Ownrshp* 2014
Sales 138.7MM^E *EMP* 800
SIC 2392 2221 5719

D-U-N-S 02-933-0792
HOLLANDIA DAIRY INC
622 E Mission Rd, San Marcos, CA 92069-1999
Tel (760) 744-3222 *Founded/Ownrshp* 1950
Sales 43.1MM^E *EMP* 200
SIC 0241 Dairy farms; Milk production; Dairy farms; Milk production
Pr: Arie H Dejong
COO: Ken May
**VP:* Peter De Jong
VP: Rudy De Jong
VP: Rhonda Fuller
VP: Bert Ton
IT Man: Angela Escalle
Mktg Dir: Lee Hodge

D-U-N-S 05-148-0887 IMP
HOLLANDIA PRODUCE LP
1545 Santa Monica Rd, Carpinteria, CA 93013
Tel (805) 684-8739 *Founded/Ownrshp* 2013
Sales 38.7MM^E *EMP* 160
SIC 0182 Vegetable crops grown under cover
Pt: Pete Overgaag

D-U-N-S 06-255-4134
HOLLAR AND GREENE PRODUCE CO INC (NC)
230 Cabbage Row, Boone, NC 28607-6020
Tel (828) 264-2177 *Founded/Ownrshp* 1962
Sales 52.0MM *EMP* 90
SIC 5148 Fresh fruits & vegetables; Fresh fruits & vegetables
Pr: Dale L Greene
**VP:* Jeffrey M Green
Exec: Barry Greene
Sales Exec: Keith Honeycutt
Sls Dir: Danny Critcher
Sls Dir: Jeff Greene
Sls Dir: Tony Greene

HOLLEY
See HIGH PERFORMANCE INDUSTRIES HOLDINGS INC

D-U-N-S 07-943-0122
■ **HOLLEY ARC COURT LLC**
(*Suby of* AMERICAN RETIREMENT CORP) ★
111 Westwood Pl Ste 400, Brentwood, TN 37027-5057
Tel (615) 221-2250 *Founded/Ownrshp* 2001
Sales 4.0MM^E *EMP* 669^E
SIC 8051 Skilled nursing care facilities

D-U-N-S 04-214-3714 IMP
HOLLEY PERFORMANCE PRODUCTS INC
(*Suby of* HIGH PERFORMANCE INDUSTRIES HOLDINGS INC) ★
1801 Russellville Rd, Bowling Green, KY 42101-3542
Tel (270) 782-2900 *Founded/Ownrshp* 1996
Sales 73.2MM^E *EMP* 605^E
SIC 3714 3592 Fuel pumps, motor vehicle; Carburetors; Fuel pumps, motor vehicle; Carburetors
Pr: Tom Tomlinson
**VP:* Terrill M Rutledge
**VP:* Stephen Trussell
VP: Steve Trussell
Netwrk Mgr: John Law
Sftwr Eng: Evan Tedder
VP Opers: Tom Flynn
Mtls Mgr: Jesus Marin
Sfty Mgr: Bill Durrett
Opers Mgr: Randy Chisholm
Plnt Mgr: Bill Christopher

D-U-N-S 02-655-3149
HOLLI-TEX SUPPLY CO LTD
131 E Olive St, Holliday, TX 76366
Tel (940) 586-1271 *Founded/Ownrshp* 1968
Sales 40.1MM *EMP* 14
SIC 5084 Oil well machinery, equipment & supplies; Oil well machinery, equipment & supplies
Mng Pt: Freddie Crampton
Pt: Gary Schaeffer

D-U-N-S 01-963-0016
■ **HOLLIDAY FENOGLIO FOWLER LP**
H F F
(*Suby of* HFF INC) ★
9 Greenway Plz Ste 700, Houston, TX 77046-0914
Tel (713) 852-3500 *Founded/Ownrshp* 2003
Sales NA *EMP* 198^E
SIC 6162 Mortgage bankers & correspondents; Mortgage bankers & correspondents
Pt: John H Pelusi Jr
Dir Surg: Jeff Hollinden
Assoc Dir: Cullen Aderhold
Assoc Dir: Greg Brown
Assoc Dir: Corbin Chaffin
Assoc Dir: Mark Damiani
Assoc Dir: Jeffrey Haag
Assoc Dir: Charity Hadley
Assoc Dir: David Lee
Assoc Dir: Charles Osbrink
Mng Dir: Davis Adams

D-U-N-S 04-778-9862
HOLLIDAY ROCK CO INC
1401 N Benson Ave, Upland, CA 91786-2166
Tel (909) 982-1553 *Founded/Ownrshp* 1959
Sales 67.0MM^E *EMP* 54^E
SIC 5032 Asphalt mixture; Concrete mixtures; Stone, crushed or broken; Sand, construction
CEO: Penny Holliday
**Pr:* Ethel Holliday
**VP:* Fredrick N Holliday
Genl Mgr: Dean Browning
Mtls Mgr: Jamison Soule

HOLLIDAY'S FASHIONS
See HOLLIDAYS GENERAL SERVICE CORP

D-U-N-S 03-433-7147
HOLLIDAYS GENERAL SERVICE CORP
HOLLIDAY'S FASHIONS
4841 Summer Ave, Memphis, TN 38122-4733
Tel (901) 522-1983 *Founded/Ownrshp* 1950
Sales 27.0MM^E *EMP* 480
SIC 5621

D-U-N-S 10-006-9616
HOLLIDAYSBURG AREA SCHOOL DISTRICT
405 Clark St, Hollidaysburg, PA 16648-2100
Tel (814) 695-5585 *Founded/Ownrshp* 1966
Sales 45.0MM *EMP* 537
Accts Young Oakes Brown & Company
SIC 8211 Public elementary school; Public junior high school; Public senior high school; Public elementary school; Public junior high school; Public senior high school
Pr: Ronald Yoder
IT Man: Karen Weise
Pr Dir: Linda Russo

D-U-N-S 95-674-1235
HOLLIDAYSBURG VETERAN HOME
MILITARY AND VETERNS AFFAIRS
Municipal Dr Rr 220, Duncansville, PA 16635
Tel (814) 696-5201 *Founded/Ownrshp* 1996
Sales 7.6MM^E *EMP* 550
SIC 8059 8051 Nursing home, except skilled & intermediate care facility; Skilled nursing care facilities; Nursing home, except skilled & intermediate care facility; Skilled nursing care facilities
Prin: David Langguth
Pharmcst: Linda Pleshko

D-U-N-S 07-533-3062
HOLLINGSEAD INTERNATIONAL LLC (CA)
(*Suby of* PATS AIRCRAFT LLC) ★
21583 Baltimore Ave, Georgetown, DE 19947-6313
Tel (302) 855-5888 *Founded/Ownrshp* 2011
Sales 58.1MM^E *EMP* 406^E
SIC 3679 8748 Electronic switches; Harness assemblies for electronic use: wire or cable; Systems analysis & engineering consulting services
Pr: Roger Wolfe
Genl Mgr: Tim Maurer
Genl Mgr: Tom Winte

D-U-N-S 00-100-6360 IMP/EXP
HOLLINGSWORTH & VOSE CO INC (MA)
112 Washington St, East Walpole, MA 02032-1098
Tel (508) 850-2000 *Founded/Ownrshp* 1892
Sales 721.2MM^E *EMP* 1,700
SIC 2621 3053 2297 Filter paper; Gasket materials; Nonwoven fabrics; Filter paper; Gasket materials; Nonwoven fabrics
Pr: Val Hollingsworth
CFO: Joseph Sherer
Treas: William Crowe
VP: Josh Ayer
VP: Jochem Hofstetter
VP: Jean Fran Ois
VP: Kevin Porter
VP: David Von Loesecke
Genl Mgr: Daryl Ives
Dir IT: Lea Macnider
IT Man: Scott Thompson
Board of Directors: Arthur Hollingsworth, Schuyler Hollingsworth Jr, Daniel T V Huntoon III, William Smart

D-U-N-S 79-151-9770
HOLLINGSWORTH INC
HOLLINGSWORTH LOGISTICS GROUP
14225 W Warren Ave, Dearborn, MI 48126-1456
Tel (313) 768-1400 *Founded/Ownrshp* 1925
Sales 70.3MM^E *EMP* 499
SIC 4225 4783 4213 General warehousing; Packing & crating; Trucking, except local; General warehousing; Packing & crating; Trucking, except local
Ch: Stephen Barr
**Pr:* R James Lapointe
**CFO:* Michael T McNamara
Sls Mgr: Scott Motherwell

D-U-N-S 00-335-3018 IMP
HOLLINGSWORTH JOHN D ON WHEELS INC
3309 Laurens Rd, Greenville, SC 29607-5237
Tel (864) 297-1000 *Founded/Ownrshp* 1895
Sales 27.6MM^E *EMP* 375
SIC 3552 7629 Textile machinery; Electrical repair shops; Textile machinery; Electrical repair shops
Pr: Carl Martin
**VP:* Bill Henderson
VP: Henderson E William
IT Man: Steve Dubuc
Sls Mgr: Steve Wilson

HOLLINGSWORTH LOGISTICS GROUP
See HOLLINGSWORTH INC

D-U-N-S 84-980-3572 IMP
HOLLINGSWORTH LOGISTICS MANAGEMENT LLC
EXOS PROMAT SYSTEMS
(*Suby of* LOGISTICS HOLLINGSWORTH GROUP LLC) ★
14225 W Warren Ave, Dearborn, MI 48126-1456
Tel (313) 768-1400 *Founded/Ownrshp* 1993
Sales 180.3MM *EMP* 700
SIC 4225 4783 General warehousing & storage; Packing & crating; General warehousing & storage; Packing & crating
CEO: Stephen S Barr
Ql Cn Mgr: Doug Burns

D-U-N-S 03-489-6712
HOLLINGSWORTH OIL CO INC
1503 Memorial Blvd Ste B, Springfield, TN 37172-3269
Tel (615) 242-8466 *Founded/Ownrshp* 1980
Sales 547.4MM *EMP* 300
Accts Robinson Hughes & Christopher
SIC 5171 Petroleum bulk stations; Petroleum bulk stations
Ch Bd: Glenn Hollingsworth
**Pr:* Ronnie H Hollingsworth
**VP:* Jennifer Johnston
Mktg Mgr: Tammy Palmore

HOLLINGSWORTH-RICHARDS FORD
See RIVER CITY FORD INC

D-U-N-S 05-820-5220
HOLLINS UNIVERSITY CORP
7916 Williamson Rd, Roanoke, VA 24019-4421
Tel (540) 362-6000 *Founded/Ownrshp* 1926
Sales 32.6MM *EMP* 380^E
Accts Brown Edwards & Company Ll
SIC 8221 College, except junior; College, except junior
Pr: Nancy Oliver Gray
**Pr:* Nora K Bell
CFO: Carrie Edmunds
**Ch:* Whitmore Suzanne
**Treas:* Kerry J Edmonds
Assoc Dir: Hannah Alley
Assoc Dir: Elizabeth Courter
Assoc Dir: Amy Hunt
Assoc Dir: Beverley Witt
Ex Dir: Wyona Lynchmcwhite
Ex Dir: Brenda McDaniel

HOLLIS
See FEDERAL COMPRESS & WAREHOUSE CO INC

D-U-N-S 01-013-5986
HOLLIS D SEGUR INC
H D SEGUR
156 Knotter Dr, Cheshire, CT 06410-1136
Tel (203) 699-4500 *Founded/Ownrshp* 1890
Sales NA *EMP* 72
SIC 6411 Insurance agents
Pr: Carl Temme
**Pr:* James B Mullen Jr
VP: James Herlihy
**VP:* William Morris
**VP:* Nicholas Pannullo
CIO: Roy Badstuebner

D-U-N-S 94-676-3695
HOLLIS TELEPHONE CO INC
TDS
515 Junction Rd, Madison, WI 53717-2151
Tel (608) 831-1000 *Founded/Ownrshp* 1984
Sales 853.0MM *EMP* 2,700
SIC 4813 Telephone communication, except radio; Telephone communication, except radio
Pr: David Wittwer

D-U-N-S 60-300-1921
HOLLISTER CONSTRUCTION SERVICES LLC
HCS
339 Jefferson Rd, Parsippany, NJ 07054-3707
Tel (201) 393-7500 *Founded/Ownrshp* 2004
Sales 56.1MM *EMP* 45^E
SIC 8741 Construction management; Construction management
CEO: Christopher A Johnson
Owner: Cherise Dovi
**Pr:* Kieran D Flanagan
**Sr VP:* Dominick Aquilina
**VP:* Mike Bartow
VP: Russell Coniglio
VP: Brendan Murray
**VP:* Vincent Solano
Dir IT: Stephen Knapp
VP Opers: Robert Sander
Mktg Dir: Selena Perry

D-U-N-S 00-552-7098 IMP/EXP
HOLLISTER INC (IL)
2000 Hollister Dr, Libertyville, IL 60048-3781
Tel (847) 680-1000 *Founded/Ownrshp* 1959, 1968
Sales 728.6MM^E *EMP* 2,400
SIC 3841 3842 Surgical & medical instruments; Surgical appliances & supplies; Surgical & medical instruments; Surgical appliances & supplies
Pr: George Maliekel
**CFO:* Sam Brilliant
Bd of Dir: Sam Falla
**VP:* Denis R Chevaleau

**VP:* Robert A Crowe
VP: John McCarthy
Dir Bus: Ken Kolakowski
Mng Dir: Klaus Grunau
Dept Mgr: Lori Fijalkowski
Dept Mgr: Joanne Gresavage
Dept Mgr: Colleen Groff

D-U-N-S 14-163-5503 IMP
■ HOLLISTER OHIO LLC
(*Suby of* ABERCROMBIE & FITCH MANAGEMENT CO) ★
6301 Fitch Path, New Albany, OH 43054-9269
Tel (614) 283-6500 *Founded/Ownrshp* 2002
Sales 52.4MM^E^ *EMP* 500
SIC 5611 5621 Men's & boys' clothing stores; Women's clothing stores; Men's & boys' clothing stores; Women's clothing stores
Dir IT: Jo Campbell

D-U-N-S 12-481-1548
HOLLISTER SCHOOL DISTRICT
2690 Cienega Rd, Hollister, CA 95023-9687
Tel (831) 630-6300 *Founded/Ownrshp* 1900
Sales 30.7MM^E^ *EMP* 543
SIC 8211 Public elementary & secondary schools; Public elementary & secondary schools
Trst: Margie Barrios
Snr Mgr: Jack Bachofer

HOLLISTER-STIER LABORATORIES
See JUBILANT HOLLISTERSTIER LLC

D-U-N-S 00-628-2214 IMP
HOLLISTER-WHITNEY ELEVATOR CORP (IL)
2603 N 24th St, Quincy, IL 62305-1215
Tel (217) 222-0466 *Founded/Ownrshp* 1900, 1959
Sales 100.8MM^E^ *EMP* 250
SIC 3534 Elevators & moving stairways; Elevators & moving stairways
VP: Herbert W Glaser
VP: Frank Musholk
**VP:* Frank H Musholt
CIO: Bill Schuering
Dir IT: Bill Schuering
Sfty Mgr: Chris Barrey
Sfty Mgr: Nick Poepping
Prd Mgr: Terry Brassfield

D-U-N-S 80-640-3395 IMP
HOLLISTON LLC
ICG HOLLISTON
(*Suby of* VERSA CAPITAL MANAGEMENT LLC) ★
905 Holliston Mills Rd, Church Hill, TN 37642-4506
Tel (423) 357-6141 *Founded/Ownrshp* 2007
Sales 42.5MM^E^ *EMP* 150
SIC 2295 2672 Coated fabrics, not rubberized; Coated & laminated paper; Coated fabrics, not rubberized; Coated & laminated paper
CEO: Lawrence Maston
**Pr:* Steve W Lister
**COO:* Keith A Polak
Chf Mktg O: Jennifer Anderson
**Sr VP:* Gary F Sweeney
**VP:* William D Chapman

HOLLMAN COURT SYSTEMS
See HOLLMAN INC

D-U-N-S 14-769-0663 IMP
HOLLMAN INC
HOLLMAN COURT SYSTEMS
1825 W Walnut Hill Ln # 110, Irving, TX 75038-4453
Tel (972) 815-4000 *Founded/Ownrshp* 1968
Sales 57.2MM^E^ *EMP* 100^E^
SIC 1629 2541 2435 2411 Athletic & recreation facilities construction; Lockers, except refrigerated: wood; Hardwood veneer & plywood; Logging
Pr: Travis Hollman
**CFO:* Vl Ho
Dir IT: Mike Wheeler
Mktg Mgr: Rebecca Tearman

D-U-N-S 04-162-2598
HOLLOMAN CORP
333 N Sam Houston Pkwy E, Houston, TX 77060-2414
Tel (281) 878-2600 *Founded/Ownrshp* 2002
Sales 1.0MMM^E^ *EMP* 1,500
SIC 1541 1623 1389 Industrial buildings & warehouses; Oil & gas pipeline construction; Roustabout service; Industrial buildings & warehouses; Oil & gas pipeline construction; Roustabout service
Ch Bd: Sam E Holloman
**Pr:* Mark Stevenson
**COO:* Bryce Harrell
**CFO:* Jim Ebeling
**VP:* Eric Prim
**VP:* Colin Young
Dir Bus: Wayne Stewart
Dir IT: Ben Wilson
Sfty Dirs: David Harris
Mtls Mgr: John Holden
Mtls Mgr: Andrew Holloman

D-U-N-S 02-639-2787
HOLLON OIL CO
OIL CAN HARRYS
1300 Davenport St, Weslaco, TX 78596-6538
Tel (956) 968-9581 *Founded/Ownrshp* 1946
Sales 23.9MM^E^ *EMP* 50
SIC 5172 7549 Petroleum products; Lubrication service, automotive; Petroleum products; Lubrication service, automotive
Pr: Bill Hollon
**Sec:* Cynthia Hollon
**VP:* Steven Wilson
Exec: Daniel Arriaga

D-U-N-S 61-937-4374
HOLLOWAY DISTRIBUTING INC
210 E Owen Ave, Puxico, MO 63960-9160
Tel (573) 222-6255 *Founded/Ownrshp* 1982
Sales 103.8MM *EMP* 90
Accts Maloney Wright & Robbins Far
SIC 5145 5194 5149 Candy; Tobacco & tobacco products; Groceries & related products; Candy; Tobacco & tobacco products; Groceries & related products
Pr: Terry Holloway
**Sec:* Debbie Holloway
IT Man: Sherry Thompson
Opers Mgr: Ron Carr

D-U-N-S 82-871-2273 IMP/EXP
HOLLOWAY DRILLING EQUIPMENT INC
HOLLOWAY RENTAL
101 Rue Napoleon, Broussard, LA 70518-5712
Tel (337) 856-8700 *Founded/Ownrshp* 1992
Sales 25.0MM *EMP* 9
SIC 5084 Oil well machinery, equipment & supplies; Oil well machinery, equipment & supplies
Pr: Rickey Holloway
Opers Mgr: Damian Domingue

HOLLOWAY RENTAL
See HOLLOWAY DRILLING EQUIPMENT INC

D-U-N-S 00-426-0097 IMP
HOLLOWAY SPORTSWEAR INC
(*Suby of* AUGUSTA SPORTSWEAR INC) ★
2633 Campbell Rd, Sidney, OH 45365-8863
Tel (937) 494-2505 *Founded/Ownrshp* 2006
Sales 71.8MM^E^ *EMP* 700
SIC 2329 2339 2392 Men's & boys' leather, wool & down-filled outerwear; Men's & boys' sportswear & athletic clothing; Women's & misses' outerwear; Blankets: made from purchased materials

D-U-N-S 02-660-4280 IMP/EXP
HOLLOWAY-HOUSTON INC
H H I
5833 Armour Dr, Houston, TX 77020-8195
Tel (713) 674-5631 *Founded/Ownrshp* 1960
Sales 146.2MM^E^ *EMP* 215
SIC 5072 Hardware; Hardware
**Treas:* Eileen Dutton
Telecom Ex: Javier Martinez
Mktg Dir: Ezequiel Ortuno
Mktg Mgr: Bob Knight
Sales Asso: Robert Dill
Sales Asso: Jordan Hamilton

D-U-N-S 80-447-0359
HOLLSTADT & ASSOCIATES INC
1333 Northland Dr Ste 220, Saint Paul, MN 55120-1344
Tel (952) 892-3660 *Founded/Ownrshp* 1990
Sales 23.7MM^E^ *EMP* 175
SIC 7379 Computer related consulting services; Computer related consulting services
CEO: Molly Jungbauer
**Pr:* James Jungbauer
**Sr VP:* William Bring
**VP:* Maxine Thomas
Sls Mgr: Aimee Krebsbach
Sls Mgr: Samantha Savage
Snr PM: Betty Knutson
Snr PM: Jennifer Lambert

D-U-N-S 00-777-1448
HOLLY AREA SCHOOL DISTRICT
920 Baird St, Holly, MI 48442-1735
Tel (248) 328-3140 *Founded/Ownrshp* 2010
Sales 15.6MM^E^ *EMP* 516^E^
SIC 8211 Public elementary & secondary schools
Dir Sec: Timothy Houck

D-U-N-S 08-833-0550
HOLLY AREA SCHOOLS
920 Baird St, Holly, MI 48442-1735
Tel (248) 328-3151 *Founded/Ownrshp* 1860
Sales 30.9MM^E^ *EMP* 550
Accts Yeo & Yeo Pc Flint Michig
SIC 8211 Public elementary school; Public junior high school; Public senior high school; Public adult education school; Public elementary school; Public junior high school; Public senior high school; Public adult education school
Pr: Tony Mayhew
**Treas:* Kevin Diviney
**VP:* Sue Julian

D-U-N-S 14-481-8395
▲ HOLLY ENERGY PARTNERS LP
2828 N Harwood St # 1300, Dallas, TX 75201-2174
Tel (214) 871-3555 *Founded/Ownrshp* 2004
Sales 332.5MM *EMP* 257^E^
Tkr Sym HEP *Exch* NYS
SIC 5171 4612 4613 Petroleum terminals; Crude petroleum pipelines; Refined petroleum pipelines; Petroleum terminals; Crude petroleum pipelines; Refined petroleum pipelines
CEO: Michael C Jennings
Genl Pt: Holly Logistic Services
Pr: Bruce R Shaw
Bd of Dir: Michael Rose
Ofcr: Kenneth Norwood
VP: Mark Cunningham
VP: Nancy Hartmann
VP: Rob Jamieson
VP: Denise McWatters
VP: Mike Mirbagheri
VP: Dean Ridenour
VP: James Townsend
VP: Gregory A White
VP: Philip Youngblood
VP Bus Dev: Mark Plake

HOLLY HILL HOSPITAL
See HOLLY HILL/CHARTER BEHAVIORAL HEALTH SYSTEM LLC

D-U-N-S 78-334-6257
HOLLY HILL HOUSE INC
HOLLY HILL NURSING & REHAB
100 Kingston Rd, Sulphur, LA 70663-4016
Tel (337) 625-5843 *Founded/Ownrshp* 1963
Sales 480.3MM *EMP* 40
SIC 8051 Skilled nursing care facilities; Skilled nursing care facilities
CEO: Charles Fellows
**Pr:* Beth Fellows
**VP:* Hugh D Fellows

HOLLY HILL NURSING & REHAB
See HOLLY HILL HOUSE INC

D-U-N-S 08-089-1351
■ HOLLY HILL/CHARTER BEHAVIORAL HEALTH SYSTEM LLC
HOLLY HILL HOSPITAL
(*Suby of* PSYCHIATRIC SOLUTIONS INC) ★
3019 Falstaff Rd, Raleigh, NC 27610-1812
Tel (919) 250-7000 *Founded/Ownrshp* 1974, 1995
Sales 45.6MM^E^ *EMP* 419
SIC 8063 Psychiatric hospitals; Psychiatric hospitals
CEO: Ron Howard
**CEO:* Robert Turner
Ex VP: Kathy Bolmer
Ex VP: Brent Turner
Nrsg Dir: Lisa Jones

D-U-N-S 06-747-0443 IMP
■ HOLLY HUNT ENTERPRISES INC
HOLLY HUNT STUDIO
(*Suby of* KNOLL INC) ★
801 W Adams St Ste 700, Chicago, IL 60607-3068
Tel (312) 329-5999 *Founded/Ownrshp* 2014
Sales 130.1MM^E^ *EMP* 250
SIC 5021 Office & public building furniture; Office & public building furniture
CEO: Holly Hunt
**Pr:* David Schutte
Genl Mgr: Victoria Lopez
IT Man: Mary Kelly
Netwrk Eng: Justin Latta
Prd Mgr: Monica Riley
VP Sls: Dan Campbell
Sales Asso: Ruben Bautista
Sales Asso: Terry Campos
Sales Asso: Trey Gonzales
Sales Asso: Kristen Greenberg

HOLLY HUNT STUDIO
See HOLLY HUNT ENTERPRISES INC

D-U-N-S 10-116-8789
HOLLY MANAGEMENT AND SUPPLY CORP
297 North St Ste 121, Hyannis, MA 02601-5133
Tel (508) 775-9316 *Founded/Ownrshp* 1984
Sales 36.7MM^E^ *EMP* 680
SIC 6531 Real estate managers; Real estate managers
Pr: Stuart Bornstein
**Treas:* Jamila Bornstein

D-U-N-S 00-309-9777
HOLLY POULTRY INC
2221 Berlin St, Baltimore, MD 21230-1637
Tel (410) 727-6210 *Founded/Ownrshp* 1992
Sales 145.1MM^E^ *EMP* 195
SIC 5144 5147 Poultry products; Meats & meat products; Poultry products; Meats & meat products
Pr: Mike Fine
**CFO:* Roy Tarash
IT Man: Tim Cheche
Sls Mgr: John Finnegan

D-U-N-S 12-153-3728
■ HOLLY REFINING & MARKETING CO-WOODS CROSS
(*Suby of* HOLLYFRONTIER CORP) ★
1070 W 500 S, West Bountiful, UT 84087-1442
Tel (801) 299-6600 *Founded/Ownrshp* 2003
Sales 64.3MM^E^ *EMP* 146
SIC 2911 Petroleum refining; Petroleum refining
Ch Bd: Matthew P Clifton

HOLLYFRONTIER
See FRONTIER REFINING & MARKETING LLC

D-U-N-S 00-896-5808 EXP
▲ HOLLYFRONTIER CORP
2828 N Harwood St # 1300, Dallas, TX 75201-2174
Tel (214) 871-3555 *Founded/Ownrshp* 1947
Sales 19.7MMM *EMP* 2,662^E^
Accts Ernst & Young Llp Dallas Tex
Tkr Sym HFC *Exch* NYS
SIC 2911 4613 Petroleum refining; Gasoline; Jet fuels; Diesel fuels; Refined petroleum pipelines; Petroleum refining; Gasoline; Jet fuels; Diesel fuels; Refined petroleum pipelines
Ch Bd: Michael C Jennings
COO: George J Damiris
CFO: Douglas S Aron
Bd of Dir: Dean Ridenour
Sr VP: Gary Fuller
Sr VP: Denise C McWatters
Sr VP: James M Stump
VP: Nellson D Burns
VP: Tom Shetina
Exec: Joe Akins
CIO: James Harvey
Board of Directors: Douglas Y Bech, George Damiris, R Kevin Hardage, Robert J Kostelnik, James H Lee, Franklin Myers, Michael E Rose, Tommy A Valenta

D-U-N-S 83-066-7726
■ HOLLYFRONTIER REFINING & MARKETING LLC
(*Suby of* HOLLYFRONTIER CORP) ★
2828 N Harwood St # 1300, Dallas, TX 75201-1518
Tel (214) 871-3555 *Founded/Ownrshp* 2009
Sales 176.5MM^E^ *EMP* 2,642^E^
SIC 2911 4612 Petroleum refining; Gasoline; Jet fuels; Diesel fuels; Crude petroleum pipelines
Ch Bd: Michael C Jennings
**CFO:* Bruce R Shaw
**Sr VP:* George J Damiris
**Sr VP:* Denise C McWatters
**Sr VP:* James M Stump
**VP:* P Dean Ridenour
VP: Henry Teichholz
Dir IT: Paul Sheth

D-U-N-S 02-936-2225 IMP
HOLLYMATIC CORP
600 E Plainfield Rd, Countryside, IL 60525-6900
Tel (708) 579-3700 *Founded/Ownrshp* 1937, 1988
Sales 36.2MM^E^ *EMP* 55
SIC 5113 3556 2672 Industrial & personal service paper; Meat processing machinery; Mixers, commercial, food; Grinders, commercial, food; Sausage stuffers; Coated & laminated paper
Pr: James D Azzar
Genl Mgr: Marilyn Krische
IT Man: Stan Skowronski
Mfg Mgr: J Wacaser
Mktg Dir: Susan Liskey
Menager: Larry Warshavsky

D-U-N-S 14-124-2607
HOLLYWOOD AMOEBA INC
AMOEBA MUSIC
6400 W Sunset Blvd, Los Angeles, CA 90028-7307
Tel (323) 465-6403 *Founded/Ownrshp* 2001
Sales 29.2MM^E^ *EMP* 240
SIC 5961 Record &/or tape (music or video) club, mail order; Record &/or tape (music or video) club, mail order
Pr: Dave Prinz
Sales Exec: Marc Weinstin
Mktg Mgr: Rachael McGovern

D-U-N-S 00-824-6118 IMP
HOLLYWOOD BED & SPRING MFG CO INC
5959 Corvette St, Commerce, CA 90040-1601
Tel (323) 887-9500 *Founded/Ownrshp* 1981
Sales 21.0MM^E^ *EMP* 90
SIC 2514 3429 2515 2511 Metal household furniture; Frames for box springs or bedsprings: metal; Manufactured hardware (general); Mattresses & bedsprings; Wood household furniture
CEO: Larry Harrow
**Pr:* Jason Harrow

HOLLYWOOD CASINO
See INDIANA GAMING CO LP

HOLLYWOOD CASINO
See MOUNTAINVIEW THOROUGHBRED RACING ASSOCIATION

HOLLYWOOD CASINO
See MOUNTAINVIEW THOROUGHBRED RACING ASSOCIATION LLC

D-U-N-S 85-873-6838
■ HOLLYWOOD CASINO - AURORA INC
(*Suby of* PENN NATIONAL GAMING INC) ★
1 W New York St, Aurora, IL 60506-4120
Tel (630) 801-1234 *Founded/Ownrshp* 2004
Sales 47.5MM^E^ *EMP* 905
SIC 7999 Gambling establishment; Gambling establishment
Pr: Timothy Wilmott
**CEO:* Peter M Carlino
**CFO:* Wandy Kashe
Genl Mgr: Pat Medchill

HOLLYWOOD CASINO BAY ST LOUIS
See BSLO LLC

D-U-N-S 80-101-5199
■ HOLLYWOOD CASINO CORP
(*Suby of* PENN NATIONAL GAMING INC) ★
825 Berkshire Blvd # 200, Reading, PA 19610-1247
Tel (610) 373-2400 *Founded/Ownrshp* 2003
Sales 39.2MM^E^ *EMP* 3,000
SIC 7011 8741 Hotels; Casino hotel; Hotel or motel management; Hotels; Casino hotel; Hotel or motel management
Pr: Edward Pratt III
**Pr:* Robert D Sheldon
**CFO:* Paul C Yates
**VP:* Walter E Evans
**VP:* Charles F Lafrano III
VP: Donald A Shapiro
VP: Walter E Vans

HOLLYWOOD CASINO JOLIET
See EMPRESS CASINO JOLIET CORP

HOLLYWOOD CASINO ST LOUIS
See ST LOUIS GAMING VENTURES LLC

HOLLYWOOD CHRYSLER JEEP
See HOLLYWOOD CHRYSLER PLYMOUTH INC

D-U-N-S 03-253-9850 EXP
HOLLYWOOD CHRYSLER PLYMOUTH INC
HOLLYWOOD CHRYSLER JEEP
2100 N State Road 7, Hollywood, FL 33021-3805
Tel (305) 696-8600 *Founded/Ownrshp* 1987
Sales 50.0MM^E^ *EMP* 128
SIC 5511 5013 5531 7538 Automobiles, new & used; Automotive supplies & parts; Automotive parts; General automotive repair shops; Automobiles, new & used; Automotive supplies & parts; Automotive parts; General automotive repair shops
Pr: Faisal Y Ahmed
**CFO:* Douglas Bernard
**VP:* Ali Ahmed
**VP:* Robert P Lambdin Jr
Genl Mgr: Jeff Silverberg

D-U-N-S 07-602-2136
HOLLYWOOD CITY OF (INC)
2600 Hollywood Blvd Ste B, Hollywood, FL 33020-4800
Tel (954) 921-3231 *Founded/Ownrshp* 1925
Sales NA *EMP* 1,294
Accts Mcgladrey Llp Fort Lauderdale
SIC 9111 City & town managers' offices; City & town managers' offices;
Ofcr: Rick Eddy
Ofcr: Sherry Stability
Plng Mgr: Leslie Del Monte
CIO: Kenneth R Fields
CTO: John Moss

HOLLYWOOD CMNTY HOSP HOLLYWOOD
See HOLLYWOOD COMMUNITY HOSPITAL MEDICAL CENTER INC

D-U-N-S 07-292-7254
HOLLYWOOD COMMUNITY HOSPITAL MEDICAL CENTER INC
HOLLYWOOD CMNTY HOSP HOLLYWOOD
6245 De Longpre Ave, Los Angeles, CA 90028-8253
Tel (323) 462-2271 *Founded/Ownrshp* 1982
Sales 75.2MM^E^ *EMP* 220
SIC 8062 General medical & surgical hospitals; General medical & surgical hospitals
CEO: Robert Starling

Pr: Ron Messenger
**V Ch Bd:* Manfred Krukemeyer
Dir Lab: Cecilia Militante
Dir Rad: Clive Nagatani
Dir Rx: David Kalamikian
Chf Nrs Of: Claudia Hayes
Chf Nrs Of: Madeline Williams
Nrsg Dir: John Blenkinsopp

D-U-N-S 19-610-2438
HOLLYWOOD ENTERTAINMENT CORP
HOLLYWOOD VIDEO
(*Suby of* MOVIE GALLERY INC) ★
9275 Sw Peyton Ln, Wilsonville, OR 97070-9200
Tel (503) 214-4600 *Founded/Ownrshp* 2005
Sales 1.0MMM^E *EMP* 19,000
SIC 5735 7841 Record & prerecorded tape stores; Video disk/tape rental to the general public
Pr: Joe Malugen
COO: Lawrence Plotnick
Bd of Dir: S Todd
Ofcr: Lynn Fletcher
Sr VP: Richard Maicki
Sr VP: Michael D Robinson
VP: Theodore Allen
VP: John Scales
Rgnl Mgr: Brett Baker
Brnch Mgr: Lana Hudnut
Dist Mgr: Joe Elizondo

D-U-N-S 01-103-1952
HOLLYWOOD GRILL RESTAURANT INC
HAMPTON INN
1811 Concord Pike, Wilmington, DE 19803-2901
Tel (302) 655-1348 *Founded/Ownrshp* 1955
Sales 11.7MM^E *EMP* 300
SIC 7011 5812 5813 6531 Hotels & motels; Restaurant, family: independent; Restaurant, family: chain; Drinking places; Cocktail lounge; Real estate agents & managers; Hotels & motels; Restaurant, family: independent; Restaurant, family: chain; Drinking places; Cocktail lounge; Real estate agents & managers

HOLLYWOOD HILLS NURSING HOME
See HOLLYWOOD HILLS REHABILITATION CENTER LLC

D-U-N-S 07-604-0633
HOLLYWOOD HILLS REHABILITATION CENTER LLC
HOLLYWOOD HILLS NURSING HOME
1200 N 35th Ave, Hollywood, FL 33021-5413
Tel (954) 981-5511 *Founded/Ownrshp* 2015
Sales 29.6MM^E *EMP* 200
SIC 8063 8051 Psychiatric hospitals; Skilled nursing care facilities; Psychiatric hospitals; Skilled nursing care facilities
CEO: Sandy Sosa-Guerrero

D-U-N-S 01-735-1446
HOLLYWOOD HOLDING CO LLC
HOLLYWOOD SUPER MARKET
2670 W Maple Rd, Troy, MI 48084-7133
Tel (248) 643-0309 *Founded/Ownrshp* 1950, 2011
Sales 108.0MM^E *EMP* 600^E
SIC 5921 5141 5411 Beer (packaged); Wine; Groceries, general line; Supermarkets, chain; Beer (packaged); Wine; Groceries, general line; Supermarkets, chain
Pr: William D Welch
VP: Kim Welch Harlan
VP: Tom Welch

D-U-N-S 05-013-7645 EXP
■ **HOLLYWOOD IMPORTS LIMITED INC**
MAROONE HONDA
(*Suby of* AUTONATION INC) ★
1450 N State Road 7, Hollywood, FL 33021-4501
Tel (954) 989-1600 *Founded/Ownrshp* 1998
Sales 44.7MM^E *EMP* 150
SIC 5511 5531 Automobiles, new & used; Automotive parts; Automobiles, new & used; Automotive parts

D-U-N-S 05-882-8760
HOLLYWOOD MEDICAL CENTER LP
HOLLYWOOD PRESBYTERIAN MED CTR
(*Suby of* CHA HEALTH SYSTEMS INC) ★
1300 N Vermont Ave, Los Angeles, CA 90027-6005
Tel (213) 413-3000 *Founded/Ownrshp* 2005
Sales 281.2MM *EMP* 1,250
SIC 8062 General medical & surgical hospitals; General medical & surgical hospitals
Pt: Jeff Nelson

D-U-N-S 06-992-8745
HOLLYWOOD MOTOR CARS LLC
TOYOTA LNCOLN MRCURY HOLLYWOOD
6000 Hollywood Blvd, Los Angeles, CA 90028-5412
Tel (323) 860-5500 *Founded/Ownrshp* 1997
Sales 43.8MM^E *EMP* 130
SIC 5511 Automobiles, new & used; Automobiles, new & used
Sls Mgr: Christopher Abrahms

HOLLYWOOD PARK CASINO
See PARK HOLLYWOOD CASINO

HOLLYWOOD PRESBYTERIAN MED CTR
See HOLLYWOOD MEDICAL CENTER LP

HOLLYWOOD PRESBYTERIAN MED CTR
See CHA HOLLYWOOD MEDICAL CENTER LP

D-U-N-S 05-227-5591 IMP/EXP
HOLLYWOOD RIBBON INDUSTRIES INC (CA)
9000 Rochester Ave, Rancho Cucamonga, CA 91730-5522
Tel (323) 266-0670 *Founded/Ownrshp* 2015
Sales NA *EMP* 400
SIC 2241 Ribbons

HOLLYWOOD SUPER MARKET
See HOLLYWOOD HOLDING CO LLC

HOLLYWOOD THEATERS
See WALLACE THEATER HOLDINGS INC

HOLLYWOOD VIDEO
See BOARDS VIDEO CO LLC

HOLLYWOOD VIDEO
See HOLLYWOOD ENTERTAINMENT CORP

D-U-N-S 04-274-1637
HOLLYWOOD WOODWORK INC
2951 Pembroke Rd, Hollywood, FL 33020-5634
Tel (954) 920-0800 *Founded/Ownrshp* 1968
Sales 20.1MM^E *EMP* 100
SIC 2431 Millwork
CEO: Yves Desmarais
VP: Bob Hacker
**VP:* Paul Des Marais
VP: Paul Marais
IT Man: Sebastien Desmarais
Prd Mgr: Ryan Chamberland
Snr PM: Bill Knight

HOLM INDUSTRIES
See ILPEA INDUSTRIES INC

D-U-N-S 96-164-5574
HOLMAN AUTOMOTIVE GROUP INC
(*Suby of* HOLMAN ENTERPRISES INC) ★
244 E Kings Hwy, Maple Shade, NJ 08052-3400
Tel (856) 663-5200 *Founded/Ownrshp* 2001
Sales 551.5MM^E *EMP* 2,000^E
SIC 5511 New & used car dealers; New & used car dealers
CEO: Carl A Ortell
**Ch Bd:* Melinda K Holman
Pr: Bill Cariss
Pr: Chris Conroy
**COO:* Brian R Bates
CFO: Steve Haindl
**Ch:* Joseph S Holman
Treas: Brian Horwith
Sr VP: Bill Kwelty
VP: Frank Beideman
VP: Glenn Gardner

D-U-N-S 03-227-2643 EXP
HOLMAN AUTOMOTIVE INC
SOUTH FLORIDA LEASING & RENTAL
(*Suby of* HOLMAN ENTERPRISES INC) ★
12 E Sunrise Blvd, Fort Lauderdale, FL 33304-1951
Tel (954) 764-1100 *Founded/Ownrshp* 1955
Sales 92.7MM^E *EMP* 234
SIC 5511 5531 Automobiles, new & used; Automotive parts; Automobiles, new & used; Automotive parts
Pr: Melinda K Holman
**Ch Bd:* Joseph S Holman
**CFO:* Brian R Bates
Treas: Gaye Rankin
**VP:* Robert R Campbell
**VP:* William J Cariss
**VP:* Angelo J Nori
Genl Mgr: Larry Oden
Mktg Mgr: Matthew McGowan
Sls Mgr: Rick Saul
Sales Asso: Gabe Camel

D-U-N-S 00-893-4192
HOLMAN DISTRIBUTION CENTER OF OREGON INC
2300 Se Beta St Ste A, Portland, OR 97222-7373
Tel (503) 652-1912 *Founded/Ownrshp* 1950
Sales 45.7MM^E *EMP* 316
SIC 4225 4213 General warehousing; Trucking, except local; General warehousing; Trucking, except local
Ch: Elizabeth Heosti
**Pr:* Robert Downie
**CFO:* Robert B Harrington
Genl Mgr: Steve Little
Mktg Dir: Peter George

D-U-N-S 02-182-7423 IMP
HOLMAN DISTRIBUTION CENTER OF WASHINGTON INC
22430 76th Ave S, Kent, WA 98032-2406
Tel (253) 872-7140 *Founded/Ownrshp* 1965
Sales 57.1MM^E *EMP* 200
SIC 4225 4213

D-U-N-S 06-570-2847 IMP/EXP
HOLMAN ENTERPRISES INC
HOLMAN FORD
7411 Maple Ave, Pennsauken, NJ 08109-2946
Tel (856) 662-1042 *Founded/Ownrshp* 1946
Sales 990.8MM^E *EMP* 2,751
SIC 5511 New & used car dealers; New & used car dealers
Pr: Mindy Holman
**Ch Bd:* Joseph S Holman
**Pr:* M K Holman
VP: Frank Beideman
Brnch Mgr: Chuck Wilkins
Sls Mgr: Henry Tomassini
Snr Mgr: Melinda Homan

HOLMAN FORD
See HOLMAN ENTERPRISES INC

D-U-N-S 05-910-6997
HOLMAN MOTORS INC
4387 Elick Ln, Batavia, OH 45103-1599
Tel (513) 752-3123 *Founded/Ownrshp* 1994
Sales 25.7MM^E *EMP* 90
SIC 5561 5511 5521

D-U-N-S 00-979-0395
HOLMAN MOVING SYSTEMS LLC
20 E Commons Blvd, New Castle, DE 19720-1734
Tel (302) 323-9000 *Founded/Ownrshp* 1885, 1992
Sales 24.1MM^E *EMP* 275
Accts Rowland Johnson & Company Pa
SIC 4213 4214 Household goods transport; Local trucking with storage; Household goods transport; Local trucking with storage
CFO: Robert Webster
Comm Dir: Paige Holden

D-U-N-S 01-987-5137
HOLMAN TRANSPORTATION SERVICES INC (ID)
1010 Holman Ct, Caldwell, ID 83605-3971
Tel (208) 454-0779 *Founded/Ownrshp* 1997
Sales 37.6MM *EMP* 112
SIC 4213 Trucking, except local; Trucking, except local
Pr: Robert Holman
**VP:* Sherry Holman

D-U-N-S 83-090-3691
HOLMANS USA LLC
6201 Jefferson St Ne, Albuquerque, NM 87109-3431
Tel (505) 343-0007 *Founded/Ownrshp* 2008
Sales 27.5MM *EMP* 4
Accts John Howard Cpa Pc Albuque
SIC 5734 Computer peripheral equipment; Computer peripheral equipment

D-U-N-S 02-099-4703
HOLMBERG FARMS INC
13430 Hobson Simmons Rd, Lithia, FL 33547-1912
Tel (813) 689-3601 *Founded/Ownrshp* 1974
Sales 22.7MM^E *EMP* 150
SIC 5193 Flowers & florists' supplies; Flowers & florists' supplies
Pr: Douglas A Holmberg

HOLMDEL TOWNSHIP BOARD EDUCATN
See BOARD OF EDUCATION OF TOWNSHIP OF HOLMDEL INC

D-U-N-S 79-897-5319
HOLMDEL TOWNSHIP SCHOOL DISTRICT
4 Crawfords Corner Rd, Holmdel, NJ 07733-1908
Tel (732) 946-1800 *Founded/Ownrshp* 2007
Sales 61.1MM *EMP* 99^E
Accts Holman Frenia Allison Pc Fre
SIC 8211 Public elementary & secondary schools; Public elementary & secondary schools
Prin: Peter Mikos

D-U-N-S 07-407-4238
HOLME ROBERTS & OWEN LLP
1700 N Lincoln St # 4100, Denver, CO 80203-4541
Tel (303) 861-7000 *Founded/Ownrshp* 2012
Sales NA *EMP* 475
SIC 8111

D-U-N-S 06-911-4408 IMP
HOLMES & BRAKEL INTERNATIONAL INC
3901 Coconut Palm Dr # 102, Tampa, FL 33619-8362
Tel (813) 229-6869 *Founded/Ownrshp* 1974
Sales 43.4MM^E *EMP* 120
SIC 5021 1799 Furniture; Furniture; Office furniture; Office furniture installation
Pr: Richard J Holmes
**Pr:* W Mark Holmes
**Genl Mgr:* Terry Shields

D-U-N-S 00-690-7562
■ **HOLMES & NARVER INC**
(*Suby of* AECOM) ★
999 W Town And Country Rd, Orange, CA 92868-4713
Tel (714) 567-2400 *Founded/Ownrshp* 1933, 1972
Sales 19.4MM^E *EMP* 450
SIC 8711 8742 8741 1542 Engineering services; Training & development consultant; Construction management; Nonresidential construction; Engineering services; Training & development consultant; Construction management; Nonresidential construction
CEO: Danny Seal
**Pr:* Raymond Landy
**CFO:* Dennis Deslatte
VP: William Autrey
VP: Michel Flynn
VP: Jeryl Jalsin
**Prin:* Tina Clugston

HOLMES AUTOMOTIVE GROUP
See GREGG YOUNG CHEVROLET OF NORWALK INC

D-U-N-S 83-774-6676
HOLMES AUTOMOTIVE GROUP INC
11344 Hickman Rd, Des Moines, IA 50325-3746
Tel (515) 253-3000 *Founded/Ownrshp* 1986
Sales 41.5MM^E *EMP* 180
SIC 5511 Automobiles, new & used; Automobiles, new & used
Pr: Max Holmes
CFO: Frederick W Lie

D-U-N-S 13-411-0860
HOLMES BUILDING SYSTEMS LLC
2863 Plank Rd, Robbins, NC 27325-7335
Tel (910) 948-2516 *Founded/Ownrshp* 2003
Sales 30.7MM^E *EMP* 150
SIC 2451 Mobile homes, except recreational; Mobile homes, except recreational
Pr: Henry Quint
Sls Mgr: Barou Golbell

HOLMES COMMUNICATIONS
See HOLMES ELECTRIC CO

D-U-N-S 07-193-6348
HOLMES COMMUNITY COLLEGE
9216 Hwy 14, Goodman, MS 39079
Tel (662) 472-2312 *Founded/Ownrshp* 1912
Sales 21.4MM^E *EMP* 500
SIC 8222 Junior college; Junior college
Pr: Glenn Boyce
**Ex VP:* Steve Caldwell
Comm Dir: Steve Diffey
Store Mgr: Jody Matthews
DP Exec: Kevin Baker
HC Dir: Don Burnham

D-U-N-S 02-597-2423
HOLMES CONSTRUCTION CO LP
7901 Sw 34th Ave, Amarillo, TX 79121-1057
Tel (806) 376-8629 *Founded/Ownrshp* 1962
Sales 34.9MM^E *EMP* 115
SIC 1611 1629 1771 Highway & street paving contractor; Land preparation construction; Concrete work; Curb construction; Highway & street paving contractor; Land preparation construction; Concrete work; Curb construction
Genl Pt: Julie Farrar
Treas: Shirley Holmes
VP: Rory Farrar
VP: James Holmes
Sfty Mgr: Bill Kimmell

D-U-N-S 18-894-5638
HOLMES COUNTY SCHOOL BOARD
701 E Pennsylvania Ave, Bonifay, FL 32425-2349
Tel (850) 547-6674 *Founded/Ownrshp* 1930
Sales 25.3MM *EMP* 500
SIC 8211 Public elementary & secondary schools; Public elementary & secondary schools

D-U-N-S 07-979-9742
HOLMES COUNTY SCHOOL DISTRICT
701 E Pennsylvania Ave, Bonifay, FL 32425-2349
Tel (850) 547-9341 *Founded/Ownrshp* 2015
Sales 7.8MM^E *EMP* 404^E
SIC 8211 Public elementary & secondary schools
MIS Dir: Phillip Byrd
Pr Dir: Christy English
Schl Brd P: Rusty Williams

D-U-N-S 10-003-9809
HOLMES COUNTY SCHOOL DISTRICT
313 Olive St, Lexington, MS 39095
Tel (662) 834-2175 *Founded/Ownrshp* 1957
Sales 31.5MM *EMP* 528
SIC 8211 Public elementary & secondary schools; Public elementary & secondary schools
IT Man: Merchell Ross

HOLMES DISTRIBUTORS
See HORIZON SOLUTIONS LLC

D-U-N-S 02-982-7318
HOLMES DRYWALL SUPPLY INC
1701 W 25th St, Kansas City, MO 64108-2242
Tel (816) 215-7924 *Founded/Ownrshp* 1969
Sales 24.4MM^E *EMP* 30^E
SIC 5039 5211 Prefabricated structures; Lumber & other building materials
Pr: Jeanne McGrath
**VP:* Barbara Schneider
Brnch Mgr: Dennis Massey

D-U-N-S 00-283-6773
HOLMES ELECTRIC CO
HOLMES COMMUNICATIONS
600 Washington Ave S, Kent, WA 98032-5708
Tel (253) 479-4000 *Founded/Ownrshp* 1946
Sales 31.0MM^E *EMP* 200^E
SIC 1731

HOLMES EXPARATION
See PANTHER ENERGY CO LLC

D-U-N-S 00-812-0883
HOLMES FOODS INC
101 S Liberty Ave, Nixon, TX 78140-2401
Tel (830) 582-1551 *Founded/Ownrshp* 1962
Sales 76.8MM^E *EMP* 275
SIC 2015 Poultry, processed; Poultry, slaughtered & dressed; Poultry, processed; Poultry, slaughtered & dressed
Pr: Phillip Morris
**CEO:* Phillip A Morris
**Sec:* Tommy Lester
**Sr VP:* Philip Hartung
**VP:* Fred Barlow
Genl Mgr: Frederick Barlow
QA Dir: Angela Salinas

HOLMES HONDA WORLD
See HOLMES MOTORS INC

D-U-N-S 18-955-4546
HOLMES MOTORS INC
HOLMES HONDA WORLD
1331 E Bert Kouns Industrl, Shreveport, LA 71105-5632
Tel (318) 212-1200 *Founded/Ownrshp* 1985
Sales 38.3MM^E *EMP* 100
SIC 5511 Automobiles, new & used; Automobiles, new & used
Owner: Charlton C Holmes
**Pr:* Mara Johnson
VP: Keith Hightower
Sales Asso: Jason Soignier
Sales Asso: Wade Strahan

HOLMES MURPHY
See HMA INC

D-U-N-S 07-347-4389
HOLMES MURPHY AND ASSOCIATES LLC
(*Suby of* HMA INC) ★
3001 Westown Pkwy, West Des Moines, IA 50266-1395
Tel (515) 223-6800 *Founded/Ownrshp* 1971
Sales NA *EMP* 300
SIC 6411 Insurance agents; Insurance agents
CEO: Daniel T Keough
**COO:* Nickolas J Henderson
Chf Mktg O: Scott Conard
Sr VP: Craig Hansen
Sr VP: Lori Wiederin
**VP:* Clifford Augspurger
VP: Eric Bolduc
**VP:* Chris Boyd
**VP:* Steve Flood
**VP:* Laure Guisinger
**VP:* John A Hurley II
VP: Kris Manning
VP: Doug Muth
VP: Randy Northrop
VP: Kurt Ratzlaff
VP: Amber Shaddox
VP: Jeffrey Shald
VP: Gail Steffen
Comm Dir: Mark Fitzgibbons
Board of Directors: Mike Foley, Wally Gomaa

D-U-N-S 00-281-2436
HOLMES OIL CO INC (NC)
100 Europa Dr Ste 550, Chapel Hill, NC 27517-2394
Tel (919) 929-9979 *Founded/Ownrshp* 1936, 1997
Sales 37.2MM^E *EMP* 190
SIC 5411 6512 5171

D-U-N-S 04-705-2790
HOLMES OLDSMOBILE CO INC
HOLMES OLDSMOBILE HONDA AUTOS
11344 Hickman Rd, Clive, IA 50325-3746
Tel (515) 253-3000 *Founded/Ownrshp* 1986
Sales 27.0MM^E *EMP* 130
SIC 5511 5013 Automobiles, new & used; Pickups, new & used; Automotive supplies & parts; Automobiles, new & used; Pickups, new & used; Automotive supplies & parts
Pr: Max H Holmes

HOLMES OLDSMOBILE HONDA AUTOS
See HOLMES OLDSMOBILE CO INC

D-U-N-S 09-892-8898
HOLMES REGIONAL MEDICAL CENTER INC
HEALTH FIRST HEALTH PLANS
(*Suby of* HEALTH FIRST HEALTH PLANS) ★
1350 Hickory St, Melbourne, FL 32901-3224
Tel (321) 434-7000 *Founded/Ownrshp* 1937
Sales 412.4MM *EMP* 2,778
SIC 8062 General medical & surgical hospitals; General medical & surgical hospitals
CEO: Steve Johnson
Chf Rad: Jose Ramos
Pr: Jerry Senne
CFO: Robert C Galloway
Treas: William C Potter
Ex VP: Stuart Mitchell
VP: Nadine Bobick
VP: Kent Brown
VP: Joseph G Felkner
VP: James S Mitchell III
Mktg Dir: Keith Lunquist

D-U-N-S 13-418-8759
HOLMES ROAD RECYCLING CO INC
2820 Holmes Rd, Houston, TX 77051-1024
Tel (713) 799-9960 *Founded/Ownrshp* 2002
Sales 50.0MM *EMP* 74
SIC 4953 Recycling, waste materials
Pr: Joseph Schneider
**VP:* Norman Harris
Opers Mgr: Gerald Schneider

D-U-N-S 03-596-6472
HOLMES TUTTLE FORD INC
660 W Auto Mall Dr, Tucson, AZ 85705-6009
Tel (520) 292-3600 *Founded/Ownrshp* 1973
Sales 66.5MM^E *EMP* 215
SIC 5511 5521 Automobiles, new & used; Used car dealers; Automobiles, new & used; Used car dealers
Prin: Cecilia Sierra
**CFO:* Susan Artaz
Sales Asso: Ron Wall

D-U-N-S 11-263-3060
■ **HOLOCAUST MEMORIAL MUSEUM UNITED STATES**
INDEPENDENT ESTABLISHMENT OF
(*Suby of* EXECUTIVE OFFICE OF UNITED STATES GOVERNMENT) ★
100 Roul Wallenberg Pl Sw, Washington, DC 20024-2126
Tel (202) 488-0400 *Founded/Ownrshp* 1980
Sales NA *EMP* 400
Accts Kpmg Llp Mclean Va
SIC 9411 8412 8231 Administration of educational programs; ; Museum; Specialized libraries; Administration of educational programs; ; Museum; Specialized libraries
Ch: Thomas Burnstein
**Ch Bd:* Tom Bernstein
**V Ch:* Joshua Bolten
**CEO:* Sara Bloomfield
COO: Aletta Schaap
Ofcr: Angela Brown
Ofcr: Rachael Fenton
Assoc Dir: Barri-Sue Black
Assoc Dir: Lisa Evans
Assoc Dir: Diana Presley
Assoc Dir: Robert Tanen
Dir Soc: Anastasia Dieter
Dir Soc: Nadia Ficara

D-U-N-S 93-223-7423
■ **HOLOGIC FOREIGN SALES CORP**
(*Suby of* HOLOGIC INC) ★
35 Crosby Dr Ste 101, Bedford, MA 01730-1411
Tel (781) 999-7300 *Founded/Ownrshp* 1989
Sales 35.6MM^E *EMP* 870
SIC 3844 X-ray apparatus & tubes; X-ray apparatus & tubes
MIS Mgr: S Ellenbogen

D-U-N-S 15-362-3137 IMP/EXP
▲ **HOLOGIC INC**
250 Campus Dr, Marlborough, MA 01752-3020
Tel (508) 263-2900 *Founded/Ownrshp* 1985
Sales 2.7MMM *EMP* 5,290^E
Accts Ernst & Young Llp Boston Mas
Tkr Sym HOLX *Exch* NGS
SIC 3845 3844 3841 Ultrasonic medical equipment, except cleaning; Electrotherapeutic apparatus; X-ray apparatus & tubes; Medical instruments & equipment, blood & bone work; Ultrasonic medical equipment, except cleaning; Electrotherapeutic apparatus; X-ray apparatus & tubes; Medical instruments & equipment, blood & bone work
Ch Bd: Stephen P Macmillan
COO: Eric B Compton
CFO: Robert W McMahon
Sr VP: Mark D Myslinski
Sr VP: Jay A Stein
VP: David Brady
VP: Meg Eckenroad
VP: Paul Malenchini
VP: Karleen M Oberton
VP: Joe Ywuc
CIO: David Rudzinsky
Board of Directors: Wayne Wilson, Jonathan Christodoro, Sally W Crawford, Scott T Garrett, David R Lavance Jr, Nancy L Leaming, Lawrence M Levy, Samuel Merksamer, Christiana Stamoulis, Elaine S Ullian

D-U-N-S 01-519-2505
■ **HOLOGIC LIMITED PARTNERSHIP**
(*Suby of* HOLOGIC INC) ★
250 Campus Dr, Marlborough, MA 01752-3020
Tel (508) 263-2900 *Founded/Ownrshp* 2002
Sales 37.0MM^E *EMP* 500
SIC 7389 Personal service agents, brokers & bureaus; Personal service agents, brokers & bureaus
Pr: John W Cumming
CFO: Glenn Muir

D-U-N-S 60-364-0251 IMP/EXP
■ **HOLOPHANE CORP**
(*Suby of* ACUITY BRANDS INC) ★
3825 Columbus Rd Bldg A, Granville, OH 43023-8604
Tel (740) 345-9631 *Founded/Ownrshp* 1989
Sales 196.2MM^E *EMP* 2,050^E
SIC 3646 3648 Commercial indusl & institutional electric lighting fixtures; Outdoor lighting equipment; Commercial indusl & institutional electric lighting fixtures; Outdoor lighting equipment
CEO: Vernon J Nagel
VP: Tom Abbott
VP: Rick Clark
VP: Bob Petro
VP Sls: Rick Simon
S&M/VP: Randy Crothers

HOLSTED JEWELERS
See HOLSTED MARKETING INC

D-U-N-S 07-326-8195 IMP
HOLSTED MARKETING INC
HOLSTED JEWELERS
112 W 34th St Ste 1405, New York, NY 10120-6727
Tel (212) 686-8537 *Founded/Ownrshp* 1971
Sales 30.4MM *EMP* 25^E
SIC 5963

D-U-N-S 00-108-6123
HOLSTEIN ASSOCIATION USA INC (NY)
1 Holstein Pl, Brattleboro, VT 05301-3304
Tel (802) 254-4551 *Founded/Ownrshp* 1885
Sales 20.7MM *EMP* 126
Accts Gallagher Flynn & Company Bu
SIC 8699 8748 Personal interest organization; Agricultural consultant; Personal interest organization; Agricultural consultant
Ex Dir: John Meyer
**CFO:* Barbara Casna
VP: Richard Chichester
VP: Glen D Vondrick
Ex Dir: Dan Meihak
Ex Dir: Rich Rogers
Sftwr Eng: Eduardo Sagrnaga

D-U-N-S 11-980-0845
HOLSTEIN-FRIESIAN SERVICES INC
HFS
(*Suby of* HOLSTEIN ASSOCIATION USA INC) ★
1 Holstein Pl, Brattleboro, VT 05301-3304
Tel (802) 254-4551 *Founded/Ownrshp* 1968
Sales 20.3MM *EMP* 8
Accts Gallagher Flynn & Company Plc
SIC 8748 Agricultural consultant; Agricultural consultant
CEO: John M Meyer
**Treas:* Barbara Casna
Treas: Thaddeus G Kuchinski Jr
Treas: Thaddeus Kuchinski
Div/Sub He: James Cooper

HOLSTON ARMY AMUNITION PLANT
See HOLSTON DEFENSE CORP

D-U-N-S 00-337-7231
■ **HOLSTON DEFENSE CORP** (VA)
HOLSTON ARMY AMUNITION PLANT
(*Suby of* EASTMAN CHEMICAL CO) ★
4509 W Stone Dr, Kingsport, TN 37660-9009
Tel (423) 578-6000 *Founded/Ownrshp* 1949, 1993
Sales 56.2MM^E *EMP* 420
SIC 2892 Secondary high explosives; Secondary high explosives
Ch Bd: Larry Munsey
**Pr:* A L King
**Treas:* R E Davis
Board of Directors: D J Kinlin

D-U-N-S 05-557-6912
HOLSTON DISTRIBUTING CO (TN)
310 Lafe Cox Dr, Johnson City, TN 37604-7444
Tel (423) 975-5200 *Founded/Ownrshp* 1934, 1971
Sales 21.7MM^E *EMP* 80
SIC 5181 Beer & other fermented malt liquors; Beer & other fermented malt liquors
Pr: Stuart E Wood Jr

D-U-N-S 07-491-1322
HOLSTON ELECTRIC COOPERATIVE INC
1200 W Main St, Rogersville, TN 37857-2493
Tel (423) 235-6811 *Founded/Ownrshp* 1939
Sales 33.7MM^E *EMP* 73
Accts Rodefer Moss & Co Pllc Green
SIC 4911 Distribution, electric power; Distribution, electric power
Pr: Lynn Parker
**Pr:* Otis Munsey
**Sec:* Melvin Greene
**VP:* Gordell Ely
Genl Mgr: Larry E Elkins
Genl Mgr: James Sandlin
Dir IT: Nathan Franklin

D-U-N-S 03-469-7276 IMP
HOLSTON GASES INC
545 W Baxter Ave, Knoxville, TN 37921-6846
Tel (865) 573-1917 *Founded/Ownrshp* 1958
Sales 112.2MM^E *EMP* 184
SIC 5169 5084 2813 Gases, compressed & liquefied; Oxygen; Acetylene; Welding machinery & equipment; Industrial gases; Gases, compressed & liquefied; Oxygen; Acetylene; Welding machinery & equipment; Industrial gases
CEO: Bill Baxter
**Pr:* Robert Anders
VP: Phil Kirby
Brnch Mgr: Hank Hodge
IT Man: Tammy White
VP Opers: Melvin Gay
Opers Mgr: Robert Parsons
Sls Dir: Dave Korte
Sales Asso: Derek McCullah

D-U-N-S 78-243-6067
HOLSTON MEDICAL GROUP PC
H M G
2323 N John B Dennis Hwy, Kingsport, TN 37660-4771
Tel (423) 857-2000 *Founded/Ownrshp* 1987
Sales 126.2MM^E *EMP* 955^E
SIC 8011 General & family practice, physician/surgeon; General & family practice, physician/surgeon
Pr: Jerry L Miller MD
Exec: Lee Chase
Rgnl Mgr: Sue Addington
Off Mgr: Beth Medlin
CTO: Wesley Combs
IT Man: Bonnie Drew
Netwrk Mgr: Gary Rowland
Web Dev: Gina Galetti
Netwrk Eng: Tim Parsons
Netwrk Eng: Michael Stout
Doctor: Eric Schwartz

D-U-N-S 00-839-6426 IMP/EXP
■ **HOLSUM BAKERY INC** (AZ)
(*Suby of* FLOWERS FOODS INC) ★
2322 W Lincoln St, Phoenix, AZ 85009-5827
Tel (602) 252-2351 *Founded/Ownrshp* 1881, 2008
Sales 45.3MM^E *EMP* 580
SIC 2051

D-U-N-S 06-102-1312 IMP/EXP
HOLSUM DE PUERTO RICO INC
CARIBE BAKERS
Carr 2 Km 20 1 Bo Cndlria St Ca, TOA Baja, PR 00949
Tel (787) 798-8282 *Founded/Ownrshp* 1998
Sales 105.1MM *EMP* 900
Accts Llm&D Psc San Juan Puerto R
SIC 2051 Bread, cake & related products; Bread, cake & related products
Pr: Ramon Calderon
**Treas:* Raul Buso
**Ex VP:* Julio Vigoreaux
VP: Consuelo Abries

D-U-N-S 02-164-1121
HOLSUM OF FORT WAYNE INC
(*Suby of* LEWIS BROTHERS BAKERIES INC) ★
136 Murray St, Fort Wayne, IN 46803-2333
Tel (260) 456-2130 *Founded/Ownrshp* 1977
Sales 209.3MM^E *EMP* 2,500
SIC 2051 Bread, all types (white, wheat, rye, etc): fresh or frozen; Bread, all types (white, wheat, rye, etc): fresh or frozen
Pr: Lewis Jr Jack
**Treas:* Jeffery J Sankovitch
**VP:* Rodger Lesh

HOLT & BUGBEE
See HOLT AND BUGBEE CO

D-U-N-S 00-799-7364 IMP
HOLT AND BUGBEE CO (MA)
HOLT & BUGBEE
1600 Shawsheen St, Tewksbury, MA 01876-1595
Tel (978) 851-7201 *Founded/Ownrshp* 1906
Sales 65.9MM^E *EMP* 180
Accts Fay & Associates Quincy Ma
SIC 5031 2431 2421 Lumber: rough, dressed & finished; Molding, all materials; Millwork; Sawmills & planing mills, general; Lumber: rough, dressed & finished; Molding, all materials; Millwork; Sawmills & planing mills, general
Pr: Phillip T Pierce
**Ch:* Mary Pierce
CIO: Bill Robinson
Opers Mgr: Wayne Blaisdell
VP Sls: Thomas Wisniowski
Sales Asso: Bob Baldwin
Sales Asso: Peter Burns

D-U-N-S 03-392-9944
HOLT AND HOLT INC (GA)
1286 Hawthorne Ave Se A, Smyrna, GA 30080-8313
Tel (404) 990-4500 *Founded/Ownrshp* 1981
Sales 21.8MM^E *EMP* 200
SIC 1742 Acoustical & ceiling work; Drywall; Insulation, buildings; Acoustical & ceiling work; Drywall; Insulation, buildings
CEO: James Michael Holt
**Sec:* Elizabeth Kellogg
**VP:* Joshua Holt
**VP:* Jason Wagner
Off Mgr: Ana Mejia

D-U-N-S 07-871-8707
HOLT CONSTRUCTION CORP
50 E Washington Ave, Pearl River, NY 10965-2308
Tel (845) 735-4054 *Founded/Ownrshp* 1919
Sales 208.6MM *EMP* 180
Accts Anchin Block & Anchin Llp Ne
SIC 1541 8742 Industrial buildings & warehouses; Industrial buildings, new construction; Construction project management consultant; Industrial buildings & warehouses; Industrial buildings, new construction; Construction project management consultant
CEO: Jack Holt
Pr: Christopher Asaro
COO: Phil Stiller
CFO: Matthew Anselmi
VP: Dennis Berg
VP: Jay Holt
Genl Mgr: John Coppinger
Off Mgr: Jen Cogliano
Snr PM: Mark Phillips
Snr Mgr: John Haelen

D-U-N-S 00-648-3978
HOLT ELECTRICAL SUPPLIES INC (MO)
1943 S Vandeventer Ave, Saint Louis, MO 63110-3219
Tel (314) 533-5555 *Founded/Ownrshp* 1963
Sales 55.1MM^E *EMP* 56^E
SIC 5063 Electrical supplies
Pr: Sylvan Holtzman
VP: Douglas Holtzman
Off Mgr: Vicki Serfling
Opers Mgr: Tom Graham
Sales Exec: Mike Holt
Sales Asso: Tim Eaves

D-U-N-S 08-179-9194
HOLT EQUIPMENT CO LLC
4508 River Rd, Louisville, KY 40222-6113
Tel (502) 899-7513 *Founded/Ownrshp* 1999
Sales 107.5MM^E *EMP* 500
SIC 5082 General construction machinery & equipment; General construction machinery & equipment
Manager: Kent Able

D-U-N-S 00-323-0174 IMP/EXP
HOLT HOSIERY MILLS INC (NC)
733 Koury Dr, Burlington, NC 27215-6720
Tel (336) 227-1431 *Founded/Ownrshp* 1947
Sales 30.5MM^E *EMP* 200
SIC 2252

D-U-N-S 96-986-4305
HOLT LUNSFORD COMMERCIAL INC
5055 Keller Springs Rd # 300, Addison, TX 75001-5997
Tel (972) 241-8300 *Founded/Ownrshp* 1992
Sales 21.3MM^E *EMP* 79
SIC 6531 Real estate leasing & rentals
Pr: Richard H Lunsford
**COO:* David Parker
**CFO:* Douglas A Lueders
Sr VP: Kirt Rimpela
VP: David Cason
VP: Ken Newman
Mktg Dir: Chance Olin
Mktg Dir: Donnie Rohde
Snr Mgr: John McGee
Snr Mgr: Cris Ruiz
Snr Mgr: Keith Shankle

D-U-N-S 02-865-9787 IMP
HOLT OF CALIFORNIA
(*Suby of* HOC HOLDINGS INC) ★
7310 Pacific Ave, Pleasant Grove, CA 95668-9708
Tel (916) 991-8200 *Founded/Ownrshp* 1999
Sales 384.9MM^E *EMP* 734
SIC 5082 5084 5083 7359 Construction & mining machinery; Tractors, construction; Materials handling machinery; Agricultural machinery; Equipment rental & leasing; Construction & mining machinery; Tractors, construction; Materials handling machinery; Agricultural machinery; Equipment rental & leasing
Pr: Kenneth Monroe
**Ch Bd:* Victor Wykoff Jr
**CFO:* Daniel Johns
**V Ch Bd:* Gordon Beatie
**Ex VP:* Ronald Monroe
VP: Cary Roulet
Brnch Mgr: Chad Reed
Sfty Dirs: Sean Sasser
Sfty Mgr: Nathan Ladd
Manager: Bart Millard
Sls Mgr: Julian Ramirez

D-U-N-S 02-266-5731
HOLT PAPER AND CHEMICAL CO INC
31375 John Deere Dr, Salisbury, MD 21804-1412
Tel (410) 742-7577 *Founded/Ownrshp* 1961
Sales 86.1MM^E *EMP* 90
SIC 5142 5087 5113 5147 Packaged frozen goods; Janitors' supplies; Industrial & personal service paper; Cups, disposable plastic & paper; Towels, paper; Meats & meat products; Packaged frozen goods; Janitors' supplies; Industrial & personal service paper; Cups, disposable plastic & paper; Towels, paper; Meats & meat products
Ch Bd: John T Holt III
**Treas:* Scott Booth
Sls Mgr: Alicha Toms

D-U-N-S 04-056-9030
HOLT PUBLIC SCHOOLS
5780 Holt Rd, Holt, MI 48842-1197
Tel (517) 699-1106 *Founded/Ownrshp* 1880
Sales 32.2MM^E *EMP* 588
SIC 8211 Elementary & secondary schools; Elementary & secondary schools

D-U-N-S 17-545-1962 IMP
HOLT SALES AND SERVICE INC
EXCEL DISTRIBUTORS
2000 E Walnut St, Des Moines, IA 50317-2267
Tel (515) 266-6406 *Founded/Ownrshp* 1997
Sales 26.7MM^E *EMP* 37
SIC 5013 3714 Truck parts & accessories; Wheel rims, motor vehicle
Pr: Samuel M Holt
Sls Mgr: Clark Symington

D-U-N-S 00-321-3410
HOLT SUBLIMATION PRINTING & PRODUCTS INC
2208 Airpark Rd, Burlington, NC 27215-8824
Tel (336) 222-3600 *Founded/Ownrshp* 2000
Sales 38.9MM^E *EMP* 160
SIC 2261 2262 2789 Printing of cotton broadwoven fabrics; Printing: manmade fiber & silk broadwoven fabrics; Bookbinding & related work; Printing of cotton broadwoven fabrics; Printing: manmade fiber & silk broadwoven fabrics; Bookbinding & related work
CEO: Frank Holt III
IT Man: Sean Finnerty
IT Man: Carin Ludlow

D-U-N-S 00-813-4959 EXP
HOLT TEXAS LTD
ENERGY COMPRESSION SYSTEMS
3302 S Ww White Rd, San Antonio, TX 78222-4830
Tel (210) 648-1111 *Founded/Ownrshp* 1987
Sales 617.5MM^E *EMP* 1,700
SIC 3531 5082 7353 7699 Dozers, tractor mounted: material moving; Road construction & maintenance machinery; Excavating machinery & equipment; Heavy construction equipment rental; Construction equipment repair; Dozers, tractor mounted: material moving; Road construction & maintenance machinery; Excavating machinery & equipment; Heavy construction equipment rental; Construction equipment repair
CEO: Peter M Holt
**Pr:* Allyn Archer
**CFO:* Paul Hensley
CFO: Kenneth Kamp
**Ch:* Benjamin D Holt
Sr VP: Edward Craner
VP: Charles Strickland
VP: Chuck Strickland
Genl Mgr: Patrick Ereynolds
Genl Mgr: Patrick Reynolds
Genl Mgr: Scott Serrine

D-U-N-S 17-553-7810 IMP/EXP
HOLTEC INTERNATIONAL
1 Holtec Dr, Marlton, NJ 08053-3462
Tel (856) 797-0900 *Founded/Ownrshp* 2006
Sales 305.3MM *EMP* 800
Accts Ernst & Young Llp Philadelph
SIC 2819 8711 Engineering services; Nuclear fuel scrap, reprocessing; Nuclear fuel scrap, reprocessing; Engineering services
CEO: Kris Singh
**CFO:* Frank Bongrazio
**Ex VP:* Alan Soler
**Sr VP:* Pierre Paul Oneid
**Sr VP:* William S Woodward
Sr VP: William Woodward
VP: Bruce Hinkley
Prgrm Mgr: Holtec Tindal
CTO: Carmen Mazzagatti
Ql Cn Mgr: Mark Solars

D-U-N-S 02-542-9861
HOLTEN MEAT INC
(*Suby of* BRANDING IRON HOLDINGS INC) ★
1682 Sauget Business Blvd, Sauget, IL 62206-1454
Tel (618) 337-8400 *Founded/Ownrshp* 1960
Sales 20.2MM^E *EMP* 90
SIC 2013 Frozen meats from purchased meat; Frozen meats from purchased meat
Pr: Michael Holten
COO: Robert S Hudspeth
COO: Scott Hudspeth
**CFO:* Craig Allen
VP: Bryan Long
Rgnl Mgr: Earl Lavelle
Area Mgr: Tripp James
Area Mgr: Rich Larose
QA Dir: Patrick Flanigan
QA Dir: Patrick Muellerkalin
VP Mfg: Bill Gwinn

D-U-N-S 02-318-8774
HOLTGER BROS INC
H B I
950 W Main Ave, De Pere, WI 54115-9349
Tel (920) 337-9980 *Founded/Ownrshp* 1963
Sales 33.1MM^E *EMP* 98
SIC 1623 Telephone & communication line construction; Cable laying construction; Electric power line construction
Pr: Donald J Holtger
**Treas:* Lorraine Holtger
**VP:* Jeffrey Holtger
Genl Mgr: Dave Winkler

D-U-N-S 78-553-0635
HOLTHOUSE CARLIN VAN TRIGT LLP
11444 W Olympic Blvd # 11, Los Angeles, CA 90064-1500
Tel (310) 477-5551 *Founded/Ownrshp* 1991
Sales 36.1MM^E *EMP* 250
SIC 8721 Certified public accountant; Certified public accountant
Mng Pt: Philip Holthouse
Sr Pt: Julie Miller
**Pt:* David Bierhorst
**Pt:* James Carlin
**Pt:* Blake Christian
**Pt:* Greg Hutchins
**Pt:* Zach Shuman
**Pt:* Norman Tamkin
**Pt:* John Van Trigt
**Pt:* William Warburton
Sr VP: James Heinz
VP: Bill Dreker
Exec: Jim Heinz

D-U-N-S 00-424-2864
HOLTON INC
ICC COLLISION CENTER
3131 S Standard Ave, Santa Ana, CA 92705-5642
Tel (714) 444-3100 *Founded/Ownrshp* 2008
Sales 24.9MM *EMP* 1
SIC 7532 Top & body repair & paint shops; Top & body repair & paint shops
Pr: Hamid Hojati

D-U-N-S 09-504-5720
HOLTON PUBLIC SCHOOLS USD 336
515 Pennsylvania Ave, Holton, KS 66436-1859
Tel (785) 364-4853 *Founded/Ownrshp* 1965
Sales 14.8M *EMP* 277
SIC 8211 Public elementary & secondary schools; Public elementary & secondary schools
Instr Medi: Cynthia Cummings

D-U-N-S 07-264-0121
HOLTON-ARMS SCHOOL INC
7303 River Rd, Bethesda, MD 20817-4697
Tel (301) 365-5300 *Founded/Ownrshp* 1901
Sales 33.4MM *EMP* 171
Accts Mcgladrey Llp Gaithersburg M
SIC 8211 Private combined elementary & secondary school
Pr: Susanna A Jones
**CFO:* Kathleen Defranco
Exec: Dorothy Durden
Prgrm Mgr: Mary Warth
DP Exec: Laura Greer
Dir IT: Brad Rathgeber
Board of Directors: Anthony Shawe

HOLT'S CIGAR CO
See HOLTS CIGAR HOLDINGS INC

D-U-N-S 00-507-4674 IMP
HOLTS CIGAR HOLDINGS INC (DE)
HOLT'S CIGAR CO
12270 Townsend Rd, Philadelphia, PA 19154-1203
Tel (215) 676-8778 *Founded/Ownrshp* 1993
Sales 33.1MM^E *EMP* 75
SIC 5194 5993 Cigars; Cigar store; Cigars; Cigar store
Pr: Robert G Levin
**COO:* Michael Pitkow
**Bd of Dir:* Carlos P Fuente Sr
**Bd of Dir:* Marvin B Sharfstein
IT Man: Rick George
IT Man: Marc Radovich
IT Man: Andrew Wise
Opers Mgr: Debbie Crawford
Sls Dir: Michael Walter

D-U-N-S 01-439-0582
HOLTZBRINCK PUBLISHERS LLC
MACMILLAN
(*Suby of* M P S) ★
175 5th Ave, New York, NY 10010-7703
Tel (646) 307-5151 *Founded/Ownrshp* 1998
Sales 166.6MM^E *EMP* 1,446^E
SIC 2731

D-U-N-S 00-895-8563
HOLTZINGER FRUIT CO INC
1312 N 6th Ave, Yakima, WA 98902-1420
Tel (509) 457-5115 *Founded/Ownrshp* 1955
Sales 99.7MM^E *EMP* 500
SIC 5148 4222 Fruits, fresh; Warehousing, cold storage or refrigerated; Fruits, fresh; Warehousing, cold storage or refrigerated
Pr: Charles Holtzinger
Sls Mgr: Steve Black

HOLTZMAN EQUIPMENT & CNSTR DIV
See HOLTZMAN OIL CORP

D-U-N-S 05-917-0829
HOLTZMAN OIL CORP
HOLTZMAN EQUIPMENT & CNSTR DIV
5534 Main St, Mount Jackson, VA 22842-9508
Tel (540) 477-3131 *Founded/Ownrshp* 1972
Sales 65.1MM^E *EMP* 110
SIC 5172 Petroleum products; Petroleum products
Pr: Bill Holtzman
**VP:* Richard Koontz

D-U-N-S 06-432-4069
HOLY ANGELS RESIDENTIAL FACILITY
10450 Ellerbe Rd, Shreveport, LA 71106-7730
Tel (318) 797-9070 *Founded/Ownrshp* 2001
Sales 14.8MM *EMP* 300
Accts Deborah D Dees Cpa/Cff Mba
SIC 8741 Nursing & personal care facility management; Nursing & personal care facility management
Pr: Gary Loftin
Dir Vol: Elizabeth Buhler
**CEO:* Laurie Boswell

D-U-N-S 96-405-7710
HOLY AVERA FAMILY
AVERA HOLY FAMILY HEALTH
826 N 8th St, Estherville, IA 51334-1528
Tel (712) 362-2631 *Founded/Ownrshp* 2010
Sales 26.1MM *EMP* 4
Accts Eide Bailly Llp Minneapolis
SIC 8011 Offices & clinics of medical doctors; Offices & clinics of medical doctors
Prin: Connie Thackery
CFO: Shannon Adams
Cmptr Lab: Julie Duitsman
VP Opers: Sean Halligan
Pharmcst: April Krull

D-U-N-S 19-601-5648
HOLY CARITAS FAMILY HOSPITAL INC
HOLY FAMILY HOSPITAL & MED CTR
(*Suby of* CARITAS CHRISTI HEALTH CARE) ★
70 East St, Methuen, MA 01844-4597
Tel (978) 687-0156 *Founded/Ownrshp* 1984
Sales 103.1MM^E *EMP* 1,700
Accts Feeley & Driscoll Pc Boston
SIC 8062 General medical & surgical hospitals; General medical & surgical hospitals
Ch Bd: Peter Gori
**Pr:* Thomas Sager
Trst: William Edwards
Trst: Thomas Hoerner
Ex VP: Joseph Maher Jr
Dir Rad: Katherine Miller
Chf Nrs Of: Kathleen Veilleux
Dir Sec: Jim Deroche
Mktg Dir: Danielle Perry
Doctor: Dhirendra Pathak
Pharmcst: Tracy Martino

HOLY CROSS CATHOLIC CHURCH
See DIOCESE OF LITTLE ROCK

HOLY CROSS CHILDREN'S SERVICES
See BOYSVILLE OF MICHIGAN INC

D-U-N-S 00-477-5599
HOLY CROSS ELECTRIC ASSOCIATION INC
HOLY CROSS ENERGY
3799 Highway 82, Glenwood Springs, CO 81601-9349
Tel (970) 945-5491 *Founded/Ownrshp* 1939
Sales 121.3MM *EMP* 155
Accts Dreyer & Kelso Pc Pa Glenwood
SIC 4911 Distribution, electric power; Distribution, electric power
Pr: Michael Glass
**Treas:* Robert Gardner
Treas: Dave Munk
Bd of Dir: Hal Clark
**VP:* Megan Gilman
Mng Dir: Steve Casey
Off Mgr: Monica Holmes
IT Man: Rick Arnhold
IT Man: Ted Jessup
Sfty Dirs: Thomas Maddalone

HOLY CROSS ENERGY
See HOLY CROSS ELECTRIC ASSOCIATION INC

D-U-N-S 07-429-6930
HOLY CROSS HEALTH INC
CATHOLIC HEALTH EAST
(*Suby of* CATHOLIC HEALTH EAST) ★
1500 Forest Glen Rd, Silver Spring, MD 20910-1460
Tel (301) 754-7000 *Founded/Ownrshp* 1978
Sales 442.7MM *EMP* 3,270
Accts Deloitte & Touche Llp Philade
SIC 8062 General medical & surgical hospitals; General medical & surgical hospitals
Pr: Kevin Sexton
Chf Path: R Snyder
COO: Khoury Bernie
CFO: Stephen Bush
**CFO:* Anne Dgillis
**VP:* Eileen Cahill
**VP:* Patrick Connely
Dir Case M: Jan Deroche
Dir Case M: Ed Grant
Dir Lab: Jay Marchwinski
Dir Lab: Mary Milling
Dir Rad: Mike Hanbury

HOLY CROSS HOSPITAL
See TAOS HEALTH SYSTEMS INC

D-U-N-S 01-059-1055
HOLY CROSS HOSPITAL
2701 W 68th St, Chicago, IL 60629-1882
Tel (773) 884-9000 *Founded/Ownrshp* 1928
Sales 132.9MM *EMP* 1,600
Accts Mcgladrey Llp Chicago Il
SIC 8062 8011 General medical & surgical hospitals; Offices & clinics of medical doctors; General medical & surgical hospitals; Offices & clinics of medical doctors
Pr: Mark Clement
Chf Path: Adil Zarif
Chf Rad: Frank Marmo
CFO: Rene' Suntay
Ofcr: Lori Pacura
VP: Neil Murphy
Exec: Katherine Roddy
Dir Risk M: Georgiana Barley
Dir Lab: Catherine Matula
Dir Rx: Nosakhare Osayamwen
Mng Ofcr: Anthony Bozzano

D-U-N-S 07-222-8851
HOLY CROSS HOSPITAL INC
CATHOLIC HEALTH EAST
(*Suby of* CATHOLIC HEALTH EAST) ★
4725 N Federal Hwy, Fort Lauderdale, FL 33308-4668
Tel (954) 771-8000 *Founded/Ownrshp* 1998
Sales 20.9MM *EMP* 2,300
SIC 8062 General medical & surgical hospitals; General medical & surgical hospitals
CEO: Patrick Taylor
Dir Recs: Jay Schatz
Dir Vol: Abbie Klaits
**COO:* Richard Brown
**CFO:* Linda Wilford
Ofcr: Taren Ruggiero
VP: Dennis Ryan
Dir Lab: Valerie Conigilio
Dir Lab: Bart Musial
Dir Rad: Cindy Siegel
Chf Nrs Of: Sheila Mischke

D-U-N-S 88-487-2102
HOLY CROSS HOSPITAL INC
CARONDELET HOLY CROSS HOSPITAL
1171 W Target Range Rd A, Nogales, AZ 85621-2415
Tel (520) 287-2771 *Founded/Ownrshp* 1987
Sales 27.8MM^E *EMP* 245
Accts Deloitte Tax Llp Cincinnati
SIC 8062 8051 General medical & surgical hospitals; Skilled nursing care facilities; General medical & surgical hospitals; Skilled nursing care facilities
Pr: Wanona Fritz
**Ch Bd:* Juby Bell
COO: Roberta B Kaemmerling
CFO: Carlos Carreon
CFO: Tom R Pepping
**VP:* Rich Polehber
VP: Rich Pulhepur
Dir OR: Catharine Fairbanks
Dir Rad: Connie Smith
Dir Env Sv: Maritza Gonzalez
IT Man: Bob Dupre

HOLY CROSS MCC
See HOLY CROSS METROPOLITAN COMMUNITY CHURCH INC

D-U-N-S 82-769-2617
HOLY CROSS METROPOLITAN COMMUNITY CHURCH INC
HOLY CROSS MCC
3130 W Fairfield Dr, Pensacola, FL 32505-4966
Tel (850) 469-9090 *Founded/Ownrshp* 1977
Sales 5.1MM^E *EMP* 300
SIC 8661 Community church; Community church

D-U-N-S 08-301-6829
HOLY CROSS SERVICES CORP
100 Lourdes Hall, Notre Dame, IN 46556-5014
Tel (574) 284-5660 *Founded/Ownrshp* 1997
Sales 7.7MM^E *EMP* 300
SIC 8059 8661 8052 Nursing home, except skilled & intermediate care facility; Religious organizations; Intermediate care facilities; Nursing home, except skilled & intermediate care facility; Religious organizations; Intermediate care facilities
CEO: Judith Johns
**Pr:* Sr Aline Marie
Treas: Marilyn Zugish
**VP:* Sr Anna Mae
**VP:* Sr Joan Marie
**VP:* Sr M Veronique
Off Admin: Kim Brunner

D-U-N-S 10-234-3662
HOLY FAMILY CONVENT
2409 S Alverno Rd, Manitowoc, WI 54220-9340
Tel (920) 682-7728 *Founded/Ownrshp* 1867
Sales 10.2MM^E *EMP* 600
SIC 8661 8051 Convent; Skilled nursing care facilities; Convent; Skilled nursing care facilities
Prin: Sister Greta Peter

HOLY FAMILY HOSPITAL
See PROVIDENCE HEALTH CARE

HOLY FAMILY HOSPITAL & MED CTR
See HOLY CARITAS FAMILY HOSPITAL INC

D-U-N-S 09-421-2446
HOLY FAMILY INSTITUTE
8235 Ohio River Blvd, Pittsburgh, PA 15202-1594
Tel (412) 766-4030 *Founded/Ownrshp* 1943
Sales 12.1MM *EMP* 300
Accts Grossman Yanak & Ford Llp Pit
SIC 8361 Home for the emotionally disturbed; Home for the emotionally disturbed
Ch: Allen Woods
**Pr:* Sister Linda Yankoski
**CFO:* Mark Palastro

D-U-N-S 06-831-9755
HOLY FAMILY MEMORIAL INC (WI)
WOODLAND CLINIC
2300 Western Ave, Manitowoc, WI 54220-3712
Tel (920) 320-2011 *Founded/Ownrshp* 1890
Sales 123.9MM *EMP* 1,300
SIC 8062 General medical & surgical hospitals; General medical & surgical hospitals
CEO: Mark Herzog
Pr: Charles Laham
CFO: Patricia Huettl
**Ch:* William Casey
**Treas:* Donald Brisch
Bd of Dir: Jane Pfeffer
Ofcr: Andria Pekarek
Ex VP: Jane Curran-Meuli
**VP:* Pat Brandel
VP: Marcia Donlon
Dir OR: Lisa Sherman
Dir Lab: Linda Couron
Dir Rx: Greg Unertl
Dir Rx: Darlene Wiegand

HOLY FAMILY REG SCH-S CAMPUS
See ARCHDIOCESE OF DETROIT ED OFF

D-U-N-S 82-644-7237
HOLY FAMILY UNIVERSITY
9801 Frankford Ave, Philadelphia, PA 19114-2094
Tel (215) 637-7700 *Founded/Ownrshp* 1982
Sales 60.4MM *EMP* 637
Accts O Connell & Company Jenkintow
SIC 8221 Colleges universities & professional schools; Colleges universities & professional schools
Pr: Sister Maureen McGarrity
VP: Patrice Feher
VP: Mark Galgano
VP: Marilyn Gennett
VP: Robert Lafond
VP: Jim Trusdell
VP: Ann Vickery
Assoc Dir: Gidget Montelibano
CTO: Michelle Foley
Mktg Dir: Allen Arndt

D-U-N-S 15-102-3439
HOLY INNOCENTS EPISCOPAL SCHOOL INC
805 Mount Vernon Hwy, Atlanta, GA 30327-4338
Tel (404) 303-2150 *Founded/Ownrshp* 1959
Sales 27.4MM^E *EMP* 225
SIC 8211 Private elementary & secondary schools; Private elementary & secondary schools
CEO: David Galloway
VP: Kathryn Edmunds
Ex Dir: Ruth Donahoo
Dir IT: Alison Schultz
Pr Dir: Peggy Shaw
Psych: Jean Jordan

D-U-N-S 07-544-0149 EXP
HOLY NAME MEDICAL CENTER INC
718 Teaneck Rd, Teaneck, NJ 07666-4245
Tel (201) 833-3000 *Founded/Ownrshp* 1925
Sales 313.1MM *EMP* 1,800^E
Accts Withumsmithbrown Pc Morristow
SIC 8062 General medical & surgical hospitals; Hospital, professional nursing school; General medical & surgical hospitals; Hospital, professional nursing school
Pr: Michael Maron
Chf Rad: Jacquelin Brunetti
Pr: Jill Valdec
**CFO:* Gregory Adams
VP: Jane Ellis
VP: Cynthia Kaufhold
VP: Celeste Oranchak
VP: Beverly Sanborn
VP: Patricia White
Exec: Steven Cicala
Prac Mgr: Juliana Avalo

D-U-N-S 07-907-9893
HOLY NAMES UNIVERSITY (CA)
3500 Mountain Blvd, Oakland, CA 94619-1699
Tel (510) 436-1000 *Founded/Ownrshp* 1868
Sales 41.9MM *EMP* 740
Accts Rk Taylor & Associates Walnut
SIC 8221 College, except junior; College, except junior
CEO: William Hynes
**Pr:* Sister Rosemarie Nassif
VP: Josh Hammer

D-U-N-S 15-091-3234
HOLY REDEEMER HEALTH SYSTEM INC
667 Welsh Rd Ste 300, Huntingdon Valley, PA 19006-6308
Tel (215) 938-0180 *Founded/Ownrshp* 1985
Sales 287.2MM *EMP* 3,800
SIC 8082 Visiting nurse service; Visiting nurse service
Pr: Michael B Laign
COO: Mark Jones
COO: Lawrence Roth
CFO: John Morozin
**CFO:* Russell Wagnes
Ofcr: Nicholas Murphy
Ex VP: Anthony Coletta
**Sr VP:* Denise Collins
Sr VP: Patrick Kennedy
Sr VP: John Kepner
VP: Teresa Giannetti
VP: Nancy Mandes
Dir: Barbara Tantum
Dir Rx: Randie Oberlender

D-U-N-S 15-091-2517
HOLY REDEEMER HEALTHCARE SYSTEM
(*Suby of* HOLY REDEEMER HEALTH SYSTEM INC) ★
667 Welsh Rd Ste 300, Huntingdon Valley, PA 19006-6308
Tel (215) 938-0180 *Founded/Ownrshp* 1999
Sales 30.8MM[E] *EMP* 2,000
SIC 8099 Blood related health services; Blood related health services
Pr: Michael Laign
COO: Mark Jones

HOLY ROSARY EXTENDED CARE
See HOLY ROSARY HEALTHCARE FOUNDATION INC

D-U-N-S 01-036-3570
HOLY ROSARY HEALTHCARE FOUNDATION INC (MT)
HOLY ROSARY EXTENDED CARE
(*Suby of* SCL HEALTH SYSTEM) ★
2600 Wilson St Stop 1, Miles City, MT 59301-5095
Tel (406) 233-2600 *Founded/Ownrshp* 1910
Sales 834.0M *EMP* 426
Accts Ernst & Young Us Llp Clayton
SIC 8062 8051 8011 General medical & surgical hospitals; Skilled nursing care facilities; Offices & clinics of medical doctors; General medical & surgical hospitals; Skilled nursing care facilities; Offices & clinics of medical doctors
CEO: Gregory Nielsen
Genl Mgr: Calvin Carey
Genl Mgr: Sharan Taylor

HOLY ROSARY MEDICAL CENTER
See DOMINICAN SISTERS OF ONTARIO INC

D-U-N-S 06-485-1223
HOLY SPIRIT ASSOCIATION FOR UNIFICATION OF WORLD CHRISTIANITY
HSA-UWC
4 W 43rd St, New York, NY 10036-7408
Tel (212) 997-0050 *Founded/Ownrshp* 1961
Sales 33.4MM[E] *EMP* 300
SIC 8661 Religious organizations; Religious organizations
Pr: Tatiana Moon
Treas: Eric Holt
VP: Joshua Cotter

D-U-N-S 07-119-5630
HOLY SPIRIT HOSPITAL OF SISTERS OF CHRISTIAN CHARITY
503 N 21st St, Camp Hill, PA 17011-2288
Tel (717) 763-2100 *Founded/Ownrshp* 1956
Sales 364.2MM[E] *EMP* 2,698
Accts Parentebeard Llc Williamsport
SIC 8062 General medical & surgical hospitals; General medical & surgical hospitals
Pr: Romaine Niemeyer
Chf Rad: Paul Licata
Dir Recs: Stacey Nolte
**Pr:* Sister Romaine Niemeyer
COO: Richard A Schaffner
CFO: Manny Evans
CFO: Rhonda Hake
Ofcr: Amy Cook
Ofcr: AMI Zumkhawala-Cook
VP: Thomas Yucha
Exec: Kelly McMillan
Exec: Dennis Michaels
Dir Inf Cn: Joanne Adkins
Dir Risk M: Ellen Feidt
Dir Risk M: Kay Tipton
Dir Lab: Michael McCurdy
Dir Lab: Jeff Seiple
Dir Rad: Anna Kinney
Dir Rx: Charles Arrison
Board of Directors: Sara Brooks

D-U-N-S 87-804-2548
HOLYOKE COMMUNITY COLLEGE
(*Suby of* MASSACHUSETTS BOARD OF HIGHER EDUCATION SYSTEM) ★
303 Homestead Ave, Holyoke, MA 01040-1091
Tel (413) 538-7000 *Founded/Ownrshp* 1946
Sales 2.3MM *EMP* 360
Accts O Connor & Drew Pc Braintre
SIC 8221 9199 College, except junior; ; College, except junior;
Pr: William Messner
Pr: Colleen Cameron
**CFO:* William Fogarty
VP: Erica Broman
VP: Anthony Pellegrino
Store Mgr: Steven Duffany
CTO: Ted Steensen
CTO: Ted Steesen
CTO: Linda Szalankiewicz
CTO: Linda Szlankiewicz
IT Man: Luanne Neves

HOLYOKE FINE HOMES
See LEWIS LEASE CRUTCHER WA LLC

D-U-N-S 15-361-6263
HOLYOKE HEALTH CENTER INC
230 Maple St Ste 1, Holyoke, MA 01040-5140
Tel (413) 420-2200 *Founded/Ownrshp* 1970
Sales 36.6MM *EMP* 120
Accts Bkd Llp Springfield Missour
SIC 8093 Specialty outpatient clinics; Specialty outpatient clinics
CEO: Jay Breines
**Pr:* Benjamin Cartagena
**CFO:* Michael Germani
CFO: Patrick Lavelle
**Treas:* William Rosario
Dir Rx: Tracey Cole
Doctor: Lois C Albury MD
Pharmcst: Linda Robins

D-U-N-S 06-697-5657
HOLYOKE MEDICAL CENTER INC
(*Suby of* VALLEY HEALTH SYSTEMS INC) ★
575 Beech St, Holyoke, MA 01040-2223
Tel (413) 534-2554 *Founded/Ownrshp* 1984
Sales 120.8MM *EMP* 1,250
Accts Pricewaterhousecoopers Llp Ha
SIC 8062 General medical & surgical hospitals; General medical & surgical hospitals
Pr: Spiridon E Hatiras
**Pr:* Hank J Porten
**Treas:* Antonio Correia
VP: Clark Fenn
VP: Michael A Zwirko
Dir OR: Patricia Tobey
Dir Lab: Thomas Gould
Dir Rx: David Gamblin
Genl Mgr: Gina Lucchesi
Off Mgr: Cynthia Gervais
MIS Dir: Todd McDermott

D-U-N-S 00-143-5908
HOLYOKE NEWS CO INC (MA)
720 Main St Ste 1, Holyoke, MA 01040-5397
Tel (413) 534-4537 *Founded/Ownrshp* 1958, 1977
Sales 26.6MM[E] *EMP* 85
SIC 5192 Magazines; Newspapers; Books
Pr: Eitan Evan
**Treas:* Malka Evan
**VP:* Michael Putira

D-U-N-S 10-003-1863
HOLYOKE PUBLIC SCHOOLS
57 Suffolk St Ste 101, Holyoke, MA 01040-5015
Tel (413) 534-2000 *Founded/Ownrshp* 1983
Sales 10.6MM[E] *EMP* 946[E]
SIC 8211 Public elementary & secondary schools
**Prin:* Eduardo Carballo
Dir IT: Ramon Rivera
Teacher Pr: Jennifer Boulias

D-U-N-S 02-325-7363
HOLZ MOTORS INC
5961 S 108th Pl, Hales Corners, WI 53130-2501
Tel (414) 425-2400 *Founded/Ownrshp* 1949
Sales 100.0MM *EMP* 190
SIC 5012 All-terrain vehicles; Dunebuggies; Automotive parts; Body shop, automotive; Automobiles & other motor vehicles
Pr: Jerome J Holz
**VP:* Douglas Nalbert
Sls Mgr: Mark Fleischmann

D-U-N-S 09-972-8776
HOLZER CLINIC LLC
HOLZER HEALTH CENTER
90 Jackson Pike, Gallipolis, OH 45631-1562
Tel (740) 446-5411 *Founded/Ownrshp* 1950
Sales 73.6MM[E] *EMP* 842
SIC 8011 8741 Physicians' office, including specialists; Management services; Physicians' office, including specialists; Management services
CEO: Christopher T Meyer
**Pr:* Craig Strafford
Treas: Jon Sullivan
IT Man: Doris Runyon
Surgeon: Ronn Grandia
Opthamlgy: Naci I Bozkir
Podiatrist: Nathan Clark
Diag Rad: Michael Myers

D-U-N-S 06-493-4081
HOLZER CONSOLIDATED HEALTH SYSTEMS INC
100 Jackson Pike, Gallipolis, OH 45631-1560
Tel (740) 446-5060 *Founded/Ownrshp* 1985
Sales 175.9MM *EMP* 1,500
Accts Plante & Moran Pllc Columbus
SIC 8062 General medical & surgical hospitals; General medical & surgical hospitals
Pr: Brent Saundrs

HOLZER HEALTH CENTER
See HOLZER CLINIC LLC

D-U-N-S 04-964-5104
HOLZER HOSPITAL FOUNDATION INC
HOLZER MEDICAL CENTER
100 Jackson Pike, Gallipolis, OH 45631-1560
Tel (740) 446-5000 *Founded/Ownrshp* 1929
Sales 140.7MM *EMP* 1,000
Accts Plante & Moran Pllc Columbus
SIC 8062 General medical & surgical hospitals; General medical & surgical hospitals
Pr: James Phillippe
Chf Rad: Phillip Long
COO: Ronald Saunders
**CFO:* Kevin Yeager
Ex VP: John Cunningham
Dir OR: Sue Gilliam
Dir Teleco: Kevin Waller
Dir Lab: Shari Kebler
Dir Rx: Matt Scola
IT Man: Mike Lavalle
Software D: Susan King

HOLZER MEDICAL CENTER
See HOLZER HOSPITAL FOUNDATION INC

D-U-N-S 79-029-5286
HOLZER MEDICAL CENTER - JACKSON
500 Burlington Rd, Jackson, OH 45640-9360
Tel (740) 288-4625 *Founded/Ownrshp* 2000
Sales 35.2MM *EMP* 285
SIC 8062 General medical & surgical hospitals; General medical & surgical hospitals
Pr: Ross A Matlack
**VP:* Rhonda Dailey
Exec: Hope Bauer
Doctor: Morgan Paul
Phys Thrpy: Traci Good

D-U-N-S 96-952-7915
HOLZER MEDICAL CENTER - JACKSON
100 Jackson Pike, Gallipolis, OH 45631-1560
Tel (740) 446-5060 *Founded/Ownrshp* 2011
Sales 35.2MM *EMP* 4[E]
Accts Plante & Moran Pllc Columbus
SIC 8011 General & family practice, physician/surgeon; General & family practice, physician/surgeon
Ch: Brent A Saunders

D-U-N-S 02-568-1768
HOLZHAUER CITY FORD-MERCURY INC
17933 Hlzhuer Automall Dr, Nashville, IL 62263-3413
Tel (618) 327-8264 *Founded/Ownrshp* 1993
Sales 23.6MM *EMP* 42
SIC 5511 Automobiles, new & used; Automobiles, new & used
Owner: Allan Holzhauer
**Pr:* Brad Holzhauer

D-U-N-S 01-042-2897 IMP
HOM FURNITURE INC
JC IMPORTS
10301 Woodcrest Dr Nw, Minneapolis, MN 55433-6519
Tel (763) 767-3600 *Founded/Ownrshp* 1973
Sales 222.2MM[E] *EMP* 950
SIC 5712 Furniture stores; Furniture stores
Ch Bd: Wayne Johansen
**Pr:* Rodney Johansen
Store Dir: Greg Bailey
Genl Mgr: Cameron Johnston
Store Mgr: Ken Coyne
QA Dir: Stacy Czapiewski
Merch Mgr: Kyle Johansen
Sls Mgr: Brenda Becker
Sls Mgr: Brian Gaspard
Sls Mgr: John Nelson
Sls Mgr: Pamela Pike

HOMAN LUMBER MART I
See HOMAN LUMBER MART INC

D-U-N-S 01-626-8765
HOMAN LUMBER MART INC
HOMAN LUMBER MART I
1650 W Lusher Ave, Elkhart, IN 46517-1420
Tel (574) 293-6595 *Founded/Ownrshp* 1972
Sales 30.8MM[E] *EMP* 50
SIC 5031 Lumber: rough, dressed & finished
Pr: Robert William Homan
**VP:* Edna Homan
Mktg Dir: Christopher Ferro

D-U-N-S 00-142-6477 IMP
■ **HOMANS ASSOCIATES LLC**
(*Suby of* BAKER DISTRIBUTING CO LLC) ★
250 Ballardvale St Ste 4, Wilmington, MA 01887-1058
Tel (978) 988-9692 *Founded/Ownrshp* 2007
Sales 37.7MM[E] *EMP* 133
SIC 5033 Insulation materials; Insulation materials
Ofcr: Wayne Bailey
**Ex VP:* Rich Iandoli
**VP:* Greg Morin
Brnch Mgr: Jim Gogarty
Brnch Mgr: Jeff Macclintic
Sls Mgr: Gilles Dionne
Sls Mgr: Larry Giunta
Sales Asso: Roger Bourassa
Sales Asso: Steve Lento

D-U-N-S 00-232-8250
HOMASOTE CO (INC) (NJ)
932 Lower Ferry Rd, Ewing, NJ 08628-3298
Tel (609) 883-3300 *Founded/Ownrshp* 1909
Sales 20.7MM *EMP* 107
Tkr Sym HMTC *Exch* OTO
SIC 2493 Insulation board, cellular fiber; Paper coated or laminated for packaging
Pr: Warren L Flicker
CFO: Ron Fafano
**CFO:* Ronald Fasano
Dir IT: Richard Mangan
**VP Opers:* Pete Tindall
Sfty Mgr: Bob Coleman
Mktg Dir: Greg O'Driscoll
Manager: Jon Downey
Manager: Paul Volkoff
Sls Mgr: Mike Sullivan

D-U-N-S 80-838-1722 IMP
■ **HOMAX GROUP INC**
(*Suby of* PPG INDUSTRIES INC) ★
1835 Barkley Blvd Ste 101, Bellingham, WA 98226-3200
Tel (360) 733-9029 *Founded/Ownrshp* 2014
Sales 42.5MM[E] *EMP* 270[E]
SIC 2851 2879 5198 2813 Paint removers; Insecticides & pesticides; Paints, varnishes & supplies; Aerosols; Paint removers; Insecticides & pesticides; Paints, varnishes & supplies; Aerosols
Pr: Ross Clawson
VP: Manu Bettegowda
**Prin:* Carolyn Resar
VP Sls: Katie Deegan

D-U-N-S 09-276-6278
HOMAX OIL SALES INC
CONOCO BULK DLR HOMAX OIL SLS
605 S Poplar St, Casper, WY 82601-2309
Tel (307) 237-5800 *Founded/Ownrshp* 1978
Sales 38.4MM[E] *EMP* 100
SIC 5172 5541 5411 Gasoline; Lubricating oils & greases; Filling stations, gasoline; Convenience stores, independent; Gasoline; Lubricating oils & greases; Filling stations, gasoline; Convenience stores, independent
Pr: Darren W Homer

HOMAX PRODUCTS
See PPG ARCHITECTURAL FINISHES INC

D-U-N-S 06-394-1850 IMP
■ **HOMAX PRODUCTS INC**
MAGIC HOMAX
(*Suby of* FLUID ENTERPRISES INC) ★
1835 Barkley Blvd Ste 101, Bellingham, WA 98226-3200
Tel (360) 733-9029 *Founded/Ownrshp* 1988
Sales 22.3MM[E] *EMP* 50[E]
SIC 5198 Paint brushes, rollers, sprayers
Pr: Ross W Clawson
**VP:* Manu Bettegowda
VP: Ray Mazur
**VP:* Jason Miller

HOMCO ACE HOME CENTER
See ODDS-N-ENDS INC

HOME & FLOWER SHOW
See MARKETPLACE EVENTS LLC

D-U-N-S 95-999-7602 IMP
HOME & GARDEN PARTY LTD
CELEBRATING HOME
2938 Brown Rd, Marshall, TX 75672-5373
Tel (903) 935-6643 *Founded/Ownrshp* 1992
Sales 65.0MM[E] *EMP* 325
SIC 5963 Direct selling establishments; Direct selling establishments
Genl Pt: Steve Carlile
Pt: Penny Carlile
Pt: Heather Chastain
CFO: Terry Kenyon
Ex VP: Jerry Benson
Ex VP: John Kiple
VP: Tony Phillips
VP: Wayne Wright
CIO: Curtis Grant
Dir IT: David Ingram
Dir IT: Jim Yauch

D-U-N-S 01-947-2331
HOME & HOSPICE CARE OF RHODE ISLAND (RI)
1085 N Main St, Providence, RI 02904-5719
Tel (401) 415-4202 *Founded/Ownrshp* 1976
Sales 32.5MM *EMP* 315[E]
Accts Marcum Llp Hartford Ct
SIC 8082 Home health care services; Home health care services
Ch: Kenneth Kermes
**Pr:* Diana Franchitto
**CFO:* Mary Macintosh
**VP:* Charles Iacono
**VP:* Tricia Keane
QC Dir: Virginia White

D-U-N-S 01-708-6836
HOME ACRES BUILDING SUPPLY CO LLC
5203 Division Ave S, Grand Rapids, MI 49548-5605
Tel (616) 534-4903 *Founded/Ownrshp* 1923
Sales 57.4MM[E] *EMP* 200
SIC 5211 5032 5033 5039

HOME AGAIN
See WELCOME HOME LLC

D-U-N-S 03-071-7891
HOME AIDE SERVICE OF EASTERN NEW YORK INC
433 River St Ste 3000, Troy, NY 12180-2250
Tel (518) 271-5000 *Founded/Ownrshp* 1958
Sales 34.2MM *EMP* 350
SIC 8082 Home health care services; Home health care services
VP: Michelle T Mazzacco

D-U-N-S 95-739-8618
HOME ATTENDANT SERVICE OF HYDE PARK INC
1273 53rd St, Brooklyn, NY 11219-3865
Tel (718) 972-1029 *Founded/Ownrshp* 2008
Sales 24.2MM *EMP* 1
Accts Rolando A Blancocpa Pllc Bald
SIC 8999 Services; Services
Prin: Hershel Bedansky

D-U-N-S 62-111-9650
HOME ATTENDANT VENDOR AGENCY INC
3036 Nostrand Ave, Brooklyn, NY 11229-1821
Tel (718) 253-3071 *Founded/Ownrshp* 1979
Sales 22.8MM *EMP* 31[E]
Accts Perelson Weiner Llp New York
SIC 8082 Home health care services; Home health care services
Pr: Kenneth A Rankin

D-U-N-S 82-878-9789
▲ **HOME BANCORP INC**
503 Kaliste Saloom Rd, Lafayette, LA 70508-4203
Tel (337) 237-1960 *Founded/Ownrshp* 2008
Sales NA *EMP* 182[E]
Tkr Sym HBCP *Exch* NGM
SIC 6035 Savings institutions, federally chartered; Savings institutions, federally chartered
Pr: John W Bordelon
**Ch Bd:* Michael P Maraist
COO: Jason P Freyou
CFO: Joseph B Zanco
Ex VP: Darren E Guidry
Ex VP: Joseph Zanco

D-U-N-S 14-181-8919
▲ **HOME BANCSHARES INC**
719 Harkrider St Ste 100, Conway, AR 72032-5619
Tel (501) 339-2929 *Founded/Ownrshp* 1989
Sales NA *EMP* 1,376[E]
Tkr Sym HOMB *Exch* NGS
SIC 6022 State commercial banks; State commercial banks

Pr: C Randall Sims
**Ch Bd:* John W Allison
COO: John Tipton
CFO: Brian S Davis
**V Ch Bd:* Robert H Adcock Jr
VP: Tish Cartwright
VP: Jenni Holbrook
IT Man: Mike Posey
Snr Mgr: Lamonica Johnston
Board of Directors: Milburn Adams, Richard H Ashley, Dale A Bruns, Richard A Buckheim, Jack E Engelkes, Tracy M French, James G Hinkle, Alex R Lieblong, Thomas J Longe

D-U-N-S 95-865-4907
■ HOME BANK NA
(*Suby of* HOME BANCORP INC) ★
503 Kaliste Saloom Rd, Lafayette, LA 70508-4203
Tel (337) 237-1960 *Founded/Ownrshp* 1908
Sales NA *EMP* 110
SIC 6035 Federal savings banks; Federal savings banks
Pr: John Bordelon
**Pr:* Sandi Chalmers
COO: Scott Sutton
Treas: David Kirkley
Ofcr: Judy Briscoe
Ofcr: Cindy Herpin
**Ex VP:* Darren E Guidry
**Ex VP:* Mary H Hopkins
Ex VP: Ben Strecker
Ex VP: Joseph Zanco
Sr VP: Lisa Arnold
VP: Gary L Broussard
VP: Ralph Edwards
VP: Eddie Gammon
VP: Dee Green
VP: Vangie Jolivette
VP: Karla McGibboney
VP: June Picard
VP: Dennis Pontiff
VP: Celeste Rushing
VP: Maggie Sonnier

D-U-N-S 13-824-4731 IMP
■ HOME BOX OFFICE INC
H B O
(*Suby of* WARNER COMMUNICATIONS INC) ★
1100 Ave Of The Ameri 42, New York, NY 10036-6712
Tel (212) 512-1000 *Founded/Ownrshp* 2003
Sales 456.8MM^E *EMP* 2,000
SIC 4841 7812

D-U-N-S 84-173-7455 IMP
HOME BREW MART INC
BALLAST PT BREWING & SPIRITS
9045 Carroll Way, San Diego, CA 92121-2405
Tel (858) 790-6900 *Founded/Ownrshp* 1992
Sales 180.6MM^E *EMP* 425
SIC 2082 5999 Ale (alcoholic beverage); Alcoholic beverage making equipment & supplies
CEO: Jim Buechler
**CEO:* Jack White
**COO:* Yuseff Cherney
**CFO:* Rick Morgan
VP: Colby Chandler
Board of Directors: James Buechler, Jack White Jr

HOME BUILDERS ASSN LOCAL
See UPPER PENINSULA BUILDERS ASSOCIATION

D-U-N-S 10-793-8771
HOME BUILDERS INSTITUTE
H B I
1201 15th St Nw Fl 6, Washington, DC 20005-2899
Tel (407) 846-5294 *Founded/Ownrshp* 1981
Sales 25.9MM *EMP* 250
Accts Tate & Tryon Washington Dc
SIC 8331 Job training services; Job training services
Ex Dir: Frederick Humphreys
**CFO:* Edward Harrison
CFO: Faye Harrison
Ex VP: C J Tirone
VP: Page Browning
VP: Lynne Harris
VP: Tadar Muhammad
VP: Faye Nock
VP: Dennis Torbett
Prgrm Mgr: Stephen Cousins
Prgrm Mgr: Paul Johnson

D-U-N-S 05-549-3902
HOME BUYERS WARRANTY CORP
2-10 HOME BUYERS WARRANTY
10375 E Harvard Ave # 100, Denver, CO 80231-3966
Tel (720) 747-6000 *Founded/Ownrshp* 2002
Sales NA *EMP* 600
SIC 6351 1531 Warranty insurance, home; Speculative builder, single-family houses; Warranty insurance, home; Speculative builder, single-family houses
CFO: Mark Lewis
Treas: I L Likes
Sr VP: Scott Zinn
VP: Henry B Allen
VP: Mike Bartosch
VP: Maurice Edney
VP: Glenn Findley
VP: Charles Nail Jr
VP: James W Prather
VP: Alison Short
VP: Bart Wares

HOME CARE
See MYSTIC VALLEY ELDER SERVICES INC

D-U-N-S 94-682-5197
HOME CARE ADVANTAGE INC
HOMECARE ADVANTAGE C H C
165 Burnside St, Cranston, RI 02910-1149
Tel (401) 781-1603 *Founded/Ownrshp* 1995
Sales 8.6MM^E *EMP* 300
SIC 8082 Home health care services; Home health care services
Pr: Elaine M Riley
**CFO:* Jim Riley

HOME CARE AMERICA
See MARY WASHINGTON HEALTHCARE SERVICES INC

D-U-N-S 17-927-2927
HOME CARE DELIVERED INC
H C D
11013 W Broad St Ste 400, Glen Allen, VA 23060-6017
Tel (804) 200-7300 *Founded/Ownrshp* 1996
Sales 28.2MM^E *EMP* 110^E
SIC 5047 Medical & hospital equipment; Medical & hospital equipment
Pr: Gordon L Fox Jr
Pr: Steve Krickovic
**CEO:* Craig Weber
**CFO:* Mark Cassidy
Ofcr: Deanna Callahan
Ofcr: Lucas Gordon
Ofcr: Patrick Morin
**Ex VP:* Richard Wells
Sr VP: Jacques F Vonbechmann III
VP: Lauren Carroll
**VP:* Darcy Furr

D-U-N-S 94-268-3202
HOME CARE FOR MAINE INC
347 Maine Ave, Farmingdale, ME 04344-2900
Tel (207) 582-8001 *Founded/Ownrshp* 1994
Sales 7.8MM *EMP* 424
Accts Albin Randall & Bennett Cpa
SIC 8052 8082 Personal care facility; Home health care services; Personal care facility; Home health care services
CEO: Molly Baldwin
**CFO:* Mike Payne

D-U-N-S 03-330-9451 IMP
HOME CARE INDUSTRIES INC
1 Lisbon St, Clifton, NJ 07013-2003
Tel (973) 365-1600 *Founded/Ownrshp* 1980
Sales 60.3MM^E *EMP* 250
SIC 2674 3052 5087 5169 Bags: uncoated paper & multiwall; Vacuum cleaner bags: made from purchased materials; Vacuum cleaner hose, rubber; Vacuum cleaner hose, plastic; Carpet & rug cleaning equipment & supplies, commercial; Vacuum cleaning systems; Specialty cleaning & sanitation preparations; Sanitation preparations; Bags: uncoated paper & multiwall; Vacuum cleaner bags: made from purchased materials; Vacuum cleaner hose, rubber; Vacuum cleaner hose, plastic; Carpet & rug cleaning equipment & supplies, commercial; Vacuum cleaning systems; Specialty cleaning & sanitation preparations; Sanitation preparations
CEO: Robert Logemann
CFO: Anthony Gigante
**CFO:* Tony Gigante
**Sr VP:* Charley Hoover
**VP:* Rose Foti
Opers Mgr: Victoria Mackin

D-U-N-S 18-968-3084
HOME CARE MANAGEMENT INC
HOME CARE NETWORK EAST
1701 N Hampton Rd Ste G, Desoto, TX 75115-2387
Tel (972) 270-2000 *Founded/Ownrshp* 2002
Sales 10.0MM^E *EMP* 300
SIC 8082 Home health care services; Home health care services
Pr: Tina Howell
**Mng Pt:* Belinda May
Advt Dir: Joe Russell

HOME CARE NETWORK EAST
See HOME CARE MANAGEMENT INC

D-U-N-S 96-680-7562
HOME CARE NETWORK INC
190 E Spring Valley Pike A, Dayton, OH 45458-3803
Tel (937) 435-1142 *Founded/Ownrshp* 1994
Sales 23.3MM^E *EMP* 521^E
SIC 8082 7361 Home health care services; Nurses' registry; Home health care services; Nurses' registry
Pr: Betty Martin
**VP:* Betty Adams
Dir IT: Carter Ledbetter
Dir IT: Todd Tobe

D-U-N-S 17-124-3603
HOME CARE OF CENTRAL CAROLINA INC
ADVANCED HOME CARE
4001 Piedmont Pkwy, High Point, NC 27265-9402
Tel (336) 878-8822 *Founded/Ownrshp* 1984
Sales 108.9MM *EMP* 400
SIC 8082 Home health care services; Home health care services
Pr: Joel C Mills
**CFO:* James P Hogan

D-U-N-S 11-476-2656
HOME CARE OPTIONS
1610 S Second St, Gallup, NM 87301-5836
Tel (505) 722-6250 *Founded/Ownrshp* 2002
Sales 6.0MM^E *EMP* 320
SIC 8052 Personal care facility; Personal care facility
Pr: Grace Laurence

D-U-N-S 09-390-3581
■ HOME CARE PHARMACY LLC
OMNICARE OF CINCINNATI
(*Suby of* OMNICARE HOLDING COMPANY)
5549 Spellmire Dr, West Chester, OH 45246-4841
Tel (513) 874-0009 *Founded/Ownrshp* 1988
Sales NA *EMP* 468
SIC 5122 Pharmaceutical preparations; Drugs, proprietaries & sundries; Drugs, proprietaries & sundries
COO: Mike Arnold

D-U-N-S 15-075-5007
HOME CARE PRODUCTS & PHARMACY
(*Suby of* EVANGELICAL COMMUNITY HOSPITAL) ★
1 Hospital Dr, Lewisburg, PA 17837-9350
Tel (570) 522-2000 *Founded/Ownrshp* 1985
Sales 104.5MM *EMP* 1,000
Accts Parenterandolph Llc Pa
SIC 5912 7352 5999 Drug stores & proprietary stores; Medical equipment rental; Medical apparatus & supplies; Drug stores & proprietary stores; Medical equipment rental; Medical apparatus & supplies
Pr: Michael Okeef
**Pr:* Michael Ikeef

D-U-N-S 11-938-5714
HOME CARE RESEARCH OF ROCHESTER INC
HCR
85 Metro Park, Rochester, NY 14623-2607
Tel (585) 272-1930 *Founded/Ownrshp* 1979
Sales 25.6M *EMP* 500
Accts Freed Maxick Cpas Pc Buffalo
SIC 8082 8733 Home health care services; Noncommercial research organizations; Home health care services; Noncommercial research organizations
CEO: Mark Maxim
**Ch Bd:* Louise Woerner
CFO: Rich Glickman
VP: Elizabeth Zicari

HOME CARE SERVICES
See CAPITAL OPPORTUNITIES INC

D-U-N-S 96-730-3822
HOME CARE SERVICES FOR INDEPENDENT LIVING INC
2044 Ocean Ave Ste B4, Brooklyn, NY 11230-7328
Tel (718) 627-1150 *Founded/Ownrshp* 2011
Sales 35.2MM *EMP* 2
Accts The Barson Group Pa Somervill
SIC 8322 Individual & family services; Individual & family services

HOME CARE TEAM, THE
See MEDICAL TEAM INC

D-U-N-S 78-175-7315
HOME CARPET INVESTMENT INC
AMERICAS FINEST CARPET CO
730 Design Ct Ste 401, Chula Vista, CA 91911-6160
Tel (619) 262-8040 *Founded/Ownrshp* 1998
Sales 26.4MM^E *EMP* 111
SIC 1752 7217 Carpet laying; Carpet & upholstery cleaning; Carpet & upholstery cleaning on customer premises; Carpet & upholstery cleaning plants; Carpet laying; Carpet & upholstery cleaning; Carpet & upholstery cleaning on customer premises; Carpet & upholstery cleaning plants
CEO: Carlos Ledesma
Off Mgr: Verionca Mendova

HOME CHOICE HOME HEALTH CARE
See SIOUX VALLEY MEMORIAL HOSPITAL ASSOCIATION

HOME CITY GRAIN
See LEWIS SEED & FERTILIZER INC

D-U-N-S 00-426-1913
HOME CITY ICE CO
6045 Bridgetown Rd Ste 1, Cincinnati, OH 45248-3047
Tel (513) 574-1800 *Founded/Ownrshp* 1956
Sales 270.6MM^E *EMP* 1,225
SIC 2097 Ice cubes; Ice cubes
Prin: Joseph H Head
**Pr:* Thomas E Sedler
**COO:* Edward T Sedler
CFO: James Stautburg
**Treas:* Thomas F Sedler
Rgnl Mgr: Jason Niewohner
Off Admin: Stacie Ross
Sfty Dirs: Kathy Winters
Trfc Dir: Scott Geiter
Sfty Mgr: Joe Whitaker
Plnt Mgr: Robert Eberly

D-U-N-S 93-215-4222 IMP
HOME CONSIGNMENT CENTER LLC
1901 Cmino Ramon Danville, Danville, CA 94526
Tel (925) 838-0113 *Founded/Ownrshp* 1994
Sales 43.8MM^E *EMP* 200
SIC 5712 5932 5094 Furniture stores; Furniture, secondhand; Antiques; Art objects, antique; Jewelry & precious stones; Furniture stores; Furniture, secondhand; Antiques; Art objects, antique; Jewelry & precious stones
Genl Pt: Chris Reilly
Pt: Johnny Crowell
Pt: Jamece Fondnazio
Pt: John Fondnazio

D-U-N-S 60-357-0412 IMP
HOME DECOR CO
STANLEY HOME DECOR
1141 Ryder St, Tupelo, MS 38804-5815
Tel (662) 844-7191 *Founded/Ownrshp* 2004
Sales 23.7MM^E *EMP* 250
SIC 3231 Mirrored glass; Mirrored glass
CEO: Richard Daendurand
**Pr:* Jeff Tartamella
**CFO:* James Bennett

D-U-N-S 61-827-6237 IMP
HOME DECOR HOLDING CO
NBGHOME
(*Suby of* NIELSEN & BAINBRIDGE LLC) ★
4325 Executive Dr Ste 150, Southaven, MS 38672-8124
Tel (662) 996-2440 *Founded/Ownrshp* 2014
Sales 58.6MM^E *EMP* 255^E
SIC 5023 Decorative home furnishings & supplies; Decorative home furnishings & supplies
CEO: Scott Slater
**Pr:* Mark Biggers
**CFO:* Gary Golden
Natl Sales: Danielle Dowdy

D-U-N-S 12-467-1368 IMP
HOME DECOR LIQUIDATORS LLC
9875 Medlock Bridge Pkwy # 200, Johns Creek, GA 30022-6640
Tel (770) 381-6100 *Founded/Ownrshp* 2002
Sales 27.0MM^E *EMP* 150
SIC 5712 Furniture stores; Furniture stores

D-U-N-S 15-205-7618 IMP
HOME DELIVERY INCONTINENT SUPPLIES CO
HDIS
9385 Dielman Indus Dr, Saint Louis, MO 63132-2214
Tel (314) 997-8771 *Founded/Ownrshp* 1985
Sales 64.3MM^E *EMP* 300^E
SIC 5961 Mail order house; Mail order house
Pr: Bruce Eric Grench
CFO: Brian Flint
Dir IT: Lynda Mashburn
IT Man: Roger Williams
VP Opers: Stacy Davis
VP Opers: Stacy Flint
Mktg Dir: Matt Murphy
Mktg Mgr: Elizabeth Kirkpatrick

HOME DEPOT, THE
See HOME DEPOT INTERNATIONAL INC

HOME DEPOT, THE
See HOME DEPOT USA INC

D-U-N-S 07-227-1711 IMP/EXP
▲ HOME DEPOT INC
HOME DEPOT, THE
2455 Paces Ferry Rd Nw, Atlanta, GA 30339
Tel (770) 433-8211 *Founded/Ownrshp* 1978
Sales 83.1MMM *EMP* 375,300
Accts Kpmg Llp Atlanta Georgia
Tkr Sym HD *Exch* NYS
SIC 5211 5231 5251 5261 1752 1751 Lumber & other building materials; Lumber products; Door & window products; Masonry materials & supplies; Paint, glass & wallpaper; Glass; Paint & painting supplies; Wallcoverings; Hardware; Tools; Nurseries & garden centers; Lawn & garden equipment; Lawn & garden supplies; Floor laying & floor work; Window & door installation & erection; Lumber & other building materials; Lumber products; Door & window products; Masonry materials & supplies; Paint, glass & wallpaper; Glass; Paint & painting supplies; Wallcoverings; Hardware; Tools; Nurseries & garden centers; Lawn & garden equipment; Lawn & garden supplies; Floor laying & floor work; Window & door installation & erection
Ch Bd: Craig A Menear
CFO: Paul Gunderman
CFO: Noel Murphy
CFO: Carol B Tom
CFO: Carol B Tome
Ex VP: Francis S Blake
Ex VP: Matthew A Carey
Ex VP: Timothy M Crow
Ex VP: Edward P Decker
Ex VP: Marvin Ellison
Ex VP: Mark Q Holifield
Ex VP: Bill Lennie
Ex VP: Teresa Wynn Roseborough
Sr VP: Lyne Castonguay
Sr VP: Trish Mueller
VP: John F Phillips
Board of Directors: Karen L Katen, Gerard J Arpey, Mark Vadon, Ari Bousbib, Gregory D Brenneman, J Frank Brown, Albert P Carey, Armando Codina, Helena B Foulkes, Linda R Gooden, Wayne M Hewett

D-U-N-S 62-424-2293 IMP/EXP
■ HOME DEPOT INTERNATIONAL INC
HOME DEPOT, THE
(*Suby of* HOME DEPOT INC) ★
2455 Paces Ferry Rd Se, Atlanta, GA 30339-1834
Tel (770) 384-3889 *Founded/Ownrshp* 1989
Sales 39.8MMM^E *EMP* 300,000^E
SIC 5211 Home centers; Home centers
Pr: Kelly Caffarelli
**Treas:* Marshall Day
**VP:* Daniel J Paris
**VP:* Lawrence A Smith
**VP:* Carol Tome
Area Mgr: Buddy Pearce
Dist Mgr: Stephanie Ours
Store Mgr: Eric Bosley
Store Mgr: Douglas Campbell
Store Mgr: Charles Hilliard
Store Mgr: Gary Wilson

HOME DEPOT, THE
See HOME DEPOT INC

D-U-N-S 78-326-6950 IMP/EXP
■ HOME DEPOT USA INC
HOME DEPOT, THE
(*Suby of* HOME DEPOT) ★
2450 Cumberland Pkwy Se, Atlanta, GA 30339-4502
Tel (573) 581-2222 *Founded/Ownrshp* 1989
Sales 39.8MMM^E *EMP* 300,000
SIC 3699 5999 Home centers; Construction management; Electrical equipment & supplies; Plumbing & heating supplies
CEO: Craig A Menear
**Pr:* Lyne Castonguay
**CFO:* Carol B Tome
**Sr VP:* Giles Bowman
**VP:* Matt Carey
**VP:* Christopher Duffy
Corp Couns: Jill U Edmondson

HOME DESIGN PRODUCTS
See RESIN PARTNERS INC

D-U-N-S 79-698-0071
HOME DIALYSIS OF MUHLENBERG COUNTY INC
(*Suby of* FRESENIUS MEDICAL CARE CARDIOVASCULAR RESOURCES INC) ★
95 Hayden Ave, Lexington, MA 02421-7942
Tel (781) 402-9000
Sales 26.3MM^E *EMP* 2,496^E
SIC 7389 Business services
Prin: Jim McCammon

D-U-N-S 18-184-1560 IMP/EXP
HOME DYNAMIX LLC
1 Carol Pl Ste 1, Moonachie, NJ 07074-1318
Tel (201) 807-0111 *Founded/Ownrshp* 1986
Sales 62.7MM^E *EMP* 150
SIC 5713 Floor covering stores; Floor covering stores
CEO: Rami Evar
Sr VP: Daniel Gabay
VP: Yuval Evar
VP: Julie Gitelman
Merch Mgr: Donna Green

HOME EMERGENCY SOLUTIONS
See HOMESERVE USA CORP

D-U-N-S 02-952-3750
HOME ENTERTAINMENT DISTRIBUTORS INC (MA)
INSURERS WORLD
(*Suby of* ENSERVIO INC) ★
95 Shawmut Rd Ste 3, Canton, MA 02021-1429
Tel (781) 821-0087 *Founded/Ownrshp* 1981
Sales 32.3MM^E *EMP* 56
Accts Laurence M Perlmutter Cpa Sl
SIC 5064 High fidelity equipment; Radios; Television sets; Video cassette recorders & accessories
Pr: Nicky Breitstein
**CFO:* Martin Goldstein
Rgnl Mgr: Lou Ayres
IT Man: Jeff Carter
VP Sls: Donald Stafford

HOME ENTERTAINMENT DIV
See FOX INC

D-U-N-S 82-475-2596 IMP/EXP
HOME ESSENTIALS & BEYOND INC
200 Theodore Conrad Dr, Jersey City, NJ 07305-4616
Tel (732) 590-3600 *Founded/Ownrshp* 2014
Sales 32.0MM^E *EMP* 120^E
SIC 5023 5199 Home furnishings; Gifts & novelties
Ch Bd: Izidore Godinger
**CFO:* Reuben Kenigsberg
Ex VP: Jay Soled
Genl Mgr: Hanna Assoulin
VP Sls: John Falzer
Mktg Mgr: Joseph Young
Sls Mgr: Amy Baldinger
Art Dir: David Mercado

D-U-N-S 61-595-7156 IMP
HOME ETC INC
4535 Mcewen Rd, Dallas, TX 75244-5208
Tel (972) 701-8802 *Founded/Ownrshp* 1988
Sales 37.8MM^E *EMP* 550
SIC 5099 Novelties, durable; Novelties, durable
Ch Bd: Ronnie Tsao
**Sec:* Alex Tsao

D-U-N-S 08-857-2938 IMP
HOME FASHIONS DISTRIBUTOR INC
HOME FASHIONS OUTLET
655 Post Rd, Wells, ME 04090-4028
Tel (207) 646-1949 *Founded/Ownrshp* 1977
Sales 25.0MM *EMP* 48^E
SIC 5719 5699 5023

HOME FASHIONS OUTLET
See HOME FASHIONS DISTRIBUTOR INC

D-U-N-S 09-312-4485
HOME FEDERAL BANK
500 12th Ave S, Nampa, ID 83651-4250
Tel (208) 468-5100 *Founded/Ownrshp* 1920
Sales NA *EMP* 329
SIC 6022

D-U-N-S 08-706-6569
■ **HOME FEDERAL BANK**
(*Suby of* HF FINANCIAL CORP) ★
225 S Main Ave, Sioux Falls, SD 57104-6309
Tel (605) 333-7556 *Founded/Ownrshp* 1992
Sales NA *EMP* 285
SIC 6035 Federal savings banks; Federal savings banks
CEO: Curtis L Hage
**COO:* Jack P Hearst
**CFO:* Darrel L Posegate
Ofcr: Steve Johnson
Ofcr: Tammi Soehl
Sr VP: Julie Nelson
Sr VP: Brent Olthoff
Sr VP: Natalie A Sundvold
VP: Barry Byrd
VP: Steven J Carnes
VP: Rita Edwards
VP: Mike Flint
VP: Travis Franklin
VP: Kristi Metzger
VP: Rick Rysavy
VP: Becky Stritecky
VP: Kirk Waugh
Board of Directors: Thomas Steen Trawick Jr

D-U-N-S 07-491-6354
HOME FEDERAL BANK OF TENNESSEE
515 Market St, Knoxville, TN 37902-2145
Tel (865) 546-0330 *Founded/Ownrshp* 1924
Sales NA *EMP* 460
SIC 6035 Federal savings & loan associations; Federal savings & loan associations
Pr: Dale Keasling
**CFO:* Raymond D Thomas
VP: Bobby Castle
VP: Barry Harr
VP: Christa McNeely
VP: Chris Rohwer
VP: Bill Sutphin
IT Man: Berry Byrd
IT Man: Deanna Davis
Mktg Mgr: Jan Evridge
Corp Couns: Rita Edwards

D-U-N-S 09-708-4081
■ **HOME FEDERAL SAVINGS BANK**
(*Suby of* HMN FINANCIAL INC) ★
1016 Civic Center Dr Nw # 1, Rochester, MN 55901-1893
Tel (507) 285-1707 *Founded/Ownrshp* 1934
Sales NA *EMP* 192
SIC 6035 Federal savings banks; Federal savings banks
Pr: Bradley C Krehbiel
Ch Bd: Hugh C Smith
Sr VP: Dwain C Jorgensen
Sr VP: Susan Kolling
VP: Robert Baudhuin
VP: Marty Mixell
VP: Eric Oftedahl
Brnch Mgr: Donna Brown

D-U-N-S 78-746-8680
HOME FEDERAL SAVINGS BANK OF TENNESSEE
515 Market St, Knoxville, TN 37902-2145
Tel (865) 544-3995 *Founded/Ownrshp* 2006
Sales NA *EMP* 1
SIC 6022 State commercial banks; State commercial banks
Prin: Tracy Flynn

D-U-N-S 03-357-9426
HOME FOLKS WHOLESALE CO INC
AFW DISTRIBUTORS
2001 Westside Dr, Augusta, GA 30907-9254
Tel (706) 868-0055 *Founded/Ownrshp* 1938
Sales 41.5MM^E *EMP* 60
SIC 5194 5145 5141 5113 Smoking tobacco; Confectionery; Groceries, general line; Industrial & personal service paper; Smoking tobacco; Confectionery; Groceries, general line; Industrial & personal service paper
Pr: Donald D Childers
**CFO:* Jerry F Weeks
**VP:* Miller M Weeks
Admn Mgr: Murray Giles

D-U-N-S 07-952-7271
HOME FOR LITTLE WANDERERS INC
10 Guest St Ste 300, Brighton, MA 02135-2066
Tel (617) 232-8610 *Founded/Ownrshp* 1865
Sales 55.1MM *EMP* 600
SIC 8351 8322 8361 8741 8093 Child day care services; Child related social services; Residential care for children; Management services; Specialty outpatient clinics; Child day care services; Child related social services; Residential care for children; Management services; Specialty outpatient clinics
Pr: Joan Wallace-Benjamin
**CFO:* Kenneth Hamberg
**Treas:* James Burrows
Ex VP: Michael Pearis
**VP:* Meredith Bryan
CTO: Antoine Duffaut
Dir IT: Frank Chiacchieri
Pr Mgr: Heather Macfarlane
Psych: Carmen Aviles
Psych: Jocelyn Baulier
Psych: Keshelle Dolly

HOME FUNRITURE
See A-AMERICA INC

D-U-N-S 05-884-8243 IMP
HOME FURNITURE CO OF LAFAYETTE INC
909 W Pont Des Mouton Rd, Lafayette, LA 70507-4007
Tel (337) 291-7900 *Founded/Ownrshp* 2012
Sales 50.5MM^E *EMP* 201
SIC 5712 Furniture stores; Furniture stores
CEO: Karol Fleming
**Pr:* Randy Paul
**COO:* Tony Kemp
**Treas:* Lori Berwick
**VP:* Ross Dees
Sfty Mgr: Craig Holston

D-U-N-S 10-584-5390 IMP
HOME GUARD INDUSTRIES INC
13101 Main St, Grabill, IN 46741-2021
Tel (260) 627-6060 *Founded/Ownrshp* 1983
Sales 25.7MM^E *EMP* 100
SIC 3442 3089 Metal doors; Windows, plastic
Pr: Brian G Barbieri
**VP:* Joseph Barbieri Jr
Plnt Mgr: Bill Parrish
Board of Directors: Joseph Barbieri Sr, Katheryn Barbieri

HOME HARDWARE CENTER
See NATCHEZ HARDWARE CENTER INC

D-U-N-S 36-091-2315
HOME HEALTH & HOSPICE CARE
7 Executive Park Dr, Merrimack, NH 03054-4058
Tel (603) 423-9089 *Founded/Ownrshp* 1973
Sales 16.3MM *EMP* 340
Accts Brad Borbidge Pa Concord Nh
SIC 8082 Visiting nurse service; Visiting nurse service
Pr: Karen Baranowskil
V Ch: Marcia Donaldson
CFO: Daryl Cady
Treas: Paul Marsolais
Ex Dir: Janice McDermott
CTO: Elizabeth Parker
Dir IT: Ellen Sorensen
Nrsg Dir: Ana Alfonso

HOME HEALTH AGENCY
See SOUTHCOAST VISITING NURSE ASSOCIATION INC

D-U-N-S 00-958-1546
HOME HEALTH AGENCY-ARIZONA INC
TEAM SELECT HOME CARE
2999 N 44th St Ste 100, Phoenix, AZ 85018-7247
Tel (602) 382-8500 *Founded/Ownrshp* 2004
Sales 26.3MM^E *EMP* 503
SIC 8082 Home health care services
Pr: Michael Lovell

D-U-N-S 10-173-3053
HOME HEALTH AND HOSPICE CARE INC
HH&HC
2402 Wayne Memorial Dr, Goldsboro, NC 27534-1728
Tel (919) 735-1387 *Founded/Ownrshp* 1981
Sales 31.6MM *EMP* 800
Accts Cliftonlarsonallen Llp Charlo
SIC 8059 Personal care home, with health care; Personal care home, with health care
Pr: Beverly Withrow
**Ch Bd:* Gary Lyon
Treas: Michelle Connor
VP: Lou Jones
Off Mgr: Loretta Burton
Dir IT: Larry Wuertzer
Mktg Dir: Edgar Holt

D-U-N-S 94-478-6375
■ **HOME HEALTH CARE AFFILIATES INC**
(*Suby of* GENTIVA HEALTH SERVICES INC) ★
106 Riverview Dr, Flowood, MS 39232-8908
Tel (601) 362-7801 *Founded/Ownrshp* 2008
Sales 12.8MM^E *EMP* 1,000
SIC 8082 Home health care services; Home health care services
Pr: Steven J Bell
**CFO:* Brent W Jorgeson

D-U-N-S 93-080-8670
HOME HEALTH CARE OF MISSISSIPPI INC
CAMELLIA HEALTHCARE
135 Mayfair Rd, Hattiesburg, MS 39402-1464
Tel (601) 939-6428 *Founded/Ownrshp* 1975
Sales 16.6MM^E *EMP* 400
SIC 8082 Home health care services; Home health care services
Pr: Wilford Payne
**Pr:* Wilford A Payne Sr
**VP:* Wilford A Payne Jr

D-U-N-S 02-706-5585 IMP
HOME HEALTH DEPOT INC
MEDICAL MOBILITY
9245 N Meridian St # 200, Indianapolis, IN 46260-1832
Tel (317) 347-6400 *Founded/Ownrshp* 2004
Sales 63.0MM^E *EMP* 202
SIC 5999 Medical apparatus & supplies; Medical apparatus & supplies
Pr: David Hartley
**Pr:* Nathan Feltman
**CFO:* Chuck Gaskins
**VP:* Jim Duncan
**VP:* Derek Miller
VP: Rich Zieba
Brnch Mgr: Jeff Hesse
Dir IT: Robbie Kibler

HOME HEALTH EQUIPMENT SERVICE
See BOTHWELL REGIONAL HEALTH CENTER FOUNDATION

D-U-N-S 62-599-4629
HOME HEALTH FOUNDATION INC
HOME HEALTH VNA
360 Merrimack St Ste 9, Lawrence, MA 01843-1764
Tel (978) 552-4000 *Founded/Ownrshp* 1984
Sales 2.4MM *EMP* 760
SIC 8082 8322 8051 7361 Home health care services; Homemakers' service; Extended care facility; Nurses' registry; Home health care services; Homemakers' service; Extended care facility; Nurses' registry
CEO: John Albert
**Treas:* John G Albert
Sr VP: Anthony J Jorge
VP: Donna Beaudin
**VP:* Deborah Chiaravalloti
VP: Meg Hogan
**VP:* Patricia Palermo
Comm Man: Beth Vimitruk
Brnch Mgr: Jean Le Bla
Brnch Mgr: Jean Leblanc
Nurse Mgr: Lisa Mom
Board of Directors: Joel Hellmann, David J Laflamme, Barbara Moody

HOME HEALTH OF RANDOLPH HOSPIT
See RANDOLPH HOSPITAL INC

HOME HEALTH OFFICE
See CAMERON REGIONAL MEDICAL CENTER

D-U-N-S 11-911-8305
HOME HEALTH SERVICES FOUNDATION INC
154 Hindman Rd, Butler, PA 16001-2417
Tel (724) 282-6806 *Founded/Ownrshp* 1983
Sales 20.1MM^E *EMP* 293
Accts Marcum Llp New Haven Connec
SIC 8082 7352 5047 Home health care services; Visiting nurse service; Medical equipment rental; Medical equipment & supplies; Home health care services; Visiting nurse service; Medical equipment rental; Medical equipment & supplies
Pr: Kristy Wright
**COO:* Elizabeth Powell

D-U-N-S 18-571-8418
HOME HEALTH SPECIALIST INC
349 W State St, Media, PA 19063-2615
Tel (610) 566-2700 *Founded/Ownrshp* 1984
Sales 6.9MM^E *EMP* 370
SIC 8082 Visiting nurse service; Visiting nurse service
Pr: Edward J Raiburn
**Pr:* Ed Raiburn

HOME HEALTH SPECIALTIES
See EASTERN MONTANA HEALTH CO

D-U-N-S 15-186-0384
HOME HEALTH UNITED INC
4639 Hammersley Rd, Madison, WI 53711-2706
Tel (608) 242-1516 *Founded/Ownrshp* 1985
Sales 22.7MM *EMP* 450
SIC 8082 8011 Visiting nurse service; Offices & clinics of medical doctors; Visiting nurse service; Offices & clinics of medical doctors
Pr: Richard Bourne
**CFO:* Alfred Stucki
**Ch:* Steve Olson
VP: Gregory Griffin

HOME HEALTH VNA
See HOME HEALTH FOUNDATION INC

D-U-N-S 03-767-9883
HOME HEALTH VNA OF HAVERHILL
(*Suby of* HOME HEALTH FOUNDATION INC) ★
360 Merrimack St Ste 9, Lawrence, MA 01843-1764
Tel (978) 552-4000 *Founded/Ownrshp* 1968
Sales 34.6MM *EMP* 437
Accts Brad Borbidge Pa
SIC 8082 Visiting nurse service; Visiting nurse service
CEO: Joan Stygles Hull
**Treas:* John Albert
VP: Antony Jorge
Board of Directors: Paul Teplitz

D-U-N-S 04-850-1936
HOME HEALTHCARE HOSPICE AND COMMUNITY SERVICES INC
312 Marlboro St, Keene, NH 03431-4163
Tel (603) 352-2253 *Founded/Ownrshp* 1981
Sales 4.6MM *EMP* 380
SIC 8082 8361 Home health care services; Residential care; Home health care services; Residential care
Pr: Cathy Sorenson
**CFO:* Richard Skeels
**Treas:* Wesley Clark
**Ex VP:* Barbara R Duckett
**VP:* Cynthia Q Woods
**Brnch Mgr:* Susan Ashworth
**IT Man:* Chad Rancourt

HOME INFSION /PRVDNCE PORTLAND
See SISTERS OF PROVIDENCE IN OREGON

HOME INFUSION SOLUTIONS
See HOME SOLUTIONS HOLDINGS LLC

D-U-N-S 15-289-6833
HOME INSTEAD INC
HOME INSTEAD SENIOR CARE
13323 California St, Omaha, NE 68154-5240
Tel (402) 498-4466 *Founded/Ownrshp* 1994
Sales 72.9MM^E *EMP* 100^E
SIC 6794 8082 Franchises, selling or licensing; Home health care services
Ch: Paul Hogan
**Pr:* Jeff Hubber
**Pr:* Jeff Huber
**CEO:* Roger Baumgart
**COO:* John Hogan
COO: Nell-Neal
CFO: Renee Macarthur
**Chf Mktg O:* Scott Dingfield
**Sr VP:* Yoshino Nakajima
VP: Jisella Dolan
Exec: Renee Smith
Comm Dir: Jami Hahn

HOME INSTEAD SENIOR CARE
See HOME INSTEAD INC

D-U-N-S 01-334-7740
HOME INSTEAD SENIOR CARE (WI)
901 Anderson Dr, Green Bay, WI 54304-5010
Tel (920) 965-1600 *Founded/Ownrshp* 1997
Sales 5.0MM *EMP* 450
SIC 8082 Home health care services; Home health care services
Pr: Steve Nooyen
Ex VP: Jason Crane
Dir Bus: James Nooyen

HOME JUICE CO OF MEMPHIS
See H J M P CORP

HOME LIGHTING CENTER
See ELECTRICAL WHOLESALE SUPPLY CO INC

D-U-N-S 06-624-2269
■ **HOME LOAN CENTER INC**
(*Suby of* LENDINGTREE LLC) ★
163 Technology Dr Ste 100, Irvine, CA 92618-2486
Tel (949) 885-3100 *Founded/Ownrshp* 2000
Sales NA *EMP* 700^E
SIC 6162 Mortgage bankers; Mortgage bankers
Pr: Anthony Hsieh
CFO: Michael Churchill
**CFO:* John H Lee
CFO: Matthew Packey
Treas: John Lacey
**Ex VP:* Jim Svinth
**Sr VP:* Rob Hill
**VP:* Alex Shin
VP: Tim Weiler
**VP:* Tomo Yebisu

D-U-N-S 00-694-2437
HOME LUMBER & SUPPLY CO
DO IT BEST
106 W 8th St, Ashland, KS 67831
Tel (620) 635-2207 *Founded/Ownrshp* 1905
Sales 21.5MM *EMP* 85
SIC 5211 Lumber & other building materials; Lumber & other building materials
Pr: John Humphreys
**Sec:* Fred Johnston
**VP:* Thom Berryman
Off Mgr: Kim Hazen
IT Man: Vince Friess

HOME LUMBER COMPANY
See MDJ INC

HOME MADE FOR HEALTHY HOMES
See DIRT PROS OF FT LAUDERDALE

D-U-N-S 01-926-5073
HOME MARKET FOODS INC
140 Morgan Dr Ste 100, Norwood, MA 02062-5076
Tel (781) 948-1500 *Founded/Ownrshp* 1996
Sales 402.5MM^E *EMP* 1,707
SIC 2013 Frozen meats from purchased meat; Frozen meats from purchased meat
Pr: Douglas K Atamian
**Pr:* Wesley L Atamian
CFO: Hilary Simons
**VP:* Rocky Schroeder
VP: Mike Weiermiller
QA Dir: Al Depaoli
QA Dir: John Peck
Opers Mgr: Patty Carr
Prd Mgr: Rick Manda
Ql Cn Mgr: Chitsanzo Kachaje
Sls Dir: Scott Lubow

HOME MEDICAL
See PHARMACY COUNTER LLC

HOME MEDICAL EQUIPMENT
See PROVIDENCE HOMES SERVICES

D-U-N-S 55-610-9499 IMP
HOME MERIDIAN HOLDINGS INC
PULASKI FURNITURE
2485 Penny Rd, High Point, NC 27265-8375
Tel (336) 887-1985 *Founded/Ownrshp* 2000
Sales 30.8MM^E *EMP* 200^E
SIC 2511 Wood household furniture; Wood bedroom furniture; Kitchen & dining room furniture; Wood household furniture; Wood bedroom furniture; Kitchen & dining room furniture
CEO: George Revington
**Pr:* Lee Boone
**Pr:* Shawn Cantrell
**COO:* Lamont Hope
**CFO:* Dough Townsend
**CFO:* Dave Wisniewski

D-U-N-S 00-313-1588 IMP
HOME MERIDIAN INTERNATIONAL INC
(*Suby of* HOME MERIDIAN HOLDINGS INC) ★
2485 Penny Rd, High Point, NC 27265-8375
Tel (336) 819-7200 *Founded/Ownrshp* 2000
Sales 23.5MM^E *EMP* 113
SIC 2511 Wood household furniture; Wood bedroom furniture; Kitchen & dining room furniture
Pr: George Revington
**COO:* Lamont Hope
CFO: Dave Wisniewski
Chf Mktg O: Edward M Tashjian
**Ex VP:* Doug Townsend
VP: Douglas Estremadoyro
IT Man: Clint Webb

HOME MOTORS
See HAL MCBRIDE CAR SALES INC

HOME NEWS & TRIBUNE
See ASBURY PARK PRESS INC

D-U-N-S 00-603-8913
HOME NEWS ENTERPRISES LLC (IN)
333 2nd St, Columbus, IN 47201-6709
Tel (800) 876-7811 *Founded/Ownrshp* 1994
Sales 55.8MM^E *EMP* 425
SIC 2711 2752

HOME NURSE
See HOMENURSE INC

D-U-N-S 02-543-8524
HOME NURSERY INC
1230 University Dr, Edwardsville, IL 62025-5558
Tel (618) 223-3063 *Founded/Ownrshp* 1977
Sales 22.6MM^E *EMP* 100
Accts Edward W Small Edwardsville
SIC 0181 5261 Ornamental nursery products; Nurseries & garden centers
Pr: Charles J Tosovsky
COO: Jeff Van Buren
**CFO:* Dennis Molitor
**Sr VP:* Mark Luchtefeld
**Sr VP:* Paul Vanoteghem
**VP:* Ann Tosovsky
IT Man: Elvin Martinez
VP Prd: Paul Van Oteghem

D-U-N-S 07-495-8935
HOME NURSING AGENCY
HOME NURSING AGENCY AFFILIATES
201 Chestnut Ave, Altoona, PA 16601-4927
Tel (724) 254-3500 *Founded/Ownrshp* 1986
Sales 3.4MM *EMP* 835
SIC 8082 Home health care services; Home health care services
CEO: Robert R Packer
COO: Phil Freeman
CFO: Gregg Laverick
**Ch:* Bernard Coettage
**Treas:* Kathy Wagner
Dir: Pamela Seasoltz
Dir IT: Dianne Worley
IT Man: Chad Myers
Psych: April Tennis
Nutrtnst: Nicole Helm
Doctor: Yousufuddin Alimd

HOME NURSING AGENCY AFFILIATES
See HOME NURSING AGENCY

D-U-N-S 19-277-2325
HOME NURSING AGENCY AFFILIATES
HOME NURSING AGENCY VISITING
201 Chestnut Ave, Altoona, PA 16601-4927
Tel (814) 946-5411 *Founded/Ownrshp* 1986
Sales 33.6MM^E *EMP* 720
SIC 8741 8082 5047 7372 6519 Hospital management; Nursing & personal care facility management; Home health care services; Medical equipment & supplies; Prepackaged software; Real property lessors; Hospital management; Nursing & personal care facility management; Home health care services; Medical equipment & supplies; Prepackaged software; Real property lessors
Ch Bd: John R Beyer
**Pr:* Robert Packer
**Treas:* Bernard Creppage
**Treas:* James Drenning

D-U-N-S 19-450-9055
HOME NURSING AGENCY COMMUNITY SERVICES
HOME NURSING AGENCY VISITING N
201 Chestnut Ave, Altoona, PA 16601-4927
Tel (814) 946-5411 *Founded/Ownrshp* 1986
Sales 15.6MM *EMP* 650
Accts Reilly Creppage & Co Inc Cpa S
SIC 8082 8322 Visiting nurse service; Individual & family services; Substance abuse counseling; Visiting nurse service; Individual & family services; Substance abuse counseling
Pr: Robert Packer
**Ch Bd:* Merle Evey
**Treas:* Steven Seltzer
**VP:* Bruce Erb
Genl Mgr: Donna Kensinger

HOME NURSING AGENCY VISITING
See HOME NURSING AGENCY AFFILIATES

HOME NURSING AGENCY VISITING N
See HOME NURSING AGENCY COMMUNITY SERVICES

D-U-N-S 03-182-9179 IMP
HOME OF ECONOMY INC
1508 N Washington St, Grand Forks, ND 58203-1458
Tel (701) 772-6611 *Founded/Ownrshp* 1946
Sales 59.1MM *EMP* 300
SIC 5311 Department stores, discount; Department stores, discount
CEO: Scott Pearson
**Pr:* Wade Pearson
**Co-Pr:* Robert Scott Pearson
**VP:* Brian Cox
**VP:* Virginia Eelkema
VP Opers: David Jones

D-U-N-S 05-075-2021
HOME OF GUIDING HANDS CORP
1825 Gillespie Way # 200, El Cajon, CA 92020-0501
Tel (619) 938-2850 *Founded/Ownrshp* 1961
Sales 16.1MM *EMP* 320
Accts Cbiz Mhm Llc San Diego Ca
SIC 8361 8052 Residential care for the handicapped; Intermediate care facilities; Residential care for the handicapped; Intermediate care facilities
CEO: Mark Klaus
**CFO:* Jan Adams
Treas: Karen Lanning
**Ex Dir:* Carol A Fitzgibbons
VP Opers: Ana Parra

D-U-N-S 08-057-4999
HOME OF HOPE INC
HOPE HOUSING SCRAPER
960 W Hope Ave, Vinita, OK 74301-5126
Tel (918) 256-8144 *Founded/Ownrshp* 1968
Sales 12.8MM *EMP* 400
Accts Bkd Llp Tulsa Ok
SIC 8361 8052 8331 Residential care; Home for the mentally retarded, with health care; Job training & vocational rehabilitation services; Residential care; Home for the mentally retarded, with health care; Job training & vocational rehabilitation services
CEO: Dianna Hoover
**COO:* Dena Pitts
**Prin:* O W Dehart
**Prin:* Jane Hartley
**Prin:* Ed Shanahan Jr

D-U-N-S 08-238-5352
HOME OF INNOCENTS INC
1100 E Market St, Louisville, KY 40206-1838
Tel (502) 596-1000 *Founded/Ownrshp* 1930
Sales 32.9MM *EMP* 320^E
Accts Deming Malone Livesay & Ostrof
SIC 8069 8322 Children's hospital; Emergency shelters; Children's hospital; Emergency shelters
Pr: Gordon Brown
CFO: David McDonald
CFO: Madelyn K Pressey
**Ch:* Joni Way
**Treas:* Phil McCauley
VP: Jeff Lewis
VP: Jean Obrien
Dir IT: Gerald Raizor
Dir IT: Lori Vaught
Psych: Lucie Erlebachova
Nrsg Dir: Karen Bender

HOME OFFICE COMMUNICATION SUP
See TELECO INC

D-U-N-S 00-799-2282
HOME OIL & GAS CO (KY)
300 Atkinson St, Henderson, KY 42420-3704
Tel (270) 826-3925 *Founded/Ownrshp* 1925
Sales 65.7MM *EMP* 34
Accts Brad Parrott Cpa Pllc Hender
SIC 5172 Engine fuels & oils; Engine fuels & oils
Ch Bd: Sara Crafton
**Pr:* James M Crafton Jr
**Treas:* Robert G Crafton
**VP:* James A Crafton
Plnt Mgr: Stewart Lyons

D-U-N-S 00-586-9359
HOME OIL CO (AR)
2096 W State Highway 158, Manila, AR 72442-9172
Tel (870) 570-0700 *Founded/Ownrshp* 1945
Sales 45.8MM^E *EMP* 45
Accts Thomas Speight & Noble Cpa S
SIC 5191 5171 5984 5541 5531 Chemicals, agricultural; Fertilizer & fertilizer materials; Petroleum bulk stations & terminals; Liquefied petroleum gas dealers; Gasoline service stations; Automotive tires; Chemicals, agricultural; Fertilizer & fertilizer materials; Petroleum bulk stations & terminals; Liquefied petroleum gas dealers; Gasoline service stations; Automotive tires
Pr: J L Price
**Treas:* Wade Castleberry
**VP:* Mike McCarty

D-U-N-S 03-148-1294
HOME OIL CO INC (AL)
HOBO PANTRY FOOD STORES
5744 E Us Highway 84, Cowarts, AL 36321-9085
Tel (334) 793-1544 *Founded/Ownrshp* 1966
Sales 102.7MM *EMP* 200
Accts Carpenter Wiggins Jordan Th
SIC 5171 5411 5541 5172 Petroleum bulk stations; Convenience stores, chain; Filling stations, gasoline; Petroleum products; Petroleum bulk stations; Convenience stores, chain; Filling stations, gasoline; Petroleum products
Pr: Tim Shirley
**Ch Bd:* Thomas A Shirley
**CFO:* Jeff D Groover
CFO: Jeff Groover
VP: Al Shirley
**VP:* Christopher A Shirley

D-U-N-S 16-253-3355
HOME ORGANIZERS INC
CLOSET WORLD, THE
3860 Capitol Ave, City of Industry, CA 90601-1733
Tel (562) 699-9945 *Founded/Ownrshp* 2001
Sales 68.8MM^E *EMP* 660
SIC 3089 Organizers for closets, drawers, etc.: plastic; Organizers for closets, drawers, etc.: plastic
Pr: Frank Melkonian

D-U-N-S 02-364-7407
HOME PARAMOUNT PEST CONTROL COMPANIES INC
YORK DISTRIBUTORS
2011 Rock Spring Rd, Forest Hill, MD 21050-2601
Tel (410) 638-0800 *Founded/Ownrshp* 1986
Sales 66.1MM^E *EMP* 600
SIC 7342 5191 Pest control services; Fertilizers & agricultural chemicals; Pest control services; Fertilizers & agricultural chemicals
Pr: Walter A Tilley
CFO: Dan Butz
**VP:* Walt A Tilley III

HOME PLUS
See JONES CASSITY INC

D-U-N-S 00-506-3532
HOME PRODUCTS INTERNATIONAL - NORTH AMERICA INC
(*Suby of* HOME PRODUCTS INTERNATIONAL INC) ★
4501 W 47th St, Chicago, IL 60632-4407
Tel (773) 890-1010 *Founded/Ownrshp* 1952
Sales 156.0MM^E *EMP* 400
SIC 3089 3499 Boxes, plastic; Organizers for closets, drawers, etc.: plastic; Ironing boards, metal; Boxes, plastic; Organizers for closets, drawers, etc.: plastic; Ironing boards, metal
CEO: George Hamilton
**CFO:* Dennis Doheny
**Sr VP:* Grant Fagan
**VP:* John Deruntz
**VP:* Kathy Evans
**VP:* John Pugh

D-U-N-S 15-293-5193 IMP/EXP
HOME PRODUCTS INTERNATIONAL INC
HPI
4501 W 47th St, Chicago, IL 60632-4407
Tel (773) 890-1010 *Founded/Ownrshp* 2007
Sales 516.7MM^E *EMP* 400
SIC 6719 Investment holding companies, except banks; Investment holding companies, except banks
Pr: George Hamilton
Pr: Randy Chambers
COO: Richard A Hssert
**CFO:* Dennis Doheny
**Sr VP:* John Deruntz
VP: Jose Cabanin
VP: Park Owens
VP: Charles Veselits
Dir IT: Tom Lammers
Dir IT: Bruce May
Mtls Mgr: Jan Engel
Board of Directors: Thomas Ferguson, Gene Moriarty, Lewis Mick Solimene

D-U-N-S 86-101-6046
▲ **HOME PROPERTIES INC**
850 Clinton Sq, Rochester, NY 14604-1795
Tel (585) 546-4900 *Founded/Ownrshp* 1993
Sales 671.9MM *EMP* 1,200
Tkr Sym HME *Exch* NYS
SIC 6798 Real estate investment trusts; Real estate investment trusts
Pr: Edward J Pettinella
Pr: Cynthia Burrell
CFO: David P Gardner
Ofcr: Robert J Luken
Ex VP: Ann M McCormick
Sr VP: Scott Doyle
Sr VP: Donald Haque
Sr VP: Janine Schue
Sr VP: John E Smith
VP: Christopher Berson
VP: Bill Brown
VP: Lesley Darling
VP: Michael Eastwood
VP: Jodi Falk
VP: Donald R Hague
VP: Karen Lejman
VP: Paul H O'Leary
VP: Biography Photo
VP: Bill Revers
VP: Charis W Warshof

D-U-N-S 87-441-8106
■ **HOME PROPERTIES LIMITED PARTNERSHIP**
(*Suby of* HOME PROPERTIES INC) ★
850 Clinton Sq, Rochester, NY 14604-1795
Tel (585) 546-4900 *Founded/Ownrshp* 1993
Sales 12.8MM^E *EMP* 1,000
SIC 6513 Apartment building operators; Apartment building operators
CFO: David P Gardner

HOME RESPITORY & INFUSION SVCS
See HEALTH CARE SOLUTIONS INC

D-U-N-S 06-397-3515
HOME RUN INC
1299 Lavelle Dr, Xenia, OH 45385-7402
Tel (800) 543-9198 *Founded/Ownrshp* 1985
Sales 31.6MM^E *EMP* 140
SIC 4213 4212 Building materials transport; Local trucking, without storage; Building materials transport; Local trucking, without storage
Pr: Gary Harlow
**VP:* Thomas Baker
**VP:* Dennis Harlow
VP Opers: Chad Harlow

D-U-N-S 82-553-0009
HOME RUN INN FROZEN FOODS CORP
1300 Internationale Pkwy, Woodridge, IL 60517-4928
Tel (630) 783-9696 *Founded/Ownrshp* 1993
Sales 27.2MM^E *EMP* 100
SIC 2038 Pizza, frozen; Pizza, frozen
Pr: Joseph Perrino
**Pr:* Marilyn Carlson
**Pr:* Lucretia Costello
**CFO:* Steven E Larek
VP: Tom Dangelo
Prd Mgr: Mike Kelly
Board of Directors: Marilyn Carlson, Lucretia Costello

D-U-N-S 07-691-3045
■ **HOME SAVINGS AND LOAN CO OF YOUNGSTOWN OHIO**
(*Suby of* UNITED COMMUNITY FINANCIAL CORP) ★
275 W Federal St, Youngstown, OH 44503-1200
Tel (330) 742-0500 *Founded/Ownrshp* 1889
Sales NA *EMP* 490^E
SIC 6036 6163 Savings & loan associations, not federally chartered; Loan brokers; Savings & loan associations, not federally chartered; Loan brokers
Pr: Patrick W Bevack
Pr: Kimberly Clark
COO: Mike Garmone
CFO: Timothy W Esson
Treas: Diana Lewis
Sr Cor Off: Preston Bair
Ofcr: Karen Feiler
Ofcr: Chuck Gole
Ofcr: Gregory G Krontiris
Ofcr: Bryan Sahli
Ex VP: James R Reske
Sr VP: Thomas R Poe
Sr VP: Barbara Radis
VP: Mark Bobbitt
VP: Anthony Dantuono
VP: Thomas Gacse
VP: Kevin Gluntz
VP: Ken Goldsboro
VP: Bob Hackler
VP: Andrew D Jone
VP: Jude Nohra
Board of Directors: Marty E Adams, Lee J Burdman, Ellen J Tressel

HOME SECURITY
See GUARDIAN PROTECTION SERVICES INC

D-U-N-S 00-633-5871
HOME SERVICE OIL CO (MO)
EXPRESS MART
6910 Front St, Barnhart, MO 63012-1508
Tel (636) 464-5266 *Founded/Ownrshp* 1930
Sales 31.8MM^E *EMP* 150
Accts Greshamsmith Llc St Louis M
SIC 5411 5171 Convenience stores, independent; Petroleum bulk stations; Convenience stores, independent; Petroleum bulk stations
Pr: David Mangelsdorf
**Sec:* Sandra Overberg
Ex VP: Bryan Goeforth
**VP:* Bryan Goforth
Genl Mgr: Tom Denman
IT Man: Jim Meese
Opers Mgr: John Ficken

D-U-N-S 03-983-9111
HOME SOLUTIONS HOLDINGS LLC
HOME INFUSION SOLUTIONS
1001 Grand St S Ste A, Hammonton, NJ 08037-3384
Tel (609) 383-6111 *Founded/Ownrshp* 2011
Sales 16.6MM^E *EMP* 500
SIC 8082 Home health care services; Home health care services
CEO: Daniel Greenleaf
**COO:* Dave Tomasello
**CFO:* Paul Sorensen Jr
**Ex VP:* Joseph Malatesta
VP: Joseph Jesuele
Brnch Mgr: John Magalla
Genl Mgr: Michelle Meinke
Dir IT: Chris Herron
Sls Mgr: Joe McArdle

D-U-N-S 09-461-7607 IMP/EXP
HOME SOURCE INTERNATIONAL INC (GA)
3595 Industrial Park Dr, Marianna, FL 32446-8092
Tel (404) 663-0647 *Founded/Ownrshp* 2000
Sales 25.0MM *EMP* 40
SIC 5023 Linens & towels
Pr: Keith R Sorgeloos
COO: Scott Sorgeloos
CFO: Mike Beard
VP Mfg: Dennis Rudd

HOME STAFF
See MASSACHUSETTS HEALTH CARE SERVICES INC

D-U-N-S 82-812-6040
HOME STATE BANCORP
2695 W Eisenhower Blvd, Loveland, CO 80537-4337
Tel (970) 669-4040 *Founded/Ownrshp* 2003
Sales NA *EMP* 425
SIC 6712 6022 Bank holding companies; State commercial banks; Bank holding companies; State commercial banks
Off Admin: Nancy Packard

D-U-N-S 12-127-3700
HOME STATE BANCORP INC
40 Grant St, Crystal Lake, IL 60014-4314
Tel (815) 459-2000 *Founded/Ownrshp* 1983
Sales NA *EMP* 191^E
SIC 6022 State commercial banks; State commercial banks
Pr: Joseph T Morrow
**Treas:* Kathleen Narusas
Sr VP: Bill Baldoni
Sr VP: Keith Leathers
**VP:* Douglas Bean
VP: Marcia Geike
**VP:* Christopher Morrow
**VP:* Steven Slack
Dist Mgr: Jack Green
CIO: Pamela Narusis
CTO: Kathleen Narusis

D-U-N-S 00-742-7768
HOME STATE BANK
(*Suby of* HOME STATE BANCORP) ★
2695 W Eisenhower Blvd # 100, Loveland, CO 80537-4338
Tel (970) 669-4040 *Founded/Ownrshp* 1950
Sales NA *EMP* 225
SIC 6022 7374 State commercial banks; Data processing service; State commercial banks; Data processing service
Ch Bd: Jack Devereaux
**Pr:* Harry Devereaux
COO: Kenneth Porter
**CFO:* Mark Bower
Sr VP: Patricia Jan
Sr VP: Mary McCambridge
VP: Dan Gavato
VP: Audrey Ketchum
VP: Scott Malan
VP: Norm Rehme
VP: Joyce Spight
VP: Scott Woods

D-U-N-S 00-693-3436
HOME STATE BANK NATIONAL ASSOCIATION (INC)
HS BANK
(*Suby of* HOME STATE BANCORP INC) ★
40 Grant St, Crystal Lake, IL 60014-4367
Tel (815) 459-2000 *Founded/Ownrshp* 1983
Sales NA *EMP* 185
SIC 6021 National commercial banks; National commercial banks
Pr: Steven L Slack
**CFO:* Kathleen Narusis
Sr VP: Bill Baldoni
Sr VP: Robert Cormier
**VP:* Douglas Bean
VP: Jeanie Bye
VP: Charles J Feck Jr
VP: Marcia Geike
VP: Bill Hartman
VP: Andrew Killinger
**VP:* Joseph T Morrow
VP: Bill Pann
VP: Mike Russotto
VP: Jim Sorenson
VP: Paul Vasquez
VP: Flo Vitale
Mng Ofcr: Keith Leathers

D-U-N-S 03-231-2257
■ **HOME STATE HEALTH PLAN INC**
(*Suby of* CENTENE CORP) ★
16090 Swingley Ridge Rd # 450, Chesterfield, MO 63017-6028
Tel (314) 725-4477 *Founded/Ownrshp* 2011
Sales NA *EMP* 158ᴱ
SIC 6324 Hospital & medical service plans
Pr: Michael F Neidorff
VP: Wendy Faust

D-U-N-S 04-291-9998
HOME SWEET HOME HOLDINGS INC
6111 S 228th St, Kent, WA 98032-1849
Tel (253) 850-6111 *Founded/Ownrshp* 1998
Sales 37.4MMᴱ *EMP* 88ᴱ
SIC 5023 6719 Home furnishings; Kitchenware; Investment holding companies, except banks
Pr: William P Reibl
**CFO:* James W Campbell
VP: Mark Kibbe
Exec: Sonia Shu

HOME TELECOM
See HOME TELEPHONE CO INC

D-U-N-S 00-279-7900
HOME TELEPHONE CO INC (SC)
HOME TELECOM
579 Stony Landing Rd, Moncks Corner, SC 29461-3307
Tel (843) 761-9101 *Founded/Ownrshp* 1953, 1962
Sales 60.4MMᴱ *EMP* 160
SIC 4813 Telephone communication, except radio; Telephone communication, except radio
CEO: Robert L Helmly Sr
**Pr:* William S Helmly
Ex VP: Helmly William
**Sr VP:* H Keith Oliver
**VP:* E L Barnes
Genl Mgr: Huey Sessions
Mktg Dir: Gina Shuler
Mktg Mgr: Gina Hutson
Sls Mgr: Mark Davis

HOME TOWN HEALTH NETWORK
See MASSILLON COMMUNITY HOSPITAL HEALTH PLAN

D-U-N-S 07-365-4472
HOME WARRANTY OF AMERICA INC
HWA
(*Suby of* DIRECT ENERGY INC) ★
1371 Abbott Ct Ste A, Buffalo Grove, IL 60089-2367
Tel (847) 325-5143 *Founded/Ownrshp* 2011
Sales NA *EMP* 95
SIC 6351 Warranty insurance, home
CEO: Marc Roth
**Pr:* Eddy Collier
**Pr:* Scott Ruby
Mktg Mgr: Monica O'Neill
Manager: Harry Keifer

HOME-STYLE INDUSTRIES
See LIPPERT COMPONENTS INC

D-U-N-S 02-435-5338
■ **HOMEADVISOR INC**
(*Suby of* IAC/INTERACTIVECORP) ★
14023 Denver West Pkwy, Lakewood, CO 80401-3253
Tel (303) 963-8066 *Founded/Ownrshp* 1999
Sales 20.9MMᴱ *EMP* 120ᴱ
SIC 7699 Caliper, gauge & other machinists' instrument repair
CEO: Chris Terrill
**Pr:* Craig Smith
**COO:* Kirk Schreck
VP: Nate Burford
**VP:* Tom Durant
VP: Daniel Grisinger
VP: John Humphreys
VP: Rob Levy
VP: Eric Smith
VP: Paul Zeckser
VP: Sarah Zoden

D-U-N-S 18-951-8033
HOMEAWAY INC
1011 W 5th St Ste 300, Austin, TX 78703-5363
Tel (512) 684-1100 *Founded/Ownrshp* 2004
Sales 446.7MM *EMP* 1,780ᴱ
SIC 6531 7389 7375 Real estate listing services; Real estate leasing & rentals; Accomodation locating services; On-line data base information retrieval; Real estate listing services; Real estate leasing & rentals; Accomodation locating services; On-line data base information retrieval
Pr: Brian H Sharples
Pt: Martin Slagter
COO: Thomas E Hale
CFO: Lynn Atchison
Chf Mktg O: Mariano Dima
VP: William Bowles
VP: Jeff Hurst
VP: Michael Osborn
VP: Venu Venugopal
CTO: Ross A Buhrdorf
Board of Directors: Lanny Baker, Simon Breakwell, Jeffrey D Brody, Kevin Krone, Simon Lehmann, Woody Marshall, Tina Sharkey

D-U-N-S 80-043-3448
HOMEBANC NATIONAL ASSOCIATION
(*Suby of* HOMEBANCORP INC) ★
3701 W Lake Mary Blvd, Lake Mary, FL 32746-3393
Tel (407) 278-0270 *Founded/Ownrshp* 2007
Sales NA *EMP* 11
SIC 6021 National commercial banks; National commercial banks
CEO: Jerry Campbell
Ofcr: Scott Jannasch
Sr VP: Maureen T Britz
VP: Michael Bottiglio
Brnch Mgr: Brian Locke

D-U-N-S 02-614-4799
HOMEBANCORP INC
101 E Kennedy Blvd, Tampa, FL 33602-5179
Tel (813) 228-8300 *Founded/Ownrshp* 2004
Sales NA *EMP* 116ᴱ
SIC 6029 Commercial banks; Commercial banks
CEO: Jerry D Campbell
CFO: Jeffrey D Saunders
Chf Cred: Courtenay Marshall
Chf Cred: William L Thorpe
Ofcr: Bethany Flores
Sr VP: Michael Alea
Sr VP: Brenda Bowers
Sr VP: Maureen T Britz
VP: Margaret Arnao
VP: David Bohlander
VP: Kristine Bredeau
VP: Maureen Cancelino
VP: Scott Carter
VP: John J Coffey
VP: Charles J Coury
VP: Nikki Digiovanni
VP: Michael Folino
VP: Tommy Gainer
VP: Amy Ganson
VP: Joanne W Jolin
VP: Jeffery S Katz

D-U-N-S 82-639-9305
HOMEBRIDGE FINANCIAL SERVICES INC
194 Wood Ave S Fl 9, Iselin, NJ 08830-2761
Tel (201) 498-9300 *Founded/Ownrshp* 1991
Sales NA *EMP* 1,250ᴱ
SIC 6162 Mortgage bankers; Mortgage bankers
Pr: Douglas Rotella
CFO: John Soricelli
Ofcr: Mary Harper
Ofcr: Tia Holloway
**VP:* Dorothy Tracy
**Prin:* Gianni Cerretani
Area Mgr: Tod Mershon
Brnch Mgr: Edward Bocchino
Brnch Mgr: Ruby Guimbard
Brnch Mgr: David Mackey
IT Man: Ian Orevillo

D-U-N-S 79-466-1793
HOMEBRIDGE MORTGAGE BANKERS CORP
REFINANCE.COM
60 Oak Dr, Syosset, NY 11791-4647
Tel (516) 682-9100 *Founded/Ownrshp* 1993
Sales NA *EMP* 125
Accts Deloitte & Touche Llp New Yor
SIC 6141 8742 6162 Financing: automobiles, furniture, etc., not a deposit bank; Financial consultant; Mortgage bankers & correspondents; Financing: automobiles, furniture, etc., not a deposit bank; Financial consultant; Mortgage bankers & correspondents
CEO: Nicholas Bratsafolis
**COO:* Paul Levine
**Treas:* Frank McBrien
Sr VP: Laurence Liebowitz
**Ex Dir:* Glenn Feldstein
CTO: Adeel Saeed

D-U-N-S 07-828-6614
■ **HOMECALL INC** (MD)
(*Suby of* LHC GROUP INC) ★
4701 Mount Hope Dr Ste A, Baltimore, MD 21215-3246
Tel (410) 644-0105 *Founded/Ownrshp* 1974, 1994
Sales 21.5MMᴱ *EMP* 650
SIC 8082 Home health care services; Home health care services
Pr: Artie Esworthy Jr
VP: Michael Hogan

HOMECARE ADVANTAGE C H C
See HOME CARE ADVANTAGE INC

D-U-N-S 94-494-4693
HOMECARE DIMENSIONS INC
12500 Network Blvd # 210, San Antonio, TX 78249-3301
Tel (210) 696-2626 *Founded/Ownrshp* 1995
Sales 22.9MMᴱ *EMP* 230
SIC 8082 Home health care services; Home health care services
Pr: John Olivas
**Pr:* Joe Williams
COO: Cathy Hosek
**VP:* Keith Sanders
Brnch Mgr: Rodolfo Blain
Off Mgr: Bryana White
Opers Mgr: Cindy Garcia

D-U-N-S 84-930-8614
HOMECARE MANAGEMENT CORP
315 Wilkesboro Blvd Ne 2a, Lenoir, NC 28645-4498
Tel (828) 754-3665 *Founded/Ownrshp* 1993
Sales 16.7MMᴱ *EMP* 700
SIC 8082 8093 Home health care services; Mental health clinic, outpatient; Home health care services; Mental health clinic, outpatient
Pr: Rankin A Whittington
CFO: Laurie McDaniel
**VP:* Sandra Whittington

HOMECARE NURSING SERVICE
See UNLIMITED CARE INC

HOMECARE OPTIONS
See VISITING HOMEMAKER SERVICE OF PASSAIC COUNTY INC

D-U-N-S 04-322-8324
HOMECARE PREFERRED CHOICE INC
BEVERLY HEALTHCARE
(*Suby of* GOLDEN LIVING) ★
1000 Fianna Way, Fort Smith, AR 72919-9008
Tel (479) 201-2000 *Founded/Ownrshp* 1997, 2008
Sales 36.6MMᴱ *EMP* 1,200
SIC 8082 Home health care services; Home health care services
Pr: Cindy H Susienka
**VP:* Bob Donovan

HOMECREST
See MASTERBRAND CABINETS INC

HOMECREST CABINETRY
See H-C LIQUIDATING CORP

D-U-N-S 82-589-9078 IMP
HOMECREST OUTDOOR LIVING LLC
1250 Homecrest Ave Se, Wadena, MN 56482-1877
Tel (218) 631-1000 *Founded/Ownrshp* 1953
Sales 37.4MMᴱ *EMP* 75
SIC 5023 Home furnishings
**CFO:* Chris Fox
VP: Laurie Swiler
Genl Mgr: Tim Dejong
CTO: Michael Kellen
CTO: John Motschenbacher
Mktg Dir: Mary Heltemes

D-U-N-S 13-048-0981
HOMEDELIVERYAMERICA.COM INC
333 Mdwlands Pkwy Ste 406, Secaucus, NJ 07094-1821
Tel (201) 617-1800 *Founded/Ownrshp* 1965
Sales 25.0MM *EMP* 90
SIC 4214 8741 4215 Local trucking with storage; Management services; Courier services, except by air; Local trucking with storage; Management services; Courier services, except by air
Ch Bd: Richard Merians
**CFO:* David L Boyne
**VP:* Jane Quan-Shau

D-U-N-S 04-049-0513
HOMEDELIVERYLINK INC
32236 Paseo Adelanto C, San Juan Capistrano, CA 92675-3609
Tel (949) 248-7501 *Founded/Ownrshp* 2000
Sales 23.1MMᴱ *EMP* 96
SIC 4212 Delivery service, vehicular
CEO: Robert E Fleisher

HOMEDICS
See FKA DISTRIBUTING CO LLC

D-U-N-S 16-441-4364 IMP
HOMEDICS USA LLC
NATIONWIDE DISTRIBUTING
(*Suby of* FKA DISTRIBUTING CO LLC) ★
3000 N Pontiac Trl, Commerce Township, MI 48390-2720
Tel (248) 863-3000 *Founded/Ownrshp* 1987
Sales 47.1MMᴱ *EMP* 300
SIC 2844 7991 7922 Toilet preparations; Spas; Beauty contest production; Toilet preparations; Spas; Beauty contest production
CEO: Alon Kaufman
Chf Mktg O: Barb Westfield
VP: Mike Mathews
VP: Katherine Matson
Genl Mgr: Ed Gatt
Dir IT: Kevin Johnson
Mktg Mgr: Herb Conroy

D-U-N-S 05-109-2716
HOMEDIRECT INC
HOMEDIRECTUSA
2001 Bttrfeld Rd Ste 1400, Downers Grove, IL 60515
Tel (708) 649-7500 *Founded/Ownrshp* 1998, 2005
Sales 54.0MMᴱ *EMP* 240
SIC 4213 4789 Household goods transport; Cargo loading & unloading services; Household goods transport; Cargo loading & unloading services
Pr: Brian Gallagher
**COO:* Frank Gaura
CFO: Jaclyn Nohren
Sr VP: James Vargo
**VP:* Tony Coletto
VP: Frank Craven
**VP:* Jim Mikrut
VP: Steve Stayduhar
**Prin:* Jeff Frederick
Dir IT: Alan McRae
IT Man: Mike Dieter

HOMEDIRECTUSA
See HOMEDIRECT INC

HOMEFABRICS & RUGS
See SQUARE YARD INC

D-U-N-S 19-975-4961
■ **HOMEFED CORP**
(*Suby of* LEUCADIA NATIONAL CORP) ★
1903 Wright Pl Ste 220, Carlsbad, CA 92008-6584
Tel (760) 918-8200 *Founded/Ownrshp* 1988
Sales 59.5MM *EMP* 27ᴱ
Tkr Sym HOFD *Exch* OTO
SIC 6514 Residential building, four or fewer units: operation
Pr: Paul J Borden
**Ch Bd:* Joseph S Steinberg
**Treas:* Erin N Ruhe
**VP:* John K Aden Jr
VP: Kent Aden
**VP:* Christian E Foulger
VP: Curt Noland
Mktg Dir: Hale Richardson

D-U-N-S 62-685-4335
HOMEFIX CORP
1506 Joh Ave Ste 188, Halethorpe, MD 21227-1083
Tel (410) 760-1777 *Founded/Ownrshp* 1990
Sales 42.3MMᴱ *EMP* 200
SIC 1521 General remodeling, single-family houses; General remodeling, single-family houses
Pr: Tope M Lala
Bd of Dir: James Wilson
Genl Mgr: Jonathan Morse
Mktg Dir: Graham North
Sales Asso: Jimmie Bennett

D-U-N-S 00-480-2310
HOMEFRONT HOME IMPROVEMENT CENTER LLC (MS)
715 Highway 82 W, Greenwood, MS 38930-5027
Tel (662) 453-4371 *Founded/Ownrshp* 1959
Sales 24.3MMᴱ *EMP* 30
SIC 5211 Lumber & other building materials

D-U-N-S 80-591-0650 IMP/EXP
■ **HOMEGOODS INC**
HG BUYING
(*Suby of* TJ MAXX) ★
770 Cochituate Rd, Framingham, MA 01701-4666
Tel (508) 390-3199 *Founded/Ownrshp* 1992
Sales 393.5MMᴱ *EMP* 1,500
SIC 5719 Kitchenware; Kitchenware
CEO: Carol Meyrowitz
**Ch Bd:* Alex Smith
**Pr:* Ken Canestrari
**Pr:* John Ricciuti
**Treas:* Jamie Lowell
**Treas:* Mary B Reynolds
**Sr VP:* Robert Cataldo
**Sr VP:* Richard Sherr
**VP:* Alfred Appel
**VP:* Jeffrey Naylor
VP: George Stephatos

HOMEGROWN NATURALS
See ANNIES INC

HOMELAND
See HAC INC

D-U-N-S 04-011-0108 IMP/EXP
HOMELAND BUILDERS INC
465 Sykes Rd, Fall River, MA 02720-4749
Tel (508) 677-0401 *Founded/Ownrshp* 1975
Sales 28.0MMᴱ *EMP* 85
SIC 1542 Nonresidential construction; Commercial & office buildings, renovation & repair; Nonresidential construction; Commercial & office buildings, renovation & repair
Pr: Eduardo V Ribeiro
Sfty Mgr: Paul Carvalho
Mktg Dir: Brian Ribera

D-U-N-S 01-417-7548
HOMELAND ENERGY SOLUTIONS LLC
2779 Highway 24, Lawler, IA 52154
Tel (563) 238-5555 *Founded/Ownrshp* 2005
Sales 330.4MM *EMP* 46
Accts Mcgladrey Llp Des Moines Iow
SIC 2869 2085 2046 Ethyl alcohol, ethanol; Distillers' dried grains & solubles & alcohol; Corn oil products; Ethyl alcohol, ethanol; Distillers' dried grains & solubles & alcohol; Corn oil products
Ch Bd: Patrick Boyle
CFO: David A Finke
**V Ch Bd:* Maurice Hyde
VP: Stan Wubbena
Board of Directors: Randy Bruess, Mathew Driscoll, Keith Eastman, Stephen Eastman, Leslie Hansen, Edward Hatten, Chad Kuhlers

D-U-N-S 01-402-3837
HOMELAND HEALTHCARE INC (TX)
825 Market St Ste 300, Allen, TX 75013-3778
Tel (214) 871-2118 *Founded/Ownrshp* 1997, 2008
Sales NA *EMP* 260
SIC 6321 Accident & health insurance; Accident & health insurance
CEO: Ron Fields
**Pr:* Robert Byrnes Jr
**CFO:* Willam Keys
Ofcr: Latonya Cole
Ofcr: Christy Fortenberry
VP: Thomas Blomberg
**VP:* Reba J Leonard
VP Admn: Mike Wood
IT Man: Steve Cross
VP Mktg: Jennifer Casey
Mktg Mgr: Tammy Kazmierczak

HOMELAND SECURITY EMRGNCY MGT
See COUNTY OF KENTON

D-U-N-S 12-915-2844
HOMELAND SECURITY SERVICES INC
201 E Center St D, Anaheim, CA 92805-7204
Tel (714) 956-2200 *Founded/Ownrshp* 2001
Sales 437.9M *EMP* 400
SIC 7382 7381 Protective devices, security; Detective & armored car services; Detective services; Protective devices, security; Detective & armored car services; Detective services
Pr: Leonard Bacani
**VP:* Florencia Bacani

D-U-N-S 13-109-8563
HOMELAND SECURITY SOLUTIONS INC
3130a Nasa Dr, Hampton, VA 23666
Tel (757) 722-4726 *Founded/Ownrshp* 2014
Sales 47.0MM *EMP* 850
SIC 7382 Security systems services; Security systems services
Pr: Stephen Cameron
COO: Richard B Neville
CFO: Julia Byron
IT Man: Alex Fernandez
Opers Mgr: Mike Kernan

D-U-N-S 87-674-1828
HOMELAND VINYL PRODUCTS INC
3300 Pinson Valley Pkwy, Birmingham, AL 35217-1816
Tel (205) 854-4330 *Founded/Ownrshp* 1993
Sales 14.6MM^E *EMP* 350^E
SIC 3081 Unsupported plastics film & sheet; Unsupported plastics film & sheet
Pr: Randall D Heath
Pr: Bill McGinness
**Sec:* Larry Frost
Dir IT: Steve Heath
Sales Exec: Judy Williams
Mktg Dir: Doug House
Manager: Don Discipio
Sls Mgr: Don Hardekopf

D-U-N-S 18-832-0279 IMP/EXP
HOMELEGANCE INC
A G A
48200 Fremont Blvd, Fremont, CA 94538-6509
Tel (510) 933-6888 *Founded/Ownrshp* 1985
Sales 34.0MM^E *EMP* 90
SIC 5021 Household furniture; Household furniture
CEO: Puhsien C Chao
**Pr:* Rosa Chao
**VP:* Hutch Chao

D-U-N-S 01-549-1970 IMP/EXP
HOMELEGANCE LA INC
HOMERICA
10506 Shoemaker Ave, Santa Fe Springs, CA 90670-4036
Tel (562) 903-5668 *Founded/Ownrshp* 1996
Sales 23.8MM *EMP* 25
Accts Huang & Huang Cpas Walnut Ca
SIC 5021 Furniture; Furniture
CEO: Yu-Hung Chen

HOMELESS CASE MANAGEMENT
See COMMUNITY RESIDENCES INC

HOMELITE CONSUMER PRODUCTS
See RYOBI TECHNOLOGIES INC

D-U-N-S 08-695-9157 IMP/EXP
HOMELITE CONSUMER PRODUCTS INC
(*Suby of* TECHTRONIC INDUSTRIES NORTH AMERICA INC) ★
1428 Pearman Dairy Rd, Anderson, SC 29625-2000
Tel (864) 226-6511 *Founded/Ownrshp* 2003
Sales 256.3MM^E *EMP* 650^E
SIC 5083 Lawn machinery & equipment; Lawn machinery & equipment
Pr: Lee Sowell
CFO: Philippe Duisson
**CFO:* Ken Faith
**Treas:* Bette Ann Braeutigam
Exec: Steve Moore
VP Mktg: Mike Sarrah
Sls Mgr: Eric Baier
Sls Mgr: Bethany Hawkins
Sls Mgr: Brian Madson

D-U-N-S 83-326-8634
HOMEMAKER HEALTH CARE INC
718 E Capitol Ave, Jefferson City, MO 65101-4009
Tel (573) 635-3900 *Founded/Ownrshp* 1973
Sales 2.3MM *EMP* 279
Accts Graves & Associates Cpas Llc
SIC 8082 Home health care services; Home health care services
Nrsg Dir: Trish Beckman

HOMEMAKER SERVICE
See FAMILY & CHILDRENS AID INC

HOMEMAKERS FURNITURE
See HOMEMAKERS PLAZA INC

D-U-N-S 10-222-2924
HOMEMAKERS INC OF OSHKOSH WISCONSIN
CAREGIVERS HOME HEALTH
(*Suby of* RES-CARE INC) ★
2020 W 9th Ave, Oshkosh, WI 54904-8072
Tel (920) 233-2081 *Founded/Ownrshp* 2008
Sales 5.2MM^E *EMP* 325
SIC 8082 Home health care services; Home health care services
Pr: George Tucker
**VP:* Jett Schuler

D-U-N-S 06-961-5938 IMP
■ **HOMEMAKERS PLAZA INC** (IA)
HOMEMAKERS FURNITURE
(*Suby of* NEBRASKA FURNITURE MART INC) ★
10215 Douglas Ave, Des Moines, IA 50322-5406
Tel (888) 818-7283 *Founded/Ownrshp* 1974, 2000
Sales 71.8MM^E *EMP* 316
SIC 5712 5719 Furniture stores; Lighting fixtures; Pictures & mirrors; Furniture stores; Lighting fixtures; Pictures & mirrors
Pr: David Merschman
CFO: Jim Reed
**Sec:* INA Merschman
**VP:* Alan Merschman
**VP:* Constance Merschman
**VP:* Roger Merschman
**VP:* Teresa Merschman
Mktg Mgr: Janet Cole

D-U-N-S 03-020-5363
HOMEMAKERS UPSTATE GROUP INC
CAREGIVERS
2465 Sheridan Dr, Tonawanda, NY 14150-9407
Tel (716) 838-6060 *Founded/Ownrshp* 1971
Sales 8.0MM *EMP* 800
SIC 8742 8082 Management consulting services; Home health care services; Management consulting services; Home health care services
Pr: Tim McGorry
**VP:* Anne-Marie Warda
**Prin:* Bader Reynolds

D-U-N-S 96-268-8776
HOMENURSE INC
HOME NURSE
2920 N Expressway, Griffin, GA 30223-6495
Tel (770) 229-9431 *Founded/Ownrshp* 1995
Sales 11.9MM^E *EMP* 500^E
SIC 8082 7361 Home health care services; Nurses' registry; Home health care services; Nurses' registry
Pr: Miranda Roberson

D-U-N-S 07-781-3723
HOMEOWNERS WARRANTY INSURANCE CO
C/O PALOMAR FINANCIAL
7501 N Cpitl Of Texas Hwy, Austin, TX 78731-1773
Tel (512) 404-6555 *Founded/Ownrshp* 1974
Sales NA *EMP* 504
SIC 6351 Warranty insurance, home; Warranty insurance, home

D-U-N-S 79-074-8276
HOMEOWNERSHIP PRESERVATION FOUNDATION
7645 Lyndale Ave S # 250, Minneapolis, MN 55423-6008
Tel (612) 230-4020 *Founded/Ownrshp* 2003
Sales 34.2MM *EMP* 4
Accts Eide Bailly Llp Minneapolis
SIC 8322 General counseling services; General counseling services
Pr: Colleen Hernandez
Off Mgr: Susan Anderson

D-U-N-S 04-986-0505
■ **HOMEQ SERVICING CORP**
(*Suby of* OCWEN LOAN SERVICING LLC) ★
4837 Watt Ave, North Highlands, CA 95660-5108
Tel (916) 339-6192 *Founded/Ownrshp* 2010
Sales NA *EMP* 1,200
SIC 6162 6163 6111 6159 Mortgage bankers; Agents, farm or business loan; Student Loan Marketing Association; Automobile finance leasing; Mortgage bankers; Agents, farm or business loan; Student Loan Marketing Association; Automobile finance leasing
Pr: Arthur Lyon
**COO:* Keith G Becher
Treas: John A Hollstien
**Sec:* Mark K Metz

D-U-N-S 01-077-7845
HOMER CENTRAL SCHOOL DISTRICT
HCDS
80 S West St, Homer, NY 13077-1599
Tel (607) 749-7241 *Founded/Ownrshp* 1949
Sales 38.3MM *EMP* 389
Accts Ciaschi Dietershagen Little
SIC 8211 Public elementary & secondary schools; Public junior high school; Public senior high school; Public elementary & secondary schools; Public junior high school; Public senior high school
**Prin:* Douglas Vanetten
Schl Brd P: Sonia Apker

D-U-N-S 07-923-7786 IMP
HOMER CITY GENERATION LP
1750 Power Plant Rd, Homer City, PA 15748-8009
Tel (724) 479-9011 *Founded/Ownrshp* 2012
Sales 65.6MM^E *EMP* 74^E
SIC 4931 Electric & other services combined

D-U-N-S 04-746-1504
HOMER COMMUNITY CONSOLIDATED SCHOOL DISTRICT 33 C
CCSD 33C
15733 S Bell Rd, Homer Glen, IL 60491-8404
Tel (708) 226-7600 *Founded/Ownrshp* 1956
Sales 57.6MM *EMP* 497
SIC 8211 Public elementary school; Public elementary school
Dir IT: Candis Gasa
Dir IT: Arlene Siefert
Pr Dir: Charla Brautigam

D-U-N-S 04-133-3931
HOMER ELECTRIC ASSOCIATION INC
HEA
3977 Lake St, Homer, AK 99603-7680
Tel (907) 283-5831 *Founded/Ownrshp* 1946
Sales 47.4MM *EMP* 123
SIC 4911 Distribution, electric power; Distribution, electric power
CEO: Bradley Janorschke
**Pr:* Debbie Debnam
**Pr:* Richard Waisanen
**VP:* William Fry
VP: Maynard Smith
IT Man: Kim Gallagher
Sfty Dirs: Eddie Tauton
Plnt Mgr: Jim Kingrey

D-U-N-S 00-432-3481 IMP/EXP
HOMER LAUGHLIN CHINA CO (DE)
FOODSERVICE DIVISION
672 Fiesta Dr, Newell, WV 26050-1299
Tel (304) 387-1300 *Founded/Ownrshp* 1927
Sales 85.5MM^E *EMP* 1,000^E
SIC 3262 5719

D-U-N-S 06-973-6601
HOMER MEMORIAL HOSPITAL
620 E College St, Homer, LA 71040-3202
Tel (318) 927-2024 *Founded/Ownrshp* 2005
Sales 29.2MM^E *EMP* 250
SIC 8062 General medical & surgical hospitals; General medical & surgical hospitals
CFO: Amy Legendre
Ex Dir: Vance Robinson
Nurse Mgr: Melody Checcarelli
Dir IT: Landon Dick

HOMER SKELTON AUTO SALES
See HOMER SKELTON FORD INC

D-U-N-S 00-781-5108
HOMER SKELTON FORD INC (MS)
HOMER SKELTON AUTO SALES
6950 Hannah Cv, Olive Branch, MS 38654-2128
Tel (662) 895-6700 *Founded/Ownrshp* 1989
Sales 47.7MM^E *EMP* 100^E
SIC 5511 Automobiles, new & used; Automobiles, new & used
CEO: Homer Skeleton
**Pr:* Michelle Chapman
**CEO:* Homer Skelton
Sls Mgr: Jody Archer

D-U-N-S 00-796-7466
HOMER T HAYWARD LUMBER CO (CA)
2511 Garden Rd, Monterey, CA 93940-5330
Tel (831) 643-1900 *Founded/Ownrshp* 1919
Sales 59.4MM^E *EMP* 200
SIC 5211 Lumber & other building materials; Lumber & other building materials
Ch Bd: Marshall Perry
Pr: William E Hayward
COO: Jim Stockman
CFO: Steve Nangelfen
Dir IT: Ed Davis
Sales Exec: Mark MEI
Mktg Dir: Suzanne Moore
Snr Mgr: Peter Grossman

D-U-N-S 87-802-0114
HOMEREACH INC
(*Suby of* OHIOHEALTH CORP) ★
404 E Wilson Bridge Rd, Worthington, OH 43085-2369
Tel (614) 566-0850 *Founded/Ownrshp* 1993
Sales 14.6MM^E *EMP* 300
SIC 8082 Home health care services; Home health care services
Pr: Frances Baby
CFO: Mike Lazar
Off Mgr: Mary Shoemaker
MIS Dir: Susan Rising

HOMERICA
See HOMELEGANCE LA INC

HOMER'S BUFFETT
See DUFFS RESTAURANTS INC

HOMES AND LAND PUBLISHING
See ENDURANCE BUSINESS MEDIA HOLDINGS LLC

D-U-N-S 96-723-2489
HOMES BY WILLIAMSCRAFT INC
4985 Lower Roswell Rd, Marietta, GA 30068-4337
Tel (678) 987-1530 *Founded/Ownrshp* 1998
Sales 64.3MM *EMP* 33
Accts Crouse & Company Pc Atlant
SIC 1521 Single-family housing construction
Pr: B Wilmont Williams
**VP:* Stacy Hanley
VP: Jamey Pugh

D-U-N-S 19-589-3719
HOMES DIRECT OF ALBUQUERQUE
2710 Karsten Ct Se, Albuquerque, NM 87102-5082
Tel (505) 242-7555 *Founded/Ownrshp* 2002
Sales 40.0MM^E *EMP* 15
SIC 1521 New construction, single-family houses; New construction, single-family houses
Pt: Ray Gritton

D-U-N-S 15-479-7070
HOMES FOR HOMELESS INC
50 Cooper Sq Fl 4, New York, NY 10003-7144
Tel (212) 529-5252 *Founded/Ownrshp* 1986
Sales 20.6MM *EMP* 370
Accts Eisneramper Llp New York Ny
SIC 8361 Self-help group home; Self-help group home
Prin: Ralph Nunez
**VP:* Denise Scaravella
IT Man: Harrish Anthony

D-U-N-S 79-601-4798
HOMES FOR INDEPENDENT LIVING OF WISCONSIN LLC
(*Suby of* OCONOMOWOC RESIDENTIAL PROGRAMS INC) ★
1746 Executive Dr, Oconomowoc, WI 53066-4830
Tel (262) 569-5520 *Founded/Ownrshp* 1999
Sales 41.1MM *EMP* 550
Accts Bdo Usa Llp Milwaukee Wi
SIC 8052 Intermediate care facilities; Home for the mentally retarded, with health care
Dir IT: Tim Hornak

D-U-N-S 01-994-4042
HOMESALE REAL ESTATE SERVICES INC
BERKSHIRE HTHAWAY HOMESERVICES
215 S Centerville Rd, Lancaster, PA 17603-8831
Tel (717) 393-0783 *Founded/Ownrshp* 1997
Sales 39.6MM^E *EMP* 250
SIC 6531 Real estate agent, residential; Real estate agent, residential
Pr: Sharon Kress
Treas: William Wolverton
Ofcr: Sarah Tompos
VP: Alicia Motter
Exec: Ronda Zeigler
Ex Dir: Doug Rebert
Sales Exec: Diana Gabardi
Mktg Mgr: Mark Ginder
Sales Asso: Richard Angstadt
Sales Asso: Mitchell Darcourt

D-U-N-S 16-662-4655
HOMESERVE USA CORP
HOME EMERGENCY SOLUTIONS
(*Suby of* HOMESERVE PLC)
601 Merritt 7 Fl 6, Norwalk, CT 06851-1174
Tel (203) 351-4924 *Founded/Ownrshp* 2003
Sales 300.0MM *EMP* 700
SIC 8741 1521 Administrative management; Administrative management; Single-family home remodeling, additions & repairs
Pr: Thomas Rusin
**CFO:* Rich Gannon
**Treas:* Chris Miller
VP: Jason Barnes
**VP:* Neil Grant
**CIO:* Dave Berry
Board of Directors: Mike Frosch, Betty Montgomery

D-U-N-S 94-223-2463
HOMESERVICES LENDING LLC
333 S 7th St Fl 27, Minneapolis, MN 55402-2438
Tel (952) 928-5300 *Founded/Ownrshp* 1995
Sales NA *EMP* 200
SIC 6162 Mortgage bankers & correspondents; Mortgage bankers & correspondents
COO: Todd Johnson
Natl Sales: Mark McGoldrick

D-U-N-S 07-692-9699
■ **HOMESERVICES OF AMERICA INC**
(*Suby of* BERKSHIRE HATHAWAY ENERGY CO) ★
333 S 7th St Fl 27, Minneapolis, MN 55402-2438
Tel (612) 336-5900 *Founded/Ownrshp* 1999
Sales NA *EMP* 2,172
SIC 6351 6531 6361 Real estate title insurance; Warranty insurance, home; Real estate brokers & agents; Warranty insurance, home; Real estate brokers & agents; Real estate title insurance
CEO: Ronald Peltier
**Pr:* R Michael Knapp
**Pr:* Robert Moline
Pr: J P Peltier
**Sr VP:* Dana Strandmo
**Sr VP:* Micheal Warmka
**Sr VP:* Mike Warmka
VP: Patty Czetowski
VP: C J Deike
**VP:* Jim Lamphere
**VP:* Patty Smejkal

D-U-N-S 13-522-5626
■ **HOMESERVICES OF CALIFORNIA INC**
(*Suby of* HOMESERVICES OF AMERICA INC) ★
6800 France Ave S Ste 600, Minneapolis, MN 55435-2017
Tel (952) 928-5900 *Founded/Ownrshp* 2002
Sales 15.3MM^E *EMP* 672
SIC 6531 Real estate agents & managers; Real estate agents & managers
Pr: Ronald Peltier
**VP:* Galen K Johnson

D-U-N-S 06-947-3163
■ **HOMESERVICES OF ILLINOIS LLC**
BERKSHIRE HATHAWAY HOME
(*Suby of* HOMESERVICES OF AMERICA INC) ★
1370 Meadow Rd, Skokie, IL 60076
Tel (847) 853-5000 *Founded/Ownrshp* 2009
Sales NA *EMP* 510
SIC 6162 Mortgage bankers & correspondents; Mortgage bankers & correspondents
Pr: Nancy Agy
COO: Bob Harroun
VP: Jeani Jernstedt
VP: George H Moloney III
VP: George Moloney
Off Mgr: Becky Hauser
IT Man: Chris Bolling
Sls&Mrk Ex: Donna August
VP Sls: Shirley Amico
S&M/VP: Connie Atterbury

D-U-N-S 05-335-1230
HOMESITE GROUP INC
HOMESITE INSURANCE
(*Suby of* AMERICAN FAMILY INSURANCE) ★
1 Federal St Fl 4, Boston, MA 02110-2003
Tel (617) 832-1300 *Founded/Ownrshp* 2014
Sales NA *EMP* 41
SIC 6411 Property & casualty insurance agent
Pr: Fabian J Fondriest
COO: Douglas Batting
Ofcr: Maureen Fidler
Ex VP: Andrew McElwee
**VP:* Randall Dyen
VP: Kristine Kash
VP: Jim Morahan
VP: Alex Punsalan
Exec: Monique Bartolo
Prgrm Mgr: Brian Pond
Snr Sftwr: Dennis Medeiros

HOMESITE INSURANCE
See HOMESITE GROUP INC

D-U-N-S 55-613-9801
HOMESITE SERVICES INC
6611 Preston Ave Ste E, Livermore, CA 94551-5108
Tel (925) 237-3050 *Founded/Ownrshp* 2004
Sales 39.4MM^E *EMP* 170
SIC 5713 5211 5023 Floor covering stores; Flooring contractor; Floor covering stores; Counter tops; Window covering parts & accessories
CEO: Tina Tomei
**COO:* Darryl Phelps

HOMESMART
See AARONS INC

D-U-N-S 11-279-0071
HOMESTAR FINANCIAL CORP
332 Washington St Nw, Gainesville, GA 30501-8517
Tel (770) 503-0380 *Founded/Ownrshp* 2002
Sales NA *EMP* 306

SIC 6162 Mortgage bankers
Pr: Wesley T Hunt
Treas: Ann C Thomsen
Ofcr: Donna Broderick
VP: Robert Messer
VP: Norman Thibault
Brnch Mgr: Paul Abraham
Brnch Mgr: Rhonda Busby
Brnch Mgr: Patti Hale
Brnch Mgr: Debra Johnston
Brnch Mgr: Nancy Presley
Brnch Mgr: John Price

D-U-N-S 07-920-1284
HOMESTAR NORTH AMERICA LLC
607 Meacham Rd, Statesville, NC 28677-2979
Tel (704) 873-3106 *Founded/Ownrshp* 2013
Sales 20.5MM^E *EMP* 100
SIC 2519 5021 2511 Household furniture, except wood or metal: upholstered; Office furniture; Wood bedroom furniture
VP: Steve Miller
**Pr:* Steve Liu

D-U-N-S 95-682-3116
HOMESTEAD
HOMESTEAD SOLDIERS SAILORS MEM
418 N Main St Ste 1, Penn Yan, NY 14527-1070
Tel (315) 531-2700 *Founded/Ownrshp* 1996
Sales 29.8MM *EMP* 2
SIC 8322 Individual & family services; Individual & family services
CEO: James Dooley
**CEO:* James Dully

D-U-N-S 00-120-0542
HOMESTEAD BAKING CO (RI)
145 N Broadway, Rumford, RI 02916-2801
Tel (401) 434-0551 *Founded/Ownrshp* 1920
Sales 20.9MM^E *EMP* 95
SIC 2051 Rolls, bread type: fresh or frozen; Bread, all types (white, wheat, rye, etc): fresh or frozen
Pr: Peter Vican
**Treas:* Bill Vican
**Treas:* William Vican Jr

D-U-N-S 06-583-2516
HOMESTEAD CHARTER FOUNDATION INC
KEYS GATE CHARTER SCHOOL
800 Corporate Dr Ste 124, Fort Lauderdale, FL 33334-3618
Tel (954) 202-3500 *Founded/Ownrshp* 2000
Sales 31.8MM *EMP* 180
SIC 8211 Private elementary & secondary schools; Private elementary & secondary schools
Pr: Eduardo Berrones
**VP:* Corey Gold

HOMESTEAD CHEESE
See STEVES WHOLESALE LLC

D-U-N-S 60-099-0985
HOMESTEAD CRAFTSMEN ASSOCIATION
HERITAGE RESTORATIONS
608 Dry Creek Rd, Waco, TX 76705-5409
Tel (254) 754-9600 *Founded/Ownrshp* 2005
Sales 28.3MM^E *EMP* 150
SIC 1542 1521 5712 2511 5812 0191 Nonresidential construction; Single-family housing construction; Furniture stores; Wood household furniture; Eating places; General farms, primarily crop; Nonresidential construction; Single-family housing construction; Furniture stores; Wood household furniture; Eating places; General farms, primarily crop

D-U-N-S 01-904-4999
HOMESTEAD ENTERPRISES INC
BUD'S SHOP N SAVE
44 Moosehead Trl, Newport, ME 04953-4108
Tel (207) 368-4733 *Founded/Ownrshp* 1985
Sales 23.4MM^E *EMP* 240
SIC 5411 8741 Supermarkets, chain; Management services; Supermarkets, chain; Management services
Pr: Charles Daniel Hill
**Treas:* Dean A Homestead

D-U-N-S 92-866-0489
HOMESTEAD FUNDING CORP
FIRST NIAGARA MORTGAGE
8 Airline Dr Ste 200, Albany, NY 12205-1019
Tel (518) 250-5641 *Founded/Ownrshp* 1994
Sales NA *EMP* 132
SIC 6162 Mortgage bankers; Mortgage bankers
Pr: Michael Rutherford
Ofcr: Kristine Wood
**VP:* Paul Rutherford
VP Mktg: Jill Flaherty
Corp Couns: Michael Solodar

D-U-N-S 07-830-2254 IMP
HOMESTEAD GARDENS INC (MD)
HOMESTEAD GARDENS LDSCPG SVCS
743 W Central Ave, Davidsonville, MD 21035-1935
Tel (410) 798-5000 *Founded/Ownrshp* 1972
Sales 63.2MM^E *EMP* 250
Accts Sturn Wagner Lombardo & Comp
SIC 5261 0181 Nurseries; Nursery stock, seeds & bulbs; Nursery stock, growing of; Nurseries; Nursery stock, seeds & bulbs; Nursery stock, growing of
Pr: Brian Riddle
**VP:* Steven Flury
IT Man: Brenda Fuentes
Manager: Roberta Zimmerman

HOMESTEAD GARDENS LDSCPG SVCS
See HOMESTEAD GARDENS INC

D-U-N-S 96-450-0214
HOMESTEAD GROUP
30 Cumberland St Ste 4, Woonsocket, RI 02895-3342
Tel (401) 775-1500 *Founded/Ownrshp* 2010
Sales 23.3MM^E *EMP* 2
Accts Kahn Litwin Renza Providenc
SIC 8322 Social service center; Social service center
Prin: Lee Ann Beaupre

D-U-N-S 07-984-3765
HOMESTEAD HOSPITAL INC
(*Suby of* BAPTIST HEALTH SOUTH FLORIDA INC) ★
975 Baptist Way, Homestead, FL 33033-7600
Tel (786) 243-8000 *Founded/Ownrshp* 1940
Sales 174.6MM *EMP* 1^E
Accts Deloitte & Touche Llp
SIC 8062 General medical & surgical hospitals
CEO: William M Duquette

D-U-N-S 82-824-4165
HOMESTEAD LONG TERM CARE MANAGEMENT LLC
1725 Old Brandon Rd, Hillsboro, TX 76645-2702
Tel (325) 854-1429 *Founded/Ownrshp* 2008
Sales 16.6MM^E *EMP* 301
SIC 8051 Services; Skilled nursing care facilities

HOMESTEAD MATERIALS HDLG CO
See JEFFERDS CORP

HOMESTEAD NURSING HOME
See HEALTHCARE RESOURCES CORP

D-U-N-S 82-702-4808
HOMESTEAD OPERATING CO INC
1766 Homestead Dr, Hot Springs, VA 24445-2910
Tel (540) 839-1766 *Founded/Ownrshp* 2006
Sales 21.7MM^E *EMP* 856
SIC 7011 Resort hotel; Resort hotel
VP: Peter Faraone

HOMESTEAD REHAB AND LIVING CTR
See DEER RIVER HEALTH CARE CENTER INC

HOMESTEAD SOLDIERS SAILORS MEM
See HOMESTEAD

D-U-N-S 00-694-1207
HOMESTEADERS LIFE CO
5700 Westown Pkwy Ofc, West Des Moines, IA 50266-8214
Tel (515) 440-7777 *Founded/Ownrshp* 1906
Sales NA *EMP* 170
SIC 6311 Legal reserve life insurance; Legal reserve life insurance
CEO: Stephen Lang
**Ch Bd:* Graham Cook
COO: Steve Shaffer
CFO: Steve W Pick
Ex VP: Judy Ralsten
VP: Will Bischoff
VP: Bonnie Gerst
**VP:* Glen Hare
VP: Kevin Kubik
VP: Marla G Lacey
Exec: Joyce Wisgerhof

D-U-N-S 15-146-8873
■ **HOMESTREET BANK**
HOMESTREET MORTGAGE CENTER
(*Suby of* HOMESTREET INC) ★
601 Union St Ste 2000, Seattle, WA 98101-2326
Tel (206) 623-3050 *Founded/Ownrshp* 1985
Sales NA *EMP* 473
SIC 6036 State savings banks, not federally chartered; State savings banks, not federally chartered
CEO: Mark K Mason
**Ch Bd:* Bruce Williams
**V Ch:* Brian Dempsey
**CFO:* Debra L Johnson
Ofcr: Webber Debbie
Ofcr: Nancy Dennehy
Ofcr: Amanda Finnegan
Ofcr: Steve Morgensen
**Ex VP:* Howard Bell
**Ex VP:* Robert Saito
**Ex VP:* Martin A Steele
Ex VP: Cory Stewart
Sr VP: Randy Daniels
**Sr VP:* Rose Marie David
VP: Mark Ahlstedt
VP: Richard Bennion
VP: Patricia Leach
VP: Paulette Lemon
VP: Tom Snyder
VP: John Sprague
VP: Sharon Todhunter
Board of Directors: Thomas E King, Donald R Voss

D-U-N-S 07-924-7268
▲ **HOMESTREET INC** (WA)
601 Union St Ste 2000, Seattle, WA 98101-1378
Tel (206) 623-3050 *Founded/Ownrshp* 1921
Sales NA *EMP* 1,611
Tkr Sym HMST *Exch* NGM
SIC 6036

HOMESTREET MORTGAGE CENTER
See HOMESTREET BANK

D-U-N-S 01-562-8356 IMP
HOMESTRETCH HOLDINGS LLC
146 Furniture Dr, Nettleton, MS 38858-6124
Tel (662) 963-2494 *Founded/Ownrshp* 2009
Sales 63.6MM^E *EMP* 300
SIC 2512 Upholstered household furniture; Upholstered household furniture
Pr: William Holliman

D-U-N-S 04-556-4861
HOMESTYLE DINING LLC
BENNIGAN'S
6500 Intl Pkwy Ste 1000, Plano, TX 75093
Tel (972) 244-8900 *Founded/Ownrshp* 1993
Sales 409.8MM^E *EMP* 10,525
SIC 5812 6794 Restaurant, family: chain; Franchises, selling or licensing; Restaurant, family: chain; Franchises, selling or licensing
COO: Howard Finkelstein
VP: Scott Neice
Dir Bus: Mike Jackson

D-U-N-S 07-103-7204
HOMESURE SERVICE INC
(*Suby of* CROSS COUNTRY HOME SERVICES INC) ★
1625 Nw 136th Ave Ste 200, Sunrise, FL 33323-2842
Tel (954) 845-9100 *Founded/Ownrshp* 1988
Sales NA *EMP* 400^E
SIC 6351 Warranty insurance, home; Warranty insurance, home
Pr: Sandra C Finn
VP: Howard Wolk

HOMETEAM ENVIRONMENTAL SVCS
See HOMETEAM PEST DEFENSE INC

D-U-N-S 95-727-9011
■ **HOMETEAM PEST DEFENSE INC**
HOMETEAM ENVIRONMENTAL SVCS
(*Suby of* ROLLINS INC) ★
3100 Mckinnon St Ste 120, Dallas, TX 75201-1111
Tel (214) 665-8700 *Founded/Ownrshp* 2008
Sales 64.0MM^E *EMP* 1,400
SIC 7342 Disinfecting & pest control services; Disinfecting & pest control services
Pr: Jerry Gahlhoff
Pr: Dennis Cone
Pr: Mike Johnson
**CFO:* Kevin Wolf
**Sr VP:* Craig Innes
**VP:* Julie Bimmerman
**VP:* Brady Camp
VP: Steve Hammond
Genl Mgr: Duane Alewine
Genl Mgr: Jim Blaney
Genl Mgr: Justin Burlingame

D-U-N-S 02-340-6759
HOMETOWN AMERICA LLC
HOMETOWN AMERICA MANAGEMENT
150 N Wacker Dr Ste 2800, Chicago, IL 60606-1610
Tel (312) 604-7515 *Founded/Ownrshp* 1997
Sales 38.3MM^E *EMP* 1,000
SIC 6512 Nonresidential building operators; Nonresidential building operators
CEO: Richard Cline
VP: Peter Hepner
Exec: Pat Kerber
Manager: Hta Crochetta
Sls Mgr: Liz Picon

HOMETOWN AMERICA MANAGEMENT
See HOMETOWN AMERICA LLC

D-U-N-S 01-963-3523
HOMETOWN AMERICA MANAGEMENT CORP
(*Suby of* HOMETOWN AMERICA LLC) ★
150 N Wacker Dr Ste 2800, Chicago, IL 60606-1610
Tel (312) 604-7500 *Founded/Ownrshp* 2002
Sales 17.5MM^E *EMP* 1,000
SIC 6515 Mobile home site operators; Mobile home site operators
CEO: Richard Cline
**COO:* Greg Oberry

D-U-N-S 02-577-3693
HOMETOWN AUTO RETAILERS INC
1230 Main St, Watertown, CT 06795-3128
Tel (203) 756-8908 *Founded/Ownrshp* 1997
Sales 233.0MM *EMP* 297
SIC 5511 Automobiles, new & used; Pickups, new & used; Automobiles, new & used; Pickups, new & used
Pr: Corey Shaker
CFO: Charles F Schwartz
Bd of Dir: Bernard J Dzinski
**VP:* William C Muller Jr
**VP:* Joseph Shaker
Board of Directors: Bernard J Dzinski Jr, Steven A Fournier, Timothy C Moynahan

D-U-N-S 04-685-1465
HOMETOWN BANK NA
1801 45th St, Galveston, TX 77550-6542
Tel (409) 763-1271 *Founded/Ownrshp* 1966
Sales NA *EMP* 45
SIC 6021 National commercial banks; National commercial banks
Pr: A J Rasmussen
**Ch Bd:* Jack Miller
**Pr:* Jimmy Rasmussen
**Sr VP:* Gary Gilliland
**Sr VP:* Linda Jones

D-U-N-S 55-644-3711
HOMETOWN BUFFET INC
OLD COUNTRY BUFFET
(*Suby of* BUFFETS INC) ★
1020 Discovery Rd Ste 100, Eagan, MN 55121-2096
Tel (651) 994-8608 *Founded/Ownrshp* 1998
Sales 124.9MM^E *EMP* 5,364
SIC 5812 Buffet (eating places); Steak restaurant; Buffet (eating places); Steak restaurant
VP: Paul Holovnia
**CFO:* A Keith Wall

D-U-N-S 15-707-8705
HOMETOWN COMMUNITY DEVELOPMENT CORP
8711 Monroe Ct Ste A, Rancho Cucamonga, CA 91730-4898
Tel (877) 647-8764 *Founded/Ownrshp* 2004
Sales 55.3MM *EMP* 2
Accts Kho & Patel San Dimas Ca
SIC 6531 Real estate agents & managers
CEO: Jed Davis
**Pr:* Scott Choppin

D-U-N-S 19-498-8965
HOMETOWN CONVENIENCE LLC
DOUBLE KWIK
51 Highway 2034, Whitesburg, KY 41858-7686
Tel (606) 633-2525 *Founded/Ownrshp* 2002
Sales 89.6MM^E *EMP* 700
SIC 5172 Gasoline; Gasoline

D-U-N-S 10-332-3234
HOMETOWN DISTRIBUTING CO INC
4841 S California Ave, Chicago, IL 60632-2094
Tel (773) 650-9200 *Founded/Ownrshp* 1983
Sales 20.6MM^E *EMP* 95
SIC 5181 Beer & other fermented malt liquors; Beer & other fermented malt liquors
Pr: James W Taylor
**Sec:* Terrence Bell

D-U-N-S 05-617-7413
HOMETOWN ENTERPRISES INC
KFC
18815 139th Ave Ne Ste C, Woodinville, WA 98072-3565
Tel (425) 486-6336 *Founded/Ownrshp* 1994
Sales 45.1MM^E *EMP* 1,000
SIC 5812 Fast-food restaurant, chain; Fast-food restaurant, chain
CEO: Sam Sibert

D-U-N-S 07-549-0222 IMP/EXP
HOMETOWN FOODS USA INC
11800 Nw 102nd Rd Ste 6, Medley, FL 33178-1030
Tel (305) 887-5200 *Founded/Ownrshp* 1996
Sales 30.6MM^E *EMP* 95
SIC 2051 Bagels, fresh or frozen
Pr: Troy Schwartzberg
**Ex VP:* Gary J Schwartzberg
**VP:* Bryan Schwartzberg

HOMETOWN HEARTH & GRILL
See GAS CONNECTION LLC

D-U-N-S 03-151-1152
HOMETOWN IMPROVEMENT CO
1430 Halfhill Way, Columbus, OH 43207-4494
Tel (614) 846-1060 *Founded/Ownrshp* 1994
Sales 35.0MM *EMP* 25
SIC 1521 General remodeling, single-family houses
Owner: Richard Hatfield

D-U-N-S 06-920-4456
HOMETOWN NEWBURGH INC (NY)
NEWBURGH TOYOTA
(*Suby of* HOMETOWN AUTO RETAILERS INC) ★
218 Route 17k, Newburgh, NY 12550-8306
Tel (845) 561-0340 *Founded/Ownrshp* 1999
Sales 23.8MM^E *EMP* 80
SIC 5511 Automobiles, new & used; Automobiles, new & used
Pr: Joseph Shaker
Genl Mgr: Richard Gaillard

D-U-N-S 04-057-3888
HOMETOWN PHARMACY INC
60 E 82nd St, Newaygo, MI 49337-8005
Tel (231) 652-7810 *Founded/Ownrshp* 1996
Sales 54.0MM^E *EMP* 250
SIC 5912 Drug stores; Drug stores
Pr: Fred Grice Jr
COO: Jim Mathews
Dir Rx: Doug Josephson
Dir Rx: Dave Pontious
Opers Mgr: Brad Pressley
Opers Mgr: Clem Shea
Opers Mgr: Kelly Snider
Opers Mgr: Tiffany Varner
Sls Mgr: Amber Gorby
Pharmcst: Alyssa Cavanaugh
Pharmcst: Ann Rooney

D-U-N-S 11-910-5021
HOMETOWN PIZZA INC
111 E Adams St, La Grange, KY 40031-1229
Tel (502) 222-4444 *Founded/Ownrshp* 1982
Sales 12.1MM^E *EMP* 350
SIC 5812 Pizzeria, chain; Pizzeria, chain
Pr: Michael Foster
**VP:* Mary J Foster

D-U-N-S 10-395-0283
HOMETOWN PLUMBING & HEATING CO
13606 118th Ave, Davenport, IA 52804-9201
Tel (563) 381-4800 *Founded/Ownrshp* 1983
Sales 23.6MM^E *EMP* 80
SIC 1711 Plumbing contractors; Heating & air conditioning contractors
Pr: Michael O Day
**VP:* Kirk Baker
**VP:* Michael Manion
VP: Simon Possin
Exec: Michael Day
Sfty Dirs: Roy Smith

D-U-N-S 62-487-7093
HOMETOWN PROVISIONS INC
201 W Kendig Rd, Willow Street, PA 17584-9514
Tel (717) 464-4165 *Founded/Ownrshp* 2005
Sales 20.5MM^E *EMP* 29
SIC 5141 Food brokers
Pr: Barry E Mellinger
**Treas:* Kevin Adams
**Treas:* Daniel R Rote
**VP:* Paul C Rote
**Prin:* Kristy Mellinger

D-U-N-S 13-724-2322
HOMETOWN URGENT CARE
2400 Corp Exchange Dr # 102, Columbus, OH 43231-7605
Tel (614) 505-7633 *Founded/Ownrshp* 2000
Sales 66.5MM^E *EMP* 1,904^E
SIC 8062 General medical & surgical hospitals
CFO: Don Cain
Ql Cn Mgr: Elizabeth Blair

D-U-N-S 07-916-9938
▲ **HOMETRUST BANCSHARES INC**
10 Woodfin St, Asheville, NC 28801-3022
Tel (828) 259-3939 *Founded/Ownrshp* 2012
Sales NA *EMP* 505^E
Accts Dixon Hughes Goodman Llp Char
Tkr Sym HTBI *Exch* NGS
SIC 6035 Federal savings banks; Federal savings banks
Ch Bd: Dana L Stonestreet
CFO: Tony J Vuncannon
Chf Cred: Keith Houghton
Ofcr: Parrish Little
Ofcr: Teresa White
Ex VP: Howard L Sellinger
Ex VP: C Hunter Westbrook

D-U-N-S 07-631-6160
■ **HOMETRUST BANK**
(Suby of HOMETRUST BANCSHARES INC) ★
10 Woodfin St, Asheville, NC 28801-3022
Tel (828) 254-8144 Founded/Ownrshp 1996
Sales NA EMP 274
SIC 6021 National commercial banks; National commercial banks
Ch Bd: Dana L Stonestreet
*CFO: Tony Vuncannon
*V Ch Bd: Larry S McDevitt
Ofcr: Dave Baylis
Assoc VP: Pedro Velazquez
*Ex VP: R Parrish Little
*Sr VP: William Coleman III
Sr VP: Eric Edgison
Sr VP: Sallie Jarosz
Sr VP: John Sprink
Sr VP: Darrin Williams
VP: Stephen Anderson
VP: Trey Coleman
VP: Justin Dunn
VP: Ron Gooding
VP: Kevin Pashke
VP: Greg Sullins
VP: John Tench
VP: Wade White

D-U-N-S 09-888-6294
HOMETRUST MORTGAGE CO
5353 W Alabama St Ste 500, Houston, TX 77056-5922
Tel (713) 369-4000 Founded/Ownrshp 1986
Sales NA EMP 125
SIC 6162 Mortgage bankers; Mortgage bankers
Pr: Lynn Nunez
*Sec: Marvin Bendle
Ofcr: Terri Commiato
Ofcr: Connie Tharp
*VP: William Knapp
VP: Kevin Nunez
Brnch Mgr: David Falk
Brnch Mgr: Bradley Rife
Brnch Mgr: Mary Titel
Dir IT: Betty Magee
Dir IT: Georgeann Mahaffey

D-U-N-S 00-507-0339
■ **HOMETTE CORP**
SKYLINE MAINSFIELD
(Suby of SKYLINE CORP) ★
2520 Bypass Rd, Elkhart, IN 46514-1518
Tel (574) 294-6521 Founded/Ownrshp 1962
Sales 101.2MM^E EMP 650
SIC 2452 3792 Modular homes, prefabricated, wood; Travel trailers & campers; Modular homes, prefabricated, wood; Travel trailers & campers
Ch Bd: Thomas Deranek
*CFO: John Pilarski

D-U-N-S 17-846-5522
HOMEVESTORS OF AMERICA INC
(Suby of FRANCHISE BRANDS LLC) ★
6500 Greenville Ave # 400, Dallas, TX 75206-1014
Tel (972) 761-0046 Founded/Ownrshp 2008
Sales 34.5MM EMP 20^E
Accts Bkd Llp Dallas Texas
SIC 6794 Franchises, selling or licensing; Franchises, selling or licensing
Pr: David Hicks
*Co-Pr: Kenneth Channell
*VP: Bonnie Depasse
Off Mgr: Kristie Haukland
Off Mgr: Melissa Perez
Off Admin: Jessie Kraftsow
Opers Mgr: Andrea Morris
Sales Asso: Chad McKinney

D-U-N-S 83-652-9920
■ **HOMEWARD RESIDENTIAL HOLDINGS INC**
(Suby of OCWEN FINANCIAL CORP) ★
1525 S Belt Line Rd, Coppell, TX 75019-4913
Tel (877) 304-3100 Founded/Ownrshp 2012
Sales 94.5MM^E EMP 1,713^E
SIC 7389 Financial services
Pr: Ronald M Faris
*VP: Mark Zeidman

D-U-N-S 82-531-1231
■ **HOMEWARD RESIDENTIAL INC**
(Suby of HOMEWARD RESIDENTIAL HOLDINGS INC) ★
1525 S Belt Line Rd, Coppell, TX 75019-4913
Tel (877) 304-3100 Founded/Ownrshp 2011
Sales NA EMP 1,700
SIC 6162 Mortgage bankers & correspondents; Mortgage bankers & correspondents
Pr: David M Applegate
*CFO: John V Britti
*Treas: Ellen Coleman
*Sr VP: Joel Gendron
*VP: Barry J Bier
*VP: Mark Zeidman

D-U-N-S 78-791-6019 IMP
HOMEWERKS WORLDWIDE LLC
500 Bond St, Lincolnshire, IL 60069-4207
Tel (224) 543-1500 Founded/Ownrshp 2006
Sales 50.0MM EMP 25
SIC 5074 3564 Plumbing & hydronic heating supplies; Exhaust fans: industrial or commercial; Plumbing & hydronic heating supplies; Exhaust fans: industrial or commercial
Pr: Peter Berkman
*CFO: Richard Wild
Sr VP: Randy Altmann
VP Sls: Jeff Pischke

D-U-N-S 96-641-2731
HOMEWOOD AT FREDERICK MD INC
10500 Bower Ave, Williamsport, MD 21795-4000
Tel (301) 582-1626 Founded/Ownrshp 2011
Sales 25.2MM EMP 4^E
Accts Smith Elliott Kearns & Company
SIC 8011 General & family practice, physician/surgeon; General & family practice, physician/surgeon
Pr: Ernest W Angell

D-U-N-S 96-641-4596
HOMEWOOD AT HANOVER PA INC
10500 Bower Ave, Williamsport, MD 21795-4000
Tel (301) 582-1626 Founded/Ownrshp 2011
Sales 26.4MM EMP 2^E
Accts Smith Elliott Kearns & Company
SIC 6531 Real estate agent, commercial; Real estate agent, commercial

D-U-N-S 10-000-0504
HOMEWOOD CITY SCHOOL DISTRICT
CITY BOARD OF EDUCATION
450 Dale Ave, Birmingham, AL 35209-3401
Tel (205) 870-4203 Founded/Ownrshp 1970
Sales 24.6MM^E EMP 485
SIC 8211 Public elementary & secondary schools; Public elementary school; Public junior high school; Public elementary & secondary schools; Public elementary school; Public junior high school
*Pr: Christopher L Hawkins
*Pr: Bruce Limbaugh
*CFO: Elizabeth Nesmith
*VP: Nancy Ferren

D-U-N-S 04-231-2819
HOMEWOOD CORP
2700 E Dublin Granville R, Columbus, OH 43231-4089
Tel (614) 898-7200 Founded/Ownrshp 1964
Sales 49.8MM^E EMP 140
SIC 1522 Apartment building construction; Apartment building construction
CEO: John H Bain
*Pr: George Anthony Skestos
Dir IT: Robert Story

D-U-N-S 06-490-3974
HOMEWOOD RETIREMENT CENTERS OF UNITED CHURCH OF CHRIST INC (MD)
16107 Elliott Pkwy, Williamsport, MD 21795-4084
Tel (301) 582-1626 Founded/Ownrshp 1932
Sales 3.8MM EMP 1,075
Accts Smith Elliott Kearns & Company
SIC 8051 8361 Skilled nursing care facilities; Home for the aged; Skilled nursing care facilities; Home for the aged
Pr: Ernest W Angell
*VP: George Mc Cullough Jr
MIS Dir: Gary Recher
Board of Directors: Lisa Bethel

HOMEWOOD SUITES
See PROMUS HOTELS LLC

D-U-N-S 07-688-7637
HOMEWOOD-FLOSSMOOR COMMUNITY HIGH SCHOOL DISTRICT 233
COOK COUNTY SCHOOL DST 233
999 Kedzie Ave, Flossmoor, IL 60422-2248
Tel (708) 799-3000 Founded/Ownrshp 1959
Sales 32.4MM^E EMP 300
Accts Thomas Havey Llp
SIC 8211 Public senior high school; Public senior high school

HOMEWORKS
See TRI-COUNTY ELECTRIC CO-OPERATIVE INC

HOMEWORLD
See C S WO & SONS LIMITED

HOMICIDE SPT SVCS OF ANE
See HOSPICE OF CHESAPEAKE BEREAVEMENT CENTER

D-U-N-S 10-235-1541 IMP/EXP
HOMIER DISTRIBUTING CO INC
H D C
84 Commercial Rd, Huntington, IN 46750-8885
Tel (260) 356-9477 Founded/Ownrshp 1983
Sales 40.1MM^E EMP 260
SIC 5251 5072 Hardware; Hardware; Hardware; Hardware
Pr: Charles Homier F
*Sec: Pam Homier
*VP: Ron Scarpa
Ex Dir: Steve Shoemaker

HOMMEL MOVOMATIC
See JENOPTIK INDUSTRIAL METROLOGY NORTH AMERICA LLC

D-U-N-S 04-654-2684 IMP
■ **HOMOGENEOUS METALS INC**
HMI METAL POWDERS
(Suby of UNITED TECHNOLOGIES CORP) ★
2395 Main St, Clayville, NY 13322-1102
Tel (315) 839-5421 Founded/Ownrshp 1965
Sales 21.6MM^E EMP 60^E
SIC 3312 Billets, steel
Ch Bd: Mark Hewko
*Ch Bd: Greg Treacy
Treas: John Lapinski
*Genl Mgr: Mark Huwko
IT Man: Leslie Murphy
Sfty Mgr: Keith Sterling
Plnt Mgr: Jim Coyle

D-U-N-S 05-689-0528
HOMRICH WRECKING INC
200 Matlin Rd, Carleton, MI 48117-9799
Tel (734) 654-9800 Founded/Ownrshp 1965
Sales 25.7MM^E EMP 60
SIC 1795 Demolition, buildings & other structures
Pr: Roger Homrich
*CFO: Nick Straub
*VP: Michael Brant
*VP: Scott Homrich

D-U-N-S 62-652-5463 IMP
HOMTEX INC
DREAMFIT
15295 Al Highway 157, Vinemont, AL 35179-9077
Tel (256) 734-3937 Founded/Ownrshp 1987
Sales 32.0MM EMP 250
SIC 2211 Sheets, bedding & table cloths: cotton; Sheets, bedding & table cloths: cotton
CEO: Gerald Jerry Wootten Jr
Pr: Gerald Jeremy Wootten III
COO: Kenny Hines
Sec: Kathy Wootten
Exec: James Bradford

D-U-N-S 14-781-4735 IMP
■ **HON CO LLC**
(Suby of HNI CORP) ★
200 Oak St, Muscatine, IA 52761-4341
Tel (563) 272-7100 Founded/Ownrshp 1999
Sales 583.2MM^E EMP 4,000
SIC 2521 Wood office furniture; Wood office furniture
VP: Jason Helmer
VP: Jerry L Vande Kieft
VP: Jean Reynolds
VP: Robert Spears
Dir Bus: Greg Berkebile
Dir Bus: Dawn Pence
IT Man: Don Hirsch
VP Opers: Dave Gardner
Ql Cn Mgr: John Hayes
Ql Cn Mgr: Ivan Marti

D-U-N-S 60-423-6757 IMP
HON HAI PRECISION INDUSTRY CO LTD
NSG-CISCO
288 S Mayo Ave, Walnut, CA 91789-3091
Tel (713) 983-2500 Founded/Ownrshp 1999
Sales 39.6MM^E EMP 120
SIC 3571 Electronic computers
CEO: Tai Ming Guo
*CFO: Yu Huang Chiu Lian
Sr VP: Peter Woo
VP: Steven Marcher
Off Mgr: Jean Chang

D-U-N-S 18-837-4060 IMP/EXP
HONAN HOLDINGS USA INC
MANILDRA MILLING
(Suby of HONAN HOLDINGS PTY LTD)
4210 Shawnee Mission Pkwy 312a, Fairway, KS 66205-2531
Tel (913) 362-0777 Founded/Ownrshp 1982
Sales 29.8MM^E EMP 38
SIC 5153 2869 Wheat; Alcohols, non-beverage
Pr: Gerard Degnan
*Treas: Paul Mall

D-U-N-S 78-747-5110
HONAT BANCORP INC
HONESDALE NATIONAL BANK
733 Main St, Honesdale, PA 18431-1844
Tel (570) 253-3355 Founded/Ownrshp 1987
Sales NA EMP 100
Accts Snodgrass Ac Wexford Pennsy
SIC 6712 Bank holding companies; Bank holding companies
CEO: William Schweighofer
COO: Thomas E Sheridan Jr
COO: Sheridan Thomas
*Ch: John P Burlein
Mktg Dir: Mark Graziadio

HONDA
See DOUG RICHERT PONTIAC CADILLAC INC

HONDA
See AUTOMANAGE LLC

HONDA
See J/R HILO ACQUISITION LLC

D-U-N-S 78-532-8167 IMP/EXP
HONDA AIRCRAFT CO INC
HONDAJET
(Suby of HONDA MOTOR CO., LTD.)
6430 Ballinger Rd, Greensboro, NC 27410-9063
Tel (336) 662-0246 Founded/Ownrshp 2011
Sales 228.8MM^E EMP 450
SIC 3728 Aircraft parts & equipment; Aircraft parts & equipment
VP: Samuel Hill
VP: Michael Paquee
Prgrm Mgr: Paul Benjamin
Prgrm Mgr: Junichi Kondo
Dept Mgr: Kazutoshi Oi
Dept Mgr: Hiroshi Yamanouchi
Dir IT: Jon Weaver
IT Man: Steve Johnston
IT Man: Jolynn Shaw
Tech Mgr: Ken Schaelchlin
Netwrk Eng: Joseph Meyer

HONDA BLOOMFIELD
See MICHIGANH1 LLC

HONDA CAR COMPANY
See MESA IMPORTS INC

HONDA CAR LAND
See WMW INC

HONDA CARS BY MARKLEY
See MARKLEY MOTORS INC

HONDA CARS OF BELLEVUE
See SCHWORER MOTOR CO

HONDA CARS OF BOSTON
See ATALA CORP

D-U-N-S 80-784-5904
HONDA CARS OF CORONA
1080 Pomona Rd, Corona, CA 92882-1834
Tel (951) 734-8400 Founded/Ownrshp 1983
Sales 32.8MM^E EMP 132
SIC 5511 New & used car dealers; New & used car dealers
Genl Pt: Hendrick Automotive Group
Genl Pt: Hage Automotive Investments
Sls Mgr: Greg Fisher
Sls Mgr: Tanal Hassoun
Sls Mgr: Sam Khoury
Sales Asso: Boris Rekhlis

HONDA CARS OF KATY
See KEMOSABE MOTORS LP

HONDA CARS OF MADEVILLE
See STREETTRACK N TRAIL INC

HONDA CARS OF MC KINNEY
See MCKINNEY AUTOMOTIVE CO LIMITED PARTNERSHIP

HONDA CARS OF ROCK HILL
See ROCK HILL AUTOMOTIVE CO

HONDA CITY
See JAB & CO INC

HONDA DE SAN JUAN
See BELLA INTERNATIONAL CORP

D-U-N-S 80-849-6574 IMP
HONDA ENGINEERING NORTH AMERICA INC
(Suby of HONDA ENGINEERING CO.,LTD.)
24000 Honda Pkwy, Marysville, OH 43040-9251
Tel (937) 642-5000 Founded/Ownrshp 1988
Sales 191.5MM^E EMP 350
SIC 3544 Special dies & tools; Industrial molds; Special dies & tools; Industrial molds
Pr: Akira Takeshita
Manager: Ryan Ramos
Sls Mgr: Tim Luoma
Snr Mgr: Dan Jacoby
Snr Mgr: Dave King
Snr Mgr: William Meddles
Snr Mgr: David Nye
Snr Mgr: Kevin Rhoades
Snr Mgr: Mike Saunders
Snr Mgr: Theron Short

D-U-N-S 19-699-8322
HONDA FEDERAL CREDIT UNION
19701 Hamilton Ave # 130, Torrance, CA 90502-1368
Tel (310) 217-0509 Founded/Ownrshp 1966
Sales NA EMP 132
SIC 6061 Federal credit unions; Federal credit unions
Ex Dir: James Updike
Brnch Mgr: Laura Brandewie
Brnch Mgr: Melissa Danner
Sys Admin: Bill D'Camp
Snr Mgr: Jeannie Leis

HONDA FINANCIAL SERVICES
See AMERICAN HONDA FINANCE CORP

HONDA LOCK OF AMERICA
See HL-A CO INC

D-U-N-S 07-984-6360
HONDA LOGISTICS NORTH AMERICA INC
(Suby of HONDA LOGISTICS INC.)
11590 Township Road 298, East Liberty, OH 43319-9487
Tel (937) 642-0335 Founded/Ownrshp 2013
Sales 145.1MM^E EMP 1,245
SIC 4226 Special warehousing & storage
Pr: Tamaki Hashimoto

HONDA MALL OF GEORGIA, THE
See ATLANTA UAG H1 LLC

D-U-N-S 82-796-1264 EXP
HONDA MANUFACTURING OF ALABAMA LLC
HMA
(Suby of AMERICAN HONDA MOTOR CO INC) ★
1800 Honda Dr, Lincoln, AL 35096-5107
Tel (205) 355-5000 Founded/Ownrshp 1999
Sales 228.8MM^E EMP 2,300
SIC 3711 Automobiles, new & used; Automobile assembly, including specialty automobiles
Pr: Jeff Tomko
IT Man: Bob Edrizendine
Opers Mgr: Rodney Moon

D-U-N-S 79-205-0838 IMP/EXP
HONDA MANUFACTURING OF INDIANA LLC
(Suby of AMERICAN HONDA MOTOR CO INC) ★
2755 N Michigan Ave, Greensburg, IN 47240-9341
Tel (812) 222-6000 Founded/Ownrshp 2007
Sales 228.8MM^E EMP 2,000
SIC 3711 Automobile assembly, including specialty automobiles
Pr: Bob Nelson
*VP: Kiyoshi Ikeyama
VP: Rick Schostek
Dir IT: Sam Labarbara
IT Man: Jeremy Stallsmith
Sftwr Eng: Hirohide Nakano
Ql Cn Mgr: Wendy Hartwell

HONDA NORTH
See PALMIERO AUTOMOTIVE OF BUTLER INC

HONDA NORTH
See INTERNATIONAL CARS LTD INC

D-U-N-S 18-770-0604
HONDA NORTH AMERICA INC
(Suby of HONDA MOTOR CO., LTD.)
700 Van Ness Ave, Torrance, CA 90501-1486
Tel (310) 781-4961 Founded/Ownrshp 1987
Sales 5.2MMM^E EMP 40,000
SIC 3711 8748 Automobile assembly, including specialty automobiles; Business consulting; Automobile assembly, including specialty automobiles; Business consulting
*Pr: Takuji Yamada
*Pr: Tetsuo Iwamura
Ex VP: Erik Berkman
Ex VP: Kihachiro Kawashima
Ex VP: Takashi Sekiguchi
VP: Charlie Baker
VP: Raymond Blank
VP: Kathy Jones
*VP: Hiroshi Soda
VP: Bob Taft
Genl Mgr: Bob Fegan

D-U-N-S 07-883-0998
HONDA NORTH AMERICA SERVICES LLC
(Suby of HONDA MOTOR CO., LTD.)
24000 Honda Pkwy, Marysville, OH 43040-9251
Tel (937) 642-5000 Founded/Ownrshp 2013
Sales 31.3MM^E EMP 58^E
SIC 5511 Automobiles, new & used

D-U-N-S 09-216-2643 IMP/EXP
HONDA OF AMERICA MFG INC
MARYSVILLE AUTO PLANT
(*Suby of* AMERICAN HONDA MOTOR CO INC) ★
24000 Honda Pkwy, Marysville, OH 43040-9251
Tel (937) 642-5000 *Founded/Ownrshp* 1978
Sales 2.5MMM^E *EMP* 13,500
SIC 3711 Automobile assembly, including specialty automobiles; Automobile assembly, including specialty automobiles
Pr: Akio Hamada
Pr: Larry Jutte
**CEO:* Tomomi Kosaka
COO: Steve Mortimer
VP: James Wehrman
**Prin:* John Adams
VP Admn: Tim Garrett
Mng Dir: Satoshi Aoki
Admn Mgr: Dave Reed
Dept Mgr: Rich Chesnut
Dept Mgr: Donald Moore

HONDA OF CLEAR LAKE
See LAKE CLEAR PARTNERS LTD

HONDA OF DANBURY
See DANBURY AUTO PARTNERSHIP

HONDA OF THE DESERT
See DESERT AUTO MALL INC

D-U-N-S 82-760-7594
HONDA OF DOWNTOWN LOS ANGELES
VELOCITY MOTORS
1540 S Figueroa St, Los Angeles, CA 90015-2887
Tel (213) 749-2331 *Founded/Ownrshp* 2011
Sales 27.7MM^E *EMP* 50
SIC 5511 Automobiles, new & used
Prin: Joseph Shuster
**Prin:* Ted Benson
Off Mgr: Antonia Grant
Sales Asso: Scott Goldner

HONDA OF EL CERRITO
See EL CERRITO AUTOMOTIVE CO

HONDA OF FIFE
See DEAN LEE INC

HONDA OF FRONTENAC
See EH LLC

HONDA OF GREELEY
See DAVIS-MOORE INC

HONDA OF HOLLYWOOD
See BILL ROBERTSON & SONS INC

HONDA OF NEW ROCHELLE
See WESTCHESER AUTOPLEX INC

HONDA OF OAKLAND
See OAKLAND AUTOMOTIVE CO LLC

HONDA OF PASADENA
See HOP LLC

HONDA OF PRINCETON
See KENT MOTORCAR CO INC

D-U-N-S 02-941-7201
■ **HONDA OF SANTA MONICA**
(*Suby of* SONIC AUTOMOTIVE INC) ★
1720 Santa Monica Blvd, Santa Monica, CA 90404-1907
Tel (310) 264-4900 *Founded/Ownrshp* 1951
Sales 22.4MM^E *EMP* 90
SIC 5511 Automobiles, new & used; Automobiles, new & used
Genl Mgr: Andy Ham
Genl Mgr: Sean Ramezani
Sls Mgr: Glen Garland

HONDA OF SCOTTSDALE
See DWW PARTNERS LLP

HONDA OF SEATTLE
See MILLER-NICHOLSON CO

HONDA OF SEATTLE
See M N ONE INC

D-U-N-S 01-216-5564 IMP/EXP
HONDA OF SOUTH CAROLINA MFG INC
(*Suby of* AMERICAN HONDA MOTOR CO INC) ★
1111 Honda Way, Timmonsville, SC 29161-9421
Tel (843) 346-2887 *Founded/Ownrshp* 1998
Sales 228.8MM^E *EMP* 600
SIC 3799 All terrain vehicles (ATV); All terrain vehicles (ATV)
Pr: Katsumi Fujimoto
Pt: Masataka Fujil
Pr: Don Brown
Pr: Kenichi Inoue
Ex VP: Satoshi Aoki
Sr VP: Dane Espenschied
VP: Bill Kalp
VP: Koichi Nagashima
**VP:* Brian Newman
VP: Kenji Sato
Div Mgr: Scott McKenzie

D-U-N-S 02-058-5674 EXP
HONDA OF SOUTH CAROLINA MFG INC
(*Suby of* HONDA MOTOR CO., LTD.)
1111 Honda Way, Timmonsville, SC 29161-9421
Tel (843) 346-8000 *Founded/Ownrshp* 1997
Sales 32.3MM^E *EMP* 65^E
SIC 3799 3999 All terrain vehicles (ATV); Atomizers, toiletry

HONDA OF TENAFLY
See D & C CHEVROLET CO

HONDA OF THOUSAND OAKS
See THOUSAND OAKS IMPORTS

D-U-N-S 55-758-8097
HONDA OF TIFFANY SPRINGS
9200 Nw Prairie View Rd, Kansas City, MO 64153-1856
Tel (816) 452-7000 *Founded/Ownrshp* 2005
Sales 20.9MM^E *EMP* 65
SIC 5511 Automobiles, new & used; Automobiles, new & used
Pr: Bobby Hennessey
Exec: Jennifer Jennings
Genl Mgr: Patrick Deery
Sls Mgr: Tim Minter

D-U-N-S 10-789-3067 IMP/EXP
HONDA POWER EQUIPMENT MFG INC
(*Suby of* AMERICAN HONDA MOTOR CO INC) ★
3721 Nc Hwy 119, Swepsonville, NC 27359
Tel (336) 578-5300 *Founded/Ownrshp* 1984
Sales 114.6MM^E *EMP* 335^E
SIC 3524 Lawn & garden mowers & accessories; Lawn & garden mowers & accessories
Pr: Yoshi Toyozumi
**Treas:* Taku Kitamura
Sls Dir: Chris Farmer

D-U-N-S 19-855-0605 IMP/EXP
HONDA PRECISION PARTS OF GEORGIA LLC
(*Suby of* AMERICAN HONDA MOTOR CO INC) ★
550 Honda Pkwy, Tallapoosa, GA 30176-4344
Tel (770) 574-3400 *Founded/Ownrshp* 2005
Sales 129.1MM^E *EMP* 500
SIC 3089 Automotive parts, plastic; Automotive parts, plastic
Genl Mgr: Jim Wise
IT Man: Greg Smith
Netwrk Eng: Matthew Lail
QI Cn Mgr: James Hendricks

D-U-N-S 15-750-9696 IMP
HONDA R&D AMERICAS INC
1900 Harpers Way, Torrance, CA 90501-1521
Tel (310) 781-5500 *Founded/Ownrshp* 2015
Sales 226.5MM^E *EMP* 1,537
SIC 8732 Market analysis or research; Market analysis or research
CEO: Frank Paluch
**Pr:* Erik Berkman
CFO: Michael Ryan
CFO: Ravi Sud
VP: Charles Allen
Genl Mgr: Morishi Horiuchi
Dir IT: Ed Dimayuga
IT Man: C Perry
Software D: Chris Sible
Snr Mgr: Anthony Arcuri
Snr Mgr: Ken Miyako

HONDA STORE
See RON BOUCHARDS AUTO SALES INC

D-U-N-S 06-458-9773 IMP/EXP
HONDA TRADING AMERICA CORP
H T A
(*Suby of* HONDA TRADING CORPORATION)
19210 Van Ness Ave, Torrance, CA 90501-1102
Tel (310) 787-5000 *Founded/Ownrshp* 2009
Sales 225.2MM^E *EMP* 150
SIC 5013 Automotive supplies & parts; Automotive supplies & parts
CEO: Nobuhiko Shiozaki
**Pr:* Hiroyuki Yamada
Treas: Sninichi Sakamoto
Ex VP: Tadashi Takeda
Opers Mgr: Michael Zarrilli
Plnt Mgr: Charles Harmon
Mktg Mgr: Karen Kim
Snr Mgr: George Tanaka

D-U-N-S 02-244-2727 IMP
HONDA TRANSMISSION MANUFACTURING OF AMERICA INC
(*Suby of* AMERICAN HONDA MOTOR CO INC) ★
6964 State Route 235 N, Russells Point, OH 43348-9703
Tel (937) 843-5555 *Founded/Ownrshp* 1981
Sales 228.8MM^E *EMP* 1,200
SIC 3714 Motor vehicle parts & accessories; Wheels, motor vehicle; Frames, motor vehicle; Exhaust systems & parts, motor vehicle; Motor vehicle parts & accessories; Wheels, motor vehicle; Frames, motor vehicle; Exhaust systems & parts, motor vehicle
Pr: Yuji Takahashi
**Pr:* Masanori Kato
**COO:* Steve Mortimer
**VP:* Gary Hand
Exec: Michael Snyder
IT Man: David Burgess
Sfty Dirs: Jerry Cline

HONDA VILLAGE
See VILLAGE MOTORS GROUP INC

HONDA WEST
See ED MELZER INC

HONDA WEST
See FAA LAS VEGAS H INC

D-U-N-S 78-136-5036
HONDA WORLD WESTMINSTER
(*Suby of* PIERCEY AUTOMOTIVE GROUP) ★
13600 Beach Blvd, Westminster, CA 92683-3202
Tel (714) 890-8900 *Founded/Ownrshp* 1989
Sales 61.9MM^E *EMP* 175
SIC 5511 7539 5015 5012 Automobiles, new & used; Automotive repair shops; Motor vehicle parts, used; Automobiles & other motor vehicles; Automobiles, new & used; Automotive repair shops; Motor vehicle parts, used; Automobiles & other motor vehicles
Pr: Jim Kitzmiller
**CFO:* Tom Chadwell
Sls Mgr: Daniele Martin
Sls Mgr: Daniel Tran

D-U-N-S 83-752-8129
HONDA-YA CITY OF INDUSTRY INC
2878 N Wyngate Rd, Orange, CA 92867-1721
Tel (714) 974-5230 *Founded/Ownrshp* 2009
Sales 24.5MM^E *EMP* 150
SIC 5511 Automobiles, new & used; Automobiles, new & used
CEO: Yumi Takashio

HONDAJET
See HONDA AIRCRAFT CO INC

D-U-N-S 08-628-3918
HONDO INDEPENDANT SCHOOL DISTRICT
2604 Avenue E, Hondo, TX 78861-3137
Tel (830) 426-3311 *Founded/Ownrshp* 1902
Sales 20.4MM *EMP* 350
Accts Coleman Horton & Company Llp
SIC 8211 Public elementary & secondary schools; Public elementary & secondary schools
IT Man: Maryjo Peters

HONDROS COLLEGE
See NATIONAL EDUCATION SEMINARS INC

D-U-N-S 60-257-1978
HONDRU DODGE INC
2005 S Market St, Elizabethtown, PA 17022-9209
Tel (888) 415-2610 *Founded/Ownrshp* 1989
Sales 25.0MM *EMP* 25
SIC 5511 Automobiles, new & used; Pickups, new & used; Vans, new & used; Automobiles, new & used; Pickups, new & used; Vans, new & used
Pr: Peter J Hondru

HONDRU FORD
See FORD HONDRU INC

HONEE BEAR CANNING CO
See PACKERS CANNING CO INC

D-U-N-S 07-937-8916
HONEOYE FALLS-LIMA CENTRAL SCHOOL DISTRICT
20 Church St, Honeoye Falls, NY 14472-1206
Tel (585) 624-7000 *Founded/Ownrshp* 2014
Sales 10.6MM^E *EMP* 277^E
SIC 8211 Elementary & secondary schools
Prin: Mike Koss

D-U-N-S 10-037-7308
HONEOYE FALLS-LIMA SCHOOL DISTRICT
20 Church St, Honeoye Falls, NY 14472-1294
Tel (585) 624-7000 *Founded/Ownrshp* 1929
Sales 16.6MM^E *EMP* 320
SIC 8211 School board; School board
**Prin:* Renee Williams
Pr Dir: Jennifer Meisenzahl
HC Dir: Stephanie Bemish

D-U-N-S 80-997-6884
HONEOYE FUNDING LLC
FIRST AMERICAN
Woodcliff Dr Bldg 255, Fairport, NY 14450
Tel (585) 643-3272 *Founded/Ownrshp* 2008
Sales NA *EMP* 5
SIC 6159 Equipment & vehicle finance leasing companies; Equipment & vehicle finance leasing companies
CFO: Mike Ziezelnann

HONESDALE NATIONAL BANK
See HONAT BANCORP INC

D-U-N-S 00-893-6262
HONESDALE NATIONAL BANK
(*Suby of* HONAT BANCORP INC) ★
733 Main St, Honesdale, PA 18431-1844
Tel (570) 253-5465 *Founded/Ownrshp* 1987
Sales NA *EMP* 100
SIC 6021 National commercial banks; National commercial banks
Pr: William Schweighofer
**Ch Bd:* John P Burleine
CFO: Roger A Shermn
Ofcr: Lisa Bonham
Ofcr: Kevin Colgan
Ex VP: Thomas Sheridan
Sr VP: Raymond Ceccotti
VP: Charles Curtin
VP: Michael Rollison
**VP:* Luke Woodmansee
Brnch Mgr: Nick Dalberto

HONEST CHARLEY SPEED SHOP
See COKER TIRE CO

D-U-N-S 96-996-2757 IMP
HONEST CO INC
2700 Penn Ave Ste 1200, Santa Monica, CA 90404-4065
Tel (310) 917-9199 *Founded/Ownrshp* 2011
Sales 67.2MM^E *EMP* 304
SIC 2341 2833 Panties: women's, misses', children's & infants'; Vitamins, natural or synthetic: bulk, uncompounded
CEO: Brian Lee
**Pr:* Jessica Alba
**COO:* David Parker
**Ofcr:* Christopher Gavigan
**Prin:* Sean Kane
Rgnl Mgr: Queenie Hilfer
Off Mgr: Carly Jansen
CTO: Oleg Pylnev
QA Dir: Jesus Monarrez
IT Man: Mahdi Farrokhzad
Sftwr Eng: Ariel Deitcher

D-U-N-S 01-293-3276
■ **HONEST TEA INC**
(*Suby of* COCA-COLA CO) ★
4827 Bethesda Ave Fl 2, Bethesda, MD 20814-7911
Tel (301) 652-3556 *Founded/Ownrshp* 1998
Sales 39.6MM^E *EMP* 95
SIC 2086 Carbonated beverages, nonalcoholic: bottled & canned; Carbonated beverages, nonalcoholic: bottled & canned
Pr: Seth Goldman
**Ch Bd:* Barry Nalebuff
Mktg Mgr: Jeremy Kugel
Mktg Mgr: Kristen Laffler
Mktg Mgr: Ross Resnick
Mktg Mgr: Lizzie Weiland

D-U-N-S 04-605-1025
HONEY BAKED HAM INC
29 Musick, Irvine, CA 92618-1638
Tel (949) 830-9050 *Founded/Ownrshp* 1973
Sales 21.1MM^E *EMP* 145
SIC 5421

D-U-N-S 07-923-6641
HONEY CHILD LLC (AL)
24710 Highway 41, Brewton, AL 36426-9049
Tel (251) 248-2983 *Founded/Ownrshp* 2013
Sales 70.0MM *EMP* 2
SIC 5812 American restaurant; American restaurant
Pt: Susan Burch

D-U-N-S 04-613-4888
HONEY FARMS INC
505 Pleasant St, Worcester, MA 01609-1894
Tel (508) 753-7678 *Founded/Ownrshp* 1969
Sales 74.3MM^E *EMP* 362
SIC 5411 Convenience stores, chain; Convenience stores, chain
Pr: Wilfred L Iandoli
**VP:* David A Murdock
Dist Mgr: Eli Houle
Mktg Dir: Karen Campbell

HONEY GROVE NURSING CENTER
See SENIOR CARE MANAGEMENT INC

D-U-N-S 07-834-3282 IMP
HONEY MADHAVA LTD
MADHAVA NATURAL SWEETENERS
14300 E I25 Frontage Rd, Longmont, CO 80504-9626
Tel (303) 823-9900 *Founded/Ownrshp* 1977
Sales 32.0MM *EMP* 62
Accts Ehrhardt Keefe Steiner & Hottm
SIC 5149 Honey
CEO: Debbie Carosella
Board of Directors: Brandi Curtis

HONEY ROCK CAMP
See TRUSTEES OF WHEATON COLLEGE

D-U-N-S 80-819-8647 IMP
HONEY-CAN-DO INTERNATIONAL LLC
5300 Saint Charles Rd, Berkeley, IL 60163-1344
Tel (708) 240-8100 *Founded/Ownrshp* 2007
Sales 43.9MM *EMP* 100
SIC 5085 Bins & containers, storage
COO: Deborah Gerfy
CFO: Tony Mazzocco
VP Sls: Paul Michalowski
Mktg Mgr: Arielle Dunn

HONEYBUCKETS
See NORTHWEST CASCADE INC

D-U-N-S 00-410-5904
HONEYCOMB CO OF AMERICA INC
(*Suby of* OVERALL-HONEYCOMB, LLC)
1950 Limbus Ave, Sarasota, FL 34243-3900
Tel (941) 756-8781 *Founded/Ownrshp* 2013
Sales 40.8MM^E *EMP* 112
SIC 3728 Panel assembly (hydromatic propeller test stands), aircraft; Aircraft body assemblies & parts; Panel assembly (hydromatic propeller test stands), aircraft; Aircraft body assemblies & parts
Pr: Steven J Walker
**COO:* Dan G Judge III
CFO: Ryan Blust
**CFO:* Harold Osban Jr
Dir Bus: Bill Bryson

HONEYVILLE FOOD PRODUCTS
See HONEYVILLE INC

D-U-N-S 05-242-5246 IMP
HONEYVILLE INC
HONEYVILLE FOOD PRODUCTS
1080 N Main St Ste 101, Brigham City, UT 84302-1470
Tel (435) 494-4193 *Founded/Ownrshp* 1951
Sales 180.1MM^E *EMP* 200
SIC 5153 Wheat; Corn; Wheat; Corn
Ch Bd: Lowell Sherratt
**Pr:* Robert W Anderson
**Treas:* Steven T Christensen
**VP:* Tyler Christensen
CIO: Chris McMasters

D-U-N-S 00-548-0876
HONEYVILLE METAL INC
4200 S 900 W, Topeka, IN 46571-9142
Tel (260) 593-2266 *Founded/Ownrshp* 1951
Sales 30.3MM^E *EMP* 67
SIC 3523 3564 Farm machinery & equipment; Dust or fume collecting equipment, industrial
Ch: Ora Hochstetler
**Pr:* Mark Hochstetler
**Treas:* Matthew Beachy
**Sr VP:* Ivan Birky
**VP:* Melvin Gingerich
Mktg Mgr: John Jones

HONEYWELL
See GRIMES AEROSPACE CO

HONEYWELL
See NOVAR CONTROLS CORP

HONEYWELL
See METROLOGIC INSTRUMENTS INC

D-U-N-S 08-190-0615
■ **HONEYWELL**
(*Suby of* HONEYWELL INTERNATIONAL INC) ★
135 W Forest Hill Ave, Oak Creek, WI 53154-2901
Tel (414) 762-5136 *Founded/Ownrshp* 1989
Sales 22.2MM^E *EMP* 250
SIC 3699 Security control equipment & systems; Security control equipment & systems
Pr: Joel Konicek
**Ch Bd:* Louis B Thalheimer
**Sec:* Charles Baker
VP: Jonathan Klinger
Genl Mgr: Lorenty John
Sales Exec: Bill Vowler

D-U-N-S 02-081-0502
■ **HONEYWELL AEROSPACE DE PUERTO RICO INC**
(*Suby of* HONEYWELL INTERNATIONAL INC) ★
1000 Carr 110, San Antonio, PR 00690-1000
Tel (787) 658-2493 *Founded/Ownrshp* 2006

Sales 24.7MM^E *EMP* 820
SIC 7389 Financial services; ; Financial services;
Pr: Vicente Nazario

D-U-N-S 06-862-3032 IMP
■ HONEYWELL ANALYTICS INC
(*Suby of* HONEYWELL INTERNATIONAL INC) ★
405 Barclay Blvd, Lincolnshire, IL 60069-3609
Tel (847) 955-8200 *Founded/Ownrshp* 2005
Sales 147.6MM^E *EMP* 1,045
SIC 3491 3829 Process control regulator valves; Gas detectors; Process control regulator valves; Gas detectors
Pr: Carl Johnson
**Treas:* John J Tus
**VP:* Paul H Brownstein
**VP:* John Hakanson
Genl Mgr: Clint Palmer
IT Man: Arnold Bowman
Sls&Mrk Ex: Patrick Hogan
VP Mktg: Ron Walczak
Mktg Mgr: Nelson Rivera

D-U-N-S 78-413-1625
■ HONEYWELL ASIA PACIFIC INC
(*Suby of* HONEYWELL INTERNATIONAL INC) ★
101 Columbia Rd, Morristown, NJ 07960-4658
Tel (973) 455-2000 *Founded/Ownrshp* 1974
Sales 24.0MM^E *EMP* 58^E
SIC 3822 Auto controls regulating residntl & coml environmt & applncs
Pr: John Tus

D-U-N-S 62-332-5057
■ HONEYWELL BUILDING SOLUTIONS SES CORP
(*Suby of* HONEYWELL INTERNATIONAL INC) ★
1250 W Sam Houston Pkwy S, Houston, TX 77042-1941
Tel (832) 252-3308 *Founded/Ownrshp* 2006
Sales 20.3MM^E *EMP* 200
SIC 1711 Mechanical contractor; Mechanical contractor
Pr: Kevin Madden
Sr VP: Harold Buchanan
VP: Ajaz Lateef
Mng Dir: Ash Gupta

D-U-N-S 09-149-1548
■ HONEYWELL DMC SERVICES LLC
(*Suby of* HONEYWELL INTERNATIONAL INC) ★
199 Rosewood Dr, Danvers, MA 01923-1398
Tel (978) 774-3007 *Founded/Ownrshp* 1995
Sales 21.9MM^E *EMP* 410
SIC 8748 7363 7372 Energy conservation consultant; Office help supply service; Application computer software; Energy conservation consultant; Office help supply service; Application computer software
Pr: Kent Anson
Treas: Sue Knight
VP: Kevin Gilligan
VP: Kevin McDonough
VP: Steve Smith

HONEYWELL ECC CALLIDUS
See CALLIDUS TECHNOLOGIES LLC

D-U-N-S 60-701-7449 IMP
■ HONEYWELL ELECTRONIC MATERIALS INC
(*Suby of* HONEYWELL INTERNATIONAL INC) ★
15128 E Euclid Ave, Spokane Valley, WA 99216-1801
Tel (509) 252-2200 *Founded/Ownrshp* 1999
Sales 232.3MM^E *EMP* 1,100
SIC 3679 3674 3643 Electronic circuits; Semiconductors & related devices; Current-carrying wiring devices; Electronic circuits; Semiconductors & related devices; Current-carrying wiring devices
Pr: David Diggs
Treas: John J Tus
VP: James M Di Stefano
VP: Ezra Eckhardt
Dir Lab: Ron Fleming
IT Man: Srinivas Chada
IT Man: Fred Hidden
IT Man: Fukuyama Ken
IT Man: Mike Piotrowski
IT Man: Brent Wilcox
QC Dir: Tom Herrington

D-U-N-S 07-939-5928
HONEYWELL FEDERAL MANUFACTURING & TECHNOLOGIES LLC
14520 Botts Rd, Kansas City, MO 64147-1302
Tel (816) 488-7007 *Founded/Ownrshp* 2000
Sales 213.8MM^E *EMP* 153^E
SIC 5191 2899 Chemicals, agricultural; Chemical preparations
CEO: Jim Turley
CTO: Mike Bloomer
IT Man: Dan Brantley
IT Man: Doug Schieber
Mtls Mgr: Emmett Helm
Trfc Mgr: Steve Kerr

HONEYWELL FIRST RESPONDER PDTS
See MORNING PRIDE MFG LLC

HONEYWELL IMAGING AND MOBILITY
See HAND HELD PRODUCTS INC

D-U-N-S 00-132-5240 IMP/EXP
■ HONEYWELL INC
(*Suby of* HONEYWELL INTERNATIONAL INC) ★
101 Columbia Rd, Morristown, NJ 07960-4658
Tel (973) 455-2000 *Founded/Ownrshp* 1927
Sales 5.7MMM^E *EMP* 50,143^E
SIC 3823 3812 3669 3491 3699 3822 Industrial instrmnts msrmnt display/control process variable; Temperature instruments: industrial process type; Controllers for process variables, all types; Programmers, process type; Aircraft control systems, electronic; Aircraft/aerospace flight instruments & guidance systems; Space vehicle guidance systems & equipment; Fire alarm apparatus, electric; Gas valves & parts, industrial; Security control equipment & systems; Auto controls regulating residntl & coml environmt & applncs; Energy cutoff controls, residential or commercial types; Thermostats, except built-in; Humidistats: wall, duct & skeleton; Industrial instrmnts msrmnt display/control process variable; Temperature instruments: industrial process type; Controllers for process variables, all types; Programmers, process type; Aircraft control systems, electronic; Aircraft/aerospace flight instruments & guidance systems; Space vehicle guidance systems & equipment; Fire alarm apparatus, electric; Gas valves & parts, industrial; Security control equipment & systems; Auto controls regulating residntl & coml environmt & applncs; Energy cutoff controls, residential or commercial types; Thermostats, except built-in; Humidistats: wall, duct & skeleton
Ch Bd: Michael R Bonsignore
V Ch: David Larson
Pr: Nance Katherine Dicciani
Pr: Jeff Laufatte
COO: Giannantonio Ferrari
CFO: Daniel Darazsdi
CFO: William M Hjerpe
CFO: Larry Stranghoener
CFO: William L Trubeck
Sr VP: James T Porter
VP: Karen O Bachman
VP: Linda Capuano
VP: Richard Diemer
VP: Jeff Donnell
VP: Edward D Grayson
VP: Susan Hewett
VP: Stephen Hirshfeld
VP: Philip M Palazzari
VP: Allen C Riess
VP: Dale Wallis
VP: Arnie Weimerskirch

D-U-N-S 19-641-0088 IMP
■ HONEYWELL INC
(*Suby of* HONEYWELL INTERNATIONAL INC) ★
550 State Route 55, Urbana, OH 43078-9482
Tel (937) 484-2000 *Founded/Ownrshp* 1986
Sales 40.9MM^E *EMP* 800
SIC 3728 Aircraft parts & equipment; Aircraft parts & equipment

D-U-N-S 13-969-1877 IMP/EXP
▲ HONEYWELL INTERNATIONAL INC
115 Tabor Rd, Morris Plains, NJ 07950-2546
Tel (973) 455-2000 *Founded/Ownrshp* 1920
Sales 40.3MMM *EMP* 127,440
Accts Pricewaterhousecoopers Llp Fl
Tkr Sym HON *Exch* NYS
SIC 3724 3812 3585 2824 2821 3714 Aircraft engines & engine parts; Turbines, aircraft type; Research & development on aircraft engines & parts; Aircraft control systems, electronic; Cabin environment indicators; Radar systems & equipment; Aircraft flight instruments; Air conditioning equipment, complete; Heating equipment, complete; Humidifiers & dehumidifiers; Nylon fibers; Polyester fibers; Polyethylene resins; Motor vehicle parts & accessories; Filters: oil, fuel & air, motor vehicle; Motor vehicle brake systems & parts; PVC valves; Aircraft engines & engine parts; Turbines, aircraft type; Research & development on aircraft engines & parts; Aircraft control systems, electronic; Cabin environment indicators; Radar systems & equipment; Aircraft flight instruments; Air conditioning equipment, complete; Heating equipment, complete; Humidifiers & dehumidifiers; Nylon fibers; Polyester fibers; Polyethylene resins; Motor vehicle parts & accessories; Filters: oil, fuel & air, motor vehicle; Motor vehicle brake systems & parts; PVC valves
Ch Bd: David M Cote
V Ch: Andreas C Kramvis
Pr: Darius Adamczyk
Pr: Alex Ismail
Pr: Tim Mahoney
CEO: Dr Nance K Dicciani
COO: Kathryn Freytag
COO: Elizabeth Jennison
CFO: Alfred Jones
CFO: Greg Lewis
CFO: Thomas A Szlosek
Chf Mktg O: Mark Winston
Sr VP: Katherine L Adams
Sr VP: William Sanders
VP: Carlos Aguirre
VP: Jerry Walker
Exec: Andrew Akers
Board of Directors: George Paz, William S Ayer, Bradley T Sheares, Gordon M Bethune, Robin L Washington, Kevin Burke, D Scott Davis, Linnet F Deily, Judd Gregg, Clive Hollick, Grace D Lieblein, Jaime Chico Pardo

D-U-N-S 62-283-0933 IMP
■ HONEYWELL INTERNATIONAL INC
(*Suby of* EMS TECHNOLOGIES INC) ★
125 Technology Pkwy, Norcross, GA 30092-2913
Tel (770) 447-4224 *Founded/Ownrshp* 1989
Sales 40.9MM^E *EMP* 400
SIC 3663 Microwave communication equipment; Microwave communication equipment
Pr: Paul Domorski
CEO: Dr Thomas E Sharon
CFO: Don T Scartz
Treas: Donald T Scarz
Sr Cor Off: Thomas Sharon
VP: John Broughton
Sftwr Eng: Dave Reynolds
Ql Cn Mgr: Sean Chancy
VP Sls: Joanne Walker
Mktg Mgr: Mats Lindeberg

D-U-N-S 07-973-8645
HONEYWELL RESINS & CHEMICALS LLC
101 Columbia Rd, Morristown, NJ 07960-4658
Tel (877) 370-7007 *Founded/Ownrshp* 2003
Sales 65.2MM^E *EMP* 260^E
SIC 5162 5169 Resins; Chemicals & allied products

D-U-N-S 16-688-9498 IMP/EXP
■ HONEYWELL RESINS & CHEMICALS LLC
(*Suby of* HONEYWELL INTERNATIONAL INC) ★
905 E Randolph Rd Bldg 97, Hopewell, VA 23860-2413
Tel (804) 541-5000 *Founded/Ownrshp* 2003
Sales 27.6MM^E *EMP* 300
SIC 2824 2869 2819 Organic fibers, noncellulosic; Industrial organic chemicals; Industrial inorganic chemicals; Organic fibers, noncellulosic; Industrial organic chemicals; Industrial inorganic chemicals
CFO: Barnie Glenn

HONEYWELL SAFETY PRODUCTS
See SPERIAN PROTECTION USA INC

HONEYWELL SAFETY PRODUCTS
See NORCROSS SAFETY PRODUCTS LLC

D-U-N-S 07-924-5827 EXP
■ HONEYWELL SAFETY PRODUCTS USA INC
(*Suby of* HONEYWELL INTERNATIONAL INC) ★
2711 Centerville Rd, Wilmington, DE 19808-1660
Tel (302) 636-5401 *Founded/Ownrshp* 2010
Sales 444.0MM^E *EMP* 2,878^E
SIC 5099 Lifesaving & survival equipment (non-medical)
CEO: David M Cote
**Pr:* Roger Fradin
**Pr:* Terrence Hahn
**Pr:* Alex Ismail
**Pr:* Andreas Kramvis
**Pr:* Tim Mahoney

D-U-N-S 19-854-1331 IMP
■ HONEYWELL SAFETY PRODUCTS USA INC
(*Suby of* HONEYWELL INTERNATIONAL INC) ★
900 Douglas Pike Ste 100, Smithfield, RI 02917-1879
Tel (401) 233-0333 *Founded/Ownrshp* 2010
Sales 42.4MM^E *EMP* 200^E
SIC 3851 Ophthalmic goods; Ophthalmic goods
CEO: Mark Levy
Sr VP: Francis Allirot
Sr VP: Christophe Lamoine
VP: Paul Breves
VP: Kirk Thompson
**Prin:* Bruce Spencer
Ex Dir: Sean Herrin
Rgnl Mgr: Hans Ng
Area Mgr: Alex Higginson
Telecom Ex: Cynthia Crook-Pick
Dir IT: Alain Desmarais

D-U-N-S 62-306-4300 EXP
■ HONEYWELL SPECIALTY WAX & ADDITIVES INC
(*Suby of* HONEYWELL INTERNATIONAL INC) ★
101 Columbia Rd, Morristown, NJ 07960-4658
Tel (973) 455-2000 *Founded/Ownrshp* 1997
Sales 107.0MM^E *EMP* 1,200^E
SIC 2999 5169 Waxes, petroleum: not produced in petroleum refineries; Waxes, except petroleum; Waxes, petroleum: not produced in petroleum refineries; Waxes, except petroleum
CEO: David Cote
**Pr:* John Gottshall
Bd of Dir: D S Davis
Bd of Dir: George Paz
VP: Elena Doom
VP: Paul Vasington

D-U-N-S 04-101-4242
■ HONEYWELL TECHNOLOGY SOLUTIONS INC
(*Suby of* HONEYWELL INTERNATIONAL INC) ★
7000 Columbia Gateway Dr # 100, Columbia, MD 21046-3151
Tel (410) 964-7000 *Founded/Ownrshp* 1985
Sales 710.8MM^E *EMP* 4,000
SIC 4899 8711 Satellite earth stations; Satellite earth stations; Engineering services
Pr: Carey Smith
**CFO:* Robert B Topolski
**Treas:* Sandra B Murray
**Sr VP:* Peter M Kreindler
**VP:* David J Anderson
**VP:* Paul H Brownstein
**VP:* John Tus
VP: Jerry Wellman
Genl Mgr: Jerry Hager
CIO: Alexander Batson
CIO: Greg Martis
Board of Directors: Eric K Shinseki, Gordon M Bethune, John R Stafford, Clive Hollick, James Howard, Bruce Karatz, Monte Krauze, Thomas F Larkins, Thomas Larkins, Ivan G Seidenberg, Bradley T Sheares

D-U-N-S 79-931-7404 IMP/EXP
HONG CHANG CORP
CALIFORNIA FOOD INTERNATIONAL
10155 Painter Ave, Santa Fe Springs, CA 90670-3017
Tel (562) 309-0068 *Founded/Ownrshp* 1994
Sales 25.0MM^E *EMP* 40
SIC 5146 5149 Seafoods; Groceries & related products; Seafoods; Groceries & related products
CEO: Hai Hua Li
**VP:* Hong J Luo

D-U-N-S 01-325-3834
HONG HING RESTAURANT DESIGN AND CONSTRUCTION INC
5380 New Peachtree Rd, Atlanta, GA 30341-2849
Tel (770) 457-0889 *Founded/Ownrshp* 2012
Sales 200.0M *EMP* 425
SIC 7389 5039 Design, commercial & industrial; Prefabricated structures; Design, commercial & industrial; Prefabricated structures

Owner: Tung Kong
Off Mgr: Ailin Mao

D-U-N-S 01-518-7414
HONG HOLDINGS LLC
CONICO MANAGEMENT
2815 Townsgate Rd Ste 225, Westlake Village, CA 91361-3092
Tel (805) 777-7938 *Founded/Ownrshp* 2003
Sales 43.8MM^E *EMP* 230^E
SIC 6719 Personal holding companies, except banks; Personal holding companies, except banks

D-U-N-S 17-785-0737 IMP/EXP
HONGHUA AMERICA LLC
HH RIGS AND SERVICES
(*Suby of* HONGHUA INTERNATIONAL CO., LTD.)
8300 Mchard Rd, Houston, TX 77053-4821
Tel (832) 448-8100 *Founded/Ownrshp* 2004
Sales 28.4MM^E *EMP* 40
SIC 3441 Floor jacks, metal
VP: Frank Ao
VP: Jace Chen
Brnch Mgr: Carlos Ju
VP Sls: Jessica Jiang

D-U-N-S 02-009-3779
HONIGMAN MILLER SCHWARTZ AND COHN LLP
660 Woodward Ave Ste 2290, Detroit, MI 48226-3583
Tel (313) 465-7000 *Founded/Ownrshp* 1948
Sales 75.7MM^E *EMP* 500
SIC 8111 General practice law office; General practice law office
CEO: David Foltyn
Pt: Joscelyn C Boucher
Pt: Amy M Brooks
Pt: Noel E Day
Pt: Andrew Doctoroff
Pt: Andrew Gerdes
Pt: William Hammond
Pt: Wayne D Hillyard
Pt: Kelly T Murphy
Pt: Jonathan P O'Brien
Pt: Richard W Paige
Pt: Kathryn D Soulier
Pt: Michelle Epstein Taigman
Pt: Phillip D Torrence
Pt: Andrew N Weber
Pt: Thomas A Wootton
Pt: Lisa Budyk Zimmer
Mng Pt: Bonnie Schneider
V Ch: Kenneth Gold
COO: Pamela Mullen
**V Ch Bd:* Alan Stuart Schwartz
Board of Directors: William O Hochkammer, Alan Stuart Schwartz V Ch

D-U-N-S 07-810-0948
HONKAMP KRUEGER & CO PC
2345 John F Kennedy Rd, Dubuque, IA 52002-2835
Tel (563) 556-0123 *Founded/Ownrshp* 1947
Sales 38.9MM^E *EMP* 251
SIC 8721 Certified public accountant; Certified public accountant
Pr: Arnold N Honkamp
Pt: Douglas D Funke
Pt: Ryan J Hauber
Pt: Michael P Moes
Pt: Michael P Weaverling
Pt: Michael P Welbes
Mng Pt: Gregory C Burbach
Pr: Natalie B Hoffmann
Prin: Karen G Ridings
Opers Mgr: Joann Kramer
Natl Sales: Judd Driscoll

D-U-N-S 03-193-8079
HONNEN EQUIPMENT CO
JOHN DEERE
5055 E 72nd Ave, Commerce City, CO 80022-1513
Tel (303) 287-7506 *Founded/Ownrshp* 1963
Sales 94.9MM^E *EMP* 280
SIC 5082 5084 Construction & mining machinery; Industrial machinery & equipment; Construction & mining machinery; Industrial machinery & equipment
Pr: Mark Honnen
**CFO:* Scott Long
Sls Mgr: Jason Bird
Sls Mgr: Rich Smith

D-U-N-S 00-643-6166
HONOLD & LA PAGE INC (WI)
1128 S 11th St, Sheboygan, WI 53081-4907
Tel (920) 457-7755 *Founded/Ownrshp* 1933
Sales 24.3MM^E *EMP* 32
SIC 5074 5063 5085 Heating equipment (hydronic); Plumbing fittings & supplies; Electrical supplies; Industrial supplies
Pr: William P Honold
**VP:* John Kuznacic

HONOLULU BUICK GMC CADILLAC
See LITHIA OF HONOLULU-BGMCC LLC

D-U-N-S 06-064-5710 IMP
HONOLULU COMMUNITY ACTION PROGRAM INC
HCAP
33 S King St Ste 300, Honolulu, HI 96813-4323
Tel (808) 521-4531 *Founded/Ownrshp* 1968
Sales 21.3MM *EMP* 500
Accts N&K Cpas Inc Honolulu Hi
SIC 8322 General counseling services; General counseling services
Ex Dir: Robert Ne Piper
Dir Vol: Richard Wells
V Ch: Ella Abe
Treas: Isaac W Choy
Dir: Michael Hane
IT Man: Corinne Murashige

D-U-N-S 04-440-3566
HONOLULU FREIGHT SERVICE (CA)
1400 Date St, Montebello, CA 90640-6323
Tel (323) 887-6777 *Founded/Ownrshp* 1945, 1978
Sales 31.3MM^E *EMP* 95

SIC 4731 Freight forwarding; Domestic freight forwarding; Freight forwarding; Domestic freight forwarding
Pr: Michael Biedleman
**CFO:* Dorene Beidleman
**VP:* Thomas Biedleman
Off Mgr: Elaine Bradley
Sls Dir: Roark Beckstead
Sales Asso: Angela Garcia
Snr Mgr: John Seaholt

HONOLULU HOMELOANS
See HHL HOLDINGS INC

D-U-N-S 18-389-2579
HONOLULU SCHOOL DISTRICT
(*Suby of* EDUCATION BOARD) ★
4967 Kilauea Ave, Honolulu, HI 96816-5731
Tel (808) 733-4950 *Founded/Ownrshp* 1967
Sales 56.9MM^E *EMP* 1,530
SIC 8211 Public elementary & secondary schools; Public elementary & secondary schools
Board of Directors: Pauline Kokubun

HONOLULU STAR ADVERTISER
See OAHU PUBLICATIONS INC

D-U-N-S 09-456-4689
HONOR CREDIT UNION (MI)
2920 Lakeview Ave, Saint Joseph, MI 49085-2317
Tel (269) 983-6357 *Founded/Ownrshp* 1934
Sales NA *EMP* 50
SIC 6062 State credit unions, not federally chartered; State credit unions, not federally chartered
CEO: Scott McFarland
**Ch:* Larry Olson
**Treas:* Mark Fry
Ofcr: Shari Weber
VP: Kent Figy
**Prin:* Brian Brown
Rgnl Mgr: Chris Jacobs
Brnch Mgr: Kellie Eldridge
Brnch Mgr: Laura Suhr
Brnch Mgr: Patrick Swem
Brnch Mgr: Courtney Waechter

HONOR FOODS
See HONOR HOLDINGS INC

D-U-N-S 05-472-3697 IMP
HONOR HOLDINGS INC (PA)
HONOR FOODS
(*Suby of* BURRIS LOGISTICS) ★
1801 N 5th St, Philadelphia, PA 19122-2198
Tel (215) 769-6800 *Founded/Ownrshp* 1946
Sales 133.1MM^E *EMP* 110
SIC 5141 5142 Groceries, general line; Packaged frozen goods; Groceries, general line; Packaged frozen goods
Pr: Richard J Singer
VP: Karen Kappra
Exec: Dave Pomroy
Genl Mgr: Greg Cyganiewicz
Dir IT: Joe Windfelder
VP Sls: Joe Adams
VP Sls: Marjorie Rossiter
Manager: Gene Overcash
Sls Mgr: Keith Blake
Sales Asso: Bruce Banning
Sales Asso: Ronnie Bortnicker

D-U-N-S 15-984-0946
HONORED CITIZENS CHOICE HEALTH PLAN INC
(*Suby of* ALIGNMENT HEALTHCARE LLC) ★
1100 W Town And Cntry Rd, Orange, CA 92868-4600
Tel (323) 728-7232 *Founded/Ownrshp* 2014
Sales NA *EMP* 90
SIC 6324 Hospital & medical service plans; Health maintenance organization (HMO), insurance only
Pr: Chuck Weber
**COO:* Elizabeth Tejada
CIO: Kerry Matsumoto
IT Man: Augi Oyola
Pharmcst: Joette Sweeney

D-U-N-S 07-768-9974
HONPA HONGWANJI HAWAII BETSUIN
1727 Pali Hwy, Honolulu, HI 96813-1612
Tel (808) 536-7044 *Founded/Ownrshp* 1923
Sales 16.3MM^E *EMP* 1,700
SIC 8661 Buddhist Temple; Buddhist Temple
Pr: Alan Goto

D-U-N-S 78-581-0222 IMP
HONSADOR LUMBER LLC
91-151 Malakole St, Kapolei, HI 96707-1893
Tel (808) 479-3071 *Founded/Ownrshp* 2004
Sales 129.4MM^E *EMP* 250
SIC 5031 5211 Lumber, plywood & millwork; Lumber & other building materials; Lumber, plywood & millwork; Lumber & other building materials
CEO: Carl Liliequist
**Pr:* Terris Inglett
**Treas:* Brian Moore
**Sr VP:* Errol Nii
VP: Randy Boyer
**VP:* Wayne Lincoln
IT Man: Karen Matsuura
VP Opers: Erik Nagli
Opers Mgr: Kevin Kwan
Sales Asso: Gene Demello
Sales Asso: John Hanohano

D-U-N-S 07-967-6005
HONSTEIN OIL & DISTRIBUTING LLC
11 Paseo Real, Santa Fe, NM 87507-8482
Tel (505) 471-1800 *Founded/Ownrshp* 2013
Sales 22.3MM^E *EMP* 99
SIC 5172 Engine fuels & oils

D-U-N-S 00-852-0967
HOOBER INC
KUBOTA
3452 Old Philadelphia Pike, Intercourse, PA 17534-7005
Tel (302) 629-3075 *Founded/Ownrshp* 1965
Sales 143.4MM^E *EMP* 224
SIC 5999 7699 5083

HOOD AUTOMOTIVE
See HOOD MOTOR CO

HOOD CABLES
See TAL-PORT INDUSTRIES LLC

D-U-N-S 55-672-9937
HOOD CHEVROLET LLC
HOOD NORTHLAKE
69020 Highway 190 Svc Rd, Covington, LA 70433
Tel (985) 892-4663 *Founded/Ownrshp* 1991
Sales 25.5MM^E *EMP* 67
SIC 5511 5531 7538 5521 Automobiles, new & used; Automotive parts; General automotive repair shops; Used car dealers; Automobiles, new & used; Automotive parts; General automotive repair shops; Used car dealers
Genl Mgr: Mike Scarle
Sls Mgr: Michael Kilbride

D-U-N-S 06-938-2778
HOOD COLLEGE OF FREDERICK MARYLAND (MD)
401 Rosemont Ave, Frederick, MD 21701-8575
Tel (301) 663-3131 *Founded/Ownrshp* 1893
Sales 45.9MM *EMP* 371
Accts Mcgladrey Llp Gaithersburgh
SIC 8221 College, except junior; College, except junior
Pr: Ron Volpe
**CFO:* Charles G Mann
VP: Jennifer Bentz
VP: Nancy Gillece
VP: Flavius Lilly
VP: Edgar Schick
Assoc Dir: Coleen Yazurlo
**CIO:* Cornelius Fay
Dir IT: Jeff Whipp
HC Dir: Jennifer Decker
Pgrm Dir: Rachel Bagni
Board of Directors: Jason Brennan, Michael Pasquerette

D-U-N-S 83-047-9478 IMP/EXP
HOOD COMPANIES INC
623 N Main St Ste 300, Hattiesburg, MS 39401-3464
Tel (601) 582-1545 *Founded/Ownrshp* 1998
Sales 673.4MM^E *EMP* 1,350^E
SIC 3086 2952 6719 Insulation or cushioning material, foamed plastic; Roofing materials; Investment holding companies, except banks; Insulation or cushioning material, foamed plastic; Roofing materials; Investment holding companies, except banks
Pr: Warren Hood
**CFO:* Larry D Davis
CFO: John Johnson
Opers Mgr: Chuck Oliver
Plnt Mgr: Tim Williams

D-U-N-S 62-156-7478
HOOD CONSTRUCTION CO INC
1050 Shop Rd Ste A, Columbia, SC 29201-5401
Tel (803) 765-2940 *Founded/Ownrshp* 1986
Sales 22.9MM^E *EMP* 49
SIC 1542 Commercial & office building, new construction; Commercial & office buildings, renovation & repair
CEO: Mark Hood
**VP:* Susan H Hood
Dir Bus: Margaret Tonkin

D-U-N-S 07-855-6251
HOOD CONTAINER CORP
(*Suby of* HOOD COMPANIES INC) ★
623 N Main St Ste 100, Hattiesburg, MS 39401-3464
Tel (601) 582-1545 *Founded/Ownrshp* 2012
Sales 66.5MM^E *EMP* 250^E
SIC 2673 Bags: plastic, laminated & coated
Pr: Warren A Hood Jr
**CFO:* John A Johnson

D-U-N-S 96-270-6151
HOOD CONTAINER OF LOUISIANA LLC
2105 Highway 964, Saint Francisville, LA 70775-7473
Tel (225) 336-2530 *Founded/Ownrshp* 2010
Sales 112.4MM^E *EMP* 250
SIC 2621 Paper mills; Paper mills
VP: Wayne Morgan
IT Man: Earl Thornton
Mill Mgr: Dan Perkins

D-U-N-S 80-389-9397
HOOD DISTRIBUTION INC
(*Suby of* HOOD INDUSTRIES INC) ★
15 Professional Pkwy # 8, Hattiesburg, MS 39402-2647
Tel (601) 264-2962 *Founded/Ownrshp* 2008
Sales 130.0MM *EMP* 196
SIC 8741 Business management
Pr: Chris Norris
Plnt Mgr: Jim Benefield
Plnt Mgr: Stan Majure
Plnt Mgr: Larry Stephens
Sales Asso: David Stump

D-U-N-S 03-307-5284 IMP
HOOD INDUSTRIES INC (MS)
MCEWEN LUMBER CO
15 Professional Pkwy # 8, Hattiesburg, MS 39402-2647
Tel (601) 264-2962 *Founded/Ownrshp* 1983
Sales 346.5MM^E *EMP* 1,150
SIC 2436 2421 5031 Panels, softwood plywood; Resawing lumber into smaller dimensions; Kiln drying of lumber; Lumber, plywood & millwork; Paneling, wood; Panels, softwood plywood; Resawing lumber into smaller dimensions; Kiln drying of lumber; Lumber, plywood & millwork; Paneling, wood
Pr: Donald Grimm
Treas: Warren Hood Jr
VP: Fran Eck
VP: John Hammack
VP: John Johnson
VP: Bill Wislocki
Mng Dir: Christopher C Norris
Brnch Mgr: Perry Rutkowski
Genl Mgr: Sondra Jones
Sales Exec: Tim Cochran

D-U-N-S 06-034-1679
HOOD LANDSCAPING PRODUCTS INC
203 W Mitchell St, Adel, GA 31620-1176
Tel (229) 896-4942 *Founded/Ownrshp* 1999
Sales 26.4MM^E *EMP* 70
SIC 5083 Landscaping equipment
Pr: Leon Hood

D-U-N-S 62-279-1606
HOOD MOTOR CO
HOOD AUTOMOTIVE
17068 Eastwood Dr, Amite, LA 70422-4500
Tel (985) 748-7118 *Founded/Ownrshp* 1989
Sales 23.3MM^E *EMP* 80
SIC 5511 Automobiles, new & used; Automobiles, new & used
Pr: William K Hood
**Treas:* Earl Cefalu Jr
**VP:* Arthur E Hood Jr

HOOD NORTHLAKE
See HOOD CHEVROLET LLC

D-U-N-S 09-210-4470 IMP
HOOD PACKAGING CORP
(*Suby of* HOOD COMPANIES INC) ★
25 Woodgreen Pl, Madison, MS 39110-9531
Tel (601) 853-7260 *Founded/Ownrshp* 1976
Sales 184.5MM^E *EMP* 750
SIC 2674 Bags: uncoated paper & multiwall; Bags: uncoated paper & multiwall
Pr: Robert Morris
Treas: Warren A Hood Jr
VP: John Johnson
Genl Mgr: Matthew Hegstrom
Genl Mgr: Michael Vidler
Mktg Dir: Todd Kimbrell

D-U-N-S 15-119-0774 EXP
HOOD PACKAGING CORP
2410 N Lyndon Ave, Tyler, TX 75702-2539
Tel (903) 593-1793 *Founded/Ownrshp* 1986
Sales 32.3MM^E *EMP* 90^E
SIC 2673 2671 3089 Plastic bags: made from purchased materials; Packaging paper & plastics film, coated & laminated; Blow molded finished plastic products; Plastic bags: made from purchased materials; Packaging paper & plastics film, coated & laminated; Blow molded finished plastic products
Pr: Robert Morris
CFO: Warren A Hood Jr
**VP:* John Johnson
**Prin:* Gulam Harji

D-U-N-S 01-074-1353
HOOD RIVER COUNTY SCHOOL DISTRICT
1011 Eugene St, Hood River, OR 97031-1499
Tel (541) 386-2511 *Founded/Ownrshp* 1966
Sales 144.3M *EMP* 550
SIC 8211 Public elementary & secondary schools; School board; Public elementary & secondary schools; School board
CFO: Saundra Buchanan

D-U-N-S 11-088-9925
HOOD RIVER JUICE CO INC
RYAN'S JUICE
550 Riverside Dr, Hood River, OR 97031-1190
Tel (541) 386-3003 *Founded/Ownrshp* 2000
Sales 33.5MM^E *EMP* 140
SIC 2099 Cider, nonalcoholic; Cider, nonalcoholic
Pr: David Ryan
VP Opers: Brian Petros
Opers Mgr: Eric Meyer
Ql Cn Mgr: Laurie Brown

D-U-N-S 08-956-6699
HOOGENDOORN CONSTRUCTION INC
47895 Us Highway 18, Canton, SD 57013-5803
Tel (605) 987-4319 *Founded/Ownrshp* 1977
Sales 25.9MM *EMP* 40
SIC 1542 Commercial & office building contractors; Commercial & office building contractors
Pr: Peter Hoogendoorn
**Treas:* Connie Hoogendoorn
Off Mgr: Pam Devries

D-U-N-S 19-895-2715 IMP/EXP
HOOGWEGT US INC
(*Suby of* HOOGWEGT GROEP B.V.)
100 Saunders Rd Ste 200, Lake Forest, IL 60045-2502
Tel (847) 918-8787 *Founded/Ownrshp* 1988
Sales 138.3MM^E *EMP* 62
SIC 5084 Dairy products manufacturing machinery; Dairy products manufacturing machinery
CEO: Dalyn L Dye
**CFO:* Arthur A Rauch
**VP:* Jill De Lio
VP: Jill Delio
**VP:* Arjen Opt Hof
VP: Sander Hulsebos

D-U-N-S 00-755-7668
HOOHANA ENTERPRISES LTD
A AKAMAI EMPLOYMENT AGENCY
1043 Makawao Ave Ste 203, Makawao, HI 96768-9468
Tel (808) 573-6675 *Founded/Ownrshp* 2001
Sales 6.2MM^E *EMP* 300
SIC 7361 Employment agencies; Employment agencies
CEO: Robin Rohrer

D-U-N-S 80-849-1695
■ **HOOK-SUPERX LLC**
(*Suby of* CVS HEALTH CORP) ★
1 Cvs Dr, Woonsocket, RI 02895-6146
Tel (401) 765-1500 *Founded/Ownrshp* 2012
Sales 62.6MM^E *EMP* 22^E
SIC 5912 Drug stores & proprietary stores
Prin: Elizabeth Jesse
Treas: Larry Solberg

D-U-N-S 55-733-8386
HOOKER CREEK COMPANIES LLC
95 Sw Scalehouse Loop # 100, Bend, OR 97702-1224
Tel (541) 389-0981 *Founded/Ownrshp* 2000
Sales 39.1MM^E *EMP* 250
SIC 1611 Highway & street construction; Highway & street construction
CFO: Scott Carlson
IT Man: Michelle Mattis
IT Man: Glenn Olson
IT Man: Keith Rasmussen
Sfty Dirs: Don Hamon
Sales Exec: Dave Hamrick
Sales Asso: John Nason

D-U-N-S 00-747-8423
HOOKER EQUITY EXCHANGE
302 E Hwy 54, Hooker, OK 73945
Tel (580) 652-2432 *Founded/Ownrshp* 1915
Sales 29.2MM *EMP* 22
Accts Lindburg Vogel Pierce Faris D
SIC 5153 5999 Grains; Farm equipment & supplies; Grains; Farm equipment & supplies
Pr: Bill Lines
Genl Mgr: John Vanmeter

D-U-N-S 00-312-0748 IMP/EXP
▲ **HOOKER FURNITURE CORP** (VA)
440 Commonwealth Blvd E, Martinsville, VA 24112-2040
Tel (276) 632-0459 *Founded/Ownrshp* 1924
Sales 244.3MM *EMP* 674^E
Accts Kpmg Llp Charlotte North Car
Tkr Sym HOFT *Exch* NGS
SIC 2511 2512 2517 2521 Wood household furniture; Wood bedroom furniture; Wood desks, bookcases & magazine racks; End tables: wood; Upholstered household furniture; Home entertainment unit cabinets, wood; Wood office furniture; Wood household furniture; Wood bedroom furniture; Wood desks, bookcases & magazine racks; End tables: wood; Upholstered household furniture; Home entertainment unit cabinets, wood; Wood office furniture
Ch Bd: Paul B Toms Jr
Pr: Michael W Delgatti Jr
CFO: Paul A Huckfeldt
Ex VP: Michael P Spece
Ex VP: Sekar Sundararajan
Sr VP: Anne M Jacobsen
Sr VP: Henry P Long
VP: Sandi Teague
VP: Pat Watson
Exec: Randy Sigmon
Board of Directors: W Christopher Beeler Jr, John L Gregory III, E Larry Ryder, David G Sweet, Ellen Connelly Taaffe, Henry G Williamson Jr

D-U-N-S 04-023-5236
HOOKSETT KAWASAKI INC
HKP POWERSPORTS
1354 Hooksett Rd, Hooksett, NH 03106-1816
Tel (603) 668-4343 *Founded/Ownrshp* 1976
Sales 30.2MM^E *EMP* 80
SIC 5571 5599 5551 Motorcycle dealers; Motorcycle parts & accessories; Snowmobiles; Boat dealers; Motorcycle dealers; Motorcycle parts & accessories; Snowmobiles; Boat dealers
Pr: Michael Whalley
**Pr:* Steven Whalley
**Treas:* Stephen Whalley
Board of Directors: George Whalley

D-U-N-S 01-301-6542 EXP
HOOLEY FAMILY MANAGEMENT INC
PLANTATION FORD
707 N State Road 7, Plantation, FL 33317-2157
Tel (954) 584-2400 *Founded/Ownrshp* 2008
Sales 22.4MM^E *EMP* 47^E
SIC 5511 Automobiles, new & used
Pr: Jack Sheeran
Sr VP: Billy White
Exec: Deena O'Brien
Sls Mgr: Allen Biskup
Sls Mgr: Lester Nunez
Sls Mgr: Jim Williamson

D-U-N-S 04-546-2066
HOOLEY INVESTMENTS LIMITED PARTNERSHIP
707 N State Road 7, Plantation, FL 33317-2157
Tel (954) 584-2400 *Founded/Ownrshp* 1967
Sales 27.2MM^E *EMP* 165
SIC 5511 Automobiles, new & used; Automobiles, new & used
Pt: Michael Hooley Jr
Pt: Patricia Hooley
Pt: Stuart Podel

D-U-N-S 14-122-7657
HOOMAN PONTIAC GMC BUICK INC
6101 W Slauson Ave, Culver City, CA 90230-6419
Tel (310) 636-4800 *Founded/Ownrshp* 2003
Sales 39.3MM^E *EMP* 150
SIC 5511 Automobiles & other motor vehicles; New & used car dealers; Automobiles, new & used
Pr: Hooman Nissani
IT Man: Dave Arnold
Sales Exec: Luis Santillan
Sls Mgr: Ryan Lee
Sls Mgr: Sherice Mann
Sls Mgr: Bijan Rezapour

HOOMAN TOYOTA OF LONG BEACH
See HTL AUTOMOTIVE INC

D-U-N-S 07-464-7165
HOOPA VALLEY TRIBAL COUNCIL
Hwy 96, Hoopa, CA 95546
Tel (530) 625-4211 *Founded/Ownrshp* 1860
Sales 35.1MM^E *EMP* 350
SIC 7389 ; Indian reservation
CFO: Jerry Davis
**Ch:* Leonard Masten Jr

D-U-N-S 02-447-6442
HOOPAUGH GRADING CO LLC (NC)
303 Forsyth Hall Dr, Charlotte, NC 28273-5816
Tel (704) 588-2284 *Founded/Ownrshp* 1953
Sales 34.2MM^E *EMP* 100
SIC 1794 Excavation & grading, building construction
Opers Mgr: Paul Heape

D-U-N-S 15-228-6142
HOOPER BAY CAFE
TOP OF THE WORLD RESTAURANT
500 W 3rd Ave, Anchorage, AK 99501-2210
Tel (907) 265-7111 *Founded/Ownrshp* 1977
Sales 4.1MM^E *EMP* 300
SIC 5812 Cafe; Cafe
**Ex Dir:* Susan Hilbers

D-U-N-S 00-192-6971
HOOPER CORP
2030 Pennsylvania Ave, Madison, WI 53704-4746
Tel (608) 249-0451 *Founded/Ownrshp* 1959
Sales 220.7MM *EMP* 350
Accts Mcgladrey Llp Madison Wi
SIC 1623 1711 Electric power line construction; Pipe laying construction; Mechanical contractor; Electric power line construction; Pipe laying construction; Mechanical contractor
Pr: G Frederick Davie
CFO: Bob Schaller
**CFO:* Robert Schaller
Sr VP: Eddee Alvarez
**VP:* Jerry A Diebling
**VP:* Keith J Judenis
**VP:* Steven Lindley
**VP:* Dave P Miller
**VP:* David Orr

D-U-N-S 06-072-2915
▲ HOOPER HOLMES INC
560 N Rogers Rd, Olathe, KS 66062-1211
Tel (913) 764-1045 *Founded/Ownrshp* 1899
Sales 28.5MM *EMP* 300
Tkr Sym HH *Exch* ASE
SIC 8099 6411 7375 Physical examination service, insurance; Information bureaus, insurance; Information retrieval services; Physical examination service, insurance; Information bureaus, insurance; Information retrieval services
Pr: Henry E Dubois
Pr: Chris Behling
Pr: Richard Whitbeck
COO: Mary Anderson
CFO: Steven Balthazor
CFO: Steven R Balthazor
Ofcr: Steve Marin
Ex VP: Bill Roberts
Sr VP: Susheel K Jain
Sr VP: Raymond A Sinclir
Sr VP: Guenther Weydauer
VP: John Bond
VP: Daren Khouri
VP: Judith Levine
VP: Joseph Malecki
Exec: Helena Santoya
Board of Directors: Ronald V Aprahamian, Mark J Emkjer, Larry Ferguson, Charles M Gillman, Gus D Halas, Thomas A Watford

D-U-N-S 60-628-4560
HOOSIER CARE INC
VERNON MANOR CHILDRENS HOME
1050 Chinoe Rd Ste 350, Lexington, KY 40502-6571
Tel (859) 255-0075 *Founded/Ownrshp* 1989
Sales 36.6MM *EMP* 650
Accts Reznick Group Pc Baltimore M
SIC 8059 Nursing home, except skilled & intermediate care facility; Nursing home, except skilled & intermediate care facility
Pr: Bruce Hutson
**Treas:* Steven Wood
VP: James R Johnson

D-U-N-S 06-280-2574 IMP
HOOSIER ENERGY RURAL ELECTRIC COOPERATIVE INC
CO-OP COMFORT CREDIT
2501 S Cooperative Way, Bloomington, IN 47403-5175
Tel (812) 356-4291 *Founded/Ownrshp* 1935
Sales 667.9MM *EMP* 475
Accts Deloitte & Touche Llp Indian
SIC 4911 Generation, electric power; Transmission, electric power; Distribution, electric power; Generation, electric power; Transmission, electric power; Distribution, electric power
Ch Bd: Charlie Meier
**Pr:* James S Weimer
**CEO:* J Steven Smith
VP: Robert C Hochstetler
VP: Robert I Richhart
VP: Tom Van Paris
Comm Man: Claire Gregory
Genl Mgr: Bill Harding
MIS Dir: Lance Davis
Dir IT: Ed Karas
IT Man: Bobby Asbell
Board of Directors: Robert D Stroup, Harry Althoff, Vaughn Tucker, August A Bauer, Dale Walther, Donald Braun, James Weimer, Darin Duncan, Herbert C Haggard, Jerry C Jackle, Emil Page, Larry Peters, Jerry Pheifer

D-U-N-S 07-203-1404
HOOSIER MOTOR CLUB
AAA HOOSIER MOTOR CLUB
3750 Guion Rd Ste 390, Indianapolis, IN 46222-1696
Tel (317) 923-1500 *Founded/Ownrshp* 1902
Sales 40.0MM^E *EMP* 295
SIC 8699 6331 Automobile owners' association; Automobile insurance; Automobile owners' association; Automobile insurance
Pr: Terry Farias
**Ch:* Philip Genetos
Opers Mgr: Tari Plump

HOOSIER OXYGEN COMPANY
See INDIANA OXYGEN CO INC

HOOSIER PARK CASINO
See HOOSIER PARK LLC

D-U-N-S 83-441-9772
HOOSIER PARK LLC
HOOSIER PARK CASINO
(*Suby of* CENTAUR LLC) ★
4500 Dan Patch Cir Xxx, Anderson, IN 46013-3161
Tel (765) 642-7223 *Founded/Ownrshp* 2007
Sales 220.0MM *EMP* 1,112^E
SIC 7948 Racing, including track operation; Racing, including track operation
Pt: Roderick Ratcliff
CFO: Kurt Wilson
VP: Thomas F Bannon
VP: Bonnie McDowell
VP: Rich Ruden
Exec: Ginger Shaw
Genl Mgr: James Brown
Genl Mgr: Angelique Davis-Boyle
CIO: Richard Moore
Dir IT: Larry Kaufmann
Sls&Mrk Ex: Mark Thacker
Board of Directors: Ralph Brown, Gene Ciscell, Rudy McMillan, Jeff Smith

D-U-N-S 09-643-7462
HOOSIER PLASTIC FABRICATION INC (CA)
1152 California Ave, Corona, CA 92881-3324
Tel (951) 272-3070 *Founded/Ownrshp* 1979, 1997
Sales 40.8MM^E *EMP* 145
SIC 2821 Machine parts, stamped or pressed metal; Thermoplastic materials
CEO: Robert G Simms
Exec: Shannon Sims
IT Man: Willie Abundez
IT Man: Shanna Garcia
IT Man: Abundez Willie
VP Opers: Mitchell McCall

D-U-N-S 04-899-0543 IMP/EXP
HOOSIER RACING TIRE CORP
HOOSIER TIRE
65465 Hc 931, Lakeville, IN 46536
Tel (574) 784-3152 *Founded/Ownrshp* 1979
Sales 79.1MM^E *EMP* 75
SIC 5014 5531 3011 5699 Tires & tubes; Automotive tires; Tires & inner tubes; Tires & tubes; Automotive tires; Tires & inner tubes; Sports apparel
Pr: Joyce L Newton
VP: Craig E Benninghoff
VP: John Desalle
VP: Scotty L Merrill
VP: Marjorie D Newton
VP: Dennis Sherman
IT Man: Tim Slater
VP Opers: Craig Benninghoff
Sfty Mgr: Mike Hammond
Manager: Joe Sherron
Plnt Mgr: Brad Hicks

HOOSIER TANK & MFG INC
See HOOSIER TANK AND MANUFACTURING INC

D-U-N-S 80-585-6184
HOOSIER TANK AND MANUFACTURING INC
HOOSIER TANK & MFG INC
1710 N Sheridan St, South Bend, IN 46628-1523
Tel (574) 232-8368 *Founded/Ownrshp* 1991
Sales 20.1MM^E *EMP* 90
SIC 3443 3469 Tanks, standard or custom fabricated: metal plate; Metal stampings
Pr: Thomas R Kinnucan Jr
**VP:* William R Welsch Jr
Sls Mgr: Andy Kinnucan

D-U-N-S 00-605-7780
HOOSIER TIMES INC
HERALD TIMES
(*Suby of* SCHURZ COMMUNICATIONS INC) ★
1900 S Walnut St, Bloomington, IN 47401-7720
Tel (800) 422-0070 *Founded/Ownrshp* 1966
Sales 33.6MM^E *EMP* 490
SIC 2711 4813 2791 2752 Newspapers: publishing only, not printed on site; ;Typesetting; Commercial printing, lithographic; Newspapers: publishing only, not printed on site; ;Typesetting; Commercial printing, lithographic
Pr: Scott C Schurz
**Treas:* Eric McIntosh
**VP:* Mayer Malloney
VP: Lolly Quigley
Genl Mgr: Andre Murray
Plnt Mgr: Bob Zaltsberg

HOOSIER TIRE
See HOOSIER RACING TIRE CORP

D-U-N-S 00-603-5273
HOOSIER TOOL & DIE CO INC
H T D
2860 N National Rd Ste B, Columbus, IN 47201-3746
Tel (812) 376-8286 *Founded/Ownrshp* 1949, 1999
Sales 21.2MM^E *EMP* 80
SIC 3545 3544 Machine tool accessories; Special dies, tools, jigs & fixtures
Pr: Robert Bosar

D-U-N-S 01-630-9817
HOOSIER TRAILER ACQUISITION CORP
HOOSIER TRAILER AND TRUCK EQP
4830 Todd Dr, Fort Wayne, IN 46803-1748
Tel (260) 422-7564 *Founded/Ownrshp* 2002
Sales 32.8MM^E *EMP* 72
SIC 5012 7539 5013 Trailers for trucks, new & used; Truck bodies; Trailer repair; Trailer parts & accessories
Pr: Dean Phillips

HOOSIER TRAILER AND TRUCK EQP
See HOOSIER TRAILER ACQUISITION CORP

D-U-N-S 09-446-9582
HOOSIER UPLANDS ECONOMIC DEVELOPMENT CORP
SERENITY NOW PSYCHTRC & COUNSL
521 W Main St, Mitchell, IN 47446-1410
Tel (812) 849-4457 *Founded/Ownrshp* 1966
Sales 21.9MM *EMP* 240
Accts Mccauley Nicolas & Company Llc
SIC 8399 8082 Community action agency; Home health care services; Community action agency; Home health care services
Ex Dir: David L Miller

HOOSIER VILLAGE RETIREMENT CTR
See SENIOR BHI LIVING INC

HOOT AEROBIC SYSTEMS
See MURPHY CORMIER GENERAL CONTRACTOR INC

HOOT MCINERNEY CADILLAC-TOYOTA
See MC INERNEY INC

D-U-N-S 03-308-7958
HOOTEN OIL CO INC (OK)
12583 S Highway 99, Seminole, OK 74868-5800
Tel (405) 382-1166 *Founded/Ownrshp* 1942
Sales 22.1MM^E *EMP* 18
SIC 5172 Service station supplies, petroleum
Pr: David Hooten

HOOTERS
See CORNETT HOSPITALITY LLC

HOOTERS
See RMD CORP

HOOTERS
See TEXAS WINGS INC

HOOTERS
See RESTAURANTS OF AMERICA INC

HOOTERS CASINO HOTEL
See 155 EAST TROPICANA LLC

D-U-N-S 12-094-6041
HOOTERS OF AMERICA LLC
1815 The Exchange Se, Atlanta, GA 30339-2027
Tel (770) 951-2040 *Founded/Ownrshp* 2011
Sales 260.9MM^E *EMP* 5,600
SIC 5812 6794 American restaurant; Franchises, selling or licensing; American restaurant; Franchises, selling or licensing
Pr: Coby Brooks
COO: Erica Eklind
**COO:* Jim Parrish
CFO: Rodney Foster
CFO: Matt Wickesberg
Chf Mktg O: Jason Abelkop
**Ofcr:* Claudia Levitas
VP: Tad Dixon
VP: Mark Doran
VP: Dan Macrenaris
VP: Greg Michael
VP: Rebecca Sinclair
VP: Kevin Vandiver
Dir Risk M: John Chlebak
Dir Risk M: Sandy Oltman

D-U-N-S 12-252-0877
HOOVEN - DAYTON CORP
H D C
511 Byers Rd, Miamisburg, OH 45342-5337
Tel (937) 233-4473 *Founded/Ownrshp* 2007
Sales 22.0MM *EMP* 101
SIC 2679 2672 2671 2759 Tags & labels, paper; Tape, pressure sensitive: made from purchased materials; Packaging paper & plastics film, coated & laminated; Labels & seals: printing
Pr: Christopher Che
COO: Kim Wright
CFO: David Nolan
**Sr VP:* Al Abolofia
VP: Mark Strauss
Genl Mgr: Mindy App
IT Man: Steve Barth
IT Man: Steve Bath
VP Mfg: Chuck Hester
Opers Mgr: Latif Affini
Opers Mgr: Spencer Cones

D-U-N-S 00-211-1318
HOOVER & STRONG INC (VA)
10700 Trade Rd, North Chesterfield, VA 23236-3000
Tel (804) 794-3700 *Founded/Ownrshp* 1912, 1989
Sales 29.0MM^E *EMP* 118
Accts Cherry Bekaert & Holland Ll
SIC 3341 Secondary precious metals; Secondary precious metals
Ch Bd: George F Hoover
**Pr:* Torrance D Hoover
**CFO:* F Daniel Pharr
Treas: Jeffery Hoover
Sr Cor Off: James McCarty
VP: Britt F Ragle
Dir IT: Norman Thornton
Plnt Mgr: Bill Tomlinson
Sales Exec: Lisa Flint

D-U-N-S 06-369-9177
HOOVER & WELLS INC
REZ STONE
2011 Seaman St, Toledo, OH 43605-1908
Tel (419) 691-9220 *Founded/Ownrshp* 1978
Sales 23.9MM *EMP* 65
SIC 1752 2891 2851 Floor laying & floor work; Adhesives & sealants; Paints & allied products; Floor laying & floor work; Adhesives & sealants; Paints & allied products
Pr: Margaret Hoover
Pr: James M Collu
**VP:* John Corsini
**VP:* James Mc Collum
VP: James McCollum
**Prin:* Robert E Hoover
**Prin:* Dennis Wells
Sfty Dirs: James Noble

D-U-N-S 05-294-8577
HOOVER CHRYSLER-JEEP LIMITED PARTNERSHIP (SC)
2250 Savannah Hwy, Charleston, SC 29414-5314
Tel (843) 763-0040 *Founded/Ownrshp* 1970
Sales 28.9MM^E *EMP* 87
SIC 5511 Automobiles, new & used; Automobiles, new & used
Genl Pt: Ronald E Hoover
**Pt:* INA R Hoover

D-U-N-S 61-347-7652
HOOVER CITY SCHOOL DISTRICT
HOOVER CITY SCHOOLS
2810 Metropolitan Way, Birmingham, AL 35243-2944
Tel (205) 439-1000 *Founded/Ownrshp* 1987
Sales 81.7MM^E *EMP* 1,500
SIC 8211 Public elementary & secondary schools; Public elementary & secondary schools
**Pr:* Earl Cooper
Pr: William Veitch
Exec: Kara Walker
Adm Dir: James Knichredom
Dir IT: Jonathan Sandlin
IT Man: Troy McCraw
Schl Brd P: Donna Frazier
Teacher Pr: Mary Veal

HOOVER CITY SCHOOLS
See HOOVER CITY SCHOOL DISTRICT

D-U-N-S 00-881-8684
HOOVER CONSTRUCTION CO INC
302 Hoover Rd S, Virginia, MN 55792-3430
Tel (218) 741-3280 *Founded/Ownrshp* 1956
Sales 37.3MM^E *EMP* 150
SIC 1611 Grading; Grading
CEO: Peter G Johnson
**Pr:* Richard Spry
**Sec:* Michael P Riley
VP: Dick Freeberg
**VP:* Richard Freeberg
Sfty Dirs: Nicholas Johnson

HOOVER CONTAINER GROUP
See HOOVER GROUP INC

HOOVER CONTAINER SOLUTIONS
See HOOVER MATERIALS HANDLING GROUP INC

D-U-N-S 14-815-0212 IMP/EXP
HOOVER GROUP INC
HOOVER CONTAINER GROUP
2135 Highway 6 S, Houston, TX 77077-4319
Tel (281) 870-8402 *Founded/Ownrshp* 1985
Sales 108.5MM^E *EMP* 230
Accts Habif Arogeti & Wyne Llp
SIC 3496 3412 3443 3089 7359 3411 Miscellaneous fabricated wire products; Metal barrels, drums & pails; Industrial vessels, tanks & containers; Tanks, lined: metal plate; Tanks, standard or custom fabricated: metal plate; Plastic containers, except foam; Plastic & fiberglass tanks; Equipment rental & leasing; Metal cans; Miscellaneous fabricated wire products; Metal barrels, drums & pails; Industrial vessels, tanks & containers; Tanks, lined: metal plate; Tanks, standard or custom fabricated: metal plate; Plastic containers, except foam; Plastic & fiberglass tanks; Equipment rental & leasing; Metal cans
CEO: Donald W Young
Pr: Paul Lewis
VP: Conrad A Arnold
VP: Scott T Meints
VP: Johan Wramsby
Netwrk Mgr: Travis Conley
Opers Mgr: Robbie Monlezun

D-U-N-S 00-446-2131 IMP
HOOVER INC
TTI FLOORCARE
(*Suby of* TECHTRONIC INDUSTRIES COMPANY LIMITED)
7005 Cochran Rd, Solon, OH 44139-4303
Tel (330) 499-9200 *Founded/Ownrshp* 2007
Sales 287.4MM^E *EMP* 600
SIC 5064 Vacuum cleaners, household; Vacuum cleaners, household
Pr: Chris Gurreri
**Pr:* Dan Gregory
**CFO:* Matt Shene
VP: D A Gault
VP: Frank Wittman
VP: Thomas Yu
VP Admn: Lynn Dragomier
IT Man: Keith Minton
Opers Mgr: Skip Lawton
Sls&Mrk Ex: Peter McCormick
Pr Mgr: Claudia Chiquillo

D-U-N-S 03-483-4218
HOOVER INC
HOOVER INC CRUSHED STONE
371 Waldron Rd, La Vergne, TN 37086-3253
Tel (615) 793-2919 *Founded/Ownrshp* 1961
Sales 29.8MM^E *EMP* 158
SIC 3273 Ready-mixed concrete; Ready-mixed concrete
Pr: Thomas S Hoover
**Ex VP:* E H Hoover III
Sls Mgr: Brian Higgins

HOOVER INC CRUSHED STONE
See HOOVER INC

D-U-N-S 04-438-1775
HOOVER JEEP CHRYSLER INC
195 Marymeade Dr, Summerville, SC 29483-5273
Tel (843) 871-8791 *Founded/Ownrshp* 1998
Sales 26.6MM *EMP* 40
SIC 5511 Automobiles, new & used; Automobiles, new & used
Pr: Ronald Hoover

D-U-N-S 96-283-2796 IMP/EXP
HOOVER MATERIALS HANDLING GROUP INC
HOOVER CONTAINER SOLUTIONS
(*Suby of* HOOVER CONTAINER GROUP) ★
2135 Highway 6 S, Houston, TX 77077-4319
Tel (800) 844-8683 *Founded/Ownrshp* 1992
Sales 101.7MM^E *EMP* 102
SIC 5113 3089 Containers, paper & disposable plastic; Plastic containers, except foam; Containers, paper & disposable plastic; Plastic containers, except foam
Ch Bd: Donald W Young
**Pr:* Paul Lewis
CFO: Joseph Levy
**VP:* Conrad A Arnold
VP: Rod Branch
**VP:* Scott T Meints
IT Man: Sharif Taha
Software D: Barry Bucher
Mfg Dir: Carlos Mendez
Ql Cn Mgr: Michael Corey
Advt Dir: Bill Terry

D-U-N-S 61-034-0705 IMP
HOOVER PRECISION PRODUCTS INC
(*Suby of* TSUBAKI NAKASHIMA CO.,LTD.)
2200 Pendley Rd, Cumming, GA 30041-6448
Tel (770) 889-9223 *Founded/Ownrshp* 1990
Sales 151.6MM^E *EMP* 1,300
SIC 3399 Steel balls; Steel balls
CEO: Kenji Yamada
**Pr:* Eric Sturdy
**CEO:* Takanori Kondo
COO: Takashige Suehiro
**CFO:* James W Brandon Jr
**CFO:* Gary Duran
Netwrk Eng: Richard Mishoe

D-U-N-S 13-330-3797
HOOVER TOYOTA LLC
(*Suby of* STEWART MANAGEMENT GROUP INC) ★
2686 John Hawkins Pkwy, Hoover, AL 35244-4000
Tel (205) 823-3720 *Founded/Ownrshp* 1999
Sales 31.7MM^E *EMP* 120
SIC 5511 Automobiles, new & used; Automobiles, new & used
VP: Tim Tuttle
Sales Exec: Dale Cox
Sales Asso: Christian Ackerman
Sales Asso: Michael Andrews
Sales Asso: Dwayne Currier
Sales Asso: Randy Lyon

D-U-N-S 10-864-3479 IMP/EXP
HOOVER TREATED WOOD PRODUCTS INC
(*Suby of* HOOVER WOOD PRODUCTS HOLDINGS INC) ★
154 Wire Rd, Thomson, GA 30824-7988
Tel (706) 595-5058 *Founded/Ownrshp* 2002
Sales 65.3MM^E *EMP* 220
SIC 2491 2899 Wood products, creosoted; Chemical preparations; Wood products, creosoted; Chemical preparations
CEO: Barry Holden
CFO: Thomas E Dickson
VP: Timothy Borris
VP: Bready Richard L
IT Man: Rick Rakoczy
Opers Mgr: Chris Clark
Opers Mgr: Brian Davis
Ql Cn Mgr: Ricky Broach
VP Mktg: Trivis Hixon
Mktg Mgr: Johnathan Richards
Mktg Mgr: Doc Young

D-U-N-S 00-537-9425 IMP
■ **HOOVER UNIVERSAL INC**
JOHNSON CONTROLS-BATTLE CREEK
(*Suby of* JOHNSON CONTROLS INC) ★
49200 Halyard Dr, Plymouth, MI 48170-2481
Tel (734) 254-5000 *Founded/Ownrshp* 1985
Sales 364.4MM^E *EMP* 2,000
SIC 2531 Seats, automobile; Seats, automobile
Pr: Keith E Wandell
Treas: Thomas Jeppson
VP: Jeffrey S Edwards
VP: William J Kohler
VP: John David Major
**VP:* Jerome D Okarma
VP: Clare Renshaw
**VP:* Stephen Allen Roell

D-U-N-S 13-210-0376 IMP/EXP
HOOVER WOOD PRODUCTS HOLDINGS INC
154 Wire Rd, Thomson, GA 30824-7988
Tel (706) 595-5058 *Founded/Ownrshp* 2002
Sales 65.3MM^E *EMP* 220^E
SIC 2491 Wood products, creosoted; Wood products, creosoted
CEO: J Eric Hanson
**Pr:* Barry Holden
**CFO:* Thomas Dickson
**VP:* Thomas E Dickson

D-U-N-S 61-124-1688
■ **HOOVERS INC**
(*Suby of* D&B) ★
5800 Airport Blvd, Austin, TX 78752-3826
Tel (512) 374-4500 *Founded/Ownrshp* 2003
Sales 72.9MM^E *EMP* 380
SIC 7375 Information retrieval services; Information retrieval services
Pr: Laura Kelly
Pr: Kris RAO
Pr: Russell Secker
COO: Carl G Shepherd
CFO: Lynn Atchison
Ex VP: Jean Blackwell
Ex VP: Carl Sheperd
Ex VP: Gregory Smith
VP: Thomas M Ballard
VP: Rachel Brush
VP: Daniel V Iannotti
VP: Sally Mascorro
**VP:* Michael Umbach
VP: Mel Yarbrough
Exec: Meg McCarthy
Exec: Hiroyuki Mitani
Exec: Jon Olson
Exec: Daniel Smith
Board of Directors: Susan D Beriont

HOOVERWOOD
See INDIANAPOLIS JEWISH HOME INC

D-U-N-S 12-787-6139 IMP
HOP AND WINE BEVERAGES LLC
22714 Glenn Dr Ste 130, Sterling, VA 20164-4482
Tel (703) 421-2337 *Founded/Ownrshp* 1998
Sales 45.6MM^E *EMP* 90
SIC 5181 Beer & other fermented malt liquors; Beer & other fermented malt liquors
**VP:* Lorea Wetten

D-U-N-S 07-829-0362
HOP CALIFORNIA ENTERTAINMENT LLC
SLATE MEDIA GROUP CALIFORNIA
1111 S Victory Blvd, Burbank, CA 91502-2550
Tel (818) 846-9381 *Founded/Ownrshp* 2011
Sales 22.5MM^E *EMP* 383^E
SIC 7929 Entertainment service
Pr: Josh Rizzo
Prd Mgr: Tyler Christiansen

D-U-N-S 96-268-3038
HOP ENERGY HOLDINGS INC
4 W Red Oak Ln Ste 310, White Plains, NY 10604-3606
Tel (914) 304-1300 *Founded/Ownrshp* 2006
Sales 165.9MM^E *EMP* 867
SIC 5983 Fuel oil dealers; Fuel oil dealers
CEO: Richard Nota
Treas: Fred Lord
**Prin:* Michael Anton
**Prin:* Steve Zambito

D-U-N-S 83-712-2753
HOP ENERGY LLC
KEYSER ENERGY
(*Suby of* HOP ENERGY HOLDINGS INC) ★
4 W Red Oak Ln Ste 310, White Plains, NY 10604-3606
Tel (914) 304-1300 *Founded/Ownrshp* 2006
Sales 165.9MM^E *EMP* 865
SIC 5983 Fuel oil dealers; Fuel oil dealers
Pr: Michael Anton
**CFO:* Richard Nota
Treas: Fred Lord
**Sr VP:* Laura Cicchelli
**Sr VP:* Steve Loizeaux
**Sr VP:* Matthew J Ryan
VP: John Kuebler
VP: Elaine Sheldon
Admn Mgr: Cindie Gagnon
Genl Mgr: Rich Hyland
Off Mgr: Kathy Lang

D-U-N-S 08-689-4730
HOP INDUSTRIES CORP (NY)
H I C
1251 Valley Brook Ave, Lyndhurst, NJ 07071-3509
Tel (201) 438-6200 *Founded/Ownrshp* 1977
Sales 53.9MM^E *EMP* 70
Accts Goldstein Lieberman & Company
SIC 5162 5111 5084 Plastics materials & basic shapes; Plastics sheets & rods; Printing & writing paper; Printing trades machinery, equipment & supplies
CEO: Spencer Lin
**Pr:* Robert Noetzel
**COO:* Maria Viray
**Sr VP:* Jack Smith
**VP:* Russell Lauricilla
**VP:* Ted Lin
Sls Mgr: Craig Kleinfield
Snr Mgr: Yung Lin

D-U-N-S 05-080-4822
HOP LLC (CA)
HONDA OF PASADENA
1965 E Foothill Blvd, Pasadena, CA 91107-3218
Tel (626) 683-5888 *Founded/Ownrshp* 1997
Sales 20.8MM^E *EMP* 85
SIC 5511 Automobiles, new & used; Automobiles, new & used

D-U-N-S 05-526-9583
HOPATCONG BOROUGH SCHOOL DISTRICT
HOPATCONG HIGH SCHOOL
2 Windsor Ave, Hopatcong, NJ 07843-1221
Tel (973) 398-8801 *Founded/Ownrshp* 1930
Sales 27.1MM^E *EMP* 555
SIC 8211 Public elementary & secondary schools; Public elementary & secondary schools
Pr: Clifford Lundin
**Pr:* Margaret Bongiorno
**Pr:* Richard Lavery
Pr: Sylvia Tetillo
Treas: Kelley Anne McGann
Bd of Dir: Peter Karpiak
Bd of Dir: Robert Nicholson
Bd of Dir: Sarah Schindelar
VP: Anthony Fasano
**VP:* Dolores Krowl
Schl Brd P: Frank Padula
Board of Directors: Alan Gilbert, Martha Krieger, Sylvia Petillo, Lou Ricca V President, Madeline Yound

HOPATCONG HIGH SCHOOL
See HOPATCONG BOROUGH SCHOOL DISTRICT

D-U-N-S 96-981-2812
HOPE CHILDRENS ALLIANCE
158 Grandfather Home Rd, Banner Elk, NC 28604-6154
Tel (828) 898-5465 *Founded/Ownrshp* 2014
Sales 28.2MM^E *EMP* 375
SIC 8322 Individual & family services; Residential care for children
Pr: John Koppelmeyer

D-U-N-S 13-512-7277
HOPE CHRISTIAN COMMUNITY FOUNDATION
4515 Poplar Ave Ste 324, Memphis, TN 38117-7507
Tel (901) 682-6201 *Founded/Ownrshp* 1998
Sales 65.8MM *EMP* 4
Accts Fouts & Morgan Cpas Memphis
SIC 8661 Religious organizations; Religious organizations
VP Opers: Brian Cochrane

D-U-N-S 05-094-7084
HOPE COLLEGE
141 E 12th St, Holland, MI 49423-3607
Tel (616) 395-7000 *Founded/Ownrshp* 1866
Sales 111.0MM *EMP* 650^E
Accts Plante & Moran Pllc Grand Ra
SIC 8221 Colleges universities & professional schools; Colleges universities & professional schools
Pr: Dr John C Knapp
**Pr:* James Bultman
**CFO:* Thomas Bylsma
Trst: Barb Depree
Ofcr: Jason Guthaus
Sr VP: Abby Reeg
**VP:* Tom Bylsma
**VP:* Richard Frost
**VP:* William C Vanderbilt
**VP:* Dave Vanderwel
VP: Scott Wolterink
Exec: Lori Bouwman
Exec: Cristina Ivey
Dir Lab: Abe Anaya
Dir Rx: Lina Lash
Dir Rx: Ross Mathesius

D-U-N-S 02-024-1063
HOPE COMMUNITY RESOURCES INC
540 W Intl Airport Rd, Anchorage, AK 99518-1105
Tel (907) 561-5335 *Founded/Ownrshp* 1968
Sales 65.3MM *EMP* 805
Accts Kpmg Llp Anchorage Ak
SIC 8361 7361 8322 8082 Residential care for the handicapped; Employment agencies; Individual & family services; Home health care services; Residential care for the handicapped; Employment agencies; Individual & family services; Home health care services
VP: Phil Candaff
**Treas:* Eugene Bates
**VP:* Mary Bolin
**VP:* John Dittrich
**VP:* Richard Edwards
**VP:* Robert Owens
Ex Dir: Stephen Lesko
IT Man: Jim Haacke
IT Man: Jim Hacky
Doctor: Tracie Kingsland
HC Dir: Cyndee Johnson

D-U-N-S 06-959-7508
HOPE ENTERPRISES FOUNDATION INC
2401 Reach Rd, Williamsport, PA 17701-9108
Tel (570) 326-3745 *Founded/Ownrshp* 1952
Sales 952.1M *EMP* 540
Accts Parentebeard Llc Williamsport
SIC 8331 Job training services; Vocational rehabilitation agency; Job training services; Vocational rehabilitation agency
Pr: James Campbell
VP: Carol Durmheiser
VP: Susan R Smith
VP: Joel Weaver

D-U-N-S 83-100-3231
HOPE ENTERPRISES INC
2401 Reach Rd, Williamsport, PA 17701-9108
Tel (570) 326-3745 *Founded/Ownrshp* 1984
Sales 22.9MM *EMP* 590
Accts Parente Beard Llc Williamspor
SIC 8361 8322 Residential care for the handicapped; Social services for the handicapped; Residential care for the handicapped; Social services for the handicapped
Pr: James F Campbell
Sr VP: Susan Smith
**VP:* Carol Drumheiser
**VP:* Lorraine Gates
**VP:* Frank Porshe
**VP:* Joel Weaver
Genl Mgr: Joe Wise

D-U-N-S 07-276-1299
HOPE FOCUS (MI)
1355 Oakman Blvd, Detroit, MI 48238-2849
Tel (313) 494-5500 *Founded/Ownrshp* 1968
Sales 29.2MM *EMP* 312
Accts Focus Hope Detroit Mi
SIC 8399 3714 8249 8299 Neighborhood development group; Motor vehicle parts & accessories; Vocational schools; Educational services; Neighborhood development group; Motor vehicle parts & accessories; Vocational schools; Educational services
Pr: William F Jones Jr
**COO:* Timothy M Duperron
Board of Directors: Glenda Price

D-U-N-S 14-735-4138 IMP
HOPE FOCUS COMPANIES INC
FOCUS HOPE LOGISTICS
(*Suby of* HOPE FOCUS) ★
1355 Oakman Blvd, Detroit, MI 48238-2849
Tel (313) 494-5500 *Founded/Ownrshp* 1984
Sales 29.3MM *EMP* 300
SIC 3545 Precision tools, machinists'; Precision tools, machinists'
CEO: Timothy Duperron
**Treas:* Martha Schultz
Software D: Rodney Smith

D-U-N-S 14-418-2313
HOPE FOR CITY
7003 Oxford St Ste A, Minneapolis, MN 55426-4525
Tel (952) 829-5239 *Founded/Ownrshp* 2001
Sales 41.8MM *EMP* 4
Accts Boulay Heutmaker Zibell & Co
SIC 8699 Charitable organization; Charitable organization
Ofcr: Quenton Marty
Prin: Joe Lahti

D-U-N-S 00-794-4721
■ **HOPE GAS INC** (WV)
DOMINION HOPE
(*Suby of* DOMINION RESOURCES INC) ★
Bank One Center W 3rd St, Clarksburg, WV 26301
Tel (304) 623-8600 *Founded/Ownrshp* 1898
Sales 102.0MM^E *EMP* 505
SIC 4924 4923 Natural gas distribution; Gas transmission & distribution; Natural gas distribution; Gas transmission & distribution
Pr: William A Fox
**VP:* Gary A Nicholas
**VP:* R M Owens

HOPE GLOBAL DIV
See NFA CORP

D-U-N-S 01-025-6881
HOPE HAVEN AREA DEVELOPMENT CENTER CORP (IA)
828 N 7th St Ste 1, Burlington, IA 52601-4921
Tel (319) 752-0110 *Founded/Ownrshp* 1970
Sales 10.7MM *EMP* 290
SIC 8361 Rehabilitation center, residential: health care incidental; Rehabilitation center, residential: health care incidental
Ex Dir: Bob Bartles
IT Man: Cheryl Enger

D-U-N-S 07-804-1340 IMP/EXP
HOPE HAVEN INC (IA)
PARKVIEW INDUSTRIES
1800 19th St, Rock Valley, IA 51247-1058
Tel (712) 476-3281 *Founded/Ownrshp* 1965
Sales 38.5MM *EMP* 700
Accts Van Bruggen & Vande Vegte Pc
SIC 8331 Vocational rehabilitation agency; Vocational rehabilitation agency
Pr: Kent Eric Eknes
**COO:* Kelvin Helmus
**CFO:* Duane Obbink
Assoc Dir: Calvin Helmus
Comm Man: Marlowe Vanginkel
Off Mgr: April Metzger
IT Man: Terry Meyer

D-U-N-S 18-827-7693
HOPE HOSPICE & COMMUNITY SERVICES INC
9470 Healthpark Cir, Fort Myers, FL 33908-3600
Tel (239) 482-4673 *Founded/Ownrshp* 1981
Sales 30.0MM^E *EMP* 537
SIC 8082 Home health care services; Home health care services
CEO: Samira Beckwith
**CFO:* Jill Lampley
Exec: Charlotte King
Dir IT: John Rivera
IT Man: Randy Retecker
IT Man: Paul Sissons
Mktg Dir: Heather Chester
Pr Dir: John Strickling
Obsttrcn: Farida Ghoghawala
Corp Couns: Bob Griffin
Snr Mgr: Luis Cortes

HOPE HOUSING SCRAPER
See HOME OF HOPE INC

D-U-N-S 94-771-9639
HOPE INTERMEDIATE RESIDENCES INC
136 Catawissa Ave, Williamsport, PA 17701-4114
Tel (570) 326-3745 *Founded/Ownrshp* 1983
Sales 3.9MM^E *EMP* 450
Accts Parente Randolph Pc Williamsp
SIC 8361 Residential care; Residential care
Pr: James F Campbell

D-U-N-S 07-604-7414
HOPE INTERNATIONAL UNIVERSITY
PACIFIC CHRISTIAN COLLEGE
2500 Nutwood Ave, Fullerton, CA 92831-3102
Tel (714) 879-3901 *Founded/Ownrshp* 1928
Sales 21.1MM *EMP* 350^E
Accts Capin Crouse Lp Brea Ca
SIC 8221 College, except junior; College, except junior
Pr: John L Derry
COO: Ron Archer
**VP:* Paul Alexander
**VP:* Russell Mark Comeaux
VP: Steven Edgington
**VP:* Michael Mulryan
**VP:* Frank Scotti
**VP:* Teresa Smith
Store Mgr: Robert Mercado
Mktg Mgr: Katie Gladding
Snr Mgr: Michele Kleeman

HOPE LAKE HOLDINGS
See GREEK PEAK HOLDINGS LLC

D-U-N-S 80-780-9681
HOPE MARKETING INTERNATIONAL INC
2526 Jefferson Ave, Baton Rouge, LA 70802-2855
Tel (225) 505-5085 *Founded/Ownrshp* 2004
Sales 10.3MM^E *EMP* 400
SIC 8732 Survey service: marketing, location, etc.; Survey service: marketing, location, etc.
CEO: Sherman G Ruth

D-U-N-S 08-368-9315
HOPE NETWORK
COMMUNITY PARTNERSHIP CENTER
3075 Orchard Vista Dr Se # 100, Grand Rapids, MI 49546-7069
Tel (616) 301-8000 *Founded/Ownrshp* 2000
Sales 123.6MM *EMP* 2,162
Accts Beene Garter Llp Grand Rapids
SIC 8331 Vocational rehabilitation agency; Sheltered workshop; Vocational rehabilitation agency; Sheltered workshop
Pr: Phill W Weaver
Pr: Phil Hickmon
CFO: Richard Fabbrini
**CFO:* Marc Kole
Ofcr: Keri Jaynes
Ex VP: Patricia Howe
VP: Lona Litson
Ex Dir: Stacey Beck
Ex Dir: David Smith
Prac Mgr: Mary Schwyn
Prgrm Mgr: Jerri Bozeman

D-U-N-S 78-600-4572
HOPE NETWORK BEHAVIORAL HEALTH SERVICE INC
1256 Walker Ave Nw, Grand Rapids, MI 49504-4067
Tel (616) 235-2910 *Founded/Ownrshp* 1987
Sales 22.8MM *EMP* 490
SIC 8052 Home for the mentally retarded, with health care; Home for the mentally retarded, with health care
Ex Dir: Allen Jansen
**Ch Bd:* Jerry Johnson
**Treas:* Mark Augustyn
**VP:* Nan Hunt
Ex Dir: Al Gansen
Sls&Mrk Ex: Steve Canum

D-U-N-S 95-790-4030
HOPE NETWORK REHABILITATION SERVICES INC
MICHAEL ADOLESCENT PROGRAM
1490 E Beltline Ave Se, Grand Rapids, MI 49506-4336
Tel (616) 940-0040 *Founded/Ownrshp* 1983
Sales 16.8MM[E] *EMP* 325
SIC 8052 Intermediate care facilities; Intermediate care facilities
Ex Dir: Margaret Kroese
Creative D: Chris McMorrow
Dir Rx: Shane Kistler
Off Mgr: Shana Dykstra
Pgrm Dir: Dawn Brunner
Pgrm Dir: Herbert Winfrey

D-U-N-S 01-009-3677
HOPE NETWORK WEST MICHIGAN
(*Suby of* COMMUNITY PARTNERSHIP CENTER) ★
795 36th St Se, Grand Rapids, MI 49548-2319
Tel (616) 248-5900 *Founded/Ownrshp* 1996
Sales 38.0MM *EMP* 700
SIC 8331 Sheltered workshop; Sheltered workshop
Pr: Roberto Saenz
VP: Dan Holbert

D-U-N-S 03-470-0523
HOPE PEDIATRICS LLC
1420 W Mockingbird Ln # 550, Dallas, TX 75247-4973
Tel (214) 396-4673 *Founded/Ownrshp* 2013
Sales 5.0MM *EMP* 290
SIC 8082 Home health care services
Pr: Carl Willis
**COO:* Lucinda Lawton

HOPE PUBLIC SCHOOL
See HOPE SCHOOL DISTRICT

D-U-N-S 06-742-0331
HOPE SCHOOL
15 East Hazel Dell Ln, Springfield, IL 62712-4210
Tel (217) 585-5437 *Founded/Ownrshp* 1957
Sales 40.4MM *EMP* 480
SIC 8211 School for physically handicapped; School for physically handicapped
Pr: Joseph Nyre
**CFO:* Allan Boesdorfer
**Treas:* Don W Templeman
Sls&Mrk Ex: Mark Schmidt

D-U-N-S 07-566-8517
HOPE SCHOOL DISTRICT
HOPE PUBLIC SCHOOL
117 E 2nd St, Hope, AR 71801-4402
Tel (870) 722-2700 *Founded/Ownrshp* 1870
Sales 23.3MM[E] *EMP* 425
SIC 8211 9411 Public elementary & secondary schools; Administration of educational programs; Public elementary & secondary schools; Administration of educational programs
Bd of Dir: Denny Dickinson
Dir Sec: Maurice Henry
Cmptr Lab: Dale Daugherty
HC Dir: Renee Sells

D-U-N-S 07-719-0742
HOPE SERVICES (CA)
30 Las Colinas Ln, San Jose, CA 95119-1212
Tel (408) 284-2850 *Founded/Ownrshp* 1952
Sales 38.5MM *EMP* 600
Accts Abbott Stringham & Lynch San
SIC 8331 Vocational rehabilitation agency; Vocational rehabilitation agency
CEO: John C Christensen
**Pr:* Fred Gawlick
**CFO:* Ray Abe
**CFO:* Ric Lnd
CFO: Gregory Steelman
VP: Ken Toren
**VP:* Rex Zimmerman
Exec: Susan Bell
IT Man: Michael Nguyen
Sls&Mrk Ex: Paul Tomaro

D-U-N-S 62-708-9808
HOPE SERVICES INC
8506 Shrimpers Row, Dulac, LA 70353-2206
Tel (985) 563-7801 *Founded/Ownrshp* 1989
Sales 24.8MM[E] *EMP* 80
SIC 3731 Tenders, ships: building & repairing; Tugboats, building & repairing; Barges, building & repairing; Offshore supply boats, building & repairing
Pr: Rocky Henderson
**Sec:* Robert L Picou Jr
**VP:* Jay Henderson
**VP:* Shana Jones
**VP:* Lou Parker
Exec: Marilyn Melancon

HOPE TRACTOR COMPANY
See TEXARKANA TRACTOR CO

HOPE VALLEY INDUSTRIES
See HV INDUSTRIES INC

HOPEDALE HOSPITAL
See HOPEDALE MEDICAL FOUNDATION

D-U-N-S 07-561-2978
HOPEDALE MEDICAL FOUNDATION
HOPEDALE HOSPITAL
107 Tremont St, Hopedale, IL 61747-7525
Tel (309) 449-3321 *Founded/Ownrshp* 1955
Sales 22.2MM *EMP* 310[E]
Accts Mcgladrey Llp Des Moines Ia
SIC 8062 8059 5912 8052 7991 8011 General medical & surgical hospitals; Nursing home, except skilled & intermediate care facility; Drug stores; Intermediate care facilities; Physical fitness facilities; Offices & clinics of medical doctors; General medical & surgical hospitals; Nursing home, except skilled & intermediate care facility; Drug stores; Intermediate care facilities; Physical fitness facilities; Offices & clinics of medical doctors
CEO: Alfred N Rossi
**COO:* Mark Rossi
CFO: Dwight Johnson
**Treas:* Matthew B Rossi
VP: Peggie Rossi
Prac Mgr: Peggy Rossi
CIO: Melissa Enderlin
Nrsg Dir: Timothy Sondag
Occ Thrpy: Emily Whitson
HC Dir: Shelbie Bontemps

D-U-N-S 14-033-8612
HOPEHEALTH INC
765 Attucks Ln, Hyannis, MA 02601-1867
Tel (508) 957-0200 *Founded/Ownrshp* 1988
Sales 28.2MM *EMP* 232[E]
Accts Marcum Llp New Haven Ct
SIC 8082 Home health care services; Home health care services
Ch: Patricia Cahill
Ch Bd: David Nunheimer
**Pr:* David W Rehm
**CFO:* Jean Dawson
**Ch:* Lawrence Capodilupo
**Treas:* Joseph R Valle
**Bd of Dir:* Elizabeth Warren
Ofcr: Susan Strauss
Dir IT: John Titus
Board of Directors: Monika Jakubicka

D-U-N-S 92-711-3464
HOPEHEALTH INC
360 N Irby St, Florence, SC 29501
Tel (843) 667-9414 *Founded/Ownrshp* 1999
Sales 30.9MM *EMP* 18[E]
Accts Burch Oxner Seale Co Cpa S Pa
SIC 8399 Advocacy group
Ex Dir: Carl M Humphries
CIO: Mark Spurling
Dir QC: Jayson Grice
Site Mgr: Ann Mays
Mktg Dir: Tiffany Rife
Sls Dir: Trac Ramine

D-U-N-S 09-677-2090
HOPELINK (WA)
10675 Willows Rd Ne # 275, Redmond, WA 98052-2447
Tel (425) 869-6000 *Founded/Ownrshp* 1971
Sales 62.5MM *EMP* 300
SIC 8322

D-U-N-S 06-395-5397 IMP
HOPES WINDOWS INC
84 Hopkins Ave, Jamestown, NY 14701-2223
Tel (716) 665-5124 *Founded/Ownrshp* 1982
Sales 62.4MM[E] *EMP* 250
SIC 3442 Sash, door or window: metal; Sash, door or window: metal
Ch Bd: Frank A Farrell Jr
Treas: Dave Gerringer
**Treas:* David Gerringer
VP: John Brown
VP: John Fafinski
**VP:* Mary C Lausterer
**VP:* Randall P Manitta
Rgnl Mgr: Jim Cave
QA Dir: Ken Warren
Mtls Mgr: Daniel Lausterer
Manager: Scott Nelson
Board of Directors: Mick Yates

D-U-N-S 96-685-5744
HOPESTAR ORTHOPEDIC GROUP
6560 Fannin St Ste 400, Houston, TX 77030-2730
Tel (713) 986-5670 *Founded/Ownrshp* 1996
Sales 4.0MM[E] *EMP* 299
SIC 8069 8011 Orthopedic hospital; Offices & clinics of medical doctors; Orthopedic hospital; Offices & clinics of medical doctors
Ch Bd: Michael Kaldis

D-U-N-S 06-068-6482
HOPEWELL AREA SCHOOL DISTRICT
2354 Brodhead Rd Ste 2, Aliquippa, PA 15001-4501
Tel (724) 375-2348 *Founded/Ownrshp* 1968
Sales 24.2MM[E] *EMP* 350
SIC 8211 Public combined elementary & secondary school; School board; Public combined elementary & secondary school; School board
Dir IT: Susan Todd
Psych: Oliver Kellee

D-U-N-S 19-307-5827
HOPEWELL CITY PUBLIC SCHOOLS
103 N 12th Ave, Hopewell, VA 23860-2310
Tel (804) 541-6400 *Founded/Ownrshp* 1904
Sales 34.0MM[E] *EMP* 585
SIC 8211 Public elementary & secondary schools; Public elementary & secondary schools
Schl Brd P: William Henry

D-U-N-S 14-720-9894
HOPEWELL HEALTH CENTERS INC
LINCOLN PARK MEDICAL CENTER
1049 Western Ave, Chillicothe, OH 45601-1104
Tel (740) 773-1006 *Founded/Ownrshp* 1986
Sales 22.4MM *EMP* 245
SIC 8099 Medical services organization; Medical services organization
Pr: Diane Lewe
**CEO:* Mark Bridenbaugh
**VP:* Kathy Cecil

D-U-N-S 36-292-0365 IMP
HOPEWELL NURSERY INC
309 Woodruff Rd, Bridgeton, NJ 08302-5945
Tel (856) 451-5552 *Founded/Ownrshp* 1988
Sales 31.0MM *EMP* 250
Accts Joseph L Gil Cpa Pc P
SIC 5193 Nursery stock; Nursery stock
Ch Bd: Robert Ench
**VP:* Robert Zentner
Sls Mgr: Doug Reach
Sales Asso: Bethany Bernard

D-U-N-S 07-059-3058
HOPEWELL VALLEY REGIONAL SCHOOL DISTRICT
ADMINISTRATION OFFICE
425 S Main St, Pennington, NJ 08534-2716
Tel (609) 737-4002 *Founded/Ownrshp* 1965
Sales 33.2MM[E] *EMP* 400
SIC 8211 Public combined elementary & secondary school; Public combined elementary & secondary school
Ofcr: Joseph Lenarski
**Prin:* Dominic Lorenzetti
IT Man: John Hagar
IT Man: Jane Lennon
IT Man: Tracy Norris
Teacher Pr: Anthony Suozzo
Psych: Cecelia Cardano
Psych: Kevin Kirwan
Psych: Amy Parker
Psych: Georgette Rogers
Psych: Terri Stimmler

D-U-N-S 83-663-5169
HOPEWEST
3090 N 12th St Unit B, Grand Junction, CO 81506-2804
Tel (970) 241-2212 *Founded/Ownrshp* 1992
Sales 36.4MM *EMP* 300
Accts Dalby Wendland & Co Pc G
SIC 8082 Home health care services; Home health care services
Pr: Christy Whitney
Dir Vol: Diane Dickey
**VP:* Sarah Walsh

D-U-N-S 01-638-0206
HOPF EQUIPMENT INC
KUBOTA
506 E 19th St, Huntingburg, IN 47542-9169
Tel (812) 683-2763 *Founded/Ownrshp* 1974
Sales 56.7MM *EMP* 46
SIC 5083 5261 Farm implements; Lawn & garden equipment; Farm implements; Lawn & garden equipment
Pr: Michael B Hopf
COO: Othmar Wagner
Treas: Glen E Hopf
VP: Charles E Hopf
VP: Linda Hopf
VP Mktg: Todd Biggs

D-U-N-S 00-431-7934
▲ HOPFED BANCORP INC
4155 Lafayette Rd, Hopkinsville, KY 42240-5366
Tel (270) 885-1171 *Founded/Ownrshp* 1997
Sales NA *EMP* 256[E]
Accts Rayburn Bates & Fitzgerald P
Tkr Sym HFBC *Exch* NGM
SIC 6022 State commercial banks; State commercial banks
Pr: John E Peck
**Ch Bd:* Harry Dempsey
CFO: Billy C Duvall
Sr VP: Boyd M Clark
VP: Michael F Stalls
Exec: Keith Bennett

HOPI TRIBAL COUNCIL
See HOPI TRIBE

D-U-N-S 07-753-0954
HOPI TRIBAL COUNCIL
1 Main St, Kykotsmovi Village, AZ 86039
Tel (928) 734-2445 *Founded/Ownrshp* 1997
Sales NA *EMP* 400[E]
SIC 9131 Indian reservation; ; Indian reservation;
Ch: Wayne Taylor Jr
**Treas:* Mary Nabanick
Ex Dir: Luann Leonard

D-U-N-S 11-613-6961
HOPI TRIBE
HOPI TRIBAL COUNCIL
1 Main St, Kykotsmovi Village, AZ 86039
Tel (928) 734-3000 *Founded/Ownrshp* 1997
Sales NA *EMP* 301
SIC 9131 Indian reservation; Indian reservation
Pr: Russell Mockta Jr
Off Mgr: Mary Felter
IT Man: Lillian Dennis

D-U-N-S 04-495-2331
HOPKINS AIRPORT LIMOUSINE SERVICE INC
HOPKINS TRANSPORTATION SVCS
13315 Brookpark Rd, Cleveland, OH 44142-1822
Tel (216) 267-8810 *Founded/Ownrshp* 1964
Sales 4.5MM *EMP* 279
SIC 4111 Airport limousine, scheduled service; Airport limousine, scheduled service
Pr: Tom Goebel
**Sec:* Mike Goebel
**VP:* Chris Goebel
**VP:* Jack Goebel

D-U-N-S 60-908-1182 IMP
HOPKINS COUNTY COAL LLC
35 Frank Cox Rd, Madisonville, KY 42431-7753
Tel (270) 326-4000 *Founded/Ownrshp* 1997
Sales 39.8MM[E] *EMP* 170
SIC 5052 Coal; Coal

D-U-N-S 06-898-8856
HOPKINS COUNTY HOSPITAL DISTRICT
HOPKINS COUNTY MEMORIAL HOSP
115 Airport Rd, Sulphur Springs, TX 75482-2105
Tel (903) 439-4052 *Founded/Ownrshp* 1952
Sales 43.1MM *EMP* 640
SIC 8062 General medical & surgical hospitals; General medical & surgical hospitals
CEO: Michael McAndrew
Pr: Joe Bob Burgin
CFO: Donna Wallace
Ofcr: Roberta Vanderburg
Sr VP: Joseph Benbeneck
Dir Lab: Gaylon Barrett
Chf Nrs Of: Terri Bunch
Dir Sec: Brent Smith
DP Exec: Brandon Gauntt
Mtls Dir: Wilt Parker
Sls&Mrk Ex: Sherry Moore

HOPKINS COUNTY MEMORIAL HOSP
See HOPKINS COUNTY HOSPITAL DISTRICT

D-U-N-S 10-065-0175
HOPKINS COUNTY SCHOOL DISTRICT
320 S Seminary St, Madisonville, KY 42431-2424
Tel (270) 825-6000 *Founded/Ownrshp* 1800
Sales 39.7MM[E] *EMP* 1,050
SIC 8211 Public combined elementary & secondary school; Public combined elementary & secondary school
**Ch:* Randy Franklin
**Prin:* Steve Faulk
**Prin:* Charles Hoskins
**Prin:* Mike Morgan
HC Dir: Charles Gant

D-U-N-S 11-388-8986
HOPKINS FINANCIAL CORP
100 E Havens Ave, Mitchell, SD 57301-4026
Tel (605) 996-7775 *Founded/Ownrshp* 1980
Sales NA *EMP* 145
SIC 6022 State commercial banks; State commercial banks
Pr: Boyd D Hopkins
**Sec:* Doloris J Hopkins
Sr VP: Terry Torgerson

D-U-N-S 01-414-9959
HOPKINS FORD INC
FORD RENT-A-CAR SYSTEM
1650 The Fairway, Jenkintown, PA 19046-1671
Tel (215) 886-5900 *Founded/Ownrshp* 1972
Sales 28.4MM[E] *EMP* 92
SIC 5511 7538 7532 5521 Automobiles, new & used; Trucks, tractors & trailers: new & used; General automotive repair shops; Top & body repair & paint shops; Used car dealers; Automobiles, new & used; Trucks, tractors & trailers: new & used; General automotive repair shops; Top & body repair & paint shops; Used car dealers
Pr: John Mac Kenzie
VP: Kevin Glinch
**VP:* G Kevin Mc Glinchey

D-U-N-S 02-943-9184
HOPKINS JOHNS COMMUNITY PHYSICIANS INC
JHCP
(*Suby of* JOHNS HOPKINS HEALTH SYS CORP) ★
3100 Wyman Park Dr, Baltimore, MD 21211-2803
Tel (410) 338-3421 *Founded/Ownrshp* 1986
Sales 22.0MM[E] *EMP* 284[E]
SIC 8062 General medical & surgical hospitals
Pr: Barbara Cook MD
Doctor: Barbara Drummond

D-U-N-S 06-939-0037
HOPKINS JOHNS MEDICAL SERVICES CORP (MD)
WYMAN PARK MEDICAL CTR
(*Suby of* JOHNS HOPKINS HEALTH SYS CORP) ★
3100 Wyman Park Dr, Baltimore, MD 21211-2803
Tel (410) 338-3071 *Founded/Ownrshp* 1941
Sales 84.7MM[E] *EMP* 1,487
SIC 8011 8741 Health maintenance organization; Management services; Health maintenance organization; Management services
COO: Barbara Cook MD
**Pr:* Steven Kravet MD
COO: Linda Gilligan
MIS Dir: Cathy Zager

D-U-N-S 60-306-9592
HOPKINS JOHNS PHARMAQUIP INC
(*Suby of* JOHNS HOPKINS HOME CARE GROUP INC) ★
5901 Holabird Ave Ste A, Baltimore, MD 21224-6015
Tel (410) 288-8000 *Founded/Ownrshp* 1992
Sales 59.0MM *EMP* 350[E]
SIC 8082 Home health care services; Home health care services
Pr: Dan Smith

D-U-N-S 08-175-8526
HOPKINS LUMBER CONTRACTORS INC
680 Old Sand Rd, Ridgeway, VA 24148-4358
Tel (276) 956-3022 *Founded/Ownrshp* 1936
Sales 23.1MM[E] *EMP* 62
SIC 5031 2448 2441 2426 2421 Lumber: rough, dressed & finished; Pallets, wood; Wood pallets & skids; Nailed wood boxes & shook; Hardwood dimension & flooring mills; Sawmills & planing mills, general
Pr: John W Hopkins
Sec: Michelle Belcher
**Sec:* Shelley C Turner
**VP:* Jerry Hopkins
Off Mgr: Shelley Turner

D-U-N-S 00-711-8318 IMP/EXP
HOPKINS MANUFACTURING CORP
428 Peyton St, Emporia, KS 66801-3722
Tel (620) 342-7320 *Founded/Ownrshp* 2011
Sales 202.4MM[E] *EMP* 650
SIC 3714 Motor vehicle parts & accessories; Motor vehicle parts & accessories
Pr: Brad Kraft
**CFO:* Jim Daniels
Chf Mktg O: Michael S Williams
**Sr VP:* Randy Kuntz
**VP:* Ken Braaten
VP: Jim Garton
**VP:* Gary Kaminski
VP: Mary Volland
Dir IT: Brian Curtiss
Sfty Dirs: Dallas Sedtwick
Sfty Mgr: Dallas Sedgwiek

D-U-N-S 05-277-9287
HOPKINS PUBLIC SCHOOL DISTRICT
1001 Highway 7, Hopkins, MN 55305-4737
Tel (952) 988-4000 *Founded/Ownrshp* 1900
Sales 126.6MM *EMP* 1,334
Accts Cliftonlarsonallen Llp Minne
SIC 8211 Public combined elementary & secondary school; School board; Public combined elementary & secondary school; School board
Treas: Barbara Klaas
Bd of Dir: Kara Amos

Exec: Donna Montgomery
Dir IT: Kathy Israel
IT Man: John Wetter
Board of Directors: Curt Wallman

D-U-N-S 07-212-0637
HOPKINS SCHOOL
986 Forest Rd, New Haven, CT 06515-2501
Tel (203) 397-1001 *Founded/Ownrshp* 1660
Sales 37.7MM *EMP* 118
Accts Cohnreznick Llp Hartford Ct
SIC 8211 Preparatory school
Prin: William W Bakke
IT Man: Heather Volosin
HC Dir: Dana Blanchard
HC Dir: Pamela McKenna
Snr Mgr: David Baxter

HOPKINS TRANSPORTATION SVCS
See HOPKINS AIRPORT LIMOUSINE SERVICE INC

HOPKINSVILLE ELECTRIC SYSTEM
See ELECTRIC PLANT BOARD OF CITY OF HOPKINSVILLE

D-U-N-S 04-993-8913
HOPKINSVILLE ELEVATOR CO INC
1040 Skyline Dr, Hopkinsville, KY 42240-5068
Tel (270) 886-5191 *Founded/Ownrshp* 1968
Sales 31.5MM^E *EMP* 57
SIC 5153 5191 Grain elevators; Animal feeds; Seeds: field, garden & flower; Fertilizer & fertilizer materials; Grain elevators; Animal feeds; Seeds: field, garden & flower; Fertilizer & fertilizer materials
Genl Mgr: Jerry Good
**Treas:* Jerry L Good
**VP:* John Young

HOPKINSVILLE WTR & ENVMT AUTH
See CITY OF HOPKINSVILLE SEWERAGE & WATER WORKS COMMISSION

D-U-N-S 07-846-5079
HOPKINTON PUBLIC SCHOOLS
89 Hayden Rowe St, Hopkinton, MA 01748-2507
Tel (508) 417-9360 *Founded/Ownrshp* 2012
Sales 10.8MM^E *EMP* 297^E
SIC 8211 Elementary & secondary schools
V Ch: Ellen Scordino
Netwrk Mgr: Linda Henderson
Teacher Pr: Kim Pulnik
Psych: Jim Casey

D-U-N-S 17-755-3963 IMP
HOPPE NORTH AMERICA INC
HARDWARE TECHNOLOGIES
(*Suby of* HOPPE HOLDING AG)
205 E Blackhawk Dr, Fort Atkinson, WI 53538-1268
Tel (920) 563-2626 *Founded/Ownrshp* 1991
Sales 31.7MM^E *EMP* 85
SIC 5072 3429 Hardware; Manufactured hardware (general); Hardware; Manufactured hardware (general)
Pr: Jeffrey T Shilakis
**Ch:* Christoph Hoppe
VP: Tamara Brown
**VP:* Ed Corby
VP: Amy Hoppe
**VP:* Michael Pasternak
**VP:* Kurt Strenke
VP: Patrick J Unker

D-U-N-S 00-112-3801 IMP
HOPPE TECHNOLOGIES INC (MA)
(*Suby of* TRIMASTER/HTECH HOLDING, LLC)
107 First Ave, Chicopee, MA 01020-4620
Tel (413) 592-9213 *Founded/Ownrshp* 1941, 2011
Sales 25.3MM^E *EMP* 75
SIC 3544 3545 Special dies, tools, jigs & fixtures; Precision tools, machinists'
Pr: Eric D Hagopian
CFO: Eric Wisnefsky
**Treas:* Douglas M Hagopian
IT Man: Rob Esposito
Mtls Mgr: Stacy Pease
Ql Cn Mgr: Jeremy Topor
Ql Cn Mgr: Steve Wojtas
Sls&Mrk Ex: Melissa Pereira

D-U-N-S 61-862-8689
HOPS GRILL & BAR INC
HOPS GRILL & BREWERY
(*Suby of* DON PABLOS) ★
Hancock At Washington St, Madison, GA 30650
Tel (706) 342-4552 *Founded/Ownrshp* 2009
Sales 139.0MM^E *EMP* 3,500
SIC 5813 5812 Bar (drinking places); Eating places; Bar (drinking places); Eating places
CEO: Tom E Dupree
VP: Tim Ligon
VP Opers: Duncan McLean

HOPS GRILL & BREWERY
See HOPS GRILL & BAR INC

D-U-N-S 02-359-1845
HOPSON OIL CO INC
MARQUARDT HEATING
1225 Whiterock Ave, Waukesha, WI 53186-3711
Tel (262) 542-5343 *Founded/Ownrshp* 1960
Sales 135.0MM *EMP* 35
SIC 5171 5983 1711 Petroleum bulk stations; Fuel oil dealers; Heating systems repair & maintenance; Petroleum bulk stations; Fuel oil dealers; Heating systems repair & maintenance
Pr: Terry Nagel
**VP:* Clint Wendet

HOPSTEINER
See S S STEINER INC

D-U-N-S 07-831-3394 IMP
HOPUNION LLC
203 Division St, Yakima, WA 98902-4622
Tel (509) 453-4792 *Founded/Ownrshp* 2006
Sales 140.0MM *EMP* 154
SIC 5181 Beer & ale
Prd Mgr: Delmar Rowden
Mktg Mgr: Melody Meyer

D-U-N-S 01-258-0247
HOQUIAM SCHOOL DISTRICT 28
305 Simpson Ave, Hoquiam, WA 98550-2419
Tel (360) 538-8200 *Founded/Ownrshp* 1900
Sales 16.4MM^E *EMP* 300
SIC 8211 Public elementary & secondary schools; School board; Public elementary & secondary schools; School board
Dir IT: Patti Reynvaan
IT Man: Lori Coady
IT Man: Kay Rotter

D-U-N-S 02-463-3653
HORACE G ILDERTON LLC (NC)
IDERTON DODGE CHRYSLER JEEP
701 S Main St, High Point, NC 27260-7513
Tel (336) 841-2020 *Founded/Ownrshp* 1926, 2004
Sales 35.3MM^E *EMP* 70
SIC 5511 7532 Automobiles, new & used; Pickups, new & used; Customizing services, non-factory basis; Automobiles, new & used; Pickups, new & used; Customizing services, non-factory basis
CFO: Christine Dowdy
Sales Exec: Murray Buck
Sls Mgr: Odell McBride

HORACE GREELEY HIGH SCHOOL
See CHAPPAQUA CENTRAL SCHOOL DISTRICT INC

D-U-N-S 11-524-2430
HORACE MANN EDUCATIONAL ASSOCIATES INC
HMEA
8 Forge Pkwy Ste 1, Franklin, MA 02038-3138
Tel (508) 298-1100 *Founded/Ownrshp* 1961
Sales 34.8MM *EMP* 700^E
Accts Cbiz Tofias Boston Ma
SIC 8299 8331 8361 Personal development school; Vocational rehabilitation agency; Home for the mentally handicapped; Personal development school; Vocational rehabilitation agency; Home for the mentally handicapped
CEO: Michael Moloney
**Pr:* Jule Noack
CFO: Nancy McDonald
**CFO:* John Moran
Bd of Dir: Michael Quink
Doctor: David Felper

D-U-N-S 06-234-2324
▲ **HORACE MANN EDUCATORS CORP**
1 Horace Mann Plz, Springfield, IL 62715-0001
Tel (217) 789-2500 *Founded/Ownrshp* 1945
Sales NA *EMP* 1,500^E
Accts Kpmg Llp Chicago Illinois
Tkr Sym HMN *Exch* NYS
SIC 6311 6331 6411 Life insurance; Property damage insurance; Property & casualty insurance agent; Pension & retirement plan consultants; Life insurance; Property damage insurance; Property & casualty insurance agent; Pension & retirement plan consultants
Pr: Marita Zuraitis
Mng Pt: John Thompson
**Ch Bd:* Gabriel L Shaheen
Pr: Joel Abrahamson
Pr: Twanna Amos
Pr: Celestine Gates
Pr: Scott Keeshin
Pr: Matt Kietzman
Pr: Angel Plaza
Pr: Kelly Ruwe
Pr: Beth Smith
Pr: Jennifer Turley
Pr: Adam Wendling
Pr: Charlton Young
COO: Christina Thompson
CFO: Dwayne D Hallman
CFO: Peter Heckman
Chf Mktg O: Stephen P Cardinal
Ofcr: Ann M Caparros
Ofcr: Ann Caparros
Ofcr: John P McCarthy
Board of Directors: Daniel A Domenech, Mary H Futrell, Stephen J Hasenmiller, Ronald J Helow, Beverley J McClure, Robert Stricker, Steven O Swyers

D-U-N-S 07-561-0402
■ **HORACE MANN LIFE INSURANCE CO**
(*Suby of* EDUCATORS LIFE INSURANCE CO OF AMERICA) ★
1 Horace Mann Plz, Springfield, IL 62715-0001
Tel (217) 789-2500 *Founded/Ownrshp* 1989
Sales NA *EMP* 1^E
SIC 6411 Insurance agents, brokers & service; Insurance agents, brokers & service
Pr: Louis G Lower II
**CFO:* Peter H Heckman
Chf Mktg O: Dan Jensen
VP: Richard Atkinson
VP: Kelvin Hubbard
**VP:* George J Zock

D-U-N-S 61-103-2751
■ **HORACE MANN PROPERTY & CASUALTY INSURANCE CO**
(*Suby of* HORACE MANN EDUCATORS CORP) ★
1 Horace Mann Plz, Springfield, IL 62715-0001
Tel (217) 789-2500 *Founded/Ownrshp* 2005
Sales NA *EMP* 10
SIC 6331 Fire, marine & casualty insurance; Fire, marine & casualty insurance
Pr: Louis G Lower II
Ex VP: Stephen P Cardinal
Sr VP: Bret A Conklin
IT Man: Fred Baskett

D-U-N-S 96-940-1855
HORACE MANN SCHOOL
231 W 246th St, Bronx, NY 10471-3430
Tel (718) 432-3416 *Founded/Ownrshp* 1887
Sales 76.8MM *EMP* 407
SIC 8211 Elementary & secondary schools; Elementary & secondary schools
Ch: Steven M Friedman
Off Mgr: Karen Bauert
Dir IT: Adam Kenner

D-U-N-S 03-056-5147
■ **HORACE MANN SERVICE CORP**
(*Suby of* HORACE MANN EDUCATORS CORP) ★
1 Horace Mann Plz, Springfield, IL 62715-0001
Tel (217) 789-2500 *Founded/Ownrshp* 1945
Sales NA *EMP* 200
SIC 6411 Insurance agents, brokers & service; Insurance agents, brokers & service
CEO: Peter H Heckman
IT Exec: Mark Hansen

D-U-N-S 07-142-6837
■ **HORACE MANN SERVICE CORP**
(*Suby of* HORACE MANN EDUCATORS CORP) ★
1 Horace Mann Plz, Springfield, IL 62715-0001
Tel (217) 789-2500 *Founded/Ownrshp* 1989
Sales NA *EMP* 350
SIC 6411 Insurance agents, brokers & service; Insurance adjusters; Insurance agents, brokers & service; Insurance adjusters
Ch Bd: Lou Lower
**Pr:* Peter H Heckman
Assoc VP: Jack Dickinson
VP: David Baumgardner
**VP:* Ann Mary Caparros
VP: Jim Strebler
CIO: Mark Hansen
Dir IT: Don Randle
Mktg Dir: Kristian Anderson

D-U-N-S 02-956-0864
HORACIO HOJMAN MD
UNIVERSITY EMERGENCY MEDICINE
593 Eddy St Ste 122, Providence, RI 02903-4923
Tel (401) 444-3842 *Founded/Ownrshp* 2000
Sales 42.2MM *EMP* 2
SIC 8011 Offices & clinics of medical doctors; Offices & clinics of medical doctors
Owner: Horacio Hojman MD
Off Mgr: Kim Roun

HORAK COMPANY, THE
See F P HORAK CO

D-U-N-S 14-005-4425
HORBRAUHAUF NEWPORT LLC
200 E 3rd St, Newport, KY 41071-1612
Tel (859) 491-7200 *Founded/Ownrshp* 2003
Sales 5.0MM *EMP* 320^E
SIC 5812
Prin: Nicholes Ellison

D-U-N-S 17-781-2609
HORGAN BROTHERS INC
2188 Detwiler Rd, Harleysville, PA 19438-2931
Tel (215) 513-9300 *Founded/Ownrshp* 1986
Sales 21.4MM^E *EMP* 150
SIC 1771 1794 1611 Concrete work; Excavation work; Surfacing & paving; Concrete work; Excavation work; Surfacing & paving
Pr: John F Horgan
**CFO:* Quentin Dancer
**VP:* Joseph A Horgan
Genl Mgr: Iain Macmillan
Snr Mgr: Steve Lewis

HORIBA AUTOMOTIVE TEST SYSTEMS
See HORIBA INSTRUMENTS INC

D-U-N-S 05-284-5583 IMP
HORIBA INSTRUMENTS INC (CA)
HORIBA AUTOMOTIVE TEST SYSTEMS
(*Suby of* HORIBA INTERNATIONAL CORP) ★
9755 Research Dr, Irvine, CA 92618-4626
Tel (949) 250-4811 *Founded/Ownrshp* 1998
Sales 43.4MM^E *EMP* 210
SIC 3823 3826 3829 3511 3825 5047 Industrial instrmnts msrmnt display/control process variable; Industrial process measurement equipment; Analyzers, industrial process type; Controllers for process variables, all types; Analytical instruments; Measuring & controlling devices; Turbines & turbine generator sets; Instruments to measure electricity; Diagnostic equipment, medical; Medical laboratory equipment; Hospital equipment & supplies; Physician equipment & supplies; Industrial instrmnts msrmnt display/control process variable; Industrial process measurement equipment; Analyzers, industrial process type; Controllers for process variables, all types; Analytical instruments; Measuring & controlling devices; Turbines & turbine generator sets; Instruments to measure electricity; Diagnostic equipment, medical; Medical laboratory equipment; Hospital equipment & supplies; Physician equipment & supplies
Pr: Jai Hakhu
COO: Frank A Buttcvoli
**CFO:* Richard Marting
VP: Axel Wendorff
Exec: Ted Niederecker
Genl Mgr: Rex Tapp
IT Man: Ashoke Bhat
Mfg Mgr: Lenny Betto
Opers Mgr: Justin Armao
Mktg Dir: Andrew Whitley

D-U-N-S 10-653-9513 IMP
HORIBA INSTRUMENTS INC
(*Suby of* HORIBA AUTOMOTIVE TEST SYSTEMS) ★
3880 Park Ave, Edison, NJ 08820-3012
Tel (732) 494-8660 *Founded/Ownrshp* 2009
Sales 30.2MM^E *EMP* 198
SIC 3826 Spectrographs; Spectrometers; Spectrographs; Spectrometers
Pr: Steve Slutter
CFO: Ann Marumoto
Bd of Dir: Kanji Ishizumi
VP: Michael Pohl
**Prin:* Michel Baudron
Ex Dir: Keith Swarm
Div Mgr: Philippe Hunault
Genl Mgr: George Setola
MIS Dir: Bryan Johnson
IT Man: Lorraine Lover
IT Man: John Pasquella

D-U-N-S 06-221-8859
HORIBA INTERNATIONAL CORP
(*Suby of* HORIBA,LTD.)
9755 Research Dr, Irvine, CA 92618-4626
Tel (949) 250-4811 *Founded/Ownrshp* 1998
Sales 154.3MM^E *EMP* 774^E
SIC 3829 Measuring & controlling devices; Measuring & controlling devices
Ch Bd: Atsushi Horiba
Pr: Riad Abuelafiya
**Pr:* Masayuki Adachi
**CEO:* Jai Hakhu
**VP:* Richard Marting

D-U-N-S 01-189-2510
■ **HORIZON AIR INDUSTRIES INC**
(*Suby of* ALASKA AIR GROUP INC) ★
19521 International Blvd, Seatac, WA 98188-5402
Tel (206) 241-6757 *Founded/Ownrshp* 1986
Sales 211.5MM^E *EMP* 3,900
SIC 4512 4522 Air passenger carrier, scheduled; Air cargo carrier, scheduled; Flying charter service; Air passenger carrier, scheduled; Air cargo carrier, scheduled; Flying charter service
Pr: Jeffrey D Pinneo
Treas: John F Schaefer Jr
**Treas:* Rudi H Schmidt
**Sr VP:* Thomas M Gerharter
Sr VP: Eugene Hahn
**Sr VP:* Andrea L Schneider
VP: Yvonne Daverin
**VP:* Eugene C Hahn
**VP:* Jean Hahn
VP: Dan Russo
VP: Daniel Scott
**VP:* Diana Shaw
**VP:* Arthur E Thomas

D-U-N-S 60-505-2310 IMP
HORIZON APPAREL MANUFACTURING INC
115 Bayside Dr, Atlantic Beach, NY 11509-1608
Tel (516) 361-4878 *Founded/Ownrshp* 2003
Sales 25.0MM *EMP* 5
SIC 2211 Apparel & outerwear fabrics, cotton; Apparel & outerwear fabrics, cotton
Pr: Mark Hassin
**VP:* Bonnie Hassin

D-U-N-S 11-974-7624
▲ **HORIZON BANCORP**
515 Franklin St, Michigan City, IN 46360-3328
Tel (219) 879-0211 *Founded/Ownrshp* 1983
Sales NA *EMP* 421^E
Tkr Sym HBNC *Exch* NGM
SIC 6021 National commercial banks; National commercial banks
Ch Bd: Craig M Dwight
CFO: Mark E Secor
Ex VP: Kathie A Deruiter
Ex VP: James Neff
Ex VP: Dave G Rose

D-U-N-S 00-693-9326
■ **HORIZON BANK NATIONAL ASSOCIATION**
(*Suby of* HORIZON BANCORP) ★
515 Franklin St, Michigan City, IN 46360-3328
Tel (219) 873-2640 *Founded/Ownrshp* 1872
Sales NA *EMP* 290
SIC 6021 National commercial banks; National commercial banks
Ch Bd: Craig M Dwight
**Pr:* Thomas H Edwards
**CFO:* Mark Secor
Treas: Cindy Pressinell
Sr VP: Carla Kanney
VP: Barb Bialko
VP: David Bly
VP: Becky Doperalski
VP: Sandy Moffett
**VP:* James Neff Sr
VP: Kori Riggs
VP: Brad Smith
VP: Keene Taylor

D-U-N-S 80-100-7803
HORIZON BANK SSB
(*Suby of* FRONTIER BANCSHARES, INC.)
600 Congress Ave Ste 400, Austin, TX 78701-2923
Tel (512) 637-5730 *Founded/Ownrshp* 1905
Sales NA *EMP* 9^E
SIC 6021 National commercial banks; National commercial banks
CEO: Paul Trylko
COO: Paula Rose
Chf Cred: Kerry Wiggins
Ofcr: Gregg Bennett
Sr VP: Charlie Avant
Sr VP: Jeff O'Jibway
VP: John Crandall
VP: Mary Wright
Ex Dir: Barbara Bozon
Dept Mgr: Bradford Smith
Brnch Mgr: Tomeka Kinne

D-U-N-S 80-041-6864
■ **HORIZON BAY MANAGEMENT LLC**
HORIZON BAY SENIOR COMMUNITIES
(*Suby of* BROOKDALE SENIOR LIVING) ★
5426 Bay Center Dr # 600, Tampa, FL 33609-3440
Tel (813) 287-3900 *Founded/Ownrshp* 2011
Sales 108.9MM^E *EMP* 3,500
SIC 8611 6531 1522 Community affairs & services; Real estate agents & managers; Residential construction; Community affairs & services; Real estate agents & managers; Residential construction
VP: Dotty J Bollinger
VP: Mary Sue Patchet
Ex Dir: Shannon East

HORIZON BAY SENIOR COMMUNITIES
See HORIZON BAY MANAGEMENT LLC

HORIZON BC/BS OF NJ
See HORIZON HEALTHCARE SERVICES INC

D-U-N-S 61-003-3235
HORIZON BEHAVIORAL HEALTH
CENTRAL VIRGINIA CMNTY SVCS
2241 Langhorne Rd, Lynchburg, VA 24501-1114
Tel (434) 847-8050 Founded/Ownrshp 1968
Sales 29.8MM^E EMP 500
SIC 8093 8322 Mental health clinic, outpatient; Social services for the handicapped; Substance abuse counseling; Mental health clinic, outpatient; Social services for the handicapped; Substance abuse counseling
CEO: Damien Cabezas
CFO: Andre McDaniel
Prgrm Mgr: Judy Hedrick
Dir IT: Rob Viohl
Opers Mgr: Aaron Lassiter
Doctor: Ralph Chester

D-U-N-S 00-695-3558 IMP
HORIZON BEVERAGE CO INC (MA)
PREMIUM BEVERAGE CO
45 Commerce Way, Norton, MA 02766-3313
Tel (508) 587-1110 Founded/Ownrshp 1932
Sales 182.4MM^E EMP 310
SIC 5181 5182 Beer & other fermented malt liquors; Wine; Liquor; Beer & other fermented malt liquors; Wine; Liquor
CEO: Robert L Epstein
*CFO: James L Rubenstein
VP: Jim Hogan
Exec: Justin Gorton
Area Mgr: Dave Castro
MIS Dir: Lou Pollock
Opers Mgr: Stephen Arrighi
VP Sls: James Tsiumis
Sls Dir: Bill Ehrhardt
Sls Mgr: Kevin Compagna
Sls Mgr: Sean Irving

D-U-N-S 78-699-4582 IMP
HORIZON BEVERAGE CO LP
8380 Pardee Dr, Oakland, CA 94621-1481
Tel (510) 465-2212 Founded/Ownrshp 1988
Sales 27.1MM^E EMP 94
SIC 5149 Groceries & related products; Groceries & related products
Pr: Mike Thomas
CFO: Paul Wong
Genl Mgr: Sam Cappione
Sls Dir: Steve Ottaviano
Sls Mgr: James Williams

HORIZON BLUE CROSS BLUE SHIELD
See HORIZON NJ HEALTH

D-U-N-S 08-153-5338
HORIZON BUILDERS INC
2131 Espey Ct Ste 3, Crofton, MD 21114-2474
Tel (410) 721-4877 Founded/Ownrshp 1982
Sales 23.1MM^E EMP 110
SIC 1521 General remodeling, single-family houses; New construction, single-family houses
Pr: Joseph Bohm
VP: Abe Sari
IT Man: Gino Gullace

D-U-N-S 92-949-5711
HORIZON CASUALTY SERVICES
(Suby of HORIZON BC/BS OF NJ) ★
33 Washington St Fl 11, Newark, NJ 07102-3120
Tel (973) 642-5280 Founded/Ownrshp 1995
Sales NA EMP 55
SIC 6321 Accident & health insurance
CEO: Christopher Lepre
IT Man: Carlos Broncano
IT Man: John Grochowski

D-U-N-S 07-862-2398
HORIZON COACH LINES
17810 Meeting House Rd # 200, Sandy Spring, MD 20860-1002
Tel (301) 260-2060 Founded/Ownrshp 2011
Sales 105.5MM^E EMP 2,500^E
SIC 4141 Local bus charter service; Local bus charter service
CEO: Francis Sherman
CFO: Adam Marr
Snr Mgr: Chris O'Connor

D-U-N-S 15-852-8401
HORIZON COMMUNICATION TECHNOLOGIES INC
30 Fairbanks Ste 110, Irvine, CA 92618-1668
Tel (714) 982-3900 Founded/Ownrshp 1998
Sales 25.6MM^E EMP 80^E
SIC 4899 Data communication services
CEO: Micheal Degraw
*Pr: Anthony Turrentine
VP: Chris Heublein
*VP: Alex Hisa
CTO: Jim Cortens
Opers Mgr: Ismael Melendrez
Sls Dir: Joe Cruz
Mktg Mgr: B J Scott

D-U-N-S 55-689-7981
HORIZON CONSTRUCTION CO
415 Winkler Dr Ste B, Alpharetta, GA 30004-0740
Tel (770) 772-0303 Founded/Ownrshp 1991
Sales 33.8MM EMP 26
Accts Whirley & Associates Alpharet
SIC 1542 Commercial & office building, new construction; Commercial & office buildings, renovation & repair; Commercial & office building, new construction; Commercial & office buildings, renovation & repair
CEO: Stephen D Micham
*CFO: Wade J White
*VP: Patty Lyons
VP: Andy Micham

HORIZON CONSTRUCTION GROUP
See HORIZON DEVELOPMENT GROUP INC

D-U-N-S 13-022-8625
HORIZON CONSTRUCTION GROUP INC
5201 E Terrace Dr Ste 300, Madison, WI 53718-8362
Tel (608) 354-0900 Founded/Ownrshp 1996
Sales 145.3MM EMP 44
Accts Sva Cpas Sc
SIC 1542 1522 Commercial & office building contractors; Residential construction; Commercial & office building contractors; Residential construction
CEO: John Faust
*Pr: Daniel Fitzgerald

D-U-N-S 08-335-7202
HORIZON CREDIT UNION
13224 E Mansfield Ave, Spokane Valley, WA 99216-1661
Tel (509) 928-6494 Founded/Ownrshp 1948
Sales NA EMP 30
SIC 6062 State credit unions; State credit unions
Pr: Jack Saulis
VP: Yvonne Middleton
Brnch Mgr: Joanna Kellerstraff
Prd Mgr: Mike Fredericks
Secur Mgr: Kevin Stirtz

D-U-N-S 15-084-4991
HORIZON DEVELOPMENT GROUP INC
HORIZON CONSTRUCTION GROUP
5201 E Terrace Dr Ste 300, Madison, WI 53718-8362
Tel (608) 354-0900 Founded/Ownrshp 1996
Sales 36.7MM^E EMP 6
SIC 6552 Land subdividers & developers, residential; Land subdividers & developers, commercial
Pr: Charles V Heath

HORIZON DISPLAY
See HORIZON TECHNOLOGY LLC

D-U-N-S 00-794-4093 IMP
HORIZON DISTRIBUTION INC (WA)
HDI
811 Summitview Ave, Yakima, WA 98902-7203
Tel (509) 453-3181 Founded/Ownrshp 1881
Sales 57.2MM^E EMP 68^E
SIC 5072 5085 5051 5063 5198 5191 Shelf or light hardware; Industrial supplies; Steel; Electrical supplies; Paints; Farm supplies; Shelf or light hardware; Industrial supplies; Steel; Electrical supplies; Paints; Farm supplies
Pr: Kenneth R Marble
*COO: Dan Marples
Exec: Tom Nunes
VP Sls: Mike Dawson
Advt Mgr: Connie Alseth
Sls Mgr: Eddie Anderson
Sales Asso: Eric Duffield
Sales Asso: Jay Underdahl
Sales Asso: Wes Vinsant

D-U-N-S 02-866-4472 IMP
■ HORIZON DISTRIBUTORS INC
(Suby of POOL CORP) ★
5214 S 30th St, Phoenix, AZ 85040-3730
Tel (480) 337-6700 Founded/Ownrshp 2005
Sales 259.2MM^E EMP 427
SIC 4971 5083 Irrigation systems; Farm & garden machinery; Irrigation equipment; Irrigation systems; Farm & garden machinery; Irrigation equipment
Pr: James W Ross
Treas: Terry Speth
VP: Mark W Joslin
VP: Manuel J Perez De La Mesa
VP: Stephen C Nelson
Opers Mgr: Dale Headley
Sls Mgr: Chris Husband
Sls Mgr: Scott Jones
Sales Asso: Jeff Bauer
Sales Asso: Lee Diller
Board of Directors: Manuel J Perez De La Mesa

D-U-N-S 04-460-1899
HORIZON ENERGY SERVICES LLC
203 E 80th St, Stillwater, OK 74074
Tel (405) 533-4800 Founded/Ownrshp 2011
Sales 203.4MM^E EMP 350
Accts Wilsey Meyer Eatmon Tate Pllc
SIC 1381 Drilling oil & gas wells; Drilling oil & gas wells

D-U-N-S 04-375-6225
HORIZON ENGINEERING ASSOCIATES LLP
30 Broad St Fl 15, New York, NY 10004-2304
Tel (212) 400-3700 Founded/Ownrshp 2000
Sales 23.6MM^E EMP 103
SIC 8711 Engineering services; Engineering services
Pt: Michael English
CFO: Rick Madarasz
Exec: Jane Barrett
Dir Bus: Emily Crandall
Off Admin: Tersa Baiardi
Mktg Dir: Josephine Lobello
Board of Directors: E Thomas Lillie

D-U-N-S 07-106-7128
HORIZON EYE CARE PA
135 S Sharon Amity Rd # 100, Charlotte, NC 28211-2842
Tel (704) 365-0555 Founded/Ownrshp 1998
Sales 20.3MM^E EMP 200
SIC 8011 Ophthalmologist; Ophthalmologist
Prin: Lewis R Gaskin MD
*Prin: Joseph Krug
*Prin: James Presley
*Prin: David N Ugland MD
*Prin: Rick H Weidman MD
IT Man: James Ivey
Opthamlgy: Royce R Syacuse
Doctor: Joseph Biber
Doctor: Judy Hustead
Doctor: Gerald Rosen
Doctor: Royce Syracuse

D-U-N-S 61-725-9916 IMP/EXP
HORIZON FABRICS INC
(Suby of HORIZON GROUP USA INC) ★
45 Technology Dr, Warren, NJ 07059-5184
Tel (908) 687-0999 Founded/Ownrshp 2000
Sales 47.9MM^E EMP 225
SIC 5131 Ribbons; Narrow fabrics; Trimmings, apparel
CEO: Roshan Wijerama
*Ch Bd: James H Cash
*CFO: Holli Gabler
VP: Steven Littman
CTO: Mark Friedberg
Dir IT: Will Beamon
S&M/VP: Linda Dow

HORIZON FLEET SERVICE
See EQUIPMENT TECHNOLOGY LLC

D-U-N-S 13-582-6985
HORIZON FOOD GROUP INC
(Suby of HORIZON HOLDINGS LLC) ★
1 Bush St Ste 650, San Francisco, CA 94104-4412
Tel (415) 394-9700 Founded/Ownrshp 1999
Sales 16.1MM^E EMP 450
SIC 5461 Cakes; Cakes
CEO: Robert M Sharp
*CFO: Lee Rucker
Off Mgr: Martha Parriott

D-U-N-S 12-210-0829
HORIZON FOOD SERVICE INC
BURGER KING
6101 S 58th St Ste B, Lincoln, NE 68516-3652
Tel (402) 421-6400 Founded/Ownrshp 1983
Sales 37.1MM^E EMP 1,200
SIC 5812 Fast-food restaurant, chain; Fast-food restaurant, chain
Pr: Dennis Erickson
*VP: Dave Schmidt
Genl Mgr: Liz Thomashide

D-U-N-S 79-308-1167 IMP
HORIZON FOREST PRODUCTS LP
(Suby of AMERICAN LUMBER CO) ★
4115 Commodity Pkwy, Raleigh, NC 27610-2973
Tel (919) 424-8265 Founded/Ownrshp 1993
Sales 22.4MM^E EMP 40
SIC 5031 Lumber: rough, dressed & finished
Pr: Jeff Myer
Chf Mktg O: Holly Williams
*VP: David Williams
Brnch Mgr: Carl Bahn
Brnch Mgr: Paul Wimer
Sales Asso: Lori Garner
Sales Asso: John Rendleman
Snr Mgr: Bev Farah
Snr Mgr: Wes Vicars

D-U-N-S 10-153-2695
HORIZON FREIGHT SYSTEM INC
6600 Bessemer Ave, Cleveland, OH 44127-1804
Tel (216) 341-7410 Founded/Ownrshp 1982
Sales 50.9MM^E EMP 100
SIC 4213 Trucking, except local
Pr: David Ferrante
*CFO: James Gifford
Sfty Dirs: Tracy Green
Sfty Dirs: Carmen Laboy
Sfty Mgr: Janet Fraley

D-U-N-S 07-980-1125
▲ HORIZON GLOBAL CORP
39400 Woodward Ave # 100, Bloomfield Hills, MI 48304-5150
Tel (248) 593-8810 Founded/Ownrshp 2015
Sales 626.8MM^E EMP 2,800^E
Tkr Sym HZN Exch NYS
SIC 3714 3711 5531 Trailer hitches, motor vehicle; Motor vehicle electrical equipment; Wreckers (tow truck), assembly of; Automobile & truck equipment & parts
Pr: Mark Zeffiro
Pr: John Aleva
Pr: Carl Bizon
CFO: David Rice
Sr VP: Paul Caruso
VP: Maria Duey

D-U-N-S 08-001-8012
HORIZON GRAIN CORP
23 Cheshire Ln, Scarsdale, NY 10583-1654
Tel (914) 441-1818 Founded/Ownrshp 2014
Sales 30.0MM EMP 1
SIC 5153 Grains
CEO: Hayman Hegazy

D-U-N-S 04-132-0909
▲ HORIZON GROUP PROPERTIES INC
5000 Hakes Dr Ste 500, Norton Shores, MI 49441-5574
Tel (231) 798-9100 Founded/Ownrshp 1998
Sales 34.1MM^E EMP 129
Tkr Sym HGPI Exch OTO
SIC 6798 Real estate investment trusts; Real estate investment trusts
Ch Bd: Gary J Skoien
*CFO: David R Tinkham
*Treas: James S Brien
*Ex VP: Andrew Pelmoter
*VP: Thomas A Rumptz
*VP: Gina Slechta

D-U-N-S 02-915-8008 IMP
HORIZON GROUP USA INC
45 Technology Dr, Warren, NJ 07059-5184
Tel (908) 810-1111 Founded/Ownrshp 2000
Sales 225.1MM^E EMP 404
SIC 5092 Toys & hobby goods & supplies; Toys & hobby goods & supplies
Pr: James H Cash
*CFO: Holli Gabler
Ex VP: Evan Buzzerio
Ex VP: Cara Costa
Ex VP: Lawrence Fine
Ex VP: Jim Neitzel
VP: Diana Castellanos
VP: Ruben Cordero
VP: Laura Crlencic
*VP: Roshan Wijerama
IT Man: Lynn Bicher

HORIZON HEALTH & SUBACUTE CENT
See TDC CONVALESCENT INC

D-U-N-S 78-594-2426
HORIZON HEALTH AND WELLNESS INC
MOUNTAIN HEALTH & WELLNESS
625 N Plaza Dr, Apache Junction, AZ 85120-5501
Tel (480) 983-0065 Founded/Ownrshp 1986
Sales 15.8MM EMP 630
Accts Metz & Associates Pllc Apache
SIC 8093 8063 8741 Mental health clinic, outpatient; Hospital for the mentally ill; Management services; Mental health clinic, outpatient; Hospital for the mentally ill; Management services
CEO: Norman Mudd
Dir IT: Dave Waldron
IT Man: Charles Staeheli

D-U-N-S 60-859-0105
■ HORIZON HEALTH CORP
(Suby of PSYCHIATRIC SOLUTIONS INC) ★
1965 Lakepointe Dr 100, Lewisville, TX 75057-6424
Tel (972) 420-8200 Founded/Ownrshp 2007
Sales 163.6MM^E EMP 2,914
SIC 8093 8069 Rehabilitation center, outpatient treatment; Alcoholism rehabilitation hospital; Drug addiction rehabilitation hospital; Rehabilitation center, outpatient treatment; Alcoholism rehabilitation hospital; Drug addiction rehabilitation hospital
Pr: Joey A Jacobs
Pr: Jack Devaney
CFO: Jack E Polson
Chf Mktg O: Bill Mulcahy
Sr VP: Doug Johnson
VP: John Coleman
VP: Denise Dailey
VP: Steven T Davidson
VP: Palma Flamino
*VP: Christopher L Howard
VP: Joyce Keegan
VP: Matthew Lisagor
VP: Dan McCarthy
VP: John Piechocki
VP: Brent Turner
VP: Anthony J Vadella

D-U-N-S 10-861-1971
HORIZON HEALTH SERVICES INC
3020 Bailey Ave, Buffalo, NY 14215-2814
Tel (716) 831-0200 Founded/Ownrshp 1974
Sales 25.4MM EMP 214
SIC 8322 8093 Substance abuse counseling; Alcoholism counseling, nontreatment; Substance abuse clinics (outpatient); Alcohol clinic, outpatient; Substance abuse counseling; Alcoholism counseling, nontreatment; Substance abuse clinics (outpatient); Alcohol clinic, outpatient
CEO: Anne D Constantino
*VP: Lisa Arnet
*VP: Brenda John Banach
*VP: Michelle Curto
VP: Brenda John-Banach
VP: Brenda Johnbanach
*VP: Paige K Prentice
VP: Paige Prentice
VP: Herbert M Weis PH
VP: Donald Will
Prgrm Mgr: Melissa Brown

D-U-N-S 15-413-1924
HORIZON HEALTHCARE PLAN HOLDING
HMO BLUE
(Suby of HORIZON BC/BS OF NJ) ★
3 Penn Plz E Ste 15-D, Newark, NJ 07105-2258
Tel (973) 466-4000 Founded/Ownrshp 1984
Sales 1.1MMM EMP 575
SIC 8011 Health maintenance organization; Health maintenance organization
*Pr: Christy Bell
*Treas: Robert Pures
VP: John Lynch
VP: Dennis Marco
VP: Pamela Miller

D-U-N-S 00-256-9564
HORIZON HEALTHCARE SERVICES INC
HORIZON BC/BS OF NJ
3 Penn Plz E Ste 1, Newark, NJ 07105-2200
Tel (973) 466-4000 Founded/Ownrshp 1932
Sales NA EMP 4,700
SIC 6324 6411 6321 Hospital & medical service plans; Health maintenance organization (HMO), insurance only; Group hospitalization plans; Dental insurance; Insurance agents, brokers & service; Accident & health insurance; Hospital & medical service plans; Health maintenance organization (HMO), insurance only; Group hospitalization plans; Dental insurance; Insurance agents, brokers & service; Accident & health insurance
CEO: Robert A Marino
Pr: Roy Kaptein
*CEO: Robert A Marino
COO: Robert Marino
*CFO: Robert J Pures
Sr Cor Off: Brian Peterson
Chf Mktg O: Glenn D Pomerantz
*Ex VP: Christy W Bell
*Sr VP: Mark Barnard
*Sr VP: Douglas E Blackwell
*Sr VP: Kevin P Conlin
*Sr VP: Margaret Coons
*Sr VP: Christopher M Lepre
*Sr VP: Linda A Willett
VP: James F Albano
VP: Lawrence B Altman
VP: Carol A Banks
VP: Philip M Bonaparte
VP: Charles A Bowles
VP: Kenneth A Brause
VP: Colleen D Brennan

D-U-N-S 14-432-4571 IMP/EXP
HORIZON HOBBY LLC
4105 Fieldstone Rd, Champaign, IL 61822-8800
Tel (217) 352-1913 Founded/Ownrshp 1985
Sales 231.9MM^E EMP 700
SIC 5092 Hobby goods; Hobby goods
CEO: Joe Ambrose
CFO: Robert Peak
*CFO: Roger Rhodes
*Ch: Rick L Stephens
*Ex VP: Kurt Bock
*Ex VP: Janet Ottmers
VP: Paul Beard
VP: Ed Delaporte
*VP: Steve Hall
Off Mgr: Terri Kirby
Software D: Joe Chrisman

D-U-N-S 08-296-4847
HORIZON HOLDINGS INC (NE)
6101 S 58th St Ste B, Lincoln, NE 68516-3652
Tel (402) 421-6400 Founded/Ownrshp 1985
Sales 25.0MM^E EMP 1,000
SIC 5812 Fast-food restaurant, chain; Fast-food restaurant, chain
Pr: Dennis Ericson

D-U-N-S 62-510-8956
HORIZON HOLDINGS LLC
1 Bush St Ste 650, San Francisco, CA 94104-4412
Tel (415) 788-2000 Founded/Ownrshp 1989
Sales 87.5MM^E EMP 515
SIC 6799 2053 Investment clubs; Cakes, bakery: frozen; Investment clubs; Cakes, bakery: frozen
VP: Victor Reed
Off Mgr: Martha Parriott

HORIZON HOME CARE
See EVERGREEN BEHAVIORAL MANAGEMENT INC

D-U-N-S 07-384-3864
HORIZON HOME CARE & HOSPICE INC
BROWN DEER
11400 W Lake Park Dr, Milwaukee, WI 53224-3035
Tel (414) 359-1503 Founded/Ownrshp 1990
Sales 34.0MM EMP 460
SIC 8082 8322 Home health care services; Individual & family services; Home health care services; Individual & family services
Ex Dir: Mary Haynor
*CFO: Laura Krause

D-U-N-S 19-448-4817
HORIZON HOSPITALITY LLC
FOUR POINT
5216 Messer Airport Hwy, Birmingham, AL 35212-3033
Tel (205) 591-0961 Founded/Ownrshp 2003
Sales 18.6MM^E EMP 500
SIC 8741 Hotel or motel management; Hotel or motel management
Genl Mgr: Robert Larn
Sales Exec: Linda Wherla

D-U-N-S 09-740-1095
HORIZON HOTELS LTD
99 Corbett Way Ste 302, Eatontown, NJ 07724-4261
Tel (732) 935-9553 Founded/Ownrshp 1994
Sales 34.3MM^E EMP 750
SIC 7011 7997 8741 Hotels & motels; Country club, membership; Hotel or motel management; Hotels & motels; Country club, membership; Hotel or motel management
Pr: Cynthia Cox
COO: Michael Olcott
*CFO: Robert Sacco
*Treas: Diane Sacco
VP: Donna Post

D-U-N-S 07-665-9978
HORIZON HOUSE
900 University St Ofc, Seattle, WA 98101-2789
Tel (206) 624-3700 Founded/Ownrshp 1962
Sales 30.5MM EMP 220
SIC 6513 Retirement hotel operation; Retirement hotel operation
Ex Dir: Robert Anderson
COO: Ed Mawe
*CFO: Carl Siver
*Ch: Sue Jones
Off Mgr: Christine Seymour
CTO: Brad D'Emidio
Dir IT: Lee Atherton
Mktg Dir: Bill Clancy
Nrsg Dir: Julie Jorgenson
HC Dir: Roma Cassel
Dietician: Mandy Chan

D-U-N-S 96-944-1869
HORIZON HOUSE DEVELOPMENTAL SVCS
120 S 30th St, Philadelphia, PA 19104-3403
Tel (215) 386-3838 Founded/Ownrshp 2011
Sales 20.0MM^E EMP 2
Accts Bdo Usa Llp Philadelphia Pa
SIC 8322 Individual & family services; Individual & family services
Prin: Jeffrey Wilush

D-U-N-S 07-146-1362
HORIZON HOUSE INC
120 S 30th St, Philadelphia, PA 19104-3403
Tel (215) 386-3838 Founded/Ownrshp 1952
Sales 11.7MM EMP 1,200
Accts Asher & Company Ltd Philadelp
SIC 8361 6512 8322 8093 Rehabilitation center, residential: health care incidental; Commercial & industrial building operation; Individual & family services; Specialty outpatient clinics; Rehabilitation center, residential: health care incidental; Commercial & industrial building operation; Individual & family services; Specialty outpatient clinics
Ch: Gabriel Ross
*Ch Bd: Gregory O Bruce
*Pr: Jeffrey W J Wilush
COO: Carolyn Pastore
*CFO: Jeff Wilush
*Sr VP: Gerald F Skillings
*VP: Thomas L Bailey
*VP: David C Dunbeck
Exec: Denise Bernier
MIS Dir: Kariemah White-Mack
QA Dir: Angela Griffin

D-U-N-S 84-206-8702
HORIZON HOUSE REHABILITATION SERVICES
2137 N 33rd St, Philadelphia, PA 19121-1106
Tel (215) 236-0224 Founded/Ownrshp 1994
Sales 35.8MM EMP 2^E
Accts Asher & Company Ltd Philade
SIC 8322 Individual & family services; Individual & family services

HORIZON INDUSTRIES
See EAST TEXAS LIGHTHOUSE FOR BLIND

D-U-N-S 02-766-8935
HORIZON INTERNATIONAL CARGO INC
(Suby of HORIZON INTERNATIONAL CARGO LIMITED)
5422 W Rosecrans Ave, Hawthorne, CA 90250-6609
Tel (310) 297-9069 Founded/Ownrshp 2008
Sales 25.4MM EMP 35
SIC 4731 6111 Freight transportation arrangement; Export/Import Bank
Pr: Nigel Davies
Pr: Andy Nicholls

D-U-N-S 19-330-5187
■ **HORIZON LINES HOLDING CORP**
(Suby of MATSON ALASKA INC) ★
2550 W Tyvola Rd Ste 530, Charlotte, NC 28217-4551
Tel (704) 973-7000 Founded/Ownrshp 2008
Sales 71.6MM^E EMP 1,598
SIC 4731 6512 Freight transportation arrangement; Nonresidential building operators; Freight transportation arrangement; Nonresidential building operators
CFO: M Mark Urbania
*COO: John V Keenan
*Ex VP: Michael T Avara
*Ex VP: Michael F Zendan II
*Sr VP: William A Hamlin
*VP: Marion Davis
*VP: Robert S Zuckerman

D-U-N-S 12-064-0508 IMP/EXP
HORIZON LINES LLC
2550 W Tyvola Rd Ste 530, Charlotte, NC 28217-4551
Tel (877) 678-7447 Founded/Ownrshp 1998
Sales 193.0MM^E EMP 1,020
SIC 4424 4783 4731 4412 Deep sea domestic transportation of freight; Packing & crating; Freight transportation arrangement; Deep sea foreign transportation of freight

D-U-N-S 07-861-1955 EXP
HORIZON MAC COOPERATIVE (CA)
1625 Shaw Ave Ste 101, Clovis, CA 93611-4089
Tel (559) 458-7272 Founded/Ownrshp 2011
Sales 40.0MM EMP 17
SIC 5145 Nuts, salted or roasted; Nuts, salted or roasted
Pr: Gary R Smith
*CEO: Jim Zion
*COO: Mark Dutra
Sls Mgr: Paul Reynolds

D-U-N-S 03-333-7523
HORIZON MANAGEMENT INC (OH)
821 Kentwood Dr Ste D, Youngstown, OH 44512-5061
Tel (330) 965-1542 Founded/Ownrshp 2000
Sales 28.1MM^E EMP 125
SIC 5411 Grocery stores
Pr: Henry Nemenz

D-U-N-S 17-189-9842
HORIZON MANAGEMENT SERVICES LLC
HORIZON STAFFING SERVICES
1169 Main St Ste 2, East Hartford, CT 06108-2295
Tel (860) 282-6124 Founded/Ownrshp 1998
Sales 16.2MM^E EMP 800^E
SIC 7361 Employment agencies; Employment agencies
VP: Whitney Miller
Mng Dir: Naz Qureshi
Off Mgr: Marge Lemieux

D-U-N-S 60-471-9690
HORIZON MEDIA INC
75 Varick St Ste 1404, New York, NY 10013-1917
Tel (212) 220-5000 Founded/Ownrshp 1988
Sales 175.8MM^E EMP 630
SIC 7319 Media buying service; Media buying service
Pr: William A Koenigsberg
*Pt: Serena Duff
*Pt: Eva Kantrowitz
Pt: Paul Santello
Pt: Jon Venison
*Mng Pt: Rich Simms
*COO: Vincent O'Toole
CFO: Vinnie O'Toole
CFO: Zach Rosenberg
*Ofcr: Taylor Valentine
*Ofcr: Rick Watrall
Ofcr: Donnie Williams
*Ex VP: Marianne Gambelli
Sr VP: Cliff Cree
*Sr VP: Jake Phillips
VP: Gianna Albors
VP: Sarah Bachman
VP: Jim Blauvelt
VP: Niki Decou
VP: Chris Fitzgerald
VP: Michelle Gordon

HORIZON MEDICAL CENTER
See CENTRAL TENNESSEE HOSPITAL CORP

D-U-N-S 07-974-3426
HORIZON MOVING GROUP LLC
6595 N Oracle Rd Ste 117, Tucson, AZ 85704-5645
Tel (520) 355-7641 Founded/Ownrshp 2010
Sales 26.0MM^E EMP 275
SIC 6719 Investment holding companies, except banks
CEO: Bruce Dusenberry
*CFO: Douglas Allen

D-U-N-S 00-279-3545
HORIZON MOVING SYSTEMS INC (AZ)
(Suby of HORIZON MOVING GROUP LLC) ★
6595 N Oracle Rd Ste 117, Tucson, AZ 85704-5645
Tel (520) 747-1400 Founded/Ownrshp 1925
Sales 23.9MM^E EMP 275
SIC 4214 4213 Household goods moving & storage, local; Household goods transport; Household goods moving & storage, local; Household goods transport
CEO: Bruce E Dusenberry
CFO: Doug Allen
*CFO: Ellen Carolan
*Treas: Kathryn H Dusenberry
Area Mgr: Lynette Wells

Brnch Mgr: Jose Conchas
Genl Mgr: Rick Shelley
IT Man: Denise Decker

D-U-N-S 07-818-1948
HORIZON MUD CO INC (TX)
500 W Wall St Ste 200, Midland, TX 79701-5093
Tel (432) 687-1171 Founded/Ownrshp 1980
Sales 29.7MM^E EMP 38
SIC 1389 5169 3533 Oil field services; Drilling mud; Oil field machinery & equipment
Pr: Anthony W Farish
CFO: Luke Blackwell
*Treas: Penny R Farish
*VP: Charles R Farish
Dist Mgr: Jason Merrick
Off Admin: Jennifer Shultz
Dir IT: Jake Pickett
Opers Mgr: Jeremy Pate
Opers Mgr: Steven Wilson

D-U-N-S 61-345-9866 IMP
HORIZON MUSIC INC
RAPCOHORIZON COMPANY
(Suby of RHC HOLDING CORP) ★
3581 Larch Ln, Jackson, MO 63755-7121
Tel (573) 243-1433 Founded/Ownrshp 1992
Sales 20.6MM^E EMP 140
SIC 3651 5735 5099 3357 Household audio & video equipment; Speaker monitors; Records, audio discs & tapes; Musical instruments; Nonferrous wiredrawing & insulating; Household audio & video equipment; Speaker monitors; Records, audio discs & tapes; Musical instruments; Nonferrous wiredrawing & insulating
Pr: Lisa Williams
*Pr: Lisa Williams
*CFO: Scott Wachter
Natl Sales: David R Boyer
Manager: James Woodard

D-U-N-S 83-469-0075
HORIZON NJ HEALTH
HORIZON BLUE CROSS BLUE SHIELD
(Suby of HORIZON BC/BS OF NJ) ★
210 Silvia St, Ewing, NJ 08628-3242
Tel (609) 718-9001 Founded/Ownrshp 1994
Sales NA EMP 275
SIC 6321 Mutual accident & health associations; Mutual accident & health associations
Pr: Karen L Clark
COO: Jai Pillai
CFO: James Dalessio
CFO: James Valessio
*Chf Mktg O: Mark Calderon
Ex VP: Christy Bell
VP: Phil Bonaparte
VP: Peggy Coons
Dir Rx: Sam Currie
Dir IT: Tyrone Shiu
Software D: Rhonda Tyson

D-U-N-S 13-397-9898
HORIZON PAYROLL SERVICES INC
2700 Miamisburg Centervil, Dayton, OH 45459-3705
Tel (937) 434-8244 Founded/Ownrshp 1981
Sales 40.0MM EMP 300
SIC 7371 5045 Custom computer programming services; Computers, peripherals & software; Custom computer programming services; Computers, peripherals & software
Pr: Marilynne Saliwanchik
*VP: Alan Saliwanchik
Opers Mgr: Stephanie Webster

D-U-N-S 17-129-9642
HORIZON PCS INC
(Suby of HORIZON TELCOM INC) ★
68 E Main St, Chillicothe, OH 45601-2503
Tel (740) 772-8200 Founded/Ownrshp 2000
Sales 32.2MM^E EMP 285
SIC 4812 Radio telephone communication; Radio telephone communication
Ch Bd: William A McKell
*COO: Alan G Morse
CFO: Stebbins B Chandor
*Sec: Steven Burkhardt
VP: Kate L Gayord
Sls&Mrk Ex: Joseph J Watson
VP Sls: Stephen Piekarski
Pr Dir: Mary Elsass

D-U-N-S 96-461-3413
■ **HORIZON PHARMA INC**
(Suby of HORIZON PHARMA PUBLIC LIMITED COMPANY)
520 Lake Cook Rd Ste 520, Deerfield, IL 60015-5633
Tel (224) 383-3000 Founded/Ownrshp 2014
Sales 296.9MM EMP 304^E
Accts Pricewaterhousecoopers Llp Ch
Tkr Sym HZNP Exch NGM
SIC 2834 Pharmaceutical preparations; Pharmaceutical preparations
Pr: Timothy P Walbert
Pr: Robert Metz
Pr: Joe Whalen
CFO: Paul W Hoelscher
CFO: Bill Iskos
Ex VP: Robert F Carey
Ex VP: David Kelly
Ex VP: John J Kody
Ex VP: Barry J Moze
Ex VP: Jeffrey W Sherman
Sr VP: John Devane
Sr VP: Terry Evans
Sr VP: Mary Martin
VP: Brian Andersen
VP: Cara Hales
VP: Ingrid Hoos
VP: Vikram Karnani
VP: Michelle Parsons
VP: Hans-Peter Zobel
Assoc Dir: Jon Eller

HORIZON PHARMACEUTICALS
See HORIZON THERAPEUTICS INC

D-U-N-S 13-473-0642
HORIZON PUBLICATIONS (2003) INC
1120 N Carbon St Ste 100, Marion, IL 62959-1055
Tel (618) 993-1711 Founded/Ownrshp 2003
Sales 27.4MM^E EMP 400
SIC 2711 Newspapers; Newspapers
Pr: David Radler
*Ex VP: Roland McBride
*VP: Mark Kipnis

D-U-N-S 03-117-8119
HORIZON PUBLICATIONS INC
1120 N Carbon St Ste 100, Marion, IL 62959-1055
Tel (618) 993-1711 Founded/Ownrshp 1997
Sales 78.0MM^E EMP 440
SIC 2711 Newspapers; Newspapers
Pr: David Radler
*CFO: Roland McBride
MIS Dir: Steve Jones

D-U-N-S 00-892-6255
HORIZON RESOURCES (ND)
317 2nd St W, Williston, ND 58801-5903
Tel (701) 572-2171 Founded/Ownrshp 1929
Sales 470.9MM EMP 150
Accts Junkermier Clark Campanella
SIC 5172 5541 5411 5191 Petroleum products; Filling stations, gasoline; Convenience stores; Farm supplies; Fertilizers & agricultural chemicals; Petroleum products; Filling stations, gasoline; Convenience stores; Farm supplies; Fertilizers & agricultural chemicals
CEO: Jeff Wagner
*Ch Bd: Wagner Harmon
*Ch Bd: Dennis Stromme
*CFO: James Radtke
*Sec: Myron Lee
*VP: Les Bean

D-U-N-S 80-898-5204
HORIZON RETAIL CONSTRUCTION INC
1500 Horizon Dr, Sturtevant, WI 53177-2066
Tel (262) 638-6000 Founded/Ownrshp 2005
Sales 146.8MM^E EMP 195^E
SIC 1542 Commercial & office building contractors; Commercial & office building contractors
Pr: Patrick Christensen
*VP: Daniel Siudak

D-U-N-S 79-604-4410
HORIZON SERVICES INC
320 Century Blvd, Wilmington, DE 19808-6270
Tel (302) 762-1200 Founded/Ownrshp 1997
Sales 79.2MM^E EMP 199
SIC 1711 Plumbing, heating, air-conditioning contractors; Plumbing, heating, air-conditioning contractors
Pr: David Geiger
*VP: Mark Aitken
CIO: Dustin Lausch
Advt Dir: Tara Brown
Sls Mgr: John Cameron

D-U-N-S 36-428-4042 IMP
HORIZON SHIPBUILDING INC
CRIMSON YACHT
13980 Shell Belt Rd, Bayou La Batre, AL 36509-2306
Tel (251) 824-1660 Founded/Ownrshp 1997
Sales 63.5MM^E EMP 244
SIC 3731 Shipbuilding & repairing; Shipbuilding & repairing
Pr: Travis R Short Sr
*VP: Ron Gunter
IT Man: Jason Hinkofer
Sfty Mgr: Jack Manche
Sfty Mgr: George Nash

D-U-N-S 80-831-5824
■ **HORIZON SOFTWARE INTERNATIONAL LLC**
(Suby of ROPER TECHNOLOGIES INC) ★
2915 Premiere Pkwy # 300, Duluth, GA 30097-3720
Tel (770) 554-6353 Founded/Ownrshp 2008
Sales 24.3MM^E EMP 181^E
SIC 7371 Computer software development; Computer software development
Pr: Randy Eckels
CFO: Calvin Jackman
Sr VP: Robbie Payne
VP: Tina Bennett
VP: Andrew Eggleston
VP: Schelley Hollyday
VP: Amy Huff
VP: Jarrell Newhouse
Prgrm Mgr: Matthew Hyde
Off Mgr: Julie Denmon
IT Man: Ryan Heard

D-U-N-S 80-461-5438 IMP
HORIZON SOLUTIONS LLC
HOLMES DISTRIBUTORS
2005 Brghtn Henriett Town, Rochester, NY 14623-2509
Tel (585) 274-8295 Founded/Ownrshp 2007
Sales 216.8MM^E EMP 280
SIC 5063 5085 Electrical apparatus & equipment; Industrial supplies; Electrical apparatus & equipment; Industrial supplies
Pr: Jim Newton
Ch Bd: J Richard Wilson
Sec: Michael C Herrmann
Sr VP: Karen Baker
Sr VP: Kathy Biesecker
Sr VP: Don Harrington
Sr VP: John Salvadore
VP: Tim Bridge
VP: Peter B Roby
Area Mgr: Matt Anderson
Area Mgr: Tom Mattice

HORIZON STAFFING SERVICES
See HORIZON MANAGEMENT SERVICES LLC

D-U-N-S 10-217-6260 IMP/EXP
HORIZON STEEL CO
350 Northgate Pkwy, Wheeling, IL 60090-2665
Tel (847) 291-0440 Founded/Ownrshp 1983
Sales 70.0MM EMP 73
SIC 5051 Steel; Steel

Pr: John Chirikas
**Pr:* Richard Nicolay
**CFO:* Mark Rohde
**VP:* Mike Cushard
Exec: Scott Fleming

D-U-N-S 96-330-4170
▲ HORIZON TECHNOLOGY FINANCE CORP
312 Farmington Ave, Farmington, CT 06032-1913
Tel (860) 676-8654 *Founded/Ownrshp* 2008
Sales 31.2MM[E] *EMP* 5[E]
Tkr Sym HRZN *Exch* NGS
SIC 6799 Financial services; Venture capital companies
Ch Bd: Robert D Pomeroy Jr
**Pr:* Gerald A Michaud
CFO: Christopher M Mathieu
Chf Cred: Daniel S Devorsetz
Sr VP: John C Bombara
Counsel: Eric Darmofal

D-U-N-S 96-524-4031 IMP
HORIZON TECHNOLOGY LLC
HORIZON DISPLAY
1 Rancho Cir, Lake Forest, CA 92630-8324
Tel (949) 595-8244 *Founded/Ownrshp* 1996
Sales 42.2MM[E] *EMP* 98
SIC 5045 7373 Computer peripheral equipment; Office computer automation systems integration; Computer peripheral equipment; Office computer automation systems integration
CEO: Kurt Johnson
**COO:* Stephen Buckler
CFO: Michael Feffer
**VP:* Michael Cannestra
Opers Mgr: Oselo Hinlo
Mktg Mgr: Steve Gladden

D-U-N-S 93-358-1456
HORIZON TELCOM INC
68 E Main St, Chillicothe, OH 45601-2503
Tel (740) 772-8200 *Founded/Ownrshp* 1995
Sales 117.0MM[E] *EMP* 285
SIC 4813 Local telephone communications; Local telephone communications
Ch Bd: Robert Mc Kell
**Pr:* Thomas Mc Kell
**CFO:* Jack Thompson
Genl Mgr: Narty Forde
S&M/VP: Joey Holibaugh

D-U-N-S 62-334-6538
HORIZON THERAPEUTICS INC
HORIZON PHARMACEUTICALS
520 Lake Cook Rd Ste 520, Deerfield, IL 60015-5633
Tel (224) 383-3000 *Founded/Ownrshp* 2005
Sales 34.9MM[E] *EMP* 166[E]
SIC 8733 Medical research
Pr: Timothy P Walbert
Pr: Chris Murphy
**CFO:* Robert J De Vaere
**Founder:* Barry L Golombik
Bd of Dir: Jeff Himawan
**Ofcr:* Jeffrey W Sherman
Ex VP: Robert Carey
Sr VP: Jeffrey Kent
Sr VP: Gerry McCluskey
VP: Brian Anderson
VP: Brian Beeler
VP: Iain Duncan
VP: Amy Grahn
VP: Ingrid Hoos
VP: Vikram Karani
VP: Merrell Magelli
VP: Cara Weyker

D-U-N-S 80-713-0500
■ HORIZON THERAPEUTICS INC
RAVICTI
(*Suby of* HORIZON PHARMA INC) ★
2000 Sierra Point Pkwy # 400, Brisbane, CA 94005-1845
Tel (650) 745-7802 *Founded/Ownrshp* 2015
Sales 113.5MM *EMP* 54
SIC 2834 Pharmaceutical preparations; Pharmaceutical preparations
Pr: Timothy P Walbert
**CFO:* Paul W Hoelscher
Sr VP: Ashley Gould
VP: Jitendra Ganju
VP: Sylvia Wheeler
IT Man: Wesley Winn
Natl Sales: Dan Niedbalski
Board of Directors: Bo Jesper Hansen, Jake R Nunn, Theodore Schroeder, Daniel G Welch

D-U-N-S 07-609-0232
HORIZON WEST HEALTHCARE INC
(*Suby of* HORIZON WEST INC) ★
4020 Sierra College Blvd # 190, Rocklin, CA 95677-3906
Tel (916) 624-6230 *Founded/Ownrshp* 1977
Sales 46.4MM[E] *EMP* 1,791[E]
SIC 8051 Convalescent home with continuous nursing care
CEO: Martine D Harmon
Dir Recs: Jeffrey Graine
Dir Recs: Mandy Johnson
**Sec:* Dennis Roccaforte
Ofcr: Linda Lutz
**VP:* Bernice Schrabeck
Dir Soc: Vickie Amerson
Dir Soc: Stephanie Barnes
Dir Soc: Jessica Dunn
Dir Soc: Kathryn Galuppo
Dir Soc: Dorothy Lyon
Dir Soc: Debby McFarland

D-U-N-S 60-515-1737
HORIZON WEST INC
4020 Sierra College Blvd, Rocklin, CA 95677-3906
Tel (916) 624-6230 *Founded/Ownrshp* 1987
Sales 98.4MM[E] *EMP* 2,500
SIC 8051 Skilled nursing care facilities; Skilled nursing care facilities
Pr: Ken McGuire
**CFO:* Alan MA
Nrsg Dir: Aletta Prinsloo

D-U-N-S 00-385-3926 IMP
HORIZON WINE & SPIRITS - NASHVILLE INC (TN)
3851 Industrial Pkwy, Nashville, TN 37218-3629
Tel (615) 320-7292 *Founded/Ownrshp* 1947, 1992
Sales 56.4MM[E] *EMP* 112
SIC 5182 Wine & distilled beverages; Wine & distilled beverages
Pr: Thomas E Bernard
VP: Greg Clarke
Exec: Henry McKinnon
Opers Mgr: Mike Harrison
Sales Exec: James Armstrong
Sales Exec: Ken Jean
S&M/VP: Tyler Brown

HORIZONS CAFE
See DOYON UNIVERSAL SERVICES LLC

D-U-N-S 16-756-8224
HORIZONS EMPLOYMENT SERVICES LLC
APPLE A DAY HEALTHCARE SVCS
1811 N Reynolds Rd # 102, Toledo, OH 43615-3533
Tel (419) 254-9644 *Founded/Ownrshp* 2007
Sales 3.5MM *EMP* 300
SIC 7361 Employment agencies; Employment agencies
Ex Dir: Patricia A Parker

D-U-N-S 00-422-0398 IMP
HORIZONS INC (OH)
IMAGING SYSTEMS
18531 S Miles Rd, Cleveland, OH 44128-4237
Tel (216) 475-0555 *Founded/Ownrshp* 1967, 1988
Sales 32.9MM[E] *EMP* 140
SIC 3861 Plates, photographic (sensitized); Plates, photographic (sensitized)
Pr: Herbert A Wainer
**VP:* Robert Miller
**VP:* Micheal Rish
IT Man: Ron Fersky
IT Man: Kevin Hocevar
Opers Mgr: Brian Fitzwater
Prd Mgr: Dan Fitzwater
Ql Cn Mgr: Robbie Pellon
Sales Exec: Karly Baldi
Mktg Mgr: Randy Uveges
Sls Mgr: Jon Keserich

HORIZONS UNLIMITED
See PETERSEN HEALTH CARE OF WISCONSIN INC

D-U-N-S 07-426-9408
HORIZONTAL BORING & TUNNELING CO
505 S River, Exeter, NE 68351-4109
Tel (402) 266-5347 *Founded/Ownrshp* 1982
Sales 22.1MM[E] *EMP* 80
SIC 1629 Trenching contractor
Pr: Brent L Moore
**Sec:* Lori B Moore
Sfty Dirs: Lonnie Shoup

HORIZONTAL DIRECTIONAL DRLG
See BROTHERTON PIPELINE INC

HORIZONTAL INTEGRATION
See GLOBAL MARKETS INC

D-U-N-S 00-523-6849 IMP
HORMANN LLC
(*Suby of* HORMANN KG VERKAUFSGESELLSCHAFT)
5050 Baseline Rd, Montgomery, IL 60538-1125
Tel (630) 859-3000 *Founded/Ownrshp* 1961
Sales 55.5MM[E] *EMP* 300
SIC 3442 Garage doors, overhead: metal; Garage doors, overhead: metal
Pr: Frank Weber
CFO: Bagher Dorch
Exec: Jean Alaniz
Mktg Mgr: Paul Kim
Manager: Jeffrey Siulborski
Manager: V Valliquette

D-U-N-S 07-663-8006
HORMANN NORTHWEST DOOR LLC
19000 Canyon Rd E, Puyallup, WA 98375-9746
Tel (253) 375-0700 *Founded/Ownrshp* 2015
Sales 34.7MM[E] *EMP* 222
SIC 3442

D-U-N-S 00-614-7383
▲ HORMEL FOODS CORP
1 Hormel Pl, Austin, MN 55912-3680
Tel (507) 437-5611 *Founded/Ownrshp* 1891
Sales 9.2MMM *EMP* 20,400
Tkr Sym HRL *Exch* NYS
SIC 2011 2013 2032 Meat packing plants; Sausages from meat slaughtered on site; Hams & picnics from meat slaughtered on site; Frankfurters from meat slaughtered on site; Canned meats (except baby food) from purchased meat; Beef stew from purchased meat; Corned beef from purchased meat; Spreads, sandwich: meat from purchased meat; Chili with or without meat: packaged in cans, jars, etc.; Meat packing plants; Sausages from meat slaughtered on site; Hams & picnics from meat slaughtered on site; Frankfurters from meat slaughtered on site; Canned meats (except baby food) from purchased meat; Beef stew from purchased meat; Corned beef from purchased meat; Spreads, sandwich: meat from purchased meat; Chili with or without meat: packaged in cans, jars, etc.
Ch Bd: Jeffrey M Ettinger
Pr: Steven G Binder
Pr: Glenn R Leitch
**Pr:* James P Snee
Pr: Larry L Vorpahl
COO: Lori Pirkl
**CFO:* Jody H Feragen
Treas: Roland G Gentzler
Sr VP: Bryan D Farnsworth
VP: Deanna T Brady
VP: Thomas R Day
VP: Brian D Johnson
VP: Donald H Kremin
VP: Lori J Marco
VP: Kevin L Myers
VP: James N Sheehan
VP: James M Splinter
Comm Dir: Mark Zelle
Board of Directors: Sally J Smith, Gary C Bhojwani, Steven A White, Terrell K Crews, Glenn S Forbes, Stephen M Lacy, John L Morrison, Elsa A Murano, Robert C Nakasone, Susan K Nestegard, Christopher J Policinski

D-U-N-S 60-838-9115
■ HORMEL FOODS CORPORATE SERVICES LLC
(*Suby of* HORMEL FOODS CORP) ★
1 Hormel Pl, Austin, MN 55912-3680
Tel (507) 437-5611 *Founded/Ownrshp* 2004
Sales 112.2MM[E] *EMP* 500
SIC 5147 Meats & meat products; Meats & meat products
CEO: Jeffrey Ettinger
VP Mktg: Whitney Velasco-Aznar
Corp Couns: Sarah Nelsen
Snr Mgr: Rick Stoulil

D-U-N-S 06-800-8283 EXP
■ HORMEL FOODS INTERNATIONAL CORP
(*Suby of* HORMEL FOODS CORP) ★
1 Hormel Pl, Austin, MN 55912-3680
Tel (507) 437-5611 *Founded/Ownrshp* 1967
Sales 43.9MM[E] *EMP* 80
SIC 5147 8742 Meats & meat products; Food & beverage consultant; Meats & meat products; Food & beverage consultant
Pr: Richard Broff
Pr: Phillip L Minerich
Area Mgr: Brian Pitzele
Mktg Mgr: Mark Mayer
Corp Couns: Sarah L Nelsen

D-U-N-S 06-358-0844
HORMUTH GROUP INC
436 W Rialto Ave, Rialto, CA 92376-5845
Tel (909) 421-1244 *Founded/Ownrshp* 1987
Sales 21.6MM[E] *EMP* 120
SIC 5031 5211 Lumber: rough, dressed & finished; Lumber products; Lumber: rough, dressed & finished; Lumber products
Pr: Richard W Hormuth

D-U-N-S 02-440-8676 IMP
HORN EQUIPMENT CO LLC
131 N Sunnylane Rd, Moore, OK 73160-8818
Tel (405) 793-9101 *Founded/Ownrshp* 1979
Sales 21.6MM[E] *EMP* 43
SIC 5084 7353 Oil well machinery, equipment & supplies; Oil field equipment, rental or leasing
Pr: Hoby Horn
**Prin:* Faye E Countryman
**Prin:* George W Countryman
**Prin:* Carl W Moore

HORN INDUSTRIAL SERVICES
See HORN INTERMEDIATE HOLDINGS INC

D-U-N-S 83-167-5926
HORN INTERMEDIATE HOLDINGS INC
HORN INDUSTRIAL SERVICES
2205 Ragu Dr, Owensboro, KY 42303-1437
Tel (270) 683-6564 *Founded/Ownrshp* 2007
Sales 33.0MM[E] *EMP* 127[E]
SIC 6719 Investment holding companies, except banks
Pr: Brent Smith

D-U-N-S 05-120-4014
HORN WELL DRILLING INC NOAH
1070 Sandy Valley Ln, Oakwood, VA 24631-9651
Tel (276) 935-5902 *Founded/Ownrshp* 1950
Sales 23.7MM[E] *EMP* 150
SIC 1381 1781 Drilling oil & gas wells; Water well drilling; Drilling oil & gas wells; Water well drilling
Pr: Jeffery A Horn
**Treas:* Marianne H Gibson
**VP:* Suzen Johnson
**VP:* Boyd Leon
Sfty Dirs: Dave Wilson

D-U-N-S 00-725-7603 IMP/EXP
HORNADY MANUFACTURING CO
3625 W Old Potash Hwy, Grand Island, NE 68803-4905
Tel (308) 382-1390 *Founded/Ownrshp* 1949
Sales 135.8MM[E] *EMP* 260
SIC 3482 3559 3483 Small arms ammunition; Ammunition & explosives, loading machinery; Ammunition, except for small arms; Ammunition loading & assembling plant; Small arms ammunition; Ammunition & explosives, loading machinery; Ammunition, except for small arms; Ammunition loading & assembling plant
Pr: Steve Hornady
CFO: Mark Kroeker
VP: Jason Hornady
Comm Man: Neal Emery
Genl Mgr: Scott Catlett
CTO: Leland Nichols
Sfty Mgr: Nat Spencer
Sfty Mgr: Doug Wilkinson
Plnt Mgr: Pat Langer
Natl Sales: Katie Glover

D-U-N-S 12-883-6181
HORNADY TRANSPORTATION LLC
(*Suby of* DASEKE INC) ★
1736 S Highway 21 Byp, Monroeville, AL 36460-3065
Tel (251) 743-5260 *Founded/Ownrshp* 2015
Sales 26.0MM[E] *EMP* 400
SIC 7363 Truck driver services; Truck driver services
Pr: Chris Hornady
VP: Joe Booker
VP: Judy Martorana
CTO: Janice McKenzie

D-U-N-S 03-404-5526
HORNADY TRUCK LINE INC
1736 S Highway 21 Byp, Monroeville, AL 36460-3065
Tel (251) 575-4811 *Founded/Ownrshp* 1928
Sales 46.8MM[E] *EMP* 506
SIC 4213

D-U-N-S 03-181-6952
■ HORNBACHERS FOODS (ND)
(*Suby of* SUPERVALU INC) ★
4151 45th St S, Fargo, ND 58104-4312
Tel (701) 281-8111 *Founded/Ownrshp* 1975
Sales 42.4MM[E] *EMP* 600[E]
SIC 5411 Grocery stores; Grocery stores
Genl Mgr: Dean Hornbacher
**Ch Bd:* Michael Wright
**VP:* Jeff Noddle
Store Dir: Mike Sunderland

D-U-N-S 94-729-9590
▲ HORNBECK OFFSHORE SERVICES INC
103 Northpark Blvd # 300, Covington, LA 70433-6111
Tel (985) 727-2000 *Founded/Ownrshp* 1997
Sales 634.7MM *EMP* 1,641
Tkr Sym HOS *Exch* NYS
SIC 4499 Boat & ship rental & leasing, except pleasure; Chartering of commercial boats; Boat & ship rental & leasing, except pleasure; Chartering of commercial boats
Ch Bd: Todd M Hornbeck
Pr: David Burns
Pr: Larry Francios
COO: Carl G Annessa
CFO: James O Harp Jr
Treas: Mark Myrtue
Ofcr: Lauren Babin
Ofcr: Erick Brown
Ofcr: Thomas Fowler
Ofcr: David Macdonald
Ofcr: Thomas Marshall
Ofcr: Iran Pagan
Ofcr: Tyler Spaulding
Ex VP: John S Cook
Ex VP: Samuel A Giberga
VP: Andrew Bruzdzinski
VP: Peter Fortier
VP: D Wallace
VP Bus Dev: Larry Francois
Board of Directors: Larry D Hornbeck, Bruce W Hunt, Steven W Krablin, Patricia B Melcher, Kevin M Meyers, John T Rynd, Bernie W Stewart, Nicholas L Swyka Jr

D-U-N-S 02-604-7410 EXP
■ HORNBECK OFFSHORE SERVICES LLC
HOS
(*Suby of* HORNBECK OFFSHORE SERVICES INC) ★
103 Northpark Blvd # 300, Covington, LA 70433-6111
Tel (985) 727-2000 *Founded/Ownrshp* 1996, 2001
Sales 97.1MM[E] *EMP* 700[E]
SIC 1382 Oil & gas exploration services; Oil & gas exploration services
Pr: Todd M Hornbeck
**Treas:* Mark S Myrtue
**Ex VP:* Carl G Annessa
**Ex VP:* John S Cook
**Ex VP:* Samuel A Giberga
**Ex VP:* James O Harp Jr

D-U-N-S 13-502-9168
■ HORNBECK OFFSHORE TRANSPORTATION LLC
(*Suby of* HORNBECK OFFSHORE SERVICES INC) ★
103 Northpark Blvd # 300, Covington, LA 70433-6111
Tel (985) 727-2000 *Founded/Ownrshp* 2002
Sales 26.0MM[E] *EMP* 350
SIC 4492 Towing & tugboat service; Towing & tugboat service
CFO: James Harp
Ofcr: Paul Ordogne

HORNBLOWER CRUISES & EVENT
See HORNBLOWER YACHTS INC

D-U-N-S 06-656-9823
HORNBLOWER YACHTS INC
HORNBLOWER CRUISES & EVENT
On The Embarcadero Pier 3 St Pier, San Francisco, CA 94111
Tel (415) 788-8866 *Founded/Ownrshp* 1984
Sales 100.2MM[E] *EMP* 350
Accts Rina Accountancy Corporation C
SIC 4489 Excursion boat operators; Excursion boat operators
Pr: Terry Macrae
Pr: Briant Stewart
VP: Andreas Sappok
VP: Annabella Stagner
Exec: Jim Unger
Sls Dir: Mia Falkenstein
Sls Mgr: Monica Antola
Sls Mgr: Christina Domino
Sls Mgr: Charlotte McAuliffe
Sls Mgr: Alicia Slater

D-U-N-S 02-852-2019
HORNBURG JAGUAR INC
(*Suby of* PENDRAGON PLC)
9176 W Sunset Blvd, Los Angeles, CA 90069-3109
Tel (310) 274-5133 *Founded/Ownrshp* 1948, 2001
Sales 43.1MM[E] *EMP* 160
SIC 5511 7538 Automobiles, new & used; General automotive repair shops; Automobiles, new & used; General automotive repair shops
Pr: Russell Smith
**VP:* Gwendolyn Hornburg
**Genl Mgr:* Martin Dodsworth
Sls Mgr: Hamid Aliyev

D-U-N-S 13-057-5012
HORNE AUTO CENTER INC
651 W Deuce Of Clubs, Show Low, AZ 85901-5811
Tel (928) 537-5500 *Founded/Ownrshp* 1991
Sales 25.2MM[E] *EMP* 75
SIC 5511 Automobiles, new & used; Automobiles, new & used
Pr: Robert C Horne
**Treas:* Cheryl K Horne
**VP:* Robert A Horne
Genl Mgr: Andrew Horne
Store Mgr: Dan Macleod

D-U-N-S 01-708-7065
HORNE BUILDING SPECIALTIES INC
PELLA WINDOW STORE
2120 Oak Industrial Dr Ne, Grand Rapids, MI 49505-6014
Tel (616) 235-3600 *Founded/Ownrshp* 1997
Sales 22.3MM^E *EMP* 90
SIC 5031 Windows; Door frames, all materials; Windows; Door frames, all materials
Pr: John Estabrook
**VP:* Michael Freiburger
**VP:* Thomas Schepperly

D-U-N-S 07-507-1548
HORNE LLP
HORNE WEALTH ADVISORS
1020 Highland Colony Pkwy # 400, Ridgeland, MS 39157-2129
Tel (601) 948-0940 *Founded/Ownrshp* 2003
Sales 78.4MM^E *EMP* 479
SIC 8721 8742 Certified public accountant; Certified public accountant; Financial consultant
Pt: Hugh J Parker
**Pt:* Wendy F Eversole
Mng Pt: Roy Ward
COO: Terry Traylor
Exec: Joel Bobo
Exec: John Scott
Exec: Charlie Shields
Off Mgr: Debbie Wyatt
CTO: Dave Buskins
IT Man: Karla Bennett
IT Man: Johnny Sanders

HORNE WEALTH ADVISORS
See HORNE LLP

D-U-N-S 08-045-3657
HORNELL BREWING CO INC
FEROLITO, VULTAGGIO & SONS
60 Crossways Park Dr W # 400, Woodbury, NY 11797-2018
Tel (516) 812-0300 *Founded/Ownrshp* 1979
Sales 67.8MM^E *EMP* 170
SIC 5149 5181 3585 Soft drinks; Beer & other fermented malt liquors; Beer dispensing equipment; Soft drinks; Beer & other fermented malt liquors; Beer dispensing equipment
Ch Bd: David K Menashi
**Ch Bd:* Don Vultaggio
**Pr:* John Ferolito
CFO: Rick Adonilla
CFO: David K Menashi
Ex VP: Robert Marciano
Ex VP: David Menashi
VP: Paul O'Donnell
VP: Bart Venza
Exec: Christine Russo
IT Man: Randy Berling

D-U-N-S 09-813-0693
HORNELL CITY SCHOOL DISTRICT
BOARD OF EDUCATION
25 Pearl St, Hornell, NY 14843-1622
Tel (607) 324-1302 *Founded/Ownrshp* 1950
Sales 13.8MM^E *EMP* 346
SIC 8211 Public elementary school; Public junior high school; Public senior high school; Public elementary school; Public junior high school; Public senior high school
**Treas:* Susan Brown
Schl Brd P: Richard Scavco
Schl Brd P: Richard Scavo
Schl Brd P: Lawrence Vetter

D-U-N-S 80-013-2057
HORNER ELECTRIC INC
1521 E Washington St, Indianapolis, IN 46201-3899
Tel (317) 639-4261 *Founded/Ownrshp* 2004
Sales 51.6MM^E *EMP* 71^E
SIC 5063 7694 7699 Electrical supplies; Electric motor repair; Pumps & pumping equipment repair; Welding equipment repair
Prin: Alan Horner
Dir IT: Kevin Cokus
Mktg Mgr: Fred Roth

D-U-N-S 01-641-5655
HORNER INDUSTRIAL SERVICES INC
INDIANA FAN & FABRICATION
1521 E Washington St, Indianapolis, IN 46201-3848
Tel (317) 639-4261 *Founded/Ownrshp* 1949
Sales 36.3MM^E *EMP* 200
SIC 3625 7694 7699 7629 5063

HORNER MILLWK
See HORNER MILLWORK CORP

D-U-N-S 00-141-0943 IMP
HORNER MILLWORK CORP (MA)
HORNER MILLWK
1255 Grand Army Hwy, Somerset, MA 02726-1203
Tel (508) 679-6479 *Founded/Ownrshp* 1957, 1981
Sales 43.8MM^E *EMP* 180
SIC 5031 5211 2431 Millwork; Millwork & lumber; Millwork; Millwork; Millwork & lumber; Millwork
Pr: Peter D Humphrey
**Treas:* Irving D Humphrey III
IT Man: Glenn Brown
Netwrk Mgr: Susan Atkinson

D-U-N-S 04-602-9518 IMP/EXP
HORNERXPRESS INC
5755 Powerline Rd, Fort Lauderdale, FL 33309-2001
Tel (954) 772-6966 *Founded/Ownrshp* 1969
Sales 113.2MM^E *EMP* 200^E
SIC 5091 3949 3561 Swimming pools, equipment & supplies; Spa equipment & supplies; Sporting & athletic goods; Pumps & pumping equipment; Swimming pools, equipment & supplies; Spa equipment & supplies; Sporting & athletic goods; Pumps & pumping equipment
Pr: William A Kent
**Treas:* Gary Chisling

D-U-N-S 04-085-4601 IMP
HORNERXPRESS-SOUTH FLORIDA INC
AUTO PILOT
5755 Powerline Rd, Fort Lauderdale, FL 33309-2001
Tel (954) 958-2560 *Founded/Ownrshp* 1969
Sales 211.7MM^E *EMP* 400
SIC 5091 Swimming pools, equipment & supplies; Swimming pools, equipment & supplies
Pr: Bill Kent
COO: Ross Champion
**Treas:* Gary Chisling
**VP:* Don Detwiler
VP: Mike Dooley
**VP:* Darren Goldstein
**VP:* Eric Levine
Genl Mgr: Chuck Schilling
CTO: William Ken
IT Man: Joanne Senko

D-U-N-S 11-313-3953
HORNOR TOWNSEND & KENT INC
(*Suby of* PENN MUTUAL LIFE INSURANCE CO) ★
600 Dresher Rd, Horsham, PA 19044-2204
Tel (215) 957-7300 *Founded/Ownrshp* 1969
Sales 84.9MM^E *EMP* 1,100
SIC 6211 Security brokers & dealers; Security brokers & dealers
Pr: Michelle A Barry
Mng Pt: Michael Geary
Mng Pt: Peter Lovley
Mng Pt: Graham Self
**Treas:* Stacey N Polakowski
Ofcr: Jason Albino
Ex VP: Joseph Radovic
VP: Rob Lazarus
**VP:* Nancy S Rush
IT Man: Ravi Patel
Opers Supe: Robert Sherman

D-U-N-S 00-314-7550 IMP/EXP
HORNWOOD INC (NC)
766 Haileys Ferry Rd, Lilesville, NC 28091-6051
Tel (704) 848-4121 *Founded/Ownrshp* 1945, 1986
Sales 47.7MM *EMP* 370
Accts Anderson Smith & Wike Pllc R
SIC 2258 Cloth, warp knit; Cloth, warp knit
Pr: Charles D Horne
**Treas:* Paula Tice
**Ex VP:* Kenneth W Horne Jr
**VP:* Larry W Adams
Off Mgr: Jerry Johnson

D-U-N-S 93-373-2955
HORNY GOAT BREWING CO
1120 S Barclay St, Milwaukee, WI 53204-2419
Tel (414) 383-6900 *Founded/Ownrshp* 2009
Sales 24.5MM^E *EMP* 53^E
SIC 5181 Beer & ale
Prin: Jim Sorenson
Sls Mgr: Richard Sprink

D-U-N-S 00-465-0426
HORONA INC
(*Suby of* ROSEN SWISS HOLDING AG)
14120 Interdrive E, Houston, TX 77032-3324
Tel (281) 442-8282 *Founded/Ownrshp* 2006
Sales 31.1MM^E *EMP* 170
SIC 7389 4731 Pipeline & power line inspection service; Industrial & commercial equipment inspection service; Building inspection service; Freight forwarding
Pr: Hermann Rosen

HOROWITZ
See MANISCHEWITZ CO

D-U-N-S 07-311-1676
HORROCKS ENGINEERS INC
2162 Grove Pkwy Ste 400, Pleasant Grove, UT 84062-6728
Tel (801) 763-5100 *Founded/Ownrshp* 1995
Sales 37.3MM *EMP* 296
Accts Squire & Company Pc Orem Ut
SIC 8711 8713 Consulting engineer; Civil engineering; Surveying services; Consulting engineer; Civil engineering; Surveying services
Ch Bd: Gilbert Horrocks
Pr: Mark Clark
**Pr:* James R Horrocks
**Ex VP:* Rex Harrison
Ex VP: Larry Reasch
IT Man: Mike Dobry
Software D: Cameron Degroff
Mktg Mgr: Sandi Lampshire

D-U-N-S 01-719-4168
HORROCKS FARM MARKET INC
7420 W Saginaw Hwy, Lansing, MI 48917-1104
Tel (517) 323-3782 *Founded/Ownrshp* 1959
Sales 34.4MM^E *EMP* 280
SIC 5431 5261 5992 5947 Fruit & vegetable markets; Lawn & garden supplies; Flowers, fresh; Gifts & novelties; Fruit & vegetable markets; Lawn & garden supplies; Flowers, fresh; Gifts & novelties
Pr: Kirk Horrocks
**Sec:* Jerald D Horrocks
**VP:* Kim Horrocks

D-U-N-S 06-221-5777
HORRY COUNTY SCHOOLS DISTRICT
335 Four Mile Rd, Conway, SC 29526-4506
Tel (843) 488-6700 *Founded/Ownrshp* 1952
Sales 273.8MM^E *EMP* 5,000
Accts Mcgregor & Company Llp Colum
SIC 8211 Public elementary & secondary schools; Public elementary & secondary schools
Ofcr: William Latham
Ex Dir: Sandra Cannon
Ex Dir: Donna Gramstad
Ex Dir: Arlene Ray
Ex Dir: Melissa Schamel
Ex Dir: Denise Vereen
Off Mgr: Katie Bomyea
IT Man: David Knight
Pr Dir: Teal Harding
Teacher Pr: Mary Anderson

D-U-N-S 78-210-9532
HORRY COUNTY SOLID WASTE AUTHORITY INC
1886 Highway 90, Conway, SC 29526-7540
Tel (843) 347-1651 *Founded/Ownrshp* 1992
Sales 50.9MM^E *EMP* 110^E
SIC 4953

D-U-N-S 00-978-8811
HORRY TELEPHONE COOPERATIVE INC
H T C
3480 Highway 701 N, Conway, SC 29526-5702
Tel (843) 365-2151 *Founded/Ownrshp* 1952
Sales 177.1MM *EMP* 690
SIC 4813 4841 7382 ; Local & long distance telephone communications; Cable & other pay television services; Security systems services; ; Local & long distance telephone communications; Cable & other pay television services; Security systems services
Ch Bd: Charles Whaoey
**Ch Bd:* Charles Whaley
**CEO:* Mike Hagg
**CFO:* Duane Carlton Lewis Jr
CFO: Oniel Miller
**Treas:* Cynthia Cannon
**VP:* Delain Stevens
Telecom Ex: Nicole Clark
CIO: Sid Blackwelder
DP Exec: Becky Causey
Dir IT: Jim Forbes

D-U-N-S 00-419-5996 IMP
HORSBURGH & SCOTT CO
5114 Hamilton Ave, Cleveland, OH 44114-3985
Tel (216) 432-5858 *Founded/Ownrshp* 2007
Sales 80.4MM^E *EMP* 200
SIC 3566 Gears, power transmission, except automotive; Speed changers (power transmission equipment), except auto; Gears, power transmission, except automotive; Speed changers (power transmission equipment), except auto
Pr: Christopher Kete
Pr: Gary Thomas
**CFO:* Mike Brown
VP: Robert Ciszak
VP: Ken Lonsberry
VP: Dean McClelland
Sls Dir: Steve Lyncha
Sls Dir: Ryan Milosh
Mktg Mgr: Gary Santavicca
Manager: Eric Chandler
Sls Mgr: Richard Cronin

HORSE & RIDER
See ACTION INC

D-U-N-S 60-907-4703 IMP/EXP
■ **HORSEHEAD CORP**
(*Suby of* HORSEHEAD HOLDING CORP) ★
4955 Steubenville Pike, Pittsburgh, PA 15205-9604
Tel (724) 774-1020 *Founded/Ownrshp* 2004
Sales 288.0MM^E *EMP* 838
SIC 3339 3629 Zinc smelting (primary), including zinc residue; Mercury arc rectifiers (electrical apparatus); Zinc smelting (primary), including zinc residue; Mercury arc rectifiers (electrical apparatus)
Pr: James Hensler
**Sr VP:* Greg Belland
**VP:* Ali Alavi
VP: William Flatley
VP: Richard Krablin
**VP:* Robert Scherich
VP Opers: Bob Elwell

D-U-N-S 80-708-0077
▲ **HORSEHEAD HOLDING CORP**
4955 Steubenville Pike, Pittsburgh, PA 15205-9604
Tel (724) 774-1020 *Founded/Ownrshp* 2003
Sales 453.9MM *EMP* 747
Tkr Sym ZINC *Exch* NGS
SIC 3339 Primary nonferrous metals; Zinc refining (primary), including slabs & dust; Zinc smelting (primary), including zinc residue; Nickel refining (primary); Primary nonferrous metals; Zinc refining (primary), including slabs & dust; Zinc smelting (primary), including zinc residue; Nickel refining (primary)
Ch Bd: James M Hensler
CFO: Robert D Scherich
VP: Ali Alavi
VP: Timothy Basilone
VP: Thomas E Janck
VP: Gary R Whitaker
VP Mfg: Lee Burkett
VP Sls: James A Totera

D-U-N-S 19-520-4581
HORSEHEAD RESOURCE DEVELOPMENT CO INC
3010 Westchester Ave, Purchase, NY 10577-2535
Tel (865) 742-0329 *Founded/Ownrshp* 2002
Sales 41.5MM^E *EMP* 405
SIC 4953 3589 2951 Hazardous waste collection & disposal; Sewage & water treatment equipment; Paving mixtures
Pr: William M Quirk
**Ch Bd:* William E Flaherty
COO: Robert Sunderman
Ex VP: William A Smelas
Sr VP: Peter W Nelson
VP: Ronald Statile

D-U-N-S 07-369-0489
HORSEHEADS CENTRAL SCHOOL DISTRICT (INC)
1 Raider Ln, Horseheads, NY 14845-2344
Tel (607) 739-5601 *Founded/Ownrshp* 1950
Sales 71.5MM *EMP* 700
Accts Bonadio & Co Llp Pittsford
SIC 8211 Public elementary & secondary schools; Public elementary & secondary schools
Treas: Melissa Yearick
Dir IT: Matt Middlebrook

D-U-N-S 07-692-6211
HORSESHOE BAY RESORT & CONFERENCE CENTER
APPLE
(*Suby of* HORSESHOE BAY RESORT INC) ★
200 Hi Cir N, Horseshoe Bay, TX 78657-5824
Tel (830) 598-2511 *Founded/Ownrshp* 1978
Sales 17.4MM^E *EMP* 399
SIC 7997 Country club, membership; Country club, membership
Ch Bd: Douglas Jaffe
**Pr:* Ron Mitchell
Off Mgr: Phillip Hill
Dir IT: David Olson

D-U-N-S 01-266-4181
HORSESHOE BAY RESORT INC
200 Hi Cir N, Horseshoe Bay, TX 78657-5824
Tel (830) 598-2511 *Founded/Ownrshp* 1970, 1996
Sales 35.7MM^E *EMP* 400
SIC 7997 Country club, membership; Country club, membership
CEO: Morris D Jaffe Jr
**Pr:* Ron L Mitchell
Dir IT: Lyle Worthington
IT Man: Cindy Iwasiuk
IT Man: Darnell Mills

HORSESHOE BOSSIER CITY
See HORSESHOE ENTERTAINMENT

HORSESHOE CASINO HOTEL
See CAESARS RIVERBOAT CASINO LLC

D-U-N-S 83-145-7395
HORSESHOE CONSTRUCTION INC
2309 S Battleground Rd, La Porte, TX 77571-9475
Tel (281) 478-5477 *Founded/Ownrshp* 1992
Sales 24.8MM^E *EMP* 111
SIC 1623 Sewer line construction; Water main construction; Sewer line construction; Water main construction
Pr: James R Holt
**VP:* Jesse R Holt

D-U-N-S 82-524-8073
■ **HORSESHOE ENTERTAINMENT**
HORSESHOE BOSSIER CITY
(*Suby of* CAESARS ENTERTAINMENT CORP) ★
711 Horseshoe Blvd, Bossier City, LA 71111-4472
Tel (318) 742-0711 *Founded/Ownrshp* 2004
Sales 79.5MM^E *EMP* 2,532
SIC 7011 Casino hotel; Casino hotel
Genl Pt: Harriahs Ent
CFO: David Eisendrath
VP: Tim Compton
VP: Shawn Matthews
Exec: Albert Washington
Dir Risk M: Tom Kokandy
IT Man: Jamie Fretwell
Secur Mgr: Greg Jackson
Mktg Dir: Scott Harris

D-U-N-S 84-313-6821 IMP
■ **HORSESHOE HAMMOND LLC**
(*Suby of* CAESARS ENTERTAINMENT CORP) ★
777 Casino Center Dr, Hammond, IN 46320-1003
Tel (866) 711-7463 *Founded/Ownrshp* 1992
Sales 53.7MM^E *EMP* 1,700
SIC 7999 5947 5812 Gambling establishment; Gift, novelty & souvenir shop; Eating places; Gambling establishment; Gift, novelty & souvenir shop; Eating places
**Pr:* Gary Loveman
Sr VP: Kevin Kline
**VP:* Thomas Lambrecht

HORSEY FAMILY, THE
See DAVID G HORSEY & SONS INC

D-U-N-S 07-146-5215
■ **HORSHAM CLINIC INC**
(*Suby of* UNIVERSAL HEALTH SERVICES INC) ★
722 E Butler Pike, Ambler, PA 19002-2310
Tel (215) 643-7800 *Founded/Ownrshp* 1996
Sales 38.4MM^E *EMP* 250
SIC 8063 Psychiatric hospitals; Psychiatric hospitals
CEO: Phyllis Weisfield
Pr: Ron Fincher
CFO: Robert Schebett
Dir Risk M: Peg Mocharnuk
Doctor: Syed Ali
Doctor: James Congdon
Nrsg Dir: Robert Kovar
HC Dir: Melissa Santarelli

D-U-N-S 61-281-0903
HORST & SON INC
120 N Pointe Blvd Ste 101, Lancaster, PA 17601-4130
Tel (717) 560-9095 *Founded/Ownrshp* 1988
Sales 30.0MM *EMP* 25
SIC 1521 Single-family housing construction; Single-family housing construction
Pr: Gerald Horst

D-U-N-S 01-486-2239
HORST CONSTRUCTION CO INC
HORST MASONRY
(*Suby of* HORST GROUP INC) ★
320 Granite Run Dr, Lancaster, PA 17601-6806
Tel (717) 581-9900 *Founded/Ownrshp* 1979
Sales 53.7MM^E *EMP* 150
SIC 1542 1541 1522 1741 1721 Commercial & office building, new construction; Industrial buildings, new construction; Multi-family dwelling construction; Masonry & other stonework; Painting & paper hanging; Commercial & office building, new construction; Industrial buildings, new construction; Multi-family dwelling construction; Masonry & other stonework; Painting & paper hanging
Pr: Harry F Scheid II
**Sec:* David C King
**Sec:* John Rose
**Sr VP:* John Kerchener
VP: Thomas M Chervanick
**VP:* Kenneth J Fetterolf
VP: Abram S Horst
**Prin:* Roger Josephian

*Prin: Beth Mack
Sls Dir: Terry Kile

D-U-N-S 09-873-1318
HORST GROUP INC
320 Granite Run Dr, Lancaster, PA 17601-6806
Tel (717) 560-1919 Founded/Ownrshp 1979
Sales 139.5MM^E EMP 360
SIC 1542 1541 6531 Commercial & office building, new construction; Industrial buildings, new construction; Real estate agents & managers; Commercial & office building, new construction; Industrial buildings, new construction; Real estate agents & managers
Pr: Randall L Horst
*VP: Richard A Watson Jr
Mng Dir: Shirlee Barlow

HORST MASONRY
See HORST CONSTRUCTION CO INC

HORTA CRAFT DIVISION
See LANSING MPS INC

HORTICA
See FLORISTS MUTUAL INSURANCE CO

D-U-N-S 03-034-3689 IMP/EXP
HORTIFRUT IMPORTS INC
(Suby of HORTIFRUT S.A.)
9450 Corkscrew Palms Cir, Estero, FL 33928-6422
Tel (239) 552-4453 Founded/Ownrshp 2010
Sales 123.4MM EMP 35^E
Accts Davidson & Nick Cpas Naples
SIC 5148 Fruits, fresh; Fruits, fresh
Ch: Victor Moller
*Pr: Gonzalo Canessa
*VP: Aribel Aguirre-Beck
VP: Aribel Beck

HORTON EMERGENCY VEHICLES
See HALCORE GROUP INC

D-U-N-S 02-406-4040 IMP
HORTON FRUIT CO INC (KY)
4701 Jennings Ln, Louisville, KY 40218-2967
Tel (502) 969-1371 Founded/Ownrshp 1940
Sales 85.7MM^E EMP 175
SIC 5148 Fruits, fresh; Vegetables, fresh; Fruits, fresh; Vegetables, fresh
Pr: Albert C Horton
*Treas: Steve Edelen
VP: Bill Benoit
*VP: William R Benoit
Exec: Norma Wood
Plnt Mgr: John Belcher

D-U-N-S 08-587-2497
HORTON GROUP INC
HORTON INSURANCE AGENCY
10320 Orland Pkwy, Orland Park, IL 60467-5658
Tel (708) 845-3000 Founded/Ownrshp 1971
Sales NA EMP 350
SIC 6411 6331 6321 6311 Insurance agents, brokers & service; Fire, marine & casualty insurance; Accident & health insurance; Life insurance; Insurance agents, brokers & service; Fire, marine & casualty insurance; Accident & health insurance; Life insurance
Pr: Steven J Topel
*Pr: Glenn M Horton
Pr: Rob McIntyre
*COO: George Daly
*CFO: Jim Farmer
CFO: Tim Scott
Ex VP: Rae Beaudry
Sr VP: Bob Dechene
Sr VP: Poppie Frank
Sr VP: Fred Garfield
Sr VP: Luis Paz
Sr VP: Paul Shaheen
Sr VP: Michael Wojcik
Sr VP: Edward Young
VP: Christiane Bouret
VP: Gary Fitzgerald
VP: Doug Henderson
VP: Patrick Johnson
VP: Rick Klein
VP: Dan Kline
VP: Steve Mannos

D-U-N-S 05-101-0973 EXP
HORTON HOMES INC
(Suby of HORTON INDUSTRIES INC) ★
101 Industrial Blvd, Eatonton, GA 31024-7254
Tel (706) 485-8506 Founded/Ownrshp 1970
Sales 54.8MM^E EMP 200^E
SIC 2451 1521 2452 Mobile homes, except recreational; Single-family housing construction; Prefabricated wood buildings; Mobile homes, except recreational; Single-family housing construction; Prefabricated wood buildings
Pr: N Dudley Horton Jr
*CFO: Steve M Sinclair
Treas: Maude M Horton
*Sec: Maude H Hicks
Ex VP: William Weeks
*VP: R W Hicks
VP: Helen N Horto
Genl Mgr: Frank Thompson
Dir IT: Dudley Horton
Sls Mgr: Dan Haley
Board of Directors: N D Horton Sr

D-U-N-S 15-444-7341 IMP
HORTON INC
(Suby of HORTON INC) ★
10840 423rd Ave, Britton, SD 57430-5649
Tel (605) 448-2244 Founded/Ownrshp 1971
Sales 111.0M^E EMP 300
SIC 5084 Engines & parts, air-cooled; Engines & parts, air-cooled
Ch Bd: Hugh K Schilling Sr
*CEO: G Henk Touw
VP: Tom Nelson
Netwrk Mgr: Laurel Behnke
Software D: Steven Henricks
Mfg Dir: Jim Boyko
QI Cn Mgr: Adrian Heitmann

D-U-N-S 62-322-3245
HORTON INC
2565 Walnut St, Saint Paul, MN 55113-2522
Tel (651) 361-6400 Founded/Ownrshp 1990
Sales 203.6M EMP 550
SIC 3714 3568 Clutches, motor vehicle; Clutches, except vehicular; Clutches, motor vehicle; Clutches, except vehicular
CEO: G Henk Touw
Sr VP: Doug Bassinger
VP: Rosalyn Fineran
VP: Nels Johnson
VP: Humberto Monesi
VP: Steve Wardleworth
Area Mgr: Tony Libby
Telecom Ex: Laurel Behnke
Dir IT: Rich Johnson
IT Man: Wayne Johnson
IT Man: Kyle Trenberth

D-U-N-S 15-336-9228
HORTON INDUSTRIES INC
101 Industrial Blvd, Eatonton, GA 31024-7254
Tel (706) 485-8506 Founded/Ownrshp 1984
Sales 202.5MM^E EMP 1,481^E
SIC 2451 5271 Mobile homes; Mobile homes; Mobile homes; Mobile homes
Pr: N Dudley Horton Jr
*Sec: Maude H Hicks
*VP: Steve Sinclair
Sls Mgr: Dan Haley

HORTON INSURANCE AGENCY
See HORTON GROUP INC

D-U-N-S 04-894-5005
HORTON VANS INC (GA)
(Suby of HORTON INDUSTRIES INC) ★
130 Coleman Dr, Eatonton, GA 31024-6703
Tel (706) 484-2241 Founded/Ownrshp 1998
Sales 119.1MM^E EMP 1,450
SIC 3713 3792 Car carrier bodies; Travel trailers & campers; Car carrier bodies; Travel trailers & campers
Pr: N Dudley Horton Jr

D-U-N-S 01-861-4842
HORTONVILLE AREA SCHOOL DISTRICT
246 N Olk St, Hortonville, WI 54944-9433
Tel (920) 779-7900 Founded/Ownrshp 1906
Sales 28.5MM^E EMP 452
SIC 8211 Public elementary & secondary schools; School board; Public elementary & secondary schools; School board
Ofcr: Brian Bahr
Prin: Sharon Becker
Prin: John Brattlund
Prin: Bruce A Carew
Prin: Laurie Hintzmann
*Prin: Bob McIntosh
Prin: Larry Sikowski
Dir Sec: Andy Koloso
Dir IT: Scott Colantonio
HC Dir: Sandy Schulz

D-U-N-S 96-903-9846
HORTONWORKS INC
5470 Great America Pkwy, Santa Clara, CA 95054-3644
Tel (408) 916-4121 Founded/Ownrshp 2011
Sales 46.0MM EMP 601
Tkr Sym HDP Exch NGS
SIC 7372 Custom computer programming services; Prepackaged software
Ch Bd: Robert Bearden
Pr: Herbert Cunitz
Pr: Steven Dean
Pr: Ferguson Mitch
CFO: Scott Davidson
Ofcr: ARI Zilka
VP: Shaun Connolly
VP: Mark Ledbetter
VP: Jeff Miller
VP: Arun Murthy
VP: Bob Page
VP: Scott Reasoner
VP: Ulf Sandberg
Board of Directors: Peter Fenton, Martin Fink, Kevin Klausmeyer, Jay Rossiter, Michelangelo Volpi

D-U-N-S 82-943-3841
HORVE CONTRACTORS INC
330 W Marion Ave, Forsyth, IL 62535-1064
Tel (217) 875-1362 Founded/Ownrshp 2003
Sales 50.0MM EMP 30
SIC 1542 Nonresidential construction; Nonresidential construction
Pr: Steve R Horve

D-U-N-S 00-512-8871 IMP
HORWEEN LEATHER CO
2015 N Elston Ave, Chicago, IL 60614-3943
Tel (773) 772-2026 Founded/Ownrshp 1905
Sales 32.7MM^E EMP 175
SIC 3111 Hides: tanning, currying & finishing; Hides: tanning, currying & finishing
Pr: Arnold Horween Jr
*Sec: Thomas Culliton
*Ex VP: Arnold Horween III
*VP: John Culliton
VP Prd: Christopher Koelblinger

D-U-N-S 06-403-5819 EXP
HORWITH TRUCKS INC
1449 Nor Bath Blvd, Northampton, PA 18067-9700
Tel (610) 261-2220 Founded/Ownrshp 1960
Sales 60.8MM EMP 130
Accts Fegley & Associates Pc Ply
SIC 5511 4213 7699 Trucks, tractors & trailers: new & used; Trucking, except local; Industrial truck repair; Trucks, tractors & trailers: new & used; Trucking, except local; Industrial truck repair
Pr: Regina Grim
CFO: Frank Horwith
*VP: Sheila Horwith
Genl Mgr: Adam Horwith
IT Man: K A Bedics

D-U-N-S 05-761-3341
HORWITZ INC
NSI
4401 Quebec Ave N Ste B, New Hope, MN 55428-4980
Tel (763) 533-1900 Founded/Ownrshp 1983
Sales 41.3MM^E EMP 110
SIC 1711 Plumbing contractors; Heating & air conditioning contractors; Process piping contractor; Mechanical contractor; Plumbing contractors; Heating & air conditioning contractors; Process piping contractor; Mechanical contractor
CEO: William McKoskey
*VP: Joe O'Shaughnessy
Off Mgr: Mary Pundt

D-U-N-S 80-143-3314
HORZION CASINO RESORT LAKE TAHOE
FOOD AND BEVERAGE
Hwy 50, Stateline, NV 89449
Tel (775) 588-6211 Founded/Ownrshp 2007
Sales 2.3MM^E EMP 300
SIC 7011 Resort hotel; Resort hotel
Genl Mgr: Wendi Elvin

HOS
See HORNBECK OFFSHORE SERVICES LLC

D-U-N-S 00-283-6013
HOS BROTHERS CONSTRUCTION INC
7733 W Bostian Rd, Woodinville, WA 98072-9787
Tel (425) 481-5569 Founded/Ownrshp 1955, 1982
Sales 86.4MM^E EMP 400
SIC 1611 1629 Grading; Earthmoving contractor; Grading; Earthmoving contractor
Pr: John Caunt
*VP: Branston J Weyer
Sfty Dirs: Kate Wicks
Opers Mgr: Jim Soushek
Snr Mgr: Shannan Cambern
Snr Mgr: Rob Williams

D-U-N-S 08-987-6825 IMP
HOSE & FITTINGS ETC INC (CA)
1811 Enterprise Blvd, West Sacramento, CA 95691-3423
Tel (916) 372-3888 Founded/Ownrshp 1978
Sales 36.7MM^E EMP 65
SIC 5074 Plumbing fittings & supplies
Prin: Edward Dail
*Prin: Linda Dail

D-U-N-S 02-742-3672 IMP/EXP
HOSE MASTER LLC
1233 E 222nd St, Cleveland, OH 44117-1104
Tel (216) 481-2020 Founded/Ownrshp 1982
Sales 53.6MM EMP 305
SIC 3599

D-U-N-S 14-691-9662 IMP/EXP
HOSE OF SOUTH TEXAS INC
4515 Agnes St, Corpus Christi, TX 78405-3323
Tel (361) 884-9335 Founded/Ownrshp 1978
Sales 31.2MM^E EMP 37
SIC 5085 Hose, belting & packing
Pr: Hensley K Batey III
*VP: Craig D Glasson

D-U-N-S 79-169-5885
HOSEA PROJECT MOVERS LLC
3951 Madison Pike, Covington, KY 41017-9437
Tel (859) 356-8900 Founded/Ownrshp 1984
Sales 28.4MM^E EMP 150
SIC 4212 Local trucking, without storage; Local trucking, without storage
VP: Earl Flummer
*VP: David Todd Hosea

D-U-N-S 01-352-7163
HOSELTON CHEVROLET INC
909 Fairport Rd, East Rochester, NY 14445-1991
Tel (585) 419-4349 Founded/Ownrshp 1969
Sales 43.1MM^E EMP 105
SIC 5511 7538 5521 Automobiles, new & used; Pickups, new & used; General automotive repair shops; Used car dealers; Automobiles, new & used; Pickups, new & used; General automotive repair shops; Used car dealers
Ch Bd: David C Hoselton
*Pr: Coralie B Hoselton
*Pr: Nicholas Warto
CFO: Dennis Segrue
*Treas: Neil D Hoselton
VP: John Love
VP: Paul Schmitt
Adm Dir: Martha Matthaidess
Genl Mgr: Mark Broncatello
Genl Mgr: Dave Foringer
*Genl Mgr: Ron Palmer

HOSELTON NISSAN
See NISSAN HOSELTON INC

D-U-N-S 06-436-5802 IMP
HOSHINO (USA) INC
(Suby of HOSHINO GAKKI HANBAI K.K.)
1726 Winchester Rd, Bensalem, PA 19020-4542
Tel (215) 638-4501 Founded/Ownrshp 1972
Sales 32.0MM^E EMP 100^E
SIC 5099 Musical instruments; Musical instruments
Pr: Shogo Hayashi
*Pr: William Reim
*CEO: Yoshihiro Hoshino
CFO: David Dittmer
CFO: Jeff Goldstein
*VP: Yuji Kitazoe
Exec: Diane Murasky
IT Man: Jim Donahue
Natl Sales: Jon Romanowski
Sls&Mrk Ex: Jim Gallagher

D-U-N-S 06-158-6129 IMP/EXP
HOSHIZAKI AMERICA INC
(Suby of HOSHIZAKI ELECTRIC CO.,LTD.)
618 Highway 74 S, Peachtree City, GA 30269-3016
Tel (770) 227-7511 Founded/Ownrshp 1981
Sales 160.6MM^E EMP 550
SIC 3585 5078 Ice making machinery; Ice boxes, industrial; Ice making machines; Ice making machinery; Ice boxes, industrial; Ice making machines
CEO: Tetsuya Yamamoto
Pr: Chris Leader
Sec: Tatsuya Hirano
Sr VP: Carter Davis
VP: Bill Anderson
VP: Greg Cavender
VP: Katsutoshi Matsushima
VP: Bob McFarland
Dist Mgr: Kevin Caudill
Natl Sales: Bret Eldridge
Sls Mgr: Steve Bragg

D-U-N-S 83-108-7270 EXP
HOSHIZAKI USA HOLDINGS INC
(Suby of HOSHIZAKI ELECTRIC CO.,LTD.)
618 Highway 74 S, Peachtree City, GA 30269-3016
Tel (770) 487-2331 Founded/Ownrshp 2006
Sales 83.7MM^E EMP 600^E
SIC 3589 Dishwashing machines, commercial; Dishwashing machines, commercial
Pr: Yukihiko Suzuki
*Pr: Tetsuya Yamamoto
*CFO: William C Anderson Jr
Dist Mgr: Robert Marsden

D-U-N-S 02-919-9858 IMP
HOSKIN & MUIR INC
CARDINAL SHOWER ENCLOSURES
6611 Preston Ave Ste C, Livermore, CA 94551-5108
Tel (925) 373-1135 Founded/Ownrshp 1972
Sales 78.0MM^E EMP 240
SIC 5031 Molding, all materials; Molding, all materials
Pr: Don Ross
*VP: Mikel Kinser

D-U-N-S 12-151-5209
HOSLER MECHANICAL INC
PROGRESSIVE MECHANICAL
10800 Galaxie Ave, Ferndale, MI 48220-2132
Tel (248) 399-4200 Founded/Ownrshp 2006
Sales 28.0MM^E EMP 100
SIC 1623 Pipe laying construction
Pr: Randy E Hosler
VP: Charles J Hosler
Snr Mgr: Steve Hammond

D-U-N-S 78-032-8402 IMP
HOSLEY INTERNATIONAL INC
6750 Daniel Burnham Dr, Portage, IN 46368-1694
Tel (708) 758-1000 Founded/Ownrshp 1984
Sales 22.0MM EMP 60
SIC 5023 Home furnishings
Ch: Piush Kumar
CFO: Pankaj Dave
VP: Khalid Muhammad
Ex Dir: Tina Hummel
DP Exec: Sean Walbran
IT Man: Paul Knutsen
Sls&Mrk Ex: Don Hunt

D-U-N-S 05-744-2725 IMP
HOSMER-DORRANCE CORP
(Suby of FILLAUER INC) ★
2710 Amnicola Hwy, Chattanooga, TN 37406-3603
Tel (408) 379-5151 Founded/Ownrshp 1996
Sales 30.3MM^E EMP 177
SIC 3842 Prosthetic appliances; Cotton & cotton applicators; Prosthetic appliances; Cotton & cotton applicators
Pr: Karl Hovland
*VP: Fran Jenkins
*VP: Richard Platt
VP: Fran Varner-Jenkins
IT Man: Jerry Stark
VP Opers: Rich Platt
Sls&Mrk Ex: Jackie Bradford

D-U-N-S 14-463-5182 IMP/EXP
HOSOKAWA MICRON INTERNATIONAL INC
HOSOKAWA MICRON POWDER SYSTEMS
(Suby of HOSOKAWA MICRON CORPORATION)
10 Chatham Rd, Summit, NJ 07901-1310
Tel (908) 277-9300 Founded/Ownrshp 1986
Sales 38.0MM^E EMP 1,500
SIC 3559 Chemical machinery & equipment; Plastics working machinery; Chemical machinery & equipment; Plastics working machinery
Pr: Isao Sato
*Ch Bd: Masuo Hosokawa
*CEO: Rob Boorhees
Chf Mktg O: Suha Osylu
*Ex VP: William J Brennan
*Ex VP: Yoshio Hosokawa
Ex VP: Holger Niemeier
*Sr VP: Fumio Sawamura
*VP: Simon H Baker
*VP: Achim Vogel
VP: Rob Voorhes

HOSOKAWA MICRON POWDER SYSTEMS
See HOSOKAWA MICRON INTERNATIONAL INC

D-U-N-S 82-882-8660
HOSPARUS INC
3532 Ephraim Mcdowell Dr, Louisville, KY 40205-3224
Tel (502) 456-6200 Founded/Ownrshp 1976
Sales 54.5MM EMP 400^E
Accts Crowe Horwath Llp Louisville
SIC 8082 Home health care services; Home health care services
Pr: Scott Bartelt
*Pr: Philip Marshell
*Sr VP: David Cook
*Sr VP: Jim Gaffney
*VP: Heather Allen
*VP: Jim Fugitte
*VP: Terri Graham
CIO: David Benefiel
Board of Directors: Rosemary Ray

HOSPECO
See HOSPITAL SPECIALTY CO

D-U-N-S 07-754-2561 IMP
HOSPI-TEL MFG CO
545 N Arlington Ave Ste 7, East Orange, NJ 07017-4005
Tel (973) 678-7100 *Founded/Ownrshp* 1983
Sales 26.5MM^E *EMP* 80
Accts Naskret Selzer & Associates
SIC 5047 Medical & hospital equipment
Pr: David L Freedland
**Ex VP:* Robert Damiano
**VP:* Joseph Freedland

D-U-N-S 62-491-4230
HOSPICE & COMMUNITY CARE
685 Good Dr, Lancaster, PA 17601-2426
Tel (717) 391-2421 *Founded/Ownrshp* 1979
Sales 29.0MM *EMP* 375
Accts Rsel Kuntz Lesher Llp Lancast
SIC 8051 8082 Extended care facility; Home health care services; Extended care facility; Home health care services
Pr: Steven M Knaub
CFO: Krista Hazen
Exec: Bonnie Lopane
IT Man: Michael Link

HOSPICE & HOME CARE BY THE SEA
See HOSPICE BY SEA INC

D-U-N-S 09-922-4891
HOSPICE & PALLIATIVE CARE CENTER
GRIEF CENTER
101 Hospice Ln, Winston Salem, NC 27103-5766
Tel (336) 768-3972 *Founded/Ownrshp* 1981
Sales 30.9MM *EMP* 375
SIC 8082 Home health care services; Home health care services
CEO: Brian Payne
Bd of Dir: Linda Darden
VP: Diane Spaugh
Mng Dir: Mark Corbett
Telecom Ex: Kathy Cecil
Dir IT: Troy Chappell
Mktg Mgr: Ann Gauthreaux
Nrsg Dir: Anita Ford
Pharmcst: Donna Brooks

D-U-N-S 16-294-6693
HOSPICE & PALLIATIVE CARE CHARLOTTE REGION
HOSPICE OF CHARLOTTE
1420 E 7th St, Charlotte, NC 28204-2448
Tel (704) 375-0100 *Founded/Ownrshp* 1978
Sales 42.8MM *EMP* 350
Accts Cherry Bekaert Llp Charlotte
SIC 8082 Home health care services; Home health care services
Pr: Janet Fortner
**Pr:* Peter A Brunnick
CFO: Joaquin Soria
Ex VP: Cindy Tilley
VP: Lisa Hood
Dir IT: Pete Davies
Doctor: Erin Carnes
Doctor: Janet Crook

D-U-N-S 18-563-5757
HOSPICE ADVANTAGE LLC
(*Suby of* CLOVERLEAF PARTNERS) ★
401 Center Ave Ste 130, Bay City, MI 48708-5939
Tel (989) 891-2200 *Founded/Ownrshp* 2015
Sales 55.3MM^E *EMP* 1,900
SIC 8052 8082 Personal care facility; Personal care facility; Home health care services
Pr: Rodney A Hildebrant
CFO: Douglas McGuire
VP: Gaylon Foresee
Ex Dir: Beverly Avello

HOSPICE AUSTIN FOUNDATION
See AUSTIN HOSPICE

D-U-N-S 13-791-5963
HOSPICE BUFFALO INC
225 Como Park Blvd, Cheektowaga, NY 14227-1480
Tel (716) 686-1900 *Founded/Ownrshp* 1974
Sales 37.7MM *EMP* 550
Accts Rsm Mcgladrey Inc Buffalo Ny
SIC 8082 Home health care services; Home health care services
Pr: William E Finn
VP: Patrick Flynn
VP: James Ptak

HOSPICE BUTLER AND WARREN CNTY
See HOSPICE OF DAYTON INC

D-U-N-S 01-227-3710
HOSPICE BY BAY
HOSPICE OF MARIN
17 E Sir Francis Drake Bl, Larkspur, CA 94939-1708
Tel (415) 927-2273 *Founded/Ownrshp* 1975
Sales 41.0MM *EMP* 265
Accts Bunker & Company Llp San Rafa
SIC 8082 Home health care services; Home health care services
CEO: Kitty Whitaker
**Pr:* Mary Taverna
COO: Mary Whitaker
**CFO:* Denis Viscek
**Ch:* Dennis A Gilardi
**Treas:* Michael R Dailey
**Prin:* Sandra Lew
**Prin:* Kenneth Meislin
Dir IT: Will Jones
Dir IT: David Norris
Dir IT: Dan Wolf
Board of Directors: Linda Simpson, Katherine M Beacock, Stephen A Thal, Michael R Dailey, Mary L Taverna Hospice By, Col Robert V Kane, Jeffrey D Kirshbaum, Robert P Kowal, Kenneth Meislin, William C Metzer Jr MD, Gerald R Peters Esq, Richard S Riede Esq

D-U-N-S 16-110-6596
HOSPICE BY SEA INC
HOSPICE & HOME CARE BY THE SEA
5300 East Ave, West Palm Beach, FL 33407-2387
Tel (561) 395-5031 *Founded/Ownrshp* 1979
Sales 26.7MM *EMP* 600
Accts Crowe Horwath Llp Chicago Il
SIC 8082 8051 Home health care services; Skilled nursing care facilities; Home health care services; Skilled nursing care facilities
Pr: Paula Alderson
Dir Vol: Sue Gallup
**COO:* Gilbert Brown
CFO: Jay Edelson
**CFO:* Jacob Spruit
**Chf Mktg O:* Dr Lenord Hock
Off Mgr: Soledad Starr
Dir IT: Seth Hirsh
Dir IT: Bivek Pathak
Sls Mgr: Tina Dayberry

D-U-N-S 78-064-9596
HOSPICE CARE NETWORK
HOSPICE CARE OF LONG ISLAND
99 Sunnyside Blvd Ste 2, Woodbury, NY 11797-2946
Tel (631) 666-4804 *Founded/Ownrshp* 1988
Sales 51.1MM *EMP* 260
SIC 8082 Home health care services; Home health care services
Ch: Patrick R Edwards
**Pr:* Maureen Hinkleman
CFO: Maureen Hickelman
**Treas:* Richard Tretler
VP: Nan Toelstedt
VP: Kristine Vogt
IT Man: Letizia Cinelli
MIS Mgr: Jeff Mohammad

HOSPICE CARE OF LONG ISLAND
See HOSPICE CARE NETWORK

HOSPICE CARE OF LOUISIANA
See COMMUNITY HOSPICES OF AMERICA INC

D-U-N-S 15-131-4499
HOSPICE CARE OF SOUTHEAST FLORIDA INC
150 S Pine Island Rd # 200, Plantation, FL 33324-2695
Tel (954) 467-7423 *Founded/Ownrshp* 1981
Sales 21.5MM *EMP* 250
SIC 8082 Home health care services; Home health care services
CEO: Susan G Telli
CFO: Barbara Blazer
**CFO:* Kathleen M Palmer
**Treas:* Jose R Pagan
**VP:* Karin Rhodes

D-U-N-S 01-669-7074
HOSPICE COMPASSUS
12 Cadillac Dr Ste 360, Brentwood, TN 37027-5361
Tel (615) 377-7022 *Founded/Ownrshp* 2009
Sales 60.0MM^E *EMP* 1,500^E
SIC 8052 Personal care facility
CEO: Jim Deal
Dir Vol: Alma Clark
Dir Vol: Kendra Edwards
Dir Vol: Dale Willis
**CFO:* Anthony James
VP: Chris Dale
VP: Kerry Massey
VP Sls: Chris Thurlow
Sls Dir: Aimee McCloud

D-U-N-S 01-752-0953
HOSPICE FOUNDATION OF ARKANSAS INC
2200 Fort Roots Dr, North Little Rock, AR 72114-1709
Tel (501) 257-3400 *Founded/Ownrshp* 1992
Sales 28.9MM *EMP* 30
SIC 8051 Skilled nursing care facilities; Skilled nursing care facilities
Ex Dir: Michael Aureli
Off Mgr: Gail Cardwell

HOSPICE HM HLTH OLATHE MED CTR
See OLATHE MEDICAL CENTER INC

D-U-N-S 78-596-4602
HOSPICE HOME CARE INC
HOSPICE HOME CARE OF CONWAY
1501 N University Ave, Little Rock, AR 72207-5242
Tel (501) 221-3338 *Founded/Ownrshp* 1994
Sales 27.1MM^E *EMP* 600
SIC 8082 Home health care services; Home health care services
Pr: Cecilia Troppoli
**Pr:* Michael Tankersley
CFO: David Rector
**Treas:* Peggy Bodeman
Off Mgr: Tracy White
Nrsg Dir: Melissa Keesee

HOSPICE HOME CARE OF CONWAY
See HOSPICE HOME CARE INC

D-U-N-S 00-381-4072
HOSPICE NAPLES INC
1095 Whippoorwill Ln, Naples, FL 34105-3847
Tel (239) 261-4404 *Founded/Ownrshp* 2009
Sales 23.5MM *EMP* 2
SIC 8052 Personal care facility
Pr: Diane Cox
VP: Karen Stevenson
Dir Pat Ac: Rebecca Molina

D-U-N-S 94-634-3886
HOSPICE OF ALAMANCE-CASWELL FOUNDATION INC
HSPCE CARE CNTR ALMNCE-CSWLL
914 Chapel Hill Rd, Burlington, NC 27215-6715
Tel (336) 532-0124 *Founded/Ownrshp* 1982
Sales 21.7MM *EMP* 60
Accts Stout Stuart Mcgowen & King Ll
SIC 8082 8051 Home health care services; Skilled nursing care facilities; Home health care services; Skilled nursing care facilities
**Oper/Dir:* Ralph Cagle

D-U-N-S 92-747-0732
HOSPICE OF ARIZONA LC
(*Suby of* AMERICAN HOSPICE HOLDINGS LLC) ★
19820 N 7th Ave Ste 130, Phoenix, AZ 85027-4743
Tel (602) 678-1313 *Founded/Ownrshp* 2004
Sales 14.8MM^E *EMP* 300
SIC 8059 Nursing home, except skilled & intermediate care facility; Nursing home, except skilled & intermediate care facility

HOSPICE OF THE BIG COUNTRY
See WEST TEXAS REHABILITATION CENTER

D-U-N-S 19-574-6581
HOSPICE OF BLUEGRASS INC
EXTRA CARE
2312 Alexandria Dr, Lexington, KY 40504-3277
Tel (859) 276-5344 *Founded/Ownrshp* 1997
Sales 61.2MM *EMP* 650
Accts Crowehorwath Llp Lexington K
SIC 8082 Home health care services; Home health care services
CEO: Elizabeth Durst Fowler
Dir Vol: Turner West
**Ch Bd:* Laura Boison
Pr: Susan Ware
**CFO:* Carol Ruggles
**Treas:* Jen Shah
**V Ch Bd:* Melba Bjornson
**VP:* Deede Byrne
**VP:* Todd Cote
VP: Ann Prewitt
VP: Janet Snapp

D-U-N-S 19-931-2919
HOSPICE OF CATAWBA VALLEY
PALLACIVE CARE CENTER
3975 Robinson Rd, Newton, NC 28658-9715
Tel (828) 466-0466 *Founded/Ownrshp* 1988
Sales 20.2MM^E *EMP* 100
Accts Mast Evans & Isenhour Llp
SIC 8051 8082 Skilled nursing care facilities; Home health care services; Skilled nursing care facilities; Home health care services
Ex Dir: David Clark

HOSPICE OF CENTRAL GEORGIA
See NAVICENT HEALTH INC

HOSPICE OF CHARLOTTE
See HOSPICE & PALLIATIVE CARE CHARLOTTE REGION

D-U-N-S 61-487-4634
HOSPICE OF CHATTANOOGA INC
4411 Oakwood Dr, Chattanooga, TN 37416-2367
Tel (423) 553-1823 *Founded/Ownrshp* 1981
Sales 27.8MM *EMP* 250^E
Accts Burk Pearlman Nebben & Huggins
SIC 8082 Home health care services; Home health care services
Med Dir: Terry Melvin
Dir Vol: Julie Devlin
**CEO:* Ben Johnston
**CFO:* David Rawiszer
**Chf Mktg O:* Theersa Davis
Sr VP: David Winchester
IT Man: Leif Buckner

D-U-N-S 93-837-2075
HOSPICE OF CHESAPEAKE BEREAVEMENT CENTER
HOMICIDE SPT SVCS OF ANE
90 Ritchie Hwy, Pasadena, MD 21122-4303
Tel (410) 987-2129 *Founded/Ownrshp* 1990
Sales 24.1MM *EMP* 100
SIC 8741 Nursing & personal care facility management; Nursing & personal care facility management
VP: Joyce Gooldy
Exec: Jeffery L McKnight Sr
Pr Mgr: Dana Disborough

D-U-N-S 03-887-0705
HOSPICE OF CHESAPEAKE INC
90 Ritchie Hwy, Pasadena, MD 21122-4303
Tel (443) 837-1554 *Founded/Ownrshp* 1979
Sales 24.1MM *EMP* 94
Accts Mullen Sondberg Wimbish & St
SIC 8082 7363 Home health care services; Medical help service; Home health care services; Medical help service
Pr: Erwin Abrams
**Ch Bd:* John Rhody
COO: Ben Marcantonio
**Treas:* Jeff McKnight
Board of Directors: John Rothamel Jr

D-U-N-S 09-182-5042
HOSPICE OF CINCINNATI INC
(*Suby of* TRIHEALTH INC) ★
4360 Cooper Rd Ste 300, Cincinnati, OH 45242-5636
Tel (513) 891-7700 *Founded/Ownrshp* 1977
Sales 50.1MM *EMP* 500
SIC 8082 8051 Home health care services; Skilled nursing care facilities; Home health care services; Skilled nursing care facilities
Pr: Sandra Lobert
Doctor: James Kahl
Pharmcst: Tom Hadaway
Snr Mgr: Pamela Hart

D-U-N-S 83-018-8934 IMP
HOSPICE OF CITRUS COUNT INC
COMFORT HOME CARE
10 Regina Blvd, Beverly Hills, FL 34465-4085
Tel (352) 527-2020 *Founded/Ownrshp* 1983
Sales 41.1MM *EMP* 123
Accts Moore Stephens Lovelace Pa Cl
SIC 8059 8082 8361 Personal care home, with health care; Home health care services; Visiting nurse service; Children's home; Personal care home, with health care; Home health care services; Visiting nurse service; Children's home
Ex Dir: Cassandra Donovan
**CEO:* Anthony J Palumbo
**COO:* Bonnie Saylor
**CFO:* Ted Dunbar

D-U-N-S 96-989-2467
HOSPICE OF CITRUS COUNTY INC
3264 W Audubon Park Path, Lecanto, FL 34461-8450
Tel (352) 746-6578 *Founded/Ownrshp* 2011
Sales 48.4MM *EMP* 113^E
Accts Moore Stephens Lovelace Pa Mi
SIC 8052 Personal care facility
Prin: Anthony J Palumbo

D-U-N-S 78-541-8591
HOSPICE OF COMFORTER INC
480 W Central Pkwy, Altamonte Springs, FL 32714-2415
Tel (407) 682-0808 *Founded/Ownrshp* 1989
Sales 25.0MM *EMP* 480
Accts Cliftonlarsonallen Llp Orland
SIC 8082 Home health care services; Home health care services
Ch Bd: Terry R Owen
Dir Vol: Susan Brydon
Pr: Bill Avery
**Pr:* Robert Wilson
COO: Dean Handy
Bd of Dir: Peggy Thomas
Bd of Dir: Kim Tuero
Ofcr: Jeff White
Ex VP: Mitchell Mikkonen
VP: Lee Tenaglia
Dir Bus: Sid Soonasra

D-U-N-S 11-289-3680
HOSPICE OF DAYTON INC
HOSPICE BUTLER AND WARREN CNTY
324 Wilmington Ave, Dayton, OH 45420-1890
Tel (937) 256-0371 *Founded/Ownrshp* 2000
Sales 53.2MM *EMP* 500
Accts Clark Schaefer Hackett & Co M
SIC 8082 Home health care services; Home health care services
Pr: Deborah Dailey
**CFO:* Jerry Durst
VP: Vicky Forrest
VP: Kim Vesey
Exec: Amy Wagner
Dir Rx: Rebecca Bledsoe
**Prin:* William H Macbeth
Dir IT: Lisa Balster
Dir IT: Ed Ruff
IT Man: Joe Bledsoe
IT Man: Sandy Rowlison

D-U-N-S 03-989-8978
HOSPICE OF FLORIDA SUNCOAST
SUNCOAST HOSPICE
5771 Roosevelt Blvd # 400, Clearwater, FL 33760-3415
Tel (727) 527-4483 *Founded/Ownrshp* 1977
Sales 87.0MM^E *EMP* 1,400
Accts Crowe Horwath Llp South Bend
SIC 8399 Health systems agency; Health systems agency
Pr: Rafael Sciullo
Dir Vol: Debbie Williams
**CFO:* Anne Hochsprung
**Ch:* Kelli E Hanley Crabb
**Treas:* Charles Whetstone
Trst: Hugh Parker
VP: Lynne Craver
VP: Becky McDonald
VP: Scott Mha
VP: Jane Schafer
Exec: Dee Touhey

D-U-N-S 80-762-9071
HOSPICE OF LAKE & SUMTER INC
2445 Lane Park Rd, Tavares, FL 32778-9605
Tel (352) 343-1341 *Founded/Ownrshp* 2007
Sales 52.2MM *EMP* 21^E
SIC 8059 Nursing & personal care; Nursing & personal care
CEO: Charles Chuck Lee
VP: Donna Loyko

D-U-N-S 78-987-0771
HOSPICE OF LAKE AND SUMTER INC
12300 Lane Park Rd, Tavares, FL 32778
Tel (352) 343-1341 *Founded/Ownrshp* 1984
Sales 58.6MM *EMP* 135
Accts Greenlee Kurras Rice & Brown P
SIC 8069 Specialty hospitals, except psychiatric; Specialty hospitals, except psychiatric
CEO: Patricia Lehotsky
**CFO:* Tom Grimmer
Sr VP: Wayne Bailey
Sr VP: Scott Hindman
VP: Bud Beucher
VP: Carolyn Thomas
Admn Mgr: Michael Metcals

HOSPICE OF MARIN
See HOSPICE BY BAY

D-U-N-S 15-271-5363
HOSPICE OF MARION COUNTY INC
3231 Sw 34th Ave, Ocala, FL 34474-8489
Tel (352) 873-7400 *Founded/Ownrshp* 1983
Sales 32.5MM *EMP* 434
SIC 8082 Home health care services; Home health care services
CEO: Mary Ellen Poe
**COO:* Alice Watts
CFO: Bill Kauffman
**CFO:* Mike Knox
Ofcr: Anne Favre
Dir Bus: Karen Loerzel
Dir IT: Dave Ritter
IT Man: Darrell Poteet
Obsttrcn: Ronald Spencer
Snr Mgr: Mery Lossada

D-U-N-S 00-285-5070
HOSPICE OF METRO DENVER INC
DENVER HOSPICE, THE
501 S Cherry St Ste 700, Denver, CO 80246-1328
Tel (303) 321-2828 *Founded/Ownrshp* 1977
Sales 39.0MM *EMP* 300
Accts Crowe Horwath Llp Chicago Il
SIC 8082 Home health care services; Home health care services
CEO: Tim Bowen
**COO:* Janelle McCallum
**CFO:* Julie Gustafson
**Ch:* John Horan
Bd of Dir: Sarah Dixon
Ex VP: William Bishop

VP: Phillip Heath
VP: Kelly Ipson
VP: Catherine Kendall
**VP:* Brenda Ritter
Dir Soc: Kristen Tucker
Board of Directors: Robin Rich, Lewis Sapiro

D-U-N-S 03-877-7041
HOSPICE OF MICHIGAN INC
HOSPICE SOUTHEASTERN MICHIGAN
400 Mack Ave, Detroit, MI 48201-2136
Tel (313) 578-5000 *Founded/Ownrshp* 1980
Sales 66.0MM *EMP* 500
Accts Crowe Chizek And Company Llc
SIC 8082 Home health care services; Home health care services
CEO: Dottie Deremo
**CFO:* Robert Cahill
Chf Cred: Patrick Miller
VP: Carol Barker
VP: Michael Jasperson
VP: Delphine Tessmar
Genl Mgr: Shirley Haan
Dir IT: Eric Kaplan
Netwrk Eng: Brad Van Horn
Opers Mgr: Deborah Martin
Mktg Dir: Tracey Pierce

D-U-N-S 60-274-6745
HOSPICE OF NORTHWEST OHIO
30000 E River Rd, Perrysburg, OH 43551-3429
Tel (419) 661-4001 *Founded/Ownrshp* 1978
Sales 29.5MM *EMP* 450
Accts William Vaughan Company Maume
SIC 8099 Medical services organization; Medical services organization
Ex Dir: Judy Seibenick
Comm Dir: Judy Lang

D-U-N-S 10-768-7022
HOSPICE OF PALM BEACH COUNTY INC
5300 East Ave, West Palm Beach, FL 33407-2270
Tel (561) 848-5200 *Founded/Ownrshp* 1978
Sales 22.9MM *EMP* 864
Accts Crowe Horwarth Llp South Bend
SIC 8059 Personal care home, with health care; Personal care home, with health care
Pr: David Fielding
**COO:* Randy Prange
**CFO:* Richard Calcote
CFO: Gregory M Kiel
Chf Cred: Jackie Lopez-Devine
VP: Faustino Gonzales
**VP:* Fred Watson
Dir Soc: Lauren Barry
Dir Bus: Bob Burwen
Prgrm Mgr: Kathleen Crum
CIO: Debra Rosamelia

D-U-N-S 18-088-0957
HOSPICE OF RED RIVER VALLEY INC
1701 38th St S Ste 101, Fargo, ND 58103-4499
Tel (701) 356-1500 *Founded/Ownrshp* 1981
Sales 23.3MM *EMP* 30
SIC 8082 Home health care services
Ex Dir: Susan Fuglie

D-U-N-S 83-254-4688
HOSPICE OF SPOKANE
121 S Arthur St, Spokane, WA 99202-2253
Tel (509) 456-0438 *Founded/Ownrshp* 1976
Sales 21.3MM *EMP* 75
Accts Dingus Zarecor & Associates P
SIC 8051 Skilled nursing care facilities; Skilled nursing care facilities
Ex Dir: Gina Drummond
Dir Vol: Dave McDougall
Nurse Mgr: Gayle Podratz
CTO: Steve Olvera

D-U-N-S 80-771-6543
HOSPICE OF TREASURE COAST INC
HEALTH AND PALLIATIVE SERVICES
(*Suby of* HEALTH AND PALLIATIVE SERVICES OF TREASURE COAST INC) ★
5090 Dunn Rd, Fort Pierce, FL 34981-4941
Tel (772) 403-4500 *Founded/Ownrshp* 1981
Sales 46.6MM *EMP* 400
SIC 8082 Home health care services; Home health care services
CEO: Louis P Benson
Ex Dir: Gail Gerntrup
IT Man: Carl Martello

D-U-N-S 14-876-8732
HOSPICE OF VALLEY
1510 E Flower St, Phoenix, AZ 85014-5698
Tel (602) 530-6900 *Founded/Ownrshp* 1977
Sales 83.0MM^E *EMP* 1,600
Accts Ernst & Young Us Llp Phoenix
SIC 8082 Home health care services; Home health care services
CEO: Susan Levine
Dir Vol: Jodie Jacobs
Dir Vol: Joy Pesuti
Dir Vol: Sherry Wachter
Bd of Dir: Judith Mitchell
Bd of Dir: Theresa Reth
**Sr VP:* Gregory K Mayer
**Sr VP:* Debbie Shumway
VP: Carol Crockett
VP: Rita Meiser
Exec: Sabrina Hoffman
Exec: Joy Pefuti
Exec: Jerry Smithson

D-U-N-S 79-181-5194
HOSPICE OF VALLEY INC
5190 Market St, Youngstown, OH 44512-2198
Tel (330) 788-1992 *Founded/Ownrshp* 1979
Sales 22.0MM *EMP* 75
SIC 8069 8322 Specialty hospitals, except psychiatric; Individual & family services

D-U-N-S 17-221-9214
HOSPICE OF WAKE COUNTY INC
250 Hospice Cir, Raleigh, NC 27607-6372
Tel (919) 828-0890 *Founded/Ownrshp* 1979
Sales 27.2MM *EMP* 73
Accts Koonce Wooten & Haywood Llp R
SIC 8082 8322 Home health care services; Individual & family services; Home health care services; Individual & family services
CEO: John Thoma
Pr: Mel Finch
Treas: Gordon Crawford
Sr VP: Glenn Anderson Jr
VP: David Wolf
Ex Dir: David Moye
IT Man: Corey Bossert

D-U-N-S 12-627-3445
HOSPICE OF WASHTENAW II
SAINT JOSEPH MERCY LVNGSTON HO
(*Suby of* CATHOLIC HEALTH EAST) ★
620 Byron Rd, Howell, MI 48843-1002
Tel (517) 545-6000 *Founded/Ownrshp* 1926
Sales 79.5MM^E *EMP* 1^E
SIC 8062 General medical & surgical hospitals
VP: Lauren Smoker
Off Mgr: Joan Lutowski
Cmptr Lab: Joan Lutovsky
Mktg Mgr: Mary Letters
Pathlgst: Dave Sadler
Pathlgst: Matthew J Wasco
Doctor: Marla Mikelait

D-U-N-S 16-749-1489
HOSPICE OF WESTERN RESERVE INC
17876 Saint Clair Ave, Cleveland, OH 44110-2602
Tel (216) 383-2222 *Founded/Ownrshp* 1978
Sales 88.9MM *EMP* 800
Accts Howard Wershbabe & Co Clevela
SIC 8059 Personal care home, with health care; Personal care home, with health care
CEO: William E Finn
V Ch: James L Hambrick
V Ch: James Hambrick
**CEO:* David Simpson
**CFO:* John E Harvan Jr
Treas: Mary Kocurko
VP: William Springer
Dir IT: Todd Benenati
IT Man: Gary Popella
Sls&Mrk Ex: Jane Van Bergen
Pr Mgr: Kimberly Tutolo

D-U-N-S 93-371-5369
HOSPICE PREFERRED CHOICE INC
ASERACARE HOSPICE
(*Suby of* BEVERLY HEALTHCARE) ★
1000 Fianna Way, Fort Smith, AR 72919-9008
Tel (479) 201-2000 *Founded/Ownrshp* 1995
Sales 22.8MM^E *EMP* 800
SIC 8051 Skilled nursing care facilities; Skilled nursing care facilities
Pr: Cindy H Susienka
VP: Jeanne Beckler
Ex Dir: Pennie Potter
VP Sls: Lee Cassell

D-U-N-S 07-931-9016
HOSPICE SOURCE LLC
1200 Commerce Dr Ste 100, Plano, TX 75093-5800
Tel (214) 572-0520 *Founded/Ownrshp* 2014
Sales 30.3MM^E *EMP* 130
SIC 5047 Medical equipment & supplies
CFO: Anthony Rosich
Prin: Kenny W Baker

HOSPICE SOUTHEASTERN MICHIGAN
See HOSPICE OF MICHIGAN INC

HOSPICE TOUCH-TOMAH MEM HOSP
See TOMAH MEMORIAL HOSPITAL INC

D-U-N-S 01-122-3265
HOSPICE TREASURE CHEST
COMMUNITY HOSPICE N E FLORIDA
4266 Sunbeam Rd Ste 100, Jacksonville, FL 32257-2426
Tel (904) 596-6278 *Founded/Ownrshp* 2004
Sales 96.1MM *EMP* 2
SIC 5932 Used merchandise stores; Used merchandise stores

HOSPICECARE
See KANAWHA HOSPICE CARE INC

D-U-N-S 80-863-4351 IMP
■ **HOSPIRA BOULDER INC**
(*Suby of* HOSPIRA INC) ★
4876 Sterling Dr, Boulder, CO 80301-2350
Tel (303) 442-2825 *Founded/Ownrshp* 2003
Sales 37.8MM^E *EMP* 126^E
SIC 5122 Proprietary (patent) medicines
CEO: Mike Ball
Brnch Mgr: Julie Nelson
Mfg Dir: Martin Meyer

D-U-N-S 14-158-8017 IMP/EXP
■ **HOSPIRA INC**
(*Suby of* PFIZER INC) ★
275 N Field Dr, Lake Forest, IL 60045-2510
Tel (224) 212-2000 *Founded/Ownrshp* 2015
Sales 4.4MMM *EMP* 19,000
Tkr Sym HSP *Exch* NYS
SIC 2834 3841 Pharmaceutical preparations; Proprietary drug products; Tablets, pharmaceutical; Diagnostic apparatus, medical; Medical instruments & equipment, blood & bone work; IV transfusion apparatus; Pharmaceutical preparations; Proprietary drug products; Tablets, pharmaceutical; Diagnostic apparatus, medical; Medical instruments & equipment, blood & bone work; IV transfusion apparatus
CEO: F Michael Ball
CFO: Thomas E Werner
Bd of Dir: Karen King
Sr VP: Royce R Bedward
Sr VP: John B Elliot
VP: Henry Weishaar
Dir Bus: Michael Gibbons
Rgnl Mgr: Patti Langley
IT Man: Gary Abbott
IT Man: Floyd Boozer
IT Man: Hector Candelario

HOSPITAL
See GETTYSBURG HEALTH CARE CORP

D-U-N-S 07-142-7447
HOSPITAL & MEDICAL FOUNDATION OF PARIS INC
PARIS COMMUNITY HOSPITAL
721 E Court St, Paris, IL 61944-2460
Tel (217) 465-4141 *Founded/Ownrshp* 1958
Sales 40.1MM^E *EMP* 285
Accts Larsson Woodyard & Henson Llp
SIC 8062 General medical & surgical hospitals; General medical & surgical hospitals
Pr: Randy Simmons
Chf Rad: Bruce Houle
**Ch Bd:* Lisa Ellis
**V Ch:* Nolan Longest
V Ch: Doug Smittkamp
**CEO:* Jeffrey Buckley
**Treas:* Keith Perry
Ofcr: Oliver Smith
VP: Terry Brinkley
VP: Robin Gordon
Dir OR: Kim Vester
Dir Lab: David Galbreath
Dir Rad: Don Held

D-U-N-S 03-052-1249
HOSPITAL ADMINISTRATION DISTRICT 4 (ME)
MAYO REGIONAL HOSPITAL
897 W Main St, Dover Foxcroft, ME 04426-1029
Tel (207) 564-8401 *Founded/Ownrshp* 1978
Sales 42.3MM *EMP* 460
SIC 8062 General medical & surgical hospitals; General medical & surgical hospitals
Pr: Edward J Hannon
COO: Dori Farrenkopf
CFO: Dennis H Allen
**CFO:* Jeff Provenzano
VP: George Barton
Exec: Robert Wright
IT Man: Mike Beane
IT Man: Daniel Forgues
IT Man: Nicole Kane
Mfg Dir: Dennis Roy
Surgeon: Robert Livingston

HOSPITAL AT WESTLAKE MED CTR
See WESTLAKE SURGICAL LP

D-U-N-S 07-247-0842
HOSPITAL AUTHORITY OF BEN HILL COUNTY
DORMINY MEDICAL CENTER
200 Perry House Rd, Fitzgerald, GA 31750-8857
Tel (229) 424-7252 *Founded/Ownrshp* 1948
Sales 65.2MM^E *EMP* 325
Accts Draffin & Tucker Albany Ga
SIC 8062 General medical & surgical hospitals; General medical & surgical hospitals
CEO: Mel Pyne
**CFO:* Paige Wynn
Dir Lab: Suzanne Brown
**Prin:* Warren Manley
CTO: Bruce Shepard
Mktg Dir: Alicia Anderson
Pathlgst: James McDonald

D-U-N-S 06-536-1826
HOSPITAL AUTHORITY OF CANDLER COUNTY INC
CANDLER COUNTY HOSPITAL
400 Cedar St, Metter, GA 30439-3338
Tel (912) 685-5741 *Founded/Ownrshp* 1961
Sales 42.9MM^E *EMP* 180
SIC 8062 8011 General medical & surgical hospitals; Offices & clinics of medical doctors
CEO: Michael Alexanderm
Dir Recs: Rhonda Brown
**CFO:* Danny Moxley
VP: Jim Anderson
Dir OR: Nancy Wrenn
Dir Inf Cn: Teal Jeffers
Dir Risk M: Linda P Whitfield
Dir Lab: Mary Spahos
Dir Rad: Kelly Morris
Dir Rx: Robert R Bowen
Dir Pat Ac: Nicole Brinson

D-U-N-S 07-247-3812
HOSPITAL AUTHORITY OF COLQUITT COUNTY (GA)
COLQUITT REGIONAL MEDICAL CTR
3131 S Main St, Moultrie, GA 31768-6925
Tel (229) 985-3420 *Founded/Ownrshp* 1939
Sales 92.1MM *EMP* 725^E
Accts Draffin & Tucker Llp Cpas A
SIC 8062 General medical & surgical hospitals; General medical & surgical hospitals
Pr: James R Lowry
V Ch: James Jeter
COO: Robert Howe
COO: Lorene Wallace
CFO: Larry Simms
**CFO:* Larry W Sims
Ofcr: James Matney
**VP:* Greg K Johnson
**VP:* Shamb Purohit
VP: Madis Spires
**VP:* Dena Zinker
Dir Lab: Cary Cardwell
Dir Lab: Anthony Moser
Dir Rad: Matthew Paine
Dir Rx: Matthew Clifton
Dir Rx: Wayne Evans

D-U-N-S 19-450-6796
HOSPITAL AUTHORITY OF COLUMBUS GEORGIA
MUSCOGEE MNOR NRSING RHAB CNTR
7150 Manor Rd, Columbus, GA 31907-3110
Tel (706) 561-3218 *Founded/Ownrshp* 1967
Sales 20.9MM *EMP* 375
Accts Mauldin & Jenkins Llc Macon
SIC 8051 Skilled nursing care facilities; Skilled nursing care facilities
**Pr:* Frank Morast III

D-U-N-S 07-247-2798
HOSPITAL AUTHORITY OF EFFINGHAM COUNTY
EFFINGHAM HOSPITAL
459 Ga Highway 119 S, Springfield, GA 31329-3021
Tel (912) 754-6451 *Founded/Ownrshp* 1969
Sales 53.5MM^E *EMP* 432
SIC 8062 General medical & surgical hospitals; General medical & surgical hospitals
CEO: Norma Jean Morgan
Chf Path: Peter White
Chf Rad: Janine Dodds
**CFO:* Ed Brown
CFO: Edward Brown
Dir OR: Patricia Parrish
Dir Case M: Edith Morris
Dir Rad: Nancy Flemming
Dir Rx: Durwin Logan
Dir Sec: Jeff Utley
CIO: Mary Pizzino

D-U-N-S 06-921-1449
HOSPITAL AUTHORITY OF HABERSHAM COUNTY
HABERSHAM COUNTY MEDICAL CTR
541 Hwy 441 N, Demorest, GA 30535
Tel (706) 754-2161 *Founded/Ownrshp* 1952
Sales 44.7MM *EMP* 600
Accts Dixon Hughes Goodman Llp Atl
SIC 8062 8051 General medical & surgical hospitals; Convalescent home with continuous nursing care; General medical & surgical hospitals; Convalescent home with continuous nursing care
Ch: Kenneth David Kerby
**CEO:* Jerry Wise
Ofcr: Evelyn McClain
Dir Lab: Christy Wall
Dir Rx: Allison Bentley
**Prin:* J Michael Shirley
Off Mgr: Regina Carter
Doctor: Brenda Garland

D-U-N-S 10-325-4967
HOSPITAL AUTHORITY OF JEFFERSON COUNTY AND CITY OF LOUISVILLE GEORGIA
JEFFERSON HOSPITAL
1067 Peachtree St, Louisville, GA 30434-1558
Tel (478) 625-7200 *Founded/Ownrshp* 1978
Sales 28.7MM^E *EMP* 200
Accts Draffin & Tucker Llp Cpas A
SIC 8062 General medical & surgical hospitals; General medical & surgical hospitals
CEO: Ray Davis
CFO: Michael Sombar
Dir Lab: Julie Bailey
Ex Dir: James Polhill
CIO: Sabrina Manning
IT Man: Jessica Guy
IT Man: James Heitzenrater
HC Dir: Amanda Smith
Board of Directors: Ted Johnson

HOSPITAL AUTHORITY OF LIBERTY
See LIBERTY REGIONAL MEDICAL CENTER INC

D-U-N-S 08-490-5561
HOSPITAL AUTHORITY OF PUTNAM COUNTY
PUTNAM GENERAL HOSPITAL
101 Greensboro Rd, Eatonton, GA 31024-6054
Tel (706) 485-2711 *Founded/Ownrshp* 1963
Sales 31.5MM^E *EMP* 134
SIC 8062 General medical & surgical hospitals
**CFO:* Brenda Jarrett
Dir OR: Christine Luke
Dir Risk M: Pam Douglas
CIO: Vickie Holder
DP Exec: April Hicks
Dir IT: Steven Kasen
Sfty Dirs: Larry Strange

D-U-N-S 07-587-7076
HOSPITAL AUTHORITY OF VALDOSTA AND LOWNDES COUNTY GEORGIA
SOUTH GEORGIA MEDICAL CENTER
2501 N Patterson St, Valdosta, GA 31602-1735
Tel (229) 333-1000 *Founded/Ownrshp* 1955
Sales 417.1MM^E *EMP* 3,000
SIC 8062 General medical & surgical hospitals; General medical & surgical hospitals
CEO: Randy Sauls
Chf OB: T Hank Moseley
Chf Rad: W Cameron Wright
Dir Recs: Deborah Cooper
V Ch: Cameron Hickman
COO: Andrew Flemer
CFO: Ray Snead
Treas: Paula Carter
Ofcr: Carolyn Blanton
Dir Rad: Teresa Tenery
Dir Rx: Bill Brannen

D-U-N-S 09-363-5527
HOSPITAL AUXILIARY OF MORGAN CITY INC
TECHE REGIONAL MEDICAL CENTER
1125 Marguerite St, Morgan City, LA 70380-1855
Tel (985) 384-2200 *Founded/Ownrshp* 2001
Sales 52.4MM^E *EMP* 350
SIC 8062 General medical & surgical hospitals; General medical & surgical hospitals
Pr: Linda Crappell
**Pr:* Larry Graham
CFO: Michael Mayeux
CFO: Michael Mayeux
**VP:* Mike Mayeux
Dir Inf Cn: Belinda Wilber
Chf Nrs Of: Vanessa Peters
CIO: Cheryl Lipari
Dir QC: Pamela Aud
Pathlgst: Gillian C Redlich
Surgeon: Tammy Clements
Board of Directors: Glenn Carney

D-U-N-S 14-700-2661
HOSPITAL BILLING & COLLECTION SERVICE LTD
HBCS
118 Lukens Dr, New Castle, DE 19720-2727
Tel (302) 552-8000 *Founded/Ownrshp* 1984
Sales 29.6MM *EMP* 382
Accts Grant Thornton Llp Philadelph
SIC 7322 Adjustment bureau, except insurance; Adjustment bureau, except insurance
Pr: Brain J Wasilewski
Pr: Joanne Courtney
Pr: Karen Troiani
VP: Jason Bullock
VP: Eric Reyes
VP: Stephen Wing
Exec: Joanne Countney
**Prin:* Kevin Haggerty
**Prin:* Robert Siensa
Dir IT: Steve Eccleston
Dir IT: Victoria Ostrow

HOSPITAL BUILDING & EQP CO
See HBE CORP

D-U-N-S 12-050-9117
HOSPITAL CAYETANO COLLY TOSTE INC
(*Suby of* DOCTOR SUSONI HEALTH COMMUNITY SERVICES CORP)
San Luis Ave Rr 129, Arecibo, PR 00613
Tel (787) 650-7272 *Founded/Ownrshp* 1996
Sales 57.4MM *EMP* 50
SIC 8062 General medical & surgical hospitals; General medical & surgical hospitals
**Prin:* Homar Perez

D-U-N-S 06-403-0216
HOSPITAL CENTRAL SERVICES COOPERATIVE INC
HCSC-LAUNDRY
2171 28th St Sw, Allentown, PA 18103-7073
Tel (610) 791-2222 *Founded/Ownrshp* 1967
Sales 31.6MM^E *EMP* 800
SIC 7218 7213 Industrial launderers; Linen supply; Industrial launderers; Linen supply
Ch: Thomas Byrnes
**CEO:* Peter J Castagna Jr
**CFO:* Thomas Fenstermacher
**Ex VP:* Timothy Crimmins Sr
**Sr VP:* Janet Busse
**VP:* Mark Angeny
**VP:* Steve Gergar
**VP:* D Kip Kuttner
VP: Mark Smoyer

D-U-N-S 06-856-9953
HOSPITAL CENTRAL SERVICES INC
2171 28th St Sw, Allentown, PA 18103-7093
Tel (610) 791-2222 *Founded/Ownrshp* 1970
Sales 103.4MM *EMP* 1,200
SIC 8741 Management services; Management services
CEO: Peter J Castagna Jr
Pr: J Michael Lee
CFO: Thomas D Fenstermacher
Ex VP: Timothy Crimmins

D-U-N-S 07-168-4559
HOSPITAL COMMITTEE FOR LIVERMORE-PLEASANTON AREAS
VALLEY CARE HEALTH SYSTEM, THE
(*Suby of* STANFORD HEALTH CARE) ★
5555 W Las Positas Blvd, Pleasanton, CA 94588-4000
Tel (925) 847-3000 *Founded/Ownrshp* 2015
Sales 148.4MM^E *EMP* 1,200
SIC 8062 8741 General medical & surgical hospitals; General medical & surgical hospitals; Hospital management
CEO: Scott Gregerson
Chf Rad: Ruby Chang
Mng Pt: Michael Ranahan
COO: Cindy Noonan
CFO: Benjie Loanzon
Bd of Dir: Tom Bramell
Trst: Ryan Chance
VP: Jessica Jordan
VP: Doreen Maples
Exec: Karen Moundsbury
Exec: Magda Ursu
Dir Rx: Karol Matsune
Dir Rx: Dennis Ong

D-U-N-S 85-998-5129
HOSPITAL COMMITTEE FOR LIVERMORE-PLEASANTON AREAS
VALLEYCARE HEALTH SYSTEM
1111 E Stanley Blvd, Livermore, CA 94550-4115
Tel (925) 447-7000 *Founded/Ownrshp* 1994
Sales 269.2MM *EMP* 1,000
SIC 8741 Administrative management; Hospital management; Administrative management; Hospital management
CEO: Marcelina L Feit

D-U-N-S 11-310-4017
HOSPITAL COMUNITARIO BUEN SAMARITANO INC
Carr 2 Avenida Severia, Aguadilla, PR 00605
Tel (787) 819-0800 *Founded/Ownrshp* 2000
Sales 47.5MM *EMP* 450
SIC 8062 General medical & surgical hospitals; General medical & surgical hospitals
Prin: Aurora Nieves
Mtls Mgr: Jessica Rios

HOSPITAL COPORATION OF AMERICA
See HCA INC

D-U-N-S 05-066-8656
■ **HOSPITAL CORP OF AMERICA**
HCA THE HEALTHCARE COMPANY
(*Suby of* HCA INC) ★
1 Park Plz, Nashville, TN 37203-6527
Tel (615) 344-9551 *Founded/Ownrshp* 1989
Sales 136.1MM^E *EMP* 800
Accts Ernst & Young Nashville Tn
SIC 8062 8063 General medical & surgical hospitals; Psychiatric hospitals; General medical & surgical hospitals; Psychiatric hospitals
CEO: R Milton Johnson
**Ch Bd:* Thomas F Frist Jr
**COO:* Jack O Bovender Jr
**Ch:* Richard M Bracken
Sr VP: Thomas H Cato
**Sr VP:* John O Colton
**Sr VP:* Joseph L Di Lorenzo
**Sr VP:* Donald W Fish
Sr VP: Eugene C Fleming
**Sr VP:* Paul J McKnight Jr
Sr VP: Joseph D Moore
Sr VP: Philip R Patton
**VP:* Donald J Israel
Board of Directors: Charles T Harris III, Carl E Reichardt, Frank S Royal, John L Thornton

D-U-N-S 96-296-6081
■ **HOSPITAL CORP OF SMITH AND OVERTON COUNTY**
LIVINGSTON REGIONAL HOSPITAL
(*Suby of* HISTORIC LIFEPOINT HOSPITALS INC) ★
315 Oak St, Livingston, TN 38570-1728
Tel (931) 823-5611 *Founded/Ownrshp* 1999
Sales 33.2MM *EMP* 329
SIC 8062 8361 8011 General medical & surgical hospitals; Rehabilitation center, residential: health care incidental; General & family practice, physician/surgeon; General medical & surgical hospitals; Rehabilitation center, residential: health care incidental; General & family practice, physician/surgeon
CEO: Timothy Mc Gill
Dir Recs: Donna Branham
**CFO:* Joe Ross
Dir Lab: Diane Robbins
Dir Rad: Todd Radford
Off Mgr: Julie Hayes
Mtls Dir: Billy Ledbetter
Doctor: Kenneth D Beaty MD
Doctor: Michael Casal
Doctor: Stephen Chapman
Doctor: Kenneth L Colburn MD
Board of Directors: Billy Ledbetter, Andrea Oliver, Scott Watson, Brad Whitson

D-U-N-S 18-791-3298
■ **HOSPITAL CORP OF UTAH**
LAKEVIEW HOSPITAL
(*Suby of* HCA INC) ★
630 Medical Dr, Bountiful, UT 84010-4908
Tel (801) 299-2200 *Founded/Ownrshp* 1961
Sales 79.0MM^E *EMP* 550
SIC 8062 8099 General medical & surgical hospitals; Medical services organization; General medical & surgical hospitals; Medical services organization
Pr: Samuel N Hazen
Chf Rad: Richard Hartbigsen
**Treas:* David G Anderson
**VP:* John M Franck II
Dir Lab: Gail D Cunningham
Chf Nrs Of: Leisha Sanders
Off Mgr: Laurie Wilson
Mtls Mgr: Margo Smith
Pharmcst: Greg Mendiola
Phys Thrpy: Robert Braun

D-U-N-S 79-542-8551
HOSPITAL COURIERS CORP
MEDICAL COURIERS
7200 S Alton Way Ste A270, Centennial, CO 80112-2249
Tel (303) 663-2498 *Founded/Ownrshp* 2005
Sales 23.6MM^E *EMP* 100
SIC 4119 Ambulance service
Pr: Peter Case
**VP:* Randall Cain

D-U-N-S 18-985-6404
HOSPITAL DAMAS INC
(*Suby of* DAMAS FOUNDATION, INC)
2213 Ponce Byp, Ponce, PR 00717-1313
Tel (787) 840-8686 *Founded/Ownrshp* 1987
Sales 59.8MM^E *EMP* 1,000
SIC 8062 General medical & surgical hospitals
Pr: Mariano McConnie Angel
**VP:* Dr Felix Colon
Dir Rx: Silma Homs

D-U-N-S 07-539-4080
HOSPITAL DANBURY INC (CT)
24 Hospital Ave, Danbury, CT 06810-6077
Tel (203) 739-7000 *Founded/Ownrshp* 1885
Sales 504.4MM *EMP* 3,000
SIC 8062 Hospital, medical school affiliated with residency; Hospital, medical school affiliated with residency
Ch Bd: John M Murphy
**Ch Bd:* James Kennedy
**Ch Bd:* Ervin Shames
**COO:* Michael Daglio
COO: Mike Daglio
CFO: Colleen Scott
**Sr VP:* Moreen O Donahue
**Sr VP:* Matthew A Miller
**Sr VP:* Phyllis F Zappala
Dir Rx: Mark Zonenshine
CIO: Peter Courtay

D-U-N-S 06-244-1480
HOSPITAL DESIGNERS INC
(*Suby of* HBE CORP) ★
11330 Olive Blvd Stop 1, Saint Louis, MO 63141-7149
Tel (314) 993-3324 *Founded/Ownrshp* 1969
Sales 14.9MM^E *EMP* 300
Accts Pricewaterhousecoopers Llp
SIC 8712 Architectural engineering; Architectural engineering
Pr: Frederick S Kummer
VP: Brad Gordon

D-U-N-S 03-013-9547
HOSPITAL DEVELOPMENT CO
ROANE GENERAL HOSPITAL
200 Hospital Dr, Spencer, WV 25276-1050
Tel (304) 927-4444 *Founded/Ownrshp* 1966
Sales 26.9MM *EMP* 275
Accts Arnett Carbis Toothman Llp Ch
SIC 8082 8062 Home health care services; General medical & surgical hospitals; Home health care services; General medical & surgical hospitals
Pr: Doug Bentz
COO: Ann Kindle
VP: Julie Carr
**VP:* Louise Ward
Dir OR: Ramonia Mc Cann
Mktg Dir: Tony Keith
Doctor: Carroll Christiansen
Doctor: Laura Cogar
Doctor: John Harrah MD
Doctor: Dixie Nichols
Pharmcst: Erin Nichols

D-U-N-S 08-485-7309
HOSPITAL DISTRICT 1 OF DICKINSON COUNTY KANSAS (KS)
VILLAGE MANOR
511 Ne 10th St, Abilene, KS 67410-2153
Tel (785) 263-2100 *Founded/Ownrshp* 1921
Sales 28.5MM *EMP* 300
Accts Wendling Noe Nelson & Johnson
SIC 8062 General medical & surgical hospitals; General medical & surgical hospitals
CEO: Mark Miller
COO: Bob Brazil
**CFO:* Elgin Glanzer
Dir Rx: Lisa Wright
QA Dir: Paula Dinkel
Opers Mgr: Wade Needham
Mktg Dir: Ann Brussow
Nrsg Dir: Patricia Berns

HOSPITAL DR PILA
See FUNDACION DR MANUEL DE LA PILA IGLESIAS INC

D-U-N-S 09-035-5280
HOSPITAL DR SUSONI INC
(*Suby of* METRO PAVIA HEALTH SYSTEM)
55 Calle Palma, Arecibo, PR 00612-4526
Tel (787) 650-1030 *Founded/Ownrshp* 1911, 2004
Sales 48.0MM *EMP* 450
SIC 8062 General medical & surgical hospitals; General medical & surgical hospitals
Prin: Eduardo Artau
VP Admn: Bibin Solidan

D-U-N-S 10-797-4540
HOSPITAL ESPANOL AUXILIO MUTUO DE PUERTO RICO INC
SOCIEDAD ESPANOLA DE AUXILIO M
(*Suby of* SOCIEDAD ESPAOLA DE AUXILIO MUTUO Y BENEFICENCIA DE PUERTO RICO) ★
Ave Ponce De Leon, San Juan, PR 00918-1000
Tel (787) 758-2000 *Founded/Ownrshp* 1992
Sales NA *EMP* 2,000
Accts Fpv & Galindez Cpas Psc San J
SIC 6324 Hospital & medical service plans
Pr: Enrique Fierres
**Pr:* Angel Cocero
**Treas:* Luis Cid
**VP:* Amador Perdido
**VP:* Angel Sanchez
**VP:* Donato Vigil
Prin: Myriam Colon
Dir IT: Edgard Rodriguez

D-U-N-S 07-780-3641
HOSPITAL FOR SICK CHILDREN PEDIATRIC CENTER (DC)
HSC PEDIATRIC CENTER
(*Suby of* H S C FOUNDATION INC) ★
1731 Bunker Hill Rd Ne, Washington, DC 20017-3096
Tel (202) 832-4400 *Founded/Ownrshp* 1883
Sales 47.8MM *EMP* 350
Accts Dixon Hughes Goodman Rockvill
SIC 8069 Children's hospital; Children's hospital
Pr: Thomas W Chapman
Dir Recs: Stephanie Gray
COO: Bruce Goldman
Ex VP: John Mathewson
VP: Rebecca Cully
VP: Nancy Doellgast
VP: Audrey Monsanto
Dir Rx: Carlyle Mark
Off Mgr: Barbara Butler
Dir IT: Eugene Greer
Opers Mgr: Nancy Doelgast

D-U-N-S 08-333-7360
HOSPITAL FOR SPECIAL CARE
(*Suby of* CENTER OF SPECIAL CARE INC) ★
2150 Corbin Ave, New Britain, CT 06053-2298
Tel (860) 827-4924 *Founded/Ownrshp* 1960
Sales 92.2MM *EMP* 25
Accts Blum Shapiro & Company Pc
SIC 8069 Chronic disease hospital; Chronic disease hospital
Pr: Jhon J Votto
Dir Vol: Lyn Robinson
**Pr:* David Crandall
CFO: Lori Whelen
Bd of Dir: Samuel Paul
Sr VP: Felicia Dedominicis
VP: Carl Ficks
VP: Vicki Golab
VP: Stan Jankowski
VP: George Olt
Dir Risk M: Donna Reinholdt
Dir Lab: Jill Perrone

HOSPITAL FOR SPECIAL SURGERY
See NEW YORK SOCIETY RELIEF RUPT CRIPPLD

D-U-N-S 07-998-8047
HOSPITAL FOR SPECIAL SURGERY LLC
ONECORE HEALTH
1044 Sw 44th St Ste 350, Oklahoma City, OK 73109-3625
Tel (405) 631-3085 *Founded/Ownrshp* 2015
Sales 25.0MM *EMP* 70
SIC 8062 8099 General medical & surgical hospitals; Childbirth preparation clinic
CEO: Steve Hockert

HOSPITAL FORMS & SYSTEMS
See HFS HOLDING CORP

D-U-N-S 15-541-8908 IMP
■ **HOSPITAL GROUP OF NEW JERSEY INC**
UHS
(*Suby of* UNIVERSAL HEALTH SERVICES INC) ★
650 Rancocas Rd, Westampton, NJ 08060-5613
Tel (609) 518-2100 *Founded/Ownrshp* 1983
Sales 19.7MM^E *EMP* 330^E
SIC 8063 Psychiatric hospitals; Psychiatric hospitals
CEO: Craig Hilton
**CFO:* Art Randell
Dir Soc: Diane Rottcamp
Dir Rx: Scott Bell
Dir Opers: Karen Irwin
Mktg Dir: Brian Levin
Psych: Ann Marie Albert
Surgeon: Christopher J Wilbur

HOSPITAL HOME HEALTH
See CRITTENDEN HOSPITAL ASSOCIATION INC

D-U-N-S 09-511-1274
HOSPITAL HOUSEKEEPING SYSTEMS INC
811 Barton Springs Rd # 300, Austin, TX 78704-8702
Tel (512) 478-1888 *Founded/Ownrshp* 1975
Sales 64.7MM^E *EMP* 3,200
SIC 7349 Janitorial service, contract basis; Janitorial service, contract basis
CEO: Tom Spry
**COO:* Roy Thorton
**CFO:* Craig Holmes
VP: Bill Rose

D-U-N-S 10-537-5799
HOSPITAL HOUSEKEEPING SYSTEMS LLC
H H S
216 E 4th St, Austin, TX 78701-3610
Tel (512) 478-1888 *Founded/Ownrshp* 2000
Sales 98.4MM^E *EMP* 4,500
SIC 7349 Cleaning service, industrial or commercial; Cleaning service, industrial or commercial
CEO: Joe Terry
Pr: Bruce Moore
CEO: Ryan Williams
COO: Bobby Floyd
CFO: Jared Hughes
CFO: Gary Link
VP: Scott Alexander
VP: Tommy Gray
VP: Sabrina Jones
VP: Dan Montoya
VP: Boyd Schultz
VP: Jim Sturman
Dir Bus: Amy Fritzer
Dir Bus: Zach Hjornevik

HOSPITAL INTERAMERICANO
See CENTRO MEDICO DEL TURABO INC

D-U-N-S 09-009-6587
HOSPITAL MATILDE BRENES INC
2 St Block J 9 Ext, Bayamon, PR 00959
Tel (787) 622-5420 *Founded/Ownrshp* 1970
Sales 11.7MM^E *EMP* 300
SIC 8062

HOSPITAL METROPOLITA
See METRO PONCE INC

HOSPITAL METROPOLITANO
See METROHEALTH INC

HOSPITAL METROPOLITANO
See METROPADIA HEALTH SYSTEM INC

HOSPITAL METROPOLITANO DR TITO
See YAUCO HEALTHCARE CORP

HOSPITAL MTRPLITANO SAN GERMAN
See SOUTHWEST HEALTH CORP

D-U-N-S 10-771-5146
■ **HOSPITAL OF BARSTOW INC**
BARSTOW COMMUNITY HOSPITAL
(*Suby of* COMMUNITY HEALTH SYSTEMS INC) ★
820 E Mountain View St, Barstow, CA 92311-3004
Tel (760) 256-1761 *Founded/Ownrshp* 1993
Sales 68.3MM^E *EMP* 215
SIC 8062 Hospital, affiliated with AMA residency; Hospital, affiliated with AMA residency
CEO: Sean Fowler
Pr: Michelle Brooks
**Pr:* Michael T Portacci
Dir Sec: Chris Duarte
CIO: Scott Bullock
QA Dir: Diane Sheriff
Nrsg Dir: Julie Pellman
HC Dir: Cindy Mays

D-U-N-S 06-925-5172
HOSPITAL OF CENTRAL CONNECTICUT
(*Suby of* CENTRAL CONNECTICUT HEALTH ALLIANCE INC) ★
100 Grand St, New Britain, CT 06052-2016
Tel (860) 224-5011 *Founded/Ownrshp* 1983
Sales 360.4MM *EMP* 2,500
Accts Saslow Lufkin & Buggy Llp Av
SIC 8062 General medical & surgical hospitals; General medical & surgical hospitals
Pr: Clarence J Silvia
Chf Rad: Sidney Ulreich
**CFO:* Ralph Becker
Ofcr: Sabrin Gregrich
Ofcr: Matteo J Lopreiato
Ofcr: Debra A Muscio
VP: Pat Hamel
VP: Brian A Rogoz
VP: Bridget A Wheeler
Dir Risk M: Linda Tompkin
Dir Lab: Nancy Bienkowski
Dir Lab: Joe Vaccarelli
Dir Rad: Edward Lombardo

D-U-N-S 88-413-0048
■ **HOSPITAL OF FULTON INC**
PARKWAY REGIONAL HOSPITAL
(*Suby of* COMMUNITY HEALTH SYSTEMS INC) ★
1000 Elm St, Fulton, KY 42041-7702
Tel (270) 472-2522 *Founded/Ownrshp* 1999

Sales 20.0MM^E *EMP* 199
SIC 8062 General medical & surgical hospitals; General medical & surgical hospitals
CEO: Rob Calhoun
CFO: Dirk Morgan
Sr VP: Brian Craven
**VP:* Mark Buford
Dir Env Sv: Angela West
Off Mgr: Dick Swader
Phys Thrpy: Tanya Thomas
Board of Directors: Kim Dillingham, Ginna Simpson

D-U-N-S 88-412-8455
■ **HOSPITAL OF LOUISA INC**
THREE RIVERS MEDICAL CENTER
(*Suby of* COMMUNITY HEALTH SYSTEMS INC) ★
2485 Highway 644, Louisa, KY 41230-9242
Tel (606) 638-0508 *Founded/Ownrshp* 1996
Sales 61.0MM^E *EMP* 340
SIC 8062 General medical & surgical hospitals; General medical & surgical hospitals
Pr: Larry Cash
Chf Rad: Donald Lewis
**CFO:* Mike Ackley
Ofcr: Heidi Maynard
Dir OR: Chandra Stroth
Phys Thrpy: Delinda Adkins

D-U-N-S 07-540-6579 IMP
HOSPITAL OF ST RAPHAEL PHYSICIANS IPA II INC
YALE-NEW HAVEN HOSPITAL SAINT
1450 Chapel St, New Haven, CT 06511-4405
Tel (203) 789-3000 *Founded/Ownrshp* 1907
Sales 203.4MM^E *EMP* 3,426
SIC 8062 8011 Hospital, affiliated with AMA residency; Health maintenance organization; Hospital, affiliated with AMA residency; Health maintenance organization
Ch Bd: Sister Barbara Conroy
**Pr:* David Benfer
Ofcr: Nancy Havill
Adm Dir: Linda Pettine
Pathlgst: Irwin Nash
Surgeon: Alfredo Axtmayer
Surgeon: Emilia Genova
Obsttrcn: Ravi Kaza
Obsttrcn: Howard Shaw
Diag Rad: Stefan Mansourian
Diag Rad: Angelo Marino

HOSPITAL ONCOLOGICO ISAAC GONZ
See LIGA PUERTORRIQUENA CONTRA EL CANCER INC

HOSPITAL PAVIA
See FERNANDEZ M PAVIA INC

D-U-N-S 09-017-0705
HOSPITAL PEREA INC
15 Calle Dr Basora N, Mayaguez, PR 00680-4833
Tel (787) 834-0101 *Founded/Ownrshp* 1997
Sales 22.5MM^E *EMP* 400
SIC 8062 General medical & surgical hospitals; General medical & surgical hospitals
Ch Bd: Donald Dizney
**Pr:* James English

D-U-N-S 09-115-5689
HOSPITAL SAN CARLOS INCORPORADO
HOSPITAL SAN CRLOS DE BORROMEO
550 Calle Concepcion Vera, Moca, PR 00676-5005
Tel (787) 877-8000 *Founded/Ownrshp* 1981
Sales 28.3MM *EMP* 423
SIC 8062 General medical & surgical hospitals; General medical & surgical hospitals
Pr: Randy Gonzalez
**Pr:* Richard Monice
**Treas:* Orlando Gonzales
**VP:* Rosie Torres
IT Man: Eva Cordero

HOSPITAL SAN CRISTOBAL
See QUALITY HEALTH SERVICES OF PUERTO RICO INC

HOSPITAL SAN CRLOS DE BORROMEO
See HOSPITAL SAN CARLOS INCORPORADO

HOSPITAL SAN JORGE
See U M C OF PUERTO RICO INC

HOSPITAL SAN JUAN BAUTISTA
See SAN JUAN BAUTISTA MEDICAL CENTER CORP

D-U-N-S 07-313-1773
HOSPITAL SERVICE ASSOCIATION OF NORTHEASTERN PENNSYLVANIA
BLUE CROSS
19 N Main St, Wilkes Barre, PA 18711-0300
Tel (570) 825-5700 *Founded/Ownrshp* 1938
Sales NA *EMP* 958
SIC 6321 Accident & health insurance

D-U-N-S 00-981-5499
HOSPITAL SERVICE DISTRICT 1 INC
WEST JEFFERSON MEDICAL CENTER
1101 Medical Center Blvd, Marrero, LA 70072-3147
Tel (504) 349-1124 *Founded/Ownrshp* 1956
Sales 59.4MM *EMP* 2,000
Accts Bkd Llp Dallas Texas
SIC 8062 General medical & surgical hospitals; General medical & surgical hospitals
CEO: Nancy R Cassagne
COO: Michael Adcock
CFO: Nancy Bassagne
CFO: Madeline Browning
CFO: Nancy Cassagne
Sr VP: Nick Thimis
VP: James Callaghan
VP: Frank Martinez
Dir Surg: Ron Bailey
Dir Lab: Renell Dore
Chf Nrs Of: Anthony J Digerolamo

D-U-N-S 07-789-1851
HOSPITAL SERVICE DISTRICT 1 OF EAST BATON ROUGE PARISH
LANE REGIONAL MEDICAL CENTER
6300 Main St, Zachary, LA 70791-4037
Tel (225) 654-1147 *Founded/Ownrshp* 1957
Sales 102.0MM^E *EMP* 605
SIC 8062 Hospital, affiliated with AMA residency; Hospital, affiliated with AMA residency
CEO: Randalt Olson
V Ch: Robert Williams
**COO:* David Beck
CFO: David Bleck
**CFO:* Michael Zimmerman
Ofcr: Kathy Pearrs
Dir Lab: David Broussard
Dir Lab: Rob Lawrence
Dir Rad: Greg Dickinson
Dir Rx: Johnny W Johnson
Dir IT: Scarlet Collier

D-U-N-S 62-213-8774
HOSPITAL SERVICE DISTRICT 2 OF BEAUREGARD PARISH
BEAUREGARD MEMORIAL HOSPITAL
600 S Pine St, Deridder, LA 70634-4942
Tel (337) 462-7100 *Founded/Ownrshp* 1950
Sales 52.1MM^E *EMP* 350^E
SIC 8062 General medical & surgical hospitals; General medical & surgical hospitals
CEO: Bob Charron
Pr: Bonnie Peterson
COO: Chris Goddard
Treas: Robert Beauregard
VP: Ronald Lafitte
Dir OR: Kie McNabb
Dir Inf Cn: Jo Blankenship
Dir Lab: Elizabeth Lewis
Dir Rad: Amy Amer
**Prin:* Ted Badger
Off Mgr: Denita Moses

D-U-N-S 06-953-6381
HOSPITAL SERVICE DISTRICT 3 LAFOURCHE PARISH (LA)
THIBODAUX REGIONAL MEDICAL CTR
602 N Acadia Rd, Thibodaux, LA 70301-4823
Tel (985) 493-4740 *Founded/Ownrshp* 1967
Sales 162.8MM *EMP* 800
SIC 8062 8051 8082 General medical & surgical hospitals; Skilled nursing care facilities; Home health care services; General medical & surgical hospitals; Skilled nursing care facilities; Home health care services
CEO: Greg Stock
COO: Scott Flowers
CFO: Steven C Gaubert
CFO: Shawn Vincent
Bd of Dir: Jake Giardina
Ofcr: Oliver Bourgeois
Ofcr: Dana Rodrigue
Dir Lab: Anne Guidry
Dir Rx: Monica Sanchez
Off Mgr: Robyn Toups
Nurse Mgr: Ellen Matthews

D-U-N-S 11-742-3277
HOSPITAL SERVICE DISTRICT NO 1
TERREBONNE GENERAL MEDICAL CTR
8166 Main St, Houma, LA 70360-3404
Tel (985) 873-4141 *Founded/Ownrshp* 1954
Sales 210.4MM^E *EMP* 1,400
SIC 8062 General medical & surgical hospitals; General medical & surgical hospitals
Pr: Phyllis L Peoples
Dir Recs: Jada Songy
**Pr:* Phyllis Peoples
VP: Sidney Hutchinson
VP: Teresita McNabb
Exec: Rose Cuneo
Dir Lab: Jacque Blanchard
Dir Lab: Cathy Kohmann
Dir Rad: Michael Muntz
Dir Rx: Cindy Duet
Dir Sec: Dean Marcel

D-U-N-S 92-765-7619
HOSPITAL SERVICE DISTRICT NO 1 OF IBERIA PARISH
IBERIA MEDICAL CENTER
2315 E Main St, New Iberia, LA 70560-4031
Tel (337) 276-5856 *Founded/Ownrshp* 2000
Sales 15.6MM^E *EMP* 500
SIC 8062 General medical & surgical hospitals; General medical & surgical hospitals
Pr: James H Youree

D-U-N-S 07-944-7561
HOSPITAL SERVICE DISTRICT NO 1 OF TANGIPAHOA PARISH
NORTH OAKS HEALTH SYSTEM
15770 Paul Vega Md Dr, Hammond, LA 70403-1475
Tel (985) 230-6934 *Founded/Ownrshp* 1960
Sales 292.7MM *EMP* 1,825
SIC 8062

D-U-N-S 07-976-5582
HOSPITAL SERVICE DISTRICT NO 2 OF LASALLE
LAFALLE GENERAL HOSPITAL
187 Ninth St, Jena, LA 71342-3900
Tel (318) 992-9200 *Founded/Ownrshp* 1966
Sales 24.6MM *EMP* 231
Accts Lester Miller & Wells Cpa A
SIC 8062 General medical & surgical hospitals; General medical & surgical hospitals
CEO: Douglas A Newman
**V Ch Bd:* Harlon Nobles
Mng Ofcr: Matthew Erickson

D-U-N-S 06-973-6544
HOSPITAL SERVICE DISTRICT NUMBER ONE OF PARISH OF LA SALLE
HARDTNER MEDICAL CENTER
1102 N Pine Rd, Olla, LA 71465-4804
Tel (504) 349-1124 *Founded/Ownrshp* 1986
Sales 21.3MM *EMP* 92
SIC 8062 General medical & surgical hospitals; General medical & surgical hospitals
Ch Bd: Lee Richardel
CFO: Paul Mathews
Off Mgr: Elissa Parker
Nrsg Dir: Fran Dick
Pharmcst: Jamie Tubre

D-U-N-S 05-333-6347
HOSPITAL SERVICE DISTRICT OF PARISH OF ST BERNARD STATE OF LA
ST. BERNARD PARISH HOSPITAL
8000 W Judge Perez Dr, Chalmette, LA 70043-1668
Tel (504) 826-9500 *Founded/Ownrshp* 2011
Sales 38.3MM *EMP* 11
SIC 8062 General medical & surgical hospitals
CEO: Wayne J Landry
**Ch Bd:* Jim Difatta
**COO:* Charlie Lindell
CFO: Joseph Kempka
**Sec:* Andrew Sercovich
Dir OR: Samantha Bocage
Dir Lab: Rafat Alkurd
Dir Rad: Ricky Arbuckle
Dir Rx: Kathy Nicolay
Chf Nrs Of: Scott Dassau
Dir Sec: Mark Grelle

HOSPITAL SHARED SERVICES
See HSS INC

D-U-N-S 05-800-6537
HOSPITAL SISTERS HEALTH SYSTEM
4936 Laverna Rd, Springfield, IL 62707-9797
Tel (217) 523-4747 *Founded/Ownrshp* 1978
Sales 166.7MM *EMP* 40^E
Accts Kpmg Llp Columbus Oh
SIC 8082 Home health care services; Home health care services
CEO: Mary Starmann-Perharrison
Chf Rad: Shawn Shekar
**Pr:* Sister J Trstensky
**COO:* Larry Schumacher
CFO: Michael W Cottrell
CFO: Patricia Huettl
CFO: Greg Simia
Treas: James Pawlak
**Sec:* Lisa Rusciolelli
Ofcr: Jay Justice
VP: Leah Busch
VP: Nicole Holst
VP: Peter Mannix
VP: Daniel McCormack
VP: Phil Mears
VP: Mark Novak
VP: Jeff Ogletree
VP: Chris Pensinger
Exec: Frank Mikell
Dir Rad: Steve Sabo
Dir Rx: Michael Murbarger

HOSPITAL SISTERS OF THE THIRD
See ST MARYS HOSPITAL & MEDICAL CENTER

D-U-N-S 83-241-6387 EXP
HOSPITAL SPECIALTY CO
HOSPECO
26301 C Wright Pkwy 200, Richmond Heights, OH 44143
Tel (800) 321-9832 *Founded/Ownrshp* 2011
Sales 85.9MM^E *EMP* 600
SIC 5113 Industrial & personal service paper; Industrial & personal service paper
Pr: Ken Vuylsteke
**CFO:* Patrick Fitzmaurice
VP: Vic Hodges
Sls Dir: Tony Maida
Sls Dir: Robert Stewart

D-U-N-S 06-873-4466
HOSPITAL UNIONTOWN INC
500 W Berkeley St, Uniontown, PA 15401-5596
Tel (724) 430-5000 *Founded/Ownrshp* 1965
Sales 126.9MM *EMP* 1,100^E
Accts Bkd Llp Springfield Mo
SIC 8062 General medical & surgical hospitals; General medical & surgical hospitals
CEO: Steve Handy
Chf Mktg O: Richard Pish
VP: Dan Glover
VP: Don Record
Chf Nrs Of: Rebecca Amberosini
Adm Dir: Elaine Bell
Adm Dir: Richard Hancock
Ex Dir: Donald Eckhart
Dir Sec: Vincent Traynor
CTO: Anthony Dalessio
QA Dir: Lisa Manetta

HOSPITAL UPR
See SERVICIOS MEDICOS UNIVERSITARIOS

HOSPITAL WING
See MEMPHIS MEDICAL CENTER AIR AMBULANCE SERVICE INC

HOSPITAL-NORTH MISS MED CTR
See NORTH MISSISSIPPI HEALTH SERVICES INC

HOSPITAL-NORTH MISSISSIPPI MED
See NORTH MISSISSIPPI MEDICAL CENTER INC

HOSPITALIST SERVICES OF TEXAS
See SCHUMACHER GROUP OF TEXAS THE INC

D-U-N-S 80-804-1045
HOSPITALISTS MANAGEMENT GROUP LLC
COGENT-HMG
4535 Dressler Rd Nw, Canton, OH 44718-2545
Tel (866) 464-7497 *Founded/Ownrshp* 2011
Sales 98.4MM^E *EMP* 2,739
SIC 8741 Hospital management; Hospital management
**CFO:* Susan Brownie
Chf Mktg O: Ronnie Jacobs MD
Chf Mktg O: M F Maida MD
Ofcr: Michael Friedlander MD
Ofcr: Ronald Greeno
Ofcr: Russell L Holman
Ofcr: Julia Wright MD
VP: Andrea Funk
**VP:* David Hess
VP: Elizabeth Yanko

HOSPITALISTS NORTHERN MICHIGAN
See INDIGO SERVICES PLC

D-U-N-S 05-753-3523
HOSPITALITY ASSOCIATES INC
16114 E Ind Ave Ste 200, Spokane Valley, WA 99216
Tel (509) 928-3736 *Founded/Ownrshp* 1978
Sales 21.7MM^E *EMP* 750
SIC 8741 Hotel or motel management; Hotel or motel management
CEO: Terry Wynia
**VP:* Jeff Lyman

D-U-N-S 16-927-0993
HOSPITALITY ASSOCIATES OF LANCASTER LP
LANCASTER HOST RESORT
2300 Lincoln Hwy E, Lancaster, PA 17602-1114
Tel (717) 299-5500 *Founded/Ownrshp* 2005
Sales 35.2MM^E *EMP* 460
SIC 7011 Hotels & motels; Hotels & motels
Genl Pt: Sander Mednick
Genl Mgr: Michelle Weinhold
IT Man: Linda Wilcox
VP Opers: Matt English
Mktg Mgr: Kevin Bergman

D-U-N-S 07-981-2838
HOSPITALITY ENGAGEMENT CORP
WHEEDLE
812 Huron Rd E Ste 322, Cleveland, OH 44115-1123
Tel (844) 943-3353 *Founded/Ownrshp* 2014
Sales 30.0MM *EMP* 4
SIC 7371 Computer software development & applications
CEO: John Weston
Pr: Brian Stein
COO: Evan Cooper

D-U-N-S 83-761-2258
HOSPITALITY ENTERPRISES INC
4220 Howard Ave, New Orleans, LA 70125-1327
Tel (504) 587-1650 *Founded/Ownrshp* 1995
Sales 50.0MM *EMP* 800
SIC 4725 Arrangement of travel tour packages, wholesale; Arrangement of travel tour packages, wholesale
Pr: James E Smith Jr
**Ch Bd:* James Smith Sr
**Treas:* Craig Smtih
VP: Bob Bourg
MIS Dir: Fred Sidhva

D-U-N-S 03-979-9148 IMP
HOSPITALITY FURNISHINGS AND DESIGN INC
HFD
146 Chestnut St, Zelienople, PA 16063-1005
Tel (724) 452-2114 *Founded/Ownrshp* 2001
Sales 31.6MM^E *EMP* 43
SIC 5046 7389 Hotel equipment & supplies; Interior design services
Pr: Robert M Cormier

D-U-N-S 18-651-7157
HOSPITALITY GROUP MANAGEMENT INC
926 2nd St Ne Ste 307, Hickory, NC 28601-3876
Tel (828) 323-1531 *Founded/Ownrshp* 1995
Sales 18.0MM^E *EMP* 350
SIC 7011 Hotel, franchised; Hotel, franchised
Pr: James Tarlton
**Sec:* Barry Whisnant
Ex Dir: Cindy Long

D-U-N-S 00-446-5934
HOSPITALITY INC
HOSPITALITY SUPPLY COMPANY
16011 Sw 42nd Ter, Miami, FL 33185-3801
Tel (888) 539-9330 *Founded/Ownrshp* 2009
Sales 48.0MM *EMP* 56
SIC 5087 Janitors' supplies; Janitors' supplies
VP: Alex F Obando

D-U-N-S 61-136-5479
HOSPITALITY INVESTMENTS LIMITED PARTNERSHIP
3808 N Sullivan Rd # 34, Spokane Valley, WA 99216-1608
Tel (509) 928-3736 *Founded/Ownrshp* 1989
Sales 57.7MM^E *EMP* 1,200
SIC 6799 Real estate investors, except property operators; Real estate investors, except property operators
Genl Pt: Terry Wynia

D-U-N-S 12-557-0569
HOSPITALITY INVESTORS LLC
4257 Haines Rd Ste A, Hermantown, MN 55811-4136
Tel (218) 729-9445 *Founded/Ownrshp* 1997
Sales 27.9MM^E *EMP* 300
SIC 6798 6799 Real estate investment trusts; Investors; Real estate investment trusts; Investors
Ex VP: Ed Miranda

D-U-N-S 78-733-8607
HOSPITALITY MANAGEMENT ADVISORS INC
277 German Oak Dr, Cordova, TN 38018-7221
Tel (901) 755-9501 *Founded/Ownrshp* 1988
Sales 4.4MM *EMP* 900^E
SIC 8741 Hotel or motel management; Hotel or motel management
CEO: Larry F Wright Jr
**COO:* David Martin
**VP:* Brandon T Birkhead

D-U-N-S 00-315-7963 IMP/EXP
HOSPITALITY MINTS LLC
213 Candy Ln, Boone, NC 28607-6713
Tel (828) 264-3045 *Founded/Ownrshp* 1976
Sales 29.2MM^E *EMP* 135
SIC 2064 Candy & other confectionery products; Candy & other confectionery products
Pr: Allen Peterson

**CFO:* Walter Kaudelka
**Ch:* Eric Bacon
VP: Lee Wilkie
VP Opers: Richard Townsend
VP Prd: Forrest Sanders
Sls Dir: Stephanie Engler
Sls Mgr: Chrystine Desmond
Sales Asso: Betty Norris

D-U-N-S 02-246-9448
HOSPITALITY PARKING SERVICES INC
1010 Common St, New Orleans, LA 70112-2401
Tel (312) 919-5711 Founded/Ownrshp 2008
Sales 5.2MM^E EMP 380^E
SIC 7299 Valet parking
CEO: James Maclean

D-U-N-S 36-295-0750
HOSPITALITY PARTNERS LLC
3 Bethesda Metro Ctr M025, Bethesda, MD 20814-6343
Tel (301) 718-6161 Founded/Ownrshp 1986
Sales 33.7MM^E EMP 500
SIC 7011 Hotels; Hotels
Pr: Michael James
Netwrk Mgr: Debbie Reindollar
**VP Opers:* John Vernon
Mktg Dir: Amy Harris

D-U-N-S 07-875-9454
HOSPITALITY PATTON MANAGEMENT LLC
1 Vance Gap Rd, Asheville, NC 28805-1227
Tel (855) 572-8866 Founded/Ownrshp 2007
Sales 31.9MM^E EMP 350
SIC 8741 Hotel or motel management; Hotel or motel management
CEO: William Horton

HOSPITALITY PROFESSIONALS
See HOSPITALITY SERVICES OF HARAHAN

D-U-N-S 92-687-8810
▲ HOSPITALITY PROPERTIES TRUST
255 Washington St Ste 300, Newton, MA 02458-1634
Tel (617) 964-8389 Founded/Ownrshp 1995
Sales 1.7MMM EMP 400
Tkr Sym HPT Exch NYS
SIC 6798 Real estate investment trusts; Real estate investment trusts
Pr: John G Murray
CFO: Mark L Kleifges
Trst: John Harrington
Sr VP: Ethan S Bornstein
VP: Aaron Chamberland
Comm Man: Jennifer Clark
Prin: David Lepore
DP Exec: Richard Hamm
Dir IT: Carlos Flores

D-U-N-S 60-916-7580
HOSPITALITY PURCHASING GROUP INTERNATIONAL LLC
HPG INTERNATIONAL
1600 Riviera Ave Ste 100, Walnut Creek, CA 94596-3567
Tel (925) 949-5706 Founded/Ownrshp 1989
Sales 34.1MM^E EMP 100
SIC 7389 Purchasing service
CEO: Cary T Schirmer
**Pr:* Benjamin O'Connor
Snr PM: Cruz Barrera
Snr PM: Tiffany Caturegli

D-U-N-S 07-973-4139
HOSPITALITY SERVICES OF HARAHAN (LA)
HOSPITALITY PROFESSIONALS
190 Hickory Ave Ste 9, Harahan, LA 70123-4069
Tel (504) 336-4044 Founded/Ownrshp 2004
Sales 30.0MM EMP 132
SIC 8331 Community service employment training program; Job counseling
Pr: Brandin Prevost

D-U-N-S 01-703-4716
HOSPITALITY SERVICES UNLIMITED INC
10450 Nw 41st St Ste 101, Doral, FL 33178-2373
Tel (305) 463-8650 Founded/Ownrshp 1989
Sales 28.8MM EMP 11
SIC 7011 Resort hotel; Resort hotel
Pr: Thomas Tyler
Ofcr: Selma Dala
Genl Mgr: Amy Davis
Off Mgr: Karen Balda

HOSPITALITY SHOP
See KENT COUNTY MEMORIAL HOSPITAL

HOSPITALITY STAFF OF METRO DC
See L C RAMNARAIN

D-U-N-S 10-834-0857
HOSPITALITY STAFFING SOLUTIONS LLC
100 Glenridge Point Pkwy, Atlanta, GA 30342-1442
Tel (770) 612-0054 Founded/Ownrshp 2000
Sales 45.5MM^E EMP 250^E
SIC 7363 Help supply services; Help supply services
CEO: Rick M Holliday
**Pr:* Rick Holliday
**Pr:* Katheryne King
**COO:* Keith M Lieberman
**CFO:* Jim Woodward
Treas: Kevin Murphy
**VP:* Naveen Ahuja
VP: David Bell
**VP:* Conrad Helms
**VP:* Martin Mazy
**VP:* Randy Olloffson
**VP:* Mauricio Ramirez

HOSPITALITY SUPPLY COMPANY
See HOSPITALITY INC

D-U-N-S 36-365-6802
HOSPITALITY SYRACUSE INC
TACO BELL
745 S Garfield Ave Ste A, Traverse City, MI 49686-3479
Tel (231) 941-5052 Founded/Ownrshp 1988
Sales 27.2MM^E EMP 870
SIC 5812 Fast-food restaurant, chain; Fast-food restaurant, chain
Pr: Wayne Lobdell
**VP:* Ken Underwood

D-U-N-S 03-650-3738
HOSPITALITY SYSTEMS INC (PA)
BONANZA RESTAURANT
45 N 4th St, Shamokin, PA 17872-5205
Tel (570) 648-8634 Founded/Ownrshp 1992
Sales 6.2MM^E EMP 300
SIC 5812 8741 6794 Fast-food restaurant, chain; Management services; Patent owners & lessors; Fast-food restaurant, chain; Management services; Patent owners & lessors
Pr: Gene A Welsh Jr

D-U-N-S 78-657-8885
HOSPITALITY VENTURES LLC
UMSTEAD HOTEL AND SPA, THE
100 Woodland Pond Dr, Cary, NC 27513-2131
Tel (919) 447-4000 Founded/Ownrshp 2006
Sales 24.6MM^E EMP 300
SIC 7011 Hotels; Hotels
Exec: Steven Greene
Off Mgr: Andrea Coakley
Sls Mgr: Janele Reynolds
Sls Mgr: Sarah To

D-U-N-S 03-557-5724
HOSPITALITY WEST LLC
PIZZA HUT
745 S Garfield Ave Ste A, Traverse City, MI 49686-3479
Tel (231) 941-5052 Founded/Ownrshp 1998
Sales 20.4MM EMP 1,800
SIC 5812 Pizzeria, chain; Pizzeria, chain

HOSPITALITYSTAFF
See PODZAMSKY LLC

HOSPITALITYSTAFF
See RAMNARAIN II LLC

HOSPITALS OF PROVIDENCE SIERRA
See TENET HOSPITALS LIMITED

HOSS
See VOSS AUTO NETWORK INC

D-U-N-S 94-386-7507
HOSSS STEAK & SEA HOUSE INC
170 Patchway Rd, Duncansville, PA 16635-8431
Tel (814) 695-7600 Founded/Ownrshp 1995
Sales 120.1MM^E EMP 3,000
SIC 5812 5146 5046 Steak restaurant; Seafood restaurants; Fish & seafoods; Restaurant equipment & supplies; Steak restaurant; Seafood restaurants; Fish & seafoods; Restaurant equipment & supplies
CEO: Willard E Campbell
**CFO:* Carl Raup
**VP:* Bob Pleva
VP: Mark Spinazzola
VP Bus Dev: Bill Bratton
Genl Mgr: Dan Isenberg
Dir IT: Carl Swope
Opers Mgr: Rob Billet
Opers Mgr: Jim Fogle
Opers Mgr: Chip Gapshes
Opers Mgr: Pat Imler

D-U-N-S 06-586-4055
HOST ANALYTICS INC
101 Redwood Shores Pkwy # 101, Redwood City, CA 94065-1177
Tel (650) 249-7100 Founded/Ownrshp 2000
Sales 26.1MM^E EMP 50
SIC 7372 Application computer software
CEO: Dave Kellogg
**Pr:* Jim Eberlin
CFO: Ian Charles
**CFO:* Ian Halifax
**Chf Mktg O:* Lance Walter
Sr VP: Bryan Katis
Sr VP: Kulo Rajasekaran
VP: Cory Ayres
VP: Ron Baden
**VP:* Aravind Balakrishnan
**VP:* Keri Brooke
VP: Nick Ezzo
VP: Alison Holmlund
VP: John O'Rourke
VP: Sreedhar Peddineni
**VP:* John Perkins
**VP:* Richard Ratkowski
VP: Andrew Ross

D-U-N-S 00-691-9872 EXP
▲ HOST HOTELS & RESORTS INC
6903 Rockledge Dr # 1500, Bethesda, MD 20817-1818
Tel (240) 744-1000 Founded/Ownrshp 1929
Sales 5.3MMM EMP 251
Accts Kpmg Llp Mclean Virginia
Tkr Sym HST Exch NYS
SIC 6798 7011 Real estate investment trusts; Hotels & motels; Real estate investment trusts; Hotels & motels
Pr: W Edward Walter
**Ch Bd:* Richard E Marriott
CFO: Gregory J Larson
Ex VP: Elizabeth A Abdoo
Ex VP: Minaz B Abji
Ex VP: James F Risoleo
Ex VP: Struan B Robertson
Sr VP: David Buckley
Sr VP: Rogerio Miranda De Souza
Sr VP: Joe Gosland
Sr VP: Brian G Macnamara
VP: Matthew Ahrens
VP: Michael Rock
VP: Georgina Sussan
Board of Directors: Mary L Baglivo, Sheila C Bair, Terence C Golden, Ann McLaughlin Korologos, John B Morse Jr, Walter C Rakowich, Gordon H Smith

D-U-N-S 08-072-8152
■ HOST HOTELS & RESORTS LP
(*Suby of* HOST HOTELS & RESORTS INC) ★
6903 Rockledge Dr # 1500, Bethesda, MD 20817-1818
Tel (240) 744-1000 Founded/Ownrshp 1998
Sales 5.3MMM EMP 251
SIC 6798 7011 Real estate investment trusts; Hotels; Real estate investment trusts; Hotels
Pr: W Edward Walter
Genl Pt: Host Hotels Resorts
CFO: Gregory J Larson
Sr VP: Jeffrey Clark
Sr VP: Doug Henry
VP: Matthew Ahrens
VP: Doug Link
Exec: Elisa Gois

D-U-N-S 00-690-7646 IMP
HOST INTERNATIONAL INC
(*Suby of* HMSHOST CORP) ★
6905 Rockledge Dr Fl 1, Bethesda, MD 20817-7826
Tel (240) 694-4100 Founded/Ownrshp 1995
Sales 614.4MM^E EMP 23,000
SIC 5812 5813 5994 5947 Snack bar; Fast-food restaurant, chain; Cafeteria; American restaurant; Cocktail lounge; Newsstand; Gift shop; Snack bar; Fast-food restaurant, chain; Cafeteria; American restaurant; Cocktail lounge; Newsstand; Gift shop
CEO: Tom Fricke
**Pr:* Joe P Martin
**Treas:* Mark T Ratych
Genl Mgr: Larry Jenkins
Snr Mgr: Matt McGill

HOST LANE
See DOTSTER INC

D-U-N-S 93-875-1310
HOST MARRIOTT SERVICES CORP
(*Suby of* HMSHOST CORP) ★
6711 Democracy Blvd, Bethesda, MD 20817-1128
Tel (240) 344-1000 Founded/Ownrshp 1995
Sales 250.8MM^E EMP 23,000
SIC 7011 Hotels & motels; Hotels & motels
Pr: William W McCarten
VP: Kent Duffie
VP: Kerry Nickerson
Genl Mgr: Deborah Mitchell

D-U-N-S 15-309-1132
HOSTDIME.COM INC
2603 Challenger Tech Ct, Orlando, FL 32826-2716
Tel (407) 467-2053 Founded/Ownrshp 2003
Sales 80.5MM^E EMP 290^E
SIC 4813 ;
CEO: Miguel Torres
**Pr:* Emmanuel Vivar
**VP:* Ray Fernandez
VP: Mark Gregan
VP: Dennis Henry
**VP:* David Vivar
VP Sls: Dan Silber
Mktg Dir: Vikki Fraser
Sls Mgr: Joshua Daniels

HOSTELLING INTERNATIONAL USA
See AMERICAN YOUTH HOSTELS INC

HOSTELS
See ST LAWRENCE COUNTY CHAPTER OF NEW YORK ASSOCIATION FOR RETARDED CHILDREN

HOSTESS BRANDS
See OLD HB INC

D-U-N-S 07-879-7211
HOSTESS BRANDS LLC
1 E Armour Blvd, Kansas City, MO 64111-1201
Tel (816) 701-4600 Founded/Ownrshp 2013
Sales 800.0MM^E EMP 1,100
SIC 2051 Bread, cake & related products; Bread, cake & related products
Pr: William Toler
VP: Scott Gray
VP: Curtis Miller
VP: Charlie Smith
Rgnl Mgr: Rod Burk
Dist Mgr: Mike Young
Sls Mgr: Michael Paquette

D-U-N-S 05-999-5431
HOSTETLER SALES & CONSTRUCTION LLC
210 Kelly Rd, Buffalo, MO 65622-4141
Tel (417) 345-7418 Founded/Ownrshp 1966
Sales 25.1MM^E EMP 75
SIC 1611 5082 3441 1791 General contractor, highway & street construction; General construction machinery & equipment; Fabricated structural metal; Structural steel erection
Off Mgr: Ken Hostetler
Sls Mgr: Clive Hustler

D-U-N-S 09-684-4220
HOSTETTER GRAIN INC (PA)
TRAPPE LANDING ELEVATOR
481 Limestone Rd, Oxford, PA 19363-1293
Tel (610) 932-4484 Founded/Ownrshp 1968
Sales 70.0MM EMP 3
SIC 5153 Grains; Soybeans; Grains; Soybeans
Pr: Wilmer L Hostetter

HOSTEXCELLENCE.COM
See ECOMMERCE INC

D-U-N-S 82-640-4258
HOSTGATOR.COM LLC
5005 Mitchelldale St # 200, Houston, TX 77092-7244
Tel (713) 574-5287 Founded/Ownrshp 2004
Sales 33.3MM^E EMP 175
SIC 4813 ;
**CEO:* Adam Farrar
**COO:* Patrick Pelanne
Ex Dir: Shashank Wagh
CTO: David Collins
QA Dir: Angela Reynolds
IT Man: Jarvis Gilmore
Mktg Mgr: Chris Whitling
Sls Mgr: Chris Zak

D-U-N-S 06-950-2693
HOSTING.COM INC
900 S Broadway Ste 400, Denver, CO 80209-4286
Tel (720) 389-3800 Founded/Ownrshp 1997
Sales 108.4MM^E EMP 335^E
SIC 7379 Computer related consulting services; Computer related consulting services
CEO: Art Zeile
**COO:* Joel Daly
CFO: Jonathan Gaunt
**CFO:* Chris Wheeler
**Ex VP:* Don Barlow
Ex VP: Scott Filion
**Ex VP:* Bill Santos
VP: Sean Bruton
VP: Will Greenhalgh
Area Mgr: Brandon Ivey
Area Mgr: Chris McCracken

D-U-N-S 78-529-2681
HOSTMARK INVESTORS LIMITED PARTNERSHIP
HOSTMARK MANAGEMENT GROUP, THE
1300 E Wdfield Rd Ste 400, Schaumburg, IL 60173
Tel (847) 517-9100 Founded/Ownrshp 1994
Sales 111.7MM^E EMP 1,800
SIC 8741 Hotel or motel management; Hotel or motel management
Mng Pt: C A Cataldo
Pt: Jerome F Cataldo
Pt: William D Gingrich
Ex VP: Peter Connolly
Ex VP: Charles A Gavzer

HOSTMARK MANAGEMENT GROUP, THE
See HOSTMARK INVESTORS LIMITED PARTNERSHIP

HOST.NET,
See BROADBANDONE INC

D-U-N-S 01-901-1373
■ HOSTWAY CORP
(*Suby of* LITTLEJOHN & CO LLC) ★
100 N Riverside Plz # 800, Chicago, IL 60606-1564
Tel (312) 238-0125 Founded/Ownrshp 2013
Sales 142.7MM^E EMP 347
SIC 4813 ;
CEO: Robert Boles
Pt: Jim Ciampaglio
**COO:* John Martis
CFO: Kurt A Phillips
**Ex VP:* John Hanjoo
**VP:* Todd Benjamin
VP: John Lee
**VP:* Mike Robski
VP: Tony Savoy
Genl Mgr: John Enright
Off Admin: Khadijah Coleman

D-U-N-S 80-803-3851 IMP
HOT COTTON INC
2931 S Alameda St, Vernon, CA 90058-1326
Tel (323) 233-4500 Founded/Ownrshp 2007
Sales 40.0MM EMP 55^E
SIC 2339 Service apparel, washable: women's; Service apparel, washable: women's
Pr: Marc Ware
**CFO:* John Andreas

HOT DOG ON A STICK
See HDOS ACQUISITION LLC

HOT DOG ON A STICK
See BOHICA LIQUIDATION INC

HOT HANDS
See HEATMAX INC

D-U-N-S 05-824-7840
HOT HEAD BURRITOS
2795 Culver Ave, Dayton, OH 45429-3723
Tel (937) 395-3611 Founded/Ownrshp 2010
Sales 8.5MM^E EMP 332^E
SIC 5812 Mexican restaurant
Prin: Matt Curtis

D-U-N-S 18-055-8207
HOT LINE CONSTRUCTION INC
9020 Brentwood Blvd Ste H, Brentwood, CA 94513-4049
Tel (925) 634-9333 Founded/Ownrshp 1986
Sales 158.5MM^E EMP 425
Accts Wayne Long & Co Bakersfield
SIC 1731 1799 Electric power systems contractors; Cable splicing service; Electric power systems contractors; Cable splicing service
Pr: Carol Bade
**CFO:* Kelly G Kutchera
**VP:* Troy Myers
Off Mgr: Cruz Munos

D-U-N-S 05-328-5888
HOT MELT TECHNOLOGIES INC
H M T
1723 W Hamlin Rd, Rochester Hills, MI 48309-3368
Tel (248) 853-2011 Founded/Ownrshp 1981
Sales 25.5MM^E EMP 30
SIC 5084 3569 3565 Industrial machinery & equipment; Packaging machinery & equipment; Assembly machines, non-metalworking; Packaging machinery
Pr: Bryan J Tanury
**VP:* Ester C Tanury

HOT MIX ASPHALT
See J J FERGUSON SAND & GRAVEL INC

HOT ROD CAFE
See BEST WINGS USA INC

HOT SPOT
See R L JORDAN OIL CO OF NORTH CAROLINA INC

D-U-N-S 01-861-9994
HOT SPRING COUNTY MEDICAL CENTER
HSC MEDICAL CENTER
1001 Schneider Dr, Malvern, AR 72104-4811
Tel (501) 332-1000 Founded/Ownrshp 1977
Sales 26.1MM^E EMP 250
Accts Hughes Welch & Milligancpasltd
SIC 8062 General medical & surgical hospitals; General medical & surgical hospitals
Ofcr: Debby Hunt

HOT SPRINGS ACE HARDWARE
See BLATCHFORDS INC

D-U-N-S 18-243-8465
HOT SPRINGS COUNTY SCHOOL DISTRICT NO 1
415 Springview St, Thermopolis, WY 82443-2244
Tel (307) 864-6500 *Founded/Ownrshp* 1970
Sales 17.2MM^E *EMP* 300
SIC 8211 Public elementary & secondary schools; Public elementary school; Public junior high school; Public senior high school; Public elementary & secondary schools; Public elementary school; Public junior high school; Public senior high school
Instr Medi: Dan Syluberget
Psych: Liz Ryan
Psych: Cortney Thoren
HC Dir: Janet Chimenti

D-U-N-S 01-001-8123
HOT SPRINGS NATIONAL PARK HOSPITAL HOLDINGS LLC
NATIONAL PARK MEDICAL CENTER
1910 Malvern Ave, Hot Springs, AR 71901-7752
Tel (501) 620-1185 *Founded/Ownrshp* 2008
Sales 17.2MM^E *EMP* 700
SIC 8011 Medical centers

D-U-N-S 94-309-5489
HOT SPRINGS SCHOOL DISTRICT 6
400 Linwood Ave, Hot Springs, AR 71913-3749
Tel (501) 624-3372 *Founded/Ownrshp* 1965
Sales 34.1MM^E *EMP* 600^E
SIC 8211 Public elementary & secondary schools; Public elementary & secondary schools
Teacher Pr: Doug Upshaw
Psych: Cherri Mertz
Psych: Danielle Pitts
Genl Couns: Charles White

D-U-N-S 07-563-4477
HOT SPRINGS VILLAGE PROPERTY OWNERS ASSOCIATION (AR)
895 Desoto Blvd, Hot Springs Village, AR 71909-7656
Tel (501) 922-5530 *Founded/Ownrshp* 1970
Sales 25.4MM^E *EMP* 539^E
Accts Frost Pllc Little Rock Arka
SIC 8641 Homeowners' association; Homeowners' association
Pr: Keith Keck
CFO: Don Yucuis
**VP:* John Cooney
**Genl Mgr:* Linda Mayhood

D-U-N-S 80-201-4014
HOT SPUR RESORTS NEVADA LIMITED
(*Suby of* HOTSPUR RESORTS NEVADA INC) ★
221 N Rampart Blvd, Las Vegas, NV 89145-5722
Tel (702) 869-7175 *Founded/Ownrshp* 2005
Sales 1.8MM^E *EMP* 500
SIC 7011 Resort hotel; Resort hotel
Pr: Thaddas Alston

D-U-N-S 03-324-8514
HOT TACOS INC
TACO BELL
5825 S 35th Ave, Phoenix, AZ 85041-4302
Tel (602) 268-9266 *Founded/Ownrshp* 1997
Sales 34.2MM *EMP* 900
SIC 5812 Fast-food restaurant, chain; Fast-food restaurant, chain
Pr: Mark Peterson
**VP:* Krystal Burge

D-U-N-S 60-322-6986 IMP
HOT TOPIC INC
TORRID
(*Suby of* 212F HOLDINGS LLC)
18305 San Jose Ave, City of Industry, CA 91748-1237
Tel (626) 839-4681 *Founded/Ownrshp* 2013
Sales 1.2MMM^E *EMP* 5,000
SIC 5621 5632 5699 Women's clothing stores; Apparel accessories; Designers, apparel; Men's & boys' clothing stores; Record &/or tape (music or video) club, mail order; Women's clothing stores; Apparel accessories; Designers, apparel
CEO: Lisa Harper
CFO: George Wehlitz
Treas: Brenda Morris
Sr VP: Jeff Allison
Sr VP: Robin Elledge
VP: Elizabeth Haynes
VP: Tricia Higgins
VP: Jerome Kahn
VP: Alain Krakirian
VP: Kelly McGuire-Diehl
VP: Sue McPherson-Spissu
VP: Sue Spiss
VP: Steve Vranes
Board of Directors: Steven Becker, Evelyn Dan, Matthew Drapkin, Terri Funk Graham, W Scott Hedrick, John Kyees, Andrew Schuon, Thomas Vellios

D-U-N-S 03-784-3310 IMP
HOT TOPICS INC
HTI COLLECTION
515 Madison Ave Rm 2310, New York, NY 10022-5430
Tel (212) 750-5542 *Founded/Ownrshp* 1988
Sales 21.6MM^E *EMP* 120
SIC 5122 5621 Cosmetics; Women's clothing stores; Cosmetics; Women's clothing stores
Pr: Byron D Donics
Off Mgr: Josette Monico

D-U-N-S 60-920-4573
HOT-LINE FREIGHT SYSTEM INC
W2197 County Road B, West Salem, WI 54669-9401
Tel (608) 486-1600 *Founded/Ownrshp* 1988
Sales 58.9MM^E *EMP* 195
SIC 4213

D-U-N-S 80-812-2071
HOT-SHOT EXPRESS INC
STRAIGHT SHOT EXPRESS
800 Kuehn Ct, Neenah, WI 54956-1667
Tel (920) 722-0956 *Founded/Ownrshp* 1995
Sales 20.8MM^E *EMP* 100^E
SIC 4212 6794 4213 Delivery service, vehicular; Patent owners & lessors; Trucking, except local
Pr: Pat Curran
IT Man: John Dominowski
Sfty Dirs: Wendy Santkuyl
Opers Mgr: Ron Burns
Opers Mgr: Jim Van Den Heuvel

D-U-N-S 02-087-1828
HOTARD COACHES INC (LA)
HOTARD DESTINATION SERVICES
2838 Touro St, New Orleans, LA 70122-3601
Tel (504) 944-0253 *Founded/Ownrshp* 1960, 2008
Sales 44.5MM^E *EMP* 247
SIC 4119 4142 Sightseeing bus; Bus charter service, except local; Sightseeing bus; Bus charter service, except local
Pr: Callen Hotard
VP: Dwight Lebla
**Prin:* Jim Zizaski
IT Man: Mike Rainey
Mktg Mgr: John Abbotte
Mktg Mgr: Lin Kiger

HOTARD DESTINATION SERVICES
See HOTARD COACHES INC

HOTBOX
See STREAMRAY INC

D-U-N-S 03-718-2961
HOTCHKIS AND WILEY CAPITAL MANAGEMENT LLC
725 S Figueroa St # 3900, Los Angeles, CA 90017-5439
Tel (213) 430-1000 *Founded/Ownrshp* 2001
Sales 21.5MM^E *EMP* 145^E
SIC 8741 6211 Financial management for business; Security brokers & dealers
Exec: George Davis
COO: Anna Lopez
CFO: Jay Menvielle
Ofcr: Tina Kodama
Sls&Mrk Ex: Bob Dochterman

D-U-N-S 10-258-0792
HOTCHKISS INSURANCE AGENCY LLC
4120 Intl Pkwy Ste 2000, Carrollton, TX 75007
Tel (972) 512-7700 *Founded/Ownrshp* 1975
Sales NA *EMP* 100
SIC 6411 Property & casualty insurance agent; Life insurance agents
CEO: Mike Hotchkiss
**Pr:* Douglas G Hotchkiss
**COO:* Gregory S Hotchkiss
VP: Wayne Bishop
**VP:* Bradley W Burnham
VP: Farrah Carlton
VP: Ann Davis
VP: Greg Hotchkiss
VP: Pat Janosky
VP: Tye Justice
VP: Wes Weatherred

D-U-N-S 07-731-3773
HOTCHKISS SCHOOL
CYNTHIA WHITE CHILDREN'S CENTE
11 Interlaken Rd, Lakeville, CT 06039-2130
Tel (860) 435-2591 *Founded/Ownrshp* 1893
Sales 83.5MM *EMP* 243
Accts Cohnreznick Llp Glastonbury
SIC 8211 Boarding school; Boarding school
**Pr:* Jean Weinberg
**Treas:* William B Tyree
Trst: John Ellis
Top Exec: Charles Frankenbach
**VP:* William R Elfers
Comm Dir: Roberta Jenckes
Genl Mgr: Andrew Cox
Off Mgr: Joanne Lakin
Off Mgr: Gail Schroder
Store Mgr: Guy Gnerre
Dir IT: Peter Chizinski

D-U-N-S 03-339-2614 IMP
HOTEL & RESTAURANT SUPPLY INC
5020 Arundel Rd, Meridian, MS 39307-9431
Tel (601) 482-7127 *Founded/Ownrshp* 1989
Sales 31.0MM *EMP* 195
SIC 5719 Commercial cooking & food service equipment; Kitchenware
Pr: Jerry R Greene
**Sec:* Marilyn Greene
**VP:* William C Wolfe
Sales Asso: Greg Ray
Sales Asso: Ann Sensing

D-U-N-S 85-981-7660
HOTEL 57 LLC
FOUR SEASONS HOTEL NEW YORK
57 E 57th St Frnt 1, New York, NY 10022-2081
Tel (212) 758-5700 *Founded/Ownrshp* 1999
Sales 39.4MM^E *EMP* 600
SIC 7011 7299 5812 Hotels & motels; Banquet hall facilities; Eating places; Hotels & motels; Banquet hall facilities; Eating places
Genl Mgr: Christoph Schmidinger
Dir Sec: Michael Lacouture
Genl Mgr: Chris Schmidinger
Dir IT: Nur Hassan
Dir IT: Roger Ingersoll
Dir IT: Ray San Jaun
Dir IT: Jamie Murphy
Dir IT: Ray Vargas
IT Man: William Chan

D-U-N-S 83-247-9419
HOTEL ACQUISITION CO LLC
THAYER LODGING GROUP
1997 Annapolis Exch Pkwy, Annapolis, MD 21401-3271
Tel (410) 268-0515 *Founded/Ownrshp* 2009
Sales 1.6MMM^E *EMP* 19,100
SIC 8741 7011 Hotel or motel management; Hotels; Hotel or motel management; Hotels

HOTEL ALLEGRO
See CLPF - BISMARCK HOTEL OPERATING CO LLC

HOTEL ALYESKA, THE
See ALYESKA RESORT MANAGEMENT CO

HOTEL CAPTAIN COOK, THE
See HICKEL INVESTMENT CO

D-U-N-S 07-955-7347
HOTEL CIRCLE PROPERTY LLC
500 Hotel Cir N, San Diego, CA 92108-3005
Tel (619) 291-7131 *Founded/Ownrshp* 2014
Sales 5.1MM^E *EMP* 500
SIC 7011 Resort hotel; Resort hotel

D-U-N-S 92-780-2868
HOTEL CLEANING SERVICES INC
9609 N 22nd Ave, Phoenix, AZ 85021-1806
Tel (602) 588-0864 *Founded/Ownrshp* 1994
Sales 30.0MM *EMP* 1,500
SIC 7349 Building maintenance services; Building & office cleaning services; Building maintenance services; Building & office cleaning services
Pr: John Knoepker
**CEO:* Debra Knoepker
**VP:* Tim Bottoms
Area Mgr: Sheila Adams
Natl Sales: Jim Cardennis
Snr Mgr: Jeff Brynsaas

HOTEL CRESCENT COURT
See RRCC LIMITED PARTNERSHIP

HOTEL DISCOUNT
See HOTELS.COM LP

D-U-N-S 96-489-7545
HOTEL EMPLOYEES RESTAURANT EMP
2815 2nd Ave, Seattle, WA 98121-3209
Tel (206) 441-7574 *Founded/Ownrshp* 2010
Sales 21.8MM *EMP* 14^E
Accts Lindquist Llp San Ramon Ca
SIC 5812 Eating places; Eating places

D-U-N-S 80-563-8272
HOTEL EQUITIES INC
41 Perimeter Ctr E # 510, Atlanta, GA 30346-1910
Tel (770) 934-2170 *Founded/Ownrshp* 2004
Sales 119.7MM^E *EMP* 700
SIC 6799 8741 Investors; Hotel or motel management; Investors; Hotel or motel management
CEO: Frederick W Cerrone
CFO: Alan Bennett

D-U-N-S 03-883-2093
HOTEL EQUITY FUND II LP
FOUR SEASONS HOTEL HOUSTON
1300 Lamar St, Houston, TX 77010-3017
Tel (713) 650-1300 *Founded/Ownrshp* 2006
Sales NA *EMP* 450
SIC 5813 5812

HOTEL GROUP, THE
See HOTEL GROUP INC

D-U-N-S 18-864-1849
HOTEL GROUP INC
HOTEL GROUP, THE
201 5th Ave S Ste 200, Edmonds, WA 98020-3481
Tel (425) 771-1788 *Founded/Ownrshp* 1984
Sales 119.7MM^E *EMP* 1,500
SIC 7011 Hotels & motels; Hotels & motels
CEO: Douglas N Dreher
Pr: Molly Bruder
**Ex VP:* Lara R Latture
VP: Richard Freebourn
**VP:* Robert E Lee
VP: Robert Lee
**Prin:* Edmond A Lee
Rgnl Mgr: Nancy Mark
Genl Mgr: Amanda Anderson
Genl Mgr: Diane Bates
Genl Mgr: Jerry Beach

D-U-N-S 10-398-8655
HOTEL INTER-CONTINENTAL DALLAS
REGISTRY DALLAS ASSOCIATES
15201 Dallas Pkwy, Addison, TX 75001-4676
Tel (972) 386-6000 *Founded/Ownrshp* 1982
Sales 21.5MM^E *EMP* 400
SIC 7011 5812 7299

HOTEL INTER-CONTINENTAL NY
See IHC INTER-CONTINENTAL (HOLDINGS) CORP

D-U-N-S 80-921-1167
HOTEL INVESTMENTS LP
GRAND HYATT CONVENTION CENTER
600 E Market St, San Antonio, TX 78205-2600
Tel (210) 224-1234 *Founded/Ownrshp* 2005
Sales 37.4MM^E *EMP* 500
SIC 7011 Hotels & motels; Hotels & motels
Sls Mgr: Allyson Anderson
Sls Mgr: Michelle Chiles

HOTEL KING KAMEHAMEHA
See HTH INC

D-U-N-S 04-193-4287
HOTEL MANAGERS GROUP LLC
11590 W Bernardo Ct # 211, San Diego, CA 92127-1624
Tel (858) 673-1534 *Founded/Ownrshp* 1996
Sales 36.0MM^E *EMP* 400
SIC 8741 7011 7041 Hotel or motel management; Hotels & motels; Membership-basis organization hotels; Hotel or motel management; Hotels & motels; Membership-basis organization hotels
Ex VP: Cha M Demayo
**Ex VP:* Michelle Demayo
VP: Alan Bowles
VP: Jerry Gruber
Genl Mgr: Mike Hensley
Genl Mgr: Patrick Sampson

D-U-N-S 00-589-3474
HOTEL MONACO
MONACO HOTEL
1101 4th Ave, Seattle, WA 98101-3003
Tel (206) 621-1770 *Founded/Ownrshp* 1996
Sales 16.3MM^E *EMP* 300
SIC 7011 5812 5813 Hotels & motels; Eating places; Drinking places; Hotels & motels; Eating places; Drinking places
Genl Mgr: Sandy Burkett
Pt: F S Seattle LP
Genl Mgr: Doug Logan
Genl Mgr: Dave Ruehlmann
Sls Dir: Kristi Klein

D-U-N-S 17-707-0315
HOTEL NIKKO OF SAN FRANCISCO INC
(*Suby of* JAL HOTELS CO.,LTD.)
222 Mason St, San Francisco, CA 94102-2115
Tel (415) 394-1111 *Founded/Ownrshp* 1999
Sales 26.4MM^E *EMP* 260
SIC 7011 5812 5813 7991 7299 Hotels; Eating places; Bar (drinking places); Health club; Banquet hall facilities; Hotels; Eating places; Bar (drinking places); Health club; Banquet hall facilities
CEO: Hiroshi Oishi
**VP:* Anna Marie Presutti

HOTEL PARAMOUNT
See CENTURY PARAMOUNT CORP

D-U-N-S 78-847-5580
HOTEL REPRESENTATIVE INC
(*Suby of* HOTEL REPRESENTATIVE AG)
99 Park Ave Fl 10, New York, NY 10016-1500
Tel (212) 515-5600 *Founded/Ownrshp* 1989
Sales 53.9MM^E *EMP* 300
SIC 7389 8742 7311 Hotel & motel reservation service; Marketing consulting services; Advertising agencies; Hotel & motel reservation service; Marketing consulting services; Advertising agencies
Pr: Paul Mc Manus
COO: Paul McManus
**CFO:* Lee Andrews

D-U-N-S 07-862-2164
HOTEL RESTAURANT & CLUB EMPLOYEES & BARTENDERS UNION LOCAL 6 AFL CIO
AFL-CIO
709 8th Ave, New York, NY 10036-7111
Tel (212) 957-8000 *Founded/Ownrshp* 1938
Sales 20.6MM *EMP* 50
Accts Armao Costa & Ricciardi Cpa S
SIC 8631 Labor unions & similar labor organizations; Labor unions & similar labor organizations
Pr: Michael Simo

D-U-N-S 01-912-3764
HOTEL ROANOKE LLC
110 Shenandoah Ave Ne, Roanoke, VA 24016-2025
Tel (540) 985-5900 *Founded/Ownrshp* 1993
Sales 10.0MM^E *EMP* 335
SIC 7011 Hotels & motels; Hotels & motels
Pt: Eileen Pevarski
Chf Mktg O: Sandra Holt
IT Man: Bruce Keiser
Sls Mgr: Eric Sawyer

D-U-N-S 61-532-0769
HOTEL TEMPLE SQUARE CORP
THE INN AT TEMPLE SQUARE
(*Suby of* DESERET MANAGEMENT CORP) ★
15 E South Temple, Salt Lake City, UT 84150-9002
Tel (801) 531-1000 *Founded/Ownrshp* 1987
Sales 13.1MM^E *EMP* 568
SIC 7011 5812 8412 Hotels; Eating places; Museums & art galleries; Hotels; Eating places; Museums & art galleries
Pr: Brent Shingleton
VP: Clark Stenquist
Genl Mgr: Marge Taylor

HOTEL VALLEY HO
See MSR PROPERTIES LLC

D-U-N-S 60-415-1311
HOTEL WEST II LP
HOLIDAY INN BILLINGS
1140 Reservoir Ave, Cranston, RI 02920-6032
Tel (401) 946-4600 *Founded/Ownrshp* 2005
Sales 12.0MM^E *EMP* 449
SIC 7011 Hotels & motels; Hotels & motels
VP: Kim Benevides

HOTEL ZAZA HOUSTON
See TRANSFORMATION 5701 LP

HOTELBEDS ACCOMODATION &
See HOTELBEDS USA INC

D-U-N-S 19-864-1839
HOTELBEDS USA INC
HOTELBEDS ACCOMODATION &
(*Suby of* FIRST CHOICE HOLIDAYS LIMITED)
5422 Carrier Dr Ste 201, Orlando, FL 32819-8323
Tel (407) 926-5344 *Founded/Ownrshp* 1988
Sales 48.0MM^E *EMP* 100^E
SIC 7389 Brokers' services
Pr: Sheila S Sheehan
Exec: Elena Acua
Exec: Josh Dworsky
Exec: Nadia Mohammed
Exec: Greg Muenzmay

HOTELS & HOSPITALITY GROUP
See JONES LANG LASALLE AMERICAS INC

D-U-N-S 10-729-5169
■ **HOTELS.COM LP**
HOTEL DISCOUNT
(*Suby of* EXPEDIA INC) ★
5400 Lyndon B Johnson Fwy # 500, Dallas, TX 75240-1019
Tel (214) 361-7311 *Founded/Ownrshp* 2005
Sales 87.6MM^E *EMP* 1,150
SIC 7389 7375 Reservation services; Hotel & motel reservation service; Information retrieval services; Reservation services; Hotel & motel reservation service; Information retrieval services
CEO: David Litman
Pr: Scott Booker
CFO: Mel Robinson
Sr VP: Jack Richards
VP: Heath Hammett
VP: Neha Parikh

Dir Soc: Becky Williamson
Genl Mgr: Aliette Parfonry
QA Dir: Allison Faucett
Software D: Matt Brown
Mktg Dir: Abhiram Chowdhry

D-U-N-S 95-983-4917
HOTH INC
RAVN AIR GROUP
4700 Old Intl Airport Rd, Anchorage, AK 99502-1020
Tel (907) 266-8300 *Founded/Ownrshp* 2015
Sales 85.0MM^E *EMP* 520^E
SIC 4522 4512 Flying charter service; Air transportation, scheduled; Flying charter service; Air transportation, scheduled
Pr: Robert Hajdukovich
Sec: Michael Hageland

HOTSCHEDULES
See RED BOOK CONNECT LLC

D-U-N-S 09-214-5858
HOTSPUR RESORTS NEVADA INC
RAMPART CASINO
221 N Rampart Blvd, Las Vegas, NV 89145-5722
Tel (702) 869-7777 *Founded/Ownrshp* 2001
Sales 31.7MM^E *EMP* 500
SIC 7011 Resort hotel; Resort hotel
Pr: Thaddas L Alston
Dir Sec: Tim Fox
Genl Mgr: Patrick Hughes

D-U-N-S 00-906-2332
HOTSTART INC (WA)
5723 E Alki Ave, Spokane Valley, WA 99212-0965
Tel (509) 534-6171 *Founded/Ownrshp* 1942, 1958
Sales 24.8MM^E *EMP* 195
SIC 3443

D-U-N-S 00-140-3245 EXP
HOTWATT INC (MA)
128 Maple St, Danvers, MA 01923-2096
Tel (978) 777-0070 *Founded/Ownrshp* 1952
Sales 26.2MM^E *EMP* 120
SIC 3822 Electric heat proportioning controls, modulating controls; Electric heat proportioning controls, modulating controls
Ch Bd: Robert S Lee
**Pr:* William E Lee
**Treas:* Robert F Cummings
**Ex VP:* Samuel Sayward
VP Opers: G Rust

D-U-N-S 16-787-3855 IMP
HOTWIRE COMMUNICATIONS LLC
1 Belmont Ave Ste 1100, Bala Cynwyd, PA 19004-1614
Tel (610) 642-8570 *Founded/Ownrshp* 2005
Sales 123.3MM^E *EMP* 300^E
SIC 4813 Telephone communication, except radio; Telephone communication, except radio
Pr: Kristin Johnson
Dir Soc: Isaac Mualem
Dir IT: Nick Fuhs
Dir IT: Chris Rios
Mktg Mgr: Amanda Brown
Art Dir: Carolina Carezis

D-U-N-S 16-993-6023
■ HOTWIRE INC
(*Suby of* EXPEDIA INC) ★
655 Montgomery St Ste 600, San Francisco, CA 94111-2627
Tel (415) 645-7350 *Founded/Ownrshp* 1999
Sales 58.2MM^E *EMP* 175
SIC 4813 ;
CEO: Dara Khosrowshahi
**Pr:* Clem Bason
VP: Brenda Barnes
VP: Taek Kwon
Assoc Dir: Laura Macdonald
Mng Dir: Leslie Campisi
Mng Dir: Suzanne Hewitt
Genl Mgr: Hamish Anderson
Genl Mgr: Jasmine L Kim
Snr Sftwr: Sanjay Assao
Snr Sftwr: Sundeep Cheedhella

D-U-N-S 60-398-1895
HOU-SCAPE INC
17725 Telge Rd, Cypress, TX 77429-7048
Tel (281) 579-6741 *Founded/Ownrshp* 1988
Sales 33.5MM^E *EMP* 250
SIC 1629 0781 0782 Irrigation system construction; Landscape counseling & planning; Landscape services; Landscape contractors; Irrigation system construction; Landscape counseling & planning; Landscape services; Landscape contractors
Pr: Paula Hill
CFO: Burt Wilson

D-U-N-S 19-015-3791
HOU-TRA INTERNATIONAL
HUNTON GROUP, THE
10555 Westpark Dr, Houston, TX 77042-5232
Tel (713) 266-3551 *Founded/Ownrshp* 1997
Sales 43.5MM^E *EMP* 140
SIC 5075 Air conditioning equipment, except room units; Air conditioning equipment, except room units
Pr: Richard Hunton Sr
Sls Mgr: Matt Rister

D-U-N-S 19-491-4602 IMP
HOUALLA ENTERPRISES LTD
METRO BLDRS & ENGINEERS GROUP
2610 Avon St, Newport Beach, CA 92663-4706
Tel (949) 515-4350 *Founded/Ownrshp* 1987
Sales 32.1MM^E *EMP* 85
SIC 1542 Commercial & office building, new construction; Specialized public building contractors; Commercial & office building, new construction; Specialized public building contractors
Pr: Fouad Houalla

D-U-N-S 00-694-4565 IMP/EXP
HOUCHENS FOOD GROUP INC (KY)
HOUCHENS MARKETS
(*Suby of* HOUCHENS INDUSTRIES INC) ★
700 Church St, Bowling Green, KY 42101-1816
Tel (270) 843-3252 *Founded/Ownrshp* 1918, 1988
Sales 2.2MMM *EMP* 10,335
SIC 5411 5541 5093

D-U-N-S 78-620-4722
HOUCHENS INDUSTRIES INC
700 Church St, Bowling Green, KY 42101-1816
Tel (270) 843-3252 *Founded/Ownrshp* 1988
Sales 3.2MMM *EMP* 16,000
Accts Bkd Llp Bowling Green Kentu
SIC 6719 Investment holding companies, except banks; Investment holding companies, except banks
CEO: James P Gipson
CFO: Gordon Minter
**Treas:* Mike Givens
Top Exec: David Burnett
VP: Clark Gipson
Rgnl Mgr: Donnie Gipson
Rgnl Mgr: Jeff Grinstead
Brnch Mgr: Joe Skaggs
Dist Mgr: Keith Sherfey
Dist Mgr: Tracy Worley
Div Mgr: Ricky Lay
Board of Directors: Chester Gregory, Sarah Glenn Grise, W Ruel Houchens, Peter Mahurin

HOUCHENS MARKETS
See HOUCHENS FOOD GROUP INC

D-U-N-S 08-244-2005
HOUCK SERVICES INC
7464 Linglestown Rd, Harrisburg, PA 17112-9432
Tel (717) 657-0212 *Founded/Ownrshp* 1977
Sales 23.1MM^E *EMP* 90
SIC 1761 1542 1541 Roofing contractor; Commercial & office buildings, renovation & repair; Renovation, remodeling & repairs: industrial buildings
Pr: Gary L Houck
**CFO:* Brian K Walker
**VP:* John A Dorfler
Opers Supe: Lee Firestone

D-U-N-S 15-752-8068 IMP/EXP
HOUDINI INC
WINE COUNTRY GIFT BASKETS
4225 N Palm St, Fullerton, CA 92835-1045
Tel (714) 525-0325 *Founded/Ownrshp* 1983
Sales 48.3MM^E *EMP* 260
SIC 5947 5199 Gift baskets; Gift baskets
Pr: Timothy J Dean
**CFO:* Dan Maguire
**VP:* John Obrien
VP: Bill Shea
VP: Hillary Spater
Genl Mgr: Wayne Avjian
CIO: Tammy Miyata
Prd Mgr: Rick De Leon
Ql Cn Mgr: Kurt Ohlander
Mktg Dir: Bill Martin
Sls Dir: Dave Casares

D-U-N-S 00-982-0101
HOUFF TRANSFER INC (VA)
46 Houff Rd, Weyers Cave, VA 24486-2315
Tel (540) 234-9233 *Founded/Ownrshp* 1937
Sales 36.9MM *EMP* 200
Accts Elmore Hupp & Company Plc C
SIC 4213 Trucking, except local; Trucking, except local
CEO: Doug Houff
**Pr:* Douglas Z Houff
CFO: Sterling Herbst
**Sec:* Grant Doyle
**VP:* Mike Fulk
**VP:* Roxie H White
Trfc Dir: Mark Bowman
Trfc Dir: Adam Cash
Trfc Dir: Greg Gilkerson
Trfc Dir: Dave Grant
Trfc Dir: Dave Russell

D-U-N-S 00-539-6973 IMP/EXP
HOUGEN MANUFACTURING INC (MI)
3001 Hougen Dr, Swartz Creek, MI 48473-7935
Tel (810) 635-7111 *Founded/Ownrshp* 1959
Sales 90.8MM^E *EMP* 130
SIC 5084 3545 3546 3541 Machine tools & metalworking machinery; Drill bits, metalworking; Broaches (machine tool accessories); Power-driven handtools; Machine tools, metal cutting type; Machine tools & metalworking machinery; Drill bits, metalworking; Broaches (machine tool accessories); Power-driven handtools; Machine tools, metal cutting type
CEO: Randall Hougen
**Pr:* Gregory Phillips
CFO: Bob Maguffee
**Treas:* Therese Y Hougen
**VP:* Victor Hougen
CTO: Jeffrey Gill
IT Man: Sarah Starkel
Mtls Mgr: Steven Tift
Plnt Mgr: Dan Piggott

D-U-N-S 01-178-8130
HOUGH PETROLEUM CORP
340 4th St, Ewing, NJ 08638-2750
Tel (609) 771-1022 *Founded/Ownrshp* 1992
Sales 31.4MM^E *EMP* 18
Accts Padden Cooper Lawson Denn Drew
SIC 5172 Gasoline; Diesel fuel; Lubricating oils & greases
Pr: Gary W Hough
**VP:* Richard S Hough

D-U-N-S 19-717-4055
HOUGH-GUIDICE REALTY ASSOCIATES INC
200 Middle Country Rd, Middle Island, NY 11953-2520
Tel (631) 345-5600 *Founded/Ownrshp* 1988
Sales 12.0MM *EMP* 400
SIC 6531 Real estate brokers & agents; Real estate brokers & agents
Pr: Anthony Guidice
**VP:* Shawn Hough

D-U-N-S 00-102-4058 IMP
HOUGHTON CHEMICAL CORP (MA)
52 Cambridge St, Allston, MA 02134-1850
Tel (617) 254-1010 *Founded/Ownrshp* 1926
Sales 32.1MM^E *EMP* 46
SIC 5074 5013 3589 Heating equipment (hydronic); Automotive supplies; Water treatment equipment, industrial
Pr: Bruce E Houghton
**Sr VP:* Patricia Kincade
**VP:* Deborah J Gavin
**VP:* Joseph Lima
VP: Joseph Warchol
Admn Mgr: Jean Fratta
IT Man: Rendy Hunter

D-U-N-S 07-148-5346
HOUGHTON COLLEGE
1 Willard Ave, Houghton, NY 14744-8732
Tel (800) 777-2556 *Founded/Ownrshp* 1883
Sales 41.6MM *EMP* 285
Accts Bonadio & Co Llp Pittsford N
SIC 8221 5942 College, except junior; College book stores; College, except junior; College book stores
Pr: Jeffrey B Spear
**VP:* Eric Alcott
**VP:* Tim Fuller
VP: Wayne Macbeth
**VP:* Ronald Oakerson
VP: Linda Woolsey
Psych: Wendy Baxter
Snr Mgr: Bob Vanwicklin

D-U-N-S 00-226-1535 IMP/EXP
HOUGHTON INTERNATIONAL INC (PA)
(*Suby of* GH HOLDINGS INC) ★
945 Madison Ave, Norristown, PA 19403-2306
Tel (610) 666-4000 *Founded/Ownrshp* 1910, 2012
Sales 433.9MM^E *EMP* 1,600
SIC 2869 2992 Hydraulic fluids, synthetic base; Lubricating oils & greases; Hydraulic fluids, synthetic base; Lubricating oils & greases
Pr: Paul Devivo
**CFO:* Keller Arnold
**Ex VP:* Michael J Shannon
**Sr VP:* Richard R Lovely
**Sr VP:* Dave Slinkman
VP: Jeewat Bijlani
VP: Dominik Elsaesser
VP: Charles E Santangelo
VP: Robert Summerhayes
VP: Steve M Taylor
VP: Joseph Warchol

HOUGHTON LAKE HEALTH PARK
See MIDMICHIGAN HEALTH SERVICES

HOUGHTON MIFFLIN HARCOURT
See HOUGHTON MIFFLIN HOLDING CO INC

D-U-N-S 07-848-0960
▲ HOUGHTON MIFFLIN HARCOURT CO
222 Berkeley St, Boston, MA 02116-3748
Tel (617) 351-5000 *Founded/Ownrshp* 2010
Sales 1.3MMM *EMP* 4,100^E
Tkr Sym HMHC *Exch* NGS
SIC 3999 2731 Education aids, devices & supplies; Education aids, devices & supplies; Book publishing
Pr: Linda Zecher
Ch Bd: Lawrence K Fish
Pr: Linda K Zecher
CFO: Eric L Shuman
CFO: Eric Shuman
Chf Cred: Mary J Cullinane
Bd of Dir: Anthony Artuso
Chf Mktg O: John K Dragoon
Ex VP: Bill Bayers
Ex VP: William F Bayers
Ex VP: William Bayers
Ex VP: Joanne Karimi
Ex VP: Margery Mayer
Ex VP: Lee Ramsayer
Ex VP: Rita H Schaefer
Sr VP: Leigh Zarelli
VP: Vicki McCraw-Payne
Board of Directors: L Gordon Crovitz, Jill A Greenthal, John F Killian, John R McKernan Jr, Jonathan F Miller, E Rogers Novak Jr

D-U-N-S 96-828-5903
■ HOUGHTON MIFFLIN HARCOURT PUBLISHERS INC
(*Suby of* HOUGHTON MIFFLIN HARCOURT CO) ★
222 Berkeley St, Boston, MA 02116-3748
Tel (617) 351-5000 *Founded/Ownrshp* 2013
Sales 306.1MM^E *EMP* 3,300^E
SIC 2731 Textbooks: publishing & printing; Textbooks: publishing & printing
Pr: Linda Zecher
**CFO:* Eric Shuman
**Treas:* Joseph Flaherty
**Ex VP:* William Bayers
**Sr VP:* Michael Dolan

D-U-N-S 00-101-5924 IMP
■ HOUGHTON MIFFLIN HARCOURT PUBLISHING CO
HOUGHTON MIFFLIN PUBLISHING
(*Suby of* HOUGHTON MIFFLIN HARCOURT CO) ★
222 Berkeley St, Boston, MA 02116-3748
Tel (617) 351-5000 *Founded/Ownrshp* 2002
Sales 926.7MM^E *EMP* 3,300
SIC 2731 Books: publishing only; Textbooks: publishing only, not printed on site; Books: publishing only; Textbooks: publishing only, not printed on site
CEO: Linda K Zecher
**Pr:* Gary Gentel
**Pr:* James G Nicholson
**Pr:* Lesa Scott
**CFO:* Eric Shuman
**Treas:* Joseph Flaherty
Treas: William Kesler
**Chf Cred:* Mary Cullinane
**Chf Mktg O:* John K Dragoon
Ex VP: Bill Bayers
**Ex VP:* William Bayers
**Ex VP:* Tim Cannon
Ex VP: John Dragoon
**Ex VP:* Joanne Karimi
Sr VP: Lance Benzley
Sr VP: Rick Blake
**Sr VP:* Brook Colangelo
Sr VP: Catherine Crowelile
Sr VP: Paul Despins
**Sr VP:* Michael Dolan
Sr VP: Don Gagnon
Board of Directors: Eric Shuman, Linda Zecher

D-U-N-S 78-709-0096
HOUGHTON MIFFLIN HOLDING CO INC
HOUGHTON MIFFLIN HARCOURT
222 Berkeley St, Boston, MA 02116-3748
Tel (617) 351-5000 *Founded/Ownrshp* 2009
Sales NA *EMP* 3,550
SIC 2731

D-U-N-S 13-202-2513 IMP
HOUGHTON MIFFLIN HOLDINGS INC
222 Berkeley St, Boston, MA 02116-3748
Tel (617) 351-5000 *Founded/Ownrshp* 2002
Sales 631.5MM^E *EMP* 3,550
SIC 2731 Book publishing; Textbooks: publishing only, not printed on site; Book publishing; Textbooks: publishing only, not printed on site
Ex VP: Stephen Richards
Ex VP: Bill Bayers
VP: Paul Donovan
Assoc Dir: Carla Gray
Sales Exec: Wendy Wooldridge
Mktg Dir: Sue Cowden
Mktg Dir: Margaret Deboer
Mktg Dir: Linda Magram
Snr Mgr: Scott Olson

HOUGHTON MIFFLIN PUBLISHING
See HOUGHTON MIFFLIN HARCOURT PUBLISHING CO

D-U-N-S 07-954-9738
HOULIHAN LOKEY HOWARD & ZUKIN INC
10250 Constellation Blvd, Los Angeles, CA 90067-6200
Tel (310) 553-8871 *Founded/Ownrshp* 2014
Sales 35.3MM^E *EMP* 192^E
SIC 6211 Security brokers & dealers
Prin: Benjamin Levy
Sr VP: John Bodine
Sr VP: Gary Brewster
Sr VP: Lyle Chastaine
Sr VP: Vescio Fredrick
Sr VP: David Frost
Sr VP: Michael McElhenney
Sr VP: Kevin Salmini
VP: Cheryl Carter
VP: Helen Cheng
VP: Stephen Hardin
VP: Justin Holland
VP: Mark Johnson
**VP:* Fony Leonard
VP: Gerard Nealon
VP: Yoon Song
VP: Malte Wulfetange
Exec: Mark Bradt
Exec: Christopher Foley
Exec: Linda Kuester
Exec: Sunil Panikkath

D-U-N-S 07-189-4554
▲ HOULIHAN LOKEY INC
10250 Constellation Blvd # 5, Los Angeles, CA 90067-6205
Tel (310) 553-8871 *Founded/Ownrshp* 1972
Sales 396.4MM^E *EMP* 981
Tkr Sym HLI *Exch* NYS
SIC 6211 6282 Investment bankers; Security brokers & dealers; Investment bankers; Investment advice
Ch: Irwin N Gold
Pr: Scott J Adelson
Pr: David A Preiser
CEO: Scott L Beiser
CFO: J Lindsey Alley
Sr VP: Hector Calzada
Sr VP: Mark Melancon
Sr VP: Glenn Neblett
VP: Richard Billovits
VP: Deirdre Johnson
VP: Jimmy Page

HOULIHAN'S
See VALLEY HOSPITALITY SERVICES LLC

HOULIHAN'S
See CLANCYS INC

D-U-N-S 04-509-2277
HOULIHANS RESTAURANTS INC
8700 State Line Rd # 100, Leawood, KS 66206-1572
Tel (913) 901-2500 *Founded/Ownrshp* 1989
Sales 195.2MM^E *EMP* 4,200
SIC 5812 5813 Restaurant, family: chain; Cocktail lounge; Restaurant, family: chain; Cocktail lounge
CEO: Robert Hartnett
**Pr:* Brian Dailey
**CFO:* Robert Ellis
VP: Cindy Parres
Exec: Dan Essex
Genl Mgr: Josh Deery
Genl Mgr: Erin Dreiling
Dir IT: Jason Clark
Mktg Mgr: Misty Stocksdale
Mktg Mgr: Chris Wirt

D-U-N-S 07-746-2265
HOULTON REGIONAL HOSPITAL
20 Hartford St Ofc, Houlton, ME 04730-1859
Tel (207) 532-2900 *Founded/Ownrshp* 1972
Sales 46.9MM *EMP* 355
SIC 8062 8051 General medical & surgical hospitals; Skilled nursing care facilities; General medical & surgical hospitals; Skilled nursing care facilities
CEO: Tom Moakler
Chf OB: Robert Mosenfelder
CFO: Cynthia Thompson
Chf Mktg O: Lisa Perfitt
Dir OR: Gina Brown
Dir Rx: Rebecca Melesciuk
Dir Rx: Paul Sjoberg

Dir Env Sv: Glenda Crandall
CIO: Tammy McGary
Software D: Ellen Bartlett
Psych: Bart Peters

D-U-N-S 14-659-2550
HOUMA INDUSTRIES LLC
1725 Destrehan Ave, Harvey, LA 70058-1115
Tel (504) 347-4585 *Founded/Ownrshp* 2005
Sales 20.0MM^E *EMP* 176
SIC 3441 Fabricated structural metal

HOUR DETROIT MAGAZINE
See HOUR MEDIA LLC

D-U-N-S 96-545-9183
HOUR MEDIA LLC
HOUR DETROIT MAGAZINE
5750 New King Dr Ste 100, Troy, MI 48098-2696
Tel (248) 691-1800 *Founded/Ownrshp* 1996
Sales 20.4MM^E *EMP* 102
SIC 2721 Periodicals
Pt: David Christensen
VP: Mike Muszall
Genl Mgr: Roxanne Mullins
Genl Mgr: Ed Peabody
Off Mgr: Kathie Gorecki
Prd Dir: Trudie Cloyd
Prd Dir: Jon Reynolds
Sales Exec: Jason Hosko
Assoc Ed: Casey Nesterowich

D-U-N-S 80-842-7327
■ **HOURGLASS HOLDINGS LLC**
(*Suby of* US SILICA HOLDINGS INC) ★
8490 Progress Dr Ste 300, Frederick, MD 21701-4996
Tel (301) 682-0600 *Founded/Ownrshp* 2007
Sales 26.8MM^E *EMP* 701
SIC 1446 Silica sand mining; Silica sand mining
CEO: Bryan Shinn
**Treas:* Michael Thompson
**Sec:* Christine Marshall

D-U-N-S 04-144-6451
HOURIGAN CONSTRUCTION CORP
4429 Bonney Rd Ste 200, Virginia Beach, VA 23462-3877
Tel (757) 499-3434 *Founded/Ownrshp* 1993
Sales 46.5MM^E *EMP* 99
Accts Sullivan Andrews & Taylor Pc
SIC 1542 1541 Commercial & office building, new construction; Industrial buildings, new construction; Commercial & office building, new construction; Industrial buildings, new construction
Pr: Mark J Hourigan
**Treas:* Ron McIntosh
**VP:* Todd Donaldson
**VP:* Janie Smith
Ql Cn Mgr: Greg Alexander
Ql Cn Mgr: Elizabeth Michaels
Snr PM: Ronald Caswell

D-U-N-S 18-163-2696
HOUSE HUNTERS INC
14340 Memorial Dr, Houston, TX 77079-6707
Tel (281) 493-3880 *Founded/Ownrshp* 1999
Sales 8.9MM^E *EMP* 400
SIC 6531 Real estate brokers & agents; Real estate brokers & agents
Ch Bd: Lynn Zarr
**Pr:* Robin Mueck

HOUSE LAND DEVELOPEMENT CO
See LAND HOUSE CO LLC

D-U-N-S 05-075-9026 IMP
HOUSE OF BATTERIES (CA)
10910 Talbert Ave, Fountain Valley, CA 92708-6038
Tel (714) 962-7600 *Founded/Ownrshp* 1965, 1990
Sales 22.7MM *EMP* 70
SIC 5063

HOUSE OF BLUES
See HOB ENTERTAINMENT LLC

D-U-N-S 61-120-5543
■ **HOUSE OF BLUES CONCERTS INC**
(*Suby of* HOB ENTERTAINMENT LLC) ★
6255 W Sunset Blvd Fl 16, Los Angeles, CA 90028-7403
Tel (323) 769-4977 *Founded/Ownrshp* 1978
Sales 11.8MM^E *EMP* 300
SIC 7929 Entertainers & entertainment groups; Entertainers & entertainment groups
Pr: Joe Kazoworski
Treas: Joseph Kaczorowski
Ex VP: Adam Friedman
VP: Jennifer Vernon
VP: John Zeebroeck

HOUSE OF BURGUNDY NEWYORK
See EBER BROS WINE AND LIQUOR CORP

D-U-N-S 05-419-4055 EXP
HOUSE OF CHEATHAM INC
CHEATHAM CHEMICAL COMPANY
1445 Rock Mountain Blvd, Stone Mountain, GA 30083-1505
Tel (770) 414-7283 *Founded/Ownrshp* 1971
Sales 42.8MM^E *EMP* 136
SIC 2844 Hair preparations, including shampoos; Toilet preparations; Hair preparations, including shampoos; Toilet preparations
CEO: Robert H Bell
**CFO:* Tom Landrus
**CFO:* Charles Yarbrough
**V Ch Bd:* Alfred C Warrington IV
Mng Dir: Jeff Carson
Snr Mgr: Shirley Yarbrough

HOUSE OF CORRECTIONS
See COUNTY OF MERRIMACK

D-U-N-S 02-951-9725
HOUSE OF FABRICS INC
FABRICLAND
(*Suby of* JO-ANN FABRICS & CRAFTS) ★
5555 Darrow Rd, Hudson, OH 44236-4011
Tel (330) 656-2600 *Founded/Ownrshp* 1998
Sales 69.5MM^E *EMP* 3,000
SIC 5949 5945 5722 Fabric stores piece goods; Sewing supplies; Notions, including trim; Arts & crafts supplies; Sewing machines; Fabric stores piece goods; Sewing supplies; Notions, including trim; Arts & crafts supplies; Sewing machines
Ch Bd: Alan Rosskamm
V Ch: Robert Norton
**Treas:* James Kerr
Sr VP: Anthony C Dissinger
Sr VP: Fred Johnson
**Sr VP:* Betty Rosskamm
Sr VP: Justin Zimmerman
VP: David Bolen
**VP:* Brian Carney
VP: Peter El Ginol
VP: John Stec
**VP:* Donald Tomoff
Comm Dir: Thomas E Connors

D-U-N-S 00-654-6089 EXP
HOUSE OF FLAVORS INC
(*Suby of* PROTEIN HOLDINGS INC) ★
110 N William St, Ludington, MI 49431-2092
Tel (231) 845-7369 *Founded/Ownrshp* 1999
Sales 84.8MM^E *EMP* 150
SIC 2024 Ice cream, packaged: molded, on sticks, etc.; Ice cream, packaged: molded, on sticks, etc.
Pr: Whit Gallagher
VP: Pat Calder
VP: Jay Sherman
Sfty Dirs: Doug Klinger
Ql Cn Mgr: Jake Smith

D-U-N-S 07-728-9635
HOUSE OF GOOD SHEPHERD
1550 Champlin Ave, Utica, NY 13502-4828
Tel (315) 235-7600 *Founded/Ownrshp* 1872
Sales 23.9MM *EMP* 410
Accts Bonadio & Co Llp Syracuse Ny
SIC 8361 Home for the emotionally disturbed; Home for the emotionally disturbed
Prin: William Holicky
**Pr:* James Humphrey
**VP:* Gregory McLean
Pr Dir: Graceann Guzski

D-U-N-S 07-830-0225
HOUSE OF GOOD SHEPHERD OF CITY OF BALTIMORE
GOOD SHEPHERD CENTER
4100 Maple Ave, Halethorpe, MD 21227-4007
Tel (410) 247-2770 *Founded/Ownrshp* 1865
Sales 20.2MM *EMP* 300
Accts Stegman & Company Towson Md
SIC 8361 Residential care; Residential care
CEO: Michele Wyman

D-U-N-S 02-794-2390 EXP
■ **HOUSE OF IMPORTS INC**
HOUSE OF IMPORTS MERCEDES-BENZ
(*Suby of* AUTONATION INC) ★
6862 Auto Center Dr, Buena Park, CA 90621-3691
Tel (714) 562-1100 *Founded/Ownrshp* 2006
Sales 62.2MM^E *EMP* 193
SIC 5511 Automobiles, new & used; Automobiles, new & used
Genl Mgr: Pat Lustig
Genl Mgr: Sean Davisson
Genl Mgr: Steve Kwak
IT Man: Christophe Ryba

HOUSE OF IMPORTS MERCEDES-BENZ
See HOUSE OF IMPORTS INC

D-U-N-S 03-945-6348
HOUSE OF LA ROSE CLEVELAND INC (OH)
6745 Southpointe Pkwy, Brecksville, OH 44141-3267
Tel (440) 746-7500 *Founded/Ownrshp* 1979
Sales 129.6MM^E *EMP* 210
SIC 5181 Beer & other fermented malt liquors; Beer & other fermented malt liquors
Ch Bd: Thomas A La Rose
**Pr:* James P La Rose
CFO: Mark Yakubowski
**V Ch Bd:* Joseph F La Rose
**VP:* Peter C La Rose
VP: Norman Mackelly
DP Exec: Dan Brinegar
IT Man: Fred Stewart
VP Sls: Art Sunday
Sls Dir: Mitch Merriman
Mktg Mgr: Heather Popa

D-U-N-S 00-319-9346 IMP/EXP
HOUSE OF RAEFORD FARMS INC
(*Suby of* NASH JOHNSON & SONS FARMS INC) ★
1000 E Central Ave, Raeford, NC 28376-3039
Tel (910) 875-8600 *Founded/Ownrshp* 1958
Sales 1.0MMM^E *EMP* 6,000
Accts Morre Stephens Frost Cpa
SIC 2015 Turkey, slaughtered & dressed; Turkey, processed: frozen; Chicken, slaughtered & dressed; Chicken, processed: frozen; Turkey, slaughtered & dressed; Turkey, processed: frozen; Chicken, slaughtered & dressed; Chicken, processed: frozen
Pr: Donald Taber
**CEO:* Robert Johnson
CFO: Mike McLeod
**CFO:* Ken Qualls
**Ch:* Marvin Johnson
Treas: Doug Senogles
VP: Steve Dunn
Genl Mgr: Steve Stefanick
Dir IT: Chuck Robison
IT Man: Andy Spivey
Opers Mgr: Ron Briggs

D-U-N-S 00-761-0843 EXP
HOUSE OF RAEFORD FARMS OF LOUISIANA LLC
(*Suby of* NASH JOHNSON & SONS FARMS INC) ★
3867 2nd St, Arcadia, LA 71001-5376
Tel (318) 263-9004 *Founded/Ownrshp* 1997
Sales 116.6MM^E *EMP* 700
SIC 0251 2015 Broiling chickens, raising of; Chicken, slaughtered & dressed; Chicken, processed: fresh; Broiling chickens, raising of; Chicken, slaughtered & dressed; Chicken, processed: fresh
Genl Mgr: Kelly Garris
Off Mgr: Christy Jackson
Plnt Mgr: Darrell McBroom
Sls Mgr: Kenneth Brasher
Sls Mgr: Ross Hickman

HOUSE OF REFUGE CHURCH
See HOUSE OF REGUGE OF ROCKFORD INC

D-U-N-S 60-805-7444
HOUSE OF REGUGE OF ROCKFORD INC
HOUSE OF REFUGE CHURCH
1401 W State St, Rockford, IL 61102-2006
Tel (815) 968-0026 *Founded/Ownrshp* 1980
Sales 8.6MM^E *EMP* 325
SIC 8661 Non-denominational church; Non-denominational church

D-U-N-S 80-987-5362
HOUSE OF REPRESENTATIVES ALASKA
(*Suby of* LEGISLATIVE OFFICE OF THE STATE OF ALASKA)
State Capitol, Juneau, AK 99801
Tel (907) 465-3720 *Founded/Ownrshp* 1959
Sales NA *EMP* 400^E
SIC 9121 Legislative bodies, state & local; ; Legislative bodies, state & local;

D-U-N-S 80-938-5669
HOUSE OF REPRESENTATIVES FLORIDA
(*Suby of* LEGISLATIVE OFFICE OF FLORIDA) ★
402 S Monroe St Ste 420, Tallahassee, FL 32399-6526
Tel (850) 488-1450 *Founded/Ownrshp* 1845
Sales NA *EMP* 695
SIC 9121 Congress; ; Congress;
Prin: Jonny Byrd
V Ch: Bill Galvano
CFO: Charlie Crist
Comm Dir: Kristen McDonald
Adv Bd Mbr: Rodd D Brickell
**Prin:* Tom Fenney
Snr Mgr: Ned Luczynski

D-U-N-S 80-882-0518
HOUSE OF REPRESENTATIVES IOWA
(*Suby of* GOVERNORS OFFICE) ★
1015 State Cpitol Bldg G2, Des Moines, IA 50319
Tel (515) 281-5879 *Founded/Ownrshp* 1846
Sales NA *EMP* 300
SIC 9121 ;
Prin: Pat Murphy
Counsel: Charles Teas

D-U-N-S 80-992-7809
HOUSE OF REPRESENTATIVES LOUISIANA STATE
(*Suby of* LEGISLATIVE OFFICE OF STATE OF LOUISIANA INC) ★
900 N 3rd St, Baton Rouge, LA 70802-5236
Tel (225) 342-7259 *Founded/Ownrshp* 1812
Sales NA *EMP* 457
SIC 9121 Legislative bodies; ; Legislative bodies;
Prin: Charlie Dewitt
Treas: John Kennedy

D-U-N-S 82-488-1254
HOUSE OF REPRESENTATIVES MASSACHUSETTS
(*Suby of* LEGISLATIVE OFFICE OF COMMONWEALTH OF MASSACHUSETTS) ★
24 Beacon St Rm 356, Boston, MA 02133-1039
Tel (617) 722-2500 *Founded/Ownrshp* 1788
Sales NA *EMP* 550
SIC 9121 Legislative bodies, state & local; ; Legislative bodies, state & local;

D-U-N-S 80-533-5528
HOUSE OF REPRESENTATIVES MICHIGAN
(*Suby of* LEGISLATIVE OFFICE OF MICHIGAN) ★
124 N Capitol Ave Fl 2, Lansing, MI 48933-1343
Tel (517) 373-1747 *Founded/Ownrshp* 1837
Sales NA *EMP* 670
SIC 9121 Legislative bodies, state & local; ; Legislative bodies, state & local;
CFO: Christine Hammond
Brnch Mgr: Mith Bean

D-U-N-S 80-517-1378
HOUSE OF REPRESENTATIVES MINNESOTA
(*Suby of* LEGISLATIVE OFFICE OF STATE OF MINNESOTA) ★
100 Revernd M Luther King, Saint Paul, MN 55155-0001
Tel (651) 296-2146 *Founded/Ownrshp* 1966
Sales NA *EMP* 737
SIC 9121 Legislative bodies; ; Legislative bodies;
MIS Dir: Laurie A Lashbrook
MIS Dir: Laurie Lashbrook

D-U-N-S 87-807-4863
HOUSE OF REPRESENTATIVES MISSOURI
(*Suby of* LEGISLATIVE OFFICE OF STATE OF MISSOURI) ★
State Capitol House Po, Jefferson City, MO 65101
Tel (573) 751-3829 *Founded/Ownrshp* 1821
Sales NA *EMP* 400^E
SIC 9121 Congress; ; Congress;

D-U-N-S 80-834-2935
HOUSE OF REPRESENTATIVES NEW HAMPSHIRE
GENERAL COURT, NEW HAMPSHIRE
(*Suby of* GOVERNORS OFFICE) ★
107 N Main St Rm 312, Concord, NH 03301-4951
Tel (603) 271-3661 *Founded/Ownrshp* 1788
Sales NA *EMP* 400
SIC 9121 Legislative bodies; ; Legislative bodies;
Prin: Terie Norelli
Prin: Gene Chandler
Prin: Linda Foster
Prin: Mary Jane Wallner
Prin: Michael Whlley

D-U-N-S 80-937-5991
HOUSE OF REPRESENTATIVES OHIO
(*Suby of* LEGISLATIVE OFFICE OF THE STATE OF OHIO)
77 S High St Fl 4, Columbus, OH 43215-6108
Tel (614) 466-4308 *Founded/Ownrshp* 1803
Sales NA *EMP* 300
SIC 9121 Legislative bodies; Legislative bodies
Comm Dir: Shannon Boston

D-U-N-S 82-470-1288
HOUSE OF REPRESENTATIVES OKLAHOMA
(*Suby of* LEGISLATIVE OFFICE OF THE STATE OF OKLAHOMA)
2300 N Lincoln Blvd B23, Oklahoma City, OK 73105-4885
Tel (405) 521-2711 *Founded/Ownrshp* 1907
Sales NA *EMP* 300^E
SIC 9121 Legislative bodies, state & local; ; Legislative bodies, state & local;
Prin: Chris Benge
Comm Dir: Damon Gardenhire
MIS Dir: Theodore J Robinson

D-U-N-S 61-845-5265
HOUSE OF REPRESENTATIVES PENNSYLVANIA
(*Suby of* LEGISLATIVE OFFICE OF COMMONWEALTH OF PENNSYLVANIA) ★
Main Capitol Bldg Rm 132, Harrisburg, PA 17120-0001
Tel (717) 787-3607 *Founded/Ownrshp* 1776
Sales NA *EMP* 2,000
SIC 9121 Legislative bodies, state & local; ; Legislative bodies, state & local;
Genl Mgr: Rep Samuel Smith
**Genl Mgr:* Representative Samuel Smith
MIS Dir: Kathy Sullivan
Counsel: Leeann Murray
Snr Mgr: James Mann

D-U-N-S 08-467-2596
HOUSE OF REPRESENTATIVES RHODE ISLAND
(*Suby of* LEGISLATIVE OFFICE OF STATE OF RHODE ISLAND) ★
82 Smith St Ste 323, Providence, RI 02903-1122
Tel (401) 222-2466 *Founded/Ownrshp* 1790
Sales NA *EMP* 300
SIC 9121 Legislative bodies, state & local; ; Legislative bodies, state & local;

D-U-N-S 87-843-3556
HOUSE OF REPRESENTATIVES TENNESSEE
(*Suby of* LEGISLATIVE OFFICE OF TENNESSEE) ★
6th & Un Legislative Plz, Nashville, TN 37243-0001
Tel (615) 741-3774 *Founded/Ownrshp* 1796
Sales NA *EMP* 523
SIC 9121 Legislative bodies, state & local; Legislative bodies, state & local;
Prin: James O Naifeh

D-U-N-S 80-719-7744
HOUSE OF REPRESENTATIVES TEXAS
(*Suby of* LEGISLATIVE OFFICE TEXAS) ★
105 W 15th St, Austin, TX 78701-1933
Tel (512) 463-0865 *Founded/Ownrshp* 1845
Sales NA *EMP* 1,000
SIC 9121 Legislative bodies, state & local; ; Legislative bodies, state & local;
Prin: Joe Straus
Adm Dir: William Gray

D-U-N-S 93-335-1660
■ **HOUSE OF REPRESENTATIVES UNITED STATES**
(*Suby of* CONGRESS UNITED STATES) ★
The Capitol, Washington, DC 20515-0001
Tel (202) 224-3121 *Founded/Ownrshp* 1787
Sales NA *EMP* 10,000
Accts Cotton & Company Llp/Matthew
SIC 9121 Congress; ; Congress;
Prin: John A Boehner
Bd of Dir: Justin Stevens
**Ofcr:* Daniel Beard
Ofcr: James Eagen
Comm Dir: Michael Hartigan
Comm Dir: Richard Rapoza
Dir Bus: Sweeney David
**Prin:* Karen Lehman Haas
**Prin:* Dan Strodell
Admn Mgr: Robert Thorsen
Off Mgr: Pearl Mangrum

D-U-N-S 80-888-2153
HOUSE OF REPRESENTATIVES WASHINGTON
(*Suby of* LEGISLATIVE OFFICE OF STATE OF WASHINGTON) ★
416 Sid Snyder Ave Sw, Olympia, WA 98501-1347
Tel (360) 786-7750 *Founded/Ownrshp* 1889
Sales NA *EMP* 300
SIC 9121 Legislative bodies, state & local; ; Legislative bodies, state & local;
Prin: Frank Chopp

D-U-N-S 03-145-2782
HOUSE OF SCHWAN INC
3636 N Comotara St, Wichita, KS 67226-1301
Tel (316) 636-9100 *Founded/Ownrshp* 1960
Sales 27.5MM^E *EMP* 75
SIC 5181 Beer & other fermented malt liquors; Beer & other fermented malt liquors
Pr: Barry L Schwan
**VP:* Robert B Schwan
Dir IT: Ron Smith
Opers Mgr: Mike Daniel

D-U-N-S 05-641-4584 IMP
HOUSE OF SPICES (INDIA) INC
12740 Willets Point Blvd, Flushing, NY 11368-1506
Tel (718) 507-4900 *Founded/Ownrshp* 1970
Sales 114.2MM^E *EMP* 230

SIC 5149 2099 5153 2033 2024 Pasta & rice; Food preparations; Grain & field beans; Vegetable pastes: packaged in cans, jars, etc.; Ice cream & frozen desserts; Pasta & rice; Food preparations; Grain & field beans; Vegetable pastes: packaged in cans, jars, etc.; Ice cream & frozen desserts
Ch Bd: Gordhandas L Soni
CFO: Chetan Soni
*VP: Niel Soni

HOUSE OF THE TEMPLE, THE
See SUPREME COUNCIL OF THIRTY-THIRD DEGREE OF SCOTTISH RITE MASONRY OF SJ USA

HOUSE OF THREADS CO
See HOUSE OF THREADS INC

D-U-N-S 00-440-3143 IMP/EXP
HOUSE OF THREADS INC (GA)
HOUSE OF THREADS CO
144 Industrial Dr, Birmingham, AL 35211-4466
Tel (205) 916-2512 Founded/Ownrshp 1996
Sales 59.9MME EMP 188
SIC 5072

D-U-N-S 02-978-6472
HOUSE OF TOOLS AND ENGINEERING INC
HTE TECHNOLOGIES
2021 Congressional Dr, Saint Louis, MO 63146-4103
Tel (314) 731-4444 Founded/Ownrshp 1959
Sales 94.1MME EMP 95
SIC 5084 Pneumatic tools & equipment; Hydraulic systems equipment & supplies; Pneumatic tools & equipment; Hydraulic systems equipment & supplies
Pr: R K Shearburn
VP: Tom Bielicki
*VP: Jean M Shearburn
VP: Marion Strickland
Info Man: Scott McBrady
Sfty Mgr: Jim Grace
Sls Mgr: Marvin Dixon
Sales Asso: Mike Doedli
Sales Asso: Russ Gilliland
Sales Asso: Bob Hanebrink
Sales Asso: Pat Town

HOUSE OF TUDOR
See BAKED IN SUN

D-U-N-S 02-332-0047
HOUSE OF WYOMING VALLEY INC
HOUSE ON THE ROCK
5754 State Road 23, Spring Green, WI 53588-8912
Tel (608) 935-3639 Founded/Ownrshp 1958
Sales 15.5MME EMP 500
SIC 7999 8412 Tourist attraction, commercial; Museums & art galleries; Tourist attraction, commercial; Museums & art galleries
Pr: Susan Donaldson
*Treas: Arthur Donaldson

HOUSE ON THE ROCK
See HOUSE OF WYOMING VALLEY INC

HOUSE WARNINGS
See EVERBURN MANUFACTURING INC

D-U-N-S 00-792-1372 EXP
HOUSE-HASSON HARDWARE CO (TN)
3125 Water Plant Rd, Knoxville, TN 37914-6640
Tel (865) 525-0471 Founded/Ownrshp 1906
Sales 359.1MME EMP 375
Accts Pugh & Company Pc Knoxville
SIC 5072 5031 Hardware; Lumber, plywood & millwork; Hardware; Lumber, plywood & millwork
CEO: Don Hasson
*VP: David Helfenberger
*VP: Steve Henry
*VP: Don M McLean
VP: Don Phillips
*VP: Mike Woolf
Rgnl Mgr: David Baumberger
Rgnl Mgr: Mike Hardin
Rgnl Mgr: Dick Morgan
CIO: Larry Fennell
Dir IT: Dennis Quilliams

D-U-N-S 79-631-7977
HOUSE-HASSON HARDWARE CO PERSINGER DIVISION INC
(Suby of HOUSE-HASSON HARDWARE CO) ★
122 Prichard Indus Pk Rd, Prichard, WV 25555-4002
Tel (304) 486-5401 Founded/Ownrshp 2007
Sales 42.2MME EMP 82
SIC 5072 Hardware
Pr: Don C Hasson
*Treas: Vernice Deskins
*VP: Beverly Perry
Sls Mgr: Gary Keck

HOUSECALL HOME HEALTH
See HOUSECALL MEDICAL RESOURCES INC

D-U-N-S 79-321-7204
■ **HOUSECALL HOME HEALTH INC**
(Suby of AMEDISYS INC) ★
5959 S Shrwood Frest Blvd, Baton Rouge, LA 70816
Tel (225) 292-2031 Founded/Ownrshp 1983
Sales 6.3MME EMP 522E
SIC 8082 Home health care services

D-U-N-S 84-996-7518
■ **HOUSECALL MEDICAL RESOURCES INC**
HOUSECALL HOME HEALTH
(Suby of AMEDISYS INC) ★
1400 Cntrpint Blvd St 100, Knoxville, TN 37932
Tel (865) 689-7123 Founded/Ownrshp 2005
Sales 25.0MME EMP 2,000
SIC 8082 8741 5999 Home health care services; Nursing & personal care facility management; Medical apparatus & supplies
CEO: John Heller
VP: Michael Hall

D-U-N-S 78-126-9022
HOUSECHEM INC
21-25 Indl Park, Waldwick, NJ 07463
Tel (201) 445-8808 Founded/Ownrshp 1986
Sales 24.0MME EMP 80
SIC 5162 8111 Plastics products; Legal services; Plastics products; Legal services
Pr: Lee Fantone
CFO: Fred Fiorentino
Genl Mgr: Knut Menshen
VP Sls: Jeffrey Stern

D-U-N-S 15-370-0133
HOUSEHOLD COMMERCIAL FINANCIAL SERVICES INC
(Suby of HOUSEHOLD GROUP, INC)
2700 Sanders Rd, Prospect Heights, IL 60070-2701
Tel (847) 564-5000 Founded/Ownrshp 1986
Sales NA EMP 525
SIC 6153 Short-term business credit; Short-term business credit
VP: Robert Walsh
*Pr: William Aldinger
*VP: Doug Friedrich

D-U-N-S 96-158-3791 IMP
HOUSEHOLD ESSENTIALS LLC
H E
5895 N Lindbergh Blvd, Hazelwood, MO 63042-3119
Tel (314) 428-5657 Founded/Ownrshp 2010
Sales 23.7MME EMP 42
SIC 5023 Home furnishings
Creative D: Chris Smith
Sales Exec: Jim Nay
Natl Sales: Tim Condon
Natl Sales: Jerry Jones
Mktg Mgr: Jo Ceresia
Sls Mgr: Tom Nance

HOUSEHOLD FINANCE
See HOUSEHOLD RECOVERY SERVICES CORP

D-U-N-S 00-693-0598
HOUSEHOLD FINANCE CORP
HFC
(Suby of HSBC FINANCE CORP) ★
2700 Sanders Rd, Prospect Heights, IL 60070-2701
Tel (847) 790-1590 Founded/Ownrshp 1925
Sales NA EMP 2,199
SIC 6141 6162 6351 6153 6159 6311 Consumer finance companies; Mortgage bankers; Credit & other financial responsibility insurance; Mercantile financing; Equipment & vehicle finance leasing companies; Life insurance carriers; Consumer finance companies; Installment sales finance, other than banks; Mortgage bankers; Credit & other financial responsibility insurance; Mercantile financing; Equipment & vehicle finance leasing companies; Life insurance carriers
Ch Bd: David A Schoenholz
*Pr: Tomothey M Detelich
*CEO: W F Aldinger
*CFO: S C Penney
Sr VP: Bruce Fletcher
Sr VP: Richard Klesse
*VP: Colin Kelly

D-U-N-S 04-278-4488 EXP
HOUSEHOLD INDUSTRIAL TRADING CORP
993 Belleville Tpke, Kearny, NJ 07032-4411
Tel (201) 997-3700 Founded/Ownrshp 1972
Sales 50.0MM EMP 100
SIC 5023 Sheets, textile; Linens, table; Sheets, textile; Linens, table
Pr: Nazar Nazarian
*VP: W Kenneth Albright

D-U-N-S 86-873-1027
HOUSEHOLD RECOVERY SERVICES CORP
HOUSEHOLD FINANCE
(Suby of HSBC NORTH AMERICA HOLDINGS INC) ★
2929 Walden Ave, Depew, NY 14043-2602
Tel (636) 227-2000 Founded/Ownrshp 1993
Sales 17.7MME EMP 500
SIC 8748 7322 Business consulting; Adjustment & collection services
VP: David Grimme
*VP: George Wilson

D-U-N-S 06-256-0917 IMP
HOUSER SHOES INC
GB SHOES
5418 Asheville Hwy, Hendersonville, NC 28791-9097
Tel (828) 254-0054 Founded/Ownrshp 1972
Sales 26.0MME EMP 148
SIC 5661 Shoe stores
Pr: Gary E Houser
*VP: Christopher Scott Houser
Exec: Maxine Ward
CTO: Celeste McKinney

D-U-N-S 03-053-8227
HOUSER TRANSPORT INC
2809 Sam Houser Rd, Vale, NC 28168-9367
Tel (704) 462-2820 Founded/Ownrshp 1996
Sales 22.0MME EMP 80
SIC 4213 Trucking, except local
Pr: Sherry Lee
*CFO: Denise Truett
*VP: Samuel C Houser
Dir Bus: Patty Toler

HOUSESURGEONS
See AOI CORP

D-U-N-S 18-671-4085 IMP
■ **HOUSEWARES HOLDING CO INC**
(Suby of NACCO INDUSTRIES INC) ★
14785 Preston Rd Ste 1100, Dallas, TX 75254-6823
Tel (440) 449-9600 Founded/Ownrshp 1988
Sales 2.0MMME EMP 5,500
SIC 3634 5719 Toasters, electric: household; Kitchenware; Toasters, electric: household; Kitchenware
CEO: Alfred M Rankin Jr
Treas: J Butler Jr

D-U-N-S 96-155-3273
HOUSING AND HEALTHCARE FINANCE LLC
HHC
2 Wisconsin Cir Ste 540, Chevy Chase, MD 20815-7012
Tel (301) 941-1667 Founded/Ownrshp 2007
Sales NA EMP 14
SIC 6162 Mortgage bankers & correspondents

HOUSING AND NEIGHBOR SVCS DEPT
See CITY OF CHICO

HOUSING AUTH OF THE CY PTERSON
See PATERSON HOUSING AUTHORITY

HOUSING AUTHORITY INSURANCE GR
See HOUSING AUTHORITY RISK RETENTION GROUP INC

D-U-N-S 07-546-4289
HOUSING AUTHORITY OF BIRMINGHAM DISTRICT (INC)
1826 3rd Ave S, Birmingham, AL 35233-1905
Tel (205) 324-0641 Founded/Ownrshp 1935
Sales NA EMP 314
SIC 9531 ; Housing authority, non-operating: government;
Ex Dir: Naomi Truman
*Ch: Mary E Robinson
Ofcr: Ronald Williams
*VP: Bob Friedman
*Ex Dir: Ralph Ruggs
IT Man: Toraine Clausell

D-U-N-S 07-452-3176
HOUSING AUTHORITY OF CITY OF CHARLOTTE NC
400 East Blvd, Charlotte, NC 28203-5584
Tel (704) 336-5822 Founded/Ownrshp 1938
Sales 87.1MM EMP 203
Accts Cohnreznick Llp Charlotte No
SIC 6531 Housing authority operator; Housing authority operator
CEO: A Fulton Meachen Jr
COO: Larry Padilla
COO: Troy White
*CFO: Heather Franklin
Ofcr: Jennifer Gallman
Ofcr: Henri Smith
VP: Ralph Vestuti
Rgnl Mgr: Kay Basar

D-U-N-S 03-745-7991
HOUSING AUTHORITY OF CITY OF DALLAS
DALLAS HOUSING AUTHORITY
3939 N Hampton Rd, Dallas, TX 75212-1630
Tel (214) 951-8300 Founded/Ownrshp 1937
Sales NA EMP 384
Accts Yeager & Boyd Birmingham Ala
SIC 9531 ;
Pr: Maryann Russ
*Prin: Ann Lott
*Ex Dir: Broussard Troy
Snr Mgr: Tim Lott

D-U-N-S 05-972-1324
HOUSING AUTHORITY OF CITY OF EL PASO
5300 E Paisano Dr, El Paso, TX 79905-2931
Tel (915) 849-3742 Founded/Ownrshp 1938
Sales NA EMP 500
Accts Dunbar Broaddus Gibson Llp
SIC 9531 Housing agency, government; ; Housing agency, government;
Pr: Pabalo Salcido
Pr: Vincent Dodds
CEO: Gerald Cichon
COO: Michael Kramer
COO: Stan Waterhouse
CFO: Satish Bhaskar
Bd of Dir: Reyna Brantner
Ex Dir: P E Montiel
Area Supr: George Navarro

D-U-N-S 10-760-3342
HOUSING AUTHORITY OF CITY OF LINCOLN
LINCOLN HOUSING AUTHORITY
5700 R St, Lincoln, NE 68505-2332
Tel (402) 434-5500 Founded/Ownrshp 1994
Sales 23.5MM EMP 87
Accts Niewedde & Wiens Cpa S York
SIC 6513 Apartment building operators; Apartment building operators
Ch: Orville Jones III
Ex Dir: Doug Marthaler
*Ex Dir: Larry Potratz
Dir IT: Janet Love

D-U-N-S 07-723-3732
HOUSING AUTHORITY OF CITY OF LOS ANGELES
HACLA
2600 Wilshire Blvd, Los Angeles, CA 90057-3400
Tel (213) 252-2500 Founded/Ownrshp 1938
Sales NA EMP 1,184
SIC 9531

D-U-N-S 03-349-1911
HOUSING AUTHORITY OF CITY OF NEWARK
500 Broad St, Newark, NJ 07102-3112
Tel (973) 273-6000 Founded/Ownrshp 1938
Sales NA EMP 1,922
SIC 9531 Housing authority, non-operating: government; Housing authority, non-operating: government
Ex Dir: Keith Kinard
CFO: Marvin Walton
Ofcr: Sibyl Bryant
VP: Larry Howell
Ex Dir: Harold Lucas
IT Man: Venancio Vannydiaz
Opers Supe: Andre McNair
Snr Mgr: Ellen Harris
Snr Mgr: Michelle Lewis

D-U-N-S 10-181-9712
HOUSING AUTHORITY OF CITY OF ORLANDO
390 N Bumby Ave, Orlando, FL 32803-6026
Tel (407) 895-3300 Founded/Ownrshp 1938
Sales 45.1MME EMP 145
Accts Ac&C Llp Cpa Coralgables F
SIC 1521 Single-family housing construction; Single-family housing construction
Ch Bd: Ed Carson
*CFO: Barbara Chen
Brnch Mgr: Margarita Rofario
Pr Dir: Ed Frazier

D-U-N-S 01-019-8117
HOUSING AUTHORITY OF CITY OF SEATTLE
SEATTLE HOUSING AUTHORITY
190 Queen Anne Ave N # 100, Seattle, WA 98109-4982
Tel (206) 615-3351 Founded/Ownrshp 1939
Sales NA EMP 602
Accts Kpmg Llp Seattle Wa
SIC 9531 Housing authority, non-operating: government; ; Housing authority, non-operating: government;
Ex Dir: Andrew Lofton
*CFO: Shelly Yapp
Exec: Linda J Brosell
Exec: Kerri Fitch
*Ex Dir: Thomas Tierney
Prgrm Mgr: Jodell Speer
CIO: Steve McDowell
IT Man: Dominique Hampton
Info Man: Butch Proffitt
Opers Mgr: Judi Carter
Genl Couns: Linda Wandell

D-U-N-S 07-003-3105
HOUSING AUTHORITY OF CITY OF TULSA
TULSA HOUSING AUTHORITY
415 E Independence St, Tulsa, OK 74106-5727
Tel (918) 581-5720 Founded/Ownrshp 1967
Sales 51.7MM EMP 227
Accts Adam Stump
SIC 6514 6531 Dwelling operators, except apartments; Housing authority operator; Dwelling operators, except apartments; Housing authority operator
Ch Bd: Ruth K Nelson
*Pr: Chea Redditt
*CFO: Don Hammons
Exec: Ladeanna Anderson

D-U-N-S 02-024-4976
HOUSING AUTHORITY OF COUNTY OF KING
KCHA
600 Andover Park W, Tukwila, WA 98188-3326
Tel (206) 574-1100 Founded/Ownrshp 1939
Sales NA EMP 300
Accts Brian Sonntag Cgfm
SIC 9531 Housing programs, planning & development: government; Housing programs, planning & development: government
Ex Dir: Stephen J Norman
*Ch: Nancy Holland Young
Dir Risk M: Mark Abernathy
Off Admin: Shawna Broeker
CIO: Gary Leaf
IT Man: Craig Violante
Sls&Mrk Ex: Jeff Friend

D-U-N-S 04-323-8971
HOUSING AUTHORITY OF COUNTY OF MERCED (CA)
405 U St, Merced, CA 95341-6548
Tel (209) 722-3501 Founded/Ownrshp 1946
Sales 27.7MM EMP 2
SIC 6513 Apartment building operators; Apartment building operators
Ex Dir: Rennise Ferrerio
Ex Dir: Carlos Araujo
Ex Dir: Nicholas Benjamin

D-U-N-S 04-034-8872
HOUSING AUTHORITY OF COUNTY OF SANTA BARBARA
HACSB
815 W Ocean Ave, Lompoc, CA 93436-6526
Tel (805) 736-3423 Founded/Ownrshp 1941
Sales 41.7MM EMP 75E
SIC 6531 Housing authority operator; Housing authority operator
Ex Dir: Frederick C Lamont
*CFO: Robert Havlicek
*Prin: Fran Clow
*Prin: Robert Dickerson
*Prin: Mickey Flacks
*Prin: John Lizarraga
*Prin: Thomas Miller

D-U-N-S 07-911-9448
HOUSING AUTHORITY OF COUNTY OF SANTA CLARA
505 W Julian St, San Jose, CA 95110-2300
Tel (408) 275-8770 Founded/Ownrshp 2013
Sales 304.3MM EMP 4
SIC 6531 Housing authority operator
Ex Dir: Alex Sanchez

D-U-N-S 01-092-3928
HOUSING AUTHORITY OF COUNTY OF SANTA CRUZ
2931 Mission St, Santa Cruz, CA 95060-5709
Tel (831) 454-9455 Founded/Ownrshp 1969
Sales 58.0MM EMP 65
SIC 6531 Real estate managers; Real estate managers
Ex Dir: Ken Cole

D-U-N-S 07-805-1299
HOUSING AUTHORITY OF GREENVILLE INC
GREENVILLE HOUSING AUTHORITY
122 Edinburgh Ct, Greenville, SC 29607-2530
Tel (864) 467-4250 Founded/Ownrshp 1938
Sales 24.0MM EMP 58
SIC 6531 Real estate agents & managers; Real estate agents & managers
Ex Dir: C Herrera
*Ex Dir: Cindi Herrera
Ex Dir: Ivory Mathews

D-U-N-S 01-040-1495
HOUSING AUTHORITY OF NEW ORLEANS
4100 Touro St, New Orleans, LA 70122-3143
Tel (504) 670-3300 *Founded/Ownrshp* 1937
Sales NA *EMP* 550
SIC 9531 Housing authority, non-operating: government; Housing authority, non-operating: government
Ex Dir: Gregg Fortner
CFO: Sieglinde Chambliss
**CFO:* Andrea Hartt
VP: Phylis Smith
VP: Wilbert Thomas Sr
Ex Dir: Michael Kelly
**Ex Dir:* HUD Receiver Team
Dir Sec: Mitchel Dusset
Genl Couns: Kim R Variste

HOUSING AUTHORITY OF THE CITY
See CITY OF RIVERSIDE

D-U-N-S 61-880-8216
HOUSING AUTHORITY RISK RETENTION GROUP INC
HOUSING AUTHORITY INSURANCE GR
189 Commerce Ct, Cheshire, CT 06410-1253
Tel (203) 272-8220 *Founded/Ownrshp* 1987
Sales NA *EMP* 103
Accts Saslow Lufkin & Buggy Llp Av
SIC 6411 6331 Advisory services, insurance; Fire, marine & casualty insurance; Advisory services, insurance; Fire, marine & casualty insurance
CEO: Dan Labrie
**CFO:* Mark Wilson
**Ch:* Richard Collins
VP: Janet Carter
VP: Pat Hosick
VP: Randall Irwin
**VP:* William Lewellyn
**VP:* Edmund Malaspina
**VP:* Dominic Mazzoccoli
VP: Miriam Robinson
**VP:* David Sagers
VP: Bob Sullivan
**VP:* Robert Sullivan

HOUSING BRIDGE
See HOUSING PARTNERS OF NEW YORK INC

D-U-N-S 08-774-3191
HOUSING DEVELOPMENT AUTHORITY MICHIGAN STATE
M.S.H.D.A.
(*Suby of* DEPARTMENT OF LICENSING AND REGULATORY AFFAIRS) ★
735 E Michigan Ave, Lansing, MI 48912-1474
Tel (517) 373-8370 *Founded/Ownrshp* 1966
Sales NA *EMP* 320
Accts Plante & Moran Pllc
SIC 9531 Housing authority, non-operating: government; ; Housing authority, non-operating: government;
Treas: Bob Kleine
Bd of Dir: Anthony Estell
Ofcr: John Walter
Exec: Donna McMillan
Assoc Dir: Andrew Haan
Admn Mgr: Bouvy Mark
Dir IT: Debra Patterson
IT Man: Janell Thelen

HOUSING FOR INDEPENDENT LIVING
See SOUTH SHORE HOUSING DEVELOPMENT CORP

D-U-N-S 04-831-3613
HOUSING OPPORTUNITIES COMMISSION OF MONTGOMERY COUNTY MARYLAND
10400 Detrick Ave Ste 407, Kensington, MD 20895-2484
Tel (240) 773-9000 *Founded/Ownrshp* 1966
Sales NA *EMP* 335
Accts Cliftonlarsonallen Llp Baltim
SIC 9531 Housing programs, planning & development: government; ; Housing programs, planning & development: government;
Ex Dir: Stacy Spann
**CFO:* Gail Willison
Netwrk Mgr: David Brody
Tech Mgr: Sylvia Seuss

D-U-N-S 87-756-9676
HOUSING PARTNERS OF NEW YORK INC
HOUSING BRIDGE
1363 Coney Island Ave, Brooklyn, NY 11230-4119
Tel (718) 252-3200 *Founded/Ownrshp* 2006
Sales 29.2MM *EMP* 30^E
SIC 8322 Family service agency
Founder: Isaac Leshinsky
**COO:* Harry Fried

D-U-N-S 62-785-3146
HOUSING WORKS INC
57 Willoughby St Fl 2, Brooklyn, NY 11201-5290
Tel (347) 473-7400 *Founded/Ownrshp* 1990
Sales 18.7MM *EMP* 474
Accts Grant Thornton Llp New York
SIC 8399 Advocacy group; Advocacy group
Pr: Charles King
Pr: Ankur Patel
**COO:* Linney Smith
**Sr VP:* Andrew Coamey
Sr VP: Maria Gbur
**VP:* Andrew Greene
Creative D: Juan Astasio
Prac Mgr: Monica Perez
Opers Mgr: Melissa Hoskey

D-U-N-S 80-360-2072
HOUSING WORKS INC
57 Willoughby St Fl 2, Brooklyn, NY 11201-5290
Tel (347) 473-7400 *Founded/Ownrshp* 1990
Sales 37.2MM *EMP* 3^E
SIC 8733 5942 Noncommercial research organizations; Book stores; Noncommercial research organizations; Book stores
Pr: Charles King
Exec: Douglan Sandern
Ex Dir: Cyndy Cook

D-U-N-S 79-640-6713
HOUSING WORKS THRIFT SHOP
122 Montague St, Brooklyn, NY 11201-3481
Tel (718) 237-0521 *Founded/Ownrshp* 2007
Sales 24.4MM *EMP* 3
SIC 5932 Used merchandise stores; Used merchandise stores
Prin: Robin Gross

D-U-N-S 05-750-0506
HOUSLEY COMMUNICATIONS INC
HOUSLEY GROUP
3550 S Bryant Blvd, San Angelo, TX 76903-9310
Tel (325) 944-9905 *Founded/Ownrshp* 1980
Sales 55.5MM^E *EMP* 250
SIC 1731 4213 1623 Telephone & telephone equipment installation; Household goods transport; Transmitting tower (telecommunication) construction; Telephone & telephone equipment installation; Household goods transport; Transmitting tower (telecommunication) construction
Pr: Robert D Housley
**Ex VP:* David Meek
IT Man: Pat Real
Mktg Mgr: M Weeks

HOUSLEY GROUP
See HOUSLEY COMMUNICATIONS INC

D-U-N-S 05-445-2776 EXP
HOUSTON - PASADENA APACHE OIL CO LP (TX)
5136 Spencer Hwy, Pasadena, TX 77505-1510
Tel (281) 487-5400 *Founded/Ownrshp* 1972
Sales 73.0MM^E *EMP* 50
SIC 5171 5172 Petroleum bulk stations; Lubricating oils & greases; Petroleum bulk stations; Lubricating oils & greases
Pt: Johnny Isbell Sr
Pt: Johnny Isbell Jr
Pt: Ken Isbell
VP: David Albright
Genl Mgr: Bill Records
Mtls Mgr: Dennis Whetzel
Opers Mgr: Ray Loftin
Sls Mgr: Jay Britt
Sls Mgr: Jack Kennedy
Sls Mgr: Pat Shipp

D-U-N-S 80-094-5193
HOUSTON AIRPORT HOSPITALITY LP
HOLIDAY INN
(*Suby of* PACIFICA ENTERPRISES) ★
15222 Jfk Blvd, Houston, TX 77032-2306
Tel (281) 449-2311 *Founded/Ownrshp* 2007
Sales 21.8MM^E *EMP* 452^E
SIC 7011 Hotels & motels
CEO: Sushil Israni

HOUSTON ASSOCIATES
See HOUSTON ENTERPRISES INC

D-U-N-S 13-963-0800
■ **HOUSTON ASSOCIATES INC**
(*Suby of* RAYTHEON CO) ★
22260 Pacific Blvd, Sterling, VA 20166-6916
Tel (703) 284-8700 *Founded/Ownrshp* 1982
Sales 40.0MM *EMP* 145
Accts Aronson Fetridge & Weigle Cpa
SIC 8748 7373 8742 7374 4813 1731 Telecommunications consultant; Systems analysis & engineering consulting services; Computer integrated systems design; Local area network (LAN) systems integrator; Systems engineering, computer related; Management consulting services; Data processing & preparation; Telephone communication, except radio; Electrical work; Telecommunications consultant; Systems analysis & engineering consulting services; Computer integrated systems design; Local area network (LAN) systems integrator; Systems engineering, computer related; Management consulting services; Data processing & preparation; Telephone communication, except radio; Electrical work
Ch Bd: John R Houston
**Pr:* General Alonzo Short
**CEO:* Tom Kennedy
**CFO:* John L Bjork
Off Mgr: Ann Seitz
Mktg Mgr: David Butt
Mktg Mgr: Shila Harley
Snr Mgr: Bryan Bass

D-U-N-S 86-835-4767
■ **HOUSTON AUTO M IMPORTS GREENWAY LTD**
MERCEDES BENZ HOUSTON GREENWAY
(*Suby of* AUTONATION INC) ★
3900 Southwest Fwy, Houston, TX 77027-7518
Tel (713) 489-2111 *Founded/Ownrshp* 1999
Sales 47.9MM^E *EMP* 200
SIC 5511 Automobiles, new & used; Automobiles, new & used
Genl Mgr: Karl Stonberg
Opers Mgr: Gail Melton
Sls Mgr: Jay Bertrand

D-U-N-S 01-528-0550
■ **HOUSTON AUTO M IMPORTS NORTH LTD**
MERCEDES-BENZ OF HOUSTON NORTH
(*Suby of* AUTONATION INC) ★
17510 North Fwy, Houston, TX 77090-4902
Tel (281) 305-8970 *Founded/Ownrshp* 1999
Sales 38.1MM^E *EMP* 125
SIC 5511 5521 Automobiles, new & used; Used car dealers; Automobiles, new & used; Used car dealers
Pr: Walter Weibel

D-U-N-S 03-184-9656
HOUSTON AVOCADO CO INC
2224 Airline Dr, Houston, TX 77009-2422
Tel (713) 880-9210 *Founded/Ownrshp* 1974
Sales 58.6MM *EMP* 135
SIC 5148 Vegetables, fresh; Fruits; Vegetables, fresh; Fruits
Pr: E Alex Flores
Sec: Elma Flores
Genl Mgr: Mark Flores

D-U-N-S 07-939-4946 IMP
HOUSTON BALLET FOUNDATION
601 Preston St, Houston, TX 77002-1605
Tel (713) 226-7685 *Founded/Ownrshp* 1955
Sales 23.1MM *EMP* 250
Accts Uhy Llp Houston Tx
SIC 7911 7922 Dance studio & school; Ballet production; Dance studio & school; Ballet production
Ex Dir: James Nelson
**Pr:* James M Jordan
**Ch:* Karl S Stern
**Trst:* Leticia Loya
Trst: Michael Parmet
**VP:* Joseph A Hafner Jr
**VP:* Daniel M McClure
VP: Daniel McClure
VP: Robert B Tudor III
Assoc Dir: Shelly Power
Pr Mgr: Sarah Lam

D-U-N-S 01-080-3559
HOUSTON BAPTIST UNIVERSITY
7502 Fondren Rd, Houston, TX 77074-3298
Tel (281) 649-3000 *Founded/Ownrshp* 1960
Sales 87.9MM *EMP* 250
Accts Fitts Roberts & Co Pc Houston
SIC 8221 8661 University; Religious organizations; University; Religious organizations
Pr: Robert B Sloan Jr
Trst: J Randle
Ofcr: Phillip Rhodes
Genl Mgr: Lacie Hinkle
HC Dir: Eduardo Borges

D-U-N-S 00-963-3538 IMP
HOUSTON BAZZ CO
BAZZ HOUSTON CO
12700 Western Ave, Garden Grove, CA 92841-4017
Tel (714) 898-2666 *Founded/Ownrshp* 1957
Sales 20.3MM^E *EMP* 85
SIC 3469 3495 3493 Machine parts, stamped or pressed metal; Mechanical springs, precision; Steel springs, except wire
Pr: Javier Castro
**Sec:* Chester O Houston
Div Mgr: Don Scuteri
IT Man: Manuel Lopez
QI Cn Mgr: Erickson Bareng

D-U-N-S 13-090-9000
HOUSTON BENCHMARK BUILDER LP
500 Westcott St Ste 290, Houston, TX 77007
Tel (713) 921-2500 *Founded/Ownrshp* 2002
Sales 60.0MM *EMP* 25
SIC 1542 Commercial & office building contractors; Commercial & office buildings, prefabricated erection
Pr: Thomas Dadoly
Pr: Craig Harden
VP: Jason Boeker
Off Mgr: Terry Johnson

D-U-N-S 10-766-2280
■ **HOUSTON CASUALTY CO**
HCC SERVICE
(*Suby of* HCC INSURANCE HOLDINGS INC) ★
13403 Northwest Fwy, Houston, TX 77040-6006
Tel (713) 462-1000 *Founded/Ownrshp* 1988
Sales NA *EMP* 169
SIC 6331 Property damage insurance; Fire, marine & casualty insurance & carriers; Property damage insurance; Fire, marine & casualty insurance & carriers
CEO: Frank J Bramanti
**Ch Bd:* Stephen L Way
**Pr:* Thomas Kaiser
CFO: Stephen Macdonough
Treas: Susan Nicosia
**Ex VP:* Frank Bramanti
Ex VP: Mike Lee
Sr VP: Barry Aframe
Sr VP: Frank Argondizzo
Sr VP: Mark Barry
Sr VP: James Bechter
Sr VP: George Blume
Sr VP: Shelly Iacobell
Sr VP: Eric Mihailovich
Sr VP: Frank Pedicini
Sr VP: Jay Ritchie
Sr VP: Richard Ruffee
Sr VP: Todd Ruyak
Sr VP: Albert Wagenen
VP: Steve Hansen
VP: Susan King

D-U-N-S 80-589-3984
HOUSTON CENTER VALVE & FITTING LP
SWAGELOK
10110 Frbnks N Houston Rd, Houston, TX 77064-3414
Tel (713) 527-0233 *Founded/Ownrshp* 2006
Sales 21.0MM^E *EMP* 42
SIC 5085 Valves & fittings
Pt: Brian H Payne
Sls Mgr: Lionel Huerta
Sls Mgr: Vance King

HOUSTON CHRONICLE
See HEARST NEWSPAPERS LLC

D-U-N-S 05-802-8352
HOUSTON CHRONICLE
(*Suby of* HEARST NEWSPAPERS LLC) ★
10635 Richmond Ave, Houston, TX 77042-4989
Tel (713) 362-7171 *Founded/Ownrshp* 2010
Sales 18.9MM^E *EMP* 652^E
SIC 2711 Newspapers
Pr: John T O'Loughlin
Sales Asso: Don Moser

D-U-N-S 13-772-5433
HOUSTON COMMUNITY CALL CENTER LP
CCC INTERACTIVE TEXAS
600 Jefferson St Ste 400, Houston, TX 77002-7379
Tel (713) 830-1400 *Founded/Ownrshp* 1999
Sales 11.6MM^E *EMP* 445
SIC 7389 Telemarketing services; Telemarketing services
Pt: Steven Hamaker
Pt: Terence Healy

D-U-N-S 07-416-2462
HOUSTON COMMUNITY COLLEGE INC
3100 Main St Ste Mc1148, Houston, TX 77002-9331
Tel (713) 718-5001 *Founded/Ownrshp* 1967
Sales 99.8MM *EMP* 5,000
SIC 8222 Community college; Community college
V Ch: Neeta Sane
Trst: Bruce A Austin
Trst: Diane O Guzm N
Trst: Richard M Schechter
Trst: Robert M Worsham
Exec: Janet May
Dir Bus: Marshall McGhee
Ex Dir: Ricardo Solis
Prgrm Mgr: Katherine Clancy
Prgrm Mgr: August Mancuso
Prgrm Mgr: Bessy Williams

HOUSTON COMPUTER CENTER
See CHANG - SHENG INC

D-U-N-S 03-949-7011
HOUSTON COUNTY BOARD OF EDUCATION
HCBOE
1100 Main St, Perry, GA 31069-3531
Tel (478) 988-6200 *Founded/Ownrshp* 1925
Sales 281.7MM *EMP* 3,856
Accts Greg S Griffin State Auditor
SIC 8211 Public elementary school; Public junior high school; Public senior high school; Sectarian school; Public elementary school; Public junior high school; Public senior high school; Sectarian school
Ch Bd: Fred Wilson
Bd of Dir: Gillis Dawkins
Bd of Dir: Charles Hill
Bd of Dir: Jim Maddox
Ofcr: Gary Copa
VP: Walt Downing
Admn Mgr: David Carpenter
Admn Mgr: Rodney Champion
Admn Mgr: Patsy Hutto
Admn Mgr: Peggy Jackson
Admn Mgr: Pat Witt

D-U-N-S 07-847-6489
HOUSTON COUNTY BOARD OF EDUCATION
1100 Main St, Perry, GA 31069-3531
Tel (478) 988-6200 *Founded/Ownrshp* 2012
Sales 4.8MM^E *EMP* 2,966^E
SIC 8211 Public elementary & secondary schools

D-U-N-S 18-385-9230
HOUSTON COUNTY BOARD OF EDUCATION
404 W Washington St, Dothan, AL 36301-2520
Tel (334) 792-8331 *Founded/Ownrshp* 1905
Sales 53.0MM *EMP* 725
SIC 8211 Public elementary & secondary schools; Public elementary & secondary schools
Dir IT: Dennis Pitts

HOUSTON COUNTY COMMISSION
See COUNTY OF HOUSTON

D-U-N-S 00-577-7206
HOUSTON COUNTY ELECTRIC COOPERATIVE INC
1701 Se Loop 304, Crockett, TX 75835-3502
Tel (936) 544-5641 *Founded/Ownrshp* 1939
Sales 43.9MM *EMP* 64
Accts Knuckols Duvall Hallum & Co
SIC 4911 Distribution, electric power; Distribution, electric power
Pr: Billy Carlton
CFO: Kathy Calvert
VP: Kennon Kellum
Off Mgr: Shirley Rayford
IT Man: Tara Young
Sfty Mgr: Charlie Gardner
Opers Mgr: Jack Vickers

D-U-N-S 07-911-1423
HOUSTON COUNTY HEALTHCARE AUTHORITY
SOUTHEAST ALABAMA MEDICAL CENT
1108 Ross Clark Cir, Dothan, AL 36301-3022
Tel (334) 793-8111 *Founded/Ownrshp* 1949
Sales 290.2MM *EMP* 2,500
SIC 8062 General medical & surgical hospitals; General medical & surgical hospitals
CEO: Ronald S Owen
Chf Path: Mark E Shertzer
**COO:* Charlie Brannon
**CFO:* Derek Miller
CFO: Terri Parsons
CFO: David Pike
**VP:* Diane Buntyn
**VP:* Ronnie Dean
VP: Susan Esslinger
VP: Peggy Sease-Fair
VP: Rick Smith
VP: Kenneth B Tucker
Exec: Sharon Bussey
Exec: Cecilia Land
Dir Rx: Philip Atkinson
Dir Rx: Sharon Perry

D-U-N-S 93-840-3938
HOUSTON COUNTY PUBLIC WORKS DEPT
2018 Kings Chapel Rd, Perry, GA 31069-2828
Tel (478) 987-4280 *Founded/Ownrshp* 1980
Sales NA *EMP* 500^E
SIC 9511 Air, water & solid waste management; Air, water & solid waste management

D-U-N-S 07-979-9005
HOUSTON COUNTY SCHOOL DISTRICT
404 W Washington St, Dothan, AL 36301-2540
Tel (334) 792-8331 *Founded/Ownrshp* 2015
Sales 28.3MM^E *EMP* 778^E
SIC 8211 Public elementary & secondary schools
HC Dir: Cas Haddock

D-U-N-S 60-098-9078
HOUSTON CREATIVE RESOURCE GROUP INC
12859 Highway 146 101, Dayton, TX 77535-2870
Tel (713) 947-0721 *Founded/Ownrshp* 2005
Sales 26.3MM^E *EMP* 200
SIC 1799 Building mover, including houses; Building mover, including houses
Pr: William K Taylor
**CFO:* Robert Nickelson
**VP:* Bill Taylor

D-U-N-S 05-827-4911 IMP
HOUSTON DISTRIBUTING CO INC (TX)
7100 High Life Dr, Houston, TX 77066-3713
Tel (281) 583-4800 *Founded/Ownrshp* 1968
Sales 60.4MM *EMP* 392
Accts Tiller And Company Bayton Te
SIC 5181 Beer & other fermented malt liquors; Beer & other fermented malt liquors
Ch Bd: Joe O Huggins III
CFO: Debra Bagget
CFO: Debra J Baggett
Ex VP: Scott Heckel
Sr VP: Richard Roberts
VP: James Garland
Exec: Tommy Harmon
VP Prd: Eric Brener
Sfty Dirs: Phil Vaello
Prd Mgr: Kenneth McGaughey
Sls&Mrk Ex: Scotty Hickle

D-U-N-S 95-924-8852
HOUSTON ENERGY LP
1200 Smith St Ste 2400, Houston, TX 77002-4315
Tel (713) 650-8008 *Founded/Ownrshp* 1988
Sales 24.5MM^E *EMP* 42
SIC 1382 Oil & gas exploration services; Oil & gas exploration services
Owner: Ronald E Neal
**Owner:* Frank W Harrison III
Pr: He-Jay McGregor
**Ex VP:* P David Amend
**VP:* Dale Coulthard
**VP:* Jay McGregor
Snr Mgr: Betsy Breier

D-U-N-S 07-534-4031 IMP
HOUSTON ENTERPRISES INC
HOUSTON ASSOCIATES
679 Grant Ferry Rd, Brandon, MS 39047
Tel (601) 992-1503 *Founded/Ownrshp* 1988
Sales 27.4MM^E *EMP* 300
SIC 5094 5199 Clocks; Candles; Clocks; Candles
Pr: Robert Q Houston
**CFO:* Joe Dempson
**Treas:* James Ernest
**VP:* Brad Houston

HOUSTON EYE ASSOCIATES
See HEA CLINIC PA

HOUSTON FIRST BAPTIST CHURCH
See FIRST BAPTIST CHURCH OF HOUSTON

D-U-N-S 13-613-0056
HOUSTON FIRST CORP
HILTON AMERICAS-HOUSTON
1600 Lamar St, Houston, TX 77010-5012
Tel (713) 739-8000 *Founded/Ownrshp* 2000
Sales 38.4MM^E *EMP* 130^E
Accts Deloitte & Touche Llp Housto
SIC 8748 Urban planning & consulting services; Urban planning & consulting services
Ch Bd: Richard J Campo
**CEO:* Dawn R Ullrich
**COO:* Mario Ariza
**COO:* Peter McStravick
**CFO:* Brenda Bazan
Admn Mgr: Joel St John

D-U-N-S 05-247-5027 IMP/EXP
HOUSTON FOAM PLASTICS INC
2019 Brooks St, Houston, TX 77026-7297
Tel (713) 224-3484 *Founded/Ownrshp* 1970
Sales 87.0MM^E *EMP* 300
SIC 3086 Insulation or cushioning material, foamed plastic; Packaging & shipping materials, foamed plastic; Insulation or cushioning material, foamed plastic; Packaging & shipping materials, foamed plastic
Pr: K E Kurtz II
**Treas:* Patty Harrington
VP: Bob Kurtz
**VP:* Robert Kurtz
Exec: Rene Gonzalez
IT Man: Tracy Beekman
Opers Mgr: Mauricio Zapata
Sales Exec: Roy Duggan
Sales Asso: Cot Cottingham
Sales Asso: Erin Juarez
Sales Asso: Leighla Mautz

D-U-N-S 16-484-5869
HOUSTON FOOD BANK
535 Portwall St, Houston, TX 77029-1332
Tel (713) 223-3700 *Founded/Ownrshp* 1981
Sales 155.4MM *EMP* 108^E
Accts Blazek & Vetterling Houston
SIC 8399 Community action agency; Community action agency
Pr: Brian Greene
Dir Vol: Oleg Jolic
**COO:* Stan Edde
CFO: Beth Tanner
**Treas:* Janet Matura
Ofcr: Jennifer Reeves
Exec: Glenda Bates
Dir Soc: Carrie Grzelak
Comm Dir: Adele Brady
CTO: Olivia McDaniel
Dir IT: Al Jimenez

D-U-N-S 83-148-3834
HOUSTON FOODS INC
BURGER KING
4415 Highway 6, Sugar Land, TX 77478-4476
Tel (281) 201-2700 *Founded/Ownrshp* 1993
Sales 29.2MM^E *EMP* 906^E
SIC 5812 Fast-food restaurant, chain
Pr: Shoukat Dhanani

D-U-N-S 07-921-8240
HOUSTON FORENSIC SCIENCE CENTER INC (TX)
HOUSTON FRNSIC SCIENCE LGC INC
(*Suby of* CITY OF HOUSTON) ★
1200 Travis St Fl 20, Houston, TX 77002-6001
Tel (713) 929-6760 *Founded/Ownrshp* 2012
Sales 26.0MM *EMP* 180
SIC 8734 Forensic laboratory; Forensic laboratory
CEO: Daniel Garner
**Ch Bd:* Scott Hochberg
**CFO:* David Leach
**VP:* Peter Stout

D-U-N-S 61-839-9893 IMP
HOUSTON FREIGHTLINER INC
(*Suby of* SELECTRANSPORTATION RESOURCES LLC) ★
9550 North Loop E, Houston, TX 77029-1230
Tel (713) 672-4115 *Founded/Ownrshp* 1997
Sales 71.8MM^E *EMP* 170
SIC 5511 5521 5012 5013 7532 7537 Trucks, tractors & trailers: new & used; Trucks, tractors & trailers: used; Commercial vehicles; Ambulances; Fire trucks; Trucks, commercial; Motor vehicle supplies & new parts; Top & body repair & paint shops; Body shop, trucks; Mobile home & trailer repair; Automotive transmission repair shops; Trucks, tractors & trailers: new & used; Trucks, tractors & trailers: used; Commercial vehicles; Ambulances; Fire trucks; Trucks, commercial; Motor vehicle supplies & new parts; Top & body repair & paint shops; Body shop, trucks; Mobile home & trailer repair; Automotive transmission repair shops
Co-Pr: Rick Stewart
**CFO:* John Ellsworth
**Prin:* Bob Garwood
Genl Mgr: Gary Fenn
Genl Mgr: Tommy Rollins
Genl Mgr: Wade Tyler
IT Man: Carrie Richards
Manager: Jackson Dawn
Sls Mgr: Bill Bruss
Sls Mgr: David Bryant

HOUSTON FRNSIC SCIENCE LGC INC
See HOUSTON FORENSIC SCIENCE CENTER INC

HOUSTON FUEL OIL TERMINAL CO
See HFOTCO LLC

HOUSTON GARDEN CENTERS
See QUALITY CHRISTMAS TREE LTD

D-U-N-S 07-420-0684 IMP
HOUSTON GRAND OPERA ASSOCIATION INC
510 Preston St, Houston, TX 77002-1504
Tel (713) 546-0200 *Founded/Ownrshp* 1955
Sales 27.9MM *EMP* 120^E
SIC 7922 Opera company; Opera company
Ch Bd: Beth Madison
**Pr:* James Hackett
Comm Dir: Judith Kurnick
Comm Man: Christine Lee
Ex Dir: Ann Owens
Mktg Dir: Steve Kelley
Mktg Mgr: Kelly Buchanan

D-U-N-S 19-018-6981
HOUSTON GREENSPOINT HOTEL ASSOCIATES
WYNDAM GREENSPOINT HOTEL
12400 Greenspoint Dr, Houston, TX 77060-1902
Tel (281) 875-2222 *Founded/Ownrshp* 1984
Sales 6.5MM^E *EMP* 300
SIC 7011 Hotels; Hotels
Pt: Wyndam Hotels Resorts
Pt: Trammel Crow Companies

D-U-N-S 78-311-9084
HOUSTON HOSPICE
1905 Holcombe Blvd, Houston, TX 77030-4123
Tel (713) 677-7100 *Founded/Ownrshp* 1980
Sales 21.7MM *EMP* 185^E
Accts Blazek & Vetterling Houston
SIC 5047 Medical & hospital equipment; Medical & hospital equipment
Pr: James Faucett Jr
VP: Christine Blackmon
Ex Dir: James Monahann

D-U-N-S 03-264-0486
HOUSTON HOSPITALS INC
1601 Watson Blvd, Warner Robins, GA 31093-3431
Tel (478) 929-9544 *Founded/Ownrshp* 2008
Sales 245.2MM *EMP* 35^E
Accts Pershing Yoakley Knoxville T
SIC 8062 General medical & surgical hospitals; General medical & surgical hospitals
CEO: Cary W Martin
**CFO:* Sean Whilden

HOUSTON HOTEL
See STERLING HOSPITALITY INC

D-U-N-S 07-420-4496
HOUSTON HOUSING AUTHORITY
2640 Ftn View Dr Ste 400, Houston, TX 77057
Tel (713) 260-0800 *Founded/Ownrshp* 1939
Sales NA *EMP* 285
SIC 9531 Housing programs; ; Housing programs;
Pr: Tory Gunsolley
Pr: Skyler Quintero
Ofcr: Anna Simotas
VP: Kenneth Acey
VP: Mark Thiele
Dir IT: Wendy Caesar
Mktg Dir: Horace Allison
Snr Mgr: Jose Benavides
Snr Mgr: Lupe Carmona
Snr Mgr: Marilyn Jenkins

D-U-N-S 06-129-2124
HOUSTON INDEPENDENT SCHOOL DISTRICT (TX)
H I S D
4400 W 18th St, Houston, TX 77092-8501
Tel (713) 556-6005 *Founded/Ownrshp* 1923
Sales 2.1MMM *EMP* 22,440
Accts Deloitte & Touche Llp Houston
SIC 8211 School board; School board
Pr: Michael Lunceford
**CFO:* Melinda Garrett
**Sec:* Diana Davila
Exec: Jackie Cayton
Exec: Andrew Monzon
Exec: Alice Reuter
Exec: Daniel Serenil
Exec: Larry Trout
Ex Dir: Randy Tullos
Dir IT: Lori Nichols
Dir IT: Ben Willson

D-U-N-S 83-174-9671
HOUSTON INTERNATIONAL INSURANCE GROUP LTD
HIIG
(*Suby of* WESTAIM HIIG LIMITED PARTNERSHIP)
800 Gessner Rd Ste 600, Houston, TX 77024-4538
Tel (713) 935-4800 *Founded/Ownrshp* 2014
Sales NA *EMP* 92^E
SIC 6331 Fire, marine & casualty insurance
CEO: Stephen L Way
**CFO:* Rhonda Kemp
**CFO:* Peter Presperin
Treas: Cindy Casale
**Ex VP:* Ed Ellis
Sr VP: Lynn Cordes
Sr VP: Kirby Hill
Sr VP: Ahmad Mian
Sr VP: Mark Rattner
**Sr VP:* Michael Schmidt
Sr VP: L Byron Way
VP: Janet Yienger

D-U-N-S 02-453-2011
HOUSTON ISD
(*Suby of* H I S D) ★
6801 Bennington St, Houston, TX 77028-5816
Tel (713) 225-7525 *Founded/Ownrshp* 2009
Sales 33.9MM^E *EMP* 1^E
SIC 8211 Public elementary & secondary schools
Genl Mgr: Ray Danilowicz

HOUSTON ISUZU TRUCK
See HOUSTON MACK SALES & SERVICE INC

D-U-N-S 95-643-5119
HOUSTON KIK INC
KIK COSTUM PRODUCTS
(*Suby of* KIK INTERNATIONAL HOUSTON INC) ★
2921 Corder St, Houston, TX 77054-3401
Tel (713) 747-8710 *Founded/Ownrshp* 1970
Sales 31.4MM^E *EMP* 114
SIC 2842 3085 Bleaches, household: dry or liquid; Plastics bottles; Bleaches, household: dry or liquid; Plastics bottles
Pr: David Cynamon
**CFO:* Roy Pearce
Ex VP: Brodie Howard
Exec: Richard Kepp
Plnt Mgr: Bob Ietkowski

D-U-N-S 09-248-7172 IMP/EXP
HOUSTON LBC L P
(*Suby of* LBC BELGIUM HOLDING NV)
11666 Port Rd, Seabrook, TX 77586-1603
Tel (281) 474-4433 *Founded/Ownrshp* 1998
Sales 140.6MM^E *EMP* 130
SIC 5171 Petroleum bulk stations; Petroleum terminals; Petroleum bulk stations; Petroleum terminals
Pt: Rory Moran
Pt: David Knowles
Pt: Michael S McKinney
Opers Supe: Brett Rushton
Sfty Mgr: Glenn Davis
Opers Mgr: Kevin Duncan
Sls Mgr: Paulo Leal

D-U-N-S 07-844-2175
HOUSTON LIVESTOCK SHOW AND RODEO EDUCATIONAL FUND
8334 Nrg Park Fl 2, Houston, TX 77054-2930
Tel (832) 667-1000 *Founded/Ownrshp* 1932
Sales 23.4MM *EMP* 1,200
Accts Pricewaterhousecoopers Llp H
SIC 7999 Rodeo operation; Rodeo operation
CEO: Joel Cowley
**Pr:* R H Stevens
**COO:* Leroy Shafer
**CFO:* Jennifer Hazelton
**VP:* Andrew Sloan
**Prin:* Paul G Somerville

D-U-N-S 96-684-9684
HOUSTON LIVESTOCK SHOW AND RODEO INC
8400 Kirby Dr, Houston, TX 77054-1504
Tel (832) 667-1000 *Founded/Ownrshp* 1932
Sales 122.5MM *EMP* 2
Accts Pricewaterhousecoopers Llp Ho
SIC 7313 Radio, television, publisher representatives
Ch Bd: Rh Stevens Jr
CFO: Jennifer Hazelton
Mng Dir: Melissa Hernlund
Mng Dir: Paula Urban
Mng Dir: Johnnie Westerhaus
Mng Dir: Julie Wood

D-U-N-S 14-991-6921
HOUSTON MAC HAIK DODGE CHRYSLER JEEP LTD
MAC HAIK CHRYSLER JEEP
11000 North Fwy, Houston, TX 77037-1008
Tel (281) 447-9500 *Founded/Ownrshp* 2004
Sales 35.4MM^E *EMP* 95
SIC 5511 Automobiles, new & used; Automobiles, new & used
Pr: Mac Haik
CFO: Jeff Heath
Sales Exec: Ron Bailey
Sls Mgr: Don Ruguleiski

D-U-N-S 60-247-2441
HOUSTON MACK SALES & SERVICE INC
HOUSTON ISUZU TRUCK
5216 N Mccarty St, Houston, TX 77013-2504
Tel (713) 673-1444 *Founded/Ownrshp* 1989
Sales 38.0MM^E *EMP* 65^E
SIC 5511 7538 7513 Trucks, tractors & trailers: new & used; General truck repair; Truck leasing, without drivers; Trucks, tractors & trailers: new & used; General truck repair; Truck leasing, without drivers
CEO: Thomas E Graddy
**Pr:* Thomas E Ewing Jr
**CFO:* Nathan Rawlins
Exec: Linda Rich
Genl Mgr: James Borchett
Genl Mgr: Mitch Casey
Off Mgr: Joyce Sunderland
IT Man: Robert Beier
Sales Asso: Tim Yacovone

HOUSTON MARRIOTT WESTCHASE
See GEPA HOTEL OWNER HOUSTON LLC

D-U-N-S 07-950-1911
HOUSTON METHODIST HOSPITAL
6565 Fannin St, Houston, TX 77030-2703
Tel (713) 790-3311 *Founded/Ownrshp* 2014
Sales 40.3MM^E *EMP* 245^E
SIC 8051 8011 0783 Skilled nursing care facilities; Medical centers; Surgery services, ornamental tree
CEO: Marc L Boom
**Ch:* Ewing Werlein Jr
**Treas:* Carlton E Baucum

HOUSTON METRO TRNST AUTH
See METROPOLITAN TRANSIT AUTHORITY OF HARRIS COUNTY

D-U-N-S 07-417-7296 IMP
HOUSTON MUSEUM OF NATURAL SCIENCE
WORTHAM IMAX THEATRE
5555 Hermann Park Dr, Houston, TX 77030-1718
Tel (713) 639-4629 *Founded/Ownrshp* 1909
Sales 33.2MM *EMP* 202
Accts Blazek & Vetterling Houston
SIC 8412 Museum; Planetarium; Museum; Planetarium
Pr: Joel A Bartsch
Pr: Victoria Smith
**CFO:* Stephen Satchnik
**Ch:* Randa Duncan Williams
**Treas:* Patrick Burke
Dir: Barbara Hawthorn
Prin: John McAlein
CTO: Emilie Thok
Merch Mgr: Jennifer King

D-U-N-S 93-294-9027
HOUSTON NFL HOLDINGS LP
HOUSTON TEXANS
2 Nrg Park, Houston, TX 77054-1573
Tel (832) 667-2000 *Founded/Ownrshp* 1990
Sales 21.7MM^E *EMP* 100
SIC 7941 Football club
Pt: Robert C McNair
V Ch: Philip Burguieres
Sr VP: Charley Casserly
Sr VP: Jamey Rootes
VP: Robert Outhwaite
VP: Greg Watson
Comm Man: Charles Hampton
Opers Mgr: Jason Lowrey
Snr Mgr: Adrienne Saxe

D-U-N-S 05-445-6546
■ **HOUSTON NORTH POLE LINE L P**
(*Suby of* QUANTA SERVICES INC) ★
1608 Margaret St, Houston, TX 77093-4010
Tel (713) 691-3616 *Founded/Ownrshp* 2001
Sales 757.2MM^E *EMP* 2,373
SIC 1623 Electric power line construction; Electric power line construction
Pr: Earl C Austin Jr
**Pr:* Elton G Sackett
CFO: Leslie Shackett
**VP:* Martha K Austin
**VP:* Bryan Michalsky

D-U-N-S 10-268-2150
■ **HOUSTON NORTH WEST MEDICAL CENTER INC**
HOUSTON NORTHWEST MEDICAL CTR
(*Suby of* TENET HEALTHCARE FOUNDATION) ★
710 Cypress Creek Pkwy # 34, Houston, TX 77090-3402
Tel (281) 440-1000 *Founded/Ownrshp* 1974
Sales 140.8MM^E *EMP* 1,600
SIC 8062 General medical & surgical hospitals; General medical & surgical hospitals
CEO: Tim Puthoff
**Pr:* Louis Garcia
CFO: Ron Watson
Ofcr: Melba Bright

D-U-N-S 61-275-5801
■ **HOUSTON NORTHWEST MEDICAL CENTER INC**
HNMC
(*Suby of* TENET HEALTHCARE CORPORATION)
710 Cypress Creek Pkwy # 340, Houston, TX 77090-3421
Tel (281) 440-1000 *Founded/Ownrshp* 1997
Sales 193.4MM^E *EMP* 2,100
SIC 8062 General medical & surgical hospitals; General medical & surgical hospitals
CEO: Tim Puthoff C
COO: Allyn Glenn
COO: Susan Jadlouski
CFO: Sean Gallager
CFO: Mark Runyon
Dir OR: Jan Rasco
Dir Rad: Madan Kulkarni
Dir Rad: Hai Nguyen
Dir Rad: Ralph Norton

Mng Dir: Susan J Dewitt
Nurse Mgr: Claudia M Neil

HOUSTON NORTHWEST MEDICAL CTR
See HOUSTON NORTHWEST MEDICAL CENTER INC

D-U-N-S 18-053-0060
HOUSTON OFFSHORE ENGINEERING LLC
WS ATKINS
(*Suby of* WS ATKINS PLC)
17220 Katy Fwy Ste 200, Houston, TX 77094-1485
Tel (281) 436-6200 *Founded/Ownrshp* 2014
Sales 20.4MM^E *EMP* 150
SIC 8711 Engineering services; Engineering services
Pr: John Chianis
IT Man: Baldemar Ramirez

D-U-N-S 05-496-0681
HOUSTON PARKS BOARD INC
300 N Post Oak Ln, Houston, TX 77024-5904
Tel (713) 942-8500 *Founded/Ownrshp* 2010
Sales 24.3MM *EMP* 7
Accts Blazek & Vetterling Houston
SIC 1629 Athletic & recreation facilities construction
Prin: Jim Elkins
Mng Dir: Chip Place

HOUSTON PHYSICIANS' HOSPITAL
See WEBSTER SURGICAL SPECIALTY HOSPITAL LTD

D-U-N-S 00-478-8188
■ **HOUSTON PIPE LINE CO LP**
(*Suby of* ENERGY TRANSFER PARTNERS LP) ★
800 E Sonterra Blvd, San Antonio, TX 78258-3940
Tel (713) 222-0414 *Founded/Ownrshp* 1925
Sales 131.7MM^E *EMP* 266
SIC 4922 Pipelines, natural gas; Pipelines, natural gas
Pt: Kelcy L Warren
Pr: Marshall S McCrea
CFO: Martin Salinas
Sr VP: Thomas P Mason
Exec: Nick Moshou
VP Opers: Greg McElwayne
Sls Dir: Lee Papayoti

D-U-N-S 92-684-3319
HOUSTON PIZZA VENTURE LLP
PAPA JOHN'S
13131 Champions Dr # 110, Houston, TX 77069-3220
Tel (281) 580-6088 *Founded/Ownrshp* 1994
Sales 24.7MM^E *EMP* 500
SIC 5812 Pizzeria, chain; Pizzeria, chain
Pr: Keith Sullins
VP: Jack A Laughery

D-U-N-S 09-820-0439
HOUSTON POLY BAG I LTD
11726 Holderrieth Rd, Tomball, TX 77375-7399
Tel (281) 351-1726 *Founded/Ownrshp* 1979
Sales 30.2MM^E *EMP* 67
SIC 2673 Trash bags (plastic film): made from purchased materials
Genl Pt: William E Sumner Jr

D-U-N-S 80-632-2210 IMP/EXP
HOUSTON REFINING LP
LYONDELLBASELL
(*Suby of* LYONDELL CHEMICAL CO) ★
12000 Lawndale St, Houston, TX 77017-2740
Tel (713) 321-4111 *Founded/Ownrshp* 2006
Sales 15.5MM^E *EMP* 920
SIC 2911

D-U-N-S 00-484-2267
HOUSTON RIVERKIDS THERAPY LLC (TX)
RIVERKIDS PEDIATRIC HOME HLTH
2540 Broadway St Ste K, Pearland, TX 77581-4913
Tel (281) 997-8509 *Founded/Ownrshp* 2007
Sales 12.0MM *EMP* 300
SIC 8082 Home health care services
CFO: Stephen Covey
COO: Keith Rockwell

HOUSTON ROCKETS, THE
See ROCKET BALL LTD

D-U-N-S 07-417-9806
HOUSTON SAM STATE UNIVERSITY
SHSU
(*Suby of* TEXAS STATE UNIVERSITY SYSTEM) ★
1806 Ave J, Huntsville, TX 77340
Tel (936) 294-1111 *Founded/Ownrshp* 1879
Sales 183.6MM *EMP* 2,200^E
SIC 8221 University; University
Pr: Dana Hoyt
Pr: Kathy Gilcrease
Assoc VP: Roy Adams
Assoc VP: David Hammonds
VP: Shirin Edwin
VP: Kolby Flowers
**VP:* Jaimie Hebert
VP: Jamie Hebert
**VP:* Frank R Holmes
VP: Frank Holmes
**VP:* Al Hooten
VP: Alvin Hooten
**VP:* Frank Parker
VP: Randall Powell
**VP:* Heather Thielemann
VP: Richard Ward
Assoc Dir: Edgar Smith
Assoc Dir: Angie Taylor

D-U-N-S 10-033-4721
HOUSTON SCHOOL DISTRICT LEASING AUTHORITY INC
636 Starkville Rd, Houston, MS 38851-9303
Tel (662) 456-5630 *Founded/Ownrshp* 2005
Sales 21.1MM^E *EMP* 512
SIC 8211 Public elementary & secondary schools; Public elementary & secondary schools
Pr: Bill Klauser
Schl Brd P: Bart Munlin
HC Dir: Christy Barnett

D-U-N-S 19-436-1986
HOUSTON SERIES OF LOCKTON COMPANIES LLC
(*Suby of* LOCKTON INC) ★
5847 San Felipe St # 320, Houston, TX 77057-3000
Tel (713) 458-5200 *Founded/Ownrshp* 1986
Sales NA *EMP* 600
SIC 6411 Insurance agents & brokers; Insurance agents & brokers
COO: Bob Bobo
**Pr:* David Lockton
Assoc VP: Jeff Estrada
Ex VP: Anthony Scott Convery
Ex VP: Kenneth Gould
Ex VP: Stacy Seaberg
Sr VP: James Arcidiacono
Sr VP: Robert Bruce
Sr VP: Gary Dort
Sr VP: Jeff Higgins
Sr VP: Albert Martin
Sr VP: Kent Peden
Sr VP: Michael Sorge
Sr VP: Gardner Thornton
VP: Clay Brooks
VP: John Canter
VP: Brian Norrie
VP: Roy Tristan
VP: Jack Watson

D-U-N-S 06-071-2437 IMP/EXP
HOUSTON SERVICE INDUSTRIES INC
H S I
(*Suby of* ATLAS COPCO NORTH AMERICA LLC) ★
15045 Lee Rd, Houston, TX 77032-4001
Tel (713) 947-1623 *Founded/Ownrshp* 2012
Sales 22.7MM^E *EMP* 50
SIC 3564 5084 Blowers & fans; Industrial machinery & equipment
Pr: Richard Pearsall
**VP:* James Pearsall

D-U-N-S 13-953-0539 IMP
HOUSTON SHUTTERS LLC
ROCKWOOD SHUTTERS
7052 Grand Blvd Ste 120, Houston, TX 77054-2223
Tel (713) 723-7100 *Founded/Ownrshp* 1998
Sales 50.7MM^E *EMP* 150
SIC 5023 Window furnishings; Window furnishings
CFO: Stephen Baur
Genl Mgr: Mike Blackburn

D-U-N-S 87-724-5142
■ **HOUSTON SPECIALTY HOSPITAL INC**
PLAZA SPECIALTY HOSPITAL
(*Suby of* TENET HEALTHCARE FOUNDATION) ★
1445 Ross Ave Ste 1400, Dallas, TX 75202-2703
Tel (469) 893-2000 *Founded/Ownrshp* 1994
Sales 14.6MM *EMP* 800
SIC 8069 Specialty hospitals, except psychiatric; Specialty hospitals, except psychiatric
CEO: James M Murphy
**Pr:* Trevor Fetter
**CFO:* Stephen Ferber
**Treas:* Dennis Dent
Dir Risk M: Maria Corzo
Dir Risk M: Luckner Denord

HOUSTON STAFFORD ELECTRICAL
See IES RESIDENTIAL INC

D-U-N-S 18-530-7147 IMP
HOUSTON SUPPLY & MFG CO
6825 Fulton St, Houston, TX 77022-4832
Tel (713) 694-6868 *Founded/Ownrshp* 1987
Sales 22.0MM^E *EMP* 16
SIC 5085 5082 Hose, belting & packing; Valves, pistons & fittings; Bearings, bushings, wheels & gears; Oil field equipment
Pr: William T Sirman
VP: Jason Sirman
**VP:* Vernon E Sirman Jr

D-U-N-S 02-081-3739
HOUSTON SYMPHONY SOCIETY
615 Louisiana St Ste 102, Houston, TX 77002-2715
Tel (713) 224-7575 *Founded/Ownrshp* 1913
Sales 27.7MM *EMP* 142
Accts Blazek & Vetterling Houston
SIC 7929 Symphony orchestras; Symphony orchestras
CEO: Mark C Hanson
**Pr:* Robert A Peiser
**CFO:* Michael Pawson
Ofcr: Agnieszka Rakhmatullaev
Assoc Dir: Jennifer Schoppe
Ex Dir: Mark Hanson
Genl Mgr: Steven Brosvik
Genl Mgr: Jeff Woodruff
Mktg Dir: Melissa Lopez

D-U-N-S 00-842-6439
■ **HOUSTON SYSCO INC**
(*Suby of* SYSCO CORP) ★
10710 Grens Crossing Blvd, Houston, TX 77038
Tel (713) 672-8080 *Founded/Ownrshp* 1953, 1970
Sales 485.0MM^E *EMP* 750
SIC 5149 5142 5046 5141 2099 Canned goods: fruit, vegetables, seafood, meats, etc.; Packaged frozen goods; Commercial cooking & food service equipment; Groceries, general line; Food preparations; Canned goods: fruit, vegetables, seafood, meats, etc.; Packaged frozen goods; Commercial cooking & food service equipment; Groceries, general line; Food preparations
CEO: Bill Delaney
**Pr:* David Devane
**Pr:* Michael W Green
Pr: Barry Robinson
**COO:* Thomas E Lankford
**CFO:* Scott Klienver
**Sr VP:* Greg Bertrand
**Sr VP:* Scott Charlton
VP: David Graham
Exec: Leonard Bryan
Admn Mgr: Betty Lawrence

HOUSTON TECHNOLOGY CENTER
See MULTI-CHEM INC

HOUSTON TEXANS
See HOUSTON NFL HOLDINGS LP

D-U-N-S 05-361-8782
HOUSTON TRIBOLOGY SALES & MARKETING OFFICE
A L S
10450 Stncliff Rd Ste 210, Houston, TX 77099
Tel (281) 599-1242 *Founded/Ownrshp* 2010
Sales 98.4MM^E *EMP* 11,000
SIC 8742 Marketing consulting services; Marketing consulting services
Genl Mgr: Rhonda Holstien
IT Man: Fran Christopher

D-U-N-S 05-869-5743 IMP
HOUSTON TUBULARS INC
13600 Hatfield Rd, Pearland, TX 77581-2729
Tel (281) 485-4014 *Founded/Ownrshp* 1981
Sales 80.4MM^E *EMP* 150
SIC 1389 Pipe testing, oil field service; Pipe testing, oil field service
Pr: Dennis J Hayden
**Sec:* Kathleen Hayden
Off Mgr: Mary Sires

D-U-N-S 96-612-9587
■ **HOUSTON VILLAGE BUILDERS INC**
(*Suby of* LENNAR CORP) ★
550 Greens Pkwy Ste 111, Houston, TX 77067-4538
Tel (281) 873-4663 *Founded/Ownrshp* 1996
Sales 28.6MM^E *EMP* 200
SIC 1521 Single-family housing construction; Single-family housing construction
Pr: Don Luke

D-U-N-S 00-808-1044 IMP/EXP
■ **HOUSTON WELL SCREEN CO**
WEATHERFORD
(*Suby of* WEATHERFORD INTERNATIONAL LLC) ★
11939 Aldine Westfield Rd, Houston, TX 77093-1095
Tel (281) 449-7261 *Founded/Ownrshp* 1946
Sales 22.8MM^E *EMP* 70
SIC 3533 Oil & gas drilling rigs & equipment
Pr: Peter Thomas Fontan
**Pr:* William T Rouse
**Sr VP:* Curtis W Huff
**VP:* James M Hudgins
Genl Mgr: Pete Olenick
Genl Mgr: John Sladic

D-U-N-S 60-560-9379
HOUSTON WEST INFINITI LTD
WEST HOUSTON INFINITI
12200 Katy Fwy, Houston, TX 77079-1500
Tel (281) 589-8900 *Founded/Ownrshp* 1989
Sales 21.7MM^E *EMP* 52
Accts Vacek Lange & Westerfield Ho
SIC 5511 7514 Automobiles, new & used; Rent-a-car service; Automobiles, new & used; Rent-a-car service
Pr: J B Gentry
**Sec:* Ron Wilson
Genl Mgr: Hart Oshman
Sales Asso: Dwayne Dimaria

D-U-N-S 01-079-1390 IMP/EXP
▲ **HOUSTON WIRE & CABLE CO INC**
10201 North Loop E, Houston, TX 77029-1415
Tel (713) 609-2100 *Founded/Ownrshp* 1975
Sales 390.0MM *EMP* 360^E
Accts Ernst & Young Llp Houston Te
Tkr Sym HWCC *Exch* NGS
SIC 5063 Electronic wire & cable; Electronic wire & cable
Pr: James L Pokluda III
Pr: Andrew Hall
CFO: Nicol G Graham
Sr VP: Christopher R McLeod
VP: Philomena Buxton
VP: Kayla Draper
VP: Armando Gonzales
Brnch Mgr: Craig Hebert
Brnch Mgr: Chad McGee
Brnch Mgr: Mike Musselman
IT Man: Craig Ortego
Board of Directors: Michael T Campbell, I Stewart Farwell, Mark A Ruelle, Wilson B Sexton, William H Sheffield, Scott L Thompson, Gary Yetman

D-U-N-S 07-418-8533
HOUSTON ZOO INC (TX)
6200 Hermann Park Dr, Houston, TX 77030-1710
Tel (713) 533-6500 *Founded/Ownrshp* 1967
Sales 50.1MM *EMP* 375
SIC 8699 Charitable organization; Charitable organization
Pr: Deborah M Cannon
COO: Chris Lyons
**CFO:* Leslie Forestier
Ofcr: Sarah Cornor
VP: David Bell
**VP:* Sharon Joseph
**VP:* Peter Riger

D-U-N-S 07-218-8840
HOUSTON-GALVESTON AREA COUNCIL
H-G A C
3555 Timmons Ln Ste 120, Houston, TX 77027-6466
Tel (713) 627-3200 *Founded/Ownrshp* 1966
Sales NA *EMP* 200
Accts Whitley Penn Llp Houston Tex
SIC 6035 Federal savings & loan associations; Federal savings & loan associations
CEO: Jack Steele
**CFO:* Nancy Haussler
Ex Dir: Nydia Delagarza
Prgrm Mgr: Mike Temple
Snr Mgr: Thomas Gray
Snr Mgr: Graciela Lubertino
Snr Mgr: Bill Tobin

D-U-N-S 80-561-0599
HOUSTONIAN CAMPUS LLC
HOUSTONIAN HOTEL CLUB AND SPA
111 N Post Oak Ln, Houston, TX 77024-7703
Tel (713) 680-2626 *Founded/Ownrshp* 1992
Sales 49.9MM^E *EMP* 450
SIC 7011 7997 Hotels & motels; Membership sports & recreation clubs; Hotels & motels; Membership sports & recreation clubs
CEO: Robert F Henricksen
**Ch Bd:* David Solomon
**Ex VP:* Pam Hayes
**Ex VP:* Steven D Lerner
**Sr VP:* Mark Yanke
Dir Sec: Sydney Blankenship
Genl Mgr: Mark Stevens

HOUSTONIAN HOTEL CLUB AND SPA
See HOUSTONIAN CAMPUS LLC

D-U-N-S 02-773-0001 IMP
HOUSTONS INC (OR)
9799 Sw Freeman Dr, Wilsonville, OR 97070-9221
Tel (503) 582-9711 *Founded/Ownrshp* 1933
Sales 65.5MM^E *EMP* 185
SIC 5046 5141 5087 Restaurant equipment & supplies; Groceries, general line; Restaurant supplies; Restaurant equipment & supplies; Groceries, general line; Restaurant supplies
CEO: John Houston
**Pr:* Bill Paolo
CFO: Paul Henderson
Treas: Dennis Anderson
**Ex VP:* Greg Dann
VP: Greg Estes
**VP:* Renee Houston
Rgnl Mgr: Jarrod Bowren
Div Mgr: Bob Baldwin
IT Man: Gary Pierce

D-U-N-S 94-938-3780 IMP
HOUWELING NURSERIES OXNARD INC
HOUWELING'S TOMATOES
645 Laguna Rd, Camarillo, CA 93012-8523
Tel (805) 488-8832 *Founded/Ownrshp* 1996
Sales 221.8MM^E *EMP* 450
Accts Kpmg Llp Burnaby Canada
SIC 5141 Groceries, general line; Groceries, general line
Pr: Casey Houweling
**CFO:* Christopher Brocklesby
Opers Mgr: Corey Rawlings
Opers Mgr: Jacqueline Rodriguez
Opers Mgr: Ben Vazquez
**VP Sls:* William Wilber

HOUWELING'S TOMATOES
See HOUWELING NURSERIES OXNARD INC

D-U-N-S 96-524-3129
HOV SERVICES INC
(*Suby of* SOURCEHOV LLC) ★
2701 E Grauwyler Rd, Irving, TX 75061-3414
Tel (248) 837-7100 *Founded/Ownrshp* 2011
Sales 87.7MM^E *EMP* 1,035^E
SIC 7374 7334 7389 2752 7331 7379 Data processing & preparation; Photocopying & duplicating services; Microfilm recording & developing service; Decals, lithographed; Mailing service; Data processing consultant
Pr: Suresh Yannamani
Pr: Dale Harn
**CFO:* James G Reynolds
**Ex VP:* Kenneth L Shaw
Sr VP: Mark Trivette
VP: Susan Stallings
Off Mgr: Nancy Montoya
Snr Ntwrk: Rick Moran
Opers Mgr: Patricia C Watson
Sales Exec: Jesse Singh
Mktg Dir: Gary Elrod

D-U-N-S 61-215-8766
HOVCHILD HOMES INC
4000 State Route 66, Tinton Falls, NJ 07753-7300
Tel (732) 922-6100 *Founded/Ownrshp* 1997
Sales 32.0MM *EMP* 50
SIC 8741 Construction management
Pr: Hirair Hovnanian
**VP:* Adele Hovnanian

D-U-N-S 04-742-6569 EXP
HOVENSA LLC
1 Estate Hope, Christiansted, VI 00820
Tel (340) 692-3000 *Founded/Ownrshp* 1999
Sales 57.6MM^E *EMP* 1,300
Accts Ernst & Young Llp New York N
SIC 1382 Oil & gas exploration services; Oil & gas exploration services
VP: Steve Beamer
VP: Joseph Hazewski
VP: Nithia Thaver

D-U-N-S 78-900-3365 IMP
HOVEROUND CORP
6010 Cattleridge Dr, Sarasota, FL 34232-6060
Tel (941) 739-6200 *Founded/Ownrshp* 1992
Sales 94.3MM^E *EMP* 437
SIC 3842 Wheelchairs; Wheelchairs
Pr: Thomas E Kruse
COO: Joyce Boyle
**CFO:* George W Kruse
CFO: Robert Munch
**Treas:* Lisa W Ondrula
VP: Christine Bullock
VP: Tony Digiovanni
VP: Margaret A Hollowy
**VP:* Gordon L Nelson
VP: Shani Reardon
VP: Don Shapiro
VP: Deb Silvers

D-U-N-S 04-525-8626
HOVIS AUTO SUPPLY INC
5074 Emlenton Clint Rd, Emlenton, PA 16373-6708
Tel (724) 867-0242 *Founded/Ownrshp* 1987
Sales 31.0MM^E *EMP* 60
SIC 5013 Automotive supplies & parts; Truck parts & accessories
Pr: Clifford J Hovis
**VP:* Curtis D Hovis

D-U-N-S 04-665-0388
▲ HOVNANIAN ENTERPRISES INC
K HOVNANIAN
110 W Front St, Red Bank, NJ 07701-5997
Tel (732) 747-7800 *Founded/Ownrshp* 1959
Sales 2.1MMM *EMP* 2,006E
Accts Deloitte & Touche Llp New Yor
Tkr Sym HOV *Exch* NYS
SIC 1521 1531 1522 6162 6361 Single-family housing construction; Condominium developers; Townhouse developers; Speculative builder, single-family houses; Residential construction; Mortgage bankers; Title insurance; Single-family housing construction; Condominium developers; Townhouse developers; Speculative builder, single-family houses; Residential construction; Mortgage bankers; Title insurance
Ch Bd: ARA K Hovnanian
Pr: Barry Edelman
COO: Thomas J Pellerito
COO: Peter Reinhart
**CFO:* J Larry Sorsby
Treas: David G Valiaveedan
VP: David Friend
VP: Catherine Gentle
VP: Brad G O'Connor
VP: David Orlando
VP: Dean Potter
VP: Joseph Riggs
VP: James Vanderwoud
Exec: Corin Elvic
Exec: Gail Murphy
Board of Directors: Robert B Coutts, Edward A Kangas, Joseph A Marengi, Vincent Pagano Jr, Stephen D Weinroth

HOW
See WORLDWIDE INTEGRATED SUPPLY CHAIN SOLUTIONS INC

D-U-N-S 07-800-3944
■ HOWALT+MCDOWELL INSURANCE INC
(*Suby of* MARSH & MCLENNAN AGENCY LLC) ★
300 Cherapa Pl Ste 601, Sioux Falls, SD 57103-2277
Tel (605) 339-3874 *Founded/Ownrshp* 2012
Sales NA *EMP* 80
SIC 6411 Insurance agents
CEO: Jeff Scherschligt
**CFO:* Paul Rickert
VP: Bill Townsend
IT Man: Jay Shank
Mktg Dir: Drew Reaves

D-U-N-S 11-136-6266
HOWARD & HOWARD ATTORNEYS PLLC
450 W 4th St, Royal Oak, MI 48067-2557
Tel (248) 645-1483 *Founded/Ownrshp* 2003
Sales 34.2MME *EMP* 251
SIC 8111 General practice law office; General practice law office
Pr: Mark Davis
Off Admin: Thomas Paukovitz
MIS Dir: Darren Ginter
IT Man: Samuel Bryant
Mktg Dir: Cindy Richards
Counsel: John Pollock

D-U-N-S 05-783-2040
HOWARD AUTO GROUP INC
HOWARD BUICK
364 W Grand Ave, Elmhurst, IL 60126-1137
Tel (630) 832-9500 *Founded/Ownrshp* 1962
Sales 23.4MME *EMP* 55
SIC 5511 Automobiles, new & used; Vans, new & used; Pickups, new & used; Automobiles, new & used; Vans, new & used; Pickups, new & used
Pr: Steven Zazove
Sls Mgr: Rich Marsili
Sales Asso: Glen Ballantyne
Sales Asso: Joe Cardenas
Sales Asso: Maurice Corral
Sales Asso: Taylor Else
Sales Asso: Todd Froehlich
Sales Asso: Tony Losacco
Sales Asso: Al Pacheco
Sales Asso: Harry Sonn

D-U-N-S 04-194-8134
HOWARD BAER INC
1301 Foster Ave, Nashville, TN 37210-4425
Tel (615) 255-7351 *Founded/Ownrshp* 1962
Sales 29.1MME *EMP* 225
SIC 4213

D-U-N-S 80-030-2882
▲ HOWARD BANCORP INC
6011 University Blvd # 370, Ellicott City, MD 21043-6074
Tel (410) 750-0020 *Founded/Ownrshp* 2005
Sales NA *EMP* 218E
Tkr Sym HBMD *Exch* NAS
SIC 6022 National commercial banks; Bank holding companies; State commercial banks
Ch Bd: Mary Ann Scully
CFO: George C Coffman
Ex VP: Robert A Altieri
Ex VP: Paul G Brown
Ex VP: Charles E Schwabe

D-U-N-S 15-925-5178
HOWARD BANK
6011 University Blvd # 370, Ellicott City, MD 21043-6074
Tel (410) 750-3285 *Founded/Ownrshp* 2004
Sales NA *EMP* 54E
SIC 6021 National commercial banks; National commercial banks
CEO: Mary Ann Scully
Pr: Shannon Boswell
Pr: Lisa Singleton
Treas: Randall James
**Ex VP:* Robert A Altieri
**Ex VP:* Paul Brown
**Ex VP:* George Coffman
**Sr VP:* Rosa Scharf
VP: Christopher Infantino
VP: Tim Kelley
VP: Barbara Knickman
VP: Christopher Marasco
VP: Danielle Mullin
VP: Michael Munoz
VP: Steven Poynot
VP: Jennifer Scully
VP: Richard Story
VP: Anthony SOS

D-U-N-S 14-465-7384
HOWARD BEEF PROCESSORS INC
ELLISON MEAT COMPANY
1401 Sioux Dr, Pipestone, MN 56164-9400
Tel (507) 825-5486 *Founded/Ownrshp* 1977
Sales 34.5MME *EMP* 220
SIC 2011 Beef products from beef slaughtered on site; Pork products from pork slaughtered on site; Beef products from beef slaughtered on site; Pork products from pork slaughtered on site
CEO: Brian Karels
**CFO:* Tom Finke
**VP:* Alan Sheldon
Exec: Alicia Ard
CTO: Michelle Jones
Dir IT: Kent Ellison

D-U-N-S 02-152-4509 IMP/EXP
HOWARD BERGER CO LLC
(*Suby of* HBC HOLDINGS LLC) ★
324a Half Acre Rd, Cranbury, NJ 08512-3254
Tel (609) 860-9990 *Founded/Ownrshp* 2012
Sales 240.6MM *EMP* 180E
Accts Mayer Hoffman Mccann New York
SIC 5072 5087 5074 Hardware; Shelf or light hardware; Security devices, locks; Janitors' supplies; Plumbing & hydronic heating supplies; Hardware; Shelf or light hardware; Security devices, locks; Janitors' supplies; Plumbing & hydronic heating supplies
Treas: John Imszennik
Sr VP: Rob Munin
VP: Michele Hudec
**VP:* Jack Imszennik
VP: Michael McLaughlin
CIO: John Mitterko
QA Dir: Vincent Rotella
Natl Sales: Howard Green
Natl Sales: Tim Slavicek
Natl Sales: Melissa Takacs
VP Sls: Elliot Piltzer

D-U-N-S 01-091-1980
HOWARD BROWN HEALTH CENTER
4025 N Sheridan Rd, Chicago, IL 60613-2010
Tel (773) 388-1600 *Founded/Ownrshp* 1976
Sales 27.7MM *EMP* 190
Accts Crowe Horwath Llp Chicago Il
SIC 8733 8322 Research institute; Individual & family services; Research institute; Individual & family services
CEO: David Ernesto Munar
**Pr:* Jamal M Edwards
COO: Magda Houlberg
**Ch:* Karna Israelsen
**Treas:* Bs Jenetta Mason
**Ex VP:* JD Duke Alden
**Sr VP:* Michelle Wetzel
VP: Janet Henderson
VP: Chandler Howell
VP: Barb Tieder
**VP:* Barbara Tieder

HOWARD BUICK
See HOWARD AUTO GROUP INC

D-U-N-S 10-666-0483
HOWARD BUILDING CORP
707 Wilshire Blvd # 3750, Los Angeles, CA 90017-3535
Tel (213) 683-1850 *Founded/Ownrshp* 1983
Sales 39.5MME *EMP* 85
SIC 1542 Nonresidential construction; Nonresidential construction
Pr: Gary Conrad
**CEO:* Paul McGunnigle
**Founder:* Michael Howard

HOWARD COLLEGE
See HOWARD COUNTY JUNIOR COLLEGE DISTRICT

D-U-N-S 07-493-8804
HOWARD COMMUNITY COLLEGE
HOWARD COMMUNITY COLLEGE BOOKS
10901 Lttle Patuxent Pkwy, Columbia, MD 21044-3197
Tel (410) 518-1000 *Founded/Ownrshp* 1966
Sales 34.3MM *EMP* 800
Accts Bdo Usa Llp Bethesda Md
SIC 8222 8221 8211 Community college; Colleges universities & professional schools; Finishing school, secondary; Community college; Colleges universities & professional schools; Finishing school, secondary
Pr: Kathleen B Hetherington
Ofcr: Patty Bylsma
Assoc VP: Joann Hawkins
VP: Alison Buckley
VP: Sharon Pierce
Assoc Dir: Minah Woo
Ex Dir: Dorothy Moore
Off Mgr: Colleen Haspert
Mktg Mgr: Katie Turner
Art Dir: Lorriana Markovic

HOWARD COMMUNITY COLLEGE BOOKS
See HOWARD COMMUNITY COLLEGE

D-U-N-S 03-033-4544
HOWARD COUNTY GENERAL HOSPITAL INC
HCGH HOWARD COUNTY GEN HOSP
(*Suby of* JOHNS HOPKINS HEALTH SYS CORP) ★
5755 Cedar Ln, Columbia, MD 21044-2999
Tel (410) 740-7935 *Founded/Ownrshp* 1969
Sales 236.0MM *EMP* 1,800E
Accts Pricewaterhousecoopers Llp B
SIC 8062 General medical & surgical hospitals; General medical & surgical hospitals
Pr: Vic Broccolino
V Ch: Gary Blechman
**CFO:* James E Young
Chf Mktg O: Michael Macon
Ofcr: Linda Holley
Sr VP: Judy Brown
Sr VP: Paul Gleichauf
Sr VP: Carl Humphreys
Sr VP: Kathryn Lloyd
**VP:* Eric Aldrich
VP: Mark Applestein
VP: Lynn Bell
**VP:* Jay H Blackman
VP: Sandra Harriman
Dir Risk M: Digna Wheatley
Dir Rx: Masoomeh Khamesian

D-U-N-S 80-856-9289
HOWARD COUNTY HOUSING COMMISSION
6751 Columbia Gateway Dr # 300, Columbia, MD 21046-3138
Tel (410) 313-6316 *Founded/Ownrshp* 1990
Sales 30.6MM *EMP* 30
Accts Clifton & Gunderson Llp Balti
SIC 8748 Urban planning & consulting services; Urban planning & consulting services

D-U-N-S 07-318-0309
HOWARD COUNTY JUNIOR COLLEGE DISTRICT
HOWARD COLLEGE
1001 Birdwell Ln, Big Spring, TX 79720-5015
Tel (432) 264-5000 *Founded/Ownrshp* 1945
Sales 10.8MM *EMP* 560
Accts Lee Reynolds Welch & Co P
SIC 8221 8222 Colleges universities & professional schools; Junior college; Colleges universities & professional schools; Junior college
Pr: Cheryl T Sparks
**Pr:* Terry Hansen
Ex Dir: Terry Hanson

D-U-N-S 18-069-3335
HOWARD COUNTY OF MARYLAND (INC)
3430 Court House Dr # 100, Ellicott City, MD 21043-4300
Tel (410) 313-2195 *Founded/Ownrshp* 1800
Sales NA *EMP* 3,463
Accts Cohn Reznick Llp Baltimore
SIC 9111 Executive offices; ; Executive offices;
Exec: Ken Ulman
Pr: Mark Miller
Ofcr: Amy Frasier
Ofcr: Sarah Miller
**Ofcr:* Raquel Sanodo
Ofcr: Vickie Shaffer
Ofcr: David Sharpe
Snr Mgr: Josh Russin

D-U-N-S 07-962-8849
HOWARD COUNTY PUBLIC SCHOOL SYSTEM
HCPSS
10910 State Route 108, Ellicott City, MD 21042-6106
Tel (410) 313-6600 *Founded/Ownrshp* 2014
Sales 225.1MME *EMP* 8,084E
SIC 8211 School board
Bd of Dir: David Bruzga
Bd of Dir: Kathleen Hanks
Bd of Dir: Joy Menkemeir
Bd of Dir: Rob Slopek
Exec: Donald White
Adm Dir: Daniel Michaels
Adm Dir: Marion Miller
Ex Dir: Katrina Burton
Ex Dir: Anne Yenchko
Dir Sec: Ron Miller
Area Mgr: Monica Pringle

D-U-N-S 00-604-9001
HOWARD E NYHART CO INC
8415 Allison Pointe Blvd # 300, Indianapolis, IN 46250-4159
Tel (317) 845-3500 *Founded/Ownrshp* 1955
Sales NA *EMP* 76E
SIC 6411 Insurance information & consulting services
CEO: Thomas Totten
COO: Tayt Odom
CFO: Lisa Hague
VP: Craig Harrell

HOWARD ENERGY PARTNERS
See HOWARD MIDSTREAM ENERGY PARTNERS LLC

D-U-N-S 00-405-6651 IMP/EXP
HOWARD FERTILIZER & CHEMICAL CO INC
8306 S Orange Ave, Orlando, FL 32809-7853
Tel (407) 855-1841 *Founded/Ownrshp* 1931
Sales 37.6MME *EMP* 106
SIC 2874 Plant foods, mixed: from plants making phosphatic fertilizer; Plant foods, mixed: from plants making phosphatic fertilizer
Pr: Robert M Howard Jr
**Treas:* Daniel D Grabhorn
**VP:* Kathy Larsen
**VP:* Charles Palmer

D-U-N-S 11-323-3691
HOWARD FINISHING LLC
HF
32565 Dequindre Rd, Madison Heights, MI 48071-1520
Tel (248) 588-9050 *Founded/Ownrshp* 1947
Sales 21.4MME *EMP* 200
SIC 3449 Miscellaneous metalwork; Miscellaneous metalwork
Pr: James E Grimes
Plnt Mgr: Dave Ludeke

HOWARD FRANK R MEMORIAL HOSP
See WILLITS HOSPITAL INC

D-U-N-S 14-603-1146
HOWARD G BUFFETT FOUNDATION
145 N Merchant St Apt 1, Decatur, IL 62523-1216
Tel (217) 429-3988 *Founded/Ownrshp* 2007
Sales 152.7MM *EMP* 1
SIC 7389 Fund raising organizations; Fund raising organizations
Prin: Howard G Buffett
Sr VP: Megan Quitkin

D-U-N-S 78-676-4225
HOWARD HANNA CO
(*Suby of* HANNA HOLDINGS INC) ★
1090 Freeport Rd Ste 1a, Pittsburgh, PA 15238-4170
Tel (412) 967-9000 *Founded/Ownrshp* 1977
Sales 57.4MME *EMP* 23
SIC 6531 Real estate brokers & agents
Pr: Howard W Hanna
COO: Natalie Guiler
**Treas:* Tracy E Rossettidelvaux
Sr VP: Howard Cramer
VP: Ron Dishler
VP: Jean Hayes
Exec: Jennifer Quattrone
Creative D: Shannon Barr
IT Man: Donna Marrone
Sales Exec: Rae Piniarczyk
Sls Mgr: Jay Hitt

HOWARD HANNA REAL ESTATE
See HANNA HOLDINGS INC

D-U-N-S 07-674-9068
HOWARD HANNA SMYTHE CRAMER
(*Suby of* HANNA HOLDINGS INC) ★
6000 Parkland Blvd, Cleveland, OH 44124-6120
Tel (216) 447-4477 *Founded/Ownrshp* 1972, 2005
Sales 21.5MME *EMP* 310
SIC 6531 Real estate brokers & agents; Real estate brokers & agents
Ch Bd: Lucius B Mc Kelvey
**Pr:* David C Paul
**Sr VP:* Alan C Chandler
VP: Bill Askin
CIO: David Ciraldo

D-U-N-S 06-305-2153
HOWARD HINMAN & LLP KATTELL
CEPARANO, LAURIE M
80 Exchange St Ste 700, Binghamton, NY 13901-3425
Tel (607) 231-6794 *Founded/Ownrshp* 1901
Sales 21.9MME *EMP* 140E
SIC 8111 General practice law office; General practice law office
Pt: James S Gleason
Pr: Chrissondra Six
CFO: Pat Price
Bd of Dir: Paul Prasarn
CIO: James Orvand
Counsel: John Keeler
Counsel: Keith Osber
Counsel: Richard Pille
Snr Mgr: Delphine O'Rourke

D-U-N-S 96-561-4626
▲ HOWARD HUGHES CORP
13355 Noel Rd Fl 22, Dallas, TX 75240-6602
Tel (214) 741-7744 *Founded/Ownrshp* 2010
Sales 634.5MM *EMP* 1,100E
Tkr Sym HHC *Exch* NYS
SIC 6798 Real estate investment trusts; Real estate investment trusts
CEO: David R Weinreb
Pr: Grant Herlitz
CFO: Andrew Richardson
Sr VP: David Kautz
Sr VP: Venkat Mittal
Sr VP: Peter Riley
Sr VP: David Striph
Sr VP: Nicholas D Vanderboom
VP: Ron Bogard
VP: Mark G Bulmash
VP: Peggy Chandler
VP: Peter Doyle
VP: Dara Engle
VP: Greg Fitchitt
VP: Robert Jenkins
VP: Caryn Kboudi
VP: Bulmash Mark
VP: Jim McCaffrey
VP: Adam Meister
VP: Mark Putney
VP: Joyce Roberts
Board of Directors: William A Ackman, Adam Flatto, Jeffrey Furber, Gary Krow, Allen Model, R Scot Sellers, Steven Shepsman, Burton M Tansky, Mary Ann Tighe

D-U-N-S 07-386-2773
HOWARD HUGHES MEDICAL INSTITUTE INC
4000 Jones Bridge Rd, Chevy Chase, MD 20815-6720
Tel (301) 215-8500 *Founded/Ownrshp* 1953
Sales 2.7MMM *EMP* 3,000
SIC 8733

HOWARD HUGHES REALTY
See HUGHES CORP

D-U-N-S 00-978-3325
HOWARD IMMEL INC
1820 Radisson St, Green Bay, WI 54302-2057
Tel (920) 468-8208 *Founded/Ownrshp* 1978
Sales 79.2MM *EMP* 70
Accts Wipfli Llp Green Bay Wiscons
SIC 1541 1542 Industrial buildings, new construction; Commercial & office building, new construction; Industrial buildings, new construction; Commercial & office building, new construction
Pr: Kelly Hafeman
**VP:* Pete Smits

D-U-N-S 02-852-2811
HOWARD INDUSTRIES INC
8855 Washington Blvd, Culver City, CA 90232-2323
Tel (310) 837-9191 *Founded/Ownrshp* 1989
Sales 24.1MME *EMP* 43
SIC 5075 5078 Air conditioning equipment, except room units; Warm air heating equipment & supplies; Refrigerators, commercial (reach-in & walk-in)
Pr: Linda Tabor Howard
**Pr:* Abraham Winter
**VP:* Esther Winter
**VP:* Jeff Winter
Sls Mgr: Steve Zoller

D-U-N-S 04-341-7476 IMP/EXP
HOWARD INDUSTRIES INC (MS)
HOWARD MEDICAL
36 Howard Dr, Ellisville, MS 39437-9020
Tel (601) 425-3151 *Founded/Ownrshp* 1968
Sales 45.0MM^E *EMP* 5^E
SIC 3629 3577

HOWARD JOHNSON
See LARK INNS LP UNIVERSITY INN

HOWARD JOHNSON
See RESORT HOSPITALITY ENTERPRISES LTD

D-U-N-S 05-512-8599
HOWARD JOHNSON
1380 S Harbor Blvd, Anaheim, CA 92802-2310
Tel (714) 776-6120 *Founded/Ownrshp* 1968
Sales 43.2MM^E *EMP* 125
SIC 5146 Seafoods; Seafoods
Pr: James P Edmondson

D-U-N-S 09-391-8159
HOWARD LAKE-WAVERLY-WINSTED PUBLIC SCHOOLS (MN)
HOWARD LK WAVERLY-WINSTED HS
8 St & 8th Ave, Howard Lake, MN 55349
Tel (320) 543-4600 *Founded/Ownrshp* 1970
Sales 13.7MM^E *EMP* 401
SIC 8211 9411 Public elementary & secondary schools; Administration of educational programs; Public elementary & secondary schools; Administration of educational programs
HC Dir: Jolie Holland

HOWARD LK WAVERLY-WINSTED HS
See HOWARD LAKE-WAVERLY-WINSTED PUBLIC SCHOOLS

D-U-N-S 00-481-1725
HOWARD LUMBER & HARDWARE INC (GA)
(*Suby of* CLAUDE HOWARD LUMBER CO) ★
600 Gentilly Rd, Statesboro, GA 30458-5153
Tel (912) 764-5621 *Founded/Ownrshp* 1910, 1988
Sales 23.5MM *EMP* 35
SIC 5211 5251 Lumber & other building materials; Paneling; Doors, wood or metal, except storm; Roofing material; Builders' hardware; Lumber & other building materials; Paneling; Doors, wood or metal, except storm; Roofing material; Builders' hardware
CEO: C Arthur Howard
**Sec:* Cecil B Howard
Sr Cor Off: Rose McKeanen
Sales Asso: Dale Hampton

HOWARD MEDICAL
See HOWARD INDUSTRIES INC

D-U-N-S 87-753-7097
HOWARD MIDSTREAM ENERGY PARTNERS LLC
HOWARD ENERGY PARTNERS
(*Suby of* ALINDA CAPITAL PARTNERS LLC) ★
17806 W Ih 10 Ste 210, San Antonio, TX 78257-8222
Tel (210) 298-2222 *Founded/Ownrshp* 2013
Sales 143.7MM^E *EMP* 130^E
SIC 5085 Pipeline wrappings, anti-corrosive; Pipeline wrappings, anti-corrosive
CEO: Mike Howard
**Pr:* Brad Bynum
**CFO:* Scott Archer
Sr VP: Jack Helmbrecht
**Sr VP:* Mark Helmke
**Sr VP:* Mike Spears
**Sr VP:* Josh Weber
VP: Canevari Castan
VP: Steve Cruse
IT Man: Sean McMillan

HOWARD MILLER CLOCK COMPANY
See HOWARD MILLER CO

D-U-N-S 00-601-1316 IMP
HOWARD MILLER CO (MI)
HOWARD MILLER CLOCK COMPANY
860 E Main Ave, Zeeland, MI 49464-1365
Tel (616) 772-9131 *Founded/Ownrshp* 1946
Sales 97.1MM^E *EMP* 500
SIC 3873 2511 3829 3823 Clocks, except timeclocks; Wood household furniture; Measuring & controlling devices; Industrial instrmnts msrmnt display/control process variable; Clocks, except timeclocks; Wood household furniture; Measuring & controlling devices; Industrial instrmnts msrmnt display/control process variable
Ch Bd: Philip Miller
**Pr:* Howard C Miller
**VP:* Dennis Palasek
Sls Mgr: Bill Papoosha

D-U-N-S 19-327-8116
HOWARD MOTORS INC
HOWARD RV SUPERCENTER
(*Suby of* RAROVIDE LLC) ★
6200 Heimos Indus Pk Dr, Saint Louis, MO 63129-6300
Tel (314) 487-8000 *Founded/Ownrshp* 2002
Sales 34.0MM *EMP* 74
SIC 5561 7538 7519 Motor homes; Recreational vehicle repairs; Motor home rental; Motor homes; Recreational vehicle repairs; Motor home rental
Pr: Randy L Howard
**VP:* Ron Howard
Off Mgr: Sara Gunnett
Sales Asso: Mark Minnela

D-U-N-S 02-531-8775 IMP
HOWARD ORLOFF IMPORTS INC (IL)
LAND ROVER CHICAGO
1924 N Paulina St, Chicago, IL 60622-1127
Tel (773) 227-3200 *Founded/Ownrshp* 1959
Sales 54.9MM^E *EMP* 105
SIC 5511 7538 5013 5531 7532 Automobiles, new & used; General automotive repair shops; Motor vehicle supplies & new parts; Automotive accessories; Body shop, automotive; Automobiles, new & used; General automotive repair shops; Motor vehicle supplies & new parts; Automotive accessories; Body shop, automotive
Pr: Howard Orloff
CFO: Jerry Burns
**Sec:* Jeff Orloff
**VP:* David Orloff
Genl Mgr: Joseph Colecta
Dir IT: Jason Pavalon
IT Man: Jason Cavalon
Sls Mgr: Christopher Moran
Sls Mgr: Shawn Snyder
Sls Mgr: Sean Stringer
Sales Asso: Christina Alvarez

D-U-N-S 05-236-5335
HOWARD PACKAGING LLC
3462 W Touhy Ave, Skokie, IL 60076-6217
Tel (847) 675-7650 *Founded/Ownrshp* 1959
Sales 23.4MM^E *EMP* 35
SIC 5113 Cardboard & products
Mktg Dir: Cathy Adams
Sales Asso: Mary Tyson

D-U-N-S 07-856-1818
HOWARD PAYNE UNIVERSITY
1000 Fisk Ave, Brownwood, TX 76801-2715
Tel (325) 649-8020 *Founded/Ownrshp* 1889
Sales 35.9MM *EMP* 185
Accts Davis Kinard & Co Pc Abilene
SIC 8221 University; University
Pr: William Ellis
Pr: Paul Dunne
VP: Magen Bunyard
Pr Dir: Coby Kestner
Sls Mgr: Karalee Fikes
Snr Mgr: Bob Pacatte

D-U-N-S 09-159-8045
■ **HOWARD PONTIAC-GMC INC**
(*Suby of* GROUP 1 AUTOMOTIVE INC) ★
13300 Broadway Ext, Oklahoma City, OK 73114-2249
Tel (405) 936-8800 *Founded/Ownrshp* 1978, 1995
Sales 52.8MM^E *EMP* 250^E
SIC 5511 Automobiles, new & used; Pickups, new & used; Vans, new & used; Automobiles, new & used; Pickups, new & used; Vans, new & used
Pr: Robert Howard
**Sec:* Brooks O'Hars
VP: Cliff Buster
**VP:* Scott Thompson
Exec: Truman Kellam
IT Man: Frank Keller
Mktg Dir: Gary Williams

D-U-N-S 00-643-6406 IMP
HOWARD PRECISION METALS INC (WI)
8058 N 87th St, Milwaukee, WI 53224-2802
Tel (414) 355-9611 *Founded/Ownrshp* 1928, 1982
Sales 35.0MM *EMP* 62
SIC 5051 Aluminum bars, rods, ingots, sheets, pipes, plates, etc.; Aluminum bars, rods, ingots, sheets, pipes, plates, etc.
CEO: Donald Howard
**Pr:* Robert A Howard
CFO: Ernest Fraser
**Treas:* Mark Howard
Opers Mgr: Robert Shey

HOWARD REGIONAL HEALTH SYSTEMS
See COMMUNITY HOWARD REGIONAL HEALTH FOUNDATION INC

HOWARD RV SUPERCENTER
See HOWARD MOTORS INC

D-U-N-S 96-213-4979
HOWARD S WRIGHT CONSTRUCTION CO
(*Suby of* BALFOUR BEATTY CONSTRUCTION GROUP INC) ★
425 Nw 10th Ave Ste 200, Portland, OR 97209-3128
Tel (503) 220-0895 *Founded/Ownrshp* 2011
Sales 56.6MM^E *EMP* 100
SIC 1542 Nonresidential construction; Nonresidential construction
Pr: Mitchell Hornecker
VP: Harlan Bixby
VP: Gordon Childress
VP: Dan Pelissier
VP: Jim Rowley
**Prin:* John Tremper
Admn Mgr: Brooke Giuffre
Dir IT: Greg Bronemann
VP Mktg: Marshall Cutting
Snr PM: Bob Barlish

D-U-N-S 18-621-8462
HOWARD S WRIGHT CONSTRUCTORS LP
501 Eastlake Ave E # 100, Seattle, WA 98109-5572
Tel (206) 447-7654 *Founded/Ownrshp* 2004
Sales NA *EMP* 479
SIC 1542

HOWARD SALES CO DIVISION
See OCEAN DESERT SALES INC

D-U-N-S 04-689-0703
HOWARD SHEPPARD INC
755 Waco Dr, Sandersville, GA 31082-7039
Tel (478) 552-5127 *Founded/Ownrshp* 1947
Sales 61.3MM^E *EMP* 350
SIC 4213 Trucking, except local; Trucking, except local
Pr: H Clifford Sheppard Jr
COO: Eric Holmes
**Treas:* Barbara Sheppard
VP: Howard Brantley
VP: Mike Rice
VP: Mitch Sheppard
**VP:* Trey Sheppard III
Dir IT: Lisa McCurdy
S&M/VP: Hoyt Sanders

D-U-N-S 15-538-5867 IMP
HOWARD SUPPLY CO LLC
HSC
4100 Intl Plz Ste 850, Fort Worth, TX 76109
Tel (817) 529-9950 *Founded/Ownrshp* 1985
Sales 93.9MM^E *EMP* 125
SIC 5084 5082 Oil well machinery, equipment & supplies; Oil field equipment; Oil well machinery, equipment & supplies; Oil field equipment
Pr: Michael Barber
**Pr:* Wayne Moody
COO: Baron Lukas
**COO:* Juergen Baron Lukas
**VP:* Mike Taylor
Store Mgr: Matt Beddoe
Store Mgr: Timothy Bender
Store Mgr: Zed Nelson
Store Mgr: Sid Shepard
Store Mgr: Mike Smith
Store Mgr: Brian Wilson

D-U-N-S 08-042-0862
HOWARD SYSTEMS INTERNATIONAL INC
QUESTCON TECHNOLOGIES
2777 Summer St Ste 505, Stamford, CT 06905-4323
Tel (203) 324-4600 *Founded/Ownrshp* 1975
Sales 28.8MM *EMP* 125
Accts Philips Gold & Company Llp N
SIC 7371 7373 8742 Custom computer programming services; Computer integrated systems design; Management consulting services; Custom computer programming services; Computer integrated systems design; Management consulting services
Pr: Howard Persky
CFO: James Malski
Sr VP: Marc Haskelson
Sr VP: Michael McMahon
VP: Jeffrey Martinik
VP: Cindy Robbins
Mng Dir: Garrett Chelius

HOWARD T HERBER MIDDLE SCHOOL
See MALVERNE UNION FREE SCHOOL DISTRICT 12

D-U-N-S 07-296-7581
HOWARD TAYLOR & SONS INC
7891 S Yellowstone Hwy, Idaho Falls, ID 83402-5809
Tel (208) 522-7770 *Founded/Ownrshp* 1970
Sales 34.8MM^E *EMP* 100
SIC 5148 Potatoes, fresh; Potatoes, fresh
Pr: Carl Taylor

D-U-N-S 00-980-7652
HOWARD TERNES PACKAGING CO
35275 Industrial Rd, Livonia, MI 48150-1231
Tel (734) 793-4130 *Founded/Ownrshp* 1948
Sales 93.3MM^E *EMP* 450
SIC 4783 6512 6552 Packing goods for shipping; Commercial & industrial building operation; Land subdividers & developers, commercial; Land subdividers & developers, residential; Packing goods for shipping; Commercial & industrial building operation; Land subdividers & developers, commercial; Land subdividers & developers, residential
Ch Bd: Howard A Ternes Jr
**Pr:* Charles E Ross
**VP:* Richard Everhart
VP: Adele Hughes
Prgrm Mgr: Lauren Turner
Dir IT: Tony Beddow
Opers Mgr: Randy Marshall
Plnt Mgr: Robert Kidd

HOWARD TIRE
See BRUCES TIRES INC

D-U-N-S 05-628-2296
HOWARD UNIVERSITY
2400 6th St Nw, Washington, DC 20059-0002
Tel (202) 806-6100 *Founded/Ownrshp* 1867
Sales 398.9MM *EMP* 5,600
SIC 8221 University; University
Pr: Dwayne Frederick
COO: Agnes Day
CFO: Rufus Blackwell
CFO: John Grish
Trst: John J Howard
Assoc VP: Michael Harris
Sr VP: Hassan Minor
Sr VP: Carol Winston
VP: Cicely Cottrell
VP: James Mitchell
VP: Florence Prioleau
VP: Harry Robinson
Assoc Dir: Rufus Erobinson
Assoc Dir: Precious Smith
Dir: Keith Witherspoon

D-U-N-S 79-410-7099
HOWARD UNIVERSITY HOSPITAL
DEPARTMENT OF SURGERY
2041 Georgia Ave Nw, Washington, DC 20060-0002
Tel (202) 865-1441 *Founded/Ownrshp* 2007
Sales 185.5MM^E *EMP* 2,000
SIC 8062

D-U-N-S 00-701-4640
HOWARD W PENCE INC (KY)
342 E Dixie Ave, Elizabethtown, KY 42701-1106
Tel (270) 737-8723 *Founded/Ownrshp* 1966
Sales 21.5MM^E *EMP* 65
SIC 1542 1731 Commercial & office building, new construction; General electrical contractor
Pr: Howard W Pence
**Sec:* Patsy Pence
**VP:* David Pence

D-U-N-S 15-186-1184
HOWARD YOUNG HEALTH CARE INC
240 Maple St, Woodruff, WI 54568-9190
Tel (715) 356-8000 *Founded/Ownrshp* 1984
Sales 2.0MM *EMP* 840
SIC 8082 Home health care services; Home health care services
CEO: Brian Kief
Ch Bd: David Klimisch
Pr: Sheila Clough
CFO: Cathy Bukowski
Treas: Thomas Ellis

D-U-N-S 07-479-4710
HOWARD YOUNG MEDICAL CENTER INC
240 Maple St, Woodruff, WI 54568-9190
Tel (715) 356-8000 *Founded/Ownrshp* 1947
Sales 62.2MM *EMP* 650
SIC 8062 General medical & surgical hospitals; General medical & surgical hospitals
Pr: Patricia Richardson
Chf Rad: Timothy L Swan
**Pr:* Sheila Clough
**CFO:* Cathy Bukowski
Treas: Greg Kopp
Pathlgst: Bruce Hertel
Pathlgst: James Lau
Doctor: Stephen Lindsey
Doctor: Vincent Moore
Pharmcst: Jack Berginz
Pharmcst: Tim Lerch

D-U-N-S 03-304-0023
■ **HOWARD-GM II INC**
SMICKLAS CHEVROLET
(*Suby of* GROUP 1 AUTOMOTIVE INC) ★
8900 Nw Expressway, Oklahoma City, OK 73162-6018
Tel (405) 470-8800 *Founded/Ownrshp* 2001
Sales 45.9MM^E *EMP* 155
SIC 5511 Automobiles, new & used; Pickups, new & used; Vans, new & used; Automobiles, new & used; Pickups, new & used; Vans, new & used
Pr: Robert Howard
Store Mgr: Bill Dooley
Telecom Ex: Maxine Kapp
IT Man: Terryl Dequire

D-U-N-S 08-618-8315
HOWARD-SUAMICO SCHOOL DISTRICT
2700 Lineville Rd, Green Bay, WI 54313-7151
Tel (920) 662-7871 *Founded/Ownrshp* 1961
Sales 37.5MM^E *EMP* 650
SIC 8211 Public elementary & secondary schools; High school, junior or senior; Public elementary & secondary schools; High school, junior or senior
Exec: Angela Sorenson
Schl Brd P: Mark Ashley
Psych: Tracy Vandenbusch

D-U-N-S 17-089-0172
HOWARDCENTER INC
208 Flynn Ave Ste 3j, Burlington, VT 05401-5420
Tel (802) 488-6900 *Founded/Ownrshp* 1884
Sales 80.2MM *EMP* 1,128
Accts Kittell Branagan & Sargent Cpa
SIC 8322 Individual & family services; Individual & family services
CEO: Todd Centybear
**Pr:* Karen Oniel
**CFO:* Charles Stringer
**Treas:* John Mc Soley
VP: Hal Colston
**VP:* Peter McCarthy
Exec: Barbara Graf
Ex Dir: Lorraine Jenne
Prgrm Mgr: Katie Dorey
Prgrm Mgr: Ashley Freeman
Prgrm Mgr: Tina Hatin

D-U-N-S 02-926-6731
HOWARDS APPLIANCES INC
901 E Imperial Hwy Ste E, La Habra, CA 90631-7443
Tel (714) 871-2700 *Founded/Ownrshp* 1949
Sales 39.6MM^E *EMP* 185
SIC 5722 5731 Electric household appliances, major; Television sets; High fidelity stereo equipment; Video cameras, recorders & accessories; Electric household appliances, major; Television sets; High fidelity stereo equipment; Video cameras, recorders & accessories
CEO: Judy Lawrence
**CEO:* William Pleasant
**VP:* Cecilia Pan
**VP:* Bill Pleasant
**VP:* Howard Roach
Brnch Mgr: Miguel Carranza
Mktg Dir: Ray Bowman

HOWARD'S EXPRESS
See RIST TRANSPORT LTD

HOWCO ENVIRONMENTAL SERVICES
See HAGAN HOLDING CO

HOWCO GROUP
See HOWCO METALS MANAGEMENT LLC

D-U-N-S 94-221-8116 IMP/EXP
HOWCO METALS MANAGEMENT LLC
HOWCO GROUP
9611 Telge Rd, Houston, TX 77095-5114
Tel (281) 649-8800 *Founded/Ownrshp* 2002
Sales 114.2MM^E *EMP* 150
Accts Ernst & Young Glasgow Scotla
SIC 5051 Steel; Steel
Pr: John Ferguson
COO: Dave Davidson
**CFO:* Kenneth Ness
Sr VP: Douglas Ferguson
**VP:* Keith Itzel
VP: Joe Klumpyan
**VP:* David Meyer
Mng Dir: David Birch
Mng Dir: M N Howat
Genl Mgr: Kevin McCabe
Dir IT: Stanton Fraser

D-U-N-S 07-927-1190 IMP
HOWDEN AMERICAN FAN CO
(*Suby of* FLAKT WOODS GROUP SA)
2933 Symmes Rd, Fairfield, OH 45014-2001
Tel (513) 773-0103 *Founded/Ownrshp* 2013
Sales 54.0MM^E *EMP* 162^E
SIC 3564 Exhaust fans: industrial or commercial; Turbo-blowers, industrial; Blowing fans: industrial or commercial; Ventilating fans: industrial or commercial; Exhaust fans: industrial or commercial; Turbo-blowers, industrial; Blowing fans: industrial or commercial; Ventilating fans: industrial or commercial

Pr: Greg Card
**VP:* Dave Nadler
**VP:* Kathy Parry
**VP:* Jeff Robinson

D-U-N-S 05-484-3438 IMP
■ HOWDEN NORTH AMERICA INC (MI)
HOWDENS
(*Suby of* ANDERSON GROUP INC) ★
7909 Parklane Rd Ste 300, Columbia, SC 29223-5667
Tel (803) 741-2700 *Founded/Ownrshp* 1980
Sales 221.9MM^{E} *EMP* 506
SIC 3564 3568 Exhaust fans: industrial or commercial; Couplings, shaft: rigid, flexible, universal joint, etc.; Exhaust fans: industrial or commercial; Couplings, shaft: rigid, flexible, universal joint, etc.
CEO: Matthew Ingle
**Pr:* Karl Kimmerling
**Ch:* Will Samuel
VP: Grahame Gurney
IT Man: Tara Vannorman
Plnt Mgr: David Smith
Manager: George Junor
Sales Asso: Stephanie Barie

D-U-N-S 96-593-2692 IMP
■ HOWDEN NORTH AMERICA INC
(*Suby of* HOWDEN NORTH AMERICA INC) ★
2933 Symmes Rd, Fairfield, OH 45014-2001
Tel (513) 874-2400 *Founded/Ownrshp* 2010
Sales 61.0MM^{E} *EMP* 170
SIC 5084 Industrial machinery & equipment; Industrial machinery & equipment
Pr: Karl Kimmerling
Chf Mktg O: Per Olesen
VP Mfg: David Nadler
VP Mktg: James Miller

D-U-N-S 07-990-9584
■ HOWDEN ROOTS LLC
(*Suby of* COLFAX CORP) ★
900 W Mount St, Connersville, IN 47331-1675
Tel (765) 827-9200 *Founded/Ownrshp* 2015
Sales 33.5MM^{E} *EMP* 235
SIC 3564 3563 Blowers & fans; Air & gas compressors

HOWDENS
See HOWDEN NORTH AMERICA INC

HOWDY HONDA
See ADNOH INC

HOWE COFFEE CO
See GEORGE JHOWE CO

D-U-N-S 07-876-5682
HOWE ELECTRIC INC
4682 E Olive Ave, Fresno, CA 93702-1689
Tel (559) 255-8992 *Founded/Ownrshp* 1949
Sales 29.6MM^{E} *EMP* 185
SIC 1731 General electrical contractor; General electrical contractor
CEO: Clinton Howe
**Pr:* Harry S Truman
**VP:* Clifford J Howe
Exec: Patricia McMurtrey
IT Man: Marjorie Montes
Sfty Dirs: Rod Tice

D-U-N-S 96-208-7607
HOWE FINANCIAL TRUST
2616 Glenview Dr, Elkhart, IN 46514-9243
Tel (574) 264-2935 *Founded/Ownrshp* 1972
Sales 32.0MM *EMP* 3
Accts Art Edelman Co-Trustee
SIC 1531 Operative builders; Operative builders
Co-Trst: Julie Griggs
**Co-Trst:* Len Bieber
**Co-Trst:* Art Edelman
**Co-Trst:* Steve Gaby
Trst: Raymond Balogh Jr
Trst: Arthur Edelman

D-U-N-S 02-716-1330 IMP/EXP
HOWE-BAKER ENGINEERS LTD
CHICAGO BRIDGE & IRON COMPANY
(*Suby of* CHICAGO BRIDGE & IRON CO) ★
3102 E 5th St, Tyler, TX 75701-5145
Tel (903) 597-0311 *Founded/Ownrshp* 1974
Sales 35.5MM^{E} *EMP* 500
SIC 1629 Industrial plant construction; Oil refinery construction; Chemical plant & refinery construction; Industrial plant construction; Oil refinery construction; Chemical plant & refinery construction
Pt: Luke Scorsone
Pt: Mitchell M Bernhard
Pt: Dennis C Planic

D-U-N-S 07-784-3308
HOWELL CHILD CARE CENTER INC
3738 Howell Day Care Rd, La Grange, NC 28551-6808
Tel (252) 566-9011 *Founded/Ownrshp* 1970
Sales 1.1MM *EMP* 1,400
SIC 8361 8052 Children's home; Intermediate care facilities; Children's home; Intermediate care facilities
Pr: Sandra Hedrick
**VP:* Jim Panton

HOWELL CONSTRUCTION
See JAMES R HOWELL & CO INC

D-U-N-S 00-810-7476
HOWELL INDUSTRIES INC
1650 Swisco Rd, Sulphur, LA 70665-8208
Tel (337) 533-8941 *Founded/Ownrshp* 1965
Sales 25.7MM^{E} *EMP* 95
SIC 1799 3599 Welding on site; Machine shop, jobbing & repair
Pr: Douglas Landry
**Sr VP:* Rodney Fruge
Genl Mgr: Guy Smith

D-U-N-S 00-110-9685 IMP
HOWELL LABORATORIES INC (ME)
188 Harrison Rd, Bridgton, ME 04009-4748
Tel (207) 647-3327 *Founded/Ownrshp* 1964, 1995
Sales 47.5MM^{E} *EMP* 70^{E}
SIC 5551 3663 Marine supplies & equipment; Antennas, transmitting & communications
Pr: David Allen
**Pr:* Paul A Wescott
**Treas:* Carl H Bishop
Ex VP: Joseph McDonnell
**VP:* Martyn Gregory
Dir IT: Al Friend
Dir IT: Norman Hutchins
Sls Mgr: Jonathan Clark
Board of Directors: Gordon Drisko, Richard E Lewis, Linda Rollins, Gary Somers, James Stevens

D-U-N-S 04-101-4770
■ HOWELL METAL CO
(*Suby of* MUELLER COPPER TUBE PRODUCTS INC) ★
574 New Market Depot Rd, New Market, VA 22844-2000
Tel (540) 740-4700 *Founded/Ownrshp* 2013
Sales 4.9MM^{E} *EMP* 340
SIC 3351

D-U-N-S 08-912-0026
HOWELL OIL CO
808 Nw 12th St, Belle Glade, FL 33430-1738
Tel (561) 996-2787 *Founded/Ownrshp* 1949
Sales 25.0MM *EMP* 9
SIC 5171 Petroleum bulk stations; Petroleum bulk stations
Pr: Christine Howell
**Sec:* Warren Keith Howell
**VP:* Greg Howell

HOWELL PACKAGING
See F M HOWELL & CO

D-U-N-S 08-774-9313
HOWELL PUBLIC SCHOOLS (MI)
411 N Highlander Way, Howell, MI 48843-1021
Tel (517) 548-6200 *Founded/Ownrshp* 1853
Sales 67.2MM^{E} *EMP* 1,740
SIC 8211 Public elementary school; Public elementary school
Bd of Dir: Mark Leahy
VP: Ann Routt
Exec: Mark Sharp
Exec: John Tiefenbach
**Prin:* Lynn Parrish
Pr Dir: Tom Gould
Schl Brd P: Michael Witt
Psych: Catherine Deschenes
Psych: Caroline Grabowski

D-U-N-S 06-502-3657
HOWELL SAND CO INC
2300 E Hastings Ave, Amarillo, TX 79108-5410
Tel (806) 383-1721 *Founded/Ownrshp* 1979
Sales 20.5MM^{E} *EMP* 60
SIC 1442 Sand mining
Pr: James R Howell Jr
**VP:* Josh Howell

D-U-N-S 05-425-4602
HOWELL TOWNSHIP BOARD OF EDUCATION
HOWELL TWP PUBLIC SCHOOLS
200 Sqnkum Yellowbrook Rd, Howell, NJ 07731
Tel (732) 751-2480 *Founded/Ownrshp* 1890
Sales 49.5MM^{E} *EMP* 1,000
Accts Robert A Hulsart And Company
SIC 8211 Public elementary school; Public senior high school; Public elementary school; Public senior high school

D-U-N-S 07-979-9772
HOWELL TOWNSHIP PUBLIC SCHOOLS
200 Sqnkum Yellowbrook Rd, Howell, NJ 07731
Tel (732) 751-2480 *Founded/Ownrshp* 2015
Sales 21.7MM^{E} *EMP* 644^{E}
SIC 8211 Public elementary & secondary schools
MIS Dir: Thomas Aquino
HC Dir: Patricia Callander

HOWELL TWP PUBLIC SCHOOLS
See HOWELL TOWNSHIP BOARD OF EDUCATION

D-U-N-S 00-890-9384
HOWELL-OREGON ELECTRIC COOPERATIVE INC
6327 Us Highway 63, West Plains, MO 65775-5345
Tel (417) 256-2131 *Founded/Ownrshp* 1939
Sales 39.3MM *EMP* 83
SIC 4911 Distribution, electric power; Distribution, electric power
CEO: Dan Singletary
Opers Mgr: Jeff West

D-U-N-S 02-605-3546 IMP
HOWELLS FURNITURE CO LTD (TX)
HOWELL'S FURNITURE GALLERIES
6095 Folsom Dr, Beaumont, TX 77706-7268
Tel (409) 832-2544 *Founded/Ownrshp* 1959
Sales 32.2MM^{E} *EMP* 100
Accts Wathen Deshong & Juncker Ll
SIC 5712 Furniture stores
Pr: Tom Schwaab
**CFO:* Donna Dibattispa
**Treas:* Carol Brantley
**VP:* Jeff Witt
Genl Mgr: Brian Berni
Store Mgr: Rene Jackson

HOWELL'S FURNITURE GALLERIES
See HOWELLS FURNITURE CO LTD

D-U-N-S 00-779-2138
HOWELLS MOTOR FREIGHT INC
51 Simmons Dr, Cloverdale, VA 24077-3131
Tel (540) 966-3200 *Founded/Ownrshp* 1957
Sales 56.9MM^{E} *EMP* 300
SIC 4213 Trucking, except local; Trucking, except local
Pr: Harry G Norris
**Sec:* Timothy S Shepard
**Ex VP:* Betty G Norris
Sr VP: Sherry Lockhart
VP: Tim Shephard

HOWL AT THE MOON
See HOWL USA LLC

D-U-N-S 92-612-7627 IMP/EXP
HOWL USA LLC
HOWL AT THE MOON
30 W Hubbard St Ste 200, Chicago, IL 60654-7389
Tel (513) 475-4001 *Founded/Ownrshp* 2007
Sales 43.2MM^{E} *EMP* 338^{E}
SIC 5813 Night clubs
CFO: Lee Jerousek
COO: Bradd O'Brien
Genl Mgr: Peter Benton
Genl Mgr: Rob Bernstein
Genl Mgr: Becky Callahan
Genl Mgr: Donnie Cox
Genl Mgr: Emily Duncan
Genl Mgr: Matt Malliski

D-U-N-S 07-691-7475
HOWLAND LOCAL SCHOOL DISTRICT
8200 South St Se, Warren, OH 44484-2447
Tel (330) 856-8200 *Founded/Ownrshp* 1890
Sales 33.0MM *EMP* 396
Accts Dave Yost Youngstown Ohio
SIC 8211 Public elementary & secondary schools; Public elementary & secondary schools
Treas: Thomas Krispinsky
Schl Brd P: Warner Bacak

D-U-N-S 00-225-0892
HOWLAND PUMP AND SUPPLY CO INC (NY)
WATERTOWN SUPPLY COMPANY
7611 State Highway 68, Ogdensburg, NY 13669-4443
Tel (315) 393-3791 *Founded/Ownrshp* 1880
Sales 50.7MM^{E} *EMP* 62
SIC 5074 5084 Plumbing & hydronic heating supplies; Pumps & pumping equipment; Plumbing & hydronic heating supplies; Pumps & pumping equipment
CEO: Steve Larose
**Pr:* Russell Mc Donald
Pr: Bob Whalen
**VP:* Dawn Mc Donald
Snr Mgr: Stephen Larose

D-U-N-S 05-831-1945 IMP
■ HOWMEDICA OSTEONICS CORP
STRYKER ORTHOPAEDICS
(*Suby of* STRYKER CORP) ★
325 Corporate Dr, Mahwah, NJ 07430-2006
Tel (201) 831-5000 *Founded/Ownrshp* 1998
Sales 523.7MM^{E} *EMP* 3,950^{E}
SIC 3842 5047 Surgical appliances & supplies; Orthopedic equipment & supplies; Surgical appliances & supplies; Orthopedic equipment & supplies
Pr: Kevin A Lobo
**CFO:* William R Jellison
**Treas:* Jeanne M Blondia
**VP:* Yin C Becker
**VP:* Steven P Benscoter
**VP:* Dean H Bergy
**VP:* William E Berry Jr
Board of Directors: Stephen P Macmillan

D-U-N-S 55-545-2481
■ HOWMET ALUMINUM CASTING INC
SIGMA DIV
(*Suby of* ALCOA INC) ★
1600 Harvard Ave, Newburgh Heights, OH 44105-3040
Tel (216) 641-4340 *Founded/Ownrshp* 2000
Sales 36.2MM^{E} *EMP* 501
SIC 3365 Aluminum & aluminum-based alloy castings; Aluminum & aluminum-based alloy castings
Pr: Raymond B Mitchell
Genl Couns: Janet Duderstadt

D-U-N-S 01-476-8660
■ HOWMET CASTINGS & SERVICES INC
(*Suby of* ALCOA POWER & PROPULSION) ★
1616 Harvard Ave, Newburgh Heights, OH 44105-3040
Tel (216) 641-4400 *Founded/Ownrshp* 2004
Sales 482.9MM^{E} *EMP* 3,954^{E}
SIC 3324 Commercial investment castings, ferrous
Pr: Eric M Brzostek
VP: Natalie Schilling

D-U-N-S 02-090-0049 IMP/EXP
■ HOWMET CORP
ALCOA POWER & PROPULSION
(*Suby of* HOWMET HOLDINGS CORP) ★
1616 Harvard Ave, Newburgh Heights, OH 44105-3040
Tel (216) 641-6124 *Founded/Ownrshp* 1975, 1995
Sales 1.3MMM^{E} *EMP* 10,000
SIC 3324 3542 5051 3479 Commercial investment castings, ferrous; Machine tools, metal forming type; Ferroalloys; Ingots; Coating of metals & formed products; Commercial investment castings, ferrous; Machine tools, metal forming type; Ferroalloys; Ingots; Coating of metals & formed products
Pr: David L Squier
**Sr VP:* Marklin Lasker
**Sr VP:* James R Stanley
**VP:* Roland A Paul
**VP Mfg:* B Dennis Albrechtsen

D-U-N-S 00-657-5799 IMP
■ HOWMET HOLDINGS CORP
(*Suby of* ALCOA INC) ★
1 Misco Dr, Whitehall, MI 49461-1799
Tel (231) 894-5686 *Founded/Ownrshp* 1970
Sales 1.3MMM^{E} *EMP* 10,000
SIC 3324 3542 5051 3479 Commercial investment castings, ferrous; Machine tools, metal forming type; Ferroalloys; Ingots; Coating of metals & formed products; Commercial investment castings, ferrous; Machine tools, metal forming type; Ferroalloys; Ingots; Coating of metals & formed products
CEO: Mario Longhi
**Pr:* Raymond B Mitchell
**VP:* James R Stanley

D-U-N-S 15-034-7862
HOWRED CORP
7887 San Felipe St # 122, Houston, TX 77063-1620
Tel (713) 781-3980 *Founded/Ownrshp* 1985
Sales 31.4MM^{E} *EMP* 200
SIC 5033 Insulation, thermal; Insulation, thermal
Pr: Howard Watson

D-U-N-S 07-480-1598
HOWREY LLP
1299 Pennsylvania Ave Nw # 300, Washington, DC 20004-2400
Tel (202) 783-0800 *Founded/Ownrshp* 2000
Sales 49.0MM^{E} *EMP* 1,540
SIC 8111 Corporate, partnership & business law; Antitrust & trade regulation law; Environmental law; Administrative & government law
Genl Pt: Robert Ruyak
Pt: Bernhard Darren B
Pt: Froemming John G
Pt: Forsythe Vanessa H
Pt: Bodner John
COO: Ralph E Allen Jr
CIO: Daniel Garparro
IT Man: John Stright

D-U-N-S 07-822-4179
HOWROYD-WRIGHT EMPLOYMENT AGENCY INC
APPLE ONE EMPLOYMENT
(*Suby of* ACT 1 GROUP INC) ★
327 W Broadway, Glendale, CA 91204-1301
Tel (818) 240-8688 *Founded/Ownrshp* 1964
Sales 76.2MM^{E} *EMP* 1,300
SIC 7361 Labor contractors (employment agency); Executive placement; Labor contractors (employment agency); Executive placement
CEO: Janice Bryant Howroyd
**Pr:* Bernard Howroyd
**CFO:* Michael Hoyal
CFO: Lynda Lindsey
Ofcr: Monir Syed
VP: Michael A Howroyd
Brnch Mgr: Jessica Elkins
Brnch Mgr: Linda Peets
Brnch Mgr: Jazmin Williamson
Software D: Jason Watts
Netwrk Eng: Al Candelaria

D-U-N-S 06-116-7834
HOWS MARKETS LLC
3035 Huntington Dr, Pasadena, CA 91107-5516
Tel (626) 535-9091 *Founded/Ownrshp* 1999
Sales 31.8MM^{E} *EMP* 325
SIC 5411 Supermarkets; Supermarkets

D-U-N-S 00-819-8160 IMP
HOWSE IMPLEMENT CO INC (MS)
AGRIMOTIVE DIVISION
2013 Highway 184, Laurel, MS 39443-8302
Tel (601) 428-0841 *Founded/Ownrshp* 1964, 1997
Sales 38.0MM^{E} *EMP* 120
Accts Philip M Stevens Cps Pa La
SIC 3523 Grounds mowing equipment; Haying machines: mowers, rakes, stackers, etc.; Harrows: disc, spring, tine, etc.; Grounds mowing equipment; Haying machines: mowers, rakes, stackers, etc.; Harrows: disc, spring, tine, etc.
Pr: Benjamin T Howse
**Treas:* Barry D Howse
Exec: Charlott Sanderson
VP Mfg: Paul Starr

D-U-N-S 00-779-4910
HOY CONSTRUCTION INC
3495 Progress Rd, Norfolk, VA 23502-1929
Tel (757) 853-8861 *Founded/Ownrshp* 1961
Sales 31.1MM^{E} *EMP* 48
SIC 1542 1541 Commercial & office building, new construction; Commercial & office buildings, renovation & repair; Industrial buildings, new construction; Renovation, remodeling & repairs: industrial buildings
Pr: James L Craig III
**Sec:* Robert Melancon
**VP:* Jeff W Knowles
**VP:* Adam W Ritt
**Prin:* Robert D Melancon

HOY FOX TOYOTA
See VISCOUNT PROPERTIES II LP

D-U-N-S 10-730-0246 IMP
HOYA CORP
HOYA VISION CARE
(*Suby of* HOYA CORPORATION)
651 E Corporate Dr, Lewisville, TX 75057-6403
Tel (972) 221-4141 *Founded/Ownrshp* 1981
Sales 97.7MM^{E} *EMP* 560
SIC 3851 Ophthalmic goods; Ophthalmic goods
Ch Bd: Bill C Benedict
**Pr:* Hiroshi Suzuki
VP: Iggy Fernandez
Genl Mgr: Mark Evett
Genl Mgr: James Sandige
Genl Mgr: Buster Wallof
Genl Mgr: Rodney Webb
IT Man: Steve Richards
Netwrk Eng: Monty Weaver
VP Opers: Sandy Morgan
Sls Dir: Ken Harden

D-U-N-S 61-962-1978 IMP
HOYA HOLDINGS INC
(*Suby of* HOYA CORPORATION)
680 N Mccarthy Blvd # 120, Milpitas, CA 95035-5120
Tel (408) 654-2309 *Founded/Ownrshp* 1973
Sales 93.4MM^{E} *EMP* 600
SIC 3861 3825 3827 Photographic sensitized goods; Test equipment for electronic & electric measurement; Optical instruments & lenses; Photographic sensitized goods; Test equipment for electronic & electric measurement; Optical instruments & lenses
CEO: Hiroshi Suzuki
**COO:* Eiichiro Ikeda
**CFO:* Ryo Hirooka
MIS Dir: Andy Wong

D-U-N-S 05-501-2350 IMP
HOYA LENS OF AMERICA INC
(*Suby of* HOYA HOLDINGS INC) ★
651 E Corporate Dr, Lewisville, TX 75057-6403
Tel (972) 221-4141 *Founded/Ownrshp* 1999
Sales 32.1MM^E *EMP* 120
SIC 5048 3851 Ophthalmic goods; Lens grinding, except prescription: ophthalmic
Pr: Paul B Dougher
**CFO:* Yuji Eshii
**Prin:* Michael Ness
IT Man: Thomas Burnett

HOYA VISION CARE
See HOYA CORP

D-U-N-S 18-553-5531 IMP/EXP
HOYER GLOBAL (USA) INC
(*Suby of* SULLIVAN UNIVERSITY SYSTEM INC) ★
2100 Space Park Dr, Houston, TX 77058-3693
Tel (281) 853-1000 *Founded/Ownrshp* 1999
Sales 40.7MM^E *EMP* 115^E
SIC 4731 Freight transportation arrangement; Freight transportation arrangement
Prin: Christa Silberstorf
**Ch Bd:* Michael Loscalzo
**Pr:* Heiko Peitsch
**Treas:* Subhas Chakrabarti

HOYFOX AUTOMOTIVE
See AIRWAY PROPERTIES MANAGERS LLC

HOY'S 5 & 10
See B J STORES INC

D-U-N-S 01-326-0070
HOYT HAYNER CORP
H H
625 Erie Blvd W, Syracuse, NY 13204-2424
Tel (315) 455-5941 *Founded/Ownrshp* 1993
Sales 39.6MM^E *EMP* 85
SIC 1542 1541 1522 Commercial & office building, new construction; Commercial & office buildings, renovation & repair; Industrial buildings, new construction; Apartment building construction
Ch Bd: Gary Thurston
**Pr:* Jeremy Thurston
**VP:* Michael George
Sfty Mgr: Mark Foley

D-U-N-S 00-627-3361 IMP
HOYT USA INC
(*Suby of* JAS D EASTON INC) ★
593 N Wright Brothers Dr, Salt Lake City, UT 84116-2847
Tel (801) 363-2990 *Founded/Ownrshp* 1946, 1983
Sales 35.9MM^E *EMP* 175
SIC 3949 Archery equipment, general; Archery equipment, general
Pr: Randy Walk
CFO: Todd Erickson
**VP:* John Cramer
VP: Jeff Howard
Plnt Mgr: Steve Memmott
Sls&Mrk Ex: Jeremy Eldredge
Mktg Mgr: Terry James
Mktg Mgr: Laura Powell

HOYT WIRE CLOTH DIV
See LUMSDEN CORP

D-U-N-S 96-249-8445
HOYU AMERICA CO
SAMY CO
(*Suby of* HOYU CO.,LTD.)
6265 Phyllis Dr, Cypress, CA 90630-5240
Tel (714) 230-3000 *Founded/Ownrshp* 2004
Sales 35.0MM *EMP* 58
SIC 5122 5999 Cosmetics, perfumes & hair products; Hair care products; Cosmetics, perfumes & hair products; Hair care products
Pr: Yoshihiro Sasaki
**Sr VP:* Minoru Tsuda

HP
See HEWLETT-PACKARD CREDIT CORP

HP BEDFORD HOUS
See MOODY NATIONAL MORTGAGE CORP

D-U-N-S 09-060-9483
HP COMMUNICATIONS INC (CA)
13341 Temescal Canyon Rd, Corona, CA 92883-4980
Tel (951) 471-1919 *Founded/Ownrshp* 1998
Sales 122.7MM^E *EMP* 240^E
Accts Steven A Flores Placentia C
SIC 1623 Communication line & transmission tower construction; Communication line & transmission tower construction
Pr: Nicholas Goldman
**Ex VP:* Ahmad Olomi
**VP:* Chris Price
Dir Bus: Hank Goldmann
Netwrk Eng: Adela Corona
Netwrk Eng: Veronica Ohr

D-U-N-S 00-583-9394
HP CUMMINGS CONSTRUCTION CO (MA)
14 Prospect St, Ware, MA 01082-1116
Tel (413) 967-6251 *Founded/Ownrshp* 1879, 1960
Sales 40.6MM^E *EMP* 125
Accts Livingston & Haynes Pc War
SIC 1542 1541 School building construction; Hospital construction; Commercial & office building, new construction; Industrial buildings & warehouses; School building construction; Hospital construction; Commercial & office building, new construction; Industrial buildings & warehouses
CEO: Dallas Folk
**Pr:* Benjamin D Harrington Jr
**Treas:* John G Harrington
**VP:* Paul Hamel
**VP:* Brian Hobart
**VP:* Michael Hulbert
**VP:* John Scott
**VP:* Dan Smith
**Prin:* Mike Hricko

D-U-N-S 04-666-7523
■ **HP ENTERPRISE SERVICES LLC**
ELECTRONIC DATA SYSTEMS
(*Suby of* HEWLETT PACKARD ENTERPRISE CO) ★
5400 Legacy Dr, Plano, TX 75024-3105
Tel (972) 604-6000 *Founded/Ownrshp* 2008
Sales 13.2MMM^E *EMP* 139,500
SIC 7374 7371 8742 Data processing service; Custom computer programming services; Marketing consulting services; Business planning & organizing services; Management engineering; Materials mgmt. (purchasing, handling, inventory) consultant; Data processing service; Custom computer programming services; Marketing consulting services; Business planning & organizing services; Management engineering; Materials mgmt. (purchasing, handling, inventory) consultant
Pr: Dennis Stolkey
**Pr:* Ronald A Rittenmeyer
CFO: Ron Bargo
CFO: Michelle Colombo
**CFO:* Catherine A Lesjak
CFO: Jerin Stransky
**CFO:* Ronald P Vargo
CFO: Trace Woodward
**Treas:* James T Murrin
Ofcr: David Morrow
Ex VP: Coley Clark
Ex VP: Martin Fink
**Ex VP:* Storrow M Gordon
Ex VP: John Visentin
Sr VP: Pete Karolczak
Sr VP: Sean Kenny
**Sr VP:* Tina M Sivinski
Sr VP: Dennis Stolkey
VP: Alan Atchison
**VP:* Cherri Musser
Exec: Jeffrey Heller

D-U-N-S 00-100-8697 IMP/EXP
HP HOOD LLC
6 Kimball Ln Ste 400, Lynnfield, MA 01940-2685
Tel (617) 887-8441 *Founded/Ownrshp* 1846
Sales 2.0MMM^E *EMP* 4,500
Accts Pricewaterhousecoopers Llp Bo
SIC 2026 2024 2022 Fluid milk; Cream, sweet; Yogurt; Ice cream & frozen desserts; Processed cheese; Fluid milk; Cream, sweet; Yogurt; Ice cream & frozen desserts; Processed cheese
CFO: Gary R Kaneb
VP: Sorin Hilgen
Dir Risk M: Jane Riley
Creative D: Esan Sivalingam
Genl Mgr: Marilyn Pieczarka
Mtls Mgr: Wandette Chin
Opers Supe: Josh Johnson
Opers Mgr: Andre Frey-Thomas
Plnt Mgr: Mike Farino
Plnt Mgr: John Marchildon
Prd Mgr: Jason Humphrey

D-U-N-S 00-912-2532
▲ **HP INC**
1501 Page Mill Rd, Palo Alto, CA 94304-1126
Tel (650) 857-1501 *Founded/Ownrshp* 1939
Sales 103.3MMM *EMP* 302,000
Tkr Sym HPQ *Exch* NYS
SIC 3571 7372 3861 3577 3572 3575 Personal computers (microcomputers); Minicomputers; Prepackaged software; Cameras, still & motion picture (all types); Diazotype (whiteprint) reproduction machines & equipment; Printers, computer; Optical scanning devices; Computer storage devices; Computer terminals; Personal computers (microcomputers); Minicomputers; Prepackaged software; Cameras, still & motion picture (all types); Diazotype (whiteprint) reproduction machines & equipment; Printers, computer; Optical scanning devices; Computer storage devices; Computer terminals
CEO: Dion Weisler
CFO: Catherine A Lesjak
Chf Mktg O: Henry Gomez
Ex VP: Martin Fink
Ex VP: John M Hinshaw
Ex VP: Abdo George Kadifa
Ex VP: Tracy S Keogh
Ex VP: Michael G Nefkens
Ex VP: John F Schultz
Ex VP: Dion J Weisler
Ex VP: Robert Youngjohns
Sr VP: Jeff T Ricci
Board of Directors: Carl Bass, Robert R Bennett, Charles V Bergh, Stephanie Burns, Mary Anne Citrino, Stacey Mobley, Stacy Brown-Philpot, Margaret C Whitman

D-U-N-S 04-303-2978
HP KOPPLEMANN INC (CT)
140 Van Block Ave, Hartford, CT 06106-2845
Tel (860) 549-6210 *Founded/Ownrshp* 1893, 1991
Sales 26.0MM^E *EMP* 125
SIC 5192 Newspapers; Newspapers
Pr: Neil K Hauss
**Treas:* Stanley Leven

D-U-N-S 92-980-0118 IMP
HP PELZER AUTOMOTIVE SYSTEMS INC
(*Suby of* HP PELZER HOLDING GMBH)
1175 Crooks Rd, Troy, MI 48084-7136
Tel (248) 280-1010 *Founded/Ownrshp* 1995
Sales 220.0MM *EMP* 900
SIC 3061 2273 Automotive rubber goods (mechanical); Carpets & rugs; Automotive rubber goods (mechanical); Carpets & rugs
CEO: John Pendleton
**CFO:* Wayne Robinson
Prgrm Mgr: Rod Duignan
Prgrm Mgr: John Nestle
Prgrm Mgr: Faris Qussar
Prgrm Mgr: Antonio Salinas
Prgrm Mgr: Pat Wundrach
Sys Mgr: Lori Murdick
Mtls Mgr: Stephen Allen
Mtls Mgr: Ginger Fryberger
Mtls Mgr: Lori Post

D-U-N-S 96-705-5331
HP THERAPEUTICS FOUNDATION INC
65 Livingston Ave, Roseland, NJ 07068-1725
Tel (973) 597-2510 *Founded/Ownrshp* 2011
Sales 30.0MM *EMP* 2
Accts Kpmg Llp New York Ny
SIC 8699 Charitable organization

D-U-N-S 00-918-5943 IMP
HPC FOODS LTD
288 Libby St, Honolulu, HI 96819-3950
Tel (808) 841-8705 *Founded/Ownrshp* 1952
Sales 21.8MM^E *EMP* 190
SIC 2099 5148 5149 Food preparations; Vegetables, fresh; Specialty food items; Food preparations; Vegetables, fresh; Specialty food items
Ch Bd: Ernest Tottori
**Pr:* Eric Enomoto
**VP:* Miriam Tottori
VP: Paul Tottori
IT Man: Terry Taira
Opers Mgr: Richard Vidinha
Opers Mgr: Ron Yamauchi
Ql Cn Mgr: Hui Wang

HPC FOODSERVICE
See HARTFORD PROVISION CO

D-U-N-S 96-869-3502
■ **HPC HOLDINGS LLC**
COMPOSITE GROUP, THE
(*Suby of* CITADEL PLASTICS HOLDINGS INC) ★
6151 Wilson Mills Rd, Highland Heights, OH 44143-2153
Tel (440) 224-1209 *Founded/Ownrshp* 2014
Sales 123.9MM^E *EMP* 430^E
SIC 2821 2655 Molding compounds, plastics; Cans, composite: foil-fiber & other: from purchased fiber; Molding compounds, plastics; Cans, composite: foil-fiber & other: from purchased fiber
CEO: Terry Morgan
CFO: Tom Meola

D-U-N-S 96-610-0252 IMP
HPC3 FURNITURE INC
BARCALOUNGER
(*Suby of* HANCOCK PARK ASSOCIATES II LP) ★
2829 W Andrew Johnson Hwy, Morristown, TN 37814-3216
Tel (423) 353-1288 *Founded/Ownrshp* 1940
Sales 25.0MM *EMP* 8
SIC 5021 Furniture
Pr: Larry L Smith

HPE
See HEATING AND PLUMBING ENGINEERS INC

D-U-N-S 55-574-5975 EXP
HPE INC
2985 Madison Rd, Cincinnati, OH 45209-2027
Tel (513) 351-9966 *Founded/Ownrshp* 1995
Sales 26.0MM^E *EMP* 17
SIC 5113 Paperboard & products
Pr: Richard G Donohoo
CFO: Earl Lindholz
**VP:* William G Donohoo
Genl Mgr: Dennie Campbell
IT Man: Craig Zobrist

HPFI
See HIGH POINT FURNITURE INDUSTRIES INC

HPG INTERNATIONAL
See HOSPITALITY PURCHASING GROUP INTERNATIONAL LLC

HPG RESTAURANT
See HYDE PARK RESTAURANT SYSTEMS INC

HPH HOSPICE
See HERNANDO-PASCO HOSPICE INC

HPI
See HERNDON PRODUCTS LLC

H.P.I.
See HENRY PRODUCTS INC

HPI
See HOME PRODUCTS INTERNATIONAL INC

HPI
See HEALTHCARE PARTNERS INVESTMENTS LLC

D-U-N-S 87-479-1841 IMP
HPI DIRECT INC
785 Goddard Ct, Alpharetta, GA 30005-2263
Tel (678) 942-1800 *Founded/Ownrshp* 1993
Sales 26.3MM *EMP* 73
SIC 2395

HPI RACING
See HOBBY PRODUCTS INTERNATIONAL INC

D-U-N-S 07-929-2847
■ **HPL HOUSTON PIPE LINE CO LLC**
(*Suby of* ENERGY TRANSFER EQUITY LP) ★
800 E Sonterra Blvd, San Antonio, TX 78258-3940
Tel (713) 222-0414 *Founded/Ownrshp* 2014
Sales 8.3MM^E *EMP* 838^E
SIC 4922 Pipelines, natural gas
Pr: Michael S McConnell

HPM BUILDING SUPPLY
See HAWAII PLANING MILL LTD

D-U-N-S 07-851-7870
HPM CONSTRUCTION LLC
(*Suby of* HENSEL PHELPS CONSTRUCTION CO) ★
17911 Mitchell S, Irvine, CA 92614-6015
Tel (949) 474-9170 *Founded/Ownrshp* 2012
Sales 300.0MM *EMP* 100
SIC 1542 Nonresidential construction; Nonresidential construction
Pr: Karen Price
Sec: Cuyler McGinley
VP: Cindy McMackin

D-U-N-S 88-309-0169
HPM INC
HPM NETWORKS
3231 Osgood Cmn, Fremont, CA 94539-5029
Tel (510) 353-0770 *Founded/Ownrshp* 1994
Sales 60.9MM^E *EMP* 33
SIC 5045 7378 Computers, peripherals & software; Computer peripheral equipment repair & maintenance
CEO: Romi Randhawa
**Sec:* Prabhjot K Randhawa
**VP:* Charles Miano
VP: Johnny Miano
**VP:* Shawn Scanlon
CTO: Nea Vongsy
IT Man: Lang Phan
IT Man: Jenny Tran
Opers Mgr: Michael Chantigian
Sales Exec: Victor Ahuja
Mktg Dir: Angela Restani

D-U-N-S 03-006-7367
HPM INDUSTRIES INC (PA)
ATLAS PRESSED METALS
125 Tom Mix Dr, Du Bois, PA 15801-2541
Tel (814) 371-4800 *Founded/Ownrshp* 1980
Sales 20.9MM^E *EMP* 70
SIC 3399 Powder, metal
Pr: Jude M Pfingstler
**Treas:* Richard L Pfingstler
**VP:* Christine A Pfingstler
Opers Mgr: Jen Rhines
Ql Cn Mgr: Richard Smochek

HPM NETWORKS
See HPM INC

D-U-N-S 94-293-2310
HPM STADCO INC
107 S Avenue 20, Los Angeles, CA 90031-1709
Tel (323) 227-8888 *Founded/Ownrshp* 1941
Sales 34.8MM^E *EMP* 603
SIC 3599 3559 3542 Machine & other job shop work; Machine shop, jobbing & repair; Plastics working machinery; Die casting machines; Machine & other job shop work; Machine shop, jobbing & repair; Plastics working machinery; Die casting machines
Pr: William Flickinger
**Ch Bd:* Parviz Nazarian
**Co-Ch Bd:* Neil Kadisha
IT Man: Jasmine Mapplethorpe
QC Dir: Jon Mitcham
S&M/VP: Bret Matta
Sls Dir: Jim Hickman

HPMI
See HENRY PLASTIC MOLDING INC

D-U-N-S 08-676-8814
HPR PARTNERS LLC
801 Warrenville Rd # 550, Lisle, IL 60532-1396
Tel (630) 737-0788 *Founded/Ownrshp* 1998
Sales 119.9MM^E *EMP* 2,000
SIC 5141 Food brokers; Food brokers
CEO: Phillip J Mason

HPS
See HAMTRAMCK PUBLIC SCHOOLS

D-U-N-S 01-712-2193
HPS LLC
3275 N M 37 Hwy, Middleville, MI 49333-9126
Tel (269) 795-3308 *Founded/Ownrshp* 1949
Sales 960.9MM *EMP* 38
Accts Meyaard Tolman & Venlet Pc C
SIC 7389 Purchasing service; Purchasing service
**CFO:* Thomas J La Pres
**Treas:* Dwith Gascho
**Treas:* Joseph Schodde
VP: Thomas Lapres
VP: Mike Sandy
IT Man: Brian McKinley
Mktg Mgr: Kendra Tossava
Manager: Bryan Brauer
Manager: Preston Fouts
Manager: Jackie Hepler
Manager: Emley Navarro
Board of Directors: Marvin Baird

D-U-N-S 12-547-3400
HPS MECHANICAL INC
3100 E Belle Ter, Bakersfield, CA 93307-6830
Tel (661) 397-2121 *Founded/Ownrshp* 1959
Sales 31.9MM^E *EMP* 130^E
SIC 1711 Plumbing contractors; Plumbing contractors
Pr: Les Denherder
**VP:* Scott Denherder
Assoc Dir: Chad Kinsey
Sys Mgr: Al Martinez
Sfty Dirs: Doug Degroot

D-U-N-S 12-083-1560
HPS PLUMBING SERVICE INC
3100 E Belle Ter, Bakersfield, CA 93307-6830
Tel (661) 324-2121 *Founded/Ownrshp* 1995
Sales 26.2MM^E *EMP* 300
SIC 1623 1711 Water, sewer & utility lines; Plumbing contractors; Water, sewer & utility lines; Plumbing contractors
Pr: Leslie Denherder

HPSA
See MITSUBISHI HITACHI POWER SYSTEMS AMERICA-ENERGY AND ENVIRONMENT LTD

D-U-N-S 00-246-7090
■ **HPSC INC** (DE)
H P S C FINANCIAL SERVICES
(*Suby of* GE HEALTHCARE FINANCIAL SERVICES INC) ★
1 Beacon St Fl 2, Boston, MA 02108-3121
Tel (617) 720-3600 *Founded/Ownrshp* 1975, 2004
Sales NA *EMP* 132
SIC 6159 Machinery & equipment finance leasing; Machinery & equipment finance leasing
VP: Catherine Estrampes
VP: Steve Spinelli
Off Mgr: Sharon Clarke

HPSD
See HATTIESBURG PUBLIC SCHOOL DISTRICT

D-U-N-S 79-077-3092
HPTTRS IHG-1 INC
255 Washington St Ste 300, Newton, MA 02458-1634
Tel (978) 686-2000 Founded/Ownrshp 2003
Sales NA EMP 599
SIC 7011

D-U-N-S 07-945-0246
■ HPTTRS IHG-2 INC
(Suby of HOSPITALITY PROPERTIES TRUST) ★
255 Washington St Ste 300, Newton, MA 02458-1634
Tel (617) 964-8389 Founded/Ownrshp 2005
Sales 114.3MM^E EMP 2,815^E
SIC 7011 Hotels & motels
COO: John Murray

D-U-N-S 07-833-1421
HQC HOLDINGS INC
HEALTH CATALYST
3165 E Millrock Dr # 400, Salt Lake City, UT 84121-4772
Tel (801) 708-6800 Founded/Ownrshp 2011
Sales 63.4MM^E EMP 302^E
Accts Ernst & Young Llp Salt Lake C
SIC 7373 Systems software development services
CEO: Dan Burton
*Ch Bd: Fraser Bullock
*Pr: Brent Dover
*COO: Paul Horstmeier
*CFO: Jeff Selander
*Sr VP: David A Burton
*VP: Brian Eliason
*VP: Jeff Jarvie
Prgrm Mgr: Tali Ramos
Prgrm Mgr: Tori Reimers
Prgrm Mgr: Brandi Stevenson

HQP EXPORT
See CRIMSON STAR ENTERPRISES INC

D-U-N-S 09-839-7078
HR ALLEN INC
HRA
2675 Rourk St, Charleston, SC 29405-7410
Tel (843) 747-4281 Founded/Ownrshp 2005
Sales 55.3MM^E EMP 250
SIC 1731 General electrical contractor; General electrical contractor
Ch Bd: Herbert R Allen Sr
*Pr: Rod Allen Jr
*VP: Guy Hancock
*VP: Brian Violette
Exec: Richard Runnels

D-U-N-S 80-701-5763
HR AMERICA INC
1102 Chestnut Hills Pkwy # 101, Fort Wayne, IN 46814-8728
Tel (260) 436-3878 Founded/Ownrshp 1991
Sales 61.0MM^E EMP 26
SIC 7363 8742 8741 Employee leasing service; Management consulting services; Management services; Employee leasing service; Management consulting services; Management services
Ch Bd: Doug Curtis
*Pr: Ryan Stoneburner
*VP: Jennifer Garcia
*Prin: Robert Curtis
Manager: Gary Siela

H.R. BEEBE
See BEEBE CONSTRUCTION SERVICES INC

HR CAPITAL MANAGEMENT
See PAY STAFF

H.R. EWELL
See HERMAN R EWELL INC

HR GREEN DEVELOPMENT
See GREEN COMPANIES INC

D-U-N-S 10-894-0420
HR LEWIS PETROLEUM CO
BEAUCLERC EXPRESSWAY
1432 Cleveland St, Jacksonville, FL 32209-6400
Tel (904) 356-0731 Founded/Ownrshp 1974
Sales 46.5MM^E EMP 75
Accts Kirby Burnett Simpsonville S
SIC 5172 5013 5541 Gasoline; Automotive supplies & parts; Gasoline service stations; Gasoline; Diesel fuel; Lubricating oils & greases; Automotive supplies & parts; Gasoline service stations
CEO: Harry R Lewis Sr
*CFO: Brain Lewis
VP: Anthony B Lewis
VP: Ron Reale
Trfc Dir: John Rauch

D-U-N-S 80-918-6729
HR PHYSICIAN SERVICES
(Suby of HOLY REDEEMER HEALTHCARE SYSTEM) ★
1602 Huntingdon Pike, Jenkintown, PA 19046-8001
Tel (215) 947-3000 Founded/Ownrshp 1999
Sales 29.6MM^E EMP 20^E
SIC 6512 Commercial & industrial building operation; Commercial & industrial building operation
*Treas: John J Morozin

D-U-N-S 83-199-3501
HR SOLUTIONS LLC
47632 Loweland Ter, Sterling, VA 20165-5143
Tel (703) 493-0084 Founded/Ownrshp 2006
Sales 10.0MM EMP 5,000
SIC 8742 Human resource consulting services; Human resource consulting services
CEO: Paul Sandhu

HR STRATEGIES
See ALLSTAFF MANAGEMENT INC

D-U-N-S 17-602-4586 IMP
HR TECHNOLOGIES INC
32500 N Avis Dr, Madison Heights, MI 48071-1558
Tel (248) 284-1170 Founded/Ownrshp 1996
Sales 33.9MM^E EMP 144
SIC 2273 Mats & matting
Pr: Tushar Patel

HRA
See HR ALLEN INC

D-U-N-S 10-112-9497 IMP
HRAP INC
AL & ED'S AUTOSOUND
11256 Bradley Ave, Pacoima, CA 91331-2323
Tel (818) 908-5700 Founded/Ownrshp 2015
Sales 20.0MM^E EMP 160
SIC 5999 5731 7539 Alarm signal systems; Telephone & communication equipment; Sound equipment, automotive; Automotive sound system service & installation; Electrical services; Alarm signal systems; Telephone & communication equipment; Sound equipment, automotive; Automotive sound system service & installation; Electrical services
CEO: Hamid Razipour
Opers Mgr: Barry Hodis
Pdt Mgr: John Haynes

D-U-N-S 02-636-2842
HRB TAX GROUP INC
1 H And R Block Way, Kansas City, MO 64105-1905
Tel (800) 472-5625 Founded/Ownrshp 1999
Sales 26.6MM^E EMP 142^E
SIC 8741 Management services
Pr: Jason Houseworth

D-U-N-S 06-267-5611
■ HRB TAX GROUP INC (MO)
(Suby of H&R BLOCK GROUP INC) ★
4400 Main St, Kansas City, MO 64111-1812
Tel (816) 753-6900 Founded/Ownrshp 1999
Sales 43.7MM^E EMP 400
SIC 8741 Business management; Business management
Pr: Jeff Yubiki
*VP: Steven A Christiansen

D-U-N-S 03-410-2785
HRC AL INVESTORS II
2250 Mcgilchrist St Se, Salem, OR 97302-1147
Tel (503) 370-7071 Founded/Ownrshp 1999
Sales 15.6MM EMP 400^E
SIC 8059 Personal care home, with health care; Personal care home, with health care
CEO: Jack Callison

D-U-N-S 62-086-4053
HRC HOTELS LLC
3495 Coolidge Rd, East Lansing, MI 48823-6374
Tel (517) 333-1597 Founded/Ownrshp 2004
Sales 44.4MM EMP 150^E
Accts Hall & Romkema Plc
SIC 7011 Hotels; Hotels
VP: Rebecca Keenan

D-U-N-S 09-528-5169
HRC MENTAL HEALTH CENTER INC
1500 N 34th St Ste 200, Superior, WI 54880-4477
Tel (715) 392-8216 Founded/Ownrshp 1978
Sales 25.4M EMP 300
SIC 8361 8093 Rehabilitation center, residential: health care incidental; Specialty outpatient clinics; Rehabilitation center, residential: health care incidental; Specialty outpatient clinics
CFO: Lynn Laplante
Ex Dir: Richard Klun

HRCA
See HIGHLANDS RANCH COMMUNITY ASSOCIATION INC

HRDI
See HUMAN RESOURCES DEVELOPMENT INSTITUTE INC

D-U-N-S 00-793-3328
▲ HRG GROUP INC
450 Park Ave Fl 29, New York, NY 10022-2640
Tel (212) 906-8555 Founded/Ownrshp 1999
Sales 5.8MMM EMP 15,900
Accts Kpmg Llp New York New York
Tkr Sym HRG Exch NYS
SIC 3691 3634 3999 6311 Storage batteries; Batteries, rechargeable; Electric household cooking appliances; Pet supplies; Life insurance; Storage batteries; Batteries, rechargeable; Electric household cooking appliances; Pet supplies; Life insurance
Pr: Omar M Asali
CFO: Thomas A Williams
*Ex VP: David M Maura
VP: Gus Cheliotis
Counsel: Brendan Doyle

HRG NORTHAMERICA
See HOGG ROBINSON USA LLC

D-U-N-S 00-421-2908
HRH DOOR CORP
WAYNE DALTON
1 Door Dr, Mount Hope, OH 44660
Tel (850) 208-3400 Founded/Ownrshp 2009
Sales 669.5MM^E EMP 2,500
SIC 3442 2431 Garage doors, overhead: metal; Garage doors, overhead: wood; Garage doors, overhead: metal; Garage doors, overhead: wood
CEO: Willis Mullet
*Pr: Thomas B Bennett III
CFO: Joseph Selogy
Dir Risk M: Bennett Kalie

D-U-N-S 07-452-1675
■ HRH OF NC INC
DUKE LIFEPOINT HEALTHCARE
(Suby of DLP HEALTHCARE LLC) ★
68 Hospital Rd, Sylva, NC 28779-2722
Tel (828) 586-7000 Founded/Ownrshp 2014
Sales 186.4MM^E EMP 1,144^E
SIC 8062 General medical & surgical hospitals; General medical & surgical hospitals
CEO: William F Carpenter III
Exec: Steven Rice
Dir OR: Tim Bell
Dir Lab: Kimberly Saunooke
Dept Mgr: Daren Carley
IT Man: Jason Daniels
Sfty Dirs: Garnett Coke
Pathlgst: Joe Hurt
Doctor: Rachel Downey

D-U-N-S 93-094-3951
HRHH HOTEL/CASINO LLC
HARD ROCK HOTEL AND CASINO
(Suby of BREF HR LLC) ★
4455 Paradise Rd, Las Vegas, NV 89169-6574
Tel (702) 693-5000 Founded/Ownrshp 2011
Sales 200.4MM^E EMP 1,363
SIC 7011 Hotels; Hotels
CEO: Dean Boswell
*Ch Bd: Peter A Morton
*Pr: Frederick Kleisner
*Sr VP: Brian D Ogaz

D-U-N-S 07-718-9541
HRI INC
(Suby of COLAS INC) ★
1750 W College Ave, State College, PA 16801-2719
Tel (814) 238-5071 Founded/Ownrshp 1998
Sales 280.3MM^E EMP 700
SIC 1611 Highway & street construction; Highway & street construction
Pr: Jeff Lamb
*VP: Kent Wible
VP: Jake Zeller
Assoc Dir: Roger Diehl
Area Mgr: Ron Barger
Sfty Dirs: Chris McHugh
Opers Mgr: Jason Lemire
Sales Asso: Randy Caldwell

D-U-N-S 05-873-6075
HRIBAR CORP
HRIBAR THOMAS TRUCK & EQP
1821 Se Frontage Rd, Mount Pleasant, WI 53177-2147
Tel (262) 886-3757 Founded/Ownrshp 1968
Sales 20.0MM^E EMP 54
SIC 5511 7519 Pickups, new & used; Trailer rental; Pickups, new & used; Trailer rental
Pr: Thomas A Hribar
*VP: Karen Kristopeit

HRIBAR THOMAS TRUCK & EQP
See HRIBAR CORP

D-U-N-S 83-630-1622
HRL LABORATORIES LLC
3011 Malibu Canyon Rd, Malibu, CA 90265-4797
Tel (310) 317-5000 Founded/Ownrshp 1998
Sales 47.8MM^E EMP 400
SIC 8731 8711 8733 Electronic research; Professional engineer; Research institute; Electronic research; Professional engineer; Research institute
Prin: P Albright
*CEO: Dr Penrose Parney C Albright
*CEO: William Jeffrey
CFO: Mary Y Asui-Amabe
CFO: Charles Fields
*CFO: Roger Gronwald
Top Exec: Dan Irvin
Prin: Albert Cosand
Brnch Mgr: Susan Rosen
Genl Mgr: Robert Kurkjian
CIO: Charles South

D-U-N-S 07-778-5087 IMP
HRM ENTERPRISES INC
TRUE VALUE
1015 Edison St Nw, Hartville, OH 44632-8509
Tel (330) 877-9353 Founded/Ownrshp 1974
Sales 71.8MM^E EMP 250
SIC 5947 5812 7389 Gift shop; American restaurant; Flea market; Gift shop; American restaurant; Flea market
Pr: William J Howard
CFO: Gary Sommers
*VP: Wayne Miller
Dir IT: Scott Micale
IT Man: Marion Coblentz
IT Man: Scott McHale
VP Sls: Jason Bare

D-U-N-S 08-378-0304 EXP
HRONIS INC A CALIFORNIA CORP
10443 Hronis Rd, Delano, CA 93215-9556
Tel (661) 725-2503 Founded/Ownrshp 1945
Sales 42.6MM^E EMP 150^E
SIC 0174 0172 Citrus fruits; Grapes
Pr: Kosta Hronis
*VP: Pete Hronis
Off Mgr: Shelley Molica

D-U-N-S 10-396-8327
HRP ASSOCIATES INC
HRP ENGINEERING
197 Scott Swamp Rd, Farmington, CT 06032-3149
Tel (860) 674-9570 Founded/Ownrshp 1982
Sales 28.0MM^E EMP 110
SIC 8748 Environmental consultant
CEO: L Andrew White
*Pr: Robert H Leach
*COO: Howard S Hurd
*CFO: Richard D McFee
Mktg Mgr: Alicia Mojica
Snr PM: Michael Ainsworth

HRP ENGINEERING
See HRP ASSOCIATES INC

HRSA
See HEALTH RESOURCES & SERVICES ADMINISTRATION

HRSD
See HAMPTON ROADS SANITATION DISTRICT (INC)

D-U-N-S 84-357-0073
HRSMART INC
(Suby of DELTEK INC) ★
2929 N Central Expy # 110, Richardson, TX 75080-2003
Tel (972) 783-3000 Founded/Ownrshp 2015
Sales 27.4MM^E EMP 200
SIC 7371 Computer software development; Computer software development
CEO: Mark Hamdan
Ex VP: David Alcaraz
Ex VP: Tom McKeown
Sr VP: Chris Knight
VP: Lynn Hoffman
QA Dir: Mohammad Shehab
Manager: Wissam Charaf
Manager: Debbie Imboden
Manager: Zachary Scruggs
Manager: Tracy Wright
Sls Mgr: Andy Najjar

D-U-N-S 13-126-1448
HRU INC -TECHNICAL RESOURCES
3451 Dunckel Rd Ste 200, Lansing, MI 48911-4298
Tel (517) 272-5888 Founded/Ownrshp 1980
Sales 14.5MM EMP 394
SIC 7361 7363 Labor contractors (employment agency); Employee leasing service; Temporary help service; Labor contractors (employment agency); Employee leasing service; Temporary help service
Pr: Judy A Daniels
*CFO: Justin Himebaugh
*VP: Tim Sackett
IT Man: Ken Evans

D-U-N-S 84-840-5234
HRUFKA ROMAN L US MEAT ANIMAL RESEARCH CENTER
Fpur 18 D, Clay Center, NE 68933
Tel (402) 762-4100 Founded/Ownrshp 1966
Sales 21.6MM^E EMP 250
SIC 8733 Research institute; Research institute
Snr Mgr: Ronald Christenson

HS BANK
See HOME STATE BANK NATIONAL ASSOCIATION (INC)

D-U-N-S 93-121-9120
HSA COMMERCIAL INC
HSA COMMERCIAL REAL ESTATE
233 S Wacker Dr Ste 350, Chicago, IL 60606-6405
Tel (312) 332-3555 Founded/Ownrshp 1981
Sales 33.7MM^E EMP 200
SIC 6552 6531 Subdividers & developers; Real estate agents & managers; Subdividers & developers; Real estate agents & managers
CEO: Robert E Smietana
V Ch: Robert Smietana
*Pr: Daniel F Miranda
*Ch: Jack Schaffer
*Sec: Mary Charchut
Ex VP: Christine Muszynski
Ex VP: Timothy Stanton
*Sr VP: Jason Klein
Sr VP: Eric Ogden
Sr VP: Mark Tegrootenhuis
VP: John Mangel
VP: Wanda Melendez
Board of Directors: Jack Newsom, Tena Vogt

HSA COMMERCIAL REAL ESTATE
See HSA COMMERCIAL INC

HSA ENGINEERS & SCIENTISTS
See RARE EARTH SCIENCES INC

HSA HAVENWYCK HOSPITAL
See HAVENWYCK HOSPITAL INC

HSA-UWC
See HOLY SPIRIT ASSOCIATION FOR UNIFICATION OF WORLD CHRISTIANITY

HSAA
See HWASEUNG AUTOMOTIVE AMERICA HOLDINGS INC

D-U-N-S 01-661-2660
HSB GROUP INC
(Suby of MUNICH-AMERICAN HOLDING CORP) ★
1 State St, Hartford, CT 06102
Tel (860) 722-1866 Founded/Ownrshp 2009
Sales NA EMP 2,428^E
SIC 6331 6411 6799 8711 8742 Fire, marine & casualty insurance; Insurance agents, brokers & service; Investors; Engineering services; Management consulting services; Fire, marine & casualty insurance; Insurance agents, brokers & service; Investors; Engineering services; Management consulting services
CEO: Gregory Barats
Pr: Denis M O'Shea
Chf Inves: James C Rowan
Ofcr: W Heckles
Ex VP: Normand Mercier
VP: Christophe McConnell
VP: J A Smith
VP: Thomas Tucker
Exec: Richard Booth
CTO: Barry Dexter
MIS Dir: Diane Swanson
Board of Directors: Theodore Kmiecik, Roberta O'brien, Nancy Onken, Peter Richter

HSB INDUSTRIAL RISK INSURERS
See WESTPORT INSURANCE CORP

HSBA
See HEALTH SERVICES & BENEFIT ADMINISTRATORS INC

HSBC ARENA
See CROSSROADS ARENA LLC

D-U-N-S 02-629-9667
HSBC BANK
1410 Flat Shoals Rd Se, Conyers, GA 30013-1802
Tel (507) 269-9138 Founded/Ownrshp 2009
Sales NA EMP 137^E
SIC 6099 Functions related to deposit banking
Ch: Douglas Flint
Sr VP: Jorge Escobar

D-U-N-S 13-168-2015 IMP/EXP
HSBC BANK USA
(Suby of HSBC USA INC) ★
1105 N Market St Fl 1, Wilmington, DE 19801-1237
Tel (302) 778-0169 Founded/Ownrshp 1999

Sales NA *EMP* 6,500
SIC 6022 State commercial banks; State commercial banks
Pr: Irene Dorner
Pr: David Goeden
Pr: Andy Ireland
CFO: Robert M Butcher
Sr VP: Irene Grant
Sr VP: Vincent J Mancuso
Sr VP: Daniel A Nissenbaum
Exec: Janet L Burak
Exec: George T Wendler
Prin: Martin J G Glynn
Mng Dir: Daniel O Minerva

D-U-N-S 82-587-1820
HSBC BANK USA NATIONAL ASSOCIATION
(*Suby of* HSBC USA INC) ★
1800 Tysons Blvd Ste 50, Mc Lean, VA 22102-4267
Tel (302) 652-4673 *Founded/Ownrshp* 1990
Sales NA *EMP* 17^E
SIC 6021 National commercial banks; National commercial banks
Pr: Irene Dorner
Sr VP: Lori Vetters
VP: Gary Houston

D-U-N-S 08-521-3007
HSBC BUSINESS CREDIT (USA) INC
(*Suby of* HSBC BANK USA) ★
452 5th Ave Fl 4, New York, NY 10018-2706
Tel (800) 511-1918 *Founded/Ownrshp* 1999
Sales NA *EMP* 344
SIC 6153 Short-term business credit; Factoring services; Short-term business credit; Factoring services
Ch Bd: Gerald A Nagle
**Ex VP:* Tom Revello
VP: David Choppolla

D-U-N-S 87-299-1674
HSBC CARD SERVICES INC
(*Suby of* HSBC FINANCE CORP) ★
26525 N Riverwoods Blvd, Mettawa, IL 60045-3440
Tel (224) 544-2000 *Founded/Ownrshp* 1989
Sales NA *EMP* 300
SIC 6141 7389 Consumer finance companies; Financial services; Consumer finance companies; Financial services
Pr: Joseph W Saunders

D-U-N-S 05-555-7276
HSBC FINANCE CORP
(*Suby of* HSBC INVESTMENTS (NORTH AMERICA) INC) ★
26525 N Riverwoods Blvd, Mettawa, IL 60045-3440
Tel (224) 880-7000 *Founded/Ownrshp* 1981
Sales NA *EMP* 1,700^E
SIC 6141 Consumer finance companies; Consumer finance companies
CEO: Kathryn G Madison
**Ch Bd:* Patrick J Burke
**COO:* Vittorio Severino
COO: Eli Sinyak
**CFO:* Michael A Reeves
**Ofcr:* Steven G Ekert
**Ex VP:* Ian T Leroni
Sr VP: Dan Cobb
VP: Mike Banyas
VP: Mark Seter
**Exec:* Rhydian H Cox
Board of Directors: Phillip D Ameen, Jeffrey A Bader, Robert K Herdman, Samuel Minzberg, Thomas K Whitford

HSBC FOUNDATION
See HEALTH SCIENCE CENTER AT BROOKLYN FOUNDATION INC

D-U-N-S 62-311-2914
HSBC INVESTMENTS (NORTH AMERICA) INC
(*Suby of* HSBC NORTH AMERICA HOLDINGS INC) ★
2700 Sanders Rd, Prospect Heights, IL 60070-2701
Tel (847) 564-5000 *Founded/Ownrshp* 2003
Sales NA *EMP* 15,650
SIC 6141 7389 6351 6159 6162 6311 Consumer finance companies; Credit card service; Credit & other financial responsibility insurance; Machinery & equipment finance leasing; Mortgage bankers; Life insurance carriers; Consumer finance companies; Credit card service; Credit & other financial responsibility insurance; Machinery & equipment finance leasing; Mortgage bankers; Life insurance carriers
Ch Bd: William F Aldinger
V Ch: Sandra Derickson
COO: Brendan McDonagh
Ofcr: Jomi Thomas
Assoc VP: Adrian Martinez
Ex VP: Terri Pearce
Sr VP: Cecilia Smith
Sr VP: Mitchell Weinstein
VP: Thomas Arduino
VP: Thomas P Richardson
VP: Pilar Rodriguez
Comm Man: Tony Burkhart

D-U-N-S 11-833-1446
HSBC MORTGAGE CORP (USA)
(*Suby of* HSBC BANK USA) ★
2929 Walden Ave, Depew, NY 14043-2690
Tel (716) 651-6100 *Founded/Ownrshp* 1985
Sales NA *EMP* 800
SIC 6162 Mortgage bankers; Mortgage bankers
Ch Bd: Michael J Maser
**Pr:* David J Hunter Jr
CFO: Paula Mann
Ex VP: Steve Tich
VP: Thomas Scanlon
VP: Daniel Szymanski
**VP:* David Travis
Mng Dir: Thomas M Kible
**VP Sls:* Kelly Rumings

D-U-N-S 00-408-0861
HSBC NATIONAL B
(*Suby of* HSBC NORTH AMERICA HOLDINGS INC) ★
415 John Carlyle St, Alexandria, VA 22314-6817
Tel (703) 837-9022 *Founded/Ownrshp* 2009
Sales NA *EMP* 355^E
SIC 6021 National commercial banks
Prin: Tucker Snyder

D-U-N-S 14-666-8061 IMP/EXP
HSBC NORTH AMERICA HOLDINGS INC
(*Suby of* HSBC HOLDINGS PLC)
452 5th Ave 7, New York, NY 10018-2706
Tel (224) 544-2000 *Founded/Ownrshp* 2004
Sales NA *EMP* 25,151^E
SIC 6351 Credit & other financial responsibility insurance; Credit & other financial responsibility insurance
CEO: Irene Dorner
CEO: Joseph W Hoff
CFO: Edgar D Ancona
Ofcr: Kunal Patel
Ex VP: Thomas M Kimble
Ex VP: Gerard Mattia
Ex VP: Beverley A Sibblies
Sr VP: James Benoit
Sr VP: Anthony Capece
Sr VP: Frances Cartagena
Sr VP: Ignacio Del Carril
Sr VP: Bruce A Fletcher
Sr VP: Barbara Tsarnas
VP: Jorge Escobar
VP: Richard Federbusch
VP: Helen Foo
VP: Patricia Gardner
VP: John Sheehan
Exec: Stephen Bottomley
Exec: Thomas M Detelich
Dir Risk M: Jonathan Lidster
Board of Directors: William R P Dalton, Anthea Disney, Robert K Herdman, Louis Hernandez Jr, Richard A Jalkut, George A Lorch, Samuel Minzberg, Beatriz R Perez, John L Thornton

D-U-N-S 07-279-6535
HSBC NORTH AMERICA INC
(*Suby of* HSBC INVESTMENTS (NORTH AMERICA) INC) ★
1 Hsbc Ctr Ste 1, Buffalo, NY 14203-2842
Tel (716) 841-2424 *Founded/Ownrshp* 1999
Sales NA *EMP* 15,650
SIC 6021 6035 6221 6091 6211 National commercial banks; Federal savings banks; Commodity brokers, contracts; Nondeposit trust facilities; Security brokers & dealers; National commercial banks; Federal savings banks; Commodity brokers, contracts; Nondeposit trust facilities; Security brokers & dealers
Ch Bd: Irene M Dorner
**COO:* Stephen P Fitzmaurice Rpa
**CFO:* Gerard Mattia

D-U-N-S 05-046-8156
HSBC SECURITIES (USA) INC
(*Suby of* HSBC NORTH AMERICA HOLDINGS INC) ★
452 5th Ave Fl 22, New York, NY 10018-2323
Tel (212) 525-5000 *Founded/Ownrshp* 2005
Sales 150.2MM^E *EMP* 813
SIC 6211 Security brokers & dealers; Security brokers & dealers
Ch Bd: Patrick Nolan
**Pr:* Mark Bucknall
CFO: Karen Almquist
Sr Cor Off: Michael Reeves
Ofcr: Bruce Pomerantz
Top Exec: David Nelson
Ex VP: Sumeet Chabria
Ex VP: Glenn Grimaldi
Ex VP: Josh Neyer
Sr VP: Hiro Atsumi
Sr VP: Peter Dawson
Sr VP: John Deluca
Sr VP: Vince Ferrentino
Sr VP: Thomas Halpin
Sr VP: Steven Kline
Sr VP: Kieran Patel
Sr VP: Craig Pattinson
Sr VP: Mark Pollack
Sr VP: Douglas Yorke
VP: Ramesh Akurati
VP: Randeep Brar

D-U-N-S 00-697-6732
HSBC USA INC
(*Suby of* HSBC NORTH AMERICA INC) ★
107 Iris Glen Dr Se, Conyers, GA 30013-1675
Tel (212) 525-5000 *Founded/Ownrshp* 1973
Sales NA *EMP* 6,500
Accts Kpmg Llp New York New York
SIC 6021 National commercial banks; National commercial banks
Ch Bd: Irene M Dorner
COO: Martyn T Brush
COO: Timothy Hinsdale
**COO:* Gregory T Zeeman
CFO: Cian Burke
**CFO:* Eric K Ferren
CFO: John T McGinnis
Top Exec: Mario Romaldini
Sr Ex VP: Steven A Bottomley
Sr Ex VP: Patrick A Cozza
Sr Ex VP: Patrick M Nolan
Sr Ex VP: Gary E Peterson
Sr Ex VP: Gregory Zeeman
Ex VP: Mary E Bilbrey
Ex VP: Loren C Klug
**Ex VP:* Patrick D Schwartz
Ex VP: Lisa M Sodeika
Sr VP: Suzanne Brienza
Sr VP: Deanna Larkin
Sr VP: John Murray
Sr VP: Malcolm West
Board of Directors: Philip Ameen, Jeffrey A Bader, Kevin M Blakely, William R P Dalton, Anthea Disney, Robert K Herdman, Richard A Jalkut, Samuel Minzberg, Nancy G Mistretta

HSBCT
See HARTFORD STEAM BOILER INSPECTION AND INSURANCE CO OF CONNECTICUT

HSBIIC
See HARTFORD STEAM BOILER INSPECTION AND INSURANCE CO

HSC
See HOWARD SUPPLY CO LLC

HSC BUILDERS & CNSTR MANAGERS
See HEALTH SCIENCES CONSTRUCTION GROUP LTD

D-U-N-S 86-958-8769
HSC COMMUNITY SERVICES INC
411 Osgood Ave, New Britain, CT 06053-2228
Tel (860) 827-4822 *Founded/Ownrshp* 2009
Sales 20.5MM *EMP* 1^E
SIC 8999 Services; Services
Prin: Ella L James

HSC INDUSTRIAL
See HUGHES SUPPLY CO

HSC MEDICAL CENTER
See HOT SPRING COUNTY MEDICAL CENTER

HSC PEDIATRIC CENTER
See HOSPITAL FOR SICK CHILDREN PEDIATRIC CENTER

D-U-N-S 78-653-3109
HSC REAL ESTATE INC
(*Suby of* CAS RESIDENTIAL LLC) ★
3101 Western Ave Ste 400, Seattle, WA 98121-3017
Tel (206) 282-5200 *Founded/Ownrshp* 1989
Sales 11.1MM^E *EMP* 600
SIC 6513 Apartment building operators; Apartment building operators
CEO: Walt Smith
**Pr:* Terry Danner
**COO:* Marysusan Wanich
**Ex VP:* Gardner Rees
**VP:* Pal Ottesen

D-U-N-S 12-375-6574
HSCB FOUNDATION INC
450 Clarkson Ave, Brooklyn, NY 11203-2012
Tel (718) 270-3041 *Founded/Ownrshp* 2002
Sales 94.1MM *EMP* 1
SIC 8699 Charitable organization; Charitable organization
Pr: Ivan Lintiver
**Pr:* Ivan Lisntziver
**Treas:* Frederick Hammond

D-U-N-S 07-547-4775
HSD HOLDING CO
HOLLAND SPECIAL DELIVERY
3068 Highland Blvd, Hudsonville, MI 49426-9455
Tel (616) 667-5100 *Founded/Ownrshp* 1973
Sales 30.5MM^E *EMP* 175
SIC 4213 4212

D-U-N-S 61-977-6537
HSF ENTERPRISES INC
MERCEDES-BENZ OF CHERRY HILL
2151 Marlton Pike W, Cherry Hill, NJ 08002-2732
Tel (856) 663-3200 *Founded/Ownrshp* 1979
Sales 81.2MM^E *EMP* 250
SIC 5511 7538 7515 Automobiles, new & used; General automotive repair shops; Passenger car leasing; Automobiles, new & used; General automotive repair shops; Passenger car leasing
Pr: Michael Hartung
Sls Mgr: Jay Romer
Sales Asso: Keri Cordero
Sales Asso: Nancy Kovler

HSF PROGRAMME
See SAN FRANCISCO HEALTH AUTHORITY

D-U-N-S 07-961-6463
HSG CONSTRUCTORS LLC
(*Suby of* BRAND ENRGY INFRSTRUCTURE SVCS) ★
5730 Fm 646 Rd E, Dickinson, TX 77539-2417
Tel (832) 226-5150 *Founded/Ownrshp* 2012
Sales 19.7MM^E *EMP* 883^E
SIC 1541 Industrial buildings, new construction

D-U-N-S 15-606-5393
HSG RESOURCES INC
(*Suby of* LIST & CLARK COMPANY)
9660 Legler Rd, Shawnee Mission, KS 66219-1291
Tel (913) 492-5920 *Founded/Ownrshp* 1983
Sales 128.1MM^E *EMP* 115
SIC 1442

D-U-N-S 96-543-0734
HSHS MEDICAL GROUP INC
3215 Executive Park Dr, Springfield, IL 62703-4514
Tel (217) 492-9696 *Founded/Ownrshp* 2008
Sales 112.4MM *EMP* 600
Accts Crowe Horwath Llp Chicago Il
SIC 8011 Medical centers; Medical centers
CEO: Richard Rolston
Dir: Craig Brace

HSI
See HABILITATIVE SERVICES INC

D-U-N-S 00-909-5134 IMP
■ **HSI LIQUIDATION INC**
RESTLINE PRODUCTS
(*Suby of* HOME-STYLE INDUSTRIES) ★
1323 11th Ave N, Nampa, ID 83687-6708
Tel (208) 466-8481 *Founded/Ownrshp* 2011
Sales 46.4MM^E *EMP* 300
SIC 2512 2515 2391 2591 2392 Upholstered household furniture; Mattresses, innerspring or box spring; Curtains & draperies; Drapery hardware & blinds & shades; Household furnishings; Upholstered household furniture; Mattresses, innerspring or box spring; Curtains & draperies; Drapery hardware & blinds & shades; Household furnishings
CEO: Jason D Lippert
**Pr:* Scott Mereness
**CFO:* Gary Ross McPhail
**Prin:* Randy D Raptosh
Rgnl Mgr: Debra Lopez
CIO: Jamie Schnur

HSI READY MIX
See HUEY STOCKSTILL INC

HSI SENSING
See HERMETIC SWITCH INC

D-U-N-S 15-032-7674
HSL AUTOMOTIVE INC
PINEHURST TOYATA - HYUNDAI
10760 S Us Highway 15 501, Southern Pines, NC 28387-5147
Tel (910) 692-2424 *Founded/Ownrshp* 1997
Sales 24.6MM^E *EMP* 65
SIC 5511 Automobiles, new & used; Pickups, new & used; Automobiles, new & used; Pickups, new & used
Pr: Philip P Smith
**Sec:* Mike Dayhoff
**VP:* Tom Holderfield

HSL CONSTRUCTION SERVICES
See HSL PROPERTIES INC

D-U-N-S 09-601-6274
HSL PROPERTIES INC
HSL CONSTRUCTION SERVICES
3901 E Broadway Blvd, Tucson, AZ 85711-3452
Tel (520) 322-6994 *Founded/Ownrshp* 1978
Sales 22.3MM^E *EMP* 40
SIC 6799 6513 Investors; Apartment building operators
Pr: Humberto S Lopez
Ex VP: Mike Censky
Ex VP: Chris Evans
**VP:* Glen Toyoshima
Rgnl Mgr: Bob Lebsack
Area Supr: Shelly Holliday

HSM SOLUTIONS
See HICKORY SPRINGS MANUFACTURING CO

HSM SOLUTIONS
See SPRING SPILLER CO

D-U-N-S 00-925-2227
HSMTX/REUNION PLAZA LLC
REUNION INNS
1401 Rice Rd, Tyler, TX 75703-3233
Tel (903) 561-6060 *Founded/Ownrshp* 1994
Sales 9.4MM^E *EMP* 303
SIC 8051 Skilled nursing care facilities; Skilled nursing care facilities
Pr: John V Rich
**CFO:* Lawanda Rich

D-U-N-S 13-043-3407 IMP/EXP
■ **HSN IMPROVEMENTS LLC**
(*Suby of* CORNERSTONE BRANDS INC) ★
16501 Rockside Rd, Maple Heights, OH 44137-4323
Tel (216) 662-6553 *Founded/Ownrshp* 2001
Sales 138.3MM^E *EMP* 1,500^E
SIC 5961 Catalog sales; Catalog sales

D-U-N-S 82-818-3140 IMP
▲ **HSN INC**
1 Hsn Dr, Saint Petersburg, FL 33729-0001
Tel (727) 872-1000 *Founded/Ownrshp* 1981
Sales 3.5MMM *EMP* 6,900^E
Tkr Sym HSNI *Exch* NGS
SIC 5961 5331 5712 Catalog & mail-order houses; Variety stores; Furniture stores; Catalog & mail-order houses; Variety stores; Furniture stores
CEO: Mindy Grossman
**Ch Bd:* Arthur C Martinez
COO: Judy A Schmeling
Chf Mktg O: William C Brand
Ex VP: Steve Armstrong
Ex VP: John Aylward
Ex VP: Brian Bradley
Ex VP: Lisa Letizio
Ex VP: Robert Monti
Ex VP: Peter Ruben
Sr VP: Chuck Anderson
VP: Brad Bohnert
VP: Sid Nasr
VP: Art Singleton
VP: Ron Williams
Dir: Jane Logan
Dir: Tammy Nolen
Creative D: Daniel Chen
Creative D: James Huggins
Dir Bus: Austin Elkins
Board of Directors: William Costello, James M Follo, Stephanie Kugelman, Thomas J McInerney, John B Morse Jr, Matthew E Rubel, Ann Sarnoff

D-U-N-S 07-690-2113 IMP
■ **HSN LLC**
(*Suby of* HSN INC) ★
1 Hsn Dr, Saint Petersburg, FL 33729-0001
Tel (727) 872-1000 *Founded/Ownrshp* 1982
Sales 1.0MMM^E *EMP* 3,650
SIC 4833 5961 Television broadcasting stations; Mail order house; Television broadcasting stations; Mail order house
CEO: Mindy F Grossman
Pt: Jeff Beck
Pr: Bill Brand
COO: Mark Ethier
COO: Judy Schmeling
CFO: Michael Attinella
Ex VP: Mary Ellen Pollin
Sr VP: Jay Herratti
Sr VP: Ryan Ross
VP: Kris Kulesza
VP: Lisa Letizio
VP: Jane Smith
VP: Roderick White

D-U-N-S 10-429-9628
■ **HSNI LLC**
(*Suby of* HSN INC) ★
1 Hsn Dr, Saint Petersburg, FL 33729-0001
Tel (727) 872-1000 *Founded/Ownrshp* 2010
Sales 67.1MM^E *EMP* 2,100
SIC 5961 Television, home shopping; Television, home shopping
CEO: Mindy Grossman
**COO:* Judy Schmeling

*CFO: Michael J Attinella
*Ex VP: Robert Monti
*Ex VP: Rob Solomon

D-U-N-S 07-884-1917
HSP EPI ACQUISITION LLC
ENTERTAINMENT
1401 Crooks Rd Ste 150, Troy, MI 48084-7106
Tel (248) 404-1520 *Founded/Ownrshp* 2013
Sales 237.5MM^E *EMP* 542^E
SIC 2731 Books: publishing only
Mktg Mgr: Lindy Rumon

HSPCE CARE CNTR ALMNCE-CSWLL
See HOSPICE OF ALAMANCE-CASWELL FOUNDATION INC

HSR BUSINESS TO BUSINESS
See GYRO LLC

D-U-N-S 07-341-5267
HSS INC
HOSPITAL SHARED SERVICES
900 S Broadway Ste 100, Denver, CO 80209-4269
Tel (303) 603-3000 *Founded/Ownrshp* 1967
Sales 119.8MM *EMP* 2,600
Accts Hein & Associates Llp Denver
SIC 8082 7381 7382 Home health care services; Home health care services; Security guard service; Protective devices, security
Pr: Wayne Schell
**CFO:* Mike Ratkiewicz
Ofcr: Adam Cornett
Ofcr: Tevita Mahe
Ofcr: Samir Singh
Sr VP: Tony York
Mng Dir: Michael Killeen
Mng Dir: Jon Overman
Mng Dir: Mark Winfield
Prgrm Mgr: Kirk Dunham
Rgnl Mgr: Robert Dyson

D-U-N-S 05-759-8729
HSS LLC
VALUEPOINT MATERIAL SOLUTIONS
5310 Hampton Pl Ste 1, Saginaw, MI 48604-8202
Tel (989) 777-2983 *Founded/Ownrshp* 1999
Sales 144.0MM^E *EMP* 139
SIC 8741 Management services; Management services
Pt: Eric Larson
**Pt:* Robert Fuller
**Pt:* Phil Shaltz
**Pt:* Scott Shively
Site Mgr: Stephen Tokar

D-U-N-S 79-468-3888
HSS PROPERTIES CORP
535 E 70th St, New York, NY 10021-4823
Tel (212) 606-1323 *Founded/Ownrshp* 1985
Sales 38.4MM *EMP* 5
Accts Ernst & Young Us Llp Indianap
SIC 6512 8069 Nonresidential building operators; Specialty hospitals, except psychiatric; Nonresidential building operators; Specialty hospitals, except psychiatric
Pr: Louis Shapiro
**CFO:* Stacey Malakoff

D-U-N-S 03-795-1907
■ **HSS SYSTEMS LLC**
WEST FLORIDA SUPPLY CHAIN SVCS
(*Suby of* HCA INC) ★
12901 Starkey Rd, Largo, FL 33773-1435
Tel (727) 533-3400 *Founded/Ownrshp* 2001
Sales 20.1MM^E *EMP* 100
SIC 8741 Management services

HST LESSEE
See ROCKLEDGE HOTEL PROPERTIES INC

D-U-N-S 01-925-3160
■ **HST LESSEE BOSTON LLC**
SHERATON BOSTON
(*Suby of* STARWOOD HOTELS & RESORTS WORLDWIDE INC) ★
39 Dalton St, Boston, MA 02199-3901
Tel (617) 236-2000 *Founded/Ownrshp* 1998
Sales 72.6MM^E *EMP* 1,140
SIC 7011 5812 7299 5813 Hotels & motels; Eating places; Banquet hall facilities; Drinking places; Hotels & motels; Eating places; Banquet hall facilities; Drinking places
Treas: Gregory Larson
VP: Lloyd Macneil
VP: Susan McDonnell
Mng Dir: Colleen Keating

D-U-N-S 10-316-4331
HST LESSEE SAN DIEGO LP
SHERATON SAN DIEGO HT & MARINA
1380 Harbor Island Dr, San Diego, CA 92101-1007
Tel (619) 291-2900 *Founded/Ownrshp* 2006
Sales 49.8MM^E *EMP* 800
SIC 6531 7011 5812 5947 5813 4493 Real estate agent, commercial; Real estate managers; Hotels & motels; Eating places; Gift, novelty & souvenir shop; Drinking places; Marinas; Real estate agent, commercial; Real estate managers; Hotels & motels; Eating places; Gift, novelty & souvenir shop; Drinking places; Marinas
Prin: Joe Tursey
Exec: Terry Guise
Sls Mgr: Lori Torio

D-U-N-S 83-276-4752
■ **HST LESSEE WEST SEATTLE LLC**
WESTIN SEATTLE
(*Suby of* HST LESSEE) ★
1900 5th Ave, Seattle, WA 98101-1204
Tel (206) 728-1000 *Founded/Ownrshp* 2006
Sales 33.5MM^E *EMP* 500
SIC 7011 Hotels & motels; Hotels & motels
Genl Mgr: Elisabeth James
Sls Mgr: Kelly Piha

HSU GROWING SUPPLY
See HSUS GINSENG ENTERPRISES INC

D-U-N-S 05-725-0243 IMP
HSUS GINSENG ENTERPRISES INC
HSU GROWING SUPPLY
T6819 County Rd W, Wausau, WI 54403-9461
Tel (715) 675-2325 *Founded/Ownrshp* 1981
Sales 37.7MM^E *EMP* 89
SIC 5149 5961 2844 2834 2099 0831 Spices & seasonings; Catalog & mail-order houses; Toilet preparations; Pharmaceutical preparations; Food preparations; Forest products; Spices & seasonings; Catalog & mail-order houses; Toilet preparations; Pharmaceutical preparations; Food preparations; Forest products
Pr: Paul C Hsu
VP: Tony Guo
**VP:* Sharon Hsu
**VP:* William Hsu
Sfty Mgr: Dennis Sciplor
Sls Mgr: Clint Kroening

D-U-N-S 61-181-6828
■ **HT AUTOMOTIVE LLC**
TEMPE HONDA
(*Suby of* PENSKE AUTOMOTIVE GROUP INC) ★
8030 S Autoplex Loop, Tempe, AZ 85284-1007
Tel (480) 893-7900 *Founded/Ownrshp* 1999
Sales 40.2MM^E *EMP* 125
SIC 5511 Automobiles, new & used; Automobiles, new & used
Pr: George Brochick
Store Mgr: David Willis
Sls Mgr: Rich Edis
Sls Mgr: Aaron Floman
Sls Mgr: Jim Franchini
Sls Mgr: Gene Penna
Sls Mgr: Dan Wickham

D-U-N-S 07-929-1995 IMP
HT INTERMEDIATE CO LLC
9825 Spectrum Dr Bldg 3, Austin, TX 78717-4930
Tel (512) 328-2892 *Founded/Ownrshp* 2014
Sales 39.3MM^E *EMP* 658
SIC 3845 Lithotripters; Lithotripters

HT SYSTEMS
See FINNCHEM USA INC

HTC
See HARRIS TRANSPORTATION CO LLC

D-U-N-S 15-668-0717
HTC AMERICA INC
(*Suby of* HTC CORPORATION)
13920 Se Eastgate Way, Bellevue, WA 98005-4440
Tel (425) 861-9174 *Founded/Ownrshp* 2003
Sales 66.5MM^E *EMP* 150
SIC 7378 Computer maintenance & repair; Computer maintenance & repair
Ch Bd: Peter Chou
**Pr:* Fred Liu
VP: Charlie Diecker
VP: Tai Ito
**VP:* Jason Mackenzie
Ex Dir: Jonathan Cocklin
Area Mgr: Alex White
Sftwr Eng: Raymond Pao
Sls Dir: Brent Kopp
Sls Dir: Grace Lewis
Manager: Dan Care

D-U-N-S 06-464-3619
HTC AMERICA INNOVATION INC
13920 Se Eastgate Way # 400, Bellevue, WA 98005-4440
Tel (425) 679-5318 *Founded/Ownrshp* 2010
Sales 56.8MM^E *EMP* 500
SIC 3661 Headsets, telephone; Telephone sets, all types except cellular radio; Headsets, telephone; Telephone sets, all types except cellular radio
CEO: Peter Chou
Top Exec: Charleen Fang
VP: Ricardo Gaibor
VP: Craig Parietti
Ex Dir: Marty McGinley
Area Mgr: Scott Sherer
Genl Mgr: Chu Nguyen
Off Admin: Yan Chen
Off Admin: Jeremy Prim
IT Man: Steve Lin
IT Man: Frank Woo

HTC EXPRESS
See HTC EXPRESS INC

D-U-N-S 78-586-5937
HTC EXPRESS INC
HTC EXPRESS
120 N Hickory, Roff, OK 74865-9001
Tel (580) 456-7159 *Founded/Ownrshp* 1996
Sales 48.3MM^E *EMP* 100
SIC 5012 Truck bodies
Pr: Gene Garrett
Genl Mgr: Brent Crawford
Genl Mgr: Jason Ingram
Opers Mgr: Willy Sanchez

D-U-N-S 80-109-5696
HTC GLOBAL SERVICES INC
HI TECH CONSULTANTS
3270 W Big Beaver Rd # 100, Troy, MI 48084-2901
Tel (248) 786-2500 *Founded/Ownrshp* 1990
Sales 187.1MM^E *EMP* 1,200
SIC 7379 Computer related consulting services; Computer related consulting services
CEO: Madhava Reddy
Ex VP: Shami Khorana
**Ex VP:* Chary Mudumby
Ex VP: Venu Vaishya
**VP:* Girish Arora
**VP:* Fredric Hagelton
**VP:* James Joseph
VP: Krishna Prasad
VP: Sutbir Randhawa
**VP:* Narayan Renga
VP: Shyam Valloornatt
Dir Bus: Binoj Varghese
Board of Directors: Sunil Jacob- Dir Laurie Ma

D-U-N-S 05-348-0047
HTC HOLDING CO
213 S Main St, Waterloo, IL 62298-1325
Tel (618) 939-6112 *Founded/Ownrshp* 1996
Sales 25.8MM *EMP* 122
Accts Keisling Associates Llp West
SIC 4813 Telephone communication, except radio; Telephone communication, except radio
Pr: H R Gentsch
**Ex VP:* Karen G Bergman
**VP:* Craig A Hern
**VP:* Lee H Whitcher

HTE CONTRACTORS
See HI-TECH ELECTRIC INC

HTE TECHNOLOGIES
See HOUSE OF TOOLS AND ENGINEERING INC

D-U-N-S 11-541-5663
HTH COMPANIES INC
239 Rock Industrial Blvd, Union, MO 63084-3139
Tel (636) 583-8698 *Founded/Ownrshp* 1984
Sales 26.8MM^E *EMP* 105
SIC 1799 1542 Insulation of pipes & boilers; Specialized public building contractors
CEO: Gregory E Hoberock
**Pr:* Dale Winters
**VP:* Eric Wilson

D-U-N-S 08-455-6661
HTH CORP (HI)
1668 S King St Fl 2, Honolulu, HI 96826-2074
Tel (808) 469-4111 *Founded/Ownrshp* 1975, 2004
Sales 75.4MM^E *EMP* 1,250
SIC 7011 5812 6512 Resort hotel; Eating places; Commercial & industrial building operation; Resort hotel; Eating places; Commercial & industrial building operation
CEO: Corine Watanabe
**Pr:* John Hayashi
**CFO:* Lauralei Taraka
**VP:* Robert Minicola
Dir IT: Frederic Chau
Board of Directors: Corine Hayashi

D-U-N-S 55-590-6031
HTH INC
HOTEL KING KAMEHAMEHA
(*Suby of* HTH CORP) ★
2490 Kalakaua Ave, Honolulu, HI 96815-3286
Tel (808) 922-1233 *Founded/Ownrshp* 1990
Sales 10.2MM^E *EMP* 500
SIC 7011 5812 5813 Hotels; Restaurant, family: independent; Cocktail lounge; Hotels; Restaurant, family: independent; Cocktail lounge
Pr: Corine Hayashi
**Prin:* Daryl Lee

D-U-N-S 82-950-7248
HTH LEARNING
2861 Womble Rd, San Diego, CA 92106-6025
Tel (619) 814-5084 *Founded/Ownrshp* 2001
Sales 36.2MM *EMP* 266^E
Accts Christy White Acct Corp San D
SIC 8299 Educational services; Educational services
CEO: Larry Rosenstock
**CFO:* Kay McElrath

HTH WORLDWIDE
See HIGHWAY TO HEALTH INC

HTI
See HUMAN TECHNOLOGIES INC

HTI COLLECTION
See HOT TOPICS INC

D-U-N-S 80-860-5179 IMP
HTI HYDRAULIC TECHNOLOGIES LLC
(*Suby of* LIGON INDUSTRIES LLC) ★
1483 Highway 3, Hampton, IA 50441-7467
Tel (419) 462-2300 *Founded/Ownrshp* 2007
Sales 31.4MM^E *EMP* 118
SIC 3593 Fluid power cylinders, hydraulic or pneumatic; Fluid power cylinders, hydraulic or pneumatic
Chf Mktg O: Keith Nicley
VP: Glen Campbell
IT Man: Condrea Lewis
Plnt Mgr: Ronnie Cottle
Plnt Mgr: Mike Lear

D-U-N-S 11-849-2768
HTI LTD
HUNTON TRANE
10555 Westpark Dr, Houston, TX 77042-5232
Tel (713) 266-3900 *Founded/Ownrshp* 1999
Sales 219.3MM^E *EMP* 450
SIC 5075 Air conditioning equipment, except room units; Warm air heating equipment & supplies; Air conditioning equipment, except room units; Warm air heating equipment & supplies
Pr: Richard Hunton
Pr: Craig Becker
COO: Richard O Hunton Jr
CFO: Bruce Seher
Sr VP: Brad Lacy
VP: Larry Bower
VP: Albert Mireles
VP: Kevin Murphy
VP: Ron Shepherd
VP: Robert Tyler
CTO: Paul Wallace

D-U-N-S 06-713-4502
■ **HTI MEMORIAL HOSPITAL CORP** (TN)
TRISTAR SKYLINE MEDICAL CENTER
(*Suby of* HCA INC) ★
3441 Dickerson Pike, Nashville, TN 37207-2539
Tel (615) 769-2000 *Founded/Ownrshp* 1959, 1995
Sales 97.6M^E *EMP* 1,250
SIC 8062 General medical & surgical hospitals; General medical & surgical hospitals
Pr: Steve Otto
Ansthlgy: Macgregor Poll
Ansthlgy: Daniel Scokin

HTI PLASTICS
See HEINKE TECHNOLOGY INC

D-U-N-S 07-915-3956
HTK AUTOMOTIVE USA CORP
DECODED USA
5218 Rivergrade Rd, Irwindale, CA 91706-1336
Tel (888) 998-9366 *Founded/Ownrshp* 2011
Sales 28.3MM *EMP* 18
SIC 3694 Automotive electrical equipment
Pr: Karim Boumajdi

D-U-N-S 87-938-6191
HTK CONSULTANTS INC
450 Gears Rd Ste 125, Houston, TX 77067-4522
Tel (218) 320-8269 *Founded/Ownrshp* 1991
Sales 23.0MM *EMP* 8
SIC 8711 Petroleum engineering; Petroleum engineering
Pr: Jeffrey R Hughes
Bd of Dir: Preston Moore
**Sr VP:* Jay Davis
VP: Rusty Ritz
VP: Doug White
VP: Kris Zaunbrecher
**VP:* Robert Zaunbrecher
Mng Dir: Tom Stroud
IT Man: Bill Hyde

D-U-N-S 80-595-1709
HTL AUTOMOTIVE INC
HOOMAN TOYOTA OF LONG BEACH
4401 E Pacific Coast Hwy, Long Beach, CA 90804-2117
Tel (562) 494-4444 *Founded/Ownrshp* 2007
Sales 38.8MM^E *EMP* 150
SIC 5511 Automobiles, new & used
CEO: Kevin Golshan
**Pr:* Hooman Michael Nissani
Sls Mgr: Ron Baldizon
Sls Mgr: Troy Feltis
Sls Mgr: Vincent Franco
Sls Mgr: Sam Hafez
Sls Mgr: Matt Hansen
Sls Mgr: Eddie Hojjat
Sls Mgr: Mark Mercado
Sls Mgr: Tony Moayed
Sls Mgr: Derik Motevosian

D-U-N-S 07-248-9763
HTL EMPLOYEES & RESTAURAN
A B P A
1630 S Commerce St, Las Vegas, NV 89102-2705
Tel (702) 733-9938 *Founded/Ownrshp* 2001
Sales 32.1MM *EMP* 14^E
SIC 5812 Eating places
Prin: Dan Maier

D-U-N-S 82-553-2088 IMP
HTM USA HOLDINGS INC
HEAD TYROLIA WINTER SPORTS
(*Suby of* HEAD SPORT GMBH)
3125 Sterling Cir Ste 101, Boulder, CO 80301-2394
Tel (800) 874-3235 *Founded/Ownrshp* 1993
Sales 152.9MM^E *EMP* 600
SIC 5091 5139 3949 Racquet sports equipment & supplies; Golf equipment; Diving equipment & supplies; Skiing equipment; Footwear, athletic; Sporting & athletic goods; Racquet sports equipment & supplies; Golf equipment; Diving equipment & supplies; Skiing equipment; Footwear, athletic; Sporting & athletic goods
Pr: David Haggerty
**Treas:* Ralf Bernhart
**VP:* Klaus Hotter
**VP Sls:* Robert Langlois

HTNA
See HAYASHI TELEMPU NORTH AMERICA CORP

HTO
See HUDSON TRAIL OUTFITTERS LTD

D-U-N-S 08-480-5860 IMP
HTP INC (MA)
HEAT TRANSFER PRODUCTS
272 Duchaine Blvd, New Bedford, MA 02745-1222
Tel (508) 763-8071 *Founded/Ownrshp* 1983
Sales 182.2MM^E *EMP* 200
SIC 5084 3443 Heat exchange equipment, industrial; Heat exchangers, condensers & components; Heat exchange equipment, industrial; Heat exchangers, condensers & components
CEO: David B Davis
**Pr:* Dave R Martin
Sr VP: Todd Romig
Sfty Mgr: Mike Leger
Natl Sales: Brad Monaghan
Manager: Doug McElwain

D-U-N-S 82-838-1520
■ **HTP RELO LLC**
(*Suby of* HARRIS TEETER LLC) ★
701 Crestdale Rd, Matthews, NC 28105-1700
Tel (704) 845-3100 *Founded/Ownrshp* 2008
Sales 24.6MM^E *EMP* 1^E
SIC 5411 Supermarkets, chain
Prin: Jeff Sherman

HTPG
See HEAT TRANSFER PRODUCTS GROUP LLC

D-U-N-S 79-150-5626
HTS ACQUISITION INC
HIGHWAY TECHNOLOGIES GROUP
915 Harger Rd, Oak Brook, IL 60523-1497
Tel (630) 368-0920 *Founded/Ownrshp* 2007
Sales NA *EMP* 1,500
SIC 3646 3229 3645

D-U-N-S 15-186-1341
HTT INC
1828 Oakland Ave, Sheboygan, WI 53081-5659
Tel (920) 453-5300 *Founded/Ownrshp* 2000
Sales 33.9MM^E *EMP* 122
SIC 3469 3544 Stamping metal for the trade; Special dies, tools, jigs & fixtures; Machine shop, jobbing & repair; Stamping metal for the trade; Special dies, tools, jigs & fixtures
Ch: David Sachse
Pr: Greg Noble
VP: Gary Fick

D-U-N-S 07-981-2890
HTX INDUSTRIAL LLC (TX)
2000 S Dairy Ashford Rd, Houston, TX 77077-5700
Tel (832) 300-0303 Founded/Ownrshp 2015
Sales 35.0MM EMP 80
SIC 1541 Industrial buildings, new construction; Renovation, remodeling & repairs: industrial buildings

D-U-N-S 06-204-3690
HU FRIEDY MANUFACTURING CO INC (NY)
3232 N Rockwell St, Chicago, IL 60618-5935
Tel (773) 975-6100 Founded/Ownrshp 1972, 1994
Sales 33.1MM^E EMP 500
SIC 5047 Medical & hospital equipment; Medical & hospital equipment
Pr: Richard Saslow

D-U-N-S 00-508-5972 IMP
HU-FRIEDY MFG CO LLC (IL)
AMERICAN DENTAL
3232 N Rockwell St, Chicago, IL 60618-5935
Tel (773) 975-3975 Founded/Ownrshp 1908
Sales 112.3MM^E EMP 625^E
SIC 3843 Dental hand instruments; Dental hand instruments
Ch Bd: Ron Saslow
*Pr: Ken Serota
*Ch: Dick Saslow
VP: Claude Brown
VP: Normand Desforges
VP: Patricia Parker
CIO: Diana Walker
QA Dir: Rich Shapiro
Dir IT: Mike Ongchangco
IT Man: Dolly Ayala
IT Man: Naeem Shah

D-U-N-S 84-891-4016
HUALALAI INVESTORS LLC
100 Kaupulehu Dr, Kailua Kona, HI 96740-5699
Tel (808) 325-8400 Founded/Ownrshp 2006
Sales 256.8MM^E EMP 758^E
SIC 6552 Land subdividers & developers, commercial; Land subdividers & developers, commercial

D-U-N-S 96-633-1944 IMP
HUALALAI RESORT CORP
FOUR SEASONS RESORT HUALALAI
72-100 Kaupulehu Dr, Kailua Kona, HI 96740-5610
Tel (808) 325-8000 Founded/Ownrshp 1996
Sales 38.5MM^E EMP 550
SIC 7011 7997 Resort hotel; Golf club, membership; Resort hotel; Golf club, membership
CEO: Eiji Iwahashi
*Pr: Pat Nagy
*Pr: Russell Schoon
*Sec: Hideto Okazeri
*Sr VP: Richard Albrecht
*VP: James Cook
Genl Mgr: John Freitas

D-U-N-S 83-913-8799
HUALAPAI ENTERPRISES
GRAND CANYON RESORT
16500 E Hwy 66, Peach Springs, AZ 86434
Tel (928) 769-2419 Founded/Ownrshp 1994
Sales NA EMP 650
SIC 7999 Resort hotel; Tourist attraction, commercial
CEO: Mark Mortenson
COO: Rory Majenty
CFO: Steven Maylin
Bd of Dir: Neil Goodell
IT Man: Ken Zachreson
Mktg Mgr: Kurtis Shaul

D-U-N-S 03-588-3487
HUALAPAI TRIBAL COUNCIL
941 Hualapai Way, Peach Springs, AZ 86434
Tel (928) 769-2216 Founded/Ownrshp 1938
Sales NA EMP 300
SIC 9131 Indian reservation; ; Indian reservation;
Ch: Sherry Counts
V Ch: Philbert Watahomigie
Ofcr: Brian Frayer
Snr Mgr: Calvin Smith

D-U-N-S 07-828-4967 IMP
HUAWEI DEVICE USA INC
(Suby of HUAWEI INVESTMENT & HOLDING CO., LTD.)
5700 Tennyson Pkwy # 500, Plano, TX 75024-7157
Tel (214) 919-6688 Founded/Ownrshp 2010
Sales 115.0MM^E EMP 500^E
SIC 3663 Cellular radio telephone; Cellular radio telephone
Pr: Zhiqiang Xu
*Treas: Ailing Lin
*Prin: Jiangao Cui

D-U-N-S 07-839-5419 IMP
HUAWEI TECHNOLOGIES CO LTD
5700 Tennyson Pkwy # 500, Plano, TX 75024-7157
Tel (214) 919-6000 Founded/Ownrshp 2012
Sales 89.5MM^E EMP 185^E
SIC 4899 8748 Communication signal enhancement network system; Communications consulting
CEO: Ren Zhengfei
Snr Mgr: Kelly Gormley

D-U-N-S 05-848-1986
HUAWEI TECHNOLOGIES USA INC
(Suby of HUAWEI TECHNOLOGIES CO., LTD.)
5700 Tennyson Pkwy # 500, Plano, TX 75024-7157
Tel (214) 545-3700 Founded/Ownrshp 2011
Sales 115.5MM^E EMP 860^E
SIC 8748 Telecommunications consultant; Telecommunications consultant
Pr: Ming He
*Pr: Charles Ding
Top Exec: Suresh Vaidyanathan
Sr VP: George Reed
VP: Jerry Meng
VP: Jerry Prestinario
Mng Dir: Zhan Bo
VP Sls: Bill Gerski
Mktg Dir: Joy Tan
Mktg Dir: Jiang Yishan
Pr Mgr: Sing Wang

D-U-N-S 07-939-8004
HUB BUICK CO
HUB HYUNDAI HWY 290
19300 Northwest Fwy, Jersey Village, TX 77065-4716
Tel (281) 894-5200 Founded/Ownrshp 1989
Sales 70.0MM EMP 120
SIC 5511 Automobiles, new & used; Automobiles, new & used
Pr: Robert C Cox
Genl Mgr: Mark Odat
Off Mgr: Julie Smith
Sls Mgr: John Lowe

D-U-N-S 00-821-3282
HUB CITY FORD INC
2909 Nw Evangeline Trwy, Lafayette, LA 70507-3422
Tel (337) 232-0090 Founded/Ownrshp 1943
Sales 52.3MM^E EMP 139
SIC 5511 5531 Automobiles, new & used; Pickups, new & used; Automotive parts; Automobiles, new & used; Pickups, new & used; Automotive parts
Ch Bd: R Jarvis Fortier
*Pr: D E Citron III
*Sec: Todd Citron
VP: Gary Angelle
*VP: Marcelle Citron
VP: Chris Daggs
Genl Mgr: Richard Fortier
Store Mgr: Andy Citron
Sales Asso: Alfred Archangel
Sales Asso: Shane Broussard
Sales Asso: Mike Cutright

D-U-N-S 05-527-6554
HUB CITY FORD-MERCURY INC
4060 S Ferdon Blvd, Crestview, FL 32536-5219
Tel (850) 682-2721 Founded/Ownrshp 1986
Sales 23.2MM^E EMP 43
SIC 5511 Automobiles, new & used; Trucks, tractors & trailers: new & used; Automobiles, new & used; Trucks, tractors & trailers: new & used
Pr: Leon Daggs Jr
*VP: Christopher Daggs
Sales Asso: Ron Branson

D-U-N-S 60-127-7940 IMP
■ **HUB CITY INC**
(Suby of REGAL-BELOIT CORP) ★
2914 Industrial Ave, Aberdeen, SD 57401-3345
Tel (605) 225-0360 Founded/Ownrshp 1989
Sales 45.1MM^E EMP 303
SIC 3568 Power transmission equipment; Power transmission equipment
Pr: Mark Gliebe
*VP: James Campbell
VP: Duke Sims
Exec: Nancy Kinder
Plnt Mgr: Phil Mitzel
Plnt Mgr: Wayne Tourdot

D-U-N-S 61-862-8556 IMP
HUB CITY INDUSTRIAL SUPPLY INC
HUB INDUSTRIAL SUPPLY
371 Sw Ring Ct Ste 101, Lake City, FL 32025-3192
Tel (386) 755-9401 Founded/Ownrshp 1990
Sales 45.8MM^E EMP 45
SIC 5085 Industrial supplies; Fasteners, industrial: nuts, bolts, screws, etc.; Industrial supplies; Fasteners, industrial: nuts, bolts, screws, etc.
Pr: Gabriel Curry
Treas: Tammy Magstadt
*VP: Stuart Johnson
*VP: Kevin Kock
*VP: Scott Stewart

D-U-N-S 62-224-4721
HUB CITY PBE INC
COLORMATCH
344 S Royal St, Jackson, TN 38301-7057
Tel (731) 424-7008 Founded/Ownrshp 1985
Sales 43.2MM^E EMP 92
SIC 5013 Body repair or paint shop supplies, automotive; Body repair or paint shop supplies, automotive
Pr: Wesley Richardson
*VP: Jim Richardson
Exec: Tony Nethery
IT Man: Robert McKenzie

D-U-N-S 06-997-8062
■ **HUB CITY TERMINALS INC**
(Suby of HUB GROUP INC) ★
2000 Clearwater Dr, Oak Brook, IL 60523-8809
Tel (630) 271-3600 Founded/Ownrshp 1971
Sales 74.9MM^E EMP 664
SIC 4731 Agents, shipping; Agents, shipping
Ch Bd: David P Yeager
VP: Terri Pizzuto

D-U-N-S 02-907-9472
HUB CONSTRUCTION SPECIALTIES INC
HUB CONSTRUCTION SUPS & EQP
379 S I St, San Bernardino, CA 92410-2409
Tel (909) 235-4100 Founded/Ownrshp 1958
Sales 48.4MM^E EMP 130
SIC 7359 5082 Equipment rental & leasing; Construction & mining machinery; Equipment rental & leasing; Construction & mining machinery
Pr: Robert T Gogo
CFO: Edward Dainko
*Sec: Bernice Gogo
Sfty Dirs: Anthony Blacksher
Opers Mgr: Tom Holod
Trfc Mgr: Debbie Ramos
Sls Mgr: Ana Toache
Sales Asso: Luis Navarro
Sales Asso: Will Pope
Sales Asso: James Thorton

HUB CONSTRUCTION SUPS & EQP
See HUB CONSTRUCTION SPECIALTIES INC

D-U-N-S 04-477-4782
HUB CONVENIENCE STORES INC
191 40th W, Dickinson, ND 58601
Tel (701) 483-3835 Founded/Ownrshp 2014
Sales 26.0MM EMP 10
SIC 5411 Convenience stores; Convenience stores
Mng Dir: Jared Scheeler

D-U-N-S 02-883-0115 IMP
HUB DISTRIBUTING INC
ANCHOR BLUE
(Suby of SUN CAPITAL PARTNERS INC) ★
1260 Corona Pointe Ct, Corona, CA 92879-5013
Tel (951) 340-3149 Founded/Ownrshp 2003
Sales 231.1MM^E EMP 3,000
SIC 5611 5621 5632 5137 5136 5094 Men's & boys' clothing stores; Women's clothing stores; Apparel accessories; Women's & children's clothing; Men's & boys' clothing; Jewelry & precious stones; Men's & boys' clothing stores; Women's clothing stores; Apparel accessories; Women's & children's clothing; Men's & boys' clothing; Jewelry & precious stones
CEO: Thomas Sands
Treas: Scott Rosner
*Treas: Thomas Shaw
VP: Andrew Boada
VP Mktg: Erik Forsell

D-U-N-S 60-653-6217
HUB ENTERPRISES INC
406 E Madison St Ste 2002, Broussard, LA 70518-4649
Tel (337) 837-2074 Founded/Ownrshp 1977
Sales 19.1MM^E EMP 500
SIC 7381 Security guard service; Security guard service
Pr: James H Romero
CFO: Robert Mouton
*VP: Dwayne Regan
Sfty Mgr: Dustin Mosley
Manager: Caroleann Defrancis
Manager: Theresa Petersen

D-U-N-S 00-102-3613 IMP
HUB FOLDING BOX CO INC (MA)
PLASTIC TECHNOLOGY DIVISION
774 Norfolk St, Mansfield, MA 02048-1826
Tel (508) 339-0005 Founded/Ownrshp 1921
Sales 140.9MM^E EMP 315
SIC 2657 Folding paperboard boxes; Folding paperboard boxes
Pr: Alfred Dirico
CFO: Hal Wilmot
*VP: Anthony H Dirico
Dir IT: Carl Schneider
Sfty Mgr: Fred Slavin
Ql Cn Mgr: John Proterra
Mktg Mgr: Tony Dirico
Sls Mgr: Lucy Gilligan
Snr Mgr: Paul Barnes

D-U-N-S 15-514-3480
▲ **HUB GROUP INC**
2000 Clearwater Dr, Oak Brook, IL 60523-8809
Tel (630) 271-3600 Founded/Ownrshp 1971
Sales 3.5MMM EMP 2,568
Tkr Sym HUBG Exch NGS
SIC 4731 Agents, shipping; Truck transportation brokers; Freight forwarding; Railroad freight agency; Transportation agents & brokers; Brokers, shipping; Truck transportation brokers; Freight forwarding
Ch Bd: David P Yeager
Pr: James J Damman
Pr: Donald G Maltby
CFO: Terri A Pizzuto
Chf Mktg O: Christopher R Kravas
Ofcr: Daniel W Burke
Ofcr: David L Marsh
Ex VP: James B Gaw
VP: Roger Paulsen
Exec: Stephen Cosgrove
Sfty Mgr: Darcy Reasoner
Board of Directors: Gary D Eppen, Charles R Reaves, Martin P Slark, Jonathan P Ward

D-U-N-S 10-180-2072
■ **HUB GROUP TRUCKING INC**
HGT
(Suby of HUB CITY TERMINALS INC) ★
2000 Clearwater Dr, Oak Brook, IL 60523-8809
Tel (630) 271-3600 Founded/Ownrshp 2006
Sales 73.9MM^E EMP 1,435
SIC 4212 Local trucking, without storage; Trucking, except local; Management services; Local trucking with storage; Draying, local: without storage
Pr: David P Yeager
*COO: Mark A Yeager
*VP: Bob Rhodes
Opers Mgr: Larry Collier
Opers Mgr: Ron Lundgren

HUB HYUNDAI HWY 290
See HUB BUICK CO

HUB INDUSTRIAL SUPPLY
See HUB CITY INDUSTRIAL SUPPLY INC

D-U-N-S 06-120-4012
HUB INTERNATIONAL GROUP NORTHEAST INC
HUB INTERNATIONAL NE
(Suby of HUB INTERNATIONAL LIMITED) ★
5 Bryant Park Fl 4, New York, NY 10018
Tel (212) 338-2000 Founded/Ownrshp 2013
Sales NA EMP 346
SIC 6411 Insurance brokers; Insurance brokers
CEO: Mark Cohen
Bd of Dir: Martin Hughes
*Sr VP: James E Hutchinson
Sr VP: Robert Shcolnik
VP: Joe Augello
VP: Robert Fiorito
VP: Rachel Romero
VP: Chester Swalm
*VP: Lucille Feldman Warner

D-U-N-S 60-965-7056
HUB INTERNATIONAL INSURANCE SERVICES INC
PETERSON MILANEY INSUR ASSOC
(Suby of HUB INTERNATIONAL LIMITED) ★
3390 University Ave # 300, Riverside, CA 92501-3325
Tel (951) 788-8500 Founded/Ownrshp 1988
Sales NA EMP 1,100
SIC 6411 Insurance agents, brokers & service; Insurance agents, brokers & service
CEO: Roy H Taylor
*Pr: Kirk Christ
*Ex VP: Travis McElvany
*Exec: Andrew Forchelli

D-U-N-S 78-436-8586
HUB INTERNATIONAL LIMITED
(Suby of HELLMAN & FRIEDMAN LLC) ★
300 N La Salle Dr Ste 17, Chicago, IL 60654-3406
Tel (312) 596-7522 Founded/Ownrshp 2013
Sales NA EMP 7,853
SIC 6411 Insurance agents, brokers & service; Property & casualty insurance agent; Insurance agents, brokers & service; Property & casualty insurance agent
Ch Bd: Martin P Hughes
Pr: Richard A Gulliver
Pr: Erica Richardson
Pr: Tim Tarwater
CFO: Joseph C Hyde
Ofcr: Ralph Colao
Ofcr: Lauren Davy
Ex VP: Jerry Gillikin
Ex VP: Carla Moradi
Ex VP: Chip Stuart
VP: Dan Abraham
VP: Timothy Aguilar
VP: Mickey Ahearn
VP: Kevin L Allgood
VP: Ronda Anderson
VP: Lyn Chacon
VP: Normand Coutu
VP: John Donahue
VP: James Foster
VP: Thom Freismuth
VP: Daniel Goldsmith

D-U-N-S 09-594-2371
HUB INTERNATIONAL MIDWEST LTD
(Suby of HUB INTERNATIONAL LIMITED) ★
55 E Jackson Blvd 1400a, Chicago, IL 60604-4102
Tel (312) 922-5000 Founded/Ownrshp 2006
Sales NA EMP 700
SIC 6411 Insurance agents; Life insurance agents; Insurance agents; Life insurance agents
Pr: Neil R Hughes
Ex VP: Rick Havron
Ex VP: Bobby Simms
Sr VP: Sam Valeo
VP: Philip Adler
VP: Linda Balisteri
VP: Neil Ferguson
VP: Saroj Mohanty
VP: Jason Romick
VP: Peter L Scavetta
VP: Steve Simms

HUB INTERNATIONAL NE
See HUB INTERNATIONAL GROUP NORTHEAST INC

D-U-N-S 84-057-0183
HUB INTERNATIONAL NORTHWEST LLC
(Suby of HUB INTERNATIONAL LIMITED) ★
12100 Ne 195th St Ste 200, Bothell, WA 98011-5768
Tel (425) 489-4500 Founded/Ownrshp 2000
Sales NA EMP 140^E
SIC 6411 Insurance agents; Insurance brokers
Pr: Andy Prill
COO: Steve Clark
Ex VP: Carl Lovsted III
Sr VP: Dean Young
VP: Rick English
VP Opers: Brian Roberts

D-U-N-S 07-414-7232
HUB INTERNATIONAL OF CALIFORNIA INC
(Suby of HUB INTERNATIONAL LIMITED) ★
6701 Center Dr W Ste 1500, Los Angeles, CA 90045-1561
Tel (310) 568-5900 Founded/Ownrshp 2002
Sales NA EMP 158^E
SIC 6411 Insurance brokers
Pr: Frank C Hayes
*VP: Kathy Quintana

D-U-N-S 06-849-8625
HUB INTERNATIONAL OF ILLINOIS LIMITED
MACK AND PARKER
(Suby of HUB INTERNATIONAL LIMITED) ★
300 N Lslle St Fl 17, Chicago, IL 60654
Tel (312) 922-5000 Founded/Ownrshp 2006
Sales NA EMP 500
SIC 6411 Insurance brokers; Insurance brokers
Pr: Mike Ahlert
*Pr: Richard A Gulliver
*CFO: Tom Musson
*Ch: Martin P Hughes
*Sr VP: Sam Valeo
*VP: Richard Babb
*VP: Kenneth Rosinski

D-U-N-S 15-626-0189
HUB INTERNATIONAL OF INDIANA LTD
420 Main St Ste 1100, Evansville, IN 47708-1513
Tel (812) 485-2800 Founded/Ownrshp 1999
Sales NA EMP 300
SIC 6411 Insurance agents, brokers & service; Insurance agents, brokers & service
Prin: Charles Burnham
*CEO: Charles Burnham
*CFO: Richards Philps
*VP: Ed Burnham

HUB INTERNATIONAL RIGG
See WM RIGG CO

D-U-N-S 09-758-5913 IMP/EXP
HUB LABELS INC
18223 Shawley Dr, Hagerstown, MD 21740-2462
Tel (301) 790-1660 Founded/Ownrshp 1978
Sales 43.3MM^E EMP 160
SIC 2679 Tags & labels, paper; Labels, paper: made from purchased material; Tags & labels, paper; Labels, paper: made from purchased material
Pr: Thomas Dahbura
*CFO: Ed Jacobs

*Sec: Mary Dahbura
*VP: Anton T Dahbura
*VP: Gladys Socks
Dir Bus: Fran Nicklas
*Prin: Abbud S Dahbura
IT Man: Scott Barron
Manager: Amanda Miller
Sales Asso: Lisa EBY

D-U-N-S 01-910-5484 IMP
HUB METALS AND TRADING INC
1141 S Acacia Ave, Fullerton, CA 92831-5312
Tel (714) 871-8020 Founded/Ownrshp 2007
Sales 20.0MME EMP 22
SIC 5051 Metals service centers & offices
Pr: Kirk Harman

D-U-N-S 00-100-9000 IMP
HUB PEN CO INC (MA)
1525 Washington St Ste 1, Braintree, MA 02184-7533
Tel (781) 535-5500 Founded/Ownrshp 1954
Sales 30.3MME EMP 250
SIC 3951 Ball point pens & parts
Pr: Joseph A Fleming
Treas: Mary McGaughey
VP: Robert Mc Gaughey
Sls Mgr: Melissa Bettua
Sales Asso: Joseph Owens

HUBACHER BODY SHOP
See HUBACHER CADILLAC INC

D-U-N-S 02-903-2083
HUBACHER CADILLAC INC
HUBACHER BODY SHOP
2341 Fulton Ave, Sacramento, CA 95825-0364
Tel (916) 929-2777 Founded/Ownrshp 1981
Sales 30.3MME EMP 97
SIC 5511 7538 Automobiles, new & used; General automotive repair shops; Automobiles, new & used; General automotive repair shops
CEO: Gregory A Goodwin
*Pr: Bob Foster
Exec: Brian Castongay
Mktg Dir: Steve Fries

HUBBARD & CRAVENS COFFEE
See SUNCOAST COFFEE INC

D-U-N-S 15-359-3975
HUBBARD & DRAKE GENERAL - MECHANICAL CONTRACTORS INC
1002 5th Ave Se, Decatur, AL 35601-3914
Tel (256) 353-9244 Founded/Ownrshp 1984
Sales 56.9MME EMP 141
SIC 1541 1711 Industrial buildings, new construction; Renovation, remodeling & repairs: industrial buildings; Mechanical contractor; Process piping contractor; Industrial buildings, new construction; Renovation, remodeling & repairs: industrial buildings; Mechanical contractor; Process piping contractor
Pr: Scott Hubbard
*VP: Chris Howard

D-U-N-S 01-653-0768
HUBBARD AUTO CENTER INC
HUBBARD GM CENTER
901 W Broadway St, Monticello, IN 47960-1815
Tel (574) 583-7121 Founded/Ownrshp 1977
Sales 21.1MME EMP 46
SIC 5511 Automobiles, new & used; Pickups, new & used; Vans, new & used
Pr: Richard M Hubbard
Sales Asso: Jonathan Timm

D-U-N-S 00-696-1932
HUBBARD BROADCASTING INC (MN)
3415 University Ave W, Saint Paul, MN 55114-2099
Tel (651) 642-4656 Founded/Ownrshp 1921
Sales 300.7MME EMP 1,200
SIC 4833 7812 4832

D-U-N-S 00-692-3197
HUBBARD CONSTRUCTION CO (FL)
MID-FLORIDA MATERIALS DIVISION
(Suby of HUBBARD GROUP INC) ★
1936 Lee Rd Ste 101, Winter Park, FL 32789-7201
Tel (407) 645-5500 Founded/Ownrshp 1920
Sales 286.3MME EMP 712
Accts Deloitte & Touche Llp Tampa
SIC 1611 2951 1623 General contractor, highway & street construction; Highway & street paving contractor; Asphalt & asphaltic paving mixtures (not from refineries); Sewer line construction; General contractor, highway & street construction; Highway & street paving contractor; Asphalt & asphaltic paving mixtures (not from refineries); Sewer line construction
CEO: Alan M Cahill
*CFO: P Frederick O DEA Jr
CFO: Fred Odea
*Ch: Pierre Anjolras
VP: Phil Anderson
VP: Paul Giles
Exec: Roberta Weaver
Div Mgr: Lupe Aranda
Dir IT: Scott Place

HUBBARD COUNTY
See HUBBARD COUNTY OF INC

D-U-N-S 08-252-4653
HUBBARD COUNTY OF INC
HUBBARD COUNTY
301 Court Ave, Park Rapids, MN 56470-1483
Tel (218) 732-3196 Founded/Ownrshp 1883
Sales NA EMP 334
Accts Hoffman Dale & Swenson Pllc
SIC 9111 Executive offices; ; Executive offices;
Off Mgr: Linda Eischens

HUBBARD GM CENTER
See HUBBARD AUTO CENTER INC

D-U-N-S 36-111-4861
HUBBARD GROUP INC
(Suby of GECOS INC) ★
1936 Lee Rd Ste 101, Winter Park, FL 32789-7201
Tel (407) 645-5500 Founded/Ownrshp 1988
Sales 476.6MME EMP 900
Accts Deloitte & Touche Llp Tampa
SIC 1611 2951 1623 General contractor, highway & street construction; Asphalt & asphaltic paving mixtures (not from refineries); Sewer line construction; General contractor, highway & street construction; Asphalt & asphaltic paving mixtures (not from refineries); Sewer line construction
Pr: William J Capehart
CFO: P Frederick Odea Jr
Sec: P Frederick O'Dea Jr
VP: Bill Capehart
Div Mgr: Tony Geach
Mtls Mgr: Ray Birko
Mtls Mgr: Theo Creighton
Snr Mgr: Paul Bonser

D-U-N-S 00-142-6063 IMP
HUBBARD ISA LLC
(Suby of AVIAGEN TURKEYS LIMITED)
195 Main St, Walpole, NH 03608-4516
Tel (603) 756-3311 Founded/Ownrshp 1974
Sales 45.4MME EMP 700
SIC 0254 8731 Poultry hatcheries; Commercial physical research; Poultry hatcheries; Commercial physical research

D-U-N-S 05-851-7202
HUBBARD PIPE AND SUPPLY INC
463 Robeson St, Fayetteville, NC 28301-5685
Tel (910) 484-0187 Founded/Ownrshp 2002
Sales 37.6MME EMP 60
SIC 5074 Plumbing & hydronic heating supplies
Pr: Wilson Teachey
*VP: David M Hubbard
Brnch Mgr: Michael Bailey
Off Mgr: David Runkel
Opers Mgr: Dave Runkle
Sales Asso: Daniel Hart
Sales Asso: Nolan Johnson

D-U-N-S 04-392-7024
HUBBARD RADIO CHICAGO LLC
WILV -FM
130 E Randolph St # 2700, Chicago, IL 60601-6307
Tel (312) 946-4700 Founded/Ownrshp 1998, 2011
Sales 42.5MME EMP 150E
SIC 4832 Radio broadcasting stations
Ch Bd: Ginny Morris
Ex VP: Drew Horowitz
Ex Dir: Ted Jakubiak
Dir IT: Wayne Braithwaite
Dir IT: William Cress
Mktg Dir: Dave Karwoski
Snr Mgr: Kent Lewin

D-U-N-S 00-890-1431
HUBBARD SUPPLY CO
901 W 2nd St, Flint, MI 48503-2680
Tel (810) 234-8681 Founded/Ownrshp 2007
Sales 73.9MME EMP 80
SIC 5084 Industrial machinery & equipment; Industrial machinery & equipment
Pr: Jeff Bigelow
*COO: Tim Brooks
CFO: Robert S Fuller
Brnch Mgr: Philip Fent
Brnch Mgr: Rose Peer
Genl Mgr: Mike Obert
Sales Asso: Amy Dinninger
Sales Asso: Tony Magalski
Sales Asso: Lyndsey Rigsby
Snr Mgr: Owen Dixon

D-U-N-S 05-531-0759 IMP
HUBBARD-HALL INC
563 S Leonard St, Waterbury, CT 06708-4316
Tel (203) 756-5521 Founded/Ownrshp 1971
Sales 50.3MM EMP 111
SIC 5169 3471 2899 2842 Chemicals, industrial & heavy; Finishing, metals or formed products; Chemical preparations; Specialty cleaning, polishes & sanitation goods; Chemicals, industrial & heavy; Finishing, metals or formed products; Chemical preparations; Specialty cleaning, polishes & sanitation goods
Pr: Molly Kellogg
*COO: Gerard Mastropietro
*Ch: Charles T Kellogg
*Sr VP: Jeff Davis
*Sr VP: Robert Farrell
Off Mgr: W Brent

D-U-N-S 77-994-9387 IMP
HUBBARDTON FORGE LLC
154 Route 30 S, Castleton, VT 05735-9521
Tel (802) 468-3090 Founded/Ownrshp 2013
Sales 47.2MME EMP 225
SIC 3645 5063 3446 Residential lighting fixtures; Lighting fixtures; Architectural metalwork; Residential lighting fixtures; Lighting fixtures; Architectural metalwork
CEO: Bob Dillon
CFO: Shelley Roop
VP: Reed Hampton
IT Man: Kelly Murphy
Natl Sales: Bruce Hathaway
Mktg Mgr: Loree Gunn
Sls Mgr: Jeannie Parker
Art Dir: Wendy Fannin
Snr Mgr: Sharron Freese
Snr Mgr: Stacey Orourke

HUBBEL KILLARK
See KILLARK ELECTRIC MANUFACTURING CO INC

D-U-N-S 15-203-9421
■ **HUBBELL CABLE ACCESSORIES**
(Suby of HUBBELL INC) ★
210 N Allen St, Centralia, MO 65240-1302
Tel (573) 682-8414 Founded/Ownrshp 1996
Sales 38.1MME EMP 157
SIC 3643 Current-carrying wiring devices; Current-carrying wiring devices
Pr: William Haines
VP: Ron Salberg
QA Dir: Gary Dickerson
Dir IT: Brad Davis
Dir IT: Gary Van Riper
IT Man: Luis Delavega
Ql Cn Mgr: Dave Dickerson
Natl Sales: Rosemary Long
VP Mktg: Jeff Thomas
Mktg Mgr: Dick Erdel
Mktg Mgr: Christy Johnson

D-U-N-S 00-118-1858 IMP
▲ **HUBBELL INC**
40 Waterview Dr, Shelton, CT 06484-4300
Tel (475) 882-4000 Founded/Ownrshp 1888
Sales 3.3MMM EMP 15,400
Accts Pricewaterhousecoopers Llp Ha
Tkr Sym HUBB Exch NYS
SIC 3643 Current-carrying wiring devices; Current-carrying wiring devices
Ch Bd: David G Nord
CFO: William R Sperry
Treas: James H Biggart Jr
Ex VP: Gary Amato
Sr VP: W Robert Murphy
VP: Joseph A Capozzoli
VP: Jim Dietrich
VP: An-Ping Hsieh
VP: An-Ping U Hsieh
VP: Paul Lewis
VP: Ron Salberg
VP: Mike Shovlin
VP: Charles M Tencza

D-U-N-S 00-510-5994 IMP
■ **HUBBELL INC (DELAWARE)**
HUBBELL RACO DIVISION
(Suby of HUBBELL INC) ★
3902 W Sample St, South Bend, IN 46619-2933
Tel (574) 234-7151 Founded/Ownrshp 1933, 1981
Sales 253.1MME EMP 2,300
SIC 3644 3699 3613 Outlet boxes (electric wiring devices); Electrical equipment & supplies; Switchgear & switchboard apparatus; Outlet boxes (electric wiring devices); Electrical equipment & supplies; Switchgear & switchboard apparatus
Pr: Timothy H Powers
*Pr: Gary N Amato
CFO: Bob Bates
*Treas: James H Biggart
VP: Wesson M Brown
Dist Mgr: Joe Devito
Natl Sales: Joseph Dani
Mktg Mgr: Wanda Korcz
Sls Mgr: Bryan Pfeifer
Sls Mgr: Anthony Stetson

D-U-N-S 19-246-4436
■ **HUBBELL INC (DELAWARE)**
(Suby of HUBBELL INC) ★
40 Waterview Dr, Shelton, CT 06484-4300
Tel (475) 882-4000 Founded/Ownrshp 2010
Sales 30.2MME EMP 613E
SIC 3643 Current-carrying wiring devices
CEO: Gary Amato
Sls Mgr: John Flynn

D-U-N-S 18-817-6499 IMP/EXP
■ **HUBBELL INDUSTRIAL CONTROLS INC**
FEMCO RADIO CONTROLS
(Suby of HUBBELL INC) ★
4301 Cheyenne Dr, Archdale, NC 27263-3246
Tel (336) 434-2800 Founded/Ownrshp 1985
Sales 76.5MME EMP 350
SIC 3625 Motor controls, electric; Motor controls, electric
Pr: Timothy Powers
*Ch Bd: G J Ratcliffe
*CFO: William Tolley
*Treas: James Biggart Jr
*VP: Gary Amato
Off Mgr: Linda Seba
IT Man: John Jones
Mtls Mgr: Linda Saba
Sfty Mgr: Pamela Johnson
Opers Mgr: D King
Natl Sales: Paul Savage

D-U-N-S 80-453-8817 IMP
■ **HUBBELL LIGHTING INC**
(Suby of HUBBELL INC) ★
701 Millennium Blvd, Greenville, SC 29607-5251
Tel (864) 599-6000 Founded/Ownrshp 1985
Sales 303.8MME EMP 1,215
SIC 3648 Lighting equipment; Outdoor lighting equipment; Lighting equipment; Outdoor lighting equipment
Pr: Scott H Muse
*Treas: James H Biggart
Ofcr: Nicole Hill
VP: Tom Benton
*VP: Wayne A Cable
*VP: Richard W Davies
VP: Ravi Koil
VP: Ron Newbold
VP: Kenneth Page
VP: Paul Ross
VP: William Sperry
VP: Kent Welke

D-U-N-S 04-826-5974 IMP/EXP
■ **HUBBELL POWER SYSTEMS INC**
(Suby of HUBBELL INC) ★
200 Center Point Cir # 200, Columbia, SC 29210-5894
Tel (803) 216-2600 Founded/Ownrshp 1994
Sales 232.1MME EMP 1,000
SIC 3643 Current-carrying wiring devices; Current-carrying wiring devices
Pr: William Tolley
VP: Patrick Clemente
VP: Mike Estes
*VP: Kevin Potts
VP: Brian Serati
IT Man: Mark Admar
Mktg Mgr: Richard Hesson
Manager: Thomas Beattie

HUBBELL PRPTS III LC SERIES A
See HUBBELL REALTY CO

HUBBELL RACO DIVISION
See HUBBELL INC (DELAWARE)

D-U-N-S 07-808-5743
HUBBELL REALTY CO
HUBBELL PRPTS III LC SERIES A
6900 Westown Pkwy, West Des Moines, IA 50266-2520
Tel (515) 276-2349 Founded/Ownrshp 1903
Sales 30.5MME EMP 175
SIC 6531 6552 8741 Real estate brokers & agents; Land subdividers & developers, commercial; Business management
Ch Bd: James W Hubbell III
*Pr: Rick Tollakson
*CFO: Jim Weber
Sr VP: Kyle Gamble
Sr VP: Todd Millang
VP: Krista Capp
Dir Risk M: Jim Sarcone
Off Admin: Sarah Riesberg
Web Dev: Almir Kazazic
Mktg Dir: Tina Hadden
Corp Couns: Ashley Aust

D-U-N-S 04-607-0223
HUBBELL ROTH & CLARK INC
555 Hulet Dr, Bloomfield Hills, MI 48302-0360
Tel (248) 454-6300 Founded/Ownrshp 1999
Sales 34.3MME EMP 151
SIC 8711 Consulting engineer; Consulting engineer
Pr: George E Hubbell
*CFO: J Bruce McFarland
*Treas: Peter T Roth
*Ex VP: Thomas E Biehl
*VP: Walter H Alix
*VP: Curt A Christenson
VP: Curt Christeson
*VP: Keith D McCormack
*VP: Michael D Waring
Exec: Nancy Faught
Exec: Bowdan Joel

D-U-N-S 00-630-2764 IMP
■ **HUBBELL WIEGMANN INC**
(Suby of HUBBELL INC) ★
501 W Apple St, Freeburg, IL 62243-1389
Tel (618) 539-3542 Founded/Ownrshp 1928
Sales 46.9MME EMP 350
SIC 3644 Junction boxes, electric; Junction boxes, electric
Pr: Timothy H Powers
*VP: Richard W Davies
Sfty Mgr: Brad Niebruegge
Opers Mgr: Paul Fix
Opers Mgr: Charlie Rogers

HUBBLE ELEMENTARY
See MARSHFIELD R-1 SCHOOL DISTRICT

HUBELL CARIBE LIMITED
See HARVEY HUBBELL CARIBE INC

D-U-N-S 15-531-7522 IMP
HUBER + SUHNER INC
(Suby of HUBER + SUHNER (USA) CORPORATION)
8530 Steele Creek Place D, Charlotte, NC 28273-4280
Tel (704) 790-7300 Founded/Ownrshp 1986
Sales 120.0MM EMP 75
SIC 3679 3678 3357 5065 Microwave components; Electronic connectors; Nonferrous wiredrawing & insulating; Electronic parts & equipment; Microwave components; Electronic connectors; Nonferrous wiredrawing & insulating; Electronic parts & equipment
Pr: Andy Hollywood
COO: URS Ryffel
CFO: Bernhard Schwarzer
CFO: Ivo Wechsler
*Treas: Sean Thomas
Ofcr: Peter Schmid
VP: Stephan Hofstetter
VP: Drew Nixon
Genl Mgr: Mike Canfield
CTO: Peter Baumann
IT Man: Sam Higgins

D-U-N-S 88-474-1877
HUBER CADILLAC INC
HUBER CHEVROLET CADILLAC
11102 W Dodge Rd, Omaha, NE 68154-2616
Tel (402) 496-0220 Founded/Ownrshp 1986
Sales 36.5MM EMP 175
SIC 5511 Automobiles, new & used; Automobiles, new & used
Pr: Ron Huber
*Treas: Jerry Schomers

HUBER CHEVROLET CADILLAC
See HUBER CHEVROLET CO INC

HUBER CHEVROLET CADILLAC
See HUBER CADILLAC INC

D-U-N-S 03-511-4644
HUBER CHEVROLET CO INC
HUBER CHEVROLET CADILLAC
11102 W Dodge Rd, Omaha, NE 68154-2691
Tel (402) 496-0220 Founded/Ownrshp 1976
Sales 62.9MM EMP 125
SIC 5511 Automobiles, new & used; Automobiles, new & used
Pr: Ronald E Huber
Treas: Jerry M Schoers
*Sec: Jerry M Schomers

D-U-N-S 15-129-4696 EXP
HUBER ENGINEERED WOODS LLC
(Suby of JM HUBER CORP) ★
10925 David Taylor Dr, Charlotte, NC 28262-1040
Tel (704) 547-0671 Founded/Ownrshp 2003
Sales 120.1MME EMP 515
SIC 2493 Reconstituted wood products; Reconstituted wood products
Pr: Brian Carlson
Pr: Albert Landers
VP: Mark Hopkins
VP: Kurt Koch
Dir IT: David Babin
IT Man: Ben Bynoe
IT Man: Todd Hair
Tech Mgr: Kevin Warshaw
Plnt Mgr: Mike Walker

VP Sls: James Denny
S&M/VP: Matthew Obrien

D-U-N-S 07-128-7502
HUBER HEIGHTS CITY SCHOOL
5954 Longford Rd, Dayton, OH 45424-2998
Tel (937) 236-8990 *Founded/Ownrshp* 1916
Sales 47.2MM^E^ *EMP* 823
SIC 8211 Public junior high school; Public senior high school; Public junior high school; Public senior high school
**CFO:* Marie Ann Bernardo
Dir IT: Clifton Bauer
IT Man: Chris Mandich
Schl Brd P: Kelly Bledsoe
Teacher Pr: Derrick Williams
Psych: Cheryl Fenton

D-U-N-S 11-857-8504 IMP
HUBER TECHNOLOGY INC
(*Suby of* HUBER SE)
9735 Northcross Center Ct, Huntersville, NC 28078-7326
Tel (704) 949-1010 *Founded/Ownrshp* 2005
Sales 31.1MM^E^ *EMP* 50
SIC 5084 Industrial machinery & equipment; Industrial machinery & equipment
Pr: Henk-Jan Van Ettekoven
**Treas:* Jennifer Covington
VP: Tracy Johnson
Mng Dir: Franz Heindl
Dir IT: Rudi Bogner
Dir IT: Bernhard Schmid

D-U-N-S 13-565-5327 IMP
HUBERGROUP USA INC
(*Suby of* HUBERGROUP INDIA PRIVATE LIMITED)
2850 Festival Dr, Kankakee, IL 60901-8937
Tel (815) 929-9293 *Founded/Ownrshp* 2006
Sales 32.8MM^E^ *EMP* 155
SIC 2893 Printing ink; Printing ink
CEO: Martin Weber
**Pr:* Thomas Hensel
CFO: Mahadevan Valdyanathan
VP: Aniruddha Joshi
Rgnl Mgr: Michel Aubry
Rgnl Mgr: Bob Yontz
**CTO:* Debu Sengupta

D-U-N-S 00-427-0997 IMP/EXP
HUBERT CO LLC
(*Suby of* TAKKT AG)
9555 Dry Fork Rd, Harrison, OH 45030-1994
Tel (513) 367-8600 *Founded/Ownrshp* 1946, 2000
Sales 231.1MM^E^ *EMP* 309
SIC 5046 Store fixtures; Store equipment; Display equipment, except refrigerated; Store fixtures; Store equipment; Display equipment, except refrigerated
Pr: Bert Kohler
VP: Charles Dennis
VP: Mark Rudy
VP: Brad Sherman
VP: Richard Thoene
VP: Pam Williams
Exec: Lisa Sant
Off Mgr: Liz Oneill
Dir IT: Mark Hopkins
Dir IT: Dave Norris
IT Man: Cheryl Meiser

D-U-N-S 01-731-5581
HUBERT DISTRIBUTORS INC
1200 Auburn Ave, Pontiac, MI 48342-3312
Tel (248) 858-2340 *Founded/Ownrshp* 1937
Sales 26.9MM^E^ *EMP* 120
SIC 5181 Beer & other fermented malt liquors; Beer & other fermented malt liquors
Pr: Thomas Vella
**CFO:* Peter Ferguson
Store Mgr: Tom O'Callaghan
Opers Mgr: Ben Labita
Sls Mgr: Mark Helzer
Sls Mgr: Denny Sturza

HUBERT VESTER CHEVROLET
See HUBERT VESTER OPERATING CO LLC

D-U-N-S 96-020-5292
HUBERT VESTER HONDA
3701 Raleigh Road Pkwy W, Wilson, NC 27896-9743
Tel (252) 243-3382 *Founded/Ownrshp* 1996
Sales 23.7MM^E^ *EMP* 65
SIC 5511 5521 Automobiles, new & used; Used car dealers; Automobiles, new & used; Used car dealers
Pr: Hubert Vester
**Sec:* Stephanie Vester
**VP:* Brenda Vester
Sales Asso: Chad Blake
Sales Asso: Markeis Howard
Sales Asso: George Myers

D-U-N-S 80-981-8235
HUBERT VESTER OPERATING CO LLC
HUBERT VESTER CHEVROLET
3717 Raleigh Road Pkwy W, Wilson, NC 27896-9743
Tel (252) 291-2111 *Founded/Ownrshp* 2003
Sales 51.4MM^E^ *EMP* 180
SIC 5511 Automobiles, new & used; Automobiles, new & used
Off Mgr: Debbie Travis

D-U-N-S 01-643-1793
HUBLER CHEVROLET INC
8220 Us 31 S, Indianapolis, IN 46227-0991
Tel (317) 882-4389 *Founded/Ownrshp* 1961
Sales 72.6MM^E^ *EMP* 157^E^
SIC 5511 7538 Automobiles, new & used; Trucks, tractors & trailers: new & used; General automotive repair shops; Automobiles, new & used; Trucks, tractors & trailers: new & used; General automotive repair shops
Pr: Brad Hubler
**VP:* John Hubler
Mktg Mgr: Jon Faust
Sls Mgr: Josh Davis
Sls Mgr: Kevin Kessinger
Sls Mgr: Rob Mohr
Sales Asso: Brian Copenhaver

HUBLER MAZDA WEST
See NISSAN HUBLER INC

D-U-N-S 94-294-1352 IMP
HUBNER MANUFACTURING CORP
(*Suby of* HUBNER HOLDING GMBH)
450 Wando Park Blvd, Mount Pleasant, SC 29464-7845
Tel (843) 849-9400 *Founded/Ownrshp* 1995
Sales 35.3MM^E^ *EMP* 115
SIC 3053 3069 Gaskets, packing & sealing devices; Expansion joints, rubber; Gaskets, packing & sealing devices; Expansion joints, rubber
CEO: Ron Paquette
**Pr:* Ron Hubner
**VP:* Patricia Hubner
Plnt Mgr: Edgar Posso
QI Cn Mgr: Bryan Hook

D-U-N-S 00-531-5233
▲ HUBSPOT INC
25 1st St Ste 200, Cambridge, MA 02141-1826
Tel (888) 482-7768 *Founded/Ownrshp* 2005
Sales 115.8MM *EMP* 785
Accts Deloitte & Touche Llp Boston
Tkr Sym HUBS *Exch* NYS
SIC 7372 ; Prepackaged software; Business oriented computer software
Ch Bd: Brian Halligan
**Pr:* J D Sherman
CFO: John Kinzer
Chf Mktg O: Kipp Bodnar
Sr VP: Hunter Madeley
VP: Joe Chernov
VP: David McNeil
CIO: Jim O'Neill
**CTO:* Dharmesh Shah
QA Dir: Waqas Younas
Dir IT: Jason Webber
Board of Directors: Stacey Bishop, Larry Bohn, Ron Gill, Lorrie Norrington, Michael Simon, David Skok

D-U-N-S 05-298-6312
HUCK FINN CLOTHES INC
LABEL SHOPPER
952 Troy Schenectady Rd # 1, Latham, NY 12110-1693
Tel (518) 785-1650 *Founded/Ownrshp* 1970
Sales 57.5MM^E^ *EMP* 450
SIC 5621 5611

D-U-N-S 80-684-6239
HUCK GROUP INC
HGI
4501 Tamiami Trl N # 214, Naples, FL 34103-3060
Tel (239) 692-8470 *Founded/Ownrshp* 2007
Sales 24.3MM^E^ *EMP* 238
SIC 2541 Wood partitions & fixtures
Pr: Mark Flegel
VP: Michelle Carter
**Mng Dir:* Leslie Flegel

D-U-N-S 00-535-4436 IMP
■ HUCK INTERNATIONAL INC
ALCOA FASTENING SYSTEMS RINGS
(*Suby of* ALCOA FASTENING SYSTEMS RINGS) ★
3724 E Columbia St, Tucson, AZ 85714-3410
Tel (520) 519-7400 *Founded/Ownrshp* 1940, 1991
Sales 166.4MM^E^ *EMP* 1,600
SIC 3429 3452 Aircraft hardware; Metal fasteners; Nuts, metal; Aircraft hardware; Metal fasteners; Nuts, metal
Pr: Olivier Jarrault
**Treas:* Peter Hong
VP: Terry Keenaghan
Genl Mgr: Ken Paine
Plnt Mgr: Laurinda Mackinnon

D-U-N-S 79-999-4673
HUCKABEE & ASSOCIATES INC
801 Cherry St 500, Fort Worth, TX 76102-6803
Tel (817) 377-2969 *Founded/Ownrshp* 1995
Sales 34.0MM *EMP* 100^E^
Accts Boucher Morgan & Young Apc S
SIC 8712 Architectural services; Architectural services
CEO: Christopher Huckabee
**Pr:* Thomas Lueck
**CFO:* Jerry Hammerlun
**Ex VP:* Paul Svacek
**VP:* Jennifer Brown
**VP:* Josh C Brown
**VP:* Nicolai Gurov
**VP:* Daren Kirbo
**VP:* Gary Rademacher

HUCKLEBERRY'S FRESH MARKETS
See ROSAUERS SUPERMARKETS INC

HUCK'S
See MARTIN & BAYLEY INC

HUDD TRANSPORATION
See DAMCO DISTRIBUTION SERVICES INC

HUDDLE HOUSE
See HH HOLDINGS INC

D-U-N-S 06-646-8497
HUDDLE HOUSE INC
5901b Pchtree Dunwoody Rd, Atlanta, GA 30328
Tel (770) 325-1300 *Founded/Ownrshp* 2012
Sales 32.6MM^E^ *EMP* 400
SIC 5812 Fast-food restaurant, chain; Fast-food restaurant, chain
CEO: Michael ABT
**COO:* Tyrone Counts
**CFO:* Thomas Cossuto
CFO: Tom Cussuto
VP: Christina Chambers
VP: Mike Wiemers
Genl Mgr: Michelle Sexton

D-U-N-S 03-302-9547
HUDIBURG AUTO GROUP
6000 Tinker Diagonal, Oklahoma City, OK 73110-2830
Tel (405) 737-6641 *Founded/Ownrshp* 1957
Sales NA *EMP* 900
SIC 5511 Automobiles, new & used; Automobiles, new & used
Pr: David Hudiburg
**Sec:* H Jean Hudiburg
Ex VP: Jeff Robinson
VP: Steve Hudiburg
Genl Mgr: Steve Blake
Genl Mgr: Jim Patch
DP Exec: Kurt Kassner
Dir IT: Kurt Kasner
Sales Exec: Greg Ryan

D-U-N-S 94-195-9082
HUDIBURG CHEVROLET LLC
HUDIBURG TOYOTA
6000 Tinker Diagonal, Midwest City, OK 73110-2830
Tel (405) 737-6641 *Founded/Ownrshp* 2010
Sales 71.8MM^E^ *EMP* 300
SIC 5511 Automobiles, new & used; Automobiles, new & used
Pr: David Hudiburg
**Sec:* Jeanie Wear
**VP:* Steve Hudiburg
Exec: Marla Martin
Telecom Ex: Dan Garrett

HUDIBURG COLLISION CENTER S
See NISSAN HUDIBURG INC

HUDIBURG TOYOTA
See HUDIBURG CHEVROLET LLC

D-U-N-S 80-705-1222
HUDSON ADVISORS LP
2711 N Haskell Ave # 1800, Dallas, TX 75204-2921
Tel (214) 754-8400 *Founded/Ownrshp* 1995
Sales 29.4MM^E^ *EMP* 2
SIC 6512 Investment advice; Commercial & industrial building operation
Pr: Robert Corcoran
Ofcr: Jena Bjornson
Ofcr: Joel Sauer
Sr VP: Cindy Kuhlman
VP: Stewart Motley

D-U-N-S 80-863-0888
HUDSON CHARLESTON ACQUISITION LLC
HUDSON NISSAN
7331 Rivers Ave, North Charleston, SC 29406-4612
Tel (843) 553-1000 *Founded/Ownrshp* 2007
Sales 37.5MM^E^ *EMP* 90
SIC 5511 Automobiles, new & used; Automobiles, new & used
Genl Mgr: Thomas Downing
Sls Mgr: Terry Breedlove
Sls Mgr: Jeff Jacobs
Sls Mgr: Hudson Jordan
Sls Mgr: Tommy Russell
Sales Asso: Caey Jiles
Sales Asso: Mikey Lam
Sales Asso: Timon Marohn
Sales Asso: Richardo Purdie
Sales Asso: Conor Stickney

D-U-N-S 05-915-4968
HUDSON CITY BANCORP INC
W80 Century Rd, Paramus, NJ 07652
Tel (201) 967-1900 *Founded/Ownrshp* 1999
Sales NA *EMP* 1,581^E^
SIC 6035 Federal savings & loan associations

D-U-N-S 07-514-1309
HUDSON CITY SAVINGS BANK
80 W Century Rd, Paramus, NJ 07652-1478
Tel (201) 967-1900 *Founded/Ownrshp* 1999
Sales NA *EMP* 1,260
SIC 6035 6163 Loan brokers; Savings institutions, federally chartered

D-U-N-S 08-046-2856
HUDSON CITY SCHOOLS
215 Harry Howard Ave, Hudson, NY 12534-1606
Tel (518) 828-4360 *Founded/Ownrshp* 1920
Sales 29.5MM^E^ *EMP* 525
Accts Raymond G Preusser Cpa Pc
SIC 8211 Public elementary & secondary schools; Public elementary & secondary schools
Dir IT: Doug Fenson
Schl Brd P: Peter Rice
Psych: Kerri Appelbaum
Psych: Joanne Lanuto
Psych: Katharine Vera

D-U-N-S 83-049-2596
HUDSON CLEAN ENERGY PARTNERS (CAYMAN MASTER) LP
400 Frank W Burr Blvd, Teaneck, NJ 07666-6839
Tel (201) 287-4100 *Founded/Ownrshp* 2007
Sales 30.1MM^E^ *EMP* 110
SIC 6282 Investment advice
Pt: John Cavalier
Pt: Neil Auerbach
Pr: Juanita Batts
VP: Wilson Chang
Mng Dir: Paul Ho

D-U-N-S 06-131-2807
HUDSON CO OF TENNESSEE
17347 Al Highway 75, Henagar, AL 35978-5628
Tel (256) 657-6100 *Founded/Ownrshp* 1971
Sales 57.9MM *EMP* 80
Accts Joseph Decosimo And Company P
SIC 1542 Commercial & office building, new construction; Commercial & office building, renovation & repair; Commercial & office building, new construction; Commercial & office buildings, renovation & repair
Pr: Winston Alan Wilks Sr
CFO: James Gunter
**CFO:* Jim Gunter
**Treas:* Winston Alan Wilks Jr
**VP:* Kevin L Wilks

D-U-N-S 00-350-1640 EXP
HUDSON CONSTRUCTION CO (TN)
JAMES C HUDSON CONSTRUCTION CO
1615 Sholar Ave, Chattanooga, TN 37406-2800
Tel (423) 624-2631 *Founded/Ownrshp* 1956
Sales 132.9MM^E^ *EMP* 60
Accts Johnson Hickey Murchison Chat
SIC 1542 Commercial & office building, new construction; Commercial & office building, new construction
Pr: Steven T Hudson
Treas: William Hines
**Sec:* Wanda Padgett
**VP:* Stanley Hendon
Mng Dir: Ralph Maddux
Site Mgr: Leslee Edwards-Moore
Sales Exec: John Blinn

D-U-N-S 10-631-3166
HUDSON CONSTRUCTION INC
1625 Dutch Ln, Hermitage, PA 16148-3010
Tel (724) 962-1980 *Founded/Ownrshp* 1991
Sales 22.8MM *EMP* 45
Accts Hill Barth & King Llc Hermi
SIC 1542 Commercial & office building, new construction; Commercial & office buildings, renovation & repair; Commercial & office building, new construction; Commercial & office buildings, renovation & repair
Pr: Mark S Hudson

D-U-N-S 01-090-3318
HUDSON COUNTY COMMUNITY COLLEGE FOUNDATION INC
26 Journal Sq Fl 14, Jersey City, NJ 07306-4102
Tel (201) 360-4051 *Founded/Ownrshp* 1991
Sales 20.6MM^E^ *EMP* 500
SIC 8222 Community college; Community college
Pr: Glen Gabert PHD
VP: Ann Frenche
Exec: Kevin Omalley
VP Admn: Tom Brodowski
Ex Dir: Paul Dillon
Prgrm Mgr: Michael Ascolese
**CIO:* Pamela Scully
HC Dir: Jose Olivares

D-U-N-S 13-796-7782
HUDSON COUNTY MEADOWVIEW HOSPITAL
MEADOWVIEW NURSING CENTER
595 County Ave, Secaucus, NJ 07094-2605
Tel (201) 319-3660 *Founded/Ownrshp* 1916
Sales 22.1MM^E^ *EMP* 500
SIC 8063 8093 Psychiatric hospitals; Detoxification center, outpatient; Psychiatric hospitals; Detoxification center, outpatient
CFO: Sam Bassily
Ofcr: Nuzhat Iqbal
QA Dir: Marissa Feldman
Sfty Dirs: Patrick Donnelly

D-U-N-S 10-037-7597
HUDSON FALLS CENTRAL SCHOOL DISTRICT
1153 Burgoyne Ave, Fort Edward, NY 12828-1137
Tel (518) 747-2121 *Founded/Ownrshp* 1884
Sales 34.0MM *EMP* 442
Accts Mc Carthy & Canlon By Fax On M
SIC 8211 Public elementary & secondary schools; Public elementary & secondary schools

D-U-N-S 03-220-3077
HUDSON FOOD STORES INC
JIFFY FOOD STORES
1904 N Young Blvd, Chiefland, FL 32626-1951
Tel (352) 493-2104 *Founded/Ownrshp* 1931
Sales 25.4MM^E^ *EMP* 150
SIC 5411 Convenience stores, chain; Convenience stores, chain
Pr: Whitney Smith
Genl Mgr: Stoney Smith

D-U-N-S 03-620-8007
HUDSON FORD JIM
1201 W Main St, Lexington, SC 29072-2405
Tel (803) 359-4114 *Founded/Ownrshp* 1964
Sales 23.9MM^E^ *EMP* 51
SIC 5511 Automobiles, new & used; Automobiles, new & used
Pr: Jim Hudson
IT Man: Thomas Blackwell
**Sls Mgr:* Jesse Gouvin
Sls Mgr: Brian Risner
Sales Asso: Jennifer Hanby

HUDSON GARDENS
See AAH HUDSON LP

D-U-N-S 12-913-3463
▲ HUDSON GLOBAL INC
1325 Avenue Of The Amer F, New York, NY 10019-6026
Tel (212) 351-7300 *Founded/Ownrshp* 2003
Sales 581.1MM *EMP* 1,800^E^
Tkr Sym HSON *Exch* NGS
SIC 7361 7363 Employment agencies; Executive placement; Help supply services; Temporary help service; Employment agencies; Executive placement; Help supply services; Temporary help service
CEO: Stephen A Nolan
Mng Pt: John Baker
**Ch Bd:* David G Offensend
CEO: Lori Hock
COO: Robert Morgan
CFO: Patrick Lyons
Bd of Dir: Melissa Connell
Ofcr: Peg Buchenroth
Ex VP: Neil Funk
Ex VP: Mary Raymond
Ex VP: Eric Samargedlis
Ex VP: Josh Sorkin
Ex VP: Gary J Valentine
Ex VP: Mark Yacano
VP: Tony Caputo
VP: Raymond Christiansen
VP: Neil J Funk
VP: Jonathan Monheit
VP: Debbie Nowicki
VP: Wade Pearson
VP: Keith Warren
Board of Directors: Richard J Coleman Jr, Jeffrey E Eberwein, Ian V Nash

D-U-N-S 96-879-0811 IMP
HUDSON GROUP (HG) INC
(*Suby of* DUFRY AG)
1 Meadowlands Plz, East Rutherford, NJ 07073-2150
Tel (201) 939-5050 *Founded/Ownrshp* 2007
Sales 1.0MMM^E *EMP* 5,000^E
SIC 2731 Newspapers, home delivery, not by printers or publishers; Snack shop; Variety stores; Book publishing
Pt: Joseph Didomizio
Pt: Courtney Thornton
Mng Pt: Joe Hudson
Pr: Raquel Aguila
Pr: James Wilson
COO: Julian Diaz
**COO:* Roger Fordyce
CFO: Luis Otaola
**Treas:* William Wolf
Chf Mktg O: Michael Levy
**Ex VP:* Michael Mullaney
Sr VP: Gary Macrae
Sr VP: Andy Rattner
Sr VP: Hope Remoundos
Sr VP: Steven Silver
Sr VP: Bobby Watson
Sr VP: Bill Wolf Sr
VP: Laura Alphran
VP: Joe Davis
VP: Cubie Dawson
VP: Robin Diaz

D-U-N-S 96-879-0829
HUDSON GROUP (HG) RETAIL LLC
(*Suby of* DUFRY AG)
1 Meadowlands Plz Ste 902, East Rutherford, NJ 07073-2100
Tel (201) 939-5050 *Founded/Ownrshp* 2010
Sales 2.4MM^E *EMP* 300
SIC 5331 5812 5963 Variety stores; Snack shop; Newspapers, home delivery, not by printers or publishers
CEO: Joseph Didomizio
Sr VP: Rick Yockelson
VP: Laura Samuels
VP Sls: Mike Maslen

D-U-N-S 11-976-5204
HUDSON HEADWATERS HEALTH NETWORK
9 Carey Rd, Queensbury, NY 12804-7880
Tel (518) 761-0300 *Founded/Ownrshp* 1981
Sales 63.7MM *EMP* 350
Accts Cohnreznick Llp New York Ny
SIC 8011 Primary care medical clinic; Primary care medical clinic
CEO: John Rugge
**CFO:* Christopher Ctournier
Ofcr: Deborah Bardin
VP: Lori Gravelle
VP: Christopher Tournier
Exec: Stuart Chapman
**Prin:* George Purdue
**Prin:* Edward Shannon
Off Mgr: Michelle Aubin
Nurse Mgr: Mary Bayliss
Doctor: Mary Kilayko

D-U-N-S 16-162-4853
HUDSON HEALTH PLAN INC
MVP HEALTH CARE
303 S Broadway Ste 321, Tarrytown, NY 10591-5455
Tel (800) 339-4557 *Founded/Ownrshp* 1985
Sales NA *EMP* 225
Accts Pricewaterhousecoopers Llp Ha
SIC 6321 Accident & health insurance; Accident & health insurance
Pr: Georganne Chapin
**COO:* Kevin Nelson
**CFO:* Howard Birnbaum
Treas: Lindsay Farrell
**Treas:* Anne K Nolon
Sr VP: Mark Santiago
VP: Cheryl Bordes
VP: Ted Herman
VP: Margaret Leonard
VP: Susan Montgomery
Mktg Mgr: Karen Pfeifer

D-U-N-S 06-580-7059
HUDSON HEALTHCARE INC
HOBOKEN UNIVERSITY MEDICAL CTR
(*Suby of* HUMC OPCO LLC) ★
308 Willow Ave, Hoboken, NJ 07030-3808
Tel (201) 418-1000 *Founded/Ownrshp* 2011
Sales NA *EMP* 1,125
SIC 8062 General medical & surgical hospitals

HUDSON HIGH SCHOOL
See HUDSON LOCAL SCHOOL DISTRICT

D-U-N-S 10-895-2524
HUDSON HOME HEALTH CARE INC
151 Rockwell Rd, Newington, CT 06111-5535
Tel (860) 666-7500 *Founded/Ownrshp* 1989
Sales 30.7MM^E *EMP* 135
SIC 5047 5999 Medical equipment & supplies; Medical apparatus & supplies; Medical equipment & supplies; Medical apparatus & supplies
Pr: Shirley Curley
**Sec:* Edward Curley Sr
IT Man: David Zielke
Opers Mgr: Ron Sperry

D-U-N-S 17-949-4935
HUDSON HONDA AUTO SALES INC
6608 Kennedy Blvd, West New York, NJ 07093-1798
Tel (201) 868-9500 *Founded/Ownrshp* 2002
Sales 20.3MM^E *EMP* 50
SIC 5511 5521 Automobiles, new & used; Automobiles, used cars only; Automobiles, new & used; Automobiles, used cars only
Pr: Carmelo Giuffre
**Prin:* Ignazio Giuffre
**Prin:* John Iacono
**Prin:* Marilyn Oszustowicz
**Prin:* Mark Parry
**Prin:* Michelle Tropiano
Off Mgr: Olga Cotos
Sls Mgr: Jason Dechert
Sls Mgr: Eddie Munoz
Sls Mgr: Yirko Salgado
Sales Asso: Fernando Batista

HUDSON HOSPITAL
See HUDSON MEMORIAL HOSPITAL INC

HUDSON HOSPITAL & CLINICS
See HUDSON HOSPITAL INC

D-U-N-S 80-366-2928
HUDSON HOSPITAL INC
HUDSON HOSPITAL & CLINICS
405 Stageline Rd, Hudson, WI 54016-1793
Tel (715) 531-6700 *Founded/Ownrshp* 2007
Sales 50.3MM *EMP* 3
Accts Kpmg Llp Minneapolis Mn
SIC 8062 8031 General medical & surgical hospitals; Offices & clinics of osteopathic physicians
Ch: Richard O'Connor
**CEO:* Marian Furlong
**Treas:* Mike Leverty
VP: Jenna Thom
**Prin:* Linda Zeits
VP Opers: Ann Ripley
Plas Surg: Frank Pilney
Doctor: Ryan Karlstad
Doctor: Jon Paulson
Doctor: Heather Rocheford
Pharmcst: Roberta Bybee

D-U-N-S 07-854-1051
HUDSON HOSPITAL OPCO LLC
CHRIST HOSPITAL
176 Palisade Ave, Jersey City, NJ 07306-1121
Tel (201) 795-8200 *Founded/Ownrshp* 2012
Sales 125.2MM^E *EMP* 1,350
SIC 8062 General medical & surgical hospitals; General medical & surgical hospitals
CEO: Peter Kelly
Pr: Doreen Wilde
CFO: George Popco
**CFO:* Patrick Ryan
Ofcr: Margaret Casey
**VP:* William Atkinson
**VP:* Nizar Kifaieh
**VP:* Allyson Miller
Pharmcst: Lisette Acevedo

D-U-N-S 82-673-8051
HUDSON HOTEL BAR
356 W 58th St, New York, NY 10019-1804
Tel (212) 554-6000 *Founded/Ownrshp* 2008
Sales 72.9MM^E *EMP* 5,000
SIC 7011 Hotels & motels; Hotels & motels
CEO: Michael Gross
Board of Directors: Michael Gross

D-U-N-S 61-476-7713
HUDSON HOTELS CORP
400 Linden Oaks Ste 120, Rochester, NY 14625-2818
Tel (585) 419-4000 *Founded/Ownrshp* 1996
Sales 7.0MM^E *EMP* 1,500
SIC 7011 8741 Hotels; Hotel or motel management; Hotels; Hotel or motel management
Pr: Thomas W Blank

D-U-N-S 07-192-8642
HUDSON INC
27 Neil Gunn Rd, Ellisville, MS 39437
Tel (601) 477-4951 *Founded/Ownrshp* 1974
Sales 28.5MM^E *EMP* 350
SIC 5331 Variety stores; Variety stores
Pr: George A Hudson Jr
**Sec:* Melissa H Callahan

D-U-N-S 79-462-8573
HUDSON INDEPENDENT SCHOOL DISTRICT
HUDSON ISD
6735 Ted Trout Dr, Lufkin, TX 75904-6641
Tel (936) 875-3351 *Founded/Ownrshp* 2007
Sales 26.3MM *EMP* 368
Accts Axley & Rode Llp Lufkin Tex
SIC 8211 Public elementary & secondary schools; Public elementary & secondary schools
Exec: Julie Kimble
Exec: Misty Pena
IT Man: Mal Frazier
HC Dir: Shalana Hyde

HUDSON INSURANCE GROUP
See HUDSON SPECIALTY INSURANCE CO

HUDSON ISD
See HUDSON INDEPENDENT SCHOOL DISTRICT

HUDSON, JIM TOYOTA
See JIM HUDSON SUPERSTORE INC

D-U-N-S 06-534-7044
HUDSON LEASECO LLC
356 W 58th St, New York, NY 10019-1804
Tel (212) 247-2353 *Founded/Ownrshp* 2000
Sales 150.0MM *EMP* 535
SIC 6719 Investment holding companies, except banks; Investment holding companies, except banks
Chf Mktg O: Laura Turk

D-U-N-S 00-178-3307 IMP
HUDSON LIQUID ASPHALTS INC (RI)
89 Ship St, Providence, RI 02903-4218
Tel (401) 274-2200 *Founded/Ownrshp* 1955
Sales 30.9MM^E *EMP* 325
SIC 2951 Asphalt paving mixtures & blocks; Asphalt paving mixtures & blocks
Owner: Tom Hudson
**Pr:* Matthew J Gill
**Pr:* Francis J O'Brien
**CFO:* Douglas E Scala
CFO: Douglas Scala
**Sr VP:* Edward R Lodge Jr
**VP:* John J Hudson

D-U-N-S 08-177-8375
HUDSON LOCAL SCHOOL DISTRICT
HUDSON HIGH SCHOOL
2400 Hudson Aurora Rd, Hudson, OH 44236-2322
Tel (330) 342-4922 *Founded/Ownrshp* 1886
Sales 23.4MM^E *EMP* 700
SIC 8211 Public elementary school; Public junior high school; Public senior high school; Public elementary school; Public junior high school; Public senior high school

D-U-N-S 08-518-9236
HUDSON M R & EVELYN FOUNDATION
675 Randol Mill Ave, Southlake, TX 76092-8471
Tel (817) 431-4800 *Founded/Ownrshp* 1991
Sales 32.7MM *EMP* 6
SIC 8699 8641 Charitable organization; Civic social & fraternal associations; Charitable organization; Civic social & fraternal associations
CEO: M K Larson
VP: John Hooser

D-U-N-S 09-917-5903
HUDSON MANAGEMENT CORP
MCDONALD'S
144 S Thomas St Ste 208, Tupelo, MS 38801-5337
Tel (662) 841-7770 *Founded/Ownrshp* 1977
Sales 16.2MM^E *EMP* 450
SIC 5812 Fast-food restaurant, chain; Fast-food restaurant, chain
Pr: Robert Hudson

HUDSON MANOR
See SENIOR CITIZENS CORP OF BORO OF FREEHOLD INC

D-U-N-S 07-866-8175
HUDSON MEMORIAL HOSPITAL INC
HUDSON HOSPITAL
405 Stageline Rd, Hudson, WI 54016-7848
Tel (715) 531-6000 *Founded/Ownrshp* 1953
Sales 49.5MM *EMP* 311
SIC 8062 8011

D-U-N-S 13-883-1925 IMP
HUDSON MERIDIAN CONSTRUCTION GROUP LLC
H M
40 Rector St Fl 18, New York, NY 10006-1705
Tel (212) 608-6600 *Founded/Ownrshp* 2002
Sales 37.9MM^E *EMP* 85^E
SIC 1542 Commercial & office building contractors
CFO: Alton Rowe
Sr VP: Noel Hayes
**VP:* Luis Gutierrezv
**VP:* Walter Haass
**VP:* Daniel Hookerv
**VP:* Gregory Rinaldi
**VP:* Richard Santosky
**VP:* Robert Schwartz
Snr PM: Paul Cava
Snr PM: Luis Gutierrez

D-U-N-S 80-986-7799
HUDSON MOTORS PARTNERSHIP
HUDSON TOYOTA
599 State Rt 440, Jersey City, NJ 07305-4878
Tel (201) 433-0009 *Founded/Ownrshp* 1992
Sales 48.9MM^E *EMP* 180
SIC 5511 Automobiles, new & used; Automobiles, new & used
Pt: Joseph C Difeo

D-U-N-S 00-385-5715
HUDSON NEWS CO
(*Suby of* DUFRY AG)
701 Jefferson Rd, Parsippany, NJ 07054-3718
Tel (201) 867-3600 *Founded/Ownrshp* 1960
Sales 1.1MMM^E *EMP* 1,146^E
SIC 5192 5942 5994 5947 Magazines; Book stores; Newsstand; Greeting cards; Magazines; Books; Newspapers; Book stores; Newsstand; Greeting cards
Ch Bd: Robert B Cohen
**Pr:* James S Cohen
COO: Ronald Clark
CFO: Catherine Berg
Treas: Al Ruddy
Sr VP: Michael Mullaney
Sr VP: Hope Remoundos
VP: Mike Bartow
VP: Catherine Ryan Dp
MIS Dir: Tom Oakley
Opers Mgr: Ross Falisi

HUDSON NISSAN
See HUDSON CHARLESTON ACQUISITION LLC

D-U-N-S 07-515-3049
HUDSON NORTH COMMUNITY ACTION CORP
800 31st St Fl 1, Union City, NJ 07087-2428
Tel (201) 866-9320 *Founded/Ownrshp* 1965
Sales 46.1MM *EMP* 750^E
Accts Wiss & Company Llp Livingston
SIC 8399 8011 Health systems agency; Primary care medical clinic; Health systems agency; Primary care medical clinic
CEO: Jone Quigley
CFO: John Reinhardt
**CFO:* Michael Shababb
Treas: Robert Divincent
VP: Edmundo De Vera
Off Mgr: Deborah Pulido
CIO: Gregory Specht
Snr Mgr: Karen Lazarowitz

D-U-N-S 96-360-8265
▲ **HUDSON PACIFIC PROPERTIES INC**
11601 Wilshire Blvd # 600, Los Angeles, CA 90025-1797
Tel (310) 445-5700 *Founded/Ownrshp* 2009
Sales 253.4MM *EMP* 151^E
Tkr Sym HPP *Exch* NYS
SIC 6798 Real estate investment trusts; Real estate investment trusts
Ch Bd: Victor J Coleman
COO: Mark T Lammas
Ofcr: Steve Jaffe
Ex VP: Christopher Barton
Ex VP: Dale Shimoda
Ex VP: Kay L Tidwell
Sr VP: Drew Gordon
Sr VP: Gary Hansel
Sr VP: Joshua Hatfield
Sr VP: Arthur Suazo
Sr VP: David Tye
Board of Directors: John Schreiber, Theodore R Antenucci, Frank Cohen, Richard B Fried, Jonathan M Glaser, Robert L Harris II, Mark D Linehan, Robert M Moran Jr, Michael Nash, Barry A Porter

D-U-N-S 00-167-7988 IMP
HUDSON PAPER CO
HUPACO
1341 W Broad St Ste 4, Stratford, CT 06615-5761
Tel (203) 378-8759 *Founded/Ownrshp* 1908
Sales 20.2MM^E *EMP* 49
SIC 5113 5199 5947 2674 2652 Bags, paper & disposable plastic; Boxes & containers; Paper & products, wrapping or coarse; Packaging materials; Party favors; Bags: uncoated paper & multiwall; Boxes, newsboard, metal edged: made from purchased materials
Pr: Richard Wilk
**Treas:* Brian Wilk
VP: Anne Oneill
**VP:* Bonnie S Wilk

D-U-N-S 78-794-5042
HUDSON POINTE CENTER FOR NURSING & REHABILATION
(*Suby of* NATIONAL HEALTH CARE ASSOCIATES INC) ★
3220 Henry Hudson Pkwy, Bronx, NY 10463-3211
Tel (718) 514-2000 *Founded/Ownrshp* 2006
Sales 87.3MM^E *EMP* 1,402^E
SIC 8741 Management services
Dir Recs: Shona Kelly
Dir Soc: Amy Schwartz
Off Mgr: Laura Canty
Nrsg Dir: Cheikh Fall
HC Dir: Thomas Berry

HUDSON PRIMARY SCHOOL
See W F PEAVY PRIMARY SCHOOL

D-U-N-S 06-146-7254
HUDSON PRINTING CO
241 W 1700 S, Salt Lake City, UT 84115-5235
Tel (801) 486-4611 *Founded/Ownrshp* 1972
Sales 35.0MM *EMP* 200
SIC 2752 Commercial printing, offset; Commercial printing, offset
Pr: Paul B Hudson
**CFO:* Wayne Devincent
**VP:* Jeremy King
Dir Bus: Bill Sattree
Opers Mgr: Aleleaanga Moli
Sales Exec: Mike Anderson
Sales Asso: Dave Carrigan
Sales Asso: Darren Peterson
Sales Asso: Blaine Robinson

D-U-N-S 02-660-6863 IMP/EXP
HUDSON PRODUCTS CORP
(*Suby of* HUDSON PRODUCTS CORP) ★
9660 Grunwald Rd, Beasley, TX 77417-8600
Tel (281) 396-8195 *Founded/Ownrshp* 2008
Sales 161.9MM^E *EMP* 505
SIC 3443 Heat exchangers, condensers & components; Heat exchangers, condensers & components
Pr: Grady Walker
Pr: Richard Ketchum
CFO: Steve Brewer
CFO: Terry Brown
VP: Robert Giammaruti
**VP:* Darrell Zahn
Exec: Janardhan Reddy
Sfty Dirs: Jo Admire
Natl Sales: Brian Hanel
Mktg Mgr: Stephen Boes
Sales Asso: Rick Lopez

D-U-N-S 82-826-0146
HUDSON PRODUCTS CORP
9660 Grunwald Rd, Beasley, TX 77417-8600
Tel (281) 396-8100 *Founded/Ownrshp* 2006
Sales 189.2MM^E *EMP* 727
SIC 3443 Air coolers, metal plate; Air coolers, metal plate
CEO: Grady Walker
**Pr:* Sam Chapple
COO: Terry Brown
**VP:* Bob Giammaruti
Dept Mgr: Lynn Bennett
Sls Mgr: Sam George

D-U-N-S 07-979-9232
HUDSON PUBLIC SCHOOLS
155 Apsley St, Hudson, MA 01749-1645
Tel (978) 567-6100 *Founded/Ownrshp* 2015
Sales 4.2MM^E *EMP* 302^E
SIC 8211 Public elementary & secondary schools
Teacher Pr: Catherine Kilcoyne
HC Dir: Lee Waingortin

D-U-N-S 83-066-6223
HUDSON RANCH POWER I LLC
409 W Mcdonald St, Calipatria, CA 92233-9701
Tel (858) 509-0150 *Founded/Ownrshp* 2006
Sales 52.2MM^E *EMP* 55
SIC 4911 Generation, electric power
**Treas:* George Donlou
Genl Mgr: Matt Kelley
IT Man: Dana Krzyston
IT Man: Toni Pelligrino

D-U-N-S 02-019-8318
HUDSON RIVER BANCORP INC
1 Hudson City Ctr, Hudson, NY 12534-2354
Tel (518) 828-4600 *Founded/Ownrshp* 1998
Sales NA *EMP* 664
SIC 6036 Savings institutions, not federally chartered; Savings institutions, not federally chartered
Pr: Carl A Florio
**CFO:* Timothy E Blow
MIS Mgr: Carol Wiggin

HUDSON RIVER COMMUNITY HEALTH
See HUDSON RIVER HEALTHCARE INC

D-U-N-S 01-095-0624
HUDSON RIVER HEALTHCARE INC
HUDSON RIVER COMMUNITY HEALTH
1200 Brown St Ste 12, Peekskill, NY 10566-3622
Tel (914) 734-8800 *Founded/Ownrshp* 1975
Sales 95.8MM *EMP* 713
Accts Cohnreznick Llp New York New
SIC 8011 Medical centers; Medical centers
CEO: Anne Nolon
**COO:* Allison Dubois
**CFO:* Thomas Sexton
**Ex VP:* Paul Kaye
**Ex VP:* Jeanette Phillips
**Ex VP:* James D Sinkoff
Dir Lab: Mary King
Off Mgr: Nancy Lenhert
Doctor: Wendy Sylvester
Doctor: Suneela Tandra
Doctor: Laura Toner

D-U-N-S 05-783-6850 EXP
HUDSON SCENIC STUDIO INC
130 Fernbrook St, Yonkers, NY 10705-1764
Tel (914) 375-0900 *Founded/Ownrshp* 1980
Sales 23.3MM^E *EMP* 130^E
SIC 3999 Theatrical scenery; Theatrical scenery
CEO: Neil Mazzella
**VP:* John C Boyd

D-U-N-S 02-813-6844
HUDSON SCHOOL DISTRICT
20 Library St, Hudson, NH 03051-4240
Tel (603) 886-1258 *Founded/Ownrshp* 1969
Sales 37.0MM^E *EMP* 600
SIC 8211 Public elementary & secondary schools; Public elementary & secondary schools
Teacher Pr: Joyce Coll

D-U-N-S 07-937-6007
HUDSON SCHOOL DISTRICT
644 Brakke Dr, Hudson, WI 54016-8322
Tel (715) 377-3700 *Founded/Ownrshp* 2014
Sales 12.9MM^E *EMP* 529^E
SIC 8211 Elementary school
Schl Brd P: Jamie Johnson

D-U-N-S 10-864-9716
HUDSON SECURITIES INC
(*Suby of* HHC ACQUISITION, INC.)
111 Town Square Pl # 1500, Jersey City, NJ 07310-2784
Tel (201) 216-0100 *Founded/Ownrshp* 2011
Sales 25.4MM^E *EMP* 123^E
SIC 6211 Traders, security; Traders, security
Pr: Keith Knox
**CEO:* Anthony Sanfilippo
**CFO:* Peter Nielsen
**Ofcr:* Ajay Sareen
**Ex VP:* Mark Leventhal
**Ex VP:* Andrew Lewin
**Ex VP:* Daisy Minott
VP: Stephanie Underwood
Mng Dir: Steve Bonebrake

HUDSON SERVICES
See HBS INC

D-U-N-S 78-734-8718
HUDSON SPECIALTY INSURANCE CO
HUDSON INSURANCE GROUP
(*Suby of* ODYSSEY RE HOLDINGS CORP) ★
100 William St Fl 5, New York, NY 10038-5044
Tel (212) 978-2800 *Founded/Ownrshp* 2005
Sales NA *EMP* 39
SIC 6411 Insurance information & consulting services
Pr: Christopher Gallagher
**CFO:* John Verbich
**Ex VP:* Christopher Suarez
Sr VP: Marc Garganigo
Sr VP: Ronald Honken
Sr VP: John Morrow
VP: Kelly Bramwell
VP: Courtney Greene
VP: Blair Holl
VP: Brian O'Neill
Genl Mgr: Ben Eison

HUDSON TECHNOLOGIES
See HUDSON TOOL & DIE CO INC

D-U-N-S 78-261-9647 IMP
▲ HUDSON TECHNOLOGIES INC
1 Blue Hill Plz Ste 1541, Pearl River, NY 10965-3110
Tel (845) 735-6000 *Founded/Ownrshp* 1991
Sales 55.8MM *EMP* 131^E
Tkr Sym HDSN *Exch* NAS
SIC 7623 Refrigeration service & repair; Refrigeration service & repair
Ch Bd: Kevin J Zugibe
**Pr:* Brian F Coleman
CFO: James R Buscemi
VP: Stephen P Mandracchia
VP Sls: Charles F Harkins Jr
Board of Directors: Vincent P Abbatecola, Dominic J Monetta, Otto C Morch, Richard Parrillo, Eric A Prouty

D-U-N-S 05-488-0216
HUDSON TOOL & DIE CO INC (MI)
HUDSON TECHNOLOGIES
(*Suby of* JSJ CORP) ★
1327 N Us Highway 1, Ormond Beach, FL 32174-2900
Tel (386) 672-2000 *Founded/Ownrshp* 1940, 1984
Sales 63.3MM^E *EMP* 220
SIC 3469 Metal stampings; Metal stampings
Pr: Bret Schmitz
**Pr:* Mark Andrews
VP: Barry Lemay
CTO: Paul Clare
Ql Cn Mgr: Bradley Schuh

HUDSON TOYOTA
See HUDSON MOTORS PARTNERSHIP

D-U-N-S 05-736-4986
HUDSON TRAIL OUTFITTERS LTD
HTO
12085 Rockville Pike, Rockville, MD 20852-1603
Tel (240) 268-0797 *Founded/Ownrshp* 1971
Sales 23.3MM^E *EMP* 200
SIC 5941 Sporting goods & bicycle shops; Bait & tackle
Pr: Henry F Cohan
**CFO:* Susan Strain
**Treas:* Stacey Cohan
**VP:* Gale Cohan

D-U-N-S 01-141-5296
HUDSON TRANSIT LINES INC
SHORTLINE
(*Suby of* COACH USA INC) ★
66 Tetz Rd, Chester, NY 10918-1830
Tel (201) 529-3666 *Founded/Ownrshp* 1998
Sales 26.0MM^E *EMP* 345
SIC 4131 Interstate bus line; Interstate bus line
Pr: George Grieve

D-U-N-S 06-106-6569
HUDSON UNITED BANK (NJ)
(*Suby of* TD BANK US HOLDING CO) ★
1000 Macarthur Blvd, Mahwah, NJ 07430-2035
Tel (201) 236-2600 *Founded/Ownrshp* 1890, 2004
Sales NA *EMP* 1,280
SIC 6141 6022 Personal credit institutions; State commercial banks; Personal credit institutions; State commercial banks
Pr: Kenneth T Neilson
Ex VP: James Mayo
Ex VP: James W Nall

HUDSON VALLEY APPLE PRODUCTS
See BROOKLYN BOTTLING OF MILTON NEW YORK INC

D-U-N-S 03-048-3531
HUDSON VALLEY BANK
21 Scarsdale Rd, Yonkers, NY 10707-3204
Tel (914) 961-6100 *Founded/Ownrshp* 1972
Sales NA *EMP* 418
SIC 6029 Commercial banks

D-U-N-S 02-066-3415
HUDSON VALLEY COMMUNITY COLLEGE
(*Suby of* STATE UNIVERSITY OF NEW YORK) ★
80 Vandenburgh Ave Ste 1, Troy, NY 12180-6096
Tel (518) 629-4822 *Founded/Ownrshp* 1953
Sales 40.8MM *EMP* 1,200^E
Accts Uhy Llp Albany New York
SIC 8222 9411 Community college; Administration of educational programs; ; Community college; Administration of educational programs;
Pr: Andrew J Matonak
Bd of Dir: Kelly Klopfer
Ofcr: Steven Denio
Ofcr: David Plunkett
VP: William Jojo
IT Man: Maureen Ferraro-Davis

D-U-N-S 18-173-6547
HUDSON VALLEY FEDERAL CREDIT UNION
137 Boardman Rd, Poughkeepsie, NY 12603-4821
Tel (845) 463-3011 *Founded/Ownrshp* 1963
Sales NA *EMP* 875^E
SIC 6061 Federal credit unions; Federal credit unions
Pr: Mary D Madden
CFO: Elizabeth Lisikatos
Cfo: Betty Moran
Ofcr: Keith Hamilton
Ofcr: Michele Rizzi
VP: John Dwyer
VP: Shannon Harkins
VP: Lisa Malone
VP: Chelen Reyes
VP: Tony Rohrmeier
Brnch Mgr: Julie Barr

D-U-N-S 11-279-0803
HUDSON VALLEY HOLDING CORP
21 Scarsdale Rd, Yonkers, NY 10707-3204
Tel (914) 961-6100 *Founded/Ownrshp* 1982
Sales NA *EMP* 421^E
SIC 6022 State commercial banks

D-U-N-S 07-667-4787
HUDSON VALLEY HOSPITAL CENTER
1980 Crompond Rd, Cortlandt Manor, NY 10567-4182
Tel (914) 737-9000 *Founded/Ownrshp* 1889
Sales 153.2MM *EMP* 527^E
Accts Vanacoredebenedictusdigovanni&
SIC 8062 General medical & surgical hospitals; General medical & surgical hospitals
Ch Bd: Edward Macdonald
**Pr:* John C Federspiel
**V Ch Bd:* Minerva Benjamin Abramson
Dir Sec: Kevin McConville
Doctor: David Horgan MD
Pharmcst: Joseph Barletti
Pharmcst: Dominick Corbi

HUDSON- SHARP MACHINE COMPANY
See THIELE TECHNOLOGIES INC

D-U-N-S 78-878-1362
HUDSON-RPM DISTRIBUTORS LLC
150 Blackstone River Rd # 6, Worcester, MA 01607-1482
Tel (617) 328-9500 *Founded/Ownrshp* 1999
Sales 173.7MM^E *EMP* 700
SIC 5192 Magazines; Magazines
Opers Mgr: Dave Dwelly
Mktg Dir: Chris Tracy

D-U-N-S 02-795-2196 IMP
HUDSON-SHARP MACHINE CO
(*Suby of* HUDSON- SHARP MACHINE CO) ★
975 Lombardi Ave, Green Bay, WI 54304-3735
Tel (920) 494-4571 *Founded/Ownrshp* 2009
Sales 62.9MM^E *EMP* 200
SIC 3565 3556 3554 3555 Wrapping machines; Food products machinery; Paper industries machinery; Printing trades machinery; Wrapping machines; Food products machinery; Paper industries machinery; Printing trades machinery
Ch Bd: Stewart Kohl
**Pr:* Kim Davis
**CFO:* Gary Reinert
Dir IT: Matthew Tordeur
**VP Mktg:* Dennis Ankcorn
**VP Mktg:* Johan Mertens
Sls Mgr: Raymundo Ortega

D-U-N-S 78-000-7410
HUDSONALPHA INSTITUTE FOR BIOTECHNOLOGY
601 Genome Way, Huntsville, AL 35806-2908
Tel (256) 971-5998 *Founded/Ownrshp* 2004
Sales 35.7MM *EMP* 155
SIC 8733 Noncommercial research organizations; Noncommercial research organizations
Pr: Richard M Myers
**CFO:* Traci Tyree
VP: John De Michele
VP: Elizabeth Newton
VP: Pete Yanul
Dir Soc: Tiffany McDaniel
Dir IT: Scott Couch
Mtls Mgr: Robert Shanafelt
Mktg Dir: Beth Pugh
Snr Mgr: Mike Frizzell
Snr Mgr: David Sims

D-U-N-S 78-598-9109
HUDSONS BAY TRADING CO LP
3 Manhattanville Rd, Purchase, NY 10577-2116
Tel (914) 694-4444 *Founded/Ownrshp* 2009
Sales 625.8MM^E *EMP* 9,000^E
SIC 5311 Department stores, non-discount; Department stores, non-discount
Mng Pt: Richard Baker
Pt: Robert Baker
Pt: Francis Casale
Pt: Donald Hutchison
Pt: Christina Johnson
Pt: William Mack
Pt: Lee Neibart
Pt: Brian Pall
Pt: Donald Watros
Board of Directors: Donald Watros

D-U-N-S 05-829-3549 IMP
HUDSONS FURNITURE SHOWROOM INC
3290 W 1st St, Sanford, FL 32771-8845
Tel (407) 708-5635 *Founded/Ownrshp* 1982
Sales 23.4MM^E *EMP* 70
SIC 5712 Furniture stores
Pr: Fred C Hudson
**CFO:* Joseph C Ellingham

HUDSON'S SUPERMARKET
See G W FOODS INC

HUDSONVILLE BOX & BASKET DIV
See FARMERS COOPERATIVE ELEVATOR CO

D-U-N-S 08-589-8450
HUDSONVILLE PUBLIC SCHOOLS INC (MI)
3886 Van Buren St, Hudsonville, MI 49426-1038
Tel (616) 669-1740 *Founded/Ownrshp* 1910
Sales 34.8MM^E *EMP* 525
SIC 8211 Public elementary & secondary schools; School board; Public elementary & secondary schools; School board
Instr Medi: Linda Boeve
Psych: Ronald Derrer

D-U-N-S 18-557-4436
HUDSPETH & ASSOCIATES INC
4775 S Santa Fe Cir, Englewood, CO 80110-6477
Tel (303) 791-5562 *Founded/Ownrshp* 2005
Sales 20.7MM^E *EMP* 75
SIC 1521 Single-family housing construction
Pr: Robert M Levitt
COO: Foster Kenney
Dir Bus: Allen Gallogly
Off Mgr: Esmeralda Garcia
Sfty Dirs: Jerry McFadden
Opers Mgr: Dave Vangraefschepe

D-U-N-S 04-620-0424
HUDSPETH COUNTY
HUDSPETH COUNTY COURTHOUSE
109 Millican St, Sierra Blanca, TX 79851
Tel (915) 369-2321 *Founded/Ownrshp* 1918
Sales NA *EMP* 290
SIC 9111 County supervisors' & executives' offices; ; County supervisors' & executives' offices;
Prin: Jim Kiehne
Brnch Mgr: Juan Gomez

HUDSPETH COUNTY COURTHOUSE
See HUDSPETH COUNTY

HUDSPETH GROUP HOME
See HUDSPETH REGIONAL CENTER

D-U-N-S 11-303-3323
HUDSPETH REGIONAL CENTER
HUDSPETH GROUP HOME
3986 Highway 80, Morton, MS 39117-3304
Tel (601) 664-6000 *Founded/Ownrshp* 2003
Sales 13.5MM^E *EMP* 870^E
SIC 8361 Home for the physically handicapped; Home for the physically handicapped
Pr: Nancy Cline
Dir Recs: Lawana Ainsworth

D-U-N-S 01-326-0138
HUEBER-BREUER CONSTRUCTION CO INC
148 Berwyn Ave, Syracuse, NY 13210-3523
Tel (315) 476-7917 *Founded/Ownrshp* 1880
Sales 31.5MM^E *EMP* 75
SIC 1542 Commercial & office building, new construction; Commercial & office buildings, renovation & repair
Pr: James V Breuer
CFO: Joe Cotter
**VP:* J Andrew Breuer
VP: Kenneth Czarnecki
VP: John Kogut
VP: J O Marshall
VP: Otis Marshall
**VP:* Nathan Podkaminer
IT Man: Dave Wilson
Sls&Mrk Ex: Breuer James
Snr PM: Dave Mehlbaum
Board of Directors: James Breuer

HUEBNER CHEVROLET
See CABOL INC

D-U-N-S 96-481-3273 IMP
HUECK FOILS HOLDING CO
(*Suby of* HC BETEILIGUNGSGES. MBH)
1955 State Route 34 3c, Wall Township, NJ 07719-9735
Tel (732) 974-4100 *Founded/Ownrshp* 1995
Sales 64.2MM^E *EMP* 72
Accts Gray Hunter Stenn Llp
SIC 3497 Zinc foil
Pr: Dietmar Wohlfart
Treas: Herbert Schwemmer
CTO: William Smoak
Dir IT: Timothy ManiguaIt

D-U-N-S 10-585-2925
HUEN ELECTRIC INC
1801 W 16th St, Broadview, IL 60155-3955
Tel (708) 343-5511 *Founded/Ownrshp* 1993
Sales 80.6MM^E *EMP* 500
SIC 1731

D-U-N-S 12-113-7785
HUEN NEW YORK INC
6695 Old Collamer Rd, East Syracuse, NY 13057-1232
Tel (315) 432-5060 *Founded/Ownrshp* 2000
Sales 70.2MM^E *EMP* 800
SIC 1731 8711 Electrical work; Engineering services; Electrical work; Engineering services
Ch Bd: Michel F Hughes
VP: Mike Osborne

D-U-N-S 07-881-6758
HUENEME ELEMENTARY SCHOOL DIST
205 N Ventura Rd, Port Hueneme, CA 93041-3065
Tel (805) 488-3588 *Founded/Ownrshp* 1872
Sales 44.6MM^E *EMP* 800
SIC 8211 Public elementary & secondary schools; Public elementary school; Public elementary & secondary schools; Public elementary school
**Ex Dir:* Suzan Henery
IT Man: Nansi McCarroll
Psych: Brian Medel

D-U-N-S 96-275-6748
HUERFANO COUNTY HOSPITAL DISTRICT
SPANISH PEAK REGIONAL HLTH CTR
23500 Us Highway 160, Walsenburg, CO 81089-9524
Tel (719) 738-5186 *Founded/Ownrshp* 1993
Sales 27.0MM *EMP* 260
SIC 8062 General medical & surgical hospitals; General medical & surgical hospitals
IT Man: Cindy Campbell

D-U-N-S 16-956-6502
HUERFANO-LAS ANIMAS AREA COUNCIL OF GOVERNMENTS
SOUTH CNTL COUNCIL GOVERNMENTS
300 S Bonaventure Ave, Trinidad, CO 81082-2047
Tel (719) 846-1133 *Founded/Ownrshp* 1988
Sales 17.5MM^E *EMP* 385
SIC 8322 Geriatric social service; Geriatric social service
Ex Dir: Walt Boulden
**CFO:* Lonnie Medina

D-U-N-S 04-729-8062
HUEY STOCKSTILL INC
HSI READY MIX
130 Huey Stockstill Rd, Picayune, MS 39466-8361
Tel (601) 798-2981 *Founded/Ownrshp* 1960
Sales 57.9MM^E *EMP* 195
Accts Carr Riggs & Ingram Llc R
SIC 1611 3272 Highway & street paving contractor; Building materials, except block or brick: concrete; Highway & street paving contractor; Building materials, except block or brick: concrete
CEO: Huey Stockstill Jr
**Pr:* Huey P Stockstill Sr
**CEO:* Huey P Stockstill Jr
**CFO:* David Stockstill
**VP:* Richard W Stockstill
**VP:* Ricky Stockstill
Off Mgr: Linda Harris

D-U-N-S 95-839-9412
HUEY T LITTLETON CLAIMS SERVICE OF WEST TEXAS INC
LITTLETON GROUP
2224 Walsh Tarlton Ln # 110, Austin, TX 78746-7761
Tel (512) 328-4447 *Founded/Ownrshp* 1985
Sales NA *EMP* 150
SIC 6411 Insurance agents, brokers & service
Pr: Steve Streetman
**VP:* Phil Meaux

D-U-N-S 92-764-4294 IMP
HUF NORTH AMERICA AUTOMOTIVE PARTS MANUFACTURING CORP
(*Suby of* HUF HULSBECK & FURST GMBH & CO. KG)
9020 W Dean Rd, Milwaukee, WI 53224-2853
Tel (414) 365-4950 *Founded/Ownrshp* 1995
Sales 114.7MM^E *EMP* 450
SIC 3714 Motor vehicle parts & accessories; Motor vehicle parts & accessories
Pr: George Haeussler
**CFO:* Leslie Carbine
MIS Dir: Patrick Dickey
IT Man: Daniel Perez
Plnt Mgr: John Brown
Sls Dir: Christopher Buchanan
Sales Asso: Gerri Ruffing

HUFCO
See STACEY SUPPLY CORP

HUFCOR AIRWALL SINCE 1900
See HUFCOR CALIFORNIA INC

D-U-N-S 18-363-5846
HUFCOR CALIFORNIA INC
HUFCOR AIRWALL SINCE 1900
(*Suby of* HUFCOR INC) ★
2380 E Artesia Blvd, Long Beach, CA 90805-1708
Tel (562) 634-3116 *Founded/Ownrshp* 1987
Sales 46.7MM^E *EMP* 600

SIC 2542 5046 Partitions & fixtures, except wood; Partitions; Partitions & fixtures, except wood; Partitions
Pr: Andy Espineira
**CEO:* J Michael Borden
**Ch:* Mike Borden
**Treas:* Frank Scott
Genl Mgr: Michael Dunn
Sls Mgr: Scott Goza

D-U-N-S 00-606-9223 IMP/EXP
HUFCOR INC (WI)
2101 Kennedy Rd, Janesville, WI 53545-0824
Tel (608) 756-1241 *Founded/Ownrshp* 1901, 1978
Sales 135.1MM^E *EMP* 600
SIC 2542 3442

D-U-N-S 00-232-0331 EXP
HUFF PAPER CO (PA)
HUFF UNITED
10 Crk Pky Namns Crk Ctr Namns Crk Cntr, Boothwyn, PA 19061
Tel (610) 497-5100 *Founded/Ownrshp* 1922, 1977
Sales 77.9MM^E *EMP* 75
SIC 5113 Industrial & personal service paper; Bags, paper & disposable plastic; Paper & products, wrapping or coarse; Industrial & personal service paper; Bags, paper & disposable plastic; Paper & products, wrapping or coarse
Ch Bd: W Lloyd Snyder III
**Pr:* Paul Burns
**Ex VP:* Fred Hilbert
**VP:* Robert E Ward
Sls Mgr: Michael Mirarchi

HUFF UNITED
See HUFF PAPER CO

D-U-N-S 02-674-4904
HUFFINES CHEVROLET SUBARU INC
1400 S Stemmons Fwy, Lewisville, TX 75067-6309
Tel (972) 221-8686 *Founded/Ownrshp* 1971
Sales 33.9MM^E *EMP* 100^E
SIC 5511 Automobiles, new & used; Automobiles, new & used
Pr: S Ray Huffines
**CFO:* Eric Harrter
Sls Mgr: Aaron Brown
Sales Asso: Greg Sikes
Sales Asso: Scott Spiegel

HUFFINES CHEVY
See HUFFINES HYUNDAI PLANO INC

HUFFINES CHRYSLER DODGE
See HUFFINES DODGE LEWISVILLE INC

D-U-N-S 15-467-6134
HUFFINES DODGE LEWISVILLE INC
HUFFINES CHRYSLER DODGE
1024 S Stemmons Fwy, Lewisville, TX 75067-5354
Tel (972) 434-2288 *Founded/Ownrshp* 1985
Sales 43.4MM^E *EMP* 111
SIC 5511 Automobiles, new & used; Automobiles, new & used
Pr: S Ray Huffines
**Pr:* J L Huffines Jr
**Pr:* James R Huffines
**CFO:* Eric Hartter
Ex Dir: Joe McBeth

D-U-N-S 10-515-3857
HUFFINES DODGE PLANO LP
4500 W Plano Pkwy, Plano, TX 75093-5607
Tel (972) 867-6000 *Founded/Ownrshp* 2000
Sales 27.9MM^E *EMP* 100
SIC 5511 Automobiles, new & used; Automobiles, new & used
Mng Pt: Ray Huffines
CFO: Eric Harter
Dir Risk M: Randy Rogers
Genl Mgr: Thomas Hervey
Sls Mgr: Shane Dove
Sls Mgr: Steve Olenak
Sls Mgr: Larry Smith
Sales Asso: Greg Gulotta
Sales Asso: Bud Johnson
Sales Asso: Brett Kelley

D-U-N-S 61-016-7066
HUFFINES HYUNDAI PLANO INC
HUFFINES CHEVY
909 Coit Rd, Plano, TX 75075-5812
Tel (972) 867-5000 *Founded/Ownrshp* 1984
Sales 38.8MM^E *EMP* 119
SIC 5511 Automobiles, new & used; Automobiles, new & used
Pr: S Ray Huffines
**CFO:* Eric Hartter
Exec: Eddie Erangy
Exec: Tom Hollett

D-U-N-S 00-315-8151 IMP
HUFFMAN FINISHING CO INC (NC)
4919 Hickory Blvd, Granite Falls, NC 28630-8390
Tel (828) 396-1741 *Founded/Ownrshp* 1945
Sales 28.6MM^E *EMP* 300
SIC 2252 2251 2262 2261 Dyeing & finishing hosiery; Men's, boys' & girls' hosiery; Women's hosiery, except socks; Finishing plants, manmade fiber & silk fabrics; Finishing plants, cotton; Dyeing & finishing hosiery; Men's, boys' & girls' hosiery; Women's hosiery, except socks; Finishing plants, manmade fiber & silk fabrics; Finishing plants, cotton
Pr: A W Huffman Jr
**VP:* A W Huffman III
**VP:* Paul Marshall

D-U-N-S 03-777-8693
HUFFMAN INDEPENDENT SCHOOL DISTRICT
HUFFMAN ISD
24302 Fm 2100 Rd, Huffman, TX 77336-2657
Tel (281) 324-1871 *Founded/Ownrshp* 1969
Sales 25.7MM^E *EMP* 400
SIC 8211 Public elementary & secondary schools; Public junior high school; Public senior high school; Public elementary & secondary schools; Public junior high school; Public senior high school
**CFO:* Tim Brittain
Dir Sec: Shannon Jones
HC Dir: Holly Oliphant

HUFFMAN ISD
See HUFFMAN INDEPENDENT SCHOOL DISTRICT

D-U-N-S 02-444-6916
HUFFMAN OIL CO INCORPORATION (NC)
1021 Queen Ann St, Burlington, NC 27217-7040
Tel (336) 227-8881 *Founded/Ownrshp* 1932, 1966
Sales 50.2MM^E *EMP* 268
SIC 5172 5541 5411 5983

D-U-N-S 80-095-9082
HUFFMASTER MANAGEMENT INC
1300 Combermere Dr, Troy, MI 48083-2703
Tel (248) 588-1600 *Founded/Ownrshp* 1989
Sales 26.4MM^E *EMP* 200
SIC 8741 8742 7381 Management services; Management consulting services; Detective & armored car services; Management services; Management consulting services; Detective & armored car services
CEO: Raymond E Huffmaster
Pr: Peter Johnson
VP Sls: Craig Cassady

HUFFY BICYCLE COMPANY
See HUFFY CORP

D-U-N-S 00-424-6500 IMP/EXP
HUFFY CORP (OH)
HUFFY BICYCLE COMPANY
6551 Centervl Bus Pkwy, Centerville, OH 45459-2686
Tel (937) 865-2800 *Founded/Ownrshp* 1928
Sales 50.2MM^E *EMP* 106
Accts Kpmg Llp Cincinnati Oh
SIC 3949 3751 Basketball equipment & supplies, general; Motor scooters & parts; Basketball equipment & supplies, general; Motor scooters & parts
Pr: William A Smith
Ch Bd: Zhidong Liang
Pr: John Collins
CFO: Steven D Lipton
Sr VP: Nancy A Michaud
VP: Dave Duff
VP: John Fowler
VP: Gary Gombita
VP: Timothy G Howard
VP: Tim Lavallee
VP: Michael Ogara
Board of Directors: Raymond Kintzley Andb Barr, Michael Buenzow, Kenny Chou

D-U-N-S 79-705-1885
HUG CO
GOURMET FOODS
(*Suby of* GOURMET FOODS INC) ★
2557 Barrington Ct, Hayward, CA 94545-1174
Tel (510) 887-0340 *Founded/Ownrshp* 1988
Sales 22.8MM^E *EMP* 90
SIC 5141 Food brokers; Food brokers
Pr: Uwe Henze

D-U-N-S 84-085-8554
■ **HUGE LLC**
(*Suby of* INTERPUBLIC GROUP OF COMPANIES INC) ★
45 Main St Ste 220, Brooklyn, NY 11201-1019
Tel (718) 625-4843 *Founded/Ownrshp* 2000
Sales 74.0MM^E *EMP* 350
SIC 7371 Custom computer programming services; Custom computer programming services
CEO: Aaron Shapiro
Pr: Jarrod Bull
VP: Holly Petitjean
VP: Mike Russell
Exec: Natalie Taylor
Assoc Dir: Stephen Chan
Creative D: Richard Bloom
Creative D: Ian Burns
Creative D: Jessie Caldwell
Creative D: Martha Dixon
Creative D: Lucas Hirata
Creative D: Kurt Jaskowiak
Creative D: Ryan Kellogg
Creative D: Mick Sutter
Creative D: Chad Tafolla
Creative D: Blake Tannery
Creative D: Andy Thomas
Creative D: Dave Tupper
Creative D: Tom Westerlin
Comm Dir: Michelle Pulman
Comm Man: Laura Fanjoy

D-U-N-S 05-196-1589 IMP
HUGG AND HALL EQUIPMENT CO (AR)
7201 Scott Hamilton Dr, Little Rock, AR 72209-3147
Tel (501) 562-1262 *Founded/Ownrshp* 1970
Sales 235.5MM^E *EMP* 318
Accts Ferguson Cobb & Associates P
SIC 5084 5082 7353 7699 5083 3531 Industrial machinery & equipment; Lift trucks & parts; Materials handling machinery; Road construction equipment; General construction machinery & equipment; Heavy construction equipment rental; Industrial machinery & equipment repair; Construction equipment repair; Landscaping equipment; Backhoes, tractors, cranes, plows & similar equipment; Industrial machinery & equipment; Lift trucks & parts; Materials handling machinery; Road construction equipment; General construction machinery & equipment; Heavy construction equipment rental; Industrial machinery & equipment repair; Construction equipment repair; Landscaping equipment; Backhoes, tractors, cranes, plows & similar equipment
Ch: John C Hugg
**Pr:* Robert M Hall
**Treas:* John Hugg
VP: Jonathan Brown
**VP:* Mike Clark
VP: Jim Hancock
VP: Rod Rhodes
VP: Karen Smith
VP: Tim Waychoff
Admn Mgr: Michelle Morris
Brnch Mgr: Jim Greenlee

HUGGINS HONDA
See GENE HUGGINS IMPORTS INC

D-U-N-S 07-396-2466
HUGGINS HOSPITAL
240 S Main St, Wolfeboro, NH 03894-4455
Tel (603) 569-7500 *Founded/Ownrshp* 1907
Sales 44.2MM *EMP* 480
SIC 8062 General medical & surgical hospitals; General medical & surgical hospitals
Treas: William Marsh
Pr: John Hammond
COO: Angela Closson
CFO: Jeremy Roberge
VP: Sandra McKenzie
Exec: Maureen Vaccaro
Dir Lab: Michael Wilkes
Dir Soc: Jerry Vasil
Dir Rx: Lee Carver
Doctor: Issam Bizri MD
Doctor: Martin Boucher

HUGH CHATHAM MEM HOSP NURSING
See HUGH CHATHAM MEMORIAL HOSPITAL INC

D-U-N-S 06-744-1436
HUGH CHATHAM MEMORIAL HOSPITAL INC
HUGH CHATHAM MEM HOSP NURSING
180 Parkwood Dr, Elkin, NC 28621-2430
Tel (336) 835-3722 *Founded/Ownrshp* 1929
Sales 96.3MM *EMP* 750
SIC 8062 8051 8361 General medical & surgical hospitals; Convalescent home with continuous nursing care; Geriatric residential care; General medical & surgical hospitals; Convalescent home with continuous nursing care; Geriatric residential care
CEO: Paul H Hammes
COO: Lee Powe
CFO: Mary Greene
Bd of Dir: Judy Snyder
Dir Lab: Diane Rocotta
Chf Nrs Of: Donna Parsons
Dir Sec: Brent Slate
CTO: Robert Peterson
QC Dir: Charlotte Lawson
Pharmcst: James Hobeck
Pharmcst: Eugenia Key

D-U-N-S 94-591-2756
HUGH DUNCAN & ASSOCIATES INC
26908 Mlibu Cove Colny Dr, Malibu, CA 90265-4321
Tel (310) 457-7432 *Founded/Ownrshp* 1995
Sales 150.0MM *EMP* 50
SIC 7311 Advertising consultant; Advertising consultant
CEO: Hugh Duncan
**Pr:* Bobby Wentworth

D-U-N-S 11-745-3514
HUGH M CUNNINGHAM INC
2029 Westgate Dr Ste 120, Carrollton, TX 75006-6474
Tel (972) 888-3808 *Founded/Ownrshp* 1948
Sales 104.1MM^E *EMP* 85
SIC 5074 5085 5083 5199 Plumbing fittings & supplies; Industrial supplies; Irrigation equipment; Architects' supplies (non-durable); Plumbing fittings & supplies; Industrial supplies; Irrigation equipment; Architects' supplies (non-durable)
Pr: David A Cunningham
COO: Hal Haas
VP: Brad Feldman
VP: Mathieu Mark
VP: Dan Townsend
Opers Mgr: Drey Hayford
VP Sls: Ted Parker
Mktg Mgr: Jonathan Bunch
Sls Mgr: Billy Parker
Sales Asso: Patricia Cozart
Sales Asso: Shannon Morykwas

D-U-N-S 01-217-1898 IMP/EXP
HUGH OKANE ELECTRIC CO FIBEROPTICS INC
90 White St, New York, NY 10013-3527
Tel (212) 334-0847 *Founded/Ownrshp* 2011
Sales 32.2MM^E *EMP* 150
SIC 1731 Electrical work; General electrical contractor; Sound equipment specialization; Voice, data & video wiring contractor; Electrical work; General electrical contractor; Sound equipment specialization; Voice, data & video wiring contractor
Ch: Hugh O'Kane
Pr: Michael Joyce
**Pr:* Hugh R Okane
CFO: Michael Brescio
**Ex VP:* Kevin O'Kane
**VP:* Larry Lundy
**VP:* John O'Kane
VP: Dennis Oliva
Snr Mgr: Chen Sridhar

D-U-N-S 07-647-7801
HUGH WOOD INC
55 Broadway Fl 24, New York, NY 10006-3747
Tel (212) 509-3777 *Founded/Ownrshp* 1982
Sales NA *EMP* 52
SIC 6411 Insurance brokers
Ch: Hugh W Wood
**V Ch:* Kenneth F Lennon
Treas: Leonard Eisenberg
Ex VP: Gary Ferrazzano
**Ex VP:* Jack Fisher
Ex VP: Jack R Fisher
**Ex VP:* Libor Hon
Sr VP: Jill Bull
Sr VP: Tom Garone
Sr VP: Richard Haverlin
**Sr VP:* Takahito Ishikawa
Sr VP: Anthony Marangiello
Sr VP: Edwin Porter
Sr VP: Heidi Solem
VP: Mike Salazar
VP: Catherine Theologis
VP: Elliot Williams

D-U-N-S 07-673-3880
HUGHES & LUCE LLP
1201 Elm St, Dallas, TX 75270-2102
Tel (214) 319-6067 *Founded/Ownrshp* 1973
Sales 16.7MM^E *EMP* 300
SIC 8111 General practice attorney, lawyer; General practice attorney, lawyer
Genl Pt: Edward Coultas
Owner: John W Patton
Pt: Aaron R Allred
Pt: Robert E Davis
Pt: Floyd R Hartley Jr
Pt: Scott Kline
Pt: G James Landon
Pt: Weston C Loegering
Pt: Gregory P Sapire
Pt: Keith A Shuley
Pt: Kirk P Watson

D-U-N-S 00-727-3279 IMP/EXP
HUGHES BROTHERS INC
210 N 13th St, Seward, NE 68434-1900
Tel (402) 643-2991 *Founded/Ownrshp* 1921
Sales 3.4MM^E *EMP* 295
SIC 2499 3441 3082

D-U-N-S 05-954-8458
HUGHES CIRCUITS INC
HCI
546 S Pacific St, San Marcos, CA 92078-4070
Tel (760) 744-0300 *Founded/Ownrshp* 1999
Sales 61.5MM^E *EMP* 185
SIC 3672 Printed circuit boards; Printed circuit boards
CEO: Barbara Hughes
**Pr:* Jerry Hughes
**VP:* Michelle Glatts
**VP:* Joe Hughes
**Prin:* Jeff Hughes

D-U-N-S 60-612-2138
■ **HUGHES COMMUNICATIONS INC**
(*Suby of* ECHOSTAR SATELLITE SERVICES LLC) ★
11717 Exploration Ln, Germantown, MD 20876-2711
Tel (301) 428-5500 *Founded/Ownrshp* 2011
Sales 1.3MM *EMP* 2,254
SIC 4813 4899 3663 Telephone communication, except radio; Data telephone communications; ; Satellite earth stations; Satellites, communications; Space satellite communications equipment; Telephone communication, except radio; Data telephone communications; ; Satellite earth stations; Satellites, communications; Space satellite communications equipment
Pr: Pradman P Kaul
CFO: Grant A Barber
Treas: Deepak V Dutt
Treas: Ren Lapidario
Ex VP: Grant A Brber
Ex VP: T Paul Gaske
Ex VP: Adrian Morris
Ex VP: Bahram Pourmand
Sr VP: Bob Buschman
Sr VP: John Corrigan
Sr VP: Dan Fraley
Sr VP: Dean A Manson
Sr VP: John McEwan
Sr VP: Dave Zatloukal
VP: Edward Fitzpatrick
VP: Steven Kee

D-U-N-S 01-858-3922
■ **HUGHES CORP**
HOWARD HUGHES REALTY
(*Suby of* ROUSE CO LP) ★
10801 W Charleston Blvd # 300, Las Vegas, NV 89135-1200
Tel (702) 791-4000 *Founded/Ownrshp* 1996
Sales 191.7MM *EMP* 70
SIC 6552 Subdividers & developers; Subdividers & developers
Pr: Kevin T Orrock
Assoc VP: Jeff Geen
Ex VP: W S Gibbons
Sr VP: Peggy Chandler
VP: Chuck Kubat
VP: John Potts
VP: Michelle Waak
Comm Man: Michael Fredericks
Ex Dir: Randy Ecklund
Genl Couns: Peter Riley
Genl Couns: Sandra Turner
Board of Directors: John Goolsby, William R Lummis, E R Vacchina, Milton H West Jr

D-U-N-S 04-106-9006
HUGHES CORP
WESCHLER INSTRUMENTS
16900 Foltz Pkwy, Strongsville, OH 44149-5520
Tel (954) 755-7111 *Founded/Ownrshp* 1968
Sales 40.1MM^E *EMP* 100
SIC 5063 3825 Electrical apparatus & equipment; Instruments to measure electricity; Electrical apparatus & equipment; Instruments to measure electricity
Pr: David E Hughes
**Ex VP:* Michael F Dorman
Sr VP: Matthew Hughes
**VP:* Douglas Hughes
**Prin:* Esther Carpenter
Manager: Ron Wood

D-U-N-S 04-476-9651
HUGHES DAN A CO LP (TX)
DAN A. HUGHES COMPANY
208 E Houston St, Beeville, TX 78102-4820
Tel (361) 358-3752 *Founded/Ownrshp* 1960, 1987
Sales 29.5MM^E *EMP* 30
SIC 1311 Crude petroleum production; Natural gas production
Pt: Dan A Hughes Sr
Pt: Dan A Hughes Jr
Off Mgr: Jim Scott
IT Man: Larry Cantrell

D-U-N-S 06-622-2308 IMP
HUGHES ENTERPRISES INC
CUSTOM APPL WHOLESALERS DIV
300 W North Ave Ste A, Lombard, IL 60148-1255
Tel (630) 932-4700 *Founded/Ownrshp* 1961
Sales 79.9MM^E *EMP* 150
SIC 5087 7215 5064 Laundry equipment & supplies; Laundry, coin-operated; Electrical appliances, television & radio; Ranges; Microwave ovens, non-commercial; Dishwashers; Laundry equipment & supplies; Laundry, coin-operated; Electrical appliances, television & radio; Ranges; Microwave ovens, non-commercial; Dishwashers
Pr: Gordon S Hughes
Exec: Bruce Levin

D-U-N-S 79-442-4937
HUGHES ENTERPRISES INC
2 Industrial Dr, Trenton, NJ 08619-3298
Tel (609) 586-7200 *Founded/Ownrshp* 1988
Sales 22.0MM^E *EMP* 35
Accts Altenburger Uris Caglioti &
SIC 5087 5199 Janitors' supplies; Packaging materials; Janitors' supplies; Packaging materials
Pr: Stephen L Polin
Ex VP: Jon Knee
Ex VP: Neal Magaziner
IT Man: Robert Weber

D-U-N-S 10-402-8162
HUGHES FEDERAL CREDIT UNION INC
971 W Wetmore Rd, Tucson, AZ 85705-1551
Tel (520) 205-5605 *Founded/Ownrshp* 1951
Sales NA *EMP* 150
SIC 6061 Federal credit unions; Federal credit unions
Pr: Robert Swick
Ch: John Sansbury
Bd of Dir: Juan Gonzalez
Sr VP: Joseph Rose
VP: Andrew Britton
IT Man: Michael Rogers
S&M/VP: Ke Terhune
Mktg Mgr: Kathy Hippensteel
Mktg Mgr: Elisa Ross

D-U-N-S 08-485-4442
HUGHES FURNITURE INDUSTRIES INC
U EDGE FURNITURES
101 Fox St, Randleman, NC 27317-1863
Tel (336) 498-6200 *Founded/Ownrshp* 2002
Sales 60.0MM *EMP* 2
SIC 5023 Slip covers (furniture); Slip covers (furniture)
Pr: Bruce Hughes

D-U-N-S 60-623-1363 IMP/EXP
HUGHES FURNITURE INDUSTRIES INC
H F I
952 S Stout Rd, Randleman, NC 27317-7638
Tel (336) 498-8700 *Founded/Ownrshp* 2002
Sales 92.0MM^E *EMP* 337
SIC 2512 7641 2426 Living room furniture: upholstered on wood frames; Upholstery work; Furniture stock & parts, hardwood; Living room furniture: upholstered on wood frames; Upholstery work; Furniture stock & parts, hardwood
VP: Bruce Hughes
**Prin:* Rita Spencer
DP Dir: Jim Crawford
Sales Exec: Dean Hoover

D-U-N-S 14-256-2102
HUGHES GENERAL CONTRACTORS INC
900 N Redwood Rd, North Salt Lake, UT 84054-2627
Tel (801) 292-1411 *Founded/Ownrshp* 2001
Sales 34.8MM^E *EMP* 99
SIC 1542 Nonresidential construction; Nonresidential construction
Pr: Todd A Hughes
**Treas:* Glenn E Hughes
Chf Mktg O: Allen Clemons
VP: John Burggraf
**VP:* Scott G Hughes
Exec: Travis Davis
Mtls Mgr: Doug Allred
Sfty Mgr: Monty Mortensen

D-U-N-S 19-285-0717
HUGHES GROUP INC
6200 E Highway 62 # 100, Jeffersonville, IN 47130-8769
Tel (812) 285-4156 *Founded/Ownrshp* 1949
Sales 41.0MM^E *EMP* 120
SIC 1622 1623 1795 1771 5013 Bridge construction; Highway construction, elevated; Water, sewer & utility lines; Wrecking & demolition work; Concrete work; Automotive supplies & parts; Automotive servicing equipment; Bridge construction; Highway construction, elevated; Water, sewer & utility lines; Wrecking & demolition work; Concrete work; Automotive supplies & parts; Automotive servicing equipment
CEO: James P Hughes
**CEO:* George E Hughes Jr
**CFO:* Roger W Denny

D-U-N-S 94-703-3999
HUGHES GROUP LLC
HG SOLTNS DIA-MO CLEAN TOP
3701 S Lawrence St, Tacoma, WA 98409-5717
Tel (253) 588-2626 *Founded/Ownrshp* 1999
Sales 21.2MM^E *EMP* 153
SIC 8742 Management consulting services; Management consulting services
VP: Michael Hampson

D-U-N-S 96-704-6558
HUGHES HARDWOOD INTERNATIONAL INC
500 Highway 13 S, Collinwood, TN 38450-4693
Tel (931) 724-6258 *Founded/Ownrshp* 1925
Sales 25.0MM^E *EMP* 120
SIC 5031 Lumber, plywood & millwork; Lumber, plywood & millwork
Pr: William H Hughes
**VP:* Parkes Hughes

D-U-N-S 07-327-4185
HUGHES HUBBARD & REED LLP
(*Suby of* HUGUES HUBBARD ET REED)
1 Battery Park, New York, NY 10004-1438
Tel (212) 837-6000 *Founded/Ownrshp* 1925
Sales 120.2MM^E *EMP* 766
SIC 8111 General practice attorney, lawyer; General practice attorney, lawyer
Pt: Charles H Scherer
Pt: William L Allinder
Pt: Ned H Bassen
Pt: Candace Beinecke
Pt: George A Davidson
Pt: Merrikay S Hall
Pt: John K Hoyns
Pt: Norman C Kleinberg
Pt: Theodore H Latty
Pt: Kenneth A Lefkowitz
Pt: William R Maguire
Pt: Timothy J McCarthy
Pt: James Modlin
Pt: Yasuo Okamoto
Pt: William R Stein
Pt: Nick Swerdloff
Mng Pt: Theodore V H Mayer
COO: Gerard F Cruse
CFO: Frederick O'Dea

HUGHES KITCHEN & BATH COLLECTN
See HUGHES SUPPLY INC

D-U-N-S 03-291-4608
HUGHES LUMBER CO
5611 Bird Creek Ave, Catoosa, OK 74015-3006
Tel (918) 266-9140 *Founded/Ownrshp* 1960
Sales 23.6MM^E *EMP* 90
SIC 5211 Lumber & other building materials
Pr: Robert L Hughes
**Ch:* Thomas J Hughes III
**VP:* Tammy Rubin
Sales Asso: Garrett Sullivan

D-U-N-S 00-785-6495
HUGHES MACHINERY CO (MO)
(*Suby of* FCX PERFORMANCE INC) ★
14400 College Blvd, Lenexa, KS 66215-2063
Tel (913) 492-0355 *Founded/Ownrshp* 1924, 2011
Sales 25.9MM^E *EMP* 65
SIC 5084 5074 Industrial machinery & equipment; Boilers, power (industrial); Industrial machinery & equipment; Boilers, power (industrial)
Pr: Tim Powell
**CFO:* Jill Peterson
VP: Dave Fisher
Opers Mgr: Sara Andersen
Opers Mgr: Jeff Flora
Sls Mgr: Jim Wonderly
Sales Asso: Darren Garrison
Sales Asso: Ron Hampton
Sales Asso: Gary Iseminger
Sales Asso: Seth Junge

D-U-N-S 03-608-2428
HUGHES MOTORS INC (SC)
6841 Bulldog Dr, Charleston, SC 29406-4733
Tel (843) 553-6410 *Founded/Ownrshp* 1939, 1957
Sales 30.3MM^E *EMP* 60
SIC 5511 New & used car dealers; New & used car dealers
Ch Bd: X O Bunch Jr
**Pr:* David W Bunch
**CFO:* James W Youmans
**Ex VP:* W Dexter X O Bunch
**VP:* Wayne Geiger
**Prin:* Julian Garris
IT Man: Jim McKelvey

D-U-N-S 62-142-5867
■ **HUGHES NETWORK SYSTEMS INTERNATIONAL SERVICES CO INC**
(*Suby of* HUGHES NETWORK SYSTEMS LLC) ★
11717 Exploration Ln, Germantown, MD 20876-2799
Tel (301) 428-5500 *Founded/Ownrshp* 2001
Sales 30.2MM^E *EMP* 60
SIC 4899 Communication signal enhancement network system
CEO: Pradmin Kaul
Pr: Lin-Nan Lee
Sr VP: John Kenyon
Sr VP: Vinod Shukla
VP: Dan Hamel
Creative D: Chuck Keeler
Prgrm Mgr: Dave Ehrlinger
Snr Sftwr: Yi Liu
Snr Sftwr: Sonia Thakur
QA Dir: Rafael Delgado
Dir IT: Richard Magin

D-U-N-S 05-688-6380 IMP
■ **HUGHES NETWORK SYSTEMS LLC**
(*Suby of* HUGHES COMMUNICATIONS INC) ★
11717 Exploration Ln, Germantown, MD 20876-2799
Tel (301) 428-5500 *Founded/Ownrshp* 2005
Sales 120.0MM *EMP* 1,924
SIC 4899 Data communication services; Data communication services
Pr: Pradman P Kaul
COO: Bill Humes
COO: Chuck McClain
COO: Sylvia McLaughlin
CFO: Ilya Alter
**CFO:* Grant A Barber
CFO: James Lucchese
**Treas:* Deepak V Dutt
Treas: Deepak Dutt
Bd of Dir: Michael T Dugan
Assoc VP: Ashok D Mehta
Ex VP: Grant A Brber
Ex VP: Adrian Morris
Ex VP: Bahram Pourmand
Sr VP: Sandi Kerentoff
**Sr VP:* Dean A Manson
**Sr VP:* Thomas J McElroy
VP: Robert O Feierbach
Exec: Dennis Conti
Board of Directors: Andrew D Africk, Jeffrey A Leddy, Aaron J Stone

HUGHES PARKER INDUSTRIES
See JM CONSOLIDATED INDUSTRIES LLC

D-U-N-S 08-607-7950
HUGHES PETROLEUM PRODUCTS INC
103 N Home St, Corrigan, TX 75939-2552
Tel (936) 398-2840 *Founded/Ownrshp* 1978
Sales 25.0MM^E *EMP* 50
SIC 5172 Petroleum products; Petroleum products
Pr: Marlin W Hughes

D-U-N-S 07-835-6154
HUGHES SATELLITE SYSTEMS CORP
100 Inverness Ter E, Englewood, CO 80112-5308
Tel (303) 706-4000 *Founded/Ownrshp* 2012
Sales 1.8MMM *EMP* 2
Accts Kpmg Llp Denver Colorado
SIC 4813 ;
CEO: Michael T Dugan

D-U-N-S 13-120-0297
HUGHES SUPPLY CO
HSC INDUSTRIAL
300 Rural Acres Dr, Beckley, WV 25801-3041
Tel (304) 252-1918 *Founded/Ownrshp* 1985
Sales 28.0MM^E *EMP* 53
SIC 1731 Energy management controls; Energy management controls
Pr: Thomas T Hughes
**Sec:* Jane Hughes
**VP:* John Hughes

D-U-N-S 00-692-3205 EXP
HUGHES SUPPLY INC
HUGHES KITCHEN & BATH COLLECTN
(*Suby of* HAJOCA CORP) ★
1 Hughes Way, Orlando, FL 32805
Tel (407) 841-4755 *Founded/Ownrshp* 2011
Sales 221.8MM^E *EMP* 3,500
SIC 5063 5074 5075 5085 Electrical apparatus & equipment; Electronic wire & cable; Wiring devices; Conduits & raceways; Plumbing & hydronic heating supplies; Pipes & fittings, plastic; Plumbing & heating valves; Warm air heating & air conditioning; Industrial supplies; Electrical apparatus & equipment; Electronic wire & cable; Wiring devices; Conduits & raceways; Plumbing & hydronic heating supplies; Pipes & fittings, plastic; Plumbing & heating valves; Warm air heating & air conditioning; Industrial supplies
CEO: Thomas I Morgan
**CFO:* David Bearman
**Ch:* David H Hughes
Ofcr: David English
Mktg Mgr: Jenny Kemphaget
Sales Asso: Edwards Cristina
Sales Asso: Chuck Prickett

D-U-N-S 80-705-2563
HUGHES TELEMATICS INC
2002 Summit Blvd Ste 1800, Brookhaven, GA 30319-1497
Tel (404) 573-5800 *Founded/Ownrshp* 2012
Sales NA *EMP* 374^E
SIC 4899 Data communication services

D-U-N-S 05-395-6066 IMP/EXP
HUGHES-ANDERSON HEAT EXCHANGERS INC
1001 N Fulton Ave, Tulsa, OK 74115-6445
Tel (918) 836-1681 *Founded/Ownrshp* 1971
Sales 37.4MM *EMP* 126
SIC 3443 Heat exchangers: coolers (after, inter), condensers, etc.; Heat exchangers: coolers (after, inter), condensers, etc.
Ch: Monte Stewart
**Pr:* Jeff Gilbert
**CFO:* Michael Longo
**Ex VP:* Kevin Gordon
IT Man: Mike Longo

HUGHES-PETERS
See MJO INDUSTRIES INC

D-U-N-S 08-591-1261
HUGHESLEAHYKARLOVIC INC
HLK
1141 S 7th St, Saint Louis, MO 63104-3623
Tel (314) 571-6300 *Founded/Ownrshp* 1977
Sales 21.1MM^E *EMP* 80
SIC 7311 Advertising consultant
Ch: James Schnurbusch
Mng Pt: Bill Hughes
**Pr:* William Hughes
Chf Mktg O: Ray Ward
**VP:* Joan Hughes
**VP:* Kathy Schrage
Creative D: Joe Leahy
Web Dev: Jacob Fisher
Prd Mgr: Angie Sucher
Mktg Mgr: Toni Edinger
Mktg Mgr: Amy George

D-U-N-S 14-471-9523 IMP/EXP
HUGHSON NUT INC
1825 Verduga Rd, Hughson, CA 95326-9675
Tel (209) 883-0403 *Founded/Ownrshp* 1985
Sales 75.9MM^E *EMP* 375
SIC 2099 Food preparations; Food preparations
Pr: Martin Pohl
CFO: Jeff Mollett
Sr VP: Mory Cobrain
Sfty Mgr: Miguel Lopez
Plnt Mgr: Butch Coburn
Prd Mgr: Ivan Gutierrez

D-U-N-S 07-812-5457
HUGHSTON CLINIC P C
6262 Veterans Pkwy, Columbus, GA 31909-3540
Tel (706) 324-6661 *Founded/Ownrshp* 1949
Sales 54.1MM^E *EMP* 450
SIC 8011 Orthopedic physician; Clinic, operated by physicians; Orthopedic physician; Clinic, operated by physicians
Pr: John Waldrop
CEO: Mark Baker
COO: David Glassburn
CFO: Angela Buchanan
CFO: Chris Wiggins
Ex Dir: Joseph Belle
Ex Dir: Linda Moore
Off Mgr: Erica Huddleston
Surgeon: Augustine Conduah
Surgeon: Garland Gudger
Surgeon: Stefan Sinco

D-U-N-S 96-962-9463
HUGHSTON HOSPITAL INC
707 Center St, Columbus, GA 31901-1575
Tel (706) 660-6303 *Founded/Ownrshp* 2011
Sales 69.3MM *EMP* 27^E
Accts Pershing Yoakley & Associates
SIC 8062 General medical & surgical hospitals; General medical & surgical hospitals
Prin: Vibhuti Ansar
Sr VP: Andrew Morley Jr

D-U-N-S 00-508-6454 IMP
HUGO BOSS CLEVELAND INC
(*Suby of* HUGO BOSS USA INC) ★
200 Public Sq Ste 3820, Cleveland, OH 44114-2321
Tel (216) 671-8100 *Founded/Ownrshp* 1841
Sales 48.7MM^E *EMP* 450
SIC 2311 2325 Suits, men's & boys': made from purchased materials; Tailored dress & sport coats: men's & boys'; Topcoats, men's & boys': made from purchased materials; Men's & boys' trousers & slacks; Suits, men's & boys': made from purchased materials; Tailored dress & sport coats: men's & boys'; Topcoats, men's & boys': made from purchased materials; Men's & boys' trousers & slacks
Pr: Anthony Lucia

D-U-N-S 36-409-8970 IMP
HUGO BOSS FASHIONS INC
(*Suby of* HUGO BOSS USA INC) ★
55 Water St Fl 48, New York, NY 10041-3204
Tel (212) 940-0600 *Founded/Ownrshp* 1988
Sales 22.5MM^E *EMP* 1^E
SIC 5136 Men's & boys' clothing
Pr: Johjochim Beer
**CFO:* Annette Schwaer

D-U-N-S 19-717-5862 IMP/EXP
HUGO BOSS USA INC
(*Suby of* HUGO BOSS AG)
55 Water St Fl 48, New York, NY 10041-3204
Tel (212) 940-0600 *Founded/Ownrshp* 2002
Sales 200.7MM^E *EMP* 900
SIC 2311 2325 2337 5136 5611 6794 Men's & boys' suits & coats; Men's & boys' trousers & slacks; Women's & misses' suits & coats; Suits: women's, misses' & juniors'; Skirts, separate: women's, misses' & juniors'; Jackets & vests, except fur & leather: women's; Men's & boys' suits & trousers; Men's & boys' sportswear & work clothing; Men's & boys' outerwear; Men's & boys' clothing stores; Franchises, selling or licensing; Men's & boys' suits & coats; Men's & boys' trousers & slacks; Women's & misses' suits & coats; Suits: women's, misses' & juniors'; Skirts, separate: women's, misses' & juniors'; Jackets & vests, except fur & leather: women's; Men's & boys' suits & trousers; Men's & boys' sportswear & work clothing; Men's & boys' outerwear; Men's & boys' clothing stores; Franchises, selling or licensing
Pr: Anthony Lucia
**Pr:* Gretchen Ruoillard
**CEO:* Andre Maeder
COO: William Scott
CFO: Dr Karsten Koelsch
Sr VP: Karine Schnapp
Exec: Fiona Choi
Creative D: Jason Wu
**Mng Dir:* Mark Brashear
Mng Dir: Matthew Keighran
Mng Dir: Endre Pech

HUGO NATURALS
See DM NATURAL PRODUCTS INC

D-U-N-S 15-534-2439
HUGO W MOSER RESEARCH INSTITUTE AT KENNEDY KRIEGER INC
707 N Broadway, Baltimore, MD 21205-1832
Tel (443) 923-9302 *Founded/Ownrshp* 1986
Sales 30.3MM *EMP* 275
Accts Sc&H Tax & Advisory Services L
SIC 8733 Research institute; Research institute
Pr: Gary Goldstein MD
**CFO:* James M Anders Jr
**CFO:* Michael Neuman

HUGO'S
See VALLEY MARKETS INC

HUGULEY MEMORIAL MEDICAL CTR
See ADVENTIST HEALTH SYSTEMS/ SUN BELT

D-U-N-S 10-661-7074 IMP
HUHTAMAKI AMERICAS INC
(*Suby of* HUHTAMAKI BEHEER V B.V.)
9201 Packaging Dr, De Soto, KS 66018-8600
Tel (913) 583-3025 *Founded/Ownrshp* 2000
Sales 167.9MM^E *EMP* 400
SIC 3089 Plastic containers, except foam; Plastic containers, except foam
CEO: Jukka Moisio
Ofcr: Timo Salonen
Ofcr: Hannu Tikkanen
**Ex VP:* Clay Dunn
**Ex VP:* Suresh Gupta
**Ex VP:* Olli Koponen
**Ex VP:* Shashank Sinha
**Sr VP:* Sari Lindholm
VP: Frank Hofenbetzer
**Prin:* Norman Botwinik
**Prin:* Steve Lyons

D-U-N-S 08-671-4149 IMP/EXP
HUHTAMAKI FILMS INC
(*Suby of* HUHTAMAKI OYJ)
9201 Packaging Dr, De Soto, KS 66018-8600
Tel (913) 583-3025 *Founded/Ownrshp* 2002
Sales 132.0MM^E *EMP* 647
SIC 3089 Plastic containers, except foam; Plastic containers, except foam
CEO: Clay Dunn
**Treas:* Earlene A Sells

*VP: John Odea
Genl Mgr: Athos Ikonomous

D-U-N-S 04-114-3850 IMP
HUHTAMAKI INC
(Suby of HUHTAMAKI OYJ)
9201 Packaging Dr, De Soto, KS 66018-8600
Tel (913) 583-3025 Founded/Ownrshp 2000
Sales 801.3MM^E EMP 3,000
SIC 2656 3565 Sanitary food containers; Ice cream containers: made from purchased material; Labeling machines, industrial; Sanitary food containers; Ice cream containers: made from purchased material; Labeling machines, industrial
CEO: Jukka Moisio
*CEO: Clay Dunn
Treas: Earlene Seales
Bd of Dir: Anthony Simon
Ofcr: Suraj Sawant
Ofcr: Jennifer Young
VP: Tom Anderza
VP: Fred Betzen
*VP: John O'Dea
Mng Dir: Ulf Wienboker
Genl Mgr: Philip Woolsey

D-U-N-S 11-540-5586
HUISKEN MEAT CO
(Suby of BRANDING IRON HOLDINGS INC) ★
245 Industrial Blvd, Sauk Rapids, MN 56379-1238
Tel (320) 259-0305 Founded/Ownrshp 2007
Sales 38.0MM^E EMP 90
SIC 5147 Meats & meat products; Meats & meat products
CEO: R Scott Hudspeth
*Pr: Michael H Holten
COO: Cliff Albertson
CFO: Craig Allen
Opers Mgr: Tim Kortuem
Ql Cn Mgr: Jeannie Meehl
Mktg Mgr: Dave Holm

D-U-N-S 02-725-2294 IMP/EXP
HUISMAN NORTH AMERICA SERVICES LLC
(Suby of HUISMAN US INC) ★
2502 Wehring Rd, Rosenberg, TX 77471-9688
Tel (832) 490-1111 Founded/Ownrshp 2008
Sales 28.5MM^E EMP 70
SIC 1389 Oil field services
*Treas: Jack O'Connor
*VP: Robert Thompson

D-U-N-S 00-274-7078
HUISMAN US INC (TX)
(Suby of ACE INNOVATION HOLDING B.V.)
2502 Wehring Rd, Rosenberg, TX 77471-9688
Tel (832) 490-1111 Founded/Ownrshp 1999
Sales 28.5MM^E EMP 75^E
SIC 5085 Industrial supplies
Pr: Anne K De Groot
VP: Robert Van Kuilenburg
Genl Mgr: Steve Bernard
VP Sls: Patrick O'Neill

D-U-N-S 08-074-7660
HUITT - ZOLLARS INC (TX)
1717 Mckinney Ave # 1400, Dallas, TX 75202-1239
Tel (214) 871-3311 Founded/Ownrshp 1975
Sales 62.6MM^E EMP 500
SIC 8713 8711 Surveying services; Consulting engineer; Surveying services; Consulting engineer
Ch Bd: Robert Zollars
*CFO: Cliff Wall
Bd of Dir: Larry Huitt
Bd of Dir: Isabel Vasquez
Chf Mktg O: Cooper Rita
*Sr VP: James Congdon
Sr VP: Louis Lagamarsino
*Sr VP: George Marks
Sr VP: Stephen E Shepard
Sr VP: Stephen E Shpard
*Sr VP: Greg Wine
VP: Charles Aldredge
VP: James Brown
VP: Flavel Chastain
VP: Scott Eddings
VP: Mark R Edgren
VP: Marc Haslinger
VP: Kenneth J Hughes
VP: Monica Kent
*VP: Robert McDermott
VP: Bonnie Obrien

D-U-N-S 05-397-1644
HULCHER SERVICES INC
(Suby of FIRST FINANCIAL RESOURCES INC) ★
611 Kimberly Dr, Denton, TX 76208-6300
Tel (940) 387-0099 Founded/Ownrshp 1978
Sales 373.8MM^E EMP 650
SIC 4953 4789 Hazardous waste collection & disposal; Railroad maintenance & repair services; Hazardous waste collection & disposal; Railroad maintenance & repair services
Pr: Frank Given
*CEO: Greg Bristow
*Treas: Curry Vogelsang
*Ex VP: Ron Ewing
Sr VP: Robert Brown
Sr VP: Hillen Robert
VP: Steve Adams
VP: Don Franks
VP: Dwain Pinkston
VP: Brett Siedelmann
VP: Rick Turner
Exec: Peter Tilton

D-U-N-S 07-600-7657
HULETT ENVIRONMENTAL SERVICES INC
7670 Okeechobee Blvd, West Palm Beach, FL 33411-2100
Tel (561) 626-9244 Founded/Ownrshp 1968
Sales 20.1MM^E EMP 92
SIC 7342 Pest control services
Pr: Hulett Timothy M
*Treas: Elizabeth Hulett
Genl Mgr: Michael Braman
Genl Mgr: Mike Fearns

D-U-N-S 12-059-1235
HULL & ASSOCIATES INC
6397 Emerald Pkwy Ste 200, Dublin, OH 43016-2231
Tel (419) 385-2018 Founded/Ownrshp 1980
Sales 47.6MM^E EMP 160
SIC 8711 Consulting engineer; Consulting engineer
Pr: Craig A Kasper
*Ch Bd: John H Hull
VP: Michael Cermak
*VP: David L Richards

D-U-N-S 07-602-1252
■ **HULL & CO INC**
(Suby of BROWN & BROWN INC) ★
1815 Griffin Rd Ste 300, Dania Beach, FL 33004-2252
Tel (954) 920-6790 Founded/Ownrshp 2005
Sales NA EMP 465
SIC 6411 Insurance brokers; Insurance brokers
Pr: Anthony T Strianese
*CFO: William N Simons
Treas: Joseph S Failla Jr
Sr VP: Erik Halvorsen
*VP: Cory T Walker
*Exec: Edwin Calabrese
*Prin: Richard Hull
Brnch Mgr: Patti Argo
Mktg Dir: Bob Briggs
Mktg Dir: Casey Pechin

D-U-N-S 02-219-4419
HULL COOPERATIVE ASSOCIATION
1206 Railroad St, Hull, IA 51239-7654
Tel (712) 439-2831 Founded/Ownrshp 1908
Sales 70.5MM EMP 42^E
Accts Burdorf Parrott & Associates
SIC 5999 5153 Feed & farm supply; Fire extinguishers; Alarm signal systems; Grain elevators; Feed & farm supply; Fire extinguishers; Alarm signal systems; Grain elevators
Pr: Tom Reuvers
*Sec: Merrill Nettinga
*VP: Galen Breuer
*Genl Mgr: Ed Westra
Off Mgr: Loren Reyelts

D-U-N-S 02-219-4542
HULL FEED AND PRODUCE INC
826 14th St, Hull, IA 51239-7438
Tel (712) 439-1851 Founded/Ownrshp 1990
Sales 26.1MM EMP 4
SIC 5191 Feed; Feed
Pr: Jay Dewitt
*VP: Doug Pollema

D-U-N-S 07-731-0423 IMP/EXP
HULL FOREST PRODUCTS INC
101 Hampton Rd, Pomfret Center, CT 06259-1712
Tel (860) 974-0127 Founded/Ownrshp 1965
Sales 26.5MM^E EMP 42
SIC 5031 2421 2426 Lumber, plywood & millwork; Paneling, wood; Sawmills & planing mills, general; Hardwood dimension & flooring mills
CEO: William Boston Hull
*Pr: Jeffrey M Durst
*VP: Samuel I Hull
Exec: Benjamin Hull
Mill Mgr: David Foisy

D-U-N-S 00-553-9945
HULL LIFT TRUCK INC
BOBCAT OF MICHIANA
28747 Old Us 33, Elkhart, IN 46516-1699
Tel (260) 482-7288 Founded/Ownrshp 1960
Sales 80.0MM^E EMP 140
SIC 5084 5999 5943 Materials handling machinery; Cleaning equipment & supplies; Office forms & supplies; Materials handling machinery; Cleaning equipment & supplies; Office forms & supplies
Pr: Brian R Hull
*CFO: Carey Bert
*VP: Thomas F Evard
VP: Douglas Simcox
Sls Mgr: David Buck
Sls Mgr: Kim Zuber
Sales Asso: Joe Kaler

D-U-N-S 09-511-2769
HULL SUPPLY CO INC (TX)
LAMRITE COMPLETE
5117 E Cesar Chavez St, Austin, TX 78702-5142
Tel (512) 385-1262 Founded/Ownrshp 1979, 1985
Sales 23.0MM^E EMP 52
SIC 5031 1751 Doors; Window & door (prefabricated) installation
Pr: Rick Hull
*VP: Dan Snyder
Off Mgr: Philip Cook
IT Man: Gabriel Cunningham
Sales Exec: Matt Southard

D-U-N-S 00-606-1683
HULMAN & CO
CLABBER GIRL
900 Wabash Ave, Terre Haute, IN 47807-3208
Tel (812) 232-9446 Founded/Ownrshp 1916
Sales 41.7MM^E EMP 160
SIC 2099 Baking powder; Baking powder
Ch Bd: Mary H George
*Pr: Jeffery G Belskus
*CFO: Jeffrey G Belskus
VP: Eric Gloe
*VP: Gary Morris

D-U-N-S 12-509-5435
HULT INTERNATIONAL BUSINESS SCHOOL INC
1 Education St, Cambridge, MA 02141-1805
Tel (617) 746-1990 Founded/Ownrshp 1997
Sales 34.7MM EMP 32
Accts Leonard Mulherin & Greene P
SIC 8244 Business college or school
Pr: Stephen J Hodges
CFO: Anders Ljungdahl
Treas: Lisa Sousa
Ex Dir: Fernando Mora
HC Dir: Deanna Fillhouer
HC Dir: Casey Rillahan

D-U-N-S 02-219-6604
HULTGREN IMPLEMENT INC
JOHN DEERE
5655 State Highway 175, Ida Grove, IA 51445-8092
Tel (712) 364-3105 Founded/Ownrshp 1976
Sales 53.8MM EMP 45
SIC 5083 7699 Farm implements; Farm equipment parts & supplies; Agricultural equipment repair services; Farm implements; Farm equipment parts & supplies; Agricultural equipment repair services
CEO: Larry Hultgren
*Pr: Jeffrey Hultgren
*Treas: Todd Conover
VP: Keith Hultgren
*VP: Dewayne Ricklens

D-U-N-S 80-853-4163
HULU LLC
2500 Broadway, Santa Monica, CA 90404-3065
Tel (310) 571-4700 Founded/Ownrshp 2007
Sales 1.0MMM EMP 725
SIC 4833 4813 Television broadcasting stations; ; Television broadcasting stations;
CEO: Mike Hopkins
*CEO: Jason Kilar
CFO: Elaine Paul
Sr VP: Tim Connolly
Sr VP: Craig Erwich
Sr VP: Peter R Naylor
Sr VP: Jenny Wall
VP: Tiffany Bollin
VP: Jim O'Gorman
VP: Eugene WEI
Assoc Dir: Angie Kang

D-U-N-S 61-934-4393
HUMAN ARC CORP
1457 E 40th St, Cleveland, OH 44103-1103
Tel (216) 431-5200 Founded/Ownrshp 1984
Sales 58.3MM^E EMP 600
SIC 8742

HUMAN CAPITAL
See METROPOLITAN NASHVILLE PUBLIC SCHOOLS

D-U-N-S 10-507-6228
HUMAN DEVELOPMENT ASSOCIATION INC
HDA
12 Heyward St Ste 4, Brooklyn, NY 11249-7839
Tel (718) 422-4700 Founded/Ownrshp 1980
Sales 28.4MM EMP 50
Accts Roth & Company Llp Brooklyn
SIC 8082 Home health care services; Home health care services
Board of Directors: Abraham Friedland, Eugene Weiss

D-U-N-S 10-821-7654
HUMAN FACTORS APPLICATIONS INC
(Suby of TERRANEAR PMC LLC) ★
1000 Burr Ridge Pkwy, Burr Ridge, IL 60527-0849
Tel (630) 850-6900 Founded/Ownrshp 2010
Sales 11.7MM^E EMP 1,000
SIC 7363 8748 Engineering help service; Business consulting; Engineering help service; Business consulting
Pr: Amar Raval
*Treas: Theresa Doyle
*Ex VP: Kenneth Fillman
IT Man: Belton Williams

D-U-N-S 19-462-6735
HUMAN FACTORS INTERNATIONAL INC
1680 Highway 1 Ste 3600, Fairfield, IA 52556-9114
Tel (641) 469-3347 Founded/Ownrshp 1988
Sales 41.3MM^E EMP 250^E
SIC 7379 Computer related consulting services; Computer related consulting services
Pr: Vijay More
Ofcr: Elisa Del Galdo
Top Exec: Reshmy Kurian
VP: Mike Flood
VP: April McGee
Creative D: Gordon Akwera
Dir Rx: Jane Martin
Dir Bus: Chris Allen
Dir Bus: Arek Reeder
Genl Mgr: Kartika Damon
Web Prj Mg: Sheri Poulson

D-U-N-S 79-705-7437
HUMAN GENOME SCIENCES INC
(Suby of GLAXOSMITHKLINE PLC)
14200 Shady Grove Rd, Rockville, MD 20850-7464
Tel (301) 309-8504 Founded/Ownrshp 2012
Sales 81.8MM^E EMP 1,100
SIC 8731 2834 Biotechnical research, commercial; Medical research, commercial; Pharmaceutical preparations; Biotechnical research, commercial; Medical research, commercial; Pharmaceutical preparations
Pr: H Thomas Watkins
CFO: David P Southwell
Bd of Dir: Ngoc T Ha
Ex VP: James H Davis PHD
Sr VP: Susan D Bateson
Sr VP: Perry Karsen
Sr VP: Craig C Parker
Sr VP: Curran M Simpson
VP: Robert Benson
VP: Alain D Cappeluti
VP: Michael R Fannon
VP: Margery B Fischbein
VP: Vincent Gogh
VP: Daniel Gold
VP: Art Mandell
VP: Kevin P McRaith
VP: Tuomo Patsi
VP: Tuomo PTsi
Dir Surg: Bill Hannon
Assoc Dir: Stephen Currier
Assoc Dir: Marge Musumeci
Board of Directors: Allan Baxter Phd, Richard J Danzig, Colin Goddard Phd, Maxine Gowen Phd, John L Lamattina Phd, Augustine Lawlor, George J Morrow, Gregory Norden, Robert C Young

D-U-N-S 08-964-5352 IMP
HUMAN KINETICS INC
YMCA PROGRAM STORE
1607 N Market St, Champaign, IL 61820-2220
Tel (217) 351-5076 Founded/Ownrshp 1974
Sales 33.2MM EMP 234^E
SIC 2731

HUMAN RESOURCE AUTHORITY
See MENOMINEE-DELTA-SCHOOLCRAFT COMMUNITY ACTION AGENCY

HUMAN RESOURCES
See CITY OF DEARBORN HEIGHTS

HUMAN RESOURCES
See STATE AUDITOR OHIO

D-U-N-S 14-700-7173
HUMAN RESOURCES DEVELOPMENT INSTITUTE INC
HRDI
222 S Jefferson St, Chicago, IL 60661-5603
Tel (312) 441-9009 Founded/Ownrshp 1978
Sales 23.9MM EMP 380
Accts Kpmg Llp Chicago Il
SIC 8322 Family counseling services; Family counseling services
CEO: Joel K Johnson
*COO: Miller Anderson
*CFO: Evelyn Willis
*Ex Dir: Tammie McCurry
Off Mgr: Margarita Reyes

D-U-N-S 07-263-1799
HUMAN RESOURCES RESEARCH ORGANIZATION (HUMRRO)
66 Canal Center Plz # 700, Alexandria, VA 22314-1591
Tel (703) 549-3611 Founded/Ownrshp 1951
Sales 24.1MM EMP 120
Accts Bdo Usa Llp Mclean Va
SIC 8733 Noncommercial research organizations; Noncommercial research organizations
Pr: William J Strickland
Pr: Steve Sellman
*CFO: Thomas R Kracker
*Treas: Charles McKay
*VP: Deirdre J Knapp
*VP: W S Sellman
*VP: Suzanne Tsacoumis
Software D: Olga Fridman

D-U-N-S 07-123-4439
HUMAN RIGHTS CAMPAIGN INC
FEDERAL PAC
1640 Rhode Island Ave Nw, Washington, DC 20036-3200
Tel (202) 628-4160 Founded/Ownrshp 1982
Sales 38.5MM EMP 248
Accts Gelman Rosenberg & Freedman B
SIC 8651 Political action committee; Political action committee
CEO: Chad Griffin
Pr: Ryan Dillon
*COO: Ana M MA
*CFO: Jim Rinefierd
Treas: James Rinefierd
Ofcr: Adam Marquez
Ofcr: Joe Tapp
Ofcr: David Yu
VP: Fred Sainz
VP: Jodee Winterhof
Exec: Jeff Krehely
Assoc Dir: Eric Bloem
Assoc Dir: Candace Gingrich
Assoc Dir: Candace Gingrich-Jones
Assoc Dir: Tari Hanneman
Assoc Dir: David Swanson
Assoc Dir: Cassandra Thomas
Dir Soc: Colette Schabram

D-U-N-S 10-309-3480 IMP
HUMAN RIGHTS WATCH INC
350 5th Ave Fl 34, New York, NY 10118-3499
Tel (212) 290-4700 Founded/Ownrshp 1976
Sales 74.2MM EMP 348
Accts Bdo Usa Llp New York Ny
SIC 8399 Social change association; Social change association
Ex Dir: Kenneth Roth
COO: Chuck Lustig
Ofcr: Matthew Myers
Ofcr: Hanss Neira
VP: Kiran D'Amico
VP: Richard Dicker
Exec: Selwan Salman
Assoc Dir: Jane Buchanan
Assoc Dir: Jacqueline McKay
Admn Mgr: Christina Pe A
Off Mgr: Anna Chaplin-Fischer

D-U-N-S 06-086-0863
HUMAN SERVICE CENTER
228 Ne Jefferson Ave, Peoria, IL 61603-3802
Tel (309) 671-8000 Founded/Ownrshp 1976
Sales 16.4MM EMP 350
Accts Cliftonlarsonallen Llp Peoria
SIC 8322 Alcoholism counseling, nontreatment; Alcoholism counseling, nontreatment
CEO: John Gilligan
CFO: Gerd Prewett
*VP: Mike Kennedy
Doctor: Arun Pinto
Doctor: Narayana Reddy
Board of Directors: Ali Bahaj, David Gorenz, Mary Heller, Brad McMillan, John Sahn, James Stevenson, Vicky Stewart, Don Welch

D-U-N-S 93-308-3446
HUMAN SERVICES ASSOCIATES INC
4001 Pelee St Ste 200, Orlando, FL 32817-3100
Tel (407) 422-0880 Founded/Ownrshp 1993
Sales 12.7MM EMP 385
Accts James Moore & Co Pl Tallahass
SIC 8322 Individual & family services; Rehabilitation services; Individual & family services; Rehabilitation services
Pr: Frank Francisco
*CEO: Lori Tomlin

*COO: Debbie Dain
*Sec: Joe Behnke
*VP: Melanie Fletcher

HUMAN SERVICES, DEPARTMENT OF
See SOUTH DAKOTA DEPARTMENT OF HUMAN SERVICES

D-U-N-S 07-367-2482
HUMAN SOLUTIONS INC (FL)
600 Maryland Ave Sw 800e, Washington, DC 20024-2539
Tel (202) 347-9728 Founded/Ownrshp 1997
Sales 32.7MM EMP 96
SIC 8711 8734 8731 8744 Engineering services; Testing laboratories; Commercial physical research; Facilities support services
Pr: Brenda G Boone
*VP: Michael Prichard
*VP: Mary Pritchard

D-U-N-S 07-581-4673 IMP
HUMAN TECHNOLOGIES CORP (NY)
H T C
2260 Dwyer Ave, Utica, NY 13501-1193
Tel (315) 735-3532 Founded/Ownrshp 1954
Sales 16.4MM EMP 330
Accts Fitzgerald Depietro & Wojnas C
SIC 8331 2262 7349 7361 8093 Sheltered workshop; Screen printing: manmade fiber & silk broadwoven fabrics; Acoustical tile cleaning service; Employment agencies; Mental health clinic, outpatient; Sheltered workshop; Screen printing: manmade fiber & silk broadwoven fabrics; Acoustical tile cleaning service; Employment agencies; Mental health clinic, outpatient
Pr: Richard E Sebastian Jr
COO: Gregory Frank
Exec: Linda Forth
DP Exec: Mike Kowiateak
Dir IT: Sara Norvis

D-U-N-S 14-004-3303
HUMAN TECHNOLOGIES INC
HTI
105 N Spring St Ste 200, Greenville, SC 29601-2862
Tel (864) 467-0330 Founded/Ownrshp 1999
Sales 21.6MM^E EMP 75^E
SIC 8742 Human resource consulting services
Prin: Herbert W Dew III
Dir IT: Karen Howard
VP Opers: David Sewell
QC Dir: Leisa Hulme
Sls Dir: Nat Banks

D-U-N-S 01-911-7691 IMP/EXP
HUMAN TOUCH LLC
3030 Walnut Ave, Long Beach, CA 90807-5222
Tel (562) 426-8700 Founded/Ownrshp 2003
Sales 53.5MM^E EMP 80
SIC 5021 Chairs; Chairs
Pr: Andrew Cohen
CEO: David Wood
COO: Craig Womack
CFO: Thomas Fragpotto
CFO: Rosy Gu
Ofcr: James Benson
Sr VP: Rick Hill
Sr VP: David A Temeles Jr
*VP: Bruce Maccallum
Prin: Chang Han
Dir IT: Andrew Corkill

HUMANA
See HUMCO INC

D-U-N-S 07-925-2241
HUMANA BENEFIT PLAN OF ILLINOIS INC
7915 N Hale Ave Ste D, Peoria, IL 61615-2088
Tel (502) 580-1000 Founded/Ownrshp 1994
Sales NA EMP 99
SIC 6321 Health insurance carriers
Pr: Pattie Dale Tye

D-U-N-S 60-261-1092
■ **HUMANA DENTAL**
(Suby of HUMANA INC) ★
1100 Employers Blvd, Green Bay, WI 54344-0002
Tel (920) 337-7674 Founded/Ownrshp 2005
Sales NA EMP 11^E
SIC 6324 Dental insurance
Pr: Jerry Ganoni

D-U-N-S 07-925-2210
HUMANA EMPLOYERS HEALTH PLAN OF GEORGIA INC
900 Ashwood Pkwy Ste 500, Atlanta, GA 30338-6997
Tel (502) 580-1000 Founded/Ownrshp 1995
Sales NA EMP 99
SIC 6321 Health insurance carriers
Pr: Pattie Dale Tye

D-U-N-S 36-414-6311
HUMANA FOUNDATION INC
421 W Main St, Frankfort, KY 40601-1815
Tel (502) 580-4140 Founded/Ownrshp 2005
Sales 47.3MM EMP 2^E
SIC 6733 Trusts; Trusts
Pr: Michael B McCallister

D-U-N-S 80-534-9198
■ **HUMANA GOVERNMENT BUSINESS INC**
(Suby of HUMANA INC) ★
305 N Hurstbourne Pkwy 1b, Louisville, KY 40222-8533
Tel (502) 318-0935 Founded/Ownrshp 1993
Sales NA EMP 19,000
SIC 6321 Health insurance carriers; Health insurance carriers
CEO: Tim McClain
*Pr: Orie Mullen
*CFO: David Lewis

D-U-N-S 15-722-0732
■ **HUMANA HEALTH BENEFIT PLAN OF LOUISIANA INC**
HUMANA OCHNSER
(Suby of HUMANA INSURANCE CO OF KENTUCKY) ★
1 Galleria Blvd Ste 850, Metairie, LA 70001-7542
Tel (504) 219-6600 Founded/Ownrshp 2004
Sales NA EMP 472
SIC 6324 Hospital & medical service plans; Hospital & medical service plans
Pr: Terry Shilling
*Sec: Lisa Blume
*Sr VP: George Renaudin

D-U-N-S 08-246-3647
■ **HUMANA HEALTH PLAN INC**
(Suby of HUMANA INC) ★
8431 Fredericksburg Rd # 340, San Antonio, TX 78229-3455
Tel (210) 615-5100 Founded/Ownrshp 1981
Sales NA EMP 1,247
SIC 6324 6321 8011 Health maintenance organization (HMO), insurance only; Accident & health insurance; Offices & clinics of medical doctors; Health maintenance organization (HMO), insurance only; Accident & health insurance; Offices & clinics of medical doctors
CEO: Michael B McCallister
COO: Greg Wolf
Dir IT: Niel Berman
Dir IT: Zhong Liu
Info Man: Molly Freeman
Sales Exec: Christina M Candler

D-U-N-S 78-793-4397
■ **HUMANA HEALTH PLAN OF KANSAS INC**
(Suby of HUMANA INC) ★
500 W Main St Ste 300, Louisville, KY 40202-4268
Tel (502) 580-1000 Founded/Ownrshp 1982
Sales NA EMP 1,800
SIC 6324 6321 Health maintenance organization (HMO), insurance only; Health insurance carriers; Health maintenance organization (HMO), insurance only; Health insurance carriers
CFO: James E Murray
*Treas: James W Doucette
VP: Marsden Connolly
VP: Mark Iorio
VP: Jaewon Ryu
Prgrm Mgr: Joan Majors
IT Man: Beau Jameson
Mktg Dir: David Gabbard
Sales Asso: Evys Rodriguez
Snr Mgr: Mary Barnes
Snr Mgr: Kevin Barry

D-U-N-S 78-681-3709
■ **HUMANA HEALTH PLAN OF OHIO INC**
(Suby of HUMANA INC) ★
640 Eden Park Dr, Cincinnati, OH 45202-6056
Tel (513) 784-5200 Founded/Ownrshp 1986
Sales NA EMP 100
SIC 6324 Health maintenance organization (HMO), insurance only
Pr: Wayne Thomas Smith
VP: Steve Ringel
Exec: Stacie Webster
CTO: Ted Nime
IT Man: Paul Bartel
Sales Exec: Marci Durkin
S&M/VP: Frank Armstrong
Sls Dir: Mike Brooks
Mktg Mgr: Brad Conrad
Mktg Mgr: Charles Jackson
Sls Mgr: James Stines
Board of Directors: Philip Brent Garmon, Donald Sovey Lankford MD

D-U-N-S 04-994-4143
▲ **HUMANA INC**
500 W Main St Ste 300, Louisville, KY 40202-4268
Tel (502) 580-1000 Founded/Ownrshp 1961
Sales NA EMP 57,000
Accts Pricewaterhousecoopers Llp L
Tkr Sym HUM Exch NYS
SIC 6324 6321 6411 Hospital & medical service plans; Health maintenance organization (HMO), insurance only; Health insurance carriers; Medical insurance claim processing, contract or fee basis; Hospital & medical service plans; Health maintenance organization (HMO), insurance only; Health insurance carriers; Medical insurance claim processing, contract or fee basis
Pr: Bruce D Broussard
Pr: Jim Brown
Pr: Craig Drablos
Pr: Mark El-Tawil
Pr: Dan Feruck
Pr: Deborah Gracey
Pr: Jim Laughlin
Pr: Tim Love
Pr: Tim McClain
Pr: Timothy O'Rourke
Pr: Bruce D Perkins
Pr: Dave Reynolds
Pr: Oraida Roman
Pr: Pattie Dale Tye
COO: James E Murray
CFO: Brian A Kane
Chf Mktg O: Jay Morris
Ofcr: Jonathan T Lord MD
Sr VP: Steven E McCulley
Sr VP: Thomas J Noland
Sr VP: R Eugene Shields
Board of Directors: Frank A D'amelio, W Roy Dunbar, Kurt J Hilzinger, David A Jones Jr, William J McDonald, William E Mitchell, David B Nash, James J O'brien, Marissa T Peterson

D-U-N-S 08-618-1922
■ **HUMANA INSURANCE CO**
(Suby of HUMANA INC) ★
1100 Employers Blvd, Green Bay, WI 54344-0002
Tel (502) 580-1000 Founded/Ownrshp 1986
Sales NA EMP 2,200
SIC 6311 6321 Life insurance carriers; Health insurance carriers; Accident insurance carriers; Life insurance carriers; Health insurance carriers; Accident insurance carriers
CEO: Bruce D Broussard
*Pr: Michael McAllister
*Ex VP: James E Murray
*Sr VP: Roy A Beveridge
*Sr VP: Jody L Bilney
*Sr VP: Christopher H Hunter
VP: Sandy Ganoni
VP: Brenda Roubal
*VP: Ronald Edward Van Thiel
VP: Mark Wernicke
*VP: Tod James Zacharias

D-U-N-S 78-793-5162
■ **HUMANA INSURANCE CO OF KENTUCKY**
(Suby of HUMANA INC) ★
500 W Main St Ste 300, Louisville, KY 40202-4268
Tel (502) 580-1000 Founded/Ownrshp 1985
Sales NA EMP 1,500
SIC 6321 8741 Health insurance carriers; Management services; Health insurance carriers; Management services
Pr: Michael B McCallister
*Treas: James H Bloem
VP: George Bauernfeind
VP: Effie Sandblom
Dir IT: Kishore Maranganti
Board of Directors: James E Murray

D-U-N-S 07-949-9306
HUMANA INSURANCE CO OF NEW YORK
500 W Main St Ste 300, Louisville, KY 40202-4268
Tel (800) 486-2620 Founded/Ownrshp 2014
Sales NA EMP 86^E
SIC 6321 Health insurance carriers

D-U-N-S 14-065-2806
■ **HUMANA MARKETPOINT INC**
(Suby of HUMANA INC) ★
500 W Main St Fl 7, Louisville, KY 40202-2946
Tel (502) 580-1000 Founded/Ownrshp 2000
Sales NA EMP 600^E
SIC 6324 6321 6411 Hospital & medical service plans; Health maintenance organization (HMO), insurance only; Health insurance carriers; Medical insurance claim processing, contract or fee basis; Hospital & medical service plans; Health maintenance organization (HMO), insurance only; Health insurance carriers; Medical insurance claim processing, contract or fee basis
Prin: W Fred Wheeler
VP: Patrick O Toole
Exec: John Kelly
Sls Mgr: Jory Clebanoff
Sls Mgr: Victor Crumity
Sls Mgr: Jeff Digioa
Sls Mgr: Jon Kaufman
Sls Mgr: Ruben Rodriguez
Sls Mgr: Keisha Smith

D-U-N-S 07-925-2309
HUMANA MEDICAL PLAN INC
3501 Sw 160th Ave, Miramar, FL 33027-4695
Tel (502) 580-1000 Founded/Ownrshp 1986
Sales NA EMP 99
SIC 6321 Health insurance carriers; Health insurance carriers
Prin: Denise Haynes

D-U-N-S 15-465-2549
■ **HUMANA MEDICAL PLAN INC**
(Suby of HUMANA INC) ★
3501 Sw 160th Ave, Miramar, FL 33027-4695
Tel (954) 626-5775 Founded/Ownrshp 1987
Sales NA EMP 150
SIC 6324 Health maintenance organization (HMO), insurance only; Health maintenance organization (HMO), insurance only
Pr: Wayne Smith
VP: Lee Bowers
Opers Supe: Lilian Nebiu
VP Mktg: Barbara Menendez
Pharmcst: Michael Busatto
Board of Directors: Karen Ann Couglin, Philip B Garson

HUMANA OCHNSER
See HUMANA HEALTH BENEFIT PLAN OF LOUISIANA INC

D-U-N-S 83-144-8894
■ **HUMANA PHARMACY INC**
(Suby of HUMANA INC) ★
9843 Windisch Rd, West Chester, OH 45069-3826
Tel (513) 483-8007 Founded/Ownrshp 2001
Sales 44.7MM^E EMP 14^E
SIC 5912 Drug stores
Prin: Scott Greenwell

HUMANE SOCIETY INTERNATIONAL
See HUMANE SOCIETY OF UNITED STATES

D-U-N-S 07-711-7745
HUMANE SOCIETY OF MISSOURI
1201 Macklind Ave, Saint Louis, MO 63110-1481
Tel (314) 647-8800 Founded/Ownrshp 1870
Sales 23.9MM EMP 180
Accts Rubin Brown Llp Saint Louis
SIC 8699 Animal humane society; Animal humane society
Pr: Kathryn Warnick
*CFO: Anne Goeckner

D-U-N-S 07-265-5970
HUMANE SOCIETY OF UNITED STATES
HUMANE SOCIETY INTERNATIONAL
2100 L St Nw Ste 500, Washington, DC 20037-1595
Tel (202) 452-1100 Founded/Ownrshp 1954
Sales 169.9MM EMP 600^E
SIC 8699 Animal humane society; Animal humane society
CEO: Wayne Pacelle
*COO: Laura Maloney
*CFO: G Thomas Waite III

*Ex VP: Patricia A Forkan
*VP: Michael Markarian
Mng Dir: Phil Redmond
Dir Sec: Richard Ladez
Prgrm Mgr: Nancy Peterson
Prgrm Mgr: Rebecca Regnery
Prgrm Mgr: Jay Sabatucci
Pr Mgr: Pepper Van Tassell

D-U-N-S 06-880-2045 IMP
HUMANETICS II LTD
(Suby of C H INDUSTRIES INC) ★
1700 Columbian Club Dr, Carrollton, TX 75006-5534
Tel (972) 416-1304 Founded/Ownrshp 1992
Sales 79.6MM^E EMP 337
SIC 3444 3599 Sheet metalwork; Custom machinery; Sheet metalwork; Custom machinery
CEO: Art Holbrook
Pr: Robert Hasty
CFO: Danny Goodwin
VP: Laurie Hasty
Dir Bus: Shane Thornton
Genl Mgr: Kevin Shaw
Prd Mgr: Saul Cervantes
Snr Mgr: John Fersch

D-U-N-S 96-259-8467 IMP
HUMANETICS INNOVATIVE SOLUTIONS INC
FIRST TECHNOLOGY SAFETY SYSTEM
47460 Galleon Dr, Plymouth, MI 48170-2467
Tel (734) 451-7878 Founded/Ownrshp 2013
Sales 32.4MM^E EMP 140^E
SIC 3829 Testing equipment: abrasion, shearing strength, etc.; Testing equipment: abrasion, shearing strength, etc.
Pr: Christopher O'Connor
COO: Cary Nicholson
*CFO: Tom Harris
*VP: Jim Davis
*VP: Michael Jarouche
VP: Janis Major
Prgrm Mgr: Joe Bastian
Prgrm Mgr: Shiva Shetty
Genl Mgr: Lin Pan
CIO: Doug Luttrell
*CTO: Mike Beebe
Board of Directors: Terry Theodore

D-U-N-S 08-056-9841
HUMANIM INC
6355 Woodside Ct, Columbia, MD 21046-1071
Tel (410) 381-7172 Founded/Ownrshp 1970
Sales 29.1MM EMP 350^E
SIC 8322 Social services for the handicapped; Social services for the handicapped
CEO: Henry Posko

D-U-N-S 03-051-6675
HUMANITY UNITED
1 Letterman Dr Bldg D, San Francisco, CA 94129-1494
Tel (650) 587-2000 Founded/Ownrshp 2012
Sales 30.0MM EMP 30
SIC 8733 Noncommercial social research organization; Noncommercial social research organization
CEO: Randy Newcomb
*COO: Kurt Kroemer
Treas: Kevin Luu
*VP: David Abramowitz
VP: Lawrence Mendenhall
Assoc Dir: Julia Thornton
Counsel: Emiliano Martinez

D-U-N-S 15-350-0434 IMP/EXP
HUMANSCALE CORP
11 E 26th St Fl 8, New York, NY 10010-1425
Tel (212) 725-4749 Founded/Ownrshp 1981
Sales 179.9MM^E EMP 400
Accts Lawrence B Goodman & Co Pa Fa
SIC 3577 2521 Computer peripheral equipment; Wood office furniture; Computer peripheral equipment; Wood office furniture
CEO: Robert King
*Pr: Heather Fennimore
*Pr: Paul Levy
*VP: Michele Gerards
VP: Daniel Gilbert
Exec: Marie Le
Mng Dir: Tim Hutchings
Dist Mgr: Elliot Balis
Dist Mgr: Paul Morris
IT Man: Amy Lindhorst
QI Cn Mgr: Ronald Hon

D-U-N-S 84-391-9197
HUMANTOUCH LLC
7918 Jones Branch Dr # 800, Mc Lean, VA 22102-3347
Tel (703) 910-5090 Founded/Ownrshp 1998
Sales 31.0MM EMP 248^E
SIC 8748 Systems analysis & engineering consulting services; Systems analysis & engineering consulting services
CEO: Moe Jafari
VP: Methta Tran

D-U-N-S 08-791-7808 IMP
HUMAX USA INC
(Suby of HUMAX CO., LTD.)
15641 Red Hill Ave # 150, Tustin, CA 92780-7327
Tel (949) 251-5200 Founded/Ownrshp 2000
Sales 448.8MM EMP 41
SIC 5064 Electrical appliances, television & radio; Electrical appliances, television & radio
Pr: Yong Min Son
Sr VP: Frank Romeo
VP Bus Dev: Nara Won

D-U-N-S 09-013-9478 IMP
HUMBERTO VIDAL INC
112 Calle Arzuaga # 1001, San Juan, PR 00925-3320
Tel (787) 751-7070 Founded/Ownrshp 1971
Sales 20.1MM^E EMP 250
SIC 5661 Shoe stores; Shoe stores
Pr: Humberto V Nadal
*Treas: Rosita P Salgado
*VP: Luis V Pagan

D-U-N-S 02-235-6737
HUMBLE INDEPENDENT SCHOOL DISTRICT
HUMBLE ISD
20200 Eastway Village Dr, Humble, TX 77338-2405
Tel (281) 641-1000 *Founded/Ownrshp* 1919
Sales 397.0MM *EMP* 5,000
Accts Whitley Penn Llp Houston Tex
SIC 8211 Public elementary & secondary schools; Public elementary school; Public junior high school; Public senior high school; Public elementary & secondary schools; Public elementary school; Public junior high school; Public senior high school
CFO: Elizabeth Lynn
Bd of Dir: Dave Martin
Trst: Carol Atwood
Dir Sec: Cheryl Vitale
MIS Dir: Arthur Allen
IT Man: Jerri Monbaron
Pr Dir: Jamie Mount
Schl Brd P: Robert Scarfo
Psych: Denise Toro

HUMBLE ISD
See HUMBLE INDEPENDENT SCHOOL DISTRICT

D-U-N-S 09-518-7043 IMP
HUMBLE MACHINE WORKS INC
134 Wilson Rd, Humble, TX 77338-4985
Tel (281) 446-3057 *Founded/Ownrshp* 1964
Sales 23.0MM *EMP* 83
SIC 3533

HUMBOLDT COUNTY OFFICE OF EDUC
See HUMBOLDT COUNTY SUPERINTENDENT OF SCHOOLS

D-U-N-S 07-983-6259
HUMBOLDT COUNTY OFFICE OF EDUCATION
901 Myrtle Ave, Eureka, CA 95501-1219
Tel (707) 445-7000 *Founded/Ownrshp* 2015
Sales 41.8MM *EMP* 116ᴱ
SIC 8211 Public elementary & secondary schools

D-U-N-S 10-004-9394
HUMBOLDT COUNTY SCHOOL DISTRICT
310 E 4th St, Winnemucca, NV 89445-2831
Tel (775) 623-8100 *Founded/Ownrshp* 1880
Sales 26.6MMᴱ *EMP* 420
SIC 8211 9411 Public elementary & secondary schools; Administration of educational programs; Public elementary & secondary schools; Administration of educational programs
Dir IT: Jeanne Moline
IT Man: Teresa Braun
IT Man: Lisa Conn
HC Dir: Marian Tyree

D-U-N-S 19-321-1000
HUMBOLDT COUNTY SUPERINTENDENT OF SCHOOLS
HUMBOLDT COUNTY OFFICE OF EDUC
901 Myrtle Ave, Eureka, CA 95501-1219
Tel (707) 445-7000 *Founded/Ownrshp* 1900
Sales 1.2MM *EMP* 370
SIC 8211 Public elementary & secondary schools; Public elementary & secondary schools
Bd of Dir: Marc Rowley
Dir Rx: Beth Wylie
Dir IT: Robert Gearhart
Dir IT: Becky Giacomini
Dir IT: Charity Walker
Pgrm Dir: James Malloy

HUMBOLDT CREAMERY ASSOCIATION
See FOSTER DAIRY FARMS

D-U-N-S 61-471-4681
HUMBOLDT GENERAL HOSPITAL DISTRICT
118 E Haskell St, Winnemucca, NV 89445-3299
Tel (775) 623-5222 *Founded/Ownrshp* 1884
Sales 28.7MMᴱ *EMP* 170ᴱ
SIC 8062 General medical & surgical hospitals
CEO: Jim Parrish
**CFO:* Larrry Hutcheson
Doctor: Bill Besainti
Board of Directors: Darlene Bryan, Shelly Eubanks, Rose Marie Green, Nicole Maher, Crystal Mattson

D-U-N-S 00-509-1707 IMP
HUMBOLDT MFG CO (IL)
875 Tollgate Rd, Elgin, IL 60123-9351
Tel (708) 456-6300 *Founded/Ownrshp* 1925, 1990
Sales 30.0MM *EMP* 60
Accts Rvg Partners Llc Oak Brook
SIC 3829 3821 Surveying & drafting equipment; Bunsen burners; Laboratory equipment: fume hoods, distillation racks, etc.; Surveying & drafting equipment; Bunsen burners; Laboratory equipment: fume hoods, distillation racks, etc.
Pr: Dennis E Burgess
**CFO:* Joe Bryk
**Sec:* Joseph Bryk
IT Man: Jeanne Stahmer
Mtls Mgr: Jim Lindberg
VP Sls: Ed Hall
Sls Mgr: Alejandro Alvarez
Sls Mgr: Grant Graff

D-U-N-S 02-814-6140
HUMBOLDT NEWSPAPER INC
TIMES-STANDARD
930 6th St, Eureka, CA 95501-1112
Tel (707) 442-1711 *Founded/Ownrshp* 1854
Sales 26.6MMᴱ *EMP* 526
SIC 2711 Newspapers: publishing only, not printed on site; Newspapers: publishing only, not printed on site

D-U-N-S 02-129-3766
HUMBOLDT PARK ASSOCIATES INC
FIRST HEALTH CARE ASSOCIATES
8140 River Dr 1, Morton Grove, IL 60053-2637
Tel (847) 583-0100 *Founded/Ownrshp* 1976
Sales 33.1MMᴱ *EMP* 619
SIC 8742 6552 Business consultant; Subdividers & developers; Business consultant; Subdividers & developers
Pr: Shael Bellows

D-U-N-S 05-960-6970
HUMBOLDT PETROLEUM INC
1324 5th St, Eureka, CA 95501-0661
Tel (707) 443-3069 *Founded/Ownrshp* 1974
Sales 37.9MMᴱ *EMP* 140
SIC 5541 5172 Filling stations, gasoline; Petroleum products; Filling stations, gasoline; Petroleum products
Pr: M J Costelo
Exec: Hillary McClurg

D-U-N-S 82-813-1982
HUMBOLDT REDWOOD CO LLC
(*Suby of* MENDOCINO REDWOOD CO LLC) ★
108 Main St, Scotia, CA 95565
Tel (707) 764-4472 *Founded/Ownrshp* 2008
Sales 71.1MMᴱ *EMP* 300ᴱ
SIC 5031 Lumber, plywood & millwork; Lumber, plywood & millwork
VP: Pierce Baymiller
IT Man: Tom Schultz
Mill Mgr: Doug McIsaac
Sls Mgr: Kristen Lockhart

D-U-N-S 05-615-1244
HUMBOLDT STATE UNIVERSITY
(*Suby of* CALIFORNIA STATE UNIVERSITY SYSTEM) ★
1 Harpst St, Arcata, CA 95521-8299
Tel (707) 826-3311 *Founded/Ownrshp* 1966
Sales 50.0MMᴱ *EMP* 350ᴱ
SIC 8221 University; University
Pr: Lisa Rossbacher
Ofcr: Paul Mann
Assoc VP: Carol Terry
VP: Rock Braithwaite
VP: Carl Coffey
Exec: Don Wolski
Assoc Dir: Anne Kimbrow
Assoc Dir: Carolyn Lehman
Ex Dir: Jane Anderson
Ex Dir: Roy Furshpan
Ex Dir: Juanita Wilson

D-U-N-S 00-290-3201
HUMBOLDT UNIFIED SCHOOL DISTRICT 22
6411 N Robert Rd, Prescott Valley, AZ 86314-9146
Tel (928) 759-4000 *Founded/Ownrshp* 1908
Sales 34.3MMᴱ *EMP* 600
SIC 8211 Public elementary & secondary schools; Public elementary school; Public junior high school; Public senior high school; Public elementary & secondary schools; Public elementary school; Public junior high school; Public senior high school
Psych: Sandra Ebeltoft

D-U-N-S 79-737-4154 IMP
HUMBOLDT WEDAG INC
(*Suby of* KHD HUMBOLDT WEDAG GMBH)
400 Technology Pkwy, Norcross, GA 30092-3406
Tel (770) 810-7300 *Founded/Ownrshp* 2001
Sales 80.0MM *EMP* 60
SIC 3559 3823 Refinery, chemical processing & similar machinery; Industrial process measurement equipment
Pr: Richard Cusick
**Treas:* Reimund Berner
VP: Berner Reimund

D-U-N-S 07-875-9348
HUMC HOLDCO LLC
308 Willow Ave, Hoboken, NJ 07030-3808
Tel (201) 418-1000 *Founded/Ownrshp* 2010
Sales 242.2MMᴱ *EMP* 1,140ᴱ
SIC 6211 Investment firm, general brokerage
Prin: Yasmine Thomas

D-U-N-S 07-831-1985
HUMC OPCO LLC
(*Suby of* HUMC HOLDCO LLC) ★
308 Willow Ave, Hoboken, NJ 07030-3808
Tel (201) 418-1000 *Founded/Ownrshp* 2011
Sales 170.1MM *EMP* 1,125ᴱ
Accts Bdo Usa Llp
SIC 8062 General medical & surgical hospitals; General medical & surgical hospitals
CEO: Philip Schaengold
**VP:* Vincent Riccitelli

D-U-N-S 82-567-2884 IMP
HUMCO HOLDING GROUP INC
(*Suby of* P L P LTD) ★
7400 Alumax Rd, Texarkana, TX 75501-0282
Tel (903) 831-7808 *Founded/Ownrshp* 1993
Sales 51.0MMᴱ *EMP* 102
SIC 2834 2899 2844 Pharmaceutical preparations; Chemical preparations; Toilet preparations; Pharmaceutical preparations; Chemical preparations; Toilet preparations
Pr: Gregory C Pulido
**CFO:* Steven B Woolf
**VP:* Alan Fyke
**VP:* Susan Hickey
VP: Francisco Lozano
**VP:* Ken Reese
Dir IT: Matt Helms
Dir IT: John Ryther
Sls Mgr: Cynthia Brown

D-U-N-S 86-763-2234
■ **HUMCO INC**
HUMANA
(*Suby of* HUMANA INC) ★
500 W Main St Ste 300, Louisville, KY 40202-2943
Tel (502) 580-1000 *Founded/Ownrshp* 2008
Sales NA *EMP* 200
SIC 6321 Accident & health insurance; Accident & health insurance
Pr: Michael Mc Callister
Exec: Tim Neely
Exec: Mark Russell
Prgrm Mgr: Brenda Renier
Software D: Joel Arbic
Sales Exec: Nick Kompara

HUMILITY OF MARY HEALTH PARTNERS
See ST JOSEPH HEALTH CENTER

HUMMEL, JOHN CONSTRUCTION
See JOHN HUMMEL CUSTOM BUILDERS INC

D-U-N-S 03-104-9588 IMP/EXP
HUMMERT INTERNATIONAL INC
4500 Earth City Expy, Earth City, MO 63045-1329
Tel (314) 506-4500 *Founded/Ownrshp* 1934
Sales 43.3MMᴱ *EMP* 72
SIC 5191 Greenhouse equipment & supplies; Insecticides; Pesticides; Fertilizer & fertilizer materials; Greenhouse equipment & supplies; Insecticides; Pesticides; Fertilizer & fertilizer materials
Pr: August H Hummert III
Brnch Mgr: Joe Farrell
Dir IT: Holly Taylor
IT Man: Shannon Dieckman
IT Man: Brandon King
Natl Sales: Chris Erwin
Sls Mgr: James Duever
Sls Mgr: Leigh Johnson

HUMMINBIRD
See JOHNSON OUTDOORS MARINE ELECTRONICS INC

D-U-N-S 17-120-2786
HUMPERDINKS TEXAS LLC
2208 W Northwest Hwy # 200, Dallas, TX 75220-4305
Tel (214) 358-4159 *Founded/Ownrshp* 1996
Sales 23.5MMᴱ *EMP* 450
SIC 8741 Restaurant management; Restaurant management
Exec: Jose Penaloza
Genl Mgr: Kevin Ehrenfried
Genl Mgr: Mike Jones

D-U-N-S 08-331-8527
HUMPHREY & ASSOCIATES INC (TX)
11235 Shady Trl, Dallas, TX 75229-4636
Tel (972) 620-1075 *Founded/Ownrshp* 1977
Sales 81.9MM *EMP* 400
Accts Weaver And Tidwell Llp Dalla
SIC 1731 Electrical work; Electrical work
Pr: Steve Humphrey Sr
Ex VP: Randall P Humhrey
**Ex VP:* Jackie Humphrey
**Ex VP:* Jacquelyn Humphrey
**Ex VP:* Randall Humphrey
**Ex VP:* Stephen Humphrey Jr
**Sr VP:* Ed West
**VP:* Scott Fletcher
**VP:* Doug Gauntt
**VP:* Roy E Kirkland
VP: Linda Moore
**VP:* Steve Schmear
Exec: Martha Sanchez

D-U-N-S 00-592-8551
HUMPHREY CO LTD (TX)
6877 Wynnwood Ln, Houston, TX 77008-5023
Tel (713) 686-8606 *Founded/Ownrshp* 1951
Sales 44.6MM *EMP* 150
SIC 1711

D-U-N-S 11-516-8010
HUMPHREY COMPANIES LLC
2851 Prairie St Sw, Grandville, MI 49418-2179
Tel (616) 530-1717 *Founded/Ownrshp* 1984
Sales 141.3MMᴱ *EMP* 695
SIC 3537 3714 3089 5023 5162 Industrial trucks & tractors; Motor vehicle parts & accessories; Molding primary plastic; Home furnishings; Plastics sheets & rods; Industrial trucks & tractors; Motor vehicle parts & accessories; Molding primary plastic; Home furnishings; Plastics sheets & rods
CEO: James A Humphrey
**CFO:* James D Green
**Ch:* John W Humphrey

D-U-N-S 00-537-8658 IMP
HUMPHREY PRODUCTS CO (MI)
5070 E N Ave, Kalamazoo, MI 49048-9785
Tel (269) 381-5500 *Founded/Ownrshp* 1901
Sales 34.0MM *EMP* 225ᴱ
SIC 3492 Control valves, fluid power: hydraulic & pneumatic; Control valves, fluid power: hydraulic & pneumatic
Pr: Robert P Humphrey
**CFO:* Tom Gambon
IT Man: Luanne Cali
Opers Mgr: Larry Tutt
Prd Mgr: John Nappo
Sls Mgr: Michael Hammond
Snr Mgr: Amie Meints

D-U-N-S 13-083-2970 IMP
HUMPHREY RICH CONSTRUCTION GROUP INC
10200 Old Columbia Rd K, Columbia, MD 21046-2305
Tel (301) 330-1650 *Founded/Ownrshp* 2002
Sales 32.0MMᴱ *EMP* 85
SIC 1541 Industrial buildings & warehouses
Pr: Mark R Humphrey
**VP:* Lawrence A Rich

D-U-N-S 62-747-8233
HUMPHREYS & PARTNERS ARCHITECTS LP
HUMPHREYS PARTNERS ARCHITECTS
5339 Alpha Rd Ste 300, Dallas, TX 75240-7307
Tel (972) 239-4563 *Founded/Ownrshp* 1991
Sales 32.5MMᴱ *EMP* 125
SIC 8712 Architectural services; Architectural services
Pr: Greg Faulkner
CFO: Bruce Myers
Sr VP: Pete Robinson
VP: Karla Cavazos
VP: Walter Hudhes
Genl Mgr: Jeri Bradshaw
DP Exec: Paul Burnes
Dir IT: Martin Koch
Prd Mgr: J K Russel

D-U-N-S 10-007-2982
HUMPHREYS CO SCHOOL DISTRICT
2443 Highway 70 E, Waverly, TN 37185-2223
Tel (931) 296-2568 *Founded/Ownrshp* 1800
Sales 16.0MM *EMP* 600
SIC 8211 Public elementary & secondary schools; School board; Public elementary & secondary schools; School board
VP: Wally Ward
Dir Sec: Kristi Brown
HC Dir: Shane Foster

D-U-N-S 87-483-6893
HUMPHREYS COUNTY SCHOOL DISTRICT
401 Fourth St, Belzoni, MS 39038-3103
Tel (662) 247-6000 *Founded/Ownrshp* 1920
Sales 15.0MMᴱ *EMP* 300
Accts Cunningham Cpas Pllc Fairhope
SIC 8211 School board; School board
Brnch Mgr: Frank Richardson

HUMPHREYS PARTNERS ARCHITECTS
See HUMPHREYS & PARTNERS ARCHITECTS LP

D-U-N-S 05-085-5618
HUMPHRIES AND CO LLC
4581 S Cobb Dr Se Ste 200, Smyrna, GA 30080-6906
Tel (770) 434-1890 *Founded/Ownrshp* 1981
Sales 133.0MM *EMP* 90
SIC 1542 Commercial & office buildings, renovation & repair; Store front construction; Commercial & office buildings, renovation & repair; Store front construction
VP: P Scott Moore
COO: Jimmy Humpries
Sec: Mike Kiblinger
Ofcr: William G Snider
VP: Paul M King Jr
VP: Scott Moore
VP: Bobby Sharitz
VP: Charles R Sharitz
VP: J Kirk Thompson Jr
Mktg Mgr: Katherine Tirrell
Genl Couns: Garth Snider

D-U-N-S 07-375-5712
HUN SCHOOL OF PRINCETON
HUN SCHOOL SUMMER DAY CAMP
176 Edgerstoune Rd, Princeton, NJ 08540-6799
Tel (609) 921-7600 *Founded/Ownrshp* 1943
Sales 31.6MM *EMP* 130
Accts Withumsmithbrownpc Red Bank
SIC 8211 Preparatory school; Preparatory school
CFO: Richard L Feck
**CFO:* Rick Fleck
**Ch:* F Kevin Tylus
Top Exec: Jeffrey Snow
Assoc Dir: Meredith Gal
Assoc Dir: Patrick Quirk
Comm Dir: Maureen Leming
Prin: Gary Gruber
Ex Dir: Bonnie Beach
Mng Dir: Kelli Sanchez
Off Admin: Lynn Watson

HUN SCHOOL SUMMER DAY CAMP
See HUN SCHOOL OF PRINCETON

HUNAN ROYAL
See ROYAL HUNAN SEAFOOD CORP

HUNGER
See SECOND HARVEST FOODBANK OF SOUTHERN WISCONSIN INC

D-U-N-S 79-711-0467
HUNGER SOLUTIONS MINNESOTA
555 Park St Ste 400, Saint Paul, MN 55103-2276
Tel (651) 486-9860 *Founded/Ownrshp* 2001
Sales 55.3MM *EMP* 9
SIC 8322 Individual & family services; Individual & family services
Pr: Colleen Moriarty

D-U-N-S 00-232-9837 EXP
HUNGERFORD & TERRY INC
H & T
226 N Atlantic Ave, Clayton, NJ 08312-1335
Tel (856) 881-3200 *Founded/Ownrshp* 1909, 1982
Sales 25.3MMᴱ *EMP* 50ᴱ
SIC 1499 3589 Greensand mining; Water treatment equipment, industrial
Pr: Thomas Carrocino
**VP:* Harold Aronovitch
**VP:* Kenneth M Sayell
CTO: Frank Caligiuri
Sales Exec: James Tamburini

D-U-N-S 15-734-9127
HUNGRY HOWIES DISTRIBUTING INC
30300 Stephenson Hwy Lowr, Madison Heights, MI 48071-1628
Tel (248) 414-3300 *Founded/Ownrshp* 1999
Sales 43.0MMᴱ *EMP* 65
SIC 5141 Groceries, general line
Pr: Thomas Jackson
Store Mgr: Brad Malvin

D-U-N-S 02-344-3478
HUNINGTON LIBRARY
1151 Oxford Rd, San Marino, CA 91108-1299
Tel (626) 405-2267 *Founded/Ownrshp* 2010
Sales 100.5MM *EMP* 3ᴱ
SIC 8231 Libraries; Libraries

D-U-N-S 01-764-4543
HUNKAR TECHNOLOGIES INC (OH)
2368 Victory Pkwy Ste 210, Cincinnati, OH 45206-2810
Tel (513) 272-1010 *Founded/Ownrshp* 1962, 1999
Sales 29.7MMᴱ *EMP* 145
SIC 3565 3823 3577 3441 Labeling machines, industrial; Controllers for process variables, all types; Bar code (magnetic ink) printers; Fabricated structural metal; Labeling machines, industrial; Controllers for process variables, all types; Bar code (magnetic ink) printers; Fabricated structural metal

Pr: Eric R Thiemann
CFO: Clayton Wynn
**Treas:* C Kevin Whaley
VP: Mike Barker
**VP:* Jeannine Martin
Exec: Dale Lucas
Genl Mgr: Eric J Rulli

D-U-N-S 08-117-1894
HUNSAKER & ASSOCIATES IRVINE INC
3 Hughes, Irvine, CA 92618-2021
Tel (949) 583-1010 *Founded/Ownrshp* 1976
Sales 55.8MM^E *EMP* 400
SIC 8711 8713 Civil engineering; Surveying services; Civil engineering; Surveying services
CEO: Richard Hunsaker
**Pr:* Douglas Snyder
VP: Chuck Cater
**VP:* Kamal Karam
VP: Steve McCutchan
VP: Mohammed Rowther
**VP:* Doug Staley
Exec: Maria Lopera
Dir IT: Sargon Pavour
Dir IT: Sargon Tavour
IT Man: Marcy Martinez

D-U-N-S 11-304-9845
HUNT & ASSOCIATES ASSISTED LIVING CORP
100 Abingdon Pl, Abingdon, VA 24211-6122
Tel (276) 676-3300 *Founded/Ownrshp* 1981
Sales 11.6MM^E *EMP* 400
SIC 8051 6513 Skilled nursing care facilities; Retirement hotel operation; Skilled nursing care facilities; Retirement hotel operation
Prin: W Hammond Hunt
**Prin:* Charles O Byrd
**Prin:* Dennis R Owens
DP Exec: Bill Hunt
IT Man: Randy Robertson

D-U-N-S 00-796-7169 EXP
HUNT & BEHRENS INC (CA)
H & B
30 Lakeville St, Petaluma, CA 94952-3125
Tel (707) 762-4594 *Founded/Ownrshp* 1921, 1966
Sales 26.1MM^E *EMP* 42
SIC 5191 5999 Feed; Feed & farm supply
CEO: Daniel J Figone
**Pr:* Dan Figone
VP: Bob Falco
**VP:* Robert J Falco
Sfty Mgr: Cheryl Aguirre

D-U-N-S 07-377-7245
HUNT & SONS INC
5750 S Watt Ave, Sacramento, CA 95829-9349
Tel (916) 383-4868 *Founded/Ownrshp* 1963
Sales 37.6MM^E *EMP* 63
SIC 5541 5171 Truck stops; Petroleum bulk stations
Pr: R Dean Hunt
**CEO:* Audrey Hunt
**Treas:* Joshua Hunt
Treas: Warren N Hut
**VP:* Warren N Hunt III
Dir IT: Jim Bramlett
Opers Mgr: Pat Webster

HUNT BROTHERS PIZZA
See BRITT HUNT CO LLC

D-U-N-S 00-800-1349 IMP
■ **HUNT BUILDING CO LTD** (TX)
(*Suby of* HUNT COMPANIES INC) ★
4401 N Mesa St Ste 201, El Paso, TX 79902-1150
Tel (915) 533-1122 *Founded/Ownrshp* 1947
Sales 165.1MM^E *EMP* 416
SIC 1522 6531 1542 Multi-family dwellings, new construction; Real estate managers; Shopping center construction; Multi-family dwellings, new construction; Real estate managers; Shopping center construction
Ch Bd: W L Hunt
**Genl Pt:* Hbc Construction Managers
**Ltd Pt:* Hunt Building Corporation
**Pr:* M L Hunt
Pr: Ronald Hutchison
**Pr:* William Kell
CFO: Steve De Bara
**CFO:* William C Sanders CPA
**Treas:* James C Hunt
**Ex VP:* Gary B Sapp
**Sr VP:* Robert R Cabello
**Sr VP:* Steve Colon
Sr VP: Christopher Lawton-Smith
**Sr VP:* Richard J Marshall
**Sr VP:* Johnny E McFarlin
**Sr VP:* John T Philley
**Sr VP:* Robin G Vaughn CPA
**Sr VP:* Ken Wall
**Sr VP:* David K Wray
**Sr VP:* K Douglas Wright
**VP:* Alfredo Aguayo
Board of Directors: Brion Georges, Richard Gleichauf, Matt Myllykangas

D-U-N-S 13-611-5255
▲ **HUNT COMPANIES INC**
4401 N Mesa St, El Paso, TX 79902-1150
Tel (915) 533-1122 *Founded/Ownrshp* 1977
Sales 467.5MM^E *EMP* 680^E
SIC 1522 6531 1542 Multi-family dwellings, new construction; Real estate managers; Shopping center construction; Multi-family dwellings, new construction; Real estate managers; Shopping center construction
Pr: Chris Hunt
Pr: Steve Coln
**Pr:* M L Hunt
Pr: Gary Sapp
Pr: Nicole Wideman
COO: Paul Kopsky Jr
CFO: William Kell
CFO: Clay Parker
**Chf Inves:* James C Hunt
Ofcr: Steve Kraynick
Ex VP: Tom Philley
Ex VP: William C Sanders
Ex VP: David Wray
Sr VP: Clarence Ansley
Sr VP: Karl Becker
Sr VP: Brenda Christman
Sr VP: Juan Gonzalezgarza
Sr VP: Jacki Hampton
Sr VP: Rick Marshall
Sr VP: Anne Scharm
Sr VP: Ken Wall

D-U-N-S 10-399-4109
HUNT CONSOLIDATED INC
H C I
(*Suby of* RRH CORP) ★
1900 N Akard St, Dallas, TX 75201-2300
Tel (214) 978-8000 *Founded/Ownrshp* 1980
Sales 13.5MMM^E *EMP* 2,571
SIC 6799 1311 2911 1382 0212

D-U-N-S 00-693-8179
■ **HUNT CONSTRUCTION GROUP INC**
(*Suby of* AECOM) ★
6720 N Scottsdale Rd, Scottsdale, AZ 85253-4400
Tel (480) 368-4700 *Founded/Ownrshp* 1944, 2014
Sales 186.1MM^E *EMP* 700^E
SIC 8741 Construction management; Construction management
CEO: Robert G Hunt
**Pr:* Michael Fratianni
**Treas:* David Smith
Treas: David B Smith
**Ex VP:* Stephen W Atkins
**Ex VP:* Robert S Aylesworth
**Ex VP:* Robert Hart
**Ex VP:* William Hornbake
**Ex VP:* Kenneth Johnson
**Ex VP:* Mark E Lavoy
**Ex VP:* William Morthland
**Ex VP:* Jose M Pienknagura
**VP:* Matthew Barnes
**VP:* Scott Blanchard
**VP:* Belinda Burke
VP: Belinda D Burke
**VP:* Kevin J Cain
VP: Peter Clark
**VP:* Richard Dejean
**VP:* Frank Devlin
**VP:* Christopher Freed

D-U-N-S 07-957-1683
■ **HUNT CORP**
(*Suby of* AECOM TECHNICAL SERVICES INC) ★
6720 N Scottsdale Rd # 300, Scottsdale, AZ 85253-4460
Tel (480) 368-4755 *Founded/Ownrshp* 2014
Sales 229.1MM^E *EMP* 550
SIC 1542 1541 6552 6531 Commercial & office building, new construction; Industrial buildings, new construction; Subdividers & developers; Real estate managers; Commercial & office building, new construction; Industrial buildings, new construction; Subdividers & developers; Real estate managers
Pr: Michael Fratianni
**Treas:* David Smith
**Ex VP:* Stephen Atkins
Ex VP: Robert M Decker
**Ex VP:* Jose Pienknagura
VP: Peter Clark
VP: Richard Dejean
VP: Troy Hoberg
VP: William D Mott
**VP:* Lucinda S New
VP: William Palmer
VP: Warner Peck
VP: Jack E Sovern
VP: Monte J Thurmond
VP: Ronald Wildermuth
VP: Robert B Woods

D-U-N-S 16-091-1848
HUNT DOMINION CORP
1601 Elm St Ste 3900, Dallas, TX 75201-4708
Tel (214) 880-8400 *Founded/Ownrshp* 2000
Sales 175.4MM^E *EMP* 175
SIC 1311 1382 1241 Crude petroleum production; Natural gas production; Oil & gas exploration services; Coal mining services; Crude petroleum production; Natural gas production; Oil & gas exploration services; Coal mining services
Pr: Bruce Hunt
VP: Tom Nelson
Board of Directors: D H Hunt

D-U-N-S 02-303-8482
HUNT ELECTRIC CORP
MIDWAY TECHNOLOGY SOLUTIONS
2300 Territorial Rd, Saint Paul, MN 55114-1614
Tel (651) 646-2911 *Founded/Ownrshp* 1965
Sales 227.8MM^E *EMP* 600
Accts Mcgladrey
SIC 1731 General electrical contractor; General electrical contractor
Pr: Michael Hanson
CFO: Ron Somerville
**VP:* James J Basara
**VP:* Lamont Herman
**VP:* Timothy Holmberg
VP: Todd Lyden
**VP:* Curtis Southward
Exec: Michelle Sissferle
Sfty Dirs: Tom Hunt
Sfty Dirs: Diana Nelson
S&M/VP: Jack Galvin

D-U-N-S 05-703-3516
HUNT ELECTRIC SUPPLY CO
1215 Maple Ave, Burlington, NC 27215-6958
Tel (336) 229-5351 *Founded/Ownrshp* 1971
Sales 89.6MM^E *EMP* 85
SIC 5063 5211 Electrical apparatus & equipment; Electrical supplies; Electrical construction materials; Electrical apparatus & equipment; Electrical supplies; Electrical construction materials
Ch Bd: R Sam Hunt III
Pr: R Samuel Hunt IV
Pr: Vicky S Hunt
VP: Rodney Sharpe

D-U-N-S 09-816-4122 IMP
HUNT ENGINE INC
14805 Main St, Houston, TX 77035-6412
Tel (713) 721-9400 *Founded/Ownrshp* 1979
Sales 26.9MM *EMP* 65
Accts Postlethwaite & Netterville M
SIC 3533 7699 7629 Oil & gas field machinery; Industrial equipment services; Electrical repair shops; Oil & gas field machinery; Industrial equipment services; Electrical repair shops
Pr: Frank Doonan
**Sec:* John Biggs
VP: Robert Copeland
Board of Directors: John Biggs, Frank Doonan

D-U-N-S 06-474-6274 IMP
HUNT ENTERPRISES INC
MCDONALD'S
10 Rabro Dr, Hauppauge, NY 11788-4233
Tel (631) 582-6665 *Founded/Ownrshp* 1971
Sales 28.8MM^E *EMP* 700
SIC 5812 8742 Fast-food restaurant, chain; Restaurant & food services consultants; Fast-food restaurant, chain; Restaurant & food services consultants
Pr: Peter Hunt
**VP:* Veronica Hunt

HUNT FOODS COMPANY
See CONAGRA GROCERY PRODUCTS CO LLC

D-U-N-S 01-283-6610
HUNT GUILLOT & ASSOCIATES LLC
HGA
603 E Reynolds Dr, Ruston, LA 71270-2822
Tel (318) 255-6825 *Founded/Ownrshp* 1997
Sales 98.8MM^E *EMP* 375
SIC 8711 Engineering services; Engineering services
CFO: Glen Mitchell
Ex VP: Don Plummer
VP: Walter Ballard
VP: Jay Guillot
VP: Don Olson
Genl Mgr: Deborah Gorman
Genl Mgr: Don Plumber
Dir IT: John Estes
IT Man: Keith Cranford
IT Man: Marjorie Torres
Mktg Mgr: Fredrick Moore

D-U-N-S 07-321-5774 IMP/EXP
HUNT INC
GULF COAST THERMAL KING
7802 Us Highway 301 N, Tampa, FL 33637-6774
Tel (813) 985-8502 *Founded/Ownrshp* 1994
Sales 26.2MM^E *EMP* 62
SIC 5511 5013 7513 Trucks, tractors & trailers: new & used; Truck parts & accessories; Truck leasing, without drivers; Trucks, tractors & trailers: new & used; Truck parts & accessories; Truck leasing, without drivers
Pr: Tommy J Koulouris
**Sec:* Irene Ranger

D-U-N-S 07-487-8968 IMP
HUNT MEMORIAL HOSPITAL DISTRICT
HUNT REGIONAL MEDICAL CENTER
4215 Joe Ramsey Blvd E, Greenville, TX 75401-7852
Tel (903) 408-5000 *Founded/Ownrshp* 1960
Sales 114.6MM *EMP* 900
Accts Bkd Llp Dallas Texas
SIC 8062 8071 8082 General medical & surgical hospitals; Medical laboratories; Home health care services; General medical & surgical hospitals; Medical laboratories; Home health care services
CEO: Richard Carter
V Ch: Joe Johnson
COO: John Heatherly
**CFO:* Jerii Rich
Off Mgr: Tammy Ballard
CTO: Kelli Caldwell
Dir IT: Rick Gibson
Dir IT: Jonathan Schafft
Netwrk Mgr: Steven Jones
Psych: Wade Barker
Psych: Matthew Barrow

D-U-N-S 09-923-9634
HUNT MIDWEST ENTERPRISES INC
8300 Ne Underground Dr # 100, Kansas City, MO 64161-9767
Tel (816) 454-7711 *Founded/Ownrshp* 1979
Sales 82.9MM^E *EMP* 310
SIC 6552 1422 6211 Subdividers & developers; Lime rock, ground; Investment firm, general brokerage; Subdividers & developers; Lime rock, ground; Investment firm, general brokerage
Ch Bd: Jim Holland
**Pr:* Lee A Derrough
**Pr:* Ora Reynolds
**CFO:* Don Hagan
**Ch:* Jack W Steadman
**VP:* Lamar Hunt
Genl Mgr: Mike Bell
Off Mgr: Sarah Jones

D-U-N-S 06-217-9698
■ **HUNT MORTGAGE GROUP LLC**
(*Suby of* HUNT COMPANIES INC) ★
230 Park Ave Fl 19, New York, NY 10169-2199
Tel (212) 317-5700 *Founded/Ownrshp* 2014
Sales NA *EMP* 200^E
SIC 6162 Mortgage bankers & correspondents; Mortgage bankers & correspondents
Pr: Robert A Wrzosek
**CFO:* Michael Larsen
Chf Cred: Daniel J Wolins
VP: Dana Blair
VP: Jeff Jones
VP: Jordan Kilbury

HUNT NURSING AND RETIREMENT HM
See DANVERS MANAGEMENT SYSTEMS INC

D-U-N-S 00-735-3402
HUNT OIL USA INC
(*Suby of* H C I) ★
1900 N Akard St, Dallas, TX 75201-2300
Tel (214) 978-8000 *Founded/Ownrshp* 1934
Sales 12.1MMM^E *EMP* 2,074
SIC 1311 1382 2911

D-U-N-S 00-792-6827
■ **HUNT PETROLEUM CORP** (DE)
(*Suby of* XTO ENERGY INC) ★
110 W 7th St, Fort Worth, TX 76102-7018
Tel (214) 880-8400 *Founded/Ownrshp* 1983
Sales 57.3MM^E *EMP* 267
SIC 1382 1311 2911 Oil & gas exploration services; Crude petroleum production; Natural gas production; Petroleum refining; Oil & gas exploration services; Crude petroleum production; Natural gas production; Petroleum refining
VP: David Levy
Treas: Max J Gardner
**Treas:* J A Gentry
**Ex VP:* Keith A Hutton
Sr VP: Peter Vogel
**VP:* Randy J Cleveland
**VP:* J A Podraza
**VP:* Robert N Schleckser
IT Man: Steve Fischer

D-U-N-S 17-526-1817
HUNT REFINING CO
(*Suby of* HUNT INVESTMENT CORPORATION)
2200 Jack Warner Pkwy, Tuscaloosa, AL 35401-1009
Tel (205) 391-3300 *Founded/Ownrshp* 1946
Sales 47.1MM^E *EMP* 300
SIC 2911

HUNT REGIONAL MEDICAL CENTER
See HUNT MEMORIAL HOSPITAL DISTRICT

HUNT TECHNOLOGIES
See LANDIS+GYR TECHNOLOGIES LLC

D-U-N-S 04-415-0381
HUNT VALLEY INN
245 Shawan Rd, Hunt Valley, MD 21031-1099
Tel (410) 785-7000 *Founded/Ownrshp* 1964
Sales 15.0MM *EMP* 400
SIC 7011 5812 Hotel, franchised; Eating places; Hotel, franchised; Eating places
Ltd Pt: Boykin Hotel Properties LP
Genl Mgr: Martin Svigir
Sls Mgr: Kevin Bergman
Sls Mgr: Mike Elliott
Sls Mgr: John Lanahan
Sls Mgr: Todd Yohn

D-U-N-S 00-677-1307
HUNT WILLIAM HERBERT TRUST ESTATE
1601 Elm St Ste 3900, Dallas, TX 75201-4708
Tel (214) 880-8400 *Founded/Ownrshp* 1954
Sales 5.0MMM^E *EMP* 251^E
SIC 8742 6799 Management consulting services; Investors; Management consulting services; Investors
Owner: William Herbert Hunt

D-U-N-S 82-491-6126
■ **HUNTAIR INC**
(*Suby of* NORTEK AIR SOLUTIONS LLC) ★
19855 Sw 124th Ave, Tualatin, OR 97062-8007
Tel (503) 639-0113 *Founded/Ownrshp* 2006
Sales 168.9MM^E *EMP* 300
SIC 3585 Refrigeration & heating equipment; Refrigeration & heating equipment
Pr: Dave E Benson
**Ch Bd:* Ed Hunt
QA Dir: Jason Wilkinson
IT Man: Allen Mills
Software D: Marc Shapiro
Opers Mgr: Mark Andersen
Opers Mgr: Mark Anderson
Natl Sales: John Hobson
Natl Sales: Mark Montesanto
Natl Sales: Mark Zabala
Sls Mgr: Harry Scott

D-U-N-S 60-840-0990
HUNTE CORP
121 N Roy Hill Blvd, Goodman, MO 64843-9765
Tel (417) 364-8597 *Founded/Ownrshp* 1991
Sales 82.6MM^E *EMP* 250
SIC 5199 Cats; Dogs; Pet supplies; Cats; Dogs; Pet supplies
CEO: Ryan Boyle
**CFO:* Patrick Fitzgerald
**Sec:* Angelina Hunte
Sr VP: Angie Stone

HUNTER BUILDINGS & MFG
See HUNTER BUILDINGS LLC

D-U-N-S 60-254-9094 IMP
HUNTER BUILDINGS LLC
HUNTER BUILDINGS & MFG
14935 Jacintoport Blvd, Houston, TX 77015-6523
Tel (281) 452-9800 *Founded/Ownrshp* 2006
Sales 130.9MM^E *EMP* 120
SIC 1542 Commercial & office building contractors; Commercial & office building contractors
Mng Pt: Michael Leblanc
CFO: Rachel Massey
VP: Bob Bills
VP: Buddy Tucker
VP: Glenn Whitlock
IT Man: Johnerick Cintrn
Sys Mgr: Jose Barragan
Mktg Mgr: Crystal Cedro
Manager: Bucky Crowson
Manager: Clay Efferson
Manager: Brian Lefebure

D-U-N-S 00-582-9601
HUNTER CONTRACTING CO (AZ)
701 N Cooper Rd, Gilbert, AZ 85233-3703
Tel (480) 892-0521 *Founded/Ownrshp* 1961
Sales 217.3MM^E *EMP* 620
SIC 1611 1629 1622 General contractor, highway & street construction; Dams, waterways, docks & other marine construction; Waste water & sewage treatment plant construction; Bridge, tunnel & elevated highway; General contractor, highway & street construction; Dams, waterways, docks & other marine construction; Waste water & sewage treatment plant construction; Bridge, tunnel & elevated highway
Pr: Steve Padilla

*CFO: Samuel J Napolitano
*Treas: Max Taddei
*Sr VP: Allen Andrews
*VP: Chuck English

D-U-N-S 02-461-8852
HUNTER CORP
HUNTER RENTALS
2520 Asheville Hwy, Hendersonville, NC 28791-1410
Tel (866) 260-8202 Founded/Ownrshp 1940
Sales 62.6MM^E EMP 140
SIC 5511 Automobiles, new & used; Automobiles, new & used
Pr: Thomas D Hunter III
*Ch: Hal M Hunter
*Treas: Mary Collins
Sr VP: Cheryl Mauleon
VP: Jerry Oshinski
Genl Mgr: Debra Hammond
IT Man: James Hall
Info Man: Hank Martin
Sls Mgr: Ryan Decker
Sls Mgr: Scott Laffin

D-U-N-S 80-779-4206 EXP
HUNTER DEFENSE TECHNOLOGIES INC
HDT ENGINEERED TECHNOLOGIES
(Suby of HDT GLOBAL INC) ★
30500 Aurora Rd Ste 100, Solon, OH 44139-2776
Tel (216) 438-6111 Founded/Ownrshp 2009
Sales 239.1MM^E EMP 650
SIC 3433 3569 3822 8331 8711 3549 Room & wall heaters, including radiators; Filters; Auto controls regulating residntl & coml environmt & applncs; Sheltered workshop; Engineering services; Assembly machines, including robotic; Room & wall heaters, including radiators; Filters; Auto controls regulating residntl & coml environmt & applncs; Sheltered workshop; Engineering services; Assembly machines, including robotic
CEO: R Andrew Hove
Pr: Mike Stolarz
*CFO: Anthony Dilucente
CFO: Tony Dilucente
Sr VP: Doug Childress
*Sr VP: Prabha Gopinath
*Sr VP: Greg Miller
*Sr VP: Carl Pates
Dir IT: Jeff Dunn
IT Man: Robin Carney
IT Man: Ryan Podger

HUNTER DISPLAYS
See HUNTER METAL INDUSTRIES INC

HUNTER DODGE CHRYSLER JEEP RAM
See H W HUNTER INC

D-U-N-S 03-738-6588 EXP
HUNTER DOUGLAS FABRICATION CO
(Suby of HUNTER DOUGLAS INC) ★
11420 Reeder Rd, Dallas, TX 75229-2108
Tel (972) 484-9771 Founded/Ownrshp 1986
Sales 50.8MM^E EMP 350
SIC 2591 Venetian blinds; Venetian blinds
Pr: Randy Liken
*CFO: Gordon Khan
*Ex VP: Ajit Mehra
Sls Mgr: Mark Mendoza

D-U-N-S 00-915-5045
HUNTER DOUGLAS FABRICATIONS
WIN-GLO WINDOW COVERINGS
(Suby of HUNTER DOUGLAS N.V.)
1880 Milmont Dr, Milpitas, CA 95035-2512
Tel (408) 435-8844 Founded/Ownrshp 1930, 1988
Sales 35.4MM^E EMP 275
SIC 2591 Drapery hardware & blinds & shades; Blinds vertical; Venetian blinds; Window shades; Drapery hardware & blinds & shades; Blinds vertical; Venetian blinds; Window shades
Pr: Jerry Fuchs
*Treas: Ajit Mehra
VP: Wayne Morrison
*VP: Brad Nelson
*VP: Steve Pirylis
VP: Brian Quirk
MIS Mgr: Mark Petter
Tech Mgr: Roger Burns
Info Man: Jim Wood
Mtls Mgr: John Martin
VP Sls: Dan Murphy
Board of Directors:

D-U-N-S 04-618-8165 IMP
HUNTER DOUGLAS INC
(Suby of HUNTER DOUGLAS N.V.)
1 Blue Hill Plz Ste 1569, Pearl River, NY 10965-6101
Tel (845) 664-7000 Founded/Ownrshp 1976
Sales 1.4MMM^E EMP 8,625
SIC 2591 3444 5084 Window blinds; Window shades; Venetian blinds; Sheet metalwork; Industrial machinery & equipment; Window blinds; Window shades; Venetian blinds; Sheet metalwork; Industrial machinery & equipment
Pr: Marvin B Hopkins
*Ch Bd: Ralph Sonnenberg
*Pr: David H Sonnenberg
*CFO: Leen Reijtenbagh
*Ex VP: Ajit Mehra
VP: Dilip Joglekar
Adm Dir: Mary Lonergan
Genl Mgr: Bryan Clabeaux
Off Admin: Kyle Finley
Dir IT: Craig Pedersen
IT Man: Jeff Boh

D-U-N-S 05-975-6197 IMP/EXP
HUNTER DOUGLAS METALS LLC
(Suby of INDUSTRIE- EN HANDELSONDERNEMING "BUISMETAAL" B.V.)
915 175th St Fl 2, Homewood, IL 60430-4575
Tel (708) 799-0800 Founded/Ownrshp 1988
Sales 57.3MM^E EMP 30
SIC 5051 Nonferrous metal sheets, bars, rods, etc.
Pr: Marvin B Hopkins
*Ch Bd: Ralph Sonnenberg
*Pr: George Ribet

*CFO: Richard H Sfura
VP: Neil Hoffman

D-U-N-S 15-807-1766 IMP/EXP
HUNTER DOUGLAS WINDOW FASHIONS INC
(Suby of HUNTER DOUGLAS INC) ★
1 Duette Way, Broomfield, CO 80020-1090
Tel (303) 466-1848 Founded/Ownrshp 1998
Sales 228.8MM^E EMP 950
SIC 2591 Drapery hardware & blinds & shades; Drapery hardware & blinds & shades
Pr: Marv Hopkins
Pr: Michael Buttitta
*Ex VP: Ajit Mehra
VP: Tim Daviau
VP: Keith Garmyn
VP: Dilip Joglekar
VP: Tom Morrissey
VP: Richard Pellett
VP: Sheryl Wisecup
Creative D: Sally Morse
Dir Bus: Ken Witherell

D-U-N-S 00-628-8203 IMP/EXP
HUNTER ENGINEERING CO INC (MO)
11250 Hunter Dr, Bridgeton, MO 63044-2391
Tel (314) 731-3020 Founded/Ownrshp 1948
Sales 141.9MM^E EMP 700
SIC 3559

D-U-N-S 15-724-2132 IMP/EXP
HUNTER FAN CO
CASABLANCA FAN COMPANY
7130 Goodlett Farms Pkwy Ste 400, Memphis, TN 38103
Tel (901) 743-1360 Founded/Ownrshp 1984
Sales 152.2MM^E EMP 350
SIC 5064 3634 3645 Fans, household: electric; Ceiling fans; Residential lighting fixtures; Fans, household: electric; Ceiling fans; Residential lighting fixtures
CEO: John Alexander
Pr: Tom Breeden
*CFO: Charles Turner
Chf Mktg O: Rick Brandl
Ex VP: Chase Davenport
Sr VP: Michael Ritter
VP: James Barrett
VP: Kenneth Garvey
VP: Tammy Judd
VP: Tim Norton
VP: Alan Walter

D-U-N-S 15-379-4867
■ **HUNTER FARMS-HIGH POINT DIVISION INC**
(Suby of HARRIS TEETER LLC) ★
1900 N Main St, High Point, NC 27262-2132
Tel (336) 822-2300 Founded/Ownrshp 1917
Sales 34.2MM^E EMP 130
SIC 2024 Dairy based frozen desserts; Dairy based frozen desserts
VP: Dwight Moore
*VP: Chester Marsh
Ql Cn Mgr: Gale Walton

D-U-N-S 78-772-9235
HUNTER FOOD INC
3707 E La Palma Ave, Anaheim, CA 92806-2121
Tel (714) 666-1888 Founded/Ownrshp 1991
Sales 27.9MM EMP 14
Accts Hou J Yen Cpa Fullerton Ca
SIC 5147 5144 4789 Lard; Eggs; Cargo loading & unloading services; Lard; Eggs; Cargo loading & unloading services
CEO: Huan Hua Le
*Prin: Barry Le
*Prin: Hsin Jung Lin Le
*Prin: Hsu Chiu Lin
S&M/Mgr: WEI Then Le

D-U-N-S 86-874-7247 IMP/EXP
HUNTER INDUSTRIES INC
1940 Diamond St, San Marcos, CA 92078-5190
Tel (800) 383-4747 Founded/Ownrshp 1993
Sales 672.3MM^E EMP 1,300^E
SIC 5087 3084 Sprinkler systems; Plastics pipe; Sprinkler systems; Plastics pipe
Pr: Gregory Hunter
Treas: Kari Pelters
Area Mgr: Vineet Upadhyay
Ql Cn Mgr: Jeffrey Guziejka
Ql Cn Mgr: Marco Lopez
Sls Mgr: Lorenzo Arcangeli
Sls Mgr: Tony Newton

D-U-N-S 03-858-0064 EXP
HUNTER INDUSTRIES L P
1940 Diamond St, San Marcos, CA 92078-5190
Tel (760) 744-5240 Founded/Ownrshp 1981
Sales 124.5MM^E EMP 800^E
SIC 1629 Irrigation system construction; Earthmoving contractor; Irrigation system construction; Earthmoving contractor
Pt: Richard E Hunter
Pt: Ann K Hunter-Welborn

D-U-N-S 06-643-4648
HUNTER INDUSTRIES LTD
COLORADO MATERIALS
5080 Fm 2439, New Braunfels, TX 78132
Tel (512) 353-7757 Founded/Ownrshp 1997
Sales 222.8MM^E EMP 500
SIC 1611 2951 1442 General contractor, highway & street construction; Asphalt & asphaltic paving mixtures (not from refineries); Gravel mining; General contractor, highway & street construction; Asphalt & asphaltic paving mixtures (not from refineries); Gravel mining
Ch Bd: John R Weisman
*Treas: Walter Ulbricht
*VP: Ronnie Jones
*VP: Mark D Reininger
Genl Mgr: John Yanek
Sfty Mgr: Orlando Castillega

D-U-N-S 78-835-4330
HUNTER INTERESTS
28 Cousteau Ln, Austin, TX 78746-3126
Tel (512) 284-8968 Founded/Ownrshp 1984
Sales 30.0MM^E EMP 4
SIC 6531 Real estate agent, commercial; Real estate agent, commercial
Owner: Douglas Hunter

D-U-N-S 06-001-8603
HUNTER MANAGEMENT CO INC
SUBWAY
551 E State Rd Ste 201, American Fork, UT 84003-2225
Tel (801) 492-4344 Founded/Ownrshp 1980
Sales 15.3MM^E EMP 300
SIC 5812 Sandwiches & submarines shop; Sandwiches & submarines shop
Pr: Logan Hunter
*Treas: J Delbert Bell
*VP: Shawn Cook
*VP: Reid Hunter

HUNTER MARINE TRANSPORT
See HMT HOLDINGS INC

D-U-N-S 00-204-1986
HUNTER METAL INDUSTRIES INC (NY)
HUNTER DISPLAYS
14 Hewlett Ave, East Patchogue, NY 11772-5499
Tel (631) 475-5900 Founded/Ownrshp 1951
Sales 21.2MM^E EMP 100
SIC 2542 2541 Fixtures: display, office or store: except wood; Display fixtures, wood
CEO: Harry Stoll
*Sr VP: Sandy Stoll
*VP: Ken Kasper
Sls Mgr: James Reed

HUNTER MOUNTAIN SKI RESORT
See SHANTY HOLLOW CORP

HUNTER OIL
See GW HUNTER INC

D-U-N-S 00-887-1365
■ **HUNTER PANELS LLC**
(Suby of CARLISLE CONSTRUCTION MATERIALS INC) ★
15 Franklin St Ste B2, Portland, ME 04101-7119
Tel (207) 761-5678 Founded/Ownrshp 2002
Sales 81.4MM^E EMP 250
SIC 3086 Insulation or cushioning material, foamed plastic; Insulation or cushioning material, foamed plastic
*VP: Jim Whitton
VP Mktg: Alma Garnett
Mktg Mgr: Steve Pavey
Sls Mgr: Selene Labbe
Sls Mgr: Rick Mockler

HUNTER RENTALS
See HUNTER CORP

D-U-N-S 18-904-7975
HUNTER ROBERTS CONSTRUCTION GROUP LLC
55 Water St Fl 51, New York, NY 10041-3201
Tel (212) 321-6800 Founded/Ownrshp 2005
Sales 762.3MM^E EMP 260
SIC 8742 1542 Construction project management consultant; Commercial & office building contractors; Construction project management consultant; Commercial & office building contractors
Pr: James C McKenna
COO: Austin Dimech
Chf Mktg O: Christopher Phillips
*Ex VP: Paul Andersen
Ex VP: Paul Anderson
*Sr VP: John Alicandri
VP: Bill Allan
*VP: Kevin Barrett
*VP: Alex Craig
VP: Jeff Crompton
*VP: Tim Dillon
*VP: Dan Dirscherl
VP: Jenny Freeman
VP: Eric Hook
*VP: Mark Lamble
VP: K Lindsey
VP: Robert Masucci
*VP: Chuck Petrusky
VP: Brian Weisser
*Exec: Brian Aronne
Exec: Thomas Ascher

D-U-N-S 00-208-2436 IMP
HUNTER SPICE INC (CA)
(Suby of SAUER CO C F) ★
184 Suburban Rd, San Luis Obispo, CA 93401-7502
Tel (805) 597-8900 Founded/Ownrshp 1984
Sales 21.4MM EMP 65
Accts Ernst & Young
SIC 2099 Seasonings & spices
Pr: Conrad Sauer
*CFO: William Uhlik
IT Man: Kevin Watkins

D-U-N-S 05-051-6962
■ **HUNTER TECHNOLOGY CORP**
(Suby of SPARTON CORP) ★
1940 Milmont Dr, Milpitas, CA 95035-2578
Tel (408) 957-1300 Founded/Ownrshp 2015
Sales 38.4MM^E EMP 200^E
SIC 3679 Microwave components; Engineering services; Microwave components
Pr: Joseph F O'Neil
COO: Mark Evans
VP: Greg Edgmon
VP: Ian Grover
VP: Tony Nguyen
Exec: Lisa Hunt
Prgrm Mgr: Billy Chen
Prgrm Mgr: Carmen Gonzalez
Prgrm Mgr: Renee Rocca
Prgrm Mgr: Monica Sierra
Dir IT: Jason Ortiz

D-U-N-S 01-405-6014 EXP
HUNTER TRUCK SALES & SERVICE INC
480 Pittsburgh Rd, Butler, PA 16002-7654
Tel (724) 586-5770 Founded/Ownrshp 1938
Sales 106.2MM^E EMP 233
SIC 5511 5531 7538 Trucks, tractors & trailers: new & used; Truck equipment & parts; General truck repair; Trucks, tractors & trailers: new & used; Truck equipment & parts; General truck repair
Pr: Homer Hunter
COO: Jeffrey Hunter
*CFO: Raff Fischer
*Sec: William Hunter
*VP: Harry Hunter
Genl Mgr: David Hunter
IT Man: Mark Rollinson
S&M/VP: Jerry Davis

D-U-N-S 00-399-3854
HUNTER-DAVISSON INC
1800 Se Pershing St, Portland, OR 97202-2338
Tel (503) 234-0477 Founded/Ownrshp 1965
Sales 26.6MM^E EMP 85
SIC 1711

D-U-N-S 17-419-9687
HUNTERDON CARE CENTER INC
1 Leisure Ct, Flemington, NJ 08822-5724
Tel (908) 788-9292 Founded/Ownrshp 1986
Sales 21.2MM EMP 175
SIC 8051 8069 8093 8049 8011 Skilled nursing care facilities; Specialty hospitals, except psychiatric; Rehabilitation center, outpatient treatment; Physical therapist; Occupational & industrial specialist, physician/surgeon
Pr: Edmund J Nagle
*VP: Gary Nagle
Nrsg Dir: Sharon Slockbower
HC Dir: Maryann Monahan
Dietician: Sue Durkin

D-U-N-S 08-569-6771
HUNTERDON CENTRAL REGIONAL SCHOOL DISTRICT
HUNTERDON CNTL RGNAL HIGH SCHL
84 State Route 31, Flemington, NJ 08822-1251
Tel (908) 782-5727 Founded/Ownrshp 1954
Sales 63.5MM EMP 9^E
SIC 8211 Public elementary & secondary schools; Public elementary & secondary schools
VP: Jacqueline Cole
Psych: Julie Blake
Psych: Caitlin Burton
Psych: Linda Childs
Psych: Jaclyn Coppola
Psych: Kevin Cubberly
Psych: Catherine Curry
Psych: Katey Edgar
Psych: Kerry Kelly

HUNTERDON CNTL RGNAL HIGH SCHL
See HUNTERDON CENTRAL REGIONAL SCHOOL DISTRICT

D-U-N-S 07-551-4927
HUNTERDON COUNTY YMCA
DEER-PATH FAMILY YMCA
144 W Woodschurch Rd, Flemington, NJ 08822-7016
Tel (908) 782-1030 Founded/Ownrshp 1914
Sales 7.8MM EMP 350
Accts Rich Gelwarg & Lampf Llp Edis
SIC 8641 8322 Youth organizations; Individual & family services; Youth organizations; Individual & family services
Ch: Bruce Black
*V Ch: James Lewey

HUNTERDON HEALTH CARE
See HUNTERDON MEDICAL CENTER (INC)

HUNTERDON HEALTH CARE
See HUNTERDON HEALTHCARE SYSTEM

D-U-N-S 62-049-7792
HUNTERDON HEALTHCARE SYSTEM
HUNTERDON HEALTH CARE
(Suby of HUNTERDON HEALTH CARE) ★
2100 Wescott Dr, Flemington, NJ 08822-4603
Tel (908) 788-6100 Founded/Ownrshp 1986
Sales 3.1MM EMP 1,720^E
SIC 8741 8011 8062 Hospital management; Offices & clinics of medical doctors; General medical & surgical hospitals; Hospital management; Offices & clinics of medical doctors; General medical & surgical hospitals
Pr: Robert P Wise
Chf Path: Steven Diamond
Dir Vol: Lynne Danik
V Ch: James H Griffit
COO: Larry Grand
*CFO: Daniel J Deets
Trst: Mkendra Lewis
Trst: Hugh Prentice
VP: Robert Coates
VP: Neil H Fache
VP: Patricia Steingall
Dir OR: Donna Cole
Dir Rx: David Adelman

D-U-N-S 06-988-6216
HUNTERDON MEDICAL CENTER (INC) (NJ)
HUNTERDON HEALTH CARE
2100 Wescott Dr, Flemington, NJ 08822-4604
Tel (908) 788-6100 Founded/Ownrshp 1948
Sales 264.4MM EMP 2,200
Accts Parentebeard Llc Clark New J
SIC 8062 General medical & surgical hospitals; General medical & surgical hospitals
CEO: Robert P Wise
*COO: Lawrence Grand
COO: Don Pinner
*CFO: Gail Kosyla
Ex VP: Christopher Sickels
*VP: Deborah Hoskins
Exec: Ross Miller
Dir OR: Donna Cole
Dir Teleco: Deirdre Meade
Dir Risk M: Stephanie Dougherty
Genl Mgr: Keia McMillan

Board of Directors: William Atwater

D-U-N-S 09-658-1475
HUNTERS RUN PROPERTY OWNERS ASSOCIATION INC
3500 Clubhouse Ln, Boynton Beach, FL 33436-6002
Tel (561) 735-4002 *Founded/Ownrshp* 1989
Sales 25.5MM *EMP* 250
Accts Mcgladrey Llp Fort Lauderdale
SIC 7997 5812 7992 Golf club, membership; Tennis club, membership; Racquetball club, membership; Eating places; Public golf courses; Golf club, membership; Tennis club, membership; Racquetball club, membership; Eating places; Public golf courses
**Pr:* Harvey Newman
**CEO:* Steven Hagedorn
COO: Mary Watkins
**Treas:* Martin Meyerson
**Treas:* Bernard Silver
**VP:* Carl Sloan

D-U-N-S 08-348-9971 IMP/EXP
HUNTERS SPECIALTIES INC
H S INDUSTRIES
6000 Huntington Ct Ne, Cedar Rapids, IA 52402-1268
Tel (319) 395-0321 *Founded/Ownrshp* 2014
Sales 76.5MM[E] *EMP* 393[E]
SIC 2844 3949 3421 2851 Face creams or lotions; Shampoos, rinses, conditioners: hair; Hunting equipment; Game calls; Cutlery; Paints & allied products; Face creams or lotions; Shampoos, rinses, conditioners: hair; Hunting equipment; Game calls; Cutlery; Paints & allied products
Pr: Larry Bildstein
COO: John Brockardt
CFO: Jim McGoldrick
**VP:* Carman Forbes
Exec: Dave Forbes
Genl Mgr: Brad Wicher
CTO: Ron Bean
Dir IT: Rick Holtz
IT Man: Steve Kimm
Opers Mgr: Jeff Martin
Ql Cn Mgr: Sam Kadura

D-U-N-S 13-841-7774
HUNTERSVILLE FORD LLC
13825 Statesville Rd, Huntersville, NC 28078-9040
Tel (704) 875-6547 *Founded/Ownrshp* 2002
Sales 24.3MM[E] *EMP* 65
SIC 5511 Automobiles, new & used; Automobiles, new & used
Sales Asso: Todd Jones

D-U-N-S 10-168-1687
HUNTGTN BCH HSP BDU OUTPATIENT
HUNTINGTON BEACH HOSPITAL
8201 Newman Ave, Huntington Beach, CA 92647-7020
Tel (714) 375-5405 *Founded/Ownrshp* 2002
Sales 50.4MM *EMP* 1
SIC 8062 8093 General medical & surgical hospitals; Mental health clinic, outpatient; General medical & surgical hospitals; Mental health clinic, outpatient
Prin: Beverly Hatch

D-U-N-S 09-936-9944
HUNTING DEARBORN INC
(*Suby of* HUNTING PLC)
6 Dearborn Dr, Fryeburg, ME 04037-1609
Tel (207) 935-2171 *Founded/Ownrshp* 2011
Sales 80.4MM[E] *EMP* 250
SIC 3599 Machine shop, jobbing & repair; Machine shop, jobbing & repair
Pr: Bill Findeisen
**Ch Bd:* Thomas Shaffner
CFO: Mel Davies
**CFO:* Robert F Newton
**VP:* Kenneth Dearborn
Genl Mgr: David Pasquale
IT Man: Robert Newton
Sfty Mgr: Kandra Kincaid
Ql Cn Mgr: Justin Bartlett
Ql Cn Mgr: Greg Cunningham
Sls Mgr: Frank Lawrence

HUNTING ENERGY SERVICES
See NATIONAL COUPLING CO INC

D-U-N-S 80-851-4517 IMP
HUNTING ENERGY SERVICES INC
HUNTING OILFIELD SERVICES.
(*Suby of* HUNTING PLC)
2 Northpoint Dr Ste 400, Houston, TX 77060-3233
Tel (281) 820-3838 *Founded/Ownrshp* 1993
Sales 261.3MM[E] *EMP* 577
SIC 1389 8741 Oil field services; Management services; Oil field services; Management services
CEO: Dennis L Proctor
Pr: Will Oliver
VP: Keith Crews
VP: Gene McBride
Exec: Yovita Christianti
Ex Dir: Jim Johnson
Mng Dir: Scott George
Area Mgr: Blair Ask
Genl Mgr: Mike Hooper
IT Man: Robert Bingham
IT Man: Roger Lenz

D-U-N-S 06-930-6553 IMP/EXP
HUNTING ENERGY SERVICES LP
HUNTING IBERIA
3817 Melancon Rd, Broussard, LA 70518-8242
Tel (337) 367-9296 *Founded/Ownrshp* 1972
Sales 20.6MM[E] *EMP* 150
SIC 3498 3599 Fabricated pipe & fittings; Machine & other job shop work
CEO: Ivan Jennings
Ofcr: Charlie Braus
**VP:* Robert Halphen
Genl Mgr: Klane Kirby
QC Dir: David Guidry
Prd Mgr: Kerry Derouen

HUNTING IBERIA
See HUNTING ENERGY SERVICES LP

D-U-N-S 61-028-0307 IMP
HUNTING INNOVA INC
INNOVA ELECTRONICS
(*Suby of* HUNTING PLC)
8383 N Sam Houston Pkwy W, Houston, TX 77064-3452
Tel (281) 653-5500 *Founded/Ownrshp* 1989
Sales 102.8MM[E] *EMP* 350
SIC 3672 3613 8711 Printed circuit boards; Power switching equipment; Engineering services; Printed circuit boards; Power switching equipment; Engineering services
CEO: Dennis Proctor
Pr: Leon Chenn
CFO: Robert Snider
Rgnl Mgr: Sandra Park
CTO: Dennis Wilson
Prd Mgr: Mary Leamons

HUNTING OILFIELD SERVICES.
See HUNTING ENERGY SERVICES INC

D-U-N-S 07-839-1908
HUNTING PLC USA
(*Suby of* HUNTING PLC)
24 Waterway Ave Ste 700, The Woodlands, TX 77380-3391
Tel (713) 595-2950 *Founded/Ownrshp* 2012
Sales 59.3MM[E] *EMP* 590
SIC 1382 Oil & gas exploration services; Oil & gas exploration services
CEO: Dennis Proctor
COO: Jim Johnson

D-U-N-S 17-087-9915
HUNTING SPECIALTY SUPPLY LP
(*Suby of* HUNTING ENERGY SERVICES INC) ★
13730 Cypress N Huston Rd, Cypress, TX 77429-3237
Tel (281) 970-8444 *Founded/Ownrshp* 2011
Sales 22.1MM[E] *EMP* 50
SIC 3533 Oil & gas drilling rigs & equipment
Pt: Gerald Byrd
Genl Pt: James Chambers
Pt: Gerald R Byrd

D-U-N-S 00-738-7178 IMP/EXP
HUNTING TITAN LTD
(*Suby of* HUNTING PLC USA) ★
11785 Highway 152, Pampa, TX 79065-1414
Tel (806) 665-3781 *Founded/Ownrshp* 1966, 1997
Sales 59.3MM[E] *EMP* 363
SIC 3533

D-U-N-S 10-384-1763 IMP
HUNTING U S HOLDINGS INC
(*Suby of* HUNTING ENERGY HOLDINGS LIMITED)
1610 Woodstead Ct Ste 310, The Woodlands, TX 77380-3403
Tel (281) 363-2406 *Founded/Ownrshp* 1982
Sales 30.5MM[E] *EMP* 495
SIC 2399 Parachutes; Parachutes
Pr: D Keith Crews

D-U-N-S 08-214-5608
HUNTINGDON COLLEGE
UNITED METHODIST CHURCH
(*Suby of* ALABAMA-WEST FLORIDA CONFERENCE OF UNITED METHODIST CHURCH INC) ★
1500 E Fairview Ave, Montgomery, AL 36106-2148
Tel (334) 833-4222 *Founded/Ownrshp* 1911
Sales 29.9MM *EMP* 185[E]
SIC 8221 College, except junior; College, except junior
Pr: J Cameron West
Ex VP: Frank C Montealvo
VP: Renee Carlisle
VP: Kyle Fedler
VP: Anthony Leigh
VP: Suellen Ofe
VP: Frank Parsons
Exec: Adrienne Gaines
Exec: Cate Holbrook
Dir Soc: William Davis
Dir IT: Bruner Rick

HUNTINGDON LIFE SCIENCES INC.
See ENVIGO CRS INC

D-U-N-S 07-682-6015 IMP
■ **HUNTINGTON ALLOYS CORP**
PART OF SPECIAL METALS
(*Suby of* PCC) ★
3200 Riverside Dr, Huntington, WV 25705-1764
Tel (304) 526-5100 *Founded/Ownrshp* 1928
Sales 244.8MM[E] *EMP* 1,000
SIC 3356 Nickel & nickel alloy: rolling, drawing or extruding; Nickel & nickel alloy: rolling, drawing or extruding
Pr: Kenneth D Buck
Pr: Keith Dabbs
Pr: Brett McBrayer
Sr VP: Steve Tassen
**VP:* Roger P Becker
**VP:* Darrin Bird
VP: Chad Gallentine
VP: Shailesh Patel
VP: Michael Williams
**VP:* Steve Zylstra
Area Supr: Jerry Blevins

D-U-N-S 04-643-1227
▲ **HUNTINGTON BANCSHARES INC**
41 S High St, Columbus, OH 43215-6170
Tel (614) 480-8300 *Founded/Ownrshp* 1966
Sales NA *EMP* 11,873[E]
Accts Deloitte & Touche Llp Columbu
Tkr Sym HBAN *Exch* NGS
SIC 6021 National commercial banks; National commercial banks
Ch Bd: Stephen D Steinour
Pr: Paul Baldwin
Pr: Amy Beck
Pr: Angela Buchwald
Pr: Emily Dahs
Pr: Michael Dicecco
Pr: Mike Fezzey
Pr: David Hammer
Pr: James H Nicholson
Pr: Andrew Paterno
Pr: Anne Pyle
Pr: Joseph Rezabek
Pr: Susan Baker Shipley
Pr: Cari Waugh
Pr: Jeff Young
CFO: Angela Campbell
CFO: Howell D McCullough II
Ch: Roger L Mann
Chf Mktg O: William Eiler
Chf Mktg O: Tom Ohara
Chf Inves: Randy Bateman
Board of Directors: Kathleen H Ransier, Ann B Crane, Steven G Elliott, Michael J Endres, John B Gerlach Jr, Peter J Kight, Jonathan A Levy, Eddie R Munson, Richard W Neu, David L Porteous

D-U-N-S 07-359-3584
HUNTINGTON BEACH CITY SCHOOL DISTRICT
17011 Beach Blvd Ste 560, Huntington Beach, CA 92647-7492
Tel (714) 964-8888 *Founded/Ownrshp* 1903
Sales 32.4MM[E] *EMP* 600
SIC 8211 Public elementary & secondary schools; Public elementary & secondary schools
Top Exec: Bruce Wright
Dir IT: Debbie Bartlett
Dir IT: James Lincoln
IT Man: Jon Archibald

D-U-N-S 17-579-7026
HUNTINGTON BEACH CONVALESCENT HOSPITAL
SEA CLIFF HEALTH CARE
18811 Florida St, Huntington Beach, CA 92648-1920
Tel (714) 847-3515 *Founded/Ownrshp* 2004
Sales 9.3MM[E] *EMP* 300
SIC 8051 Convalescent home with continuous nursing care; Convalescent home with continuous nursing care
Nrsg Dir: Evelyn Aranton Rn

D-U-N-S 05-980-5853
HUNTINGTON BEACH DODGE INC
16701 Beach Blvd, Huntington Beach, CA 92647-4814
Tel (714) 847-5515 *Founded/Ownrshp* 1998
Sales 34.3MM[E] *EMP* 100
SIC 5511 Automobiles, new & used; Automobiles, new & used
Pr: Clay James
Sls Mgr: Gregg Greco
Sls Mgr: Alen Hurst

HUNTINGTON BEACH FORD
See YORK ENTERPRISES SOUTH INC

HUNTINGTON BEACH HOSPITAL
See PRIME HEALTHCARE HUNTINGTON BEACH LLC

HUNTINGTON BEACH HOSPITAL
See HUNTGTN BCH HSP BDU OUTPATIENT

D-U-N-S 07-954-5703
HUNTINGTON BEACH UNION HIGH SCHOOL DISTRICT
5832 Bolsa Ave, Huntington Beach, CA 92649-1181
Tel (714) 903-7000 *Founded/Ownrshp* 1991
Sales 89.4MM[E] *EMP* 1,552
SIC 8211 Public elementary & secondary schools; Public elementary & secondary schools
**Pr:* Bonnie Castrey
Bd of Dir: Matthew Harper
**VP:* Kathleen Iverson
Adm Dir: John Klungreseter
Instr Medi: Shirley Bowen
Board of Directors: Bonnie Bruce, Bonnie Castrey, Sallie Dashiell, Matthew Harper, Michael Simons

D-U-N-S 07-268-4152
HUNTINGTON CABELL HOSPITAL INC
CABELL HOME HEALTH SERVICES
1340 Hal Greer Blvd, Huntington, WV 25701-0195
Tel (304) 526-2000 *Founded/Ownrshp* 1955
Sales 417.6MM *EMP* 2,300[E]
SIC 8062 Hospital, professional nursing school with AMA residency; Hospital, professional nursing school with AMA residency
Pr: Brent A Marsteller
Treas: Pat Cromwell
**Treas:* Floyd Eharlow Jr
**VP:* David Graley
VP: Paul Smith
VP: Mark Twilla
Dir Case M: Christine Maniskas
Ex Dir: Michele Conley
QA Dir: Valerie Hopkins-Smith
Tech Mgr: Garry Atkins
VP Opers: Glen Washington

D-U-N-S 01-275-8512
HUNTINGTON CHEVROLET INC (NY)
370 Oakwood Rd, Huntington Station, NY 11746-7214
Tel (631) 427-0900 *Founded/Ownrshp* 1945, 1999
Sales 73.0MM *EMP* 107
SIC 5511 Automobiles, new & used
Pr: Gregory Williams

D-U-N-S 04-765-0585
HUNTINGTON COACH CORP
64 Bayville Ave, Bayville, NY 11709-1656
Tel (631) 423-0400 *Founded/Ownrshp* 1956
Sales 29.0MM[E] *EMP* 250
SIC 4151 School buses; School buses
Pr: Kevin Clifford

D-U-N-S 07-891-5303
HUNTINGTON COUNTY COMMUNITY SCHOOL CORP
2485 Waterworks Rd, Huntington, IN 46750-4145
Tel (260) 356-8312 *Founded/Ownrshp* 1966
Sales 57.5MM[E] *EMP* 1,000
SIC 8211 Public combined elementary & secondary school; Public combined elementary & secondary school
Treas: Edette Eckert
**Treas:* Sheila Hall

MIS Dir: Nick Vickrey
Dir IT: Tom Ashley

D-U-N-S 79-495-8538 EXP
HUNTINGTON FOAM LLC
101 N 4th St, Jeannette, PA 15644-3331
Tel (724) 522-5144 *Founded/Ownrshp* 2008
Sales 39.9MM[E] *EMP* 248
SIC 3086 Plastics foam products; Plastics foam products
Pr: Ed Flynn
**CFO:* Thomas Kuehl

D-U-N-S 04-607-8911
HUNTINGTON FORD INC
2890 S Rochester Rd, Rochester Hills, MI 48307-5801
Tel (248) 852-4500 *Founded/Ownrshp* 1968
Sales 38.0MM[E] *EMP* 110
SIC 5511 Automobiles, new & used; Automobiles, new & used
Pr: Patrick Scoggin
**Pr:* John T Huntington
Store Mgr: Paul Pearcy
Sls Mgr: Dan Saunders

HUNTINGTON HERALD-DISPATCH
See CHAMPION PUBLISHING INC

HUNTINGTON HILLS CENTER
See EAST NORTHPORT RESIDENTIAL HEALTH CARE FACILITY INC

HUNTINGTON HONDA/SAAB
See L & S MOTORS INC

D-U-N-S 06-911-6521
HUNTINGTON HOSPITAL
100 W California Blvd, Pasadena, CA 91105-3010
Tel (626) 397-5000 *Founded/Ownrshp* 2011
Sales 513.4MM *EMP* 237[E]
SIC 8062 General medical & surgical hospitals
Prin: Peter W Corrigan
CFO: Jim Noble
VP: Bonnie Kass
VP: Debbie Tafoya
Dir Lab: Jessica Graves
Dir Rx: Berina Leslie
CTO: Sheryl Rudie
Dir IT: Henry Jenkins
IT Man: Weldon Clark
Surgeon: Magdi Alexander
Obsttrcn: Joseph Ll

D-U-N-S 04-919-0598
HUNTINGTON HOSPITAL AUXILIARY
270 Park Ave, Huntington, NY 11743-2799
Tel (631) 351-2257 *Founded/Ownrshp* 1917
Sales 325.5MM *EMP* 6
SIC 5947 5499 8322 Gift shop; Coffee; Social service center; Gift shop; Coffee; Social service center
Pr: Barbara Mawra

D-U-N-S 06-802-0726
HUNTINGTON HOSPITAL DOLAN FAMILY HEALTH CENTER INC
270 Park Ave, Huntington, NY 11743-2799
Tel (631) 351-2000 *Founded/Ownrshp* 1915
Sales 325.5MM *EMP* 2,000
SIC 8062 General medical & surgical hospitals; General medical & surgical hospitals
CEO: Michael J Dowling
Dir Recs: Robert Coelho
Dir Vol: Gina Torchon
**Ch Bd:* Irving Klein
**CEO:* Kevin Lawlor
**Treas:* Gordon Hargraves
Bd of Dir: Douglas Byrnes
Bd of Dir: Robert Zingale
Top Exec: Joseph G Gavin Jr
**VP:* Michael J Alesandro
VP: Robert Mottola
VP: Michael Quartier
Exec: Sue Schmeising
Dir OR: Jeanette Brown
Dir Lab: Jeanne Thompson
Dir Rx: Mateyunas Jack
Dir Rx: Jack Mateyunas

D-U-N-S 00-130-7495 IMP
■ **HUNTINGTON INGALLS INC**
(*Suby of* HUNTINGTON INGALLS INDUSTRIES INC) ★
4101 Washington Ave, Newport News, VA 23607-2734
Tel (757) 380-2000 *Founded/Ownrshp* 2011
Sales 3.3MMM[E] *EMP* 19,000[E]
SIC 3731 Shipbuilding & repairing; Submarines, building & repairing; Military ships, building & repairing; Tankers, building & repairing; Shipbuilding & repairing; Submarines, building & repairing; Military ships, building & repairing; Tankers, building & repairing
Pr: Mike Peters
**Treas:* D R Wyatt
VP: William Ermatinger
VP: Douglass Fontaine
VP: Dennis Gallimore
**VP:* Alene Kaufman
**VP:* Barbara A Niland
Genl Mgr: Janet Barker
Genl Mgr: Jim Kaltenschnee
MIS Dir: Bobby Tolbert
IT Man: Richard Clabbers
Board of Directors: Ken Mahler

D-U-N-S 96-736-2331
▲ **HUNTINGTON INGALLS INDUSTRIES INC**
4101 Washington Ave, Newport News, VA 23607-2734
Tel (757) 380-2000 *Founded/Ownrshp* 1886
Sales 6.9MMM *EMP* 38,000[E]
Tkr Sym HII *Exch* NYS
SIC 3731 Military ships, building & repairing; Military ships, building & repairing
Pr: C Michael Petters
CFO: Barbara A Niland
CFO: Thomas Stiehle
Ofcr: Chavis Harris
Ofcr: Kenneth Rogers
VP: Carolyn E Apostolou
VP: Daniel L Arczynski

VP: Ray Bagley
VP: Bill Bell
VP: Dwayne B Blake
VP: Gerald Boyd
VP: Jerri Fuller Dickseski
VP: John Donnelly
VP: Irwin F Edenzon
VP: Bill Ermatinger
VP: Tim Farrell
VP: Andy Green
VP: Daniel P Holloway
VP: George Jones
VP: Christopher D Kastner
VP: Ren Mathieu
Board of Directors: Robert F Bruner, Thomas B Fargo, Victoria D Harker, Anastasia D Kelly, Paul D Miller, Thomas C Schievelbein, Karl M Von Der Heyden, John K Welch, Stephen R Wilson

D-U-N-S 78-101-1999
■ HUNTINGTON INGALLS INDUSTRIES INTERNATIONAL SHIPBUILDING INC
(*Suby of* HUNTINGTON INGALLS INC) ★
1000 Access Rd, Pascagoula, MS 39567-4485
Tel (228) 935-1122 *Founded/Ownrshp* 2011
Sales 185.3MM^E *EMP* 1^E
SIC 3731 Combat vessels, building & repairing
Pr: Philip Teek
**Treas:* James L Sanford
VP: Lori Harper
VP: Richard Schenk

D-U-N-S 00-541-7522
■ HUNTINGTON INSURANCE INC
(*Suby of* HUNTINGTON NATIONAL BANK) ★
519 Madison Ave, Toledo, OH 43604-1206
Tel (419) 720-7900 *Founded/Ownrshp* 1898
Sales NA *EMP* 189
SIC 6411 Insurance agents; Insurance agents
Pr: Paul Baldwin
COO: Alan Thomas
CFO: Dennis Raab
Treas: Pamela M Alspach
Sr VP: Robert C Hawker Cpcu Arm
Sr VP: Ralph Burkley
Sr VP: William Fether
Sr VP: Robert Hawker
Sr VP: Ronald L Murray
Sr VP: Leslie Talkington
VP: A D Story

HUNTINGTON INTNL MED GRP
See ULTIMATE HEALTH SERVICES INC

HUNTINGTON LEARNING CENTER
See HUNTINGTON LEARNING CORP

D-U-N-S 08-975-0780
HUNTINGTON LEARNING CORP
HUNTINGTON LEARNING CENTER
496 Kinderkamack Rd G01, Oradell, NJ 07649-1512
Tel (201) 261-8400 *Founded/Ownrshp* 1986
Sales 173.5MM^E *EMP* 15,000
SIC 8299 Tutoring school; Tutoring school
Ch: Raymond J Huntington
**VP:* Eileen C Huntington

D-U-N-S 06-384-0797
HUNTINGTON LIBRARY ART COLLECTIONS AND BOTANICAL GARDEN
1151 Oxford Rd, San Marino, CA 91108-1218
Tel (626) 405-2100 *Founded/Ownrshp* 1919
Sales 24.2MM^E *EMP* 380
SIC 8231 8412 8422 Public library; Art gallery, noncommercial; Botanical garden; Public library; Art gallery, noncommercial; Botanical garden
Ch Bd: Robert F Erburu
**Pr:* Steve Koblik
**Pr:* Robert Skotheim
CFO: Alison Snowden
Trst: Scott Jordan
Ofcr: Rebecca Shea
VP: Susan Campi
VP: Coreen Rodgers
**VP:* Laurie Sowd
Dir Soc: Jessica Visu
Opers Mgr: Loren Alison

HUNTINGTON MED PATHOLOGY GROUP
See PASADENA CYTO PATHOLOGY LABORATORY INC

D-U-N-S 87-927-5428
HUNTINGTON MEDICAL FOUNDATION
PASADENA COMMUNITY URGENT CARE
133 N Altadena Dr Ste 201, Pasadena, CA 91107-7328
Tel (626) 397-8322 *Founded/Ownrshp* 1995
Sales 25.9MM *EMP* 250
Accts Ernst & Young Us Llp Irvine
SIC 8099 Medical services organization; Medical services organization
CEO: David Lee
Off Mgr: Diane Taylor
Doctor: Laura Mabie

D-U-N-S 06-474-9732
HUNTINGTON MEDICAL GROUP P C
180 E Pulaski Rd, Huntington Station, NY 11746-1915
Tel (631) 425-2175 *Founded/Ownrshp* 1946
Sales 31.5MM^E *EMP* 270
SIC 8011 Pediatrician; Pediatrician
Ex Dir: Fred Weinstein
**Pr:* Thomas Mc Donagh MD
Ofcr: Kelly Fontana
**VP:* Faisal Siddiqui
**VP:* Joel Sive MD
Opthamlgy: Shaul Debbi
Doctor: Abu Ahmed
Doctor: Thomas McDonough
Doctor: Caludette Poole
Doctor: Sara V Siddique

HUNTINGTON MEMORIAL HOSPITAL
See PASADENA HOSPITAL ASSOCIATION LTD

D-U-N-S 06-975-9520
HUNTINGTON MEMORIAL HOSPITAL INC
PARKVIEW HUNTINGTON HOSPITAL
2001 Stults Rd, Huntington, IN 46750-1282
Tel (260) 355-3000 *Founded/Ownrshp* 1900
Sales 59.1MM *EMP* 300
SIC 8062 General medical & surgical hospitals; General medical & surgical hospitals
Ch Bd: Janet McElhaney
Pr: Kelly Hesting
Pr: Laura Hughes
**COO:* Darlene Garrett
**CFO:* Michael Browning
Doctor: Anil RAO

D-U-N-S 09-972-8669 IMP
■ HUNTINGTON NATIONAL BANK
(*Suby of* HUNTINGTON BANCSHARES INC) ★
41 S High St Fl 1, Columbus, OH 43215-6167
Tel (614) 480-8300 *Founded/Ownrshp* 1979
Sales NA *EMP* 10,100
SIC 6029 Commercial banks; Commercial banks
Pr: Stephen D Steinour
Pr: Renee Csuhran
Pr: Sadhana Mohan
Pr: William C Shivers
COO: Paul Heller
CFO: Howell D McCullough III
Sr Tst Off: Brian Wolfe
Assoc VP: Timothy Bender
Ex VP: David S Anderson
Ex VP: Barbara Benham
Ex VP: Richard A Cheap
Ex VP: Jeff Sturm
Sr VP: William R Adon
Sr VP: Dave Bartlett
Sr VP: Susan Brueckman
Sr VP: Joel Coursey
Sr VP: Chris Daniels
Sr VP: Laurens J De Kort
Sr VP: Diane L Dougherty
Sr VP: Bryan Fialkowski
Sr VP: William Harris
Board of Directors: David L Porteous, Dave Anderson, Kathleen H Ransier, Don M Casto III, Ann B Crane, Steven G Elliott, Michael J Endres, John B Gerlach Jr, Peter J Kight, Jonathan A Levy, Richard W Neu

HUNTINGTON PENNYSAVER
See STAR COMMUNITY PUBLISHING GROUP LLC

D-U-N-S 08-552-3769
HUNTINGTON SANITARY BOARD
555 7th Ave, Huntington, WV 25701-1931
Tel (304) 696-5564 *Founded/Ownrshp* 1935
Sales 26.5MM^E *EMP* 75
SIC 4952 Sewerage systems; Sewerage systems
Sfty Dirs: Martin Shelton
Snr Mgr: Scott Kelley

HUNTINGTON TOWN HALL
See TOWN OF HUNTINGTON

D-U-N-S 07-751-3117
HUNTINGTON UNION FREE SCHOOL DISTRICT 3
50 Tower St, Huntington Station, NY 11746-1233
Tel (631) 673-2121 *Founded/Ownrshp* 1657
Sales 42.7MM^E *EMP* 795
Accts Cullen & Danowski Llp Port J
SIC 8211 Public elementary & secondary schools; Public elementary & secondary schools
Pr Dir: James Hoops
Instr Medi: Mike Tudisco

D-U-N-S 05-286-4972
HUNTINGTON UNIVERSITY INC
2303 College Ave, Huntington, IN 46750-1237
Tel (260) 356-6000 *Founded/Ownrshp* 1897
Sales 25.9MM *EMP* 170^E
Accts Bkd Llp Fort Wayne Indiana
SIC 8221 College, except junior; College, except junior
Pr: Sherilyn Emberton
**CFO:* Thomas W Ayers
**CFO:* Greg Smitley
VP: Michael Wanous
Genl Mgr: Blair Stairs
Pr Dir: Mark Schenkel
Pgrm Dir: Susie Boyer
Snr Mgr: Kyle Shondell

HUNTLEIGH MCGEEHEE
See CLJM LLC

D-U-N-S 06-321-9607
HUNTLEIGH USA CORP
545 E John Carpenter Fwy, Irving, TX 75062-3931
Tel (972) 719-9180 *Founded/Ownrshp* 2011
Sales 123.5MM^E *EMP* 2,300
SIC 4581

D-U-N-S 80-432-7505
HUNTLEY JOHN INC
MILLS ELECTRIC CO
4430 Pacific Hwy, Bellingham, WA 98226-9068
Tel (360) 734-0730 *Founded/Ownrshp* 2006
Sales 35.0MM *EMP* 220
Accts Moss-Adams Llp Bellingham Wa
SIC 1731 Electrical work; Electrical work
Pr: John Huntley
Opers Mgr: Josh Huntley

HUNTNGTON BEACH CHRYSLER
See SURF CITY AUTO GROUP INC

D-U-N-S 07-475-1827
HUNTON & WILLIAMS LLP
951 E Byrd St Riverfro Riverfront, Richmond, VA 23219
Tel (804) 788-8200 *Founded/Ownrshp* 1901
Sales 395.5MM^E *EMP* 1,541
SIC 8111 General practice law office; General practice law office
Mng Pt: Walfrido Martinez
Pt: W Christopher Arbery
Pt: Steven H Becker
Pt: Ken Bell
Pt: Stephen Bennett
Pt: Lawrence J Bracken II
Pt: Emerson V Briggs
Pt: Tyler P Brown
Pt: Christopher Graffiin Browning
Pt: Eric R Burner
Pt: Terence G Connor
Pt: Cyane Crump
Pt: J Mark Debord
Pt: Robert H Edwards Jr
**Pt:* Juan Enjamio
Pt: Edward J Fuhr
Pt: Robert J Grey Jr
Pt: Robert J Hahn
Pt: Doug Heffner
Pt: Matthew C Henry
Pt: Louanna O Heuhsen
Board of Directors: William Brownell

HUNTON AND WILLIAM
See SUSAN F WILTSIE

HUNTON GROUP, THE
See HOU-TRA INTERNATIONAL

HUNTON TRANE
See HTI LTD

HUNTON TRANE SERVICES
See HVAC MECHANICAL SERVICES OF TEXAS LTD

HUNTS PHOTO & VIDEO
See W B HUNT CO INC

D-U-N-S 08-464-4335
HUNTS POINT COOPERATIVE MARKET INC
355 Food Center Dr, Bronx, NY 10474-7000
Tel (718) 328-0179 *Founded/Ownrshp* 1990
Sales 25.5MM^E *EMP* 50
SIC 5141 5147 Groceries, general line; Meats & meat products
Ch Bd: Steven Schwartzreich
**Sec:* Vincent Pacifico

D-U-N-S 00-197-2363
HUNTSINGER FARMS INC (WI)
2424 Alpine Rd, Eau Claire, WI 54703-9562
Tel (715) 832-9739 *Founded/Ownrshp* 1929
Sales 47.3MM^E *EMP* 200
SIC 2035 0161 2099 Horseradish, prepared; Mustard, prepared (wet); Rooted vegetable farms; Food preparations; Horseradish, prepared; Mustard, prepared (wet); Rooted vegetable farms; Food preparations
VP: Nancy J Bartusch
Mktg Mgr: Eric Rygg

HUNTSMAN ADVANCED MATERIALS
See RUBICON LLC

D-U-N-S 15-926-0202 IMP/EXP
■ HUNTSMAN ADVANCED MATERIALS AMERICAS LLC
(*Suby of* HUNTSMAN ADVANCED MATERIALS LLC) ★
500 S Huntsman Way, Salt Lake City, UT 84108-1235
Tel (801) 584-5700 *Founded/Ownrshp* 2003
Sales 73.0MM^E *EMP* 490
SIC 2821 Plastics materials & resins; Plastics materials & resins
Pr: Peter Huntsman
Ch: Jon M Huntsman
Bd of Dir: Michael K Young
Ex VP: Robert Haight
VP: Curtis Dowd
Admn Mgr: Carol Hollinshead
Opers Mgr: Dennis Ivins

D-U-N-S 14-145-8583 EXP
■ HUNTSMAN ADVANCED MATERIALS LLC
(*Suby of* HUNTSMAN CORP) ★
500 S Huntsman Way, Salt Lake City, UT 84108-1235
Tel (801) 584-5700 *Founded/Ownrshp* 2008
Sales 73.0MM^E *EMP* 491
SIC 2821 2891 3087 Plastics materials & resins; Adhesives & sealants; Custom compound purchased resins; Plastics materials & resins; Adhesives & sealants; Custom compound purchased resins
VP: Maria Csiba-Womersley
VP: Maria Csiba-Womersly
VP: Kevin Hardman

D-U-N-S 83-017-5274
HUNTSMAN CANCER FOUNDATION
500 S Huntsman Way, Salt Lake City, UT 84108-1235
Tel (801) 584-5700 *Founded/Ownrshp* 2009
Sales 47.0MM *EMP* 35^E
Accts Deloitte Tax Llp Salt Lake Ci
SIC 8069 Cancer hospital
CEO: Peter R Huntsman

D-U-N-S 61-111-5721
HUNTSMAN CANCER HOSPITAL
HUNTSMAN COMPREHENSIVE BREAST
1950 Circle Of Hope Dr, Salt Lake City, UT 84112-5500
Tel (801) 587-7000 *Founded/Ownrshp* 2005
Sales NA *EMP* 81^E
SIC 6324 Hospital & medical service plans; Hospital & medical service plans
Prin: Michael Kelly
Ex Dir: Ray Linch
Ex Dir: Rayn Lych
Ex Dir: Raymond Lynch
IT Man: Blue Macelwee
Surgeon: Esther Kannapel
Surgeon: Jason J Schwartz
Doctor: Ali Choucair

HUNTSMAN COMPREHENSIVE BREAST
See HUNTSMAN CANCER HOSPITAL

D-U-N-S 18-257-5584 IMP
▲ HUNTSMAN CORP
500 S Huntsman Way, Salt Lake City, UT 84108-1235
Tel (801) 584-5700 *Founded/Ownrshp* 1970
Sales 11.5MMM *EMP* 16,000
Accts Deloitte & Touche Llp Houston
Tkr Sym HUN *Exch* NYS
SIC 2821 3081 2869 2816 2865 Polystyrene resins; Polyethylene film; Ethylene; Propylene, butylene; Titanium dioxide, anatase or rutile (pigments); Dyes & pigments; Polystyrene resins; Polyethylene film; Ethylene; Propylene, butylene; Titanium dioxide, anatase or rutile (pigments); Dyes & pigments
Pr: Peter R Huntsman
Ch Bd: Jon M Huntsman
CFO: J Kimo Esplin
CFO: David Huntsman
V Ch Bd: Nolan D Archibald
Ofcr: Kimo Esplin
Ofcr: Maria Womersley
Ex VP: Edwin Clement
Ex VP: Bob Haight
Ex VP: David Stryker
VP: Maria Csiba-Womersley
VP: Curt Ogdon
VP: Eric Phillips
VP: Randy W Wright
Exec: Kevin Huntsman
Exec: Rick Kovacich
Exec: Vivi Sutardi

D-U-N-S 13-162-8534 EXP
■ HUNTSMAN HOLDINGS LLC
(*Suby of* HUNTSMAN CORP) ★
500 S Huntsman Way, Salt Lake City, UT 84108-1235
Tel (801) 584-5700 *Founded/Ownrshp* 2005
Sales 320.2MM^E *EMP* 11,595
SIC 2821 2911 3081 2869 Polystyrene resins; Petroleum refining; Polyethylene film; Ethylene; Propylene, butylene; Polystyrene resins; Petroleum refining; Polyethylene film; Ethylene; Propylene, butylene
CEO: Peter R Huntsman
CFO: J Kimo Esplin
Ch: Jon M Huntsman
Ex VP: Samuel D Scruggs

D-U-N-S 08-737-6146 IMP/EXP
■ HUNTSMAN INTERNATIONAL LLC
(*Suby of* HUNTSMAN CORP) ★
500 S Huntsman Way, Salt Lake City, UT 84108-1235
Tel (801) 584-5700 *Founded/Ownrshp* 1999
Sales 11.5MMM *EMP* 16,000
Accts Deloitte & Touche Llp Houston
SIC 2821 3081 2869 2816 2865 Polystyrene resins; Polyethylene film; Ethylene; Propylene, butylene; Titanium dioxide, anatase or rutile (pigments); Dyes & pigments; Polystyrene resins; Polyethylene film; Ethylene; Propylene, butylene; Titanium dioxide, anatase or rutile (pigments); Dyes & pigments
Pr: Peter R Huntsman
**Ch Bd:* Jon M Huntsman
CFO: J Kimo Esplin
Ex VP: David M Stryker
VP: Randy W Wright
Dir IT: Deon Hill
Dir IT: Brenda Keeler
Board of Directors: Nolan D Archibald, Mary C Beckerle, M Anthony Burns, Patrick Harker, Jon M Huntsman Jr, Robert Margetts, Wayne A Reaud, Alvin V Shoemaker

D-U-N-S 92-605-7969
■ HUNTSMAN INTERNATIONAL TRADING CORP
(*Suby of* HUNTSMAN PETROCHEMICAL LLC) ★
10003 Woodloch Forest Dr # 260, The Woodlands, TX 77380-1955
Tel (281) 719-6000 *Founded/Ownrshp* 1994
Sales 599.5MM^E *EMP* 300
SIC 5169 Chemicals & allied products; Chemicals & allied products
CEO: Peter R Huntsman
**Ch:* Jon M Huntsman
**VP:* Sean Douglas
**Pr:* J Kimo Esplin
**VP:* Kevin C Hardman
**VP:* John R Heskett
VP: James H Huntsman
Exec: Becky Rieger
CTO: Christopher Cox
Dir IT: Brian McIntosh
IT Man: Shii Lee

D-U-N-S 04-754-7690 IMP/EXP
■ HUNTSMAN P&A AMERICAS LLC
HUNTSMAN PIGMENTS & ADDITIVES
(*Suby of* HUNTSMAN CORP) ★
7101 Muirkirk Rd, Beltsville, MD 20705-1333
Tel (301) 210-3400 *Founded/Ownrshp* 2014
Sales 2.7MM^E *EMP* 585
SIC 2895 2816 2299 5169 Carbon black; Zinc pigments: zinc oxide, zinc sulfide; Chrome pigments: chrome green, chrome yellow, zinc yellow; Iron oxide pigments (ochers, siennas, umbers); Yarn, metallic, ceramic or paper fibers; Chemicals & allied products; Concrete additives; Carbon black; Zinc pigments: zinc oxide, zinc sulfide; Chrome pigments: chrome green, chrome yellow, zinc yellow; Iron oxide pigments (ochers, siennas, umbers); Yarn, metallic, ceramic or paper fibers; Chemicals & allied products; Concrete additives
Mng Dir: Andrew M Ross
VP: Dennis Turner
Genl Mgr: Mike Corcoran
CIO: Matt Davis
IT Man: Jonathan Ellis
Tech Mgr: John Kurnas
Tech Mgr: Peter Wright
VP Mfg: Harry Reid
Sfty Mgr: Ramesh Patel
Ql Cn Mgr: Brian Golden
Manager: Jeff Bourne

D-U-N-S 14-717-3017 EXP
■ HUNTSMAN PETROCHEMICAL LLC
(*Suby of* HUNTSMAN INTERNATIONAL LLC) ★
500 S Huntsman Way, Salt Lake City, UT 84108-1235
Tel (801) 584-5700 *Founded/Ownrshp* 1994
Sales 599.5MM^E *EMP* 1,500
SIC 2911 Petroleum refining; Petroleum refining
**Pr:* Peter R Huntsman
**CFO:* J Kimo Esplin
Treas: Jena Howland
**Ex VP:* James R Moore
**VP:* Kevin C Hardman
**VP:* L Russell Healy
VP: Karen Huntsman

HUNTSMAN PIGMENTS & ADDITIVES
See HUNTSMAN P&A AMERICAS LLC

D-U-N-S 07-835-4818 IMP/EXP
■ HUNTSMAN-COOPER LLC (UT)
(*Suby of* HUNTSMAN INTERNATIONAL LLC) ★
500 S Huntsman Way, Salt Lake City, UT 84108-1235
Tel (801) 584-5700 *Founded/Ownrshp* 1982
Sales 110.1MM^E^ *EMP* 1,000
SIC 2821 Polystyrene resins; Polystyrene resins
VP: Curt Ogdon

HUNTSVILLE AUTOPLEX
See HUNTSVILLE DODGE INC

D-U-N-S 07-765-3269
HUNTSVILLE CITY BOARD OF EDUCATION (INC)
200 White St Se, Huntsville, AL 35801-4104
Tel (256) 428-6800 *Founded/Ownrshp* 1890
Sales 189.4MM^E^ *EMP* 3,000
SIC 8211 Public elementary & secondary schools; School board
Pr: Laurie Mc Caulley
Exec: Kenneth Carpenter
Pr Dir: Rena Anderson
Schl Brd P: Topper Birney

D-U-N-S 03-620-4402
HUNTSVILLE CITY OF WATER SYSTEM
HUNTSVILLE UTILITIES
112 Spragins St Sw, Huntsville, AL 35895-0001
Tel (256) 535-1200 *Founded/Ownrshp* 1954
Sales 25.8MM *EMP* 119
Accts Carr Riggs & Ingram Llc Ente
SIC 4941 Water supply; Water supply
Pr: William Pippin
CFO: Tim McKee
CFO: Timothy D McKee
Sec: James S Wall

D-U-N-S 07-846-3427
HUNTSVILLE CITY SCHOOLS
200 White St Se, Huntsville, AL 35801-4104
Tel (256) 428-6800 *Founded/Ownrshp* 2012
Sales 28.3MM^E^ *EMP* 2,937^E^
SIC 8211 Elementary & secondary schools

HUNTSVILLE DIVISION
See BENCHMARK ELECTRONICS HUNTSVILLE INC

D-U-N-S 61-492-4835
HUNTSVILLE DODGE INC
HUNTSVILLE AUTOPLEX
6580 University Dr Nw, Huntsville, AL 35806-1718
Tel (256) 824-8000 *Founded/Ownrshp* 1995
Sales 25.9MM^E^ *EMP* 65
SIC 5511 Automobiles, new & used; Automobiles, new & used
Pr: Elena Fairhurst
**Sec:* Mike Fox
Sales Asso: Willie Aaron
Sales Asso: Doug Jones

D-U-N-S 12-061-6008
HUNTSVILLE EMERGENCY MEDICAL SERVICES INC
HEMSI
2700 6th Ave Sw, Huntsville, AL 35805-3755
Tel (256) 518-2245 *Founded/Ownrshp* 1981
Sales 22.3MM *EMP* 180
Accts Mda Professional Group Pc Hu
SIC 4119 Local passenger transportation; Local passenger transportation
CEO: Jon Howell
**Pr:* Mr Stan Chapman
**VP:* John Brown
VP: Bob Wagner

HUNTSVILLE HOSP WOMEN CHILDREN
See HEALTH CARE AUTHORITY OF CITY OF HUNTSVILLE

D-U-N-S 14-458-8811
HUNTSVILLE HOUSING AUTHORITY
200 Washington St Ne, Huntsville, AL 35801-4843
Tel (256) 539-0774 *Founded/Ownrshp* 1941
Sales 20.5MM *EMP* 96
SIC 6531 8322 Housing authority operator; Individual & family services; Housing authority operator; Individual & family services
Ex Dir: Michael Lundy
IT Man: Sandra Eddlemon
IT Man: Teresa Wade

D-U-N-S 09-938-6146
HUNTSVILLE INDEPENDENT SCHOOL DISTRICT
ADMINSTRATION OFFICE
441 Fm 2821 Rd E, Huntsville, TX 77320-9223
Tel (936) 435-6300 *Founded/Ownrshp* 1875
Sales 56.5MM^E^ *EMP* 1,000
Accts Kenneth C Davis & Company Hu
SIC 8211 Public elementary & secondary schools; Public elementary & secondary schools
Exec: Emily Demilliano
Exec: Shannon Duncan
Cmptr Lab: Joeann Bon-Jorno
IT Man: Cesar Trevino
Pr Dir: Emily Demillianl
Teacher Pr: Debora Homann
Psych: Julie Picket

HUNTSVILLE INTERNATIONAL ARPRT
See HUNTSVILLE MADISON CTY AIRPRT

D-U-N-S 06-368-0789
HUNTSVILLE MADISON CTY AIRPRT
HUNTSVILLE INTERNATIONAL ARPRT
1000 Glenn Hearn Blvd Sw # 20008, Huntsville, AL 35824-2107
Tel (256) 772-9395 *Founded/Ownrshp* 1956
Sales 28.4MM *EMP* 115
Accts Mercer & Associates Pc Hunts
SIC 4581 6531 Airport; Hangars & other aircraft storage facilities; Real estate agent, commercial; Airport; Hangars & other aircraft storage facilities; Real estate agent, commercial
Ch: Carl J Gessler Jr
**Sec:* William H Johnston Jr
**VP:* Dallas W Fanning
**VP:* Luther Roberts
**Ex Dir:* Richard Tucker
IT Man: Shelaine Luttrell
Sftwr Eng: Tom Perry
Sls Dir: Peggy Tiemann

HUNTSVILLE MEMORIAL HOSPITAL
See WALKER COUNTY HOSPITAL CORP

D-U-N-S 07-417-9300
HUNTSVILLE MEMORIAL HOSPITAL AUXILIARY
110 Memorial Hospital Dr, Huntsville, TX 77340-4940
Tel (936) 291-3411 *Founded/Ownrshp* 1927
Sales 84.2MM *EMP* 600
Accts Bkd Llp Houston Texas
SIC 8062 General medical & surgical hospitals; General medical & surgical hospitals
CEO: Ralph Beaty
CFO: Dorothy Nevill
Opers Mgr: Liz McGinty

D-U-N-S 12-826-5493
HUNTSVILLE PUBLIC SCHOOL DISTRICT 1
570 W Main St, Huntsville, AR 72740-9244
Tel (479) 738-2011 *Founded/Ownrshp* 1900
Sales 19.8MM^E^ *EMP* 350
SIC 8211 Public elementary & secondary schools; Public elementary & secondary schools

D-U-N-S 02-806-3048
HUNTSVILLE REHABILITATION FOUNDATION INC
PHOENIX
2939 Johnson Rd Sw, Huntsville, AL 35805-5844
Tel (256) 880-0671 *Founded/Ownrshp* 1967
Sales 40.6MM *EMP* 720
Accts Breland & Hemenway Todd Pc
SIC 8331 Vocational rehabilitation agency; Vocational rehabilitation agency
Pr: Bryan Dodson
**VP:* David Perez
**VP:* Tim Stickley
**VP:* Wes Tyler
Comm Dir: David Person
Sales Exec: Helen Miller

HUNTSVILLE UTILITIES
See HUNTSVILLE CITY OF WATER SYSTEM

HUNTSVILLE UTILITIES
See CITY OF HUNTSVILLE ELECTRIC SYSTEMS

D-U-N-S 16-236-1245
HUNTSVILLE WHOLESALE FURNITURE INC
ASHLEY HOMESTORE
3020 Memorial Pkwy Sw, Huntsville, AL 35801-5303
Tel (256) 519-4600 *Founded/Ownrshp* 2004
Sales 26.8MM *EMP* 120^E^
Accts Seaman Shinkunas & Lindgren
SIC 5712 Furniture stores; Furniture stores
Pr: Allen W Marks
CFO: Mark Kimbrough

D-U-N-S 01-193-3033
HUNTSVILLE-MADISON COUNTY MENTAL HEALTH BOARD INC
WELLSTONE BEHAVIORAL HEALTH
4040 Memorial Pkwy Sw C, Huntsville, AL 35802-4364
Tel (256) 533-1970 *Founded/Ownrshp* 1968
Sales 13.7MM *EMP* 300
Accts Mercer & Associates Pc Huntsv
SIC 8093 Mental health clinic, outpatient; Mental health clinic, outpatient
Ex Dir: Brian Davis
**CFO:* Donna Saunders
CFO: Andrew Skelton
**Mng Dir:* Jeremy Blair

D-U-N-S 16-504-7783
HUNTSWORTH HEALTH NORTH AMERICA LLC
800 Town Line Rd Ste 100, Yardley, PA 19067
Tel (215) 550-8300 *Founded/Ownrshp* 1999
Sales 30.8MM^E^ *EMP* 200^E^
SIC 8742 Management consulting services; Management consulting services
CEO: Neil W Matheson
Pr: Kevin Kruse
COO: Mike Brown
CFO: Richard Neave
Sr VP: David Avitabile
VP: Rob Diefenderfer
VP: Philip Sjostedt
Mng Dir: Andy Abbott
Snr Mgr: Carolyn Hicks

HUNTWOOD INDUSTRIES
See TRA INDUSTRIES INC

D-U-N-S 82-485-2524
HUNTZINGER MANAGEMENT GROUP INC
670 N River St Ste 401, Wilkes Barre, PA 18705-1028
Tel (570) 824-4721 *Founded/Ownrshp* 2006
Sales 28.6MM *EMP* 32
SIC 7379 8742 Computer related consulting services; Management consulting services; Computer related consulting services; Management consulting services
Pr: Bob Kitts
Ch Bd: George Huntzinger
Pr: Tanya Freeman
CEO: Robert Kitts
CFO: David Dichiara
VP: William C Reed
VP Mktg: Craig Kasper
Board of Directors: William C Reed, Richard Sorensen

D-U-N-S 00-720-5065
HUNZICKER BROTHERS INC (OK)
501 N Virginia Ave, Oklahoma City, OK 73106-2638
Tel (405) 239-7771 *Founded/Ownrshp* 1920, 1989
Sales 150.9MM^E^ *EMP* 145
SIC 5063 Electrical supplies; Electrical supplies
CEO: Myers Lockard
Mng Pt: Julie Edmondson
**Ch Bd:* F W Hunzicker
Ofcr: John Zher
**Ex VP:* John D Henderson
**VP:* Richard Dean
VP: Steve Evans
VP: Robert M Kinniburgh
Brnch Mgr: Bob Boydstun
Off Mgr: Barb Parsons
**VP Sls:* Jerry Young

D-U-N-S 00-794-6841
HUNZINGER CONSTRUCTION CO (WI)
21100 Enterprise Ave, Brookfield, WI 53045-5226
Tel (262) 797-0797 *Founded/Ownrshp* 1907
Sales 82.4MM^E^ *EMP* 175
Accts The Vanderbloemen Group Llc W
SIC 1542 8741 Commercial & office building, new construction; Shopping center construction; Design & erection, combined: non-residential; Construction management; Commercial & office building, new construction; Shopping center construction; Design & erection, combined: non-residential; Construction management
Pr: John C Hunzinger
Treas: Anthony A Klein
Ex VP: James R Hunzinger
Ex VP: Kevin O 'toole
VP: Joel Becker
VP: Tim Van Dyn Hoven
VP: Tim Hoven
VP: Jon Jansen
VP: Larry Palank
Exec: Mike Huebner
VP Opers: Tim Vandynhoven

HUPACO
See HUDSON PAPER CO

D-U-N-S 00-530-2583 IMP
HUPP ELECTRIC MOTORS INC (IA)
275 33rd Ave Sw, Cedar Rapids, IA 52404-4690
Tel (319) 398-4800 *Founded/Ownrshp* 1912
Sales 39.2MM^E^ *EMP* 195
SIC 5722 Electric household appliances; Electric household appliances
Ch Bd: Robert T Hupp
**Pr:* Kevin Hupp
**Treas:* Nelson Craig
**VP:* Terry Dolezal
**VP:* Chuck Rutledge
Mktg Mgr: Connie Hupp
Sls Mgr: Ladd Wessels

D-U-N-S 02-750-7268 EXP
HUPPINS HI-FI PHOTO & VIDEO INC
ONECALL
421 W Main Ave, Spokane, WA 99201-0655
Tel (509) 747-6486 *Founded/Ownrshp* 1987
Sales 42.9MM *EMP* 87
Accts Moss Adams Llp Spokane Wash
SIC 5946 5731 5961 Camera & photographic supply stores; Cameras; High fidelity stereo equipment; Video recorders, players, disc players & accessories; Catalog & mail-order houses; Camera & photographic supply stores; Cameras; High fidelity stereo equipment; Video recorders, players, disc players & accessories; Catalog & mail-order houses
Pr: Murray Huppin
**VP:* Joel Huppin

D-U-N-S 02-324-7612
HURCKMAN MECHANICAL INDUSTRIES INC
1450 Velp Ave, Green Bay, WI 54303-4418
Tel (920) 499-8771 *Founded/Ownrshp* 1975
Sales 42.8MM^E^ *EMP* 120
SIC 1711 3444 Mechanical contractor; Sheet metalwork; Mechanical contractor; Sheet metalwork
Pr: Brad Hurckman
**CFO:* Mike Terrien
**Treas:* James Vercauteren
IT Man: John Hurckman
**IT Man:* David Porter

D-U-N-S 04-458-1734 IMP
▲ HURCO COMPANIES INC
1 Technology Way, Indianapolis, IN 46268-5106
Tel (317) 293-5309 *Founded/Ownrshp* 1968
Sales 222.3MM *EMP* 730^E^
Tkr Sym HURC *Exch* NGS
SIC 3823 7372 Computer interface equipment for industrial process control; Prepackaged software; Computer interface equipment for industrial process control; Prepackaged software
Ch Bd: Michael Doar
Pr: Gregory S Volovic
COO: Chad Back
CFO: Sonja K McClelland
Bd of Dir: Andrew Lewis
Ex VP: John P Donlon
VP: Joe Braun
VP: Lyn Hudson
VP: Himat Patel
Snr Sftwr: Todd Musall
Dir IT: Kristen Hayes
Board of Directors: Robert W Cruickshank, Andrew Niner, Richard Porter, Ronald Strackbein

D-U-N-S 07-991-6215
■ HURCO USA INC
(*Suby of* HURCO COMPANIES INC) ★
1 Technology Way, Indianapolis, IN 46268-5106
Tel (317) 293-5309 *Founded/Ownrshp* 2015
Sales 33.0MM^E^ *EMP* 114^E^
SIC 3823 7372 Computer interface equipment for industrial process control; Prepackaged software
CEO: Michael Doar

HURD AUTO MALL
See HURD CHEVROLET INC

D-U-N-S 01-855-9427
HURD BUICK PONTIAC GMC TRUCK LLC
REGINE PONTIAC G M C
1669 Hartford Ave, Johnston, RI 02919-3202
Tel (401) 751-7890 *Founded/Ownrshp* 2001
Sales 22.7MM^E^ *EMP* 118
SIC 5511 Automobiles, new & used; Automobiles, new & used
Genl Mgr: Wendy Bowen

D-U-N-S 01-854-4213
HURD CHEVROLET INC (RI)
HURD AUTO MALL
1705 Hartford Ave, Johnston, RI 02919-3203
Tel (401) 751-6000 *Founded/Ownrshp* 1935
Sales 39.9MM^E^ *EMP* 101
SIC 5511 7515 7513 7539 7538 5012 Automobiles, new & used; Trucks, tractors & trailers: new & used; Passenger car leasing; Truck leasing, without drivers; Automotive repair shops; General automotive repair shops; Automobiles & other motor vehicles; Automobiles, new & used; Trucks, tractors & trailers: new & used; Passenger car leasing; Truck leasing, without drivers; Automotive repair shops; General automotive repair shops; Automobiles & other motor vehicles
Pr: Christopher Hurd
**Ch Bd:* F Judson Hurd
Off Mgr: Maria Conti
Sls Mgr: Matt Lafazia
Sls Mgr: Keith Lincoln
Sls Mgr: Ron Mandeville
Sls Mgr: Shane Young

HURD WINDOWS & DOORS
See HWD ACQUISITION INC

THE HURLBUT
See ROBERT H HURLBUT

D-U-N-S 01-358-8333
HURLEY ENTERPRISE INC
HURLEY'S OILFIELD SERVICE
208 Dakota Ave, Fairview, MT 59221
Tel (406) 742-5312 *Founded/Ownrshp* 2005
Sales 25.5MM^E^ *EMP* 115
SIC 1389 Oil field services
Pr: Vass Hurley

D-U-N-S 09-870-8352 IMP/EXP
■ HURLEY INTERNATIONAL LLC
(*Suby of* NIKE INC) ★
1945 Placentia Ave, Costa Mesa, CA 92627-3420
Tel (949) 548-9375 *Founded/Ownrshp* 2002
Sales 81.1MM^E^ *EMP* 201
SIC 2329 5137 Men's & boys' sportswear & athletic clothing; Men's & boys' leather, wool & down-filled outerwear; Men's & boys' furnishings; Knickers, dress (separate): men's & boys'; Women's & children's clothing
CEO: Robert M Hurley
Sr VP: John Cherpas
Sr VP: Marie Takeshita
Sr VP: Selma Taygan
VP: Paul Barfoot
VP: Bob Campbell
VP: Dwight Dunn
VP: Tony Gonzalez
VP: Bill Hurley
VP: George Malovrazich
VP: Ryan Mangan
VP: Alex Messmer
VP: Natasha Thomsen
VP: Sean Vali
Creative D: Joseph Whitmarsh

D-U-N-S 07-423-2273
HURLEY MEDICAL CENTER
GERIATRIC OTRACH CLNC/CARE MGT
1 Hurley Plz, Flint, MI 48503-5902
Tel (810) 257-9000 *Founded/Ownrshp* 1905
Sales 461.3MM^E^ *EMP* 2,884
SIC 8062 Hospital, professional nursing school with AMA residency; Hospital, professional nursing school with AMA residency
CEO: Melanie Devalac
Chf Path: Cathy Blight
Chf Rad: Apparao Mukkamala
**CFO:* Kevin Murphy
CFO: Cass Wisniewski
Treas: Thomas James
Treas: Maryann Turouske
Bd of Dir: Michael Marulli
Ofcr: Denise Denington
Ex VP: William Smith
VP: Michael Burnett
VP: Michael Jaggi
VP: Karen M Lopez
Dir Rad: Dawn Hiller
Board of Directors: James Wheeler, Delores Ennis, Anthony Whittbrodt, Chris Flores, Thomas James, Joel Kleiner, Thomas Landall, Pamela Loving, Ira Rutherford, Judy Samelson, Ernest Vahala

D-U-N-S 04-086-8049
HURLEY OF AMERICA INC
803 Linden Ave Ste 3, Rochester, NY 14625-2723
Tel (781) 438-7830 *Founded/Ownrshp* 1998
Sales 11.7MM^E^ *EMP* 1,200^E^
SIC 7349 7382 Janitorial service, contract basis; Security systems services; Janitorial service, contract basis; Security systems services
Pr: Barton L Munro Jr
Dir Bus: Ronald O'Brien

D-U-N-S 06-097-0191
HURLEY SERVICES CORP
NORTHWEST CLINIC
1125 S Linden Rd Ste 210, Flint, MI 48532-4069
Tel (810) 230-3350 *Founded/Ownrshp* 1988
Sales 15.6MM^E^ *EMP* 300
SIC 8741 5047 5999 8071 Management services; Medical equipment & supplies; Medical apparatus & supplies; Medical laboratories; Management services; Medical equipment & supplies; Medical apparatus & supplies; Medical laboratories
Pr: Phillip C Dutcher

D-U-N-S 15-015-0055
HURLEY/BINSONS MEDICAL EQUIPMENT INC
H CARE
G 4433 Miller Rd, Flint, MI 48507
Tel (810) 733-0280 *Founded/Ownrshp* 1980
Sales 51.3MM^E^ *EMP* 100^E^
SIC 5047 Medical equipment & supplies
Pr: Phillip Thom

HURLEY'S OILFIELD SERVICE
See HURLEY ENTERPRISE INC

D-U-N-S 10-136-9937
HURON CAPITAL PARTNERS LLC
500 Griswold St Ste 2700, Detroit, MI 48226-4485
Tel (313) 962-5800 Founded/Ownrshp 1999
Sales 100.1MM^E EMP 826
SIC 6211 Investment bankers; Investment bankers
Pr: Heather Madland
COO: Gerard A Loftus
*CFO: David Reynolds
Bd of Dir: Edward Shellard
VP: Mark Miller
VP: Gretchen Perkins

D-U-N-S 08-221-2721 IMP
HURON CASTING INC
H C I
7050 Hartley St, Pigeon, MI 48755-5190
Tel (989) 453-3933 Founded/Ownrshp 1976
Sales 96.4MM^E EMP 450^E
SIC 3325 3369 Alloy steel castings, except investment; Nonferrous foundries; Alloy steel castings, except investment; Nonferrous foundries
Pr: Leroy Wurst
*CFO: Matt Davis
*VP: Devere Sturm
Off Mgr: Terry Waitt
Plnt Mgr: Chris Wurst
Trfc Mgr: Linda Wolfram
Snr Mgr: Dave Beachy

D-U-N-S 14-897-0184
▲ **HURON CONSULTING GROUP INC**
550 W Van Buren St # 1600, Chicago, IL 60607-3827
Tel (312) 583-8700 Founded/Ownrshp 2002
Sales 889.2MM EMP 2,870^E
Tkr Sym HURN Exch NGS
SIC 8742 8748 Hospital & health services consultant; Financial consultant; School, college, university consultant; Educational consultant; Hospital & health services consultant; Financial consultant; School, college, university consultant; Educational consultant
Pr: James H Roth
COO: C Mark Hussey
Chf Mktg O: Debbie Murphy
Ex VP: Diane E Ratekin
Admn Mgr: Suzan Kharputly
CTO: Sara Flanagan
Board of Directors: James D Edwards, H Eugene Lockhart, George E Massaro, John F McCartney, John S Moody, Debra Zumwalt

D-U-N-S 11-136-7897
■ **HURON CONSULTING SERVICES LLC**
(Suby of HURON CONSULTING GROUP INC) ★
550 W Van Buren St # 1600, Chicago, IL 60607-3827
Tel (312) 583-8700 Founded/Ownrshp 2002
Sales 80.5MM^E EMP 1,757
SIC 8748 Business consulting; Business consulting
CEO: James H Roth
Pr: Natalia Delgado
*Pr: Mary Sawall
*Ex VP: C Mark Hussey
*VP: John D Kelly
*VP: Diane E Ratekin
Mng Dir: Terry Lloyd

D-U-N-S 11-928-2978
HURON HEALTH CARE CENTER INC
ADMIRALS PNTE NRSNG RHBLTTION
1920 Cleveland Rd W, Huron, OH 44839-1211
Tel (419) 433-4990 Founded/Ownrshp 1993
Sales 584.9MM EMP 125
SIC 8051 Skilled nursing care facilities; Skilled nursing care facilities
Off Mgr: Jackie Schaffer
IT Man: Mari Engelhardt
Mktg Dir: Jody Corsillas
HC Dir: Robin Dunlap
HC Dir: Mary Willgrube

D-U-N-S 11-306-2848 IMP
HURON INC
TUBE ASSEMBLY MANUFACTURING CO
6554 Lakeshore Rd, Lexington, MI 48450-9763
Tel (810) 359-5344 Founded/Ownrshp 2015
Sales 40.3MM^E EMP 280
SIC 3498 3451 Screw machine products; Fabricated pipe & fittings; Fabricated pipe & fittings; Screw machine products
Pr: Jerry Solar
CFO: Rick Cook
VP: George Duditch
Plnt Mgr: George Moss
Ql Cn Mgr: Dave Farr
Sls Mgr: John Bowns

D-U-N-S 04-494-4791
HURON LIME INC (OH)
100 Meeker St, Huron, OH 44839-1713
Tel (419) 433-2141 Founded/Ownrshp 1966, 2002
Sales 22.8MM EMP 30
Accts Deimling Forbes Willoughby O
SIC 3274 Quicklime; Quicklime
Pr: Edward Gordon
*Ch: Jerome Osborne
*VP: Nancy J Case
Genl Mgr: Christopher Kitts

HURON MEDICAL CENTER
See HURON MEMORIAL HOSPITAL

D-U-N-S 07-276-6835
HURON MEMORIAL HOSPITAL
HURON MEDICAL CENTER
1100 S Van Dyke Rd, Bad Axe, MI 48413-9799
Tel (989) 269-9521 Founded/Ownrshp 1906
Sales 41.1MM EMP 274
SIC 8062

D-U-N-S 00-615-7275
HURON NEWSPAPERS LLC (SD)
HURON PLAINSMAN
(Suby of NEWS MEDIA CORP) ★
49 3rd St Se, Huron, SD 57350-2015
Tel (605) 353-7401 Founded/Ownrshp 1886
Sales 20.1MM^E EMP 570
SIC 2711 Newspapers, publishing & printing; Newspapers, publishing & printing
Pr: Tom Hawley
*VP: Keith Haugland
VP: Loretta McDonald

HURON PLAINSMAN
See HURON NEWSPAPERS LLC

D-U-N-S 07-869-2712
HURON REGIONAL MEDICAL CENTER INC
172 4th St Se, Huron, SD 57350-2590
Tel (605) 353-6200 Founded/Ownrshp 1978
Sales 32.0MM^E EMP 250^E
Accts Harrington & Associates Ltd H
SIC 8062 General medical & surgical hospitals; General medical & surgical hospitals
CEO: David Dick
Chf OB: Nathan Loewen
*Pr: John Single
*CFO: Marcia Zwanzige
VP: Marcia Zwanziger
Dir Lab: Owen Baine
Dir IT: Irene Hale
QC Dir: Janice Farrar
Sls Mgr: Jim Rieger
Doctor: Michael Guerin MD
Dir Heelth: Stacey Thorsen

D-U-N-S 03-986-7288
HURON SCHOOL DISTRICT (MI)
32044 Huron River Dr, New Boston, MI 48164-9282
Tel (734) 782-1436 Founded/Ownrshp 1946
Sales 25.9MM EMP 483
Accts Rehmann Robson Jackson Mi
SIC 8211 Public elementary & secondary schools; Public elementary school; Public elementary & secondary schools; Public elementary school
Bd of Dir: Alice Ferguson
VP: Jack Richert
Schl Brd P: Colleen Lazere
Psych: Valari Ambrose
Psych: Laura Lee
Psych: Jason Pliska
Snr Mgr: Michael Gill

D-U-N-S 07-650-1295
HURON SCHOOL DISTRICT 2-2
88 3rd St Se, Huron, SD 57350-2501
Tel (605) 353-6995 Founded/Ownrshp 1889
Sales 15.6MM^E EMP 350
SIC 8211 Public elementary & secondary schools; School board; Public elementary & secondary schools; School board
Dir Sec: Cory Borg
IT Man: Lennie Symes

D-U-N-S 83-195-2069
■ **HURON TECHNOLOGIES INC**
(Suby of HURON CONSULTING GROUP INC) ★
1925 Nw Amberglen Pkwy, Beaverton, OR 97006-6945
Tel (503) 748-3900 Founded/Ownrshp 2010
Sales 15.3MM^E EMP 317
SIC 7371 7372 Custom computer programming services; Educational computer software; Custom computer programming services; Educational computer software
Pr: Nick Stier
Pr: Dan Gillespie
*COO: Gary Raetz
VP: Arnaud Poujardieu
Off Mgr: Kerry Bryant
VP Sls: Gary Whitney
Snr PM: Scott Weinstein

D-U-N-S 01-112-1514
HURON VALLEY AMBULANCE INC (MI)
1200 State Cir, Ann Arbor, MI 48108-1691
Tel (734) 971-4420 Founded/Ownrshp 1978
Sales 29.7MM^E EMP 400^E
SIC 4119 Ambulance service; Ambulance service
Pr: Dale Berry
COO: Jerry Zapolnik
CFO: Barbara Bachman
VP: Paul Hood

D-U-N-S 06-984-3852
HURON VALLEY BOARD OF EDUCATION
2390 S Milford Rd, Highland, MI 48357-4934
Tel (248) 684-8000 Founded/Ownrshp 1946
Sales 113.5MM EMP 1,400
Accts Plante & Moran Pllc Auburn Hi
SIC 8211 Public elementary school; Public junior high school; Public senior high school; School board; Public elementary school; Public junior high school; Public senior high school; School board
Pr: Lindsay Cotter
Prin: Peg Sell
Teacher Pr: Scott Lindberg

D-U-N-S 07-982-7308
HURON VALLEY SCHOOLS
2390 S Milford Rd, Highland, MI 48357-4934
Tel (248) 684-8000 Founded/Ownrshp 2015
Sales 118.3MM EMP 1,895^E
SIC 8211 Public elementary & secondary schools
Netwrk Eng: Stephanie Anderson
Pr Dir: Kim Root
Psych: Lynne Burton
Psych: Beverly Groth
Psych: Gina Pryor

D-U-N-S 00-533-7332 IMP/EXP
HURON VALLEY STEEL CORP (MI)
1650 W Jefferson Ave, Trenton, MI 48183-2136
Tel (734) 479-3500 Founded/Ownrshp 1961
Sales 120.3MM^E EMP 260
Accts Baker Tilly Verchow Krause Llp
SIC 5093 3341 3559 Nonferrous metals scrap; Zinc smelting & refining (secondary); Aluminum smelting & refining (secondary); Recycling machinery; Nonferrous metals scrap; Zinc smelting & refining (secondary); Aluminum smelting & refining (secondary); Recycling machinery
Pr: Eric R Fritz
*Pr: Ronald Dalton
COO: Richard Wolanski
CFO: Dick Anderson
Sr VP: Ron Dalton
*VP: Mark Gaffney

HURON VENTURES
See CANO PETROLEUM INC

HURON-CLINTON METROPARKS
See HURON-CLINTON METROPOLITAN AUTHORITY

D-U-N-S 07-423-3917
HURON-CLINTON METROPOLITAN AUTHORITY
HURON-CLINTON METROPARKS
13000 Highridge Dr, Brighton, MI 48114-9058
Tel (810) 227-2757 Founded/Ownrshp 1939
Sales NA EMP 1,000
Accts Rehmann Robson Troy Mi
SIC 9512 Recreational program administration, government; ; Recreational program administration, government;
CEO: Anthony V Marrocco
*Treas: John P McCulloch
Dir IT: Kimberly Jarvis
Mktg Mgr: Kassie Kretzschmar

D-U-N-S 04-943-5427
HURR LAW OFFICE PC
4717 Fletcher Ave Ste 101, Fort Worth, TX 76107-7830
Tel (817) 210-0144 Founded/Ownrshp 2010
Sales 54.0MM EMP 3
SIC 8111 Legal services; Legal services
Pr: Randall L Hurr
Psych: Michele Delotto
Psych: Melissa Wilks

HURRICANE COMPRESSOR COMPANY
See K GRIMMER INDUSTRIES INC

D-U-N-S 92-885-9529
HURRICANE CONSULTING INC
HCI INTEGRATED SOLUTIONS
4035 Ridge Top Rd Ste 325, Fairfax, VA 22030-7454
Tel (703) 537-3151 Founded/Ownrshp 1995
Sales 32.4MM^E EMP 275
SIC 8744

D-U-N-S 86-721-3704 IMP
HURRICANE ELECTRIC LLC
760 Mission Ct, Fremont, CA 94539-8204
Tel (510) 580-4100 Founded/Ownrshp 1988
Sales 38.3MM^E EMP 90
SIC 4813 7375 Telephone communication, except radio; ; Information retrieval services
Exec: Benny Ng
Mktg Mgr: Matthew Leber

D-U-N-S 61-139-8561
HURRICANE FOOD INC
WENDY'S
800 E Thompson Rd, Indianapolis, IN 46227-1670
Tel (317) 789-4000 Founded/Ownrshp 1989
Sales 13.0MM^E EMP 438
SIC 5812 Fast-food restaurant, chain; Fast-food restaurant, chain
CEO: Gerald F Gowan
*Ch Bd: Jerry Gowan
*Pr: David Gowan
*CFO: David Poling

D-U-N-S 08-878-7205
HURRICANE LOUNGE INC
HURRICANE SEAFOOD RESTAURANT
809 Gulf Way, St Pete Beach, FL 33706-4218
Tel (727) 360-9558 Founded/Ownrshp 1977
Sales 8.5MM^E EMP 300
SIC 5812 5813 Steak restaurant; Seafood restaurants; Cocktail lounge; Steak restaurant; Seafood restaurants; Cocktail lounge
Pr: Mary B Falkenstein
*VP: Domonick J Falkenstein

HURRICANE SEAFOOD RESTAURANT
See HURRICANE LOUNGE INC

D-U-N-S 04-869-5746 EXP
HURST BOILER & WELDING CO INC
21971 Us Highway 319 N, Coolidge, GA 31738-3743
Tel (229) 346-3545 Founded/Ownrshp 1967
Sales 76.1MM^E EMP 231
SIC 3443 3625 Boilers: industrial, power, or marine; Relays & industrial controls; Boilers: industrial, power, or marine; Relays & industrial controls
Pr: Thomas E Hurst
*Sec: Theresa H White
*VP: Hayward L Hurst
Div Mgr: Hayward Hurst
IT Man: Chuck Ray
VP Opers: Gary Hunter
Sales Exec: Bruce Coffee
Sls Mgr: Gene Zebley

D-U-N-S 78-196-7062
HURST DEALERSHIP ACQUISITION LTD
FREEMAN PONTIAC MAZDA
204 Ne Loop 820, Hurst, TX 76053-7327
Tel (817) 287-5200 Founded/Ownrshp 1991
Sales 33.9MM^E EMP 102
SIC 5511 Automobiles, new & used; Automobiles, new & used
Pt: James Freeman
*Pt: Jerald W Freeman Jr
Genl Mgr: Dan Miner
Genl Mgr: Dain Minor
Genl Mgr: Don Woodruff
Sls Mgr: Mike Allen
Sls Mgr: Russell Hossain
Sales Asso: Dillon Martinez

D-U-N-S 02-667-6536 IMP
HURST ELECTRIC LP
229 W Hurst Blvd, Hurst, TX 76053-7898
Tel (817) 268-3000 Founded/Ownrshp 1953
Sales 34.5MM EMP 40
Accts Milbern Ray And Company Grape
SIC 1731 General electrical contractor; General electrical contractor
Genl Pt: N L Jordan
Pt: Gerald L Jordan
Pt: Mary C Jordan

HURST MANUFACTURING DIVISION
See NIDEC MOTOR CORP

D-U-N-S 03-534-6147 IMP
HURST STORES INC
ACE HARDWARE
160 N Bluff St, St George, UT 84770-4546
Tel (435) 673-6141 Founded/Ownrshp 1946
Sales 40.4MM^E EMP 160
SIC 5251 5941 5945 5311 Hardware; Sporting goods & bicycle shops; Hobby, toy & game shops; Department stores, discount; Hardware; Sporting goods & bicycle shops; Hobby, toy & game shops; Department stores, discount
Pr: Jason Hurst
*Sec: Julie Hurst
*VP: Robin Faldmo
Store Mgr: Lynne Gillett
Store Mgr: Bart Hillier
Store Mgr: Vera Novak
Store Mgr: Zara Shallbetter

D-U-N-S 07-316-2935
HURST-EULESS-BEDFORD INDEPENDENT SCHOOL DISTRICT
HEB ISD
1849 Central Dr, Bedford, TX 76022-6017
Tel (817) 267-3311 Founded/Ownrshp 1955
Sales 216.9MM EMP 2,322
Accts Weaver And Tidwell Llp Fort
SIC 8211 Public elementary & secondary schools; Public elementary & secondary schools
Exec: Ellen Jones
Dir IT: Kathryn Craker
Dir IT: Kiera Elledge
IT Man: Ana Natal
Teacher Pr: Jodie Hawkins
Psych: Dana Cox

HURT COMPANY, THE
See A J HURT JR INC

D-U-N-S 04-349-8633
HURTT FABRICATING CORP (MO)
26707 E Scott Rd, Marceline, MO 64658-8188
Tel (660) 376-3501 Founded/Ownrshp 1966
Sales 23.9MM^E EMP 65
SIC 3312 3441 3444 3353 Rods, iron & steel: made in steel mills; Fabricated structural metal; Sheet metalwork; Aluminum sheet, plate & foil
Ch Bd: Robert J Hurtt Sr
CFO: Robert Walton
*Treas: Darren Buckner
*VP: Charles D Haley
Sfty Mgr: Andy North

D-U-N-S 61-033-9025 EXP
HUSA MANAGEMENT INC
SHERLOCK'S BAKER ST PUB
1414a Upland Dr, Houston, TX 77043-4721
Tel (713) 461-0608 Founded/Ownrshp 2005
Sales 47.4MM^E EMP 960^E
SIC 5812 American restaurant; American restaurant
Pr: Larry Martin
COO: Steve Riley
*CFO: Tammy Cepeda
*VP: Edgar Carlson
*VP: William Dearing
*VP: Lawrence Martin
VP: Pat McGinity
Genl Mgr: Trey White
VP Opers: Bob Allison
Mktg Dir: Holly Spillers

D-U-N-S 82-543-9651
HUSCH BLACKWELL LLP
4801 Main St Ste 1000, Kansas City, MO 64112-2551
Tel (816) 983-8000 Founded/Ownrshp 2008
Sales 274.6MM^E EMP 1,390
SIC 8111 General practice law office; General practice law office
Pt: Gregory Smith
Pt: Lisa J Berns
Pt: James Borthwick
Pt: Caroline G Chicoine
Pt: Joseph Conran
Pt: Joseph W Cornelison
Pt: Samuel Digirolamo
Pt: Joyce Dixon
Pt: Bradley Hiles
Pt: Ralph Kalish
Pt: Benjamin Mann
Pt: John R Phillips
Pt: Ronald Schowalter
Pt: James Warden
Pt: Maurice Watson
Pt: Ralph G Wrobley
Mng Pt: Thomas H Dahlk
Mng Pt: Virginia L Fry
Mng Pt: Winn W Halverhout
Mng Pt: Caroline L Hermeling
Mng Pt: Steven M Kupka

D-U-N-S 83-180-1381
HUSCO AUTOMOTIVE HOLDINGS LLC
(Suby of HUSCO INTERNATIONAL INC) ★
2239 Pewaukee Rd, Waukesha, WI 53188-1638
Tel (262) 953-6400 Founded/Ownrshp 2008
Sales 20.1MM^E EMP 140^E
SIC 3694 Engine electrical equipment; Engine electrical equipment
S&M/VP: Carl Jensen

D-U-N-S 14-774-3983 IMP/EXP
HUSCO INTERNATIONAL INC
2239 Pewaukee Rd, Waukesha, WI 53188-1638
Tel (262) 513-4200 Founded/Ownrshp 1985
Sales 296.3MM^E EMP 1,200
SIC 3492 Control valves, fluid power: hydraulic & pneumatic; Control valves, fluid power: hydraulic & pneumatic
Pr: Austin Ramirez
COO: Jim Gannon
CFO: Todd Hoytink
Ofcr: Harshad Sonawane
VP: Gregg Heller

VP: Bob Mortensen
VP: Jason Schuetz
VP: Rick Sievert
Dir Lab: Craig Hopp
IT Man: Terry Balsewicz
Sftwr Eng: Mike Fossell

D-U-N-S 05-367-0899
■ HUSH PUPPIES RETAIL INC
(*Suby of* WOLVERINE WORLD WIDE INC) ★
9341 Courtland Dr Ne, Rockford, MI 49351-0001
Tel (616) 866-5500 *Founded/Ownrshp* 1970
Sales 41.6MMᴱ *EMP* 500
SIC 5661 Shoe stores; Shoe stores
Pr: Timothy J O'Donovan
CFO: Stephen L Gulis Jr
Sls Dir: Michael Bohnsack

D-U-N-S 02-254-6639
HUSKER AG LLC
54048 Highway 20, Plainview, NE 68769-4072
Tel (402) 582-4446 *Founded/Ownrshp* 2000
Sales 199.1MM *EMP* 52ᴱ
Accts Eide Bailly Llp Minneapolis
SIC 2869 Ethanolamines; Ethyl alcohol, ethanol; Ethanolamines; Ethyl alcohol, ethanol
Ch Bd: Robert Brummels

D-U-N-S 03-507-1869
HUSKER AUTOMOTIVE INC
BMW OF LINCOLN
6833 Telluride Dr, Lincoln, NE 68521-8981
Tel (402) 479-7500 *Founded/Ownrshp* 2000
Sales 52.8MMᴱ *EMP* 175
SIC 5511 7532 5531 5521 Automobiles, new & used; Top & body repair & paint shops; Automotive & home supply stores; Used car dealers; Automobiles, new & used; Top & body repair & paint shops; Automotive & home supply stores; Used car dealers
Pr: Thomas M Malone
**Pr:* Cecil Van Tuyl
**CFO:* Jim Thayer
**VP:* Elias Khalil
**VP:* John Morford

D-U-N-S 03-483-4655
HUSKEY BUILDING SUPPLY INC
HUSKEY TRUSS
424 Lewisburg Ave, Franklin, TN 37064-2801
Tel (615) 791-0100 *Founded/Ownrshp* 1948
Sales 42.7MMᴱ *EMP* 220
SIC 5211 Lumber & other building materials; Lumber & other building materials
Pr: Jim Huskey
CFO: Neil Gossman
Opers Mgr: Travis Woodside
Sales Asso: Mike Sandman

HUSKEY TRUSS
See HUSKEY BUILDING SUPPLY INC

D-U-N-S 08-206-9949 IMP
HUSKIE TOOLS INC
198 N Brandon Dr, Glendale Heights, IL 60139-2025
Tel (630) 893-7755 *Founded/Ownrshp* 2015
Sales 29.0MMᴱ *EMP* 43
Accts Baloun & Company Palatine Il
SIC 5084 Hydraulic systems equipment & supplies
Pr: Loralee Pearson
Pr: Thomas J Itrich
Sec: Donna Lee Itrich
VP: Roger Richter
Genl Mgr: Deanna Dazzo
IT Man: Louis Rivera
Manager: Nick Koch

D-U-N-S 03-475-7045
HUSKIES LESSEE LLC
SIR FRANCIS DRAKE HOTEL
450 Powell St, San Francisco, CA 94102-1504
Tel (415) 392-7755 *Founded/Ownrshp* 2010
Sales 32.0MM *EMP* 375
SIC 7011 Hotels; Hotels
Genl Mgr: John Price
IT Man: Stacey Bradetich

D-U-N-S 00-632-8959
HUSKY CORP (MO)
2325 Husky Way, Pacific, MO 63069-3634
Tel (636) 825-7200 *Founded/Ownrshp* 1947
Sales 33.8MM *EMP* 113
SIC 3499 Nozzles, spray: aerosol, paint or insecticide; Nozzles, spray: aerosol, paint or insecticide
Pr: Grenville G Sutcliffe
**Ex VP:* Brad Baker
CIO: Jill Whitworth
Ql Cn Mgr: Steve Baynham
Ql Cn Mgr: Rich Bishop

D-U-N-S 01-087-6845
HUSKY ENVELOPE PRODUCTS INC
1225 E West Maple Rd, Walled Lake, MI 48390-3764
Tel (248) 624-7070 *Founded/Ownrshp* 1986
Sales 28.8MMᴱ *EMP* 100
SIC 2677 2759 Envelopes; Commercial printing; Envelopes; Commercial printing
Pr: William Reske
**Treas:* Brian S Tabaczka
**VP:* Robert Muehl

HUSKY HARDWOOD FLOORS
See LUMBER LIQUIDATORS INC

HUSKY IDEALEASE
See HUSKY INTERNATIONAL TRUCKS INC

D-U-N-S 10-126-4414 IMP
HUSKY INJECTION MOLDING SYSTEMS INC
(*Suby of* HUSKY INJECTION MOLDING SYSTEMS LTD)
55 Amherst Villa Rd, Buffalo, NY 14225-1432
Tel (905) 951-5000 *Founded/Ownrshp* 1964
Sales 218.3MMᴱ *EMP* 668
SIC 5084 7699 Plastic products machinery; Industrial equipment services; Plastic products machinery; Industrial equipment services
Pr: Michael McKendry
**Pr:* George Haltsis
**CEO:* John Galt
**CFO:* Daniel Gagnon
VP: David Cook
**VP:* Dirk Schlimm
**VP:* Richard Sieradzki
Mng Dir: Michael Kirschnick
Genl Couns: Micael McKendry

D-U-N-S 14-765-5401
HUSKY INTERNATIONAL TRUCKS INC
HUSKY IDEALEASE
13123 48th Ave S, Tukwila, WA 98168-3305
Tel (206) 433-3466 *Founded/Ownrshp* 1985
Sales 65.6MMᴱ *EMP* 150
SIC 5511 5531 7538 7513 Pickups, new & used; Trucks, tractors & trailers: new & used; Truck equipment & parts; Truck engine repair, except industrial; Truck rental, without drivers; Pickups, new & used; Trucks, tractors & trailers: new & used; Truck equipment & parts; Truck engine repair, except industrial; Truck rental, without drivers
Ch Bd: Mike D Mc Devitt
**VP:* Lloyd Wright
Genl Mgr: Chris McDevitt
IT Man: Kalyn Ellis
Site Mgr: Mike McDevitt
Manager: Fred Schilling
Mktg Mgr: Don Hogan
Sls Mgr: John Gru

HUSKY LINERS
See WINFIELD CONSUMER PRODUCTS INC

D-U-N-S 55-547-0798 IMP/EXP
HUSQVARNA CONSTRUCTION PRODUCTS NORTH AMERICA INC
DIMAS DIVISION
(*Suby of* HUSQVARNA HOLDING AB)
17400 W 119th St, Olathe, KS 66061-7740
Tel (913) 928-1000 *Founded/Ownrshp* 2007
Sales 114.0MMᴱ *EMP* 500
SIC 3541 3291 5085 5082 3425 2951 Saws & sawing machines; Abrasive products; Abrasives; Contractors' materials; Saw blades & handsaws; Asphalt paving mixtures & blocks; Saws & sawing machines; Abrasive products; Abrasives; Contractors' materials; Saw blades & handsaws; Asphalt paving mixtures & blocks
Pr: Anders Strobe
Pr: Scott Clifford
Sr VP: Trevor Singleton
VP: Jack Fish
Dist Mgr: Glen Bulloss
Dist Mgr: Craig Caliva
Dist Mgr: Phil Crull
Dist Mgr: Jeff Iafornaro
Dist Mgr: Ryan Yonkers
Genl Mgr: Tony Cochran
Software D: Anthony Skinner

HUSQVARNA CONSUMER OUTDOOR PRO
See HUSQVARNA OUTDOOR PRODUCTS INC

D-U-N-S 61-802-7424 EXP
HUSQVARNA CONSUMER OUTDOOR PRODUCTS NA INC
(*Suby of* HUSQVARNA AB)
9335 Harris Corners Pkwy P, Charlotte, NC 28269-3818
Tel (704) 597-5000 *Founded/Ownrshp* 2006
Sales 1.7MMMᴱ *EMP* 6,000
SIC 3524 Lawn & garden tractors & equipment; Lawn & garden tractors & equipment
CEO: Alan Shaw
Pr: Alankar Naik
CFO: Fredric Ostman
CFO: Robert Tish
Treas: Drew Moody
Treas: Ted D Parks
Sr VP: Lennie Rhoades
VP: Simon Howard
VP: Anthony Marchese
VP: Kandy Rudd
Mng Dir: Matt McNally

D-U-N-S 07-929-5459
HUSQVARNA FORESTRY PRODUCTS NA INC
HUSQVARNA OUTDOOR PRODUCTS
1 Poulan Dr, Nashville, AR 71852-3305
Tel (870) 845-1234 *Founded/Ownrshp* 2007
Sales 30.6MMᴱ *EMP* 1,000
SIC 0831 ; Forest products
Pr: Steve Harvill
**Treas:* Magnus Ekesund
**VP:* Earl Bennett
**VP:* Myron Lottman
**Prin:* Judy Moore
IT Man: Adam West
Prd Mgr: Todd Jamison
Ql Cn Mgr: Keith Satterfield

HUSQVARNA OUTDOOR PRODUCTS
See HUSQVARNA FORESTRY PRODUCTS NA INC

D-U-N-S 07-999-4894
HUSQVARNA OUTDOOR PRODUCTS INC
263 E Oak St, Mc Rae, GA 31055-4342
Tel (229) 868-5641
Sales 18.8MMᴱ *EMP* 860
SIC 3524

D-U-N-S 62-644-9636
HUSQVARNA OUTDOOR PRODUCTS INC
HUSQVARNA CONSUMER OUTDOOR PRO
(*Suby of* HUSQVARNA CONSUMER OUTDOOR PRODUCTS NA INC) ★
1 Poulan Dr, Nashville, AR 71852-3305
Tel (870) 845-1234 *Founded/Ownrshp* 2005
Sales 228.8MMᴱ *EMP* 853ᴱ
SIC 3524 Lawn & garden equipment
Prin: Richey Lagrone
Plnt Mgr: Steve Harvill

D-U-N-S 82-866-0519 IMP/EXP
HUSQVARNA PROFESSIONAL PRODUCTS INC
(*Suby of* HUSQVARNA AB)
9335 Harris Corners Pkwy, Charlotte, NC 28269-3818
Tel (704) 597-5000 *Founded/Ownrshp* 2008
Sales 50.2MMᴱ *EMP* 70
SIC 5083 Lawn & garden machinery & equipment; Lawn & garden machinery & equipment
Pr: Dave Zerfoss
**CEO:* Kai Warn
**CFO:* Michael Parkins
Plnt Mgr: Giuseppe Manacorda

D-U-N-S 13-619-4789 IMP
HUSQVARNA US HOLDING INC
(*Suby of* HUSQVARNA AB)
20445 Emerald Pkwy, Cleveland, OH 44135-6009
Tel (216) 898-1800 *Founded/Ownrshp* 2001
Sales 100.4MMᴱ *EMP* 1,400
SIC 3582 Dryers, laundry: commercial, including coin-operated; Dryers, laundry: commercial, including coin-operated
CFO: George Weigand
**Treas:* Marie-Louise Wingard
**Sr VP:* Richard Pietch
**Sr VP:* Ronald Zajaczkowski

HUSSEY COPPER
See LIBERTAS COPPER LLC

D-U-N-S 01-189-7204 IMP
HUSSEY CORP
HUSSEY SEATING CO
38 Dyer St Ext, North Berwick, ME 03906-6763
Tel (207) 676-2271 *Founded/Ownrshp* 1835
Sales 61.7MMᴱ *EMP* 300ᴱ
SIC 2531 Stadium seating; Bleacher seating, portable; Chairs, portable folding; Stadium seating; Bleacher seating, portable; Chairs, portable folding
Pr: Tim Hussey
**VP:* Garri Marill
**VP:* Todd M Pierce
**VP:* Jack F Rogers
Mtls Mgr: Eric Baum
Plnt Mgr: Rick Glover
Natl Sales: Jim Chadbourne
Natl Sales: Steve Luttazi
Natl Sales: Mike Slater
Sls&Mrk Ex: Chris Robinson
Manager: Jeff Saucier

HUSSEY FABRICATED PRODUCTS
See HCL LIQUIDATION LTD

HUSSEY SEATING CO
See HUSSEY CORP

D-U-N-S 00-109-5777 IMP/EXP
HUSSEY SEATING CO (ME)
(*Suby of* HUSSEY CORP) ★
38 Dyer St Ext, North Berwick, ME 03906-6763
Tel (207) 676-2271 *Founded/Ownrshp* 1835
Sales 26.5MMᴱ *EMP* 260
SIC 2531 Stadium seating; Bleacher seating, portable; Chairs, portable folding; Stadium seating; Bleacher seating, portable; Chairs, portable folding
Pr: Timothy B Hussey
CFO: Gary Merrill
VP: Todd Pierce
VP Sls: Jack Rogers

D-U-N-S 00-696-7731 IMP
HUSSMANN CORP
HUSSMANN REFRIGERATION
(*Suby of* HUSSMANN INTERNATIONAL INC) ★
12999 St Charles Rock Rd, Bridgeton, MO 63044-2483
Tel (314) 291-2000 *Founded/Ownrshp* 2004
Sales 394.1MMᴱ *EMP* 900
SIC 3585 Refrigeration & heating equipment; Refrigeration equipment, complete; Lockers, refrigerated; Counters & counter display cases, refrigerated; Refrigeration & heating equipment; Refrigeration equipment, complete; Lockers, refrigerated; Counters & counter display cases, refrigerated
CEO: Dennis Gibson
Pr: Dave Martin
CFO: Tom Cordy
VP: Tom Ryan
Brnch Mgr: Grant Payne
Dist Mgr: Steve Reber
Plnt Mgr: Daniel Tellez
Sales Exec: Raymond Winchell
Snr Mgr: David Denney
Snr Mgr: Daniel Schnur

D-U-N-S 13-614-7027 IMP
HUSSMANN INTERNATIONAL INC
(*Suby of* CLAYTON DUBILIER & RICE LLC) ★
12999 St Charles Rock Rd, Bridgeton, MO 63044-2419
Tel (314) 291-2000 *Founded/Ownrshp* 2011
Sales 1.3MMMᴱ *EMP* 9,100ᴱ
SIC 3585 5963 Refrigeration equipment, complete; Food services, direct sales; Refrigeration equipment, complete; Food services, direct sales
CEO: Dennis Gipson
**Pr:* D G Gipson
**Pr:* L R Rauzon
**COO:* John Gialouris
**CFO:* Tim Figge
Treas: P Hong
**Treas:* Mike Lages
Treas: Gary Shmerler
VP: J A Cutillo
VP: Steve Douglas
**VP:* Brian J Hostetler
**VP:* P Nachtigal
VP: M C Schaefer
VP: G E Swimmer

HUSSMANN REFRIGERATION
See HUSSMANN CORP

D-U-N-S 07-173-7159
HUSSON UNIVERSITY
NESCOM
1 College Cir, Bangor, ME 04401-2929
Tel (207) 941-7000 *Founded/Ownrshp* 1898
Sales 57.0MM *EMP* 520
Accts Macpage Llc South Portland M
SIC 8221 College, except junior; College, except junior
Pr: Robert A Clark
**Ch Bd:* Carol C Kanar
**CFO:* Craig Hadley
Ofcr: Lewis Beal
Ofcr: Thomas Conlon
Ofcr: Amanda Gifford
Ofcr: Wendy Morrill
Ofcr: Matthew Parkhurst
**Sr VP:* Lynne Coy Ogan
VP: Thomas Martz
**VP:* Tom Martz
VP: Barbara Moody
Assoc Dir: Liana Fellis
Assoc Dir: Lisa Mazzarelli

D-U-N-S 09-404-2017 IMP
HUSSONG MANUFACTURING CO INC
KOZY HEAT FIREPLACES
204 Industrial Park Rd, Lakefield, MN 56150-1285
Tel (507) 662-6641 *Founded/Ownrshp* 1976
Sales 22.9MMᴱ *EMP* 100
SIC 3433 Heating equipment, except electric; Stoves, wood & coal burning; Logs, gas fireplace
Ch Bd: Dudley Hussong
**Pr:* Jim Hussong
**Sec:* Betty Hussong
Ofcr: David Harwood

D-U-N-S 02-406-4552
HUSSUNG MECHANICAL CONTRACTORS INC (KY)
H M C
6913 Enterprise Dr Ste B, Louisville, KY 40214-4398
Tel (502) 375-0440 *Founded/Ownrshp* 1966
Sales 55.8MMᴱ *EMP* 175
SIC 1711 Mechanical contractor; Mechanical contractor
Pr: David L Hussung
VP: Scott Dixon
IT Man: Imogene Gravenstreter

HUSTLER CASINO
See EL DORADO ENTERPRISES INC

D-U-N-S 09-966-6430 IMP
HUSTLER CONVEYOR CO
(*Suby of* AMERICAN PULVERIZER CO) ★
4101 Crusher Dr, O Fallon, MO 63368-8695
Tel (636) 441-8600 *Founded/Ownrshp* 1979
Sales 23.3MMᴱ *EMP* 80
SIC 3535 Belt conveyor systems, general industrial use
Pr: Chris Griesedieck
**CFO:* Brian Catlett
**CFO:* Christopher Shy
**VP:* Paul Griesedieck
Off Mgr: Laura Young
Plnt Mgr: Mike Smith
VP Mktg: David Guyton

HUSTLER TURF EQUIPMENT
See EXCEL INDUSTRIES INC

D-U-N-S 06-127-3777
HUSTON BOHANNAN INC
7500 Jefferson St Ne # 1, Albuquerque, NM 87109-4335
Tel (505) 823-1000 *Founded/Ownrshp* 1971
Sales 26.8MMᴱ *EMP* 168ᴱ
Accts Redw Llc Albuquerque New Mex
SIC 8711 7371 Consulting engineer; Computer software development
Pr: Brian G Burnett
**Mng Pt:* Kevin Patton
**Mng Pt:* Leslie Small
**Mng Pt:* Kurt Thorson
Pr: Jeff Mulbery
**COO:* Leslie L Small
**Treas:* Kerry L Davis
**Treas:* David A Larson
VP: Todd Burt
VP: Loretta Davis
VP: Sean Melville
VP: Matt Santistevan

D-U-N-S 01-647-1690
HUSTON ELECTRIC INC
1915 E North St, Kokomo, IN 46901-3169
Tel (765) 457-9137 *Founded/Ownrshp* 1962
Sales 47.0MMᴱ *EMP* 160
SIC 1731 1799 General electrical contractor; Sign installation & maintenance; General electrical contractor; Sign installation & maintenance
Pr: Jeff Cardwell
Pr: Jack Snyder
**COO:* Jon Huston
**Ex VP:* Jason Huston
VP: Matt Boor
VP: Steven Houston
Brnch Mgr: Sarah Hill
Off Mgr: Fredrick Cantrell
Telecom Mg: Chuck Huston
Sfty Dirs: Ryan Hasser

HUSTON PATTERSON PRINTERS
See HUSTON-PATTERSON CORP

D-U-N-S 00-517-5021
HUSTON-PATTERSON CORP (IL)
HUSTON PATTERSON PRINTERS
123 W North St Fl 4, Decatur, IL 62522-3396
Tel (217) 429-5161 *Founded/Ownrshp* 1895
Sales 28.6MMᴱ *EMP* 115
SIC 2752 2791 Commercial printing, offset; Typesetting; Commercial printing, offset; Typesetting
Pr: Thomas W Kowa
**COO:* Stephen E Frantz
**VP:* Donald Ellis
VP: Tonya Kowa-Morelli
**VP:* Tonya Kowa Morelli
Dir IT: Richard Hathaway
S&M/VP: Joe Morelli

D-U-N-S 04-996-7631 IMP
HUTCHENS CHEVROLET INC
12920 Jefferson Ave, Newport News, VA 23608-1694
Tel (757) 243-1947 *Founded/Ownrshp* 1986

Sales 31.6MM^E *EMP* 77
SIC 5511 Automobiles, new & used; Automobiles, new & used
Pr: Brian P Hutchens
**Sec:* Frederick Reams
**VP:* Kevin B Hutchens

D-U-N-S 02-972-2303
HUTCHENS CONSTRUCTION CO
1007 Main St, Cassville, MO 65625-1335
Tel (417) 847-2489 *Founded/Ownrshp* 2004
Sales 32.4MM *EMP* 90
Accts Bkd Llp Springfield Mo
SIC 1611 1422 Highway & street paving contractor; Crushed & broken limestone; Highway & street paving contractor; Crushed & broken limestone
Pr: Phil Hutchens
**CFO:* Kayla Ragsdale
**VP:* Valarie Hutchens
VP Mfg: Brandon Finn
Sls&Mrk Ex: Rachel Fuller

D-U-N-S 04-395-0807 IMP
HUTCHENS INDUSTRIES INC
215 N Patterson Ave, Springfield, MO 65802-2296
Tel (417) 862-5012 *Founded/Ownrshp* 1926
Sales 123.5MM^E *EMP* 700
SIC 3714 Shock absorbers, motor vehicle; Shock absorbers, motor vehicle
Pr: Jeffrey C Hutchens
VP: Jim Cantrell
VP: J Detherage
Rgnl Mgr: Geoff Stanford
CTO: Russ Brazeal
IT Man: John Junkel
Snr Mgr: Joel Lancaster

D-U-N-S 02-397-0346
HUTCHENS PETROLEUM CORP
22 Performance Dr, Stuart, VA 24171-5150
Tel (276) 694-7000 *Founded/Ownrshp* 1975
Sales 89.8MM *EMP* 36
Accts Sells Hogg & Associates Cpas
SIC 5172 5541 5983 Petroleum products; Gasoline service stations; Fuel oil dealers; Petroleum products; Gasoline service stations; Fuel oil dealers
Pr: Timothy Hutchens

D-U-N-S 80-542-1104
HUTCHENS SENTER KELLAM & PETTIT PA
HUTCHENS SENTER KELLAM PETTIT
4317 Ramsey St, Fayetteville, NC 28311-2133
Tel (910) 864-6888 *Founded/Ownrshp* 1993
Sales 27.1MM^E *EMP* 180
SIC 8111 General practice law office; General practice law office
Pr: H Terry Hutchens
**Pt:* William Senter

HUTCHENS SENTER KELLAM PETTIT
See HUTCHENS SENTER KELLAM & PETTIT PA

D-U-N-S 06-377-3378
HUTCHESON MEDICAL CENTER INC
100 Gross Crescent Cir, Fort Oglethorpe, GA 30742-3669
Tel (706) 858-2000 *Founded/Ownrshp* 1953
Sales 56.5MM *EMP* 530^E
SIC 8051 8011 8062 Skilled nursing care facilities; Medical centers; General medical & surgical hospitals; Skilled nursing care facilities; Medical centers; General medical & surgical hospitals
CEO: Farrell Hayes
Chf Rad: John F Nelson
**Ch Bd:* T Darrell Weldon
V Ch: Bill Cohen
**Pr:* Debbie Reeves
CFO: Denise Baker
CFO: Steve Ledbetter
CFO: Bill J Otting
VP: Pat Conley
VP: Scott Radeker
Dir OR: Patricia Conley
Dir Inf Cn: Sylvia Mc Crary
Dir Case M: Sandra Siniard
Dir Rad: Linda Case
Dir Rad: Jerry Jeffers
Dir Rx: Jerry Hale
Dir Rx: Holly Trotter

HUTCHIN COOP ELEVATOR
See HUTCHINSON CO-OP

D-U-N-S 79-990-8066 IMP/EXP
HUTCHINGS AUTOMOTIVE PRODUCTS INC
2041 Nw 15th Ave, Pompano Beach, FL 33069-1405
Tel (954) 958-9866 *Founded/Ownrshp* 1998
Sales 72.8MM *EMP* 995
SIC 3465 Body parts, automobile: stamped metal
CEO: James L Hutchings
**Pr:* Donald J Hutchings
**VP:* William O Hood
VP: William Hood
Ql Cn Mgr: Franco Seravalli

D-U-N-S 08-269-2997
HUTCHINGS COURT REPORTERS LLC (CA)
400 N Tustin Ave Ste 301, Santa Ana, CA 92705-3852
Tel (702) 314-7200 *Founded/Ownrshp* 1953
Sales 25.8MM *EMP* 50
SIC 7338 Court reporting service
IT Man: Bill Jimenez
Sys/Mgr: Jane Van Der Veen

D-U-N-S 07-662-1895
HUTCHINS & WHEELER A PROFESSIONAL CORP
101 Federal St Fl 13, Boston, MA 02110-1858
Tel (617) 345-1000 *Founded/Ownrshp* 1844
Sales 12.8MM^E *EMP* 328
SIC 8111 General practice law office; General practice law office
Pr: John H Clymer
COO: Peter Furness
MIS Dir: Mary O Mara
Board of Directors: Richard M Stein

D-U-N-S 84-800-6383
HUTCHINS DRYWALL INC
2335 Silver Wolf Dr, Henderson, NV 89011-4431
Tel (702) 565-5317 *Founded/Ownrshp* 1989
Sales 32.0MM^E *EMP* 80
SIC 1742 Drywall

D-U-N-S 01-898-0235
HUTCHINS MOTORS INC (ME)
O'CONNOR MOTRO COMPANY
187 Riverside Dr, Augusta, ME 04330-4133
Tel (207) 622-3191 *Founded/Ownrshp* 1947, 2005
Sales 88.6MM^E *EMP* 200^E
SIC 5511 5012 Automobiles, new & used; Trucks, commercial; Automobiles, new & used; Trucks, commercial
CEO: Randall Hutchins
**CFO:* Troy Knowlan
Exec: Anna Starrett

D-U-N-S 07-190-8735
HUTCHINSON & BLOODGOOD LLP
550 N Brand Blvd Fl 14, Glendale, CA 91203-1952
Tel (818) 637-5000 *Founded/Ownrshp* 1953
Sales 22.0MM^E *EMP* 125
SIC 8721 Accounting, auditing & bookkeeping; Accounting, auditing & bookkeeping
Mng Pt: Richard Preciado
Pt: Michael Benneian
Pt: Gary Carruthers
Pt: Jenny Chen
Pt: Juan Daukowski
Pt: Bill Eckenrod
Pt: Lee Hanna
Pt: John Hoyte
Pt: Doug Kawamura
Pt: Sahak Loussinian
Pt: Mica Miyamoto
Pt: Elizabeth Moore
Pt: Joseph Muriello
Pt: Sergio Santos
Pt: Duane Sharpe
Pt: Steve Throop
Pt: Peter Weir
Mng Pt: Richard A Precido
CFO: Kalena Rebollar

D-U-N-S 00-102-3704 IMP
■ **HUTCHINSON AEROSPACE & INDUSTRY INC**
(*Suby of* HUTCHINSON CORP) ★
82 South St, Hopkinton, MA 01748-2205
Tel (508) 417-7000 *Founded/Ownrshp* 1943, 2000
Sales 79.3MM^E *EMP* 421
SIC 3714 3061 3724 Shock absorbers, motor vehicle; Mechanical rubber goods; Aircraft engines & engine parts; Shock absorbers, motor vehicle; Mechanical rubber goods; Aircraft engines & engine parts
CEO: Cedric Duclos
CFO: Laurent Godbillot
Treas: Shano Cristilli
VP: Ron Lassy
VP: Paul Stupinski
Prin: Grant Hintze
Admn Mgr: Brenda Tomlinson
Genl Mgr: Tom Foley
VP Opers: Pierre Acker
VP Opers: Scott Pollock

D-U-N-S 00-601-5382 IMP
■ **HUTCHINSON ANTIVIBRATION SYSTEMS INC** (MI)
HUTCHINSON AUTOMOTIVE
(*Suby of* HUTCHINSON CORP) ★
460 Fuller Ave Ne, Grand Rapids, MI 49503-1912
Tel (616) 459-4541 *Founded/Ownrshp* 1986, 1988
Sales 134.0MM^E *EMP* 673
SIC 3069 3061 Molded rubber products; Mechanical rubber goods; Molded rubber products; Mechanical rubber goods
CEO: Jacques Maign
VP: Jim Todoroff
Prgrm Mgr: David Blissett
Info Man: Douglas Mauk
Plnt Mgr: Eric Jamet
Plnt Mgr: Tom Kelly
Ql Cn Mgr: Roger Wayt
S&M/VP: Bruce Aittama
Snr Mgr: Jerome Joly
Snr Mgr: Russ Olson

D-U-N-S 96-482-3868
HUTCHINSON AREA HEALTH CARE INC
HUTCHINSON COMMUNITY HOSPITAL
1095 Highway 15 S, Hutchinson, MN 55350-5000
Tel (320) 234-5000 *Founded/Ownrshp* 1934
Sales 80.9MM *EMP* 630
SIC 8062 General medical & surgical hospitals; General medical & surgical hospitals
Pr: Dr Steven Mulder
**CFO:* Pamela Larson
VP: Brendan Keilan
Exec: John Curtiss
Exec: Cheryl Wiener
Dir Inf Cn: Lynette Wendlandt
Chf Nrs Of: Jan Manary
CIO: John Curtis
CTO: Robin Erickson
Sfty Dirs: Karen Ober
Mktg Mgr: Mary E Wells
Board of Directors: Cary Lindere, Kara Neubarth

HUTCHINSON AUTO MALL
See HUTCHINSON AUTOMOTIVE INC

HUTCHINSON AUTOMOTIVE
See HUTCHINSON ANTIVIBRATION SYSTEMS INC

D-U-N-S 04-711-8786
HUTCHINSON AUTOMOTIVE INC
HUTCHINSON AUTO MALL
3989 River Place Dr, Macon, GA 31210-1730
Tel (478) 757-2190 *Founded/Ownrshp* 2008
Sales 27.0MM^E *EMP* 65
SIC 5511 Automobiles, new & used; Automobiles, new & used
CEO: Forest Hutchinson
**CFO:* Michael Hutchinson

D-U-N-S 07-332-5425
HUTCHINSON CLINIC PA
LYONS MEDICAL CENTER
2101 N Waldron St, Hutchinson, KS 67502-1197
Tel (620) 669-2500 *Founded/Ownrshp* 1967
Sales 64.0MM^E *EMP* 700
SIC 8011 8071 5912 5999 Clinic, operated by physicians; Radiologist; Medical laboratories; Drug stores & proprietary stores; Hearing aids; Clinic, operated by physicians; Radiologist; Medical laboratories; Drug stores & proprietary stores; Hearing aids
CEO: Michael Heck
**Pr:* Stanton Barker
**COO:* Darryl Serpen
COO: Benjamin Vallier
**CFO:* Michael Harms
CFO: Belinda Mahoney
VP: Ginger Morrell
Dir Lab: Stacy Gasper
Dir Rad: Daren Beltz
Dir IT: Kathy Both
IT Man: Robert Davidson

D-U-N-S 02-282-7596
HUTCHINSON CO-OP
HUTCHIN COOP ELEVATOR
1060 5th Ave Se, Hutchinson, MN 55350-7028
Tel (320) 587-4647 *Founded/Ownrshp* 1955
Sales 52.4MM *EMP* 17
Accts Carlson Highland & Co Llp N
SIC 5191 5171 5541 Fertilizer & fertilizer materials; Chemicals, agricultural; Seeds: field, garden & flower; Petroleum bulk stations; Filling stations, gasoline; Fertilizer & fertilizer materials; Chemicals, agricultural; Seeds: field, garden & flower; Petroleum bulk stations; Filling stations, gasoline
CEO: Michael Conner
Pr: Lynn Mackedanz
Sec: Joe Tauer
Bd of Dir: Joe Mallak
VP: Tina Huebner
VP: Rodney Kurth
Prin: Morris Rettman
Prin: Gary Warner

D-U-N-S 07-625-5322
HUTCHINSON COMMUNITY COLLEGE
1300 N Plum St, Hutchinson, KS 67501-5831
Tel (620) 665-3423 *Founded/Ownrshp* 1928
Sales 22.0MM *EMP* 521
Accts Swindoll Janzen Hawk & Loyd
SIC 8222 Community college; Community college
Pr: Edward Berger
**Pr:* Carter File
**Sec:* Cindy Andsager
**VP:* Julie Blanton
VP: Cindy Hoss
IT Man: Glenn Acheson
Psych: Debbie Gieselman
Pgrm Dir: Travis Booe

HUTCHINSON COMMUNITY HOSPITAL
See HUTCHINSON AREA HEALTH CARE INC

D-U-N-S 08-108-7892 EXP
■ **HUTCHINSON CORP**
(*Suby of* HUTCHINSON)
460 Fuller Ave Ne, Grand Rapids, MI 49503-1912
Tel (616) 459-4541 *Founded/Ownrshp* 2006
Sales 887.3MM^E *EMP* 3,175
SIC 3069 3011 Molded rubber products; Mittens, rubber; Tires, cushion or solid rubber; Molded rubber products; Mittens, rubber; Tires, cushion or solid rubber
Ch Bd: Yves Rene Manot
**Pr:* Gerard Gehin
**Treas:* Thomas Popma
Netwrk Mgr: Sam Aiuto
Plnt Mgr: Jim Johnston
Mktg Mgr: Walt Jenkins

D-U-N-S 36-108-1623 IMP
■ **HUTCHINSON FTS INC**
(*Suby of* HUTCHINSON CORP) ★
1060 Centre Rd, Auburn Hills, MI 48326-2600
Tel (248) 589-7710 *Founded/Ownrshp* 1996
Sales 226.3MM^E *EMP* 1,075
SIC 3714 3061 3567 3492 3443 3429 Air conditioner parts, motor vehicle; Mechanical rubber goods; Industrial furnaces & ovens; Fluid power valves & hose fittings; Fabricated plate work (boiler shop); Manufactured hardware (general); Air conditioner parts, motor vehicle; Mechanical rubber goods; Industrial furnaces & ovens; Fluid power valves & hose fittings; Fabricated plate work (boiler shop); Manufactured hardware (general)
CEO: Paul H Campbell
**VP:* Sean Canty
Prgrm Mgr: Robert Cerant
Tech Mgr: Carlos Enriquez
Mtls Mgr: Sue Kesty
Plnt Mgr: Paul Macdonald
Ql Cn Mgr: John Macuga
Ql Cn Mgr: Efrain Varela
Ql Cn Mgr: Mark Woolwine
S&M/VP: Bruce Aittama
Manager: Keith Hanson

D-U-N-S 83-013-3794
HUTCHINSON HEALTH CARE
1095 Highway 15 S, Hutchinson, MN 55350-5000
Tel (320) 234-5000 *Founded/Ownrshp* 2006
Sales 80.8MM^E *EMP* 99
Accts Mcgladrey Llp Minneapolis Mn
SIC 8082 Home health care services
Pr: Steve Mulder
IT Man: Pat Spaude
HC Dir: Tammy Gohl
Dietician: Karen Gensemer

HUTCHINSON HEART
See HUTCHINSON REGIONAL MEDICAL CENTER INC

HUTCHINSON IND SCHL DST NO 423
See COUNTY OF MCLEOD IND SCHOOL DIST 423

D-U-N-S 19-860-4852 IMP
■ **HUTCHINSON INDUSTRIES INC**
(*Suby of* HUTCHINSON CORP) ★
460 Southard St, Trenton, NJ 08638-4224
Tel (609) 394-1010 *Founded/Ownrshp* 1988
Sales 117.5MM^E *EMP* 450
SIC 3069 Rubber automotive products; Rubber automotive products
Pr: Pascal Seraderian
Off Admin: Harriet H Zipper

D-U-N-S 04-940-2753
HUTCHINSON OIL CO INC
HUTCHIS
515 S Main St, Elk City, OK 73644-6700
Tel (580) 225-0301 *Founded/Ownrshp* 1969
Sales 124.7MM^E *EMP* 150
SIC 5171 5541 Petroleum bulk stations; Filling stations, gasoline; Petroleum bulk stations; Filling stations, gasoline
Pr: David Hutchinson
**Treas:* Linda Hutchinson

D-U-N-S 60-459-1495
HUTCHINSON PLUMBING HEATING COOLING LLC
621 Chapel Ave E Ste E, Cherry Hill, NJ 08034-1412
Tel (856) 429-5807 *Founded/Ownrshp* 1948
Sales 28.9MM^E *EMP* 200
SIC 6512 Nonresidential building operators; Nonresidential building operators
Pr: Ed Hutchinson
Prin: George H Hutchinson

HUTCHINSON PUBLIC SCHOOLS
See HUTCHINSON USD 308

D-U-N-S 07-626-2955
HUTCHINSON REGIONAL MEDICAL CENTER INC
HUTCHINSON HEART
(*Suby of* HEALTH CARE INC) ★
1701 E 23rd Ave, Hutchinson, KS 67502-1105
Tel (620) 665-2000 *Founded/Ownrshp* 1967
Sales 25.2MM^E *EMP* 1,000
Accts Wendling Noe Nelson & Johnson
SIC 8062 Skilled nursing care facilities; General medical & surgical hospitals
CFO: Cassandra Dolen
Pr: Michael Krach
**CEO:* Kendall Johnson
COO: Mike Connell
VP: Robyn Chadwick
VP: Todd Laffoon
VP: Dan Stafford
Exec: Rita Blackburn
Exec: Carl Caton
Exec: Chris Hill
Exec: Gary Holderman
Dir Teleco: Randy Miller

HUTCHINSON SALES
See HUTCHINSON SEALING SYSTEMS INC

D-U-N-S 96-550-8224
HUTCHINSON SCHOOL DISTRICT
30 Glen St Nw, Hutchinson, MN 55350-1618
Tel (320) 587-2860 *Founded/Ownrshp* 2010
Sales 16.7MM^E *EMP* 550^E
SIC 8211 Elementary & secondary schools

D-U-N-S 94-455-7115
■ **HUTCHINSON SEAL CORP**
NATIONAL O RINGS
(*Suby of* HUTCHINSON CORP) ★
11634 Patton Rd, Downey, CA 90241-5212
Tel (248) 375-4190 *Founded/Ownrshp* 1996
Sales 91.8MM^E *EMP* 900
SIC 3053 Gaskets & sealing devices; Gaskets & sealing devices
Pr: Christian Groche
Pr: Robert Hanson
CFO: Cedric Duclos
DP Exec: Steve Orlowicz
IT Man: Marcelo Lewin

D-U-N-S 08-558-2505 IMP
■ **HUTCHINSON SEALING SYSTEMS INC**
HUTCHINSON SALES
(*Suby of* HUTCHINSON CORP) ★
1060 Centre Rd, Auburn Hills, MI 48326-2600
Tel (248) 375-3720 *Founded/Ownrshp* 1999
Sales 238.2MM^E *EMP* 1,075
SIC 3069 Rubber automotive products; Rubber automotive products
Pr: Robert C Hanson
**Treas:* John Attard
S&M/VP: Bob Hanson
Snr Mgr: Paul Leason

D-U-N-S 00-645-6768 IMP
▲ **HUTCHINSON TECHNOLOGY INC** (MN)
40 W Highland Park Dr Ne, Hutchinson, MN 55350-9300
Tel (320) 587-3797 *Founded/Ownrshp* 1965
Sales 252.8MM *EMP* 2,489^E
Tkr Sym HTCH *Exch* NGS
SIC 3679 8731 Electronic circuits; Electronic research; Electronic circuits; Electronic research
Pr: Richard J Penn
**Ch Bd:* Wayne M Fortun
COO: Wendy Wick
CFO: David P Radloff
VP: Nancy Fischer
VP: Beatrice Graczyk
VP: Peter Ickert
VP: Mark Jelkin
VP: Dale M Ruzicka
Exec: John Farmerie
Exec: Matthew Lang
Exec: Paul Pesavento
Exec: Karen Raske
Exec: Randy Seifert
Board of Directors: Martha Goldberg Aronson, Russell Huffer, Frank P Russomanno, Phil E Soran, Thomas R Verhage

D-U-N-S 05-046-5509
HUTCHINSON USD 308
HUTCHINSON PUBLIC SCHOOLS
1520 N Plum St, Hutchinson, KS 67501-5854
Tel (620) 665-4400 *Founded/Ownrshp* 1876
Sales 46.6MM^E *EMP* 800
SIC 8211 Public combined elementary & secondary school; Public combined elementary & secondary school
Prin: Janis Bair
Prin: Michael Ellegood
Prin: Glenn Fortmayer
Prin: Marietta L Gray
Prin: Laura McLemore
Prin: Randy Norwood
Prin: Elizabeth Peirce
Prin: Rod Rathbun
Prin: Tamara Sullivan
Prin: M M Young

HUTCHIS
See HUTCHINSON OIL CO INC

D-U-N-S 05-978-4983
HUTCHISON CORP
INNER SPACE CONSTRUCTORS DIV
6107 Obispo Ave, Long Beach, CA 90805-3799
Tel (310) 763-7991 *Founded/Ownrshp* 1971
Sales 22.2MM^E *EMP* 80
SIC 1542 1742 1521 Nonresidential construction; Commercial & office building, new construction; Acoustical & ceiling work; Single-family housing construction; Nonresidential construction; Commercial & office building, new construction; Acoustical & ceiling work; Single-family housing construction
Ch Bd: Robert J Hutchison
**Sec:* Linda Mc Dannold
**VP:* Stephen Mc Dannold
Exec: Norma Herrera

D-U-N-S 96-778-5361 IMP/EXP
HUTCHISON HAYES SEPARATION INC
3520 E Sam Houston Pkwy N, Houston, TX 77015-3247
Tel (713) 455-9600 *Founded/Ownrshp* 2007
Sales 22.1MM^E *EMP* 40
SIC 5084 Food industry machinery
Pr: Jack Krahe
**Ch Bd:* Michael Dunson
**CFO:* Carl Wedemeyer

D-U-N-S 02-223-2581
HUTCHISON INC
HUTCHISON LUMBER
7460 Hwy 85, Adams City, CO 80022
Tel (303) 287-2826 *Founded/Ownrshp* 1952
Sales 50.1MM^E *EMP* 190
SIC 3523 5051 Farm machinery & equipment; Bale ties, wire; Farm machinery & equipment; Bale ties, wire
CEO: George G Hutchison
CFO: Bill Dodson
**VP:* Blake Hutchison
**VP:* Doug Jacks
Genl Mgr: Jon Starry
Sales Asso: Bill Kullbom

HUTCHISON LUMBER
See HUTCHISON INC

D-U-N-S 08-134-5852
HUTCHISON SCHOOL
1740 Ridgeway Rd, Memphis, TN 38119-5314
Tel (901) 761-2220 *Founded/Ownrshp* 2004
Sales 20.6MM *EMP* 180
Accts Reynolds Bone & Griesbeck Plc
SIC 8211 Private elementary & secondary schools; Private elementary & secondary schools
Dir IT: Jesse Cresswell
IT Man: Sandy Benson
Pr Dir: Cathy Barber
HC Dir: Candy Covington
HC Dir: Dorothy Sisnett

D-U-N-S 82-871-2232
HUTCO INC
114 Park Center Dr, Broussard, LA 70518-3605
Tel (337) 837-5594 *Founded/Ownrshp* 1986
Sales 45.1MM^E *EMP* 1,300
SIC 7363 Help supply services; Help supply services
Pr: James M Hutchison Jr
CFO: Bernard J Barilleaux
**Sec:* Bernard Barilleaux
**VP:* Scott Hutchison

D-U-N-S 96-947-6019 IMP
HUTSON INC
JOHN DEERE
1201 Fulton Rd, Mayfield, KY 42066-2963
Tel (270) 247-0125 *Founded/Ownrshp* 1996
Sales 72.6MM^E *EMP* 189
SIC 5083 Agricultural machinery & equipment; Tractors, agricultural; Agricultural machinery & equipment; Tractors, agricultural
Pr: Barry Carson
CFO: Tracy Martin
**Treas:* Gay Grogan
IT Man: Aaron Pitman

D-U-N-S 06-258-8751
HUTSON MOTOR CO INC
2316 1st Ave Se, Moultrie, GA 31788-6215
Tel (229) 891-4000 *Founded/Ownrshp* 1970
Sales 25.2MM^E *EMP* 80
SIC 5511 Automobiles, new & used; Automobiles, new & used
Pr: Robert Hutson
**Sec:* Peggy Hutson
IT Man: Annette Tillman

D-U-N-S 15-142-7143
HUTT TRUCKING CO INC
H T C
1362 Lincoln Ave, Holland, MI 49423-9381
Tel (616) 928-2300 *Founded/Ownrshp* 1976
Sales 39.4MM^E *EMP* 105
SIC 4213

D-U-N-S 06-674-7346
HUTTER CONSTRUCTION CORP
HUTTER HOMES
810 Turnpike Rd, New Ipswich, NH 03071-3845
Tel (603) 878-2300 *Founded/Ownrshp* 1973
Sales 90.0MM *EMP* 150
SIC 1541 1542 Industrial buildings & warehouses; Nonresidential construction; Industrial buildings & warehouses; Nonresidential construction
Pr: Lars A Traffie
CFO: Rich Upsall
**CFO:* Richard Upsall
**Treas:* James J Traffie
**VP:* Gary Bertram
**VP:* Quentin Jones
Genl Mgr: Dwayne White
IT Man: Jay Lewis
Sales Exec: Diane Cooper
Sls Mgr: Nels Traffie

HUTTER HOMES
See HUTTER CONSTRUCTION CORP

D-U-N-S 00-630-6740 IMP
▲ HUTTIG BUILDING PRODUCTS INC
HUTTIG SASH & DOOR CO
555 Maryville University, Saint Louis, MO 63141-5805
Tel (314) 216-2600 *Founded/Ownrshp* 1885
Sales 623.7MM *EMP* 1,000
Tkr Sym HBP *Exch* NAS
SIC 5031 5033 Millwork; Door frames, all materials; Doors, combination, screen-storm; Doors; Roofing & siding materials; Insulation materials; Millwork; Door frames, all materials; Doors, combination, screen-storm; Doors; Roofing & siding materials; Insulation materials
Pr: Jon P Vrabely
**Ch Bd:* Delbert H Tanner
VP: Greg Gurley
VP: Gregory W Gurley
VP: Hank J Krey
VP: Brian D Robinson
Genl Mgr: Wes Coffee
Genl Mgr: John Drinen
Genl Mgr: Brian Laplaga
Genl Mgr: Jason White
Off Mgr: Owen Pengelly
Board of Directors: E Thayer Bigelow, Richard S Forte, Donald L Glass, James Hibberd, Gina Hoagland, Patrick Larmon, J Keith Matheney, Delbert H Tanner

HUTTIG SASH & DOOR CO
See HUTTIG BUILDING PRODUCTS INC

D-U-N-S 18-662-3976 EXP
HUTTIG-TEXAS LIMITED PARTNERSHIP
SOUTHWEST ROOFING SUPPLY
2115 Valley View Ln, Dallas, TX 75234-8934
Tel (972) 620-9097 *Founded/Ownrshp* 2005
Sales 22.1MM^E *EMP* 120^E
SIC 5031 Lumber, plywood & millwork; Building materials, interior; Building materials, exterior; Molding, all materials
Sls Mgr: Bill Washerlesky

D-U-N-S 10-007-5134
HUTTO INDEPENDENT SCHOOL DIST
200 College St, Hutto, TX 78634-4525
Tel (512) 759-3771 *Founded/Ownrshp* 1993
Sales 25.8MM^E *EMP* 345
SIC 8211 Public elementary & secondary schools; Public elementary & secondary schools
HC Dir: Brandi Baker

D-U-N-S 78-846-0509
HUTTON CONSTRUCTION CORP
2229 S West St, Wichita, KS 67213-1113
Tel (316) 942-8855 *Founded/Ownrshp* 1992
Sales 107.3MM^E *EMP* 185^E
SIC 1542 Commercial & office building, new construction; Commercial & office buildings, renovation & repair; Commercial & office building, new construction; Commercial & office buildings, renovation & repair
Pr: Ben Hutton
COO: Philip Augustino
**CFO:* Peggy West
**Ofcr:* Jim Keusler
**VP:* Josh Herrman
VP: Jack Schulte
Mtls Mgr: Brett Budd

D-U-N-S 07-639-2331
HUTZEL HOSPITAL
WOMENS CENTER
3980 John R St, Detroit, MI 48201-2018
Tel (313) 745-7555 *Founded/Ownrshp* 1985
Sales 44.1MM^E *EMP* 1,884
SIC 8062 General medical & surgical hospitals; General medical & surgical hospitals
CEO: Mike Duggin
Mtls Mgr: Butch Johnson

D-U-N-S 61-915-3559 EXP
HUVEPHARMA INC
525 Westpark Dr Ste 230, Peachtree City, GA 30269-3578
Tel (770) 486-7212 *Founded/Ownrshp* 2005
Sales 90.0MM *EMP* 85
SIC 5122 Animal medicines
Pr: Glen Wilkinson

D-U-N-S 88-312-8204 IMP
HUVEPHARMA INC
3360 Maury Ave, Saint Louis, MO 63116-2029
Tel (314) 752-3521 *Founded/Ownrshp* 2007
Sales 21.8MM^E *EMP* 38^E
SIC 5122 Pharmaceuticals
Pr: Kiril Doumschiev
Site Mgr: Doug Haight
Site Mgr: Ralph Staiert
Mktg Mgr: Ivan Gospodinov

D-U-N-S 11-425-7728 IMP
HUXTABLES KITCHEN INC
2100 E 49th St, Vernon, CA 90058-2825
Tel (323) 923-2900 *Founded/Ownrshp* 2001
Sales 24.7MM^E *EMP* 100
SIC 5812 2099 2015 2013 Eating places; Ready-to-eat meals, salads & sandwiches; Poultry slaughtering & processing; Sausages & other prepared meats
Pr: Kenneth F Hayes
S&M/VP: Neil Merritt
Mktg Mgr: Karen Mitchell

HV
See HIDDEN VALLEY COMPANIES INC

D-U-N-S 12-889-4909 IMP/EXP
HV INDUSTRIES INC
HOPE VALLEY INDUSTRIES
222 Exeter Rd, North Kingstown, RI 02852-6406
Tel (401) 295-4404 *Founded/Ownrshp* 2002
Sales 45.3MM^E *EMP* 150
SIC 3081 Unsupported plastics film & sheet; Unsupported plastics film & sheet
Pr: Thomas Melucci
**VP:* Craig Melucci
VP: Dana White
Creative D: Paul Bierce

D-U-N-S 17-905-7674
HVAC DISTRIBUTORS INC
2 Old Market St, Mount Joy, PA 17552-1320
Tel (717) 653-6674 *Founded/Ownrshp* 1987
Sales 147.5MM^E *EMP* 98
Accts Hatter Harris & Beittel Llp
SIC 5075 Warm air heating & air conditioning; Warm air heating & air conditioning
Pr: David W Mcllwaine
**Sec:* William B Mcllwaine
Trfc Dir: Tony Eberly
Mktg Mgr: Heather Seitz
Sls Mgr: Eric Rodenhauser
Sales Asso: Eric Germer

D-U-N-S 15-474-7265
HVAC MECHANICAL SERVICES OF TEXAS LTD
HUNTON TRANE SERVICES
(*Suby of* HTI LTD) ★
10555 Westpark Dr, Houston, TX 77042-5232
Tel (713) 266-3900 *Founded/Ownrshp* 1997
Sales 64.0MM^E *EMP* 300
SIC 3599 1711 3441 3585 3444 Air intake filters, internal combustion engine, except auto; Warm air heating & air conditioning contractor; Fabricated structural metal; Refrigeration & heating equipment; Sheet metalwork; Air intake filters, internal combustion engine, except auto; Warm air heating & air conditioning contractor; Fabricated structural metal; Refrigeration & heating equipment; Sheet metalwork
Pr: Richard Hunton
**CFO:* Larry Bower
**VP:* Michael Deatherage

D-U-N-S 06-610-6394
HVAC SALES & SUPPLY CO INC
2015 Thomas Rd, Memphis, TN 38134-6316
Tel (901) 365-1137 *Founded/Ownrshp* 1982
Sales 22.2MM^E *EMP* 57
SIC 5075 Warm air heating equipment & supplies; Furnaces, warm air; Heat exchangers; Air conditioning & ventilation equipment & supplies
Pr: William D Bomar
**VP:* Dale C Smith
Genl Mgr: Robert Hayes
Sales Asso: Torin Gladney
Sales Asso: Jimmy Greenhaw
Sales Asso: Adam Lunsford

D-U-N-S 04-475-6844
HVB AMERICA INC
(*Suby of* UNICREDIT BANK AG)
150 E 42nd St Fl 29, New York, NY 10017-5632
Tel (212) 672-6000 *Founded/Ownrshp* 1996
Sales NA *EMP* 600
SIC 6082 Foreign trade & international banking institutions; Foreign trade & international banking institutions
COO: Christopher Wrenn
Top Exec: Mark Bowles
VP: James Cochrane
VP: Danielle Scarola
Mng Dir: Thomas Rubbert
Mng Dir: Curt Schade
IT Man: Harm Bandholz

HVCA
See DEAN TECHNOLOGY INC

HVCC-USA
See HANON SYSTEMS USA LLC

D-U-N-S 04-109-5555
HVH TRANSPORTATION INC
181 E 56th Ave Ste 200, Denver, CO 80216-1748
Tel (303) 292-3656 *Founded/Ownrshp* 1977
Sales 86.3MM^E *EMP* 540
Accts Marrs Sevier & Company Llc
SIC 4213 Trucking, except local; Less-than-truckload (LTL) transport; Trucking, except local; Less-than-truckload (LTL) transport
Ch Bd: Robert L Holder
**Pr:* Bruce Holder
**Treas:* Wayne Holder
VP: Jack Egger
VP: David Felton
Genl Mgr: Jim Pirano
DP Exec: Harold Hajoway
IT Man: Heath Reeves
Mktg Dir: Dave Antonio

D-U-N-S 16-010-4873
HVHC INC
(*Suby of* HIGHMARK BLUE CRSS-BLUE SHIELD) ★
100 Senate Ave, Camp Hill, PA 17011-2309
Tel (717) 760-9680 *Founded/Ownrshp* 1996
Sales NA *EMP* 6,350
SIC 6324 Hospital & medical service plans; Hospital & medical service plans
Pr: Walter F Froh
**Ch Bd:* Robert C Gray
**CFO:* Michael Kincaid
**CFO:* Douglas C Shepard
Sr VP: Bob Cox

VP: Cheryl Grobelny
Snr Mgr: Michael Thibdeau

D-U-N-S 18-959-3275
■ HVM LLC
EXTENDED STAY HOTELS
(*Suby of* ESA MANAGEMENT LLC) ★
11525 N Community House R, Charlotte, NC 28277-3610
Tel (980) 345-1600 *Founded/Ownrshp* 2013
Sales 395.2MM^E *EMP* 9,300
SIC 7011 Hotels & motels; Hotels & motels
CEO: James L Donald
Ex VP: Hugh Wall
VP: Mark D Mahoney
Dir IT: Ben Hall

D-U-N-S 13-676-9705
■ HVPH MOTOR CORP
LEXUS DE SAN JUAN
(*Suby of* PENSKE AUTOMOTIVE GROUP INC) ★
Ave John F Kennedy Km, San Juan, PR 00929
Tel (787) 273-3000 *Founded/Ownrshp* 1993
Sales 28.7MM^E *EMP* 120
SIC 5511 Automobiles, new & used; Automobiles, new & used
Pr: Charles Vaillant
**Sec:* Jose Gregorio Velez

HVUD
See HARPETH VALLEY UTILITIES DISTRICT OF DAVIDSON AND WILLIAMSON COUNTIES

D-U-N-S 09-133-1835
HW HOLDCO LLC
BUILDER MAGAZINE
1 Thomas Cir Nw Ste 600, Washington, DC 20005-5803
Tel (202) 452-0800 *Founded/Ownrshp* 1976
Sales 192.4MM^E *EMP* 630
SIC 2721 7389 Trade journals: publishing only, not printed on site; Trade show arrangement; Trade journals: publishing only, not printed on site; Trade show arrangement
CEO: Peter Goldstone
Pr: Joe Carroll
**CFO:* Matthew Flynn
Ex VP: Thomas Rousseau
VP: Nick Cavnar
VP: Ray Giovine
VP: Neal Kielar
VP: Nelson Wischovit
VP: Nelson Wischovitch
VP: Nelson Wiscovitch
Exec: Craig Webb
Assoc Dir: Amie Gilmore
Creative D: David Beveridge
Creative D: Dobby Gibson

HWA
See HOME WARRANTY OF AMERICA INC

D-U-N-S 07-983-3496
HWASEUNG AUTOMOTIVE ALABAMA LLC
(*Suby of* HSAA) ★
100 Sonata Dr, Enterprise, AL 36330-7338
Tel (334) 348-9516 *Founded/Ownrshp* 2015
Sales 72.3MM *EMP* 356
SIC 3714 Air conditioner parts, motor vehicle
Pr: Hyeong Jin Kim
CFO: Kang Chan Park

D-U-N-S 15-196-4025 IMP
HWASEUNG AUTOMOTIVE AMERICA HOLDINGS INC
HSAA
(*Suby of* HWASEUNG R&A CO., LTD.)
100 Sonata Dr, Enterprise, AL 36330-7338
Tel (334) 348-9516 *Founded/Ownrshp* 2003
Sales 177.3MM *EMP* 185
Accts Rodl Warren Averett Llc Montg
SIC 3069 5085 Weather strip, sponge rubber; Hose, belting & packing; Weather strip, sponge rubber; Hose, belting & packing
Pr: Harry Kim
CFO: Paul Park
VP: J K Lee
Admn Mgr: David Kim
Dir IT: Brian Oates
IT Man: Gerald Cross
Sfty Mgr: Julie Feeney
Sfty Mgr: Gary Jordan
Prd Mgr: James Hwang
Ql Cn Mgr: Amy Thrash
Snr Mgr: Chuck Patterson

D-U-N-S 07-983-3491
HWASEUNG AUTOMOTIVE USA LLC
(*Suby of* HSAA) ★
101 Development Ln, Enterprise, AL 36330-7381
Tel (334) 348-9516 *Founded/Ownrshp* 2015
Sales 104.9MM *EMP* 43^E
SIC 3714 Air conditioner parts, motor vehicle
Pr: Hyeong Jin Kim
**CFO:* Kang Chan Park

D-U-N-S 14-508-4849 IMP
HWASHIN AMERICA CORP
(*Suby of* HWASHIN CO., LTD.)
661 Montgomery Hwy, Greenville, AL 36037-3527
Tel (334) 382-1100 *Founded/Ownrshp* 2003
Sales 368.0MM *EMP* 470
SIC 5531 Automotive parts; Automotive parts
Ch: Ho Jeong
**Pr:* Seojin Jeong
**Pr:* Hyun Park
**CFO:* Milton Park
Snr Mgr: Nam Ko

D-U-N-S 13-079-9406
HWC LOGISTICS INC
5300 Kennedy Rd, Forest Park, GA 30297-2505
Tel (678) 705-6002 *Founded/Ownrshp* 1981
Sales 23.1MM^E *EMP* 111^E
SIC 4214 4226 Local trucking with storage; Special warehousing & storage
Pr: Michael Owens
Pr: Rodney Brennan
**COO:* Kevin Snell

*VP: David Ireland
Opers Mgr: Walter McElwaney

D-U-N-S 78-082-0580 IMP
■ HWC WIRE & CABLE CO
HAYNES WIRE ROPE
(Suby of HOUSTON WIRE & CABLE CO INC) ★
10201 North Loop E, Houston, TX 77029-1415
Tel (713) 609-2160 Founded/Ownrshp 1985
Sales 115.0MM^E EMP 282^E
SIC 5063 Electrical apparatus & equipment; Transformers & transmission equipment; Electrical apparatus & equipment; Transformers & transmission equipment
CEO: James L Pokluda III
*CFO: Nicol G Graham
*VP: John Marchiando
Admn Mgr: Lynda Danna
Natl Sales: Eric Jacques

D-U-N-S 62-486-8568 EXP
HWD ACQUISITION INC
HURD WINDOWS & DOORS
(Suby of SIERRA PACIFIC INDUSTRIES) ★
575 S Whelen Ave, Medford, WI 54451-1738
Tel (715) 748-2011 Founded/Ownrshp 2014
Sales 110.5MM^E EMP 500
SIC 2431 Window frames, wood; Window frames, wood
Pr: Dominic Truniger
*CFO: Dave Roland
VP: David Kochendorfer
*CTO: Bill Schultz
Plnt Mgr: Brad Sackett
Ql Cn Mgr: Mike Czerniak

D-U-N-S 10-528-6905
HWF CONSTRUCTION INC
3685 Fruitvale Ave, Bakersfield, CA 93308-5107
Tel (661) 587-3590 Founded/Ownrshp 1997
Sales 32.2MM EMP 15
SIC 2721 Magazines: publishing only, not printed on site; Magazines: publishing only, not printed on site
Pr: Robert Hinelsy

D-U-N-S 06-104-5027 IMP
HWH CORP (MT)
H W H
2096 Moscow Rd, Moscow, IA 52760-9603
Tel (563) 724-3715 Founded/Ownrshp 1967
Sales 37.7MM^E EMP 125
SIC 3714 Hydraulic fluid power pumps for auto steering mechanism; Hydraulic fluid power pumps for auto steering mechanism
Pr: Paul E Hanser
*VP: Francis Brinkmeyer
*VP: Kurt Brinkmeyer
Plnt Mgr: Tim Rumler
Sls Mgr: Carol Frerichs

HWH INDUSTRIAL
See WE BUILD INC

HWI DO IT CENTER
See SCHILLING BROTHERS LUMBER & HARDWARE INC

D-U-N-S 18-734-0489
HWP DEVELOPMENT LLC
SIX FLAGS GREAT ESCAPE LODGE A
89 Six Flags Dr, Queensbury, NY 12804-6215
Tel (518) 824-6060 Founded/Ownrshp 2003
Sales 15.2MM^E EMP 425
SIC 7996 7011 Theme park, amusement; Hotels; Theme park, amusement; Hotels
Genl Mgr: Kerry Claus
IT Man: Babette Donlon

HWRSD
See HAMILTON-WENHAM REGIONAL SCHOOL DISTRICT

D-U-N-S 14-465-8478
HWRT OIL CO LLC
1 Piasa Ln, Hartford, IL 62048-1504
Tel (618) 254-2855 Founded/Ownrshp 2004
Sales 2.8MMM EMP 22
Accts Uhy Llc St Louis Missouri
SIC 5172 Petroleum products; Petroleum products
Pr: Matthew Schrimpf
*Treas: Susan Hatfield
*VP: Bryan Hatfield
Area Mgr: Russell Andrews
Area Mgr: William Weirich

D-U-N-S 07-947-2609
HWSTAR HOLDINGS CORP
(Suby of ADS WASTE HOLDINGS INC) ★
90 Fort Wade Rd Ste 200, Ponte Vedra, FL 32081-5112
Tel (904) 737-7900 Founded/Ownrshp 2006
Sales 27.0MM^E EMP 104^E
SIC 4953 6719 Refuse systems; Personal holding companies, except banks
CEO: Richard Burke
*COO: John Spegal
*CFO: Steve Carn
*VP: Jaime Marini

HWY 10 & 45 CITGO
See OUTAGAMIE CO-OP SERVICES INC

D-U-N-S 00-618-2307
HWY AG SERVICES
HIGHWAY AG SVC & CONVIENCE STR
290 W Derrynane St, Le Center, MN 56057-2600
Tel (507) 357-6868 Founded/Ownrshp 1916
Sales 76.9MM EMP 48
Accts Carlson Highland & Co Llp
SIC 5191 5171 Feed; Seeds: field, garden & flower; Fertilizer & fertilizer materials; Petroleum bulk stations; Feed; Petroleum bulk stations
Genl Mgr: Joe Spinler
*Pr: Luke Retka

D-U-N-S 15-776-8214
HWZ DISTRIBUTION GROUP LLC
NEXGEN BUILDING SUPPLY
(Suby of NEXGEN BUILDING SUPPLY) ★
3274 Spring Grove Ave, Cincinnati, OH 45225-1338
Tel (513) 618-0300 Founded/Ownrshp 2004
Sales 143.6MM^E EMP 135
SIC 5032 Drywall materials; Drywall materials
CEO: Robert Hoge
*Pr: Richard Wolgemuth
*CFO: Bruce Fhaey

D-U-N-S 02-332-0005 IMP
HY CITE ENTERPRISES LLC
ROYAL PRESTIGE
333 Holtzman Rd, Madison, WI 53713-2109
Tel (608) 273-3373 Founded/Ownrshp 1963
Sales 86.2MM^E EMP 350
SIC 5023 Home furnishings; Stainless steel flatware; Decorative home furnishings & supplies; Glassware; Home furnishings; Stainless steel flatware; Decorative home furnishings & supplies; Glassware
Pr: Erik Johnson
*COO: Peter Johnson Jr
*VP: Arin Brost
VP: Angella Gordillo
*VP: James Martin
*VP: Larry Schauff
*VP: Anna Stebbins
CIO: Jesse Brud
Opers Supe: Pam Wolter
VP Sls: Steve Owen
Mktg Mgr: Ruben Santiago

HY CONNECT
See HOFFMAN YORK INC

D-U-N-S 01-886-4561
HY LABONNE AND SONS INC
LABONNE'S EPICURE MARKET
43 Falls Ave, Waterbury, CT 06708
Tel (203) 263-1940 Founded/Ownrshp 1962
Sales 29.5MM^E EMP 210
SIC 5411 Grocery stores, independent; Grocery stores, independent
Ch Bd: Robert H Labonne Jr
*Treas: Dorothy Labonne
*VP: Terri Plourde

D-U-N-S 04-697-4788
HY LEE PAVING CORP
2100 Quarry Hill Rd, Rockville, VA 23146-2229
Tel (804) 360-9066 Founded/Ownrshp 1956
Sales 27.7MM^E EMP 140
SIC 2951 1611 5032 Asphalt paving mixtures & blocks; Highway & street paving contractor; Asphalt mixture; Asphalt paving mixtures & blocks; Highway & street paving contractor; Asphalt mixture
CEO: Gordon F Penick III
*Pr: Joseph B Penick
*Treas: Cynthia G Hill
*VP: Claude B Daniels
*VP: Harold Gatewood
*VP: Cr Langhorne
*VP: Charles R Langhorne
*VP: Frederick M Luck
*VP: Stanley B Snellings

D-U-N-S 00-801-1744
■ HY-BON ENGINEERING CO INC
(Suby of REGAL-BELOIT CORP) ★
2404 Commerce Dr, Midland, TX 79703-7549
Tel (432) 697-2292 Founded/Ownrshp 2014
Sales 33.6MM^E EMP 156^E
SIC 3533 Oil field machinery & equipment; Oil field machinery & equipment
Pr: Inayat Virani
*CFO: Richard Snow
*Sr VP: Jay Pottmeyer
*Sr VP: James K Sidebottom
Dir IT: Nathan Neilitz
VP Opers: Dave Latch
Sls Dir: Darin Nelson
Sales Asso: Ray Calhoun

D-U-N-S 00-627-0946 IMP
HY-C CO INC
10950 Linpage Pl, Saint Louis, MO 63132-1038
Tel (314) 241-1214 Founded/Ownrshp 1947, 1988
Sales 22.9MM^E EMP 75
SIC 3444 Metal housings, enclosures, casings & other containers
Pr: Robert A Jacobson
*Ex VP: David Walters
*Sr VP: Deborah Jacobson
Snr Mgr: John Salmon

D-U-N-S 09-310-0238
HY-LINE NORTH AMERICA LLC
(Suby of EW GROUP GMBH)
1755 West Lakes Pkwy A, West Des Moines, IA 50266-8227
Tel (515) 225-6030 Founded/Ownrshp 1978
Sales 78.6MM^E EMP 700
SIC 0254 Chicken hatchery; Chicken hatchery
Pr: Dennis Casey
*Pr: Harold Block
*CFO: Charles Bingman
Off Admin: Ivy Clawson
Dir IT: Gerald Fitzgerald
Sales Asso: Petek Settar

HY-MILER
See DISTRICT PETROLEUM PRODUCTS INC

HY-POWER
See HYPOWER INC

D-U-N-S 17-559-1320 IMP
HY-PRO CORP
HY-PRO FILTRATION
6810 Layton Rd, Anderson, IN 46011-9494
Tel (765) 635-2300 Founded/Ownrshp 1986
Sales 37.0MM^E EMP 100
SIC 3569 Filter elements, fluid, hydraulic line; Lubrication equipment, industrial; Filter elements, fluid, hydraulic line; Lubrication equipment, industrial
Pr: Larry Hoeg
*Treas: Aaron Hoeg

*IT Man: Ronald Huseman
Ql Cn Mgr: Curt Martin

HY-PRO FILTRATION
See HY-PRO CORP

D-U-N-S 04-409-1676 IMP
HY-PRODUCTION INC
6000 Grafton Rd, Valley City, OH 44280-9330
Tel (330) 273-2400 Founded/Ownrshp 1966
Sales 32.3MM^E EMP 124
SIC 3519 3492 3451 3594 3599 Engines, diesel & semi-diesel or dual-fuel; Control valves, fluid power: hydraulic & pneumatic; Screw machine products; Fluid power pumps & motors; Machine shop, jobbing & repair; Engines, diesel & semi-diesel or dual-fuel; Control valves, fluid power: hydraulic & pneumatic; Screw machine products; Fluid power pumps & motors; Machine shop, jobbing & repair
Ch Bd: William Kneebusch
*Pr: Mathew Roach
CFO: Brian B Gill
CFO: Brian Kushinski
*VP: Keith Koprowski
Exec: Jeff Kneebusch
QA Dir: Eugene Waller
Dir IT: Josh Cornett
Dir IT: Pam Cox

D-U-N-S 05-136-8439 EXP
HY-TEK MATERIAL HANDLING INC
2222 Rickenbacker Pkwy W, Columbus, OH 43217-5002
Tel (614) 497-2500 Founded/Ownrshp 1989
Sales 83.0MM^E EMP 130
SIC 5084 5013 7538 7513 1796 Materials handling machinery; Conveyor systems; Lift trucks & parts; Truck parts & accessories; Truck engine repair, except industrial; Truck rental, without drivers; Machinery installation; Materials handling machinery; Conveyor systems; Lift trucks & parts; Truck parts & accessories; Truck engine repair, except industrial; Truck rental, without drivers; Machinery installation
Pr: Samuel Grooms
*CFO: David Tumbas
*VP: Mark Bruner
*VP: Donnie Johnson
VP: Tony Murray
VP: David Price
Dir Bus: Al Marchionda
IT Man: Tim Stewart
IT Man: Susan Wright
Mktg Dir: Claire Rigot
Sls Mgr: Scott Moe

D-U-N-S 96-488-9641
HY-VEE AND AFFILIATES BENEFIT PLAN AND TRUST
5820 Westown Pkwy, West Des Moines, IA 50266-8223
Tel (515) 267-2800 Founded/Ownrshp 2010
Sales NA EMP 2^E
Accts Rsm Mcgladrey Inc Des Moine
SIC 6411 Pension & retirement plan consultants; Pension & retirement plan consultants
Prin: Charlie Bridges

D-U-N-S 92-957-9837
HY-VEE CONSTRUCTION LC
(Suby of HY-VEE FOOD AND DRUG) ★
5605 Ne 22nd St, Des Moines, IA 50313-2531
Tel (515) 645-2300 Founded/Ownrshp 1995
Sales 33.1MM^E EMP 100
SIC 1542 1541 Nonresidential construction; Industrial buildings & warehouses; Nonresidential construction; Industrial buildings & warehouses
VP: Marty Ison

HY-VEE FOOD AND DRUG
See HY-VEE INC

D-U-N-S 00-692-5671 IMP
HY-VEE INC (IA)
HY-VEE FOOD AND DRUG
5820 Westown Pkwy, West Des Moines, IA 50266-8223
Tel (515) 267-2800 Founded/Ownrshp 1930
Sales 8.0MMM EMP 72,000
SIC 5411 5912 5921 Supermarkets, chain; Convenience stores, chain; Drug stores; Liquor stores; Supermarkets, chain; Convenience stores, chain; Drug stores; Liquor stores
CEO: Randy Edeker
Pr: Mark Brauer
Pr: Pat Hensley
*Pr: Jay Marshall
Pr: Mark Millsap
Pr: Chuck Seaman
Pr: Lisa Stowater
Pr: Donna Tweeten
*Ofcr: Andy McCann
*Ex VP: Mike Skokan
*Ex VP: Tom Watson
*Ex VP: Jon Wendel
Sr VP: Charles M Bell
*Sr VP: Sheila Laing
VP: Dennis A Ausenhus
VP: Jane Esbeck
VP: Freddie L Housman
VP: Jane B Knaack-Esbeck
VP: Rose E Kleyweg Mitchell
VP: Michael G Tetmeyer
Comm Dir: Tara Hunter

D-U-N-S 86-859-3682
HY-WAY INC
HIGHWAY OIL
534 S Kansas Ave Ste 1205, Topeka, KS 66603-3451
Tel (785) 357-6161 Founded/Ownrshp 1994
Sales 29.0MM EMP 80
SIC 5541 Gasoline service stations; Gasoline service stations
Pr: Tom Platis
*Treas: Paul McFann

D-U-N-S 13-807-0800
HYANNIS AIR SERVICE INC
CAPE AIR
660 Barnstable Rd, Hyannis, MA 02601-1927
Tel (508) 790-3122 Founded/Ownrshp 1988
Sales 50.2MM^E EMP 400
SIC 4512 4522 Air transportation, scheduled; Air transportation, nonscheduled; Air transportation, scheduled; Air transportation, nonscheduled
CEO: Daniel Wolf
*Pr: Dave Bushy
*Pr: Linda A Markham
*CFO: Michael A Migliore
*Treas: Thomas J Raftery

HYANNIS HONDA
See XIPHIAS ENTERPRISES INC

HYATT
See SANDSABAR & GRILL

HYATT AT THE BELLEVUE
See HYATT CORP AS AGENT OF BELLEVUE LL INC A PENNSYLVANIA CORP

D-U-N-S 12-004-0683
HYATT AUTOMOTIVE LLC
HYUNDAI - ISUZU
1887 Highway 501, Myrtle Beach, SC 29577-9768
Tel (843) 626-3657 Founded/Ownrshp 1999
Sales 180.0MM EMP 110
SIC 5511 Automobiles, new & used; Automobiles, new & used
Pt: Charles F Hyatt

HYATT CENTER
See HYATT CORP

HYATT CENTER
See DORADO BEACH HOTEL CORP

D-U-N-S 00-690-4783 IMP
■ HYATT CORP
HYATT CENTER
(Suby of HYATT EQUITIES LLC) ★
71 S Wacker Dr Ste 1, Chicago, IL 60606-4716
Tel (312) 750-1234 Founded/Ownrshp 1967, 1979
Sales 2.7MMM^E EMP 35,700
SIC 7011 Hotels & motels; Hotels & motels
Ch Bd: Thomas J Pritzker
Pr: Dan Azark
Pr: Eric Fish
*Pr: Doug Geoga
*Pr: Mark S Hoplamazian
Pr: Katie Meyer
Pr: Cliff Tamplin
CFO: Harmit J Singh
Chf Mktg O: Angela Perry
*Sr VP: Harold Handelsman
Sr VP: Susan T Smith
VP: Bill Bernahl
VP: Cheryl L Phelps
*VP: Kenneth R Posner
Exec: Eric Damidot
Dir Soc: Tammy Brent
Dir Soc: Stuart Enselein
Dir Soc: Amy Johnson
Dir Soc: Tish Lew
Dir Soc: Jennifer McLeroy
Dir Soc: Mweiser Mwohear

D-U-N-S 36-060-8236
■ HYATT CORP
HYATT REGENCY DFW
(Suby of HYATT CENTER) ★
2334 N International Pkwy, Dallas, TX 75261-4031
Tel (972) 453-8400 Founded/Ownrshp 2001
Sales 50.0MM EMP 300^E
SIC 7011 5812 5813 5947 7992 7299 Hotels & motels; Eating places; Drinking places; Gifts & novelties; Public golf courses; Banquet hall facilities; Hotels & motels; Eating places; Drinking places; Gifts & novelties; Public golf courses; Banquet hall facilities
CEO: Mark S Hoplamazian
*Ch: Thomas J Pritzker
*VP: Rena Hozore Reiss
Dir Soc: George Maldonado
Comm Man: Phillip Pierce
Genl Mgr: Tim Dant
Mktg Dir: Joe Masser
Sls Mgr: Trent Culler
Sls Mgr: Susan Wegner

D-U-N-S 60-099-7980
HYATT CORP
GRAND HYATT DFW INTL ARPRT
(Suby of H GROUP HOLDING INC) ★
2337 S International Pkwy, Dallas, TX 75261
Tel (972) 973-1234 Founded/Ownrshp 2005
Sales 24.0MM^E EMP 200
SIC 8741 Hotel or motel management; Hotel or motel management
Genl Mgr: George Vizer
*Prin: Keith Spinden

D-U-N-S 19-635-4732
HYATT CORP AS AGENT OF BELLEVUE LL INC A PENNSYLVANIA CORP
HYATT AT THE BELLEVUE
1415 Chancellor St, Philadelphia, PA 19102-3801
Tel (215) 893-1234 Founded/Ownrshp 1988
Sales 24.0MM EMP 180
SIC 7011 5812 5813 7991 Hotels & motels; Eating places; Drinking places; Physical fitness facilities; Hotels & motels; Eating places; Drinking places; Physical fitness facilities
CEO: George Rubin
Genl Mgr: Stephen Buenaga

D-U-N-S 17-540-5448
HYATT CORP AS AGENT OF CCHH GHDC LLC A DELAWARE LIMITED LIABILITY CO
GRAND HYATT WASHINGTON
1000 H St Nw, Washington, DC 20001-4520
Tel (202) 637-4790 Founded/Ownrshp 1980
Sales 36.5MM^E EMP 600
SIC 7011 Hotels; Hotels
VP: Mark Ellen MD
Mktg Mgr: Nisha Patel

D-U-N-S 12-882-3031
HYATT CORP AS AGENT OF CCHH MAUI LLC
HYATT REGENCY MAUI
200 Nohea Kai Dr, Lahaina, HI 96761-1942
Tel (808) 661-1234 *Founded/Ownrshp* 2008
Sales 42.2MM^E *EMP* 800
SIC 7011 Hotels & motels; Hotels & motels
Board of Directors: Jean Ewing

D-U-N-S 03-948-8440
■ **HYATT CORPORATON AS AGENT OF AP-APMC SAVANNAH LP**
HYATT HOTEL
(*Suby of* HYATT CENTER) ★
2 W Bay St, Savannah, GA 31401-1107
Tel (912) 238-1234 *Founded/Ownrshp* 1997
Sales 20.8MM^E *EMP* 240
SIC 7011 5813 5812 Hotels & motels; Drinking places; Eating places; Hotels & motels; Drinking places; Eating places
Pr: Michael Gallegos
Dir Soc: Chad Laskowski
Genl Mgr: Andaz Amsterdam
Genl Mgr: Sheldon Fox
Genl Mgr: Becky Reeve
Off Mgr: Walter Brown
Mktg Mgr: Allison Marrero
Sls Mgr: Scott Edwards

D-U-N-S 00-831-8073
HYATT DIE CAST AND ENGINEERING CORP - SOUTH
4656 Lincoln Ave, Cypress, CA 90630-2650
Tel (714) 826-7550 *Founded/Ownrshp* 1956
Sales 23.5MM^E *EMP* 163
SIC 3363

D-U-N-S 03-760-3297 IMP/EXP
■ **HYATT EQUITIES LLC**
(*Suby of* HYATT HOTELS CORP) ★
71 S Wacker Dr Fl 14, Chicago, IL 60606-4637
Tel (312) 750-1234 *Founded/Ownrshp* 2004
Sales 2.7MMM^E *EMP* 36,760
SIC 7011 Hotels; Hotels
Ch Bd: Thomas J Pritzker
**CFO:* Gebhard F Rainer

HYATT HOTEL
See HYATT CORPORATON AS AGENT OF AP-APMC SAVANNAH LP

HYATT HOTEL
See HYATT INTERNATIONAL CORP

HYATT HOTEL
See HYATT REGENCY HOTEL

HYATT HOTEL
See GREENWICH HOTEL LIMITED PARTNERSHIP

HYATT HOTEL
See CLASSIC RIVERDALE INC

HYATT HOTEL
See JWMCC LIMITED PARTNERSHIP

HYATT HOTEL
See MANCHESTER GRAND RESORTS LP

HYATT HOTEL
See CC-NAPLES INC

HYATT HOTEL
See 2301 SE 17TH ST LLC

HYATT HOTEL
See CRESCENT REAL ESTATE L P

D-U-N-S 60-249-5579
▲ **HYATT HOTELS CORP**
71 S Wacker Dr Ste 1000, Chicago, IL 60606-4716
Tel (312) 750-1234 *Founded/Ownrshp* 1957
Sales 4.4MMM *EMP* 45,000^E
Tkr Sym H *Exch* NYS
SIC 7011 6794 Hotels & motels; Franchises, selling or licensing; Hotels & motels; Franchises, selling or licensing
Pr: Mark S Hoplamazian
**Ch Bd:* Thomas J Pritzker
CFO: Atish Shah
Chf Mktg O: Maryam Banikarim
Ofcr: Robert W K Webb
Ex VP: H Charles Floyd
Ex VP: Peter Fulton
Ex VP: Stephen G Haggerty
Ex VP: Rena Hozore Reiss
Ex VP: Peter J Sears
Ex VP: David Udell
Sr VP: Samie Barr
VP: Lara Migliassi
VP: Candace Mueller
Board of Directors: William Wrigley Jr, Richard A Friedman, Susan D Kronick, Mackey J McDonald, Cary D McMillan, Pamela M Nicholson, Jason Pritzker, Michael A Rocca, Richard C Tuttle, James H Wooten Jr

D-U-N-S 80-941-6373
■ **HYATT HOTELS CORP**
GRAND HYATT DENVER
(*Suby of* HYATT HOTELS CORP) ★
1750 Welton St, Denver, CO 80202-3940
Tel (303) 295-1234 *Founded/Ownrshp* 2006
Sales 23.4MM^E *EMP* 280
SIC 7011 Hotels & motels; Hotels & motels
CEO: Mark Hoplamazian
Exec: John Treusein
**Genl Mgr:* Greg Leonard
Genl Mgr: Janell Peterson
Sls Mgr: September Boscia
Sls Mgr: Deanna Brown

D-U-N-S 03-773-0348
■ **HYATT HOTELS CORP OF MARYLAND**
HYATT REGENCY BALTIMORE
(*Suby of* HYATT EQUITIES LLC) ★
300 Light St, Baltimore, MD 21202-1012
Tel (410) 528-1234 *Founded/Ownrshp* 1981
Sales 29.2MM^E *EMP* 400
SIC 7011 Hotels & motels; Hotels & motels
Pr: Kenneth Posner
**VP:* Harold Handelsman

D-U-N-S 11-416-4197 IMP/EXP
■ **HYATT HOTELS MANAGEMENT CORP**
(*Suby of* HYATT CENTER) ★
71 S Wacker Dr Ste 1000, Chicago, IL 60606-4716
Tel (312) 750-1234 *Founded/Ownrshp* 1977
Sales 855.4MM^E *EMP* 35,700
SIC 7011 Hotels & motels; Hotels & motels
CEO: Mark Hoplamazian
Sr Cor Off: Frank Orc
Ex VP: Labelle Van
**Sr VP:* Frank Borg
**Sr VP:* Chuck Floyd
Sr VP: David Tarr
VP: Linda R Olson
Exec: Tracy Gainer

D-U-N-S 14-771-0644
■ **HYATT HOTELS OF FLORIDA INC**
HYATT REGENCY ORLANDO
(*Suby of* HYATT HOTELS CORP) ★
9801 International Dr, Orlando, FL 32819-8104
Tel (407) 352-4000 *Founded/Ownrshp* 2013
Sales 60.3MM^E *EMP* 1,800
SIC 7011 5812 5813

D-U-N-S 04-739-1206
■ **HYATT INTERNATIONAL CORP**
HYATT HOTEL
(*Suby of* HYATT HOTELS CORP) ★
200 W Mdson Str Mdson Plz Madison, Chicago, IL 60606
Tel (312) 750-1234 *Founded/Ownrshp* 1969
Sales 539.8MM^E *EMP* 30,996
SIC 7011 Hotels & motels; Hotels & motels
Pr: Bernd Chorengel
**Pr:* Mark S Hoplamazian
CFO: Ken Posner
CFO: Gary Smith
Sr VP: Chuck Floyd
Sr VP: Michelle Kincaid
**VP:* Michael Evanoff
VP: Gebhard Rainer
VP: Robert V Schnitz
VP: Len Stoga
Sales Exec: Sara Kearney

D-U-N-S 62-607-7093
■ **HYATT LEGAL PLANS INC**
(*Suby of* METLIFE) ★
1111 Superior Ave E # 800, Cleveland, OH 44114-2541
Tel (216) 241-0022 *Founded/Ownrshp* 1997
Sales NA *EMP* 96
SIC 6411 Insurance agents, brokers & service; Advisory services, insurance; Information bureaus, insurance; Policyholders' consulting service
Pr: William H Brooks
**CFO:* Mike Penzner
**VP:* Andrew Kohn
Dir IT: Robert Nettgen
Mktg Dir: Ted Holcomb
Sls Dir: Marcia Messett

D-U-N-S 02-731-7857
HYATT LODGE
2815 Jorie Blvd, Oak Brook, IL 60523-2161
Tel (630) 568-1234 *Founded/Ownrshp* 2009
Sales 11.5MM^E *EMP* 300
SIC 7011 Hostels; Hostels
Genl Mgr: Norm Canfield

HYATT PLACE SAN JOSE HOTEL
See WEST SAN CARLOS HOTEL PARTNERS LLC

HYATT REGEN PITTS INTER AIRPO
See MHF PIT OPERATING IV LLC

HYATT REGENCY BALTIMORE
See HYATT HOTELS CORP OF MARYLAND

D-U-N-S 78-885-4300
HYATT REGENCY CENTURY PLAZA
2025 Avenue Of The Stars, Los Angeles, CA 90067-4701
Tel (310) 228-1234 *Founded/Ownrshp* 2005
Sales 33.8MM^E *EMP* 650
SIC 7011 Hotels & motels; Hotels & motels
CEO: Rakesh Sarna
**Pr:* Ken Cruse
Sls Mgr: Adam Smith

HYATT REGENCY CHESAPEAKE BAY
See MARYLAND ECONOMIC DEVELOPMENT CORP

HYATT REGENCY CHICAGO
See KATO KAGAKU CO LTD

D-U-N-S 09-972-6986
HYATT REGENCY COLUMBUS
350 N High St, Columbus, OH 43215-2006
Tel (614) 463-1234 *Founded/Ownrshp* 1978
Sales 16.6MM^E *EMP* 325
SIC 7011 Hotels & motels; Hotels & motels
**Genl Pt:* Hyatt Columbus Corp

HYATT REGENCY DFW
See HYATT CORP

D-U-N-S 12-487-5142
HYATT REGENCY HOTEL
HYATT HOTEL
122 N 2nd St, Phoenix, AZ 85004-2379
Tel (602) 440-3166 *Founded/Ownrshp* 2000
Sales 9.0MM^E *EMP* 400
SIC 7011 Hotels & motels; Hotels & motels

D-U-N-S 80-718-5392
HYATT REGENCY LAKE TAHOE
111 Country Club Dr, Incline Village, NV 89451-9305
Tel (775) 832-1234 *Founded/Ownrshp* 1975
Sales 34.5MM^E *EMP* 600^E
SIC 8741 Hotel or motel management; Restaurant management; Hotel or motel management; Restaurant management
Genl Mgr: Mark Pardue
**Treas:* Ken Posner
Ex Dir: Tony Salah
**Genl Mgr:* Fred Euler

HYATT REGENCY MAUI
See HYATT CORP AS AGENT OF CCHH MAUI LLC

HYATT REGENCY MCCORMICK PLACE
See METROPOLITAN PIER AND EXPOSITION AUTHORITY

HYATT REGENCY MISSION BAY SPA
See H C T INC

HYATT REGENCY ORLANDO
See HYATT HOTELS OF FLORIDA INC

HYATT REGENCY SACRAMENTO
See CAPITOL REGENCY LLC

HYATT SELECT HOTELS GROUP
See SELECT HOTELS GROUP LLC

HYATT-REGENCY BUFFALO
See WEST GENESEE HOTEL ASSOCIATES LP

D-U-N-S 02-586-2160
HYB INC (TN)
HARPER PORSCHE
9735 Kingston Pike, Knoxville, TN 37922-3346
Tel (865) 691-0393 *Founded/Ownrshp* 1981
Sales 22.1MM^E *EMP* 40
SIC 5511 Automobiles, new & used
Pr: Thomas Harper
**Sec:* Janet Harper
**VP:* Dale Underwood

D-U-N-S 83-301-4108
HYBRA ADVANCE TECHNOLOGY INC
1249 Woodmere Ave Unit D, Traverse City, MI 49686-4299
Tel (231) 392-3661 *Founded/Ownrshp* 2005
Sales 26.6MM^E *EMP* 300
SIC 5065 Electronic parts; Electronic parts
Pr: Joseph Thiel
**CFO:* Ryan Wells
Natl Sales: Scott Anton

HYBRID APPAREL
See HYBRID PROMOTIONS LLC

D-U-N-S 12-967-1165 IMP
HYBRID PROMOTIONS LLC
HYBRID APPAREL
10711 Walker St, Cypress, CA 90630-4750
Tel (714) 952-3866 *Founded/Ownrshp* 1999
Sales 450.0MM *EMP* 400^E
Accts Richardson Kontogouris Emerson
SIC 5136 5137 5611 Men's & boys' clothing; Women's & children's clothing; Men's & boys' clothing stores
CEO: Jarrod Dogan
**COO:* David Lederman
VP: Derrick Baca
Creative D: Kirk Ewing

HYCLONE BIOPROCESSES CONT DIV
See HYCLONE LABORATORIES INC

D-U-N-S 08-183-2461 IMP/EXP
■ **HYCLONE LABORATORIES INC** (UT)
HYCLONE BIOPROCESSES CONT DIV
(*Suby of* GENERAL ELECTRIC CO) ★
925 W 1800 S, Logan, UT 84321-6241
Tel (435) 792-8000 *Founded/Ownrshp* 1975, 2014
Sales 117.3MM^E *EMP* 636
SIC 2836 8071

D-U-N-S 05-434-5181 EXP
HYCO ALABAMA LLC
(*Suby of* WEBER-HYDRAULIK INC) ★
218 Arad Thompson Rd Ne, Arab, AL 35016-2783
Tel (256) 586-8152 *Founded/Ownrshp* 2011
Sales 54.9MM^E *EMP* 125
SIC 3561 Cylinders, pump; Cylinders, pump
Pr: Ron Whitaker
IT Man: Greg Ennis
Mtls Mgr: Jennifer Marion

D-U-N-S 79-432-8260
HYCOMP LLC
(*Suby of* SMS SIEMAG LLC) ★
17960 Englewood Dr Ste A, Cleveland, OH 44130-8496
Tel (440) 234-2002 *Founded/Ownrshp* 2001
Sales 26.4MM^E *EMP* 94
SIC 3089 Injection molding of plastics
Area Mgr: Ken Schiefer
IT Man: Becky Crozier
Ql Cn Mgr: Todd McGregor
Sls Mgr: Brian Bosworth

D-U-N-S 15-340-3035
HYCROFT RESOURCES & DEVELOPMENT INC
(*Suby of* ALLIED NEVADA GOLD CORP) ★
54980 Jungo Rd, Winnemucca, NV 89445
Tel (775) 321-0780 *Founded/Ownrshp* 2013
Sales 44.3MM^E *EMP* 22
SIC 1041 1044 Open pit gold mining; Open pit silver mining
Pr: Randy Buffington
**Pr:* Scott A Caldwell
**Sec:* Roger L Smith
Mng Dir: Roderick Williams

D-U-N-S 07-916-8191 IMP
HYDAC TECHNOLOGY CORP
2260 City Line Rd 2280, Bethlehem, PA 18017-2130
Tel (610) 266-0100 *Founded/Ownrshp* 1975
Sales 156.8MM^E *EMP* 500
SIC 3569 Filter elements, fluid, hydraulic line; Filter elements, fluid, hydraulic line
Pr: Matthias Mueller
CFO: Ted Dikeman
**VP:* Ilek Ozsoy
VP: Thomas Thielen
Area Mgr: Mark Haake
Div Mgr: Eric Ramseyer
Div Mgr: John Welch
Genl Mgr: Randall Symes
IT Man: Ed Woll
Mtls Mgr: Earl Roberts
Prd Mgr: Dina Parris

D-U-N-S 00-656-6475
HYDAKER-WHEATLAKE CO (MI)
(*Suby of* UTILITY SUPPLY AND CONSTRUCTION CO) ★
420 S Roth St Ste B, Reed City, MI 49677-9115
Tel (231) 832-2258 *Founded/Ownrshp* 1924, 2007
Sales 53.6MM^E *EMP* 200
SIC 1623 Electric power line construction; Electric power line construction
CEO: Charles Holmquist
COO: Mark Pellerito
Sr VP: Jeff D Stauffer

D-U-N-S 09-756-8968
HYDE & HYDE INC
300 El Sobrante Rd, Corona, CA 92879-5757
Tel (951) 279-5239 *Founded/Ownrshp* 1984
Sales 65.8MM^E *EMP* 250
SIC 7389 Packaging & labeling services; Packaging & labeling services
Pr: Tim Hyde
Sr VP: Jenie Aguilera
Plnt Mgr: John Shaughnessy
Plnt Mgr: Charlie Turner

D-U-N-S 08-046-6774
HYDE ALICE MEDICAL CENTER
AHMC
133 Park St Ste 1, Malone, NY 12953-1243
Tel (518) 483-3000 *Founded/Ownrshp* 1905
Sales 74.5MM *EMP* 480
Accts Freed Maxick Cpas Pc Buffalo
SIC 8062 8051 General medical & surgical hospitals; Skilled nursing care facilities; General medical & surgical hospitals; Skilled nursing care facilities
CEO: Douglas F Divello
V Ch: Brian Monette
Treas: Dean Johnston
Bd of Dir: Dan Clark
**Sr VP:* Ginger Carriero
**VP:* Sean Curtin
**VP:* Julie Marshall
VP: Tammy Reynolds
Dir Rad: Amy Oconnor
Off Mgr: Amy Fleury
Off Mgr: Jeff Mauer

HYDE ATHLETIC INDUSTRIES
See SAUCONY INC

HYDE CLOTHES DIV
See BAYER CLOTHING GROUP INC

D-U-N-S 07-831-1601
HYDE PARK BANCORP INC
1196 River St, Boston, MA 02136-2906
Tel (617) 361-6900 *Founded/Ownrshp* 2011
Sales NA *EMP* 142^E
SIC 6036

D-U-N-S 08-227-0653
HYDE PARK CENTRAL SCHOOL DISTRICT
11 Boice Rd, Hyde Park, NY 12538-1632
Tel (845) 229-4065 *Founded/Ownrshp* 1961
Sales 36.5MM^E *EMP* 615
SIC 8211 Public elementary school; Public junior high school; Public senior high school; Public elementary school; Public junior high school; Public senior high school
Treas: Linda Steinberg
Bd of Dir: Steven Mittermaier
Dir IT: Forrest Addor
Netwrk Mgr: Rita Accardi
Schl Brd P: Doug Hieter
HC Dir: Amy McArdle

D-U-N-S 07-959-0527
HYDE PARK CONVALESCENT HOSPITAL INC
6520 West Blvd, Los Angeles, CA 90043-4393
Tel (323) 753-1354 *Founded/Ownrshp* 1965
Sales 275.7MM *EMP* 50
SIC 8051 Skilled nursing care facilities; Skilled nursing care facilities
Pr: Jeff Mendell

HYDE PARK GRILLE
See COVENTRY RESTAURANT SYSTEMS INC

D-U-N-S 94-936-0168
HYDE PARK RESTAURANT SYSTEMS INC
HPG RESTAURANT
9724 Ravenna Rd 100, Twinsburg, OH 44087-2144
Tel (330) 405-5658 *Founded/Ownrshp* 1986
Sales 27.3MM^E *EMP* 600
SIC 8741 Restaurant management; Restaurant management
Pr: Joe Saccone
**VP:* Richard Hauck

D-U-N-S 08-019-5134 IMP/EXP
HYDE SHIPPING CORP
10025 Nw 116th Way Ste 2, Medley, FL 33178-9104
Tel (305) 913-4933 *Founded/Ownrshp* 1976
Sales 61.1MM^E *EMP* 110
Accts Socarras & Associates Coral G
SIC 4731 Agents, shipping; Agents, shipping
Pr: David Hyde
**Pr:* Meade D Hyde
CFO: Carlos Morera
**Treas:* Kern Hyde
MIS Dir: Linda Brown
Opers Mgr: Mike Young
Sls Mgr: Joe Koger
Snr PM: Shane Ciriago

D-U-N-S 12-398-3322
HYDER CLAY TRUCKING LINES INC
CLAY HYDER TRANSPORTATION
(*Suby of* COMCAR INDUSTRIES INC) ★
8814 Dietz Ave Ste A, Hickory, NC 28602-8607
Tel (828) 397-7673 *Founded/Ownrshp* 1998
Sales 40.6MM^E *EMP* 460
SIC 4213 Contract haulers; Contract haulers
Pr: Toby Tate

D-U-N-S 00-880-1771
HYDER CONSTRUCTION INC
543 Santa Fe Dr, Denver, CO 80204-5048
Tel (303) 825-1313 *Founded/Ownrshp* 1987
Sales 32.1MM^E *EMP* 55
SIC 1542 1541

HYDRA POOLS
See PI INC

D-U-N-S 00-228-8694 IMP
HYDRA-MATIC PACKING CO INC (PA)
FABRICS FOR INDUSTRY DIVISION
2992 Franks Rd, Huntingdon Valley, PA 19006-4283
Tel (215) 947-5802 *Founded/Ownrshp* 1945, 1986
Sales 71.8MM^E *EMP* 80
SIC 5033 3564 2821 Fiberglass building materials; Insulation, thermal; Blowers & fans; Plastics materials & resins; Fiberglass building materials; Insulation, thermal; Blowers & fans; Plastics materials & resins
VP: Marguerite McKenna
**Pr:* Gerald McKenna
**Pr:* Joseph T McKenna
IT Man: Kathleen Tressel

D-U-N-S 05-361-0804 IMP
HYDRA-POWER SYSTEMS INC (OR)
5445 Ne 122nd Ave, Portland, OR 97230-1092
Tel (206) 621-9259 *Founded/Ownrshp* 1970
Sales 69.7MM^E *EMP* 105
Accts Fellner & Kuhn Pc Portland
SIC 5084 3594 Hydraulic systems equipment & supplies; Pumps, hydraulic power transfer; Hydraulic systems equipment & supplies; Pumps, hydraulic power transfer
CEO: Lynn A Stuart
**Pr:* Jeffery R Stuart
VP: Michael Achterman
**VP:* Dan Sowards
**VP:* Paul D Sowards Jr
Genl Mgr: Lori Anderson
Dir IT: Bob Jablonski
Sales Asso: Jana Darr
Sales Asso: Doug Duvall
Sales Asso: Kris Lavigne
Sales Asso: Patrick Sheppard

D-U-N-S 05-437-9383
HYDRADYNE HYDRAULICS INC
7330 W Sam Houston Pkwy N, Houston, TX 77040-3100
Tel (713) 937-8111 *Founded/Ownrshp* 1971
Sales 26.1MM^E *EMP* 65
SIC 5084 7699 3441 Hydraulic systems equipment & supplies; Hydraulic equipment repair; Fabricated structural metal
Pr: Richard Kohl
VP: David Parks

D-U-N-S 19-520-0212 IMP
HYDRADYNE LLC
15050 Faa Blvd, Fort Worth, TX 76155-2215
Tel (817) 391-1547 *Founded/Ownrshp* 2003
Sales 379.9MM^E *EMP* 590
SIC 5084 Hydraulic systems equipment & supplies; Hydraulic equipment repair; Hydraulic systems equipment & supplies
Pr: David Parks
Exec: Donna Breaux
Comm Man: Sherri Smith
Sfty Mgr: Jeff O'Connor

D-U-N-S 13-120-1493 IMP
HYDRAFORCE INC
500 Barclay Blvd, Lincolnshire, IL 60069-4314
Tel (847) 793-2300 *Founded/Ownrshp* 1987
Sales 202.9MM^E *EMP* 850^E
SIC 3492 Control valves, fluid power: hydraulic & pneumatic; Control valves, fluid power: hydraulic & pneumatic
Pr: James Brizzolara
Pr: David Roberts
VP: Bernhard Biederma
VP: Arthur Smith
Mng Dir: Chuck Kloser
Mng Dir: Peter McDonald
Snr Sftwr: Chris James
QA Dir: Ali Mohammed
Dir IT: Bill Bouxsein
VP Opers: Greg Balog
Opers Mgr: Butch Kretsch
Board of Directors: John Pepe

D-U-N-S 11-048-0279 IMP
■ **HYDRALIFT AMCLYDE INC**
(*Suby of* NATIONAL OILWELL VARCO INC) ★
240 Plato Blvd E, Saint Paul, MN 55107-1609
Tel (651) 293-4646 *Founded/Ownrshp* 2008
Sales 34.5MM^E *EMP* 125
SIC 3536 3533 Cranes & monorail systems; Oil field machinery & equipment; Cranes & monorail systems; Oil field machinery & equipment

D-U-N-S 06-715-2868 IMP
HYDRAMASTER
CLEANMASTER
11015 47th Ave W, Mukilteo, WA 98275-5019
Tel (479) 750-8380 *Founded/Ownrshp* 1971
Sales 20.7MM^E *EMP* 125
SIC 3635 Household vacuum cleaners; Carpet shampooer; Household vacuum cleaners; Carpet shampooer
Pr: Steven Brandt
**VP:* Michael C Palmer
**VP:* Phil SIS
Exec: Mark Barker
Mktg Dir: Bill Jensen
Mktg Dir: Tracy Johnson
Sls Dir: Wayne Boone

D-U-N-S 05-923-1126 IMP/EXP
HYDRANAUTICS
(*Suby of* NITTO AMERICAS INC) ★
401 Jones Rd, Oceanside, CA 92058-1216
Tel (760) 901-2500 *Founded/Ownrshp* 1987
Sales 133.5MM *EMP* 450
SIC 2899 3589 Chemical preparations; Water treatment equipment, industrial; Chemical preparations; Water treatment equipment, industrial
CEO: Brett Andrews
**COO:* Upen Bharwada
Bd of Dir: Ben Freeman
VP: Craig Bartels
**VP:* Ellen Class
**VP:* Michael Concannon
**VP:* Norio Ikeyama
**VP:* Karin Stink
**VP:* Randolph Truby
**VP:* Marek Wilf
VP Opers: Randy Tribi

D-U-N-S 02-068-0331 IMP
HYDRAPOWER INTERNATIONAL INC
950 N Collier Blvd # 202, Marco Island, FL 34145-2725
Tel (239) 642-5379 *Founded/Ownrshp* 1973
Sales 88.4MM^E *EMP* 1,100
SIC 3542 Shearing machines, power; Press brakes; Presses: hydraulic & pneumatic, mechanical & manual; Shearing machines, power; Press brakes; Presses: hydraulic & pneumatic, mechanical & manual
Pr: Robin F Wissing

HYDRAQUIP
See EMPLOYEE OWNED HOLDINGS INC

D-U-N-S 00-389-7949 IMP
HYDRAQUIP INC (TX)
HDI
(*Suby of* EMPLOYEE OWNED HOLDINGS INC) ★
4723 Pinemont Dr, Houston, TX 77092-3527
Tel (713) 680-1951 *Founded/Ownrshp* 1951, 2007
Sales 190.6MM^E *EMP* 117
SIC 5084 Hydraulic systems equipment & supplies; Pneumatic tools & equipment; Hydraulic systems equipment & supplies; Pneumatic tools & equipment
Pr: Tim Nichols
**Treas:* David Tyler
**VP:* William Boyle
**Prin:* Richard Neels
Brnch Mgr: Bill Cross
Dir IT: Chad Ferreira
Opers Mgr: Jason Berger
Opers Mgr: Troy Ottmer
Sls&Mrk Ex: Ruth Robinson
Sales Asso: Joshua Bennett
Sales Asso: Tim Campbell

D-U-N-S 02-862-4070 EXP
HYDRASERVICE INC
JOHN DEERE
2104 State Highway 160, Warrior, AL 35180-4510
Tel (205) 647-5326 *Founded/Ownrshp* 1982
Sales 36.3MM^E *EMP* 80
SIC 5084 7699 7359 Water pumps (industrial); Pumps & pumping equipment repair; Equipment rental & leasing; Water pumps (industrial); Pumps & pumping equipment repair; Equipment rental & leasing
CEO: F J Doyle II
COO: Liz Sherbert
**CFO:* Marlene Green
IT Man: Hal Midkiff
Sls Mgr: John Scott

D-U-N-S 15-998-8794
■ **HYDRATIGHT OPERATIONS INC**
(*Suby of* ACTUANT CORP) ★
1102 Hall Ct, Deer Park, TX 77536-1870
Tel (713) 860-4200 *Founded/Ownrshp* 2005
Sales 38.1MM^E *EMP* 275
SIC 7359 Tool rental
Pr: Don A Fancher
**Sec:* Mark J Pike
Ofcr: Wanda Preston
IT Man: Wesley Harris

HYDRAULEX GLOBAL
See HYDRAULIC REPAIR AND DESIGN CORP

HYDRAULEX GLOBAL
See HYDRAULEX INTERNATIONAL HOLDINGS INC

D-U-N-S 96-472-5605
HYDRAULEX INTERNATIONAL HOLDINGS INC
HYDRAULEX GLOBAL
48175 Gratiot Ave, Chesterfield, MI 48051-2604
Tel (914) 682-2700 *Founded/Ownrshp* 2011
Sales 52.1MM^E *EMP* 150^E
SIC 6719 Investment holding companies, except banks; Investment holding companies, except banks
CEO: Shirish Pareek

D-U-N-S 02-879-3917 IMP
HYDRAULIC CONTROLS INC
4700 San Pablo Ave, Emeryville, CA 94608-3097
Tel (510) 658-8300 *Founded/Ownrshp* 1965
Sales 51.6MM^E *EMP* 140
SIC 5084

D-U-N-S 01-021-1415 IMP/EXP
HYDRAULIC REPAIR AND DESIGN CORP
HYDRAULEX GLOBAL
(*Suby of* HYDRAULEX GLOBAL) ★
701 N Levee Rd, Puyallup, WA 98371-3205
Tel (253) 872-8900 *Founded/Ownrshp* 2011
Sales 59.8MM^E *EMP* 80
SIC 5084 7699 Alcoholic beverage making equipment & supplies; Hydraulic equipment repair; Alcoholic beverage making equipment & supplies; Hydraulic equipment repair
Pr: Shirish Pareek
**Ch:* David Schopp
**VP:* Cathy Ayers
Exec: Nickolas Nesland
Sales Exec: Rick Edmondson

HYDRAULIC SUPPLY CO
See AERO HARDWARE & SUPPLY INC

D-U-N-S 04-037-0249 IMP/EXP
HYDRAULICS INTERNATIONAL INC
9201 Independence Ave, Chatsworth, CA 91311-5905
Tel (818) 998-1231 *Founded/Ownrshp* 1976
Sales 75.7MM *EMP* 360^E
Accts Roschke & Wall Agura Hills C
SIC 3728 Aircraft parts & equipment; Aircraft parts & equipment
CEO: Nicky Ghaemmaghami
**CFO:* Shah Banifazl
CFO: Shah Banisazl
**VP:* Linda Ghaemmaghami

HYDREL
See KILPATRICK TOWNSEND & STOCKTON LLP

D-U-N-S 96-582-6774 IMP
HYDRIL CO
TENARIS HYDRIL
(*Suby of* MAVERICK TUBE CORP) ★
302 Mccarty St, Houston, TX 77029-1140
Tel (713) 670-3500 *Founded/Ownrshp* 2006
Sales 89.9MM^E *EMP* 747
SIC 3533 Oil & gas field machinery
Pr: Brad Lowe
Mng Dir: Alberto Agostini
Board of Directors: Chris North

HYDRIL PRESSURE CONTROL
See HYDRIL USA DISTRIBUTION LLC

D-U-N-S 06-205-6288 IMP/EXP
■ **HYDRIL USA DISTRIBUTION LLC**
HYDRIL PRESSURE CONTROL
(*Suby of* GE AERO ENERGY PRODUCTS) ★
3300 N Sam Houston Pkwy E, Houston, TX 77032-3411
Tel (281) 449-2000 *Founded/Ownrshp* 2008
Sales 447.6MM^E *EMP* 1,700
SIC 3533 Oil & gas field machinery; Oil & gas field machinery
Pr: Charles Chauvier
**VP:* Chuck Chauviere
**Genl Mgr:* Mat R Castaneda
IT Man: Michael Seghers
Mfg Dir: Desi Barreto
Snr Mgr: Frank Emerich

D-U-N-S 82-896-4341 IMP
■ **HYDRIL USA MANUFACTURING LLC**
(*Suby of* GE AERO ENERGY PRODUCTS) ★
3300 N Sam Houston Pkwy E, Houston, TX 77032-3411
Tel (281) 449-2000 *Founded/Ownrshp* 2008
Sales 228.8MM^E *EMP* 1,000
SIC 3069 Rubber automotive products; Rubber automotive products

D-U-N-S 10-269-2972
HYDRILL LLC
2200 West Loop S Ste 800, Houston, TX 77027-3532
Tel (281) 449-2000 *Founded/Ownrshp* 2001
Sales 42.5MM^E *EMP* 444
SIC 3533 3625 Oil & gas field machinery; Relays & industrial controls; Oil & gas field machinery; Relays & industrial controls
CEO: Chuck Chauvare
CFO: Chris North
Treas: Andrew Ricks

D-U-N-S 00-643-5887 IMP/EXP
HYDRITE CHEMICAL CO (WI)
300 N Patrick Blvd Fl 2, Brookfield, WI 53045-5816
Tel (262) 792-1450 *Founded/Ownrshp* 1929
Sales 501.2MM^E *EMP* 800
SIC 5169 2819 2841 2869

D-U-N-S 61-527-8520 IMP
HYDRO ALUMINUM ADRIAN INC
100 Gus Hipp Blvd, Rockledge, FL 32955-4701
Tel (321) 636-8147 *Founded/Ownrshp* 2012
Sales 28.8MM^E *EMP* 174
SIC 3354 3463 Aluminum extruded products; Aluminum forgings; Aluminum extruded products; Aluminum forgings
Pr: Greg Hall

D-U-N-S 07-874-9484 IMP/EXP
HYDRO ALUMINUM METALS USA LLC
(*Suby of* NORSK HYDRO ASA)
1500 Whetstone Way # 103, Baltimore, MD 21230-5148
Tel (443) 835-3133 *Founded/Ownrshp* 2012
Sales 26.3MM^E *EMP* 130
SIC 3354 Aluminum extruded products
CEO: Svein Richard Brandtzg
**CFO:* Eivind Kallevik
IT Man: Marco Celano
Sls Mgr: Jennifer Mann

D-U-N-S 14-032-3424 IMP
HYDRO CARBIDE INC
(*Suby of* HBD INDUSTRIES INC) ★
4439 State Route 982, Latrobe, PA 15650-3700
Tel (724) 539-9701 *Founded/Ownrshp* 1974
Sales 21.1MM^E *EMP* 170
SIC 2819 Carbides; Carbides
CEO: Randy L Greely
**CEO:* Thomas Pozda
**CFO:* Mark R Dyll
**Treas:* Robert Sirac
VP: Paul Kuhns

D-U-N-S 07-852-3381
HYDRO CONDUIT CORP (GA)
CEMEX
(*Suby of* CEMEX MATERIALS LLC) ★
1501 Belvedere Rd, West Palm Beach, FL 33406-1501
Tel (903) 784-8652 *Founded/Ownrshp* 1963
Sales 34.8MM^E *EMP* 110^E
SIC 3272 Concrete products
Prin: Adrian Driver
Ex VP: Jose Garcia
VP: Michael Carlson
VP: Ryane Mahoney
VP Opers: Jerry Haught
Opers Mgr: Bryan Drake
Opers Mgr: Louie Figueroa
Opers Mgr: Brandon Town
Plnt Mgr: Marvin Jenson
Plnt Mgr: Ramon Neilson
Plnt Mgr: Ralph Prickett

D-U-N-S 96-382-0522
HYDRO CONDUIT OF TEXAS LP
RINKER MATERIALS CON PIPE DIV
(*Suby of* CEMEX MATERIALS LLC) ★
6560 Langfield Rd 3-H, Houston, TX 77092-1008
Tel (832) 590-5400 *Founded/Ownrshp* 2000
Sales 28.4MM^E *EMP* 150
SIC 3272 Pressure pipe, reinforced concrete; Pressure pipe, reinforced concrete
Pt: David Clarke
VP: Dave Fordyce
VP: Steve Seamore
Genl Mgr: Janet Cobb

D-U-N-S 03-778-3032 IMP
HYDRO ENGINEERING INC
865 W 2600 S, South Salt Lake, UT 84119-2429
Tel (801) 972-1181 *Founded/Ownrshp* 1980
Sales 27.5MM^E *EMP* 75^E
SIC 5084

D-U-N-S 05-226-9230
HYDRO INC
834 W Madison St, Chicago, IL 60607-2630
Tel (312) 738-3000 *Founded/Ownrshp* 1978
Sales 80.5MM^E *EMP* 200
SIC 8711 5084 7699 Engineering services; Pumps & pumping equipment; Pumps & pumping equipment repair; Engineering services; Pumps & pumping equipment; Pumps & pumping equipment repair
Pr: George Harris
Top Exec: Einar Glomnes
Ex VP: Wenche Agerup
Ex VP: Donald Fitch
Ex VP: Hans-Joachim Kock
VP: Michelle Carrera
VP: Jesse Stinson
Exec: Birgitte Holter
Dir Bus: Matt Landis
Mng Dir: Arnd Brinkmann
Mng Dir: Bill Painter

D-U-N-S 01-002-6271
HYDRO RESOURCES HOLDINGS INC (TX)
2245 Texas Dr Ste 250, Sugar Land, TX 77479-1102
Tel (713) 622-4033 *Founded/Ownrshp* 1999, 2002
Sales 67.9MM^E *EMP* 250
SIC 1781 Water well drilling; Water well drilling
Pr: Alton Cherry
**VP:* Mark McWatters

D-U-N-S 04-896-2393
HYDRO SERVICE & SUPPLIES INC
513 United Dr, Durham, NC 27713-1477
Tel (919) 544-3744 *Founded/Ownrshp* 1967
Sales 23.0MM^E *EMP* 63
SIC 3589 7699 Water treatment equipment, industrial; Industrial equipment services
Pr: Dave Currin
**Ch Bd:* Charles S Atwater
**Pr:* Wes Robbins
**VP:* Darrell Baber
**VP:* Paul Rigsbee
**VP:* Charles Riley
Sales Asso: Tony Abduramani
Sales Asso: John Bentley

D-U-N-S 79-138-9893 EXP
HYDRO SPA PARTS AND ACCESSORIES INC
6101 45th St N, Saint Petersburg, FL 33714-1038
Tel (727) 573-9611 *Founded/Ownrshp* 1992
Sales 41.2MM^E *EMP* 400^E
SIC 5091 3088 3949 Spa equipment & supplies; Hot tubs, plastic or fiberglass; Sporting & athletic goods; Spa equipment & supplies; Hot tubs, plastic or fiberglass; Sporting & athletic goods
Pr: Brian K Wiley
**Pr:* Charles S Wiley
**Pr:* Robert M Wiley
CFO: Darcy Buckley
**CFO:* Art Zelenak
IT Man: Mike Fritz Inactive

D-U-N-S 96-697-1673 IMP
■ **HYDRO SYSTEMS CO**
(*Suby of* OPW FLUID TRANSFER GROUP) ★
3798 Round Bottom Rd, Cincinnati, OH 45244-2498
Tel (513) 271-8800 *Founded/Ownrshp* 1998
Sales 59.3MM^E *EMP* 321^E
SIC 3586 Measuring & dispensing pumps
CEO: Jeff Rowe
**CFO:* Steve Vogel
**VP:* Gordon Thomas
Exec: David Demske
Sls Dir: Gary Pratt
Manager: Paul Cusworth
Sls Mgr: James Stephens
Sales Asso: Scott Chapman

D-U-N-S 09-900-7684
HYDRO SYSTEMS INC
29132 Avenue Paine, Valencia, CA 91355-5402
Tel (661) 775-0686 *Founded/Ownrshp* 1999
Sales 22.7MM^E *EMP* 96
SIC 3431 3432 3088 Bathtubs: enameled iron, cast iron or pressed metal; Plumbing fixture fittings & trim; Plastics plumbing fixtures; Bathtubs: enameled iron, cast iron or pressed metal; Plumbing fixture fittings & trim; Plastics plumbing fixtures
Pr: Scott G Steinhardt
Ex VP: David Ortwein
**VP:* Larry Burroughs
**VP:* Dave Ortwein
Natl Sales: Ramiro Ponce

D-U-N-S 00-452-0185 IMP
HYDRO TUBE ENTERPRISES INC (OH)
137 Artino St, Oberlin, OH 44074-1265
Tel (440) 774-1022 *Founded/Ownrshp* 1922, 2007
Sales 20.8MM^E *EMP* 105
SIC 3498 Tube fabricating (contract bending & shaping); Tube fabricating (contract bending & shaping)
Pr: Mike Prokop
**VP:* Richard Cooks
**VP:* Thomas E Hamel
VP Opers: Tim Althaus

VP Opers: Richard Cook
Mtls Mgr: Michael McCartney

D-U-N-S 06-396-8754 IMP
HYDRO-AIR COMPONENTS INC
ZEHNDER RITTLING
(*Suby of* ZEHNDER GROUP AG)
100 Rittling Blvd, Buffalo, NY 14220-1885
Tel (716) 827-6510 *Founded/Ownrshp* 2006
Sales 40.3MM^E *EMP* 130
SIC 3585 1711 Refrigeration & heating equipment; Plumbing, heating, air-conditioning contractors; Refrigeration & heating equipment; Plumbing, heating, air-conditioning contractors
CEO: Scott Pallotta
COO: Tony Scime
**VP:* Robert Daigler
Sls&Mrk Ex: Julius Atkins
Sls Mgr: Dave Clouden
Sls Mgr: Wayne Mayer
Sls Mgr: Clark Zacaroli

D-U-N-S 96-413-2864 IMP
■ **HYDRO-AIRE INC**
(*Suby of* CRANE AEROSPACE INC) ★
3000 Winona Ave, Burbank, CA 91504-2540
Tel (818) 526-2600 *Founded/Ownrshp* 1999
Sales 104.7MM^E *EMP* 602^E
SIC 3728 Aircraft parts & equipment; Aircraft parts & equipment
CEO: Brendan J Curran
**Treas:* Tazewell Rowe
VP: Mike Brady
Ex Dir: Stuart Johnson
Sftwr Eng: Herman Yih
Opers Mgr: Dale Beymer

D-U-N-S 01-012-2661
HYDRO-CHEM PROCESSING INC
125 Hckory Sprng Indus Dr, Canton, GA 30115-8897
Tel (770) 345-2222 *Founded/Ownrshp* 1968
Sales 39.5MM^E *EMP* 250
Accts Ross Lane & Company
SIC 1541 Industrial buildings, new construction; Industrial buildings, new construction
CEO: Norton Dennis
**VP:* Joseph D Borg
**VP:* C V Dinsmore
Mfg Mgr: Tony Bybee
Ql Cn Mgr: Bruce Salonek

D-U-N-S 62-157-7188 IMP
HYDRO-GEAR INC
(*Suby of* DANFOSS A/S)
1411 S Hamilton St, Sullivan, IL 61951-2264
Tel (217) 728-2581 *Founded/Ownrshp* 1975
Sales 75.0MM^E *EMP* 350^E
SIC 3594 Hydrostatic drives (transmissions); Hydrostatic drives (transmissions)
Pr: Ray Hauser
Pt: Agri Fab
Pt: Ronald D Harshman
Pt: Gary Harvey
Pt: Jack Obiala
QA Dir: Jason Shoemaker
Ql Cn Mgr: Justin Adcock
Ql Cn Mgr: Curt Allen
Ql Cn Mgr: Shawn Fagin
Ql Cn Mgr: Mark Trowbridge
Sales Exec: Mike McCoy

D-U-N-S 09-137-8679
HYDRO-KLEAN LLC
333 Nw 49th Pl, Des Moines, IA 50313-2233
Tel (515) 283-0500 *Founded/Ownrshp* 2011
Sales 20.1MM^E *EMP* 125
SIC 7699 Waste cleaning services; Sewer cleaning & rodding
Genl Mgr: Dennis Bailey
CFO: Wade Anderson

HYDRO-POWER SYSTEM
See TULSA RIG IRON INC

D-U-N-S 05-569-4905 EXP
HYDRO-SCAPE PRODUCTS INC (CA)
5805 Kearny Villa Rd, San Diego, CA 92123-1172
Tel (858) 560-1600 *Founded/Ownrshp* 1969, 2003
Sales 65.7MM^E *EMP* 189
SIC 5083 5087 5193 5191 5261

HYDRO-VAC
See HITECMETAL GROUP INC

D-U-N-S 06-707-6802
■ **HYDROAIR HUGHES LLC**
(*Suby of* APPLIED INDUSTRIAL TECHNOLOGIES INC) ★
330 Garnet Way Ste 1212, Pittsburgh, PA 15224-2006
Tel (203) 248-8863 *Founded/Ownrshp* 2008
Sales 37.6MM^E *EMP* 78
SIC 5084 Pneumatic tools & equipment; Hydraulic systems equipment & supplies
VP: Bill Pueschel

D-U-N-S 83-828-5880 IMP
HYDROBLEND INC
HB SPECIALTY FOODS
1801 N Elder St, Nampa, ID 83687-3079
Tel (208) 467-7441 *Founded/Ownrshp* 1997
Sales 41.1MM^E *EMP* 195
SIC 2045 2041 2051 2099 Flours & flour mixes, from purchased flour; Flour mixes; Bread, cake & related products; Seasonings: dry mixes; Bread crumbs, not made in bakeries; Flours & flour mixes, from purchased flour; Flour mixes; Bread, cake & related products; Seasonings: dry mixes; Bread crumbs, not made in bakeries
Pr: Mike Guthrie
Ex VP: John Diteman
VP: Chris Berger
VP: Bill Cyr
VP: Randy Hobert
Dir IT: Mike Emery
Plnt Mgr: Casey Guthrie
Ql Cn Mgr: Brady Guthrie
Snr Mgr: Sharon Hansen

D-U-N-S 16-872-5054
HYDROCARBON EXCHANGE CORP
5910 N Cntrl Expy # 1380, Dallas, TX 75206-5126
Tel (214) 987-0257 *Founded/Ownrshp* 2004
Sales 340.2MM *EMP* 8
Accts Bdo Usa Llp Dallas Texas
SIC 4924 Natural gas distribution; Natural gas distribution
Pr: R Scott Hopkins

D-U-N-S 87-938-1697
■ **HYDROCARBON TECHNOLOGIES INC**
(*Suby of* HEADWATERS INC) ★
1501 New York Ave, Lawrenceville, NJ 08648-4635
Tel (609) 394-3102 *Founded/Ownrshp* 2001
Sales 26.8MM^E *EMP* 85
SIC 8731 Energy research
Pr: Craig Hickman
**VP:* Lap-Keung Lee

D-U-N-S 10-267-3886
HYDROCHEM LLC
(*Suby of* AQUILEX HOLDINGS LLC) ★
900 Georgia Ave, Deer Park, TX 77536-2518
Tel (713) 393-5600 *Founded/Ownrshp* 2007
Sales 400.0MM *EMP* 2,086
SIC 7349 Cleaning service, industrial or commercial; Cleaning service, industrial or commercial
CEO: Gary Noto
**Pr:* Gregory G Rice
CFO: Judy Shields
Sr VP: Gregory Ric
Sr VP: Doug Vail
VP: Steve Akkerman
VP: Willie Jones
VP: Don Millet
Rgnl Mgr: Mike Madden
Rgnl Mgr: Bob Tsiffer
Area Mgr: D Gunter

D-U-N-S 10-908-2255 EXP
HYDROFORM USA INC
2848 E 208th St, Carson, CA 90810-1101
Tel (310) 632-6353 *Founded/Ownrshp* 1982
Sales 35.0MM *EMP* 154
SIC 3728 Aircraft parts & equipment; Aircraft parts & equipment
CEO: Chester K Jablonski
**CFO:* Mauricio Salazar
VP: Rick Gardless
VP: Scott McCormack
Genl Mgr: Jorge Curiel
QA Dir: Keith Krause
Dir IT: Steven Hsu
Dir IT: Rick McCandless
Dir IT: Steven Stansbury
**Counsel:* Jeffrey Lake

D-U-N-S 19-394-2604
HYDROGEOLOGIC INC
11107 Sunset Hills Rd # 400, Reston, VA 20190-5375
Tel (703) 478-5186 *Founded/Ownrshp* 2001
Sales 74.9MM^E *EMP* 375
SIC 8744 ;
Pr: Peter Huyakorn
Pr: Jonathan Sperka
**COO:* Scott Schulein
**VP:* Dr Jan Kool
**VP:* Cathy Nelson
Rgnl Mgr: Tony Gogel
CTO: Timothy Hazlett
Snr PM: Justin Barker
Snr PM: Robert Keskonis

HYDROHOIST BOAT LIFTS
See HYDROHOIST MARINE GROUP INC

D-U-N-S 05-395-5837 EXP
HYDROHOIST MARINE GROUP INC
HYDROHOIST BOAT LIFTS
915 W Blue Starr Dr, Claremore, OK 74017-2802
Tel (918) 341-6811 *Founded/Ownrshp* 1985
Sales 37.4MM^E *EMP* 100
SIC 3536 3537 3534 Boat lifts; Industrial trucks & tractors; Elevators & moving stairways

D-U-N-S 03-409-7126
HYDROID LLC
(*Suby of* SIMRAD NORTH AMERICA INC)
6 Benjamin Nye Cir, Pocasset, MA 02559-4900
Tel (508) 563-6565 *Founded/Ownrshp* 2001, 2008
Sales 31.5MM^E *EMP* 32^E
SIC 3731 Submarine tenders, building & repairing

HYDROLEVEL DIV
See C COWLES & CO

D-U-N-S 09-673-2706 IMP
HYDROMAT INC (MO)
11600 Adie Rd, Maryland Heights, MO 63043-3510
Tel (314) 432-0070 *Founded/Ownrshp* 1979
Sales 81.8MM^E *EMP* 187
Accts Deloitte & Touche Llp
SIC 5084 Metalworking machinery; Metalworking machinery
Pr: Bruno Schmitter
Pr: Rich Vales
**CFO:* Bruce Falconer
Rgnl Mgr: Urban Meloche
CIO: Scott Frisby
Dir IT: Carl Milligan
Plnt Mgr: Rudy Bieri
Manager: Bill Nuetzel

D-U-N-S 02-432-8457 EXP
HYDROMATIC PUMPS INC
1101 Myers Pkwy, Ashland, OH 44805-1969
Tel (419) 289-1144 *Founded/Ownrshp* 1971
Sales 56.0MM^E *EMP* 600
SIC 3561 Pumps, domestic: water or sump; Pumps, domestic: water or sump
Pr: Keith Lang
Treas: Michael Meyer

HYDROMATION COMPANY
See FILTRA-SYSTEMS CO

D-U-N-S 06-181-8688 IMP
■ **HYDROMOTION INC**
(*Suby of* PRECISE HARD CHROME) ★
85 E Bridge St, Spring City, PA 19475-1404
Tel (610) 948-4150 *Founded/Ownrshp* 1971, 2000
Sales 21.7MM^E *EMP* 87
SIC 3599 3621 3594 Machine shop, jobbing & repair; Motors & generators; Fluid power pumps & motors
Pr: Mike Klute
QC Dir: Jeff Laub
Mtls Mgr: Ellen Groller

D-U-N-S 10-234-8901
HYDRONIC & STEAM EQUIPMENT CO INC
8950 Bash St, Indianapolis, IN 46256-1277
Tel (317) 577-8326 *Founded/Ownrshp* 1984
Sales 24.4MM^E *EMP* 35
SIC 5074 5075 5084 Heating equipment (hydronic); Air conditioning & ventilation equipment & supplies; Industrial machinery & equipment
Pr: Dennis L Kring
**Sec:* Al E Madden
Bd of Dir: Jack Kibort
Off Mgr: Chris Thompson
Sales Asso: Denise Clute
Sales Asso: Ernie Retek
Sales Asso: Kevin Weddle
Sales Asso: Don Werner

D-U-N-S 04-332-5984 IMP/EXP
HYDROTECH INC (OH)
ENPRO
10052 Commerce Park Dr, West Chester, OH 45246-1338
Tel (513) 881-7000 *Founded/Ownrshp* 1967
Sales 38.2MM^E *EMP* 84
SIC 5084 3492

D-U-N-S 10-931-3598
HYDROTHERM INC
260 N Elm St, Westfield, MA 01085-1614
Tel (413) 564-5515 *Founded/Ownrshp* 2003
Sales 33.8MM^E *EMP* 400
SIC 3443 Boilers: industrial, power, or marine; Boilers: industrial, power, or marine
CEO: John Reed
Sales Asso: Paul A Mattingly

D-U-N-S 02-516-4302 IMP
HYDROX CHEMICAL CO INC (IL)
HYDROX LABORATORIES
825 Tollgate Rd Ste B, Elgin, IL 60123-9326
Tel (847) 468-9400 *Founded/Ownrshp* 1913, 1981
Sales 40.8MM^E *EMP* 65
SIC 2844 2819 2834 2869 Shampoos, rinses, conditioners: hair; Peroxides, hydrogen peroxide; Veterinary pharmaceutical preparations; Industrial organic chemicals
Pr: Kappana Ramanandan
COO: John Polydoros
**CFO:* Brian Gaare
CFO: Brian Garre
Exec: Lisa Seyller
IT Man: Nick Srivastava
Ql Cn Mgr: Keith Robertson

HYDROX LABORATORIES
See HYDROX CHEMICAL CO INC

D-U-N-S 01-471-9421
HYGEIA PAPER CO
DUBIN PAPER
41 Conshohocken State Rd # 305, Bala Cynwyd, PA 19004-2412
Tel (215) 462-7907 *Founded/Ownrshp* 1932
Sales 33.0MM *EMP* 80
SIC 5113 5046 Industrial & personal service paper; Restaurant equipment & supplies; Industrial & personal service paper; Restaurant equipment & supplies
Pr: Frank Dubin
**VP:* Norman Hockman

D-U-N-S 84-918-1706
HYGEN PHARMACEUTICALS INC
8635 154th Ave Ne, Redmond, WA 98052-3564
Tel (425) 451-9178 *Founded/Ownrshp* 1993
Sales 25.0MM *EMP* 28
SIC 5122 Pharmaceuticals
CEO: Nishit Mehta
IT Man: Josiah Ward
Opers Mgr: Ranjani Kamath
Natl Sales: Tim Lapworth
Natl Sales: Michael Ramirez
Mktg Mgr: Nishit RAO

HYGENIA
See MEDICAL PACKAGING CORP

D-U-N-S 00-416-3390 IMP/EXP
HYGENIC CORP
(*Suby of* COGR INC) ★
1245 Home Ave, Akron, OH 44310-2575
Tel (330) 633-8460 *Founded/Ownrshp* 2000
Sales 94.0MM^E *EMP* 324
SIC 3069 3061 Medical & laboratory rubber sundries & related products; Mechanical rubber goods; Medical & laboratory rubber sundries & related products; Mechanical rubber goods
Pr: Marshall Dahneke
**CFO:* Niels Lichti
**VP:* Ralph Buster
VP: Dwayne Hofstatter
VP: Jim Loudin
VP: John Vatalaro
Rgnl Mgr: Xinghai Liu
CTO: Carlos Albinana
Dir IT: John Rutter
IT Man: Bob Crabbs
Web Dev: Greg Sloane

D-U-N-S 62-489-7047 EXP
HYGRADE OCEAN PRODUCTS INC
86 Macarthur Dr, New Bedford, MA 02740-7214
Tel (508) 993-5700 *Founded/Ownrshp* 1991
Sales 24.6MM^E *EMP* 45
SIC 5146 Seafoods

Pr: Albert Santos
CFO: Linda C Wisniewski
**Treas:* Carmine Romano
Trst: Doreen Santos

D-U-N-S 10-685-2072 IMP
HYI
222 N Vincent Ave, Covina, CA 91722-3904
Tel (626) 332-8989 *Founded/Ownrshp* 1979
Sales 60.0MM *EMP* 60
Accts Peter Liou El Monte Ca
SIC 5139 5091 Footwear; Sporting & recreation goods; Footwear; Sporting & recreation goods
Ch Bd: Jennie Kiang
**Ch:* Raymond Kiang
Off Mgr: Joanne Loh
VP Opers: Melanie Estandia
Natl Sales: Robert Walsh
Mktg Mgr: Mike Fingleton

D-U-N-S 84-847-5328
HYLA INC
ERECYCLING CORP
(*Suby of* HYLA MOBILE (BELGIQUE) SA)
1507 Lyndon B Ste 500, Farmers Branch, TX 75234
Tel (972) 573-0300 *Founded/Ownrshp* 2010
Sales 60.0MM *EMP* 125
SIC 5084 Recycling machinery & equipment
Ch: Ronald T Lemay
**Pr:* Biju Nair
CFO: Gary Stone
Ofcr: Jim Fredericks
**Sr VP:* Rich Jones
Sr VP: Tod Mertes
Sr VP: Giulio Pappalardo
**VP:* Shad Spears

D-U-N-S 09-190-6313
HYLAND ENTERPRISES INC
3770 Puritan Way Unit J, Frederick, CO 80516-9463
Tel (307) 328-0668 *Founded/Ownrshp* 2005
Sales NA *EMP* 300
SIC 4212 1389

D-U-N-S 09-990-4435 IMP
HYLAND HILLS PARK & RECREATION DISTRICT
HYLAND HLLS GOLF CRS/WTER WRLD
8801 Pecos St, Denver, CO 80260-5038
Tel (303) 427-7873 *Founded/Ownrshp* 1955
Sales 50.4MM^E *EMP* 1,600
SIC 7999 Recreation services; Recreation services
Pr: Donald Cciancio II
**Pr:* Donald C Ciancio II
**Treas:* Sarah Heil
**VP:* Nicholas J McCoy
**Ex Dir:* Greg Mastriona

HYLAND HLLS GOLF CRS/WTER WRLD
See HYLAND HILLS PARK & RECREATION DISTRICT

D-U-N-S 18-657-8936 IMP
HYLAND SANDERS CORP
1640 Varner Dr, Mobile, AL 36693-5643
Tel (251) 661-1952 *Founded/Ownrshp* 1988
Sales 22.3MM^E *EMP* 90
SIC 1752 Floor laying & floor work
Pr: Michael D Sanders
**VP:* Hugh F Hyland
Div Mgr: Phillip Thompson

D-U-N-S 78-751-5550
HYLAND SOFTWARE INC
(*Suby of* TCB) ★
28500 Clemens Rd, Westlake, OH 44145-1145
Tel (440) 788-5000 *Founded/Ownrshp* 2007
Sales 443.5MM^E *EMP* 1,660
SIC 7372 Application computer software; Application computer software
CEO: Bill Priemer
**Ch Bd:* Christopher J Hyland
COO: Sheila Lowe
Assoc VP: Valt Vesikallio
**Ex VP:* Miguel Zubizarreta
VP: Drew Chapin
**VP:* Noreen Kilbane
VP: Andy Kuyper
**VP:* Timothy Pembridge
VP: Bill Premier
Comm Man: Erin Kupcak

HYLAND'S HOMEOPATHIC
See STANDARD HOMEOPATHIC CO

D-U-N-S 80-829-1236
HYLANT GROUP
8 Cadillac Dr Ste 230, Brentwood, TN 37027-5392
Tel (615) 732-6500 *Founded/Ownrshp* 2007
Sales NA *EMP* 600
SIC 6361 Title insurance; Title insurance
Prin: Kimberly Riley

D-U-N-S 06-809-5702
HYLANT GROUP INC
811 Madison Ave Fl 11, Toledo, OH 43604-5626
Tel (419) 255-1020 *Founded/Ownrshp* 1985
Sales NA *EMP* 610
SIC 6411 Insurance agents; Insurance agents
CEO: Michael Hylant
**Ch Bd:* Patrick Hylant
Pr: Todd Belden
**Pr:* William F Buckley
**Pr:* John W Chaney
Pr: Scott Dillabaugh
Pr: Tony Evans
Pr: Michael Gilbert
Pr: Clay Jennings
Pr: Thomas O'Connell
Pr: Kim Riley
Pr: Kimberly L Riley
Pr: Frank Treco
COO: Christine Mahboob
COO: Morrie Sanderson
COO: Patrick Savage
CFO: Bill Pridgeon
**CFO:* William P Pridgeon
**Ex VP:* Lisa G Hawker
Ex VP: Lisa Hawker
**Ex VP:* Richard C Hylant

D-U-N-S 05-917-9275
HYLTON ENTERPRISES (VIRGINIA) INC
HYLTON GROUP
5593 Mapledale Plz, Woodbridge, VA 22193-4527
Tel (703) 590-1111 *Founded/Ownrshp* 1989
Sales 20.5MM^E *EMP* 100
SIC 1531 Speculative builder, single-family houses
Ch Bd: Conrad C Hylton
Pr: George A Halfpap Jr
CFO: Paula Hall
Sec: Norris Sisson
VP: Hylton Jr Cecil D
VP: John E Walvius

HYLTON GROUP
See HYLTON ENTERPRISES (VIRGINIA) INC

D-U-N-S 87-820-6630 IMP
HYMAN COMPANIES INC
LANDAU
727 N Meadow St Ste A, Allentown, PA 18102-1936
Tel (610) 433-4114 *Founded/Ownrshp* 1995
Sales 35.3MM^E *EMP* 320
SIC 5632 Costume jewelry; Costume jewelry
Pr: Nat L Hyman

HYMAN KAPLAN PAVILLION
See GOOD SAMARITAN PHYSICIAN SERVICES

D-U-N-S 06-090-3150 IMP
HYMAN LEWIS INC
860 Sandhill Ave, Carson, CA 90746-1221
Tel (310) 532-5700 *Founded/Ownrshp* 1976
Sales 20.3MM^E *EMP* 60
SIC 5023 Window furnishings; Floor coverings; Fireplace equipment & accessories; Rugs
CEO: James Hyman
**COO:* Robert Le Blanc
**COO:* Wolfgang Moeller
CFO: Joseph Orlando
Netwrk Eng: Don Grindle
Sales Asso: Twyla Burks

D-U-N-S 02-516-4385
HYMANS AUTO SUPPLY CO
EZMIX
8600 S Commercial Ave, Chicago, IL 60617-2535
Tel (773) 978-8221 *Founded/Ownrshp* 1927
Sales 33.0MM^E *EMP* 70^E
SIC 5198 5531 5251 Paints; Automotive parts; Hardware
Pr: Richard E Hyman
**Treas:* Martyn Hyman
**VP:* Dennis E Hyman
Genl Mgr: Steve Hyman

HYNES CONVENTION CENTER
See MASSACHUSETTS CONVENTION CENTER AUTHORITY

D-U-N-S 00-416-8951 IMP
HYNES INDUSTRIES INC
ROLL FORMED PRODUCTS CO DIV
3805 Hericks Rd, Austintown, OH 44515
Tel (330) 799-3221 *Founded/Ownrshp* 1966
Sales 58.0MM^E *EMP* 150^E
SIC 5051 3449 3316 3441 Metals service centers & offices; Strip, metal; Custom roll formed products; Wire, flat, cold-rolled strip: not made in hot-rolled mills; Fabricated structural metal; Metals service centers & offices; Strip, metal; Custom roll formed products; Wire, flat, cold-rolled strip: not made in hot-rolled mills; Fabricated structural metal
CEO: D R Golding
**Ch Bd:* William W Bresnahan
**Pr:* William J Bresnahan
**Treas:* Edmond C Clarke
**VP:* Jim Blair
VP: Ted Clark
**VP:* Dick Evans
**VP:* Mike Giambattista
**VP:* Pat Montana
Opers Mgr: Judy Patton

D-U-N-S 07-866-9398 IMP
HYOSUNG HOLDINGS USA INC
(*Suby of* HYOSUNG CORPORATION)
15800 John J Delaney Dr, Charlotte, NC 28277-2832
Tel (704) 790-6100 *Founded/Ownrshp* 2009
Sales NA *EMP* 508
SIC 2299 2296 Fabrics: linen, jute, hemp, ramie; Tire cord & fabrics; Fabrics: linen, jute, hemp, ramie; Tire cord & fabrics
Pr: Keiho Lee
**CFO:* Hyeong Seob Jeong

D-U-N-S 18-320-8727
HYOSUNG USA INC
(*Suby of* HYOSUNG HOLDINGS USA INC) ★
15801 Brixham Hill Ave, Charlotte, NC 28277-4644
Tel (704) 790-6136 *Founded/Ownrshp* 1993
Sales 550.6MM *EMP* 500
Accts Kpmg Llp New York Ny
SIC 2221 2296 Broadwoven fabric mills, manmade; Cord for reinforcing rubber tires; Broadwoven fabric mills, manmade; Cord for reinforcing rubber tires
Pr: Terry Swanner
**CFO:* Hyeong Seob Jeong
Adm Dir: J Walker
Mng Dir: Young Choi
Genl Mgr: Yung Kim
Sls Mgr: Stefano Choi
Sls Mgr: Neeraj Handa
Snr Mgr: Ilnur Algushaev
Snr Mgr: Jong Lee

HYPAC
See BOMAG AMERICAS INC

D-U-N-S 07-840-1339
■ **HYPER MARKETING INC**
(*Suby of* ALLIANCE DATA SYSTEMS CORP) ★
104 S Michigan Ave # 1500, Chicago, IL 60603-5915
Tel (312) 263-2558 *Founded/Ownrshp* 2012
Sales 117.4MM^E *EMP* 1,100^E
SIC 6211 7311 Investment firm, general brokerage; Advertising agencies; Investment firm, general brokerage; Advertising agencies
CEO: Zain Raj
**Pr:* Paul Kramer
**CFO:* Christopher Averill
**Chf Mktg O:* Michael Miller

D-U-N-S 80-841-4226
HYPER NETWORK SOLUTIONS LLC
HEALTH NATURAL SYSTEMS
11780 Us Highway 1 # 400, North Palm Beach, FL 33408-3007
Tel (561) 863-5408 *Founded/Ownrshp* 2006
Sales 50.0MM^E *EMP* 15
SIC 5122 Vitamins & minerals; Vitamins & minerals

HYPERACTIVE
See E & J LAWRENCE CORP

D-U-N-S 92-986-1052 IMP
HYPERCEL CORP
NAZTECH
28385 Constellation Rd, Valencia, CA 91355-5048
Tel (661) 310-1000 *Founded/Ownrshp* 1995
Sales 27.8MM^E *EMP* 50
SIC 5065 Telephone & telegraphic equipment
Pr: David Nazar
VP: Sam Onda
Dir IT: Andrew Caddy
Mktg Dir: Lili Miura
Sls Dir: Shoshanna Lefcourt
Mktg Mgr: Robbie Cabral
Sls Mgr: Walter Lopez

D-U-N-S 18-179-2714
■ **HYPERCOM CORP**
HYPERCOM NETWORK SYSTEMS
(*Suby of* VERIFONE SYSTEMS INC) ★
8888 E Raintree Dr # 300, Scottsdale, AZ 85260-3951
Tel (480) 642-5000 *Founded/Ownrshp* 2011
Sales 95.5MM^E *EMP* 1,431
SIC 3578 7372 7299 5065 Point-of-sale devices; Automatic teller machines (ATM); Application computer software; Information services, consumer; Electronic parts; Point-of-sale devices; Automatic teller machines (ATM); Application computer software; Information services, consumer; Electronic parts
CEO: Philippe Tartavull
Pr: Heidi R Goff
CFO: Grant Lyon
CFO: Robert M Vreeland
Ch: Norman Stout
Ex VP: Jennifer Miles
Sr VP: John H Andrews
Sr VP: O B Rawls
Sr VP: Ob Rawls IV
Sr VP: Douglas J Reich
Sr VP: Ronald R Rhodes
Sr VP: William Rossiter
Sr VP: Scott Tsujita
VP: Lloyd Baylard
VP: Tk Cheung
VP: Chris Dismukes
VP: Gary Franza
VP: Chris Henry
VP: Ulf Hnick
VP: Tim Jones
VP: Don Kingsborough
Board of Directors: Daniel D Diethelm, Johann J Dreyer, Keith B Geeslin, Thomas Ludwig, Ian K Marsh, Phillip J Riese, Norman Stout

HYPERCOM NETWORK SYSTEMS
See HYPERCOM CORP

D-U-N-S 14-188-3582
HYPERION CAPITAL GROUP LLC
5885 Meadows Rd Ste 850, Lake Oswego, OR 97035-8650
Tel (503) 597-1800 *Founded/Ownrshp* 2003
Sales NA *EMP* 37
Accts Schwindt & Co Portland Oreg
SIC 6162 Mortgage bankers & correspondents; Mortgage bankers & correspondents

D-U-N-S 14-482-1860
HYPERQUALITY INC
(*Suby of* INTELLISIST INC) ★
10900 Ne 8th St Ste 1101, Bellevue, WA 98004-4456
Tel (206) 428-6044 *Founded/Ownrshp* 2012
Sales 29.4MM^E *EMP* 650^E
SIC 8742 Quality assurance consultant; Quality assurance consultant
Pr: Mike Mattsen
**CEO:* Howard Lee
Ex VP: Joe Caliro
Ex VP: Urmindra Shukla
VP: Matt Bixler
VP: Stephanie Rainwater
CTO: Anil Goel
VP Sls: Pat Gamido
S&M/VP: Chrystal Lewark

HYPERTAC
See HYPERTRONICS CORP

HYPERTEC GROUP
See HYPERTEC USA INC

D-U-N-S 06-272-8590
HYPERTEC USA INC
HYPERTEC GROUP
(*Suby of* HYPERTEC SYSTEMES INC)
10601 N Frank Lloyd Wrigh, Scottsdale, AZ 85259-2659
Tel (480) 626-9000 *Founded/Ownrshp* 2006
Sales 28.9MM^E *EMP* 100
SIC 5734 5045 3577 Computer peripheral equipment; Computers, peripherals & software; Bar code (magnetic ink) printers
Pr: Robert Ahdoot
**VP:* Shan Ahdoot
VP: Reine Karam
**VP:* Mike Marracino
Off Mgr: Denise Marracino
VP Sls: Jean Carufel

D-U-N-S 05-632-9527 IMP/EXP
HYPERTHERM INC
21 Great Hollow Rd, Hanover, NH 03755-3124
Tel (603) 643-3441 *Founded/Ownrshp* 1971
Sales 571.5MM^E *EMP* 1,350
SIC 3541 Machine tools, metal cutting type; Machine tools, metal cutting type
Ch Bd: Richard W Couch Jr
**Pr:* Evan Smith
**CFO:* Cary Chan
**VP:* Barbara Couch
**VP:* Jeffrey Deckrow
**VP:* Peter Vickers
Mng Dir: Brooke Freeland
Dist Mgr: Jeff Ellingson
Dist Mgr: Tommy Hanchette
Genl Mgr: Dean Lizotte
Off Mgr: Jean Dickerson

D-U-N-S 05-348-1123
HYPERTRONICS CORP
HYPERTAC
(*Suby of* SMITHS INTERCONNECT GROUP LIMITED)
16 Brent Dr, Hudson, MA 01749-2978
Tel (978) 568-0451 *Founded/Ownrshp* 1995
Sales 58.5MM^E *EMP* 135
SIC 3678 Electronic connectors; Electronic connectors
Pr: Vadim Radunsky
CFO: Stephen Webster
**Treas:* Margaret S McDonald
VP: Garry Macdonald
IT Man: Edmund Uzar
Mtls Mgr: Judy Harris
Mfg Mgr: Stephen Sullivan
Opers Mgr: Caeser Berardinelli
Ql Cn Mgr: Mark Warshofsky
VP Sls: Rosa Chaves
Sls Mgr: Peter Osborn

D-U-N-S 09-457-2005
■ **HYPONEX CORP** (GA)
SCOTTS- HYPONEX
(*Suby of* SCOTTS CO LLC) ★
14111 Scottslawn Rd, Marysville, OH 43040-7800
Tel (937) 644-0011 *Founded/Ownrshp* 1980, 1988
Sales 444.1MM^E *EMP* 3,000
SIC 2873 2875 Fertilizers: natural (organic), except compost; Plant foods, mixed: from plants making nitrog. fertilizers; Fertilizers, mixing only; Potting soil, mixed; Fertilizers: natural (organic), except compost; Plant foods, mixed: from plants making nitrog. fertilizers; Fertilizers, mixing only; Potting soil, mixed
Pr: James Hagedorn
**CFO:* David C Evans
**Ex VP:* David M Brockman
**Ex VP:* Christopher Nagel

HYPOVEREINSBANK
See BAYERISCHE HYPO-UND VEREINSBANK INC

D-U-N-S 36-171-1542
HYPOWER INC
HY-POWER
5913 Nw 31st Ave, Fort Lauderdale, FL 33309-2207
Tel (954) 978-9300 *Founded/Ownrshp* 1991
Sales 138.9MM^E *EMP* 250
Accts Mcgladrey & Pullen Llp Fort L
SIC 1623 1731 Pipe laying construction; Electrical work; Pipe laying construction; Electrical work
Pr: Bernard Paul-Hus
**CFO:* Stephen Cassetta
**Ex VP:* Eric Paul-Hus
Sfty Dirs: David Weingarten
Mktg Dir: Petar Stoykov
Snr PM: Adam Johnson
Snr PM: John Mitcheltree

D-U-N-S 05-026-4621 IMP
HYPRO INC
600 S Jefferson St, Waterford, WI 53185-4218
Tel (608) 348-4810 *Founded/Ownrshp* 1969
Sales 382.0MM^E *EMP* 1,000
SIC 3599 Machine shop, jobbing & repair; Machine shop, jobbing & repair
Pr: Robert Schildt
CFO: Michelle Burgess
**Sec:* Dorothy Schildt
**VP:* Gary Schildt
VP: Kirk Schildt
CIO: Roy Nelson
Sfty Dirs: Terry Roberts
QC Dir: Ron Ruebensam
QC Dir: Ronald Ruebensum
Plnt Mgr: Rick Brey
Plnt Mgr: Steve Knurr

D-U-N-S 02-932-7541
HYSEN - JOHNSON FORD INC
12200 Los Osos Valley Rd, San Luis Obispo, CA 93405-7222
Tel (805) 544-5200 *Founded/Ownrshp* 1993
Sales 20.8MM^E *EMP* 75
SIC 5511 Automobiles, new & used; Automobiles, new & used
Pr: Perry Falk

D-U-N-S 82-572-4065
HYSITRON INC
9625 W 76th St Ste 150, Eden Prairie, MN 55344-3775
Tel (952) 835-6366 *Founded/Ownrshp* 1993
Sales 29.5MM^E *EMP* 125
SIC 3826 8731 3829 Analytical instruments; Commercial physical research; Measuring & controlling devices; Analytical instruments; Commercial physical research; Measuring & controlling devices
Ch Bd: Jerzy Wyrobek
**Pr:* Oden Warren
**CEO:* Thomas Wyrobek
Off Mgr: Stephanie Long
S&M/VP: Dan Carlson
Mktg Mgr: Michael Berg
Mktg Mgr: James Burkstrand
Mktg Mgr: Katie Fisher
Mktg Mgr: Randy Ward
Manager: Josh Mack
Sls Mgr: Jeffrey Rollings

D-U-N-S 04-364-7130 IMP/EXP
HYSPAN PRECISION PRODUCTS INC
1685 Brandywine Ave, Chula Vista, CA 91911-6097
Tel (619) 421-1355 *Founded/Ownrshp* 1968
Sales 94.4MM^E *EMP* 450
SIC 3568 3496 3441 Ball joints, except aircraft & automotive; Woven wire products; Expansion joints (structural shapes), iron or steel; Ball joints, except aircraft & automotive; Woven wire products; Expansion joints (structural shapes), iron or steel
Pr: Donald R Heye
**CFO:* Eric Barnes
**CFO:* Phillip Ensz

D-U-N-S 04-306-0532
HYSPECO INC
1729 S Sabin St, Wichita, KS 67209-2750
Tel (316) 943-0254 *Founded/Ownrshp* 1987
Sales 71.8MM^E *EMP* 94
SIC 5084 Hydraulic systems equipment & supplies; Pneumatic tools & equipment; Hydraulic systems equipment & supplies; Pneumatic tools & equipment
Pr: Dave Zavala
**CFO:* Bryan J Webb
VP: Ted Barney
Sls Mgr: David Tawater

HYSTER
See NACCO MATERIALS HANDLING GROUP INC

HYSTER AND YALE
See NMHG HOLDING CO

D-U-N-S 05-599-2804
HYSTER NEW ENGLAND INC
159 Rangeway Rd, North Billerica, MA 01862-2013
Tel (978) 670-3000 *Founded/Ownrshp* 1996
Sales 21.9MM^E *EMP* 175
SIC 5084 7353

D-U-N-S 60-247-2573
▲ **HYSTER-YALE MATERIALS HANDLING INC**
5875 Landerbrook Dr # 300, Cleveland, OH 44124-6511
Tel (440) 449-9600 *Founded/Ownrshp* 1989
Sales 2.7MMM *EMP* 5,400
Accts Ernst & Young Llp Cleveland
Tkr Sym HY *Exch* NYS
SIC 3537 Lift trucks, industrial: fork, platform, straddle, etc.; Lift trucks, industrial: fork, platform, straddle, etc.
Ch Bd: Alfred M Rankin Jr
CFO: Kenneth C Schilling
Treas: Brian K Frentzko
Sr VP: Lauren E Miller
Sr VP: Rajiv K Prasad
Sr VP: Victoria L Rickey
Sr VP: Harry Sands
VP: Charles A Bittenbender
VP: Jennifer M Langer
Board of Directors: Eugene Wong, J C Butler Jr, Carolyn Corvi, John P Jumper, Dennis W Labarre, Joseph Loughrey, Claiborne R Rankin, Michael E Shannon, John M Stropki, Britton T Taplin

HYTECH SPRING AND MACHINE CO.
See TOKUSEN HYTECH INC

D-U-N-S 60-590-3285
■ **HYTEK FINISHES CO**
ESTERLINE
(*Suby of* ESTERLINE TECHNOLOGIES CORP) ★
8127 S 216th St, Kent, WA 98032-1996
Tel (253) 872-7160 *Founded/Ownrshp* 1989
Sales 32.5MM^E *EMP* 200
SIC 3471 Cleaning, polishing & finishing; Cleaning, polishing & finishing
CEO: Curtis C Reusser
**Pr:* Alain Durand
**VP:* Robert D George
**VP:* Tom Heine
**VP:* Marcia J Mason
QC Dir: Eric Carlson

D-U-N-S 09-347-1431
HYTERA AMERICA INC
(*Suby of* HYTERA COMMUNICATIONS CORPORATION LIMITED)
3315 Commerce Pkwy, Miramar, FL 33025-3954
Tel (954) 846-1011 *Founded/Ownrshp* 1979
Sales 23.0MM^E *EMP* 22
SIC 5065 Communication equipment; Communication equipment
Pr: Zhenhai Zhao
**VP:* Carlos Cordova
Mktg Mgr: Eric Izurieta
Sls Mgr: Janine Rives

HYTORC DIVISION
See UNEX CORP

D-U-N-S 96-294-4950
HYTORC WIND LIMITED LIABILITY CO
218 Island Rd, Mahwah, NJ 07430
Tel (201) 512-9500 *Founded/Ownrshp* 2009
Sales 29.0MM^E *EMP* 50
SIC 5084 Hydraulic systems equipment & supplies
CEO: John Junkers
Genl Mgr: Stephen Clark
Off Mgr: Tangi Banks

HYUNDAI
See GATEWAY MOTORS INC

HYUNDAI
See HILLCREST FORD LINCOLN-MERCURY INC

HYUNDAI - ISUZU
See HYATT AUTOMOTIVE LLC

D-U-N-S 16-106-9646
HYUNDAI AMERICA TECHNICAL CENTER INC
HATCI
(*Suby of* HYUNDAI MOTOR COMPANY)
6800 Geddes Rd, Ypsilanti, MI 48198-9670
Tel (734) 337-2500 *Founded/Ownrshp* 1986
Sales 51.2MM^E *EMP* 145
SIC 8711 8734 Designing: ship, boat, machine & product; Automobile proving & testing ground; Designing: ship, boat, machine & product; Automobile proving & testing ground
Pr: Won Suk Cho

**Treas:* Seong Song
Mng Dir: John Suh
Ql Cn Mgr: Tyler Dennis
Ql Cn Mgr: Mike Dziamski
Counsel: Zach Dunlap
Snr Mgr: Joel Crowell
Snr Mgr: Paul Haight
Snr Mgr: John Juriga
Snr Mgr: Gary Kozlowski
Snr Mgr: Dae OH

D-U-N-S 60-739-7783
HYUNDAI CAPITAL AMERICA
HYUNDAI FINANCE
(*Suby of* HYUNDAI MOTOR AMERICA) ★
3161 Michelson Dr # 1900, Irvine, CA 92612-4418
Tel (714) 965-3000 *Founded/Ownrshp* 1989
Sales NA *EMP* 540ᴱ
SIC 6141 Automobile loans, including insurance; Automobile loans, including insurance
CEO: Sam Sanghyuk Suh
Pr: Rick Christensen
**Pr:* Sukjoon Won
**CEO:* Jwa Jin Cho
COO: Daniel Kwon
**CFO:* Minsok Randy Park
VP: Kwansun Ahn
VP: Katherine Cassidy
VP: James Cisneros
VP: Annie Fallows
VP: Hristo Malchev
VP: Carol Moore
VP: Pierric Senay
VP: Min Sok
VP: Bryan Utley
VP: Adem Yilmaz
VP: David Zuchowski

HYUNDAI CONSTRUCTION EQP USA
See HYUNDAI CONSTRUCTION EQUIPMENT AMERICAS INC

D-U-N-S 84-743-2135
HYUNDAI CONSTRUCTION EQUIPMENT AMERICAS INC
HYUNDAI CONSTRUCTION EQP USA
(*Suby of* HYUNDAI HEAVY INDUSTRIES CO., LTD.)
6100 Atlantic Blvd, Norcross, GA 30071-1305
Tel (877) 509-2254 *Founded/Ownrshp* 1991
Sales 36.3MMᴱ *EMP* 65ᴱ
SIC 5082 Construction & mining machinery
Pr: Ms Kang
**VP:* Kirk Gillette
VP: Chuck Leone
**Prin:* John Lim

HYUNDAI FINANCE
See HYUNDAI CAPITAL AMERICA

D-U-N-S 94-937-1116 IMP/EXP
HYUNDAI IDEAL ELECTRIC CO
IDEAL ELECTRIC COMPANY
(*Suby of* HYUNDAI HEAVY INDUSTRIES CO., LTD.)
330 E 1st St, Mansfield, OH 44902-7756
Tel (419) 520-3314 *Founded/Ownrshp* 2007
Sales 70.0MM *EMP* 208
Accts Deloitte And Touche Llp Chica
SIC 3621 3613 3625 Generators & sets, electric; Motors, electric; Switchgear & switchgear accessories; Relays & industrial controls; Generators & sets, electric; Motors, electric; Switchgear & switchgear accessories; Relays & industrial controls
Pr: Justin Lim
Treas: Suyong Ham
**Treas:* Albert Ohk
VP: Harry Lim
VP: Robert Ortasic
CIO: Robert Blankenhorn
IT Man: Janet Durre
Plnt Mgr: Mike Buck
Ql Cn Mgr: Erin Rankin

D-U-N-S 61-471-1760 IMP/EXP
HYUNDAI MERCHANT MARINE (AMERICA) INC
(*Suby of* UNDAI MERCHANT MARINE CO., LTD.??)
222 Las Colinas Blvd W, Irving, TX 75039-5421
Tel (972) 501-1100 *Founded/Ownrshp* 1982
Sales 86.4MMᴱ *EMP* 520
Accts Kpmg Llp Los Angeles Ca
SIC 4731 Agents, shipping; Agents, shipping
CEO: Seock Dong Lee
Sr VP: Brian Black
VP: Stephen Barnett
VP: David Kalata
VP: Lamont Petersen
VP: Hyunjong Shin
IT Man: Young Hong
Sls Mgr: C W Lee
Sales Asso: Murry Shipman
Snr Mgr: Yh Park
Board of Directors: Jae Lee

D-U-N-S 13-193-6494 IMP/EXP
HYUNDAI MOTOR AMERICA
(*Suby of* HYUNDAI MOTOR COMPANY)
10550 Talbert Ave, Fountain Valley, CA 92708-6032
Tel (714) 965-3000 *Founded/Ownrshp* 1985
Sales 416.3MMᴱ *EMP* 600
Accts Kpmg Llp Los Angeles Califor
SIC 5013 5511 6141 6153 Automotive supplies & parts; Automobiles, new & used; Automobile & consumer finance companies; Short-term business credit; Automotive supplies & parts; Automobiles, new & used; Automobile & consumer finance companies; Short-term business credit
Pr: David Zuchowski
CEO: B H Lee
CEO: Gail Lee
CFO: J Suh
Ofcr: Paul Koh
Ex VP: Jerry Flannary
VP: Bill Demaree
VP: Derrick Hatami
VP: Michael O'Brien
Dir Risk M: Kenneth Gang
VP Admn: John Krafcik
Board of Directors: J K Choi, M K Chung, N M Kim, K A Lee

D-U-N-S 11-001-2890 IMP/EXP
HYUNDAI MOTOR MANUFACTURING ALABAMA LLC
HMMA
(*Suby of* HYUNDAI MOTOR COMPANY)
700 Hyundai Blvd, Montgomery, AL 36105-9626
Tel (334) 387-8000 *Founded/Ownrshp* 2002
Sales 71.8MMᴱ *EMP* 3,300
SIC 5511 Automobiles, new & used; Automobiles, new & used
Pr: Young Deuk Lim
CFO: Lashanda Griffin
VP: John Kalson
VP: Byung-Kwan Kim
VP: Moon-Hee Lee
IT Man: Khang Martin
Ql Cn Mgr: Yvette Gilkey-Shuford
Ql Cn Mgr: Chris Horton
Secur Mgr: Larry Pugh
Secur Mgr: Cassandra Williams
Sales Asso: Kevin Ohnemus

HYUNDAI OF EL PASO
See SOUTHWEST HYUNDAI LP

D-U-N-S 13-583-1811
HYUNDAI OF NEW PORT RICHEY LLC
3936 Us Highway 19, New Port Richey, FL 34652-6152
Tel (727) 569-0999 *Founded/Ownrshp* 2002
Sales 239.0MM *EMP* 85
SIC 5511 7549 Automobiles, new & used; Automotive maintenance services; Automobiles, new & used; Automotive maintenance services
**CFO:* Michael R Macarthur
Sls Mgr: Warren Blackburn
Sls Mgr: Alan Wooldrige

D-U-N-S 05-047-8424
HYUNDAI OF TEMPE LLC (AZ)
8050 S Autoplex Loop, Tempe, AZ 85284-1007
Tel (480) 961-4800 *Founded/Ownrshp* 2001
Sales 26.0MMᴱ *EMP* 75
SIC 5511 Automobiles, new & used; Automobiles, new & used
Genl Mgr: Mike Wasserman
IT Man: Eric Barcus

D-U-N-S 02-465-4599
HYUNDAI OF WESLEY CHAPEL LLC
3936 Us Highway 19, New Port Richey, FL 34652-6152
Tel (813) 751-0999 *Founded/Ownrshp* 2007
Sales 27.0MM *EMP* 35
SIC 5511 Automobiles, new & used; Automobiles, new & used

D-U-N-S 05-471-0916 IMP
HYUNDAI POWER TRANSFORMERS USA INC
215 Folmar Pkwy, Montgomery, AL 36105-5513
Tel (334) 481-2000 *Founded/Ownrshp* 2010
Sales 53.2MMᴱ *EMP* 101
SIC 3612 Transformers, except electric
Pr: Gyou Chul Lee
**CFO:* Hyung Jo Ahn
QA Dir: Leonardo Moreno
Sales Asso: Kat Collins

D-U-N-S 61-453-1622 IMP
HYUNDAI TRANSLEAD
(*Suby of* HYUNDAI MOTOR COMPANY)
8880 Rio San Diego Dr # 600, San Diego, CA 92108-1634
Tel (619) 574-1500 *Founded/Ownrshp* 1989
Sales 664.1MMᴱ *EMP* 2,092
SIC 3443 3715 3412 Industrial vessels, tanks & containers; Semitrailers for truck tractors; Metal barrels, drums & pails; Industrial vessels, tanks & containers; Semitrailers for truck tractors; Metal barrels, drums & pails
CEO: KS Lee
**COO:* Glen Harney
CFO: Steve Choi
**CFO:* Sb Yoon
Sr VP: Gihwan Kim
VP: Sung-SOO Park
VP: Brian Prall
VP: Garry Shidler
VP: Howard Yurgevich
Genl Mgr: Younghag Choi
Genl Mgr: Rogelio Lapez

D-U-N-S 61-023-1099 IMP
HYUNDAM AMERICA INC
(*Suby of* HYUNDAM INDUSTRIAL CO., LTD.)
195a Commerce Ctr, Greenville, SC 29615-5817
Tel (864) 288-3008 *Founded/Ownrshp* 2004
Sales 44.1MM *EMP* 28
SIC 3465 Automotive stampings; Automotive stampings

D-U-N-S 10-163-4160
HZ INDUSTRIES INC
706 Bond Ave Nw, Grand Rapids, MI 49503-1434
Tel (616) 453-4491 *Founded/Ownrshp* 1985
Sales 50.0MM *EMP* 350
SIC 3469 3495 Machine parts, stamped or pressed metal; Wire springs; Machine parts, stamped or pressed metal; Wire springs
Ch Bd: James J Zawacki
**Pr:* Merele Emery

I

I & E TECHNOLOGIES
See INSTRUMENTATION & ELECTRICAL TECHNOLOGIES LLC

I & G BELLEVUE
See LASALLE INCOME & GROWTH FUND IV

I & K DISTRIBUTORS
See COUNTRYSIDE FOODS LLC

D-U-N-S 06-890-5272
I & M J GROSS CO
GROSS BUILDERS
14300 Ridge Rd Ste 100, Cleveland, OH 44133-4936
Tel (440) 237-1681 *Founded/Ownrshp* 1916
Sales 92.4MMᴱ *EMP* 200
SIC 1522 Multi-family dwellings, new construction; Multi-family dwellings, new construction
Pr: Gary Gross
**VP:* Harley Gross
Genl Mgr: Dick Devaney
Off Mgr: Debbie Baran
Opers Mgr: Linda Brooks
Opers Mgr: Nicole Lacianci
Opers Mgr: Christopher Sheely
Sls&Mrk Ex: Kris Kutz
Mktg Dir: Beth Bakker

D-U-N-S 11-987-9729
I & S ACQUISITION CORP
(*Suby of* INGLETT & STUBBS INTERNATIONAL HOLDINGS PTY LIMITED)
5200 Riverview Rd Se, Mableton, GA 30126-2953
Tel (404) 881-1199 *Founded/Ownrshp* 2005
Sales 167.5MMᴱ *EMP* 1,455ᴱ
SIC 1731 General electrical contractor; General electrical contractor
Pr: Jeffrey Giglio
**CFO:* Kimberly Warren
**VP:* J Terry Frierson

I 2 M
See CRESTWOOD MEMBRANES INC

I 3
See INTEGRATION INNOVATION INC

I 5 TOYOTA SCION
See UHLMANN MOTORS INC

I A C
See INDUSTRIAL ACOUSTICS CO INC

I A C
See IAC TROY LLC

I A C
See IRVINE APARTMENT COMMUNITIES LP

D-U-N-S 94-456-5811
I A C GROUP INC
2400 W 75th St Ste 201, Shawnee Mission, KS 66208-3511
Tel (913) 432-1451 *Founded/Ownrshp* 1995
Sales NA *EMP* 200
SIC 6311 6321 Life insurance; Accident & health insurance; Life insurance; Accident & health insurance
Pr: Robert E Stroud
Treas: Charles E Cain
Ex VP: Sue Ann Wright
Sr VP: Ronald F Jones

D-U-N-S 80-826-4027 EXP
I A C SPRINGFIELD LLC
INTERNTNL AUTOMOTVE COMPONENTS
(*Suby of* IAC GROUP) ★
801 Bill Jones Indus Dr, Springfield, TN 37172-5014
Tel (615) 384-6265 *Founded/Ownrshp* 2007
Sales 22.4MMᴱ *EMP* 170
SIC 3089 Automotive parts, plastic; Automotive parts, plastic
Pr: James K Kamsickas

I A I
See INTERNATIONAL ASSEMBLY INC

D-U-N-S 07-779-3842
I A M NATIONAL PENSION FUND
1300 Conn Ave Nw Ste 300, Washington, DC 20036-1707
Tel (202) 785-2658 *Founded/Ownrshp* 1960
Sales NA *EMP* 130
SIC 6371 Pension funds
**CFO:* Lori Kuan

I A P
See INTEGRATED AGRIBUSINESS PROFESSIONALS COOPERATIVE INC

I A S
See INSURANCE ADMINISTRATIVE SOLUTIONS LLC

I A S
See INTEGRATED ARCHIVE SYSTEMS INC

I AT
See ILLINOIS AUTO TRUCK CO INC

D-U-N-S 00-286-6630
I B ABEL INC (GA)
620 Edgar St, York, PA 17403-2854
Tel (717) 845-1639 *Founded/Ownrshp* 1913
Sales 53.7MMᴱ *EMP* 100
SIC 1731 General electrical contractor; General electrical contractor
Pr: Patrick A Kinsley
**Ch Bd:* Robert Kinsley
**CFO:* Mathew Poff
CFO: Jeff Zarfoss
**Sec:* Mary Linebaugh
VP: Denny Geiger
VP: Willard Wolf
Exec: Thomas Tacconelli

I B B
See INTERNATIONAL BULLION AND METAL BROKERS (USA) INC

I B C
See INTERNATIONAL BONDED COURIERS INC

D-U-N-S 07-589-7397
I B E W LOCAL 1 APPRENTICE & TRAINING FUND
ELECTRICAL INDUST TRAINING CTR
3260 Hampton Ave, Saint Louis, MO 63139-2357
Tel (314) 752-2330 *Founded/Ownrshp* 1941
Sales 57.8MM *EMP* 10
SIC 8249 1731 Trade school; Electrical work; Trade school; Electrical work

D-U-N-S 00-467-6857
I B E W LOCAL 1249 INSURANCE FUND
6518 Fremont Rd, East Syracuse, NY 13057-9441
Tel (315) 656-8390 *Founded/Ownrshp* 2008
Sales NA *EMP* 1
SIC 6371 Pensions; Pensions
Prin: William Boire

I B M L
See IMAGING BUSINESS MACHINES LLC

D-U-N-S 08-019-2883
I B M SOUTHEAST EMPLOYEES FEDERAL CREDIT UNION
790 Park Of Commerce Blvd, Boca Raton, FL 33487-3619
Tel (561) 982-4700 *Founded/Ownrshp* 1969
Sales NA *EMP* 235
SIC 6061 Federal credit unions; Federal credit unions
Pr: Larry B Mc Cants
**CFO:* Lynn Wilderman
**Ch:* Donald Lee
Treas: James Dorman
IT Man: William C Sarborough

I B S
See IRWIN BUILDERS SUPPLY CORP

I B S
See INTERACTIVE BUSINESS SYSTEMS INC

I B S
See IBS ENTERPRISE USA INC

D-U-N-S 08-417-3764
I B S A INC
INDEPENDENT BUILDERS SUP ASSN
1801 Wal Pat Rd, Smithfield, NC 27577-9436
Tel (919) 934-7616 *Founded/Ownrshp* 1977
Sales 55.7MMᴱ *EMP* 40
SIC 5031 5033 Lumber, plywood & millwork; Roofing, siding & insulation
Pr: Tim Johnson
**Ch Bd:* Ray Gaster
**Pr:* Ray Price
**CFO:* Bert Radford
**Sec:* Mike Christain
**VP:* Johnny Hicks

I B S DIRECT
See INTERNATIONAL BUSINESS SYSTEMS INC

I BT
See INTERNATIONAL BROTHERHOOD OF TEAMSTERS

D-U-N-S 13-100-4962
I BT LOCAL 191
I BT LOCAL 191 HLTH SVC/INSUR
1139 Fairfield Ave Ste 1, Bridgeport, CT 06605-4109
Tel (203) 366-5849 *Founded/Ownrshp* 1954
Sales 20.4MM *EMP* 12
SIC 8631 Labor union; Labor union
Pr: Joseph Bennetta

I BT LOCAL 191 HLTH SVC/INSUR
See I BT LOCAL 191

I B-TECH
See IMASEN BUCYRUS TECHNOLOGY INC

I BEIGEL BAKING CO
See SGFW BAKERS INC

I C
See I C SYSTEM INC

I, C & E RAILROAD
See IOWA CHICAGO & EASTERN RAILROAD CORP

I C A
See INFRASTRUCTURE CORP OF AMERICA

I C A NN
See INTERNET CORP FOR ASSIGNED NAMES AND NUMBERS

I C B A
See INDEPENDENT COMMUNITY BANKERS OF AMERICA

I C B S
See INTER-COMMERCIAL BUSINESS SYSTEMS INC

I C C
See ILLINOIS CENTRAL COLLEGE

I C C
See INTERNATIONAL CODE COUNCIL INC

I C C
See INTERSTATE CONNECTING COMPONENTS INC

I C C
See INNOVATIVE COMMUNICATION CONCEPTS INC

D-U-N-S 14-717-9717 IMP
I C CLASS COMPONENTS CORP
CLASSIC
23605 Telo Ave, Torrance, CA 90505-4028
Tel (310) 539-5500 *Founded/Ownrshp* 1985
Sales 86.7MMᴱ *EMP* 250
SIC 5065 Electronic parts & equipment; Electronic parts & equipment
Pr: Jeff Klein
**COO:* Chris Klein
**COO:* Kris Klein
CFO: Nasser Shamsian
**Sec:* Emma Klein
VP: Joseph Jareck
**VP:* Perry Klein
**VP:* Ray Liston
Brnch Mgr: Carlos Ismerio
Dir IT: Daniel Lee
IT Man: Al C Camacho

D-U-N-S 80-288-8107
I C E SERVICES INC
2606 C St, Anchorage, AK 99503-2640
Tel (907) 644-0385 *Founded/Ownrshp* 1986
Sales 13.1MMᴱ *EMP* 450

SIC 5812 7349 Caterers; Janitorial service, contract basis; Hospital housekeeping; Cleaning service, industrial or commercial
Pr: Thomas Bourdon
Sec: Deborah Bourdon

I C G
See INTERNATIONAL CASINGS GROUP INC

I C GROUP
See IC SECURITY PRINTERS INC — MARKETING

I C I
See INVESTMENT CO INSTITUTE

I C I
See INTERVEST CONSTRUCTION OF ORLANDO INC

I C I
See INTERNATIONAL CRANKSHAFT INC

I C L
See INDEPENDENT CONTAINER LINE LIMITED

I C M
See INTERNATIONAL CREATIVE MANAGEMENT INC

I C M
See INDUSTRIAL CONSTRUCTORS/MANAGERS INC

I C M
See INDEPENDENT CAPITAL MANAGEMENT INC

I C O
See INTER CITY OIL CO INC

I C P R JUNIOR COLLEGE
See INSTITUTO COMERCIAL DE PUERTO RICO INC

I C S
See INFORMATION & COMPUTING SERVICES INC

I C S
See INTEGRATED CIRCUIT SYSTEMS INC

I C S
See INFINITY CONSULTING SOLUTIONS INC

I C S
See ICS NETT INC

I C S
See INNOVATIVE CONTROL SYSTEMS INC

I C S
See INTERNATIONAL CONTROL SERVICES INC

I C S GENERAL CONTRACTORS
See C S I INC

D-U-N-S 07-135-1985
I C SYSTEM INC (MN)
I C
444 Highway 96 E, Saint Paul, MN 55127-2557
Tel (651) 483-8201 *Founded/Ownrshp* 1941
Sales 88.9MM^E *EMP* 1,000
SIC 7322

I CT
See INNOVATIVE CHEMICAL TECHNOLOGIES INC

D-U-N-S 04-811-6891
I C THOMASSON ASSOCIATES INC (TN)
2950 Kraft Dr Ste 500, Nashville, TN 37204-3683
Tel (615) 346-3400 *Founded/Ownrshp* 1942
Sales 25.5MM *EMP* 160
SIC 8711 Consulting engineer; Consulting engineer
Ch Bd: George R Bratton
**Pr:* Joseph J Wimberly IV
**Treas:* William Tinnell
**Sr VP:* Cliff Harville
Sys Mgr: Daniel Gunter

I C W
See INSURANCE CO OF WEST

D-U-N-S 13-657-1325 IMP
I CERCO INC
DIAMONITE PLANT
453 W Mcconkey St, Shreve, OH 44676-9769
Tel (330) 567-2145 *Founded/Ownrshp* 2003
Sales 56.9MM^E *EMP* 300
SIC 3567 Ceramic kilns & furnaces; Ceramic kilns & furnaces
Pr: Byron Anderson
COO: Jim Jaskowiak
Ql Cn Mgr: Sharen Brigham

I COMM SOLUTIONS
See INTOUCH WIRELESS

D-U-N-S 00-891-5613
I D BOOTH INC (NY)
BOOTH ELECTRICAL SUPPLY DIV
620 William St, Elmira, NY 14901-2545
Tel (607) 733-9121 *Founded/Ownrshp* 1875, 1958
Sales 33.8MM *EMP* 142
SIC 5074 5085 5063 5072 5169 Plumbing & hydronic heating supplies; Pipes & fittings, plastic; Boilers, power (industrial); Industrial supplies; Electrical construction materials; Electrical supplies; Hardware; Nuts (hardware); Bolts; Screws; Salts, industrial; Plumbing & hydronic heating supplies; Pipes & fittings, plastic; Boilers, power (industrial); Industrial supplies; Electrical construction materials; Electrical supplies; Hardware; Nuts (hardware); Bolts; Screws; Salts, industrial
Pr: John Seeley Booth Jr
**VP:* John S Booth III
**VP:* Peter S Booth
Brnch Mgr: Bob Torrey
Sls Mgr: Adam Bowes
Sls Mgr: Mike Herrick
Sls Mgr: Jeff Monroe
Sales Asso: David Sawyer

I D C
See IDC RESEARCH INC

I D C
See INDUSTRIAL DOOR CONTRACTORS INC

I D C
See INDUSTRIAL DESIGN & CONSTRUCTION INC

D-U-N-S 07-177-5779
I D D D INC
TRUCKERS INN
6162 Us Highway 51, Deforest, WI 53532-2958
Tel (608) 246-3040 *Founded/Ownrshp* 1977
Sales 29.7MM^E *EMP* 100
SIC 5541 5812 Truck stops; Diner; Truck stops; Diner
Pr: Dean Mantel
**Sec:* Ingred Mantel

D-U-N-S 06-330-5734
I D E A INC
1 Idea Way, Caldwell, ID 83605-6999
Tel (208) 459-6357 *Founded/Ownrshp* 1969
Sales 27.6MM^E *EMP* 105
SIC 2752 Commercial printing, lithographic; Commercial printing, lithographic
Ch Bd: Robert McDonagh
**CEO:* Paul L Kaye
**VP:* Anita Kiser
Sfty Mgr: Sally Warner

I D F
See INTERNATIONAL DEHYDRATED FOODS INC

I D G
See INDUSTRIAL DISTRIBUTION GROUP INC

I D I
See INTRASTATE DISTRIBUTORS INC

D-U-N-S 17-712-8295
I D INDUSTRIES INC
2755 E Philadelphia St, Ontario, CA 91761-8547
Tel (909) 591-9597 *Founded/Ownrshp* 1987
Sales 31.5MM^E *EMP* 36
Accts Brendzel & Company Upland Ca
SIC 5084 Hydraulic systems equipment & supplies
Pr: Ramiro Donoso
**VP:* Linda Donoso
Off Mgr: Candy McLain

I D L
See RYAN DIRECTIONAL SERVICES INC

I D M CONTROLS
See OMRON OILFIELD AND MARINE INC

D-U-N-S 00-652-8335 IMP
I D N - HARDWARE SALES INC
IDN DOOR AND HARDWARE
(*Suby of* H HOFFMAN IDN INC) ★
35950 Industrial Rd, Livonia, MI 48150-1274
Tel (734) 466-4088 *Founded/Ownrshp* 1994
Sales 22.9MM^E *EMP* 64
SIC 5087 Locksmith equipment & supplies; Locksmith equipment & supplies
Pr: Arnold Goldman
**Sec:* Dan Loewe
**VP:* Alvin M Hoffman
**VP:* Karen Hoffman
Sls Mgr: Neil Cronk

I D PENNOCK BRANCH
See YMCA OF ROCK RIVER VALLEY

I D T
See INTEGRATED DNA TECHNOLOGIES INC

I D W
See INNOVATIVE DISPLAYWORKS INC

I E A
See IMPERIAL ELECTRONIC ASSEMBLY INC

I E A
See INFRASTRUCTURE AND ENERGY ALTERNATIVES LLC

I E C
See WALKER COMPONENT GROUP INC

I E I
See IEI GENERAL CONTRACTORS INC

I E I
See INTERCONTINENTAL EXPORT IMPORT INC

D-U-N-S 10-244-1169
I E MILLER OF EUNICE INC
I.E. MILLER & COMPANY
826 Industrial Rd, Eunice, LA 70535-3934
Tel (337) 457-2216 *Founded/Ownrshp* 2011
Sales NA *EMP* 430
SIC 4213

I E R INDUSTRIES
See IER FUJIKURA INC

I F A
See INTERMOUNTAIN FARMERS ASSOCIATION

I F A
See INDEPENDENT FINANCIAL AGENTS INC

I F A C
See INTERNATIONAL FEDERATION OF ACCOUNTANTS

I F C
See INDUSTRIAL FUMIGANT CO LLC

I F C O SYSTEMS
See IFCO SYSTEMS NORTH AMERICA INC

I F H
See INSTITUTION FOOD HOUSE INC

I F N
See INDIANA FIBER NETWORK LLC

I F T
See ILLINOIS FEDERATION OF TEACHERS

I G BURTON IMPORTS
See IG BURTON & CO INC

D-U-N-S 01-206-9043
I G FEDERAL ELECTRICAL SUPPLY CORP (NY)
4720 30th St, Long Island City, NY 11101-3444
Tel (718) 729-5700 *Founded/Ownrshp* 1932
Sales 63.2MM^E *EMP* 58
Accts Israeloff Trattner & Co Pc
SIC 5063 Electrical supplies; Wiring devices; Electrical supplies; Wiring devices
CEO: Meryl R Berger
Sec: Jodi B Ehren
Ex VP: Ira M Friedman

I G I
See INTERNATIONAL GROUP INC

I G M
See INTERNATIONAL GRANITE & MARBLE CORP

I G T
See INTERNATIONAL GAME TECHNOLOGY INC

D-U-N-S 94-851-2116
■ I GENCO INC
GENCO ATC
(*Suby of* GENCO ATC) ★
100 Papercraft Park, Pittsburgh, PA 15238-3200
Tel (800) 677-3110 *Founded/Ownrshp* 1995
Sales 292.5MM^E *EMP* 1,000
SIC 4225 4111 5045 General warehousing & storage; Local & suburban transit; Computers, peripherals & software; General warehousing & storage; Local & suburban transit; Computers, peripherals & software
Prin: Arthur Smuck
**Pr:* David Mabon
Pr: John Marx
**Pr:* Joseph Salamunovich
**Pr:* Andy Smith
**CEO:* Laurie Barkman
**CEO:* Todd R Peters
**COO:* Art Smuck
**CFO:* Rick Roadarmel
**Ch:* Herb Shear
**Ex VP:* Pete Rector
VP: Marc Sherman
Dir Bus: Rich Otterman

D-U-N-S 55-651-8181
I GRACE CO INC
37-18 Nthrn Blvd Ste 500, Long Island City, NY 11101
Tel (212) 987-1900 *Founded/Ownrshp* 1988
Sales 51.2MM *EMP* 115
Accts Anchin Block & Anchin Llp Ne
SIC 8741 7299 Construction management; Home improvement & renovation contractor agency
CEO: David J Cohen
**COO:* Keith D Kirkpatrick
Mng Dir: Timothy Hanes
Mng Dir: Ron Johns
Dir IT: Benjamin BJ Lambert
Snr PM: Nick Angione
Snr PM: Ron Ortiz
Snr Mgr: Andon George

I H A
See ILLINOIS HOSPITAL ASSOCIATION

I H C
See INTERSTATE HIGHWAY CONSTRUCTION INC

I H D
See INDUSTRIAL HARDWARE DISTRIBUTORS INC

I H G
See SIX CONTINENTS HOTELS INC

D-U-N-S 05-417-0204
I H MISSISSIPPI VALLEY CREDIT UNION
2121 47th St, Moline, IL 61265-3663
Tel (309) 793-6200 *Founded/Ownrshp* 1936
Sales NA *EMP* 200
SIC 6062 State credit unions, not federally chartered; State credit unions, not federally chartered
Pr: Dennis Hall
**Sec:* Eli McDermand
Ofcr: Laurie Burkholder
Ofcr: Crystal Cutkomp
Ofcr: Jeff Hitt
Ofcr: Brittany McAninch
Ofcr: Josh Peterson
Ofcr: Brook Viktor
Ofcr: Christine Wiegel
Ofcr: Lindsay Williams
Sr VP: Kristi Riffe
VP: Morgan Dunn
**VP:* Randy Neumann

I H P
See IHP INDUSTRIAL INC

D-U-N-S 79-387-0700
I HERITAGE INC
HERITAGE MAZDA
(*Suby of* ATLANTIC AUTOMOTIVE CORP) ★
1 Olympic Pl Ste 700, Towson, MD 21204-4112
Tel (410) 356-2277 *Founded/Ownrshp* 1991
Sales 21.7MM^E *EMP* 70
SIC 5511 Automobiles, new & used; Automobiles, new & used
Pr: Jerome Fader

D-U-N-S 04-909-7203
I HOSPITAL
2108 W Kennedy Blvd, Tampa, FL 33606-1535
Tel (813) 286-2120 *Founded/Ownrshp* 2010
Sales 8.0MM^E *EMP* 303^E
SIC 8062 General medical & surgical hospitals
Prin: Ross J Newman
CFO: Brenden Crampton

I I C
See INDOTRONIX INTERNATIONAL CORP

I I D
See IMPERIAL IRRIGATION DISTRICT

I I F
See IIF DATA SOLUTIONS INC

I I R
See INSTITUTE FOR INTERGOVERNMENTAL RESEARCH IN

I I T
See ILLINOIS INSTITUTE OF TECHNOLOGY

D-U-N-S 00-121-1275
I J WHITE CORP (NY)
20 Executive Blvd, Farmingdale, NY 11735-4710
Tel (631) 293-3788 *Founded/Ownrshp* 1919
Sales 23.2MM^E *EMP* 70
SIC 3556 3535 Food products machinery; Conveyors & conveying equipment
Ch Bd: Peter J White
VP: Joyce Bridges
Mtls Mgr: Nick Oster
Plnt Mgr: Roy Berntsen
VP Sls: Jim Souza

I K E A
See IKEA TRADING SERVICES INC

I K ELECTRIC COMPANY
See JSK CO INC

I K O
See GOLDIS ENTERPRISES INC

I K O PRODUCTIONS
See GOLDIS HOLDINGS INC

I. KEATING FURNITURE WORLD
See I KEATING INC

D-U-N-S 03-185-3393 IMP
I KEATING INC
I. KEATING FURNITURE WORLD
10 S Broadway, Minot, ND 58701-3816
Tel (701) 852-3536 *Founded/Ownrshp* 1961
Sales 43.2MM *EMP* 162
SIC 5712 5713 Furniture stores; Bedding & bedsprings; Mattresses; Waterbeds & accessories; Floor covering stores; Carpets; Floor tile; Linoleum; Household appliance stores; Electric household appliances, major; Furniture stores; Bedding & bedsprings; Mattresses; Waterbeds & accessories; Floor covering stores; Carpets; Floor tile; Linoleum
Pr: Chuck Kramer
**Treas:* Matthew Kramer
**Sec:* Tim Kramer
**VP:* Mark Kramer

D-U-N-S 61-638-8976
I KESTREL ACQUISITION CORP
1035 Swabia Ct, Durham, NC 27703-8462
Tel (919) 990-7500 *Founded/Ownrshp* 2005
Sales 551.3MM^E *EMP* 1,567
SIC 2821 2822 2869 2899 2891 2851 Plastics materials & resins; Butadiene-acrylonitrile, nitrile rubbers, NBR; Vinyl acetate; Rosin sizes; Adhesives; Paints & allied products; Plastics materials & resins; Butadiene-acrylonitrile, nitrile rubbers, NBR; Vinyl acetate; Rosin sizes; Adhesives; Paints & allied products
Ch Bd: John S Gaither
**COO:* Douglas E Frey
**CFO:* Roger L Willis
VP: Bethy Cassidy

D-U-N-S 36-409-4821 IMP
I KRUGER INC
(*Suby of* VEOLIA WATER TECHNOLOGIES) ★
4001 Weston Pkwy, Cary, NC 27513-2311
Tel (919) 677-8310 *Founded/Ownrshp* 2005
Sales 75.4MM^E *EMP* 122^E
SIC 5084 Pollution control equipment, water (environmental); Pollution control equipment, water (environmental)
Pr: Mike Gutshall
**Treas:* Leigh A Joyce
VP: Sun Hong
**VP:* Sun-Nan Hong
VP: Joy Lipinski
Dir IT: Mario Silva
IT Man: Sherri Moore
Site Mgr: Elmer Williams
Mktg Dir: Denisse Ike
Manager: Ken Krupa
Sls Mgr: Brian Frewerg

D-U-N-S 02-682-0159
I KUNIK CO
2000 Industrial Dr, McAllen, TX 78504-4003
Tel (956) 686-4324 *Founded/Ownrshp* 2007
Sales 25.4MM *EMP* 225
SIC 5148

I L 2000
See INTEGRATED LOGISTICS 2000 LLC

I L B
See INTERNATIONAL LINE BUILDERS INC

I L C
See ILC INDUSTRIES LLC

D-U-N-S 05-349-1247
I L LONG CONSTRUCTION CO INC
4117 Indiana Ave, Winston Salem, NC 27105-3460
Tel (336) 661-1616 *Founded/Ownrshp* 1969
Sales 69.3MM^E *EMP* 140
SIC 1542 1541 1521 Nonresidential construction; Industrial buildings & warehouses; Single-family housing construction; Nonresidential construction; Industrial buildings & warehouses; Single-family housing construction
VP: Edwin L Welch Jr
**Treas:* Sue Welch
**VP:* Robert E Welch
Exec: Dolly Llewellyn

I L S
See SUPPLY TECHNOLOGIES LLC

I L W U
See INTERNATIONAL LONGSHORE & WAREHOUSE UNION

I M A
See INDIANAPOLIS MUSEUM OF ART INC

I M A
See IMA DAIRY & FOOD USA INC

I M A
See INTEGRATED MANUFACTURING & ASSEMBLY LLC

I M A TOOL DISTRIBUTORS
See ROBERTS TOOL & SUPPLY CO INC

I M E A
See ILLINOIS MUNICIPAL ELECTRIC AGENCY

I M G
See INTERNATIONAL MEDICAL GROUP INC

I M I
See IRVING MATERIALS INC

I M N G
See INTERNATIONAL MEDICAL NEWS GROUP LLC

I M S
See INTEGREON MANAGED SOLUTIONS INC

I M S ELECTONICS RECYCLING
See IMS ELECTRONICS RECYCLING INC

I M S G
See IM SYSTEMS GROUP INC

I M S STEEL
See CCC STEEL INC

I MARLIN
See MARLIN NETWORK INC

D-U-N-S 06-384-1526
I MEGLIO CORP
151 Alkier St, Brentwood, NY 11717-5135
Tel (631) 617-6900 *Founded/Ownrshp* 2013
Sales 67.0MM *EMP* 30
SIC 2431 5031 Millwork; Millwork
Pr: Barbara Khanat
**VP:* David Suarez

D-U-N-S 14-181-9578
I N C BUILDERS INC
ACME STAFFING
550 E 32nd St Ste 2, Yuma, AZ 85365-3431
Tel (928) 344-8367 *Founded/Ownrshp* 2003
Sales 8.0MM^E^ *EMP* 500
SIC 7363 Temporary help service; Temporary help service
Pr: Mary Ellerman
**Sec:* Kim Ellerman

I N G
See ING FINANCIAL SERVICES LLC

I N G
See NEWPORT APPAREL CORP

I N G
See ING FINANCIAL HOLDINGS CORP

D-U-N-S 80-978-9266
I N I HOLDINGS INC
110 Galaxy Dr, Dover, DE 19901-9262
Tel (302) 674-3600 *Founded/Ownrshp* 1991
Sales 46.1MM^E^ *EMP* 400
SIC 2711 2752 Newspapers: publishing only, not printed on site; Newspapers, publishing & printing; Commercial printing, offset; Newspapers: publishing only, not printed on site; Newspapers, publishing & printing; Commercial printing, offset
**Bd of Dir:* Chris Engel

D-U-N-S 11-171-8516
I N X S INC
MAGIC TOYOTA
21300 Highway 99, Edmonds, WA 98026-7747
Tel (425) 556-4422 *Founded/Ownrshp* 1983
Sales 38.8MM^E^ *EMP* 90
SIC 5511 5521 Automobiles, new & used; Used car dealers; Automobiles, new & used; Used car dealers
Pr: David Broadus
Exec: Darlene Nex
Sales Exec: Oscar Navarro
Sls Mgr: Mojo Giron
Sls Mgr: Athena Halverson
Sales Asso: Ron Felder
Sales Asso: Joon Song

I O
See IO DATA CENTERS LLC

D-U-N-S 17-828-5599 IMP
I O INTERCONNECT LTD
I/O INTERCONNECT
1202 E Wakeham Ave, Santa Ana, CA 92705-4145
Tel (714) 564-1111 *Founded/Ownrshp* 1986
Sales 223.6MM^E^ *EMP* 1,500
SIC 3678 3679 Electronic connectors; Harness assemblies for electronic use: wire or cable; Electronic connectors; Harness assemblies for electronic use: wire or cable
CEO: Gary Kung
Sls Dir: Roland Balusek

I P
See INDUSTRY PRODUCTS CO

I P A
See INTERMOUNTAIN POWER AGENCY

I P E C
See INTEGRATED PROCESS ENGINEERS & CONSTRUCTORS INC

I P E G
See INDUSTRIAL PROCESS EQUIPMENT CO

I P G
See INTEGRATED PRINT & GRAPHICS INC

I P G
See INTERTAPE POLYMER CORP

D-U-N-S 82-498-5378
I P L COMMUNICATIONS CORP
701 Seneca St Ste 500, Buffalo, NY 14210-1358
Tel (716) 854-1811 *Founded/Ownrshp* 1994
Sales 22.0MM *EMP* 175
SIC 8748 1731 Telecommunications consultant; Electrical work; Telecommunications consultant; Electrical work
Pr: George Schlemmer
**Ex VP:* Rick Lombard
VP: Norm Hartman

I P M
See INDEPENDENT PAPERBOARD MARKETING LLC

D-U-N-S 15-693-1248 IMP
I P R PHARMACEUTICAL INC
(*Suby of* ASTRAZENECA PLC)
San Isdro Indus Park Lot, Canovanas, PR 00729
Tel (787) 957-1400 *Founded/Ownrshp* 1986
Sales 122.8MM^E^ *EMP* 800
SIC 2834 Tablets, pharmaceutical; Tablets, pharmaceutical
Pr: Ruben Freyre
CFO: James Lovell

I P S
See INTELLIGENT PRODUCT SOLUTIONS INC

I P S
See INDUSTRIAL POWER SYSTEMS INC

I P S
See INTEGRATED POWER SERVICES LLC

I P T
See INTEGRATED PROCUREMENT TECHNOLOGIES INC

I P W
See IMAGE PROJECTIONS WEST INC

D-U-N-S 07-342-4728
I PHOENIX RESTORATION & CONSTRUCTION
14032 Distribution Way, Dallas, TX 75234-3439
Tel (214) 902-0111 *Founded/Ownrshp* 1999
Sales 37.0MM *EMP* 210
Accts Colburn & Peterson Pc
SIC 1542 Specialized public building contractors; Specialized public building contractors
CEO: Dale C Sellers

I Q C
See INGREDIENT QUALITY CONSULTANTS INC

I R D
See INTEGRITY RETAIL DISTRIBUTION INC

I R I
See INTERNATIONAL REPUBLICAN INSTITUTE

I R M
See AUFHAUSER CORP

I R S
See INTERNAL REVENUE SERVICE

I R T
See INTERACTIVE RESPONSE TECHNOLOGIES INC

I R T C
See INTUITIVE RESEARCH AND TECHNOLOGY CORP

I S A
See INTEGRATED SYSTEMS ANALYSTS INC

I S A
See INTERVIEWING SERVICE OF AMERICA INC

I S C
See ISC CONSTRUCTORS LLC

I S C O
See ISCO INDUSTRIES INC

I S D
See GARLAND INDEPENDENT SCHOOL DISTRICT

I S D
See COMMERCE INDEPENDENT SCHOOL DISTRICT

I S D 181 COMMUNITY EDUCATION
See BRAINERD PUBLIC SCHOOLS

I S I
See INTERCONNECT SYSTEMS INC

I S M
See INDUSTRIAL SALES & MFG INC

I S O
See ISO SERVICES INC

I S O
See INTELLIGENT SWITCHGEAR ORGANIZATION LLC

D-U-N-S 60-643-6959
I S O INDUSTRIES INC
5353 E Princess Anne Rd F, Norfolk, VA 23502-1861
Tel (757) 855-0900 *Founded/Ownrshp* 2004
Sales 171.0MM *EMP* 15
Accts Goodman & Company Norfolk Vi
SIC 5172 Fuel oil; Fuel oil
Pr: Robert G Powell
Genl Mgr: Kathy Wright
Off Mgr: Mike Sano

D-U-N-S 00-571-3953
I S Q INC
QUALITY INDUSTRIAL SERVICES
(*Suby of* QUALITY INDUSTRIAL SERVICE) ★
27481 Beverly Rd Ste 100, Romulus, MI 48174-2049
Tel (313) 295-9000 *Founded/Ownrshp* 1993
Sales 23.6MM^E^ *EMP* 600
SIC 8742 Quality assurance consultant; Quality assurance consultant
Pr: Tom Taulbee
**VP:* Stewart Christian

I S S
See INTERNATIONAL SCHOOLS SERVICES INC

I S S
See INTERNET SECURITY SYSTEMS INC

I S S
See INTELLIGENT SOFTWARE SOLUTIONS INC

D-U-N-S 10-796-8773
I S TECHNOLOGIES LLC
COMPUTER SYSTEM DESIGNERS
8221 S Walker Ave, Oklahoma City, OK 73139-9451
Tel (405) 604-3277 *Founded/Ownrshp* 2002
Sales 25.5MM^E^ *EMP* 220
SIC 7379 Computer related consulting services; Computer related consulting services
CEO: Iva Salmon
CFO: Donald Young
IT Man: Patti Harrison

D-U-N-S 15-270-9494
I S U RESEARCH PARK CORP
2501 N Loop Dr Ste 1600, Ames, IA 50010-8651
Tel (515) 296-7275 *Founded/Ownrshp* 1988
Sales 21.7MM^E^ *EMP* 900
Accts Schnurr & Company Llp Cpa S &
SIC 8733 Research institute; Research institute
Pr: Steven T Carter

D-U-N-S 00-419-9204 IMP/EXP
I SCHUMANN & CO LLC
22500 Alexander Rd, Bedford, OH 44146-5576
Tel (440) 439-2300 *Founded/Ownrshp* 1917, 1978
Sales 28.4MM^E^ *EMP* 115^E^
SIC 3341 Brass smelting & refining (secondary); Bronze smelting & refining (secondary); Copper smelting & refining (secondary); Nickel smelting & refining (secondary); Brass smelting & refining (secondary); Bronze smelting & refining (secondary); Copper smelting & refining (secondary); Nickel smelting & refining (secondary)
Ch Bd: Michael A Schumann
**Pr:* Scott Schumann
**CFO:* Don Robertson
**Ex VP:* David Schumann
Natl Sales: Jim Shiltz

D-U-N-S 00-591-1966 IMP
I STERN AND CO INC
49 Brant Ave Ste 7&8, Clark, NJ 07066-1561
Tel (732) 382-9666 *Founded/Ownrshp* 1992
Sales 20.3MM^E^ *EMP* 13
SIC 5162 Plastics resins
Pr: Brian Miles
**Prin:* Todd Stein
Natl Sales: Peter Lang
Sales Asso: Wes Baird

D-U-N-S 00-884-7782
I SUPPLY CO (OH)
1255 Spangler Rd, Fairborn, OH 45324-9768
Tel (937) 878-5240 *Founded/Ownrshp* 1974
Sales 188.3MM^E^ *EMP* 175
SIC 5087 5113 Janitors' supplies; Containers, paper & disposable plastic; Janitors' supplies; Containers, paper & disposable plastic
CEO: Jerry Parisi
**Pr:* Gerald Parisi
**Treas:* Anita Boshears
**VP:* Tim Detrick
VP: Paul Droullard
**VP:* Joseph Parisi
**VP:* Gene Shepard
**VP:* Dan Strawn
Exec: Michael Kristin
CTO: Diane Cantrell
Dir IT: Denise Lovejoy

I T C
See INTERNATIONAL TRADE COMMISSION UNITED STATES

I T C
See ITC SERVICE GROUP INC

I T C
See INTERSTATE TELECOMMUNICATIONS COOPERATIVE INC

I T C
See ITC ACCEPTANCE CO

D-U-N-S 82-871-5867
I T C W INC
ARTGANIKS
584 Beaconsfield Ave, Naperville, IL 60565-4316
Tel (630) 305-8849 *Founded/Ownrshp* 2004
Sales 14.5MM^E^ *EMP* 330
SIC 8742 3999 Management consulting services; Framed artwork; Management consulting services; Framed artwork
Pr: Margaret Thomas

I T G
See INTEGRATION TECHNOLOGIES GROUP INC

I T G
See ITG HOLDINGS INC

I T S
See INTERNATIONAL THERMAL SYSTEMS LLC

I T S
See INTERNATIONAL TRANSPORTATION SERVICE INC

I T S
See SGS AUTOMOTIVE SERVICES INC

I T V
See INTERNATIONAL TIMBER AND VENEER LLC

D-U-N-S 00-425-2482 IMP
I T VERDIN CO (OH)
VERDIN COMPANY
444 Reading Rd, Cincinnati, OH 45202-1432
Tel (513) 241-4010 *Founded/Ownrshp* 1842, 1968
Sales 20.4MM^E^ *EMP* 105
SIC 3931 3699 3873 Carillon bells; Bells, electric; Clocks, except timeclocks; Carillon bells; Bells, electric; Clocks, except timeclocks
CEO: F B Wersel
**Pr:* James R Verdin
**CEO:* Robert R Verdin Jr
**VP:* David E Verdin
**Prin:* Stanley A Hittner
**Prin:* I T Verdin
Ex Dir: Ed Sullivan
IT Man: Dolores Hinton

Mktg Dir: Bob Santoro
Sls Mgr: Susan Sizer

I T W FOILS
See FOILMARK INC

D-U-N-S 96-437-3948
■ **I T W INC**
(*Suby of* ILLINOIS TOOL WORKS INC) ★
155 Harlem Ave, Glenview, IL 60025-4075
Tel (847) 657-6171 *Founded/Ownrshp* 2002
Sales 57.3MM^E^ *EMP* 221^E^
SIC 3565 Packing & wrapping machinery
Pr: Michael Larsen
VP: Mike Potempa

I U CREDIT UNION
See INDIANA UNIVERSITY EMPLOYEES FEDERAL CREDIT UNION INC

I U O E
See INTERNATIONAL UNION OF OPERATING ENGINEERS JOINT WELFARE FUND

I V D
See INTERNATIONAL VIDEO DISTRIBUTORS LLC

I V I
See INDUSTRIAL VENTILATION INC

D-U-N-S 08-993-9479
I VKC L P (TX)
322 Julie Rivers Dr, Sugar Land, TX 77478-3179
Tel (281) 240-4308 *Founded/Ownrshp* 2000
Sales 18.2MM^E^ *EMP* 400^E^
SIC 5812 Sandwiches & submarines shop; Sandwiches & submarines shop
Pt: Sunita Agrawal
**Pr:* Brij Agrawal

I W C
See INSTITUTIONAL WHOLESALE CO INC

I W I MOTOR PARTS
See FALEY ENTERPRISES INC

D-U-N-S 83-020-7648
I WMI
17100 Pioneer Blvd # 230, Artesia, CA 90701-2776
Tel (562) 977-4906 *Founded/Ownrshp* 2007
Sales 40.0MM *EMP* 280
SIC 1542 Commercial & office building contractors; Commercial & office building contractors
Pr: David T Gajdzik
**CFO:* Chris Gajdzik

D-U-N-S 08-623-5538
I WPC INC
WINTER PARK CONSTRUCTION CO
221 Circle Dr, Maitland, FL 32751-6456
Tel (407) 644-8923 *Founded/Ownrshp* 1974
Sales 92.1MM^E^ *EMP* 135
SIC 1542 Commercial & office building, new construction; Commercial & office building, new construction
CEO: Tracy S Forrest
CFO: Steffanie Mills
**CFO:* Adam D Nickerson
**VP:* Jeff Forrest
**VP:* Charles Reynolds
MIS Dir: Harry Rogers

D-U-N-S 03-239-1161
I-10 RV INC
RIVER RV
10626 General Ave, Jacksonville, FL 32220-2108
Tel (904) 783-0313 *Founded/Ownrshp* 1978
Sales 29.8MM *EMP* 46
SIC 5561

I-20 CADDO COUNTY
See ANADARKO PUBLIC SCHOOLS

I-57 SERVICE CENTER
See JBS PACKERLAND INC

D-U-N-S 12-157-3216
I-69 AUTO TRUCK PLAZA INC
220 E Centennial Ave, Muncie, IN 47303-2902
Tel (765) 288-7795 *Founded/Ownrshp* 1983
Sales 53.5MM^E^ *EMP* 286
SIC 5541 5812 5947 Gasoline service stations; Truck stops; Restaurant, family: independent; Gift shop; Gasoline service stations; Truck stops; Restaurant, family: independent; Gift shop
Pr: Hoyt Neal
MIS Dir: Chris Donnellan

I-69 TRAILER CENTER
See NOVAE CORP

I-90 NISSAN
See MD AUTO GROUP LLC

I-BANK
See INDEPENDENT BANK

I-CAR
See INTER-INDUSTRY CONFERENCE ON AUTO COLLISION REPAIR

I-CONVERT
See INTERNATIONAL CONVERTER (CALDWELL) INC

I-DEAL
See IPREO LLC

D-U-N-S 17-510-1625
■ **I-FLOW CORP**
(*Suby of* KIMBERLY-CLARK CORP) ★
43 Discovery Ste 100, Irvine, CA 92618-3773
Tel (800) 448-3569 *Founded/Ownrshp* 2009
Sales 69.8MM^E^ *EMP* 1,100^E^
SIC 3841 Surgical instruments & apparatus; Surgical instruments & apparatus
Pr: Donald Earhart
**COO:* James J Dal Porto
**CFO:* James R Talevich
VP: Roger Massenger
VP: Brock Thompson
CTO: Julie Schneider

VP Mktg: Alan Dine
Sls Mgr: Jackie Fecher
Sls Mgr: Jody Kohutek
Sls Mgr: Tom McMurtry
Sls Mgr: Chad Miller

I-FRAN
See MSI INVENTORY SERVICE CORP

D-U-N-S 36-110-8459
I-HEALTH INC
AMERIFIT BRANDS
(*Suby of* D S M) ★
55 Sebethe Dr Ste 102, Cromwell, CT 06416-1054
Tel (800) 722-3476 *Founded/Ownrshp* 2011
Sales 79.9MM^E *EMP* 65
SIC 5122 Vitamins & minerals
CEO: Wes Parris
**Pr:* Victor H Emerson Jr
Pr: Wes Paris
**Treas:* Kenneth OH
**Treas:* Jurgen Paulis
**VP:* David M Feitel
VP: Jeff Shirley
Mktg Dir: Susan Lewis
Sales Asso: Rhonda Cornett

D-U-N-S 00-642-7462
I-K-I MANUFACTURING CO INC
116 Swift St, Edgerton, WI 53534-1891
Tel (608) 884-3411 *Founded/Ownrshp* 1955
Sales 30.9MM^E *EMP* 115
SIC 7389 3441 Filling pressure containers; Fabricated structural metal
CEO: Stanley O Midtbo
**CFO:* William Moore
VP: Ryun Bibro
**Prin:* Larry Midtbo
**Prin:* Marilyn Midtbo
Dir IT: Jeff Kron

I-ZONE
See UNITED VISION GROUP INC

I.COMM
See ICOMM CORP

D-U-N-S 18-290-3625 IMP
I/N TEK LP
(*Suby of* ACRELORMITTAL US LLC) ★
30755 Edison Rd, New Carlisle, IN 46552-9695
Tel (574) 654-1000 *Founded/Ownrshp* 2002
Sales 111.5MM^E *EMP* 250
SIC 3316 Strip steel, cold-rolled: from purchased hot-rolled; Strip steel, cold-rolled: from purchased hot-rolled

I/O INTERCONNECT
See I O INTERCONNECT LTD

D-U-N-S 06-546-6997 IMP
■ **I/O MARINE SYSTEMS INC**
ION
(*Suby of* ION GEOPHYSICAL CORP) ★
5000 River Rd, New Orleans, LA 70123-5314
Tel (504) 733-6061 *Founded/Ownrshp* 1968
Sales 21.7MM^E *EMP* 107^E
SIC 3812 3999 Navigational systems & instruments; Navigational systems & instruments; Atomizers, toiletry
Pr: D Brian Hanson
**Pr:* Dave Moffat
Treas: Girish Hemrajani
**Ex VP:* Steve Bate
**Ex VP:* Chris Usher
**VP:* David L Roland

D-U-N-S 01-284-3235 IMP
I2 ASIA LLC
21983 W 83rd St, Shawnee, KS 66227-3133
Tel (913) 422-1600 *Founded/Ownrshp* 2007
Sales 110.0MM *EMP* 10
SIC 5084 Industrial machinery & equipment; Industrial machinery & equipment

D-U-N-S 62-232-6684
I2 TECHNOLOGIES INC
(*Suby of* JDA SOFTWARE GROUP INC) ★
11701 Luna Rd, Dallas, TX 75234-6072
Tel (469) 357-1000 *Founded/Ownrshp* 2010
Sales 72.6MM^E *EMP* 1,280^E
SIC 7372 Business oriented computer software; Business oriented computer software
CEO: Jackson L Wilson Jr
Pr: Raymond B Greer
CFO: Michael J Berry
Bd of Dir: Berry Cash
Bd of Dir: James D Maikranz
Ex VP: Hiten D Varia
Sr VP: John Harvey
Sr VP: Nancy J Litzler
Sr VP: Graham C Newland
Sr VP: Surku Sinnadurai
Sr VP: Aditya Srivastava
Sr VP: M Miriam Wardak
VP: Ken Coulter
VP: Chris Dorr
VP: Steven Minisini
Board of Directors: Stephen P Bradley Phd, J Coley Clark, Richard L Clemmer, Richard Hunter, Michael J Simmons, Lloyd G Waterhouse

D-U-N-S 00-379-5551
I2C INC
1300 Island Dr Ste 105, Redwood City, CA 94065-5170
Tel (650) 480-5222 *Founded/Ownrshp* 2000
Sales 154.0MM^E *EMP* 400
SIC 5045 Computers, peripherals & software; Computers, peripherals & software
CEO: Amir Wain
Pr: Usman Baig
**CFO:* Charlie Noreen
Chf Mktg O: Marc Winitz
**Sr VP:* Jim Ackerson
**Sr VP:* Stephan Koukis
**Sr VP:* Jon Round
**VP:* Maryann Allison
VP: Nancy Baunis
**VP:* Steve Diamond
VP: Henry Gage Jr
**VP:* Khalid Hameed
**VP:* Ed Kelly
**VP:* Zohair Mustafeez
VP: Lori Thomas

D-U-N-S 62-164-7085
I2K HOLDINGS INC
160 Sansome St Fl 6, San Francisco, CA 94104-3788
Tel (415) 249-4000 *Founded/Ownrshp* 2003
Sales 54.0MM^E *EMP* 532
SIC 7373 8721 8742 Computer integrated systems design; Payroll accounting service; Human resource consulting services
CEO: Craig D Morris
CFO: Grant Morris
**Ch:* Dr Kwok Kah Kie

I2SYSTEMS
See INTEGRATED ILLUMINATION SYSTEMS INC

I2TECH
See INNOVATIVE INJECTION TECHNOLOGIES INC

D-U-N-S 07-918-3701
I3 ELECTRONICS INC (NY)
1701 North St, Endicott, NY 13760-5553
Tel (866) 820-4820 *Founded/Ownrshp* 2013
Sales 70.0MM^E *EMP* 420^E
SIC 3674 Semiconductors & related devices; Semiconductors & related devices
Pr: Jim Matthews Jr
Prgrm Mgr: Mark Pichette
Ql Cn Mgr: Ron Arno

D-U-N-S 87-801-6443
I3 GROUP INC
INTERIOR INVESTMENTS
550 Bond St, Lincolnshire, IL 60069-4207
Tel (847) 325-1000 *Founded/Ownrshp* 1994
Sales 140.0MM^E *EMP* 120
Accts Miller Cooper & Co Ltd
SIC 5021 1799 Office & public building furniture; Office furniture installation; Office & public building furniture; Office furniture installation
Pr: Don Shannon
**VP:* Michael Greenberg

D-U-N-S 07-000-5851
I3 LLC
1150 Gateway Dr W, Shakopee, MN 55379-3819
Tel (952) 697-4850 *Founded/Ownrshp* 2010
Sales 20.4MM^E *EMP* 146
SIC 5251 Builders' hardware

D-U-N-S 12-908-6331
I3G LLC
755 Main St Ste 7, Monroe, CT 06468-2830
Tel (203) 445-2000 *Founded/Ownrshp* 1999
Sales 14.3MM^E *EMP* 285
SIC 8748 Telecommunications consultant; Telecommunications consultant
Pt: Ilhan Bagoren

D-U-N-S 07-881-7666
I3PL LLC
LOGISTICS TEAM
218 Machlin Ct, Walnut, CA 91789-3026
Tel (909) 839-2600 *Founded/Ownrshp* 2012
Sales 25.0MM *EMP* 100
SIC 4731 Freight transportation arrangement; Freight transportation arrangement

D-U-N-S 02-022-2633
IA AMERICAN LIFE INSURANCE CO
(*Suby of* INDUSTRIELLE ALLIANCE, ASSURANCE ET SERVICES FINANCIERS INC)
17550 N Perimeter Dr # 210, Scottsdale, AZ 85255-7833
Tel (480) 473-5540 *Founded/Ownrshp* 2009
Sales 45.0MM^E *EMP* 20^E
SIC 7389 6311 Financial services; Life insurance
Pr: Mike Stickney
Sls Mgr: Mary Dinkel
Corp Couns: Greg Morris

D-U-N-S 00-233-3136
IA CONSTRUCTION CORP (PA)
(*Suby of* BARRETT INDUSTRIES CORP) ★
24 Gibb Rd, Franklin, PA 16323-6225
Tel (814) 432-3184 *Founded/Ownrshp* 1924, 2003
Sales 83.2MM^E *EMP* 250
SIC 1611 2951 1622 1623 General contractor, highway & street construction; Road materials, bituminous (not from refineries); Bridge construction; Highway construction, elevated; Water main construction; Sewer line construction; General contractor, highway & street construction; Road materials, bituminous (not from refineries); Bridge construction; Highway construction, elevated; Water main construction; Sewer line construction
Pr: Robert Doucet
**Treas:* Fred Shelton
VP: Randy Eller
VP: Robert S Field
**VP:* Donald Rosenbarger
**VP:* Dennis States
Sfty Dirs: Larry Hirchak
Board of Directors: Dominique J Leveille

IAA CONCRETE
See SUNTEC CONCRETE INC

IAAI
See INSURANCE AUTO AUCTIONS INC

D-U-N-S 01-975-5628
IAB FINANCIAL BANK
(*Suby of* INDEPENDENT ALLIANCE BANKS INC) ★
118 E Ludwig Rd Ste 100, Fort Wayne, IN 46825-4245
Tel (260) 469-6262 *Founded/Ownrshp* 1946
Sales NA *EMP* 120
SIC 6022 6163 State commercial banks; Loan brokers; State commercial banks; Loan brokers
Pr: Mike Marhenke
Pr: Jeffery Krivacs
Ofcr: Neal Toussaint
Ex VP: Dave Arnold
Ex VP: Karen Cameron
Ex VP: Paul Grandlienard
Ex VP: Michael Rice
Sr VP: Bob Michael
VP: Doug Meyer
VP: Jeff Rolfsen
VP: Kevin Roth
VP: David Young

IABA
See INSTITUTE FOR APPLIED BEHAVIOR ANALYSIS A PSYCHOLOGICAL CORP

IAC GROUP
See INTERNATIONAL AUTOMOTIVE COMPONENTS GROUP NORTH AMERICA INC

D-U-N-S 80-116-8548 IMP
IAC MENDON LLC
(*Suby of* IAC GROUP) ★
236 Clark St, Mendon, MI 49072-9794
Tel (269) 496-2215 *Founded/Ownrshp* 2007
Sales 71.8MM^E *EMP* 907
SIC 5531 Automotive & home supply stores
CEO: Robert S Miller
**CFO:* Dennis E Richardville
**Ex VP:* Janis N Acosta

D-U-N-S 84-474-9127
■ **IAC SEARCH & MEDIA INC**
ASK.COM
(*Suby of* IAC/INTERACTIVECORP) ★
555 12th St Ste 500, Oakland, CA 94607-3699
Tel (510) 985-7400 *Founded/Ownrshp* 2005
Sales 133.3MM^E *EMP* 505
SIC 7375 Information retrieval services; Information retrieval services
CEO: Doug Leeds
Pr: George S Lichter
**COO:* Shane McGilloway
**CFO:* Dominic Butera
**CFO:* Steven J Sordello
Ofcr: Steven Pickering
**Ex VP:* Tuoc Luong
**Ex VP:* Brett M Robertson
VP: Jared Cluff
VP: Valerie Combs
VP: Scott Garrell
VP: Deborah Jenkins
VP: Elizabeth McMillan
VP: Adam Richards
VP: Lisa Ross
VP Bus Dev: Oliver Hill

D-U-N-S 87-435-4434 IMP
IAC SPARTANBURG INC
(*Suby of* IAC GROUP) ★
1 Austrian Way, Spartanburg, SC 29303-2478
Tel (864) 591-0000 *Founded/Ownrshp* 2010
Sales 46.7MM^E *EMP* 300
SIC 3714 8711 3296 Motor vehicle parts & accessories; Acoustical engineering; Mineral wool; Motor vehicle parts & accessories; Acoustical engineering; Mineral wool
Pr: Oliver Hafner
**Sec:* Clarence Crews
**VP:* Oliver Storbeck

D-U-N-S 80-826-3581
IAC TROY LLC
I A C
(*Suby of* IAC GROUP) ★
163 Glen Rd, Troy, NC 27371-8320
Tel (910) 572-3721 *Founded/Ownrshp* 2007
Sales 30.0MM^E *EMP* 70
SIC 3089 Automotive parts, plastic; Automotive parts, plastic
CEO: Robert S Steve Miller
**Ex VP:* Janis N Acosta
**Ex VP:* Dennis E Richardville
Ql Cn Mgr: Ryan Payne

D-U-N-S 17-518-0819
▲ **IAC/INTERACTIVECORP**
555 W 18th St, New York, NY 10011-2822
Tel (212) 314-7300 *Founded/Ownrshp* 1986
Sales 3.1MMM *EMP* 4,000
Tkr Sym IACI *Exch* NGS
SIC 7372 7375 5961 Prepackaged software; Information retrieval services; On-line data base information retrieval; Catalog & mail-order houses; Prepackaged software; Information retrieval services; On-line data base information retrieval; Catalog & mail-order houses
CEO: Joseph Levin
**Ch Bd:* Barry Diller
V Ch: Victor A Kufmn
Pr: Scott Garell
Pr: Jay Herratti
Pr: Jon Miller
Pr: Bret Violette
CEO: Mandy Ginsberg
CEO: Darren Macdonald
CEO: Sean Moriarty
CEO: Jason Rapp
CEO: Jim Safka
CEO: Sam Yagan
CFO: Jeffrey W Kip
**V Ch Bd:* Victor A Kaufman
Ofcr: Jason Stewart
Ex VP: Chuck Geiger
Sr VP: Mary Osako
Sr VP: Michael Schwerdtman
Sr VP: Gregg Winiarski
VP: Lance Barton
Board of Directors: Edgar Bronfman Jr, Chelsea Clinton, Michael D Eisner, Bonnie S Hammer, David Rosenblatt, Alan G Spoon, Alexander Von Furstenberg, Richard F Zannino

D-U-N-S 13-447-0595
IACCESS TECHNOLOGIES INC
1251 E Dyer Rd Ste 160, Santa Ana, CA 92705-5655
Tel (714) 922-9158 *Founded/Ownrshp* 2003
Sales 26.6MM *EMP* 57
SIC 8711 8748 Engineering services; Business consulting
CEO: Hasan I Ramlaoui
Dir Bus: Marie Fujita
Prgrm Mgr: Chris Overman
Snr Sftwr: Dung Nguyen
Snr Sftwr: Michael Steven
IT Man: Neil Duong
Sftwr Eng: Jeremy Whitcher
Board of Directors: Rey Ryan

D-U-N-S 78-287-0091
IACOBONI SITE SPECIALISTS INC
9301 Philadelphia Rd, Baltimore, MD 21237-4101
Tel (410) 686-2100 *Founded/Ownrshp* 1991
Sales 27.2MM^E *EMP* 94
SIC 1623 1611

D-U-N-S 18-327-8126
IAE INTERNATIONAL AERO ENGINES AG
400 Main St Ms121-10, East Hartford, CT 06108-0968
Tel (860) 565-1773 *Founded/Ownrshp* 1983
Sales 66.0MM^E *EMP* 150
SIC 3724 Aircraft engines & engine parts; Aircraft engines & engine parts
Pr: Jon Beatty
Pr: Chris Bewley
**CFO:* Dave Avery
**CFO:* Charles Ayer
**Sr VP:* Rick Deurloo
**Sr VP:* Jim Guiliano
VP: Annalie Brown
VP: Martin Brown
**VP:* Steve Burrill
**VP:* John Green
Sls Dir: Martyn Holmes

IAFF
See INTERNATIONAL ASSOCIATION OF FIRE-FIGHTERS

IAIS
See IOWA INTERSTATE RAILROAD LTD

D-U-N-S 96-744-4766
IAM ACQUISITION LLC
COREGISTICS
240 Northpoint Pkwy, Acworth, GA 30102-2083
Tel (609) 395-6934 *Founded/Ownrshp* 2011
Sales 34.0MM *EMP* 90
SIC 7389 Packaging & labeling services; Packaging & labeling services
CEO: Eric Wilhelm
Pr: Tim Budic
**COO:* Chris Gaffney
**COO:* Kevin Hail
**CFO:* Chris Ristau
Opers Mgr: Robert Brogan
VP Mktg: Greg Rose

D-U-N-S 00-424-3184 IMP
IAMS CO
(*Suby of* MARS INC) ★
8700 S Masn Montgomery Rd, Mason, OH 45040-9760
Tel (800) 675-3849 *Founded/Ownrshp* 2014
Sales 145.0MM^E *EMP* 1,000
SIC 2047 2048 Dog food; Cat food; Prepared feeds; Dog food; Cat food; Prepared feeds
CEO: AG Losley
CFO: Brian Robson

D-U-N-S 02-185-9124
IANYWHERE SOLUTIONS INC
(*Suby of* SYBASE INC) ★
1 Sybase Dr, Dublin, CA 94568-7976
Tel (519) 883-6898 *Founded/Ownrshp* 2000
Sales 17.0MM^E *EMP* 400
SIC 7371 Computer software development & applications; Computer software development & applications
Pr: Terry Stepien
Snr Sftwr: Steve Chaput
Sls Dir: Robert Spinks
Sls Dir: Kerry Youker

D-U-N-S 07-949-2183
IAP GLOBAL SERVICES LLC
7315 N Atlantic Ave, Cape Canaveral, FL 32920-3721
Tel (321) 784-7100 *Founded/Ownrshp* 2014
Sales 622.4MM^E *EMP* 1,659^E
SIC 6726 Investment offices
CFO: Terrance Derosa
**Sr VP:* Rochelle Cooper
**VP:* Barbara Jerich
Prgrm Mgr: Lee Michlin

D-U-N-S 01-081-6486
IAP WORLD SERVICES INC
(*Suby of* IAP WORLDWIDE SERVICES INC) ★
7315 N Atlantic Ave, Cape Canaveral, FL 32920-3721
Tel (321) 868-7851 *Founded/Ownrshp* 2005
Sales 159.0MM^E *EMP* 835^E
SIC 4731 4581 8744 4911 1541 4813 Freight transportation arrangement; Airports, flying fields & services; Airport control tower operation, except government; Facilities support services; Transmission, electric power; ; ; Industrial buildings & warehouses; Wire telephone; Freight transportation arrangement; Airports, flying fields & services; Airport control tower operation, except government; Facilities support services; Transmission, electric power; ; ; Industrial buildings & warehouses; Wire telephone
Pr: Douglas Kitani
**Treas:* Ann Gonzalez
**VP:* Rochelle L Cooper
Genl Couns: David Craig
Board of Directors: Barbara Jerich

D-U-N-S 78-433-0677
IAP WORLDWIDE SERVICES INC
WATER WORKS PLUMBING HEATING
(*Suby of* IAP GLOBAL SERVICES LLC) ★
7315 N Atlantic Ave, Cape Canaveral, FL 32920-3721
Tel (973) 633-5115 *Founded/Ownrshp* 2004
Sales 551.2MM *EMP* 1,647
Accts Mcgladrey Llp Mclean Virgini
SIC 4731 4581 8744 4911 Freight transportation arrangement; Airports, flying fields & services; Facilities support services; ; Transmission, electric power; Distribution, electric power; Freight transportation arrangement; Airports, flying fields & services; Facilities support services; ; Transmission, electric power; Distribution, electric power

CEO: Douglas Kitani
CFO: Terry Derosa
Ofcr: Russell Ehlinger
Ofcr: Pamela Williams
Sr VP: Rochelle Cooper
VP: Pascal Budge
VP: Charles Dominy
VP: James Duffy
VP: Barbara Jerich
VP: Richard Sloop
Comm Dir: Maureen Fitzgerald
Dir Bus: Bob Hammerle
Comm Man: Arlene Mellinger

D-U-N-S 08-109-7425
IAP-HILL LLC
(*Suby of* IAP WORLD SERVICES INC) ★
7315 N Atlantic Ave, Cape Canaveral, FL 32920-3721
Tel (321) 784-7100 *Founded/Ownrshp* 2013
Sales 11.4MM^E *EMP* 350
SIC 8744 4911 4931 4939 Facilities support services; Base maintenance (providing personnel on continuing basis); ; Electric & other services combined; Combination utilities; Facilities support services; Base maintenance (providing personnel on continuing basis); ; Electric & other services combined; Combination utilities
Ch: Fredrick Nohmer
Treas: Ann Gonzalez
Genl Mgr: David Craig
Genl Mgr: Barbara A Jerich

D-U-N-S 07-316-6196
IAPMO RESEARCH AND TESTING INC
INTERNATIONAL ASSOCIATION OF P
5001 E Philadelphia St, Ontario, CA 91761-2816
Tel (909) 472-4100 *Founded/Ownrshp* 1994
Sales 31.7MM *EMP* 65
Accts Miller Giangrande Llp Brea C
SIC 8611 Contractors' association
Ex Dir: G P Russ Chaney
Exec: Russ Chaney
**Dir Surg:* Shahin Moinian
Ex Dir: Steven Chatfield
**Genl Couns:* Neil Bogatz

IAS
See INTERNATIONAL AMERICAN SUPERMARKETS CORP

IAS ADMINISTRATION
See CHURCH OF SCIENTOLOGY INTERNATIONAL

IASAIR
See INTEGRATED AIRLINE SERVICES INC

D-U-N-S 96-589-6140
IASIS GLENWOOD REGIONAL MEDICAL CENTER LP
(*Suby of* IASIS HEALTHCARE LLC) ★
503 Mcmillan Rd, West Monroe, LA 71291-5327
Tel (318) 329-4200 *Founded/Ownrshp* 2010
Sales 42.7MM^E *EMP* 5,014^E
SIC 8011 Medical centers
CEO: Ron Elder
Ofcr: Susan Humphries

IASIS HEALTHCARE
See ST JOSEPH MEDICAL CENTER CORP

IASIS HEALTHCARE
See MEDICAL CENTER OF SOUTHEAST TEXAS L P

D-U-N-S 04-381-1228
IASIS HEALTHCARE CORP
(*Suby of* IASIS INVESTMENT LLC) ★
117 Seaboard Ln Bldg E, Franklin, TN 37067-2855
Tel (615) 844-2747 *Founded/Ownrshp* 1994
Sales 3.8MMM^E *EMP* 12,395
SIC 8062 General medical & surgical hospitals; General medical & surgical hospitals
CEO: David R White
Pr: Sandra McRee
Pr: W Carl Whitmer
COO: Phillip J Mazzuca
CFO: John M Doyle
Bd of Dir: Charlene Jackson
Ofcr: Julie Heath
Ofcr: Greg Jahn
Sr VP: Jorge Munoz
VP: Bob Reinhardt
Exec: Gladstone Jones
Dir Case M: Timothy Wardle
Dir Lab: Judy Barnes
Dir Lab: Kevin Brown
Dir Lab: Scott Croft
Dir Lab: Jim McBride
Dir Rad: Dianne Cueto
Board of Directors: Thomas C Geiser

D-U-N-S 82-775-6078
IASIS HEALTHCARE LLC
(*Suby of* IASIS HEALTHCARE CORP) ★
117 Seaboard Ln Bldg E, Franklin, TN 37067-2855
Tel (615) 844-2747 *Founded/Ownrshp* 2004
Sales 2.7MMM *EMP* 12,395^E
Accts Ernst & Young Llp Nashville
SIC 8062 General medical & surgical hospitals; General medical & surgical hospitals
Pr: W Carl Whitmer
**COO:* Phillip J Mazzuca
**COO:* Sandra K McRee
**CFO:* John M Doyle
Sr VP: James Hoffman
VP: Russ Follis
VP: Michele M Peden
CIO: Brian Loflin
CTO: Chris Dahl

D-U-N-S 15-202-8325
IASIS INVESTMENT LLC
113 Seaboard Ln Ste 200a, Franklin, TN 37067-4830
Tel (615) 844-2747 *Founded/Ownrshp* 2004
Sales 3.9MMM^E *EMP* 12,396^E
Accts Ernst & Young Llp Nashville
SIC 8062 General medical & surgical hospitals; General medical & surgical hospitals
Tech Mgr: Beverly McKenzie

D-U-N-S 16-892-0499 IMP
IAT INTERNATIONAL INC
555 E Main St Ste 1101, Norfolk, VA 23510-2232
Tel (757) 622-7239 *Founded/Ownrshp* 1997
Sales 90.0MM *EMP* 6
SIC 5088 Railroad equipment & supplies; Railroad equipment & supplies
Pr: Avraham Ashkenazi
**Sec:* Patricia Ashkenazi

IAT SPECIALTY INSURANCE
See ACCEPTANCE INDEMNITY INSURANCE CO

D-U-N-S 14-337-2329
IATRIC SYSTEMS INC
27 Great Pond Dr, Boxford, MA 01921-1635
Tel (978) 805-4100 *Founded/Ownrshp* 1990
Sales 40.5MM^E *EMP* 235
SIC 5734 7379 Computer software & accessories; Computer related consulting services; Computer software & accessories; Computer related consulting services
CEO: Joel Berman
**Pr:* Frank Fortner
Sr VP: Marc Andiel
**Sr VP:* Joe Cocuzzo
**Sr VP:* John Danahey
**Sr VP:* Sandy Rosenbaum
VP: Chris Hanson
VP: Ken Hoffman
VP: Jeff McGeath
VP: Jason Whiteside
Creative D: Lee Sorg

D-U-N-S 79-029-0915
IATSE NATIONAL HEALTH AND WELFARE FUND
55 W 39th St Fl 5, New York, NY 10018-3850
Tel (212) 580-9092 *Founded/Ownrshp* 2007
Sales 177.7MM *EMP* 4
Accts Schultheis & Panettieri Llp H
SIC 8011 Offices & clinics of medical doctors
Ch: Steven Rapaport

IAUTOMATION
See AUTOMATIONSOLUTIONS INC

D-U-N-S 07-967-1892
IAV AUTOMOTIVE ENGINEERING INC
(*Suby of* IAV GMBH INGENIEURGESELLSCHAFT AUTO UND VERKEHR)
15620 Technology Dr, Northville, MI 48168-2849
Tel (734) 233-3300 *Founded/Ownrshp* 1998
Sales 22.7MM^E *EMP* 100
SIC 8711 Engineering services
Pr: Utz-Jens Beister
Pr: Chris Hennessy
IT Man: Craig Henriksen
Sftwr Eng: Yi Jiang
S&M/VP: Jeremy Goddard
Genl Couns: Connor Bacon
Snr Mgr: Ryan Beehler
Snr Mgr: Christophe Laurent

IB AMERICAS
See INTERNATIONAL BACCALAUREATE ORGANIZATION INC

D-U-N-S 11-836-8369
IB OFT WELFARE FUND 945
585 Hamburg Tpke, Wayne, NJ 07470-2024
Tel (973) 942-9463 *Founded/Ownrshp* 2002
Sales 20.9MM *EMP* 3
Accts Ennis Prezioso & Company Clif
SIC 8631 Labor union; Labor union

D-U-N-S 18-493-1392
IB ROOF SYSTEMS INC
8181 Jetstar Dr Ste 150, Irving, TX 75063-2846
Tel (541) 242-2871 *Founded/Ownrshp* 2005
Sales 29.0MM^E *EMP* 50
SIC 5033 Roofing & siding materials; Roofing & siding materials
Prin: Larry Stanley
**CEO:* Jason Stanley
**CFO:* Tim Luck
CFO: John Sprague
CFO: Jens Verloop
**Ch:* Shawn Stanley
Tech Mgr: Brian Martineau
Board of Directors: Bill Batershell, Dennis Hungerford

D-U-N-S 96-488-2463
IBA GROUP INSURANCE TRUST
8909 Purdue Rd Ste 102, Indianapolis, IN 46268-3147
Tel (317) 879-4040 *Founded/Ownrshp* 2010
Sales NA *EMP* 2
Accts Lm Henderson & Company Llp In
SIC 6411 Insurance agents, brokers & service; Insurance agents, brokers & service

D-U-N-S 03-861-8039
IBA HEALTH & LIFE ASSURANCE (INC)
(*Suby of* BRONSON MANAGEMENT SERVICES CORP) ★
106 Farmers Aly Ste 300, Kalamazoo, MI 49007-4825
Tel (269) 341-8000 *Founded/Ownrshp* 1990
Sales NA *EMP* 239
Accts Ernst & Young Grand Rapids M
SIC 6321 6311 Health insurance carriers; Life insurance carriers; Health insurance carriers; Life insurance carriers
Pr: David Kibbe
Sls Mgr: John Specter

D-U-N-S 96-811-3634
IBA HOLDINGS LLC
VIDARIS
(*Suby of* COGR INC) ★
360 Park Ave S Fl 15, New York, NY 10010-1731
Tel (212) 689-5389 *Founded/Ownrshp* 2015
Sales 37.6MM^E *EMP* 205
SIC 8711 8712 6719 Building construction consultant; Architectural services; Building construction consultant; Architectural services; Investment holding companies, except banks
Pr: Israel Berger

COO: Marc Weissbach
Sr VP: Alexander Argento
Snr PM: Catherine Bobenhausen

D-U-N-S 95-770-4737 IMP
IBA MOLECULAR NORTH AMERICA INC
(*Suby of* ILLINOIS HEALTH AND SCIENCE) ★
21000 Atl Blvd Ste 730, Dulles, VA 20166
Tel (703) 547-8173 *Founded/Ownrshp* 2015
Sales 180.8MM^E *EMP* 400
SIC 5122 5047 Pharmaceuticals; Medical & hospital equipment; Pharmaceuticals; Medical & hospital equipment
CEO: Renaud Dehareng
Pr: L Lee Karras
COO: Anthony Stagnolia
VP: Peter Burke

D-U-N-S 05-317-8823 IMP
IBAHN CORP
SUITE TECHNOLOGY
(*Suby of* IBAHN GENERAL HOLDINGS CORP) ★
126 W 10000 S Ste 100, Sandy, UT 84070
Tel (801) 952-2000 *Founded/Ownrshp* 1999
Sales 75.7MM^E *EMP* 200
SIC 4813 ;
CEO: David W Garrison
Pr: Lawrence Dustin
Pr: Harry Hollines
CFO: David Roshak
**Ch:* Michael Yagemann
VP: Ijames Jones
VP: Jeff Selander
VP: Michelle Vargas
Exec: Monica Gabler
Snr Sftwr: Donald Corbett
Snr Sftwr: Doug Johnson

D-U-N-S 05-044-4574
IBAHN GENERAL HOLDINGS CORP
2755 E Cttnwd Pkwy 400, Salt Lake City, UT 84121
Tel (801) 952-2000 *Founded/Ownrshp* 2000
Sales 75.7MM^E *EMP* 200^E
SIC 4813 ;
Pr: David W Garrison
COO: Gregg Hodges
COO: Frank W King
Sec: Jeff Barton
VP: Bonnie Hughes
VP: James E Jones
VP: James E Jons
Mng Dir: Paul Sullivan
S&M/VP: Joseph J Rook
Sls Dir: Greg McMurdie
Mktg Mgr: San Francisco

D-U-N-S 62-319-1533
IBASET FEDERAL SERVICES LLC
SOLUMINA
27442 Portola Pkwy # 300, Foothill Ranch, CA 92610-2823
Tel (949) 598-5200 *Founded/Ownrshp* 1986
Sales 50.8MM^E *EMP* 215
SIC 7379 Computer related maintenance services; Computer related maintenance services
Ch: Ladeira Poonian
**Pr:* Vic Sial
Ofcr: Terri Carson
VP: Louis Columbus
VP: Bob Joyce
VP: Todd Roark
VP: Vicki Slusiewicz
Exec: Chris Wheeler
Prgrm Mgr: Jeff Neylon
Snr Sftwr: Greg Stevenson
IT Man: Marc Leclerc

D-U-N-S 11-171-4812
IBASIS INC
(*Suby of* KONINKLIJKE KPN N.V.)
10 Maguire Rd 3, Lexington, MA 02421-3110
Tel (781) 505-7500 *Founded/Ownrshp* 1996
Sales 193.3MM^E *EMP* 372
SIC 4813 Long distance telephone communications; Telephone communications broker; Long distance telephone communications; Telephone communications broker
Pr: Willem Offerhaus
Pr: Michael Hughes
CFO: D J Long
Treas: Jorg De Graaf
Bd of Dir: Izhar Armony
Sr VP: Edwin Ierland
Sr VP: Edwin Van
VP: Oubay Atassi
VP: Michael Crimmins
VP: Julia Frevold
VP: Brad Guth
VP: Ardjan Konijnenberg
VP: Patrick Meijer
VP: Jayesh Patel
VP: Mark Saponar
VP: Tim Walsh
Dir Bus: Mark Fuller
Board of Directors: Robert H Brumley, Charles N Corfield, W Frank King Phd

D-U-N-S 05-848-5939
■ **IBBOTSON ASSOCIATES INC**
(*Suby of* MORNINGSTAR INC) ★
22 W Washington St, Chicago, IL 60602-1605
Tel (312) 616-1620 *Founded/Ownrshp* 2006
Sales 34.0MM^E *EMP* 150
SIC 6282 5045 Investment counselors; Computer software; Investment counselors; Computer software
Pr: Peng Chen
Sr VP: Kishore Gangwani
Sales Asso: Joe Falkenberg

IBBS
See INTEGRATED BROADBAND SERVICES LLC

IBC
See INTERNATIONAL BISCUITS & CONFECTIONS LLC

IBC A DBS COMPANY
See DOMINION BUSINESS SOLUTIONS INC

IBC BANK
See INTERNATIONAL BANK OF COMMERCE

IBC BANK
See INTERNATIONAL BANK OF COMMERCE - ZAPATA

IBC-HEARTHWARE
See HEARTHWARE INC

IBC/ WORLDWIDE
See INTERNATIONAL BUSINESS COMMUNICATIONS INC

D-U-N-S 83-264-2693
■ **IBERDROLA RENEWABLES HOLDINGS INC**
(*Suby of* IBERDROLA, SOCIEDAD ANONIMA)
1125 Nw Couch St Ste 700, Portland, OR 97209-4129
Tel (503) 796-7000 *Founded/Ownrshp* 2003
Sales 177.7MM^E *EMP* 220^E
SIC 4932 4931 Gas & other services combined; Electric & other services combined; Gas & other services combined; Electric & other services combined
Pr: Martin Mugica

D-U-N-S 94-737-6422 IMP
■ **IBERDROLA RENEWABLES LLC**
(*Suby of* IBERDROLA RENEWABLES HOLDINGS INC) ★
1125 Nw Couch St Ste 700, Portland, OR 97209-4129
Tel (503) 227-3468 *Founded/Ownrshp* 2007
Sales 177.6MM^E *EMP* 220^E
SIC 4932 4931 Gas & other services combined; Electric & other services combined; Gas & other services combined; Electric & other services combined
Pr: Martin Mugica
**Pr:* Andrew P Haller
**Pr:* Terry Hudgens
Pr: John McStravick
CFO: Pablo Canales
**CFO:* I Merrick Kerr
**Sr VP:* Matthew K Morrow
**Sr VP:* Peter C Van Alderwerelt
VP: Jeff Ballard
VP: David Degabriele
VP: Tim McCabe
**VP:* Allan Query
**VP:* Donald J Winslow
Dir Risk M: Alfred Frakes
Dir Risk M: Julian Johnson

D-U-N-S 00-697-7763
■ **IBERDROLA USA INC**
(*Suby of* IBERDROLA, SOCIEDAD ANONIMA)
52 Farm View Dr, New Gloucester, ME 04260-5100
Tel (207) 688-6300 *Founded/Ownrshp* 2008
Sales 2.5MMM^E *EMP* 5,837
Accts Pricewaterhousecoopers Llp Ph
Tkr Sym AGR *Exch* NYS
SIC 4911 4922 4924 Distribution, electric power; Generation, electric power; Transmission, electric power; Natural gas transmission; Natural gas distribution; Distribution, electric power; Generation, electric power; Transmission, electric power; Natural gas transmission; Natural gas distribution
Ch Bd: Robert D Kump
Pr: Ignacio Estella
**COO:* Kevin Walker
**CFO:* Daniel Alcain
**Sr VP:* F Michael McClain
VP: Steven R Adams
VP: Neil Clitheroe
VP: Paul K Connolly
VP: Gene Jensen
VP: Franklyn Reynolds
VP: Mary Smith
VP Bus Dev: Thorn Dickinson

D-U-N-S 14-241-9964
■ **IBERDROLA USA MANAGEMENT CORP**
(*Suby of* IBERDROLA USA INC) ★
52 Farm View Dr, New Gloucester, ME 04260-5100
Tel (207) 688-6300 *Founded/Ownrshp* 2003
Sales 221.8MM^E *EMP* 450
SIC 5063 Power transmission equipment, electric; Power transmission equipment, electric
CEO: Robert D Kump
**COO:* Kevin Walker
**CFO:* Jose Maria Torres
**VP:* Sheri Lamoureux
Netwrk Eng: Donald Holling
Mktg Mgr: Laney Brown

D-U-N-S 15-071-3779
■ **IBERDROLA USA MANAGEMENT CORP**
(*Suby of* IBERDROLA USA INC) ★
89 East Ave, Rochester, NY 14649-0001
Tel (585) 771-2112 *Founded/Ownrshp* 2003
Sales 22.4MM^E *EMP* 99
SIC 7389 Personal service agents, brokers & bureaus
CEO: Sara J Burns
VP: Patrick Neville
Dir IT: John Streett
IT Man: Donna Sellers

IBERIA FINANCIAL SERVICES
See IBERIABANK

D-U-N-S 08-840-8323 IMP
IBERIA FOODS CORP
(*Suby of* BROOKLYN BOTTLING OF MILTON NEW YORK INC) ★
1900 Linden Blvd, Brooklyn, NY 11207-6806
Tel (718) 272-8900 *Founded/Ownrshp* 2003
Sales 32.3MM^E *EMP* 140
SIC 2032 Ethnic foods: canned, jarred, etc.; Ethnic foods: canned, jarred, etc.
Pr: Eric Miller
**CFO:* William Schneible
Area Mgr: Ciro Castillo
Sls Mgr: Luis Botero

D-U-N-S 19-393-2147
IBERIA INVESTMENT GROUP LLC
2807 Teal Dr, New Iberia, LA 70560-1455
Tel (337) 364-8183 *Founded/Ownrshp* 2005
Sales 68.3MM^E *EMP* 354

SIC 1731 General electrical contractor; General electrical contractor
Pr: Philip B Breaux
Ch: Ernest P Breaux Jr
Ex VP: Johny P Barom Jr

IBERIA MEDICAL CENTER
See HOSPITAL SERVICE DISTRICT NO 1 OF IBERIA PARISH

D-U-N-S 07-193-0952
IBERIA MEDICAL CENTER FOUNDATION
2315 E Main St, New Iberia, LA 70560-4031
Tel (337) 364-0441 *Founded/Ownrshp* 1960
Sales 52.5MM *EMP* 360
SIC 8062 8011 General medical & surgical hospitals; Offices & clinics of medical doctors; General medical & surgical hospitals; Offices & clinics of medical doctors
CEO: Jim Youree
Pr: Brennon Lebla
**Pr:* Parker Templeton
**COO:* Shane Myers
**CFO:* Stephanie Kirk
**CFO:* Wally Piekarczyk
CFO: Walter Pierkarczyk
Ofcr: Kelly Kalk
VP: Carrie Templeton
IT Man: Tim Fletcher
Orthpdst: Harold Hebert

D-U-N-S 01-039-7545
IBERIA PARISH LIBRARY
445 E Main St, New Iberia, LA 70560-3730
Tel (337) 364-7150 *Founded/Ownrshp* 1947
Sales 22.6MM *EMP* 22ᴱ
SIC 8231 Public library; Public library

D-U-N-S 07-945-2934
IBERIA PARISH SCHOOL DISTRICT
1500 Jane St, New Iberia, LA 70563-1544
Tel (337) 685-4395 *Founded/Ownrshp* 1879
Sales 109.3MMᴱ *EMP* 2,000
Accts Kolder Champagne Slaven & Co
SIC 8211 Public elementary & secondary schools; Public elementary & secondary schools
MIS Dir: Gwen Migues
Teacher Pr: Jacklene Jones
HC Dir: Barbara Hitter

D-U-N-S 09-269-0288
■ **IBERIABANK**
IBERIA FINANCIAL SERVICES
(*Suby of* IBERIABANK CORP) ★
200 W Congress St, Lafayette, LA 70501-6873
Tel (800) 682-3231 *Founded/Ownrshp* 1995
Sales NA *EMP* 798
SIC 6036 6163 Savings & loan associations, not federally chartered; Loan brokers; Savings & loan associations, not federally chartered; Loan brokers
Pr: Daryl G Byrd
Pr: Gregory A King
Pr: Kevin P Rafferty
COO: Michael J Brown
CFO: Marilyn W Burch
Ch: William H Fenstermaker
Ex VP: Elizabeth A Ardoin
Ex VP: George J Becker III
Ex VP: J Randolph Bryan
Ex VP: John Davis
Ex VP: John R Davis
Ex VP: Donna Kasmiersky
Ex VP: Michael Naquin
Ex VP: David Shutley
Sr VP: Anthony J Restel
VP: Beth Ardoin
VP: Mark D Evans
VP: Winifred Stamps
VP: Pat Trahan
VP: Pete M Yuan

D-U-N-S 92-725-8202
▲ **IBERIABANK CORP**
200 W Congress St, Lafayette, LA 70501-6873
Tel (337) 521-4003 *Founded/Ownrshp* 1994
Sales NA *EMP* 2,825ᴱ
Tkr Sym IBKC *Exch* NGS
SIC 6022 State commercial banks; State commercial banks
Pr: Daryl G Byrd
**Ch Bd:* William H Fenstermaker
Pr: Lawrence G Ford
Pr: Karl Hoefer
Pr: Gregory A King
Pr: Dawn Primeaux
Pr: Rhonda Prosser
Pr: Rick Pullum
Pr: Kevin Rafferty
Pr: Jeannie Rotolo
Pr: Heidi Young
COO: Michael J Brown
CFO: Jim McLemore
CFO: Anthony J Restel
**V Ch Bd:* E Stewart Shea III
Bd of Dir: Michael Naquin
Bd of Dir: Melanie Savell
Ofcr: Mike Jordan
Ofcr: Ernest Lawrence
Ofcr: Sarah Oliver
Ofcr: Mark Reiber
Board of Directors: Elaine D Abell, Harry V Barton Jr, Ernest P Breaux Jr, John N Casbon, Angus R Cooper II, John E Koerner III, O Miles Pollard Jr, David H Welch

D-U-N-S 06-791-1305
IBERO-AMERICAN ACTION LEAGUE INC
817 E Main St, Rochester, NY 14605-2722
Tel (585) 256-8900 *Founded/Ownrshp* 1968
Sales 9.0MM *EMP* 280
Accts Bonadio & Co Llp Pittsford
SIC 8399 6159 Council for social agency; Small business investment companies; Council for social agency; Small business investment companies
Pr: Hilda Rosario Escher
COO: Ruth N Colon
CFO: George Dickinson
**Sr VP:* Gladys Santiago
**VP:* Jose Cruz
VP: Elisa Dejesus
VP: Aida N Veras
Mktg Dir: Ruth Colon

D-U-N-S 00-799-8230
IBERVILLE INSULATIONS LLC (LA)
11621 Sun Belt Ct, Baton Rouge, LA 70809-4209
Tel (225) 752-2194 *Founded/Ownrshp* 1981
Sales 68.9MM *EMP* 200
SIC 1799 Insulation of pipes & boilers; Insulation of pipes & boilers
Opers Mgr: Jeff Starkey

D-U-N-S 08-655-8574
IBERVILLE MOTORS INC
23085 Highway 1, Plaquemine, LA 70764-2312
Tel (225) 687-9244 *Founded/Ownrshp* 2000
Sales 24.0MMᴱ *EMP* 25
SIC 5511 7538 7532 7515 Automobiles, new & used; General automotive repair shops; Top & body repair & paint shops; Passenger car leasing; Automobiles, new & used; General automotive repair shops; Top & body repair & paint shops; Passenger car leasing
Pr: Stan Anders
**VP:* Bobby Roussel
Genl Mgr: David Montoya

IBERVILLE PARISH
See PARISH OF IBERVILLE

D-U-N-S 09-858-8163
IBERVILLE PARISH SCHOOL BOARD (INC)
58030 Plaquemine St, Plaquemine, LA 70764-2522
Tel (225) 687-4341 *Founded/Ownrshp* 1800
Sales 42.8MMᴱ *EMP* 750
SIC 8211 Public elementary & secondary schools; Public elementary & secondary schools
VP: Darlene Ourso
HC Dir: John Knipmyer

IBEW
See INTERNATIONAL BROTHERHOOD OF ELECTRICAL WORKERS

D-U-N-S 01-439-0324
IBEW 292 HEALTH CARE PLAN
6900 Wedgwood Rd N, Osseo, MN 55311-3552
Tel (763) 493-8830 *Founded/Ownrshp* 2010
Sales 44.3MM *EMP* 2
Accts Legacy Professionals Llp Edin
SIC 8099 Health & allied services; Health & allied services
Prin: Elizabeth Ashbaugh

D-U-N-S 96-488-2521
IBEW ELECTRIAL WORKERS GENERAL WELFARE FUND
28600 Della Vista Pkwy, Warrenville, IL 60555
Tel (630) 393-1701 *Founded/Ownrshp* 2010
Sales 32.4MM *EMP* 3
Accts Levinson Sirrion Hein & Bilkey
SIC 8631 Labor unions & similar labor organizations; Labor unions & similar labor organizations

D-U-N-S 16-726-7756
IBEW LOCAL 18
4189 W 2nd St, Los Angeles, CA 90004-4340
Tel (213) 387-8274 *Founded/Ownrshp* 1947
Sales 96.1MM *EMP* 18
Accts Miller Kaplan Arase Llp North
SIC 8631 Labor unions & similar labor organizations; Labor unions & similar labor organizations
Pr: Frank Miramontes

IBEW LOCAL 38
See CLEVELAND ELECTRICAL JATC

D-U-N-S 02-650-4605
IBEW LOCAL 716 PENSION TRUST
ELECTRIAL MEDICAL TRUST
8441 Gulf Fwy Ste 304, Houston, TX 77017-5066
Tel (713) 643-9300 *Founded/Ownrshp* 1969
Sales 22.0MM *EMP* 7
SIC 6733 Trusts, except educational, religious, charity: management; Trusts, except educational, religious, charity: management
Co-Ownr: Sandy Heck
Prin: Hazel Sheppard

D-U-N-S 96-490-1859
IBEW LOCAL 98 HEALTH & WELFARE FUND
1719 Spring Garden St, Philadelphia, PA 19130-3915
Tel (215) 599-6436 *Founded/Ownrshp* 2010
Sales NA *EMP* 3
Accts Novak Francella Llc Bala Cynw
SIC 6371 Pension, health & welfare funds; Pension, health & welfare funds

D-U-N-S 80-717-1967
IBEW-NECA SOUTHWESTERN HEALTH BENEFIT FUND
4040 Mcewen Rd Ste 100, Dallas, TX 75244-5092
Tel (972) 980-1123 *Founded/Ownrshp* 2007
Sales 61.6MM *EMP* 2
Accts Edwards And Leathers Pc Dalla
SIC 8099 Health & allied services
Owner: Harriet Langston
Treas: Stephen Mack
Sales Exec: Harold Dias

D-U-N-S 07-875-2105
IBEX CONSTRUCTION CO LLC
1 Whitehall St Fl 7, New York, NY 10004-2119
Tel (646) 366-6200 *Founded/Ownrshp* 2003
Sales 57.6MMᴱ *EMP* 90
SIC 1542 8741 Nonresidential construction; Construction management
CFO: Neil Wegman
VP: Bob Linsky
Exec: Robert Postlethwaite

D-U-N-S 08-156-0922
IBEX ENTERPRISES
RESOURCE DESIGN INTERIORS
747 Front St Ste 100, San Francisco, CA 94111-1969
Tel (415) 777-0202 *Founded/Ownrshp* 1989
Sales 22.0MM *EMP* 35
SIC 5021 5023 7389 Office & public building furniture; Window furnishings; Floor coverings; Interior design services
CEO: Kathryn Abbassi
**Treas:* Mohammad Abbassi
**VP:* Firouzeh Abbassi
**VP:* Maryann McCarthy
**VP:* Ann Pantera
**VP:* Kalee Woo

IBEX GLOBAL
See TRG CUSTOMER SOLUTIONS INC

D-U-N-S 96-349-3916
IBEX STAFFING SOLUTIONS INC
805 Media Luna St 41, Brownsville, TX 78520-4056
Tel (956) 574-9787 *Founded/Ownrshp* 2008
Sales 400.0M *EMP* 341
SIC 7361 Employment agencies; Employment agencies
Pr: Jorge Varcena

IBG
See INTERACTIVE BROKERS GROUP INC

D-U-N-S 07-016-8039
■ **IBG LLC** (CT)
(*Suby of* IBG) ★
1 Pickwick Plz, Greenwich, CT 06830-5551
Tel (203) 618-5800 *Founded/Ownrshp* 1994, 2007
Sales 2.0MMM *EMP* 421ᴱ
Accts Deloitte & Touche Llp New Yor
SIC 6211 8732 Dealers, security; Commercial nonphysical research; Dealers, security; Commercial nonphysical research
**CFO:* Paul Brody
CFO: Bill Cavagnaro

IBI
See INGLE-BARR INC

IBI
See ILLINOIS BLOWER INC

D-U-N-S 94-882-6891
IBI ACQUISITIONS INC
3250 W 114th Cir Unit D, Westminster, CO 80031-8002
Tel (303) 469-7758 *Founded/Ownrshp* 2008
Sales 27.2MM *EMP* 2
SIC 6799 Investors; Investors
Prin: Patsy Sessions

IBI ARMORED SERVICES
See BII INC

D-U-N-S 05-614-8968
IBI GROUP (US) INC
(*Suby of* IBI GROUP INC)
18401 Von Karman Ave # 110, Irvine, CA 92612-8543
Tel (949) 477-5030 *Founded/Ownrshp* 1979
Sales 21.7MMᴱ *EMP* 50ᴱ
SIC 8711 0781 Civil engineering; Consulting engineer; Landscape architects
CEO: Scott Stewart
**Pr:* Alistair Baillie
**Pr:* David Thom
**CFO:* Tony Long
**VP:* David Chow
Snr PM: Terry Belcher

D-U-N-S 12-598-7235 IMP
■ **IBI LLC**
(*Suby of* GLOBAL POWER EQUIPMENT GROUP INC) ★
20394 Pinto Rd, Caldwell, ID 83607-8000
Tel (208) 459-6077 *Founded/Ownrshp* 2013
Sales 20.9MMᴱ *EMP* 60
SIC 3443 Tanks, standard or custom fabricated: metal plate
CEO: Dave Erlebach
COO: Tom Weisenbuehler
Off Mgr: Linda Florczyk
Ql Cn Mgr: Jose Flores
Manager: Ray Bishop

D-U-N-S 05-310-0702
IBIQUITY DIGITAL CORP
6711 Columbia Gateway Dr, Columbia, MD 21046-2294
Tel (443) 539-4291 *Founded/Ownrshp* 1998
Sales 31.8MMᴱ *EMP* 150
SIC 8731 Commercial physical research; Radio broadcasting stations
Pr: Robert J Struble
COO: Jeffrey P Jury
CFO: James Spencer
Sr VP: Stephen T Baldacci
Sr VP: Joseph D'Angelo
Sr VP: Gene Parrella
Sr VP: Albert D Shuldiner
VP: Kathi Cover
VP: Bob Dillon
VP: Judith L Kennedy
Snr Sftwr: Catherine Gooi

IBIS
See INTERACTIVE BUSINESS INFORMATION SYSTEMS INC

IBIS GOLF AND COUNTRY CLUB
See IBIS WEST PALM PARTNERS LP

D-U-N-S 00-356-9949 IMP
IBIS TEK LLC (PA)
912 Pittsburgh Rd, Butler, PA 16002-8913
Tel (724) 586-6005 *Founded/Ownrshp* 2000, 2002
Sales 85.7MMᴱ *EMP* 400ᴱ
SIC 3699 Security devices; Security devices
CEO: Tom Buckner
CFO: Harry Kramer
Ex VP: John Buckner
Ex VP: John Owens
Sr VP: Bill Rosemeyer
Exec: Sharon Latini
Prgrm Mgr: Jack Doyle
QA Dir: Jon Robins
Dir IT: Chet Hosey
IT Man: Ron Zulick
Manager: David Herbeck

D-U-N-S 87-970-9897
IBIS WEST PALM PARTNERS LP
IBIS GOLF AND COUNTRY CLUB
8225 Ibis Blvd, West Palm Beach, FL 33412-1575
Tel (561) 625-8500 *Founded/Ownrshp* 1996
Sales 36.0MMᴱ *EMP* 322
SIC 7997 Country club, membership; Country club, membership
Pt: Stewart Tyrrell
Genl Pt: Blackstone Real Estate Investo
Genl Pt: Mskp I LLC
VP: Chuck Gill
Exec: Christopher Park
Genl Mgr: Gale Wentworth Dillon
Genl Mgr: Stephen Logiudice
DP Exec: Logiudice Stephen
Dir IT: Roy Parks

D-U-N-S 62-690-2316 IMP
IBL LIMITED LLC
4001 International Pkwy, Carrollton, TX 75007-1914
Tel (972) 360-9000 *Founded/Ownrshp* 1990
Sales NA *EMP* 17,800
SIC 7011 Hotels & motels

IBM
See INTERNATIONAL BUSINESS MACHINES CORP

IBM
See KENEXA CORP

D-U-N-S 03-751-8412
■ **IBM CREDIT LLC**
(*Suby of* IBM) ★
1 North Castle Dr, Armonk, NY 10504-1725
Tel (914) 765-1900 *Founded/Ownrshp* 1981
Sales NA *EMP* 1,500
SIC 6153 6159 Installment paper; Equipment & vehicle finance leasing companies; Installment paper; Equipment & vehicle finance leasing companies
Pr: Joseph C Lane
**Pr:* Mark Loughridge
**Treas:* Michael Cromar
**Treas:* Daniel Zuchelli
**VP:* James W Boyken
**VP:* Jesse J Greene
VP: Bob John
**VP:* John J Shay Jr
**VP:* Paula L Summa
Board of Directors: Robert F Woods

D-U-N-S 00-169-7945
■ **IBM WORLD TRADE CORP** (DE)
(*Suby of* IBM) ★
1 New Orchard Rd Ste 1, Armonk, NY 10504-1722
Tel (914) 765-1900 *Founded/Ownrshp* 1923
Sales 28.1MMMᴱ *EMP* 113,000
SIC 3571 3577 7377 7379 Electronic computers; Computer peripheral equipment; Computer rental & leasing; Computer related maintenance services; Electronic computers; Computer peripheral equipment; Computer rental & leasing; Computer related maintenance services
CEO: Virginia M Rometty
Pt: Asif Samad
V Ch: Samuel Prabhakar
**CFO:* Mark Loughridge
**Treas:* Martin J Schroeter
Sr VP: Steven A Mills
VP: Larry Bowden
VP: Michael Daniels
VP: Raj Desai
VP: Jan Janick
**VP:* David L Johnson
VP: Abby Kohnstamm
VP: Paul Ledak
VP: Farid Metwaly
VP: Tim Ravey
VP: Walker Royce
VP: Bob Sutor
VP: Eric Tsou
VP: Anthony Yu
Exec: John Maciver

D-U-N-S 07-991-1503
IBP CORP HOLDINGS INC
495 S High St Ste 50, Columbus, OH 43215-5689
Tel (614) 692-6360 *Founded/Ownrshp* 2015
Sales 46.6MMᴱ *EMP* 2,000ᴱ
SIC 1742 6719 Insulation, buildings; Investment holding companies, except banks
Pr: William Jenkins

D-U-N-S 00-101-1746
IBRAHIM SARAYA MD (NY)
6134 188th St Ste 214, Fresh Meadows, NY 11365-2726
Tel (718) 454-4600 *Founded/Ownrshp* 2003
Sales 45.7MM *EMP* 15
SIC 8011 Offices & clinics of medical doctors
Pr: Ibraham Saraya MD

D-U-N-S 92-954-3531
IBRIDGE LLC
12725 Sw Millikan Way # 200, Beaverton, OR 97005-1679
Tel (888) 490-3282 *Founded/Ownrshp* 2004
Sales 39.4MMᴱ *EMP* 600
SIC 7374 Data processing & preparation; Data entry service; Data processing service; Data processing & preparation; Data entry service; Data processing service
Genl Couns: Simeon D Rapoport

IBS
See INTEGRATED BAGGING SYSTEMS CORP

D-U-N-S 10-311-8659 IMP
IBS ELECTRONICS INC
3506 W Lake Center Dr D, Santa Ana, CA 92704-6985
Tel (714) 751-6633 *Founded/Ownrshp* 1982
Sales 41.0MM *EMP* 160
SIC 5065 5045 Printed circuit boards; Electronic parts; Computer peripheral equipment; Electronic parts; Computer peripheral equipment
CEO: Hamid B Tavakoli
**Pr:* Bahman R Tavi
Ofcr: Sandy Zhang
Mng Dir: Ollie Gray

Genl Mgr: Jimmy Au
Genl Mgr: Beth Dureza
Mktg Mgr: Yassi Tavakoli

D-U-N-S 78-894-7950
IBS ENTERPRISE USA INC
I B S
(*Suby of* IBS AB)
90 Blue Ravine Rd, Folsom, CA 95630-4728
Tel (916) 542-2820 *Founded/Ownrshp* 1978
Sales 32.8MM^E *EMP* 158
SIC 7371 5045 Custom computer programming services; Computer software; Custom computer programming services; Computer software
CEO: Doug Braun
**COO:* Christian Paulsson
CFO: Aimee J Lasserre
**CFO:* Fredrik Sandelin
CFO: Mark Vincenzini
VP: Lee Donnelly
VP: Dan Grimm
**VP:* David Rode
**VP:* Hiten Varia
CTO: Mike Verdeyen
VP Mktg: Dan Wells

D-U-N-S 78-376-4434 EXP
▲ IBS PARTNERS LTD
1 N University Dr Ut400a, Plantation, FL 33324-2038
Tel (954) 581-0922 *Founded/Ownrshp* 1985
Sales 645.8MM^E *EMP* 1,600
SIC 2086 Soft drinks: packaged in cans, bottles, etc.; Soft drinks: packaged in cans, bottles, etc.
Genl Pt: Nick A Caporella
Ex VP: Edward Knecht

D-U-N-S 07-847-2502 IMP
IBS PHARMA LLC
LGM PHARMA
3200 West End Ave Ste 500, Nashville, TN 37203-1322
Tel (615) 783-2185 *Founded/Ownrshp* 2008
Sales 24.0MM *EMP* 12
SIC 5122 Pharmaceuticals; Pharmaceuticals
CEO: Leah Chitrik
COO: Mendy Schurder

IBS USA
See INTEGRATED BUSINESS ANALYSIS INC

IBT GLOBAL
See INTEGRATED BOOK TECHNOLOGY INC

D-U-N-S 16-982-0383
IBT HOLDINGS CORP
1600 S Azusa Ave Unit 700, City of Industry, CA 91748-1683
Tel (626) 854-9700 *Founded/Ownrshp* 2006
Sales NA *EMP* 95^E
SIC 6022 State commercial banks
Prin: Henry W Peng

D-U-N-S 80-846-9493
IBT HOLDINGS LLC
600 Pinnacle Ct Ste 655, Norcross, GA 30071-3663
Tel (770) 381-2023 *Founded/Ownrshp* 2007
Sales 53.1MM *EMP* 4^E
Accts Robins Eskew Smith & Jordan
SIC 6719 Personal holding companies, except banks; Personal holding companies, except banks
Pr: Donald T Harvey

D-U-N-S 00-385-4437 IMP/EXP
IBT INC (MO)
9400 W 55th St, Shawnee Mission, KS 66203-2042
Tel (913) 677-3151 *Founded/Ownrshp* 1949
Sales 161.5MM *EMP* 320
SIC 5085 5084

D-U-N-S 87-749-0149
IBT MEDIA INC
INTERNATIONAL BUSINESS TIMES
7 Hanover Sq Fl 5, New York, NY 10004-2674
Tel (646) 867-7100 *Founded/Ownrshp* 2006
Sales 45.1MM^E *EMP* 200^E
SIC 2741 ;
Pr: Etienne Uzac
Chf Mktg O: Mitchell Caplan
Sr VP: Thomas Hammer
Pr Dir: Emily Scheer

IBTS
See INSTITUTE FOR BUILDING TECHNOLOGY AND SAFETY INC

IBTX RISK SERVICES
See INSURANCE & BONDS AGENCY OF TEXAS

IBUYPOWER
See AMERICAN FUTURE TECHNOLOGY CORP

D-U-N-S 03-666-9968
IBW FINANCIAL CORP
4812 Georgia Ave Nw, Washington, DC 20011-4522
Tel (202) 722-2000 *Founded/Ownrshp* 1996
Sales NA *EMP* 159
Accts Stegman & Company Baltimore
SIC 6021 National commercial banks; National commercial banks
Pr: B Doyle Mitchell Jr
**Ch:* Clinton W Chapman
Ex VP: Patricia Mitchell

D-U-N-S 02-134-4700
■ IC BUS LLC
(*Suby of* NAVISTAR INC) ★
600 Dave Ward Dr, Conway, AR 72034-7083
Tel (501) 327-7761 *Founded/Ownrshp* 1995
Sales NA *EMP* 1,100
SIC 3713 3711 Bus bodies (motor vehicles); Chassis, motor vehicle; Bus bodies (motor vehicles); Chassis, motor vehicle
VP: Don Ferran
VP: Debbie Isaacs

D-U-N-S 00-203-3988
■ IC BUS OF OKLAHOMA LLC
(*Suby of* IC BUS LLC) ★
2322 N Mingo Rd, Tulsa, OK 74116-1218
Tel (918) 833-4000 *Founded/Ownrshp* 2000
Sales 228.8MM^E *EMP* 1,000
SIC 3711 3713 Motor vehicles & car bodies; Truck & bus bodies; Motor vehicles & car bodies; Truck & bus bodies
Pr: Grant Tick
**VP:* Michael Cancelliere

D-U-N-S 17-608-1537
IC COMPLIANCE LLC
ICON PROFESSIONAL SERVICES
1065 E Hillsdale Blvd # 300, Foster City, CA 94404-1613
Tel (650) 378-4150 *Founded/Ownrshp* 2015
Sales 276.9MM^E *EMP* 5,500
SIC 7371 8721 Accounting, auditing & bookkeeping; Computer software development & applications; Payroll accounting service
CEO: Teresa Creech
COO: Dana Shaw
CFO: Keith Corbin
CIO: Lynn Dunn

IC GROUP
See IC SECURITIES PRINTERS INC

D-U-N-S 61-682-7739 EXP
IC INDUSTRIES INC
1101 E 33rd St, Hialeah, FL 33013-3528
Tel (305) 696-8330 *Founded/Ownrshp* 1990
Sales 27.3MM^E *EMP* 85
SIC 2653 Boxes, corrugated: made from purchased materials; Boxes, corrugated: made from purchased materials
Pr: Joel Bachelor
**Ch Bd:* Harvey Rothstein
Treas: Victor Diaz
**VP:* Matthew Rothstein
**VP:* Wendy Rothstein
Exec: Zidalia Bencosme
Prd Mgr: Jim Short
Sls&Mrk Ex: Angela Metzger

D-U-N-S 07-929-0742
IC INTRACOM HOLDINGS LLC
550 Commerce Blvd, Oldsmar, FL 34677-2810
Tel (813) 855-0550 *Founded/Ownrshp* 2014
Sales 33.7MM^E *EMP* 60^E
SIC 6799 Investors
COO: Betsy Bennette

IC INTRACOM USA
See INTRACOM USA INC

IC POTASH
See INTERCONTINENTAL POTASH CORP (USA)

D-U-N-S 11-340-3307
IC SECURITIES PRINTERS INC
IC GROUP
4080 S 500 W, Salt Lake City, UT 84123-1358
Tel (801) 265-8100 *Founded/Ownrshp* 1983
Sales 25.3MM^E *EMP* 145
SIC 2759 Business forms: printing; Business forms: printing
Ch Bd: James L Macfarlane
**Pr:* David L Macfarlane
CFO: David Jackson
Dir IT: Steve Thompson

D-U-N-S 07-844-4957
IC SECURITY PRINTERS INC – MARKETING
I C GROUP
4080 S 500 W, Salt Lake City, UT 84123-1358
Tel (801) 265-8100 *Founded/Ownrshp* 1982
Sales 59.2MM^E *EMP* 150
SIC 5111 5162 Printing paper; Plastics products; Printing paper; Plastics products
Pr: Dave Jackson
**Ch Bd:* James L Mac Farlane
**Pr:* David P Jackson
**Pr:* David P Macfarlane
COO: Russell G Chew
**VP:* John Kellogg
**VP:* Alan Lake
**VP:* Greg Tait
Genl Mgr: Matt Butler
CIO: Steve Thomas
Dir IT: Jim Doherty

I.C.A.
See INTERLOCHEN CENTER FOR ARTS

D-U-N-S 10-582-8532
ICA CONSTRUCCION URBANA SA DE CV
MIRAMAR CONSTRUCTION CO
85 Ave De Diego Villas, San Juan, PR 00927-6349
Tel (787) 763-9625 *Founded/Ownrshp* 1998
Sales 22.9MM *EMP* 250
SIC 1611 1622 1522 1629 Highway & street construction; Bridge construction; Hotel/motel, new construction; Dam construction; Highway & street construction; Bridge construction; Hotel/motel, new construction; Dam construction
Admn Mgr: Agustin Morales Sanchez

D-U-N-S 17-958-4255
ICA DE PUERTO RICO INC
85 Ave De Diego Ste 230, San Juan, PR 00927-6349
Tel (787) 622-3040 *Founded/Ownrshp* 1996
Sales 60.0MM *EMP* 450
SIC 1611 General contractor, highway & street construction; General contractor, highway & street construction
Pr: Felipe Martinez Alvarez
**VP:* Arturo Gonzalez Huerta

ICA ENGINEERING, INC.
See HDR ICA

D-U-N-S 10-887-0254
▲ ICAD INC
98 Spit Brook Rd Ste 100, Nashua, NH 03062-5734
Tel (603) 882-5200 *Founded/Ownrshp* 2001
Sales 43.9MM *EMP* 144^E
Tkr Sym ICAD *Exch* NAS
SIC 3841 Pharmaceutical preparations; Surgical & medical instruments; Surgical instruments & apparatus
CEO: Kenneth Ferry
**Ch Bd:* Lawrence Howard
Pr: Kevin Burns
Sr VP: Jonathan Go
Sr VP: Stacey Stevens
Board of Directors: Rachel Brem, Anthony Ecock, Robert Goodman, Steven Rappaport, Elliot Sussman

D-U-N-S 04-015-9147
ICAFS INC
GENERAL SERVICES
2922 Hathaway Rd, Richmond, VA 23225-1724
Tel (804) 320-7101 *Founded/Ownrshp* 1971
Sales 14.0MM^E *EMP* 350
SIC 6513 6512 Apartment building operators; Commercial & industrial building operation; Apartment building operators; Commercial & industrial building operation
Pr: Jonathan S Perel
**CFO:* Norman Van Ferguson
**VP:* Wood Bonnie L
**VP:* Marianne Phillips
Sales Exec: Frank Zauner

D-U-N-S 07-866-1219
ICAHAN MEDICAL INSTITUE
MOUNT SINAI MEDICAL CENTER
1425 Madison Ave Flrs 8/9, New York, NY 10029-6514
Tel (212) 241-6500 *Founded/Ownrshp* 2012
Sales 22.2MM^E *EMP* 101^E
SIC 8011 Offices & clinics of medical doctors
Dir Rx: Ravi Iyengar
Dir IT: David Holloway
IT Man: Daniel Selch
IT Man: Betty Zhang
Netwrk Eng: Brian Bragg
Sls Mgr: Elena Rahona
Pathlgst: Shabnam Jaffer
Doctor: Lawrence Baruch
Doctor: Alan Schiller

ICAHN
See FEDERAL-MOGUL HOLDINGS CORP

ICAHN
See IEH FM HOLDINGS LLC

D-U-N-S 18-580-7088
■ ICAHN ENTERPRISES HOLDINGS LP
(*Suby of* ICAHN ENTERPRISES LP) ★
767 5th Ave Fl 17, New York, NY 10153-0028
Tel (212) 702-4300 *Founded/Ownrshp* 1987
Sales 19.1MMM *EMP* 59,559
SIC 6512 5719 6211 5093 Nonresidential building operators; Beddings & linens; Security brokers & dealers; Security brokers & dealers; Scrap & waste materials; Nonresidential building operators; Beddings & linens; Security brokers & dealers; Security brokers & dealers; Scrap & waste materials
Ch Bd: Carl C Icahn
CFO: Andrew Skobe
VP: Rainer Bostel
VP: Robert Egan
VP: Brad Norton
VP: Keith Power
VP: Andrew Sexton
VP: Edward Szubielski
Genl Mgr: Michael Hedderich
Genl Mgr: Richard Llope
Genl Mgr: Janice Maiden

D-U-N-S 55-589-7164
▲ ICAHN ENTERPRISES LP
767 5th Ave Ste 4700, New York, NY 10153-0108
Tel (212) 702-4300 *Founded/Ownrshp* 1987
Sales 19.1MMM *EMP* 65,577
Accts Grant Thornton Llp New York
Tkr Sym IEP *Exch* NGS
SIC 6722 3714 7999 3743 5093 6531 Management investment, open-end; Motor vehicle parts & accessories; Gambling establishment; Railroad equipment; Ferrous metal scrap & waste; Real estate leasing & rentals; Management investment, open-end; Motor vehicle parts & accessories; Gambling establishment; Railroad equipment; Ferrous metal scrap & waste; Real estate leasing & rentals
Pr: Keith Cozza
CFO: Sunghwan Cho
Treas: John Saldarelli
Ofcr: Peter Reck
Dir IT: Won-Hyuk Hong
Genl Couns: Mark Weitzen
Counsel: Jesse Lynn
Snr Mgr: Joseph Mattina

D-U-N-S 07-886-1598
ICAHN SCHOOL OF MEDICINE AT MOUNT SINAI (NY)
MOUNT SINAI HOSPITAL, THE
(*Suby of* MOUNT SINAI HOSPITAL) ★
1 Gustave L Levy Pl, New York, NY 10029-6504
Tel (212) 241-6500 *Founded/Ownrshp* 1968
Sales 1.7MMM *EMP* 7,000
Accts Ernst & Young Llp New York N
SIC 8249 Medical training services; Medical training services
CEO: Ken Davis
**CFO:* Stephen Harvey
VP: Teri Willey
Dir Lab: Gomathi Jayaraman
Assoc Dir: Alan Krissoff
Assoc Dir: Abby Livingston
Adm Dir: Shinolia Brown
Tech Mgr: Andrew Pizzimenti
VP Sls: Thomas Ahn
Pathlgst: Shabnam Jaffer
Obsttrcn: Angela Bianco

ICAI
See ITOCHU CHEMICALS AMERICA INC

D-U-N-S 01-346-2120
ICAN BENEFIT GROUP LLC
5300 Broken Sound Blvd Nw, Boca Raton, FL 33487-3520
Tel (800) 530-4226 *Founded/Ownrshp* 2005
Sales NA *EMP* 150^E
SIC 6411 Insurance information & consulting services
**Pr:* Sam Shatz
Ex VP: Victor Scavo

ICAP
See INSTITUTIONAL CAPITAL LLC

D-U-N-S 05-359-1566
ICAP CAPITAL MARKETS LLC
(*Suby of* ICAP PLC)
5 Harborside Fincl Ctr, Jersey City, NJ 07311
Tel (212) 341-9900 *Founded/Ownrshp* 2007
Sales NA *EMP* 600^E
SIC 6099 Deposit brokers; Foreign currency exchange; Deposit brokers; Foreign currency exchange
Sr VP: Edward Brown
Sr VP: Robert Nagle
VP: Luis Rangel
Mng Dir: Lisa Nelson
Opers Mgr: Vincent Mancini
Snr Mgr: Ron Wexler

D-U-N-S 18-614-9964
ICAP ENERGY LLC
(*Suby of* ICAP PLC)
9931 Corporate Campus Dr # 3000, Louisville, KY 40223-4035
Tel (502) 327-1400 *Founded/Ownrshp* 2001
Sales 48.7MM^E *EMP* 173^E
SIC 5172 Crude oil
Pr: Rosenberg Richard
COO: Ron Purpora
CFO: Todd Creek
Treas: Luciano Soldiviero
Ex VP: Jeffery Knott
Sr VP: Jonathan Simone
VP: Mark Luppino
Exec: Loren Miller
Comm Dir: Ivette Collazo
Mng Dir: Laurent Gonelle
Mng Dir: Paul Newman

D-U-N-S 07-887-5465
ICAP SERVICES NORTH AMERICA LLC
GARBAN INTERCAP
(*Suby of* ICAP PLC)
1100 Plaza Five Fl 12, Jersey City, NJ 07311-4003
Tel (212) 341-9900 *Founded/Ownrshp* 1998
Sales 252.7MM^E *EMP* 804
SIC 6211 Brokers, security; Brokers, security
CEO: Michael Spencer
**COO:* Ken Pigaga
COO: Ron Purpora
CFO: Philip Curpy
Ofcr: Lou Lombardi
Sr VP: Kevin Doherty
VP: Mike Accolla
VP: Christopher Balzotti
VP: Grant Morrow
VP: Virgil Ranaudo
VP: Lisa Reaves
VP: Brian Salonsky

D-U-N-S 04-401-8349
ICARE INDUSTRIES INC
4399 35th St N Ste 100, Saint Petersburg, FL 33714-3700
Tel (727) 512-3000 *Founded/Ownrshp* 1968
Sales 49.7MM^E *EMP* 300
SIC 3851 5995 Ophthalmic goods; Contact lenses, prescription; Eyeglasses, prescription; Ophthalmic goods; Contact lenses, prescription; Eyeglasses, prescription
Pr: James S Payne
**CFO:* Cy Stankiewicz
Chf Mktg O: Don Cook
**VP:* Robert Stevens
CTO: Ted Schneider

D-U-N-S 78-815-6995
ICAT HOLDINGS LLC
3665 Discovery Dr Fl 3, Boulder, CO 80303-7820
Tel (303) 447-1155 *Founded/Ownrshp* 2005
Sales 30.4MM^E *EMP* 119^E
SIC 6719 Investment holding companies, except banks
VP: Eric Heringer
Dir Risk M: Chris Austin
Snr Sftwr: Brennock Jerry
Snr Sftwr: Mike Krell
CIO: Mike Ferber
Software D: Jack Crews
Software D: Jimmy Wu
Software D: Erin Young
Sftwr Eng: Lin George
Sales Exec: Steve Lemon
Sls Dir: Sonny Spearman

D-U-N-S 80-763-1825
ICAT LOGISTICS INC
6805 Douglas Legum Dr # 3, Elkridge, MD 21075-6262
Tel (443) 459-8070 *Founded/Ownrshp* 1992
Sales 43.7MM^E *EMP* 120
SIC 4731 Freight transportation arrangement; Freight transportation arrangement
Pr: Richard L Campbell
**CFO:* Jim Vespa
**VP:* Jeanie Perkins

ICAT MANAGERS
See INTERNATIONAL CATASTROPHE INSURANCE MANAGERS LLC

D-U-N-S 86-718-4129
ICBA BANCARD INC
(*Suby of* I C B A) ★
1615 L St Nw Ste 900, Washington, DC 20036-5623
Tel (202) 659-8111 *Founded/Ownrshp* 1998
Sales NA *EMP* 37^E
SIC 6153 Credit card services, central agency collection
Pr: Linda Echard
Ex VP: Liang Han
**VP:* Alvin Eisenrauch
**VP:* David Petro
Off Mgr: Susan Meizenhal

D-U-N-S 19-281-3111 EXP
ICC CHEMICAL CORP
PRIOR CHEMICAL
(*Suby of* ICC INDUSTRIES INC) ★
460 Park Ave Fl 7, New York, NY 10022-1841
Tel (212) 521-1700 *Founded/Ownrshp* 2007
Sales 248.7MM^E *EMP* 50
SIC 5169 5122 5162 Chemicals & allied products; Pharmaceuticals; Plastics materials & basic shapes; Chemicals & allied products; Pharmaceuticals; Plastics materials & basic shapes
Ch: Naveen Chandra
**Ch Bd:* John J Farber
**Pr:* William R Brunger
CFO: Blaise Sarcone
**Treas:* Susan Aibinder
VP: Sandra Farber

ICC COLLISION CENTER
See HOLTON INC

D-U-N-S 04-617-7341 IMP/EXP
ICC INDUSTRIES INC
460 Park Ave Fl 7, New York, NY 10022-1841
Tel (212) 521-1700 *Founded/Ownrshp* 1950
Sales 770.8MM^E *EMP* 2,528
SIC 2821 2869 2911 2899 3081 2834

D-U-N-S 19-702-2049
■ **ICC LOWE LLC**
(*Suby of* FCB WORLDWIDE INC) ★
5 Sylvan Way Ste 110, Parsippany, NJ 07054-3813
Tel (973) 984-2755 *Founded/Ownrshp* 2015
Sales 35.4MM^E *EMP* 320
SIC 7311 Advertising agencies; Advertising agencies
CEO: Steven Viviano
**COO:* Frank Galella
Ex VP: Ken Jordan
Sr VP: Karina Costantino
Sr VP: Bobby Defino
Sr VP: Serge Eisenberg
Sr VP: Brian Raineri
Sr VP: Steve Sobel
VP: Bill Ablaschai
VP: Karan Bredenbeck
VP: Neil Goldberg
VP: Mark Goodson
VP: James Hutchinson
VP: Ruth Markowitz
VP: Christian Nazar
VP: Karen Neale
VP: Jim Saccento
VP: Dina Scanlon
VP: Scott Thompson
VP: Andrew Thorn
VP: Bill Wenzel

ICC NEXERGY
See ICC-NEXERGY INC

D-U-N-S 96-797-0968 IMP
ICC-NEXERGY INC
ICC NEXERGY
1200 Internationale Pkwy # 101, Woodridge, IL 60517-4976
Tel (708) 836-3800 *Founded/Ownrshp* 2014
Sales 556.6MM^E *EMP* 1,595^E
SIC 3629 Battery chargers, rectifying or nonrotating; Battery chargers, rectifying or nonrotating
Pr: Stephen McClure
**CFO:* Kenneth J Wroblewski
Ofcr: Sean Harrigan
Off Mgr: Debbie Panzica
Sales Exec: Stuart Oakes

ICCI
See INTERNATIONAL COMMODITY CARRIERS INC

ICCNEXERGY
See NEXERGY INC

D-U-N-S 00-166-6643 IMP
ICCO-CHEESE CO INC (NY)
1 Olympic Dr, Orangeburg, NY 10962-2514
Tel (845) 359-1370 *Founded/Ownrshp* 1932
Sales 31.7MM^E *EMP* 35
SIC 5143 Cheese
Pr: Joseph Angiolillo
**Prin:* Joe Angiolillo

D-U-N-S 07-878-8813 IMP
ICD ALLOYS AND METALS LLC
ICD GROUP INTERNATIONAL
3946 Westpoint Blvd, Winston Salem, NC 27103-6719
Tel (336) 793-2222 *Founded/Ownrshp* 2013
Sales 75.0MM *EMP* 15
SIC 5093 Metal scrap & waste materials
Owner: Alexander Leviant
**Pr:* Ian Machent

D-U-N-S 84-736-2688 EXP
ICD AMERICA LLC
145 Huguenot St Ste 106, New Rochelle, NY 10801-5240
Tel (914) 633-4200 *Founded/Ownrshp* 2007
Sales 76.0MM *EMP* 7
Accts Mathew V John New York Ny
SIC 5169 Chemicals & allied products; Chemicals & allied products

ICD GROUP INTERNATIONAL
See ICD ALLOYS AND METALS LLC

D-U-N-S 07-101-5366
ICD INTERNATIONAL CENTER FOR DISABLED (NY)
INSTITUTE FOR CAREER DEV
123 William St Fl 5, New York, NY 10038-3821
Tel (212) 585-6009 *Founded/Ownrshp* 1920
Sales 31.3MM *EMP* 42
Accts Rsm Mcgladrey Inc New York N
SIC 8099 8331 Medical services organization; Job training & vocational rehabilitation services
Pr: Les Halpert
**Ch Bd:* Justin Wender
**V Ch Bd:* Richard Weber
**V Ch Bd:* Christopher Wu
**Ex Dir:* Dawn Mastoridis

ICDC COLLEGE
See INTERNATIONAL CAREER DEVELOPMENT CENTER INC

ICE
See INTERNATIONAL CONSTRUCTION EQUIPMENT INC

ICE
See INTERCONTINENTAL EXCHANGE INC

D-U-N-S 18-064-8115
ICE BUILDERS INC
GRAY
(*Suby of* GRAY INC) ★
421 E Cerritos Ave, Anaheim, CA 92805-6320
Tel (714) 491-1317 *Founded/Ownrshp* 2001
Sales 84.8MM^E *EMP* 180
SIC 1541

ICE CASTLE FISH HOUSE MFG
See AMERICAN SURPLUS & MANUFACTURING INC

D-U-N-S 00-627-8428 EXP
ICE CREAM SPECIALTIES INC (MO)
NORTH STAR DISTRIBUTING
(*Suby of* PRAIRIE FARMS DAIRY INC) ★
8419 Hanley Industrial Ct, Saint Louis, MO 63144-1917
Tel (314) 962-2550 *Founded/Ownrshp* 1957
Sales 83.7MM^E *EMP* 412
SIC 2024 Ice cream & frozen desserts; Ice cream & frozen desserts
Pr: Leonard Southwell
Off Mgr: Mary Luebbert
Sales Exec: Bob Apple
Mktg Dir: Bill Montgomery

D-U-N-S 82-693-3645 IMP
ICE FLOE LLC
NICHOLS BROTHERS BOAT BUILDERS
5400 Cameron Rd, Freeland, WA 98249-9782
Tel (360) 331-5500 *Founded/Ownrshp* 2007
Sales 60.9MM^E *EMP* 161
SIC 3732 Boat building & repairing; Boat building & repairing
Ofcr: Charlotte Whitaker
Prgrm Mgr: Fran Lafond
Snr Mgr: Fred Becker
Snr Mgr: Peter Sinclair

D-U-N-S 09-778-6230
ICE FOLLIES & HOLIDAY ON ICE INC
DISNEY ON ICE
(*Suby of* GREATEST SHOW ON EARTH) ★
8607 Westwood Center Dr # 500, Vienna, VA 22182-7506
Tel (703) 448-4000 *Founded/Ownrshp* 1979
Sales 4.0MM^E *EMP* 400
SIC 7999 Exhibition operation; Exhibition operation
Ch Bd: Kenneth Feld
Off Mgr: Ellen McCree
CIO: Fred Wade

ICE GALLERY
See INTERNATIONAL CRUISE & EXCURSION GALLERY INC

ICE HOUSE
See BILLS DISTRIBUTING INC

D-U-N-S 14-739-0558
ICE HOUSE AMERICA LLC
(*Suby of* ULYSSES MANAGEMENT LLC) ★
1597 The Greens Way # 101, Jacksonville Beach, FL 32250-1402
Tel (904) 241-7535 *Founded/Ownrshp* 2011
Sales 23.0MM^E *EMP* 100
SIC 3581 6794 Automatic vending machines; Franchises, selling or licensing; Automatic vending machines; Franchises, selling or licensing
CEO: Pete Cotter
**CFO:* Robert Ball
VP: Craig McIlroy
IT Man: Bob McManus
VP Mktg: Michael Little

D-U-N-S 61-078-1051 IMP
ICE INDUSTRIES INC
3810 Herr Rd, Sylvania, OH 43560-8925
Tel (419) 842-3600 *Founded/Ownrshp* 2002
Sales 223.9MM^E *EMP* 450
SIC 3469 Metal stampings; Metal stampings
Ch: Howard Ice
**COO:* Paul Bishop
CFO: David McGranahan
**Ex VP:* Jeff Boger
Prgrm Mgr: Vince Curtis
Mtls Mgr: Nikki Edingfield
Plnt Mgr: Shawn Kerns

D-U-N-S 07-595-5575
ICE MILLER LLP
1 American Sq Ste 2900, Indianapolis, IN 46282-0019
Tel (317) 236-2100 *Founded/Ownrshp* 1910
Sales 89.9MM^E *EMP* 600
SIC 8111 Legal services; Legal services
Pt: Phillip Bayt
Pt: Steven Humke
Pt: Byron Myers
Pt: Phillip Scaletta
Pt: Myra Selby
Pt: Richard Thrapp
COO: Mitchell Hopwell
COO: Mitchell E Hopwood
CFO: John Daniels
Dir Bus: John Gilligan
CIO: Tim Eckenrode

ICE MOBILITY
See ICE SERVICES LLC

D-U-N-S 96-817-2556
ICE RECYCLING LLC
431 Cedar St, Lake City, SC 29560-2601
Tel (843) 374-0217 *Founded/Ownrshp* 2008
Sales 22.3MM^E *EMP* 75
SIC 4953 Recycling, waste materials
Plnt Mgr: Wesley Ballou

D-U-N-S 80-034-4116
ICE RIVER SPRINGS USA INC
ICE SERVICE SPRINGS WATER CO
(*Suby of* ICE RIVER SPRINGS WATER CO. INC)
100 Ceramic Tile Dr, Morganton, NC 28655-6772
Tel (519) 925-2929 *Founded/Ownrshp* 2008
Sales 46.5MM^E *EMP* 250^E
SIC 2086 Water, pasteurized: packaged in cans, bottles, etc.; Water, pasteurized: packaged in cans, bottles, etc.
Pr: James Fallis Gott
**Ex VP:* Sandy Gott

ICE SERVICE SPRINGS WATER CO
See ICE RIVER SPRINGS USA INC

D-U-N-S 05-149-2901
ICE SERVICES LLC
ICE MOBILITY
800 Corporate Woods Pkwy, Vernon Hills, IL 60061-3154
Tel (847) 821-6901 *Founded/Ownrshp* 2010
Sales 32.8MM *EMP* 37
SIC 4899 4812 Data communication services; Radio telephone communication
CEO: Mike Mohr

ICE-O-MATIC
See MILE HIGH EQUIPMENT LLC

ICE-PS
See INTELLIGENCE COMMUNICATIONS AND ENGINEERING INC

ICEBERG ENTERPRISES
See CP CO

D-U-N-S 13-253-8443 IMP
ICEBERG ENTERPRISES LLC
2700 S River Rd Ste 303, Des Plaines, IL 60018-4107
Tel (847) 685-9500 *Founded/Ownrshp* 1999
Sales 41.4MM^E *EMP* 175
SIC 3089 Blow molded finished plastic products; Blow molded finished plastic products
CEO: Howard Green
Pr: Richard Gilbert
VP: Richard Fox
VP: David Parzynski Sr
VP: Shawn Reniker
Exec: Ed Wu
VP Sls: Darren Fischer
Sales Asso: Kathy Cline

D-U-N-S 16-363-5837 IMP
ICEBREAKER NATURE CLOTHING INC
(*Suby of* ICEBREAKER LIMITED)
1330 Nw 14th Ave, Portland, OR 97209-2815
Tel (503) 229-7380 *Founded/Ownrshp* 2004
Sales 20.2MM^E *EMP* 25
SIC 5137 5136 Women's & children's clothing; Men's & boys' clothing
CEO: Jeremy Moon
**Pr:* Lisa Thompson
Opers Mgr: Seth Dennis

ICEC
See OXBOW SULPHUR INC

D-U-N-S 04-742-6747 IMP
■ **ICEE CO**
(*Suby of* J & J SNACK FOODS CORP) ★
1205 S Dupont Ave, Ontario, CA 91761-1536
Tel (909) 390-4233 *Founded/Ownrshp* 1987
Sales 174.9MM^E *EMP* 700
SIC 2038 5145 3559 2087 Frozen specialties; Popcorn & supplies; Plastics working machinery; Flavoring extracts & syrups; Frozen specialties; Popcorn & supplies; Plastics working machinery; Flavoring extracts & syrups
Pr: Gerald B Shreiber
**Pr:* Dan Fachner
**CFO:* Kent Galloway
CFO: Debbie Todd
VP: Scott Carter
**VP:* Rodney N Sexton
Trfc Dir: Richard DOE
Trfc Dir: Vanessa Gutierrez
Trfc Dir: Denise Valenzuela
Opers Mgr: Ernesto Gonzalez
Opers Mgr: Bill Haines

D-U-N-S 04-319-9371
ICEE DISTRIBUTORS LLC
ICEE OF ALABAMA
1513 Swan Lake Rd, Bossier City, LA 71111-5335
Tel (318) 746-4895 *Founded/Ownrshp* 1965, 1978
Sales 49.0MM^E *EMP* 60
SIC 5142 Fruit juices, frozen
Pr: Jarrel Dan Festervan
VP: Carl Deroche

ICEE OF ALABAMA
See ICEE DISTRIBUTORS LLC

ICEF PUBLIC SCHOOLS
See INNER CITY EDUCATION FOUNDATION

D-U-N-S 80-408-6903 IMP/EXP
ICELANDIC NORTHWEST INC
(*Suby of* ICELANDIC GROUP HF.)
14615 Ne N Wodinville Way, Woodinville, WA 98072-8499
Tel (425) 398-9246 *Founded/Ownrshp* 2006
Sales 35.0MM *EMP* 5
SIC 5146 Seafoods; Seafoods
Pr: Peter Trost

D-U-N-S 62-104-8227
ICENHOWER OIL & GAS INC
5916 Industrial Drive Ext, Bossier City, LA 71112-2623
Tel (318) 752-2293 *Founded/Ownrshp* 2007
Sales 179.1MM^E *EMP* 380^E
SIC 1382 Oil & gas exploration services; Oil & gas exploration services
Pr: Tim Icenhower

D-U-N-S 36-117-3321 IMP/EXP
ICEROCK INC
EARTH CORE
6899 Phillips Indus Blvd, Jacksonville, FL 32256-3029
Tel (904) 363-3417 *Founded/Ownrshp* 1988
Sales 34.9MM^E *EMP* 100
SIC 5074 Fireplaces, prefabricated; Fireplaces, prefabricated
CEO: Carl R Spadaro

D-U-N-S 07-618-3909
■ **ICF CONSULTING GROUP INC**
(*Suby of* ICF INTERNATIONAL INC) ★
9300 Lee Hwy, Fairfax, VA 22031-6050
Tel (703) 934-3000 *Founded/Ownrshp* 1969
Sales 949.3MM *EMP* 4,000
SIC 8742 Management consulting services; Management consulting services
CEO: Sudhakar Kesavan
CFO: James C Morgan
Treas: Terrance Mc Govern
Sr VP: Sal Fazzolari
Sr VP: Abyd Karmali
VP: Gray F Michael
VP: Paul Weeks
Prin: Troy Barker
Prin: Rinaldo A Campana
Prgrm Mgr: David Birken

D-U-N-S 07-264-8579
■ **ICF INC LLC**
(*Suby of* ICF CONSULTING GROUP INC) ★
9300 Lee Hwy Ste 200, Fairfax, VA 22031-6051
Tel (703) 934-3000 *Founded/Ownrshp* 1985
Sales 150.4MM^E *EMP* 2,470
SIC 8742 8748 Management consulting services; Business consulting; Management consulting services; Business consulting
Ch Bd: Sudhakar Kesavan
Pr: John Wasson
CFO: James C Morgan
Treas: Terrance Mc Govern
Sr VP: Douglas Beck
Sr VP: James E Daniel
Sr VP: Barbara Rudin

D-U-N-S 02-080-2733
ICF INDUSTRIES INC
617 Main St, Pleasant Hill, MO 64080-1707
Tel (816) 540-4200 *Founded/Ownrshp* 2007
Sales 20.5MM^E *EMP* 90
SIC 3441 Fabricated structural metal
CEO: Robert Krug

D-U-N-S 13-900-1544
▲ **ICF INTERNATIONAL INC**
9300 Lee Hwy Ste 200, Fairfax, VA 22031-6051
Tel (703) 934-3000 *Founded/Ownrshp* 1969
Sales 1.0MMM *EMP* 5,000
Tkr Sym ICFI *Exch* NGS
SIC 8742 8748 Management consulting services; Business consulting; Management consulting services; Business consulting
Ch Bd: Sudhakar Kesavan
Pr: John Wasson
CFO: James C Morgan
Bd of Dir: Edward H Bersoff
Bd of Dir: Larry Kocot
Ex VP: Ellen Glover
Ex VP: Isabel S Reiff
Sr VP: Philip Mihlmester
VP: David Bauer
VP: Douglas Beck
VP: Lisa Bendixen
VP: Erik Buice
VP: Uday Desai
VP: Rick Fioravanti
VP: Courtney Foster
VP: Lisa Gagne
VP: Jeanette Hercik
VP: Ross Kiddie
VP: Kevin Petak
VP: Robert Toth
VP: Irvin Towson
Board of Directors: Eileen O'shea Auen, Edward H Bersoff, Cheryl Grise, Sanjay Gupta, Peter Schulte

D-U-N-S 07-155-5015
■ **ICF JONES & STOKES INC**
(*Suby of* ICF CONSULTING GROUP INC) ★
630 K St Ste 400, Sacramento, CA 95814-3331
Tel (916) 737-3000 *Founded/Ownrshp* 1970, 2008
Sales 49.0MM^E *EMP* 743
SIC 8748 Environmental consultant; Environmental consultant
Pr: Sergio Ostria
**CFO:* Sandra Murray
**Treas:* Terrance Mc Govern

D-U-N-S 06-678-3721
■ **ICF MACRO INC**
(*Suby of* ICF CONSULTING GROUP INC) ★
530 Gaither Rd Ste 500, Rockville, MD 20850-1478
Tel (301) 315-2800 *Founded/Ownrshp* 2009
Sales 47.9MM^E *EMP* 644
SIC 8742 8732 7373 Training & development consultant; Incentive or award program consultant; Hospital & health services consultant; Market analysis, business & economic research; Computer systems analysis & design; Training & development consultant; Incentive or award program consultant; Hospital & health services consultant; Market analysis, business & economic research; Computer systems analysis & design
Pr: Jeanne Townend
COO: Bill Younger
**CFO:* Sandra Murray
**Treas:* Terrance Mc Govern
Sr VP: Mildred Ambrosia
VP: Teri Hunt
IT Man: Leo Shen
Info Man: Kevin Pyles
Board of Directors: John Wasson

D-U-N-S 61-738-8087
■ ICF RESOURCES LLC
(*Suby of* ICF CONSULTING GROUP INC) ★
9300 Lee Hwy, Fairfax, VA 22031-6050
Tel (703) 934-3000 *Founded/Ownrshp* 1999
Sales 39.4MM^E *EMP* 440
SIC 8748 Business consulting; Business consulting
Treas: Debra Lewis
Board of Directors: John Wasson

D-U-N-S 04-827-7800
■ ICF SH&E INC
(*Suby of* ICF CONSULTING GROUP INC) ★
630 3rd Ave Fl 11, New York, NY 10017-6925
Tel (212) 682-8455 *Founded/Ownrshp* 2007
Sales 22.5MM *EMP* 65
SIC 8732 8741 8742 Economic research; Financial management for business; Transportation consultant; Economic research; Financial management for business; Transportation consultant
Ch Bd: Sergio Ostria
CFO: Sandra Murray
Treas: Terrance Mc Govern
VP: Donald S Garvett

D-U-N-S 78-829-1789
■ ICF Z-TECH INC
(*Suby of* ICF CONSULTING GROUP INC) ★
530 Gaither Rd, Rockville, MD 20850-1381
Tel (301) 315-2800 *Founded/Ownrshp* 2007
Sales 48.5MM *EMP* 72
SIC 8742 Management consulting services; Management consulting services
Pr: John Wasson
CFO: Sandra Murray
Treas: Terrance McGovern
VP: Donald McMaster
VP: Candice Mendenhall
VP: John Smith
VP: Clyde A Wurster
Board of Directors: Ellen Glover

ICG
See INTERNATIONAL CRISIS GROUP

I.C.G.
See INTERSTATE CONSTRUCTION GROUP INC

D-U-N-S 11-910-1269
ICG ADDCAR SYSTEMS LLC
(*Suby of* UGM HOLDINGS PTY LIMITED)
No1 Hwm Dr, Ashland, KY 41102
Tel (606) 928-7244 *Founded/Ownrshp* 2014
Sales 35.5MM^E *EMP* 125
SIC 3532 Mining machinery; Mining machinery
Pr: Neil Novak

ICG HOLLISTON
See HOLLISTON LLC

D-U-N-S 78-517-9602
■ ICG ILLINOIS LLC
(*Suby of* INTERNATIONAL COAL GROUP INC) ★
8100 E Main St, Williamsville, IL 62693-9187
Tel (217) 566-3006 *Founded/Ownrshp* 2011
Sales 31.3MM^E *EMP* 300
SIC 1241 Coal mining services; Coal mining services
Pr: Robert Gardiner

D-U-N-S 61-484-4590
■ ICG LLC
(*Suby of* INTERNATIONAL COAL GROUP INC) ★
114 Smiley Dr, Saint Albans, WV 25177-1504
Tel (304) 760-2400 *Founded/Ownrshp* 2004
Sales 147.2MM^E *EMP* 3,500
SIC 1241 Coal mining services; Coal mining services
Pr: Bennett K Hatfield
VP Sls: Bud Runyon

D-U-N-S 88-398-0179
ICH GROUP LLC
500 Kuwili St Ste 100, Honolulu, HI 96817-5355
Tel (808) 531-6671 *Founded/Ownrshp* 1988
Sales 8.5MM *EMP* 300
SIC 5141 Food brokers; Food brokers
CEO: Kenneth long
**Pr:* Glenn Wong
**VP:* Dorothy Yung

ICHABOD CRANE CENTRAL SCHOOL
See KINDERHOOK CENTRAL SCHOOL DISTRICT

D-U-N-S 80-978-0141 IMP
ICHIA USA INC
(*Suby of* ICHIA TECHNOLOGIES, INC.)
509 Telegraph Canyon Rd, Chula Vista, CA 91910-6436
Tel (619) 482-2222 *Founded/Ownrshp* 1993
Sales 23.7MM^E *EMP* 200
SIC 3674 Semiconductors & related devices
Genl Mgr: Simon Goh

D-U-N-S 61-708-6512
ICHOR SYSTEMS INC
3185 Laurelview Ct, Fremont, CA 94538-6535
Tel (510) 897-5200 *Founded/Ownrshp* 2009
Sales 10.4MM^E *EMP* 500
SIC 3674 Semiconductors & related devices
CEO: Tom Rohrs
Pr: Mark Hutson
CFO: Maurice Carson
Sr VP: Phil Barros

D-U-N-S 83-253-6796 IMP
ICHOR SYSTEMS INC
(*Suby of* FP) ★
9660 Sw Herman Rd, Tualatin, OR 97062-7905
Tel (503) 625-2251 *Founded/Ownrshp* 2012
Sales 106.7MM^E *EMP* 426
SIC 3559 5984 Semiconductor manufacturing machinery; Liquefied petroleum gas dealers; Semiconductor manufacturing machinery; Liquefied petroleum gas dealers
Pr: Andrew Kowal
**Pr:* Maurice Carson
Pr: Peter English
**Pr:* Mark Hutson
**CEO:* Thomas M Rohrs
**Sr VP:* Phil R Barros
**Sr VP:* Mark A Thomas
Snr Sftwr: Kelly Pustejovsky
IT Man: Huey Burke
VP Opers: Kim McGuire
Opers Mgr: Faisal Bholat

D-U-N-S 79-786-5540 IMP
ICI AMERICA INC
(*Suby of* ICI AMERICAN HOLDINGS LLC) ★
10 Finderne Ave, Bridgewater, NJ 08807-3365
Tel (908) 203-2800 *Founded/Ownrshp* 1966
Sales 106.1MM^E *EMP* 3,000
SIC 2821 3081 2869 2843 2865 Acrylic resins; Polyurethane resins; Unsupported plastics film & sheet; Industrial organic chemicals; Surface active agents; Cyclic crudes & intermediates; Acrylic resins; Polyurethane resins; Unsupported plastics film & sheet; Industrial organic chemicals; Surface active agents; Cyclic crudes & intermediates
Ch Bd: William H Power
CFO: Tim Brownlee
**CFO:* R J Forrest
**Treas:* R Timothy Brownlee
**VP:* Clive A Grannum
Mng Dir: Ken Dowling

D-U-N-S 79-867-2218 IMP
ICI AMERICAN HOLDINGS LLC
PERMABOND AMERICAS
(*Suby of* IMPERIAL CHEMICAL INDUSTRIES LIMITED)
10 Finderne Ave, Bridgewater, NJ 08807-3365
Tel (908) 203-2800 *Founded/Ownrshp* 1992
Sales 550.9MM^E *EMP* 14,800
SIC 2851 2821 3081 2869 2843 2865 Paints & allied products; Paints: oil or alkyd vehicle or water thinned; Enamels; Lacquer: bases, dopes, thinner; Acrylic resins; Polyurethane resins; Unsupported plastics film & sheet; Industrial organic chemicals; Surface active agents; Cyclic crudes & intermediates; Paints & allied products; Paints: oil or alkyd vehicle or water thinned; Enamels; Lacquer: bases, dopes, thinner; Acrylic resins; Polyurethane resins; Unsupported plastics film & sheet; Industrial organic chemicals; Surface active agehts; Cyclic crudes & intermediates
VP: Stephen Bradford
Genl Mgr: Tony Woodiwiss

D-U-N-S 19-457-5619
ICI BINDING CORP
8834 Mayfield Rd Ste A, Chesterland, OH 44026-2696
Tel (440) 729-2445 *Founded/Ownrshp* 1957
Sales 43.3MM^E *EMP* 540
SIC 2789 Bookbinding & related work; Bookbinding & related work
Pr: Jay Fairfield

D-U-N-S 06-114-4291 EXP
ICI CONSTRUCTION INC
24715 W Hardy Rd, Spring, TX 77373-5764
Tel (281) 355-5151 *Founded/Ownrshp* 1982
Sales 165.7MM *EMP* 102
Accts Cornwell Jackson Pllc Plano
SIC 1542 Commercial & office building, new construction; School building construction; Commercial & office buildings, renovation & repair; Commercial & office building, new construction; School building construction; Commercial & office buildings, renovation & repair
Pr: Russell Cobb
**Treas:* Tom Cobb
**Sr VP:* Chris Sidwa
**VP:* B J Cobb
VP: Chris Graves
**VP:* Steve Williams

D-U-N-S 36-409-8566 IMP
ICI METALS INC
12609 Alameda Dr, Strongsville, OH 44149-3028
Tel (440) 846-9500 *Founded/Ownrshp* 1975
Sales 20.5MM^E *EMP* 20
SIC 5051 Steel; Aluminum bars, rods, ingots, sheets, pipes, plates, etc.; Copper products
Pr: Daniel P Caine
Sales Asso: John Murrey

D-U-N-S 96-734-2510
ICI SEEDS INC
SYNGENTA
2369 330th St, Slater, IA 50244-7798
Tel (515) 685-5000 *Founded/Ownrshp* 2004
Sales NA *EMP* 625
SIC 2899 8731 5191 0723

D-U-N-S 09-512-9859
ICI SERVICES CORP
500 Viking Dr Ste 200, Virginia Beach, VA 23452-7487
Tel (757) 340-6970 *Founded/Ownrshp* 1999
Sales 63.6MM^E *EMP* 360
Accts Wall Einhorn & Chernitzer Pc
SIC 8711 Professional engineer; Professional engineer
Pr: Dennis M McCarley
**Treas:* Jay Harrison
Ofcr: Kirsten Wilson
Ex VP: Lynda Badran
Sr VP: Robin Mickle
VP: Sandra Besora
**VP:* Clifford Campbell
VP: Donald Frahler
VP: Ted Fredrick
VP: Mike Harmon
VP: Kevin Lees
VP: Rich Miner
VP: Karen Teets

ICIA
See INTERNATIONAL COMMUNICATIONS INDUSTRIES ASSOCIATION INC

D-U-N-S 00-948-4908 IMP/EXP
ICICLE SEAFOODS INC
SEWARD FISHERIES
4019 21st Ave W Ste 300, Seattle, WA 98199-1299
Tel (206) 282-0988 *Founded/Ownrshp* 1965
Sales 241.3MM^E *EMP* 500
SIC 2092 2091 Shellfish, frozen: prepared; Fish, frozen: prepared; Salmon: packaged in cans, jars, etc.; Shellfish, frozen: prepared; Fish, frozen: prepared; Salmon: packaged in cans, jars, etc.
CEO: Chris Ruettgers
Ch Bd: Amy Humphreys
Pr: Guhlke Dennis J
Pr: Ladon Johnson
COO: Tony Jolley
CFO: Robert Vonneveld
Treas: Zonneveld Robert
Treas: Robert Zonneveld
Ex VP: Tammy French
VP: Alan Cook
VP: Woodruff John
VP: John Woodruff
VP Bus Dev: Christopher Ruettgers

D-U-N-S 01-979-7468
ICIMS.COM INC
90 Matawan Rd Fl 500, Matawan, NJ 07747-2624
Tel (732) 847-1941 *Founded/Ownrshp* 1999
Sales 47.4MM *EMP* 240^E
Accts Deloitte & Touche Llp Parsipp
SIC 7371 Custom computer programming services; Custom computer programming services
Pr: Colin Day
**COO:* Adam Feigenbaum
**Ch:* Gwo Ching Liou
Bd of Dir: Amir Goldman
Sr VP: Michael Wilczak
VP: Jess Gaetano
VP: Tyler Kimble
VP: Devon Quaglietta
VP: Al Smith
Off Admin: Ciara Lake
Snr Sftwr: Leonard Cacciatore

ICL
See INSTITUTE FOR COMMUNITY LIVING INC

ICL INDUSTRIAL PRODUCTS
See ICL-IP AMERICA INC

D-U-N-S 96-226-5885 IMP/EXP
ICL NORTH AMERICA INC
(*Suby of* ISRAEL CHEMICALS LTD.)
622 Emerson Rd Ste 500, Saint Louis, MO 63141-6742
Tel (314) 983-7500 *Founded/Ownrshp* 2010
Sales 132.9MM^E *EMP* 550^E
SIC 2819 Chemicals, high purity: refined from technical grade; Chemicals, high purity: refined from technical grade
CEO: Charles M Weidhas
**VP:* Anantha Desikan
**VP:* Paul M Schlessman

D-U-N-S 08-527-1638
ICL PERFORMANCE PRODUCTS LP
(*Suby of* ISRAEL CHEMICALS LTD.)
622 Emerson Rd Ste 500, Saint Louis, MO 63141-6742
Tel (314) 983-7500 *Founded/Ownrshp* 2005
Sales 245.0MM^E *EMP* 550
SIC 2819 Chemicals, high purity: refined from technical grade; Chemicals, high purity: refined from technical grade
Pr: Mark Volmer
Pr: Thomas York
CFO: Paul Schlessman
VP: Michael Bork
VP: Bruene Cremer
VP: Heather Luther
VP: Deborah Tallo
VP: Terry Zerr
Dir Lab: Markadams Adams
CIO: Christy M Barker
QA Dir: Gary Heiserman

D-U-N-S 83-277-4413 IMP/EXP
ICL-IP AMERICA INC
ICL INDUSTRIAL PRODUCTS
(*Suby of* ICL NORTH AMERICA INC) ★
622 Emerson Rd Ste 500, Saint Louis, MO 63141-6742
Tel (877) 661-4272 *Founded/Ownrshp* 2007
Sales 65.1MM^E *EMP* 168
SIC 2819 Industrial inorganic chemicals; Industrial inorganic chemicals
CEO: Charles Weidhas
**Pr:* Willem Hofland
**Ch:* Paul Schlessman
**Sr VP:* Allen Tillman
S&M/VP: Mike Goode
Counsel: Steven Smart

ICM
See IMPROVED CONSTRUCTION METHODS INC

ICM
See INTERNATIONAL CONTROLS & MEASUREMENTS CORP

D-U-N-S 78-059-4458
ICM DISTRIBUTING CO INC
INVENTORY CONTROLLED MDSG
(*Suby of* SANDUSCO INC) ★
1755 Entp Pkwy Ste 200, Twinsburg, OH 44087
Tel (234) 212-3030 *Founded/Ownrshp* 2006
Sales 29.8MM^E *EMP* 35
SIC 5122 5049 5199 5092 Hair preparations; Cosmetics; School supplies; General merchandise, nondurable; Toys
Pr: Harry Singer
**VP:* Phillip B Singer
VP Sls: Mark Rosemeyer

D-U-N-S 05-353-8260
ICM HOLDINGS INC (NY)
40 W 57th St Fl 16, New York, NY 10019-4001
Tel (212) 556-5600 *Founded/Ownrshp* 1966, 1988
Sales 30.3MM^E *EMP* 727
SIC 7922 Talent agent, theatrical; Talent agent, theatrical
Ch: Jeffrey Berg
Pr: James A Wiatt
CFO: Robert Murphy
V Ch Bd: Samuel C Cohn
V Ch Bd: Ralph Mann
Counsel: Wayne Kabak

D-U-N-S 83-468-3369
ICM INC
310 N 1st St, Colwich, KS 67030-9655
Tel (316) 796-0900 *Founded/Ownrshp* 1995
Sales 58.5MM^E *EMP* 440
SIC 8748 5153 8711 Marketing consulting services; Grain & field beans; Consulting engineer; Construction & civil engineering; Energy conservation consultant; Grain & field beans; Consulting engineer; Construction & civil engineering
CEO: David Vander Griend
COO: Eric Mork
CFO: Andy Bulloch
Ex VP: Jill Mitchell
VP: Brock Beach
VP: Brad Box
VP: Jeff Roskam
Dir Lab: Jackie Lissolo
Area Mgr: Adam Anderson
Off Mgr: Reva Carlson
IT Man: Mike Spellman

ICMA
See INTERNATIONAL CITY/COUNTY MANAGEMENT ASSOCIATION

ICMA RETIREMENT
See INTERNATIONAL CITY MANAGEMENT ASSOCIATION RETIREMENT CORP

D-U-N-S 07-079-6743 IMP/EXP
■ ICO - SCHULMAN LLC
(*Suby of* A SCHULMAN INC) ★
24624 Interstate 45, Spring, TX 77386-4084
Tel (832) 663-3131 *Founded/Ownrshp* 2010
Sales 246.4MM^E *EMP* 3,000^E
SIC 2821 Plastics materials & resins; Plastics materials & resins
Pr: Joseph Gingo
Pr: David J Phillips
Treas: Joseph J Levanduski
Bd of Dir: Charles T McCord
VP: Paul Giddens
VP: Andy Ubhi

ICO BUSINESS OUTFITTERS
See ICO COMPANIES INC

D-U-N-S 13-539-5627 IMP/EXP
ICO COMPANIES INC
ICO BUSINESS OUTFITTERS
6330 Ne 4th Ct, Miami, FL 33138-6108
Tel (305) 751-6133 *Founded/Ownrshp* 2002
Sales 25.2MM^E *EMP* 58
SIC 5136 5699 2326 Men's & boys' clothing; Uniforms; Work uniforms
Pr: James Turk
VP: Mike Scornavacca
**VP:* Scott Turk
CTO: Kalila Moorehead

D-U-N-S 07-867-2448
ICO LLC
70 E Main St Ste B, Greenwood, IN 46143-4201
Tel (317) 865-9700 *Founded/Ownrshp* 1995
Sales 16.7MM^E *EMP* 600
SIC 5431 Fruit & vegetable markets; Fruit & vegetable markets
CEO: William Vidal
Genl Mgr: Vincent Morel

D-U-N-S 36-149-9064 IMP
■ ICO POLYMERS NORTH AMERICA INC
ICO TECHNOLOGIES
(*Suby of* ICO - SCHULMAN LLC) ★
24624 Interstate 45, Spring, TX 77386-4084
Tel (832) 663-3131 *Founded/Ownrshp* 1996
Sales 40.4MM^E *EMP* 300
SIC 3089 Extruded finished plastic products; Extruded finished plastic products
CEO: Joseph Gingo
**Ch Bd:* Gregory T Barmore
**CFO:* Jon Biro
**Sr VP:* Joseph Levanduski
**Sr VP:* David Minc
Plnt Mgr: Johan Lemarchand
Sls Mgr: Joel Porter

ICO RALLY
See INSULATION SOURCES INC

ICO TECHNOLOGIES
See ICO POLYMERS NORTH AMERICA INC

ICOFFEE BY REMINGTON
See REMINGTON DESIGNS LLC

D-U-N-S 03-799-9331 IMP/EXP
ICOM AMERICA INC
(*Suby of* ICOM INCORPORATED)
12421 Willows Rd Ne # 200, Kirkland, WA 98034-8736
Tel (425) 454-8155 *Founded/Ownrshp* 1979
Sales 76.7MM^E *EMP* 110
SIC 5065 Communication equipment; Amateur radio communications equipment; Radio & television equipment & parts; Communication equipment; Amateur radio communications equipment; Radio & television equipment & parts
Pr: Hiroshi Nakaoka
VP: Bob Carey
Exec: Deborah Paulsson
Prin: Rick Burke
Div Mgr: Ray Novak
MIS Dir: Dean Benidict
IT Man: Rob Johnson
Opers Mgr: Dick Varbero
Natl Sales: Joe Collica
Sls&Mrk Ex: Masahiro Hiranuma
Advt Dir: David Kruzic

D-U-N-S 03-462-6325
ICOM MECHANICAL INC
477 Burke St, San Jose, CA 95112-4101
Tel (408) 292-4968 *Founded/Ownrshp* 1981
Sales 66.6MM^E *EMP* 225
SIC 1711 Plumbing, heating, air-conditioning contractors; Mechanical contractor; Plumbing, heating, air-conditioning contractors; Mechanical contractor
CEO: Donald George Isaacson
**Pr:* Dane Littleton

*CFO: Elizabeth Wozniak
*VP: Alan Glace
VP: Alan Grace
*VP: Tom Radich
Sys Mgr: Brett Erickson

ICOMM
See CREATIVE COMMERCE LLC

D-U-N-S 00-777-5752
ICOMM CORP (MI)
I.COMM
24600 N Industrial Dr, Farmington Hills, MI 48335-1553
Tel (248) 960-3700 Founded/Ownrshp 1943, 1989
Sales 23.0MM^E EMP 75
SIC 1731 Sound equipment specialization
Pr: Fred Shuart
*VP: Ray Gries
*VP: Ewa Kaczmarczyk
Brnch Mgr: John Hill
IT Man: Laurie Moore
Sls Dir: John Flanagan
Board of Directors: John J Harvey

ICON
See INDUSTRIAL CONSTRUCTION AND DESIGN INC

D-U-N-S 96-773-4158
ICON ACQUISITION HOLDINGS LP
680 N Lake Shore Dr, Chicago, IL 60611-4546
Tel (312) 751-8000 Founded/Ownrshp 2010
Sales 61.3MM^E EMP 550^E
SIC 7812 4841 2721 Motion picture production; Cable & other pay television services; Periodicals; Motion picture production; Cable & other pay television services; Periodicals
Genl Pt: Scott N Flanders

D-U-N-S 82-693-5699
ICON AG SOLUTIONS LLC
JOHN DEERE
4511 Eagle Ave, Ireton, IA 51027-7560
Tel (712) 278-2351 Founded/Ownrshp 2006
Sales 21.2MM^E EMP 90
SIC 5083 7699 Farm implements; Farm machinery repair; Farm implements; Farm machinery repair
Store Mgr: Mark Pierce
Store Mgr: Tom Winter
Sls Mgr: Denny O'Bryan

D-U-N-S 78-848-1039
ICON AIRCRAFT INC
2141 Icon Way, Vacaville, CA 95688-8766
Tel (707) 564-4000 Founded/Ownrshp 2006
Sales 24.1MM^E EMP 55
SIC 3728 Aircraft parts & equipment
CEO: Kirk Hawkins
COO: Chris Dawson
COO: Steen Strand
CFO: David Crook
CFO: Chris King
VP: Craig Bowers
VP: Matthew Gionta
VP: Bill James
VP: Klaus Tritschler
VP: Thomas Wieners
Prgrm Mgr: Michael Emanuel
Board of Directors: Bart Becht

D-U-N-S 79-880-0343
ICON BANK OF TEXAS NATIONAL ASSOCIATION
7908 N Sam Houston Pkwy S, Houston, TX 77064
Tel (281) 517-2400 Founded/Ownrshp 2007
Sales NA EMP 68^E
SIC 6021 National commercial banks; National commercial banks
Prin: Chris B Kelley
Pr: Jessica Cassidy
COO: Mark Reiley
CFO: Chris Kelley
Treas: Barbara Middlebrook
Ex VP: KY Troyer
Sr VP: Tracy Dixon
Sr VP: Jamie Elmore-Kelly
Sr VP: Chuck Harris
Sr VP: Nathan Kerr
Sr VP: John Shirley
Sr VP: Gordon Stinson
VP: Leigh Martinez
VP: Julie Zaleski

D-U-N-S 15-480-6012
ICON CAPITAL CORP
ICON INVESTMENTS
(Suby of ICON HOLDINGS CORP) ★
3 Park Ave Fl 36, New York, NY 10016-5902
Tel (646) 845-2585 Founded/Ownrshp 1996
Sales 20.5MM^E EMP 108
SIC 7359 Equipment rental & leasing; Equipment rental & leasing
CEO: Micheal A Reisner
*Pr: Mark Gatto
Chf Cred: Jason Ng
*Ex VP: Douglas Crossman
*Ex VP: Derek O'Leary
VP: John Abney
VP: John Cardillo
VP: Drew Frevert
VP: Craig Jackson
VP: Lucas Kraft
VP: Derek Schwartz
VP: Nicholas Sinigaglia
VP: Beth Wilson
Assoc Dir: Dana Elder
Assoc Dir: Mark Llewellyn
Assoc Dir: Sooji Park

D-U-N-S 17-930-8267
ICON CENTRAL LABORATORIES INC
(Suby of ICON PUBLIC LIMITED COMPANY)
123 Smith St, Farmingdale, NY 11735-1004
Tel (631) 777-8833 Founded/Ownrshp 1994
Sales 199.8MM^E EMP 8,500
SIC 8071 8734 Medical laboratories; Testing laboratories; Medical laboratories; Testing laboratories
CEO: Ciaran Murray
*Pr: Robert Scott Edwards
Ex VP: Andrew Kraus
VP: Eimear Kenny
*VP: Dr Nuala Murphy
VP: Jim Wagner
Assoc Dir: Steve Ioannou
Dir Bus: Brian Colfer
Dir Bus: Charlie Keyes
Genl Mgr: Clare Osullivan
IT Man: Jessica Reres

ICON CLINICAL RESEARCH
See ICON DEVELOPMENT SOLUTIONS LLC

D-U-N-S 87-288-5173
ICON CLINICAL RESEARCH LLC
ICON DEVELOPMENT SOLUTIONS
(Suby of ICON CLINICAL RESEARCH LIMITED)
2100 Pennbrook Pkwy, North Wales, PA 19454-4105
Tel (215) 616-3000 Founded/Ownrshp 1992
Sales 125.3MM^E EMP 654
SIC 8731 Commercial physical research; Commercial physical research
CEO: Bill Taaffe
Pr: Laura Johnson
*Pr: William Taaffe
*COO: John W Hubbard
CFO: George McMillan
*Treas: David Peters
Sr VP: Jody Fleisig
VP: Ray Briggs
VP: Todd Czajka
VP: Robert Hughes
VP: Eimear Kenny
VP: Tom Ludden
VP: Scott Neff
VP: Adrian Pencak
VP: Kate Tranotti
Assoc Dir: Laura Capicchioni
Assoc Dir: Tom McCloskey

ICON DEVELOPMENT SOLUTIONS
See ICON CLINICAL RESEARCH LLC

D-U-N-S 83-041-8658
ICON DEVELOPMENT SOLUTIONS LLC
ICON CLINICAL RESEARCH
(Suby of ICON PUBLIC LIMITED COMPANY)
820 W Diamond Ave Ste 100, Gaithersburg, MD 20878-1419
Tel (301) 944-6810 Founded/Ownrshp 1997
Sales 15.0MM EMP 10,000
SIC 8733 Noncommercial research organizations
CEO: Ciaran Murray
Ch: Thomas Lynch
Sr VP: Stuart Madden
VP: Ralf Brueckner
VP: Adrian Pencak
Assoc Dir: Chad Pollio
Mng Dir: Timothy J Myers
IT Man: Candy Dehn

D-U-N-S 96-833-3174
ICON ECI FUND FIFTEEN LP
100 5th Ave Fl 4, New York, NY 10011-6910
Tel (212) 418-4700 Founded/Ownrshp 2011
Sales 37.3MM EMP 2
Accts Ernst & Young Llp New York N
SIC 7359 Equipment rental & leasing; Equipment rental & leasing

D-U-N-S 88-300-3113
ICON ENTERPRISES INC
CIVICPLUS
302 S 4th St Ste 500, Manhattan, KS 66502-6410
Tel (785) 587-1853 Founded/Ownrshp 1994
Sales 37.4MM^E EMP 200
SIC 7374 Computer graphics service; Computer graphics service
CEO: Ward Morgan
V Ch: Hal Rose
Bd of Dir: Eric Ames
*VP: Tony Gagnon
VP: John Pagen
Creative D: Jeff Baker
CIO: Warren Bert
CTO: Keith Womack
IT Man: Lindsey Rogge
Software D: Luis Carranco
Software D: Matt Flavin

D-U-N-S 83-038-7374
ICON EQUIPMENT AND CORPORATE INFRASTRUCTURE FUND FOURTEEN LP
100 5th Ave Fl 4, New York, NY 10011-6910
Tel (212) 418-4700 Founded/Ownrshp 2009
Sales 40.8MM EMP 2^E
Accts Ernst & Young Llp New York N
SIC 7359 Equipment rental & leasing; Equipment rental & leasing
Prin: Cheryl Brown

D-U-N-S 80-817-7661 IMP
ICON EYEWEAR INC
5 Empire Blvd, South Hackensack, NJ 07606-1805
Tel (201) 330-9333 Founded/Ownrshp 1993
Sales 130.2MM^E EMP 130^E
Accts Josephson Luxenberg Kance And
SIC 5099 Sunglasses; Sunglasses
Ch Bd: Michael Chang
*Pr: Bruce Bartley
*Ex VP: Julie Chang
Ex VP: Karen Goh
Ex VP: George Hanley
*Ex VP: Joe Massa
*VP: Mike Cotton
CIO: Jack Woods
Natl Sales: Dyanne Baldwin

D-U-N-S 08-392-2229 EXP
ICON HEALTH & FITNESS INC
HEALTHRIDER
1500 S 1000 W, Logan, UT 84321-8206
Tel (435) 750-5000 Founded/Ownrshp 2006
Sales 1.1MMM^E EMP 3,263
SIC 3949 Treadmills; Exercising cycles; Gymnasium equipment; Treadmills; Exercising cycles; Gymnasium equipment
Ch Bd: Scott R Watterson
*Pr: David J Watterson
COO: M Brough
CFO: Fred Beck
*CFO: S Fred Beck
*V Ch Bd: Robert C Gay
*Chf Mktg O: Matthew N Allen
Sr VP: Jay Kirkham
Sr VP: Jon M White
VP: William Dalebout
VP: Rick Dawson
VP: Ryan Dunkley
VP: Tann Tueller
VP: Blake Watterson
Comm Man: Melanie Jensen
Board of Directors: W Steve Albrecht, Gregory Benson, Alan H Freudenstein, Lester W B Moore, Gary E Stevenson, Scott R Watterson

D-U-N-S 15-030-4855
■ **ICON HOLDING CORP**
ICON INTERNATIONAL
(Suby of OMNICOM GROUP INC) ★
107 Elm St Fl 15, Stamford, CT 06902-3834
Tel (203) 328-2300 Founded/Ownrshp 2000
Sales 797.3MM^E EMP 200
SIC 7389 7319 Barter exchange; Media buying service; Barter exchange; Media buying service
Pr: John P Kramer
*CFO: Clarence V Lee III
Chf Cred: Christopher Levy

D-U-N-S 96-947-9179
ICON HOLDINGS CORP
3 Park Ave Fl 36, New York, NY 10016-5902
Tel (212) 418-4700 Founded/Ownrshp 1996
Sales 31.7MM^E EMP 200^E
SIC 6211 Brokers, security; Dealers, security; Brokers, security; Dealers, security
CEO: Michael A Reisner
*Ex VP: Douglas Crossman
VP: Gregory Schill
*Prin: Mark Gatto

D-U-N-S 00-511-9714
ICON IDENTITY SOLUTIONS INC (IL)
1418 Elmhurst Rd, Elk Grove Village, IL 60007-6417
Tel (847) 364-2250 Founded/Ownrshp 1925, 1997
Sales 102.5MM EMP 450
Accts Mcgladrey Llp Chicago Il
SIC 3993 Signs & advertising specialties; Neon signs; Signs & advertising specialties; Neon signs
Pr: Kurt Ripkey
*CFO: John Callan
Ex VP: Thomas Hunt
*Ex VP: Tom Hunt
*Ex VP: Melanee Jech
Ex VP: Douglas Long
*Ex VP: John Noonan
Sr VP: Evan Wollak
VP: Matt Czyl
VP: Jeff Dickinson
VP: Jim Erickson
VP: Gus Holt
VP: Laura Monroe
VP: Bill Reavey
VP: Jeff Skoumal

D-U-N-S 01-402-9925
ICON INFORMATION CONSULTANTS LP
100 Waugh Dr Ste 300, Houston, TX 77007-5962
Tel (713) 438-0919 Founded/Ownrshp 1997
Sales 53.2MM^E EMP 716
SIC 7361 7363 7374 Placement agencies; Labor contractors (employment agency); Temporary help service; Data processing & preparation; Placement agencies; Labor contractors (employment agency); Temporary help service; Data processing & preparation
CEO: Pamela A Chambers O Rourke
Pt: Timothy L O'Rourke
Ex Dir: Pamela Orouke
Software D: Dawn Peck

ICON INTERNATIONAL
See ICON HOLDING CORP

D-U-N-S 13-175-7304
■ **ICON INTERNATIONAL INC**
(Suby of ICON HOLDING CORP) ★
4 Stamford Plz 15th, Stamford, CT 06902-3834
Tel (203) 328-2300 Founded/Ownrshp 1985
Sales 797.3MM EMP 200
SIC 7389 7319 Barter exchange; Media buying service; Barter exchange; Media buying service
CEO: John P Kramer
Chf Cred: Christopher Levy
Ex VP: Peter Benassi
*Ex VP: Clarence V Lee III
Ex VP: John Matluck
Ex VP: Ed McCarrick
Ex VP: Richard Upton
VP: Tom Bartholomew
VP: Joanne Cancro
VP: Kelly Emmert
VP: Jerry Padilla
*VP: Gary Perlman
VP: Steven Raider
VP: Bob Schindele
VP: John Stofka
VP: William Sullivan
VP: Jack Testani
VP: Maureen Walsh
VP Bus Dev: Daniel Barutio
Assoc Dir: Sean Kornfeld

ICON INVESTMENTS
See ICON CAPITAL CORP

D-U-N-S 96-253-7275
ICON LEASING FUND TWELVE LLC
100 5th Ave Fl 4, New York, NY 10011-6910
Tel (212) 418-4700 Founded/Ownrshp 2010
Sales 91.2MM EMP 4
SIC 6722 Money market mutual funds

ICON MATERIALS
See CPM DEVELOPMENT CORP

D-U-N-S 88-419-6106
ICON MECHANICAL CONSTRUCTION AND ENGINEERING LLC
1616 Cleveland Blvd, Granite City, IL 62040-4401
Tel (618) 452-0035 Founded/Ownrshp 1995
Sales 59.0MM EMP 250
Accts Crowe Horwath Llp South Bend
SIC 8711 3498 Engineering services; Fabricated pipe & fittings; Engineering services; Fabricated pipe & fittings
Pr: Michael F Bieg
VP: Todd Jeffries
VP: Timothy Schaeffer
Sfty Dirs: Mike Buchana
Snr PM: Matt Lanahan

D-U-N-S 18-141-7572
ICON METAL FORMING LLC
(Suby of MARTINREA INDUSTRIES INC) ★
2190 Landmark Ave Ne, Corydon, IN 47112-2016
Tel (812) 738-5900 Founded/Ownrshp 2005
Sales 84.5MM^E EMP 380
SIC 3714 1761 Motor vehicle parts & accessories; Sheet metalwork; Motor vehicle parts & accessories; Sheet metalwork
Genl Mgr: John Munroe
Ql Cn Mgr: Darrel Patterson
Ql Cn Mgr: Leroy Sparks

D-U-N-S 05-665-3884
ICON METALCRAFT INC
940 Dillon Dr, Wood Dale, IL 60191-1233
Tel (630) 766-5600 Founded/Ownrshp 1971
Sales 26.5MM^E EMP 105
SIC 3444 3544 Sheet metal specialties, not stamped; Special dies & tools
CEO: Silvia McLain
*VP: Saul Soto
Plnt Mgr: Tom Harman

ICON PROFESSIONAL SERVICES
See IC COMPLIANCE LLC

ICONECTIV
See TELCORDIA TECHNOLOGIES INC

D-U-N-S 12-500-1149 EXP
ICONICS INC
100 Foxborough Blvd # 130, Foxboro, MA 02035-2883
Tel (508) 543-8600 Founded/Ownrshp 1986
Sales 31.4MM^E EMP 125
SIC 7371 7372

D-U-N-S 09-482-5262
▲ **ICONIX BRAND GROUP INC**
1450 Broadway Fl 3, New York, NY 10018-2232
Tel (212) 730-0030 Founded/Ownrshp 1978
Sales 461.2MM EMP 150^E
Tkr Sym ICON Exch NGS
SIC 6794 3143 3144 Patent buying, licensing, leasing; Men's footwear, except athletic; Women's footwear, except athletic; Patent buying, licensing, leasing; Men's footwear, except athletic; Women's footwear, except athletic
Ch Bd: Peter Cuneo
CFO: David Blumberg
CFO: David K Jones
Ofcr: Carla Crawford
Ex VP: Jason Schaefer
Ex VP: Andrew Tarshis
Sr VP: Marc San Angelo
VP: Ericka Alford
VP: Aaron Kopelowitz
VP: Kimberly Lee Minor
VP: Lanie Pilnock
VP: Deborah Stehr
Board of Directors: Drew Cohen, F Peter Cuneo, Barry Emanuel, Mark Friedman, Sue Gove, James A Marcum

D-U-N-S 00-649-3691
ICONMA LLC (OR)
850 Stephenson Hwy, Troy, MI 48083-1127
Tel (248) 583-1930 Founded/Ownrshp 2000
Sales 142.4MM^E EMP 1,556
SIC 7363 Help supply services; Temporary help service; Help supply services; Temporary help service
CEO: Claudine S George
*VP: William Pelletier
*VP: Sat Yalaman
VP Bus Dev: Tracey Larowe
Exec: Vijaya Lakshmi
Genl Mgr: Bhaskar RAO
Opers Mgr: Deepak Kumar
Natl Sales: Lauren Clark
Natl Sales: Jessica Snow
Natl Sales: Autumn Warman

D-U-N-S 01-094-1540
ICORE INTERNATIONAL INC
(Suby of ZODIAC US CORP) ★
3780 Flightline Dr, Santa Rosa, CA 95403-1054
Tel (707) 535-2750 Founded/Ownrshp 2004
Sales 92.2MM^E EMP 205
SIC 3089 Molding primary plastic; Molding primary plastic
CEO: Ted Perdue
*CFO: Arnold Nixon
VP: Ian Humphries
*VP: Mark McGrath
Sls Dir: Gail Isobe

D-U-N-S 55-680-7944
ICORE NETWORKS INC
7900 Westpark Dr Ste A315, Mc Lean, VA 22102-4235
Tel (703) 673-1350 Founded/Ownrshp 2001
Sales 46.6MM EMP 190
SIC 4813 7379 Telephone communication, except radio; Computer related consulting services

ICP
See ISLAND COMPUTER PRODUCTS INC

D-U-N-S 01-642-5816
ICR INC
1 Ocean Blvd, Long Branch, NJ 07740-6754
Tel (732) 571-4000 Founded/Ownrshp 2000
Sales 2.7MM^E EMP 400^E
SIC 7011 5813 5812

Genl Mgr: Scott Span

ICR SERVICES
See INDUSTRIAL CONTROL REPAIR INC

D-U-N-S 61-079-0276 IMP
ICRCO INC
26 Coromar Dr, Goleta, CA 93117-3024
Tel (310) 530-5035 *Founded/Ownrshp* 2004
Sales 24.7MM^E *EMP* 110
SIC 3845 Laser systems & equipment, medical; Laser systems & equipment, medical
CEO: Stephen Neushul
Pr: Janet Burki
**Pr:* Mark Valentine
CFO: Linda Pahl
CFO: Linda Paul
Dir Lab: MO Duwaik
CTO: Daniel Valentino
Tech Mgr: Abhinav Sing
Web Dev: Shelton Johnson
Sftwr Eng: Dhaval Joshi
VP Sls: Felipe Carrera

D-U-N-S 00-722-3964 IMP/EXP
ICREST INTERNATIONAL LLC
JCP
(*Suby of* ITOCHU CORPORATION)
725 S Figueroa St # 3050, Los Angeles, CA 90017-5524
Tel (213) 488-8303 *Founded/Ownrshp* 2000
Sales 458.9MM *EMP* 33
Accts Deloitte & Touche Llp Los An
SIC 5148 5147 Fresh fruits & vegetables; Meats & meat products; Fresh fruits & vegetables; Meats & meat products
CEO: Takeshi Yagubhi
**Bd of Dir:* Makoto Sawanoi
Mktg Dir: Yasuaki Sagara
Sls Mgr: Ken Park

D-U-N-S 11-444-2648
ICROSSING INC
(*Suby of* HEARST CORP) ★
300 W 57th St Fl 20f, New York, NY 10019-3741
Tel (212) 649-3900 *Founded/Ownrshp* 2011
Sales 115.0MM^E *EMP* 900
SIC 8742 7311 Marketing consulting services; Advertising consultant; Marketing consulting services; Advertising consultant
Pr: Brian Powley
Sr Pt: Diana Gordon
Pt: Laura Kuhn
Pr: Mark Mulhern
Pr: Mike Parker
**CFO:* Michael J Jackson
**Ofcr:* Brian Haven
**Ofcr:* Dave Johnson
**Ofcr:* David Santos
Ofcr: Patrick Stern
**Ex VP:* Rod Lenniger
**Sr VP:* Darren Prock
**Sr VP:* Paramjeet Sanghera
Sr VP: Gary Stein
Sr VP: Shoshana Winter
VP: Christopher Andrew
VP: Jeffrey Harouche
VP: Anne Keenan
VP: Mary Matyas
VP: Andrew Schmeling
VP: Steven Shay

D-U-N-S 15-138-7420
ICS BUILDERS INC
108 W 39th St Fl 14, New York, NY 10018-8257
Tel (212) 633-1300 *Founded/Ownrshp* 1980
Sales 28.4MM *EMP* 50^E
Accts Connolly & Company Warren Nj
SIC 1542 8741 Commercial & office building, new construction; Construction management; Commercial & office building, new construction; Construction management
Ch Bd: Pat Herbert
**Ch Bd:* John O'Rourke Jr
**Pr:* John O'Rourke
VP Opers: Edward Oarourke

D-U-N-S 15-652-4808
ICS BUILDERS INC
11 Glenmere Dr, Chatham, NJ 07928-1305
Tel (212) 633-1300 *Founded/Ownrshp* 2004
Sales 20.6MM *EMP* 1
Accts Connolly & Company Pc Warr
SIC 1521 New construction, single-family houses; New construction, single-family houses
Owner: Patrick Herbert

D-U-N-S 14-990-5668
ICS CONSOLIDATED INC
640 Brooker Creek Blvd # 465, Oldsmar, FL 34677-2929
Tel (352) 650-4338 *Founded/Ownrshp* 1999
Sales 65.9MM^E *EMP* 30^E
SIC 5065 Electronic parts & equipment
CEO: Marty Poad
VP: Margo Bystedt
CIO: Victor Berggren

ICS CONSTRUCTION SERVICES
See INTERIOR CONSTRUCTION SERVICES LTD

D-U-N-S 62-535-0371
ICS CONTRACT SERVICES LLC
1251 Marietta Blvd Nw, Atlanta, GA 30318-4140
Tel (404) 367-8286 *Founded/Ownrshp* 2005
Sales 18.3MM^E *EMP* 1,000
SIC 7349 Janitorial service, contract basis; Janitorial service, contract basis
Area Mgr: Joe Thomas

D-U-N-S 04-175-1520
ICS CORP
2225 Richmond St Ste 3, Philadelphia, PA 19125-4368
Tel (215) 427-3355 *Founded/Ownrshp* 1965
Sales 32.4MM^E *EMP* 225
SIC 7374 2759 7331 Data processing & preparation; Commercial printing; Direct mail advertising services; Data processing & preparation; Commercial printing; Direct mail advertising services

Pr: Richard Bastian
**Treas:* Catharine Radomicki
**VP:* Richard Prendergast
Mtls Mgr: Fran King
Prd Mgr: Frank Strenger

D-U-N-S 17-862-1848
ICS ENTERPRISES LLP
ICS VMI GROUP
12273 Gateway Blvd W, El Paso, TX 79936-7809
Tel (915) 239-9256 *Founded/Ownrshp* 1996
Sales 33.9MM^E *EMP* 300
SIC 2653 2449 4225 Corrugated boxes, partitions, display items, sheets & pad; Rectangular boxes & crates, wood; General warehousing; Corrugated boxes, partitions, display items, sheets & pad; Rectangular boxes & crates, wood; General warehousing
Prin: Albert Lanza

D-U-N-S 78-760-8694
ICS INC
INDUSTRIAL CONTRACT SERVICES
2500 State Mill Rd, Grand Forks, ND 58203
Tel (701) 775-8480 *Founded/Ownrshp* 2009
Sales 27.3MM^E *EMP* 75^E
SIC 1542 1771 1623 Commercial & office building, new construction; Concrete work; Water & sewer line construction
CEO: Astrew Molstad
**Treas:* Jon Kearns
**VP:* Gary Bridgeford
**VP:* Kip Langei
IT Man: George Olson

D-U-N-S 17-183-8480
ICS NETT INC
I C S
2677 Prosperity Ave # 400, Fairfax, VA 22031-4929
Tel (703) 342-4260 *Founded/Ownrshp* 2003
Sales 60.9MM^E *EMP* 120
SIC 4731 7379 Freight transportation arrangement; ; Freight transportation arrangement;
Pr: Shehraze Shah
CFO: Rebecca Lewis
**Ofcr:* Khurram Shah
Ofcr: Samantha Zeisler
Ex VP: Khaled Amro
VP: Becky Lewis
VP: Chan Park
VP: Eric Smith
VP: Kwasi Speede
Prgrm Mgr: Jared Dean
Prgrm Mgr: Ben Theis

ICS PROJECT HEADSTART
See INSTITUTE FOR COMMUNITY SERVICES INC

ICS VMI GROUP
See ICS ENTERPRISES LLP

ICSC
See INTERNATIONAL COUNCIL OF SHOPPING CENTERS INC

ICTC USA
See INTERCONNECT CABLE TECHNOLOGIES CORP

D-U-N-S 05-806-8052 IMP
▲ ICTV BRANDS INC
489 Devon Park Dr Ste 315, Wayne, PA 19087-1809
Tel (484) 598-2300 *Founded/Ownrshp* 1998
Sales 32.3MM *EMP* 15^E
Tkr Sym ICTV *Exch* OTO
SIC 5961 7812 Catalog & mail-order houses; Television, home shopping; Commercials, television: tape or film; Catalog & mail-order houses; Television, home shopping; Commercials, television: tape or film
Ch Bd: Kelvin Claney
Pr: Richard Ransom
CFO: Ryan Lebon

D-U-N-S 00-195-2241 IMP/EXP
ICU EYEWEAR INC (CA)
FISHERMAN EYEWEAR
1440 4th St Ste A, Berkeley, CA 94710-1315
Tel (831) 637-9300 *Founded/Ownrshp* 1956, 2010
Sales 23.4MM^E *EMP* 60
SIC 5099

D-U-N-S 11-838-0146 IMP
▲ ICU MEDICAL INC
951 Calle Amanecer, San Clemente, CA 92673-6212
Tel (949) 366-2183 *Founded/Ownrshp* 1984
Sales 309.2MM *EMP* 2,280^E
Tkr Sym ICUI *Exch* NGS
SIC 3841 3845 IV transfusion apparatus; Catheters; Pacemaker, cardiac; IV transfusion apparatus; Catheters; Pacemaker, cardiac
CEO: Vivek Jain
CFO: Scott E Lamb
CFO: Francis Obrien
VP: Alison D Burcar
VP: Tom McCall
VP: Steven C Riggs
Prgrm Mgr: Joe Perry
IT Man: Doug Bregman
Mktg Dir: Scott Seewald
Sls Dir: Rob Houde
Sales Asso: William Leek
Board of Directors: Jack W Brown, John J Connors, David C Greenberg, Joseph R Saucedo, Richard H Sherman, Robert S Swinney

ICUBA
See INDEPENDENT COLLEGES AND UNIVERSITIES BENEFIT ASSOCIATION INC

D-U-N-S 05-874-4512
ICV CAPITAL PARTNERS LLC
ICV PARTNERS
810 7th Ave Fl 35, New York, NY 10019-5818
Tel (212) 455-9600 *Founded/Ownrshp* 1999
Sales 90.1MM^E *EMP* 484^E
SIC 6282 6211 Investment advisory service; Investment firm, general brokerage; Investment advisory service; Investment firm, general brokerage
Pr: Willie Woods

Ofcr: David Maue
VP: Zeena H RAO
VP: Ashley Smith

ICV PARTNERS
See ICV CAPITAL PARTNERS LLC

D-U-N-S 06-559-5796
ICV SOLUTIONS INC
BEDROC
3351 Aspen Ste 350, Franklin, TN 37067
Tel (615) 815-1785 *Founded/Ownrshp* 2009
Sales 32.0MM *EMP* 40
SIC 7379
Pr: Gregory Chase Wilkinson
**CEO:* Cameron Plato
Ex VP: Jud Wells
**VP:* Judson Wells
Dir Bus: Josh Drummond
Dir Bus: Will Harris
Dir Bus: Chace Herndon
Dir Bus: Jeff McCance
Netwrk Eng: Mike Burns

ICVGC
See INDEPENDENCE CONSTRUCTION CO OF VA

D-U-N-S 09-148-9716
ICW GROUP HOLDINGS INC
11455 El Camino Real, San Diego, CA 92130-2088
Tel (858) 350-2400 *Founded/Ownrshp* 1981
Sales NA *EMP* 550^E
SIC 6331 6411 Fire, marine & casualty insurance & carriers; Insurance brokers; Fire, marine & casualty insurance & carriers; Insurance brokers
CEO: Kevin M Prior
**Ch Bd:* Ernest Rady
**Treas:* Sariborz Rostamian
Sr VP: Richard Manship
VP: John Gustafson
VP: James Senior
Web Dev: Mark Dailey

D-U-N-S 00-339-9636
■ ID ANALYTICS INC
(*Suby of* LIFELOCK INC) ★
15253 Ave Of Science, San Diego, CA 92128-3437
Tel (858) 312-6200 *Founded/Ownrshp* 2002, 2012
Sales 23.7MM^E *EMP* 140
SIC 7382 Protective devices, security; Protective devices, security
CEO: Scott Carter
COO: Peter Boyes
Ofcr: George Gelly
Ofcr: Daniel Rawlings
VP: Steve Dyrhahl
VP: Garient Evans
VP Mktg: Laura Trotter
Sls Dir: Eric Gunderson

D-U-N-S 00-248-3543
ID GRIFFITH INC
735 S Market St Ste A, Wilmington, DE 19801-5246
Tel (302) 656-8253 *Founded/Ownrshp* 1945
Sales 38.4MM^E *EMP* 85
SIC 1711 Mechanical contractor; Warm air heating & air conditioning contractor; Process piping contractor
Pr: David L Zarrilli
**Treas:* Richard A Murphy
**VP:* Michael H Treml

D-U-N-S 87-802-9701 IMP
ID IMAGES LLC
2991 Interstate Pkwy, Brunswick, OH 44212-4327
Tel (330) 220-7300 *Founded/Ownrshp* 2007
Sales 21.6MM^E *EMP* 108
SIC 2672 Adhesive papers, labels or tapes: from purchased material; Adhesive papers, labels or tapes: from purchased material
Pr: Brian Gale
Prd Mgr: Scott Beaujon
Ql Cn Mgr: Paul Parish
Mktg Mgr: Nancy Klaar
Manager: Dave Oliverio
Sls Mgr: Mark Mallory
Sales Asso: Carrie Jarvis

ID LINE, THE
See IDENTIFICATION PLATES INC

ID ON DEMAND
See IDONDEMAND INC

D-U-N-S 84-901-3537 IMP
▲ ID SYSTEMS INC
123 Tice Blvd, Woodcliff Lake, NJ 07677-7670
Tel (201) 996-9000 *Founded/Ownrshp* 1994
Sales 45.6MM *EMP* 123^E
Tkr Sym IDSY *Exch* NGM
SIC 3663 ;
Ch Bd: Kenneth S Ehrman
COO: David Andrews
COO: Norman L Ellis
CFO: Ned Mavrommati
CFO: Ned Mavrommatis
Ex VP: Todd Felker
Ex VP: Brett Kirkpatrick
Ex VP: Tim Parker
VP: Adam Ghidali
VP: Andrea Jacobs
VP: Gene Merlo
VP: Dan Romary
VP Bus Dev: Kevin Franz
Exec: Dennis Oury
Board of Directors: Kenneth Brakebill, Michael Brodsky, Ron Konezny, Tony Trousset

D-U-N-S 60-586-7753 IMP
ID TECHNOLOGY LLC
(*Suby of* PRO MACH INC) ★
2051 Franklin Dr, Fort Worth, TX 76106-2204
Tel (817) 624-6838 *Founded/Ownrshp* 2007
Sales 76.4MM^E *EMP* 170
SIC 5084 3565 3953 2759 Industrial machinery & equipment; Labeling machines, industrial; Marking devices; Commercial printing; Industrial machinery & equipment; Labeling machines, industrial; Marking devices; Commercial printing
**CFO:* William M Schult
Treas: Dawn Zuilhof

Ex VP: Mike Eddinger
**VP:* Mark W Anderson
**VP:* Robert Zuilhof
Exec: Kevin Kremer
Rgnl Mgr: David Rapoza
Sls&Mrk Ex: Amy James
VP Sls: Allan Shipman

IDA
See NOVA MUD INC

D-U-N-S 00-692-6323
IDA CASON CALLAWAY FOUNDATION
CALLAWAY GARDENS
17800 Us Highway 27, Pine Mountain, GA 31822-2393
Tel (706) 663-2281 *Founded/Ownrshp* 1936
Sales 68.7MM^E *EMP* 750^E
Accts Dougherty Mckinnon & Luby Llc
SIC 7011 Resort hotel; Resort hotel
Ch Bd: Edward C Callaway
V Ch: Hal Northrop
VP: Richard Waterhouse
Exec: Joe Malone
Genl Mgr: Bob Sykora
Dir IT: Sherman Thompson
Mktg Dir: Kathy Tilley
Mktg Dir: Sylmarie Trowbridge
Sls Dir: Pat Horan
Sls Mgr: Will Porter

IDA FARMER'S CO-OP ELEVATOR CO
See IDA FARMERS CO-OPERATIVE

D-U-N-S 01-714-3314
IDA FARMERS CO-OPERATIVE
IDA FARMER'S CO-OP ELEVATOR CO
2953 Lewis Ave, Ida, MI 48140-9581
Tel (734) 269-3325 *Founded/Ownrshp* 1921
Sales 27.6MM *EMP* 15
Accts Osbourne March Condon & Co
SIC 5153 5191 Grain & field beans; Farm supplies; Grain & field beans; Farm supplies
Pr: Larry Metz
**Sec:* Lyle Schafer
Genl Mgr: Michael Dick
Off Mgr: Mary Gerwick

D-U-N-S 96-684-6131
IDA GROVE BANCSHARES INC
501 2nd St, Ida Grove, IA 51445-1304
Tel (712) 364-3393 *Founded/Ownrshp* 1981
Sales NA *EMP* 71^E
SIC 6712 Bank holding companies
Pr: Kenneth Van Kekerix

D-U-N-S 13-118-8419
IDA TOWER
1010 12th St Apt 813, Altoona, PA 16601-3453
Tel (814) 944-4055 *Founded/Ownrshp* 1974
Sales 43.4MM^E *EMP* 3,900
SIC 6513 Apartment building operators; Apartment building operators
Pt: Roger Bunnell
Pt: Leeann Morein
Pt: Nancy Walters
Prin: Jennifer Hardee

D-U-N-S 01-047-7925
IDABEL INDEPENDENT SCHOOL DISTRICT 5
IDABEL PUBLIC SCHOOLS
200 Ne Ave C, Idabel, OK 74745-3226
Tel (580) 286-7639 *Founded/Ownrshp* 1908
Sales 9.0MM *EMP* 619
SIC 8211 Public combined elementary & secondary school; School board; Public combined elementary & secondary school; School board
Pgrm Dir: Tammy Blackard

IDABEL PUBLIC SCHOOLS
See IDABEL INDEPENDENT SCHOOL DISTRICT 5

D-U-N-S 03-545-0571
▲ IDACORP INC (ID)
1221 W Idaho St, Boise, ID 83702-5627
Tel (208) 388-2200 *Founded/Ownrshp* 1998
Sales 1.2MMM *EMP* 2,029^E
Accts Deloitte & Touche Llp Boise
Tkr Sym IDA *Exch* NYS
SIC 4911 Electric services; Distribution, electric power; Generation, electric power; Transmission, electric power; Electric services; Distribution, electric power; Generation, electric power; Transmission, electric power
Pr: Darrel T Anderson
**Ch Bd:* Robert A Tinstman
CFO: Steven R Keen
Ofcr: Lori D Smith
Sr VP: Rex Blackburn
VP: Jeffrey L Malmen
VP: Kenneth W Petersen
Board of Directors: Joan H Smith, Thomas Carlile, Thomas J Wilford, Richard J Dahl, Ronald W Jibson, Judith A Johansen, Dennis L Johnson, J Lamont Keen, Christine King, Richard J Navarro, Jan B Packwood

D-U-N-S 06-755-3073
IDAHO BEVERAGES INC
PEPSI COLA BTLG CO LEWISTON
2108 1st Ave N, Lewiston, ID 83501-1604
Tel (208) 743-6535 *Founded/Ownrshp* 1974
Sales 30.3MM^E *EMP* 70
SIC 5149 2086 Soft drinks; Soft drinks: packaged in cans, bottles, etc.
Pr: Gary Prasil
**Sec:* Cheri Prasil
VP: Jason Dickerson
**VP:* Robert Walter Prasil Jr

IDAHO BRAND BOARD
See STATE POLICE IDAHO

D-U-N-S 10-813-5278
IDAHO CENTRAL CREDIT UNION
4400 Central Way, Pocatello, ID 83202-5096
Tel (208) 239-3000 *Founded/Ownrshp* 1940
Sales NA *EMP* 335^E

SIC 6062 State credit unions, not federally chartered; State credit unions, not federally chartered
CEO: Kent Oram
Ofcr: Jessica Anderson
Ofcr: Jeremy Haney
Ofcr: Russel Hill
Ofcr: Jeff May
Ofcr: Shelli Pardsley
Ofcr: Nickole Romriell
Ofcr: Rick Tolman
Ofcr: Alawna Towns-Atherton
Ofcr: Lisa Walsh
Ofcr: Daniel Wyler
VP: Jeremy Bowcut
VP: Corey Dahle
VP: Ben Davidson
VP: Edward Tierney

D-U-N-S 02-024-3684
IDAHO DEPARTMENT OF ENVIRONMENTAL QUALITY
D E Q
(*Suby of* EXECUTIVE OFFICE OF STATE OF IDAHO) ★
1410 N Hilton St, Boise, ID 83706-1253
Tel (208) 373-0502 *Founded/Ownrshp* 2000
Sales NA *EMP* 350
SIC 9511 Environmental protection agency, government; ; Environmental protection agency, government;

D-U-N-S 82-520-1486
IDAHO DEPARTMENT OF HEALTH AND WELFARE
(*Suby of* EXECUTIVE OFFICE OF STATE OF IDAHO) ★
450 W State St Fl 9, Boise, ID 83702-6056
Tel (208) 334-5500 *Founded/Ownrshp* 1972
Sales NA *EMP* 3,100^E
SIC 9431 Administration of public health programs; ; Administration of public health programs;
Prgrm Mgr: Matt Wimmer

D-U-N-S 02-646-7840
IDAHO DEPARTMENT OF JUVENILE CORRECTIONS
954 W Jefferson St, Boise, ID 83702-5436
Tel (208) 334-5100 *Founded/Ownrshp* 1997
Sales 8.6MM^E *EMP* 402^E
SIC 8361 Juvenile correctional facilities; Juvenile correctional facilities
Prin: Larry Callicutt
**Prin:* Sharon Harrigfelb
**Prin:* Brent Renkie

D-U-N-S 82-501-7395
IDAHO DEPARTMENT OF TRANSPORTATION
(*Suby of* EXECUTIVE OFFICE OF STATE OF IDAHO) ★
3311 W State St, Boise, ID 83703-5879
Tel (208) 334-8000 *Founded/Ownrshp* 1974
Sales NA *EMP* 2,760^E
SIC 9621 Regulation, administration of transportation;
Ch: Darrell Manning
**V Ch:* Gary Blick
Ofcr: Kelly Dirocco
Ofcr: Jon Pope
Exec: Jeff Stratten
Rgnl Mgr: Aaron Bauges
Rgnl Mgr: Jason Brinkman
Rgnl Mgr: Bruce Christensen
Rgnl Mgr: Chad Clawson
Rgnl Mgr: Tom Cole
Rgnl Mgr: Jayme Coonce

D-U-N-S 82-520-1510
IDAHO DEPT OF FISH AND GAME
(*Suby of* EXECUTIVE OFFICE OF STATE OF IDAHO) ★
600 S Walnut St, Boise, ID 83712-7729
Tel (208) 334-3781 *Founded/Ownrshp* 1938
Sales NA *EMP* 500
SIC 9512 Wildlife conservation agencies; ; Wildlife conservation agencies;
**CFO:* Jim Lau
IT Man: Michael Pearson
Snr Mgr: Sara Focht

IDAHO DISTRIBUTING
See C STEIN INC

D-U-N-S 14-004-0713
IDAHO DIVISION OF VETERANS SERVICES
351 N Collins Rd, Boise, ID 83702-4519
Tel (208) 577-2310 *Founded/Ownrshp* 2003
Sales NA *EMP* 500^E
SIC 9451 Administration of veterans' affairs; ; Administration of veterans' affairs;
Dir Soc: Gwen Thornfeldt

IDAHO ELKS REHAB HOSPITAL
See IDAHO ELKS REHABILITATION HOSPITAL INC

D-U-N-S 84-910-5887
IDAHO ELKS REHABILITATION HOSPITAL
600 N Robbins Rd, Boise, ID 83702-4565
Tel (208) 489-4444 *Founded/Ownrshp* 1994
Sales 29.0MM *EMP* 640
SIC 8049 8011 Audiologist; Offices & clinics of medical doctors; Audiologist; Offices & clinics of medical doctors
CFO: Doug Lewis
COO: Melissa Honsinger
Dir Rad: Susan Abraham
Dir Rx: Debbie Rothstein
IT Man: Dan Vilner
Mktg Mgr: Christine Bubb
Psych: Jason Southwick
Pharmcst: Alfred Hogenauer
Pharmcst: Grace Lawrence
Cert Phar: Karisa Baker
HC Dir: Judy Davenport

D-U-N-S 08-680-4705
IDAHO ELKS REHABILITATION HOSPITAL INC
IDAHO ELKS REHAB HOSPITAL
600 N Robbins Rd, Boise, ID 83702-4565
Tel (208) 343-2583 *Founded/Ownrshp* 1946
Sales 29.0MM *EMP* 400
SIC 8093 Rehabilitation center, outpatient treatment

D-U-N-S 83-274-0471
IDAHO FALLS PETERBILT INC
(*Suby of* PETERBILT OF UTAH INC) ★
4460 Andco Dr, Idaho Falls, ID 83402-5871
Tel (208) 528-0004 *Founded/Ownrshp* 2008
Sales 36.0MM *EMP* 45
SIC 7538 7532 5531 5511 General truck repair; Body shop, trucks; Truck equipment & parts; Trucks, tractors & trailers: new & used
CEO: Eric Jackson
**Pr:* Blake Jackson
**CFO:* Cary Davis
Sls Mgr: John Carpenter

D-U-N-S 02-964-2717
IDAHO FALLS SCHOOL DISTRICT NO 91 EDUCATION FOUNDATION INC
690 John Adams Pkwy, Idaho Falls, ID 83401-4073
Tel (208) 525-7500 *Founded/Ownrshp* 1953
Sales 67.2MM *EMP* 1,100
SIC 8211 Public elementary & secondary schools; School board; Public elementary & secondary schools; School board
Dir IT: Nancy Baumgart
Dir IT: Rene Miller

IDAHO FOODBANK , THE
See IDAHO FOODBANK WAREHOUSE INC

D-U-N-S 03-308-8167
IDAHO FOODBANK WAREHOUSE INC
IDAHO FOODBANK , THE
3562 S Tk Ave, Boise, ID 83705-5278
Tel (208) 336-9643 *Founded/Ownrshp* 1994
Sales 29.2MM *EMP* 32
Accts Dorothy Ann Snowball Cpa Bois
SIC 8322 Individual & family services; Individual & family services
Pr: Karen L Vauk
**CFO:* Edward O Loggins
**Ex Dir:* Roger Simon
Brnch Mgr: Cari Miller
CTO: Kathryn Buxton
VP Opers: Roy Lacey
VP Opers: Marco Valle

D-U-N-S 02-191-6034 EXP
IDAHO FOREST GROUP LLC
687 W Cnfield Ave Ste 100, Coeur D Alene, ID 83815
Tel (208) 255-3200 *Founded/Ownrshp* 2008
Sales 119.6MM^E *EMP* 800
SIC 5211 Lumber products; Lumber products
CFO: Kevin Esser
VP: Erol Deren
Mill Mgr: Mike Henley
Mill Mgr: Chris Pease

D-U-N-S 82-847-5264
IDAHO FOREST GROUP LLC
4447 E Chilco Rd, Athol, ID 83801-8477
Tel (208) 255-3200 *Founded/Ownrshp* 2008
Sales 153.8MM^E *EMP* 750
SIC 2421 Sawmills & planing mills, general; Sawmills & planing mills, general
Pr: Scott Atkison
**Ch Bd:* Marc A Brinkmeyer
**CFO:* Kevin Esser
CFO: Jay Mclsaac
**VP:* Beti Becker
**VP:* Erol Deren
Genl Mgr: Carmen Ruiffes
IT Man: Cheryl Murdock

D-U-N-S 00-908-3973
IDAHO FRESH-PAK INC
529 N 3500 E, Lewisville, ID 83431-5034
Tel (208) 754-4686 *Founded/Ownrshp* 1960
Sales 38.1MM^E *EMP* 300
SIC 2034 Potato products, dried & dehydrated; Potato products, dried & dehydrated
Pr: Ryan Clement
**CFO:* Rodney Roberts
**Treas:* Brad Bowen
**VP:* Todd Clement

D-U-N-S 82-618-0119
▲ IDAHO INDEPENDENT BANK
IIB
8882 N Government Way L, Hayden Lake, ID 83835-9282
Tel (208) 772-6399 *Founded/Ownrshp* 1993
Sales NA *EMP* 55
Tkr Sym IIBK *Exch* OTC
SIC 6022 State commercial banks; State commercial banks
CEO: Jack W Gustavel
**Chf Cred:* Vander Ploeg
**Ex VP:* Rod Colwell
**VP:* Craig Burkhart
**VP:* Lynn Gustavel
VP: Steve Jungen
VP: Paul Montreuil

D-U-N-S 09-667-9865
IDAHO MATERIAL HANDLING INC
(*Suby of* HOJ ENGINEERING & SALES CO INC) ★
4655 S Federal Way, Boise, ID 83716-5531
Tel (208) 336-4400 *Founded/Ownrshp* 1977
Sales 32.2MM^E *EMP* 100
SIC 5084

D-U-N-S 82-859-8065 EXP
IDAHO MILK PRODUCTS INC
2249 S Tiger Dr, Jerome, ID 83338-5080
Tel (208) 644-2871 *Founded/Ownrshp* 2007
Sales 24.0MM^E *EMP* 50
SIC 2026 Milk processing (pasteurizing, homogenizing, bottling)
Pr: Ron Aardema
**Sec:* Rick Omaindia
**VP:* Russell Visser
Exec: Patti Schaefer
Sftwr Eng: Ed Webb
Ql Cn Mgr: Chad Larsen
Mktg Mgr: Jessica Henry
Sls Mgr: Patty Rusch

D-U-N-S 18-410-7696
IDAHO MILK TRANSPORT INC
745 W Bedke Blvd, Burley, ID 83318
Tel (208) 878-5000 *Founded/Ownrshp* 1986
Sales 24.1MM *EMP* 90
SIC 4212 Liquid haulage, local; Liquid haulage, local
CEO: Robert Brice
**Pr:* Gene Brice
Opers Mgr: Kraig Franks
Sls&Mrk Ex: Xana Brice

D-U-N-S 16-456-6932 IMP/EXP
IDAHO PACIFIC HOLDINGS INC
4723 E 100 N, Ririe, ID 83443
Tel (208) 538-6971 *Founded/Ownrshp* 2004
Sales 47.0MM^E *EMP* 390
SIC 2034 Potato products, dried & dehydrated; Potato products, dried & dehydrated
CEO: Wally Browning III
Plnt Mgr: Billy Penny
Plnt Mgr: Tim Ruggles
**VP Sls:* John Schodde

D-U-N-S 09-880-3265
IDAHO PACIFIC LUMBER CO INC
7255 W Franklin Rd, Boise, ID 83709-0926
Tel (208) 375-8052 *Founded/Ownrshp* 1979
Sales 190.5MM *EMP* 44
SIC 5031 Lumber: rough, dressed & finished; Lumber: rough, dressed & finished
Pr: Eric D Grandeen
Mng Pt: Jonathan Nagle
CFO: Sharon Jensen
**CFO:* Patrick J Sullivan
**VP:* Keith S Berg
Off Mgr: Niki Robin
Off Mgr: Ginny Wekall
IT Man: Ron Meeuf

D-U-N-S 07-842-8810
IDAHO POTATO PACKERS CORP (ID)
(*Suby of* NONPAREIL CORP) ★
40 N 400 W, Blackfoot, ID 83221-5632
Tel (208) 785-3030 *Founded/Ownrshp* 1944, 1973
Sales 100.3MM^E *EMP* 300
SIC 5148 Potatoes, fresh; Potatoes, fresh
CEO: Harold M Abend
**CFO:* John Fullmer
**Treas:* Eileen Abend
**VP:* Howard Phillips

D-U-N-S 00-692-7271
■ IDAHO POWER CO (ID)
(*Suby of* IDACORP INC) ★
1221 W Idaho St, Boise, ID 83702-5627
Tel (208) 388-2200 *Founded/Ownrshp* 1989, 1998
Sales 1.2MMM^E *EMP* 2,029^E
Accts Deloitte & Touche Llp Boise
SIC 4911 Electric services; Transmission, electric power; Generation, electric power; Distribution, electric power; Electric services; Transmission, electric power; Generation, electric power; Distribution, electric power
Pr: Darrel T Anderson
**Ch Bd:* Robert A Tinstman
**CFO:* Steven R Keen
Bd of Dir: Lana Skouras
Bd of Dir: Dawn Thompson
**Sr VP:* Rex Blackburn
Sr VP: Lisa A Grow
VP: Jim Burdick
**VP:* Lonnie Krawl
VP: Lonnie G Krawl
VP: Tracie Metcalf
**VP:* Kenneth W Petersen
VP: Lori D Smith
Board of Directors: Robert A Tinstman, C Stephen Allred, Thomas J Wilford, Richard J Dahl, Ronald W Jibson, Judith A Johansen, Dennis L Johnson, J Lamont Keen, Christine King, Jan B Packwood, Joan H Smith

D-U-N-S 07-834-1468
IDAHO STATE UNIVERSITY
FINANCE AND ADMINISTRATION
921 S 8th Ave, Pocatello, ID 83209-0001
Tel (208) 282-0211 *Founded/Ownrshp* 1901
Sales 130.5MM *EMP* 1,900
Accts Moss Adams Llp Eugene Oregon
SIC 8221 University; University
Pr: Arthur C Vilas
Pr: Debbie Henrickson
Pr: V Mitchell
Bd of Dir: Eric Bell
Bd of Dir: Emily Kvamme
Ofcr: James Dixon
Ofcr: Doug Schelk
VP: Barbara A Adamcik
VP: Jameson Bastow
VP: Donald J Colby
Assoc Dir: Stephen Bezdeka
Assoc Dir: Chad Gross

D-U-N-S 16-918-9396
IDAHO STATE UNIVERSITY
AIRCRAFT TECHNOLOGY
1455 Flightline, Pocatello, ID 83204-7550
Tel (208) 232-8485 *Founded/Ownrshp* 1936
Sales 130.5MM *EMP* 3
Accts Moss Adams Llp Eugene Oregon
SIC 8249 Vocational schools; Vocational schools
Pr: Richard Bowen
Ex Dir: Veronica Hapgood

D-U-N-S 00-909-1422 IMP
IDAHO STEEL PRODUCTS INC (ID)
255 E Anderson St, Idaho Falls, ID 83401-2016
Tel (208) 522-1275 *Founded/Ownrshp* 1918, 1991
Sales 30.9MM *EMP* 80
SIC 3556 3599 Food products machinery; Machine shop, jobbing & repair; Food products machinery; Machine shop, jobbing & repair
CEO: Delynn Bradshaw
**Pr:* Lynn Bradshaw
**CEO:* Alan Bradshaw
**CEO:* Davis Christensen
**CFO:* Craig A Parker
Sls Mgr: Bruce Ball

D-U-N-S 11-750-6964
IDAHO SUPREME POTATOES INC
614 E 800 N, Firth, ID 83236-1112
Tel (208) 346-6841 *Founded/Ownrshp* 1966
Sales 44.1MM^E *EMP* 350
SIC 2034 5148 0211 Potato products, dried & dehydrated; Potatoes, fresh; Beef cattle feedlots; Potato products, dried & dehydrated; Potatoes, fresh; Beef cattle feedlots
Pr: Wilford Chapman
CFO: Bill Chapmin
**CFO:* Steve Prescott
VP: Vondel Chapman
Exec: Sandra Vega
**Genl Mgr:* Wade Chapman
Software D: Pam Vouk
Sls Dir: Brad Chapman

D-U-N-S 79-009-9530
■ IDAHO TIMBER CORP
(*Suby of* IDAHO TIMBER LLC) ★
1844 Joe Brown Hwy S, Chadbourn, NC 28431-8502
Tel (910) 654-5555 *Founded/Ownrshp* 2007
Sales 20.0MM^E *EMP* 251^E
SIC 5031 Lumber, plywood & millwork
Exec: Michael Jacobs

D-U-N-S 09-467-7994 IMP/EXP
■ IDAHO TIMBER LLC
(*Suby of* LEUCADIA NATIONAL CORP) ★
3540 E Longwing Ln # 270, Meridian, ID 83646-1104
Tel (208) 377-3000 *Founded/Ownrshp* 2005
Sales 116.9MM^E *EMP* 450
SIC 0831 Forest products; Forest products
CEO: Ted Ellis
**CFO:* Scott Beechie
**VP:* Brock Lenon
**VP:* Dave Taugher

D-U-N-S 03-376-8300
■ IDAHO TIMBER OF TEXAS LLC
(*Suby of* LEUCADIA NATIONAL CORP) ★
900 W Risinger Rd, Fort Worth, TX 76140-5335
Tel (817) 293-1001 *Founded/Ownrshp* 1981
Sales 20.8MM^E *EMP* 82
SIC 5031 2421 Lumber: rough, dressed & finished; Lumber: rough, sawed or planed
Sls Mgr: Mitch Renfro

D-U-N-S 82-922-8753
■ IDAHO TREATMENT GROUP LLC
(*Suby of* BWX TECHNOLOGIES INC) ★
850 Energy Pl Ste 100, Idaho Falls, ID 83401-1503
Tel (208) 557-0973 *Founded/Ownrshp* 2009
Sales NA *EMP* 600
SIC 8741 Management services; Management services
Pr: Dan Swaim
Genl Mgr: Jim Simonds

D-U-N-S 04-130-9196
IDAHO TROUT PROCESSORS CO
1301 S Vista Ave Ste 200, Boise, ID 83705-2576
Tel (208) 345-3505 *Founded/Ownrshp* 1959
Sales 23.5MM^E *EMP* 214
SIC 2092 Fish, fresh: prepared; Fish, frozen: prepared; Fish, fresh: prepared; Fish, frozen: prepared
Pr: Anita Kay Hardy
**VP:* Gregory Kaslo

D-U-N-S 07-301-7006
IDAHO YOUTH RANCH INC
IDAHO YOUTH RANCH THRIFT STORE
5465 W Irving St, Boise, ID 83706-1213
Tel (208) 377-2613 *Founded/Ownrshp* 1953
Sales 19.7MM *EMP* 370
Accts Cliftonlarsonallen Llp Boise
SIC 8361 8322 5932 Home for the emotionally disturbed; Halfway group home, persons with social or personal problems; Adoption services; Used merchandise stores; Home for the emotionally disturbed; Halfway group home, persons with social or personal problems; Adoption services; Used merchandise stores
Pr: Michael Jones
**CFO:* Nancy Proctor
**Ch:* Jaris Collins
**Ch:* Bud Sickinger
**Treas:* Gil Walker
Assoc Dir: Kristin Matthews
Store Mgr: Cindy Oberg
Psych: Laura Cook

IDAHO YOUTH RANCH THRIFT STORE
See IDAHO YOUTH RANCH INC

D-U-N-S 18-121-8660
■ IDAHO-PACIFIC CORP
(*Suby of* OTTER TAIL CORP) ★
4723 E 100 N, Rigby, ID 83442-5811
Tel (208) 538-6971 *Founded/Ownrshp* 1987
Sales 34.6MM^E *EMP* 250
SIC 2034

D-U-N-S 80-680-5441 IMP/EXP
IDAHOAN FOODS LLC
357 Constitution Way, Idaho Falls, ID 83402-3538
Tel (208) 542-3700 *Founded/Ownrshp* 2009
Sales 175.4MM^E *EMP* 590
SIC 2034 Potato products, dried & dehydrated; Potato products, dried & dehydrated
VP: Ryan Carter
VP: Marc Desmarais
VP: Glen Walter
Exec: David Macfarlane
CIO: Jim Bramlette
Dir IT: Devin McCarthy
VP Mfg: Samuel Huffman
Plnt Mgr: Kenny Kniep
Prd Mgr: Shane Williams
Ql Cn Mgr: Phil Geraci
Ql Cn Mgr: Trevor Grunig

IDB BANK OF NEW YORK
See ISRAEL DISCOUNT BANK OF NEW YORK

D-U-N-S 62-527-5706 IMP
IDB HOLDINGS INC
(*Suby of* ADAMS FOODS LTD)
601 S Rockefeller Ave, Ontario, CA 91761-7871
Tel (909) 390-5624 *Founded/Ownrshp* 1997
Sales 909.5MM[E] *EMP* 1,500
SIC 5143 2022 Dairy products, except dried or canned; Cheese; Processed cheese; Dairy products, except dried or canned; Cheese; Processed cheese
CEO: Jim Dekeyser
**Sec:* Peter Dolan
VP: Jackie Thomas
Dir IT: Elizabeth Ocasio
IT Man: Greg Jensen
Opers Mgr: Sam Lopez

D-U-N-S 11-082-9926
IDC CONSTRUCTION MANAGEMENT INC
(*Suby of* CH2M HILL ENGINEERS INC) ★
2020 Sw 4th Ave Ste 300, Portland, OR 97201-4973
Tel (503) 224-6040 *Founded/Ownrshp* 2008
Sales 228.0MM *EMP* 250
SIC 8741 Construction management; Construction management
Pr: Kenneth Durant

D-U-N-S 80-515-9969
IDC LTD
1511 Route 22 Ste C25, Brewster, NY 10509-4085
Tel (702) 450-1000 *Founded/Ownrshp* 1974
Sales 12.7MM[E] *EMP* 303
SIC 8742 Management consulting services; Management consulting services
Pt: L Gregg Carlson
Pt: Brad Carlson
CFO: Michelle Verrone
IT Man: Katarina Rojko

D-U-N-S 00-176-5395
IDC RESEARCH INC (MA)
I D C
(*Suby of* EXECUTRAIN) ★
5 Speen St, Framingham, MA 01701-4674
Tel (508) 872-8200 *Founded/Ownrshp* 1964
Sales 117.4MM[E] *EMP* 1,700
SIC 8732 Market analysis or research; Market analysis or research
Pr: Kirk Campbell
COO: Michelle Kloss
COO: Lindsey Vangulden
**CFO:* Mark Sullivan
**Ch:* Patrick J McGovern
**Ex VP:* Crawford Del Prete
**Sr VP:* Frank Gens
Sr VP: Alexa McCloughan
Sr VP: Henry Morris
Sr VP: Vernon Turner
**VP:* Debra Bernardi
**VP:* Ed Bloom
VP: Laura Brady
VP: Bill Casey
VP: Lance Castonguay
VP: Bradley Christenson
VP: Kristen Kim
VP: Scott Langdoc
VP: Rebecca Levitt
VP: Rick Nicholson
VP: Sally Reinfeld

D-U-N-S 80-083-8224
IDC TECHNOLOGIES INC
1851 Mccarthy Blvd # 116, Milpitas, CA 95035-7448
Tel (408) 383-0155 *Founded/Ownrshp* 2003
Sales 37.7MM[E] *EMP* 150
SIC 7379 ;
Pr: Prateek Gattani
Exec: Mandeep Kaur
Mng Dir: Roma Singh
IT Man: Galvin Jha
Software D: Asif Equabal
Sls Dir: Aniket Srivastava
Manager: Ashu Dubey
Sls Mgr: Prashant Bhardwaj
Sls Mgr: Aashish Bhatia
Sls Mgr: Samiran Das
Sls Mgr: Gaurav Sharma

IDC-AUTOMATIC
See INDUSTRIAL DOOR CO INC

D-U-N-S 92-910-9585
IDD AEROSPACE CORP
(*Suby of* ZODIAC US CORP) ★
18225 Ne 76th St, Redmond, WA 98052-5021
Tel (425) 885-0617 *Founded/Ownrshp* 1995
Sales 53.2MM[E] *EMP* 160
SIC 3728 3647 3812 Panel assembly (hydromatic propeller test stands), aircraft; Aircraft lighting fixtures; Search & navigation equipment; Panel assembly (hydromatic propeller test stands), aircraft; Aircraft lighting fixtures; Search & navigation equipment
Pr: Elizabeth Deyoung
CFO: Joel Higgins
**CFO:* Cheryl St Paul
VP: Yannick Assouad
VP: Roger Ellis
VP: Mike Ralston
Exec: Michelle King
Dir IT: John Rodie

D-U-N-S 00-437-0243
IDDINGS TRUCKING INC (OH)
741 Blue Knob Rd, Marietta, OH 45750-8275
Tel (740) 568-1780 *Founded/Ownrshp* 1966
Sales 32.8MM[E] *EMP* 105
Accts Brunei-Cox Llp Canton Ohio
SIC 4212 4213 Coal haulage, local; Dump truck haulage; Heavy hauling
Prin: George C Loeber
Ex VP: Donn Kerr
**VP:* Thomas E Hall
**Prin:* Raymond E Waters
Genl Mgr: Richard Gessel
Genl Mgr: Brad Loeber
Sfty Mgr: Robin Buckley

IDE
See INTERNATIONAL DEVELOPMENT ENTERPRISES

D-U-N-S 05-158-5495
IDE PONTIAC INC
DICK IDE HONDA
875 Panorama Trl S, Rochester, NY 14625-2309
Tel (585) 586-2820 *Founded/Ownrshp* 1970
Sales 35.3MM[E] *EMP* 100
SIC 5511

IDEA NUOVA GLOBAL
See IDEA NUOVA INC

D-U-N-S 17-724-6337 IMP
IDEA NUOVA INC
IDEA NUOVA GLOBAL
302 5th Ave Fl 5, New York, NY 10001-3604
Tel (212) 643-0680 *Founded/Ownrshp* 1987
Sales 165.0MM *EMP* 150
SIC 5021 Hair accessories; Beds & bedding
Pr: Nathan Accad
CFO: Issac Ades
Ex VP: Karen Brown
VP: Benjamin Accad
Sls Dir: Ruben Araya

D-U-N-S 00-304-1915
IDEA PUBLIC SCHOOLS (TX)
505 Angelita Dr Ste 9, Weslaco, TX 78599-8694
Tel (956) 377-8000 *Founded/Ownrshp* 2000
Sales 170.0MM *EMP* 2,381
Accts Padgett Stratemann & Co Ll
SIC 8211 Private elementary school; Private junior high school; Private elementary school; Private junior high school
Ch: Mike Rhodes
**Pr:* Thomas E Torkelson
**CFO:* Wyatt Truscheit
**Treas:* Bill Carrera
Sr Cor Off: Matthew Randazzo
VP: Debbie Brient
**VP:* Carlo Hershberger
VP: Lindsey Schaefer
VP: Leslie Whitworth
Comm Man: Anne Sykes
Mktg Mgr: Kisella Cardenas

D-U-N-S 96-948-0792
IDEA SOLUTIONS INC
2099 Gateway Pl Ste 340, San Jose, CA 95110-1017
Tel (408) 436-3800 *Founded/Ownrshp* 2011
Sales NA *EMP* 375
SIC 7379

D-U-N-S 08-883-4288
IDEA TRAVEL CO
13145 Byrd Ln Ste 101, Los Altos Hills, CA 94022-3211
Tel (650) 948-0207 *Founded/Ownrshp* 1973
Sales 84.6MM[E] *EMP* 1,100
SIC 4724 Travel agencies; Travel agencies
CEO: Michael Schoendorf
CTO: Ram Bodapati
Software D: Beverly Hoh

D-U-N-S 19-263-6889 EXP
IDEAITALIA CONTEMPORARY FURNITURE CORP
1902 Emmanuel Church Rd, Conover, NC 28613-7301
Tel (828) 464-1000 *Founded/Ownrshp* 2004
Sales 40.0MM *EMP* 140
SIC 2426 5712 4226 Turnings, furniture: wood; Furniture stores; Household goods & furniture storage; Turnings, furniture: wood; Furniture stores; Household goods & furniture storage
Pr: Carlo Bargagli

IDEAL ACCESSORIES
See IDEAL FASTENER CORP

D-U-N-S 00-709-0228
IDEAL AEROSMITH INC
3001 S Washington St, Grand Forks, ND 58201-6716
Tel (701) 757-3400 *Founded/Ownrshp* 1938, 1994
Sales 23.8MM[E] *EMP* 110
SIC 8734 3826 3825

IDEAL ALUMINUM
See IDEAL DEALS LLC

IDEAL BOX COMPANY
See HARVARD FOLDING BOX CO INC

D-U-N-S 00-509-1749 IMP
IDEAL BOX CO (IL)
4800 S Austin Ave, Chicago, IL 60638-1484
Tel (708) 594-3100 *Founded/Ownrshp* 1924
Sales 80.0MM *EMP* 200[E]
SIC 2653 3993 Boxes, corrugated: made from purchased materials; Display items, corrugated: made from purchased materials; Signs & advertising specialties; Boxes, corrugated: made from purchased materials; Display items, corrugated: made from purchased materials; Signs & advertising specialties
Ch: Stephen Eisen
**Pr:* Scott Eisen
**COO:* Yale Eisen
CFO: Scott Clary
VP: Jeff Craig
Genl Mgr: William McFarland
MIS Dir: Robert Ross
VP Opers: Mike Sebring

D-U-N-S 96-967-2950 EXP
IDEAL BOX CO
15 Union St Ste 555, Lawrence, MA 01840-1823
Tel (978) 683-2802 *Founded/Ownrshp* 2011
Sales 22.1MM *EMP* 8
Accts Sklar Carmosin & Company Jenk
SIC 5113 Folding paperboard boxes
Pr: David Simkins
**CFO:* Anthony Battaglia
**Sec:* Barbara Camera
**Prin:* Steven Gadon
**Prin:* Michael Simkins
**Prin:* Michelle Simkins-Rubell
Manager: Katie Kiley

D-U-N-S 00-704-0348 IMP
IDEAL CHEMICAL AND SUPPLY CO
4025 Air Park St, Memphis, TN 38118-9036
Tel (901) 363-7720 *Founded/Ownrshp* 1932
Sales 95.1MM[E] *EMP* 104
SIC 5169 7389 Industrial chemicals; Laundry soap chips & powder; Packaging & labeling services; Industrial chemicals; Laundry soap chips & powder; Packaging & labeling services
CEO: Sam Block Jr
**CFO:* Terri Vaugh
CFO: Linda Wax
**VP:* Jeffrey Block
VP: Lisa Logan
**VP:* Kelly McCabe
Dir IT: Moore Glyn
IT Man: Terri Vaughan
Sfty Mgr: Megan Mims
Mktg Mgr: Dennis Whipple

D-U-N-S 05-379-5241 IMP
IDEAL CLAMP PRODUCTS INC
8100 Tridon Dr, Smyrna, TN 37167-6603
Tel (615) 459-5800 *Founded/Ownrshp* 2011
Sales 218.1MM[E] *EMP* 800
SIC 3429 Clamps, metal; Clamps, metal
Pr: Mike Reese
VP: Thomas Reeve
Off Mgr: Lara Kilpatrick
Dir IT: Joe Wilkerson
IT Man: Michael Sichel
Sfty Mgr: Janice Boren
Opers Mgr: Jorge Alvarez
Plnt Mgr: Mike Priddy

D-U-N-S 04-448-5183
IDEAL CONSTRUCTION CO
803 W 1st Ave, Crossett, AR 71635-2707
Tel (870) 364-4185 *Founded/Ownrshp* 1997
Sales 32.2MM[E] *EMP* 75
SIC 1542 1611 Commercial & office building, new construction; General contractor, highway & street construction
Pr: Mike Webb
Treas: Donna Rice
**VP:* Charles Fricke

D-U-N-S 01-429-6052
IDEAL CONTRACTING LLC
2525 Clark St, Detroit, MI 48209-1337
Tel (313) 551-2263 *Founded/Ownrshp* 1998
Sales 39.7MM[E] *EMP* 50
SIC 1542 1742 1771 1791 Nonresidential construction; Plastering, drywall & insulation; Concrete work; Structural steel erection
Pr: Loren Venegas
CFO: Rachael Morton
**VP:* Robert Kohut P E
**VP:* Kevin Foucher
VP Opers: Greg Sorrentino

D-U-N-S 96-581-1271 IMP/EXP
IDEAL DEALS LLC
IDEAL ALUMINUM
3200 Parker Dr, Saint Augustine, FL 32084-0891
Tel (386) 736-1700 *Founded/Ownrshp* 2010
Sales 35.7MM[E] *EMP* 70
SIC 3334 3479 Primary aluminum; Aluminum coating of metal products
Exec: Walter Lehmann
Natl Sales: Glenn Spilling

D-U-N-S 03-459-2766
IDEAL DISTRIBUTING CO INC
BUDWEISER OF CLARKSVILLE
2059 Wilma Rudolph Blvd, Clarksville, TN 37040-6621
Tel (931) 552-3300 *Founded/Ownrshp* 1964
Sales 54.6MM[E] *EMP* 130
SIC 5181 Beer & other fermented malt liquors; Beer & other fermented malt liquors
CEO: Charles W Hand
**Pr:* Charles Hand Jr
**CFO:* William Mosely
Snr Mgr: Barry Batson

IDEAL DOOR
See CLOPAY BUILDING PRODUCTS CO INC

IDEAL ELECTRIC COMPANY
See HYUNDAI IDEAL ELECTRIC CO

D-U-N-S 78-057-5015
IDEAL ELECTRICAL SUPPLY CORP
2230 Adams Pl Ne, Washington, DC 20018-3601
Tel (202) 526-7500 *Founded/Ownrshp* 1991
Sales 44.0MM *EMP* 27
Accts Penan & Scott Pc Rockville
SIC 5063 5065 5084 Electrical apparatus & equipment; Electronic parts & equipment; Industrial machinery & equipment
Pr: Cora Williams
**CFO:* Anil Chavan
**Sr VP:* Dennis Harris
**Sr VP:* Ken Rogers

D-U-N-S 05-255-5315 IMP/EXP
IDEAL FASTENER CORP
IDEAL ACCESSORIES
603 W Industry Dr, Oxford, NC 27565-3593
Tel (919) 693-3115 *Founded/Ownrshp* 1936, 1963
Sales 55.4MM[E] *EMP* 275
SIC 3965 Zipper; Zipper
Pr: Ralph Gut
**VP:* Carol Critcher
VP: Mary Gut
Genl Mgr: Gary Davis
Genl Mgr: Dan Spivey
Mfg Mgr: David Spitler
VP Sls: Larry Phillips

IDEAL GERIT DRUM RING MFG
See MEYER STEEL DRUM INC

D-U-N-S 62-113-7942
IDEAL HOMES OF NORMAN LP
1320 N Porter Ave, Norman, OK 73071-6619
Tel (405) 364-1152 *Founded/Ownrshp* 1989
Sales 20.4MM[E] *EMP* 120
SIC 6552 6531 Land subdividers & developers, residential; Real estate managers; Real estate brokers & agents
Genl Pt: Gene McKown
Pt: Todd Booze
Pt: Vernon McKown
Pr: Russ Gammill
VP: Donna Widener
Div Mgr: Bill Fleming
Div Mgr: Tim Sullivan
IT Man: Chad Tolle
VP Opers: Brice Rice
Prd Mgr: Michael Hogan
Prd Mgr: Kent Moore

D-U-N-S 02-725-1793
IDEAL IMAGE DEVELOPMENT INC
(*Suby of* STEINER US HOLDINGS INC) ★
4830 W Kennedy Blvd # 440, Tampa, FL 33609-2548
Tel (813) 286-8100 *Founded/Ownrshp* 2006
Sales 15.0MM[E] *EMP* 315[E]
SIC 7231 Hairdressers
CEO: Leonard Fluxman
**Pr:* Bruce Fabel
**CFO:* Stephen Lazarus
VP: Jay Haley
**VP:* Rob Lazar
Dir IT: Nathan Russell
Mktg Dir: Jenny Sutter
Mktg Mgr: Evan Frangos
Sales Asso: Ashley Demers
Sales Asso: Amanda Michaud
Sales Asso: Andie Riffle

D-U-N-S 00-509-4685 IMP/EXP
IDEAL INDUSTRIES INC
1375 Park Ave, Sycamore, IL 60178-2429
Tel (815) 895-5181 *Founded/Ownrshp* 1916
Sales 347.9MM[E] *EMP* 1,225
SIC 3825 3643 Electrical power measuring equipment; Current-carrying wiring devices; Electrical power measuring equipment; Current-carrying wiring devices
Pr: Jim James
**Ch Bd:* David W Juday
COO: Byron Pollock
CFO: Jim Faltonower
**CFO:* Cannelle Giblin
**Sr VP:* Vicki Slomka
VP: Duke Given
VP: Brad Lindsay
VP: Erwin Pietsch
Area Mgr: Justin Halsema
Area Mgr: Robert Hoag

D-U-N-S 04-766-5075
IDEAL INNOVATIONS INC
950 N Glebe Rd Ste 800, Arlington, VA 22203-4199
Tel (703) 528-9101 *Founded/Ownrshp* 1999
Sales 64.9MM[E] *EMP* 350
SIC 8742 9711 Management consulting services; ; Management consulting services; National security
CEO: Robert W Kocher Jr
**CFO:* Richard Syretz
**Sr VP:* R J Kolton
**Sr VP:* Rebecca Perlman
**Sr VP:* Michael Smith
**VP:* Hope Farmer
VP: Vicky Steward

IDEAL PAPER TUBES & CORES
See US PAPER MILLS CORP

IDEAL SALES
See UNIQUE SALES OF USA INC

D-U-N-S 78-057-3403
IDEAL SETECH LLC
1415 Durant Dr, Howell, MI 48843-8572
Tel (517) 545-9250 *Founded/Ownrshp* 2005
Sales 27.4MM *EMP* 99[E]
SIC 8741 Management services
CEO: Frank Venegas
Genl Mgr: Jesse Venegas

D-U-N-S 01-402-8091 IMP/EXP
IDEAL SNACKS CORP
89 Mill St, Liberty, NY 12754-2038
Tel (845) 292-7000 *Founded/Ownrshp* 1998
Sales 53.9MM[E] *EMP* 200
SIC 2096 Potato chips & similar snacks; Potato chips & similar snacks
Pr: Zeke Alenick
**CFO:* Joseph Talmage
VP: Miriam Ehrenberg
**VP:* Steven Van Poucke
Dir IT: Dennis Norberg
Sls&Mrk Ex: Jim Pietro
VP Sls: Rick Fishman

D-U-N-S 01-623-1974
IDEAL SOLUTIONS INC
31 Boland Ct, Greenville, SC 29615-5730
Tel (864) 286-9009 *Founded/Ownrshp* 1998
Sales 32.2MM[E] *EMP* 800
Accts Mckinley Cooper & Co Llp
SIC 7361 8721 7363 Executive placement; Accounting, auditing & bookkeeping; Help supply services; Executive placement; Accounting, auditing & bookkeeping; Help supply services
Pr: Steve Ivester
**VP:* Mike Surprenant

D-U-N-S 18-573-2526
IDEAL STEEL INC
90693 Link Rd, Eugene, OR 97402-9647
Tel (541) 689-0901 *Founded/Ownrshp* 1987
Sales 33.9MM[E] *EMP* 125
SIC 7389 Metal cutting services; Metal cutting services
Pr: Ronald Duquette
VP: Michele Lucas
Dir IT: Elaine Duquette
Plnt Mgr: Ron Norman
Sales Exec: Paul Duquette
Sls&Mrk Ex: Randy Etter

D-U-N-S 12-060-7044
IDEAL STEEL LLC
1289 Smede Hwy, Broussard, LA 70518-8032
Tel (337) 560-9667 *Founded/Ownrshp* 2002
Sales 43.7MM^E *EMP* 85
SIC 5039 Metal buildings
Genl Mgr: Gene Rodrigue
**CFO:* John Tolson IV
VP Sls: Chad Fleming
Sls Mgr: Rodrigue Kevin

D-U-N-S 00-896-4249
IDEAL SUPPLY CO OF NEW YORK
445 Communipaw Ave, Jersey City, NJ 07304-3620
Tel (201) 333-2600 *Founded/Ownrshp* 1930
Sales 21.3MM^E *EMP* 60
SIC 5051 5074

D-U-N-S 09-217-8040
IDEAL SYSTEM SOLUTIONS INC
5610 Rowland Rd Ste 150, Minnetonka, MN 55343-8982
Tel (763) 425-8163 *Founded/Ownrshp* 1996
Sales 48.1MM^E *EMP* 30^E
SIC 5045 3571 7373 5734 Computers, peripherals & software; Electronic computers; Value-added resellers, computer systems; Computer & software stores
CEO: Elise M Hernandez
Ex VP: John Maquire
**VP:* John McGuire
Mktg Dir: Carol Irish

D-U-N-S 17-579-0252 IMP
■ **IDEAL TAPE CO INC**
IDEAL TAPE CO-A DIV AMERCN BIL
(*Suby of* AMERICAN BILTRITE INC) ★
1400 Middlesex St, Lowell, MA 01851-1296
Tel (978) 458-6833 *Founded/Ownrshp* 1986
Sales 30.7MM^E *EMP* 70
SIC 2672 2671 Tape, pressure sensitive: made from purchased materials; Packaging paper & plastics film, coated & laminated; Tape, pressure sensitive: made from purchased materials; Packaging paper & plastics film, coated & laminated
Pr: Richard G Marcus
**Treas:* William M Marcus
**Sec:* Henry W Winkleman
**VP:* Howard N Feist III
**VP:* Skip Feist
**VP:* Roger Marcus
VP: Louis Miller
VP: John Poulton
Dir IT: Joe Mariani

IDEAL TAPE CO-A DIV AMERCN BIL
See IDEAL TAPE CO INC

D-U-N-S 00-132-9218
IDEAL WINDOWS MANUFACTURING INC
100 W 7th St, Bayonne, NJ 07002-1133
Tel (201) 437-4300 *Founded/Ownrshp* 1924
Sales 47.4MM^E *EMP* 287
SIC 3089

D-U-N-S 94-124-9930 IMP
IDEALAB
(*Suby of* IDEALAB HOLDINGS LLC) ★
130 W Union St, Pasadena, CA 91103-3628
Tel (626) 356-3654 *Founded/Ownrshp* 2006
Sales 97.7MM^E *EMP* 650
SIC 6726 5511 Investment offices; New & used car dealers; Investment offices; New & used car dealers
Ch Bd: Bill Gross
V Ch: Larry Gross
**Pr:* Marcia Goodstein
**CFO:* Craig Chrisney
**VP:* Teresa Bridwell
**VP:* Kristen Ding
Mng Dir: Allen Morgan
CTO: Jerome Budzik
Dir IT: Doeppel Dave
IT Man: Raj Dhaka
Web Dev: Douglas Tally
Board of Directors: Benjamin M Rosen, Jon F Welch Jr

D-U-N-S 02-231-8245
IDEALAB HOLDINGS LLC
130 W Union St, Pasadena, CA 91103-3628
Tel (626) 585-6900 *Founded/Ownrshp* 1996
Sales 102.6MM^E *EMP* 825
SIC 6799 5045 5734 Venture capital companies; Computer software; Computer software & accessories; Venture capital companies; Computer software; Computer software & accessories
CEO: Bill Gross
**Pr:* Marcia Goodstein
**CFO:* Craig Chrisney
Bd of Dir: Allen Morgan
**VP:* Kristen Ding
**VP:* Wes Ferrari

IDEALEASE OF BALTIMORE
See BELTWAY INTERNATIONAL LLC

IDEALEASE OF CENTRAL WISCONSIN
See MID-STATE TRUCK SERVICE INC

IDEALEASE OF HOUSTON
See TEXAS TRUCK CENTERS OF HOUSTON LTD

IDEALEASE OF MIAMI
See RECHTIEN INTERNATIONAL TRUCKS INC

IDEALEASE OF NORTH EAST WI
See PACKER CITY INTERNATIONAL TRUCKS INC

IDEALEASE OF OCALA
See MAUDLIN INTERNATIONAL TRUCKS INC

IDEALEASE OF RENO-SPARKS
See BIG D INTERNATIONAL TRUCKS INC

IDEALEASE OF SAN DIEGO
See DION INTERNATIONAL TRUCKS LLC

IDEALEASE OF TAMPA
See SUN STATE INTERNATIONAL TRUCKS LLC

IDEAS
See INTEGRATED DECISIONS AND SYSTEMS INC

IDEASPHERE
See TWINLAB HOLDINGS INC

D-U-N-S 12-484-6598
IDEASTREAM
WVIZ/PBS HD
1375 Euclid Ave, Cleveland, OH 44115-1826
Tel (216) 916-6100 *Founded/Ownrshp* 2001
Sales 25.9MM *EMP* 151
Accts Maloney Novotny Llc Cleveland
SIC 4833 Television broadcasting stations; Television broadcasting stations
Mng Pt: Larry Pollock
Dir Vol: Siomara Marquetti
**CEO:* Jerry F Wareham
**COO:* Kit Jensen
**CFO:* Bob Calsin
**CFO:* John Phillips
**Treas:* Kevin McMullen
Prgrm Mgr: Liesl Bonneau
IT Man: John Debarr
Prd Mgr: Mike Vendeland
Snr Mgr: Karen Kasler

D-U-N-S 02-476-4584
IDEAUSA PRODUCTS INC
2370 E Artesia Blvd, Long Beach, CA 90805-1708
Tel (310) 860-6076 *Founded/Ownrshp* 2013, 2012
Sales 30.0MM *EMP* 5
SIC 3571 Electronic computers; Electronic computers
Pr: FAI Wong
**Pr:* Dennis Wong

D-U-N-S 12-425-9503 IMP
IDEAVILLAGE PRODUCTS CORP
155 Us Highway 46 Fl 4, Wayne, NJ 07470-6831
Tel (973) 826-8400 *Founded/Ownrshp* 2002
Sales 200.0MM^E *EMP* 38
SIC 5961 General merchandise, mail order; General merchandise, mail order
Pr: Anand Khubani
**CFO:* David M Epstein
Sys Mgr: Alfredo Sanoguel
VP Mktg: Robin Bonnema
VP Sls: Mike Govindani
Snr Mgr: Jane Gilmartin

D-U-N-S 07-715-1991 IMP
IDEC CORP
(*Suby of* IDEC CORPORATION)
1175 Elko Dr, Sunnyvale, CA 94089-2209
Tel (408) 747-0550 *Founded/Ownrshp* 1975
Sales 52.2MM^E *EMP* 117
SIC 5065 Electronic parts; Electronic parts
CEO: Toshiyuki Funaki
**Pr:* Mikio Funaki
**CFO:* Donald L Scrivner
Sr VP: Nabil Hanna
VP: Sada Ohara
Ex Dir: Felicia Gustin
IT Man: Alvin Chen
VP Sls: Wally Baldwin
Manager: Brian Orell

D-U-N-S 82-514-0986 IMP/EXP
■ **IDEELI INC**
(*Suby of* GROUPON INC) ★
620 8th Ave Fl 45, New York, NY 10018-1741
Tel (646) 745-1000 *Founded/Ownrshp* 2014
Sales 61.1MM^E *EMP* 180
SIC 2741 ;
CEO: Stefan Pepe
**Sr VP:* Joel Greengrass
**Sr VP:* Janee Ries
VP: Eduardo Frias
**Dir Risk M:* David Manela

D-U-N-S 00-890-7537
IDEKER INC
4614 S 40th St, Saint Joseph, MO 64503-2151
Tel (816) 364-3970 *Founded/Ownrshp* 1947
Sales 24.9MM^E *EMP* 75^E
SIC 1622 Highway construction, elevated
Ch Bd: Ronald Ideker
**Pr:* Paul Ideker
**Pr:* Roger Ideker
Treas: Watkins Miner
**VP:* Ken Ideker
**VP:* Cody Phillips
Sfty Mgr: Rusty Thiulman

D-U-N-S 78-575-0373 IMP/EXP
IDEMITSU LUBRICANTS AMERICA CORP
(*Suby of* APOLLO IDEMITSU CORP) ★
701 Port Rd, Jeffersonville, IN 47130-8425
Tel (812) 284-3300 *Founded/Ownrshp* 1992
Sales 208.3MM *EMP* 85
Accts Deloitte & Touche Llp Detroi
SIC 2992 Lubricating oils & greases; Lubricating oils & greases
Pr: Masashi Yokomura
**VP Admn:* Shinji Otsubo
IT Man: Jacob Apperson
**VP Mfg:* Tammi Walts
Sfty Dirs: Sandra Vargas
Mtls Mgr: Kristi Hunter
Ql Cn Mgr: Takuma Kimura
Natl Sales: Jim Muehlman
**VP Sls:* Shukichi Shimoda
Snr Mgr: Tony Kosicki

D-U-N-S 17-481-0218
IDENTCO INTERNATIONAL CORP
28164 W Concrete Dr, Ingleside, IL 60041-8836
Tel (815) 385-0011 *Founded/Ownrshp* 1988
Sales 49.0MM^E *EMP* 70
SIC 5131 2672 Labels; Coated & laminated paper
Pr: Scott B Lucas

D-U-N-S 17-011-6839
IDENTIDAD ADVERTISING DEVELOPMENT LLC
IDENTIDAD TELECOM
7950 Nw 53rd St Ste 132, Doral, FL 33166-4636
Tel (786) 242-2224 *Founded/Ownrshp* 2002
Sales 55.0MM^E *EMP* 18
SIC 4813 Telephone communication, except radio; Telephone communication, except radio
**COO:* Andres Sanchez
**CFO:* James Merced
Treas: Maria Merced

IDENTIDAD TELECOM
See IDENTIDAD ADVERTISING DEVELOPMENT LLC

D-U-N-S 00-731-8892 IMP/EXP
IDENTIFICATION PLATES INC
ID LINE, THE
1555 High Point Dr, Mesquite, TX 75149-9009
Tel (972) 216-1616 *Founded/Ownrshp* 1959
Sales 24.8MM^E *EMP* 68
SIC 5051 3479 2759

D-U-N-S 04-408-0468 IMP
IDENTISYS INC (MN)
7630 Commerce Way, Eden Prairie, MN 55344-2002
Tel (952) 294-1200 *Founded/Ownrshp* 1999
Sales 38.6MM^E *EMP* 105
SIC 3699 Electrical equipment & supplies; Electrical equipment & supplies
CEO: Michael R Shields
CFO: Tony Dick
VP Sls: Tate Preston
Mktg Dir: Darlene Swan
Sls Dir: Lindia Roth
Mktg Mgr: Charles Nelson
Mktg Mgr: Michael Shields II
Sls Mgr: Jim Amberg
Sls Mgr: Shelli Bartlett
Sls Mgr: Laurie Bosu
Sls Mgr: Jon Burgoon

IDENTITY GROUP
See IDENTITY HOLDING CO LLC

D-U-N-S 07-874-5534
IDENTITY GROUP HOLDINGS CORP
1480 Gould Dr, Cookeville, TN 38506-4152
Tel (931) 432-4000 *Founded/Ownrshp* 2014
Sales 199.4MM^E *EMP* 940
SIC 3089 3086 3993 3953 Injection molding of plastics; Plastics foam products; Signs & advertising specialties; Marking devices; Injection molding of plastics; Plastics foam products; Signs & advertising specialties; Marking devices
CEO: Brad Wolf
**CFO:* Brian Mogensen

D-U-N-S 07-874-5506
IDENTITY GROUP HOLDINGS LLC
(*Suby of* IDENTITY GROUP HOLDINGS CORP) ★
1480 Gould Dr, Cookeville, TN 38506-4152
Tel (931) 432-4000 *Founded/Ownrshp* 2007
Sales 91.2MM^E *EMP* 615
SIC 3953 Marking devices; Marking devices
CEO: Brad Wolf
**CFO:* Brian Mogensen

D-U-N-S 80-076-9551 IMP/EXP
IDENTITY HOLDING CO LLC
IDENTITY GROUP
1480 Gould Dr, Cookeville, TN 38506-4152
Tel (931) 432-4000 *Founded/Ownrshp* 2007
Sales 117.6MM^E *EMP* 600
SIC 3953 2672 Marking devices; Labels (unprinted), gummed: made from purchased materials; Marking devices; Labels (unprinted), gummed: made from purchased materials
Pr: Brad Wolf
**CFO:* Brian Mogensen
**VP:* Lee Brantley
**VP:* David Durfee
VP: Ron Jarvis
**VP:* Warren Soltis
Exec: Chris Thompson
VP Mktg: Liz Kelsey

D-U-N-S 85-966-6471 IMP
▲ **IDENTIV INC**
39300 Civic Center Dr # 140, Fremont, CA 94538-2338
Tel (949) 250-8888 *Founded/Ownrshp* 1990
Sales 81.2MM *EMP* 308^E
Accts Bdo Usa Llp San Jose Califo
Tkr Sym INVE *Exch* NGM
SIC 3577 7372 Computer peripheral equipment; Prepackaged software; Computer peripheral equipment; Prepackaged software
CEO: Steven Humphreys
**Pr:* Jason Hart
CFO: Melvin Denton
CFO: Brian Nelson
Bd of Dir: Manuel Cubero
Ex VP: Sour Chhor
Ex VP: Stephen Healy
VP: Mark Allen
VP: Brent Archer
VP: Roger Hornstra
VP: John Piccininni
VP: Jeff Rowland
VP: Mathew Smith
VP: Stephen Summerill
VP: Robert Zivney
Board of Directors: Gary Kremen, James E Ousley, Daniel S Wenzel

D-U-N-S 10-210-6952
IDENTIX INC
MORPHOTRUST
(*Suby of* MORPHOTRUST USA LLC) ★
5705 W Old Shakopee Rd # 100, Bloomington, MN 55437-3127
Tel (952) 932-0888 *Founded/Ownrshp* 2006
Sales 39.8MM^E *EMP* 370
SIC 3577 Magnetic ink & optical scanning devices; Magnetic ink & optical scanning devices
Pr: Richard Agostinelli
COO: Linda Howard
Ex VP: Grant Evans
Ex VP: Sunday Lewis
VP: Charles W Archer
VP: Daniel Dellegrotti
VP: Allen Ganz
VP: Daniel Maase
VP: Yuri Shapiro
VP: William J Spence
Off Mgr: Lynn Olstad

D-U-N-S 03-814-4739
IDEO LP
150 Forest Ave, Palo Alto, CA 94301-1614
Tel (650) 289-3400 *Founded/Ownrshp* 2010
Sales 68.3MM^E *EMP* 145
SIC 7336 7389 8711 Design services; Commercial art & graphic design; Design, commercial & industrial; Engineering services
Pr: Tim Brown
Pt: Gretchen Addi
Pt: Peter Coughlan
Pt: Fred Dust
Pt: Tom Eich
Pt: Chris Flink
Pt: Richard Kelly
Pt: Ilya Prokopoff
Pt: Iain Roberts
Pt: Philipp Schaefer
Mng Dir: Davide Agnelli

D-U-N-S 01-145-5446
IDERA INC
POINTSECURE
2950 North Loop W Ste 700, Houston, TX 77092-8806
Tel (713) 523-4433 *Founded/Ownrshp* 2014
Sales 145.3MM^E *EMP* 405^E
SIC 7371 7372 Computer software development & applications; Software programming applications; Application computer software; Computer software development & applications; Software programming applications; Application computer software
CEO: Randy Jacops
**COO:* Chris Smith
CFO: Trey Chambers
**CFO:* York Richards
VP: Josh Stephens
Software D: Robert Wilkinson
Sftwr Eng: Mark Slavens
Natl Sales: Matt Daigger
VP Mktg: Heidi Farris
VP Sls: Jerry Morgan
Sls Dir: Mark Berglund

IDERTON DODGE CHRYSLER JEEP
See HORACE G ILDERTON LLC

D-U-N-S 18-358-0844 IMP
▲ **IDEX CORP**
1925 W Field Ct Ste 200, Lake Forest, IL 60045-4862
Tel (847) 498-7070 *Founded/Ownrshp* 1987
Sales 2.1MMM *EMP* 6,712^E
Accts Deloitte & Touche Llp Chicago
Tkr Sym IEX *Exch* NYS
SIC 3561 3563 3594 Industrial pumps & parts; Air & gas compressors; Fluid power pumps & motors; Industrial pumps & parts; Air & gas compressors; Fluid power pumps & motors
Ch Bd: Andrew K Silvernail
Pr: Ivy B Suter
COO: Eric Ashleman
CFO: Elizabeth Hernandez
CFO: Heath A Mitts
Chf Mktg O: Walter Aranton
Ofcr: Garin Bergman
Ofcr: Jeffrey D Bucklew
Ex VP: Brian Ayling
Ex VP: Jeff Krautkramer
Sr VP: Denise Cade
Sr VP: James Maclennan
Sr VP: Frank J Notaro
Sr VP: Daniel J Salliotte
VP: Michael J Yates
Board of Directors: Bradley J Bell, William M Cook, Katrina Helmkamp, Gregory F Milzcik, Ernest J Mrozek, David C Parry, Livingston L Satterthwaite, Michael T Tokarz, Cynthia J Warner

D-U-N-S 01-452-6276
IDEX GLOBAL SERVICES INC (CA)
(*Suby of* I2K HOLDINGS INC) ★
505 Montgomery St # 1250, San Francisco, CA 94111-6512
Tel (415) 249-3400 *Founded/Ownrshp* 1997, 2002
Sales 47.4MM^E *EMP* 500
SIC 1731 7373 Communications specialization; Computer integrated systems design; Communications specialization; Computer integrated systems design
CEO: Craig D Morris
**CFO:* Grant Morris
Sr Cor Off: Robert White
Dir IT: Lama Beckett

D-U-N-S 07-393-1891 IMP
■ **IDEX HEALTH & SCIENCE LLC**
(*Suby of* IDEX CORP) ★
600 Park Ct, Rohnert Park, CA 94928-7906
Tel (707) 588-2000 *Founded/Ownrshp* 2002
Sales 124.8MM^E *EMP* 781
SIC 3821 3829 3826 3823 3494 Laboratory apparatus & furniture; Measuring & controlling devices; Analytical instruments; Industrial instrmnts msrmnt display/control process variable; Valves & pipe fittings; Laboratory apparatus & furniture; Measuring & controlling devices; Analytical instruments; Industrial instrmnts msrmnt display/control process variable; Valves & pipe fittings
Pr: Jeff Cannon
VP: Heath A Mitts
VP: Dominic A Romeo
VP: Daniel J Salliotte
VP: Lisa Walsh
Sftwr Eng: Steve Carlson
Ql Cn Mgr: Eric Bond
Sls Dir: Marty McCoy
Manager: Khong Cheong
Manager: Thomas Mikhail

D-U-N-S 00-515-1006
■ **IDEX MPT INC**
FITZPATRICK COMPANY, THE
(*Suby of* IDEX CORP) ★
832 N Industrial Dr, Elmhurst, IL 60126-1132
Tel (630) 530-3333 *Founded/Ownrshp* 1912, 2010
Sales 21.9MM^E *EMP* 112

SIC 3599 Amusement park equipment; Amusement park equipment
Pr: Anthony Divito
*Pr: Peter Ruck
Ex VP: Richard Murphy
*Genl Mgr: Sam Mawley
Genl Mgr: Andrea Panico
VP Opers: Lee Brooks
Mtls Mgr: Jamie Yusko
Ql Cn Mgr: Josaa Molinar
Natl Sales: Kim Dietrich
Manager: Viviana Aguilera
Manager: Hilda Dickinson

D-U-N-S 07-510-6562
IDEXCEL INC
459 Herndon Pkwy Ste 11, Herndon, VA 20170-6221
Tel (703) 230-2600 Founded/Ownrshp 2005
Sales 32.4MM^E EMP 200
SIC 8748 Business consulting; Business consulting
Pr: Prasad Alapati

IDEXX CVD
See IDEXX REFERENCE LABORATORIES INC

D-U-N-S 10-818-3757 IMP
▲ IDEXX LABORATORIES INC
1 Idexx Dr, Westbrook, ME 04092-2041
Tel (207) 556-0300 Founded/Ownrshp 1983
Sales 1.4MMM EMP 6,400
Accts Pricewaterhousecoopers Llp Bo
Tkr Sym IDXX Exch NGS
SIC 3826 2834 5047 Blood testing apparatus; Electrolytic conductivity instruments; Water testing apparatus; Veterinary pharmaceutical preparations; Instruments, surgical & medical; Blood testing apparatus; Electrolytic conductivity instruments; Water testing apparatus; Veterinary pharmaceutical preparations; Instruments, surgical & medical
Ch Bd: Jonathan W Ayers
CFO: Brian P McKeon
Treas: Rick Holt
Ex VP: Jay Mazelsky
Ex VP: Johnny D Powers
Ex VP: Michael J Williams
Sr VP: Louis W Pollock
VP: Jacqueline L Studer
VP: Robert Suva
Exec: Carol Paolino
Dir Bus: Serge Leterme
Board of Directors: Bruce L Claflin, Thomas Craig, William T End, Rebecca M Henderson, Barry C Johnson, Daniel M Junius, Robert J Murray, M Anne Szostak, Sophie V Vandebroek

D-U-N-S 00-681-8561
■ IDEXX REFERENCE LABORATORIES INC (GA)
IDEXX CVD
(Suby of IDEXX LABORATORIES INC) ★
1 Idexx Dr, Westbrook, ME 04092-2040
Tel (207) 856-0300 Founded/Ownrshp 1996
Sales 25.4MM^E EMP 430
SIC 8071 Testing laboratories; Testing laboratories
Pr: David Shaw
CEO: Bruce Gardner
VP: Giovani Twigge
IT Man: Chris Weekes
Snr Mgr: Eduard De Vries

IDG CHARLOTTE
See IDG USA LLC

D-U-N-S 15-779-0791
IDG COMMUNICATIONS INC
INFOWORLD PUBLISHING COMPANY
(Suby of EXECUTRAIN) ★
5 Speen St, Framingham, MA 01701-4674
Tel (508) 875-5000 Founded/Ownrshp 1987
Sales 83.8MM^E EMP 1,200
SIC 2721 2731 Trade journals: publishing only, not printed on site; Magazines: publishing & printing; Books: publishing & printing; Trade journals: publishing only, not printed on site; Magazines: publishing & printing; Books: publishing & printing
CEO: Michael Friedenberg
*Pr: David Hill
Pr: Bob Melk
CEO: Matthew Yorke
*Treas: Edward B Bloom
Sr VP: Pam Stenson
VP: Rajeev Agarwal
VP: Joel Martin
VP: Eric Owen
VP: Mike Romoff
Mktg Mgr: Matt Kim

D-U-N-S 08-955-0487 IMP/EXP
IDG LLC
U S STAMP & SIGN
(Suby of IDENTITY GROUP HOLDINGS LLC) ★
1480 Gould Dr, Cookeville, TN 38506-4152
Tel (931) 432-4000 Founded/Ownrshp 2007
Sales 47.1MM^E EMP 530
SIC 3953

D-U-N-S 00-192-2681 IMP
IDG USA LLC
IDG CHARLOTTE
(Suby of I D G) ★
2100 The Oaks Pkwy, Belmont, NC 28012
Tel (704) 398-5600 Founded/Ownrshp 2000
Sales 497.6MM^E EMP 1,200
SIC 5084 5085

D-U-N-S 80-702-2483
IDHASOFT INC
SEMAFOR TECHNOLOGIES USA
(Suby of IDHASOFT LIMITED)
6 Concourse Pkwy Ste 500, Atlanta, GA 30328-5360
Tel (770) 248-2999 Founded/Ownrshp 2007
Sales 122.9MM^E EMP 1,200
SIC 7379 Computer related consulting services; Computer related consulting services
CEO: Alok Pathak
CEO: Murali Anantharaman
*CFO: Purnima Kaddi
Ex VP: Ashish Dayal
Ex VP: Karen Mills
Ex VP: Hiren Shah
Ex VP: Jim Waites
*Sr VP: Roger Cunningham
Sr VP: Dave Kilzer
VP: Dermot Barry
VP: Philip Brennan
VP: Nagesh Doddaka
VP: Stephen Graef
VP: Vic Gupta
VP: Srikanth Kari
VP: Marc Nolan

IDHS
See INDIANA DEPARTMENT OF HOMELAND SECURITY

IDI
See INDUSTRIAL DIELECTRICS HOLDINGS INC

IDI COMPOSITES INTERNATIONAL
See INDUSTRIAL DIELECTRICS INC

IDI DISTRIBUTORS
See INSULATION DISTRIBUTORS INC

D-U-N-S 96-172-9642
IDI FABRICATION INC
14444 Herriman Blvd, Noblesville, IN 46060-4900
Tel (317) 776-6577 Founded/Ownrshp 2010
Sales 26.3MM^E EMP 100^E
SIC 3567 Induction & dielectric heating equipment; Induction & dielectric heating equipment
Pr: Scott Doll
*VP: Peter Jarosz
Natl Sales: Jerry Short

D-U-N-S 04-895-9811
IDI VBMJR CORP
1105 N New Hope Rd, Raleigh, NC 27610-1415
Tel (919) 231-6355 Founded/Ownrshp 2003
Sales 24.6MM^E EMP 250^E
SIC 5033 5031 Insulation materials; Building materials, interior; Insulation materials; Building materials, interior
Brnch Mgr: John Krawczyk

D-U-N-S 80-583-1422
IDIRECT GOVERNMENT LLC
IGT
(Suby of IDIRECT TECHNOLOGIES) ★
13921 Park Center Rd # 600, Herndon, VA 20171-3237
Tel (703) 648-8118 Founded/Ownrshp 2007
Sales 20.2MM^E EMP 77
SIC 4899 Satellite earth stations; Ccmmunication signal enhancement network system
Pr: John Ratigan
*Pr: Karl Fuchs
Ex VP: Mike Fraser
Sr VP: David Bettinger
*Sr VP: Greg Walker
*VP: Jim Hanlon
*Prin: Richard Gallivan
Sales Exec: Brad Mack
Sales Exec: Craig Masters
Mktg Mgr: Keri Spencer
Sls Mgr: Joe Bender
Board of Directors: Vincent E Boles, Robert T Dail, John G Meyer Jr

IDIRECT TECHNOLOGIES
See VT IDIRECT INC

IDL
See INGENIOUS DESIGNS LLC

D-U-N-S 06-956-2941 IMP
IDL TOOLS INTERNATIONAL LLC
30 Boright Ave, Kenilworth, NJ 07033-1015
Tel (908) 276-2330 Founded/Ownrshp 2004
Sales 31.8MM^E EMP 140
SIC 5251 Tools
CEO: Sean M Quinn
*CFO: Mike Donath

D-U-N-S 00-433-3738 IMP
■ IDL WORLDWIDE INC (PA)
(Suby of MATTHEWS INTERNATIONAL CORP) ★
500 Grant Ave, East Butler, PA 16029-2111
Tel (724) 431-0606 Founded/Ownrshp 1937, 2004
Sales 98.7MM^E EMP 753
SIC 3993 2752

D-U-N-S 01-118-9006
IDLE FREE SYSTEMS INC
(Suby of PHILLIPS & TEMRO INDUSTRIES INC) ★
7617 Mineral Point Rd # 201, Madison, WI 53717-1623
Tel (608) 237-6311 Founded/Ownrshp 2003, 2014
Sales 13.8MM^E EMP 348^E
SIC 3621 Control equipment for buses or trucks, electric
CEO: Robert Hopton

D-U-N-S 02-553-2458
IDLEWOOD ELECTRIC SUPPLY INC (IL)
114 Skokie Valley Rd, Highland Park, IL 60035-4404
Tel (847) 831-3600 Founded/Ownrshp 1959
Sales 49.4MM^E EMP 100
SIC 5063 5719 Electrical apparatus & equipment; Lighting fixtures; Lighting fixtures; Electrical apparatus & equipment; Lighting fixtures
CEO: Barbara Scheinman Lansing
*Ch Bd: Isidore Scheinman
*Pr: Jeffery Scheinman
VP: David Lansing
Off Mgr: Jennifer Grant

IDM TRUCKING
See RAILSIDE ENTERPRISES INC

D-U-N-S 08-200-2957 IMP
IDN - ACME INC
INTERNATIONAL DIST NETWORK-IDN
(Suby of IDN INC) ★
1504 Justin Rd, Metairie, LA 70001-5985
Tel (504) 837-7315 Founded/Ownrshp 1995
Sales 20.9MM^E EMP 62
SIC 5099 Locks & lock sets
Pr: William B Johnson
VP: Hope Blanco
*VP: Karen Hoffman Kahl
VP: Brian Salles
VP Admn: Delno Mullins

D-U-N-S 00-254-4393 IMP/EXP
IDN - ARMSTRONGS INC (GA)
(Suby of H HOFFMAN IDN INC) ★
3589 Broad St, Atlanta, GA 30341-2203
Tel (404) 875-0136 Founded/Ownrshp 1966
Sales 24.5MM^E EMP 59
SIC 5087 Locksmith equipment & supplies
CEO: John M Burke
*CFO: Fred Michael Groover
Brnch Mgr: Jorge De La Paz
IT Man: Susan Richards
Sls&Mrk Ex: Wayne Morris

IDN DOOR AND HARDWARE
See I D N - HARDWARE SALES INC

D-U-N-S 10-333-1179 IMP
IDN INC
2401 Mustang Dr Ste 100, Grapevine, TX 76051-8640
Tel (817) 421-5470 Founded/Ownrshp 1978
Sales 40.7MM^E EMP 195
SIC 5087 Locksmith equipment & supplies; Locksmith equipment & supplies
Pr: F Michael Groover
*Sec: Karen Huffman Kahl
*VP: Alvin M Hoffman
Opers Mgr: Paul Ranieri
Mktg Mgr: Kathleen Schuster-Kempf

D-U-N-S 82-955-9231
■ IDONDEMAND INC
ID ON DEMAND
(Suby of IDENTIV INC) ★
1900 Carnegie Ave Ste B, Santa Ana, CA 92705-5557
Tel (415) 200-4546 Founded/Ownrshp 2008
Sales 76.5MM^E EMP 290^E
SIC 7373 Local area network (LAN) systems integrator; Local area network (LAN) systems integrator
VP: Jennifer A Grigg
VP: Jack Bubany
*Prin: Matthew Herscovitzh
Off Mgr: Anna Ruggiero

D-U-N-S 96-164-3785 IMP
IDQ HOLDINGS INC
100 S Bedford Rd Ste 300, Mount Kisco, NY 10549-3444
Tel (888) 318-5454 Founded/Ownrshp 2013
Sales NA EMP 300^E
SIC 3714

IDS
See INTEGRATED DISTRIBUTION SERVICES INC

IDS
See IMPERIAL DESIGN SERVICE INC

IDS
See INTEGRATED DEICING SERVICES LLC

IDS
See INNOVATIVE DESIGN SOLUTIONS INC

D-U-N-S 04-032-7306
IDS ENGINEERING GROUP INC
13333 Northwest Fwy # 300, Houston, TX 77040-6016
Tel (713) 462-3178 Founded/Ownrshp 1970
Sales 41.3MM^E EMP 260
SIC 8711 Consulting engineer; Consulting engineer
Pr: Gerry E Pate
Treas: Jeff E Ross
VP: Chad Abram
VP: Debra L Anglin
*VP: Lois Pate
VP: Jess Swaim
Dir IT: Greg Goodman
Mktg Mgr: Michelle Cazares
Snr PM: Eric Johnson
Snr PM: Frank Olshefski
Snr PM: Timothy Talaga

D-U-N-S 96-375-8375
IDS GROUP INC
INTERNATIONAL DECISION SYSTEMS
220 S 6th St Ste 700, Minneapolis, MN 55402-1497
Tel (612) 851-3200 Founded/Ownrshp 2003
Sales 33.2MM^E EMP 390^E
SIC 7372 Prepackaged software
CEO: Michael Campbell
VP: Ng Leong
Snr Sftwr: Debrah Vitelli
Dir IT: Craig Debban
IT Man: Herry Fernandez
IT Man: Jill Zimmer
Tech Mgr: Rob Takkunen
Tech Mgr: Matt Weum
Software D: Sara Larsen
Sftwr Eng: Alex Brekken
Sftwr Eng: Mike Norgaard

IDS.COM
See INTELLIGENT DOCUMENT SOLUTIONS INC

D-U-N-S 80-609-5217 IMP
■ IDSC HOLDINGS LLC
SNAP-ON INDUSTRIAL
(Suby of SNAP-ON INC) ★
2801 80th St, Kenosha, WI 53143-5656
Tel (262) 656-5200 Founded/Ownrshp 1920
Sales 449.7MM^E EMP 4,010
SIC 3423 3559 7372 6794 5013 3546 Mechanics' hand tools; Automotive maintenance equipment; Prepackaged software; Patent owners & lessors; Motor vehicle supplies & new parts; Power-driven handtools; Mechanics' hand tools; Automotive maintenance equipment; Prepackaged software; Patent owners & lessors; Motor vehicle supplies & new parts; Power-driven handtools
Pr: Nick Pinchuk
Pr: Anthony Roberts
CFO: Martin M Ellen
Genl Mgr: Andrea Ehlert
Off Admin: Joanne Valentini
Sls Mgr: Richard Simmons

IDT 911
See IDT911 LLC

D-U-N-S 80-903-9910 IMP
▲ IDT CORP
550 Broad St Ste 500, Newark, NJ 07102-4536
Tel (973) 438-1000 Founded/Ownrshp 1990
Sales 1.6MMM EMP 1,250
Accts Grant Thornton Llp New York
Tkr Sym IDT Exch NYS
SIC 4813 Telephone communication, except radio; Local & long distance telephone communications; ; Telephone communication, except radio; Local & long distance telephone communications;
CEO: Shmuel Jonas
*Ch Bd: Howard S Jonas
Ofcr: Marcelo Fischer
Ex VP: Menachem Ash
Ex VP: Joyce J Mason
VP: Joe Caldarone
VP: Moshe Gabay
VP: Emilio RAO
VP: Michelle Wandzilak
VP: Esti Witty
DP Dir: Sergey Altman
Board of Directors: Michael Cosentino, Bill Pereira, Judah Schorr

D-U-N-S 80-286-4061
■ IDT DOMESTIC TELECOM INC
(Suby of IDT CORP) ★
520 Broad St Fl 5, Newark, NJ 07102-3111
Tel (973) 438-1000 Founded/Ownrshp 2001
Sales 214.9MM^E EMP 1,200
SIC 4813 Telephone communication, except radio; Telephone communication, except radio
CEO: Bill Pereira
Ex VP: Sab Ventola
Exec: Theodore Tewksbury

D-U-N-S 60-415-4778
IDT911 LLC
IDT 911
7580 N Dobson Rd Ste 201, Scottsdale, AZ 85256-2702
Tel (480) 355-8500 Founded/Ownrshp 2003
Sales 21.2MM^E EMP 72
SIC 8741 6289 Management services; Security custodians
CEO: Matt Cullina
*Pr: Sean Daly
*Pr: Scott Frazee
COO: Judd Rousseau
Sr VP: Michael Milligan
VP: Betty Chan-Bauza
VP: Peter Moraga
VP: Michael Pooley
Dir IT: Jeffrey Rosenthal
Pr Mgr: Kelly Santos
Mktg Mgr: Jennifer Holm

IDVA
See ILLINOIS DEPARTMENT OF VETERANS AFFAIRS

IDVILLE
See BAUDVILLE INC

IDX
See PACIFIC COAST SHOWCASE INC

D-U-N-S 04-949-8363 IMP/EXP
IDX - BALTIMORE INC
(Suby of IDX CORP) ★
8901 Snowden River Pkwy, Columbia, MD 21046-1673
Tel (410) 551-3600 Founded/Ownrshp 1969, 2005
Sales 32.8MM^E EMP 125
SIC 2542 Fixtures: display, office or store: except wood; Fixtures: display, office or store: except wood
CEO: Terry Schultz
Ex VP: Mark Pritchard
*VP: Julian Nicole
VP Opers: Haresh Raitaita
VP Opers: Haresh Raithatha

D-U-N-S 12-442-4826 IMP
IDX CORP
TRIANGLE SYSTEMS
1 Rider Trail Plaza Dr, Earth City, MO 63045-1313
Tel (314) 801-6304 Founded/Ownrshp 2001
Sales 393.0MM^E EMP 1,045
SIC 2542 Office & store showcases & display fixtures; Office & store showcases & display fixtures
CEO: Terry Schultz
Pr: Terri Boettigheimer
Pr: Bruce Moco
Pr: Tony Volpe
*CFO: Fritz Baumgartner
Ex VP: Bill Delaney
*Ex VP: Bob Heditsian
*Ex VP: Scott Norvell
*Ex VP: Mark Pritchard
VP: Gordon Bjorkman
VP: Jim Comarata
VP: John Morehead
VP: Bill Rapagnani

D-U-N-S 02-066-6681
■ IDX SYSTEMS CORP (VT)
GE
(Suby of GENERAL ELECTRIC CO) ★
40 Idx Dr, South Burlington, VT 05403-7771
Tel (802) 658-2664 Founded/Ownrshp 1969, 2006
Sales 98.4MM^E EMP 2,409
SIC 7371 Computer software systems analysis & design, custom; Computer software systems analysis & design, custom
Pr: John Dineen
VP: Nan O'Leary
IT Man: Bruce Hoversland
Sftwr Eng: David Banks
Sftwr Eng: Brian Coles
Sftwr Eng: Alex Fong
Sftwr Eng: Praveen Kysetti
Sftwr Eng: Renu Sharma
Mktg Mgr: Ramiro Roman
Genl Couns: Robert Baker

IDYLLWILD ARTS ACADEMY, THE
See IDYLLWILD ARTS FOUNDATION

D-U-N-S 10-405-2048
IDYLLWILD ARTS FOUNDATION
IDYLLWILD ARTS ACADEMY, THE
52500 Temecula Rd, Idyllwild, CA 92549
Tel (951) 659-2171 *Founded/Ownrshp* 1946
Sales 26.0MM *EMP* 175
Accts Singerlewak Llp Los Angeles
SIC 8211 8299 Elementary & secondary schools; Music & drama schools; Elementary & secondary schools; Music & drama schools
Pr: Brian D Cohen
Ch Bd: Jeffrey Borak
Pr: Pamela G Jordan
CEO: Faith Raiguel
CFO: John Newman
Trst: Paula Moore
Ofcr: Scott Schroeder
VP: Steve Fraider
Store Mgr: Jeremy Teeguarden
Mktg Dir: Benjamin Brookes
Snr Mgr: Shannon Jacobs

IDYLWOOD CARE CENTER
See HELIOS HEALTHCARE LLC

I.E. MILLER & COMPANY
See I E MILLER OF EUNICE INC

IEA
See ENGENDREN CORP

D-U-N-S 02-341-4968 IMP/EXP
IEA LLC
(*Suby of* ENGENDREN CORP) ★
9625 55th St, Kenosha, WI 53144-7811
Tel (262) 942-1414 *Founded/Ownrshp* 2012
Sales 38.6MM^E *EMP* 200
SIC 3433 3634 Radiators, except electric; Radiators, electric; Radiators, except electric; Radiators, electric
**COO:* Donald Chambers
**CFO:* Patricia Frieman
VP: George Newell
Exec: Craig Seifert
Genl Mgr: David Oshefsky
Opers Mgr: Ron Shaffer

D-U-N-S 09-302-6672
IEA RENEWABLE ENERGY INC (WI)
RESIDUAL MANAGEMENT TECHNOLOGY
(*Suby of* I E A) ★
1212 Deming Way Ste 200, Madison, WI 53717-1981
Tel (608) 831-4444 *Founded/Ownrshp* 1977, 2013
Sales 135.2MM^E *EMP* 562
SIC 8711 8748 Engineering services; Environmental consultant; Engineering services; Environmental consultant
Pr: David Kutcher
Pr: David Bostwick
**CFO:* Tracy Pearson
VP: Steve Johannsen
**VP:* Kenneth Knecht
Dir Bus: Jake Brewster

IEC
See INTERNATIONAL ENVIRONMENTAL CORP

IEC
See INTERSTATE ELECTRIC CO INC

D-U-N-S 00-246-3305
▲ IEC ELECTRONICS CORP
105 Norton St, Newark, NY 14513-1298
Tel (315) 331-7742 *Founded/Ownrshp* 1966
Sales 127.0MM *EMP* 994^E
Tkr Sym IEC *Exch* ASE
SIC 3672 3679 Printed circuit boards; Electronic circuits; Printed circuit boards; Electronic circuits
Pr: Jeffery T Schlarbaum
CFO: Michael T Williams
Board of Directors: Florence D Hudson, John Carlton Johnson, Edward W Kay Jr, Eben S Moulton, James C Rowe, Jerold L Zimmerman

D-U-N-S 01-458-4296 IMP
■ IEC ELECTRONICS CORP-ALBUQUERQUE
(*Suby of* IEC ELECTRONICS CORP) ★
1450 Mission Ave Ne, Albuquerque, NM 87107-4925
Tel (505) 345-5591 *Founded/Ownrshp* 2009
Sales 53.0MM^E *EMP* 98
SIC 3679 3672 Electronic circuits; Printed circuit boards; Electronic circuits; Printed circuit boards
Pr: John T Boone
VP: Chris Cook
VP: Ed Fuhr
Exec: Marianne Lorcher
Genl Mgr: Donald Haynes

D-U-N-S 09-202-1369
IEC GROUP INC (ID)
IEC MANAGEMENT RESOURCE GROUP
3449 E Copper Point Dr, Meridian, ID 83642-6731
Tel (208) 947-9226 *Founded/Ownrshp* 1958, 1997
Sales 50.3MM^E *EMP* 241^E
SIC 8742 6411 Human resource consulting services; Labor & union relations consultant; Compensation & benefits planning consultant; Medical insurance claim processing, contract or fee basis; Human resource consulting services; Labor & union relations consultant; Compensation & benefits planning consultant; Medical insurance claim processing, contract or fee basis
CEO: T Andrew Fujimoto
**COO:* Carrie Hatch
**CFO:* Benjamin Wright
**Ex VP:* Jon Aubrey
Ex Dir: Andy Fujimoto
CTO: Nate Johnson
QA Dir: Leslie Emery
IT Man: Roger Belnap
IT Man: Jim Negomir
IT Man: Kelly Simper
Manager: Lee Lewis

IEC MANAGEMENT RESOURCE GROUP
See IEC GROUP INC

IECP
See INCLUSIVE EDUCATION AND COMMUNITY PARTNERSHIP

IEE
See INDUSTRIAL ELECTRONIC ENGINEERS INC

D-U-N-S 08-039-9595
IEEE FOUNDATION INC
LEEE FOUNDATION
3 Park Ave Fl 17, New York, NY 10016-5997
Tel (212) 419-7900 *Founded/Ownrshp* 1973
Sales 36.8MM^E *EMP* 560^E
Accts Ernst & Young Llp Cpa S Isel
SIC 8621 Engineering association; Engineering association
Pr: Emerson W Pugh
V Ch: Yuan Lee
**Treas:* Dr David A Conner
Treas: Peter Meyer
Bd of Dir: Patrick Chan
VP: Michael Edds
Prgrm Mgr: Holly Brown
CIO: Gabriel Brown
Dir IT: Affif Siddique
IT Man: Fred Bauer
IT Man: Sunil Dubey

D-U-N-S 14-763-5940 IMP
■ IEH BA LLC
BECK/ARNLEY
(*Suby of* ICAHN ENTERPRISES LP) ★
2375 Midway Ln, Smyrna, TN 37167-5881
Tel (615) 220-3200 *Founded/Ownrshp* 2015
Sales 52.9MM^E *EMP* 100
SIC 5013 Automotive supplies & parts; Automotive supplies & parts
Pr: Randy St John
**Pr:* Max C Dull
VP: Bob Anderson
**VP:* Paul Farwick
VP: John Murphy
IT Man: Tammy Williams
Opers Mgr: Pat Freeman
Mktg Dir: Tina Hunt
Sls Dir: Bob Timoney

D-U-N-S 82-744-3552
■ IEH FM HOLDINGS LLC
ICAHN
(*Suby of* ICAHN ENTERPRISES HOLDINGS LP) ★
767 5th Ave Ste 4700, New York, NY 10153-0108
Tel (212) 702-4300 *Founded/Ownrshp* 2008
Sales 7.3MMM^E *EMP* 59,559^E
SIC 3462 3559 3694 3812 3674 Automotive & internal combustion engine forgings; Railroad, construction & mining forgings; Degreasing machines, automotive & industrial; Automotive electrical equipment; Acceleration indicators & systems components, aerospace; Computer logic modules; Automotive & internal combustion engine forgings; Railroad, construction & mining forgings; Degreasing machines, automotive & industrial; Automotive electrical equipment; Acceleration indicators & systems components, aerospace; Computer logic modules

IEH LBRTORIES CONSULTING GROUP
See INSTITUTE FOR ENVIRONMENTAL HEALTH INC

IEHP
See INLAND EMPIRE HEALTH PLAN

IEI
See INTERNATIONAL EXPORTS INC

D-U-N-S 36-076-4724
IEI GENERAL CONTRACTORS INC
I E I
1725 Midway Rd, De Pere, WI 54115-8607
Tel (920) 337-2111 *Founded/Ownrshp* 1989
Sales 26.6MM^E *EMP* 75
SIC 1542 1541 Commercial & office building, new construction; Commercial & office buildings, renovation & repair; Industrial buildings, new construction; Renovation, remodeling & repairs: industrial buildings
Pr: Mike Johnson
**Sec:* Brad Deprez
**VP:* Chris T Berg
VP: Rick Geurts

IEM
See INTERNATIONAL ENGINEERING & MANUFACTURING INC

IEM
See INNOVATIVE EMERGENCY MANAGEMENT INC

D-U-N-S 06-956-5113
IEP HOLDINGS LLC
INTERSTATE ENERGY PARTNERS
3033 Campus Dr Ste W125, Minneapolis, MN 55441-2686
Tel (763) 432-6552 *Founded/Ownrshp* 2011
Sales 40.0MM^E *EMP* 6^E
SIC 5211 Sand & gravel
CEO: William Frothinger
**Pr:* Nate Holmberg
**VP:* Mitch Theisen

IEPA
See ILLINOIS ENVIRONMENTAL PROTECTION AGENCY

D-U-N-S 05-482-8514
IER A WOLF INDUSTRIES COMAPNY
5910 Hamblen Dr, Humble, TX 77396-3215
Tel (281) 441-9321 *Founded/Ownrshp* 1999
Sales 24.5MM^E *EMP* 45
SIC 5063 Electrical supplies
Pr: Michael Wolf
Sls Mgr: Dave Lewis

D-U-N-S 80-738-3831 IMP
IER FUJIKURA INC
I E R INDUSTRIES
8271 Bavaria Dr E, Macedonia, OH 44056-2259
Tel (330) 425-7121 *Founded/Ownrshp* 1993
Sales 34.0MM^E *EMP* 170
SIC 3069 3061 3053 2821 Molded rubber products; Mechanical rubber goods; Gaskets, packing & sealing devices; Plastics materials & resins; Molded rubber products; Mechanical rubber goods; Gaskets, packing & sealing devices; Plastics materials & resins
Pr: Carol Braunschweig
**Ch Bd:* Gerald J Breen
**Pr:* John Elsley
**Pr:* Athur E Lange
Sls Mgr: Pat Breen
Sls Mgr: Matt Mueller

IES
See INDUSTRIAL ELECTRONICS SERVICES INC

IES ABROAD
See INSTITUTE FOR INTERNATIONAL EDUCATION OF STUDENTS

D-U-N-S 07-843-3037
■ IES COMMERCIAL & INDUSTRIAL LLC
(*Suby of* INTEGRATED ELECTRICAL SERVICES INC) ★
5433 Westheimer Rd # 500, Houston, TX 77056-5399
Tel (713) 860-1500 *Founded/Ownrshp* 2011
Sales 25.1MM^E *EMP* 120^E
SIC 1731 Electrical work
Prin: Michael J Caliel

D-U-N-S 05-241-7230
■ IES COMMERCIAL INC
(*Suby of* INTEGRATED ELECTRICAL SERVICES INC) ★
5433 Westheimer Rd # 500, Houston, TX 77056-5399
Tel (713) 860-1500 *Founded/Ownrshp* 2007
Sales 540.9MM^E *EMP* 2,583^E
SIC 1731 Electrical work; Electrical work
VP: William Albright
Sr VP: Bobby Stalvey
VP: Robert Callahan
VP: Leslie Stubbs
Mktg Dir: Lisa Marshall

IES INTER/REALTIMETECH
See FAAC INC

D-U-N-S 07-420-7655 EXP
■ IES RESIDENTIAL INC
HOUSTON STAFFORD ELECTRICAL
(*Suby of* INTEGRATED ELECTRICAL SERVICES INC) ★
10203 Mula Cir, Stafford, TX 77477-3326
Tel (281) 498-2212 *Founded/Ownrshp* 1998
Sales 209.4MM^E *EMP* 1,000
SIC 1731 Electrical work; Electrical work
Pr: Richard Nix
Pr: Christine Kirklin
VP: Robert Callahan
VP: Dwayne Collier
Div Mgr: Bob Conn
Div Mgr: Armando Lozano
IT Man: Christina Phagan
VP Opers: William Wilks
Sfty Dirs: Randall Allen

D-U-N-S 07-915-2465
■ IES SUBSIDIARY HOLDINGS INC
(*Suby of* INTEGRATED ELECTRICAL SERVICES INC) ★
5433 Westheimer Rd # 500, Houston, TX 77056-5399
Tel (713) 860-1500 *Founded/Ownrshp* 2013
Sales 57.7MM^E *EMP* 269^E
SIC 1731 Electrical work; Electrical work

IESC
See INTERNATIONAL EXECUTIVE SERVICE CORPS

IESCO
See INTERNATIONAL ELECTRICAL SALES CORP

D-U-N-S 06-370-5635
IESI MD CORP
PROGRESSIVE WASTE SOLUTIONS
(*Suby of* PROGRESSIVE WASTE SOLUTIONS LTD) ★
2911 52nd Ave Ste A, Hyattsville, MD 20781-1134
Tel (410) 768-1900 *Founded/Ownrshp* 2011
Sales 197.2MM^E *EMP* 320^E
SIC 4953 4212 Refuse collection & disposal services; Garbage collection & transport, no disposal; Refuse collection & disposal services; Garbage collection & transport, no disposal
CEO: Joseph Quarin
Sls Mgr: Jason Rumsey
Sls Mgr: Michael Werk

D-U-N-S 02-660-9367 IMP
IESI NY CORP
(*Suby of* PROGRESSIVE WASTE SOLUTIONS LTD) ★
99 Wood Ave S Ste 1001, Iselin, NJ 08830-2713
Tel (201) 443-3000 *Founded/Ownrshp* 1997
Sales 229.8MM^E *EMP* 520
SIC 4953 Refuse systems; Refuse systems
VP: Stephen T Moody
**CFO:* Thomas J Cowee
**VP:* Edward L Apuzzi
**VP:* Thomas L Brown
MIS Dir: Raymond Digioia
Board of Directors: Jeffrey J Keenan

D-U-N-S 61-657-2389
IESMART SYSTEMS LLC
15200 E Hardy Rd, Houston, TX 77032-2718
Tel (281) 447-6278 *Founded/Ownrshp* 2000
Sales 22.0MM *EMP* 115
Accts Karlins Ramey & Tompkins Llc
SIC 1799 Cable splicing service; Cable splicing service
CEO: Douglas D Colvin
Pr: Gary W Colvin
COO: Chad Gross
COO: David Snider
CFO: Rick Dittemore
CFO: Ron Wade
VP: Kim Colvin
Opers Mgr: Nathanael Hill

D-U-N-S 06-355-2180
IET-MECO
DONCASTERS
2121 S Main St, Paris, IL 61944-2965
Tel (217) 465-6575 *Founded/Ownrshp* 2011
Sales 35.0MM *EMP* 125
SIC 3519 Internal combustion engines
Pr: Marvin Miller

D-U-N-S 00-234-6443
IEW CONSTRUCTION GROUP INC
75 Sculptors Way, Trenton, NJ 08619-3427
Tel (609) 586-5005 *Founded/Ownrshp* 1925
Sales 82.4MM *EMP* 175
SIC 1622 3441 1611 1796 1541

D-U-N-S 04-201-4977 IMP
IEWC CORP (WI)
INDUSTRIAL ELECTRIC WIRE CABLE
5001 S Towne Dr, New Berlin, WI 53151-7956
Tel (262) 782-2255 *Founded/Ownrshp* 1961
Sales 161.1MM^E *EMP* 196
SIC 5063 Wire & cable; Wire & cable
Pr: David Nestingen
COO: Jim Clarke
Ex VP: Paul Bryant
Ex VP: Kyle Spader
VP: Tom Artinian
VP: Roger Caynor
Sls Mgr: Barbara Rael
Sales Asso: Tomasa Darling

D-U-N-S 03-997-9303
IEX GROUP INC
4 World Trade Ctr Fl 44, New York, NY 10007-5200
Tel (646) 568-2320 *Founded/Ownrshp* 2011
Sales 26.0MM *EMP* 61^E
SIC 6231 Stock exchanges
CEO: Brad Katsuyama
**COO:* John Schwall
**Prin:* Sophia Lee
Off Mgr: Tara McKee
**CTO:* Robert Park
Netwrk Eng: James Cape

IF
See INDUSTRIAL FABRICS INC

D-U-N-S 07-874-6723
▲ IF BANCORP INC
201 E Cherry St, Watseka, IL 60970-1661
Tel (815) 432-2476 *Founded/Ownrshp* 2011
Sales NA *EMP* 99^E
Accts Bkd Llp Decatur Illinois
Tkr Sym IROQ *Exch* NAS
SIC 6035 Savings institutions, federally chartered; Savings institutions, federally chartered
Pr: Walter H Hasselbring III
**Ch Bd:* Gary Martin
COO: Linda L Hamilton
CFO: Pamela J Verkler
Ex VP: Terry W Acree
Ex VP: Thomas J Chamberlain

D-U-N-S 12-247-6877
IF HOLDING INC
INITIATIVE FOOD COMPANY
1117 K St, Sanger, CA 93657-3200
Tel (559) 875-3354 *Founded/Ownrshp* 2002
Sales 33.1MM^E *EMP* 130^E
SIC 6719 Investment holding companies, except banks; Investment holding companies, except banks
Pr: John Ypma
VP: Jeff Jankovic
VP: John P Mulvaney
Dir Bus: Karen Rose
VP Opers: Brad Johnson
Sfty Dirs: Richard Aguirre
Prd Mgr: Marvin Canales
Sls Dir: Bill Astin

D-U-N-S 83-023-3321
IF MUSIC INC
401 Orange St, Palm Harbor, FL 34683-5449
Tel (727) 515-3004 *Founded/Ownrshp* 2008
Sales 47.6MM^E *EMP* 2,000
SIC 2741 ;
CEO: Kent White
**Pr:* Michael A Boyd

D-U-N-S 03-684-5329
IF&P FOODS INC
INDIANAPOLIS FRUIT COMPANY
4501 Massachusetts Ave, Indianapolis, IN 46218-3160
Tel (317) 546-2425 *Founded/Ownrshp* 1987, 1997
Sales 184.7MM^E *EMP* 380
SIC 5148 Fruits; Fruits
Pr: Mike Mascari
**Sec:* Greg Corsaro
Ex VP: Kevin Guilfoy
**VP:* Danny Corsaro
**VP:* Chris Mascari
**VP:* Christopher Mascari
**VP:* Peter Piazza
Area Mgr: Marc Jones
IT Man: Christopher Bradley
Prd Mgr: Rebecca Contreras
Mktg Mgr: Antonia Mascari

IFA
See INTERNATIONAL FOOD ASSOCIATES INC

D-U-N-S 06-003-4469
IFA INSURANCE CO (INC)
INDEPENDENT FINANCIAL AGENTS
(*Suby of* I F A) ★
14 Walnut Ave, Clark, NJ 07066-1606
Tel (732) 815-1201 *Founded/Ownrshp* 1972
Sales NA *EMP* 50
SIC 6331 Automobile insurance
Pr: Patrick J Walsh
IT Man: Justin Blanding
Genl Couns: Adam Marshall

D-U-N-S 14-769-2214
IFA NURSERIES INC
9450 Sw Commerce Cir # 370, Wilsonville, OR 97070-9692
Tel (503) 855-3358 *Founded/Ownrshp* 1985

Sales 24.3MM^E EMP 175
SIC 0181 Ornamental nursery products; Ornamental nursery products
Pr: Thomas E Jackman
*CFO: David Colgrove
*Sec: Howard Dew

D-U-N-S 12-349-5884 IMP
IFA ROTORION - NORTH AMERICA LLC
(Suby of IFA ROTORION - HOLDING GMBH)
9770 Patriot Blvd Ste 100, Ladson, SC 29456-6703
Tel (843) 486-5400 Founded/Ownrshp 2009
Sales 49.9MM^E EMP 500
SIC 3714 Drive shafts, motor vehicle; Drive shafts, motor vehicle
CEO: Felix Von Nathusius
Pr: Mauro Amarante
Pr: Erik Manning
COO: Jeff Peterson
Mng Dir: John Gallagher
Snr Mgr: Uwe Linz

IFAW
See INTERNATIONAL FUND FOR ANIMAL WELFARE INC

D-U-N-S 13-272-7137
IFC HOLDINGS INC
8745 Henderson Rd Ste 300, Tampa, FL 33634-1148
Tel (813) 289-0722 Founded/Ownrshp 1982
Sales 28.4MM^E EMP 320
Accts Kpmg Llp
SIC 6722 Management investment, open-end; Management investment, open-end
CEO: Steve Dowden
*Prin: Lynn R Niedermeier

I.F.C. MANAGEMENT SERVICES
See INDIANAPOLIS FRUIT CO INC

D-U-N-S 08-005-2973
■ IFCTV LLC
(Suby of AMC NETWORKS INC) ★
11 Penn Plz Fl 2, New York, NY 10001-2028
Tel (212) 324-8500 Founded/Ownrshp 1994
Sales 1.2MM^E EMP 500
SIC 4833 Television broadcasting stations

D-U-N-S 96-860-6970 IMP/EXP
IFCO SYSTEMS NORTH AMERICA INC
I F C O SYSTEMS
(Suby of IFCO SYSTEMS B.V.)
13100 Nw Fwy Ste 625, Houston, TX 77040-6340
Tel (713) 332-6145 Founded/Ownrshp 2000
Sales 813.8MM^E EMP 3,636
SIC 2448 Pallets, wood; Pallets, wood
Pr: David S Russell
CFO: Vance Maultsby Jr
CFO: Michael W Nimtsch
Sr VP: Dan Helmick
VP: Andy Hamilton
VP: Rich Hamlin
VP: Gregg Mihallik
VP: Edward Rhyne
Assoc Dir: Randy Webb
Dir Bus: Jon Holthaus
Admn Mgr: Tammy Neill

D-U-N-S 94-515-6115 EXP
IFCO SYSTEMS US LLC
(Suby of BRAMBLES LIMITED)
3030 N Rocky Point Dr W # 300, Tampa, FL 33607-5903
Tel (813) 287-8940 Founded/Ownrshp 2000
Sales 22.5MM^E EMP 75
SIC 3081 Packing materials, plastic sheet; Packing materials, plastic sheet
Pr: Daniel Walsh
Genl Mgr: Bryan Truett
Off Mgr: Dottie Latimer

IFDC
See INTERNATIONAL FERTILIZER DEVELOPMENT CENTER

IFES
See INTERNATIONAL FOUNDATION FOR ELECTORAL SYSTEMS

D-U-N-S 62-678-0977
IFES INC
1850 K St Nw Lbby 5, Washington, DC 20006-2255
Tel (202) 350-6750 Founded/Ownrshp 1987
Sales 87.7MM EMP 300
Accts Argy Wiltse & Robinson Pc
SIC 8733 Research institute; Research institute
Pr: William Sweeney
COO: Wyatt A Stewart III
Prgrm Mgr: Homeyra Mokhtarzada

IFF
See INTERNATIONAL FLAVORS & FRAGRANCES INC

IFG COMPANIES
See ALAMANCE SERVICES INC

IFG COMPANIES
See FIRST FINANCIAL INSURANCE CO INC

D-U-N-S 14-463-2411 IMP/EXP
IFG CORP
1400 Broadway Rm 2202, New York, NY 10018-5222
Tel (212) 239-8615 Founded/Ownrshp 1986
Sales 46.3MM^E EMP 200^E
SIC 2329 2339

D-U-N-S 04-427-3279 EXP
IFH GROUP INC
3300 E Rock Falls Rd, Rock Falls, IL 61071-3708
Tel (815) 626-1018 Founded/Ownrshp 1998
Sales 27.0MM^E EMP 100
SIC 3594 3443 Fluid power pumps; Fuel tanks (oil, gas, etc.): metal plate; Fluid power pumps; Fuel tanks (oil, gas, etc.): metal plate
Pr: Keith D Ellefsen
*Treas: John Nagy
*VP: John Pope

IFIC
See INTERNATIONAL FIDELITY INSURANCE CO

D-U-N-S 11-746-5930
IFL GROUP INC
(Suby of SHADRACK LLC)
6860 S Service Dr, Waterford, MI 48327-1652
Tel (248) 666-1961 Founded/Ownrshp 1997
Sales 24.2MM EMP 80
SIC 4522 5172

D-U-N-S 01-529-6659
IFLEXION
115 Wild Basin Rd, West Lake Hills, TX 78746-3303
Tel (512) 402-5287 Founded/Ownrshp 1999
Sales 10.1MM^E EMP 370
SIC 7371 Computer software development; Computer software development
Prin: Dmitry Azarov

D-U-N-S 17-503-3356 IMP
IFM EFECTOR INC
(Suby of IFM ELECTRONIC GMBH)
1100 Atwater Dr, Malvern, PA 19355-8731
Tel (800) 441-8246 Founded/Ownrshp 1987
Sales 40.2MM^E EMP 212
SIC 3679 Electronic switches; Electronic switches
Pr: Roger Zarma
Sec: Vincent R Zagar
VP: Joseph T Kelly
IT Man: Lori Thomas
Mtls Mgr: Tim Frey
Sales Exec: Carolyn Hettrich
Advt Mgr: Judy Gersh
Sls Mgr: Cary Grimmer
Sls Mgr: John Ibbetson
Sls Mgr: Chad Terry
Sls Mgr: Kevin Vanderslice
Board of Directors: Ludger Tismer

D-U-N-S 07-986-5905
IFM GLOBAL INFRASTRUCTURE FUND
114 W 47th St Fl 26, New York, NY 10036-1511
Tel (212) 784-2260 Founded/Ownrshp 2015
Sales 97.3MM^E EMP 394^E
SIC 6799 1623 Investors; Water, sewer & utility lines
CEO: Brett Himbury
Ofcr: Joshua Lim

D-U-N-S 03-446-5629 IMP
IFN.COM INC (CA)
TOLLFREEFORWARDING.COM
9841 Airport Blvd Fl 9, Los Angeles, CA 90045-5421
Tel (310) 337-1305 Founded/Ownrshp 2009
Sales 21.1MM^E EMP 74^E
SIC 4813 Local & long distance telephone communications; Voice telephone communications
CEO: Travis May
COO: Jason Obrien
VP: Bill Ellis
VP Sls: Matt Hemingway
Sls Dir: John Carter
Sales Asso: Krystina Gage
Sales Asso: Suri Mendoza
Sales Asso: Erica Simpson

D-U-N-S 00-102-9123
IFP INC (MN)
INNOVATIVE FOOD PROCESSORS
2125 Airport Dr, Faribault, MN 55021-7798
Tel (507) 334-2730 Founded/Ownrshp 1981
Sales 24.0MM^E EMP 180
SIC 2099 Food preparations; Food preparations
CEO: Ephraim Eyal

D-U-N-S 15-444-9912
IFP INC
(Suby of ESI HOLDING CORP) ★
2125 Airport Dr, Faribault, MN 55021-7798
Tel (507) 365-8463 Founded/Ownrshp 1985
Sales 20.9MM^E EMP 130^E
SIC 6512 7359 Commercial & industrial building operation; Tool rental
CEO: Ephi Eyal
*VP: Carin Draper
*VP: Craig Siefken
IT Man: Joe Apling
Plnt Mgr: Mike Pollesch
Ql Cn Mgr: Charlie Bohl
Ql Cn Mgr: Dusty Wermers
Mktg Dir: Walter Zackowitz
Sls Dir: Rainer Schindler
Sales Asso: Jeanne Ghorley

IFPRI
See INTERNATIONAL FOOD POLICY RESEARCH INSTITUTE

D-U-N-S 04-693-6337
IFREEDOM DIRECT CORP
124 N Chrles Lindbergh Dr, Salt Lake City, UT 84116-2820
Tel (801) 493-2700 Founded/Ownrshp 1998
Sales NA EMP 304
SIC 6163 6162 Mortgage brokers arranging for loans, using money of others; Mortgage bankers & correspondents; Mortgage brokers arranging for loans, using money of others; Mortgage bankers & correspondents
CEO: Kevin T Gates
*Pr: Richard Bailey
*CFO: Terry Turville
Exec: Keri Thomas

D-U-N-S 83-078-6195 IMP
IFS COATINGS INC
3601 N Interstate 35, Gainesville, TX 76240-1939
Tel (940) 668-1062 Founded/Ownrshp 1999
Sales 49.2MM^E EMP 116^E
SIC 2899 2851 2821 Chemical preparations; Epoxy coatings; Polyesters
Pr: Glynn Mason
*VP: Patrick H Donahue
Sls Mgr: Brian Money

D-U-N-S 78-831-4839
IFS FINANCIAL SERVICES INC
(Suby of WESTERN & SOUTHERN LIFE INSURANCE CO) ★
303 Broadway St Ste 1100, Cincinnati, OH 45202-4220
Tel (513) 362-8000 Founded/Ownrshp 1991
Sales 25.4MM^E EMP 224
SIC 6211 6282 Security brokers & dealers; Investment advice; Security brokers & dealers; Investment advice
Pr: Jill T McGruder
Pr: Mark E Caner

D-U-N-S 01-449-8109 IMP
IFS INDUSTRIES INC (PA)
(Suby of ONA POLYMERS LLC)
400 Orton Ave, Reading, PA 19603
Tel (610) 378-1381 Founded/Ownrshp 1963, 1977
Sales 69.4MM^E EMP 28
SIC 3255 2899 2891 2851 3297 2992 Core wash or wax; Flooring, wood; Paving stones; Paints & allied products; Nonclay refractories; Lubricating oils & greases
Pr: Patrick H Donahue
*VP: Craig D Weidenhammer
IT Man: Richard Stanley
Manager: Brad Coleman

D-U-N-S 95-746-7848
IFS NORTH AMERICA INC
(Suby of INDUSTRIAL AND FINANCIAL SYSTEMS, IFS AB)
300 Park Blvd Ste 555, Itasca, IL 60143-2635
Tel (888) 437-4968 Founded/Ownrshp 1995
Sales 68.6MM^E EMP 250
SIC 7372 7379 8243 Prepackaged software; Data processing consultant; Software training, computer; Prepackaged software; Data processing consultant; Software training, computer
CEO: Cindy Jaudon
COO: Eric Delong
CFO: Mitch Dwight
VP: Jan Brunaes
VP: Kevin Deal
VP: Ronny Frey
Dir Bus: Len Iseldyke
CIO: Bjorn Wetterlin
CTO: Richard Pankratz
Sftwr Eng: Dinesh Kumar
Sftwr Eng: Mathias Nilsson

D-U-N-S 79-787-9934
IFURS HOLDINGS INC
IMAGE FRST HLTHCARE SPECIALIST
900 E 8th Ave Ste 300, King of Prussia, PA 19406-1347
Tel (513) 965-9488 Founded/Ownrshp 1989
Sales 14.3MM^E EMP 325
SIC 7213 Linen supply; Linen supply
Pr: Jerry Berstein
*COO: Joe Geraghty
*CFO: Jim Malandra
*Treas: Murray Berstein
*VP: David Burnette
Plnt Mgr: David Wyrick
Manager: Brad Rader

D-U-N-S 13-513-2913 EXP
IFWE INC
TAGGED.COM
840 Battery St, San Francisco, CA 94111-1504
Tel (415) 946-1850 Founded/Ownrshp 2005
Sales 41.6MM^E EMP 110^E
SIC 4899 Data communication services; Data communication services
Ch Bd: Reid Hoffman
*CEO: Greg Tseng
VP: Andrew Pedersen
VP: James Takazawa
Snr Sftwr: Misha Nasledov
CTO: Johann Schleier-Smith
*CTO: Johann Schleier Smith
QA Dir: Diana Nasledov
Dir IT: Alex Kaplan
IT Man: Tim Miller
Sftwr Eng: Andrew Neilson

D-U-N-S 14-831-5088
IFX CORP
(Suby of UBS CAPITAL LLC) ★
15050 Nw 79th Ct, Miami Lakes, FL 33016-5810
Tel (305) 512-1100 Founded/Ownrshp 2001
Sales 91.3MM^E EMP 420
SIC 4813 ;
Ch Bd: Michael Shalom
*CEO: Samuel Mezrahi
*CFO: Michael Abramowitz
Sr VP: Jack Roepers
Mktg Dir: Lynn Gomez

IFX INTERNATIONAL CARRIER SVCS
See NEUTRONA NETWORKS INTERNATIONAL LLC

D-U-N-S 08-419-3580
IG BURTON & CO INC
I G BURTON IMPORTS
793 Bay Rd, Milford, DE 19963-6122
Tel (302) 422-3041 Founded/Ownrshp 1960
Sales 225.0MM^E EMP 245
SIC 5511 7538 Automobiles, new & used; Pickups, new & used; Trucks, tractors & trailers: new & used; General automotive repair shops; Automobiles, new & used; Pickups, new & used; Trucks, tractors & trailers: new & used; General automotive repair shops
Pr: Charles Burton
*VP: Irwin G Burton III

D-U-N-S 96-979-0281
IG STAFFING HOLDINGS LLC
4170 Ashford Dnwody Rd Ne, Brookhaven, GA 30319-1442
Tel (404) 257-7900 Founded/Ownrshp 2007
Sales 173.1MM^E EMP 1,000
SIC 7361 Employment agencies; Employment agencies
CEO: Rich Lingle

IGA
See KIRBY FOODS INC

IGA
See GIANT EAGLE

D-U-N-S 07-994-3132
IGA (PR) INC
4m40 Calle Petrea, Bayamon, PR 00956-2971
Tel (800) 242-6167 Founded/Ownrshp 1963
Sales 9.8MM^E EMP 499
SIC 2051 6719 Bakery: wholesale or wholesale/retail combined; Investment holding companies, except banks
Ch Bd: Manuel Dos Santos
CEO: Andrew Rogers
COO: Richard Earl Beach
VP: Isaac Effrom
VP: Ariel Jabionski
VP: Ricardo Landenkoff
Exec: Pascual Ros Aguado

D-U-N-S 00-543-9237 IMP
IGA INSTITUTE EDUCATIONAL FOUNDATION (DE)
8745 W Higgins Rd Ste 350, Chicago, IL 60631-2773
Tel (773) 693-4520 Founded/Ownrshp 1926, 1968
Sales 24.4MM^E EMP 48
SIC 5113 5046 6411 Sanitary food containers; Store fixtures; Insurance agents
Pr: Paulo Goelzer
*Ch Bd: Thomas S Haggai
*Pr: Paulo G Goelzer
*Pr: Vincent Kong
*CFO: Bob Grottke
*Ex VP: Bill Benzing
Sr VP: David Bennett
Sr VP: Doug Fritsch
VP: Nicolas Liakopolus
CTO: Paulo Golzer
Sales Exec: Mike Ladato

D-U-N-S 06-659-9101
IGATE AMERICAS INC
1 Broadway Fl 13, Cambridge, MA 02142-1100
Tel (617) 914-8000 Founded/Ownrshp 2011
Sales NA EMP 2,300
SIC 7371 7373

D-U-N-S 36-154-7370
IGATE CLINICAL RESEARCH INTERNATIONAL INC
1000 Commerce Dr Ste 500, Pittsburgh, PA 15275-1039
Tel (412) 506-1131 Founded/Ownrshp 2005
Sales 30.0MM^E EMP 451^E
SIC 8071 Medical laboratories
Prin: Micheal Zugay
CFO: Bruce Haney
Assoc VP: Ronald Edwards
Assoc VP: Biju John
Assoc VP: Ajith Madhavan
Assoc VP: Vikram Nayak
Assoc VP: John Petrakis
Exec: Asmita Mahashabde
Exec: Kaori Sakai
Assoc Dir: Rajesh Bapnad
Assoc Dir: Atul Deshpande
Assoc Dir: Mohita Dubey
Assoc Dir: Antony Eda
Assoc Dir: Anirban Ghosh
Assoc Dir: Rohit G Koshie
Assoc Dir: Albert Mathew
Assoc Dir: Varughese Mathew
Assoc Dir: Abid Mohammad
Assoc Dir: Hari Narayana
Assoc Dir: Shailesh Padgaonkar
Assoc Dir: Nilesh Panditrao

D-U-N-S 18-175-9119
■ IGATE CORP
(Suby of CAPGEMINI CONSULTING) ★
100 Somerset Corp Blvd # 5000, Bridgewater, NJ 08807-2842
Tel (908) 219-8050 Founded/Ownrshp 2015
Sales 1.2MMM^E EMP 33,484^E
Tkr Sym IGTE Exch NGS
SIC 7371 7374 7389 Computer software development; Data processing service; Process serving service; Computer software development; Data processing service; Process serving service
Pr: Ashok Vemuri
CFO: Sujit Sircar
Ex VP: Derek Kemp
Ex VP: Sanjay Tugnait
Sr VP: Srikanth Iyengar
Sls Dir: David Sullivan
Board of Directors: W Roy Dunbar, Goran Lindahl, Martin G McGuinn, Salim Nathoo, William G Parrett, Naomi O Seligman S

D-U-N-S 05-435-6303
■ IGATE INC
(Suby of IGATE CORP) ★
1305 Cherrington Pkwy, Moon Township, PA 15108-4355
Tel (412) 787-2100 Founded/Ownrshp 1986
Sales 98.4MM^E EMP 5,000
SIC 7373 Computer integrated systems design
Pr: Ashok Vemuri
*Ch Bd: Ashok Trivedi
*Treas: Ram S Prasad
*VP: Sujit Sircar
Assoc Dir: Mahesh Shahane
Prgrm Mgr: Santosh Kinikar
Prgrm Mgr: Sameer Marathe
Snr Sftwr: Prasad Aruva
Snr Sftwr: Prasad Dalvi
Snr Sftwr: Sandhya Gadgoli
Snr Sftwr: Jeriel Gladson

D-U-N-S 14-872-8368 IMP
■ IGATE TECHNOLOGIES INC
(Suby of IGATE CORP) ★
100 Somerset Corp Blvd # 5000, Bridgewater, NJ 08807-2842
Tel (908) 219-8050 Founded/Ownrshp 2000
Sales 195.6MM^E EMP 3,000
SIC 7371 Custom computer programming services; Custom computer programming services
CEO: Ashok Vemuri
*CFO: Sujit Sircar
Treas: Suresh Nair
Assoc VP: Sharad Mohan

*Ex VP: Srinivas Kandula
*Ex VP: Derek Kemp
*Ex VP: Sanjay Tugnait
VP: Sandip Parekh
Exec: Arjun Nandi
Prgrm Mgr: Sreenivas Jayaraja
Prgrm Mgr: Suyog Joshi

IGC
See INTERMOUNTAIN GAS CO

IGGY'S SPORTS GRILL
See IPAK HOSPITALITY GROUP INC

D-U-N-S 15-387-8595
IGH SOLUTIONS INC
TRAVEL TAGS
(Suby of TAYLOR CORP) ★
5842 Carmen Ave, Inver Grove Heights, MN 55076-4413
Tel (651) 450-1201 Founded/Ownrshp 2005
Sales 36.4MM^E EMP 380^E
SIC 2759 Commercial printing; Commercial printing
Pr: Al Rausch
*Pr: Barb Cederberg
Mktg Mgr: Rosa Hermoza

D-U-N-S 00-235-8455 IMP/EXP
IGI INTERNATIONAL GROUP INC
INTERNATIONAL WAXES
(Suby of I G I) ★
1007 E Spring St, Titusville, PA 16354-7826
Tel (814) 827-3609 Founded/Ownrshp 1943
Sales 141.2MM^E EMP 275
SIC 2999 Waxes, petroleum: not produced in petroleum refineries; Waxes, petroleum: not produced in petroleum refineries
CEO: W Ross Reucassel
Pr: Kenneth Reucassel
CFO: David Imrie
VP: Christopher J Robinson

D-U-N-S 01-103-6910 IMP
▲ IGI LABORATORIES INC
105 Lincoln Ave, Buena, NJ 08310
Tel (856) 697-1441 Founded/Ownrshp 1977
Sales 33.7MM EMP 52^E
Accts Eisneramper Llp Iselin New J
Tkr Sym TLGT Exch NGS
SIC 2834 Pharmaceutical preparations; Dermatologicals; Pharmaceutical preparations; Dermatologicals
Pr: Jason Grenfell-Gardner
V Ch: Eman Barrada
CFO: Jenniffer Collins
Ex VP: Nadya Lawrence
Ex VP: Charles E Moore
Sr VP: Kenneth Miller
Dir Sec: Stephen Richardson
IT Man: Shawn McMorrow
Opers Mgr: Sanjay Samudre
Snr Mgr: Jayme Candelario
Snr Mgr: Meghan Heffernan
Board of Directors: John Celentano, James C Gale, Steven Koehler

IGI PRINTING
See GOODWAY GRAPHICS INC

D-U-N-S 10-179-8015
IGLESIA CRISTIANA DISCIPULOS DECRISTO INC
Km 19 Hm Rr 167, Bayamon, PR 00957
Tel (787) 799-7878 Founded/Ownrshp 1940
Sales 1.6MM EMP 307
SIC 8661 Miscellaneous denomination church; Miscellaneous denomination church

D-U-N-S 09-106-9856
IGLESIA EPISCOPAL PUERTORRIQUENA INC
COLEGIO SAN JUSTO
Carr 848 Km 1 1 Bo Sait J St Ca, Trujillo Alto, PR 00978
Tel (787) 761-9800 Founded/Ownrshp 1971
Sales 12.0MM^E EMP 1,350
SIC 8661 Episcopal Church; Episcopal Church
Pr: Bishop David Alvarez
*Treas: Darling Martinez
Treas: Eileen Rosado

D-U-N-S 14-692-8114
IGLESIA EPISCOPAL PUERTORRIQUENA INC
ST LUKES HOME CARE & HOSPICE
Piso 4 Ave Bldg A, Ponce, PR 00733
Tel (787) 843-4185 Founded/Ownrshp 1971
Sales 42.7MM EMP 940
SIC 8082 8399 Home health care services; Health systems agency; Home health care services; Health systems agency
Ex Dir: Guillermo Martin
*Ex Dir: Annie Alvarado

D-U-N-S 96-457-2726
IGLOO HOLDINGS CORP
32 Crosby Dr, Bedford, MA 01730-1448
Tel (781) 687-8500 Founded/Ownrshp 2010
Sales 939.2MM^E EMP 2,600^E
SIC 6289 7375 Financial reporting; Information retrieval services; Financial reporting; Information retrieval services

D-U-N-S 96-457-2791
IGLOO INTERMEDIATE CORP
(Suby of IGLOO HOLDINGS CORP) ★
32 Crosby Dr, Bedford, MA 01730-1448
Tel (781) 687-8500 Founded/Ownrshp 2010
Sales 939.2MM^E EMP 2,600^E
SIC 6289 7375 Financial reporting; Information retrieval services; Financial reporting; Information retrieval services

D-U-N-S 06-211-8427 IMP/EXP
IGLOO PRODUCTS CORP
777 Igloo Rd, Katy, TX 77494-2972
Tel (203) 922-7500 Founded/Ownrshp 2014
Sales 524.1MM^E EMP 1,050
SIC 3086 Ice chests or coolers (portable), foamed plastic; Ice chests or coolers (portable), foamed plastic
CEO: Gary Kiedaisch
Pr: Mark Parrish
CFO: Laura Snyder
Ex VP: Tony Carfagno
Sr VP: Fred Lewis
VP: Angela Sizemore
VP: Candi Whitsel
Off Mgr: Janette Martinez

IGM
See INTERSTATE GAS MARKETING INC

D-U-N-S 96-474-9134 IMP/EXP
IGM RESINS USA INC
(Suby of I.G.M. HOLDING B.V.)
3300 Westinghouse Blvd, Charlotte, NC 28273-6521
Tel (704) 945-8722 Founded/Ownrshp 2010
Sales 23.6MM^E EMP 60
SIC 2851 Coating, air curing
Pr: Tim Tip Pett
*CEO: Edward Frindt
*CFO: Timothy Fagan
Tech Mgr: Dipak Shah
Opers Mgr: Jon Wojcio
Manager: Jack Hallman
Sls Mgr: Jeffrey Testerman

D-U-N-S 60-229-4154
IGM SOLUTIONS INC
1900 Enterprise Ct, Libertyville, IL 60048-9737
Tel (847) 918-1790 Founded/Ownrshp 2005
Sales 22.8MM^E EMP 50
SIC 3441 Fabricated structural metal
Pr: Paul Kelly
*CFO: Jane Mohapp
Board of Directors: Ross Hinrichsen

IGNACIOUS BEAN MEMORIAL SCHOOL
See LOWER YUKON SCHOOL DISTRICT INC

D-U-N-S 02-001-2647
IGNATIAN CORP (CA)
ST IGNTIUS COLLEGE PREPARATORY
2001 37th Ave, San Francisco, CA 94116-1165
Tel (415) 731-7500 Founded/Ownrshp 1855
Sales 35.0MM^E EMP 120
SIC 8211 Catholic senior high school; Preparatory school; Catholic senior high school; Preparatory school
Pr: John M Knight
*CEO: Edwin Harris
*CFO: Mary Cillon
*CFO: Terry Dillon
Ofcr: Ed Evert
*Prin: Father Ed Harris
Psych: Brice Campoverdi
Psych: Julie Clair
Psych: Amy Harms
Psych: Brian Kelly
Psych: Sarah Merrell

IGNIFY CONSULTING
See IGNIFY INC

D-U-N-S 11-146-8992
IGNIFY INC
IGNIFY CONSULTING
200 Pine Ave Ste 400, Long Beach, CA 90802-3039
Tel (562) 219-2000 Founded/Ownrshp 2015
Sales 31.1MM^E EMP 210
SIC 5734 7373 7372 Software, business & non-game; Computer integrated systems design; Business oriented computer software; Software, business & non-game; Computer integrated systems design; Business oriented computer software
Pr: Sandeep Walia
*Treas: Craig Griffith
*VP: Bhavesh Ashani
VP: Nina Gonzalez
*VP: Pankaj Kumar
VP: Kevin Stallings
Dir IT: Kathleen Cotecson
Dir IT: Danny MAI
Dir IT: Rohan Wali
IT Man: Guneet Singh
Tech Mgr: Khushhal Garg

D-U-N-S 78-824-5681 IMP
■ IGNITE RESTAURANT GROUP INC
(Suby of JH WHITNEY VI LP) ★
9900 Westpark Dr Ste 300, Houston, TX 77063-5287
Tel (713) 366-7500 Founded/Ownrshp 1991
Sales 837.1MM EMP 10,900
Accts Pricewaterhousecoopers Llp Ho
Tkr Sym IRG Exch NGS
SIC 5812 Grills (eating places); Grills (eating places)
CEO: Robert S Merritt
Pr: David Catalano
Pr: John Gilbert
COO: David G Catalano
CFO: Brad A Leist
*CFO: Jeffrey L Rager
*Ofcr: Robin N Ahearn
*Ofcr: Kevin T Cottingim
*Sr VP: Edward W Engel
VP: Ellen Clarry
VP: Jim Doak
VP: Deanna Parr
Board of Directors: Richard P Bermingham, Brian N Cherry, John F Gilbert III, Ann Iverson, Robert S Merritt, Paul R Vigano, Fritzi Woods

D-U-N-S 08-717-7338
IGNITED LLC
2150 Park Pl Ste 100, El Segundo, CA 90245-4714
Tel (310) 773-3100 Founded/Ownrshp 1999
Sales 180.0MM EMP 126
SIC 7311 Advertising agencies; Advertising agencies
CEO: Eric Johnson
COO: Bill Rosenthal
*COO: William Rosenthal
CFO: Whitney Stephenson
VP: Dave Martin
Exec: David Lock
Dir: Alexandria Oliver
Snr PM: Todd Kenman
Snr Mgr: Lena Lotsey

D-U-N-S 07-849-8871
IGNITIONONE INC
200 Park Ave Fl 27, New York, NY 10166-0005
Tel (888) 744-6483 Founded/Ownrshp 2013
Sales 51.1MM^E EMP 345^E
SIC 7319 Display advertising service; Media buying service; Display advertising service; Media buying service
CEO: Will Margiloff
*Pr: Roger Barnette
*COO: Jonathan Ragals
*CFO: Scott Levine
*Sr VP: Eric Carlyle
Sr VP: Barry Schnur
*CTO: Craig Pohan
Sls Dir: Frank Goldberg
Mktg Mgr: Tommy Marzella
Mktg Mgr: Cat Prestipino

IGOV.COM
See MA FEDERAL INC

IGP
See INTERNATIONAL GARDEN PRODUCTS INC

D-U-N-S 02-066-6256
IGP INDUSTRIES LLC
INDUSTRIAL GROWTH PARTNERS
101 Mission St Ste 1500, San Francisco, CA 94105-1731
Tel (415) 882-4550 Founded/Ownrshp 1997
Sales 208.1MM^E EMP 2,584
SIC 7389 Brokers, business: buying & selling business enterprises; Brokers, business: buying & selling business enterprises
VP: Daniel Delaney
VP: Karen Greaves
Mng Dir: Jeffrey Webb

D-U-N-S 07-916-2909
IGPS LOGISTICS LLC
225 E Robinson St Ste 200, Orlando, FL 32801-4321
Tel (321) 281-9200 Founded/Ownrshp 2013
Sales 31.6MM^E EMP 60^E
SIC 7359 Pallet rental services; Pallet rental services
CEO: Jeff Liebesman
CFO: Greg Anderson
*Co-CEO: Robert Liebesman
Opers Mgr: Ellwood Iacobs

IGS
See INTERGRAPH GOVERNMENT SOLUTIONS CORP

D-U-N-S 00-437-3692 IMP
IGS INDUSTRIES INC (PA)
200 Country Club Rd, Meadow Lands, PA 15347
Tel (724) 222-5800 Founded/Ownrshp 1961
Sales 35.3MM^E EMP 110
SIC 3499 3469 3053 Shims, metal; Stamping metal for the trade; Gaskets, all materials
Ch Bd: Richard Disalle
*Pr: David C Sphar
*VP: Dan Bird

D-U-N-S 79-868-7737 IMP
IGS STORE FIXTURES INC
345 S Main St Ste 3, Providence, RI 02903-2984
Tel (978) 532-0010 Founded/Ownrshp 1992
Sales 62.6MM^E EMP 180
SIC 2541 Wood partitions & fixtures; Wood partitions & fixtures
Pr: Dominic Butera
*Pr: Dominic I Butera Jr
*CFO: Harvey Gordon
*Sec: Harvey J Gordon

IGT
See IDIRECT GOVERNMENT LLC

D-U-N-S 78-744-6962 IMP/EXP
■ IGT
(Suby of I GT) ★
9295 Prototype Dr, Reno, NV 89521-8986
Tel (775) 448-7777 Founded/Ownrshp 1980
Sales 177.5MM^E EMP 762^E
SIC 3999 5099 Slot machines; Game machines, coin-operated; Slot machines; Game machines, coin-operated
Pr: Patti S Hart
Pr: Thomas J Matthews
CEO: G Thomas Baker
CFO: Maureen Mullarkey
CFO: Maureen Mullarky
Ex VP: Robert Bittman
Ex VP: Joe Kaminkow
Ex VP: Paul Mathews
Sr VP: Sarah Beth Brown
Sr VP: Ward Chilton
Sr VP: Anthony Ciorciari
Sr VP: Rich Pennington
VP: Don Gromer
VP: Randy Kirner
VP: Jim Vasquez
VP: Eric Vetter
VP: Matt Wilkerson
Exec: Andrew Wood
Creative D: Kevin Melahn

D-U-N-S 08-935-4583 IMP/EXP
■ IGT GLOBAL SOLUTIONS CORP
(Suby of INTERNATIONAL GAME TECHNOLOGY PLC)
10 Memorial Blvd, Providence, RI 02903-1160
Tel (401) 392-1000 Founded/Ownrshp 1980
Sales 317.6MM^E EMP 4,920
SIC 7999 3575 7372 7378 2752 7374

D-U-N-S 82-715-8606
IGT SOLUTIONS INC
303 5th Ave Rm 1608, New York, NY 10016-6601
Tel (212) 684-8601 Founded/Ownrshp 2007
Sales 23.0MM EMP 32
SIC 7371 Computer software development; Computer software development
*Pr: Rahul Bhatia
Ofcr: Uday Shah
*VP: Stephen Smith

D-U-N-S 14-783-2521 IMP
IGUS BEARINGS INC
(Suby of IGUS GMBH)
257 Ferris Ave, Rumford, RI 02916-1033
Tel (401) 438-2200 Founded/Ownrshp 1985
Sales 68.4MM^E EMP 150
SIC 5063 5085 Wire & cable; Bearings; Wire & cable; Bearings
Pr: Frank Blase
*VP: Carsten Blase
*VP: Mohammad Salim Shafi
Mfg Dir: Wayne Murphy
Manager: Adam Anderson
Manager: Wes Beavers
Manager: Jeremy Biltz
Manager: Herman Burmeister
Manager: Joe Costanzo
Manager: Chris Doerr
Manager: Shannon Douglas

IH
See INVITATION HOMES LP

D-U-N-S 04-755-7145
IH SERVICES INC
127 Tanner Rd, Greenville, SC 29607-5918
Tel (864) 297-3748 Founded/Ownrshp 1955
Sales 60.0MM^E EMP 2,700
SIC 7349 5014 7217 Janitorial service, contract basis; Tires & tubes; Carpet & rug cleaning plant; Janitorial service, contract basis; Tires & tubes; Carpet & rug cleaning plant
CEO: Ryan Hendley
*Ch Bd: Dickson L Hendley
*Pr: Taylor M Bruce
*CFO: Michael G Putnam
*Sec: Lucille Hendley
VP: Todd Hendley
VP: Edwin White
Dir Bus: Seth Bruce
Brnch Mgr: James Clary
Dist Mgr: Duane Norman
Opers Mgr: David Murphy

IHA
See INTEGRATED HEALTH ASSOCIATES INC

D-U-N-S 07-927-7688
IHA HEALTH SERVICES CORP
ANN ARBOR NEUROLOGY
24 Frank Lloyd Wright Dr, Ann Arbor, MI 48105-9484
Tel (734) 747-6766 Founded/Ownrshp 2010
Sales 207.8MM EMP 3
SIC 8011 Obstetrician; Obstetrician
Pr: William J Fileti
*VP: Richard Duffy
*VP: Chris Holda
*VP: Linda Macellven
*VP: Martin Murray

D-U-N-S 08-930-9843
■ IHC ADMINISTRATIVE SERVICES INC
INSURERS ADMINISTRATIVE CORP
(Suby of INDEPENDENCE HOLDING CO) ★
2101 W Peoria Ave Ste 100, Phoenix, AZ 85029-4925
Tel (602) 870-1400 Founded/Ownrshp 1978
Sales NA EMP 250
Accts Wolf Weis & Horowitz Llc Ro
SIC 6411 Medical insurance claim processing, contract or fee basis; Insurance claim processing, except medical; Medical insurance claim processing, contract or fee basis; Insurance claim processing, except medical
Ch: Stephen A Wood
Pr: Peter Wirski
CFO: Bruce D Robbins
Sr VP: Rick A Faucher
VP: Michael K Brown
VP: Edward Carney
VP: Constantine Costas
VP: Frank Fugiel
VP: Stacy B Ketcham
VP: Brad Waldrop
VP: Christy Wood
VP: Christy L Wood
VP: Daryl J Zee

D-U-N-S 00-779-9745
IHC CONSTRUCTION COMPANIES LLC
1500 Executive Dr, Elgin, IL 60123-9311
Tel (847) 742-1516 Founded/Ownrshp 2002
Sales 66.3MM^E EMP 175
SIC 1629 1542 1541 1623

IHC HEALTH SERVICES
See INTERMOUNTAIN HEALTH CARE INC

D-U-N-S 01-319-6598
IHC HEALTH SERVICES INC
INTERMOUNTAIN LIFE FLIGHT
250 N 2370 W, Salt Lake City, UT 84116-2936
Tel (801) 321-3333 Founded/Ownrshp 1976
Sales 25.0MM EMP 250
SIC 4522 Nonscheduled charter services; Air taxis; Nonscheduled charter services; Air taxis
Prin: Kent Johnson
*Ex Dir: Pam Moore

D-U-N-S 18-362-1390
IHC HEALTH SERVICES INC
DIXIE MEDICAL CENTER
(Suby of IHC HEALTH SERVICES) ★
1380 E Medical Center Dr, St George, UT 84790-2123
Tel (801) 442-5000 Founded/Ownrshp 1972
Sales 383.1MM^E EMP 4,000
Accts Kpmg Llp Salt Lake City Ut
SIC 8062 8011 8322 8049 8093 8069 General medical & surgical hospitals; Offices & clinics of medical doctors; Pathologist; Individual & family services; Speech specialist; Substance abuse clinics (outpatient); Specialty hospitals, except psychiatric; General medical & surgical hospitals; Offices & clinics of medical doctors; Pathologist; Individual & family services; Speech specialist; Substance abuse clinics (outpatient); Specialty hospitals, except psychiatric
Pr: William Nelson
*Pr: Charles Sorenson
*CFO: Bert Zimmerli
Dir Risk M: Teri Chase-Dunn

Dir Sec: Scot Newbrough
Orthpdst: Zachary Leitze
Pharmcst: Suzanne Jones

D-U-N-S 83-447-6350
IHC INTER-CONTINENTAL (HOLDINGS) CORP
HOTEL INTER-CONTINENTAL NY
(*Suby of* IHC UNITED STATES (HOLDINGS) CORP) ★
747 3rd Ave Fl 26, New York, NY 10017-2803
Tel (212) 852-6400 *Founded/Ownrshp* 1988
Sales 50.6MM^E *EMP* 520
SIC 7011 Hotels; Hotels
Pr: J T Kuhlman
**Ofcr:* Albert J Puccianelli

D-U-N-S 14-290-8412
IHC UNITED STATES (HOLDINGS) CORP
(*Suby of* INTERCONTINENTAL HOTELS GROUP RESOURCES INC) ★
3 Ravinia Dr, Atlanta, GA 30346-2118
Tel (770) 604-5000 *Founded/Ownrshp* 2004
Sales 50.6MM^E *EMP* 526^E
SIC 7011 Hotels & motels

D-U-N-S 17-614-1059
■ IHC/CONSHOHOCKEN CORP
(*Suby of* WYNDHAM HOTELS & RESORTS) ★
680 Andersen Dr, Pittsburgh, PA 15220-2759
Tel (610) 941-5600 *Founded/Ownrshp* 1998
Sales 4.3MM^E *EMP* 700
SIC 7011 Hotels; Hotels
Genl Pt: IHC R Corporation

IHCC
See INVER HILLS COMMUNITY COLLEGE

D-U-N-S 08-646-7672
IHEALTH TECHNOLOGIES INC
115 Prmter Ctr Pl Ste 700, Atlanta, GA 30346-1280
Tel (770) 379-2800 *Founded/Ownrshp* 2014
Sales NA *EMP* 300
SIC 8742 Business consulting

D-U-N-S 06-945-6655 IMP
■ IHEARTCOMMUNICATIONS INC
(*Suby of* IHEARTMEDIA CAPITAL I LLC) ★
200 E Basse Rd, San Antonio, TX 78209-4489
Tel (210) 822-2828 *Founded/Ownrshp* 1974, 2008
Sales 6.3MMM *EMP* 19,200
SIC 4832 4833 7312 Radio broadcasting stations; Television broadcasting stations; Outdoor advertising services; Radio broadcasting stations; Television broadcasting stations; Outdoor advertising services
Ch Bd: Robert W Pittman
**Pr:* Richard J Bressler
Bd of Dir: Brian Jay
Bd of Dir: Mark Sobolewski
Bd of Dir: Gary Sullivan
Ex VP: John Partilla
Ex VP: Gayle Troberman
Ex VP: Robert H Walls Jr
Sr VP: Brian Glicklich
Sr VP: Scott D Hamilton
Sr VP: Kenneth E Wyker
VP: William Feehan
VP: Namon Jones
VP: Paul Livornese
Creative D: Scott Stanley
Adv Bd Mbr: Henry Flores

D-U-N-S 07-851-1866
■ IHEARTMEDIA CAPITAL I LLC
(*Suby of* IHEARTMEDIA CAPITAL II LLC) ★
200 E Basse Rd, San Antonio, TX 78209-4489
Tel (210) 822-2828 *Founded/Ownrshp* 2008
Sales 6.3MMM *EMP* 20,800^E
SIC 4813 4899 Telephone communication, except radio; Data communication services; Communication signal enhancement network system; Telephone communication, except radio; Data communication services; Communication signal enhancement network system
Ch Bd: Robert W Pittman
Pr: Richard J Bressler
Sr VP: Scott D Hamilton

D-U-N-S 96-813-8813
■ IHEARTMEDIA CAPITAL II LLC
(*Suby of* IHEARTMEDIA INC) ★
200 E Basse Rd, San Antonio, TX 78209-4489
Tel (210) 822-2828 *Founded/Ownrshp* 2008
Sales 6.8MMM^E *EMP* 20,800^E
SIC 4899 4813 Communication signal enhancement network system; Telephone communication, except radio; Communication signal enhancement network system; Telephone communication, except radio
Ch Bd: Robert W Pittman

D-U-N-S 82-776-1300
▲ IHEARTMEDIA INC
200 E Basse Rd, San Antonio, TX 78209-4489
Tel (210) 822-2828 *Founded/Ownrshp* 2007
Sales 6.3MMM *EMP* 19,200
Accts Ernst & Young Llp San Antonio
Tkr Sym CCMO *Exch* OTO
SIC 4832 7312 Radio broadcasting stations; Outdoor advertising services; Billboard advertising; Poster advertising, outdoor; Radio broadcasting stations; Outdoor advertising services; Billboard advertising; Poster advertising, outdoor
Ch Bd: Robert W Pittman
Ch Bd: John Hogan
**Pr:* Richard J Bressler
Pr: Sara McClure
Ex VP: Wendy Goldberg
Ex VP: Gayle Troberman
Ex VP: Robert H Walls Jr
Sr VP: Scott D Hamilton
Exec: Pat Connor
Exec: Debbie Wagner
Exec: Kim Williams

D-U-N-S 07-136-9826 IMP
IHERB INC
17825 Indian St, Moreno Valley, CA 92551-9533
Tel (951) 616-3600 *Founded/Ownrshp* 1996
Sales 44.7MM^E *EMP* 110^E
SIC 5499 5122 Vitamin food stores; Drugs, proprietaries & sundries
Pr: Reza Faraee
CTO: Eiman Zabihi
Software D: Nicholas Donnelly
Software D: Gary Maccie
Software D: Amin Pashna
Software D: Mehrak Vahidi
Sftwr Eng: Brad Oldham
Sftwr Eng: Jay Sun
Sfty Mgr: Renee Botello

IHG
See INTER-CONTINENTAL HOTELS CORP

D-U-N-S 60-382-0718
IHGC OPERATORS INC
200 Inverness Dr W, Englewood, CO 80112-5200
Tel (303) 397-7201 *Founded/Ownrshp* 1995
Sales 8.7MM^E *EMP* 350
SIC 7011 Hotels & motels; Hotels & motels
Mng Dir: George Fisher

IHI
See INSTITUTE FOR HEALTHCARE IMPROVEMENT

IHI
See INTERCARE HOLDINGS INSURANCE SERVICES INC

IHI COMPACT EXCAVATOR SALES
See COMPACT EXCAVATOR SALES LLC

D-U-N-S 07-861-0098
IHI E&C INTERNATIONAL CORP
(*Suby of* IHI INC) ★
1080 Eldridge Pkwy, Houston, TX 77077-2575
Tel (713) 270-3100 *Founded/Ownrshp* 2012
Sales 353.6MM *EMP* 500^E
SIC 8711 Jet propulsion engines; Engineering services
Pr: Glyn Rodgers
**COO:* Rod McCracken
**CFO:* Sean Johnston
VP: Keith Carter
VP: Larry Redden
VP: Kamal Shah
Comm Man: Lindsay Szeszycki
Ex Dir: Jay Grimes
Genl Mgr: Takuya Nakano
IT Man: Dan Mater
Tech Mgr: Augusto Duque

D-U-N-S 10-111-3975 IMP
IHI INC
(*Suby of* IHI CORPORATION)
150 E 52nd St Fl 24, New York, NY 10022-6246
Tel (212) 599-8100 *Founded/Ownrshp* 1977
Sales 367.8MM^E *EMP* 500
Accts Ernst & Young Llp New York N
SIC 5099 8732 8711 5084 Firearms & ammunition, except sporting; Market analysis, business & economic research; Engineering services; Industrial machinery & equipment; Firearms & ammunition, except sporting; Market analysis, business & economic research; Engineering services; Industrial machinery & equipment
Pr: Kazuaki Kama
**Ex VP:* Ichiro Hashimoto
**Ex VP:* Yuji Hiruma
**Ex VP:* Tamotsu Saito

D-U-N-S 82-675-9503
IHI POWER SERVICES CORP
RIO BRAVO ROCKLIN
3100 Thunder Valley Ct, Lincoln, CA 95648-9579
Tel (916) 645-3383 *Founded/Ownrshp* 2012
Sales 50.3MM^E *EMP* 67^E
SIC 4911 Generation, electric power
CFO: Stephen B Gross
Plnt Mgr: Charles Odrechowski

D-U-N-S 05-089-4583 IMP
IHI TURBO AMERICA CO
(*Suby of* IHI CORPORATION)
1598 Ste Rte 16, Shelbyville, IL 62565
Tel (217) 774-9571 *Founded/Ownrshp* 1980
Sales 24.2MM^E *EMP* 79
SIC 3724 3999 Turbo-superchargers, aircraft; Turbo-superchargers, aircraft; Atomizers, toiletry
Pr: Hiromu Furukawa
**Sec:* Michael Price
Genl Mgr: Bruce Renton
Opers Mgr: Tom Rezinas
Sls Mgr: Michael Sinclair

IHILANI RESORT & SPA
See KO OLINA INTANGIBLES LLC

IHMS
See INTERNATIONAL HOTEL MANAGEMENT SERVICES INC

D-U-N-S 79-136-9197
IHMS (BOSTON) LLC
TAJ BOSTON HOTEL
(*Suby of* IHMS) ★
15 Arlington St, Boston, MA 02116-3417
Tel (617) 536-5700 *Founded/Ownrshp* 2006
Sales 22.4MM^E *EMP* 300
SIC 7011 Hotels & motels; Hotels & motels
Genl Mgr: Nitin Bengani
VP Mktg: Deepa Harris
Pr Dir: Sarita Roy

D-U-N-S 61-440-9972
IHMS LLC
PIERRE, THE
(*Suby of* IHMS) ★
2 E 61st St, New York, NY 10065-8401
Tel (212) 838-8000 *Founded/Ownrshp* 2005
Sales 75.0MM *EMP* 525
SIC 7011 Hotels & motels; Hotels & motels

IHOP
See SUNSHINE RESTAURANT MERGER SUB LLC

IHOP
See INTERNATIONAL HOUSE OF PANCAKES LLC

IHOP
See FERTITTA HOSPITALITY LLC

IHOP
See KMG ENTERPRISES INC

IHOP
See JUNIOR SENIOR INC

IHOP
See ROMULUS INC

IHOP
See LORRAINE ENTERPRISES LC

D-U-N-S 03-443-7795
■ IHP I OWNER JV LLC
(*Suby of* NORTHSTAR REALTY FINANCE CORP) ★
399 Park Ave, New York, NY 10022-4614
Tel (212) 547-2640 *Founded/Ownrshp* 2014
Sales 49.7MM^E *EMP* 1,524^E
SIC 8741 Hotel or motel management
CEO: David Hamamoto
CFO: Debra Hess
Ex VP: Ronald Lieberman

D-U-N-S 00-717-3719 IMP
IHP INDUSTRIAL INC (MO)
I H P
1701 S 8th St, Saint Joseph, MO 64503-2631
Tel (816) 236-2552 *Founded/Ownrshp* 1923
Sales 30.2MM^E *EMP* 112
Accts Sigman & Co Kansas City Mis
SIC 1711 1623 1629 3498 3443 Mechanical contractor; Warm air heating & air conditioning contractor; Pipeline construction; Dam construction; Fabricated pipe & fittings; Fabricated plate work (boiler shop); Mechanical contractor; Warm air heating & air conditioning contractor; Pipeline construction; Dam construction; Fabricated pipe & fittings; Fabricated plate work (boiler shop)
Pr: Daniel J Fitzpatrick
Treas: Bob Fitzpatrick
**Sec:* Robert J Fitzpatrick Jr
**VP:* David L Fitzpatrick

D-U-N-S 83-012-6178 IMP
IHP OPERATIONS LLC
INNOVATIVE HEARTH PRODUCTS
(*Suby of* INNOVATIVE HEARTH HOLDINGS LLC) ★
2701 S Harbor Blvd, Santa Ana, CA 92704-5803
Tel (714) 549-7782 *Founded/Ownrshp* 2012
Sales 147.2MM^E *EMP* 347
SIC 3433 Heating equipment, except electric; Heating equipment, except electric
CEO: Mark Klein
**CFO:* Linda Pahl
VP: Gerardo Lozano
Rgnl Mgr: Pilar Garcia
CIO: Andreas Fellner
Dir IT: Amy Cho
Plnt Mgr: Mike Feist
Plnt Mgr: Sam Scarbrough
Plnt Mgr: Albert Talamantes
Prd Mgr: Ansel Garcia
Manager: Brent Weber

D-U-N-S 06-267-8529
IHRIE SUPPLY CO INC (NC)
1605 Cargill Ave S, Wilson, NC 27893-6642
Tel (252) 291-5521 *Founded/Ownrshp* 1964, 1972
Sales 36.5MM^E *EMP* 68
Accts Bunch & Company Llp Rocky
SIC 5074 Plumbing & hydronic heating supplies; Heating equipment (hydronic); Plumbing fittings & supplies
CEO: Edward C Ihrie
IT Man: Wanda Taylor
S&M/VP: Earl Young
Sales Asso: Ernie Carson
Sales Asso: Ike Christian
Sales Asso: Kevin Harrell

IHRIG MOVING AND STORAGE
See COOK MOVING SYSTEMS INC

IHS
See INDIAN HEALTH SERVICE

D-U-N-S 00-353-6755
IHS DIALYSIS INC (FL)
6001 Broken Sound Pkwy Nw # 508, Boca Raton, FL 33487-2766
Tel (561) 443-0743 *Founded/Ownrshp* 2005
Sales 56.3MM^E *EMP* 5,000^E
SIC 8092 Kidney dialysis centers; Kidney dialysis centers
CEO: Nelson R Shaller
**Pr:* Kathleen McDonnell

D-U-N-S 62-036-5023
■ IHS GLOBAL INC
(*Suby of* IHS HOLDING INC) ★
15 Inverness Way E, Englewood, CO 80112-5710
Tel (303) 790-0600 *Founded/Ownrshp* 1987
Sales 155.3MM^E *EMP* 2,000
SIC 7299 8732 8748 7375 Information services, consumer; Market analysis, business & economic research; Business analysis; Business consulting; Information retrieval services; Information services, consumer; Market analysis, business & economic research; Business analysis; Business consulting; Information retrieval services
CEO: Jerre Stead
**Pr:* Scott Key
Dir Soc: David Maus
Sls Dir: Laura Lamb
Snr Mgr: Jim Dorsey

D-U-N-S 02-051-4852
■ IHS GLOBAL INSIGHT INC
(*Suby of* IHS INC) ★
24 Hartwell Ave Ste 6, Lexington, MA 02421-3139
Tel (781) 301-9100 *Founded/Ownrshp* 2008
Sales 67.5MM^E *EMP* 552
SIC 8731 Commercial physical research; Commercial physical research
Pr: Greg Hart
COO: Jeff Caldwell
Ex VP: Kenneth J McGill
VP: Mack Brothers
VP: Patrick G Richmond
Dir Bus: Vik Barodia
Dir Bus: Chiaki Komine
Dir Bus: Christian Schena
Dir Bus: Diana Wyman
Mng Dir: Frederic Avierinos
Mng Dir: Paul Bingham

D-U-N-S 19-733-1002
■ IHS HOLDING INC
(*Suby of* IHS INC) ★
15 Inverness Way E, Englewood, CO 80112-5710
Tel (303) 790-0600 *Founded/Ownrshp* 1992
Sales 155.3MM^E *EMP* 2,300
SIC 7299 8732 8748 7375 Information services, consumer; Market analysis, business & economic research; Business analysis; Business consulting; Information retrieval services; Information services, consumer; Market analysis, business & economic research; Business analysis; Business consulting; Information retrieval services
CEO: Richard G Walker
COO: Robert Carpenter
COO: Bob Lockwood
COO: Mike McCrory
Co-COO: Jeff Tarr
Sr VP: Ernesto Ramirez
Sr VP: Mark Rose
VP: Paul Everson
VP: Steve Foreman
VP: Jonathan Gear
**VP:* Stephen Green
VP: George Guo
VP: Todd Hyatt
VP: Scott Key
VP: Jo Labbienti
VP: Don Lesem
VP: Thomas Littman
VP: Ed Mattix
VP: Randal Meske
VP: George Nagy
VP: Mike Neal

D-U-N-S 19-015-1993
■ IHS INC
(*Suby of* IHS INC) ★
8584 Katy Fwy Ste 400, Houston, TX 77024-1856
Tel (713) 464-6188 *Founded/Ownrshp* 2011
Sales 24.6MM^E *EMP* 170
SIC 7371 Computer software development; Computer software development
Pr: Arshad Matin
Pr: Randy Harvey
**CFO:* Jake Pyles
VP: Stan Abele
VP: Hank Chambers
VP: Christopher Lewis
Adm Dir: Michael Dang
Dir IT: Ken Moore
Software D: Konrad Bisch
Software D: Judy Hopkins
Software D: Yun Xu
Board of Directors: Thomas A Smith

D-U-N-S 19-822-4532
▲ IHS INC
15 Inverness Way E, Englewood, CO 80112-5710
Tel (303) 790-0600 *Founded/Ownrshp* 1959
Sales 2.2MMM *EMP* 8,980^E
Accts Ernst & Young Denver Colorad
Tkr Sym IHS *Exch* NYS
SIC 7299 8732 8748 7375 Information services, consumer; Market analysis, business & economic research; Business analysis; Business consulting; Information retrieval services; Information services, consumer; Market analysis, business & economic research; Business analysis; Business consulting; Information retrieval services
CEO: Jerre Stead
CFO: Todd Hyatt
Ex VP: Stephen Green
Ex VP: Murray Mercier
Sr VP: Jaspal Chahal
Sr VP: Heather Matzke-Hamlin
Exec: Dave Hopkins
Assoc Dir: Ana Gamboa
Dir: Rob Harman
CIO: Becky Kilpatrick
CIO: Lili Seidman

IHSS CONSORTIUM, THE
See IN-HOME SUPPORTIVE SERVICES CONSORTIUM OF SAN FRANCISCO INC

D-U-N-S 07-910-2243
IHT PROFESSIONAL SERVICES LLC
(*Suby of* CONNOLLY LLC) ★
115 Prmter Ctr Pl Ste 700, Atlanta, GA 30346-1280
Tel (770) 379-2800 *Founded/Ownrshp* 2011
Sales 14.2MM^E *EMP* 550
SIC 7376 8748 7363 Computer facilities management; Test development & evaluation service; Medical help service; Computer facilities management; Test development & evaluation service; Medical help service
CFO: Curtis A Cain

II
See INSULATIONS INC

D-U-N-S 60-570-4519
II DIAMOND MOTORS INC
DIAMOND MAZDA
10968 Airline Hwy, Baton Rouge, LA 70816-4214
Tel (225) 295-3900 *Founded/Ownrshp* 1988
Sales 22.6MM *EMP* 38
SIC 5511 Automobiles, new & used; Automobiles, new & used
Pr: Robert B Andre
**Treas:* Kelly Brooks
Exec: Shaun Efferson
Sls Mgr: Kris Morales

D-U-N-S 14-830-5675
II IN ONE CONTRACTORS INC
4344 W 45th St, Chicago, IL 60632-4309
Tel (773) 847-2100 *Founded/Ownrshp* 1984

Sales 26.1MM[E] *EMP* 150
SIC 1771 1611 1751 1794 Foundation & footing contractor; Highway & street paving contractor; Carpentry work; Excavation work; Foundation & footing contractor; Highway & street paving contractor; Carpentry work; Excavation work
Pr: Robert J McGee Jr
**VP:* Oliver Fifer
IT Man: Danny Cooney

D-U-N-S 04-168-3767
II MAYA LLC MESO
(*Suby of* FIREBIRD RESTAURANT GROUP LLC) ★
1611 Mckinney Ave, Dallas, TX 75202-1227
Tel (972) 241-2171 *Founded/Ownrshp* 2015
Sales 53.7M[E] *EMP* 673[E]
SIC 5812 Eating places

D-U-N-S 02-788-7703
II ORLANDO LLC FS
FOUR SEASONS RESORT ORLANDO
10100 Dream Tree Blvd, Golden Oak, FL 32836-4012
Tel (800) 267-3046 *Founded/Ownrshp* 2013
Sales 23.8MM[E] *EMP* 500
SIC 7011 Resort hotel; Resort hotel
Off Mgr: Ben Shank

D-U-N-S 15-192-8512 IMP
II STANLEY CO INC
(*Suby of* STANLEY ELECTRIC CO.,LTD.)
1500 Hill Brady Rd, Battle Creek, MI 49037-7320
Tel (269) 660-7777 *Founded/Ownrshp* 1985
Sales 251.7MM[E] *EMP* 800
SIC 5063 4911 Motor vehicle lighting equipment; Electronic circuits; Electrical fittings & construction materials; Distribution, electric power
Pr: Satoshi Nakamura
CFO: Jerry Hammond
**CFO:* Glenn Kirk
**Sec:* Shoji Ichikawa
**Ex VP:* Mike Isham
Ex VP: Zygadlo Rich
Dir Rx: Ashish Stefano
Dept Mgr: Setsu Okubo
Div Mgr: Dave Knickerbocker
IT Man: Susan Cummings
Sfty Dirs: Tim Menzie

D-U-N-S 05-552-9333 IMP
▲ II-VI INC (PA)
375 Saxonburg Blvd, Saxonburg, PA 16056-9499
Tel (724) 352-4455 *Founded/Ownrshp* 1971
Sales 741.9MM *EMP* 8,490
Accts Ernst & Young Llp Pittsburgh
Tkr Sym IIVI *Exch* NGS
SIC 3827 3229 3674 3699 Optical instruments & lenses; Optical elements & assemblies, except ophthalmic; Optical glass; Fiber optics strands; Semiconductors & related devices; Laser welding, drilling & cutting equipment; Optical instruments & lenses; Optical elements & assemblies, except ophthalmic; Optical glass; Fiber optics strands; Semiconductors & related devices; Laser welding, drilling & cutting equipment
Ch Bd: Francis J Kramer
**Pr:* Vincent D Mattera Jr
CFO: Mary Jane Raymond
VP: Giovanni Barbarossa
QC Dir: Bob Morris
Snr Mgr: Ryan Brolley
Snr Mgr: Michael Oates
Board of Directors: Joseph J Corasanti, Wendy F Dicicco, Thomas E Mistler, Marc Y E Pelaez, William Schromm, Peter W Sognefest, Howard H Xia

D-U-N-S 00-833-9988
■ II-VI OPTICAL SYSTEMS INC (CA)
(*Suby of* II-VI INC) ★
36570 Briggs Rd, Murrieta, CA 92563-2387
Tel (951) 926-2994 *Founded/Ownrshp* 1961, 2000
Sales 23.1MM[E] *EMP* 170[E]
SIC 3812 3827

IIA, THE
See INSTITUTE OF INTERNAL AUDITORS-RESEARCH FOUNDATION

IIB
See IDAHO INDEPENDENT BANK

IICC
See INTERNATIONAL INDUSTRIAL CONTRACTING CORP

D-U-N-S 01-022-3894
IIDON INC
IIDON SECURITY ASSOCIATES
4055 Valley View Ln # 150, Dallas, TX 75244-5040
Tel (972) 620-2344 *Founded/Ownrshp* 2000
Sales 16.0MM *EMP* 500
SIC 7381 Security guard service; Security guard service
Pr: Hans S Yoo
**CFO:* Aziz Noorali
Sr VP: Jesse Penn II
Dir Sec: William Katt
IT Man: Annie Um
Secur Mgr: Michael Buckner

IIDON SECURITY ASSOCIATES
See IIDON INC

IIE COMMUNICATIONS DIVISION
See INSTITUTE OF INTERNATIONAL EDUCATION INC

D-U-N-S 11-470-6695
IIF DATA SOLUTIONS INC
I I F
14850 Conference Center D, Chantilly, VA 20151-3844
Tel (703) 531-1180 *Founded/Ownrshp* 1998
Sales 51.3MM[E] *EMP* 400
SIC 7379 7371 Computer related consulting services; Software programming applications; Computer related consulting services; Software programming applications
Pr: Charles R Patten Sr
CFO: Heath West
Prgrm Mgr: Xavier Stewart

Board of Directors: Christopher Kachouroff, Charles Patten

III OFFSHORE ADVISORS
See AVM LP

IIMAK
See INTERNATIONAL IMAGING MATERIALS INC

D-U-N-S 09-557-5523
IIT INC
6 Cornish Ct Ste 101, Dix Hills, NY 11746-6002
Tel (631) 254-8600 *Founded/Ownrshp* 1995
Sales 26.0MM *EMP* 85[E]
Accts Nazareth Consulting Inc Har
SIC 7379 Computer related consulting services; Computer related consulting services
CEO: Dinesh Gulati
Sr VP: Joseph Ziccardi
VP: Ken Frank

D-U-N-S 07-914-1418
IJKG LLC
BAYONNE MEDICAL CENTER
714 Bergen Ave, Jersey City, NJ 07306-4802
Tel (201) 858-5000 *Founded/Ownrshp* 2007
Sales 168.3MM[E] *EMP* 1,058
SIC 8741 Hospital management; Hospital management
Chf Path: Raoul Rudelli
Chf Rad: James Brown
Chf Rad: Edward Fobben
COO: Nizar Kifaieh
CFO: David Paulosky
Ex VP: Jakey Ccti
Sr VP: Jerry Bass
Sr VP: Mark Spektor
Sr VP: Pat Whipkey
VP: Orest Padkowsky
Dir Risk M: Pat Hoffman
Dir Case M: Eileen Popola
Dir Lab: Ricardo Binsol
Dir Lab: Alan Wiseman
Dir Rx: Jay Horowitz
Dir Rx: Gene Rader

D-U-N-S 82-528-0352
IJKG OPCO LLC
BAYONNE MEDICAL CENTER
(*Suby of* BAYONNE MEDICAL CENTER) ★
714 Bergen Ave, Jersey City, NJ 07306-4802
Tel (201) 858-5000 *Founded/Ownrshp* 2007
Sales 168.3MM *EMP* 1,058
SIC 8741 Hospital management; Hospital management
**Pr:* Dr Mark Spektor Dl
**CFO:* Patrick Ryan
Chf Nrs Of: Rita Poss
Opers Mgr: Veronica S Maria
Doctor: Gregory Anselmi
Doctor: Barry Elkind MD
Doctor: Raul Rudelli
Pharmcst: Tony Fazio

D-U-N-S 79-251-8826
IJN INC
BETH'S BARRICADES
1623 Middle Road Ext, Gibsonia, PA 15044-7913
Tel (412) 559-1396 *Founded/Ownrshp* 2005
Sales 21.0MM[E] *EMP* 60
SIC 3499 Barricades, metal
Pr: Elizabeth N Nury

D-U-N-S 03-025-2949 IMP
IJOT DEVELOPMENT INC
1300 Clay St Ste 600, Oakland, CA 94612-1427
Tel (925) 258-9909 *Founded/Ownrshp* 1982
Sales 122.6MM[E] *EMP* 1,600
SIC 2531 2599 Public building & related furniture; Work benches, factory; Public building & related furniture; Work benches, factory
Pr: Michael Gompertz

D-U-N-S 62-701-8133
IJS GLOBAL HOLDINGS INC
(*Suby of* BRYNWOOD PARTNERS II LIMITED PARTNERSHIP) ★
1055 Stevenson Ct, Roselle, IL 60172-4316
Tel (847) 734-6805 *Founded/Ownrshp* 2005
Sales 40.7MM[E] *EMP* 112
SIC 4731 Freight forwarding
CEO: Giorgio Laccona
**Treas:* Mark Atzbi

D-U-N-S 06-453-1088
IJS GLOBAL INC
1055 Stevenson Ct, Roselle, IL 60172-4316
Tel (847) 734-6805 *Founded/Ownrshp* 2006
Sales 54.2MM[E] *EMP* 23[E]
SIC 4731 Freight transportation arrangement
CFO: George Menz
Opers Mgr: Cesar Castro

D-U-N-S 79-098-2826
IJS GLOBAL INC
(*Suby of* IJS GLOBAL HOLDINGS INC) ★
1055 Stevenson Ct, Roselle, IL 60172-4316
Tel (847) 734-6805 *Founded/Ownrshp* 2004
Sales 30.0MM[E] *EMP* 109
SIC 4731 Freight forwarding; Freight forwarding
Pr: Dennis Dolan
Sr VP: Margaret Bradford
Dist Mgr: Joseph Lance

D-U-N-S 19-336-7625
IJUS LLC
INNOVATIVE JOINT UTILITY SVCS
690 Taylor Rd Ste 100, Gahanna, OH 43230-3520
Tel (614) 470-9882 *Founded/Ownrshp* 2005
Sales 20.0MM[E] *EMP* 127
SIC 8711 Engineering services; Engineering services
Pr: William Schulze
Area Mgr: Eric Young
Genl Mgr: Brett Willitt
Dir IT: Lennie Phipps
IT Man: Kevin Hoover
Sfty Dirs: Scott Schulze
Opers Supe: Marty Cowie

Opers Supe: Kerry Jonker
Opers Supe: Tom Ogle

D-U-N-S 18-827-3262
IK SYSTEMS INC
7625 Main Street Fishers, Victor, NY 14564-8963
Tel (585) 924-9000 *Founded/Ownrshp* 1986
Sales 30.1MM[E] *EMP* 34
SIC 5065 5999 1731 Security control equipment & systems; Communication equipment; Communication equipment; Safety & security specialization; Communications specialization
Ch Bd: Melkon Babigian
IT Man: Matt Mahoney

D-U-N-S 93-973-4497
IKANO COMMUNICATIONS INC
A & S TECHNOLOGIES
9221 Corbin Ave Ste 260, Northridge, CA 91324-1625
Tel (801) 924-0900 *Founded/Ownrshp* 1998
Sales 36.3MM[E] *EMP* 184
SIC 7374 Data processing & preparation; Data processing & preparation
CEO: Jim Murphy
**Pr:* Sam Ghahremanpour
**COO:* George Mitsopoulos
Ex VP: Kevin Childre
**VP:* Dean Russ

D-U-N-S 08-662-7218 IMP
■ IKANOS COMMUNICATIONS INC
(*Suby of* QUALCOMM ATHEROS INC) ★
47669 Fremont Blvd, Fremont, CA 94538-6577
Tel (510) 979-0400 *Founded/Ownrshp* 2015
Sales 48.3MM *EMP* 235[E]
Tkr Sym IKAN *Exch* NGM
SIC 3674 Semiconductors & related devices; Semiconductors & related devices
Pr: Rahul Patel
CFO: Sanjay Mehta
Treas: Akash Palkhiwala
VP: Daniel D Vrechek

D-U-N-S 96-401-0482 IMP
■ IKANOS COMMUNICATIONS INC
(*Suby of* IKANOS COMMUNICATIONS INC) ★
100 Schult Dr, Red Bank, NJ 07701-6775
Tel (732) 345-7500 *Founded/Ownrshp* 2004
Sales 42.3MM[E] *EMP* 283
SIC 3674 8711 Semiconductors & related devices; Engineering services; Semiconductors & related devices; Engineering services
Genl Mgr: Lawrence Ciaccia
CTO: Daniel Amrany
Pr Mgr: Morgan Small

D-U-N-S 78-040-0102
IKARIA INC
53 Frontage Rd Fl 3, Hampton, NJ 08827-4032
Tel (908) 238-6600 *Founded/Ownrshp* 2005
Sales NA *EMP* 375
SIC 8731 8732 Commercial physical research; Biotechnical research, commercial; Commercial nonphysical research

D-U-N-S 02-985-3015
IKASYSTEMS CORP
132 Turnpike Rd, Southborough, MA 01772-2129
Tel (508) 251-3182 *Founded/Ownrshp* 2003
Sales 180.5MM[E] *EMP* 175[E]
SIC 5045 Computer software
CEO: Joe Marabito
**Ch Bd:* Ravi Ika
**COO:* Alisha Bloom
**CFO:* Bradley T Miller
**CFO:* John Rogers
CFO: Edward Saraiva
**Sr VP:* Brian Kim
**Sr VP:* Dave Lucey
Sr VP: Madu Narahari
**Sr VP:* Philip J Spinelli
VP: Dean Ascioti
VP: Stuart Greenspan
VP: John Jacobsen
VP: Chinmay Nanavati
VP: Jeff Rimpas
VP: Sandy Shroyer
Exec: Stacy Coggeshall

D-U-N-S 62-543-8809
IKE AUTO PARK INC
IKE HONDA CARS
4407 W Deyoung St, Marion, IL 62959-7727
Tel (618) 997-4000 *Founded/Ownrshp* 1984
Sales 48.7MM[E] *EMP* 62
SIC 5511 Automobiles, new & used; Automobiles, new & used
Pr: Edward F Eigenrauch
**Sec:* Lori Miller
**VP:* Brian Egenraugh
**Genl Mgr:* Lori Sisulak
Mktg Dir: Jason Eigenrauch
Sls Mgr: Brian Eigenrauch
Sales Asso: Andrew Corderman
Sales Asso: Michelle Laird

IKE BEHAR
See REGINA BEHAR ENTERPRISES

D-U-N-S 11-278-7742 IMP
IKE BEHAR APPAREL & DESIGN INC
13955 Nw 60th Ave, Miami Lakes, FL 33014-3126
Tel (305) 557-5212 *Founded/Ownrshp* 1975
Sales 34.1MM[E] *EMP* 214
SIC 5136 Shirts, men's & boys'; Sportswear, men's & boys'; Shirts, men's & boys'; Sportswear, men's & boys'
Pr: Isaac Behar
**Treas:* Alan Behar
**VP:* Lawrence Behar
**VP:* Regina Behar
**VP:* Steve Behar
Mktg Dir: Shaliza Deen

D-U-N-S 04-933-8858
IKE GAMING INC
EL CORTEZ HOTEL
600 Fremont St, Las Vegas, NV 89101-5614
Tel (702) 385-5200 *Founded/Ownrshp* 1962

Sales 83.6MM[E] *EMP* 1,400
SIC 7011 Casino hotel; Casino hotel
Pr: Ike Lawrence Epstein
**Pr:* John D Gaughan
CFO: Joe Woody
**Sec:* Alan J Woody
**VP:* Kenneth Espstien
**VP:* Brady Exber
**VP:* Wayne Starker
Exec: Jose Garcia
Genl Mgr: Tomg Kiminski
Genl Mgr: Jack Thalgott
Dir IT: Randy Grijalva

IKE HONDA CARS
See IKE AUTO PARK INC

D-U-N-S 55-609-1544
IKEA DISTRIBUTION SERVICES INC
(*Suby of* IKEA HOLDING US INC) ★
100 Ikea Dr, Westampton, NJ 08060-5112
Tel (609) 261-1208 *Founded/Ownrshp* 1989
Sales 42.5MM[E] *EMP* 215
SIC 5712 Furniture stores; Furniture stores
Pr: Keith Keller
**Treas:* John Robinson
**VP:* Donald Stewart

D-U-N-S 11-847-0939 IMP/EXP
IKEA HOLDING US INC
(*Suby of* INGKA HOLDING OVERSEAS B.V.)
1105 N Market St Ste 1044, Wilmington, DE 19801-1216
Tel (302) 655-4126 *Founded/Ownrshp* 1984
Sales 1.2MMM[E] *EMP* 13,000
SIC 5021 5712

D-U-N-S 79-257-4050 IMP
IKEA INDUSTRY DANVILLE LLC
100 Ikea Dr, Ringgold, VA 24586-1101
Tel (434) 822-6080 *Founded/Ownrshp* 2006
Sales 79.1MM[E] *EMP* 275
SIC 2511 Wood household furniture; Wood household furniture
IT Man: Niklas Osslen
Manager: Jim Meyer
Prd Mgr: Charles Myrick

D-U-N-S 79-307-5920
IKEA NORTH AMERICA SERVICES LLC
(*Suby of* IKEA HOLDING US INC) ★
420 Alan Wood Rd, Conshohocken, PA 19428-1141
Tel (610) 834-0180 *Founded/Ownrshp* 1989
Sales 290.8MM[E] *EMP* 350[E]
SIC 6794 5712 Franchises, selling or licensing; Furniture stores; Franchises, selling or licensing; Furniture stores
Pr: Mike Ward
Pr: Odd Friis
COO: Hans Ljungberg
COO: Rick Wilson
CFO: Soren Hansen
Treas: Jim Quinn
Treas: John Robinson
Chf Mktg O: Leontyne Green
Comm Man: Christine Whitehawk
Prin: Antoine Jackson
Area Mgr: Jan Andersson

D-U-N-S 11-847-0871 IMP/EXP
IKEA PENNSYLVANIA INC
(*Suby of* IKEA HOLDING US INC) ★
496 W Germantown Pike, Plymouth Meeting, PA 19462-1302
Tel (610) 834-0180 *Founded/Ownrshp* 1984
Sales 44.6MM[E] *EMP* 250[E]
SIC 5712 Furniture stores; Furniture stores
Pr: Bjorn Bayley
**Pr:* Bjorn Baylay
**Treas:* Michael Mc Donald
Store Mgr: Jim Tilley
Dir IT: Marco Sousa
Info Man: Monica Grinchis
Netwrk Eng: Chris Jackson
Sales Exec: Anders Elmeskov
VP Mktg: Julie Wainwright
Pr Mgr: Karolina Horoszczak
Mktg Mgr: Stefanie Smith

IKEA SAN DIEGO
See HAUSTEN LLC

D-U-N-S 61-410-1079 IMP
IKEA TRADING SERVICES INC
I K E A
(*Suby of* IKEA SUPPLY AG)
7810 Katy Fwy, Houston, TX 77024-2006
Tel (713) 263-0689 *Founded/Ownrshp* 1989
Sales 82.3MM[E] *EMP* 645
SIC 5712 Furniture stores; Furniture stores
Pr: Eva Maria Johansson
**CEO:* Mikael Ohlsson
**Treas:* Keith Keller

IKEA-SEATTLE
See ELMHULT LIMITED PARTNERSHIP

IKE'S
See MID AMERICAN RESTAURANTS INC

D-U-N-S 04-916-6986 IMP
IKO INTERNATIONAL INC
(*Suby of* NIPPON THOMPSON CO., LTD.)
91 Walsh Dr, Parsippany, NJ 07054-1098
Tel (973) 402-0254 *Founded/Ownrshp* 1969, 2005
Sales 23.0MM[E] *EMP* 66
SIC 5085 Bearings
Pr: Sadato Sugihara

IKO MANUFACTURING
See IKO PRODUCTION INC

D-U-N-S 60-328-0491 IMP
IKO MIDWEST INC
(*Suby of* GOLDIS ENTERPRISES INC) ★
235 W South Tec Dr, Kankakee, IL 60901-8426
Tel (815) 936-9600 *Founded/Ownrshp* 2003
Sales 25.1MM[E] *EMP* 65
SIC 2429 Shingle & shingle mills
Pr: David Koschitzky

Treas: Ronald Healey
QA Dir: Allen Montalto

D-U-N-S 78-780-9458
IKO PRODUCTION INC
IKO MANUFACTURING
(*Suby of* GOLDIS HOLDINGS INC) ★
120 Hay Rd, Wilmington, DE 19809-3509
Tel (302) 764-3100 *Founded/Ownrshp* 1992
Sales 30.1MM^E *EMP* 127
SIC 2952 Roofing materials; Roofing materials
Pr: David Koschitzky

IKON FINANCIAL SERVICES
See GECITS

IKPS
See INTEGRITY KOKOSING PIPELINE SERVICES LLC

IKS
See INTERNATIONAL KNIFE & SAW INC

IL DEPT CMMRCE ECNOMIC OPRTNTY
See ILLINOIS DEPARTMENT OF COMMERCE AND ECONOMIC OPPORTUNITY

D-U-N-S 80-681-1972
IL DEPT OF CHILDREN & FAMILY
(*Suby of* EXECUTIVE OFFICE OF GOVERNOR) ★
406 E Monroe St 412, Springfield, IL 62701-1411
Tel (217) 785-2509 *Founded/Ownrshp* 1964
Sales 20.6MM^E *EMP* 300
SIC 8322 9441 Child related social services; Administration of social & manpower programs; ; Child related social services; Administration of social & manpower programs;
Ex Dir: Jess McDonald
Genl Couns: Elizabeth Yore
Snr Mgr: Judy Yeager

D-U-N-S 03-442-0455 IMP
IL FORNAIO (AMERICA) CORP
(*Suby of* ROARK CAPITAL GROUP INC) ★
770 Tamalpais Dr Ste 400, Corte Madera, CA 94925-1795
Tel (415) 945-0500 *Founded/Ownrshp* 2012
Sales 219.5MM^E *EMP* 6,600
SIC 5812 5813 5149 5461 2051 Italian restaurant; Drinking places; Bakery products; Bakeries; Bread, cake & related products; Italian restaurant; Drinking places; Bakery products; Bakeries; Bread, cake & related products
CEO: Michael Hislop
Mng Pt: Dalton Archie
**Pr:* Michael J Beatrice
**CFO:* Sean K Maloney
VP: Frank Licata
Exec: Maurizio Mazzon
Brnch Mgr: Fabio Terzi
Genl Mgr: Chamal Perera
Mktg Mgr: Alison Bianchetti
Mktg Mgr: Alison Weese
Sls Mgr: Dina Ardizzone

D-U-N-S 86-809-1448
IL VICINO HOLDING CO INC
IL VICINO WOOD OVEN PIZZA
2201 San Pedro Dr Ne 2, Albuquerque, NM 87110-4133
Tel (505) 262-4717 *Founded/Ownrshp* 1993
Sales 10.7MM^E *EMP* 300
SIC 5812 Pizza restaurants; Pizza restaurants
Pr: Gregory Atkin
**VP:* Richard Post
**VP:* Thomas White

IL VICINO WOOD OVEN PIZZA
See IL VICINO HOLDING CO INC

D-U-N-S 16-012-9011
ILAND INTERNET SOLUTIONS CORP
1235 North Loop W Ste 800, Houston, TX 77008-1764
Tel (800) 697-7088 *Founded/Ownrshp* 1995
Sales 29.9MM^E *EMP* 50^E
SIC 4813
CEO: Scott R Sparvero
Pr: Dante Orsini
**Pr:* Eduardo B Ussher
CFO: Bill Warrick
Sr VP: Jennifer Brenner
VP: Julien Anguenot
VP: Lilac Schoenbeck
Comm Dir: Kellie Willman
Snr Ntwrk: Charlton Tulud
CTO: Justin Giardina
Sys Mgr: Bakul Brahmbhatt

ILB
See INTERNATIONAL LINE BUILDERS INC

D-U-N-S 18-726-6259 IMP
ILC DOVER LP
(*Suby of* NEW ILC DOVER INC) ★
1 Moonwalker Rd, Frederica, DE 19946-2080
Tel (302) 335-3911 *Founded/Ownrshp* 2011
Sales 74.9MM^E *EMP* 475
SIC 3842 3721 7389 Personal safety equipment; Space suits; Balloons, hot air (aircraft); Design services; Personal safety equipment; Space suits; Balloons, hot air (aircraft); Design services
Genl Pt: William Wallach
Pt: Dan Herring
VP: Scott Patterson
Prgrm Mgr: Tony Asti
Prgrm Mgr: Catherine Dodgen
IT Man: Mary Downes
VP Opers: Brad Walters
Mfg Mgr: Jeff Tricarico
Opers Mgr: Bob Hudson
VP Mktg: Ilc Dover
VP Sls: Rhonda Haller

D-U-N-S 00-250-1005 IMP
ILC INDUSTRIES LLC (NY)
I L C
105 Wilbur Pl, Bohemia, NY 11716-2426
Tel (631) 567-5600 *Founded/Ownrshp* 2010
Sales 100.9MM^E *EMP* 354^E
SIC 3674 Semiconductors & related devices; Semiconductors & related devices
CEO: Clifford P Lane
CFO: Ken Sheedy
Exec: S Millman
Exec: A W Trapani
Genl Mgr: Rodrigo Araoz
Mktg Dir: Ivette Cruz
Pdt Mgr: Jerry Kessler

ILC RESOURCES
See IOWA LIMESTONE CO

D-U-N-S 78-764-8054 IMP
ILCO UNICAN HOLDING CORP
400 Jeffreys Rd, Rocky Mount, NC 27804-6624
Tel (252) 446-3321 *Founded/Ownrshp* 1988
Sales 108.1MM^E *EMP* 1,000
SIC 3429 Keys, locks & related hardware; Keys & key blanks; Locks or lock sets; Keys, locks & related hardware; Keys & key blanks; Locks or lock sets
Ch Bd: Aaron M Fish

D-U-N-S 79-055-5028
ILD HOLDINGS INC
5000 Sawgrass Village Cir, Ponte Vedra Beach, FL 32082-5045
Tel (904) 273-2440 *Founded/Ownrshp* 2004
Sales 45.4MM *EMP* 200
SIC 4813 Long distance telephone communications; Long distance telephone communications
Ch Bd: Michael Lewis
**Pr:* Dennis Stoutenburgh
**CFO:* H Edward Brooks Jr
CFO: Christopher A Dyrek
**Sec:* C Read Morton Jr

D-U-N-S 82-971-1501
ILEX CAPITAL GROUP LLC
23 West St, Annapolis, MD 21401-2420
Tel (410) 897-0701 *Founded/Ownrshp* 2007
Sales 38.1MM^E *EMP* 140^E
SIC 6282 Investment advisory service; Investment advisory service

D-U-N-S 15-699-0434
ILEX CONSTRUCTION AND DEVELOPMENT INC
433 Park St, Charlottesville, VA 22902-4737
Tel (410) 820-4393 *Founded/Ownrshp* 1986
Sales 68.0MM^E *EMP* 140
SIC 1542 1521 1751 Commercial & office buildings, renovation & repair; New construction, single-family houses; Single-family home remodeling, additions & repairs; Carpentry work; Commercial & office buildings, renovation & repair; New construction, single-family houses; Single-family home remodeling, additions & repairs; Carpentry work
Ch: Douglas V Croker III
**Pr:* Mark Guedri
**VP:* Margaret Oxnam
Exec: Talli Oxnam
VP Opers: Neil Middlesworth

ILGWU LOCAL 23 25
See METROPOLITAN JOINT BOARD UNITED

ILIKAI
See ANEKONA MANAGEMENT LLC

D-U-N-S 78-854-7784
ILITCH HOLDINGS INC
LITTLE CAESAR'S
2211 Woodward Ave, Detroit, MI 48201-3467
Tel (313) 983-6000 *Founded/Ownrshp* 1997
Sales 824.0MM^E *EMP* 6,828
SIC 7941 7922 5812 Sports clubs, managers & promoters; Theatrical producers & services; Eating places; Sports clubs, managers & promoters; Theatrical producers & services; Eating places
Ch Bd: Michael Ilitch
Pr: Christopher Ilitch
CFO: Scott Fisher
CFO: Todd Seroka
Treas: David Agius
V Ch Bd: Malina Ilitch
Ex VP: Craig Turnbull
VP: Stanford P Berenbaum
VP: Stuart Degeus
VP: Richard Fenton
VP: Rick Fenton
VP: John Kotlar
VP: Doug Kuiper
VP: Bill Lee
VP: Steve Marquardt
VP: Karen Mullen
VP: Joan Rivard
VP: Joshua Sanborn
Comm Man: Liz Ford

D-U-N-S 03-173-3136 IMP
ILJIN ALABAMA CORP
(*Suby of* ILJIN GLOBAL CO., LTD.)
14 Downing Dr, Phenix City, AL 36869-3341
Tel (334) 297-4494 *Founded/Ownrshp* 2010
Sales 63.1MM *EMP* 21^E
SIC 5531 Automotive parts; Automotive parts
Prin: Steve B Park

D-U-N-S 10-391-2879
ILLCO INC
535 S River St, Aurora, IL 60506-5549
Tel (630) 892-7904 *Founded/Ownrshp* 1982
Sales 40.0MM *EMP* 94
SIC 5075 5078 Air conditioning & ventilation equipment & supplies; Refrigeration equipment & supplies; Air conditioning & ventilation equipment & supplies; Refrigeration equipment & supplies
Ch Bd: John Glass III
**Pr:* William Bergamini
**CFO:* Karen Madonia
Sales Exec: Ron Meyer
Mktg Dir: Bill Bergamini

D-U-N-S 00-732-6630
ILLES FOOD INGREDIENTS LTD
ILLES SEASONINGS & FLAVORS
2200 Luna Rd Ste 120, Carrollton, TX 75006-6559
Tel (214) 689-1300 *Founded/Ownrshp* 1987
Sales 26.3MM^E *EMP* 92
SIC 2087 2099 Flavoring extracts & syrups; Powders, drink; Pastes, flavoring; Concentrates, drink; Food preparations
Ch Bd: George M Illes Jr
**CFO:* Greg Nystrom
Treas: Jimmy McDonald
**VP:* Marc Aymond
**VP:* Tom Bailey
VP: John Dale
**VP:* Cristin Kahale
**VP:* Linda Mullin
VP: Vicki Peterlin
**VP:* Dave Schauf
**VP:* Curt Woods

ILLES SEASONINGS & FLAVORS
See ILLES FOOD INGREDIENTS LTD

D-U-N-S 04-657-5494
■ **ILLIANA DISPOSAL SERVICE INC**
ALLIED WASTE SERVICES NW IND
(*Suby of* ALLIED WASTE INDUSTRIES INC) ★
865 Wheeler St, Crown Point, IN 46307-2766
Tel (219) 662-8600 *Founded/Ownrshp* 1991
Sales 89.9MM^E *EMP* 400
SIC 4953 Refuse collection & disposal services; Recycling, waste materials; Refuse collection & disposal services; Recycling, waste materials
Pr: Dave Schutt
**VP:* Doug Rosenbum

D-U-N-S 02-339-7110
ILLING CO INC
N114 W 18937 Clinton Dr N 114 W, Germantown, WI 53022
Tel (262) 250-7566 *Founded/Ownrshp* 1931
Sales 57.8MM^E *EMP* 48
SIC 5099 7336 3411 Containers: glass, metal or plastic; Silk screen design; Metal cans
Pr: James Stein
**Pr:* Michael Alber
**Treas:* Ken Schroeder
**VP:* Kyle Whaley
Opers Mgr: John Kroll

D-U-N-S 05-820-6745
■ **ILLINGWORTH-KILGUST MECHANICAL INC**
(*Suby of* EMCOR GROUP INC) ★
11217 W Becher St, Milwaukee, WI 53227-1032
Tel (414) 476-6850 *Founded/Ownrshp* 1998
Sales 31.6MM^E *EMP* 105^E
SIC 1711 Mechanical contractor
Pr: Dan Pfeifer
**Ex VP:* Michael F Mamayek
**VP:* Ralph Boldt
VP: David Leed
**VP:* John Schmitz

ILLINI COMMUNITY HOSPITAL
See BLESSINGCARE CORP

D-U-N-S 11-748-2422
▲ **ILLINI CORP**
3200 W Iles Ave, Springfield, IL 62711-9680
Tel (217) 787-5111 *Founded/Ownrshp* 1983
Sales NA *EMP* 110
Tkr Sym ILII *Exch* OTO
SIC 6022 State commercial banks; State commercial banks
Pr: Burnard McHone
**Ch Bd:* Thomas A Black
**COO:* James L Adkins
**CFO:* Dennis Guthrie
**V Ch Bd:* N Ronald Thunman
Bd of Dir: Robert Olson
VP: Jennifer Obrien
VP Opers: Juanita Mathis
Snr Mgr: Jennifer Watret

D-U-N-S 60-886-6364
ILLINI MANORS INC
285 S Farnham St, Galesburg, IL 61401-5323
Tel (309) 343-1550 *Founded/Ownrshp* 1988
Sales 11.4MM^E *EMP* 447
SIC 8051 Skilled nursing care facilities; Skilled nursing care facilities
Pr: Donald Fike

D-U-N-S 00-542-0518
ILLINI MEDIA CO (IL)
WPGU-FM
512 E Green St Fl 3, Champaign, IL 61820-6483
Tel (217) 337-8300 *Founded/Ownrshp* 1911
Sales 1.9MM *EMP* 414
Accts Cliftonlarsonallen Llp Champa
SIC 2711 4832 2741 2721 Newspapers: publishing only, not printed on site; Radio broadcasting stations; Yearbooks: publishing & printing; Periodicals; Newspapers: publishing only, not printed on site; Radio broadcasting stations; Yearbooks: publishing & printing; Periodicals
VP: Amara Enyia
Dir Rx: Melissa Pasco
Genl Mgr: Lil Levant
Off Mgr: Cathy Jordan
Dir IT: Todd Rigg
Advt Dir: Nancy Elliott

D-U-N-S 60-820-2243
ILLINI MEDICAL ASSOCIATES SC
101 N State St, Jerseyville, IL 62052-1754
Tel (618) 498-7518 *Founded/Ownrshp* 2005
Sales 31.0MM^E *EMP* 861^E
SIC 8062 General medical & surgical hospitals
Pr: David Harmon
Off Mgr: Dawn Stump

D-U-N-S 78-598-4428
ILLINOIS ACTION FOR CHILDREN
4753 N Broadway St # 1200, Chicago, IL 60640-4982
Tel (773) 769-8005 *Founded/Ownrshp* 2004
Sales 36.7MM *EMP* 400
Accts Crowe Horwath Llp Chicago Il
SIC 8322 8399 General counseling services; Referral service for personal & social problems; Advocacy group; General counseling services; Referral service for personal & social problems; Advocacy group
Ch Bd: Monica Moss
**Pr:* Maria Whelan
VP: Sessy Nyman
Dir IT: Jeff Hanneman
Netwrk Eng: Marc Eallonardo
Snr Mgr: Mike Middendorf

D-U-N-S 06-740-8856
ILLINOIS AGRICULTURAL ASSOCIATION
ILLINOIS FARM BUREAU
1701 Towanda Ave, Bloomington, IL 61701-2050
Tel (309) 557-2111 *Founded/Ownrshp* 1919
Sales 48.1MM *EMP* 5,050
SIC 8611 6722 8742 6311 7514

ILLINOIS AUTO CENTRAL
See ILLINOIS AUTO ELECTRIC CO

D-U-N-S 00-693-0648 IMP
ILLINOIS AUTO ELECTRIC CO
ILLINOIS AUTO CENTRAL
700 Enterprise St, Aurora, IL 60504-8148
Tel (630) 862-3300 *Founded/Ownrshp* 1915
Sales 110.5MM *EMP* 240
SIC 5084 5013 5083 5078 7699 3519

D-U-N-S 02-516-5424 EXP
ILLINOIS AUTO TRUCK CO INC (IL)
I AT
1669 Marshall Dr, Des Plaines, IL 60018-1840
Tel (847) 299-1100 *Founded/Ownrshp* 1935, 1963
Sales 32.2MM^E *EMP* 75
Accts Gimbel Abrams & Singer Chicag
SIC 5013 Clutches
Pr: Richard H Stein
**Treas:* Leonard F Stein
VP: Steve Saaf
**VP:* Jordan R Stein
VP: Jordan Stein
VP: Terri Stein
MIS Dir: James Jarvis
Natl Sales: John Ellison

D-U-N-S 02-576-9878
ILLINOIS AYERS OIL CO
AYERCO CONVENIENCE CENTERS
Jct Hwy 24 & I 172, Quincy, IL 62306
Tel (217) 434-8662 *Founded/Ownrshp* 1964
Sales 69.4MM^E *EMP* 250
SIC 5541 5411 5171 Filling stations, gasoline; Convenience stores, chain; Petroleum bulk stations; Filling stations, gasoline; Convenience stores, chain; Petroleum bulk stations
Ch: Robert E Ayers
**Pr:* Carl W Adams
**Treas:* Ronald M Clark

D-U-N-S 00-693-0655
■ **ILLINOIS BELL TELEPHONE CO**
AT&T ILLINOIS
(*Suby of* AT&T MIDWEST) ★
225 W Randolph St Fl Ll, Chicago, IL 60606-1839
Tel (618) 344-9077 *Founded/Ownrshp* 1881, 1984
Sales 2.3MMM^E *EMP* 14,929
SIC 4813 8721 6512 Local & long distance telephone communications; Local telephone communications; Voice telephone communications; Data telephone communications; Billing & bookkeeping service; Commercial & industrial building operation; Local & long distance telephone communications; Local telephone communications; Voice telephone communications; Data telephone communications; Billing & bookkeeping service; Commercial & industrial building operation
Pr: Carrie Hightman
Ex VP: Stanley Dennis
IT Man: Mike Brown

D-U-N-S 08-908-1384 IMP
ILLINOIS BLOWER INC
IBI
750 Industrial Dr Ste E, Cary, IL 60013-1988
Tel (224) 888-2052 *Founded/Ownrshp* 1999
Sales 41.0MM^E *EMP* 47
SIC 3564 Blowing fans: industrial or commercial; Exhaust fans: industrial or commercial; Ventilating fans: industrial or commercial
Pr: Tyler S Barth
**Sec:* Craig Cummins
VP: Bill Howarth
QI Cn Mgr: David Magart
Sales Exec: Rick Bursh

D-U-N-S 78-726-8853
ILLINOIS BONE & JOINT INSTITUTE
LAKE SHORE ORTHOPEDICS
350 S Greenleaf St # 405, Gurnee, IL 60031-5709
Tel (847) 336-2344 *Founded/Ownrshp* 1985
Sales 85.0MM *EMP* 800
SIC 8011 Offices & clinics of medical doctors; Offices & clinics of medical doctors
Prin: Edward Hamming
VP: Ira Kornblatt
**Prin:* Robert Dugan MD
**Prin:* Bruce Hamming MD
**Prin:* Edward Logue MD
**Prin:* Bruce Summerville MD
Orthpdst: Edward G Hammin
Orthpdst: Bruce A Hmming
Podiatrist: Garo Emerzian

D-U-N-S 78-973-3029
ILLINOIS BONE AND JOINT INSTITUTE LLC
900 Rand Rd Ste 300, Des Plaines, IL 60016-2359
Tel (847) 375-3000 *Founded/Ownrshp* 1991
Sales 154.8MM^E *EMP* 700
SIC 8011 Orthopedic physician; Orthopedic physician
Pr: Wayne M Goldstein MD
Rgnl Mgr: Annette Egel
Surgeon: Taizoon Baxamusa
Surgeon: Marc Breslow
Surgeon: Brian Donahue
Surgeon: Alexander Gordon
Surgeon: Francis Lamberta

Surgeon: Alan League
Surgeon: ARI Youderian
Doctor: Michael Kornblatt
Doctor: David Morgan

ILLINOIS BRICK COMPANY
See SOUTHFIELD CORP

ILLINOIS BRICK COMPANY
See SOUTHFIELD CORP

D-U-N-S 87-933-3623
ILLINOIS BUREAU OF COMMUNICATIONS AND COMPUTER SERVICES
INFORMATION SERVICES
(*Suby of* ILLINOIS DEPARTMENT OF CENTRAL MANAGEMENT SERVICES) ★
120 W Jefferson St Fl 3, Springfield, IL 62702-5170
Tel (217) 782-3570 *Founded/Ownrshp* 1989
Sales NA *EMP* 300
SIC 9199 General government administration; General government administration

ILLINOIS CANCERCARE
See ONCOLOGY-HEMATOLOGY ASSOCIATES OF CENTRAL ILLINOIS PC

D-U-N-S 06-325-2738
ILLINOIS CASUALTY CO
225 20th St, Rock Island, IL 61201-8810
Tel (309) 793-1700 *Founded/Ownrshp* 1950
Sales NA *EMP* 30
SIC 6331 Fire, marine & casualty insurance & carriers; Fire, marine & casualty insurance & carriers
Pr: John Klockau
CFO: Arron Sutherland
**Sec:* Leona M Peterson-Spear
**VP:* Christopher J Klockau
**VP:* Richard Mc Carthy
Prgrm Mgr: Anne Thomas
Dir IT: Norm Schmeichel
Snr Mgr: Julia Jackson

D-U-N-S 06-523-7463 IMP
■ **ILLINOIS CEMENT CO LLC**
(*Suby of* EAGLE MATERIALS INC) ★
1601 Rockwell Rd, La Salle, IL 61301-9600
Tel (815) 224-2112 *Founded/Ownrshp* 1990
Sales 30.9MM^E *EMP* 150
SIC 3241 Masonry cement; Masonry cement
Pr: Steven R Rowley

D-U-N-S 04-192-9217
ILLINOIS CENTRAL COLLEGE
I C C
1 College Dr, Peoria, IL 61635-0002
Tel (309) 694-5011 *Founded/Ownrshp* 1966
Sales 59.9MM^E *EMP* 1,800
SIC 8222 Community college; Community college
Pr: John S Erwin
**VP:* Rita Ali
**VP:* Bruce Budde
VP: Tracy Morris
VP: Margaret Swanson

D-U-N-S 05-944-7961
ILLINOIS CENTRAL RAILROAD CO
CANADIAN NATIONAL ILL CENTL RR
(*Suby of* COMPAGNIE DES CHEMINS DE FER NATIONAUX DU CANADA)
17641 Ashland Ave, Homewood, IL 60430-1339
Tel (708) 332-3500 *Founded/Ownrshp* 1989
Sales 304.3MM^E *EMP* 3,600
SIC 4011 Railroads, line-haul operating; Railroads, line-haul operating
Ch Bd: Paul Tellier
**Pr:* E Hunter Harrison
**Pr:* Claude Mongeau
CFO: Dale W Phillips
Sr VP: Donald Skelton

D-U-N-S 17-207-1818
ILLINOIS CENTRAL SCHOOL BUS LLC
MINNESOTA CENTRAL SCHOOL BUS
78 N Chicago St 2, Joliet, IL 60432-4421
Tel (815) 744-4800 *Founded/Ownrshp* 2004
Sales 200.0MM^E *EMP* 1,500^E
SIC 4151 School buses; School buses
COO: Ron Howard
CFO: Patrick Earley
Exec: Jen Varner
Dir Bus: Dan O'Brien

ILLINOIS CMNTY COLLEGE DST 523
See KISHWAUKEE COLLEGE

D-U-N-S 03-057-3596
ILLINOIS COLLEGE
1101 W College Ave, Jacksonville, IL 62650-2299
Tel (217) 245-3000 *Founded/Ownrshp* 1829
Sales 29.6MM *EMP* 200
Accts Sikich Llp Springfield Illin
SIC 8221 College, except junior; College, except junior
CEO: John R Fairfield
Pr: Ann Marie Stahel
**Pr:* Axel D Steuer
VP: Malinda Carlson
**VP:* Robert J Lane
VP: Robert B Thomson III
Assoc Dir: Kristen Reed
Dir Sec: Mark Lawson
Dir IT: Craig Steenerson
IT Man: Sherry Turpin

D-U-N-S 01-028-5898
ILLINOIS COLLEGE OF OPTOMETRY
3241 S Michigan Ave Ste 1, Chicago, IL 60616-3878
Tel (312) 225-1700 *Founded/Ownrshp* 1947
Sales 39.4MM *EMP* 290
SIC 8011 8221 Clinic, operated by physicians; Colleges universities & professional schools; Clinic, operated by physicians; Colleges universities & professional schools
Ex Dir: Dr Arol Augsburger
**Pr:* Richard S Kattouf
**CFO:* John Budzynski
CFO: Peter Sander
**Treas:* Chuck Quattrochi

**VP:* Mark Colip
**VP:* Valarie Conrad
**VP:* Leonard Messner
Web Dev: Jonathan McIntire

ILLINOIS COMMUNITY COLLEGE BD
See ILLINOIS COMMUNITY COLLEGE SYSTEM

ILLINOIS COMMUNITY COLLEGE BOA
See ROCK VALLEY COLLEGE

ILLINOIS COMMUNITY COLLEGE BOA
See ELGIN COMMUNITY COLLEGE

ILLINOIS COMMUNITY COLLEGE BOA
See ILLINOIS COMMUNITY COLLEGE DISTRICT NO 515

D-U-N-S 06-996-6414
ILLINOIS COMMUNITY COLLEGE DISTRICT NO 515
ILLINOIS COMMUNITY COLLEGE BOA
(*Suby of* ILLINOIS COMMUNITY COLLEGE BD) ★
202 S Halsted St, Chicago Heights, IL 60411-8200
Tel (708) 709-3500 *Founded/Ownrshp* 1957
Sales 6.8MM *EMP* 500^E
Accts Crowe Horwath Llp Oak Brook
SIC 8222 8221 9411 Community college; Colleges universities & professional schools; Administration of educational programs; Community college; Colleges universities & professional schools; Administration of educational programs
Pr: Dr Eric Radtke
**Ch Bd:* Jacqueline Agee
**CFO:* Dr Alan Robertson
Ofcr: Sam Pavesich
Exec: John Flannigan
Ex Dir: David Cronan
Store Mgr: Jennifer Murdie
IT Man: William Carlborg
Mktg Dir: Jennifer Stoner

D-U-N-S 00-920-1943
ILLINOIS COMMUNITY COLLEGE SYSTEM
ILLINOIS COMMUNITY COLLEGE BD
(*Suby of* ILLINOIS STATE BOARD OF EDUCATION) ★
401 E Capitol Ave, Springfield, IL 62701-1706
Tel (217) 528-2858 *Founded/Ownrshp* 1965
Sales 264.9MM^E *EMP* 1,300
SIC 8221 9411 Colleges universities & professional schools; Administration of educational programs; Colleges universities & professional schools; Administration of educational programs
Pr: Geoffrey Obrzut
**VP:* Elaine S Johnson
Assoc Dir: Robert Brice
Dir: Jeff Newell
Off Admin: Marie Nolden

D-U-N-S 13-309-9338
■ **ILLINOIS CONSOLIDATED TELEPHONE CO**
CONSOLIDATED COMMUNICATIONS
(*Suby of* CONSOLIDATED COMMUNICATIONS HOLDINGS INC) ★
121 S 17th St, Mattoon, IL 61938-3915
Tel (217) 235-3311 *Founded/Ownrshp* 1924
Sales 100.2MM^E *EMP* 309
SIC 4813 Local & long distance telephone communications; ; Local & long distance telephone communications;
Pr: Richard Lumpkin
**Pr:* Robert J Currey
VP: Brian Carr
DP Dir: Jeff Ritke
IT Man: Rob Koester

D-U-N-S 01-022-1109
ILLINOIS CONSTRUCTORS CORP
39w866 Fabyan Pkwy, Elburn, IL 60119-9801
Tel (630) 232-7280 *Founded/Ownrshp* 1975
Sales 23.1MM^E *EMP* 75
SIC 1622 Bridge construction; Highway construction, elevated
Pr: John Mackanin Pe
**Treas:* Larry Slad
Genl Mgr: Rusy Mitcheff

D-U-N-S 96-166-6257
ILLINOIS CORN PROCESSING LLC
1301 S Front St, Pekin, IL 61554-4065
Tel (309) 353-3990 *Founded/Ownrshp* 2009
Sales 200.0MM *EMP* 75
SIC 2085 Grain alcohol for beverage purposes
Pr: Donald Oldham
**Pr:* Randy Schrick
Opers Mgr: Tom Belk
Ql Cn Mgr: Doug Leathers

D-U-N-S 80-681-2368
ILLINOIS DEPARTMENT OF CENTRAL MANAGEMENT SERVICES
(*Suby of* EXECUTIVE OFFICE OF GOVERNOR) ★
401 S Spring St Rm 715, Springfield, IL 62706-4002
Tel (217) 782-2141 *Founded/Ownrshp* 1982
Sales NA *EMP* 550
SIC 9199 9111 General government administration; Executive offices; General government administration; ; Executive offices;
V Ch: Robyn Gabel
Genl Couns: Jeffrey Shuck

D-U-N-S 80-681-1931
ILLINOIS DEPARTMENT OF COMMERCE AND ECONOMIC OPPORTUNITY
IL DEPT CMMRCE ECNOMIC OPRTNTY
(*Suby of* EXECUTIVE OFFICE OF GOVERNOR) ★
500 E Monroe St, Springfield, IL 62701-1643
Tel (217) 782-7500 *Founded/Ownrshp* 1978
Sales NA *EMP* 300
SIC 9611 Administration of general economic programs; ; Administration of general economic programs;
**COO:* Emily Monk
**CFO:* Anita Eatel
**Prin:* Adam Pollet

D-U-N-S 80-681-0529
ILLINOIS DEPARTMENT OF EMPLOYMENT SECURITY
(*Suby of* EXECUTIVE OFFICE OF GOVERNOR) ★
607 E Adams St Fl 10, Springfield, IL 62701-2037
Tel (217) 785-5070 *Founded/Ownrshp* 1980
Sales NA *EMP* 643
SIC 9441 Income maintenance programs; ; Income maintenance programs;

D-U-N-S 16-726-6241
ILLINOIS DEPARTMENT OF FINANCIAL AND PROFESSIONAL REGULATION
DIV OF BANKS AND REAL ESTATE
(*Suby of* EXECUTIVE OFFICE OF GOVERNOR) ★
320 W Washington St Fl 3, Springfield, IL 62701-1142
Tel (217) 782-3000 *Founded/Ownrshp* 2004
Sales NA *EMP* 800
Accts Sikich Llp Aurora Illinois
SIC 9311 Finance, taxation & monetary policy; ; Finance, taxation & monetary policy;
IT Man: Greg Doerfler
Snr Mgr: Miller Paul

D-U-N-S 80-671-5603
ILLINOIS DEPARTMENT OF HUMAN SERVICES
(*Suby of* EXECUTIVE OFFICE OF GOVERNOR) ★
401 S Clinton St, Chicago, IL 60607-3800
Tel (312) 793-1547 *Founded/Ownrshp* 1974
Sales NA *EMP* 2,800
SIC 9431 Mental health agency administration, government; ; Mental health agency administration, government;
MIS Dir: Gene Hagerman
IT Man: Sharon Zahorodnyj
Tech Mgr: Kevin Spurlock
Ql Cn Mgr: Lisa Leeper
Snr Mgr: Steven Washburn

D-U-N-S 80-632-8373
ILLINOIS DEPARTMENT OF MILITARY AFFAIRS
ILLINOIS MILITARY AFFAIRS
(*Suby of* EXECUTIVE OFFICE OF GOVERNOR) ★
1301 N Macarthur Blvd, Springfield, IL 62702-2317
Tel (217) 761-3910 *Founded/Ownrshp* 1818
Sales NA *EMP* 1,265
SIC 9711 National Guard; ; National Guard;

D-U-N-S 80-681-0313
ILLINOIS DEPARTMENT OF NATURAL RESOURCES
(*Suby of* EXECUTIVE OFFICE OF GOVERNOR) ★
1 Natural Resources Way # 100, Springfield, IL 62702-1290
Tel (217) 782-6302 *Founded/Ownrshp* 1913
Sales NA *EMP* 2,000
SIC 9512 9111 Land, mineral & wildlife conservation; ; Executive offices; ; Land, mineral & wildlife conservation; ; Executive offices;

D-U-N-S 80-666-0296
ILLINOIS DEPARTMENT OF PUBLIC HEALTH
(*Suby of* EXECUTIVE OFFICE OF GOVERNOR) ★
535 W Jefferson St Lbby, Springfield, IL 62702-5058
Tel (217) 785-4302 *Founded/Ownrshp* 1877
Sales NA *EMP* 6,406
SIC 9431 Administration of public health programs; ; Administration of public health programs;
CEO: Lamar Hasbrouck
**CFO:* Gary T Robinson

D-U-N-S 80-681-2467
ILLINOIS DEPARTMENT OF TRANSPORTATION
(*Suby of* EXECUTIVE OFFICE OF GOVERNOR) ★
2300 S Dirksen Pkwy, Springfield, IL 62764-0001
Tel (217) 782-7820 *Founded/Ownrshp* 1972
Sales NA *EMP* 22,897^E
SIC 9621 Regulation, administration of transportation;
**Ch Bd:* David Vaught
Ofcr: Colleen Caton
Ofcr: Kathleen Michals
Off Admin: Phyllis Dixon
IT Man: Kitty Adye
Genl Couns: Daniel Kelber
Genl Couns: Roma Larson
Genl Couns: Vivian Toliver
Snr Mgr: Craig Emberton
Snr Mgr: Mike Healy
Snr Mgr: Lance Jones

D-U-N-S 80-681-2582
ILLINOIS DEPARTMENT OF VETERANS AFFAIRS
IDVA
(*Suby of* EXECUTIVE OFFICE OF GOVERNOR) ★
833 S Spring St, Springfield, IL 62704-2617
Tel (217) 782-6641 *Founded/Ownrshp* 1970
Sales NA *EMP* 1,200
SIC 9451 Administration of veterans' affairs; ; Administration of veterans' affairs
Ex Dir: Dan Grant
**CFO:* Deborah Miller
CIO: Steven Depooter

D-U-N-S 80-671-5629
ILLINOIS DEPT OF HEALTHCARE & FAMILY SERVICES
(*Suby of* EXECUTIVE OFFICE OF GOVERNOR) ★
201 S Grand Ave E, Springfield, IL 62763-1000
Tel (217) 782-1200 *Founded/Ownrshp* 1877
Sales NA *EMP* 862
SIC 9441 9111 Administration of social & manpower programs; ; Executive offices; ; Administration of social & manpower programs; ; Executive offices;
Brnch Mgr: Theresa Eagleson
Snr Mgr: Lynne Thomas

D-U-N-S 07-198-8737
ILLINOIS EASTERN COMMUNITY COLLEGE DISTRICT 529
233 E Chestnut St, Olney, IL 62450-2227
Tel (618) 393-2982 *Founded/Ownrshp* 1968
Sales 15.9MM^E *EMP* 330
SIC 8222 5942 8221 Junior college; Book stores; Colleges universities & professional schools; Junior college; Book stores; Colleges universities & professional schools
CEO: Terry L Bruce
**CFO:* Roger Browning
CFO: Ed Wright

D-U-N-S 87-932-4861
ILLINOIS ENVIRONMENTAL PROTECTION AGENCY
IEPA
(*Suby of* EXECUTIVE OFFICE OF GOVERNOR) ★
1021 North Grand Ave E, Springfield, IL 62702-4059
Tel (217) 782-3397 *Founded/Ownrshp* 1970
Sales NA *EMP* 1,487
SIC 9511 Air, water & solid waste management; Air, water & solid waste management
Ex Dir: Douglas Scott
CFO: Kathy Griffin
Ofcr: Brad Halloran
Ofcr: Tonya Janecek
Ofcr: Teresa Rademacher
**VP:* William Child
Snr Mgr: Tom Johnson
Snr Mgr: Steven Young

ILLINOIS FARM BUREAU
See ILLINOIS AGRICULTURAL ASSOCIATION

D-U-N-S 08-102-8946
ILLINOIS FEDERATION OF TEACHERS
I F T
500 Oakmont Ln, Westmont, IL 60559-5520
Tel (630) 468-4080 *Founded/Ownrshp* 1937
Sales 22.4MM *EMP* 93
SIC 8631 Labor union; Labor union
Pr: Daniel Montgomery
Comm Dir: Gail Purkey

D-U-N-S 00-280-3120
ILLINOIS GAS CO (IL)
1927 Miller Dr, Olney, IL 62450-4744
Tel (618) 395-8588 *Founded/Ownrshp* 1916
Sales 20.2MM^E *EMP* 45
SIC 4924 Natural gas distribution
Pr: Roger C Avery
**Treas:* Jonathan Avery
**VP:* Robert Avery

D-U-N-S 08-204-3951
ILLINOIS GROWTH ENTERPRISES INC
7200 Clinton Rd, Loves Park, IL 61111-3806
Tel (815) 962-8333 *Founded/Ownrshp* 1970
Sales 88.7M *EMP* 450
Accts Cliftonlarsonallen Llp Peori
SIC 8331 Vocational rehabilitation agency; Vocational training agency; Work experience center; Sheltered workshop; Vocational rehabilitation agency; Vocational training agency; Work experience center; Sheltered workshop
CEO: Don Thayer
**Ch Bd:* Bob Gough
**Ch Bd:* Loren Heinzeroth
**CFO:* Jennifer Dunlap
Opers Mgr: Mike Miller
Board of Directors: Charles Box, Chris Budde, Paul Logli, Tom Martenson, Fred Muehlfelder, Vivienne Schorr, Jim Starnes, Karl Swanson, Michael Wilcop

D-U-N-S 18-056-7232
ILLINOIS HEALTH AND SCIENCE
2300 N Edward St, Decatur, IL 62526-4163
Tel (217) 876-8121 *Founded/Ownrshp* 1984
Sales 448.9MM^E *EMP* 2,300^E
SIC 8062 General medical & surgical hospitals; General medical & surgical hospitals
Pr: Kenneth Smithmier
**COO:* Tim Stone
**CFO:* Al Naqvi
**Ex VP:* Gary Peacock
Exec: Jeanine Garner
Doctor: Cesar Arguelles
Doctor: Cohen Carol
Doctor: Arguelles Cesar
Doctor: Ellington Charles
Doctor: Facchini Frank
Doctor: Gordon Gregory

ILLINOIS HEALTH MAINTENANCE
See ILLINOIS LIFE & HEALTH INSURANCE GUARANTEE ASSOCIATION INC

D-U-N-S 06-847-4378
ILLINOIS HOSPITAL ASSOCIATION
I H A
1151 E Warrenville Rd M, Naperville, IL 60563-9393
Tel (630) 276-5400 *Founded/Ownrshp* 1940
Sales 21.2MM^E *EMP* 147
SIC 8621 8742 4724 7322 7371 Professional membership organizations; Hospital & health services consultant; Group hospitalization plans; Travel agencies; Collection agency, except real estate; Software programming applications; Professional membership organizations; Hospital & health services consultant; Travel agencies; Collection agency, except real estate; Software programming applications
CEO: Maryjane A Wurth
**Sr VP:* Terri L Allen
Sr VP: A J Wilhelmi
Ex Dir: Derek Robinson
IT Man: Joe Connell
Genl Couns: Mark D Deaton

D-U-N-S 62-803-2898 IMP
ILLINOIS INDUSTRIAL TOOL INC
GREAT LAKES WHOLESALE GROUP
530 W North Frontage Rd B, Bolingbrook, IL 60440-5095
Tel (708) 597-6000 *Founded/Ownrshp* 1991
Sales 34.8MM^E *EMP* 45

SIC 5072 5141 5149 5087 Hand tools; Groceries, general line; Health foods; Beauty salon & barber shop equipment & supplies; Hand tools; Groceries, general line; Health foods; Beauty salon & barber shop equipment & supplies
Pr: Lance Ericson
CFO: Mike Stengel
Sls Mgr: Eric Brandstatter

ILLINOIS INST OF ART-CHICAGO
See ILLINOIS INSTITUTE OF ART INC

D-U-N-S 07-231-5377
■ ILLINOIS INSTITUTE OF ART INC (IL)
ILLINOIS INST OF ART-CHICAGO
(*Suby of* EDUCATION MANAGEMENT CORP) ★
350 N Orleans St Ste 800, Chicago, IL 60654-1529
Tel (312) 280-3500 *Founded/Ownrshp* 1916, 1995
Sales 11.0MM^E *EMP* 412
SIC 8249 8221 Commercial art school; Colleges universities & professional schools; Commercial art school; Colleges universities & professional schools
Pr: John B Jenkins
**Treas:* Dorinda Pannozzo
Ex VP: David Ray
Mktg Dir: Lia Miller

D-U-N-S 04-208-4434
ILLINOIS INSTITUTE OF TECHNOLOGY (IL)
I I T
10 W 35th St, Chicago, IL 60616-3717
Tel (312) 567-3000 *Founded/Ownrshp* 1891
Sales 261.9MM *EMP* 1,662
Accts Kpmg Llp Chicago Il
SIC 8221 University; University
Pr: John L Anderson
Recvr: Maurice Barnette
CFO: Susan Wallace
**Ch:* Robert Pritzker
Assoc VP: Ronald Staudt
VP: Gerald Doyle
VP: Jeanne Hartig
VP: Patricia Laughlin
VP: Bruce Watts
Dir Teleco: Virginia Bentley
Assoc Dir: Faye Bulaclac
Assoc Dir: John Grimes
Assoc Dir: Kamara Jackson
Assoc Dir: Ryan Nelson
Assoc Dir: Jeffrey Wat
Comm Man: Vince Laconte

D-U-N-S 08-295-0163
ILLINOIS INSURANCE GUARANTY FUND (IL)
150 S Wacker Dr Ste 2970, Chicago, IL 60606-4207
Tel (312) 422-9700 *Founded/Ownrshp* 1972
Sales NA *EMP* 19
SIC 6411 Insurance agents, brokers & service; Insurance agents, brokers & service
Ex Dir: Tim Schotke

D-U-N-S 94-806-2336
ILLINOIS LIFE & HEALTH INSURANCE GUARANTEE ASSOCIATION INC
ILLINOIS HEALTH MAINTENANCE
1520 Kensington Rd # 112, Oak Brook, IL 60523-2140
Tel (773) 714-8050 *Founded/Ownrshp* 1993
Sales 31.1MM *EMP* 6
SIC 8399 Social service information exchange

ILLINOIS MADISON INSUR AGCY
See MADISON MUTUAL INSURANCE CO

D-U-N-S 96-969-0515
ILLINOIS MASONIC CHARITIES FUND
2866 Via Verde St, Springfield, IL 62703-4388
Tel (217) 529-8900 *Founded/Ownrshp* 2011
Sales 132.9MM *EMP* 2
Accts Eck Schafer & Punke Llp Sprin
SIC 8322 Individual & family services
Ch: James D Williams

D-U-N-S 05-786-4449
ILLINOIS MASONIC MEDICAL CENTER
ADVOCATE HEALTH CARE
(*Suby of* ADVOCATE HEALTH CARE NETWORK) ★
836 W Wellington Ave, Chicago, IL 60657-5147
Tel (773) 975-1600 *Founded/Ownrshp* 1909
Sales 245.0MM^E *EMP* 3,460
SIC 8062 General medical & surgical hospitals; General medical & surgical hospitals
CEO: Susan Nordstrom Lopez
**VP:* Dr William Wener
Off Mgr: Maryann Wasner
Obsttrcn: Irma Sodini
Ansthlgy: Deepti Agarwal
Ansthlgy: Sahar Honari
Doctor: Toni-Denise Espina
Doctor: Edwin Feldman MD
Doctor: Kamala A Ghey MD
Doctor: John P Kirby MD
Doctor: Sunil N Patel MD

D-U-N-S 12-257-0526 EXP
ILLINOIS METER INC
IMCO SUPPLY
4390 Jeffory St, Springfield, IL 62703-5344
Tel (217) 529-1672 *Founded/Ownrshp* 1985
Sales 38.8MM^E *EMP* 48
SIC 5084 Water pumps (industrial)
Pr: Dennis J Sheley
**Sec:* James H Sheley
Opers Mgr: Jason Cozadd

ILLINOIS MILITARY AFFAIRS
See ILLINOIS DEPARTMENT OF MILITARY AFFAIRS

D-U-N-S 12-231-9072
ILLINOIS MUNICIPAL ELECTRIC AGENCY
I M E A
3400 Conifer Dr, Springfield, IL 62711-8301
Tel (217) 789-4632 *Founded/Ownrshp* 1984
Sales 327.1MM *EMP* 28
Accts Baker Tilly Virchow Krause Ll
SIC 4911 Distribution, electric power; Distribution, electric power
Pr: Kevin M Gaden
CFO: Bob Chidres
**CFO:* Bob Childers
**Sr VP:* Phillip Doc Mueller
**VP:* Troy Fodor
**VP:* Kevin Wagner
Secur Mgr: Alice Schum

D-U-N-S 09-317-2104
ILLINOIS MUNICIPAL RETIREMENT FUND
IMRF
2211 York Rd Ste 500, Oak Brook, IL 60523-2337
Tel (630) 368-1010 *Founded/Ownrshp* 1939
Sales NA *EMP* 186
SIC 6371

D-U-N-S 00-693-5324
ILLINOIS MUTUAL LIFE INSURANCE CO
300 Sw Adams St, Peoria, IL 61634-0002
Tel (309) 674-8255 *Founded/Ownrshp* 1910
Sales NA *EMP* 212
SIC 6321 6311 Disability health insurance; Life insurance carriers; Disability health insurance; Life insurance carriers
Pr: Katy McCord
**Ch Bd:* Michel A Mc Cord
Pr: Susan Reitz
Treas: Sheryl Baker
**Ex VP:* W E Palmatier
VP: Christopher Connor
VP: Mary Gensel
VP: J W Marshall
VP: Pamela Murrell
VP: Lawrence P Smith
VP: Lawrence Smith
VP: Jeffrey Wann
Exec: Judith McCord
Exec: Bill Palmatier

D-U-N-S 80-702-9256
ILLINOIS NATIONAL BANK
322 E Capitol Ave, Springfield, IL 62701-1710
Tel (217) 747-5500 *Founded/Ownrshp* 1983
Sales NA *EMP* 15^E
SIC 6712 Bank holding companies; Bank holding companies
Pr: Richard K McCord
Sr VP: Andrew Herrera
Sr VP: Jeffrey L Raes
Sr VP: Deborah J Shelton

D-U-N-S 02-574-1455
ILLINOIS OIL MARKETING EQUIPMENT INC (IL)
850 Brenkman Dr, Pekin, IL 61554-1523
Tel (309) 253-5428 *Founded/Ownrshp* 1954, 1995
Sales 22.1MM *EMP* 59
SIC 3443 Service station equipment installation, maintenance & repair; Tanks, standard or custom fabricated: metal plate
Pr: Kevin Lane
**Sec:* Joyce Hale
**VP:* Brad Rodgers
VP: John Schumaker

D-U-N-S 60-621-2678
ILLINOIS PAPER CO
ILLINOUS PAPER AND COPIER
6 Territorial Ct, Bolingbrook, IL 60440-4662
Tel (630) 679-9090 *Founded/Ownrshp* 1976
Sales 55.5MM^E *EMP* 73
SIC 5044 5112 Copying equipment; Computer & photocopying supplies
Pr: Terry R Yormark
VP: Matt Lichius
Genl Mgr: Sheryl Gregory
Off Mgr: Cassie Walling
Sls Dir: Scott Schiffner

D-U-N-S 02-110-4786
■ ILLINOIS POWER GENERATING CO
NEW AMEREN ENERGY RESOURCES
(*Suby of* ILLINOIS POWER RESOURCES LLC) ★
601 Travis St Ste 1400, Houston, TX 77002-3253
Tel (713) 507-6400 *Founded/Ownrshp* 2013
Sales 648.0MM *EMP* 384^E
Accts Ernst & Young Llp Houston Te
SIC 4911 Generation, electric power; Generation, electric power
Pr: Robert C Flexon
**Ch Bd:* Kevin Howell
CFO: Clint C Freeland
VP: J Clinton Walden
Mng Dir: Robert Hallett
Board of Directors: Mario Alonso, Marjorie Bowen, Carolyn J Burke, Julius Cox

D-U-N-S 07-923-8300
■ ILLINOIS POWER HOLDINGS LLC
(*Suby of* IPH II LLC) ★
601 Travis St Ste 1400, Houston, TX 77002-3253
Tel (713) 507-6400 *Founded/Ownrshp* 2013
Sales 658.9MM^E *EMP* 477^E
SIC 4911 Electric services; Generation, electric power; Electric services; Generation, electric power

D-U-N-S 15-300-5306
■ ILLINOIS POWER RESOURCES LLC
NEW AMEREN ENERGY RESOURCES
(*Suby of* ILLINOIS POWER HOLDINGS LLC) ★
1901 Chouteau Ave, Saint Louis, MO 63103-3003
Tel (314) 554-4110 *Founded/Ownrshp* 2013
Sales 658.9MM^E *EMP* 421^E
SIC 4911 Electric services; Electric services
**Pr:* Daniel F Cole
**CEO:* Thomas R Voss
**CFO:* Martin J Lyons Jr
**Sr VP:* Gregory L Nelson
**VP:* Jerre E Birdsong

D-U-N-S 80-295-4529
ILLINOIS QUAD CITY CIVIC CENTER AUTHORITY
IWIRELESS CENTER
1201 River Dr, Moline, IL 61265-1303
Tel (309) 764-2001 *Founded/Ownrshp* 1984
Sales 5.3MM *EMP* 525
Accts Mcgladrey Davenport Ia
SIC 6512 Nonresidential building operators; Nonresidential building operators
Ex Dir: Scott Mullen
**Ch Bd:* Paul Mulcahey
**CFO:* Rocky Jones
Treas: Albert Van Tieghem
Sls&Mrk Ex: Arron Roof
Mktg Dir: Stephani Nagle
Mktg Dir: Charlie Schilling

D-U-N-S 00-798-2168
ILLINOIS ROAD CONTRACTORS INC
520 N Webster Ave, Jacksonville, IL 62650-1115
Tel (217) 245-6181 *Founded/Ownrshp* 1925
Sales 37.1MM^E *EMP* 120
Accts Kerber Eck & Braeckel Llp Sp
SIC 1611 2951 4213 Highway & street maintenance; Asphalt & asphaltic paving mixtures (not from refineries); Trucking, except local; Highway & street maintenance; Asphalt & asphaltic paving mixtures (not from refineries); Trucking, except local
CEO: Devon Davidsmeyer
**Pr:* Jeffry Davidsmeyer
Treas: Earl L Forrer
Treas: Earl Forrler
**Sec:* R Thomas Slaybeck
**Ex VP:* Thomas L Atkins

D-U-N-S 00-381-0835
ILLINOIS RURAL ELECTRIC COOPERATIVE
2 S Main St, Winchester, IL 62694-1218
Tel (217) 243-8700 *Founded/Ownrshp* 1936
Sales 28.5MM *EMP* 33
Accts Cliftonlarsonallen Llp Austin
SIC 4911 Distribution, electric power; Distribution, electric power
Pr: Robert A Brown
**Treas:* Ronald Myers
**VP:* F Alan Heaton

D-U-N-S 17-569-4736 IMP
ILLINOIS SLEEP PRODUCTS INC
ENGLANDER OF ILLINOIS, CO
3428 W 48th Pl, Chicago, IL 60632-3027
Tel (773) 927-0888 *Founded/Ownrshp* 1986
Sales 22.4MM^E *EMP* 55
SIC 5021 2515

D-U-N-S 60-513-7884
ILLINOIS SPORT FACILITATES AUTHORITIES
333 W 35th St, Chicago, IL 60616-3621
Tel (312) 674-5590 *Founded/Ownrshp* 1988
Sales 41.9MM *EMP* 5
SIC 8741 Management services; Management services
Pr: Perri L Irmer
Bd of Dir: Alvin Boutte Jr

D-U-N-S 80-681-2558
ILLINOIS STATE BOARD OF EDUCATION
ISBE
(*Suby of* EXECUTIVE OFFICE OF GOVERNOR) ★
100 N 1st St Ste 1, Springfield, IL 62702-5011
Tel (217) 782-4321 *Founded/Ownrshp* 1975
Sales NA *EMP* 1,300
SIC 9411 ; Executive offices; ;
Pr Dir: Matthew Vanover

D-U-N-S 07-704-2869
ILLINOIS STATE MEDICAL SOCIETY
20 N Michigan Ave Ste 700, Chicago, IL 60602-4890
Tel (312) 782-2749 *Founded/Ownrshp* 1850
Sales 173.1MM^E *EMP* 226
SIC 8621 Medical field-related associations; Medical field-related associations
CEO: Alexander Lerner
VP: Audrey Vanagunas
CIO: Suzanne Nelson

D-U-N-S 80-681-0164
ILLINOIS STATE OF STATE POLICE
(*Suby of* EXECUTIVE OFFICE OF GOVERNOR) ★
801 S 7th St, Springfield, IL 62703-2487
Tel (217) 782-7263 *Founded/Ownrshp* 1941
Sales NA *EMP* 2,800
SIC 9221 State police; ; State police;
Bd of Dir: Jan Bowsher
Bd of Dir: Ralph Caldwell
Ofcr: Timothy Tripp
Exec: Scott Compton
Exec: Rick Hector
Dir Lab: Jan Johnson
Off Mgr: Cathy Gullo
CTO: Carol Gibbs
IT Man: Matthew Burger
Snr Mgr: Jamie Blakley
Snr Mgr: Lambert Fleck

D-U-N-S 07-233-2430
ILLINOIS STATE OF TOLL HIGHWAY AUTHORITY
(*Suby of* EXECUTIVE OFFICE OF GOVERNOR) ★
2700 Ogden Ave, Downers Grove, IL 60515-1703
Tel (630) 241-6800 *Founded/Ownrshp* 1953
Sales NA *EMP* 1,750
Accts Mcgladrey & Pullen Llp Schau
SIC 9621 Regulation, administration of transportation; ; Regulation, administration of transportation;
Pr: John Mitola
COO: Karen Burke
**CFO:* Mike Colsch
Ex Dir: Jeffrey S Dailey
Ex Dir: Jack Hartman
IT Man: Christine Benn
IT Man: Wendy Maka
Genl Couns: Tom Bamonte
Snr Mgr: Joseph Kambich
Snr Mgr: John Wagner

D-U-N-S 80-764-8597
■ ILLINOIS STUDENT ASSISTANCE COMMISSION
(*Suby of* UNITED STATES DEPT OF EDUCATION) ★
500 W Monroe St Ste 300, Springfield, IL 62704-1990
Tel (217) 782-6767 *Founded/Ownrshp* 1957
Sales NA *EMP* 591
SIC 9411 Administration of educational programs; Administration of educational programs
Mng Dir: Eric Zarnikow

D-U-N-S 00-514-6428 IMP
▲ ILLINOIS TOOL WORKS INC
155 Harlem Ave, Glenview, IL 60025-4075
Tel (847) 724-7500 *Founded/Ownrshp* 1912
Sales 14.4MMM *EMP* 49,000
Accts Deloitte & Touche Llp Chicag
Tkr Sym ITW *Exch* NYS
SIC 3089 3965 3499 2891 3585 Injection molded finished plastic products; Closures, plastic; Synthetic resin finished products; Fasteners; Strapping, metal; Adhesives & sealants; Refrigeration & heating equipment; Injection molded finished plastic products; Closures, plastic; Synthetic resin finished products; Fasteners; Strapping, metal; Adhesives & sealants; Refrigeration & heating equipment
Pr: E Scott Santi
V Ch: Christopher O'Herlihy
Pr: Jack Shirrell
CFO: Michael M Larsen
Bd of Dir: Susan Crown
Ofcr: Mary K Lawler
Ex VP: John R Hartnett
Ex VP: Thomas Mackey
Ex VP: Roland M Martel
Ex VP: Steven L Martindale
Ex VP: Chris Oaherlihy
Ex VP: Juan Valls
Ex VP: Michael R Zimmerman
Sr VP: Maria C Green
VP: Ben Anthony
VP: Bob Callahan
VP: Ben Collason
VP: Joy Maros
VP: George Mondane
VP: Randall J Scheuneman
Exec: Michael Klear
Board of Directors: Daniel J Brutto, Susan Crown, James W Griffith, Richard H Lenny, Robert S Morrison, James A Skinner, David B Smith Jr, Pamela B Strobel, Kevin M Warren

D-U-N-S 61-501-7654 EXP
ILLINOIS TRUCK AND EQUIPMENT CO INC
320 Briscoe Dr, Morris, IL 60450-6854
Tel (815) 941-1483 *Founded/Ownrshp* 1989
Sales 37.6MM^E *EMP* 44
SIC 5511 5082 Trucks, tractors & trailers: new & used; Construction & mining machinery; Heavy construction equipment rental; Trucks, tractors & trailers: new & used; Construction & mining machinery
Pr: Rolf Helland

D-U-N-S 80-788-6627
ILLINOIS VALLEY CENTRAL HIGH SCHOOL
IVC HIGH SCHOOL
1300 W Sycamore St, Chillicothe, IL 61523-1373
Tel (309) 274-5481 *Founded/Ownrshp* 1967
Sales 15.5MM^E *EMP* 350
SIC 8211 Public elementary & secondary schools; Public elementary & secondary schools
Dir IT: Tom Morris

D-U-N-S 07-688-6654
ILLINOIS VALLEY COMMUNITY COLLEGE
COMMUNITY COLLEGE DST 513
(*Suby of* ILLINOIS COMMUNITY COLLEGE BD) ★
815 N Orlando Smith St, Oglesby, IL 61348-9692
Tel (815) 224-2720 *Founded/Ownrshp* 1924
Sales 24.1MM^E *EMP* 500
SIC 8222 8221 9411 Junior colleges & technical institutes; Colleges universities & professional schools; Administration of educational programs; Junior colleges & technical institutes; Colleges universities & professional schools; Administration of educational programs
Pr: Jerome Corcoran
Dir Recs: Tracy Morris
Ofcr: Mona Smith
VP: Deborah Anderson
VP: Harriet Custer
VP: William Marshall
VP: Jeanette Maurice
VP: Lori Scroggs
Comm Man: Cathy Bangert
Store Mgr: Lauren Sandberg
IT Man: Richard Pearce

ILLINOIS VALLEY COMMUNITY HOSP
See IV HEALTHCORP INC

D-U-N-S 03-055-2913
ILLINOIS VALLEY COMMUNITY HOSPITAL INC
925 West St, Peru, IL 61354-2757
Tel (815) 223-3300 *Founded/Ownrshp* 1986
Sales 16.2MM^E *EMP* 650
SIC 8062 General medical & surgical hospitals; General medical & surgical hospitals
CEO: Tommy Hobbs
**Pr:* Kris Paul
**CFO:* Steve Davis
**VP:* James Loveland
**VP:* Bobby Smith

ILLINOIS VALLEY PLASTICS
See IPLASTICS LLC

D-U-N-S 07-069-1472
ILLINOIS VEHICLE INSURANCE AGENCY INC
1s450 Summit Ave Ste 370, Oakbrook Terrace, IL 60181-3976
Tel (773) 774-9404 *Founded/Ownrshp* 1975
Sales NA *EMP* 396
SIC 6411 6331 Insurance brokers; Automobile insurance; Insurance brokers; Automobile insurance
Pr: Roger G Wolf

D-U-N-S 04-895-2246
ILLINOIS WESLEYAN UNIVERSITY
1312 Park St, Bloomington, IL 61701-1773
Tel (309) 556-1000 *Founded/Ownrshp* 1850
Sales 91.5MM *EMP* 500
Accts Kpmg Llp Chicago Illinois

SIC 8221 University; University
Ch Bd: Craig Hart
Pr: Susan Bassi
**Pr:* Minor Myers Jr
Treas: William Walsh
Trst: Michael Clark
Trst: Kathleen Lewton
Trst: Robert Pag
VP: Jean Baird
VP: Kenneth C Browning
VP: Patrick McLane
**VP:* Robert Reardon
VP: Catherine Spitz
Creative D: Lewis Williams

ILLINOIS WHL CASH REGISTER
See ILLINOIS WHOLESALE CASH REGISTER INC

D-U-N-S 04-677-7504 IMP/EXP
ILLINOIS WHOLESALE CASH REGISTER INC
ILLINOIS WHL CASH REGISTER
2790 Pinnacle Dr, Elgin, IL 60124-7943
Tel (847) 310-4200 *Founded/Ownrshp* 1976
Sales 27.7MM *EMP* 95
SIC 5044 Cash registers; Cash registers
Pr: Al Moorhouse
**VP:* Bonnie Moorhouse
**VP:* Dan Moorhouse
**VP:* Bob Tracy

D-U-N-S 00-693-5407
■ **ILLINOIS-AMERICAN WATER CO** (IL)
(*Suby of* AMERICAN WATER WORKS CO INC) ★
300 N Water Works Dr, Belleville, IL 62223-8601
Tel (618) 236-1181 *Founded/Ownrshp* 1800, 1946
Sales 149.0MM^E *EMP* 430
SIC 4941 Water supply; Water supply
Pr: Karla Olson Teasley
Treas: Charles Overath
VP: Mark Johnson
VP: R D Michem
VP: Frederick Ruckman
Genl Mgr: Patti Davis
VP Opers: Mike Smyth
VP Opers: Barry Suits

ILLINOUS PAPER AND COPIER
See ILLINOIS PAPER CO

ILLUME CANDLES
See STARLUME INC

D-U-N-S 03-330-5264 IMP
▲ **ILLUMINA INC**
5200 Illumina Way, San Diego, CA 92122-4616
Tel (858) 202-4500 *Founded/Ownrshp* 1998
Sales 1.8MMM *EMP* 3,700^E
Tkr Sym ILMN *Exch* NGS
SIC 3826 3821 Analytical instruments; Clinical laboratory instruments, except medical & dental; Analytical instruments; Clinical laboratory instruments, except medical & dental
CEO: Jay T Flatley
**Ch Bd:* William H Rastetter
**Pr:* Francis Desouza
CFO: Marc A Stapley
Ofcr: Mostafa Ronaghi
Sr VP: Sanjay Chikarmane
Sr VP: Charles Dadswell
Sr VP: Alex Dickinson
Sr VP: Gregory F Heath
Sr VP: Arthur L Holden
Sr VP: Mark Lewis
Dir Lab: Jason Jackson
Assoc Dir: Josh Bernd
Assoc Dir: Cosmin Deciu
Assoc Dir: Kumar Duraiswamy
Assoc Dir: Dan Headon
Assoc Dir: Michael O'Neill
Assoc Dir: Kathleen Pierce
Assoc Dir: Jeff Sabo
Assoc Dir: Bryan Schneider
Assoc Dir: Andrew Summers
Board of Directors: A Blaine Bowman, Daniel M Bradbury, Karin Eastham, Robert S Epstein, Jeff Huber, Gerald Moller, David R Walt, Roy A Whitefield

D-U-N-S 96-874-5435
ILLUMINATE 360 LLC
4555 Mansell Rd Ste 300, Alpharetta, GA 30022-8279
Tel (770) 521-4277 *Founded/Ownrshp* 2007
Sales 50.0MM *EMP* 20
SIC 5734 5251 8742 Computer & software stores; Hardware; Management information systems consultant; Computer & software stores; Hardware; Management information systems consultant
Mng Pt: Tripp Cox
Sr VP: Jeff Glattstein
Sr VP: Mike Marett
VP: Kelly Gilstrap
VP: Jeff Newman
Sls Dir: Catherine Ashford

D-U-N-S 07-564-8139
ILLUMINATING CONCEPTS LTD
30733 W 10 Mile Rd, Farmington Hills, MI 48336-2605
Tel (248) 478-2525 *Founded/Ownrshp* 1982
Sales 24.1MM^E *EMP* 53
SIC 5063 8748 Lighting fixtures; Lighting consultant
CEO: Ron Harwood
CFO: Geanne Quigle
Treas: Keith Irtenkauf
VP: Rochelle Harwood
Genl Mgr: Sheila Kerr
Sftwr Eng: Martin Banks
Sftwr Eng: Adam Magaluk
Sls&Mrk Ex: Sheila Shaw
Mktg Dir: Nick Priest
Mktg Dir: Penny Ziskind

D-U-N-S 94-584-5048 IMP
ILLUMINATIONS.COM INC
1736 Corporate Cir, Petaluma, CA 94954-6924
Tel (707) 776-2000 *Founded/Ownrshp* 2004
Sales 61.4MM^E *EMP* 1,049
SIC 5961 5947 Mail order house; Novelties; Mail order house; Novelties
Pr: Wallis D Arnold

D-U-N-S 08-560-6205
ILLY CAFE
800 Westchester Ave S440, Rye Brook, NY 10573-1358
Tel (877) 469-4559 *Founded/Ownrshp* 1992
Sales 23.0MM^E *EMP* 70^E
SIC 5149 Coffee, green or roasted
Pr Mgr: Laura Bachrach
Sls Mgr: Vicki Lorillard

ILM GROUP, THE
See INDIANA LUMBERMENS MUTUAL INSURANCE CO INC

D-U-N-S 00-543-6332 IMP/EXP
ILMO PRODUCTS CO (IL)
7 Eastgate Dr, Jacksonville, IL 62650-6761
Tel (217) 245-2183 *Founded/Ownrshp* 1913, 1985
Sales 41.9MM^E *EMP* 100
SIC 5084 2813 Welding machinery & equipment; Industrial gases; Welding machinery & equipment; Industrial gases
CEO: Linda Standley
**Pr:* Brad Floreth
CFO: John Damaro
Brnch Mgr: Greg Collins
Store Mgr: Winston Farmer
Store Mgr: Jasen Friedrich
Store Mgr: Tracy Hutmacher
Store Mgr: Terry Jack
Store Mgr: Penny McCormick
Store Mgr: Scotty Mikovich
Store Mgr: Tim Pennell

D-U-N-S 62-516-8463 IMP
ILMOR ENGINEERING INC
ILMOR HIGH PERFORMANCE MARINE
43939 Plymouth Oaks Blvd, Plymouth, MI 48170-2557
Tel (734) 456-3600 *Founded/Ownrshp* 1990
Sales 42.8MM *EMP* 85
Accts Plante & Moran Pllc Southfie
SIC 3714 Motor vehicle engines & parts; Motor vehicle engines & parts
Pr: Paul Ray
**VP:* Julie Bernard
IT Man: Dan Darnoziak
Opers Mgr: Wayne Bennett

ILMOR HIGH PERFORMANCE MARINE
See ILMOR ENGINEERING INC

D-U-N-S 02-691-4418 IMP
ILMOR MARINE LLC
(*Suby of* ILMOR ENGINEERING INC) ★
186 Penske Way, Mooresville, NC 28115-8094
Tel (704) 360-1900 *Founded/Ownrshp* 2008
Sales 23.6MM^E *EMP* 25
Accts Plante & Moran Pllc Southfiel
SIC 3519 Marine engines; Marine engines
Pr: Paul Ray
**Pr:* Ronald Brown
**COO:* Edwin Baumgartner
**Treas:* John Fraas
**VP:* Julie Bernard

D-U-N-S 19-845-3953
ILONA FINANCIAL GROUP INC
1807 S Washington St, Naperville, IL 60565-2446
Tel (630) 699-6147 *Founded/Ownrshp* 2003
Sales NA *EMP* 150^E
SIC 6311 Life insurance carriers; Life insurance carriers
Pr: Peter Fitzpatrick
**Treas:* Norman Fair

ILOVETOCREATE A DUNCAN ENTPS
See DUNCAN ENTERPRISES

D-U-N-S 09-327-0262 IMP
ILPEA INDUSTRIES INC
HOLM INDUSTRIES
(*Suby of* ILPEA INDUSTRIES INC) ★
745 S Gardner St, Scottsburg, IN 47170-2178
Tel (812) 752-1245 *Founded/Ownrshp* 2001
Sales 150.1MM^E *EMP* 700
SIC 3053 3089 Gaskets, all materials; Window frames & sash, plastic; Gaskets, all materials; Window frames & sash, plastic
Pr: Wayne Heverly
**VP:* Ken Chenoweth
Plnt Mgr: Jim Arndt
Ql Cn Mgr: Amy Phillis
Sls Mgr: Russell Murray

D-U-N-S 83-115-7651
ILPEA INDUSTRIES INC
745 S Gardner St, Scottsburg, IN 47170-2178
Tel (812) 752-2526 *Founded/Ownrshp* 2009
Sales 269.3MM^E *EMP* 700^E
SIC 5085 Gaskets
Pr: Wayne Heverly
**Sec:* Gary L Barrigar
**VP:* Paul Schiefley
Off Mgr: Gary Barrigar

D-U-N-S 60-849-8064
ILS CO LLC
8350 E Old Vail Rd, Tucson, AZ 85747-9197
Tel (520) 618-4309 *Founded/Ownrshp* 2001
Sales 54.4MM^E *EMP* 150
SIC 4731 Freight transportation arrangement; Freight forwarding; Freight transportation arrangement; Freight forwarding
CEO: Luis F Seldner
Pr: Juan Carlos Seldner
COO: Juan Seldner

D-U-N-S 01-759-3596
ILS NATIONAL LLC
ILSN
1570 S Mahaffie Cir, Olathe, KS 66062-3432
Tel (913) 888-9191 *Founded/Ownrshp* 1996
Sales 40.0MM *EMP* 18
SIC 7389 Purchasing service; Purchasing service

D-U-N-S 07-770-0198
ILSC HOLDINGS LC
(*Suby of* KATMAI GOVERNMENT SERVICES LLC) ★
700 W Airport Rd, Payson, AZ 85541-3665
Tel (928) 474-0092 *Founded/Ownrshp* 2010
Sales 40.0MM *EMP* 800^E
SIC 3812 Search & navigation equipment; Search & navigation equipment
CEO: Dave Shephens
Ofcr: Candace Hendrickson

ILSCO
See BARDES CORP

D-U-N-S 00-424-9843 IMP
ILSCO CORP (OH)
UTILCO DIV
(*Suby of* BARDES CORP) ★
4730 Madison Rd, Cincinnati, OH 45227-1426
Tel (513) 871-4000 *Founded/Ownrshp* 1894
Sales 68.2MM^E *EMP* 470
SIC 3643 3369 3451 3678 3544 3469

ILSN
See ILS NATIONAL LLC

ILTS CALIFORNIA
See INTERNATIONAL LOTTERY & TOTALIZATOR SYSTEMS INC

ILTS DELAWARE
See INTERNATIONAL LOTTERY & TOTALIZATOR SYSTEMS INC

D-U-N-S 15-302-2798 EXP
ILUKA RESOURCES INC
(*Suby of* ILUKA RESOURCES INC) ★
4505 Emperor Blvd Ste 220, Durham, NC 27703-8457
Tel (904) 284-9832 *Founded/Ownrshp* 1984
Sales 20.9MM^E *EMP* 350
SIC 1499 Peat mining & processing; Peat mining & processing
Pr: Matthew Blackwell
Pr: Darren Smith
VP: Des Alfred
VP: Allan Sale

D-U-N-S 80-446-5115 IMP/EXP
ILUKA RESOURCES INC
(*Suby of* ILUKA RESOURCES LIMITED)
12472 St John Church Rd, Stony Creek, VA 23882-3239
Tel (434) 348-4300 *Founded/Ownrshp* 2007
Sales 160.2MM^E *EMP* 495^E
SIC 1481 Nonmetallic mineral services
Prin: Matthew B Blackwell
Opers Mgr: John Goroncy
Prd Mgr: David Hill

D-U-N-S 61-735-5990 IMP
■ **IM FLASH TECHNOLOGIES LLC**
(*Suby of* MICRON TECHNOLOGY INC) ★
4000 N Flash Dr, Lehi, UT 84043-5148
Tel (801) 767-4000 *Founded/Ownrshp* 2005
Sales 225.9MM^E *EMP* 450
SIC 3674 Integrated circuits, semiconductor networks, etc.; Integrated circuits, semiconductor networks, etc.
Pr: Amy Rawlinson
**Ex Ofcr:* Keyvan Esfarjani
Bd of Dir: Sysongkham Hansana
Dir: Paul Whitlock
Prgrm Mgr: Mark Ball
QA Dir: Ben Chung
Netwrk Mgr: Rod Keyes
Sys Mgr: Kevin Call
Secur Mgr: Jeff Sheppard
Mktg Mgr: Justin Harnish

D-U-N-S 07-860-6887
IM SOLUTIONS LLC
TEXAS IMS
(*Suby of* LEADINGRESPONSE LLC) ★
15150 Preston Rd, Dallas, TX 75248-4877
Tel (214) 736-1493 *Founded/Ownrshp* 2012
Sales 203.8M^E *EMP* 339^E
SIC 7311 Advertising consultant

D-U-N-S 62-282-7525
IM SYSTEMS GROUP INC
I M S G
3206 Tower Oaks Blvd # 300, Rockville, MD 20852-4220
Tel (240) 833-1889 *Founded/Ownrshp* 1987
Sales 29.3MM *EMP* 271
Accts Aronson Llc Rockville Maryla
SIC 7373 8748 8731 7389 8999 8742 Computer integrated systems design; Communications consulting; Telecommunications consultant; Natural resource research; Environmental research; Marine reporting; Weather related services; Industrial & labor consulting services; Computer integrated systems design; Communications consulting; Telecommunications consultant; Natural resource research; Environmental research; Marine reporting; Weather related services; Industrial & labor consulting services
CEO: Vance Hum
**CFO:* Nina Chow
CFO: Wyatt Tinsley
VP: Sean Lam
Dir Bus: Brian Mischel
Prgrm Mgr: Bryan Oles
IT Man: Patti Porter

I.M.A.
See INTERCHURCH MEDICAL ASSISTANCE INC

D-U-N-S 07-992-4104
IMA DAIRY & FOOD USA INC
I M A
(*Suby of* IM.A. SPA)
523 Raritan Center Pkwy, Edison, NJ 08837-3918
Tel (732) 343-7619 *Founded/Ownrshp* 1961
Sales 221.8MM^E *EMP* 4,600
SIC 5083 Dairy machinery & equipment

D-U-N-S 82-602-2233 IMP/EXP
IMA LIFE NORTH AMERICA INC
(*Suby of* I.M.A. INDUSTRIA MACCHINE AUTOMATICHE SPA)
2175 Military Rd, Tonawanda, NY 14150-6001
Tel (716) 695-6354 *Founded/Ownrshp* 2013
Sales 70.0MM *EMP* 150
SIC 2834 Druggists' preparations (pharmaceuticals); Druggists' preparations (pharmaceuticals)
Pr: Giovanni Pecchioli
**Sec:* Sergio Marzo
**Ex VP:* Jose Ruiz
VP: Laura Opera
**VP:* Ernesto Renzi

D-U-N-S 05-706-6540 IMP/EXP
IMA NORTH AMERICA INC
NOVA PACKAGING SYSTEM
(*Suby of* I.M.A. INDUSTRIA MACCHINE AUTOMATICHE SPA)
7 New Lancaster Rd, Leominster, MA 01453-5224
Tel (978) 537-8534 *Founded/Ownrshp* 2001
Sales 35.6MM^E *EMP* 60
SIC 5112 Office supplies
Pr: Stewart Harvey
**Pr:* Warren Roman
**CFO:* Gerard Krouchick
**Treas:* Barry Collins
Dir IT: Dana Blanchard
IT Man: Lee Villeneuve
Sfty Mgr: Harry Ahlawat
Sls Dir: Tom Wyzykowski
Manager: Michael Bersani
Manager: Alan Hymas
Manager: James McKee

D-U-N-S 15-846-7840
IMA OF KANSAS INC
8200 E 32nd St N, Wichita, KS 67226-2606
Tel (316) 267-9221 *Founded/Ownrshp* 2011
Sales NA *EMP* 196
SIC 6411 Insurance agents, brokers & service; Insurance agents, brokers & service
Pr: Jeff Grace
VP: Paul Davis
**VP:* Raymond J Merz
VP: Glenn Nyberg
Admn Mgr: Stacey Faber
Dir IT: Jeffory Curtis

D-U-N-S 11-818-4118
IMACC CORP
MYERS CONTAINER
2303 Dalton Industrial Ct, Dalton, GA 30721-1911
Tel (706) 270-8635 *Founded/Ownrshp* 1984
Sales 43.2MM^E *EMP* 350
SIC 3412 3089

D-U-N-S 80-232-4384 IMP
IMAEX TRADING CO
A & D FOODS
65 Crestridge Dr, Suwanee, GA 30024-3573
Tel (678) 541-0234 *Founded/Ownrshp* 1994
Sales 35.0MM^E *EMP* 40^E
SIC 5142 Fish, frozen: packaged
CEO: Sengiri Angkawijana

D-U-N-S 80-178-3192
IMAGE 2000
7510 Hazeltine Ave, Van Nuys, CA 91405-1419
Tel (818) 781-2200 *Founded/Ownrshp* 1992
Sales 42.1MM^E *EMP* 135
SIC 5999 7699 Photocopy machines; Photographic equipment repair; Photocopy machines; Photographic equipment repair
CEO: Richard Campbell
**VP:* Joe Blatchford
Brnch Mgr: Joe Veres
Sls Mgr: Kenneth Mann

D-U-N-S 17-512-0724 EXP
IMAGE ACCESS CORP
22 Paris Ave Ste 108, Rockleigh, NJ 07647-2600
Tel (201) 342-7878 *Founded/Ownrshp* 1986
Sales 20.6MM^E *EMP* 43
SIC 5044 7389 Microfilm equipment; Micrographic equipment; Microfilm recording & developing service
Pr: Robert Feulner
Mng Pt: Tish Goodspeed
**Treas:* Marilyn Bresnak
**VP:* William Bresnak Jr
**VP:* Claire Feulner

D-U-N-S 87-994-3769
IMAGE API LLC
2002 Old Saint Augustine, Tallahassee, FL 32301-4883
Tel (850) 222-1400 *Founded/Ownrshp* 2012
Sales 22.8MM *EMP* 150
Accts Mcgladrey Llp Jacksonville F
SIC 7374 Data processing & preparation; Data processing & preparation
CEO: Dan Nellius
VP: Patrick Menjor
VP: John Schmidt
Tech Mgr: Jason Hickey
Software D: Nengmou Wang
Mktg Dir: Rick Johnston
Snr PM: Brian Walsh
Board of Directors: Richard Griffith

D-U-N-S 79-578-2247
IMAGE BY J & K LLC
1039 Blue Ridge View Cir, Forest, VA 24551-4379
Tel (888) 667-6929 *Founded/Ownrshp* 2006
Sales 58.7MM^E *EMP* 400
SIC 3589 7217 7349 7342 Floor washing & polishing machines, commercial; Carpet & upholstery cleaning; Building & office cleaning services; Service station cleaning & degreasing; Air duct cleaning; Rest room cleaning service; Floor washing & polishing machines, commercial; Carpet & upholstery cleaning; Building & office cleaning services; Service station cleaning & degreasing; Air duct cleaning; Rest room cleaning service

D-U-N-S 08-619-8405
IMAGE CONTROL INC
(*Suby of* CLIPPARD INSTRUMENT LABORATORY INC) ★
3121 Clifty Dr, Madison, IN 47250-1644
Tel (812) 273-5551 *Founded/Ownrshp* 1970
Sales 25.1MM^E *EMP* 237
SIC 3823 3625

D-U-N-S 01-803-8252
IMAGE DIRECT LLC
200 Monroe Ave Ste 4, Frederick, MD 21701-3145
Tel (301) 620-9900 *Founded/Ownrshp* 2000
Sales 22.8MM^E^ *EMP* 150
SIC 7331 Direct mail advertising services; Direct mail advertising services
Ofcr: Carl Richmond
Dir IT: Rexrode Dennis

D-U-N-S 18-763-1163 IMP
IMAGE DUTY-FREE SERVICES INC
7300 Nw 19th St Ste 704, Miami, FL 33126-1233
Tel (305) 591-0123 *Founded/Ownrshp* 1992
Sales 22.0MM *EMP* 180
SIC 5399 Duty-free goods; Duty-free goods
Ch Bd: Leon Tenenbaum
**Pr:* Antoine Goetgheluck

D-U-N-S 06-154-1802
IMAGE FIRST HEALTHCARE LAUNDRY SPECIALISTS INC
900 E 8th Ave Ste 300, King of Prussia, PA 19406-1347
Tel (484) 253-7200 *Founded/Ownrshp* 1997
Sales 27.2MM^E^ *EMP* 500^E^
SIC 7218 Industrial clothing launderers; Industrial clothing launderers
Pr: Jeffrey Berstein
**COO:* Joe Geraghty
**CFO:* James Malandra
Ofcr: Mary Ann McGowan
**VP:* David Burnette
**VP:* Bill Roberts
Manager: Travis Margo

D-U-N-S 01-134-3121
IMAGE FLOORING LLC
14720 W 105th St, Lenexa, KS 66215-4414
Tel (314) 432-3000 *Founded/Ownrshp* 2000
Sales 22.0MM^E^ *EMP* 99
SIC 5023 Floor coverings; Floor coverings
Pr: Melissa Miller
**Treas:* Cathy Wilkinson
**VP:* Jim Wilkinson

IMAGE FRST HLTHCARE SPECIALIST
See IFURS HOLDINGS INC

D-U-N-S 83-080-8270
IMAGE HOLDINGS CORP
2750 Sw Pkwy Ave, Wilsonville, OR 97070
Tel (503) 685-8888 *Founded/Ownrshp* 2009
Sales 43.8MM^E^ *EMP* 337^E^
SIC 3861 Projectors, still or motion picture, silent or sound; Projectors, still or motion picture, silent or sound
Prin: John Hui
**Pr:* Lap Shun Hui

D-U-N-S 05-246-8584
IMAGE IV SYSTEMS INC
512 S Varney St, Burbank, CA 91502-2196
Tel (323) 849-3049 *Founded/Ownrshp* 1984
Sales 21.6MM^E^ *EMP* 85
SIC 5044 Photocopy machines; Copying equipment
Pr: Ronald Warren
VP: Norma Henkel
**VP:* Sue Warren
VP: Susan Warren
Rgnl Mgr: Kelsey Goodrich

D-U-N-S 08-218-6045
IMAGE ONE LLC
AWNING INNOVATIONS
11899 Exit 5 Pkwy, Fishers, IN 46037-7938
Tel (877) 352-8014 *Founded/Ownrshp* 1999
Sales 122.7MM^E^ *EMP* 160
SIC 5039 Awnings; Awnings
**CFO:* Todd Hayes

IMAGE PRINTING
See VIVID IMPACT CO LLC

D-U-N-S 96-324-9891 IMP
IMAGE PROJECTIONS WEST INC
I P W
14135 E 42nd Ave Ste 40, Denver, CO 80239-4984
Tel (303) 576-9476 *Founded/Ownrshp* 1996
Sales 66.2MM^E^ *EMP* 139
SIC 5112 3955 Laserjet supplies; Laserjet supplies; Print cartridges for laser & other computer printers
Pr: Kedar Morarka
**COO:* John Arnold
**CFO:* Brian Grady
Chf Mktg O: Tony Telesmanic
**Ex VP:* Keith Arnold
QI Cn Mgr: Zane Kindred

D-U-N-S 62-160-7514
▲ IMAGE SENSING SYSTEMS INC
1600 University Ave W # 500, Saint Paul, MN 55104-3893
Tel (651) 603-7700 *Founded/Ownrshp* 1984
Sales 23.0MM *EMP* 124^E^
Tkr Sym ISNS *Exch* NAS
SIC 3861 Aerial cameras; Cameras & related equipment; Aerial cameras; Cameras & related equipment
COO: Dale E Parker
**Ch Bd:* James W Bracke
VP: Kenneth S Shain
Board of Directors: Andrew T Berger, Melissa B Fisher, Thomas G Hudson, Paul F Lidsky

D-U-N-S 84-913-8508
■ IMAGE SOLUTIONS INC
CSC REGULATORY SERVICE GROUP
(*Suby of* COMPUTER SCIENCES CORP) ★
100 S Jefferson Rd # 300, Whippany, NJ 07981-1055
Tel (973) 560-0404 *Founded/Ownrshp* 2011
Sales 86.7MM^E^ *EMP* 500^E^
SIC 7374 Computer processing services; Computer processing services
Pr: Jinsoo Kim
**COO:* Paul Chung
**CFO:* Peter Kim

IMAGE SOURCE
See COPIER SOURCE INC

D-U-N-S 13-636-9746
IMAGE STREAM MEDICAL INC
1 Monarch Dr Ste 102, Littleton, MA 01460-1440
Tel (978) 486-8494 *Founded/Ownrshp* 2002
Sales 21.2MM^E^ *EMP* 90
SIC 3841 3669 5047 Diagnostic apparatus, medical; Visual communication systems; Surgical equipment & supplies; Medical laboratory equipment
Pr: Eddie Mitchell
COO: Michael Miller
CFO: Mark Oppenheim
Bd of Dir: Flagg Flanagan
Prgrm Mgr: Fred Harvey
Prgrm Mgr: Anthony Sacramone
Snr Sftwr: Maria Mirkis
CTO: Pete Renzi
Opers Mgr: Rick Mongeau
Snr Mgr: Nicholas Grogan

D-U-N-S 61-330-3684 IMP
IMAGE TECHNOLOGY CHEMICAL
1380 N Knollwood Cir, Anaheim, CA 92801-1311
Tel (714) 252-0160 *Founded/Ownrshp* 1991
Sales 23.1MM^E^ *EMP* 35
SIC 5169 Chemicals, industrial & heavy
CEO: Abbas Emtiaz
**Pr:* Tom Emtiaz
**VP:* Harry Emtiaz

D-U-N-S 09-845-9357
IMAGENET CONSULTING LLC
913 N Broadway Ave, Oklahoma City, OK 73102-5810
Tel (405) 232-1264 *Founded/Ownrshp* 2005
Sales 80.0MM *EMP* 330
SIC 5999 5044

D-U-N-S 12-609-4585
IMAGENET LLC
6411 S 216th St, Kent, WA 98032-1392
Tel (253) 395-0110 *Founded/Ownrshp* 2002
Sales 23.9MM^E^ *EMP* 150^E^
SIC 7374 4226 6411 Data processing & preparation; Data processing service; Computer processing services; Optical scanning data service; Document & office records storage; Medical insurance claim processing, contract or fee basis
Mng Pt: John Mattingly
Genl Mgr: Scott Needham
Opers Mgr: Lynn Burke
Opers Mgr: Oliver Levy
Prd Mgr: Audrey Hoover
Manager: Steve Ortiz

D-U-N-S 80-196-7170 IMP
IMAGEONE INDUSTRIES INC
677 Dunksferry Rd, Bensalem, PA 19020-5929
Tel (215) 826-0880 *Founded/Ownrshp* 2007
Sales 46.0MM *EMP* 140
SIC 5046 Signs, electrical; Signs, electrical
Pr: James Mikula
VP: Tom Gianni
VP: Valentin Sanchez
Genl Mgr: Dawn Clark
Mtls Mgr: Mary Heitmann
Natl Sales: Rich Russo
Sls Mgr: Allyse Mikula
Art Dir: Kevin Shaw

D-U-N-S 79-129-4874
IMAGES DANCE CO
12851 Barrett Ln, Santa Ana, CA 92705-1371
Tel (714) 573-8114 *Founded/Ownrshp* 2006
Sales 56.7MM *EMP* 7
SIC 7911 Dance studios, schools & halls; Dance studios, schools & halls
Ex Dir: Deb Reynolds

D-U-N-S 78-998-4069
IMAGETEC L P
4509 Prime Pkwy, McHenry, IL 60050-7000
Tel (815) 759-6000 *Founded/Ownrshp* 1992
Sales 24.0MM^E^ *EMP* 150
SIC 7629 5044 7378 5045 Business machine repair, electric; Office equipment; Copying equipment; Duplicating machines; Computer maintenance & repair; Computers, peripherals & software
Pt: Rich Normann
**Pt:* James J Cook
**Pt:* Carl Cucco
VP: Mark Dodge
Genl Mgr: Mike Fahey
IT Man: Daniel Burke
Trfc Dir: Carolyn Hendler
Mktg Mgr: John Stephenson
Sls Mgr: Larry Dolendi
Sls Mgr: Derek Edwards
Sls Mgr: Kevin Linklater

IMAGETEK OFFICE SYSTEMS
See IMAGETEK PARTNERS LLC

D-U-N-S 00-102-0978
IMAGETEK PARTNERS LLC (TX)
IMAGETEK OFFICE SYSTEMS
220 Westway Pl Ste 150, Arlington, TX 76018-5673
Tel (817) 465-2450 *Founded/Ownrshp* 2000
Sales 29.4MM^E^ *EMP* 54
SIC 5044 7641 Office equipment; Photocopy machines; Office furniture repair & maintenance
VP: Danny Munoz
Exec: Monica Ratliff
Off Mgr: Beverly Oakes
Sales Exec: Anthony Arnold
S&M/VP: Brandon Chick
Sls Dir: Peggy Brown
Sls Dir: Linda Narcho
Sls Mgr: Lisa Caranci
Sls Mgr: Cyndi Crumpton
Sls Mgr: Drew Grace

IMAGEWEAR, ULTRA OPTICS
See WALMAN OPTICAL CO

IMAGEWORKS
See MAILSOUTH INC

D-U-N-S 95-883-0499
IMAGEWORKS DISPLAY AND MARKETING GROUP INC
415 Wachovia St, Winston Salem, NC 27101-5082
Tel (336) 750-0089 *Founded/Ownrshp* 1996
Sales 39.0MM^E^ *EMP* 36
SIC 7319 Display advertising service; Display advertising service
Pr: David Abbruzzese
**Treas:* Mark Beeler
**VP:* Brian Walker
Dir Bus: Michael Purviance
QA Dir: Roberto Mendoza
Snr PM: Stephen Foerster

D-U-N-S 80-884-6299 IMP
IMAGINATION TECHNOLOGIES INC
IMAGINATION TECHNOLOGIES LTD
(*Suby of* IMAGINATION TECHNOLOGIES LIMITED)
3201 Scott Blvd, Santa Clara, CA 95054-3008
Tel (408) 530-5000 *Founded/Ownrshp* 2015
Sales 26.5MM^E^ *EMP* 161^E^
SIC 3674 6794 Microprocessors; Franchises, selling or licensing; Microprocessors; Franchises, selling or licensing
CEO: Hossein Yassaie
**Pr:* Ravikrishna Cherukuri
Pr: Ravi Krishna
**Pr:* Sandeep Vij
CFO: Jose Franca
**CFO:* William Slater
**CFO:* Richard Smith
VP: Victor Castellucci
VP: Jim Finch
**VP:* Brad Holtzinger
VP: Jim Kurkowski
VP: Cesar Martin-Perez
VP: Derek Meyer
VP: Kevin Meyer
VP: Jos Maria Moniz
VP: Victor Peng
VP: Kate Hunt Rundle
VP Bus Dev: Mark Tyndall

IMAGINATION TECHNOLOGIES LTD
See IMAGINATION TECHNOLOGIES INC

D-U-N-S 07-876-4119
IMAGINE COMMUNICATIONS CORP
HARRIS BROADCAST
(*Suby of* GORES GROUP LLC) ★
3001 Dallas Pkwy Ste 300, Frisco, TX 75034-8639
Tel (469) 803-4900 *Founded/Ownrshp* 2012
Sales 476.9MM^E^ *EMP* 2,177
SIC 3663 Radio broadcasting & communications equipment; Television broadcasting & communications equipment; Radio broadcasting & communications equipment; Television broadcasting & communications equipment
CEO: Charlie Vogt
Pr: Steve Foreman
Pr: Pablo Gargiulo
**Pr:* Harris Morris
**CFO:* Mike Behling
**CFO:* Skip Sorenson
**Ex VP:* Jeff Liening
**Sr VP:* Robert Duncan
VP: Ajay Kapoor
Prgrm Mgr: David Ellis
**CTO:* Steve Reynolds

D-U-N-S 79-892-9597
IMAGINE COMMUNICATIONS CORP
(*Suby of* HARRIS BROADCAST) ★
101 W Colfax Ave, Denver, CO 80202-5315
Tel (303) 476-4590 *Founded/Ownrshp* 2014
Sales NA *EMP* 1,400
SIC 8731 7373 Computer (hardware) development; Systems software development services; Computer (hardware) development; Systems software development services
CEO: Charles Vogt
**Pr:* Pablo Gargiulo
**CFO:* Bruce Warren
**Founder:* Ron Gutman
**Founder:* Doron Segev
**Chf Mktg O:* Ramnik Kamo
Ofcr: Chuck Gilbert
Rgnl VP: Brian Cotter
Ex VP: Sean Huurman
**Sr VP:* Marc Tayer
**VP:* Brian Bentley
**VP:* Lorenzo Bombelli
**VP:* Mark Davis
VP: Marc Formisano
VP: Mark Jordan
VP: John McNamara
VP: Jamey Munroe
**VP:* Zeev Prokopets
VP: David Rubin
VP: Bob Stankosh

D-U-N-S 18-854-8742 IMP
IMAGINE NATION BOOKS LTD
BOOKS ARE FUN
282 Century Pl Ste 2000, Louisville, CO 80027-1677
Tel (303) 516-3400 *Founded/Ownrshp* 2004
Sales 44.9MM^E^ *EMP* 120
SIC 5942 Book stores
Pr: Ben Kaplan
**Treas:* James Walker
VP: Allan Shook
Rgnl Mgr: Matthew Tanner
Off Mgr: Susan Orourke
CTO: Sharon Blanton
CTO: Timothy Chester
CTO: Alfred Essa
CTO: Christopher Gill
CTO: Gary Ham
CTO: Edward Mahon

D-U-N-S 60-592-8741
IMAGINE ONE TECHNOLOGY & MANAGEMENT LTD
416 Colonial Ave Ste 200, Colonial Beach, VA 22443-2210
Tel (804) 224-1555 *Founded/Ownrshp* 2002
Sales 28.5MM^E^ *EMP* 220

SIC 8711 7371 Engineering services; Custom computer programming services; Engineering services; Custom computer programming services
Pr: Nancie Lumpkins
Pr: James Krout
**Sr VP:* Reynald Bald
VP: Philipp Charles
VP: Jim Fahlsing
Pgrm Dir: Craig Hampson
Snr Mgr: Fred Severson

D-U-N-S 18-750-7660 IMP
IMAGINE PRINT SOLUTIONS INC
1000 Valley Park Dr, Shakopee, MN 55379-1879
Tel (952) 903-4400 *Founded/Ownrshp* 1988
Sales 320.8MM^E^ *EMP* 1,240
Accts Larson Allen Llp Minneapolis
SIC 2759 Promotional printing; Promotional printing
CEO: Robert J Lothenbach
Sr VP: Chris White
VP: Rick Neumann
VP: Renee Scheier
VP: Mary Sheehan
Plng Mgr: Patrick Wilkes
Dir IT: Michael Potter
IT Man: Nick Fiorenza
Software D: Andrew Adams
Software D: Darryl Drozdik
VP Opers: Jim Gustafson

D-U-N-S 83-296-9773
IMAGINE SCHOOL ON BROADWAY
2320 Broadway, Fort Wayne, IN 46807-1104
Tel (260) 458-8311
Sales 3.6MM^E^ *EMP* 336
SIC 8211 Public elementary & secondary schools

D-U-N-S 96-321-6259
IMAGINE SCHOOLS NON-PROFIT INC
1005 N Glebe Rd Ste 610, Arlington, VA 22201-5758
Tel (703) 527-2600 *Founded/Ownrshp* 2004
Sales 93.7MM *EMP* 3,500^E^
SIC 8299 Educational services; Educational services
Pr: Dennis Bakke
**VP:* Eileen Bakke
VP: James McFadden

D-U-N-S 12-030-3438
IMAGINE SCHOOLS OF DELAWARE INC
(*Suby of* IMAGINE SCHOOLS ON BROADWAY) ★
8071 Nw 54th St, Doral, FL 33166-4004
Tel (305) 648-5962 *Founded/Ownrshp* 2004
Sales 112.1M^E^ *EMP* 1,700
SIC 8211 Private combined elementary & secondary school; Private combined elementary & secondary school
Ch: Octavio J Visiedo
**Pr:* Wade Dyke
**CFO:* Javier Montiel

D-U-N-S 14-911-0806
IMAGINE SCHOOLS ON BROADWAY
1005 N Glebe Rd Ste 610, Arlington, VA 22201-5758
Tel (703) 527-2600 *Founded/Ownrshp* 2003
Sales 1.4MM *EMP* 3,600
Accts Berman Hopkins Wright Laham Cp
SIC 8211 Elementary & secondary schools; Elementary & secondary schools
Pr: Dennis W Bakke
CFO: Rob Huey
Off Mgr: Barbara Mecca
Off Admin: Lisa Bukke
Dir IT: Thomas Henderson

D-U-N-S 80-739-0315
IMAGINE SOFTWARE INC
DERIVATIVES.COM
22 Cortlandt St Fl 32, New York, NY 10007-3167
Tel (212) 317-7600 *Founded/Ownrshp* 1993
Sales 22.8MM^E^ *EMP* 80^E^
SIC 7371 Computer software development
CEO: Lance Smith
**Pr:* Steven Harrison
CFO: Cary Dorsi
Ofcr: Yvonne Dahl
VP: Jeff Hayes
VP: Boris Khanales
**VP:* David Miller
VP: Gene Reznik
**VP:* Scott Sherman
VP: Frank Squeri
Mng Dir: Jonathan Richards

D-U-N-S 08-008-0185
IMAGINETICS HOLDINGS LLC
3410 A St Se, Auburn, WA 98002-8807
Tel (253) 735-0156 *Founded/Ownrshp* 2012
Sales 54.4MM^E^ *EMP* 87^E^
SIC 3444 3469 3545 Sheet metalwork; Metal stampings; Machine tool attachments & accessories
CEO: Scott Strong

D-U-N-S 78-111-3477
IMAGINETICS LLC
(*Suby of* IMAGINETICS HOLDINGS LLC) ★
3410 A St Se, Auburn, WA 98002-8807
Tel (253) 735-0156 *Founded/Ownrshp* 2013
Sales 26.5MM^E^ *EMP* 87
SIC 3444 3469 3545 Sheet metalwork; Metal stampings; Machine tool attachments & accessories
CEO: Scott Strong
COO: Patrick Prince
CFO: Robert Mazzacavallo
VP: Michael Honey
DP Exec: Scott Mitchell

IMAGINEU
See DEVELOPMENTAL DISABILITIES CENTER

D-U-N-S 04-773-4467
IMAGING ALLIANCE GROUP LLC
IMAGING PATH
2601 Minnehaha Ave, Minneapolis, MN 55406-1530
Tel (612) 588-9944 *Founded/Ownrshp* 1997
Sales 28.6MM^E^ *EMP* 85
SIC 5044 Copying equipment
CEO: Jim Loffler
CFO: Harold Lederman
**Sr VP:* John Hastings

*VP: Joel Nelson
VP: Pat Sepnieski
*VP: Gary Volbert
IT Man: Paul Rehovsky

IMAGING AND SENSING TECHNOLOGY
See MIRION TECHNOLOGIES (IST) CORP

D-U-N-S 62-164-6710 EXP
IMAGING ASSOCIATES INC
11110 Westlake Dr, Charlotte, NC 28273-3781
Tel (704) 522-8094 Founded/Ownrshp 1991
Sales 27.2MM^E EMP 29
SIC 5047 Medical & hospital equipment
Pr: Michael E Masterman
*VP: Sandra B Masterman
*VP: Sandy Masterman

D-U-N-S 79-143-3568
IMAGING BUSINESS MACHINES LLC
I B M L
2750 Crestwood Blvd, Irondale, AL 35210-1227
Tel (205) 314-1821 Founded/Ownrshp 1992
Sales 44.8MM^E EMP 180
SIC 3579 8711 3577 Canceling machinery, post office; Paper handling machines; Engineering services; Computer peripheral equipment; Optical scanning devices; Canceling machinery, post office; Paper handling machines; Engineering services; Computer peripheral equipment; Optical scanning devices
Pr: Derrick Murphy
CFO: Russell Smith
CFO: T Summersell
VP: Terry Sherwin
Exec: Ben Fell
CTO: Joseph Pizzitola
IT Man: Karen Burnham
Software D: Allen Davis
Netwrk Eng: Barry Moore

THE IMAGING CENTER
See OBSTETRICAL AND GYNECOLOGICAL ASSOCIATES PLLC

D-U-N-S 80-882-8222
IMAGING CENTER OF N CENTRAL INDIANA
2201 W Boulevard, Kokomo, IN 46902-6070
Tel (765) 452-0808 Founded/Ownrshp 1993
Sales 122.1MM EMP 19
Accts Bucheri Mccarty & Metz Llp Ko
SIC 8071 X-ray laboratory, including dental; X-ray laboratory, including dental

D-U-N-S 78-681-1740
IMAGING HEALTHCARE SPECIALISTS LLC
150 W Washington St, San Diego, CA 92103-2005
Tel (619) 295-9729 Founded/Ownrshp 2005
Sales 27.6MM^E EMP 105^E
SIC 8011 Offices & clinics of medical doctors
Pr: Thomas D Cleary
Mktg Dir: Kim Brandt
Doctor: John Lubisich
Diag Rad: David Buckley
Diag Rad: Sloane Chen
Diag Rad: John Doemeny
Diag Rad: Brian Moffit
Diag Rad: Marray Reicher

D-U-N-S 06-470-5866
IMAGING OFFICE SYSTEMS INC
4505 E Park 30 Dr, Columbia City, IN 46725-8869
Tel (260) 248-9696 Founded/Ownrshp 1995
Sales 24.8MM^E EMP 100
SIC 5999 8742 Business machines & equipment; Management information systems consultant
CEO: Paul Black
*Pr: E Brian Kopack
*COO: Gary G Gushard
*Sr VP: Bob Barkley
*VP: John Trimble

IMAGING PATH
See IMAGING ALLIANCE GROUP LLC

IMAGING SYSTEMS
See HORIZONS INC

IMAGING SYSTEMS
See ACCESS PRODUCTS INC

IMAGING TECHNOLOGIES
See AMERICAN REPROGRAPHICS SOUTHEAST LLC

IMAGINIT TECHNOLOGIES
See RAND WORLDWIDE SUBSIDIARY INC

IMAGINIT TECHNOLOGIES
See RAND WORLDWIDE FOREIGN HOLDINGS INC

D-U-N-S 02-160-5191
IMARK GROUP INC
4201 Northview Dr Ste 303, Bowie, MD 20716-2660
Tel (301) 567-8888 Founded/Ownrshp 1996
Sales 58.2MM^E EMP 15^E
SIC 5063 Electrical supplies
Sr VP: Bob Smith

D-U-N-S 00-934-8376 IMP/EXP
IMASEN BUCYRUS TECHNOLOGY INC (OH)
I B-TECH
(Suby of IMASEN ELECTRIC INDUSTRIAL CO., LTD.)
260 Crossroads Blvd, Bucyrus, OH 44820-1363
Tel (419) 563-9590 Founded/Ownrshp 1997
Sales 62.7MM^E EMP 220
SIC 3714 Motor vehicle parts & accessories; Motor vehicle parts & accessories
Pr: Katsumi Ito
*VP: Joe Downing
*VP: Koichi Fukui

D-U-N-S 93-358-8691 IMP/EXP
▲ **IMATION CORP**
1 Imation Way, Oakdale, MN 55128-3414
Tel (651) 704-4000 Founded/Ownrshp 1996
Sales 729.5MM EMP 910^E
Tkr Sym IMN Exch NYS
SIC 3695 3572 Magnetic & optical recording media; Computer software tape & disks: blank, rigid & floppy; Optical disks & tape, blank; Video recording tape, blank; Computer storage devices; Computer tape drives & components; Disk drives, computer; Magnetic storage devices, computer; Magnetic & optical recording media; Computer software tape & disks: blank, rigid & floppy; Optical disks & tape, blank; Video recording tape, blank; Computer storage devices; Computer tape drives & components; Disk drives, computer; Magnetic storage devices, computer
CEO: Robert B Fernander
CFO: Scott J Robinson
Sr VP: Greg J Bosler
Sr VP: Gregory J Bosler
VP: Karen R Beadie
VP: John P Breedlove
VP: Randy J Christoffersen
VP: James C Ellis
VP: Patricia A Hamm
VP: N Kawasaki
VP: Stephen F Moss
*Int Pr: Barry L Kasoff
Board of Directors: Geoff S Barrall, Joseph A Deperio, L White Matthews III, Tracy McKibben, Robert Searing, Alex Spiro, David B Stevens

D-U-N-S 15-972-1794
■ **IMATION ENTERPRISES CORP**
(Suby of IMATION CORP) ★
1 Imation Way, Oakdale, MN 55128-3414
Tel (651) 704-4000 Founded/Ownrshp 1996
Sales 60.4MM^E EMP 1,115
SIC 3695 3845 5112 Magnetic disks & drums; Magnetic tape; Electromedical equipment; Data processing supplies; Magnetic disks & drums; Magnetic tape; Electromedical equipment; Data processing supplies
CEO: Mark E Lucas
CFO: Paul R Zeller
Sr VP: Gregory J Bosler
Sr VP: John L Sullivan
VP: John P Breedlove
VP: Randy J Christofferson
VP: Patricia Hamm
VP: Nobuyoshi Kawasaki
VP: Subodh K Kulkarni
VP: Brian J Plummer
Board of Directors: Lawrence E Eaton, Michael S Fields, William W George, Linda W Hart, Ronald T Lemay, Marvin L Mann, Glen Taylor, Daryl J White

D-U-N-S 12-122-8662 IMP
IMAX CORP
IMAX WORLDWIDE IMPORTS
12502 E 55th St, Tulsa, OK 74146-6225
Tel (918) 665-7715 Founded/Ownrshp 1984
Sales 51.2MM^E EMP 135^E
SIC 5023 Decorative home furnishings & supplies; Decorative home furnishings & supplies
Pr: Al Bulak
CEO: Jiande Chen
*Sr VP: Faye Bulak
Opers Mgr: Clayton Doner

IMAX WORLDWIDE IMPORTS
See IMAX CORP

IMB
See INTERNATIONAL MISSION BOARD OF SOUTHERN BAPTIST CONVENTION

D-U-N-S 07-443-7252 IMP
IMBERT INTERNATIONAL INC
IMBERT LOUIS
7030 N Austin Ave, Niles, IL 60714-4602
Tel (847) 588-3170 Founded/Ownrshp 1978
Sales 29.5MM^E EMP 29
SIC 5084 5085 Industrial machinery & equipment; Industrial supplies
Pr: William S Toth
*CFO: Lisa Acosta
VP: John Grzeskowski
VP: Gary Stern

IMBERT LOUIS
See IMBERT INTERNATIONAL INC

IMBRANDED
See AUTOMOTIVE MEDIA LLC

IMC
See INTERAMERICAN MOTOR CORP

IMC
See INTERNATIONAL MULCH CO INC

IMC
See INDUSTRIAL MOLDING CORP

IMC
See INSULATION MATERIALS CORP

IMC
See ISLANDS MECHANICAL CONTRACTOR INC

IMC CONSTRUCTION
See INTERNATIONAL MANAGEMENT CONSULTANTS INC

IMC FINANCIALS MARKET
See IMC-CHICAGO LLC

D-U-N-S 00-516-8526
IMC GROUP USA HOLDINGS INC
300 Westway Pl, Arlington, TX 76018-1021
Tel (817) 258-3200 Founded/Ownrshp 2000
Sales 87.5MM^E EMP 485
SIC 6719 Investment holding companies, except banks; Investment holding companies, except banks
Pr: Jacob Harbaz
CFO: Reggie Lowder

D-U-N-S 01-743-9894
IMC INC (VA)
11480 Comm Pk Dr, Reston, VA 20191
Tel (703) 871-8700 Founded/Ownrshp 1981
Sales 38.4MM EMP 323^E
SIC 7371 7373 8711 Custom computer programming services; Systems integration services; Engineering services; Custom computer programming services; Systems integration services; Engineering services
Ch Bd: Sudhakar V Shenoy
*Pr: Louis Matrone
*Ex VP: Surresh Shenoy
*Sr VP: John Rita
VP: Raymond Boyle
VP: Atul Mathur
Exec: Matthew Killmeyer
Dir Bus: Gill Maggs
Prgrm Mgr: Tom Green
Prgrm Mgr: Michael Reep
Prgrm Mgr: Quentin Robinson

D-U-N-S 07-943-6294
IMC MANAGER LLC
495 S Grand Ste 2203, Las Vegas, NV 89106
Tel (702) 599-3314 Founded/Ownrshp 2011
Sales 23.0MM^E EMP 200
SIC 6798 Real estate investment trusts; Real estate investment trusts
Treas: Kenneth Landfield
VP: Dana Andrew
VP: James Nail
VP: Jimmy Palmer
Dir Sec: Kempen Olivier
Secur Mgr: Homer Haithcock
Secur Mgr: Virginia Ramos
Advt Dir: John Emerick

D-U-N-S 19-826-6277
IMC-CHICAGO LLC
IMC FINANCIALS MARKET
233 S Wacker Dr Ste 4300, Chicago, IL 60606-6377
Tel (312) 244-3300 Founded/Ownrshp 2000
Sales 139.7MM^E EMP 131
SIC 6231 Stock exchanges; Stock exchanges
Mng Dir: Emir Al-Rawi
*Mng Dir: Robin Van Boxsel
CTO: Henk Kamphuis
Software D: Michael Hansen

D-U-N-S 83-270-2976 IMP/EXP
IMC-METALSAMERICA LLC
(Suby of PMR) ★
135 Old Boiling Sprng Rd, Shelby, NC 28152-0648
Tel (704) 482-8200 Founded/Ownrshp 2009
Sales 125.0MM EMP 75
SIC 3331 Primary copper; Primary copper smelter products; Bars (primary), copper; Slabs (primary), copper; Primary copper; Primary copper smelter products; Bars (primary), copper; Slabs (primary), copper
Pr: Bernard C Shilberg

IMC2 SQUARED
See INTERNET UNIVERSITY INC

D-U-N-S 96-398-2327
IMCA GROUP INC
PROGRESSION ADVANCE PLG GROUP
1 E Uwchlan Ave Ste 411, Exton, PA 19341-1282
Tel (610) 594-4320 Founded/Ownrshp 1995
Sales 40.0MM EMP 5
SIC 7389 8742 Financial services; Marketing consulting services; Financial services; Marketing consulting services
Pr: Edward K Miller

IMCB
See INTERMOUNTAIN COMMUNITY BANCORP

IMCENTRIC
See VENAFI INC

IMCG
See INTERMODAL CARTAGE CO INC

D-U-N-S 13-134-5761 IMP/EXP
■ **IMCLONE SYSTEMS LLC**
(Suby of ELI LILLY AND CO) ★
440 Us Highway 22, Bridgewater, NJ 08807-2477
Tel (908) 541-8000 Founded/Ownrshp 2008
Sales 225.3MM^E EMP 1,128
SIC 2836 2834 Biological products, except diagnostic; Pharmaceutical preparations; Biological products, except diagnostic; Pharmaceutical preparations
CEO: John H Johnson
*Ch Bd: Carl C Icahn
CFO: Ana I Stancc
CFO: Harlan W Mdcoo
*CFO: Kenneth J Zuerblis
Bd of Dir: Ronald Martell
Bd of Dir: Larry Witte
*Sr VP: Richard Crowley
Sr VP: Ronald A Mrtell
Sr VP: Sjoseph Tarnowski
VP: Benjamin Anderson
VP: Michael Barry
VP: Paul A Goldstein
*VP: Gregory T Mayes
VP: Dorit Moell
VP: Ruth Schulz
Assoc Dir: Robert Morrison
Assoc Dir: Scott Stachowski
Assoc Dir: Bill Strong

IMCO
See INTERNATIONAL MUFFLER CO

D-U-N-S 09-217-7534
IMCO CARBIDE TOOL INC
TOLEDO CUTTING TOOLS
28170 Cedar Park Blvd, Perrysburg, OH 43551-4872
Tel (419) 661-6313 Founded/Ownrshp 1983
Sales 28.4MM^E EMP 90
SIC 3545 5084 Machine tool accessories; Tools & accessories for machine tools; Machine tools & accessories
Ch Bd: Perry L Osburn
*VP: Matthew S Osburn
Sales Asso: Tammy Deselms

D-U-N-S 08-993-6686 EXP
IMCO GENERAL CONSTRUCTION INC (WA)
2116 Buchanan Loop, Ferndale, WA 98248-9801
Tel (360) 671-3936 Founded/Ownrshp 1978
Sales 114.7MM^E EMP 180^E
SIC 1541 1629 1542 Waste water & sewage treatment plant construction; Nonresidential construction; Industrial buildings, new construction; Industrial buildings, new construction; Waste water & sewage treatment plant construction; Nonresidential construction
Ch: Frank Imhof
*Treas: Tyler Kimberley
*VP: Courtney Imhof
*VP: Patti Imhof
IT Man: Kurt Rutgers
Sfty Mgr: Lisa Young
Mktg Dir: Ashley Kimberley
Snr PM: C J Handforth
Snr PM: Mark Rocha

D-U-N-S 83-110-0037 IMP
IMCO RECYCLING OF OHIO LLC
(Suby of ALERIS INTERNATIONAL INC) ★
7335 Newport Rd Se, Uhrichsville, OH 44683-6368
Tel (740) 922-2373 Founded/Ownrshp 2010
Sales 24.2MM^E EMP 164
SIC 3341 4953 Aluminum smelting & refining (secondary); Recycling, waste materials; Aluminum smelting & refining (secondary); Recycling, waste materials
Pr: Denis W Ray
*VP: Robert R Holian

IMCO SUPPLY
See ILLINOIS METER INC

IMCOPEX
See FBA HOLDING INC

IMCOR
See INTERSTATE MECHANICAL CORP

IMCTV
See INTER MOUNTAIN CABLE INC

D-U-N-S 80-741-9051
IMDS HOLDINGS CORP
MEDICINE LODGE HOLDINGS
867 W 400 N, Logan, UT 84321-3798
Tel (435) 753-7675 Founded/Ownrshp 2012
Sales 39.3MM^E EMP 241
SIC 3599 3549 3545 3544 3542 Personal holding companies, except banks; Machine & other job shop work; Metalworking machinery; Machine tool accessories; Special dies, tools, jigs & fixtures; Machine tools, metal forming type
Pr: T Wade Fallin
*Ch Bd: Harold Linville
*Pr: Brady R Shirley

IME
See INTERMOUNTAIN ELECTRIC INC

IMEC
See INTERNATIONAL MEDICAL EQUIPMENT COLLABORATIVE

D-U-N-S 08-675-8356
IMECO INC
1590 Dutch Rd, Dixon, IL 61021-8624
Tel (815) 288-7771 Founded/Ownrshp 1992
Sales 22.2MM^E EMP 205
SIC 5013 Motor vehicle supplies & new parts

D-U-N-S 13-658-2108
IMEDX INC
6 Concourse Pkwy Ste 1475, Atlanta, GA 30328-5367
Tel (404) 418-0096 Founded/Ownrshp 2009
Sales 54.3MM^E EMP 351
SIC 7371 7372 7373 7374 7379 7338 Custom computer programming services; Prepackaged software; Computer integrated systems design; Calculating service (computer); Computer related consulting services; Secretarial & court reporting; Custom computer programming services; Prepackaged software; Computer integrated systems design; Calculating service (computer); Computer related consulting services; Secretarial & court reporting
CEO: Christopher Foley
*Pr: Venkat Sharma
CFO: Bob Attanasio
*CFO: Robert Attanasio
*Ofcr: Michael Kimball
VP: Earl Flannery
*VP: Chris Lally
*VP: Brad Runyon
CTO: Patti Clements
Mktg Mgr: Herini Betha
Manager: Pat Mahoney

D-U-N-S 96-252-6799 IMP/EXP
IMERYS CARBONATES LLC
(Suby of IMERYS USA INC) ★
1301 Gene Stewart Blvd, Sylacauga, AL 35150
Tel (256) 249-4901 Founded/Ownrshp 1999
Sales 25.7MM^E EMP 300^E
SIC 2819 Calcium compounds & salts, inorganic

D-U-N-S 79-501-0792 IMP/EXP
IMERYS FILTRATION MINERALS INC
(Suby of IMERYS USA INC) ★
1732 N 1st St Ste 450, San Jose, CA 95112-4579
Tel (800) 893-4445 Founded/Ownrshp 2005
Sales 691.6MM^E EMP 1,499
SIC 1499 Diatomaceous earth mining; Diatomaceous earth mining
CEO: Douglas A Smith
*Pr: John Oskan
CFO: Leslie Zimmer
*Treas: Fred Weber
*V Ch Bd: Paul Woodberry
Exec: Kim Rivera
Genl Mgr: George Christoferson
Mktg Dir: Tom Sulpizio

D-U-N-S 83-496-6368 IMP/EXP
IMERYS FUSED MINERALS GREENEVILLE INC
(Suby of IMERYS)
109 Coile St, Greeneville, TN 37745-5830
Tel (423) 787-0333 Founded/Ownrshp 2008
Sales 25.9MM^E EMP 60

SIC 3339 Lead & zinc
CFO: Phil Matthews
**VP:* Sam Akers
QI Cn Mgr: Rick Hawk

D-U-N-S 78-056-5636 EXP
IMERYS MINERALS CALIFORNIA INC
(*Suby of* IMERYS FILTRATION MINERALS INC) ★
2500 San Miguelito Rd, Lompoc, CA 93436-9743
Tel (805) 736-1221 *Founded/Ownrshp* 1991
Sales 588.2MM^E *EMP* 1,145
SIC 1499 3295 Diatomaceous earth mining; Minerals, ground or treated; Diatomaceous earth mining; Minerals, ground or treated
Pr: Douglas A Smith
**CEO:* John Oskam
**CFO:* John Leichty
VP: Jack Murray
VP: Ken Schweigert
VP: Bruno Van Herpen
VP: Charles Vogelsang
MIS Dir: Bill Kinman

D-U-N-S 00-954-1780 EXP
IMERYS PERLITE USA INC
HARBORLITE
(*Suby of* IMERYS FILTRATION MINERALS INC) ★
1732 N 1st St Ste 450, San Jose, CA 95112-4579
Tel (919) 562-0031 *Founded/Ownrshp* 1992
Sales 100.3MM^E *EMP* 173
SIC 1499 Perlite mining; Perlite mining
CFO: John Liechty
Off Mgr: Paul Sowards

D-U-N-S 79-052-2791 EXP
IMERYS TALC AMERICA INC
(*Suby of* IMERYS)
1732 N 1st St Ste 450, San Jose, CA 95112-4579
Tel (805) 562-0260 *Founded/Ownrshp* 1992
Sales 155.2MM^E *EMP* 562^E
SIC 3295 1499 Talc, ground or otherwise treated; Talc mining; Talc, ground or otherwise treated; Talc mining
Pr: Brian Hanrahan

D-U-N-S 06-149-0140 IMP/EXP
IMERYS USA INC (DE)
(*Suby of* IMERYS)
100 Mansell Ct E Ste 300, Roswell, GA 30076-4860
Tel (770) 645-3300 *Founded/Ownrshp* 1979, 1999
Sales 1.0MMM^E *EMP* 4,069
SIC 1455 1459 1429 1422 2819 Kaolin mining; Clays (common) quarrying; Marble, crushed & broken-quarrying; Lime rock, ground; Calcium carbide; Kaolin mining; Clays (common) quarrying; Marble, crushed & broken-quarrying; Lime rock, ground; Calcium carbide
Pr: Gerard Buffiere
Pr: Richard Hatcher
Treas: Jeffrey C Hicks
Ofcr: Merilee Long
Ex VP: Richard D Ryan
Ex VP: Thierry Salmona
VP: Antoinette Forrester
VP: Phil Jones
VP: Mikko Likitalo
VP: Daniel Moncino
Exec: Anna Kucherenko
Exec: Joan Malit
Dir Bus: Tim Chen

IMET
See INDUSTRIAL METALS RECYCLING CORP

IMETCO
See INNOVATIVE METALS CO INC

D-U-N-S 80-879-5348 IMP
IMEX AMERICA CORP
(*Suby of* IMEX CO.,LTD.)
3560 Fairview Indus Dr Se, Salem, OR 97302-1154
Tel (503) 391-1500 *Founded/Ownrshp* 1993
Sales 50.0MM *EMP* 33
SIC 5112 Photocopying supplies
Pr: Yuithiro Kitaoka
**Ch Bd:* Akira Kitaoka

D-U-N-S 07-869-8931
IMEX GLOBAL SOLUTIONS HOLDINGS LLC
(*Suby of* LION EQUITY HOLDINGS LLC) ★
1501 Morse Ave, Elk Grove Village, IL 60007-5723
Tel (847) 640-7776 *Founded/Ownrshp* 2013
Sales 41.8MM^E *EMP* 205^E
SIC 6719 Investment holding companies, except banks; Investment holding companies, except banks
CEO: Brian Fleisher

D-U-N-S 07-872-1272
IMEX GLOBAL SOLUTIONS LLC
(*Suby of* IMEX GLOBAL SOLUTIONS HOLDINGS LLC) ★
400 Comm Blvd Ste A2, Carlstadt, NJ 07072
Tel (973) 776-7555 *Founded/Ownrshp* 2012, 2013
Sales 30.6MM^E *EMP* 200^E
SIC 7389 Mailing & messenger services; Mailing & messenger services
VP: Carlos Barbosa

IMG
See INTEGRATED MANUFACTURING GROUP LLC

D-U-N-S 19-418-8645
IMG
DEMO DELUXE
4560 Dorinda Rd, Yorba Linda, CA 92887-1800
Tel (714) 974-1700 *Founded/Ownrshp* 1983
Sales 76.8MM^E *EMP* 4,000
SIC 7389 Demonstration service; Demonstration service
Pr: Jim Smith
IT Man: Pat Stamatelatos

D-U-N-S 96-663-0019 IMP
IMG ACADEMY LLC
5500 34th St W, Bradenton, FL 34210-3506
Tel (941) 755-1000 *Founded/Ownrshp* 2012
Sales 45.4MM^E *EMP* 700
SIC 7999 Sports instruction, schools & camps; Sports instruction, schools & camps
COO: Geoffrey Healy
Sr VP: Gary Swain
VP: Neil McGinness
Dir Bus: Jay Kim
Genl Mgr: Rick Barakat
HC Dir: Sabra Pacheco

D-U-N-S 14-605-6358
IMG ARTISTS LLC
7 W 54th St, New York, NY 10019-3433
Tel (212) 994-3500 *Founded/Ownrshp* 2003
Sales 32.1MM^E *EMP* 285
SIC 7389 Artists' agents & brokers; Artists' agents & brokers
COO: Lorna Aizlewood
CFO: Susie Holliday
Sr VP: Ramona Jaroff
Sr VP: David Lai
VP: Wray Armstrong
VP: Gilles Demonet
VP: Matthew Horner
VP: Anthony Howard
VP: John Martyn
VP: Jenny Palmer
VP: Dean Schultz
VP: Manfred Seipt
VP: Elizabeth Sobol
VP: Alec Treuhaft
VP: Jeffrey Vanderveen
VP: Maurice Whitaker
Exec: Parveen Sandhu

D-U-N-S 96-525-4654
IMG COLLEGE LLC
(*Suby of* INTERNATIONAL MERCHANDISING) ★
540 N Trade St, Winston Salem, NC 27101-2915
Tel (336) 831-0748 *Founded/Ownrshp* 2014
Sales 38.7MM^E *EMP* 150^E
SIC 8742 Marketing consulting services
Pr: Ben C Sutton Jr
**VP:* Rick Barakat
Genl Mgr: Matt Reynolds

D-U-N-S 80-058-1527
IMG ENTERPRISES INC
CHERRY LAKE TREE FARM
7836 Cherry Lake Rd, Groveland, FL 34736-9007
Tel (352) 429-2171 *Founded/Ownrshp* 1982
Sales 50.6MM^E *EMP* 450^E
SIC 0174 0181 Grapefruit grove; Orange grove; Ornamental nursery products; Grapefruit grove; Orange grove; Ornamental nursery products
CEO: Michel Sallin
**Treas:* Melanie S Ressler
VP: Timothee Sallin
Off Admin: Novella Crosby
Prd Mgr: Austin Spivey
Mktg Mgr: Chloe Gentry
Sales Asso: Hope Beck
Sales Asso: Jason Gibson
Sales Asso: Caren Humphries

D-U-N-S 61-022-9200 IMP/EXP
IMG HOLDINGS INC
DANA CLASSIC FRAGRANCES
400 Lyster Ave, Saddle Brook, NJ 07663-5910
Tel (201) 881-8550 *Founded/Ownrshp* 2003
Sales 46.5MM *EMP* 67
Accts Mc Gladrey & Pullen Llp Fort
SIC 5122 Perfumes; Cosmetics; Perfumes; Cosmetics
Pr: Isaac Florens Cohen
**COO:* Gina Zamarelli
**Ex VP:* Jeffrey B McGovern
**CIO:* Scott Gruskin

IMG MEDIA
See TRANSWORLD INTERNATIONAL INC

D-U-N-S 96-439-3743
IMH FINANCIAL CORP
7001 N Scottsdale Rd # 2050, Paradise Valley, AZ 85253-3698
Tel (480) 840-8400 *Founded/Ownrshp* 2009
Sales NA *EMP* 15
Accts Bdo Usa Llp Phoenix Arizona
SIC 6162 Mortgage bankers & correspondents; Mortgage bankers & correspondents
CEO: William Meris
Pr: Dawn Douglass
**COO:* Steven Derak
**CFO:* Lisa Jack
**Ex VP:* Jonathan Brohard
VP: Tim Keenan
VP: Ryan Muranaka

IMH SHELDON CLINIC
See IROQUOIS MEMORIAL HOSPITAL

D-U-N-S 18-877-0416 IMP/EXP
IMI AMERICAS INC
(*Suby of* IMI PLC)
5400 S Delaware St, Littleton, CO 80120-1663
Tel (763) 488-5400 *Founded/Ownrshp* 1981
Sales 608.5MM^E *EMP* 4,000
SIC 2542 Partitions & fixtures, except wood; Partitions & fixtures, except wood
Pr: Robert Guerra
**Pr:* Greg Croydon
**Treas:* Jim Etter
VP: Pat Burgoyne
Off Mgr: Pam Brown

IMI PRECISION ENGINEERING
See NORGREN INC

D-U-N-S 00-638-1537
IMI SOUTH LLC
(*Suby of* I M I) ★
1440 Selinda Ave, Louisville, KY 40213-1954
Tel (502) 456-6930 *Founded/Ownrshp* 2009
Sales 82.4MM^E *EMP* 510
SIC 3273 Ready-mixed concrete; Ready-mixed concrete

IMIC HOTELS
See INTERSTATE MANAGEMENT & INVESTMENT CORP

D-U-N-S 02-433-0821
IMLAY CITY COMMUNITY SCHOOLS
634 W Borland Rd, Imlay City, MI 48444-1416
Tel (810) 724-9861 *Founded/Ownrshp* 1873
Sales 21.1MM *EMP* 269
Accts Lewis & Knopf Cpas Pc Flint
SIC 8211 Public elementary & secondary schools; Public elementary & secondary schools
Prin: Monica Bickel
Psych: Jim Owen

D-U-N-S 60-522-0672
IMLAY CITY FORD INC
LINCOLN MERCURY
1788 S Cedar St, Imlay City, MI 48444-9779
Tel (810) 724-5900 *Founded/Ownrshp* 1989
Sales 22.6MM^E *EMP* 51
SIC 5511 Automobiles, new & used; Vans, new & used; Pickups, new & used
Pr: Paul A Lafontaine
Sls Mgr: Dustin Thammavongsa

D-U-N-S 01-403-5752
IMLERS POULTRY LP (PA)
IMLERS POULTRY TRANSPORTATION
1887 Route 764, Duncansville, PA 16635-7952
Tel (814) 943-5563 *Founded/Ownrshp* 1903, 1968
Sales 100.0MM *EMP* 170
SIC 5144 5147 5141 5142 Poultry: live, dressed or frozen (unpackaged); Meats & meat products; Groceries, general line; Packaged frozen goods; Poultry: live, dressed or frozen (unpackaged); Meats & meat products; Groceries, general line; Packaged frozen goods
CFO: Melissa Lovrich
**Pt:* Brian Imler
**Pt:* Fred Imler Jr
Exec: Frank Dombroski
Dir IT: Chris Pechtold
IT Man: Bob Williams
Mktg Dir: Clyde Monahan
Sls Mgr: Jody Clemenson
Sales Asso: Dave Dolinger

IMLERS POULTRY TRANSPORTATION
See IMLERS POULTRY LP

D-U-N-S 08-188-1633
IMMACULATA UNIVERSITY
1145 King Rd, Immaculata, PA 19345-9903
Tel (610) 647-4400 *Founded/Ownrshp* 1920
Sales 54.4MM *EMP* 225
SIC 8221

IMMACULATE CONCEPTION CONVENT
See SISTERS OF ST FRANCIS

D-U-N-S 08-569-5468
IMMACULATE MARY HOME
2990 Holme Ave, Philadelphia, PA 19136-1830
Tel (215) 335-2100 *Founded/Ownrshp* 1976
Sales 30.5MM *EMP* 350
SIC 8051 Convalescent home with continuous nursing care; Convalescent home with continuous nursing care
Nrsg Dir: Kim Griffies

D-U-N-S 03-092-9744
IMMANUEL
1044 N 115th St Ste 500, Omaha, NE 68154-4410
Tel (402) 829-2900 *Founded/Ownrshp* 1990
Sales 25.4MM^E *EMP* 460
SIC 8661 Religious organizations; Religious organizations
CEO: Eric Gurley
Pr: Tom Garvey
**CFO:* Dan Friedlund
Ex Dir: Jill Wheeler

IMMANUEL CAMPUS OF CARE
See IMMANUEL CARING MINISTRIES INC

D-U-N-S 05-930-3045
IMMANUEL CARING MINISTRIES INC
IMMANUEL CAMPUS OF CARE
11301 N 99th Ave, Peoria, AZ 85345-5466
Tel (623) 977-8373 *Founded/Ownrshp* 1998
Sales 12.7MM *EMP* 350
Accts Beachfleischman Pc Tucson Az
SIC 8069 Specialty hospitals, except psychiatric; Specialty hospitals, except psychiatric
Pr: Jim Shaner
Ex Dir: Dean Kidder
HC Dir: Victoria Medina

D-U-N-S 04-164-1588
IMMANUEL RETIREMENT COMMUNITIES
6757 Newport Ave Ste 200, Omaha, NE 68152-2191
Tel (402) 829-2912 *Founded/Ownrshp* 2009
Sales 27.2MM *EMP* 1^E
Accts Seim Johnson Llp Omaha Ne
SIC 8661 Religious organizations; Religious organizations
Prin: John Hewitt
VP: Andrew Fisher
VP: Peggy Hall
VP: Roxann Meyer

D-U-N-S 15-072-3125 IMP
IMMEDIA INC
(*Suby of* LIBERTY DIVERSIFIED INTERNATIONAL INC) ★
3311 Broadway St Ne Ste A, Minneapolis, MN 55413-1891
Tel (612) 524-3400 *Founded/Ownrshp* 2011
Sales 31.2MM^E *EMP* 195
SIC 2396 7336 Screen printing on fabric articles; Commercial art & graphic design; Screen printing on fabric articles; Commercial art & graphic design
Ch Bd: Michael Fiterman
Pr: Mike Redding
**COO:* Daniel Zdon
**CFO:* Byron Wieberdink
**Ex VP:* David Lenzen
**VP:* Ronda Bayer
**VP:* Michael Snowball
Genl Mgr: Alla Johnson
Genl Mgr: Justin Raney

IMMEDIATE CARE CENTER
See GREAT FALLS CLINIC REALTY LLP

D-U-N-S 01-855-7605
■ **IMMEDIATE CLINIC HEALTHCARE INC**
(*Suby of* ENSIGN GROUP INC) ★
27101 Puerta Real Ste 450, Mission Viejo, CA 92691-8566
Tel (949) 487-9500 *Founded/Ownrshp* 2012
Sales 358.9M^E *EMP* 519^E
SIC 8082 Home health care services
Pr: Mike Dalton
Treas: Soon Burnam

D-U-N-S 19-635-6786
IMMEDIATE MAILING SERVICES INC
IMS
245 Commerce Blvd, Liverpool, NY 13088-4541
Tel (315) 437-4189 *Founded/Ownrshp* 1986
Sales 20.9MM^E *EMP* 150
SIC 7331 Mailing service; Mailing service
Ch Bd: W Lee Vanderpool Jr
**CEO:* John Mashia Jr
Sr VP: Chris Buell
Mktg Mgr: Randy Kahn
Manager: Mark Vanderpool

D-U-N-S 80-009-0300
IMMEDIENT CORP
88 Centennial Ave, Piscataway, NJ 08854-3906
Tel (732) 980-1800 *Founded/Ownrshp* 2005
Sales 27.6MM^E *EMP* 480
SIC 7379 Computer related consulting services; Computer related consulting services
CEO: Arthur Byrd
**CFO:* Julia K Kellberg
VP: Anthony Volpi
Prin: Christopher Ambrose
Prin: Kit Ambrose
Prin: Richard Dreher
Mng Dir: Mark Corgan
CIO: Ian Thorne
CTO: Tim Harris
CTO: Robert Schwartz
IT Man: Anton Korenev

D-U-N-S 82-584-5027
▲ **IMMERSION CORP**
50 Rio Robles, San Jose, CA 95134-1806 ★
Tel (408) 467-1900 *Founded/Ownrshp* 1993
Sales 52.9MM *EMP* 141
Tkr Sym IMMR *Exch* NGS
SIC 3577 7371 Computer peripheral equipment; Computer software development & applications; Computer peripheral equipment; Computer software development & applications
CEO: Victor Viegas
**Ch Bd:* Carl Schlachte
CFO: Paul Norris
Sr VP: Dennis Sheehan
VP: Daniel Brongiel
VP: Jason Patton
VP: Richard Stacey
VP: Mahesh Sundaram
VP: Chris Ulrich
VP: Craig Vachon
Dir Bus: Michael Blicher
Board of Directors: David Habiger, Jack Saltich, David Sugishita, John Veschi

IMMI
See INDIANA MILLS & MANUFACTURING INC

D-U-N-S 15-980-3972
■ **IMMIXGROUP INC**
(*Suby of* ARROW ELECTRONICS INC) ★
8444 Westpark Dr Ste 200, Mc Lean, VA 22102-5112
Tel (703) 752-0610 *Founded/Ownrshp* 2015
Sales 416.3MM^E *EMP* 201^E
SIC 7371 7379 Computers, peripherals & software; Custom computer programming services; Computer hardware requirements analysis
Pr: Art Richer
CFO: Noel N Samuel
Ofcr: Don Logan Jr
Ex VP: Stephen Charles
VP: Bob Laclede
VP: Skip Liesegang
VP: Phill Magaro
Mng Dir: Steve Michael
VP Opers: William Bottoms
VP Mktg: Lou Brossman
VP Sls: Craig Harper
Board of Directors: Nelson Carbonell, Thomas B Newell

D-U-N-S 09-869-2374
■ **IMMIXTECHNOLOGY INC**
(*Suby of* IMMIXGROUP INC) ★
8444 Westpark Dr Ste 200, Mc Lean, VA 22102-5112
Tel (703) 752-0610 *Founded/Ownrshp* 1997
Sales 221.8MM^E *EMP* 201
SIC 5045 Computers, peripherals & software; Computers, peripherals & software
CEO: Art Richer
**CFO:* Noel Samuel
**Ex VP:* Steve Charles
**VP:* Bill Bottoms
**VP:* Skip Liesegang
**VP:* Phill Magaro
VP Mktg: Lou A Brossman

D-U-N-S 60-603-4197
■ **IMMUCOR GTI DIAGNOSTICS INC**
(*Suby of* GEN-PROBE INC) ★
20925 Crossroads Cir, Waukesha, WI 53186-4054
Tel (262) 754-1000 *Founded/Ownrshp* 2010
Sales 32.0MM^E *EMP* 100
SIC 2835 In vitro diagnostics; In vitro diagnostics
Pr: Jim Tidey
Ex VP: Gian Visentin
Mfg Dir: Marilyn Clarke
Board of Directors: Tina Bethhauser

D-U-N-S 06-144-6282 IMP/EXP
IMMUCOR INC
(*Suby of* IVD INTERMEDIATE HOLDINGS B INC) ★
3130 Gateway Dr, Peachtree Corners, GA 30071-1189
Tel (770) 441-2051 *Founded/Ownrshp* 2011

Sales 389.3MM *EMP* 1,090^E
Accts Grant Thornton Llp Atlanta G
SIC 2835 In vitro & in vivo diagnostic substances; Blood derivative diagnostic agents; In vitro diagnostics; In vivo diagnostics; In vitro & in vivo diagnostic substances; Blood derivative diagnostic agents; In vitro diagnostics; In vivo diagnostics
Pr: Jeffrey R Binder
CFO: R Deible
CFO: Dominique Petitgenet
CFO: Dominique Petitgent
VP: Michele Howard
VP: Michael Poynter
VP: Daniel L Ruckman
VP: Hiroshi Uchida
VP: Scott Webber
Exec: Wayne Guthrie
Telecom Ex: Connie Vinson
Board of Directors: Jeffrey K Rhodes, Todd B Sisitsky

D-U-N-S 05-970-9394
IMMUNE DISEASE INSTITUTE INC
3 Blackfan Cir Fl 3, Boston, MA 02115-5713
Tel (617) 713-8000 *Founded/Ownrshp* 1953
Sales 29.9MM *EMP* 275
SIC 8071

D-U-N-S 02-813-4799
■ IMMUNEX CORP
(*Suby of* AMGEN INC) ★
51 University St, Seattle, WA 98101-3614
Tel (206) 551-5169 *Founded/Ownrshp* 2002
Sales 91.2MM^E *EMP* 700
SIC 2834 8731 2836 Pharmaceutical preparations; Drugs affecting parasitic & infective diseases; Biotechnical research, commercial; Biological products, except diagnostic; Pharmaceutical preparations; Drugs affecting parasitic & infective diseases; Biotechnical research, commercial; Biological products, except diagnostic
Pr: Roger Pearlmutter
Pr: Michael Mumford
Pr: Douglas E Williams
COO: Bruce Phillips
COO: Peggy V Phillips
CFO: Michael Aguir
Sr Cor Off: Scott Bailey
Ex VP: Gail Kerber
VP: Valoree E Dowll
VP: Steven Gillis
VP: David A Mann
VP: Kendall Mohler
**VP:* Steve M Odre
VP: D Sassenfeld
Assoc Dir: Douglas Hostler

D-U-N-S 01-199-1874
▲ IMMUNOGEN INC (MA)
830 Winter St Ste 6, Waltham, MA 02451-1477
Tel (781) 895-0600 *Founded/Ownrshp* 1981
Sales 85.5MM *EMP* 317^E
Accts Ernst & Young Llp Boston Mas
Tkr Sym IMGN *Exch* NGS
SIC 2834 Pharmaceutical preparations; Pharmaceutical preparations
Pr: Daniel M Junius
**Ch Bd:* Stephen McCluski
CFO: David B Johnston
Ex VP: Richard J Gregory
Ex VP: John M Lambert
Ex VP: Charles Morris
Sr VP: Sandra E Poole
VP: Godfrey Amphlett
VP: Craig Barrows
VP Bus Dev: Peter Williams
CTO: Susan Sullivan
Board of Directors: Mark Goldberg, Dean Mitchell, Nicole Onetto, Kristine Peterson, Howard H Pien, Joseph J Villafranca, Richard J Wallace

D-U-N-S 07-952-3506
IMMUNOTEC RESEARCH INC
5895 Rickenbacker Rd, Commerce, CA 90040-3027
Tel (450) 424-9992 *Founded/Ownrshp* 2003
Sales 54.8MM^E *EMP* 130
SIC 5963 Direct sales, telemarketing; Direct sales, telemarketing
CEO: Charles L Orr
**COO:* Robert Felton
**VP:* John Molson
**VP:* Patrick Montpetit
**VP:* Gabriela Moreno

D-U-N-S 00-122-5275 IMP
■ IMO INDUSTRIES INC
(*Suby of* COLFAX CORP) ★
10571 Telg Rd Ste 201, Glen Allen, VA 23059
Tel (804) 560-4070 *Founded/Ownrshp* 1997, 1998
Sales 104.7MM^E *EMP* 479^E
SIC 3561 3714 3829 Pumps & pumping equipment; Motor vehicle parts & accessories; Motor vehicle transmissions, drive assemblies & parts; Aircraft & motor vehicle measurement equipment; Pressure transducers; Pumps & pumping equipment; Motor vehicle parts & accessories; Motor vehicle transmissions, drive assemblies & parts; Aircraft & motor vehicle measurement equipment; Pressure transducers
Pr: Brannan Charles Scott
**VP:* Lehman Mark Paul

IMO PUMP
See COLFAX PUMP GROUP

IMOBILE
See AWI USA LLC

D-U-N-S 96-784-5467
IMOBILE LLC
206 Terminal Dr, Plainview, NY 11803-2312
Tel (516) 433-9300 *Founded/Ownrshp* 2006
Sales 57.1MM^E *EMP* 5,000^E
SIC 5999 Mobile telephones & equipment; Mobile telephones & equipment
CEO: Sarabjit Lamba
Pr: Chetan Sharma
Sr VP: Ravi Bansal
VP: Jim Radack

D-U-N-S 80-943-2391
IMOBILE OF USA LLC
(*Suby of* IMOBILE LLC) ★
207 Terminal Dr, Plainview, NY 11803-2301
Tel (516) 813-9593 *Founded/Ownrshp* 2008
Sales 1.1MM^E *EMP* 350^E
SIC 5999 Mobile telephones & equipment
CEO: Sarabjit Lamba
Pr: Chetan Sharma

D-U-N-S 79-102-8983
IMON COMMUNICATIONS LLC
625 1st St Se Ste 250, Cedar Rapids, IA 52401-2032
Tel (319) 298-6484 *Founded/Ownrshp* 2006
Sales 22.3MM *EMP* 86
Accts Mcgladrey Llp Cedar Rapids
SIC 4813 4841 Communications specialization; ; Cable television services
CEO: Patrice Carroll
Netwrk Eng: Tony Bennett

D-U-N-S 08-829-7150
IMORTGAGE.COM INC
4800 N Scottsdale Rd # 3800, Scottsdale, AZ 85251-7618
Tel (480) 627-0100 *Founded/Ownrshp* 1999
Sales NA *EMP* 55
SIC 6163 Mortgage brokers arranging for loans, using money of others
CEO: Dan Hanson
Ofcr: Christal Allemand
Ex VP: Darien Evans
Ex VP: Dan Hanson
Sr VP: Dan Pena
Brnch Mgr: Sue Barry
Brnch Mgr: Kurt Baugher
Brnch Mgr: Maria Bauman
Brnch Mgr: Jannine Bielesch
Brnch Mgr: Sandy Boatwright
Brnch Mgr: Rick Brown

IMO'S COUNTRY STORE
See FRONK OIL CO INC

IMP
See INTERNATIONAL MARINE PRODUCTS INC

IMP
See INTERNATIONAL MASTERS PUBLISHERS INC

IMPA
See INDIANA MUNICIPAL POWER AGENCY

D-U-N-S 16-001-1516
■ IMPAC GROUP INC
(*Suby of* WESTROCK MWV LLC) ★
1950 N Ruby St, Melrose Park, IL 60160-1110
Tel (708) 344-9100 *Founded/Ownrshp* 2002
Sales 78.3MM^E *EMP* 1,526
SIC 2657 Folding paperboard boxes; Folding paperboard boxes
Pr: Richard Block

D-U-N-S 02-595-2958
IMPAC LOGISTIC SERVICES LLC
ADVANCED SHIPG & CONSOLIDATION
1 American Way Ste 1, Secaucus, NJ 07094-2421
Tel (201) 617-7777 *Founded/Ownrshp* 2001
Sales 15.9MM^E *EMP* 450
SIC 4222 8741 4225 Warehousing, cold storage or refrigerated; Management services; General warehousing & storage; Warehousing, cold storage or refrigerated; Management services; General warehousing & storage
Mng Dir: Janya Thana-Athiporn
Genl Mgr: Tommy Lui

D-U-N-S 61-818-9443
IMPAC MEDICAL SYSTEMS INC
(*Suby of* ELEKTA AB (PUBL))
100 Mathilda Pl Fl 5, Sunnyvale, CA 94086-6017
Tel (408) 830-8000 *Founded/Ownrshp* 2005
Sales 51.8MM^E *EMP* 430
SIC 7372 7373 Business oriented computer software; Computer integrated systems design; Business oriented computer software; Computer integrated systems design
Pr: James P Hoey
**Ex VP:* David A Auerbach
**Ex VP:* Joseph K Jachinowski
VP: Scott Soehl
Snr Sftwr: Rhonda Ludwico
Snr Sftwr: John Weston
Snr Ntwrk: Jason McCurry
Web Dev: Art Woods
Software D: Sanjay Bari
Software D: Derek Lane
Sftwr Eng: Carla Frazior

D-U-N-S 96-347-7778
■ IMPAC MORTGAGE CORP
EXCEL MORTGAGE SERVICING, INC.
(*Suby of* IMPAC MORTGAGE HOLDINGS INC) ★
19500 Jamboree Rd, Irvine, CA 92612-2401
Tel (949) 475-3600 *Founded/Ownrshp* 2008
Sales NA *EMP* 1,400
SIC 6162 Mortgage bankers & correspondents
Pr: Joseph R Tomkinson
Ex VP: Sean McCluskey

D-U-N-S 93-774-8440
▲ IMPAC MORTGAGE HOLDINGS INC
19500 Jamboree Rd, Irvine, CA 92612-2401
Tel (949) 475-3900 *Founded/Ownrshp* 1995
Sales 45.1MM *EMP* 298^E
Tkr Sym IMH *Exch* ASE
SIC 6798 6162 Real estate investment trusts; Mortgage bankers & correspondents; Real estate investment trusts; Mortgage bankers & correspondents
Ch Bd: Joseph R Tomkinson
**Pr:* William S Ashmore
CFO: Todd R Taylor
Ex VP: Andrew McCormick
Ex VP: William C Morris
Ex VP: Ronald M Morrison
Sr VP: Jim Dickinson
CIO: Jeff Ratter
Sls Dir: Michael Rago
Board of Directors: Leigh J Abrams, Frank P Filipps, Stephan R Peers, James Walsh

D-U-N-S 05-227-7008
IMPACT CHEMICAL TECHNOLOGIES INC
PRODUCTION CHEMICALS
10501 E Hwy 80, Midland, TX 79706
Tel (432) 458-3500 *Founded/Ownrshp* 1994
Sales 82.3MM^E *EMP* 152
SIC 5169 Chemicals & allied products; Chemicals & allied products
Pr: Autry C Stephens
**VP:* Brandon Martin

D-U-N-S 11-291-2753
IMPACT COMMUNICATION PARTNERS INC
IMPACT COMMUNICATIONS
360 Madison Ave Fl 4, New York, NY 10017-7148
Tel (212) 490-2300 *Founded/Ownrshp* 1981
Sales 21.1MM^E *EMP* 165
SIC 8742 Marketing consulting services; Marketing consulting services
Pr: James Bargon
**CFO:* Michael Cerrato
Assoc Ed: Patricia Long

IMPACT COMMUNICATIONS
See IMPACT COMMUNICATION PARTNERS INC

D-U-N-S 08-064-7134 IMP/EXP
IMPACT CONFECTIONS INC
4017 Whitney St, Janesville, WI 53546-1003
Tel (608) 208-1100 *Founded/Ownrshp* 1982
Sales 39.6MM^E *EMP* 200
SIC 2064 Candy & other confectionery products; Management services; Candy & other confectionery products
Pr: Jeffrey Rome
Treas: William Henry
VP: Terence C O'Brien

IMPACT CUTOFF DIV
See HAMMILL MANUFACTURING CO

D-U-N-S 13-181-9224
IMPACT DESIGN LLC
301 E Kansas St, Lansing, KS 66043-1619
Tel (913) 727-6556 *Founded/Ownrshp* 2005
Sales 8.2MM^E *EMP* 300
SIC 2395 2759 Embroidery & art needlework; Screen printing; Embroidery & art needlework; Screen printing

D-U-N-S 55-594-5125
IMPACT FLUID SOLUTIONS LLC
2800 Post Oak Blvd # 2000, Houston, TX 77056-6100
Tel (713) 964-7736 *Founded/Ownrshp* 2005
Sales 23.5MM *EMP* 35
Accts Bkd Llp Houston Texas
SIC 1381 Drilling oil & gas wells
CEO: Curtis W Huff
Mng Pt: Jake Yates
Mng Pt: Rowdy Yates
**COO:* Alan Gilmour
**CFO:* Harnad Bhat
**CTO:* Andy Bradbury

D-U-N-S 62-110-5936
IMPACT FORGE GROUP LLC
(*Suby of* HEPHAESTUS HOLDINGS INC) ★
2805 Norcross Dr, Columbus, IN 47201-4911
Tel (812) 342-4437 *Founded/Ownrshp* 2006
Sales 158.3MM^E *EMP* 500
SIC 3462 3463 Iron & steel forgings; Nonferrous forgings; Iron & steel forgings; Nonferrous forgings
CEO: George Thanopolous
**VP:* Dennis Potter
Admn Mgr: Lisa Krebs
Genl Mgr: Walter Powers
Dir IT: Terry McInerney
Dir IT: Francis Walker
QC Dir: John Williamson
Prd Mgr: Andy Larrison
Ql Cn Mgr: Jeff Cornn
Ql Cn Mgr: Joe Keeley

D-U-N-S 06-180-9641
IMPACT FULFILLMENT SERVICES(INC)
1601 Anthony Rd, Burlington, NC 27215-8979
Tel (336) 227-1130 *Founded/Ownrshp* 1998
Sales 55.7MM^E *EMP* 126
SIC 3999 Advertising display products
Pr: J T Porterfield
**CFO:* Dave Forsyth
**Treas:* Perry Nichols
**Ex VP:* T Zone
VP: Malcolm Barnes
Genl Mgr: Michael Palmer
QA Dir: Veronica Bolinger
QA Dir: Tracy Suggs
Manager: Michele Mabee
Opers Mgr: Antony Settle
Prd Mgr: Bill Hill

D-U-N-S 78-250-2850
IMPACT INDUSTRIAL SUPPLIES INC
7020 Anderson Rd, Tampa, FL 33634-4410
Tel (813) 885-2343 *Founded/Ownrshp* 1991
Sales 20.9MM^E *EMP* 20
SIC 5085 Industrial supplies
Pr: John Diaz
Genl Mgr: Dan Irvine
Sales Asso: Pete Diaz

D-U-N-S 62-650-8246
■ IMPACT INNOVATIONS GROUP LLC
(*Suby of* DYNAMICS RESEARCH CORP) ★
2 Tech Dr, Andover, MA 01810-2434
Tel (410) 872-5400 *Founded/Ownrshp* 2004
Sales 8.5MM^E *EMP* 300
SIC 7379 7376 Computer related consulting services; Computer facilities management; Computer related consulting services; Computer facilities management
Pr: Ellen Glover
Dir IT: Shane Sedate

D-U-N-S 14-425-7651 IMP
IMPACT INNOVATIONS INC
223 1st Ave Se, Clara City, MN 56222
Tel (320) 847-1210 *Founded/Ownrshp* 1968
Sales 39.1MM^E *EMP* 150
SIC 2241 5023 7299 Lace & decorative trim, narrow fabric; Home furnishings; Gift wrapping services; Lace & decorative trim, narrow fabric; Home furnishings; Gift wrapping services
CEO: John Dammermann
**CFO:* Ron Noyes
**VP:* John Crider
**VP:* Jane Hagert
**VP:* Gerard Wypyszynski
Dir Bus: Lee Williams
Mng Dir: Phoebe Yuen
Genl Mgr: Jill Citrowske
Mktg Dir: Debbie Donovan

D-U-N-S 08-707-5586 IMP
IMPACT INSTRUMENTATION INC
IMPACT MEDICAL
27 Fairfield Pl, West Caldwell, NJ 07006-6206
Tel (973) 882-1212 *Founded/Ownrshp* 1977
Sales 36.8MM^E *EMP* 150
SIC 3845 Respiratory analysis equipment, electromedical; Respiratory analysis equipment, electromedical
Pr: Leslie H Sherman
**Sec:* Mel Chettum
VP: Todd Powell
IT Man: Vishal Patel
Sftwr Eng: Henry Chuang
Sftwr Eng: Erik Klein
Sftwr Eng: Andrew Stakiwicz
Prd Mgr: Michael Natelli
Ql Cn Mgr: Gloria Bernstein
Natl Sales: Greg Grubaugh
Sls Mgr: Anthony Altamore

IMPACT LIGHTING & PRODUCTION
See HARTMANN STUDIOS INC

D-U-N-S 94-416-1942
IMPACT LOGISTICS INC
7980 N Bro Blvd Ste 104, Memphis, TN 38133
Tel (901) 377-5298 *Founded/Ownrshp* 1986
Sales 71.9MM^E *EMP* 850
Accts Mark Layne Horne Llp Cpas
SIC 4225 General warehousing & storage; General warehousing & storage
CEO: David S Hamilton
**CFO:* Wayne D Vandersteeg
Ex VP: Wayne Vandersteeg
**VP:* Ruth Hamilton
Dir IT: Shawn Troxel

IMPACT MEDICAL
See IMPACT INSTRUMENTATION INC

D-U-N-S 12-623-3324 IMP
IMPACT NETWORKING LLC
13875 W Boulton Blvd, Mettawa, IL 60045
Tel (224) 207-3050 *Founded/Ownrshp* 1999
Sales 41.0MM *EMP* 150
Accts Frost Ruttenberg & Rothblatt
SIC 5112 5065 5043 Computer & photocopying supplies; Telephone & telegraphic equipment; Photographic processing equipment; Computer & photocopying supplies; Telephone & telegraphic equipment; Photographic processing equipment
CEO: Frank Cucco
**Pr:* Dan Meyer
CFO: Nick Cosmano
Treas: Susan Kubichek
VP: Jeremy Fordemwalt
VP: John Larson
Off Mgr: Tarah Ostrander
Web Dev: Martin Blase
Opers Mgr: Steve Buchholz
Sls&Mrk Ex: Philip Waugh
VP Sls: Tom Pieters

IMPACT PARTNERSHIP, THE
See IMPACT PARTNERSHIP LLC

D-U-N-S 87-439-5002
IMPACT PARTNERSHIP LLC
IMPACT PARTNERSHIP, THE
3550 Georg Busbe Pkwy Ste, Kennesaw, GA 30144
Tel (678) 784-2000 *Founded/Ownrshp* 2011
Sales NA *EMP* 114
SIC 6311 Life insurance
Pr: Stephen Odom
CFO: Ed Williams
Chf Mktg O: Ford Stokes
Ofcr: Derrick Vermillion
VP: Ron Eastman
Off Mgr: Teena Celler

D-U-N-S 61-774-8277 IMP
IMPACT PLASTICS CORP
11419 Smith Dr, Huntley, IL 60142-9602
Tel (847) 669-6407 *Founded/Ownrshp* 1999
Sales 33.3MM^E *EMP* 75^E
SIC 5093 Scrap & waste materials
Prin: Scott Lemajeur
VP: Gary Cardoza
Opers Mgr: Lonnie Timmerman
Plnt Mgr: John Sousa
Sls Mgr: Scott Myers

D-U-N-S 18-403-8545 IMP
IMPACT PLASTICS INC
1070 S Industrial Dr A, Erwin, TN 37650-3656
Tel (423) 743-3561 *Founded/Ownrshp* 1988
Sales 21.5MM^E *EMP* 97
SIC 3089 Injection molded finished plastic products
Pr: Gerald M O'Connor Jr
Prd Mgr: Anita Hensley

D-U-N-S 00-505-2360 IMP
■ IMPACT PRODUCTS LLC
(*Suby of* S P RICHARDS CO) ★
2840 Centennial Rd, Toledo, OH 43617-1898
Tel (419) 841-2891 *Founded/Ownrshp* 2001, 2014
Sales 106.4MM^E *EMP* 151

SIC 5084 5087 2392 3089 Safety equipment; Janitors' supplies; Mops, floor & dust; Buckets, plastic; Tissue dispensers, plastic; Safety equipment; Janitors' supplies; Mops, floor & dust; Buckets, plastic; Tissue dispensers, plastic
CEO: Terry Neal
**CFO:* Jeff Beery
VP: John Irwin
VP: James Kenchtges
Genl Mgr: Jim Beadles
IT Man: Bryan Byczynski
Natl Sales: John Daschner
Natl Sales: Adam Siegel
VP Mktg: Jeannie McCarthy
Mktg Dir: Kaiko Zureich
Manager: Scott Erwin

IMPACT RESOURCE GROUP
See WERE READY TO ASSEMBLE INC

D-U-N-S 06-334-5656
IMPACT SALES INC
ISI
915 W Jefferson St Ste A, Boise, ID 83702-5483
Tel (208) 343-5800 *Founded/Ownrshp* 1998
Sales 34.8MM^E *EMP* 150
SIC 5141 5142 Food brokers; Packaged frozen goods; Food brokers; Packaged frozen goods
CEO: Carl Pennington
VP: Tim Clare
Off Mgr: Teresa Miller
Board of Directors: Paul Pennington, Jeff Russell

IMPACT SAND AND GRAVEL
See WADLEY CONSTRUCTION INC

D-U-N-S 92-685-9026
■ IMPACT SCIENCE & TECHNOLOGY INC
ITT EXELIS
(*Suby of* EDO CORP) ★
85 Northwest Blvd Ste B, Nashua, NH 03063-4068
Tel (603) 459-2200 *Founded/Ownrshp* 2006
Sales 27.4MM^E *EMP* 215
Accts Manzi & Assoc N Andover Ma
SIC 8748 3679 7371 Systems engineering consultant, ex. computer or professional; Electronic circuits; Custom computer programming services; Systems engineering consultant, ex. computer or professional; Electronic circuits; Custom computer programming services
CEO: David F Melcher
**Pr:* Christopher Bernhardt
**Treas:* Joe Daniel
CTO: Brad Baharian
Sftwr Eng: Andy Vuong
Board of Directors: Christopher Bernhardt, David Melcher

D-U-N-S 12-476-7075
IMPACT SOLUTIONS CONSULTING INC
1300 Ridenour Blvd Nw # 202, Kennesaw, GA 30152-4501
Tel (770) 795-9525 *Founded/Ownrshp* 2002
Sales 23.5MM^E *EMP* 100
SIC 7379 Computer related consulting services
Pr: Russel Forde
CFO: Young Nashlee
**CFO:* Nashlee Young
VP: Richard Stocks
VP: Michael Trocki
Ex Dir: Mark Kubicek
Rgnl Mgr: Diane Herrera
IT Man: Steven Lakes
VP Opers: Lynn Schneider
Manager: Todd Caras
Snr PM: Sara Loya

D-U-N-S 04-364-6657
IMPACT STEEL INC (MI)
255 S Old Woodward Ave # 330, Birmingham, MI 48009-6185
Tel (248) 414-6100 *Founded/Ownrshp* 1998
Sales 63.0MM^E *EMP* 23
SIC 5051 Steel; Steel
CEO: Mike Easlick
VP: Rob Feldman
**Prin:* Jeff Jay

IMPACT STRATEGIES, INC.
See HINRICHS GROUP INC

D-U-N-S 07-550-7392
IMPACT SYSTEMS INC (PA)
KEYSTONE
(*Suby of* KEYSTONE HUMAN SERVICES) ★
124 Pine St, Harrisburg, PA 17101-1208
Tel (717) 232-7509 *Founded/Ownrshp* 1972, 2008
Sales 228.9M *EMP* 450
Accts Keystone Service System Inc H
SIC 8361 Home for the mentally handicapped; Home for the mentally handicapped
Pr: Dennis Felty

D-U-N-S 06-315-3100 IMP
IMPACT UNLIMITED INC
IMPACT XM
250 Ridge Rd, Dayton, NJ 08810-1502
Tel (732) 274-2000 *Founded/Ownrshp* 1973
Sales 37.1MM^E *EMP* 165
SIC 2541 Store & office display cases & fixtures; Drainboards, plastic laminated; Store & office display cases & fixtures; Drainboards, plastic laminated
Pr: Jared Pollacco
**CFO:* Joseph Haggerty
**Ex VP:* Sandie Stransky
VP: Steve Mapes
VP: Sandra Stansky
Creative D: Bruce Dickerson
Creative D: Wayne Netzel
Creative D: Paul Spadafora
IT Man: Allan Hall
Info Man: Edward Salge
S&M/VP: Nicholaos Papadopoulos
Board of Directors: David Acharya, James Illikman, Charles Pollacco

IMPACT XM
See IMPACT UNLIMITED INC

D-U-N-S 05-596-7069
IMPACTASSETS INC
7315 Wisconsin Ave 1000w, Bethesda, MD 20814-3218
Tel (855) 482-2946 *Founded/Ownrshp* 2008
Sales 35.0MM *EMP* 14
SIC 7389 Financial services; Financial services
Pr: Timothy Freundlich

D-U-N-S 02-154-3124
IMPACTRX INC
(*Suby of* SYMPHONY TECHNOLOGY GROUP LLC) ★
550 Blair Mill Rd Ste 100, Horsham, PA 19044-2376
Tel (215) 444-8700 *Founded/Ownrshp* 2011
Sales 30.5MM^E *EMP* 500
SIC 8743 7361 Promotion service; Employment agencies; Promotion service; Employment agencies
Pr: Gregory Ellis
**Founder:* Terry Overton
Ex VP: Ron Timmerman
Sr VP: ADI K Asavaid
Sr VP: Rob Delghiaccio
VP: Peter Bittinger
VP: Martin Glogowski
VP: John C Kain
VP: Rosemarie Maglietta
VP: Jill Mundinger
VP: Kjell Nygren
VP: Joan Phillips
VP: David N Stievater
Dir Surg: Susan Grosso

D-U-N-S 08-865-6512
IMPAQ INTERNATIONAL LLC
10420 Little Patuxent Pkw, Columbia, MD 21044-3636
Tel (410) 715-6799 *Founded/Ownrshp* 2001
Sales 49.7MM^E *EMP* 175
SIC 8733 7371 7373 7379 8742 Noncommercial research organizations; Custom computer programming services; Computer integrated systems design; Computer related maintenance services; Industrial & labor consulting services; Human resource consulting services; Noncommercial research organizations; Custom computer programming services; Computer integrated systems design; Computer related maintenance services; Industrial & labor consulting services; Human resource consulting services
VP: Norma Gavin
VP: Jeff Mike
VP: Raman Ponos
VP: Janet Robb
Assoc Dir: Morgan Barnes
Mng Dir: Stephen Coy
Mng Dir: Ines Vigil
Genl Mgr: Mia Blecher
Snr Sftwr: Balaji Regoti
Snr Sftwr: Sumegha Shaw
Dir IT: Kourosh Razavi

IMPAX
See WILSON TOOL INTERNATIONAL INC

D-U-N-S 00-259-5734 IMP
▲ IMPAX LABORATORIES INC
30831 Huntwood Ave, Hayward, CA 94544-7003
Tel (510) 240-6000 *Founded/Ownrshp* 1993
Sales 596.0MM *EMP* 973
Accts Kpmg Llp Philadelphia Pennsy
Tkr Sym IPXL *Exch* NGS
SIC 2834 Pharmaceutical preparations; Pharmaceutical preparations
Pr: G Frederick Wilkinson
**Ch Bd:* Robert L Burr
CFO: Arthur Koch
**CFO:* Bryan M Reasons
**Ofcr:* Deborah M Penza
Sr VP: Mark Fitch
Sr VP: Donna M Hughes
Sr VP: Andrew Schaschl
**Sr VP:* Mark A Schlossberg
VP: Koch Arthur
VP: Goff Baker
VP: Marcy Macdonald
VP: Italo Pennella
VP: Bryan Reasons
VP: Brandon Smith
VP: Meg Snowden
VP: Richard Ting
Assoc Dir: Marsha Glenn
Assoc Dir: Felix Lai
Assoc Dir: Maria Messina
Assoc Dir: Aravind Mittur
Board of Directors: Leslie Z Benet, Allen Chao, Michael Markbreiter, Mary K Pendergast, Peter R Terreri, Janet S Vergis, Nigel Ten Fleming

IMPCO
See GODFREY & WING INC

D-U-N-S 09-463-3120 IMP
■ IMPCO TECHNOLOGIES INC
(*Suby of* FUEL SYSTEMS SOLUTIONS INC) ★
3030 S Susan St, Santa Ana, CA 92704-6435
Tel (714) 656-1200 *Founded/Ownrshp* 2006
Sales 86.8MM^E *EMP* 540
SIC 3714 3592 7363 Fuel systems & parts, motor vehicle; Carburetors; Engineering help service; Fuel systems & parts, motor vehicle; Carburetors; Engineering help service
Genl Mgr: Massimo Fracchia
Pr: Brian Olson
COO: Peter Chase
COO: Brad E Garner
Sr Cor Off: Richard Baverstock
VP: R O Blackwood
VP: Colleen Woo
Exec: Bruno Balocco
CTO: Doug Donaldson
Dir IT: Elo Sarafian
Sls Mgr: Rob Mercer

D-U-N-S 95-686-9085
IMPEL MANAGEMENT SERVICES LLC
MEDICAL CLINIC OF NORTH TEXAS
9003 Arprt Fwy 3 Ste 100, North Richland Hills, TX 76180
Tel (817) 514-5200 *Founded/Ownrshp* 1994
Sales 37.3MM^E *EMP* 350^E

SIC 8741 Management services; Management services
CFO: Daniel Gutschenritter
Dir Soc: Cynthia Puente
**Prin:* Michael Yerrid
IT Man: Khanh McCall
Site Mgr: Amy Atkins
Site Mgr: Darlene Bell
Site Mgr: Delores Talbott
Psych: Susan Clifford
Psych: Bryan Demarie
Psych: Carrie Jones
Psych: Vincent McColm

D-U-N-S 14-724-8306
IMPERATIS CORP
2231 Crystal Dr Ste 1114, Arlington, VA 22202-3727
Tel (703) 413-4900 *Founded/Ownrshp* 1986
Sales 46.1MM^E *EMP* 130
SIC 7373 8711 8742 Computer integrated systems design; Engineering services; Business consultant; Computer integrated systems design; Engineering services; Business consultant
Pr: Mastin M Robeson
**Ch Bd:* Charles R Henry
**CFO:* Joe Kuhlmann
VP: Dave Dieugenio
VP: Heidi Garner
VP: Matthew Kunst
Dir Bus: Melinda Byrd
IT Man: John Latasse
Tech Mgr: Mulvaney Patrick
Sftwr Eng: Andrew Ivy
Mktg Dir: Tom Morgan

IMPERIAL - SAVANNAH
See IMPERIAL SUGAR CO

D-U-N-S 13-797-7224 IMP
IMPERIAL BAG & PAPER CO LLC
255 Us Highway 1 And 9, Jersey City, NJ 07306-6727
Tel (201) 437-7440 *Founded/Ownrshp* 2006
Sales 2.3MMM^E *EMP* 275^E
SIC 5087 Janitors' supplies; Janitors' supplies
CEO: Robert Tillis
**Pr:* Jason Tillis
**CFO:* Paul Cervino
CFO: Robert De Gregorio
**Sr VP:* Jeffery Burdick
**VP:* Chris Freeman
Dir Bus: Charlie Delia
Dir Bus: Daniel Plaut
Snr Mgr: Harry Westfall

IMPERIAL BEVERAGE
See CKL CORP

D-U-N-S 78-111-5659 IMP
IMPERIAL BRANDS INC
(*Suby of* MARIE BRIZARD WINE AND SPIRITS)
11505 Fairchild Ste 204, Palm Beach Gardens, FL 33410
Tel (561) 624-5662 *Founded/Ownrshp* 2006
Sales 69.6MM^E *EMP* 32
SIC 5182 2084 Wine & distilled beverages; Wines, brandy & brandy spirits; Wine & distilled beverages; Wines, brandy & brandy spirits
Pr: Nicolas Guillant
**Treas:* Sandy Morriss
VP: Christian Castren
VP: Mike Meany
VP: James Ron Quick
VP: Timo Sutinen
Dir IT: Carrie Rogina
Info Man: Sean Krause

D-U-N-S 06-877-3530
IMPERIAL BROWN INC
R-PLUS DOORS
2271 Ne 194th Ave, Portland, OR 97230-7437
Tel (503) 665-5539 *Founded/Ownrshp* 1970
Sales 24.4MM^E *EMP* 110^E
SIC 3585 Refrigeration equipment, complete; Refrigeration equipment, complete
Pr: Rick Schermerhorn
**Ch Bd:* Allen T Zell
**Pr:* Richard Schermerhorn
**Sec:* Judith Zell
**VP:* Justin Sandall
**VP:* David Zell
Opers Mgr: Chris Straughn
Manager: Brian Baxter
Sales Asso: John Karleskint

D-U-N-S 15-414-8642
IMPERIAL CAPITAL LLC
2000 Avenue Of The Stars 900s, Los Angeles, CA 90067-4716
Tel (310) 246-3700 *Founded/Ownrshp* 1997
Sales 30.9MM^E *EMP* 118
SIC 6211 Investment bankers; Investment bankers
CEO: Randall Wooster
Pr: Tom Corcoran
CEO: Randall E Wooster
COO: Mark Martis
CFO: Harry Chung
Ofcr: Catherine Schafer
Ofcr: Todd Wiench
Ex VP: Paul Aronzon
Ex VP: John Mack
Sr VP: Glenn Blitzer
Sr VP: Adam Braham
Sr VP: Tim Coughlin
Sr VP: Alex Fonti
Sr VP: Nicole Fry
Sr VP: Gayle Grant
Sr VP: Dan Guay
Sr VP: Erich Hobelmann
Sr VP: Sebastian Hoppe
Sr VP: Christopher Jacobs
Sr VP: Brian Kaufman
Sr VP: Peter Lukas

IMPERIAL CHEVROLET
See MEEHAN AUTOMOBILES INC

D-U-N-S 00-601-5085 EXP
IMPERIAL CLINICAL RESEARCH SERVICES INC (MI)
IMPERIAL GRAPHICS
3100 Walkent Dr Nw, Grand Rapids, MI 49544-1402
Tel (616) 784-0100 *Founded/Ownrshp* 1965, 2000
Sales 27.2MM^E *EMP* 150
SIC 2761 5112 2759 2732 Manifold business forms; Stationery & office supplies; Commercial printing; Book printing; Manifold business forms; Stationery & office supplies; Commercial printing; Book printing
Pr: Matthew Bissell
COO: Amanda Falicki
**VP:* Steven Balk
IT Man: Terry Yax
Netwrk Eng: Scott Waldo
Sfty Mgr: John Calvetti
Prd Mgr: Karlton Gray
Mktg Mgr: Scott Scheidel
Sls Mgr: Paul Kehoe
Sls Mgr: Dave Woodard

D-U-N-S 00-698-5543 IMP
IMPERIAL COMMODITIES CORP
BERNS & KOPPSTEIN DIV
(*Suby of* N.V. DELI MAATSCHAPPIJ)
17 Battery Pl Ste 723, New York, NY 10004-1198
Tel (212) 837-9400 *Founded/Ownrshp* 2009
Sales 26.2MM^E *EMP* 45
SIC 5149 5159 Canned goods: fruit, vegetables, seafood, meats, etc.; Coffee & tea; Rubber, crude
Ch Bd: John M Morley

D-U-N-S 07-874-5197
IMPERIAL COMMUNITY COLLEGE DISTRICT (INC)
IMPERIAL VALLEY COLLEGE
380 E Aten Rd, Imperial, CA 92251-9653
Tel (760) 352-8320 *Founded/Ownrshp* 2008
Sales 19.7MM^E *EMP* 508
SIC 8222 8221 Junior college; Colleges universities & professional schools; Junior college; Colleges universities & professional schools
Pr: Ed Gould
Psych: Gilbert Campos
Psych: Said Canez
Psych: Lorraine Mazeroll

D-U-N-S 07-831-6761
IMPERIAL CONTRACTING
695 De Long Ave Ste 101, Novato, CA 94945-3350
Tel (480) 892-9157 *Founded/Ownrshp* 2003
Sales 60.7MM^E *EMP* 150^E
SIC 1522 Multi-family dwelling construction; Multi-family dwelling construction
Pr: Kevin Heselton

D-U-N-S 08-498-0176
IMPERIAL COUNTY OFFICE OF EDUCATION FOUNDATION
1398 Sperber Rd, El Centro, CA 92243-9621
Tel (760) 312-6464 *Founded/Ownrshp* 1947
Sales 18.5MM^E *EMP* 530^E
Accts Wilkinson Hadley King & Co L
SIC 8299 8211 Educational services; Elementary & secondary schools; Educational services; Elementary & secondary schools
Pr: Cristi Mamer
Treas: Claudia Guzman
Ofcr: Damon Smith
VP: Annette Buttner
Prin: John Caltagirone
Off Mgr: Cynthia Trujillo
Dir IT: Ariel Cecena
Mktg Dir: Martha Cruz
Psych: Chris Hawkins

D-U-N-S 06-849-9334
IMPERIAL CRANE SERVICES INC
7500 Imperial Dr, Bridgeview, IL 60455-2395
Tel (708) 598-2300 *Founded/Ownrshp* 1969
Sales 33.1MM^E *EMP* 150
SIC 7353 5084 7699 Cranes & aerial lift equipment, rental or leasing; Cranes, industrial; Industrial machinery & equipment repair; Cranes & aerial lift equipment, rental or leasing; Cranes, industrial; Industrial machinery & equipment repair
Pr: Berkshire Bohne
Pr: Jeff Bohne
COO: William Tierney
CFO: David A Dobson
CFO: David Dobson
VP: Tierney Bill
VP: Jay Fisher
VP: Bill Tierney
Genl Mgr: John Tierney
CTO: Mark Priepot
VP Sls: Wesley Austin

D-U-N-S 02-262-2617
IMPERIAL DESIGN SERVICE INC
IDS
1958 Wilson Ave Sw, Grand Rapids, MI 49534-2196
Tel (616) 791-1900 *Founded/Ownrshp* 1980
Sales 22.8MM^E *EMP* 165
SIC 8711 7361 Engineering services; Employment agencies; Engineering services; Employment agencies
Pr: Wayne Walcott
**Pr:* Rex Baker
**VP:* Thomas Mathews
Sls Mgr: Chad Scholl

D-U-N-S 00-184-3127 EXP
IMPERIAL DISTRIBUTORS INC (MA)
33 Sword St, Auburn, MA 01501-2146
Tel (508) 756-5156 *Founded/Ownrshp* 1939
Sales 835.9MM^E *EMP* 750
Accts Mcgladrey Llp Boston Massach
SIC 5122 Toiletries; Toiletries
CEO: Michael Sleeper
**Pr:* Herbert L Daitch
VP: Ralph Cruz
VP: Joe Kirby
VP: Sandra Noonan
VP: Don Polsi
VP: Tammy Remillard
CTO: Steven Perry

Dir IT: Dovid Kashnow
Sftwr Eng: Fazal Alam
Opers Mgr: Derek Potter

D-U-N-S 00-416-3945 IMP
IMPERIAL ELECTRIC CO
(*Suby of* KINETEK INDUSTRIES INC) ★
1503 Exeter Rd, Akron, OH 44306-3889
Tel (575) 434-0633 *Founded/Ownrshp* 2006
Sales 44.5MM^E *EMP* 270
SIC 3621 Motors, electric; Generators & sets, electric; Motors, electric; Generators & sets, electric
Pr: David Molnar
**CFO:* Mark Schoolcraft
MIS Dir: Gannon William
Plnt Mgr: Srdjan Sudar
Ql Cn Mgr: Elena Shue
S&M/VP: David Chippi
S&M/VP: Gary Ward
Sales Asso: Bob Caputo

D-U-N-S 36-450-6949 IMP
IMPERIAL ELECTRONIC ASSEMBLY INC
I E A
1000 Federal Rd, Brookfield, CT 06804-1123
Tel (203) 740-8425 *Founded/Ownrshp* 1989
Sales 35.5MM^E *EMP* 93
SIC 3679 Electronic circuits; Electronic circuits
Pr: Tony Conte
**VP:* Edward O'Donnell
Mtls Mgr: Frank Cassaniti
Opers Mgr: Mark Bohacs
Ql Cn Mgr: Peter Bockiaro

IMPERIAL EXPRESS
See VALCO LOGISTICS INC

IMPERIAL FASTENER
See MIDWEST EQUIPMENT & SUPPLY CO INC

D-U-N-S 00-737-9226
IMPERIAL FIRE & CASUALTY INS CO
(*Suby of* IMPERIAL MANAGEMENT CORP) ★
4670 I 49 N Service Rd, Opelousas, LA 70570-0882
Tel (337) 942-5691 *Founded/Ownrshp* 2007
Sales NA *EMP* 8^E
SIC 6411 Insurance agents, brokers & service
CFO: Dirk Boudreaux

D-U-N-S 96-004-1986
IMPERIAL FIRE AND CASUALTY INSURANCE CO
(*Suby of* IMPERIAL MANAGEMENT CORP) ★
304 W Landry St, Opelousas, LA 70570-5120
Tel (337) 942-5691 *Founded/Ownrshp* 1990
Sales NA *EMP* 50
SIC 6411 Insurance agents, brokers & service; Insurance agents, brokers & service
CEO: H Marcus Carter Jr
CIO: Scott Proctor
Dir IT: Jill Tucker

IMPERIAL FROZEN FOODS
See H P SKOLNICK INC

IMPERIAL GRAPHICS
See IMPERIAL CLINICAL RESEARCH SERVICES INC

D-U-N-S 07-910-2043
IMPERIAL GROUP MANUFACTURING INC
4545 Airport Rd, Denton, TX 76207-3927
Tel (940) 565-8505 *Founded/Ownrshp* 2013
Sales 649.6MM^E *EMP* 1,892
SIC 3715 Truck trailers; Trailer bodies; Truck trailer chassis; Truck trailers; Trailer bodies; Truck trailer chassis
Pr: Brian Crumbaugh
**VP:* John Hatherly
**VP:* Ian Kirson
Sfty Dirs: Melanie Parker

D-U-N-S 60-989-5248
IMPERIAL GUARD AND DETECTIVE SERVICES INC
IMPERIAL GUARD SERVICE
2555 Poplar Ave, Memphis, TN 38112-3822
Tel (866) 840-2066 *Founded/Ownrshp* 1968
Sales 41.7MM^E *EMP* 2,000
SIC 7381 Security guard service; Security guard service
Pr: R Q Brewer
**Sec:* Robin Todd
**VP:* William Brinson
VP: Don Stewart
Rgnl Mgr: Justin Burd
MIS Mgr: Jack Tardy
Secur Mgr: Nick Anderson
Secur Mgr: Kevlin Parker

IMPERIAL GUARD SERVICE
See IMPERIAL GUARD AND DETECTIVE SERVICES INC

D-U-N-S 82-694-8499 IMP
IMPERIAL HEADWEAR INC
17101 E Ohio Dr, Aurora, CO 80017-3878
Tel (303) 597-0206 *Founded/Ownrshp* 1993
Sales 27.8MM^E *EMP* 200
SIC 2353 Hats, caps & millinery; Hats & caps; Caps: cloth, straw & felt; Uniform hats & caps

D-U-N-S 08-268-9274
IMPERIAL HEALTH LLP
CLINIC
501 Dctor Mchael Dbkey Dr, Lake Charles, LA 70601-5724
Tel (337) 433-8400 *Founded/Ownrshp* 1985
Sales 51.5MM^E *EMP* 300
SIC 8011 Clinic, operated by physicians; Clinic, operated by physicians
CEO: Kris Hickingbottom
Pt: Raphael C Chan MD
CFO: Lisa Bussell
Ch: Arthur Primeax
Ex Dir: Donzella Lee
Off Mgr: Lisa Conner
Off Mgr: Wanda Lemelle
CTO: C J Lejeune
Doctor: Harold G Bienvenu MD
Doctor: Donna Buckles
Doctor: Albert Chinn

D-U-N-S 15-393-5374
IMPERIAL HOTEL GROUP INC
SHERATON IMPERIAL HOTEL & CONV
4700 Emperor Blvd, Durham, NC 27703-8424
Tel (919) 941-5050 *Founded/Ownrshp* 1985
Sales 22.5MM^E *EMP* 290
SIC 7011 Hotel, franchised; Hotel, franchised
Pr: Robert L Jones
**VP:* Keith R Harrod
Exec: Elhaj Tayouga
Genl Mgr: Rachane Dangrojana
Genl Mgr: Namchai Paladsongkram
Sales Exec: Danielle Parsons
Mktg Mgr: Richard Humbles
Sls Mgr: K Adam

D-U-N-S 02-907-9712 IMP
IMPERIAL IMPORTS INC
TOYOTA OF SAN BERNARDINO
765 Showcase Dr N, San Bernardino, CA 92408-2729
Tel (909) 381-4444 *Founded/Ownrshp* 1966
Sales 61.6MM^E *EMP* 200
SIC 5511 Automobiles, new & used
Pr: Clifford R Cummings

D-U-N-S 16-132-0700 IMP
IMPERIAL INDUSTRIAL SUPPLY CO
MAXTOOL
5798 Ontario Mills Pkwy, Ontario, CA 91764-5116
Tel (909) 592-6888 *Founded/Ownrshp* 1984
Sales 75.8MM^E *EMP* 45
Accts Khandelwal & Associates An Ac
SIC 5072 5251 Hand tools; Tools
Pr: Robert W Raskin

D-U-N-S 03-876-2969
IMPERIAL INDUSTRIES INC
(*Suby of* WAUSAU TILE INC) ★
505 W Industrial Park Ave, Rothschild, WI 54474-7917
Tel (715) 359-0200 *Founded/Ownrshp* 1984
Sales 48.8MM^E *EMP* 128
SIC 3443 Tanks, standard or custom fabricated: metal plate; Tanks, standard or custom fabricated: metal plate
Pr: Edward Creske
**VP:* William Creske
Genl Mgr: Russ Putnam
Sls&Mrk Ex: Tom Aerts

D-U-N-S 04-399-0191
IMPERIAL INVESTMENT CO INC
THE MARTENS COMPANIES
4800 Wisconsin Ave Nw, Washington, DC 20016-4612
Tel (202) 537-3000 *Founded/Ownrshp* 1953
Sales 23.8MM^E *EMP* 90
SIC 5511 Automobiles, new & used; Automobiles, new & used
Pr: Harry Martens III
**VP:* John C Martens
**VP:* Virginia S Martens

D-U-N-S 00-958-4624 IMP
IMPERIAL IRRIGATION DISTRICT
I I D
333 E Barioni Blvd, Imperial, CA 92251-1773
Tel (800) 303-7756 *Founded/Ownrshp* 1911
Sales 1.0MMM^E *EMP* 1,300
SIC 4911 4971 4931 ; Water distribution or supply systems for irrigation; Electric & other services combined; ; Water distribution or supply systems for irrigation; Electric & other services combined
Pr: Stephen Benson
Pr: Anthony Sanchez
CEO: Keven Kelly
Ofcr: Jamie Asbury
Ofcr: Raquel Lopez
Ofcr: Belen Valenzuela
Ofcr: Donald Vargas
VP: Mike Abatti
VP: Norma Sierra Galindo
VP: Stella Mendoza
Prgrm Mgr: Henry Beltran

D-U-N-S 08-058-9492
IMPERIAL LLC (OK)
2020 N Mingo Rd, Tulsa, OK 74116-1220
Tel (918) 437-1300 *Founded/Ownrshp* 1988
Sales 63.4MM^E *EMP* 300
SIC 2095 5962 5812 Roasted coffee; Sandwich & hot food vending machines; Beverage vending machines; Candy & snack food vending machines; Cigarettes vending machines; Eating places; Roasted coffee; Sandwich & hot food vending machines; Beverage vending machines; Candy & snack food vending machines; Cigarettes vending machines; Eating places
Pr: Lance Whorton
**Pr:* Paul Mark Tims
CFO: Nancy Hettcher
CFO: Craig Johnston
**VP:* Kevin Hinds
Genl Mgr: Stacey Whisenhunt
Opers Mgr: John Slaughter
Sales Asso: Margaret Motley

IMPERIAL LUMBER & SUPPLY
See MARONDA HOMES INC

D-U-N-S 04-910-9734
IMPERIAL MANAGEMENT CORP
(*Suby of* SOUTHPORT LANE MANAGEMENT LLC) ★
4670 I 49 N Service Rd, Opelousas, LA 70570-0882
Tel (337) 942-5691 *Founded/Ownrshp* 2013
Sales NA *EMP* 190^E
SIC 6331 Fire, marine & casualty insurance & carriers; Fire, marine & casualty insurance & carriers
CEO: H Marcus Carter Jr
**Pr:* Je Brignac
**CFO:* Dirk Boudreaux

D-U-N-S 09-728-3212
IMPERIAL MARBLE CORP
327 E Lasalle St, Somonauk, IL 60552-9561
Tel (815) 498-2303 *Founded/Ownrshp* 1979
Sales 32.5MM^E *EMP* 170
SIC 3281 2542 Bathroom fixtures, cut stone; Cabinets: show, display or storage: except wood; Bathroom fixtures, cut stone; Cabinets: show, display or storage: except wood
Pr: Richard Williams
**CFO:* Kim Williams
Sfty Dirs: Barbara Abbott

D-U-N-S 10-840-7669 IMP
IMPERIAL MARKETING INC
LOGOED MERCHANDISE
21238 Bridge St, Southfield, MI 48033-4089
Tel (248) 353-0950 *Founded/Ownrshp* 1991
Sales 22.8MM^E *EMP* 55
SIC 5199 Advertising specialties
Pr: John R Slavsky III
Treas: Raymond Deegan
Ex VP: Kenneth Olivier
VP: Ira Levin
Prin: Teresa Chui
Rgnl Mgr: Richard Asci
Dir IT: Doug Tolman
Sls&Mrk Ex: Frank Calabro
VP Sls: Frank Hutton
Mktg Dir: Steven Rogge
Mktg Mgr: Philip Peters

IMPERIAL MARKING SYSTEMS
See BEST LABEL CO INC

IMPERIAL MFG CO
See SPENUZZA INC

IMPERIAL MOTOR PARTS-DIVISION
See BATTERY USA INC

IMPERIAL PALACE HOTEL & CASINO
See IMPERIAL PALACE OF MISSISSIPPI LLC

D-U-N-S 93-947-6370
IMPERIAL PALACE OF MISSISSIPPI LLC
IMPERIAL PALACE HOTEL & CASINO
850 Bayview Ave, Biloxi, MS 39530-1701
Tel (228) 432-3243 *Founded/Ownrshp* 1997
Sales NA *EMP* 2,300^E
SIC 7011 5812 5813 7832

D-U-N-S 60-413-6192 EXP
IMPERIAL PARKING (US) LLC
MARCPARC AND MARCPARC VALET
(*Suby of* IMPERIAL PARKING CANADA CORPORATION)
510 Walnut St Ste 420, Philadelphia, PA 19106-3623
Tel (212) 736-7171 *Founded/Ownrshp* 2002
Sales 226.2MM^E *EMP* 4,620
Accts Kpmg Llp Vancouver Canada
SIC 7521 Parking structure; Parking lots; Parking structure; Parking lots
Pr: Allan Copping
**Treas:* Bradley Yen

IMPERIAL PIPE & SUPPLY
See BAKERSFIELD PIPE AND SUPPLY INC

IMPERIAL PIZZA
See RANDOLPH PACKING CO

D-U-N-S 04-596-0218 IMP
IMPERIAL PLASTICS INC
21320 Hamburg Ave, Lakeville, MN 55044-9032
Tel (952) 469-4951 *Founded/Ownrshp* 1996
Sales 127.3MM^E *EMP* 570^E
SIC 3089

D-U-N-S 00-291-0800 IMP/EXP
IMPERIAL POOLS INC (NY)
33 Wade Rd, Latham, NY 12110-2613
Tel (518) 786-1200 *Founded/Ownrshp* 1966
Sales 64.1MM^E *EMP* 213
SIC 3949 5091 Swimming pools, except plastic; Swimming pools, equipment & supplies; Swimming pools, except plastic; Swimming pools, equipment & supplies
CEO: William Churchman
**Pr:* John V Maiuccoro
VP: Robert Burke
**VP:* Gary Maiuccoro
**Prin:* Katie Maiuccoro
Brnch Mgr: Dean Ferriola
Brnch Mgr: Charlie Renna
IT Man: Joe Mogul
Sfty Mgr: Dave Carl
Mktg Dir: Jeff Mazzone
Sls Dir: Bob Moskos

D-U-N-S 06-948-7924
IMPERIAL SERVICE SYSTEMS INC
200 W 22nd St Ste 201, Lombard, IL 60148-4883
Tel (630) 925-1800 *Founded/Ownrshp* 1973
Sales 20.1MM^E *EMP* 500
SIC 7349 Janitorial service, contract basis; Janitorial service, contract basis
Pr: Vito Cavallo

D-U-N-S 05-842-5471
IMPERIAL SPRINKLER SUPPLY INC
1485 N Manassero St, Anaheim, CA 92807-1938
Tel (714) 792-2925 *Founded/Ownrshp* 1980
Sales 44.6MM^E *EMP* 40^E
SIC 5087 Sprinkler systems
Pr: Gabriel Moriel
**Sec:* Dolores Moriel
Brnch Mgr: Gene Cools
Brnch Mgr: Robert Reyes
IT Man: Katie Berstler
Sales Exec: Ed Pongs
Sls Mgr: Bob Barrett
Sls Mgr: Mike Perilman
Sales Asso: Don Remington

D-U-N-S 00-808-6472 IMP
IMPERIAL SUGAR CO (TX)
IMPERIAL - SAVANNAH
(*Suby of* LOUIS DREYFUS COMMODITIES LLC) ★
3 Sugar Creek Center Blvd # 500, Sugar Land, TX 77478-2210
Tel (281) 491-9181 *Founded/Ownrshp* 1905, 2012
Sales 600.0MM *EMP* 530
SIC 2062 5149 Cane sugar refining; Granulated cane sugar from purchased raw sugar or syrup; Powdered cane sugar from purchased raw sugar or syrup; Sugar, refined; Cane sugar refining; Granulated cane sugar from purchased raw sugar or syrup; Powdered cane sugar from purchased raw sugar or syrup; Sugar, refined
Pr: Michael Gorrell
**CEO:* John C Sheptor
CFO: Douglas Brewster
**CFO:* H P Mechler
Treas: Ed Cox
**Treas:* J Eric Story
Ex VP: W Scher
**Sr VP:* Louis T Bolognini
VP: Luciano Cocito
VP: Greig P Debow Jr
VP: H P Machler
**VP:* George Muller
VP: John Reinert
**VP:* Jeffrey Zanchelli
Exec: Mark Yunker

D-U-N-S 02-324-7661 IMP/EXP
■ **IMPERIAL SUPPLIES LLC**
(*Suby of* WW GRAINGER INC) ★
789 Armed Forces Dr, Green Bay, WI 54304-4527
Tel (920) 494-7474 *Founded/Ownrshp* 2009
Sales 61.1MM^E *EMP* 184
SIC 5013 5085

IMPERIAL TOOLS
See STRIDE TOOL INC

D-U-N-S 04-933-7249 IMP/EXP
IMPERIAL TOY LLC
16641 Roscoe Pl, North Hills, CA 91343-6104
Tel (818) 536-6500 *Founded/Ownrshp* 2006
Sales 211.0MM^E *EMP* 800
SIC 3944 Games, toys & children's vehicles; Games, toys & children's vehicles
VP: Lee Loetz
VP: Carolyn Matthews
VP: Tim Nolan
Comm Dir: Janis Van Tine
IT Man: Leone Zion
Natl Sales: Susan Vigil
VP Sls: David Opell
Genl Couns: Stefanie Schaeffer

D-U-N-S 60-733-3221 IMP
IMPERIAL TRADING CO LLC
701 Edwards Ave, Harahan, LA 70123-3120
Tel (504) 733-1400 *Founded/Ownrshp* 1916
Sales 183.7MM^E *EMP* 230^E
SIC 5194 5141 5145 Cigarettes; Groceries, general line; Candy; Cigarettes; Groceries, general line; Candy
Pr: Emile Cantrell
COO: Bill Kearney IV
CFO: Gil Stroud Jr
Sr VP: Gilbert Stroud
Exec: John Georges
VP Admn: Cheryl Analla
Info Man: Brandon Pham
VP Opers: Richard Duhon
Sales Exec: Lee Farrell

IMPERIAL TURF PRODUCTS
See JAMES MORIEL

D-U-N-S 07-999-3164
IMPERIAL TURF PRODUCTS INC (CA)
1485 N Manassero St, Anaheim, CA 92807-1938
Tel (714) 696-7501 *Founded/Ownrshp* 2005
Sales 54.0MM^E *EMP* 40^E
SIC 3523 Cabs, tractors & agricultural machinery
CEO: Gabriel Moriel

D-U-N-S 01-229-4153
IMPERIAL UNIFIED SCHOOL DISTRICT
219 N E St, Imperial, CA 92251-1176
Tel (760) 355-3200 *Founded/Ownrshp* 1906
Sales 29.8MM *EMP* 300
Accts Wilkinson Hadley & Co Llp E
SIC 8211 Public elementary & secondary schools; High school, junior or senior; School board; Public elementary & secondary schools; High school, junior or senior; School board
Pr: Jill Tucker

IMPERIAL VALLEY COLLEGE
See IMPERIAL COMMUNITY COLLEGE DISTRICT (INC)

D-U-N-S 82-517-6105 IMP
IMPERIAL VALLEY FOODS INC
1961 Buchanan Ave, Calexico, CA 92231-4306
Tel (760) 203-1896 *Founded/Ownrshp* 2006
Sales 38.4MM^E *EMP* 300
SIC 2037 Frozen fruits & vegetables; Frozen fruits & vegetables
Pr: Gustavo Cabellero Jr
**Treas:* Edna Cabellero
**VP:* Fernando Cabellero

IMPERIAL VENDING
See ESTEY CORP

D-U-N-S 04-659-2515 EXP
IMPERIAL WESTERN PRODUCTS INC
BIOTANE PUMPING
86600 Avenue 54, Coachella, CA 92236-3812
Tel (760) 398-0815 *Founded/Ownrshp* 1966
Sales 138.4MM^E *EMP* 289
SIC 5159 2841 2869

D-U-N-S 00-514-1684 IMP
IMPERIAL WOODWORKING CO
310 N Woodwork Ln, Palatine, IL 60067-4933
Tel (847) 221-2107 *Founded/Ownrshp* 1963
Sales 45.4MM^E *EMP* 200
SIC 2541 Store fixtures, wood; Store fronts, prefabricated: wood; Store fixtures, wood; Store fronts, prefabricated: wood
Ch Bd: Frank Huschitt Sr
**Pr:* Frank Huschitt III
VP: Marcus Burggraf
VP: Paul Garvin

*VP: Marion Huschitt
VP: Richard Stiers
Plnt Mgr: Mike Wright

D-U-N-S 87-985-0840 IMP
IMPERIAL ZINC CORP
1031 E 103rd St, Chicago, IL 60628-3007
Tel (773) 264-5900 Founded/Ownrshp 1994
Sales 27.2MM^E EMP 85
SIC 3341 Secondary nonferrous metals; Secondary nonferrous metals
Pr: David Kozin
*Sec: Michael Weinger
Genl Mgr: Dave Goss
VP Sls: Aaron Stankewicz

D-U-N-S 00-328-9444 IMP/EXP
IMPERIAL-SAVANNAH LP
(Suby of IMPERIAL - SAVANNAH) ★
201 Oxnard Dr, Savannah, GA 31407-2409
Tel (912) 721-3329 Founded/Ownrshp 1916, 1997
Sales 24.5MM^E EMP 125
SIC 2062 2063 4225 4213 Cane sugar refining; Granulated cane sugar from purchased raw sugar or syrup; Beet sugar from beet sugar refinery; Granulated sugar from sugar beets; Liquid sugar from sugar beets; General warehousing; Trucking, except local; Cane sugar refining; Granulated cane sugar from purchased raw sugar or syrup; Beet sugar from beet sugar refinery; Granulated sugar from sugar beets; Liquid sugar from sugar beets; General warehousing; Trucking, except local
Pt: James M Kelly
*Pt: Walter Kress
*Pt: Benjamin A Oxnard Jr
*Pt: David H Roche
*Pt: William F Schwer
*Pt: J Eric Story

D-U-N-S 14-077-9922
▲ IMPERVA INC
3400 Bridge Pkwy Ste 200, Redwood City, CA 94065-1195
Tel (650) 345-9000 Founded/Ownrshp 2002
Sales 164.0MM EMP 723^E
Tkr Sym IMPV Exch NYS
SIC 7371 Computer software development & applications; Computer software development & applications
Pr: Anthony J Bettencourt
*Ch Bd: Shlomo Kramer
*Pr: Anthony Bettencourt
CFO: Terrence J Schmid
Chf Mktg O: Kim Decarlis
Ofcr: Michael Mooney
Sr VP: Meg Bear
Sr VP: Merav Davidson
Sr VP: Brett Hooper
Sr VP: Mark Kraynak
Sr VP: Tram T PHI
VP: Anthony Dumont
VP: Jason Huey
VP: Kurt Michael
VP: Gary Pfeiffer
VP: Enrique Pla
VP: Karl Soderlund
Board of Directors: Greg Clark, Geraldine Elliott, Charles Giancarlo, Theresia Gouw, Steven Krausz, Albert A Pimentel, Frank Slootman, Allan Tessler, James Tolonen

D-U-N-S 04-248-7116
IMPEX SYSTEMS GROUP INC
667 Nw 29th St, Miami, FL 33127-3826
Tel (305) 573-0163 Founded/Ownrshp 1982
Sales 23.9MM^E EMP 200
SIC 5072 2842 Hardware; Specialty cleaning, polishes & sanitation goods; Hardware; Specialty cleaning, polishes & sanitation goods
Pr: David Weck
*VP: Steve Berenson
VP: Michel Delmas

D-U-N-S 01-558-0249 IMP
IMPINJ INC
400 Frview Ave N Ste 1200, Seattle, WA 98109
Tel (206) 517-5300 Founded/Ownrshp 2000
Sales 41.2MM^E EMP 130^E
SIC 3674 Semiconductor circuit networks; Semiconductor circuit networks
V Ch: Chris Diorio
Pr: Bill Ashley
Pr: Eric Brodersen
Pr: Bill Colleran
Pr: William T Colleran
CFO: Evan Fein
Bd of Dir: Clinton Bybee
Sr VP: Scott Medford
Sr VP: Walter X Palhetas
VP: Craig Cotton
VP: Vince Moretti
Comm Dir: Kerstin Kurth
Board of Directors: Steve Arnold

D-U-N-S 86-885-6969
IMPLANT DIRECT SYBRON MFG LLC
3050 E Hillcrest Dr, Westlake Village, CA 91362-3171
Tel (818) 444-3300 Founded/Ownrshp 2007
Sales 40.1MM^E EMP 200
SIC 8021 Dental clinic; Dental clinic
Pr: Gerald A Niznick
Ex VP: Tom Stratton
VP: Philip Davis
Exec: Ginger Page
CTO: Kevin Corcoran
QA Dir: Fenton Harvey
IT Man: Erika Coffin
Mtls Mgr: Vicki Pualengco
Mktg Mgr: Robin Reck
Manager: Thomas Gregor
Manager: Dan Krapf

D-U-N-S 83-138-4883
IMPLICIT OIL & GAS LP
8150 N Cntrl Expy # 1200, Dallas, TX 75206-1991
Tel (214) 891-8558 Founded/Ownrshp 2005
Sales 22.0MM EMP 2
SIC 1382 Oil & gas exploration services; Oil & gas exploration services
Ltd Pt: Ed Boutte
Genl Pt: B K Funds GP

D-U-N-S 36-153-1585 IMP/EXP
IMPLUS FOOTCARE LLC
2001 Tw Alexander Dr, Durham, NC 27709-0184
Tel (919) 544-7900 Founded/Ownrshp 1989
Sales 120.0MM^E EMP 251
SIC 5139 Shoe accessories; Shoe accessories
CEO: Seth Richards
Pr: Steve Couder
*Pr: Todd Vore
*CFO: Bill Alfano
*Ex VP: Steve Head
Ex VP: Alden Mills
VP: Matt Carter
VP: Ian Maccoll
Genl Mgr: Elizabeth Henley
Natl Sales: Matt Brucker
Natl Sales: Drew Davies

D-U-N-S 19-396-3469
IMPORT CITY INC
EGLIN BMW-MAZDA
1006 Beal Pkwy Nw, Fort Walton Beach, FL 32547-1404
Tel (850) 863-2161 Founded/Ownrshp 1963
Sales 47.3MM^E EMP 150
SIC 5511 7538 Automobiles, new & used; General automotive repair shops; Automobiles, new & used; General automotive repair shops
Pr: Gerald M Hollingsworth
*Sec: Doyle Reeves
VP: Vince Wiggins

D-U-N-S 08-717-7879 IMP
IMPORT COLLECTION
TIC
7885 Nelson Rd, Panorama City, CA 91402-6045
Tel (818) 782-3060 Founded/Ownrshp 1967
Sales 27.5MM^E EMP 70
Accts Magidof Sadat & Gilmore Llp
SIC 5199 Gifts & novelties
CEO: David Mehdyzadeh
*Sec: Sina Mehdyzadeh
*VP: Samy Mehdyzadeh

IMPORT DIRECT
See E & S INTERNATIONAL ENTERPRISES INC

D-U-N-S 07-942-4232
IMPORT FRONT ENDS & PARTS
LEROY WILLIAMS JR
7009 Estate Tutu, St Thomas, VI 00802-1739
Tel (340) 514-4331 Founded/Ownrshp 2012
Sales 50.0MM EMP 2
SIC 7389 Automobile recovery service; Automobile recovery service
Owner: Leroy Williams Jr

D-U-N-S 17-591-2286
IMPORT MEX DISTRIBUTORS INC
IMPORT-MEX DISTRIBUTOR
1240 W 13th St Bay 2, Riviera Beach, FL 33404-6639
Tel (561) 881-5581 Founded/Ownrshp 1996
Sales 29.1MM^E EMP 42
SIC 5141 Food brokers
Pr: Lorenzo G Aedo
*Treas: Leyda Solorzano
*VP: Lorenzo J Aedo
*VP: Luis E Solorzano

D-U-N-S 02-804-2836
IMPORT MOTORS INC
BMW CONCORD
1967 Market St, Concord, CA 94520-2626
Tel (925) 682-3577 Founded/Ownrshp 1967
Sales 71.8MM^E EMP 250
SIC 5511 Automobiles, new & used; Automobiles, new & used
Pr: Robert Day
*VP: Mark Day
Sales Asso: Gary Boynton

D-U-N-S 17-497-4865 IMP
IMPORT SPECIALTIES INC
HEARTLAND AMERICA
8085 Century Blvd, Chaska, MN 55318-3056
Tel (952) 361-3640 Founded/Ownrshp 1985
Sales 80.1MM^E EMP 325
SIC 7549 High performance auto repair & service; High performance auto repair & service
Ch Bd: Bruce Brekke
*Pr: Mark Platt
VP: Thomas Bulver
Netwrk Mgr: Gina Deboer
Web Dev: Marc Mutchler
Web Dev: Johann Speer
Mktg Mgr: Sue Mendenhall
Genl Couns: Dan Maertens

IMPORT-MEX DISTRIBUTOR
See IMPORT MEX DISTRIBUTORS INC

IMPORTED AUTOMOTIVE PARTS
See A P I INC

D-U-N-S 05-824-9426
IMPORTED CAR STORE INC
VOLVO
(Suby of DINGMAN GROUP INC) ★
1432 S Harbor City Blvd, Melbourne, FL 32901-3211
Tel (321) 727-3788 Founded/Ownrshp 1975
Sales 32.6MM^E EMP 105
SIC 5511 5521 Automobiles, new & used; Used car dealers; Automobiles, new & used; Used car dealers
Owner: William Dingman
*Sec: Richard Dingman

D-U-N-S 09-869-2643
IMPORTED CARS OF MARYLAND INC
COLLEGE PARK HONDA
9500 Baltimore Ave, College Park, MD 20740-1360
Tel (301) 441-1313 Founded/Ownrshp 1991
Sales 55.2MM^E EMP 150
SIC 5511 5521 Automobiles, new & used; Used car dealers; Automobiles, new & used; Used car dealers
Ch Bd: Robert M Rosenthal
*Pr: Richard Patterson
*Treas: Donald Bavely
Sls Mgr: Harold Stephens
Sales Asso: Pia Glenn

IMPORTED TREASURES
See ARTERIORS IMPORT TRADING CO

IMPORTEX
See FIBREWORKS CORP

D-U-N-S 06-255-9216 EXP
IMPORTS AUTOMOTIVE CO
HENDRICK BMW
6950 E Independence Blvd, Charlotte, NC 28227-9417
Tel (704) 535-0885 *Founded/Ownrshp 1975, 1986
Sales 21.3MM^E EMP 68
SIC 5511 5531 7538 Automobiles, new & used; Automotive parts; General automotive repair shops; Automobiles, new & used; Automotive parts; General automotive repair shops
Pt: John Desmond
Pr Mgr: John Dennison
Sls Mgr: Joe Pagano

D-U-N-S 96-908-5518
IMPOSSIBLE FOODS INC
525 Chesapeake Dr, Redwood City, CA 94063-4724
Tel (650) 461-4385 Founded/Ownrshp 2011
Sales 47.2MM^E EMP 60
SIC 5141 Food brokers
CEO: Patrick Brown

D-U-N-S 14-657-4673 IMP
IMPREMEDIA LLC
LA RAZA
(Suby of US HISPANIC MEDIA INC) ★
1 Metrotech Ctr Fl 18, Brooklyn, NY 11201-3949
Tel (212) 807-4785 Founded/Ownrshp 2012
Sales 87.8MM^E EMP 566
SIC 2711 Newspapers: publishing only, not printed on site; Newspapers: publishing only, not printed on site
*COO: Francisco Seghezzo
VP: Jorge Ayala
VP: Olga Casabona
Sls Mgr: Leslie Russell

D-U-N-S 01-118-2784
IMPRES TECHNOLOGY SOLUTIONS INC
10330 Pioneer Blvd # 280, Santa Fe Springs, CA 90670-8226
Tel (562) 298-4030 Founded/Ownrshp 2001
Sales 29.0MM^E EMP 28
SIC 5045 Computers, peripherals & software; Systems engineering, computer related; Value-added resellers, computer systems; Custom computer programming services; Systems engineering consultant, ex. computer or professional; Computers, peripherals & software
Pr: Richard Fu
*VP: Carl Nolasco
VP: John Podolak
Mktg Dir: Teresa Wang

D-U-N-S 06-458-0129
IMPRESA AEROSPACE LLC
344 W 157th St, Gardena, CA 90248-2135
Tel (310) 354-1200 Founded/Ownrshp 1987
Sales 103.3MM^E EMP 320
SIC 3728 3444 Aircraft parts & equipment; Sheet metalwork; Aircraft parts & equipment; Sheet metalwork
CEO: Scott Smith
VP: Dennis Fitzgerald
*VP: David Hirsch
Genl Mgr: Jose Banuelos
Genl Mgr: John Byon
QA Dir: Peter Billante
QC Dir: Ron Williams
Ql Cn Mgr: Vince Flores

D-U-N-S 02-136-6930 IMP/EXP
▲ IMPRESO INC
TSTIMPRESO
652 Southwestern Blvd, Coppell, TX 75019-4419
Tel (972) 462-0100 Founded/Ownrshp 2000
Sales 83.3MM EMP 170
Tkr Sym ZCOM Exch OTO
SIC 2761 2679 2086 Manifold business forms; Telegraph, teletype & adding machine paper; Paper products, converted; Water, pasteurized: packaged in cans, bottles, etc.; Manifold business forms; Telegraph, teletype & adding machine paper; Paper products, converted; Water, pasteurized: packaged in cans, bottles, etc.
Ch Bd: Marshall D Sorokwasz
*VP: Susan M Atkins
*VP: Jeff Boren
*VP: John L Graves
Trfc Mgr: Debbie Gomez
Manager: Greg Allred
Manager: Don Cozzi
Manager: Clint Howard
Manager: Adam Smith

D-U-N-S 12-935-7757 IMP
IMPRESSION INKS LTD
7333 Jack Newell Blvd N, Fort Worth, TX 76118-7100
Tel (817) 590-9711 Founded/Ownrshp 1999
Sales 20.4MM^E EMP 37
SIC 2893 Printing ink; Printing ink
Pr: Jesse Samaniego
VP: Gilly Bain

D-U-N-S 04-539-2925
IMPRESSIONS INC
1050 Westgate Dr, Saint Paul, MN 55114-1067
Tel (651) 646-1050 Founded/Ownrshp 1967
Sales 26.5MM^E EMP 250
SIC 3086 2759

D-U-N-S 07-125-9436 IMP
IMPRESSIONS MARKETING GROUP INC
7951 Angleton Ct, Lorton, VA 22079-1012
Tel (703) 550-6902 Founded/Ownrshp 1982
Sales 50.9MM^E EMP 280
Accts E Cohen And Company Cpa S R
SIC 2541 2431 2521 2434 1751 7336 Store fixtures, wood; Showcases, except refrigerated: wood; Millwork; Wood office furniture; Wood kitchen cabinets; Carpentry work; Store fixture installation; Graphic arts & related design; Store fixtures, wood; Showcases, except refrigerated: wood; Millwork; Wood office furniture; Wood kitchen cabinets; Carpentry work; Store fixture installation; Graphic arts & related design
Pr: Eric T Gerber
*CFO: Kevin R Goodale
*VP: John J Hendley
IT Man: Ted Stout

D-U-N-S 04-098-0182
IMPRESSIONS SOLUTIONS INC
1705 Industrial Park Rd, Columbus, MS 39701-8619
Tel (662) 329-5250 Founded/Ownrshp 2000
Sales 38.8MM EMP 30
SIC 5734 Printers & plotters: computers; Printers & plotters: computers
Pr: Ron Harper
*CFO: Randy McDade
*Genl Mgr: Lance Moore
Mktg Dir: Alicia Harper
Sls Dir: Greg Frost
Sales Asso: Amberly Starks

IMPRESSIVE LABELS
See DRG TECHNOLOGIES INC

D-U-N-S 07-687-7117
IMPRINT ENTERPRISES INC
VISION BUSINESS PRODUCTS
555 N Commons Dr, Aurora, IL 60504-4112
Tel (630) 505-1700 Founded/Ownrshp 1975
Sales 39.8MM^E EMP 50
SIC 5049 5045 5021 Bank equipment & supplies; Computer peripheral equipment; Office furniture; Bank equipment & supplies; Computer peripheral equipment; Office furniture
Pr: Robert L Conti Jr
IT Man: Robert Vickers
Opers Mgr: Louise Bewig
Natl Sales: Michael Freeman
Mktg Dir: Cindy Pawlowski
Sales Asso: Gara Dunmore

D-U-N-S 17-489-3412 EXP
IMPRINTS WHOLESALE INC
4690 Florence St, Denver, CO 80238-5001
Tel (303) 333-3200 Founded/Ownrshp 1992
Sales 39.6MM^E EMP 120
SIC 5136 5137 Sportswear, men's & boys'; Sportswear, women's & children's; Sportswear, men's & boys'; Sportswear, women's & children's
CEO: Scott Lynes
*Prin: Chas Roudebush

D-U-N-S 10-539-4956
▲ IMPRIVATA INC
10 Maguire Rd Ste 125, Lexington, MA 02421-3110
Tel (781) 674-2700 Founded/Ownrshp 2001
Sales 96.9MM EMP 429^E
Tkr Sym IMPR Exch NYS
SIC 7372 Prepackaged software; Application computer software; Business oriented computer software; Prepackaged software; Application computer software; Business oriented computer software
Pr: Omar Hussain
CFO: Jeffrey Kalowski
Chf Mktg O: Clay Ritchey
Ofcr: Sean Kelly
Sr VP: Thomas Brigiotta
Sr VP: Carina Edwards
Sr VP: Geoff Hogan
Sr VP: Christopher Shaw
VP: John Milton
Genl Mgr: Edward Gaudet
Snr Sftwr: Jay Tucker
Board of Directors: David Barrett, John Blaeser, John Halamka, Paul Maeder, David Orfao, Rodger Weismann

D-U-N-S 00-900-0191
■ IMPROMED LLC (WI)
(Suby of BUTLER ANIMAL HEALTH SUPPLY LLC) ★
304 Ohio St, Oshkosh, WI 54902-5888
Tel (920) 236-7070 Founded/Ownrshp 1981, 2011
Sales 48.8MM^E EMP 130
SIC 5045 Computer software; Computer peripheral equipment; Computer software; Computer peripheral equipment
Pr: Hallie A Detjen
VP: Terry Hendrickson
VP: William Randolph
Dir IT: Matt Kempf
Sftwr Eng: Bradley Bogenschutz
Sftwr Eng: Scott Chamberlain
Sls Dir: Patrick Curran
Sales Asso: Christopher Maas
Snr Mgr: Rory Karle

IMPROV ELECTRONICS
See KENT DISPLAYS INC

D-U-N-S 05-196-2090
IMPROVED CONSTRUCTION METHODS INC
ICM
1040 N Redmond Rd, Jacksonville, AR 72076-3656
Tel (501) 982-7715 Founded/Ownrshp 1970
Sales 35.6MM^E EMP 55^E
SIC 5082 General construction machinery & equipment; General construction machinery & equipment
Pr: Bruce McFadden
*CFO: Jeff Jackson
Rgnl Mgr: Jack Sikes
Snr Mgr: Nathan Elam
Board of Directors: Roy Brown, Mark McFadden

IMPROVING ENTERPRISES
See IMPROVING HOLDINGS LLC

D-U-N-S 61-731-4542
IMPROVING HOLDINGS LLC
IMPROVING ENTERPRISES
16633 Dallas Pkwy Ste 100, Addison, TX 75001-6894
Tel (214) 613-4444 Founded/Ownrshp 2007

Sales 24.1MM^E *EMP* 171^E
SIC 8742 7371 Training & development consultant; Computer software systems analysis & design, custom; Computer software development & applications; Training & development consultant; Computer software systems analysis & design, custom; Computer software development & applications
Pr: Curtis A Hite
**Sr VP:* Barry Rogers
VP: Michelle Cook
**VP:* Ricardo Deanda
**VP:* Todd Girvin
Mktg Dir: Melissa Meeker

D-U-N-S 00-997-1727
■ **IMPSAT FIBER NETWORKS INC**
(*Suby of* LEVEL 3 GC LIMITED)
2040 N Dixie Hwy, Wilton Manors, FL 33305-2255
Tel (954) 779-7171 *Founded/Ownrshp* 2007
Sales 111.0MM^E *EMP* 1,352
SIC 4899 Communication signal enhancement network system; Communication signal enhancement network system
Ch Bd: Ricardo Verdagaer
COO: Hector Alonzo
CFO: Hector Alonso
Ex VP: Marcelo Girotti
Ex VP: Mariano Torre Gomez
Sr VP: Rodolfo Arroyo
Sr VP: Guillermo V Pardo
Sr VP: Jose Torres
VP: Laurinda Pang

D-U-N-S 78-055-3632 IMP
IMPULSE MANUFACTURING INC
55 Impulse Industrial Dr, Dawsonville, GA 30534-0926
Tel (706) 216-1700 *Founded/Ownrshp* 1987
Sales 47.0MM^E *EMP* 140^E
SIC 3444 3441 3449 7699 3469 3317 Sheet metalwork; Fabricated structural metal; Custom roll formed products; Industrial machinery & equipment repair; Metal stampings; Welded pipe & tubes

D-U-N-S 13-856-7065
IMPULSE MONITORING INC
10420 Lttle Ptxnt Pkwy, Columbia, MD 21044-3533
Tel (410) 740-2370 *Founded/Ownrshp* 2003
Sales 30.0MM *EMP* 170
SIC 7363 Medical help service; Medical help service
CEO: Gene Cattarina
Rgnl Mgr: Jim Persyn
Rgnl Mgr: Bobby Tasky
VP Sls: Christopher Brown

IMPULSE SHOPPER
See PENNYSAVER

IMRA
See RETAIL INDUSTRY LEADERS ASSOCIATION INC

D-U-N-S 61-522-9150
IMRA AMERICA INC
(*Suby of* AISIN SEIKI CO., LTD.)
1044 Woodridge Ave, Ann Arbor, MI 48105-9774
Tel (734) 669-7377 *Founded/Ownrshp* 1990
Sales 40.7MM *EMP* 60
Accts Pricewaterhousecoopers Llp De
SIC 8732 8731 3699 Research services, except laboratory; Commercial physical research; Electrical equipment & supplies; Research services, except laboratory; Commercial physical research; Electrical equipment & supplies
Pr: Takashi Omitsu
VP: Gyu Cho
Mktg Mgr: Len Deskalon
Doctor: Andrius Marcinkevicius

D-U-N-S 04-085-1255
IMREX LLC
55 Sandy Hill Rd, Oyster Bay, NY 11771-3110
Tel (516) 479-3675 *Founded/Ownrshp* 1997
Sales 48.1MM^E *EMP* 412
SIC 3679 Electronic circuits; Electronic circuits

IMRF
See ILLINOIS MUNICIPAL RETIREMENT FUND

IMRI
See INFORMATION MANAGEMENT RESOURCES INC

IMRIS
See DEERFIELD IMAGING INC

IMS
See INTERNATIONAL MEDICATION SYSTEMS LTD

IMS
See INTERNATIONAL MILL SERVICE INC

IMS
See INDUSTRIAL MAINTENANCE SERVICES INC

IMS
See IMMEDIATE MAILING SERVICES INC

IMS
See INTEGRATED MEDICAL SYSTEMS INTERNATIONAL INC

IMS
See INTERMODAL MANAGEMENT SYSTEM LLC

IMS
See INTEGRATED MEDICAL SYSTEMS INC

IMS BUHRKE-OLSON
See OLSON METAL PRODUCTS LLC

IMS BUHRKE-OLSON
See BUHRKE INDUSTRIES LLC

D-U-N-S 00-418-4909 IMP/EXP
IMS CO (OH)
INJECTION MOLDERS SUPPLY
10373 Stafford Rd, Chagrin Falls, OH 44023-5296
Tel (440) 543-1615 *Founded/Ownrshp* 1960
Sales 34.8MM^E *EMP* 60
SIC 5084 Industrial machinery & equipment; Plastic products machinery
CEO: Brad G Morse
**COO:* Jeffrey Sawicki
**Co-CEO:* Mary Ann Morris
Sales Asso: Dave Doyle
Sales Asso: Rolando Monzon

D-U-N-S 17-786-0801 EXP
IMS COMPANIES LLC
IMS COMPANIES, LLC OF DELAWARE
1 Innovation Dr, Des Plaines, IL 60016-3161
Tel (847) 391-8100 *Founded/Ownrshp* 2002
Sales 700.0MM^E *EMP* 2,191^E
SIC 3469 8711 Metal stampings; Engineering services

IMS COMPANIES, LLC OF DELAWARE
See IMS COMPANIES LLC

D-U-N-S 17-535-6265
IMS ELECTRONICS RECYCLING INC
I M S ELECTONICS RECYCLING
12455 Kerran St Ste 300, Poway, CA 92064-8834
Tel (360) 750-8883 *Founded/Ownrshp* 2007
Sales 43.4MM^E *EMP* 102
SIC 5065 Sound equipment, electronic; Sound equipment, electronic
CEO: Robert M Davis
**Pr:* Bob Davis
**CFO:* Teddy Davis
Brnch Mgr: Ed Seigel

D-U-N-S 00-512-3013 IMP
IMS ENGINEERED PRODUCTS LLC
AMCO ENGINEERING CO
(*Suby of* IMS COMPANIES LLC) ★
1 Innovation Dr, Des Plaines, IL 60016-3161
Tel (847) 391-8100 *Founded/Ownrshp* 2005
Sales 50.8MM^E *EMP* 163
SIC 3444 2522 3699 3469 2542 Housings for business machines, sheet metal; Office cabinets & filing drawers: except wood; Filing boxes, cabinets & cases: except wood; Office desks & tables: except wood; Electrical equipment & supplies; Metal stampings; Partitions & fixtures, except wood; Housings for business machines, sheet metal; Office cabinets & filing drawers: except wood; Filing boxes, cabinets & cases: except wood; Office desks & tables: except wood; Electrical equipment & supplies; Metal stampings; Partitions & fixtures, except wood
S&M/VP: Kevin Groom
Treas: Edward V Anderson
IT Man: Don Gorz

D-U-N-S 79-128-7746
IMS ENVIRONMENTAL SERVICES INC
HEPACO
1301 Marsh St, Norfolk, VA 23523-1735
Tel (757) 543-5718 *Founded/Ownrshp* 2005
Sales 24.6MM^E *EMP* 204^E
SIC 8748 4959 1799 8744 Environmental consultant; Oil spill cleanup; Dewatering; Facilities support services; Environmental consultant; Oil spill cleanup; Dewatering; Facilities support services
Pr: Ronald Horton Jr
**Pr:* Horton Jr Ron
**CEO:* Horton Sr Ron
**Treas:* Horton Richard G
**Treas:* Vonda Hall
VP: Robert May
**VP:* May Robert W
Genl Mgr: Brenda Hanbury
Sfty Mgr: Larry Brittain

D-U-N-S 79-121-3692 IMP
IMS GEAR GEORGIA INC
(*Suby of* IMS GEAR GMBH)
1234 Palmour Dr Ste B, Gainesville, GA 30501-6857
Tel (770) 840-9600 *Founded/Ownrshp* 2005
Sales 75.3MM^E *EMP* 300
SIC 3089 3449 Plastic processing; Miscellaneous metalwork; Plastic processing; Miscellaneous metalwork
CEO: Greg Vitek
**Pr:* Norbert Willman
**CFO:* Tim A Corbin
**Treas:* Knut Heidelback
**VP:* Bernd Schilling

D-U-N-S 88-362-1153 IMP
IMS GEAR HOLDING INC
(*Suby of* IMS GEAR GMBH)
1234 Palmour Dr Ste B, Gainesville, GA 30501-6857
Tel (770) 840-9600 *Founded/Ownrshp* 1994
Sales 24.6MM^E *EMP* 100
SIC 3089 Injection molding of plastics
Pr: Clemens Rosenstiel
**Treas:* Knut Heidelbach
VP: Juergen Moller
VP: Greg Vitek
Genl Mgr: Tom Paladino
Mfg Mgr: Dextory Smith
Opers Mgr: Ken Turk
Sls Mgr: Gerald Valentine

D-U-N-S 79-347-7923 IMP
IMS GEAR VIRGINIA INC
489 Progress Ln, Virginia Beach, VA 23454-3477
Tel (757) 468-8810 *Founded/Ownrshp* 2007
Sales 34.3MM^E *EMP* 105
SIC 5013 Automotive supplies & parts
Pr: Guenter Weissenseel
**CFO:* Andreas Steiert
**Sec:* Hans-Michael Weissenseel

D-U-N-S 07-935-5550
▲ **IMS HEALTH HOLDINGS INC**
83 Wooster Hts Fl 5, Danbury, CT 06810-7552
Tel (203) 448-4600 *Founded/Ownrshp* 2009
Sales 2.6MMM *EMP* 10,200^E
Accts Pricewaterhousecoopers Llp N
Tkr Sym IMS *Exch* NYS
SIC 7374 Data processing & preparation; Data processing & preparation
Pr: ARI Bousbib
CFO: Ronald E Bruehlman
Sr VP: Harvey A Ashman
Sr VP: Robert Chu
Sr VP: Kevin C Knightly
Sr VP: Stefan Linn
Sr VP: Jos Luis Fern Ndez
Sr VP: Satwinder Sian
VP: Harshan Bhangdia
VP: Jon Resnick
VP: Mason Tenaglia

D-U-N-S 02-302-0097
■ **IMS HEALTH INC**
(*Suby of* HEALTHCARE TECHNOLOGY INTERMEDIATE HOLDINGS INC) ★
83 Wooster Hts Fl 5, Danbury, CT 06810-7552
Tel (203) 448-4600 *Founded/Ownrshp* 2010
Sales 2.6MMM *EMP* 7,275
SIC 7379 Business consultant; Market analysis or research; Computer related maintenance services
CEO: ARI Bousbib
Pr: Adel Al-Saleh
CFO: Christos Drakapoulos
**Treas:* Jeffrey Ford
**Sr VP:* Harvey A Ashman
Sr VP: Bruce Boggs
VP: Kabir Shahani
Exec: Bill Hiter
Comm Dir: Phil N Oliva
Brnch Mgr: Thomas Pacilio
Genl Mgr: Patty Obermaier
Board of Directors: Karen Katen

D-U-N-S 10-395-5035 IMP
■ **IMS INC**
(*Suby of* ANIXTER INTERNATIONAL INC) ★
340 Progress Dr, Manchester, CT 06042-2282
Tel (860) 649-4415 *Founded/Ownrshp* 1982
Sales 36.1MM^E *EMP* 99
SIC 5051 5063 5251 Wire; Cable conduit; Hardware; Wire; Cable conduit; Hardware
Pr: Giulio Berardesca
Pr: William Hale
Opers Mgr: Richard McKinnon
Sls Mgr: Charlie Moran

D-U-N-S 15-888-1078
IMS MARKETING INC
INSURANCE MANAGEMENT SERVICES
731 N Taylor St Ste 100, Amarillo, TX 79107-5281
Tel (806) 371-7877 *Founded/Ownrshp* 1983
Sales NA *EMP* 91
SIC 6411 Insurance claim processing, except medical
Pr: Joe Clark
**VP:* Stephen Willingham

D-U-N-S 78-430-1657
IMS MASONRY INC
335 S 1250 W, Lindon, UT 84042-1638
Tel (801) 796-8420 *Founded/Ownrshp* 1977
Sales 20.3MM *EMP* 165
Accts Squire & Company Pc Orem Uta
SIC 1741 Masonry & other stonework; Masonry & other stonework
Pr: Alan Johnson
**VP:* Richard H Holdaway
Ex Dir: Jeff Buczkiewicz

IMS PET INDUSTRIES
See IMS TRADING CORP

D-U-N-S 02-913-6058 EXP
IMS RECYCLING SERVICES INC
2697 Main St, San Diego, CA 92113-3612
Tel (619) 231-2521 *Founded/Ownrshp* 1954
Sales 51.3MM^E *EMP* 173
SIC 5093 Ferrous metal scrap & waste; Ferrous metal scrap & waste
CEO: Robert M Davis
CFO: Teddy Davis
**CFO:* Theodora Davis Inman
**Ch:* Ruth Davis
**VP:* Deborah Odle
Opers Mgr: Kathrine Rehder

D-U-N-S 60-412-3158 IMP
■ **IMS TRADING CORP**
IMS PET INDUSTRIES
(*Suby of* BREEDERS CHOICE) ★
34 Passaic St, Wood Ridge, NJ 07075-1004
Tel (973) 249-0026 *Founded/Ownrshp* 2015
Sales 28.4MM^E *EMP* 50^E
SIC 5191 Animal feeds
Pr: Samuel Blackorsky
CFO: Barry Granite
**VP:* Milton Gittelman
Software D: Steve Zembriski

D-U-N-S 83-581-2264
IMSA FUND FOR ADVANCEMENT OF EDUCATION
1500 W Sullivan Rd, Aurora, IL 60506-1000
Tel (630) 907-5000 *Founded/Ownrshp* 1986
Sales 1.7MM *EMP* 300
SIC 7389 Fund raising organizations; Fund raising organizations
Pr: Glenn Max McGee

D-U-N-S 11-845-5349
IMSA STEEL CORP
STEELSCAPE
(*Suby of* BLUESCOPE STEEL LIMITED)
222 W Kalama River Rd, Kalama, WA 98625-9420
Tel (360) 673-8200 *Founded/Ownrshp* 2008
Sales 17.2MM^E *EMP* 316
SIC 3479 3441 Coating of metals & formed products; Fabricated structural metal; Coating of metals & formed products; Fabricated structural metal
Pr: Cesar Jarero

IMSCO
See INTERNATIONAL MANAGEMENT SERVICES CO INC

D-U-N-S 95-764-3976 IMP
IMSCORP
603 L St, Lincoln, NE 68508-2432
Tel (402) 474-6603 *Founded/Ownrshp* 1995
Sales 37.2MM^E *EMP* 200

SIC 3949 3544 2851 Softball equipment & supplies; Basketball equipment & supplies, general; Special dies, tools, jigs & fixtures; Jigs & fixtures; Epoxy coatings; Polyurethane coatings; Softball equipment & supplies; Basketball equipment & supplies, general; Special dies, tools, jigs & fixtures; Jigs & fixtures; Epoxy coatings; Polyurethane coatings
Pr: Elmer Wessel
**VP:* Nicholas J Cusick
IT Man: Karl Schlitt

IMT
See INNOVATIVE MICRO TECHNOLOGY INC

IMT GROUP
See IMT INSURANCE CO

D-U-N-S 06-962-7883
IMT INSURANCE CO
IMT GROUP
4445 Corporate Dr Ste 100, West Des Moines, IA 50266-5999
Tel (515) 327-2777 *Founded/Ownrshp* 1883
Sales NA *EMP* 189
SIC 6331 7374 Property damage insurance; Fire, marine & casualty insurance & carriers; Data processing service; Property damage insurance; Fire, marine & casualty insurance & carriers; Data processing service
VP: Sean Kennedy
**Treas:* Gregory J Blythe
**Sr VP:* Dennis Patterson
**VP:* Brad Buchanan
**VP:* Chris Owenson
**VP:* Mark Vasey
Dir IT: Tom Minger
Dir IT: Anne West
IT Man: Terry Staton
Opers Mgr: Jeff Wilson
VP Mktg: Rich Nauman
Board of Directors: Sharon K Heaton, Wilmer D Honnold, Richard M Willis

IMTAS
See INNOVATIVE MANAGEMENT & TECHNOLOGY APPROACHES INC

D-U-N-S 10-309-7556
IMTECH CORP
ACTIVU
301 Round Hill Dr, Rockaway, NJ 07866-1224
Tel (973) 366-5550 *Founded/Ownrshp* 1983
Sales 25.0MM *EMP* 65
SIC 7373 Systems integration services
CEO: Paul Noble
CFO: Rich Aguinaldo
VP: Mark Roy
VP: John Stark
Off Mgr: Louisa Valentin
CTO: Krzysztof Bryczkowski
Sftwr Eng: Kevin Anthony
Sftwr Eng: Joseph Delgado
Sftwr Eng: Matthew Ferreira
Sftwr Eng: Sasha Rukodanov
Opers Mgr: Henry Carabba

D-U-N-S 61-609-4348
IMTECH GRAPHICS INC
545 Dell Rd, Carlstadt, NJ 07072-2211
Tel (201) 933-8002 *Founded/Ownrshp* 1994
Sales 35.4MM^E *EMP* 120
SIC 2796 Color separations for printing; Color separations for printing
Pr: Gary Cordovano
Pr: Vincent Gathmann
**CFO:* Mark Cunningham
Sr VP: Jose Diaz
VP: John Adamus
VP: Mike Cordovano
VP: Michael Puccio
Info Man: Andrew Kazmierski
Prd Dir: Joe Lisella
VP Sls: Ralph Papaleo

D-U-N-S 02-648-5631 IMP
IMTECH MARINE USA INC
R H TRADING
(*Suby of* IMTECH MARINE B.V.)
8943 Gulf Fwy, Houston, TX 77017-7004
Tel (713) 941-2290 *Founded/Ownrshp* 1997
Sales 48.9MM^E *EMP* 110
SIC 5088 Marine supplies; Marine supplies
Pr: URS Rathgeb
**Ex VP:* Jeff Bigler
**Prin:* Jack C Haynie
Rgnl Mgr: Sam Boyd
Rgnl Mgr: Alexander Gimenez
Rgnl Mgr: Ugo Piasevoli
Ql Cn Mgr: Richard Beattie
Sls Mgr: Esther Aguirre
Sls Mgr: Mark Lane

IMTT
See INTERNATIONAL-MATEX TANK TERMINALS

IMW
See INDUSTRIAL MAINTENANCE WELDING & MACHINING CO INC

D-U-N-S 09-604-6474
IN CELEBRATION OF GOLF MANAGEMENT LLC
6440 N 56th St, Paradise Valley, AZ 85253-4141
Tel (480) 951-5771 *Founded/Ownrshp* 1999
Sales 6.8MM^E *EMP* 650
SIC 7992 Public golf courses; Public golf courses

D-U-N-S 07-843-2512
IN CORR ENERGY GROUP LLC
13275 E Fremont Pl # 200, Centennial, CO 80112-3986
Tel (720) 974-1657 *Founded/Ownrshp* 2012
Sales 26.8MM *EMP* 3
Accts Eks&H Lllp Denver Colorado
SIC 5172 Crude oil; Crude oil
Pr: Joe Purdy

D-U-N-S 12-766-6621
IN DEMAND LLC
345 Hudson St Fl 17, New York, NY 10014-4520
Tel (646) 638-8200 *Founded/Ownrshp* 1999

Sales 69.0MM^E EMP 150^E
SIC 4841 Cable & other pay television services; Cable & other pay television services
*Ex VP: Michael Berman
VP: James Dettman
VP: Tony Dunaif
VP: Emilio R N EZ
VP: David Ludder
VP: Jessica Marrone
VP: Emilio Nunez
VP: John Schultz
VP: Lori Wengrofsky
Creative D: Brendan Connors
Off Admin: Terry Brown

D-U-N-S 05-478-1841
IN DESIGN KITCHENS PLUS LLC
277 Main St Ste A, Millburn, NJ 07041-1174
Tel (973) 315-3155 Founded/Ownrshp 2010
Sales 57.2MM EMP 1
SIC 5722 Kitchens, complete (sinks, cabinets, etc.)
Pr: Andrea Costa

IN EVERYWAY GOURMET
See CELEBRITY FOODS INC

D-U-N-S 55-603-0641 IMP/EXP
IN GEAR FASHIONS INC
INGEAR
4401 Nw 167th St, Miami Gardens, FL 33055-4311
Tel (305) 830-2900 Founded/Ownrshp 1990
Sales 22.7MM^E EMP 150
SIC 2339 2329 Sportswear, women's; Beachwear: women's, misses' & juniors'; Men's & boys' sportswear & athletic clothing; Sportswear, women's; Beachwear: women's, misses' & juniors'; Men's & boys' sportswear & athletic clothing
Pr: Kevin N Frija
*VP: Jacob Levy

D-U-N-S 83-174-0464
■ **IN HOME HEALTH LLC**
HEARTLAND HM HALTHCARE HOSPICE
(Suby of MANOR CARE OF AMERICA INC) ★
333 N Summit St, Toledo, OH 43604-1531
Tel (419) 252-5500 Founded/Ownrshp 2010
Sales 19.4MM^E EMP 1,905^E
SIC 8082 Home health care services

D-U-N-S 36-127-4608
IN LINE COMMERCIAL CONSTRUCTION INC
18880 Sw Shaw St, Beaverton, OR 97078-1248
Tel (503) 642-5117 Founded/Ownrshp 1983
Sales 29.9MM EMP 68
Accts Akt Cpa And Business Consultan
SIC 1742 1542 Acoustical & ceiling work; Drywall; Nonresidential construction; Acoustical & ceiling work; Drywall; Nonresidential construction
CEO: Dave Flint
Sfty Mgr: Pat McLean
Board of Directors: Miranda Corrigan

D-U-N-S 96-779-3816
IN MOTION HOLDINGS LLC
19336 N 1425 East Rd, Hudson, IL 61748-7674
Tel (309) 452-4426 Founded/Ownrshp 2010
Sales 61.5MM EMP 270^E
Accts Heinold Banwart Ltd East Peor
SIC 4213 Trucking, except local; Trucking, except local
CFO: Bill Wettstein

IN SHAPE HEALTH CLUBS
See IN SHAPE MANAGEMENT CO

D-U-N-S 93-386-6295
IN SHAPE MANAGEMENT CO
IN SHAPE HEALTH CLUBS
6 S El Dorado St, Stockton, CA 95202-2804
Tel (209) 472-2231 Founded/Ownrshp 1993
Sales 9.0MM EMP 300
SIC 7991 Health club; Health club
Pr: Morton Rothbard
*CEO: Paul Rothbard
*CFO: Rob Farrens

IN STEP FOODSERVICE
See CHAIN LINK SERVICES LP

IN THE SWIM
See CORTZ INC

D-U-N-S 10-203-3461 IMP
IN TOUCH MINISTRIES INC
INTOUCH MINISTRY
3836 Dekalb Tec Pkwy, Atlanta, GA 30340-3604
Tel (770) 451-1001 Founded/Ownrshp 1982
Sales 88.5MM EMP 200
Accts Habif Arogeti & Wynne Llp Atl
SIC 7922 Television program, including commercial producers; Radio producers; Television program, including commercial producers; Radio producers
CEO: Phillip Bowen
*Pr: Charles F Stanley
CFO: Anita Clift
*CFO: Mitch Crowe
Ex VP: Brad Cornell
Ex VP: Corrin Fink
Sr VP: Van Mylar
VP: Keith Hurd
Creative D: Randy Drake
Ex Dir: Ian Currey
Brnch Mgr: Greg Peters

IN VENTIVE COMMERCIAL SERVICES
See VENTIV HEALTH INC

D-U-N-S 83-614-2224
IN-HOME SUPPORTIVE SERVICES CONSORTIUM OF SAN FRANCISCO INC
IHSS CONSORTIUM, THE
1035 Market St Ste L1, San Francisco, CA 94103-1666
Tel (415) 255-2079 Founded/Ownrshp 1994
Sales 20.5MM EMP 500
Accts Le Ho& Company Llp Daly City
SIC 8322 Individual & family services; Homemakers' service; Individual & family services; Homemakers' service
CEO: Gay Kaplan

Prin: Margaret Baran
Prin: Mark Burns
Prin: Debra J Dolch
Ex Dir: Donna Calame
Ex Dir: Andrew Gaines

D-U-N-S 02-914-4821
IN-N-OUT BURGERS
4199 Campus Dr Ste 900, Irvine, CA 92612-8604
Tel (949) 509-6200 Founded/Ownrshp 1963
Sales 386.9MM^E EMP 10,000
SIC 5812 Fast-food restaurant, chain; Fast-food restaurant, chain
Pr: Lynsi Martinez
CFO: Roger Kotch
CFO: Annette Neeley
*Treas: Tom Martin
*Ex VP: Darrell Chambliss
*Ex VP: Ken Iriart
*Sr VP: Kenneth Rose
*VP: Jim Little
VP: Arnold Wensinger
Dir Soc: Jennifer Knox
Dir Soc: Monique Macalinao
Dir Soc: Jordan Visu
Dir Soc: Laurie Visu

D-U-N-S 15-513-7524
IN-PACT INC
INDIANA EPILEPSY SERVICES
12300 Marshall St, Crown Point, IN 46307-4808
Tel (219) 464-8062 Founded/Ownrshp 1980
Sales 12.8MM EMP 330
SIC 8322 Social service center; Social service center
Pr: Mike Jones
*CFO: Ray Giacomin
*VP: Barbara Gillan

D-U-N-S 06-688-4172 IMP
IN-PLACE MACHINING CO INC
3811 N Holton St, Milwaukee, WI 53212-1213
Tel (414) 562-2000 Founded/Ownrshp 1955
Sales 20.3MM^E EMP 100
SIC 3599 3542 7692 Machine shop, jobbing & repair; Machine tools, metal forming type; Welding repair; Machine shop, jobbing & repair; Machine tools, metal forming type; Welding repair
Pr: Jonathan Eder
*Ch Bd: Ralph Eder
*VP: Dan Eder
*VP: Roger Norgel
VP: John Vretenar
Mktg Dir: Debbie Lentz

D-U-N-S 84-477-2199
IN-ROADS CREATIVE PROGRAMS INC
7955 Webster St Ste 7, Highland, CA 92346-3880
Tel (909) 864-1551 Founded/Ownrshp 2000
Sales 13.1MM^E EMP 763^E
SIC 8322 Children's aid society; Children's aid society
CEO: Sharon Barton

IN-SHAPE CITY
See IN-SHAPE HEALTH CLUBS LLC

D-U-N-S 07-877-8040
IN-SHAPE HEALTH CLUBS LLC
IN-SHAPE CITY
6 S El Dorado St Ste 700, Stockton, CA 95202-2804
Tel (209) 472-2231 Founded/Ownrshp 1981
Sales 25.1MM^E EMP 180
SIC 7991 Health club
CEO: Paul Rothbard
*Pr: Morton Rothbard
*VP: Rob Farrens
VP Opers: Steve Saxton

D-U-N-S 14-476-7043
IN-STORE OPPORTUNITIES INC
SUPERFRIDGE
362 Industrial Park Rd # 5, Middletown, CT 06457-1548
Tel (860) 632-8880 Founded/Ownrshp 1991
Sales 27.7MM^E EMP 400
SIC 7389 Design, commercial & industrial; Design, commercial & industrial
CEO: Leonard Rosinski
*CFO: Lisa Shattuck
*VP: Sherri Hult
*VP: Ira Lewis
Exec: Karen Longo
Mng Dir: Steve Frenda

D-U-N-S 07-917-0205
■ **IN-TER-SPACE SERVICES INC** (PA)
LICENSED AS CLEAR CHANNEL
(Suby of CLEAR CHANNEL OUTDOOR HOLDINGS INC) ★
7450 Tilghman St Ste 104, Allentown, PA 18106-9034
Tel (610) 395-8002 Founded/Ownrshp 1974, 2006
Sales 22.5MM^E EMP 145
SIC 7319 7311 Display advertising service; Advertising agencies; Display advertising service; Advertising agencies
CEO: Toby Sturek
*Treas: Brian Coleman
*VP: Scott Bick
*VP: Melissa Cleary
*VP: Pam Horn
IT Man: Raymond Frisch
VP Opers: Robert Lovell

IN-TOYS
See KIDS PREFERRED INC

D-U-N-S 01-525-2468
INA ACE HOLDINGS INC
(Suby of A C E) ★
436 Walnut St, Philadelphia, PA 19106-3703
Tel (215) 640-1000 Founded/Ownrshp 1998
Sales NA EMP 250
SIC 6411 Property & casualty insurance agent; Property & casualty insurance agent
CEO: Dominic Frederico
Pr: John Moore
*Pr: Susan Rivera
*Ex VP: Bruce L Kessler
Sr VP: Deborah Alleyne
Sr VP: Mark Gadaire

Sr VP: Connie Germano
Sr VP: Craig Hanrahan
Sr VP: Robert Omrod
Sr VP: Bryan Tedford
Sr VP: Alexander Wells
VP: Burt Carver
VP: Peter Demallie
VP: Mike Driscoll
VP: Lana Gurevich
VP: Diane Herkness
VP: Mary Kannon
VP: Henry Minissale
VP: Kelly Ravanis
*VP: Steven Reiss
VP: David Smith

D-U-N-S 09-613-8664 IMP
INABATA AMERICA CORP
(Suby of INABATA & CO., LTD.)
1270 Avenue Of The Americ, New York, NY 10020-1705
Tel (212) 586-7764 Founded/Ownrshp 1978
Sales 28.9MM^E EMP 34
SIC 5169 5065 5142 Chemicals, industrial & heavy; Electronic parts & equipment; Modems, computer; Meat, frozen: packaged
Pr: Masaru Inoue
*Pr: Naobumi Matsuki
*Genl Mgr: Taku Inoue

D-U-N-S 80-854-9216
INALERT SECURITY DISTRIBUTION INC
402 N 29th St, McAllen, TX 78501-7503
Tel (956) 687-1002 Founded/Ownrshp 1993
Sales 20.7MM EMP 6
SIC 5072 Security devices, locks
Pr: Lucy Rivero
*Sec: Rosa Maria Rivero
Genl Mgr: Terry Maldonado
Off Mgr: Diana Luevano

D-U-N-S 18-735-4233 IMP
INALFA ROAD SYSTEM INC
1370 Pacific Dr, Auburn Hills, MI 48326-1569
Tel (248) 371-3060 Founded/Ownrshp 1997
Sales 33.9MM^E EMP 464
Accts Plante & Moran Pllc Auburn H
SIC 3714 3231 Sun roofs, motor vehicle; Products of purchased glass; Sun roofs, motor vehicle; Products of purchased glass
Pr: Frederick L M Welschen
*Sec: Mary S Drexler

D-U-N-S 16-189-3557 IMP/EXP
INALFA ROOF SYSTEMS INC
INALFA-HOLLANDIA
(Suby of INALFA ROOF SYSTEMS GROUP B.V.)
1370 Pacific Dr, Auburn Hills, MI 48326-1569
Tel (248) 371-3060 Founded/Ownrshp 2011
Sales 270.0MM^E EMP 630
SIC 3714 Sun roofs, motor vehicle; Sun roofs, motor vehicle
Pr: Ton Hougen
Pr: Matthew Sosnoski
CFO: Wim Das
*CFO: Mary S Drexler
*Ex VP: Mike Smith
VP: Jarrod Fiengo
VP: Peter Lenkens
Prgrm Mgr: Frank Kuipers
CTO: Mike Schulte
MIS Dir: John Binerski
Tech Mgr: Kevin Deras

INALFA-HOLLANDIA
See INALFA ROOF SYSTEMS INC

D-U-N-S 10-749-4960
INAMAR LTD
(Suby of A C E) ★
1601 Chestnut St, Philadelphia, PA 19192-0003
Tel (215) 640-1000 Founded/Ownrshp 1977
Sales NA EMP 1,000
SIC 6321 Accident & health insurance; Accident & health insurance
CEO: Bryan Dowd

D-U-N-S 78-908-9989
INASMUCH FOUNDATION
210 Park Ave Ste 3150, Oklahoma City, OK 73102-5604
Tel (405) 604-5292 Founded/Ownrshp 2006
Sales 24.9MM EMP 3
Accts Ronald J Heusel Cpa Oklahom
SIC 8733 Noncommercial research organizations; Noncommercial research organizations
Prin: Robert Ross
CFO: Julie Jividen
Ofcr: Nancy Hodgkinson
Ofcr: Sarah Roberts

D-U-N-S 10-011-8236
INB FINANCIAL CORP
(Suby of BANORTE USA CORP) ★
1801 S 2nd St, McAllen, TX 78503-1353
Tel (956) 664-8406 Founded/Ownrshp 1987
Sales NA EMP 50^E
SIC 6019 Federal home loan banks
Pr: Samuel J Munafo
*Chf Cred: Dana Michael Long
*Ex VP: Mark Barker
*Ex VP: Horacio Cortes
*Ex VP: Marin Espinosa
*Ex VP: Karen Valdez
*Ex VP: Jesus A Zambrano
Sr VP: Mary Lou Vicencio

D-U-N-S 19-609-4283
■ **INC AEROJET ROCKETDYNE OF DE**
(Suby of AEROJET ROCKETDYNE HOLDINGS INC) ★
8900 De Soto Ave, Canoga Park, CA 91304-1967
Tel (818) 586-1000 Founded/Ownrshp 2013
Sales 564.8MM^E EMP 2,000^E
SIC 2869 3724 Rocket engine fuel, organic; Aircraft engines & engine parts; Rocket engine fuel, organic; Aircraft engines & engine parts
Pr: Eileen Drake
Sr VP: Paul Meyer
VP: Pete Gleszer

QA Dir: Thomas Parrill
IT Man: Yvette Velasquez
Snr Mgr: Jeff Jensen

D-U-N-S 07-555-6373
INC CITY OF ROCKY MOUNT
331 Faf Franklin St, Rocky Mount, NC 27802
Tel (252) 972-1200 Founded/Ownrshp 1867
Sales NA EMP 930
Accts Martin Starnes & Associates C
SIC 9111 Mayors' offices; ; Mayors' offices;
Ofcr: Ala Alzer
Ofcr: Daniel Joyner
Ofcr: Matthew Tillery
Exec: Tameka Kenan-Norman
Snr Mgr: Brian Sasser

INC CSE W-INDUSTRIES
See W CSE INDUSTRIES INC

INC ESSENTRA FILTER PRODUCTS
See ESSENTRA FILTER PRODUCTS INC

INC, MODEC INTERNATIONAL
See MODEC (USA) INC

D-U-N-S 18-327-7938
INC RESEARCH INSTITUTIONS FOR SEISMOLOGY
IRIS
1200 New York Ave Nw # 400, Washington, DC 20005-3928
Tel (202) 682-2220 Founded/Ownrshp 1985
Sales 39.1MM EMP 59
Accts Mcgladrey Llp Gaithersburg
SIC 8733 Scientific research agency; Scientific research agency
Pr: Robert Betrick
*CFO: Candy Shin
Dir: Ray Willemann
*Prin: David Simpson
Prgrm Mgr: John Taber
Info Man: Robert Newman
Sftwr Eng: Yazan Suleiman

D-U-N-S 96-362-1776
INC RESEARCH LLC
3201 Beechleaf Ct Ste 600, Raleigh, NC 27604-1500
Tel (919) 876-9300 Founded/Ownrshp 2010
Sales 1.1MMM^E EMP 5,119
SIC 8731 Medical research, commercial; Medical research, commercial
CEO: Jamie Macdonald
*Pr: John Potthoff
*CEO: James T Ogle
*COO: Alistair Macdonald
*CFO: David Gill
CFO: Dan Harnett
CFO: Gregory S Rush
CFO: Jim Stelten
Ofcr: Michael L Corrado
Ofcr: Malcolm Fletcher
Ex VP: John Barker
*Ex VP: Neil Ferguson
Ex VP: Nicholas Kenny
Ex VP: Neil Macallister
Ex VP: Mark Roseman
Ex VP: Judy Swilley
Sr VP: Richard Mark
Sr VP: Chris Smyth
Sr VP: Tom Zoda
VP: Tim Dietlin
VP: Hans-Peter Guler

INC SGS INTERNATIONAL
See PLASTIC PACKAGING INC

D-U-N-S 06-472-4958
INC VILLAGE OF FREEPORT
46 N Ocean Ave, Freeport, NY 11520-3023
Tel (516) 377-2200 Founded/Ownrshp 1892
Sales NA EMP 330
SIC 9111 Mayors' offices; ; Mayors' offices;
Treas: Ismaela Hernandez
Trst: Jorge Martinez
Trst: Carmen Pineyro

D-U-N-S 06-034-5626
INC VILLAGE OF GARDEN CITY
351 Stewart Ave, Garden City, NY 11530-4528
Tel (516) 742-5800 Founded/Ownrshp 1919
Sales NA EMP 312
Accts Albrecht Viggiano Zureck & Co
SIC 9111 Mayors' offices; ; Mayors' offices;
Treas: Frank Kelly
Treas: Robert L Schoee
*Treas: Robert L Schoelle

D-U-N-S 04-745-6025
INC VILLAGE OF HEMPSTEAD
99 Nichols Ct, Hempstead, NY 11550-3166
Tel (516) 483-6200 Founded/Ownrshp 1853
Sales NA EMP 470^E
Accts Nawrocki Smith Llp Melville
SIC 9111 Mayors' offices; ; Mayors' offices;
*Treas: Ray Calame
*Treas: Baldwin Hamilton

D-U-N-S 01-600-5229
INCAPITAL HOLDINGS LLC
1800 N Military Trl # 400, Boca Raton, FL 33431-6364
Tel (561) 361-1100 Founded/Ownrshp 2000
Sales 21.2MM^E EMP 140
SIC 6211 Bond dealers & brokers; Bond dealers & brokers
Pr: David Ajifu
Pr: John Blanton
Pr: Laurie Bricker
Pr: Bill Consolino
Pr: Gerrit Gerritsen
Pr: John Marone
Pr: Mike Murphy
Pr: Justin Plante
Pr: Stephen Powers
Pr: John Swenson
Pr: Evan Zlotnick
VP: Marcia Fellerturnoy
VP: Tom Goin
VP: Daniel McGouran
VP: Carmen Palladino
VP: Paul Wexler

D-U-N-S 07-971-8931
INCARE HOME HEALTH CARE GROUP LLC
1820 Gravesend Neck Rd, Brooklyn, NY 11229-4511
Tel (718) 646-3777 Founded/Ownrshp 2013
Sales 10.0M EMP 374
SIC 8082 Oxygen tent service

D-U-N-S 02-701-5213
INCE DISTRIBUTING INC (TX)
2233 Nw Loop 410, San Antonio, TX 78230-5308
Tel (210) 341-7161 Founded/Ownrshp 1957
Sales 55.1MM^E EMP 200
SIC 5075 5064 Air conditioning equipment, except room units; Electrical heating equipment; Electrical appliances, television & radio; Air conditioning equipment, except room units; Electrical heating equipment; Electrical appliances, television & radio
Pr: Raymond B Ince Sr
*VP: Nancy L Ince
IT Man: Sandy Collins
VP Mktg: Nancy Ince
Sls Mgr: Stephen Cotton

D-U-N-S 60-545-0758
INCENTIVE CONCEPTS LLC
2645 Metro Blvd, Maryland Heights, MO 63043-2411
Tel (314) 739-5489 Founded/Ownrshp 2005
Sales 50.0MM EMP 30
SIC 8742 Incentive or award program consultant; Distribution channels consultant; Incentive or award program consultant; Distribution channels consultant
Pr: Jeffery Reinberg
Pr: Joseph Liuzza
*Pr: Joseph Reinberg
*Pr: Brian Rivolta
COO: Shelby Anderson
*CFO: Dick Bueckman
*Ex VP: I Joseph Liuzza
VP: Vince McDonald
Dir Soc: Lauren Emge
CTO: Justin McDowell
Natl Sales: Marvel Jasnoch

D-U-N-S 96-018-7623
INCEPT CORP
4150 Belden Village St Nw # 205, Canton, OH 44718-3643
Tel (330) 649-9086 Founded/Ownrshp 1992
Sales 21.7MM^E EMP 200
SIC 7389 Telemarketing services; Telemarketing services
Pr: Jeffrey White
*Pr: Sam Falletta
VP: Wendy Afee
VP: Billie Johnson
VP: Mark Skolosh
VP: Dave Walter
*VP: Brad White
Dir IT: Mike Gashash
Dir IT: Brian Smith
Opers Mgr: Tom Moore

INCHCAPE SHIPPING SERVICES
See ISS MARINE SERVICES INC

D-U-N-S 01-136-3913 IMP/EXP
INCHEM CORP (NC)
(Suby of TOLL SOLUTIONS LLC) ★
12345 Steele Creek Rd, Charlotte, NC 28273-3738
Tel (803) 329-8000 Founded/Ownrshp 1993, 1997
Sales 25.5MM^E EMP 83^E
SIC 2821 2899 Plastics materials & resins; Chemical preparations; Plastics materials & resins; Chemical preparations
Pr: Stephen Crownshaw
*CFO: Craig M Mazzucca

D-U-N-S 78-496-5563
INCIPE LLC
HAWK FORD OF OAK LAWN
6100 W 95th St, Oak Lawn, IL 60453-2784
Tel (708) 599-6000 Founded/Ownrshp 2006
Sales 71.8MM^E EMP 117
SIC 5511 Automobiles, new & used; Automobiles, new & used
CEO: John Crane
Off Mgr: Mary Crawford
Sales Asso: John Swets

D-U-N-S 14-912-0243 IMP
INCIPIO TECHNOLOGIES INC
6001 Oak Cyn, Irvine, CA 92618-5200
Tel (949) 250-4929 Founded/Ownrshp 2000
Sales 46.1MM^E EMP 80^E
SIC 3577 Computer peripheral equipment; Computer peripheral equipment
CEO: Andy Fathollahi
Pr: Kristen Roney
Creative D: Vincent Lo
Dir IT: Kevin Suda
Opers Mgr: Mike Scaglione
Natl Sales: Rachel Dejong
Natl Sales: Macenzie Hadley

D-U-N-S 00-301-8710 IMP
INCLINATOR CO OF AMERICA (PA)
601 Gibson Blvd, Harrisburg, PA 17104-3215
Tel (717) 939-8420 Founded/Ownrshp 1923, 1943
Sales 24.5MM^E EMP 58
SIC 3534 Elevators & moving stairways
Pr: Melvyn R Bowman
Div Mgr: Paul Chance
Prd Mgr: Rick Hoffman
Manager: Mark Crispen

INCLINE EQUITY PARTNERS
See INCLINE MANAGEMENT CORP

D-U-N-S 04-346-7126
INCLINE MANAGEMENT CORP (PA)
INCLINE EQUITY PARTNERS
625 Liberty Ave, Pittsburgh, PA 15222-3110
Tel (412) 762-9244 Founded/Ownrshp 2010
Sales 26.1MM^E EMP 190
SIC 6726 Investment offices; Investors syndicates; Investment offices; Investors syndicates
Pr: Jack Glover
*VP: Wali Bacdayan
*VP: Justin Bertram
Exec: Cale Grove
Exec: Lauren McKibben
Exec: Charles Rossetti
Off Mgr: Michele Toomey

D-U-N-S 04-048-6375
INCLINE VILLAGE GENERAL IMPROVEMENT DISTRICT
GOLF COURSES AT INCLINE VLG
893 Southwood Blvd, Incline Village, NV 89451-7425
Tel (775) 832-1100 Founded/Ownrshp 1961
Sales 2.6MM EMP 650
Accts Kafoury Armstrong & Co Fall
SIC 7999 7011 7992 4941 4952 Picnic ground operation; Bathing beach, non-membership; Ski lodge; Public golf courses; Water supply; Sewerage systems; Picnic ground operation; Bathing beach, non-membership; Ski lodge; Public golf courses; Water supply; Sewerage systems
Ch: Joe Wolfe
*Ch: Jim Smith
*Treas: Bill Devine
Genl Mgr: Bill Horn
Genl Mgr: Steve Pinkerton
Genl Mgr: Ferrato Wilson
CIO: Mike Lane
Dir IT: Tim Hagan
Sls Mgr: Carl Strohschein

D-U-N-S 83-688-6390
INCLUSION INC
3067 E Copper Point Dr, Meridian, ID 83642-1740
Tel (208) 888-1758 Founded/Ownrshp 1995
Sales 18.4MM^E EMP 300
SIC 8082 Home health care services; Home health care services
Pr: Janna Miller
VP: Lyle Miller

D-U-N-S 11-479-2703
INCLUSIVE EDUCATION AND COMMUNITY PARTNERSHIP
IECP
2323 Roosevelt Blvd Apt 3, Oxnard, CA 93035-4480
Tel (805) 985-4808 Founded/Ownrshp 2002
Sales 343.1M^E EMP 300
SIC 8211 8351 Specialty education; Preschool center
Pr: Rick B Clemens

INCLUSIVE HEALTH
See NORTH CAROLINA HEALTH INSURANCE RISK POOL INC

D-U-N-S 06-266-9213
INCO INC
1200 Atlantic Ave, Rocky Mount, NC 27801-2710
Tel (800) 672-4626 Founded/Ownrshp 1972
Sales 43.0MM^E EMP 389
SIC 1541 7363 3599 7389 Industrial buildings, new construction; Industrial help service; Machine & other job shop work; Crane & aerial lift service; Industrial buildings, new construction; Industrial help service; Machine & other job shop work; Crane & aerial lift service
Pr: De Leon Parker Sr
*Treas: Gwen Rigsby
*Ex VP: De Leon Parker Jr
*VP: Jack Banning

D-U-N-S 14-760-3492
INCO SERVICES INC
3550 Francis Cir, Alpharetta, GA 30004-3921
Tel (770) 740-1837 Founded/Ownrshp 1985
Sales 35.0MM EMP 200
SIC 1541 Industrial buildings, new construction; Industrial buildings, new construction
Pr: Doug Davis
*CFO: Michael V Lampert
VP: Steven Hayes
*VP: Steven Hays
*VP: John T King
CIO: Barry Driggers
Sales Exec: Gary Smith
Sls Mgr: Clay Hales

D-U-N-S 95-940-7479 IMP
INCOBRASA INDUSTRIES LTD
540 E Us Highway 24, Gilman, IL 60938-6078
Tel (815) 265-4803 Founded/Ownrshp 1995
Sales 45.7MM^E EMP 120
SIC 2075 Soybean oil mills; Soybean oil mills
Pr: R B Ribeiro D Pedro II
Off Mgr: Rick Ashelmen
Plnt Mgr: Sergio Baruffi
Ql Cn Mgr: Kerry Fogarty
Sls&Mrk Ex: Joe Czernik

D-U-N-S 00-550-2976
INCOE CORP (MI)
1740 E Maple Rd, Troy, MI 48083-4209
Tel (248) 616-0220 Founded/Ownrshp 1958, 1963
Sales 40.3MM^E EMP 180
SIC 3544 3823 3499 3625 3432 3429 Dies, plastics forming; Temperature instruments: industrial process type; Nozzles, spray: aerosol, paint or insecticide; Relays & industrial controls; Plumbing fixture fittings & trim; Manufactured hardware (general); Dies, plastics forming; Temperature instruments: industrial process type; Nozzles, spray: aerosol, paint or insecticide; Relays & industrial controls; Plumbing fixture fittings & trim; Manufactured hardware (general)
CEO: Eric J Seres Jr
Dist Mgr: Tony Bylo
Dist Mgr: Larry McCormack
IT Man: Jim Bott
Plnt Mgr: Kurt Curtis
Sls Dir: David Lange
Sls Mgr: David Boyle
Sls Mgr: Dave Daugherty
Sls Mgr: Eddie Fike
Sls Mgr: Robert Mouzas
Sls Mgr: Chad Posey

D-U-N-S 05-573-9791 IMP
INCOM INC
294 Southbridge Rd, Charlton, MA 01507-5238
Tel (508) 909-2200 Founded/Ownrshp 1976
Sales 34.6MM^E EMP 167
SIC 3229 Fiber optics strands; Fiber optics strands
Ch Bd: Anthony M Detarando
Pr: Michael Detarando
*Sec: Anthony J Detarando
VP: John Lewis
*Prin: Michael A Detarando
Off Mgr: Denise Gendreau
Prd Mgr: Michael Leblanc
Sls Mgr: Darlene Green

D-U-N-S 60-623-5000
INCOME RESEARCH & MANAGEMENT INC
INCOME RESEARCH MANAGEMENT
100 Federal St Fl 30, Boston, MA 02110-1884
Tel (617) 330-9333 Founded/Ownrshp 1987
Sales 21.8MM^E EMP 110
SIC 8741 Financial management for business
Pr: John A Sommers
Ofcr: Richard Kizik
Sr VP: Jonathan Barnet
Sr VP: Jamie Gordon
Sr VP: John Mohr
Sr VP: Sue Synodis
VP: Robert Gentile
VP: Michael Litchfield
VP: Rob Lund
VP: William Omalley
VP: Hiten Patel
VP: Lisa Viale

INCOME RESEARCH MANAGEMENT
See INCOME RESEARCH & MANAGEMENT INC

INCOMM
See INTERACTIVE COMMUNICATIONS INTERNATIONAL INC

D-U-N-S 13-521-7334
INCOMM AGENT SOLUTIONS INC
11900 Biscayne Blvd # 300, North Miami, FL 33181-2743
Tel (305) 381-7729 Founded/Ownrshp 2003
Sales 55.7MM^E EMP 230
SIC 4813 Telephone communication, except radio; Telephone communication, except radio
CEO: AMI Shashoua
Sr VP: Adam Landry
VP: Miriam Guraryа
Exec: David Hattie
QA Dir: Jose Rodriguez
Dir IT: Daniel Sharp
Netwrk Mgr: Ronald Pintado
Sls Mgr: Darryn Law

INCOMM DIGITAL SOLUTIONS
See GIFTANGO LLC

D-U-N-S 13-182-5510
INCOMM HOLDINGS INC
250 Williams St Nw # 5000, Atlanta, GA 30303-1041
Tel (770) 240-6100 Founded/Ownrshp 2002
Sales NA EMP 884
SIC 6099 Clearinghouse associations, bank or check; Clearinghouse associations, bank or check
CEO: M Brooks Smith
*Pr: Phil Graves
*CFO: Scott Meyerhoff
CFO: Ken Taylor
Treas: Kirk Callwood
Ex VP: Robert Skiba
Ex VP: Frank Squill
Off Mgr: Dasha Lackey

INCON
See INTELLIGENT CONTROLS INC

D-U-N-S 05-810-0772
▲ INCONTACT INC
UCN
7730 S Union Park Ave # 500, Midvale, UT 84047-5571
Tel (801) 320-3200 Founded/Ownrshp 1997
Sales 171.7MM EMP 607^E
Tkr Sym SAAS Exch NAS
SIC 7372 4813 Prepackaged software; Application computer software; Local & long distance telephone communications; Prepackaged software; Application computer software; Local & long distance telephone communications
Pr: Paul Jarman
*Ch Bd: Theodore Stern
CFO: Gregory Ayers
Chf Mktg O: Mariann McDonagh
Ofcr: Trent Savage
Ex VP: Julian Critchfield
Ex VP: Bill Robinson
Ex VP: William Robinson
Ex VP: Bassam Salem
Sr VP: Rajeev Shrivastava
VP: Jeff Canter
VP: Jarrett Cummings
VP: Ken O'Donnell
Comm Dir: Heather Hurst
Board of Directors: Steve Barnett, Mark J Emkjer, Blake O Fisher Jr, Paul F Koeppe

D-U-N-S 96-533-9609
INCORP INC
ECOQUIP
(Suby of R E KRAMIG & CO INC) ★
3020 Diego Dr, Evansville, IN 47715-2903
Tel (812) 485-0035 Founded/Ownrshp 1999
Sales 24.8MM^E EMP 200
SIC 1799 Insulation of pipes & boilers; Asbestos removal & encapsulation; Insulation of pipes & boilers; Asbestos removal & encapsulation
Pr: Brad Solem
*CFO: Ryan Schenk
Sfty Dirs: Byron Marksberry
Opers Mgr: Juan Garza
Sls Dir: Jimmy Guessfeld
Board of Directors: Ryan Schenk

INCREDIBLE CHRISTMAS PLACE
See CHRISTMAS PLACE INC

D-U-N-S 13-256-2278
INCREDIBLE PIZZA CO INC
2522 S Campbell Ave, Springfield, MO 65807-3502
Tel (417) 890-1408 Founded/Ownrshp 1999
Sales 22.1MM^E EMP 450
SIC 5812 7929 Pizza restaurants; Pizza restaurants; Entertainment service
CEO: Rick Barsness
CFO: Vickey Crow
*CFO: George Ward
*VP: Cheryl Barsness
VP: Mary Clapp
Tech Mgr: Mark Thomas
Opers Mgr: Joy Wollek

D-U-N-S 17-789-4052
INCREDIBLE TECHNOLOGIES INC
200 Corporate Woods Pkwy, Vernon Hills, IL 60061-3171
Tel (847) 870-7027 Founded/Ownrshp 1985
Sales 27.4MM^E EMP 125
SIC 7371 Custom computer programming services; Computer software development
Pr: Elaine A Hodgson
*COO: James Dore
COO: James Dort
CFO: Gay Milano
*Treas: Gay A Milano
VP: Beena Blake
VP: Robert Fay
VP: Scott Jacobson
VP: Steven Jaskowiak
*VP: Scott Morrison
VP: Jim Palermo

INCREDIBLEFRESH
See COLLIER COUNTY PRODUCE INC

D-U-N-S 07-970-2196
INCREDIMAIL INC
PERION
15809 Bear Creek Pkwy, Redmond, WA 98052-1542
Tel (206) 201-0099 Founded/Ownrshp 2006
Sales 10.7MM^E EMP 350
SIC 7373 7371 Systems software development services; Computer software development & applications
Ch Bd: Tamar Gottlieb

D-U-N-S 16-725-3314
INCREDITEK INC
1205 Belmar Dr, Belcamp, MD 21017-1206
Tel (410) 273-0360 Founded/Ownrshp 2004
Sales 38.9MM EMP 40
SIC 7379 8711 Computer related maintenance services; Engineering services; Computer related maintenance services; Engineering services
CEO: Adam Pattisall
Pr: Sal Leggio
*CFO: Pamela Pippin
Prgrm Mgr: Matthew Eisenhuth

D-U-N-S 13-618-9631
INCREMEDICAL LLC
8259 Wicker Ave, Saint John, IN 46373-8878
Tel (219) 365-6560 Founded/Ownrshp 1999
Sales 24.7MM^E EMP 155
SIC 8741 Hospital management
CFO: Chuck Taylor

D-U-N-S 01-278-5745 IMP
INCSTORES LLC
FLOORINGINC.COM
120 E Corporate Pl Ste 20, Chandler, AZ 85225-1060
Tel (800) 613-0996 Founded/Ownrshp 2007
Sales 31.3MM EMP 50
SIC 5713 Floor covering stores
CEO: Chuck Chan
*COO: Kurt Leitinger
*CFO: Anthony Schmidt
VP: Justin Hoverson
Software D: Mark Ferrante

D-U-N-S 55-696-7347
▲ INCYTE CORP
1801 Augustine Cut Off, Wilmington, DE 19803-4404
Tel (302) 498-6700 Founded/Ownrshp 1991
Sales 511.5MM EMP 481^E
Accts Ernst & Young Llp Philadelphi
Tkr Sym INCY Exch NGS
SIC 8731 Commercial physical research; Commercial physical research
Pr: Herve Hoppenot
*Ch Bd: Richard U De Schutter
CFO: David W Gryska
*V Ch Bd: Julian C Baker
Ofcr: Reid M Huber
Ofcr: David Stoilman
Ex VP: James M Daly
Ex VP: Barry P Flannelly
Ex VP: Richard S Levy
Ex VP: Brian Metcalf
Ex VP: Patricia Schreck
Ex VP: Eric H Siegel
Ex VP: Paula J Swain
Sr VP: Steven H Stein
VP: Pamela Muiphy
VP: Victor Sandor
VP: Swamy Yeleswaram
Exec: Joseph Glenn
Assoc Dir: Ankur Shah
Assoc Dir: Trupti Sheth
Board of Directors: Barry M Ariko, Paul A Brooke, Paul J Clancy, Wendy L Dixon, Paul A Friedman

D-U-N-S 07-973-4158
IND SCHOOL DIST 191
ADMINISTRATIVE SERVICES CENTER
100 River Ridge Ct, Burnsville, MN 55337-1695
Tel (952) 707-2000 Founded/Ownrshp 1955
Sales 69.2MM^E EMP 1,300
Accts Malloy Montague Karnowski R
SIC 8211 Public elementary school; Public junior high school; Public senior high school; Public elementary & secondary schools
Dir IT: Doug Johnson
Pr Dir: Gary Kubat
Pr Dir: Aldo Sicoli
Pr Dir: Tom Umhoefer

D-U-N-S 07-026-1144
IND SCHOOL DIST 621
MOUNDS VIEW SCHOOL DISTRICT 62
350 Highway 96 W, Saint Paul, MN 55126-1951
Tel (651) 621-6000 Founded/Ownrshp 1952

Sales 159.0MM *EMP* 1,450
Accts Malloy Montague Karnowski R
SIC 8211 8742 Public senior high school; Public special education school; Public junior high school; Public elementary school; Management consulting services; Public senior high school; Public special education school; Public junior high school; Public elementary school; Management consulting services
V Ch: Amy Jones
Bd of Dir: Marre Sager
Prgrm Mgr: Lindsey Boumgarden

IND. SCHOOL DIST. 813
See WABASHA & GOODHUE COS

INDAK GROUP, THE
See INDAK MANUFACTURING CORP

D-U-N-S 00-524-6392 IMP
INDAK MANUFACTURING CORP
INDAK GROUP, THE
1915 Techny Rd, Northbrook, IL 60062-5382
Tel (847) 272-0343 *Founded/Ownrshp* 1947
Sales 33.4MM^E *EMP* 250
SIC 3625

D-U-N-S 82-556-8082 IMP
INDAK MANUFACTURING CORP
701 Enterprise Dr, Delavan, WI 53115-1313
Tel (262) 728-5531 *Founded/Ownrshp* 1994
Sales 23.2MM^E *EMP* 250
SIC 3873

D-U-N-S 82-857-3944 IMP/EXP
INDALEX WEST INC
18111 Railroad St, City of Industry, CA 91748-1216
Tel (626) 964-3411 *Founded/Ownrshp* 2006
Sales 75.2MM^E *EMP* 1,500
SIC 3354 Aluminum extruded products; Pipe, extruded, aluminum; Tube, extruded or drawn, aluminum; Aluminum extruded products; Pipe, extruded, aluminum; Tube, extruded or drawn, aluminum
CEO: Mark Russell
**Treas:* Pat Simmons
**VP:* Robert Leckie
Opers Mgr: Pat Meyer
Sales Asso: Debbie Lyttle

D-U-N-S 13-120-3945
INDECK ENERGY SERVICES INC
600 N Buffalo Grove Rd # 300, Buffalo Grove, IL 60089-2432
Tel (847) 520-3212 *Founded/Ownrshp* 1985
Sales 305.1MM^E *EMP* 301
SIC 4911 Distribution, electric power; Distribution, electric power; Generation, electric power
Pr: Lawrence A Lagowski
**Ch Bd:* Gerald Forsythe
Pr: David Hicks
CFO: Thomas M Capone
Sr VP: Lawrence A Lgowski
VP: Michael Dubois
**VP:* Joseph M Oskorep
VP: James Thompson
VP Opers: John E Har
Opers Mgr: Tim Oconnor
Plnt Mgr: Scott Harmeson

D-U-N-S 02-566-2586
INDECK POWER EQUIPMENT CO
1111 Willis Ave, Wheeling, IL 60090-5841
Tel (847) 541-8300 *Founded/Ownrshp* 1985
Sales 79.1MM^E *EMP* 93^E
Accts Bdo Seidman Llp Chicago Ill
SIC 5084 5074 7359 Power plant machinery; Engines & parts, diesel; Boilers, power (industrial); Equipment rental & leasing; Power plant machinery; Engines & parts, diesel; Boilers, power (industrial); Equipment rental & leasing
Pr: Marsha Forsythe Fournier
**Ch Bd:* Gerald Forsythe
**CFO:* Lawrence A Lagowski
CFO: Lawrence A Lgowski
Sr VP: Patrick Delmonico
VP: Elizabeth Harrison
Sls&Mrk Ex: Lisa Lindell
Sls Dir: Dale Pfaff

D-U-N-S 05-529-1389
INDECO SALES INC
805 E 4th Ave, Belton, TX 76513-2769
Tel (254) 939-5742 *Founded/Ownrshp* 1971
Sales 30.1MM^E *EMP* 56
SIC 5021 2531 2522 2521 School desks; Public building & related furniture; Office furniture, except wood; Wood office furniture
Pr: Byron L Mays
**Sec:* Doris Mays
**VP:* Patrick Lynn Mays
Genl Mgr: Lynn Mays

INDECOMM GLOBAL SERVICES
See INDECOMM HOLDINGS INC

D-U-N-S 96-546-7298
INDECOMM HOLDINGS INC
INDECOMM GLOBAL SERVICES
(*Suby of* INDECOMM CORPORATION)
379 Thornall St Ste 2, Edison, NJ 08837-2226
Tel (732) 404-0081 *Founded/Ownrshp* 2014
Sales 60.0MM *EMP* 500^E
SIC 7371 Custom computer programming services; Custom computer programming services
CEO: Venu Raghavan
Pr: Neil Armstrong
**Pr:* Rajan Nair
**CEO:* K P Ponnapa
**CFO:* Balaji Venkatachalam
Sr VP: Judy Wheatley
VP: Paul Patti
VP: Hari Prasad
Snr Mgr: Dan Harrison
Snr Mgr: Mathew Panayil

D-U-N-S 06-538-3788
■ **INDECOR GROUP INC**
VIRGINIA PAINT COMPANY
(*Suby of* BENJAMIN MOORE & CO) ★
4307 W Broad St, Richmond, VA 23230-3305
Tel (804) 359-5088 *Founded/Ownrshp* 1954, 2000
Sales 36.2MM^E *EMP* 113
SIC 5198 5231 Paints; Paint
Genl Mgr: John Tatum
**Prin:* Julie Colgin

INDECOR HOME DESIGN
See BENTEX GROUP INC

D-U-N-S 00-626-4394
INDEECO LLC (MO)
(*Suby of* ASPEQ HEATING GROUP LLC) ★
425 Hanley Industrial Ct, Saint Louis, MO 63144-1511
Tel (314) 644-4300 *Founded/Ownrshp* 1926
Sales 45.9MM^E *EMP* 125
SIC 3567

D-U-N-S 61-382-5806
INDEED INC
INDEED.COM
(*Suby of* RECRUIT HOLDINGS CO.,LTD.)
7501 N Capital Of Texas H, Austin, TX 78731-1776
Tel (203) 328-2691 *Founded/Ownrshp* 2005
Sales 20.4MM^E *EMP* 50^E
SIC 7361 Employment agencies
CEO: Hisayuki Idekoba
Pr: Douglas Gray
**Pr:* Rony Kahan
**CEO:* Paul Forster
VP: Angela Conklin
Off Mgr: Rachel Bryant
IT Man: Cameron Davison
IT Man: Ben Rose
IT Man: Geoff Traugott
Software D: Justin Capogna
Software D: Dan Heller
Board of Directors: Brad Burnham, Kenneth A Richieri

INDEED.COM
See INDEED INC

D-U-N-S 00-233-8713 IMP/EXP
INDEL INC
(*Suby of* ROWAN TECHNOLOGIES, INC.)
10 Indel Ave, Rancocas, NJ 08073
Tel (609) 267-9000 *Founded/Ownrshp* 1956
Sales 495.3MM^E *EMP* 4,000^E
SIC 3567 3548 3822 3541 3563

D-U-N-S 09-173-2818 IMP
INDELCO PLASTICS CORP
6530 Cambridge St, Minneapolis, MN 55426-4484
Tel (952) 925-5075 *Founded/Ownrshp* 1978
Sales 49.0MM^E *EMP* 51
SIC 5162 5084 Plastics sheets & rods; Plastics products; Pumps & pumping equipment
Pr: Trent L Dore
Treas: Nick Peura
**VP:* Steven B Dore
Sales Exec: Dave Beery
Sls Mgr: Brian Foran

D-U-N-S 05-222-1694 EXP
INDEPAK INC (OR)
2136 Ne 194th Ave, Portland, OR 97230-7440
Tel (503) 661-6774 *Founded/Ownrshp* 1967
Sales 25.2MM^E *EMP* 95
SIC 3089 Blister or bubble formed packaging, plastic
Pr: Edavid Aho
**Sec:* Jan Aho

D-U-N-S 01-334-7489
INDEPENDANT PROPANE CO
FARMERS LP GAS CO
4209 State Highway 64 W, Henderson, TX 75652
Tel (903) 657-5511 *Founded/Ownrshp* 1981
Sales 17.8MM^E *EMP* 300^E
SIC 5984 Liquefied petroleum gas, delivered to customers' premises; Liquefied petroleum gas, delivered to customers' premises
Pr: Ken Stibler

D-U-N-S 06-264-2871
INDEPENDANT SCHOOL DISTRICT 2752
FAIRMONT AREA SCHOOL DIST 2752
714 Victoria St Ste 103, Fairmont, MN 56031-4372
Tel (507) 238-4234 *Founded/Ownrshp* 1900
Sales 16.4MM^E *EMP* 350
SIC 8211 Public elementary & secondary schools; Public elementary & secondary schools
IT Man: Greg King

D-U-N-S 03-582-2071
INDEPENDENCE BANK
425 E 18th St, Owensboro, KY 42303-3850
Tel (270) 684-4445 *Founded/Ownrshp* 1910
Sales NA *EMP* 120
SIC 6022 State commercial banks; State commercial banks
Pr: Christopher Reid
**Sr VP:* Terry Roark
VP: Kyle Aud

D-U-N-S 06-154-2486
INDEPENDENCE BANK
(*Suby of* MONTANA SECURITY, INC.)
435 3rd St, Havre, MT 59501-3613
Tel (406) 265-1241 *Founded/Ownrshp* 1972
Sales NA *EMP* 73^E
Accts Federal Deposit Insurance Corp
SIC 6022 6021 State commercial banks; National commercial banks; State commercial banks; National commercial banks
Pr: Miles Hamilton
VP: Dawn Crowder
**VP:* Bill Keller

INDEPENDENCE BUSINESS SUPPLY
See INDEPENDENCE OFFICE AND BUSINESS SUPPLY CO INC

D-U-N-S 10-225-5416
INDEPENDENCE CARE SYSTEMS INC
257 Park Ave S Fl 2, New York, NY 10010-7381
Tel (212) 614-1213 *Founded/Ownrshp* 2002
Sales 266.9MM *EMP* 1^E
Accts Baker Tilly Virchow Krause Llp
SIC 8748 Business consulting
Pr: Rick Surpin
VP: Ann Berson
VP: Kathryn Haslanger
Exec: Regina Estela
Off Mgr: Yvette Gonzalez
Dir IT: Kerri Lopez
Dir IT: Miguel Soares

D-U-N-S 78-959-5451
■ **INDEPENDENCE COAL CO INC**
(*Suby of* ALPHA NATURAL RESOURCES INC) ★
782 Robinson Creek Rd, Madison, WV 25130-9372
Tel (304) 369-7108 *Founded/Ownrshp* 1995
Sales 79.8MM^E *EMP* 385^E
SIC 1222 Bituminous coal-underground mining; Bituminous coal-underground mining
Pr: Mark Clemens
**Treas:* G Scott Cole
**Treas:* Jeffrey M Jarosinski

D-U-N-S 15-322-4902
INDEPENDENCE CONSTRUCTION CO OF VA
ICVGC
301 Cleveland Pl Ste 103, Virginia Beach, VA 23462-6571
Tel (757) 490-1500 *Founded/Ownrshp* 1995
Sales 22.3MM^E *EMP* 36
Accts Sullivan Andrews & Taylor Pc
SIC 1542 1541 Commercial & office building, new construction; Design & erection, combined: non-residential; Industrial buildings & warehouses; Industrial buildings, new construction
Pr: Thomas H Watts
Treas: Donna J Luce
**VP:* Richard Pettruny
**VP:* Terry L Thompson
Sfty Dirs: Adam Watts

INDEPENDENCE CONSTRUCTION MTLS
See ALLAN MYERS LP

D-U-N-S 07-841-8792
INDEPENDENCE CONTRACT DRILLING INC
11601 N Galayda St, Houston, TX 77086-3617
Tel (281) 598-1230 *Founded/Ownrshp* 2012
Sales 70.3MM *EMP* 250
Tkr Sym ICD *Exch* NYS
SIC 1381 3561 Drilling oil & gas wells; Drilling oil & gas wells; Pumps, oil well & field
Pr: Byron Dunn
**COO:* Ed Jacob III
**CFO:* Philip Choyce
Sr VP: J Scott Thompson
**VP:* Dave Brown
**VP:* Michael J Harwell
**VP:* Aaron W Mueller
**VP Bus Dev:* Chris Menefee
Board of Directors: Matthew Fitzgerald, Daniel F McNease

D-U-N-S 00-452-5580 IMP
INDEPENDENCE EXCAVATING INC (OH)
5720 E Schaaf Rd, Independence, OH 44131-1396
Tel (216) 524-1700 *Founded/Ownrshp* 1956, 1962
Sales 162.9MM *EMP* 350
Accts Ciuni & Panichi Cleveland Oh
SIC 1629 1794 1611 1771 1795 Land preparation construction; Excavation work; General contractor, highway & street construction; Building board-up contractor; Concrete repair; Demolition, buildings & other structures; Land preparation construction; Excavation work; General contractor, highway & street construction; Concrete repair; Demolition, buildings & other structures
Pr: Victor Digeronimo Jr
**VP:* Rick Digeronimo
VP: Mike Orlando
Genl Mgr: Don Digeronimo
CTO: Jeff Wisniewski
Netwrk Mgr: James Reeves
Sfty Dirs: Theresa Ross
Sfty Dirs: Tom Steblinski
Trfc Dir: Mike Digeronimo
Snr PM: Greg Digeronimo
Snr Mgr: Justin King

D-U-N-S 04-423-3666
INDEPENDENCE FIRST INC
540 S 1st St, Milwaukee, WI 53204-1605
Tel (414) 291-7520 *Founded/Ownrshp* 1979
Sales 35.1MM *EMP* 975^E
Accts Ritz Holman Llp Milwaukee Wi
SIC 8322 Association for the handicapped; Association for the handicapped
Ex Dir: Lee Schulz
**CFO:* Andy Dalint

D-U-N-S 07-950-4061
INDEPENDENCE HEALTH GROUP INC
1901 Market St, Philadelphia, PA 19103-1480
Tel (215) 241-2400 *Founded/Ownrshp* 2014
Sales NA *EMP* 9,500^E
SIC 6321 Accident & health insurance
Pr: Daniel J Hilferty
**CFO:* Alan Krigstein
**Ex VP:* Christopher Cashman
**Ex VP:* Richard J Neeson
**Ex VP:* Paul A Tufano
**Ex VP:* I Steven Udvarhelyi
**VP:* Yvette D Bright

D-U-N-S 02-660-3407
■ **INDEPENDENCE HOLDING CO**
(*Suby of* GENEVE HOLDINGS INC) ★
96 Cummings Point Rd, Stamford, CT 06902-7919
Tel (203) 358-8000 *Founded/Ownrshp* 1980
Sales NA *EMP* 600^E
Accts Kpmg Llp New York New York
Tkr Sym IHC *Exch* NYS

SIC 6311 6321 Life insurance; Accident & health insurance; Life insurance; Accident & health insurance
Ch Bd: Roy T K Thung
**COO:* David T Kettig
CFO: Teresa A Herbert
Ofcr: Michael A Kemp
Ex VP: Gumbiner Ken
**Sr VP:* Larry R Graber
Sr VP: Michael Kemp
VP: Peter Doran
VP: Colleen McGuire
VP: Brian R Schlier
VP: Brad Waldrop
Board of Directors: Allan C Kirkman, John L Lahey, Steven B Lapin, James G Tatum

INDEPENDENCE HONDA
See INDEPENDENCE LINCOLN-MERCURY INC

INDEPENDENCE HOSPITAL
See COMPSERVICES INC

D-U-N-S 00-173-5091
INDEPENDENCE HOSPITAL INDEMNITY PLAN INC (PA)
BLUE CROSS
1901 Market St, Philadelphia, PA 19103-1480
Tel (215) 241-2400 *Founded/Ownrshp* 1938
Sales NA *EMP* 9,500
SIC 6321 Accident & health insurance; Accident & health insurance
Pr: Daniel J Hilferty
Pr: Brett A Mayfield
COO: Christopher D Butler
COO: Toni Wise
CFO: Alan Krigstein
Ch: Robert H Young
Treas: Gene Brown
Ofcr: Karen Lessin
Ex VP: Yvette Bright
Sr VP: Stephen P Fera
Sr VP: Kathryn A Galarneau
Sr VP: Mucheal A Green
Sr VP: John Janney
Sr VP: John R Janney
Sr VP: Brian Lobley
Sr VP: Carolyn W Luther
Sr VP: Daniel Lyons
Sr VP: Kathleen A McEndy
Sr VP: Donna O Moore
Sr VP: Richard L Snyder
Sr VP: Paul A Tufano

D-U-N-S 05-070-6076 IMP
INDEPENDENCE LINCOLN-MERCURY INC
INDEPENDENCE HONDA
9400 W 65th St, Shawnee, KS 66203-3662
Tel (816) 833-4790 *Founded/Ownrshp* 1967, 1990
Sales 22.2MM^E *EMP* 110^E
SIC 5511 Automobiles, new & used; Automobiles, new & used
Pr: Joseph L Messner
CFO: Kevin Killilea
**Ch:* Anthony Soave
Sls Mgr: John Howden
Sls Mgr: Doug Spencer

D-U-N-S 10-824-8642
INDEPENDENCE LUMBER INC
407 Lumber Ln, Independence, VA 24348-4057
Tel (276) 773-3744 *Founded/Ownrshp* 1985
Sales 23.0MM^E *EMP* 100
SIC 2421 Sawmills & planing mills, general
Pr: Eller Randall
**CFO:* Mike Bolling
**CFO:* Bolling Charles M
**Ex VP:* Nelson D Weaver
VP: Damon Eller
**VP:* Eller Damon Randell

INDEPENDENCE MEDICAL
See RGH ENTERPRISES INC

INDEPENDENCE MISSION SCHOOLS
See PHILADELPHIA INDEPENDENT MISSION SCHOOLS

D-U-N-S 79-548-4708
INDEPENDENCE MOTEL PROPERTIES LIMITED PARTNERSHIP
RAMADA INN
8325 N Armada Ave, Kansas City, MO 64152-1007
Tel (816) 891-7250 *Founded/Ownrshp* 1992
Sales 7.8MM^E *EMP* 300
SIC 7011 Hotels & motels; Hotels & motels

D-U-N-S 10-153-4600
INDEPENDENCE OFFICE AND BUSINESS SUPPLY CO INC
INDEPENDENCE BUSINESS SUPPLY
4550 Hinckley Indus Pkwy, Cleveland, OH 44109-6010
Tel (216) 398-8880 *Founded/Ownrshp* 1983
Sales 38.8MM^E *EMP* 55
SIC 5112 5021 Stationery & office supplies; Office supplies; Furniture
Pr: Steven Gordon
**VP:* Tony Angelo
VP: Pat Bova
**VP:* James Connelly
**VP:* Phillip Dubiel
Off Mgr: Judy Zitzman
Sls Dir: Mark Warszawski
Sls Mgr: Greg Ryb

D-U-N-S 01-583-6974 IMP
■ **INDEPENDENCE OILFIELD CHEMICALS LLC**
(*Suby of* INNOSPEC INC) ★
1450 Lake Robbins Dr # 400, The Woodlands, TX 77380-3263
Tel (713) 936-4340 *Founded/Ownrshp* 2012, 2014
Sales 64.1MM^E *EMP* 200
SIC 2899 5169 Chemical preparations; Chemicals & allied products
Pr: Jeff Hibbeler
**CFO:* Corbin Barnes
**Ex VP:* Jaime De Los Santos
Ex VP: Jaime Santos
**Sr VP:* Jeff Dawson
Sr VP: Clark Emrich

*Sr VP: Butch Gothard
Off Mgr: Brenda Gorski

D-U-N-S 60-723-4085 IMP
INDEPENDENCE PLUS INC
720 Enterprise Dr, Oak Brook, IL 60523-1908
Tel (708) 366-4500 Founded/Ownrshp 1987
Sales 26.4MM^E EMP 450
SIC 8082 Home health care services; Home health care services
CEO: Tamara Muller
*CFO: Les Weiss
Comm Dir: Whitney Grabowski
CTO: Troy Monthye
Mktg Mgr: Kurt Lumsden
Doctor: Chris Evans
Nrsg Dir: Nancy Flynn
Nrsg Dir: Nancy Tafoya

D-U-N-S 96-727-8057
INDEPENDENCE REALTY TRUST INC
2929 Arch St Ste 1650, Philadelphia, PA 19104-2864
Tel (215) 243-9000 Founded/Ownrshp 2011
Sales 49.2MM EMP 300^E
SIC 6798 Real estate investment trusts; Real estate investment trusts
Ch Bd: Scott F Schaeffer
Pr: Farrell M Ender
CFO: James J Sebra

D-U-N-S 80-192-5181
INDEPENDENCE RESIDENCES INC
11240 Francis Lewis Blvd, Queens Village, NY 11429-2235
Tel (718) 805-6796 Founded/Ownrshp 1988
Sales 20.6MM EMP 263
Accts Bdo Usa Llp New York Ny
SIC 8361 Residential care for the handicapped; Residential care for the handicapped
Ex Dir: Ray Denatale
Assoc Dir: Ravi Dahiya
Dir IT: Rakesh Moore
Dir IT: Rakesh Pardeshi
Snr Mgr: Philip Wagner

D-U-N-S 07-626-0082
INDEPENDENCE SCHOOL BOARD OF EDUCATION
201 N Forest Ave, Independence, MO 64050-2696
Tel (816) 521-5300 Founded/Ownrshp 1866
Sales 182.8MM EMP 1,800
SIC 8211 Public elementary & secondary schools; High school, junior or senior; School board
Pr: Ann Franklin
*Treas: Jill Esry
Genl Mgr: Dan Sherman
Pr Dir: Jana Corrie
Teacher Pr: Linda G Gray Smith
HC Dir: Lori Halsey

D-U-N-S 07-998-8284
INDEPENDENCE SCHOOL DISTRICT
201 N Forest Ave Ste 30, Independence, MO 64050-2697
Tel (816) 521-5300 Founded/Ownrshp 2015
Sales 51.6MM^E EMP 1,800^E
SIC 8211 Public elementary & secondary schools

D-U-N-S 05-583-4642
INDEPENDENCE TELEVISION CO INC
W D R B TV-CHANNEL 41
(Suby of BCI) ★
624 W Muhammad Ali Blvd, Louisville, KY 40203-1915
Tel (502) 584-6441 Founded/Ownrshp 1984
Sales 34.7MM^E EMP 190
SIC 4833 Television broadcasting stations; Television broadcasting stations
Pr: Bill Lamd
CFO: Steve Ballard
Treas: Rick Roberts
VP: Barry Fulmer
VP: Barry Fumer
Creative D: Antonio Pantoja
Creative D: Brandon Smith
IT Man: Ken Logsdon
Sls Mgr: Marti Hazel
Sls Mgr: Scott Raby

D-U-N-S 06-337-5086
INDEPENDENCE TITLE CO
ITCOA
5900 Sheph Mount Cove Bld, Austin, TX 78730
Tel (512) 372-8455 Founded/Ownrshp 2006
Sales NA EMP 159^E
SIC 6361 Title insurance
CEO: Jay Southworth
*COO: Brian Pitman
Ofcr: Laura Brookshire
*Sr VP: Chad Decker
*Sr VP: Terri Morrison
*Sr VP: Judith Sullings
VP: Denise Holmes
Area Mgr: Jason L Bragg

D-U-N-S 06-863-3494 IMP/EXP
INDEPENDENCE TUBE CORP
6226 W 74th St, Chicago, IL 60638-6196
Tel (708) 496-0380 Founded/Ownrshp 1972
Sales 52.8MM^E EMP 220
SIC 3317 Tubes, wrought: welded or lock joint; Tubes, wrought: welded or lock joint
Ch Bd: David F Grohne
Pr: Rick Werner
CFO: Michael Dustmann
VP: David Gast
VP: John A Helinski
VP: John J Koschwanez
CIO: Alan Goldenberg
IT Man: Neil Taylor
Netwrk Eng: Joseph Brauer
VP Mktg: Lee Mancheschi
Mktg Mgr: John Tassone

D-U-N-S 04-943-2446
■ **INDEPENDENT ADVERTISING INC**
HILL HOLLIDAY
(Suby of INTERPUBLIC GROUP OF COMPANIES INC) ★
53 State St, Boston, MA 02109-2820
Tel (617) 437-1600 Founded/Ownrshp 1998
Sales 95.6MM^E EMP 767
SIC 7311 7331 7389 8732 Advertising agencies; Direct mail advertising services; Promoters of shows & exhibitions; Market analysis or research; Advertising agencies; Direct mail advertising services; Promoters of shows & exhibitions; Market analysis or research
CEO: Mike Sheehan
*Pr: Karen Kaplan
*CFO: Steve Andrews
*Treas: Ellen Johnson
*V Ch Bd: Richard Pantano
*Ofcr: Dirk Herbert
Ex VP: Leslie Howard
Ex VP: Graham Ritchie
Ex VP: Chris Wallrapp
Sr VP: Andrew Barnett
Sr VP: Jeff Nowak
Sr VP: Kim Portrate
Sr VP: Chris Sherrill
VP: Rowena Alston
VP: Allison Baker
VP: Brad Blake
VP: Suzanne Brunner
VP: Adam Cahill
VP: Chris D'Amico
VP: Wilma Epstein
VP: Mary Gallagher

D-U-N-S 80-403-0422
INDEPENDENT ALLIANCE BANKS INC
118 E Ludwig Rd Ste 103, Fort Wayne, IN 46825-4245
Tel (260) 482-5480 Founded/Ownrshp 2007
Sales NA EMP 2^E
Accts Bkd Llp Fort Wayne In
SIC 6712 Bank holding companies; Bank holding companies
Prin: Lynn Bierlein
Ex VP: Karen Cameron
VP: Michael Chapman

D-U-N-S 03-632-6163
■ **INDEPENDENT BANK** (TX)
(Suby of INDEPENDENT BANK ANNA) ★
331 W Main St, Denison, TX 75020-3124
Tel (903) 465-7744 Founded/Ownrshp 1892
Sales NA EMP 25
SIC 6021 National commercial banks; National commercial banks
Pr: Scott Bandemier
*Ex VP: Peggy Partridge
VP: Ronald Corcoran
*VP: Jeff Hood

D-U-N-S 13-955-2678
INDEPENDENT BANK
I-BANK
(Suby of INDEPENDENT HOLDINGS INC) ★
5050 Poplar Ave Ste 2200, Memphis, TN 38157-2200
Tel (901) 844-5050 Founded/Ownrshp 1998
Sales NA EMP 100
SIC 6029 Commercial banks; Commercial banks
CEO: Charles B Dudley III
Pr: Micah Brafford
Pr: Doug Pittman
*Pr: Susan S Stephenson
CFO: Robert Shuster
CFO: Hugh M Stephens Jr
Ofcr: Venice Lennard
Ofcr: Joanne Silk
*Ex VP: William C Butler
*Ex VP: Kevin Trainor
*Ex VP: H Allen Whittsitt
Sr VP: Stacy Bramlett
*Sr VP: D E Grubbs
Sr VP: Hank Risley
VP: Bob Ballance
VP: Linda Barnes
VP: Forrest Bowman
VP: Dan Brooks
VP: Phil Clacko
VP: Louis D'Eri
VP: Melissa Evans

D-U-N-S 03-632-0299
■ **INDEPENDENT BANK ANNA**
(Suby of FIRST INDEPENDENT BNK MCKINNEY) ★
1427 W White St, Anna, TX 75409-5353
Tel (972) 924-3361 Founded/Ownrshp 1913
Sales NA EMP 25
SIC 6021 National commercial banks
CEO: Dan Brooks
*CFO: Jan Webb

D-U-N-S 05-585-7395
■ **INDEPENDENT BANK CORP**
(Suby of INDEPENDENT BANK CORP) ★
230 W Main St, Ionia, MI 48846-1655
Tel (616) 527-2400 Founded/Ownrshp 1973
Sales NA EMP 896^E
Accts Crowe Horwath Llp Grand Rapi
SIC 6022 State commercial banks; State commercial banks
Pr: William B Kessel
V Ch: Patrick Rokosz
*Pr: William J Boer
CFO: William R Kohls
CFO: Robert Shuster
Assoc VP: Coni Burns
Ex VP: Stefanie M Kimball
Ex VP: Dennis Mack
Ex VP: A Perry
Ex VP: David Reglin
Ex VP: Akhil Sheikh
Sr VP: Richard Butler
Sr VP: Gary Dawley
Sr VP: Charles Schadler
VP: Larry Arendt
VP: Sherry Conklin
VP: Melissa Hewlett
VP: Keith Lightbody
VP: Hofmeyer Mark
VP: Pamela Martin
VP: Cheryl McKellar
Board of Directors: William J Boer

D-U-N-S 06-586-9216
▲ **INDEPENDENT BANK CORP** (MI)
4200 E Beltline Ave Ne, Grand Rapids, MI 49525-9783
Tel (616) 527-5820 Founded/Ownrshp 1973
Sales NA EMP 896^E
Tkr Sym IBCP Exch NGS
SIC 6022 State commercial banks; State commercial banks
Pr: William B Kessel
Ch Bd: Michael M Magee Jr
CFO: Robert N Shuster
Ofcr: Maria Fernette
Ofcr: Dennis J Mack
Ofcr: Bernie Marvin
Ofcr: Tamara Pearson
Ex VP: Mark L Collins
Ex VP: Stefanie M Kimball
Ex VP: James Mack
Ex VP: David C Reglin
Sr VP: Richard E Butler
Sr VP: Chad Crozier
Sr VP: Peter R Graves
Sr VP: Steve Potter
Sr VP: James J Twarozynski
VP: Steve Broda
VP: Jordan Glassco
VP: Deborah Herman
VP: Susan Johnson
VP: Tom McKowen
Board of Directors: William J Boer, Joan A Budden, Stephen L Gulis Jr, Terry L Haske, Robert L Hetzler, James E McCarty, Matthew J Missad, Charles A Palmer, Charles C Van Loan

D-U-N-S 15-216-0768
▲ **INDEPENDENT BANK CORP**
2036 Washington St, Hanover, MA 02339-1617
Tel (781) 878-6100 Founded/Ownrshp 1985
Sales NA EMP 984^E
Tkr Sym INDB Exch NGS
SIC 6022 State commercial banks; State commercial banks
Pr: Christopher Oddleifson
*Ch Bd: Donna L Abelli
Pr: Bruce Bumpus
Pr: David Emmons
Pr: Charlie Rigney
CFO: Robert Cozzone
CFO: Dennis Sheahan
Ofcr: Jeremy Kimbrell
Ex VP: Jane L Lundquist
Ex VP: Gerard F Nadeau
Sr VP: Robert D Cozzone
Sr VP: Kevin Inkley
Sr VP: Tracey Scalata
VP: Thomas Banks
VP: John Barron
VP: Joel Cavness
VP: Nanette Davidson
VP: Scott Ewing
VP: Jeffrey Guimond
VP: Pasqual Kioumejian
VP: Elizabeth Lynch
Board of Directors: Brian S Tedeschi, William P Bissonnette, Thomas R Venables, Kevin J Jones, Eileen C Miskell, John J Morrissey, Daniel F O'brien, Carl Ribeiro, John H Spurr Jr, Maurice H Sullivan Jr, Frederick Taw

D-U-N-S 83-005-0170
▲ **INDEPENDENT BANK GROUP INC**
FIRST INDEPENDENT BNK MCKINNEY
1600 Redbud Blvd Ste 400, McKinney, TX 75069-3258
Tel (972) 548-5910 Founded/Ownrshp 1974
Sales NA EMP 38
Tkr Sym IBTX Exch NGM
SIC 6021 National commercial banks; National commercial banks
CEO: David R Brooks
V Ch: Daniel W Brooks
V Ch: Brian E Hobart
V Ch: James D Stein
V Ch: Courtney Williams
*Pr: Torry Berntsen
Ofcr: Jennifer Conkle
Ofcr: Tiffany Hernandez
Ofcr: Sam Thielepape
Ofcr: James Tippit
Ex VP: Tim Baker
Ex VP: Patrick Blossom
*Ex VP: Michelle Hickox
Ex VP: Phil Mevawala
Ex VP: Mike Phillips
Ex VP: James Schafer
Ex VP: Jan C Webb
Sr VP: Randy Masters
Sr VP: Barbara Peiffer
Sr VP: Hector Salazar
VP: Chris Bielss

D-U-N-S 01-976-5403
■ **INDEPENDENT BANK-EAST MICHIGAN**
(Suby of INDEPENDENT BANK CORP) ★
1111 W Caro Rd Ste B, Caro, MI 48723-8807
Tel (989) 673-5656 Founded/Ownrshp 1904, 1993
Sales NA EMP 182
SIC 6022 State commercial banks; State commercial banks
Pr: Ronald Long
Ofcr: Mary Gurley
Sr VP: Robert Camp
*Sr VP: Dale Van De Vuss
*VP: Mike Furst
VP: Connie Hanna
VP: Scott Lewis
VP: John Stemmler
*VP Opers: Bonnie Hanna

D-U-N-S 96-375-2464
INDEPENDENT BANKERS BANK INC
(Suby of BANKER'S BANCORP, INC.)
2151 W White Oaks Dr, Springfield, IL 62704-6495
Tel (217) 585-0734 Founded/Ownrshp 1986
Sales NA EMP 69^E
SIC 6021 National commercial banks; National commercial banks
V Ch: John Schneider
*Pr: John Jones
*CFO: Mark Rivelin
*VP: Jerry Sheley

D-U-N-S 13-039-4521
INDEPENDENT BANKERS FINANCIAL CORP
11701 Luna Rd, Farmers Branch, TX 75234-6026
Tel (972) 650-6000 Founded/Ownrshp 1983
Sales NA EMP 626
SIC 6712 Bank holding companies; Bank holding companies
Pr: Michael O'Rourke
*Sec: Patricia Blackshear

INDEPENDENT BANKERSBANK THE
See TIB INDPENDENT BANKERSBANK

D-U-N-S 62-748-7689 EXP
INDEPENDENT BEVERAGE CORP
3936 Corporation Cir, Charlotte, NC 28216-3421
Tel (704) 399-2504 Founded/Ownrshp 1991
Sales 38.2MM^E EMP 90
SIC 2086 Bottled & canned soft drinks; Bottled & canned soft drinks
Ch Bd: C Cliff Ritchie
*Pr: Marc K Robinson
*Sec: David Barker
Dir IT: Bill Barten

D-U-N-S 01-954-8368
INDEPENDENT BREWERS UNITED CORP
MAGIC HAT BREWING COMPANY
(Suby of NORTH AMERICAN BREWERIES INC) ★
431 Pine St Ste G12, Burlington, VT 05401-5093
Tel (802) 862-6114 Founded/Ownrshp 2010
Sales 82.9MM^E EMP 573^E
SIC 2082 2084 Malt beverages; Wines; Malt beverages; Wines
Pr: Martin R Kelly
Treas: Eric Peterson
*VP: Steve Hood

INDEPENDENT BUILDERS SUP ASSN
See I B S A INC

D-U-N-S 00-307-0000 IMP/EXP
INDEPENDENT CAN CO
1300 Brass Mill Rd, Belcamp, MD 21017-1236
Tel (410) 272-0090 Founded/Ownrshp 1949
Sales 64.6MM^E EMP 270
SIC 3411 2752 Tin cans; Commercial printing, lithographic; Tin cans; Commercial printing, lithographic
Ch: H Douglas Huether
*Pr: Richard Huether
*COO: Frank Currens
*Ex VP: Robert D McClelland
Ex VP: Robert McClelland
Admn Mgr: Cathy McClelland
Brnch Mgr: Joyce Sutton
IT Man: Lori Heitzenrater
Mtls Mgr: Page Edwards
Plnt Mgr: Deb Sheets
Plnt Mgr: Toby Shiens

D-U-N-S 79-017-0146
INDEPENDENT CAPITAL MANAGEMENT INC
I C M
8383 Wilshire Blvd # 210, Beverly Hills, CA 90211-2432
Tel (310) 557-9850 Founded/Ownrshp 1988
Sales 38.7MM^E EMP 150
SIC 6282 Investment counselors; Investment counselors
Pr: Drew Marloe
*CFO: Lance Stanley
Dist Mgr: Nikola March
Div Mgr: Michael Gallop
Div Mgr: Pamela Rodriguez

D-U-N-S 00-699-2820 IMP/EXP
INDEPENDENT CHEMICAL CORP (NY)
7951 Cooper Ave, Glendale, NY 11385-7529
Tel (718) 326-6620 Founded/Ownrshp 1945
Sales 25.6MM^E EMP 40^E
Accts R Wertheim & Co Syosses Ny
SIC 5169 Industrial chemicals; Sealants
Pr: Jonathan Spielman
VP: William Spielman
Snr Mgr: Stanley Spielman

D-U-N-S 00-191-8077
INDEPENDENT COACH CORP (NY)
25 Wanser Ave, Inwood, NY 11096-2389
Tel (516) 239-1100 Founded/Ownrshp 1941, 1999
Sales 29.6MM^E EMP 340
SIC 4151 4141 School buses; Local bus charter service; School buses; Local bus charter service
Pr: Nick Fabrizio
*Sec: Nancy Quas

D-U-N-S 13-883-2493
INDEPENDENT COLLEGES AND UNIVERSITIES BENEFIT ASSOCIATION INC
ICUBA
4850 Millenia Blvd, Orlando, FL 32839-6012
Tel (407) 354-4646 Founded/Ownrshp 2002
Sales 77.3MM EMP 5
Accts Oswald & Scott Pa Orlando Fl
SIC 8742 School, college, university consultant
Ex Dir: Mark S Weinstein

D-U-N-S 07-958-0577
INDEPENDENT COLLEGES OF INDIANA
101 W Ohio St Ste 440, Indianapolis, IN 46204-1906
Tel (317) 236-6090 Founded/Ownrshp 1948
Sales 20.7MM EMP 10
SIC 8743 Lobbyist; Lobbyist
Pr: Hans C Giesecke

D-U-N-S 07-071-6907
INDEPENDENT COLLEGES OF INDIANA INC
30 S Meridian St Ste 800, Indianapolis, IN 46204-3567
Tel (317) 236-6090 Founded/Ownrshp 1952, 2005
Sales 22.5MM EMP 13

SIC 8399 8611 Fund raising organization, non-fee basis; Business associations; Fund raising organization, non-fee basis; Business associations
Pr: Hans C Giesecke
Comm Dir: Mary Hamer
Ex Dir: Robert Hodge
Off Mgr: Nanette Dumm

D-U-N-S 06-816-0274
INDEPENDENT COMMUNITY BANKERS OF AMERICA
I C B A
1615 L St Nw Ste 900, Washington, DC 20036-5623
Tel (202) 659-8111 *Founded/Ownrshp* 1930
Sales 36.4MM[E] *EMP* 143
Accts Witt Mares Plc Richmond Vir
SIC 8611 6211 7372 8742 6162 7389 Trade associations; Security brokers & dealers; Business oriented computer software; Financial consultant; Mortgage bankers & correspondents; Charge account service; Trade associations; Security brokers & dealers; Business oriented computer software; Financial consultant; Mortgage bankers & correspondents; Charge account service
CEO: Camden R Fine
COO: Mark A Raitor
CFO: Patricia Hopkins
Ch: Steve Stenehjem
Assoc VP: Michael Lahr
Ex VP: Ken Guenther
Ex VP: Terry J Jorde
VP: Mike Beck
VP: Abigail Bresett
VP: Chris Cole
VP: Timothy Cook
VP: Alvin Eisenrauch
VP: Ronald Ence
VP: Ann Grochala
VP: John Hand
VP: Julie Hanson
VP: David Hibbs
VP: Ike Jones
VP: Jason Kratovil
VP: Amy A Miller
VP: Renee Rappaport
Board of Directors: Salvatore Marranea, Cynthia Blankenship, R Michael S Menzies, Thomas G Caldwell, Mark A Raitor, Wayne A Cottle, Kathy Underwood, Dennis Doyle, Larry W Winum, Charles F Harper, David E Hayes, Jack E Hopkins, Terry J Jorde, James D Mac Phee

INDEPENDENT CONSTRUCTION CO
See D A MCCOSKER CONSTRUCTION CO

D-U-N-S 14-467-0981 IMP/EXP
INDEPENDENT CONTAINER LINE LIMITED
I C L
(*Suby of* ICL HOLDING GMBH & CO. KG)
5620 Cox Rd, Glen Allen, VA 23060-9266
Tel (804) 222-2220 *Founded/Ownrshp* 1991
Sales 48.5MM[E] *EMP* 170
SIC 4412 Deep sea foreign transportation of freight; Deep sea foreign transportation of freight
CEO: John Kirkland
**Pr:* Jesse N Pope
CFO: Steve Gohlke
**VP:* Guillermo Esteves
VP: Sarah Gaillard
**VP:* Dale R Ross
CIO: Mark Workman
Dir IT: Deon Price
IT Man: George Evans
Sfty Mgr: John Gillies
Mktg Mgr: Valerie Gunn

D-U-N-S 03-612-8320
INDEPENDENT DISPATCH INC (OR)
214 Ne Middlefield Rd, Portland, OR 97211-1299
Tel (503) 285-4251 *Founded/Ownrshp* 1980
Sales 75.9MM *EMP* 78
Accts Thompson Kessler Wiest & Borqu
SIC 4731 Domestic freight forwarding; Foreign freight forwarding; Domestic freight forwarding; Foreign freight forwarding
CEO: Michael Gilbert
**Pr:* Gregory M Gilbert

INDEPENDENT EDUCATION PRE K-12
See MONTCLAIR KIMBERLEY ACADEMY

D-U-N-S 79-545-4834
INDEPENDENT ELECTRIC SUPPLY CORP
41 Innerbelt Rd, Somerville, MA 02143-4417
Tel (617) 625-5155 *Founded/Ownrshp* 1992
Sales 85.1MM[E] *EMP* 70
Accts Markovitz Dugan & Associates
SIC 5063 Electrical apparatus & equipment; Electrical apparatus & equipment
Pr: Daniel H Gray
**CEO:* William L Gray
**Treas:* Bruce Gray
VP: Marc Reisfelt
Sales Asso: Tom Day
Sales Asso: Andrew Metzler

D-U-N-S 06-912-8924
INDEPENDENT ELECTRIC SUPPLY INC (CA)
(*Suby of* SONEPAR MANAGEMENT US INC) ★
2001 Marina Blvd, San Leandro, CA 94577-3204
Tel (520) 908-7900 *Founded/Ownrshp* 1973
Sales 636.6MM[E] *EMP* 525[E]
SIC 5063 Electrical apparatus & equipment; Wiring devices; Electrical construction materials; Cable conduit; Electrical apparatus & equipment; Wiring devices; Electrical construction materials; Cable conduit
Pr: Doug Walo
**Prin:* Timothy Birky
IT Man: Jeff Chow
Sales Asso: Ana Abreu
Sales Asso: Alonzo Pangilinan
Sales Asso: Brian Smartt

INDEPENDENT ESTABLISHMENT OF
See HOLOCAUST MEMORIAL MUSEUM UNITED STATES

INDEPENDENT FINANCIAL AGENTS
See IFA INSURANCE CO (INC)

D-U-N-S 06-428-5125
INDEPENDENT FINANCIAL AGENTS INC
I F A
14 Walnut Ave, Clark, NJ 07066-1606
Tel (732) 815-1201 *Founded/Ownrshp* 1967
Sales NA *EMP* 55
SIC 6141 7374 6411 5045 Mutual benefit associations; Data processing service; Insurance agents; Computers; Mutual benefit associations; Data processing service; Insurance agents; Computers
Pr: Patrick J Walsh Jr
**VP:* David Walsh
Dir IT: Justin Blanding

D-U-N-S 55-630-3840
INDEPENDENT FINANCIAL MARKETING GROUP INC
(*Suby of* SUN LIFE FINANCIAL INC)
100 Manhattanville Rd # 7, Purchase, NY 10577-2134
Tel (800) 873-4374 *Founded/Ownrshp* 2001
Sales 26.6MM[E] *EMP* 665
SIC 8742 6211 6411 Marketing consulting services; Bond dealers & brokers; Dealers, security; Insurance agents, brokers & service; Life insurance agents; Marketing consulting services; Bond dealers & brokers; Dealers, security; Insurance agents, brokers & service; Life insurance agents
Pr: Robert L Spadafora
**COO:* Joanne K Novak
**CFO:* Robert J McKenna
**Sr VP:* Patrick J Connelly
**VP:* Richard Koll
VP: Salley Love

D-U-N-S 96-871-1767
INDEPENDENT FINANCIAL PARTNERS
3030 N Rocky Point Dr W # 150, Tampa, FL 33607-7200
Tel (813) 341-0960 *Founded/Ownrshp* 2011
Sales 18.9MM[E] *EMP* 300
SIC 7389 Financial services; Financial services
CEO: William E Hamm Jr
COO: Erik Aschenbrenner
Ofcr: Jennifer Tanck
Snr Mgr: Mark Duran

D-U-N-S 78-237-1017 EXP
INDEPENDENT FOOD CORP
INDEPENDENT MEAT COMPANY
2072 Orchard Dr E, Twin Falls, ID 83301-7992
Tel (208) 733-0980 *Founded/Ownrshp* 1983
Sales 51.1MM[E] *EMP* 250
SIC 2011 Beef products from beef slaughtered on site; Pork products from pork slaughtered on site; Cured meats from meat slaughtered on site; Beef products from beef slaughtered on site; Pork products from pork slaughtered on site; Cured meats from meat slaughtered on site
Pr: Patrick Florence
Ofcr: Rob Stephens
Plnt Mgr: Chris Schmahl

D-U-N-S 06-333-9592 IMP
INDEPENDENT FOODS LLC (WA)
311 N 4th St Ste 204, Yakima, WA 98901-2467
Tel (509) 457-6487 *Founded/Ownrshp* 1972
Sales 40.9MM[E] *EMP* 250
SIC 2033 Fruits: packaged in cans, jars, etc.; Fruits: packaged in cans, jars, etc.
**COO:* Jeff Goshorn

D-U-N-S 08-693-2266 IMP
INDEPENDENT FURNITURE SUPPLY CO INC
3609 W Jackson St, Tupelo, MS 38801-7060
Tel (662) 844-8411 *Founded/Ownrshp* 2001
Sales 60.3MM *EMP* 285
Accts Franks Franks Jarrell & Wile
SIC 3086 Plastics foam products; Plastics foam products
Pr: James E Wiygul III
**Sec:* Michael R Thomas

D-U-N-S 09-933-0227
INDEPENDENT HEALTH ASSOCIATION INC
511 Farber Lakes Dr Ste 2, Williamsville, NY 14221-8272
Tel (716) 631-3001 *Founded/Ownrshp* 1980
Sales NA *EMP* 1,050
Accts Deloitte & Touche Llp Buffalo
SIC 6324 Health maintenance organization (HMO), insurance only; Health maintenance organization (HMO), insurance only
Pr: Michael C D
**CFO:* Mark Johnson

D-U-N-S 12-849-1706
INDEPENDENT HEALTH CORP
(*Suby of* INDEPENDENT HEALTH ASSOCIATION INC) ★
511 Farber Lakes Dr Ste 2, Buffalo, NY 14221-8272
Tel (716) 631-3001 *Founded/Ownrshp* 1984
Sales NA *EMP* 900[E]
SIC 6324 Hospital & medical service plans; Hospital & medical service plans
CEO: Michael C D
COO: Janet Stoeckl
**CFO:* Mark Johnson
Bd of Dir: Jim Pokoj
Chf Mktg O: John Rodgers
Ex VP: Jill Syracuse
VP: Eric Decker
CIO: Judith Feldman
CTO: John Iusi
Dir IT: John Okeefe
IT Man: Herb Zastrow

D-U-N-S 80-686-1394
INDEPENDENT HOLDINGS INC
5050 Poplar Ave Ste 2200, Memphis, TN 38157-2200
Tel (901) 844-5050 *Founded/Ownrshp* 2007
Sales NA *EMP* 178[E]
SIC 6712 Bank holding companies
Prin: Dorothy Carsten

D-U-N-S 61-695-8596
INDEPENDENT II LLC
7825 National Tpke, Louisville, KY 40214-4901
Tel (502) 315-2525 *Founded/Ownrshp* 2005
Sales 25.2MM[E] *EMP* 64
SIC 2653 Corrugated & solid fiber boxes
CEO: Neil Macdonald
Plnt Mgr: Vern Jennings

D-U-N-S 79-097-6588
INDEPENDENT INSURANCE INVESTMENTS INC
(*Suby of* INVERNESS MANAGEMENT LLC) ★
1000 River Rd Ste 300, Conshohocken, PA 19428-2440
Tel (610) 832-4940 *Founded/Ownrshp* 2005
Sales NA *EMP* 820
SIC 6331 6411 Automobile insurance; Property damage insurance; Insurance agents, brokers & service; Automobile insurance; Property damage insurance; Insurance agents, brokers & service
CEO: William Lockhorn

D-U-N-S 17-431-1142 IMP
INDEPENDENT LIVING ASSOCIATION INC
110 York St Fl 3, Brooklyn, NY 11201-1446
Tel (718) 852-2000 *Founded/Ownrshp* 1984
Sales 36.5MM *EMP* 500
SIC 8051 8361 Extended care facility; Mental retardation hospital; Residential care; Extended care facility; Mental retardation hospital; Residential care
Pr: Michael Kass
CFO: Frank Delucia
**Ch:* Jay Tinter
**Treas:* John Welch
Ex Dir: Arthur Palevsky
QA Dir: Richard Gruber
Sales Exec: John Degroot

INDEPENDENT LIVING FOR SENIORS
See ELDER ONE

D-U-N-S 01-237-2728
INDEPENDENT LIVING SERVICES INC (AR)
1615 Independence Ave, Conway, AR 72034-3975
Tel (501) 327-5234 *Founded/Ownrshp* 1970
Sales 7.6MM *EMP* 292
Accts Conner & Sartain Cpas Pa Conw
SIC 8322 Social services for the handicapped; Social services for the handicapped
Ex Dir: Jackie Fliss
QA Dir: Sindy Gomes
Pgrm Dir: Barbara Spradlin

INDEPENDENT MEAT COMPANY
See INDEPENDENT FOOD CORP

D-U-N-S 00-520-6081
INDEPENDENT MECHANICAL INDUSTRIES INC
4155 N Knox Ave, Chicago, IL 60641-1915
Tel (773) 282-4500 *Founded/Ownrshp* 1923
Sales 51.0MM[E] *EMP* 125
SIC 1711 Mechanical contractor; Refrigeration contractor; Warm air heating & air conditioning contractor; Ventilation & duct work contractor; Mechanical contractor; Refrigeration contractor; Warm air heating & air conditioning contractor; Ventilation & duct work contractor
Pr: Joseph P Reynolds
**Pr:* Victor Giometti
Treas: Ronald Marshall
**VP:* John M Reynolds
**Genl Mgr:* Rudolph Umlauf
Sfty Mgr: Mike Differding
Opers Mgr: Hal Strider

INDEPENDENT NATIONAL CAR RENTL
See MIDWEST CAR CORP

D-U-N-S 00-234-7011 IMP
INDEPENDENT NEWSPAPERS INC
DELAWARE PRINTING COMPANY
(*Suby of* I N I HOLDINGS INC) ★
110 Galaxy Dr, Dover, DE 19901-9262
Tel (302) 674-3600 *Founded/Ownrshp* 1991
Sales 46.1MM[E] *EMP* 300
SIC 2711 2752 Newspapers: publishing only, not printed on site; Newspapers, publishing & printing; Commercial printing, offset; Newspapers: publishing only, not printed on site; Newspapers, publishing & printing; Commercial printing, offset
CEO: Joe Smyth
Pr: Ed Dulin
**CFO:* Christopher Engel
Sr VP: Darel La Prade

D-U-N-S 80-013-3522 IMP
INDEPENDENT NEWSPAPERS INC
THE DAILY TRIBUNE
(*Suby of* 21ST CENTURY NEWSPAPERS INC) ★
100 Macomb Daily Dr, Mount Clemens, MI 48043-5802
Tel (586) 469-4510 *Founded/Ownrshp* 1997
Sales 21.7MM[E] *EMP* 400
SIC 2711 Newspapers, publishing & printing; Newspapers, publishing & printing
Pr: Ronald J Wood
**VP:* Jerry Bammel

D-U-N-S 80-227-3029
INDEPENDENT OPPORTUNITIES INC
6202 S Lewis Ave Ste P, Tulsa, OK 74136-1064
Tel (918) 744-5067 *Founded/Ownrshp* 1989
Sales 27.2MM *EMP* 900
SIC 8361 Home for the mentally handicapped; Home for the mentally handicapped
CFO: Kendra Robinson
IT Man: Paul Herrman

D-U-N-S 60-876-3918
INDEPENDENT OPPORTUNITIES OF MICHIGAN INC
I.O.M.
45199 Cass Ave, Utica, MI 48317-5508
Tel (586) 739-2911 *Founded/Ownrshp* 1987
Sales 6.5MM *EMP* 300
SIC 8361 8741 8082 Home for the mentally handicapped; Management services; Home health care services; Home for the mentally handicapped; Management services; Home health care services
Ex Dir: Leslie Salvani
Ex Dir: Cindy White

D-U-N-S 15-552-8946
INDEPENDENT OPTIONS INC
391 Corporate Terrace Cir, Corona, CA 92879-6028
Tel (951) 279-2585 *Founded/Ownrshp* 1984
Sales 15.4MM[E] *EMP* 325
SIC 8361 Home for the mentally handicapped; Home for the mentally handicapped
Pr: P Dennis Mattson

D-U-N-S 10-849-2638
INDEPENDENT ORDER OF ODD FELLOWS
PIKES PEAK LODGE 38
575 S Union Blvd, Colorado Springs, CO 80910-3458
Tel (719) 633-2002 *Founded/Ownrshp* 1880
Sales 514.7MM[E] *EMP* 171[E]
SIC 8641 Fraternal associations
Sales Exec: George Epperson
**Prin:* Craig Highland

D-U-N-S 07-916-8954
INDEPENDENT PAPERBOARD MARKETING LLC
I P M
19950 Overseas Hwy, Summerland Key, FL 33042-3166
Tel (305) 745-1636 *Founded/Ownrshp* 2013
Sales 26.2MM[E] *EMP* 19[E]
SIC 5113 Paper tubes & cores
Pr: Michael Greene

D-U-N-S 17-788-3816
INDEPENDENT PHARMACY COOPERATIVE
1550 Columbus St, Sun Prairie, WI 53590-3901
Tel (608) 825-9556 *Founded/Ownrshp* 1984
Sales 1.0MMM *EMP* 65
Accts Grant Thornton Llp Appleton
SIC 5122 7299 Drugs & drug proprietaries; Buyers' club; Drugs & drug proprietaries; Buyers' club
Pr: Don Anderson
CFO: Chuck Benjamin
VP: Mark Kinney
VP: Tom Scono
VP: Rob Tinsley
Exec: Michelle Johnson
Trfc Mgr: Janet Spellbring
Sls&Mrk Ex: Mike Dulas
VP Sls: Dan Hanekamp
Sls Dir: Tim Knight
Sls Dir: Mike Mitchell

D-U-N-S 00-176-5932 IMP
INDEPENDENT PIPE & SUPPLY BUSINESS TRUST
6 Whitman Rd, Canton, MA 02021-2706
Tel (781) 828-8500 *Founded/Ownrshp* 1930
Sales 77.5MM[E] *EMP* 100
SIC 5074 Heating equipment (hydronic); Plumbing fittings & supplies; Pipes & fittings, plastic; Plumbing & heating valves; Heating equipment (hydronic); Plumbing fittings & supplies; Pipes & fittings, plastic; Plumbing & heating valves
CEO: Jeffrey Nierman
**Ch Bd:* Edward J Nierman
**Ch Bd:* Sheldon Nierman
CFO: Sharon Norton
**Ex VP:* Alan H Mirson
Sls Mgr: Jim Hunter

D-U-N-S 00-613-1718 IMP
INDEPENDENT PRINTING CO INC (DE)
CHECK ADVANTAGE
1801 Lawrence Dr, De Pere, WI 54115-9129
Tel (920) 336-7731 *Founded/Ownrshp* 1935
Sales 65.1MM[E] *EMP* 200[E]
SIC 2782 2752 2759 2732 Blankbooks & looseleaf binders; Checkbooks; Commercial printing, offset; Commercial printing; Book printing; Blankbooks & looseleaf binders; Checkbooks; Commercial printing, offset; Commercial printing; Book printing
Ch Bd: Peter Thomson
**Pr:* William Ziemendorf
**Ex VP:* Michael Pollatz
**VP:* Daniel Simons
**VP:* James Verhoeven
Genl Mgr: Jim Bruce
Genl Mgr: Marybeth Van Gruensven
VP Mfg: Julie Newhouse
Mktg Mgr: Brock O'Leary
Sales Asso: Wayne Nemecek

D-U-N-S 62-344-0591 EXP
INDEPENDENT PROCUREMENT ALLIANCE PROGRAM LLC
IPAP
1650 Tri Park Way Ste B, Appleton, WI 54914-1698
Tel (920) 832-1100 *Founded/Ownrshp* 1998
Sales 425.0MM *EMP* 25
SIC 5143 Dairy products, except dried or canned
Pr: Scott Eithun
Sls Mgr: Liz Bunker

D-U-N-S 10-510-4900
INDEPENDENT PROFESSIONAL SERVICES INC
IPROFESSIONAL
(*Suby of* CONNER ENTERPRISES INC) ★
3921 Route 202, Doylestown, PA 18902-1621
Tel (215) 340-3470 *Founded/Ownrshp* 1997
Sales 30.0MM *EMP* 240
SIC 8721 Payroll accounting service; Payroll accounting service
Pr: Michael O'Connor
**COO:* Matt Zimmerman
**Treas:* Tommas Conners
**VP:* Barbara Oconnor

D-U-N-S 78-279-6346
INDEPENDENT PROJECT ANALYSIS INC
IPA
44426 Atwater Dr, Ashburn, VA 20147-3364
Tel (703) 729-8300 *Founded/Ownrshp* 1987
Sales 45.0MM *EMP* 140
SIC 8748 Business consulting; Business consulting
Pr: Edward W Merrow
COO: Mary Ellen Yarossi
CFO: Ken Ingersoll
Treas: Loretta M Errow
**Sec:* Loretta M Merrow
Bd of Dir: Rolando Gachter
Bd of Dir: Margit Jochmann
Bd of Dir: David Rosenberg
Snr PM: Lynn Dickey
Snr Mgr: Jennifer Carr

D-U-N-S 02-825-4493
INDEPENDENT PROPANE CO LLC
(*Suby of* INDEPENDENT PROPANE COMPANY HOLDINGS)
2591 Dallas Pkwy Ste 105, Frisco, TX 75034-8543
Tel (972) 712-8877 *Founded/Ownrshp* 1996
Sales 32.6MM^E *EMP* 450
SIC 5984 Propane gas, bottled; Propane gas, bottled
Pr: David L Scott
VP: Rick Maier
VP: Jay McClung
VP: James Payne
Sls&Mrk Ex: Craig Roepke

D-U-N-S 05-433-1868 IMP
■ **INDEPENDENT PROPANE CO LLC**
(*Suby of* INERGY PROPANE LLC) ★
2591 Dallas Pkwy Ste 105, Frisco, TX 75034-8543
Tel (972) 731-5454 *Founded/Ownrshp* 1996
Sales 124.1MM^E *EMP* 1,008
SIC 5984 5172 Propane gas, bottled; Gases, liquefied petroleum (propane); Propane gas, bottled; Gases, liquefied petroleum (propane)
Pr: William R Moler
**Ch:* John J Sherman

D-U-N-S 00-523-0594 EXP
INDEPENDENT PROTECTION CO INC
TURTLE TOP
1607 S Main St, Goshen, IN 46526-4721
Tel (574) 533-4116 *Founded/Ownrshp* 1934
Sales 35.3MM^E *EMP* 240
SIC 3643 7532 3711 3446 3444 Lightning protection equipment; Van conversion; Buses, all types, assembly of; Architectural metalwork; Sheet metalwork; Lightning protection equipment; Van conversion; Buses, all types, assembly of; Architectural metalwork; Sheet metalwork
Pr: Robert E Cripe
**VP:* Richard D Cripe
**VP:* Robert E Cripe Jr
**VP:* Phillip Tom Jr
Dir IT: Jeff Gowdy
VP Opers: Gerry Lawton
Mfg Dir: Michael Potis
Sfty Mgr: Mary Bowman
Plnt Mgr: Glen Homes
Prd Mgr: Tony Bradley
Sls Mgr: Kim Bledsoe

INDEPENDENT PUBLISHERS GROUP
See CHICAGO REVIEW PRESS INC

D-U-N-S 95-992-1529
INDEPENDENT PURCHASING COOPERATIVE INC
9200 S Dadeland Blvd # 800, Miami, FL 33156-2758
Tel (305) 670-0041 *Founded/Ownrshp* 1996
Sales 191.0MM^E *EMP* 100^E
Accts Bdo Usa Llp Miami Florida
SIC 7389 Purchasing service; Purchasing service
Pr: Jan Risi
Pr: Dennis Clabby
**CFO:* Ceoroger Trombino
CFO: Roger Trombino
Treas: Juliet Dibenedetto
Bd of Dir: Bill Cornelius
VP: Moises Cassidy
VP: Aaron Staflus
Comm Dir: Robert Hopkins
Prgrm Mgr: Kelly-Ann Pinnock
Prgrm Mgr: Don Purser

INDEPENDENT PWR SYSTEMS & LGE
See LGE ELECTRICAL SALES INC

D-U-N-S 08-876-7850 IMP
INDEPENDENT QUALITY CARE INC
WOODLAND LFYTTE CNVLSCENT HOSP
3 Crow Canyon Ct, San Ramon, CA 94583-1619
Tel (925) 855-0881 *Founded/Ownrshp* 1988
Sales 18.4MM^E *EMP* 627
SIC 8059 Convalescent home; Convalescent home
Pr: Daniel W Alger
VP: Jeremy Grimes

D-U-N-S 00-195-9691
INDEPENDENT SALT CO (KS)
1126 20th Rd, Kanopolis, KS 67454-9560
Tel (785) 472-4421 *Founded/Ownrshp* 1913
Sales 23.5MM^E *EMP* 50
SIC 2899 Chemical preparations
Pr: Brian G Keener
**VP:* Michelle Janssen
Trfc Mgr: Chrys Lamatsch

D-U-N-S 07-175-3248
INDEPENDENT SCHOOL DIST 625
ST. PAUL PUBLIC SCHOOLS
360 Colborne St, Saint Paul, MN 55102-3228
Tel (651) 767-8100 *Founded/Ownrshp* 1856
Sales 166.2MM^E *EMP* 6,500
Accts Kpmg Llp Minneapolis Mn
SIC 8299 Educational services; Educational services
Bd of Dir: John Brodrick
Prgrm Mgr: Faye Norton
CIO: Julie Huppertz
DP Exec: Steve Fox
IT Man: Nancy Demars-Wolfe
IT Man: Susan Hollingsworth
IT Man: Greg Renner
Teacher Pr: Laurin Cathey

D-U-N-S 07-177-6108
INDEPENDENT SCHOOL DISTRICT #535
ROCHESTER PUBLIC SCHOOLS
615 7th St Sw, Rochester, MN 55902-2052
Tel (507) 328-3000 *Founded/Ownrshp* 1859
Sales 218.0MM *EMP* 2,500
Accts Cliftonlarsonallen Llp Austin
SIC 8211 Public combined elementary & secondary school; Public special education school; Public combined elementary & secondary school; Public special education school
**Treas:* John Carlson
Off Mgr: Sandra Gibson

D-U-N-S 07-239-6823
INDEPENDENT SCHOOL DISTRICT 1 OF TULSA COUNTY
TULSA PUBLIC SCHOOLS
3027 S New Haven Ave, Tulsa, OK 74114-6131
Tel (918) 746-6800 *Founded/Ownrshp* 1907
Sales 411.5MM^E *EMP* 6,115
SIC 8211 Public elementary & secondary schools; Public elementary & secondary schools
Pr: Mr Gary Percefull
COO: Steve Mayfield
Treas: Mark A Poole
**Treas:* Joe Stoeptelwerth
Bd of Dir: Charles Greenough
Bd of Dir: David G Page
Bd of Dir: Barry L Steichen
Ofcr: Jana Rodriguez
**VP:* Ms Anna America
Exec: Robert Burton
Comm Man: Randy Wallace

D-U-N-S 09-595-5373
INDEPENDENT SCHOOL DISTRICT 15
ISD 15 ST FRANCIS
4115 Ambassador Blvd Nw, Saint Francis, MN 55070-9368
Tel (763) 753-7040 *Founded/Ownrshp* 1888
Sales 53.0MM *EMP* 788
SIC 8211 Public combined elementary & secondary school; Public combined elementary & secondary school
MIS Dir: Corey Tramm
IT Man: Joann Neve
Teacher Pr: David Lindberg
HC Dir: Lillian Levine

D-U-N-S 07-651-0668
INDEPENDENT SCHOOL DISTRICT 152
MOORHEAD PUBLIC SCHOOLS
2410 14th St S Ste 1, Moorhead, MN 56560-4622
Tel (218) 284-3300 *Founded/Ownrshp* 1916
Sales 42.4MM^E *EMP* 900
SIC 8211 Public elementary & secondary schools; Public junior high school; Public senior high school; Public elementary & secondary schools; Public junior high school; Public senior high school

D-U-N-S 07-176-6745
INDEPENDENT SCHOOL DISTRICT 181
804 Oak St, Brainerd, MN 56401-3755
Tel (218) 454-6900 *Founded/Ownrshp* 1920
Sales 84.6MM *EMP* 700
SIC 8211 Public elementary & secondary schools; Public elementary & secondary schools
IT Man: Debra Silgjord
Schl Brd P: Ruth Nelson
Doctor: Barb McColgan

D-U-N-S 06-653-7218
INDEPENDENT SCHOOL DISTRICT 197
1897 Delaware Ave, Mendota Heights, MN 55118-4338
Tel (651) 403-7000 *Founded/Ownrshp* 1961
Sales 47.5MM^E *EMP* 750
Accts Malloy Montague Karnowski R
SIC 8211 Public elementary & secondary schools; Public junior high school; Secondary school; Public elementary & secondary schools; Public junior high school; Secondary school
Prin: Carolyn Hartwigsen
Prin: Susan Powell
Ex Dir: Aaron Kapaun

D-U-N-S 09-710-4582
INDEPENDENT SCHOOL DISTRICT 241
ALBERT LEA AREA SCHOOLS
211 W Richway Dr, Albert Lea, MN 56007-2164
Tel (507) 379-4800 *Founded/Ownrshp* 1921
Sales 50.6MM *EMP* 499
SIC 8211 Public junior high school; Public elementary school; Vocational high school; Elementary school; Kindergarten
V Ch: Mark Ciota
Treas: David Klatt
Ofcr: Jenny Hanson
Dir IT: Jim Quiram
Schl Brd P: Linda Laurie
Psych: Kristen Erkkila
Psych: Traci Jasperson

D-U-N-S 07-148-9827
INDEPENDENT SCHOOL DISTRICT 271
BLOOMINGTON PUB SCHL DST 271
1350 W 106th St, Bloomington, MN 55431-4152
Tel (952) 681-6400 *Founded/Ownrshp* 1918
Sales 108.0MM^E *EMP* 2,200
Accts Kern Dewenter Viere Ltd B
SIC 8211 Public elementary & secondary schools; Public elementary school; Public junior high school; Public senior high school; Public elementary & secondary schools; Public elementary school; Public junior high school; Public senior high school
Ex Dir: Tim Anderson
MIS Dir: John Weisser
Psych: Gretchen Johnson
Psych: Lauri Munoz
Psych: Nathan Schoch
Psych: Annie Stroup

D-U-N-S 09-391-6252
INDEPENDENT SCHOOL DISTRICT 273
EDINA PUBLIC SCHOOLS
5701 Normandale Rd, Edina, MN 55424-2401
Tel (952) 848-3900 *Founded/Ownrshp* 1949
Sales 85.1MM^E *EMP* 1,200
Accts Malloy Montague Karnowski R
SIC 8211 Public elementary & secondary schools; Public elementary & secondary schools
Prin: Carol Meyer

D-U-N-S 07-175-7397
INDEPENDENT SCHOOL DISTRICT 279
OSSEO AREA PUBLIC SCHOOLS
11200 93rd Ave N, Maple Grove, MN 55369-3669
Tel (763) 391-7000 *Founded/Ownrshp* 1952
Sales 292.1MM *EMP* 2,700
Accts Malloy Montague Karnowski R
SIC 8211 Public elementary & secondary schools; Public elementary & secondary schools
**Ch:* Dean G Henke
Teacher Pr: Judy McDonald

D-U-N-S 07-649-2578
INDEPENDENT SCHOOL DISTRICT 281
ROBBINSDALE AREA SCHOOLS
4148 Winnetka Ave N, Minneapolis, MN 55427-1210
Tel (763) 504-8000 *Founded/Ownrshp* 1915
Sales 120.9MM^E *EMP* 2,000
Accts Larsonallen Llp Minneapolis
SIC 8211 Public elementary school; Public junior high school; Public senior high school; Public special education school; Public elementary school; Public junior high school; Public senior high school; Public special education school
Ofcr: Alex Weber
**Ex Dir:* Stephanie Crosby
**Ex Dir:* Al Ickler
**Ex Dir:* Jeff Priess
**Ex Dir:* Lori Simon
Prgrm Mgr: Cynthia Smith
Pr Dir: Latisha Gray
Psych: Rosinta Stromquist
Psych: Sarah Warner
Psych: Amie Wold
Psych: Dan Woodbury

D-U-N-S 02-048-9977
INDEPENDENT SCHOOL DISTRICT 465
LITCHFIELD PUBLIC SCHOOLS
307 E 6th St 100, Litchfield, MN 55355-1808
Tel (320) 693-2444 *Founded/Ownrshp* 1999
Sales 12.0MM *EMP* 450
SIC 8211 Public elementary & secondary schools; Public elementary & secondary schools
**CFO:* Todd Swanson

D-U-N-S 10-003-8058
INDEPENDENT SCHOOL DISTRICT 482
LITTLE FALLS COMMUNITY SCHOOLS
1001 5th Ave Se, Little Falls, MN 56345-3357
Tel (320) 632-2000 *Founded/Ownrshp* 1903
Sales 18.0MM^E *EMP* 380
SIC 8211 9511 Public elementary & secondary schools; School board; Air, water & solid waste management; Public elementary & secondary schools; School board; Air, water & solid waste management
CFO: Nancy Henderson

D-U-N-S 08-450-1246
INDEPENDENT SCHOOL DISTRICT 492
AUSTIN PUBLIC SCHOOLS
401 3rd Ave Nw, Austin, MN 55912-2378
Tel (507) 460-1900 *Founded/Ownrshp* 1920
Sales 36.6MM^E *EMP* 725
SIC 8211 Public elementary school; Public junior high school; Public senior high school; Public elementary school; Public junior high school; Public senior high school
Bd of Dir: Daniel Heins
Ofcr: Kelley Lang
Ofcr: James Lunt
DP Dir: Yawo Kpelevi
MIS Dir: Corey Haugen
Dir IT: Don Jones
IT Man: Dan Noss
Teacher Pr: Brad Berghstrom
HC Dir: Tricia Browning

D-U-N-S 10-003-9163
INDEPENDENT SCHOOL DISTRICT 518
WORTHINGTON PUBLIC SCHOOL
1117 Marine Ave, Worthington, MN 56187-1610
Tel (507) 372-2172 *Founded/Ownrshp* 1950
Sales 19.4MM^E *EMP* 450
SIC 8211 Public elementary & secondary schools; School board; Public elementary & secondary schools; School board

D-U-N-S 03-798-9860
INDEPENDENT SCHOOL DISTRICT 52
7217 Se 15th St, Oklahoma City, OK 73110-5235
Tel (405) 737-4461 *Founded/Ownrshp* 1942
Sales 22.7MM^E *EMP* 1,350
SIC 8211 Public elementary & secondary schools; Public elementary & secondary schools

D-U-N-S 10-003-7498
INDEPENDENT SCHOOL DISTRICT 544
FERGUS FALLS PUBLIC SCHOOLS
601 Randolph Ave, Fergus Falls, MN 56537-1669
Tel (218) 998-0544 *Founded/Ownrshp* 2001
Sales 21.1MM^E *EMP* 450
SIC 8211 Public elementary & secondary schools; Public elementary & secondary schools

D-U-N-S 96-744-9468
INDEPENDENT SCHOOL DISTRICT 544
4b East Dr, Fergus Falls, MN 56537
Tel (218) 998-0544 *Founded/Ownrshp* 2015
Sales 7.9MM^E *EMP* 350
SIC 8211 Elementary & secondary schools
Trst: Sue Lewis

D-U-N-S 07-178-4649
INDEPENDENT SCHOOL DISTRICT 578
PINE CITY PUBLIC SCHOOLS
1400 Main St S, Pine City, MN 55063-2155
Tel (320) 629-4020 *Founded/Ownrshp* 1912
Sales 19.2MM *EMP* 304
Accts Althoff & Nordquist Llc Pine
SIC 8211 Public elementary school; Public senior high school; Vocational high school; Public elementary school; Public senior high school; Vocational high school
Bd of Dir: Tim Geisler
Bd of Dir: Wendy Leibel
Instr Medi: Diana Fedder

D-U-N-S 04-082-3809
INDEPENDENT SCHOOL DISTRICT 595
EAST GRAND FORKS PUB SCHL 595
203 14th St Ne, East Grand Forks, MN 56721-1626
Tel (218) 773-2405 *Founded/Ownrshp* 1900
Sales 23.2MM^E *EMP* 300
SIC 8211 Public elementary school; Public junior high school; Public senior high school; Public vocational/technical school; Public elementary school; Public junior high school; Public senior high school; Public vocational/technical school
Ex Dir: James Richter
Schl Brd P: Tony Palmoscino
HC Dir: Christy Carlstrom

D-U-N-S 03-001-6422
INDEPENDENT SCHOOL DISTRICT 622 (MN)
2520 12th Ave E, Saint Paul, MN 55109-2420
Tel (651) 748-7560 *Founded/Ownrshp* 1942
Sales NA *EMP* 1,458
SIC 9411 Administration of educational programs; Administration of educational programs
Dir Vol: Roxanne Berfeldt
Bd of Dir: Kim Cavallaro
Bd of Dir: Betti Marx
Ex Dir: Theresa Auge
Ex Dir: Scott Duddeck

D-U-N-S 10-225-0867
INDEPENDENT SCHOOL DISTRICT 623 (INC)
ROSEVILLE AREA SCHOOLS
1251 County Road B2 W, Saint Paul, MN 55113-3299
Tel (651) 635-1600 *Founded/Ownrshp* 1949
Sales 109.8MM *EMP* 962
Accts Cliftonlarsonallen Llp Minnea
SIC 8211 Public combined elementary & secondary school; Public senior high school; Public adult education school; Public combined elementary & secondary school; Public senior high school; Public adult education school
**CFO:* Barbara Anderson
Treas: Lori Oberstar
Sftwr Eng: Mary Schifsky
Psych: Lisa Valerius
Snr Mgr: Heather Brian
Snr Mgr: Jacob Mack
Snr Mgr: Shannon Renne
Snr Mgr: Teresa Taylor

D-U-N-S 01-034-7839
INDEPENDENT SCHOOL DISTRICT 624 (INC)
WHITE BEAR LAKE AREA SCHOOLS
4855 Bloom Ave, White Bear Lake, MN 55110-5418
Tel (651) 407-7562 *Founded/Ownrshp* 1957
Sales 113.5MM *EMP* 1,000
Accts Malloy Montague Karnowski R
SIC 8211 Public elementary & secondary schools; Public elementary & secondary schools
Prin: Kristine Wehrkamp
VP: Krist Ide
Ex Dir: Pete Willcoxon Sr
MIS Dir: Mark Garrison
IT Man: Steve Allen
Teacher Pr: Linda Goers
Psych: Aleta Schulte

D-U-N-S 07-134-6191
INDEPENDENT SCHOOL DISTRICT 656
FARIBAULT PUBLIC SCHOOLS
2800 1st Ave Nw, Faribault, MN 55021-1909
Tel (507) 333-6059 *Founded/Ownrshp* 1879
Sales 57.0MM *EMP* 525
Accts Larson Allen Weishair & Co
SIC 8211 Public elementary & secondary schools; Specialty education; Public elementary & secondary schools; Specialty education
IT Man: Andi Johnson
Psych: Michelle Breun
Psych: Dawn Peanasky
Board of Directors: A Seven Member Board

D-U-N-S 05-023-3097
INDEPENDENT SCHOOL DISTRICT 659
1400 Division St S, Northfield, MN 55057-2799
Tel (507) 663-0629 *Founded/Ownrshp* 1876
Sales 55.9MM *EMP* 500
Accts Peterson & Company Pa Mank
SIC 8211 Public combined elementary & secondary school; Public combined elementary & secondary school
Schl Brd P: Ellan Iverson

D-U-N-S 79-645-1425
INDEPENDENT SCHOOL DISTRICT 701
800 E 21st St, Hibbing, MN 55746-1803
Tel (218) 208-0849 *Founded/Ownrshp* 1992
Sales 16.8MM^E *EMP* 320
Accts Sterle & Co Ltd Hibbing M
SIC 8211 Public elementary & secondary schools; Public elementary & secondary schools
HC Dir: Deanna Linholm

D-U-N-S 07-150-1092
INDEPENDENT SCHOOL DISTRICT 709
DULUTH PUBLIC SCHOOLS
215 N 1st Ave E, Duluth, MN 55802-2058
Tel (218) 336-8700 *Founded/Ownrshp* 1908
Sales 126.9MM *EMP* 2,300
Accts Wipfli Llp Duluth Minnesota

SIC 8211 Elementary school; Secondary school; Elementary school; Secondary school
Prac Mgr: Sandy Halteman
MIS Dir: William Beyer
Teacher Pr: Tim Sworsky
Nrsg Dir: Sherry Iverson
HC Dir: Jason Crane

D-U-N-S 08-248-0435
INDEPENDENT SCHOOL DISTRICT 71
PONCA CITY PUBLIC SCHOOLS
111 W Grand Ave, Ponca City, OK 74601-5211
Tel (580) 767-8010 *Founded/Ownrshp* 1910
Sales 41.5MM^E *EMP* 749
SIC 8211 Public elementary & secondary schools; High school, junior or senior; Public elementary & secondary schools; High school, junior or senior
Prin: David Pennington
VP: Jerry Jantz
**Prin:* Nancy Nenimann
**Prin:* Mike White
Dir Sec: Brett Smith
Dir IT: Jason Ridenour
Pr Dir: Mary Ladd
Sls Dir: Frank Lucus
Mktg Mgr: Dale Dewitt

D-U-N-S 03-747-0655
INDEPENDENT SCHOOL DISTRICT 829
WASECA PUBLIC SCHOOLS
501 Elm Ave E, Waseca, MN 56093-3360
Tel (507) 835-2500 *Founded/Ownrshp* 1920
Sales 25.1MM *EMP* 350
Accts Cliftonlarsonallen Llp Austin
SIC 8211 Public elementary & secondary schools; Public elementary & secondary schools
Teacher Pr: Denise Seberson

D-U-N-S 07-651-0304
INDEPENDENT SCHOOL DISTRICT 831
FOREST LAKE AREA SCHOOL
6100 210th St N, Forest Lake, MN 55025-9617
Tel (651) 982-8100 *Founded/Ownrshp* 1918
Sales 80.8MM *EMP* 1,100
Accts Malloy Montague Karnowski R
SIC 8211 Public elementary school; Public junior high school; Public senior high school; Public elementary school; Public junior high school; Public senior high school
Schl Brd P: Rob Rapheal
Teacher Pr: Donna Friedmann

D-U-N-S 07-178-3930
INDEPENDENT SCHOOL DISTRICT 834
STILLWATER AREA SCHOOL DST
1875 Greeley St S, Stillwater, MN 55082-6079
Tel (651) 351-8340 *Founded/Ownrshp* 1955
Sales 53.4MM^E *EMP* 1,000
SIC 8211 Public elementary & secondary schools; Public elementary & secondary schools
Bd of Dir: Becky Webb

D-U-N-S 06-046-6554
INDEPENDENT SCHOOL DISTRICT 861 (INC)
903 Gilmore Ave, Winona, MN 55987-2580
Tel (507) 494-0800 *Founded/Ownrshp* 1900
Sales 22.1MM^E *EMP* 700
SIC 8211 Public elementary & secondary schools; Public elementary & secondary schools

D-U-N-S 01-040-2758
INDEPENDENT SCHOOL DISTRICT 877 (INC) (MN)
214 1st Ave Ne, Buffalo, MN 55313-1602
Tel (763) 682-5200 *Founded/Ownrshp* 1970
Sales 68.9MM *EMP* 681
Accts Kern Dewenter Viere Ltd S
SIC 8211 Public elementary school; Public senior high school; Public elementary school; Public senior high school
Prin: Jim Bauck-Sup't

D-U-N-S 07-864-5561
INDEPENDENT SCHOOL DISTRICT 9 TULSA COUNTY OK
UNION SCHOOL DISTRICT
8506 E 61st St, Tulsa, OK 74133-1926
Tel (918) 357-4321 *Founded/Ownrshp* 1923
Sales 132.6MM *EMP* 1,250
Accts Cole & Reed Pc Oklahoma Ci
SIC 8211 Public elementary & secondary schools; Public elementary & secondary schools
CEO: Ed Payton
Off Mgr: Rhonda Duke
Off Mgr: Diane Smith
CTO: Joshua Starks
Pr Dir: Gretchen H Bethell
Psych: Kay Martin
Psych: Kulsum Siddiqui
Psych: Kim Strom

D-U-N-S 02-071-1842
INDEPENDENT SCHOOL DISTRICT I-29
NORMAN BOARD OF EDUCATION
131 S Flood Ave, Norman, OK 73069-5463
Tel (405) 364-1339 *Founded/Ownrshp* 1891
Sales 128.1MM *EMP* 1,889
Accts Eide Bailly Llp Oklahoma Cit
SIC 8211 Public elementary school; Public junior high school; Public senior high school; Public elementary school; Public junior high school; Public senior high school
**CFO:* Brenda R Burkett
**Treas:* Janine Warren
Off Admin: Cara Simonton
Off Admin: Lynne Thompson
Off Admin: Roberta White
MIS Dir: Jack Green
IT Man: Lyndon Berglan
Pr Dir: Alesha Leemaster
Psych: Sarah Kirk
Psych: Shirley Moore
Psych: Sara Smith

D-U-N-S 96-210-0660
INDEPENDENT SCHOOL DISTRICT NO 271
1350 W 106th St, Minneapolis, MN 55431-4152
Tel (952) 681-6400 *Founded/Ownrshp* 2010
Sales 146.6MM *EMP* 7^E
Accts Kern Dewenter Viere Ltd Blo
SIC 8211 Elementary & secondary schools; Elementary & secondary schools

D-U-N-S 96-339-1680
INDEPENDENT SCHOOL DISTRICT NO 413
401 S Saratoga St, Marshall, MN 56258-3172
Tel (507) 537-6924 *Founded/Ownrshp* 2010
Sales 32.5MM *EMP* 10^E
Accts Hoffman & Brobts Pllp Marsha
SIC 8211 Elementary & secondary schools; Elementary & secondary schools

D-U-N-S 07-134-0830
INDEPENDENT SCHOOL DISTRICT NO 77
MANKATO AREA PUBLIC SCHOOL
10 Civic Center Plz Ste 1, Mankato, MN 56001-7795
Tel (507) 387-5077 *Founded/Ownrshp* 1874
Sales 101.9MM *EMP* 1,200
Accts Larson Allen Llp Austin Minn
SIC 8211 Public elementary & secondary schools; Public elementary & secondary schools
**CFO:* Jerry Kolander
Pr Dir: Shelly Schultz
HC Dir: Joe Meixl

D-U-N-S 12-274-0046
INDEPENDENT SCHOOL DISTRICT OF BOISE CITY
BOISE SCHOOL DISTRICT
8169 W Victory Rd, Boise, ID 83709-4164
Tel (208) 854-4000 *Founded/Ownrshp* 1881
Sales 234.4MM *EMP* 3,025
Accts Eide Bailly Llp Boise Idaho
SIC 8211 Public elementary & secondary schools; Public elementary & secondary schools
Trst: Aj Balukoff
Trst: Troy Rohn
Trst: Dave Wagers
VP: Maria Greeley
Psych: Lori Lodge
Psych: Shelli Metcalf

INDEPENDENT SCHOOL DST 129
See MONTEVIDEO SCHOOL DISTRICT 129

INDEPENDENT SCHOOL DST 347
See WILLMAR SCHOOL DISTRICT 347

INDEPENDENT SCHOOL DST 719
See PRIOR LAKE - SAVAGE AREA SCHOOLS

D-U-N-S 96-659-2268
INDEPENDENT SCHOOL HEALTH ASSN INC
1 Elm St, Byfield, MA 01922-2734
Tel (978) 499-3123 *Founded/Ownrshp* 2011
Sales 43.3MM *EMP* 3
SIC 8211 Elementary & secondary schools; Elementary & secondary schools
Pr: Rebecca Smith
Treas: Penny Aham

INDEPENDENT SEAFOOD
See JOWDY INDUSTRIES INC

D-U-N-S 15-058-8002
INDEPENDENT SHEET METAL CO INC
233 Central Ave, Hawthorne, NJ 07506-1820
Tel (973) 423-1150 *Founded/Ownrshp* 1956
Sales 26.7MM^E *EMP* 100
SIC 3444 1761 Sheet metalwork; Sheet metalwork
Pr: Edward Rebenack
**VP:* Stephen Pucilowski
VP: Mark Walker

D-U-N-S 08-562-5200 EXP
INDEPENDENT STATIONERS INC
IS.GROUP
250 E 96th St Ste 510, Indianapolis, IN 46240-3730
Tel (317) 845-9155 *Founded/Ownrshp* 1977
Sales 202.0MM *EMP* 36
Accts Greenwalt Cpas Inc Indianap
SIC 5112 5021 Stationery & office supplies; Office furniture; Stationery & office supplies; Office furniture
Pr: Michael Gentile
**CFO:* Bruce A Campbell
CFO: Bruce Campbell
**Ch:* Kenny Sayes
**Treas:* Bryan Kristenson
**Ex VP:* Charles Forman
**VP:* Kevin France
VP: France Kevin
Admn Mgr: Cora Lienemann
IT Man: Angela Fenoglio
Merch Mgr: Ty Blankenbaker

INDEPENDENT STAVE COMPANY
See ISCO HOLDING CO INC

D-U-N-S 00-626-8494 IMP/EXP
INDEPENDENT STAVE CO LLC
LEBANON SUPPLY COMPANY
(*Suby of* INDEPENDENT STAVE CO) ★
1078 S Jefferson Ave, Lebanon, MO 65536-3601
Tel (417) 588-4151 *Founded/Ownrshp* 1945
Sales 257.2MM^E *EMP* 1,000
SIC 2449 5947 2499 Barrels, wood: coopered; Gift shop; Kitchen, bathroom & household ware: wood; Barrels, wood: coopered; Gift shop; Kitchen, bathroom & household ware: wood
CEO: John Joseph Boswell
**Pr:* Brad Boswell
**Sec:* W Paul Walker
VP: Amie Dewane
IT Man: James Ledbetter
Opers Mgr: Tammy Ross

D-U-N-S 00-452-7966 IMP
INDEPENDENT STEEL CO LLC (IL)
(*Suby of* ESMARK STEEL GROUP LLC) ★
615 Liverpool Dr, Valley City, OH 44280-9717
Tel (330) 225-7741 *Founded/Ownrshp* 1957, 2010
Sales 23.7MM^E *EMP* 50
SIC 5051 7389 3316 Steel; Metal cutting services; Cold finishing of steel shapes
Pr: Mark Schwertner
VP: Mark A Schwertner

D-U-N-S 13-766-6934
INDEPENDENT SUPPORT SERVICES INC
20 Crystal St, Monticello, NY 12701-1323
Tel (845) 794-5218 *Founded/Ownrshp* 2002
Sales 32.2MM *EMP* 2^E
Accts Knack Pavloff & Company Llp M
SIC 8322 Individual & family services; Individual & family services
Ex Dir: Alan Kulchinsky

D-U-N-S 78-480-6747
INDEPENDENT TELEVISION SERVICE INC
651 Brannan St Ste 410, San Francisco, CA 94107-1535
Tel (415) 356-8383 *Founded/Ownrshp* 1989
Sales 20.1MM *EMP* 16
SIC 8611 Business associations; Business associations
CEO: Sally Jo Fifer
**Ex VP:* Judy Tam
**Sr VP:* Tamara Gould
**Sr VP:* Jim Sommers
**VP:* Pamm Higgins
Dir Bus: Sharan Sklar
**Ex Dir:* Jim Yee
Mng Dir: Sreedevi Sripathy
Dir IT: Eric Paul
Dir IT: Roger Vansleet
IT Man: Roger V Fleet

INDEPENDENT TRADING COMPANY
See BRAD RAMBO & ASSOCIATES INC

D-U-N-S 60-261-2681
INDEPENDENT TRANSPORTERS OF HANDICAPPED INC
221 N Sunrise Service Rd, Manorville, NY 11949-9604
Tel (631) 878-9270 *Founded/Ownrshp* 1978
Sales 60.5MM^E *EMP* 1,300
Accts Grant Thornton Llp New York
SIC 8361 4729 Home for the mentally handicapped; Carpool/vanpool arrangement; Home for the mentally handicapped; Carpool/vanpool arrangement
CEO: Walter W Stockton
**CFO:* Mary Beth Maag
**Treas:* Bruce Fuhrmann
Dir Surg: Tom Traklval
Dir IT: Mike Napolitano
Opers Mgr: Robert Dubester

D-U-N-S 02-952-4816
INDERBITZIN DISTRIBUTORS INC
901 Valley Ave Nw, Puyallup, WA 98371-2517
Tel (253) 922-2592 *Founded/Ownrshp* 1979
Sales 36.3MM^E *EMP* 60
SIC 5141 Groceries, general line; Groceries, general line
Pr: Jhon Inderbitzin
**Pr:* John Inderbitzin
**VP:* Glen J Inderbitzin
**VP:* Paul Inderbitzin

D-U-N-S 06-243-0145
INDEVCO INC
MID AMERICA TRUSS
9826 Big Meadows Rd, Jefferson City, MO 65101-8518
Tel (573) 395-3400 *Founded/Ownrshp* 1969
Sales 20.6MM^E *EMP* 85
SIC 2439 Trusses, except roof: laminated lumber; Trusses, wooden roof
Pr: Ferdinand A Lehmen
**VP:* Curt Lehmen
Genl Mgr: Mike Pfahl

D-U-N-S 10-112-8577 IMP
INDEX CORP
(*Suby of* INDEX-WERKE GMBH & CO. KG HAHN & TESSKY)
14700 N Pointe Blvd, Noblesville, IN 46060-4171
Tel (317) 770-6300 *Founded/Ownrshp* 1982
Sales 22.7MM^E *EMP* 55
SIC 5084 Machine tools & accessories
Pr: Jeffrey Reinert
**VP:* Kevin Tretter
Tech Mgr: Guenter Schad
Natl Sales: Mark Webster
**VP Sls:* Michael Huggett
Mktg Mgr: Gary A Jones
Manager: Bob Ayers
Manager: Mike Czyzak
Manager: Pierre Michaud
Manager: Tim Pottridge
Manager: David Stevens

INDEX DIGITAL MEDIA, INC.
See ATLUS USA INC

D-U-N-S 02-834-9678 EXP
INDEX FRESH INC
3880 Lemon St Ste 210, Riverside, CA 92501-3355
Tel (909) 877-0999 *Founded/Ownrshp* 1914
Sales 30.2MM^E *EMP* 57
SIC 0723 Crop preparation services for market
Pr: Dana L Thomas
V Ch: Stephen Miller
**COO:* Giovanni Cavaletto
**CFO:* Merrill Causey
VP: Kevin Thron
Mktg Mgr: Debbie Willmann

INDEX MILLWORK
See INDEX PACKAGING INC

D-U-N-S 00-798-7134 IMP
INDEX NOTION CO INC
WOODEN KEY
136 W Carmel Dr, Carmel, IN 46032-2526
Tel (317) 573-3990 *Founded/Ownrshp* 1911, 1989
Sales 31.0MM^E *EMP* 300
Accts Kehlenbrink Laurence & Pauckne
SIC 5947 Greeting cards; Gift shop; Greeting cards; Gift shop
Pr: James G Sinclair
**Sec:* Jennifer Sinclair

D-U-N-S 05-158-8085 EXP
INDEX PACKAGING INC
INDEX MILLWORK
1055 White Mountain Hwy, Milton, NH 03851-4443
Tel (603) 350-0018 *Founded/Ownrshp* 1968
Sales 30.8MM^E *EMP* 160
SIC 2449 3086 3412 2441 2431 Wood containers; Plastics foam products; Metal barrels, drums & pails; Nailed wood boxes & shook; Planing mill, millwork; Wood containers; Plastics foam products; Metal barrels, drums & pails; Nailed wood boxes & shook; Planing mill, millwork
Pr: Bruce Lander
**Ex VP:* William M Lander
Sls Dir: Dave Bechard
Sls Dir: Chris Brooks
Sales Asso: Todd Blaisdell

D-U-N-S 87-757-0648
INDEXX INC
303 Haywood Rd, Greenville, SC 29607-3426
Tel (864) 234-1024 *Founded/Ownrshp* 1992
Sales 22.2MM^E *EMP* 90
Accts Cherry Bekaert & Holland Llp
SIC 2752 2675 Commercial printing, lithographic; Die-cut paper & board
Pr: Jordan R Finn
**VP:* Lewis Dibridge
Exec: Gina Morgan
Dir IT: Charlie Evans
Dir IT: Charlie Mayfield
VP Opers: Mike Lawing
Mktg Dir: Mike Miller
Sls Dir: Mike Robinson
Sales Asso: Russell Fortney
Sales Asso: Sherry Jenkins
Pgrm Dir: Mitch Odom

INDIAN CREEK HYDRO
See LVDE CORP

D-U-N-S 12-598-7974
INDIAN CREEK SCHOOL DISTRICT
587 Bantam Ridge Rd, Steubenville, OH 43953-4267
Tel (740) 264-3502 *Founded/Ownrshp* 1966
Sales 27.2MM^E *EMP* 325
Accts Mary Taylor Cpa Youngstown
SIC 8211 9411 Public elementary & secondary schools; Administration of educational programs; Public elementary & secondary schools; Administration of educational programs

D-U-N-S 00-790-5607
INDIAN ELECTRIC COOPERATIVE INC
Us Hwy 64, Cleveland, OK 74020
Tel (918) 295-9500 *Founded/Ownrshp* 1939
Sales 49.6MM *EMP* 80
SIC 4911 Distribution, electric power; Distribution, electric power
CEO: Jack Clinkscale
**Pr:* Loris Peckenpaugh
Treas: Berry Keeler
IT Man: Donald Lawrence
Sfty Dirs: Bill Graham
Opers Mgr: Rick Davis

D-U-N-S 10-217-9678 IMP
INDIAN GROCERIES & SPICES INC
NIRAV
8051 Central Park Ave, Skokie, IL 60076-2904
Tel (847) 674-2480 *Founded/Ownrshp* 1982
Sales 43.0MM^E *EMP* 57
SIC 5149 Specialty food items; Spices & seasonings
Pr: Shirish N Sanghavi
**VP:* Nirav Sanghavi

D-U-N-S 11-512-6518 IMP/EXP
INDIAN HEAD INDUSTRIES INC
MGM BRAKES
8530 Cliff Cameron Dr, Charlotte, NC 28269-5906
Tel (704) 547-7411 *Founded/Ownrshp* 1989
Sales 58.4MM^E *EMP* 400
SIC 3593 3714 Fluid power cylinders & actuators; Motor vehicle brake systems & parts; Fluid power cylinders & actuators; Motor vehicle brake systems & parts
CEO: Ron Parker
**VP:* Jeffery Parker
**VP:* Susan Pfeiffr

D-U-N-S 96-187-6737
INDIAN HEALTH COUNCIL
50100 Golsh Rd, Valley Center, CA 92082-5338
Tel (760) 749-1410 *Founded/Ownrshp* 1970
Sales 21.2MM *EMP* 99
Accts Rsm Mcgladrey Inc Los Angeles
SIC 8611 Business associations; Business associations
Dir Rx: Robert Schostag
Ex Dir: Connie Kirk
Ex Dir: Deven Parlikar

D-U-N-S 92-764-5234
■ **INDIAN HEALTH SERVICE**
IHS
(*Suby of* UNITED STATES DEPARTMENT OF HEALTH & HUMAN SERVICES) ★
801 Thompson Ave Ste 120, Rockville, MD 20852-1627
Tel (301) 443-1083 *Founded/Ownrshp* 1955
Sales NA *EMP* 15,800
SIC 9431 Administration of public health programs; ; Administration of public health programs;
CEO: John Molina
Ex VP: Arshad Matin
VP: Jane O Bomba
VP: Jo Moon
Dir Risk M: Robert Valandra
Assoc Dir: Eric Brody
Adm Dir: Michelle Antone
Adm Dir: Farrel Smith
Adm Dir: Vicki Snell
Ex Dir: Gwen Steelman
Prgrm Mgr: Merle Botone

D-U-N-S 87-948-6298
INDIAN HILLS COMMUNITY COLLEGE FOUNDATION INC
525 Grandview Ave Bldg 1, Ottumwa, IA 52501-1359
Tel (641) 683-5111 *Founded/Ownrshp* 1967
Sales 1.5MM^E *EMP* 398
Accts Anderson Larkin & Co Pc Ottum
SIC 8222 Junior colleges & technical institutes; Junior colleges & technical institutes
CEO: Matt Thompson
**Pr:* Shelly Harvey
Pr: Robert Morissey
CFO: Bill Meck
**Prin:* F James Lindenmayer
VP Admn: Jim Lindenmayer
IT Man: Neil Alertsen
Netwrk Mgr: Shane Molyneu
Mktg Dir: Kevin Pink
Pgrm Dir: Denise Kluever
Snr Mgr: James Anderson

D-U-N-S 00-636-8815 IMP/EXP
■ **INDIAN INDUSTRIES INC**
ESCALADE SPORTS
(*Suby of* ESCALADE INC) ★
817 Maxwell Ave, Evansville, IN 47711-3870
Tel (812) 467-1200 *Founded/Ownrshp* 1927, 1973
Sales 84.3MM^E *EMP* 486
SIC 3949 Ping-pong tables; Archery equipment, general; Billiard & pool equipment & supplies, general; Basketball equipment & supplies, general; Ping-pong tables; Archery equipment, general; Billiard & pool equipment & supplies, general; Basketball equipment & supplies, general
Pr: Robert Keller
**Ch Bd:* Robert E Griffin
VP: James Allshouse
Natl Sales: Jason Borg
Mktg Dir: Patrick Griffin
Mktg Dir: David Vogrin
Mktg Dir: Ken Young
Sls Dir: Jack Bowman
Sls Mgr: Doug Hunter
Sales Asso: Bob Keller
Board of Directors: B E Matthews Jr, A Graves Williams Jr

D-U-N-S 05-677-5679 IMP
INDIAN JEWELERS SUPPLY CO
601 E Coal Ave, Gallup, NM 87301-6005
Tel (505) 722-4451 *Founded/Ownrshp* 1968
Sales 21.7MM^E *EMP* 57
SIC 5094 Jewelry
Pr: David Vining
**Treas:* Jack Dill
**VP:* Steve Turner
Genl Mgr: William C Caldes
IT Man: Joe Ward
Board of Directors: Jack Dill, Ray Jones, Luis Ortega, Steve Turner, David Vining

D-U-N-S 19-302-4155
INDIAN LAKE LOCAL SCHOOL DISTRICT
6210 State Route 235 N, Lewistown, OH 43333-9704
Tel (937) 686-8601 *Founded/Ownrshp* 1962
Sales 21.6MM *EMP* 103
SIC 8211 Public elementary & secondary schools; Public elementary & secondary schools
Prin: Dennis Shaner
Psych: Luann Lause

INDIAN MOTORCYCLE REDWOOD CITY
See BOARDWALK CARS INC

INDIAN MOUND MALL
See GLIMCHER PROPERTIES LIMITED PARTNERSHIP

INDIAN NATION WHOLESALE
See STEPHENSON WHOLESALE CO INC

INDIAN OAKS LIVING CENTER
See PM MANAGEMENT - KILLEEN II NC LLC

D-U-N-S 96-284-8255
INDIAN PATH HOSPITAL INC
INDIAN PATH MEDICAL CENTER
(*Suby of* MOUNTAIN STATES HEALTH ALLIANCE) ★
2000 Brookside Dr, Kingsport, TN 37660-4682
Tel (423) 857-7000 *Founded/Ownrshp* 1998
Sales 53.9MM^E *EMP* 640
SIC 8062 General medical & surgical hospitals; General medical & surgical hospitals
CEO: Martin McLorain
**CFO:* John Doyle
CTO: Rachel Bishop
Doctor: Sherrie Arrants
Doctor: Mark Jenkins MD
Pharmcst: Julia Blair
Pharmcst: Dan Gmyrek
Pharmcst: Ed Minor
Diag Rad: Jeffrey Honeycutt
Diag Rad: Bradley Miller

INDIAN PATH MEDICAL CENTER
See INDIAN PATH HOSPITAL INC

D-U-N-S 06-860-8983
INDIAN PRAIRIE COMMUNITY UNIT SCHOOL DISTRICT
INDIAN PRAIRIE SCHOOL DISTRICT
780 Shoreline Dr, Aurora, IL 60504-6192
Tel (630) 375-3000 *Founded/Ownrshp* 1972
Sales 122.7MM^E *EMP* 3,000
SIC 8211 Public elementary school; Public combined elementary & secondary school; Public senior high school; Public elementary school; Public combined elementary & secondary school; Public senior high school
CIO: David Zoner
Web Dev: Peg Grommon
Plnt Mgr: Adrienne Morgan
Board of Directors: Kathleen H Baldwin, Jeannette A Clark, Deanne M Harzinski, Mark Metzger, Pete Neumeister, Judith S Sotir, Owen Wavrinek

INDIAN PRAIRIE SCHOOL DISTRICT
See INDIAN PRAIRIE COMMUNITY UNIT SCHOOL DISTRICT

D-U-N-S 10-374-2078
INDIAN RIDGE PROVISIONS INC
400 Emlen Way, Telford, PA 18969-1700
Tel (215) 723-3164 *Founded/Ownrshp* 1983
Sales 27.2MM^E *EMP* 55
SIC 5146 5147 Seafoods; Meats, fresh
Pr: Joseph W Hinderliter
**Pr:* John Demito
**CFO:* Boris Borichevsky
**VP:* Steve Polscan

D-U-N-S 01-505-4646
INDIAN RIVER CENTRAL SCHOOL DISTRICT
DISTRICT OFFICE
32735 County Route 29 B, Philadelphia, NY 13673-4210
Tel (315) 642-3441 *Founded/Ownrshp* 1957
Sales 84.3MM *EMP* 679
Accts Poulsen & Podvin Pc Watert
SIC 8211 Public elementary & secondary schools; School board; Public elementary & secondary schools; School board
Pr: Donald Brumfield
**CFO:* James Koch
Bd of Dir: Rhonda Calhoun
Bd of Dir: Thomas Lapp
Schl Brd P: Frank Laverghetta

D-U-N-S 18-190-3816
INDIAN RIVER COLONY CLUB INC
1936 Freedom Dr, Melbourne, FL 32940-6876
Tel (321) 255-6000 *Founded/Ownrshp* 1986
Sales 20.9MM^E *EMP* 110
SIC 6552 1521 7997 Land subdividers & developers, residential; New construction, single-family houses; Golf club, membership
CFO: Julie A Roberts
**Pr:* Jim Moseley
**VP:* Cynthia Morgan

D-U-N-S 07-920-8989
INDIAN RIVER COUNTY
1800 27th St Bldg B, Vero Beach, FL 32960-0310
Tel (772) 567-8000 *Founded/Ownrshp* 1926
Sales NA *EMP* 1,500
Accts Rehmann Robson Llc Vero Beach
SIC 9111 Executive offices; ; Executive offices;
Ofcr: John Duran
Ex Dir: John King
Telecom Mg: Terry Smith
Snr Mgr: Harold Seeley

D-U-N-S 61-171-0427
INDIAN RIVER MEMORIAL HOSPITAL INC
1000 36th St, Vero Beach, FL 32960-6592
Tel (772) 567-4311 *Founded/Ownrshp* 1984
Sales 182.2MM *EMP* 1,400
SIC 8062 8011 General medical & surgical hospitals; Offices & clinics of medical doctors; General medical & surgical hospitals; Offices & clinics of medical doctors
Ch Bd: Thomas Segura
Dir Vol: Mary Jane Stewart
Ch Bd: Charles Sheehan
CEO: Jeffrey L Susi
CFO: Gregory Gardner
Treas: Jack Pastor
Treas: Jack Weisbaum
Ex Dir: Jan Donlan
Brnch Mgr: Dee Boshaw
Psych: Mariamma Pyngolil
Obsttrcn: Donna Fabean

D-U-N-S 87-807-1638
INDIAN RIVER SCHOOL DISTRICT
31 Hosier St, Selbyville, DE 19975-9300
Tel (302) 436-1000 *Founded/Ownrshp* 1969
Sales 75.0MM^E *EMP* 1,650^E
SIC 8211 Public elementary & secondary schools; Public elementary & secondary schools

D-U-N-S 07-222-0825
INDIAN RIVER STATE COLLEGE FOUNDATION INC
3209 Virginia Ave, Fort Pierce, FL 34981-5541
Tel (772) 462-7340 *Founded/Ownrshp* 1960
Sales 10.5MM *EMP* 5,000
Accts Berger Toombs Elam Gaines &
SIC 8222 Community college; Community college
**Ex Dir:* Ann L Decker

D-U-N-S 05-302-4758
INDIAN RIVER TRANSPORT CO
2580 Executive Rd, Winter Haven, FL 33884-0929
Tel (863) 324-2430 *Founded/Ownrshp* 1993
Sales 102.5MM^E *EMP* 500^E
SIC 4213 Refrigerated products transport; Refrigerated products transport
Ch: John J Harned
**Pr:* Marguerite Harned
Dir IT: Matt Hurst
Dir IT: William Youngberg
Sfty Dirs: Anthony Black
Sfty Dirs: Mark Gresset
Opers Mgr: William Wolven

D-U-N-S 05-605-5957
INDIAN SPRINGS SCHOOL DISTRICT 109
7540 S 86th Ave, Justice, IL 60458-1168
Tel (708) 496-8700 *Founded/Ownrshp* 1876
Sales 34.7MM *EMP* 300
Accts Baker Tilly Virchow Krause Ll
SIC 8211 Public elementary & secondary schools; School board; Public elementary & secondary schools; School board

D-U-N-S 87-763-6092 EXP
INDIAN SUMMER CARPET MILLS INC
CHEROKEE CARPET INDUSTRIES
601 Callahan Rd Se, Dalton, GA 30721-5004
Tel (706) 259-3386 *Founded/Ownrshp* 1994
Sales 54.3MM *EMP* 350
Accts Gilbert Crump & Associates P
SIC 2273 Carpets, hand & machine made; Carpets, hand & machine made
Pr: Ann Eaton
**CFO:* James L Orr
S&M/VP: Tim Gilmore
S&M/VP: Dan Haglund
Sls Mgr: Tony Giglio

D-U-N-S 06-587-7888 EXP
INDIAN SUMMER COOPERATIVE INC
3958 W Chauvez Rd Ste 1, Ludington, MI 49431-8200
Tel (231) 845-6248 *Founded/Ownrshp* 1973
Sales 101.3MM^E *EMP* 400
SIC 2033 0723 4213 2035 Apple sauce: packaged in cans, jars, etc.; Fruit juices: packaged in cans, jars, etc.; Fruits: packaged in cans, jars, etc.; Fruit (fresh) packing services; Trucking, except local; Contract haulers; Pickles, sauces & salad dressings; Apple sauce: packaged in cans, jars, etc.; Fruit juices: packaged in cans, jars, etc.; Fruits: packaged in cans, jars, etc.; Fruit (fresh) packing services; Trucking, except local; Contract haulers; Pickles, sauces & salad dressings
Pr: Roy D Hackert
**Sec:* Steven Hull
Opers Mgr: Doyle Fenner

D-U-N-S 05-503-5534
INDIANA ACCOUNTS STATE BOARD
(*Suby of* EXECUTIVE OFFICE OF STATE OF INDIANA) ★
302 W Washington St E418, Indianapolis, IN 46204-2769
Tel (317) 232-2513 *Founded/Ownrshp* 2002
Sales NA *EMP* 339^E
SIC 9311 Finance, taxation & monetary policy;
Prin: Bruce Hartman
Plnt Mgr: Paul Joyce

INDIANA AMERICAN WATER
See INDIANA-AMERICAN WATER CO INC

D-U-N-S 14-039-2650
INDIANA ANNUAL UNITED METHODIST CHURCH
301 Pennsylvania Pkwy, Indianapolis, IN 46280-1397
Tel (317) 924-1321 *Founded/Ownrshp* 2003
Sales 13.8MM^E *EMP* 1,100
SIC 8661 Methodist Church; Methodist Church
Ofcr: Jim Milner
**Ex Dir:* Nick Yarde

D-U-N-S 12-720-2989 IMP
INDIANA ARCELORMITTAL HARBOR LLC
ARCELLORMITTAL INDIANA HBR W
(*Suby of* ACRELORMITTAL US LLC) ★
3210 Watling St, East Chicago, IN 46312-1716
Tel (219) 399-1200 *Founded/Ownrshp* 2002
Sales 228.8MM^E *EMP* 900
SIC 3312 Blast furnaces & steel mills; Blast furnaces & steel mills
CEO: Rodney B Mott
**Prin:* Louis Schorsch
Div Mgr: Tracy Brough
Genl Mgr: Richard Morris
Sls Mgr: Thomas Furjanic
Sls Mgr: Marc-Andre Guay
Board of Directors: Wendy Boos

D-U-N-S 03-896-2486
INDIANA AREA SCHOOL DISTRICT INC
501 E Pike Rd, Indiana, PA 15701-2234
Tel (724) 463-8567 *Founded/Ownrshp* 1966
Sales 25.1MM^E *EMP* 410
Accts Clay & Gascoine Llc Indiana
SIC 8211 Public combined elementary & secondary school; Public junior high school; Public senior high school; Public combined elementary & secondary school; Public junior high school; Public senior high school
MIS Dir: Andrew Shubra

D-U-N-S 12-158-5822
INDIANA ASPIRE INC
9615 E 148th St Ste 1, Noblesville, IN 46060-4371
Tel (317) 587-0500 *Founded/Ownrshp* 1973
Sales 31.3MM *EMP* 410^E
SIC 8093 Mental health clinic, outpatient; Mental health clinic, outpatient
Pr: C Richard De Haven
**Pr:* Bryan Brenner
**COO:* Barbara Scott
**CFO:* Craig Baird
**Treas:* Douglas Prince
**VP:* Jerry Landers
**VP:* Jeffrey L Reed
**Prin:* Larry Burch
CIO: Virginia Nelson
**Doctor:* Jerry Sheward

D-U-N-S 94-695-5648 IMP
INDIANA AUTOMOTIVE FASTENERS INC
(*Suby of* AOYAMA SEISAKUSHO CO.,LTD.)
1300 Anderson Blvd, Greenfield, IN 46140-7934
Tel (317) 467-0100 *Founded/Ownrshp* 1996
Sales 120.1MM^E *EMP* 401
SIC 3452 3714 Bolts, nuts, rivets & washers; Motor vehicle parts & accessories; Bolts, nuts, rivets & washers; Motor vehicle parts & accessories
Pr: Heisaburo Hidaka
**VP:* Pete Murray
VP: Satoshi Takeda
Ql Cn Mgr: Derek Brown
Snr Mgr: Mike Lee

INDIANA BLOOD CENTER
See CENTRAL INDIANA REGIONAL BLOOD CENTER INC

D-U-N-S 15-450-4237
INDIANA BRIDGE-MIDWEST STEEL INC
1810 S Macedonia Ave, Muncie, IN 47302-3669
Tel (765) 288-1985 *Founded/Ownrshp* 2002
Sales 23.4MM^E *EMP* 56
SIC 3441 Fabricated structural metal
Pr: Chunilal H Gala
**Pr:* Christian Klink
**Treas:* Ken Crismore
VP: Sheryl Bronnenberg

D-U-N-S 00-508-1328 IMP
INDIANA CARTON CO INC
1721 W Bike St, Bremen, IN 46506-2123
Tel (574) 546-3848 *Founded/Ownrshp* 1933, 1970
Sales 49.4MM^E *EMP* 90
Accts Kruggel Lawton & Co South B
SIC 2657 Folding paperboard boxes
CEO: David L Petty
**Ch Bd:* Kenneth Petty
**Ex VP:* James C Petty
**VP:* John Hummer
**VP:* Scott Marsh
VP: Matthew Petty

D-U-N-S 12-552-3345
INDIANA COMPREHENSIVE HEALTH INSURANCE ASSOCIATION
9465 Counselors Row # 200, Indianapolis, IN 46240-3817
Tel (317) 877-5376 *Founded/Ownrshp* 1981
Sales 160.9MM *EMP* 3
Accts Ksm Business Services Inc Ind
SIC 8641 Social associations; Social associations
Ex Dir: Douglas Stratton
**Ch:* Dennis Casey

D-U-N-S 07-206-0353
INDIANA CREDIT UNION LEAGUE INC
5975 Castle Creek Pkwy North, Indianapolis, IN 46250
Tel (317) 594-5300 *Founded/Ownrshp* 1935
Sales 1.9MM *EMP* 287
Accts Bkd Llp Indianapolis In
SIC 8611 5943 Trade associations; Office forms & supplies; Trade associations; Office forms & supplies
Ch: Randy Glassburn
**Pr:* John W Mc Kenzie
**CFO:* Dan Davis
Ofcr: Chuck Barr
VP: Chris Beaumont
VP: Leeanne Fisher
VP: Joe Guilfoy
VP: Anne Jester
VP: Kristi Lowell
Comm Man: Lynley Chapin
Snr Mgr: John McKenzie

D-U-N-S 82-479-9209
INDIANA DEPARTMENT OF EDUCATION
SUPERINTENDENT PUB INSTRUCTION
(*Suby of* EXECUTIVE OFFICE OF STATE OF INDIANA) ★
115 W Washington St 600s, Indianapolis, IN 46204-3471
Tel (317) 232-6610 *Founded/Ownrshp* 1984
Sales NA *EMP* 300
SIC 9441 Administration of social & manpower programs; ; Administration of social & manpower programs;
Brnch Mgr: George Frampton
IT Man: Gary Grist

D-U-N-S 82-479-9217
INDIANA DEPARTMENT OF ENVIRONMENTAL MANAGEMENT
(*Suby of* EXECUTIVE OFFICE OF STATE OF INDIANA) ★
100 N Senate Ave Rm N1255, Indianapolis, IN 46204-2222
Tel (800) 451-6027 *Founded/Ownrshp* 1986
Sales NA *EMP* 900
SIC 9511 Air, water & solid waste management; ; Air, water & solid waste management;
**CFO:* Claira Farrow
CFO: Beth McMinn
Exec: Barry Sneed
Sls&Mrk Ex: Michael Mendyk
Snr Mgr: Dave Cline
Snr Mgr: John Guerrettaz
Snr Mgr: Nancy Johnston
Snr Mgr: Liz Melvin
Snr Mgr: Pam O'Rourke
Snr Mgr: Rex Osborn
Snr Mgr: Christine Pedersen

D-U-N-S 87-829-8520
INDIANA DEPARTMENT OF HOMELAND SECURITY
IDHS
(*Suby of* EXECUTIVE OFFICE OF STATE OF INDIANA) ★
302 W Washington St E208, Indianapolis, IN 46204-2767
Tel (317) 232-1921 *Founded/Ownrshp* 2005
Sales NA *EMP* 280
SIC 9229
Ex Dir: John Hill
Pr: Lee Shirkey
Pr: Len Woolard
Ofcr: Dionne Chisolm
Ofcr: Steven Gonzalez
Ofcr: Chris Tomokane
Opers Mgr: Abdas Ortiz
Snr Mgr: Ryan Chandler
Snr Mgr: Debbie Frye
Snr Mgr: Christy Riccardi

D-U-N-S 82-479-9381
INDIANA DEPARTMENT OF NATURAL RESOURCES
(*Suby of* EXECUTIVE OFFICE OF STATE OF INDIANA) ★
402 W Washington St W299, Indianapolis, IN 46204-2243
Tel (317) 232-4020 *Founded/Ownrshp* 1938
Sales NA *EMP* 1,510
SIC 9512 Land, mineral & wildlife conservation; ; Land, mineral & wildlife conservation;
Brnch Mgr: Steve Lucas

D-U-N-S 82-479-9308
INDIANA DEPARTMENT OF REVENUE
COMMISSIONERS OFFICE
(*Suby of* EXECUTIVE OFFICE OF STATE OF INDIANA) ★
100 N Senate Ave Rm N105, Indianapolis, IN 46204-2217
Tel (317) 232-2240 *Founded/Ownrshp* 1947

Sales NA *EMP* 800[E]
SIC 9311 Finance, taxation & monetary policy; ; Finance, taxation & monetary policy;

D-U-N-S 82-479-9555
INDIANA DEPARTMENT OF TRANSPORTATION
(*Suby of* EXECUTIVE OFFICE OF STATE OF INDIANA) ★
100 N Senate Ave Rm N758, Indianapolis, IN 46204-2219
Tel (317) 232-3166 *Founded/Ownrshp* 1989
Sales NA *EMP* 3,600
SIC 9621 Regulation, administration of transportation; Regulation, administration of transportation;
Prin: Karl Browning
**CFO:* Dan Brassard
**Prin:* Mitchell E Daniels Jr

D-U-N-S 80-989-6780
INDIANA DEPT OF CORRECTION
(*Suby of* EXECUTIVE OFFICE OF STATE OF INDIANA) ★
302 W Washington St E334, Indianapolis, IN 46204-4701
Tel (317) 232-2430 *Founded/Ownrshp* 1958
Sales NA *EMP* 6,000
SIC 9223 Prison, government; ; Prison, government;
CEO: Randy Koester
**Ch:* Christopher Meloi
Ofcr: Jaime Raderstorf

D-U-N-S 82-479-9613
INDIANA DEPT OF WORKFORCE DEVELOPMENT
(*Suby of* EXECUTIVE OFFICE OF STATE OF INDIANA) ★
10 N Senate Ave, Indianapolis, IN 46204-2277
Tel (317) 233-5661 *Founded/Ownrshp* 1991
Sales 58.3MM[E] *EMP* 1,650
SIC 7389 ;
**CFO:* Randy Gillespie
CFO: Scott Sanders

D-U-N-S 06-470-3812
INDIANA DLZ INC
(*Suby of* DLZ CORP) ★
6121 Huntley Rd, Columbus, OH 43229-1003
Tel (614) 848-4333 *Founded/Ownrshp* 1992
Sales 24.7MM[E] *EMP* 425
Accts Longanbach Giusti Kuck & Hornb
SIC 8711 8712 Consulting engineer; Sanitary engineers; Architectural engineering; Consulting engineer; Sanitary engineers; Architectural engineering
Ch Bd: Vikram Rajadhyaksha
Pr: Joseph Zwierzyski
**COO:* Pratap Rajadhyaksha
**VP:* Brian Glaze
**VP:* Michael Keevan
**VP:* Robert Kirkley
Div Mgr: Mike Trevino
Snr PM: Steve Pelto
Snr Mgr: Brian Bratcher
Snr Mgr: Randy Hardy
Snr Mgr: Brian Kinney

INDIANA DOWNS
See INDIANAPOLIS DOWNS LLC

INDIANA ELECTRICAL WORKERS PEN
See ELECTRICAL WORKERS BENEFITTR FUND

D-U-N-S 09-812-2252 IMP
INDIANA ENBI INC
1703 Mccall Dr, Shelbyville, IN 46176-9783
Tel (317) 398-3267 *Founded/Ownrshp* 2015
Sales 37.1MM[E] *EMP* 150
SIC 3069 Printers' rolls & blankets: rubber or rubberized fabric; Printers' rolls & blankets: rubber or rubberized fabric
Pr: James Maulucci
Genl Mgr: Dominique Eusebe
Opers Mgr: Marvin Talbot
Plnt Mgr: Jim Maulucci

INDIANA EPILEPSY SERVICES
See IN-PACT INC

D-U-N-S 82-479-9225
INDIANA FAMILY AND SOCIAL SERVICES ADMINISTRATION
FSSA
(*Suby of* EXECUTIVE OFFICE OF STATE OF INDIANA) ★
402 W Washington St W461, Indianapolis, IN 46204-2243
Tel (317) 233-4454 *Founded/Ownrshp* 1991
Sales NA *EMP* 9,700
SIC 9441 ;
CEO: Debra Minott
IT Man: Gregory Jinks
Snr Mgr: Kevin Jones

INDIANA FAN & FABRICATION
See HORNER INDUSTRIAL SERVICES INC

INDIANA FARM BUREAU
See UNITED FARM FAMILY MUTUAL INSURANCE CO

D-U-N-S 07-957-0479
INDIANA FARM BUREAU INC
225 S East St, Indianapolis, IN 46202-4002
Tel (317) 692-7851 *Founded/Ownrshp* 1919
Sales 756.6MM[E] *EMP* 1,200[E]
SIC 8611 Trade associations; Trade associations
Pr: Donald Villwock
**VP:* Isabella Chism
**VP:* Randy L Kron
VP: Randy Spurlock
VP: Sherry Wayne
IT Man: Kim Bray
Software D: Leslie Thompson
Netwrk Eng: Debbie Katterhenry

D-U-N-S 07-204-6550
INDIANA FARMERS MUTUAL INSURANCE CO
FARMERS INSURANCE
10 W 106th St, Indianapolis, IN 46290-1002
Tel (317) 846-4211 *Founded/Ownrshp* 1877
Sales NA *EMP* 156
SIC 6411 Insurance agents, brokers & service; Insurance agents, brokers & service
Ch: F Neal Johnson
**Pr:* Daniel E Stone
**CFO:* Paul Seppel
Ofcr: W Campbell
VP: Bart Anderson
VP: Rick Casilvafil
VP: Cyndy Mehrtens
VP: Glenn Toren
Dir Soc: Lisa Marlow
IT Man: Harry Taylor
Mktg Dir: Scott Miller

D-U-N-S 55-547-1838 IMP
INDIANA FCC INC
(*Suby of* F.C.C. CO., LTD.)
555 Industrial Dr, Portland, IN 47371-9399
Tel (260) 726-8023 *Founded/Ownrshp* 1988
Sales 228.8MM[E] *EMP* 450
SIC 3714 Clutches, motor vehicle; Clutches, motor vehicle
Pr: Yoshitaka Saito
VP Admn: Jeff Bailey
Telecom Ex: Diane Parr
QA Dir: Mike Bell
IT Man: Michael Hunt
VP Prd: Motoyuki Hino
VP Prd: Mamoru Yamaguchi
Prd Mgr: Mike Shephard
Ql Cn Mgr: Kevin Barcus
Mktg Mgr: Allan Martin
Snr Mgr: Makoto Amano

D-U-N-S 14-352-0083
INDIANA FIBER NETWORK LLC
I F N
5520 W 76th St, Indianapolis, IN 46268-5109
Tel (317) 733-8538 *Founded/Ownrshp* 2002
Sales 21.7MM[E] *EMP* 39
SIC 1731 Communications specialization; Communications specialization
VP: Tom Bechtel

D-U-N-S 00-636-6108 IMP
INDIANA FURNITURE INDUSTRIES INC
1224 Mill St, Jasper, IN 47546-2852
Tel (812) 482-5727 *Founded/Ownrshp* 1905, 1928
Sales 36.1MM[E] *EMP* 275
SIC 2521 2531 2512

D-U-N-S 01-592-2552
■ **INDIANA GAMING CO LP**
HOLLYWOOD CASINO
(*Suby of* PENN NATIONAL GAMING INC) ★
777 Hollywood Blvd, Lawrenceburg, IN 47025-2503
Tel (812) 539-8000 *Founded/Ownrshp* 2008
Sales 78.7MM[E] *EMP* 1,700
SIC 7011 Casino hotel; Casino hotel
Genl Pt: G Argosy
Dir Soc: Elizabeth Doll

D-U-N-S 00-693-8211
■ **INDIANA GAS CO INC**
VECTREN
(*Suby of* VECTREN UTILITY HOLDINGS INC) ★
20 Nw 4th St, Evansville, IN 47708-1724
Tel (812) 491-4000 *Founded/Ownrshp* 1945
Sales 307.3MM[E] *EMP* 875[E]
SIC 4924 Natural gas distribution; Natural gas distribution
Ch Bd: Neil C Ellerbrook
**CEO:* Carl Chapman
**CFO:* Jerome A Benkert Jr
Sr VP: John Little
**VP:* M Susan Hardwick
VP: Tim Hewitt
VP: Rick Schach
IT Man: Pat Russell
Opers Supe: Josh Sargent
VP Mktg: Steve Williams
Board of Directors: Ronald E Christian, William S Duty

INDIANA GAZETTE
See INDIANA PRINTING AND PUBLISHING CO

INDIANA GRAND
See CENTAUR ACQUISITION LLC

INDIANA HAND CENTER
See HAND SURGERY ASSOCIATES OF INDIANA INC

D-U-N-S 05-330-3889
INDIANA HARBOR BELT RAILROAD CO
2721 161st St, Hammond, IN 46323-1099
Tel (219) 989-4703 *Founded/Ownrshp* 1896
Sales 83.1MM[E] *EMP* 750[E]
Accts Mcgladrey Llp Chicago Illino
SIC 4013 4011 Switching & terminal services; Railroads, line-haul operating; Switching & terminal services; Railroads, line-haul operating
CEO: Jim Roots
**Pr:* Cindy Sanborn
**CFO:* Derek Smith
Ex Dir: Mark Manion
Genl Mgr: Chuck Allen
Sls Dir: Leo Pauwels
Genl Couns: R Serpe
Snr Mgr: John Szamatowicz

D-U-N-S 00-417-9110
■ **INDIANA HARBOR COKE CO LP** (IN)
(*Suby of* SUNCOKE ENERGY INC) ★
3210 Watling St, East Chicago, IN 46312-1716
Tel (219) 397-5769 *Founded/Ownrshp* 1996, 2012
Sales 66.1MM[E] *EMP* 122
SIC 3312 Blast furnaces & steel mills; Blast furnaces & steel mills
CEO: Kenneth J Schuett

D-U-N-S 85-846-9067
INDIANA HEALTHCARE CORP
835 Hospital Rd, Indiana, PA 15701-3629
Tel (724) 357-7000 *Founded/Ownrshp* 1987
Sales 32.7M *EMP* 1,100
Accts Ernst & Young Llp Pittsburgh
SIC 8741 Hospital management; Hospital management
CEO: Steven Wolf
**CFO:* Larry Marshall
**Prin:* Robert Parker
Board of Directors: Mrs Susan Delaney, Robert D Duggan, Robert G Goldstrohm MD, Herbert L Hanna MD, Alan Holsinger, Robert T Jack, James Miller

D-U-N-S 87-695-0031
INDIANA HEALTHCARE FOUNDATION
835 Hospital Rd, Indiana, PA 15701-3629
Tel (724) 357-7000 *Founded/Ownrshp* 1987
Sales 400.0M *EMP* 900
Accts Parentebeard Llc Philadelphia
SIC 7389 Fund raising organizations; Fund raising organizations
Pr: Stephen Wolfe
**CFO:* Larry Marshall
CIO: Ken Reily

D-U-N-S 60-362-5419
INDIANA HEAT TRANSFER CORP
500 W Harrison St, Plymouth, IN 46563-1399
Tel (574) 936-3171 *Founded/Ownrshp* 1985
Sales 50.1MM[E] *EMP* 213
SIC 3714 Radiators & radiator shells & cores, motor vehicle; Radiators & radiator shells & cores, motor vehicle
Pr: Daniel B Altman
COO: Ian Hite
COO: Rick Hite
Ql Cn Mgr: Joseph Mersch

D-U-N-S 96-381-6397
INDIANA HOSPITAL
823 Hospital Rd, Indiana, PA 15701
Tel (724) 357-7125 *Founded/Ownrshp* 2010
Sales 132.3MM[E] *EMP* 3
SIC 8741 Hospital management; Hospital management
Prin: Ali Tunio
Doctor: Durre S Ahmed MD

INDIANA INDUSTRIAL CONTRACTORS
See INDUSTRIAL CONTRACTORS SKANSKA INC

D-U-N-S 04-533-7771
INDIANA INSTITUTE OF TECHNOLOGY INC
INDIANA TECH
1600 E Washington Blvd, Fort Wayne, IN 46803-1297
Tel (260) 422-5561 *Founded/Ownrshp* 1930
Sales 84.6MM *EMP* 450
Accts Bkd Llp Fort Wayne In
SIC 8221 College, except junior; College, except junior
CEO: Arthur E Snyder
Board of Directors: A Nineteen Member Board

D-U-N-S 00-693-8229
INDIANA INSURANCE CO
(*Suby of* LIBERTY MUTUAL INSURANCE CO) ★
6281 Tri Ridge Blvd # 1, Loveland, OH 45140-8345
Tel (816) 216-5313 *Founded/Ownrshp* 1851
Sales NA *EMP* 750
SIC 6331 Fire, marine & casualty insurance; Fire, marine & casualty insurance
Pr: Richard Bell
Sls Mgr: Maureen Paul
Snr Mgr: Barth Fisher
Snr Mgr: Joan Grade
Snr Mgr: Celeste Sanford

D-U-N-S 07-913-6496
INDIANA INTERGROUP
5641 E 72nd St, Indianapolis, IN 46250-2601
Tel (317) 840-0304 *Founded/Ownrshp* 2013
Sales 11.0M *EMP* 500
SIC 8322 Self-help organization; Self-help organization
**Prin:* Richard Otis Stamm

D-U-N-S 62-658-0302
INDIANA INTERNAL MEDICINE CONSULTANTS PC
701 E County Line Rd, Greenwood, IN 46143-1072
Tel (317) 885-2860 *Founded/Ownrshp* 1990
Sales 20.2MM[E] *EMP* 80
SIC 8011 Internal medicine, physician/surgeon
CEO: William C Buffie MD
Doctor: Michael Dubois
Board of Directors: Robert S Daly MD, Steven M Samuels MD, Sanjay Vyas MD

D-U-N-S 83-157-6041
INDIANA L RCG L C
(*Suby of* RENAL CARE GROUP INC) ★
920 Winter St, Waltham, MA 02451-1521
Tel (781) 699-4404 *Founded/Ownrshp* 1997
Sales 8.9MM[E] *EMP* 516[E]
SIC 8092 Kidney dialysis centers

D-U-N-S 07-977-0307
INDIANA LABORERS WELFARE FUND
413 Swan St, Terre Haute, IN 47807-4224
Tel (812) 238-2551 *Founded/Ownrshp* 2015
Sales NA *EMP* 3[E]
SIC 6371 Pension, health & welfare funds

D-U-N-S 11-072-4122 IMP
INDIANA LLC ADVICS MANUFACTURING
ABI
(*Suby of* ADVICS NORTH AMERICA INC) ★
10550 James Adams St, Terre Haute, IN 47802-9294
Tel (812) 298-1617 *Founded/Ownrshp* 2010
Sales 118.8MM[E] *EMP* 400
SIC 3714 Air brakes, motor vehicle; Air brakes, motor vehicle
**Pr:* Atsushi Takenaga
**Treas:* Kazuza Tsukamoto
Exec: Dennis Hanshu

Ql Cn Mgr: Darrin Johnson
Ql Cn Mgr: Michael Woldahl

D-U-N-S 00-604-1933
INDIANA LUMBERMENS MUTUAL INSURANCE CO INC
ILM GROUP, THE
8888 Keyst Cross Ste 250, Indianapolis, IN 46240
Tel (317) 875-3600 *Founded/Ownrshp* 1897
Sales NA *EMP* 70[E]
SIC 6331 Property damage insurance; Property damage insurance
Pr: John F Wolf
**Treas:* Donald Blackwell
**VP:* Raymond Kampisi
**VP:* Susan Knotts
VP: Greg Pianko
**VP:* Gregory Pienco

INDIANA MASONIC HOME
See GRAND LODGE OF INDIANA F & A M SCHOLARSHIP BOARD INC

D-U-N-S 07-205-1212
INDIANA MASONIC HOME INC
ACACIA HOME HEALTH CARE
690 S State St, Franklin, IN 46131-2553
Tel (317) 736-6141 *Founded/Ownrshp* 1916
Sales 26.7MM[E] *EMP* 250
Accts Ksm Business Services Inc Ind
SIC 8361 Geriatric residential care; Residential care for the handicapped; Geriatric residential care; Residential care for the handicapped
Pr: James L Chesney
**CEO:* John Rose
**CFO:* Michael Malandrakis
**VP:* Robert R Stevens
Dir Bus: Kate Cline
HC Dir: Drema Simmons

D-U-N-S 18-606-4077
INDIANA MEMBERS CREDIT UNION OF INDIANAPOLIS INDIANA
5103 Madison Ave, Indianapolis, IN 46227-4239
Tel (317) 788-4693 *Founded/Ownrshp* 1956
Sales NA *EMP* 250
SIC 6062 State credit unions; State credit unions
Pr: Ron Collier
Brnch Mgr: Scott Mann
Brnch Mgr: Stephanie Roesner

D-U-N-S 00-698-5584 IMP
■ **INDIANA MICHIGAN POWER CO**
(*Suby of* AMERICAN ELECTRIC POWER CO INC) ★
1 Riverside Plz, Columbus, OH 43215-2355
Tel (614) 716-1000 *Founded/Ownrshp* 1907
Sales 2.2MMM *EMP* 2,551[E]
SIC 4911 Electric services; Distribution, electric power; Generation, electric power; Transmission, electric power; Electric services; Distribution, electric power; Generation, electric power; Transmission, electric power
Ch Bd: Nicholas K Akins
**Pr:* Paul Chodak III
**CFO:* Brian X Tierney
**VP:* Thomas A Kratt
VP: Mark Peifer
Mktg Mgr: Ron Kalie
Snr Mgr: Paul Higginbotham
Board of Directors: Lisa M Barton, Marc E Lewis, Mark C McCullough, Robert P Power, Carla E Simpson, Barry O Wiard

D-U-N-S 00-606-3101 IMP
INDIANA MILLS & MANUFACTURING INC
IMMI
18881 Immi Way, Westfield, IN 46074-3001
Tel (317) 896-9531 *Founded/Ownrshp* 1961
Sales 205.8MM[E] *EMP* 700
SIC 3731 2399 Marine rigging; Belting & belt products; Marine rigging; Belting & belt products
CEO: Larry Gray
**Pr:* James T Anthony
Prgrm Mgr: Paul Britton
Prgrm Mgr: Dan Crowe
Mtls Mgr: Steve Ahler

D-U-N-S 83-112-8231 IMP
INDIANA MULTIMATIC MFG INC
(*Suby of* MULTIMATIC INC)
201 Re Jones Rd, Butler, IN 46721-9570
Tel (260) 868-1000 *Founded/Ownrshp* 2009
Sales 113.1MM[E] *EMP* 200
SIC 3465 Body parts, automobile: stamped metal; Body parts, automobile: stamped metal
Pr: Peter Czapka
**VP:* Martin Bressel
Prgrm Mgr: Curt Bremmer
Prgrm Mgr: Jim Woltman
Dir IT: Geoff Studdard
Ql Cn Mgr: Lisa Goodman

D-U-N-S 05-721-4579
INDIANA MUNICIPAL POWER AGENCY
IMPA
11610 N College Ave, Carmel, IN 46032-5602
Tel (317) 573-9955 *Founded/Ownrshp* 1983
Sales 456.5MM *EMP* 84[E]
SIC 4911 Distribution, electric power; Generation, electric power; Distribution, electric power; Generation, electric power
CEO: Raj RAO
**Treas:* William Grahm
**V Ch Bd:* David Osburne
Ex VP: David C Forward
**Sr VP:* Jack Alvey
**Sr VP:* Doug Buresh
**Sr VP:* Chris Rettig
VP: Larry Brown
VP: Richard Foltz
**VP:* Maria T Grossman
VP: Bev Matthews
VP: Christian Rettig
VP: Frank Smardo
Exec: Scott Berry

D-U-N-S 00-603-7436
■ INDIANA NEWSPAPERS INC (IN)
INDIANAPOLIS STAR, THE
(*Suby of* TEGNA INC) ★
130 S Meridian St, Indianapolis, IN 46225-1046
Tel (317) 444-4000 *Founded/Ownrshp* 1998, 2000
Sales 145.4MM[E] *EMP* 1,300
SIC 2711 2752 Newspapers, publishing & printing; Commercial printing, lithographic; Newspapers, publishing & printing; Commercial printing, lithographic
Pr: Karen Crotchfelt
Treas: Dawn Fisher
**Treas:* Michael A Hart
VP: Dawn Fisher-Polomski
**VP:* Gracia C Martore
VP: Peter Ricker
MIS Dir: Glen Berryman
IT Man: Steve Walker
Board of Directors: Robert J Dickey

D-U-N-S 80-989-5717
INDIANA OFFICE OF ADJUTANT GENERAL
ADJUTANT GENERAL'S OFFICE
(*Suby of* EXECUTIVE OFFICE OF STATE OF INDIANA) ★
2002 S Holt Rd, Indianapolis, IN 46241-4804
Tel (317) 247-3559 *Founded/Ownrshp* 1816
Sales NA *EMP* 1,992
SIC 9711 ;

D-U-N-S 62-304-1530
INDIANA ORGAN PROCUREMENT ORGANIZATION INC
3760 Guion Rd, Indianapolis, IN 46222-1618
Tel (317) 685-0389 *Founded/Ownrshp* 1987
Sales 27.4MM *EMP* 50
SIC 8099 Organ bank; Organ bank
Pr: Lynn Driver
VP: Ken Sheetz
Exec: Dave Murphy
IT Man: Jonathan Tanzer

D-U-N-S 83-037-4695
INDIANA ORTHOPAEDIC HOSPITAL LLC
8450 Northwest Blvd, Indianapolis, IN 46278-1381
Tel (317) 956-1000 *Founded/Ownrshp* 2002
Sales 141.0MM *EMP* 200[E]
SIC 8069 Orthopedic hospital; Orthopedic hospital
CEO: Jane Keller
CFO: Anthony Gioia
Dir Inf Cn: Heather Hohenberger
Dir Risk M: Tiffini White
Dir Lab: Tiffany Moody
Ansthlgy: Joseph Lafnitzegger
Doctor: David Kaehr
Doctor: Michael Kramer

D-U-N-S 00-603-6776
INDIANA OXYGEN CO INC
HOOSIER OXYGEN COMPANY
6099 Corporate Way, Indianapolis, IN 46278-2923
Tel (317) 290-0003 *Founded/Ownrshp* 1915
Sales 70.2MM[E] *EMP* 91
SIC 5169 5084 2813 Industrial gases; Welding machinery & equipment; Industrial gases; Industrial gases; Welding machinery & equipment; Industrial gases
Ch Bd: Walter L Brant
**Pr:* Anne Hayes
**Ex VP:* Michael Gunnels
**Ex VP:* Gary Halter
Ex VP: David L Kapan
Brnch Mgr: Tim Meranda
Genl Mgr: Pamela Sutton
IT Man: Dave Jackson
VP Sls: James Fuller
Sls Mgr: Ty Guernsey
Sls Mgr: Dan Latham

D-U-N-S 61-396-3131 IMP/EXP
INDIANA PACKERS CORP
(*Suby of* MITSUBISHI CORPORATION)
Hwy 421 S & Cr 100 N, Delphi, IN 46923
Tel (765) 564-3680 *Founded/Ownrshp* 1994
Sales 276.8MM[E] *EMP* 1,540
SIC 2011 2013 Pork products from pork slaughtered on site; Bacon, slab & sliced from meat slaughtered on site; Sausages & other prepared meats; Pork products from pork slaughtered on site; Bacon, slab & sliced from meat slaughtered on site; Sausages & other prepared meats
Pr: Russ Yearwood
**Pr:* Edward J Nelson
**CEO:* Masao Watanabe
CFO: James Miller
VP: James B Garrison
**VP:* James Hardison
VP: Dave Murray
VP: John Revord
**VP:* Randy Toleman
QA Dir: Rachael Royer
QA Dir: R Tinnell

D-U-N-S 78-552-8076
INDIANA PHOENIX INC
PHOENIX MIXERS
200 Dekko Dr, Avilla, IN 46710
Tel (260) 897-4397 *Founded/Ownrshp* 2000
Sales 25.8MM[E] *EMP* 90
SIC 3713 Cement mixer bodies
Pr: Carl Stockberger
**CFO:* Jay Carrison
**Sec:* Wyne Klink
**Prin:* Hartkey Hyder
Prd Mgr: Aren Hansen
Manager: Edward Johnson

D-U-N-S 82-479-9597
INDIANA POLICE STATE
(*Suby of* EXECUTIVE OFFICE OF STATE OF INDIANA) ★
100 N Senate Ave Rm N340, Indianapolis, IN 46204-2213
Tel (317) 232-8241 *Founded/Ownrshp* 1933
Sales NA *EMP* 1,900
SIC 9221 State police; ; State police;
Prgrm Mgr: Gayle Hicks

Pgrm Dir: Robert Paglia
Snr PM: Ram Annamalai

D-U-N-S 00-437-6109
INDIANA PRINTING AND PUBLISHING CO (PA)
INDIANA GAZETTE
899 Water St, Indiana, PA 15701-1705
Tel (724) 465-5555 *Founded/Ownrshp* 1890
Sales 50.7MM[E] *EMP* 320
SIC 2752 2711 Commercial printing, lithographic; Commercial printing & newspaper publishing combined; Commercial printing, lithographic; Commercial printing & newspaper publishing combined
CEO: Michael J Donnelly
**Treas:* Stacy Donnelly Gottfredson
VP: Joseph Geary
DP Exec: Mark Bender
Prd Mgr: Donna Rethi
Mktg Dir: John Buckshaw

D-U-N-S 15-209-4355
■ INDIANA RAIL ROAD CO
(*Suby of* MIDLAND UNITED CORP) ★
8888 Keystone Xing # 1600, Indianapolis, IN 46240-4606
Tel (888) 596-2121 *Founded/Ownrshp* 1989
Sales 39.9MM[E] *EMP* 180
SIC 4011 4013 Railroads, line-haul operating; Switching & terminal services; Railroads, line-haul operating; Switching & terminal services
Pr: Thomas G Hoback
Pr: Larry Kaelin
Pr: Peter Ray
**CFO:* Mike Engel
Sr VP: Robert Babcock
Pr Dir: Chris Rund
Sls Mgr: Yvonne Dunlea

D-U-N-S 07-496-1061
INDIANA REGIONAL MEDICAL CENTER
835 Hospital Rd, Indiana, PA 15701-3629
Tel (724) 357-7000 *Founded/Ownrshp* 1914
Sales 151.1MM *EMP* 1,100
Accts Parentebeard Llc Pittsburgh
SIC 8062 8011 General medical & surgical hospitals; Offices & clinics of medical doctors; General medical & surgical hospitals; Offices & clinics of medical doctors
Pr: Stephen A Wolfe
**CFO:* Larry Marshall
**Ch:* Todd Brice
**Ch:* Beverly Gazza
**Treas:* Joseph Geary
Ofcr: Ernest Lemoi
Sr VP: Dominique Pacctaniccia
Dir OR: Jeanne Stelmak
Dir Rx: Adam Kochman
Dir Sec: Danny Sacco
Off Mgr: Dawn Landis

INDIANA RESTAURANT EQP CO
See PENGUIN POINT FRANCHISE SYSTEMS INC

D-U-N-S 05-044-7477
INDIANA SCHOOL FOR DEAF
1200 E 42nd St, Indianapolis, IN 46205-2004
Tel (317) 493-0462 *Founded/Ownrshp* 2010
Sales 32.2MM[E] *EMP* 99
SIC 5192 Books
Prin: Dawniela A Halischak
Bd of Dir: Kim Majeri
Bd of Dir: Christine Wood
Ofcr: James Ryals
**Prin:* John Skjeveland
Mtls Mgr: Jim Hoglind
Mtls Mgr: Shaun Ray

D-U-N-S 12-907-8379
INDIANA SCHOOL FOR DEAF ALUMNI ASSOCIATION INC
1200 E 42nd St, Indianapolis, IN 46205-2004
Tel (317) 924-4374 *Founded/Ownrshp* 2000
Sales 28.3M *EMP* 302
SIC 8211 School for physically handicapped; School for the retarded; School for physically handicapped; School for the retarded
Bd of Dir: Sandra Wascher
**Prin:* Jeff Richards

D-U-N-S 01-123-4267
INDIANA SECONDARY MARKET FOR EDUCATION LOANS INC
11595 N Meridian St # 200, Carmel, IN 46032-6924
Tel (317) 715-9000 *Founded/Ownrshp* 1980
Sales NA *EMP* 120
SIC 6111 Student Loan Marketing Association; Student Loan Marketing Association
Pr: Stephen W Clinton
**Ch Bd:* Robert Macgille
**CFO:* Joseph Wood
Genl Mgr: Stewart Bick

D-U-N-S 05-895-7077 IMP
INDIANA SOUTHERN TIRE INC
1342 W 100 N, Princeton, IN 47670-8550
Tel (812) 386-8473 *Founded/Ownrshp* 1971
Sales 34.5MM[E] *EMP* 65
SIC 5531 5014 Automotive tires; Automobile tires & tubes
Pr: Paul Weaver
**Treas:* Larry Zurcher
**VP:* Paul Zurcher
Exec: Jeff Coleman
Mktg Mgr: Jason Mulkey
Sales Asso: Anna Smith

D-U-N-S 82-479-9407
INDIANA STATE DEPARTMENT OF HEALTH
(*Suby of* EXECUTIVE OFFICE OF STATE OF INDIANA) ★
2 N Meridian St Ste 1, Indianapolis, IN 46204-3010
Tel (317) 233-1325 *Founded/Ownrshp* 1991
Sales NA *EMP* 2,217
SIC 9431 Administration of public health programs; ; Administration of public health programs;
Genl Mgr: Howard Cundif
Off Mgr: Joeann Gupton

IT Man: Rebecca Chauhan
Pr Dir: Jennifer Dunlap

D-U-N-S 07-595-3448
INDIANA STATE UNIVERSITY
200 N 7th St, Terre Haute, IN 47809-1902
Tel (812) 237-6311 *Founded/Ownrshp* 1865
Sales 128.6MM *EMP* 1,700
Accts Paul D Joyce Cpa Indianapol
SIC 8221 University; University
Pr: Daniel J Bradley
**Pr:* Lyod Benjamins
**Treas:* Dianne McKee
Ofcr: Joshua Clifford
Ofcr: David Glick
Ofcr: Christopher Heleine
Ofcr: Jeffery Stinson
Assoc Dir: Carol A Reed
Ex Dir: John Sanders
CIO: Lisa Spence
Netwrk Eng: Robert Depasse

INDIANA STEEL AND TUBE
See E & H TUBING INC

D-U-N-S 00-174-7609 IMP
INDIANA SUGARS INC
911 Virginia St, Gary, IN 46402-2705
Tel (219) 886-9151 *Founded/Ownrshp* 1983
Sales 426.9MM[E] *EMP* 170
SIC 5149 Groceries & related products; Sugar, refined; Salt, edible; Flavourings & fragrances; Groceries & related products; Sugar, refined; Salt, edible; Flavourings & fragrances
Ch Bd: Ronald Yonover
**Treas:* John Yonover
VP: Vito Jasinevicius
VP: James Oconnell
IT Man: John Witt
S&M/VP: Scott Sievers

D-U-N-S 01-657-0665
INDIANA SUPERMARKETS INC
PARK-N-SHOP
3501 Edison Rd, South Bend, IN 46615-3713
Tel (574) 247-4400 *Founded/Ownrshp* 1955
Sales 22.6MM[E] *EMP* 210
SIC 5411 5541 Supermarkets; Convenience stores; Filling stations, gasoline; Supermarkets; Convenience stores; Filling stations, gasoline
Pr: Dennis Rhodes
**VP:* William Rhodes

D-U-N-S 01-641-7230
INDIANA SUPPLY CORP
6751 E 30th St, Indianapolis, IN 46219-1139
Tel (317) 359-5451 *Founded/Ownrshp* 1955
Sales 27.4MM[E] *EMP* 97
SIC 5075 5051 Warm air heating equipment & supplies; Air conditioning & ventilation equipment & supplies; Sheets, metal; Warm air heating equipment & supplies; Air conditioning & ventilation equipment & supplies; Sheets, metal
Ch Bd: Stanley Hurt
**Pr:* David M Draga
CFO: Tracey Gisell
IT Man: Andy Cord
Genl Couns: Pearson Smith

D-U-N-S 07-596-6341
INDIANA SYMPHONY SOCIETY INC
ISO MUSIC STAND
32 E Washington St # 600, Indianapolis, IN 46204-3513
Tel (317) 262-1100 *Founded/Ownrshp* 1930
Sales 22.3MM *EMP* 170
Accts Blue & Co Llc Carmel In
SIC 7929 Symphony orchestras; Symphony orchestras
Pr: Simon P Crookall
**Ch Bd:* Robert Anker
**Treas:* Robert Kaspar
Bd of Dir: Ralph Wilhelm
Ofcr: Lauren Laski
VP: Steve Hamilton
Exec: Rita Martin
Genl Mgr: Gary Ginstling
CIO: Ken Fitzgerald
Mktg Dir: Sarah Ross
Sls Mgr: Margaret Henney

INDIANA TECH
See INDIANA INSTITUTE OF TECHNOLOGY INC

INDIANA TICKET COMPANY
See MUNCIE NOVELTY CO INC

INDIANA TOLL ROAD
See ITR CONCESSION CO LLC

INDIANA TOOL & DIE
See JASPER ENGINE EXCHANGE INC

D-U-N-S 00-542-2134 IMP
INDIANA TOOL & MFG CO INC (IN)
ITAMCO COMPANY
6100 Michigan Rd, Plymouth, IN 46563-7798
Tel (574) 936-5548 *Founded/Ownrshp* 1955
Sales 29.0MM[E] *EMP* 100
SIC 3462 3545 Gear & chain forgings; Machine tool attachments & accessories
CEO: Donald K Neidig
**Pr:* Noble L Neidig
**VP:* Gary L Neidig

D-U-N-S 17-077-2144
INDIANA TRUMP REALTY LLC
(*Suby of* TRUMP ENTERTAINMENT RESORTS INC) ★
1 Buffington Harbor Dr, Gary, IN 46406-3000
Tel (609) 441-8406 *Founded/Ownrshp* 2004
Sales 2.4MM[E] *EMP* 469[E]
SIC 7011 Casino hotel
Prin: Scott Hubbard

D-U-N-S 06-833-1750 EXP
■ INDIANA TUBE CORP (DE)
(*Suby of* HANDY & HARMAN) ★
2100 Lexington Rd, Evansville, IN 47720-1234
Tel (812) 467-7155 *Founded/Ownrshp* 1973, 1998
Sales 30.0MM[E] *EMP* 350

SIC 3317 Steel pipe & tubes; Steel pipe & tubes
Pr: John Whitenack
**VP Opers:* Ron Hawkins
Ql Cn Mgr: Gary Frank
**VP Sls:* Ron Tenbarge

D-U-N-S 07-847-8339
INDIANA UNIVERSITY
1020 E Kirkwood Ave, Bloomington, IN 47405-7103
Tel (812) 855-7581 *Founded/Ownrshp* 2012
Sales 2.2MMM *EMP* 31[E]
SIC 8221 Colleges universities & professional schools
Prin: Eliza Pavalko
Bd of Dir: Steven Janowiecki
Art Dir: Chelsea Coleman
Assoc Ed: Elisa Gross
Assoc Ed: T Rowley

D-U-N-S 83-304-1267
INDIANA UNIVERSITY CREDIT UNION
105 E Winslow Rd, Bloomington, IN 47401-8689
Tel (812) 855-7823 *Founded/Ownrshp* 2009
Sales NA *EMP* 4
SIC 6061 Federal credit unions; Federal credit unions
Prin: Robert Newcomb

D-U-N-S 08-153-5981
INDIANA UNIVERSITY EMPLOYEES FEDERAL CREDIT UNION INC
I U CREDIT UNION
105 E Winslow Rd, Bloomington, IN 47401-8689
Tel (812) 855-7823 *Founded/Ownrshp* 1956
Sales NA *EMP* 56
SIC 6061 Federal credit unions; Federal credit unions
Pr: Robert Newcomb
**CFO:* Brian Price
IT Man: Mark Weigle

D-U-N-S 01-639-3092
INDIANA UNIVERSITY FOUNDATION INC
1500 N State Road 46 Byp, Bloomington, IN 47408
Tel (812) 855-8311 *Founded/Ownrshp* 1936
Sales 222.7MM *EMP* 240
Accts Deloitte & Touche Llp Indiana
SIC 6732 Educational trust management; Educational trust management
Pr: Gene Tempel
**CFO:* James Perin
Off Mgr: Beth Gillespie

D-U-N-S 09-201-7060
INDIANA UNIVERSITY HEALTH
IU HEALTH BLACKFORD HOSPITAL
(*Suby of* INDIANA UNIVERSITY HEALTH INC) ★
410 Pilgrim Blvd, Hartford City, IN 47348-1382
Tel (765) 348-0300 *Founded/Ownrshp* 2008
Sales 5.2MMM *EMP* 150
Accts Ernst & Young Llp Indianapoli
SIC 8062 General medical & surgical hospitals
CEO: Steven West
Cert Phar: Dianna Davis

D-U-N-S 07-597-4899
INDIANA UNIVERSITY HEALTH BALL MEMORIAL HOSPITAL INC
IU HEALTH ALBANY PHARMACY
(*Suby of* INDIANA UNIVERSITY HEALTH INC) ★
2401 W University Ave, Muncie, IN 47303-3428
Tel (765) 751-1449 *Founded/Ownrshp* 2009
Sales 395.1MM *EMP* 3,000
SIC 8062 Hospital, medical school affiliated with nursing & residency; Hospital, medical school affiliated with nursing & residency
Pr: Michael Haley
Dir Recs: Piper Hawk
CFO: Carol Fields
Chf Mktg O: Jeff Bird
VP: Terry Pence
Dir Lab: Debbie Garner
Dir Mgr: Jill Carter
Dir QC: Claire Lee
IT Man: Shawna White
Netwrk Mgr: Mark Constant
Opers Mgr: Kim Koss

D-U-N-S 07-206-2003
INDIANA UNIVERSITY HEALTH BEDFORD INC
BEDFORD HOSPITAL
2900 16th St, Bedford, IN 47421-3510
Tel (812) 275-1200 *Founded/Ownrshp* 1967
Sales 50.6MM *EMP* 385
SIC 8062 General medical & surgical hospitals; General medical & surgical hospitals
CEO: Bradford W Dykes
Chf Rad: Timothy Lach
**VP:* Brenda Davis
VP: David Murphy
**VP:* James Pittman
**VP:* Charles Shetler
**Exec:* Cindy Smale
Dir Case M: Teresa Mathis
Dir Lab: Valerie Knight
Dir Rx: Tobie Rogers
Genl Mgr: Geneva French

D-U-N-S 07-205-2137
INDIANA UNIVERSITY HEALTH BLOOMINGTON INC
IU HEALTH BLOOMINGTON HOSPITAL
601 W 2nd St, Bloomington, IN 47403-2317
Tel (812) 353-5252 *Founded/Ownrshp* 1905
Sales 355.6MM *EMP* 3,200
SIC 8062 General medical & surgical hospitals; General medical & surgical hospitals
Pr: Mark E Moore
CFO: Michael Craig
CFO: David Massengale
CFO: James Myers
Chf Mktg O: Michael Niemeier
VP: Teri Dematas
VP: Chris Molloy
VP: Holly Vonderheit
Dir Teleco: Nancy Jacobs
Dir Rad: Bruce N Monson
Nurse Mgr: Jason Crouch

D-U-N-S 96-524-8321
INDIANA UNIVERSITY HEALTH INC
INDIANA UNIVERSITY HOSPITAL
1701 Senate Blvd, Indianapolis, IN 46202-1239
Tel (317) 962-2000 *Founded/Ownrshp* 2010
Sales 2.0MMM^E *EMP* 17,242
Accts Ernst & Young Llp Indianapoli
SIC 8062 6324 General medical & surgical hospitals; Health maintenance organization (HMO), insurance only; General medical & surgical hospitals; Health maintenance organization (HMO), insurance only
Pr: Daniel F Evans Jr
Chf Mktg O: Richard Graffis MD
Ofcr: Karlene Kerfoot
VP: Catherine Cooper - Weidner
Exec: Linda Q Everett
Adm Dir: Max Barnhart
Adm Dir: Karen Brenner
Adm Dir: H George
Adm Dir: Sheila Ogden
Adm Dir: Michelle Schafer
Prgrm Mgr: Sue Dunham
Board of Directors: V William Hunt, Sara E Barker, James E Lingeman MD, Myles Brand, Angela B McBride, D Craig Brater MD, Thomas W Chapman, Bishop Michael J Coyner, Stephen L Ferguson, Charles E Golden, David W Goodrich, Adam Herbert Jr

D-U-N-S 07-891-8976
INDIANA UNIVERSITY HEALTH LA PORTE HOSPITAL INC
LA PORTE HOSPITAL & HLTH SVCS
1007 Lincolnway, La Porte, IN 46350-3201
Tel (219) 326-1234 *Founded/Ownrshp* 1966
Sales 648.0MM *EMP* 1,500
SIC 8062 General medical & surgical hospitals; General medical & surgical hospitals
CEO: Thor Thordarson
COO: Linda Satkofki
CFO: Dan Elmer
**CFO:* Mark Rafalski
CFO: Mark Rasalski
CFO: Jerry Wasserstein
Treas: Allison Hertges
Chf Mktg O: Bill Houston
Ex VP: Maria Fruth
Dir OR: Heather Manley
Dir Rad: Matthew Shebel
Dir Rx: Leonid Slobodskoy

D-U-N-S 95-899-9815
INDIANA UNIVERSITY HEALTH LA PORTE PHYSICIANS INC
1100 Lincolnway, La Porte, IN 46350-3289
Tel (219) 326-2469 *Founded/Ownrshp* 1983
Sales 25.8MM *EMP* 280
SIC 8011 Clinic, operated by physicians; Clinic, operated by physicians
VP: Rhonda Volk

D-U-N-S 07-889-3420
INDIANA UNIVERSITY HEALTH MORGAN HOSPITAL INC
2209 John R Wooden Dr, Martinsville, IN 46151-1840
Tel (765) 842-8441 *Founded/Ownrshp* 2011
Sales 39.9MM *EMP* 380
Accts Blue & Co Llc Indianapolis I
SIC 8062 General medical & surgical hospitals; General medical & surgical hospitals
CEO: Doug Puckett
**CFO:* Scott Andritsch
Obsttrcn: Lynn Reynolds
HC Dir: Melissa Deckard

D-U-N-S 07-406-6036
INDIANA UNIVERSITY HEALTH PAOLI INC
642 W Hospital Rd, Paoli, IN 47454-9672
Tel (812) 723-2811 *Founded/Ownrshp* 2000
Sales 30.1MM^E *EMP* 200
SIC 8062 General medical & surgical hospitals; General medical & surgical hospitals
CEO: Larry Bailey
CFO: Sue Brock
IT Man: Sara Meyers
Surgeon: Rexene Slayton
Pharmcst: Teri Dorsett
HC Dir: John Lee

D-U-N-S 07-845-5878
INDIANA UNIVERSITY HEALTH PLANS INC
IU HEALTH
(*Suby of* INDIANA UNIVERSITY HEALTH INC) ★
950 N Meridian St Ste 950, Indianapolis, IN 46204-1161
Tel (317) 963-9700 *Founded/Ownrshp* 2008
Sales NA *EMP* 30
SIC 6321 Accident & health insurance carriers
Pr: James T Parker
**COO:* Dennis Murphy
**CFO:* Ryan C Kitchell
**Ex VP:* John C Kohne
VP: Scott Brenton
Dir Rx: Mary Odonnell
Sales Asso: Thad Thompson
Pharmcst: Lora Ertmoed
Snr PM: Tom Zmyslo
Snr Mgr: Judy Coleman

D-U-N-S 11-486-1938
INDIANA UNIVERSITY HEALTH SOUTHERN INDIANA PHYSICIANS INC
1302 S Rogers St, Bloomington, IN 47403-4752
Tel (812) 353-5866 *Founded/Ownrshp* 1994
Sales 4.1MM *EMP* 440
Accts Pricewaterhousecoopers Llp Ch
SIC 8011 Medical centers; Medical centers
Pr: Gene Perry
**Prin:* Mark Moore

D-U-N-S 80-833-4119
INDIANA UNIVERSITY HEALTH STARKE HOSPITAL LLC
IU HEALTH STARKE HOSPITAL
102 E Culver Rd, Knox, IN 46534-2216
Tel (574) 772-6231 *Founded/Ownrshp* 2009
Sales 22.9MM *EMP* 8^E

SIC 8062 8322 General medical & surgical hospitals; Community center
Pr: Craig Felty
Chf Rad: Josephine Klicek
Dir OR: Heather Manley
Dir Soc: Kim Welsh
**Prin:* Linda Satkoski
Phys Thrpy: Becky Alwood-Wallace

D-U-N-S 94-156-0364 IMP
INDIANA UNIVERSITY HEALTH TIPTON HOSPITAL INC
1000 S Main St, Tipton, IN 46072-9753
Tel (765) 675-8500 *Founded/Ownrshp* 2008
Sales 45.7MM *EMP* 300
SIC 8062 General medical & surgical hospitals; General medical & surgical hospitals
Pr: Michael Harlowe
CFO: Vern Schmaltz
Doctor: Kevin Condict
HC Dir: Rich Young

INDIANA UNIVERSITY HOSPITAL
See INDIANA UNIVERSITY HEALTH INC

D-U-N-S 07-313-0049
INDIANA UNIVERSITY OF PENNSYLVANIA
STATE SYSTEM OF HGHR
(*Suby of* STATE SYSTEM HIGHER EDUCATN PA) ★
1011 S Dr 201 Sutton, Indiana, PA 15705-0001
Tel (724) 357-2200 *Founded/Ownrshp* 1875
Sales 175.9MM^E *EMP* 1,846
Accts Cliftonlarsonallen Llp Plymo
SIC 8221 9411 University; Administration of educational programs; ; University; Administration of educational programs;
Pr: Michael Driscoll
**VP:* James Begany
VP: Evan Bohnen
**VP:* Gerald Intemann
**VP:* Rhonda Luckey
**VP:* William Speidel
**VP:* Cornelius Wooten

D-U-N-S 07-865-7507
INDIANA UNIVERSITY OF SOUTH EAST
4201 Grant Line Rd, New Albany, IN 47150-2158
Tel (812) 941-2000 *Founded/Ownrshp* 2012
Sales 50.9MM^E *EMP* 700
SIC 8221 University; University
Dir Vol: Claudia Crump
Ofcr: Ruben Borrego
VP: Cory Dixon
Assoc Dir: Julie Ingram
Store Mgr: Julie Faulds
Off Admin: Heather Rife
Mktg Dir: Steven Krolak
Doctor: Mary Baker

D-U-N-S 07-880-5837
INDIANA UNIVERSITY PRESS
1320 E 10th St, Bloomington, IN 47405-3907
Tel (800) 842-6796 *Founded/Ownrshp* 2013
Sales 40.0MM^E *EMP* 290^E
SIC 5192 Books, periodicals & newspapers
V Ch: Richard Gunderman
Sr VP: David Hopkins
VP: Bryan Povlinski
VP: Andrew Ramos
Exec: Thomas Wieligman
Dir Lab: Steve Studley
Assoc Dir: Bridget Balint
Assoc Dir: Nancy Bannister
Assoc Dir: Michael Denunzio
Assoc Dir: Olga Kalentzidou
Assoc Dir: Sarah Rathbun
Assoc Dir: Kathy Sideli

D-U-N-S 11-734-3145
INDIANA UNIVERSITY RADIOLOGY ASSOCIATES INC
550 University Blvd # 663, Indianapolis, IN 46202-5149
Tel (317) 274-2881 *Founded/Ownrshp* 1980
Sales 21.8MM *EMP* 40
Accts Larry E Nunn & Associates L
SIC 8011 Radiologist; Radiologist
Pr: Valerie Jackson
**VP:* Huen Yune MD
**Prin:* Michael La Masters
Doctor: Dean Maglinte

D-U-N-S 14-704-1789
INDIANA UNIVERSITY RADIOLOGY ASSOCIATES INC
714 N Senate Ave Ste 100, Indianapolis, IN 46202-3297
Tel (317) 715-6425 *Founded/Ownrshp* 1979
Sales 50.4MM *EMP* 70
SIC 8011 Radiologist; Radiologist
Podiatrist: William Berry

D-U-N-S 07-207-8199
INDIANA WESLEYAN UNIVERSITY
4201 S Washington St, Marion, IN 46953-4974
Tel (765) 674-6901 *Founded/Ownrshp* 1919
Sales 226.1MM *EMP* 1,000
Accts Bkd Llp Fort Wayne In
SIC 8221 Colleges & universities; Colleges & universities
Pr: David Wright
Pr: Terry Munday
VP: Darlene Bressler
VP: Brian Gardner
**VP:* Duane Kilty
VP: Mandy Ogunnowo
VP: Thomas E Phillippe Sr
Dir Lab: Juanita Higley
Assoc Dir: Jeanne Craig
**Prin:* Henry Smith
CTO: Melissa Sprock
Board of Directors: Tiffany Lewis

D-U-N-S 19-995-5014
INDIANA WESTERN EXPRESS INC
IWX MOTOR FREIGHT
2750 N Barnes Ave, Springfield, MO 65803-4921
Tel (417) 873-1000 *Founded/Ownrshp* 1990
Sales 74.8MM *EMP* 500
Accts Wilson & Mee Cpas Springfiel
SIC 4213 Trucking, except local; Trucking, except local
Pr: Stephen J Coulter

D-U-N-S 07-829-5759
INDIANA WHITESELL CORP
(*Suby of* WHITESELL CORP) ★
5101 Decatur Blvd Ste W, Indianapolis, IN 46241-9529
Tel (317) 279-3278 *Founded/Ownrshp* 2011
Sales 36.9MM^E *EMP* 400^E
SIC 3399 5085 3429 4212 4225

D-U-N-S 00-693-8930
■ **INDIANA-AMERICAN WATER CO INC**
INDIANA AMERICAN WATER
(*Suby of* AMERICAN WATER WORKS CO INC) ★
555 E County Line Rd # 201, Greenwood, IN 46143-1064
Tel (800) 492-8373 *Founded/Ownrshp* 1872
Sales NA *EMP* 363
SIC 4941 Water supply; Water supply
Pr: Alan Deboy

D-U-N-S 00-777-7915
INDIANA-KENTUCKY ELECTRIC CORP
OVEC
(*Suby of* OHIO VALLEY ELECTRIC CORP) ★
3932 Us Rte 23, Piketon, OH 45661
Tel (740) 289-7200 *Founded/Ownrshp* 1952
Sales 199.1MM *EMP* 320
Accts Deloitte & Touche Llp Cincinn
SIC 4911 Generation, electric power; Transmission, electric power; Generation, electric power; Transmission, electric power
Pr: Nicholos Akins
**COO:* Mark Peifer
**CFO:* John Brodt

D-U-N-S 06-281-1757
INDIANAPOLIS AIRPORT AUTHORITY
7800 Col Weircook Dr # 100, Indianapolis, IN 46241-8009
Tel (317) 487-9594 *Founded/Ownrshp* 1962
Sales 75.6MM^E *EMP* 480
Accts Bkd Llp Indianapolis In
SIC 4581 Airports, flying fields & services; Airports, flying fields & services
Pr: Lacy M Johnson
**Pr:* Mike Wells
COO: Mike Medvescek
**Treas:* Stu Grauel
**Treas:* Robert Thomson
**VP:* Patrick Callahan
**VP:* Kelly Flynn
**Ex Dir:* Robert Duncan

D-U-N-S 08-561-9922
INDIANAPOLIS CAR EXCHANGE INC (IN)
5161 S Indianapolis Rd, Whitestown, IN 46075-9377
Tel (317) 769-4858 *Founded/Ownrshp* 1978, 1986
Sales 75.0MM *EMP* 120
SIC 5012 Automobile auction; Automobile auction
Pr: Daniel Hockett

D-U-N-S 11-904-8119
INDIANAPOLIS DOWNS LLC
INDIANA DOWNS
(*Suby of* CENTAUR HOLDINGS LLC) ★
4200 N Michigan Rd, Shelbyville, IN 46176-8515
Tel (317) 421-0000 *Founded/Ownrshp* 1999
Sales 28.7MM^E *EMP* 800^E
SIC 7948 Horse race track operation; Horse race track operation
Ch: Rod Rapeliff
Pr: Tricia Lavore
**Ch:* Ross Mangano
Genl Mgr: Jon Schuster
Dir IT: Ted Mazotas
Mktg Mgr: Jamie Rucker

INDIANAPOLIS DRY STRIPPING
See MCCOY INVESTMENTS INC

D-U-N-S 06-280-7318
INDIANAPOLIS ELECTRICAL JOINT APPRENTICESHIP TRAINING CENTER INC
ELECTRICAL TRAINING INSTITUTE
1751 S Lawndale Ave, Indianapolis, IN 46241-4315
Tel (317) 270-5282 *Founded/Ownrshp* 1946
Sales 1.9MM *EMP* 450
SIC 8249 Vocational apprentice training; Vocational apprentice training
Ch Bd: James Bewsey
Dir IT: Jon Tekulve

INDIANAPOLIS FRUIT COMPANY
See IF&P FOODS INC

D-U-N-S 01-641-7529
INDIANAPOLIS FRUIT CO INC
I.F.C. MANAGEMENT SERVICES
(*Suby of* IF&P FOODS INC) ★
4501 Massachusetts Ave, Indianapolis, IN 46218-3176
Tel (317) 546-2425 *Founded/Ownrshp* 1997
Sales 54.0MM^E *EMP* 180
SIC 5148 Fruits, fresh; Vegetables, fresh; Fruits, fresh; Vegetables, fresh
Owner: Mike Mascari
**CFO:* Gregory P Corsaro
**Sec:* Greg Corsaro
**Ex VP:* Danny Corsaro
**VP:* Joe Corsaro
**VP:* Chris Mascari
**VP:* Peter Piazza

D-U-N-S 07-204-0587
INDIANAPOLIS INDIANA HOTELS PARTNERSHIP
14185 Dallas Pkwy # 1100, Dallas, TX 75254-1319
Tel (972) 490-9600 *Founded/Ownrshp* 1993
Sales 13.2MM^E *EMP* 470
SIC 8741 Hotel or motel management; Hotel or motel management
CEO: Monty Bennett
Genl Pt: Indiana Hotels III Corp

D-U-N-S 09-321-8907
INDIANAPOLIS JEWISH HOME INC
HOOVERWOOD
7001 Hoover Rd, Indianapolis, IN 46260-4169
Tel (317) 251-2261 *Founded/Ownrshp* 1946
Sales 16.9MM *EMP* 300
Accts Crowe Horwath Llp Indianapoli
SIC 8051 Skilled nursing care facilities; Skilled nursing care facilities
VP: Greg Hylton
VP: Thomas Zupancic
Pr Dir: Barb Rettig
Mktg Mgr: Dee Rolland

D-U-N-S 62-356-5582
INDIANAPOLIS METROPOLITAN HIGH SCHOOLS
INDIANPLIS MTRO CREER ACDEMIES
(*Suby of* GOODWILL INDUSTRIES OF CENTRAL INDIANA INC) ★
1635 W Michigan St, Indianapolis, IN 46222-3852
Tel (317) 524-4638 *Founded/Ownrshp* 2003
Sales 25.5MM *EMP* 60
SIC 8211 Private senior high school; Private senior high school
Pr: James M McClelland
**Pr:* Dan Riley
Snr Mgr: Daniel Stevens

D-U-N-S 06-554-8273 IMP
INDIANAPOLIS MUSEUM OF ART INC
I M A
4000 Michigan Rd, Indianapolis, IN 46208-3326
Tel (317) 923-1331 *Founded/Ownrshp* 1882
Sales 28.2MM *EMP* 300
Accts Bkd Llp Indianapolis In
SIC 8412 5947 Museum; Gift shop; Museum; Gift shop
V Ch: June McCormack
**CEO:* Charles Venable
**COO:* Nick Cameron
**CFO:* Jennifer Bartenbach
CFO: Jeremiah Wise
**Treas:* Daniel Cantor
Treas: Lawrence A O'Connor Jr
Ofcr: Andra Walters
IT Man: Kris Arnold
Mktg Dir: Jessica Di Santo
Mktg Dir: Jessica Disanto

D-U-N-S 07-207-3943
INDIANAPOLIS OSTEOPATHIC HOSPITAL INC
WESTVIEW HOSPITAL
3630 Guion Rd, Indianapolis, IN 46222-1616
Tel (317) 920-8439 *Founded/Ownrshp* 1961
Sales 61.3MM *EMP* 453
Accts Blue & Co Llc Indianapolis I
SIC 8062 General medical & surgical hospitals; General medical & surgical hospitals
Pr: David C Williams
**CEO:* Jerry Porter
COO: Randy White
**CFO:* John Anderson
CFO: Roger Boruff
CFO: Jerry Marks
Chf Mktg O: Deborah Lee
Exec: Patty Heffner
Dir Lab: Matt Chaille
Dir Lab: Laury Dodds
Dir Rx: Brad Philbrick

D-U-N-S 00-693-8310
■ **INDIANAPOLIS POWER & LIGHT CO**
(*Suby of* IPALCO ENTERPRISES INC) ★
1 Monument Cir, Indianapolis, IN 46204-2901
Tel (317) 261-8261 *Founded/Ownrshp* 1926
Sales 740.1MM^E *EMP* 1,250
SIC 4911 Generation, electric power; Generation, electric power
CEO: Ken Zagzebski
Pr: Kelly M Huntington
Pr: Sandi Vasel
COO: Ronald E Talbot
Treas: Anita M Hill
VP: William Henley
VP: Jim Sadtler
IT Man: Erick Jones
Sls&Mrk Ex: Danielle Harbor

INDIANAPOLIS PUBLIC LIBRARY
See INDIANAPOLIS-MARION COUNTY PUBLIC LIBRARY FOUNDATION INC

D-U-N-S 07-596-7992
INDIANAPOLIS PUBLIC SCHOOLS
IPS
120 E Walnut St, Indianapolis, IN 46204-1389
Tel (317) 226-4000 *Founded/Ownrshp* 1835
Sales 448.1MM^E *EMP* 8,000
SIC 8211 Public elementary & secondary schools; Public elementary & secondary schools
Ex Dir: Joseph Smith
IT Man: Stan Cork
IT Man: Aaron Groves
Pr Dir: Lee Boler
Schl Brd P: Amy Roof

D-U-N-S 07-208-3116
INDIANAPOLIS PUBLIC TRANSPORTATION CORP
INDYGO
1501 W Washington St A, Indianapolis, IN 46222-4574
Tel (317) 614-9221 *Founded/Ownrshp* 1965
Sales 12.1MM *EMP* 550
Accts Crowe Horwath Llp Indianapoli
SIC 4111 Bus line operations; Bus line operations
CEO: Michael A Terry
CFO: Wayne Oteham Sr
Treas: Erica Morgan
**VP:* Mike Birch
**VP:* Roscoe Brown
**VP:* Phalease Crichlow
**VP:* Andy Jackson
VP: Nancy Manley
Dir: Annette Darrow
Genl Mgr: Virginia Dunnigan

INDIANAPOLIS STAR, THE
See INDIANA NEWSPAPERS INC

D-U-N-S 07-205-6773 IMP
INDIANAPOLIS ZOOLOGICAL SOCIETY INC
1200 W Washington St, Indianapolis, IN 46222-4552
Tel (317) 630-2001 Founded/Ownrshp 1944
Sales 32.3MM EMP 199
Accts Bkd Llp Indianapolis In
SIC 8422 Zoological garden, noncommercial; Zoological garden, noncommercial
Ch: Michael Wells
*Pr: Michael I Crowther
*CFO: Claudia Willis
*Treas: James Powers
Ofcr: Julie McDearmon
Ofcr: J Sandifer
VP: Mike Alley
VP: Ali Malek
VP: Brent Ridenour
VP: J Ridenour
Dir Soc: Liz Mok
Creative D: Jo Hohlbein
Comm Dir: Judith L Gagen
Board of Directors: Timothy Ardillo, Will Key

D-U-N-S 06-280-7391
INDIANAPOLIS-MARION COUNTY PUBLIC LIBRARY FOUNDATION INC
INDIANAPOLIS PUBLIC LIBRARY
2450 N Meridian St, Indianapolis, IN 46208-5732
Tel (317) 269-1700 Founded/Ownrshp 1873
Sales 53.8MM EMP 640
Accts Paul D Joyce Cpa Indianapol
SIC 8231 Public library; Public library
CEO: Jackie Nytes
*CFO: Becky Dixon
VP: Gary J Meyer
Dir Soc: Eric Houghtalen
*Prin: Laura Bramble
Area Mgr: Sharon Bernhardt
Dir IT: Debra Champ
IT Man: Carolyn Adams
Web Dev: Brian Dunten

INDIANHEAD CASH & CARRY
See INDIANHEAD FOODSERVICE DISTRIBUTOR INC

D-U-N-S 01-916-8970
INDIANHEAD COMMUNITY ACTION AGENCY INC
1000 College Ave W, Ladysmith, WI 54848-2118
Tel (715) 532-4222 Founded/Ownrshp 1966
Sales 12.9MM EMP 1,200ᴱ
Accts Wipfli Llp Madison Wisconsin
SIC 8399 Community action agency; Community action agency
CEO: Brett Gerber
*Ex Dir: Jerome Drahos
Dir IT: Bob Carter

D-U-N-S 02-321-2079
INDIANHEAD FOODSERVICE DISTRIBUTOR INC
INDIANHEAD CASH & CARRY
313 N Hastings Pl, Eau Claire, WI 54703-3440
Tel (715) 834-2777 Founded/Ownrshp 1976
Sales 129.1MMᴱ EMP 90
SIC 5142 5141 5147 5143 Packaged frozen goods; Groceries, general line; Meats, fresh; Dairy products, except dried or canned; Packaged frozen goods; Groceries, general line; Meats, fresh; Dairy products, except dried or canned
Pr: Thomas Gillett
*Treas: Elizabeth Gillett
Sls Mgr: Mark Danielson

D-U-N-S 04-145-3473
INDIANOLA COMMUNITY SCHOOL DISTRICT
1304 E 2nd Ave, Indianola, IA 50125-2898
Tel (515) 961-9500 Founded/Ownrshp 1870
Sales 22.9MMᴱ EMP 490
SIC 8211 Public elementary & secondary schools; Public elementary & secondary schools
IT Man: Brad Germond
Schl Brd P: Carolynn Lantewalter

D-U-N-S 04-707-9736
INDIANOLA SCHOOL DISTRICT
702 Highway 82 E, Indianola, MS 38751-2322
Tel (662) 884-1200 Founded/Ownrshp 1920
Sales 14.7MMᴱ EMP 400
Accts Watkins Ward And Stafford Ja
SIC 8211 Public elementary school; Public junior high school; Public senior high school; Public elementary school; Public junior high school; Public senior high school

INDIANPLIS MTRO CREER ACDEMIES
See INDIANAPOLIS METROPOLITAN HIGH SCHOOLS

D-U-N-S 94-709-9396
INDIANTOWN COGENERATION FUNDING CORP
(Suby of INDIANTOWN COGENERATION LP) ★
13303 Sw Silver Fox Ln, Indiantown, FL 34956
Tel (772) 597-6500 Founded/Ownrshp 1998
Sales 42.4MMᴱ EMP 60
SIC 4911 Generation, electric power; Generation, electric power

D-U-N-S 86-127-5568
INDIANTOWN COGENERATION LP
13303 Sw Silver Fox Ln, Indiantown, FL 34956
Tel (772) 597-6500 Founded/Ownrshp 2007
Sales 42.4MMᴱ EMP 60
SIC 4911 Generation, electric power; Generation, electric power
Plnt Mgr: Gary Willer
Sfty Mgr: Chris Fitzpatrick
Opers Mgr: Chris Curry

D-U-N-S 15-119-5682
INDICOM BUILDINGS INC
721 N Burleson Blvd, Burleson, TX 76028-2912
Tel (817) 447-1213 Founded/Ownrshp 1986
Sales 24.7MMᴱ EMP 90
SIC 2452 3448 Prefabricated buildings, wood; Buildings, portable: prefabricated metal
CEO: Ron Procunier

D-U-N-S 87-317-6911
INDICON CORP
6125 Center Dr, Sterling Heights, MI 48312-2667
Tel (586) 274-0505 Founded/Ownrshp 1993
Sales 55.9MMᴱ EMP 225
SIC 3613 3625 Control panels, electric; Relays & industrial controls; Control panels, electric; Relays & industrial controls
Pr: Paul Duhaime
*Sec: Andrew T Conti

D-U-N-S 82-463-1873 IMP
■ **INDIGO AMERICA INC**
HEWLETT PACKARD
(Suby of HP INC) ★
165 Dascomb Rd 1, Andover, MA 01810-5886
Tel (978) 474-2000 Founded/Ownrshp 2001
Sales 256.8MMᴱ EMP 420
SIC 5049 Scientific & engineering equipment & supplies; Scientific & engineering equipment & supplies
Pr: Catherine Lesjak
CFO: Alon Bar-Shany
*Treas: Charles N Charnas
Sr Cor Off: Franc Gentili
*VP: Ann O Baskins
VP: Brian Larose
VP: Jane Shea Seitz
Comm Dir: Cory Pforzheimer
Comm Dir: Sarah Pompei
Comm Man: Fred Van Buiten
*Ex Dir: Todd Cromwell

D-U-N-S 82-748-9183
INDIGO ENERGY PARTNERS LLC
222 Main St Sw, Gainesville, GA 30501-3708
Tel (678) 513-9114 Founded/Ownrshp 2008
Sales 40.5MMᴱ EMP 17
SIC 5172 Fuel oil
CEO: John E Mansfield Jr
COO: Martin N Underwood Jr
CFO: Blake W Shirley Sr
IT Man: Martin Underwood

D-U-N-S 79-560-2866
INDIGO MINERALS LLC
600 Travis St Ste 5500, Houston, TX 77002-3008
Tel (713) 237-5000 Founded/Ownrshp 2007
Sales 43.1MMᴱ EMP 30
SIC 1481 Mine development, nonmetallic minerals
CEO: William E Pritchard III
*Pr: Keith E Jordan
*CFO: Becky Bayless
*Sr VP: Fred Bakun
*Sr VP: Bradley J Rome
*VP: Marc Dellamea
*VP: Chris Whitten
Dir IT: Lance Kirk

D-U-N-S 02-287-4118
INDIGO SERVICES PLC
HOSPITALISTS NORTHERN MICHIGAN
10850 E Traverse Hwy # 4400, Traverse City, MI 49684-1364
Tel (231) 346-6800 Founded/Ownrshp 2009
Sales 24.0MMᴱ EMP 65
SIC 8011 Orthopedic physician; Orthopedic physician
CEO: David Friar
CEO: Deb Blashill
VP: James Levy
VP: Richard Woodbury
Prin: Troy Ahlstrom

D-U-N-S 15-085-2960 IMP
INDIO PRODUCTS INC
SEVEN SISTERS OF NEW ORLEANS
5331 E Slauson Ave, Commerce, CA 90040-2916
Tel (323) 720-1188 Founded/Ownrshp 2011
Sales 63.2MMᴱ EMP 150
SIC 5049 3999

D-U-N-S 00-222-7296
INDIUM CORP OF AMERICA (NY)
34 Robinson Rd, Clinton, NY 13323-1419
Tel (800) 446-3486 Founded/Ownrshp 1934
Sales 215.0MMᴱ EMP 780
SIC 3356 Solder: wire, bar, acid core, & rosin core; Solder: wire, bar, acid core, & rosin core
Ch Bd: William N Macartney III
*Pr: Gregory P Evans
COO: Lee Kresge
CFO: Leslie E Schenk
VP: Ross Berntson
VP: James A Slattery
Rgnl Mgr: Tom Pearson
Genl Mgr: Paul Gassensmith
CTO: Bob Jarrett
Dir IT: Dawn Glenn
Plnt Mgr: Tom Becker

D-U-N-S 04-460-4374
INDIVIDUAL ADVOCACY GROUP INC
1289 Windham Pkwy, Romeoville, IL 60446-1763
Tel (630) 759-0201 Founded/Ownrshp 1995
Sales 24.7MMᴱ EMP 430
Accts Sikich Llp Naperville Il
SIC 8322 Social services for the handicapped; Social services for the handicapped
Ex Dir: Charlene Bennett

D-U-N-S 79-740-8549
INDIVIOR INC
(Suby of INDIVIOR PLC)
10710 Midlothian Tpke, North Chesterfield, VA 23235-4722
Tel (804) 379-1090 Founded/Ownrshp 2014
Sales 194.7MMᴱ EMP 330
SIC 5122 Pharmaceuticals; Pharmaceuticals
CEO: Shaun Thaxter
CEO: Richard Simkin
Sr VP: Bob Banks
VP: Sandy Mellis
VP: Javier Rodriguez
Dir Bus: Rolley Johnson
CIO: Ingo Elfering
Dir IT: Ray Gabehart
IT Man: Brad Ashby
Info Man: Artemisa Villalba
Natl Sales: Brianne Broeker

D-U-N-S 05-748-8660 IMP/EXP
INDO-EUROPEAN FOODS INC
1000 Air Way, Glendale, CA 91201-3030
Tel (818) 247-1000 Founded/Ownrshp 1966
Sales 21.2MMᴱ EMP 35
SIC 5141 Groceries, general line
CEO: Albert Bezjian

D-U-N-S 05-494-6025 IMP/EXP
INDOFF INC
11816 Lackland Rd Ste 200, Saint Louis, MO 63146-4248
Tel (314) 997-1122 Founded/Ownrshp 1971
Sales 245.2MMᴱ EMP 450
SIC 5021 5044 5084 Office furniture; Office equipment; Materials handling machinery; Office furniture; Office equipment; Materials handling machinery
Pr: Jim Malkus
Pt: Annette Martin
*Ch Bd: Dennis Mourning
*CFO: Julie Frank
*Ch: John S Ross
Bd of Dir: Golda Whitten
*VP: Pam Hake
*VP: Robin Migdal
VP: Robin Migdoff
VP: Dave Schmitt
VP: John Vasquez
VP: Jo Warfield
Exec: Candice Vandertuig
Dir Bus: Amanda Goedken

INDOOR CAFE
See FIRST MERIDIAN MANAGEMENT & CONSULTING LLC

INDOOR ENVIRONMENTAL SERVICES
See FAMAND INC

D-U-N-S 00-151-9230 IMP
INDOPCO INC
NATIONAL STARCH AND CHEMICAL
(Suby of ICI AMERICAN HOLDINGS LLC) ★
10 Finderne Ave Ste A, Bridgewater, NJ 08807-3365
Tel (908) 685-5000 Founded/Ownrshp 1997
Sales 444.8MMᴱ EMP 9,748ᴱ
SIC 2891 2046 2821 2869 2899 2099 Adhesives; Sealants; Industrial starch; Edible starch; Plastics materials & resins; Industrial organic chemicals; Perfume materials, synthetic; Flavors or flavoring materials, synthetic; Fatty acid esters, aminos, etc.; Chemical preparations; Food preparations; Adhesives; Sealants; Industrial starch; Edible starch; Plastics materials & resins; Industrial organic chemicals; Perfume materials, synthetic; Flavors or flavoring materials, synthetic; Fatty acid esters, aminos, etc.; Chemical preparations; Food preparations
Ch Bd: John McAdam
Pr: Rama Chandran
CFO: R J Forrest
VP: Ingrid Cole
VP: Christine B Gibson
VP: Peter C Maloff
VP: Peter A Salis
IT Man: Tom Merritt
Snr Mgr: Alicia Martin

D-U-N-S 13-782-5159 IMP/EXP
INDORAMA VENTURES USA INC
(Suby of INDORAMA POLYMERS PUBLIC COMPANY LIMITED)
801 Pineview Rd, Asheboro, NC 27203-3192
Tel (336) 672-0101 Founded/Ownrshp 2003
Sales 69.8MMᴱ EMP 95
SIC 5023 Decorative home furnishings & supplies; Decorative home furnishings & supplies
Pr: DK Agarwal
*CFO: Stephen C Edwards
Sr VP: Shankar Srinivasan
*VP: Sanjay Ahuja
*VP: Hussam Awad

D-U-N-S 17-722-2023
INDOTRONIX INTERNATIONAL CORP
IIC
331 Main St Ste 108, Poughkeepsie, NY 12601-3145
Tel (845) 473-1137 Founded/Ownrshp 1986
Sales 88.8MMᴱ EMP 550
Accts Vanacore Debenedictus Digova
SIC 7379 7371 7372 Computer related consulting services; Custom computer programming services; Computer software development; Prepackaged software; Computer related consulting services; Custom computer programming services; Computer software development; Prepackaged software
Ch Bd: Babu R Mandava
*Treas: RAO Chintapalli
VP: Ritu Thakur
VP Bus Dev: A Potluri
IT Man: Ashwani Goel
IT Man: Tammy Lindsey
Opers Supe: Cas Kuchinsky
Genl Couns: Elizabeth Baldizzi
Board of Directors: Shashi Kapur

D-U-N-S 01-872-2781
INDRA USA INC
(Suby of INDRA SISTEMAS THALES INFORMATION SYSTEMS S. A. AT)
800 Brickell Ave Ste 1270, Miami, FL 33131-2971
Tel (305) 373-7749 Founded/Ownrshp 2008
Sales 22.5MMᴱ EMP 98
Accts Cliftonlarsonallen Llp Orlan
SIC 8731 Computer (hardware) development
Ex VP: Emilio Diaz Exposito
*Pr: Edenilson Fleischmann
COO: Gabriel Machado
Ofcr: Abdulaziz Qambar
Dir Bus: Felix Gil

INDRAMAT DIV
See BOSCH REXROTH CORP

D-U-N-S 14-844-4701
INDRATECH LLC
1212 E Maple Rd, Troy, MI 48083-2817
Tel (248) 377-1877 Founded/Ownrshp 2003
Sales 25.6MMᴱ EMP 70
SIC 2515 Mattresses & foundations
Dir IT: Surendra Khambete

D-U-N-S 19-720-4290 IMP/EXP
■ **INDSPEC CHEMICAL CORP**
(Suby of OCCIDENTAL PETROLEUM CORP) ★
133 Main St, Petrolia, PA 16050-9717
Tel (724) 756-2370 Founded/Ownrshp 1996
Sales 75.8MMᴱ EMP 300
SIC 2865 2819 Resorcinol; Sodium & potassium compounds, exc. bleaches, alkalies, alum.; Sodium sulfate, glauber's salt, salt cake; Sodium sulfides; Resorcinol; Sodium & potassium compounds, exc. bleaches, alkalies, alum.; Sodium sulfate, glauber's salt, salt cake; Sodium sulfides
Pr: Mark Koppel
IT Man: Al Wourst
Tech Mgr: John Heckman
Sfty Mgr: Mike Dailey
Plnt Mgr: Dave Dorko

D-U-N-S 79-748-0100 IMP
INDUCTORS INC
CENTRAL TECHNOLOGIES
140 Technology Dr Ste 500, Irvine, CA 92618-2427
Tel (949) 623-2460 Founded/Ownrshp 1991
Sales 22.1MMᴱ EMP 50
SIC 5065 Electronic parts & equipment
CEO: Judy Macdonald
Sls Mgr: John Thompson
Art Dir: Bianca Montoya

D-U-N-S 08-477-7630 IMP/EXP
INDUCTOTHERM CORP
(Suby of ROWAN TECHNOLOGIES, INC.)
10 Indel Ave, Rancocas, NJ 08073
Tel (609) 267-3537 Founded/Ownrshp 1974
Sales 39.6MMᴱ EMP 210
SIC 3567 Induction heating equipment; Induction heating equipment
VP: John B Maher
*Ch Bd: John H Mortimer
*CEO: Satyen N Prabhu
Treas: Manning Smith
*VP: Asia T H Kim
VP: John O'Meara
VP: Virginia R Smith
VP: Byron L Taylor
Mng Dir: Jagat Shah
Dist Mgr: Peter Brunetzky
Dist Mgr: Bill Newbold

INDULAC
See INDUSTRIA LECHERA DE PUERTO RICO INC

INDUPLATE
See GREYSTONE OF LINCOLN INC

D-U-N-S 06-984-8067
INDUPLATE INC
GREYSTONE
1 Greystone Ave Ste 1, North Providence, RI 02911-1082
Tel (401) 231-5770 Founded/Ownrshp 1932
Sales 31.3MMᴱ EMP 190
SIC 3471 3398 Chromium plating of metals or formed products; Plating of metals or formed products; Metal heat treating; Chromium plating of metals or formed products; Plating of metals or formed products; Metal heat treating
CEO: John Maconi
*Pr: Everett Fernald Jr
CFO: Norman Chartier
*VP: David Lippy
*Prin: Susan Marie Piccolomini
Plnt Mgr: Butch Wegimont

D-U-N-S 00-427-6150 EXP
INDURON COATINGS LLC (AL)
3333 Richard Arrington N, Birmingham, AL 35234
Tel (205) 324-9584 Founded/Ownrshp 1947, 1985
Sales 22.5MMᴱ EMP 28
SIC 5198 2851 Paints; Paints & allied products
Pr: David D Hood

D-U-N-S 85-844-0097
INDUS CAPITAL PARTNERS LLC
888 7th Ave Fl 26, New York, NY 10106-2700
Tel (212) 909-2888 Founded/Ownrshp 2000
Sales 28.1MMᴱ EMP 100
SIC 6211 Security brokers & dealers; Security brokers & dealers
CFO: James Weiner
Ofcr: Kathleen Olin
VP: Stephen Gonzalez
VP: Alona Strait
VP: Robert Szpiczynski
Ex Dir: Robert Morier

D-U-N-S 19-384-6362
INDUS CONSTRUCTION LP
6060 Brookglen Dr Ste A, Houston, TX 77017-5098
Tel (713) 454-1148 Founded/Ownrshp 2003
Sales 28.8MMᴱ EMP 200
SIC 1611 Highway & street construction; Highway & street construction

D-U-N-S 80-293-9454
INDUS CORP
1951 Kidwell Dr Fl 8, Vienna, VA 22182-3930
Tel (703) 506-6700 Founded/Ownrshp 1991
Sales 51.4MM EMP 450
SIC 4813 8742 Telephone communication, except radio; Management consulting services; Telephone communication, except radio; Management consulting services
Pr: Shivram Krishnan
*COO: Michael Bowers
*CFO: Donald Shoff
*Sr VP: Bart Yeager

VP: Dan Moore
VP: William Yeager
Prgrm Mgr: Ron Johnson
Snr Sftwr: Scott Kocher
CIO: Hariharan Suryanarayanan
QA Dir: Rhonda Holder
Web Dev: Jhuma Chakraborty

D-U-N-S 78-959-1302
INDUS ENTERPRISES INC
TEXAS JASMINE WHOLESALE
7051 Southwest Fwy, Houston, TX 77074-2007
Tel (713) 784-4335 *Founded/Ownrshp* 1992
Sales 113.9MM *EMP* 98
SIC 5149 5194 5912 Groceries & related products; Tobacco & tobacco products; Proprietary (non-prescription medicine) stores; Groceries & related products; Tobacco & tobacco products; Proprietary (non-prescription medicine) stores
Pr: Zulfiqar A Momin
**VP:* Khowaja Barkat A
**VP:* Barkat A Khowaja
**Prin:* Jamshed Momin

INDUS FINIS SERVI POWDE PLANT
See INDUSTRIAL FINISHING SERVICES INC

D-U-N-S 19-409-1682
INDUS FOODS INC
PONDEROSA STEAKHOUSE
1080 Pittsford Victor Rd # 201, Pittsford, NY 14534-3805
Tel (585) 248-2440 *Founded/Ownrshp* 1988
Sales 24.7MM^E *EMP* 550
SIC 5812 Steak restaurant; Steak restaurant
Pr: Bhoopinder Mehta
**Treas:* Shrawan K Singh
Off Mgr: Pam Ebert
MIS Dir: Julie Burke
VP Opers: Martin Woodarek

INDUS INFOTECH
See DANLAW INC

D-U-N-S 15-979-2662
INDUS TECHNOLOGY INC
2243 San Diego Ave # 200, San Diego, CA 92110-2069
Tel (619) 299-2555 *Founded/Ownrshp* 2004
Sales 44.3MM^E *EMP* 230
SIC 8711 Engineering services; Engineering services
Pr: James B Lasswell
**CFO:* Rebecca Spane
Sr VP: Robin Mickle
**Sr VP:* Will Nevilles
VP: Steve Chiodini
**VP:* Eric Macgregor
**VP:* Jan Perez
Dir Bus: Tony Lopez
Prgrm Mgr: Lee Dennison
Prgrm Mgr: Richard Hart
Prgrm Mgr: Danl Thomas
Board of Directors: Tony Lopez

D-U-N-S 78-375-1878
INDUSA INDUSTRIAL SUPPLIES INC
105 Calle San Andres, San Juan, PR 00901-2807
Tel (787) 723-3450 *Founded/Ownrshp* 1990
Sales 20.9MM^E *EMP* 40
Accts Diaz Bergnes Jacobo Gonzalez V
SIC 5085 5074 5084 Valves & fittings; Plumbing fittings & supplies; Pumps & pumping equipment
Pr: Ramon Riancho
**Treas:* Irene Garcia
**VP:* Marime Riancho
**VP:* Ramom Riancho

INDUSCO WIRE ROPE & RIGGING
See INDUSTRIAL SALES CO INC

D-U-N-S 09-004-3811 IMP/EXP
INDUSTRIA LECHERA DE PUERTO RICO INC
INDULAC
(*Suby of* FONDO FOMENTO INDUSTRIA LECHERA)
198 Ave Carlos Chardon, San Juan, PR 00918-1744
Tel (787) 753-0974 *Founded/Ownrshp* 1952
Sales 48.8MM *EMP* 98
Accts Rsm Roc & Company San Juan P
SIC 2021 2023 2022 Creamery butter; Powdered skim milk; Cheese, natural & processed; Creamery butter; Powdered skim milk; Cheese, natural & processed
Pr: Larry Lugo

D-U-N-S 17-348-0443
INDUSTRIAL ACCESSORIES CO
4800 Lamar Ave Ste 203, Shawnee Mission, KS 66202-1711
Tel (913) 384-5511 *Founded/Ownrshp* 1987
Sales 61.2MM^E *EMP* 90^E
SIC 5075 5084 8711 Air pollution control equipment & supplies; Pneumatic tools & equipment; Industrial engineers; Air pollution control equipment & supplies; Pneumatic tools & equipment; Industrial engineers
Pr: Glenn A Smith Jr
**Sec:* Robert M Frye
Ex VP: Pramodh Nijhawan
VP: Bob Frye
Genl Mgr: Darrell Childress
CTO: Connie Cunningham
Dir IT: Jason Dowse
IT Man: Jacob Her
IT Man: Rob Oconor
Mktg Mgr: Rebecca Moles
Sales Asso: Kerry Brown

D-U-N-S 00-130-6547 IMP
INDUSTRIAL ACOUSTICS CO INC (NY)
I A C
3901 W Kearney St, Lincoln, NE 68524-2201
Tel (718) 931-8000 *Founded/Ownrshp* 1949, 1998
Sales 149.5MM^E *EMP* 600
SIC 3448 1742 Prefabricated metal buildings; Acoustical & ceiling work; Prefabricated metal buildings; Acoustical & ceiling work
Pr: Kenneth Delasho
VP: Mike Walsh
IT Man: Lloyd Attree
IT Man: Irma Cordero
Sales Exec: Dan Obrien

D-U-N-S 78-580-0426
INDUSTRIAL AIR CENTERS INC
731 E Market St, Jeffersonville, IN 47130-3923
Tel (812) 280-7070 *Founded/Ownrshp* 1991
Sales 32.1MM^E *EMP* 73
SIC 5084 Compressors, except air conditioning; Compressors, except air conditioning
Pr: George Burch
CFO: Tom Clare
**VP:* Scott Carpenter
**VP:* Stan Street
Area Mgr: Jeff Bray
Area Mgr: Jim Graessle

D-U-N-S 02-459-2727
INDUSTRIAL AIR INC
428 Edwardia Dr, Greensboro, NC 27409-2608
Tel (336) 292-1030 *Founded/Ownrshp* 1964
Sales 51.6MM^E *EMP* 125
SIC 1711 3443

D-U-N-S 17-136-8553 IMP/EXP
INDUSTRIAL AIRTOOL LP LLP
(*Suby of* PIPELINE SUPPLY & SERVICE LLC) ★
1305 W Jackson Ave, Pasadena, TX 77506-1709
Tel (409) 948-3527 *Founded/Ownrshp* 2014
Sales 112.7MM^E *EMP* 108
SIC 5084 Industrial machinery & equipment; Industrial machinery & equipment
Pr: Andy Gessner
Pt: William Pinkley
VP: Scott Whigham
IT Man: Sandra Cavazos
Sls Mgr: Darrell Sump
Sales Asso: Gabriel Arredondo
Sales Asso: Steve Hand
Sales Asso: Rolando Rodriguez
Sales Asso: Harold Schmidt

D-U-N-S 11-334-0095
INDUSTRIAL ALLOYS INC
3013 Eaton Ave, Indian Trail, NC 28079-8830
Tel (704) 882-2887 *Founded/Ownrshp* 1983
Sales 24.3MM^E *EMP* 18
SIC 5051 3312 Iron or steel semifinished products; Primary finished or semifinished shapes
VP: Chris Cauthen
**Treas:* Joye Cauthen
**VP:* Kim Garner
VP: Kimberly Garner
Sales Asso: Frank McManus

D-U-N-S 06-814-7990
INDUSTRIAL AND COMMERCIAL BANK OF CHINA (USA) NA
BEA-USA
(*Suby of* INDUSTRIAL AND COMMERCIAL BANK OF CHINA LIMITED)
202 Canal St, New York, NY 10013-4517
Tel (212) 238-8208 *Founded/Ownrshp* 1995, 2013
Sales NA *EMP* 188
SIC 6021 National commercial banks; National commercial banks
Pr: Tang Peng-Wah
CFO: Francis Wong
Chf Cred: Douglas Price
Ex VP: David Willner
Sr VP: Helen Cams
**VP:* Donald Lai
VP: Robert Lee
Brnch Mgr: Xintao Luo

D-U-N-S 96-148-0340
INDUSTRIAL ASPHALT HOLDINGS INC
(*Suby of* SUMMIT MATERIALS LLC) ★
9020 N Cpitl Of Texas Hwy, Austin, TX 78759-7279
Tel (512) 251-3713 *Founded/Ownrshp* 2011
Sales 45.9MM^E *EMP* 160
SIC 3531 Asphalt plant, including gravel-mix type; Asphalt plant, including gravel-mix type
Pr: Jill Shachelford

INDUSTRIAL AUTOMATED SYSTEMS
See SHAW ELECTRIC INC

D-U-N-S 82-471-8209 IMP
INDUSTRIAL AUTOMATION LLC
2968 Waterview Dr, Rochester Hills, MI 48309-3484
Tel (248) 598-5900 *Founded/Ownrshp* 1992
Sales 20.4MM^E *EMP* 80^E
SIC 3549 5084 Metalworking machinery; Industrial machinery & equipment
Co-Ownr: Mark Gust
**Co-Ownr:* Jim McMahon
Prgrm Mgr: Todd Chadick
Prgrm Mgr: Dave Collier
Prgrm Mgr: Andy Popchock
Prgrm Mgr: Greg Schaff
Genl Mgr: Jeff Kotila
Genl Mgr: Paul Valenti

D-U-N-S 07-963-0775
INDUSTRIAL AXLE CO LLC
(*Suby of* DEXTER AXLE CO) ★
21608 Protecta Dr, Elkhart, IN 46516-9532
Tel (574) 295-6077 *Founded/Ownrshp* 2014
Sales 67.1MM^E *EMP* 395^E
SIC 3714 Axles, motor vehicle; Axles, motor vehicle
Pr: Adam Dexter
CFO: Bernie Bolka

D-U-N-S 00-797-2680
INDUSTRIAL BANK (DC)
INDUSTRIAL BANK OF WASHINGTON
(*Suby of* IBW FINANCIAL CORP) ★
4812 Georgia Ave Nw, Washington, DC 20011-4522
Tel (202) 722-2000 *Founded/Ownrshp* 1934, 1996
Sales NA *EMP* 126
SIC 6021 National commercial banks; National commercial banks
Pr: B Doyle Mitchell Jr
Pr: Rodney Epps
Pr: Judy A McKenzie
COO: Patricia Mitchell
COO: Andrella Williams
CFO: Thomas Wilson
Ofcr: Mashon Butler
Ofcr: Connie Smith
Ex VP: Thomas McLaurin
VP: Lynn Rowe
VP: Roydell Stephens

INDUSTRIAL BANK OF WASHINGTON
See INDUSTRIAL BANK

D-U-N-S 08-687-1837 IMP
INDUSTRIAL BATTERY & CHARGER INC (NC)
5831 Orr Rd, Charlotte, NC 28213-6347
Tel (865) 525-2841 *Founded/Ownrshp* 1977
Sales 38.9MM^E *EMP* 125
SIC 5063 Storage batteries, industrial; Storage batteries, industrial
Pr: Terry K Earnhardt
VP: Rodney Broome
Brnch Mgr: Lisa Bond

D-U-N-S 08-681-8531
INDUSTRIAL BATTERY PRODUCTS INC
1250 Ambassador Blvd, Saint Louis, MO 63132-1706
Tel (314) 473-2200 *Founded/Ownrshp* 1997
Sales 38.0MM *EMP* 75
SIC 5063

D-U-N-S 08-239-0469 IMP
INDUSTRIAL BELTING & TRANSMISSION INC
4061 Mccollum Ct, Louisville, KY 40218-3107
Tel (502) 456-6100 *Founded/Ownrshp* 1994
Sales 27.6MM^E *EMP* 40
SIC 5085 Hose, belting & packing; Power transmission equipment & apparatus; Pistons & valves
Pr: Mark Deich
Sales Asso: Steve Eddington
Sales Asso: Jeff Rutledge

D-U-N-S 00-386-8650
INDUSTRIAL BUILDERS INC (ND)
1307 County Road 17 N, West Fargo, ND 58078-3818
Tel (701) 282-4977 *Founded/Ownrshp* 1953
Sales 126.5MM^E *EMP* 318
SIC 1629 1622 1542 1611 1623 Dam construction; Bridge construction; Commercial & office building, new construction; Commercial & office buildings, renovation & repair; School building construction; Institutional building construction; Resurfacing contractor; Pipeline construction; Dam construction; Bridge construction; Commercial & office building, new construction; Commercial & office buildings, renovation & repair; School building construction; Institutional building construction; Resurfacing contractor; Pipeline construction
Pr: Paul W Diederich
**Ex VP:* Donn O Diederich
**VP:* Roger Haberman
**VP:* Ron Mack

D-U-N-S 61-821-3495
INDUSTRIAL BUILDERS INC
D-BACH INDUSTRIAL
1711 Slipstream Way, Caldwell, ID 83605-5462
Tel (208) 795-5670 *Founded/Ownrshp* 2013
Sales 26.6MM^E *EMP* 25
Accts Eide Bailly Llp Boise Idaho
SIC 1623 Water, sewer & utility lines; Sewer line construction; Water main construction
Pr: Dave Erlebach
Exec: Penny Johnson

INDUSTRIAL BUILDING SERVICES
See LENNOX NATIONAL ACCOUNT SERVICES LLC

D-U-N-S 05-238-0748
INDUSTRIAL BUS LINES INC
ALL ABOARD AMERICA
(*Suby of* ALL ABOARD AMERICA HOLDINGS INC) ★
230 S Country Club Dr, Mesa, AZ 85210-1248
Tel (480) 962-6202 *Founded/Ownrshp* 1948
Sales 25.7MM^E *EMP* 232
SIC 4111 Bus transportation
CEO: Jack D Wigley
Pr: John Montgomery
VP: Kathy Vincent
Sls Mgr: Lesleigh Camtise

INDUSTRIAL CABLES
See NEXANS ENERGY USA INC

D-U-N-S 03-999-9412 IMP
INDUSTRIAL CHEMICAL CORP
CUSTOM PAK
885 W Smith Rd, Medina, OH 44256-2424
Tel (330) 725-0800 *Founded/Ownrshp* 1946
Sales 39.0MM^E *EMP* 47
SIC 5169 7389 Chemicals, industrial & heavy; Caustic soda; Packaging & labeling services
Pr: Ron Camaglia
**VP:* Frederick Camaglia
Off Mgr: Renee Brandt

D-U-N-S 03-198-8728
INDUSTRIAL CHEMICALS CORP
4631 W 58th Ave, Arvada, CO 80002-7004
Tel (303) 427-2727 *Founded/Ownrshp* 1975
Sales 33.9MM *EMP* 32
Accts Kenneth R Jorgensen Denver
SIC 5169 Industrial chemicals; Industrial chemicals
CEO: Gary W Biesemeier
**Pr:* Robert L Wilson II
**VP:* Dorene Biesemeier
VP: Joyce Winn
Mfg Mgr: Rich Petz
Board of Directors: Dorene Biesemeier, Gary Biesemeier, Thomas Helgeson

D-U-N-S 04-996-6583 EXP
INDUSTRIAL CHEMICALS INC
2540 Bellwood Rd, North Chesterfield, VA 23237-1308
Tel (804) 275-9292 *Founded/Ownrshp* 1970
Sales 26.6MM^E *EMP* 46^E
SIC 5169 Industrial chemicals
Pr: William K Lane III
Opers Mgr: Jason Bassett
VP Sls: James Graham

D-U-N-S 05-097-8329 IMP
INDUSTRIAL CHEMICALS INC
2042 Montreat Dr Ste A, Vestavia, AL 35216-4040
Tel (205) 823-7330 *Founded/Ownrshp* 1970
Sales 99.5MM *EMP* 130
Accts Warren Averett Llc Birmingha
SIC 5169 Chemicals, industrial & heavy; Chemicals, industrial & heavy
Pr: William L Welch
**VP:* L B Welch
IT Man: Mark Jeter

D-U-N-S 00-714-8380 EXP
INDUSTRIAL CHROME INC (KS)
834 Ne Madison St, Topeka, KS 66608-1128
Tel (785) 235-3463 *Founded/Ownrshp* 1955, 1992
Sales 29.4MM^E *EMP* 85
SIC 3714 3471 Motor vehicle parts & accessories; Chromium plating of metals or formed products; Decorative plating & finishing of formed products; Plating of metals or formed products
CEO: Ellis Needham
COO: Ray Ortega
**Sec:* Naomi Needham
Exec: Gordon Yetter
Genl Mgr: Chris Needham
IT Man: Max Guffy

D-U-N-S 18-790-5864
INDUSTRIAL COATINGS CONTRACTORS INC
(*Suby of* APACHE INDUSTRIAL SERVICES INC) ★
36545 Perkins Rd, Prairieville, LA 70769-3209
Tel (225) 673-4490 *Founded/Ownrshp* 2012
Sales 23.0MM^E *EMP* 170
SIC 1799 Coating, caulking & weather, water & fireproofing; Coating, caulking & weather, water & fireproofing
Pr: Michael Knigin
**CFO:* John David
**Sec:* Pete David
VP: David Cohen
**VP:* T David Cohen
Sfty Dirs: Scott Gomez
Opers Mgr: Teddy Dupuy

D-U-N-S 05-747-2623
INDUSTRIAL COMMERCIAL SYSTEMS INC
SAN MARCOS MECHANICAL
1165 Joshua Way, Vista, CA 92081-7840
Tel (760) 300-4094 *Founded/Ownrshp* 1982
Sales 51.3MM^E *EMP* 160
SIC 1711 Ventilation & duct work contractor; Warm air heating & air conditioning contractor; Ventilation & duct work contractor; Warm air heating & air conditioning contractor
Pr: Robin Sides
**VP:* Matt Harbin
Snr Mgr: Karen Case

D-U-N-S 88-499-4088
INDUSTRIAL COMMISSION ARIZONA
(*Suby of* EXECUTIVE OFFICE OF STATE OF ARIZONA) ★
800 W Washington St Bsmt, Phoenix, AZ 85007-2903
Tel (602) 542-4411 *Founded/Ownrshp* 1925
Sales NA *EMP* 315
SIC 9651 Regulation, miscellaneous commercial sectors; ; Regulation, miscellaneous commercial sectors;
Ofcr: Janine Locke
Off Mgr: Teresa Hilton
Snr Mgr: Randy Austin

D-U-N-S 04-438-3474
INDUSTRIAL COMMISSION OF OHIO
(*Suby of* EXECUTIVE OFFICE STATE OF OHIO) ★
30 W Spring St Fl 30, Columbus, OH 43215-2233
Tel (614) 466-2765 *Founded/Ownrshp* 1911
Sales NA *EMP* 600
SIC 9441 Administration of social & manpower programs; ; Administration of social & manpower programs

D-U-N-S 08-653-2397
INDUSTRIAL COMMUNICATIONS AND ELECTRONICS INC
INDUSTRIAL TOWER AND WIRELESS
40 Lone St, Marshfield, MA 02050-2102
Tel (781) 319-1111 *Founded/Ownrshp* 1971
Sales 31.8MM^E *EMP* 115
SIC 4812 5065 7622 1731

D-U-N-S 11-514-9668
INDUSTRIAL CONSTRUCTION AND DESIGN INC
ICON
2807 N 10th St, Saint Augustine, FL 32084-1871
Tel (904) 827-9795 *Founded/Ownrshp* 1981
Sales 37.0MM^E *EMP* 185^E
SIC 3554 Paper mill machinery: plating, slitting, waxing, etc.; Paper mill machinery: plating, slitting, waxing, etc.
Pr: Steve T Jenkins
**VP:* James C Dewitt

D-U-N-S 10-848-9337
INDUSTRIAL CONSTRUCTORS/MANAGERS INC
I C M
1432 Stockyard Rd, Pueblo, CO 81001-4536
Tel (719) 545-0296 *Founded/Ownrshp* 1991
Sales 25.5MM *EMP* 200^E
SIC 1541 Industrial buildings, new construction; Industrial buildings, new construction
Pr: Burnell Zercher
Sec: Pamela Zercher
Sr VP: John Luckett
Sfty Dirs: Dave Montoya

INDUSTRIAL CONSULTANTS
See AM PM STAFFING SERVICES

INDUSTRIAL CONTAINER & SUPPLY
See PROFESSIONAL PACKAGING CORP

D-U-N-S 03-536-6467 IMP
INDUSTRIAL CONTAINER AND SUPPLY CO
(*Suby of* INDUSTRIAL CONTAINER & SUPPLY) ★
1845 S 5200 W, Salt Lake City, UT 84104-4706
Tel (801) 972-1561 *Founded/Ownrshp* 1996
Sales 28.3MM^E *EMP* 50
SIC 5085 Drums, new or reconditioned; Pails, metal; Barrels, new or reconditioned
Pr: Daryl Jay Macbeth
**VP:* Robert L Hall
**VP:* J Mitchell Hill
**Prin:* Arnold Ashby
Genl Mgr: Danton Butters

D-U-N-S 17-485-3416
INDUSTRIAL CONTAINER SERVICES - CA NORTH LLC
(*Suby of* INDUSTRIAL CONTAINER SERVICES LLC) ★
749 Galleria Blvd, Roseville, CA 95678-1331
Tel (916) 781-2775 *Founded/Ownrshp* 2014
Sales 21.6MM^E *EMP* 52
SIC 5085 2655 Commercial containers; Fiber cans, drums & similar products

D-U-N-S 11-202-5445 IMP
INDUSTRIAL CONTAINER SERVICES - FL LLC
(*Suby of* INDUSTRIAL CONTAINER SERVICES LLC) ★
6191 Jones Ave, Zellwood, FL 32798
Tel (407) 889-5500 *Founded/Ownrshp* 2001
Sales 214.0MM *EMP* 930
SIC 5085 Drums, new or reconditioned; Drums, new or reconditioned
**Pr:* Charles Veniez
**CFO:* Kevin Breheny

D-U-N-S 13-163-0399
INDUSTRIAL CONTAINER SERVICES - NC LLC
(*Suby of* INDUSTRIAL CONTAINER SERVICES LLC) ★
2810 W Trade St, Charlotte, NC 28208-3249
Tel (704) 392-5386 *Founded/Ownrshp* 2001
Sales 67.8MM^E *EMP* 90
SIC 5085 Commercial containers
CEO: Calvin G Lee
Pr: Charles Veniez
COO: Gerald Butler
CFO: Kevin Breheny
Chf Mktg O: Kurt Richardson

D-U-N-S 03-991-3699 IMP
INDUSTRIAL CONTAINER SERVICES LLC
(*Suby of* AURORA CAPITAL GROUP) ★
1540 S Greenwood Ave, Montebello, CA 90640-6536
Tel (323) 724-8500 *Founded/Ownrshp* 2011
Sales 353.8MM^E *EMP* 930
SIC 3412 3443 3411 Fabricated plate work (boiler shop); Metal cans; Metal barrels, drums & pails; Metal barrels, drums & pails; Fabricated plate work (boiler shop); Metal cans
Genl Mgr: Edward Disilets
Opers Mgr: Moses Kingsbury
Opers Mgr: Rick Trull
Sls Mgr: Chris Garrelts
Sls Mgr: Kellie Simpson

INDUSTRIAL CONTRACT SERVICES
See ICS INC

D-U-N-S 10-850-0000
INDUSTRIAL CONTRACTORS INC
(*Suby of* API GROUP INC) ★
701 Channel Dr, Bismarck, ND 58501-7706
Tel (701) 258-9908 *Founded/Ownrshp* 1981
Sales 81.4MM *EMP* 175
Accts Kpmg Llp Minneapolis Mn
SIC 1711 1731 Mechanical contractor; General electrical contractor; Mechanical contractor; General electrical contractor
Pr: Lloyd Bushong
**Treas:* Gregory Keup
VP: Jeff Hammes
Off Mgr: Laura Sollman
IT Man: Adam Pascoe

D-U-N-S 00-700-9889 IMP/EXP
INDUSTRIAL CONTRACTORS SKANSKA INC
INDIANA INDUSTRIAL CONTRACTORS
(*Suby of* SKANSKA USA INC) ★
401 Nw 1st St, Evansville, IN 47708-1001
Tel (812) 423-7832 *Founded/Ownrshp* 2013
Sales 378.8MM^E *EMP* 1,000
SIC 1541 1542

INDUSTRIAL CONTROL COMPONENTS
See BELL ELECTRICAL SUPPLY INC

D-U-N-S 85-861-1080
INDUSTRIAL CONTROL REPAIR INC
ICR SERVICES
28601 Lorna Ave, Warren, MI 48092-3931
Tel (586) 751-3335 *Founded/Ownrshp* 1992
Sales 39.0MM^E *EMP* 121^E
SIC 7629 Electronic equipment repair; Circuit board repair
Pr: Paul Gutierrez
**VP:* Don Czerniewski
**VP:* Glenn Dantes
Site Mgr: Suzanne Perrey

D-U-N-S 08-095-4308
INDUSTRIAL CONTROLS DISTRIBUTORS LLC
JOHNSON CONTROLS
(*Suby of* ERIKS N.V.)
17 Christopher Way, Eatontown, NJ 07724-3325
Tel (732) 918-9000 *Founded/Ownrshp* 1976
Sales 78.4MM^E *EMP* 125
SIC 5075 5074 Air conditioning equipment, except room units; Heating equipment (hydronic); Air conditioning equipment, except room units; Heating equipment (hydronic)
Pr: Tom Comstock
CFO: Pat Larosa
VP: John Perry
Dept Mgr: Paul Rector

VP Mktg: Paul Barsa
Sales Asso: Michael Barnwell
Sales Asso: Tony Biondi
Sales Asso: David Cohen
Sales Asso: Stephen Guyon
Sales Asso: John Marinko
Sales Asso: Brian McBroom

D-U-N-S 09-186-9552
INDUSTRIAL DATA EXCHANGE INC
AUTO LOCATER
(*Suby of* ENGLE ONLINE) ★
1425 W Main St, Mount Joy, PA 17552-9589
Tel (717) 653-1833 *Founded/Ownrshp* 1985
Sales 13.0MM^E *EMP* 300
SIC 2721 Periodicals: publishing only

D-U-N-S 36-289-9684
INDUSTRIAL DESIGN & CONSTRUCTION INC
I D C
14061 Highway 73, Prairieville, LA 70769-3612
Tel (225) 343-1145 *Founded/Ownrshp* 1988
Sales 78.5MM *EMP* 250
SIC 1541 1629 Industrial buildings & warehouses; Chemical plant & refinery construction

D-U-N-S 36-461-8777
INDUSTRIAL DEVELOPMENTS INTERNATIONAL LLC
INDUSTRIAL DEVELOPMENTS INTL
1100 Peachtree S, Atlanta, GA 30309
Tel (404) 479-4000 *Founded/Ownrshp* 2012
Sales 176.8MM *EMP* 167
SIC 6552 6531 Land subdividers & developers, commercial; Real estate managers; Land subdividers & developers, commercial; Real estate managers
CEO: Timothy J Gunter
**Pr:* Henry D Gregroy Jr
Ofcr: Tim Moore
Ex VP: Karl Knauff
VP: John Benson
**VP:* David R Birdwell
**VP:* Linda Booker
VP: Bert Calvert
VP: Ben Chrin
VP: Joe Goss
VP: Scott Helms
VP: Jason Holland
VP: Jon Kelly
VP: Jeff Lanaghan
VP: Chris Lee
VP: Paulina Marvan
VP: Gary Minor
**VP:* Matthew C O'Sullivan
VP: Paul Pontius
VP: Paul Roeser
VP: Michael Salisbury

INDUSTRIAL DEVELOPMENTS INTL
See INDUSTRIAL DEVELOPMENTS INTERNATIONAL LLC

D-U-N-S 00-493-9229 IMP/EXP
INDUSTRIAL DIELECTRICS HOLDINGS INC
IDI
407 S 7th St, Noblesville, IN 46060-2708
Tel (317) 773-1766 *Founded/Ownrshp* 1966
Sales 183.7MM^E *EMP* 630
SIC 3644 Insulators & insulation materials, electrical; Insulators & insulation materials, electrical
Pr: Thomas K Merrell
**VP:* John D Merrell

D-U-N-S 96-732-9314 IMP/EXP
INDUSTRIAL DIELECTRICS INC
IDI COMPOSITES INTERNATIONAL
(*Suby of* IDI) ★
407 S 7th St, Noblesville, IN 46060-2708
Tel (317) 773-1766 *Founded/Ownrshp* 2009
Sales 40.5MM^E *EMP* 85
SIC 2821 Molding compounds, plastics
Pr: Thomas K Merrell
CFO: Terry Doll
VP: Thomas Flood
Dir Bus: Chris McClure
IT Man: Ken Burns
VP Mktg: Paul Rhodes

D-U-N-S 12-235-8617 IMP/EXP
INDUSTRIAL DIESEL INC
8705 Harmon Rd, Fort Worth, TX 76177-7501
Tel (817) 232-1071 *Founded/Ownrshp* 1983
Sales 24.7MM^E *EMP* 35
SIC 5084 Engines & parts, diesel
Pr: Ed Hale
**VP:* Sam Bonar
**VP:* Chris Stevens
Genl Mgr: Rodney Anderson

D-U-N-S 02-987-0664 IMP
INDUSTRIAL DISTRIBUTION GROUP INC
I D G
(*Suby of* EIGER HOLDCO LLC) ★
2100 The Oaks Pkwy, Belmont, NC 28012
Tel (704) 398-5600 *Founded/Ownrshp* 2014
Sales 818.2MM^E *EMP* 932
Accts Securities And Exchange Commis
SIC 5084 7699 Industrial machinery & equipment; Industrial machinery & equipment repair; Industrial machinery & equipment; Industrial machinery & equipment repair
Pr: Charles A Lingenfelter
Pr: Will Brummett
**CFO:* James C Melton
**Ex VP:* Edward C Gerber
VP: Russ Smith
VP: Darryl Wilges
Brnch Mgr: Mark Mihalik
Web Dev: Bradford Nock
Site Mgr: Bill Lamar
Opers Mgr: Will Caldwell
Opers Mgr: Mark Garmon

INDUSTRIAL DIVISION
See FEDERAL FOAM TECHNOLOGIES INC

D-U-N-S 07-868-8215 IMP
INDUSTRIAL DOOR CO INC
IDC-AUTOMATIC
360 Coon Rapids Blvd Nw, Minneapolis, MN 55433-5622
Tel (763) 786-4730 *Founded/Ownrshp* 1974
Sales 34.4MM^E *EMP* 160
SIC 1751 3495 Garage door, installation or erection; Sash balances, spring; Garage door, installation or erection; Sash balances, spring
CEO: Jodi Boldenow
CFO: Kathy Wall
Treas: Jodi Olson
**VP:* Jeremy Sizer
Plnt Mgr: Karl Lundahl
Plnt Mgr: Tony Steppat

D-U-N-S 10-177-1111
INDUSTRIAL DOOR CONTRACTORS INC
I D C
820 Mayberry Springs Rd, Columbia, TN 38401-9339
Tel (931) 540-1234 *Founded/Ownrshp* 1983
Sales 21.2MM^E *EMP* 60
Accts Cooper Travis & Company Plc
SIC 3442 3441 Metal doors; Hangar doors, metal; Fabricated structural metal
Pr: James Dillard
VP: Larry Castleberry
**VP:* Timothy Talbot
Plnt Mgr: David Doss
Sales Exec: Joe Moran
VP Mktg: Andrea Arnold

D-U-N-S 00-829-3417
INDUSTRIAL DYNAMICS CO LTD (CA)
FILTEC
3100 Fujita St, Torrance, CA 90505-4007
Tel (310) 325-5633 *Founded/Ownrshp* 1960
Sales 35.1MM^E *EMP* 216^E
SIC 3559 3829 Screening equipment, electric; Measuring & controlling devices; Screening equipment, electric; Measuring & controlling devices
Pr: David Storey
CFO: Janet Caldwell
VP: Bruce Hoerning
**Prin:* Steve M Calhoun
Admn Mgr: Dennis Dizon
Genl Mgr: Jackson Chad
Telecom Ex: Ken Hudson
Sftwr Eng: Leonid Orlov
Sfty Mgr: Ruth Villaros
Sls Dir: Georg Buch
Mktg Mgr: Lindsey Saletta
Board of Directors: Steve Calhoun

INDUSTRIAL ELECTRIC MFG
See NEW IEM LLC

INDUSTRIAL ELECTRIC MFG
See ABD EL & LARSON HOLDINGS LLC

D-U-N-S 07-545-8612 IMP
INDUSTRIAL ELECTRIC MOTOR WORKS INC
1551 Redman Rd, Meridian, MS 39305-8428
Tel (601) 679-5500 *Founded/Ownrshp* 1965
Sales 26.6MM *EMP* 38
Accts Culpepper And Culpepper Cpa M
SIC 5063 7694 Motors, electric; Electric motor repair; Motors, electric; Electric motor repair
Ch Bd: Thomas E Mc Daniel
**Ch Bd:* Thomas E McDaniel
**Pr:* Thomas A McDaniel
**Sec:* Kathy M Temple
**VP:* Stephen McDaniel
Mktg Dir: Mitch Malone
Mktg Dir: Ricky Pounders
Sales Asso: Madison Hike
Sales Asso: Glenda Hughes
Sales Asso: Rachel Starks

INDUSTRIAL ELECTRIC MOTORS
See INTERSTATE ELECTRIC MOTORS AND CONTROL INC

INDUSTRIAL ELECTRIC WIRE CABLE
See IEWC CORP

D-U-N-S 00-836-2543 IMP
INDUSTRIAL ELECTRONIC ENGINEERS INC
IEE
7723 Kester Ave, Van Nuys, CA 91405-1105
Tel (818) 787-0311 *Founded/Ownrshp* 1947
Sales 58.5MM^E *EMP* 100
SIC 3577 3575 Graphic displays, except graphic terminals; Keyboards, computer, office machine; Graphic displays, except graphic terminals; Keyboards, computer, office machine
Pr: Thomas Whinfrey
Pr: Steve Motter
COO: Steve White
Ch: Donald G Gumpertz
VP: Arthur Bradley
VP: Sandra Hsia
VP: Jerri Schafer
VP: Michael Tubbs
VP Bus Dev: Michael Klass
Dir IT: Donna Mayne
Ql Cn Mgr: Robert Acosta

D-U-N-S 00-842-3535
INDUSTRIAL ELECTRONIC SUPPLY INC
2321 Texas Ave, Shreveport, LA 71103-3660
Tel (318) 222-9459 *Founded/Ownrshp* 1978
Sales 26.0MM^E *EMP* 64
SIC 5065 4731

D-U-N-S 80-919-0747
INDUSTRIAL ELECTRONICS SERVICES INC
IES
213 Suncrest St, Gray, TN 37615-3499
Tel (423) 467-3377 *Founded/Ownrshp* 1992
Sales 26.9MM^E *EMP* 80
SIC 3672 7629 Printed circuit boards; Circuit board repair
Pr: Kathy Mullins
CFO: Glen Allen
**Sec:* Larry Mullins
Exec: Laura Tomlinson

IT Man: Tim Coleman
Plnt Mgr: Tom Denison
Ql Cn Mgr: Steve Andrews

D-U-N-S 03-524-2411
INDUSTRIAL ENGINE SERVICE CO
HKT BIG SKY MOTORS
2515 W Towne St, Glendive, MT 59330-9602
Tel (406) 377-3350 *Founded/Ownrshp* 1962
Sales 27.4MM^E *EMP* 91
SIC 5511 Automobiles, new & used; Pickups, new & used; Vans, new & used; Automobiles, new & used; Pickups, new & used; Vans, new & used
Prin: Wencytoepke
Sales Asso: Joe Kessel

D-U-N-S 11-621-5096
INDUSTRIAL FABRICATION SERVICES INC
460 Commerce St, Lake Crystal, MN 56055-4589
Tel (507) 726-6000 *Founded/Ownrshp* 1984
Sales 22.3MM *EMP* 70
SIC 3441 Fabricated structural metal; Fabricated structural metal
Pr: Kenneth Wilmes
**Sec:* Tim Stokes
**VP:* Duane Boomgarden
**VP:* Mathew Doherty
**VP:* Steve Leuck
Off Mgr: Marilyn Paulsen

INDUSTRIAL FABRICATORS
See TSGC INC

D-U-N-S 87-718-2865
INDUSTRIAL FABRICATORS INC
4328 York Hwy, Gastonia, NC 28052-6801
Tel (704) 864-5026 *Founded/Ownrshp* 1994
Sales 121.1MM^E *EMP* 210
Accts Miller Sherrill Blake Eagle Cp
SIC 3441 Fabricated structural metal; Fabricated structural metal
Pr: Roger Bingham
**VP:* Pat Bingham
Sfty Mgr: Amy Shirley
Opers Mgr: Robin Craig
Prd Mgr: Keith Campbell
Ql Cn Mgr: Jack Herndon

D-U-N-S 06-654-0733 IMP
INDUSTRIAL FABRICS CORP
CREAREDGE TECHNICAL FABRICS
(*Suby of* CLEAR EDGE FILTRATION HOLDING B.V.)
7160 Northland Cir N B, Minneapolis, MN 55428-1532
Tel (763) 535-3220 *Founded/Ownrshp* 2007
Sales 23.1MM^E *EMP* 65
SIC 3089 2282 2824 2821 Monofilaments, nontextile; Polypropylene filament yarn: twisting, winding, etc.; Nylon fibers; Polyesters
CEO: Richard Jordan
**Pr:* Rolf W Muehlenhaus
Sales Asso: Jim Slonina

D-U-N-S 10-243-1335 IMP
INDUSTRIAL FABRICS INC
IF
510 O Neal Ln Ext, Baton Rouge, LA 70819
Tel (225) 273-9600 *Founded/Ownrshp* 1981
Sales 22.3MM^E *EMP* 75
SIC 8711

D-U-N-S 02-762-9476 IMP
INDUSTRIAL FINISHES & SYSTEMS INC
SOUTHERN ABRASIVES
3455 W 1st Ave, Eugene, OR 97402-5449
Tel (541) 485-1503 *Founded/Ownrshp* 1958
Sales 112.8MM^E *EMP* 160
Accts Moss Adams Llp Cpa S
SIC 5085 5198 Abrasives; Paints, varnishes & supplies; Abrasives; Paints, varnishes & supplies
Pr: Glenn Duckworth
**Ch:* Stuart W Barr
Mktg Dir: Mike Duncan

D-U-N-S 93-848-7246
INDUSTRIAL FINISHING SERVICES INC
INDUS FINIS SERVI POWDE PLANT
710 1st St Ne, Perham, MN 56573-1845
Tel (218) 346-3975 *Founded/Ownrshp* 1995
Sales 24.3MM^E *EMP* 80
SIC 3471 3479 Electroplating & plating; Painting, coating & hot dipping
CEO: Terry Welle
**Pr:* Dwayne Roberts
**CFO:* Joe Askew
**VP:* Steve Campbell

D-U-N-S 00-892-8178
INDUSTRIAL FIRST INC
25840 Miles Rd Ste 2, Bedford, OH 44146-1426
Tel (216) 991-8605 *Founded/Ownrshp* 1989
Sales 36.1MM^E *EMP* 250
SIC 1741 1761 1791 Masonry & other stonework; Siding contractor; Roofing contractor; Sheet metalwork; Structural steel erection; Masonry & other stonework; Siding contractor; Roofing contractor; Sheet metalwork; Structural steel erection
Pr: Steven F Lau
**Ex VP:* Frank Burkosky
VP: Brendan Rose

D-U-N-S 02-984-5161
■ **INDUSTRIAL FUMIGANT CO LLC**
I F C
(*Suby of* ROLLINS INC) ★
13420 W 99th St, Lenexa, KS 66215-1365
Tel (913) 782-7600 *Founded/Ownrshp* 2005
Sales 22.1MM^E *EMP* 300
SIC 7342 Exterminating & fumigating; Pest control services; Exterminating & fumigating; Pest control services
Pr: Gary Rollins
**Treas:* Harry J Cynkus
**Ex VP:* Dan Ponton
**Sr VP:* Tom Walters
VP: Thomas R Beck
VP: Brad Henry
VP: Chris Mueller
VP Admn: Lynn Hansel

Sls Mgr: Doug Canoy
Sls Mgr: Joe Chapin
Sls Mgr: Frank Healy

INDUSTRIAL GROWTH PARTNERS
See IGP INDUSTRIES LLC

D-U-N-S 00-517-1368
INDUSTRIAL HARD CHROME LTD (IL)
501 Fluid Power Dr, Geneva, IL 60134-1181
Tel (630) 208-7000 *Founded/Ownrshp* 1955
Sales 20.5MM^E *EMP* 120
SIC 3471 Electroplating of metals or formed products
Pr: C G Therkildsen
VP: Fred Parker
VP Mfg: Bruce Busse
VP Opers: Rich Peterson
Sales Exec: Steve Schaus
Sls Mgr: Donna Horgan

D-U-N-S 80-743-1291 IMP
INDUSTRIAL HARDWARE DISTRIBUTORS INC
I H D
1201 Burlington St, Kansas City, MO 64116-4022
Tel (816) 221-9700 *Founded/Ownrshp* 1993
Sales 22.6MM^E *EMP* 35
SIC 5085 Fasteners, industrial: nuts, bolts, screws, etc.; Industrial tools
Pr: Rick Simon
**Sec:* Ron Jenkins
**Ex VP:* Arell Wasson
VP: Nathan Finney

D-U-N-S 00-151-3076 EXP
INDUSTRIAL HEATER CORP
30 Knotter Dr, Cheshire, CT 06410-1122
Tel (203) 250-0500 *Founded/Ownrshp* 1921, 1991
Sales 20.9MM^E *EMP* 80
SIC 3567 Heating units & devices, industrial: electric
Pr: Thomas A McGwire Jr
**Pr:* Ted McGwire
Exec: Helen Lespier
VP Mfg: Jim Czarzasty
Board of Directors: Thomas A McGwire Sr

INDUSTRIAL HIGH SCHOOL
See INDUSTRIAL INDEPENDENT SCHOOL DISTRICT

D-U-N-S 83-133-1165
INDUSTRIAL INCOME TRUST INC
518 17th St Ste 17, Denver, CO 80202-4130
Tel (303) 228-2200 *Founded/Ownrshp* 2009
Sales NA *EMP* 30^E
SIC 6091 Nondeposit trust facilities

D-U-N-S 02-081-5114
INDUSTRIAL INDEPENDENT SCHOOL DISTRICT
INDUSTRIAL HIGH SCHOOL
511 5th St, Vanderbilt, TX 77991-5000
Tel (361) 284-3226 *Founded/Ownrshp* 1947
Sales 12.0MM *EMP* 25,144
Accts Sliva & Reed Pc Bay City
SIC 8211 Public elementary school; Public junior high school; Public senior high school; Public elementary school; Public junior high school; Public senior high school
VP: Tim Garcia
Schl Brd P: Missy Klimitchek
Psych: Melody Vickery

D-U-N-S 11-809-8219
INDUSTRIAL INFO RESOURCES INC
2277 Plaza Dr Ste 300, Sugar Land, TX 77479-6601
Tel (713) 783-5147 *Founded/Ownrshp* 1983
Sales 28.8MM^E *EMP* 91^E
SIC 8732 8742 2741 Market analysis or research; Industry specialist consultants; Technical manuals: publishing & printing
Pr: Edward Lewis
Pr: Tom Fordham
**COO:* Edward Fox
CFO: Niesha Kovich
Sr VP: Robert Bugg
Sr VP: Gene Dewree
VP: Tammy Bankhead
**VP:* Michael Bergen
**VP:* Paul Copello
VP: Rich Cottingham
VP: Alfredo Delangel
VP: Christine Garcia
**VP:* Sheila Goods
VP: Gordon Gorrie
VP: Federico Iwakawa-Shiga
VP: Anna Jenkins
VP: Christopher Keister
VP: Alex Moneyhun
VP: Shane Mullins
VP: Thomas Nguyen
**VP:* Chris Paschall

D-U-N-S 12-092-8841 IMP
■ **INDUSTRIAL INSULATION GROUP LLC**
SPROULE MANUFACTURING
(*Suby of* JOHNS MANVILLE CORP) ★
2100 Line St, Brunswick, GA 31520-2784
Tel (912) 264-6372 *Founded/Ownrshp* 2012
Sales 79.8MM^E *EMP* 350
SIC 3296 3086 Insulation: rock wool, slag & silica minerals; Plastics foam products; Insulation: rock wool, slag & silica minerals; Plastics foam products
Pr: Fred Stephan
Ex Dir: Cindy Mobley
Plnt Mgr: Paul Davidson
Prd Mgr: Allan Lowery

D-U-N-S 04-614-4192
INDUSTRIAL IRON WORKS INC
ADAMS FERTILIZER EQUIPMENT
1503 S Whitehead Dr, De Witt, AR 72042
Tel (870) 946-2494 *Founded/Ownrshp* 1976
Sales 38.5MM^E *EMP* 220
SIC 3523 Fertilizing machinery, farm; Fertilizing machinery, farm
Pr: Billy C Adams
**Sec:* William W Adams

Chf Mktg O: Joe Thurman
Sfty Dirs: Gary Morris

D-U-N-S 02-169-5276
INDUSTRIAL KILN & DRYER GROUP INC
12711 Townepark Way # 100, Louisville, KY 40243-2390
Tel (502) 244-4031 *Founded/Ownrshp* 1999
Sales 20.9MM^E *EMP* 25^E
SIC 5084 Industrial machinery & equipment
Pr: Randall S Young
Chf Mktg O: David Curtis
**VP:* Leonard A Loesch
**VP:* Jerry W Young
Mtls Mgr: Tom McCune
Sales Asso: Donna Sipes

D-U-N-S 94-987-8722 IMP
INDUSTRIAL LAMINATES/NORPLEX INC
(*Suby of* IDI) ★
665 Lybrand St, Postville, IA 52162-7792
Tel (563) 864-7321 *Founded/Ownrshp* 2002
Sales 85.0MM^E *EMP* 180
SIC 3089 3081 Laminating of plastic; Unsupported plastics film & sheet; Laminating of plastic; Unsupported plastics film & sheet
Pr: Thomas K Merrell
**Sec:* Terrence M Doll
**Sec:* Lawrence Henss
VP: Denny Ford
**VP:* Jay Merrell
Mktg Dir: Robert O Smail
Sls Mgr: Brett Koelle

D-U-N-S 04-427-6646 IMP
■ **INDUSTRIAL LIGHT & MAGIC (VANCOUVER) LLC**
(*Suby of* LUCASFILM COML PRODUCTIONS) ★
1110 Gorgas Ave, San Francisco, CA 94129-1406
Tel (415) 292-4671 *Founded/Ownrshp* 2011
Sales 36.0MM^E *EMP* 156^E
SIC 7699 Industrial equipment services
CEO: Steve Condiotti
Sr VP: Chrissie England
Plng Mgr: Yves Metraux
Dir IT: Robert Molholm
IT Man: Doug Luberts
Prd Mgr: Ryan Wiederkehr
Mktg Dir: Miles Perkins
Art Dir: Aaron McBride

D-U-N-S 14-717-5074 IMP
INDUSTRIAL LIGHTING PRODUCTS LLC
519 Codisco Way, Sanford, FL 32771-6618
Tel (407) 478-3759 *Founded/Ownrshp* 2012
Sales 40.1MM^E *EMP* 100
SIC 3646 Commercial indusl & institutional electric lighting fixtures
Natl Sales: Dave Weinberg
Manager: Torey Brewer
Manager: Devin Jernigan
Sls Mgr: Turner Nabors

D-U-N-S 02-280-6251
INDUSTRIAL LUBRICANT CO INC
35108 Us Highway 2, Grand Rapids, MN 55744-4752
Tel (218) 328-0602 *Founded/Ownrshp* 1944
Sales 73.8MM^E *EMP* 132
SIC 5172 Lubricating oils & greases
CEO: James J Hoolihan
**Pr:* Gary D Oja
Genl Mgr: Kathy Hoolihan
Off Mgr: Geri Leidholm

D-U-N-S 05-602-9424
INDUSTRIAL MACHINE & MANUFACTURING CORP
MOTOR PARTS BARRINGS
1816 Rapides Ave, Alexandria, LA 71301-7211
Tel (318) 442-0463 *Founded/Ownrshp* 1971
Sales 36.5MM *EMP* 3
SIC 5085 Bearings, bushings, wheels & gears; Bearings, bushings, wheels & gears
Pr: Barbara Brister
**VP:* J Rodney Brister

D-U-N-S 00-640-3067 IMP
INDUSTRIAL MAGNETICS INC (MI)
1385 S M 75, Boyne City, MI 49712-9689
Tel (231) 582-3100 *Founded/Ownrshp* 1961
Sales 28.5MM^E *EMP* 145
SIC 3499 Magnets, permanent: metallic
CEO: Walter J Shear III
CFO: Robin Stanley
Manager: Collins McGeorge

D-U-N-S 07-314-1749
INDUSTRIAL MAINTENANCE CONTRACTORS INC
INDUSTRIAL MINT CONTRS HOUSTON
2301 Garden City Hwy, Midland, TX 79701-1549
Tel (432) 682-3745 *Founded/Ownrshp* 1997
Sales 31.3MM *EMP* 125
Accts Sproles Woodard Llp Midland
SIC 1721 7699 1389 Aircraft painting; Tank repair; Oil field services; Aircraft painting; Tank repair; Oil field services
Pr: Jerry W Bushman
**VP:* David Lesco
**VP:* Kathy Oglesby
Exec: Kathy O'Glesby
Sfty Dirs: Jessie Engbrock

D-U-N-S 11-729-7366
INDUSTRIAL MAINTENANCE SERVICES INC
IMS
1920 20th Ave N, Escanaba, MI 49829-9577
Tel (906) 789-9021 *Founded/Ownrshp* 1997
Sales 31.2MM *EMP* 40^E
Accts Anderson Tackman & Company P
SIC 1541 Renovation, remodeling & repairs: industrial buildings; Renovation, remodeling & repairs: industrial buildings
Pr: John R Soper Jr
**CFO:* Brenda S Soper
Sfty Dirs: Aaron Johnsen
Sfty Dirs: Tim Martineau

D-U-N-S 07-433-1273 IMP
INDUSTRIAL MAINTENANCE WELDING & MACHINING CO INC
IMW
2nd & Hupp Rd, Kingsbury, IN 46345
Tel (219) 393-5531 *Founded/Ownrshp* 1975
Sales 29.5MM^E *EMP* 150
SIC 3569 3599 4212 Assembly machines, non-metalworking; Machine shop, jobbing & repair; Heavy machinery transport, local; Assembly machines, non-metalworking; Machine shop, jobbing & repair; Heavy machinery transport, local
Pr: Matthew Sularski
**Pr:* Gene Berchem
**Treas:* Stephen Sularski
**VP:* Robert Sularski

D-U-N-S 01-526-8944
INDUSTRIAL MANAGEMENT OF MATERIALS OF CAROLINAS LLC
815 State Rd, Cheraw, SC 29520-2131
Tel (843) 537-5231 *Founded/Ownrshp* 2000
Sales 35.0MM^E *EMP* 126
SIC 5051 5085 Pipe & tubing, steel; Valves & fittings; Pipe & tubing, steel; Valves & fittings

D-U-N-S 00-235-0593 IMP/EXP
INDUSTRIAL MANUFACTURING CO LLC
(*Suby of* SUMMA HOLDINGS INC) ★
8223 Brecksville Rd Ste 1, Brecksville, OH 44141-1367
Tel (440) 838-4700 *Founded/Ownrshp* 1979, 2000
Sales 572.2MM^E *EMP* 1,600
SIC 2542 3728 3566 Lockers (not refrigerated): except wood; Cabinets: show, display or storage: except wood; Shelving, office & store: except wood; Aircraft body & wing assemblies & parts; Aircraft assemblies, subassemblies & parts; Speed changers, drives & gears; Lockers (not refrigerated): except wood; Cabinets: show, display or storage: except wood; Shelving, office & store: except wood; Aircraft body & wing assemblies & parts; Aircraft assemblies, subassemblies & parts; Speed changers, drives & gears
CEO: James Benenson Jr
**Pt:* Clement Benenson
**Pr:* James Benenson III
**CFO:* John E Cvetic

D-U-N-S 08-163-6524
INDUSTRIAL MARKETING INC (MO)
SLAY INDUSTRIES
(*Suby of* J S LEASING CO INC) ★
1441 Hampton Ave, Saint Louis, MO 63139-3115
Tel (314) 647-7529 *Founded/Ownrshp* 1965, 1979
Sales 20.1MM^E *EMP* 270
SIC 8741 8721 Financial management for business; Accounting, auditing & bookkeeping; Financial management for business; Accounting, auditing & bookkeeping
Pr: Guy Slay
**Treas:* Jeanne M Rhodes
**VP:* Tim Tahan Jr

INDUSTRIAL MATERIAL
See STEVEN-SHARON CORP

INDUSTRIAL MECHANICAL COMPANY
See CCC GROUP INC

D-U-N-S 62-488-1777
INDUSTRIAL MEDICINE ASSOCIATES PC
660 White Plains Rd # 630, Tarrytown, NY 10591-5107
Tel (914) 323-0316 *Founded/Ownrshp* 1990
Sales 28.5MM *EMP* 259
SIC 8011 Offices & clinics of medical doctors; Offices & clinics of medical doctors
Pr: David Pulver MD
**CFO:* Jeanine Delong

INDUSTRIAL METAL PDTS IMPCO
See CONTINENTAL EAGLE CORP

D-U-N-S 00-105-9369
INDUSTRIAL METAL PRODUCTS CO INC (MA)
INMETAL
15 Merchant St, Sharon, MA 02067-1614
Tel (781) 762-3330 *Founded/Ownrshp* 1959
Sales 22.5MM^E *EMP* 84
SIC 3444 3441 Sheet metalwork; Fabricated structural metal
Pr: Evelyn E Hurlbut
Sfty Mgr: Stephen Harradon
Ql Cn Mgr: Ed Aldrich
Sales Exec: Sumner Eagerman

INDUSTRIAL METAL SALES
See CAMBRIDGE-LEE INDUSTRIES LLC

INDUSTRIAL METAL SUPPLY CO
See NORMAN INDUSTRIAL MATERIALS INC

D-U-N-S 60-341-7254 EXP
INDUSTRIAL METALS RECYCLING CORP
IMET
955 Brandt Dr, Elgin, IL 60120-1601
Tel (847) 214-2800 *Founded/Ownrshp* 1987
Sales 40.5MM^E *EMP* 45
SIC 5093 Nonferrous metals scrap
Pr: Marc J Gordon
**VP:* Thomas O'Brien
**VP:* Michael Obrien

INDUSTRIAL MINT CONTRS HOUSTON
See INDUSTRIAL MAINTENANCE CONTRACTORS INC

D-U-N-S 04-316-1512
■ **INDUSTRIAL MOLDING CORP**
IMC
(*Suby of* NN INC) ★
616 E Slaton Rd, Lubbock, TX 79404-5897
Tel (806) 474-1000 *Founded/Ownrshp* 1947, 1999
Sales 22.0MM^E *EMP* 151^E
SIC 3089 Injection molded finished plastic products; Injection molded finished plastic products
CEO: Richard Holder
DP Exec: Johnny Upchurch

D-U-N-S 04-390-8177 IMP
INDUSTRIAL MOLDS INC
TRUE-CUT WIRE EDM DIV
5175 27th Ave, Rockford, IL 61109-1783
Tel (815) 397-2971 *Founded/Ownrshp* 1973
Sales 20.9MM^E *EMP* 115
SIC 3544 Forms (molds), for foundry & plastics working machinery
Pr: Jack D Peterson
VP: Tim Peterson
Prd Mgr: Eric Peterson

D-U-N-S 86-924-2958 IMP
■ **INDUSTRIAL MOTION CONTROL LLC**
DE-STA-CO CAMCO PRODUCTS
(*Suby of* DE-STA-CO) ★
1444 S Wolf Rd, Wheeling, IL 60090-6514
Tel (847) 459-5200 *Founded/Ownrshp* 2007
Sales 40.0MM *EMP* 150
SIC 3568 3535 3625 3566 Power transmission equipment; Conveyors & conveying equipment; Relays & industrial controls; Speed changers, drives & gears; Power transmission equipment; Conveyors & conveying equipment; Relays & industrial controls; Speed changers, drives & gears
CFO: Ian Nilson
Plnt Mgr: Greg Gallina

D-U-N-S 06-311-3633 IMP/EXP
INDUSTRIAL NETTING INC
(*Suby of* FRANDSEN CORP) ★
7681 Setzler Pkwy N, Brooklyn Park, MN 55445-1883
Tel (763) 504-4360 *Founded/Ownrshp* 1999
Sales 22.0MM *EMP* 35
Accts Boulay Heutmaker Zibell
SIC 3089 Netting, plastic; Netting, plastic
Pr: Greg Frandsen
Plnt Mgr: Mike Rog
S&M/VP: Dave Brentz
Sls Mgr: Sheila Katusky
Sls Mgr: Karen Slater

D-U-N-S 00-416-6526 IMP
INDUSTRIAL NUT CORP (OH)
1425 Tiffin Ave, Sandusky, OH 44870-2054
Tel (419) 625-8543 *Founded/Ownrshp* 1908, 1950
Sales 23.6MM^E *EMP* 100
Accts Frank Seringer & Chaney Inc
SIC 3452 Nuts, metal
Pr: William Springer
Pr: David Springer
Bd of Dir: David Voight
**VP:* John E Moffitt
**VP:* James B Springer
**VP:* John William Springer III
VP: Stephen Springer
Sfty Mgr: Greg Bartemes
Sls Mgr: Gary Schuster

INDUSTRIAL OILS UNLIMITED
See OILS UNLIMITED LLC

D-U-N-S 08-508-5108
INDUSTRIAL OPPORTUNITIES INC
ELASTIC PRODUCTS
2586 Business 19, Andrews, NC 28901-8044
Tel (828) 321-4754 *Founded/Ownrshp* 1974
Sales 3.0MM *EMP* 300
SIC 2211 2395 8331

D-U-N-S 82-946-1198
INDUSTRIAL OPPORTUNITY PARTNERS LP
1603 Orrington Ave # 700, Evanston, IL 60201-3880
Tel (847) 556-3466 *Founded/Ownrshp* 2006
Sales 20.8MM^E *EMP* 473
SIC 8741 Management services; Management services
Pt: Michael J Hering

D-U-N-S 03-353-4991
INDUSTRIAL PACKAGING CORP
300 Villanova Dr Sw, Atlanta, GA 30336-2526
Tel (404) 346-5800 *Founded/Ownrshp* 1950
Sales 37.9MM *EMP* 54^E
SIC 5113 5199 5087 Corrugated & solid fiber boxes; Pressure sensitive tape; Packaging materials; Janitors' supplies; Corrugated & solid fiber boxes; Pressure sensitive tape; Packaging materials; Janitors' supplies
Pr: Mark J Lichtenstein
**CFO:* Glenn Yesner
Div Mgr: Steve Taylor
IT Man: Marvin Cox
Sales Exec: Dave Lewis
Mktg Mgr: Sharon Roper

D-U-N-S 03-008-9585 IMP/EXP
INDUSTRIAL PACKAGING SUPPLIES INC
IPS PACKAGING
10 Jack Casey Ct, Fountain Inn, SC 29644-9000
Tel (864) 862-1500 *Founded/Ownrshp* 1976
Sales 70.5MM *EMP* 122
SIC 5113 5084 5085 Shipping supplies; Packaging machinery & equipment; Industrial supplies; Shipping supplies; Packaging machinery & equipment; Industrial supplies
Pr: Jerry Murdock
**CFO:* Tony Dumit
IT Man: Gilbert Bowman
IT Man: Becky Cannady
IT Man: Alison Whitted
Sls Mgr: Brad Murdock
Sales Asso: Craig McAvoy

D-U-N-S 02-870-1092 IMP
INDUSTRIAL PARTS DEPOT LLC
IPD
(*Suby of* STORM INDUSTRIES INC) ★
23231 Normandie Ave, Torrance, CA 90501-5096
Tel (310) 530-1900 *Founded/Ownrshp* 2008
Sales 46.2MM^E *EMP* 95
SIC 5084 3519 Engines & parts, diesel; Parts & accessories, internal combustion engines; Engines & parts, diesel; Parts & accessories, internal combustion engines
Pr: Russell Kneipp
CFO: Marshall Berliner
Ofcr: Lou Romano

CTO: Clarke Ashton
Dir IT: John Furgerson
Info Man: Mark Tu
Opers Mgr: Rick Niemeyer
Prd Mgr: Albert Shehata
VP Sls: Bob Straw
Mktg Dir: Reza Khamsi
Sls Mgr: Eddie Tostado

INDUSTRIAL PERFORMANCE PDTS
See CHROMATE INDUSTRIAL CORP

D-U-N-S 04-107-6693
INDUSTRIAL PIPE & STEEL LLC
IPS
9936 Rush St, South El Monte, CA 91733-2684
Tel (626) 443-9467 Founded/Ownrshp 2004
Sales 31.1MM^E EMP 40^E
SIC 5051 Steel
Genl Mgr: Art Raygoza

D-U-N-S 82-476-6158 IMP
INDUSTRIAL PIPE FITTINGS LLC
IPF
6020 Osborn St, Houston, TX 77033-1016
Tel (800) 241-4175 Founded/Ownrshp 1997
Sales 41.8MM^E EMP 133
SIC 3084 Plastics pipe; Plastics pipe
Ch Bd: Drew Berkman
*CFO: Justin Traurig
Mfg Mgr: Tim Tipton

D-U-N-S 00-378-1127 IMP
INDUSTRIAL PIPING INC
(Suby of IPI ACQUISITION LLC) ★
13504 S Point Blvd Ste M, Charlotte, NC 28273-6763
Tel (704) 588-1100 Founded/Ownrshp 1952
Sales 44.1MM^E EMP 650
Accts Cherry Bekaert Llp Charlotte
SIC 3599 3569 Machine shop, jobbing & repair; Sprinkler systems, fire: automatic; Machine shop, jobbing & repair; Sprinkler systems, fire: automatic
CEO: Stephen Boord
COO: Kevin Walsh
CFO: Robert Coston
CFO: Blair Swogger
Chf Mktg O: Matt Ryan
VP: Scott Brady
VP: David Brakefield
VP: Stacie Lacour
VP: Bill McClung
VP: Scott Rice
Div Mgr: Chris Shea

D-U-N-S 16-143-4576 IMP/EXP
INDUSTRIAL PIPING SPECIALISTS INC
IPS
606 N 145th East Ave, Tulsa, OK 74116-2111
Tel (918) 437-9100 Founded/Ownrshp 1986
Sales 74.8MM^E EMP 184
SIC 5051 5085

D-U-N-S 00-934-9127
INDUSTRIAL PLANT SERVICES INC
95 Sbelt Industrial Dr, Houston, TX 77047
Tel (713) 433-7049 Founded/Ownrshp 1987
Sales 71.8MM EMP 250
SIC 1752 7699 Floor laying & floor work; Boiler & heating repair services; Floor laying & floor work; Boiler & heating repair services; Boiler repair shop
Pr: Jeff Duncombe
*CFO: Greg Fussel
*VP: Gregory C Geisen

D-U-N-S 19-776-5241 IMP
INDUSTRIAL POLISHING SERVICES INC
(Suby of ADHARA INC) ★
9465 Customhouse Plz H1, San Diego, CA 92154-7655
Tel (619) 661-1691 Founded/Ownrshp 1984
Sales 24.0MM EMP 9
SIC 3471 Finishing, metals or formed products
Pr: Enrique Mereles Sr
Mng Dir: Jose Almaraz

D-U-N-S 00-478-6448
INDUSTRIAL POWER AND LIGHTING CORP
60 Depot St, Buffalo, NY 14206-2204
Tel (716) 854-1811 Founded/Ownrshp 1960, 1989
Sales 26.4MM^E EMP 130
SIC 1731 General electrical contractor; General electrical contractor
Pr: George R Schlemmer
*Ex VP: Richard Lombard
*VP: Paul Rautenstrauch
VP: Brandon Schlemmer
Dir IT: Jason Mack
Snr PM: Ray Taylor

D-U-N-S 88-493-9232
INDUSTRIAL POWER GENERATING CO LLC
INGENCO
2250 Dabney Rd, Richmond, VA 23230-3323
Tel (804) 354-9500 Founded/Ownrshp 1995
Sales 22.9MM^E EMP 120
SIC 3612 Transformers, except electric; Transformers, except electric
CEO: Charles Packard
*COO: Thomas Kennedy
*CFO: Richard Putney
*Treas: Raymond Yerly
Sr VP: Dave Palumbo
Sfty Mgr: Gary Leake
Secur Mgr: Michael Ellison

INDUSTRIAL POWER ISUZU TRUCK
See INDUSTRIAL POWER LLC

D-U-N-S 06-088-7135
INDUSTRIAL POWER LLC
INDUSTRIAL POWER ISUZU TRUCK
712 N Beach St, Fort Worth, TX 76111-5943
Tel (817) 834-7473 Founded/Ownrshp 1996
Sales 27.1MM^E EMP 60^E
SIC 5084 5511 5012

D-U-N-S 13-946-6908
INDUSTRIAL POWER SYSTEMS INC
IPS
129 Dixie Hwy, Rossford, OH 43460-1241
Tel (419) 531-3121 Founded/Ownrshp 1985
Sales 69.1MM EMP 250
SIC 1711 1796 1731 Mechanical contractor; Machinery installation; Electrical work; Mechanical contractor; Machinery installation; Electrical work
Pr: Kevin Gray
CFO: Kirk Guy
*CFO: Gary Haas
*VP: John Gray
*VP: Jeremiah Johnson
Sfty Dirs: William Norris
Snr PM: Eric Baumgartner

D-U-N-S 04-129-7094 IMP
INDUSTRIAL PROCESS EQUIPMENT CO
IPEG
(Suby of OHIO TRANSMISSION CORP) ★
6823 Hazelwood Ave, Saint Louis, MO 63134-1019
Tel (314) 534-3100 Founded/Ownrshp 2013
Sales 26.6MM^E EMP 53
SIC 5084 3599 Chemical process equipment; Machine shop, jobbing & repair
Opers Mgr: Jeff Horton
Sales Asso: Peggy Bauer

INDUSTRIAL PRODUCTS
See BEHLEN MFG CO

D-U-N-S 04-015-6432 IMP
INDUSTRIAL PRODUCTS CO
124 Fastener Dr, Lynchburg, VA 24502-3948
Tel (434) 525-0319 Founded/Ownrshp 1976
Sales 27.6MM^E EMP 65^E
SIC 5084 Industrial machinery & equipment; Derricks
CEO: Jeffrey Scott Wolf
*CEO: Kieran McGrane
*CFO: George F Raymond
Mtls Mgr: Matt Hankins
Ql Cn Mgr: Randy Maddox
Sls Mgr: Van Fry
Sales Asso: Renee Ferguson

INDUSTRIAL PRODUCTS DIV
See HAGERTY BROTHERS CO

INDUSTRIAL PRODUCTS DVN
See TENAX CORP

D-U-N-S 08-652-7546
INDUSTRIAL PROTECTION PRODUCTS INC
INDUSTRIAL PROTECTION SERVICES
220 Ballardvale St Ste I, Wilmington, MA 01887-1050
Tel (978) 657-4740 Founded/Ownrshp 1977
Sales 36.1MM^E EMP 50
SIC 5084 Safety equipment
Pr: Richard F Murphy III
*Sec: Ellen M Murphy
Rgnl Mgr: Jonathan Marshall
Rgnl Mgr: Cliff Plourde
Rgnl Mgr: Jon Usher
IT Man: Cindy Murphy
Opers Mgr: Mary Almeida
VP Sls: Don Speicher
VP Sls: Don Speicher

INDUSTRIAL PROTECTION SERVICES
See INDUSTRIAL PROTECTION PRODUCTS INC

INDUSTRIAL RAW MATERIALS
See IRM LLC

D-U-N-S 78-932-5321
INDUSTRIAL REFRIGERATION SERVICES INC
INNOVATED MECHANICAL SERVICES
613 Se Magazine Rd, Ankeny, IA 50021-3744
Tel (515) 964-1810 Founded/Ownrshp 1992
Sales 20.9MM EMP 52
Accts Meriwether Wilson And Company
SIC 1711 1731 Refrigeration contractor; Mechanical contractor; Electrical work
Pr: Rodney Heston
*Sec: Brenda Heston
*VP: John Heston
*VP: Katherine Walker

D-U-N-S 08-756-6535 IMP
INDUSTRIAL RESOURCES INC
(Suby of VICTORY OF WEST VIRGINIA INC) ★
Industrial Contracting Rd, Fairmont, WV 26554
Tel (304) 363-4100 Founded/Ownrshp 2006
Sales 41.1MM^E EMP 140
SIC 1629 3537 3535 3532 3494 3441 Mine loading & discharging station construction; Industrial trucks & tractors; Conveyors & conveying equipment; Mining machinery; Valves & pipe fittings; Fabricated structural metal; Mine loading & discharging station construction; Industrial trucks & tractors; Conveyors & conveying equipment; Mining machinery; Valves & pipe fittings; Fabricated structural metal
Ch Bd: Wayne Stanley
*Pr: Charles J Miller
*Treas: William J Harvey
Plnt Mgr: Greg Watkins

D-U-N-S 01-341-8694 IMP
INDUSTRIAL RIVET & FASTENER CO
200 Paris Ave, Northvale, NJ 07647-2205
Tel (201) 750-1040 Founded/Ownrshp 1912
Sales 22.0MM^E EMP 54^E
SIC 5072 5085 3452 Miscellaneous fasteners; Bolts; Rivets; Industrial supplies; Bolts, nuts, rivets & washers; Miscellaneous fasteners; Bolts; Rivets; Industrial supplies; Bolts, nuts, rivets & washers
Pr: William Goodman
Sec: Joanne Sherman

D-U-N-S 09-009-3824 IMP
■ **INDUSTRIAL RUBBER & MECHANICS INC**
INRUMEC
(Suby of KAMAN INDUSTRIAL TECHNOLOGIES CORP) ★
8 Carr 189, Gurabo, PR 00778-3047
Tel (787) 687-1200 Founded/Ownrshp 1963, 2008
Sales 21.8MM^E EMP 58
Accts Diaz Berger Jacobo Gonzalez Vi
SIC 5085 5063 Rubber goods, mechanical; Power transmission equipment, electric
Pr: Steven J Smidler
*Treas: Robert D Starr
VP: Roger S Jorgensen
Pgrm Dir: Marcos Lugo

INDUSTRIAL RUBBER APPLICATORS
See IRACORE INTERNATIONAL INC

INDUSTRIAL RUBBER WORKS
See ABBOTT RUBBER CO INC

D-U-N-S 01-632-7043
INDUSTRIAL SAFETY TECHNOLOGIES LLC
(Suby of SCOTT SAFETY) ★
4055 Tech Forest Blvd, The Woodlands, TX 77381-2007
Tel (713) 559-9200 Founded/Ownrshp 2015
Sales 57.4MM^E EMP 560^E
SIC 3829 Gas detectors; Gas detectors
CEO: Adam Markin
CEO: Dave Rutter
VP: Kevin McKeigue

D-U-N-S 05-094-2044 IMP
INDUSTRIAL SALES & MFG INC
ISM
2609 W 12th St, Erie, PA 16505-4343
Tel (814) 833-9876 Founded/Ownrshp 1967
Sales 24.1MM^E EMP 80
SIC 3599 Machine shop, jobbing & repair
Pr: James J Rutkowski Sr
*Treas: James J Rutkowski Jr
VP: Thomas Luteran
*VP: Robert Charlie G Rutkowski
IT Man: Jim Adams
Sfty Mgr: Laurie Dever
Mfg Mgr: Gary Prescott
Ql Cn Mgr: John Orr
Sales Exec: Charlie Rutkorwski
Sls Mgr: Ed Bolt
Snr Mgr: Michael Zoth

D-U-N-S 00-885-9878 IMP
INDUSTRIAL SALES CO INC
INDUSCO WIRE ROPE & RIGGING
(Suby of MAZELLA COMPANIES) ★
1200 W Hamburg St, Baltimore, MD 21230-1991
Tel (410) 244-6365 Founded/Ownrshp 1983
Sales 22.9MM^E EMP 70
SIC 5051 5085 5088 5072 Rope, wire (not insulated); Industrial supplies; Marine supplies; Builders' hardware; Rope, wire (not insulated); Industrial supplies; Marine supplies; Builders' hardware
CEO: Anthony Mazzella
*Pr: Craig Hayward
*CFO: Stephanie Miller
*VP: Gayle Protzko
Sls Mgr: Keith Dennis
Sls Mgr: Howard Scloloss
Board of Directors: Anthony Mazzella

D-U-N-S 11-913-0938 IMP
INDUSTRIAL SCIENTIFIC CORP
1 Life Way, Pittsburgh, PA 15205-7500
Tel (412) 788-4353 Founded/Ownrshp 1984
Sales 276.7MM^E EMP 700
SIC 3829 Measuring & controlling devices; Gas detectors; Measuring & controlling devices; Gas detectors
Ch Bd: Kent D McElhattan
*Pr: Eva Yi Chen
*Pr: Justin McElhattan
*COO: Kevin Miller
*VP: Harry A Griffith
*VP: Garth F Miller
Exec: Jeffrey Higgs
Dir Lab: Bob Kuzmich
Prgrm Mgr: Kelly Copeland
Prgrm Mgr: Chad Neville
Rgnl Mgr: Hani Qronfleh
Board of Directors: James E Cashman

D-U-N-S 04-346-2282
INDUSTRIAL SECURITY SERVICE INC
(Suby of UNITED AMERICAN SECURITY LLC) ★
4525 W 160th St, Cleveland, OH 44135-2627
Tel (216) 898-9970 Founded/Ownrshp 2010
Sales 15.4MM^E EMP 700
SIC 7381 Security guard service; Private investigator; Security guard service; Private investigator
Pr: John P Andrews
VP: James Hughes
Dir IT: Jennifer Taylor
Opers Mgr: Ryan Spriggs

INDUSTRIAL SERVICE
See NORTHWESTERN PLASTICS LTD

D-U-N-S 78-535-2519
INDUSTRIAL SERVICE AND INSTALLATION INC
290 Emig Rd, Emigsville, PA 17318
Tel (717) 767-1129 Founded/Ownrshp 1988
Sales 29.1MM^E EMP 60
SIC 3535 Belt conveyor systems, general industrial use
Pr: Steven Smith
*Treas: Roy McCloskey
*VP: Victor Prevost
IT Man: Garvey Blymire

D-U-N-S 01-065-6403
INDUSTRIAL SERVICES CO INC (MO)
3648 W Nichols St, Springfield, MO 65803-5669
Tel (417) 831-3459 Founded/Ownrshp 2011
Sales 29.6MM EMP 50^E
Accts Kpm Cpas Pc Springfield Mis
SIC 1541 1542 Industrial buildings, new construction; Commercial & office building, new construction; Industrial buildings, new construction; Commercial & office building, new construction
CEO: Darin Wilken
Off Mgr: April Isley

INDUSTRIAL SERVICES DIVISION
See JOHNSTON CONSTRUCTION CO

D-U-N-S 01-327-1967
INDUSTRIAL SERVICES GROUP INC
BLASTCO
318 Neeley St, Sumter, SC 29150-7452
Tel (803) 773-6388 Founded/Ownrshp 2001
Sales 32.6MM EMP 500
Accts Bauknight Pietras & Stormer P
SIC 1799 Coating of metal structures at construction site; Coating of metal structures at construction site
Pr: Joe Vandiver
*CFO: Danny Hollis

D-U-N-S 11-910-4677 EXP
▲ **INDUSTRIAL SERVICES OF AMERICA INC**
7100 Grade Ln, Louisville, KY 40213-3424
Tel (502) 368-1661 Founded/Ownrshp 1984
Sales 117.4MM EMP 96^E
Tkr Sym IDSA Exch NAS
SIC 5093 4953 Scrap & waste materials; Metal scrap & waste materials; Ferrous metal scrap & waste; Wire & cable scrap; Recycling, waste materials; Non-hazardous waste disposal sites; Scrap & waste materials; Metal scrap & waste materials; Ferrous metal scrap & waste; Wire & cable scrap; Recycling, waste materials; Non-hazardous waste disposal sites
Ch Bd: Orson Oliver
*Pr: Sean Garber
CFO: Todd L Phillips
Ex VP: Daniel C Gascoyne
Dir IT: Mike Dart
Opers Mgr: Nolan Brock
Board of Directors: Albert Cozzi, Francesca Scarito, Ronald Strecker, Vincent J Tyra, William B Yarmuth

D-U-N-S 01-330-9500
INDUSTRIAL SITE SERVICES INC
11510 State Hwy 188 E, Sinton, TX 78387
Tel (361) 364-3022 Founded/Ownrshp 2000
Sales 30.2MM^E EMP 200
SIC 7389 Pipeline & power line inspection service; Pipeline & power line inspection service
Pr: Richard Gingirch
Genl Mgr: Jerry Brister

D-U-N-S 14-240-0733
INDUSTRIAL SOLUTIONS GROUP LLC
OQSG
600 Jefferson St Ste 1200, Lafayette, LA 70501-6949
Tel (337) 769-9608 Founded/Ownrshp 2002
Sales 32.7MM^E EMP 200
SIC 1389 Gas field services; Oil field services; Gas field services; Oil field services
Sfty Dirs: Malcolm Wise

D-U-N-S 09-728-7478
INDUSTRIAL SPECIALTIES LLC
3500 S Macarthur Blvd A2, Oklahoma City, OK 73179-7613
Tel (405) 672-1221 Founded/Ownrshp 1979
Sales 25.0MM EMP 47^E
SIC 3492 5085

D-U-N-S 05-321-7592 IMP
INDUSTRIAL STEEL & WIRE CO OF ILLINOIS LLC
1901 N Narragansett Ave, Chicago, IL 60639-3841
Tel (773) 804-0404 Founded/Ownrshp 1966
Sales 55.3MM^E EMP 55^E
SIC 5051 Wire; Wire
*Pr: Dr Brian K Furlong
*CFO: Wayne Benett
*CFO: Scott Weldon
Sfty Mgr: Tom Howlett

INDUSTRIAL STEEL CO DIVISION
See FLEXCO PRODUCTS INC

D-U-N-S 04-831-0825
INDUSTRIAL STEEL CONSTRUCTION INC
413 Old Kirk Rd, Geneva, IL 60134
Tel (630) 232-7473 Founded/Ownrshp 1969
Sales 44.3MM^E EMP 225
SIC 3441 Fabricated structural metal; Fabricated structural metal for bridges
Pr: Joseph R Hish
*Treas: Michael Mariano
*Sec: Dorothy Avigiano

D-U-N-S 12-965-3312
INDUSTRIAL STEEL PRODUCTS LLC
8517 Herrington Ct, Pevely, MO 63070-1658
Tel (636) 475-4441 Founded/Ownrshp 2002
Sales 21.2MM^E EMP 20
SIC 5051 Steel
VP: David Harrell
Off Mgr: Lisa Eckstein
Ql Cn Mgr: Tiffany Waller

D-U-N-S 00-549-8845
INDUSTRIAL STEEL TREATING CO
IST
613 Carroll Ave, Jackson, MI 49202-3169
Tel (517) 787-6312 Founded/Ownrshp 1950
Sales 24.2MM^E EMP 85
SIC 3398 Metal heat treating
Pr: Timothy Levy
IT Man: Jeff Thomas
VP Opers: Tim Levy
Ql Cn Mgr: Rich Polin

D-U-N-S 00-798-7274
INDUSTRIAL SUPPLY CO
322 N 9th St 328, Terre Haute, IN 47807-3009
Tel (217) 446-5029 Founded/Ownrshp 1915
Sales 32.2MM^E EMP 56
SIC 5085 5074 Industrial supplies; Plumbing fittings & supplies; Heating equipment (hydronic)
Pr: Donald M Ireland
Treas: Suzanne K Rukes
VP: Jack Simpson
Board of Directors: Cathy Dickerman, Dr Richard Ireland

D-U-N-S 00-895-4661 IMP/EXP
INDUSTRIAL SUPPLY CO INC
1635 S 300 W, Salt Lake City, UT 84115-5107
Tel (801) 484-8644 Founded/Ownrshp 1927
Sales 99.6MM^E EMP 130
SIC 5084 5085 Safety equipment; Machine tools & accessories; Welding machinery & equipment; Abrasives; Fasteners, industrial: nuts, bolts, screws, etc.; Rubber goods, mechanical; Safety equipment; Machine tools & accessories; Welding machinery & equipment; Abrasives; Fasteners, industrial: nuts, bolts, screws, etc.; Rubber goods, mechanical
CEO: Chris Bateman
*Pr: Randy Y Evans
*Ch: Phil Thompson
*VP: Shawn Newell
*VP: Jessica Polychronis
VP: Jessica Yurgaitis
Brnch Mgr: Diamond Fullmer
Brnch Mgr: Cortney McKee
IT Man: Tony Kittere
Sales Asso: Kerry Binggeli
Sales Asso: Krisha Bird

D-U-N-S 60-486-4017 EXP
INDUSTRIAL SUPPLY SOLUTIONS INC
ISSI
804 Julian Rd, Salisbury, NC 28147-9080
Tel (704) 636-4241 Founded/Ownrshp 1988
Sales 59.8MM EMP 160
Accts Suttle & Stalnaver Pllc
SIC 5084 5085 Industrial machinery & equipment; Industrial supplies; Industrial machinery & equipment; Industrial supplies
Pr: R Frank Carmazzi
*VP: Perry Bernhardt
*VP: Joe Carmazzi
*VP: Mike Lear
Opers Mgr: Joe Dooly
Opers Mgr: Wade Figard
Sales Asso: Lou Cisneros

D-U-N-S 80-066-4401
INDUSTRIAL SUPPORT SERVICES INC
2600 N 42nd St, Quincy, IL 62305-7682
Tel (217) 223-6180 Founded/Ownrshp 1992
Sales 24.8MM^E EMP 300
SIC 7389 Packaging & labeling services; Packaging & labeling services
Pr: Nicholas E Lansing
*Genl Mgr: Jeffery Gibson

D-U-N-S 62-075-4283
■ INDUSTRIAL TECTONICS BEARINGS CORP
(Suby of R B C) ★
18301 S Santa Fe Ave, E Rncho Dmngz, CA 90221-5519
Tel (310) 537-3750 Founded/Ownrshp 1990
Sales 25.9MM^E EMP 150^E
SIC 3562 5085 Roller bearings & parts; Bearings; Roller bearings & parts; Bearings
CEO: Michael J Hartnett
Genl Mgr: Phil Beausoleil
Genl Mgr: Karen Santacruz
Dir IT: Mary Atkinson
IT Man: Ricardo Perez
Sfty Mgr: David Goldsmith
Plnt Mgr: Sean Williams
Snr Mgr: Albert Lopez

D-U-N-S 00-535-5219 IMP
INDUSTRIAL TECTONICS INC
ITI
(Suby of KAYDON CORP) ★
7222 Huron River Dr, Dexter, MI 48130-1099
Tel (734) 426-4681 Founded/Ownrshp 1945, 1994
Sales 25.0MM^E EMP 82^E
SIC 3399 Steel balls
Pr: Michael Purchase
*Treas: Peter C De Chants
Ql Cn Mgr: Doug Nummerdor

D-U-N-S 61-178-9272
INDUSTRIAL TEST SYSTEMS INC
1875 Langston St, Rock Hill, SC 29730-7314
Tel (803) 329-9712 Founded/Ownrshp 1989
Sales 69.0MM EMP 46
SIC 3826 3829 Environmental testing equipment; Geiger counters
Pr: Ivars Jaunakais
*Sec: Dayrl Jaunakais
*VP: George Bailey
*VP: Lea Jaunakais
*VP: Maris Jaunakais
Genl Mgr: Joni Moss
Ql Cn Mgr: Elizabeth Allen
Mktg Mgr: Jay Anand
Mktg Mgr: Mike McBride
Sls Mgr: Andrew Roberts

INDUSTRIAL TIMBER & LUMBER CO
See ITL CORP

INDUSTRIAL TIMBER AND LBR LLC
See ITL LLC

D-U-N-S 04-692-5728
INDUSTRIAL TIMBER INC
330 White Plains Rd, Hiddenite, NC 28636-8767
Tel (828) 632-6338 Founded/Ownrshp 1999
Sales 30.8MM^E EMP 177
SIC 2493 5031 Reconstituted wood products; Lumber, plywood & millwork; Reconstituted wood products; Lumber, plywood & millwork
Pr: Craig Larsen
*COO: Michael Ruch
CFO: Bill Lassell
*VP: Jimmy Hunt

INDUSTRIAL TIRE & BATTERY
See SUMMIT HANDLING SYSTEMS INC

D-U-N-S 06-327-0466
INDUSTRIAL TOOL DIE & ENGINEERING INC
4765 S Overland Dr, Tucson, AZ 85714-3431
Tel (520) 745-8771 Founded/Ownrshp 1972
Sales 28.5MM^E EMP 79
SIC 3829 3544 Measuring & controlling devices; Special dies, tools, jigs & fixtures; Measuring & controlling devices; Special dies, tools, jigs & fixtures
CEO: Guy M Theriault
*Pr: Donald L Theriault
VP: Chris Fulk
*VP: Michelle Jensen
Ql Cn Mgr: Dan Igoe
Ql Cn Mgr: Jim Young

D-U-N-S 07-149-3407
INDUSTRIAL TOOL INC
ITI
(Suby of MARUKA USA INC) ★
9210 52nd Ave N, Minneapolis, MN 55428-4098
Tel (763) 533-7244 Founded/Ownrshp 2012
Sales 26.8MM^E EMP 30^E
SIC 5084 3541 Industrial machinery & equipment; Machine tools, metal cutting type
CEO: Dick Leuck
CEO: Dick Lueck
Ch: Edgar J McDonald
Plnt Mgr: Ingvar Larsen

INDUSTRIAL TOWER AND WIRELESS
See INDUSTRIAL COMMUNICATIONS AND ELECTRONICS INC

D-U-N-S 05-849-4634
INDUSTRIAL TRACTOR CO INC
6870 Philips Hwy, Jacksonville, FL 32216-6036
Tel (904) 296-5000 Founded/Ownrshp 1983
Sales 31.7MM^E EMP 200
SIC 5084 5082 Industrial machinery & equipment; General construction machinery & equipment; Industrial machinery & equipment; General construction machinery & equipment
Pr: Richard Cassidy Jr

D-U-N-S 80-124-5465
INDUSTRIAL TRANSPORT SERVICES LLC
2101 Hwy 69 S, Mount Vernon, IN 47620
Tel (812) 831-4053 Founded/Ownrshp 1987
Sales 25.4MM^E EMP 150^E
SIC 4213 4225 Trucking, except local; General warehousing & storage; Trucking, except local; General warehousing & storage
CFO: Jeff Denning

D-U-N-S 00-452-0284 IMP
INDUSTRIAL TUBE AND STEEL CORP (OH)
4658 Crystal Pkwy, Kent, OH 44240-8020
Tel (330) 474-5530 Founded/Ownrshp 1956, 1999
Sales 85.2MM^E EMP 100
SIC 5051 Tubing, metal; Bars, metal; Tubing, metal; Bars, metal
Pr: Dick Siess
*Prin: Frederick H Gillen
*Prin: H William Kranz Jr

D-U-N-S 00-968-6643
■ INDUSTRIAL TUBE CO LLC
HARTZELL AEROSPACE
(Suby of ITT CORP) ★
3091 Indian Ave, Perris, CA 92571-3228
Tel (951) 657-2611 Founded/Ownrshp 2015
Sales 25.0MM^E EMP 99
SIC 3492 3812 3728 Aircraft parts & equipment; Control valves, aircraft: hydraulic & pneumatic; Acceleration indicators & systems components, aerospace; Aircraft body & wing assemblies & parts; Aircraft assemblies, subassemblies & parts; Aircraft power transmission equipment; Aircraft propellers & associated equipment

D-U-N-S 60-633-3599
INDUSTRIAL TURNAROUND CORP
ITAC
13141 N Enon Church Rd, Chester, VA 23836-3120
Tel (804) 414-1100 Founded/Ownrshp 1988
Sales 64.4MM EMP 350^E
SIC 1541 8711 Industrial buildings & warehouses; Engineering services; Industrial buildings & warehouses; Engineering services
CEO: Sidney Harrison
*Pr: Jon Loftis
VP: Glenn Harper
VP: Ernie Langevin
*VP: Richard Starnes
Dir Bus: Walt Johnson
Off Mgr: Nancy Dinkle
CTO: Andy Mutter

D-U-N-S 15-185-4650 IMP
INDUSTRIAL VALCO INC
3135 E Ana St, Compton, CA 90221-5606
Tel (310) 635-0711 Founded/Ownrshp 1983
Sales 53.9MM^E EMP 50
SIC 5085 3498 Valves & fittings; Pipe fittings, fabricated from purchased pipe
Pr: Rob C Raban
Brnch Mgr: Eddie Lujan
Brnch Mgr: Vernon Preston
Manager: Cindy Renkowiecki

D-U-N-S 07-790-1619
INDUSTRIAL VALVE SALES & SERVICE INC
5310 Highway 45, Eight Mile, AL 36613-8529
Tel (800) 523-2159 Founded/Ownrshp 1975
Sales 44.6MM^E EMP 250
SIC 7699 5085 Valve repair, industrial; Valves & fittings; Valve repair, industrial; Valves & fittings
Pr: Donald F Williams
*VP: James G Harrell Jr
Ex Dir: Clyde Collins
Off Mgr: Kate Yarman
Plnt Mgr: Stan Harris
Sls Mgr: Kenya Dennis
Sls Mgr: John Harper

D-U-N-S 05-242-7325 EXP
INDUSTRIAL VENTILATION INC
I V I
723 E Karcher Rd, Nampa, ID 83687-3044
Tel (509) 545-9751 Founded/Ownrshp 1970
Sales 23.5MM^E EMP 90
SIC 3444 5191 3564 Metal ventilating equipment; Chemicals, agricultural; Blowers & fans
Pr: Frank H Bushman
*CFO: Jerry Bertels
VP: Joyce Popp

D-U-N-S 79-923-4893
INDUSTRIAL VENTILATION INC
IVI NORTH
W6395 Specialty Dr, Greenville, WI 54942-8026
Tel (920) 757-6001 Founded/Ownrshp 1993
Sales 25.0MM EMP 160
SIC 1711 Mechanical contractor; Ventilation & duct work contractor; Mechanical contractor; Ventilation & duct work contractor
CEO: Gerald Auler
*Pr: Jim Hanegraaf
*Treas: Renae Langel

D-U-N-S 05-589-9926
INDUSTRIAL WAREHOUSE SERVICES INC
IWS-MAHRT
502 Bear Creek Cutoff Rd, Tuscaloosa, AL 35405-6443
Tel (205) 759-1286 Founded/Ownrshp 1968
Sales 43.5MM EMP 153
Accts Jamison Money Farmer Pc Tusca
SIC 4225 7389 4213 General warehousing & storage; Packaging & labeling services; Trucking, except local; General warehousing & storage; Packaging & labeling services; Trucking, except local
Ch: Fred Hahn
*Pr: Gregg Hahn
Genl Mgr: Rodger Collins

D-U-N-S 11-629-1832
INDUSTRIAL WASTE UTILIZATION INC
5601 State St, Montclair, CA 91763-6241
Tel (909) 984-9984 Founded/Ownrshp 1981
Sales 23.7MM^E EMP 45
SIC 4959 Environmental cleanup services
Pr: Charles Templer

D-U-N-S 07-924-5638
INDUSTRIAL WATER TREATMENT SOLUTIONS CORP
(Suby of PRAIRIE CAPITAL LP) ★
16880 Lathrop Ave, Harvey, IL 60426-6031
Tel (708) 339-1313 Founded/Ownrshp 2011
Sales 28.2MM^E EMP 159
SIC 6719 3589 2899 Personal holding companies, except banks; Water treatment equipment, industrial; Chemical preparations
Pr: Christopher Dooley

D-U-N-S 05-095-8362
INDUSTRIAL WELDING SUPPLY CO OF HARVEY INC
GAS & SUPPLY
111 Buras Rd, Belle Chasse, LA 70037-3175
Tel (504) 392-2400 Founded/Ownrshp 1981
Sales 49.1MM^E EMP 132
SIC 5084 5085 5169

INDUSTRIAS LANCERMEX SA DE CV
See LANCER CORP

D-U-N-S 09-030-6929 IMP/EXP
INDUSTRIAS VASSALLO INC
VASSALLO INDUSTRIES
1000 Carr 506, Coto Laurel, PR 00780-2935
Tel (787) 848-1515 Founded/Ownrshp 1969
Sales 39.3MM^E EMP 307
SIC 3084 3089 2519 Plastics pipe; Fittings for pipe, plastic; Plastic hardware & building products; Furniture, household: glass, fiberglass & plastic; Plastics pipe; Fittings for pipe, plastic; Plastic hardware & building products; Furniture, household: glass, fiberglass & plastic
Pr: Rafael V Vassallo
*CFO: Peter Lectora
*VP: Jose Valls Eng
*VP: Olga Vassallo
VP Opers: Jose Valls

D-U-N-S 02-881-9303
INDUSTRIES OF BLIND INC
WINSTON SALEM INDS FOR BLIND
7730 N Point Blvd, Winston Salem, NC 27106-3310
Tel (336) 759-0551 Founded/Ownrshp 1957
Sales 8.1MM^E EMP 300
SIC 8331 Sheltered workshop; Sheltered workshop
Pr: David Horton
VP Opers: Dan Kelly

D-U-N-S 13-124-1960
INDUSTRIOUS MOTORS LLC
NISSAN OF BUENA PARK
6501 Auto Center Dr, Buena Park, CA 90621-2901
Tel (714) 739-0800 Founded/Ownrshp 2003
Sales 34.6MM^E EMP 55
SIC 5511 Automobiles, new & used; Automobiles, new & used
CEO: Greg Brown
Ex VP: Stephen T Palmer
Dir IT: Robert Lawicki
Sls Mgr: Tom D'Aquila
Sls Mgr: Chris Jones
Sls Mgr: Jacob Little
Sales Asso: C A Eloy

INDUSTRL MNGT OF MATERIALS OF
See AMERICAN STAINLESS LLC

D-U-N-S 00-454-5208
INDUSTRY PRODUCTS CO (OH)
I P
500 W Statler Rd, Piqua, OH 45356-8281
Tel (937) 778-0585 Founded/Ownrshp 1966
Sales 51.2MM^E EMP 402
SIC 7692 3053 3714 3544 3081 Automotive welding; Gaskets, all materials; Motor vehicle parts & accessories; Motor vehicle body components & frame; Special dies, tools, jigs & fixtures; Unsupported plastics film & sheet; Automotive welding; Gaskets, all materials; Motor vehicle parts & accessories; Motor vehicle body components & frame; Special dies, tools, jigs & fixtures; Unsupported plastics film & sheet
Pr: Linda Cleveland
Telecom Ex: Tammie Skikus
CTO: Verla Pautsch
MIS Dir: James Bailey
IT Man: Jeremy Sharp
Info Man: Dave Jacomet
VP Opers: Bob Axe
Mfg Dir: Tom Craft
Ql Cn Mgr: Jeff Montgomery
Ql Cn Mgr: Mike Patrick
Manager: Malcolm Kidd

D-U-N-S 14-449-2824
INDUSTRY SERVICES CO INC OF LOUISIANA
6265 Rangeline Rd, Theodore, AL 36582-5245
Tel (251) 443-6900 Founded/Ownrshp 2000
Sales 24.3MM EMP 45
Accts Rhodes Young Black & Duncan
SIC 1629 1741 Industrial plant construction; Refractory or acid brick masonry; Industrial plant construction; Refractory or acid brick masonry
Pr: Shawn Hunter

INDUSTRY SOURCE , THE
See TNG WORLDWIDE INC

D-U-N-S 08-647-4079
INDUSTRY STATE BANK
16886 Fordtran Blvd, Industry, TX 78944-5053
Tel (979) 992-3391 Founded/Ownrshp 1911
Sales NA EMP 33
SIC 6022 State commercial banks; State commercial banks
Ch Bd: James Lindmann
*Pr: Ervin Mieth Jr
CFO: Bradley Lindemann
*Ex VP: Lew Ellyn Gross
Ex VP: Margaret Kubala
*Sr VP: Pamela Cernoch
*Sr VP: Bonnie Schultz
VP: Bonnie Schulz

D-U-N-S 82-847-4630 IMP
INDY EQUIPMENT INDEPENDENCE RECYCLING INC
6220 E Schaaf Rd, Independence, OH 44131-1332
Tel (216) 524-0999 Founded/Ownrshp 2008
Sales 250.0MM EMP 250
SIC 3531 Construction machinery; Construction machinery
Pr: Victor Digeronimo
Sec: Robert Digeranimo
Off Mgr: Ronald Brocco
VP Mktg: Shannon Carlisle

INDY HONDA
See INDY ROHR MOTORS INC

INDY ROC
See AIMCO APARTMENT INVESTMENT AND MANAGEMENT CO

D-U-N-S 61-555-3435
INDY ROHR MOTORS INC
INDY HONDA
8455 Us 31 S, Indianapolis, IN 46227-6277
Tel (317) 887-0800 Founded/Ownrshp 1990
Sales 33.4MM^E EMP 93
SIC 5511 7538 5531 5521 5012 Automobiles, new & used; General automotive repair shops; Automotive & home supply stores; Used car dealers; Automobiles & other motor vehicles; Automobiles, new & used; General automotive repair shops; Automotive & home supply stores; Used car dealers; Automobiles & other motor vehicles
Pr: Robert V Rohrman
*Sec: Linda Rohrman
Sales Asso: Brian Beck
Sales Asso: Chris Belt
Sales Asso: Scott Hall
Sales Asso: Glenn Nesta

D-U-N-S 18-190-0473 IMP
INDY TIRE CENTERS INC
9302 E 30th St Ste B, Indianapolis, IN 46229-1079
Tel (317) 541-2452 Founded/Ownrshp 1986
Sales 48.0MM^E EMP 100
SIC 5531 5014 Automotive tires; Automobile tires & tubes
Pr: Dennis Dickson
*Sec: Dorothy McKenzie
*VP: Christopher P Fox
*VP: Scott Monteith
*VP: Zurcher Paul W

INDY TRUCK SALES
See MCGRENHO L L C

INDYGO
See INDIANAPOLIS PUBLIC TRANSPORTATION CORP

D-U-N-S 16-190-9049
INDYNE INC
11800 Sunrise Valley Dr # 250, Reston, VA 20191-5302
Tel (703) 903-6900 Founded/Ownrshp 1999
Sales 257.4MM^E EMP 1,700
Accts Argy Wiltse & Robinson Pc M
SIC 8744 8748 7382 Base maintenance (providing personnel on continuing basis); Base maintenance (providing personnel on continuing basis); Communications consulting; Security systems services
Pr: C Donald Bishop
*Pr: Mr Donyer Miller
*COO: Jeffrey Riemer
VP: Gayle Kall
Prgrm Mgr: Stewart Price
Dir IT: Robert Trujillo
Netwrk Mgr: Kevin Andres

D-U-N-S 04-072-1776
INEOQUEST TECHNOLOGIES INC
170 Forbes Blvd, Mansfield, MA 02048-1149
Tel (508) 339-2497 Founded/Ownrshp 2001
Sales 22.3MM^E EMP 125^E
SIC 3825 Instruments to measure electricity
Pr: Calvin Harrison
Ch Bd: Peter Dawson
Pr: Gino Dion
CFO: Steve Sanford

Sr VP: Rick Ford
VP: Bruce Hammergren
VP: Sunil Kotagiri
Snr Sftwr: Paul Dao
Snr Sftwr: Rich Lorenz
Snr Sftwr: Prabhu Manickam
Snr Sftwr: Shiva Patwary

D-U-N-S 80-690-6900 IMP/EXP
INEOS ABS (USA) LLC
(*Suby of* INEOS GROUP LIMITED)
356 Three Rivers Pkwy, Addyston, OH 45001-2553
Tel (513) 467-2400 *Founded/Ownrshp* 2009
Sales 75.0MM^E *EMP* 255^E
SIC 2899 Chemical preparations; Chemical preparations
VP: Clint Herring
CFO: Clark Carter
**Treas:* Rebecca Libourel
IT Man: Joe Moehring
Sfty Mgr: Kenneth Schmidt
Opers Mgr: Karel Brabant
Opers Mgr: Bryan Mullalley
Opers Mgr: Sharon Terrell

D-U-N-S 00-398-3483 IMP/EXP
INEOS AMERICAS LLC
INEOS TECHNOLOGIES
(*Suby of* INEOS GROUP LIMITED)
2600 S Shore Blvd Ste 500, League City, TX 77573-2944
Tel (281) 535-6600 *Founded/Ownrshp* 1963
Sales 755.5MM^E *EMP* 2,600
SIC 2873 2869 Nitrogenous fertilizers; Industrial organic chemicals; Nitrogenous fertilizers; Industrial organic chemicals
Mng Pt: Daniel Moore
CFO: William Bernard
VP: Greg Musler
Dir Rx: Joe Walton
Dir IT: Joachim Pieper
IT Man: Chris Dow
IT Man: Colin Fulton
IT Man: Vincent Gauthier
IT Man: Brian Harley
IT Man: Clifton Loup
Tech Mgr: Cameron Robinson

D-U-N-S 00-818-8117 IMP/EXP
INEOS AMERICAS LLC
(*Suby of* INEOS HOLDINGS LIMITED)
7770 Rangeline Rd, Theodore, AL 36582-5212
Tel (251) 443-3000 *Founded/Ownrshp* 2003
Sales 188.5MM^E *EMP* 520
SIC 2869 2865 Phenol, alkylated & cumene; Acetone, synthetic; Acetone, synthetic; Phenol, alkylated & cumene
COO: Ron Deakins
CFO: Beverley Hoyle
IT Man: Stuart Buchman
QI Cn Mgr: Terry Quint
VP Mktg: Ben Smith

INEOS BIO AMERICAS
See INEOS BIO USA LLC

D-U-N-S 82-971-7086 EXP
INEOS BIO USA LLC
INEOS BIO AMERICAS
(*Suby of* INEOS BIO SA)
3030 Warrenville Rd # 650, Lisle, IL 60532-1000
Tel (630) 857-7000 *Founded/Ownrshp* 2012
Sales 29.9MM^E *EMP* 72^E
SIC 5169 Chemicals & allied products
CEO: Peter Williams
CFO: Bob Sokol
Snr PM: Stephen Coburn

D-U-N-S 09-289-9736 IMP
INEOS LLC
INEOS OXIDE
(*Suby of* INEOS GROUP LIMITED)
8550 United Plaza Blvd, Baton Rouge, LA 70809-2256
Tel (225) 687-1946 *Founded/Ownrshp* 2001
Sales 35.8MM^E *EMP* 50
SIC 5169 Chemicals & allied products
Comm Man: Richard Longden

D-U-N-S 62-377-0315 IMP
INEOS LLC
1900 Fort Amanda Rd, Lima, OH 45804-1827
Tel (419) 226-1200 *Founded/Ownrshp* 2002
Sales 62.6MM^E *EMP* 140^E
SIC 5162 Plastics materials & basic shapes; Plastics materials & basic shapes
Exec: Sally Duval
Sfty Mgr: Patrick Kiser

D-U-N-S 94-379-8863 IMP
INEOS NEW PLANET BIOENERGY LLC
(*Suby of* INEOS BIO SA)
925 74th Ave Sw, Vero Beach, FL 32968-9755
Tel (772) 794-7900 *Founded/Ownrshp* 2012
Sales 23.3MM^E *EMP* 65
SIC 2869 Ethanolamines; Ethanolamines
Pr: David King
**CEO:* Peter Williams
**COO:* Mark Niederschulte
**CFO:* Martin Olavesen
Dir IT: John McNally

INEOS OXIDE
See INEOS LLC

INEOS TECHNOLOGIES
See INEOS AMERICAS LLC

D-U-N-S 62-380-4809 IMP/EXP
INEOS USA LLC
(*Suby of* INEOS GROUP LIMITED)
2600 S Shore Blvd Ste 500, League City, TX 77573-2944
Tel (281) 535-6600 *Founded/Ownrshp* 2005
Sales NA *EMP* 2,449
SIC 5169 3999 Plastics materials & resins; Chemicals & allied products; Atomizers, toiletry
CEO: Robert Learman
COO: Frederick Rulander
**CFO:* Robert Sokol

**Ch:* Jim Ratcliffe
VP: Michael Nagle
VP: Gary Wallace
IT Man: Steve Vice
Sfty Mgr: Malcolm McGregor
Opers Mgr: Jose Garibay
Plnt Mgr: Danny Webb
Prd Mgr: Jeff Montgomery

D-U-N-S 07-958-7209
INERGEX LLC
50 Fountain Plz Ste 700, Buffalo, NY 14202-2218
Tel (716) 829-1000 *Founded/Ownrshp* 2014
Sales 20.4MM^E *EMP* 125^E
SIC 7379 Computer related consulting services
Pr: Tim Frank
VP: Jeffrey Lippert
VP: Loretta Nappo
Off Admin: Frauke Stoffel

D-U-N-S 18-245-4681
INERGY HOLDINGS LP
2 Brush Creek Blvd # 200, Kansas City, MO 64112-1712
Tel (816) 842-8181 *Founded/Ownrshp* 1996
Sales 221.8MM^E *EMP* 2,910
SIC 5172 6719 Petroleum products; Gases, liquefied petroleum (propane); Investment holding companies, except banks; Petroleum products; Gases, liquefied petroleum (propane); Investment holding companies, except banks
Pr: John J Sherman
Pr: Phillip L Elbert
CFO: R Brooks Sherman Jr
Sr VP: Laura L Ozenberger
VP: Phil Elbert
Opers Supe: Don Boroff
Opers Supe: Bob Williams
Board of Directors: Warren H Gfeller, Arthur B Krause, Richard T O'brien

D-U-N-S 12-576-5680
■ **INERGY PROPANE LLC**
(*Suby of* SUBURBAN PROPANE PARTNERS LP) ★
2 Brush Creek Blvd # 200, Kansas City, MO 64112-1712
Tel (816) 842-8181 *Founded/Ownrshp* 2012
Sales 157.4MM^E *EMP* 1,008
SIC 5984 5172 Propane gas, bottled; Gases, liquefied petroleum (propane); Propane gas, bottled; Gases, liquefied petroleum (propane)
Pr: Phillip L Elbert
VP: Kent Blackford
VP: Barry Cigich
VP: Don Krider
VP: Jason Reeves
VP: R B Sherman
VP: Barry Wall

D-U-N-S 17-612-7629
INETU INC
744 Roble Rd Ste 70, Allentown, PA 18109-9100
Tel (610) 266-7441 *Founded/Ownrshp* 1996
Sales 24.8MM^E *EMP* 86
SIC 7379 Computer related consulting services
CEO: Dev Chanchani
COO: Ajay Chanchani
CFO: Tim O'Keefe
VP: David Fowler
VP: Chris Kivlehan
Exec: Matthew Dejesus
Exec: John Meyer
Snr Ntwrk: Matthew Peterson
Sftwr Eng: Steven Bernard
Sftwr Eng: Steven Bernhard
Sftwr Eng: David Lamb

INEZ ELEMENTARY SCHOOL
See MARTIN COUNTY SCHOOLS

D-U-N-S 94-921-8999 IMP
INFAC NORTH AMERICA INC
(*Suby of* INFAC CORPORATION)
1 Infac Dr, Campbellsville, KY 42718-2482
Tel (270) 789-1040 *Founded/Ownrshp* 2008
Sales 35.7MM *EMP* 70
Accts Choi Kim & Park Llp Montgom
SIC 5013 Automotive supplies & parts; Automotive supplies & parts
Pr: Ohe Gil Choi
**VP:* Joong Seon Choi
Genl Mgr: Brian S Bland

D-U-N-S 04-157-0627
INFAITH COMMUNITY FOUNDATION
625 4th Ave S, Minneapolis, MN 55415-1624
Tel (612) 338-5482 *Founded/Ownrshp* 2013
Sales 29.8MM *EMP* 7^E
SIC 8641 Civic social & fraternal associations
Prin: Chris Andersen

INFANTINO
See BLUE BOX OPCO LLC

D-U-N-S 82-905-7814 IMP
■ **INFASTECH DECORAH LLC**
(*Suby of* STANLEY BLACK & DECKER INC) ★
1304 Kerr Dr, Decorah, IA 52101-2406
Tel (563) 382-4559 *Founded/Ownrshp* 2011
Sales 95.8MM^E *EMP* 475^E
SIC 3452 3965 Bolts, metal; Fasteners; Bolts, metal; Fasteners
COO: Kevin V Fernando
Genl Mgr: Nick McIntyre

D-U-N-S 80-533-7925
INFASTRUCTURE SERVICES HOLDINGS INC
4570 Orange Blvd, Sanford, FL 32771-9108
Tel (954) 973-3060 *Founded/Ownrshp* 2008
Sales 13.0MM^E *EMP* 450
SIC 1611 1623 Surfacing & paving; Underground utilities contractor; Surfacing & paving; Underground utilities contractor
Pr: Kenneth Jackson
**CFO:* Nardo Bosque

D-U-N-S 05-055-2082
INFICON INC
(*Suby of* INFICON HOLDING AG)
2 Technology Pl, East Syracuse, NY 13057-9714
Tel (315) 434-1149 *Founded/Ownrshp* 1970, 2000
Sales 124.8MM^E *EMP* 810
SIC 3823 3812 Industrial process control instruments; Search & navigation equipment; Industrial process control instruments; Search & navigation equipment
Pr: Peter Maier
Pr: Daniel Hoffman
CFO: Matthias Troendle
Chf Mktg O: Remo Klaiber
**VP:* Hoang Cao
**VP:* Stephen Chabot
**VP:* Jerry Wander
Prgrm Mgr: Kenneth Rosys
Genl Mgr: Darren Lee
Off Admin: Sandy Cheney
Off Admin: Sandy Conner

D-U-N-S 07-842-1235
INFIGEN ENERGY US DEVELOPMENT LLC
6688 N Central Expy # 500, Dallas, TX 75206-3914
Tel (214) 515-1100 *Founded/Ownrshp* 2012
Sales 35.6MM^E *EMP* 58^E
SIC 4911 Generation, electric power
VP: Andrew Flanagan
CFO: Greg Flowers
VP Opers: Hans Owens
Sfty Dirs: Kendra Smith
Sfty Mgr: John Boyle
Opers Mgr: Mat Dusenberry
Opers Mgr: Blake Holmes
Opers Mgr: Scott Martin
Plnt Mgr: Darren Duvall

D-U-N-S 06-313-6592 IMP
INFILCO DEGREMONT INC
SUEZ
(*Suby of* SUEZ ENVIRONNEMENT)
8007 Discovery Dr, Richmond, VA 23229-8605
Tel (804) 756-7600 *Founded/Ownrshp* 2009
Sales 110.5MM^E *EMP* 326
SIC 3589 Sewage & water treatment equipment; Sewage & water treatment equipment
Ch Bd: Vernon D Lucy
Pt: Kevin Smith
**Ch Bd:* Maximilien Pellegrini
**Treas:* Robert W Winslow
**Sr VP:* Paul G Davia
VP: Temple Ballard
**VP:* Albert A Pristera
Mktg Dir: Sylvie Roy
Snr Mgr: Melanie Demont
Snr Mgr: Joseph Giannone
Board of Directors: Patrice Keime, Barry Windsor

D-U-N-S 17-721-2305 IMP/EXP
INFILTRATOR WATER TECHNOLOGIES LLC
CHAMPION POLYMERS RECYCLING
(*Suby of* ONTARIO TEACHERS' PENSION PLAN BOARD)
4 Business Park Rd, Old Saybrook, CT 06475-4238
Tel (860) 577-7000 *Founded/Ownrshp* 2015
Sales 77.8MM^E *EMP* 300
SIC 3089

INFINEON TECHNOLOGIES AG
See INFINEON TECHNOLOGIES US HOLDCO INC

D-U-N-S 04-167-4912 IMP
INFINEON TECHNOLOGIES AMERICAS CORP
INTERNATIONAL RECTIFIER CORP
(*Suby of* INFINEON TECHNOLOGIES US INTERCO LLC) ★
101 N Sepulveda Blvd, El Segundo, CA 90245-4318
Tel (310) 726-8000 *Founded/Ownrshp* 2015
Sales 687.8MM^E *EMP* 1,200
SIC 3674 Semiconductors & related devices; Semiconductors & related devices
CEO: Oleg Khaykin
COO: Geremie Hopkins
CFO: Ilan Daskal
Ex VP: Petra Nagel
Ex VP: Gary Tanner
VP: Nick Brand
VP: John Burgess
VP: Henry Gao
VP: Henning Hauenstein
VP: Jeng Lue
VP: Tim McDonald
VP: Tim Phillips
VP: Pat Schreffler
VP: Michael Seidl
Exec: Graham Robertson
Exec: Rick Sivan
Dir Risk M: Phil Bahng
Dir Risk M: Mark Mason

D-U-N-S 10-323-1692 IMP
INFINEON TECHNOLOGIES NORTH AMERICA CORP
(*Suby of* INFINEON TECHNOLOGIES AG) ★
640 N Mccarthy Blvd, Milpitas, CA 95035-5113
Tel (866) 951-9519 *Founded/Ownrshp* 2015
Sales 431.9MM^E *EMP* 1,200
SIC 3674 Semiconductors & related devices; Transistors; Microprocessors; Quartz crystals, for electronic application; Microwave components; Semiconductors & related devices
CEO: Reinhard Ploss
**Pr:* Robert Lefort
**CFO:* Dominik Asam
**CFO:* Andrew Prillwitz
VP: Phil Gibson
Genl Mgr: Nick Sierra
IT Man: Frank Haase
IT Man: Wesley Swail
Sftwr Eng: Jorg Berkner
S&M/VP: Brad Royston
Mktg Dir: Paul Patterson

D-U-N-S 07-969-9553
INFINEON TECHNOLOGIES US HOLDCO INC
INFINEON TECHNOLOGIES AG
(*Suby of* INFINEON TECHNOLOGIES AG)
640 N Mccarthy Blvd, Milpitas, CA 95035-5113
Tel (408) 956-8960 *Founded/Ownrshp* 2014
Sales 1.1MMM^E *EMP* 1,200^E
SIC 3674 Integrated circuits, semiconductor networks, etc.
CEO: Reinhard Ploss
**CFO:* Andrew Prillwitz
**Prin:* Robert Lefort
Mng Dir: Albert Stritter
Dir IT: Trung Le
Dir IT: Klaudia Seiling
Dir IT: Natalie Yap
IT Man: Jorg Domaschke
IT Man: Arun Naik
Mktg Dir: Jack Artman
Mktg Dir: Matthias Halsband

D-U-N-S 07-968-8344
INFINEON TECHNOLOGIES US INTERCO LLC
(*Suby of* INFINEON TECHNOLOGIES AG) ★
640 N Mccarthy Blvd, Milpitas, CA 95035-5113
Tel (866) 951-9519 *Founded/Ownrshp* 2014
Sales 687.8MM^E *EMP* 1,200^E
SIC 3674 Integrated circuits, semiconductor networks, etc.
CFO: Andrew Prillwitz
Pr: Jean-Baptiste Loire
Prin: Cynthia Murphy

D-U-N-S 02-133-1686 EXP
▲ **INFINERA CORP**
140 Caspian Ct, Sunnyvale, CA 94089-1000
Tel (408) 572-5200 *Founded/Ownrshp* 2000
Sales 668.0MM *EMP* 1,318
Accts Ernst & Young Llp San Jose C
Tkr Sym INFN *Exch* NGS
SIC 3661 7372 Fiber optics communications equipment; Prepackaged software; Fiber optics communications equipment; Prepackaged software
CEO: Thomas J Fallon
**Ch Bd:* Kambiz Y Hooshmand
**Pr:* David F Welch
CFO: Brad Feller
Sr VP: Bob Jandro
Sr VP: Robert J Jandro
Sr VP: James L Laufman
Sr VP: Nick Walden
VP: Scott Chandler
VP: Dirk Corsus
VP: Todd Hanson
VP: Bill Jarvis
VP: Kevin Jones
VP: Michael Jung
VP: Antti Kankkunen
VP: Frederick A Kish Jr
VP: Paul Morkel
VP: Minoo Mortazavi
VP: Lonny Orona
VP: Prasad Paranjape
VP: Stan Peterson
Board of Directors: James Dolce, Marcel Gani, Paul J Milbury, Carl Redfield, Mark A Wegleitner

D-U-N-S 03-210-5889
INFINEUM USA LP
(*Suby of* INFINEUM INTERNATIONAL LIMITED)
1900 E Linden Ave, Linden, NJ 07036-1133
Tel (908) 474-2573 *Founded/Ownrshp* 1998
Sales 1.1MMM^E *EMP* 600
SIC 5169 Natural resource research; Lubricating oils; Chemical preparations; Oil additives; Chemical additives
Pt: Mark Struglinski
Pt: Bruce Arfken
Admn Mgr: Kiyoaki Nishida
IT Man: Felix Cruz
Netwrk Eng: Jean Guillou
Opers Mgr: Bryan Boyle
Plnt Mgr: John Englishman
Sls Dir: Ken Kalisky
Mktg Mgr: Shaun Harkin
Mktg Mgr: Ahmad Zareh
Counsel: Carl Howard

D-U-N-S 17-341-3154
INFINISOURCE INC
COBRA COMPLIANCE SYSTEMS
13024 Balntyn Corp Pl # 400, Charlotte, NC 28277-2113
Tel (800) 300-3838 *Founded/Ownrshp* 1991
Sales 58.7MM^E *EMP* 350^E
SIC 8742

D-U-N-S 14-809-3714
INFINITE CAMPUS INC
4321 109th Ave Ne, Minneapolis, MN 55449-6794
Tel (651) 631-0000 *Founded/Ownrshp* 1993
Sales 29.2MM^E *EMP* 130
SIC 7371 Computer software development; Computer software development
CEO: Charles Kratsch
Ofcr: Brian Page
Telecom Ex: Bob Kilian
Dir IT: Dan Orlando
IT Man: Joseph Coleman
Software D: Eric Holec
Software D: Cindy Koolmo
Software D: Neil Smeby
Sftwr Eng: Chanthy Dullum
Sftwr Eng: Joseph Fessler
Sftwr Eng: Chris Gennaula

D-U-N-S 01-106-6144 IMP
INFINITE COMPUTER SOLUTIONS INC
(*Suby of* INFINITE COMPUTER SOLUTIONS (INDIA) LIMITED)
15201 Diamondback Dr # 125, Rockville, MD 20850-3695
Tel (301) 355-7760 *Founded/Ownrshp* 2001
Sales 124.7MM^E *EMP* 630

SIC 7379 7371 Computer related consulting services; Custom computer programming services; Computer related consulting services; Custom computer programming services
Ch Bd: Sanjay Govil
*Pr: Neeraj Tewari
*CEO: Upinder Zutshi
*Ex VP: Sanjeev Gulati
*Sr VP: Sheppard Lyngdoh
Sr VP: Ravi Nimmagadda
*Sr VP: Ashoka Tankala
VP: Manish Agarwal
VP: Jay Fahey
VP: John Laskey
Exec: Kamal Kumar

D-U-N-S 07-971-1551
INFINITE DIAMONDS & JEWELLERY INC
MUNIC
12 E 46th St Fl 3, New York, NY 10017-2418
Tel (914) 255-2846 Founded/Ownrshp 2014
Sales 80.0MM EMP 14
SIC 5094 Jewelry & precious stones; Diamonds (gems)
Pr: Romil Kothari

D-U-N-S 01-425-5249
INFINITE ENERGY CONSTRUCTION INC
PROGRESS ELECTRIC
13625 Oak St, Kansas City, MO 64145-1459
Tel (816) 763-7471 Founded/Ownrshp 1996
Sales 21.0MM EMP 55E
SIC 1731 4911 Electrical work; Electric services
Pr: Nilson Goes

D-U-N-S 96-364-0557
INFINITE ENERGY HOLDINGS INC
7001 Sw 24th Ave, Gainesville, FL 32607-3704
Tel (352) 240-4121 Founded/Ownrshp 2010
Sales 153.9MME EMP 250
SIC 4911 4924 Distribution, electric power; Natural gas distribution
Pr: Darin Cook
*CEO: Richard S Blaser
*CFO: Robert Scott Thomas
*Genl Couns: Jeffrey Traynham

D-U-N-S 96-878-6749
INFINITE ENERGY INC
INTELLIGENT ENERGY
(Suby of INFINITE ENERGY HOLDINGS INC) ★
7001 Sw 24th Ave, Gainesville, FL 32607-3704
Tel (352) 331-1654 Founded/Ownrshp 1994
Sales 152.8MME EMP 10
SIC 4924 Natural gas distribution; Natural gas distribution
CEO: Darin Cook
*Pr: Richard Blaser
COO: Steve Madden
Ex VP: Xavier Yrausquin
VP: Laura Doljanica
VP: Becky Patrick
Prgrm Mgr: Laura Williamson
CIO: Sajid Hasan
QA Dir: Alex Pinillos
Dir IT: Jennifer Mueller
IT Man: Delmiro Campelo

D-U-N-S 14-230-1774 IMP
INFINITE HERBS LLC
7953 Nw 21st St, Doral, FL 33122-1616
Tel (305) 599-9255 Founded/Ownrshp 2003
Sales 30.0MM EMP 210
SIC 5149 Spices & seasonings
S&M/Mgr: Jordan Phillips

D-U-N-S 06-309-3460
INFINITE VELOCITY AUTOMOTIVE INC
FH DAILEY
800 Davis St, San Leandro, CA 94577-1512
Tel (510) 351-8800 Founded/Ownrshp 2011
Sales 22.2MME EMP 82
SIC 5511 New & used car dealers; New & used car dealers
Pr: Steve Song

INFINITI FINANCIAL SERVICE
See NISSAN MOTOR ACCEPTANCE CORP

D-U-N-S 14-213-6105
INFINITI OF ARDMORE INC
(Suby of CHESTER COUNTY NISSAN LLC) ★
130 Sibley Ave, Ardmore, PA 19003-2312
Tel (610) 896-4400 Founded/Ownrshp 2002
Sales 20.8MME EMP 60E
SIC 5511 New & used car dealers; New & used car dealers
Pr: Dave Desko

INFINITI OF BATON ROUGE
See ET INTERNATIONAL LLC

D-U-N-S 02-447-8067 EXP
■ **INFINITI OF CHARLOTTE INC** (NC)
SONIC AUTOMOTIVE
(Suby of SONIC AUTOMOTIVE INC) ★
9103 E Independence Blvd, Matthews, NC 28105-4503
Tel (704) 847-9010 Founded/Ownrshp 1981, 1998
Sales 21.7MME EMP 47
SIC 5511 7538 Automobiles, new & used; General automotive repair shops
Pr: Bruton Smith
Genl Mgr: Steve Okane
Sales Asso: Rodney Marsh

INFINITI OF COCONUT CREEK
See TT OF SAMPLE INC

INFINITI OF KIRKLAND
See SOUND INFINITI INC

D-U-N-S 80-935-1240
INFINITI OF LISLE
4325 Lincoln Ave, Lisle, IL 60532-1211
Tel (630) 241-3000 Founded/Ownrshp 1990
Sales 40.0MM EMP 90
SIC 5511 5521 Automobiles, new & used; Used car dealers; Automobiles, new & used; Used car dealers
Pr: Horst Korallus
*VP: Guenter Korallus
CTO: Nathan Carr
IT Man: Nathan Palmer
Sales Asso: Steve Johnson
Sales Asso: Sean Pelkey
Sales Asso: Joe Peters
Sales Asso: Scott Rehfeldt

INFINITI OF MISSION VIEJO
See GSM AUTO GROUP II LLC

INFINITI OF PEORIA
See PIVT MOTORS INC

D-U-N-S 05-878-5882
INFINITI OF SCOTTSDALE INC
7601 E Frank Lloyd Wrig, Scottsdale, AZ 85260-1000
Tel (480) 941-0055 Founded/Ownrshp 1972
Sales 44.6MME EMP 120
SIC 5511 Automobiles, new & used; Pickups, new & used; Automobiles, new & used; Pickups, new & used
Pr: Cecil Van Tuyl
*VP: Patricia Van Tuyl
Genl Mgr: Ken Schatsburg
VP Mktg: Chris Schatsburg
Sls Mgr: Henry Rosetti
Snr Mgr: Kathy Roznowski

INFINITI OF THOUSAND OAKS
See ACHIEVEMENT AUTOMOTIVE GROUP LLC

D-U-N-S 14-305-8514
INFINITI OF WEST CHESTER INC
1265 Wilmington Pike, West Chester, PA 19382-8446
Tel (610) 696-6700 Founded/Ownrshp 2004
Sales 23.6MME EMP 50
SIC 5511 Automobiles, new & used
Pr: Joseph Bush Jr
*Sec: Dean Bush
Genl Mgr: Leigh Timberman
Store Mgr: Brian Ferraro

D-U-N-S 00-877-2225
INFINITY AIR INC
18321 Ventura Blvd # 400, Tarzana, CA 91356-4247
Tel (818) 881-8911 Founded/Ownrshp 1997
Sales 27.4MME EMP 37
SIC 5088 Aircraft & space vehicle supplies & parts
CEO: Jimmy Wu
COO: Jack Petrasanta
*CFO: Sherie Jan
*Prin: Edvin Youhanna
Genl Mgr: Ali Djomeh
Sftwr Eng: Peter Ji

D-U-N-S 03-003-2155
■ **INFINITY CASUALTY INSURANCE CO**
ATLANTA CASUALTY
(Suby of INFINITY PROPERTY AND CASUALTY CORP) ★
11700 Great Oaks Way # 300, Alpharetta, GA 30022-2480
Tel (678) 627-7000 Founded/Ownrshp 1972, 2005
Sales NA EMP 1,000
SIC 6331 6411 Automobile insurance; Insurance agents, brokers & service; Automobile insurance; Insurance agents, brokers & service
Pr: Jim Gober
*Treas: J Thomas Brooks
*VP: Thomas B Freeland
*VP: M F Washburne
Sftwr Eng: Jay Zimmerman

D-U-N-S 80-074-5762 IMP
INFINITY CLASSICS INTERNATIONAL INC
INFINITY HOSIERY
1365 38th St, Brooklyn, NY 11218-3634
Tel (718) 851-2577 Founded/Ownrshp 1995
Sales 61.3MME EMP 351
SIC 5139 Footwear; Footwear
Ch Bd: Joe Steinberg

D-U-N-S 17-577-1570
INFINITY CONSTRUCTION SERVICES LP
622 Commerce St, Clute, TX 77531-5612
Tel (979) 388-8579 Founded/Ownrshp 2003
Sales 148.1MM EMP 1,100
SIC 1629 1542 Chemical plant & refinery construction; Institutional building construction; Chemical plant & refinery construction; Institutional building construction
Pr: Harold E Monical
VP: Jerry Monical
VP: Mark Monical
Dir IT: Chad Funk

D-U-N-S 13-676-6651
INFINITY CONSULTING SOLUTIONS INC
I C S
462 7th Ave Fl 2, New York, NY 10018-7847
Tel (212) 714-2600 Founded/Ownrshp 2001
Sales 42.1MM EMP 12E
Accts Citrin Cooperman & Company Ll
SIC 8748 Business consulting
CEO: Doug Klares
CFO: Eric Fenchel
*Treas: Michael Wainstein
Sr VP: Scott Rhodes
*VP: Robert Frome
VP: Matthew Walden
Rgnl Mgr: Jeremy Neihardt
Off Mgr: Allison Noelle
IT Man: Elisa Emeritz
Snr Mgr: John Liberatore

D-U-N-S 95-758-9708
INFINITY CONTACT INC
4700 Tama St Se Ste 1500, Cedar Rapids, IA 52403-4556
Tel (319) 378-1400 Founded/Ownrshp 1996
Sales 35.9MME EMP 400
SIC 7389 Telemarketing services; Telemarketing services
CEO: Thomas Leidigh
*Pr: Stephen Griggs
VP: Craig Sell
CIO: Greg Best
Sls Mgr: Amber Kramer

D-U-N-S 55-600-0532
INFINITY CONTRACTING SERVICES CORP
DASNY MECHANICAL
11220 14th Ave, College Point, NY 11356-1408
Tel (718) 762-3200 Founded/Ownrshp 2005
Sales 25.0MM EMP 30
SIC 1711 Plumbing, heating, air-conditioning contractors; Heating systems repair & maintenance; Heating & air conditioning contractors
CEO: Shirley W Yu
*Pr: George Wu
*VP: Keshous Yan
IT Man: Shirley Wu

D-U-N-S 60-992-7566 IMP
INFINITY GLOBAL INC
501 Bridge St, Danville, VA 24541-1405
Tel (434) 793-7570 Founded/Ownrshp 2004
Sales 20.0MME EMP 42
SIC 2673 Bags: plastic, laminated & coated
Pr: Ronald Palmer
VP: Crystal Telfian
Off Admin: Jaimie REA
Opers Mgr: Bob Devaul
Sls Mgr: Lynn Searcy

D-U-N-S 61-476-6392
■ **INFINITY GROUP INC**
(Suby of INFINITY INSURANCE CO) ★
3700 Colonnade Pkwy, Birmingham, AL 35243-3216
Tel (205) 870-4000 Founded/Ownrshp 1992
Sales NA EMP 2,000
SIC 6411 Insurance claim adjusters, not employed by insurance company; Insurance claim adjusters, not employed by insurance company
CEO: James R Gober
*Treas: Roger Prestridge

D-U-N-S 78-672-2595
INFINITY HEALTHCARE INC
111 E Wisconsin Ave # 2100, Milwaukee, WI 53202-4815
Tel (414) 290-6720 Founded/Ownrshp 1991
Sales 32.9MME EMP 250E
SIC 8011 Internal medicine practitioners; Internal medicine practitioners
CEO: Glenn Aldinger
*Pr: Thomas Reminga MD
*Prin: Gregory A Cierlik
Diag Rad: Kevin Gelshenen
Diag Rad: Jerome Quets

D-U-N-S 86-699-4804
INFINITY HOME CARE LLC
6700 Professional Pkwy W, Lakewood Ranch, FL 34240-8444
Tel (941) 378-3703 Founded/Ownrshp 2006
Sales 20.3MME EMP 500E
SIC 8082 Home health care services; Home health care services
Ch Bd: R Robert Moxley
Pr: Phyllis Mullis
Pr: Joe Rosa
*CEO: Steve Karasick
*CEO: Jeff Thompson
*CFO: Ralph Nelson
*Sr VP: Thomas Engala
*Sr VP: John J Piazza Jr
Sr VP: Irene R Tuttle
VP: Steven Brooks
*VP: Christine Lennox
*VP: Ryan Macclellan

D-U-N-S 01-601-2804
INFINITY HOME IMPROVEMENT INC (MI)
GUTTER HELMET OF MICHIGAN
852 47th St Sw, Grand Rapids, MI 49509-5138
Tel (616) 224-1140 Founded/Ownrshp 2000, 2003
Sales 28.4MME EMP 150
SIC 1521 General remodeling, single-family houses; General remodeling, single-family houses
Pr: Mark Adams
*CFO: Steve Mc Cullick
*VP: Chris Kusneske
*Genl Mgr: Bob Heilman
Netwrk Mgr: Mike Todd

INFINITY HOSIERY
See INFINITY CLASSICS INTERNATIONAL INC

D-U-N-S 19-389-5885
■ **INFINITY INSURANCE CO**
(Suby of INFINITY PROPERTY AND CASUALTY CORP) ★
3700 Colonnade Pkwy # 600, Birmingham, AL 35243-3219
Tel (205) 870-4000 Founded/Ownrshp 1979
Sales NA EMP 2,260
SIC 6331 Fire, marine & casualty insurance; Fire, marine & casualty insurance
CEO: James R Gober
*Pr: Glen N Godwin
*CFO: Roger Smith
*Treas: Roger Prestridge
Sr VP: Ralph Gravelle
*VP: William Kennedy
VP: Jim Orrison
*VP: Sheila H Williams
Dir Bus: Jim Dougherty
Brnch Mgr: Stephen Bloor
Brnch Mgr: John Burg

D-U-N-S 96-850-2026 IMP
INFINITY LAWN AND GARDEN INC
6300 75th Ave, Milan, IL 61264-3267
Tel (309) 799-7002 Founded/Ownrshp 2009
Sales 22.5MME EMP 25E
SIC 5083 Lawn & garden machinery & equipment
Pr: Ronald D Bjustrom
Ex VP: Trey George
*VP: Rick Burkamper
*Prin: Thomas J Pastrnak

INFINITY LTL
See LTL COLOR COMPOUNDERS LLC

D-U-N-S 14-911-1127
INFINITY MACHINE & ENGINEERING CORP
2249 American Blvd, De Pere, WI 54115-8490
Tel (920) 965-0222 Founded/Ownrshp 2003
Sales 45.1MME EMP 211E
SIC 8711 Engineering services
Pr: Scott Santaga

D-U-N-S 55-607-9791
INFINITY MAINTENANCE SERVICES LP
622 Commerce St, Clute, TX 77531-5612
Tel (979) 388-8574 Founded/Ownrshp 2003
Sales 45.8MM EMP 550
Accts Grant Thornton Llp Houston
SIC 1629 Industrial plant construction; Industrial plant construction
Pt: Mark Monical
Genl Pt: Imgp LLC

D-U-N-S 80-004-0206
■ **INFINITY NATIONAL INSURANCE CO**
INFINITY SELECT
(Suby of INFINITY INSURANCE CO) ★
3700 Colonnade Pkwy # 600, Birmingham, AL 35243-3219
Tel (205) 870-4000 Founded/Ownrshp 1992
Sales NA EMP 450
SIC 6411 Insurance agents & brokers; Insurance agents & brokers
Pr: Glen N Godwin
*VP: Roger Prestridge
*VP: Sheila H Williams

D-U-N-S 03-250-7836
INFINITY OILFIELD SERVICES LLC
1 Eye Center Dr, Muncy, PA 17756-9200
Tel (570) 567-7027 Founded/Ownrshp 2009
Sales 90.8MME EMP 200
SIC 5172 Crude oil; Crude oil
COO: Gary Patena
CFO: Dan Moore
Sfty Dirs: Todd Watts

D-U-N-S 83-938-7966
▲ **INFINITY PHARMACEUTICALS INC**
784 Memorial Dr, Cambridge, MA 02139-4613
Tel (617) 453-1000 Founded/Ownrshp 1995
Sales 165.0MM EMP 195E
Accts Ernst & Young Llp Boston Mas
Tkr Sym INFI Exch NGS
SIC 2834 8731 Pharmaceutical preparations; Commercial physical research; Pharmaceutical preparations; Commercial physical research
Ch Bd: Adelene Q Perkins
COO: Susan Ferrante
CFO: Lawrence E Bloch
Chf Mktg O: David A Roth
Ofcr: Sujay Kango
Ofcr: Vito J Palombella
Ex VP: Winston Lam
VP: David Baas
VP: Margaret Read
VP: Dee Rodriguez
Board of Directors: Jose Baselga, Jeffrey Berkowitz, Anthony B Evnin, Gwen A Fyfe, Eric S Lander, Norman C Selby, Ian F Smith, Michael C Venuti

D-U-N-S 12-182-2287
▲ **INFINITY PROPERTY AND CASUALTY CORP**
3700 Colonnade Pkwy # 600, Birmingham, AL 35243-3216
Tel (205) 870-4000 Founded/Ownrshp 2002
Sales NA EMP 2,200E
Tkr Sym IPCC Exch NGS
SIC 6331 Automobile insurance; Automobile insurance
Ch Bd: James R Gober
CFO: Robert H Bateman
CFO: Roger Smith
Ex VP: Samuel J Simon
Sr VP: Glen N Godwin
Sr VP: Scott C Pitrone
VP: Ralph Gravelle
VP: Amy Jordan
VP: Jim Orrison
Snr Sftwr: Anne Irwin
Dir IT: Christy Spink
Board of Directors: Teresa A Canida, Angela Brock-Kyle, Harold W Layman, E Robert Meaney, Drayton Nabers Jr, William S Starnes, James L Weidner, Samuel J Weinhoff

INFINITY REHAB
See AVAMERE REHAB SERVICES LLC

D-U-N-S 00-219-4509 IMP
INFINITY RESOURCES INC (IL)
CRITICS' CHOICE VIDEO & DVD
900 N Rohlwing Rd, Itasca, IL 60143-1161
Tel (630) 735-1000 Founded/Ownrshp 1994
Sales 79.2MME EMP 600
SIC 5961 Record &/or tape (music or video) club, mail order; Record &/or tape (music or video) club, mail order
CEO: Dennis E Abboud
*COO: Jack Datz
*CFO: Russ Huggins
*VP: Gary Rowlings
*VP: Jim Shriver
CTO: Anthony Giovingo
IT Man: Randy S Miguel

D-U-N-S 82-952-8574
INFINITY SALES GROUP LLC
5201 Congress Ave Ste 150, Boca Raton, FL 33487-3627
Tel (561) 665-4310 Founded/Ownrshp 2008
Sales 70.3MME EMP 450
SIC 5731 Antennas, satellite dish; Antennas, satellite dish
COO: Michael Hochberger
Opers Mgr: Baron Jordan

INFINITY SELECT
See INFINITY NATIONAL INSURANCE CO

D-U-N-S 78-375-0078
■ INFINITY STANDARD INSURANCE CO
(*Suby of* INFINITY PROPERTY AND CASUALTY CORP) ★
11700 Great Oaks Way # 300, Alpharetta, GA 30022-2480
Tel (678) 627-6000 *Founded/Ownrshp* 2013
Sales NA *EMP* 1,150
SIC 6331 Property damage insurance; Property damage insurance
Ch: Michael D Krause
**VP:* Keith Hefner

D-U-N-S 11-110-1528 IMP
INFINITY TRADING & SOLUTIONS LLC
ITS INFINITY TRADING
450 E Elliot Rd, Chandler, AZ 85225-1379
Tel (480) 940-1037 *Founded/Ownrshp* 2002
Sales 23.7MM^E *EMP* 25
SIC 5088 Aircraft equipment & supplies; Aircraft & space vehicle supplies & parts
Prgrm Mgr: Jeremy Chacon

D-U-N-S 96-487-8776
INFIRMARY HEALTH HOSPITALS INC
5600 Derby Rd, Mobile, AL 36693
Tel (251) 660-5120 *Founded/Ownrshp* 2010
Sales 52.4MM *EMP* 0^E
SIC 8062

D-U-N-S 12-091-3801
INFIRMARY HEALTH SYSTEM INC
5 Mobile Infirmary Cir, Mobile, AL 36607-3513
Tel (251) 435-3030 *Founded/Ownrshp* 1982
Sales 51.7MM *EMP* 5,000
SIC 8062 6512 1542 7322 5047 7389 General medical & surgical hospitals; Nonresidential building operators; Nonresidential construction; Collection agency, except real estate; Medical equipment & supplies; Fund raising organizations; General medical & surgical hospitals; Nonresidential building operators; Nonresidential construction; Collection agency, except real estate; Medical equipment & supplies; Fund raising organizations
CEO: D Mark Nix
**Pr:* E Chandler Bramlett
COO: Rick Nall
Ex VP: Alan Whaley
VP: Harry Brislin
VP: Howard H Fache
VP: Mary Geary
VP: Danny Harrison
VP: Eddy Stephens
Exec: Tom Crout
Dir Lab: Art Goodson

INFLATABLE IMAGES
See SCHERBA INDUSTRIES INC

D-U-N-S 96-179-5510
INFLECTION ENERGY LLC
1099 18th St Ste 3100, Denver, CO 80202-1931
Tel (303) 531-2300 *Founded/Ownrshp* 2008
Sales 50.7MM^E *EMP* 49
SIC 1311 Natural gas production
CEO: Mark S Sexton
**CFO:* Thomas A Coyne

D-U-N-S 61-187-8513
INFLUENCE HEALTH INC
3000 Riverchase Galleria, Hoover, AL 35244-2315
Tel (205) 982-5800 *Founded/Ownrshp* 1996
Sales 21.0MM^E *EMP* 50
Accts Sellers Richardson Holman & We
SIC 7361 7371 Employment agencies; Custom computer programming services
CEO: Gale Wilson-Steele
**Pr:* Peter Kuhn
CFO: Brian Lindstrom
Bd of Dir: Crystal Rock
Sr VP: Marc Guthrie
VP: Bill Andrae
VP: Steve Bock
VP: Anthony Chipelo
VP: Judson Englett
VP: Doug Griffin
VP: Nick Hatalski
VP: Bill Holland
VP: Jason Ingram
VP: Steve Leibforth
VP: Corey Milliman
VP: Andrew Moore
VP: Chris White

INFLUENT
See PCCW TELESERVICES (US) INC

INFO PLACE USA
See CALIFORNIA INFOPLACE INC

D-U-N-S 07-367-0135
■ INFO SYSTEMS LLC
ISI CONNECT
(*Suby of* MTM TECHNOLOGIES INC) ★
590 Century Blvd, Wilmington, DE 19808-6273
Tel (302) 633-9800 *Founded/Ownrshp* 1982
Sales 27.8MM^E *EMP* 225
SIC 5045 7373 Computers; Computer integrated systems design; Computers; Computer integrated systems design
CFO: Jennifer Kenzie

D-U-N-S 08-567-5783
INFOTECH INC
5700 Sw 34th St Ste 1235, Gainesville, FL 32608-5376
Tel (352) 375-7624 *Founded/Ownrshp* 1990
Sales 20.5MM *EMP* 240^E
SIC 7371 7379 Computer software development; Computer related consulting services; Computer software development; Computer related consulting services
Pr: James T McClave
Sr VP: Thomas Rothrock
VP: Lora Labonte
VP: Terry Sullivan
Prgrm Mgr: Jonathan Coombes
Genl Mgr: Yuji Matsuoka
Snr Sftwr: Brian Deragon
CTO: Charles Engelke
QA Dir: Paul Guidry
Dir IT: Jeff Hoover
Dir IT: Guido Lemeer

D-U-N-S 09-175-3215
INFOBAHN SOFTWORLD INC
2010 N 1st St Ste 470, San Jose, CA 95131-2039
Tel (408) 855-9616 *Founded/Ownrshp* 1996
Sales 23.8MM^E *EMP* 150
SIC 7379 7371 Computer related consulting services; Computer software development; Computer related consulting services; Computer software development
CEO: Maneesha Chandra
**Pr:* Nitin Chandra

D-U-N-S 12-600-0301 IMP
▲ INFOBLOX INC
3111 Coronado Dr, Santa Clara, CA 95054-3206
Tel (408) 986-4000 *Founded/Ownrshp* 1999
Sales 306.1MM *EMP* 772
Accts Ernst & Young Llp San Jose C
Tkr Sym BLOX *Exch* NYS
SIC 7374 7371 7379 Computer peripheral equipment; Computer related consulting services; Data processing & preparation; Data processing service; Custom computer programming services; Computer software development & applications; Software programming applications; Computer related consulting services
Pr: Jesper Andersen
**Ch Bd:* Michael L Goguen
CFO: Remo E Canessa
Chf Mktg O: Ashish Gupta
Ex VP: Thorsten Freitag
Ex VP: Scott J Fulton
Ex VP: Atul Garg
Ex VP: David N Gee
VP: Ricardo Moreno
Mng Dir: Aaron Pollet
CIO: Benny Kirsh
Board of Directors: Richard E Belluzzo, Laura C Conigliaro, Philip Fasano, Fred M Gerson, Daniel J Phelps

D-U-N-S 11-813-5995
INFOCISION MANAGEMENT CORP
325 Springside Dr, Akron, OH 44333-4504
Tel (330) 668-1400 *Founded/Ownrshp* 1982
Sales 292.5MM^E *EMP* 2,783
SIC 7389 Telemarketing services; Telemarketing services
CEO: Craig Taylor
Ch Bd: Gary Taylor
Pr: Steve Boyazis
CFO: Dave Hamrick
Ofcr: Michael Van Scyoc
Sr VP: Steve Brubaker
Sr VP: Steven R Brubaker
Sr VP: Ken Dawson
Sr VP: Mike Langenfeld
VP: Michael Cook
VP: Curt Cramblett
VP: Michael Shonk

D-U-N-S 07-481-3809
INFOCOM INTERNATIONAL CORP
11242 Waples Mill Rd # 200, Fairfax, VA 22030-6079
Tel (703) 273-7200 *Founded/Ownrshp* 1939
Sales 25.6MM^E *EMP* 130
SIC 8611 Trade associations
CEO: David Labuskes
**Pr:* Tony Warner
COO: Ai Damico
Bd of Dir: Matt Emerson
Sr VP: Jason McGraw
VP: Ann Brigida
VP: Patricia Caldwell
VP: Tom Stimson
VP: Melissa Taggart
VP: Tally Walsh
VP: Taly Walsh
Dir Soc: Bill Thomas

D-U-N-S 19-752-2659
INFOCROSSING INC
(*Suby of* WIPRO LIMITED)
2 Christie Hts, Leonia, NJ 07605-2233
Tel (201) 840-4700 *Founded/Ownrshp* 1999
Sales 138.0MM^E *EMP* 882
SIC 7374 Data processing service; Data processing service
CEO: Pinaki Kar
V Ch: Robert B Wallach
CFO: Robert Graham
CFO: Shiva Kumar
**CFO:* Yogesh Patel
Ex VP: Bridget Malone
Ex VP: Thomas Stortz
**Sr VP:* Nicholas J Letizia
Sr VP: Jim Turner
VP: Michael Bendit
VP: Mark Declemente
VP: Stephen Fangman
VP: Lisa Fauley
VP: Bob Gaus
VP: John Hammack
VP: Gary Lazarawicz
**VP:* Garry Lazarewicz
**VP:* Dan Martino
VP: Kent Micho
VP: Peter Piasentini
VP: Mitch Taks

D-U-N-S 16-151-1795 IMP
INFOCUS CORP
INFOCUS SYSTEMS
(*Suby of* IMAGE HOLDINGS CORP) ★
13190 Sw 68th Pkwy # 200, Portland, OR 97223-8368
Tel (503) 207-4700 *Founded/Ownrshp* 2009
Sales 24.0MM^E *EMP* 110
SIC 3861 3577 Projectors, still or motion picture, silent or sound; Graphic displays, except graphic terminals; Input/output equipment, computer; Projectors, still or motion picture, silent or sound; Graphic displays, except graphic terminals; Input/output equipment, computer
CEO: Mark Housley
Pr: Raymond Yu
COO: Joseph O'Sullivan
CFO: Lisa K Prentice
VP: Darron Bacal
VP: JB Daines
VP: Steve Stark
VP: David Woolf
Prin: Mark Reed
Ex Dir: Don Payne
Admn Mgr: Joanna Gebhart

INFOCUS SYSTEMS
See INFOCUS CORP

D-U-N-S 96-991-6535
INFOEXPERTS INC
300 N Coit Rd Ste 340, Richardson, TX 75080-5482
Tel (972) 671-1500 *Founded/Ownrshp* 1995
Sales 22.0MM *EMP* 46^E
SIC 7371 Computer software systems analysis & design, custom; Computer software systems analysis & design, custom
CEO: Nick Punyamurthy
VP: Kevin Nason
**VP:* Yiuling Punyamurthy
**VP:* M W Ricciardelli
IT Man: Syed Shah
Sls Dir: Charles Bright

D-U-N-S 79-164-7092 IMP
INFOGAIN CORP
485 Alberto Way Ste 100, Los Gatos, CA 95032-5476
Tel (408) 355-6000 *Founded/Ownrshp* 1990
Sales 96.8MM^E *EMP* 597
SIC 7379 7373 8742 8748 7374 1731 Computer related consulting services; Computer integrated systems design; Management information systems consultant; Systems engineering consultant, ex. computer or professional; Data processing & preparation; Electrical work; Computer related consulting services; Computer integrated systems design; Management information systems consultant; Systems engineering consultant, ex. computer or professional; Data processing & preparation; Electrical work
Pr: Kapil K Nanda
Pr: Brian Rogan
**CFO:* Phil Johnson
**CFO:* Dean Wohlwend
Sr VP: Mark De La Vega
VP: Laki Balaji
VP: Mark Collin
VP: Rakesh Goel
VP: Chris Meneze
VP: Manoj Mittal
VP: Hari Pendyla
Exec: Lokesh Joshi
Exec: Shraddha Sharma
Exec: Shashi Tekade
Dir Bus: Neha Kapoor

D-U-N-S 10-391-6201
INFOGIX INC
1240 E Diehl Rd Ste 400, Naperville, IL 60563-4802
Tel (630) 505-1800 *Founded/Ownrshp* 1982
Sales 40.8MM *EMP* 193
Accts Kathy Li
SIC 7372 8742 Business oriented computer software; Management consulting services; Business oriented computer software; Management consulting services
Pr: Sumit Nijhawan
**CEO:* Madhavan Nayar
Ex VP: Greg McTee
Exec: David Campbell
QA Dir: Eloise Butters
Sls&Mrk Ex: John Reams

D-U-N-S 06-865-1702 IMP
INFOGROUP INC
1020 E 1st St, Papillion, NE 68046-7611
Tel (402) 836-4500 *Founded/Ownrshp* 2010
Sales 577.4MM^E *EMP* 2,100
SIC 7331 Direct mail advertising services; Direct mail advertising services
Ch Bd: Michael Iaccarino
Pr: Larry Buchweitz
Pr: Mike Fisher
Pr: Robert Hylkema
Pr: Mark Litvinoff
Pr: Pankaj Mathur
Pr: Don Patrick
COO: Jim Scott
CFO: Stormy L Dean
**CFO:* Richard Hanks
**CFO:* John Hofman
Chf Mktg O: Slade Kobran
Sr VP: Vivian Ayuso
**Sr VP:* Prunda Das
Sr VP: Nicholas Dayan
**Sr VP:* Lisa Greene
Sr VP: Andrea Haldeman
Sr VP: Ann Kennedy
Sr VP: Cary Zackman
VP: Darren Amato
VP: Tom Claire
Board of Directors: Jim Sturm

D-U-N-S 07-752-5256
INFOHIGHWAY COMMUNICATIONS CORP
(*Suby of* BROADVIEW NETWORKS INC) ★
39 Broadway Fl 19, New York, NY 10006-3003
Tel (212) 404-5000 *Founded/Ownrshp* 2007
Sales 22.4MM^E *EMP* 138
SIC 4813 Local & long distance telephone communications; ; Local & long distance telephone communications;
Ch Bd: Joseph A Gregori
**Pr:* Peter Parrinello
**CEO:* Michael K Robinson
**COO:* Brian P Crotty
COO: Brian Crotty
**CFO:* Corey Rinker
Ex VP: Terrence Anderson
**Ex VP:* Charles C Hunter
VP: Guy H Lupi
**Prin:* Kenneth A Shulman
**VP Sls:* Peter Karoczki

D-U-N-S 11-818-7871
INFOIMAGE OF CALIFORNIA INC
141 Jefferson Dr, Menlo Park, CA 94025-1114
Tel (650) 473-6388 *Founded/Ownrshp* 1984
Sales 21.5MM^E *EMP* 85^E
SIC 2759 7331 7374 Laser printing; Mailing service; Data processing service
Pr: Howard Lee
**COO:* Rose Lee
**CFO:* Lilly Fong
CFO: Lenora Lee
VP: Mason Guy
VP: Guy Mason
Prgrm Mgr: David Trang
CTO: Kim Mawla
VP Opers: Mimi Lee
Opers Mgr: John Ludi
Mktg Mgr: Kelly Chan

D-U-N-S 05-379-2545
■ INFOLAB LLC (MS)
(*Suby of* PHYSICIAN SALES & SERVICE) ★
5950 Freeport Ave Ste 109, Memphis, TN 38141-8388
Tel (352) 237-9654 *Founded/Ownrshp* 1968, 2012
Sales 25.6MM^E *EMP* 233
SIC 5047 Medical & hospital equipment; Diagnostic equipment, medical; Medical laboratory equipment; Physician equipment & supplies
Pr: J Scott Spradling
VP: Lamar Buck
Off Mgr: Traci Scott
Dir IT: Shane Smith

D-U-N-S 82-504-0009
INFOMART INC
1582 Terrell Mill Rd Se, Marietta, GA 30067-6048
Tel (770) 984-2727 *Founded/Ownrshp* 1993
Sales 23.7MM^E *EMP* 130
SIC 7375 On-line data base information retrieval; On-line data base information retrieval
CEO: Tammy Cohen
COO: Adam Townsend
VP: Erica Clausen-Lee
Genl Mgr: Elizabeth Kressel
CTO: James Wilson
Natl Sales: Natalie McLain

D-U-N-S 02-211-4839
INFOMAX OFFICE SYSTEMS INC
1010 Illinois St, Des Moines, IA 50314-3090
Tel (515) 244-6002 *Founded/Ownrshp* 1958
Sales 27.4MM^E *EMP* 62
SIC 5044 7699 Office equipment; Photocopy machine repair
Pr: Stephen W Jacobs
**CFO:* Jim Reisener
VP Mktg: Steve Cox
VP Sls: Ed Schiller
Sls Mgr: Patrick Onken

D-U-N-S 14-490-4716
INFOMEDIA GROUP INC
CARENET
11845 W Interstate 10 # 400, San Antonio, TX 78230-1042
Tel (210) 595-2000 *Founded/Ownrshp* 2004
Sales 62.6MM^E *EMP* 750
SIC 7363 Medical help service; Medical help service
Pr: John W Erwin
**CFO:* Scott Schawe
**Ex VP:* Vikie Spulak
**Sr VP:* Rick Scheel
VP: Jane Binzak
**VP:* Frank Schilling
VP: Stacie Stoner
Prin: Gerald Perkins
Genl Mgr: Desiree Stanton
VP Mktg: Julie Ring

INFOMOTION
See DOBBS-STANFORD CORP

D-U-N-S 19-342-5923 IMP
INFONET SERVICES CORP
BT INFONET
(*Suby of* BRITISH TELECOMMUNICATIONS PUBLIC LIMITED COMPANY)
2160 E Grand Ave, El Segundo, CA 90245-5024
Tel (310) 335-2600 *Founded/Ownrshp* 2005
Sales 180.6MM^E *EMP* 1,085
SIC 4813 7373 7375 Data telephone communications; Computer integrated systems design; Information retrieval services; Data telephone communications; Computer integrated systems design; Information retrieval services
CEO: David Andrew
**Pr:* Jose A Collazo
**COO:* Pete Sweers
**CFO:* Akbar H Firdosy
Sr Cor Off: John Martinez
Bd of Dir: Peter Hanelt
Ofcr: Nigel Perks
Ex VP: John Boltes
**Ex VP:* John C Hoffman
**Ex VP:* Michael J Timmins
Ex VP: Michael Timmons
**Sr VP:* Paul Galleberg
Sr VP: Don Niven
VP: James Ashmore
VP: Jim Ayers
VP: Lee Bykerk
VP: John Hoffman
VP: Joseph Hold
VP: Roger Morrell
VP: Saran Snongjati
VP: Jocelyn Thompson

INFOPRINT
See RICOH PRODUCTION PRINT SOLUTIONS LLC

D-U-N-S 04-693-1940
INFOPRO CORP
103 Morgan Ln Ste 102, Plainsboro, NJ 08536-3300
Tel (609) 606-9010 *Founded/Ownrshp* 1994
Sales 28.1MM^E *EMP* 500
Accts Atul Malhotra & Co Llc Cpas

SIC 7373 7379 8742 Computer system selling services; Computer related consulting services; Management consulting services; Computer system selling services; Computer related consulting services; Management consulting services
Pr: Amit Gaur
CFO: Rakesh Shah
Ex VP: Karthik Natarajan
Ex VP: Arun Prakash
Ex VP: Sonia Wadhwa
Sftwr Eng: Atul Sharma

D-U-N-S 17-710-3918
INFOPRO CORP
6705 Odyssey Dr Nw, Huntsville, AL 35806-3301
Tel (256) 382-9700 *Founded/Ownrshp* 1986
Sales 59.8MM *EMP* 350
Accts Beason & Nalley Huntsville A
SIC 8711 7374 7373 7371 3489 Engineering services; Data processing & preparation; Computer integrated systems design; Custom computer programming services; Ordnance & accessories; Engineering services; Data processing & preparation; Computer integrated systems design; Custom computer programming services; Ordnance & accessories
CEO: Joann Longshore
**Pr:* William Billy Longshore
Treas: Bettye Longshore
**Sr VP:* Chris Jackson
**Sr VP:* William R Longshore Jr
VP: Shashikant Sinha
VP: Norm Stanley
**VP:* Roger J Young
Prgrm Mgr: Steve Tate

D-U-N-S 14-832-8607
INFOR (GA) INC
(*Suby of* INFOR (US) INC) ★
13560 Morris Rd Ste 4100, Alpharetta, GA 30004-8995
Tel (678) 319-8000 *Founded/Ownrshp* 2002
Sales 26.9MM^E *EMP* 180^E
SIC 7389 Brokers, business: buying & selling business enterprises
Pr: Ken Walters
COO: Mark Braman
CFO: Amy Shelley
**Ex VP:* Robin Pederson
Dir: Thad Roland
CIO: Kari Thron
Dir IT: Dennis Cook
Dir IT: Jeff Dyer
Dir IT: Alex Latimer
Dir IT: Tom Pfoertner
Dir IT: Bill Winner

D-U-N-S 11-146-6152
INFOR (US) INC
LILLY SOFTWARE ASSOCIATES
(*Suby of* INFOR INC) ★
13560 Morris Rd Ste 4100, Alpharetta, GA 30004-8995
Tel (678) 319-8000 *Founded/Ownrshp* 2002
Sales 1.5MMM^E *EMP* 3,980
SIC 7372 Prepackaged software; Prepackaged software
CEO: Charles Phillips
Ch Bd: Carl James Schaper
Pr: Duncan Angove
Pr: Stephan Scholl
COO: Pam Murphy
CFO: Kevin Samuelson
CFO: Maureen Thomas
Ex VP: Jim Byrnes
Ex VP: Soma Somasundaram
Sr VP: Chip Coyle
Sr VP: Thibault De Clisson
Sr VP: Gregory Giangiordano
Sr VP: Bruce Richardson
VP: David W Burton
VP: John C Levey

D-U-N-S 07-832-1398
INFOR GLOBAL SOLUTIONS INC
(*Suby of* INFOR (US) INC) ★
641 Ave Of Americas Fl 4, New York, NY 10011
Tel (646) 336-1700 *Founded/Ownrshp* 2002
Sales 35.9MM^E *EMP* 161^E
SIC 7372 Prepackaged software
CEO: James Schaper
VP: Bill Ellis
Snr Sftwr: Jayant Nayak
QA Dir: Harvey Canaan
IT Man: Pamela Driffield
IT Man: Sean Li
IT Man: Bernie McHugh
Software D: Madhuri Malepati
Sftwr Eng: Naresh Chanda
Sales Exec: Edith Bevers
Mktg Dir: Amanda Sanocki

D-U-N-S 07-847-2182
INFOR INC
(*Suby of* INFOR LUX BOND CO) ★
641 Ave Of The Americas # 4, New York, NY 10011-2038
Tel (646) 336-1700 *Founded/Ownrshp* 2009
Sales 2.7MMM^E *EMP* 12,790
SIC 7371 7372 8748 Custom computer programming services; Computer software development & applications; Business oriented computer software; Business consulting; Custom computer programming services; Computer software development & applications; Business oriented computer software; Business consulting
CEO: Charles Phillips
**Ch Bd:* Jim Schaper
Pr: Duncan Angove
Pr: Stephan Scholl
COO: Pam Murphy
CFO: Jeffrey Laborde
Sr VP: Jay Hopkins
Board of Directors: Prescott Ashe, Stewart Bloom, David Dominik, C J Fitzgerald

D-U-N-S 07-952-9385
INFOR LUX BOND CO
641 Ave Of The Americas, New York, NY 10011-2014
Tel (646) 336-1700 *Founded/Ownrshp* 2014
Sales 2.7MMM^E *EMP* 12,920^E
SIC 7371 7372 8748 Custom computer programming services; Business oriented computer software; Business consulting
CEO: Charles Phillips

D-U-N-S 14-314-7762
INFORELIANCE CORP
4050 Legato Rd Ste 700, Fairfax, VA 22033-2897
Tel (703) 246-9360 *Founded/Ownrshp* 2000
Sales 83.0MM^E *EMP* 330^E
SIC 7371 Computer software development; Computer software development
Pr: Andrew J Butler
**Ch Bd:* William T Williams
**Pr:* Andrew Butler
CFO: Chrissy Bristow
VP: John Sankovich
Exec: Matthew Toloczko
Creative D: Shab Nassirpour
Dir Bus: Aaron Faulkner
Prgrm Mgr: Joanne Morris
Prgrm Mgr: Kristie O'Shea
Prgrm Mgr: Joscph Paschall

D-U-N-S 06-738-6870
INFORMA FINANCIAL INFORMATION INC
(*Suby of* INFORMA SWITZERLAND LIMITED)
1 Research Dr Ste 400a, Westborough, MA 01581-3988
Tel (508) 616-5550 *Founded/Ownrshp* 1989
Sales 72.2MM^E *EMP* 388
SIC 2721 Periodicals: publishing only; Periodicals: publishing only
Pr: Kenneth B Bohlin
**Treas:* Kevin Donagher
**VP:* Thomas C Etter
**VP:* Marc Levine
CIO: Jonathan Earp
Sales Exec: Kevin Grist
Snr Mgr: Soontara Hayes

D-U-N-S 05-933-1277
INFORMA INVESTMENT SOLUTIONS INC
(*Suby of* INFORMA FINANCIAL INFORMATION INC) ★
4 Westchester Park Dr # 200, White Plains, NY 10604-3431
Tel (914) 640-0200 *Founded/Ownrshp* 1984
Sales 30.9MM^E *EMP* 121^E
SIC 7373 Systems software development services; Systems software development services
CEO: Leno Toich
Ch: Kenneth B Bohlin
Sr VP: Chris Volpe
VP: Ruth Calderon
VP: Maureen Farrell
VP: Michael Kagan
VP: Brandi Meeks
Mng Dir: Lac Anvuong
IT Man: Steven Isaacson
Software D: Yuri Bilas
Opers Mgr: Karen Johnson

D-U-N-S 06-570-7184
INFORMA RESEARCH SERVICES INC
(*Suby of* INFORMA FINANCIAL INFORMATION INC) ★
26565 Agoura Rd Ste 300, Calabasas, CA 91302-1942
Tel (818) 880-8877 *Founded/Ownrshp* 2000
Sales 41.2MM^E *EMP* 300
SIC 8742 Banking & finance consultant; Banking & finance consultant
Pr: Michael E Adler
**COO:* Charles A Miwa
COO: Charles Miwa
Sr VP: Brian Richards
**VP:* Lori Jomsky
Snr Sftwr: Shariq Akhtar
Dir IT: Brian McDonald
Dir IT: Abhay Sharma
Software D: Bharat Nallamothu

D-U-N-S 19-996-4883 IMP
INFORMA USA INC
(*Suby of* INFORMA GROUP PLC)
101 Arthur Andersen Pkwy, Sarasota, FL 34232-6323
Tel (508) 616-6600 *Founded/Ownrshp* 1987
Sales 153.1MM^E *EMP* 825
SIC 2731 8742 Pamphlets: publishing only, not printed on site; Business planning & organizing services; Pamphlets: publishing only, not printed on site; Business planning & organizing services
Pr: Kenneth B Bohlin
**Ch Bd:* Peter Rigby
**Treas:* Amthony Foye
**Prin:* Patricia Giardina
Mktg Mgr: Jessica Evers

D-U-N-S 82-532-0344
▲ INFORMATICA LLC
2100 Seaport Blvd, Redwood City, CA 94063-5596
Tel (650) 385-5000 *Founded/Ownrshp* 1993
Sales 1.0MMM *EMP* 3,234^E
Tkr Sym INFA *Exch* NGS
SIC 7372 Prepackaged software; Prepackaged software
CEO: Anil Chakravarthy
Pr: David Rye
CFO: Earl E Fry
Ofcr: Jo Stoner
Ex VP: Margaret Breya
Ex VP: Ivan Chong
Ex VP: Richard Hicks
Ex VP: Paul J Hoffman
Ex VP: Charles Race
Ex VP: Ansa Sekharan
Ex VP: Amit Walia
Sr VP: Graham C Burrows
Sr VP: Bart Foster
Sr VP: Jeff Moses
Sr VP: Barr Shriver
VP: Sean Oleary

D-U-N-S 06-524-5750
INFORMATICS APPLICATIONS GROUP INC
TIAG
11911 Freedom Dr Ste 1180, Reston, VA 20190-5649
Tel (703) 437-7878 *Founded/Ownrshp* 2002
Sales 32.9MM^E *EMP* 165
SIC 8742 7371 7373 Management consulting services; Computer software systems analysis & design, custom; Computer integrated systems design; Management consulting services; Computer software systems analysis & design, custom; Computer integrated systems design
Ch Bd: Dalita Harmon
**COO:* Jeff Goldberg
**CFO:* Kay Martin
Ofcr: Cynthia Roberts
**Ex VP:* Fred Goeringer
Dir Bus: Sara Byrd
Prgrm Mgr: Mary Ingeholm
Snr Ntwrk: Michael Tucciarone
IT Man: Gustavo Benitez
IT Man: Victor Jackson
Sls&Mrk Ex: Kent Toppert

D-U-N-S 60-164-0170 IMP
INFORMATICS HOLDINGS INC
(*Suby of* DATALOGIC SPA)
1400 10th St, Plano, TX 75074-8648
Tel (972) 516-1100 *Founded/Ownrshp* 2005
Sales 71.0MM^E *EMP* 113
SIC 5045 7389 Computer peripheral equipment; Computer software; Packaging & labeling services; Computer peripheral equipment; Computer software; Packaging & labeling services
Pr: Thomas O Shea
Opers Mgr: Matt Weir
Sls Dir: Paul Bowman
Mktg Mgr: Ginger Ebinger
Mktg Mgr: Jay Schofield
Sales Asso: Jonathan Farrell
Sales Asso: Aaron Graham
Sales Asso: Jared Parrish
Sales Asso: Anthony Rossini
Sales Asso: Siobhan Thompson

D-U-N-S 07-160-6404
INFORMATION & COMPUTING SERVICES INC (FL)
I C S
1650 Prudential Dr # 300, Jacksonville, FL 32207-8147
Tel (904) 399-8500 *Founded/Ownrshp* 1982
Sales 23.5MM^E *EMP* 102
SIC 7371 7379 7373 Computer software development; Custom computer programming services; Computer related consulting services; Systems integration services; Business oriented computer software
Ch Bd: Jorge F Morales
**Treas:* Michael Morales
**VP:* Aaron Ellinger
**VP:* Teresa Jackson
VP: Gina Kane
**VP:* Stephen Morgan
CTO: Matt Stueck
Dir IT: Ben Hancock
IT Man: Cheryl Rodgers
Software D: Fred Wehle
VP Opers: John P Carr

D-U-N-S 07-885-1615
INFORMATION BUILDERS INC (NY)
2 Penn Plz Fl 28, New York, NY 10121-2898
Tel (212) 736-4433 *Founded/Ownrshp* 1975
Sales 575.4MM^E *EMP* 1,500
SIC 7373 6794 Computer systems analysis & design; Patent buying, licensing, leasing; Computer systems analysis & design; Patent buying, licensing, leasing
Pr: Gerald D Cohen
Sr VP: Michael Corcoran
Sr VP: Harry J Lerner
Sr VP: Peter Mittelman
Sr VP: Sylvain Pavlowski
Sr VP: David Sandel
Sr VP: David Small
VP: Jos M Garc A-Soto
VP: Dennis Bartels
VP: Jon Deutsch
VP: Martin B Slagowitz
VP: Tom Villani
Exec: Laura Dennison
Comm Man: Kathleen Butler

D-U-N-S 09-215-6025
INFORMATION CONTROL CORP
CLUTCH INTERACTIVE
2500 Corporate Exchange D, Columbus, OH 43231-7601
Tel (614) 523-3070 *Founded/Ownrshp* 1992
Sales 86.1MM^E *EMP* 500
Accts Gbq Partners Llc Columbus Oh
SIC 7379 Computer related consulting services; Computer related consulting services
CEO: Steven Glaser
**Ch Bd:* Blane Walter
**Pr:* John Kratz
**VP:* Scot Burdette
VP: Chris Cooke
**VP:* Dave Dieterle
VP: Donald Jackson
VP: Rick Ritzler
**Prin:* Janet Arnette
**Prin:* Terry Slabaugh
Dir IT: Chris Anelick

D-U-N-S 04-366-9030
INFORMATION INNOVATORS INC
(*Suby of* TRIPLE-I HOLDINGS LLC) ★
7400 Fullerton Rd Ste 210, Springfield, VA 22153-2830
Tel (703) 635-7088 *Founded/Ownrshp* 2002
Sales 125.8MM^E *EMP* 574
SIC 7379 Computer related consulting services; Computer related consulting services
CEO: Steven C Ikirt
Pr: Brian Hall
Pr: Junji Takahashi
**Pr:* Franco Tao
COO: Edward Meagher
**CFO:* Denise Wilder
Sr VP: Daniel Matthews
VP: Rodney Caswell
**VP:* Mark Harrington
VP: Helayne Sweet
Dir Soc: Angela Jackson

D-U-N-S 80-750-5078
INFORMATION MANAGEMENT RESOURCES INC
IMRI
85 Argonaut Ste 200, Aliso Viejo, CA 92656-4105
Tel (949) 215-8889 *Founded/Ownrshp* 1992
Sales 23.2MM^E *EMP* 160^E
SIC 7373 8742 7371 Computer integrated systems design; Management consulting services; Computer software systems analysis & design, custom
CEO: Martha Daniel
VP: Mathurin Daniel
VP: Brenda Taylor
Ex Dir: Pete Furze

D-U-N-S 05-529-5026
■ INFORMATION NETWORK SYSTEMS INC
(*Suby of* SYTEX GROUP INC) ★
700 N Frederick Ave, Gaithersburg, MD 20879-3328
Tel (301) 240-7000 *Founded/Ownrshp* 2004
Sales 35.2MM^E *EMP* 1,000
SIC 7373 7363 Systems engineering, computer related; Help supply services; Systems engineering, computer related; Help supply services
Pr: June Shrewsbury
**Treas:* Kenneth Possenriede

D-U-N-S 16-950-1694
INFORMATION PROVIDERS INC
33 10th Ave S Ste 301, Hopkins, MN 55343-1309
Tel (952) 938-1400 *Founded/Ownrshp* 1996
Sales NA *EMP* 430
SIC 6411 Insurance agents, brokers & service; Insurance agents, brokers & service
Pr: Frederick Peters
Sls Mgr: John Horton
Snr Mgr: Kirk Brownfield

D-U-N-S 09-473-8267
INFORMATION RESOURCES INC
INFOSCAN
(*Suby of* NEW MOUNTAIN CAPITAL I LLC) ★
150 N Clinton St, Chicago, IL 60661-1402
Tel (312) 726-1221 *Founded/Ownrshp* 2011
Sales 498.8MM^E *EMP* 3,600
SIC 7372 Prepackaged software; Prepackaged software
Ch Bd: Rick Lenny
Pt: Ed See
**Pr:* Andrew Appel
**Pr:* Lawrence Benjamin
Pr: Craig Chapa
Pr: Doug Goodwin
**Pr:* Beverly A Grant
**Pr:* Nigel Howlett
Pr: John Lawlor
**Pr:* Bernhard Nann
Pr: Mark Parise
Pr: Thomas E Peterson
Pr: Robert I Tomei
**Pr:* Mark Tims
Pr: Derek Wiszniewski
COO: Jean Cooney
**CFO:* Mike Duffey
CFO: Mike Samuels
Div Pres: Rick Kurz
Div Pres: Marks S Parise
**Chf Mktg O:* Andrew A Salzman
Board of Directors: Jeffrey P Ansell, Matt Ebbel, Raj Gupta, Lawrence Jackson, Steven Klinsky, Mathew J Lori, Don W McGeorge

INFORMATION SERVICES
See ILLINOIS BUREAU OF COMMUNICATIONS AND COMPUTER SERVICES

D-U-N-S 79-880-9211
▲ INFORMATION SERVICES GROUP INC
281 Tresser Blvd Ste 901, Stamford, CT 06901-3246
Tel (203) 517-3100 *Founded/Ownrshp* 2006
Sales 209.6MM *EMP* 800^E
Tkr Sym III *Exch* NGM
SIC 8742 7379 Management consulting services; Computer related consulting services; Management consulting services; Computer related consulting services
Ch Bd: Michael P Connors
COO: Dru Graves
CFO: David E Berger
Ex VP: R James Cravens
VP: Randy Scheller
Board of Directors: Neil G Budnick, Gerald S Hobbs, Christine Putur, Donald C Waite III

D-U-N-S 01-386-0767
INFORMATION SYSTEMS AUDIT AND CONTROL ASSOCIATION
ISACA
3701 Algonquin Rd # 1010, Rolling Meadows, IL 60008-3124
Tel (847) 253-1545 *Founded/Ownrshp* 1969
Sales 50.1MM *EMP* 91
Accts Grant Thornton Llp Chicago I
SIC 8621 Professional membership organizations; Professional membership organizations
CEO: Susan Caldwell
Pr: Greg Grocholski
Pr: Ken Vander Wal
Treas: Peggy Arevalo
Bd of Dir: Anjay Agarwal
Bd of Dir: Gautam Amladi
Bd of Dir: Priten Bangdiwala
Bd of Dir: Dharmesh Joshi
Bd of Dir: Ravi Joy
Bd of Dir: S V Krishnan
Bd of Dir: Shashin Lotlikar
Bd of Dir: Homiyar Madan
Bd of Dir: Drupad Mahadevia
Bd of Dir: Ravikriran Mankikar
Bd of Dir: Arul Nambi
Bd of Dir: Onkar N Nath
Bd of Dir: Satish Nerkar
Bd of Dir: Haridas Raigaga
Bd of Dir: S A Sayana
Bd of Dir: Anand Shenoy
Bd of Dir: Gurudatt Shenoy
Board of Directors: Zubin Chagpar, Jo Stewart-Rattray

D-U-N-S 01-804-9692
INFORMATION SYSTEMS AUDIT AND CONTROL FOUNDATION INC
3701 Algonquin Rd # 1010, Rolling Meadows, IL 60008-3124
Tel (847) 253-1545 Founded/Ownrshp 1976
Sales 43.2MM EMP 40
SIC 8732 Educational research; Educational research
Ex Dir: Susan Caldwell
*COO: Ron Reba

D-U-N-S 10-792-8806
INFORMATION SYSTEMS LABORATORIES INC
10070 Barnes Canyon Rd, San Diego, CA 92121-2722
Tel (858) 535-9680 Founded/Ownrshp 1982
Sales 30.2MM^E EMP 120
SIC 8711 Engineering services; Engineering services
CEO: Richard G Miller
COO: William Gang
CFO: Peter Kuebler
Ofcr: Allan Brink
VP: Bill Arcieri
VP: David Honey
VP: Jim Larson
VP: James Meyer
VP: Jon Yim
Snr Sftwr: Terry Gitnick
Dir IT: Carlos Gomez

INFORMATION TECHNOLOGY EXPERTS
See CHEROKEE SERVICES GROUP LLC

D-U-N-S 08-956-3498
■ **INFORMATION TECHNOLOGY INC**
FISERV
(Suby of FISERV INC) ★
1345 Old Cheney Rd, Lincoln, NE 68512-1266
Tel (402) 423-2682 Founded/Ownrshp 1995
Sales 114.4MM^E EMP 1,200
SIC 5045 7373 7374 7371 Computer peripheral equipment; Systems software development services; Data processing & preparation; Custom computer programming services; Computer peripheral equipment; Systems software development services; Data processing & preparation; Custom computer programming services
Pr: Thomas M Cypher
Sr VP: Dave Carden
Sr VP: Jim McLoughlin
Prgrm Mgr: Jon Burmeister
Prgrm Mgr: Tezra Schmidt
Prgrm Mgr: Samual Venhaus

D-U-N-S 05-539-6717
INFORMATION TODAY INC
143 Old Marlton Pike, Medford, NJ 08055-8750
Tel (609) 654-6266 Founded/Ownrshp 1979
Sales 20.5MM^E EMP 124
SIC 2721 7389 Trade journals: publishing only, not printed on site; Convention & show services; Trade journals: publishing only, not printed on site; Convention & show services
Pr: Thomas H Hogan
*Ch Bd: Roger R Bilboul
COO: Mike Flaherty
VP: Richard Kaser
VP: John Yersak
Dir Soc: Linda Saxton
Dir Soc: Meghan Shaginaw
Dir Soc: Meghan Shott
IT Man: Bill Spence
Software D: Paul Johnston
Software D: Chris McCafferty

D-U-N-S 05-966-0238
INFORMATION TRANSPORT SOLUTIONS INC
335 Jeanette Barrett Indu, Wetumpka, AL 36092-5437
Tel (334) 567-1993 Founded/Ownrshp 1993
Sales 37.9MM EMP 90
Accts Jackson Thornton & Co Pc Mont
SIC 7373 Computer integrated systems design; Computer systems analysis & design; Systems integration services; Local area network (LAN) systems integrator; Computer integrated systems design; Computer systems analysis & design; Systems integration services; Local area network (LAN) systems integrator
Pr: Tomi J Selby
VP: Barry Carpenter
VP: Barry Franklin
VP: Mike Hall
*VP: Mike Selby
VP: Jeff Towry
VP: Justin Wasden
Dir Bus: Charlie Jackson
Snr Ntwrk: Robert Carroll
Snr Ntwrk: David Simmons
Netwrk Mgr: Zach Milstead

D-U-N-S 12-192-5390
INFORMATIX INC
2485 Natomas Park Dr # 430, Sacramento, CA 95833-2937
Tel (916) 830-1400 Founded/Ownrshp 1986
Sales 49.2MM^E EMP 170
Accts Quiroz & Company Llp San Fran
SIC 7379 7371 Computer related consulting services; Computer software development; Computer related consulting services; Computer software development
CEO: Raul Ocazionez
VP: Marge Chapman
Off Mgr: Erica Robbins
IT Man: Rafael Aguado
VP Opers: David Dean

D-U-N-S 82-604-6703
■ **INFORMEDRX INC**
(Suby of CATAMARAN CORP) ★
4805 E Thistle Landing Dr # 100, Phoenix, AZ 85044-6478
Tel (800) 282-3232 Founded/Ownrshp 2000
Sales 104.8MM^E EMP 495
SIC 8742 Management consulting services; Management consulting services
Prin: Mark Thierer

*VP: Jeffrey Park
*Prin: Gordon S Glenn

INFOSAFE
See TM INC

INFOSCAN
See INFORMATION RESOURCES INC

D-U-N-S 00-462-7316
INFOSCITEX CORP
(Suby of DCS CORP) ★
295 Foster St Ste 1, Littleton, MA 01460-2022
Tel (781) 419-6370 Founded/Ownrshp 2000, 2012
Sales 22.9MM^E EMP 150
SIC 8741 Business management
Pr: Stuart S Haber
VP: David Montella
VP: Leslie Rubin
VP Sls: Cheryl Beecher
Pgrm Dir: Mike Gilkey

D-U-N-S 19-525-5786 IMP
INFOSEAL LLC
1825 Blue Hills Cir Ne, Roanoke, VA 24012-8661
Tel (540) 981-1140 Founded/Ownrshp 2001
Sales 25.5MM^E EMP 100^E
SIC 2759 Commercial printing
Genl Mgr: David Yost
*Pt: Andy Harnett
Ofcr: Rick Bohn
Brnch Mgr: Brenda Jackson
Manager: Bob Hardig
Sls Mgr: Leo Lombardo

D-U-N-S 82-521-8902 IMP
▲ **INFOSONICS CORP**
3636 Nobel Dr Ste 325, San Diego, CA 92122-1078
Tel (858) 373-1600 Founded/Ownrshp 1994
Sales 48.1MM EMP 67^E
Tkr Sym IFON Exch NAS
SIC 3661 5065 Mobile telephone equipment; Telephones & telephone apparatus; Mobile telephone equipment
Pr: Joseph Ram
CFO: Vernon A Loforti
S&M/VP: Joe Murgo
Mktg Mgr: Natalie Fitzsimmons
Board of Directors: Randall P Marx, Robert S Picow, Kirk A Waldron

D-U-N-S 60-772-6994
INFOSPHERIX INC
(Suby of LANYON SOLUTIONS INC) ★
22530 Gtwy Ctr Dr Ste 200, Clarksburg, MD 20871-2022
Tel (301) 556-9400 Founded/Ownrshp 2007
Sales 18.8MM^E EMP 300
SIC 7311 Advertising agencies; Advertising agencies
Pr: Richard C Levin
*VP: Roger Downs
IT Man: Vipin Wagh
Opers Mgr: Kristine Vess

D-U-N-S 16-987-5858
INFOSYS LIMITED
(Suby of INFOSYS LIMITED)
6100 Tennyson Pkwy # 200, Plano, TX 75024-6104
Tel (469) 229-9400 Founded/Ownrshp 1995
Sales 49.1MM^E EMP 100^E
SIC 7371 7373 7379 7372 Custom computer programming services; Computer software development; Systems engineering, computer related; Computer related consulting services; Prepackaged software
CEO: S D Shibulal
Assoc VP: Rajeev Nayar
Assoc VP: Jason Richard
VP: Kishor Gummaraju
VP: Komal Jain
Sls Mgr: Sanjeev Bode
Snr PM: Prasanna Ramaswamy
Snr Mgr: Kevin Corr

D-U-N-S 18-485-0097
INFOSYS MCCAMISH SYSTEMS LLC
(Suby of INFOSYS LIMITED)
6425 Powers Ferry Rd, Atlanta, GA 30339-2908
Tel (770) 690-1500 Founded/Ownrshp 2011
Sales NA EMP 147
SIC 6399 7373 Warranty insurance, product; except automobile; Computer integrated systems design
Pr: J Gordon Beckham Jr
*CFO: Carol K Black
Sr VP: Mark Dephillips
VP: Samuel Sam
VP Admn: Lisa Johnson
Sftwr Eng: Mike Dyer
Sftwr Eng: Michael Lake
Pgrm Dir: Kim Wood

D-U-N-S 96-718-8702
INFOSYS PUBLIC SERVICES INC
(Suby of INFOSYS LIMITED)
800 King Farm Blvd # 505, Rockville, MD 20850-5979
Tel (301) 354-8600 Founded/Ownrshp 2009
Sales 98.4MM^E EMP 2,000
SIC 7371 7374 8742 Custom computer programming services; Computer software systems analysis & design, custom; Computer software development & applications; Optical scanning data service; Management engineering; Custom computer programming services; Computer software systems analysis & design, custom; Computer software development & applications; Optical scanning data service; Management engineering
CEO: Eric Paternoster
*Ch Bd: Jefferey Lehman
*VP: Jim Havelka

D-U-N-S 62-615-3006
■ **INFOTECH AEROSPACE SERVICES INC**
(Suby of UNITED TECHNOLOGIES CORP) ★
699 Ave Industrial, Isabela, PR 00662-3581
Tel (787) 609-4000 Founded/Ownrshp 2003
Sales 41.9MM^E EMP 600^E
Accts Kevane Grant Thornton Llp San

SIC 8711 8741 Engineering services; Management services
Pr: Rita A Peralta
Genl Mgr: Hector Rodriguez
Genl Mgr: Jeffery Tracey
IT Man: Americo Campos

D-U-N-S 01-470-2695
INFOTECH GLOBAL INC
371 Hoes Ln Ste 300a, Piscataway, NJ 08854-4143
Tel (732) 271-0600 Founded/Ownrshp 1995
Sales 22.4MM^E EMP 70^E
Accts Gaines Goldenfarb & Luongo L
SIC 7379 7371 Computer related consulting services; Computer software development & applications
CEO: Arthur Kapoor
Ex VP: Sunil Sachdev
*CIO: Sita Mehta Kapoor
Sales Exec: Nitin Verma
Mktg Dir: Reynold Wolfarth

D-U-N-S 14-883-0594
INFOTELECOM HOLDINGS LLC
BROADVOX
75 Erieview Plz Fl 4, Cleveland, OH 44114-1839
Tel (216) 373-4811 Founded/Ownrshp 2001
Sales 184.9MM^E EMP 400
SIC 4813 7373 ; ; Computer system selling services; ; ; Computer system selling services
IT Man: Thomas Jordon

D-U-N-S 17-473-3084
INFOTELECOM LLC
(Suby of BROADVOX) ★
75 Erieview Plz Fl 4, Cleveland, OH 44114-1839
Tel (216) 373-4600 Founded/Ownrshp 2005
Sales 12.0MM^E EMP 397^E
SIC 7389 Telephone services
COO: Eugene Blumin

D-U-N-S 79-889-7153 IMP
INFOTRIEVE INC
(Suby of C C C) ★
20 Westport Rd, Wilton, CT 06897-4549
Tel (203) 423-2130 Founded/Ownrshp 2014
Sales 23.9MM^E EMP 165
SIC 7375 Data base information retrieval; Data base information retrieval
Pr: Kenneth J Benvenuto
Sr VP: Richard H Weaver
VP: Mike Violano
Ex Dir: Mary Ging
*CTO: Fred Pandolfi
Dir IT: Arun Daniel
Mktg Dir: Robert Mata
Sls Mgr: Ulisse Gallo

D-U-N-S 95-691-1044
INFOUSA MARKETING INC
GOVERNMENT AND LIBRARY SECTOR
(Suby of INFOGROUP INC) ★
1020 E 1st St, Papillion, NE 68046-7611
Tel (402) 593-4500 Founded/Ownrshp 1996
Sales 36.7MM^E EMP 692
SIC 7331 Direct mail advertising services; Direct mail advertising services
VP: Fred Vakili
CFO: Alan Heckart
CFO: Steven Purcell
*Treas: Stormy Dean
Sr Cor Off: D Thayer
Bd of Dir: Loren Heckathorne
Ex VP: William Chasse
Ex VP: Todd Lowdon
Ex VP: Bob Toth
Sr VP: John Copenhaver
Sr VP: Susie Robinson
VP: Andrey Kolesnik
VP: Jayesh Patel
VP: Scott Roberts
VP: Kevin Shaughnessy
VP: Jim Winner
Exec: Don Hamlett
Exec: Pankaj Mathur
Comm Dir: Mercy Ruiz-Lugo

D-U-N-S 95-812-0552
INFOVISION INC
800 E Campbell Rd Ste 388, Richardson, TX 75081-1841
Tel (972) 234-0058 Founded/Ownrshp 1995
Sales 95.5MM^E EMP 600
Accts Perkins Dexter Sinopoli & Ha
SIC 8711 7371 Consulting engineer; Computer software systems analysis & design, custom; Consulting engineer; Computer software systems analysis & design, custom
Pr: Sean Yalamanchi
Mng Pt: Lisa Annis
*VP: Raman Kovelamudi
Admn Mgr: Jacie Hunt
Admn Mgr: Lina Lim
Off Mgr: Katie Uebele
Board of Directors: Sean Yalamanchi

INFOWORLD PUBLISHING COMPANY
See IDG COMMUNICATIONS INC

D-U-N-S 96-455-3812
INFOZEN LLC
6700 Rockledge Dr Ste 300, Bethesda, MD 20817-7834
Tel (301) 605-8000 Founded/Ownrshp 1995
Sales 52.1MM EMP 300
SIC 7371 Custom computer programming services; Custom computer programming services
CEO: Raj Ananthanpillai
Pr: William Lay
CFO: Donald Acker
*CFO: Dwight L Carmichael
Ofcr: Judy Clark
*Sr VP: Manuel Miranda
*Sr VP: Greg Mundell
Sr VP: Steve Penyak
Sr VP: Mike Stull
VP: Glenn Gargan
VP: Chet Hayes
VP: Aaron Kilinski
VP: Ron Knoblock

VP: Ronald Knoblock
Dir Bus: Diana Wilkins
Board of Directors: Michael Chertoff, Tom Davis, Norman A Willox Jr

D-U-N-S 06-783-6641
■ **INFRA SOURCE INC**
(Suby of QUANTA SERVICES INC) ★
4033 Morgan Rd, Ypsilanti, MI 48197-9637
Tel (734) 434-2000 Founded/Ownrshp 2012
Sales 638.1MM^E EMP 2,000
SIC 1521 General remodeling, single-family houses
Prin: Jack Webb

D-U-N-S 15-190-9637 EXP
■ **INFRA-METALS CO**
(Suby of RELIANCE STEEL & ALUMINUM CO) ★
580 Middletown Blvd D100, Langhorne, PA 19047-1877
Tel (215) 741-1000 Founded/Ownrshp 2006
Sales 387.8MM^E EMP 514
SIC 5051 Steel; Steel
CEO: Gregg J Mollins
Pr: Michael Dean
Pr: Mark Haight
CFO: Herb Dubrow
CFO: Christopher Moreton
Treas: Robert J Joubran
Prin: Tom Gores
IT Man: Nick Lazaridis
IT Man: Stoner William
Opers Mgr: Don Everett
Opers Mgr: Darrell Tidwell

D-U-N-S 78-202-5688
INFRAGISTICS INC
2 Commerce Dr, Cranbury, NJ 08512-3501
Tel (609) 448-2000 Founded/Ownrshp 1989
Sales 35.0MM EMP 300
SIC 5045 Computer software
Pr: Dean Guida
*COO: Christopher Larsen
*CFO: Chris Rogers
*VP: Jason Beres
VP: Connie Chen
*VP: Don Preuninger
VP: Richard Rivera
*VP: Frank Sacco
VP: Jack Schwinn

INFRARED TECHNOLOGIES DIVISION
See DRS NETWORK & IMAGING SYSTEMS LLC

INFRARED TRAINING CENTER
See FLIR SYSTEMS INC

D-U-N-S 12-406-5421
INFRAREDX INC
34 3rd Ave, Burlington, MA 01803-4414
Tel (781) 221-0053 Founded/Ownrshp 1998
Sales 29.2MM^E EMP 80
SIC 3841 Diagnostic apparatus, medical
CEO: Donald Southard
*Ch Bd: James E Muller M D
*Pr: Steve Nakashige
COO: Carolyn Rogers
*CFO: Michael Guarasci
VP: Steve Chartier
VP: Jim Dillon
*VP: Jeffrey Mazur
*VP: Bob Silva
*VP: Mark Wilder
Genl Mgr: Jennifer Cote

D-U-N-S 07-966-5657
INFRAREIT INC (MD)
1807 Ross Ave Fl 4, Dallas, TX 75201-8002
Tel (214) 855-6700 Founded/Ownrshp 2001
Sales 134.4MM EMP 4
SIC 6798 Real estate investment trusts
Ch Bd: W Kirk Baker
Pr: David Campbell
CFO: Brant Meleski
Sr VP: Benjamin D Nelson

D-U-N-S 04-072-3970
INFRASAFE HOLDING INC
ADVANTOR SYSTEMS
12612 Challenger Pkwy, Orlando, FL 32826-2759
Tel (407) 859-3350 Founded/Ownrshp 2003
Sales 21.1MM^E EMP 60
SIC 7382 7371 Security systems services; Custom computer programming services
Pr: Todd H Flemming
*COO: Richard N Clifton
*Sr VP: Jeffrey J Whirley
*VP: Grant Herring
*VP: Mike Ollivier
IT Man: Todd Holmes
IT Man: Bill Orr
Mktg Dir: Curtis Hrncirik

D-U-N-S 11-608-8837
■ **INFRASOURCE CONSTRUCTION LLC**
QS MATS
(Suby of QUANTA SERVICES INC) ★
4957 Carpenter Rd, Ypsilanti, MI 48197-9609
Tel (734) 434-2000 Founded/Ownrshp 2002
Sales 63.8MM^E EMP 200
SIC 1611 Concrete construction: roads, highways, sidewalks, etc.; Concrete construction: roads, highways, sidewalks, etc.

D-U-N-S 04-908-0799
■ **INFRASOURCE DACON LLC**
(Suby of QUANTA SERVICES INC) ★
1300 Underwood Rd, Deer Park, TX 77536
Tel (281) 479-7409 Founded/Ownrshp 2000
Sales 47.8MM^E EMP 150
SIC 1731 Electrical work; Electrical work
Prin: Henry Jackson
VP: Scott Porter

D-U-N-S 02-995-0339
■ **INFRASOURCE LLC**
INFRASOURCE UNDGRD SVCS LLC
(Suby of QUANTA SERVICES INC) ★
2936 S 166th St, New Berlin, WI 53151-3506
Tel (713) 629-7600 Founded/Ownrshp 2000

Sales 797.7MM^E *EMP* 2,500
SIC 1623 1542 Water, sewer & utility lines; Nonresidential construction

INFRASOURCE SERVICES, INC.
See QUANTA FIBER NETWORKS INC

D-U-N-S 00-981-1274
■ INFRASOURCE UNDERGROUND CONSTRUCTION INC
(*Suby of* INFRASOURCE CONSTRUCTION LLC) ★
2936 S 166th St, New Berlin, WI 53151-3506
Tel (262) 782-6160 *Founded/Ownrshp* 1945, 2004
Sales 22.8MM^E *EMP* 100
SIC 1623 5172 Water, sewer & utility lines; Petroleum products
Genl Mgr: Doug Anderson
**CFO:* Robert Cleveland
**VP:* Pete Fojtik
Opers Mgr: Robert Gahr

INFRASOURCE UNDGRD SVCS LLC
See INFRASOURCE LLC

D-U-N-S 96-978-1165
INFRASTRUCTURE AND ENERGY ALTERNATIVES LLC
I E A
2 Westbrook Corporate Ctr, Westchester, IL 60154-5702
Tel (708) 397-4200 *Founded/Ownrshp* 2011
Sales 280.9MM^E *EMP* 882
SIC 8731 1731 Energy research; Energy management controls; Energy research; Energy management controls
CEO: Paul M Daily
CFO: Creighton Early
VP: Chris Novotney
Mktg Dir: Alyson Hanson

D-U-N-S 07-440-0599
INFRASTRUCTURE AND INDUSTRIAL CONSTRUCTORSSOUTHEAST INC
2809 Crusader Cir, Virginia Beach, VA 23453-3133
Tel (757) 468-1500 *Founded/Ownrshp* 1982
Sales 21.2MM^E *EMP* 60
SIC 1629 1622 Marine construction; Pier construction; Dock construction; Bridge construction
Pr: J Randolph Sutton
**Sr VP:* G Ken Sutton
**VP:* John Greene

D-U-N-S 01-070-4695
INFRASTRUCTURE CORP OF AMERICA
I C A
(*Suby of* HDR INC) ★
750 Old Hickory Blvd # 200, Brentwood, TN 37027-4567
Tel (615) 377-4730 *Founded/Ownrshp* 2015
Sales 33.3MM^E *EMP* 700
SIC 8742 8711 8741 Management consulting services; Management consulting services; Engineering services; Financial management for business
Pr: Howard Eley
COO: Mark Acuff
Ex VP: David Rader
VP: Brad Winstead
Rgnl Mgr: Shane Parker
Off Mgr: Melondy Crain
IT Man: Stan King
Mktg Dir: Mike Shinn

D-U-N-S 83-165-3063
INFRASTRUCTURE HOLDINGS CO LLC
(*Suby of* J H WHITNEY & CO) ★
115 S 48th St, Tempe, AZ 85281-2312
Tel (480) 784-2910 *Founded/Ownrshp* 2008
Sales 164.1MM *EMP* 850^E
Accts Mcgladrey & Pullen Llp Phoen
SIC 1611 1794 2591 General contractor, highway & street construction; Concrete construction: roads, highways, sidewalks, etc.; Excavation & grading, building construction; Blinds vertical; General contractor, highway & street construction; Concrete construction: roads, highways, sidewalks, etc.; Excavation & grading, building construction; Blinds vertical
CFO: David James

D-U-N-S 07-013-2329
INFRASTRUCTURE SERVICES INC
(*Suby of* ISI ACQUISITION CORP) ★
5215 Fidelity St, Houston, TX 77029-3566
Tel (281) 233-8000 *Founded/Ownrshp* 1994
Sales 20.1MM^E *EMP* 264
SIC 1611 0782 8741 1771 Highway & street paving contractor; Guardrail construction, highways; Highway & street maintenance; Highway lawn & garden maintenance services; Construction management; Concrete pumping; Concrete repair; Grouting work; Highway & street paving contractor; Guardrail construction, highways; Highway & street maintenance; Highway lawn & garden maintenance services; Construction management; Concrete pumping; Concrete repair; Grouting work
Ch Bd: Timothy H Herbert
Dir IT: Kevin Allen

D-U-N-S 87-711-9214
INFRATECH CORP
2036 Baker Ct Nw, Kennesaw, GA 30144-6423
Tel (770) 792-8700 *Founded/Ownrshp* 1994
Sales 138.9MM^E *EMP* 300
SIC 1623 Electric power line construction; Electric power line construction
CEO: Christopher Prangley
**COO:* Derek Lee
**CFO:* James Dunn
**VP:* Jerry Wilson

D-U-N-S 00-607-7150 IMP
INFRATROL MANUFACTURING CORP
INNOVATIVE MODERN COATERS
2500 S 162nd St, New Berlin, WI 53151-2808
Tel (262) 797-8140 *Founded/Ownrshp* 1997
Sales 600.0MM *EMP* 43
SIC 3567 Industrial furnaces & ovens
Pr: Steve Onsager
Plnt Mgr: Dave Kuske
VP Sls: Mike Grande

D-U-N-S 07-873-3460 IMP/EXP
INFRICO USA CORP
(*Suby of* INFRICO SL)
7042 Nw 46th St, Miami, FL 33166-5606
Tel (305) 777-9599 *Founded/Ownrshp* 1986
Sales 28.1MM^E *EMP* 260
SIC 3585 Refrigeration & heating equipment; Refrigeration & heating equipment
Pr: Jose Torres-Tenllado

INFUND
See FIRST INSURANCE FUNDING CORP

D-U-N-S 13-611-4316
INFUSED SOLUTIONS LLC
22636 Davis Dr Ste 100, Sterling, VA 20164-4492
Tel (703) 349-0624 *Founded/Ownrshp* 2003
Sales 32.0MM *EMP* 800
SIC 7371 Computer software development; Computer software development
Pr: Marlon Johnson
**CFO:* Akber Masood
Prgrm Mgr: Belinda Lopez
Genl Mgr: Cat Wearp

D-U-N-S 11-817-7190
INFUSION DEVELOPMENT CORP
599 Broadway Fl 5, New York, NY 10012-3372
Tel (212) 732-6100 *Founded/Ownrshp* 1999
Sales 61.9MM^E *EMP* 300
SIC 7371 Computer software systems analysis & design, custom; Computer software systems analysis & design, custom
CEO: Gregory Brill
**Pr:* Alim Somani
**CFO:* Debra Johnson
VP: Kevin Dolnick
VP: Vimal Sethi
Creative D: Peter Rivera
Dir Bus: Marc Cerro
Off Mgr: Stephanie Garcia
Off Admin: April Catossela
IT Man: Tyler Davey
IT Man: Leung Jack

D-U-N-S 93-111-9895 IMP
INFUSION PARTNERS INC
TEXAS INFUSION PARTNERS
(*Suby of* DEACONESS ASSOCIATIONS INC) ★
4623 Wesley Ave Ste H, Cincinnati, OH 45212-2272
Tel (513) 396-6060 *Founded/Ownrshp* 1994
Sales 14.0MM^E *EMP* 330
SIC 8082 Home health care services; Home health care services
VP: Dana Soper
VP: Ray Di Saldo
CIO: Doug Lee
Opers Mgr: Darla Arnold
VP Mktg: Laura Burgheim
Pharmcst: John Dugan

D-U-N-S 13-806-3016
INFUSION SOFTWARE INC
INFUSIONSOFT
1260 S Spectrum Blvd, Chandler, AZ 85286-8415
Tel (480) 807-0644 *Founded/Ownrshp* 2007
Sales 178.7MM^E *EMP* 361^E
SIC 7379 7371 Computer related consulting services; Computer software development; Computer related consulting services; Computer software development
CEO: Clate Mask
**CFO:* Curtis Smith
**CFO:* Brent Stumme
Chf Mktg O: Greg Head
**Sr VP:* Hal Halladay
Sr VP: Elizabeth Pitt
**VP:* Marc Chesley
VP: Roy Kelly
VP: Dave Lee
**VP:* Scott Martineau
VP: Jo Anne Ravielli
VP: Adam Ross
**VP:* Kathy Sacks
**VP:* Aaron Stead
Creative D: Jason Plummer

D-U-N-S 07-247-7305
INFUSIONDEV CORP
599 Broadway Fl 5, New York, NY 10012-3372
Tel (212) 732-6100 *Founded/Ownrshp* 1997
Sales 18.5MM^E *EMP* 300^E
SIC 7371 Computer software systems analysis & design, custom; Computer software systems analysis & design, custom
Pr: Gregory Brill
**Ch Bd:* Deborah Johnson

INFUSIONSOFT
See INFUSION SOFTWARE INC

D-U-N-S 78-059-7980
▲ INFUSYSTEM HOLDINGS INC
31700 Research Park Dr, Madison Heights, MI 48071-4627
Tel (248) 291-1210 *Founded/Ownrshp* 2005
Sales 66.4MM *EMP* 213^E
Tkr Sym INFU *Exch* ASE
SIC 5047 Surgical equipment & supplies; Surgical equipment & supplies
Pr: Eric Steen
**Ch Bd:* Ryan Morris
COO: Janet Skonieczny
CFO: Jonathan P Foster
Ex VP: Michael McReynolds
Ex VP: Sean W Schembri
VP: John Haggerty
Mktg Mgr: Pamela Okopny

D-U-N-S 60-878-8782
■ INFUSYSTEM INC
(*Suby of* INFUSYSTEM HOLDINGS INC) ★
31700 Research Park Dr, Madison Heights, MI 48071-4627
Tel (248) 291-1210 *Founded/Ownrshp* 2007
Sales 28.3MM^E *EMP* 130
SIC 7352 Medical equipment rental; Medical equipment rental
CEO: Eric Steen
**CFO:* Jonathan Foster
VP: Richard Diiorio
VP: Don Hemperley
VP: Steve Marcus
**VP:* Jennnet Skonieczny
Rgnl Mgr: Brad Steadman
VP Opers: Keith Burmeister
Mktg Mgr: Jackie Simon
Sls Mgr: Steve Bash
Sls Mgr: Mary Fantigrossi

D-U-N-S 07-911-6451
ING (L) RENTA FUND WORLD
(*Suby of* ING INVESTMENT MANAGEMENT INC) ★
5780 Powers Ferry Rd, Atlanta, GA 30327-4390
Tel (770) 690-4600 *Founded/Ownrshp* 2013
Sales 133.2M^E *EMP* 654^E
SIC 6722 Management investment, open-end

D-U-N-S 87-775-1698
■ ING BANK FSB
ING DIRECT
(*Suby of* CAPITAL ONE FINANCIAL CORP) ★
802 Delaware Ave, Wilmington, DE 19801-1377
Tel (302) 658-2200 *Founded/Ownrshp* 2000
Sales NA *EMP* 749^E
SIC 6035 6211 Savings institutions, federally chartered; Security brokers & dealers; Savings institutions, federally chartered; Security brokers & dealers
CEO: Ralph Hamers
**COO:* Jim Kelly
**COO:* Roel Louwhoff
**CFO:* Pg Flynn
**CFO:* Patrick Flynn
Ex VP: Brian Myres
Dir IT: Lynda Baker
IT Man: Berak Thomas
Software D: Dennis Brennan
Opers Mgr: Frederick West
Advt Dir: Tim Tarr

ING DIRECT
See ING BANK FSB

D-U-N-S 83-967-4066 IMP
ING FINANCIAL HOLDINGS CORP
I N G
1325 Avenue Of The Americ, New York, NY 10019-6048
Tel (646) 424-6000 *Founded/Ownrshp* 1981
Sales NA *EMP* 526^E
SIC 6211 6221

D-U-N-S 00-225-2448
ING FINANCIAL MARKETS LLC
(*Suby of* ING GROEP N.V.)
1325 Ave Of The Amer 3, New York, NY 10019-6048
Tel (646) 424-6000 *Founded/Ownrshp* 2002
Sales 65.0MM^E *EMP* 300
SIC 6211 Security brokers & dealers
Pr: David Duffy
**COO:* John Cirrito

D-U-N-S 07-915-7824
ING FINANCIAL SERVICES LLC
I N G
(*Suby of* ING BANK N.V.)
1325 Avenue Of The Americ, New York, NY 10019-6048
Tel (646) 424-6000 *Founded/Ownrshp* 1993
Sales NA *EMP* 58^E
SIC 6141 Automobile & consumer finance companies; Installment sales finance, other than banks
CFO: John Egan
VP: Michael Fine
VP: Nick Fuchs
VP: Mark Holzweiss
VP: Yanbin Huang
VP: Gerard Mercado
Mng Dir: James Beach
Dir IT: Kelly Utley
Opers Mgr: Robert Cancellieri

D-U-N-S 78-708-5732
ING INVESTMENT MANAGEMENT ALTERNATIVE ASSETS LLC
230 Park Ave, New York, NY 10169-0005
Tel (212) 309-8200 *Founded/Ownrshp* 1999
Sales 23.2MM^E *EMP* 87^E
SIC 6722 Management investment, open-end
CEO: Jeffrey T Becker
CFO: Greg Tencza
**Ex VP:* Kevin McMahon
Sr VP: Michael Forstl
Sr VP: Richard C Kilbride
VP: Tom Applegate
VP: Elias Belessakos
VP: Michael Macdonald
Mng Dir: Mark Carrigan
IT Man: Jay Bennard
Counsel: Marie E Picard

D-U-N-S 02-007-0962
ING INVESTMENT MANAGEMENT INC
(*Suby of* ING GROEP N.V.)
230 Park Ave Rm 1532, New York, NY 10169-1532
Tel (212) 309-8200 *Founded/Ownrshp* 1997
Sales 136.3MM^E *EMP* 691^E
SIC 6211 Security brokers & dealers; Security brokers & dealers
Prin: Paul Gyra
Pr: Marti Adams
Pr: John Faron
COO: Alain Karaoglan
COO: Michael Kuchler
Ex VP: Bridget Healy
Ex VP: James Kase
Ex VP: Paul Mistretta
Ex VP: Ewout Steenbergen
Sr VP: Vincent Costa
VP: Gerard De Labry
VP: Karen Ramos
Exec: Kevin Silva
Dir Risk M: Prakash Shimpi
Comm Dir: Karen Burnsted

D-U-N-S 12-443-2134 IMP
ING USA HOLDING CORP
1 S Orange St, Wilmington, DE 19801-5006
Tel (302) 658-2200 *Founded/Ownrshp* 1999
Sales NA *EMP* 1,171
SIC 6035

D-U-N-S 00-698-5600
INGALLS & SNYDER LLC
1325 Avenue Of The Americ, New York, NY 10019-6066
Tel (212) 269-7800 *Founded/Ownrshp* 1924
Sales 29.3MM^E *EMP* 80
SIC 6211 Dealers, security; Dealers, security
CEO: Robert A Case
VP: Scott Selby
Mng Dir: H Boone
Mng Dir: Aphrodite Garrison
**Genl Couns:* J Richard Popp

D-U-N-S 14-835-6033
INGALLS HEALTH SYSTEM
INGALLS MEMORIAL HOSPITAL
1 Ingalls Dr, Harvey, IL 60426-3558
Tel (708) 333-2333 *Founded/Ownrshp* 1981
Sales 13.3MM *EMP* 2,963
Accts Crowe Horwath Llp Chicago Il
SIC 8062 General medical & surgical hospitals; General medical & surgical hospitals
Pr: Kurt E Johnson
**CFO:* Vincent Pryoor

D-U-N-S 96-679-7040
INGALLS HEALTH SYSTEM EMPLOYEE BENEFIT TRUST
1 Ingalls Dr, Harvey, IL 60426-3558
Tel (708) 333-2300 *Founded/Ownrshp* 2011
Sales 21.2MM *EMP* 2
SIC 6733 Trusts; Trusts
Prin: Amanda Campbell

INGALLS MEMORIAL HOSPITAL
See INGALLS HEALTH SYSTEM

D-U-N-S 06-744-4927
INGALLS MEMORIAL HOSPITAL
1 Ingalls Dr, Harvey, IL 60426-3558
Tel (708) 333-2300 *Founded/Ownrshp* 1922
Sales 292.0MM *EMP* 2,296
SIC 8062 General medical & surgical hospitals; General medical & surgical hospitals
Pr: Kurt Johnson
COO: Robert Czuba
**CFO:* Vince Pryor
CFO: Andy Stefo
Bd of Dir: Robert Harris
Bd of Dir: Richard King
VP: Michael Hicks
VP: David Hoddes
VP: Christine Rosner
VP Bus Dev: Scott Strausser
Exec: Aletha Ross
Dir Lab: Marilyn Nelson
Dir Rx: Martha Jelski

INGALLS PROFESSIONAL PHRM IV
See MEDCENTRIX INC

D-U-N-S 96-996-1882
INGALLS SHIPBUILDING INC
1000 Jerry St, Pascagoula, MS 39567
Tel (228) 935-1122 *Founded/Ownrshp* 2002
Sales 68.1MM^E *EMP* 153^E
SIC 3731 Shipbuilding & repairing
Pr: Brian Cuccias
Ofcr: Mark Hawthorne
**VP:* Kevin Amis
**VP:* Dave Belanger
**VP:* Tim Farrell
VP: Lori Harper
VP: Thomas Stiehle
Dir Bus: Christie Thomas
Prgrm Mgr: Kevin Jarvis
Prgrm Mgr: George Nungesser
IT Man: Kevin Falgout

D-U-N-S 06-446-9695
INGARDIA BROS PRODUCE INC
700 S Hathaway St, Santa Ana, CA 92705-4126
Tel (949) 645-1365 *Founded/Ownrshp* 1973
Sales 46.0MM^E *EMP* 190
SIC 5148 5146

INGEAR
See IN GEAR FASHIONS INC

D-U-N-S 05-025-4810
INGEN-HOUSZ LLC
(*Suby of* HOLDINGS (INGEN-HOUSZ) LLC)
113 S La Brea Ave, Los Angeles, CA 90036-2998
Tel (323) 936-9303 *Founded/Ownrshp* 2013
Sales 57.6MM^E *EMP* 455^E
SIC 6722 0762 1731 Management investment, open-end; Farm management services; Energy management controls

INGENCO
See INDUSTRIAL POWER GENERATING CO LLC

D-U-N-S 03-686-8011 IMP/EXP
INGENIA POLYMERS INC
(*Suby of* INGENIA POLYMERS CORP)
3200 Southwest Fwy # 1250, Houston, TX 77027-7568
Tel (281) 862-2111 *Founded/Ownrshp* 1993
Sales 34.6MM^E *EMP* 90^E
SIC 2821 Molding compounds, plastics; Molding compounds, plastics
Pr: John Lefas
**Pr:* Steve Galland
COO: Cheryl Wilson
**Ex VP:* Maria Lefas
**VP:* Marc Potemans
Opers Mgr: Bogdan Olejarz
Plnt Mgr: Nitin Tiwari
Manager: Belinda Waters

D-U-N-S 14-847-9173 IMP
INGENICO CORP (DELAWARE)
INGENICO NORTH AMERICA
(*Suby of* INGENICO PREPAID SERVICES FRANCE 28 32)
3025 Windward Plz Ste 600, Alpharetta, GA 30005-8734
Tel (678) 456-1200 *Founded/Ownrshp* 1983
Sales 98.1MM^E *EMP* 378
SIC 3577 Magnetic ink recognition devices; Magnetic ink recognition devices
CEO: Philip Lazar
**Pr:* Jelss Dowin
CFO: Michael Wasserfuhr
Ex VP: Patrice Durand
Ex VP: Michel Leger
Ex VP: Patrice Lemarre
Sr VP: Deborah Dixson
VP: Rhonda Boardman
VP: Alan Forgione
VP: Charles K Kovach
Mng Dir: Craig Doyle

D-U-N-S 12-139-1192 IMP
INGENICO INC
(*Suby of* INGENICO CORP (DELAWARE)) ★
3025 Windward Plz Ste 600, Alpharetta, GA 30005-8734
Tel (678) 456-1200 *Founded/Ownrshp* 1993
Sales 26.0MM^E *EMP* 200
SIC 3577 Magnetic ink recognition devices; Magnetic ink recognition devices
CEO: Barry Thomson
VP: Rhonda Boardman
VP: Alan Forgione

INGENICO NORTH AMERICA
See INGENICO CORP (DELAWARE)

D-U-N-S 61-325-6551 IMP/EXP
■ **INGENIOUS DESIGNS LLC**
IDL
(*Suby of* HSN INC) ★
2060 9th Ave, Ronkonkoma, NY 11779-6253
Tel (631) 254-3376 *Founded/Ownrshp* 2000
Sales 35.7MM^E *EMP* 110
SIC 2392 5199 3089 5099 Mops, floor & dust; Broom, mop & paint handles; Plastic containers, except foam; Containers: glass, metal or plastic
Ch Bd: Joy Mangano
**VP:* Ronni Fauci
VP: Christie Miranne

D-U-N-S 86-900-6668
INGENIUM CORP
8235 Penn Randall Pl # 207, Upper Marlboro, MD 20772-2639
Tel (301) 883-9800 *Founded/Ownrshp* 1990
Sales 28.0MM^E *EMP* 298
SIC 7379 Computer related maintenance services; Computer related maintenance services
CEO: Andre Lynch
COO: John Watkins Jr
**Ex VP:* Carolyn Lynch
VP: Watkins Bg
VP: Cheryl Devine
Exec: John O'Connor
Dir Bus: Anthony Byrd
Dir Bus: Gene Poole

D-U-N-S 12-820-4190
INGENIUM TECHNOLOGIES CORP
216 Mary Ct, Rockford, IL 61104
Tel (815) 399-8803 *Founded/Ownrshp* 2000
Sales 25.9MM^E *EMP* 130^E
SIC 8711 Consulting engineer; Consulting engineer
Pr: Duane Wingate
**CFO:* Jeffrey Schneider
**VP:* Richard Walsh
VP Opers: Ellie Taylor

INGENIX
See OPTUM GOVERNMENT SOLUTIONS INC

INGENUITY MEDIA GROUP
See MARTIN AGENCY INC

D-U-N-S 83-325-0017 IMP
INGENUS PHARMACEUTICALS LLC
4190 Millenia Blvd, Orlando, FL 32839-6408
Tel (407) 354-5365 *Founded/Ownrshp* 2009
Sales 22.7MM *EMP* 11
SIC 2834 Cough medicines
Ch: Raju Mantena
**Pr:* Andrew Gellman
**CFO:* Matthew Baumgartner

D-U-N-S 87-844-3324
INGERMAN CONSTRUCTION CO
5 Powell Ln, Collingswood, NJ 08108-1945
Tel (856) 662-1730 *Founded/Ownrshp* 1994
Sales 26.1MM *EMP* 17
Accts Isdaner & Company Llc Cpas
SIC 1522 Apartment building construction; Remodeling, multi-family dwellings; Apartment building construction; Remodeling, multi-family dwellings
Pr: M Brad Ingerman
**Pr:* Edward Coupe

D-U-N-S 10-391-6649 IMP
INGERSOLL CUTTING TOOL CO
(*Suby of* IMC GROUP USA HOLDINGS INC) ★
845 S Lyford Rd, Rockford, IL 61108-2749
Tel (815) 387-6600 *Founded/Ownrshp* 2000
Sales 74.4MM^E *EMP* 485
SIC 3545 Machine tool accessories; Machine tool accessories
Pr: Charles Elder
VP: Richard Sollich
Area Mgr: Doug Furnish
IT Man: Doug Lamb
IT Man: Brian McAuliffe
MIS Mgr: Sandie Blankenship

D-U-N-S 13-838-8652 IMP/EXP
INGERSOLL MACHINE TOOLS INC
(*Suby of* CAMOZZI SPA)
707 Fulton Ave, Rockford, IL 61103-4069
Tel (815) 987-6000 *Founded/Ownrshp* 2003
Sales 73.6MM *EMP* 331
Accts Mcgladrey Llp Rockford Ilino
SIC 3541 3545 Machine tools, metal cutting type; Machine tool accessories; Machine tools, metal cutting type; Machine tool accessories
Pr: Tino Oldani
CFO: Paul Ballweg
CFO: Larry Mocadlo
**VP:* James W Keeling
VP: Brian McIntyre
Snr Sftwr: Che Griswold
IT Man: Calvin Spruit
Sftwr Eng: Nicholas Dimick
Sftwr Eng: Kevin Fraser
Sftwr Eng: Murray Page

INGERSOLL-RAND
See THERMO KING DE PUERTO RICO INC

INGERSOLL-RAND
See ZEKS AIR DRIER CORP

D-U-N-S 00-136-8026 IMP/EXP
INGERSOLL-RAND CO (NJ)
(*Suby of* INGERSOLL-RAND PUBLIC LIMITED COMPANY)
800 Beaty St Ste B, Davidson, NC 28036-6924
Tel (704) 655-4000 *Founded/Ownrshp* 1871
Sales 5.7MMM^E *EMP* 35,560
SIC 3561 3429 3546 3563 3531 Pumps & pumping equipment; Furniture builders' & other household hardware; Keys, locks & related hardware; Power-driven handtools; Air & gas compressors including vacuum pumps; Winches; Pumps & pumping equipment; Furniture builders' & other household hardware; Keys, locks & related hardware; Power-driven handtools; Air & gas compressors including vacuum pumps; Winches
Ch Bd: Michael W Lamach
Pr: Michael D Radcliff
CFO: Susan K Carter
Sr VP: Marcia J Avedon
Sr VP: Paul Camuti
Sr VP: Robert L Katz
Sr VP: Gary Michel
Sr VP: Don H Rice
VP: Wb Gould
VP: Sean McBride
Dir Bus: Joshua Weidman
Board of Directors: Tony L White, Ann C Berzin, John Bruton, Jared L Cohon, Gary D Forsee, Edward E Hagenlocker, Constance Horner, Theodore E Martin, John P Surma, Richard J Swift

D-U-N-S 61-342-4191
INGERSOLL-RAND INTERNATIONAL HOLDING CORP
(*Suby of* INGERSOLL-RAND CO) ★
800 Beaty St, Davidson, NC 28036-9000
Tel (704) 655-4000 *Founded/Ownrshp* 1978
Sales 40.0MM^E *EMP* 300
SIC 3531 Construction machinery; Construction machinery
Ch Bd: Theodore Black
CFO: James V Gelly
**CFO:* Thomas F McBride
**Treas:* William J Armstrong
**Ex VP:* Thomas E Bennett
**Ex VP:* William G Mulligan
**Ex VP:* James E Perrella
Sr VP: Marcia J Avedon
Sr VP: James D Byglan
Sr VP: Steven B Hochhauser
VP: Ted Doheny
**VP:* Patricia Nachtigal

D-U-N-S 96-330-6712 IMP/EXP
INGERSOLL-RAND US TRANE HOLDINGS CORP
(*Suby of* INGERSOLL-RAND PUBLIC LIMITED COMPANY)
1 Centennial Ave Ste 101, Piscataway, NJ 08854-3921
Tel (732) 652-7100 *Founded/Ownrshp* 2008
Sales 5.4MMM^E *EMP* 29,000^E
SIC 3585 Refrigeration & heating equipment; Refrigeration & heating equipment
CEO: Michael W Lamach
**CFO:* Steven R Shawley
Snr Mgr: Kim Gerardi

D-U-N-S 01-791-7946 IMP
INGETEAM INC
(*Suby of* INGETEAM SA)
3550 W Canal St, Milwaukee, WI 53208-4152
Tel (414) 934-4100 *Founded/Ownrshp* 2008
Sales 40.2MM^E *EMP* 100
SIC 3569 Sprinkler systems, fire: automatic
CEO: Aitor Sotes
**Pr:* Mark Obradovich
Ex VP: Alberto Guerrero
VP: Felix Morales
VP: Rabah Rennane
IT Man: Bill Winker
Sls Mgr: Jered Diebold

D-U-N-S 60-367-8512
■ **INGEVITY SOUTH CAROLINA LLC**
(*Suby of* WESTROCK MWV LLC) ★
5255 Virginia Ave, North Charleston, SC 29406-3615
Tel (843) 740-2300 *Founded/Ownrshp* 2003
Sales 4.0MM^E *EMP* 700
SIC 2611 Kraft (sulfate) pulp; Pulp mills, chemical & semichemical processing
Exec: Awilda Quinones

D-U-N-S 04-098-0138
INGHAM & CO INC
INGHAM RETIREMENT GROUP
9155 S Dadeland Blvd # 1512, Miami, FL 33156-2740
Tel (305) 671-2200 *Founded/Ownrshp* 1981
Sales NA *EMP* 40
SIC 6371 Pension funds
Pr: Kenneth Ingham
**Treas:* Marc Eichberg
**Ex VP:* Linda M Ingham
**VP:* George Anderton
VP: Patrick Morrell
Mktg Dir: Jennifer Shelley
Snr Mgr: FCA Smith

D-U-N-S 07-840-3185
INGHAM INTERMEDIATE SCHOOL DISTRICT
2630 W Howell Rd, Mason, MI 48854-9392
Tel (517) 676-1051 *Founded/Ownrshp* 1930
Sales 20.9MM^E *EMP* 340
Accts Manner Costerisan & Ellis P
SIC 8211 Public junior high school; Public senior high school; Public special education school; Public vocational/technical school; Public junior high school; Public senior high school; Public special education school; Public vocational/technical school

D-U-N-S 80-123-5508
INGHAM REGIONAL MEDICAL CENTER
MCLAREN GREATER LANSING
(*Suby of* MCLAREN HEALTH CARE CORP) ★
401 W Greenlawn Ave, Lansing, MI 48910-0899
Tel (517) 975-7800 *Founded/Ownrshp* 1992
Sales 254.1MM *EMP* 2,500
SIC 8062 General medical & surgical hospitals; General medical & surgical hospitals
CEO: Philip Incarnati
Dir Vol: Donna Gardner
**Pr:* Dennis Litos
**CFO:* Dale Thompson
CFO: Robert Wright
Orthpdst: Kelly Coffey
Orthpdst: Floyd Goodman
Orthpdst: Erich Hornbach
Pathlgst: Neil C Caliman
Surgeon: Forrest Fredline
Surgeon: Shane Martin

INGHAM RETIREMENT GROUP
See INGHAM & CO INC

D-U-N-S 13-189-6532
INGLE & SON LANDSCAPING INC
INGLE SON LNDSCPING IRRIGATION
205 11th St Se, Conover, NC 28613-2171
Tel (828) 464-5306 *Founded/Ownrshp* 1978
Sales 27.2MM^E *EMP* 55
SIC 5083 0782 Irrigation equipment; Lawn services
Pr: John Wesley Ingle II

INGLE SON LNDSCPING IRRIGATION
See INGLE & SON LANDSCAPING INC

D-U-N-S 11-258-4180
INGLE-BARR INC
IBI
20 Plyleys Ln, Chillicothe, OH 45601-2005
Tel (740) 702-6117 *Founded/Ownrshp* 1982
Sales 36.9MM^E *EMP* 130
SIC 1541 1521 1542 Renovation, remodeling & repairs: industrial buildings; General remodeling, single-family houses; Commercial & office buildings, renovation & repair; Renovation, remodeling & repairs: industrial buildings; General remodeling, single-family houses; Commercial & office buildings, renovation & repair
Pr: Wilbur B Poole
**VP:* Jeffrey Poole
Snr PM: Mike Moss

D-U-N-S 02-441-8584 IMP/EXP
▲ **INGLES MARKETS INC** (NC)
2913 Us Highway 70, Black Mountain, NC 28711-9103
Tel (828) 669-2941 *Founded/Ownrshp* 1965
Sales 3.7MMM *EMP* 25,000
Accts Deloitte & Touche Llp Atlanta
Tkr Sym IMKTA *Exch* NGS
SIC 5411 5912 5541 2026 6512 Supermarkets, chain; Drug stores & proprietary stores; Filling stations, gasoline; Fluid milk; Shopping center, property operation only; Supermarkets, chain; Drug stores & proprietary stores; Filling stations, gasoline; Fluid milk; Shopping center, property operation only
Ch Bd: Robert P Ingle II
**Pr:* James W Lanning
**CFO:* Ronald B Freeman
VP: Joseph Ashley
VP: Steve Burnett
VP: Nathan Fisher
VP: Dale Grasso
VP: Cindy Mixon
VP: Todd Reidy
Exec: Jenny Cochran
Dir Rx: Ankit V Patel
Board of Directors: Fred D Ayers, L Keith Collins, Ernest E Ferguson, Laura Ingle Sharp, Brenda S Tudor

D-U-N-S 83-150-0280
INGLESIDE AT KING FARM
701 King Farm Blvd, Rockville, MD 20850-6165
Tel (240) 499-9015 *Founded/Ownrshp* 2009
Sales 18.4MM *EMP* 300
SIC 8051 8052 8059 Skilled nursing care facilities; Intermediate care facilities; Rest home, with health care; Skilled nursing care facilities; Intermediate care facilities; Rest home, with health care
Pr: Robert E Bell
**CEO:* Richard Woodard
**CFO:* Joseph Girardi
**Ex Dir:* Jonathan Garber

D-U-N-S 04-534-1302
INGLESIDE INDEPENDENT SCHOOL DISTRICT
2664 San Angelo Ave, Ingleside, TX 78362-5820
Tel (361) 776-7631 *Founded/Ownrshp* 1932
Sales 22.0MM *EMP* 325
Accts Gowland Strealy Morales & Co
SIC 8211 Public elementary & secondary schools; Public elementary & secondary schools
Brnch Mgr: Terri Fisher

D-U-N-S 16-856-5989 IMP
INGLETT & STUBBS INTERNATIONAL (US) LLC
(*Suby of* I & S ACQUISITION CORP) ★
5500 S Cobb Dr Se Ste 300, Atlanta, GA 30339-6704
Tel (404) 591-2100 *Founded/Ownrshp* 2008
Sales 32.5MM^E *EMP* 290
SIC 1731 1541 1542 Electrical work; Industrial buildings & warehouses; Nonresidential construction; Electrical work; Industrial buildings & warehouses; Nonresidential construction
Ch Bd: Jeffrey V Giglio
**Pr:* David Lytle
**CFO:* Christopher R Williams
Mktg Dir: Phillip Davidson

D-U-N-S 00-388-2313
INGLETT & STUBBS LLC
(*Suby of* I & S ACQUISITION CORP) ★
5200 Riverview Rd Se, Mableton, GA 30126-2953
Tel (404) 881-1199 *Founded/Ownrshp* 1953, 2001
Sales 135.0MM *EMP* 850
SIC 1731

D-U-N-S 13-360-0809
INGLEWOOD PARK CEMETERY
720 E Florence Ave, Inglewood, CA 90301-1482
Tel (310) 412-6500 *Founded/Ownrshp* 1982
Sales 26.2MM *EMP* 160^E
Accts White Nelson Diehl Evans Lp I
SIC 6553 Cemeteries, real estate operation; Cemeteries, real estate operation
Pr: Daniel Villa
**CFO:* Chris Winners
**VP:* Kevin Brown
VP: Jacqueline Gonzalez
**VP:* Cheryl Lewis
VP: Martin L Simms III
VP: Martin Simms
**VP:* David Wharmby
Sls Mgr: Ashley Madison

D-U-N-S 10-064-4343
INGLEWOOD UNIFIED SCHOOL DISTRICT
401 S Inglewood Ave, Inglewood, CA 90301-2599
Tel (310) 419-2500 *Founded/Ownrshp* 1953
Sales 82.5MM^E *EMP* 1,600
SIC 8211 Public elementary & secondary schools; High school, junior or senior; Public elementary & secondary schools; High school, junior or senior
Ofcr: Leslie Gaulden
**Prin:* Joyce Kennedy
**Prin:* Ofelia Lariviere
Ex Dir: Stephen McCray
Off Mgr: Christy Onwuemelie
Dir IT: John Wietting
Plnt Mgr: David Lindo
Teacher Pr: Sharrel Carter

D-U-N-S 96-753-5159
INGLIS FOUNDATION
2600 Belmont Ave, Philadelphia, PA 19131-2713
Tel (215) 878-5600 *Founded/Ownrshp* 1984
Sales 24.7MM *EMP* 10
Accts Cliftonlarsonallen Llp Plymou
SIC 8641 Civic social & fraternal associations; Civic social & fraternal associations
Pr: Gavin Kerr
**CFO:* Kevin S Kelly
**VP:* Lea Frontino
**VP:* Tracie B Giles
Exec: Cheryl Whitfield
Doctor: Sefi Knoble

D-U-N-S 96-350-7590
INGLIS HOUSE
2600 Belmont Ave, Philadelphia, PA 19131-2799
Tel (215) 878-5600 *Founded/Ownrshp* 2010
Sales 48.7MM *EMP* 2^E
Accts Cliftonlarsonallen Llp Plymou
SIC 6513 Apartment building operators; Apartment building operators
Prin: Sheena Rogers
CFO: Gerald Magid
VP: Lea Frontino
Ex Dir: Arthurette Stone
IT Man: Larry Jackowski

D-U-N-S 79-052-6755
INGO MONEY INC
623 Holcomb Bridge Rd, Roswell, GA 30076-1511
Tel (770) 640-0695 *Founded/Ownrshp* 2001
Sales NA *EMP* 99
Accts Mcnair Mclemore Middlebrooks
SIC 6099 7389 7291 Check cashing agencies; Financial services; Tax return preparation services
Ch Bd: Drew W Edwards
**Pr:* Luz Lopez Urrutia
**V Ch Bd:* Richard Chambers
Ofcr: Randy Simoneaux
**Ex VP:* Dickson Chu
**Ex VP:* George Hodges
Ex VP: Charles Potts
**VP:* Beth Fix
VP: Matt Hamilton
VP: Douglas Oram
Dir Risk M: Bill Roese

D-U-N-S 07-318-3642 IMP/EXP
INGOMAR PACKING CO LLC
9950 S Ingomar Grade, Los Banos, CA 93635
Tel (209) 826-9494 *Founded/Ownrshp* 1982
Sales 96.9MM^E *EMP* 251
SIC 2033 Tomato paste: packaged in cans, jars, etc.; Tomato paste: packaged in cans, jars, etc.
Pr: Gregory Pruett
COO: Larry Narbaitz
**VP:* William B Cahill Jr
QA Dir: Shawn Ketcher
VP Opers: Jim Murphy
Mktg Dir: Stephanie Harrigan
Sls Dir: Mark Stegeman
Sls Mgr: Dominic Taddeucci

D-U-N-S 13-104-4299
INGRAM BARGE CO
GREAT RIVER MARINE SERVICE DIV
(*Suby of* INGRAM INDUSTRIES INC) ★
4400 Harding Pike, Nashville, TN 37205-2204
Tel (615) 298-8200 *Founded/Ownrshp* 1984
Sales 145.8MM^E *EMP* 2,500
SIC 4449 River transportation, except on the St. Lawrence Seaway; River transportation, except on the St. Lawrence Seaway
CEO: Orrin H Ingram
Pr: Steve Porth

Pr: Kaj Shah
CFO: Crystal Taylor
Treas: Jeffrey K Belser
Chf Cred: Dan Martin
Bd of Dir: Chip Lacy
Ofcr: Dan Mecklenborg Sr
Ofcr: David G Sehrt
Ex VP: Mary Cavarra
Ex VP: Eleanor McDonald
Sr VP: Robert Barker
Sr VP: Daniel T Martin
Sr VP: Dave O'Loughlin
VP: Keith Aulson
VP: Shawn Faulkner
VP: Tom Vorholt
Exec: Jim Blackmon
Dir Risk M: Angela Angrick
Board of Directors: John R Ingram, Orrin Ingram, Eleanor McDonald

INGRAM BOOK COMPANY
See INGRAM BOOK GROUP INC

D-U-N-S 12-157-3724 IMP/EXP
INGRAM BOOK GROUP INC
INGRAM BOOK COMPANY
(*Suby of* INGRAM INDUSTRIES INC) ★
1 Ingram Blvd, La Vergne, TN 37086-3629
Tel (615) 213-5000 *Founded/Ownrshp* 1995
Sales 3.3MMM^E *EMP* 2,050
SIC 5192 Books, periodicals & newspapers; Books, periodicals & newspapers
CEO: John Ingram
**Pr:* Shawn Morin
**CFO:* Brian Dauphin
VP: Mel Carnahan
VP: Dennis Delaney
VP: David Elleman
VP: Marc Farrow
VP: Andrew Gatlin
VP: Cameron Griffith
VP: Eric Hawkins
VP: Brenda Owen
VP: Steve Pait
VP: Steve Pate
VP: David Shealy
VP: Daniel Sheehan
VP: Gerard Viveiros
VP: Marcus Woodburn
Dir Teleco: Phil Watson
Creative D: Terry Morrison

D-U-N-S 10-104-3875
INGRAM CURREY ACADEMY
6544 Murray Ln, Brentwood, TN 37027-5515
Tel (615) 507-3242 *Founded/Ownrshp* 1968
Sales 23.4MM *EMP* 125
Accts Frasier Dean & Howard Pllc Na
SIC 8211 Academy; Private special education school; Academy; Private special education school
Prin: Kathy Rayburn
Ofcr: Shannon Polk
Dir Rx: Felicia Weishaar
DP Exec: Kevin Gocha
Dir IT: Kevin Myers
HC Dir: Kathy Boles

D-U-N-S 05-231-2782 IMP
INGRAM ENTERPRISES INC
FIREWORKS OVER AMERICA
3010 Ingram Ave, Springfield, MO 65803-8805
Tel (417) 862-1931 *Founded/Ownrshp* 1968
Sales 37.6MM^E *EMP* 150
SIC 5092 Fireworks; Fireworks
Pr: Michael Ingram
**Treas:* Barbara Ingram

D-U-N-S 11-300-4696 IMP/EXP
INGRAM ENTERTAINMENT HOLDINGS INC
2 Ingram Blvd, La Vergne, TN 37089-2000
Tel (615) 287-4000 *Founded/Ownrshp* 1999
Sales 612.1MM^E *EMP* 1,000
SIC 5065 5045 Tapes, audio & video recording; Computers & accessories, personal & home entertainment; Tapes, audio & video recording; Computers & accessories, personal & home entertainment
CEO: Claire W Tucker
**Pr:* David B Ingram
**Treas:* Jeffrey D Skinner
**Treas:* Wade L Smith
**Sr VP:* W Donnie Daniel
Sr VP: Jeffrey Skinner
VP: Nancy Cowan

D-U-N-S 60-235-2676 IMP/EXP
INGRAM ENTERTAINMENT INC
(*Suby of* INGRAM ENTERTAINMENT HOLDINGS INC) ★
2 Ingram Blvd, La Vergne, TN 37089-2000
Tel (615) 287-4000 *Founded/Ownrshp* 1997
Sales 612.1MM^E *EMP* 460
SIC 5065 5092 5099 Diskettes, computer; Video games; Video & audio equipment; Diskettes, computer; Video games; Video & audio equipment
Pr: David B Ingram
V Ch: W Donnie Daniel
Pr: Robert W Webb
CFO: Donnie Daniel
Ex VP: Robert A Geistman
Sr VP: John J Fletcher
Sr VP: Bob Geistman
VP: Bill Boyle
Exec: James Ellis
Ex Dir: Philip Gaeser
Brnch Mgr: Jessie Wagley

D-U-N-S 00-894-3839 IMP/EXP
INGRAM INDUSTRIES INC (TN)
4400 Harding Pike Ste 310, Nashville, TN 37205-2314
Tel (615) 298-8200 *Founded/Ownrshp* 1962, 1978
Sales 3.7MMM^E *EMP* 5,015
SIC 5192 4449

D-U-N-S 16-830-9354
■ **INGRAM MICRO ASIA HOLDINGS INC**
(*Suby of* INGRAM MICRO INC) ★
3351 Michelson Dr Ste 100, Irvine, CA 92612-0697
Tel (714) 566-1000 *Founded/Ownrshp* 1999
Sales 84.9MM^E *EMP* 900
SIC 5045 Computer software; Computer software
Pr: Alain Monie
**CFO:* William Humes

D-U-N-S 00-491-9486 IMP/EXP
▲ **INGRAM MICRO INC** (IN)
3351 Michelson Dr Ste 100, Irvine, CA 92612-0697
Tel (714) 566-1000 *Founded/Ownrshp* 1979
Sales 46.4MMM *EMP* 21,700
Accts Pricewaterhousecoopers Llp Or
Tkr Sym IM *Exch* NYS
SIC 5045 Computers, peripherals & software; Computer peripheral equipment; Computers; Computer software; Computers, peripherals & software; Computer peripheral equipment; Computers; Computer software
CEO: Alain Monie
Pr: Eduardo Araujo
Pr: Paul Read
Pr: Felix Wong
COO: David Lorsch
COO: Alain Moni
COO: Kevin M Murai
COO: Fan Zhang
CFO: Vicki Bernstein
CFO: Diana Dimadi
CFO: Luca Farina
CFO: Craig Hewitt
CFO: William D Humes
CFO: Paul Lilley
CFO: Lisa Locklear
CFO: Heinz Ttich
CFO: Viki Van Bernstein
CFO: John Walsh
Treas: Erik Smolders
Bd of Dir: Jay Giron
Ex VP: Larry C Boyd
Board of Directors: Joe B Wyatt, Howard I Atkins, David A Barnes, Leslie S Heisz, John R Ingram, Dale R Laurence, Linda Fayne Levinson, Scott A McGregor, Carol G Mills, Wade Oosterman

INGRAM MICRO MOBILITY
See TOUCHSTONE WIRELESS REPAIR AND LOGISTICS LP

INGRAM PARK AUTO CENTER
See NISSAN BENSON INC

INGRAM PARK CHRYSLER
See CPC LEASING CO INC

D-U-N-S 60-269-7161 IMP
INGRAM PERIODICALS INC
(*Suby of* INGRAM INDUSTRIES INC) ★
1 Ingram Blvd, La Vergne, TN 37086-3629
Tel (615) 793-5000 *Founded/Ownrshp* 1986
Sales 46.0MM^E *EMP* 175^E
SIC 5192 Periodicals; Periodicals
Ch Bd: John R Ingram
**Pr:* Shawn R Everson
VP: Jeff Myrick
Exec: Jerilee Davis
Genl Mgr: Mark Ouimet

D-U-N-S 04-975-1670
INGRAM READYMIX INC
3580 Farm Market 482, New Braunfels, TX 78132
Tel (830) 625-9156 *Founded/Ownrshp* 1957
Sales 87.0MM^E *EMP* 480
SIC 3273

D-U-N-S 85-884-2958
INGREDIENT QUALITY CONSULTANTS INC
I Q C
7365 Merchant Ct Ste 2, Lakewood Ranch, FL 34240-8446
Tel (941) 907-0502 *Founded/Ownrshp* 1990
Sales 40.0MM *EMP* 4
SIC 6221 8748 Commodity brokers, contracts; Commodity traders, contracts; Agricultural consultant; Commodity brokers, contracts; Commodity traders, contracts; Agricultural consultant
Pr: Wayne Whittaker
**Sec:* Diane Whittaker

D-U-N-S 09-902-8615
INGREDIENT RESOURCE CORP
2401 Lower Hunters Trce, Louisville, KY 40216-1300
Tel (502) 448-4480 *Founded/Ownrshp* 1980
Sales 25.0MM *EMP* 5
SIC 5191 Feed; Feed
Pr: James Ford
**VP:* Steve Ford

D-U-N-S 09-932-4506 IMP
INGREDIENTRADE.COM INC
333 W 52nd St Ste 305, New York, NY 10019-6238
Tel (212) 586-1880 *Founded/Ownrshp* 2000
Sales 38.8MM^E *EMP* 200
SIC 5149 2037 Specialty food items; Frozen fruits & vegetables; Specialty food items; Frozen fruits & vegetables
Ch Bd: Phillip D Greenberg
**CFO:* Robert Patrizio
Genl Mgr: Le Thi Hong Thai

D-U-N-S 80-115-3628 IMP
INGREDIENTS SOLUTIONS INC
ISI
631 Moosehead Trl, Waldo, ME 04915-3402
Tel (207) 722-4172 *Founded/Ownrshp* 1992
Sales 50.0MM *EMP* 11
SIC 5149 Seasonings, sauces & extracts; Seasonings, sauces & extracts
CEO: Scott Rangus
**CFO:* Janine Mehuren
Opers Mgr: Patti Hays
Snr Mgr: Donna Ravin

D-U-N-S 00-481-1423 EXP
▲ **INGREDION INC**
5 Westbrook Corporate Ctr, Westchester, IL 60154-5749
Tel (708) 551-2600 *Founded/Ownrshp* 1906
Sales 5.6MMM *EMP* 11,400
Accts Kpmg Llp Chicago Illinois
Tkr Sym INGR *Exch* NYS
SIC 2046 Wet corn milling; Corn starch; Corn oil products; Corn sugars & syrups; Wet corn milling; Corn starch; Corn oil products; Corn sugars & syrups
Ch Bd: Ilene S Gordon
CFO: Jack C Fortnum
Chf Cred: Christine M Castellano
Sr VP: Anthony P Delio
VP: Neal R Christian
VP: Matthew R Galvanoni
VP: Richard O'Shanna
Exec: Dinah Diaz
Comm Dir: Claire Regan
Dir Rx: Paul Bratley
Prin: Linda Skrabutenas
Board of Directors: David B Fischer, Paul Hanrahan, Wayne M Hewett, Gregory B Kenny, Barbara A Klein, Victoria J Reich, Luis Aranguren-Trellez, Dwayne A Wilson

D-U-N-S 08-286-0842
INGUARD INC
231 W Canal St, Wabash, IN 46992-3218
Tel (866) 563-8821 *Founded/Ownrshp* 1968
Sales NA *EMP* 26
SIC 6411 Insurance agents, brokers & service; Insurance agents, brokers & service
CEO: Parker Beauchamp

D-U-N-S 18-151-5607 IMP
INGURAN LLC
SEXING TECHNOLOGIES
22575 State Highway 6 S, Navasota, TX 77868-8297
Tel (936) 870-3960 *Founded/Ownrshp* 2002
Sales 43.6MM^E *EMP* 300
Accts Ernest And Young Houston Tx
SIC 0752 Animal specialty services; Animal specialty services
CEO: Juan Moreno
VP: Thom Gilligan
Assoc Dir: Jared Templeton

INHALATION THERAPY CO DIV
See AGL WELDING SUPPLY CO INC

INHALATION TOXICOLOGY RES INST
See LOVELACE BIOMEDICAL & ENVIRONMENTAL RESEARCH INSTITUTE

INHEALTH RECORD SYSTEMS
See PROFESSIONAL FILING SYSTEMS INC

D-U-N-S 00-875-4892
INHOME CARE INC
808 W Indiana Ave, Midland, TX 79701-6610
Tel (432) 570-4475 *Founded/Ownrshp* 1989
Sales 4.4MM^E *EMP* 290
SIC 8082 Home health care services; Home health care services
Pr: Michael Waters

D-U-N-S 84-056-4723
INIT INNOVATIONS IN TRANSPORTATION INC
(*Suby of* INIT INNOVATION IN TRAFFIC SYSTEMS AG)
1420 Kristina Way Ste 101, Chesapeake, VA 23320-8927
Tel (757) 413-9100 *Founded/Ownrshp* 2001
Sales 60.2MM *EMP* 32^E
Accts Dixon Hughes Goodman Llp Vir
SIC 7371 Computer software systems analysis & design, custom; Computer software systems analysis & design, custom
Pr: Roland Staib
**Ch:* Gottfried Greschner
**VP:* David Dodson
**VP:* Linda Keith
Sftwr Eng: Ponnampal Rajakumar
Netwrk Eng: Christopher Davis
Netwrk Eng: Chris Neidig
Opers Mgr: Carl Craft
Sls Dir: Carl Commons
Mktg Mgr: Ann Derby
Snr PM: Michael Lehner

INITIAL AIRPORT SERVICES
See INITIAL CONTRACT SERVICES INC

D-U-N-S 17-442-7575
INITIAL CONTRACT SERVICES INC
INITIAL AIRPORT SERVICES
(*Suby of* RENTOKIL INITIAL UK LTD)
1780 Corporate Dr Ste 440, Norcross, GA 30093-2958
Tel (678) 812-3079 *Founded/Ownrshp* 1986
Sales 23.1MM^E *EMP* 2,500
SIC 7349 Janitorial service, contract basis
Pr: Edward S Fleury
**CFO:* Barry Collins
CFO: Deborah Hubbard

INITIATIVE FOOD COMPANY
See IF HOLDING INC

D-U-N-S 02-005-4966
INITIATIVE GROUP INC
319 Garlington Rd Ste B1, Greenville, SC 29615-4621
Tel (864) 297-4081 *Founded/Ownrshp* 2000
Sales 28.3MM^E *EMP* 450
SIC 6799 8742 Commodity investors; Management consulting services; Commodity investors; Management consulting services
Pr: Matthew Calvage
**VP:* Robert Chandler

INITIATIVE MEDIA
See MEDIABRANDS WORLDWIDE INC

INJECTION MOLDERS SUPPLY
See IMS CO

D-U-N-S 00-156-7569 IMP
INJECTRON CORP
DETAILED DESIGNS
1000 S 2nd St, Plainfield, NJ 07063-1306
Tel (908) 753-1990 *Founded/Ownrshp* 1959, 1981
Sales 57.0MM^E *EMP* 300
SIC 3089 Injection molding of plastics; Injection molding of plastics
Pr: Lou Pollak
Sr VP: Marvin Kaplan
IT Man: Steph Naude
Ql Cn Mgr: Craig Ford
VP Sls: Morris Peter

D-U-N-S 00-112-5285
INJECTRONICS CORP
1 Union St, Clinton, MA 01510-2930
Tel (978) 365-1200 *Founded/Ownrshp* 1981
Sales 21.0MM^E *EMP* 70
SIC 3089 3083 Injection molding of plastics; Laminated plastics plate & sheet
CEO: Paul A Nazzaro
Pr: Mike Simmons
**COO:* Michael Simmons
**CFO:* Michael Bowe
Genl Mgr: Scott Nickerson
MIS Dir: Harry Tock
Telecom Mg: Peter Bogert
VP Mfg: Daniel Maxfield
QC Dir: Stan Allen
QC Dir: Peter Glekas
Opers Mgr: Butch Kowalczyk

D-U-N-S 12-080-4059 IMP
INJEX INDUSTRIES INC
30559 San Antonio St, Hayward, CA 94544-7101
Tel (510) 487-4960 *Founded/Ownrshp* 1984
Sales 41.7MM^E *EMP* 375
SIC 3714 Motor vehicle body components & frame; Motor vehicle body components & frame
Prin: F Pete Petri

D-U-N-S 12-154-0749
INJURED WORKERS PHARMACY LLC
(*Suby of* ACON EQUITY PARTNERS III, L.P.)
300 Federal St, Andover, MA 01810-1038
Tel (978) 208-5401 *Founded/Ownrshp* 2014
Sales 71.8MM^E *EMP* 305
SIC 5961 5912 Pharmaceuticals, mail order; Drug stores; Pharmaceuticals, mail order; Drug stores
CEO: Kenneth Martino
**CFO:* James Standish
VP: George Cayer
VP: Michael Cirillo
VP: Chuck McKinley
Dir Rx: Roger Scandura
Mktg Dir: Cristy Beram

D-U-N-S 07-972-5113
INK ACQUISITION LLC
399 Park Ave Fl 18, New York, NY 10022-4968
Tel (212) 547-2609 *Founded/Ownrshp* 2014
Sales 38.5MM^E *EMP* 783^E
SIC 8741 Hotel or motel management
VP: Laura Benner

D-U-N-S 07-972-5245
INK ACQUISITION VI LLC
FORT WALTON BEACH FOUR POINTS
399 Park Ave Fl 18, New York, NY 10022-4968
Tel (212) 547-2609 *Founded/Ownrshp* 2014
Sales 9.7MM^E *EMP* 325^E
SIC 8741 Hotel or motel management
VP: Laura Benner

D-U-N-S 07-976-4649
INK ACQUISITION VI LLC
MORRISTOWN WESTIN
399 Park Ave Fl 18, New York, NY 10022-4968
Tel (212) 547-2609 *Founded/Ownrshp* 2011
Sales 4.0MM^E *EMP* 325
SIC 8741 Hotel or motel management
VP: Laura Benner

D-U-N-S 07-972-5270
INK ACQUISITION VII LLC
399 Park Ave Fl 18, New York, NY 10022-4968
Tel (212) 547-2609 *Founded/Ownrshp* 2014
Sales 10.1MM^E *EMP* 398^E
SIC 8741 Hotel or motel management
VP: Laura Benner

D-U-N-S 14-734-1267 IMP
INK SYSTEMS INC
2311 S Eastern Ave, Commerce, CA 90040-1430
Tel (323) 720-4000 *Founded/Ownrshp* 1985
Sales 35.5MM^E *EMP* 240
SIC 2893

D-U-N-S 80-016-4956 IMP/EXP
INKCYCLE INC
TONERCYCLE
11100 W 82nd St, Lenexa, KS 66214-1502
Tel (913) 894-8387 *Founded/Ownrshp* 1992
Sales 90.8MM^E *EMP* 490
SIC 3955 7699 7378 5045 8249 5734 Print cartridges for laser & other computer printers; Printing trades machinery & equipment repair; Computer peripheral equipment repair & maintenance; Computer peripheral equipment; Printers, computer; Computers; Business training services; Printers & plotters: computers; Personal computers; Print cartridges for laser & other computer printers; Printing trades machinery & equipment repair; Computer peripheral equipment repair & maintenance; Computer peripheral equipment; Printers, computer; Computers; Business training services; Printers & plotters: computers; Personal computers
Pr: Rick Krska
**COO:* Tom Cunningham
**CFO:* Cathy Lynch
**Ex VP:* Brad Roderick
**VP:* Bob Ehlers
**VP:* Joy James
**VP:* Carl Little
VP: Inkcycle Names
**VP:* Keith Riley
**CTO:* Tom Ashley

INKPIXI
See EARTH SUN MOON TRADING CO INC

D-U-N-S 01-075-8667
INKTEL HOLDINGS CORP
13975 Nw 58th Ct, Miami Lakes, FL 33014-3114
Tel (305) 523-1100 *Founded/Ownrshp* 1997
Sales 70.4MM^E *EMP* 420

SIC 7389 Telemarketing services; Telemarketing services
Pr: Arriola J Ricky
**COO:* Summer Dennis
**CFO:* Manuel Hernandez
**CFO:* Albert Llodra
Top Exec: Abigail Auslander
**Ex VP:* Dan Arriola
**Sr VP:* Dave Drayton
**VP:* Eduardo Arriola
**VP:* Robert J Ballwanz
**VP:* Donald Cannava
**VP:* Chris Chinni
VP: David Matthews
**VP:* Tim Sanchez
Exec: Michael Olivero

D-U-N-S 16-027-0617
■ INKTOMI CORP
(*Suby of* YAHOO INC) ★
701 First Ave, Sunnyvale, CA 94089-1019
Tel (650) 653-2800 *Founded/Ownrshp* 1996
Sales 20.4MM^E *EMP* 770
SIC 7372 7371 Application computer software; Custom computer programming services; Application computer software; Custom computer programming services
Ch Bd: David Peterschmidt
**CFO:* Randy Gottfried
Sr VP: Al Shipp
VP: Richard Pierce
Snr Mgr: Jill Reed

D-U-N-S 83-457-1986
INKWARE LLC
189 Waukewan St, Meredith, NH 03253
Tel (603) 677-3100 *Founded/Ownrshp* 2006
Sales 25.3MM^E *EMP* 275
SIC 2893 2899 Printing ink; Ink or writing fluids; Printing ink; Ink or writing fluids
Opers Mgr: Stephen Emery
Sls Mgr: James Pike

D-U-N-S 10-653-4274 IMP
INKWELL GLOBAL MARKETING CORP
600 Madison Ave, Manalapan, NJ 07726-9594
Tel (732) 617-3500 *Founded/Ownrshp* 1977
Sales 32.5MM^E *EMP* 43
SIC 5199 Advertising specialties
CEO: Carol Marder
**CFO:* Steven Marder
CFO: Stacey Resetar

D-U-N-S 07-880-2259
INLAND AMERICAN LODGING DALLAS AKARD TRS LIMITED PARTNERSHIP
FAIRMONT HOTEL DALLAS
1717 N Akard St, Dallas, TX 75201-2301
Tel (214) 720-2020 *Founded/Ownrshp* 2011
Sales 23.0MM^E *EMP* 270
SIC 7011 Hotels & motels; Hotels & motels
Genl Mgr: Michael Mussara
Genl Mgr: Mark Huntley
Sls Mgr: Ginny Burroughs

D-U-N-S 60-293-4239
INLAND BANCORP INC
2805 Butterfield Rd # 370, Oak Brook, IL 60523-1168
Tel (630) 218-8000 *Founded/Ownrshp* 2005
Sales 85.3MM *EMP* 112^E
SIC 6719 Investment holding companies, except banks; Investment holding companies, except banks
CEO: Daniel Goodwin
Sr Pt: Lawrence Aaron
**Pr:* Howard Jaffe
**VP:* Cheri Andersen

D-U-N-S 00-366-6468
INLAND BANK AND TRUST
(*Suby of* INLAND BANCORP INC) ★
2805 Butterfield Rd # 200, Oak Brook, IL 60523-1170
Tel (630) 908-6555 *Founded/Ownrshp* 1996
Sales NA *EMP* 51^E
SIC 6029 Commercial banks; Commercial banks
Pr: Howard Jaffe
Ofcr: Rosalie Bukowski
Ofcr: Chris Metcalf
**Ex VP:* David Martin
**Sr VP:* Christine E Gordon
Sr VP: Bud Schrock
VP: Paul Berley
VP: Linda Boyer
VP: Gregory Braid
VP: Sharon Follin
VP: Coby Hakalir
VP: Kevin O'Brien
VP: Hal Odonnell
VP: John Ostrem
VP: Anthony Renelli
VP: Miguel Sanchez
VP: Jocelyn Urban

D-U-N-S 16-198-5056
INLAND BANK AND TRUST
(*Suby of* INLAND BANCORP INC) ★
2225 S Wolf Rd, Hillside, IL 60162-2212
Tel (708) 562-2200 *Founded/Ownrshp* 1987
Sales NA *EMP* 35
SIC 6022 State commercial banks; State commercial banks
Pr: Thomas D Pano
**Ch Bd:* Seymour Goldgehn
Pr: Frank Binetti
Pr: Colleen Ryan
CEO: Jeffrey Vock
CFO: Joseph T Puleo
Ex VP: Mark Avis
Sr VP: Sean Gallagher
Sr VP: Charles Thomas
VP: Christine Gordon
VP: Philip Sirotzke

D-U-N-S 79-927-0392
INLAND BUILDING SYSTEMS
INLAND BUILDINGS
(*Suby of* BEHLEN MFG CO) ★
2141 2nd Ave Sw, Cullman, AL 35055-5343
Tel (256) 739-6827 *Founded/Ownrshp* 1996
Sales 25.9MM^E *EMP* 150
SIC 3448 Prefabricated metal buildings; Prefabricated metal buildings
Pr: Jim McIndoo
VP: Donnie Humphries
**VP:* Robert South
Dist Mgr: Don Clark
Dist Mgr: Dennis Parrino
Off Mgr: Loretta Hays
Sls Mgr: Bruce Hodgson
Snr Mgr: Scott Dehaan

INLAND BUILDINGS
See INLAND BUILDING SYSTEMS

INLAND CAREER CENTER
See GOODWILL SOUTHERN CALIFORNIA

D-U-N-S 02-829-4130
INLAND CHEVROLET INC (CA)
350 Carriage Cir, Hemet, CA 92545-9618
Tel (951) 658-4401 *Founded/Ownrshp* 1991
Sales 26.2MM^E *EMP* 70
SIC 5511 Automobiles, new & used; Automobiles, new & used
Pr: Eric Gosch
Sls Mgr: Ron Riccio

D-U-N-S 04-090-1555
INLAND CONSTRUCTION CO
120 W Cataldo Ave Ste 100, Spokane, WA 99201-3211
Tel (509) 474-0177 *Founded/Ownrshp* 1974
Sales 20.8MM^E *EMP* 50
SIC 1541 1542 Industrial buildings & warehouses; Nonresidential construction
Pr: Thomas E Clemson
Opers Mgr: Don Schieman

D-U-N-S 08-117-6356
INLAND COUNTIES REGIONAL CENTER INC
INLAND REGIONAL CENTER
1365 S Waterman Ave, San Bernardino, CA 92408-2804
Tel (909) 890-3000 *Founded/Ownrshp* 1971
Sales 335.1MM *EMP* 586^E
Accts Windes Inc Long Beach Ca
SIC 8741 Management services; Management services
CEO: Carol A Fitzgibbons
Trst: Gary Galosic
**Ex Dir:* Carol Fitzgibbons
Prgrm Mgr: Lawana Blair
Prgrm Mgr: Mia Gurri
Prgrm Mgr: Nancy Lee
Prgrm Mgr: Betty Tanius
Prgrm Mgr: Dorla Watson
Off Admin: Stephen Hughes
Psych: Beth Adelman
Psych: Camerina Aguirre

D-U-N-S 07-937-0518
INLAND CRUDE PURCHASING LLC
727 N Waco Ave Ste 400, Wichita, KS 67203-3900
Tel (316) 263-3201 *Founded/Ownrshp* 2012
Sales 175.0MM *EMP* 3
SIC 5172 Crude oil; Crude oil

D-U-N-S 79-705-3808
INLAND DETROIT DIESEL-ALLISON INC
INLAND POWER GROUP
13015 W Custer Ave, Butler, WI 53007-1113
Tel (262) 781-7100 *Founded/Ownrshp* 1992
Sales 21.9MM^E *EMP* 137
Accts Grant Thornton Milwaukee Wi
SIC 5084

D-U-N-S 83-270-6712
INLAND DIVERSIFIED REAL ESTATE TRUST INC
2901 Butterfield Rd, Oak Brook, IL 60523-1190
Tel (630) 218-8000 *Founded/Ownrshp* 2008
Sales 185.8MM *EMP* 4^E
Accts Kpmg Llp Chicago Illinois
SIC 6798 Real estate investment trusts; Real estate investment trusts
Pr: Barry Lazarus
**CFO:* Steven T Hippel
VP: Dan Lombardo
Opers Mgr: Sean King

D-U-N-S 09-090-2164
INLAND DREDGING CO LLC
103 N King Ave, Dyersburg, TN 38024-4609
Tel (731) 285-1995 *Founded/Ownrshp* 1997
Sales 21.4MM *EMP* 60^E
SIC 1629 Dredging contractor
Pr: Clifton Valentine
Off Mgr: Colleen Jamison
IT Man: James Mohead

D-U-N-S 82-816-4942
INLAND EMPIRE FILIPINO SDA
604 E State St, Redlands, CA 92374-3517
Tel (909) 335-1760 *Founded/Ownrshp* 2008
Sales 8.4MM^E *EMP* 300
SIC 8661 Church of God; Church of God

D-U-N-S 93-355-2804
INLAND EMPIRE HEALTH PLAN
IEHP
10801 6th St Ste 120, Rancho Cucamonga, CA 91730-5987
Tel (909) 890-2000 *Founded/Ownrshp* 1994
Sales NA *EMP* 855
Accts Moss Adams Llp Irvine Califo
SIC 6324 6321 Health maintenance organization (HMO), insurance only; Accident & health insurance; Health maintenance organization (HMO), insurance only; Accident & health insurance
CEO: Brad Gilbert
COO: Phillip W Branstetter
**CFO:* Chet Uma
**Ch:* Bob Buster
Chf Mktg O: Susan Arcidiacono
VP: Suzanne Harvey
Dir Rx: Chris Chan
CIO: Michael Deering
Dir IT: Carl Lewis
Dir IT: John Prosa
Dir IT: Terry Terr
Board of Directors: Bob Buster, Jerry Eaves, Dr Ernest Garcia, Dennis Hansburger, Tom Mullin, Tex Ritter, Drew Williams

D-U-N-S 00-906-9279
INLAND EMPIRE PAPER CO INC
(*Suby of* COWLES PUBLISHING CO) ★
3320 N Argonne Rd, Spokane, WA 99212-2099
Tel (509) 924-1911 *Founded/Ownrshp* 1935
Sales 66.9MM^E *EMP* 140
SIC 2621 Newsprint paper; Newsprint paper
Pr: Kevin Rasler
**Sec:* Steve Rector
Off Mgr: Karen Unser
Trfc Dir: Rob Hopkins
Opers Mgr: Dennis Parent

D-U-N-S 04-365-6206
INLAND EMPIRE UTILITIES AGENCY A MUNICIPAL WATER DISTRICT (INC)
6075 Kimball Ave, Chino, CA 91708-9174
Tel (909) 993-1600 *Founded/Ownrshp* 1950
Sales 264.5MM^E *EMP* 308
Accts Mayer Hoffman Mccann Pc Irv
SIC 4941 Water supply; Water supply
Pr: Terry Catlin
**Pr:* John Anderson
COO: Jon Florio
CFO: Christina Valencia
**Sec:* Ging Cookman
**Sec:* Steve Elie
Ofcr: Tina Cheng
Ofcr: Jason Gu
**VP:* Michael Camacho
VP: Angel Santiago
**VP:* Wyatt Troxel
Dir Lab: Nel Groenveld

D-U-N-S 02-893-0816
INLAND ENVELOPE CO
150 N Park Ave, Pomona, CA 91768-3835
Tel (909) 622-2016 *Founded/Ownrshp* 1966
Sales 20.6MM^E *EMP* 55
SIC 2677 Envelopes
CEO: Bernard Kloenne

D-U-N-S 18-184-5462
INLAND FOODS CORP
BURGER KING
1621 Executive Ave, Myrtle Beach, SC 29577-6501
Tel (843) 448-2646 *Founded/Ownrshp* 1986
Sales 10.8MM^E *EMP* 500
SIC 5812 Fast-food restaurant, chain; Fast-food restaurant, chain
Pr: Rick H Seagroves
Opers Mgr: David Lloyd

D-U-N-S 08-936-1620 IMP
INLAND FRESH SEAFOOD CORP OF AMERICA INC
INLAND SEAFOOD
1651 Montreal Cir, Tucker, GA 30084-6933
Tel (678) 373-4580 *Founded/Ownrshp* 1976
Sales 241.5MM^E *EMP* 325
SIC 5146 Fish & seafoods; Seafoods; Fish & seafoods; Seafoods
CEO: Joel Knox
**Pr:* Chris Rosenberger
**COO:* Bill Demmond
**VP:* William Demmond
**VP:* Stephen T Musser Jr
**VP:* Robert Novotny
VP: Michael Robins
Opers Mgr: Mike Bowen
Sls Mgr: Meteka Gilyard

INLAND GROUP
See INLAND REAL ESTATE GROUP OF COMPANIES INC

INLAND GROUP
See INLAND LITHO LLC

D-U-N-S 14-427-0584
INLAND HOSPITAL
(*Suby of* EASTERN MAINE HEALTHCARE SYSTEMS) ★
200 Kennedy Memorial Dr, Waterville, ME 04901-4595
Tel (207) 873-0731 *Founded/Ownrshp* 1943
Sales 67.5MM^E *EMP* 575
SIC 8062 Hospital, medical school affiliated with nursing & residency; Hospital, medical school affiliated with nursing & residency
CEO: John Dalton
Chf Rad: Thomas Cubberley
Sr VP: Sally Connery
Dir OR: Christopher Sylvester
Dir Rad: Tina Hintz
Dir Rad: Tina Marlowe
Mktg Dir: Sara Dyer
Surgeon: Simon Gibbs
Obsttrcn: Tina Quinn
Pharmcst: Jessica Lane-Hanson

D-U-N-S 06-771-6530
INLAND IMAGING ASSOCIATES PS
801 S Stevens St, Spokane, WA 99204-2654
Tel (509) 456-5600 *Founded/Ownrshp* 1972
Sales 24.1MM^E *EMP* 308
SIC 8011 8071 Radiologist; Medical laboratories; Radiologist; Medical laboratories
CEO: Steve Duvoisin
**Pr:* Don Cubberley
CIO: Cole Hanford
CTO: Tracy Hanford
Dir IT: Jeff Sund
Diag Rad: Elin Angeid-Backman
Diag Rad: Brad J Ratcliff
Board of Directors: Richard Beren, James Deniro, Tom Finley, Robert Fulton, Peter J Horn, Robert G Weigand

D-U-N-S 96-440-0832
INLAND IMAGING BUSINESS ASSOCIATES LLC
801 S Stevens St, Spokane, WA 99204-2654
Tel (509) 456-5600 *Founded/Ownrshp* 1996
Sales 22.1MM^E *EMP* 80^E
SIC 5047 X-ray machines & tubes
COO: Kathleen Wilson
Ofcr: Dan Hiebert
IT Man: Shan Brus
IT Man: Shelley Peterson
Art Dir: Fran Zabawa
Snr Mgr: Sarah Russell

D-U-N-S 04-278-8989
INLAND IMAGING LLC (WA)
801 S Stevens St, Spokane, WA 99204-2654
Tel (509) 363-7709 *Founded/Ownrshp* 1997
Sales 37.7MM^E *EMP* 270^E
SIC 8011 8071 Radiologist; Medical laboratories; Radiologist; Medical laboratories
CEO: Steve Duvoisin
Sr VP: Jodi Bailey
CTO: Stacie Gordon
Dir IT: Gregory Balmforth
IT Man: Dan Hiebert
IT Man: Travis Thomas
IT Man: Kathleen Wilson
Netwrk Eng: Bob Cole
Opers Mgr: Ronda Smith
Mktg Dir: Pam Pyrc
Mktg Dir: Ed Renouard

D-U-N-S 02-984-5187
INLAND INDUSTRIES INC
19841 Benson St, Bucyrus, KS 66013-8201
Tel (913) 492-9050 *Founded/Ownrshp* 1930
Sales 20.8MM^E *EMP* 231
SIC 5084 2711 2893 5999 7011 6512 Printing trades machinery, equipment & supplies; Newspapers, publishing & printing; Letterpress or offset ink; Art & architectural supplies; Tourist camps, cabins, cottages & courts; Commercial & industrial building operation; Printing trades machinery, equipment & supplies; Newspapers, publishing & printing; Letterpress or offset ink; Art & architectural supplies; Tourist camps, cabins, cottages & courts; Commercial & industrial building operation
Ch: Brian D Murray
**Pr:* Jack D Burton
CFO: D Burton
**VP:* Beau Campbell
**VP:* Craig R Murray
**VP:* Michael C Murray

D-U-N-S 00-690-7679
INLAND KENWORTH (US) INC (CA)
(*Suby of* INLAND INDUSTRIES LTD)
9730 Cherry Ave, Fontana, CA 92335-5257
Tel (909) 823-9955 *Founded/Ownrshp* 1934, 1989
Sales 130.4MM^E *EMP* 417
SIC 5012 7538 5013 7513 Trucks, commercial; Diesel engine repair: automotive; Truck parts & accessories; Truck rental & leasing, no drivers; Trucks, commercial; Diesel engine repair: automotive; Truck parts & accessories; Truck rental & leasing, no drivers
Ch: Leigh Parker
**Pr:* Jim Beidrwieden
**CEO:* William Currie
**CFO:* Les Ziegler

D-U-N-S 14-970-2750
INLAND KENWORTH (US) INC
1600 Washington Blvd, Montebello, CA 90640-5422
Tel (909) 823-9955 *Founded/Ownrshp* 2001
Sales 71.8MM^E *EMP* 407
SIC 5511 5531 7538 Trucks, tractors & trailers: new & used; Automobile & truck equipment & parts; General truck repair; Trucks, tractors & trailers: new & used; Automobile & truck equipment & parts; General truck repair
Pr: Jim Deiderwieden
**CFO:* Les Ziegler
Genl Mgr: Rich Cawley
Off Mgr: Renee Unland

D-U-N-S 00-620-5298 IMP
INLAND LABEL AND MARKETING SERVICES LLC
2009 West Ave S, La Crosse, WI 54601-6297
Tel (608) 788-5800 *Founded/Ownrshp* 1945
Sales 52.3MM^E *EMP* 250
SIC 2754 2752

D-U-N-S 10-872-6076
INLAND LITHO LLC
INLAND GROUP
4305 E La Palma Ave, Anaheim, CA 92807-1843
Tel (714) 993-6000 *Founded/Ownrshp* 1984
Sales 20.1MM^E *EMP* 60
SIC 2752 Lithographing on metal
Sales Exec: Dave Howard

D-U-N-S 02-920-1704
INLAND MARINE INDUSTRIES INC
INLAND METAL
3245 Depot Rd, Hayward, CA 94545-2709
Tel (510) 785-8555 *Founded/Ownrshp* 1986
Sales 33.9MM^E *EMP* 95
SIC 3499 Shims, metal
Pr: Stan G Sutton
QC Dir: Frank Bray
QC Dir: Keith Cranfill
Prd Mgr: Sid Perry
Ql Cn Mgr: John Robinson
Ql Cn Mgr: Troy Vandenover
Mktg Dir: Jason Stewart
Sls Mgr: Connie Bates

D-U-N-S 18-652-5895
INLAND MARINE SERVICE INC
1720 Petersburg Rd, Hebron, KY 41048-8400
Tel (859) 689-7707 *Founded/Ownrshp* 1981
Sales 22.5MM^E *EMP* 300
SIC 4492 8713 Marine towing services; Surveying services; Marine towing services
CEO: Cathy Shantz Hammond
**Pr:* David E Hammond
Opers Mgr: Dan Willis

INLAND METAL
See INLAND MARINE INDUSTRIES INC

D-U-N-S 88-423-1572
■ INLAND NORTHWEST BANK
(*Suby of* NORTHWEST BANCORPORATION INC) ★
421 W Riverside Ave # 606, Spokane, WA 99201-0402
Tel (509) 624-3042 *Founded/Ownrshp* 1989
Sales NA *EMP* 27ᴱ
SIC 6022 State commercial banks; State commercial banks
Pr: Randal L Fuewell
**Pr:* Frederick M Schunter
Chf Cred: Scott Southwick
**Sr VP:* Christopher C Jurey
VP: Cindy Bocook
**VP:* Jennifer L Johnson
Dir IT: Stuart McMath
VP Mktg: Jason Miller

D-U-N-S 07-574-6768
INLAND NORTHWEST BLOOD CENTER (WA)
210 W Cataldo Ave, Spokane, WA 99201-2217
Tel (800) 423-0151 *Founded/Ownrshp* 1945
Sales 23.6MM *EMP* 167
SIC 8099

D-U-N-S 02-989-8991
INLAND NORTHWEST HEALTH SERVICES (WA)
ST LUKES REHABILITATION INST
601 W 1st Ave, Spokane, WA 99201-3825
Tel (509) 232-8100 *Founded/Ownrshp* 1986
Sales 23.4MMᴱ *EMP* 200ᴱ
SIC 8099 Health screening service; Health screening service
Pr: R Ronald Wells
Sr Pt: James Watanabe
CFO: Jeff Thurlow
Bd of Dir: Michael Wilson
Sr VP: John Fletcher
VP: Mary Butler
**VP:* Gary Livingstonm
VP: Dean Martz
Exec: Phyllis Gabel
Comm Man: Cindy Dionne
Prin: Sharon Bishop

INLAND NORTHWEST HEALTH SVCS
See ST LUKES REHABILITATION INSTITUTE

D-U-N-S 88-471-7208
INLAND NORTHWEST RENAL CARE GROUP LLC
DIALYSIS CENTERS OF AMERICA
(*Suby of* RENAL CARE GROUP INC) ★
4 Westbrook Corporate Ctr, Westchester, IL 60154-5752
Tel (708) 498-9036 *Founded/Ownrshp* 1973
Sales 6.1MMᴱ *EMP* 330
SIC 8092 Kidney dialysis centers; Kidney dialysis centers
COO: Timothy Martin

D-U-N-S 00-605-4100
INLAND PAPERBOARD AND PACKAGING INC
1300 S Mo Pac Expy Fl 3, Austin, TX 78746-6933
Tel (512) 234-5001 *Founded/Ownrshp* 1978, 1984
Sales 1.1MMMᴱ *EMP* 9,387
Accts Ernst & Young Llp Austin Tex
SIC 2653 2631 3086 2679 2657 Corrugated boxes, partitions, display items, sheets & pad; Solid fiber boxes, partitions, display items & sheets; Linerboard; Packaging & shipping materials, foamed plastic; Corrugated paper: made from purchased material; Folding paperboard boxes; Corrugated boxes, partitions, display items, sheets & pad; Solid fiber boxes, partitions, display items & sheets; Linerboard; Packaging & shipping materials, foamed plastic; Corrugated paper: made from purchased material; Folding paperboard boxes
Ch Bd: William B Howes
**Pr:* Dale E Stahl
**CFO:* Michael H Sullivan
**Treas:* David Terpin
Treas: Joseph Tomlinson
**Ex VP:* Bart J Doney
**Ex VP:* James C Foxworthy
**Ex VP:* J Patrick Malley III
**VP:* Steve Householder
**VP:* M Richard Warner
VP: Edwin L Wilson
Board of Directors: David Dolben, Clifford J Grum, Kenneth Jastrow II, Harold Maxwell, Joseph E Turk

D-U-N-S 96-251-9760
INLAND PIPE REHABILITATION LLC
(*Suby of* STRENGTH CAPITAL PARTNERS LLC) ★
2002 Timberloch Pl # 550, The Woodlands, TX 77380-1182
Tel (281) 362-1131 *Founded/Ownrshp* 2007
Sales 88.2MMᴱ *EMP* 150ᴱ
SIC 6282 Investment advisory service; Investment advisory service
CEO: Terry Bellora
Pr: Joe Cutillo
Off Mgr: Becky Waldron

D-U-N-S 00-895-8274
INLAND POWER & LIGHT CO
10110 W Hallett Rd, Spokane, WA 99224-7435
Tel (509) 747-7151 *Founded/Ownrshp* 1938
Sales 75.4MM *EMP* 110ᴱ
SIC 4911 Distribution, electric power; Distribution, electric power
CEO: Kris Mikkelsen
**COO:* Glen Best
**CFO:* Sandi McKee
Bd of Dir: Kenneth E Jacobson
Trst: Michelle Caird
**Prin:* Chad Jenson
IT Man: Chris Cable
IT Man: Travis Rushton

INLAND POWER GROUP
See INLAND DETROIT DIESEL-ALLISON INC

D-U-N-S 00-643-3650 IMP
INLAND POWER GROUP INC
JOHN DEERE
13015 W Custer Ave, Butler, WI 53007-1113
Tel (262) 781-7100 *Founded/Ownrshp* 1958
Sales 117.6MM *EMP* 275
SIC 5084 5531 7699 Engines & parts, diesel; Automobile & truck equipment & parts; Engine repair & replacement, non-automotive

D-U-N-S 95-879-7271
INLAND PROFESSIONAL TITLE LLC
501 S Bernard St Ste 101, Spokane, WA 99204-2508
Tel (509) 922-2222 *Founded/Ownrshp* 2008
Sales NA *EMP* 65
SIC 6361 Real estate title insurance
Ofcr: Ken Vedders
Plnt Mgr: Connie Doddg
Prd Mgr: Connie Dodge

D-U-N-S 15-175-8505
INLAND PROPERTY MANAGEMENT INC
(*Suby of* INLAND GROUP) ★
2901 Butterfield Rd, Oak Brook, IL 60523-1190
Tel (630) 218-8000 *Founded/Ownrshp* 1986
Sales 17.8MMᴱ *EMP* 700
SIC 6531 Real estate managers; Real estate managers
Pr: Daniel Goodwin
**Treas:* Alan Kremin
VP: Roberta S Matlin

D-U-N-S 01-699-0074
▲ INLAND REAL ESTATE CORP (MD)
2901 Butterfield Rd, Oak Brook, IL 60523-1190
Tel (877) 206-5656 *Founded/Ownrshp* 1994
Sales 204.7MM *EMP* 129ᴱ
Accts Kpmg Llp Chicago Illinois
Tkr Sym IRC *Exch* NYS
SIC 6798 Real estate investment trusts; Real estate investment trusts
Pr: Mark E Zalatoris
Pr: Fred Kapel
CFO: Brett A Brown
Assoc VP: Eric Spiess
Ex VP: D Scott Carr
Sr VP: William W Anderson
Sr VP: Beth Sprecher Brooks
Sr VP: Janet Heintz
Sr VP: Roberta S Matlin
Sr VP: Paul Rogers
VP: Sharon Anderson-Cox
VP: Bob Edmiston
VP: Gale Evans
VP: Fred Fisher
VP: Judy Fu
VP: Jeff Hertz
VP: Kim Karas
VP: Richard Kehoe
VP: Robert Leahy
VP: Dean Lev
VP: Philip Menolascina
Board of Directors: Thomas P D'arcy, Daniel L Goodwin, Joel G Herter, Heidi N Lawton, Thomas H McAuley, Thomas R McWilliams, Meredith Wise Mendes, Joel D Simmons

D-U-N-S 10-319-0062
INLAND REAL ESTATE GROUP OF COMPANIES INC
INLAND GROUP
2901 Butterfield Rd, Oak Brook, IL 60523-1190
Tel (630) 218-8000 *Founded/Ownrshp* 1967
Sales NA *EMP* 1,114
SIC 6513 6512 6162 6282 1522 1542 Apartment building operators; Commercial & industrial building operation; Mortgage bankers; Investment advice; Multi-family dwelling construction; Commercial & office building, new construction; Apartment building operators; Commercial & industrial building operation; Mortgage bankers; Investment advice; Multi-family dwelling construction; Commercial & office building, new construction
Pr: G Joseph Cosenza
**CEO:* Daniel L Goodwin
**CFO:* Alan Kremin
**Ch:* Robert D Parks
**Treas:* Alan F Kremin
**Ex VP:* Robert H Baum
Ex VP: Robert Baum
**Sr VP:* Sharon Anderson-Cox
Sr VP: Karen Kautz
**Sr VP:* Paul Wheeler
VP: Robert Barg
VP: Chad Colombo
VP: Maureen Denard
**VP:* Janice J Fox
**VP:* Matthew Tice
Dir Risk M: Shoba Rajanahally
Board of Directors: Joann M Armenta, Catherine L Lynch

D-U-N-S 11-820-2753
INLAND REAL ESTATE INVESTMENT CORP
(*Suby of* INLAND GROUP) ★
2901 Butterfield Rd, Oak Brook, IL 60523-1190
Tel (630) 218-8000 *Founded/Ownrshp* 1987
Sales 238.3MMᴱ *EMP* 59
SIC 6211 6798 Security brokers & dealers; Real estate investment trusts
CEO: Mitchell A Sabshon
**Ch Bd:* Robert D Parks
**Pr:* Brenda G Gujral
Treas: Catherine L Ynch
**Sec:* Catherine L Lynch
**Sr VP:* Patricia Challenger
Sr VP: Guadalupe Griffin
**Sr VP:* Roberta S Matlin
VP: Ravi Bansal
Comm Man: Lindsey Schober

INLAND REGIONAL CENTER
See INLAND COUNTIES REGIONAL CENTER INC

INLAND SEAFOOD
See INLAND FRESH SEAFOOD CORP OF AMERICA INC

D-U-N-S 12-127-3023
INLAND SECURITIES CORP
(*Suby of* INLAND REAL ESTATE INVESTMENT CORP) ★
2901 Butterfield Rd, Oak Brook, IL 60523-1190
Tel (630) 218-8000 *Founded/Ownrshp* 1998
Sales 238.1MM *EMP* 45
Accts Kpmg Llp Chicago Il
SIC 6211 Brokers, security; Brokers, security
CEO: Michael T Ezzell II
Treas: Catherine Lynch
Chf Cred: Suzanne L Bond
Sr VP: Curtis Shoch
Sr VP: Shawn Vaughan
VP: James Anderson
VP: Jackie Barbera
VP: Richard Brown
VP: Rod Curtis
VP: Drew Dedelow
VP: Jay Dobbs
VP: Peter Fisher
VP: David Flamm
VP: Jeff Hertz
VP: Roberta S Matlin
VP: Kenny Miley
VP: Michael O'Shea
VP: Kathleen A Pelletier
VP: Robert Speidel
VP: Michael Vozella

D-U-N-S 05-572-1351
INLAND SERVICE CORP
14101 W Hwy 290 Ste 600, Austin, TX 78737-9343
Tel (512) 858-4558 *Founded/Ownrshp* 1975
Sales 27.2MM *EMP* 200
SIC 4953 Refuse collection & disposal services; Refuse collection & disposal services
Pr: Robert A Smith
**Pr:* Montgomery Davison
**VP:* Wayne Johnson
**VP:* David G Perry

D-U-N-S 01-399-5923
INLAND STAR DISTRIBUTION CENTERS INC (CA)
3146 S Chestnut Ave, Fresno, CA 93725-2606
Tel (559) 237-2052 *Founded/Ownrshp* 1985
Sales 44.4MMᴱ *EMP* 165
SIC 4225 4213 General warehousing & storage; General warehousing; Trucking, except local; General warehousing & storage; General warehousing; Trucking, except local
CEO: Michael K Kelton
Sr VP: Michael O'Donnell
Genl Mgr: Richard Smith
IT Man: Dave Donathan
Mktg Dir: John Neale

D-U-N-S 78-667-3764 IMP
INLAND TARP & LINER LLC
4172 N Frontage Rd E, Moses Lake, WA 98837-4901
Tel (509) 766-7024 *Founded/Ownrshp* 1991
Sales 26.4MMᴱ *EMP* 50ᴱ
SIC 5199 Tarpaulins; Tarpaulins
Sls Mgr: Glen Knopp
**Prin:* Calvin Stapleton

D-U-N-S 07-142-8379
INLAND TOOL CO
727 N Topper Rd, Mount Pulaski, IL 62548-6074
Tel (217) 792-3206 *Founded/Ownrshp* 1974
Sales 20.9MMᴱ *EMP* 50
SIC 3545 3469 3465 3544 Machine tool accessories; Metal stampings; Automotive stampings; Special dies, tools, jigs & fixtures
Pr: Kirk Evans
Off Mgr: Suzie Maxheimer
Mtls Mgr: Victor Martinek

D-U-N-S 02-290-5400
INLAND TRUCK PARTS CO INC
4400 College Blvd Ste 145, Overland Park, KS 66211-2326
Tel (913) 345-9664 *Founded/Ownrshp* 1967
Sales 138.9MMᴱ *EMP* 525
SIC 5013 7538

INLAND VALLEY CARE & REHAB CTR
See INLAND VALLEY PARTNERS LLC

D-U-N-S 08-314-7595
INLAND VALLEY CONSTRUCTION CO INC
18382 Slover Ave, Bloomington, CA 92316-2363
Tel (909) 875-2112 *Founded/Ownrshp* 1977
Sales 21.2MMᴱ *EMP* 75
SIC 1531 Operative builders
Pr: Kenneth Caruso
COO: Duke Dixon
**Treas:* Kelly Bird

INLAND VALLEY DAILY BULLETIN
See CALIFORNIA NEWSPAPERS LIMITED PARTNERSHIP

D-U-N-S 16-530-7088
INLAND VALLEY PARTNERS LLC
INLAND VALLEY CARE & REHAB CTR
250 W Artesia St, Pomona, CA 91768-1807
Tel (909) 623-7100 *Founded/Ownrshp* 1998
Sales 23.6MM *EMP* 250
SIC 8049 Nurses & other medical assistants; Nurses & other medical assistants
Dir Recs: Sylvia Johnson

D-U-N-S 17-364-2851
■ INLAND VALLEY REGIONAL MEDICAL CENTER INC
(*Suby of* UNIVERSAL HEALTH SERVICES INC) ★
36485 Inland Valley Dr, Wildomar, CA 92595-9681
Tel (951) 677-1111 *Founded/Ownrshp* 1983
Sales 49.5MMᴱ *EMP* 500ᴱ
SIC 8062 8011 General medical & surgical hospitals; Clinic, operated by physicians; General medical & surgical hospitals; Clinic, operated by physicians
CEO: Alan B Miller
CFO: Diane Moon
**CFO:* Barry Thorfinnson
Dir Inf Cn: Derek Shiba
Dir Risk M: Teri Ransbury
Div Mgr: Ann Kuss
Pathlgst: Duyet C Vo
Nrsg Dir: Ginny Ince
Pharmcst: Kim Tran

D-U-N-S 06-733-7600
INLAND WATERS POLLUTION CONTROL INC
(*Suby of* INLAND PIPE REHABILITATION LLC) ★
4086 Michigan Ave, Detroit, MI 48210-3261
Tel (313) 899-3014 *Founded/Ownrshp* 2002
Sales 21.1MMᴱ *EMP* 115ᴱ
SIC 7389 Pipeline & power line inspection service; Pipeline & power line inspection service
Pr: Joe Cutillo
**VP:* Allan Jetneak
**VP:* Dennis Oszust
Sales Asso: Lori Read

D-U-N-S 00-543-7587
INLANDER BROTHERS INC
7701 S Claremont Ave, Chicago, IL 60620-5810
Tel (773) 778-1600 *Founded/Ownrshp* 1985
Sales 68.3MMᴱ *EMP* 70
SIC 5113 5112 Industrial & personal service paper; Towels, paper; Office supplies; Industrial & personal service paper; Towels, paper; Office supplies
Pr: Lawrence Bruno
CFO: Don McClure
**VP:* Ken Beville

D-U-N-S 80-924-3553
INLANTA MORTGAGE INC
FIRST CHOICE MRTG IN WISCONSIN
611 N Barker Rd Ste 200, Brookfield, WI 53045-5930
Tel (262) 513-9853 *Founded/Ownrshp* 1993
Sales NA *EMP* 133
SIC 6163 Mortgage brokers arranging for loans, using money of others; Mortgage brokers arranging for loans, using money of others
CEO: John Knowlton
**Pr:* Nicholas J Deltorto
COO: Pete Salamone
CFO: Dennis Degrave
Ofcr: Ann Becker
Ofcr: Catherine Below
Ofcr: Mike Butler
Ofcr: Rebecca Hollander
Ofcr: Jim Mann
Ofcr: Olivera Prpa
Ofcr: Amy Walters
VP: Chris Knowlton

D-U-N-S 15-765-1928 IMP/EXP
INLET PETROLEUM CO
420 L St Ste 101, Anchorage, AK 99501-1976
Tel (907) 274-3835 *Founded/Ownrshp* 2005
Sales 40.3MMᴱ *EMP* 36
SIC 5172 Petroleum products; Lubricating oils & greases; Aircraft fueling services; Fuel oil
Pr: Joel Lawrence
**Pr:* Richard D Brew
**Treas:* Karen Griffin
**Treas:* Wendell Tuisuala
**VP:* Chris Hamey
**VP:* Amy Humphreys
**VP:* Donald L Martn
**VP:* Eric D Van Andel
Snr Mgr: Toshiro Morgan
Board of Directors: Brian Bogen, Tim Engle

INLINE DISTRIBUTING
See ALL-TEX INC

D-U-N-S 18-870-6808
INLINE ELECTRIC SUPPLY CO INC
INLINE LIGHTING
2880 Bob Wallace Ave Sw, Huntsville, AL 35805-4106
Tel (256) 533-2851 *Founded/Ownrshp* 1988
Sales 53.1MM *EMP* 150
Accts Lecroy Cpa Group Pc Huntsvil
SIC 5063 5719 Electrical supplies; Lighting, lamps & accessories; Lighting fixtures; Electrical supplies; Lighting, lamps & accessories; Lighting fixtures
Pr: Bruce Summerville
Sales Exec: Bruce Woods
Mktg Dir: Lauren Collins
Sales Asso: Jerry Gilbert
Sales Asso: Doug Halbrooks
Sales Asso: Ricky Ray
Sales Asso: Sue Thompson

INLINE LIGHTING
See INLINE ELECTRIC SUPPLY CO INC

D-U-N-S 04-517-6898 IMP/EXP
INLINE PLASTICS CORP
SURELOCK DIVISION
42 Canal St, Shelton, CT 06484-3265
Tel (203) 924-5933 *Founded/Ownrshp* 1968
Sales 73.6MMᴱ *EMP* 280
SIC 3089 Thermoformed finished plastic products; Trays, plastic; Thermoformed finished plastic products; Trays, plastic
Pr: Thomas Orkisz
VP: Dan Landan
QA Dir: Victoria Kleftogiannis
QA Dir: Brian Vogel
Sfty Mgr: Jerry Bristol
Plnt Mgr: Tam Joines
Plnt Mgr: Sam Maida
VP Sls: Jennifer Marcucci
Manager: Andrew Erskine
Manager: Kevin Gallagher
Manager: Sharon Rapp

INLINE SOLUTIONS THROUGH TECH
See CONTACT NETWORK INC

D-U-N-S 02-142-6002 IMP
■ INLINER AMERICAN INC
(*Suby of* LAYNE CHRISTENSEN CO) ★
2601 W Lake Mary Blvd # 129, Lake Mary, FL 32746-3567
Tel (407) 472-0014 *Founded/Ownrshp* 2006
Sales 24.3MMᴱ *EMP* 163

SIC 1623 Water & sewer line construction; Pipeline construction; Water & sewer line construction; Pipeline construction
Pr: Mark Harris
**Sr VP:* Michael Cannon

INMAN COAL
See BLACK CASTLE MINING CO INC

D-U-N-S 14-794-5968
INMAN HOLDING CO INC
INMAN MILLS
300 Park Rd, Inman, SC 29349-1754
Tel (864) 472-2121 *Founded/Ownrshp* 1985
Sales 182.5MM^E *EMP* 659^E
SIC 2211 2221 Broadwoven fabric mills, cotton; Broadwoven fabric mills, manmade; Broadwoven fabric mills, cotton; Broadwoven fabric mills, manmade
CEO: Robert H Chapman III
**Pr:* Norman H Chapman
**CFO:* James C Pace Jr
**VP:* William P Bowan
**VP:* Ben Truslow
**VP Mfg:* George Abbott

INMAN MILLS
See INMAN HOLDING CO INC

D-U-N-S 00-334-8471 IMP
INMAN MILLS (SC)
(*Suby of* INMAN HOLDING CO INC) ★
300 Park Rd, Inman, SC 29349-1754
Tel (864) 472-2121 *Founded/Ownrshp* 1901
Sales 172.1MM^E *EMP* 625
SIC 2281 Needle & handicraft yarns, spun; Needle & handicraft yarns, spun
Prin: Rober H Champ III
**Pr:* Norman H Chapman
**CEO:* Robert H Chapman III
COO: George Abbott
**CFO:* James C Pace Jr
VP: George Abbott
VP: William E Bowen Jr
Dir IT: David Blackwell
Plnt Mgr: George A Abbott
Plnt Mgr: Bill Hightower

D-U-N-S 14-499-8200 EXP
INMAR INC
INMAR PROMOTION SERVICES
635 Vine St, Winston Salem, NC 27101-4186
Tel (336) 631-2500 *Founded/Ownrshp* 2014
Sales 1.1MMM^E *EMP* 4,500
SIC 7389 Inventory computing service; Inventory computing service
CEO: L David Mounts
**Pr:* Bob Carter
**Pr:* Steve Dollase
**Pr:* Jeff Pepperworth
**Pr:* John Ross
**CFO:* Drew Dixon
**Chf Mktg O:* Travis Lewis
**Ex VP:* Fred Jorgenson
Ex VP: Sharon Joyner-Payne
**Ex VP:* Mark Wright
Exec: Sylvia Hutchens

INMAR PROMOTION SERVICES
See INMAR INC

D-U-N-S 07-032-2755 IMP
INMARK LLC (GA)
675 Hartman Rd Ste 100, Austell, GA 30168-7773
Tel (770) 373-3300 *Founded/Ownrshp* 1975
Sales 51.1MM^E *EMP* 70
SIC 5085 Commercial containers; Commercial containers
Pr: David S Oyler
CFO: Brad Crouch
**VP:* James E Curlee
Dir Lab: Vishnu Chetluru
Dept Mgr: Doug Perkins
Genl Mgr: Donnan Gray
Dir IT: Gail Traylor
Opers Mgr: Mark Shelpon
Ql Cn Mgr: Chuck Albert
VP Sls: Frank Orvino
Mktg Mgr: Joe Skwarek

INMARSAT
See GLOBE WIRELESS LLC

D-U-N-S 03-285-2613
INMARSAT INC
(*Suby of* INMARSAT PLC)
1101 Conn Ave Nw Ste 1200, Washington, DC 20036-4344
Tel (202) 248-5150 *Founded/Ownrshp* 1998
Sales 124.2MM^E *EMP* 1,400
SIC 3663 Satellites, communications; Satellites, communications
VP: Louise Billingsley
Pr: Alan Auckenthaler
Pr: Bruce Henoch
Sr VP: Rebecca Cowen-Hirsch
Sr VP: John Mackey
VP: Stephen Gizinski
VP Mktg: Alena Koci

INMETAL
See INDUSTRIAL METAL PRODUCTS CO INC

INMETCO
See INTERNATIONAL METAL RECLAIMING CORP

D-U-N-S 07-877-3463 IMP
INMUSIC BRANDS INC
(*Suby of* NUMARK INDUSTRIES LLC) ★
200 Scenic View Dr, Cumberland, RI 02864-1847
Tel (401) 658-3131 *Founded/Ownrshp* 2012
Sales 73.8MM^E *EMP* 62^E
SIC 5736 Musical instrument stores
Pr: John E Odonnell
COO: Paul Antrop
**CFO:* Paul Stansky
Sr VP: Costa Lakoumentas
QA Dir: Aaron Hachen
QA Dir: Bryce Kanzer
QA Dir: Jose Navedo

IT Man: Kyle Mello
Ql Cn Mgr: Adam Gay

D-U-N-S 18-610-6134 IMP/EXP
INN AMERICA HOSPITALITY
517 Us Highway 1 S # 2100, Iselin, NJ 08830-3023
Tel (732) 283-2218 *Founded/Ownrshp* 1988
Sales 12.8MM^E *EMP* 720
SIC 5812 6513 Restaurant, family: independent; Apartment hotel operation; Restaurant, family: independent; Apartment hotel operation
Pr: Randy Chick
**Prin:* Alan Winegarten
**Genl Mgr:* Lee Burtelsen-Lion

INN AT CHATEAU ELAN
See ELAN CHATEAU RESORTS LLC

INN AT PALMETTO BLUFF, THE
See PBLH LLC

THE INN AT TEMPLE SQUARE
See HOTEL TEMPLE SQUARE CORP

INN MAID PRODUCTS
See TMARZETTI CO

D-U-N-S 01-056-7469
INN MANAGEMENT SERVICES INC
EDEN RESORT
222 Eden Rd, Lancaster, PA 17601-4216
Tel (717) 569-6444 *Founded/Ownrshp* 1975
Sales 17.4MM^E *EMP* 300
SIC 8741 Hotel or motel management; Restaurant management; Hotel or motel management; Restaurant management
Pr: Drew Anthon
**Sec:* Joyce Anthon
Sls Mgr: Nicole Bader
Sls Mgr: Tara Dimattio
Sls Mgr: Merle Peduto

D-U-N-S 06-355-9728
INN OF LAKE CITY INC
COMFORT INN
3559 W Us Highway 90, Lake City, FL 32055-4869
Tel (386) 752-3901 *Founded/Ownrshp* 1965
Sales 12.0MM^E *EMP* 340
SIC 7011 Hotels & motels; Hotels & motels
VP: Mike P Sturdivant
**Pr:* Gaines P Sturdivant
**Ch:* Earl F Jones
**Treas:* Michael J Hart
Sls&Mrk Ex: Donna Paulin

D-U-N-S 17-597-0644
INN OF MOUNTAIN GODS RESORT AND CASINO
CASINO APACHE TRAVEL CENTER
287 Carrizo Canyon Rd, Mescalero, NM 88340-9641
Tel (575) 464-7777 *Founded/Ownrshp* 2004
Sales 61.4MM^E *EMP* 1,251^E
SIC 7999 7011 Gambling establishment; Casino hotel; Gambling establishment; Casino hotel
Ch Bd: Carleton Naiche-Palmer PHD
**COO:* Elizabeth Foster-Anderson
CFO: Lance Kintz
**Treas:* Hazel Botella-Spottedbird
Treas: Karen Braswell
Ofcr: Debra Gonzales
**VP:* Jackie Blaylock
**Prin:* R Miles Ledgerwood
**Prin:* Manuel Lujan Jr
CTO: Tamara Berger
Dir IT: Ray Daniel
Board of Directors: R Miles Ledgerwood, Manuel Lujan Jr

INN ON BARTON CREEK, THE
See SOUTH DAVIS COMMUNITY HOSPITAL

D-U-N-S 16-704-6478
INN ON WESTPORT LIMITED PARTNERSHIP
WWW.INNONWESTPORT.COM
4000 S Westport Ave, Sioux Falls, SD 57106-2356
Tel (605) 362-1210 *Founded/Ownrshp* 1994
Sales 25.4MM *EMP* 82
SIC 8059 Domiciliary care
Pt: John B Goodman

INNCO
See OIL STATES SYSTEMS INC

D-U-N-S 05-521-8762 IMP
INNER CITY BROADCASTING CORP
333 7th Ave Rm 1401, New York, NY 10001-5092
Tel (212) 447-1000 *Founded/Ownrshp* 1972
Sales 31.6MM^E *EMP* 200
SIC 4832 4841 Radio broadcasting stations; Cable television services; Radio broadcasting stations; Cable television services
Ch Bd: Pierre Sutton
**Pr:* Debbie Jackson
CFO: William Cooper
**V Ch Bd:* Hal Jackson
MIS Dir: Ferd Jewell
Sls Dir: Leon Van Gelder

D-U-N-S 79-161-0368
INNER CITY EDUCATION FOUNDATION
ICEF PUBLIC SCHOOLS
5120 W Goldleaf Cir # 350, Los Angeles, CA 90056-1660
Tel (323) 290-6900 *Founded/Ownrshp* 1995
Sales 23.7MM^E *EMP* 300^E
SIC 8211 Private elementary & secondary schools; Private elementary & secondary schools
CEO: Nathaniel Parker Hudnut
**COO:* Kenneth Zeff
VP: Marie Morelock
Off Mgr: Melinda Dockery
Off Mgr: Ava Onwu
Off Mgr: Kazuki Uema
Dir IT: Irving Arana
IT Man: Greg Brendel
Pr Dir: Debra Price
Psych: Amber Willis

INNER SPACE CONSTRUCTORS DIV
See HUTCHISON CORP

D-U-N-S 11-898-0184
INNER-PARISH SECURITY CORP
IPSC
43222 Pecan Ridge Dr, Hammond, LA 70403-0605
Tel (985) 542-7960 *Founded/Ownrshp* 1977
Sales 23.2MM^E *EMP* 700^E
Accts Lee Gray Cpa
SIC 7381 7382 Security guard service; Security systems services; Security guard service; Security systems services
Pr: Mark Hamilton Leto Sr
Pr: Sal Ruffino
VP: Brian Hollis
**VP:* Michael D Leto
VP: Michael Leto

D-U-N-S 00-112-8834 EXP
INNER-TITE CORP (MA)
110 Industrial Dr, Holden, MA 01520-1893
Tel (508) 829-6361 *Founded/Ownrshp* 1917, 1987
Sales 22.1MM^E *EMP* 85
SIC 3699 3429 Security devices; Locks or lock sets
Pr: George W Davis
VP: Rick Novia
Exec: Christy Mattison
Dir IT: Steve Foley
IT Man: Scott Powell
Plnt Mgr: John Mahaney
Sales Exec: Lee Holovnia
Sls Mgr: Jeremy Auger
Sls Mgr: William Brozowski
Sls Mgr: Jack Killoran
Sls Mgr: Raymond Mills

INNERASIA TRAVEL GROUP
See GEOGRAPHIC EXPEDITIONS INC

D-U-N-S 15-342-8719
INNERPAC LLC
250 N Mannheim Rd, Hillside, IL 60162-1835
Tel (630) 789-1369 *Founded/Ownrshp* 1986
Sales NA *EMP* 350
SIC 2653 7389

D-U-N-S 95-985-2810
INNERSEA DISCOVERIES LLC
AMERICAN SAFARI CRUISES
3826 18th Ave W, Seattle, WA 98119-1616
Tel (206) 284-0300 *Founded/Ownrshp* 2009
Sales 21.4MM^E *EMP* 82
SIC 4725 Tour operators
CFO: Eric Gier
**Ex VP:* Tim Jacox
VP: Tim Voss
Comm Dir: Sarah Scoltock
Dir Bus: Blanca-Stella Lanao
Sls Dir: Yolanda Brown
Sls Mgr: Mike Bollen
Sales Asso: Naomi Sture
Snr Mgr: Dan Blanchard
Snr Mgr: Jeff Coult

D-U-N-S 07-744-7964 IMP
■ **INNERWIRELESS INC**
BLACK BOX NETWORK SERVICES
(*Suby of* BLACK BOX CORP) ★
1155 Kas Dr Ste 200, Richardson, TX 75081-7213
Tel (972) 201-2532 *Founded/Ownrshp* 1998
Sales 22.9MM^E *EMP* 90
SIC 5063 Wire & cable; Wire & cable
Pr: Michael McAndrew
**CEO:* Ed Cantwell
**COO:* Darla Braun
**CFO:* Chris McCoy
Treas: Chris G Mc Coy
Sr VP: Bill Holman
**Sr VP:* James McCoy
**VP:* Timothy C Huffmyer
CTO: Frederick Robertson
IT Man: Jim Davis
Sls Dir: Paul Brown

D-U-N-S 10-135-4012 IMP/EXP
▲ **INNERWORKINGS INC**
600 W Chicago Ave Ste 750, Chicago, IL 60654-2524
Tel (312) 642-3700 *Founded/Ownrshp* 2002
Sales 1.0MMM *EMP* 1,500
Accts Ernst & Young Llp Chicago Il
Tkr Sym INWK *Exch* NGS
SIC 2752 7374 7372 Commercial printing, lithographic; Data processing & preparation; Publishers' computer software; Commercial printing, lithographic; Data processing & preparation; Publishers' computer software
Pr: Eric D Belcher
COO: John D Eisel
CFO: Joseph M Busky
CFO: Jeffrey P Pritchett
Chf Mktg O: Leigh Segall
Ex VP: Scott Frisoni
Sr VP: Jan Sevcik
Creative D: Tiffany Neuman
Dir Bus: Jessica Baldacchino
Dir Bus: John Cunningham
Dir Bus: Joe Wester
Board of Directors: Charles K Bobrinskoy, David Fisher, Daniel M Friedberg, J Patrick Gallagher Jr, Jack M Greenberg, Julie M Howard, Linda S Wolf

D-U-N-S 06-791-0907
INNFLUX LLC
(*Suby of* THINGS LLC) ★
850 W Jackson Blvd # 250, Chicago, IL 60607-3048
Tel (312) 850-3399 *Founded/Ownrshp* 2015
Sales 17.9MM^E *EMP* 442^E
SIC 4813 7011 ; Hotels & motels
Co-CEO: Brian Oconnor
**Co-CEO:* Michael Grabenstein
VP: Jeremiah Carscadden
VP: Chris Drinkall
**CTO:* Chris Wieland
VP Sls: Ken Cook

INNISBROOK WRAPS
See SHAMROCK CORP

D-U-N-S 78-331-4776
INNISFREE HOTELS INC
113 Bay Bridge Dr, Gulf Breeze, FL 32561-4470
Tel (850) 934-3609 *Founded/Ownrshp* 1985
Sales 100.0MM *EMP* 2,000
SIC 7011 Hotels & motels
CEO: Julian B Macqueen
**Pr:* Harlan Butler
Pr: Jill Miller
**CFO:* Brooks Moore
Ofcr: Al Parker
**VP:* Michael Nixon
**VP:* Carol Ruben
Genl Mgr: Gina Dudley
Genl Mgr: Sharon Ehmann
Sales Asso: Tom Rasinen

D-U-N-S 87-827-8571
INNKEEPERS HOSPITALITY INC
ISLAND HOSPITALITY MANAGEMENT
50 Cocoanut Row Ste 212, Palm Beach, FL 33480-4027
Tel (561) 655-9001 *Founded/Ownrshp* 1994
Sales 24.2MM^E *EMP* 600
SIC 7011 Hotels & motels; Hotels; Inns; Hotels & motels; Hotels; Inns
Pr: Jeffrey H Fisher
COO: Thomas Otte
**COO:* Reandy Webb
Sr VP: Walt Jeff
VP: Richard Mielbye
VP: Mark Murphy
VP Bus Dev: Laura Davidson
VP Bus Dev: Peter Willis
Dir IT: Ron Foster

D-U-N-S 01-035-1930
INNO-FLEX CORP (MN)
(*Suby of* BERYL CORP) ★
7101 31st Ave N, Minneapolis, MN 55427-2848
Tel (763) 536-1007 *Founded/Ownrshp* 1973
Sales 38.6MM^E *EMP* 190
SIC 3625 Industrial controls: push button, selector switches, pilot; Industrial controls: push button, selector switches, pilot
CEO: Zelman Levine
**Pr:* John Pesonen
**CFO:* Bruce Hilden
**VP:* Craig Levine
Sls Mgr: Paul Clemons

D-U-N-S 82-655-9101 IMP
INNO-PAK LLC
1932 Pittsburgh Dr, Delaware, OH 43015-3868
Tel (740) 363-0090 *Founded/Ownrshp* 2007
Sales 80.0MM *EMP* 43^E
SIC 5162 Plastics materials; Plastics materials

D-U-N-S 11-147-8587
INNOCEAN WORLDWIDE AMERICAS LLC
180 5th St Ste 200, Huntington Beach, CA 92648-7107
Tel (714) 861-5200 *Founded/Ownrshp* 2002
Sales 49.6MM^E *EMP* 192^E
SIC 7311 Advertising agencies; Advertising agencies
CFO: Yun Jong Beak
Sr VP: Cynthia Jensen
VP: Eddie Austin
VP: Ben Gogley
VP: Cecilia Gorman
VP: Carol Lombard
VP: Marisstella Marinkovic
VP: Miles Turpin
VP: Chang Yoo
VP: Jim Zabel
Creative D: Greg Braun
Creative D: Lon Davis
Creative D: Charles Gerstner
Creative D: Ed Gines
Creative D: David Mesfin

INNOCOR FOAM TECHNOLOGIES
See INNOCOR INC

D-U-N-S 79-649-0584
INNOCOR FOAM TECHNOLOGIES LLC
ADVANCED COMFORT PRODUCTS
(*Suby of* INNOCOR FOAM TECHNOLOGIES) ★
187 State Route 36 # 101, West Long Branch, NJ 07764-1343
Tel (732) 263-0800 *Founded/Ownrshp* 2009
Sales 135.4MM^E *EMP* 408^E
SIC 3086 Plastics foam products; Carpet & rug cushions, foamed plastic; Insulation or cushioning material, foamed plastic; Padding, foamed plastic; Plastics foam products; Carpet & rug cushions, foamed plastic; Insulation or cushioning material, foamed plastic; Padding, foamed plastic
Ch Bd: Diane Price Baker
**CEO:* Michael C Thompson
**CFO:* Stuart Stoller
VP: Judy Kelman
**VP Opers:* Steven Setzer
Board of Directors: Richard A Heller, Todd A Robinson, Fancis Scriceo

D-U-N-S 78-855-7015 IMP/EXP
INNOCOR INC
INNOCOR FOAM TECHNOLOGIES
(*Suby of* SUN CAPITAL PARTNERS INC) ★
187 Rte 36 Ste 101, West Long Branch, NJ 07764-1343
Tel (732) 263-0800 *Founded/Ownrshp* 2012
Sales 426.4MM^E *EMP* 685
SIC 2515 2392 3069 Mattresses & foundations; Cushions & pillows; Bathmats, rubber; Mattresses & foundations; Cushions & pillows; Bathmats, rubber
CEO: Carol S Eicher
**COO:* Robert West
**CFO:* Doug Vaughan
**Ex VP:* Michael Loomis
VP: Lisa Cohen
Natl Sales: Jewelee Racioppi
Sls Dir: James Harris
Board of Directors: Richard A Heller, Todd A Robinson, Francis M Scricco, Michael C Thompson

D-U-N-S 19-516-0908
▲ **INNODATA INC**
3 University Plz, Hackensack, NJ 07601-6208
Tel (201) 371-8000 *Founded/Ownrshp* 1988

Sales 59.0MM *EMP* 5,090^E
Tkr Sym INOD *Exch* NGM
SIC 7374 Data processing & preparation; Data processing & preparation; Data entry service
Ch Bd: Jack S Abuhoff
Pr: Klaas Brouwer
COO: Ashok Mishra
CFO: O'Neil Nalavadi
VP: Sperling J Martin
Div Mgr: Dave Mariano
Board of Directors: Haig S Bagerdjian, Louise C Forlenza, Stewart R Massey, Anthea C Stratigos

D-U-N-S 11-932-0781
INNOMARK COMMUNICATIONS LLC
420 Distribution Cir, Fairfield, OH 45014-5473
Tel (513) 285-1040 *Founded/Ownrshp* 2000
Sales 39.6MM^E *EMP* 98
SIC 7319 Display advertising service
Exec: Paul Molyneaux
CFO: Bill Witters
VP: Todd Garritano
Creative D: Mike Kerth
Genl Mgr: Bron Wolff
Snr Ntwrk: Greg Frimming
Plnt Mgr: Kent Johncox
Natl Sales: Sean Garry
Sls Dir: Michael Jenkins

D-U-N-S 82-781-3762
INNOPATH SOFTWARE INC
333 W El Camino Real # 230, Sunnyvale, CA 94087-1973
Tel (408) 962-9200 *Founded/Ownrshp* 1999
Sales 40.4MM^E *EMP* 210
SIC 7371 Computer software development; Computer software development
Pr: John Fazio
**VP:* Naresh Bansal
**VP:* Adrian Chan
**VP:* Mark Fazio
VP: Carla Fitzgerald
**VP:* Eric King
**VP:* Dave McCroskey
Board of Directors: Tom Bevilacqua, Edward Thompson

D-U-N-S 61-090-3960
▲ INNOPHOS HOLDINGS INC
259 Prospect Plains Rd, Cranbury, NJ 08512-3706
Tel (609) 495-2495 *Founded/Ownrshp* 2004
Sales 839.1MM *EMP* 1,427^E
Accts Pricewaterhousecoopers Llp Fl
Tkr Sym IPHS *Exch* NGS
SIC 2874 2819 Phosphatic fertilizers; Industrial inorganic chemicals; Phosphatic fertilizers; Industrial inorganic chemicals
Ch Bd: Randolph Gress
V Ch: Dennis Dean
CFO: Mark Feuerbach
VP: Charles Brodheim
VP: Bernard Carneal
VP: Cher Dacosta
VP: William Farran
VP: Joseph Golowski
Exec: Louis Calvarin
Exec: Roma Harris
Exec: Steve Schmitz
Comm Man: Jo Sterenberg
Board of Directors: Gary Cappeline, Amado Cavazos, Linda Myrick, Karen Osar, John Steitz, James Zallie

D-U-N-S 15-553-2257 IMP/EXP
■ INNOPHOS INC
(*Suby of* INNOPHOS INVESTMENTS II INC) ★
259 Prospect Plains Rd, Cranbury, NJ 08512-3706
Tel (609) 495-2495 *Founded/Ownrshp* 2004
Sales 277.5MM^E *EMP* 990
SIC 2819 2874 Industrial inorganic chemicals; Phosphates; Industrial inorganic chemicals; Phosphates
Pr: Randolph Gress
CFO: Neil Salmon
VP: Thomas Benner
VP: Louis Calvarin PHD
VP: William Farran
VP: Jose Gonzalez
VP: Karen Kennedy
CTO: Fernando Birman
QA Dir: Jane Murphy
Dir IT: Walter Matchim
Dir IT: Ali Najafi
Board of Directors: Gary Cappeline, Amado Cavazos, Linda Myrick, Karen Osar, John Steitz, Stephen Zide

D-U-N-S 07-950-7424
■ INNOPHOS INVESTMENTS II INC
(*Suby of* INNOPHOS INVESTMENTS HOLDINGS, INC.)
259 Prospect Plains Rd, Cranbury, NJ 08512-3706
Tel (609) 495-2495 *Founded/Ownrshp* 2012
Sales 277.5MM^E *EMP* 990^E
SIC 2874 2819 Phosphates; Industrial inorganic chemicals; Phosphates; Industrial inorganic chemicals
Ch Bd: Randolph Gress
CFO: Mark Feuerbach
VP: Iris Alvarado
VP: Charles Brodheim
VP: William Farran

D-U-N-S 09-378-8651 IMP
■ INNOSPEC ACTIVE CHEMICALS LLC (GA)
(*Suby of* INNOSPEC INC) ★
510 W Grimes Ave, High Point, NC 27260-6545
Tel (336) 882-3308 *Founded/Ownrshp* 2001, 2007
Sales 74.0MM *EMP* 130
SIC 2869 Industrial organic chemicals; Industrial organic chemicals
**VP:* Bruce McDonald
Exec: Lisa Hall
CTO: Jane Hall
IT Man: Katrina Parnell

D-U-N-S 07-390-1295 IMP
INNOSPEC FUEL SPECIALTIES LLC
8310 S Valley Hwy Ste 350, Englewood, CO 80112-5931
Tel (303) 792-5554 *Founded/Ownrshp* 2007
Sales 39.1MM^E *EMP* 100^E
SIC 2911 2899 Fuel additives; Chemical preparations; Fuel additives; Chemical preparations
CEO: Patrick Williams
CFO: Maher Jad
**Ex VP:* Phil Boon
**Ex VP:* Ian Cleminson
**Sr VP:* Cathy Hessner
Sr VP: Lisa Mandell
**Sr VP:* Ian McRobbie
VP: Ian Macmillan
VP: Brian Watt
Comm Man: Kate Davison
IT Man: Kevin Ellis

D-U-N-S 04-200-6515 IMP
▲ INNOSPEC INC
8310 S Valley Hwy Ste 350, Englewood, CO 80112-5931
Tel (303) 792-5554 *Founded/Ownrshp* 1938
Sales 960.9MM *EMP* 1,300
Tkr Sym IOSP *Exch* NGS
SIC 2911 2869 Fuel additives; Perfumes, flavorings & food additives; Fuel additives; Perfumes, flavorings & food additives
Pr: Patrick S Williams
CFO: Ian P Cleminson
Chf Cred: David E Williams
Ex VP: Philip J Boon
Sr VP: Catherine Hessner
Sr VP: Ian M McRobbie
VP: Brian R Watt
Sls Dir: Kevin Adamson
Snr Mgr: Andrew McKnight

INNOTEC AUTOMATION
See INNOTEC CORP

D-U-N-S 79-746-9103 IMP
INNOTEC CORP
INNOTEC AUTOMATION
441 E Roosevelt Ave, Zeeland, MI 49464-1278
Tel (616) 772-5959 *Founded/Ownrshp* 1992
Sales 29.0MM^E *EMP* 90^E
SIC 3469 3679 Metal stampings; Electronic circuits; Metal stampings; Electronic circuits
Pr: Michael Lanser
**Sec:* Pete Lanser
**VP:* Bryan Lanser

D-U-N-S 12-094-3535
INNOTRAC CORP
(*Suby of* BLUE EAGLE HOLDINGS LP) ★
6465 E Johns Xing Ste 400, Johns Creek, GA 30097-1581
Tel (678) 584-4000 *Founded/Ownrshp* 2014
Sales 218.6MM^E *EMP* 1,450^E
SIC 7389 7374 8742 Telephone services; Telemarketing services; Data processing & preparation; Marketing consulting services; Telephone services; Telemarketing services; Data processing & preparation; Marketing consulting services
CEO: Ramesh Srinivasan
**COO:* Robert J Toner
CFO: George Hare
**CFO:* Stephen G Keaveney
**Sr VP:* Larry C Hanger
**Sr VP:* Edgar L Ringer
VP: Brent Dorfman
VP: Glen Fernaux
**Dir Surg:* Christine A Herren
CIO: Matt Gross
Dir IT: John Cummings
Board of Directors: Scott Dorfman

D-U-N-S 07-963-0874
INNOVA ATLANTIC WHITE HORSE OPERATIONS LLC
HAMMONTON CENTER FOR REHABILIT
43 N White Horse Pike, Hammonton, NJ 08037-1875
Tel (609) 567-3100 *Founded/Ownrshp* 2011
Sales 20.6MM *EMP* 250
SIC 8051 Rehabilitation services; Skilled nursing care facilities; Mental retardation hospital
Owner: Kenneth Rozenberg

INNOVA ELECTRONICS
See HUNTING INNOVA INC

INNOVA HOSPITAL SAN ANTONIO
See VICTORY MEDICAL CENTER SOUTHCROSS LP

INNOVA IDEAS & SERVICES
See SIGLER COMPANIES INC

D-U-N-S 07-957-0700
INNOVA SOLUTIONS INC
4633 Old Ironsides Dr # 320, Santa Clara, CA 95054-1846
Tel (408) 889-2020 *Founded/Ownrshp* 2014
Sales 30.0MM *EMP* 88
SIC 7379 Computer related consulting services; Computer related consulting services
CEO: Rajkumar Velagapud

D-U-N-S 60-594-4870
INNOVACARE SERVICES CO LLC
173 Bridge Plz N, Fort Lee, NJ 07024-7575
Tel (201) 969-2300 *Founded/Ownrshp* 2012
Sales NA *EMP* 1,304
SIC 6324 8011 8741 8742 Group hospitalization plans; Health maintenance organization; Management services; Marketing consulting services; Group hospitalization plans; Health maintenance organization; Management services; Marketing consulting services
Pr: Rick Shinto
**Ch Bd:* Daniel E Straus
Pr: Stacy Mays
**Pr:* Timothy J O'Donnell
Pr: Timothy P O'Rourke
Pr: Raul F Montalvo Orsini
COO: Marcia Anderson
**COO:* Penelope Kokkinides
**COO:* Jess Parks
CFO: Kim Bressen
**CFO:* Douglas Malton
**Chf Cred:* Nancy Waltermire
Chf Mktg O: Rod St Clair
**Ex VP:* John S Brittain Jr
**Ex VP:* Robert G Torricelli
**Sr VP:* Eugene Huang
**VP:* Mark Cary
VP: Carol Hairston
**VP:* Howard Kamins
**VP:* Samir Mistry
VP: Samir K Mistry

D-U-N-S 96-185-2449 IMP
■ INNOVACON INC
(*Suby of* ALERE INC) ★
9975 Summers Ridge Rd, San Diego, CA 92121-2997
Tel (858) 805-8900 *Founded/Ownrshp* 2006
Sales 20.3MM^E *EMP* 70
SIC 2835 In vitro & in vivo diagnostic substances
CEO: John Bridgen
**Pr:* Jixun Lin
VP: Edward Tung
QA Dir: Sharon Chavez
Sls Mgr: Marki Andrews
Sls Mgr: Steven Smith

INNOVAGE
See TOTAL COMMUNITY OPTIONS INC

D-U-N-S 60-309-1281 IMP/EXP
INNOVAGE LLC
(*Suby of* INNOVAGE CANADA LIMITED)
4490 Von Karman Ave, Newport Beach, CA 92660-2008
Tel (949) 587-9207 *Founded/Ownrshp* 1988
Sales 65.0MM^E *EMP* 100
SIC 5112 Stationery & office supplies; Stationery & office supplies
Dir IT: Larry Tenebaum
VP: Corey Udkoff
Genl Mgr: Barry Messner
IT Man: Brian Drinkwater

D-U-N-S 07-971-5742
INNOVAIRRE COMMUNICATIONS LLC
825 Hylton Rd, Pennsauken, NJ 08110-1307
Tel (856) 663-2500 *Founded/Ownrshp* 2014
Sales 81.0MM^E *EMP* 150^E
SIC 7389 Fund raising organizations
CEO: Don McKenzie
Pr: Dean Wimer
CFO: Drew Moyer
VP: Dawn Brelsford
VP: Rebecca Sijl-Gacel

D-U-N-S 05-832-7834 IMP
INNOVANCE INC
505 W Front St, Albert Lea, MN 56007-2751
Tel (507) 377-8910 *Founded/Ownrshp* 1972
Sales 76.6MM *EMP* 730
Accts Cliftonlarsonallen Llp Austin
SIC 3599 3544 3469 Machine shop, jobbing & repair; Special dies, tools, jigs & fixtures; Metal stampings; Machine shop, jobbing & repair; Special dies, tools, jigs & fixtures; Metal stampings
Pr: Mike L W Larson
CFO: Steve Tufte
VP: Randy Eggum
Board of Directors: James Anderson, Dan Dolan, Louis S Larson, Dave Lundak, Scott Thiss

INNOVANT GROUP
See INNOVANT INC

D-U-N-S 15-341-7626 IMP
INNOVANT INC
INNOVANT GROUP
84 Ferris Hill Rd, New Canaan, CT 06840-3822
Tel (203) 966-1305 *Founded/Ownrshp* 2003
Sales 42.7MM^E *EMP* 172
SIC 2521 Wood office furniture; Wood office furniture
Pr: Charles Braham
**VP:* Garrett Pluck

D-U-N-S 05-371-9188
INNOVASIAN CUISINE ENTERPRISES INC
18251 Cascade Ave S Ste B, Tukwila, WA 98188-4700
Tel (425) 251-3706 *Founded/Ownrshp* 1999
Sales 86.5MM *EMP* 37
SIC 5149 Specialty food items
CEO: Joe Zalke

D-U-N-S 04-707-7156
INNOVASYSTEMS INTERNATIONAL LLC
2385 Northside Dr Ste 300, San Diego, CA 92108-2716
Tel (619) 756-6500 *Founded/Ownrshp* 1997
Sales 52.7MM^E *EMP* 300^E
SIC 7371 7373 7379 7376 Custom computer programming services; Computer integrated systems design; Computer related maintenance services; Computer facilities management; Custom computer programming services; Computer integrated systems design; Computer related maintenance services; Computer facilities management
CFO: Lynn Hutton
COO: Mike McCoy
Ex VP: Jan Rhu
Sr VP: David Roberts
IT Man: Ian Chase
Software D: Lynn Bastian
Software D: Micheal Slentz
Software D: Christopher Story
Sftwr Eng: William Antilla
Sftwr Eng: Devon Arrington
Sftwr Eng: Derek Blake

D-U-N-S 05-787-1147
INNOVATED MACHINE & TOOL CO INC
250 Picketts Line, Newport News, VA 23603-1366
Tel (757) 887-2181 *Founded/Ownrshp* 1985
Sales 25.1MM^E *EMP* 50
SIC 3441 Fabricated structural metal
CEO: Dwight Bryant
**Pr:* Cameron Bryant
**CFO:* Martha Bryant
**VP:* Marti Byrant
**Prin:* Ashley Bryant
**Prin:* Kirsten Gastoukian

INNOVATED MECHANICAL SERVICES
See INDUSTRIAL REFRIGERATION SERVICES INC

D-U-N-S 06-306-3747 IMP
INNOVATION ASSOCIATES INC
530 Columbia Dr Ste 101, Johnson City, NY 13790-1096
Tel (607) 798-9376 *Founded/Ownrshp* 1973
Sales 76.6MM^E *EMP* 150
SIC 3559 8711 Pharmaceutical machinery; Consulting engineer; Pharmaceutical machinery; Consulting engineer
CEO: Mary Reno
Pr: John Wilson
**COO:* Thomas Boyer
**Ch:* Joseph Harry Boyer
**Ex VP:* Doyle Jensen
VP: John Becker
VP: Phil L Samples
VP: Allan Scott
Brnch Mgr: Sandra Cole
Snr Sftwr: Mike Hostetler
Dir IT: David Zembek

D-U-N-S 06-429-6932
INNOVATION DATA PROCESSING INC
275 Paterson Ave Ste 301, Little Falls, NJ 07424-1678
Tel (973) 200-0735 *Founded/Ownrshp* 1972
Sales 25.7MM^E *EMP* 100
SIC 7374 7371 Data processing service; Custom computer programming services
Pr: Anthony Mazzone
**VP:* John Mazzone
**VP:* Thomas J Meehan
Exec: Patrickm Fitzsimmons
DP Dir: Dante Ferman
Software D: Wayne R Bumback
Software D: Ed Gilroy
Software D: Rich Morse
Software D: Terry Thomas
Software D: Ron Wright

D-U-N-S 09-190-9841 IMP
INNOVATION FIRST INC
RACKSOLUTIONS.COM
1519 Interstate Hwy 30 W, Greenville, TX 75402-4810
Tel (903) 453-0800 *Founded/Ownrshp* 1997
Sales 58.7MM^E *EMP* 150
SIC 1731 Electronic controls installation; Electronic controls installation
Pr: David Norman
**CFO:* Warren Weeks
Ex VP: Joe Astroth
VP: Dennis Feeney
**VP:* Bob Mimlitch
VP: Raul Olivera
VP: Julie Sickels
Creative D: Brandon Adams
Rgnl Mgr: Karthik Kanagasabapathy
IT Man: Brandon Martus
IT Man: Tim Norman

D-U-N-S 80-246-5948 EXP
INNOVATION GROUP LTD
409 W 76th St, Davenport, IA 52806-1322
Tel (563) 386-6201 *Founded/Ownrshp* 1993
Sales 25.0MM *EMP* 15
SIC 5099 Timber products, rough; Timber products, rough
Pr: David Suh

D-U-N-S 07-954-4160
■ INNOVATION HEALTH PLAN INC
(*Suby of* AETNA LIFE INSURANCE CO INC) ★
3130 Fairview Park Dr # 300, Falls Church, VA 22042-4529
Tel (703) 914-2925 *Founded/Ownrshp* 2012
Sales NA *EMP* 3,616^E
SIC 6324 Hospital & medical service plans
Ex Dir: Amy Turner

D-U-N-S 05-652-9852 IMP
INNOVATION INDUSTRIES INC
3500 E Main St, Russellville, AR 72802-9673
Tel (479) 968-2232 *Founded/Ownrshp* 1980
Sales 22.4MM^E *EMP* 117
Accts Anthony A D Arezzo Pc Cpa
SIC 3534 Elevators & moving stairways; Elevators & moving stairways
Pr: Paul Horney IV
**Ch:* Zola Horney
VP: Christopher Hannon
**VP:* Guy Horney
Exec: Carol Harris
IT Man: Michael Hilton
IT Man: Joe Keeton
Sls Mgr: Ray Buford

D-U-N-S 80-906-6819
INNOVATION TECHNOLOGY GROUP INC
945 Stewart Dr Ste 200, Sunnyvale, CA 94085-3940
Tel (408) 212-2700 *Founded/Ownrshp* 2007
Sales 20.1MM^E *EMP* 1^E
SIC 8742 Business consultant
Pr: Jomei Chang
VP: Marsha Thompson
Mng Dir: Jan Nielsson

D-U-N-S 16-941-7735
INNOVATION VENTURES LLC
LIVING ESSENTIALS
38955 Hills Tech Dr Ste 1, Farmington Hills, MI 48331-3431
Tel (248) 960-1700 *Founded/Ownrshp* 2000
Sales 171.9MM^E *EMP* 100
SIC 5149 Groceries & related products; Groceries & related products
CEO: Manoj Bhargava
VP: Jeff Stone
Creative D: Carl Sperber
Natl Sales: Garrett Dempsey
VP Sls: Rise Meguiar
Mktg Dir: John Griffin
Mktg Mgr: Kinga Wierzbicka
Art Dir: Kelly Gray

INNOVATIONS BY VP SUPPLY
See V P SUPPLY CORP

D-U-N-S 06-701-1781
INNOVATIONS FOR POVERTY ACTION
188 Livingston St, New Haven, CT 06511-2210
Tel (203) 432-8172 *Founded/Ownrshp* 2011
Sales 40.5MM *EMP* 2
SIC 7389
Prin: Dean Karland

D-U-N-S 80-624-0859
INNOVATIVE AFTERMARKET SYSTEMS LP
10800 Pecan Park Blvd # 410, Austin, TX 78750-1224
Tel (512) 421-8001 *Founded/Ownrshp* 2011
Sales 24.5MM^E *EMP* 100
SIC 5531 7389 Automotive accessories; Telemarketing services
Pt: Bob Corbin
Pt: Paul Clinkscales
Pt: Scott Hendrix
Pt: Jeff Jagoe
CFO: Mike Forsythe
QA Dir: Cindy Thomason
Dir IT: Peggy Howe
Dir IT: Matt Nowicki
IT Man: Bryan Farr
Mktg Dir: Stephanie Carrasquillo
Manager: Tabor Davis

D-U-N-S 61-496-7300
INNOVATIVE AG SERVICES CO
2010 S Main St, Monticello, IA 52310-7707
Tel (319) 465-3501 *Founded/Ownrshp* 2005
Sales 855.2MM *EMP* 500
Accts Meriwether Wilson And Company
SIC 5999 Feed & farm supply; Feed & farm supply
CEO: Rick Vaughan
**Pr:* Randy Blake
**CFO:* Brenda Hoefler
VP: Ron Barkema
**VP:* Paul Cook
Dir IT: Carrie Lyons
Dir IT: Bob Twining
VP Opers: Brian Kramer
VP Sls: Michael Duncomb
S&M/VP: Mike Duncomb
Snr Mgr: Mark Bradke

D-U-N-S 07-879-1912
INNOVATIVE BLOOD RESOURCES
MEMORIAL BLOOD CENTERS
737 Pelham Blvd, Saint Paul, MN 55114-1739
Tel (651) 332-7000 *Founded/Ownrshp* 2013
Sales 53.3MM *EMP* 474^E
Accts Cliftonlarsonallen Llp Minne
SIC 8099 Blood bank; Blood bank
Pr: Donald C Berglund
Pr: Ellen Disalvo
**COO:* Jeffrey D Allen
CFO: John Buske
Bd of Dir: Phil Losacker
VP: Kristine Belanger
VP: Mark Janzen
Dir IT: Pearse Ward
IT Man: Kelly Gillaspie
Pathlgst: Elizabeth Perry

D-U-N-S 96-857-4082
INNOVATIVE BUILDING SYSTEMS LLC
4900 Ritter Rd Ste 130, Mechanicsburg, PA 17055-6929
Tel (717) 458-1400 *Founded/Ownrshp* 2014
Sales 71.9MM^E *EMP* 200
SIC 2452 Prefabricated wood buildings
Ex VP: Jolene Myers

D-U-N-S 02-864-8554
INNOVATIVE CAPITAL HOLDINGS INC
225 Banyan Blvd Ste 230, Naples, FL 34102-5156
Tel (239) 228-5000 *Founded/Ownrshp* 2013
Sales 32.8MM^E *EMP* 130^E
SIC 6719 3724 Personal holding companies, except banks; Aircraft engines & engine parts

D-U-N-S 02-395-7322 IMP
INNOVATIVE CHEMICAL TECHNOLOGIES INC
I C T
103 Walnut Grove Rd Se, Cartersville, GA 30120-6427
Tel (770) 607-9340 *Founded/Ownrshp* 1998
Sales 44.9MM^E *EMP* 40
SIC 5169 2899 Chemicals & allied products; Chemical preparations
CEO: Jeffrey R Alender
VP: Bruce Baker

D-U-N-S 18-947-1642 IMP
INNOVATIVE COMMUNICATION CONCEPTS INC
I C C
519 8th Ave Frnt 4, New York, NY 10018-4517
Tel (212) 699-3200 *Founded/Ownrshp* 1982
Sales 29.7MM^E *EMP* 60^E
SIC 5065 1731 7629 Telephone equipment; Telephone & telephone equipment installation; Telephone set repair
CEO: William Wenzel
**Pr:* Edward Panzenbeck
VP: Lee Bear
VP: Robert Sese
CTO: Latchman Singh
Netwrk Mgr: Dan Dalessandro

D-U-N-S 00-596-5756 IMP
INNOVATIVE COMMUNICATIONS CORP
INNOVATIVE TELEPHONES
4611 Tutu Park Mall # 200, St Thomas, VI 00802-1735
Tel (340) 777-7700 *Founded/Ownrshp* 1997
Sales 40.8MM^E *EMP* 500
SIC 4813 4841 Telephone communication, except radio; Local & long distance telephone communications; ; Data telephone communications; Cable television services; Telephone communication, except radio; Local & long distance telephone communications; ; Data telephone communications; Cable television services
CEO: Seth Davis
**Pr:* Shawn O-Donnell
Trst: Adrian Labennett
VP: Mickey Breton
VP: Beverly Chongasing
VP: Jennifer Matarangas-King
VP: Emiel Michiels
Genl Mgr: Brent Butler
IT Man: Rene Henry
Opers Mgr: Bob Vanooyen
Pr Mgr: Willa Fils

D-U-N-S 61-939-5523 IMP
INNOVATIVE COMPANIES LLC
130 Motor Pkwy, Hauppauge, NY 11788-5107
Tel (631) 273-4445 *Founded/Ownrshp* 2002
Sales 55.4MM^E *EMP* 539
SIC 5032 Building stone; Building stone

INNOVATIVE CONCEPT
See BOARDMAN MEDICAL SUPPLY CO

D-U-N-S 78-057-7305
INNOVATIVE CONCEPTS INTERNATIONAL LLC
18706 Chopin Dr, Lutz, FL 33558-2874
Tel (813) 393-6425 *Founded/Ownrshp* 2005
Sales 30.0MM *EMP* 5
SIC 7382 1542 1799 Security systems services; Nonresidential construction; Artificial turf installation; Security systems services; Nonresidential construction; Artificial turf installation
VP: Don Zimmerman

D-U-N-S 00-865-3870
INNOVATIVE CONSTRUCTION SOLUTIONS INC (CA)
4011 W Chandler Ave, Santa Ana, CA 92704-5201
Tel (714) 893-6366 *Founded/Ownrshp* 1999
Sales 21.8MM^E *EMP* 105
SIC 8744 1795 ; Demolition, buildings & other structures
Pr: Hirad Emadi
**VP:* John R White
Snr PM: Jason Goldsbrough
Snr PM: Don Lawrence

D-U-N-S 07-976-2139
INNOVATIVE CONSTRUCTION SOLUTIONS INC (WI)
INNOVATVE CONSTRUCTION SOL INC
21675 Gateway Rd, Brookfield, WI 53045-5137
Tel (262) 790-1911 *Founded/Ownrshp* 1994
Sales 46.2MM *EMP* 35
SIC 1542 Nonresidential construction; Nonresidential construction
Pr: David Schwartz
VP: David England
VP: Robert Lumley
**VP:* Maureen Miller Schwartz
Off Mgr: Cheryl Brown
Snr PM: Brian Strandt
Snr PM: Jack Tomkiewicz

INNOVATIVE CONSUMER PACKAGING
See CRAWFORD INDUSTRIES LLC

D-U-N-S 78-301-7858
INNOVATIVE CONTROL SYSTEMS INC
I C S
1349 Jacobsburg Rd, Wind Gap, PA 18091-9716
Tel (610) 881-8000 *Founded/Ownrshp* 1988
Sales 24.9MM^E *EMP* 85
SIC 3589 Car washing machinery; Car washing machinery
Pr: Kevin W Detrick
**Sec:* Karen Miller
**Ex VP:* Brian Bath
**VP:* Rob Deal
Comm Man: Jeff Labarre
Sls Mgr: Robert Wingard

D-U-N-S 15-039-0078 IMP
■ **INNOVATIVE DESIGN SOLUTIONS INC**
IDS
(*Suby of* HOME-STYLE INDUSTRIES) ★
6801 15 Mile Rd, Sterling Heights, MI 48312-4517
Tel (248) 583-1010 *Founded/Ownrshp* 2014
Sales 50.2MM^E *EMP* 120
SIC 3571 Electronic computers
Pr: Robert Ford
**VP:* Shawn Haley

INNOVATIVE DIAGNOSTIC LAB
See HEALTH DIAGNOSTIC LABORATORY INC

D-U-N-S 14-718-7298
INNOVATIVE DIALYSIS PARTNERS INC
(*Suby of* US RENAL CARE INC) ★
1 World Trade Ctr, Long Beach, CA 90831-0002
Tel (562) 495-8075 *Founded/Ownrshp* 2013
Sales 33.8MM^E *EMP* 350
SIC 5999 8092

D-U-N-S 13-672-3314 IMP/EXP
INNOVATIVE DISPLAYWORKS INC
I D W
8825 Boston Pl, Rancho Cucamonga, CA 91730-4922
Tel (909) 447-8254 *Founded/Ownrshp* 2001
Sales 30.4MM *EMP* 40
Accts Vicente Lloyd & Stutzman Llp
SIC 5046 3441 2541 Display equipment, except refrigerated; Fabricated structural metal; Display fixtures, wood; Display equipment, except refrigerated; Fabricated structural metal; Display fixtures, wood
CEO: Leo Wills
**VP:* Nathan W Linder

D-U-N-S 94-405-5003
INNOVATIVE DRIVER SERVICES CO
4400 Stuart Andrew Blvd B, Charlotte, NC 28217-1591
Tel (704) 521-6611 *Founded/Ownrshp* 1996
Sales 17.0MM^E *EMP* 400
SIC 7361 Placement agencies; Placement agencies
CEO: Mark Weir
**Pr:* Brad Kimbirl
Prin: Lisa Fuston

D-U-N-S 11-634-3711
INNOVATIVE EDUCATION MANAGEMENT INC
1166 Broadway Ste Q, Placerville, CA 95667-5745
Tel (530) 295-3566 *Founded/Ownrshp* 1998
Sales 31.6MM *EMP* 53
Accts Feddersen & Company Llp Cpa S
SIC 8741 Management services; Management services
Pr: Randy Gaschler
VP: Jennifer Sanchez

D-U-N-S 60-127-5282
INNOVATIVE EMERGENCY MANAGEMENT INC
IEM
2801 Slater Rd Ste 110, Morrisville, NC 27560-8477
Tel (919) 990-8191 *Founded/Ownrshp* 1985
Sales 58.2MM^E *EMP* 220
SIC 8748 8742 7371 Human resource consulting services; Business consulting; Business consulting; Management consulting services; Planning consultant; Custom computer programming services
Pr: Madhu Beriwal
**Treas:* Dan Michael
VP: John Poulsen
Prd Mgr: Greg Fitzgerald

D-U-N-S 02-575-2093
INNOVATIVE EMPLOYEE SOLUTIONS INC
9665 Gran Rdge Dr Ste 420, San Diego, CA 92123
Tel (858) 715-5100 *Founded/Ownrshp* 1987
Sales 75.0MM^E *EMP* 1,500
SIC 8721 Payroll accounting service; Payroll accounting service
CEO: Karla Hertzog
**Pr:* Gaby Mergenphal
**CFO:* Peter Limone
**VP:* Darlene Bruder
**VP:* Tania Fiero
**VP:* Trevor Foster
**Prin:* Elizabeth M Rice
Off Mgr: Chris Jahn
Sales Exec: Jae Cazimero
Board of Directors: Karla Hertzog

D-U-N-S 80-714-2778
INNOVATIVE ENERGY SERVICES INC
16600 Park Row, Houston, TX 77084-5019
Tel (281) 392-5199 *Founded/Ownrshp* 1988
Sales 133.0MM^E *EMP* 107
SIC 5084 Oil well machinery, equipment & supplies; Oil well machinery, equipment & supplies
Pr: Rick Adams
**Pr:* Doug Gaither
**Sr VP:* William Clayton
Off Mgr: Sally Clayton

D-U-N-S 01-722-7956
INNOVATIVE EXAMS LLC
(*Suby of* PSI EXAMINATION SERVICES) ★
329 W 18th St Ste 613, Chicago, IL 60616-4924
Tel (312) 612-1049 *Founded/Ownrshp* 2015
Sales 18.2MM^E *EMP* 556^E
SIC 8748 Test development & evaluation service
CEO: Ruben A Garcia
VP: David Pascal
CTO: Boris Barvish

D-U-N-S 12-489-4390
INNOVATIVE EXCAVATION INC
INNOVATIVE LANDSCAPE
5403 W Wells Park Rd, West Jordan, UT 84081-5658
Tel (801) 260-1300 *Founded/Ownrshp* 2001
Sales 30.0MM^E *EMP* 120
SIC 1794 4959 0781 Excavation work; Snowplowing; Landscape services; Excavation work; Snowplowing; Landscape services
Pr: Darrin Loertscher
**CFO:* Nate McEntire
Genl Mgr: Kasey Jiron
Sls Mgr: Allen Quille

D-U-N-S 07-959-8019
INNOVATIVE FIXTURE SOLUTIONS LLC
1122 Milford Ave, Rockford, IL 61109-3636
Tel (815) 395-8500 *Founded/Ownrshp* 2014
Sales 25.0MM *EMP* 100
SIC 2511 Magazine racks: wood; Magazine racks: wood
CEO: Shaun Starbuck

D-U-N-S 10-940-9578 IMP
INNOVATIVE FLEXPAK INC
1530 Mountain Sprng Pkwy, Springville, UT 84663-3000
Tel (801) 491-3220 *Founded/Ownrshp* 2002
Sales 70.2MM^E *EMP* 150
SIC 2834 Vitamin, nutrient & hematinic preparations for human use; Vitamin, nutrient & hematinic preparations for human use
Pr: Travis Parry
Pr: Bryan Wright
CFO: Ryan Gifford
Dir Lab: Taylor Broughton
Prd Mgr: Lori Jones
Ql Cn Mgr: Chantel Wood

INNOVATIVE FOOD CREATIONS
See JAMES CALVETTI MEATS INC

D-U-N-S 55-556-7903
▲ **INNOVATIVE FOOD HOLDINGS INC**
28411 Race Track Rd, Bonita Springs, FL 34135-6845
Tel (239) 596-0204 *Founded/Ownrshp* 2004
Sales 30.8MM *EMP* 263
Tkr Sym IVFH *Exch* OTO
SIC 8322 8742 8099 8049 Meal delivery program; Food & beverage consultant; Nutrition services; Dietician; Meal delivery program; Food & beverage consultant; Nutrition services; Dietician
CEO: Sam Klepfish
**Pr:* Justin Wiernesz

INNOVATIVE FOOD PROCESSORS
See IFP INC

D-U-N-S 10-068-2298 IMP/EXP
INNOVATIVE GAS SYSTEMS INC
16250 State Highway 249, Houston, TX 77086-1014
Tel (713) 937-5200 *Founded/Ownrshp* 2001
Sales 32.8MM^E *EMP* 125
SIC 3081 Unsupported plastics film & sheet; Unsupported plastics film & sheet
Pr: Tom Jeffers
**CFO:* E J Devine
Genl Mgr: Barry Smith
Genl Mgr: Tony Troiano

INNOVATIVE HEALTH PRODUCTS
See GEOPHARMA INC

D-U-N-S 07-865-6004
INNOVATIVE HEARTH HOLDINGS LLC
INNOVATIVE HEARTH PRODUCTS IHP
1508 Elm Hill Pike # 108, Nashville, TN 37210-3635
Tel (714) 549-7782 *Founded/Ownrshp* 1971
Sales 147.2MM^E *EMP* 580
SIC 3433 Wall heaters, except electric; Wall heaters, except electric
CEO: Mark Klein
**CFO:* Linda Pahl

INNOVATIVE HEARTH PRODUCTS
See IHP OPERATIONS LLC

INNOVATIVE HEARTH PRODUCTS IHP
See INNOVATIVE HEARTH HOLDINGS LLC

D-U-N-S 05-479-4466 IMP
INNOVATIVE HEARTH PRODUCTS LLC
LENNOX
1508 Elm Hill Pike # 108, Nashville, TN 37210-3635
Tel (615) 925-3417 *Founded/Ownrshp* 2012
Sales 152.0MM^E *EMP* 349
SIC 3634 3433 Heating units, electric (radiant heat): baseboard or wall; Heating equipment, except electric; Heating units, electric (radiant heat): baseboard or wall; Heating equipment, except electric
Pr: Mark Klein
**CFO:* Linda Pahl
Mtls Mgr: William Baer
VP Sls: Thomas Krebs
Sls Mgr: Steve Evjen

D-U-N-S 96-954-7053
INNOVATIVE HESS PRODUCTS LLC
MILMOUR PRODUCTS
2605 S Clearbrook Dr, Arlington Heights, IL 60005-4625
Tel (847) 676-3260 *Founded/Ownrshp* 1966
Sales 55.9MM^E *EMP* 406
SIC 2821 Plastics materials & resins; Plastics materials & resins

D-U-N-S 82-722-5236 IMP
INNOVATIVE HOLDINGS OF IOWA INC
109 Progressive Dr, Roland, IA 50236-7705
Tel (515) 388-1011 *Founded/Ownrshp* 1993
Sales 24.7MM^E *EMP* 85
SIC 3647 Boat & ship lighting fixtures
Pr: Jerrold L Handsaker
Board of Directors: Roger Handsaker, Richard Parker

D-U-N-S 78-459-4504
INNOVATIVE HOSPITALITY SYSTEMS LLC
4333 Canal St, New Orleans, LA 70119-5944
Tel (305) 591-0413 *Founded/Ownrshp* 2005
Sales 7.9MM^E *EMP* 500
SIC 7349 2899 Janitorial service, contract basis; Chemical preparations; Janitorial service, contract basis; Chemical preparations
CEO: Julio Castro
CFO: Michael Martin

D-U-N-S 13-494-2718
INNOVATIVE IDM LLC
1625 Wallace Dr Ste 110, Carrollton, TX 75006-6654
Tel (214) 574-9500 *Founded/Ownrshp* 2000
Sales 95.9MM^E *EMP* 95
SIC 5063 7622 3699 Electrical apparatus & equipment; Antenna repair & installation; Electrical equipment & supplies; Electrical apparatus & equipment; Antenna repair & installation; Electrical equipment & supplies
Pr: Eugene Gray
VP: Adam Schiller
CTO: Tammy Gray
MIS Mgr: Kenneth Skillett
Opers Mgr: Todd Mueller
Prd Mgr: Luis Santeliz
Sls Mgr: Mike Adams

D-U-N-S 13-312-5869 IMP
INNOVATIVE INJECTION TECHNOLOGIES INC
I2TECH
2360 Grand Ave, West Des Moines, IA 50265-5731
Tel (515) 225-7878 *Founded/Ownrshp* 2003
Sales 57.0MM^E *EMP* 150
SIC 2821 3089 Molding compounds, plastics; Injection molding of plastics; Molding compounds, plastics; Injection molding of plastics
Pr: Robert Janeczko
**CFO:* Morgan Endecott

D-U-N-S 03-267-7213
INNOVATIVE INTERFACES INC
VTLS-VIRTUA
5850 Shellmound St, Emeryville, CA 94608-1966
Tel (510) 655-6200 *Founded/Ownrshp* 1978
Sales 103.7MM^E *EMP* 350
SIC 8231

INNOVATIVE JOINT UTILITY SVCS
See IJUS LLC

INNOVATIVE LANDSCAPE
See INNOVATIVE EXCAVATION INC

D-U-N-S 61-797-5862
INNOVATIVE LIVESTOCK SERVICES INC
2006 Broadway Ave Ste 2c, Great Bend, KS 67530-4043
Tel (620) 793-9200 *Founded/Ownrshp* 2005

Sales 32.1MM^E *EMP* 170
SIC 0139 0211 Alfalfa farm; Beef cattle feedlots
CEO: Lee Borck
**COO:* Andrew Murphy
VP: Stan Myers

D-U-N-S 01-993-3084
INNOVATIVE MANAGEMENT & TECHNOLOGY APPROACHES INC (VA)
IMTAS
2100 Crystal Dr Ste 750, Arlington, VA 22202-3789
Tel (571) 255-6021 *Founded/Ownrshp* 1994
Sales 32.4MM *EMP* 165
SIC 7373 4813 Computer integrated systems design; Telephone communication, except radio; Computer integrated systems design; Telephone communication, except radio
Ch Bd: Ajay Bhatia
COO: Tim Bashara
Prgrm Mgr: Michael Gregory
Genl Mgr: Allen Smith
Dir IT: Rick Martin
IT Man: Kristen Adkins
IT Man: David Borzi

D-U-N-S 06-976-9987
INNOVATIVE MANUFACTURING SOLUTIONS CORP
AMCO ENGINEERING
(*Suby of* IMS COMPANIES LLC) ★
1 Innovation Dr, Des Plaines, IL 60016-3161
Tel (847) 391-8100 *Founded/Ownrshp* 2001
Sales 25.7MM^E *EMP* 205
SIC 3444 Sheet metal specialties, not stamped; Sheet metal specialties, not stamped
Pr: Mark D Simanton
Prgrm Mgr: Devang Kadakia
Dir IT: Don Gorz
VP Opers: Kimberly Daley
Mktg Dir: Jim Walenda

D-U-N-S 83-318-5130
INNOVATIVE MATTRESS SOLUTIONS LLC
MATTRESS WHSE SLEEP OUTFITTERS
11060 Winfield Rd, Winfield, WV 25213-7934
Tel (304) 586-2863 *Founded/Ownrshp* 2002
Sales 86.2MM^E *EMP* 450
SIC 8741 Management services; Management services
CEO: Kimberly Knopf
CFO: Nathen McBrayer
Treas: Kimberly Brown
Chf Mktg O: Steve Kyger
VP: Traci Markham
Exec: Andrew Bloomfield
Mktg Mgr: Steve Plantz

D-U-N-S 86-953-0485
INNOVATIVE METALS CO INC
IMETCO
(*Suby of* GARLAND INDUSTRIES INC) ★
4648 S Old Peachtree Rd, Peachtree Corners, GA 30071-1501
Tel (770) 908-1030 *Founded/Ownrshp* 1994
Sales 26.0MM *EMP* 50^E
SIC 2952 Roofing materials; Roofing materials
CEO: Joseph Orlando
**CFO:* Charles Ripepi
VP: Bruce Rick
Genl Mgr: Scott Kraft
Sys Mgr: Bryan Wood
Plnt Mgr: Billy Tant
Manager: Mark Ricigliaino
Sls Mgr: David Bushman
Sls Mgr: Sean Holloway
Sls Mgr: Joseph Myers
Sls Mgr: Patrick Penza

D-U-N-S 00-834-2198
INNOVATIVE MICRO TECHNOLOGY INC
IMT
75 Robin Hill Rd, Goleta, CA 93117-3108
Tel (805) 681-2807 *Founded/Ownrshp* 2005
Sales 32.9MM^E *EMP* 100
SIC 3674 Semiconductors & related devices; Semiconductors & related devices
Pr: Craig H Ensley
COO: Richard Balanson
**CFO:* Peter Altavilla
CFO: Pete Altivilla
VP: Rich Brossart
**VP:* Paul Pickering
VP: Jill Wittels
Prgrm Mgr: Ryan Pooran
Prgrm Mgr: Benedikt Zeyen
Off Mgr: Bernice Williams
**CTO:* Chris Gudeman
Board of Directors: Malcolm Currie, Rob Herb, Kurt Petersen, Jose Suarez, Barry Waite

INNOVATIVE MOBILITY
See QUALITY ASSURED SERVICES INC

INNOVATIVE MODERN COATERS
See INFRATROL MANUFACTURING CORP

D-U-N-S 16-094-8048 IMP
INNOVATIVE OFFICE PRODUCTS LLC
(*Suby of* CORRIDOR CAPITAL LLC) ★
100 Kuebler Rd, Easton, PA 18040-9288
Tel (610) 559-6369 *Founded/Ownrshp* 2013
Sales 25.0MM^E *EMP* 112
SIC 2522 Office furniture, except wood; Office furniture, except wood
CEO: Joe Tosolt
**CFO:* Kevin McClelland
IT Man: Shawn Woods
Prd Mgr: Joe Mannino
Sls Dir: Tim Jancar
Sls Mgr: Kim Di Paolo
Snr Mgr: Bryan Maldony

D-U-N-S 05-124-0872
INNOVATIVE OFFICE SOLUTIONS LLC
151 Cliff Rd E Ste 40, Burnsville, MN 55337-1586
Tel (952) 808-9900 *Founded/Ownrshp* 2001
Sales 392.6MM^E *EMP* 225
SIC 5112 5021 Office supplies; Office furniture
COO: Julie Owen
CFO: Brooks Smith
Ex VP: Greg McLeod
Exec: John Townsend
CIO: Jason Player

D-U-N-S 87-663-6077 IMP
INNOVATIVE REFRIGERATION SYSTEMS INC
373 Mt Torrey Rd, Lyndhurst, VA 22952-2516
Tel (540) 941-8500 *Founded/Ownrshp* 1994
Sales 34.0MM^E *EMP* 150
SIC 7623 Refrigeration repair service
Pr: Michael J McGinnis
**CFO:* Sandra H McGinnis
Ofcr: David Piller
**VP:* Bob Curran
**VP:* Keith McGinnis
**VP:* John Stoklosa
Off Admin: Rachel Lindberg

D-U-N-S 60-502-1948
INNOVATIVE RESOURCE GROUP LLC
APS HEALTHCARE
(*Suby of* PARTNERS HEALTHCARE SOLUTIONS, INC.)
44 S Broadway Fl 12, White Plains, NY 10601-4411
Tel (800) 305-3720 *Founded/Ownrshp* 2007
Sales 5.7MM^E *EMP* 1,018
SIC 8099 Health screening service; Health screening service

INNOVATIVE RESOURCE MANAGEMENT
See INNOVATIVE WASTE MANAGEMENT INC

D-U-N-S 96-911-1210
INNOVATIVE SERVICE TECHNOLOGY MANAGEMENT SERVICES INC
IST MANAGEMENT SERVICES
934 Glenwood Ave Se # 250, Atlanta, GA 30316-1875
Tel (404) 582-8850 *Founded/Ownrshp* 1997
Sales 98.4MM^E *EMP* 1,500
SIC 8744 Facilities support services; Facilities support services
CEO: Hal Blackman
Pr: Daniel Blechinger
Pr: Chris Eckl
Pr: Ashleigh Fiora
CFO: Dale McKee
Sr VP: Craig Hamel
VP: Jason Jeray
VP Admn: Lori Mitchum
Software D: Dennis Flanagan
Software D: Page Gedney
Software D: Steve Obarowski

D-U-N-S 82-972-1344
INNOVATIVE SERVICES INC
445 S Madison St, Green Bay, WI 54301-4101
Tel (920) 431-0962 *Founded/Ownrshp* 1999
Sales 16.0MM *EMP* 600
Accts Baker Tilly Virchow Krause Ll
SIC 8059 8361 8331 Home for the mentally retarded, exc. skilled or intermediate; Residential care; Job training & vocational rehabilitation services; Home for the mentally retarded, exc. skilled or intermediate; Residential care; Job training & vocational rehabilitation services
COO: Richard Bahr
Prgrm Mgr: Kelsi Conroy

D-U-N-S 19-380-2162
▲ INNOVATIVE SOLUTIONS & SUPPORT INC
720 Pennsylvania Dr, Exton, PA 19341-1129
Tel (610) 646-9800 *Founded/Ownrshp* 1988
Sales 44.1MM *EMP* 146^E
Accts Grant Thornton Llp Philadelp
Tkr Sym ISSC *Exch* NGS
SIC 3812 7371 Aircraft/aerospace flight instruments & guidance systems; Aircraft control instruments; Computer software development & applications; Aircraft/aerospace flight instruments & guidance systems; Aircraft control instruments; Computer software development & applications
Ch Bd: Geoffrey S M Hedrick
Pr: Shahram Askarpour
CFO: Relland M Winand
**V Ch Bd:* Glen R Bressner
VP: Maureen Martin
Assoc Dir: Katherine Ellis
Prgrm Mgr: Kevin Cravens
Prgrm Mgr: Lou Morelli
Genl Mgr: Charlotte Scheld
Snr Sftwr: Bill Sun
Sftwr Eng: Weipo Chessen
Board of Directors: Winston J Churchill, Robert A Mionis, Robert E Mittelstaedt Jr, Robert H Rau

D-U-N-S 04-239-2865
■ INNOVATIVE SOLUTIONS AND SUPPORT LLC
(*Suby of* INNOVATIVE SOLUTIONS & SUPPORT INC) ★
720 Pennsylvania Dr, Malvern, PA 19355
Tel (610) 646-9800 *Founded/Ownrshp* 1988
Sales 46.0MM *EMP* 113
SIC 3728 Aircraft parts & equipment; Aircraft parts & equipment
VP: Jonathan Freiman
VP: Brian Urbanski
Sftwr Eng: Judy Cadmus
VP Opers: Roger Mitchell

D-U-N-S 02-756-3654
INNOVATIVE SOLUTIONS INSURANCE SERVICES LLC
ISISLIFE
200 N Sepulveda Blvd, El Segundo, CA 90245-4340
Tel (310) 851-8222 *Founded/Ownrshp* 1998
Sales NA *EMP* 40
SIC 6411 Insurance agents & brokers; Insurance agents & brokers
Dir IT: Lionel Gusti

D-U-N-S 00-681-5158
INNOVATIVE STAFFING INC (UT)
859 W South Jordan Pkwy # 77, South Jordan, UT 84095-5601
Tel (801) 984-0252 *Founded/Ownrshp* 2000
Sales 30.8MM^E *EMP* 1,100
SIC 7363 Employee leasing service; Employee leasing service
Pr: Michelyn Farnsworth
**VP:* John Farnsworth
VP: Ronald Messenheimer
Comm Man: Kristen Neilson

INNOVATIVE STORAGE SYSTEMS
See INNOVATIVE STORE SYSTEMS INC

D-U-N-S 06-751-1266
INNOVATIVE STORE SYSTEMS INC
INNOVATIVE STORAGE SYSTEMS
1351 S Beach Blvd Ste L, La Habra, CA 90631-1126
Tel (562) 947-4101 *Founded/Ownrshp* 1989
Sales 3.2MM *EMP* 2,019
SIC 2542 Partitions & fixtures, except wood; Partitions & fixtures, except wood
Pr: Ron Benudiz
**CFO:* Natalie Benudiz

INNOVATIVE STYLING OPTIONS
See ZOTOS INTERNATIONAL INC

INNOVATIVE SUP CHAIN SOLUTIONS
See SUPPLY CHAIN SOLUTIONS LLC

D-U-N-S 80-751-1209
INNOVATIVE SYSTEMS GROUP INC
799 Roosevelt Rd 4-109, Glen Ellyn, IL 60137-5930
Tel (630) 858-8500 *Founded/Ownrshp* 1991
Sales 26.2MM^E *EMP* 250
Accts Plante & Moran Pllc
SIC 7371 Custom computer programming services; Custom computer programming services
Pr: Joselito C Salas
Mng Pt: Tom Bryan
Off Mgr: Lisa Gorman
Sales Exec: Daniel Burns

D-U-N-S 04-263-3680
INNOVATIVE SYSTEMS LLC
1000 Innovative Dr, Mitchell, SD 57301-5516
Tel (605) 995-6120 *Founded/Ownrshp* 1998
Sales 26.0MM^E *EMP* 175
SIC 7373 Computer integrated systems design; Computer integrated systems design
Dir IT: Jim Reyne
Sftwr Eng: Caitlin Taggart
Sales Exec: Tony Kazil
Sls&Mrk Ex: Lisa Johnson
Mktg Dir: Scott Meyer

D-U-N-S 78-039-8058 IMP
INNOVATIVE TECHNOLOGY DISTRIBUTORS LLC
IT DISTRIBUTORS
30 Mayfield Ave, Edison, NJ 08837-3821
Tel (732) 476-6600 *Founded/Ownrshp* 2005
Sales 37.8MM^E *EMP* 46
SIC 5045 Computers, peripherals & software
CFO: Victor Bilak
IT Man: Bijal Patel

D-U-N-S 16-269-1823 IMP
INNOVATIVE TECHNOLOGY ELECTRONICS CORP
1 Channel Dr, Port Washington, NY 11050-2216
Tel (516) 883-8220 *Founded/Ownrshp* 2004
Sales 35.0MM^E *EMP* 14
SIC 5065 Electronic parts & equipment; Electronic parts & equipment
Ch Bd: Corey Lieblein
**CFO:* Suzanne Wollman
Creative D: Lucas Eberle

INNOVATIVE TELE - ST THOMAS
See VIRGIN ISLAND TELEPHONE CORP

INNOVATIVE TELEPHONES
See INNOVATIVE COMMUNICATIONS CORP

D-U-N-S 15-342-7088
INNOVATIVE TURNAROUND CONTROLS LTD
3512 Fairmont Pkwy, Pasadena, TX 77504-3006
Tel (281) 998-9547 *Founded/Ownrshp* 2005
Sales 30.8MM^E *EMP* 250
SIC 1382 Oil & gas exploration services; Oil & gas exploration services
Pt: Troy Cassels
VP: William Berry
VP: Sonny Best
VP: Dale E Martin
IT Man: Varghese Joshy
IT Man: Jake Soliz

D-U-N-S 06-589-7266
INNOVATIVE VEGETATION SERVICES INC
FARRENS TREE SURGEONS INC
(*Suby of* UTILITY VEGETATION SERVICES INC) ★
708 Blair Mill Rd, Willow Grove, PA 19090-1701
Tel (215) 784-4200 *Founded/Ownrshp* 1990
Sales 12.9MM^E *EMP* 432
Accts Pricewaterhousecoopers Llp
SIC 0783 Tree trimming services for public utility lines; Tree trimming services for public utility lines
Pr: Scott Asplundh
Sec: Joseph P Dwyer
**VP:* Brent D Asplundh
**VP:* Carl H J Asplundh III
**VP:* Gregg G Asplundh
VP: Matthew B Asplundh
**VP:* Steven G Asplundh
**VP:* George E Graham Jr
**VP:* James E Graham
Admn Mgr: Pat Kinney
CIO: Eric Reibsane
Board of Directors: Barr E Asplundh, E Boyd Asplundh, Paul S Asplundh, Robert H Asplundh, Hyland R Johns

D-U-N-S 11-137-6224
INNOVATIVE WASTE MANAGEMENT INC
INNOVATIVE RESOURCE MANAGEMENT
125 Crosscreek Dr, Summerville, SC 29485-8250
Tel (843) 725-2000 *Founded/Ownrshp* 1997
Sales 22.9MM^E *EMP* 29
SIC 4731 5169 4953 4959 5172 Brokers, shipping; Industrial chemicals; Aromatic chemicals; Recycling, waste materials; Environmental cleanup services; Diesel fuel
Pr: Russ Lloyd
Pr: Rusty Lloyd
**VP:* Ned Foster
Off Mgr: Ethel Erwin
Off Mgr: Carrie Faris
Sls Dir: Ty Dupree

D-U-N-S 07-954-9065
INNOVATIVE XCESSORIES & SERVICES LLC
1862 Sparkman Dr Nw, Huntsville, AL 35816-1122
Tel (877) 330-1331 *Founded/Ownrshp* 2012, 2014
Sales 121.9MM^E *EMP* 1,500
SIC 5012 3711 Automobiles & other motor vehicles; Automobile assembly, including specialty automobiles
CEO: Kevin Heronimus
Pr: Jim Scott
CFO: Tim Garner
Ex VP: Mike Boyko
Ex VP: Paul Desmet
Ex VP: Omer Gursoy
Ex VP: George Lezon
Ex VP: Joe Olivastri
VP: Steve Decker
VP: Ben Dollar
VP: Brent Kwapisz
VP: Michael Magnuson
VP: Terry Pe

INNOVATVE CONSTRUCTION SOL INC
See INNOVATIVE CONSTRUCTION SOLUTIONS INC

D-U-N-S 04-194-9520
■ INNOVEL SOLUTIONS INC
SEARS LOGISTICS SERVICES, INC.
(*Suby of* SEARS ROEBUCK AND CO) ★
3333 Beverly Rd, Hoffman Estates, IL 60179-0001
Tel (847) 286-2500 *Founded/Ownrshp* 1940
Sales 639.8MM^E *EMP* 8,000
SIC 4731 8741 8742 Agents, shipping; Management services; Management consulting services; Agents, shipping; Management services; Management consulting services
Pr: Jeffrety A Starecheski
Treas: Jim Krise
VP: Richard Mc Laughlin
VP: Mark Meloro
VP: Roger Will
Prgrm Mgr: Pratham Naik

D-U-N-S 62-623-8117
■ INNOVEX INC
(*Suby of* QUINTILES TRANSNATIONAL CORP) ★
10 Waterview Blvd Ste 100, Parsippany, NJ 07054-7605
Tel (973) 257-4500 *Founded/Ownrshp* 1999
Sales 81.6MM^E *EMP* 1,500
SIC 8734 8999 7374 Testing laboratories; Communication services; Data processing & preparation; Testing laboratories; Communication services; Data processing & preparation
Pr: Anthony Yost
VP: Edward F Heimers
IT Man: Walter Smalty
VP Mktg: Theresa Borgia
VP Mktg: Matt Carey

D-U-N-S 17-456-7540 EXP
INNOVIA FILMS INC
(*Suby of* INNOVIA FILMS LIMITED)
290 Interstate N, Atlanta, GA 30339
Tel (770) 818-3000 *Founded/Ownrshp* 2004
Sales 45.6MM^E *EMP* 207
SIC 3861 Reels, film; Reels, film
CEO: David Beeby
**Pr:* Joseph Picccione
CFO: Martin Leitch
**CFO:* David Tilston
**Ch:* Dennis Matthewman
Exec: Lucy Cowton
Mng Dir: William Lowther
Off Mgr: Katheryn Bush
Plnt Mgr: Steve Nikkel
Sales Exec: Thomas Gwin

D-U-N-S 82-746-0341
INNOVIS HEALTH LLC
(*Suby of* ESSENTIA HEALTH) ★
1702 University Dr S, Fargo, ND 58103-4940
Tel (701) 364-8989 *Founded/Ownrshp* 2007
Sales 333.8MM *EMP* 99
SIC 8093 Specialty outpatient clinics; Specialty outpatient clinics

D-U-N-S 96-939-8721
INNOVIS HEALTH LLC
3000 32nd Ave S, Fargo, ND 58103-6132
Tel (701) 364-3300 *Founded/Ownrshp* 2011
Sales 259.3MM *EMP* 4^E
Accts Ernst & Young Atlanta Ga
SIC 8011 Physical medicine, physician/surgeon; Physical medicine, physician/surgeon
Prin: Peter Jacobson

D-U-N-S 00-621-5560 IMP
INNOVIZE INC (MN)
G M L
500 Oak Grove Pkwy, Saint Paul, MN 55127-8536
Tel (651) 490-0000 *Founded/Ownrshp* 1958, 1961
Sales 24.3MM^E *EMP* 110
SIC 2759 2789 2396 3599 3089 2672 Screen printing; Bookbinding & related work; Automotive & apparel trimmings; Machine & other job shop work; Engraving of plastic; Coated & laminated paper
Pr: John Ledy
**VP:* Dave Jessen

VP: Mark Rutkiewicz
Exec: Becky Bjorgum
VP Opers: John Sopp
Ql Cn Mgr: Mike McGovern
Ql Cn Mgr: Tom Quintavalle
Ql Cn Mgr: Allen Thomsen
Sales Asso: Nancy Castillo
Sales Asso: Roxanne Thayer
Sales Asso: Britney Thew

INNOVTORS IN MCRWAVE TECHNOLGY
See CEM CORP

D-U-N-S 09-682-0642 IMP
INNOWARE PAPER INC
(Suby of INNOWARE PAPER HOLDING COMPANY, INC.)
255 Spring St, Clintonville, WI 54929-1159
Tel (678) 690-5100 Founded/Ownrshp 2007
Sales 34.6MM^E EMP 150
SIC 2656 Plates, paper: made from purchased material; Utensils, paper: made from purchased material; Plates, paper: made from purchased material; Utensils, paper: made from purchased material
Pr: Nicholas Clementi
COO: Johnd Rice
*CFO: Leo Waner
IT Man: Kent Richmond
Tech Mgr: Richard Enk

D-U-N-S 10-757-1234
INNS OF AMERICA
755 Raintree Dr Ste 200, Carlsbad, CA 92011-3298
Tel (760) 438-6661 Founded/Ownrshp 1983
Sales 17.9MM^E EMP 300
Accts William H Ling Cpa San Dieg
SIC 7011 Motels; Motels
Pr: Timothy O Conner
*COO: Terry Lathrum

D-U-N-S 10-322-1164
INNSBROOK CORPATION
INNSBROOK DIV
1 Aspen Cir, Wright City, MO 63390
Tel (636) 928-3366 Founded/Ownrshp 1964
Sales 46.1MM^E EMP 200
SIC 6552 6531 7992 7011 6513 6512 Subdividers & developers; Real estate agents & managers; Public golf courses; Hotels & motels; Apartment building operators; Nonresidential building operators; Subdividers & developers; Real estate agents & managers; Public golf courses; Hotels & motels; Apartment building operators; Nonresidential building operators
Pr: Charles Boyce
*Ch Bd: Edmund J Boyce Jr
*Pr: Warren Wobbe
*CEO: Lester J Buechele
CFO: Chris Moore
Bd of Dir: Budget Review

INNSBROOK DIV
See INNSBROOK CORPATION

D-U-N-S 14-476-2668
INNVISION HOSPITALITY INC
504 Carver Rd, Griffin, GA 30224-3936
Tel (678) 967-2020 Founded/Ownrshp 2004
Sales 80.2MM^E EMP 80
SIC 5131 5021 7389 Textiles, woven; Furniture; Interior design services
Ch: Walter Jones Jr
*Pr: Chris Parker
Sls Mgr: Emille Aboona

INNVTV SPCLTY SILICN ACQUSTN
See SPECIALTY SILICONE FABRICATORS INC

D-U-N-S 09-054-6628 IMP
INO THERAPEUTICS LLC
(Suby of THERAKOS INC) ★
Perryville I I I Corp, Hampton, NJ 08827
Tel (908) 238-6600 Founded/Ownrshp 2015
Sales 48.0MM^E EMP 99
SIC 5122 2834 Pharmaceuticals; Pharmaceutical preparations; Pharmaceuticals; Pharmaceutical preparations
CFO: Elizabeth Larkin
Dir IT: Don Romeo
VP Mktg: Ken Marshall
Snr Mgr: Anne Smith

D-U-N-S 07-953-7040
INOAC INTERIOR SYSTEMS LLC
(Suby of INOAC USA INC) ★
22670 Haggerty Rd Ste 150, Farmington Hills, MI 48335-2607
Tel (734) 254-3482 Founded/Ownrshp 2014
Sales 34.0MM EMP 44
SIC 3069 3089 8711 Rubber automotive products; Automotive parts, plastic; Engineering services; Rubber automotive products; Automotive parts, plastic; Engineering services
Prgrm Mgr: Malte Bergfeld

D-U-N-S 18-283-5900 IMP/EXP
INOAC PACKAGING GROUP INC
(Suby of INOAC USA INC) ★
901 Nutter Dr, Bardstown, KY 40004-2604
Tel (502) 348-5159 Founded/Ownrshp 2005
Sales 34.7MM^E EMP 150
SIC 3089 3085 Plastic containers, except foam; Plastics bottles; Plastic containers, except foam; Plastics bottles
Pr: Kenjiro Miwa
*Pr: Chuck Little
Sr VP: Del Felter
*VP: Yutaka Matsui
VP: Danny Rossoll
Genl Mgr: Debbie Wright
Dir IT: Michael Pecoraro
Ql Cn Mgr: Jerry Keller
Ql Cn Mgr: Joe Ramey

D-U-N-S 15-137-3891
INOAC USA INC
(Suby of DIA SEIKO CO.,LTD.)
1515 Equity Dr Ste 200, Troy, MI 48084-7129
Tel (248) 619-7031 Founded/Ownrshp 2001
Sales 120.0MM^E EMP 559
SIC 3085 3714 Plastics bottles; Motor vehicle parts & accessories; Plastics bottles; Motor vehicle parts & accessories
CEO: Toyohiko Okina
*Pr: Charles Little
*Pr: Carl D Malz
*CFO: Ed Yeaste
*Ch: Soichi Inoue
VP: Andy Dargavell
*VP: Yasutaka Haruta
*VP: Noriyoshi Suzuki
Sls Dir: Fuminori Horio

D-U-N-S 13-672-9634 IMP
▲ INOGEN INC
326 Bollay Dr, Goleta, CA 93117-5550
Tel (805) 562-0500 Founded/Ownrshp 2001
Sales 112.5MM EMP 411
Tkr Sym INGN Exch NGS
SIC 3841 Surgical & medical instruments; Surgical & medical instruments
Pr: Raymond Huggenberger
*Ch Bd: Heath Lukatch
CFO: Alison Bauerlein
Ex VP: Matt Scribner
Ex VP: Brenton Taylor
Ex VP: Scott Wilkinson
VP Mktg: Byron Myers
Board of Directors: R Scott Greer, Loren McFarland, Benjamin Anderson-Ray, Heather Rider

D-U-N-S 79-808-5890
INOLA HEALTH CARE CENTER INC
400 N Broadway, Inola, OK 74036-9424
Tel (918) 543-8800 Founded/Ownrshp 1988
Sales 300.9MM EMP 50
SIC 8011 Medical centers; Medical centers
Pr: Howard Childers
Nrsg Dir: Pam Childers
HC Dir: Rory Childers

D-U-N-S 05-976-6675 IMP/EXP
INOLEX CHEMICAL CO
(Suby of INOLEX GROUP INC) ★
2101 S Swanson St, Philadelphia, PA 19148-3497
Tel (215) 755-0766 Founded/Ownrshp 1981
Sales 109.9MM^E EMP 100
SIC 5169 Chemicals, industrial & heavy; Chemicals, industrial & heavy
CFO: Don Byrne
*CEO: Edward Heinz
*Treas: Robert E Paganelli
*VP: Tyler Housel

D-U-N-S 15-397-4555 IMP
INOLEX GROUP INC
2101 S Swanson St, Philadelphia, PA 19148-3404
Tel (215) 271-0800 Founded/Ownrshp 1984
Sales 109.9MM^E EMP 100^E
SIC 2869 2821 Industrial organic chemicals; Polyesters; Industrial organic chemicals; Polyesters
Ch: Conrad A Plimpton
*Pr: Robert E Paganelli

D-U-N-S 83-735-9520
INOMEDIC HEALTH APPLICATIONS INC
2 Eaton St Ste 908, Hampton, VA 23669-4099
Tel (757) 722-7575 Founded/Ownrshp 1994
Sales 22.2MM EMP 200
Accts Cherry Bekaert Llp Virginia B
SIC 8744 8011 Facilities support services; Offices & clinics of medical doctors; Facilities support services; Offices & clinics of medical doctors
CEO: Leroy P Gross
*Pr: Cynthia Gross
CFO: Laura Walkup
*Treas: Shirley Gross
*VP: John Anderson
*VP: Joanne Creech
*VP: Mark Patton

D-U-N-S 01-305-3002
INOTEK SAFETY CONSULTANTS LLC (TX)
1717 Turning Basin Dr, Houston, TX 77029-4050
Tel (281) 888-4283 Founded/Ownrshp 2007
Sales 27.3MM^E EMP 315
SIC 8742 Industrial & labor consulting services; Industrial & labor consulting services
CEO: Greg Robl
*Pr: Stewart Records
Exec: Trashanna Eagleton

D-U-N-S 18-835-4831 IMP
INOVA DIAGNOSTICS INC
(Suby of WERFENLIFE SA.)
9900 Old Grove Rd, San Diego, CA 92131-1638
Tel (858) 586-9900 Founded/Ownrshp 2008
Sales 98.5MM^E EMP 570
SIC 2835 8731 In vitro & in vivo diagnostic substances; In vitro diagnostics; In vivo diagnostics; Medical research, commercial; In vitro & in vivo diagnostic substances; In vitro diagnostics; In vivo diagnostics; Medical research, commercial
CEO: Roger Ingles
CFO: Pere Solagagles
CFO: Pere Solasagales
VP: Ronda Elliott
VP: Michael Mahler
Exec: Valerie Brouillette
CTO: Waler Binder
IT Man: Pedro Solesageles
VP Opers: Abe Chohan
Mfg Dir: Ron Huber
Mfg Mgr: Wendy Eads

INOVA FAIRFAX HOSPITAL
See INOVA HEALTH CARE SERVICES

INOVA FAIRFAX HOSPITAL
See INOVA VNA HOME CARE INC

D-U-N-S 03-064-2823 IMP/EXP
INOVA GEOPHYSICAL INC (TX)
12200 Parc Crest Dr # 100, Stafford, TX 77477-2449
Tel (281) 568-2000 Founded/Ownrshp 2004
Sales 100.7MM^E EMP 83^E
SIC 5046 Commercial equipment
Pr: Glenn Hauer
Pr: John Lybarger
Sr VP: Doug Allinson
Sr VP: Liang Chaoyang
*Sr VP: Tim Hladik
*Sr VP: Linda Lattimore
*Sr VP: Keith Witt
*VP: Carey Mogdan
IT Man: Guan Hao
Sls Mgr: Vince Rodych

D-U-N-S 05-442-7455
INOVA HEALTH CARE SERVICES
INOVA FAIRFAX HOSPITAL
(Suby of INOVA HEALTH SYSTEM) ★
8110 Gatehouse Rd 200e, Falls Church, VA 22042-1217
Tel (703) 289-2000 Founded/Ownrshp 1956
Sales 2.1MMM EMP 13,000
SIC 8062 8093 General medical & surgical hospitals; Specialty outpatient clinics; General medical & surgical hospitals; Specialty outpatient clinics
Ch: Nicholas Carosi
Pr: Maggie Cornett
*Pr: John Knox Singleton
Treas: Peggy Harris
*Treas: Lydia Thomas
*VP: James Hughes
*VP: Richard C Magenheimer
VP: Jennifer Siciliano
*VP: H Patrick Walters
Exec: Kylanne Green
Dir Risk M: Maureen Burke
Dir Risk M: Heidi Harrison

D-U-N-S 19-201-8141
INOVA HEALTH SYSTEM
8110 Gatehouse Rd 200e, Falls Church, VA 22042-1217
Tel (703) 289-2072 Founded/Ownrshp 1977
Sales NA EMP 16,000
SIC 8741 8011 8062 8049 8059 8051 Hospital management; Offices & clinics of medical doctors; General medical & surgical hospitals; Physical therapist; Nutrition specialist; Speech specialist; Nurses & other medical assistants; Convalescent home; Nursing home, except skilled & intermediate care facility; Skilled nursing care facilities; Hospital management; Offices & clinics of medical doctors; General medical & surgical hospitals; Physical therapist; Nutrition specialist; Speech specialist; Nurses & other medical assistants; Convalescent home; Nursing home, except skilled & intermediate care facility; Skilled nursing care facilities
CEO: John Knox Singleton
Pr: Lori Brown
COO: Daniel Jackson Fache
*COO: Mark Stauder
COO: Keith Turner
*CFO: Richard Magenheimer
*Ch: Stephen Cumbie
Ofcr: Jim Dickens
*Ex VP: Loring Flint
*Ex VP: Marshall Ruffin
VP: John Fay
VP: Nancy Gosnell
Exec: Thomas Graves
Dir Risk M: Robin Landry
Dir Lab: Amy Shoemaker
Assoc Dir: Meredith Carter
Dir Rx: Shirin Byrd

D-U-N-S 80-435-1476
INOVA HEALTH SYSTEM SERVICES
(Suby of INOVA HEALTH SYSTEM) ★
8110 Gatehouse Rd 200e, Falls Church, VA 22042-1217
Tel (703) 289-2000 Founded/Ownrshp 1987
Sales 57.6MM^E EMP 1,000^E
SIC 8062

D-U-N-S 96-182-2207
INOVA LOUDOUN AMBULATORY SURGERY CENTER LLC
(Suby of INOVA LOUDOUN HOSPITAL) ★
44045 Riverside Pkwy, Leesburg, VA 20176-5101
Tel (703) 777-3300 Founded/Ownrshp 2010
Sales 17.8MM^E EMP 937^E
SIC 8062 General medical & surgical hospitals
Prin: John Grish

INOVA LOUDOUN HOSPITAL
See LOUDOUN HOSPITAL CENTER

INOVA LOUDOUN HOSPITAL
See LOUDOUN HEALTHCARE INC

D-U-N-S 96-181-0830
INOVA RESTON MRI CENTER LLC
(Suby of INOVA FAIRFAX HOSPITAL) ★
8110 Gatehouse Rd 200e, Falls Church, VA 22042-1252
Tel (703) 289-2072 Founded/Ownrshp 2000
Sales 4.3MM^E EMP 575^E
SIC 8011 Offices & clinics of medical doctors
Prin: John Knox Singleton

D-U-N-S 14-700-6498
INOVA VNA HOME CARE INC
INOVA FAIRFAX HOSPITAL
(Suby of INOVA FAIRFAX HOSPITAL) ★
5701d General Wash Dr, Alexandria, VA 22312-2408
Tel (703) 321-6000 Founded/Ownrshp 1951
Sales 16.3MM EMP 350
Accts Reznick Group Pc Vienna V
SIC 8082 Home health care services; Home health care services
Ex Dir: Helen Cole
Treas: Robin D Brooks
VP: Richard C Magenheimer
*Ex Dir: Eileen Dohmann
Div Mgr: Jeffrey Anderson

D-U-N-S 82-947-9877
INOVA WOODBURN SURGERY CENTER LLC
(Suby of INOVA FAIRFAX HOSPITAL) ★
3289 Woodburn Rd Ste 100, Annandale, VA 22003-7343
Tel (703) 226-2640 Founded/Ownrshp 2008
Sales 52.3MM^E EMP 1,890^E
SIC 8011 Offices & clinics of medical doctors
Prin: Vannette Poole

D-U-N-S 96-181-0749
INOVACAP LLC
(Suby of INOVA FAIRFAX HOSPITAL) ★
8110 Gatehouse Rd 200e, Falls Church, VA 22042-1252
Tel (703) 289-2072 Founded/Ownrshp 2000
Sales 3.6MM^E EMP 411^E
SIC 8011 Offices & clinics of medical doctors
Prin: John Knox Singleton
Off Mgr: Carole Guerard

D-U-N-S 07-851-0797
▲ INOVALON HOLDINGS INC
4321 Collington Rd # 100, Bowie, MD 20716-2646
Tel (301) 809-4000 Founded/Ownrshp 1998
Sales 361.5MM EMP 2,609^E
Accts Deloitte & Touche Llp Mclean
Tkr Sym INOV Exch NGS
SIC 7371 7374 7372 Custom computer programming services; Data processing & preparation; Prepackaged software
Ch Bd: Keith R Dunleavy
Pr: Robert A Wychulis
CFO: Thomas R Kloster
Ofcr: Christopher E Greiner
Ofcr: Daniel L Rizzo
Ofcr: Shauna L Vernal
CTO: Joseph R Rostock

D-U-N-S 80-636-8390
INOVALON INC
4321 Collington Rd # 100, Bowie, MD 20716-2646
Tel (301) 262-3848 Founded/Ownrshp 2006
Sales 319.3MM^E EMP 900
SIC 8733 Medical research; Medical research
CEO: Keith R Dunleavy
Pr: Robert Wychulis
COO: David Finkel
CFO: Thomas Kloster
Sr VP: Stephen Decherney
Sr VP: Luis Gutierrez
VP: Kim Collins
VP: Daniel J Holohan III
VP: John Spitz
CIO: Ann Parker
CTO: Joe Rostock
Board of Directors: Denise K Fletcher, Lee D Roberts, William J Teuber Jr

D-U-N-S 83-128-2715 IMP
INOVAR INC
1073 W 1700 N, Logan, UT 84321-1713
Tel (435) 792-4949 Founded/Ownrshp 2009
Sales 71.5MM^E EMP 340
SIC 3672 Printed circuit boards; Printed circuit boards
CEO: Blake Kirby
*Pr: Tom Carlin
*Pr: Craig Rupp
VP: Issam Ata
*VP: David Griffith
*VP: Jed Jones
*VP: Debra Kaminsky
*VP: Paul Wold
Prgrm Mgr: Heidi Klopfenstein
Dir IT: Tom Sunderland
Mtls Mgr: Tracy Tagg

D-U-N-S 83-274-7997
INOVATEUS SOLAR LLC
19890 State Line Rd, South Bend, IN 46637-1553
Tel (574) 485-1400 Founded/Ownrshp 2008
Sales 23.0MM EMP 20
SIC 5211 3433 Solar heating equipment; Solar heaters & collectors

D-U-N-S 12-771-4298
INOVATIVE FACILITY SERVICES LLC
(Suby of KELLERMEYER BERGENSONS SERVICES LLC) ★
1573 Henthorne Dr, Maumee, OH 43537-1372
Tel (419) 861-1710 Founded/Ownrshp 1997
Sales 6.8MM^E EMP 400
SIC 7349 Building maintenance services; Building maintenance services

D-U-N-S 11-411-7984
■ INOVIS USA INC
(Suby of GE GLOBAL EXCHANGE SERVICES) ★
11720 Amberpark Dr # 400, Alpharetta, GA 30009-2275
Tel (770) 521-2284 Founded/Ownrshp 2010
Sales 35.0MM^E EMP 400
SIC 7374 Data processing & preparation; Data processing & preparation
Pr: Sean Feeney
Pr: Tami Morrison
Pr: Pat Salmonese
COO: Stefanie Payne
CFO: Greg Clevenger
*CFO: Kenneth Williams
Top Exec: Shelby L Davis
Sr VP: Scott Cravotta
Sr VP: John Duvall
Sr VP: Sal Mahbouba
VP: Steve Cochran
VP: Matthew Connell
VP: Sue Myers
VP: Doug Stewart

D-U-N-S 01-595-4530 IMP
INOVO INC
(Suby of DRIVE MEDICAL DESIGN & MFG) ★
401 Leonard Blvd N, Lehigh Acres, FL 33971-6302
Tel (239) 491-3516 Founded/Ownrshp 2011
Sales 22.1MM^E EMP 78
SIC 3841 Surgical & medical instruments
Pr: Richard Kocinski
*CFO: Tom San Antonio
*Treas: Harvey Diamond
VP: Charles Chaplin
VP: Kevin McCulloh
VP: Mike Mulroy
VP: Oscar Sanchez
QC Dir: Kent Dankenbring
Ql Cn Mgr: Tim Tarkington
Ql Cn Mgr: Chauncy Veopaseuth
Sls Mgr: Andrea Ortiz
Board of Directors: Michael J Endres, Ellen Hardymon

D-U-N-S 16-538-2669 IMP
INOXPA USA INC
3721 Santa Rosa Ave B4, Santa Rosa, CA 95407-8240
Tel (707) 585-3900 *Founded/Ownrshp* 2004
Sales 29.8MM^E *EMP* 300
SIC 5084 Pumps & pumping equipment; Pumps & pumping equipment
Pr: Candi Granes Campasol
Genl Mgr: Keith Van Note
Sls Mgr: Mark Sottana
Sls Mgr: Keith Vannote

D-U-N-S 01-595-9636 IMP/EXP
INPACO CORP
(*Suby of* LIQUI-BOX CORP) ★
6950 Wrthington Galena Rd, Worthington, OH 43085-2309
Tel (614) 888-9288 *Founded/Ownrshp* 1990
Sales 36.2MM^E *EMP* 426^E
SIC 2673 Plastic bags: made from purchased materials
CEO: Ken J Swanson

D-U-N-S 04-104-9169
▲ INPHI CORP
2953 Bunker Hill Ln # 300, Santa Clara, CA 95054-1131
Tel (408) 217-7300 *Founded/Ownrshp* 2000
Sales 156.1MM *EMP* 670
Accts Pricewaterhousecoopers Llp Sa
Tkr Sym IPHI *Exch* NYS
SIC 3674 Integrated circuits, semiconductor networks, etc.; Integrated circuits, semiconductor networks, etc.
Pr: Ford Tamer
**Ch Bd:* Diosdado P Banatao
CFO: John Edmunds
Sr VP: Ron Torten
VP: Scott Feller
VP: Vinod Lakhani
VP: Charles Roach
VP: Hojjat Salemi
VP: Mona Taylor
VP: Norman K Yeung
CTO: Sudeep Bhoja
Board of Directors: Nicholas E Brathwaite, David Liddle, Bruce McWilliams, Elissa Murphy, Sam S Srinivasan

D-U-N-S 86-865-3650
■ INPHYNET HOSPITAL SERVICES INC
(*Suby of* TEAM HEALTH INC) ★
14050 Nw 14th St Ste 190, Sunrise, FL 33323-2851
Tel (954) 475-1300 *Founded/Ownrshp* 1999
Sales 17.8MM^E *EMP* 532
SIC 7363 8741 Medical help service; Nursing & personal care facility management; Medical help service; Nursing & personal care facility management
Prin: Neil Principe
**Ch Bd:* Clifford Findeiss
**COO:* Erie D Chapman III
**CFO:* George W Mc Cleary Jr
**Sr VP:* Jere D Creed
**Sr VP:* Marta Prado
**Sr VP:* Neil J Principe
**Sr VP:* Victor J Weinstein
VP Sls: Tonya White
Board of Directors: Thomas E Dewey Jr, Donald C Wegmiller

D-U-N-S 80-075-8471 IMP
INPLAST INDUSTRIES USA LLC
PLASTIKON INDUSTRIES KENTUCKY
325 Embry Dr, Leitchfield, KY 42754-1727
Tel (270) 259-2400 *Founded/Ownrshp* 2006
Sales 22.8MM^E *EMP* 55
SIC 3089 Billfold inserts, plastic

INPO
See INSTITUTE OF NUCLEAR POWER OPERATIONS

D-U-N-S 10-672-2606 IMP/EXP
INPRO CORP
FIRELINE 520
S80w18766 Apollo Dr, Muskego, WI 53150-9219
Tel (262) 679-9010 *Founded/Ownrshp* 1993
Sales 120.5MM^E *EMP* 420
SIC 3081 Unsupported plastics film & sheet; Unsupported plastics film & sheet
CEO: Stephen J Ziegler
Pr: Steve Baumgautner
**Pr:* Philip J Ziegler
**CFO:* Andy Ciesielski
Sr VP: Mark Ala
**VP:* Mark Alan
VP: Steve Baumgardner
**VP:* Matt Bennett
**VP:* Steve Bumgartner
VP: Beth Gleesing
**VP:* Glenn Kennedy
**VP:* Michael R Sekula
Exec: William Kraus

D-U-N-S 03-571-7359
■ INPRO/SEAL LLC
(*Suby of* WAUKESHA BEARINGS CORP) ★
4221 81st Ave W, Rock Island, IL 61201-7336
Tel (309) 787-8940 *Founded/Ownrshp* 1966, 2009
Sales 52.7MM^E *EMP* 135
SIC 5085 3053 Bearings; Gaskets, packing & sealing devices; Bearings; Gaskets, packing & sealing devices
CEO: David C Orlowski
CFO: Stacy Holland
VP: Mark Lee
Rgnl Mgr: Chuck Medinger
Dist Mgr: Paul Christieson
Dist Mgr: Gene Jaremczuk
Sls Mgr: Phil Flesher
Snr Mgr: Brian Soloway

D-U-N-S 01-681-0095
INRECON LLC
(*Suby of* BELFOR PROPERTY RESTORATION) ★
185 Oakland Ave Ste 300, Birmingham, MI 48009-3481
Tel (248) 594-3188 *Founded/Ownrshp* 2004
Sales 28.3MM^E *EMP* 550
SIC 1521 1541 1542 Repairing fire damage, single-family houses; Renovation, remodeling & repairs: industrial buildings; Commercial & office buildings, renovation & repair; Repairing fire damage, single-family houses; Renovation, remodeling & repairs: industrial buildings; Commercial & office buildings, renovation & repair

D-U-N-S 62-671-8154
INRIX INC
10210 Ne Pints Dr Ste 400, Kirkland, WA 98033
Tel (425) 284-3800 *Founded/Ownrshp* 2004
Sales 131.1MM^E *EMP* 759^E
SIC 3651 Household audio & video equipment
Pr: Bryan Mistele
Pr: Steve Dann
**Pr:* Mark Daymond
CFO: Jeff Decillia
**CFO:* Saul Gates
**Chf Mktg O:* Steve Banfield
**Ofcr:* Rafay Khan
Sr VP: Don Butler
Sr VP: Paul Gross
**Sr VP:* Alex Meyer
Sr VP: Mark Wang
VP: Mike Arcuri
**VP:* Scott Baker
VP: Andreas Hecht
VP: Jonathan Maron
VP: Kush Parikh
VP: Danny Woolard
Board of Directors: John Connors, Mike Gerling, Diane Irvine, Tony Posawatz

INRUMEC
See INDUSTRIAL RUBBER & MECHANICS INC

INSCITE
See SHARPS COMPLIANCE INC OF TEXAS

INSCO DICO GROUP , THE
See DEVELOPERS SURETY AND INDEMNITY CO

D-U-N-S 02-703-4644 IMP
INSCO DISTRIBUTING INC
JOHNSON CONTROLS
12501 Network Blvd, San Antonio, TX 78249-3306
Tel (210) 690-8400 *Founded/Ownrshp* 1958
Sales 151.9MM^E *EMP* 272
SIC 5078 5075 Commercial refrigeration equipment; Air conditioning equipment, except room units; Warm air heating equipment & supplies; Commercial refrigeration equipment; Air conditioning equipment, except room units; Warm air heating equipment & supplies
Pr: Rudy Trevino
**CFO:* James McCann
VP: A Trevino
**VP:* B G Trevino
Dir IT: Mark Lehman
IT Man: Julio Ruiz
Advt Mgr: Kristi Lane
Mktg Mgr: Mark Sowders
Sls Mgr: Noel Gregory
Sls Mgr: Bobby Harper
Sls Mgr: Ivan Kierum

D-U-N-S 14-479-5176
■ INSCO INSURANCE SERVICES INC
DEVELOPERS SURETY INDEMNITY CO
(*Suby of* AMTRUST FINANCIAL SERVICES INC) ★
17771 Cowan Ste 100, Irvine, CA 92614-6044
Tel (949) 797-9243 *Founded/Ownrshp* 2014
Sales NA *EMP* 135
SIC 6411 6351 Property & casualty insurance agent; Surety insurance bonding; Liability insurance
Ch Bd: Harry Crowell
Sr VP: Susan Moore
VP: Sam Tobis
VP: Dan Young
Rgnl Mgr: Steve Murray
Rgnl Mgr: Dave Paloma
Brnch Mgr: Emil Askew
Brnch Mgr: Tiffany Birch
Brnch Mgr: Steve Bonilla
Brnch Mgr: Denver Branch
Brnch Mgr: Lauderdale Branch

D-U-N-S 83-087-1864
INSCO INTERMEDIATE HOLDINGS INC
17 Powder Hill Rd, Lincoln, RI 02865-4407
Tel (401) 334-6800 *Founded/Ownrshp* 2007
Sales 48.1MM^E *EMP* 86
SIC 5084 5085 Industrial machinery & equipment; Pumps & pumping equipment; Industrial supplies; Bins & containers, storage; Industrial machinery & equipment; Pumps & pumping equipment; Industrial supplies; Bins & containers, storage
Pr: Edmund M Mauro III
**CFO:* Walter R Dilling
**VP Opers:* Mary Lou Jelinek

D-U-N-S 17-295-2033
INSCOPE INTERNATIONAL INC
12018 Sunrise Valley Dr # 100, Reston, VA 20191-3432
Tel (703) 480-3200 *Founded/Ownrshp* 2003
Sales 33.3MM *EMP* 85
Accts Thompson Greenspon Fairfax V
SIC 7379 Computer related consulting services; Computer related consulting services
CEO: Michael Bruce
**Pr:* Bruce Michael
COO: Tom Martwinski
**CFO:* Gary Struzik
VP: Kevin Cassidy
VP: Steve Conner
VP: Jack Coverick
**VP:* Jason Craig
VP: Dawn Dumbeck
**VP:* Struzik Gary
IT Man: Jamie Giordano

D-U-N-S 07-981-3083
INSECT CONTROL SOLUTIONS INC (TX)
612 Spring Cypress Rd, Spring, TX 77373-2526
Tel (832) 299-2400 *Founded/Ownrshp* 2013
Sales 68.0MM *EMP* 15
SIC 2879 Insecticides & pesticides
Pr: Dave Glaffelc

D-U-N-S 78-788-1098
INSERO & CO CPAS PC
2 State St Ste 300, Rochester, NY 14614-1329
Tel (585) 454-6996 *Founded/Ownrshp* 2006
Sales NA *EMP* 70
SIC 6371 7291 8721 Pension funds; Tax return preparation services; Accounting, auditing & bookkeeping
CEO: Frank A Insero
Ofcr: Sharon Insero

D-U-N-S 01-131-0018
INSERRA SUPERMARKETS INC
SHOP-RITE
20 Ridge Rd Ste 1, Mahwah, NJ 07430-2328
Tel (201) 529-5900 *Founded/Ownrshp* 1933
Sales 524.7MM^E *EMP* 4,000
SIC 5411 5735 Supermarkets, chain; Video tapes, prerecorded; Supermarkets, chain; Video tapes, prerecorded
CEO: Lawrence R Inserra
**CFO:* Theresa Inserra
**Ex VP:* Steve Chalas
Plnt Mgr: Marguerite Turano
Snr Mgr: Nelson Ota

D-U-N-S 61-780-0425 IMP/EXP
INSERTECH LLC
711 Indl Dr, Cary, IL 60013
Tel (847) 516-6415 *Founded/Ownrshp* 2005
Sales 28.8MM^E *EMP* 170
SIC 3089 Injection molding of plastics; Plastic processing; Injection molding of plastics; Plastic processing
CFO: Ken Johnson
Mtls Mgr: Simon Foster
Plnt Mgr: Frank Drago
Ql Cn Mgr: Benjamin Baker

D-U-N-S 62-320-7826
INSERTS EAST INC
G & F GRAPHIC SERVICES
7045 Central Hwy, Pennsauken, NJ 08109-4312
Tel (856) 663-8181 *Founded/Ownrshp* 1974
Sales 63.2MM^E *EMP* 125
SIC 5043 8742 2791 2752 Photographic equipment & supplies; Printing apparatus, photographic; Management consulting services; Business planning & organizing services; Typesetting; Commercial printing, lithographic; Photographic equipment & supplies; Printing apparatus, photographic; Management consulting services; Business planning & organizing services; Typesetting; Commercial printing, lithographic
CEO: Gino Maiale
COO: Timmothy McCaffery
**CFO:* Andy Kavulic
Plnt Mgr: Matt Gooch

D-U-N-S 83-650-1544 IMP
INSERTS USA INC
FINISHING PLUS
4546 W 47th St, Chicago, IL 60632-4408
Tel (773) 254-3366 *Founded/Ownrshp* 1976
Sales 21.9MM^E *EMP* 125
SIC 2789 Bookbinding & related work; Bookbinding & related work
Pr: Frank J Puisis
Prin: Dave Defenbaugh

INSERV
See INTEGRATED SERVICE CO LLC

INSERV
See WILLBROS DOWNSTREAM LLC

INSERV
See INTEGRATED INDUSTRIAL SERVICES INC

D-U-N-S 05-581-9536 IMP
INSERVCO INC
STACI LAGRANGE
(*Suby of* STACI CORP) ★
110 Commerce Dr, Lagrange, OH 44050-9491
Tel (847) 855-9600 *Founded/Ownrshp* 2011
Sales 20.6MM^E *EMP* 119
SIC 3679 Electronic circuits; Electronic circuits
Sec: Jere Simonson
**VP:* Greg Hebson
**VP:* Mike Nargi
Exec: Georgianna Overs
Brnch Mgr: Linda Chapman
Sfty Mgr: Dennis Sudnick
Plnt Mgr: Bob Paukst
Ql Cn Mgr: Walter Hunt

D-U-N-S 18-179-9008
INSERVCO INSURANCE SERVICES INC
(*Suby of* PENN NATIONAL INSURANCE) ★
2 N 2nd St Ste 2, Harrisburg, PA 17101-1619
Tel (717) 230-8300 *Founded/Ownrshp* 1980
Sales NA *EMP* 75
SIC 6411 8093 Insurance agents, brokers & service; Rehabilitation center, outpatient treatment
CEO: Michael Scheib
Pr: Staci Ulp
Treas: Donald Casey

D-U-N-S 02-275-4225
INSERVICE AMERICA INC
ISA
129 Vista Centre Dr, Forest, VA 24551-2780
Tel (434) 316-7400 *Founded/Ownrshp* 1998
Sales 22.5MM^E *EMP* 200
SIC 7389 Telemarketing services; Telemarketing services
Pr: Carl Townsend
**CFO:* James E Fitzpatrick
CFO: Earl Nance

D-U-N-S 80-117-9800
INSIDE EDGE COMMERCIAL INTERIOR SERVICES LLC
(*Suby of* MENDOTA HOLDINGS INC) ★
2700 Blue Waters Rd, Eagan, MN 55121-1403
Tel (651) 389-3900 *Founded/Ownrshp* 2004
Sales 26.9MM^E *EMP* 130
SIC 1752 Floor laying & floor work; Floor laying & floor work
CEO: David Moeller
Sr VP: Lisa Bien-Sinz
VP: Matt Cooper
VP: Joe Dovenmuehle
VP: Kevin Riley
VP: Lisa Bien Sinz

INSIDE SALES
See INSIDESALES.COM INC

D-U-N-S 62-128-8562
INSIDE SOURCE INC
INSIDE SOURCE/YOUNG
985 Industrial Rd Ste 101, San Carlos, CA 94070-4157
Tel (650) 508-9101 *Founded/Ownrshp* 1990
Sales 81.9MM^E *EMP* 140
SIC 5021 Office & public building furniture
Pr: David Denny
COO: Kristen Haren
Sr VP: Gary Young
VP: Tina Fong
VP: Nancy Kusich
VP: David Lombardi
IT Man: Wendy Joos
Opers Mgr: Robert Robles

INSIDE SOURCE/YOUNG
See INSIDE SOURCE INC

D-U-N-S 18-998-9150
INSIDE TRACK INC
1620 Montgomery St # 230, San Francisco, CA 94111-1016
Tel (415) 243-4440 *Founded/Ownrshp* 2005
Sales 31.2MM^E *EMP* 300
SIC 8748 Educational consultant; Educational consultant
CEO: Alan Tripp
**Pr:* Kai Drekmeier
**CFO:* ARI Blum
Mktg Mgr: Tai Nicolopoulos

D-U-N-S 00-382-8296
INSIDERSREFERRAL.COM INC (CA)
JOBS2CAREERS
6433 Champion Grandvie, Austin, TX 78750-8588
Tel (512) 808-0190 *Founded/Ownrshp* 2007
Sales 23.1MM^E *EMP* 34
Accts Maxwell Locke & Ritter Llc A
SIC 7361 Employment agencies; Employment agencies
CEO: Bruce GE
**Ofcr:* Shelly Mudd

D-U-N-S 14-509-3139
INSIDESALES.COM INC
INSIDE SALES
1712 S East Bay Blvd, Provo, UT 84606-6115
Tel (385) 207-7252 *Founded/Ownrshp* 2004
Sales 20.4MM^E *EMP* 23^E
SIC 8741 Management services
CEO: David Elkington
**Pr:* Kenneth Krogue
**CFO:* Kevin Samuelson
**Chf Mktg O:* Mick Hollison
Sr VP: Brent Peters
Sr VP: Todd Riesterer
VP: Rick Baker
VP: Christopher Da Cunha
VP: Tom Milligan
VP: Dave Orrico
VP: Tom Pilkington
VP: Michael Plante
VP: Kevin White

D-U-N-S 18-925-6212
INSIDEVIEW TECHNOLOGIES INC
444 De Haro St Ste 210, San Francisco, CA 94107-2398
Tel (415) 728-9309 *Founded/Ownrshp* 2005
Sales 90.2MM^E *EMP* 150
SIC 5045 Computers, peripherals & software; Computers, peripherals & software
CEO: Umberto Milletti
Pr: Jigisha Patel
COO: James Desser
Bd of Dir: Brian Jacobs
Chf Mktg O: Tracy Eiler
Chf Mktg O: Brian Kelly
Chf Mktg O: Rand Schulman
Chf Inves: John Hawie
Ex VP: Joseba Trullos
Ex VP: Steve Young
Sr VP: Mike Delaat
VP: Mike Aguillard
VP: Gordon T Anderson
VP: Tina Babbi
VP: Susan Baker
VP: Karen Burr
VP: Jeff Croscn
VP: Mike Donofrio
VP: Paula Gaspard
VP: David Gorsuch
VP: Sylvia Kainz
Board of Directors: Jim Simons

D-U-N-S 80-440-1313 IMP/EXP
INSIGHT BEVERAGES INC
(*Suby of* KERRY GROUP PUBLIC LIMITED COMPANY)
750 Oakwood Rd, Lake Zurich, IL 60047-1519
Tel (847) 438-1598 *Founded/Ownrshp* 2015
Sales 43.4MM^E *EMP* 200^E
SIC 2087 2095 2099 5499 Beverage bases; Coffee extracts; Tea blending; Beverage stores
CEO: Andrew F Burke
Pr: Gerard A Behan
VP: Richard Bruner
VP: Bill Flack
VP: Don Lillard
VP Opers: Ray Medina
Mtls Mgr: Phil Anderson
Mktg Mgr: Maria Alarcon
Sls Mgr: Kim Lachman
Sls Mgr: John Notte
Snr Mgr: Irene Castro

INSIGHT CAPITAL PARTNERS
See INSIGHT VENTURE PARTNERS

D-U-N-S 07-153-8925
■ **INSIGHT COMMUNICATIONS CO INC**
INSIGHT MIDWEST HOLDINGS
(*Suby of* TIME WARNER CABLE INC) ★
810 7th Ave Fl 41, New York, NY 10019-5864
Tel (917) 286-2300 *Founded/Ownrshp* 2012
Sales 504.0MM^E *EMP* 4,035
SIC 4841 4813 Cable television services; Telephone communication, except radio; ; Cable television services; Telephone communication, except radio;
Pr: Michael S Willner
**Ch Bd:* Sidney R Knafel
**Pr:* Dinni Jain
**Ex VP:* John F Abbot
Ex VP: Chris Slattery
Sr VP: Mike Page
VP: Charlie Barnes
**Prin:* Satish Adige

D-U-N-S 14-799-8280
INSIGHT COMMUNICATIONS OF KENTUCKY LP
810 7th Ave Fl 28, New York, NY 10019-9000
Tel (917) 286-2300 *Founded/Ownrshp* 1985
Sales NA *EMP* 1,000
SIC 4841

D-U-N-S 15-755-2118
■ **INSIGHT DIRECT USA INC**
(*Suby of* INSIGHT NORTH AMERICA INC) ★
6820 S Harl Ave, Tempe, AZ 85283-4318
Tel (480) 333-3000 *Founded/Ownrshp* 1986
Sales 6.7MMM^E *EMP* 4,000
SIC 5045 3571 Computers, peripherals & software; Personal computers (microcomputers); Computers, peripherals & software; Personal computers (microcomputers)
CEO: Kenneth T Lamneck
**Pr:* Steven Dodenhoff
**CFO:* Glynis Bryan
**Treas:* Helen Johnson
Sr VP: Simon Taylor
**VP:* Mark N Rogers
VP: Michael Schelbert
CIO: Rick Goddard
CIO: David Rice
CIO: James Webster
IT Man: Susan Zimmerman

D-U-N-S 87-638-3589
▲ **INSIGHT ENTERPRISES INC**
6820 S Harl Ave, Tempe, AZ 85283-4318
Tel (480) 333-3000 *Founded/Ownrshp* 1988
Sales 5.3MMM *EMP* 5,406^E
Tkr Sym NSIT *Exch* NGS
SIC 5045 7379 5065 Computers, peripherals & software; Computer peripheral equipment; Computer software; Disk drives; Computer related consulting services; Modems, computer; Communication equipment; Computers, peripherals & software; Computer peripheral equipment; Computer software; Disk drives; Computer related consulting services; Modems, computer; Communication equipment
Pr: Kenneth T Lamneck
Ch Bd: Timothy A Crown
Pr: Steve Dodenhoff
CFO: Glynis A Bryan
Treas: Helen K Johnson
VP: John Carnahan
VP: Steven Dodenhoff
VP: Carolyn Haas
VP: Brian Hicks
VP: Dana A Leighty
VP: Dana Leighty
VP: Mary Sculley
VP: Carole Sowers
VP: Jeffrey Warner
Dir Bus: Audra Carter
Board of Directors: Richard E Allen, Bennett Dorrance, Michael M Fisher, Larry A Gunning, Anthony A Ibarguen, Kathleen S Pushor

INSIGHT EQUITY
See DUSTEX CORP

D-U-N-S 17-589-8936 IMP
INSIGHT EQUITY A P X L P
VISION-EASE LENS
1400 Civic Pl Ste 250, Southlake, TX 76092-7647
Tel (817) 488-7775 *Founded/Ownrshp* 2004
Sales 76.7MM^E *EMP* 1,200^E
SIC 6722 3441 3443 3556 3714 5171 Management investment, open-end; Bridge sections, prefabricated highway; Tanks, lined: metal plate; Food products machinery; Motor vehicle parts & accessories; Petroleum terminals; Management investment, open-end; Bridge sections, prefabricated highway; Tanks, lined: metal plate; Food products machinery; Motor vehicle parts & accessories; Petroleum terminals

D-U-N-S 12-846-2509 IMP/EXP
INSIGHT EQUITY ACQUISITION CO LLC
(*Suby of* INSIGHT EQUITY HOLDINGS LLC) ★
1400 Civic Pl Ste 250, Southlake, TX 76092-7647
Tel (817) 354-2715 *Founded/Ownrshp* 2003
Sales 160.1MM^E *EMP* 800
SIC 2911 6722 3851 3441 Petroleum refining; Management investment, open-end; Lenses, ophthalmic; Bridge sections, prefabricated highway; Petroleum refining; Management investment, open-end; Lenses, ophthalmic; Bridge sections, prefabricated highway
CFO: Scott Lambert

D-U-N-S 82-745-3189
INSIGHT EQUITY ACQUISITION PARTNERS LP
DIRECT FUELS
(*Suby of* INSIGHT EQUITY ACQUISITION CO LLC) ★
12625 Calloway Cmtry Rd, Euless, TX 76040-7021
Tel (817) 354-2700 *Founded/Ownrshp* 2003
Sales 43.5MM^E *EMP* 42
SIC 5171 Petroleum terminals
Pt: Ted Beneski
**Pt:* Warren Bonham
**Pt:* Scott Lambert
**Pt:* Terry Nevels
**Pt:* Victor Vescovo
Brnch Mgr: Warner Williams

D-U-N-S 62-045-7296
INSIGHT EQUITY HOLDINGS LLC
1400 Civic Pl Ste 250, Southlake, TX 76092-7647
Tel (817) 488-7775 *Founded/Ownrshp* 2000
Sales 1.4MMM^E *EMP* 4,000
SIC 6722 3851 2911 3441 Management investment, open-end; Lenses, ophthalmic; Petroleum refining; Bridge sections, prefabricated highway; Management investment, open-end; Lenses, ophthalmic; Petroleum refining; Bridge sections, prefabricated highway
VP: Brad Buser
VP: Jack Waterstreet
VP: Chris Zugaro

D-U-N-S 19-039-7401
INSIGHT EQUITY LP
(*Suby of* INSIGHT EQUITY HOLDINGS LLC) ★
1400 Civic Pl Ste 250, Southlake, TX 76092-7647
Tel (817) 488-7775 *Founded/Ownrshp* 2002
Sales 609.6MM^E *EMP* 2,402
SIC 6722 3441 3443 3556 3714 5171 Management investment, open-end; Bridge sections, prefabricated highway; Tanks, lined: metal plate; Food products machinery; Motor vehicle parts & accessories; Petroleum terminals; Petroleum bulk stations; Management investment, open-end; Bridge sections, prefabricated highway; Tanks, lined: metal plate; Food products machinery; Motor vehicle parts & accessories; Petroleum terminals; Petroleum bulk stations
Mng Pt: Ted Beneski
**Pt:* Warren Bonham
**Pt:* Eliot Kerlin
**Pt:* Victor L Vescovo
**Sr VP:* Andrew Boisseau
**Sr VP:* Jack Waterstreet
**VP:* Brad Buser
**VP:* James Jackson
**VP:* Dan Lenahan
VP: Jack Nadal
**VP:* Ben Stolbach

D-U-N-S 17-093-7697
INSIGHT FINANCIAL MANAGEMENT
7300 147th St W Ste 402, Saint Paul, MN 55124-7855
Tel (952) 388-1117 *Founded/Ownrshp* 2004
Sales 65.0MM *EMP* 600
SIC 8741 8742 Business management; Financial consultant; Business management; Financial consultant
Owner: Michael Uline

D-U-N-S 05-844-2336
INSIGHT FOR LIVING
5700 Democracy Dr # 2500, Plano, TX 75024-7275
Tel (972) 473-5000 *Founded/Ownrshp* 1979
Sales 20.1MM *EMP* 105^E
Accts Capin Crouse Llp Greenwood I
SIC 4832 Religious; Religious
Pr: Cynthia Swindoll
CFO: Jerry Foster

D-U-N-S 96-192-8400
INSIGHT GLOBAL LLC
(*Suby of* IG STAFFING HOLDINGS LLC) ★
4170 Ashford Dunwoody 250, Brookhaven, GA 30319-1457
Tel (770) 454-7990 *Founded/Ownrshp* 2001
Sales 173.1MM^E *EMP* 650
SIC 7361 Employment agencies; Employment agencies
Ch Bd: Glenn Johnson
**CEO:* Rich Lingle
**CFO:* Mike Lewis
Treas: John Harris
Sr VP: Kevin Ingham
**Prin:* Glenn Johnson
Software D: Michael Knowlin
Software D: Peri Levengood
Netwrk Eng: John Alexander
Natl Sales: Joel Givan
Mktg Mgr: Katie Catalogna

D-U-N-S 96-362-1842
■ **INSIGHT HEALTH SERVICES CORP**
INSIGHT IMAGING
(*Suby of* INSIGHT HEALTH SERVICES HOLDINGS CORP) ★
5775 Wayzata Blvd Ste 400, Minneapolis, MN 55416-1271
Tel (949) 282-6000 *Founded/Ownrshp* 2001
Sales 216.0MM^E *EMP* 1,434
SIC 5047 Diagnostic equipment, medical; Diagnostic equipment, medical
Pr: Kip Hallman
**CEO:* Robert Baumgartner
**COO:* Rick Long
**COO:* Bernie O'Rourke
CFO: Keith Kelson
Treas: Kent Tuholsky
Sec: Patricia Roberts
**Sec:* Darren Wright
**Ex VP:* Patrica Blank
Sr VP: Robert J Mentzer
VP: Gregg Daversa
Dir Risk M: Lucille Thompson

D-U-N-S 13-022-5811
▲ **INSIGHT HEALTH SERVICES HOLDINGS CORP**
26250 Entp Ct Ste 100, Lake Forest, CA 92630
Tel (949) 282-6000 *Founded/Ownrshp* 2010
Sales 216.0MM^E *EMP* 1,490^E
Accts Pricewaterhousecoopers Llp Or
Tkr Sym ISGTQ *Exch* OTO
SIC 8071 Testing laboratories; Testing laboratories
Pr: Louis E Hallman III
**CEO:* Robert V Baumgartner
**COO:* Bernard J O'Rourke
**CFO:* Keith S Kelson
**Ex VP:* Patricia R Blank
**Sr VP:* Michael C Jones
**Sr VP:* Scott A McKee
Opers Mgr: Jeffrey Hammett
Counsel: Maria Eridondo
Board of Directors: Eugene Linden, Wayne B Lowell, Richard Nevins, James A Ovenden, Keith E Rechner, Steven G Segal

INSIGHT IMAGING
See INSIGHT HEALTH SERVICES CORP

D-U-N-S 96-774-5527
INSIGHT INVESTMENTS CORP
611 Anton Blvd Fl 7, Costa Mesa, CA 92626-7005
Tel (714) 939-2300 *Founded/Ownrshp* 1987
Sales 161.8MM^E *EMP* 240
SIC 7377 5045 Computer peripheral equipment rental & leasing; Computer peripheral equipment; Computer peripheral equipment rental & leasing; Computer peripheral equipment
CEO: John Ford
**Pr:* Richard Heard
VP: Carol Boldt
VP: Michelle Conyers
VP: Michael McCoy

D-U-N-S 18-385-3795
INSIGHT INVESTMENTS LLC
INSIGHT SYSTEMS EXCHANGE
(*Suby of* INSIGHT INVESTMENTS CORP) ★
611 Anton Blvd Ste 700, Costa Mesa, CA 92626-7050
Tel (714) 939-2300 *Founded/Ownrshp* 1987
Sales 161.8MM^E *EMP* 237^E
SIC 7377 5045 Computer peripheral equipment rental & leasing; Computer peripheral equipment; Computer peripheral equipment rental & leasing; Computer peripheral equipment
CEO: John W Ford
**Pr:* Richard Heard
**CFO:* David Wang
**Ex VP:* Christopher Czaja
VP: Carol Boldt

INSIGHT MIDWEST HOLDINGS
See INSIGHT COMMUNICATIONS CO INC

D-U-N-S 09-473-3862 IMP
■ **INSIGHT NORTH AMERICA INC**
PC WHOLESALE
(*Suby of* INSIGHT ENTERPRISES INC) ★
444 Scott Dr, Bloomingdale, IL 60108-3111
Tel (630) 924-6700 *Founded/Ownrshp* 2002
Sales 6.7MMM^E *EMP* 4,500
SIC 5045

INSIGHT OPTICAL MANUFACTURING
See OPTICAL FOR EYES CO

D-U-N-S 02-054-8137
INSIGHT OPTICAL MANUFACTURING CO OF FLORIDA INC (FL)
(*Suby of* ARANON CORP) ★
285 W 74th Pl, Hialeah, FL 33014-5094
Tel (305) 557-9004 *Founded/Ownrshp* 1975, 1978
Sales 31.2MM^E *EMP* 90
SIC 5048 Ophthalmic goods; Frames, ophthalmic; Lenses, ophthalmic; Ophthalmic goods; Frames, ophthalmic; Lenses, ophthalmic
Ch: Phillip Wolman
**Pr:* Lisa M Wolman
**COO:* Adam Wolman
**VP:* Jeffry Martin
**VP:* Robert Messa
Netwrk Mgr: Paul Kudla

D-U-N-S 17-679-2315 IMP
■ **INSIGHT PHARMACEUTICALS CORP**
HERITAGE BRANDS
(*Suby of* MEDTECH PRODUCTS INC) ★
660 White Plains Rd # 250, Tarrytown, NY 10591-5171
Tel (267) 852-0505 *Founded/Ownrshp* 2014
Sales 25.3MM^E *EMP* 45^E
SIC 5122 Pharmaceuticals
CEO: Gary Downing
**CFO:* Jim Berwick
Opers Mgr: Marcelo Casadei

D-U-N-S 88-434-7568 IMP
■ **INSIGHT PUBLIC SECTOR INC**
(*Suby of* INSIGHT ENTERPRISES INC) ★
2250 W Pinehurst Blvd # 200, Addison, IL 60101-6100
Tel (630) 924-6801 *Founded/Ownrshp* 2002
Sales 147.5MM^E *EMP* 150
SIC 5045 Computers; Computers
Pr: Kenneth Lamneck
**CFO:* Glynis Bryan
**Sr VP:* Helen K Johnson
**VP:* Dana A Leighty

INSIGHT SYSTEMS EXCHANGE
See INSIGHT INVESTMENTS LLC

D-U-N-S 07-836-2947
INSIGHT VENTURE MANAGEMENT LLC
INSIGHT VENTURE PARTNERS
1114 Ave Of The Americas, New York, NY 10036-7703
Tel (212) 230-9200 *Founded/Ownrshp* 1995
Sales 31.8MM^E *EMP* 247
SIC 6799 Venture capital companies
VP: Alex Crisses
COO: Jeff Horing
CFO: Mark Lessing
Bd of Dir: Lauren Bonett
Bd of Dir: Nikitas Koutoupes
Ofcr: Edward Delk
VP: Clan Cotter
VP: Richard Wells
Exec: Jerry Murdock
Mng Dir: Blair Flicker
Mng Dir: Hilary Gosher

INSIGHT VENTURE PARTNERS
See INSIGHT VENTURE MANAGEMENT LLC

D-U-N-S 09-583-2023
INSIGHT VENTURE PARTNERS
INSIGHT CAPITAL PARTNERS
1114 Ave Of Americas 36th, New York, NY 10036
Tel (212) 230-9200 *Founded/Ownrshp* 1995
Sales 56.7MM^E *EMP* 140
SIC 6799 5045 Venture capital companies; Computer software; Venture capital companies; Computer software
Pr: Jeffrey Horing
Pt: Kaushik Das
**CFO:* Mark Lessing
**VP:* Daniel Chiou
Ex Dir: Bill Doyle
Mng Dir: George McCulloch
CTO: Steve Rabin
Dir IT: Greg Ferguson

D-U-N-S 04-573-5897
INSIGHTSQUARED INC
4 Copley Pl Ste 500, Boston, MA 02116-6513
Tel (617) 370-8100 *Founded/Ownrshp* 2010
Sales 22.5MM^E *EMP* 175^E
SIC 7371 Computer software development
CEO: Frederick Shilmover
VP: Jonathan Tushman
Sftwr Eng: T J Higgins
VP Mktg: Joe Chernov

INSIGNIA PRODUCTS
See BUY BEST PURCHASING LLC

D-U-N-S 61-595-4922
INSIGNIA SYSTEMS INC
8799 Brooklyn Blvd, Minneapolis, MN 55445-2398
Tel (763) 392-6200 *Founded/Ownrshp* 1990
Sales 26.3MM *EMP* 70^E
Tkr Sym ISIG *Exch* NAS
SIC 7389 8742 Advertising, promotional & trade show services; Merchandising consultant; Advertising, promotional & trade show services; Merchandising consultant
Pr: John C Gonsior
**Ch Bd:* Edward A Corcoran
Ofcr: Tim Halfmann
Ofcr: Timothy J Halfmann
Ex VP: Larry Mortimer
Ex VP: Gary L Vars
VP: Joshua Ahlberg
VP: Sara Batchelder
VP: Stephanie Brown
VP: Erin Callahan
VP: Steve Chase
VP: Steve Phillips
VP: Julia Schmidt
VP: John Thompson
VP: Mark Wallace
VP: Kelli Whitelaw
VP: Jeff Williams
Exec: Helen Everett
Board of Directors: Jacob J Berning, David L Boehnen, Philip L Cooley, Michael C Howe, Nicholas J Swenson, F Peter Zaballos, Steven R Zenz

D-U-N-S 78-122-9948
INSIGNIA TECHNOLOGY SERVICES LLC
610 Thimble Shoals Blvd, Newport News, VA 23606-2573
Tel (757) 591-2111 *Founded/Ownrshp* 2006
Sales 47.5MM^E *EMP* 170
SIC 3669 7371 8741 Intercommunication systems, electric; Computer software development; Management services
CEO: Fred O' Brien
**Pr:* David Laclair
Prgrm Mgr: Michael Morton
IT Man: Heather Grochowski
Snr Mgr: Derek Beavers
Snr Mgr: William Caffaro

D-U-N-S 80-453-0632
■ **INSIGNIA/ESG HOTEL PARTNERS INC**
(*Suby of* CB RICHARD ELLIS REAL ESTATE SERVICES LLC) ★
11150 Santa Monica Blvd # 220, Los Angeles, CA 90025-3380
Tel (310) 765-2600 *Founded/Ownrshp* 1998
Sales 64.5MM^E *EMP* 5,800
SIC 6512 Property operation, retail establishment; Property operation, retail establishment
CEO: Mary Ann Tighe
Pr: John Powers
Board of Directors: Andrew L Farkas

D-U-N-S 94-565-7138
INSITE REAL ESTATE LLC
1400 16th St Ste 300, Oak Brook, IL 60523-8854
Tel (630) 617-9100 *Founded/Ownrshp* 1996
Sales 22.3MM^E *EMP* 45^E
SIC 6531 6552 Real estate agents & managers; Land subdividers & developers, commercial
**Prin:* Gerald J Kostelny
Mng Dir: Larissa Addison
Mng Dir: Robin Rash
Off Mgr: Kevin Daelen
Dir IT: Tahir Sair

D-U-N-S 10-992-9526
INSITE WIRELESS GROUP LLC
1199 N Fairfax St Ste 700, Alexandria, VA 22314-1437
Tel (703) 535-3009 *Founded/Ownrshp* 2000
Sales 20.0MM^E *EMP* 32
SIC 4812 Cellular telephone services
CEO: David Weisman
COO: Richard M Grimes
**COO:* Dale Walsh
**CFO:* Lance C Cawley
**VP:* Dale Harkins
**VP:* Warren Harkins
Dir Bus: Jeff Just
Counsel: Gordon Chin

D-U-N-S 87-816-4086
■ **INSITU INC**
(*Suby of* BOEING CO) ★
118 Columbia River Way, Bingen, WA 98605-9086
Tel (509) 493-8600 *Founded/Ownrshp* 2008
Sales 108.3MM^E *EMP* 167
SIC 8711 3999 Aviation &/or aeronautical engineering; Airplane models, except toy
Pr: Ryan Hartman
Pr: Steve Norlund
**Treas:* Lra Schey
Ofcr: Mark Goodale
Ofcr: Tina Sicilia

*VP: Heidi Capozzi
*VP: Charlie Guthrie
VP: Mark Hary
VP: Paul Scott
*VP: Gary Viviani
VP Bus Dev: Matt Mazur
Exec: Brian Gates
Exec: James Hays
Exec: Glen Stebbins

D-U-N-S 10-924-3139 IMP
■ INSITUFORM MID-AMERICA INC
(Suby of INSITUFORM TECHNOLOGIES LLC) ★
702 Spirit 40 Park Dr # 105, Chesterfield, MO 63005-1195
Tel (636) 530-8000 Founded/Ownrshp 1995
Sales 62.4MM^E EMP 700
SIC 1623 1622 Water, sewer & utility lines; Sewer line construction; Water main construction; Pipeline construction; Tunnel construction; Water, sewer & utility lines; Sewer line construction; Water main construction; Pipeline construction; Tunnel construction
Ch: Jerome Kalishman
*Pr: J Richard
*VP: Robert Affholder
VP: Carroll Slusher

D-U-N-S 03-940-6616 IMP
■ INSITUFORM TECHNOLOGIES LLC
(Suby of AEGION CORP) ★
17988 Edison Ave, Chesterfield, MO 63005-3700
Tel (636) 530-8000 Founded/Ownrshp 1980
Sales 704.3MM^E EMP 3,280
SIC 1623 Pipeline construction; Underground utilities contractor; Pipeline construction; Underground utilities contractor
CEO: Charles R Gordon
*CFO: David A Martin
*Treas: Kenneth L Young
Ofcr: Charles Butler
*Ofcr: David F Morris
*Sr VP: Brian J Clarke
*Sr VP: Dorwin E Hawn
VP: Chuck Delaney
VP: Bruce A Frost
VP: Ruben Mella
VP: Robert Moorhead
VP: John Reeser
VP: Dwane Ruiz
*VP: Laura Villa
VP: Michael White
VP: Kenneth Young
Board of Directors: Stephen P Cortinovis, Stephanie A Cuskley, John P Dubinsky, Charles R Gordon, Juanita H Hinshaw, M Richard Smith, Alfred L Woods

D-U-N-S 00-686-5752
■ INSITUFORM TECHNOLOGIES USA LLC (DE)
(Suby of INSITUFORM TECHNOLOGIES LLC) ★
11351 W 183rd St Ste A, Orland Park, IL 60467-9438
Tel (630) 257-2209 Founded/Ownrshp 1920, 1993
Sales 27.7MM^E EMP 169
SIC 1623 1611 Sewer line construction; Water main construction; Highway & street maintenance; Sewer line construction; Water main construction; Highway & street maintenance
Pr: John G Marich

D-U-N-S 07-930-0369
■ INSITUFORM TECHNOLOGIES USA LLC
(Suby of AEGION CORP) ★
17988 Edison Ave, Chesterfield, MO 63005-3700
Tel (636) 530-8000 Founded/Ownrshp 2011
Sales 21.2MM^E EMP 99
SIC 1623 Water, sewer & utility lines
Sr VP: David F Morris
CFO: David A Martin
Treas: Kenneth L Young
Sr VP: Brian J Clarke
Sr VP: Dorwin E Hawn
VP: Laura Villa

INSKIP AUTO CENTER
See AUTO CENTER IMPORTS INC

INSKIP AUTOCENTER
See UAG WEST BAY AM LLC

D-U-N-S 95-859-9235
INSKIP AUTOCENTER
1515 Bald Hill Rd, West Warwick, RI 02893
Tel (401) 821-1510 Founded/Ownrshp 2007
Sales 35.1MM^E EMP 200
SIC 5511 Automobiles, new & used; Automobiles, new & used
Pr: Maicel Valois
Dir IT: Richard Palian

INSL-X
See COMPLEMENTARY COATINGS CORP

D-U-N-S 04-836-3480
INSOMNIAC GAMES INC (CA)
2255 N Ontario St Ste 550, Burbank, CA 91504-3197
Tel (818) 729-2400 Founded/Ownrshp 1994
Sales 22.7MM^E EMP 167^E
SIC 3944 Electronic games & toys
Pr: Theodore C Price
CFO: Ransom White
*VP: Alex Hastings
Dir IT: Steven Kirk

D-U-N-S 80-663-0596
INSOURCE GROUP INC
12221 Merit Dr Ste 1000, Dallas, TX 75251-2243
Tel (972) 455-1023 Founded/Ownrshp 1992
Sales 20.8MM^E EMP 200
SIC 7361 7374 7379 8741 Employment agencies; Data processing & preparation; Computer related maintenance services; Management services; Employment agencies; Data processing & preparation; Computer related maintenance services; Management services
CEO: Jim Thompson
*Pr: James Thompson
*CEO: Steven A Raab
Dir Soc: Darlene Volpe

IT Man: Chris Lee
IT Man: Jeff Woodoff

D-U-N-S 96-550-6678
INSOURCE PERFORMANCE SOLUTIONS LLC
5601 77 Center Dr Ste 240, Charlotte, NC 28217-0735
Tel (704) 643-3232 Founded/Ownrshp 2003
Sales 82.2MM^E EMP 2,000
SIC 7363 Help supply services; Help supply services
Pr: Jeff Larkin
Pr: Kevin Clark
Pr: Ken Southerland
Sfty Dirs: Drew Bobo
Opers Mgr: Daniel Cottrill
Opers Mgr: Dan Lovett

D-U-N-S 96-482-4270 IMP
INSOURCE TECHNOLOGIES INC
12124 Road 111, Paulding, OH 45879-9000
Tel (419) 399-3600 Founded/Ownrshp 1997
Sales 26.6MM EMP 170
Accts Arend Laukhuf & Stroller Inc
SIC 3699 Electrical equipment & supplies; Electrical equipment & supplies
Pr: Kenneth Manz
*VP: Roger Manz
Sftwr Eng: Jim Manz
Sls Mgr: Larry Manz

D-U-N-S 01-301-8929
INSPA CORP
4001 1st Ave S, Seattle, WA 98134-2339
Tel (425) 881-1068 Founded/Ownrshp 1994
Sales 8.2MM^E EMP 300
SIC 7991 5999 Spas; Toiletries, cosmetics & perfumes; Spas; Toiletries, cosmetics & perfumes
Pr: Colleen Stone
*CFO: Mike Ostrem
*VP: Diana Ahern

INSPECTION OILFIELD SERVICES
See IOS/PCI LLC

INSPECTION SERVICES INTL
See D & C INSPECTION SERVICES INC

D-U-N-S 07-101-7438
INSPECTORATE AMERICA CORP
(Suby of BSI INSPECTORATE AMERICA) ★
12000 Aerospace Ave # 200, Houston, TX 77034-5587
Tel (713) 944-2000 Founded/Ownrshp 1980
Sales 165.3MM^E EMP 764^E
SIC 7389 8734 8731 Petroleum refinery inspection service; Inspection & testing services; Testing laboratories; Product testing laboratory, safety or performance; Agricultural research; Petroleum refinery inspection service; Inspection & testing services; Testing laboratories; Product testing laboratory, safety or performance; Agricultural research
Pr: Kevin Somers
*CFO: Barry Benton
Ex VP: Lloyd Taylor
VP: Greg Bramhall
VP: Brad Cook
VP: Rob Lee
VP: John Nelson
*VP: Carlos Yamamoto
Dir Lab: Hector Fimbres
Rgnl Mgr: Dave Bell
Admn Mgr: Scott Arntzen

D-U-N-S 79-434-2758
INSPECTORATE AMERICA HOLDING INC
BSI INSPECTORATE AMERICA
(Suby of INSPECTORATE HOLDINGS PLC)
12000 Aerospace Ave # 200, Houston, TX 77034-5587
Tel (713) 944-2000 Founded/Ownrshp 1991
Sales 165.3MM^E EMP 764
SIC 7389 8734 Inspection & testing services; Testing laboratories; Inspection & testing services; Testing laboratories
Pr: Neil Hopkins
*CFO: Barry Benton
CFO: James Davis
VP: Alan Aronowitz
VP: Mark Esselman
VP: Brit Horncastle
VP: Randy Neck
VP: Aldo Rodriguez

D-U-N-S 07-831-4763
■ INSPECTORS GENERAL ON INTEGRITY AND EFFICIENCY COUNCIL OF
CIGIE
(Suby of G S A) ★
1717 H St Nw Ste 825, Washington, DC 20006-3920
Tel (202) 292-2604 Founded/Ownrshp 2011
Sales NA EMP 1,200
SIC 9199 General government administration; ; General government administration;
Ofcr: Brett Wilson

D-U-N-S 11-317-3269
■ INSPERITY HOLDINGS INC
ADMINISTAFF OF TEXAS, INC.
(Suby of INSPERITY INC) ★
19001 Crescent Springs Dr, Kingwood, TX 77339-3802
Tel (281) 358-8986 Founded/Ownrshp 1986
Sales 1.6MMM^E EMP 1,316^E
SIC 7363 Help supply services
Pr: Paul J Sarvadi

D-U-N-S 18-126-2080
▲ INSPERITY INC
19001 Crescent Springs Dr, Kingwood, TX 77339-3802
Tel (281) 358-8986 Founded/Ownrshp 1986
Sales 2.3MMM EMP 2,300
Accts Ernst & Young Llp Houston T
Tkr Sym NSP Exch NYS
SIC 8742 7363 7361 6311 Human resource consulting services; Employee leasing service; Employment agencies; Life insurance; Human resource consulting services; Employee leasing service; Employment agencies; Life insurance
Ch Bd: Paul J Sarvadi
*Pr: Richard G Rawson
Pr: Marilyn Warner

COO: A Steve Arizpe
CFO: Douglas S Sharp
Bd of Dir: Eli Jones
Bd of Dir: Paul S Lattanzio
Bd of Dir: Gregory E Petsch
Bd of Dir: Austin P Young III
Ofcr: Jeremy Lawson
Ex VP: Jay E Mincks
Sr VP: Ross Astramecki
Sr VP: Gregory R Clouse
Sr VP: Daniel D Herink
Sr VP: Samuel G Larson
VP: Mark W Allen
VP: Howard G Buff
VP: James Himanga
VP: Martin K Scirratt
Comm Dir: Alan Dodd
Board of Directors: Michael W Brown, Michelle McKenna-Doyle, Jack M Fields Jr, Eli Jones, Carol R Kaufman, Paul S Lattanzio, Austin P Young

D-U-N-S 01-880-9974
INSPHERE INSURANCE SOLUTIONS INC
(Suby of HEALTHMARKETS LLC) ★
9151 Boulevard 26, North Richland Hills, TX 76180-5600
Tel (817) 255-3100 Founded/Ownrshp 2009
Sales NA EMP 277^E
SIC 6411 Insurance agents, brokers & service; Insurance agents, brokers & service
CEO: Kenneth J Fasola
*Ex VP: R Scott Donovan
*Ex VP: Derrick A Duke
*Sr VP: N Lee Bedford
*Sr VP: Michael Burson
Sr VP: Jack Heller
Dir Risk M: Wes Doby
Dir Risk M: Arden Williams
Dist Mgr: Anne Miller
Sls Mgr: Douglas Buchheit
Sales Asso: Lindsay Adams

INSPIRA HEALTH CENTER BRIDGETON
See INSPIRA MEDICAL CENTERS INC

D-U-N-S 78-875-6927
INSPIRA HEALTH NETWORK INC
2950 College Dr Ste 2d, Vineland, NJ 08360-6933
Tel (856) 641-8000 Founded/Ownrshp 1983
Sales 415.1MM^E EMP 3,063
SIC 8062 General medical & surgical hospitals; General medical & surgical hospitals
Pr: John A Diangelo
Pr: Chester Kaletkowski
Ex VP: Eileen Cardile
Sr VP: Erich Florentine
VP: Carolyn Heckman
VP: Paul Lambrecht
VP: Steven Linn
Dir Bus: Joseph Alessanvrini
Obsttrcn: Peter S Konchak
Ansthlgy: Tamer A Attia
Ansthlgy: Aboulnasr Hamada

D-U-N-S 06-989-0911
INSPIRA MEDICAL CENTERS INC
INSPIRA HEALTH CENTER BRIDGETON
(Suby of INSPIRA HEALTH NETWORK INC) ★
333 Irving Ave, Bridgeton, NJ 08302-2123
Tel (856) 575-4500 Founded/Ownrshp 2010
Sales 412.1MM EMP 3,063
SIC 8062 General medical & surgical hospitals; General medical & surgical hospitals
Pr: John D'Angelo
Pr: Colleen Bodhuin
COO: Keith Bailey
*COO: Wayne Schiffner
CFO: Eric Florentine
Treas: Herb Deininger
Sr VP: Dawn Jenkins
Comm Dir: Linda Macdonald
Dir Rad: Glenda Smith
Dir Rx: Joe Alessandrini
Prac Mgr: Bernadette Battistini

INSPIRATION MINISTRIES
See INSPIRATIONAL NETWORK INC

D-U-N-S 79-090-9931
INSPIRATIONAL NETWORK INC
INSPIRATION MINISTRIES
3000 World Reach Dr, Indian Land, SC 29707-6542
Tel (803) 578-1461 Founded/Ownrshp 1992
Sales 46.7MM^E EMP 220
SIC 5961 4841 Catalog & mail-order houses; Cable television services; Catalog & mail-order houses; Cable television services
CEO: David Cerullo
Ex VP: Becky Henderson
Sr VP: Robert Brace
VP: Mitch Martin
Dir Sec: Jack Postell
VP Opers: Brack Rogers
VP Mktg: John Roos
Mktg Dir: Kathy Covington
Art Dir: Susan Sigmon
Board of Directors: Morris Cerullo, Don Gordon, John Gronke, Fred Smith

D-U-N-S 05-037-2161
INSPIRATIONAL NETWORKS
MEDIA COMMUNICATIONS
9700 Southern Pine Blvd, Charlotte, NC 28273-5559
Tel (704) 525-9800 Founded/Ownrshp 2010
Sales 5.1MM^E EMP 300
SIC 4833 Television broadcasting stations
Pr: David Cerello
VP: Rosemary Green
Dir IT: Gary Olmsted
Sls&Mrk Ex: Doug Butts
Mktg Mgr: Ossie Mills

D-U-N-S 15-938-1060
INSPIRE DEVELOPMENT CENTERS
105 S 6th St Ste B, Sunnyside, WA 98944-1448
Tel (509) 839-9762 Founded/Ownrshp 1983
Sales 34.7MM EMP 325^E
Accts Cliftonlarsonallen Llp Yakim
SIC 8322 Individual & family services; Individual & family services

CEO: Tadeo Saenz-Thompson
*CFO: Nicole Bisping
IT Man: Peggy Glossen
Snr Mgr: Jorge Castillo

INSPIRE INSURANCE GROUP
See INSPIRE INSURANCE SOLUTIONS INC

D-U-N-S 83-810-9213
INSPIRE INSURANCE SOLUTIONS INC
INSPIRE INSURANCE GROUP
300 Burnett St, Fort Worth, TX 76102-2799
Tel (817) 348-3900 Founded/Ownrshp 1997
Sales 68.8MM EMP 196^E
Accts Deloitte & Touche Llp Fort Wo
SIC 7371 Computer software development & applications; Computer software development & applications
CEO: Richard Marxen
Ch Bd: John F Pergrande
*Pr: Jeffrey W Robinson
COO: W Smith
Ch: John Pergande
Act CFO: Andrea Goodrich
Bd of Dir: James Drawert
Bd of Dir: F Dunham
Ofcr: J E Lundby
Ex VP: R Agazzi
Ex VP: Robert A Agazzi
Ex VP: John Aldredge
Ex VP: Gordon Garr
Sr VP: Bob Buatt
Sr VP: Ann Mirabito
VP: S Aldredge
VP: Christine Bass
VP: Edith Fife
VP: R Lynn
VP: Randell McKan
VP: Robert Milburn

D-U-N-S 92-672-3339
■ INSPIRE PHARMACEUTICALS INC
(Suby of OAK PHARMACEUTICALS INC) ★
1 Merck Dr, Whitehouse Station, NJ 08889-3400
Tel (908) 423-1000 Founded/Ownrshp 2013
Sales 20.2MM^E EMP 240
SIC 2836 Biological products, except diagnostic; Biological products, except diagnostic
Pr: John Canan
Treas: Mark McDonough

D-U-N-S 06-499-0047 IMP/EXP
INSPIRED BEAUTY BRANDS INC
JHIRMACK
330 7th Ave Ste 1600, New York, NY 10001-5248
Tel (212) 235-2130 Founded/Ownrshp 2010
Sales 25.4MM^E EMP 21
SIC 5122 Cosmetics; Hair preparations
CEO: Sam Maniaci
*CFO: Jeffrey Sieglen
*Ch: Peter Lafleche

D-U-N-S 11-295-2432
INSPIRITEC INC
340 N 12th St Ste 108, Philadelphia, PA 19107-1114
Tel (302) 792-8299 Founded/Ownrshp 2000
Sales 33.0MM EMP 132
Accts Eisneramper Llp Jenkintown P
SIC 8243 Software training, computer; Software training, computer
Pr: John F Connolly Jr
CFO: Dick Mahan
Snr PM: Bill Odonnell

D-U-N-S 60-507-9706
■ INSPRO CORP
RISK ADMINISTRATION & MGT
(Suby of HCC INSURANCE HOLDINGS INC) ★
2300 Clayton Rd Ste 1100, Concord, CA 94520-2157
Tel (925) 685-1600 Founded/Ownrshp 1982
Sales NA EMP 35
SIC 6411 Insurance agents, brokers & service; Insurance agents, brokers & service
Mng Dir: Grant Weaver
Ofcr: S Lee Nelson
Dir IT: David Wiley

D-U-N-S 09-339-3882
INSPRO INC (NE)
INSPRO INSURANCE
100 E 6th St, Fremont, NE 68025-5030
Tel (402) 721-9707 Founded/Ownrshp 1970
Sales NA EMP 85
SIC 6411 Insurance agents
Pr: Randall Eikmeier
COO: Kevin McCarville
Ex VP: Mike Chvatal
Ex VP: James Irvine
Sr VP: Loren Sweigard
VP: Dan Chvatal
VP: Becky Haufle
VP: Jeff Keller
Exec: Michael J Chvatal
Exec: Randall L Eikmeier
Exec: Rohn P Loyd

INSPRO INSURANCE
See INSPRO INC

INSTAFF
See BG STAFFING INC

D-U-N-S 07-928-8110
▲ INSTALLED BUILDING PRODUCTS INC
495 S High St Ste 50, Columbus, OH 43215-5689
Tel (614) 221-3399 Founded/Ownrshp 1977
Sales 518.0MM EMP 3,625^E
Tkr Sym IBP Exch NYS
SIC 1522 5033 5211 Residential construction; Insulation materials; Insulation material, building; Residential construction; Insulation materials; Insulation material, building
Ch Bd: Jeffrey W Edwards
Pr: W Jeffrey Hire
Pr: R Scott Jenkins
Pr: Matthew J Momper
Pr: Warren W Pearce
Pr: Brad A Wheeler
Pr: Randall S Williamson
COO: Jay P Elliott

*CFO: Michael T Miller
Sr VP: William W Jenkins
Sr VP: Jason R Niswonger
Board of Directors: Margot L Carter, Lawrence A Hilsheimer, Janet E Jackson, J Michael Nixon, Steven G Raich, Robert H Schottenstein, Michael H Thomas

D-U-N-S 05-285-6622
■ INSTALLED BUILDING PRODUCTS LLC
ROCKFORD INSULATION
(Suby of INSTALLED BUILDING PRODUCTS INC) ★
495 S High St Ste 50, Columbus, OH 43215-5689
Tel (614) 962-6360 Founded/Ownrshp 1954, 2002
Sales 317.5MM^E EMP 2,000^E
SIC 1742

D-U-N-S 12-284-7507
■ INSTALLED BUILDING PRODUCTS LLC
BUILDERS INSULATION NH
(Suby of INSTALLED BUILDING PRODUCTS LLC) ★
62 King St, Auburn, NH 03032-3973
Tel (603) 645-1604 Founded/Ownrshp 2001
Sales 21.1MM^E EMP 916^E
SIC 1761 5021 5719 2515 Gutter & downspout contractor; Shelving; Fireplace equipment & accessories; Foundations & platforms
Genl Mgr: Kyle Niemela
Brnch Mgr: Sean Archuleta

INSTALLOY
See TEXAS PIPE AND SUPPLY CO LTD

D-U-N-S 87-421-4182
INSTALLS INC LLC
241 Main St Ste 500, Buffalo, NY 14203-2726
Tel (716) 843-1200 Founded/Ownrshp 1993
Sales 33.2MM^E EMP 210
SIC 8741 Management services; Management services
Pr: Thomas Hunt
*COO: John T Nettina
Treas: Grashawn Shabazz
*VP: Kyle Bernard
VP: Vijay Reddy
*VP: Kirk M Rydzynski
Exec: Tim Kisker
*Co-Founder: Lee Hess
IT Man: Lay Yap
Sftwr Eng: Alex Civiletti
Sftwr Eng: Dale Neimeier

INSTANT AUTO INSURANCE
See A-AFFORDABLE INSURANCE AGENCY INC

D-U-N-S 82-901-7834
INSTANT AUTO INSURANCE AGENCY INC
INSTANT INS AGENCY
8113 Ridgepoint Dr # 214, Irving, TX 75063-3197
Tel (800) 850-6000 Founded/Ownrshp 1998
Sales NA EMP 190
SIC 6411 Insurance agents, brokers & service
Pr: Barry G Porter
*VP: Stephen Brandt

INSTANT INS AGENCY
See INSTANT AUTO INSURANCE AGENCY INC

D-U-N-S 04-816-6672
INSTANT WEB INC
IWCO DIRECT
7951 Powers Blvd, Chanhassen, MN 55317-9326
Tel (952) 474-0961 Founded/Ownrshp 1968
Sales 213.7MM^E EMP 2,200
SIC 7331 Direct mail advertising services; Direct mail advertising services
CEO: Jim Andersen
*CFO: Joe Morrison
*Chf Mktg O: Patrick Deck
VP: Don Brady
VP: Jill Burg
VP: Rick Eggers
*VP: Debora Haskel
VP: Chris Houtte
VP: Jeffrey Jurick
VP: Jerry Montella
IT Man: Len Johnson

D-U-N-S 07-935-9891
INSTANT WEB LLC
IWCO DIRECT
7951 Powers Blvd, Chanhassen, MN 55317-9326
Tel (952) 474-0961 Founded/Ownrshp 2014
Sales 140.0MM^E EMP 2,200
SIC 7331 Direct mail advertising services
Ex VP: Pat Deck
Ex VP: Joe Morrison
Sr VP: Jay Garner
VP: Dave Johannes
Dir IT: Chris Van Houtte

D-U-N-S 02-728-6282
INSTANTLY INC
USAMP
16501 Ventura Blvd # 300, Encino, CA 91436-2007
Tel (866) 872-4006 Founded/Ownrshp 2008
Sales 39.5MM^E EMP 200
SIC 8732 Market analysis or research; Market analysis or research; Market analysis, business & economic research; Survey service: marketing, location, etc.
CEO: Alan Gould
CFO: John Woolard
Chf Mktg O: Andy Jolls
Ex VP: Ted Bouzakis
Ex VP: Jim Collins
Sr VP: Michael Brezner
Sr VP: Joshua Pink
Sr VP: Robyn TAS
VP: Melanie Courtright
VP: Karyn Hall
VP: Joe Jordan
VP: Elisabeth Mischel
VP: Daniel Ross
VP: Edward J Russo
VP: Leslie Warshaw

D-U-N-S 00-428-6175
INSTANTWHIP FOODS INC (DE)
2200 Cardigan Ave, Columbus, OH 43215-1092
Tel (614) 488-2536 Founded/Ownrshp 1934
Sales 50.8MM^E EMP 146
SIC 6794 8741 2026 5143 Franchises, selling or licensing; Administrative management; Fluid milk; Dairy products, except dried or canned; Franchises, selling or licensing; Administrative management; Fluid milk; Whipped topping, except frozen or dry mix; Dairy products, except dried or canned
Pr: Douglas A Smith
*Treas: Thomas G Michaelides

D-U-N-S 86-943-8739
INSTAR SERVICES GROUP LP
(Suby of BLACK EAGLE) ★
6905 Telegraph Rd Ste 205, Bloomfield Hills, MI 48301-3159
Tel (248) 203-7714 Founded/Ownrshp 2008
Sales 40.5MM^E EMP 301
SIC 1521 1522 1542 Repairing fire damage, single-family houses; Remodeling, multi-family dwellings; Commercial & office buildings, renovation & repair; Repairing fire damage, single-family houses; Remodeling, multi-family dwellings; Commercial & office buildings, renovation & repair
CEO: Tom Denomme
CFO: James J Guillaumin
Ex VP: Jim Stanilious
Brnch Mgr: Shane Flores

D-U-N-S 04-606-8821 IMP
INSTASET CORP
INSTASET PLASTIC
10101 Marine City Hwy, Anchorville, MI 48004
Tel (586) 725-0229 Founded/Ownrshp 1997
Sales 27.0MM^E EMP 100
SIC 3089 Injection molded finished plastic products; Thermoformed finished plastic products
Pr: Douglas Burrell
VP: Patrick Hunt
Ql Cn Mgr: Melissa Visga
Sls Mgr: Rocco Messana

INSTASET PLASTIC
See INSTASET CORP

D-U-N-S 83-323-3484
INSTAWARES HOLDING CO LLC
1965 Vaughn Rd Nw, Kennesaw, GA 30144-7024
Tel (770) 517-1838 Founded/Ownrshp 2009
Sales 48.7MM^E EMP 101
SIC 5087 5719 Restaurant supplies; Cookware, except aluminum
CEO: Craig Callaway
*Pr: Bruce Brown

D-U-N-S 12-889-6151 EXP
INSTAWARES LLC
(Suby of INSTAWARES HOLDING CO LLC) ★
222 Chastain Rd Nw, Kennesaw, GA 30144-3012
Tel (770) 517-1838 Founded/Ownrshp 2010
Sales 28.8MM^E EMP 50
SIC 5719 Cookware, except aluminum
CEO: Bruce Brown
COO: Paul Stoner
CFO: Juliet Reising
VP: Fred Moss
Web Dev: Mike Newbold
Mktg Mgr: Holly Patterson
Sls Mgr: Michael Price

D-U-N-S 00-322-0225 EXP
▲ INSTEEL INDUSTRIES INC (NC)
1373 Boggs Dr, Mount Airy, NC 27030-2145
Tel (336) 786-2141 Founded/Ownrshp 1958
Sales 447.5MM EMP 790^E
Accts Grant Thornton Llp Charlotte
Tkr Sym IIIN Exch NGS
SIC 3315 Wire & fabricated wire products; Welded steel wire fabric; Wire, steel: insulated or armored; Wire & fabricated wire products; Welded steel wire fabric; Wire, steel: insulated or armored
Pr: H O Woltz III
CFO: Michael C Gazmarian
VP: Richard Burgess
VP: Chris Stauffer
VP: Richard T Wagner
VP Admn: James F Petelle
Genl Mgr: Chad Swavey
IT Man: Christi Smiley
Software D: Julia Terry
Sls Mgr: Daniel Lundeen
Sls Mgr: Wes Schrooten
Board of Directors: Louis E Hannen, Charles B Newsome, Gary L Pechota, W Allen Rogers II, Joseph A Rutkowski, C Richard Vaughn

D-U-N-S 18-329-9502 IMP/EXP
■ INSTEEL WIRE PRODUCTS CO
(Suby of INSTEEL INDUSTRIES INC) ★
1373 Boggs Dr, Mount Airy, NC 27030-2145
Tel (336) 719-9000 Founded/Ownrshp 1981
Sales 196.5MM^E EMP 685^E
SIC 3315 Concrete reinforcing mesh & wire; Welded steel wire fabric
Pr: H O Woltz III
*CFO: Michael C Gazmarian
*VP: Lyle Bullington
*VP: James F Petelle
*VP: Chris Stauffer
*VP: Richard Wagner
Sfty Mgr: Anthony Shannon
Natl Sales: Jack Wellborn
Sls Mgr: Jim Hoenig
Sales Asso: Monica Larraga
Sales Asso: Ashley Morton

D-U-N-S 14-485-1409
INSTINET CORP
(Suby of INSTINET GROUP INC) ★
1095 Avenue Of The, New York, NY 10036
Tel (212) 310-9500 Founded/Ownrshp 1968
Sales 122.0MM^E EMP 600
SIC 6211 7379 Brokers, security; Computer related maintenance services; Brokers, security; Computer related maintenance services
CEO: Fumiki Kondo
Ch Bd: Ed Nicoll
CEO: Glenn Lesko
COO: Frank M Freitas
CFO: Jacob Asbury
CFO: Nathalie Leroy
Co-CEO: Anthony Abenante
Ex VP: Alex Goor
VP: Wadood Chaudhary
CTO: Chris Rogers

D-U-N-S 02-162-3777
INSTINET GROUP INC
(Suby of NOMURA SECURITIES INTERNATIONAL INC) ★
1095 Ave Of The Americas, New York, NY 10036-6797
Tel (518) 474-4429 Founded/Ownrshp 2007
Sales 148.7MM^E EMP 600
SIC 6231 Stock exchanges; Stock exchanges
CEO: Fumiki Kondo
Ch Bd: Ian Strachan
COO: Frank M Freitas
CFO: Jacob Asbury
CFO: John F Fay
Ofcr: Francisco Soto
Sr VP: David Bellantonio
Sr VP: Richard Jones
Sr VP: Jay McEntire
VP: Eric Chaney
VP: Jesse Forster
VP: Ken Fujimoto
VP: Kenneth Gast
VP: Steven Gero
VP: David Hoffman
VP: Harry Ko
VP: Leela Kode
VP: John Lafrance
VP: Betsy McGrath
VP: Dillon McNiven
VP: William Nuckols

D-U-N-S 07-375-0135
INSTITUTE FOR ADVANCED STUDY - LOUIS BAMBERGER AND MRS FELIX FULD FOU
1 Einstein Dr, Princeton, NJ 08540-4907
Tel (609) 734-8000 Founded/Ownrshp 1930
Sales 60.4MM EMP 185
Accts Kpmg Llp Short Hills Nj
SIC 8621 Scientific membership association; Scientific membership association
Ch: Charles Simonyi
*Pr: Martin Leibowitz
Treas: Allen I Rowe
*Treas: Brian Wruble
Chf Inves: Ashvin Chhabra
Ofcr: Robbert Dijkgraaf
Ofcr: Jean Durbin
Ofcr: Brian Epstein
Ofcr: Kelly Thomas
VP: Christina Ferrara
Assoc Dir: Michael Gehret
Assoc Dir: John Masten

D-U-N-S 13-012-0967 IMP
INSTITUTE FOR APPLIED BEHAVIOR ANALYSIS A PSYCHOLOGICAL CORP
IABA
5777 W Century Blvd # 675, Los Angeles, CA 90045-5600
Tel (310) 649-0499 Founded/Ownrshp 1982
Sales 17.3MM^E EMP 375
SIC 8049 8741 8093 Clinical psychologist; Management services; Specialty outpatient clinics; Clinical psychologist; Management services; Specialty outpatient clinics
Pr: Gary W Lavigna PHD

D-U-N-S 07-011-0721
INSTITUTE FOR BUILDING TECHNOLOGY AND SAFETY INC
IBTS
45207 Research Pl Ste 100, Ashburn, VA 20147-2421
Tel (703) 481-2000 Founded/Ownrshp 2002
Sales 29.7MM EMP 140^E
Accts Halt Buzas & Powell Ltd Alex
SIC 8742 8711 Management consulting services; Engineering services; Management consulting services; Engineering services
CEO: Ashok Goswami
*COO: Shyam Choudhary
Prgrm Mgr: Rudy Saporite
Admn Mgr: Jackie Cosio
IT Man: Aseem Jaiswal
IT Man: Leslie Woodside
Mktg Mgr: Michelle Waddle
Board of Directors: Tim Nogler, Charlotte Randolph, Steven Sarkozy, Richard Sliwoski, Craig Thurmond

D-U-N-S 06-436-7329
INSTITUTE FOR CANCER RESEARCH
CHASE CANCER CENTER
(Suby of FOX CHASE CANCER CENTER FOUNDATION) ★
333 Cottman Ave, Philadelphia, PA 19111-2434
Tel (215) 728-6900 Founded/Ownrshp 1972
Sales 63.9MM EMP 350
Accts Pricewaterhousecoopers Llp Ph
SIC 8071 Testing laboratories; Testing laboratories
Pr: Michael Seiden MD
*Treas: Anthony Diasio
*Prin: John Hyde
*Genl Mgr: Thomas Albanesi

INSTITUTE FOR CAREER DEV
See ICD INTERNATIONAL CENTER FOR DISABLED

INSTITUTE FOR CAREER DEVELOPME
See GOODWILL OF SILICON VALLEY

D-U-N-S 07-726-9256
INSTITUTE FOR CHILD AND FAMILY HEALTH INC
15490 Nw 7th Ave Ste 201, Miami, FL 33169-6231
Tel (305) 685-0381 Founded/Ownrshp 1951
Sales 18.3MM EMP 375
Accts Verdeja & De Armas Llp Miami
SIC 8093 Mental health clinic, outpatient; Mental health clinic, outpatient
CEO: Juan C Gonzalez
*Pr: Henry E Landa
*Pr: Stephen J Makar
*CFO: M Ahmed Qureshi
Opers Supe: Barbara Arteaga
Opers Supe: Farah Halaby
Opers Supe: Rose Lagravere
Pgrm Dir: Maite Schenker

D-U-N-S 17-330-6457
INSTITUTE FOR COMMUNITY LIVING INC
ICL
125 Broad St, New York, NY 10004-2400
Tel (212) 385-3030 Founded/Ownrshp 1986
Sales 88.5MM EMP 1,200
Accts Grassi & Co Cpas Pc Jericho
SIC 8052 Home for the mentally retarded, with health care; Home for the mentally retarded, with health care
Pr: David Woodlock
*COO: Chris Copeland
*COO: Stella Pappas
*CFO: Dewey Howard
*Treas: Michael V Balistreri
Bd of Dir: Lisa Delduke
Bd of Dir: Alden Haffner
*Ex VP: Gina Jacobson
*Sr VP: Pamela Tindall-Obrien
VP: Constance Brown
VP: Pat Valerio

D-U-N-S 07-354-8562
INSTITUTE FOR COMMUNITY SERVICES INC
ICS PROJECT HEADSTART
160 W Valley Ave, Holly Springs, MS 38635-2218
Tel (662) 252-1582 Founded/Ownrshp 1967
Sales 35.0MM EMP 850
SIC 8351 Head start center, except in conjunction with school; Head start center, except in conjunction with school
Bd of Dir: Anita Lockhart

D-U-N-S 07-484-9589
INSTITUTE FOR DEFENSE ANALYSES INC
4850 Mark Center Dr, Alexandria, VA 22311-1882
Tel (703) 845-2000 Founded/Ownrshp 1956
Sales 218.7MM EMP 1,500
Accts Pricewaterhousecoopers Llp Mc
SIC 8733 Research institute; Research institute
CEO: David Chu
Mng Pt: Edward R Jayne II
*Ch: Suzanne H Woolsey
*Treas: Dean Graves Jr
Bd of Dir: William H Press
Bd of Dir: Rod Williams
Ofcr: Marco Quiroga
VP: Judith Hautala
VP: Dale Lichtblau
Adm Dir: Bruce Angier
IT Man: Brad Gernand

D-U-N-S 10-618-8451
INSTITUTE FOR DEVELOPMENTAL DISABILITIES INC
CRYSTAL SPRINGS SCHOOL
38 Narrows Rd, Assonet, MA 02702-1633
Tel (508) 644-3101 Founded/Ownrshp 1982
Sales 22.8MM EMP 500
Accts Leonard Mulherin & Greene P
SIC 8211 Specialty education; Specialty education
Pr: Susan A Bouchard-Young

D-U-N-S 16-473-1718
INSTITUTE FOR ENVIRONMENTAL HEALTH INC
IEH LBRTORIES CONSULTING GROUP
15300 Bothell Way Ne, Lake Forest Park, WA 98155-7634
Tel (800) 491-7745 Founded/Ownrshp 1992
Sales 22.2MM^E EMP 183
SIC 8731 Environmental research; Environmental research
Pr: Mansour Samadpour
COO: Samuel P Myoda
*VP: Dalia Alfi
VP: Sergio Sanchez
VP: Jaspreet Sidhu
VP: Jay Unverferth
Dir Lab: Jessica Williams

D-U-N-S 79-346-2284
INSTITUTE FOR FAMILY CENTERED SERVICES INC
916 Fox Ridge Trl, Chesapeake, VA 23322-6511
Tel (804) 346-0051 Founded/Ownrshp 1988
Sales 5.9MM^E EMP 300
SIC 8322 Family (marriage) counseling; Family (marriage) counseling
Pr: John P Sullivan
Ex Dir: William E Painter Jr

D-U-N-S 08-166-5374
INSTITUTE FOR FAMILY HEALTH
INSTITUTE FOR URBAN FMLY HLTH
2006 Madison Ave, New York, NY 10035-1217
Tel (212) 633-0800 Founded/Ownrshp 1985
Sales 104.1MM EMP 603
Accts O Connor Davies Llp Harrison
SIC 8011 Ambulatory surgical center; General & family practice, physician/surgeon; Ambulatory surgical center; General & family practice, physician/surgeon
Pr: Neil Calman
COO: Peter A Grisafi
CFO: Gail Shamilov
Bd of Dir: Mary Mitchell
*Sr VP: Edward Fried
*Sr VP: Maxine Golub
*Sr VP: Virna Little
*Sr VP: Nicole Nurse
Sr VP: Robert Schiller
VP: Steve Carter
VP: Yvonne Eisner
VP: Brian Flynn
VP: Kwame Kitson
VP: Kathleen McGovern-Kearns
Comm Man: Robin Lally

D-U-N-S 79-514-0805
INSTITUTE FOR GENOMIC RESEARCH
9712 Medical Center Dr, Rockville, MD 20850-3775
Tel (301) 838-0200 *Founded/Ownrshp* 1992
Sales 21.6MM[E] *EMP* 300
SIC 8733 Research institute; Research institute
Pr: Claire M Fraser
CFO: Aimee L Turner
VP: Eric Eisenstadt
VP: Robert Friedman
Ex Dir: Saul Kravitz
Ex Dir: Martin Shumway
Dir IT: Corey Irwin
Dir IT: Alex Saeed
Dir IT: Steven Salsbury
Dir IT: Sapiro Vadim
Info Man: Michael Heaney

D-U-N-S 36-345-9905
INSTITUTE FOR HEALTHCARE IMPROVEMENT
IHI
20 University Rd Ste 7, Cambridge, MA 02138-5815
Tel (617) 301-4800 *Founded/Ownrshp* 2005
Sales 39.7MM *EMP* 135[E]
SIC 8699 Charitable organization; Charitable organization
CEO: Maureen Bisognano
Pr: Carol Beasley
Pr: Paul Hamnett
CFO: Amy Hosford
Treas: Gary Mecklenburg
Bd of Dir: Molly Fubel
Ex VP: Derek Feeley
Sr VP: Kedar Mate
VP: Katharine Luther
Dir Soc: Emily Crites
Dir Soc: Lauren Showalter
Dir Soc: Beth Solomon
Dir Soc: Carly Underwood
Board of Directors: Thomas W Chapman, Enrique Ruelas, Mark D Smith

D-U-N-S 10-187-3446
INSTITUTE FOR INTERGOVERNMENTAL RESEARCH IN
I I R
2050 Centre Pointe Blvd, Tallahassee, FL 32308-7828
Tel (850) 385-0600 *Founded/Ownrshp* 1978
Sales 24.4MM *EMP* 135
SIC 8742 Industry specialist consultants; Industry specialist consultants
Pr: D Douglas Bodrero
**CFO:* Mary J Dodd
**Treas:* Emory B Williams
Bd of Dir: Henry Kan
Ex VP: Bob Cummings
**Ex VP:* Robert E Cummings
**Sr VP:* Gina W Hartsfield
**VP:* E Bruce Buckley
**VP:* Betty W Collier
**VP:* R Clay Jester
**VP:* Richard H Ward

D-U-N-S 07-231-7324
INSTITUTE FOR INTERNATIONAL EDUCATION OF STUDENTS
IES ABROAD
33 W Monroe St Ste 2300, Chicago, IL 60603-5405
Tel (312) 944-1750 *Founded/Ownrshp* 1950
Sales 86.1MM *EMP* 150
Accts Crowe Horwath Llp Chicago Il
SIC 8299 Student exchange program; Student exchange program
Pr: Mary Dwyer
COO: William Hoye
**CFO:* William Martens
Ofcr: Jennifer Skiba
VP: Bill Martens
VP: Roger Sheffield
**VP:* Michael Steinberg
CIO: Ian Ellis
Dir IT: Bill Sechen

D-U-N-S 96-727-3087
INSTITUTE FOR INTERNATIONAL RESEARCH
101 Arthur Andersen Pkwy, Sarasota, FL 34232-6323
Tel (941) 365-4471 *Founded/Ownrshp* 1996
Sales 15.0MM[E] *EMP* 350
SIC 8742 Management consulting services; Management consulting services
Genl Mgr: Linda Harkleroad
Dir IT: John Lee
Sftwr Eng: Jeff Lup
Opers Mgr: Lauren Defalco

D-U-N-S 11-849-9912
INSTITUTE FOR INTERNATIONAL RESEARCH INC
(*Suby of* INSTITUTE FOR INTERNATIONAL RESEARCH (I.I.R.) B.V.)
708 3rd Ave Fl 4, New York, NY 10017-4201
Tel (212) 661-3500 *Founded/Ownrshp* 1983
Sales 17.3MM[E] *EMP* 360
SIC 8299 8243 8742 Educational services; Data processing schools; Banking & finance consultant; Educational services; Data processing schools; Banking & finance consultant
Pr: Debra Chipman
COO: Bill Sullivan
COO: Larry Thomas
CFO: Wade Miquelon
Ex VP: Marvlieu Hall
VP: Eric Kubicka
VP: Paula Lashinsky
VP: Charlotte Sibley
VP: Greg Thomas
Dir Soc: Marina Adamsky
Dir Bus: Matthew Middleton

D-U-N-S 62-649-3576
INSTITUTE FOR JUSTICE
901 N Glebe Rd Ste 900, Arlington, VA 22203-1854
Tel (703) 682-9320 *Founded/Ownrshp* 2006
Sales 24.6MM *EMP* 7
Accts Rubino & Mcgeehin Chartered
SIC 8733 Noncommercial research organizations; Noncommercial research organizations
Pr: William H Mellor
Comm Dir: J Wilson
Ex Dir: Elizabeth Foley
Ex Dir: Lee McGrath
Corp Couns: Jenny Hoffpauir

INSTITUTE FOR LGSLATIVE ACTION
See NATIONAL RIFLE ASSOCIATION OF AMERICA

D-U-N-S 06-434-5106
INSTITUTE FOR ONE WORLD HEALTH (CA)
25 Taylor St 209, San Francisco, CA 94102-3916
Tel (650) 392-2510 *Founded/Ownrshp* 2000
Sales 30.6MM *EMP* 50
SIC 7991 Health club; Health club
Ch Bd: Victoria G Hale

D-U-N-S 07-491-3257
INSTITUTE FOR ONEWORLD HEALTH INC
IOWH
280 Utah Ave Ste 250, South San Francisco, CA 94080-6819
Tel (650) 392-2510 *Founded/Ownrshp* 2000
Sales 24.7MM *EMP* 10
Accts Gelman Rosenberg & Freedman
SIC 8699 Charitable organization
Pr: Richard Chin
COO: Ahvie Herskowitz
CFO: Robert E Farrell
Ofcr: Matthew A Wikler
Psych: Syed Hassan

D-U-N-S 07-838-3586
INSTITUTE FOR PROFESSIONAL CARE EDUCATION LLC
MEDIFECTA HEALTHCARE TRAINING
5109 Ne 82nd Ave Ste 201, Vancouver, WA 98662-6841
Tel (503) 655-4757 *Founded/Ownrshp* 2012
Sales 52.3MM[E] *EMP* 8,299
SIC 8299 Educational service, nondegree granting: continuing educ.; Educational service, nondegree granting: continuing educ.

D-U-N-S 12-221-7193
■ **INSTITUTE FOR PROFESSIONAL DEVELOPMENT INC**
(*Subsy of* APOLLO EDUCATION GROUP INC) ★
4615 E Elwood St, Phoenix, AZ 85040-1958
Tel (480) 966-5394 *Founded/Ownrshp* 1973
Sales 13.4MM[E] *EMP* 394
SIC 8742 School, college, university consultant; Merchandising consultant; School, college, university consultant; Merchandising consultant
Pr: Ron King
**Sec:* John Sperling
VP Mktg: Peter Albrecht
VP Mktg: Jack Farrell
VP Mktg: Dana Souser

D-U-N-S 07-417-3873
INSTITUTE FOR REHABILITATION & RESEARCH (TX)
MEMORIAL HERMANN MEMORIAL CITY
(*Suby of* MEMORIAL HERMANN HEALTH SYSTEM) ★
1333 Moursund St, Houston, TX 77030-3405
Tel (713) 799-5000 *Founded/Ownrshp* 1959, 2006
Sales 91.5MM *EMP* 90
SIC 8062 General medical & surgical hospitals
Pr: Dan Wolterman
CFO: David Strickler
**Ex VP:* Dale St Arnold
**VP:* Carrol Aulbaugh
Dir Risk M: Rodgie Mann

D-U-N-S 00-217-4922
INSTITUTE FOR SHIPBOARD EDUCATION
ISE
2410 Old Ivy Rd, Charlottesville, VA 22903-5084
Tel (434) 243-4072 *Founded/Ownrshp* 1971
Sales 56.9MM *EMP* 60[E]
Accts Cherry Bekaert Llp Charlotte
SIC 8299 Educational services; Educational services
Pr: Michael Segal
**COO:* Salvatore Moschella
**CFO:* Lary Grant
VP: Luke Jones

D-U-N-S 36-293-7005
INSTITUTE FOR STUDY ABROAD INC
1100 W 42nd St Ste 305, Indianapolis, IN 46208-3345
Tel (317) 940-9336 *Founded/Ownrshp* 1988
Sales 48.2MM *EMP* 50[E]
SIC 8299 Student exchange program; Student exchange program
Pr: Mark Schied
**VP:* Joanna Hovley Bowles
**VP:* Steve Seaworth
**VP:* Warren Wise

D-U-N-S 13-564-6524
INSTITUTE FOR SYSTEMS BIOLOGY
401 Terry Ave N Ste 103, Seattle, WA 98109-5263
Tel (206) 732-1200 *Founded/Ownrshp* 1999
Sales 46.6MM[E] *EMP* 240
SIC 8733 Biotechnical research, noncommercial; Biotechnical research, noncommercial
Ch Bd: Louis Lange
Bd of Dir: Bill Bowes Jr
Bd of Dir: William K Bowes
Bd of Dir: Alan Diercks
Bd of Dir: Gustavo Glusman
Ex VP: Alan Aderem
Sr VP: John Aitchison
**Sr VP:* David Galas
**Sr VP:* James Ladd
VP: Sissy Walsh Bouchard
Assoc Dir: Nathan Price
Comm Dir: Hsiao-Ching Chou

D-U-N-S 79-198-1202
INSTITUTE FOR TRANSFUSION MEDICINE
5 Parkway Ctr 875, Pittsburgh, PA 15220-3608
Tel (412) 209-7316 *Founded/Ownrshp* 1987
Sales 1.7MM *EMP* 1,200
SIC 8099 Blood bank; Blood bank
CEO: James P Covert
**COO:* Jim Fitzgerald
CFO: Mark Giaquinto
VP: Linda Hahn
VP: Andrea Hassett
**VP:* Darrell J Triulzi
Info Man: Kevin Roney
Software D: Melissa Hopkins
Secur Mgr: Patrick Nevel

INSTITUTE FOR URBAN FMLY HLTH
See INSTITUTE FOR FAMILY HEALTH

D-U-N-S 14-464-5405
INSTITUTE HOMECARE SERVICES INC
105 E 22nd St Rm 700, New York, NY 10010-5447
Tel (212) 942-6780 *Founded/Ownrshp* 1984
Sales 7.1M *EMP* 650
Accts Nadel & Pearlman Cpa S Pc Gre
SIC 8322 Individual & family services; Individual & family services
Pr: S C Drinane
**Pr:* Suleika Cabrera Drinane

D-U-N-S 01-504-3672
INSTITUTE OF COMMUNITY SERVICES INC (MS)
PROJECT HEADSTART
160 W Valley Ave, Holly Springs, MS 38635-2218
Tel (662) 252-1582 *Founded/Ownrshp* 1970
Sales 26.7MM *EMP* 850
Accts Watkins Ward And Stafford We
SIC 8351 Head start center, except in conjunction with school; Head start center, except in conjunction with school
Ex Dir: Arvern Moore
IT Man: Marcia Naylor

D-U-N-S 04-768-4758
INSTITUTE OF ELECTRICAL AND ELECTRONICS ENGINEERS INC
3 Park Ave Fl 17, New York, NY 10016-5902
Tel (732) 981-0060 *Founded/Ownrshp* 1963
Sales 167.9MM[E] *EMP* 1,068
SIC 8621 Engineering association; Engineering association
Pr: Roberto De Marca
**Pr:* Peter W Staecker
**CFO:* Thomas Siegert
**Ch:* Shu Ping Chang
Bd of Dir: Dennis Hall
Bd of Dir: Christian Pepin
Bd of Dir: Steve Strong
Chf Inves: Sandeep Pandya
Ex VP: Didier Ryelandt
VP: Moshe Kam
Exec: James Dumser
Exec: Anthony Durniak
Exec: Lawrence Hamerman
Exec: Matt Loeb
Exec: Teck Low
Exec: Levent Onural
Exec: Alexander Pasik
Exec: Peter Staecker
Exec: Cary Yang

D-U-N-S 04-506-0753 IMP/EXP
INSTITUTE OF GAS TECHNOLOGY
GAS TECHNOLOGY INSTITUTE
1700 S Mount Prospect Rd, Des Plaines, IL 60018-1800
Tel (847) 768-0500 *Founded/Ownrshp* 2000
Sales 68.9MM *EMP* 250
SIC 8731 8733 Energy research; Environmental research; Educational research agency; Energy research; Environmental research; Educational research agency
Pr: David C Carroll
**Ch Bd:* Mary Jane McCartney
COO: Chakravarth Sishtla
**CFO:* James Ingold
Treas: Christopher Herman
VP: Edward B Johnston
VP: Jack Lewnard
VP: Albert Sherman
**VP:* Ronald Snedic
VP: Ronald N Snedic
Assoc Dir: John Meek
Board of Directors: John Somerhalder II, Philip C Ackerman, John M Stinson III, Randy Barnard, Lori Traweek, Robert W Best, Michael Warren Jr, Peter A Cistaro, Charles D Davidson, Robert J Fani, Terry D McCallister,lee M, Mark T Maassel, James T McManus II

D-U-N-S 07-255-8976
INSTITUTE OF INTERNAL AUDITORS-RESEARCH FOUNDATION
IIA, THE
247 Maitland Ave, Altamonte Springs, FL 32701-4201
Tel (407) 937-1100 *Founded/Ownrshp* 1941
Sales 44.3MM *EMP* 143[E]
Accts Batts Morrison Wales & Lee Pa
SIC 8621 Professional membership organizations; Professional membership organizations
Pr: Richard Chambers
CFO: Steve Lameier
Bd of Dir: Michael Moody
Bd of Dir: Stephen Morgan
Bd of Dir: Karem Obeid
Assoc VP: Donald Sparks
VP: Jamie Dubray
VP: Tianna Dumond
VP: Greg Jaynes
VP: Ramsay Knight
VP: Roger Lemaster
VP: Charity Prentice
VP: Paul Skurecki
VP: Ghia Smith

D-U-N-S 07-103-2973 EXP
INSTITUTE OF INTERNATIONAL EDUCATION INC (NY)
IIE COMMUNICATIONS DIVISION
809 United Nations Plz, New York, NY 10017-3503
Tel (212) 883-8200 *Founded/Ownrshp* 1919
Sales 586.6MM *EMP* 450
Accts Pricewaterhousecoopers Llp Ne
SIC 8299 Educational services; Educational services
Ch: Thomas Johnson
Pr: Saul T Caisman
V Ch: Diane J Paton
**Pr:* Allan Goodman
**COO:* Peggy Blumenthal
CFO: Nancy Khan
Ofcr: Candice Homan
Ofcr: Susan Sharp
Comm Dir: Sharon Witherell
Ex Dir: Keith Miceli
Prgrm Mgr: Lina Aleryani

D-U-N-S 10-192-9933
INSTITUTE OF INTERNATIONAL FINANCE INC
1333 H St Nw Ste 800e, Washington, DC 20005-4770
Tel (202) 857-3600 *Founded/Ownrshp* 1983
Sales 33.5MM *EMP* 60
Accts Larsonallen Llp Arlington Va
SIC 8611 Trade associations; Trade associations
CEO: Timothy D Adams
V Ch: Roberto E Stubal
Bd of Dir: Mustafa Akin
**Mng Dir:* Charles H Dallara
Mng Dir: Andres Portilla
IT Man: Karen Davenport
Info Man: Charlotte Hannagan
Snr Mgr: Andrew Desouza
Snr Mgr: Richard Heffernan
Snr Mgr: Maysoon Kaibni

INSTITUTE OF MUSIC AND DANCE
See MARYGROVE COLLEGE

D-U-N-S 09-857-8834
INSTITUTE OF NUCLEAR POWER OPERATIONS
INPO
700 Galleria Pkwy Se # 100, Atlanta, GA 30339-5943
Tel (770) 644-8000 *Founded/Ownrshp* 1979
Sales 114.6MM *EMP* 365
Accts Bennett Thrasher Llp Atlanta
SIC 8999 Nuclear consultant; Nuclear consultant
Pr: Robert F Willard
**Pr:* Jim Ellis
Pr: William Webster
**CFO:* Kris Straw
VP: Rob Gambone
VP: David Garchow
VP: Kim Maza
VP: Joan Penner-Hahn
Exec: Richard Larosa
**VP Admn:* James R Morris
Prgrm Mgr: Tim Chapin

D-U-N-S 15-531-7514
INSTITUTE OF PROFESSIONAL PRACTICE INC
2096 Airport Rd, Barre, VT 05641
Tel (802) 229-9515 *Founded/Ownrshp* 1981
Sales 71.2MM *EMP* 850
Accts Kerin-Ann Black-Deegan Cpa Mo
SIC 8361 Residential care for the handicapped; Residential care for the handicapped
CEO: Louis Giramma
**CFO:* Lois Nial
Ex VP: Susan Frederickson
Ex VP: Elaine Lussier
**VP:* Elaine J Lussier

D-U-N-S 82-596-5486
INSTITUTE ON AGING
ADULT DAY CARE CENTER
3575 Geary Blvd, San Francisco, CA 94118-3212
Tel (415) 750-4101 *Founded/Ownrshp* 1999
Sales 30.1MM *EMP* 350
Accts Good & Fowler Llp South San F
SIC 8322 Geriatric social service; Geriatric social service
Pr: J Thomas Briody
**COO:* Cindy Kaufmann
**CFO:* Roxana Tsougarakis
VP: Suzanne M Harris

INSTITUTE PUERTO RICAN CULTURE
See INSTITUTO DE CULTURA PUERTORRIQUENA

D-U-N-S 07-991-8850
INSTITUTES OF APPLIED HUMAN DYNAMICS INC
32 Warren Ave, Tarrytown, NY 10591-3021
Tel (914) 220-4300 *Founded/Ownrshp* 1957
Sales 46.3MM *EMP* 650[E]
Accts Loeb & Troper Llp New York N
SIC 8361 Home for the mentally retarded; Home for the mentally retarded
Pr: Mary K St Mark
**Ex Dir:* Stanley Silverstein

D-U-N-S 02-462-4298 IMP
■ **INSTITUTION FOOD HOUSE INC** (NC)
I F H
(*Suby of* P F G) ★
543 12th Street Dr Nw, Hickory, NC 28601-4754
Tel (800) 800-0434 *Founded/Ownrshp* 1965, 2012
Sales 491.8MM[E] *EMP* 622
SIC 5141 5142 Groceries, general line; Packaged frozen goods; Groceries, general line; Packaged frozen goods
Pr: Gerald Davis
**Ch Bd:* Boyd L George
CFO: Michael J Highland
**Sec:* Ron W Knedlik
Sr VP: Jeff Sykes
**VP:* Thomas Dooley
**Prin:* Moses George
Rgnl Mgr: Tim Jones
MIS Dir: Jay Schwarz
Netwrk Mgr: Ellen Beck
Opers Mgr: Johnny Duncan

D-U-N-S 78-556-8390
INSTITUTION FOR SAVINGS IN NEWBURYPORT AND ITS VICINITY CHAR
93 State St, Newburyport, MA 01950-6695
Tel (978) 462-3106 *Founded/Ownrshp* 1997
Sales NA *EMP* 59[E]

SIC 6036 Savings institutions, not federally chartered; Savings institutions, not federally chartered
Pr: Donald D Mitchell

D-U-N-S 07-974-9099
INSTITUTIONAL CAPITAL LLC
ICAP
(*Suby of* NEW YORK LIFE INSURANCE CO) ★
225 W Wacker Dr Ste 2400, Chicago, IL 60606-1319
Tel (312) 424-9100 *Founded/Ownrshp* 1969, 2006
Sales 24.6MM^E *EMP* 50
SIC 6282 Investment advisory service
CEO: Jerrold Senser
Pr: Ryan Carroll
**Pr:* Paula L Rogers
**CFO:* Robert J Lukaszewicz
Chf Cred: Brian E Franc
Chf Mktg O: Kelly A O'Kelly
Ex VP: Kain D Cederberg
Ex VP: Michael F Citrano
Ex VP: Thomas Cole
**Ex VP:* Keith D Watson
**Ex VP:* Scott E Weisenberger
Sr VP: Benjamin H Bielawski
Sr VP: Kelly Engstrom
Sr VP: John P Garrett
Sr VP: Susan F Lippa
Sr VP: Jeffrey A Miller
Sr VP: Treasa H Moran
Sr VP: Kathleen C Pease
Sr VP: Andrew P Starr
Sr VP: Robert D Stoll
Sr VP: Matthew T Swanson

D-U-N-S 06-889-9806
INSTITUTIONAL CARE PHARMACY
1815 W County Road 54, Tiffin, OH 44883-7723
Tel (419) 447-6216 *Founded/Ownrshp* 1988
Sales 54.3MM^E *EMP* 131^E
SIC 5122 5047 5912 Patent medicines; Medical & hospital equipment; Drug stores & proprietary stores; Patent medicines; Medical & hospital equipment; Drug stores & proprietary stores
Pr: James W Unverferth
VP: Dick Sandilands
IT Man: Sue Hawkins
Pharmcst: Chad Orr

D-U-N-S 62-110-4475
INSTITUTIONAL CASEWORK INC
CAMPBELL RHEA
1865 Hwy 641 North Paris, Paris, TN 38242
Tel (731) 642-4251 *Founded/Ownrshp* 2006
Sales 56.2MM^E *EMP* 250
SIC 3821 Laboratory apparatus & furniture; Laboratory apparatus & furniture
CEO: Jim Arthurs
**VP:* Donna Milam
DP Exec: Janet Ziegner
Sales Exec: Jacqui Pingre
Snr PM: Bobby Veazey

D-U-N-S 79-884-6684
▲ INSTITUTIONAL FINANCIAL MARKETS INC
2929 Arch St Ste 1703, Philadelphia, PA 19104-2857
Tel (215) 701-9555 *Founded/Ownrshp* 1999
Sales 55.7MM *EMP* 335
Tkr Sym IFMI *Exch* ASE
SIC 6211 Security brokers & dealers; Security brokers & dealers
Pr: Lester R Brafman
**Ch Bd:* Jack J Dimaio Jr
COO: Shami J Patel
CFO: Joseph W Pooler Jr
**V Ch Bd:* Daniel G Cohen

D-U-N-S 07-682-7468
INSTITUTIONAL INVESTOR LLC
(*Suby of* EUROMONEY INSTITUTIONAL INVESTOR PLC)
225 Park Ave S Fl 7, New York, NY 10003-1605
Tel (212) 224-3300 *Founded/Ownrshp* 1997
Sales 62.9MM^E *EMP* 342
SIC 7389 2741 2721 Convention & show services; Newsletter publishing; Magazines: publishing & printing; Trade journals: publishing & printing; Convention & show services; Newsletter publishing; Magazines: publishing & printing; Trade journals: publishing & printing
**CEO:* David E Antin
COO: David Antin
**Ch:* Diane Alfano
Ex Dir: Lou Cassetta
**Ex Dir:* Lewis Knox
Ex Dir: Steven Olson
Mng Dir: Sam Knox
Prgrm Mgr: Marsha Larned
Genl Mgr: Randy Liebowitz
CTO: Harry Katz
Dir IT: Kevin Davies

D-U-N-S 83-280-7705
■ INSTITUTIONAL SHAREHOLDERS SERVICES INC
SECURITIES CLASS ACTION SVC
(*Suby of* RISKMETRICS GROUP INC) ★
702 King Farm Blvd # 400, Rockville, MD 20850-6536
Tel (301) 556-0500 *Founded/Ownrshp* 2007
Sales 56.9MM^E *EMP* 309
SIC 8742 6282 Management consulting services; Investment advice; Management consulting services; Investment advice
CEO: John Connolly
**Pr:* Gary Retelny
**COO:* Stephen Sears
**CFO:* Robert J Bear
Ofcr: Thomas Rus
VP: Ginger Castillo
**VP:* Ron Harold

D-U-N-S 19-009-5500
INSTITUTIONAL VENTURES PARTNERS
IVP
2 Embarcadero Ctr # 1680, San Francisco, CA 94111-3823
Tel (415) 765-9393 *Founded/Ownrshp* 2005
Sales 50.0MM *EMP* 15

SIC 6211 Investment bankers; Investment bankers
Pt: Sandy Miller
Pt: Todd Chaffee
Pt: Norm Fegulson
Pt: Steve Harrick
Pt: Dennis Phelps

D-U-N-S 03-460-8091
INSTITUTIONAL WHOLESALE CO INC
I W C
535 Dry Valley Rd, Cookeville, TN 38506-4937
Tel (931) 537-4000 *Founded/Ownrshp* 1997
Sales 219.4MM^E *EMP* 175
SIC 5141 5142 Groceries, general line; Packaged frozen goods; Groceries, general line; Packaged frozen goods
Owner: Jimmy W Mackie
**Sec:* John M Mackie
**VP:* James Robert Mackie
Store Mgr: Greg Hughes
Opers Mgr: Jerry Shelgren
Sls Dir: Peter Guy

D-U-N-S 09-104-8835
INSTITUTO COMERCIAL DE PUERTO RICO INC
I C P R JUNIOR COLLEGE
558 Ave Munoz Rivera, San Juan, PR 00918-3610
Tel (787) 250-6436 *Founded/Ownrshp* 1946
Sales 13.8MM *EMP* 283
Accts Rs & Assoc-Psc San Juan Pr
SIC 8222 Junior college
Ch: Ramon A Negron
**Pr:* Maribel Bayona
**CEO:* Olga E Rivera
**CFO:* Noel Ortiz
**VP:* Mg Felix A Santoni
IT Man: Jesus Baeza

D-U-N-S 13-144-7021
INSTITUTO DE CIENCIAS FORENSE
(*Suby of* EXECUTIVE OFFICE OF COMMONWEALTH OF PUERTO RICO) ★
Cond Maga, San Juan, PR 00907-1966
Tel (787) 765-0615 *Founded/Ownrshp* 1986
Sales 20.6MM^E *EMP* 326
SIC 8734 Forensic laboratory; Forensic laboratory
Ex Dir: Lyvia A Alvarez

D-U-N-S 09-036-3250
INSTITUTO DE CULTURA PUERTORRIQUENA
INSTITUTE PUERTO RICAN CULTURE
Norzagaray Final St Bo, San Juan, PR 00901
Tel (787) 724-0700 *Founded/Ownrshp* 1955
Sales NA *EMP* 380
SIC 9199 General government administration; General government administration
Ex Dir: Robert Bounds

D-U-N-S 09-059-6503
INSTITUTO INTERNACIONAL DE BANCA INC
FLORIDA TECHNICAL COLLEGE
(*Suby of* EDUK GROUP) ★
56 Carr 20, Guaynabo, PR 00966-3300
Tel (787) 982-3000 *Founded/Ownrshp* 2007
Sales 48.7MM^E *EMP* 2,000
Accts Kevane Grant Thornton Llp San
SIC 8249 8244 8243 8222 7231 Banking school, training; Business & secretarial schools; Data processing schools; Technical institute; Cosmetology school; Banking school, training; Business & secretarial schools; Data processing schools; Technical institute; Cosmetology school
Pr: Guillermo Nigaglioni
Pr: Melissa Rosario
**Pr:* Ebbesen Samuel
**CFO:* Jose Cordorva
**Ch:* Fidel Alonso Valls
**VP:* Rafael Jimenez

INSTITUTO PANAMERICANO HATO REY
See FIRST HOSPITAL PANAMERICANO INC

D-U-N-S 86-948-5169
■ INSTRON JAPAN CO LTD
(*Suby of* ILLINOIS TOOL WORKS INC) ★
825 University Ave, Norwood, MA 02062-2643
Tel (781) 828-2500 *Founded/Ownrshp* 2007
Sales 31.0MM^E *EMP* 450
SIC 3829 Measuring & controlling devices; Measuring & controlling devices
Pr: Steven Martindale
Genl Mgr: Yahya Gharagozlou

D-U-N-S 06-130-8551
INSTRUCTURE INC
6330 S 3000 E Ste 700, Salt Lake City, UT 84121-6237
Tel (801) 869-5000 *Founded/Ownrshp* 2008
Sales 70.6MM^E *EMP* 400
Tkr Sym INST *Exch* NYS
SIC 7371 Computer software development; Computer software development
CEO: Josh Coates
Pr: David Burggraaf
COO: Kevin Kopas
**CFO:* Steve Kaminsky
VP: Trey Bean
VP: Davis Bell
**VP:* Misty Frost
VP: Paul Henry
VP: Mitch Macfarlane
**VP:* Mitch McFarlane
VP: Jeff Weber
**VP:* Zach Wily
Creative D: Paul Jacobsen
Board of Directors: Byron Deeter

D-U-N-S 79-246-9868 IMP
■ INSTRUMENT & VALVE SERVICES CO
(*Suby of* FISHER CONTROLS INTERNATIONAL LLC) ★
205 S Center St, Marshalltown, IA 50158-2823
Tel (641) 754-3011 *Founded/Ownrshp* 1991
Sales 146.4MM^E *EMP* 350

SIC 3494 3825 7699 Valves & pipe fittings; Instruments to measure electricity; Valve repair, industrial; Valves & pipe fittings; Instruments to measure electricity; Valve repair, industrial
Pr: Gary Major
**Pr:* Denny Cahill
**Treas:* Phil Stafford

D-U-N-S 78-838-6084 IMP
INSTRUMENT SALES AND SERVICE INC
16427 Ne Airport Way, Portland, OR 97230-4961
Tel (503) 239-0754 *Founded/Ownrshp* 2008
Sales 35.1MM^E *EMP* 100
SIC 5013 7699 Automotive supplies & parts; Miscellaneous automotive repair services; Automotive supplies & parts; Miscellaneous automotive repair services
CEO: David Lisle
**Pr:* Scott Haugen
**CFO:* James Trumbo
Dir Bus: Lawrance Griffiths
**Prin:* Sean Kelly
Opers Mgr: David Wallace
Ql Cn Mgr: Brian Clark
Sls Mgr: Noel Allen
Sls Mgr: Eric Asp
Sls Mgr: Humberto Romero
Sls Mgr: Ron Standish

INSTRUMENT TRANSFORMERS, INC.
See INSTRUMENT TRANSFORMERS LLC

D-U-N-S 01-081-5926 IMP
■ INSTRUMENT TRANSFORMERS LLC
INSTRUMENT TRANSFORMERS, INC.
(*Suby of* GENERAL ELECTRIC CAPITAL CORP) ★
1907 Calumet St, Clearwater, FL 33765-1190
Tel (727) 461-9413 *Founded/Ownrshp* 1975
Sales 203.1MM^E *EMP* 500
SIC 3612 Instrument transformers (except portable); Instrument transformers (except portable)
**Pr:* James M Koepsell
**CFO:* Lester L McDaniel
**VP:* William Booth
IT Man: Bob Criswell
Sfty Mgr: Karl Clemons
Sales Exec: Koepsell Jim

D-U-N-S 60-973-4236
■ INSTRUMENTARIUM DENTAL INC
(*Suby of* DANAHER CORP) ★
2800 Crystal Dr, Hatfield, PA 19440-1944
Tel (414) 747-1030 *Founded/Ownrshp* 2005
Sales 38.3MM *EMP* 44
SIC 5047 Medical & hospital equipment; Medical & hospital equipment
Pr: Henrik Roos

D-U-N-S 80-161-9029
INSTRUMENTATION & ELECTRICAL SPECIALIST LLC
2417 Randolph Rd, Pasadena, TX 77503-4237
Tel (281) 470-1063 *Founded/Ownrshp* 1999
Sales 30.0MM *EMP* 150
SIC 1731 Electrical work; Electrical work
CEO: Joseph A Durso III
**Pr:* Ann Durso

D-U-N-S 01-233-5522
INSTRUMENTATION & ELECTRICAL TECHNOLOGIES LLC
I & E TECHNOLOGIES
600 Saint Etienne Rd, Broussard, LA 70518-6011
Tel (337) 289-3030 *Founded/Ownrshp* 2000
Sales 23.9MM^E *EMP* 55
SIC 3533 Oil & gas field machinery
**VP:* Virgil Hebert

D-U-N-S 55-722-3252 IMP
INSTRUMENTATION LABORATORY CO
(*Suby of* INSTRUMENTATION LABORATORY SPA)
180 Hartwell Rd, Bedford, MA 01730-2443
Tel (781) 861-0710 *Founded/Ownrshp* 1991
Sales 407.7MM^E *EMP* 1,100
SIC 3841 2819 8731 2835 Diagnostic apparatus, medical; Chemicals, reagent grade: refined from technical grade; Commercial physical research; In vitro & in vivo diagnostic substances; Diagnostic apparatus, medical; Chemicals, reagent grade: refined from technical grade; Commercial physical research; In vitro & in vivo diagnostic substances
Pr: Ramon E Benet
**CFO:* Javier Gomez
CFO: Luis Guererro
Treas: Thomas H Conway
Ofcr: Ellen Lorusso
Ex VP: Steven Trotta
Sr VP: Ramon Benet
Sr VP: Ramone Benet
VP: James Clayton
**VP:* Jose Luis Martin
VP: Stephen Trotta

INSUL-FAB
See CONCOTE CORP

D-U-N-S 06-897-1787 IMP
INSUL-THERM INTERNATIONAL INC
6651 E 26th St, Commerce, CA 90040-3215
Tel (323) 728-0558 *Founded/Ownrshp* 1982
Sales 20.0MM^E *EMP* 50^E
SIC 5033 2899 3296

INSULATED ROOFING CONTRACTORS
See URETHANE OF KENTUCKIANA INC

INSULATED SEAL
See MDC VACUUM PRODUCTS LLC

INSULATED TRANSPORT PRODUCTS
See SIGNODE INDUSTRIAL GROUP LLC

D-U-N-S 07-906-0620
INSULATING SERVICES INC
10709 Granite St Ste H, Charlotte, NC 28273-6353
Tel (704) 588-7814 *Founded/Ownrshp* 1973
Sales 29.1MM^E *EMP* 245
SIC 1799

D-U-N-S 78-313-8191
INSULATION CONTRACTORS INC
22706 58th Pl S, Kent, WA 98032-4666
Tel (253) 395-1895 *Founded/Ownrshp* 1989
Sales 23.4MM^E *EMP* 120
SIC 1742 Insulation, buildings; Exterior insulation & finish (EIFS) applicator; Insulation, buildings; Exterior insulation & finish (EIFS) applicator
Pr: Gary Trauter
**VP:* Fletcher Vinson

D-U-N-S 09-827-7759
INSULATION DISTRIBUTORS INC
IDI DISTRIBUTORS
8303 Audubon Rd, Chanhassen, MN 55317-9494
Tel (952) 279-6400 *Founded/Ownrshp* 1979
Sales 163.9MM^E *EMP* 135
SIC 5033 Insulation materials; Insulation materials
CEO: Joseph Novogratz
CFO: Gary Meier
VP: Mike Clements
VP: Christopher Novogratz
Rgnl Mgr: Wes Ruprecht
Brnch Mgr: Greg Nelson
Genl Mgr: Thomas Bird
IT Man: Jackie Nuebauer
Sales Asso: Brian Rivero

D-U-N-S 09-718-9252
INSULATION FABRICATORS INC
(*Suby of* DISTRIBUTION INTERNATIONAL INC) ★
2501 165th St Ste 3, Hammond, IN 46320-2933
Tel (219) 845-2008 *Founded/Ownrshp* 2015
Sales 53.9MM^E *EMP* 100
SIC 5033 3296 Mineral wool insulation materials; Fiberglass insulation; Mineral wool insulation materials; Fiberglass insulation
Pr: Ted McNabb
VP: Tim Black
IT Man: Jeremy Gerstenberg
VP Sls: Mark Horvat

INSULATION FOR LIFE
See DIVERSIFIED THERMAL INC

D-U-N-S 06-868-5205
INSULATION MATERIALS CORP
IMC
700 Metuchen Rd, South Plainfield, NJ 07080-4814
Tel (908) 753-6766 *Founded/Ownrshp* 1971
Sales 20.1MM^E *EMP* 35
SIC 5033 Insulation, thermal
Ch Bd: Robert A March
**CFO:* Lou Tiblk

D-U-N-S 11-996-3973 IMP
INSULATION SOURCES INC
ICO RALLY
2575 E Bayshore Rd, Palo Alto, CA 94303-3210
Tel (650) 856-9900 *Founded/Ownrshp* 1997
Sales 40.7MM^E *EMP* 90
SIC 5063 5065 Wire & cable; Electronic parts; Wire & cable; Electronic parts
CEO: Edwina M Cioffi
IT Man: Esther Constantakis
Sls Mgr: Lynn Greenholtz

D-U-N-S 03-651-3976
INSULATION SPECIALISTS OF TULSA INC (OK)
ISTI PLANT SERVICES
17207 E 21st St, Tulsa, OK 74134-2105
Tel (918) 234-1097 *Founded/Ownrshp* 1997
Sales 77.1MM^E *EMP* 150
SIC 1629 Oil refinery construction; Oil refinery construction
Pr: Jaime Barraza
**VP:* Noe Gonzalez
Site Mgr: Carter Mason
Site Mgr: Jaime Montes

D-U-N-S 80-534-6850
INSULATION UNITED STATES HOLDINGS INC
7600 Oakwood Street Ext, Mebane, NC 27302-9577
Tel (919) 304-3846 *Founded/Ownrshp* 2007
Sales 72.8MM^E *EMP* 438
SIC 3086 Plastics foam products; Plastics foam products
Pr: Ulrich Weimer

D-U-N-S 06-265-8729 IMP/EXP
INSULATIONS INC (LA)
II
1101 Edwards Ave, Harahan, LA 70123-2227
Tel (504) 733-5033 *Founded/Ownrshp* 1970
Sales 138.3MM^E *EMP* 1,000
SIC 1799 1761 1741

D-U-N-S 00-965-7891 IMP
INSULECTRO
20362 Windrow Dr Ste 100, Lake Forest, CA 92630-8140
Tel (949) 587-3200 *Founded/Ownrshp* 1991
Sales 145.8MM^E *EMP* 120
SIC 5065 Electronic parts; Electronic parts
CEO: Timothy P Redfern
**Pr:* Patrick Redfern
**CFO:* Brad Biddle
VP: Jason Marsh
**VP:* Kevin M Miller
VP: Ken Parent
**VP:* Kenneth Parent
Off Mgr: Ann Visan
IT Man: Kenny Chao
Opers Mgr: Jim McKay
Opers Mgr: Ricardo Soto

D-U-N-S 05-133-4402 IMP
▲ INSULET CORP
600 Technology Park Dr # 200, Billerica, MA 01821-4150
Tel (978) 600-7000 *Founded/Ownrshp* 2000
Sales 288.7MM *EMP* 519^E
Tkr Sym PODD *Exch* NGS
SIC 3841 Surgical & medical instruments; Surgical & medical instruments
Pr: Patrick J Sullivan

Pr: Daniel Levangie
COO: William Patrick Ryan
CFO: Carsten Boess
CFO: Michael Levitz
Ofcr: Shacey Petrovic
Ex VP: Brad Thomas
Sr VP: M Hooks
VP: Annette Brewster
VP: Stephen Bubrick
VP: Robert Campbell
VP: Ruthann Depietro
VP: Todd Durniak
VP: Christopher Gilbert
VP: Deborah Gordon
VP: Mark Licari
VP: Jason Ng
VP: Kevin Schmid
VP: Patrick Treanor
VP: Daniel Trodden
VP: Glenn Weatherley
Board of Directors: Sally Crawford, Jessica Hopfield, Timothy J Scannell, Steven Sobieski, Regina Sommer, Joseph Zakrzewski

D-U-N-S 17-487-3992
INSULFOAM LLC
6004 Westgate Blvd # 120, Tacoma, WA 98406-2503
Tel (253) 271-3056 *Founded/Ownrshp* 2007
Sales NA *EMP* 578
SIC 3086 3085

D-U-N-S 61-004-0024 IMP
INSULITE GLASS CO INC
780 W Frontier Ln, Olathe, KS 66061-7202
Tel (800) 452-7721 *Founded/Ownrshp* 1998
Sales 36.9MM^E *EMP* 90
SIC 5039 3211 Glass construction materials; Insulating glass, sealed units; Glass construction materials; Insulating glass, sealed units
Pr: Beau Guyette
Ex VP: Sam Keegan
Div Mgr: Dan Brayman
Off Mgr: Amanda Vinn

D-U-N-S 08-025-6050
INSURANCE & BONDS AGENCY OF TEXAS (TX)
IBTX RISK SERVICES
10101 Reunion Pl Ste 100, San Antonio, TX 78216-4165
Tel (210) 696-6688 *Founded/Ownrshp* 1946, 1988
Sales NA *EMP* 100
SIC 6411 Insurance agents, brokers & service
Pr: Stephen Smith
**COO:* Lori Green
**CFO:* Randy Purvis

D-U-N-S 02-036-6350
INSURANCE ADMINISTRATIVE SOLUTIONS LLC (FL)
I A S
17757 Us Highway 19 N # 660, Clearwater, FL 33764-6560
Tel (727) 584-0007 *Founded/Ownrshp* 2002
Sales NA *EMP* 72^E
SIC 6411 Insurance agents, brokers & service
Pr: Lane Kent
CFO: Rick A Gordon
Sr VP: Victor Castellanos
Sr VP: Mark Postove
IT Man: Gary Cannday
IT Man: Darcey Shaffer
Web Dev: Ryan Biscoglia

D-U-N-S 80-747-9316
INSURANCE AND SAFETY FIRE COMMISSIONER GEORGIA
(*Suby of* EXECUTIVE OFFICE OF STATE OF GEORGIA) ★
2 Martin L King Jr Se 7, Atlanta, GA 30334
Tel (404) 656-2070 *Founded/Ownrshp* 1877
Sales NA *EMP* 300
SIC 9651 Insurance commission, government; ; Insurance commission, government;

INSURANCE ANSWER CENTER
See ANSWER FINANCIAL INC

D-U-N-S 12-273-9428 EXP
■ **INSURANCE AUTO AUCTIONS INC**
IAAI
(*Suby of* KAR AUCTION SERVICES INC) ★
2 Westbrook Corporate Ctr # 1000, Westchester, IL 60154-5722
Tel (708) 492-7000 *Founded/Ownrshp* 2007
Sales 203.3MM^E *EMP* 1,089
SIC 5012 Automobile auction; Automobiles; Automobile auction; Automobiles
Pr: John Kett
COO: David R Montgomery
Sr VP: Donald J Hermanek
VP: Sidney L Kerley

INSURANCE BROKER
See PARKER SMITH & FEEK INC

D-U-N-S 03-462-8820
INSURANCE CARE DIRECT INC
ABS HEALTHCARE SERVICES
1002 E Newport Center Dr # 200, Deerfield Beach, FL 33442-7752
Tel (866) 792-5976 *Founded/Ownrshp* 2006
Sales NA *EMP* 100
Accts Bdo Usa Llp Miami Florida
SIC 6411 Insurance agents, brokers & service; Insurance agents, brokers & service
Pr: Arnold Cohen
**Treas:* Bradley Cohen

INSURANCE CENTER, THE
See INSURANCE CENTER

D-U-N-S 08-114-3109
INSURANCE CENTER
INSURANCE CENTER, THE
701 Sand Lake Rd, Onalaska, WI 54650-2442
Tel (608) 783-6441 *Founded/Ownrshp* 1950
Sales NA *EMP* 90
SIC 6411 6321 6324 6371 Insurance agents; Life insurance agents; Property & casualty insurance agent; Accident insurance carriers; Health insurance carriers; Group hospitalization plans; Pension funds
Pr: Timothy Johnson
VP: Dewayne Bierman
Exec: Jill Roesler
Mktg Dir: Katie Marti
Sls Dir: Dean Rhodes
Sls Mgr: Brian Hess
Sls Mgr: Jeff Leclaire
Sls Mgr: Bill Patzner
Sls Mgr: Shari Steele

D-U-N-S 07-923-0306
INSURANCE CENTER OF NEW ENGLAND INC
1070 Suffield St, Agawam, MA 01001-2931
Tel (413) 781-2410 *Founded/Ownrshp* 1962
Sales NA *EMP* 67
SIC 6411 Insurance agents
CEO: Dean M Florian
**Pr:* William O Trudeau Jr
**COO:* David T Florian
COO: William Trudeau
VP: Denise Remillard

D-U-N-S 83-317-3334
INSURANCE CLAIMS MANAGEMENT INC
404 S Barstow St, Eau Claire, WI 54701-3667
Tel (715) 830-6000 *Founded/Ownrshp* 2003
Sales NA *EMP* 300^E
SIC 6411 Insurance claim processing, except medical; Insurance claim processing, except medical
CEO: Paul Gross
**CFO:* Travis Wiemer
**Exec:* Michael Anderson
CTO: Hal Brown

D-U-N-S 07-050-2695
INSURANCE CO OF GREATER NEW YORK (INC)
GNY INSURANCE COMPANIES
(*Suby of* GNY INSURANCE COMPANIES) ★
200 Madison Ave Fl 3, New York, NY 10016-3901
Tel (212) 683-9700 *Founded/Ownrshp* 1967
Sales NA *EMP* 350
SIC 6331 Fire, marine & casualty insurance & carriers; Fire, marine & casualty insurance & carriers
Prin: Alexander E Rosenthal
Pr: Warren W Heck
Ex VP: Max Solomon
Sr VP: James T Ferrando
Sr VP: Lorenzo T Griffin
VP: Frank E Jaeger
VP: Robert Lowenstein
VP: John Mc Mahon
VP: John B Minner
VP: John A Reda
VP: Leonard Silkes

D-U-N-S 00-698-5659
■ **INSURANCE CO OF STATE OF PENNSYLVANIA**
(*Suby of* CHARTIS US INC) ★
175 Water St Fl 18, New York, NY 10038-4976
Tel (212) 770-7000 *Founded/Ownrshp* 1972
Sales NA *EMP* 50
SIC 6331 Fire, marine & casualty insurance & carriers
Ch Bd: Thomas R Tizzio
VP: David Bolnick
VP: Michael J Castelli
VP: Doug Wolfe
IT Man: Edwin Daniel

D-U-N-S 05-926-8409
INSURANCE CO OF WEST
I C W
(*Suby of* ICW GROUP HOLDINGS INC) ★
11455 El Camino Real # 200, San Diego, CA 92130-2047
Tel (858) 350-2400 *Founded/Ownrshp* 1974
Sales NA *EMP* 311^E
SIC 6331 Fire, marine & casualty insurance; Property damage insurance; Fire, marine & casualty insurance; Property damage insurance
Pr: Kevin Prior
**Ch Bd:* Ernest Rady
**Treas:* H Michael Freet
Treas: Michael H Freet
Sr VP: Doug Browne
VP: Krikor Derderian
VP: Veronica Meyers
VP: Cynthia Vincent

INSURANCE COMMISSIONER
See CALIFORNIA DEPARTMENT OF INSURANCE

D-U-N-S 84-976-9406
INSURANCE EXCHANGE BROKERAGE SERVICE INC
(*Suby of* PRIME HOLDINGS INC)
8722 S Harrison St, Sandy, UT 84070-1420
Tel (801) 304-5510 *Founded/Ownrshp* 1996
Sales NA *EMP* 30
SIC 6411 Insurance brokers; Insurance brokers
Pr: Rick J Lindsey
**COO:* Ted Paulson
**CFO:* Jack McDonnel
**VP:* Mark Fisher

D-U-N-S 07-862-8989
INSURANCE FUND NEW YORK STATE
NYSIF
(*Suby of* EXECUTIVE OFFICE OF STATE OF NEW YORK) ★
199 Church St Fl 13, New York, NY 10007-1100
Tel (212) 587-7390 *Founded/Ownrshp* 1914
Sales NA *EMP* 2,400^E
SIC 9199 Workers' compensation insurance; ;
CEO: Dennis Hayes
Brnch Mgr: Suzan Kornblush
CIO: Robert Sammons
Dir IT: Lori Endires
Telecom Mg: Ron Dawson
IT Man: Lori Hitchcock
IT Man: Tom Kowal
IT Man: David Moses
IT Man: Slawomir Wysocky
Snr Mgr: Randall Hinton

D-U-N-S 04-760-3444
INSURANCE HOUSE INC
1904 Drachten Dr Se, Marietta, GA 30067
Tel (770) 952-0080 *Founded/Ownrshp* 1964
Sales NA *EMP* 310^E
SIC 6331 6411 6141 Property damage insurance; Fire, marine & casualty insurance & carriers; Insurance brokers; Licensed loan companies, small; Property damage insurance; Fire, marine & casualty insurance & carriers; Insurance brokers; Licensed loan companies, small
CEO: Jill K Jinks
**Pr:* John Gordon Jinks Jr
COO: Jacqueline M Schaendorf
CFO: Kerry Buchan
Treas: Roy Little
Ofcr: Rebecca Bittinger
QA Dir: Andrea Hendry
Dir IT: Jon Santee
Software D: Mark Chen
Mktg Dir: Butch Hayes
Sls Dir: Bill Mathis

INSURANCE MANAGEMENT SERVICES
See IMS MARKETING INC

D-U-N-S 12-207-0618
INSURANCE NETWORK OF TEXAS
ALLSTATE
143 E Austin St, Giddings, TX 78942-3201
Tel (512) 472-1147 *Founded/Ownrshp* 1971
Sales NA *EMP* 65
SIC 6411 Insurance agents, brokers & service
CEO: Robert James Nitsche
**Pr:* David D Ferguson
VP: Nitsche Gary
**VP:* Ruth Nitsche
VP: Steve Swinney
CIO: McMahan Connie
Telecom Mg: Russell Spicer
IT Man: Connie McMahan
Mktg Mgr: Julie Schatte

D-U-N-S 12-736-9796
INSURANCE NETWORK SERVICES INC
1501 Lady St, Columbia, SC 29201-3401
Tel (803) 748-2400 *Founded/Ownrshp* 1995
Sales NA *EMP* 200
SIC 6411 Insurance adjusters; Insurance adjusters
Pr: Michael Culbertson

D-U-N-S 18-930-5592
INSURANCE OFFICE OF AMERICA INC
1855 W State Road 434, Longwood, FL 32750-5036
Tel (407) 788-3000 *Founded/Ownrshp* 1988
Sales NA *EMP* 750
SIC 6411 Insurance agents; Electronic media advertising representatives; Investment holding companies, except banks; Insurance agents
CEO: Heath Ritenour
Mng Pt: Christopher Labrecque
V Ch: Jeffrey Jones
**Pr:* Jeff Lagos
Pr: Richard Lott
**COO:* Mary Lawless
**CFO:* Jay Grevers
CFO: Wes Scovanner
**Ch:* John Ritenour
Ex VP: Scott Kuzmic
Ex VP: Jeffrey Miner
**Ex VP:* Jon Thurman
**Sr VP:* Danny Anderson
Sr VP: Sherry Barrett
Sr VP: Rick Collins
Sr VP: Lawrence Depalma
Sr VP: Richard Hyder
Sr VP: John Lahey
VP: Steve Esposito
VP: Bob Hamilton
VP: Paul Jemmi
Board of Directors: Wesley Scovanner

INSURANCE OUTLET
See NOLAN INSURANCE CORP

D-U-N-S 07-212-7525
INSURANCE PROGRAMMERS INC
10 Technology Dr, Wallingford, CT 06492-1955
Tel (203) 269-7741 *Founded/Ownrshp* 1966
Sales NA *EMP* 30
SIC 6371 6411 Pension, health & welfare funds; Insurance claim processing, except medical
Ch Bd: Henry L Bourland
**Pr:* Diane Klobukowski
**CEO:* Lawrence L Bourland
CFO: Cheryl Melillo
Ex VP: Richard Poulaino
**VP:* Richard M Poulaino
**VP:* John S Sardo

INSURANCE RECRUITING SPECIALIS
See DAWG INC

INSURANCE RESOURCES
See REGIONS INSURANCE GROUP

INSURANCE SERVICES DIV
See CARCO GROUP INC

D-U-N-S 05-665-9725
■ **INSURANCE SERVICES OFFICE INC**
(*Suby of* VERISK ANALYTICS INC) ★
545 Washington Blvd Fl 12, Jersey City, NJ 07310-1613
Tel (201) 469-2000 *Founded/Ownrshp* 1997
Sales 726.5MM^E *EMP* 6,495
SIC 7375 Information retrieval services; Information retrieval services
CEO: Scott Stephenson
Pr: Shawn Deane
Pr: John J Kollar
Ex VP: Mark V Anquillare
Ex VP: Carole J Banfield
Sr VP: Vincent P McCarthy
Sr VP: Kevin B Thompson
VP: Beth Fitzgerald
VP: Bill Foster
VP: Michael R Waters
Exec: Perry F Rotella
Exec: Steve Spencer

INSURANCE SYSTEMS OF TENNESSEE
See KAPLAN PROFESSIONALS

D-U-N-S 01-530-2771
INSURANCE TECHNOLOGIES LLC
2 S Cascade Ave Ste 200, Colorado Springs, CO 80903-1660
Tel (719) 442-6400 *Founded/Ownrshp* 1995
Sales 33.6MM^E *EMP* 175
SIC 7371 Computer software development & applications; Computer software development & applications
CEO: Larry Wiedeman
**Pr:* David Fenimore
Pr: Susan Wiedeman
**COO:* Tammy Shuminsky
Sr VP: Bill Aguayo
Sr VP: Jim Gates
VP: Steven Acosta
VP: Jim Ferrell
VP: Del Lang
VP: Tracy McGurran
VP: Carla Torres
VP: Jane Upton
Creative D: Laurie Anderson

D-U-N-S 15-720-2342
INSURANCE UNDERWRITERS LTD INC
2610 Edenborn Ave, Metairie, LA 70002-7016
Tel (504) 883-2500 *Founded/Ownrshp* 1986
Sales NA *EMP* 75
SIC 6411 Insurance agents, brokers & service
Pr: Jack Landry
**Ch Bd:* Ron Paulin
Pr: Charles Fontenelle
**Sr VP:* Robert J Richard

D-U-N-S 79-981-5803
INSURANCE.COM INC
COMPARISONMARKET INSUR AGCY
30775 Bnbridge Rd Ste 210, Solon, OH 44139
Tel (440) 498-0001 *Founded/Ownrshp* 2000
Sales NA *EMP* 285^E
Accts Ernst & Young Llp Cleveland
SIC 6411 Insurance agents & brokers
CEO: Robert Klapper
**Ch Bd:* David L Roush
CFO: Dennis Raab
Chf Mktg O: Steve Chiles
VP: Carrie Liber
IT Man: George Burgyan
IT Man: Burdette Chris
Sys Mgr: Jason Pasciak
Software D: Patrick Atayа
Software D: Lalitha Paladugu

INSURE EXPRESS INSURANCE SVC
See CARTEL MARKETING INC

INSURERS ADMINISTRATIVE CORP
See IHC ADMINISTRATIVE SERVICES INC

INSURERS WORLD
See HOME ENTERTAINMENT DISTRIBUTORS INC

D-U-N-S 02-071-7203
INSURICA INC
(*Suby of* NORTH AMERICAN GROUP) ★
5100 N Classen Blvd # 300, Oklahoma City, OK 73118-5263
Tel (405) 556-2205 *Founded/Ownrshp* 1959
Sales NA *EMP* 290
SIC 6411 Insurance agents; Insurance agents
Ch Bd: Bill Durrett
**Pr:* Mike Ross
**CFO:* Ed Young
**Ex VP:* Gary Jarmon
**Sr VP:* John Hester
**VP:* Jeff Nickles
**VP:* Kevin Wellfare
Dir Risk M: Judy Roof
Admn Mgr: Mary Tilford
Mktg Dir: Kevin Welfare

D-U-N-S 07-870-3731
INSURITY INC
170 Huyshope Ave, Hartford, CT 06106-2817
Tel (866) 476-2606 *Founded/Ownrshp* 2011
Sales 30.2MM^E *EMP* 1,000^E
SIC 7374 Data processing service
CEO: Jeffrey Glazer
**Ch Bd:* Danny Daniel Sr
Pr: Sylvester Mathis
COO: Marvin Karlow
**COO:* Bob Larew
**CFO:* Rick Sorensen
**Sr VP:* Lani Cathey
**Sr VP:* Kenny Lebleu
VP: Bruce Broussard
VP: Elizabeth Del Ferro
VP: James Hatch
VP: Ajay Kelshiker
VP: Clyde Owen
**VP:* Ken Safft

D-U-N-S 00-452-5937
INSURORS OF TEXAS GENERAL AGENCY LTD (TX)
225 S 5th St, Waco, TX 76701-2112
Tel (254) 759-3701 *Founded/Ownrshp* 1900, 1980
Sales NA *EMP* 75
SIC 6411 Insurance agents & brokers; Life insurance agents
CEO: Tom Chase
Pr: George Chase
Ex VP: Shane Baker
Ex VP: Doug Peacock
Sr VP: Jason Youens
VP: D J Callaway

D-U-N-S 96-893-7990
INSYNC STAFFING LLC
125 S Wacker Dr Ste 2700, Chicago, IL 60606-4475
Tel (312) 424-0300 *Founded/Ownrshp* 2011
Sales 7.7MM^E *EMP* 350
SIC 7361 Employment agencies; Employment agencies

D-U-N-S 15-617-5155
INSYS CONSULTING SERVICES INC
395 W Passaic St Ste 400, Rochelle Park, NJ 07662-3016
Tel (201) 621-4797 *Founded/Ownrshp* 2002
Sales 33.3MM^E *EMP* 160^E
SIC 7379 Computer related consulting services; Computer related consulting services
CEO: Linda Magnusson-Rosario
Mng Pt: Michael Short
**COO:* Anthony Pirozzi Jr
**CFO:* Jodi Edelson
VP: Joseph Clark
Mng Dir: John Braiman
Dir IT: Jeff Decker
Software D: Ed Friedman

D-U-N-S 92-903-3959 EXP
▲ INSYS THERAPEUTICS INC
1333 S Spectrum Blvd, Chandler, AZ 85286-8458
Tel (602) 910-2617 *Founded/Ownrshp* 1990
Sales 222.1MM *EMP* 382
Tkr Sym INSY *Exch* NGM
SIC 2836 2834 Biological products, except diagnostic; Pharmaceutical preparations; Druggists' preparations (pharmaceuticals); Biological products, except diagnostic; Pharmaceutical preparations; Druggists' preparations (pharmaceuticals)
Ch Bd: John N Kapoor
**Pr:* Michael L Babich
CFO: Darryl S Baker
CFO: Darryl Baker
CFO: Martin McCarthy
VP: Alec Burlakoff
VP: Mike Gurry
VP: Vikram Malhotra
VP: Brian Pipko
VP: Steve Sherman
Dist Mgr: Tiffany Cromartie

D-U-N-S 12-860-4035
INT TECHNOLOGIES LLC
2415 E Camelback Rd # 700, Phoenix, AZ 85016-4288
Tel (602) 508-6177 *Founded/Ownrshp* 2000
Sales 42.3MM^E *EMP* 450
SIC 7379 Computer related consulting services; Computer related consulting services
IT Man: Tod Talburt
Opers Mgr: Richard Krause

D-U-N-S 07-838-5161 IMP
INT TRADING USA LLC
261 W 35th St Ste 1100, New York, NY 10001-1900
Tel (212) 760-2338 *Founded/Ownrshp* 2004
Sales 37.3MM *EMP* 230
SIC 2325 2339 Men's & boys' trousers & slacks; Women's & misses' outerwear; Men's & boys' trousers & slacks; Women's & misses' outerwear
CEO: Sung Pak

D-U-N-S 11-559-2433
INTACCT CORP
300 Park Ave, San Jose, CA 95110-2773
Tel (408) 878-0900 *Founded/Ownrshp* 2005
Sales 29.1MM^E *EMP* 50^E
SIC 7379 7371 Computer related consulting services; Custom computer programming services
CEO: Robert K Reid
CEO: Michael A Braun
Sr VP: Vijay Iyer
VP: Larry Blair
VP: Haris Hadjiannou
VP: Taylor Macdonald
VP: Dan Miller
VP: Derek Taylor
CIO: Haris Hadjiioannou
QA Dir: Sita Valluri
Ql Cn Mgr: Eric Roth
Board of Directors: Jeff Epstein

D-U-N-S 00-844-5397
INTACT TECHNOLOGY INC
9111 Edmonston Rd Ste 300, Greenbelt, MD 20770-1552
Tel (301) 429-1923 *Founded/Ownrshp* 1996
Sales 26.9MM *EMP* 60
SIC 7379 Computer related consulting services; Computer related consulting services
CEO: Todd Johnson
Pgrm Dir: Sherrie Danquer

INTAGLIO ASSOCIATES IN DESIGN
See GEORGE P JOHNSON CO

D-U-N-S 05-731-6531 IMP
■ INTALCO ALUMINUM CORP
ALCOA INTALCO WORKS
(*Suby of* ALCOA INC) ★
4050 Mountain View Rd, Ferndale, WA 98248-9683
Tel (360) 384-7061 *Founded/Ownrshp* 1998
Sales 228.8MM^E *EMP* 1,180
SIC 3334 Primary aluminum; Ingots (primary), aluminum; Primary aluminum; Ingots (primary), aluminum
Pr: Barry S Hullett
**Treas:* Peter Hong
**VP:* Christie Breves
**VP:* John Kenna
Exec: Mike Rousseau
Nurse Mgr: Melissa Falcone

D-U-N-S 08-442-6860
INTARCIA THERAPEUTICS INC
155 Seaport Blvd 11f, Boston, MA 02210-2698
Tel (617) 936-2500 *Founded/Ownrshp* 1995
Sales 22.6MM^E *EMP* 44^E
Accts Ernst & Young Llp
SIC 8731 Biotechnical research, commercial
Ch Bd: Kurt Graves
COO: Michael Williams
CFO: James Ahlers
Bd of Dir: Joel Kellman Member
Chf Mktg O: Peter Langecker MD
Ofcr: Michelle Baron
Ofcr: Owen Hughes Jr
VP: Thomas Alessi
VP: Thomas R Alessi
VP: James P Brady
VP: David Franklin
VP: Raymond T Keane
VP: Eddie Li
VP: Curtis Scribner MD
VP: Sunita Zalani
Board of Directors: James Niedel, Gino Santini, Nancy Thornberry

D-U-N-S 19-160-0303 IMP
INTAT PRECISION INC
(*Suby of* AISIN TAKAOKA CO.,LTD.)
2148 N State Road 3, Rushville, IN 46173-9302
Tel (765) 932-5323 *Founded/Ownrshp* 1988
Sales 213.6MM^E *EMP* 400
SIC 3321 Ductile iron castings; Ductile iron castings
Pr: Donald Carson
Treas: David Reid
VP: Brad Rist
CTO: Dave Payne
Ql Cn Mgr: Mike Guffey

INTCOMEX
See SOFTWARE BROKERS OF AMERICA INC

D-U-N-S 14-588-3331 IMP/EXP
■ INTCOMEX HOLDINGS LLC
(*Suby of* INTCOMEX INC) ★
3505 Nw 107th Ave Ste 1, Doral, FL 33178-9800
Tel (305) 477-6230 *Founded/Ownrshp* 1989
Sales 182.6MM^E *EMP* 500
SIC 5045 Computers; Computer peripheral equipment; Computer software; Computers; Computer peripheral equipment; Computer software
Ch Bd: Anthony S Shalom
**CEO:* Michael Shalom
Genl Mgr: Eric Hachmann
MIS Dir: Naji Zakka
S&M/VP: Danny Schachtel

D-U-N-S 60-321-5513 IMP/EXP
■ INTCOMEX INC
(*Suby of* CVCI INTCOMEX INVESTMENT, L.P.)
3505 Nw 107th Ave Ste 1, Doral, FL 33178-9800
Tel (305) 477-6230 *Founded/Ownrshp* 2004
Sales 1.4MMM *EMP* 1,971^E
SIC 5045 Computers; Computer peripheral equipment; Computer software; Computers; Computer peripheral equipment; Computer software
Ch Bd: Anthony Shalom
Pr: Michael Shalom
COO: Leopoldo Coronado
CFO: Bert Lopez
CFO: Humberto Lopez
CFO: Russell A Olson
Treas: Russell Olson
VP: Yali Luna
Exec: Elio Rotondo
Rgnl Mgr: Marlene Novo
Genl Mgr: Jerry Plowski
Board of Directors: Enrique Bascur, Adolfo Henriques, Thomas A Madden, Juan Pablo Pallordet

INTE Q
See SHC DIRECT LLC

D-U-N-S 04-581-7103 IMP/EXP
■ INTEC BILLING INC
(*Suby of* INTEC TELECOM SYSTEMS LIMITED)
301 Perimeter Ctr N # 200, Atlanta, GA 30346-2432
Tel (404) 705-2800 *Founded/Ownrshp* 1968
Sales 80.3MM^E *EMP* 600
SIC 5045 Computers, peripherals & software; Computers, peripherals & software
CEO: Fredrick D Brott
**CFO:* Wes Hargraves
Ex VP: Gary Aviv

D-U-N-S 00-985-9147
INTEC COMMUNICATIONS LLC
1207 S White Chapel Blvd # 200, Southlake, TX 76092-9316
Tel (817) 540-6000 *Founded/Ownrshp* 2008
Sales 64.1MM^E *EMP* 300^E
SIC 4813 Data telephone communications; Data telephone communications
Sr VP: Huston Greer

D-U-N-S 00-506-7004 IMP
INTEC GROUP INC
666 S Vermont St, Palatine, IL 60067-6950
Tel (847) 358-0088 *Founded/Ownrshp* 1953
Sales 109.9MM^E *EMP* 425
SIC 3089 Molding primary plastic; Injection molding of plastics; Molding primary plastic; Injection molding of plastics
Pr: Steven M Perlman
VP: Michael Gaines
Dir Bus: Craig Richards
Off Mgr: Char Kovac
VP Opers: John Powser
QC Dir: Christy Claus
Ql Cn Mgr: Rena Drewes
Board of Directors: Stanley M Perlman, Gary C White

D-U-N-S 12-779-3987
INTEC-MEXICO LLC
(*Suby of* INTEC GROUP INC) ★
666 S Vermont St, Palatine, IL 60067-6950
Tel (847) 358-0088 *Founded/Ownrshp* 2006
Sales 84.8MM^E *EMP* 360
SIC 3089 Molding primary plastic; Molding primary plastic

D-U-N-S 05-778-8809
INTECARE INC
8604 Allisnville Rd Ste 325, Indianapolis, IN 46250
Tel (317) 791-0788 *Founded/Ownrshp* 1998
Sales 55.0MM *EMP* 14
Accts Bradley & Associates Inc In
SIC 8093 Mental health clinic, outpatient; Mental health clinic, outpatient
CEO: Larry Burch
**CFO:* Al Verberke
VP Mktg: Al Verbeke

D-U-N-S 15-379-5554
INTECH CONSTRUCTION LLC
3020 Market St Fl 2, Philadelphia, PA 19104-2999
Tel (215) 243-2000 *Founded/Ownrshp* 1986
Sales 150.0MM^E *EMP* 170
SIC 8741 Construction management; Construction management
VP: R Kelly
**VP:* David Maguire
Dir IT: Scott Force
Snr PM: Phillip Moses

D-U-N-S 78-376-6330
INTECH CONTRACTING LLC
3131 Custer Dr Ste 8, Lexington, KY 40517-4006
Tel (859) 272-0352 *Founded/Ownrshp* 1991
Sales 42.5MM *EMP* 150
Accts Ray Foley Hensley & Company
SIC 1622 1542 Bridge construction; Commercial & office building contractors; Bridge construction; Commercial & office building contractors
VP: Byron Ogger
Off Mgr: Teresa Dearinger

D-U-N-S 05-832-4336 IMP
INTECH INDUSTRIES INC
7180 Sunwood Dr Nw, Ramsey, MN 55303-5100
Tel (763) 576-8291 *Founded/Ownrshp* 1967
Sales 20.8MM^E *EMP* 99
Accts Ds&B Ltd Minneapolis Minneso
SIC 3544 Punches, forming & stamping; Dies, plastics forming
Pr: Roger A Neilson Sr
**Sec:* Jean Neilson
VP: Mark Neilson
**VP:* Mark Nielson
IT Man: Curt Renslow
Ql Cn Mgr: Sam Schiess

D-U-N-S 05-912-7485
INTECH MECHANICAL CO INC
7501 Galilee Rd, Roseville, CA 95678-6905
Tel (916) 797-4900 *Founded/Ownrshp* 1996
Sales 20.5MM *EMP* 100
Accts Bfba Llp Sacramento Califor
SIC 1711 Plumbing contractors; Plumbing contractors
Pr: Richard B Chowdry
**Sec:* Julie Chowdry

D-U-N-S 03-625-2992
INTECH PROCESS AUTOMATION INC
4903 W Sam Houston Pkwy N, Houston, TX 77041-8230
Tel (713) 849-1000 *Founded/Ownrshp* 1998
Sales 69.9MM^E *EMP* 300
SIC 1731 Access control systems specialization; Access control systems specialization
Pr: Eric Fidler
Genl Mgr: Aasim Waheed

D-U-N-S 11-300-6738
INTECSEA INC
(*Suby of* WORLEYPARSONS LIMITED)
15600 J F Kennedy Blvd # 900, Houston, TX 77032-2349
Tel (281) 987-0800 *Founded/Ownrshp* 2008
Sales 72.2MM^E *EMP* 800
SIC 8711 8742 Consulting engineer; Construction project management consultant; Consulting engineer; Construction project management consultant
CEO: Ed Smith
Pr: Neil Mackintosh
Pr: Craig Reeves
VP: David S McKeehan
VP: Chunfa Wu
CTO: Garry Mahoney
Snr PM: Tony Billick
Snr PM: Jason Harvey
Snr PM: Glenn Lanan

D-U-N-S 80-852-4920 IMP/EXP
■ INTEGER GROUP L L C
(*Suby of* OMNICOM GROUP INC) ★
7245 W Alaska Dr, Lakewood, CO 80226-3228
Tel (303) 393-3000 *Founded/Ownrshp* 1993
Sales 94.3MM^E *EMP* 805
SIC 7311 8742 8743 Advertising agencies; Advertising agencies; Marketing consulting services; Promotion service
Ch Bd: Jeremy Pagden
**CEO:* Mike Sweeney
**COO:* Frank Maher
**CFO:* Chris Stoeber
Sr VP: Nick Hoadley
Sr VP: Bryce McTavish
VP: Meg Kinney
VP: Julie Landy
VP: Molly McLaren
Assoc Dir: Matt Silvestri
Creative D: Christopher Austin
Creative D: Shannon Ball
Creative D: Leslie Bell
Creative D: Dustin Bredice
Creative D: Juan Cabrera
Creative D: Sean Coleman
Creative D: Alison Earnhardt
Creative D: Kent Fieldsend
Creative D: Gerardo Garcia-Jurado
Creative D: Shannan Garrison
Creative D: Ray Gordon

INTEGRA
See ONKYO USA CORP

D-U-N-S 01-304-9481
INTEGRA ADMINISTRATIVE GROUP INC
F & S PROPERTY MANAGEMENT CO
110 S Shipley St, Seaford, DE 19973-3714
Tel (302) 629-4168 *Founded/Ownrshp* 1971
Sales NA *EMP* 22
Accts Fleetwood Cross & Kinnamon I
SIC 6411 6531 Insurance claim processing, except medical; Insurance brokers; Real estate managers
Pr: David Smith
CFO: Linda Wainwright

D-U-N-S 14-855-4983 EXP
INTEGRA BIOTECHNICAL INC
PEDI
(*Suby of* WITCO INDUSTRIES, INC)
2731 Loker Ave W, Carlsbad, CA 92010-6601
Tel (760) 931-1844 *Founded/Ownrshp* 1985
Sales 24.0MM^E *EMP* 74
SIC 3089 Injection molded finished plastic products
CEO: Jeffrey S Goble
**Pr:* Richard D Witchey Jr
Ql Cn Mgr: Lee Eelin

INTEGRA HEALTH
See APLINGTON-PARKERSBURG FAMILY PRACTICE

D-U-N-S 10-231-6093
INTEGRA HEALTHCARE INC
INTEGRITY HEALTH CARE
3751 Ne Ralph Powell Rd, Lees Summit, MO 64064-2349
Tel (816) 254-3131 *Founded/Ownrshp* 2000
Sales 6.2MM^E *EMP* 325
SIC 8082 Home health care services; Home health care services
CEO: Phil Nelugin
**CEO:* Phil Melugin
CTO: Jon Dougherty

D-U-N-S 83-091-3153
INTEGRA HOLDINGS INC
3450 N Rock Rd Ste 100, Wichita, KS 67226-1351
Tel (316) 630-6805 *Founded/Ownrshp* 2008
Sales 28.0MM^E *EMP* 247
SIC 8734 Testing laboratories; Testing laboratories
CEO: Becky Craft
**VP Opers:* Brett Robinson

D-U-N-S 08-317-1244
■ INTEGRA LIFESCIENCES CORP (DE)
JARIT
(*Suby of* INTEGRA LIFESCIENCES HOLDINGS CORP) ★
311 Enterprise Dr, Plainsboro, NJ 08536-3344
Tel (609) 275-2700 *Founded/Ownrshp* 1994
Sales 275.2MM^E *EMP* 887
SIC 3841 Surgical & medical instruments; Surgical & medical instruments
CEO: Peter Arduini
Pr: Stuart M Essig
Pr: Ray Petersen
COO: Brian Larkin
CFO: Glenn G Coleman
Bd of Dir: Raymond Murphy
Ex VP: Jerry Backe
Sr VP: John Bostjancic
Sr VP: Richard Gorelic
VP: Mark Augusti
VP: Kenneth Burhop
VP: Les Burrows
VP: Robert T Davis Jr
VP: John B Henneman
VP: Alan Kilyk
VP: Tim Mikac
VP: Ray Peterson
VP: Joseph Vinhais

D-U-N-S 79-016-8090 EXP
▲ INTEGRA LIFESCIENCES HOLDINGS CORP
311 Enterprise Dr, Plainsboro, NJ 08536-3344
Tel (609) 275-0500 *Founded/Ownrshp* 1989
Sales 928.3MM *EMP* 3,400
Tkr Sym IART *Exch* NGS
SIC 3841 2836 3842 Surgical & medical instruments; Biological products, except diagnostic; Surgical appliances & supplies; Implants, surgical; Surgical & medical instruments; Biological products, except diagnostic; Surgical appliances & supplies; Implants, surgical
Pr: Peter J Arduini
CFO: Glenn G Coleman
Ofcr: Padma Thiruvengadam
VP: Mark Augusti
VP: Kenneth Burhop
VP: Robert T Davis Jr
VP: Richard D Gorelick
VP: Brian Larkin
VP: Debbie Leonetti
VP: John Mooradian
VP: Judith E O'Grady
VP: Dan Reuvers
VP: Joseph Vinhais
Board of Directors: Keith Bradley, Richard E Caruso, Stuart M Essig, Barbara B Hill, Lloyd W Howell Jr, Donald E Morel Jr, Raymond G Murphy, Christian S Schade, James M Sullivan

D-U-N-S 04-405-4938
■ INTEGRA LIFESCIENCES SALES LLC
(*Suby of* INTEGRA LIFESCIENCES CORP) ★
311 Enterprise Dr, Plainsboro, NJ 08536-3344
Tel (609) 529-9748 *Founded/Ownrshp* 2011
Sales 50.9MM *EMP* 300
SIC 3841 Surgical & medical instruments
CEO: Peter J Arduini

D-U-N-S 14-897-5076
INTEGRA LOGISTICS LLC
4400 Alexander Dr 1w, Alpharetta, GA 30022-3753
Tel (678) 775-5140 *Founded/Ownrshp* 2005
Sales 100.0MM *EMP* 60
SIC 4731 Freight transportation arrangement; Freight transportation arrangement
COO: Josephine Nortz
CFO: Tony Johnson
VP: Lane Woodard

D-U-N-S 16-716-3422
INTEGRA LOGISTICS SERVICES LLC
4741 World Houston Pkwy, Houston, TX 77032-2452
Tel (281) 227-8888 *Founded/Ownrshp* 2003
Sales 43.2MM^E *EMP* 70
SIC 4731 Freight transportation arrangement
**Pr:* Mark Young
Opers Mgr: Linda Brazelton

INTEGRA MILTEX
See YORK INTEGRA PA INC

INTEGRA REALTY RESOURCES
See SHELLI LOWE & ASSOCIATES

D-U-N-S 12-525-2606
INTEGRA REALTY RESOURCES INC
IRR
640 8th Ave Fl 15, New York, NY 10036-7117
Tel (212) 255-7858 *Founded/Ownrshp* 1999
Sales 54.3MM^E *EMP* 900
SIC 6531 Appraiser, real estate; Appraiser, real estate
Ch Bd: Michael Welch
Pr: Jeffrey Rogers
CFO: Mark Halter
Chf Mktg O: Andrew Ludwig
Ofcr: Jan Decker
Ex VP: Ray Cirz
VP: George Ward
Dir Bus: Buzz Walker
Mng Dir: Ken Brown
Mng Dir: David Dominy
Mng Dir: Eric Enloe

D-U-N-S 13-952-7068
INTEGRA STAFFING LLC
4601 Charlotte Park Dr # 150, Charlotte, NC 28217-1913
Tel (704) 527-9191 *Founded/Ownrshp* 2002
Sales 12.8MM^E *EMP* 300
SIC 7363 7361 Help supply services; Executive placement; Help supply services; Executive placement
COO: Robert Fish
Mktg Mgr: Julia Lamb
Mktg Mgr: Julia Orr

D-U-N-S 01-939-0504 IMP
INTEGRA TECHNOLOGIES LLC
(*Suby of* INTEGRA HOLDINGS INC) ★
3450 N Rock Rd Ste 100, Wichita, KS 67226-1351
Tel (316) 630-6800 *Founded/Ownrshp* 1998
Sales 24.4MM^E *EMP* 110
SIC 3674 Semiconductors & related devices; Semiconductors & related devices
Pr: Mark Marshall
Opers Supe: Matt Kersey
Opers Mgr: Michael Jerman
Opers Mgr: Alex Ricciardi

INTEGRA TELECOM
See ESCHELON TELECOM OF COLORADO INC

INTEGRA TELECOM
See ELECTRIC LIGHTWAVE LLC

D-U-N-S 16-012-2222
INTEGRA TELECOM HOLDINGS INC
18110 Se 34th St, Vancouver, WA 98683-9418
Tel (360) 558-6900 *Founded/Ownrshp* 2014
Sales 290.9MM^E *EMP* 1,400
SIC 4813 Local & long distance telephone communications; ; Local & long distance telephone communications;
CEO: Mark Willency
**CFO:* Jesse Selnick
Chf Mktg O: Joseph Harding
Ofcr: Jason Koenders
**Ex VP:* Michael Sharpe
**Sr VP:* Karen L Clauson
**Sr VP:* Felicity O'Herron
Sr VP: Claire Schulte
Sr VP: Daniel Stoll
VP: Aaron Capsel
VP: Steven Fisher
VP: Cindy Leiser
VP: Craig Pierce
VP: Martha Tate
Dir Surg: Jim Nieuwstraten
Board of Directors: Karen Clauson, Felicity O'herron, Craig Pierce, Jesse Selnick, Michael Sharpe, Martha Tate, Mark Willency

D-U-N-S 13-912-7117
INTEGRA TELECOM INC
18110 Se 34th St Bldg 1s, Vancouver, WA 98683-9418
Tel (360) 558-6900 *Founded/Ownrshp* 1996
Sales 591.2MM^E *EMP* 1,426
SIC 7389 4813 Telephone services; Telephone communication, except radio; Telephone services; Telephone communication, except radio
CEO: Mark Willency
COO: Michael Sharpe
CFO: Jesse Selnick
Sr VP: Karen L Clauson
Sr VP: Felicity O'Herron
Sr VP: Claire Schulte
Sr VP: Daniel Stoll
VP: Aaron Capsel
VP: Steven Fisher
VP: Cindy Leiser
VP: Craig Pierce
VP: Martha Tate
Dir Surg: Jim Nieuwstraten
Dir Surg: Chris Pike
Dir Surg: Mark Roskopt
Board of Directors: Karen Clauson, Felicity O'herron, Craig Pierce, Jesse Selnick, Michael Sharpe, Martha Tate, Mark Willency

D-U-N-S 13-936-0101
INTEGRA TELECOM OF OREGON INC
(*Suby of* INTEGRA TELECOM HOLDINGS INC) ★
18110 Se 34th St, Vancouver, WA 98683-9418
Tel (360) 558-6900 *Founded/Ownrshp* 1985
Sales 31.9MM^E *EMP* 600
SIC 4813 Local & long distance telephone communications; Local & long distance telephone communications
CEO: Mark Willency
Treas: Chris Aabert
Sr VP: Matthew Fahey
Sls Mgr: Sacha Basho
Board of Directors: Mark Willency

D-U-N-S 05-505-5573
INTEGRA US MARKETING LLC
(*Suby of* INTEGRA PETROCHEMICALS PTE. LTD.)
5075 Westheimer Rd # 790, Houston, TX 77056-5643
Tel (713) 224-2044 *Founded/Ownrshp* 2002
Sales 100.0MM^E *EMP* 4
SIC 8742 Marketing consulting services; Marketing consulting services

D-U-N-S 83-128-2772
INTEGRACARE HOLDINGS INC
2559 Sw Grapevine Pkwy, Grapevine, TX 76051-1000
Tel (817) 310-4999 *Founded/Ownrshp* 2009
Sales 606.8MM^E *EMP* 5,604^E
SIC 6719 Investment holding companies, except banks; Investment holding companies, except banks
Pr: Benjamin A Breier
**CFO:* David Hagey
**Sr VP:* Donald H Robinson
**VP:* James T Flowers
**VP:* Christopher T Gearad
VP: Rhonda Sanders
**VP:* Jeffrey P Stodghill
Brnch Mgr: Tracy Dent
Brnch Mgr: Kristine Stough
IT Man: Chris Massey
VP Sls: Michael Boggs

D-U-N-S 08-614-1892
INTEGRACE INC
7200 Third Ave, Sykesville, MD 21784-5201
Tel (410) 795-8800 *Founded/Ownrshp* 1990
Sales 24.0MM^E *EMP* 623
Accts Parente Beard Llc Lancaster
SIC 8361 6513 Geriatric residential care; Apartment building operators; Geriatric residential care; Apartment building operators
Ch Bd: William B Dulany
**Pr:* James Melhorn
**Treas:* Joseph Girardi
**V Ch Bd:* John Parham
Sls&Mrk Ex: Mindi Bryant

INTEGRACOLOR GROUP
See INTEGRACOLOR LTD

D-U-N-S 00-732-6358 IMP
INTEGRACOLOR LTD
INTEGRACOLOR GROUP
3210 Innovative Way, Mesquite, TX 75149-2756
Tel (972) 288-7655 *Founded/Ownrshp* 1988
Sales 137.1MM^E *EMP* 450
SIC 2752 2754 Commercial printing, lithographic; Commercial printing, gravure; Commercial printing, lithographic; Commercial printing, gravure
Pt: Larry King
CFO: Tony Mendoza
DP Exec: Ryan Riley
Opers Mgr: Danny Macwilliams
Board of Directors: Lorn Davis, Bill Yost

D-U-N-S 60-349-3206 IMP
INTEGRACORE LLC
6077 W Wells Park Rd, West Jordan, UT 84081-5684
Tel (801) 948-7100 *Founded/Ownrshp* 1993
Sales 47.3MM^E *EMP* 100^E
SIC 7379 2752 7389 7372 Disk & diskette conversion service; Commercial printing, lithographic; Packaging & labeling services; Prepackaged software
Pr: Kurt Flygare

D-U-N-S 83-224-5778
INTEGRAL AD SCIENCE INC
95 Morton St Fl 8, New York, NY 10014-3372
Tel (646) 278-4871 *Founded/Ownrshp* 2009
Sales 33.6MM^E *EMP* 198^E
SIC 7311 Advertising consultant
Pr: Scott Knoll
Bd of Dir: Alan Murray
Ofcr: Kiril Tsemekhman
Sr VP: David Hahn
Sr VP: Michael Iantosca
Sr VP: Sergei Izrailev
Sr VP: Kristin Leary
Sr VP: Rob Molchon
VP: Alexey Kharlamov
VP: Terance Kinsky
VP: Harmon Lyons
Board of Directors: Don Epperson

D-U-N-S 86-728-3715
INTEGRAL COMPONENTS INC
1220 Tech Ct, Westminster, MD 21157-3029
Tel (410) 848-5542 *Founded/Ownrshp* 1993
Sales 36.8MM^E *EMP* 60
SIC 5065 Electronic parts & equipment
Pr: William Keiser
**VP:* Russ Keiser

D-U-N-S 12-257-3988
INTEGRAL CONSULTING INC
719 2nd Ave Ste 700, Seattle, WA 98104-1747
Tel (206) 230-9600 *Founded/Ownrshp* 2002
Sales 24.7MM^E *EMP* 136
SIC 8748 8711 8999 4959 Environmental consultant; Engineering services; Consulting engineer; Scientific consulting; Environmental cleanup services; Environmental consultant; Engineering services; Consulting engineer; Scientific consulting; Environmental cleanup services
Pr: Lucinda Jacobs
**Treas:* Alison Monson
**VP:* Judi Durda
**VP:* Larry Marx
**Prin:* Tyler Gass
**Prin:* Laura Jones
**Prin:* Russel Keenan
**Prin:* William Locke
IT Man: Doug Carbaugh

D-U-N-S 01-819-3669
INTEGRAL CONSULTING SERVICES INC
704 Quince Orchard Rd # 290, Gaithersburg, MD 20878-1770
Tel (301) 990-0880 *Founded/Ownrshp* 1998
Sales 29.3MM^E *EMP* 200
SIC 7371 8748 7389 8742 8299 Custom computer programming services; Custom computer programming services; Business consulting; ; Management consulting services; Educational services
Pr: Renu Johri
**Ex VP:* Abhai Johri
**Sr VP:* Frank Scudder
**VP:* Mary Pearl
Creative D: Stacie Lee
Snr Sftwr: Clinton Randall
Sls Dir: Kim Amster
Pgrm Dir: Craig Goodman

D-U-N-S 83-629-3597
INTEGRAL DEVELOPMENT CORP
INTEGRAL ENGINEERING
3400 Hillview Ave, Palo Alto, CA 94304-1346
Tel (650) 424-4500 *Founded/Ownrshp* 1993
Sales 59.6MM^E *EMP* 200
SIC 7372 Prepackaged software; Prepackaged software
Pr: Harpal Sandhu
Pr: Jay Kronberg
**CFO:* Albert Yau
Ofcr: Stephanie Feldt
Mng Dir: Richard Farrell
Sftwr Eng: Pranab Das
Sftwr Eng: Jatin Verma
VP Sls: Jesse Bruno

INTEGRAL ENGINEERING
See INTEGRAL DEVELOPMENT CORP

D-U-N-S 78-798-3543
INTEGRAL GROUP LLC
191 Peachtree St Ne # 4100, Atlanta, GA 30303-1748
Tel (404) 224-1860 *Founded/Ownrshp* 1993
Sales 247.5MM^E *EMP* 310
Accts Frazier & Deeter Llc Atlanta
SIC 6552 8748 6798 6799 6722 Subdividers & developers; Business consulting; Real estate investment trusts; Real estate investors, except property operators; Management investment, open-end; Subdividers & developers; Business consulting; Real estate investment trusts; Real estate investors, except property operators; Management investment, open-end
CEO: Egbert L J Perry
COO: Kenneth Chestnut
COO: Valerie Edwards
CFO: Mitchell Powell
VP: Daryl Jones
VP: Judi Jones
VP: Cecilia Perry
VP: Eric Pinckney
QA Dir: Robert Easterling

D-U-N-S 01-852-9181
INTEGRAL HEALTH PLAN INC
INTEGRITY QUALITY CARE
4631 Woodland Corp Blvd, Tampa, FL 33614
Tel (866) 258-4326 *Founded/Ownrshp* 2011
Sales 94.2MM *EMP* 16^E
Accts Kpmg Llp Greensboro Nc
SIC 8099 Blood related health services
CEO: James Young

D-U-N-S 93-199-4297 IMP
INTEGRAL PRODUCTS INC
24030 Frampton Ave, Harbor City, CA 90710-2102
Tel (424) 250-1600 *Founded/Ownrshp* 1995
Sales 34.7MM^E *EMP* 40^E
SIC 5088 Aircraft & space vehicle supplies & parts
CEO: John Roth

INTEGRAL SOLUTIONS GROUP
See J M SMITH CORP

D-U-N-S 10-192-5139
■ **INTEGRAL SYSTEMS INC**
(*Suby of* KRATOS DEFENSE & SECURITY SOLUTIONS INC) ★
4820 Estgate Mall Ste 200, San Diego, CA 92121
Tel (443) 539-5330 *Founded/Ownrshp* 2011
Sales 84.8MM^E *EMP* 690^E
SIC 7373 Computer systems analysis & design; Systems integration services; Computer systems analysis & design; Systems integration services
Pr: Paul G Casner Jr
CFO: Bill Bambarger
CFO: William M Bambarger
CFO: Deanna Lund
CFO: Christopher Roberts
Treas: Thomas Hyman
Ex VP: R Miller Adams
Ex VP: Stuart C Daughtridge
Sr VP: Sandee Carter
Sr VP: James B Kramer
Sr VP: Don Patrick
Sr VP: John Schladweiler
VP: David Bryant
VP: Craig Dempster
VP: Joan Grewe
VP: Kathryn J Herr
VP: Roger Hiyama
VP: Ron Johnson
VP: Eric Kirby
VP: Donald Mack
VP: Levi A Royster

D-U-N-S 07-927-6973
INTEGRAL TECHNOLOGIES CORP
(*Suby of* TAC INC) ★
52 Center Dr, New Hyde Park, NY 11040-2335
Tel (516) 248-3059 *Founded/Ownrshp* 2001
Sales 12.4MM^E *EMP* 1,200^E
SIC 7389 Business services
Prin: Cassandra Lems

D-U-N-S 15-143-9767
INTEGRAMED AMERICA INC
(*Suby of* INTEGRAMED HOLDING CORP) ★
2 Manhattanville Rd, Purchase, NY 10577-2113
Tel (914) 253-8000 *Founded/Ownrshp* 2012
Sales 96.9MM^E *EMP* 1,534
SIC 8093 Specialty outpatient clinics; Specialty outpatient clinics
Ch Bd: Jay Higham
Pr: Dan P Doman
Pr: Daniel P Doman
Pr: Mark Segal
Pr: Joseph Travia
COO: Lawrence Friedman
CFO: Eugene R Curcio
CFO: John W Hlywak
CFO: Timothy P Sheehan
CFO: Timothy Sheehan
Treas: Shelly Shapiro
Ofcr: Cheryl Gilbert
Ex VP: Scott Soifer
VP: Kate Fix
VP: Jeff Futterman
VP: Jeffrey Futterman
VP: Denise Montee
VP: Mark Weinberg
VP: Claude E White

D-U-N-S 07-862-3992
INTEGRAMED HOLDING CORP
(*Suby of* SAGARD CAPITAL PARTNERS LP) ★
2 Manhattanville Rd, Purchase, NY 10577-2113
Tel (914) 253-8000 *Founded/Ownrshp* 2012
Sales 221.9MM^E *EMP* 1,534^E
SIC 6719 Investment holding companies, except banks; Investment holding companies, except banks
Pr: Jay Higham
Chf Mktg O: Shannon Delage

D-U-N-S 09-044-2864
INTEGRAND ASSURANCE CO
(*Suby of* VICTOR J SALGADO & ASSOCIATES INC) ★
Franklin D Roosevelt Ave, San Juan, PR 00921
Tel (787) 781-0707 *Founded/Ownrshp* 1988
Sales NA *EMP* 190^E
SIC 6331 Fire, marine & casualty insurance; Property damage insurance; Fire, marine & casualty insurance; Property damage insurance
Ch Bd: Victor J Salgado Jr
**VP:* Milagros M Cabrera

D-U-N-S 96-498-9367
INTEGRATE.COM INC
4900 N Scotts Rd Ste 4000, Scottsdale, AZ 85251
Tel (866) 478-0326 *Founded/Ownrshp* 2010
Sales 22.1MM^E *EMP* 80^E
SIC 7379 Computer related consulting services
Pr: Jeremy Bloom
Pr: Eugene Kobrinsky
CFO: David Tomizuka
**Chf Mktg O:* Scott Vaughan
Sr VP: David Walsh
VP: Tom Click
VP: Kyle Gale
VP: Ryan Maher
VP: Alex Viderman
Sftwr Eng: Jacob Carter
Mktg Mgr: Van Levine
Board of Directors: Reggie Bradford

D-U-N-S 78-822-6751
INTEGRATED AGRIBUSINESS PROFESSIONALS COOPERATIVE INC
I A P
7108 N Fresno St Ste 150, Fresno, CA 93720-2960
Tel (559) 440-1980 *Founded/Ownrshp* 1991
Sales 152.3MM *EMP* 8
Accts Horg & Gray Llp Fresno Calif
SIC 5191 Fertilizer & fertilizer materials; Fertilizers & agricultural chemicals; Chemicals, agricultural; Fertilizer & fertilizer materials
Ch Bd: Dean Miller
**Pr:* Bob Higby
**VP:* Melissa McQueen
**VP:* Patrick Menagh

D-U-N-S 11-882-3798
INTEGRATED AIRLINE SERVICES INC
IASAIR
(*Suby of* CARGO AIRPORT SERVICES USA LLC) ★
1639 W 23rd St Ste 240, Jamaica, NY 11430
Tel (718) 880-3453 *Founded/Ownrshp* 2013
Sales 179.0MM^E *EMP* 1,500
SIC 4581 Air freight handling at airports; Air freight handling at airports
Pr: Tom Wheeling
COO: Stephen Navin
**CFO:* Michael Labarbera
Treas: Harry B Combs
**Sr VP:* Ray Jetha
**Sr VP:* Liane Kelly
**VP:* Julio Feliciano
IT Man: Mike Cornell
IT Man: Andrew Oldham
VP Sls: Glen Avila
S&M/VP: Ken Katchen

D-U-N-S 17-375-9143
INTEGRATED ALARM SERVICES GROUP INC
(*Suby of* PROTECTION ONE INC) ★
99 Pine St Fl 3, Albany, NY 12207-2776
Tel (518) 426-1515 *Founded/Ownrshp* 2003
Sales 21.0MM^E *EMP* 837
SIC 7382 Security systems services; Security systems services
Ch Bd: Timothy M McGinn

D-U-N-S 92-646-6475
INTEGRATED ARCHIVE SYSTEMS INC
I A S
1121 San Antonio Rd D100, Palo Alto, CA 94303-4311
Tel (650) 390-9995 *Founded/Ownrshp* 1994
Sales 170.0MM *EMP* 61
SIC 8742 5045 Management information systems consultant; Computer software
CEO: Amy Joyce RAO
**CFO:* Anna Borden
IT Man: Bob Elsey
IT Man: Thomas O'Brien
IT Man: Brooke Stasiak
**VP Sls:* Karin Napier
Sls Dir: Jeff Zontos
Sales Asso: Pam Bach
Sales Asso: Frenda Chek
Sales Asso: Cindy Monroe
Sales Asso: Julia Nash

D-U-N-S 79-024-6771 IMP
INTEGRATED BAGGING SYSTEMS CORP
IBS
(*Suby of* AMTOPP DIV) ★
101 Interplast Blvd, Lolita, TX 77971-4115
Tel (361) 874-3000 *Founded/Ownrshp* 1992
Sales 111.9MM^E *EMP* 1,100^E
SIC 3081 Packing materials, plastic sheet; Packing materials, plastic sheet
Pr: Dr John Young
**Pr:* Joe Chen
CIO: Lambert Wang

D-U-N-S 12-409-8042
INTEGRATED BIOMETRIC TECHNOLOGY LLC
L-1 ENROLLMENT SERVICES DIV
(Suby of MORPHOTRUST USA LLC) ★
15 Century Blvd Ste 500, Nashville, TN 37214-4617
Tel (615) 871-0522 Founded/Ownrshp 2012
Sales 21.1MM^E EMP 300
SIC 8748 Systems analysis or design

D-U-N-S 05-049-0903 EXP
▲ INTEGRATED BIOPHARMA INC
225 Long Ave Ste 13, Hillside, NJ 07205-2368
Tel (888) 319-6962 Founded/Ownrshp 1979
Sales 37.4MM EMP 119^E
Accts Friedman Llp East Hanover Ne
Tkr Sym INBP Exch OTO
SIC 2834 Vitamin, nutrient & hematinic preparations for human use; Vitamin, nutrient & hematinic preparations for human use
Ch Bd: E Gerald Kay
CFO: Dina L Masi
*Ex VP: Christina Kay
*Ex VP: Riva Sheppard
Dir Sec: Geoffrey Schild
Board of Directors: Robert Canarick, Carl Desantis, Joseph Laplaca, William H Milmoe

D-U-N-S 79-458-2312
INTEGRATED BOOK TECHNOLOGY INC
IBT GLOBAL
22 Hamilton Way, Castleton On Hudson, NY 12033-1015
Tel (518) 271-5117 Founded/Ownrshp 1991
Sales 23.5MM^E EMP 120
SIC 2732 2789 Book printing; Binding only: books, pamphlets, magazines, etc.; Book printing; Binding only: books, pamphlets, magazines, etc.
Pr: John R Paeglow III
*VP: William J Clockel
*VP Sls: Robert Lindberg
Sls Mgr: Ken Sabol

D-U-N-S 13-695-3085
INTEGRATED BROADBAND SERVICES LLC
IBBS
222 Chastain Mdws Ste 100, Kennesaw, GA 30144-5896
Tel (678) 581-3837 Founded/Ownrshp 2001
Sales 23.1MM^E EMP 156
SIC 4813 7371 ; Computer software development; ; Computer software development
CEO: Dave Keil
*Ch Bd: Robert Buckfelder
CFO: Bill Fielder
VP: Mike Griffith
VP: Mark Hayes
VP: Bob Hobbs
VP: Sandra Jimenez
VP: Holly Misirly
VP: Ricky Moore
VP: Todd Zittrouer
Snr Ntwrk: Derek Waldroop

D-U-N-S 79-617-9026
INTEGRATED BUSINESS ANALYSIS INC
IBS USA
1275 Barclay Blvd, Buffalo Grove, IL 60089-4514
Tel (866) 629-9996 Founded/Ownrshp 1992
Sales 51.0MM^E EMP 50
SIC 8742

D-U-N-S 08-325-1876
■ INTEGRATED CIRCUIT SYSTEMS INC
I C S
(Suby of INTEGRATED DEVICE TECHNOLOGY INC) ★
820 Adams Ave Ste 100, Norristown, PA 19403-2328
Tel (610) 666-1901 Founded/Ownrshp 2005
Sales 41.0MM^E EMP 503
SIC 3674 Integrated circuits, semiconductor networks, etc.
Ch Bd: Henry I Boreen
Pr: Clyde Hosein
Pr: Hock E Tan
CFO: Justine F Lien
Sr VP: Werner Anderson
VP: Edward Hall

D-U-N-S 04-892-7672
■ INTEGRATED COMMERCIALIZATION SOLUTIONS INC
PARAGARDDIRECT
(Suby of AMERISOURCEBERGEN SPECIALTY GROUP INC) ★
3101 Gaylord Pkwy Fl 2, Frisco, TX 75034-8655
Tel (888) 285-7481 Founded/Ownrshp 2003
Sales 21.5MM^E EMP 200
SIC 8742 Business planning & organizing services; Business planning & organizing services
Pr: Peter Belden
IT Man: Karl Erickson
IT Man: Tina Ramirez
Sls Mgr: Greg Honor

D-U-N-S 93-191-8866
INTEGRATED CONTROL SYSTEMS INC
4020 Vassar Dr Ne Ste H, Albuquerque, NM 87107-2058
Tel (505) 884-3503 Founded/Ownrshp 1996
Sales 25.2MM^E EMP 110
SIC 1731 5075 1542 6552 Electronic controls installation; Thermostats; Commercial & office building contractors; Land subdividers & developers, commercial
Pr: Steven B Chavez
*COO: Eric Eckles
*CFO: Raymond Gonzales
Genl Mgr: Mark McNeal
CTO: D Leavengoo

D-U-N-S 00-842-4517 IMP
INTEGRATED CORROSION COMPANIES INC
BRANCE-KRACHY CO
4411 Navigation Blvd 3, Houston, TX 77011-1035
Tel (713) 225-6661 Founded/Ownrshp 1988
Sales 81.7MM^E EMP 77
SIC 5063 3471 Power transmission equipment, electric; Electroplating of metals or formed products; Power transmission equipment, electric; Electroplating of metals or formed products
VP: Brent Bertrant
*VP: Dale Betz
VP: Lehrmann Clark
*VP: Matthew Henning
VP: Scott Hunt
*VP: C M Nelson
*VP: John Parkins
*Prin: Jesse Marion
VP Sls: Leslie Lehrmann
Mktg Dir: Roger Richards
Sls Dir: Christi Haas

D-U-N-S 18-404-6944
INTEGRATED CROP MANAGEMENT CONSULTANTS INC
320 Elm Ave, Greenfield, CA 93927-5243
Tel (831) 674-5102 Founded/Ownrshp 1986
Sales 24.3MM^E EMP 33
SIC 5191 Chemicals, agricultural
Pr: Ed Benech

D-U-N-S 13-202-6670
INTEGRATED DATA STORAGE LLC
1111 W 22nd St Ste 510, Oak Brook, IL 60523-1936
Tel (312) 334-6400 Founded/Ownrshp 2002
Sales 27.0MM^E EMP 43
Accts Lj Soldinger Associates Llc
SIC 7373 Value-added resellers, computer systems
CEO: Matthew Massick
Ch: Alan Dorrian
VP: Vince Buscareno
IT Man: Johnathan Austin
IT Man: Jake Massick
IT Man: Justin Mescher
Mktg Dir: Chris Plunkett
Sls Dir: Michelangelo Scalera
Mktg Mgr: Brian Elles
Snr PM: Juan Martinez

D-U-N-S 62-207-6347
INTEGRATED DECISIONS AND SYSTEMS INC
IDEAS
(Suby of SAS INSTITUTE INC) ★
8500 Normandale Lake Blvd # 1200, Minneapolis, MN 55437-3813
Tel (952) 698-4200 Founded/Ownrshp 2008
Sales 20.7MM^E EMP 180^E
SIC 7371 Computer software development; Computer software development
Pr: Ravi Mehrotra
*Ch Bd: Subhash Gupta
*CFO: Mark Derus
*VP: Sanjay Nagalia
VP: Rajiv Nashikkar
*CTO: Mike Gray
VP Sls: Joseph Martino
Mktg Mgr: Amy Anderson

D-U-N-S 13-789-8362
INTEGRATED DEICING SERVICES LLC
IDS
175 Ammon Dr, Manchester, NH 03103-3311
Tel (603) 647-1717 Founded/Ownrshp 2008
Sales 129.6MM^E EMP 550
SIC 3728 Deicing equipment, aircraft; Deicing equipment, aircraft
Pr: Salvatore Calvino
*Sr VP: Karen Fortin
*VP: Patrick Brown
*VP: Michael Grantz
VP: Linda Langsten
*VP: Bryan McCreary
VP: David Thornton
Mng Dir: Gil Schuckman
Genl Mgr: James Alexander
Genl Mgr: Scott Cummings
Genl Mgr: Mike Doroshenko

D-U-N-S 03-814-2600 IMP
▲ INTEGRATED DEVICE TECHNOLOGY INC
6024 Silver Creek Vly Rd, San Jose, CA 95138-1011
Tel (408) 284-8200 Founded/Ownrshp 1980
Sales 572.9MM EMP 1,484^E
Accts Pricewaterhousecoopers Llp Sa
Tkr Sym IDTI Exch NGS
SIC 3674 Semiconductors & related devices; Semiconductors & related devices
Pr: Gregory L Waters
*Ch Bd: John Schofield
CFO: Janet Oneal
CFO: Brian C White
VP: Matthew D Brandalise
VP: Chun Chen
VP: Sailesh Chittipeddi
VP: Louise Gaulin
VP: Mario Montana
VP: Graham Robertson
VP: David R Shepard
Creative D: Mia McNamee
Board of Directors: Ken Kannappan, Gordon Parnell, Robert A Rango, Donald Schrock, Ron Smith, Norman P Taffe

D-U-N-S 12-775-2835 IMP/EXP
INTEGRATED DISTRIBUTION AND LOGISTICS DIRECT LLC
SP EXPRESS
2429 S 51st Ave Ste 10, Phoenix, AZ 85043-8022
Tel (520) 573-1100 Founded/Ownrshp 2002
Sales 23.6MM^E EMP 50
SIC 4215 4213 4225 4731 Parcel delivery, vehicular; Trucking, except local; General warehousing & storage; Freight transportation arrangement
Pr: Michael Bayley
*COO: William R Bock
CFO: Howard Schildhouse
*Ofcr: Dave Crowder
Ex VP: Scott Guilmette
Dir IT: Doug Coker
IT Man: David Lynch
Software D: Marcelo Molina
S&M/VP: Niel Randall

D-U-N-S 01-337-5005
INTEGRATED DISTRIBUTION SERVICES INC
IDS
3100 Reeves Rd, Plainfield, IN 46168-7926
Tel (317) 837-7007 Founded/Ownrshp 2007
Sales 24.7MM^E EMP 52^E
SIC 4225 8742 General warehousing & storage; Transportation consultant
Pr: Mark Defabis
VP: Robert Hartley
*VP: Michael Jones
*VP: Rick Lagore
Genl Mgr: Garry Barfuss
Opers Mgr: Dave Hudson

D-U-N-S 17-846-1687
INTEGRATED DNA TECHNOLOGIES INC
I D T
1710 Commercial Park, Coralville, IA 52241-2760
Tel (319) 626-8400 Founded/Ownrshp 1987
Sales 160.0MM^E EMP 725
SIC 8733 5047 Research institute; Diagnostic equipment, medical; Research institute; Diagnostic equipment, medical
Pr: Joseph Walder
Pr: Jen Lockhart
COO: Trey Martin
CFO: Allen Siegal
VP: Mark Behlke
VP: Mark Campbell
VP: Patrick Marschall
VP: Aaron Warner
VP: Matthew Wetzel
VP: Dawn Wilson
Web Dev: Jean Deschamps

D-U-N-S 96-828-5481
▲ INTEGRATED DRILLING EQUIPMENT HOLDINGS CORP
25311 I 45 N Bldg 6, Spring, TX 77380
Tel (281) 465-9393 Founded/Ownrshp 1981
Sales 87.2MM EMP 270
Accts Whitley Penn Llp Houston Tex
Tkr Sym IRIG Exch OTO
SIC 3533 7539 5084 Drilling tools for gas, oil or water wells; Electrical services; Drilling equipment, excluding bits; Drilling tools for gas, oil or water wells; Electrical services; Drilling equipment, excluding bits
CEO: Jim Terry
*Ch Bd: James N Mills
CFO: N Michael Dion
*V Ch Bd: Stephen Cope

D-U-N-S 83-983-2631 IMP
▲ INTEGRATED ELECTRICAL SERVICES INC
5433 Westheimer Rd # 500, Houston, TX 77056-5339
Tel (713) 860-1500 Founded/Ownrshp 2006
Sales 573.8MM EMP 2,740
Tkr Sym IESC Exch NGM
SIC 1731 Electrical work; Electrical work
Pr: Robert W Lewey
Pr: Michael Rice
CFO: Terry L Freeman
CFO: Tracy A McLauchlin
Treas: Neil Depascal
Sr VP: Bob Callahan
Sr VP: William L Fiedler
Sr VP: Terry Freeman
Sr VP: Margery M Harris
Sr VP: Gail D Makode
Sr VP: Danniel Petro
Sr VP: Bobby Stalvey
Sr VP: Jim Thurman
Sr VP: Peter Van Nort
VP: William Albright
VP: Richard China
VP: Dwayne Collier
VP: Christopher Haas
VP: Richard A Nix
VP: James A Robertson
Dir Risk M: Ryan Snell
Board of Directors: Joseph L Dowling III, David B Gendell, Joe Koshkin, Donald L Luke

D-U-N-S 06-972-5945
INTEGRATED ENERGY TECHNOLOGIES INC
DONCASTERS GCE INTEGRATED
757 Main St, Chula Vista, CA 91911-6168
Tel (619) 421-1151 Founded/Ownrshp 2004
Sales 42.4MM^E EMP 160
SIC 3562 Casters; Casters
CEO: Craig Gooding
VP: Tim Martin
Mng Dir: Richard Zalac
IT Man: Peter Gastelum
Ql Cn Mgr: Jeffrey Berry

D-U-N-S 13-390-4602 IMP/EXP
INTEGRATED EQUIPMENT INC
5701 Brittmoore Rd, Houston, TX 77041-5614
Tel (713) 785-7075 Founded/Ownrshp 2002
Sales 32.2MM^E EMP 30
SIC 5082 Oil field equipment
Pr: Ashish Sharma
COO: Mike Taylor
*VP: W Clark Harlow
Off Mgr: Nagen McDaniel
Opers Supe: Walter Washington
Manager: Cindy Amat
Sales Asso: Gary Argabright

INTEGRATED FOOD SERVICE
See LETS DO LUNCH

INTEGRATED GENETICS
See ESOTERIX GENETIC LABORATORIES LLC

D-U-N-S 96-716-1006 IMP
INTEGRATED GLOBAL SERVICES INC
7600 Whitepine Rd, North Chesterfield, VA 23237-2215
Tel (804) 794-1646 Founded/Ownrshp 2010
Sales 36.8MM^E EMP 100^E
SIC 3479 Coating, rust preventive
Pr: Richard Crawford
*Ch: Reichert Hunter J
*VP: Iain Hall

D-U-N-S 92-866-9027
INTEGRATED HEALTH ASSOCIATES INC
IHA
24 Frank Lloyd Wright Dr, Ann Arbor, MI 48105-9484
Tel (734) 747-6766 Founded/Ownrshp 1994
Sales 148.1MM^E EMP 800
SIC 8011 Offices & clinics of medical doctors; Offices & clinics of medical doctors
Pr: William J Fileti
*Ch Bd: Robert Breakey MD
*CFO: Lowell Sprague
*Treas: James L Marley
*VP: Linda Macellven
*VP: Martin Murray
Prac Mgr: Sarah Bradley
Dir IT: Chris Holda
Sales Exec: Amy Middleton
Doctor: Sharon Bihlmeyer
Doctor: Kevin Bohnsack

INTEGRATED HEALTH HOLDINGS LLC
See CENTREX REVENUE SOLUTIONS LLC

D-U-N-S 07-997-5832
INTEGRATED HEALTH HOLDINGS LLC (MD)
6021 University Blvd # 450, Ellicott City, MD 21043-6077
Tel (443) 288-0223 Founded/Ownrshp 2013
Sales 14.2MM^E EMP 471
SIC 6719 8721 Personal holding companies, except banks; Billing & bookkeeping service
Prin: Desi C LLC
Genl Mgr: Gira Shah

D-U-N-S 12-176-0243
INTEGRATED HEALTHCARE SYSTEMS INC
3311 E Murdock St, Wichita, KS 67208-3054
Tel (316) 689-9111 Founded/Ownrshp 1982
Sales 55.6MM^E EMP 1,000
SIC 7359 Equipment rental & leasing; Equipment rental & leasing

D-U-N-S 06-637-1092 IMP
INTEGRATED ILLUMINATION SYSTEMS INC
I2SYSTEMS
355 Bantam Lake Rd, Morris, CT 06763-1102
Tel (860) 567-1568 Founded/Ownrshp 2004
Sales 49.1MM^E EMP 49^E
SIC 5063 Lighting fixtures
Pr: Thomas Zampini II
Natl Sales: Colby Schlensker
Sls Mgr: Nancy Sawyer

D-U-N-S 14-818-8899
INTEGRATED INDUSTRIAL SERVICES INC
INSERV
121 Dickens Rd, Fuquay Varina, NC 27526-8302
Tel (919) 552-6355 Founded/Ownrshp 1992
Sales 53.2MM^E EMP 150
Accts Charles Bryan Cpa Pa Angi
SIC 1711 1731 Mechanical contractor; General electrical contractor; Mechanical contractor; General electrical contractor
Ch Bd: James D Romano
*Pr: Mark Youngquist
VP: Don Mingin
Exec: John Lechner

D-U-N-S 09-632-8914
INTEGRATED LOGISTICS 2000 LLC (VA)
I L 2000
4007 Atlantic Ave Ste 101, Virginia Beach, VA 23451-2658
Tel (757) 498-1895 Founded/Ownrshp 1999
Sales 27.1MM^E EMP 43
SIC 4731 8742 Freight transportation arrangement; Management consulting services
Pr: Kraig A Cesar
VP: Scott Satterfield
Dir Bus: Jon Burnham
Genl Mgr: Craig Ponton

INTEGRATED MAGNETICS
See MAGNET SALES & MFG CO INC

D-U-N-S 19-916-3627
INTEGRATED MAIL INDUSTRIES LTD
3450 W Hopkins St, Milwaukee, WI 53216-1700
Tel (414) 908-3500 Founded/Ownrshp 1987
Sales 20.1MM^E EMP 105
SIC 7331 Mailing service; Mailing service
Ch Bd: Bruce Arbit
IT Man: Kelly Ciezki
Prd Mgr: Mark Shaw

D-U-N-S 15-417-3637
INTEGRATED MANAGEMENT SYSTEMS INC
3135 S State St Ste 104, Ann Arbor, MI 48108-1653
Tel (734) 996-0500 Founded/Ownrshp 1985
Sales 8.3MM EMP 300
SIC 8748 Systems engineering consultant, ex. computer or professional; Systems engineering consultant, ex. computer or professional
Pr: Sudhir Jain
Opers Mgr: Ajit Makhecha

D-U-N-S 94-877-4492 IMP
INTEGRATED MANUFACTURING & ASSEMBLY LLC
I M A
6501 E Nevada St, Detroit, MI 48234-2833
Tel (734) 530-5600 Founded/Ownrshp 2006
Sales 220.0MM^E EMP 600
SIC 2531 Seats, automobile; Seats, automobile
Owner: James Comer
Ql Cn Mgr: Millisa Burdette
Ql Cn Mgr: Dustin Diehl
Ql Cn Mgr: Cliff Holmes
Ql Cn Mgr: Rich Umin

D-U-N-S 62-703-6325 IMP
INTEGRATED MANUFACTURING GROUP LLC
IMG
225 Mountain Vista Pkwy, Livermore, CA 94551-8210
Tel (925) 273-1100 *Founded/Ownrshp* 2004
Sales 21.8MM^E *EMP* 60
SIC 3599 Machine shop, jobbing & repair
CEO: Kam Pasha
**COO:* Lance Morford
**CFO:* Kiran Mukkamala
**VP:* Mahesh Kumar
**VP:* Allen Timmons
**VP:* Dwayne Williams
Genl Mgr: Rick Tachuk

D-U-N-S 17-633-8929
INTEGRATED MEDIA MANAGEMENT LLC
330 Dalziel Rd Ste 4, Linden, NJ 07036-6211
Tel (908) 862-6600 *Founded/Ownrshp* 1990
Sales 28.7MM^E *EMP* 40^E
SIC 5112 Business forms
Pr: Charles Klein
VP: John Levy
QA Dir: Anusha Iyer
VP Opers: Howard Klein
Sls Dir: Phillip Elwyn
Manager: Wanda Nichoalds

D-U-N-S 94-684-4925
INTEGRATED MEDICAL DELIVERY LLC
236 Nw 62nd St, Oklahoma City, OK 73118-7422
Tel (405) 775-4200 *Founded/Ownrshp* 1996
Sales 20.5MM^E *EMP* 275
SIC 8741 Hospital management; Nursing & personal care facility management; Hospital management; Nursing & personal care facility management

D-U-N-S 78-787-0505
INTEGRATED MEDICAL PROFESSIONALS PLLC
532 Broadhollow Rd # 142, Melville, NY 11747-3672
Tel (516) 931-0041 *Founded/Ownrshp* 2006
Sales 40.0MM^E *EMP* 284^E
SIC 8011 Offices & clinics of medical doctors
CEO: Deepak A Kapoor
**COO:* W Price Dunaway
Pathlgst: Savvas Mendrinos
**Doctor:* Ann E Anderson
**Doctor:* Shawn H Zimberg

D-U-N-S 83-201-5361
INTEGRATED MEDICAL SERVICES INC
INTEGRATED MEDICAL SVCS IMS
9250 N 3rd St Ste 4010, Phoenix, AZ 85020-2432
Tel (602) 633-3834 *Founded/Ownrshp* 1995
Sales 25.3MM^E *EMP* 400
SIC 8099 Medical services organization; Medical services organization
Pr: John A Dover

INTEGRATED MEDICAL SVCS IMS
See INTEGRATED MEDICAL SERVICES INC

D-U-N-S 96-236-4444
INTEGRATED MEDICAL SYSTEMS INC
IMS
12600 S Holiday Dr Ste A, Alsip, IL 60803-3250
Tel (708) 597-7105 *Founded/Ownrshp* 1995
Sales 49.8MM^E *EMP* 90
SIC 5047 Medical & hospital equipment; Medical & hospital equipment
Pr: Patrick Di Orio
**Sec:* Dan Izzo
Dir Bus: Michael Donio
Rgnl Mgr: Erik Barnett
Rgnl Mgr: Pete Brody

D-U-N-S 78-580-3404 IMP
■ INTEGRATED MEDICAL SYSTEMS INTERNATIONAL INC
IMS
(*Suby of* STERIS CORP) ★
3316 2nd Ave N, Birmingham, AL 35222-1214
Tel (205) 879-3840 *Founded/Ownrshp* 2001
Sales 117.9MM *EMP* 1,100
Accts Barfield Murphy Shank & Smit
SIC 3841 7699 Medical equipment & supplies; Professional instrument repair services; Surgical & medical instruments; Professional instrument repair services
CEO: Gene Robinson
Pr: Victor Graffeo
**CFO:* David Strevy
Ex VP: James Boyette
Ex VP: Chris Isbell
Ex VP: Lenny Jordan
VP: Brandon Bonser
VP: Andrew Edwards
VP: Eric Fabitz
VP: Sharon Hadley
VP: Jason Harrell
VP: Kyle Hunter
VP: Brian Jones
VP: Art Klebba
VP: Lynne Thomas
VP: Leslie Vanatta
VP: Dan Weber
Dir Soc: Terry Clunie

D-U-N-S 06-751-2785
■ INTEGRATED MERCHANDISING SYSTEMS LLC
GROUP II COMMUNICATIONS
(*Suby of* OMNICOM GROUP INC) ★
8338 Austin Ave, Morton Grove, IL 60053-3209
Tel (847) 583-3800 *Founded/Ownrshp* 2007
Sales 63.8MM^E *EMP* 150
SIC 7389 Advertising, promotional & trade show services; Advertising, promotional & trade show services
VP: Doug Carlson
VP: Sally Harrington
VP: David O'Grady
Creative D: Darryl Giambalvo
Off Mgr: Anne O'Keefe
IT Man: Bill Freiberg
IT Man: Terry Sams
Web Dev: Patel Unnati
Prd Mgr: Susan Barrett
Prd Mgr: Megan Mulligan

D-U-N-S 02-893-4490
INTEGRATED METAL PRODUCTS INC
2923 Old Tampa Hwy, Lakeland, FL 33803-1674
Tel (863) 687-4110 *Founded/Ownrshp* 2001
Sales 21.9MM^E *EMP* 70
SIC 3441 Fabricated structural metal
Pr: Wayne Albritton
CFO: Dewayne Watford
**VP:* Eva Albritton

D-U-N-S 02-180-4922
INTEGRATED OFFICE TECHNOLOGY LLC (CA)
IO TEC
12150 Mora Dr 2, Santa Fe Springs, CA 90670-3759
Tel (562) 236-9200 *Founded/Ownrshp* 2000, 2001
Sales 21.5MM^E *EMP* 50^E
SIC 5044 Office equipment
Mktg Mgr: Heidi Zieman

D-U-N-S 96-396-2832 IMP/EXP
INTEGRATED PACKAGING MACHINERY LLC
801 Fox Row Ct Ne, Rockford, MI 49341-7244
Tel (616) 531-7758 *Founded/Ownrshp* 1998
Sales 37.0MM^E *EMP* 60
SIC 5084 Materials handling machinery
Pr: Brad Lamb
**VP:* Kendal Malstrom

D-U-N-S 62-249-7188
■ INTEGRATED PAYMENT SYSTEMS INC
(*Suby of* FIRST DATA CORP) ★
6200 S Quebec St Ste 320b, Greenwood Village, CO 80111-4750
Tel (402) 951-7008 *Founded/Ownrshp* 1992
Sales NA *EMP* 751
SIC 6099 Money order issuance
Pr: Charles T Fote
VP: Tarcisio Bortoletto
VP: Ron Darnall
VP: George Zirkel

D-U-N-S 80-057-4167 IMP
INTEGRATED POWER SERVICES LLC
I P S
3 Independence Pt Ste 100, Greenville, SC 29615-4543
Tel (864) 451-5600 *Founded/Ownrshp* 2012
Sales 183.7MM^E *EMP* 900
SIC 7694 Motor repair services; Motor repair services
CEO: Brian Brehmer
**CEO:* John Zuleger
Plnt Mgr: Mike Renfro

D-U-N-S 05-320-0911
INTEGRATED PRINT & GRAPHICS INC
I P G
645 Stevenson Rd, South Elgin, IL 60177-1134
Tel (847) 695-6777 *Founded/Ownrshp* 1990
Sales 30.6MM^E *EMP* 130^E
SIC 2752 7331 2761 Business forms, lithographed; Direct mail advertising services; Manifold business forms; Business forms, lithographed; Direct mail advertising services; Manifold business forms
Pr: Gary Mozina
Ex VP: John Brahm
CIO: Christ Gorski
Plnt Mgr: Bill Surges
Sls Mgr: Denise Hansen
Sls Mgr: Doug Marecek

D-U-N-S 95-618-4220 IMP
INTEGRATED PROCESS ENGINEERS & CONSTRUCTORS INC
I P E C
1901 Allen Dr, Fort Atkinson, WI 53538-3142
Tel (920) 568-0475 *Founded/Ownrshp* 1996
Sales 23.7MM^E *EMP* 50
SIC 3556 3613 8711 Food products machinery; Dairy & milk machinery; Control panels, electric; Engineering services
Pr: Mark McGlynn
**Treas:* Barbara McGlynn
IT Man: Mark McGynn

D-U-N-S 94-778-3122 IMP/EXP
INTEGRATED PROCUREMENT TECHNOLOGIES INC
I P T
320 Storke Rd Ste 100, Goleta, CA 93117-2992
Tel (805) 682-0842 *Founded/Ownrshp* 1996
Sales 151.3MM^E *EMP* 48
SIC 5088 5065 Aircraft & parts; Navigation equipment & supplies; Communication equipment
CEO: Etty Yenni
**COO:* Ken Krutenat
**CFO:* Scott Heinz
Ex VP: Robert Harden
VP: Albert Yenni
Dir Bus: Tay Lai
Sls&Mrk Ex: Greg Wenclewicz
Sales Asso: Johnny Ryan

D-U-N-S 78-871-6954
■ INTEGRATED PRODUCTION SERVICES INC
(*Suby of* COMPLETE PRODUCTION SERVICES INC) ★
16800 Greenspt Pk Dr 200s, Houston, TX 77060-2300
Tel (281) 774-6700 *Founded/Ownrshp* 2007
Sales 189.0MM^E *EMP* 270
SIC 1389 3599 Construction, repair & dismantling services; Custom machinery; Construction, repair & dismantling services; Custom machinery
Pr: Jeff Kaufmann
Pr: Jose Bayardo
COO: Clinton Coldren
**Treas:* Robert S Taylor
**VP:* John Graham
VP: Richard Guerra
**VP:* Brian K Moore
VP: Scott Ritter
IT Man: John Finucan
IT Man: John Finuken
Tech Mgr: Mark Ference

D-U-N-S 04-878-7183
■ INTEGRATED REGIONAL LABORATORIES
IRL
(*Suby of* HCA-HOSPITAL CORP OF AMERICA) ★
5361 Nw 33rd Ave, Fort Lauderdale, FL 33309-6313
Tel (954) 777-0139 *Founded/Ownrshp* 1996
Sales 31.4MM^E *EMP* 800
SIC 8071 Pathological laboratory; Pathological laboratory
CEO: Joanne Trout
**COO:* Carol Sheets
**CFO:* Alma Alexander

D-U-N-S 05-832-0032
INTEGRATED SECURITY SERVICES INC
305 Madison Ave Ste 1563, New York, NY 10165-1519
Tel (212) 808-4153 *Founded/Ownrshp* 1998
Sales 7.0MM *EMP* 397
SIC 7382 Security systems services; Security systems services
Pr: Gail Schissel
**VP:* Douglas J Ingram
**VP:* Alan Schissel

D-U-N-S 07-939-6810
INTEGRATED SERVICE CO LLC
INSERV
1900 N 161st East Ave, Tulsa, OK 74116-4829
Tel (918) 234-4150 *Founded/Ownrshp* 2012
Sales 72.4MM^E *EMP* 850^E
SIC 1629 Oil refinery construction
Ch Bd: Arlo Dekraai
**Pr:* Clayton Hughes
**CFO:* Mark Dolan
VP: Oliver Stanley
Genl Mgr: Haley Henson
Off Mgr: Matthew Chrzanowski
CIO: Brett Tabbler
Sfty Dirs: Grant Dalton
Site Mgr: Bobby Hamlin
Sfty Mgr: Greg Dooley

D-U-N-S 07-915-2135
INTEGRATED SERVICE MANAGEMENT LLC
12312 Wilkins Ave, Rockville, MD 20852-1846
Tel (703) 480-2671 *Founded/Ownrshp* 2012
Sales 32.2MM^E *EMP* 3,000
SIC 7349 Building & office cleaning services; Building & office cleaning services
Ch: Fran Gali
Area Mgr: Manuel Rodriguez

D-U-N-S 18-928-9481
INTEGRATED SERVICES INC
ISI
15115 Sw Sequoia Pkwy # 110, Portland, OR 97224-7156
Tel (503) 968-8100 *Founded/Ownrshp* 1987
Sales 28.1MM^E *EMP* 73
SIC 5045 7378 7371 Computers, peripherals & software; Computer maintenance & repair; Computer software development
CEO: Steve Barram
**Pr:* Scott Nordlund
VP: Wayne Allen
VP: Dan Johnson
QA Dir: Kelvin Ngai
QA Dir: Eric Nofsinger
Software D: Michael Lynch
Mktg Dir: Suzanne Kocurek

D-U-N-S 60-820-8245 IMP
▲ INTEGRATED SILICON SOLUTION INC
1623 Buckeye Dr, Milpitas, CA 95035-7423
Tel (408) 969-6600 *Founded/Ownrshp* 1988
Sales 328.9MM *EMP* 590^E
Accts Grant Thornton Llp San Franci
Tkr Sym ISSI *Exch* NGS
SIC 3674 Semiconductors & related devices; Semiconductors & related devices
Pr: Scott D Howarth
**Ch Bd:* Jimmy S M Lee
V Ch: Kong Y Han
Pr: Chung Wang
CFO: John M Cobb
Ofcr: Shirlin Tan
Ex VP: Chang-Chaio Han
Sr VP: Sanjiv Asthana
Sr VP: Ron Kalakuntla
VP: Allen Chang
VP: Shou-Kong Fan
VP: Paul Jei-Zensong
VP: Lyn Zastrow
VP Bus Dev: Kashi Manjunatha
VP Bus Dev: Lou Yang
Dir Surg: Thomas Dolzy

D-U-N-S 55-662-1068
INTEGRATED SOLUTIONS INC
ISI ENVIRONMENTAL SERVICES
215 S Laura St, Wichita, KS 67211-1516
Tel (316) 264-7050 *Founded/Ownrshp* 1991
Sales 39.0MM^E *EMP* 165^E
SIC 8742 8748 Industry specialist consultants; Environmental consultant; Safety training service; Industry specialist consultants; Environmental consultant; Safety training service
Pr: Karma Mason
**Treas:* Gary Mason
Sls&Mrk Ex: Tamara Hadley
Board of Directors: Tamara Hadley

D-U-N-S 05-436-6463 IMP
INTEGRATED SUPPLY NETWORK LLC
ISN
2727 Interstate Dr, Lakeland, FL 33805-2304
Tel (863) 603-0777 *Founded/Ownrshp* 1997
Sales 354.9MM^E *EMP* 275
SIC 5013 5072 Tools & equipment, automotive; Power handtools; Tools & equipment, automotive; Power handtools
**Ch Bd:* F P Weber
CFO: Bill Driscoll
**CFO:* William Driscoll
**VP:* Peter D Weber

D-U-N-S 96-140-4530
INTEGRATED SUPPORT SOLUTIONS INC
RD SOLUTIONS
4283 Empress Ave, Encino, CA 91436-3504
Tel (818) 787-2116 *Founded/Ownrshp* 1996
Sales 17.0MM *EMP* 386
SIC 8748 Business consulting; Business consulting
Pr: Steve Eisner
S&M/VP: Denise Terry

D-U-N-S 01-662-6426
INTEGRATED SYSTEMS ANALYSTS INC (VA)
I S A
2001 N Beauregard St # 600, Alexandria, VA 22311-1722
Tel (703) 824-0700 *Founded/Ownrshp* 1980, 1981
Sales 22.9MM^E *EMP* 130
SIC 1731 7378 7373 Computer installation; Computer & data processing equipment repair/maintenance; Local area network (LAN) systems integrator; Systems engineering, computer related; Computer systems analysis & design
Ch Bd: C Michael Gooden
**Pr:* Edward G Sharp
**Ex VP:* Mary H Anderson
**VP:* Adrienne Geis
CIO: Peter Fry

D-U-N-S 07-884-2642
INTEGRATED TECH GROUP LLC
(*Suby of* QUALTEK USA LLC) ★
1150 1st Ave Ste 600, King of Prussia, PA 19406-1300
Tel (484) 804-4500 *Founded/Ownrshp* 2013
Sales 24.2MM^E *EMP* 400
SIC 4225 General warehousing & storage; General warehousing & storage
Prin: Montvydal Thomas

D-U-N-S 15-073-2050
INTEGRATED TECHNICAL PRODUCTS LLC
ACT INDUSTRIAL PROCESS SERVICE
12400 Coit Rd Ste 700, Dallas, TX 75251-2059
Tel (318) 675-1772 *Founded/Ownrshp* 2004
Sales 21.4MM^E *EMP* 130
Accts Wilf & Henderson Pc
SIC 8711 Mechanical engineering; Mechanical engineering

D-U-N-S 07-931-6849
INTEGRATED TECHNOLOGIES GROUP INC (CA)
11250 Playa Ct, Culver City, CA 90230-6127
Tel (424) 672-1512 *Founded/Ownrshp* 2006
Sales 10.0MM *EMP* 395^E
SIC 3499 Magnetic shields, metal; Magnetic shields, metal
CEO: Anil Anji

D-U-N-S 07-868-9582
INTEGRATED TELCOM SERVICES CORP
(*Suby of* MITEL TECHNOLOGIES INC) ★
1146 N Alma School Rd, Mesa, AZ 85201-3000
Tel (480) 961-9000 *Founded/Ownrshp* 2012
Sales 11.0MM^E *EMP* 387^E
SIC 5065 Electronic parts & equipment
Pr: Philip Keenan

D-U-N-S 96-275-1678
INTEGRATED TURF SOLUTIONS LLC
900 Circle 75 Pkwy Se, Atlanta, GA 30339-3035
Tel (877) 686-8873 *Founded/Ownrshp* 2009
Sales 66.0MM^E *EMP* 276
SIC 3523 Turf & grounds equipment; Turf & grounds equipment
COO: John Bogosian

D-U-N-S 07-230-4723
INTEGRATING TECHNOLOGY & STANDARDS INC
IRON WOMAN CONSTRUCTION
5680 Emerson St, Denver, CO 80216-1318
Tel (303) 399-5534 *Founded/Ownrshp* 1994
Sales 20.3MM^E *EMP* 50
SIC 1629 Earthmoving contractor
Pr: Shaun Egan
Off Mgr: Paul Wohlfarth

D-U-N-S 00-969-9346
INTEGRATION INNOVATION INC (AL)
I 3
689 Discovery Dr Nw # 500, Huntsville, AL 35806-2831
Tel (256) 513-5179 *Founded/Ownrshp* 2007, 2008
Sales 44.8MM *EMP* 147
Accts Hill Fogg & Associates Pc
SIC 8711 7373 7371 Engineering services; Systems integration services; Computer software development; Engineering services; Systems integration services; Computer software development
CEO: Michael W Wicks
**Pr:* Bill Looney
COO: Ken Shannon
**Ex VP:* Joseph Summers
VP: Adam Harper
Prgrm Mgr: Shannon Allen
IT Man: Benita Wheeler
Software D: David Dunson
VP Opers: Walter Strankman

D-U-N-S 09-795-7463
INTEGRATION PARTNERS CORP (MA)
12 Hartwell Ave, Lexington, MA 02421-3113
Tel (781) 357-8100 *Founded/Ownrshp* 1999
Sales 68.8MM^E *EMP* 195
SIC 7373 Local area network (LAN) systems integrator; Local area network (LAN) systems integrator
Pr: David C Nahabedian
**Treas:* Barton F Graf Jr

D-U-N-S 03-662-9841
■ INTEGRATION PARTNERS-NY CORP
(*Suby of* INTERCLOUD SYSTEMS INC) ★
1719 State Rt 10 Ste 114, Parsippany, NJ 07054-4537
Tel (973) 871-2100 *Founded/Ownrshp* 2014

Sales 16.0MM^E EMP 280^E
SIC 8741 7372 Management services; Prepackaged software

D-U-N-S 12-990-2180
INTEGRATION POINT INC
10720 Sikes Pl Ste 300, Charlotte, NC 28277-8143
Tel (704) 576-3678 Founded/Ownrshp 2000
Sales 26.5MM^E EMP 100
SIC 7373 7371 Systems integration services; Computer software development; Systems integration services; Computer software development
CEO: Tom Barnes
*Pr: Clay Perry
*Sr VP: Melissa Irmen
*VP: Angela Chamberlain
*VP: Ned Chamberlain
VP: Keith Dunn
VP: Kareem Howell
VP: Kris Kay
VP: Scott Lovin
VP: Jeffrey McCauley
VP: Scott McLaine
VP: Kevin Shoemaker
VP: Virginia Thompson

D-U-N-S 12-651-1963
INTEGRATION TECHNOLOGIES GROUP INC
ITG
2745 Hartland Rd, Falls Church, VA 22043-3541
Tel (703) 698-8282 Founded/Ownrshp 1984
Sales 24.5MM EMP 73
Accts Cohnreznick Llp Tysons Virgi
SIC 5731 7378 Television sets; Computer peripheral equipment repair & maintenance; Television sets; Computer peripheral equipment repair & maintenance
Pr: Michael Angelakis
*Pr: Burl Williams
*Ex VP: Markus Darby
*VP: Giovanni Canobbio
*VP: Regina Hwang
VP: Tom Reilly
VP: Heather Reis
Exec: Hwang Regina
Exec: William Weithman
CIO: George Harris
Software D: Briget Fellers

D-U-N-S 82-821-6270
■ **INTEGRATIONS POWER INTERNATIONAL**
(Suby of POWER INTEGRATIONS INC) ★
5245 Hellyer Ave, San Jose, CA 95138-1002
Tel (408) 414-8528 Founded/Ownrshp 2008
Sales 21.6MM^E EMP 392
SIC 3674 Integrated circuits, semiconductor networks, etc.; Integrated circuits, semiconductor networks, etc.
Pr: Balu Balakrishnan

D-U-N-S 05-065-4651
INTEGREON MANAGED SOLUTIONS INC
IMS
(Suby of INTEGREON MANAGED SOLUTIONS (INDIA) PRIVATE LIMITED)
2011 Crystal Dr Ste 200, Arlington, VA 22202-3779
Tel (201) 213-6107 Founded/Ownrshp 1998
Sales 104.8MM EMP 1,612
Accts Sr Batliboi & Associates Llp
SIC 8111 Legal services; Legal services
CEO: Robert Gogel
Pr: Marcia Goldenberg
*CFO: Kenneth Stelzer
Sr VP: Michael Dorsam
VP: Vicky Brown
VP: Mark Jewell
VP: Tara Lamy
VP: Michelle Richard
*VP: Benjamin Romualdez
VP: Mark Ross
*VP: Andrew Sims

D-U-N-S 78-966-5366
INTEGRICHAIN INC
8 Penn Ctr 1628 Jfk 300, Philadelphia, PA 19103
Tel (609) 806-5005 Founded/Ownrshp 2006
Sales 48.3MM^E EMP 102^E
SIC 5122 Pharmaceuticals
CEO: Kevin E Leininger
*Ex VP: Joshua I Halpern
*VP: Jeffrey M Borman
*VP: Dennis Omalley
*VP: Richard A Salerno
*VP: Darren Weiss
Board of Directors: Phillip Chan, Jim Gunton

D-U-N-S 96-941-2456
INTEGRIS AMBULATORY CARE CORP
5300 N Independence Ave, Oklahoma City, OK 73112-5556
Tel (405) 949-6026 Founded/Ownrshp 2011
Sales 152.6MM EMP 9^E
Accts Kpmg Llp Oklahoma City Ok
SIC 8062 General medical & surgical hospitals; General medical & surgical hospitals
Prin: Barton H Dawson

D-U-N-S 08-699-5966
INTEGRIS BAPTIST MEDICAL CENTER INC
BAPTIST MEDICAL CENTER OKLA
(Suby of INTEGRIS HEALTH INC) ★
3300 Nw Expressway, Oklahoma City, OK 73112-4418
Tel (405) 949-3011 Founded/Ownrshp 1983
Sales 582.8MM EMP 2,700
SIC 8062 General medical & surgical hospitals; General medical & surgical hospitals
Pr: Chris Hammes
CFO: David Hadley
*CFO: Wentz J Miller
Bd of Dir: William C Goad
VP: William Hood
CIO: Mark Hargrove
Mtls Mgr: Sonya Roddy
Opers Mgr: Jake Brownlow
Obsttrcn: Lynn Horton
Doctor: Jeffrey Thompson
Doctor: Brian C Williams

INTEGRIS BAPTIST REGIONAL HOSP
See BAPTIST REGIONAL HEALTH CENTER

INTEGRIS CLINTON REGIONAL HOSP
See CLINTON HMA LLC

INTEGRIS CNDIAN VLY RGNAL HOSP
See INTEGRIS RURAL HEALTH INC

D-U-N-S 12-195-6734
INTEGRIS HEALTH INC
3300 Nw Expwy, Oklahoma City, OK 73112-4418
Tel (405) 949-6066 Founded/Ownrshp 1983
Sales 50.0M EMP 9,927
SIC 8062 General medical & surgical hospitals; General medical & surgical hospitals
CEO: Bruce Lawrence
Pr: Avilla Williams
*COO: Chris Hammes
*CFO: David Hadley
Bd of Dir: David Kallenberger
Ofcr: Kathy Ellis
VP: Kathie Calbone
VP: Susan Dragoo
VP: Jerry Gardner
VP: Phil Lance
VP: Jason Thompson
Dir Lab: Theresa Schuldt
Assoc Dir: William Green
Assoc Dir: Vivek Kohli

D-U-N-S 96-967-9773
INTEGRIS HEALTH INC
5300 N Independence Ave # 280, Oklahoma City, OK 73112-5555
Tel (405) 949-6026 Founded/Ownrshp 2011
Sales 217.6MM EMP 19^E
Accts Kpmg Llp Oklahoma City Ok
SIC 8099 Health & allied services; Health & allied services
VP: Barbara Dean
CIO: George Conklin
IT Man: Karen Welke

D-U-N-S 04-110-8510
INTEGRIS JIM THORPE REHABILITATION HOSPITAL
4219 S Western Ave, Oklahoma City, OK 73109-3410
Tel (405) 644-5200 Founded/Ownrshp 2001
Sales 6.9MM^E EMP 300^E
SIC 8093 Rehabilitation center, outpatient treatment; Rehabilitation center, outpatient treatment
*VP: Phil Lance
VP: Ritchie Splitt
Nrsg Dir: Christopher Molo

D-U-N-S 82-980-0825
INTEGRIS PHYSICIANS SERVICES INC
5300 N Independence Ave # 260, Oklahoma City, OK 73112-5556
Tel (405) 951-2529 Founded/Ownrshp 1995
Sales 110.2MM EMP 3
SIC 8742 Management consulting services; Management consulting services
CEO: Stan Hupfeld
*Pr: Lisa Anderson

D-U-N-S 09-967-6400
INTEGRIS RURAL HEALTH INC
INTEGRIS CNDIAN VLY RGNAL HOSP
(Suby of INTEGRIS HEALTH INC) ★
1201 Health Center Pkwy, Yukon, OK 73099-6381
Tel (405) 717-6800 Founded/Ownrshp 1983
Sales 32.8MM^E EMP 300
SIC 8062 General medical & surgical hospitals; General medical & surgical hospitals
*Pr: Jeff Tarrant
*CEO: Bruce Lawrence
*CFO: Cindy White
*Ex VP: Chris Hammes
VP: Alyson Smith
Dir Lab: Veronda Morrison
Dir Rx: Jason Baird
Dir Env Sv: Dewayne Grant
*Prin: Wentz Miller
Sales Exec: Tracy Cain
Mktg Dir: Beverly Gossage

D-U-N-S 96-939-1072
INTEGRIS RURAL HEALTH INC
5300 N Independence Ave # 280, Oklahoma City, OK 73112-5555
Tel (405) 949-6026 Founded/Ownrshp 2011
Sales 282.0MM EMP 2^E
Accts Kpmg Llp Oklahoma City Ok
SIC 8099 Health & allied services; Health & allied services

D-U-N-S 08-256-5755
INTEGRIS RURAL HEALTHCARE OF OKLAHOMA INC
INTEGRIS RURAL HEALTHCARE OKLA
3300 Nw Expwy, Oklahoma City, OK 73112-4418
Tel (405) 949-3011 Founded/Ownrshp 1994
Sales 108.7MM^E EMP 1,896
SIC 8062 6513 General medical & surgical hospitals; Retirement hotel operation; General medical & surgical hospitals; Retirement hotel operation
CEO: Stan Hupfeld
*Pr: Bruce Lawrence
*COO: Tim Johnsen
Doctor: Rajesh Kanagala
Doctor: Paul Maton
Doctor: Robert Rankin
Doctor: Danny Smith
Doctor: Clinton Wallis

INTEGRIS RURAL HEALTHCARE OKLA
See INTEGRIS RURAL HEALTHCARE OF OKLAHOMA INC

D-U-N-S 07-888-5757
INTEGRITY AEROSPACE GROUP INC (MI)
1370 Piedmont Dr, Troy, MI 48083-1917
Tel (248) 613-4155 Founded/Ownrshp 2011
Sales 40.5MM^E EMP 300^E
SIC 7641 X-ray inspection service, industrial; Reupholstery & furniture repair
CEO: Scott Thams

D-U-N-S 04-793-9504
INTEGRITY APPLICATIONS INC
15020 Conference Ctr Dr, Chantilly, VA 20151-3868
Tel (703) 378-8672 Founded/Ownrshp 1998
Sales 111.6M EMP 485
Accts W Filipovitch & Co Carlsba
SIC 8748 7371 Systems engineering consultant, ex. computer or professional; Computer software development; Systems engineering consultant, ex. computer or professional; Computer software development
CEO: Joseph L Brickey
*Pr: Dave Dzaran
Pr: Peter Kimes
Pr: Doug Postman
*CFO: Lee Smith
*Treas: Steven M Wear
Ex VP: David Malka
Sr VP: Victor C See Jr
*VP: Kenneth A Abeloe
VP: Daniel Crisp
VP: Dick Dicsee
*VP: Paul Frommelt
VP: Michael Rigo
VP: Vic See
VP: Robert Thomas
VP: Steven Wear
Board of Directors: Ken Abeloe, Joseph Brickey, Paul Frommelt, Bill Jugus, Mike Rhodes, Steven Wear

D-U-N-S 01-333-2089
INTEGRITY BANK SSB
4040 Washington Ave, Houston, TX 77007-5606
Tel (713) 335-8700 Founded/Ownrshp 2007
Sales NA EMP 25^E
SIC 6021 National commercial banks; National commercial banks
Pr: Charles M Neff Jr
*CFO: James M McElray
Chf Cred: Phil Montgomery
Ofcr: Darla Henry
Ofcr: Chris Henson
Ofcr: Dustin Martin
Ofcr: Debbie Peterson
Ex VP: Deborah Dinsmore
Ex VP: Mike McElray
*Sr VP: Hazem Ahmed
Sr VP: Rick Clark
Sr VP: James Coleman
*Sr VP: Bob Jenkins
*Sr VP: Charlie Phillips
*Sr VP: Jim Smith
*Sr VP: Jerry Tarnopol
VP: Linda Amador-Stephens
*VP: Diane Barnes
VP: Claudia Gutierrez
*VP: Cheryl Murphy

D-U-N-S 08-321-3228
INTEGRITY BUSINESS SOLUTIONS LLC
4740 Talon Ct Se Ste 8, Grand Rapids, MI 49512-5462
Tel (616) 554-2346 Founded/Ownrshp 2001
Sales 97.8MM^E EMP 85
SIC 5112 Office supplies; Office supplies
Genl Mgr: Kevin Knolll

D-U-N-S 62-689-6567 EXP
INTEGRITY COAL SALES INC
905 Marconi Ave, Ronkonkoma, NY 11779-7211
Tel (631) 686-5692 Founded/Ownrshp 1990
Sales 30.0MM^E EMP 15
SIC 5052 5989 Coal; Coal
Pr: Gregory Licata
*Treas: Stacey Lagrega

INTEGRITY DELAWARE HOLDCO
See INTEGRITY INDUSTRIES INC

D-U-N-S 79-633-4477
INTEGRITY EXPRESS LOGISTICS LLC
4370 Malsbary Rd Ste 200, Blue Ash, OH 45242-5653
Tel (888) 374-5138 Founded/Ownrshp 2007
Sales 59.1MM^E EMP 116
SIC 4212 4731 Local trucking, without storage; Truck transportation brokers
Pr: James Steger

D-U-N-S 10-352-9447
INTEGRITY FINANCIAL CORP
39 2nd St Nw, Hickory, NC 28601-6104
Tel (828) 328-5702 Founded/Ownrshp 2001
Sales NA EMP 208
Accts Dixon Hughes Pllc Charlotte
SIC 6022 State commercial banks; State commercial banks
CEO: W Alex Hall Jr
*Ch Bd: David E Cline
*COO: Ronald S Shoemaker
CFO: Susan B Mikels
Bd of Dir: Jack Ferguson
Bd of Dir: H McKenney
Board of Directors: Loretta P Dodgen, Jack Ray Ferguson, Hal F Huffman Jr, Robert P Huntley, W Steve Ikerd, H Ray McKenney Jr, Randy D Miller, Howard Pruitt, Carl G Yale

D-U-N-S 85-887-0806
INTEGRITY FINANCIAL PARTNERS INC
(Suby of INTEGRITY SOLUTION SERVICES INC) ★
4370 W 109th St Ste 100, Overland Park, KS 66211-1316
Tel (913) 312-3333 Founded/Ownrshp 2011
Sales 10.6MM^E EMP 300^E
SIC 7322 Collection agency, except real estate; Collection agency, except real estate
CEO: A L Summerlin
*Pr: Nick Petrini
*COO: Bradley A Lantz
Ofcr: Teri Strahine
VP Sls: Greg Ferrall
VP Sls: Sergio Martinez

INTEGRITY HEALTH CARE
See INTEGRA HEALTHCARE INC

INTEGRITY HEALTH PLUS
See MASH CO SERVICES LLC

D-U-N-S 93-385-2605
INTEGRITY HOME CARE
2960 N Eastgate Ave, Springfield, MO 65803-5746
Tel (417) 889-9773 Founded/Ownrshp 2009
Sales 24.7MM^E EMP 597^E
SIC 8082 8049 Home health care services; Nurses, registered & practical
Pr: Greg Horton
VP: Tara Ferguson
Ex Dir: Sandy Ingram
Rgnl Mgr: Matt Collier
Rgnl Mgr: Lyndsey Normand
CIO: John Dougherty
IT Man: Patrick Maxwell
Doctor: Doug McNeal MD

D-U-N-S 15-408-3075 IMP
INTEGRITY INDUSTRIES INC
INTEGRITY DELAWARE HOLDCO
2710 E Corral Ave, Kingsville, TX 78363-4109
Tel (361) 595-5561 Founded/Ownrshp 2009
Sales 38.3MM^E EMP 96
SIC 2899 5169 2841 Chemical preparations; Drilling mud; Chemicals, industrial & heavy; Detergents, synthetic organic or inorganic alkaline; Chemical preparations; Drilling mud; Chemicals, industrial & heavy; Detergents, synthetic organic or inorganic alkaline
Pr: Max Duncan
*VP: Ernesto Bautista
*VP: Jefffrey L Tepera
CTO: Conrad Garcia

D-U-N-S 79-824-5684
INTEGRITY INSURANCE CO INC
625 From Rd Ste 3, Paramus, NJ 07652-3500
Tel (201) 262-9300 Founded/Ownrshp 1987
Sales NA EMP 75
SIC 6331 Fire, marine & casualty insurance

D-U-N-S 09-314-3485
INTEGRITY INTERNATIONAL SECURITY SERVICES INC
211 University Ave, Clarksville, TN 37040-5127
Tel (931) 647-5384 Founded/Ownrshp 1977
Sales 8.0MM^E EMP 300
SIC 7381 1731 7382 Security guard service; Electrical work; Security systems services; Security guard service; Electrical work; Security systems services
Pr: Rigoberto Rivera

D-U-N-S 07-859-9787
INTEGRITY KOKOSING PIPELINE SERVICES LLC (OH)
IKPS
17531 Waterford Rd, Fredericktown, OH 43019-9561
Tel (740) 694-6315 Founded/Ownrshp 2012
Sales 64.0MM EMP 175
SIC 4613 Gasoline pipelines (common carriers); Gasoline pipelines (common carriers)
CEO: Marsha Rinehart
Pr: Timothy Seibert

D-U-N-S 06-197-7484
INTEGRITY LIFE INSURANCE CO
(Suby of WESTERN & SOUTHERN LIFE INSURANCE CO) ★
400 Broadway St, Cincinnati, OH 45202-3312
Tel (513) 362-8000 Founded/Ownrshp 2000
Sales NA EMP 1^E
SIC 6311 Life insurance
Pr: John R Lindholm
*CFO: Don Cummings
*Treas: Jim Vance
Sr VP: John F O'Connell
VP: David Anderson
*VP: Ed Babbitt
*VP: Dennis L Carr
VP: Paul Kruth
VP: Charles White
Sls Mgr: Bill Diehl

D-U-N-S 86-950-4332
INTEGRITY MARKETING INC
800 W Central Rd Ste 136, Mount Prospect, IL 60056-6511
Tel (847) 632-1440 Founded/Ownrshp 1994
Sales 70.0MM EMP 5
SIC 5149 5141 Groceries & related products; Food brokers
Pr: Robert Scaramuzzi

D-U-N-S 01-624-3404
INTEGRITY METALS
115 S 1st St, Connersville, IN 47331-1948
Tel (765) 825-1136 Founded/Ownrshp 1939, 1976
Sales 69.3MM^E EMP 60^E
SIC 5093 Metal scrap & waste materials; Metal scrap & waste materials
Pr: Price Glazer
COO: Josh Carter
*VP: Martha Glazer

D-U-N-S 00-614-3580
INTEGRITY MUTUAL INSURANCE CO (WI)
2121 E Capitol Dr, Appleton, WI 54911-8726
Tel (920) 734-4511 Founded/Ownrshp 1933
Sales NA EMP 92
SIC 6331 Property damage insurance; Reciprocal interinsurance exchanges: fire, marine, casualty; Property damage insurance; Reciprocal interinsurance exchanges: fire, marine, casualty
Pr: Richard J Schinler
VP: Mary Jo Buchberger
VP: Dean Buffington
VP: Steve Klingemann
VP: Jon Match
VP: Jill Stache
VP: Mary Stadel
VP Mktg: Cathy Beaudin
S&M/VP: Brad Kelly
Mktg Mgr: Jennifer Coopman

D-U-N-S 04-643-7278
INTEGRITY NATIONAL CORP
1738 Elton Rd 311, Silver Spring, MD 20903-1725
Tel (301) 424-8405 Founded/Ownrshp 1997
Sales 13.9MM^E EMP 476^E

SIC 7349 Janitorial service, contract basis; Janitorial service, contract basis
CEO: Michael A Hines
**Pr:* Antoninus H Hines
IT Man: Cynthia Acklin

INTEGRITY NUTRACEUTICALS INTL
See FHG CORP

INTEGRITY QUALITY CARE
See INTEGRAL HEALTH PLAN INC

D-U-N-S 03-494-5326
INTEGRITY REBAR PLACERS
1345 Nandina Ave, Perris, CA 92571-9402
Tel (951) 696-6843 *Founded/Ownrshp* 2005
Sales 29.0MM^E *EMP* 200
SIC 1791 Structural steel erection; Structural steel erection
Pr: Kenneth Negrete
VP: Denise Negrete
**VP:* Richard Rabay

D-U-N-S 78-024-6315
INTEGRITY RETAIL DISTRIBUTION INC
I R D
15221 Canary Ave, La Mirada, CA 90638-5249
Tel (714) 739-2714 *Founded/Ownrshp* 2007
Sales 37.0MM *EMP* 47
SIC 4212 Delivery service, vehicular
Pr: Brad Garberich
Ex VP: Theron Garcia
**VP:* Joe Barich

D-U-N-S 92-847-3024
INTEGRITY SOLUTION SERVICES INC
NARS
20 Corporate Hills Dr, Saint Charles, MO 63301-3749
Tel (636) 530-7985 *Founded/Ownrshp* 1993
Sales 315.5MM^E *EMP* 3,300
SIC 8748 7322 Business consulting; Collection agency, except real estate; Business consulting; Collection agency, except real estate
CEO: Tim Bauer
**Pr:* Harry Jackson

D-U-N-S 17-602-5096
INTEGRITY STAFFING SOLUTIONS INC
700 Prides Xing 300, Newark, DE 19713-6102
Tel (302) 661-8770 *Founded/Ownrshp* 1997
Sales 591.6MM^E *EMP* 26,000
SIC 7363 Temporary help service; Temporary help service
Pr: Todd B Bavol
**CFO:* Sean Montgomery
VP: Deborah Pierce
Rgnl Mgr: Brandon Blanton
Brnch Mgr: Karin Price
Opers Mgr: Diana Bavetz

INTEGRITY STAINLESS
See IS ACQUISITION INC

D-U-N-S 02-326-0604 IMP
INTEGRITY TRACKING LLC (PA)
MOBILE HELP
3701 Fau Blvd Ste 300, Boca Raton, FL 33431-6491
Tel (561) 347-6255 *Founded/Ownrshp* 2006
Sales 23.5MM^E *EMP* 75
SIC 3841 Biopsy instruments & equipment; Diagnostic apparatus, medical; Medical instruments & equipment, blood & bone work; Instruments, microsurgical: except electromedical
CEO: Robert S Flippo
**Pr:* Dennis V Boyle
**CFO:* Joel Richardson
**Ch:* Scott H Adams
**Prin:* Elias Janetis
Mktg Dir: Brenda Stuglik
Board of Directors: Harry Leider

D-U-N-S 01-511-9689
INTEGRITY TRADE SERVICES
10055 W Lincoln Hwy, Frankfort, IL 60423-1272
Tel (815) 277-2914 *Founded/Ownrshp* 2008
Sales 13.0MM^E *EMP* 302
SIC 7361 Employment agencies
CEO: John Cumbee
Mng Dir: Tim Breakey
Opers Mgr: Janice Hernandez
Manager: Sandy Rongstad
Sales Asso: Debbie Nickelson

D-U-N-S 07-031-4053
■ **INTEGRITY URGENT CARE CLINICS INC**
(*Suby of* IMMEDIATE CLINIC HEALTHCARE INC) ★
4323 Integrity Center Pt, Colorado Springs, CO 80917-1683
Tel (719) 591-2558 *Founded/Ownrshp* 2014
Sales 265.5M^E *EMP* 507^E
SIC 8082 8011 8051 Home health care services; Offices & clinics of medical doctors; Skilled nursing care facilities
Pr: Mike Dalton
**Treas:* Soon Burnam

INTEGRO INSURANCE BROKERS
See INTEGRO LTD

D-U-N-S 61-164-9430
INTEGRO LTD
INTEGRO INSURANCE BROKERS
1 State St Fl 9, New York, NY 10004-1817
Tel (212) 295-8000 *Founded/Ownrshp* 2015
Sales NA *EMP* 458
SIC 6411 Insurance brokers; Insurance brokers
Pr: Peter Garvey
Bd of Dir: John Clements
Ex VP: Robert Dunn
Sr VP: Darryl Abbey
Sr VP: Brad Hendrick
Sr VP: Annacarin Jansson
Sr VP: Barbra Massina
Sr VP: Kareen Richardson
Sr VP: John Salvucci
Sr VP: Neal Wallace
VP: Patty Boylan
VP: Jim Farrell
VP: David Herson
VP: Jarrod Hitt
VP: Greg Horun
VP: Kristy Lai
VP: Ed Mascher
VP: Renae Parent
VP: Olivia Peniston
VP: Brendan Traynor
Dir Bus: Matthew Clemo

D-U-N-S 36-334-3232
INTEGRO USA INC
(*Suby of* INTEGRO INSURANCE BROKERS) ★
1 State St Fl 9, New York, NY 10004-1817
Tel (212) 295-8000 *Founded/Ownrshp* 2005
Sales NA *EMP* 300^E
SIC 6411 Insurance agents & brokers; Insurance agents & brokers
Pr: Marc Kunney
**Ch Bd:* Robert Clements
**Pr:* Peter Garvey
**CEO:* Roger Egan Sr
**CFO:* Joe Salerno
Treas: Joe Meyer
Bd of Dir: Jack Byrne

INTEGRTED SYSTEMS GROUP DIV OF
See SPEEDRACK PRODUCTS GROUP LTD

D-U-N-S 82-767-4834
■ **INTEGRYS BUSINESS SUPPORT LLC**
(*Suby of* WEC ENERGY GROUP INC) ★
200 E Randolph St # 2200, Chicago, IL 60601-6433
Tel (312) 240-3877 *Founded/Ownrshp* 2015
Sales 209.9MM^E *EMP* 1,000
SIC 8742 8721 General management consultant; Accounting, auditing & bookkeeping; General management consultant; Accounting, auditing & bookkeeping
Ch: Mark Radtke
Ofcr: Barth Wolf
**VP:* Linda Kallas
**VP:* William D Laakso
**VP:* Phillip M Mikulsky
**VP:* James F Schott
Exec: Sara Hurley

D-U-N-S 87-771-9260
INTEGRYS ENERGY GROUP INC
200 E Randolph St # 2200, Chicago, IL 60601-6433
Tel (312) 228-5400 *Founded/Ownrshp* 1993
Sales 4.1MMM *EMP* 4,888^E
SIC 4931 5172 4911 Electric & other services combined; Fuel oil; Distribution, electric power; Generation, electric power

D-U-N-S 07-989-5916
■ **INTEGRYS HOLDING INC** (WI)
(*FOMERLY: GET ACQUISITION CORP*)
(*Suby of* WEC ENERGY GROUP INC) ★
231 W Michigan St, Milwaukee, WI 53201
Tel (414) 221-2345 *Founded/Ownrshp* 1993, 2015
Sales 1.6MMM^E *EMP* 1,337^E
SIC 4931 Electric & other services combined
Ch Bd: Gale E Klappa
**Pr:* Allen L Leverett
**CFO:* J Patrick Keyes
VP: Stephen P Dickson

D-U-N-S 61-757-4889 IMP
INTEK AMERICA INC
18528 S Dminguez Hills Dr, Rancho Dominguez, CA 90220-6415
Tel (310) 213-9886 *Founded/Ownrshp* 2005
Sales 28.1MM *EMP* 24
SIC 5087 Shredders, industrial & commercial
Pr: Herman Chang
Ex VP: Seung Lee
Sls Mgr: Juan Wozniak

D-U-N-S 04-385-4876
INTEK PLASTICS INC (MN)
1000 Spiral Blvd, Hastings, MN 55033-3916
Tel (651) 437-3805 *Founded/Ownrshp* 1960, 1984
Sales 50.2MM^E *EMP* 250^E
SIC 3089 Plastic hardware & building products; Extruded finished plastic products; Plastic hardware & building products; Extruded finished plastic products
CEO: Jill Hesselroth
**Pr:* Mike Kinning
**COO:* Steve Glienke
**CFO:* Dave Watling
Sr VP: Martin McLean
Plnt Mgr: James Southcotte
Ql Cn Mgr: Jim Peterson

D-U-N-S 04-789-7855 IMP
▲ **INTEL CORP**
2200 Mission College Blvd, Santa Clara, CA 95054-1549
Tel (408) 765-8080 *Founded/Ownrshp* 1968
Sales 55.8MMM *EMP* 106,700^E
Tkr Sym INTC *Exch* NGS
SIC 3674 3577 7372 Microprocessors; Microcircuits, integrated (semiconductor); Computer logic modules; Memories, solid state; Application computer software; Telephone & telegraph apparatus; Computer peripheral equipment; Semiconductors & related devices; Microprocessors; Microcircuits, integrated (semiconductor); Memories, solid state; Computer peripheral equipment; Prepackaged software; Application computer software
CEO: Brian M Krzanich
**Ch Bd:* Andy D Bryant
Pr: Leslie L Vadasz
CFO: Stacy J Smith
Ex VP: William M Holt
Ex VP: Paul S Otellini
Sr VP: Anand Chandrasekher
Sr VP: Gregory R Pearson
Sr VP: Christopher Young
VP: Scott Coleman
VP: Deborah S Conrad
VP: Robert Crooke
VP: Aicha Evans
VP: Amir Faintuch
VP: Anne B Gundelfinger
VP: Jai K Hakhu
VP: John N Johnson
VP: Ann B Kelleher
VP: Cary Klafter
VP: Joe Mele
VP: Suzan A Miller
Board of Directors: Charlene Barshefsky, Susan L Decker, John J Donahoe, Reed E Hundt, James D Plummer, David S Pottruck, Frank D Yeary, David B Yoffie

D-U-N-S 96-017-1981
INTEL FOUNDATION
5200 Ne Elam Young Pkwy, Hillsboro, OR 97124-6497
Tel (503) 696-8080 *Founded/Ownrshp* 1988
Sales 43.5MM *EMP* 6
SIC 8699 Charitable organization; Charitable organization
Ch: Craig Barrett
**Pr:* Wendy Hawkins
**Sec:* Leslie Culbertson
**Sec:* Patty Murray
Ex Dir: Peter Broffman

D-U-N-S 05-421-5186
■ **INTEL MASSACHUSETTS INC**
(*Suby of* INTEL CORP) ★
75 Reed Rd, Hudson, MA 01749-2895
Tel (978) 553-4000 *Founded/Ownrshp* 1997
Sales 141.4MM^E *EMP* 900
SIC 3674 Integrated circuits, semiconductor networks, etc.; Integrated circuits, semiconductor networks, etc.
Pr: Arvind Sodhani
Brnch Mgr: Ed Caldwell
IT Man: Gary Reinking
IT Man: Kelly Stinson
IT Man: Jan Wilson
Tech Mgr: Shay Goyal
Tech Mgr: Tony Piscopo
Sftwr Eng: Michael Zhao
Mtls Mgr: Andrew Curtis
Opers Mgr: Sue Strittmatter
Mktg Mgr: Kristen Hardeman

D-U-N-S 07-887-2634
■ **INTEL MEDIA INC**
(*Suby of* INTEL CORP) ★
2200 Mission College Blvd, Santa Clara, CA 95054-1549
Tel (408) 765-0063 *Founded/Ownrshp* 1999
Sales 33.2M *EMP* 350
SIC 4841 Subscription television services; Subscription television services
Pr: Erik Huggers
Counsel: Brian J Fox

D-U-N-S 17-309-4004
■ **INTEL NETWORK SYSTEMS INC**
(*Suby of* INTEL CORP) ★
77 Reed Rd, Hudson, MA 01749-2809
Tel (978) 553-4000 *Founded/Ownrshp* 1999
Sales 47.1MM^E *EMP* 239
SIC 3577 7373 Computer peripheral equipment; Systems integration services; Computer peripheral equipment; Systems integration services
Ch: Craig Barrett
VP: David Lourie
VP: Angelo Santineloi
VP: Tom Smith
Prin: Dale Myers
Prgrm Mgr: Phillip Sidney
Rgnl Mgr: James Hajjar
Genl Mgr: Jeffrey Dawkins
Snr Sftwr: Saptarshi Mondal
Dir IT: Clayton Bogusky
IT Man: Madjid Far

D-U-N-S 14-156-7953
INTELENET AMERICA LLC
(*Suby of* GODREJ UPSTREAM LIMITED)
1001 28th St S, Fargo, ND 58103-2372
Tel (701) 280-5200 *Founded/Ownrshp* 2003
Sales 31.9MM^E *EMP* 670
SIC 7389 Telephone answering service; Telephone answering service
VP: Jeff Jacobson

D-U-N-S 11-262-0112
INTELEPEER CLOUD COMMUNICATIONS LLC
177 Bovet Rd Ste 400, San Mateo, CA 94402-3120
Tel (650) 525-9200 *Founded/Ownrshp* 2002
Sales 46.9MM^E *EMP* 106
SIC 4813 Data telephone communications; Telephone/video communications
Pr: Frank Fawzi
**CFO:* Andre Simone
**Sr VP:* Phil Bronsdon
Sr VP: John Hart
Off Mgr: Michael Schirmer
VP Sls: Todd Smith
Mktg Dir: Brad Parisian
Board of Directors: Lawrence Irving, Ray Smets

D-U-N-S 13-892-6998
▲ **INTELIQUENT INC**
550 W Adams St Fl 9, Chicago, IL 60661-3636
Tel (312) 384-8000 *Founded/Ownrshp* 2004
Sales 220.5MM *EMP* 160
Tkr Sym IQNT *Exch* NGS
SIC 4813 ;
Pr: Matthew Carter Jr
**Ch Bd:* James P Hynes
CFO: Kurt J Abkemeier
Ex VP: John T Bullock
Ex VP: John M Schoder
Ex VP: Brett A Scorza
Sr VP: Richard L Monto
Sr VP: Ian Neale
VP: Eric R Carlson
VP: Charles Drexler
VP: Dave Tatak
Board of Directors: Joseph A Beatty, Edward M Greenberg, Lawrence M Ingeneri, Timothy A Samples, Rian J Wren, Lauren F Wright

D-U-N-S 01-688-7346
■ **INTELISPEND PREPAID SOLUTIONS LLC**
(*Suby of* BLACKHAWK NETWORK HOLDINGS INC) ★
1400 S Highway Dr, Fenton, MO 63026-2281
Tel (636) 226-2000 *Founded/Ownrshp* 2013
Sales 29.1MM^E *EMP* 125
SIC 8742 Incentive or award program consultant
Pr: Jim Menadier
COO: Sheree Thornsberry
CFO: Russ Yergensen
VP: Deanna Baker
VP: Bill Beck
VP: Kathleen Bibbins
VP: Dan Easley
VP: Wendy Harp-Lewis
VP: Martin Hood
VP: Duwayne Milner
VP: Lawrence J Newman
VP: Dan Sanders
VP: Michele Sullender

D-U-N-S 01-174-7982
INTELLECTUAL VENTURES LLC
3150 139th Ave Se Ste 500, Bellevue, WA 98005-4046
Tel (425) 467-2300 *Founded/Ownrshp* 1999
Sales 159.7MM^E *EMP* 500^E
SIC 7379 ;
Pr: Adriane Brown
COO: Eben Frankenberg
CFO: Larry Froeber
**Ex VP:* Chris Alliegro
**Ex VP:* Andy Elder
Ex VP: Masanobu Katoh
**Ex VP:* David Kris
Ex VP: Gregory Landis
**Ex VP:* Casey T Tegreene
Ex VP: Loria Yeadon
Sr VP: Mona Locke
VP: Geoff Deane
VP: Eric Nagel
VP: Keith Schorsch
VP: Maurizio Vecchione
Exec: Camilla McMillan
Assoc Dir: John S Foster Jr
Dir Bus: Russell Hannigan

INTELLI-TECH
See INTELLIGENT VAR TECHNOLOGY

INTELLICLAIM, CLAIMSLINK
See CEI GROUP INC

D-U-N-S 04-869-0650
INTELLIDYNE LLC
2677 Prosperity Ave # 301, Fairfax, VA 22031-4928
Tel (703) 575-9715 *Founded/Ownrshp* 1998
Sales 47.9MM^E *EMP* 275
SIC 7379 Computer related consulting services; Computer related consulting services
CEO: Tony Crescenzo
Pr: Robert L Grey
COO: Ed Abner
CFO: Joseph W Kuhn
CFO: Carlos Salazar
Ex VP: Joseph G Felber
Ex VP: Shirl Jenkins
Sr VP: Michael Monroe
Sr VP: Leo Peterson
VP: Bill Boyd
VP: Shirl L Jenkins

INTELLIEPI
See INTELLIGENT EPITAXY TECHNOLOGY INC

D-U-N-S 78-700-0269
INTELLIGENCE COMMUNICATIONS AND ENGINEERING INC
ICE-PS
1850 Paseo San Luis, Sierra Vista, AZ 85635-4612
Tel (520) 458-4321 *Founded/Ownrshp* 2006
Sales 25.3MM *EMP* 230
Accts Bleachfleischaman Pc Tucson
SIC 7373 4899 8711 8748 8299 7379 Systems software development services; Computer-aided engineering (CAE) systems service; Data communication services; Engineering services; Systems engineering consultant, ex. computer or professional; Personal development school; Computer related maintenance services
CEO: Danny Avant
**Pr:* Edward Molina
**VP:* Melvin Albert
**VP:* David Olson
Sftwr Eng: James Hachtel

INTELLIGENCER, THE
See OGDEN NEWSPAPERS INC

INTELLIGENCER/RECORD THE
See CALKINS MEDIA INC

D-U-N-S 16-191-1532
INTELLIGENT AUTOMATION INC
15400 Calhoun Dr Ste 190, Rockville, MD 20855-2814
Tel (301) 294-5200 *Founded/Ownrshp* 1987
Sales 30.0MM *EMP* 115
Accts Aronson Llc Rockville Maryla
SIC 8711 Consulting engineer; Consulting engineer
Pr: Vikram Manikonda
**Ch Bd:* Joseph Schwartz
**Pr:* Leonard S Haynes
**Ex VP:* Jacqueline A Haynes
**VP:* Benjamin Bachrach
**VP:* Chujen Lin
**VP:* Roger Xu

D-U-N-S 62-699-0530 IMP
INTELLIGENT BEAUTY LLC
IQ COSMETICS
2301 Rosecrans Ave # 4110, El Segundo, CA 90245-4966
Tel (310) 683-0940 *Founded/Ownrshp* 2006
Sales NA *EMP* 550^E
SIC 5999 2844 Cosmetics; Cosmetic preparations

D-U-N-S 06-896-9984
INTELLIGENT CONSUMER HOLDINGS LLC
ALL CONNECT
980 Hammond Dr Ste 1000, Atlanta, GA 30328-8187
Tel (404) 260-2200 *Founded/Ownrshp* 1996
Sales 182.3MM^E *EMP* 830
SIC 7299 Information services, consumer; Information services, consumer
Sr VP: Ron Carpinella
VP: Matt Williams
Software D: Dmitry Dmitriev

Sftwr Eng: Gayatri Desai
VP Mktg: Jagdish N Sheth
Mktg Mgr: Mark Lister

D-U-N-S 08-688-2867 IMP
■ INTELLIGENT CONTROLS INC
INCON
(*Suby of* FRANKLIN ELECTRIC CO INC) ★
34 Spring Hill Rd, Saco, ME 04072-9651
Tel (207) 571-1123 *Founded/Ownrshp* 2002
Sales 21.6MM^E *EMP* 90^E
SIC 3829 Measuring & controlling devices
Pr: Scott Trumbull
**Pr:* Greg Sengstack
Mktg Mgr: Jeff Golarz

D-U-N-S 61-856-3720
INTELLIGENT DECISIONS INC
21445 Beaumeade Cir, Ashburn, VA 20147-6036
Tel (703) 554-1600 *Founded/Ownrshp* 1988
Sales 139.9MM^E *EMP* 400
SIC 3571 5045

D-U-N-S 80-719-8952
INTELLIGENT DOCUMENT SOLUTIONS INC
IDS.COM
747 E Whitcomb Ave, Madison Heights, MI 48071-1409
Tel (248) 588-2415 *Founded/Ownrshp* 2014
Sales 24.5MM^E *EMP* 97^E
SIC 2752 Atlas & map printing, lithographic
CEO: William Hayden
Pr: Wendy Lokken

INTELLIGENT ENERGY
See INFINITE ENERGY INC

D-U-N-S 05-980-3945 IMP
INTELLIGENT EPITAXY TECHNOLOGY INC
INTELLIEPI
1250 E Collins Blvd, Richardson, TX 75081-2401
Tel (972) 234-0068 *Founded/Ownrshp* 1998
Sales 22.0MM *EMP* 50
SIC 3674 Wafers (semiconductor devices); Semiconductor circuit networks
Pr: Yung Chung KAO
**VP:* Jenn-Ming Kuo
VP: Jenmming Kuo
VP: Paul Pinsukanjana
VP Opers: Kevin Vargason

D-U-N-S 07-940-5385
INTELLIGENT INVESTMENTS LLC (SC)
1010 Park Dr, Myrtle Beach, SC 29577-4362
Tel (980) 989-4016 *Founded/Ownrshp* 2011
Sales 765.0MM *EMP* 10
SIC 6726 7389 Investment offices;
CEO: Antonio Johnson
COO: Demarko Terrell Lee
COO: Jose Pastrana

D-U-N-S 61-479-5743
INTELLIGENT MANUFACTURING SOLUTONS LLC
645 Harvey Rd, Manchester, NH 03103-3323
Tel (603) 296-1160 *Founded/Ownrshp* 2005
Sales 25.4MM^E *EMP* 40
SIC 5065 Electronic parts

D-U-N-S 01-475-9092
INTELLIGENT PRODUCT SOLUTIONS INC (NY)
I P S
700 Veterans Hwy Ste 100, Hauppauge, NY 11788-2929
Tel (631) 676-7744 *Founded/Ownrshp* 2007
Sales 22.2MM^E *EMP* 88
SIC 8711 Engineering services
Pr: Mitch Maimen
**Ex VP:* Paul Severino
**Sr VP:* Rob Stein
**VP:* Hilary Farnsworth
**VP:* Derek Peterson
Mng Dir: Dan Blase
Prgrm Mgr: John Carricato
IT Man: Rick Isbitiren
Sftwr Eng: Justin Adams
Sftwr Eng: Hrushikesh Bhatt
Sftwr Eng: Anthony Gray

D-U-N-S 96-351-9939
INTELLIGENT SOFTWARE SOLUTIONS INC
I S S
5450 Tech Center Dr # 400, Colorado Springs, CO 80919-2339
Tel (719) 452-7000 *Founded/Ownrshp* 1997
Sales 160.4MM^E *EMP* 525
Accts Eks & H Llp Denver Colorado
SIC 7371 Computer software development; Computer software development
Pr: Jay Jesse
**CFO:* Nikki Herman
Ofcr: Wes Caldwell
**VP:* Lisa Jesse
**VP:* Dennis Linn
**VP:* Jesse Miller
VP: Laine Napier
VP: Rob Rogers

D-U-N-S 15-285-8361 EXP
INTELLIGENT SWITCHGEAR ORGANIZATION LLC
I S O
(*Suby of* EATON CORP) ★
4955 Marconi Dr, Alpharetta, GA 30005-8894
Tel (770) 442-9442 *Founded/Ownrshp* 2003
Sales 23.1MM^E *EMP* 242
SIC 3613 7629 Switchgear & switchgear accessories; Electrical repair shops; Electrical equipment repair services; Switchgear & switchgear accessories; Electrical repair shops; Electrical equipment repair services
Pr: Gustavo Cedeno
IT Man: Cristy McAdams
Mktg Mgr: Bart Cranford
Sales Asso: Jim Latimer
Sales Asso: Bruce Newhouse

D-U-N-S 01-645-3321 IMP
INTELLIGENT TECHNOLOGIES LLC
ITECH
9454 Waples St, San Diego, CA 92121-2919
Tel (858) 458-1500 *Founded/Ownrshp* 1997
Sales 28.9MM^E *EMP* 82
SIC 3829 Measuring & controlling devices; Measuring & controlling devices
CEO: Donald A Kutz
**Ex VP:* Frank Cooper
**VP:* Carl Gallenson
Prgrm Mgr: Mark Sickinger
Genl Mgr: Steven Warren
IT Man: Shari Mraz
Sls Mgr: Wayne Bolin

D-U-N-S 79-311-0446
INTELLIGENT VAR TECHNOLOGY
INTELLI-TECH
1652 Yeager Ave, La Verne, CA 91750-5853
Tel (909) 394-5188 *Founded/Ownrshp* 1992
Sales 36.3MM^E *EMP* 30
SIC 5045 7373 Computer peripheral equipment; Computer software; Computer integrated systems design
CEO: Cynthia Johnson
**Pr:* Darrell Johnson
Dir IT: Darrell Welch
Sales Asso: Nadine Peters

D-U-N-S 07-880-2844
INTELLIGRATED SOFTWARE LLC
KNIGHTED, LLC
(*Suby of* INTELLIGRATED SYSTEMS LLC) ★
555 Taxter Rd, Elmsford, NY 10523-2336
Tel (678) 366-8066 *Founded/Ownrshp* 2012
Sales 50.0MM *EMP* 200
SIC 7371 Computer software development
Ex VP: Kevin Roach
VP: Mike Barker
Sftwr Eng: Vincent Aguirre
VP Opers: Paul Allen

D-U-N-S 08-328-1845
INTELLIGRATED SYSTEMS INC
7901 Innovation Way, Mason, OH 45040-9498
Tel (866) 936-7300 *Founded/Ownrshp* 1996
Sales 1.2MMM^E *EMP* 2,800
SIC 3535 5084 7371 Conveyors & conveying equipment; Industrial machinery & equipment; Computer software development; Conveyors & conveying equipment; Industrial machinery & equipment; Computer software development
CEO: Chris Cole
**Pr:* Jim McCarthy
**CFO:* Ed Puisis
Bd of Dir: Robert Forlenza
Ex VP: Steve Ackerman
Ex VP: Gregory Cronin
Ex VP: Kevin Roach
Ex VP: Kevin V Roach
Ex VP: Jim Sharp
Sr VP: John Cullen
VP: Chris Arnold
VP: Dick Braatz
VP: Cyril Crawford
VP: Crawford Cyril
VP: Michael Hession
VP: Alan Oppenheim
VP: Eric Palotas
VP: Craig Turner
Dir Bus: Bill Natsch

D-U-N-S 06-468-1054
INTELLIGRATED SYSTEMS LLC
(*Suby of* INTELLIGRATED SYSTEMS INC) ★
7901 Innovation Way, Mason, OH 45040-9498
Tel (513) 701-7300 *Founded/Ownrshp* 2001
Sales 378.7MM^E *EMP* 2,300
SIC 3535 5084 7371 Conveyors & conveying equipment; Materials handling machinery; Computer software development; Conveyors & conveying equipment; Materials handling machinery; Computer software development
CEO: Chris Cole
Pr: Dennis Gates
**Pr:* Jim McCarthy
**CFO:* Ed Puisis
**Sr VP:* Jim McKnight
**VP:* Bryan Jones
Genl Mgr: Amy Ball
CTO: Ray Neiser
CTO: Raymond Neiser
Sales Exec: Richard Scheiring
Sls Mgr: Scott Gillette

D-U-N-S 00-626-6001 IMP
INTELLIGRATED SYSTEMS OF OHIO LLC (DE)
(*Suby of* INTELLIGRATED SYSTEMS INC) ★
7901 Innovation Way, Mason, OH 45040-9498
Tel (314) 993-4700 *Founded/Ownrshp* 2010, 2009
Sales 162.4MM^E *EMP* 2,800
SIC 3535 5084 3537 Conveyors & conveying equipment; Industrial machinery & equipment; Palletizers & depalletizers; Conveyors & conveying equipment; Industrial machinery & equipment; Palletizers & depalletizers
Pr: Jim McCarthy
**Ex VP:* Stephen Ackerman
Ex VP: Chuck Waddle
Sr VP: Bill Harton
Sr VP: Ken Thouvenot
VP: Richard Braatz
**VP:* Stephen Causey
VP: Ted Clucas
VP: Wes Goode
VP: Robert Miller
VP: Frank Pellegrino
VP: Chris Roach
VP: Matt Wicks

D-U-N-S 14-460-7160
■ INTELLINEX LLC
ACS LEARNING SERVICES
(*Suby of* XEROX BUSINESS SERVICES LLC) ★
6000 Fredom Sq Dr Ste 100, Independence, OH 44131
Tel (216) 685-6000 *Founded/Ownrshp* 2006
Sales 125.0MM *EMP* 325
SIC 4813 ;
Mng Dir: Richard Klingshirn
VP: Rachelle Ussery
VP Opers: Leo Blankenship

D-U-N-S 60-122-4512
INTELLIPOWER INC
1746 N Saint Thomas Cir, Orange, CA 92865-4247
Tel (714) 921-1580 *Founded/Ownrshp* 1988
Sales 22.0MM^E *EMP* 100
SIC 3677 Transformers power supply, electronic type
CEO: G W Bill Shipman
VP: George Vuduc
Off Mgr: Jerry Beverly

D-U-N-S 87-728-1613
INTELLIPRO GROUP INC
2905 Stender Way Ste 42, Santa Clara, CA 95054-3224
Tel (408) 200-9891 *Founded/Ownrshp* 2009
Sales 16.0MM^E *EMP* 380
SIC 7379 Computer related consulting services; Computer related consulting services
CEO: Grace MA

D-U-N-S 11-351-3753
INTELLIQUICK DELIVERY INC
4022 S 20th St, Phoenix, AZ 85040-1483
Tel (602) 224-0033 *Founded/Ownrshp* 1998
Sales 21.2MM^E *EMP* 74^E
SIC 4513 4215 7389 Air courier services; Courier services, except by air; Courier or messenger service
CEO: Keith A Spizzirri
CFO: Karen Gilette
CFO: Karen Gillette
Dir IT: Douglas Hunt
IT Man: Devon Blaylock
Trfc Dir: Alton Hardy

D-U-N-S 03-159-2467
INTELLIRISK MANAGEMENT CORP
(*Suby of* IQOR US INC) ★
335 Madison Ave Fl 27, New York, NY 10017-4653
Tel (646) 274-3030 *Founded/Ownrshp* 1998
Sales 82.4MM^E *EMP* 6,000
SIC 7322 Adjustment & collection services; Adjustment & collection services
Ex VP: Norm Meritt
**CFO:* Paul Clark
**Ex VP:* Christopher Dorval
**Ex VP:* Barry Grant
**Ex VP:* Greg Harmer
**Ex VP:* Gary Praznik
**Ex VP:* Graeme Stirrett
**Sr VP:* James Wallace
VP: Judah Kaplan

D-U-N-S 83-155-3834
INTELLISIST INC
SPOKEN COMMUNICATIONS
2101 4th Ave, Seattle, WA 98121-2352
Tel (206) 428-6044 *Founded/Ownrshp* 2005
Sales 76.0MM^E *EMP* 660^E
SIC 7389 Telemarketing services; Telemarketing services
CEO: Howard Lee
**Pr:* Cathy Bradley
CFO: Ty Graham
CFO: Robin Krueger
**Ex VP:* David Milstein
VP: Cliff Harlow
VP: Jude Kavalam
**Prin:* Dan Karr
Off Mgr: Tonia Lopez-Song
Software D: Kindah Sakkal
Netwrk Eng: Kathy Hodges
Board of Directors: Simon Crosby

D-U-N-S 09-033-8422
INTELLISOURCE LLC
1899 Wynkoop St Ste 900, Denver, CO 80202-1093
Tel (303) 692-1100 *Founded/Ownrshp* 1999
Sales 90.0MM *EMP* 7,500
SIC 8742 Management consulting services
CEO: Robyn Donahue
Pr: Brad Levy
**COO:* Ajay Bagal
**Sr VP:* Matt Pollard
Sr VP: Scott Snyder
Exec: Karen Lam
Exec: Scott Walker
Off Mgr: Jennifer Rogers
Off Admin: Selena Rivera
CTO: Hector Nunez
Mktg Mgr: Kristen Hitner

D-U-N-S 00-939-1137
INTELLISPACE EVENT MANAGEMENT
(*Suby of* KONINKLIJKE PHILIPS N.V.)
8051 Congress Ave Ste 400, Boca Raton, FL 33487-1346
Tel (561) 361-6990 *Founded/Ownrshp* 2008
Sales 50.3MM^E *EMP* 900^E
SIC 7371 5045 Computer software development; Computer software; Computer software development; Computer software
CEO: Steve Rusckowski
CFO: Peter Kammerer
**VP:* Robert Flippo
VP Sls: Moe Kirk
Mktg Dir: Katherine Overby
Mktg Mgr: James Bennett
Sls Mgr: Chris Andreski
Sls Mgr: Jeannette Gainey

D-U-N-S 10-672-4235
INTELLISWIFT SOFTWARE INC
MAGAGNINI
2201 Walnut Ave, Fremont, CA 94538-2334
Tel (510) 490-9240 *Founded/Ownrshp* 2001
Sales 96.0MM^E *EMP* 325
SIC 7379 Computer related consulting services; Computer related consulting services
CEO: Parag Patel
Ex VP: Rahul Garg
VP: John Magagnini
**Prin:* Bob Patel
Genl Mgr: Huzefa Poonawala
IT Man: Rekha Shetty
IT Man: Haimz Ukil
Opers Mgr: Amit Kansal
Sls&Mrk Ex: Tiffany Tran

D-U-N-S 83-098-5792
INTELLISYNC CORP
(*Suby of* NOKIA OYJ)
313 Fairchild Dr, Mountain View, CA 94043-2215
Tel (650) 625-2185 *Founded/Ownrshp* 2007
Sales 23.8MM^E *EMP* 456
SIC 7371 7372 Computer software development; Prepackaged software; Computer software development; Prepackaged software
Pr: Woodson Hobbs
COO: Clyde Foster
CFO: David Eichler
CFO: Kelly J Hicks
Chf Mktg O: Robert Gerber
Sr VP: Bob Apollo
VP: Steve Goldberg
VP: Richard Walker

INTELLITECH SOLUTIONS
See DRAGONE TECHNOLOGY SERVICES LLC

D-U-N-S 03-624-4114
INTELOCO
LOGISTICS ONE
33 Cady Hill Blvd, Saratoga Springs, NY 12866-9047
Tel (518) 587-3700 *Founded/Ownrshp* 1997
Sales 20.1MM^E *EMP* 196
SIC 4212 4225 Local trucking, without storage; General warehousing; Local trucking, without storage; General warehousing
Pr: William J McNeary IV
COO: Robert Feldman
CFO: Graham Goffin
**VP:* James M Benham
VP: Jonathan Madden
Sfty Dirs: John Cammarene
Opers Mgr: Joe Tubbs

D-U-N-S 83-980-9159 IMP
INTELSAT CORP
(*Suby of* INTELSAT HOLDING CORP) ★
7900 Tysons One Pl, Mc Lean, VA 22102-5971
Tel (703) 559-6800 *Founded/Ownrshp* 2006
Sales 319.6MM^E *EMP* 1,111
SIC 4841 Direct broadcast satellite services (DBS); Direct broadcast satellite services (DBS)
Ch Bd: David McGlade
**Pr:* Stephen Spengler
**CFO:* Michael McDonnell
**Treas:* Hank Courson
Treas: Kevin Watson
**Ex VP:* Michelle Bryan
**Ex VP:* Thierry Guillemin
Ex VP: Tony Trujillo Jr
Sr VP: Bruce A Haymes
Sr VP: Michael S Liebow
**Sr VP:* Kurt Riegelman
**VP:* Sajid Ajmeri
**VP:* Stephen Chernow
**VP:* Angela Galyean
**VP:* Michael Green
VP: Jay Yass
Exec: Chris Nibecker
Dir Teleco: Amy Voorhees

D-U-N-S 12-719-0358
INTELSAT GENERAL CORP
(*Suby of* INTELSAT USA SALES CORP) ★
7900 Tysons One Pl Ste 12, Mc Lean, VA 22102-5979
Tel (703) 270-4200 *Founded/Ownrshp* 2002
Sales 34.4MM^E *EMP* 90
SIC 4899 Data communication services
Pr: Kay Sears
**Prin:* David Agatston
**Prin:* Joseph Uglialoro

D-U-N-S 06-485-7527 IMP
INTELSAT GLOBAL SERVICE LLC
(*Suby of* INTELSAT SA)
7900 Tysons One Pl, Mc Lean, VA 22102-5971
Tel (703) 559-7129 *Founded/Ownrshp* 2013
Sales 311.7MM^E *EMP* 873
SIC 4899 Data communication services; Data communication services
Ch Bd: Thierry Guillemin
VP: Conny L Kuman

D-U-N-S 17-589-5452 IMP
INTELSAT HOLDING CORP
(*Suby of* INTELSAT SA)
7900 Tysons One Pl Fl 14, Mc Lean, VA 22102-5972
Tel (202) 703-5599 *Founded/Ownrshp* 2006
Sales 392.9MM^E *EMP* 1,112
SIC 4899 Satellite earth stations; Satellite earth stations
CEO: Stephen Spengler
**COO:* James B Frownfelter
COO: Thierry Guillemin
**CFO:* Jeffrey Freimark
CFO: Michael McDonnell
Ofcr: Nancy Velasquez
**Ex VP:* Michael Antonovich
**Ex VP:* James W Cuminale
**Ex VP:* Phillip Spector
Sr VP: Linda Bartlett
Sr VP: Kurt Riegelman
VP: Carrolyn Bostic
VP: Bruno Fromont
VP: Adam Levy
VP: Mohammad Marashi
VP: Peter Ostapiuk

D-U-N-S 80-104-6533
INTELSAT INTERNATIONAL SYSTEMS LLC
(*Suby of* INTELSAT CORP) ★
3400 Intl Dr Nw Ste 100, Washington, DC 20008
Tel (202) 944-6800 *Founded/Ownrshp* 1997
Sales 14.5MM^E *EMP* 500

SIC 4899 Satellite earth stations; Satellite earth stations
Pr: Joseph Wright Jr
Genl Mgr: Beverly Taylor
CIO: John Stanton

D-U-N-S 12-719-0002 IMP
INTELSAT USA SALES CORP
(*Suby of* INTELSAT GLOBAL SALES & MARKETING LTD.)
7900 Tysons One Pl, Mc Lean, VA 22102-5971
Tel (703) 559-6800 *Founded/Ownrshp* 2001
Sales 385.2MM^E *EMP* 1,300
SIC 4899 Data communication services; Data communication services
CEO: David McGlade
**CFO:* Patricia Casey
**Ex VP:* Michael McDonnell
**Ex VP:* Phillip L Spector
**Ex VP:* Stephen Spengler
**Sr VP:* Thierry Guillemin
**Sr VP:* Kurt Riegelman

D-U-N-S 05-606-2628 IMP/EXP
INTENSE LIGHTING LLC
(*Suby of* LEVITON MANUFACTURING CO INC) ★
3340 E La Palma Ave, Anaheim, CA 92806-2814
Tel (714) 630-9877 *Founded/Ownrshp* 2015
Sales 36.0MM^E *EMP* 80
SIC 3646 3645 Commercial indusl & institutional electric lighting fixtures; Residential lighting fixtures
Pr: Kenny Eidsvold
Pr: Tom Steinkraus
CFO: Shaffiq Rahim
IT Man: Yoon Daniel
VP Opers: Heath Huisken
VP Opers: Nikki Silva
Ql Cn Mgr: Carmen Rodriguez
VP Sls: Pat Jones
VP Sls: Rob Limroth
Mktg Dir: Kristian Johnson
Manager: Greg O'Connor

D-U-N-S 62-219-2362
INTENSIVIST GROUP
(*Suby of* COGENT HEALTHCARE INC) ★
830 W II Route 22, Lake Zurich, IL 60047-2560
Tel (866) 344-0543 *Founded/Ownrshp* 2011
Sales 6.4MM^E *EMP* 417^E
SIC 8011 Offices & clinics of medical doctors
Pr: Jay Cowen
**COO:* Frank M Lucas
**Chf Mktg O:* Stephen Matchett

D-U-N-S 94-818-2944 IMP/EXP
INTEPLAST BAGS AND FILMS CORP
VIAM FILMS
(*Suby of* AMTOPP DIV) ★
1 Interplast Dr, Morristown, TN 37814-2548
Tel (423) 581-6990 *Founded/Ownrshp* 2012
Sales 127.9MM^E *EMP* 170
SIC 2671 Plastic film, coated or laminated for packaging; Plastic film, coated or laminated for packaging
Pr: Homer Hesh
**VP:* Gregg Gillis
VP: Cheryl Huff
Genl Mgr: Martha Martin
Plng Mgr: Peter Schoenhoff
Telecom Ex: Doug Johnson
Prd Mgr: Jeff Burleson

D-U-N-S 78-694-1427 IMP
INTEPLAST GROUP LTD
AMTOPP DIV
9 Peach Tree Hill Rd, Livingston, NJ 07039-5702
Tel (973) 994-8000 *Founded/Ownrshp* 1998
Sales 2.2MMM *EMP* 2,000^E
SIC 3081 Polypropylene film & sheet; Polyethylene film; Polyvinyl film & sheet; Packing materials, plastic sheet; Polypropylene film & sheet; Polyethylene film; Polyvinyl film & sheet; Packing materials, plastic sheet
Pr: John Young
**Pr:* Homer Hsieh
**CFO:* Robert Wang
VP: Dick Heinle
VP: Paul Huang
VP: Victor Shen
Dir Rx: Ting Chan
Dir Rx: Andy Chen
Dir Bus: Bill Sweaney
Rgnl Mgr: Dan Taylor
CTO: Gary WEI

D-U-N-S 14-804-5701
■ **INTER AMERICAN PRODUCTS INC**
KENLAKE FOODS
(*Suby of* KROGER CO) ★
1240 State Ave, Cincinnati, OH 45204-1728
Tel (800) 645-2233 *Founded/Ownrshp* 1989
Sales 235.9MM^E *EMP* 3,000^E
SIC 2095 2099 2033 2079 2087 2022 Roasted coffee; Spices, including grinding; Jellies, edible, including imitation: in cans, jars, etc.; Preserves, including imitation: in cans, jars, etc.; Salad oils, except corn: vegetable refined; Concentrates, drink; Processed cheese; Natural cheese; Roasted coffee; Spices, including grinding; Jellies, edible, including imitation: in cans, jars, etc.; Preserves, including imitation: in cans, jars, etc.; Salad oils, except corn: vegetable refined; Concentrates, drink; Processed cheese; Natural cheese
CEO: David B Dillon
**Pr:* Rodney McMullen
**Genl Mgr:* Bill Lucia

D-U-N-S 02-276-6935 EXP
INTER CITY OIL CO INC
I C O
1923 South St, Duluth, MN 55812-2042
Tel (218) 728-3641 *Founded/Ownrshp* 1990
Sales 35.6MM^E *EMP* 183
SIC 5541 5411 5983 5172 Filling stations, gasoline; Convenience stores, chain; Fuel oil dealers; Gasoline; Filling stations, gasoline; Convenience stores, chain; Fuel oil dealers; Gasoline
Pr: Judy L Weber
**Sec:* Donna K Flesher

INTER COMMUNITY HOSPITAL
See CITRUS VALLEY HEALTH PARTNERS INC

INTER CONNECT SVCS GROUP II
See NETWORK BILLING SYSTEMS LLC

D-U-N-S 01-907-9667
INTER CONTINENTAL SAN JUAN
INTERCONTINENTAL SAN JUAN
596 Isla Verde Av Rsort C, Carolina, PR 00979
Tel (787) 982-4253 *Founded/Ownrshp* 2011
Sales 11.0MM^E *EMP* 487
SIC 7011

INTER FIT HEALTH
See REDICLINIC LLC

D-U-N-S 06-744-8142
INTER LOCAL PENSION FUND INC
455 Kehoe Blvd Ste 100, Carol Stream, IL 60188-5203
Tel (630) 752-8400 *Founded/Ownrshp* 1950
Sales NA *EMP* 5
SIC 6371 Pension funds; Pension funds
Ex Dir: Elizabeth Jacobs
Off Mgr: Carrie Paragon

D-U-N-S 04-558-2376
INTER MOUNTAIN CABLE INC
IMCTV
20 Laynesville Rd, Harold, KY 41635-9076
Tel (606) 478-9406 *Founded/Ownrshp* 1965
Sales 20.3MM *EMP* 35^E
Accts Alan M Zumstein Cpa Lexingt
SIC 4841 Cable television services
Pr: Paul R Gearheart
**CFO:* James Campbell
**Treas:* Susan Gearheart-Schmoldt
**VP:* Paul D Gearheart
Dir IT: Susan Schmoldt
Opers Mgr: Jefferson Thacker

D-U-N-S 15-181-8556
INTER NATIONAL BANK
(*Suby of* INB FINANCIAL CORP) ★
1801 S 2nd St, McAllen, TX 78503-1353
Tel (956) 664-8400 *Founded/Ownrshp* 1985
Sales NA *EMP* 50^E
SIC 6021 National commercial banks; National commercial banks
Pr: Samuel J Munafo
COO: Jorje Melendez
CFO: Edgar Maldonado
Ex VP: Marin J Espinosa
Sr VP: Valerie Cardenas
Sr VP: Manuel Casanova
Sr VP: Alberto De Llano
Sr VP: Elodia Delagarza
Sr VP: Elodia Garza
Sr VP: David Puig
Sr VP: Oscar Rodriguez
VP: Mary Campos
VP: Sonia Cano
VP: Gustavo Castro
VP: Eduardo Chavez
VP: Amelia Cisneros
VP: Yvette Corona
VP: Esmer Doughterty
VP: Heraclio Flores
VP: Esther Howard
VP: Miles Hutchinson

INTER OCEAN
See INTER-OCEAN SEAFOOD TRADER

D-U-N-S 03-317-0648
INTER PACIFIC MOTORS INC
ORCHID ISLE AUTO CENTER
1030 Kanoelehua Ave, Hilo, HI 96720-5263
Tel (808) 935-1191 *Founded/Ownrshp* 1966
Sales 34.2MM^E *EMP* 88
SIC 5511 5531 7538 New & used car dealers; Automobile & truck equipment & parts; General automotive repair shops; New & used car dealers; Automobile & truck equipment & parts; General automotive repair shops
Pr: Joseph W Hanley Sr
**Pr:* Joseph W Hanley Jr
**Treas:* Caroline Kekaualua
Sls Mgr: Jay M Blake

D-U-N-S 16-113-5447 IMP
▲ **INTER PARFUMS INC**
551 5th Ave, New York, NY 10176-0001
Tel (212) 983-2640 *Founded/Ownrshp* 1985
Sales 499.2MM *EMP* 298^E
Tkr Sym IPAR *Exch* NGS
SIC 2844 Toilet preparations; Perfumes & colognes; Cosmetic preparations; Toilet preparations; Perfumes & colognes; Cosmetic preparations
Ch Bd: Jean Madar
**V Ch:* Philippe Benacin
Pr: Andy Clarke
Pr: Kellie Como
COO: Stanislas Archambault
**CFO:* Russell Greenberg
VP: Gregory Reznik
VP Opers: Laura Marinelli
Board of Directors: Robert Bensoussan, Patrick Choel, Michel Dyens, Francois Heilbronn, Jean Levy

INTER TREND
See DEEP FOODS INC

D-U-N-S 60-964-3630
INTER-AGENCY COUNCIL OF MENTAL RETARDATION & DEVELOPMENTAL DISABILITIES AGENCIES INC
150 W 30th St Fl 15, New York, NY 10001-4138
Tel (212) 645-6360 *Founded/Ownrshp* 1974
Sales 45.4MM *EMP* 7
SIC 8621 Medical field-related associations; Medical field-related associations
Dir IT: Fausto Then
Info Man: Chanel Ramsay

D-U-N-S 00-325-4513
INTER-AMERICAN DEVELOPMENT BANK
BANCO INTERAMERICANO DE DESAR
1300 New York Ave Nw, Washington, DC 20577-0001
Tel (202) 623-1000 *Founded/Ownrshp* 1952
Sales NA *EMP* 2,000^E
Accts Kpmg Llp Washington Dc
SIC 6082 Foreign trade & international banking institutions; Foreign trade & international banking institutions
Pr: Luis A Moreno
V Ch: Robert J Deal Jr
COO: Julie T Katzman
CFO: Claudia De Colstoun
**CFO:* Gustavo De Rosa
Treas: Otto Gutierrez
Treas: Charles O Sethness
Bd of Dir: Jose Cartas
Bd of Dir: Alan Gill
Ofcr: Ellen Mitchell
VP: Santiago Levy Algazi
VP: K B Dillon
VP: Jaime Sujoy

D-U-N-S 62-755-1237
INTER-AMERICAN OIL WORKS INC
2416 N Fm 1936, Odessa, TX 79763-5980
Tel (432) 381-1757 *Founded/Ownrshp* 2008
Sales 39.1MM^E *EMP* 75
SIC 3533 Oil & gas drilling rigs & equipment; Oil & gas drilling rigs & equipment
Pr: Johnny Kidd
**Treas:* Kenny Black
**VP:* Tom Luttrell
VP: Tom Luttural
IT Man: Phil Schlecht

INTER-CHEM
See INTERNATIONAL CHEMICAL CO

D-U-N-S 01-207-1643
INTER-CITY TIRE & AUTO CENTER INC
UNDERCARE
777 Dowd Ave, Elizabeth, NJ 07201-2118
Tel (908) 354-5533 *Founded/Ownrshp* 1980
Sales 92.3MM^E *EMP* 200
SIC 5531 5013 5014 7538 Automotive tires; Automotive supplies & parts; Tires & tubes; General automotive repair shops; Automotive tires; Automotive supplies & parts; General automotive servicing equipment; Tires & tubes; General automotive repair shops
Pr: Morris Erbesh
CFO: Agnes Feltz
Board of Directors: Agnes Seltez

D-U-N-S 60-360-4513 IMP
INTER-COMMERCIAL BUSINESS SYSTEMS INC
I C B S
601 Century Pkwy Ste 100, Allen, TX 75013-8034
Tel (972) 649-4949 *Founded/Ownrshp* 1989
Sales 21.5MM^E *EMP* 30
SIC 5065 Electronic parts & equipment
CEO: Nancy Lutringer
Pr: Thomas M Lacey
VP: John Morrell
IT Man: Travis Canada

D-U-N-S 07-619-2475
INTER-CON SECURITY SYSTEMS INC
210 S De Lacey Ave # 200, Pasadena, CA 91105-2048
Tel (626) 535-2200 *Founded/Ownrshp* 1973
Sales 574.9MM^E *EMP* 25,000
SIC 7381 Guard services; Protective services, guard; Security guard service; Guard services; Protective services, guard; Security guard service
Ch Bd: Enrique Hernandez Jr
**Pr:* Neil Martau
COO: Lance Mueller
CFO: Paul Miller
CFO: Robin Simpson
Ofcr: Eric Strott
Ofcr: Andrew Thomas
Ofcr: Carlton Whiting
VP: Susana Castro
VP: John Harmke
**VP:* Roland A Hernandez
VP: Jerry Neville
VP: Rebecca Rowland
VP: Richard Stack
VP: Robert Williams
Exec: Robert Fenn

D-U-N-S 14-297-5080
INTER-CONTINENTAL HOTELS CORP
IHG
(*Suby of* HOTEL INTER-CONTINENTAL NY) ★
3 Ravinia Dr Ste 100, Atlanta, GA 30346-2121
Tel (770) 604-5000 *Founded/Ownrshp* 1946
Sales 50.4MM^E *EMP* 1,803^E
SIC 7011 Hotels & motels
CEO: Kirk Kinsell
**CFO:* Robert J Chitty
**CFO:* Robert Gunkel
Sr VP: Curt Smith
Exec: Didier Lailheugue
Exec: Andrew Rubin
Comm Dir: Giles Deards
Comm Dir: Patty Kahn
Comm Dir: Suzette Meade
Dir Bus: Clive Plummer
**Prin:* Stevan Porter

D-U-N-S 01-337-8807 IMP
INTER-COUNTY BAKERS INC
INTER-COUNTY BAKERY SUPPLY
1095 Long Island Ave A, Deer Park, NY 11729-3800
Tel (631) 957-1350 *Founded/Ownrshp* 1995
Sales 85.0MM *EMP* 91
SIC 5142 Bakery products, frozen; Bakery products, frozen
CEO: Theodore P Heim Jr
**Pr:* Theodore P Heim Sr
CFO: Laura Mulligan
VP Sls: Andy Hislop

INTER-COUNTY BAKERY SUPPLY
See INTER-COUNTY BAKERS INC

D-U-N-S 00-694-4680
INTER-COUNTY ENERGY COOPERATIVE CORP
1009 Hustonville Rd, Danville, KY 40422-2222
Tel (859) 236-4561 *Founded/Ownrshp* 1937
Sales 55.7MM *EMP* 62
SIC 4911 Distribution, electric power; Distribution, electric power
Pr: James Jacobus
Bd of Dir: Jennifer Turner
VP: Vickie Lay

D-U-N-S 01-417-7075
INTER-INDUSTRY CONFERENCE ON AUTO COLLISION REPAIR
I-CAR
5125 Trillium Blvd, Hoffman Estates, IL 60192-3600
Tel (847) 590-1191 *Founded/Ownrshp* 1979
Sales 23.5MM *EMP* 560^E
Accts Mann Weitz & Associates Llc
SIC 8331 Skill training center; Skill training center
Ch: William Brower
**Pr:* John Van Alstyne
**Ch:* Bob Keith
Dir IT: Bob Jansen
Mktg Dir: Ann Gonzalez

D-U-N-S 06-332-3331
INTER-MOUNTAIN PIPE & THREADING CO
935 Pendell Blvd, Mills, WY 82644
Tel (307) 234-2058 *Founded/Ownrshp* 1982
Sales 26.5MM *EMP* 41
SIC 5051 5131 Steel; Thread
Pr: Richard A Bonander
Sec: Jolene Bonander
VP: Greg Breed
Off Mgr: Dorothy Ray
Opers Mgr: David Johnson

D-U-N-S 01-207-2724 IMP
INTER-OCEAN INDUSTRIES LLC
BELLARNO INTERNATIONAL
1208 Avenue M, Brooklyn, NY 11230-5204
Tel (718) 375-2532 *Founded/Ownrshp* 1962
Sales 20.2MM^E *EMP* 15^E
Accts Mahoney Cohen
SIC 5065 Electronic parts & equipment; Electronic parts & equipment
Mng Pt: Donald Fishoff
Pt: AVI Fishoff
Pt: Meryl Fishoff
Pt: Barbara Gold
Pt: Regina Weinstock

D-U-N-S 61-040-4824 IMP
INTER-OCEAN SEAFOOD TRADER
INTER OCEAN
1200 Industrial Rd Ste 12, San Carlos, CA 94070-4129
Tel (650) 508-0691 *Founded/Ownrshp* 1989
Sales 61.0MM *EMP* 6
SIC 5146 Fish & seafoods
Pr: John Chen

D-U-N-S 88-473-6596 IMP
INTER-POWER CORP
TARIFA
3578 Van Dyke Rd, Almont, MI 48003-8045
Tel (810) 798-7050 *Founded/Ownrshp* 2003
Sales 20.0MM^E *EMP* 52
SIC 3567 Induction heating equipment
Pr: Gary Gariglio
Sls Mgr: Chuck L Kens

D-U-N-S 02-146-1868
INTER-RAIL TRANSPORT OF NASHVILLE LLC
WENTZVILLE AUTORAMP SERVICES
115 Lawyers Row Ste 3, Centreville, MD 21617-1061
Tel (410) 758-2893 *Founded/Ownrshp* 1979
Sales 32.5MM^E *EMP* 125
SIC 4789

D-U-N-S 05-851-0678
INTER-STATE FORD TRUCK SALES INC
INTERSTATE TRUCK CENTER
45 Brainard Rd, Hartford, CT 06114-1601
Tel (860) 706-0950 *Founded/Ownrshp* 1987
Sales 23.4MM^E *EMP* 42
SIC 5511 5012 Automobiles, new & used; Trucks, commercial
Pr: Sue Gordon

D-U-N-S 60-641-8416
INTER-STATE HARDWOODS CO INC
Rr 250 Box 92, Bartow, WV 24920
Tel (304) 456-4597 *Founded/Ownrshp* 1989
Sales 36.0MM^E *EMP* 180
Accts Maloney & Associates Pllc Kin
SIC 2426 2421 Hardwood dimension & flooring mills; Sawmills & planing mills, general; Hardwood dimension & flooring mills; Sawmills & planing mills, general
CEO: Edward G Frazee
**Pr:* Bryan Vernon
**Treas:* Karen Myers
**VP:* Barry Frazee

D-U-N-S 05-237-1499
INTER-STATE OIL CO
8221 Alpine Ave, Sacramento, CA 95826-4708
Tel (916) 457-6572 *Founded/Ownrshp* 1970
Sales 52.0MM^E *EMP* 65
SIC 5172 Lubricating oils & greases; Lubricating oils & greases
Pr: Brent Andrews
**Pr:* Terrance W Andrews
**Sec:* Laurie Andrews
Off Mgr: Sara King
Sales Exec: Todd Glader

D-U-N-S 00-717-1291
INTER-STATE STUDIO & PUBLISHING CO (MO)
3500 Snyder Ave, Sedalia, MO 65301-6871
Tel (660) 826-1764 *Founded/Ownrshp* 1933, 1952
Sales 26.1MM^E *EMP* 900

SIC 7221 2741 Photographic studios, portrait; Yearbooks: publishing & printing; Photographic studios, portrait; Yearbooks: publishing & printing
Ch Bd: Aric Snyder
**Pr:* Jeff Tilley
**Sec:* Cindy Snyder
**VP:* Rick Pettit
**Ex Dir:* Ed Sanders
Dir IT: David Lake
Software D: Joel Reid
Opers Mgr: Bill Henry
Opers Mgr: Emily Martens
Pr Dir: Milton Thompson
Mktg Mgr: Angie Howard

D-U-N-S 09-451-7216 IMP
INTER-TEL INTEGRATED SYSTEMS INC
(*Suby of* MITEL (DELAWARE) INC) ★
120 N 44th St Ste 200, Phoenix, AZ 85034-1826
Tel (480) 961-9000 *Founded/Ownrshp* 1977
Sales 25.4MM^E *EMP* 383
SIC 5065 Telephone equipment
Pr: Jeff Ford
**Ch Bd:* Steven G Mihaylo
**CFO:* Kurt Kneipe

D-U-N-S 60-471-2828
INTER-TEL TECHNOLOGIES INC
(*Suby of* MITEL (DELAWARE) INC) ★
1146 N Alma School Rd, Mesa, AZ 85201-3000
Tel (480) 858-9600 *Founded/Ownrshp* 1977
Sales 300.0MM *EMP* 118
SIC 5999 1731 5065 3661 3577 Telephone equipment & systems; Telephone & telephone equipment installation; Electronic parts & equipment; Telephone & telegraph apparatus; Computer peripheral equipment; Telephone equipment & systems; Telephone & telephone equipment installation; Electronic parts & equipment; Telephone & telegraph apparatus; Computer peripheral equipment
Pr: Craig W Rauchle

D-U-N-S 17-445-4280
INTER-TRACK PARTNERS LLC
O T B
8600 W North Ave, Melrose Park, IL 60160-1615
Tel (708) 615-1200 *Founded/Ownrshp* 1987
Sales 12.8MM^E *EMP* 852
SIC 7999 Off-track betting; Off-track betting
Top Exec: Michael Mackey

D-U-N-S 16-122-0728
INTER-TRIBAL COUNCIL OF MICHIGAN INC
2956 Ashmun St, Sault Sainte Marie, MI 49783-3720
Tel (800) 562-4957 *Founded/Ownrshp* 1970
Sales 23.5MM *EMP* 129
SIC 8331 Community service employment training program; Community service employment training program
Ex Dir: L John Lufkins
Board of Directors: L John Lufkins

D-U-N-S 12-087-1090
INTER-VALLEY HEALTH PLAN INC
300 S Park Ave Ste 300, Pomona, CA 91766-1546
Tel (909) 623-6333 *Founded/Ownrshp* 1979
Sales NA *EMP* 70
Accts Ernst & Young Us Llp Irvine
SIC 6324 8011 Hospital & medical service plans; Offices & clinics of medical doctors; Hospital & medical service plans; Offices & clinics of medical doctors
CEO: Ronald Bolding
**CFO:* Michael Nelson
IT Man: Dorothy Demandante
Software D: Tan Lee
Sls Dir: Tom Kaczmerek
Sls Mgr: Kathleen Cade
Surgeon: Vinod K Garg
Obsttrcn: Stephanie J Cropper
Obsttrcn: Simmi P Dhaliwal
Opthamlgy: Boban Joseph

INTER/MEDIA ADVERTISING
See INTER/MEDIA TIME BUYING CORP

D-U-N-S 08-651-3199
INTER/MEDIA TIME BUYING CORP
INTER/MEDIA ADVERTISING
22120 Clarendon St # 300, Woodland Hills, CA 91367-6315
Tel (818) 995-1455 *Founded/Ownrshp* 1974
Sales 27.2MM^E *EMP* 70
SIC 7311 Advertising agencies
Pr: Robert B Yallen
Pr: Jim Christensen
**VP:* Malena Cruz
VP: Rick Feldman
VP: Joseph Poulose
VP: Grant Rosenquist
VP: Kevin Szymanski
Software D: Remya Ravindran
VP Sls: Rick Sax

D-U-N-S 09-483-3290
INTERA INC
1812 Centre Creek Dr # 300, Austin, TX 78754-5153
Tel (512) 425-2000 *Founded/Ownrshp* 2001
Sales 21.2MM *EMP* 159
Accts Pmb Helin Donovan Llp Austin
SIC 8711 8748 Engineering services; Environmental consultant; Engineering services; Environmental consultant
CEO: Marsh Lavenue
**COO:* Eric Markland
**Ex VP:* Cindy Ardito
**Ex VP:* Van Kelley
Prin: John F Pickens

INTERA INTERNATIONAL
See INTERRA GROUP INC

INTERACT
See INTERCOMMUNITY ACTION INC

D-U-N-S 61-024-4878
INTERACT PUBLIC SAFETY SYSTEM
INTERACT911
(*Suby of* HARRIS, N. COMPUTER CORPORATION)
102 W 3rd St Ste 750, Winston Salem, NC 27101-3902
Tel (800) 768-3911 *Founded/Ownrshp* 2015
Sales 33.8MM^E *EMP* 233
SIC 7373 Systems integration services; Systems integration services
CEO: John McNulty
**CFO:* Doug Laux
Ex VP: Jeff Jones
**Ex VP:* Marcus Perez
Sr VP: Tim Bigwood
**Sr VP:* James Cape
**Sr VP:* Steve McDowall
**Sr VP:* Jim Simak
**Sr VP:* Terry Turner
VP: Drew Allvine
VP: Deidre Chaney
VP: Darren Dillard
VP: Tim Irelan
**VP:* Mike McGarry
**VP:* Sue Olson
VP: Scott Pate

INTERACT PUBLIC SAFETY SYSTEMS
See COLOSSUS INC

INTERACT911
See INTERACT PUBLIC SAFETY SYSTEM

D-U-N-S 78-039-5963
INTERACTIONS LLC
INTERACTIONS TECHNOLOGY SVCS
31 Hayward St Ste E, Franklin, MA 02038-2166
Tel (866) 637-9049 *Founded/Ownrshp* 2004
Sales 26.3MM^E *EMP* 57^E
SIC 7371 5961 Software programming applications; Computer software, mail order
CEO: Michael Cloran
Pr: Jim Dreher
Pr: Michael Iacobucci
COO: Dave Parkinson
CFO: Edward Durkin
Ofcr: Elizabeth Lemons
Ofcr: David Samuels
Ex VP: Jim Bandanza
Ex VP: Phil Gray
Ex VP: Mark Leonard
Sr VP: Laurie Giandomenico
Sr VP: Joseph Gildea
VP: James Nolan
VP: Sanjeev Sawai
Board of Directors: Michael Wilens

INTERACTIONS TECHNOLOGY SVCS
See INTERACTIONS LLC

D-U-N-S 79-892-9902
▲ INTERACTIVE BROKERS GROUP INC
IBG
1 Pickwick Plz Ste 100, Greenwich, CT 06830-5531
Tel (203) 618-5800 *Founded/Ownrshp* 1977
Sales 1.1MMM *EMP* 880^E
Tkr Sym IBKR *Exch* NGS
SIC 6211 Security brokers & dealers; Security brokers & dealers
Ch Bd: Thomas Peterffy
**Pr:* Milan Galik
**CFO:* Paul J Brody
**V-Ch Bd:* Earl H Nemser
Ex VP: Thomas A Frank
Sr VP: Steve Sanders
Board of Directors: Richard Gates, Lawrence E Harris, Hans R Stoll, Wayne Wagner

D-U-N-S 94-087-2591
■ INTERACTIVE BROKERS LLC
(*Suby of* IBG LLC) ★
2 Pickwick Plz Ste 210, Greenwich, CT 06830-5576
Tel (203) 618-5700 *Founded/Ownrshp* 1998
Sales 86.5MM^E *EMP* 139^E
SIC 6211 Security brokers & dealers; Security brokers & dealers
CFO: Bill Cavagnaro
Ofcr: Mike Adamski
Ofcr: Arnold J Feist
Ofcr: Anthony Seirer
Ex Dir: Drew Sultan
Mng Dir: David Friedland
Mng Dir: Steve Kelsey
Mng Dir: William McGowan
Mng Dir: Richard Roman
Off Mgr: Steven Donahue
Snr Sftwr: Vinit Goradia

D-U-N-S 61-203-4934
INTERACTIVE BUSINESS INFORMATION SYSTEMS INC
IBIS
420 Technology Pkwy # 100, Norcross, GA 30092-3414
Tel (770) 368-4000 *Founded/Ownrshp* 1989
Sales 43.2MM^E *EMP* 77
SIC 5045 Computer software; Computer peripheral equipment
CEO: J Andrew Vabulas
**COO:* Dwight Specht
CFO: Chuck Ristau
VP: Janis Braslins
**Prin:* Andy Vabulas
Rgnl Mgr: Tom Nall

D-U-N-S 11-365-5468
INTERACTIVE BUSINESS SYSTEMS INC
I B S
2625 Bttrfeld Rd Ste 114w, Oak Brook, IL 60523
Tel (630) 571-9100 *Founded/Ownrshp* 1981
Sales 64.2MM^E *EMP* 739
SIC 7379 Data processing consultant; Data processing consultant
Pr: Daniel Williams
Rgnl VP: Peggy Martinuz
Mng Dir: Jack Adams
Brnch Mgr: Mark Zimbal
CIO: Ellen Barry
CTO: Maureen Osborne
Dir IT: Owen Cooper
IT Man: Pamela Emerson

D-U-N-S 80-189-6200
INTERACTIVE COMMUNICATIONS INTERNATIONAL INC
INCOMM
(*Suby of* INCOMM HOLDINGS INC) ★
250 Williams St Nw # 5000, Atlanta, GA 30303-1032
Tel (770) 240-6100 *Founded/Ownrshp* 1992
Sales NA *EMP* 600^E
SIC 6099 Telephone services; Clearinghouse associations, bank or check
Pr: M Brooks Smith
Pr: David Vielehr
COO: Daniel Pree
**CFO:* Scott Meyerhoff
Ex VP: Jeff Baker
Dir Bus: Brian Blasius
Dir Bus: Michael Misuraca
CTO: Brian Hoffman
Tech Mgr: Venkat Yarabarla
Sftwr Eng: Srinivasa Yeramsetty
Netwrk Eng: Cliff Haas

D-U-N-S 79-283-0184
INTERACTIVE DATA CORP
(*Suby of* IGLOO INTERMEDIATE CORP) ★
32 Crosby Dr, Bedford, MA 01730-1448
Tel (781) 687-8500 *Founded/Ownrshp* 2010
Sales 939.2MM *EMP* 2,600
SIC 6289 7375 Financial reporting; Information retrieval services; Financial reporting; Information retrieval services
Pr: Stephen C Daffron
**Ch Bd:* Mason Slaine
COO: Jay Nadler
CFO: Vincent Chippari
CFO: Steven Crane
CFO: Andrew J Hajducky
CFO: Andrew Hajducky
Sr Cor Off: Andrew Koven
Ofcr: Rhonda Brier
Ex VP: Andrea H Loew
Ex VP: Tim Noble
Sr VP: Lou J Gehring
Sr VP: Carol Sweeney
VP: Ken Shibata
Exec: Gisela Morales
Exec: Neil Rudden
Dir Soc: Martina Murtagh
Dir Rx: Christen Fleming
Dir Bus: Magnus Cattan
Dir Bus: Christen Langguth

D-U-N-S 11-985-1215
INTERACTIVE DATA PRICING AND REFERENCE DATA LLC
(*Suby of* INTERACTIVE DATA CORP) ★
32 Crosby Dr, Bedford, MA 01730-1448
Tel (781) 687-8800 *Founded/Ownrshp* 1974
Sales NA *EMP* 1,765^E
SIC 6022 State commercial banks; State commercial banks
CEO: Stephen C Daffron
**Pr:* Steven Crane
**COO:* John King
**CFO:* Vincent A Chippari
Sr VP: Eric Pinstein
**VP:* Lori Hannay
Exec: Barbara Isacsson
Mng Dir: James Farrer
Snr Sftwr: Sonny Diaz
Snr Sftwr: Michael Foley
Snr Sftwr: Bruce Wisentaner

D-U-N-S 08-001-2237
INTERACTIVE HEALTH HOLDINGS CORP
1700 E Golf Rd Ste 900, Schaumburg, IL 60173-5816
Tel (847) 590-0200 *Founded/Ownrshp* 2015
Sales 21.1MM^E *EMP* 5^E
SIC 8099 Physical examination & testing services; Health screening service; Physical examination service, insurance
Pr: Cathy Kenworthy
CFO: Peter Burger

D-U-N-S 80-898-3696
INTERACTIVE HEALTH SOLUTIONS INC
(*Suby of* INTERACTIVE HEALTH HOLDINGS CORP) ★
1700 E Golf Rd Ste 900, Schaumburg, IL 60173-5816
Tel (866) 279-1636 *Founded/Ownrshp* 2011
Sales 21.1MM^E *EMP* 1,972
SIC 8099 Physical examination & testing services; Health screening service; Physical examination service, insurance
Pr: Cathy Kenworthy
Pr: Jim Batastini
Ex VP: Charlie Estey
**VP:* Richard Bi
**VP:* Aaron Money
VP: Stacey Nevara
Rgnl Mgr: Patrick Deagan
IT Man: Ken Stiple
Natl Sales: Patti Duran
VP Sls: Pat Loridas
Mktg Dir: Donna Hofmeister

D-U-N-S 07-829-8647
▲ INTERACTIVE INTELLIGENCE GROUP INC
7601 Interactive Way, Indianapolis, IN 46278-2727
Tel (317) 872-3000 *Founded/Ownrshp* 1994
Sales 341.3MM *EMP* 2,122^E
Tkr Sym ININ *Exch* NGS
SIC 7372 Application computer software; Application computer software
Ch Bd: Donald E Brown
CFO: Stephen R Head
Chf Mktg O: Jeff M Platon
Sr VP: Gary R Blough
Sr VP: Joseph A Staples
Dir Sec: Thomas J Fisher

D-U-N-S 94-114-5153
■ INTERACTIVE INTELLIGENCE INC
(*Suby of* INTERACTIVE INTELLIGENCE GROUP INC) ★
7601 Interactive Way, Indianapolis, IN 46278-2727
Tel (317) 715-8414 *Founded/Ownrshp* 1994
Sales 136.5MM^E *EMP* 849^E
SIC 7372 7371 Application computer software; Custom computer programming services; Application computer software; Custom computer programming services
Ch Bd: Donald E Brown MD
Pt: Kris Sparks
COO: Rich Guard
**CFO:* Stephen R Head
CFO: Steve Head
Bd of Dir: Safwat Shawaf
Chf Mktg O: Jeff Platon
**Chf Mktg O:* Joseph A Staples
**Ex VP:* Gary R Blough
VP: Joe Adams
**VP:* Pamela J Hynes
VP: Douglas T Shinsato
Board of Directors: Richard G Halperin, Edward L Hamburg Phd, Michael C Heim, Mark E Hill, Richard A Reck

D-U-N-S 78-072-6738 IMP
INTERACTIVE LIFE FORMS LLC
FLESHLIGHT
7000 Burleson Rd Ste C, Austin, TX 78744-3214
Tel (888) 804-4453 *Founded/Ownrshp* 1994
Sales 35.5MM^E *EMP* 100
SIC 2821 Plastics materials & resins; Plastics materials & resins
COO: Brian Shubin
CTO: David Ashley
Opers Mgr: Todd Porter
Genl Couns: Matthew Esber

D-U-N-S 62-328-6309
INTERACTIVE MARKETING SERVICES INC
BROADBAND INTERACTIVE
2716 W Montrose Ave, Chicago, IL 60618-1521
Tel (773) 267-2493 *Founded/Ownrshp* 1993
Sales 14.0MM *EMP* 300
SIC 4841 Cable & other pay television services; Cable & other pay television services
Pr: Robert Larrimore
Genl Mgr: Peter Quinton

D-U-N-S 62-799-1102
INTERACTIVE MARKETING SERVICES INC
2 N Maple Ave, Ridgely, MD 21660-1923
Tel (410) 634-2060 *Founded/Ownrshp* 1991
Sales 16.5MM^E *EMP* 550
SIC 7389 Telephone services; Advertising, promotional & trade show services; Telephone services; Advertising, promotional & trade show services
Pr: Michael Wilt
**VP:* Jack Dellose
IT Man: Jerry Daniels
IT Man: Eddie Harris
IT Man: Leroy Woomer

D-U-N-S 94-357-3246
INTERACTIVE PERFORMANCE INC
(*Suby of* OSI OUTSOURCING SERVICES, INC.)
4275 Bridge View Dr, Charleston, SC 29405-7444
Tel (843) 308-7771 *Founded/Ownrshp* 2003
Sales 10.2MM^E *EMP* 414^E
SIC 7322 Collection agency, except real estate
Prin: Dennis Grady

INTERACTIVE PRTG & PACKG CO
See IPAK INC

D-U-N-S 83-812-2950
INTERACTIVE RESPONSE TECHNOLOGIES INC
I R T
(*Suby of* CYBER CITY TELESERVICES MARKETING INC) ★
4500 N State Road 7 # 301, Lauderdale Lakes, FL 33319-5877
Tel (954) 484-4973 *Founded/Ownrshp* 2010
Sales 85.8MM^E *EMP* 2,700
SIC 7389 Telephone services; Telephone services
Pr: Richard Eychner
CFO: James M Pelky
**Ex VP:* Martin J Lehtio II
**Sr VP:* Sandra Gobbo
Dir IT: Terry Scott
Web Dev: Ian Jory
Genl Couns: Stephen Ferber

D-U-N-S 93-224-5137 EXP
INTERACTIVE SERVICES NETWORK INC
ISN COMMUNICATIONS
1035 Ne 125th St Ste 300, North Miami, FL 33161-5841
Tel (305) 573-5300 *Founded/Ownrshp* 1995
Sales 20.7MM^E *EMP* 68
SIC 4813 Telephone communication, except radio
Pr: Roberto Chmielewski
COO: Julio Abdala
CTO: Omar Barreneche
VP Sls: Stu Kolinsky
Sls Mgr: Jaime Campo
Sls Mgr: Bermudez Mariano
Sls Mgr: Janice Villano
Sls Mgr: Robert Villano

D-U-N-S 94-270-8074
INTERACTIVE SOLUTIONS INC
3860 Forest Hill Irene Rd # 101, Memphis, TN 38125-2586
Tel (901) 866-1474 *Founded/Ownrshp* 1996
Sales 26.2MM^E *EMP* 48
Accts The Marston Group Pc Memph
SIC 5099 7389 Video & audio equipment; Teleconferencing services
Pr: Jay Myers
**CFO:* Annelle Hochhauser
**VP:* Jeremy Johnson
**VP:* Derek Plummer
Exec: Linda Mathis

D-U-N-S 10-147-2970
■ INTERACTIVE TECHNOLOGY SOLUTIONS LLC
(*Suby of* ACENTIA LLC) ★
3130 Frview Pk Dr Ste 800, Falls Church, VA 22042
Tel (703) 712-4000 *Founded/Ownrshp* 2001
Sales 42.5MM^E *EMP* 775^E

SIC 7379 8742 ; Management consulting services; ; Management consulting services
CEO: Todd Stottlemyer
**Pr:* Robert McCord
COO: Lawrence Oconnor
**CFO:* Tom Weston
**Ex VP:* Mike Raymond
**Sr VP:* Tom Woteki
CTO: Chris Chroniger

D-U-N-S 00-968-1586 IMP
■ **INTERAMERICAN MOTOR CORP** (CA)
IMC
(*Suby of* AUTOZONE INC) ★
8901 Canoga Ave, Canoga Park, CA 91304-1512
Tel (818) 678-6571 *Founded/Ownrshp* 1962, 2014
Sales 293.6MM^E *EMP* 250
SIC 5013 5599 Automotive supplies & parts; Automotive supplies & parts; Dunebuggies
CEO: John Mosunic
**Treas:* Hanns Hederer
**Ex VP:* Winfred Baur
Admn Mgr: Sieclinde Pelaez
VP Opers: John Taillon
Opers Mgr: Hank Helm
Sales Asso: Ali Saleem

D-U-N-S 79-806-2709 IMP
INTERAMERICAS APPAREL INC
14100 Carlton Dr, Davie, FL 33330-4659
Tel (954) 424-7388 *Founded/Ownrshp* 1992
Sales 26.3MM^E *EMP* 500
Accts Mckean Paul Chrycy Fletcher &
SIC 2389 Men's miscellaneous accessories; Men's miscellaneous accessories
Pr: Dennis Griffis
**CFO:* Ryan G Woods

D-U-N-S 12-156-8919
INTERAUDI BANK
19 E 54th St, New York, NY 10022-3106
Tel (212) 833-1000 *Founded/Ownrshp* 1983
Sales NA *EMP* 72
SIC 6022 State commercial banks; State commercial banks
Pr: Joseph G Audi
Pr: Ming Ouyang
CFO: Stefan Johansson
**Sr VP:* Louis R Cina
VP: Mayra Egas
VP: Anthony Lopez
VP: Esther Ogrodnik
VP: Maryann Seery
Genl Mgr: Nabil Achkar

D-U-N-S 04-333-7401 IMP
INTERBAKE FOODS LLC
NORSE DAIRY SYSTEMS
(*Suby of* GEORGE WESTON LIMITED)
3951 Westerre Pkwy # 200, Henrico, VA 23233-1312
Tel (804) 755-7107 *Founded/Ownrshp* 1972
Sales 217.6MM^E *EMP* 1,031
SIC 2052 2051 Cookies; Crackers, dry; Bread, cake & related products; Breads, rolls & buns; Cakes, pies & pastries; Cookies; Crackers, dry; Bread, cake & related products; Breads, rolls & buns; Cakes, pies & pastries
Pr: Raymond Baxter
VP: Keith Gaines
VP: Rick Lee
VP: Tiffany Reeve
QC Dir: Denise Bullock

D-U-N-S 03-635-3530
INTERBANK INC
(*Suby of* OLNEY BANCSHARES OF TEXAS INC) ★
4921 N May Ave, Oklahoma City, OK 73112-6041
Tel (580) 928-5511 *Founded/Ownrshp* 1901, 1976
Sales NA *EMP* 400
SIC 6022 State commercial banks; State commercial banks
Ch Bd: John T French
Pr: C H Wyatt
CFO: Stephanie Craig
CFO: Brad Stieben
Ex VP: Brad Maddoux
Ex VP: Keith Schwandt
Sr VP: Darla Hoffman
Sr VP: Darin Schmidt
Sr VP: Mandy Wilson
VP: Sharon Forrester
VP: Scott Keeney

INTERBANK MORTGAGE COMPANY
See CHICAGO MORTGAGE SOLUTIONS CORP

D-U-N-S 00-497-8656 IMP/EXP
INTERBOND CORP OF AMERICA (FL)
BRANDSMART USA
3200 Sw 42nd St, Fort Lauderdale, FL 33312-6813
Tel (954) 797-4000 *Founded/Ownrshp* 1980
Sales 465.5MM^E *EMP* 2,400
Accts Kaufman Rossin & Co Pa Miam
SIC 5731 5722 Consumer electronic equipment; High fidelity stereo equipment; Television sets; Video cameras & accessories; Electric household appliances, major; Consumer electronic equipment; High fidelity stereo equipment; Television sets; Video cameras & accessories; Electric household appliances, major
Pr: Robert Perlman
**Treas:* Eric Beazley
Sr VP: Vincent Visco
VP: Eydie Bowe
VP: Amanda Griffin
**VP:* Lary Sinewitze
Genl Mgr: Phil Lieberman
VP Sls: Neil Anello
Mktg Dir: Lara Aronoff

D-U-N-S 17-333-7445 IMP/EXP
INTERBOND HOLDING CORP
BRANDSMART U.S.A.
3200 Sw 42nd St, Fort Lauderdale, FL 33312-6813
Tel (954) 797-4000 *Founded/Ownrshp* 1990
Sales 700.0MM^E *EMP* 2,100
Accts Kaufman Rossin And Co

SIC 7629 3699 5722 Electrical repair shops; Appliance cords for household electrical equipment; Electric household appliances; Electrical repair shops; Appliance cords for household electrical equipment; Electric household appliances
Pr: Michael Pearlman
VP: Craig Prescott
VP Mktg: Ellen Stevens
S&M/VP: Bobby Johnson

D-U-N-S 07-841-7659
INTERBORO MANAGEMENT INC
155 Mineola Blvd, Mineola, NY 11501-3920
Tel (516) 213-0286 *Founded/Ownrshp* 2011
Sales NA *EMP* 135^E
SIC 6411 Insurance agents, brokers & service
Pr: David Nichols

D-U-N-S 00-698-5667
INTERBORO MUTUAL INDEMNITY INSURANCE CO
155 Mineola Blvd, Mineola, NY 11501-3920
Tel (516) 248-1100 *Founded/Ownrshp* 1914
Sales NA *EMP* 100
SIC 6411 Insurance agents
Pr: William S Gibson
Ch Bd: Henry W Dwyer
Ofcr: Thomas Manion
VP: Susan Ende
VP: Anthony Terracciano
IT Man: Joe Leogrande
Software D: Paul Battaglia
Software D: Dmitriy Kogan
Software D: Inna Shelomyanova
Board of Directors: Edwin W Martin, Peter A Brandel, Fran Purcell, Henry W Dwyer, Martin H Renken, William L Edwards, George J Farrell, Milton F Gidge, William A Hagan Jr, Bradley Hemingway, Leonard Lazarus, William H Lister

D-U-N-S 05-712-3713
INTERBORO SCHOOL DISTRICT
900 Washington Ave, Prospect Park, PA 19076-1498
Tel (610) 461-6700 *Founded/Ownrshp* 1931
Sales 39.4MM^E *EMP* 450
SIC 8211 8661 Public elementary & secondary schools; Elementary school; High school, junior or senior; Religious organizations; Public elementary & secondary schools; Elementary school; High school, junior or senior; Religious organizations
Treas: William Phelps
VP: John N Kaelin Jr
VP: Brian Razzi
Prin: Paulette N Bradley
Prin: Michael T Didomenico
Prin: William K Miller
Prin: Michael Pladus
Prin: Ronald Reidinger
CTO: Paul Gibson
DP Exec: Chris Goldgerg
Trfc Dir: James Simmonds

D-U-N-S 07-525-6552
■ **INTERBRAND CORP**
(*Suby of* OMNICOM GROUP INC) ★
130 5th Ave Fl 4, New York, NY 10011-4305
Tel (212) 798-7500 *Founded/Ownrshp* 2007
Sales 96.1MM^E *EMP* 800
SIC 8742 7336 Marketing consulting services; Package design; Marketing consulting services; Package design
CEO: Jez Frampton
**Pr:* David Martin
CEO: Josh Feldmeth
CEO: Beth Viner
**CFO:* James Bruce
**CFO:* Kelly Gall
Ofcr: Leslie Butterfield
Ofcr: Andy Payne
**VP:* Pawel Tulin
VP: Jim Williamson
Assoc Dir: Krista Danias
Creative D: Andreas Rotzler

D-U-N-S 09-282-5397
■ **INTERBRAND DESIGN FORUM INC**
(*Suby of* INTERBRAND CORP) ★
7575 Paragon Rd, Dayton, OH 45459-5316
Tel (937) 439-4400 *Founded/Ownrshp* 1978, 2002
Sales 26.8MM^E *EMP* 225
SIC 8742 7389 Planning consultant; Merchandising consultant; Interior design services; Planning consultant; Merchandising consultant; Interior design services
CEO: D Lee Carpenter
**VP:* Scott Smith
VP: Paul Vanderburgh
Ex Dir: Tom Custer

D-U-N-S 79-347-4800
■ **INTERCALL INC**
(*Suby of* WEST CORP) ★
8420 W Bryn Mawr Ave # 1100, Chicago, IL 60631-3479
Tel (773) 399-1600 *Founded/Ownrshp* 2003
Sales 137.4MM^E *EMP* 903
SIC 7389 Teleconferencing services; Teleconferencing services
Pr: Paul Nichols
Pr: J Scott Etzler
Pr: Kevin Neville
CFO: Paul M Mendlik
Ex VP: Michael Nessler
Ex VP: Tom Priestley
Ex VP: Robert Wise
VP: Marty Dunne
VP: Susan Ferguson
Dir Bus: Amel Attif
Dir Bus: Tiina Maenpaa

D-U-N-S 10-441-1157
INTERCAMBIO EXPRESS INC
RAYO TRANSFERS
426 N Main St, Elkhart, IN 46516-3084
Tel (574) 343-5200 *Founded/Ownrshp* 1997
Sales NA *EMP* 51
SIC 6099 Electronic funds transfer network, including switching

Pr: Isaac Torres
Dir IT: Ed Manteuffel
IT Man: Adrian Soto
IT Man: Christian Velazquez
Software D: Sarah Wiseman
Mktg Mgr: Ron Deleon
Snr Mgr: Jorge Araiza
Snr Mgr: Jorge Nava

D-U-N-S 07-891-3761
INTERCARE COMMUNITY HEALTH NETWORK
50 Industrial Park Rd, Bangor, MI 49013-1246
Tel (269) 427-7937 *Founded/Ownrshp* 1971
Sales 28.6MM *EMP* 230^E
Accts Yeo & Yeo Pc Saginaw Mi
SIC 8011 Clinic, operated by physicians; Clinic, operated by physicians
CEO: Velma Hendershot
**CFO:* Patrick Sullivan
**Ex VP:* Judith Rayman
**VP:* Michael Giacalone
MIS Dir: Robin Labrecque
Nutrtnst: Adelle Shearer
Doctor: Barbara Boyd
Doctor: Suzanne Hawkins
Doctor: Asif Ishaque

INTERCARE HOLDINGS INSUR SVCS
See PACIFIC SECURED EQUITIES INC

D-U-N-S 78-507-7590
INTERCARE HOLDINGS INSURANCE SERVICES INC
IHI
(*Suby of* INTERCARE HOLDINGS INSUR SVCS) ★
3010 Lava Ridge Ct # 110, Roseville, CA 95661-3063
Tel (916) 677-2500 *Founded/Ownrshp* 1994
Sales NA *EMP* 263
SIC 6411 Insurance adjusters; Insurance adjusters
CEO: George McLeary
Ex VP: Anges Hoeberling
Ex VP: Richard R Rothman
VP: Alan Avriett
VP: Mark Gibbons
VP: Sandra Jimenez

INTERCEPT
See STRATMAR SYSTEMS INC

D-U-N-S 61-137-2681
■ **INTERCEPT INC**
INTERCEPT PAYMENT SOLUTIONS
(*Suby of* FIDELITY NATIONAL INFORMATION SERVICES INC) ★
3150 Holcomb Bridge Rd, Norcross, GA 30071-1330
Tel (770) 248-9600 *Founded/Ownrshp* 2006
Sales NA *EMP* 1,600
SIC 6099 7374 Electronic funds transfer network, including switching; Data processing & preparation; Electronic funds transfer network, including switching; Data processing & preparation
Ch Bd: William P Foley II
**CFO:* Al Stinson
VP Opers: Charlie Honaker

D-U-N-S 03-076-7821
INTERCEPT INTERACTIVE INC
UNDERTONE NETWORKS
(*Suby of* PERION NETWORK LTD)
340 Madison Ave Fl 8, New York, NY 10173-0899
Tel (212) 685-8000 *Founded/Ownrshp* 2015
Sales 46.3MM^E *EMP* 196^E
SIC 7311 Advertising agencies; Advertising agencies
CEO: Corey Ferengul
CFO: Mark Attarian
Chf Cred: Marc Ellenbogen
Sr VP: George Durden
Sr VP: Chris Henger
Sr VP: Rob Schwartz
Sr VP: Denise Stott

INTERCEPT PAYMENT SOLUTIONS
See INTERCEPT INC

D-U-N-S 09-972-0724 IMP
INTERCERAMIC INC
INTERCRAMIC TILE STONE GALLERY
(*Suby of* INTERNACIONAL DE CERAMICA, S.A.B. DE C.V.)
2333 S Jupiter Rd, Garland, TX 75041-6007
Tel (214) 503-4967 *Founded/Ownrshp* 1993
Sales 131.1MM^E *EMP* 650
SIC 3253 5032 Ceramic wall & floor tile; Tile, structural clay; Ceramic wall & floor tile; Tile, structural clay
CEO: Victor Almeida
CFO: Len Lugo
**Ex VP:* Steve Belken
**Ex VP:* Humberto Maese
**Sr VP:* Edmeerto Maese
Dir IT: Gabriel Grijalva
Software D: Alberto Rodriguez
Opers Mgr: Orlando Cappa
Opers Mgr: Frank Gomez
Opers Mgr: Todd Wilkinson
Ql Cn Mgr: M Rios

INTERCHEM AMERICAS
See INTERCHEM USA INC

D-U-N-S 78-562-8368 IMP
INTERCHEM CORP
120 N State Rt 17 Ste 115, Paramus, NJ 07652-2812
Tel (201) 261-7333 *Founded/Ownrshp* 1981
Sales 27.1MM^E *EMP* 50
SIC 5122 5169 Pharmaceuticals; Chemicals & allied products
Ch: Ron Mannino
**Pr:* Joseph Pizza
VP: Michele Scrofani
VP: Diana Tate
Dir IT: Rafael Martinez
VP Sls: Lee Armstrong
Sls Dir: Kimberly Bianco
Art Dir: Lisa Young
Snr Mgr: Kurt Stalder

D-U-N-S 94-156-6838 IMP/EXP
INTERCHEM USA INC
INTERCHEM AMERICAS
(*Suby of* INTERCHEM PTE. LTD.)
2800 Post Oak Blvd Ste 52, Houston, TX 77056-6100
Tel (713) 623-8389 *Founded/Ownrshp* 1976
Sales 27.8MM^E *EMP* 6
SIC 5172 Petroleum products
Pr: Roberto Dahlgren
**Treas:* Rob Langstraat
**VP:* Jeroen Baaima

D-U-N-S 07-521-9113
INTERCHURCH MEDICAL ASSISTANCE INC (MD)
I.M.A.
500 Main St, New Windsor, MD 21776-9770
Tel (410) 635-8720 *Founded/Ownrshp* 1960
Sales 130.9MM *EMP* 150
Accts Raffa Pc Washington Dc
SIC 8661 Religious organizations; Religious organizations
Pr: Richard Santos
**CFO:* Tracey Stevens
Ofcr: Amanda Addison
Ofcr: Jennifer Bentzel
Ofcr: Sarah Craciunoiu
Ofcr: Ramatou Hassane
Ofcr: Carol Shores
VP: Dragana Veskov
IT Man: Ryan Williams

D-U-N-S 07-321-5097 IMP/EXP
INTERCIT INC
FIRMENICH CITRUS CENTER
(*Suby of* FIRMENICH INC) ★
3919 Kidron Rd, Lakeland, FL 33811-1293
Tel (863) 646-0165 *Founded/Ownrshp* 1988
Sales 22.1MM^E *EMP* 110
SIC 2899 Oils & essential oils; Oils & essential oils
Genl Mgr: Beverly Bateman
**Treas:* Eric Jorgensen
**VP:* Don Hendrix
**VP:* Peary Marro
Sfty Mgr: Tom Pearson
Opers Mgr: Brad Farrow

INTERCITY HOME CARE
See INTERCITY HOMEMAKER SERVICE INC

D-U-N-S 06-515-7778
INTERCITY HOME CARE
11 Dartmouth St Ste 201, Malden, MA 02148-5102
Tel (781) 321-6300 *Founded/Ownrshp* 1972
Sales 65.4M *EMP* 700
Accts Baker & Co
SIC 8082 Home health care services; Home health care services
Pr: Arthur S Reinherz
**Pr:* James Katz
**Treas:* Ralph Reinherz
Board of Directors: Constance Arvanites, Rowena Band, Frank L De Marco, Mary Alice Murray, Elizabeth O'brien, Margaret Sutherland, Haig Yardumian, Abraham Zorochnick

D-U-N-S 80-259-6197
INTERCITY HOMEMAKER SERVICE INC
INTERCITY HOME CARE
11 Dartmouth St Ste 202, Malden, MA 02148-5102
Tel (781) 321-6300 *Founded/Ownrshp* 1976
Sales 12.0MM *EMP* 500
SIC 8082 Home health care services; Home health care services
Pr: Jim Katz
Treas: Ralph D Reinherz

D-U-N-S 05-015-4525
INTERCITY TRANSIT
526 Pattison St Se, Olympia, WA 98501-2076
Tel (360) 786-8585 *Founded/Ownrshp* 1981
Sales 30.1MM *EMP* 285
SIC 4131 Intercity bus line; Intercity bus line
Genl Mgr: Michael Harbour
V Ch: Ed Hildreth
Bd of Dir: Martin Thies
Plng Mgr: Dennis Bloom
IT Man: Joe Ramsauer

D-U-N-S 82-945-2916
▲ **INTERCLOUD SYSTEMS INC**
1030 Broad St Ste 102, Shrewsbury, NJ 07702-4317
Tel (732) 898-6308 *Founded/Ownrshp* 2010
Sales 76.2MM *EMP* 483^E
Tkr Sym ICLD *Exch* NAS
SIC 7378 7379 7373 Computer & data processing equipment repair/maintenance; Computer related maintenance services; Office computer automation systems integration; Computer & data processing equipment repair/maintenance; Computer related maintenance services; Office computer automation systems integration
Ch Bd: Mark Munro
Pr: Frank Jadevaia
CFO: Timothy A Larkin
Mktg Mgr: Mary Santacross
Board of Directors: Mark F Durfee, Charles K Miller, Neal L Oristano

INTERCNTNENTAL SAN JUAN RESORT
See INTERCONTINENTAL HOTELS (PUERTO RICO) INC

D-U-N-S 92-885-0759
INTERCOASTAL HEALTH SYSTEMS INC
1309 N Flagler Dr, West Palm Beach, FL 33401-3406
Tel (561) 650-6272 *Founded/Ownrshp* 2001
Sales 190.1M *EMP* 3,100
SIC 8741 8069 Hospital management; Nursing & personal care facility management; Specialty hospitals, except psychiatric; Hospital management; Nursing & personal care facility management; Specialty hospitals, except psychiatric
CEO: Robert Freymuller
CFO: Oscar Fernandez

D-U-N-S 87-922-1463
INTERCOASTAL MEDICAL GROUP INC
943 S Beneva Rd Ste 306, Sarasota, FL 34232-2499
Tel (941) 955-1108 Founded/Ownrshp 1997
Sales 26.5MM^E EMP 500^E
SIC 8069 Specialty hospitals, except psychiatric; Specialty hospitals, except psychiatric
Pr: John Steele MD
*Treas: Arthur S Dinenberg
*VP: Joseph L Bramante
*VP: Mauricio M Concha
*VP: Charles Hollen MD
Dir Lab: Gail Michaelson
Dir IT: Jean Mingari
IT Man: Mark Rehder
Opers Mgr: Linda Thomas
Surgeon: George Storey
Podiatrist: Joseph Bramante

D-U-N-S 08-325-5752
INTERCOMMUNITY ACTION INC (PA)
INTERACT
6012 Ridge Ave, Philadelphia, PA 19128-1697
Tel (215) 487-0904 Founded/Ownrshp 1969
Sales 22.9MM EMP 400
Accts Kreischer Miller Horsham Pen
SIC 8093 8361 Mental health clinic, outpatient; Rehabilitation center, residential: health care incidental; Mental health clinic, outpatient; Rehabilitation center, residential: health care incidental
Pr: David Bolin
CFO: Susan Wyland
Bd of Dir: Bernard Guet
Sr VP: Kathy Manderino
VP: Micheal Sharp
VP: Jodi Silverman
MIS Dir: Mike Mann
Netwrk Mgr: Thomas Foley

INTERCOMMUNITY HEALTH NETWORK
See INTERCOMMUNITY HEALTH PLANS INC

D-U-N-S 04-904-2398
INTERCOMMUNITY HEALTH PLANS INC
INTERCOMMUNITY HEALTH NETWORK
3600 Nw Samaritan Dr, Corvallis, OR 97330-3737
Tel (541) 757-5111 Founded/Ownrshp 1993
Sales 129.0MM EMP 10
Accts Kpmg Llp
SIC 8099 Medical services organization; Medical services organization
Pr: Kelly Kaiser

D-U-N-S 08-947-6055 IMP/EXP
INTERCOMP CO
3839 County Road 116, Medina, MN 55340-9342
Tel (763) 476-2531 Founded/Ownrshp 1978
Sales 27.2MM^E EMP 85
SIC 3596 Industrial scales; Truck (motor vehicle) scales
CEO: William Kroll
CFO: Derek Eilderts
*VP: Robert Kroll
VP: Jason Luftman
VP: Bruce Rhoe
Mktg Mgr: Aaron Vanheel

D-U-N-S 62-153-1250
INTERCON BUILDING CORP
211 Atherton St, Charlotte, NC 28203-5602
Tel (704) 522-1140 Founded/Ownrshp 1990
Sales 25.2MM^E EMP 60
SIC 1542 Commercial & office building, new construction
Pr: Curtis Trenkelbach
CFO: Nicole Fasulka
*Ex VP: Roxanne Trenkelbach
VP: David Reynolds

D-U-N-S 10-320-4970
INTERCON CHEMICAL CO
1100 Central Indus Dr, Saint Louis, MO 63110-2302
Tel (314) 771-6600 Founded/Ownrshp 1990
Sales 32.6MM^E EMP 95
SIC 2842 2841 Floor waxes; Disinfectants, household or industrial plant; Cleaning or polishing preparations; Soap: granulated, liquid, cake, flaked or chip; Detergents, synthetic organic or inorganic alkaline; Floor waxes; Disinfectants, household or industrial plant; Cleaning or polishing preparations; Soap: granulated, liquid, cake, flaked or chip; Detergents, synthetic organic or inorganic alkaline
Pr: James A Epstein
*CFO: William M Biddle
VP: Jim Smith
Rgnl Mgr: Greg Rassmussen
DP Exec: Richard Scott
VP Opers: Jeff Huber
Mfg Dir: Bryan Abernathy
Mtls Mgr: Robert Albers
Plnt Mgr: Steven Powell
Mktg Dir: Bob Nichols

D-U-N-S 12-159-1358
INTERCON CONSTRUCTION INC
INTERCON ENERGY SERVICES
5512 State Rd 19 & 113, Waunakee, WI 53597-9530
Tel (608) 850-4820 Founded/Ownrshp 2010
Sales 165.2MM EMP 625
Accts Sva Certified Public Accountan
SIC 1623 Oil & gas line & compressor station construction; Oil & gas pipeline construction; Communication line & transmission tower construction; Cable laying construction; Oil & gas line & compressor station construction; Oil & gas pipeline construction; Communication line & transmission tower construction; Cable laying construction
Pr: Anna Hillebrandt
Pr: Chris Wozniak
*Treas: Jamie De Bruin
*VP: Jeff Hillebrandt
Sfty Dirs: Tim Knaup
VP Mktg: Steve Allen
Board of Directors: Jamie De Bruin, Gail Deveau

INTERCON ENERGY SERVICES
See INTERCON CONSTRUCTION INC

INTERCON PAPER
See JR RODRIGUEZ INTERNATIONAL CORP

D-U-N-S 05-280-1750
INTERCONEX INC
(Suby of PARAMOUNT TRANSPORTATION SYSTEMS INC) ★
860 Greens Pkwy Ste 500, Houston, TX 77067-4453
Tel (281) 716-4800 Founded/Ownrshp 1969, 2005
Sales 41.0MM EMP 80
SIC 4731 4226 Foreign freight forwarding; Household goods, warehousing; Foreign freight forwarding; Household goods, warehousing
CEO: Chris Meyer
*CFO: Wil Tiongson
*Sr VP: Alex Talbot
Dir Bus: Victoria Meyer
Genl Mgr: Ephraim Hosein
Dir IT: Balaji Rayampettai

D-U-N-S 61-691-7761 IMP
INTERCONNECT CABLE TECHNOLOGIES CORP
ICTC USA
16090 Flight Path Dr, Brooksville, FL 34604-6824
Tel (352) 796-1716 Founded/Ownrshp 2007
Sales 31.4MM^E EMP 75
SIC 3643 3678 3679 5065 Current-carrying wiring devices; Electronic connectors; Harness assemblies for electronic use: wire or cable; Electronic parts & equipment
Pr: Sareet Majumdar
COO: Mary Alice Betts
Genl Mgr: Michael Carso
IT Man: Richard Maier
Sls Dir: Paul Sochacki
Board of Directors: Michael Thiel

D-U-N-S 09-826-7230 IMP
INTERCONNECT DEVICES INC
SYNERGETIX
(Suby of SMITHS INTERCONNECT GROUP LIMITED)
5101 Richland Ave, Kansas City, KS 66106-1089
Tel (913) 342-5544 Founded/Ownrshp 2010
Sales 53.2MM^E EMP 230
SIC 3679 3825 3643 3625 Electronic circuits; Instruments to measure electricity; Current-carrying wiring devices; Relays & industrial controls; Electronic circuits; Instruments to measure electricity; Current-carrying wiring devices; Relays & industrial controls
Pr: Michael Kirkman
*CFO: Mark Deuel
*Sr VP: Howard Weiner
VP: Christy Barrett
VP: Gabriel Guglielmi
CIO: Allen Henry
IT Man: Alan Henery
Tech Mgr: Kim House
Sls Dir: Bill Oxley
Sls Mgr: Kimberly Gallotello
Sls Mgr: Kimberly Rice
Board of Directors: George Moore, John Shoemaker

INTERCONNECT SOLUTIONS
See MX ELECTRONICS MANUFACTURING INC

D-U-N-S 15-370-2261 IMP
INTERCONNECT SYSTEMS INC
I S I
759 Flynn Rd, Camarillo, CA 93012-8056
Tel (805) 482-2870 Founded/Ownrshp 1988
Sales 37.6MM^E EMP 140
SIC 3674 Semiconductors & related devices; Semiconductors & related devices
Pr: William P Miller
*VP: Louis Buldain
*VP: Glen Griswold
IT Man: Joseph Bagliere
Opers Mgr: John Crawford
Prd Mgr: Gary Donovan
Ql Cn Mgr: Dave Nichols
Natl Sales: Mike Laskey
VP Mktg: Mark Gilliam
Sls Dir: Gilma Bustillos
Manager: Dave Gagnon

D-U-N-S 80-271-1887
INTERCONNECT WIRING LLP
5024 W Vickery Blvd, Fort Worth, TX 76107-7517
Tel (817) 377-9473 Founded/Ownrshp 2008
Sales 22.5MM EMP 150
Accts Bdo Usa Llp Fort Worth Texa
SIC 3694 3613 5063 3699 4581 Harness wiring sets, internal combustion engines; Panel & distribution boards & other related apparatus; Wire & cable; Flight simulators (training aids), electronic; Aircraft maintenance & repair services; Harness wiring sets, internal combustion engines; Panel & distribution boards & other related apparatus; Wire & cable; Flight simulators (training aids), electronic; Aircraft maintenance & repair services
Pr: John B Ashour
*VP: Chris Bettinger
*VP: Clare E McGarrey
*VP: Marc Piloian
VP: Matthew Ratliff
Prgrm Mgr: Thomas Kaler
IT Man: Doug Symes
IT Man: Chris Vardy
Ql Cn Mgr: Titus Ashour
Ql Cn Mgr: Jeanie Peel
Sales Exec: Bert Vergez

D-U-N-S 18-146-4152
INTERCONTINENTAL
INTERCONTINENTAL BUCKHEAD
3315 Peachtree Rd Ne, Atlanta, GA 30326-1007
Tel (404) 946-9000 Founded/Ownrshp 2005
Sales 14.3MM^E EMP 500
SIC 7011 Hotels; Hotels
Pr: John Porter
VP: Lou Fader
Exec: Terry Nackers
Genl Mgr: Patrick Birchal

INTERCONTINENTAL BUCKHEAD
See INTERCONTINENTAL

INTERCONTINENTAL CELLULOSE SLS
See EKMAN & CO INC

INTERCONTINENTAL CHICAGO OHARE
See RIVER ROAD HOTEL PARTNERS LLC

D-U-N-S 92-692-6259 IMP
INTERCONTINENTAL COFFEE TRADING INC
INTERCONTINENTAL COFFEE TRDG
110 W A St Ste 110, San Diego, CA 92101-3702
Tel (619) 338-8335 Founded/Ownrshp 2009
Sales 25.0MM^E EMP 10
SIC 2095 5499 Roasted coffee; Coffee
CEO: Lisa Colon

INTERCONTINENTAL COFFEE TRDG
See INTERCONTINENTAL COFFEE TRADING INC

D-U-N-S 07-887-0113
▲ **INTERCONTINENTAL EXCHANGE INC**
5660 New Northside Dr # 300, Atlanta, GA 30328-5823
Tel (770) 857-4700 Founded/Ownrshp 2000
Sales 4.2MMM EMP 2,902
SIC 6231 Security & commodity exchanges; Security & commodity exchanges
Ch Bd: Jeffrey C Sprecher
Pr: David Jonas
Pr: Lynn Martin
Pr: Charles A Vice
CFO: Scott A Hill
Treas: Martin Hunter
Ofcr: Scott Arkills
Ofcr: Stanislav Ivanov
Sr VP: Douglas A Foley
Sr VP: Jay Rajarathinam
VP: Tim Barry
VP: Mark Fabian
VP: Daniel Kennedy
VP: Kelly Loeffler
VP: Peter S Roberson
Exec: Julia Tenbroeck
Board of Directors: Charles R Crisp, William J Hague, Fred W Hatfield, Terrence F Martell, Robert Reid, Frederic V Salerno, Judith A Sprieser, Vincent Tese

D-U-N-S 83-569-1841
■ **INTERCONTINENTAL EXCHANGE INC**
ICE
(Suby of INTERCONTINENTAL EXCHANGE INC) ★
1415 Moonstone, Brea, CA 92821-2832
Tel (770) 857-4700 Founded/Ownrshp 2000
Sales 3.0MMM EMP 2,902
Tkr Sym ICE Exch NYS
SIC 6231 Security & commodity exchanges; Security & commodity exchanges
Ch Bd: Jeffrey C Sprecher
Pr: Ben Jackson
Pr: Bruce Tupper
Pr: Brad Vannan
Pr: Charles A Vice
CFO: Scott A Hill
Sr VP: Edwin D Marcial
Sr VP: Jonathan H Short
Prin: Charles R Crisp
Prin: Jean-Marc Forneri
Prin: Judd A Gregg

D-U-N-S 60-236-2931 IMP/EXP
INTERCONTINENTAL EXPORT IMPORT INC
I E I
8815 Centre Park Dr # 400, Columbia, MD 21045-2282
Tel (410) 674-5600 Founded/Ownrshp 1984
Sales 135.6MM^E EMP 70
SIC 5162 Plastics products; Plastics products
CEO: Saurabh Naik
*CFO: Srinath Dharmapadam
*VP: Rajiv Naik
Software D: Vinit Dedhia
Snr Mgr: Saureen Desai

D-U-N-S 96-102-3884
INTERCONTINENTAL HOLDING CO INC
ADAMS SUPER FOODS STORE
275 Schoolhouse Rd, Cheshire, CT 06410-1241
Tel (203) 272-3511 Founded/Ownrshp 1996
Sales 66.5MM^E EMP 850
SIC 5411 Grocery stores; Grocery stores
Pr: Michael A Bozzuto
Pr: Steve Heggelke
*VP: Robert Wood

INTERCONTINENTAL HOTEL
See CLEVELAND CLINIC HOTEL SERVICES INC

INTERCONTINENTAL HOTEL
See DTRS INTERCONTINENTAL CHICAGO LLC

D-U-N-S 80-662-9267
INTERCONTINENTAL HOTELS (PUERTO RICO) INC
INTERCNTNENTAL SAN JUAN RESORT
(Suby of INTERCONTINENTAL HOTELS GROUP RESOURCES INC) ★
5961 Ave Isla Verde, Carolina, PR 00979-5720
Tel (787) 791-5000 Founded/Ownrshp 2005
Sales 15.5MM^E EMP 500
SIC 7011 Hotels; Hotels
Genl Mgr: Alan S Carrette

D-U-N-S 12-598-7318
INTERCONTINENTAL HOTELS GROUP RESOURCES INC
(Suby of INTERCONTINENTAL HOTELS LIMITED)
3 Ravinia Dr Ste 100, Atlanta, GA 30346-2121
Tel (770) 604-5000 Founded/Ownrshp 1997
Sales 2.8MMM^E EMP 60,000
SIC 7011 8741 6794 Hotels & motels; Business management; Financial management for business; Hotel or motel management; Franchises, selling or licensing; Hotels & motels; Business management; Financial management for business; Hotel or motel management; Franchises, selling or licensing
CEO: Kirk Kinsell
*CFO: Robert Gunkel
Ofcr: Damali Stansbury
Exec: Joe Buentello
Exec: Rene Oskam
Dir Risk M: Douglas Austin
Comm Dir: Emma Corcoran
Prgrm Mgr: Amy Takahashi
Area Mgr: Lisa Britton
Genl Mgr: Chandra Badola
Genl Mgr: David Bixby

D-U-N-S 00-363-3562 IMP
INTERCONTINENTAL PACKAGING CO (MN)
PRESTIGE WINE & SPIRITS GROUP
(Suby of JOHNSON BROTHERS LIQUOR CO) ★
1999 Shepard Rd, Saint Paul, MN 55116-3210
Tel (651) 649-5823 Founded/Ownrshp 1969
Sales 48.8MM^E EMP 30
SIC 5182 Wine
CEO: Michael Johnson
*Pr: Doug McIntosh
*CEO: Lynn Johnson
*Treas: Scott Belsaas
Rgnl Mgr: Adam Roper
Rgnl Mgr: Peter Uliciansky
Site Mgr: Mikel Morgan
Natl Sales: Gail Dino

D-U-N-S 00-331-4728
INTERCONTINENTAL POTASH CORP (USA)
IC POTASH
(Suby of IC POTASH CORP)
600 W Bender Blvd, Hobbs, NM 88240-2287
Tel (575) 942-2799 Founded/Ownrshp 2010
Sales 25.0MM EMP 12^E
SIC 1474 Potash mining; Potash mining
Pr: Sidney Himmel
CFO: Kevin Strong
*Sr VP: Patricia Nicole
*VP: Tommy Cope

INTERCONTINENTAL SAN JUAN
See INTER CONTINENTAL SAN JUAN

INTERCONTINENTAL SERVICES
See SENIOR CARLTON LIVING INC

D-U-N-S 06-728-0073
INTERCONTINENTAL TERMINALS CO LLC
ITC
1943 Independence Pkwy S, La Porte, TX 77571-9801
Tel (281) 884-0300 Founded/Ownrshp 2007
Sales 62.9MM^E EMP 200
SIC 4226 Petroleum & chemical bulk stations & terminals for hire; Petroleum & chemical bulk stations & terminals for hire
Pr: Bernt A Netland
Mng Pt: Andy James
*CFO: Mark P Jeansonne
Sr VP: Bob Pennacchi
*Sr VP: Robert P Pennacchi
*Sr VP: Steve Turchi
VP: Roy Bass
VP: Karen Bradley
VP: Stanley King
*VP: Richard C Merz
Genl Mgr: Gary Coti

INTERCORP
See U S NITTO

D-U-N-S 88-345-7061 IMP
INTERCOS AMERICA INC
(Suby of INTERCOS SPA)
200 N Route 303, Congers, NY 10920-1772
Tel (845) 268-4400 Founded/Ownrshp 2005
Sales 35.6MM^E EMP 200
SIC 2844

D-U-N-S 01-358-2069
INTERCOUNTY APPLIANCE CORP
10 National Blvd, Medford, NY 11763-2253
Tel (631) 543-6900 Founded/Ownrshp 1956
Sales 85.8MM^E EMP 85
SIC 5064 Electric household appliances; Electric household appliances
Pr: Vito Blandi
*VP: Robert Stevens
MIS Dir: Thomas Tyers
Board of Directors: Richard Merhige

D-U-N-S 00-696-6600
INTERCOUNTY ELECTRIC COOPERATIVE ASSOCIATION INC
102 Maple Ave, Licking, MO 65542-9877
Tel (573) 674-2211 Founded/Ownrshp 1936
Sales 56.4MM EMP 115
SIC 4911 Distribution, electric power; Distribution, electric power
Genl Mgr: Dwayne Cartwright

D-U-N-S 14-467-8737
INTERCOUNTY SUPPLY INC
BORDER SALES
255 S Regent St, Port Chester, NY 10573-4724
Tel (914) 939-4350 Founded/Ownrshp 1997
Sales 66.6MM^E EMP 48
SIC 5074 Plumbing & hydronic heating supplies; Heating equipment (hydronic); Plumbing & heating valves
Ch Bd: William B Owen
*Ch Bd: Thomas Sabatino

INTERCRAMIC TILE STONE GALLERY
See INTERCERAMIC INC

D-U-N-S 60-199-6940
INTERCRUISES SHORESIDE & PORT SERVICES INC
(Suby of TUI AG)
80 Sw 8th St Ste 1800, Miami, FL 33130-3013
Tel (305) 373-5011 Founded/Ownrshp 2003
Sales 20.5MM^E EMP 115
SIC 4725 Sightseeing tour companies; Sightseeing tour companies
Pr: Celeste Gladstone
*Ex VP: Kristina Spencer

D-U-N-S 17-842-7910
INTERDENT INC
(*Suby of* HIG MIDDLE MARKET LLC) ★
9800 S La Cienega Blvd # 800, Inglewood, CA 90301-4442
Tel (310) 765-2400 *Founded/Ownrshp* 2012
Sales 126.7MME *EMP* 1,800
SIC 8021 Dentists' office; Dentists' office
Pr: Ivar S Chhina
COO: Scott Bremen
**CFO:* Robert W Hill
VP: John Bukowski
Rgnl Mgr: Cathy Lee
**CIO:* Lee Rouman
IT Man: Kathryn Leuenberger
Counsel: Gilda Breland
Counsel: Megan Wallace

D-U-N-S 79-210-1024
INTERDENT SERVICE CORP
(*Suby of* INTERDENT INC) ★
9800 S La Cienega Blvd # 800, Inglewood, CA 90301-4442
Tel (310) 765-2400 *Founded/Ownrshp* 1999
Sales 60.6MME *EMP* 1,700
SIC 8021 Dental clinics & offices; Dental clinics & offices
CEO: John Stenbrun
**CFO:* Jeff Hertzig
Sr VP: Kevin Webb
VP: Michelle Kahan

D-U-N-S 07-112-6072 IMP/EXP
INTERDESIGN INC (OH)
30725 Solon Indus Pkwy, Solon, OH 44139-4380
Tel (440) 248-0136 *Founded/Ownrshp* 1974
Sales 196.4MME *EMP* 280
SIC 5023 Home furnishings; Home furnishings
Pr: Robert Immerman
Ex VP: Robert Mountain
VP: Chris Banning
VP: Jason Shefrin
**VP:* Robert Woolnough
Dir IT: Pete Yedrzeyek
IT Man: Lesli Kelley
IT Man: Debi Sapolin
Natl Sales: Heidi Asplin
Natl Sales: Sarah Kutz
Natl Sales: Eric Lohm

D-U-N-S 05-720-7953
■ **INTERDIGITAL COMMUNICATIONS LLC**
(*Suby of* INTERDIGITAL INC) ★
200 Bellevue Pkwy Ste 300, Wilmington, DE 19809-3727
Tel (610) 878-7800 *Founded/Ownrshp* 2007
Sales 32.7MME *EMP* 200
SIC 3663 5999 Mobile communication equipment; Mobile telephones & equipment; Mobile communication equipment; Mobile telephones & equipment
Pr: William J Merritt
**Ch Bd:* Steven T Clontz
**CFO:* Richard J Brezski
Ofcr: Janet Point
**Ex VP:* Brian G Kiernan
VP: Guy M Hicks
VP: Andrew Isztwan
Counsel: Bruce G Bernstein
Snr Mgr: Alex Giladi
Board of Directors: Steven T Clontz, Edward Kamins, Robert S Roath, Robert W Shaner

D-U-N-S 80-632-9855
▲ **INTERDIGITAL INC**
200 Bellevue Pkwy Ste 300, Wilmington, DE 19809-3727
Tel (302) 281-3600 *Founded/Ownrshp* 1972
Sales 415.8MM *EMP* 320E
Accts Pricewaterhousecoopers Llp P
Tkr Sym IDCC *Exch* NGS
SIC 3663 5999 6794 Mobile communication equipment; Mobile telephones & equipment; Mobile communication equipment; Mobile telephones & equipment; Patent owners & lessors
Pr: William J Merritt
Pt: Todd Simpson
**Ch Bd:* Steven T Clontz
CFO: Richard J Brezski
Treas: Sidney D Rosenblatt
Ex VP: Jannie K Lau
Ex VP: James J Nolan
Ex VP: Lawrence Shay
Ex VP: Byung K Yi
Exec: Scott A McQuilkin
CTO: Himatlal Naresh
Board of Directors: Gilbert F Amelio, Jeffrey K Belk, S Douglas Hutcheson, Edward B Kamins, John A Kritzmacher, Kai Oistamo, Jean F Rankin, Robert S Roath

D-U-N-S 03-980-2574
INTEREUM INC
845 Berkshire Ln N, Minneapolis, MN 55441-5419
Tel (763) 238-0063 *Founded/Ownrshp* 2004
Sales 55.0MM *EMP* 114
SIC 5021 Office furniture; Office furniture
CEO: Matthew Sveen
**Pr:* Jerry Erickson
COO: Bob Mattson
**Treas:* Matt Sveen
**VP:* Bret Abbott
Exec: Penny Rosson
IT Man: Sherri Rhone
Opers Mgr: Bill Pease
Sales Asso: Sacha Sweeney
Snr Mgr: Loretta Bowes
Snr Mgr: Lori Hulzen

INTERFACE ADVNCE FRCE MSREMENT
See INTERFACE INC

D-U-N-S 87-432-2860 IMP
■ **INTERFACE AMERICAS INC**
(*Suby of* INTERFACE INC) ★
2859 Pcs Frry St 2000, Atlanta, GA 30339
Tel (770) 437-6800 *Founded/Ownrshp* 2000
Sales 305.4MME *EMP* 1,800
SIC 2273 Carpets & rugs; Carpets & rugs
Pr: John R Wells
COO: David Simmons
**CFO:* Patrick C Lynch
**Treas:* Keith Wright
VP: Buck Collett
Comm Dir: Valerie Bennett
IT Man: Brian Moran
Mktg Dir: Kristy Sherlund

D-U-N-S 79-879-0796
INTERFACE ASSOCIATES INC
INTERFACE CATHETER SOLUTIONS
(*Suby of* N D C) ★
27721 La Paz Rd, Laguna Niguel, CA 92677-3948
Tel (949) 448-7056 *Founded/Ownrshp* 2015
Sales 27.6MME *EMP* 175E
SIC 3841 5047 Surgical & medical instruments; Hospital equipment & furniture; Surgical & medical instruments; Hospital equipment & furniture
Pr: Gary D Curtis
Pr: Eric Mabry
CFO: Gayle L Arnold
VP: Nabil Jubran
CTO: Joe Stupecky
Prd Mgr: Juan Pomares
Ql Cn Mgr: Gonzalo Angalico
S&M/VP: Mark Geiger
Mktg Dir: Lucy Panzio
Mktg Mgr: Jennifer Fauria

INTERFACE CATHETER SOLUTIONS
See INTERFACE ASSOCIATES INC

D-U-N-S 05-497-6352
INTERFACE ENGINEERING INC
100 Sw Main St Ste 1600, Portland, OR 97204-3254
Tel (503) 382-2266 *Founded/Ownrshp* 2006
Sales 31.4MME *EMP* 180
SIC 8711 Mechanical engineering; Mechanical engineering; Electrical or electronic engineering
Pr: Andrew Frichtl
Prin: Richard Benney Jr
Prin: Stacey Lin
Prin: John McMichael
Admn Mgr: Hormoz Janssens
IT Man: Joe Schmid

D-U-N-S 82-641-9280
INTERFACE FLOORING SYSTEMS INC
2859 Paces Ferry Rd Se, Atlanta, GA 30339-5701
Tel (800) 336-0225 *Founded/Ownrshp* 1987
Sales 602.2MME *EMP* 1,000
SIC 3272 1771 3999 Floor slabs & tiles, precast concrete; Flooring contractor; Atomizers, toiletry
CEO: John R Wells
**CFO:* Patrick C Lynch

D-U-N-S 07-846-5199
INTERFACE HOLDINGS GROUP LIMITED LIABILITY CO
15 Kennedy Blvd, East Brunswick, NJ 08816-1250
Tel (732) 993-4141 *Founded/Ownrshp* 2010
Sales 54.3MME *EMP* 700
SIC 8743 Promotion service; Promotion service
COO: Mitchell Rubin
**VP:* Mark Buzharsky

D-U-N-S 06-108-1592 IMP
INTERFACE INC
INTERFACE ADVNCE FRCE MSREMENT
7401 E Butheruf Dr, Scottsdale, AZ 85260
Tel (480) 948-5555 *Founded/Ownrshp* 1968
Sales 24.6MME *EMP* 110
SIC 3829 3825 Physical property testing equipment; Instruments to measure electricity; Physical property testing equipment; Instruments to measure electricity
Ch Bd: Richard F Caris
**Pr:* C T Haller
CFO: Ken Gerard

D-U-N-S 06-453-9372 IMP/EXP
▲ **INTERFACE INC**
2859 Paces Ferry Rd Se # 2000, Atlanta, GA 30339-6216
Tel (770) 437-6800 *Founded/Ownrshp* 1973
Sales 1.0MMM *EMP* 3,245
Accts Bdo Usa Llp Atlanta Georgia
Tkr Sym TILE *Exch* NGS
SIC 2273 Carpets & rugs; Carpets & rugs
Ch Bd: Daniel T Hendrix
Pr: Neel Bradham
COO: Jay D Gould
CFO: Patrick C Lynch
Chf Mktg O: Jo Ann Herold
Sr VP: B L Demoura
Sr VP: Joyce D Lavalle
Sr VP: Claude Ouimet
Sr VP: Lindsey K Parnell
Sr VP: Pieter Vandertoorn
Sr VP: J H Walker
Sr VP: John R Wells
Sr VP: Raymond S Willoch
VP: Keith Armstrong
VP: George Bandy
VP: John Bradford
VP: Buck Collett
VP: Vicki Devuono
VP: Kevin Gallagher
VP: Sanjay Lall
VP: Erin Meezan
Board of Directors: John P Burke, Edward C Callaway, Andrew B Cogan, Carl I Gable, Daniel T Hendrix, Christopher G Kennedy, K David Kohler, James B Miller, Sheryl Palmer

D-U-N-S 92-608-1712 EXP
INTERFACE PERFORMANCE MATERIALS INC
216 Wohlsen Way, Lancaster, PA 17603-4043
Tel (717) 390-1886 *Founded/Ownrshp* 2012
Sales 182.5MME *EMP* 400
SIC 3053 Gasket materials; Gasket materials
Pr: Victor Swint
CFO: Bob Rathsam
Ex VP: Louis J Dannibale
Ex VP: Robert Rathsam
VP: Scott Dossey

D-U-N-S 92-922-7791
INTERFACE REHAB INC
774 S Placentia Ave # 200, Placentia, CA 92870-6838
Tel (714) 646-8300 *Founded/Ownrshp* 1995
Sales 35.1MME *EMP* 657
SIC 8049 Physical therapist; Speech specialist; Physical therapist; Speech specialist
CEO: Anant B Desai

D-U-N-S 78-099-0938 IMP
INTERFACE SEALING SOLUTIONS INC
(*Suby of* INTERFACE PERFORMANCE MATERIALS INC) ★
410 S 1st Ave, Marshalltown, IA 50158-5007
Tel (641) 752-6736 *Founded/Ownrshp* 2006
Sales 20.1MME *EMP* 135
SIC 3053 Gaskets, packing & sealing devices; Gaskets, packing & sealing devices
Ch Bd: Bill Warkentin
**CFO:* Lance Koved

D-U-N-S 14-706-2681
INTERFACE SECURITY SYSTEMS LLC
3773 Corporate Centre Dr, Earth City, MO 63045-1130
Tel (314) 595-0100 *Founded/Ownrshp* 1998
Sales 249.3MME *EMP* 538
SIC 4813 Security systems services;
CEO: Michael Shaw
COO: Michael McLeod
CFO: Ken Obermeyer
Ex VP: Chuck Moeling
Ex VP: Matt Stopa
VP: Jeffrey Frye
VP: Tim Meehling
VP: Randy Metz
Off Mgr: Dianne Offerman
Natl Sales: Kathie Milton
Mktg Mgr: Don Meadows

D-U-N-S 01-101-9496
INTERFACE SERVICES INC
106 Northpoint Pkwy 2, Acworth, GA 30102-2082
Tel (770) 975-4419 *Founded/Ownrshp* 2010
Sales 67.0MM *EMP* 29E
SIC 5713 Business consulting; Carpets
Pr: Pieter Van Der Toorn
**Prin:* John Costa

D-U-N-S 60-663-3907 IMP/EXP
■ **INTERFACEFLOR LLC**
(*Suby of* INTERFACE INC) ★
1503 Orchard Hill Rd, Lagrange, GA 30240-5709
Tel (706) 882-1891 *Founded/Ownrshp* 1981
Sales 367.0MM *EMP* 1,500
SIC 2273 Finishers of tufted carpets & rugs; Finishers of tufted carpets & rugs
VP: Steve Arbaugh
VP: John Bradford
VP: Jerry Hall
VP: Mark Iberri
VP: Cindi Oakey
VP: Timothy Riordan
VP: Pieter Van Der Toorn
VP: Chris Turk
Exec: Shannon Deluca
Exec: Mike Gutierrez
Exec: Joan Holda
Dir Bus: John Crouch

D-U-N-S 07-616-0449
INTERFAITH MEDICAL CENTER
1545 Atlantic Ave, Brooklyn, NY 11213-1122
Tel (718) 613-4000 *Founded/Ownrshp* 1982
Sales 174.7MM *EMP* 1,550
Accts Charles A Barragato & Co Llp
SIC 8062 General medical & surgical hospitals; General medical & surgical hospitals
CEO: Venra Glicpsman
COO: Amini McIntosh
CFO: Gregory Dixon
CFO: Robert Mariani
Sr VP: William Green
VP: John Goodwin
**Prin:* Gregory Dickson
**Prin:* Edward Glicpsman
Prgrm Mgr: Shontelle Ramsay
Nurse Mgr: Sharon Prawl
Nurse Mgr: Jessica Steele

INTERFAITH OF THE WOODLANDS
See WOODLAND RELIGIOUS COMMUNITY INC

D-U-N-S 06-044-3686
INTERFAITH OLDER ADULT PROGRAMS INC
600 W Virginia St Ste 300, Milwaukee, WI 53204-1551
Tel (414) 291-7500 *Founded/Ownrshp* 1975
Sales 7.9MM *EMP* 300
SIC 8322 Outreach program; Senior citizens' center or association; Outreach program; Senior citizens' center or association
CEO: Carol Eschner
Dir Vol: Kay Bloesl
**Pr:* Paul Bina
Sr VP: Samantha Garrett
**VP:* Maureen Slattery
Off Mgr: Crystal Stinemates
IT Man: Quan Booker
IT Man: Nate Gingras

D-U-N-S 05-421-8938
■ **INTERFINANCIAL INC**
(*Suby of* ASSURANT INC) ★
1 Chase Manhattan Plz # 41, New York, NY 10005-1401
Tel (212) 859-7000 *Founded/Ownrshp* 1980
Sales 238.1MME *EMP* 4,100
SIC 6719 Investment holding companies, except banks; Investment holding companies, except banks
CEO: Kerry Clayton
IT Man: William Henson

INTERFINISH
See CHICAGO METALLIC CORP

D-U-N-S 01-005-8451
INTERFLEX GROUP INC
3200 W Nc Highway 268, Wilkesboro, NC 28697-7459
Tel (336) 921-3505 *Founded/Ownrshp* 1975
Sales 51.6MME *EMP* 205
SIC 3053 Packing materials; Packing materials
Ch Bd: Stephen Doyle
**CFO:* William Elkin Jr
Ofcr: Lewis Brooks
**VP:* Eric Bumgarner
VP: Monica Murray
Ql Cn Mgr: Tina Kiefer

D-U-N-S 07-850-3454
INTERFOOD INC
(*Suby of* INTERFOOD HOLDING B.V.)
777 Brickell Ave Ste 702, Miami, FL 33131-2866
Tel (305) 456-7824 *Founded/Ownrshp* 2006
Sales 238.6MM *EMP* 25
Accts Gray Gray & Gray Cpas Westwoo
SIC 5143 Dairy products, except dried or canned; Dairy products, except dried or canned
Pr: Jason Medcalf
**Ch Bd:* Dirk Neerhoff
**CFO:* Nick Sharp
**V Ch Bd:* F C G M Van Stipdonk
**VP:* Johannes Van De Hueval

D-U-N-S 11-519-1322
INTERFOODS OF AMERICA INC
9500 S Dadeland Blvd # 800, Miami, FL 33156-2852
Tel (305) 670-0746 *Founded/Ownrshp* 1996
Sales 115.4MME *EMP* 3,576
SIC 5812 6794 Fast-food restaurant, chain; Chicken restaurant; Franchises, selling or licensing; Fast-food restaurant, chain; Chicken restaurant; Franchises, selling or licensing
Ch Bd: Robert S Berg
**COO:* Steven M Wemple
**CFO:* Francis X Maloney
CFO: Francis Maloney
VP: Mark Siragusa
Area Mgr: Gavert Bucknor
Area Supr: Sharon Mann
Dist Mgr: Willie Barnes
Dist Mgr: Tim Donnellan
Dist Mgr: Richard Thomason
Dir IT: Bryan McKinney

D-U-N-S 16-725-4486 EXP
INTERFOR US INC
(*Suby of* INTERFOR CORPORATION)
2211 Rimland Dr Ste 220, Bellingham, WA 98226-8654
Tel (360) 788-2299 *Founded/Ownrshp* 2004
Sales 440.5MME *EMP* 3,400
SIC 0811 2421 5031 Timber tracts; Lumber: rough, sawed or planed; Lumber, plywood & millwork; Lumber: rough, dressed & finished; Timber tracts; Lumber: rough, sawed or planed; Lumber, plywood & millwork; Lumber: rough, dressed & finished
Pr: Duncan K Davies
**Treas:* Norm Chow
**Sr VP:* John A Horning
**VP:* J Steven Hofer
**VP:* Otto F Schulte
**VP:* Richard J Slaco
**VP:* Mark Stock
Opers Mgr: Rick Forgaard

D-U-N-S 60-560-2606 IMP/EXP
INTERFOREST CORP
INTERFOREST PENN BEAVER DIV
(*Suby of* INTERFOREST LTD)
119 Aid Dr, Darlington, PA 16115-1637
Tel (724) 827-8366 *Founded/Ownrshp* 1987
Sales 20.2MME *EMP* 88
SIC 5031 2435 Veneer; Lumber: rough, dressed & finished; Hardwood veneer & plywood; Veneer; Lumber: rough, dressed & finished; Hardwood veneer & plywood
Pr: James Prescott
**Ch:* Hans-Joachim Danzer
**V Ch Bd:* Juergen De Gruyter
VP: Michael Morin

INTERFOREST PENN BEAVER DIV
See INTERFOREST CORP

D-U-N-S 00-438-7221
■ **INTERFORM CORP** (PA)
INTERFORM SOLUTIONS
(*Suby of* CHAMPION INDUSTRIES INC) ★
1901 Mayview Rd, Bridgeville, PA 15017-1520
Tel (412) 221-7321 *Founded/Ownrshp* 1964, 1996
Sales 41.0MME *EMP* 220
SIC 5112 2761 2791 7331 2759 2752 Manifold business forms; Computer forms, manifold or continuous; Continuous forms, office & business; Fanfold forms; Strip forms (manifold business forms); Typesetting; Direct mail advertising services; Commercial printing; Commercial printing, lithographic; Manifold business forms; Computer forms, manifold or continuous; Continuous forms, office & business; Fanfold forms; Strip forms (manifold business forms); Typesetting; Direct mail advertising services; Commercial printing; Commercial printing, lithographic
Pr: Ronald H Scott
**Treas:* E Romutis
VP: Paul Fodness
**VP:* James Rhodes
VP: Dan Rosswog
Creative D: Jeffrey Smith
Genl Mgr: John Nester
Off Mgr: Tammy Peters
Mktg Dir: Tony Redd
Sls Dir: Helen Kennedy
Sls Mgr: Kevin Mann

INTERFORM SOLUTIONS
See INTERFORM CORP

D-U-N-S 18-605-8079 IMP
INTERFRESH INC
2019 W Orangewood Ave A, Orange, CA 92868-1974
Tel (714) 449-1669 *Founded/Ownrshp* 1987
Sales 28.2MME *EMP* 50
SIC 5141 Food brokers
CEO: Craig A Smith
**Pr:* Christopher Puentes
COO: Gene Razo
**CFO:* Mary Tinkham
**Sec:* Philip Smith

Mktg Dir: Doug Stewart
Sls Mgr: Darryl Anderson

D-U-N-S 01-456-5014
INTERGALACTIC INC
BOOKMANS ENTERTAINMENT EXCHANG
3330 E Speedway Blvd, Tucson, AZ 85716-3936
Tel (520) 881-1744 *Founded/Ownrshp* 1977
Sales 26.0MM *EMP* 285
Accts Beachfleischman Pc Tucson A
SIC 5942 Book stores; Book stores
Pr: Robert Oldfather
Treas: Tom Carpenter
**Ex VP:* Sean Feeney
**VP:* James Lubinski
Store Mgr: Katie Downing
Store Mgr: Sarah McGovern

D-U-N-S 12-126-9489
INTERGEN
(*Suby of* INTERGEN SERVICES INC) ★
30 Corporate Dr Ste 400, Burlington, MA 01803-4252
Tel (781) 993-3000 *Founded/Ownrshp* 2003
Sales 45.0MM^E *EMP* 85^E
SIC 4911 Electric services
CEO: Neil H Smith
Pr: Mark Iamonaco
COO: Tim Menzie
Ofcr: Martin Gilbert
VP: Rich Coburn
VP: Susan Gonzalez
VP: Brent Gunther
VP: Mike Novelli
VP: Simo Santavirta
VP: Kathleen Sullivan
Genl Mgr: Malcolm Gamble

D-U-N-S 88-465-3734
INTERGEN SERVICES INC
(*Suby of* INTERGEN N.V.)
30 Corporate Dr Ste 400, Burlington, MA 01803-4252
Tel (781) 272-5250 *Founded/Ownrshp* 2008
Sales 45.6MM^E *EMP* 210
SIC 8748 Energy conservation consultant; Energy conservation consultant
Pr: Neil H Smith
**COO:* Tim Menzie
**CFO:* Marc Stewart
**VP:* Susan Gonzalez
**VP:* Kathleen Sullivan

D-U-N-S 05-515-7903
INTERGRAPH CORP
INTERGRAPH SEC, GOVT & INFRA
(*Suby of* HEXAGON AB)
305 Intergraph Way, Madison, AL 35758-7567
Tel (256) 799-6300 *Founded/Ownrshp* 1969, 2010
Sales 883.7MM^E *EMP* 4,000
SIC 7372 7373 7379 Application computer software; Computer integrated systems design; Computer related consulting services; Application computer software; Computer integrated systems design; Computer related consulting services
CEO: Ola Rollen
**Pr:* Gerhard Sallinger
COO: Scott Moore
**CFO:* Steven Cost
CFO: Doug Morrison
Ex VP: Patrick Holcomb
**Ex VP:* Ed Porter
VP: Mark Doherty
VP: Horst Harbauer
VP: Bart Hoogenraad
VP: Robert Mott
Dir Bus: David McDonald

D-U-N-S 96-339-5368
INTERGRAPH GOVERNMENT SOLUTIONS CORP
IGS
(*Suby of* INTERGRAPH CORP) ★
301 Cochran Rd Sw, Huntsville, AL 35824-1109
Tel (256) 799-6300 *Founded/Ownrshp* 2010
Sales 40.4MM^E *EMP* 150^E
SIC 7371 Computer software development; Computer software development
Pr: Joseph Fehrenbach
**CFO:* Ken Barnett
CFO: Tammy Brannen
**Sr VP:* Gerald King
**Sr VP:* Brad Ward

D-U-N-S 78-856-6300
INTERGRAPH PROCESS & BUILDING SOLUTIONS INC
(*Suby of* INTERGRAPH CORP) ★
1 Intergraph Corporation, Huntsville, AL 35894-0001
Tel (256) 730-2000 *Founded/Ownrshp* 2000
Sales 22.7MM^E *EMP* 700
SIC 7373 Systems software development services; Systems software development services
Pr: David Stinson
**COO:* Ed Edmondson
COO: Ed Mondson
**CFO:* Scott Moore
**VP:* Kurt Ingenthron
**VP:* Shiraz Jaffer
Dir Soc: Karen Carleton

INTERGRAPH SEC, GOVT & INFRA
See INTERGRAPH CORP

D-U-N-S 80-195-6525
INTERGRATED HEALTH SVCS OF GREEN BRIAR INC
GREEN BRIAR NURSING CENTER
9820 N Kendall Dr, Miami, FL 33176-1816
Tel (305) 412-3074 *Founded/Ownrshp* 1991
Sales 4.5MM^E *EMP* 300
SIC 8082 8051 Home health care services; Skilled nursing care facilities; Home health care services; Skilled nursing care facilities
Pr: Jim Santarsiero
**Treas:* William Krystopwicz

D-U-N-S 06-493-0886
▲ INTERGROUP CORP
10940 Wilshire Blvd # 2150, Los Angeles, CA 90024-3942
Tel (310) 889-2500 *Founded/Ownrshp* 1965
Sales 72.7MM *EMP* 319
Accts Burr Pilger Mayer Inc San F
Tkr Sym INTG *Exch* NAS
SIC 6513 Apartment building operators; Residential hotel operation; Apartment hotel operation; Apartment building operators; Residential hotel operation; Apartment hotel operation
Ch Bd: John V Winfield
Treas: David T Nguyen
VP: David C Gonzalez

D-U-N-S 60-972-9095
INTERGROUP INTERNATIONAL LTD
1111 E 200th St, Euclid, OH 44117-1134
Tel (216) 965-0257 *Founded/Ownrshp* 1999
Sales 24.4MM^E *EMP* 70
SIC 2821 Plastics materials & resins
Pt: Neil Gloger
Pt: Sarah Gatanas

D-U-N-S 61-079-4414 IMP
INTERGULF CORP
428 Highway 146 S, La Porte, TX 77571
Tel (281) 474-4210 *Founded/Ownrshp* 1989
Sales 27.0MM^E *EMP* 75^E
SIC 2911 2992 5172 4449 4212 4213 Petroleum refining; Lubricating oils & greases; Petroleum brokers; Canal & intracoastal freight transportation; Canal barge operations; Petroleum haulage, local; Liquid petroleum transport, non-local
Pr: Steve R Rhyne
**VP:* Rick R Crump
Cpers Mgr: Michael Canales
VP Sls: David Burkhardt
Sales Asso: Dawn McCain
Sales Asso: Angie Molina

D-U-N-S 06-510-6460
INTERHEALTH CORP
PIH HEALTH
12401 Washington Blvd, Whittier, CA 90602-1006
Tel (562) 698-0811 *Founded/Ownrshp* 1981
Sales 14.4MM *EMP* 1,400
SIC 8062 8011 General medical & surgical hospitals; Offices & clinics of medical doctors; General medical & surgical hospitals; Offices & clinics of medical doctors
Ch Bd: Richard Casford
**Pr:* Daniel F Adams
**CFO:* Gary Koger
**VP:* Ronald Yoshihara
CIO: Jim Pelgrin

D-U-N-S 12-496-6602
INTERIM HEALTH CARE OF COLUMBUS
INTERIM SERVICES
2680 N Columbus St Ste A, Lancaster, OH 43130-8411
Tel (740) 653-5990 *Founded/Ownrshp* 2000
Sales 23.3MM *EMP* 15
SIC 8059 Temporary help service; Rest home, with health care
Prin: Paul Sprouse

D-U-N-S 61-287-0915
INTERIM HEALTH CARE OF NORTHEAST INC
INTERIM SERVICES
608 Chestnut St, Manchester, NH 03104-3520
Tel (603) 668-6956 *Founded/Ownrshp* 1979
Sales 16.7MM^E *EMP* 500
SIC 7363 7361 8322 Medical help service; Nurses' registry; Individual & family services; Medical help service; Nurses' registry; Individual & family services
Pr: Richard A Peterson
**VP:* Elaine Peterson

D-U-N-S 87-717-9044
INTERIM HEALTH CARE OF NORTHWESTERN OHIO INC
INTERIM SERVICES
(*Suby of* INTERIM HEALTHCARE) ★
3100 W Central Ave # 250, Toledo, OH 43606-2914
Tel (419) 578-4698 *Founded/Ownrshp* 1992
Sales 9.2MM^E *EMP* 400
SIC 8082 Home health care services; Home health care services
CEO: Harold A Salo
**Pr:* Thomas Di Marco
**Pr:* Michael W Hartshorn

INTERIM HEALTHCARE
See SALO INC

INTERIM HEALTHCARE
See BAYOU HOMECARE LP

D-U-N-S 61-465-4804
INTERIM HEALTHCARE INC
INTERIM SERVICES
(*Suby of* THE HALIFAX GROUP LLC)
1601 Swgrs Corp Pkwy # 100, Sunrise, FL 33323-2827
Tel (800) 338-7786 *Founded/Ownrshp* 2012
Sales 510.4MM^E *EMP* 2,552^E
SIC 6794 7363 8082 Franchises, selling or licensing; Medical help service; Home health care services
Pr: Kathleen Gilmartin
V Ch: Allan Sorensen
CFO: Bill Bologna
**Treas:* Michael Slupecki
**V Ch Bd:* Allan C Sorensen
Ofcr: Catherine Kreston
Ofcr: Barbara McCann
**VP:* Max Hahnen
VP: David Haslup
**VP:* Barbara Mc Cann
**VP:* Satish Movva
VP: Hermanda Taylor
VP: Steven Turner
VP: Ray Umansky
VP: Keith Walsh
VP: Mike Zeshonski
Dir Risk M: Dwight Garner
Dir Bus: Sara Watson

D-U-N-S 60-462-0898
INTERIM HEALTHCARE INC
ACTIVE WAY
3020 W Willow Knolls Dr # 1, Peoria, IL 61614-8128
Tel (309) 693-7665 *Founded/Ownrshp* 1988
Sales 10.2MM^E *EMP* 580
SIC 7363 8099 8082 Medical help service; Physical examination & testing services; Physical examination service, insurance; Home health care services; Medical help service; Physical examination & testing services; Physical examination service, insurance; Home health care services
Pr: Randy Lawson
**VP:* Sandy Lawson
Off Mgr: Laura Rosecran
Nrsg Dir: Jackie Cooley

D-U-N-S 08-443-4299
INTERIM HEALTHCARE OF COLUMBUS INC
INTERIM SERVICES
(*Suby of* INTERIM HEALTHCARE) ★
784 Morrison Rd, Gahanna, OH 43230-6642
Tel (614) 888-3130 *Founded/Ownrshp* 1981
Sales 27.6MM *EMP* 800
Accts Dohner Louis & Stephens Inc
SIC 8082 Home health care services; Home health care services
Pr: Thomas J Dimarco
**Prin:* Michael W Hartshorn
**Prin:* Richard Nielsen
IT Man: Tyler Rader

D-U-N-S 07-127-8501
INTERIM HEALTHCARE OF DAYTON INC
MEDICAL PRSNNEL POOL OF DAYTON
(*Suby of* INTERIM HEALTHCARE) ★
30 W Rahn Rd Ste 2, Dayton, OH 45429-2238
Tel (937) 291-5330 *Founded/Ownrshp* 1985
Sales 6.7MM^E *EMP* 299
SIC 7363 Temporary help service; Temporary help service
Pr: Thomas J Dimarco

D-U-N-S 15-628-7120
INTERIM HEALTHCARE OF EASTERN CAROLINAS INC
(*Suby of* INTERIM HEALTHCARE INC) ★
301 Liberty St, Whiteville, NC 28472-3714
Tel (910) 642-2106 *Founded/Ownrshp* 1984
Sales 13.6MM^E *EMP* 517
SIC 7363 8082 Medical help service; Home health care services; Visiting nurse service; Medical help service; Home health care services; Visiting nurse service
Prin: Donna Lou Byrd
Nrsg Dir: Karen Warwick

D-U-N-S 78-909-1998
INTERIM HEALTHCARE OF EASTERN CONNECTICUT INC
12 Case St Ste 215, Norwich, CT 06360-2222
Tel (860) 889-3388 *Founded/Ownrshp* 1976
Sales 16.2MM^E *EMP* 800
SIC 7363 8082 Medical help service; Home health care services; Medical help service; Home health care services
Pr: Shirley Langford

D-U-N-S 78-932-9836
INTERIM HEALTHCARE OF LUBBOCK INC
INTERIM SERVICES
5224 75th St Ste D, Lubbock, TX 79424-2525
Tel (806) 791-0042 *Founded/Ownrshp* 2001
Sales 12.0MM *EMP* 500
SIC 7363 Temporary help service; Temporary help service
CEO: Jason Bullard
**Pr:* Jim Bullard

D-U-N-S 18-985-3534
INTERIM HEALTHCARE OF NORTH CENTRAL FLORIDA INC
INTERIM SERVICES
9738 Us Highway 441 # 102, Leesburg, FL 34788-3974
Tel (352) 326-0400 *Founded/Ownrshp* 1983
Sales 17.0MM^E *EMP* 800
SIC 8082 7361 Home health care services; Employment agencies; Home health care services; Employment agencies
Pr: Edward Foxx Bixby
**VP:* Ronald Jakubiak

D-U-N-S 96-453-1024
INTERIM HEALTHCARE OF NORTHERN CALIFORNIA INC
970 Executive Way, Redding, CA 96002-0630
Tel (530) 221-1300 *Founded/Ownrshp* 1995
Sales 11.9MM^E *EMP* 350
SIC 8082 Home health care services; Home health care services
Pr: Robert Seawright
Pr: Rob Chapman

D-U-N-S 12-666-9261
INTERIM HEALTHCARE OF NORTHWEST FLORIDA INC
INTERIM SERVICES
1962 Village Green Way B, Tallahassee, FL 32308-3871
Tel (850) 422-2044 *Founded/Ownrshp* 1998
Sales 10.4MM^E *EMP* 400
SIC 8082 Home health care services; Home health care services
Pr: Robert G Gaff
**VP:* Cynthia Lavoie

D-U-N-S 87-878-8236
INTERIM HEALTHCARE OF PITTSBURGH INC
512 Georgian Pl, Somerset, PA 15501-1613
Tel (814) 445-1080 *Founded/Ownrshp* 1971
Sales 62.9MM *EMP* 2
SIC 7363 Temporary help service; Temporary help service
Pr: Thomas J Dimarco
**VP:* Thomas W Caldwell

D-U-N-S 80-731-9942
INTERIM HEALTHCARE OF SPOKANE INC
INTERIM SERVICES
1625 W 4th Ave Uppr A, Spokane, WA 99201-5620
Tel (509) 456-5665 *Founded/Ownrshp* 1990
Sales 2.2MM *EMP* 350
SIC 8082 Home health care services; Home health care services
CEO: Terrance D Blanchat
**Pr:* Rick Morris
**VP:* Paula Sweeney

D-U-N-S 87-713-0211
INTERIM HEALTHCARE OF TULSA INC
2828 E 51st St Ste 102, Tulsa, OK 74105-1745
Tel (918) 746-7828 *Founded/Ownrshp* 1974
Sales 20.6MM^E *EMP* 400
SIC 7363 7361 Medical help service; Nurses' registry; Medical help service; Nurses' registry
Pr: Terri Heritage
COO: Karen Burges
Prgrm Mgr: Judy Walker
IT Man: Russ Sanders
Sls&Mrk Ex: Marilyn Rumley

D-U-N-S 82-487-4614
INTERIM HEALTHCARE PRIVATE SERVICES INC
INTERIM SERVICES
9738 Us Highway 441 # 102, Leesburg, FL 34788-3962
Tel (352) 326-0400 *Founded/Ownrshp* 1987
Sales 14.8MM^E *EMP* 700
SIC 7363 Temporary help service; Temporary help service
Pr: Edward Foxx Bixby

D-U-N-S 19-672-8075
INTERIM HOME HEALTHCARE CO
INTERIM SERVICES
2526 Ward Blvd, Wilson, NC 27893-1600
Tel (252) 243-7808 *Founded/Ownrshp* 1988
Sales 60.3MM^E *EMP* 3,000
SIC 8082 Home health care services; Home health care services
Pr: John Morris
**Sec:* June Piper
**VP:* Lisa Morris

INTERIM SERVICES
See INTERIM HEALTHCARE OF COLUMBUS INC

INTERIM SERVICES
See GARY HALGRAN

INTERIM SERVICES
See INTERIM HEALTH CARE OF COLUMBUS

INTERIM SERVICES
See INTERIM HEALTHCARE OF NORTHWEST FLORIDA INC

INTERIM SERVICES
See INTERIM HEALTHCARE OF NORTH CENTRAL FLORIDA INC

INTERIM SERVICES
See INTERIM HOME HEALTHCARE CO

INTERIM SERVICES
See INTERIM HEALTH CARE OF NORTHEAST INC

INTERIM SERVICES
See INTERIM HEALTHCARE INC

INTERIM SERVICES
See INTERIM HEALTHCARE OF LUBBOCK INC

INTERIM SERVICES
See INTERIM HEALTHCARE OF SPOKANE INC

INTERIM SERVICES
See INTERIM HEALTHCARE PRIVATE SERVICES INC

INTERIM SERVICES
See INTERIM HEALTH CARE OF NORTHWESTERN OHIO INC

D-U-N-S 84-935-7843
INTERIOR ALASKA MCDONALDS INC
1930 Airport Way, Fairbanks, AK 99701-4010
Tel (907) 452-4600 *Founded/Ownrshp* 1987
Sales 6.3MM^E *EMP* 350^E
SIC 5812 Fast-food restaurant, chain; Fast-food restaurant, chain
Pr: Kathi Cinkosky

D-U-N-S 13-051-7766
INTERIOR ARCHITECTS INC
500 Sansome St Ste 8th, San Francisco, CA 94111-3211
Tel (415) 434-3305 *Founded/Ownrshp* 1984
Sales 87.5MM *EMP* 200
SIC 8712

D-U-N-S 02-345-5785
INTERIOR CONSTRUCTION SERVICES LTD
ICS CONSTRUCTION SERVICES
2930 Market St, Saint Louis, MO 63103-2525
Tel (314) 534-6664 *Founded/Ownrshp* 1980
Sales 56.1MM *EMP* 125
Accts Rubinbrown Llp Saint Louis M
SIC 1752 1742 Floor laying & floor work; Drywall; Floor laying & floor work; Drywall
Pr: Gregory J Zavaglia
**Treas:* Dennis Beausang
**VP:* Michael Zavaglia

D-U-N-S 03-811-0995 IMP
INTERIOR DESIGN SERVICES INC
OFFICE FURNITURE NASHVILLE
(*Suby of* DEKALB OFFICE ENVIRONMENTS INC) ★
209 Powell Pl, Brentwood, TN 37027-7522
Tel (615) 340-9200 *Founded/Ownrshp* 2013
Sales 77.4MM^E *EMP* 100
SIC 5021 5712 7389 Office & public building furniture; Office furniture; Interior decorating; Office & public building furniture; Office furniture; Interior decorating
Pr: John Rasper
**VP:* Anita Baltimore

**VP:* Steve Meek
VP: Trent Sullivan
Off Mgr: Kayla Bowen
IT Man: Brett Jackson
VP Sls: Tim Carroll

D-U-N-S 03-390-4611 EXP
INTERIOR ELEMENTS GOVERNMENT SALES DIVISION INC
CAPITOL FURNITURE DISTRIBUTION
(*Suby of* CAPITOL SUPPLY INC) ★
5225 Nw 33rd Ave, Fort Lauderdale, FL 33309-6302
Tel (954) 485-5000 *Founded/Ownrshp* 1998
Sales 30.0MM *EMP* 24
SIC 5021 Office furniture; Office furniture
Pr: Harry Steinman
VP: Joan Steele
Dir IT: Gary Nelson
Mktg Mgr: Nadine Mathieu
Sls Mgr: David Ostan
Sales Asso: Mike Althoff
Sales Asso: Kim Douglas

INTERIOR EXTERIOR BUILDING SUP
See INTERIOR/EXTERIOR BUILDING SUPPLY LIMITED PARTNERSHIP

D-U-N-S 05-778-9419
■ **INTERIOR HOLDINGS LLC**
(*Suby of* PEABODY ENERGY CORP) ★
701 Market St Ste 700, Saint Louis, MO 63101-1826
Tel (314) 342-3400 *Founded/Ownrshp* 1994
Sales 20.4MM^E *EMP* 25
SIC 8731 Energy research
Pr: Irl Engelhardt

INTERIOR INVESTMENTS
See I3 GROUP INC

D-U-N-S 01-427-5445 IMP
INTERIOR INVESTMENTS LLC
(*Suby of* I3 GROUP INC) ★
550 Bond St, Lincolnshire, IL 60069-4207
Tel (847) 325-1000 *Founded/Ownrshp* 1997
Sales 35.5MM^E *EMP* 102
SIC 5712 Office furniture
VP: John Horak

D-U-N-S 83-457-5052
INTERIOR REMOVAL SPECIALIST INC
8990 Atlantic Ave, South Gate, CA 90280-3505
Tel (323) 357-6900 *Founded/Ownrshp* 1994
Sales 29.9MM^E *EMP* 150
SIC 1795 Demolition, buildings & other structures; Demolition, buildings & other structures
CEO: Carlos Herrera
**VP:* Isabel Herrera
Dir IT: Gary Shelton
Sfty Dirs: Raul Anguiano
Opers Mgr: Vicky Herrera
Opers Mgr: Roxy Rocha

INTERIOR SOLUTIONS
See NATIONAL DESIGN & TRADE NETWORK INC

D-U-N-S 10-317-2961 IMP
INTERIOR SPECIALISTS INC
(*Suby of* FARADAY HOLDINGS LLC)
1630 Faraday Ave, Carlsbad, CA 92008-7313
Tel (760) 929-6700 *Founded/Ownrshp* 2014
Sales 288.3MM^E *EMP* 1,000
SIC 1752 1799 Carpet laying; Drapery track installation; Carpet laying; Drapery track installation
Pr: Alan Davenport
Pr: Brian Reed
Pr: Lee Singer
Pr: Joe Terrana
Pr: Tom Tidmore
COO: Stephanie Heim
**CFO:* Robert Hess
**Sr VP:* Randy Bafus
**Sr VP:* Dennis Crowley
**Sr VP:* Pat Crowley
VP: John McMillen

D-U-N-S 61-149-0756
INTERIOR SPECIALISTS INC
11012 Red Lion Rd, White Marsh, MD 21162
Tel (410) 335-0381 *Founded/Ownrshp* 1990
Sales 28.8MM^E *EMP* 150
SIC 1795 Wrecking & demolition work; Demolition, buildings & other structures; Wrecking & demolition work; Demolition, buildings & other structures
Pr: Dino Trombetta
**VP:* Michael Carbaugh

D-U-N-S 10-802-8143
INTERIOR SYSTEMS CONTRACTING INC
ISC CONTRACTING
1545 S Kingshighway Blvd, Saint Louis, MO 63110-2227
Tel (314) 533-1888 *Founded/Ownrshp* 1981
Sales 28.1MM *EMP* 60
Accts Brown Smith Wallace Llc St
SIC 1542 Commercial & office building contractors; Commercial & office building contractors
Pr: Dan Green
Bd of Dir: Dan Ford
**VP:* Scott Seymour
Sfty Mgr: John Perkowski

D-U-N-S 09-854-5064 IMP
INTERIOR SYSTEMS INC
241 N Brdwy Ste 600, Milwaukee, WI 53202
Tel (414) 224-0957 *Founded/Ownrshp* 1979
Sales 73.7MM^E *EMP* 300
SIC 2599 2511 Restaurant furniture, wood or metal; Wood household furniture; Restaurant furniture, wood or metal; Wood household furniture
Ch Bd: Lindsey S Bovinet
**Pr:* Tony Lutz
**VP:* Gerald Andino
VP: Christine Braswell
Creative D: Tony Pagliuca
Sys Mgr: Kevin Paiser
VP Sls: Melanie Laspina-Bixler
Sls Dir: Jason Fredrickson
Sls Mgr: Richard Best

D-U-N-S 03-440-8617
INTERIOR/EXTERIOR BUILDING SUPPLY LIMITED PARTNERSHIP
INTERIOR EXTERIOR BUILDING SUP
730 S Scott St, New Orleans, LA 70119-6935
Tel (504) 484-6613 *Founded/Ownrshp* 1965
Sales 153.1MM^E *EMP* 130
SIC 5031 Building materials, exterior; Building materials, interior; Building materials, exterior; Building materials, interior
Pt: James Geary
IT Man: Scott Morey
Opers Mgr: Scott Cason
Sales Asso: David Adams
Sales Asso: Michael Fuselier
Sales Asso: Tuck Moon
Sales Asso: Teresa Savell

D-U-N-S 06-585-4655 IMP/EXP
INTERKAL LLC
(*Suby of* KOTOCORP (USA) INC) ★
5981 E Cork St, Kalamazoo, MI 49048-9638
Tel (269) 349-1521 *Founded/Ownrshp* 1988
Sales 34.5MM^E *EMP* 150
SIC 2531 Stadium seating; Stadium seating
Pr: Matt Lalonde
Info Man: Phil Miller
Sftwr Eng: Brian Stafford
Trfc Mgr: Brian Ellis
Sls Mgr: Larry Parrish

D-U-N-S 61-873-6557
INTERLAKE HOLDING CO
1 Landmark Sq Ste 710, Stamford, CT 06901-2670
Tel (203) 977-8900 *Founded/Ownrshp* 1987
Sales 106.4MM *EMP* 25
Accts Grant Thornton Llp Cleveland
SIC 4449 4499 Intracoastal (freight) transportation; Boat & ship rental & leasing, except pleasure; Intracoastal (freight) transportation; Boat & ship rental & leasing, except pleasure
Ch Bd: Paul R Tregurtha
Pr: James R Barker
VP: Robert F Dorn
VP: John Hopkins

D-U-N-S 11-929-8792
INTERLAKE INDUSTRIES INC
4732 E 355th St, Willoughby, OH 44094-4632
Tel (440) 942-0800 *Founded/Ownrshp* 1957
Sales 25.5MM^E *EMP* 180
SIC 3469 Stamping metal for the trade; Stamping metal for the trade
Pr: Lisa M Habe
**VP:* Dan Valentino
VP: Norm Valentino Sr

D-U-N-S 12-101-7771 IMP
INTERLAKE MECALUX INC
(*Suby of* MECALUX, SA)
1600 N 25th Ave Ste A, Melrose Park, IL 60160-1868
Tel (708) 344-9999 *Founded/Ownrshp* 2000
Sales 424.1MM^E *EMP* 650
SIC 5084 2542 Industrial machinery & equipment; Partitions & fixtures, except wood; Industrial machinery & equipment; Partitions & fixtures, except wood
Pr: Angel De Arriba
CFO: Susan Elizabeth
VP: Vinnie Depaola
VP: David Suica
Genl Mgr: Daniel Joly
Genl Mgr: Tim Kelleher
CTO: Vinod Rodrigo
Dir IT: Pete Deckert
Dir IT: Kryzsztof Zygulski
IT Man: Jose Guajardo
IT Man: John Meile

D-U-N-S 06-889-0011
INTERLAKE STEAMSHIP CO
(*Suby of* INTERLAKE HOLDING CO) ★
7300 Engle Rd, Middleburg Heights, OH 44130-3429
Tel (440) 260-6900 *Founded/Ownrshp* 1913
Sales 106.4MM *EMP* 25
SIC 4432 Freight transportation on the Great Lakes; Freight transportation on the Great Lakes
Ch: James R Barker
**Pr:* Mark W Barker
Pr: Bob Dorn
**CFO:* Andrew Langlois
CFO: William Thornton
**V Ch Bd:* Paul R Tregurtha
**Sr VP:* Robert F Dorn
Opers Mgr: Chad Kidder
Opers Mgr: Phil Moore

INTERLAKEN TECHNOLOGY
See WATER WORKS MANUFACTURING INC

D-U-N-S 11-245-0304
INTERLATIN INC
300 S Alto Mesa Dr Ste A, El Paso, TX 79912-4430
Tel (915) 298-5450 *Founded/Ownrshp* 1998
Sales 33.7MM *EMP* 342^E
Accts Pena Briones Mcdaniel And Co
SIC 5084 Printing trades machinery, equipment & supplies; Printing trades machinery, equipment & supplies
Pr: Alejandro Carillo
CFO: Brenda Martinez

D-U-N-S 61-193-7053
INTERLEMO USA INC
(*Suby of* LEMO S.A.)
635 Park Ct, Rohnert Park, CA 94928-7940
Tel (707) 578-8811 *Founded/Ownrshp* 1986
Sales 85.8MM^E *EMP* 101
SIC 5065 Connectors, electronic
Genl Mgr: Peter Mueller

D-U-N-S 06-958-9925
INTERLINC MORTGAGE SERVICES LLC
10613 W Sam Houston Pkwy, Houston, TX 77064-4657
Tel (281) 664-6437 *Founded/Ownrshp* 2011
Sales 38.9MM^E *EMP* 228^E
SIC 6211 6162 Mortgages, buying & selling; Mortgage bankers & correspondents; Mortgages, buying & selling; Mortgage bankers & correspondents

CEO: James Van Steenhouse
**CFO:* David Scheiderich
Brnch Mgr: Bob Pape
IT Man: Todd Wedlake

D-U-N-S 08-079-2989 IMP
■ **INTERLINE BRANDS INC**
SUPPLY WORKS
(*Suby of* INTERLINE BRANDS INC) ★
801 W Bay St, Jacksonville, FL 32204-1605
Tel (904) 421-1400 *Founded/Ownrshp* 2000
Sales 2.2MMM^E *EMP* 3,279^E
Accts Deloitte & Touche Llp Jackson
SIC 5074 5063 5072 Plumbing fittings & supplies; Electrical fittings & construction materials; Hardware; Plumbing fittings & supplies; Electrical fittings & construction materials; Hardware
CEO: Michael J Grebe
**Ch Bd:* Michael Grebe
**Pr:* Kenneth D Sweder
**COO:* William E Sanford
**CFO:* John K Bakewell
**CFO:* John Ebner
**CFO:* Tom Tossavainen
**Chf Mktg O:* William R Pray
**VP:* Laurence W Howard
Dist Mgr: Mike Huller
Dist Mgr: Joel Lewis
Board of Directors: Gideon Argov, Michael E Dedomenico, John J Gavin, Barry J Goldstein, Ernest K Jacquet, Christopher W Santoro, Drew T Sawyer

D-U-N-S 36-111-2936 IMP/EXP
■ **INTERLINE BRANDS INC**
(*Suby of* HOME DEPOT INC) ★
801 W Bay St, Jacksonville, FL 32204-1605
Tel (904) 421-1400 *Founded/Ownrshp* 2015
Sales 2.4MMM^E *EMP* 4,300
SIC 5074 5063 5072 Plumbing fittings & supplies; Electrical fittings & construction materials; Hardware; Plumbing fittings & supplies; Electrical fittings & construction materials; Hardware
Ch Bd: Michael J Grebe
Pr: Kenneth D Sweder
COO: Mike Canales
CFO: Federico Pensotti
Chf Mktg O: Jonathan S Bennett
Sr VP: John McDonald
VP: Michael Agliata
VP: Chad Kluko
Genl Mgr: Julie Kobliska
CIO: Lucretia D Doblado
Opers Mgr: Aaron Brooks

D-U-N-S 96-798-0558
INTERLINK
INTERLINK COMPANY THE
10940 Wilshire Blvd, Los Angeles, CA 90024-3915
Tel (310) 734-1499 *Founded/Ownrshp* 1992
Sales NA *EMP* 103
SIC 6159 8742 Intermediate investment banks; Banking & finance consultant
**V Ch:* Dr Charles Kohlhaas
**Ex VP:* Jason P Caramanis

INTERLINK COMPANY THE
See INTERLINK

D-U-N-S 78-374-6688
INTERLINK COMMUNICATION SYSTEMS INC
(*Suby of* ICS CONSOLIDATED INC) ★
700 Brooker Ste 1000, Oldsmar, FL 34677
Tel (813) 925-6021 *Founded/Ownrshp* 2000
Sales 65.8MM^E *EMP* 21
SIC 5065 Electronic parts & equipment
Ch: Marty Poad
**Pr:* Alan Higgins
COO: Daniel Fung
**COO:* Thomas W Straub
**CFO:* William Scott
**Ex VP:* Joe Serra
VP: Cynthia McLellan
VP: Grace Natividad
**VP:* Diane R Poad
Exec: Jacquie Stovern
Mktg Dir: Fabien Maisl

INTERLINK SUPPLY
See BRIDGEWATER LLC

D-U-N-S 07-928-3461
INTERLOCHEN CENTER FOR ARTS
I.C.A.
4000 M 137, Interlochen, MI 49643-8427
Tel (231) 276-7200 *Founded/Ownrshp* 1927
Sales 53.8MM *EMP* 475
Accts Bdo Usa Llp Grand Rapids Mi
SIC 8299 8211 Art school, except commercial; Preparatory school; Boarding school; Art school, except commercial; Preparatory school; Boarding school
Ex Dir: Jeffrey S Kimpton
Ofcr: Kara Francisco
Ofcr: Janet Morris
Assoc VP: Beth Stoner
VP: Timothy J Dougherty
**VP:* Edward Farraday
**VP:* Ann Hanson
**VP:* Pat Kessel
**VP:* Thomas Paulson
**VP:* Eric Snoek
**VP:* Timothy Wade

INTERLOCHEN FOR THE ARTS
See INTERLOCK & CENTER FOR ARTS

D-U-N-S 17-044-3498
INTERLOCK & CENTER FOR ARTS
INTERLOCHEN FOR THE ARTS
4000 M 137, Interlochen, MI 49643-8427
Tel (231) 276-7472 *Founded/Ownrshp* 1928
Sales 27.0MM^E *EMP* 1
SIC 8299 Art school, except commercial; Art school, except commercial
CFO: Patrick M Kessel
**CEO:* Owen Kimpton

D-U-N-S 10-213-4178 IMP/EXP
INTERLOCK INDUSTRIES INC
545 S 3rd St Ste 310, Louisville, KY 40202-1936
Tel (502) 569-2007 *Founded/Ownrshp* 1982
Sales 380.3MM^E *EMP* 1,000
SIC 3341 4121 3444 3354 2653

D-U-N-S 92-847-5276 IMP/EXP
INTERLOG USA INC
(*Suby of* NETWORK FOB) ★
9380 Central Ave Ne # 350, Minneapolis, MN 55434-3567
Tel (612) 789-3456 *Founded/Ownrshp* 2014
Sales 37.0MM^E *EMP* 150
SIC 4731 Freight transportation arrangement; Freight transportation arrangement
CEO: David Canfield
VP: Brent Koughan

D-U-N-S 00-213-7099 IMP
INTERLUDE HOME INC
25 Trefoil Dr, Trumbull, CT 06611-1330
Tel (203) 445-7617 *Founded/Ownrshp* 1961
Sales 30.8MM^E *EMP* 125
SIC 5099 Mobile home parts & accessories; Mobile home parts & accessories
Pr: Carl Phillips
CFO: David Brault
VP: Phoebe Bergenheim
VP: Jim Calhoun
VP: Georg Ching
Dir IT: Scott Flewelling
Sls Mgr: Mitchell Bernstein
S&M/Mgr: Sean McFadden

D-U-N-S 36-424-2370
INTERMAP TECHNOLOGIES INC
(*Suby of* INTERMAP TECHNOLOGIES CORPORATION)
8310 S Valley Hwy Ste 400, Englewood, CO 80112-5809
Tel (303) 708-0955 *Founded/Ownrshp* 1996
Sales 37.4MM^E *EMP* 182^E
SIC 7389 Photogrammatic mapping; Photogrammatic mapping
Pr: Todd Oseth
Sr VP: Rich Mohr
Sr VP: Richard Mohr
VP: Bob Antoniazzi
VP: Kevin Burns
VP: Bruce Engelbert
VP: Nigel Jackson
VP: Dan Lynch
VP: Walter Sedlacek
VP: J Keith Tennant
Off Mgr: Kate Bachman
Board of Directors: John C Curlander, Mike Hoehn, Howard J Nellor

D-U-N-S 00-338-0755
INTERMARINE INC (DE)
10000 Memorial Dr Ste 700, Houston, TX 77024-3412
Tel (713) 984-9999 *Founded/Ownrshp* 1982
Sales 28.8MM^E *EMP* 300
SIC 4412 4424 4492 Deep sea foreign transportation of freight; Deep sea domestic transportation of freight; Marine towing services; Deep sea foreign transportation of freight; Deep sea domestic transportation of freight; Marine towing services
Ch Bd: Marshall Cloyd
**Sec:* Jeannette Robinson Cloyd

D-U-N-S 61-155-9428 IMP/EXP
INTERMARINE LLC
1 Canal St, New Orleans, LA 70130-1152
Tel (504) 529-2100 *Founded/Ownrshp* 2004
Sales 23.0MM^E *EMP* 138
SIC 4412

D-U-N-S 00-521-4077 IMP
INTERMATIC INC
7777 Winn Rd, Spring Grove, IL 60081-9698
Tel (815) 675-2321 *Founded/Ownrshp* 1891
Sales 240.6MM^E *EMP* 795
SIC 3612 3645 Line voltage regulators; Residential lighting fixtures; Line voltage regulators; Residential lighting fixtures
Pr: David Schroeder
**Ch Bd:* Douglas M Kinney Sr
COO: Daniel Dallemolle
Ex VP: Lenay Tenburn
VP: James R Bohn
VP: Linnea T Bruin
VP: Gary Koetters
VP: William Sommers
VP: Chuck Whitmer
Exec: David Hawthorne
Exec: Connie Kinsch
Exec: Jennifer Reed
Exec: Paul Surczyn

D-U-N-S 79-924-6558 IMP
■ **INTERMEC INC**
(*Suby of* HONEYWELL INTERNATIONAL INC) ★
16201 25th Ave W, Lynnwood, WA 98087-2520
Tel (425) 348-2600 *Founded/Ownrshp* 2013
Sales 682.6MM^E *EMP* 2,312
SIC 3577 Computer peripheral equipment; Bar code (magnetic ink) printers; Optical scanning devices; Computer peripheral equipment; Bar code (magnetic ink) printers; Optical scanning devices
Ch Bd: Allen J Lauer
CFO: Robert J Driessnack
CFO: Lanny H Michael
Sr VP: James McDonnell
Sr VP: Yukio Morikubo
Sr VP: Earl R Thompson
VP: Scott Anderson
VP: Larry N Colson
VP: David W Danjczek
VP: Peter Fausel
VP: Michael E Keane
VP: Larry Klimczyk
VP: John Ourourke
VP: Ian Snadden
Exec: Darci Lee

INTERMEC MEDIA PRODUCTS
See INTERMEC ULTRA PRINT INC

D-U-N-S 00-490-8729 IMP
■ **INTERMEC TECHNOLOGIES CORP** (WA)
(*Suby of* INTERMEC INC) ★
16201 25th Ave W, Lynnwood, WA 98087-2520
Tel (425) 348-2600 *Founded/Ownrshp* 1966, 1997
Sales 449.1MM^E *EMP* 1,745
SIC 3577 2759 Computer peripheral equipment; Printers, computer; Optical scanning devices; Readers, sorters or inscribers, magnetic ink; Labels & seals: printing; Computer peripheral equipment; Printers, computer; Optical scanning devices; Readers, sorters or inscribers, magnetic ink; Labels & seals: printing
Pr: John Waldron
**Treas:* John J Tus
**VP:* Michael Colwell
VP: Bob Driessnack
VP: Earl Thompson
VP: David Yung
Prin: Gene Shultice
Prgrm Mgr: Wes Kephart
Rgnl Mgr: Tracey Jones IV
Snr Sftwr: Tony Carter
Sftwr Eng: Peter Girodat
Board of Directors: Michael Keane

D-U-N-S 06-892-9827
■ **INTERMEC ULTRA PRINT INC**
INTERMEC MEDIA PRODUCTS
(*Suby of* INTERMEC TECHNOLOGIES CORP) ★
9290 Le Saint Dr, West Chester, OH 45014-5454
Tel (513) 874-5882 *Founded/Ownrshp* 1973, 1994
Sales 27.0MM^E *EMP* 250
SIC 2759 Flexographic printing; Flexographic printing
IT Man: Al Fettes
Prd Mgr: Darell Thomas
S&M/Mgr: Dave Cashman

D-U-N-S 16-947-8984
■ **INTERMECH INC**
(*Suby of* BAHNSON INC) ★
4731 Commercial Park Ct, Clemmons, NC 27012-8700
Tel (336) 760-3111 *Founded/Ownrshp* 1980
Sales 37.5MM^E *EMP* 250
SIC 1711 Mechanical contractor; Mechanical contractor
Pr: Kevin Matz
**Treas:* Jeff Walgren
**Ex VP:* Joseph Burns
**Sr VP:* Mark Malloy
**VP:* Melvin Cromwell
VP: Tim West
Dir IT: John Canup
Sfty Mgr: Ron Scott

D-U-N-S 17-507-1398
■ **INTERMEDIA COMMUNICATIONS INC**
(*Suby of* VERIZON BUSINESS GLOBAL LLC) ★
3608 Queen Palm Dr, Tampa, FL 33619-1317
Tel (800) 940-0011 *Founded/Ownrshp* 2006
Sales 413.4MM^E *EMP* 5,073
SIC 4813 Local & long distance telephone communications; Voice telephone communications; Data telephone communications; ; Local & long distance telephone communications; Voice telephone communications; Data telephone communications;
Pr: David C Ruberg
Pr: Richard Marchant
Pr: James M Walters
Pr: Jeanne M Walters
CFO: Robert M Manning
Sr VP: Richard J Buyens
Sr VP: James F Geiger
VP: Bob Hunter
VP: Particia A Kurlin
VP: Dick Marchant
VP: Mark Tubb

D-U-N-S 61-297-6592
INTERMEDIA HOLDINGS INC
825 E Middlefield Rd, Mountain View, CA 94043-4025
Tel (650) 641-4000 *Founded/Ownrshp* 2004
Sales 52.7MM^E *EMP* 105^E
SIC 7379
CEO: Michael Gold
**COO:* Jonathan McCormick
**CFO:* Scott Allen
Sr VP: Andrew Gachechiladze
Sr VP: Doug Johnson
Sr VP: Eric Weiss
VP: Brian Shellabarger
Mng Dir: Ed Macnair
**CTO:* Jonathan Levine
VP Opers: Brent Rich
VP Sls: Luis B Curet
Board of Directors: Kevin Parker

D-U-N-S 80-442-3148
INTERMEDIA OUTDOORS HOLDINGS LLC
(*Suby of* KROENKE SPORTS & ENTERTAINMENT LLC) ★
2855 S James Dr Ste 101, New Berlin, WI 53151-3662
Tel (262) 432-9100 *Founded/Ownrshp* 2014
Sales 40.5MM^E *EMP* 160^E
SIC 7312 Outdoor advertising services

D-U-N-S 80-534-0630
INTERMEDIA OUTDOORS INC
(*Suby of* INTERMEDIA OUTDOORS HOLDINGS LLC) ★
1040 Avenue Of, New York, NY 10018
Tel (212) 852-6600 *Founded/Ownrshp* 2006
Sales 40.5MM^E *EMP* 260^E
SIC 2326 5045 Industrial garments, men's & boys'; Computer software; Industrial garments, men's & boys'; Computer software
CEO: David Koff
**CFO:* Andy Goldstein
**Ch:* Peter Kern
**Ch:* Jeff Paro

D-U-N-S 61-984-3829
INTERMEDIA PARTNERS VII LP
405 Lexington Ave Fl 48, New York, NY 10174-0002
Tel (212) 503-2850 *Founded/Ownrshp* 2005
Sales 7.1MM^E *EMP* 285
SIC 4841 Cable & other pay television services
Pt: David Koff
Mng Pt: Leo Hindery

D-U-N-S 36-421-0328
INTERMEDIANET INC
(*Suby of* TELANETIX INC) ★
825 E Middlefield Rd, Mountain View, CA 94043-4025
Tel (650) 641-4000 *Founded/Ownrshp* 2013
Sales 22.6MM^E *EMP* 100
SIC 7373 Computer integrated systems design; Computer integrated systems design
Pr: Michael Gold
**COO:* Jonathan McCormick
**CFO:* Scott Allen
VP: Diane Banner
VP: Ryan Barrett
VP: Sarat Khilnani
VP: Fyhrie Peter
VP: Brian Shellabarger
Creative D: Tyra Dumars
Opers Mgr: Yi Hong
Sales Exec: Jason Stevens

D-U-N-S 07-868-8249
INTERMEDIATE DISTRICT 287 (MN)
ISD287
1820 Xenium Ln N, Minneapolis, MN 55441-3708
Tel (763) 550-7100 *Founded/Ownrshp* 1968
Sales 80.6MM *EMP* 700
Accts Malloy Montague Karnowski R
SIC 8211 Public vocational/technical school; Public special education school; Specialty education; Public vocational/technical school; Public special education school; Specialty education
Bd of Dir: Bobbie Betz
Bd of Dir: Don Draayer
Bd of Dir: Julie B Gavaras

D-U-N-S 07-649-1075
INTERMEDIATE SCHOOL DISTRICT 917
1300 145th St E, Rosemount, MN 55068-2932
Tel (651) 423-8229 *Founded/Ownrshp* 1970
Sales 14.0MM *EMP* 325
SIC 8211 Public elementary & secondary schools; Public elementary & secondary schools
Psych: Albert Hoekstra

D-U-N-S 07-748-2438
INTERMEDIATE UNIT 1 EDUCATIONAL FOUNDATION
1 Intermediate Unit Dr, Coal Center, PA 15423-1001
Tel (724) 938-6600 *Founded/Ownrshp* 1854
Sales 54.6MM *EMP* 800
Accts Cypher & Cypher Cpas Canonsb
SIC 8211 Specialty education; Specialty education
Ex Dir: Charles F Mahoney
Ex Dir: Lawerence O Shea
MIS Dir: Stephen Smolenski
Teacher Pr: Jennifer Judge
Teacher Pr: Thomas Tano

D-U-N-S 80-940-9647
INTERMEDIX CORP
6451 N Federal Hwy # 1000, Fort Lauderdale, FL 33308-1424
Tel (954) 308-8700 *Founded/Ownrshp* 2010
Sales 250.0MM *EMP* 2,000
SIC 7372 Business oriented computer software; Business oriented computer software
CEO: Joel Portice
Pr: Thomas Hesser
Pr: Mike McHale
Pr: Steve Queen
Pr: William Ryan
Pr: Keith Tucker
**COO:* Ken Cooke
**CFO:* Michael Wallace
Ofcr: Joe McCloskey
Ex VP: Dave Poole
Ex VP: David Poole
Sr VP: Jack Donahue
Sr VP: Rick Fossier
Sr VP: Pamela Krop
Sr VP: Dan Pope
Sr VP: Calvin Rogers
VP: Gregg Lord
VP: Jim Montgomery
VP: Morris Slocum
VP: Kyle Wailes
VP: Kyle Winston
Board of Directors: Thomas H Lee

D-U-N-S 12-091-9766 IMP
INTERMET CORP
301 Commerce St Ste 2901, Fort Worth, TX 76102-4122
Tel (817) 348-9190 *Founded/Ownrshp* 2005
Sales 341.4MM^E *EMP* 2,337
SIC 3321 3714 3462 3363 3364 Ductile iron castings; Motor vehicle parts & accessories; Automotive forgings, ferrous: crankshaft, engine, axle, etc.; Aluminum & aluminum-based alloy castings; Magnesium & magnesium-base alloy die-castings; Ductile iron castings; Motor vehicle parts & accessories; Automotive forgings, ferrous: crankshaft, engine, axle, etc.; Aluminum & aluminum-based alloy castings; Magnesium & magnesium-base alloy die-castings
Pr: Jeff Mihalic
Pr: Robert Axe
Pr: Troy Jonas
Pr: Eric Showalter
CFO: William H Whalen
Ofcr: Bob Flaherty
Sls Dir: Kyle Klein
Counsel: Alan J Miller

D-U-N-S 00-303-2752 IMP/EXP
INTERMETRO INDUSTRIES CORP
(*Suby of* ALI GROUP NORTH AMERICA CORP) ★
651 N Washington St, Wilkes Barre, PA 18705-1799
Tel (570) 825-2741 *Founded/Ownrshp* 1998, 2015
Sales 519.2MM^E *EMP* 1,500
SIC 3496 2542 3537 3411 3315 2441 Miscellaneous fabricated wire products; Shelving, made from purchased wire; Grocery carts, made from purchased wire; Cabinets: show, display or storage: except wood; Dollies (hand or power trucks), industrial except mining; Metal cans; Steel wire & related products; Nailed wood boxes & shook; Miscellaneous fabricated wire products; Shelving, made from purchased wire; Grocery carts, made from purchased wire; Cabinets: show, display or storage: except wood; Dollies (hand or power trucks), industrial except mining; Metal cans; Steel wire & related products; Nailed wood boxes & shook
Pr: John Nackley
Treas: Don McAlonan
VP: Bill O'Donoghue
VP: Tom Uells
VP: John H Welsch
Netwrk Mgr: Michael Ward
Ql Cn Mgr: Carmen Nardozzi
Mktg Mgr: Carl Dymond

D-U-N-S 94-738-8617
INTERMEX WIRE TRANSFER LLC
INTERNATIONAL MONEY EXPRESS
9480 S Dixie Hwy, Miami, FL 33156-2934
Tel (305) 671-8000 *Founded/Ownrshp* 2001
Sales NA *EMP* 150
SIC 6099 4822 Foreign currency exchange; Cable, telegram & telex services; Foreign currency exchange; Cable, telegram & telex services
Pr: Robert Lisy
**CFO:* Darrell Ebbert
VP: Eduardo Azcarate
**VP:* Jose Perez
Brnch Mgr: Francisco Hernandez
CIO: William Velez
IT Man: Geraldine Schnaider
Mktg Dir: Cristiana Lacayo
Mktg Mgr: Mariana Perez
Snr Mgr: Brian Augustin

D-U-N-S 07-872-5912
■ **INTERMIX HOLDCO INC**
(*Suby of* GAP INC) ★
1440 Broadway Fl 5, New York, NY 10018-2385
Tel (212) 741-5075 *Founded/Ownrshp* 2012
Sales 27.5MM^E *EMP* 250
SIC 5651 5641 5632 5621 Family clothing stores; Children's & infants' wear stores; Women's accessory & specialty stores; Women's clothing stores; Family clothing stores; Children's & infants' wear stores; Women's accessory & specialty stores; Women's clothing stores; Women's sportswear
Pr: Jyophi RAO
**Chf Cred:* Khajak Keledjian

INTERMNTAIN SCNTFIC BIOEXPRESS
See BIOEXPRESS LLC

D-U-N-S 10-181-5314
INTERMODAL CARTAGE CO INC
IMCG
5707 E Holmes Rd, Memphis, TN 38141-8206
Tel (901) 363-0050 *Founded/Ownrshp* 1982
Sales 79.6MM^E *EMP* 300
SIC 4213 Trucking, except local; Trucking, except local
Pr: Mark H George
VP: Michael Baker
VP: Chris Morre
VP Opers: Peter Thrall
Opers Mgr: Dimitri Douklias
Opers Mgr: Susie Gresham
Opers Mgr: Jon Moss
Manager: Mike Jenkins

D-U-N-S 94-915-0965
INTERMODAL MANAGEMENT SYSTEM LLC
IMS
265 Industrial Way W, Eatontown, NJ 07724-2303
Tel (732) 935-8400 *Founded/Ownrshp* 1995
Sales 56.5MM *EMP* 70
SIC 4731 Freight forwarding; Freight forwarding
**Pt:* Michael O'Brien
VP: Robert Lanczycki
Trfc Dir: Mandie Collins
S&M/VP: James Frostick

D-U-N-S 17-930-5537 IMP/EXP
INTERMODAL TANK TRANSPORT (USA) INC
10720 W Sam Houston Pkwy, Houston, TX 77064-3569
Tel (713) 888-0501 *Founded/Ownrshp* 1997
Sales 23.3MM^E *EMP* 150
SIC 4731 Transportation agents & brokers
Pr: Ernst Schuckmann
**CEO:* Jon Hulsey
**CFO:* Ward Rivenburg
VP: Matt Caldwell
**VP:* Jordi Lorente
Tech Mgr: Ian Foulkes
Sales Asso: Tammy Leonard

D-U-N-S 36-219-2473
INTERMOLECULAR INC
3011 N 1st St, San Jose, CA 95134-2004
Tel (408) 582-5700 *Founded/Ownrshp* 2004
Sales 47.7MM *EMP* 253^E
Tkr Sym IMI *Exch* NGS
SIC 3674 Semiconductors & related devices; Semiconductors & related devices
Pr: Bruce M McWilliams
CFO: C Richard Neely Jr
CFO: Rick Neely
Sr VP: Scot A Griffin
Sr VP: Zia Malik
VP: Minh Le
VP: Sandeep Nijhawan
VP: Dipu Pramanik
Board of Directors: Thomas R Baruch, Marvin D Burkett, Irwin Federman, Wilbert Van Den Hoek, George M Scalise

D-U-N-S 17-063-2405
INTERMOOR INC
101 Youngswood Rd, Morgan City, LA 70380-2276
Tel (985) 385-3083 *Founded/Ownrshp* 2004
Sales 236.2MM^E *EMP* 120^E
SIC 1381 Drilling oil & gas wells; Drilling oil & gas wells
Pr: Thomas Fulton
**Pr:* Chuck Minton
**VP:* Larry Puckett
**VP:* Scott Thomas
IT Man: Ramus Martin

D-U-N-S 79-110-6326
■ **INTERMOOR INC**
(*Suby of* ACTEON GROUP LTD)
900 Threadneedle St # 300, Houston, TX 77079-2913
Tel (832) 399-5000 *Founded/Ownrshp* 2004
Sales 24.3MM^E *EMP* 98^E
SIC 8711 Industrial engineers
Pr: Thomas Fulton
Ofcr: Kelly Carda
Opers Mgr: Lonnie Olds
Opers Mgr: Anthony Palmature

INTERMOUNTAIN BEER DISTRG CO
See INTERMOUNTAIN DISTRIBUTING CO

D-U-N-S 13-060-6754
INTERMOUNTAIN COMMUNITY BANCORP
IMCB
414 Church St, Sandpoint, ID 83864-7002
Tel (208) 263-0505 *Founded/Ownrshp* 1998
Sales NA *EMP* 271^E
SIC 6035

D-U-N-S 03-521-2059 IMP
INTERMOUNTAIN DISTRIBUTING CO
INTERMOUNTAIN BEER DISTRG CO
1010 Intermountain St, Billings, MT 59101-7721
Tel (406) 245-7744 *Founded/Ownrshp* 1949
Sales 20.6MM^E *EMP* 60
Accts Walborn & Associates Pc Bi
SIC 5181 5182 Beer & other fermented malt liquors; Wine; Wine coolers, alcoholic
Pr: Don Brocopp
**Treas:* Marilyn Brocopp
**VP:* Tim Brocopp

D-U-N-S 79-792-1236 EXP
INTERMOUNTAIN DRILLING SUPPLY CORP
3412 W 2400 S, Salt Lake City, UT 84119-1150
Tel (801) 972-6455 *Founded/Ownrshp* 1995
Sales 39.8MM^E *EMP* 50
SIC 5084 Drilling equipment, excluding bits
CEO: Van Bohne
**VP:* Robert Bourquin
**VP:* Brook Neimi
Brnch Mgr: Phil Jensen
Sales Asso: Parker Brannon
Sales Asso: Bryan Morris
Sales Asso: Mike Perry
Sales Asso: Glen Ward
Sales Asso: Michael White
Sales Asso: Jessica Yocum

D-U-N-S 00-880-1797
■ **INTERMOUNTAIN ELECTRIC INC**
IME
(*Suby of* QUANTA SERVICES INC) ★
5050 Osage St Ste 500, Denver, CO 80221-7822
Tel (303) 733-7248 *Founded/Ownrshp* 1946, 1999
Sales NA *EMP* 400
SIC 1542 8742 3671 General electrical contractor; Commercial & office building contractors; Construction project management consultant; Cathode ray tubes, including rebuilt
Pr: Tom Allen
Ex VP: Lee Brown
**VP:* Jason Clay
**VP:* David Hoyt
VP: Steve Miller
**VP:* Tom Pourchot
Opers Mgr: Tom Sutton

D-U-N-S 07-995-4418
INTERMOUNTAIN ELECTRIC SERVICE
701 S Federal Blvd, Riverton, WY 82501-4907
Tel (307) 856-7321 *Founded/Ownrshp* 1974
Sales 24.1MM^E *EMP* 92
Accts Mckee Marburger & Fagnant P
SIC 1731 1389 1623 General electrical contractor; Oil field services; Electric power line construction; General electrical contractor; Oil field services; Electric power line construction
Pr: Donald C Larson
CFO: Bonny Medow
**Sec:* Bonny J Medow
**VP:* Thale F Ellison
Genl Mgr: Chris Jepson

D-U-N-S 17-795-0441 IMP/EXP
INTERMOUNTAIN ELECTRONICS INC OF PRICE UTAH
1511 S Highway 6, Price, UT 84501-7408
Tel (877) 544-2291 *Founded/Ownrshp* 1985
Sales 31.5MM^E *EMP* 135
SIC 3699 5063

D-U-N-S 00-895-4380 IMP
INTERMOUNTAIN FARMERS ASSOCIATION (UT)
I F A
1147 W 2100 S, South Salt Lake, UT 84119-1563
Tel (801) 972-2122 *Founded/Ownrshp* 1915
Sales 214.0MM *EMP* 400^E
SIC 5999 5191

D-U-N-S 18-191-2262
■ **INTERMOUNTAIN GAS CO**
IGC
(*Suby of* MDU RESOURCES GROUP INC) ★
555 S Cole Rd, Boise, ID 83709-0940
Tel (208) 377-6000 *Founded/Ownrshp* 2008
Sales 151.6MM^E *EMP* 210^E
SIC 4924 Natural gas distribution; Natural gas distribution
Ch Bd: Richard Hokin
**Pr:* William C Glynn
**CEO:* Nicole A Kivisto
**Ex VP:* Scott Madison
**VP:* Mark Chiles
VP: Diane Petersen

Dir Risk M: Gary Panter
Dist Mgr: Randy Morgan
Dir IT: Hart Gilchrist
IT Man: Fred Leakeas
Sfty Mgr: Robert Peterson

D-U-N-S 02-203-9596
INTERMOUNTAIN HEALTH CARE HEALTH SERVICES
INTERMOUNTAIN MEDICAL CENTER
5121 S Cottonwood St, Murray, UT 84107-5701
Tel (801) 507-5358 *Founded/Ownrshp* 2007
Sales 2.1MMM[E] *EMP* 30,000
SIC 8011

D-U-N-S 07-295-5503
INTERMOUNTAIN HEALTH CARE INC
IHC HEALTH SERVICES
36 S State St Ste 1600, Salt Lake City, UT 84111-1441
Tel (801) 442-2000 *Founded/Ownrshp* 1975
Sales 5.5MMM *EMP* 23,000
Accts Kpmg Llp Salt Lake City Ut
SIC 8062 General medical & surgical hospitals; General medical & surgical hospitals
CEO: Charles W Sorenson
**Ch Bd:* Scott Anderson
**Pr:* William H Nelson
COO: Keith Alexander
**COO:* Laura S Kaiser
COO: Gary Pherson
CFO: Brian Hickenlooper
CFO: Ron Jensen
CFO: Jeremiah Radandt
**V Ch Bd:* Bruce Reese
Trst: Penny S Brooke
Trst: Clark D Ivory
Trst: Edward G Kleyn
Trst: Joann B Seghini
Ofcr: Dean Lin
VP: Phyliss Domm
**VP:* Everett N Goodwin Jr
**VP:* Douglas J Hammer
VP: Larry D Hancock
VP: Kim Henrichsen
VP: Terri Kane
Board of Directors: Merrill Gappmayer, F Ann Millner Ph D, Scott Anderson, Robert H Garff, Joann B Seghini Ph D, Teresa Beck, Elizabeth Hammond MD, Richard R Price MD, Douglas C Black, Randy Horiuchi, Bruce T Reese, Mark R Briesacher MD, Rebecca Chavez-Houck, Marc R Udall MD, Penny S Brooke, Clark Ivory, Jane Carule, Linda C Leckman MD, Daniel W Davis MD, Lawrence S Lewin, Spencer F Eccles, Kent H Murdock, Irene S Fisher, Robert Parsons

D-U-N-S 96-454-4170
INTERMOUNTAIN HEALTHCARE FOUNDATION
36 S State St Ste 2200, Salt Lake City, UT 84111-1470
Tel (801) 442-2000 *Founded/Ownrshp* 2010
Sales 30.9MM *EMP* 2
Accts Ernst & Young Llp Roseville
SIC 8099 Health & allied services
Prin: Robert H Bischoff
CFO: Chris Randall
Dir Rad: Lisa Peters
Info Man: Mark Latkowski
Info Man: Nancy Nelson
Sls&Mrk Ex: Rebecca Nielsen
Pathlgst: Sarah Ilstrup
Doctor: Brett Parkinson

D-U-N-S 09-932-5060
INTERMOUNTAIN INDUSTRIES INC
555 S Cole Rd, Boise, ID 83709-0940
Tel (208) 377-6000 *Founded/Ownrshp* 1984
Sales 147.9MM[E] *EMP* 450
SIC 4924 Natural gas distribution; Natural gas distribution
Ch Bd: Richard Hokin
Pr: William C Glynn
Ofcr: Linda Murray
VP: Bruce West

INTERMOUNTAIN LIFE FLIGHT
See IHC HEALTH SERVICES INC

INTERMOUNTAIN MEDICAL CENTER
See INTERMOUNTAIN HEALTH CARE HEALTH SERVICES

D-U-N-S 07-310-4879 IMP
INTERMOUNTAIN ORIENT INC
7609 W Emerald St, Boise, ID 83704-9018
Tel (208) 384-5600 *Founded/Ownrshp* 1982
Sales 30.0MM *EMP* 23
SIC 5031 Lumber: rough, dressed & finished; Lumber: rough, dressed & finished
CEO: Dennis K Downer
**CFO:* Mike Clements
Dir IT: Jewel Jones

D-U-N-S 84-927-0694
INTERMOUNTAIN PLASTIC DISTRIBUTION INC
2300 S Decker Lake Blvd B, Salt Lake City, UT 84119-2048
Tel (801) 201-1212 *Founded/Ownrshp* 2000
Sales 138.0MM *EMP* 3
SIC 5162 Plastics materials & basic shapes; Plastics materials & basic shapes
**Pr:* Talley Goodson
**CFO:* Wynn Clayton

D-U-N-S 06-980-5455
INTERMOUNTAIN POWER AGENCY
I P A
10653 S River Front Pkwy # 120, South Jordan, UT 84095-3531
Tel (801) 938-1333 *Founded/Ownrshp* 1970
Sales 698.0MM *EMP* 500
SIC 4911

D-U-N-S 12-121-4985
INTERMOUNTAIN POWER SERVICE CORP
ITSC
850 W Brush Wellman Rd, Delta, UT 84624-9522
Tel (435) 864-4414 *Founded/Ownrshp* 1982
Sales 351.8MM[E] *EMP* 485
SIC 4911 Generation, electric power; Generation, electric power
Pr: Jon A Finlinson
CFO: Sam Wardle
**Sec:* Roger Stowell
**VP:* Jon P Christensen
IT Man: Lance Johnson
IT Man: Brook Pace
Sfty Dirs: Lewis Rawlinson
Opers Supe: Lloyd Leavitt

D-U-N-S 00-686-5273 IMP
INTERMOUNTAIN RURAL ELECTRIC ASSOCIATION
IREA
5496 N Us Highway 85, Sedalia, CO 80135-8600
Tel (303) 688-3100 *Founded/Ownrshp* 1938
Sales 279.9MM *EMP* 176
SIC 4911 Electric services; Electric services
Pr: Timothy White
CFO: Mandi Zimmerman
**VP:* Bruff Shea
Exec: Gerry Hacker
Genl Mgr: Stan Lewandowski
IT Man: Patty Helberg
IT Man: Martha Lord
IT Man: Anne Thomas
IT Man: Robert Youngquist
Sfty Dirs: Alex Mendez
Snr PM: Mark Jurgemeyer

D-U-N-S 18-216-4707
INTERMOUNTAIN WEST COMMUNICATIONS CO
701 S 9th St, Las Vegas, NV 89101-7068
Tel (702) 642-3333 *Founded/Ownrshp* 1983
Sales 204.9MM[E] *EMP* 650
SIC 4833 Television broadcasting stations; Television broadcasting stations
Ch Bd: James E Rogers
Sales Asso: Brett Cavanaugh

D-U-N-S 00-909-6090 IMP
INTERMOUNTAIN WOOD PRODUCTS INC
1938 S West Temple, Salt Lake City, UT 84115-1820
Tel (801) 486-5414 *Founded/Ownrshp* 1961
Sales 69.8MM[E] *EMP* 110
SIC 5031 5211 Hardboard; Plywood; Millwork; Lumber products; Hardboard; Plywood; Millwork; Lumber products
Pr: Ben E Banks
**CFO:* Scott L Miles
Bd of Dir: Tom Reece
**VP:* Brad Banks
VP: Brian Myers
Sls Mgr: Scott Jensen
Sales Asso: Sean Fogarty
Sales Asso: Lane Janke
Sales Asso: Craig Wilkinson

D-U-N-S 03-549-1294
■ **INTERMUNE INC**
(*Suby of* ROCHE HOLDINGS INC) ★
1 Dna Way, South San Francisco, CA 94080-4918
Tel (415) 466-4383 *Founded/Ownrshp* 1998, 2014
Sales 70.3MM *EMP* 353[E]
SIC 2834 8731 Pharmaceutical preparations; Medical research, commercial; Pharmaceutical preparations; Medical research, commercial
Pr: Daniel G Welch
**CFO:* John C Hodgman
**Ex VP:* Jonathan A Leff
**Ex VP:* Sean P Nolan
**Ex VP:* Andrew Powell
Sr VP: Marianne Armstrong
Sr VP: Pasquale Frega
Sr VP: Cynthia Y Robinson
Sr VP: Stephen N Rosenfield
Sr VP: Marites Sotto
Assoc Dir: Judy Chang
Assoc Dir: Robyn Eddings
Assoc Dir: Henry Garcia
Assoc Dir: Charles Li

D-U-N-S 07-912-0648
INTERNAL MEDICINE CLINIC
1600 22nd Ave, Meridian, MS 39301-3223
Tel (601) 483-5322 *Founded/Ownrshp* 1970
Sales 20.4MM[E] *EMP* 104
SIC 8011 Internal medicine, physician/surgeon
Pt: A Gary Boone
Pt: Dr Wesley S Bennett
Pt: Dr Joel T Callahan
Pt: Dr Robert E Clark
Pt: Dr Milton D Concannon
Pt: Dr Frederick T Duggan
Pt: Dr Thomas H Greer Jr
Pt: Dr John C Halbrook
Pt: Dr William F Reid
Pt: Dr Anthony L Thomas

D-U-N-S 15-312-5625
INTERNAL MEDICINE GROUP FREMONT
ST JOHNS CLINIC
1965 S Fremont Ave # 350, Springfield, MO 65804-2201
Tel (417) 820-3128 *Founded/Ownrshp* 2004
Sales 464.3MM *EMP* 30
SIC 8011 Internal medicine practitioners; Internal medicine practitioners
Off Mgr: Cindy Jackson
Obsttrcn: Christina Litherland
Obsttrcn: Barbara Wotherspoon

D-U-N-S 04-053-9587
■ **INTERNAL REVENUE SERVICE**
I R S
(*Suby of* UNITED STATES DEPT OF TREASURY) ★
1111 Constitution Ave Nw, Washington, DC 20224-0002
Tel (202) 803-9000 *Founded/Ownrshp* 1862
Sales NA *EMP* 92,800
SIC 9311 Taxation department, government; ;Taxation department, government;
Bd of Dir: Amy Nelson
Ofcr: Willie Bailey
Ofcr: Daniel Bennett
Ofcr: Lisa Boudreau
Ofcr: Cynthia Murray
Ofcr: Kevin Stam
Adm Dir: Amy Fleming
Adm Dir: Mary Newcomb
Adm Dir: Sandra Sieminski
Prgrm Mgr: Christine Adams
CIO: Bill Maglin

D-U-N-S 94-291-6578
▲ **INTERNAP CORP**
1 Ravinia Dr Ste 1300, Atlanta, GA 30346-2128
Tel (404) 302-9700 *Founded/Ownrshp* 1996
Sales 334.9MM *EMP* 700
Tkr Sym INAP *Exch* NGS
SIC 7373 7375 Computer integrated systems design; Information retrieval services; Computer integrated systems design; Information retrieval services
Pr: Michael A Ruffolo
Mng Pt: Brian Hammond
Pr: Joe Nicolosi
COO: Michel Vent
CFO: Kevin M Dotts
Bd of Dir: Jeffrey Enebrad
Sr VP: Pete Bell
Sr VP: Peter M Evans
Sr VP: Michael Higgins
Sr VP: Mike Higgins
Sr VP: Steven A Orchard
Sr VP: Christian Primeau
VP: Patricia Watkins
Exec: Steve Francis
Dir: Jason Harms
Board of Directors: Charles B Coe, Patricia L Higgins, Gary M Pfeiffer, Michael A Ruffolo, Daniel C Stanzione, Debora J Wilson

D-U-N-S 78-373-5855
INTERNATIONAL ACADEMY OF FINANCE LTD
CORDOVA INDUSTRIES
13177 Foothill Blvd, Sylmar, CA 91342-4830
Tel (818) 361-7724 *Founded/Ownrshp* 1963
Sales 59.0MM *EMP* 127
SIC 2869 3944 2879 Alcohols, industrial: denatured (non-beverage); Video game machines, except coin-operated; Insecticides, agricultural or household; Alcohols, industrial: denatured (non-beverage); Video game machines, except coin-operated; Insecticides, agricultural or household
Pr: Sam Cordova
**Pr:* Steven M Cordova
**Ex VP:* Rodrick Cordova
**VP:* Sam Scott Cordova
**VP:* Steven Schector

D-U-N-S 06-373-6193
■ **INTERNATIONAL ACADEMY OF MERCHANDISING & DESIGN LTD**
INTERNTNAL ACADEMY DESIGN TECH
(*Suby of* CAREER EDUCATION CORP) ★
1 N State St Ste 500, Chicago, IL 60602-3309
Tel (312) 346-5152 *Founded/Ownrshp* 1997
Sales 25.4MM[E] *EMP* 450
SIC 8221 Colleges universities & professional schools; Colleges universities & professional schools
Pr: Thomas McNamara
VP: Sandy Rhodes
Exec: Lori Russell
Assoc Dir: Vincent Oneal

INTERNATIONAL ACURA
See INTERNATIONAL MALL MOTOR CO

D-U-N-S 02-987-2272 IMP
INTERNATIONAL AID INC
17011 Hickory St, Spring Lake, MI 49456-9795
Tel (616) 846-7490 *Founded/Ownrshp* 1980
Sales 90.0MM *EMP* 20
Accts Monroe Sweeris & Tromp Plc
SIC 8699 Charitable organization; Charitable organization
Pr: Brian Anderson
**Ch Bd:* Luke Niewenhuis
COO: Robert J Goodwin
**Treas:* Michael Houskamp
Comm Dir: Bruce Buursma
Mng Dir: Steve Rienstra
Dir IT: Michael Okelly
Snr Mgr: Gordon Loux

D-U-N-S 02-079-0895
INTERNATIONAL AIDS VACCINE INITATIVE INC
125 Broad St Fl 9, New York, NY 10004-2743
Tel (212) 847-1111 *Founded/Ownrshp* 1996
Sales 66.3MM *EMP* 190[E]
Accts Gelman Rosenberg & Freedman B
SIC 2836 8731 Vaccines; Commercial physical research; Vaccines; Commercial physical research
Pr: Margaret McGlynn
Pt: Thomas P Monath
Ch Bd: Alex Godwin Coutinho
COO: David N Cook
CFO: Louis Schwartz
Bd of Dir: Paul A Wilson
Sr VP: Lynn Doren
Comm Man: Ulysee Huling
Ex Dir: Michel Sidibe
Ex Dir: Jane Waterman
Board of Directors: Alice P Albright, Lord Fowler, Eric Goosby, Adel A F Mahmoud

D-U-N-S 15-580-4946
INTERNATIONAL AIR TRANSPORT ASSOCIATION INC
703 Nw 62nd Ave Ste 600, Miami, FL 33126-4676
Tel (305) 264-7772 *Founded/Ownrshp* 1992
Sales 22.0MM[E] *EMP* 158
SIC 6799 Commodity contract trading companies
CEO: Tony Tyler
Sr VP: Windmuller Thomas
Rgnl Mgr: Mayumi Jantar
Snr Mgr: Gordon Wright

D-U-N-S 83-472-1649
INTERNATIONAL AIRMOTIVE HOLDING CO INC
(*Suby of* BBA AVIATION PLC)
900 Nolen Dr Ste 100, Grapevine, TX 76051-8641
Tel (214) 956-3000 *Founded/Ownrshp* 1998
Sales 15.3MM[E] *EMP* 1,571[E]
SIC 7699 3724 Aircraft & heavy equipment repair services; Aircraft engines & engine parts; Aircraft & heavy equipment repair services; Aircraft engines & engine parts
Pr: Hugh McElory
**CFO:* Douglas Meador

D-U-N-S 96-520-3636
INTERNATIONAL ALLIANCE THEATRICAL 46 IATSE
211 Donelson Pike Ste 202, Nashville, TN 37214-2932
Tel (615) 885-1058 *Founded/Ownrshp* 2010
Sales 5.0MM *EMP* 300
SIC 7363 Labor resource services; Labor resource services
Pr: Greg Barbara

D-U-N-S 18-183-0159 IMP/EXP
INTERNATIONAL AMERICAN SUPERMARKETS CORP
IAS
226 Old New Brunswick Rd, Piscataway, NJ 08854-3755
Tel (732) 981-8001 *Founded/Ownrshp* 1985
Sales 49.9MM *EMP* 45
SIC 5141 Food brokers; Food brokers
CEO: Suhayl Sauma
**Pr:* Bassam Sauma
**CFO:* Joe Sauma
CFO: Carlos Velazquez
**VP:* Abdo Sauma
**VP:* Sami Sauma
Off Mgr: Diana Vitanza
IT Man: Ginger Chop

D-U-N-S 14-907-2993 IMP
INTERNATIONAL ASSEMBLERS INC
1161 W Plcita De La Ctnia Cotonia, Green Valley, AZ 85622
Tel (520) 648-2244 *Founded/Ownrshp* 1980
Sales 29.2MM[E] *EMP* 400
SIC 3679 Electronic circuits; Electronic circuits
CEO: Richard Crocker
**Ex VP:* James Price

D-U-N-S 95-937-7995
INTERNATIONAL ASSEMBLY INC
I A I
750 E Los Ebanos Blvd A, Brownsville, TX 78520-4865
Tel (956) 499-7933 *Founded/Ownrshp* 1992
Sales 145.6MM[E] *EMP* 750[E]
SIC 5162 Plastics materials & basic shapes; Plastics materials & basic shapes
Pr: Robert Katusak

INTERNATIONAL ASSN MACHINISTS
See INTERNATIONAL ASSOCIATION OF MACHINISTS AND AEROSPACE WORKERS

D-U-N-S 07-263-2482
INTERNATIONAL ASSOCIATION OF CHIEFS OF POLICE INC
44 Canal Center Plz # 200, Alexandria, VA 22314-1579
Tel (703) 836-6767 *Founded/Ownrshp* 1893
Sales 24.4MM *EMP* 125
Accts Sarfino And Rhoades Llp Rockv
SIC 8621 Professional membership organizations; Professional membership organizations
Ex Dir: Vince Talucci
Treas: Carl Wolf

D-U-N-S 07-480-1911
INTERNATIONAL ASSOCIATION OF FIREFIGHTERS
IAFF
1750 New York Ave Nw # 300, Washington, DC 20006-5301
Tel (202) 737-8484 *Founded/Ownrshp* 1918
Sales 51.0MM *EMP* 120
Accts Renner And Company Cpa Pc Ale
SIC 8631 Trade union; Trade union
Pr: Harold Schaitberger
Pr: Paul Hufnagel
CFO: Don Copley
**Sec:* Thomas Miller
VP: Scott Barns
Ex Dir: Steven Rank
IT Man: Dennis Toney
Genl Couns: Baldwin Robertson

D-U-N-S 02-029-3916
INTERNATIONAL ASSOCIATION OF IRON WORKERS
1750 New York Ave Nw # 400, Washington, DC 20006-5301
Tel (202) 383-4800 *Founded/Ownrshp* 1896
Sales 26.1MM[E] *EMP* 125
Accts Bond Beebe Bethesda Md
SIC 8631 Labor union
Pr: Walter Wise
**Pr:* Joseph J Hunt
**Treas:* Edward McHugh
Treas: Dennis Toney

D-U-N-S 06-948-3931
INTERNATIONAL ASSOCIATION OF LIONS CLUBS INC
LIONS CLUBS INTERNATIONAL
300 W 22nd St, Oak Brook, IL 60523-8815
Tel (630) 468-6881 *Founded/Ownrshp* 1919
Sales 69.5MM *EMP* 288
Accts Mcgladrey Llp Chicago Il
SIC 8641 Civic associations; Civic associations
Pr: Barry J Palmer
Treas: Kimberly Hugo
**Treas:* Mary Allen Skerik
Bd of Dir: John Harrigan
Top Exec: Francis Fife
VP: Jeff Becker
VP: John Brown

VP: Gary Cordes
VP: Darryl Henson
VP: Sandra Mangini
VP: Rick Merlo
VP: Warren Shaffer
VP: Jeanne Stapleton
VP: Dave Waller
VP: Scott Watford
Assoc Dir: Kevin Cherep

INTERNATIONAL ASSOCIATION OF M
See AEROSPACE INDUSTRIAL DISTRICT LODGE 751

D-U-N-S 05-518-9591
INTERNATIONAL ASSOCIATION OF MACHINISTS AND AEROSPACE WORKERS
INTERNATIONAL ASSN MACHINISTS
9000 Machinists Pl, Upper Marlboro, MD 20772-2675
Tel (301) 967-4500 *Founded/Ownrshp* 1888
Sales 61.4MM^E *EMP* 400
SIC 8631 Labor union; Labor union
Pr: R Thomas Buffenbarger
Top Exec: Herbert Ries
VP: Don Kennedy
VP: Marsha Malesich
VP: Bob Martinez
Assoc Dir: Diane Dettmann
Off Admin: Terri Kenealy
Snr Mgr: Stan Pickthall

INTERNATIONAL ASSOCIATION OF P
See IAPMO RESEARCH AND TESTING INC

D-U-N-S 96-346-8447
INTERNATIONAL ASSOCIATION OF WOMEN POLICE CONFERENCE
30 S 7th St, Minneapolis, MN 55402-1601
Tel (612) 673-3586 *Founded/Ownrshp* 2010
Sales 240.0M *EMP* 500
SIC 8621 Professional membership organizations; Professional membership organizations
Prin: Kris Arneson

D-U-N-S 00-280-9924
INTERNATIONAL AUDIO VISUAL INC (DE)
MY PROJECTOR STORE
5149 Powerline Rd, Fort Lauderdale, FL 33309-3156
Tel (954) 630-9797 *Founded/Ownrshp* 1997
Sales 72.2MM^E *EMP* 42
SIC 5064 5999 Electrical appliances, television & radio; Audio-visual equipment & supplies
Pr: Wade Gilbert
Opers Mgr: Michael Arencibia
VP Sls: Patrick Laliberty
Mktg Mgr: Heather Wagaman

D-U-N-S 15-191-7101 IMP
INTERNATIONAL AUTO PROCESSING INC
1 Joe Frank Harris Blvd, Brunswick, GA 31523-7802
Tel (912) 554-8432 *Founded/Ownrshp* 1988
Sales 221.5MM^E *EMP* 350
SIC 5012 7542 7538 7532 Automobiles & other motor vehicles; Carwashes; General automotive repair shops; Top & body repair & paint shops; Automobiles & other motor vehicles; Carwashes; General automotive repair shops; Top & body repair & paint shops
Pr: James M Showalter
*CEO: Robert Miller
*CFO: Masahisa Kobayashi
Sr VP: Doug Tipton
VP: Tammy Young
Ex Dir: Jack McConnell

D-U-N-S 61-682-7796
INTERNATIONAL AUTOMATION INC
9009 Clubridge Dr, Fort Wayne, IN 46809-3000
Tel (260) 747-6151 *Founded/Ownrshp* 1986
Sales 49.0MM *EMP* 402
Accts Baden Gage & Schroeder
SIC 3593 Fluid power actuators, hydraulic or pneumatic; Fluid power actuators, hydraulic or pneumatic
Pr: Harry M Neff
Pr: Phil Friend
*Treas: Joseph Oberlin
*VP: Pete Cole

D-U-N-S 79-319-6341 IMP/EXP
INTERNATIONAL AUTOMOTIVE COMPONENTS GROUP NORTH AMERICA INC
IAC GROUP
(*Suby of* INTERNATIONAL AUTOMOTIVE COMPONENTS GROUP SA)
28333 Telegraph Rd, Southfield, MI 48034-1953
Tel (248) 455-7000 *Founded/Ownrshp* 2007
Sales 7.3MMM^E *EMP* 28,425
SIC 3089 Automotive parts, plastic; Automotive parts, plastic
CEO: Robert S Miller
*Ch Bd: Wilbur L Ross Jr
*CFO: Dennis E Richardville
*Ex VP: Janis N Acosta
Ex VP: Kathleen Sheehan
VP: Alicia Allen
Ex Dir: David Ladd
Prgrm Mgr: Clint Cheetwood
Prgrm Mgr: Allen Zacharevich
Genl Mgr: Guy Current
CIO: Kirsty Fitzner

D-U-N-S 96-808-8687
INTERNATIONAL AUTOMOTIVE COMPONENTS GROUP NORTH AMERICA LLC
(*Suby of* INTERNATIONAL AUTOMOTIVE COMPONENTS GROUP SA)
28333 Telegraph Rd, Southfield, MI 48034-1953
Tel (248) 455-7000 *Founded/Ownrshp* 2006
Sales 2.4MM^E *EMP* 15,000
SIC 5013 Motor vehicle supplies & new parts; Motor vehicle supplies & new parts
Pr: Robert Steven
*Ex VP: Janis N Acosta
*Ex VP: Dennis E Richardville
*Prin: James K Kamsickas
Dir IT: Les Tolley

Tech Mgr: Steve Molino
Mtls Mgr: Patti Stewart
Plnt Mgr: Richard Lee
Board of Directors: Patrick Machir

D-U-N-S 02-336-6578
INTERNATIONAL AUTOS INC
BERNDT CLASSIC IMPORTS
2400 S 108th St, Milwaukee, WI 53227-1904
Tel (414) 543-3000 *Founded/Ownrshp* 1995
Sales 45.1MM^E *EMP* 64
SIC 5511 Automobiles, new & used; Automobiles, new & used
Pr: Ralph Mauro
*Treas: Richard C Berndt
Genl Mgr: Tom Dexter
Off Mgr: Carol Scoville
Dir IT: David Poremba
Sls Mgr: Crystal Mirr
Sls Mgr: Shadrach Simmons
Sales Asso: Mark Donahue

D-U-N-S 04-638-1281
INTERNATIONAL BACCALAUREATE ORGANIZATION INC
IB AMERICAS
7501 Wisconsin Ave # 200, Bethesda, MD 20814-6501
Tel (301) 202-3000 *Founded/Ownrshp* 1975
Sales 166.2MM *EMP* 55
Accts Deloitte & Touche Llp
SIC 8299 Educational service, nondegree granting: continuing educ.; Educational service, nondegree granting: continuing educ.
Pr: Jeffery Beard
*Prin: Bradley Richardson

D-U-N-S 11-982-2534
▲ **INTERNATIONAL BANCSHARES CORP**
1200 San Bernardo Ave, Laredo, TX 78040-6301
Tel (956) 722-7611 *Founded/Ownrshp* 1979
Sales NA *EMP* 3,223^E
Accts Mcgladrey Llp Dallas Texas
Tkr Sym IBOC *Exch* NGS
SIC 6022 State commercial banks; State commercial banks
Ch Bd: Dennis E Nixon
*Treas: Imelda Navarro
Bd of Dir: Ignacio Urrabazo
Ex VP: Javier Villase or
Ex VP: Dalia Martinez
Ex VP: Carlos Moreno
Ex VP: Idaloia Ramirez
Ex VP: Javier Villaseor
VP: Jennifer Alvarado
VP: Alva Deletemartinez
VP: Juan Gamez
VP: Guadalupe Garcia
VP: Marvie Garcia
*VP: R David Guerra
VP: SRI Gunaratnam
VP: Ramiro Herrera
VP: Ron A Lalonde
VP: Alvaro Martinez
VP: Wilfredo Martinez
VP: Jessica Mendiola
VP: Rosie Ramirez
Board of Directors: Irving Greenblum, Doug Howland, Peggy J Newman, Larry Norton, Leonardo Salinas, Antonio R Sanchez Jr

D-U-N-S 06-202-4112
INTERNATIONAL BANK FOR RECONSTRUCTION & DEVELOPMENT
WORLD BANK, THE
1818 H St Nw, Washington, DC 20433-0001
Tel (202) 473-1000 *Founded/Ownrshp* 1945
Sales NA *EMP* 15,000
SIC 6082 Foreign trade & international banking institutions; Foreign trade & international banking institutions
Pr: Jim Yongkim
COO: SRI Mulyani Indrawati
CFO: Vincenzo La Via
Ofcr: Renee Desclaux
Ofcr: Arik Levi
Ofcr: Hiep Phan
Ofcr: Jim Rosenberg
VP: Connie Eysenck
VP: Jeoffrey Lamb
VP: Philippe Le Hou Rou
VP: Edith Ssempala
VP: Laura Tuck
VP: Hasan Tuluy
VP: Axel Van Trotsenburg
VP: Stephanie Von Friedeburg

D-U-N-S 79-227-0878
INTERNATIONAL BANK OF CHICAGO
(*Suby of* IBC BANCORP, INC)
5069 N Broadway St, Chicago, IL 60640-3015
Tel (773) 769-2899 *Founded/Ownrshp* 1997
Sales NA *EMP* 125
SIC 6022 State commercial banks; State commercial banks
Pr: Robert A Klamp
COO: John Benson
CFO: Barry Haskins
Ofcr: Mandy Quach
*Ex VP: Warren H Tai
Ex VP: Joseph Turner
Sr VP: Jovantae Willis
VP: Thomas Gehrke
IT Man: Samuel Ll
Mktg Mgr: Karina Medvedev

D-U-N-S 04-147-0519
■ **INTERNATIONAL BANK OF COMMERCE**
IBC BANK
(*Suby of* INTERNATIONAL BANCSHARES CORP) ★
1200 San Bernardo Ave, Laredo, TX 78040-6301
Tel (956) 722-7611 *Founded/Ownrshp* 1979
Sales NA *EMP* 1,622
SIC 6022 State commercial banks; State commercial banks
Pr: Dennis Nixon
Treas: Michael Saenz
Bd of Dir: Guillermo Trevino
Ofcr: Gabriela Holloway
Ex VP: William Cuellar
Ex VP: Carlos Martinez
*Ex VP: Dalia Martinez
*Ex VP: Imelda Navarro
Ex VP: Gerald Schwebel
Ex VP: J Jorge Verduzco
Sr VP: Shannon Galloway
Sr VP: Yvette Gonzalez
Sr VP: Delores Hansen
Sr VP: Chris Loeher
Sr VP: Chris Loehr
Sr VP: Chris Lohr
Sr VP: Rosie Ramirex
Sr VP: Michael Sohh
Sr VP: John A Villarreal
Sr VP: Chris Weller
Sr VP: Dustin Wells

D-U-N-S 12-150-4955
■ **INTERNATIONAL BANK OF COMMERCE - ZAPATA**
IBC BANK
(*Suby of* INTERNATIONAL BANCSHARES CORP) ★
Us Hwy 83 At 10th Ave, Zapata, TX 78076
Tel (956) 765-8361 *Founded/Ownrshp* 2003
Sales NA *EMP* 124
SIC 6022 State commercial banks; State commercial banks
Pr: Renato Ramirez
CFO: Janie De La Garza
Sr VP: Elisa Gonzalez

D-U-N-S 05-747-7515
INTERNATIONAL BAY CLUBS LLC
BALBOA BAY CLUB AND RESORT
1221 W Coast Hwy Ste 145, Newport Beach, CA 92663-5037
Tel (949) 645-5000 *Founded/Ownrshp* 2012
Sales 29.9MM^E *EMP* 500^E
SIC 7997 4493 6552 7011 Membership sports & recreation clubs; Beach club, membership; Marinas; Land subdividers & developers, residential; Hotels & motels; Membership sports & recreation clubs; Beach club, membership; Marinas; Land subdividers & developers, residential; Hotels & motels
CEO: Todd M Pickup
Pr: David Wooten
Genl Mgr: Sam El-Rabaa
Sls Mgr: Amy Cale
Sls Mgr: Kelsey Harned
Board of Directors: Mark C Doyle, Beverly Ray

D-U-N-S 18-344-7473 IMP/EXP
INTERNATIONAL BEDDING CORP
6301 Memorial Hwy Ste 101, Tampa, FL 33615-4573
Tel (954) 491-1004 *Founded/Ownrshp* 2007
Sales 25.1MM^E *EMP* 550
SIC 2515 Mattresses, innerspring or box spring; Box springs, assembled; Mattresses, innerspring or box spring; Box springs, assembled
Pr: Tony R Smith
*Ch Bd: Thomas J Allison
Treas: Mike Claru
Sr VP: Daniel J Hige
VP: Daniel Hige

D-U-N-S 14-964-6833 IMP
INTERNATIONAL BISCUITS & CONFECTIONS LLC
IBC
(*Suby of* ADVANTAGE SALES & MARKETING LLC) ★
10000 Lincoln Dr E # 102, Marlton, NJ 08053-3105
Tel (856) 813-1008 *Founded/Ownrshp* 2003
Sales 43.3MM *EMP* 22
Accts Schreiber & Calvo Cpas Pc Ne
SIC 5145 Confectionery; Candy; Confectionery; Candy
Pr: Don Demato
Treas: Gloria Shabazz
Mktg Mgr: Jill Short

INTERNATIONAL BLENDS
See PIZZA BLENDS INC

D-U-N-S 03-654-3445
INTERNATIONAL BOAT RENTALS INC (LA)
MARINER BOATS
11864 Highway 308, Larose, LA 70373-5877
Tel (985) 798-5700 *Founded/Ownrshp* 1996
Sales 32.0MM^E *EMP* 400
SIC 4492 Tugboat service; Tugboat service
Pr: Stephen Williams
*Sec: Rhonda Chiasson Williams
Off Mgr: Elizabeth Robiaux

D-U-N-S 03-281-5011
INTERNATIONAL BONDED COURIERS INC
I B C
3333 New Hyde Park Rd, New Hyde Park, NY 11042-1204
Tel (516) 627-8200 *Founded/Ownrshp* 1980
Sales 59.7MM^E *EMP* 240
SIC 4513 Air courier services; Air courier services
Pr: Joseph Costigan
*CFO: Robert Basista
*VP: Tom Costigan
*VP: Edward Kohler
*VP: Roberto Moreno
*VP: Ed Weissman
*VP: William Womick
*VP: Sara Zeidman
Exec: Cathy Pagano

D-U-N-S 60-606-9607 IMP
INTERNATIONAL BRAKE INDUSTRIES INC
CARLSON QUALITY BRAKE
(*Suby of* QUALITOR INC) ★
4300 Quality Dr, South Bend, IN 46628-9665
Tel (419) 905-7468 *Founded/Ownrshp* 1967
Sales 83.6MM^E *EMP* 862
SIC 3713 3714 Truck & bus bodies; Motor vehicle brake systems & parts; Truck & bus bodies; Motor vehicle brake systems & parts
Pr: Greg Andes
*Treas: Scott Gibaratz

D-U-N-S 01-184-2841
■ **INTERNATIONAL BROADCASTING BUREAU**
(*Suby of* UNITED STATES DEPT OF STATE) ★
3919 Voa Site B Rd, Grimesland, NC 27837-8977
Tel (252) 758-2171 *Founded/Ownrshp* 1950
Sales NA *EMP* 5,128
SIC 9199 Civil service commission, government; ; Civil service commission, government;

D-U-N-S 07-625-3715
INTERNATIONAL BROTHERHOOD OF BOILERMAKERS ARCHIVES INC
753 State Ave Ste 570, Kansas City, KS 66101-2511
Tel (913) 371-2640 *Founded/Ownrshp* 1893
Sales 21.0MM^E *EMP* 150
Accts Schnurr & Company Llp Fort D
SIC 8631 Labor union
Pr: Newton B Jones
*VP: J Tom Baca
*VP: Warren Fairley
*VP: David Haggerty
*VP: Joseph Maloney
VP: Sam May
*VP: Lawrence J McManamon
*VP: Edward Power
*VP: James Pressley

D-U-N-S 96-988-9398
INTERNATIONAL BROTHERHOOD OF BOILERMAKERS IRON SHIP BUILDERS
753 State Ave, Kansas City, KS 66101-2516
Tel (913) 371-2640 *Founded/Ownrshp* 2011
Sales 41.1MM *EMP* 3
Accts Legacy Professionals Llp Chic
SIC 8631 Labor unions & similar labor organizations; Labor unions & similar labor organizations
Prin: Carolyn Nitcher

INTERNATIONAL BROTHERHOOD OF E
See ELECTRICAL WORKERS CORP

D-U-N-S 01-834-5512
INTERNATIONAL BROTHERHOOD OF ELECTRIC WORKER LOCAL UNION 1245
AFL-CIO #1245
30 Orange Tree Cir, Vacaville, CA 95687-3105
Tel (707) 452-2700 *Founded/Ownrshp* 1948
Sales 27.8MM *EMP* 68
SIC 8631 Labor union; Labor union
Pr: Ed Mallory
*VP: James McCulley

D-U-N-S 06-927-5980
INTERNATIONAL BROTHERHOOD OF ELECTRICAL WORKERS
IBEW
900 7th St Nw Bsmt 1, Washington, DC 20001-4089
Tel (202) 833-7000 *Founded/Ownrshp* 1955
Sales 151.7MM *EMP* 970
Accts Calibre Cpa Group Pllc Bethes
SIC 8631 Labor union; Labor union
Pr: Edwin D Hill
CFO: Jeff Miller
*Sec: Salvatore J Chilia
VP: Curtis Henke
VP: Sam May
VP: John O'Rourke
Exec: Melinda Brent
Software D: Bing Ye

D-U-N-S 96-480-6710
INTERNATIONAL BROTHERHOOD OF ELECTRICAL WORKERS - PENSION BENEFIT FUND
900 7th St Nw, Washington, DC 20001-3886
Tel (202) 728-6200 *Founded/Ownrshp* 2010
Sales 171.7MM *EMP* 24^E
Accts Calibre Cpa Group Pllc Washin
SIC 8631 Trade union; Trade union
Prin: Ed Hill
CFO: Michael Franey
Treas: Richard Shereda
VP: Kenneth Cooper
VP: Joseph Davis
VP: Robert Klein
Dir IT: Victor Evans

D-U-N-S 08-643-1327
INTERNATIONAL BROTHERHOOD OF ELECTRICAL WORKERS AFL-CIO LOCAL 98 (PA)
1701 Spring Garden St, Philadelphia, PA 19130-3915
Tel (215) 563-5592 *Founded/Ownrshp* 1900
Sales 20.6MM *EMP* 13^E
Accts Elko & Associates Ltd Media
SIC 8631 Labor union; Labor union
*Treas: Todd Nielsen
*VP: James Minck
Counsel: Pat Bianculli

D-U-N-S 05-628-6222
INTERNATIONAL BROTHERHOOD OF TEAMSTERS
I B T
25 Louisiana Ave Nw, Washington, DC 20001-2130
Tel (202) 624-6800 *Founded/Ownrshp* 1903
Sales 167.8MM *EMP* 649^E
Accts Novak Francella Llc New York
SIC 8631 Labor union; Labor union
Pr: James P Hoffa
COO: Wayne Schultz
Treas: Ken Hall
Treas: C Keegel
Trst: John Manley
Ofcr: Beatrice Newbury
VP: David Cabral
VP: Dominic Chiovare
VP: Jack Cipriani
VP: Richard K Hall
VP: Carroll Haynes
VP: Ron Herrera
VP: Al Hobart
VP: Chuck Mack
VP: Rick Middleton
VP: Fred Potter
VP: David Robinson

VP: Myron Sharp
VP: Donald Siegel
VP: David Yoders
Exec: Stephan Shapiro

D-U-N-S 96-724-0297
INTERNATIONAL BROTHERHOOD OF TEAMSTERS 863 TCWH
209 Summit Rd, Mountainside, NJ 07092-2304
Tel (908) 654-6990 *Founded/Ownrshp* 2011
Sales 36.0MM *EMP* 3
Accts Ra Eberle & Company Llc
SIC 8631 Labor unions & similar labor organizations; Labor unions & similar labor organizations

D-U-N-S 60-524-6586
INTERNATIONAL BROTHERHOOD OF TEAMSTERS LOCAL UNION 947
10947 N Main St, Jacksonville, FL 32218-4954
Tel (904) 764-7756 *Founded/Ownrshp* 1989
Sales 406.7M *EMP* 450
Accts Gordon & Newsom Pa Jacksonvil
SIC 8631 Labor unions & similar labor organizations; Labor unions & similar labor organizations
Pr: Marvin Franklin
Prin: Randy Kaneer

D-U-N-S 96-456-3881
INTERNATIONAL BROTHERHOOD OF TEAMSTERS VOLUNTARY EMPLOYEE BENEFITS TRUST
25 Louisiana Ave Nw, Washington, DC 20001-2130
Tel (202) 624-6800 *Founded/Ownrshp* 2010
Sales 33.0MM *EMP* 13ᴱ
Accts Novak Francella Llc Bala Cynw
SIC 8631 Labor unions & similar labor organizations; Labor unions & similar labor organizations
VP: Ken Hall

D-U-N-S 96-421-2059
INTERNATIONAL BROTHERHOOD OF TEAMSTERS- 710 HEALTH AND WELFARE FUND
4217 S Halsted St, Chicago, IL 60609-2636
Tel (773) 254-2500 *Founded/Ownrshp* 2010
Sales 47.2MM *EMP* 3
Accts Legacy Professionals Llp Chic
SIC 8631 Labor unions & similar labor organizations; Labor unions & similar labor organizations
Prin: John Kelahan
Off Mgr: Cathy Heckle

D-U-N-S 78-494-5172
INTERNATIONAL BUILDING MATERIALS LLC
INTERNATIONAL WOOD PRODUCTS
14421 Se 98th Ct, Clackamas, OR 97015-9626
Tel (503) 650-9663 *Founded/Ownrshp* 1996
Sales 41.7MMᴱ *EMP* 55
SIC 5031 Lumber: rough, dressed & finished; Plywood
Pr: Dave Stelle
CEO: Doug Hart
CFO: Terry D Watson
Sales Asso: Terry Hagen

D-U-N-S 09-506-8003
INTERNATIONAL BULLION AND METAL BROKERS (USA) INC
I B B
14051 Nw 14th St Ste 3, Sunrise, FL 33323-2885
Tel (954) 660-6900 *Founded/Ownrshp* 2003, 1977
Sales 130.4MMᴱ *EMP* 100ᴱ
SIC 5094 Jewelry; Jewelry
Pr: Gavin M Kovacs
Pr: Stephen Kovacs

D-U-N-S 07-737-4163 IMP
INTERNATIONAL BUSINESS COMMUNICATIONS INC
IBC/ WORLDWIDE
1981 Marcus Ave Ste C105, New Hyde Park, NY 11042-2028
Tel (516) 352-4505 *Founded/Ownrshp* 1967
Sales 26.8MMᴱ *EMP* 270ᴱ
SIC 3086 2679 Packaging & shipping materials, foamed plastic; Pressed fiber & molded pulp products except food products; Packaging & shipping materials, foamed plastic; Pressed fiber & molded pulp products except food products
Pr: Norman Kay
Ex VP: Philip Schoonmaker
VP: Jeri Newman
Opers Mgr: Mike Walker

D-U-N-S 00-136-8083
▲ **INTERNATIONAL BUSINESS MACHINES CORP** (NY)
IBM
1 New Orchard Rd Ste 1, Armonk, NY 10504-1722
Tel (914) 499-1900 *Founded/Ownrshp* 1910
Sales 92.7MMM *EMP* 379,592
Tkr Sym IBM *Exch* NYS
SIC 7379 7371 3571 3572 3674 Computer related consulting services; Computer software development; Software programming applications; Minicomputers; Mainframe computers; Personal computers (microcomputers); Computer storage devices; Disk drives, computer; Tape storage units, computer; Semiconductors & related devices; Microcircuits, integrated (semiconductor); Computer related consulting services; Computer software development; Software programming applications; Minicomputers; Mainframe computers; Personal computers (microcomputers); Computer storage devices; Disk drives, computer; Tape storage units, computer; Semiconductors & related devices; Microcircuits, integrated (semiconductor)
Ch Bd: Virginia M Rometty
CFO: Martin J Schroeter
Ex VP: Steven A Mills
Sr VP: Bruno V Di Leo Allen
Sr VP: Colleen F Arnold
Sr VP: Michelle H Browdy
Sr VP: Erich Clementi
Sr VP: Diane J Gherson
Sr VP: Jon C Iwata
Sr VP: Martin Jetter
Sr VP: James J Kavanaugh
Sr VP: John E Kelly III
Sr VP: Arvind Krishna
Sr VP: Robert J Leblanc
Sr VP: Robert J Picciano
Sr VP: Michael D Rhodin
Sr VP: Thomas W Rosamilia
Sr VP: Bridget A Van Kralingen
Board of Directors: James W Owens, Alain J P Belda, Joan E Spero, William R Brody, Sidney Taurel, Kenneth I Chenault, Peter R Voser, Michael L Eskew, David N Farr, Alex Gorsky, Shirley Ann Jackson, Andrew N Liveris, W James McNerney Jr

D-U-N-S 00-227-0023
INTERNATIONAL BUSINESS SYSTEMS INC (PA)
I B S DIRECT
431 Yerkes Rd, King of Prussia, PA 19406-3556
Tel (610) 265-8210 *Founded/Ownrshp* 1932, 1969
Sales 34.0MMᴱ *EMP* 87
SIC 2761 Manifold business forms; Manifold business forms
Pr: George H Schnyder
Pr: Ted Sherwin
CFO: Shaun Buss
VP: Nicholas Martino
Plnt Mgr: Russell Kreider
VP Sls: Jaime Capacete
Sls Dir: Greg Lacava

INTERNATIONAL BUSINESS TIMES
See IBT MEDIA INC

D-U-N-S 01-978-0311
INTERNATIONAL CAREER DEVELOPMENT CENTER INC (CA)
ICDC COLLEGE
11859 Wilshire Blvd # 600, Los Angeles, CA 90025-6621
Tel (310) 482-6996 *Founded/Ownrshp* 1995
Sales 32.3MM *EMP* 269
Accts Almich & Associates Lake Fore
SIC 8222 Community college; Community college
CEO: Anna Berger
CFO: Eleanor Metshin
VP: Marvin Gomez
VP: Yael Holtcamp
Off Mgr: Alona Pariger
Opers Mgr: Alma Meza
Opers Mgr: Stephanie Perez
Mktg Mgr: Maria Logan
Sls Mgr: Revekka Geykher
HC Dir: Yvonne Zepeda

D-U-N-S 80-739-3194
INTERNATIONAL CARGO MARKETING CONSULTANTS INC
ALLIANCE AIRLINES
Cargo Bldg 517, Chicago, IL 60666
Tel (773) 917-2008 *Founded/Ownrshp* 1987
Sales 47.6MMᴱ *EMP* 500
SIC 4512 4522 Air transportation, scheduled; Air cargo carriers, nonscheduled; Air transportation, scheduled; Air cargo carriers, nonscheduled
Pr: Robert Jones
Board of Directors: Samechicago SEC

D-U-N-S 07-953-2065
INTERNATIONAL CARS LTD INC (MA)
HONDA NORTH
382 Newbury St, Danvers, MA 01923-1060
Tel (978) 539-5000 *Founded/Ownrshp* 1974, 1989
Sales 108.5MMᴱ *EMP* 260
SIC 5511 5521 Automobiles, new & used; Used car dealers; Automobiles, new & used; Used car dealers
CEO: Marshall Jespersen
CFO: Dave Dubois
CFO: David Dubois
Genl Mgr: Richard Collins
Genl Mgr: Joe Dettrey
Off Mgr: Erica Nicholas
IT Man: Devin Sullivan
Advt Mgr: Michael Nadeau
Sls Mgr: Steve Collins
Sls Mgr: Rui Moreira
Sls Mgr: Gus Noci

D-U-N-S 15-514-4728 EXP
INTERNATIONAL CASINGS GROUP INC
I C G
4420 S Wolcott Ave, Chicago, IL 60609-3159
Tel (773) 376-9200 *Founded/Ownrshp* 1986
Sales 31.3MMᴱ *EMP* 120
SIC 2013 Sausage casings, natural; Frozen meats from purchased meat; Sausage casings, natural; Frozen meats from purchased meat
Pr: Alon Nir
Pr: Rob Schouten
Genl Mgr: Jay Gotteiner
Genl Mgr: Tom Sanecki
Opers Mgr: Michael Davis

D-U-N-S 05-899-2699
INTERNATIONAL CATASTROPHE INSURANCE MANAGERS LLC
ICAT MANAGERS
(*Suby of* ICAT HOLDINGS LLC) ★
385 Interlocken Cres # 1100, Broomfield, CO 80021-3492
Tel (303) 449-1944 *Founded/Ownrshp* 1998
Sales NA *EMP* 119
SIC 6411 Property & casualty insurance agent
CFO: Derek Cochems
Sr VP: Jennifer Cohen
Sr VP: Craig Nechvatal
VP: Whitney Alt
VP: Eric Heringer
VP: Brad Pence
VP: Jean Verrier
Dir IT: Heidi McIntyre
Netwrk Mgr: Geoff Hannam
Board of Directors: Thomas W Hayes, Don Parkes, William Riker, Laura E Myers Wagner

D-U-N-S 79-468-0215
INTERNATIONAL CENTER FOR ENTREPRENEURIAL DEVELOPMENT INC
PARCEL PLUS
12715 Telge Rd, Cypress, TX 77429-2289
Tel (281) 256-4100 *Founded/Ownrshp* 1992
Sales 38.4MMᴱ *EMP* 150
SIC 6794 7331 Franchises, selling or licensing; Direct mail advertising services; Franchises, selling or licensing; Direct mail advertising services
Pr: Stephen B Hammerstein
CFO: Scott Kruger
Ch: F C Hadfield
VP: Debbie Clifford
VP: Vito Salvaggio
Advt Dir: Charmayne Redd
Mktg Dir: Jay Groot

D-U-N-S 07-986-3232
INTERNATIONAL CENTRE FOR DISPUTE RESOLUTION
AMERICAN ARBITRATION ASSN
120 Brdwy Fl 21, New York, NY 10271
Tel (212) 484-4181 *Founded/Ownrshp* 2015
Sales 18.8MMᴱ *EMP* 1,000
SIC 7389 Arbitration & conciliation service

D-U-N-S 07-003-8104 IMP/EXP
INTERNATIONAL CHEMICAL CO (OK)
INTER-CHEM
1887 E 71st St, Tulsa, OK 74136-3922
Tel (918) 496-7711 *Founded/Ownrshp* 1976
Sales 755.0MM *EMP* 42
Accts Hogan & Slovacek Tulsa Oklah
SIC 5191 Fertilizers & agricultural chemicals
Ch Bd: John R Arend
Pr: Brad Thomas
CFO: Eugene B Graves
Ex VP: Albert A Colby Jr
Sr VP: Gene Graves
VP: Martha Starr
Exec: Aaron Choquette
Prin: B P Abney
Prin: Tricia Arend
CTO: Wally Wells
Opers Mgr: Denny Arend

D-U-N-S 19-669-2821
INTERNATIONAL CHEMICAL WORKERS UNION LOCAL 95C
64 Maple St, Rouses Point, NY 12979-1424
Tel (518) 297-2312 *Founded/Ownrshp* 1975
Sales 5.0MMᴱ *EMP* 734
SIC 8631 Labor union; Employees' association; Labor union; Employees' association
Pr: Richard Rushford
Treas: Sharlene Stone

INTERNATIONAL CHILDREN'S CHARI
See HELP CHILDREN WORLD FOUNDATION

D-U-N-S 18-374-2063
INTERNATIONAL CHILDRENS FUND INC
619 Main St, Neenah, WI 54956-2430
Tel (920) 729-5721 *Founded/Ownrshp* 1978
Sales 43.2MM *EMP* 1
Accts Wipfli Llp Green Bay Wi
SIC 8699 Charitable organization; Charitable organization
Pr: Lori Fulcer
Sec: Julie Aleff
VP: Larry Oettel

D-U-N-S 00-697-6641 IMP
INTERNATIONAL CHIMNEY CORP (NY)
55 S Long St, Williamsville, NY 14221-6622
Tel (716) 634-3967 *Founded/Ownrshp* 1927
Sales 40.1MM *EMP* 250
Accts Chiampou Travis Besaw & Kershn
SIC 1741 3255 Chimney construction & maintenance; Firebrick, clay; Chimney construction & maintenance; Firebrick, clay
Ch Bd: Richard T Lohr
Sec: Thomas Sullivan
VP: Edmund Gasiecki
Rgnl Mgr: Jim Fleming
Sfty Mgr: Bob Weigand

D-U-N-S 04-115-7397
INTERNATIONAL CHURCH OF FOURSQUARE GOSPEL
FOURSQUARE INTERNATIONAL
1910 W Sunset Blvd # 200, Los Angeles, CA 90026-3275
Tel (213) 989-4234 *Founded/Ownrshp* 1921
Sales 208.2MMᴱ *EMP* 5,000
SIC 8661 6512 7032 8211 8221 Miscellaneous denomination church; Nonresidential building operators; Radio broadcasting stations; Sporting & recreational camps; Elementary & secondary schools; Colleges universities & professional schools; Miscellaneous denomination church; Nonresidential building operators; Sporting & recreational camps; Elementary & secondary schools; Colleges universities & professional schools
Pr: Glenn C Burris Jr
CFO: Ron Thigpenn
Treas: Brent Morgan
VP: Sterling Brackett
VP: Tammy Dunahoo
VP: Jared Roth
VP: James C Scott Jr
Prin: Paul Risser
Snr Sftwr: John Cashdollar

D-U-N-S 02-187-6420
INTERNATIONAL CITY MANAGEMENT ASSOCIATION RETIREMENT CORP
ICMA RETIREMENT
777 N Capitol St Ne # 600, Washington, DC 20002-4239
Tel (202) 962-4600 *Founded/Ownrshp* 1972
Sales 210.6MMᴱ *EMP* 671ᴱ
SIC 7389 6726 Financial services; Management investment funds, closed-end; Financial services; Management investment funds, closed-end
Pr: Joan McCallen
CFO: Michael Guarasci
Sr VP: Angela Montez
VP: David Braverman
Counsel: Erica McFarquhar
Board of Directors: Eric Anderson, Collette Chilton, Eric McKissack, David Mora, Robert O'neill

D-U-N-S 07-263-1831
INTERNATIONAL CITY/COUNTY MANAGEMENT ASSOCIATION
ICMA
777 N Capitol St Ne # 500, Washington, DC 20002-4239
Tel (202) 289-4262 *Founded/Ownrshp* 1933
Sales 26.4MM *EMP* 135
Accts Rubino & Company Chartered Be
SIC 8621 Education & teacher association; Education & teacher association
Ex Dir: Robert O'Neill
Exec: Regina Anderson-Ford
Creative D: Erik Sundvall
Ex Dir: Robert J O'Neill Jr
Prgrm Mgr: Nate Engle
Prgrm Mgr: Kathy Younker
Pgrm Dir: Molly Singer
Pgrm Dir: Bert Waisanen

D-U-N-S 61-484-3881
■ **INTERNATIONAL COAL GROUP INC**
(*Suby of* ARCH COAL INC) ★
114 Smiley Dr, Saint Albans, WV 25177-1504
Tel (304) 760-2400 *Founded/Ownrshp* 2011
Sales 576.2MMᴱ *EMP* 4,266ᴱ
SIC 1222 1221 Bituminous coal-underground mining; Bituminous coal & lignite-surface mining; Bituminous coal-underground mining; Bituminous coal & lignite-surface mining
Pr: Bennett K Hatfield
CFO: Bradley W Harris
Sr VP: Phillip M Hardesty
Sr VP: Oren Eugene Kitts
Sr VP: Roger L Nicholson
Sr VP: William Scott Perkins
MIS Dir: Steve Horton
IT Man: Jim Friderick
IT Man: David Schweigert
Plnt Mgr: Joe N Tussey
VP Mktg: Merritt Marc

D-U-N-S 08-492-3119
INTERNATIONAL CODE COUNCIL INC
I C C
4051 Flossmoor Rd, Country Club Hills, IL 60478-5771
Tel (202) 370-1800 *Founded/Ownrshp* 1972
Sales 50.8MM *EMP* 300
SIC 8621 Professional membership organizations; Professional membership organizations
Pr: Ronald E Piester
Pr: Stephen D Jones
CFO: John Belcik
Sec: Alex Cash Olszowy III
Sr VP: Michael Beaton
Sr VP: Sara Yerkes
VP: Guy Tomberlin
Rgnl Mgr: Steve Thorsell

D-U-N-S 83-776-9223
INTERNATIONAL CODE COUNCIL INC
500 New Jersey Ave Nw # 6, Washington, DC 20001-2005
Tel (202) 370-1800 *Founded/Ownrshp* 1994
Sales 2.8MM *EMP* 360ᴱ
Accts Bdo Usa Llp Chicago Il
SIC 8611 Regulatory associations; Regulatory associations
CEO: Rick Weirland
COO: Dominic Simms
Sr VP: Michael Armstrong
VP: Laurence Genest
VP: David Karmol
VP: Hamid Naderi
VP: Steve Skeehan
Ex Dir: David Walls
Rgnl Mgr: Roland Hall
CTO: Patrick Vandergriff
Mktg Dir: Greg West

D-U-N-S 05-531-7320 IMP
INTERNATIONAL COFFEE & TEA LLC
COFFEE BEAN & TEA LEAF, THE
1945 S La Cienega Blvd, Los Angeles, CA 90034-1601
Tel (310) 237-2326 *Founded/Ownrshp* 1998
Sales 179.7MMᴱ *EMP* 2,850
Accts Deloitte & Touche Los Angeles
SIC 5812 5499 6794 Coffee shop; Coffee; Tea; Franchises, selling or licensing; Coffee shop; Coffee; Tea; Franchises, selling or licensing
Pr: John Fuller
COO: Eric Foo Kok Cheng
COO: Lawrence Edelman
CFO: Melvin Allias
CFO: Karen Cate
Treas: John Garrow
Sr VP: Andrew Nathan
Sr VP: Adam Tabachnikoff
VP: Michael R Beck
VP: Lacy Novell Morris
VP: Daniel Osers
VP: Bill Robards

INTERNATIONAL COLD STORAGE
See RAINEY ROAD LLC

D-U-N-S 14-170-4929
INTERNATIONAL COLLEGE
215 Park Ave S Ste 2016, New York, NY 10003-1603
Tel (212) 529-3005 *Founded/Ownrshp* 2003
Sales 44.3MM *EMP* 4
Accts Mcgladrey Llp New York Ny
SIC 8742 School, college, university consultant; School, college, university consultant
Pr: John Johnson

D-U-N-S 61-465-0554
INTERNATIONAL COLLEGE
215 Park Ave S Ste 1710, New York, NY 10003-1619
Tel (212) 529-3005 *Founded/Ownrshp* 1891
Sales 39.2MM *EMP* 4

SIC 8211 Elementary & secondary schools; Elementary & secondary schools
Ch: William H Turner
**Ofcr:* Jenifer Turner
**Sr VP:* Peter Gerard

D-U-N-S 00-404-7031 IMP/EXP
■ INTERNATIONAL COMFORT PRODUCTS CORP (USA)
(*Suby of* CARRIER CORP) ★
Heil Quaker Ave Bldg 650, Lewisburg, TN 37091
Tel (931) 359-3511 *Founded/Ownrshp* 1999
Sales 56.8MM^E *EMP* 550
SIC 3585 Air conditioning units, complete: domestic or industrial; Heating & air conditioning combination units; Air conditioning units, complete: domestic or industrial; Heating & air conditioning combination units
Pr: Herman Kling
CFO: Stephen L Clanton
Sr VP: David P Cain
Sr VP: Francis C Harrell
Sr VP: James L Kirwan
Sr VP: Herman V Kling

D-U-N-S 00-404-7049
■ INTERNATIONAL COMFORT PRODUCTS LLC
(*Suby of* INTERNATIONAL COMFORT PRODUCTS CORP (USA)) ★
651 Heil Quaker Ave, Lewisburg, TN 37091-2184
Tel (931) 359-3511 *Founded/Ownrshp* 2003
Sales 56.8MM^E *EMP* 220^E
SIC 3585 3433 Air conditioning units, complete: domestic or industrial; Furnaces, domestic steam or hot water
Exec: George Lewis
Dir IT: Wayne Daniel
Dir IT: Julie Edwards
Dir IT: Mark Wade
VP Mfg: Don Clark
Sales Exec: Charlie Piranian
Sls&Mrk Ex: Lisa Townley
Mktg Dir: Jeff Anderson

D-U-N-S 61-692-0104 IMP
INTERNATIONAL COMMERCE & MARKETING CORP
POSTAL PRODUCTS UNLIMITED
500 W Oklahoma Ave, Milwaukee, WI 53207-2649
Tel (414) 290-1500 *Founded/Ownrshp* 1988
Sales 111.1MM^E *EMP* 140
SIC 5085 5961 Industrial supplies; Mail order house; Industrial supplies; Mail order house
Pr: Brian P Nelson
**CFO:* James Hess
Ex Dir: Victor Frangopoulous
Genl Mgr: John Ludwig
IT Man: Carter Carte
Web Dev: Andrew Otoo
Mktg Dir: Sean Buyeske

D-U-N-S 80-118-2838
INTERNATIONAL COMMERCE AGENCY LLC
(*Suby of* CREATIVE COMMERCE LLC) ★
1230 American Blvd, West Chester, PA 19380-4264
Tel (610) 918-1861 *Founded/Ownrshp* 2006
Sales 47.2MM *EMP* 12
SIC 8742 Marketing consulting services; Marketing consulting services

D-U-N-S 80-822-0412
INTERNATIONAL COMMODITY CARRIERS INC
ICCI
2090 Commerce Dr, Medford, OR 97504-9744
Tel (541) 734-9141 *Founded/Ownrshp* 1993
Sales 34.0MM *EMP* 70
SIC 4731

D-U-N-S 01-810-2264
INTERNATIONAL COMMUNICATIONS EXCHANGE CORP (OH)
4033 Ellery Ave, Moraine, OH 45439-2133
Tel (937) 296-9605 *Founded/Ownrshp* 1990
Sales 100.0MM *EMP* 12
SIC 8748 7379 Telecommunications consultant; Computer related consulting services; Telecommunications consultant; Computer related consulting services
Pr: Alan Doll

D-U-N-S 96-783-5500
INTERNATIONAL COMMUNICATIONS INDUSTRIES ASSOCIATION INC
ICIA
11242 Waples Mill Rd # 2, Fairfax, VA 22030-6079
Tel (703) 273-7200 *Founded/Ownrshp* 2013
Sales 28.6MM *EMP* 2
Accts Watkins Meegan Llc Bethesda
SIC 8611 Business associations; Business associations
Prin: Greg Jeffreys

D-U-N-S 06-392-8303
INTERNATIONAL COMMUNITY HEALTH SERVICES
INTERNATIONAL DISTRICT COMMUNI
720 8th Ave S Ste 100, Seattle, WA 98104-3033
Tel (206) 788-3700 *Founded/Ownrshp* 1976
Sales 27.3MM *EMP* 250
Accts Cliftonlarsonallen Llp Bellev
SIC 8099 Physical examination & testing services; Physical examination & testing services
Pr: Teresita Batayola
Dir Rx: Jon Sonoda
IT Man: Chieko Hironaga
Psych: Ellen Ngo
Pharmcst: Helen Louie

D-U-N-S 07-739-7453
INTERNATIONAL COMPUTER SYSTEMS INC
FIRST COLLECTIONS
10925 Otter Creek E Blvd, Mabelvale, AR 72103-1661
Tel (501) 455-0758 *Founded/Ownrshp* 1969
Sales 21.4MM^E *EMP* 203
SIC 7322 Collection agency, except real estate; Collection agency, except real estate
Pr: William A Dunkum
**Ex VP:* Gary Adams
VP: John Dunkum
VP Opers: Chris Dunkum

D-U-N-S 94-333-0530
INTERNATIONAL CONCORD INC
CONCORD INTERNATIONAL
(*Suby of* CHASSIX INC) ★
300 Galleria Officentre # 501, Southfield, MI 48034-8460
Tel (248) 728-8642 *Founded/Ownrshp* 2013
Sales 133.8MM^E *EMP* 150
SIC 3714 Motor vehicle parts & accessories; Motor vehicle parts & accessories
CEO: Mark Allan

D-U-N-S 15-157-2369
INTERNATIONAL CONFERENCE RESORTS OF NORTH CAROLINA INC
7700 E Mccormick Pkwy, Scottsdale, AZ 85258-3431
Tel (480) 991-9000 *Founded/Ownrshp* 1976
Sales 33.0MM *EMP* 425
SIC 7011 Resort hotel; Resort hotel
Pr: Burt Cabanas

D-U-N-S 07-969-3872
INTERNATIONAL CONSORTIUM FOR ADVANCED MANUFACTURING RESEARCH INC
3 Courthouse Sq Fl 2, Kissimmee, FL 34741-5440
Tel (407) 742-4252 *Founded/Ownrshp* 2014
Sales 120.0MM *EMP* 9
SIC 8731 Commercial physical research
Pr: Dave Saathoff
**Ex Dir:* Dan Holladay

D-U-N-S 06-631-8189
INTERNATIONAL CONSTRUCTION EQUIPMENT INC
ICE
301 Warehouse Dr, Matthews, NC 28104-8100
Tel (704) 821-8200 *Founded/Ownrshp* 1974
Sales 24.7MM^E *EMP* 50
SIC 7353 3531 Heavy construction equipment rental; Vibrators for concrete construction; Pile drivers (construction machinery); Posthole diggers, powered
Pr: T Richard Morris
CFO: Kurt Seufert
**CFO:* Kurt W Seufort
**VP:* Thomas P Cunningham
Exec: Alicia Dowling
**Prin:* Christian Cunningham
**Prin:* Dick Morris
Mng Dir: Peter Goodman
**Genl Mgr:* Brock Hemmingsen
IT Man: Mark Courey

D-U-N-S 06-585-8896
INTERNATIONAL CONTRACTORS INC
977 S Il Route 83, Elmhurst, IL 60126-4966
Tel (630) 834-8043 *Founded/Ownrshp* 1982
Sales 65.8MM *EMP* 50
SIC 1542 Commercial & office building, new construction; Institutional building construction
Pr: Bruce R Bronge
Pr: Joseph Fahey
**CFO:* Anthony Wygonski
VP: Marc Poskin
IT Man: Paul Baloun
VP Opers: Timothy Jackson
Opers Mgr: Daniel Bronge
Snr PM: Robert Peele
Snr PM: Dan REA

D-U-N-S 79-315-4014
INTERNATIONAL CONTROL SERVICES INC
I C S
606 W Imboden Dr, Decatur, IL 62521-9067
Tel (217) 422-6700 *Founded/Ownrshp* 1992
Sales 38.1MM^E *EMP* 110
SIC 3672 Printed circuit boards; Printed circuit boards
Pr: Dennis M Espinoza
**CFO:* Christopher Expinoza
**CFO:* Robert Johnston

D-U-N-S 13-074-0111 IMP
INTERNATIONAL CONTROLS & MEASUREMENTS CORP
ICM
7313 William Barry Blvd, North Syracuse, NY 13212-3384
Tel (315) 233-5266 *Founded/Ownrshp* 1984
Sales 50.0MM *EMP* 250^E
SIC 3625 Electric controls & control accessories, industrial; Electric controls & control accessories, industrial
Ch Bd: Hassan B Kadah
**Pr:* Andrew Kadah
**Treas:* Laurie Kadah
CTO: Michael Muench
MIS Dir: Charles Hunt
Sftwr Eng: Ayham Ahmad
Sftwr Eng: Tony Pan
Mtls Mgr: William Brokhoff
Ql Cn Mgr: Kim Jakway
Ql Cn Mgr: Brian Smith
Mktg Dir: Kevin Jobsky

D-U-N-S 36-151-7568 EXP
INTERNATIONAL CONVERTER (CALDWELL) INC
I-CONVERT
(*Suby of* BAGCRAFT) ★
17153 Industrial Hwy, Caldwell, OH 43724-9779
Tel (740) 732-5665 *Founded/Ownrshp* 1999
Sales 30.8MM^E *EMP* 241
SIC 3089 3353 3083 Laminating of plastic; Aluminum sheet, plate & foil; Laminated plastics plate & sheet; Laminating of plastic; Aluminum sheet, plate & foil; Laminated plastics plate & sheet
Pr: Phil Harris
**VP:* Jerry Lawrence
**VP:* Craig Lemieux
**VP:* Gerry Medlin
**VP:* Mitchell Mekaelian
**VP:* Mohammed Nadeem
Plnt Mgr: Brent Gillon
Ql Cn Mgr: Rice John
Manager: Ray Keen

D-U-N-S 60-816-9264
INTERNATIONAL COOLING TOWER USA INC
(*Suby of* BARON HOLDINGS INC)
7320 N La Cholla Blvd # 154, Tucson, AZ 85741-2309
Tel (780) 469-4900 *Founded/Ownrshp* 1989
Sales 57.0MM *EMP* 263
Accts Beachfleischman Pc Tucson Az
SIC 1629 Industrial plant construction; Industrial plant construction
Pr: Douglas A Baron
CFO: Harvey Saskiw
**VP:* M A Hafso

D-U-N-S 07-684-2269
INTERNATIONAL COPPER ASSOCIATION LTD
260 Madison Ave Fl 17, New York, NY 10016-2401
Tel (212) 251-7240 *Founded/Ownrshp* 1959
Sales 65.7MM *EMP* 23
SIC 8611 Trade associations; Trade associations
Pr: John Holland
**Ch Bd:* Oscar Groeneveld
**CFO:* John Kearns
Sr VP: Anthony Pickering
Mng Dir: Markku Ainali
VP Opers: David Brender

D-U-N-S 16-587-5928 IMP
INTERNATIONAL COSMETICS & PERFUMES
30 W 21st St Fl 7, New York, NY 10010-6959
Tel (212) 643-0011 *Founded/Ownrshp* 1996
Sales 82.2MM^E *EMP* 300^E
SIC 5122 Cosmetics, perfumes & hair products; Cosmetics, perfumes & hair products
Pr: Emmanuel Lajugie-Saujet
**Pr:* Thomas Saujet
VP: Adam Brecht
Mktg Mgr: Clementine Grenot

D-U-N-S 78-687-5757
INTERNATIONAL COUNCIL OF CRUISE LINES INC
2111 Wilson Blvd Ste 800, Arlington, VA 22201-3090
Tel (703) 522-8463 *Founded/Ownrshp* 1994
Sales 20.8MM *EMP* 3
SIC 8611 Trade associations; Trade associations
Pr: Cynthia A Colenda

D-U-N-S 06-825-8326
INTERNATIONAL COUNCIL OF SHOPPING CENTERS INC (IL)
ICSC
1221 Ave Of The Flr 41, New York, NY 10020
Tel (646) 728-3800 *Founded/Ownrshp* 1957
Sales 60.4MM^E *EMP* 400
SIC 8611 8621 2721 7389 Trade associations; Professional membership organizations; Periodicals; Convention & show services; Trade associations; Professional membership organizations; Periodicals; Convention & show services
Ch Bd: Brad M Hutensky
V Ch: David Henry
**Pr:* Valerie J Cammiso
**CEO:* Michael P Kercheval
COO: Robert M Allia
COO: Peter Dicapua
**COO:* John C Emmert
Bd of Dir: Alan Beaudette
Bd of Dir: Kevin Cantley
Trst: Joseph Hoesley
Chf Inves: Thomas Senkbeil
Sr VP: Rudolph Milian
VP: Sandhya Espitia
VP: Shirley Maloney
VP: John T McDonald
VP: Patricia Norins
VP: Rhonda Payne
VP: Rebecca Sullivan
VP: James A Tolliver
Dir Soc: Casey Adams
Dir Soc: Berivan Kockaya

D-U-N-S 96-720-6756
INTERNATIONAL COUNSELING SERVICES
LUTHERAN COMMUNITY SERVICE
115 Ne 100th St Ste 200, Seattle, WA 98125-8019
Tel (206) 694-5700 *Founded/Ownrshp* 1960
Sales 25.9MM *EMP* 80
SIC 8322 General counseling services; General counseling services
Prgrm Mgr: Lisa Lyon

D-U-N-S 62-162-6597 IMP
INTERNATIONAL CRANKSHAFT INC
I C I
(*Suby of* NIPPON STEEL & SUMITOMO METAL CORPORATION)
101 Carley Ct, Georgetown, KY 40324-9303
Tel (502) 868-0003 *Founded/Ownrshp* 2012
Sales 144.4MM *EMP* 260
Accts Deloitte & Touche Llp Louisvi
SIC 3714 Crankshaft assemblies, motor vehicle; Crankshaft assemblies, motor vehicle
Pr: Nobuaki Masuda
**Sec:* Kozo Matsumoto
**VP:* William McCurley

D-U-N-S 06-596-2094 IMP
INTERNATIONAL CREATIVE MANAGEMENT INC
I C M
(*Suby of* ICM HOLDINGS INC) ★
10250 Constellation Blvd # 1, Los Angeles, CA 90067-6241
Tel (310) 550-4000 *Founded/Ownrshp* 1988
Sales 30.3MM^E *EMP* 550
SIC 7922 8699 Talent agent, theatrical; Literary, film or cultural club; Talent agent, theatrical; Literary, film or cultural club
Ch Bd: Jeff Berg
**CFO:* Robert Murphy
**Co-Pr:* Nancy Josephson
**Co-Pr:* Ed Limato
Top Exec: Carol Goll
Ex VP: Jack Gilardi
Sr VP: Pam Brockie
Sr VP: Patrick Herold
Sr VP: Gregory Lipstone
VP: Dan Donahue
VP: Erin Oremland
VP: Jon Pleeter
VP: Michelle Suess

D-U-N-S 04-087-2785
INTERNATIONAL CRISIS GROUP
ICG
1629 K St Nw Ste 450, Washington, DC 20006-1677
Tel (202) 785-1601 *Founded/Ownrshp* 1995
Sales 23.1MM *EMP* 10
Accts Gelman Rosenberg & Freedman B
SIC 8399 Advocacy group; Advocacy group
Sr VP: Mark L Schneider
Top Exec: Tabib Huseynov
Ex VP: Stephen Druhot
Comm Dir: Scott Malcomson
Off Mgr: Jessica Hauser
Off Mgr: Pankaj Malla
Off Mgr: Anne Murambi
Off Mgr: Zachary Walko
Opers Mgr: Zaib Barlas

D-U-N-S 00-206-2052
INTERNATIONAL CRUISE & EXCURSION GALLERY INC
ICE GALLERY
15501 N Dial Blvd, Scottsdale, AZ 85260-1615
Tel (602) 395-1995 *Founded/Ownrshp* 1996
Sales 1.5MMM^E *EMP* 15,000
Accts Deloitte & Touche Llp
SIC 4724 Travel agencies; Travel agencies
Pr: John Rowley
COO: Glenn Nadel
COO: Glenn A Nadell
VP: Rendy Buness
Ex Dir: Patrick Ryan
Mng Dir: Kevin Sharp

D-U-N-S 06-148-3173 IMP/EXP
INTERNATIONAL CRUISE FOOD & HOTEL SUPPLIERS INC
470 Ne 185th St, Miami, FL 33179-4511
Tel (305) 653-2042 *Founded/Ownrshp* 1998
Sales 32.0MM *EMP* 32
SIC 5113 5149 Groceries & related products; Industrial & personal service paper; Industrial & personal service paper; Groceries & related products
Pr: Edwin A Dallow

D-U-N-S 02-290-5608 IMP
■ INTERNATIONAL DAIRY QUEEN INC
(*Suby of* BERKSHIRE HATHAWAY INC) ★
7505 Metro Blvd Ste 500, Minneapolis, MN 55439-3018
Tel (952) 830-0200 *Founded/Ownrshp* 1998
Sales 74.2MM^E *EMP* 450
SIC 5812 Ice cream stands or dairy bars; Snow cone stand; Ice cream stands or dairy bars
Pr: Charles W Mooty
CFO: James S Simpson
Ex VP: Alan Roark
VP: Lee Banbury
VP: William Barrier
VP: Keith Correia
VP: Tim Hawley
VP: Michael D Keller
VP: Scott Muyres
VP: Jodi Nyman
VP: Lane Schmiesing
VP: Ann Stone

D-U-N-S 08-156-8040 IMP/EXP
INTERNATIONAL DATA GROUP INC
EXECUTRAIN
1 Exeter Plz Fl 15, Boston, MA 02116
Tel (617) 423-9030 *Founded/Ownrshp* 1964
Sales 3.5MMM *EMP* 13,450
SIC 2721 8732 7389 Trade journals: publishing only, not printed on site; Market analysis or research; Trade show arrangement; Trade journals: publishing only, not printed on site; Market analysis or research; Trade show arrangement
Ch Bd: Patrick J McGovern
**CFO:* Edward B Bloom
Top Exec: Kevin Krull
VP: Kevin Kane
VP: Bill Laberis
VP: Charles Lee
VP: Nancy Percival
VP: Jeremy Rueb
VP: Neal Silverman
VP: Pam Stenson
VP: Jason Tenenbown
VP: Sean Weglage

INTERNATIONAL DECISION SYSTEMS
See IDS GROUP INC

D-U-N-S 07-651-9115
INTERNATIONAL DECISION SYSTEMS INC
(*Suby of* IDS GROUP INC) ★
220 S 6th St Ste 700, Minneapolis, MN 55402-1497
Tel (612) 851-3200 *Founded/Ownrshp* 2004
Sales 33.2MM^E *EMP* 350
SIC 7372 7373

D-U-N-S 00-298-0811
INTERNATIONAL DECORATORS INC
28059 W Commercial Ave, Lake Barrington, IL 60010-2443
Tel (847) 526-7477 *Founded/Ownrshp* 1952
Sales 20.3MM^E *EMP* 150
SIC 1742 1721 Drywall; Acoustical & ceiling work; Painting & paper hanging; Residential painting; Commercial painting; Wallcovering contractors
Pr: Anthony C Pintozzi Jr

Treas: James Gaszynski
**Sec:* Randall Freund
**VP:* Bill Preston
Sfty Dirs: Peter Graham
Doctor: D Stamos

D-U-N-S 04-657-1923 EXP
INTERNATIONAL DEHYDRATED FOODS INC
I D F
3801 E Sunshine St, Springfield, MO 65809-2800
Tel (417) 881-7820 *Founded/Ownrshp* 1982
Sales 46.9MM^E *EMP* 230
SIC 2015 Poultry, processed: fresh; Poultry, processed: frozen; Poultry, processed; Poultry, processed: fresh; Poultry, processed: frozen; Poultry, processed
CEO: Kurt D Hellweg
Pr: Michael J Gerke
CFO: Paul W Fry
VP: Stephanie Lynch
S&M/VP: Robert Hoopingarner

D-U-N-S 10-344-9385 IMP
INTERNATIONAL DELICACIES
2100 Atlas Rd Ste F, Richmond, CA 94806-1100
Tel (510) 669-2444 *Founded/Ownrshp* 1983
Sales 49.0MM^E *EMP* 150
SIC 5149 Pasta & rice; Cookies; Fruits, dried; Cooking oils; Pasta & rice; Cookies; Fruits, dried; Cooking oils
CEO: Hossein Banejad
CFO: Ruth Banejad
VP: Dean Wilkinson

D-U-N-S 17-515-9201 IMP
INTERNATIONAL DELIGHTS LLC
EXQUISITIES
230 Brighton Rd, Clifton, NJ 07012-1414
Tel (973) 928-5431 *Founded/Ownrshp* 1985
Sales 29.5MM^E *EMP* 130
SIC 2051 Bread, cake & related products; Bread, cake & related products

D-U-N-S 07-680-9438
INTERNATIONAL DELIVERY SOLUTIONS LLC
7340 S Howell Ave Unit 5, Oak Creek, WI 53154-7486
Tel (414) 856-1188 *Founded/Ownrshp* 1999
Sales 24.0MM *EMP* 38^E
SIC 7389 Mailing & messenger services
COO: Margaret Schneider
Opers Mgr: Richard Phillips

D-U-N-S 15-392-9625
INTERNATIONAL DEVELOPMENT ENTERPRISES
IDE
1031 33rd St Ste 270, Denver, CO 80205-2772
Tel (720) 235-3446 *Founded/Ownrshp* 1980
Sales 20.5MM *EMP* 13
Accts Clifton Gunderson Llp Greenwo
SIC 8611 Business associations; Business associations
Pr: Paul Polak
Dir Vol: Dana Cousteau
CFO: Annmarie Logue
VP: Jill Barkin
VP: Gary Zamis
Comm Man: Ilana Martin
Off Mgr: Michelle Warner
IT Man: Elizabeth Snow

D-U-N-S 80-149-9922 IMP
INTERNATIONAL DEVELOPMENT LLC
SUN GLOW
(*Suby of* SORENSON CAPITAL PARTNERS LP) ★
899 Henrietta Creek Rd, Roanoke, TX 76262-6309
Tel (817) 251-6999 *Founded/Ownrshp* 2008
Sales 54.9MM^E *EMP* 75
SIC 5063 Electrical apparatus & equipment; Electrical apparatus & equipment
CEO: John Browder
**Ch Bd:* Kathy Chang
**Pr:* Curtis Toone
CFO: Dan McWilliams
**VP:* Len Blackwell
VP: Kelli Thompson

D-U-N-S 15-709-7411
■ **INTERNATIONAL DEVELOPMENT UNITED STATES AGENCY FOR**
USAID
(*Suby of* EXECUTIVE OFFICE OF UNITED STATES GOVERNMENT) ★
1300 Penn Ave Nw 848, Washington, DC 20004-3002
Tel (202) 712-0000 *Founded/Ownrshp* 1963
Sales NA *EMP* 9,000
SIC 9611 Economic development agency, government; ; Economic development agency, government;
**CFO:* David Ostermeyer
Bd of Dir: Anne Craner
Ofcr: Tyler Beckelman
Ofcr: Maria Marigliano
Ofcr: Stephen Matzie
Ofcr: Robert Maushammer
Ofcr: Greg Olson
Ofcr: Glenn Post
Ofcr: Kevin Rafferty
Ofcr: Sandra Stajka
Assoc Dir: Joseph Ryan
Board of Directors: Paula Kohler

INTERNATIONAL DIST NETWORK-IDN
See IDN - ACME INC

D-U-N-S 17-591-3466 IMP/EXP
INTERNATIONAL DISTRIBUTORS LLC
6600 Bandini Blvd, Commerce, CA 90040-3302
Tel (323) 859-9000 *Founded/Ownrshp* 1997
Sales 42.5MM *EMP* 30
SIC 5199 5141 General merchandise, non-durable; Groceries, general line
Pr: B J Chang

INTERNATIONAL DISTRICT COMMUNI
See INTERNATIONAL COMMUNITY HEALTH SERVICES

D-U-N-S 60-973-1690 IMP
INTERNATIONAL DOTS LLC GLUE
N117w18711 Fulton Dr, Germantown, WI 53022-2439
Tel (262) 814-8500 *Founded/Ownrshp* 1999
Sales 22.8MM *EMP* 45^E
SIC 5199 5084 Packaging materials; Packaging machinery & equipment
Genl Mgr: Bruce Church
Genl Mgr: Brian Ritzow
Mfg Mgr: Joshua Smith
Ql Cn Mgr: Joseph Salmon

D-U-N-S 10-313-3625 IMP
INTERNATIONAL E-Z UP INC
1900 2nd St, Norco, CA 92860-2803
Tel (800) 457-4233 *Founded/Ownrshp* 1983
Sales 20.4MM^E *EMP* 100^E
SIC 2394 Shades, canvas: made from purchased materials
CEO: William Bradford Smith
**Ch Bd:* Mark Carter
**Pr:* Brad Smith
Store Mgr: James Gorman
Sls Mgr: Stuart Bremner

D-U-N-S 02-460-4352
INTERNATIONAL EDUCATION CORP
16485 Laguna Canyon Rd # 300, Irvine, CA 92618-3840
Tel (949) 272-7200 *Founded/Ownrshp* 1996
Sales 121.3MM^E *EMP* 1,000
Accts Almich & Associates Irvine C
SIC 8249 Vocational schools; Vocational schools
Pr: Fardad Fateri
Pr: William Murtagh Jr
**Pr:* Shoukry Tiab
**COO:* Joseph W Fox
**COO:* Janis Paulson
**CFO:* George P Harbison
**Ex VP:* Sandra N Lockwood
**Sr VP:* Aaron J Mortensen

D-U-N-S 62-362-5600
INTERNATIONAL EDUCATION SERVICES INC
AMOCO
550 W C St Ste 850, San Diego, CA 92101-3513
Tel (619) 479-2626 *Founded/Ownrshp* 2002
Sales 26.0MM *EMP* 100
SIC 2731 Book publishing
Pr: Angel C Martorell

D-U-N-S 19-445-3742
INTERNATIONAL EDUCATIONAL SERVICES INC
INTERNATIONAL EMRGNCY SHELTER
32120 Fm Rd 1847, Los Fresnos, TX 78566
Tel (956) 233-5705 *Founded/Ownrshp* 1984
Sales 34.3MM *EMP* 225
Accts Juan E Rivera Cpa Port Isab
SIC 8361 Children's boarding home; Children's boarding home
CEO: Ruben Gallegos Jr
**CFO:* Juan Gonzalez
**VP:* Lionel Perez

D-U-N-S 00-949-5628
INTERNATIONAL ELECTRIC INC
21973 W 83rd St, Lenexa, KS 66227-3133
Tel (913) 451-8458 *Founded/Ownrshp* 2009
Sales 21.4MM^E *EMP* 97
SIC 1731 Electrical work
Owner: Clifton Dodge
**CFO:* Chad Dodge
**VP:* Gary Suess

D-U-N-S 09-494-5136 IMP/EXP
INTERNATIONAL ELECTRICAL SALES CORP (FL)
IESCO
7540 Nw 66th St, Miami, FL 33166-2804
Tel (305) 591-8390 *Founded/Ownrshp* 1978
Sales 43.9MM *EMP* 34
Accts S I Gordon & Company Pa Cora
SIC 5063 Electrical apparatus & equipment; Electrical apparatus & equipment
Pr: Robert P Bernstein
**Sec:* Carlos Pino
**VP:* Juan F Bravo
VP Sls: Robert Obrian

INTERNATIONAL EMRGNCY SHELTER
See INTERNATIONAL EDUCATIONAL SERVICES INC

D-U-N-S 06-560-0991 IMP
INTERNATIONAL ENGINEERING & MANUFACTURING INC (MI)
IEM
6054 N Meridian Rd, Hope, MI 48628-9786
Tel (989) 689-4911 *Founded/Ownrshp* 1968
Sales 21.9MM^E *EMP* 96
SIC 3429 Manufactured hardware (general)
Pr: Robert Musselman
VP: Randy Oberson
Sls Dir: Larry Tiede

D-U-N-S 00-746-4753 IMP/EXP
■ **INTERNATIONAL ENVIRONMENTAL CORP**
IEC
(*Suby of* LSB INDUSTRIES INC) ★
5000 Interstate 40 W, Oklahoma City, OK 73128
Tel (405) 605-5000 *Founded/Ownrshp* 1968
Sales 88.6MM^E *EMP* 236
SIC 3585 Refrigeration & heating equipment; Refrigeration & heating equipment
Pr: Larry Jewel
Pr: Larry Jewell
Pr: Dennis F Kloster
Pr: Kim Sabatino
VP: Warren Shoulders
Off Mgr: Carol Oden
Sfty Mgr: Ann Allen
VP Sls: Robert Jaynch

D-U-N-S 80-452-3538
INTERNATIONAL EQUIPMENT INC
(*Suby of* INTERNATIONAL INDUSTRIES INC) ★
Larry Joe Harless Dr, Gilbert, WV 25621
Tel (304) 746-6021 *Founded/Ownrshp* 1989
Sales 1.1MM *EMP* 339
SIC 3715 Truck trailers; Trailer bodies; Truck trailers; Trailer bodies
Ch Bd: James Harless
**Pr:* Gary G White
**Treas:* Raymond McKinney
VP Opers: Mike Monroe
Opers Mgr: Charles Coleman

D-U-N-S 07-828-7874
INTERNATIONAL EQUIPMENT SOLUTIONS LLC
(*Suby of* KPS CAPITAL PARTNERS LP) ★
2211 York Rd Ste 320, Oak Brook, IL 60523-4030
Tel (630) 570-6880 *Founded/Ownrshp* 2011
Sales 555.7MM^E *EMP* 1,732^E
SIC 3531 Cabs, for construction machinery; Cabs, for construction machinery
CEO: Steve Andrews

D-U-N-S 07-682-9480
INTERNATIONAL EXECUTIVE SERVICE CORPS
IESC
1900 M St Nw Ste 500, Washington, DC 20036-3522
Tel (202) 326-0280 *Founded/Ownrshp* 1964
Sales 28.0MM *EMP* 50
Accts Rsm Mcgladrey Inc Vienna Va
SIC 8611 Business associations; Business associations
Pr: Spencer T King
Ch Bd: Don B Taggart
Ch Bd: John P Torell
Pr: Elizabeth K Lavach
CEO: Donald H Layton
Assoc VP: Erin Spinnell
VP: Shaun Donnelly
VP: Steve Kroll
Prgrm Mgr: Christian Klein
Snr Mgr: Andrey Yemelin

D-U-N-S 11-937-9290
INTERNATIONAL EXECUTIVE SERVICE CORPS
1900 M St Nw Ste 500, Washington, DC 20036-3522
Tel (202) 589-2600 *Founded/Ownrshp* 2000
Sales 28.0MM *EMP* 42
SIC 8748 Urban planning & consulting services
CEO: Tom Miller

D-U-N-S 96-267-8608 EXP
INTERNATIONAL EXPORTS INC
IEI
10820 Train Ct, Houston, TX 77041-7041
Tel (713) 849-2299 *Founded/Ownrshp* 2010
Sales 45.8MM^E *EMP* 48^E
SIC 5141 Groceries, general line
Prin: Hibba S Itani
**Prin:* Omar S Itani

D-U-N-S 05-881-1340
INTERNATIONAL EXTRUSIONS INC (MI)
EXCRUTION PAINTING
5800 Venoy Rd, Garden City, MI 48135-1655
Tel (734) 427-8700 *Founded/Ownrshp* 1971
Sales 30.0MM^E *EMP* 172
Accts Rehmann Troy Mi
SIC 3354 3441 Aluminum extruded products; Fabricated structural metal; Aluminum extruded products; Fabricated structural metal
Pr: Nicholas Noecker
**VP:* George Gazepis
VP Opers: Robert Hill
Sfty Mgr: Don Campbell
Opers Mgr: Edward Schaekel
Natl Sales: Jeff Aschoff
Sls&Mrk Ex: Glen Smith
Sls Mgr: Laura Walraven

D-U-N-S 04-526-3662
INTERNATIONAL EYECARE CENTER INC
2445 Broadway St, Quincy, IL 62301-3264
Tel (217) 222-9207 *Founded/Ownrshp* 1981
Sales 20.5MM^E *EMP* 100
SIC 5995 8011 Optical goods stores; Opticians; Offices & clinics of medical doctors
Pr: Dr John H Mc Dougall
Rgnl Mgr: Ashley Lay
Doctor: Timothy Leahy

D-U-N-S 60-679-5698
■ **INTERNATIONAL FAMILY ENTERTAINMENT INC**
FOX FAMILY CHANNEL
(*Suby of* ABC FAMILY WORLDWIDE INC) ★
3800 W Alameda Ave, Burbank, CA 91505-4300
Tel (818) 560-1000 *Founded/Ownrshp* 1997
Sales 30.1MM^E *EMP* 288
SIC 4841 7812 7922 7999 Cable television services; Television film production; Theatrical producers; Legitimate live theater producers; Television program, including commercial producers; Recreation services; Cable television services; Television film production; Theatrical producers; Legitimate live theater producers; Television program, including commercial producers; Recreation services
Pr: Mel Woods
Sr VP: Tom Cosgrove
MIS Dir: Tracey Stuart

D-U-N-S 09-208-5513
INTERNATIONAL FEDERATION OF ACCOUNTANTS
I F A C
529 5th Ave Fl 6, New York, NY 10017-4649
Tel (212) 286-9344 *Founded/Ownrshp* 1977
Sales 26.4MM^E *EMP* 66
Accts Citrin Cooperman & Company Ll
SIC 8611 Trade associations; Trade associations
CEO: Ian Ball
Pr: Olivia Kirtley
IT Man: Matthew Bohun-Aponte

Tech Mgr: Christopher Arnold
Tech Mgr: Beverley Bahlmann
Tech Mgr: Maria Chuvasheva
Tech Mgr: Brett James
Tech Mgr: Diane Jules
Tech Mgr: Szymon Radziszewicz
Tech Mgr: Marta Russell
Tech Mgr: Paul Thompson

D-U-N-S 78-610-5197
INTERNATIONAL FELLOWSHIP OF CHRISTIANS & JEWS INC
30 N La Salle St Ste 2600, Chicago, IL 60602-3356
Tel (312) 641-7200 *Founded/Ownrshp* 1983
Sales 110.4MM *EMP* 42
Accts Rsm Mcgladrey Inc Chicago Il
SIC 8661 Religious organizations; Religious organizations
Pr: Rabbi Yechiel Eckstein
COO: Clark Miller
COO: David Wolfard
**VP:* Yael Eckstein
VP: Sue Woodward
Comm Dir: Michael Stoltz
Web Dev: James Dalton
Mktg Dir: Ronda Henna

D-U-N-S 07-911-2777
INTERNATIONAL FERTILIZER DEVELOPMENT CENTER
IFDC
1010 Reservation Dr, Muscle Shoals, AL 35661
Tel (256) 381-6600 *Founded/Ownrshp* 1974
Sales 64.2MM *EMP* 100
Accts Cdpapc Athens Al
SIC 8731 Agricultural research
Pr: Amit H Roy
**COO:* John H Allgood
Board of Directors: Ann Tutwiler

D-U-N-S 00-256-9754
INTERNATIONAL FIDELITY INSURANCE CO
IFIC
1111 Raymond Blvd Fl 20, Newark, NJ 07102-5206
Tel (973) 286-7911 *Founded/Ownrshp* 1964
Sales NA *EMP* 240
SIC 6351 Fidelity or surety bonding; Fidelity or surety bonding
Pr: Fred Mitterhoff
**COO:* Robert Minister
**CFO:* Maria Costa
Treas: Charlotte Weiss
Treas: Charlotte S WEI
Sr VP: Anthony Demartino
Sr VP: Adrian Oddi
**Sr VP:* Jerry Watson
VP: Anna Dime
**VP:* Norman R Konvitz
VP: Robert Minster
**VP:* Daniel Mitterhoff
VP: Dorothy O'Connor
**VP:* Beatriz Sampedro
VP: Beatrib Sanpedro
VP: Brian St Clair
Board of Directors: George F Brenner

D-U-N-S 05-628-1876
INTERNATIONAL FINANCE CORP
WORLD BANK, THE
2121 Pennsylvania Ave Nw, Washington, DC 20433-0005
Tel (202) 473-3800 *Founded/Ownrshp* 1956
Sales NA *EMP* 2,100^E
SIC 6082 Foreign trade & international banking institutions; Foreign trade & international banking institutions
CEO: Jin-Yong Cai
**Pr:* Robert Zoellick
COO: Simeon Djankov
Ofcr: Azita Amjadi
Ofcr: Desmond Andrades
Ofcr: Zafar Azhar
Ofcr: Branimir Bajic
Ofcr: Masud Cader
Ofcr: Enrico Capraro
Ofcr: Richard Davis
Ofcr: Dina Elnaggar
Ofcr: Arvind Ghate
Ofcr: Nisha Goyal
Ofcr: Luisita Guanlao
Ofcr: Adrienne Kennedy
Ofcr: Bernard Lauwers
Ofcr: Maura Leary
Ofcr: Anat Lewin
Ofcr: Ming Lin
Ofcr: Santosh Maskeri
Ofcr: Julia Poblete

D-U-N-S 10-011-2478
INTERNATIONAL FINANCIAL GROUP INC
ISG COMPANIES
238 International Rd, Burlington, NC 27215-5129
Tel (336) 586-2500 *Founded/Ownrshp* 1993
Sales NA *EMP* 300
SIC 6331 Fire, marine & casualty insurance & carriers; Fire, marine & casualty insurance & carriers
Pr: Robert Linton
Dir IT: Wade Staunton

D-U-N-S 61-531-0075
INTERNATIONAL FIRE PROTECTION INC
(*Suby of* API GROUP INC) ★
243 Royal Dr, Madison, AL 35758-1788
Tel (256) 461-9988 *Founded/Ownrshp* 2007
Sales 41.7MM *EMP* 260
Accts Kpmg Llp Minneapolis Mn
SIC 1711 8711 Fire sprinkler system installation; Fire protection engineering; Fire sprinkler system installation; Fire protection engineering
Pr: Kamran Malek
VP: Ronald Davidson
VP: Brad Zurn
Dist Mgr: Matthew Gardner
Dist Mgr: Randy Smith

D-U-N-S 00-153-4833 IMP/EXP
▲ INTERNATIONAL FLAVORS & FRAGRANCES INC (NY)
IFF
521 W 57th St, New York, NY 10019-2929
Tel (212) 765-5500 *Founded/Ownrshp* 1909
Sales 3.0MMM *EMP* 6,200
Accts Pricewaterhousecoopers Llp N
Tkr Sym IFF *Exch* NYS
SIC 2869 2844 2087 Flavors or flavoring materials, synthetic; Perfume materials, synthetic; Toilet preparations; Flavoring extracts & syrups; Flavors or flavoring materials, synthetic; Perfume materials, synthetic; Toilet preparations; Flavoring extracts & syrups
CEO: Douglas D Tough
**CEO:* Andreas Fibig
COO: Cynthia Ross
CFO: Roger Blanken
CFO: Alison A Cornell
**CFO:* Richard A O'Leary
Treas: Chad Weller
Ofcr: Kevin Berryman
Ex VP: Julian W Boyden
Ex VP: Beth E Ford
Ex VP: Wayne Howard
**Sr VP:* Angelica T Cantlon
**Sr VP:* Anne Chwat
**Sr VP:* Francisco Fortanet
Sr VP: Dennis M Meany
VP: Shelley Bellisle
VP: Saumya Dwivedi
VP: David Gerics
VP: Sophia Grojsman
VP: Sophie Grossman
VP: Steve Huang
Board of Directors: Henry W Howell Jr, Marcello V Bottoli, Katherine M Hudson, Linda B Buck, Arthur C Martines, J Michael Cook, Dale F Morrison, Michael Ducker, Roger W Ferguson, John Ferraro, Andreas Fibig, Christina Gold, Alexandra A Herzan

D-U-N-S 12-091-1024 IMP
INTERNATIONAL FLOW SERVICES LP
4230 Greenbriar Dr, Stafford, TX 77477-3917
Tel (281) 240-2000 *Founded/Ownrshp* 2001
Sales 60.9MM^E *EMP* 57^E
SIC 5084 Controlling instruments & accessories
Pt: Rick Heidt
Ex VP: Daniel English
Dir IT: Bob Davis

D-U-N-S 80-561-1386 IMP
INTERNATIONAL FOOD ASSOCIATES INC
IFA
1730 Hurd Dr, Irving, TX 75038-4324
Tel (214) 351-9060 *Founded/Ownrshp* 2006
Sales 30.0MM *EMP* 39
SIC 5149 Specialty food items
CEO: Greg Figueroa
**Pr:* Donald Cook
**COO:* Gary Ruchlin
**Ex VP:* Dale Lucas
**Sr VP:* Mike Wheeler
VP: Jacqueline Peckham

D-U-N-S 02-031-3540
INTERNATIONAL FOOD POLICY RESEARCH INSTITUTE
IFPRI
2033 K St Nw Ste 400, Washington, DC 20006-1018
Tel (202) 862-5600 *Founded/Ownrshp* 1975
Sales 146.6MM *EMP* 200
SIC 8731 8733 Commercial physical research; Noncommercial research organizations; Commercial physical research; Noncommercial research organizations
Ofcr: Godwin Horlu
Ofcr: James Stevenson
Ofcr: Wondwosen Tefera
Top Exec: Andrea Pedolsky
VP: John Bongaarts
Prgrm Mgr: Amanda Wyatt
Pgrm Dir: Howarth Bouis

D-U-N-S 04-350-4356
INTERNATIONAL FOOD PRODUCTS CORP
150 Lrkin Wllams Indus Ct, Fenton, MO 63026-2409
Tel (636) 717-2100 *Founded/Ownrshp* 1974
Sales 49.4MM^E *EMP* 62
SIC 5149

D-U-N-S 14-807-4466 IMP/EXP
INTERNATIONAL FOODSOURCE LLC
VALUED NATURALS
52 Richboynton Rd, Dover, NJ 07801-2650
Tel (973) 361-7044 *Founded/Ownrshp* 2004
Sales 39.9MM^E *EMP* 90
SIC 2034 Dehydrated fruits, vegetables, soups; Dehydrated fruits, vegetables, soups
CEO: Dan Baron
Sr VP: Terry Quinn
VP Sls: Linda Johnson

D-U-N-S 07-950-4031 IMP/EXP
INTERNATIONAL FOREST PRODUCTS LLC
1 Patriot Pl, Foxboro, MA 02035-1374
Tel (508) 698-4600 *Founded/Ownrshp* 1972
Sales 89.9MM^E *EMP* 100
SIC 0831 Paper & products, wrapping or coarse; Forest products
Ch: Robert K Kraft
Pr: Larry Burton
**Pr:* Daniel Kraft
COO: Jonathan A Kraft
**COO:* Daniel Moore
CFO: Michael Quattromani
VP: Jim Cobery
VP: Terry Maceachen
VP: Eduardo Porta
VP: Rob Shepard
Mng Dir: Nairne Gray

D-U-N-S 17-537-9569
INTERNATIONAL FOUNDATION FOR ELECTORAL SYSTEMS
IFES
1850 K St Nw, Washington, DC 20006-2213
Tel (202) 350-6700 *Founded/Ownrshp* 1987
Sales 68.2MM *EMP* 1
SIC 7374 Data processing & preparation; Data processing & preparation
Pr: William Sweeney
**COO:* Jim Johnson
VP: Stephanie Hoke
**VP:* Michael Svetlik

D-U-N-S 07-893-1938
INTERNATIONAL FOUNDATION OF EMPLOYEE BENEFIT PLANS INC (WI)
18700 W Bluemound Rd, Brookfield, WI 53045-2936
Tel (262) 786-6700 *Founded/Ownrshp* 1954, 1964
Sales 29.3MM *EMP* 130
SIC 8742 Programmed instruction service; Programmed instruction service
CEO: Michael Wilson
Pt: Kenton J Klaus
Pt: Robert W Ridley
Pt: Jeff Snyder
**Pr:* Kenneth R Boyd
Pr: Cebs Davidson
**Pr:* Thomas T Holsman
COO: Sandra Becker
**CFO:* W A Hamwright Jr
**Treas:* Regina C Reardon
Prin: Lewis E Devendorf
Board of Directors: Terry Davidson L Hamwright

D-U-N-S 07-461-6996
INTERNATIONAL FREIGHT FORWARDING INC (TX)
BAZAN, RUBEN FORWARDING AGENCY
302 International Blvd, Laredo, TX 78045-7212
Tel (956) 718-7100 *Founded/Ownrshp* 1950
Sales 20.7MM^E *EMP* 136
SIC 4731 Freight forwarding; Freight forwarding
Pr: Ruben Bazan Sr
**Treas:* Ruben Bazan Jr
Mng Dir: Edmund Benson
Mng Dir: Natalie Driver
Genl Mgr: Omar Camacho
Off Mgr: Patricia Salinas
CTO: Otto Schroeder
Dir IT: Edgar Hernandez
Dir IT: Arturo Miguel
Dir IT: Elisa Trevino

D-U-N-S 07-842-2517
INTERNATIONAL FULFILLMENT SOLUTIONS LLC
INTERNATIONALFULFILLMENT.COM
2080 S Industrial Rd C, Salt Lake City, UT 84104-3858
Tel (888) 993-8534 *Founded/Ownrshp* 2011
Sales 30.0MM *EMP* 25
SIC 4731 Freight transportation arrangement
Off Mgr: Tori Tucker

D-U-N-S 09-586-7024
INTERNATIONAL FUND FOR ANIMAL WELFARE INC
IFAW
290 Summer St, Yarmouth Port, MA 02675-1734
Tel (508) 744-2000 *Founded/Ownrshp* 1969
Sales 20.3MM *EMP* 225
SIC 8699 Charitable organization; Charitable organization
Pr: Azzedine Downes
**Ch Bd:* Kathleen Savesky
CFO: John Kluza
**CFO:* Tom Maul
Ofcr: Rosemary Adler
Ofcr: Johnathan Alie
Ofcr: Andreas Dinkelmeyer
Ofcr: Mary Harrington
VP: Tereza Byrne
**VP:* Erica Martin
**VP:* Dr Ian Robinson
VP: Andrew Wilson
Exec: Kathryn Green
Comm Dir: Shawna Moos
Comm Man: Louis Cafiero
Comm Man: Jacqueline Nyagah
Comm Man: Christina Pretorius
Comm Man: Rob Rosenfeld

D-U-N-S 79-885-6829
■ INTERNATIONAL FUNERAL SERVICES INC
(*Suby of* SCI) ★
1929 Allen Pkwy, Houston, TX 77019-2506
Tel (713) 522-5141 *Founded/Ownrshp* 1993
Sales 8.0MM^E *EMP* 700
SIC 7261 Funeral service & crematories; Funeral service & crematories
Prin: Jerry Pullins

INTERNATIONAL FURNITURE
See SCHNADIG CORP

D-U-N-S 78-743-1022
INTERNATIONAL FUTURES & OPTIONS ASSOCIATES
141 W Jackson Blvd # 1685, Chicago, IL 60604-2992
Tel (312) 353-0340 *Founded/Ownrshp* 1990
Sales NA *EMP* 180
SIC 6153 6221 Mercantile financing; Commodity contracts brokers, dealers; Mercantile financing; Commodity contracts brokers, dealers
Pt: Stephen Gold
Pt: James Kavlentis
Pt: Mauray Krabitz
Pt: Sidney Rosenberg

D-U-N-S 10-230-9457
INTERNATIONAL GAMCO INC
9335 N 48th St, Omaha, NE 68152-1541
Tel (402) 571-2449 *Founded/Ownrshp* 1992
Sales 32.1MM^E *EMP* 170
SIC 2754 Cards, except greeting: gravure printing; Cards, except greeting: gravure printing
Pr: Phillip J Glassman
**Treas:* Robert P Koory
IT Man: Michael Abel
IT Man: Lee Matson
Sales Asso: Sheryl Czyz

D-U-N-S 06-502-0216 IMP
■ INTERNATIONAL GAME TECHNOLOGY INC
IGT
(*Suby of* INTERNATIONAL GAME TECHNOLOGY PLC)
6355 S Buffalo Dr, Las Vegas, NV 89113-2133
Tel (702) 669-7777 *Founded/Ownrshp* 2015
Sales 319.7MM^E *EMP* 4,400
Tkr Sym IGT *Exch* NYS
SIC 7999 Coin-operated amusement machines; Slot machines; Gambling & lottery services; Gambling machines, operation; Coin-operated video game rental; Gambling & lottery services; Lottery operation; Lottery tickets, sale of
CEO: Renato Ascoli
CFO: Alberto Fornaro
Co-CEO: Walter Bugno
Co-CEO: Michael Chambrello
Sr VP: Ken Bossingham
Sr VP: Ward Chilton
VP: Craig Churchill
VP: Toni Marteenez
Genl Couns: Neil Friedman

D-U-N-S 15-782-6843 IMP/EXP
INTERNATIONAL GARDEN PRODUCTS INC
IGP
30590 Se Kelso Rd, Boring, OR 97009-6016
Tel (503) 663-1698 *Founded/Ownrshp* 1997
Sales 28.9MM^E *EMP* 1,000
SIC 0181 Nursery stock, growing of; Nursery stock, growing of
Pr: Jay Hulbert
**CFO:* Ron Ridout

INTERNATIONAL GASKET & SUPPLY
See LEADER GASKET TECHNOLOGIES INC

INTERNATIONAL GEOTECHNICAL
See HEPHAISTOS BUILDING SUPPLIES INC

D-U-N-S 02-896-7651 IMP
INTERNATIONAL GOLD STAR INC (NY)
570 Smith St, Brooklyn, NY 11231-3820
Tel (718) 522-1545 *Founded/Ownrshp* 2002
Sales 21.5MM *EMP* 32
SIC 5149 Specialty food items; Specialty food items
Pr: Galina Pincow

D-U-N-S 00-473-2124
INTERNATIONAL GOLF CLUB LLC
159 Ballville Rd, Bolton, MA 01740-1227
Tel (978) 779-6910 *Founded/Ownrshp* 1999
Sales 11.5MM^E *EMP* 300
SIC 7997 Membership sports & recreation clubs; Golf club, membership; Membership sports & recreation clubs; Golf club, membership

D-U-N-S 87-686-3713
INTERNATIONAL GOLF MAINTENANCE INC
(*Suby of* MEADOWBROOK GOLF GROUP INC) ★
5385 Gateway Blvd Ste 12, Lakeland, FL 33811-1785
Tel (407) 589-7200 *Founded/Ownrshp* 1998
Sales 14.9MM *EMP* 600
SIC 0782 Lawn services; Lawn services
Pr: Ron E Jackson
**CFO:* K Eric Burk
Ex VP: Greg Plotner
Rgnl Mgr: Tyler Minamyer
CIO: Paul Walker

D-U-N-S 19-144-5824 IMP
INTERNATIONAL GOURMET FOODS INC
7520 Fullerton Rd, Springfield, VA 22153-2812
Tel (404) 349-6333 *Founded/Ownrshp* 1985
Sales 22.9MM^E *EMP* 87^E
SIC 5499 Groceries, general line; Gourmet food stores
Pr: Maurizio Dibenigno
**Sec:* Lori Ann Di Benigno
Div Mgr: Kelli Chapman
Genl Mgr: Chris Walsh
Sales Exec: Louis Botta

D-U-N-S 00-891-3097 IMP/EXP
INTERNATIONAL GRANITE & MARBLE CORP
I G M
2038 83rd St, North Bergen, NJ 07047-4711
Tel (201) 869-5200 *Founded/Ownrshp* 1948
Sales 26.9MM^E *EMP* 100
SIC 5032

D-U-N-S 13-643-1848 IMP/EXP
INTERNATIONAL GREETINGS USA INC
(*Suby of* INTERNATIONAL GREETINGS PLC)
338 Indl Blvd, Midway, GA 31320
Tel (912) 884-9727 *Founded/Ownrshp* 1990
Sales 93.8MM *EMP* 225
Accts Ernst & Young Llp Miami Fl
SIC 2679 Gift wrap, paper: made from purchased material; Gift wrap, paper: made from purchased material
CEO: Lawrence Louis
**CEO:* Paul Fineman
CFO: Lester Kiene
**CFO:* Anthony Lawrinson
**Ch:* John Charlton
**VP:* Wain Yarber
Mfg Mgr: Larry Garman
Opers Mgr: Otis Cloud

D-U-N-S 07-921-0685 EXP
INTERNATIONAL GROCERS INC
2007 Nw 84th Ave, Doral, FL 33122-1521
Tel (305) 597-1550 *Founded/Ownrshp* 2013
Sales 25.0MM *EMP* 100
SIC 5411 5141 Grocery stores; Groceries, general line; Grocery stores; Groceries, general line
Pr: Derek Kramer
**VP:* Robert Kramer

D-U-N-S 12-228-0092 IMP/EXP
INTERNATIONAL GROUP INC
I G I
(*Suby of* INTERNATIONAL GROUP INC,THE)
1007 E Spring St, Titusville, PA 16354-7826
Tel (814) 827-4900 *Founded/Ownrshp* 1985
Sales 112.0MM *EMP* 500
SIC 5169 2911 Waxes, except petroleum; Oils, lubricating; Petrolatums, nonmedicinal; Paraffin wax; Waxes, except petroleum; Oils, lubricating; Petrolatums, nonmedicinal; Paraffin wax
CEO: W Ross Reucassel
**Pr:* Kenneth Reucassel
CFO: David Imrie

D-U-N-S 05-251-0729
INTERNATIONAL HEALTH SERVICES INC
599 Canal St, Lawrence, MA 01840-1244
Tel (617) 605-0727 *Founded/Ownrshp* 2001
Sales 18.6MM *EMP* 950
SIC 8082 Home health care services; Home health care services
Pr: Margarita Blanter

D-U-N-S 83-079-5543
INTERNATIONAL HOTEL MANAGEMENT SERVICES INC
IHMS
(*Suby of* THE INDIAN HOTELS COMPANY LIMITED)
2 E 61st St, New York, NY 10065-8401
Tel (212) 838-8000 *Founded/Ownrshp* 1986
Sales 112.4MM^E *EMP* 700
SIC 7011 Hotels & motels; Hotels & motels
Pr: Raymond Bickson
**CFO:* Anil P Goel
**VP:* Deepa Misra Harris
**VP:* Jodi Leblanc
Ex Dir: Abhijit Mukerji
Genl Mgr: Heiko Kuenstle
Off Mgr: Corinna Luebbe
Off Mgr: Samik Sarkar
Off Mgr: Ameeya Shrimali
Dir IT: Raju Rathod
Sales Exec: Abhilash Shetty
Board of Directors: Anil P Goel, Jodi Le Balnc, Rajesh K Parekh

INTERNATIONAL HOUSE
See UNIVERSITY OF CHICAGO

D-U-N-S 04-223-2546
■ INTERNATIONAL HOUSE OF PANCAKES LLC
IHOP
(*Suby of* DINEEQUITY INC) ★
450 N Brand Blvd Fl 7, Glendale, CA 91203-2346
Tel (818) 240-6055 *Founded/Ownrshp* 1968
Sales 45.7MM^E *EMP* 897
SIC 5812 Restaurant, family: chain; Restaurant, family: chain
VP: Patrick Piccirianna

D-U-N-S 10-861-8745 IMP/EXP
INTERNATIONAL IMAGING MATERIALS INC
IIMAK
310 Commerce Dr, Amherst, NY 14228-2396
Tel (716) 691-6333 *Founded/Ownrshp* 1926
Sales 131.3MM^E *EMP* 587
SIC 3955 3555 Ribbons, inked: typewriter, adding machine, register, etc.; Printing trades machinery; Ribbons, inked: typewriter, adding machine, register, etc.; Printing trades machinery
Ch Bd: Richard Marshall
**CEO:* Douglas Wagner
**CFO:* Joe Perna
**Sr VP:* Susan R Stamp
Prgrm Mgr: John Edick
Prgrm Mgr: Gregory Gotthelf
Netwrk Eng: Neil Hickey
Opers Mgr: Mike Kopcho
Mktg Dir: Amy Schmitt
Snr Mgr: Solloway Greg
Board of Directors: David Jaffe, William Mantoague, John Paxton, Robert Scribner, Eric Wilnes

D-U-N-S 00-653-8003 IMP
INTERNATIONAL INDUSTRIAL CONTRACTING CORP (MI)
IICC
35900 Mound Rd, Sterling Heights, MI 48310-4793
Tel (586) 264-7070 *Founded/Ownrshp* 1961, 1978
Sales 49.3MM *EMP* 150
Accts Plante & Moran Pllc Clinton T
SIC 1796 Machine moving & rigging; Machine moving & rigging
Pr: Douglas W Jardine
**CFO:* Jonathan Firsht
**VP:* Ryan C Farnen
**VP:* Brian Jardine
**VP:* Martha Jardine
VP: Fred Wilson
Off Admin: Samiluah Lynch
Sfty Mgr: John Lapish
Opers Mgr: Larz Olson

D-U-N-S 19-059-1016
INTERNATIONAL INDUSTRIES INC
210 Larry Joe Harless Dr, Gilbert, WV 25621
Tel (304) 664-3227 *Founded/Ownrshp* 1987
Sales 105.5MM^E *EMP* 1,104
SIC 6211 Investment bankers; Investment bankers
Ch Bd: James Harless
**Pr:* Gary G White
**Treas:* Raymond McKinney
**VP:* C Fred Shewey

D-U-N-S 08-000-0102 EXP
INTERNATIONAL INGREDIENT CORP
150 Lrkin Williams Ind Ct, Fenton, MO 63026-2409
Tel (636) 343-4111 *Founded/Ownrshp* 1976
Sales 32.2MM^E *EMP* 130
SIC 2048 Livestock feeds; Livestock feeds
Ch Bd: Fred E Brown
**CEO:* Clayton C Brown
**COO:* Mike Rivard
VP: Jennifer Hoercher
**VP:* Kathy Langan

VP: Jim Warren
Genl Mgr: David Gerfen
Genl Mgr: Dan McNamara
MIS Mgr: Brian Cissell
Nutrtnst: Nick Shelton

D-U-N-S 60-381-7631 IMP
INTERNATIONAL INSPIRATIONS LTD
LUX ACCESSORIES
362 5th Ave Ste 601, New York, NY 10001-2210
Tel (212) 465-8500 *Founded/Ownrshp* 2005
Sales 20.4MME *EMP* 90
SIC 3961 Costume jewelry; Costume jewelry
CEO: Saul Shaya Reiter
Ex VP: Sherry Burns
Opers Mgr: Tarkan Boke

D-U-N-S 07-933-9729
INTERNATIONAL INTIMATES INC (DE)
RENE ROFE LINGERIE
31 W 34th St Fl 8, New York, NY 10001-3030
Tel (212) 213-4848 *Founded/Ownrshp* 2014
Sales 20.5MME *EMP* 275
SIC 5137 Women's & children's lingerie & undergarments
Ch Bd: Rene Rofe
**CFO:* Richard Rosenberg

D-U-N-S 17-719-2754 IMP
INTERNATIONAL JUSTICE MISSION
P.O. Box 58147, Washington DC (20037-8147)
Tel (703) 465-5495 *Founded/Ownrshp* 1994
Sales 44.8MM *EMP* 650
Accts Mcgladrey Llp Mclean Va
SIC 8399 Social change association; Social change association
Pr: Gary Haugen
**CFO:* Gary Veurnik
Chf Mktg O: Eric Asche
Ex VP: Gary Veurink
Sr VP: Sean Litton
VP: Bill Clark
VP: Jim Martin
VP: Darcy Taylor
**VP:* Lauren Weaver
Exec: Shelley Thames
Prgrm Mgr: Kirsten Singleton

D-U-N-S 78-502-4436 IMP/EXP
INTERNATIONAL KNIFE & SAW INC
IKS
(*Suby of* UCT COATINGS INC) ★
1435 N Cashua Dr, Florence, SC 29501-6950
Tel (843) 662-6345 *Founded/Ownrshp* 2006
Sales 44.1MME *EMP* 85
SIC 3423 Knives, agricultural or industrial
Pr: Don Weeks
**VP:* Terry Issac
**VP:* Jim Ranson
Exec: Kay Howard
Dist Mgr: Dean Johnston
VP Opers: George Revollo
Plnt Mgr: Mike Gray
Mktg Dir: Terry Isaacs
Sls Mgr: Dave Graham
Sales Asso: Grace Campbell
Board of Directors: Timothy Donahue, Terry Isaacs, Don Weeks

D-U-N-S 02-356-9924
■ **INTERNATIONAL LABORATORIES INC**
INTERNATIONAL LABS
(*Suby of* WESTROCK MWV LLC) ★
2701 75th St N, Saint Petersburg, FL 33710-2938
Tel (727) 322-7160 *Founded/Ownrshp* 2008
Sales 45.0MM *EMP* 209
SIC 7389 Packaging & labeling services; Packaging & labeling services
Pr: Stephen C Pohlmann
**VP:* Robert E Birkenholz
**VP:* Timothy Wojdan

INTERNATIONAL LABS
See INTERNATIONAL LABORATORIES INC

D-U-N-S 04-148-2128
INTERNATIONAL LEADERSHIP OF TEXAS
1820 N Glnvlle Dr Ste 100, Richardson, TX 75081
Tel (972) 479-9144 *Founded/Ownrshp* 2014
Sales 24.5MME *EMP* 479E
SIC 8211 Elementary & secondary schools; Elementary & secondary schools
**CFO:* Jerry McCright

D-U-N-S 06-622-5574
INTERNATIONAL LEASE FINANCE CORP
(*Suby of* AERCAP LOS ANGELES) ★
10250 Constellation Blvd, Los Angeles, CA 90067-6200
Tel (310) 788-1999 *Founded/Ownrshp* 2014
Sales 120.4MME *EMP* 564E
SIC 7359 5599 8741 Aircraft rental; Aircraft dealers; Business management; Aircraft rental; Aircraft dealers; Business management
CEO: Henri Courpron
**CFO:* Elias Habayeb
CFO: David L Herzog
Treas: Pamela Hendry
**Sr VP:* Kurt H Schwarz
VP: Steve Adams
VP: Drew Bauer
VP: Spiro Farougias
VP: Joey Johnsen
VP: David Kingsley
VP: Richard Lee
VP: Raviv Surpin
VP: Douglas Walker

D-U-N-S 04-502-6044
■ **INTERNATIONAL LIFE SUPPORT INC**
AMERICAN MEDICAL RESPONSE
(*Suby of* AMERICAN MEDICAL RESPONSE INC) ★
99-840 Iwaiwa St Unit 1, Aiea, HI 96701-3280
Tel (808) 487-4900 *Founded/Ownrshp* 1979
Sales 33.5MM *EMP* 60
SIC 4119 Ambulance service; Ambulance service
Pr: William A Sanger
**CFO:* Randel Owen
**Ex VP:* Mark Bruning
Prin: Lynne Ward
Board of Directors: William Sanger

D-U-N-S 12-238-2849
■ **INTERNATIONAL LINE BUILDERS INC**
I L B
(*Suby of* MDU RESOURCES GROUP INC) ★
19020 Sw Cipole Rd Ste A, Tualatin, OR 97062-8362
Tel (503) 692-0193 *Founded/Ownrshp* 1997
Sales 80.0MME *EMP* 300
SIC 1623 Electric power line construction; Electric power line construction
CEO: Ronald Tipton
**Pr:* Michael A Bass
**Pr:* Charles R Griffin
**VP:* Antonio Y De Ocampo
VP Admn: Marla Jordan
Div Mgr: Kevin Nelsen
Dir IT: John Paist

D-U-N-S 60-334-8236
■ **INTERNATIONAL LINE BUILDERS INC**
ILB
(*Suby of* MDU RESOURCES GROUP INC) ★
2520 Rubidoux Blvd, Riverside, CA 92509-2147
Tel (951) 682-2982 *Founded/Ownrshp* 1989
Sales 32.5MME *EMP* 180
SIC 1731 Electrical work; Electrical work
CEO: Jeffrey S Thiede
**Pr:* Mike Bass
**Sr VP:* Don McNair
Sfty Dirs: David Vail

D-U-N-S 07-186-5604
INTERNATIONAL LONGSHORE & WAREHOUSE UNION
I L W U
1188 Franklin St Fl 4, San Francisco, CA 94109-6800
Tel (415) 775-0533 *Founded/Ownrshp* 1937
Sales 7.4MM *EMP* 382
Accts The Henry Levy Group Oakland
SIC 8631 Labor unions & similar labor organizations; Labor unions & similar labor organizations
Pr: Robert McEllrath
VP: Chad Oneill
VP: Matt Ventoza
Comm Dir: Craig Merrilees

D-U-N-S 01-189-9083
INTERNATIONAL LOTTERY & TOTALIZATOR SYSTEMS INC
ILTS DELAWARE
2310 Cousteau Ct, Vista, CA 92081-8346
Tel (760) 598-1655 *Founded/Ownrshp* 1999
Sales 22.7MM *EMP* 33E
SIC 7371 7372 3572 Custom computer programming services; Prepackaged software; Computer storage devices
Pr: Jeffrey M Johnson
Ch Bd: Theodore A Johnson
Snr Sftwr: Craig Meinen
IT Man: Kent Rarick
IT Man: Gregg Wallace
Software D: Melroy D'Monty
Netwrk Eng: Greg Wallace

D-U-N-S 09-590-0064
INTERNATIONAL LOTTERY & TOTALIZATOR SYSTEMS INC
ILTS CALIFORNIA
(*Suby of* BERJAYA LOTTERY MANAGEMENT (HK) LIMITED)
2310 Cousteau Ct, Vista, CA 92081-8346
Tel (760) 598-1655 *Founded/Ownrshp* 1999
Sales 22.7MM *EMP* 33
SIC 7371 7372 3572 Custom computer programming services; Prepackaged software; Computer storage devices

D-U-N-S 07-993-0715
INTERNATIONAL LUTHERAN LAYMENS LEAGUE
LUTHERAN HOUR MINISTRIES
(*Suby of* BCTN HOLDING INC) ★
660 Mason Ridge Center Dr, Saint Louis, MO 63141-8557
Tel (314) 317-4125 *Founded/Ownrshp* 1917
Sales 34.7MM *EMP* 115
Accts Brown Smith Wallace Llc St
SIC 8661 Religious organizations; Religious organizations
Pr: Kurt Bucholz
**COO:* Larry Pritchett
CFO: Curt Wittbracht
**CFO:* Curtiss Wittbracht
Ofcr: Jackeline Ammoms
Ofcr: Bervin Mirtsching
VP: Don Bennett
Dir Soc: Phyllis Wallace
CIO: Terry Shields
Board of Directors: Michael Onnen

D-U-N-S 17-447-9352 EXP
INTERNATIONAL MALL MOTOR CO
INTERNATIONAL ACURA
10455 Nw 12th St, Doral, FL 33172-2736
Tel (305) 477-6666 *Founded/Ownrshp* 1987
Sales 45.0MME *EMP* 150
SIC 5511 Automobiles, new & used; Automobiles, new & used
Pr: Ronald Esserman
VP: John Hoctor
Genl Mgr: Pancho Rivas
Sls Mgr: Viviana Usme
Sales Asso: Vidal Nuez

D-U-N-S 08-711-4492
INTERNATIONAL MANAGEMENT CONSULTANTS INC
IMC CONSTRUCTION
3 Great Valley Pkwy # 200, Malvern, PA 19355-1478
Tel (610) 889-3600 *Founded/Ownrshp* 1974
Sales 58.4MME *EMP* 65
SIC 1542 Nonresidential construction; Nonresidential construction
Pr: Robert Cottone
**CFO:* James Kwartnik
**VP:* Michael Ryan
Dir Bus: Mark Purcell
Off Mgr: Devon Medina
Dir IT: Mark Holton
IT Man: Tim Stoltzfus
Sfty Dirs: Ken Umstead
Mktg Mgr: Ellen Davis
Snr PM: Larry Getz
Snr PM: Michael McBall

D-U-N-S 07-112-7153 IMP/EXP
INTERNATIONAL MANAGEMENT GROUP (OVERSEAS) LLC
1360 E 9th St Ste 100, Cleveland, OH 44114-1782
Tel (216) 522-1200 *Founded/Ownrshp* 2014
Sales 435.9M *EMP* 1,708
Accts Mai Wealth Advisors Llc Cleve
SIC 7941 7999 7922 Manager of individual professional athletes; Sports instruction, schools & camps; Theatrical producers & services; Manager of individual professional athletes; Sports instruction, schools & camps; Theatrical producers & services
Treas: William Prip
**Pr:* Ian Todd
**CFO:* Arthur J La Fave Jr
Ofcr: Tony Crispino
Sr VP: David Abrutyn
Sr VP: Rob Armstrong
Sr VP: Jeremy Cole
Sr VP: Mindy Coppin
Sr VP: Diarmuid Crowley
Sr VP: Graham Fry
**Sr VP:* Neil Graff
Sr VP: Martin Jolly
**Sr VP:* Peter Kuhn
Sr VP: Arthur Lafave
**Sr VP:* Kevin Lavan
Sr VP: James Leitz
Sr VP: Rob Mason
Sr VP: Bill Palant
Sr VP: Andrew Pierce
Sr VP: Gary Pluchino
Sr VP: Bobby Sharma

D-U-N-S 11-303-6755
INTERNATIONAL MANAGEMENT SERVICES CO INC
IMSCO
3633 Wheeler Rd Ste 350, Augusta, GA 30909-6545
Tel (706) 855-1014 *Founded/Ownrshp* 1993
Sales 190.5MME *EMP* 1,500E
SIC 8742 Materials mgmt. (purchasing, handling, inventory) consultant; Materials mgmt. (purchasing, handling, inventory) consultant
Ch: Nancy C Hall
**Pr:* David W Bowles
**Treas:* Tammy A Bridgers
**Sr VP:* Robert Prugar

D-U-N-S 18-734-2923 IMP/EXP
INTERNATIONAL MANUFACTURING & LOGISTICS LLC
ROYAL CREST PROMOTIONS
16163 W 45th Dr Unit E, Golden, CO 80403-2600
Tel (303) 333-8250 *Founded/Ownrshp* 2004
Sales 30.4MME *EMP* 60
SIC 5099 5091 5092 2253 Novelties, durable; Sporting & recreation goods; Toys & hobby goods & supplies; Knit outerwear mills
CEO: Jerry Shoun
**CFO:* J Churchill Owen
**VP:* Bradley E Keller
**VP:* Mark Skorpil
Genl Mgr: Joakim Sylme

D-U-N-S 80-541-5924 IMP
■ **INTERNATIONAL MANUFACTURING TECHNOLOGIES INC**
NASSCO
(*Suby of* NASSCO HOLDINGS INC) ★
2798 Harbor Dr, San Diego, CA 92113-3650
Tel (619) 544-7741 *Founded/Ownrshp* 1990
Sales 24.9MME *EMP* 140E
SIC 3312 3731 Structural & rail mill products; Shipbuilding & repairing; Structural & rail mill products; Shipbuilding & repairing
CEO: Willam J Cuddy
**Pr:* James C Scott

D-U-N-S 80-960-8578
INTERNATIONAL MARINE AND INDUSTRIAL APPLICATORS LLC
7884 Spanish Fort Blvd, Spanish Fort, AL 36527-5342
Tel (251) 626-3625 *Founded/Ownrshp* 2007
Sales 28.5MME *EMP* 166E
SIC 1799 1721 Sandblasting of building exteriors; Exterior residential painting contractor; Sandblasting of building exteriors; Exterior residential painting contractor

D-U-N-S 05-241-9959 IMP
INTERNATIONAL MARINE PRODUCTS INC
IMP
(*Suby of* EIWA INTERNATIONAL INC) ★
500 E 7th St, Los Angeles, CA 90014-2410
Tel (213) 680-0190 *Founded/Ownrshp* 1991
Sales 39.1MME *EMP* 65
SIC 5146 Fish, fresh; Fish, frozen, unpackaged
CEO: James Ho
**Pr:* Yoshihiro Momose
Sls Mgr: Johni Kusayamagi

D-U-N-S 07-957-0830
INTERNATIONAL MARKET CENTERS INC
(*Suby of* INTERNATIONAL MARKET CENTERS LP) ★
475 S Grand Central Pkwy, Las Vegas, NV 89106-4552
Tel (702) 599-9621 *Founded/Ownrshp* 2011
Sales 162.8MM *EMP* 206
SIC 6798 Real estate investment trusts
Ch Bd: Robert J Maricich
Pr: Dorothy Belshaw
COO: Pedro Zapata
CFO: William F Lacey
Ex VP: Scott Eckman
Sr VP: Carolyn Conley
Board of Directors: Ryan Cotton, Scott Graves, James P Hoffmann, Philip Loughlin, Kimberly Mc-Caslin, Eric S Rangen

D-U-N-S 96-842-8800
INTERNATIONAL MARKET CENTERS LP
495 S Grand Central Pkwy, Las Vegas, NV 89106-4555
Tel (702) 599-9621 *Founded/Ownrshp* 2011
Sales 162.8MME *EMP* 206E
SIC 8741 Management services
CEO: Robert Naricich

D-U-N-S 17-482-3740 IMP/EXP
INTERNATIONAL MARKETING SYSTEMS LTD
2 Corporate Dr Ste 136, Shelton, CT 06484-6274
Tel (203) 929-2254 *Founded/Ownrshp* 2011
Sales 81.9MM *EMP* 45E
Accts Mckenna Dyer & Company Pc
SIC 5141 8742 Food brokers; Marketing consulting services; Food brokers; Marketing consulting services
Pr: Thomas M O Hara
**Treas:* Kirsten Vincent
Opers Mgr: John Pesavento
Mktg Dir: Callie Langeland
Mktg Dir: Scott Ricci
Mktg Mgr: Kayleigh Walls

D-U-N-S 07-929-3023
INTERNATIONAL MASTER PRODUCTS CORP (MI)
MASTER TAG
9751 Us Highway 31, Montague, MI 49437-9655
Tel (231) 894-5651 *Founded/Ownrshp* 1951, 1980
Sales 24.5MME *EMP* 125E
SIC 2752 2759 2671 Tags, lithographed; Commercial printing; Packaging paper & plastics film, coated & laminated; Tags, lithographed; Commercial printing; Packaging paper & plastics film, coated & laminated
Pr: Richard K Hughes Jr
Creative D: Gerry Giorgio
Genl Mgr: Mark Jones
Ql Cn Mgr: Brad Irey
Ql Cn Mgr: Juan Loera
Sls Mgr: Richard Niklas
Sls Mgr: Joan Williamson
Sales Asso: Sherry Davis

D-U-N-S 10-772-7638 IMP
INTERNATIONAL MASTERS PUBLISHERS INC
IMP
(*Suby of* INTERNATIONAL MASTERS PUBLISHERS B.V.)
352 Park Ave S Ste 1400, New York, NY 10010-1721
Tel (212) 353-6400 *Founded/Ownrshp* 1983
Sales 24.5MME *EMP* 150
SIC 5963 7372 2731 Encyclopedias & publications, direct sales; Publishers' computer software; Book publishing
Pr: Anders Dahl
Pr: Andrew Nadsen
COO: Jan Dvorak
Sr VP: Hal Oringer
VP: Victor H Peck Jr
Genl Mgr: Johan Ller
Opers Mgr: Tony Imbimbo
VP Sls: Aysenur Topdagi
Art Dir: Ed Lopresti

D-U-N-S 18-637-5218
INTERNATIONAL MEDICAL CORPS
12400 Wilshire Blvd # 1500, Los Angeles, CA 90025-1030
Tel (310) 826-7800 *Founded/Ownrshp* 1984
Sales 232.6MM *EMP* 63E
SIC 8322 Disaster service; Disaster service
Ch: Robert Simon
**Pr:* Nancy Aossey
Treas: William Sundblad
Trst: Sarah Ahrens
Trst: Timothy Kirk
Ofcr: Elizabeth Apopo
Ofcr: Ahmad Jaran
Ofcr: Andrew Kent
Ofcr: Jennifer Naiboka
Ofcr: EMI Samata
Ofcr: Heidi Saravia
VP: David Giron
VP: Rebecca Milner
VP: Stephen Tomlin
VP: Rabih Torbay

D-U-N-S 03-312-1398
INTERNATIONAL MEDICAL EQUIPMENT COLLABORATIVE
IMEC
1600 Osgood St, North Andover, MA 01845-1048
Tel (978) 557-5510 *Founded/Ownrshp* 1994
Sales 31.6MM *EMP* 2
Accts Libby & Miner Tax & Bookkeepin
SIC 8742 5047 Hospital & health services consultant; Medical & hospital equipment
Pr: Thomas Keefe
Genl Mgr: Jennifer Keefe
IT Man: Anne Matthews

D-U-N-S 60-293-0018
INTERNATIONAL MEDICAL GROUP INC
I M G
2960 N Meridian St, Indianapolis, IN 46208-4715
Tel (317) 655-4500 *Founded/Ownrshp* 2015
Sales NA *EMP* 115
SIC 6411 Advisory services, insurance
Pr: Brian Barwick
COO: Joseph L Brougher
CFO: Kurt Kipfer
Ex VP: Todd Hancock
VP: Tom Moses

D-U-N-S 86-798-4619
INTERNATIONAL MEDICAL NEWS GROUP LLC
I M N G
7 Century Dr Ste 302, Parsippany, NJ 07054-4609
Tel (973) 290-8237 *Founded/Ownrshp* 2001
Sales 28.0MME *EMP* 73
SIC 2721 Magazines: publishing only, not printed on site; Magazines: publishing only, not printed on site

Pr: Alan Imhoff
**VP:* Sylvia Reitman
Ex Dir: Terry Rudd
Genl Mgr: Alan J Imhoff
Natl Sales: Steve Schwanz

D-U-N-S 05-575-0020 IMP
■ INTERNATIONAL MEDICATION SYSTEMS LTD
IMS
(*Suby of* AMPHASTAR PHARMACEUTICALS INC) ★
1886 Santa Anita Ave, South El Monte, CA 91733-3414
Tel (626) 442-6757 *Founded/Ownrshp* 1998
Sales 128.9MM^E *EMP* 720^E
SIC 2834 2833 3841 Drugs acting on the central nervous system & sense organs; Anesthetics, in bulk form; Surgical & medical instruments; Drugs acting on the central nervous system & sense organs; Anesthetics, in bulk form; Surgical & medical instruments
Pr: Jack Zhang
Pr: Hl Lou
COO: Mary Luo Zhang
CTO: Bernard Chu
MIS Dir: Tony Kwan
VP Opers: Paul Yu

INTERNATIONAL MERCHANDISING
See WME IMG LLC

D-U-N-S 06-890-4119
INTERNATIONAL MERCHANDISING CORP
(*Suby of* INTERNATIONAL MANAGEMENT GROUP (OVERSEAS) LLC) ★
1360 E 9th St Ste 100, Cleveland, OH 44114-1730
Tel (216) 522-1200 *Founded/Ownrshp* 1967
Sales 3.5MM^E *EMP* 764
SIC 7941 7999 Manager of individual professional athletes; Sports instruction, schools & camps; Manager of individual professional athletes; Sports instruction, schools & camps
Pr: Mark H Mc Cormack
**CFO:* Peter Kuhn
**CFO:* Arthur J La Fave Jr

D-U-N-S 15-070-1837 IMP
INTERNATIONAL MERCHANDISING SERVICE INC
USTTOOLS
1928 W Malvern Ave, Fullerton, CA 92833-2105
Tel (714) 449-0678 *Founded/Ownrshp* 1985
Sales 35.5MM^E *EMP* 25
Accts Kim & Lee Corporation Los Ang
SIC 5072 Hand tools; Hand tools
Pr: Peter I Song
Opers Mgr: Moses Chang
Genl Couns: Kris Song

INTERNATIONAL MERCHANTS
See WINEGARDNER & HAMMONS INC

D-U-N-S 08-756-1015 IMP
■ INTERNATIONAL METAL RECLAIMING CORP
INMETCO
(*Suby of* HORSEHEAD HOLDING CORP) ★
1 Inmetco Dr, Ellwood City, PA 16117-6231
Tel (724) 758-5515 *Founded/Ownrshp* 2010
Sales 39.7MM^E *EMP* 108
SIC 4953 3341 Recycling, waste materials; Secondary nonferrous metals
CEO: James M Hensler
Treas: Stephanie Anderson

D-U-N-S 06-435-2529
INTERNATIONAL MILL SERVICE INC
IMS
(*Suby of* MILL SERVICES CORP) ★
1155 Bus Ctr Dr Ste 200, Horsham, PA 19044
Tel (215) 956-5500 *Founded/Ownrshp* 2007
Sales 121.4MM^E *EMP* 1,100
SIC 3295 3341 1422 8742 Slag, crushed or ground; Secondary nonferrous metals; Cement rock, crushed & broken-quarrying; Public utilities consultant; Slag, crushed or ground; Secondary nonferrous metals; Cement rock, crushed & broken-quarrying; Public utilities consultant
Pr: Raymond S Kalouche
**Treas:* Daniel E Rosati
VP: Aarne Anderson
CIO: Michael McGraw
IT Man: Steve Helbig
Opers Mgr: Brad Brentin

D-U-N-S 94-482-4622
INTERNATIONAL MINERALS CORP
ECUADORIAN MINERALS CORP US
(*Suby of* HOCHSCHILD MINING PLC)
469 Stageline Loop, Elko, NV 89801-9545
Tel (480) 483-9932 *Founded/Ownrshp* 2013
Sales 20.9MM *EMP* 11^E
SIC 1041 Gold ores mining
Pr: Stephen J Kay
**CFO:* Scott M Brunsdon

D-U-N-S 06-235-1499
INTERNATIONAL MISSION BOARD OF SOUTHERN BAPTIST CONVENTION
IMB
3806 Monument Ave, Richmond, VA 23230-3932
Tel (804) 353-0151 *Founded/Ownrshp* 1845
Sales 103.9MM^E *EMP* 4,686
Accts Clifton Gunderson Llp Glen A
SIC 8661 2731 7812 Baptist Church; Pamphlets: publishing & printing; Audio-visual program production; Baptist Church; Pamphlets: publishing & printing; Audio-visual program production
Pr: Tom Elliff
**Ch Bd:* Jimmy Perichard
**CFO:* David A Steverson
**V Ch Bd:* O Tim Locher
Assoc VP: Cheri Spence
**Ex VP:* Claude A Meador
VP: David Mills
VP: Randy Pegues
VP: Tom Williams
VP: Ken Winter
Dir Soc: Karen Campbell

D-U-N-S 02-925-8336
INTERNATIONAL MISSIONS INC
CHRISTAR
1500 Intl Pkwy Ste 200, Richardson, TX 75081
Tel (214) 838-3800 *Founded/Ownrshp* 2010
Sales 14.2MM *EMP* 300
Accts Capin Crouse Llp Grapevine T
SIC 8661 Churches, temples & shrines; Churches, temples & shrines
**Treas:* Richard Barron

D-U-N-S 61-942-0313 IMP
INTERNATIONAL MOLD CORP
23224 Giacoma Ct, Clinton Township, MI 48036-4608
Tel (586) 615-9356 *Founded/Ownrshp* 2005
Sales 23.0MM *EMP* 100
SIC 3544 Industrial molds
Pr: James H Pelcher
**Treas:* Michael Lilla
Prgrm Mgr: John Rank

D-U-N-S 06-927-5188
INTERNATIONAL MONETARY FUND
700 19th St Nw, Washington, DC 20431-0002
Tel (202) 623-7000 *Founded/Ownrshp* 1944
Sales NA *EMP* 2,700
SIC 6082 Foreign trade & international banking institutions; Foreign trade & international banking institutions
Mng Dir: Christine Lagarde
Treas: G M Fitzpatrick
Ofcr: Bernadete Alves
Ofcr: Justin Ayres
Ofcr: Sheila Edmund
Ofcr: Thomas Howard
Ofcr: Graham Newman
Ofcr: Sharon Slattery
Ofcr: Duncan Whitcher
Exec: George Brookings
Exec: Ydahlia Metzgen
Exec: Valeria Poveda

INTERNATIONAL MONEY EXPRESS
See INTERMEX WIRE TRANSFER LLC

D-U-N-S 07-779-3206
INTERNATIONAL MOTOR CARS INC
PASSPORT AUTOMOTIVE GROUP
5000 Auth Way, Suitland, MD 20746-4205
Tel (301) 423-8400 *Founded/Ownrshp* 1975
Sales 103.8MM^E *EMP* 225
SIC 5511 7538 5521 New & used car dealers; General automotive repair shops; Used car dealers; New & used car dealers; General automotive repair shops; Used car dealers
Pr: Everett A Hellmuth III
VP: Calancy Boyd
**VP:* Bruce Dunigan
Genl Mgr: Jay McLean
CTO: Peter Swarthout
Dir IT: Greg Lemons
VP Mktg: David Comfort
Sls Mgr: Said Abdelilah
Sls Mgr: David Lee
Sls Mgr: Fersen Lominy
Sls Mgr: Joe Long

INTERNATIONAL MOTORS
See MUELLER INC PETER

D-U-N-S 09-519-2985
INTERNATIONAL MUFFLER CO
IMCO
2400 Maremont Pkwy, Loudon, TN 37774-1065
Tel (800) 882-6833 *Founded/Ownrshp* 1981
Sales 56.8MM^E *EMP* 700
SIC 3714 3317 Mufflers (exhaust), motor vehicle; Steel pipe & tubes; Mufflers (exhaust), motor vehicle; Steel pipe & tubes
Pr: Kenneth Banks
**CFO:* Pam McNew
IT Man: Kristi McBride
Mfg Dir: Lynn Vittatoe
Mfg Mgr: Robert King

D-U-N-S 03-875-0829
INTERNATIONAL MULCH CO INC
IMC
182 Nw Industrial Ct, Bridgeton, MO 63044-1276
Tel (314) 336-1030 *Founded/Ownrshp* 2000
Sales 26.7MM^E *EMP* 50
Accts Mueller Prost Pc St Louis M
SIC 3069 Medical & laboratory rubber sundries & related products
Pr: Michael Miller
**VP:* Cindy Miller
Mktg Dir: Mike Sebastian

D-U-N-S 00-625-9931 IMP/EXP
■ INTERNATIONAL MULTIFOODS CORP
J M SMUCKER
(*Suby of* J M SMUCKER CO) ★
1 Strawberry Ln, Orrville, OH 44667-1241
Tel (330) 682-3000 *Founded/Ownrshp* 2000, 2004
Sales 221.1MM^E *EMP* 1,450
SIC 5145 5149 5143 2048 2041 Candy; Snack foods; Chewing gum; Coffee, green or roasted; Tea bagging; Baking supplies; Pizza supplies; Cheese; Livestock feeds; Pizza dough, prepared; Flour; Flour mixes; Candy; Snack foods; Chewing gum; Coffee, green or roasted; Tea bagging; Baking supplies; Pizza supplies; Cheese; Livestock feeds; Pizza dough, prepared; Flour; Flour mixes
CEO: Gary Costley PHD
**Pr:* Dan C Swander
**CFO:* John E Byom
**Sr VP:* Frank W Bonvino
VP: Ralph P Hargrow
VP: Dennis R Johnson

D-U-N-S 08-957-4347 IMP/EXP
INTERNATIONAL NUTRITION INC
7706 I Plz, Omaha, NE 68127-1841
Tel (402) 331-0123 *Founded/Ownrshp* 1976
Sales 24.2MM^E *EMP* 62^E
SIC 2048 2834 Feed supplements; Feed premixes; Pharmaceutical preparations; Feed supplements; Feed premixes; Pharmaceutical preparations
Pr: Steven J Silver
VP: Kim Nguyen
IT Man: Jesse Regier
Sales Exec: Kent Loeffler

D-U-N-S 96-404-4825
INTERNATIONAL OPERATING ENGINEERS UNION 49 HEALTH AND WELFARE FUND
3001 Metro Dr Ste 500, Bloomington, MN 55425-1617
Tel (952) 854-0795 *Founded/Ownrshp* 2010
Sales 141.0MM *EMP* 11^E
Accts Legacy Professionals Llp Minn
SIC 8631 Labor unions & similar labor organizations
Prin: William Addleman

D-U-N-S 80-786-5035
INTERNATIONAL ORTHODOX CHRISTIAN CHARITIES INC
IOCC
110 West Rd Ste 360, Baltimore, MD 21204-2365
Tel (410) 243-9820 *Founded/Ownrshp* 1992
Sales 49.0MM *EMP* 125
Accts Mcgladrey Llp Baltimore Mary
SIC 8322 Emergency social services; Emergency social services
CEO: Constantine Triantafilou
**CFO:* Pamela Seagull
**Prin:* Dan Christopulos
Off Admin: Sylvia Tsakalos

D-U-N-S 80-739-6403
INTERNATIONAL OSTRICH INC
3000 Gulf To Bay Blvd # 6, Clearwater, FL 33759-4321
Tel (727) 797-2322 *Founded/Ownrshp* 1992
Sales 50.0MM *EMP* 400
SIC 6531 Appraiser, real estate; Appraiser, real estate
Pr: Maurice Wilder
**Sec:* Mary Carotenuto
**VP:* Colby Wilder

D-U-N-S 07-534-8222 IMP
■ INTERNATIONAL PACKAGING AND LOGISTICS GROUP INC
(*Suby of* STANDARD RESOURCES LIMITED)
7700 Irvine Center Dr, Irvine, CA 92618-2923
Tel (949) 861-3560 *Founded/Ownrshp* 2007
Sales 35.7MM *EMP* 34
Tkr Sym IPLO *Exch* OTO
SIC 5199 3221 Packaging materials; Packaging materials; Glass containers
CEO: Owen Naccarato
Board of Directors: William Gresher, Allen Lin

D-U-N-S 00-119-8829 IMP/EXP
INTERNATIONAL PACKAGING CORP (RI)
INTERPAK
517 Mineral Spring Ave, Pawtucket, RI 02860-3408
Tel (401) 724-1600 *Founded/Ownrshp* 1957
Sales 87.2MM^E *EMP* 600
SIC 3499 3089

D-U-N-S 00-638-2253 IMP/EXP
INTERNATIONAL PAINT LLC
(*Suby of* AKZO NOBEL INC) ★
6001 Antoine Dr, Houston, TX 77091-3503
Tel (713) 682-1711 *Founded/Ownrshp* 1921, 1987
Sales 120.8MM^E *EMP* 400
SIC 2851 Enamels; Lacquer: bases, dopes, thinner; Varnishes; Enamels; Lacquer: bases, dopes, thinner; Varnishes
Rgnl Mgr: Roger Bain
Genl Mgr: Andrew Smith
QA Dir: Steve Vento
Dir IT: Henry Vasterling
IT Man: David Harm
IT Man: Gunawan Thofandi
Opers Mgr: Jan Steg
VP Sls: Fernando Macedo
Mktg Mgr: Fred Daoust
Mktg Mgr: Jo A Plsek
Sls Mgr: Kevin Perego

D-U-N-S 83-321-6133
INTERNATIONAL PALMS RESORT AND CONFERENCE CENTER LLC
6515 International Dr, Orlando, FL 32819-8217
Tel (407) 351-3500 *Founded/Ownrshp* 2010
Sales 11.2MM^E *EMP* 300
SIC 7011 Resort hotel; Resort hotel
Exec: Michelle Wheeler
VP Sls: Jim Bullock
Sls Mgr: Stephen Rice
Sls Mgr: John Seegers

INTERNATIONAL PAPER
See TIN INC

INTERNATIONAL PAPER
See NEW-INDY CONTAINERBOARD LLC

INTERNATIONAL PAPER
See XPEDX LLC

INTERNATIONAL PAPER
See TEMPLE-INLAND INC

INTERNATIONAL PAPER
See SHOREWOOD PACKAGING CORP OF VIRGINIA

D-U-N-S 00-131-6561 IMP/EXP
▲ INTERNATIONAL PAPER CO (NY)
6400 Poplar Ave, Memphis, TN 38197-0198
Tel (901) 419-7000 *Founded/Ownrshp* 1898
Sales 23.6MMM *EMP* 58,000
Accts Deloitte & Touche Llp Memphis
Tkr Sym IP *Exch* NYS
SIC 2621 2653 2656 2631 2611 Paper mills; Printing paper; Text paper; Bristols; Boxes, corrugated: made from purchased materials; Food containers (liquid tight), including milk cartons; Cartons, milk: made from purchased material; Container, packaging & boxboard; Container board; Packaging board; Pulp mills; Paper mills; Printing paper; Text paper; Bristols; Boxes, corrugated: made from purchased materials; Food containers (liquid tight), including milk cartons; Cartons, milk: made from purchased material; Container, packaging & boxboard; Container board; Packaging board; Pulp mills
CEO: Mark S Sutton
Pr: Jean-Michel Ribieras
COO: Lawrence Beck
**CFO:* Carol L Roberts
Bd of Dir: Patrick Geiger
Ex VP: William Amick
Ex VP: Richard Lowe
Ex VP: James Melican Jr
Ex VP: Thomas J Weisenbach
Sr VP: Maura Abeln-Smith
Sr VP: Jerome N Carter
Sr VP: Jerry Carter
Sr VP: Thomas E Costello
Sr VP: Charlie Greiner
**Sr VP:* Thomas G Kadien
**Sr VP:* Paul J Karre
Sr VP: William B Lytton
**Sr VP:* Sharon R Ryan
VP: Evans Heath
VP: George A O'Brien
Board of Directors: J Steven Whisler, David J Bronczek, Ray G Young, William J Burns, Ahmet C Dorduncu, Ilene S Gordon, Jay L Johnson, Stacey J Mobley, Joan E Spero, John L Townsend III, William G Walter

D-U-N-S 02-782-7073
INTERNATIONAL PAPER COMPA
6283 Tri Ridge Blvd, Loveland, OH 45140-8318
Tel (513) 248-6000 *Founded/Ownrshp* 2011
Sales 21.9MM^E *EMP* 77^E
SIC 8111 General practice attorney, lawyer

D-U-N-S 03-827-5199
INTERNATIONAL PARTNERSHIP FOR HUMAN DEVELOPMENT INC
IPHD
722 E Market St Ste 100, Leesburg, VA 20176-4475
Tel (703) 443-1691 *Founded/Ownrshp* 1983
Sales 27.4MM *EMP* 6
Accts Mitchell & Co Pc Leesburg Va
SIC 8322 Individual & family services; Individual & family services
Pr: William Pruzensky
**Ch Bd:* C E Martin
**VP:* Lino Gussoni
**Prin:* Daniel Shaughnessy

D-U-N-S 19-124-7118
INTERNATIONAL PARTNERSHIP FOR MICROBICIDES INC
8401 Colesville Rd # 200, Silver Spring, MD 20910-3312
Tel (301) 608-2221 *Founded/Ownrshp* 2002
Sales 32.7MM *EMP* 100
Accts Mcgladrey Llp Vienna Va
SIC 8731 Commercial physical research; Commercial physical research
CEO: Dr Zeda Rosenberg
CFO: Chris Camut
Bd of Dir: Seth L Harrison
Bd of Dir: David Kessler
Bd of Dir: Anandi Yuvaraj
Ofcr: Luann Blount
Ofcr: Georgina Caswell
Ex VP: Lynn Bodarky
Ex VP: Brid Devlin
Ex VP: Prem Narang
Exec: Kathleen Ross
Assoc Dir: Tiffany Derrick
Comm Man: Holly Seltzer

D-U-N-S 06-077-8842
INTERNATIONAL PENTECOSTAL HOLINESS CHURCH
EMMANUEL COLLEGE
7300 Nw 39th Expy, Bethany, OK 73008-2340
Tel (405) 787-7110 *Founded/Ownrshp* 1911
Sales 73.9MM^E *EMP* 4,650
SIC 8661 Pentecostal Church; Pentecostal Church
Prin: James Leggett
Sr VP: Douglas Compton
VP: Doc Ron Carpenter
**Ex Dir:* Doug Beacham

D-U-N-S 05-826-4164 IMP/EXP
INTERNATIONAL PET SUPPLIES AND DISTRIBUTION INC
(*Suby of* PETCO ANIMAL SUPPLIES INC) ★
9125 Rehco Rd, San Diego, CA 92121-2270
Tel (858) 453-7845 *Founded/Ownrshp* 1991
Sales 27.1MM^E *EMP* 100
SIC 5199 Pet supplies
CEO: James Myers

INTERNATIONAL PIPING PDTS INS
See IPP USA INC

D-U-N-S 07-522-2646
INTERNATIONAL PLANNED PARENTHOOD FEDERATION - WESTERN HEMISPHERE REGION INC (NY)
IPPFWHR
125 Maiden Ln Fl 9, New York, NY 10038-5063
Tel (212) 248-6400 *Founded/Ownrshp* 1955
Sales 32.7MM *EMP* 49
Accts Kpmg
SIC 8699 Personal interest organization
**Pr:* Monty Eustace
**Ch:* Marta Trabanino
**Treas:* Jacqueline Sharpe
Ofcr: Laura Feeney
Ofcr: Rosalyn Pen
Ofcr: Karthik Srinivasan
Ofcr: Helen Young

Comm Dir: Kelly Castagnaro
CIO: Leslie Varkonyi

D-U-N-S 16-166-9593
INTERNATIONAL PLANNING ALLIANCE LLC
300 Broadacres Dr Ste 175, Bloomfield, NJ 07003-3165
Tel (973) 256-7300 *Founded/Ownrshp* 1999
Sales NA *EMP* 200
SIC 6411 7389 Insurance agents; Pension & retirement plan consultants; Financial services; Insurance agents; Pension & retirement plan consultants; Financial services
Ch: Gerald J Clericuzio
**V Ch:* Anthony J Pascazio
**Pr:* David R Alter
Ofcr: Erika Singer
Sr VP: Howard Udoff
VP: Barbara Gelber
Brnch Mgr: Harold Osman
Brnch Mgr: Melanie Werling
Sls Mgr: Anthony Campanile

D-U-N-S 78-826-1779
■ **INTERNATIONAL PLANT SERVICES LLC**
(*Suby of* TEXAS GULF ENERGY INC) ★
1602 Old Underwood Rd, La Porte, TX 77571-9649
Tel (281) 867-8400 *Founded/Ownrshp* 2012
Sales 9.5MM^E *EMP* 376
SIC 8711 7692 1629 Engineering services; Welding repair; Oil refinery construction; Engineering services; Welding repair; Oil refinery construction
Pr: Craig Crawford
**Sr VP:* Pete Kappler
Opers Mgr: Adriane Wilson

D-U-N-S 04-121-6722 IMP
INTERNATIONAL PLAYTHINGS LLC (NJ)
(*Suby of* EPOCH CO.,LTD.)
75d Lackawanna Ave, Parsippany, NJ 07054-1096
Tel (973) 316-2500 *Founded/Ownrshp* 1967, 2008
Sales 36.6MM^E *EMP* 46
SIC 5092 Toys & hobby goods & supplies
Opers Mgr: Glenn Neville
VP Sls: Bryan Bendavid
VP Sls: Bryan Dendavid
Sls Dir: Tangie Hines
Mktg Mgr: Michelle Winfrey
Sls Mgr: June Heider
Sales Asso: Geri Hamrick
Sales Asso: Robin Leib
Sales Asso: Jane Rozman
Art Dir: Ani Carpenter

INTERNATIONAL PLUS
See NOS COMMUNICATIONS INC

D-U-N-S 05-492-6076
INTERNATIONAL POLYMERS CORP
426 S Aubrey St, Allentown, PA 18109-2769
Tel (610) 841-4050 *Founded/Ownrshp* 2011
Sales 46.2MM^E *EMP* 55
SIC 5162 Resins; Plastics basic shapes
Pr: Blair Manning
**CEO:* Brian Taschler
**CFO:* Wayne Muffley
**VP:* Brad Ahner
Manager: Larry Seyller

D-U-N-S 18-970-5080
INTERNATIONAL POWER AMERICA INC
(*Suby of* INTERNATIONAL POWER LTD.)
1990 Post Oak Blvd, Houston, TX 77056-3818
Tel (713) 636-0000 *Founded/Ownrshp* 1996
Sales 89.5MM^E *EMP* 267
SIC 4911 Distribution, electric power; Generation, electric power; Transmission, electric power; Distribution, electric power; Generation, electric power; Transmission, electric power
Pr: Zin Smati
**CEO:* Bruce Levy
**Treas:* Patrick Gaussent
**VP:* Barry R Brits
**VP:* Gerald Depatoul
**VP:* David Musselman
Plnt Mgr: Mike Fields
Sales Exec: Bill J Henson
Genl Couns: Clint Steyn

D-U-N-S 95-974-6590
INTERNATIONAL PRECAST SOLUTIONS LLC
(*Suby of* PRESTRESSED SYSTEMS INCORPORATED)
60 Haltiner St, River Rouge, MI 48218-1259
Tel (313) 843-0073 *Founded/Ownrshp* 2008
Sales 29.9MM^E *EMP* 100
SIC 3272 Concrete products
CEO: Loris Collavino
**Pr:* Don Little
**VP:* Anil Mehta
**VP:* Paul Phillips

D-U-N-S 12-231-7498 IMP
INTERNATIONAL PRECISION COMPONENTS CORP
I.P.C.C.
28468 N Ballard Dr, Lake Forest, IL 60045-4508
Tel (847) 247-2050 *Founded/Ownrshp* 1984
Sales 105.1MM^E *EMP* 320
SIC 3089 Plastic processing; Plastic processing
Pr: Michael D Stolzman
COO: Erich Schuetz
CFO: Pat Cutrona
CFO: Robert Istok
**VP:* Karen M Stolzman
MIS Dir: Darius Nalborczyk
IT Man: Joeyy De Leon
Sfty Dirs: Angel Pacheco
Plnt Mgr: Stan Kalisz
Plnt Mgr: Mirek Szczesny
Plnt Mgr: Virgis Valeika

INTERNATIONAL PROACTIVE SEC
See IPS ASSOCIATES LLC

D-U-N-S 05-420-6487
INTERNATIONAL PROCESSING CORP
(*Suby of* DEXT CO) ★
233 Wilshire Blvd Ste 310, Santa Monica, CA 90401-1206
Tel (310) 458-1574 *Founded/Ownrshp* 1996
Sales 28.0MM^E *EMP* 300
SIC 2048 Prepared feeds; Prepared feeds
Pr: Bob McMullen
IT Man: Junaid Khan
IT Man: Scott Rosen

D-U-N-S 79-704-7834 IMP
■ **INTERNATIONAL PROCESSING CORP**
(*Suby of* BLACKSTONE GROUP HOLDINGS LLC) ★
1100 Enterprise Dr, Winchester, KY 40391-9668
Tel (859) 745-2200 *Founded/Ownrshp* 1991
Sales 58.2MM^E *EMP* 333
SIC 2834 Pharmaceutical preparations; Pharmaceutical preparations
Sfty Dirs: Shane Hatten

D-U-N-S 11-930-4561 IMP/EXP
INTERNATIONAL PROCESSPLANTS AND EQUIPMENT CORP
INTERNTNAL PROCESS PLANTS-IPPE
410 Prnctn Hightstown Rd, Princeton Junction, NJ 08550-3126
Tel (609) 586-8004 *Founded/Ownrshp* 1986
Sales 67.3MM^E *EMP* 150^E
SIC 5084 Industrial machinery & equipment; Chemical process equipment; Industrial machinery & equipment; Chemical process equipment
Pr: Ronald Gale
Pr: Drew Ziccardi
**Ex VP:* Jan Gale
Counsel: Matt Gottesfeld
Snr PM: Van Lewis

INTERNATIONAL PRODUCE EXCHANGE
See BALDOR SPECIALTY FOODS INC

D-U-N-S 95-748-5956
INTERNATIONAL PROTECTION GROUP LLC
INTERNTNAL PROTECTIVE SEC AGCY
483 8th Ave Ste 1570, New York, NY 10001
Tel (212) 947-1681 *Founded/Ownrshp* 1989
Sales 77.0MM^E *EMP* 350
SIC 5065 7381 Electronic parts & equipment; Security control equipment & systems; Detective & armored car services; Security guard service; Electronic parts & equipment; Security control equipment & systems; Detective & armored car services; Security guard service
Pr: Jerry Heying
**Treas:* Noriko Heying

INTERNATIONAL PUBLICATIONS SVC
See TAYLOR & FRANCIS INC

D-U-N-S 80-735-7439 EXP
INTERNATIONAL RAGS LTD
4410 Clinton Dr, Houston, TX 77020-7800
Tel (713) 491-0700 *Founded/Ownrshp* 1993
Sales 21.9MM^E *EMP* 75
SIC 5093 Waste rags
Pr: Amirali Momin

INTERNATIONAL RAM ASSOCIATES
See AIR SERV SECURITY INC

D-U-N-S 02-195-9700
INTERNATIONAL REALTY NETWORK INC
EDDIE BERNARD REALTY
17328 Ventura Blvd # 104, Encino, CA 91316-3904
Tel (818) 708-1477 *Founded/Ownrshp* 1997
Sales 37.0MM^E *EMP* 27
SIC 6531 Real estate brokers & agents; Real estate brokers & agents
Pr: Eddie Bernard
**CFO:* Tina Cossak

INTERNATIONAL RECTIFIER CORP
See INFINEON TECHNOLOGIES AMERICAS CORP

D-U-N-S 62-513-3228 IMP
INTERNATIONAL REHABILITATIVE SCIENCES INC
R S MEDICAL
14001 Se 1st St, Vancouver, WA 98684-3513
Tel (360) 892-0339 *Founded/Ownrshp* 1990
Sales 21.4MM^E *EMP* 91
SIC 3841 Surgical & medical instruments
Pr: John Konsin
**Pr:* Richard Terrell
Rgnl Mgr: Jody Chiarotti
Dist Mgr: Paul Leung
VP Sls: Peter Boicourt
Mktg Mgr: Jay Mills

D-U-N-S 04-780-2223
INTERNATIONAL RELIEF AND DEVELOPMENT INC
IRD
1621 N Kent St Ste 400, Arlington, VA 22209-2119
Tel (703) 247-3068 *Founded/Ownrshp* 1998
Sales 249.7MM *EMP* 313
Accts Raffa Pc Washington Dc
SIC 8322 Individual & family services; Individual & family services
CEO: Kris Manos
**Pr:* Arthur B Keys Jr
**CFO:* Beverly Morris-Armstrong
**CFO:* Elsie Tama
Prgrm Mgr: Michele Lemmon
IT Man: Mladen Basaric

D-U-N-S 19-776-2461
INTERNATIONAL RELIEF TEAMS INC
4560 Alvarado Canyon Rd 2g, San Diego, CA 92120-4309
Tel (619) 284-7979 *Founded/Ownrshp* 1990
Sales 31.6MM *EMP* 5
Accts Schilling & Hinzman San Diego
SIC 8611 Community affairs & services; Community affairs & services
Ex Dir: Barry La Forgia
Exec: James Weeks
**Ex Dir:* Barry Laforgia

D-U-N-S 12-651-0312
INTERNATIONAL REPUBLICAN INSTITUTE
I R I
1225 I St Nw Ste 700, Washington, DC 20005-5962
Tel (202) 408-9450 *Founded/Ownrshp* 1983
Sales 57.0MM *EMP* 70^E
Accts Mcgladrey Llp Mc Lean Va
SIC 8651 Political organizations
Pr: Loran Craner
Pt: Craig Varoga
**Pr:* Lorne Craner
CFO: Paul Beriault
Ofcr: Lindsay Arnold
Ofcr: Laura Baker
Ofcr: Matthew Baker
Ofcr: Kareina Cole
Ofcr: Jennifer Crall
Ofcr: Elizabeth Donkervoort
Ofcr: Matthew Hays
Ofcr: Preston Lindler
Ofcr: Milica Panic
Ofcr: David Sands
Ofcr: Rhett Skiles
Ofcr: John Tomaszewski
**Ex VP:* Judy Van Rest
Sr VP: Chris McDaniel

D-U-N-S 07-885-4940
INTERNATIONAL RESCUE COMMITTEE INC
IRC AND PARTNERS
122 E 42nd St Fl 12, New York, NY 10168-1299
Tel (212) 551-3000 *Founded/Ownrshp* 1933
Sales 562.0MM *EMP* 8,000
Accts Kpmg Llp New York Ny
SIC 8322 Social service center; Social service center
Pr: David Miliband
Ofcr: Alexandra Brosnan
Ofcr: Erica Depiero
Ofcr: Steven Kasoni
Ofcr: Odette Odia
Ofcr: Ellyson Perkins
Ofcr: Zoran Sredojevic
Exec: Nafisa Spaher
Ex Dir: Leslye Moore
Prgrm Mgr: Neetu Mahil
CIO: David Goodman

D-U-N-S 79-704-5846
INTERNATIONAL RESEARCH AND EXCHANGES BOARD INC
IREX
1275 K St Nw Ste 600, Washington, DC 20005-4064
Tel (202) 628-8188 *Founded/Ownrshp* 1968
Sales 70.9MM *EMP* 600^E
SIC 8733

D-U-N-S 12-594-8000 IMP
INTERNATIONAL RESISTIVE CO INC
WIRE AND FILM TECHNOLOGIES DIV
(*Suby of* TT ELECTRONICS PLC)
4222 S Staples St, Corpus Christi, TX 78411-2702
Tel (361) 992-7900 *Founded/Ownrshp* 1990
Sales 33.8MM *EMP* 300
SIC 3676 Electronic resistors; Electronic resistors
Pr: Gareth Mycock
**CFO:* Ary Dickson
Rgnl Mgr: Sandra Rivas

D-U-N-S 15-172-9357 EXP
INTERNATIONAL RESISTIVE CO OF TEXAS LP
ADVANCED FILM DIVISION
(*Suby of* INTERNATIONAL RESISTIVE CO INC) ★
4222 S Staples St, Corpus Christi, TX 78411-2702
Tel (361) 992-7900 *Founded/Ownrshp* 2001
Sales 27.5MM^E *EMP* 244^E
SIC 3676 3674 5065 Electronic resistors; Semiconductors & related devices; Electronic parts & equipment; Electronic resistors; Semiconductors & related devices; Electronic parts & equipment

D-U-N-S 11-925-9364
■ **INTERNATIONAL RESOURCES GROUP LTD**
(*Suby of* ENGILITY CORP) ★
1320 Braddock Pl, Alexandria, VA 22314-1692
Tel (703) 664-2695 *Founded/Ownrshp* 2012
Sales 21.7MM^E *EMP* 437
SIC 8748 8742 8744 Energy conservation consultant; Environmental consultant; Management consulting services; Administrative services consultant; Facilities support services; Energy conservation consultant; Environmental consultant; Management consulting services; Administrative services consultant; Facilities support services
Genl Mgr: Timothy Knight
CEO: Anthony Smeraglinolo
CFO: Michael Alber
Ofcr: Richard Eisendorf
Ofcr: Kirk Johnson
Ofcr: Stefan Medina
Sr VP: Craig Reed
VP: Michael Dallara
VP: Audie Setters
VP: Thomas Wheelock
Comm Dir: William Ogborn

INTERNATIONAL REST MGT GROUP
See INTERNATIONAL RESTAURANT MANAGEMENT GROUP INC

D-U-N-S 11-125-0031 EXP
INTERNATIONAL RESTAURANT MANAGEMENT GROUP INC
INTERNATIONAL REST MGT GROUP
4104 Aurora St, Coral Gables, FL 33146-1416
Tel (305) 476-1611 *Founded/Ownrshp* 1992
Sales 65.7MM^E *EMP* 2,000
SIC 5812 Lunchrooms & cafeterias; Lunchrooms & cafeterias
Pr: Hoi Sang Yeung
CFO: Ally Ho
Ofcr: Raymond Wong
VP: David Dinkel
**VP:* Ying Ho
**VP:* Nita Y Yeung
**VP:* Sing-Yan S Yeung
IT Man: Yeung Hoi
Mktg Dir: Johanna Wade

D-U-N-S 87-690-5654 IMP/EXP
INTERNATIONAL RESTAURANT SERVICES INC
CHILI'S
Amelia Dist Ctr 23 Ema St, Guaynabo, PR 00968
Tel (787) 273-3131 *Founded/Ownrshp* 1994
Sales 37.5MM^E *EMP* 1,200
Accts Kevane Grant Thornton Llp San
SIC 5813 5812 Bars & lounges; Eating places; Bars & lounges; Eating places
Pr: Arthur Jotic
**VP:* Ramon Leal

INTERNATIONAL RISK CONSULTANTS
See IRC INC

D-U-N-S 02-450-5613
INTERNATIONAL ROAD DYNAMICS CORP
(*Suby of* INTERNATIONAL ROAD DYNAMICS INC)
2402 Spring Ridge Dr E, Spring Grove, IL 60081-8693
Tel (815) 675-1430 *Founded/Ownrshp* 2011
Sales 42.2MM *EMP* 34
SIC 5044 Office equipment; Office equipment
Pr: Terry Bergan
**COO:* Randy Hanson
**CFO:* David Cortens
**VP:* Sharon Parker

D-U-N-S 80-030-3146
■ **INTERNATIONAL ROYALTY CORP**
(*Suby of* ROYAL GOLD INC) ★
10 Inverness Dr E Ste 104, Englewood, CO 80112-5611
Tel (303) 799-9020 *Founded/Ownrshp* 2003
Sales 41.7MM *EMP* 11
Accts Pricewaterhousecoopers Llp Va
SIC 1011 1041 1061 Iron ore mining; Gold ores mining; Cobalt ore mining; Nickel ore mining; Iron ore mining; Gold ores mining; Cobalt ore mining; Nickel ore mining
Ch Bd: Douglas B Silver
Pr: Paul H Zink
CFO: Ray W Jenner
VP: David R Hammond

D-U-N-S 62-367-6728 IMP
INTERNATIONAL RUBBER PRODUCTS INC
IRP
1035 Calle Amanecer, San Clemente, CA 92673-6260
Tel (949) 373-4510 *Founded/Ownrshp* 2005
Sales 24.6MM^E *EMP* 100^E
SIC 3061 Mechanical rubber goods; Mechanical rubber goods
CEO: Rod Trujillo
**Pr:* Casper Zublin Jr
**CEO:* Rod Trujillo
**CFO:* Susan Perkins
**Ex VP:* Jose Castro
**VP:* Ralph Mazzolini
Opers Mgr: Danny Gomez
Board of Directors: Rod Trujillo

D-U-N-S 01-062-7974
INTERNATIONAL SALES & SERVICE INC
COMMERCIAL BUILDING SERVICE
7561 S Grant St Ste A4, Littleton, CO 80122-2626
Tel (303) 730-3001 *Founded/Ownrshp* 1967
Sales 23.6MM *EMP* 18
SIC 1542 Commercial & office building, new construction
Pr: Ivar A Larsen
**VP:* Andrew Larsen
Ex Dir: Robert Krull
Snr Mgr: Mark Reid

D-U-N-S 04-089-8629 IMP
INTERNATIONAL SALT CO LLC
123 N Wacker Dr Fl 24, Chicago, IL 60606-1760
Tel (215) 428-2012 *Founded/Ownrshp* 1997
Sales 75.6MM^E *EMP* 60^E
SIC 5169

D-U-N-S 07-374-8790
INTERNATIONAL SCHOOLS SERVICES INC
I S S
15 Roszel Rd Ste 11, Princeton, NJ 08540-6248
Tel (609) 452-0990 *Founded/Ownrshp* 1989
Sales 23.5MM *EMP* 160
SIC 8211 8299 Private elementary & secondary schools; Educational services; Private elementary & secondary schools; Educational services
Pr: Roger G Hove
**COO:* James Newfrock
**CFO:* Kristin Evins
Ofcr: Anthony Maimone
**VP:* Rob Ambrogi
VP: Lila Leung
VP: Bruce McWilliams
Off Mgr: Carolyn Bethune
Dir IT: Malcolm Stitt
IT Man: Andy Craig

D-U-N-S 02-307-7154
INTERNATIONAL SECURITIES EXCHANGE HOLDINGS INC
(*Suby of* US EXCHANGE HOLDINGS INC) ★
60 Broad St Fl 26, New York, NY 10004-4138
Tel (212) 943-2400 *Founded/Ownrshp* 2007
Sales 155.1MM^E *EMP* 224^E
SIC 6231 Stock option exchanges; Stock option exchanges
CEO: Gary Katz
**V Ch:* Frank J Jones
**Ch:* David Krell
Bd of Dir: David J Young
Ofcr: Joseph W Ferraro III
VP: Mark Wille
Dir Bus: Mike Knesevitch
**Prin:* Joseph Sellitto
**Prin:* Christianna Wood
Software D: Jennifer Kam
Board of Directors: Matthew Andresen, Timothy Brennan, Stanley Choung, Thomas Eichelmann, Joseph Sellitto

D-U-N-S 83-157-9177
INTERNATIONAL SECURITIES EXCHANGE LLC
(*Suby of* INTERNATIONAL SECURITIES EXCHANGE HOLDINGS INC) ★
60 Broad St Fl 26, New York, NY 10004-2349
Tel (212) 943-2400 *Founded/Ownrshp* 2006
Sales 155.1MM^E *EMP* 224
SIC 6231 Stock option exchanges; Stock option exchanges
Pr: Gary Katz
COO: Thomas Reina
CFO: Bruce Cooperman
Exec: Jackie Gaillard
Mng Dir: Boris Ilyevsky
Snr Ntwrk: Timothy Kropp
Snr Ntwrk: James McGirr
CIO: Daniel Friel
CTO: Lawrence P Cambell
Software D: Jennifer Kam
Corp Couns: Joseph Ferraro

D-U-N-S 83-642-3558 EXP
INTERNATIONAL SECURITY AND TRADING CORP
ISTC
8880 Nw 18th Ter, Doral, FL 33172-2642
Tel (305) 594-4141 *Founded/Ownrshp* 2002
Sales 51.8MM^E *EMP* 85^E
Accts George Saenz Cpa Pa Miami
SIC 5065 Security control equipment & systems; Security control equipment & systems
CEO: Pilar Gomez
*Pr: Augusto I Perez
Pr: Patricia Barragana
CFO: Fabio Pinto
Chf Mktg O: Efrain Perez
VP Sls: Eder Bannitz
Mktg Mgr: Omar Avila
Manager: Andre Porsche
Sls Mgr: Fabiola Castillo
Sls Mgr: Ana Duque

D-U-N-S 62-049-1969
INTERNATIONAL SECURITY MANAGEMENT GROUP INC
ISMG
(*Suby of* UNIVERSAL PROTECTION SERVICE LP) ★
8215 Roswell Rd Bldg 1100, Atlanta, GA 30350-6446
Tel (770) 649-5725 *Founded/Ownrshp* 2014
Sales 19.2MM^E *EMP* 800
SIC 7382

D-U-N-S 78-491-7064
INTERNATIONAL SERVICES INC
1250 Barclay Blvd, Buffalo Grove, IL 60089-4500
Tel (847) 808-5590 *Founded/Ownrshp* 1991
Sales 60.8MM^E *EMP* 1,200
SIC 8742

D-U-N-S 02-112-2494
INTERNATIONAL SHIP REPAIR & MARINE SERVICES INC
1616 Penny St, Tampa, FL 33605-6003
Tel (813) 247-1118 *Founded/Ownrshp* 1990
Sales 22.5MM^E *EMP* 190^E
SIC 3731

D-U-N-S 92-922-5936
INTERNATIONAL SHIPBREAKING LIMITED LLC
(*Suby of* EUROPEAN METAL RECYCLING LIMITED)
18501 Rl Ostos Rd, Brownsville, TX 78521-1038
Tel (956) 831-4112 *Founded/Ownrshp* 1995
Sales 20.1MM^E *EMP* 120
SIC 4499 3341 Ship dismantling; Marine dismantling & scrapping services; Marine wrecking ships for scrap; Recovery & refining of nonferrous metals; Ship dismantling; Marine dismantling & scrapping services; Marine wrecking ships for scrap; Recovery & refining of nonferrous metals
CEO: Joel Dupre
CFO: David Farnsworth

D-U-N-S 09-491-5493 IMP/EXP
▲ INTERNATIONAL SHIPHOLDING CORP
11 N Water St Ste 18290, Mobile, AL 36602-5018
Tel (251) 243-9100 *Founded/Ownrshp* 1978
Sales 294.8MM *EMP* 625
Tkr Sym ISH *Exch* NYS
SIC 4412 4424 Deep sea foreign transportation of freight; Deep sea domestic transportation of freight; Deep sea foreign transportation of freight; Deep sea domestic transportation of freight
Ch Bd: Niels M Johnsen
*Pr: Erik L Johnsen
CFO: Manuel G Estrada
Ex VP: Peter M Johnston
VP: Sheila Dean-Rosenbohm
Dir Risk M: Ken Strong
IT Man: Sherri Bates
Board of Directors: Kenneth H Beer, H Merritt Lane III, Edwin A Lupberger, James J McNamara, Harris V Morrissette, T Lee Robinson Jr

D-U-N-S 09-000-5059
INTERNATIONAL SHIPPING AGENCY INC
INTERSHIP
500 Paseo Monaco Apt 55, Bayamon, PR 00956-9776
Tel (787) 778-2355 *Founded/Ownrshp* 1960
Sales 91.1MM^E *EMP* 1,500
SIC 4491 4731 Stevedoring; Docks, piers & terminals; Agents, shipping; Stevedoring; Docks, piers & terminals; Agents, shipping
Pr: David R Segarra Jr
*CFO: Maria Caraballo
*Treas: Pablo Jose Alvarez
*VP: Salustino Alvarez
VP: Jose Garcia
VP: Renzo Roman

D-U-N-S 14-187-5562
INTERNATIONAL SHOPPES INC
540 Rockaway Ave, Valley Stream, NY 11581-1918
Tel (516) 872-5797 *Founded/Ownrshp* 1961
Sales 18.5MM^E *EMP* 300
SIC 6519 Real property lessors; Real property lessors
Pr: Michael Halpern

D-U-N-S 06-466-9484
INTERNATIONAL SIGN & DESIGN CORP
10831 Canal St, Largo, FL 33777-1636
Tel (727) 541-5573 *Founded/Ownrshp* 1976
Sales 21.2MM^E *EMP* 156
SIC 3993 Signs & advertising specialties; Signs & advertising specialties
CEO: William Griffin
*CFO: Seth F Sekeres
*VP: Eric Sekeres
Sls Mgr: Tony Dublo

D-U-N-S 62-128-7564 IMP/EXP
■ INTERNATIONAL SNUBBING SERVICES LLC
(*Suby of* SESI LLC) ★
190 Industries Ln, Arnaudville, LA 70512-6331
Tel (337) 754-7233 *Founded/Ownrshp* 2000
Sales 200.0MM^E *EMP* 300
SIC 1389 7353 Oil field services; Oil field equipment, rental or leasing; Oil field services; Oil field equipment, rental or leasing
Pr: Mark Hardy
CFO: Jamie Kartsimas
Sr VP: Steven Courville
VP: Tony Sanders
Genl Mgr: Shane Rivette
VP Opers: Jack Hardy
Opers Mgr: Gregorio Loginow

D-U-N-S 02-041-1393
INTERNATIONAL SOS ASSISTANCE INC
(*Suby of* INTERNATIONAL SOS PTE LTD)
3600 Horizon Blvd Ste 300, Feasterville Trevose, PA 19053-4949
Tel (215) 942-8000 *Founded/Ownrshp* 1998
Sales 33.6MM^E *EMP* 154
SIC 8011 8748 General & family practice, physician/surgeon; Business consulting; General & family practice, physician/surgeon; Business consulting
Pr: Nick Peters
*Pr: Arnaud Vaissi
CFO: Gregory Bell
Sr VP: Gino Lamarca
VP: David Cameron
VP: David W Unkle
Comm Man: Colette Pilkus
Mng Dir: Grant Jeffery
Genl Mgr: Chris Lim
Genl Mgr: Philippe Maezelle
CTO: Dipak Pandya

D-U-N-S 87-301-8162 IMP/EXP
INTERNATIONAL SOURCING CO INC
CORDOVA SAFETY PRODUCTS
4025 Viscount Ave, Memphis, TN 38118-6106
Tel (901) 458-5030 *Founded/Ownrshp* 1994
Sales 81.0MM *EMP* 77
Accts Lenahan Smith & Bargiachi P
SIC 5099 Safety equipment & supplies; Safety equipment & supplies
Pr: Himanshu Varma
CFO: Abhay Bhargava
Treas: Scott Laxton
VP: Dave Kuehneman
Dir IT: Printice Kincade
VP Sls: Jimmy Garbuzinski
Sls Mgr: Daniel Bird
Sls Mgr: Eugenio Juarez
Sls Mgr: Chip Minger

D-U-N-S 13-541-2562 EXP
■ INTERNATIONAL SPECIALTY HOLDINGS INC
(*Suby of* ASHLAND INC) ★
1361 Alps Rd, Wayne, NJ 07470-3700
Tel (973) 628-4000 *Founded/Ownrshp* 2011
Sales 170.2MM^E *EMP* 2,500
SIC 2869 Industrial organic chemicals; Industrial organic chemicals
Pr: Sunil Kumar

D-U-N-S 96-437-8459 IMP/EXP
■ INTERNATIONAL SPECIALTY PRODUCTS INC
ASHLAND
(*Suby of* ASHLAND INC) ★
1361 Alps Rd, Wayne, NJ 07470-3700
Tel (973) 628-4000 *Founded/Ownrshp* 2011
Sales 413.5MM^E *EMP* 2,800
SIC 2869 2821 2843 2842 2899 Amines, acids, salts, esters; Plastics materials & resins; Surface active agents; Specialty cleaning, polishes & sanitation goods; Chemical preparations; Amines, acids, salts, esters; Plastics materials & resins; Surface active agents; Specialty cleaning, polishes & sanitation goods; Chemical preparations
Pr: Sunil Kumar
*CFO: Douglas Vaughan
*Treas: Susan B Yoss
VP: Jon Stern
Dir Lab: Carl Eckardt
Genl Mgr: Melvin W Martin
Dir IT: Robert Frey
IT Man: Justin Dunlap
Software D: Sanath Kalutota
Sls&Mrk Ex: Steven Olsen
Sls Dir: Eimear O'Connell

D-U-N-S 19-233-6964
INTERNATIONAL SPECIALTY TUBE LLC
IST
6600 Mount Elliott St, Detroit, MI 48211-2437
Tel (313) 923-2000 *Founded/Ownrshp* 2004
Sales 77.2MM^E *EMP* 108
SIC 3317 Tubes, wrought: welded or lock joint; Tubes, wrought: welded or lock joint
Sales Exec: Jason Vandeven

D-U-N-S 04-796-6643 IMP
▲ INTERNATIONAL SPEEDWAY CORP
1 Daytona Blvd, Daytona Beach, FL 32114-1252
Tel (386) 254-2700 *Founded/Ownrshp* 1953
Sales 651.9MM *EMP* 845^E
Accts Ernst & Young Llp Jacksonvil
Tkr Sym ISCA *Exch* NGS
SIC 7948 Automotive race track operation; Stock car racing; Motorcycle racing; Race track operation; Automotive race track operation; Stock car racing; Motorcycle racing; Race track operation
CEO: Lesa France Kennedy
*Ch Bd: James C France
Pr: Douglas Bolas
Pr: John R Saunders
CFO: Daniel W Houser
Chf Mktg O: Daryl Q Wolfe
Ex VP: W Crotty
Sr VP: W Garrett Crotty
Sr VP: W Grant Lynch Jr
Sr VP: Roger R Vandersnick
VP: Andrew Gurtis
VP: Laura Jackson
VP: Brett Scharback
VP: Brian K Wilson
Board of Directors: Larry Aiello Jr, J Hyatt Brown, Edsel B Ford II, Brian Z France, Wiliam P Graves, Sonia M Green, Christy F Harris, Larry D Woodard

D-U-N-S 60-486-3241
INTERNATIONAL STEEL SERVICES INC
ISSI
661 Andersen Dr Ste 7, Pittsburgh, PA 15220-2700
Tel (412) 922-9100 *Founded/Ownrshp* 1989
Sales 54.5MM^E *EMP* 110
SIC 8711 Chemical engineering; Chemical engineering
Pr: Walter J Sieckman
*Treas: Jan C Wirtner
*Ex VP: Satish Wadhawan
*Sr VP: Malvin Sander
*VP: Michael Sieckmann
*VP: Mark Stropkaj
Board of Directors: Paul Songer

D-U-N-S 94-941-2308
INTERNATIONAL STONE INC
10 Ryan Rd, Woburn, MA 01801-2444
Tel (781) 937-3300 *Founded/Ownrshp* 1995
Sales 20.9MM^E *EMP* 80
SIC 3441 5032 3281 Fabricated structural metal; Brick, stone & related material; Cut stone & stone products
Pr: Joanne Gemelarro
Genl Mgr: Nicholas Sfravara

INTERNATIONAL SUPPLIERS
See KERZNER INTERNATIONAL NORTH AMERICA INC

D-U-N-S 10-659-5937
INTERNATIONAL SUPPLY CO
2717 W North St, Edelstein, IL 61526-9530
Tel (309) 249-6211 *Founded/Ownrshp* 1983
Sales 33.9MM^E *EMP* 90
SIC 3621 Control equipment for electric buses & locomotives
Pr: E Lee Hofmann
Treas: Rebecca Hofmann
*Sec: Becky Hofmann
*VP: Duane Dean
VP: Rick Durie
Sls Mgr: Brett Dean
Sls Mgr: Lee Hofmann

D-U-N-S 17-786-7483 IMP
INTERNATIONAL SURFACE SOLUTIONS LLC
1 Cablecar Dr, Washington, MO 63090-1119
Tel (636) 239-0300 *Founded/Ownrshp* 2003
Sales 41.6MM^E *EMP* 95
SIC 5084 Safety equipment; Safety equipment

D-U-N-S 15-737-9496
INTERNATIONAL SWAPS AND DERIVATIVES ASSOCIATION INC
ISDA
360 Madison Ave Rm 1601, New York, NY 10017-7113
Tel (212) 901-6000 *Founded/Ownrshp* 1985
Sales 62.4MM *EMP* 52
Accts Pricewaterhousecoopers Llp Ne
SIC 8611 Trade associations
CEO: Robert Pickel
CEO: George Handjinicolaou
CFO: Huzefa Deesawala
Ch: Stephen Oconnor
Treas: Diane Genova
Software D: Mehboob Hoque
Counsel: Gregory Zerzan
Snr Mgr: Conrad Voldstad

D-U-N-S 04-519-6904
INTERNATIONAL SYSTEMS & CONTROLS CORP
2950 North Loop W Ste 500, Houston, TX 77092-8830
Tel (713) 526-5461 *Founded/Ownrshp* 1983
Sales 39.7MM^E *EMP* 200
SIC 3491 Pressure valves & regulators, industrial; Pressure valves & regulators, industrial
Ch Bd: R F Medina

D-U-N-S 00-799-4353
INTERNATIONAL TANK TERMINALS LLC
INTERNTNL-MATEX TANK TERMINALS
321 Saint Charles Ave, New Orleans, LA 70130-3145
Tel (504) 586-8300 *Founded/Ownrshp* 1943, 1946
Sales 21.1MM^E *EMP* 135
SIC 4226 Petroleum & chemical bulk stations & terminals for hire
Ch Bd: James J Coleman Sr
*Pr: Thomas B Coleman
*Treas: Howard Streiffer
*VP: James J Coleman Jr
Opers Supe: George Americk
Ql Cn Mgr: Jack Kennedy

D-U-N-S 10-148-9045
INTERNATIONAL TECHNEGROUP INC
5303 Dupont Cir, Milford, OH 45150-2734
Tel (513) 576-3900 *Founded/Ownrshp* 1983
Sales 34.0MM^E *EMP* 125
SIC 7371 Computer software development
Pr: Michael Lemon
*Treas: Thomas A Gregory
*VP: Donald Hemmelgarn
VP: Rendell Hughes
Dir Bus: Mark Haines
Genl Mgr: Alex Tsechansky
Snr Sftwr: Charles Fuller
Sftwr Eng: Tracey Jones
Sftwr Eng: Mark Pare
Sftwr Eng: Josh Rinaldi
Sftwr Eng: Laurine Thompson

D-U-N-S 80-728-2694 IMP/EXP
INTERNATIONAL TECHNICAL COATINGS INC
ITC
110 S 41st Ave, Phoenix, AZ 85009-4626
Tel (602) 415-1400 *Founded/Ownrshp* 2002
Sales 46.7MM^E *EMP* 150
SIC 3496 3479 Shelving, made from purchased wire; Painting, coating & hot dipping; Shelving, made from purchased wire; Painting, coating & hot dipping
Pr: Johnnie Caldwell
CFO: Torrey Peterson

D-U-N-S 04-987-1288
INTERNATIONAL TECHNIDYNE CORP
ACCRIVA DIAGNOSTICS
(*Suby of* ACCRIVA DIAGNOSTICS INC) ★
6260 Sequence Dr, San Diego, CA 92121-4358
Tel (858) 263-2300 *Founded/Ownrshp* 2015
Sales 70.0MM^E *EMP* 350
SIC 3841 3829 Diagnostic apparatus, medical; Medical diagnostic systems, nuclear; Diagnostic apparatus, medical; Medical diagnostic systems, nuclear
Pr: Scott Cramer
*COO: Tom Whalen
*CFO: Greg Tibbitts
*Sr VP: Matt Bastardi
*VP: Kimberly Ballard
VP: Lesley Traver
*Prin: Brett Giffin
Rgnl Mgr: Joel Payne
Sls Mgr: Bill Eno
Sls Mgr: Brian Maley
Sls Mgr: Regine Voegele

D-U-N-S 09-191-2303
INTERNATIONAL TECHNIFAB INC
SPECIALLY PDTS & INSTALLATION
(*Suby of* PARAGON INDUSTRIES INC) ★
6300 E 39th Ave, Denver, CO 80207-1333
Tel (303) 333-6784 *Founded/Ownrshp* 2008
Sales 44.6MM^E *EMP* 400^E
SIC 3296 Mineral wool insulation products
Pr: John Fox

D-U-N-S 13-186-2302 IMP
INTERNATIONAL TECHNOLOGIES & SYSTEMS CORP
ITSCO
10721 Walker St, Cypress, CA 90630-4720
Tel (714) 761-8886 *Founded/Ownrshp* 1985
Sales 31.4MM^E *EMP* 48^E
SIC 5065 3578 Electronic parts & equipment; Point-of-sale devices
Pr: Stanley Ning
Ex VP: Terry Conant
CTO: George Jiang
Info Man: Yvonne Yong
QC Dir: Joannes Hsuean
Opers Mgr: Grace Jin
Sales Exec: Renee Hendrick
Sls Dir: Eric Vanpoppelen
Manager: Peter Charland
Manager: Jason Hall
Manager: Robert Wang

D-U-N-S 05-846-8229
INTERNATIONAL TECHNOLOGY SOLUTIONS INC
IT SOLUTIONS
2000 Cornwall Rd, Monmouth Junction, NJ 08852-2444
Tel (732) 985-5900 *Founded/Ownrshp* 1998
Sales 22.0MM *EMP* 250
SIC 7371 Computer software systems analysis & design, custom; Computer software systems analysis & design, custom
Pr: Venu Mukkamala
*Pr: Ranga Gurrala

D-U-N-S 82-519-8484 IMP
▲ INTERNATIONAL TEXTILE GROUP INC
804 Green Valley Rd # 300, Greensboro, NC 27408-7000
Tel (336) 379-6220 *Founded/Ownrshp* 2006
Sales 595.4MM *EMP* 4,650
Accts Grant Thornton Llp Raleigh N
Tkr Sym ITXN *Exch* OTO
SIC 3714 3496 2211 2231 2221 2273 Motor vehicle parts & accessories; Fabrics, woven wire; Denims; Draperies & drapery fabrics, cotton; Upholstery fabrics, cotton; Tickings; Worsted fabrics, broadwoven; Upholstery fabrics, wool; Polyester broadwoven fabrics; Draperies & drapery fabrics, manmade fiber & silk; Upholstery fabrics, manmade fiber & silk; Carpets & rugs; Motor vehicle parts & accessories; Fabrics, woven wire; Denims; Draperies & drapery fabrics, cotton; Upholstery fabrics, cotton; Tickings; Worsted fabrics, broadwoven; Upholstery fabrics, wool; Polyester broadwoven fabrics; Draperies & drapery fabrics, manmade fiber & silk; Upholstery fabrics, manmade fiber & silk; Carpets & rugs
Pr: Kenneth T Kunberger
*CFO: Gail A Kuczkowski
*Treas: Craig J Hart
Ex VP: Dale Arnold
VP: Pete Baumann
VP: Nelson Bebo
*VP: Neil W Koonce
Mng Dir: Kevin Reardon
Genl Mgr: Julio Delgado
Dir IT: Sandy Greene
IT Man: Andrew Watakila

INTERNATIONAL THEOLOGICAL UNIV
See WESTERN FEDERATION CHURCH AND TRIBE

D-U-N-S 02-933-4336 EXP
INTERNATIONAL THERMAL SYSTEMS LLC
I T S
4697 W Greenfield Ave, Milwaukee, WI 53214-5308
Tel (414) 672-7700 *Founded/Ownrshp* 2010
Sales 22.7MM^E *EMP* 126
SIC 3567 3559 7629 3582 Industrial furnaces & ovens; Sewing machines & hat & zipper making machinery; Electrical repair shops; Commercial laundry equipment; Industrial furnaces & ovens; Sewing machines & hat & zipper making machinery; Electrical repair shops; Commercial laundry equipment
Pr: John K Zea
CFO: Alice Sonnencein
**Prin:* Roy Bruce
**Prin:* Jeffrey C Mitchell
IT Man: Charles Cash
Mtls Mgr: John Halbur
Mktg Dir: Susan Hoffmann
Sls Mgr: Matt Wingert

D-U-N-S 14-596-7415 EXP
INTERNATIONAL THERMOCAST CORP
189 Etowah Industrial Ct, Canton, GA 30114-8017
Tel (678) 445-2022 *Founded/Ownrshp* 1991
Sales 37.6MM^E *EMP* 100
SIC 2541 3088 Counter & sink tops; Plastics plumbing fixtures
Pr: Mark Anderson
Exec: Joe Blanchard
S&M/VP: Bob Schroeder

INTERNATIONAL TILE & STONE
See TILE-IT INDUSTRIES INC

D-U-N-S 96-719-5231
INTERNATIONAL TIMBER AND VENEER LLC
I T V
(*Suby of* INTERNATIONAL VENEER CO INC) ★
75 Mcquiston Dr, Jackson Center, PA 16133-1635
Tel (724) 662-0880 *Founded/Ownrshp* 1996
Sales 121.4MM^E *EMP* 170
SIC 2435 5031 Veneer stock, hardwood; Composite board products, woodboard; Veneer stock, hardwood; Composite board products, woodboard
Ex VP: Bo Edwards
**Treas:* H Tyler Howerton
**VP:* Mike Rastatter
Sfty Dirs: Jill Richardson

INTERNATIONAL TOOL & SUPPLY
See GLOBAL OILFIELD SERVICES INC

D-U-N-S 78-196-3053
INTERNATIONAL TOY INC
2151 Michelson Dr Ste 185, Irvine, CA 92612-1368
Tel (949) 333-3777 *Founded/Ownrshp* 1990
Sales 24.0MM^E *EMP* 50
SIC 5092 Toys & hobby goods & supplies
Pr: Steve Asher

D-U-N-S 55-744-5186 EXP
INTERNATIONAL TRACTOR CO INC
547 Saw Mill River Rd 1d, Ardsley, NY 10502-2143
Tel (914) 693-0300 *Founded/Ownrshp* 1991
Sales 80.0MM *EMP* 6
SIC 5082 Construction & mining machinery; Construction & mining machinery
Pr: Eilat Lav
Genl Mgr: John Cannourji

D-U-N-S 92-995-6225
■ **INTERNATIONAL TRADE ADMINISTRATION**
(*Suby of* UNITED STATES DEPARTMENT OF COMMERCE) ★
14th /Constitution Ave Nw, Washington, DC 20230-0001
Tel (202) 482-2000 *Founded/Ownrshp* 1980
Sales NA *EMP* 2,400
SIC 9611 Trade commission, government; ; Trade commission, government;
CFO: Mary Pleffner
Ofcr: Brenda Carter-Nixon
IT Man: Laura Merchant

INTERNATIONAL TRADE CENTER
See TRADE CENTER MANAGEMENT ASSOCIATES LLC

D-U-N-S 02-187-7998
■ **INTERNATIONAL TRADE COMMISSION UNITED STATES**
I T C
(*Suby of* EXECUTIVE OFFICE OF UNITED STATES GOVERNMENT) ★
500 E St Sw Ste 316, Washington, DC 20436-0004
Tel (202) 205-2000 *Founded/Ownrshp* 1916
Sales NA *EMP* 360
SIC 9611 Trade commission, government; ; Trade commission, government;
Exec: Margaret O'Laughlin
Mng Ofcr: Lynette Gabourel
Dir IT: Pamela Dyson
IT Man: Myra Lay
Psych: Juliana Cofrancesco
Counsel: Elizabeth Argenti
Counsel: Karen Driscoll
Snr Mgr: Robert Bauchspies
Snr Mgr: William Cunningham

D-U-N-S 02-431-7336 IMP/EXP
INTERNATIONAL TRADE WINDS LLC
ITW
7441 Lake Forest Dr, Clarkston, MI 48346-2571
Tel (248) 620-6333 *Founded/Ownrshp* 2000
Sales 21.7MM *EMP* 5
Accts William Vaughan Company Maume
SIC 5013 Automotive supplies & parts; Automotive supplies & parts
Pr: George Landolt
**Pr:* Richard Landolt

D-U-N-S 05-649-7493 IMP
INTERNATIONAL TRADERS INC
ITI
800 Tiffany Blvd Ste 302, Rocky Mount, NC 27804-1807
Tel (252) 407-2000 *Founded/Ownrshp* 1991
Sales 39.2MM^E *EMP* 35
SIC 5141 Food brokers
Pr: Todd Williams
Natl Sales: Joel Attoe
Natl Sales: Robert Pryately

INTERNATIONAL TRADING
See JINDAL INTERNATIONAL INC

D-U-N-S 82-978-1504
INTERNATIONAL TRAINING FUND
3 Park Pl, Annapolis, MD 21401-3687
Tel (410) 269-2000 *Founded/Ownrshp* 1956
Sales 27.1MM *EMP* 26
Accts Salter & Company Llc Bethesda
SIC 8631 6141 Labor unions & similar labor organizations; Mutual benefit associations; Labor unions & similar labor organizations; Mutual benefit associations
Prin: Michael P Arndt
**Off Mgr:* Joseline Dorsey

D-U-N-S 04-224-2826
INTERNATIONAL TRANDUCER CORP
CHANNEL TECHNOLOGIES GROUP
869 Ward Dr, Santa Barbara, CA 93111-2920
Tel (805) 683-2575 *Founded/Ownrshp* 1966, 2009
Sales 62.7MM^E *EMP* 475
SIC 3825 3812 Transducers for volts, amperes, watts, vars, frequency, etc.; Search & navigation equipment; Transducers for volts, amperes, watts, vars, frequency, etc.; Search & navigation equipment
Co-Ch Bd: R M Callahan
**Pr:* Kevin Ruelas
CFO: John Ladd
**Co-Ch Bd:* Robert F Carlson
VP: Art Campbell
VP: Gary Douville
Exec: Jon Monroe
Dir Bus: Trent Morrow
Prgrm Mgr: Joe Zaremski
Ql Cn Mgr: Curt Madison

D-U-N-S 12-892-5539
■ **INTERNATIONAL TRANSMISSION CO**
ITC TRANSMISSION
(*Suby of* ITC HOLDINGS CORP) ★
27175 Energy Way, Novi, MI 48377-3639
Tel (248) 374-7100 *Founded/Ownrshp* 2003
Sales 111.6MM^E *EMP* 100
SIC 4911 Transmission, electric power; Transmission, electric power
Pr: Joseph L Welch
**CFO:* Edward Rahill
**VP:* Linda H Blair
**VP:* Cameron M Bready
VP: Larry Bruneel
VP: Joseph Dudak
**VP:* Jon E Jipping
**VP:* Daniel J Oginsky
VP: Thomas W Vitez
CIO: Denis Desrosiers
Dir IT: Bruce Alexander

D-U-N-S 06-457-5806
INTERNATIONAL TRANSPORTATION SERVICE INC (CA)
I T S
(*Suby of* KAWASAKI KISEN KAISHA, LTD.)
1281 Pier G Way, Long Beach, CA 90802-6353
Tel (562) 435-7781 *Founded/Ownrshp* 1971
Sales 46.1MM^E *EMP* 403
SIC 4491 Marine loading & unloading services; Marine loading & unloading services
Pr: Sho Ishitobi
**Sec:* Yuji Yamamoto
**Ex VP:* John Miller
VP: Masanora Kurose
**VP:* Michael Shanks
Exec: Fumito Kawamata
CTO: Bill Ramos
Dir IT: Kiyo Kojitani
IT Man: Eric Bayani
IT Man: Gary Dalton
Netwrk Mgr: Tomo Wakamatsu

D-U-N-S 00-373-4018
INTERNATIONAL TRUCK AND ENGINE CORP
6125 Urbana Rd, Springfield, OH 45502-9279
Tel (937) 390-4045 *Founded/Ownrshp* 1999
Sales 91.1MM^E *EMP* 1,500
SIC 4212 Local trucking, without storage; Local trucking, without storage
Prin: Bob Baker
**Ch Bd:* Mr Daniel Ustian
**CEO:* John R Horne
**CFO:* Robert C Lannert
**Sr VP:* Robert A Boardman
VP: Donald Kohs
Exec: Dorothy Crump
Dir IT: Brian Powell
Mtls Mgr: Daren Martin

D-U-N-S 05-868-8318
INTERNATIONAL TRUCKS OF HOUSTON LLC
TEXAS TRUCK CENTERS OF HOUSTON
8900 North Loop E, Houston, TX 77029-1218
Tel (713) 674-3444 *Founded/Ownrshp* 1988
Sales 119.8MM^E *EMP* 250
SIC 5511 5531 Trucks, tractors & trailers: new & used; Truck equipment & parts; Trucks, tractors & trailers: new & used; Truck equipment & parts
Mktg Mgr: Rob Kumar

D-U-N-S 62-198-8302
INTERNATIONAL TURF INVESTMENT CO INC
3001 Street Rd, Bensalem, PA 19020-2006
Tel (215) 639-9000 *Founded/Ownrshp* 1990
Sales 66.3MM^E *EMP* 2,486
SIC 7948 Horse race track operation; Racehorse training; Stables, racing; Thoroughbred horse racing; Horse race track operation; Racehorse training; Stables, racing; Thoroughbred horse racing
**VP:* William Hogwood

INTERNATIONAL UN PNTRS & ALIED
See INTERNATIONAL UNION OF PAINTERS AND ALLIED TRADES

D-U-N-S 02-398-1101
INTERNATIONAL UNION AGAINST TUBERCULOSIS AND LUNG DISEASE INC
61 Broadway Rm 1720, New York, NY 10006-2710
Tel (212) 500-5720 *Founded/Ownrshp* 1995
Sales 22.4MM^E *EMP* 7
Accts O Connor Davies Munnis And Dob
SIC 8733 Medical research; Medical research
Ex Dir: Jose Luis Castro
IT Man: Mili Chowfla

D-U-N-S 07-484-8615
INTERNATIONAL UNION OF BRICKLAYERS & ALLIED CRAFTWORKERS
620 F St Nw, Washington, DC 20004-1618
Tel (202) 783-3788 *Founded/Ownrshp* 1865
Sales 41.5MM *EMP* 200
Accts Calibre Cpa Group Pllc Bethes
SIC 8631 Labor union; Labor union
Pr: James Boland
**Sec:* Henry F Kramer
**Ex VP:* Timothy Driscoll
Ex VP: Ken Lambert
Ex VP: Gerald Omalley
**Ex VP:* Gerard Scarano
Ex VP: Dominic Spano
Assoc Dir: Reid Blank
Dir IT: Melissa Wyers
Counsel: Caryn Halifax
Board of Directors: Robert Francis, Sally Sohn

D-U-N-S 96-412-4676
INTERNATIONAL UNION OF OP ENGINEERS LOCAL 181 320 AND TVA HEALTH AND WELFARE
P.O. Box 1179 (42419-1179)
Tel (270) 826-6750
Sales 38.1MM *EMP* 3^E
Accts Harding Shymanski & Co Psc Ev
SIC 8631 Labor unions & similar labor organizations

INTERNATIONAL UNION OF OPERATI
See OPERATING ENGINEERS LOCAL 49

D-U-N-S 02-030-2030
INTERNATIONAL UNION OF OPERATING ENGINEERS (DC)
IUOE
1125 17th St Nw, Washington, DC 20036-4709
Tel (202) 429-9100 *Founded/Ownrshp* 1896
Sales 72.3MM *EMP* 125
Accts Calibre Cpa Group Pllc Bethes
SIC 8631 Trade union
Pr: James Callahan
**Sec:* Brian E Hecky
Exec: Christine Simpkins
Snr Ntwrk: Carlos Alves
Dir IT: Quinton Ware
Sales Exec: Richard Griffin

D-U-N-S 06-777-8209
INTERNATIONAL UNION OF OPERATING ENGINEERS
1121 L St Ste 401, Sacramento, CA 95814-3969
Tel (916) 444-6880 *Founded/Ownrshp* 1939
Sales 44.1MM^E *EMP* 1,350
SIC 8631 Labor union; Labor union

D-U-N-S 07-212-5099
INTERNATIONAL UNION OF OPERATING ENGINEERS
LOCAL UNION 478 ACDE
1965 Dixwell Ave, Hamden, CT 06514-2407
Tel (203) 288-9261 *Founded/Ownrshp* 1911
Sales 43.8MM *EMP* 100
Accts Schultheis & Panettieri Llp H
SIC 8631 Labor union
Pr: Philip Rapuano
Exec: Judith Hart
Sls Mgr: Ted Battistone

D-U-N-S 07-582-7097
INTERNATIONAL UNION OF OPERATING ENGINEERS JOINT WELFARE FUND
I U O E
4325 S Salina St, Syracuse, NY 13205-2064
Tel (315) 492-1796 *Founded/Ownrshp* 1957
Sales NA *EMP* 23
SIC 6371 Union funds; Union funds

D-U-N-S 96-898-0149
INTERNATIONAL UNION OF OPERATING ENGINEERS LOCAL 132 HEALTH & WELFARE FD
636 4th Ave, Huntington, WV 25701-1324
Tel (304) 525-0482 *Founded/Ownrshp* 2011
Sales 26.1MM *EMP* 5
Accts Harris & Company Cpas Hunting
SIC 8631 Labor union; Labor union
Prin: Tommy Plumber

D-U-N-S 01-029-4049
INTERNATIONAL UNION OF OPERATING ENGINEERS LOCAL 150 (IL)
HOISTING PORTABLE & SHOVEL ENG
6200 Joliet Rd, Countryside, IL 60525-3957
Tel (708) 482-7300 *Founded/Ownrshp* 1936
Sales 36.9MM^E *EMP* 300
Accts Graff Ballauer & Blanski Pc N
SIC 8631 6371 5912 6512 Labor union; Union welfare, benefit & health funds; Drug stores; Commercial & industrial building operation; Labor union; Union welfare, benefit & health funds; Drug stores; Commercial & industrial building operation
Pr: James M Sweeney
**Treas:* Joseph Ward
**VP:* Jim Sweeny

D-U-N-S 02-040-6815
INTERNATIONAL UNION OF OPERATING ENGINEERS LOCAL 30 (DC)
11506 Myrtle Ave, Richmond Hill, NY 11418-1717
Tel (718) 847-8484 *Founded/Ownrshp* 1959
Sales 5.7MM *EMP* 1,000
Accts Schultheis & Panettien Llp Ha
SIC 8631 6512 Collective bargaining unit; Nonresidential building operators; Collective bargaining unit; Nonresidential building operators
IT Man: Ralph Pascarella

D-U-N-S 07-264-0626
INTERNATIONAL UNION OF PAINTERS AND ALLIED TRADES
INTERNATIONAL UN PNTRS & ALIED
7234 Parkway Dr, Hanover, MD 21076-1307
Tel (410) 564-5900 *Founded/Ownrshp* 1887
Sales 37.4MM *EMP* 97
Accts Novak Francella Llc Bala Cynwy
SIC 8631 Labor unions & similar labor organizations
Pr: James A Williams
**Sec:* George Galis

INTERNATIONAL UNION UAW
See UAW PUBLIC RELATIONS

D-U-N-S 07-313-2227
INTERNATIONAL UNION UNITED AUTOMOBILE AEROSPACE AND AGRICULTURAL IMPLEMENT WORKERS OF AM
U A W
8000 E Jefferson Ave, Detroit, MI 48214-3963
Tel (313) 926-5000 *Founded/Ownrshp* 1935
Sales 208.0MM^E *EMP* 3,000
SIC 8631 Labor union; Labor union
Pr: Dennis Williams
VP: James Settles
Ex Dir: David Hirschland
MIS Dir: Stanley Thornton
IT Man: Andrew Dunn
Snr Mgr: Cameron Wright

D-U-N-S 08-458-3715 IMP/EXP
INTERNATIONAL VENEER CO INC
(*Suby of* IVC USA INC) ★
1551 Montgomery St, South Hill, VA 23970-3920
Tel (434) 447-7100 *Founded/Ownrshp* 1975
Sales 25.0MM *EMP* 35^E
SIC 5031 Veneer; Veneer
Pr: Pitt Neukirchner
Ch Bd: Sergio Colombo
Sec: Howerton H Tyler
VP: Roberto Palvarini
CTO: Jim Cottingham
Sys Admin: James Cottingham
Snr Mgr: Tyler Howerton

D-U-N-S 14-701-8998
INTERNATIONAL VIDEO DISTRIBUTORS LLC
I V D
59 Lake Dr, East Windsor, NJ 08520-5320
Tel (609) 426-1777 *Founded/Ownrshp* 1986
Sales 25.2MM^E *EMP* 75^E
SIC 5099 Video & audio equipment; Tapes & cassettes, prerecorded; Video cassettes, accessories & supplies
Pr: Frank Koretsky
Exec: Richard Galloway
CIO: Dwight Atkinson
IT Man: Andy Green
Opers Mgr: Brian Lloyd
Mktg Dir: Adam Hasner
Genl Couns: Mary Iuliano

D-U-N-S 96-159-4343 IMP/EXP
INTERNATIONAL VITAMIN CORP
IVC
500 Halls Mill Rd, Freehold, NJ 07728-8811
Tel (732) 308-3000 *Founded/Ownrshp* 2009
Sales 148.4MM^E *EMP* 420
SIC 2834 Vitamin preparations; Vitamin preparations
Pr: Steven Dai
**COO:* Glenn Davis
**CFO:* Ran Bareket
CFO: Thomas Bocchino
CFO: Mike Colbert
**Treas:* Eva Pinto
Ofcr: Michael Krekevich
Ex VP: Mike Richtmyer
Sr VP: Thomas E Bocchino
Sr VP: Michael Durso
Sr VP: Dan Tannenbaum
Sr VP: John Torphy
VP: Richard Connor
VP: Peter Cosgrove
VP: Diane Dottavio
VP: Scott Parzych
**VP:* Stephen Rosenman
**VP:* Bart Smith
VP: John Yonkin
Creative D: Bob Wiethop
Dir Bus: Preston Zoller

INTERNATIONAL WARRANTY SVCS
See MILITARY CAR SALES INC

INTERNATIONAL WAXES
See IGI INTERNATIONAL GROUP INC

D-U-N-S 55-683-2710
INTERNATIONAL WAXES INC
(*Suby of* IGI INTERNATIONAL GROUP INC) ★
45 Route 446, Smethport, PA 16749-5413
Tel (814) 887-5501 *Founded/Ownrshp* 1990
Sales 141.2MM^E *EMP* 200
SIC 5169 Waxes, except petroleum; Waxes, except petroleum
Pr: William R Reucassel
**CFO:* David Imrie
**Treas:* James Gelly
**Treas:* John J Tus
**VP:* Kenneth Reucassel

D-U-N-S 82-633-7466 IMP/EXP
INTERNATIONAL WHOLESALE TILE LLC
(*Suby of* IWT HOLDINGS LLC)
3500 Sw 42nd Ave, Palm City, FL 34990-5613
Tel (772) 223-5151 *Founded/Ownrshp* 2008
Sales 25.2MM^E *EMP* 60
SIC 2426 Hardwood dimension & flooring mills; Hardwood dimension & flooring mills
Pr: Paul Bousher
**CFO:* Michael Dagostino
**CFO:* Mike Dagostino
VP: Forrest Jordan
VP: Grey C Perna
**Mktg Mgr:* Ken Baker

D-U-N-S 16-199-6624 IMP/EXP
■ **INTERNATIONAL WINE & SPIRITS LTD**
(*Suby of* UST LLC) ★
14111 Ne 145th St, Woodinville, WA 98072-6981
Tel (425) 488-1133 *Founded/Ownrshp* 2009
Sales 72.9MM^E *EMP* 950
SIC 2084 Wines; Wines
Pr: Theodor P Baseler
**Ch Bd:* Vincent Gierer
**Treas:* Kenneth Hopson
**Sr VP:* Douglas N Gore
**Sr VP:* Shila A Newlands
**Sr VP:* Glen D Yaffa
VP: Peter Bachman
VP: John Baker
VP: Steve Burns
VP: Patrick Hurrie
VP: Keith Love

D-U-N-S 06-712-4909 IMP
INTERNATIONAL WINES INC (AL)
301 Snow Dr, Birmingham, AL 35209-6340
Tel (205) 945-7101 *Founded/Ownrshp* 1974
Sales 48.0MM^E *EMP* 78
SIC 5182 Wine; Wine
Pr: Charles W Yeates
**Pr:* Brian Herr
**Pr:* Seth W Poole
**VP:* Dwayne Stansell
IT Man: Dewayne Stansell
Sls Mgr: Jeff Carter
Sls Mgr: Todd Edmondson

INTERNATIONAL WIRE GROUP
See CAMDEN WIRE CO INC

D-U-N-S 05-491-0935
INTERNATIONAL WIRE GROUP
12 Masonic Ave, Camden, NY 13316-1202
Tel (315) 245-3800 *Founded/Ownrshp* 2011
Sales 313.6MM^E *EMP* 1,615^E
SIC 3351 Wire, copper & copper alloy; Wire, copper & copper alloy
CEO: Rodney Kent
**CFO:* Donald Dekay

D-U-N-S 88-349-8446 IMP
INTERNATIONAL WIRE GROUP INC
BARE WIRE DIVISION
(*Suby of* INTERNATIONAL WIRE GROUP) ★
12 Masonic Ave, Camden, NY 13316-1202
Tel (315) 245-2000 *Founded/Ownrshp* 2004
Sales 284.3MM^E *EMP* 1,600
SIC 3357 Nonferrous wiredrawing & insulating; Nonferrous wiredrawing & insulating
Ch Bd: Rodney D Kent
V Ch: William L Pennington
COO: Edwin Flynn
**CFO:* Glenn J Holler
**VP:* Geoff Kent
VP: Charles Lovenguth
VP: James Mills
IT Man: Zbig Crula
Sfty Mgr: Joe Biondi
Sls Mgr: Pete Hawkes

INTERNATIONAL WOOD PRODUCTS
See INTERNATIONAL BUILDING MATERIALS LLC

INTERNATIONAL YOGURT COMPANY
See YOCREAM INTERNATIONAL INC

D-U-N-S 62-084-7210
INTERNATIONAL YOUTH FOUNDATION
32 South St Ste 500, Baltimore, MD 21202-7503
Tel (410) 951-1500 *Founded/Ownrshp* 2004
Sales 26.6MM *EMP* 70
Accts Mcgladrey & Pullen Llp Gaith
SIC 8641 Youth organizations; Youth organizations
Pr: William S Reese
**Ch Bd:* Douglas Becker
**CFO:* Samantha Barbee
Ofcr: Ruben Acosta
Ofcr: Afnan Mahmoud
Creative D: Gillian McCallion
Dir Bus: Awais Sufi
Prgrm Mgr: Jessica Elisberg
Prgrm Mgr: Jennifer Hills
Prgrm Mgr: Bassem Nasir
Prgrm Mgr: Hafez Neeno

D-U-N-S 01-038-5979
■ **INTERNATIONAL-MATEX TANK TERMINALS**
IMTT
(*Suby of* MACQUARIE INFRASTRUCTURE CORP) ★
321 Saint Charles Ave, New Orleans, LA 70130-3145
Tel (504) 586-8300 *Founded/Ownrshp* 2014
Sales 234.5MM^E *EMP* 1,000
SIC 4226 1799 Petroleum & chemical bulk stations & terminals for hire; Petroleum storage tank installation, underground; Petroleum storage tanks, pumping & draining; Dock equipment installation, industrial; Petroleum & chemical bulk stations & terminals for hire; Petroleum storage tank installation, underground; Petroleum storage tanks, pumping & draining; Dock equipment installation, industrial
Pr: Richard D Courtney
CFO: James May
VP: James E Miles III
VP: Jim Papernik
Admn Mgr: Rhonda Yelverton
IT Man: Sandra Demartini
Opers Mgr: Michael Crampton
Plnt Mgr: John Little

INTERNATIONALFULFILLMENT.COM
See INTERNATIONAL FULFILLMENT SOLUTIONS LLC

D-U-N-S 95-838-8308
INTERNET AUTO RENT & SALES INC
1220 Kietzke Ln, Reno, NV 89502-2749
Tel (775) 824-6060 *Founded/Ownrshp* 1996
Sales 27.9MM^E *EMP* 70^E
SIC 5521 7514 Automobiles, used cars only; Passenger car rental
Pr: John C Stephens
Sls Mgr: Rick Aguilar

D-U-N-S 01-055-3035
INTERNET BOOKING AGENCY.COM INC
SANTA FOR HIRE.COM
232 Via Eboli, Newport Beach, CA 92663-4604
Tel (949) 673-7707 *Founded/Ownrshp* 2000
Sales 17.8MM^E *EMP* 500
SIC 7361 7922 Employment agencies; Theatrical producers & services; Employment agencies; Theatrical producers & services
CEO: Robert Mindte
**COO:* Felicia Mindte
Opers Mgr: Donna Camp

D-U-N-S 04-441-8221 IMP
INTERNET BRANDS INC
909 N Sepulveda Blvd # 11, El Segundo, CA 90245-2727
Tel (310) 280-4000 *Founded/Ownrshp* 2014
Sales 218.6MM^E *EMP* 649^E
SIC 7374 Computer graphics service; Advertising, promotional & trade show services; Computer graphics service
CEO: Robert N Brisco
Pr: Gregory T Perrier
COO: Lisa Morita
COO: Lisa Vila
CFO: Scott Friedman
Chf Mktg O: Chuck Hoover
Ex VP: Eugene Schutt
Ex VP: B Lynn Walsh
Sr VP: Mark Miller
VP: Chris Braun
VP: Marcia Galazzi
VP: Mark McCready
VP: Rod Stoddard
Dir Bus: Eric Wellner

D-U-N-S 01-804-0704
INTERNET BROADCASTING SYSTEMS INC
355 Randolph Ave, Saint Paul, MN 55102-3610
Tel (651) 365-4000 *Founded/Ownrshp* 1996
Sales 30.1MM^E *EMP* 133
SIC 7375 Information retrieval services; Information retrieval services
CEO: Elmer Baldwin
COO: Jeffrey Kimball
**CFO:* Steve Johansen
Ex VP: Harry Hawks
VP: Dave Abbott
VP: Ken Rees
**Dir Risk M:* Luke Edson
QA Dir: Shaana Lusti
Web Dev: Drew Diller
Opers Mgr: Carrie Davenport
S&M/VP: John Sailer

D-U-N-S 04-551-1487
INTERNET CORP FOR ASSIGNED NAMES AND NUMBERS
I C A NN
12025 Waterfront Dr # 300, Los Angeles, CA 90094-2536
Tel (310) 823-9358 *Founded/Ownrshp* 1998
Sales 127.8MM *EMP* 160^E
Accts Ernst & Young Us Llp San Dieg
SIC 7373 Systems software development services; Systems software development services
CEO: Fadi Chehad
**Pr:* Paul Twomey
**COO:* Akram Atallah
CFO: Kevin Wilson
Bd of Dir: Ram Mohan
VP: Nora Abusitta
VP: Rodrigo De La Parra
VP: Veni Markovski
VP: Christopher Mondini
VP: David Olive
VP: Maguy Serad
VP: Paul Verhoef
Exec: Gabriella Schittek

D-U-N-S 88-415-1890
INTERNET GLOBAL LLC
11951 Freedom Dr Ste 1300, Reston, VA 20190-5642
Tel (571) 267-7071 *Founded/Ownrshp* 2000
Sales 62.1MM^E *EMP* 600^E
SIC 4813 7375 ; Information retrieval services; ; Information retrieval services
Pt: David Browning
COO: Pedro Detresno
Genl Mgr: Clovis Lacerda
Genl Mgr: Joern Lubkoll

D-U-N-S 95-743-9946
INTERNET PIPELINE INC
IPIPELINE
222 Valley Creek Blvd # 300, Exton, PA 19341-2385
Tel (484) 348-6555 *Founded/Ownrshp* 2015
Sales 107.6MM^E *EMP* 413^E
SIC 7372 Prepackaged software; Prepackaged software
CEO: Timothy Wallace
Pr: James Adamek
Pr: Paul Melchiorre
COO: Lawrence Berran
CFO: Larry Berran
CFO: Brian Seidman
Chf Mktg O: Michael Persiano
Ex VP: Kevin Kemmerer
Ex VP: Dan Smith
Ex VP: Daphne Thomas
VP: Roy Goodart

D-U-N-S 92-928-3547
INTERNET SECURITIES INC
ISI EMERGING MARKETS
(*Suby of* EUROMONEY INSTITUTIONAL INVESTOR PLC)
225 Park Ave S Fl 6, New York, NY 10003-1604
Tel (212) 610-2900 *Founded/Ownrshp* 1999
Sales 28.9MM^E *EMP* 240^E
SIC 7389 Financial services; Financial services
Ch: Gary Mueller
**CEO:* Brian De Lacy
CFO: Alfredo Canta
Bd of Dir: Joseph J Bellace
Bd of Dir: Kevin Breard
Ex VP: Samantha Manke
VP: Juan Amaya
VP: Sheena Amin
**VP:* Bogandra Helio
Exec: Carl Blake
Exec: ISI Mark Lambley
Exec: Idil Ozkan
Exec: Agnieszka Piwowarczyk
Exec: ISI Katrina Topham
Dir Bus: Douglas Grant

D-U-N-S 83-731-9656
■ **INTERNET SECURITY SYSTEMS INC**
I S S
(*Suby of* IBM) ★
6303 Barfield Rd, Atlanta, GA 30328-4233
Tel (404) 236-2600 *Founded/Ownrshp* 1997
Sales 54.4MM^E *EMP* 800
SIC 7371 Computer software systems analysis & design, custom; Computer software systems analysis & design, custom
CEO: Brian Truskowski
Pr: Helen Berg
**Pr:* Thomas E Noonan
**CFO:* Richard Macchia
VP: Lawrence A Constanza
**CTO:* Christopher W Klaus
Sls Dir: Anita Bailey
Sls Mgr: Yann Lereverend

D-U-N-S 03-362-0626 IMP
INTERNET SERVICES CORP (NC)
1300 Altura Rd, Fort Mill, SC 29708-7055
Tel (803) 547-9100 *Founded/Ownrshp* 1987
Sales 45.4MM^E *EMP* 150^E
SIC 5192 5065 3695 Books; Cassettes, recording; Magnetic & optical recording media; Books; Cassettes, recording; Magnetic & optical recording media
Pr: Jeff S Yager
CFO: Tom Emery
**VP:* Steven T Yager

D-U-N-S 03-981-8120
INTERNET SOCIETY
1775 Wiehle Ave Ste 200, Reston, VA 20190-5158
Tel (703) 439-2120 *Founded/Ownrshp* 1992
Sales 45.6MM *EMP* 88^E
SIC 7373 Computer integrated systems design
CEO: Lynn St Amour
COO: Leonard Kleinrock
**CFO:* Gregory M Kapfer
Top Exec: Ahmed Al Balooshi
VP: Huang Chengqing
VP: Raul Echeberria
VP: Gao Xinmin
Snr Mgr: Olaf Kolkman
Snr Mgr: Gregg Lechner
Snr Mgr: Amelia Yeo

D-U-N-S 01-518-4708
INTERNET UNIVERSITY INC
IMC2 SQUARED
12404 Park Central Dr # 400, Dallas, TX 75251-1800
Tel (214) 224-1000 *Founded/Ownrshp* 1995
Sales 12.4MM^E *EMP* 335
Accts Philip Vogel & Co Pc Dallas
SIC 7311 Advertising agencies; Advertising agencies
Pr: Doug Levy
**Chf Cred:* Michael J Davis
Sr VP: Darrell Carpenter
Sr VP: Urvashi Pitre
**VP:* Marc Blumberg
VP: Bryan Bradley
IT Man: Andrew Tuffnell

D-U-N-S 17-514-6836
INTERNEWS NETWORK
876 7th St, Arcata, CA 95521-6358
Tel (707) 826-2030 *Founded/Ownrshp* 1982
Sales 26.3MM^E *EMP* 450
Accts Gelman Rosenberg & Freedman
SIC 7812 7922 Television film production; Entertainment promotion; Television film production; Entertainment promotion
CEO: Jeanne Bourgault
**Pr:* David Hoffman
**COO:* David Creekmore
Ofcr: Sheden Alsaaty
**VP:* Erica Feldkamp
Dir IT: Ray Nelson
Software D: Richard Golebiowski

INTERNTIONAL TRNSP SPECIALISTS
See TSL CO HOLDINGS LTD

INTERNTNAL ACADEMY DESIGN TECH
See INTERNATIONAL ACADEMY OF MERCHANDISING & DESIGN LTD

INTERNTNAL PROCESS PLANTS-IPPE
See INTERNATIONAL PROCESSPLANTS AND EQUIPMENT CORP

INTERNTNAL PROTECTIVE SEC AGCY
See INTERNATIONAL PROTECTION GROUP LLC

INTERNTNAL QLTY PRDCTIVITY CTR
See PENTON LEARNING SYSTEMS LLC

INTERNTNAL RHBLTTION ASSOC INC
See CIGNA HEALTH MANAGEMENT INC

INTERNTNAL WRLDWIDE INVSTMENTS
See TREMAYNE ANTONIO WILLIAMS GLOBAL ESTATE ENTRUSTTRUST

INTERNTNL AUTOMOTVE COMPONENTS
See I A C SPRINGFIELD LLC

INTERNTNL-MATEX TANK TERMINALS
See INTERNATIONAL TANK TERMINALS LLC

INTERNTONAL CHURCH RELIEF FUND
See CHILDRENS HUNGER RELIEF FUND

D-U-N-S 12-259-7300
■ **INTERO REAL ESTATE SERVICES INC**
(*Suby of* HOMESERVICES OF AMERICA INC) ★
10275 N De Anza Blvd, Cupertino, CA 95014-2045
Tel (408) 342-3000 *Founded/Ownrshp* 2014
Sales 46.6MM^E *EMP* 305
SIC 6531 Real estate brokers & agents; Real estate brokers & agents
Co-CEO: Robert Moles
**COO:* Tom Tognoli
CFO: Stuart Blomgren
**Co-CEO:* Gino Blefari
**VP:* John Thompson
Mktg Dir: Susie Mize

D-U-N-S 80-808-7196
INTERO SOCAL PARTNERS LLC
12526 High Bluff Dr # 190, San Diego, CA 92130-2064
Tel (408) 828-0859 *Founded/Ownrshp* 2007
Sales 48.0MM *EMP* 1
SIC 8742 Real estate consultant; Real estate consultant

D-U-N-S 19-089-4761
INTEROP TECHNOLOGIES LLC
13500 Powers Ct, Fort Myers, FL 33912-4503
Tel (239) 425-6845 *Founded/Ownrshp* 2002
Sales 29.9MM^E *EMP* 105
SIC 4812 Cellular telephone services
Pr: John Dwyer
CFO: Patricia M Heath
Bd of Dir: Nancy Dwyer
VP: John Bickford
VP: Eddie Decurtis
VP: Jim Dwyer III
VP: Fred Farrell
VP: Damian Sazama
VP: Donn Wilkins
VP: Stephen J Zitnik
Prin: Margaret M Peggy Dwyer
Board of Directors: Brian Rich, Fred Tannenbaum

D-U-N-S 07-838-3128
INTEROUTE USA INC
(*Suby of* INTEROUTE COMMUNICATIONS LIMITED)
661 S Fitch Mountain Rd, Healdsburg, CA 95448-4647
Tel (707) 395-0918 *Founded/Ownrshp* 2001
Sales 50.2MM^E *EMP* 8
SIC 4822 Radio telephone communication; ; Data communication services; ; Telegraph & other communications
CEO: Robert McNeal

D-U-N-S 18-055-7811
INTERPACIFIC GROUP INC
576 Beale St, San Francisco, CA 94105-2019
Tel (415) 442-0711 *Founded/Ownrshp* 1986
Sales 48.3MM^E *EMP* 1,306
SIC 8721 Accounting, auditing & bookkeeping; Accounting, auditing & bookkeeping
Pr: Dave Smith

INTERPAK
See INTERNATIONAL PACKAGING CORP

D-U-N-S 06-193-1189
INTERPARK HOLDINGS LLC
(*Suby of* ALINDA CAPITAL PARTNERS LLC) ★
200 N Lasalle St Ste 1400, Chicago, IL 60601
Tel (312) 935-2900 *Founded/Ownrshp* 2011
Sales 56.5MM^E *EMP* 800
SIC 7521 Automobile parking; Automobile parking
Pr: J Marshall Peck
**COO:* Douglas I Poirier
CFO: Steve Beauchamp
**CFO:* Andrew Runge
**Sr VP:* Andrew R McLaughlin
**Sr VP:* Charles J Murphy
**VP:* Charles Murphy
Dir IT: Dave Nelson

D-U-N-S 96-518-7466
INTERPARK LLC
200 N La Salle St # 1400, Chicago, IL 60601-1035
Tel (312) 935-2800 *Founded/Ownrshp* 2011
Sales 63.3MM^E *EMP* 850^E
SIC 7521 Automobile parking; Automobile parking
CFO: Andrew Runge
Sr VP: Charles Murphy
VP: Andy McLaughlin
**IT Man:* John Casper
IT Man: Raj Gupta
Web Dev: Husain Raj
Opers Mgr: Ali Azhar
Opers Mgr: Olubunmi Omitoyin

D-U-N-S 03-714-6495 IMP
▲ **INTERPHARM HOLDINGS INC**
AMNEAL PHARMACEUTICALS
75 Adams Ave, Hauppauge, NY 11788-3605
Tel (631) 231-6021 *Founded/Ownrshp* 1992
Sales 126.5MM^E *EMP* 670^E
Tkr Sym IPAH *Exch* OTO
SIC 2834 Drugs affecting neoplasms & endrocrine systems; Drugs affecting neoplasms & endrocrine systems
CEO: Chintu Patel
**Ch Bd:* Maganlal K Sutaria
Pr: Jim Luce
**COO:* Raj Sutaria
**CFO:* Rochelle Fuhrmann
**CFO:* Peter Giallorenzo
Treas: Jyoti Sutaria
**Ex VP:* Kenneth Cappel
**Ex VP:* Dr Shankar Hariharan
**Ex VP:* Jim Luc
VP: Anil Chhettry
VP: Candis Edwards
VP: Robert Loewenstein
VP: David Miller
VP: Mark Patrichuk

Board of Directors: Stewart Benjamin, Kennith Johnson, Joan P Neuscheler, David Reback, Richard J Miller Perry Sut

D-U-N-S 00-615-1336 IMP
INTERPLASTIC CORP (MN)
MOLDING PRODUCTS
1225 Willow Lake Blvd, Saint Paul, MN 55110-5145
Tel (651) 481-6860 *Founded/Ownrshp* 1962
Sales 616.0MM^E *EMP* 500
SIC 5169 2821 Synthetic resins, rubber & plastic materials; Polyesters; Vinyl resins; Molding compounds, plastics; Synthetic resins, rubber & plastic materials; Polyesters; Vinyl resins; Molding compounds, plastics
CEO: James D Wallenfelsz
**CFO:* Steven Dittel
**Treas:* David Engelsgaard
**VP:* Robert De Roma
**VP:* Ivan Levy
Sfty Mgr: Tracy Baysinger
Plnt Mgr: Dave Rixen
Prd Mgr: Cory Hoang
Ql Cn Mgr: Kevin Gildea
Ql Cn Mgr: Robert Krajewski

D-U-N-S 14-413-0259 IMP
INTERPLEX INDUSTRIES INC
(*Suby of* INTERPLEX HOLDINGS LTD.)
1434 110th St Ste 301, College Point, NY 11356-1448
Tel (718) 961-6212 *Founded/Ownrshp* 2014
Sales 135.9MM^E *EMP* 10^E
SIC 3471 3825 3674 3469 Electroplating of metals or formed products; Instruments to measure electricity; Semiconductor circuit networks; Stamping metal for the trade; Electroplating of metals or formed products; Instruments to measure electricity; Semiconductor circuit networks; Stamping metal for the trade
Ch Bd: Jack Seidler
Pr: Sanjiv Chhahira
**CFO:* Belinda Lin Zijun
Opers Mgr: Peter Salvas

D-U-N-S 03-785-4148 IMP
INTERPLEX PLASTICS INC
(*Suby of* INTERPLEX INDUSTRIES INC) ★
1086 Brentwood Ct, Lexington, KY 40511-1233
Tel (859) 231-6100 *Founded/Ownrshp* 1985
Sales 26.2MM^E *EMP* 65
SIC 3089 Injection molding of plastics
Plnt Mgr: Scott Rankin
Ql Cn Mgr: Bob McGohon
Board of Directors: Jack Seidler

INTERPOINT
See CRANE ELECTRONICS INC

D-U-N-S 61-466-9430
■ **INTERPOOL INC**
TRAC INTERMODAL
(*Suby of* SEACASTLE CONTAINER LEASING) ★
50 College Rd E, Princeton, NJ 08540-6614
Tel (609) 452-8900 *Founded/Ownrshp* 2007
Sales 80.8MM^E *EMP* 285
SIC 7359 Home cleaning & maintenance equipment rental services; Equipment rental & leasing
CEO: Keith Lovetro
Pr: Sheldon Landy
CFO: Chris Annese
Sr VP: Inbal ARI
Sr VP: Val Noel
Sr VP: Carl Rodriguez
VP: Joseph Kozinski
VP: Blake Morris
VP: Barbara Pentell
VP: Alan Schmid
VP: Todd J Steiner
Board of Directors: Chris Annese, Gregg Carpene, Keith Lovetro

D-U-N-S 16-674-7233 IMP/EXP
INTERPORT LOGISTICS CORP
INTERPORT SERVICES
12950 Nw 25th St Ste 100, Miami, FL 33182-1515
Tel (305) 477-1910 *Founded/Ownrshp* 2003
Sales 35.1MM^E *EMP* 70
SIC 4731 Freight forwarding
Pr: Alberto J Marino Sr
**Treas:* Ivette C Marino
**VP:* Jorge R De Tuya
**VP:* Jose De Vivero
Dir Bus: Avelino Garcia
Mng Dir: Stephen Daal
VP Opers: Anamaria Reyes
Snr Mgr: Gary Goldfarb

INTERPORT SERVICES
See INTERPORT LOGISTICS CORP

D-U-N-S 04-002-4457 IMP
INTERPOWER CORP
100 Interpower Ave, Oskaloosa, IA 52577-1864
Tel (641) 673-5000 *Founded/Ownrshp* 1975
Sales 28.3MM^E *EMP* 70
SIC 5063 3643 3678 3677 3613 3357 Electrical apparatus & equipment; Current-carrying wiring devices; Electronic connectors; Electronic coils, transformers & other inductors; Switchgear & switchboard apparatus; Nonferrous wiredrawing & insulating
Pr: Robert D Wersen
**CFO:* David Krutzfeldt
Sr VP: Amy Sarver
QA Dir: Rob Taylor
Manager: Michelle Cooper

D-U-N-S 13-162-5691 IMP/EXP
INTERPRESS TECHNOLOGIES INC
(*Suby of* CONCEPT) ★
1120 Del Paso Rd, Sacramento, CA 95834-7737
Tel (916) 929-9771 *Founded/Ownrshp* 1988
Sales 25.0MM *EMP* 65
SIC 2631 Folding boxboard; Folding boxboard
Pr: Roderick W Miner
Pr: Peter Fox
Genl Mgr: Dave Worley
Off Mgr: Connie Worley
IT Man: John Allison

Prd Mgr: Shawn Scherer
Sls Mgr: Brian Smith

INTERPUBLIC GROUP OF CO
See GEOMENTUM INC

INTERPUBLIC GROUP OF COMPANIES
See DAILEY & ASSOCIATES

INTERPUBLIC GROUP OF COMPANIES
See JACK MORTON WORLDWIDE INC

D-U-N-S 00-698-5790
▲ **INTERPUBLIC GROUP OF COMPANIES INC**
1114 Avenue Of The Americ, New York, NY 10036-7703
Tel (212) 704-1200 *Founded/Ownrshp* 1902
Sales 7.5MMM *EMP* 47,400
Accts Pricewaterhousecoopers Llp Ne
Tkr Sym IPG *Exch* NYS
SIC 7311 8742 Advertising agencies; Advertising agencies; Marketing consulting services
Ch Bd: Michael I Roth
CEO: Sean Finnegan
CFO: Frank Mergenthaler
Bd of Dir: John Greeniaus
Chf Mktg O: Tony Bombacino
Ex VP: Richard Doomany
Ex VP: Philippe Krakowsky
Ex VP: David Rosenberg
Ex VP: Timothy Sompolsky
Sr VP: Andrew Bonzani
Sr VP: Christopher F Carroll
Sr VP: Christopher Carroll
Sr VP: Julie M Connors
Sr VP: John Halper
Sr VP: Peter Leinroth
Sr VP: Terry D Peigh
VP: Kobzev Anaka
VP: David J Weiss
Board of Directors: Deborah G Ellinger, H John Greeniaus, Mary J Steele Guilfoile, Dawn Hudson, William T Kerr, Henry S Miller, Jocelyn Carter-Miller, Jonathan F Miller, David M Thomas

INTERPUBLIC GRP OF COMPANIES
See R/GA MEDIA GROUP INC

D-U-N-S 08-457-9333
INTERRA CREDIT UNION
300 W Lincoln Ave, Goshen, IN 46526-3221
Tel (574) 534-2506 *Founded/Ownrshp* 1932
Sales NA *EMP* 160
SIC 6062 State credit unions, not federally chartered; State credit unions, not federally chartered
Pr: Jack Sheets
**Ch Bd:* Steve Warner
Treas: Martha Packer
Ofcr: Shannon Schrock
**VP:* Andrew Gangwer
**VP:* Sanford Miller
Brnch Mgr: Liz Borntrager
Brnch Mgr: Curtis Meyer
Genl Mgr: Tane Reed
CIO: Sherry Wenger
CTO: Sanford Allendach

D-U-N-S 96-278-0669 IMP
INTERRA FOOD MARKETING LLC
(*Suby of* INTERRA INTERNATIONAL LLC) ★
400 Interstate N Pkwy Ste, Atlanta, GA 30339-5017
Tel (770) 612-8101 *Founded/Ownrshp* 2009
Sales 26.2MM^E *EMP* 45
SIC 5144 5147 Poultry & poultry products; Meats & meat products
CEO: Steve T Isaf
VP: Melvin Maddux

D-U-N-S 12-580-7094 IMP/EXP
INTERRA GROUP INC
INTERA INTERNATIONAL
400 Interstate N Pkwy Ste, Atlanta, GA 30339-5017
Tel (770) 612-8101 *Founded/Ownrshp* 2000
Sales 106.7MM^E *EMP* 130
SIC 5141 6719 Food brokers; Investment holding companies, except banks
CEO: Stephen T Isaf
Ex VP: Michael Crump
VP: John Donofrio
VP: Bill Green
VP: Claudia Membreno
Rgnl Mgr: Eric Tietz
Sls Mgr: Scott Rothenberg

D-U-N-S 08-008-6451
INTERRA INTERNATIONAL LLC
(*Suby of* INTERA INTERNATIONAL) ★
400 Interstate N Pkwy Ste, Atlanta, GA 30339-5017
Tel (770) 612-8101 *Founded/Ownrshp* 2015
Sales 26.2MM^E *EMP* 130
SIC 5144 5147 5141 Poultry & poultry products; Meats & meat products; Food brokers
CEO: Stephen Isaf
VP: Claudia Membreno

D-U-N-S 01-560-3967
INTERRA SYSTEMS INC (CA)
1601 S De Anza Blvd # 212, Cupertino, CA 95014-5358
Tel (408) 579-2000 *Founded/Ownrshp* 2000
Sales 27.2MM^E *EMP* 150
SIC 7371 Computer software systems analysis & design, custom; Computer software systems analysis & design, custom
Pr: Sunil K Jain
CFO: Mark Brown
VP: Ashish Basu
VP: Krishna Uppuluri
Off Mgr: Michelle Gamboa
Prd Dir: Reena Misra
Mktg Dir: Anne Hohenberger
Sls Dir: Juanchy Mejia

D-U-N-S 04-585-6143 IMP
INTERROLL CORP
(*Suby of* INTERROLL HOLDING AG)
3000 Corporate Dr, Wilmington, NC 28405-7422
Tel (910) 799-1100 *Founded/Ownrshp* 2002
Sales 48.0MM^E *EMP* 110
SIC 3535 Conveyors & conveying equipment; Conveyors & conveying equipment

CEO: Paul Zumbuhl
S&M/VP: John Davis
Manager: Gary Essex
Manager: Steven Leong
Sales Asso: Samantha Byam

D-U-N-S 00-521-2642 IMP
INTERROLL ENGINEERING WEST INC (DE)
1 Forge Rd, Canon City, CO 81212-9671
Tel (719) 276-3750 *Founded/Ownrshp* 1928, 2013
Sales 22.4MM^E *EMP* 100^E
SIC 3535 Conveyors & conveying equipment; Belt conveyor systems, general industrial use; Passenger baggage belt loaders; Bulk handling conveyor systems; Conveyors & conveying equipment; Belt conveyor systems, general industrial use; Passenger baggage belt loaders; Bulk handling conveyor systems
Pr: Marco Oropeza
Exec: Dick Watkins
**VP Opers:* Mark Means

D-U-N-S 87-671-5355
INTERSECT ENT INC
1555 Adams Dr, Menlo Park, CA 94025-1439
Tel (650) 641-2100 *Founded/Ownrshp* 2003
Sales 38.5MM *EMP* 212
Tkr Sym XENT *Exch* NGM
SIC 3841 Surgical & medical instruments; Surgical & medical instruments
Pr: Lisa D Earnhardt
COO: Richard E Kaufman
CFO: Monika De Martini
CFO: Jeryl L Hilleman
Chf Cred: Charles S McKhann
VP: James Stambaugh
VP: Jim Stambaugh
VP: Amy C Wolbeck
Snr PM: Travis Rappleye
Board of Directors: Kieran T Gallahue, Cynthia L Lucchese, Dana G Mead Jr, Frederic H Moll, Casey M Tansey, W Anthony Vernon

D-U-N-S 94-250-0286
INTERSECT GROUP LLC
10 Glenlake Pkwy Ste 300s, Atlanta, GA 30328-3495
Tel (770) 500-3636 *Founded/Ownrshp* 2007
Sales 57.4MM^E *EMP* 270^E
SIC 8742 Management consulting services; Management consulting services
CEO: Rebecca Rogers Tijerino
Mng Pt: Wade Hughes
Mng Pt: Scott Meyerhoff
CFO: Mike Snyder
VP: Shaw Drummond
Exec: Don Zuhlke
Dir Bus: Greg Malever
Mktg Mgr: Lisa Beasley

D-U-N-S 12-772-0899
INTERSECTION MEDIA HOLDINGS INC
100 Park Ave Ste 610, New York, NY 10017-5560
Tel (212) 644-6200 *Founded/Ownrshp* 2003
Sales 152.3MM^E *EMP* 375
SIC 7312 Outdoor advertising services; Billboard advertising; Outdoor advertising services; Billboard advertising
CEO: Donald Allman
**Pr:* Scott Goldsmith
**CFO:* Craig Abolt
Ex VP: Jamie Lowe
Sr VP: David Etherington
Sr VP: Heather McGuire
Prgrm Mgr: Svetlana Shafirovich
IT Man: Cindy McNally
Netwrk Eng: Gregory Neilson

D-U-N-S 00-787-4170
INTERSECTION MEDIA LLC
(*Suby of* INTERSECTION MEDIA HOLDINGS INC) ★
100 Park Ave Ste 610, New York, NY 10017-5560
Tel (212) 644-6200 *Founded/Ownrshp* 1999
Sales 53.4MM^E *EMP* 374
SIC 7312 Outdoor advertising services; Billboard advertising; Outdoor advertising services; Billboard advertising
CEO: Donald R Allman
Pr: Ken Cozales
**CFO:* Craig Albolt
**Chf Cred:* Scott Goldsmith
Ex VP: Craig Abolt
Ex VP: Dave Etherington
Ex VP: Jamie Lowe
Sr VP: Mary Hamilton
Sr VP: Steven Hillwig
Sr VP: Heather McGuire
Sr VP: Miko Rahming
VP: Scott Christensen
VP: Mark Graham
VP: Margit Kittridge

D-U-N-S 09-414-2846
▲ **INTERSECTIONS INC**
3901 Stonecroft Blvd, Chantilly, VA 20151-1032
Tel (703) 488-6100 *Founded/Ownrshp* 1996
Sales 246.6MM *EMP* 478
Tkr Sym INTX *Exch* NGM
SIC 7323 Credit bureau & agency; Credit bureau & agency
Ch Bd: Michael R Stanfield
COO: Johan Roets
CFO: Ronald L Barden
Ex VP: Neal B Dittersdorf
Ex VP: John Scanlon
Sr VP: Joe Mason
VP: Mark Andringa
VP: Gregory Gannon
VP: Gillian Osborne
VP: Tracy M Ward
Creative D: Taruna Bajaj
Board of Directors: John M Albertine, Thomas G Amato, Steve Bartlett, James L Kempner, Thomas L Kempner, Bruce L Lev, John H Lewis, David A McGough

D-U-N-S 94-539-2137
■ **INTERSECTIONS INSURANCE SERVICES INC**
(*Suby of* INTERSECTIONS INC) ★
315 W University Dr, Arlington Heights, IL 60004-1811
Tel (847) 797-8500 *Founded/Ownrshp* 2007
Sales NA *EMP* 1^E
SIC 6411 Insurance agents, brokers & service
Pr: Michael Stanfield

INTERSHIP
See INTERNATIONAL SHIPPING AGENCY INC

D-U-N-S 19-482-0007
INTERSIGN CORP
2156 Amnicola Hwy, Chattanooga, TN 37406-3721
Tel (423) 698-3085 *Founded/Ownrshp* 1987
Sales 20.4MM^E *EMP* 102
SIC 3993 Signs, not made in custom sign painting shops
Pr: Hank Mc Mahon
**COO:* Jim Roides
Natl Sales: Crystal Simpson

D-U-N-S 08-028-3083 IMP/EXP
■ **INTERSIL COMMUNICATIONS LLC**
(*Suby of* INTERSIL CORP) ★
1001 Murphy Ranch Rd, Milpitas, CA 95035-7912
Tel (408) 432-8888 *Founded/Ownrshp* 1999
Sales 126.2MM^E *EMP* 1,017
SIC 3674 Semiconductors & related devices; Semiconductors & related devices
Pr: Necip Sayiner
**CFO:* Rick Crowley
Treas: Lisi John
**Sr VP:* Andrew Cowell
Sr VP: David Loftus
Sr VP: Andy Micallef
**Sr VP:* Thomas C Tokos
VP: Carlos Garcia
DP Dir: Tim Lok
Dir IT: Terry Brophy
IT Man: Sue Brazelton

D-U-N-S 12-485-1549 IMP
▲ **INTERSIL CORP**
1001 Murphy Ranch Rd, Milpitas, CA 95035-7912
Tel (408) 432-8888 *Founded/Ownrshp* 1999
Sales 562.5MM *EMP* 1,017^E
Tkr Sym ISIL *Exch* NGS
SIC 3674 3679 Semiconductors & related devices; Integrated circuits, semiconductor networks, etc.; Electronic circuits; Semiconductors & related devices; Integrated circuits, semiconductor networks, etc.; Electronic circuits
Ch Bd: Donald Macleod
Pr: Necip Sayiner
CFO: Richard Crowley
CFO: Minh Nguyen
Bd of Dir: Malcolm Cambra
Ex VP: Louis Dinardo
VP: Andrew Hughes
Ex Dir: Ken Dyer
Area Mgr: Wyatt Foard
Area Mgr: Pat Higgins
Area Mgr: Paolo Scarpa

D-U-N-S 01-305-1784
INTERSTATE + LAKELAND LUMBER CORP
247 Mill St, Greenwich, CT 06830-5806
Tel (203) 531-8885 *Founded/Ownrshp* 1944
Sales 28.9MM^E *EMP* 130
Accts Rebecca Fishkin
SIC 5211 5031 Lumber & other building materials; Millwork & lumber; Cabinets, kitchen; Millwork; Lumber: rough, dressed & finished; Kitchen cabinets; Lumber & other building materials; Millwork & lumber; Cabinets, kitchen; Millwork; Lumber: rough, dressed & finished; Kitchen cabinets
CEO: Sheldon Kahan
**Pr:* Jack Kahan
**CFO:* Gary Schneldmen
**VP:* Herb Kahan
**VP:* Susan Kahan Sieber

INTERSTATE ALL BATTERY CENTER
See RETAIL ACQUISITION & DEVELOPMENT INC

INTERSTATE AUTO BODY PARTS
See CERTIFIT INC

D-U-N-S 94-264-0749
INTERSTATE AUTO GROUP INC
CARHOP AUTO SALES AND FINANCE
10801 Red Circle Dr, Minnetonka, MN 55343-9135
Tel (800) 662-2746 *Founded/Ownrshp* 1995
Sales 31.4MM^E *EMP* 100
SIC 5521 Automobiles, used cars only
CEO: Eric Fosse
**Pr:* Tim Ehde
**CEO:* Donald Griffin

D-U-N-S 07-883-8762 IMP/EXP
INTERSTATE BATTERIES INC
(*Suby of* INTERSTATE BATTERY SYSTEM INTERNATIONAL INC) ★
12770 Merit Dr Ste 1000, Dallas, TX 75251-1245
Tel (972) 991-1444 *Founded/Ownrshp* 2013
Sales 150.3MM^E *EMP* 727^E
SIC 5531 Batteries, automotive & truck; Battery charging alternators & generators
Ch: Norm Miller
**Pr:* Scott Miller
VP: Karen Brown
VP: Wendell Samuel
VP: Michael Tapp
Exec: Larry Larsh
Rgnl Mgr: Scott Moore
**Genl Mgr:* Dale Herold
**Genl Mgr:* Walt Holmes
**Genl Mgr:* Tyler Reeves
Pr Mgr: Carrie Clark

D-U-N-S 96-552-6197 IMP
INTERSTATE BATTERY SYSTEM INTERNATIONAL INC
12770 Merit Dr Ste 1000, Dallas, TX 75251-1245
Tel (972) 991-1444 *Founded/Ownrshp* 1991
Sales 454.5MM^E *EMP* 1,350

SIC 5013 Automotive batteries; Automotive batteries
VP: Jeff Haddock
COO: Kevin Clinkscales
VP: Chris Antoniou
VP: Adam Colley
VP: Grant Dismore
VP: Mickey Elam
VP: Patrick Fletcher
VP: Walt Holmes
VP: Walter Holmes
VP: Paul Kunz
VP: Scott Miller
VP: Billy Norris
VP: William Norris
VP: Steve Phelps
VP: Patsy Reid
VP: Heather Swanson
VP: Chris Willis

D-U-N-S 02-625-3922 IMP/EXP
INTERSTATE BATTERY SYSTEM OF AMERICA INC
12770 Merit Dr Ste 300, Dallas, TX 75251-1402
Tel (972) 991-1444 *Founded/Ownrshp* 1991
Sales NA *EMP* 455ᴱ
SIC 5013 Automotive batteries

D-U-N-S 80-584-8926
INTERSTATE BUILDING MAINTENANCE CORP
1720 Kendarbren Dr # 721, Jamison, PA 18929-1070
Tel (215) 675-8500 *Founded/Ownrshp* 1988
Sales 10.5MMᴱ *EMP* 300
SIC 7349 Building & office cleaning services; Building & office cleaning services
Pr: Robert Weller
Opers Mgr: Richard Pagotto

D-U-N-S 03-512-4155
INTERSTATE BUSINESS EQUIPMENT INC
MODERN BANKING SYSTEMS
7655 Burlington St, Omaha, NE 68127-3939
Tel (402) 592-5500 *Founded/Ownrshp* 1965
Sales 29.2MMᴱ *EMP* 85
SIC 5045 7371 7378 Computers; Computer software; Computer software systems analysis & design, custom; Computer maintenance & repair
Owner: Mike Crown
IT Man: Glenn Stenger
IT Man: Todd Thompson
Software D: Josh Stodola

D-U-N-S 79-651-4479
INTERSTATE CARRIER XPRESS INC
3820 Wisman Ln, Quincy, IL 62305-9550
Tel (217) 224-0770 *Founded/Ownrshp* 1992
Sales 34.5MMᴱ *EMP* 125
SIC 4213 Trucking, except local
Pr: William Gully
**Sec:* Barbara Gully
**VP:* Michael Gully

D-U-N-S 04-431-3443 IMP
INTERSTATE CHEMICAL CO INC
UNITED-ERIE DIVISION
2797 Freedland Rd, Hermitage, PA 16148-9099
Tel (724) 981-3771 *Founded/Ownrshp* 1968
Sales 396.6MMᴱ *EMP* 335
SIC 5169 2819 Chemicals & allied products; Industrial inorganic chemicals; Chemicals & allied products; Industrial inorganic chemicals
Pr: Albert R Puntureri
Ex VP: Paul R Cirillo
Ex VP: Lou Razzano
VP: Meg Grober
VP: Robert McLeod
**VP:* Joseph S Puntureri
VP Opers: Trey Soates
Trfc Dir: Scott Shoup
Plnt Mgr: Trey Coates
Plnt Mgr: Joseph Mikolic
Natl Sales: Jack Verigood

D-U-N-S 12-259-8279
INTERSTATE CLEANING CORP
1566 N Warson Rd, Saint Louis, MO 63132-1106
Tel (314) 428-0566 *Founded/Ownrshp* 1984
Sales 47.4MMᴱ *EMP* 1,300ᴱ
SIC 7349 Janitorial service, contract basis; Janitorial service, contract basis
Pr: John E Brauch Jr
**Ex VP:* Michael P Brauch
**Ex VP:* Philip R Gaudy

INTERSTATE CNNCTING COMPONENTS
See HEILINDMIL - AERO LLC

D-U-N-S 06-471-5279
INTERSTATE COLD STORAGE INC
4410 New Haven Ave, Fort Wayne, IN 46803-1650
Tel (260) 428-2505 *Founded/Ownrshp* 1969
Sales 25.8MMᴱ *EMP* 80
SIC 4222 Warehousing, cold storage or refrigerated
Pr: Vincent Tippmann
IT Man: Doug Chambers
IT Man: Sharon Short

D-U-N-S 00-498-2807
INTERSTATE COMMODITIES INC (NY)
7 Madison St, Troy, NY 12180-4929
Tel (518) 272-7212 *Founded/Ownrshp* 1947
Sales 84.9MMᴱ *EMP* 20ᴱ
SIC 5191 5153 Feed; Grains
Ch Bd: Greg Oberting
**Pr:* Victor A Oberting Jr
**Sec:* Lori Alessi
VP: Carlton Hyman
**VP:* Gary Oberting
**VP:* Victor Oberting III
**VP:* Michael Piazza
Div Mgr: Cameron Charles
Genl Mgr: Harry Gillette Jr
Plnt Mgr: Rick Marr

D-U-N-S 60-251-7229
INTERSTATE COMPANIES INC
ISTATE TRUCK
(*Suby of* GDG HOLDINGS INC) ★
2601 American Blvd E, Bloomington, MN 55425-1378
Tel (952) 854-2044 *Founded/Ownrshp* 1975
Sales 450.0MM *EMP* 60
SIC 7538 8711 5085 Management services; Administrative management; Air conditioning supply services; Diesel engine repair: automotive; Trucks, tractors & trailers: new & used; Diesel engine repair: automotive; Engineering services; Power transmission equipment & apparatus
Ch Bd: Gordon D Galarneau
**CEO:* Travis Penrod
**COO:* Jeff Caswell
**CFO:* Larry Schwartz
CFO: Larry Schwartz
**Ex VP:* Bob Woodward
**VP:* Carl Brown
**VP:* Russ Dreyer
VP: Keith Yingling
Brnch Mgr: Gary Berger
Brnch Mgr: Chad Johnson

D-U-N-S 03-395-4124
INTERSTATE CONCRETE AND ASPHALT CO
(*Suby of* CPM DEVELOPMENT CORP) ★
8849 W Wyoming Ave, Rathdrum, ID 83858-9578
Tel (208) 765-1144 *Founded/Ownrshp* 1986
Sales 20.2MMᴱ *EMP* 100
SIC 1611 3271 5211 2951 3273 1442 Highway & street paving contractor; Brick, concrete; Concrete & cinder block; Concrete, bituminous; Ready-mixed concrete; Construction sand & gravel; Highway & street paving contractor; Brick, concrete; Concrete & cinder block; Concrete, bituminous; Ready-mixed concrete; Construction sand & gravel
Pr: Jeff Schaffer
Sls Mgr: Dan Benson

D-U-N-S 14-840-5863 IMP
INTERSTATE CONNECTING COMPONENTS INC
I C C
(*Suby of* HEILIND ELECTRONICS INC) ★
120 Mount Holly Byp, Lumberton, NJ 08048
Tel (856) 722-5535 *Founded/Ownrshp* 2013
Sales 62.9MMᴱ *EMP* 93
SIC 5065 3678 Connectors, electronic; Electronic connectors; Connectors, electronic; Electronic connectors
Pr: Scott Jacobs
**Treas:* Miriam Jacobs
Pgrm Dir: Cheryl Gordon

D-U-N-S 13-840-2776
INTERSTATE CONSTRUCTION GROUP INC
I.C.G.
437 29th St Ne Ste F, Puyallup, WA 98372-6784
Tel (253) 435-0949 *Founded/Ownrshp* 2002
Sales 35.0MMᴱ *EMP* 3
SIC 1542 Commercial & office building contractors; Commercial & office building contractors
Pr: Larry Prescott
Ex VP: Bob Brazier
**VP:* Ken Lorenz
Off Mgr: Lisa Boyer

INTERSTATE CONTAINER CAMBRIDGE
See INTERSTATE CORRPACK LLC

D-U-N-S 05-611-4553 IMP
INTERSTATE CONTAINER COLUMBIA LLC
128 Crews Dr, Columbia, SC 29210-7202
Tel (803) 365-0240 *Founded/Ownrshp* 2011
Sales 36.2MMᴱ *EMP* 46ᴱ
SIC 5113 Boxes & containers
Prin: Jim Lee

D-U-N-S 01-909-4908
INTERSTATE CONTAINER LOWELL LLC
(*Suby of* INTERSTATE RESOURCES INC) ★
240 Industrial Ave E, Lowell, MA 01852-5114
Tel (978) 458-4555 *Founded/Ownrshp* 1997
Sales 22.2MMᴱ *EMP* 140ᴱ
SIC 2653 Boxes, corrugated: made from purchased materials; Boxes, corrugated: made from purchased materials

D-U-N-S 02-520-5672
INTERSTATE CONTAINER READING LLC
(*Suby of* INTERSTATE RESOURCES INC) ★
100 Grace St, Reading, PA 19611-1977
Tel (610) 376-7123 *Founded/Ownrshp* 1982
Sales 95.9MMᴱ *EMP* 240
SIC 5113 Boxes & containers; Boxes & containers
CEO: Tony Frem
COO: Jim Morgan
CFO: Pierre Khattar
Genl Mgr: Jeff Coleman

D-U-N-S 95-729-5934
INTERSTATE CORRPACK LLC
INTERSTATE CONTAINER CAMBRIDGE
(*Suby of* INTERSTATE RESOURCES INC) ★
903 Woods Rd, Cambridge, MD 21613-9469
Tel (410) 221-6100 *Founded/Ownrshp* 1996
Sales 45.2MMᴱ *EMP* 100
SIC 2653 Corrugated & solid fiber boxes
IT Man: Russell Garrett
Opers Mgr: Garfield Boothe
Plnt Mgr: Bill Berg
Sales Asso: Elyse Cristos

D-U-N-S 00-452-1613 IMP
INTERSTATE DIESEL SERVICE INC (OH)
INTERSTATE-MCBEE
5300 Lakeside Ave E, Cleveland, OH 44114-3916
Tel (216) 881-0015 *Founded/Ownrshp* 1947, 1953
Sales 76.3MMᴱ *EMP* 325
SIC 5013 3714 Automotive engines & engine parts; Fuel systems & parts, motor vehicle; Fuel pumps, motor vehicle; Automotive engines & engine parts; Fuel systems & parts, motor vehicle; Fuel pumps, motor vehicle
CEO: Alfred J Buescher
**Pr:* Ann Buescher
**COO:* Brad Buescher

D-U-N-S 05-549-8216
INTERSTATE DISTRIBUTOR CO
(*Suby of* SALTCHUK RESOURCES INC) ★
11707 21st Ave Ct S, Tacoma, WA 98444-1236
Tel (253) 537-9455 *Founded/Ownrshp* 2011
Sales 335.9MMᴱ *EMP* 3,760
SIC 4213 Trucking, except local; Trucking, except local
Pr: Marc Rogers
**Treas:* Rodney A Mc Lean
VP: Todd Bailey
**VP:* Jo Borden
VP: Cathy Canonica
VP: Al Garcia
VP: Donna Hodel
**VP:* Terry S Mc Lean

D-U-N-S 03-382-7734 IMP
INTERSTATE DISTRIBUTORS OF DUNN INC
(*Suby of* B M D) ★
798 George Perry Lee Rd, Dunn, NC 28334
Tel (910) 892-4143 *Founded/Ownrshp* 2015
Sales 24.9MMᴱ *EMP* 46
SIC 5072 5031 Builders' hardware; Lumber: rough, dressed & finished
Pr: William G Lasater Jr
**Treas:* David C McLamb
Treas: David McLamb
**VP:* Jimmy Blackmon
Off Admin: Alice Stephenson
Trfc Dir: Ronald Norris
**Opers Mgr:* Monty McLamb
Sales Asso: Gail Cramer

D-U-N-S 82-522-2714
INTERSTATE DODGE INC
920 Highway 165 Byp, Monroe, LA 71203
Tel (318) 387-2665 *Founded/Ownrshp* 1993
Sales 25.0MMᴱ *EMP* 50
SIC 5511 5521 Automobiles, new & used; Used car dealers; Automobiles, new & used; Used car dealers
Pr: John Klagholz

D-U-N-S 79-806-8623
INTERSTATE DRYWALL CORP
700 Lanidex Plz Ste 101, Parsippany, NJ 07054-2705
Tel (973) 428-2800 *Founded/Ownrshp* 1986
Sales 20.4MMᴱ *EMP* 200
SIC 1742 Drywall; Drywall
Pr: Peter Di Tommaso
**Pr:* Peter Ditommaso
**VP:* Frank Ditommaso

D-U-N-S 00-958-3493 IMP
INTERSTATE ELECTRIC CO INC
IEC
2240 Yates Ave, Commerce, CA 90040-1914
Tel (323) 724-0420 *Founded/Ownrshp* 1966
Sales 71.5MMᴱ *EMP* 115
SIC 5046 Signs, electrical; Signs, electrical
Pr: Edward Urlik
CFO: Hortensia Gomez
Brnch Mgr: Arnie Binter
Brnch Mgr: Dan Carson
Opers Mgr: Michael Avery
Opers Mgr: Mike Demitchell
Mktg Mgr: Rebekah Hogan
Sls Mgr: Bill Fox

D-U-N-S 05-604-8218
INTERSTATE ELECTRIC MOTORS AND CONTROL INC
INDUSTRIAL ELECTRIC MOTORS
(*Suby of* ECHO ELECTRIC SUPPLY) ★
9770 S 142nd St Ste 1, Omaha, NE 68138-3722
Tel (402) 342-1191 *Founded/Ownrshp* 1997
Sales 16.4MMᴱ *EMP* 320
SIC 7694 5063 Electric motor repair; Motors, electric; Electric motor repair; Motors, electric
CEO: Mitch Lane
**VP:* Lowell Elliott
Brnch Mgr: Tammie Neyman

D-U-N-S 01-914-3163
INTERSTATE ELECTRICAL SERVICES CORP
70 Treble Cove Rd, North Billerica, MA 01862-2208
Tel (978) 667-5200 *Founded/Ownrshp* 1966
Sales 92.2MM *EMP* 600
Accts Mcgladrey Llp Boston Massach
SIC 1731 Electronic controls installation; Communications specialization; Electronic controls installation; Communications specialization
Pr: Jim P Alibrandi
CFO: Thomas O'Toole
**Treas:* Pasquale A Alibrandi
**Ex VP:* Carl Brand
VP: Brian Lewis
VP: Bob Parker
VP: John Sloan
**VP:* John Sloane
VP: Gary Sobolewski
Sales Asso: Donny Griffith

D-U-N-S 01-066-6618
INTERSTATE ELECTRICAL SUPPLY INC (GA)
2300 2nd Ave, Columbus, GA 31901-1022
Tel (706) 324-1000 *Founded/Ownrshp* 1972
Sales 52.1MMᴱ *EMP* 68
SIC 5063 5999 Electrical supplies; Motors, electric; Electrical supplies; Motors, electric
CEO: Jack H Tinkler III
VP: Penny Bero
Exec: Paul Grable
Brnch Mgr: John Starr
Genl Mgr: Walter Morrison
IT Man: Julie Blanton
Sls Mgr: Bob Bedingfield
Sales Asso: Sharon Hackleman
Sales Asso: Mike Moore

D-U-N-S 04-254-1250
INTERSTATE ELECTRONICS CO
600 Joliet Rd Ste E, Willowbrook, IL 60527-5684
Tel (630) 789-8700 *Founded/Ownrshp* 1964
Sales 21.7MMᴱ *EMP* 75
SIC 1731 Communications specialization
Pr: Gregory P Kuzmic
VP: Mark Woltkamp
VP Opers: Frank Debartolo

D-U-N-S 00-828-9043
■ **INTERSTATE ELECTRONICS CORP**
L-3 INTERSTATE ELECTRONICS
(*Suby of* L-3 COMMUNICATIONS CORP) ★
602 E Vermont Ave, Anaheim, CA 92805-5607
Tel (714) 758-0500 *Founded/Ownrshp* 1955
Sales 104.7MMᴱ *EMP* 1,102
SIC 3825 3812 3679 Test equipment for electronic & electric measurement; Navigational systems & instruments; Liquid crystal displays (LCD); Test equipment for electronic & electric measurement; Navigational systems & instruments; Liquid crystal displays (LCD)
Pr: Thomas L Walsh
VP: Rick Bieniak
**VP:* Carol Grogg
IT Man: Nancy Sturmer
Sftwr Eng: Mike Sanders

D-U-N-S 05-473-1380
INTERSTATE ENERGY LLC
COMO OIL & PROPANE
(*Suby of* THOMPSONS GAS & ELECTRIC SERVICE INC) ★
4330 W 1st St Ste A, Duluth, MN 55807-2239
Tel (218) 722-6666 *Founded/Ownrshp* 2015
Sales 21.1MMᴱ *EMP* 120
Accts Brady Martz & Associates Pc
SIC 5983 5984 Fuel oil dealers; Liquefied petroleum gas dealers; Fuel oil dealers; Liquefied petroleum gas dealers
Sls Mgr: Brian Raygor

INTERSTATE ENERGY PARTNERS
See IEP HOLDINGS LLC

D-U-N-S 07-685-5501
INTERSTATE FIRE & CASUALTY CO INC
(*Suby of* FIREMANS FUND INSURANCE CO) ★
33 W Monroe St Ste 1400, Chicago, IL 60603-5309
Tel (312) 346-6400 *Founded/Ownrshp* 2007
Sales NA *EMP* 320
SIC 6331 Property damage insurance; Fire, marine & casualty insurance: mutual; Property damage insurance; Fire, marine & casualty insurance: mutual
Pr: Gary R Dittman
VP: Michael P Sullivan
Board of Directors: Lauren R Bailey, Douglas E Franklin, John F Huddleston Jr, Jaffery F Johnson, Sally B Narey, Frank A Sapio, D Andrew Torrance, Kavin E Walker, David M Zona

D-U-N-S 15-883-4262 IMP
INTERSTATE FLOORING LLC
ISC SURFACES
5100 Kansas Ave, Kansas City, KS 66106-1137
Tel (913) 573-0600 *Founded/Ownrshp* 1999
Sales 61.6MMᴱ *EMP* 225
SIC 5032 5023 Ceramic wall & floor tile; Home furnishings; Ceramic wall & floor tile; Home furnishings
CFO: Jack Chalfant
Sls Mgr: Chris Schuster
Sales Asso: Kristy Gibbs

D-U-N-S 04-207-2025 IMP
INTERSTATE FOAM & SUPPLY INC (NC)
302 306 Comfort Dr Ne, Conover, NC 28613
Tel (828) 459-9700 *Founded/Ownrshp* 1981
Sales 36.9MMᴱ *EMP* 215
SIC 3069 Foam rubber; Foam rubber
Pr: Mark A Webb
**VP:* Lewis A Webb
IT Man: Rob Baker
IT Man: Doug Martin
Prd Mgr: Rob Snelgrove

D-U-N-S 01-207-2880
INTERSTATE FOODS INC
INTERSTATE POULTRY
565 West St, New York, NY 10014-1407
Tel (212) 929-3550 *Founded/Ownrshp* 1996
Sales 22.0MMᴱ *EMP* 50
SIC 5144 Poultry: live, dressed or frozen (unpackaged)
Pr: Robert Greenzeig
**Sec:* Thomas Ryan
**VP:* David Adelson

D-U-N-S 04-439-1989
INTERSTATE FORD INC
125 Alexandersville Rd, Miamisburg, OH 45342-5700
Tel (937) 866-0781 *Founded/Ownrshp* 1981
Sales 50.7MMᴱ *EMP* 130
SIC 5511 5521

D-U-N-S 03-480-9578
INTERSTATE FUEL SYSTEMS INC
8221 Alpine Ave, Sacramento, CA 95826-4708
Tel (916) 457-6572 *Founded/Ownrshp* 1978
Sales 20.5MMᴱ *EMP* 100
SIC 5172 Fuel oil; Fuel oil
Pr: Terrance Andrews
**Treas:* Laurene Andrews

D-U-N-S 17-732-8291
INTERSTATE GAS MARKETING INC
IGM
2018 S 6th St, Indiana, PA 15701-6012
Tel (724) 465-7958 *Founded/Ownrshp* 1987
Sales 150.2MMᴱ *EMP* 230
SIC 4925 5172 Gas: mixed, natural & manufactured; Gases; Gas: mixed, natural & manufactured; Gases
Pr: Michael Melnick
**Treas:* John Pisarsik
**VP:* William Gregg

D-U-N-S 62-605-8655
INTERSTATE GAS SUPPLY INC
6100 Emerald Pkwy, Dublin, OH 43016-3248
Tel (614) 659-5000 *Founded/Ownrshp* 1989
Sales 1.4MMM *EMP* 170
SIC 1311 Natural gas production; Natural gas production
Pr: Scott L White

*COO: Jim Baich
*Ex VP: Doug Austin
*VP: Larry Friedeman
VP: Mike Gatt
VP: Jason Moore
*VP: Nicole Shiring
VP: Patrick Smith
VP: Shelly Stotzer
Software D: Gibran Britt
Netwrk Eng: Eric Nussear

D-U-N-S 02-790-3681 IMP
INTERSTATE GOURMET COFFEE ROASTERS INC
43 Norfolk Ave, South Easton, MA 02375-1190
Tel (508) 238-8393 Founded/Ownrshp 1979
Sales 25.0MM EMP 98
SIC 5149 Coffee, green or roasted
Pr: Michael C Dovner

D-U-N-S 01-021-9521
INTERSTATE GRATINGS LLC
1820 W 200 S, Lindon, UT 84042-1611
Tel (801) 922-4700 Founded/Ownrshp 2007
Sales 22.0MM^E EMP 52
SIC 5051 3549 3999 Steel; Wiredrawing & fabricating machinery & equipment, ex. die; Atomizers, toiletry

D-U-N-S 87-799-2388
INTERSTATE GROUP LLC
TRAILERSPLUS
3800 Airport Rd, Nampa, ID 83687-8633
Tel (877) 808-5447 Founded/Ownrshp 2005
Sales 73.5MM^E EMP 350
SIC 3792 Travel trailers & campers; Travel trailers & campers

D-U-N-S 00-779-7657 IMP
INTERSTATE HIGHWAY CONSTRUCTION INC
I H C
7135 S Tucson Way, Centennial, CO 80112-3987
Tel (303) 790-7132 Founded/Ownrshp 1956
Sales 1.3MMM EMP 400
SIC 1611 Concrete construction: roads, highways, sidewalks, etc.; Highway & street paving contractor; General contractor, highway & street construction; Airport runway construction; Concrete construction: roads, highways, sidewalks, etc.; Highway & street paving contractor; General contractor, highway & street construction; Airport runway construction
CEO: J Kenyon Schaeffer
*Pr: James Randall
*Treas: Jeffrey C Littman
*VP: John L Edwards
*VP: John Medberry
*VP: Calvin Thomas
Ql Cn Mgr: Hassan Barzegar

D-U-N-S 87-635-4984
INTERSTATE HIGHWAY SIGN CORP
INTERSTATE SIGNWAYS
7415 Lindsey Rd, Little Rock, AR 72206-3829
Tel (501) 490-4242 Founded/Ownrshp 2005
Sales 31.6MM^E EMP 115
SIC 3993 Signs, not made in custom sign painting shops; Signs, not made in custom sign painting shops
Pr: Robert Brown
*CFO: Michael Holland
Genl Mgr: Geoffrey Quo
MIS Dir: Jeanie Toombs
Prd Mgr: Dennis Campbell
Trfc Mgr: Adam Hoover
Sls Mgr: Cathie Hamilton
Sls Mgr: Dan Wright

D-U-N-S 03-550-8816
INTERSTATE HOTELS & RESORTS INC
HAMPTON INN
(Suby of HOTEL ACQUISITION CO LLC) ★
4501 Fairfax Dr Ste 500, Arlington, VA 22203-1668
Tel (703) 387-3100 Founded/Ownrshp 2010
Sales 1.6MMM^E EMP 19,060
SIC 7011 Hotels & motels; Hotels & motels
CEO: Thomas F Hewitt
*Pr: Samuel E Knighton
*CEO: Jim Abrahamson
COO: Chris Van Der Baars
COO: Bob Morse
CFO: Hana Barsoum
*CFO: Carrie McIntyre
*CFO: Bruce A Riggins
Bd of Dir: Corde Carrillo
Bd of Dir: Nicholas Colonna
Bd of Dir: Nick Donovan
Bd of Dir: Doug Erber
Bd of Dir: Melinda Franklin
Bd of Dir: David Hauge
Bd of Dir: Paul Hernandez
Bd of Dir: Richard Hollingsworth
Bd of Dir: Deborah Jordan
Bd of Dir: Don Jue
Bd of Dir: Robert Katherman
Bd of Dir: Richard Lasater
Bd of Dir: Steve Maguin

D-U-N-S 11-099-2026
INTERSTATE IMPROVEMENT INC
16871 Canby Ave, Faribault, MN 55021-8553
Tel (507) 333-2677 Founded/Ownrshp 2001
Sales 47.0MM^E EMP 125
SIC 1611 Concrete construction: roads, highways, sidewalks, etc.; Concrete construction: roads, highways, sidewalks, etc.
Pr: Jeremy Gibbs
*VP: Tony Detomaso

D-U-N-S 07-689-2306
INTERSTATE INDEMNITY CO
(Suby of ALLIANZ GLOBAL RISKS US INSURANCE CO) ★
33 W Monroe St Ste 1200, Chicago, IL 60603-5316
Tel (312) 346-6400 Founded/Ownrshp 2007
Sales NA EMP 140
SIC 6331 Property damage insurance; Fire, marine & casualty insurance: mutual; Property damage insurance; Fire, marine & casualty insurance: mutual
Pr: Art Mossman
*Pr: Susan Albrecht
*VP: Michael P Sullivan

D-U-N-S 07-924-0916
INTERSTATE INDUSTRIAL SANDS LLC
(Suby of IEP HOLDINGS LLC) ★
3033 Campus Dr Ste W125, Plymouth, MN 55441-2686
Tel (763) 432-6552 Founded/Ownrshp 2012
Sales 40.0MM^E EMP 6
SIC 2819 Silica compounds
CEO: William J Frothinger

D-U-N-S 04-177-2195
INTERSTATE MANAGEMENT & INVESTMENT CORP
IMIC HOTELS
1 Surrey Ct, Columbia, SC 29212-3100
Tel (803) 772-2629 Founded/Ownrshp 1981
Sales 70.0MM^E EMP 1,400
SIC 7011 Hotels & motels; Hotels & motels
CEO: E L Pooser Jr
*Pr: Bert Pooser III
*VP: Jeff Buchko
*VP: Kathy Rabune
*VP: Rick Rabune
Telecom Mg: Mike McDowell

D-U-N-S 96-801-4865
INTERSTATE MANAGEMENT CO LLC
(Suby of HAMPTON INN) ★
4501 Fairfax Dr Ste 500, Arlington, VA 22203-1668
Tel (703) 387-3100 Founded/Ownrshp 1998
Sales 98.4MM^E EMP 11,000
SIC 8741 Hotel or motel management; Hotel or motel management

D-U-N-S 10-386-4518
INTERSTATE MANUFACTURING INC
68935 Union St, White Pigeon, MI 49099-9452
Tel (269) 483-7641 Founded/Ownrshp 1990
Sales 22.5MM^E EMP 80
SIC 3799 Trailers & trailer equipment
Pr: Christopher C Hamlin
*Sec: Joseph Hamlin
*VP: Doug Jenkins

INTERSTATE MCBEE
See MCBEE SUPPLY CORP

D-U-N-S 92-897-2520 IMP
INTERSTATE MEAT & PROVISION
STERLING PACIFIC MEAT COMPANY
6114 Scott Way, Commerce, CA 90040-3518
Tel (323) 838-9400 Founded/Ownrshp 1995
Sales 95.5MM^E EMP 100
SIC 5142 5147 Packaged frozen goods; Meat brokers; Packaged frozen goods; Meat brokers
CEO: Jim Asher
VP Opers: Luis Munoz

D-U-N-S 05-496-9985
INTERSTATE MEAT DISTRIBUTORS INC
9550 Se Last Rd, Clackamas, OR 97015-9595
Tel (503) 656-0633 Founded/Ownrshp 1971
Sales 64.1MM^E EMP 100
SIC 5147 Meats & meat products; Meats & meat products
Pr: Darrin Hoy
*VP: James Meng
Opers Mgr: Brian Charles
Sls Mgr: Michael Sinner

D-U-N-S 04-900-2306
INTERSTATE MECHANICAL CONTRACTORS INC
3200 Henson Rd, Knoxville, TN 37921-5345
Tel (865) 588-0180 Founded/Ownrshp 1982
Sales 45.3MM^E EMP 150
SIC 1711 Mechanical contractor; Mechanical contractor
Pr: Terry L Self
*COO: Joe R Webb
*CFO: Amanda C Yearwood

D-U-N-S 10-280-5546
INTERSTATE MECHANICAL CORP
IMCOR
1841 E Washington St, Phoenix, AZ 85034-1230
Tel (602) 257-1319 Founded/Ownrshp 1983
Sales 151.0MM^E EMP 380
SIC 1711 Mechanical contractor; Mechanical contractor
Ch Bd: Merle M Karber
CFO: Sterling Smith
*Treas: Susan Baxter
*VP: Rick Karber
Dir Bus: Jeremy Ettesvold
IT Man: David Pool
Snr PM: Brian Greer

D-U-N-S 05-465-5480
INTERSTATE MECHANICAL SERVICES INC
51 Railroad Ave Ste 5, Closter, NJ 07624-1239
Tel (201) 767-1192 Founded/Ownrshp 1997
Sales 23.0MM EMP 50
Accts Marchionda & Ferrer Pa Cli
SIC 1711 Mechanical contractor; Mechanical contractor
Owner: Richard W Tully Jr

INTERSTATE MFG & SUPPLY DIV
See SPS COMPANIES INC

D-U-N-S 03-649-4339
INTERSTATE MILLS LLC
900 30th Pl Nw, Owatonna, MN 55060-5001
Tel (507) 451-1230 Founded/Ownrshp 1998
Sales 34.2MM^E EMP 60
SIC 5153 5191 Grains; Animal feeds; Grains; Animal feeds

INTERSTATE MNROE MCHY SUPS DIV
See STATCO ENGINEERING & FABRICATORS INC

INTERSTATE MUSIC SUPPLY
See CASCIO MUSIC CO INC

D-U-N-S 09-317-2583
INTERSTATE NATIONAL CORP OF TEXAS GENERAL AGENCY (TX)
33 W Monroe St Ste 1200, Chicago, IL 60603-5316
Tel (312) 346-6400 Founded/Ownrshp 1978, 2007
Sales NA EMP 600
SIC 6411 Insurance agents; Insurance agents
Pr: Susan Albracht
*CFO: Kevin Hart
Ex VP: Breanne Morley

D-U-N-S 80-433-6709
INTERSTATE NATIONAL DEALER SERVICES INC
6120 Powers Ferry Rd S, Atlanta, GA 30339-2996
Tel (678) 894-3500 Founded/Ownrshp 2003
Sales NA EMP 140
SIC 6399 6221 Warranty insurance, automobile; Commodity contracts brokers, dealers
Pr: Mark H Mishler
Sr Pt: Richard Ocallaghan
*CFO: Geoffrey Tirone
Chf Mktg O: Ricky Wolfe
Ofcr: Stephanie Scott-Gueye
*Ex VP: Lawrence J Altman
*Ex VP: Sansone Dominic
*VP: Gerry Thanner
VP: Ronald Williams
IT Man: Robert Kollar
Sales Asso: Donna Avery

D-U-N-S 03-348-4080 IMP
INTERSTATE NATIONALEASE INC
(Suby of FRED TAYLOR CO INC) ★
2700 Palmyra Rd, Albany, GA 31707-1885
Tel (229) 883-7250 Founded/Ownrshp 1966
Sales 37.1MM^E EMP 293
Accts Sellers Richardson Holman & We
SIC 7513 Truck leasing, without drivers; Truck leasing, without drivers
Pr: Mark Taylor
VP: Paul Brown
VP: Jamy Former
VP: Joe Puff
VP: Sharon Veasey
Dir IT: Karen Roberts

D-U-N-S 03-405-4023
INTERSTATE OIL CO INC (AL)
CHEVRON
2335 S Forbes Dr, Montgomery, AL 36110-1501
Tel (334) 262-7301 Founded/Ownrshp 1921
Sales 58.6MM^E EMP 250
SIC 5541 5171

D-U-N-S 08-523-9309
INTERSTATE OPTICAL CO
(Suby of ESSILOR OF AMERICA INC) ★
680 Lindaire Ln E, Ontario, OH 44906-1760
Tel (419) 529-6800 Founded/Ownrshp 2008
Sales 21.6MM^E EMP 68^E
SIC 5048 Ophthalmic goods
Pr: John Art
*Treas: Deborah L Art
*VP: Robert Art
VP: Bud Stanton

D-U-N-S 04-949-5138
INTERSTATE PACKAGING CO
2285 Hwy 47 N, White Bluff, TN 37187-4126
Tel (615) 797-9000 Founded/Ownrshp 1969
Sales 36.5MM EMP 200
Accts Frazier & Deeter Nashville T
SIC 2673 2672 Cellophane bags, unprinted: made from purchased materials; Labels (unprinted), gummed: made from purchased materials; Cellophane bags, unprinted: made from purchased materials; Labels (unprinted), gummed: made from purchased materials
Pr: Jerald Doochin
*VP: Teri Doochin
IT Man: Mike Matt
Sfty Mgr: Paul Tucker
Opers Mgr: Tracy Jacobs
Opers Mgr: Joseph Matt
Prd Mgr: Bob Wall
Sls Mgr: Spencer Wilson
Snr Mgr: Scott Harwell

D-U-N-S 06-692-8623 EXP
INTERSTATE PAPER LLC
(Suby of INTERSTATE RESOURCES INC) ★
2366 Interstate Rd Ste 1, Riceboro, GA 31323-3934
Tel (912) 884-3371 Founded/Ownrshp 1982
Sales 148.3MM^E EMP 240
SIC 2631 Kraft linerboard; Kraft linerboard
CEO: Antoine N Frem
Pr: Charles Feghali
Sec: Ramez G Skaff

D-U-N-S 01-452-1017
INTERSTATE PAPER SUPPLY CO INC
IPSCO
103 Good St, Roscoe, PA 15477
Tel (724) 938-2218 Founded/Ownrshp 1951
Sales 21.8MM^E EMP 100
SIC 2679 3086 2671 Paper products, converted; Plastics foam products; Packaging paper & plastics film, coated & laminated; Paper products, converted; Plastics foam products; Packaging paper & plastics film, coated & laminated
Pr: Bart R Raitano Jr

D-U-N-S 09-726-1036
INTERSTATE PERSONNEL SERVICES INC
PASCHALL TRUCK LINES
3443 Us Highway 641 S, Murray, KY 42071-7112
Tel (270) 753-1717 Founded/Ownrshp 1971, 1973
Sales 162.3MM^E EMP 1,176^E
Accts Katz Sapper & Miller Llp In
SIC 4213 Trucking, except local; Trucking, except local
Pr: Randall A Waller Sr
*Treas: Judy Ingersoll
*Treas: Anthony Waller Jr
*VP: Hal T Bishop
*VP: Thomas J Stephens
*VP: Luther G Waller

INTERSTATE PLASTICS
See DONGALEN ENTERPRISES INC

D-U-N-S 62-755-1195
INTERSTATE PLUMBING & AIR CONDITIONING LLC
7201 W Post Rd, Las Vegas, NV 89113-6610
Tel (702) 367-6064 Founded/Ownrshp 1994
Sales 28.0MM^E EMP 368
Accts Fair Anderson & Lagerman Las
SIC 1711 Plumbing, heating, air-conditioning contractors; Plumbing, heating, air-conditioning contractors
Treas: Carole Vesely
VP: Paul Enix

INTERSTATE POTATO PACKERS
See OPPENHEIMER COMPANIES INC

INTERSTATE POULTRY
See INTERSTATE FOODS INC

D-U-N-S 00-681-5844
INTERSTATE POULTRY INC (CA)
3050 E 11th St, Los Angeles, CA 90023-3606
Tel (323) 264-4024 Founded/Ownrshp 2000
Sales 32.0MM EMP 145
SIC 5144 Poultry products; Poultry products
CEO: Carlos Velasco

D-U-N-S 00-694-0522 IMP
■ **INTERSTATE POWER AND LIGHT CO** (IA)
(Suby of ALLIANT ENERGY CORP) ★
200 1st St Se, Cedar Rapids, IA 52401-1409
Tel (319) 398-4411 Founded/Ownrshp 1882
Sales 1.8MMM EMP 1,766
SIC 4911 4924 4961

D-U-N-S 36-199-7740
INTERSTATE POWER SYSTEMS INC
(Suby of INTERSTATE COMPANIES INC) ★
2601 American Blvd E, Minneapolis, MN 55425-1321
Tel (952) 854-5511 Founded/Ownrshp 2005
Sales 183.7MM^E EMP 60^E
SIC 5084 Trucks, industrial; Trucks, industrial
CEO: Jeff Gaswell
*CEO: Travis Penrod
*CFO: Larry Schwartz
*Ch: Gordan Galarneau
Genl Mgr: Mike Creamer
Dir IT: Tom McHenry
IT Man: Shane Sargent
VP Opers: Mike Severson
Sls&Mrk Ex: Ken Trembath
Sls Mgr: Carl Brown

INTERSTATE POWERCARE
See POWERCARE AND SERVICE SOLUTIONS INC

D-U-N-S 05-199-6319
INTERSTATE PROTECTIVE SERVICES INC
153 Andover St Ste 209, Danvers, MA 01923-5307
Tel (978) 750-4600 Founded/Ownrshp 2010
Sales 950.0M EMP 450
SIC 8999 Services; Services
Pr: Thomas Driscoll
Prin: John Snyder

D-U-N-S 07-548-3412
INTERSTATE REALTY MANAGEMENT CO INC (NJ)
3 E Stow Rd Ste 100, Marlton, NJ 08053-3188
Tel (856) 596-0500 Founded/Ownrshp 1973
Sales 89.6MM^E EMP 1,300
SIC 6531 6513 Real estate managers; Condominium manager; Rental agent, real estate; Apartment hotel operation; Real estate managers; Condominium manager; Rental agent, real estate; Apartment hotel operation
Ch Bd: Michael J Levitt
Genl Pt: Kenneth Price
*Pr: Mark Morgan
*Treas: Jim Bleiler
VP: Michael Boettger
Mng Dir: David L Anderson
VP Opers: Paul Sassani

D-U-N-S 05-760-2187
INTERSTATE REHABILITATION CENTER INC
IRC INDUSTRIES
204 Mississippi Ave, Red Wing, MN 55066-1807
Tel (651) 388-7108 Founded/Ownrshp 1968
Sales 3.8MM^E EMP 290
SIC 8322 Social services for the handicapped; Social services for the handicapped
Ex Dir: David Leiseth

D-U-N-S 05-651-4524 IMP/EXP
INTERSTATE RESOURCES INC
(Suby of INDEVCO SAL)
1300 Wilson Blvd Ste 1075, Arlington, VA 22209-2330
Tel (703) 243-3355 Founded/Ownrshp 1988
Sales 435.7MM^E EMP 930
SIC 2631 2653 7389 Kraft linerboard; Boxes, corrugated: made from purchased materials; Purchasing service; Kraft linerboard; Boxes, corrugated: made from purchased materials; Purchasing service
CEO: Neetmat Frem
COO: James Morgan
CFO: Pierre Khattar
CFO: Pierre Khatter
VP: Charles Feghali
VP: Roger Malone
VP: David Stauffer
Rgnl Mgr: Laurie Maggio
Genl Mgr: Geoffrey Schiffenhaus
Mktg Dir: Tom Pierce
Mktg Mgr: Hiba Darazi

D-U-N-S 04-709-7410 IMP
INTERSTATE RESTORATION LLC
3401 Quorum Dr Ste 300, Fort Worth, TX 76137-3621
Tel (817) 293-0035 Founded/Ownrshp 2007
Sales 156.3MM^E EMP 160

SIC 1542 1522 7349 Commercial & office buildings, renovation & repair; Remodeling, multi-family dwellings; Building maintenance services; Commercial & office buildings, renovation & repair; Remodeling, multi-family dwellings; Building maintenance services
COO: Brian Wooley
Ex VP: Clay Mazur
VP: Ron Miles
Exec: Pat Skinner
IT Man: Kim Goss
Natl Sales: Dana Pierce
Mktg Dir: Matt Wenstrom
Manager: Doug Prokop
Manager: Gina Rouban
Manager: Synthia Wendell

D-U-N-S 00-942-8582
INTERSTATE ROCK PRODUCTS INC
42 S 850 W Ste 201, Hurricane, UT 84737-3210
Tel (435) 635-2628 *Founded/Ownrshp* 1981
Sales 54.8MM^E *EMP* 150
SIC 1611 5032 5211 General contractor, highway & street construction; Concrete mixtures; Gravel; Asphalt mixture; Cement; Sand & gravel; General contractor, highway & street construction; Concrete mixtures; Gravel; Asphalt mixture; Cement; Sand & gravel
Pr: Don Stratton
**Sec:* Craig Stratton
**VP:* Brian Stratton

D-U-N-S 03-251-4382 IMP/EXP
INTERSTATE SCREW CORP
ATLAS BOLT AND NUT
475 W 18th St, Hialeah, FL 33010-2418
Tel (305) 885-3951 *Founded/Ownrshp* 1956
Sales 20.5MM^E *EMP* 44
SIC 5072 Screws; Power handtools
Pr: Hermina J Seiden
**Pr:* Ronald Seiden
Ofcr: Dominick Menendez
**Ofcr:* Samantha Seiden
VP: Eric Seiden
Off Mgr: Jorge Martinez

INTERSTATE SIGNWAYS
See INTERSTATE HIGHWAY SIGN CORP

INTERSTATE STEEL
See NATIONAL MATERIAL LP

D-U-N-S 61-379-6226
INTERSTATE STEEL SUPPLY CO OF MARYLAND INC
50 Cabot Blvd E, Langhorne, PA 19047-1802
Tel (877) 313-6550 *Founded/Ownrshp* 1997
Sales NA *EMP* 1,600
SIC 5051

INTERSTATE STREAM COMMISSION
See ENGINEER NEW MEXICO STATE

D-U-N-S 00-696-7756 IMP/EXP
INTERSTATE SUPPLY CO (MO)
ISC SURFACES
9245 Dielman Indus Dr, Saint Louis, MO 63132-2202
Tel (314) 994-7100 *Founded/Ownrshp* 1906, 2007
Sales 27.9MM^E *EMP* 220
SIC 3996 5211

D-U-N-S 08-978-3575
INTERSTATE TELECOMMUNICATIONS COOPERATIVE INC
I T C
312 4th St W, Clear Lake, SD 57226-4102
Tel (605) 874-2181 *Founded/Ownrshp* 1953
Sales 29.4MM^E *EMP* 70
SIC 4813 4841 Telephone communication, except radio; Cable television services
Prin: Jerry Heiberger

D-U-N-S 78-861-1353
INTERSTATE TRANSPORT INC
324 1st Ave N, Saint Petersburg, FL 33701-3811
Tel (727) 822-9999 *Founded/Ownrshp* 2002
Sales 34.9MM^E *EMP* 56
SIC 4731 Freight transportation arrangement
Pr: Gloria H Higham
VP: Timothy J Higham
Sls Mgr: Andy Stein

D-U-N-S 03-612-3321
INTERSTATE TRANSPORTATION EQUIPMENT INC (SC)
2511 Trotter Rd, Columbia, SC 29290
Tel (803) 776-5041 *Founded/Ownrshp* 1947, 1982
Sales 35.5MM *EMP* 10
Accts Mcgregor & Company Llp Colum
SIC 5012 Buses; Buses
Pr: Robert D Coleman

D-U-N-S 92-621-4784
INTERSTATE TREATING INC
7141 Club Dr, Odessa, TX 79762-5451
Tel (432) 362-9291 *Founded/Ownrshp* 1987
Sales 20.8MM^E *EMP* 70
SIC 7353 1629 1389 5084 3444 3441 Oil equipment rental services; Industrial plant construction; Processing service, gas; Petroleum industry machinery; Sheet metalwork; Fabricated structural metal
Pr: Ronald D Rains

INTERSTATE TRUCK CENTER
See INTER-STATE FORD TRUCK SALES INC

D-U-N-S 07-736-1442
INTERSTATE TRUCK CENTER LLC
VALLEY PETERBILT
825 Navy Dr, Stockton, CA 95206-1169
Tel (209) 944-5821 *Founded/Ownrshp* 1974
Sales 75.0MM^E *EMP* 150
SIC 5012 7513 Trucks, commercial; Truck rental, without drivers; Trucks, commercial; Truck rental, without drivers
**CFO:* Rick Coslett
IT Man: Don Hoffman

D-U-N-S 80-899-2416
INTERSTATE TRUCKWAY INC
TRUCKWAY LEASING
1755 Dreman Ave, Cincinnati, OH 45223-2445
Tel (513) 542-5500 *Founded/Ownrshp* 1988
Sales 68.6MM *EMP* 130
Accts Deloitte & Touche Llp Cincin
SIC 7513 5012 Truck rental & leasing, no drivers; Commercial vehicles; Truck rental & leasing, no drivers; Commercial vehicles
Pr: Ron Horstman
**VP:* Jeff Barber
**VP:* Robert Jones
**VP:* Shawn Watson
Sls Mgr: Willy Walraven

D-U-N-S 05-737-0009 IMP/EXP
INTERSTATE VAN LINES INC
INTERSTATE WRLDWIDE RELOCATION
5801 Rolling Rd, Springfield, VA 22152-1099
Tel (703) 226-3320 *Founded/Ownrshp* 1943
Sales 34.3MM *EMP* 300
SIC 4213

INTERSTATE WAREHOUSE SERVICES
See FRED TAYLOR CO INC

D-U-N-S 15-209-5006 IMP
INTERSTATE WAREHOUSING OF VIRGINIA LLC
(*Suby of* TIPPMANN PROPERTIES INC) ★
9009 Coldwater Rd Ste 300, Fort Wayne, IN 46825-2072
Tel (260) 490-3000 *Founded/Ownrshp* 1997
Sales 105.9MM^E *EMP* 539
SIC 4222 Warehousing, cold storage or refrigerated; Warehousing, cold storage or refrigerated
Ch: John Tippmann
**Pr:* Charles Tippmann
**VP:* Joseph Greco
**VP:* Steven Tippmann
Rgnl Mgr: Andrew Jackson
Opers Mgr: Jarad Gerardot
Sls Dir: David Hastings

D-U-N-S 11-843-1316
INTERSTATE WASTE SERVICES INC
ADVANCED DISPOSAL
(*Suby of* ACTION CARTING ENVIRONMENTAL SERVICES INC) ★
150 Allen Rd Ste 201, Basking Ridge, NJ 07920-2977
Tel (201) 830-3250 *Founded/Ownrshp* 2013
Sales 46.0MM^E *EMP* 60
SIC 4953 Hazardous waste collection & disposal
Ch Bd: Michael J De Castro
**CFO:* Mike Gruppuso
Site Mgr: Dominick Ferrara

D-U-N-S 92-681-6356 IMP
INTERSTATE WINDOW CORP
MANNIX
345 Crooked Hill Rd Ste 1, Brentwood, NY 11717-1020
Tel (631) 231-0800 *Founded/Ownrshp* 1995
Sales 33.7MM^E *EMP* 100
SIC 3442 Metal doors, sash & trim; Metal doors, sash & trim
Pr: Robert Salzer
**VP:* Paul Greenstein
**VP:* Sue Hausner
VP: Daniel Monosson

D-U-N-S 08-514-8484
INTERSTATE WIRE CO INC
10355 Sanden Dr, Dallas, TX 75238-2440
Tel (214) 553-1311 *Founded/Ownrshp* 1977
Sales 63.6MM^E *EMP* 80
SIC 5063 Electronic wire & cable; Wire & cable; Electronic wire & cable; Wire & cable
Pr: Jeff Fleming
Chf Mktg O: Hunter Fleming
Sls Dir: Chet Easterwood
Sls Mgr: Mark Word
Sales Asso: David Cortez

INTERSTATE WRLDWIDE RELOCATION
See INTERSTATE VAN LINES INC

INTERSTATE-MCBEE
See INTERSTATE DIESEL SERVICE INC

INTERSTATES CONSTRUCTION SERVI
See HARBOR GROUP INC

D-U-N-S 04-258-2577
INTERSTATES CONSTRUCTION SERVICES INC
(*Suby of* HARBOR GROUP INC) ★
1520 N Main Ave, Sioux Center, IA 51250-2111
Tel (712) 722-1662 *Founded/Ownrshp* 1999
Sales 80.1MM *EMP* 325
Accts Nichols Rise & Company Llp S
SIC 1731 3629 Electrical work; Computerized controls installation; Electronic generation equipment; Electrical work; Computerized controls installation; Electronic generation equipment
CEO: Scott Peterson
**Ch Bd:* Larry E Den Herder
**Pr:* David A Crumrine
**COO:* Catherine Bloom
**VP:* Dave Los
**VP:* Wayne McDaniel
**VP:* Lowell Reith
**VP:* Randy Van Vorst

D-U-N-S 10-885-1353
INTERSYSTEMS CORP
1 Memorial Dr Ste 6, Cambridge, MA 02142-1356
Tel (617) 621-0600 *Founded/Ownrshp* 1978
Sales 500.0MM *EMP* 1,400
SIC 7371 Prepackaged software; Computer software development & applications
Pr: Phillip T Ragon
COO: Christine Chapman
CFO: Ryan Brenneman
VP: Jerry Bartlett
**VP:* Richard Currier
**VP:* Joe Desantis
**VP:* Paul Grabsheid
VP: Steve Hess
**VP:* Robert Nagle
**VP:* Matthew Nee
VP: John F Paladino
**VP:* Susan Ragon
VP: Larry Roth
VP: Ron Sullivan
VP: Ray Vrtiska

D-U-N-S 08-899-6947 IMP/EXP
INTERSYSTEMS INTERNATIONAL INC
(*Suby of* PRITZKER GROUP- CHICAGO LLC) ★
9575 N 109th Ave, Omaha, NE 68142-1123
Tel (402) 330-1500 *Founded/Ownrshp* 2012
Sales 54.6MM^E *EMP* 275
SIC 3523 5033

D-U-N-S 10-569-4947 IMP
INTERTAPE POLYMER CORP
I P G
(*Suby of* IPG (US) INC) ★
100 Paramount Dr Ste 300, Sarasota, FL 34232-6051
Tel (941) 727-5788 *Founded/Ownrshp* 1995
Sales 200.7MM^E *EMP* 600
SIC 2672 Tape, pressure sensitive: made from purchased materials; Tape, pressure sensitive: made from purchased materials
Pr: Gregory A Yull
CFO: Eric Johnson
VP: Jim B Carpenter
VP: Bernard J Pitz

INTERTAPE POLYMER GROUP
See IPG (US) HOLDINGS INC

D-U-N-S 83-151-7045
INTERTAPE POLYMER US INC
(*Suby of* IPG (US) INC) ★
3647 Cortez Rd W Ste 102, Bradenton, FL 34210-3195
Tel (941) 727-5788 *Founded/Ownrshp* 2004
Sales 29.0MM^E *EMP* 407^E
SIC 2675 Die-cut paper & board
Pr: Janice Loppe
Snr Mgr: Maribel Estrada

D-U-N-S 15-451-8278 IMP
INTERTEC SYSTEMS LLC
45000 Helm St Ste 200, Plymouth, MI 48170-6040
Tel (734) 254-3268 *Founded/Ownrshp* 2008
Sales 95.3MM^E *EMP* 516
SIC 3714 Motor vehicle parts & accessories; Instrument board assemblies, motor vehicle; Motor vehicle parts & accessories; Instrument board assemblies, motor vehicle

INTERTECH FLOORING
See WE IMHOFF & CO INC

D-U-N-S 10-912-3406 IMP/EXP
INTERTECH GROUP INC
4838 Jenkins Ave, North Charleston, SC 29405-4816
Tel (843) 744-5174 *Founded/Ownrshp* 1983
Sales 1.6MMM^E *EMP* 15,832
SIC 3949 Fishing equipment; Fishing equipment
CEO: Anita G Zucker
COO: Jay Tiedemann
Ex VP: Robert Johnston
Sr VP: Sarah Van Mosel
IT Man: Jerry Zucker
Mktg Dir: Mike Fewell
Counsel: Matt Garfinkle

D-U-N-S 80-832-0050
INTERTECH SECURITY GROUP LLC
1501 Preble Ave Ste 6, Pittsburgh, PA 15233-2248
Tel (724) 742-4900 *Founded/Ownrshp* 2005
Sales 162.4MM^E *EMP* 180
SIC 7382 Security systems services; Burglar alarm maintenance & monitoring; Protective devices, security
CEO: Ronald Petnuch
CFO: Bart Huchel
Ex VP: Christopher J Wetzel
VP: Matthew Petnuch

D-U-N-S 00-172-2722
INTERTECH SECURITY LLC (PA)
(*Suby of* INTERTECH SECURITY GROUP LLC) ★
1501 Preble Ave Ste 6, Pittsburgh, PA 15233-2248
Tel (412) 246-1200 *Founded/Ownrshp* 1999
Sales 160.9MM^E *EMP* 180
SIC 5065 Security control equipment & systems; Security control equipment & systems
CEO: Ronald Petnuch
CFO: Bart Huchel
**Ex VP:* Christopher J Wetzel
VP: Michael Devinney
**VP:* Matthew Petnuch
Sales Exec: Bruce Oliver

D-U-N-S 62-736-3877
INTERTEK
545 E Algonquin Rd Ste F, Arlington Heights, IL 60005-4376
Tel (847) 871-1020 *Founded/Ownrshp* 2006
Sales 418.9MM^E *EMP* 2,564^E
SIC 8748 Business consulting
CEO: Wolfhart Hauser
**Pr:* Greg Tieman
Mktg Mgr: Michael Kremer

INTERTEK AUTOMOTIVE RESEARCH
See INTERTEK USA INC

INTERTEK COMPANY
See GLOBAL X-RAY & TESTING CORP

INTERTEK ETL SEMKO
See INTERTEK TESTING SERVICES NA INC

D-U-N-S 03-769-0302
INTERTEK TESTING SERVICES NA INC
INTERTEK ETL SEMKO
(*Suby of* INTERTEK GROUP PLC)
3933 Us Route 11, Cortland, NY 13045-9715
Tel (607) 753-6711 *Founded/Ownrshp* 1996
Sales 185.4MM^E *EMP* 1,400
SIC 8734 Testing laboratories; Product testing laboratory, safety or performance; Testing laboratories; Product testing laboratory, safety or performance
CEO: Wolfhart Hauser
**Pr:* Gregg Tiemann
**CFO:* Lloyd Pitchford
**Treas:* Tim Courossi
Ofcr: Chatdao Intertek
**Ex VP:* Stefan Butz
**VP:* Nimer Hafi
**VP:* Derwyn Reuber
VP: Patrick Sweeney
**VP:* Jeff Turcotte
Dir Lab: Daniel Betancourt
Dir Lab: Jason Carter
Dir Lab: Gumaro Castillo
Dir Lab: Katie Danyko
Dir Lab: Jennifer Heath
Dir Lab: Mike Holland
Dir Lab: Charlotte Hoorne
Dir Lab: Leilani McMillan
Dir Lab: Shanley Meulens
Dir Lab: Mickey Moore
Dir Lab: Daniel Thompson

D-U-N-S 07-415-9310
INTERTEK USA INC
INTERTEK AUTOMOTIVE RESEARCH
(*Suby of* INTERTEK UK HOLDINGS LIMITED)
2 Riverway Ste 500, Houston, TX 77056-2083
Tel (713) 543-3600 *Founded/Ownrshp* 1988
Sales 957.2MM^E *EMP* 4,000
SIC 4785 8734 Surveyors, marine cargo; Inspection services connected with transportation; Calibration & certification; Surveyors, marine cargo; Inspection services connected with transportation; Calibration & certification
Pr: Jay Gutierrez
CFO: William Charles
**VP:* Graham Lees
**VP:* Mark Vise
VP: Dirk Von Czarnowski
Exec: Diane Summers
Dir Lab: Ai Khor
Brnch Mgr: Alexis Ayala
Brnch Mgr: Anulfo Duval
Brnch Mgr: Kevin Gilbert
Genl Mgr: Stephen Southern

D-U-N-S 14-868-2727
INTERTEX GENERAL CONTRACTORS INC
28338 Constellation Rd # 900, Valencia, CA 91355-5098
Tel (661) 702-2222 *Founded/Ownrshp* 1982
Sales 32.8MM *EMP* 20
SIC 1542 Commercial & office building, new construction; Commercial & office building, new construction
Pr: Dale R Donohoe
**VP:* John T J T Garrett
**VP:* Bob Lyon
Exec: Tony Tumasone
Surg Cl Rc: Omid Omhgeresteh

INTERTHERM
See NORTEK GLOBAL HVAC LLC

D-U-N-S 00-420-0445
■ **INTERTHINX INC**
(*Suby of* FIRST AMERICAN FINANCIAL CORP) ★
30005 Ladyface Ct, Agoura Hills, CA 91301-2583
Tel (818) 878-1941 *Founded/Ownrshp* 2014
Sales NA *EMP* 700^E
SIC 6163 Mortgage brokers arranging for loans, using money of others; Mortgage brokers arranging for loans, using money of others
Pr: Jeff Moyer
Ex VP: Constance Wilson
Sr VP: Paul Harris
Sr VP: David G Kittle
Sr VP: Brett Waterman
VP: Laura Buser
VP: Jim Portner
VP: Gayle Shank
VP: Shiraz Vartanian
VP: Ilya Verlinsky
VP: Nick Volpe
VP: Ashley Woodworth

INTERTON-USA
See AMERICAN HEARING SYSTEMS INC

D-U-N-S 06-277-9053
■ **INTERTRADE LIMITED CORP**
(*Suby of* ROCKWELL COLLINS INC) ★
4700 N River Blvd Ne, Cedar Rapids, IA 52411-6636
Tel (319) 378-3500 *Founded/Ownrshp* 1969
Sales 31.3MM^E *EMP* 35^E
SIC 5065 5088 Electronic parts & equipment; Aircraft & parts
Pr: Kelly Ortberg
**Treas:* Douglas E Stenske
Off Mgr: Susan Krewson
Sls Mgr: Kurt Downey
Sls Mgr: Damon Hines
Sls Mgr: Travis Kalous

D-U-N-S 02-089-6791
INTERURBAN TRANSIT PARTNERSHIP
RAPID, THE
300 Ellsworth Ave Sw, Grand Rapids, MI 49503-4005
Tel (616) 459-7701 *Founded/Ownrshp* 1977
Sales 28.3MM^E *EMP* 350
SIC 4111 Bus transportation; Bus transportation
CEO: Peter Varga
COO: Brian Pouget
Sales Exec: Jennifer Kalczuk

D-U-N-S 83-729-3943
■ **INTERVAL ACQUISITION CORP**
INTERVAL INTERNATIONAL
(*Suby of* INTERVAL INTERNATIONAL INC) ★
6262 Sunset Dr Ste 400, South Miami, FL 33143-4843
Tel (954) 431-0060 *Founded/Ownrshp* 2008
Sales 42.1MM^E *EMP* 1,700
SIC 4724 Travel agencies; Travel agencies
Pr: Craig M Nash
**COO:* Paul Rishell
**CFO:* William Carl Drew
**Treas:* Eduardo Fernandez
**Ex VP:* Jeanette E Marbert

D-U-N-S 13-211-7024
■ INTERVAL HOLDING CO INC
(*Suby of* INTERVAL ACQUISITION CORP) ★
6262 Sunset Dr Fl 6, South Miami, FL 33143-4843
Tel (305) 666-1861 *Founded/Ownrshp* 2002
Sales 5.7MM^E *EMP* 1,700
SIC 8699 8721 6531 Travel club; Billing & bookkeeping service; Escrow agent, real estate; Travel club; Billing & bookkeeping service; Escrow agent, real estate
Prin: Jeanette Marbert

INTERVAL INTERNATIONAL
See INTERVAL ACQUISITION CORP

D-U-N-S 08-359-9936 EXP
■ INTERVAL INTERNATIONAL INC
(*Suby of* INTERVAL LEISURE GROUP INC) ★
6262 Sunset Dr Ste 400, South Miami, FL 33143-4843
Tel (305) 666-1861 *Founded/Ownrshp* 2008
Sales 179.3MM^E *EMP* 2,080
SIC 8699 Travel club; Travel club
CEO: Craig M Nash
Pr: Arturo Sosa
**COO:* Jeanette E Marbert
COO: Jeanette Marbert
COO: Paul Rishell
**CFO:* William Carl Drew
Treas: Eduardo Fernandez
Bd of Dir: Robert Healey
Sr VP: Sharon Freed
Sr VP: John Galea
Sr VP: Victoria Kincke
Sr VP: Jim Marmorstone
VP: Bryan T Broek
VP: Larry Dettelis
VP: Raul Estrada
VP: Rob Gaynor
VP: David Gilbert
VP: Edrea Kaiser
VP: Katy Keusch
VP: Marie Lee
VP: Stephanie Lone

D-U-N-S 82-818-6291
▲ INTERVAL LEISURE GROUP INC
6262 Sunset Dr, South Miami, FL 33143-4843
Tel (305) 666-1861 *Founded/Ownrshp* 1976
Sales 614.3MM *EMP* 6,100^E
Tkr Sym IILG *Exch* NGS
SIC 8699 Travel club; Travel club
Ch Bd: Craig M Nash
**COO:* Jeanette E Marbert
CFO: William L Harvey
Treas: John A Galea
Ex VP: Annie Welsh
Sr VP: Victoria J Kincke
Sr VP: Victoria Kincke
VP: Lily Arteaga
IT Man: Nelson Martinez
Board of Directors: David Flowers, Victoria L Freed, Chad Hollingsworth, Gary S Howard, Lewis K Korman, Thomas J Kuhn, Thomas P Murphy Jr

D-U-N-S 06-348-8522
INTERVARSITY CHRISTIAN FELLOWSHIP/USA
TWENTY ONE HUNDRED PRODUCTIONS
635 Science Dr, Madison, WI 53711-1099
Tel (608) 274-9001 *Founded/Ownrshp* 1941
Sales 87.8MM *EMP* 1,613
Accts Capin Crouse Llp Wheaton Il
SIC 8661 2731 7032 Religious organizations; Books: publishing & printing; Bible camp; Religious organizations; Books: publishing & printing; Bible camp
Pr: Alexander Hill
**Ch:* Rudy Hernandez
**Treas:* Mark Felton
Ofcr: Mark Bogertman
VP: A Fryling
**VP:* Robert Fryling
**VP:* Andrew Ginsberg
**VP:* Tom Lin
**VP:* James Lundgren
**VP:* Karon Morton
**VP:* Kim Porter
**VP:* Paul Tokonaga
Exec: Scott Wilson
Assoc Dir: Roy Stephen

INTERVENTIONAL ASSOCIATES OF M
See UT MEDICAL GROUP INC

D-U-N-S 83-542-9861
INTERVEST BANCSHARES CORP
1 Rockefeller Plz Ste 400, New York, NY 10020-2003
Tel (212) 218-2800 *Founded/Ownrshp* 1993
Sales NA *EMP* 81^E
SIC 6021 National commercial banks

D-U-N-S 17-409-1686
INTERVEST CONSTRUCTION OF ORLANDO INC
I C I
2379 Beville Rd, Daytona Beach, FL 32119-8720
Tel (386) 788-0820 *Founded/Ownrshp* 1980
Sales 145.3MM^E *EMP* 249
SIC 1522 1521 Multi-family dwelling construction; New construction, single-family houses; Multi-family dwelling construction; New construction, single-family houses
Pr: Morteza Hosseini-Kargar
CFO: Tom McCall
CFO: Jean Trinder
VP: Judy Lawrence
VP: Dick Smith
VP: Sherrie Williams
Exec: Robert Fortier
VP Admn: Charlene Ireland
Off Mgr: Debbie Carter
Sales Asso: Christine Claus
Sales Asso: Summer Halsey

D-U-N-S 03-767-8216 IMP
■ INTERVET INC
(*Suby of* MERCK & CO INC) ★
29160 Intervet Ln, Millsboro, DE 19966-4217
Tel (302) 934-4341 *Founded/Ownrshp* 2007
Sales 78.4MM^E *EMP* 800
SIC 2836 Veterinary biological products; Veterinary biological products
Pr: Christopher Ragland
VP: Stephen Collins
Assoc Dir: Joyce Woods
Genl Mgr: David Hallas
Tech Mgr: Dominique Legeay
Opers Mgr: Bonita Taylor
Ql Cn Mgr: Arthur Bowden
Ql Cn Mgr: Arnaud Pibaleau
Natl Sales: Clayton Coder
Natl Sales: Graham Welch
Mktg Mgr: Jim Miles

D-U-N-S 16-636-6161
INTERVIEWING SERVICE OF AMERICA INC
I S A
15400 Sherman Way Fl 4, Van Nuys, CA 91406-4271
Tel (818) 989-1044 *Founded/Ownrshp* 1982
Sales 56.0MM^E *EMP* 800
SIC 8732 Market analysis, business & economic research; Market analysis, business & economic research
Ch: Arnold Fishman
**Pr:* Michael Halberstam
**COO:* Tony Kretzmer
Ex VP: Daniel Gascoyne
**VP:* John Fitzpatrick
**VP:* Gregg Stickeler

INTERVISION FOODS
See INTERVISION LLC

D-U-N-S 19-379-9942 IMP/EXP
INTERVISION LLC
INTERVISION FOODS
3060 Peachtree Rd Nw # 230, Atlanta, GA 30305-2239
Tel (404) 814-1282 *Founded/Ownrshp* 2004
Sales 27.6MM^E *EMP* 20
SIC 5142 Frozen fish, meat & poultry
**Mng Dir:* Charles H Angstadt

D-U-N-S 80-631-0306
INTERVISION SYSTEMS TECHNOLOGIES INC
2270 Martin Ave, Santa Clara, CA 95050-2704
Tel (408) 980-8550 *Founded/Ownrshp* 1993
Sales 49.1MM^E *EMP* 80
SIC 7373 8712 Systems integration services; Computer systems analysis & design; Architectural services
CEO: Jeff Kaiser
**Pr:* Jason Gress
CFO: Samantha Vo
VP: Jamie Lee
VP: James Whitemore
Prgrm Mgr: J T Welsh
CIO: Thomas Dillon
Sftwr Eng: John Wade
VP Sls: Steven Goodison
Sls Mgr: Todd Hogan
Sls Mgr: Audrey Hurtado

D-U-N-S 11-743-9273
■ INTERVOICE LLC
(*Suby of* CONVERGYS CORP) ★
201 E 4th St 102-11, Cincinnati, OH 45202-4248
Tel (972) 454-8000 *Founded/Ownrshp* 2011
Sales 97.3MM^E *EMP* 736^E
SIC 3661 Telephone & telegraph apparatus; PBX equipment, manual or automatic; Telephone & telegraph apparatus; PBX equipment, manual or automatic
V Ch: David Bradenberg
V Ch: Stanley Brannan
Pr: Jeffrey Daly
Ex VP: Ray Naeini
Ex VP: Bob Ritchey
Ex VP: Donald R Walsh
Sr VP: Dwain H Ammond
Sr VP: Gordon H Givens
Sr VP: Kenneth Goldberg
Sr VP: Dwain H Hammond
Sr VP: Mark Haris
Sr VP: Richard Herrmann
Sr VP: Marie A Jackson
Sr VP: Francis G Sherlock
VP: Marc Gardner
VP: Manuel James
VP: Phil Osborn
VP: Greg Smith
VP: Steve Wind
VP: Carol Wingard

D-U-N-S 84-800-5518
INTERVOICE SERVICES INC
17787 Waterview Pkwy, Dallas, TX 75252-8027
Tel (972) 454-8000 *Founded/Ownrshp* 1983
Sales 32.4MM^E *EMP* 600
SIC 8748 Business consulting; Business consulting
Pr: David Brandenberg
Sr VP: Richard Herrmann
VP: Y K Abernathy
VP: Y Abernathy
Sls Dir: Kurt Parker

INTERWEST CONSTRUCTION & DEV
See INTERWEST DEVELOPMENT NW INC

D-U-N-S 19-457-2723
INTERWEST CONSTRUCTION INC
609 N Hill Blvd, Burlington, WA 98233-4600
Tel (360) 757-7574 *Founded/Ownrshp* 1988
Sales 32.7MM^E *EMP* 100
SIC 1623 7353 Water, sewer & utility lines; Heavy construction equipment rental; Water, sewer & utility lines; Heavy construction equipment rental
Pr: Eben Twaddle
**CFO:* Mark Suhadolnik
**Treas:* Patti M Baker
**VP:* Sean McGuiness
Genl Mgr: Suzanne Downing

D-U-N-S 79-795-1449
INTERWEST DEVELOPMENT NW INC
INTERWEST CONSTRUCTION & DEV
28201 Stat Rr 410, Buckley, WA 98321
Tel (253) 939-9787 *Founded/Ownrshp* 1991
Sales 20.9MM^E *EMP* 100
SIC 1542 Commercial & office building, new construction; Commercial & office building, new construction
Pr: Joe Kessell
**VP:* Shane Selander
**VP:* William Selander Jr
Off Mgr: Phyllis Reich

D-U-N-S 09-952-8531
INTERWEST INSURANCE SERVICES INC
KEMPER INSURANCE
3636 American River Dr # 2, Sacramento, CA 95864-5952
Tel (916) 488-3100 *Founded/Ownrshp* 1992
Sales NA *EMP* 315
SIC 6411 Insurance brokers; Insurance brokers
Ch: Tom Williams
**Pr:* Thomas Williams
**CEO:* Keith Schuler
**COO:* Nancy Luttenbacher
**CFO:* Donald Pollard
**Ex VP:* William O'Keefe
VP: Steve Azevedo
VP: Mark Blofsky
VP: Craig Houck
VP: Tom Hughes
VP: Greg Scoville
VP: Phil Watkins
Exec: Sam Wlasiuk
Assoc Dir: Ann Quinn

D-U-N-S 06-118-0456
INTERWEST VENTURE MANAGEMENT CO
2710 Sand Hill Rd Fl 2, Menlo Park, CA 94025-7020
Tel (650) 854-8585 *Founded/Ownrshp* 1980
Sales 28.3MM *EMP* 35
SIC 8741 Business management; Business management
Pr: Philip T Gianos

INTERWIRE GROUP
See INTERWIRE PRODUCTS INC

D-U-N-S 05-730-3372 IMP
INTERWIRE PRODUCTS INC
INTERWIRE GROUP
355 Main St Ste 2, Armonk, NY 10504-1844
Tel (914) 273-6633 *Founded/Ownrshp* 1981
Sales 96.8MM *EMP* 147
Accts Bdo Usa Llp Valhalla Ny
SIC 5051 Metal wires, ties, cables & screening; Metal wires, ties, cables & screening
Pr: Frank Cardile Jr
**V Ch Bd:* Deborah Cardile
VP: Lanny Wright
Genl Mgr: Susan Cook
Dir IT: Bob Chellis
Trfc Mgr: Brian McGillicuddy
Sales Asso: Sherry Hochard
Sales Asso: David Jenkins
Sales Asso: Laura Peterson
Sales Asso: Stephanie Ramey

D-U-N-S 12-987-0007
INTERWORLD HIGHWAY LLC
TEQUIPMENT.NET
205 Westwood Ave, Long Branch, NJ 07740-6564
Tel (866) 942-6273 *Founded/Ownrshp* 2002
Sales 40.7MM *EMP* 38
Accts Mcguckin Shatz & White Llc L
SIC 5999 Educational aids & electronic training materials
Pr: Richard Wagner
**VP:* Evan Cirelli
IT Man: Jacob Petrie
Sls Mgr: Gene Bulmer
Sls Mgr: Jonathan Dolan
Sls Mgr: Hugh Macdonald

D-U-N-S 07-969-3070
INTERZAN LLC
ROMEO & JULIET COUTURE
530 7th Ave Rm 2201, New York, NY 10018-4849
Tel (310) 926-8026 *Founded/Ownrshp* 2015
Sales 22.0MM *EMP* 20
SIC 5621 Women's specialty clothing stores
CEO: David Shamouelian
**COO:* Douglas Toth

D-U-N-S 05-151-5203 IMP
▲ INTEST CORP
804 E Gate Dr Ste 200, Mount Laurel, NJ 08054-1209
Tel (856) 505-8800 *Founded/Ownrshp* 1981
Sales 41.8MM *EMP* 127^E
Tkr Sym INTT *Exch* ASE
SIC 3825 3823 Digital test equipment, electronic & electrical circuits; Semiconductor test equipment; Temperature measurement instruments, industrial; Digital test equipment, electronic & electrical circuits; Semiconductor test equipment; Temperature measurement instruments, industrial
Pr: Robert E Matthiessen
**Ch Bd:* Alyn R Holt
CFO: Hugh T Regan Jr
Sr VP: Daniel J Graham
VP: James Pelrin
Off Mgr: Susan Dawson
MIS Dir: Hugh Regan
Sls Dir: Paul Kays
Board of Directors: Steven J Abrams, Joseph W Dews IV, William Kraut

INTEST THERMAL SOLUTIONS
See TEMPTRONIC CORP

D-U-N-S 80-786-9362 IMP/EXP
INTEVA PRODUCTS LLC
(*Suby of* RENCO GROUP INC) ★
1401 Crooks Rd Ste 100, Troy, MI 48084-7106
Tel (248) 655-8886 *Founded/Ownrshp* 2007
Sales 3.0MMM^E *EMP* 11,500
SIC 3714 5085 Motor vehicle parts & accessories; Motor vehicle parts & accessories; Industrial supplies
Pr: Lon Offenbacher
CFO: William Dircks
VP: Steven Galle
VP: Jan Griffiths
VP: William Hanna
VP: Michael Maddelein
Ex Dir: Matthew Modrzejewski
CIO: Dennis Hodges
CTO: David Blankenship
Opers Supe: Allan Guerra
Counsel: Marnie Suma

D-U-N-S 62-267-0529 IMP
▲ INTEVAC INC
3560 Bassett St, Santa Clara, CA 95054-2704
Tel (408) 986-9888 *Founded/Ownrshp* 1990
Sales 65.5MM *EMP* 302^E
Accts Grant Thornton Llp San Jose
Tkr Sym IVAC *Exch* NGS
SIC 3559 Semiconductor manufacturing machinery; Semiconductor manufacturing machinery
Pr: Wendell Blonigan
**Ch Bd:* Norman H Pond
**Pr:* Wendell T Blonigan
COO: Luke Marusaik
CFO: James Moniz
CFO: James P Moniz
Treas: Christopher Smith
Bd of Dir: Ping Yang
Ex VP: Andres Brugal
Ex VP: Jay C Cho
Ex VP: Jay Cho
Ex VP: Michael A Russak
Ex VP: Michael Russak
VP: Ralph Kerns
Dir Bus: Michael Mohawk
Board of Directors: Matthew A Drapkin, David S Dury, Marc T Giles, Stanley J Hill, Thomas M Rohrs, John F Schaefer, Ping Yang

D-U-N-S 83-121-4312
INTEVATION FOOD GROUP LLC
3975 Tall Pine Dr, Plover, WI 54467-3568
Tel (715) 345-1926 *Founded/Ownrshp* 2008
Sales 62.2MM^E *EMP* 200
SIC 2038 Snacks, including onion rings, cheese sticks, etc.
Pr: Mark Arend
**VP:* Christine Arend

D-U-N-S 78-937-8879 IMP
INTEX DIY INC
100 Leggett Dr, Villa Rica, GA 30180-1523
Tel (770) 459-1800 *Founded/Ownrshp* 2004
Sales 22.0MM^E *EMP* 100
SIC 2299 5093 3291 2392 2297 Batting, wadding, padding & fillings; Textile waste; Abrasive products; Household furnishings; Nonwoven fabrics; Batting, wadding, padding & fillings; Textile waste; Abrasive products; Household furnishings; Nonwoven fabrics
Pr: Robert Dailey
**CEO:* Mitchell S Bollag
**CFO:* B Alan Hayes
Natl Sales: Edie Marks

INTEX PLASTICS SALES
See INTEX PROPERTIES PERRIS VALLEY LP

D-U-N-S 00-752-5827
INTEX PROPERTIES PERRIS VALLEY LP
INTEX PLASTICS SALES
(*Suby of* INTEX RECREATION CORP) ★
4130 Santa Fe Ave, Long Beach, CA 90810-1439
Tel (310) 549-5400 *Founded/Ownrshp* 1970
Sales 21.9MM^E *EMP* 400
SIC 3081 5162 Vinyl film & sheet; Polyethylene film; Plastics products; Vinyl film & sheet; Polyethylene film; Plastics products
Pr: Tien P Zee
**VP:* Bill Smith

D-U-N-S 06-777-0883 IMP/EXP
INTEX RECREATION CORP (CA)
(*Suby of* INTEX RECREATION CORP) ★
4001 Via Oro Ave Ste 210, Long Beach, CA 90810-1400
Tel (310) 549-1846 *Founded/Ownrshp* 1966
Sales 26.5MM^E *EMP* 100
SIC 5021 5092 5091 5162 Waterbeds; Toys; Watersports equipment & supplies; Plastics materials & basic shapes; Waterbeds; Toys; Watersports equipment & supplies; Plastics materials & basic shapes
CEO: Tien P Zee
**Pr:* Jim Lai
**VP:* Bill Smith

D-U-N-S 09-862-6062 IMP/EXP
INTEX RECREATION CORP
4001 Via Oro Ave Ste 210, Long Beach, CA 90810-1400
Tel (310) 549-5400 *Founded/Ownrshp* 1970
Sales 192.8MM^E *EMP* 679^E
SIC 5091 5092 5021 3081 Watersports equipment & supplies; Toys; Waterbeds; Vinyl film & sheet; Polyethylene film; Watersports equipment & supplies; Toys; Waterbeds; Vinyl film & sheet; Polyethylene film
Pr: Tien P Zee
Info Man: Wayne Farmer
Sls Dir: Steve DOE
Sls Dir: Ryan Slate
Counsel: Gerald Margolis

D-U-N-S 14-703-7055
INTEX SOLUTIONS INC
110 A St, Needham, MA 02494-2807
Tel (781) 453-0933 *Founded/Ownrshp* 1985
Sales 21.7MM^E *EMP* 75
SIC 5734 7371 Software, business & non-game; Computer software development
Pr: George Jigarjian
Ofcr: Aviva Figler
VP: Timothy Burr
VP: Pamela Kalmus
VP: James Wilner
Dir IT: Brian Day
Software D: Garrett Stuck
Software D: T Sung
Sftwr Eng: Matthew Feinberg
S&M/VP: Christina Lynch

D-U-N-S 05-609-5326
INTHINC INC
4225 W Lake Park Blvd # 100, Salt Lake City, UT 84120-8213
Tel (801) 886-2255 *Founded/Ownrshp* 1997
Sales 54.5MM^E *EMP* 340

SIC 3672 Printed circuit boards; Printed circuit boards
CEO: Todd W Follmer
Pr: Tom Carlin
**Pr:* Blake Kirby
Pr: Carleton Watkins
CFO: Vivek Chaturvedi
CFO: Michael Olson
Treas: Philip Swensen
**Ex VP:* Jeffrey M Harvey
Sr VP: Thomas D Williams
VP: Roy Breslawski
VP: Jeff Cummings
VP: Melissa S Rosato
VP: Larry Simmons

D-U-N-S 11-004-6310 IMP
INTHINC TECHNOLOGY SOLUTIONS INC
4225 W Lake Park Blvd # 100, West Valley City, UT 84120-8213
Tel (801) 886-2255 *Founded/Ownrshp* 1999
Sales 39.1MM^E *EMP* 85
SIC 3812 3559 Search & navigation equipment; Automotive related machinery; Search & navigation equipment; Automotive related machinery
CEO: Todd W Follmer
**CFO:* Michael Burstein
CFO: Michael Olsen
**Ex VP:* Skip Kinford
**Sr VP:* Peter Allen
**VP:* Vivek Chaturvedi
**VP:* Jeffrey M Harvey
VP: Bruce Huber
VP: Brian Meek
**VP:* Kevin Mitchell
VP: Wesley Robinson
VP: Paul Shouse
**Exec:* J Corey Catten
Board of Directors: O Jeffrey Collett, Todd W Follmer, Alan Larsen, Joseph P Urso

INTIER AUTOMOTIVE SEATING
See MAGNA SEATING OF AMERICA INC

D-U-N-S 17-557-1231
INTIGRAL INC
EST
7850 Northfield Rd, Walton Hills, OH 44146-5523
Tel (440) 945-1075 *Founded/Ownrshp* 2005
Sales 42.2MM^E *EMP* 227
SIC 3231 Insulating glass: made from purchased glass; Insulating glass: made from purchased glass
CEO: Tom Bradley
**Pr:* Jason Thomas
**Ex VP:* Jim Prete
VP: Jamey Beard
VP: Brett Beech
**VP:* Dick Dietrich
**VP:* Edmond Leopold
**VP:* Phil Marcantonio
**VP:* Deanna Negron
Exec: Susan Hamilton
Telecom Ex: Jeff Mock

D-U-N-S 82-684-8280 IMP
INTIMACY MANAGEMENT CO LLC
3980 Dekalb Tec Pkwy, Atlanta, GA 30340-2758
Tel (678) 244-0519 *Founded/Ownrshp* 2007
Sales 63.9MM^E *EMP* 189
SIC 5137 Apparel belts, women's & children's; Apparel belts, women's & children's
Pr: David Nethero
Rgnl Mgr: Isabel Baert

D-U-N-S 96-784-0369
■ INTIMATE BRANDS HOLDING LLC
(*Suby of* INTIMATE BRANDS INC) ★
3 Limited Pkwy, Columbus, OH 43230-1467
Tel (614) 415-7000 *Founded/Ownrshp* 2011
Sales 368.6MM^E *EMP* 228^E
SIC 5632 Lingerie (outerwear)
V Ch: Kenneth B Gilman
Sls Mgr: Jill Granoff

D-U-N-S 15-061-4829
■ INTIMATE BRANDS INC
(*Suby of* L BRANDS INC) ★
3 Limited Pkwy, Columbus, OH 43230-1467
Tel (614) 415-7000 *Founded/Ownrshp* 1993
Sales 368.6MM^E *EMP* 228^E
SIC 5632 Lingerie (outerwear)
CFO: Stuart Burgdoerfer

D-U-N-S 12-154-4423
INTL BUDGET PARTNERSHIP
CENTER ON BDGT PLICY PRORITIES
820 1st St Ne Ste 460, Washington, DC 20002-4243
Tel (202) 408-1080 *Founded/Ownrshp* 1981
Sales 37.5MM *EMP* 60
Accts Rhis Jones & Maresca Pa Colu
SIC 8733 Physical research, noncommercial
Ex Dir: Robert Greenstein
Bd of Dir: Henry J Aaron
Bd of Dir: Barbara Blum
Bd of Dir: Matthew Broaddus
Bd of Dir: Martha Coven
Bd of Dir: Kris Cox
Bd of Dir: Keri Fulton
Bd of Dir: Manuela Garza
Bd of Dir: James O Gibson
Bd of Dir: Pamela Gomez
Bd of Dir: Beatrix Hamburg
Bd of Dir: Deborah Harrod
Bd of Dir: Jim Horney
Bd of Dir: Elizabeth Hudgins
Bd of Dir: Josh Kaufman
Bd of Dir: Manya Khan
Bd of Dir: Jason Levitis
Bd of Dir: Harika Masud
Bd of Dir: Jason Moreira
Bd of Dir: Marion Pines
Bd of Dir: Robert D Reischauer

D-U-N-S 00-859-6490
INTL COMMUNICTS
11242 Waples Mill Rd, Fairfax, VA 22030-6079
Tel (703) 352-2409 *Founded/Ownrshp* 2007
Sales 25.7MM *EMP* 1

SIC 7389 Personal service agents, brokers & bureaus; Personal service agents, brokers & bureaus
Prin: Jay Rogina

D-U-N-S 62-079-3877
▲ INTL FCSTONE INC
708 3rd Ave Rm 1500, New York, NY 10017-4108
Tel (212) 485-3500 *Founded/Ownrshp* 1924
Sales 34.6MMM *EMP* 1,141
Tkr Sym INTL *Exch* NGS
SIC 6282 6211 6289 Investment advice; Security brokers & dealers; Mineral, oil & gas leasing & royalty dealers; Security & commodity clearinghouses; Investment advice; Security brokers & dealers; Mineral, oil & gas leasing & royalty dealers; Security & commodity clearinghouses
Pr: Sean M O'Connor
**Ch Bd:* John Radziwill
Pr: Gary Esterman
Pr: Marcelo Taborda
COO: Xuong Nguyen
CFO: William J Dunaway
Chf Inves: Jonathan Binder
Ofcr: Robert Marischen
Ofcr: Brian Sephton
Ofcr: Laura Torphy
VP: Shaun Finnerty
VP: Rene Friedman
VP: Tricia Harrod
Dir Risk M: Nate Burka
Dir Risk M: Juan Hinojosa

D-U-N-S 78-906-7241
INTONE NETWORKS INC
10 Austin Ave, Iselin, NJ 08830-2908
Tel (732) 721-3002 *Founded/Ownrshp* 2003
Sales 24.2MM^E *EMP* 400
SIC 7371 7389 Computer software development; Telephone services; Computer software development; Telephone services
Pr: Chandrakala Kodathala
VP: Srikanth Javvadi
**VP:* Kavitha Kodathala
VP: Reddy Prabsakar
**VP:* Prabhakar Reddy
Exec: Poonam Kumari
Dir Bus: Nancy Major
Sls Mgr: Prathima Devulapally

D-U-N-S 11-819-7941
INTOUCH CREDIT UNION
5640 Democracy Dr, Plano, TX 75024-3514
Tel (214) 291-1776 *Founded/Ownrshp* 2001
Sales NA *EMP* 200
SIC 6062 State credit unions; State credit unions
Pr: Kent Lugrand
CFO: Bob McDonald
Bd of Dir: Theresa Tschirky
Ofcr: Sammie Cantrell
Sr VP: Scott Alton
VP: Tarry Martin
VP: Tim McCoy
Brnch Mgr: Sheila Cullum
Brnch Mgr: Eveline Ngassa

INTOUCH HEALTH
See INTOUCH TECHNOLOGIES INC

INTOUCH MINISTRY
See INTOUCH MINISTRIES INC

D-U-N-S 09-012-1661
INTOUCH SOLUTIONS INC (KS)
7045 College Blvd Ste 300, Overland Park, KS 66211-1529
Tel (913) 317-9700 *Founded/Ownrshp* 1999
Sales 107.9MM^E *EMP* 500
SIC 8742 Marketing consulting services; Marketing consulting services
CEO: Faruk Capan
**Ex VP:* Wendy Blackburn
Ex VP: Boris Kushkuley
**Ex VP:* Angela Tenuta
**Ex VP:* David Windhausen
**Sr VP:* Megan O'Connor
Sr VP: Dirk Reinhardt
Sr VP: Eric Vollmuth
**VP:* Pat McNerney
**VP:* Connie Mullinix
VP: Greg Schutta
Exec: Connie Millinix
Dir: Joe Abella
Dir: Laura Shepherd
Creative D: Charley Aldridge
Creative D: Chris Boyer
Creative D: Erin Cwiakala
Creative D: Joanna Friel
Creative D: Kris Grazier
Creative D: Kit Hunnell
Creative D: Craig Johnston

D-U-N-S 13-303-3717
INTOUCH TECHNOLOGIES INC
INTOUCH HEALTH
6330 Hollister Ave, Goleta, CA 93117-3115
Tel (805) 562-8686 *Founded/Ownrshp* 2002
Sales 33.4MM *EMP* 54
Accts Deloitte & Touche Llp Los Ang
SIC 7372 Robots, assembly line: industrial & commercial; Prepackaged software; Business oriented computer software
CEO: Yulun Wang
**COO:* David Adornetto
**CFO:* Stephen L Wilson
**Ex VP:* Paul Evans
**VP:* Michael Chan
VP: Bill Day
**VP:* Charles S Jordan
**VP:* Steve Jordan
VP: Christopher Joslin
VP: Doug McClung
VP: Gerry Popolow
VP: Andy Puterbaugh
VP: Herb Winckelmann
**VP:* Tim Wright
VP Bus Dev: Bill Goodmen
Board of Directors: John Glaser

D-U-N-S 12-858-3098
INTOUCH WIRELESS
I COMM SOLUTIONS
7 W 30th St Fl 12, New York, NY 10001-4406
Tel (212) 279-3338 *Founded/Ownrshp* 1999
Sales 33.8MM *EMP* 15
Accts Steinbach & Sekular
SIC 5065 Telephone equipment
**Pr:* Vijayant Ghai
**Treas:* Atul Ghai
**VP:* Suresh Sachdeva

D-U-N-S 13-695-1303
INTOUCH WIRELESS OF COLOMBUS CIRCLE LLC
1940 W Corporate Way, Anaheim, CA 92801-5373
Tel (714) 829-1600 *Founded/Ownrshp* 2002
Sales 25.0MM^E *EMP* 550
Accts Grober And Company Llc Saint
SIC 5999 Mobile telephones & equipment; Mobile telephones & equipment
Brnch Mgr: Sarah Baker

D-U-N-S 79-682-3511
INTOWN HOLDING CO LLC
2727 Paces Fery Rd 2 1200, Atlanta, GA 30339
Tel (770) 799-5000 *Founded/Ownrshp* 1997
Sales NA *EMP* 0^E
Accts Deloitte & Touche Llp Atlanta
SIC 6712 Bank holding companies; Bank holding companies

INTOWN HOMES
See LOVETT CUSTOM HOMES INC

D-U-N-S 82-865-3225
INTOWN HOSPITALITY INVESTORS LP
INTOWN SUITES
980 Hammond Dr Ste 1400, Atlanta, GA 30328-8144
Tel (770) 799-5000 *Founded/Ownrshp* 2007
Sales 40.8MM^E *EMP* 1,100
SIC 6513 Apartment hotel operation; Apartment hotel operation
CFO: Dennis M Cassel
COO: Scott Griffith
CFO: Marianela Mayor
Exec: Kenneth Almy
Exec: Rich Keister
Exec: Dave Macculley
Exec: Lora Rabun
Exec: Gary Scott
Exec: Somesh Sharma
Area Mgr: A J Clay
Area Mgr: Byron Millirons

INTOWN SUITES
See INTOWN HOSPITALITY INVESTORS LP

D-U-N-S 04-526-0440
INTOWN SUITES MANAGEMENT INC
(*Suby of* INTOWN HOSPITALITY INVESTORS LP) ★
980 Hammond Dr Ste 1400, Atlanta, GA 30328-8144
Tel (800) 769-1670 *Founded/Ownrshp* 2008
Sales 39.8MM^E *EMP* 900
SIC 6513 Apartment hotel operation; Apartment hotel operation
CEO: Dennis M Cassel
CFO: Fereed Mangaliji
VP: Fereed Mangalji

D-U-N-S 09-617-3950 IMP
INTRA AMERICAN METALS INC
INTRAMETCO
14297 Bergen Blvd Ste 200, Noblesville, IN 46060-3383
Tel (317) 219-4444 *Founded/Ownrshp* 1979
Sales 118.0MM *EMP* 11
SIC 5093 Nonferrous metals scrap
Pr: Jay Stutz
**VP:* Tom Alexander
**VP:* John Town

D-U-N-S 08-503-4742
INTRA CORP
885 Manufacturers Dr, Westland, MI 48186-4036
Tel (734) 728-1688 *Founded/Ownrshp* 1977
Sales 20.3MM^E *EMP* 105
SIC 3545 3544 3823 Gauges (machine tool accessories); Special dies, tools, jigs & fixtures; Industrial instrmnts msrmnt display/control process variable
CEO: John Battista Sr
**Pr:* John Battista Jr
**Treas:* Patricia Battista
VP: Wojtek Grabinski
Sfty Dirs: Edward Malen
Ql Cn Mgr: Christopher Janutol
Snr Mgr: David Kruszewski

D-U-N-S 01-643-0246
INTRA STAFF
10751 Falls Rd Ste 275, Lutherville Timonium, MD 21093-4541
Tel (410) 583-2950 *Founded/Ownrshp* 1987
Sales 12.0MM *EMP* 650
SIC 7361 Placement agencies; Placement agencies

D-U-N-S 15-036-1632
INTRACARE HOSPITAL
7601 Fannin St, Houston, TX 77054-1905
Tel (281) 893-7200 *Founded/Ownrshp* 1984
Sales 24.3MM^E *EMP* 600
SIC 8062 General medical & surgical hospitals
Ch: Timothy Sharma MD
**CEO:* Terry Scovill
**CFO:* Deo Shanker
Pr Dir: John Pickett

D-U-N-S 09-702-4272
INTRACARE NORTH HOSPITAL
(*Suby of* INTRACARE HOSPITAL) ★
1120 Cypress Station Dr, Houston, TX 77090-3002
Tel (281) 453-8300 *Founded/Ownrshp* 2003
Sales 20.8MM *EMP* 300^E
SIC 8062 General medical & surgical hospitals; General medical & surgical hospitals
CFO: Deo Shanker
CFO: Fred Chen
**VP:* Terry Scoville

D-U-N-S 08-276-5751 EXP
INTRACO CORP
AUTOMOTIVE SERVICE INDUSTRIES
530 Stephenson Hwy Fl 2nd, Troy, MI 48083-1131
Tel (313) 345-1333 *Founded/Ownrshp* 1971
Sales 32.9MM^E *EMP* 50^E
SIC 5039 5013 5012 Exterior flat glass: plate or window; Interior flat glass: plate or window; Automobile glass; Automotive supplies & parts; Trucks, noncommercial
Ch Bd: Nicola M Antakli
**CEO:* J John Antakli
**Treas:* Mike Rousseau
**Ex VP:* Sam Antakli
**VP:* Jehad Antakli
**VP:* Mauro R Difazio
**VP:* Jeffrey Krause
**VP:* Michael F Rousseau
**VP:* Daniel W Wywoda
Opers Mgr: Raya Alperovich
Opers Mgr: Caroline Perrotta

D-U-N-S 62-422-9902 IMP/EXP
INTRACOM USA INC
IC INTRACOM USA
(*Suby of* IC INTRACOM HOLDINGS LLC) ★
550 Commerce Blvd, Oldsmar, FL 34677-2810
Tel (813) 855-0550 *Founded/Ownrshp* 1990
Sales 33.7MM^E *EMP* 50
Accts Spence Marston Bunch Morris
SIC 5063 5045 Electrical apparatus & equipment; Computers & accessories, personal & home entertainment
Pr: Michael Thiel
**CFO:* Betsy Bennett
**VP:* Sareet Majumdar
**VP:* David Sousa
**VP:* Randy Steen
Web Dev: Divyesh Mistry
Mktg Mgr: Stacey Klinger
Mktg Mgr: Michael Smith
Board of Directors: Michael Thiel, Ulrich Thiel

D-U-N-S 15-341-6883
INTRADE INDUSTRIES INC
2559 S East Ave, Fresno, CA 93706-5104
Tel (559) 274-9877 *Founded/Ownrshp* 2004
Sales 20.1MM^E *EMP* 84
SIC 4231 Trucking terminal facilities
CEO: Tejinder S Mehta
**VP:* Baljinder Kaur

INTRADECO
See REGAL WORLDWIDE TRADING LLC

INTRADECO APPAREL
See INTRADECO INC

D-U-N-S 14-070-5653
INTRADECO APPAREL INC
(*Suby of* INTRADECO APPAREL) ★
9500 Nw 108th Ave, Medley, FL 33178-2517
Tel (305) 264-8888 *Founded/Ownrshp* 2001
Sales 325.0MM *EMP* 180^E
Accts Kabat Schertzer De La Torre
SIC 2389 Men's miscellaneous accessories; Men's miscellaneous accessories
CEO: Felix J Siman
**CFO:* Jose E Siman
VP: Martha Dugan
Off Mgr: Manuel Moreno
Dir IT: Luis Marquina
IT Man: Leonor Segovia
Opers Mgr: Edgar Aguirre
S&M/VP: Hector Gutierrez

D-U-N-S 10-833-6066 IMP
INTRADECO INC
INTRADECO APPAREL
9500 Nw 108th Ave, Medley, FL 33178-2517
Tel (305) 264-6022 *Founded/Ownrshp* 2013
Sales 335.0MM^E *EMP* 180^E
SIC 5136 5199 5065 Men's & boys' clothing; Cotton yarns; Electronic parts; Men's & boys' clothing; Cotton yarns; Electronic parts
Pr: Jose E Siman
Sr VP: Terry Trofholz
VP: Luis Marquina
**VP:* Felix J Siman
**Prin:* Rolando Calsa
IT Man: Rafael Olivares
IT Man: Leonor Segovia
Natl Sales: Joel Eisenberg
VP Sls: Jay Boyett

D-U-N-S 13-086-6551
■ INTRADO INC
(*Suby of* WEST CORP) ★
1601 Dry Creek Dr Ste 250, Longmont, CO 80503-6494
Tel (303) 651-3553 *Founded/Ownrshp* 1993
Sales 190.3MM^E *EMP* 776
SIC 7373 Computer-aided system services; Computer-aided system services
Pr: Mary Hester
Pr: Christopher Borchers
**CEO:* Stephen M Meer
COO: Julie Gehring
**Sr VP:* Craig W Donaldson
**Sr VP:* Mary Hester
**Sr VP:* Dami Hummel
**Sr VP:* Steve Lowe
VP: Terry Barrett
VP: Paul Devenny
VP: Craig Donaldson
VP: Jim Keenan
VP: Marc Offutt
Exec: Johnny Alirez
Exec: Jim Antonucci
Exec: Debbie Hall

D-U-N-S 18-970-5820 IMP
INTRAHEALTH INTERNATIONAL INC
6340 Quadrangle Dr # 200, Chapel Hill, NC 27517-7891
Tel (919) 313-9100 *Founded/Ownrshp* 2005
Sales 90.4MM *EMP* 154^E
Accts Gelman Rosenberg & Freedman B

SIC 8011 Health maintenance organization; Health maintenance organization
Pr: Pape Amadou Gaye
Ofcr: Anne Fitzgerald
Ofcr: Jennifer Gloc
Ofcr: Nola Paterni
Ofcr: Aimee Phillips
Sr VP: Rebecca Kohler
VP: Maureen Corbett
VP: Scott Sherman Edd
Prgrm Mgr: Carol Cisse
Prgrm Mgr: Laura Hurley
Prgrm Mgr: Dana Singleton
Board of Directors: Todd Wohler, Walter Davenport, Joseph P Davis III, Marilyn Deluca, Sheila Leatherman, Josh Nesbit, Charles Ok Pannenborg, Nilda Peragallo, Carlos Correcha-Price, Beverly Rubin

D-U-N-S 80-323-7697
▲ INTRALINKS HOLDINGS INC
150 E 42nd St Fl 8, New York, NY 10017-5626
Tel (212) 543-7700 *Founded/Ownrshp* 1996
Sales 255.8MM *EMP* 810^E
Tkr Sym IL *Exch* NYS
SIC 7372 7382 Prepackaged software; Security systems services; Prepackaged software; Security systems services
Pr: Ronald W Hovsepian
*Ch Bd: Patrick J Wack Jr
CFO: Christopher J Lafond
Chf Mktg O: Thor Johnson
Ex VP: Jose Almandoz
Ex VP: Aditya Joshi
Ex VP: Russell Poole
Ex VP: Scott N Semel
Sr VP: Daren Glenister
VP: Ian Bruce
VP: Wade Callison
VP: Paul Cofini
VP: John Dalkiewicz
VP: Greg Langan
VP: Harry Lee
VP: Jorge Mira
VP: Leif O'Leary
VP: Peter Robinson
Board of Directors: Brian J Conway, Peter Gyenes, Thomas Hale, Habib Kairouz, Robert C McBride, Harsha Ramalingam, J Chris Scalet

D-U-N-S 94-885-4443
■ INTRALINKS INC
(*Suby of* INTRALINKS HOLDINGS INC) ★
150 E 42nd St Fl 8, New York, NY 10017-5626
Tel (212) 543-7700 *Founded/Ownrshp* 2007
Sales 199.0MM^E *EMP* 380
SIC 4899 7375 Data communication services; Information retrieval services; Data communication services; Information retrieval services
Pr: Ronald W Hovsepian
CFO: Derek Irwin
*CFO: Anthony Plesner
Ex VP: Julian Henkin
Ex VP: Rob Mullen
*Ex VP: Fahim Siddiqui
Sr VP: David Barbero
*Sr VP: Gary Hirsch
Sr VP: Dave Roy
Sr VP: Glenn Schwartz
Sr VP: Claudia Seeger
VP: Michael Baldwin
VP: Mayank Choudhary
VP: Christopher Ford
VP: Rainer Gawlick
VP: Rob Piane
VP: Jeanette Vanbelle
VP: Chris Vitti
VP: George Waidell
Dir Bus: Charles Roberts
Board of Directors: Brian J Conway, Habib Kairouz, Harry D Taylor

D-U-N-S 06-546-7052 IMP/EXP
INTRALOX LLC
(*Suby of* LAITRAM LLC) ★
301 Plantation Rd, Harahan, LA 70123-5326
Tel (504) 733-6739 *Founded/Ownrshp* 1990
Sales 158.9MM^E *EMP* 608
SIC 3535 Conveyors & conveying equipment; Conveyors & conveying equipment
Sfty Dirs: Zhinong Yan
Sfty Mgr: Gloria Bowman

INTRAMETCO
See INTRA AMERICAN METALS INC

D-U-N-S 09-229-6524
INTRANSIT INC
UTI TRANSPORT SOLUTIONS
(*Suby of* UTI UNITED STATES INC) ★
3525 Excel Dr, Medford, OR 97504-9798
Tel (541) 773-3993 *Founded/Ownrshp* 2006
Sales 64.5MM^E *EMP* 110
SIC 4731 Brokers, shipping; Brokers, shipping
Pr: Donald R Farthing
Pr: Chad Atkinson
VP: Suellen Rowe
VP: Pat Walden
Dir IT: Kevin Washington

D-U-N-S 62-252-7463 IMP
INTRAPAC (HARRISONBURG) INC
(*Suby of* INTRAPAC GROUP,THE)
4850 Crowe Dr, Mount Crawford, VA 22841-2221
Tel (540) 434-1703 *Founded/Ownrshp* 2003
Sales 45.6MM^E *EMP* 260
SIC 3499 3089 Metal household articles; Plastic containers, except foam; Metal household articles; Plastic containers, except foam
Pr: Rami Younes
*VP: Joe Forelich
Opers Mgr: David Stanlick
Plnt Mgr: Randy Churchill

D-U-N-S 07-866-0879
INTRAPAC INTERNATIONAL CORP
136 Fairview Rd Ste 320, Mooresville, NC 28117-9519
Tel (704) 360-8910 *Founded/Ownrshp* 2012
Sales 120.0MM *EMP* 900
SIC 3085 3221 Plastics bottles; Glass containers
CEO: Ray Grupinski
Dir IT: Braden Timmermann

D-U-N-S 03-878-2496 IMP
INTRASTATE DISTRIBUTORS INC
I D I
6400 E 8 Mile Rd, Detroit, MI 48234-1111
Tel (313) 893-9410 *Founded/Ownrshp* 1980
Sales 75.7MM^E *EMP* 100^E
SIC 5149 5181 Soft drinks; Beer & other fermented malt liquors; Soft drinks; Beer & other fermented malt liquors
Pr: Tim Dabish
*VP: Al Dabish
DP Exec: Bill Peck
IT Man: Laith Koja

D-U-N-S 60-708-6030
INTRATEK COMPUTER INC
9950 Irvine Center Dr, Irvine, CA 92618-4357
Tel (949) 334-4200 *Founded/Ownrshp* 1989
Sales 25.4MM *EMP* 310
SIC 7379 Computer maintenance & repair;
Ch: Allen Fahami
*CEO: Jeffrey Shyshka
COO: Rod Holdren
*CFO: Bahman Ghobbeh
*VP: Parviz Ramezani

D-U-N-S 07-921-4173
INTRAWEST RESORTS HOLDINGS INC
1621 18th St Ste 300, Denver, CO 80202-5905
Tel (303) 749-8200 *Founded/Ownrshp* 2007
Sales 587.5MM *EMP* 4,000^E
Tkr Sym SNOW *Exch* NYS
SIC 7011 7999 6531 Investors; Ski lodge; Resort hotel; Ski instruction; Ski rental concession; Real estate agents & managers
CEO: Thomas F Marano
*Ch Bd: Wesley R Edens
COO: Sky Foulkes
CFO: Travis Mayer
Ex VP: Joshua B Goldstein
Ex VP: Joshua Goldstein
Sr VP: Carl Long

D-U-N-S 95-969-1825
INTRAWEST SANDESTIN CO LLC
(*Suby of* INTRAWEST ULC)
9300 Us Highway 98 W, Destin, FL 32550-7268
Tel (850) 267-8000 *Founded/Ownrshp* 1998
Sales 13.1MM^E *EMP* 700
SIC 7011 Resort hotel; Resort hotel
Genl Mgr: Michael Stange
Off Mgr: Tamaralyn Wallace

D-U-N-S 16-457-0173
INTRAWEST SHARED SERVICES INC
1621 18th St Ste 300, Denver, CO 80202-5905
Tel (303) 749-8200 *Founded/Ownrshp* 2004
Sales 20.4MM^E *EMP* 80
SIC 6552 Land subdividers & developers, commercial
CEO: William A Jensen
*CFO: Dallas Lucas
*Prin: Ian Arthur
*Prin: Josh Goldstein
Off Mgr: Jenni Graham

INTRAWEST ULC
See INTRAWEST US HOLDINGS INC

D-U-N-S 12-316-0249
INTRAWEST US HOLDINGS INC
INTRAWEST ULC
1621 18th St Ste 300, Denver, CO 80202-5905
Tel (303) 749-8200 *Founded/Ownrshp* 1993
Sales 26.5MM^E *EMP* 15^E
SIC 8748 Industrial development planning
CEO: William Jensen
*CEO: Tom Marano
*COO: Sky Foulkes
*Ex VP: Joshua Goldstein
VP: Doug Jones
*VP: Travis Mayer
VP: Jon Simisky
Dir Bus: Jeremy Ivey
*Prin: Jeff Grayson
Dir IT: Gary De Oca
Sls Mgr: Jamie Lillard

D-U-N-S 36-155-8182 IMP
INTREN INC
TRENCH-IT
18202 W Union Rd, Union, IL 60180-9710
Tel (815) 923-2300 *Founded/Ownrshp* 1991
Sales 204.9MM *EMP* 300^E
SIC 1623 Underground utilities contractor; Underground utilities contractor
Pr: Lance Rosenmayer
Pr: Jason Combs
*CFO: Mike McArthy
Ex VP: Michael Sandberg
*VP: Rob Wiggs
IT Man: Kyle Juno
IT Man: Angela Trent
Opers Mgr: Pete Comes
Snr PM: Bill Creighton

D-U-N-S 13-827-4977
INTREPID COMPANIES INC
INTREPID USA HEALTHCARE SVCS
(*Suby of* INTREPID USA HEALTHCARE SVCS) ★
4055 Valley View Ln # 500, Dallas, TX 75244-5074
Tel (214) 455-3750 *Founded/Ownrshp* 2005
Sales 24.3MM^E *EMP* 90
SIC 8082 Home health care services
CEO: Todd Garamella
Off Mgr: Sara Ayers

D-U-N-S 83-067-1140
INTREPID GROUP INC
360 Quality Cir Nw Ste B, Huntsville, AL 35806-4549
Tel (256) 705-6800 *Founded/Ownrshp* 2009
Sales 68.7MM *EMP* 75
Accts Hall Albright Garrison & Assoc
SIC 8711 Engineering services; Engineering services
CFO: Andrew White

D-U-N-S 01-273-2421
■ INTREPID HEALTHCARE SERVICES INC
(*Suby of* TEAM HEALTH HOLDINGS INC) ★
4605 Lankershim Blvd, North Hollywood, CA 91602-1818
Tel (888) 447-2362 *Founded/Ownrshp* 2015
Sales 693.9MM *EMP* 2,841^E
Tkr Sym IPCM *Exch* NGS
SIC 8011 Physicians' office, including specialists; Physicians' office, including specialists
CEO: Adam D Singer
Pr: R Jeffrey Taylor
CFO: Richard H Kline III
Chf Mktg O: Kerry E Weiner
Ex VP: Richard G Russell
Sr VP: Glenn Appelbaum
Sr VP: Beth Hawley
Sr VP: Fernando J Sarria
Sr VP: Jeffrey Winter
VP: Felix Aguirre
VP: Mark Citron
VP: Mark C Citron
VP: John Fretz
VP: Jamie S Glazer
VP: Patrick Holmes
VP: Timothy Lary
VP: Kathleen Loya
VP: Marcie Matthews
VP: Melody Rassouli
VP: Robert Roig
VP: Cary Rosoff

D-U-N-S 12-648-3713
INTREPID LEARNING SOLUTIONS INC
411 1st Ave S Ste 300, Seattle, WA 98104-3849
Tel (206) 381-3779 *Founded/Ownrshp* 1999
Sales 25.7MM^E *EMP* 185
SIC 8732 8748 8742 Educational research; Educational consultant; Management consulting services; Educational research; Educational consultant; Management consulting services
Pr: Vikesh Mahendroo
*Pr: Sam Herring
CFO: Greg Glassman
*CFO: Jo Surbrugg
VP: Sanjay Advani
CTO: Mike Flanagan

D-U-N-S 13-657-8262
INTREPID LLC
(*Suby of* INTREPID GROUP INC) ★
360 Quality Cir Nw Ste B, Huntsville, AL 35806-4549
Tel (256) 705-6800 *Founded/Ownrshp* 2009
Sales 68.7MM *EMP* 62
Accts Hall Albright Garrison & Assoc
SIC 8711 Engineering services; Engineering services
Prin: William Best Jr
Prin: Greg Stolt

D-U-N-S 13-241-8505
INTREPID MINING
707 17th St Ste 4200, Denver, CO 80202-3432
Tel (303) 296-3006 *Founded/Ownrshp* 2000
Sales 194.2MM^E *EMP* 630
SIC 1479 1474 Salt (common) mining; Potash mining; Salt (common) mining; Potash mining

D-U-N-S 82-588-6638
▲ INTREPID POTASH INC
707 17th St Ste 4200, Denver, CO 80202-3432
Tel (303) 296-3006 *Founded/Ownrshp* 2007
Sales 410.3MM *EMP* 928^E
Accts Kpmg Llp Denver Colorado
Tkr Sym IPI *Exch* NYS
SIC 1474 Potash mining; Potash mining
Ch Bd: Robert P Jornayvaz III
COO: Patrick Avery
CFO: Brian D Frantz
Bd of Dir: Robert Jornayvaz
Ex VP: David Honeyfield
Ex VP: James N Whyte
Sr VP: John G Mansanti
VP: Ken Heisel
VP: Margaret E McCandless
VP: Rufus Moore
Genl Mgr: Robert Baldridge
Board of Directors: Terry Considine, Chris A Elliott, J Landis Martin, Barth E Whitham

D-U-N-S 14-451-6205 IMP
■ INTREPID POTASH-NEW MEXICO LLC
(*Suby of* INTREPID POTASH INC) ★
1996 Potash Mines Rd, Carlsbad, NM 88220-8965
Tel (575) 887-5591 *Founded/Ownrshp* 2004
Sales 352.6MM^E *EMP* 628^E
SIC 1474 Potash, soda & borate minerals; Potash, soda & borate minerals
Pr: David W Honeyfield
*Pr: Hugh Harvey
*Sr VP: Kelvin G Feist
*Sr VP: John G Mansanti
*VP: Rod Gloss
*VP: Robert Jornayvaz
Off Mgr: Steve McCutcheon
QA Dir: Chet Beaumont
Sfty Dirs: Barbara Bechstein
Sfty Dirs: Ronnie Crockett
Sfty Dirs: Curtis Davidson

D-U-N-S 80-013-9628
INTREPID POWERBOATS INC
(*Suby of* FULHAM INVESTORS FUND II LP) ★
11700 Belcher Rd S, Largo, FL 33773-5115
Tel (954) 922-7544 *Founded/Ownrshp* 1983
Sales 53.9MM^E *EMP* 310^E
SIC 3732 Boat building & repairing; Boat building & repairing
Pr: Charles K Clinton
Pr: Steve Wedde
*CFO: Amy Shrenko
Sr VP: Michael C Obolsky
Sr VP: Michael Obolsky
VP: Mark Beaver
VP: Amy Shranko

INTREPID USA HEALTHCARE SVCS
See INTREPID USA INC

INTREPID USA HEALTHCARE SVCS
See INTREPID COMPANIES INC

D-U-N-S 09-182-8587
INTREPID USA INC
INTREPID USA HEALTHCARE SVCS
(*Suby of* PATRIARCH PARTNERS LLC) ★
4055 Valley View Ln # 500, Dallas, TX 75244-5048
Tel (214) 445-3750 *Founded/Ownrshp* 1999
Sales 138.5MM^E *EMP* 2,500
SIC 7363 8082 Medical help service; Home health care services; Medical help service; Home health care services
CEO: Charles Sweet
*CFO: Andrew Kerr
Ex VP: William Mayes
Dir Soc: Elli Grandalen
Comm Dir: Kathy Bingham
Area Mgr: Nikki McClellan
Brnch Mgr: Debbra Gilbert
Off Mgr: Sara Ayers
Off Mgr: Colleen Bonn
Off Mgr: Vicky Brady
Off Mgr: Sonja Carter

D-U-N-S 19-102-7528
▲ INTREXON CORP
20374 Seneca Meadows Pkwy, Germantown, MD 20876-7004
Tel (301) 556-9900 *Founded/Ownrshp* 2011
Sales 71.9MM *EMP* 149
Tkr Sym XON *Exch* NYS
SIC 8731 Biotechnical research, commercial; Biotechnical research, commercial
Ch Bd: Randal J Kirk
Pt: David Kalson
Pr: Thomas J Goralski
Pr: Gerardo A Zapata
COO: Krish S Krishnan
CFO: Rick L Sterling
Chf Cred: Jack A Bobo
Ex VP: Samuel Broder
Sr VP: Sunil Chada
Sr VP: Kelly Huang
Sr VP: Corey Huck
Sr VP: Olivier R Jarry
Sr VP: Thomas R Kasser
Sr VP: Robert F Walsh III
VP: Christopher Basta
VP: Costas Loullis
VP: Cary P Moxham

D-U-N-S 15-297-8359 IMP
INTRI-PLEX TECHNOLOGIES INC
(*Suby of* IPT HOLDING INC) ★
751 S Kellogg Ave, Goleta, CA 93117-3832
Tel (805) 683-3414 *Founded/Ownrshp* 1993
Sales 20.8MM^E *EMP* 134
SIC 3469 Stamping metal for the trade; Stamping metal for the trade
CEO: Lawney J Falloon
*Ch Bd: David Janes
*CFO: Lawrence Ellis
*VP: John Sullivan
Ex Dir: Anne Casper

D-U-N-S 00-234-5767
▲ INTRICON CORP (MN)
1260 Red Fox Rd, Arden Hills, MN 55112-6944
Tel (651) 636-9770 *Founded/Ownrshp* 1930
Sales 68.3MM *EMP* 569^E
Accts Baker Tilly Virchow Krause Ll
Tkr Sym IIN *Exch* NGM
SIC 3679 3651 3674 2821 Electronic switches; Microphones; Hybrid integrated circuits; Molding compounds, plastics; Electronic switches; Microphones; Hybrid integrated circuits; Molding compounds, plastics
Pr: Mark S Gorder
*Ch Bd: Michael J McKenna
CFO: Scott Longval
Treas: J Longval
VP: Dennis L Gonsior
VP: Greg Gruenhagen
VP: Delain Wright
Telecom Ex: Lee Davis
IT Man: Jana Pargeter
Ql Cn Mgr: Brent Nieman
VP Sls: Michael P Geraci
Board of Directors: Nicholas A Giordano, Robert N Masucci, Philip N Seamon

D-U-N-S 00-694-4029
INTRUST BANK NA
(*Suby of* INTRUST FINANCIAL CORP) ★
105 N Main St, Wichita, KS 67202-1401
Tel (316) 383-1111 *Founded/Ownrshp* 1876
Sales NA *EMP* 939
SIC 6021 National trust companies with deposits, commercial; National trust companies with deposits, commercial
Ch Bd: C Q Chandler IV
V Ch: J Lentell
*Pr: Jay Smith
*CFO: Brian Heinrichs
*Chf Cred: Rick Beach
Ofcr: Jim Betts
Ofcr: Molly Darrenkamp
Ofcr: Lisa Elliott
Ofcr: Lisa Vance
Trst Ofcr: Diana Boyce
Ex VP: Anna Anderson
Ex VP: Steve L Hipp
Ex VP: Bruce Long
Ex VP: Julius Madas
Ex VP: Janeen Smalley
Sr VP: Jeff Carson
Sr VP: Roger Eastwood
Sr VP: Joe Eaton
Sr VP: Bruce Frost
Sr VP: T R Goering
Sr VP: John Goff
Board of Directors: Richard M Kerschen, C Robert Buford, Thomas D Kitch, Frank Carney, Eric T Knorr, Richard G Chance, Charles Koch, C Q Chandler III, William B Moore, George T Chandler, Paul Seymour Jr, Stephen L Clark, Kenneth Shannon, R L Darmon, Donald Slawson, Charles Dieker, John Stewart III, Martin Eby Jr, Jeffrey Turner

D-U-N-S 12-176-8790
INTRUST FINANCIAL CORP
105 N Main St, Wichita, KS 67202-1412
Tel (316) 383-1111 *Founded/Ownrshp* 1971
Sales NA *EMP* 950
Accts Bkd Llp Kansas City Mo
SIC 6712 6022 Bank holding companies; State commercial banks; Bank holding companies; State commercial banks
CEO: Charles Q Chandler III
Ch Bd: C Q Chandler III
Pr: C Q Chandler IV
COO: Rick L Beach
CFO: Jay L Smith
Chf Cred: Alicia M Guagliardo
Ofcr: Graty Bolier
Ofcr: Douglas Gaumer
Ofcr: Mark Maier
Ofcr: Cinda Pray
Ex VP: Roger Eastwood
Ex VP: Steve L Hipp
Sr VP: Dan Eilert
Sr VP: T R Goeing
VP: Deanna Boyles
VP: Blaine Carnprobst
VP: Joseph Eaton
VP: Greg Scafe
VP: Don Wilson
VP Bus Dev: Jeff Emmot

D-U-N-S 96-617-1837 IMP/EXP
INTSEL STEEL DISTRIBUTORS LLC
INTSEL STEEL WEST
(*Suby of* TRIPLE-S STEEL HOLDINGS INC) ★
11310 W Little York Rd, Houston, TX 77041-4917
Tel (713) 937-9500 *Founded/Ownrshp* 1960
Sales 205.4MM^E *EMP* 200
SIC 5051 3312 3444 Iron & steel (ferrous) products; Iron & steel (ferrous) products; Blast furnaces & steel mills; Sheet metal specialties, not stamped
**Pr:* Gary Stein
VP: Troy Arceneaux
VP: Martha Beecher
Genl Mgr: Craig Peterson
VP Opers: Mike Livergood
Opers Mgr: Austin Shirley
Sls&Mrk Ex: Mike Niederkorn
VP Sls: Paul Pierantozzi
Sales Asso: Joann Augustin
Sales Asso: David Diaz

INTSEL STEEL WEST
See INTSEL STEEL DISTRIBUTORS LLC

D-U-N-S 17-634-1139 IMP
INTSEL STEEL WEST LLC
STEELCO
(*Suby of* TRIPLE-S STEEL HOLDINGS INC) ★
1887 S 700 W, Salt Lake City, UT 84104-1705
Tel (801) 973-0911 *Founded/Ownrshp* 2006
Sales 21.2MM^E *EMP* 97^E
SIC 3444 5051 Metal roofing & roof drainage equipment; Siding, sheet metal; Structural shapes, iron or steel
Mktg Dir: Richard Mangone
Sls Mgr: Troy Arceneaux

D-U-N-S 88-387-3473
INTSEL STEEL WEST LLC
R&S STEEL
(*Suby of* TRIPLE-S STEEL HOLDINGS INC) ★
3811 Joliet St, Denver, CO 80239-3233
Tel (303) 321-9660 *Founded/Ownrshp* 1995
Sales 46.6MM^E *EMP* 72
SIC 5051 Pipe & tubing, steel; Pipe & tubing, steel
Pr: Gary Stein
**Ex VP:* Mike Rolnick
Dir IT: Lee Moody
Sls Dir: Jim Lanteri

D-U-N-S 00-958-4058
INTTRA INC
1 Upper Pond Rd Ste 1a, Parsippany, NJ 07054-1068
Tel (973) 263-5100 *Founded/Ownrshp* 2000
Sales 57.3MM^E *EMP* 250^E
SIC 4424 Deep sea domestic transportation of freight; Deep sea domestic transportation of freight
CEO: John F Fay
**Pr:* Kenneth B Bloom
**CFO:* Gary Ito
**Sr VP:* John Debenedette
Sr VP: Paul Mullins
**Sr VP:* Harry Sangree
VP: Greg Donnelly
VP: Roger Gatto
VP: Syed Majid
Genl Mgr: Albert Impink
Snr Ntwrk: Rizwan Sarkhot
Board of Directors: Jeffrey Ganek

INTUIT FINANCIAL SERVICES
See DIGITAL INSIGHT CORP

D-U-N-S 11-329-0969
▲ INTUIT INC
2700 Coast Ave, Mountain View, CA 94043-1140
Tel (650) 944-6000 *Founded/Ownrshp* 1983
Sales 4.1MMM *EMP* 7,700
Accts Ernst & Young Llp San Jose
Tkr Sym INTU *Exch* NGS
SIC 7372 Business oriented computer software; Business oriented computer software
Pr: Brad D Smith
CFO: Kiran Patel
CFO: Timothy Pistell
CFO: R Neil Williams
Bd of Dir: Peter Supernaugh
Ex VP: Laura A Fennell
Ex VP: H Tayloe Stansbury
Sr VP: Per-Kristian Halvorsen
Sr VP: Alex Lintner
Sr VP: Atticus Tysen
VP: Mark J Flournoy
Exec: Sowmya Tanudi
Dir Bus: Christine Martino
Dir Bus: Susan Steele
Comm Man: Tony Marcyes
Board of Directors: William V Campbell, Scott D Cook, Diane B Greene, Suzanne Nora Johnson, Edward A Kangas, Dennis D Powell, Jeff Weiner

D-U-N-S 94-915-7630
INTUITION SYSTEMS INC
9428 Baymeadows Rd # 600, Jacksonville, FL 32256-7969
Tel (904) 421-7220 *Founded/Ownrshp* 1996
Sales 38.3MM^E *EMP* 200
SIC 7374 Data processing service; Data processing service
CEO: Claude J Collier
**Pr:* David Graham
**Pr:* Steven R Settles
**CEO:* James H Van Horn
**CFO:* Polly Corless
**Prin:* Michael Wielgus
**CIO:* Jean Pierre Zaiter
IT Man: Latash Pennybaker
Netwrk Eng: Daryl Dressler

D-U-N-S 08-294-8303
INTUITIVE RESEARCH AND TECHNOLOGY CORP
I R T C
5030 Bradford Dr Nw # 205, Huntsville, AL 35805-1923
Tel (256) 922-9300 *Founded/Ownrshp* 1999
Sales 271.3MM *EMP* 287
SIC 8711 8748 Engineering services; Systems engineering consultant, ex. computer or professional; Engineering services; Systems engineering consultant, ex. computer or professional
CEO: Angel R Almodovar
**Pr:* Harold Brewer
VP: Albert Killen
VP: Tommie Newberry
Prgrm Mgr: Lee Odell
Snr Sftwr: Brian Bentley
IT Man: Melissa Nix

D-U-N-S 93-864-7021 IMP
▲ INTUITIVE SURGICAL INC
1020 Kifer Rd, Sunnyvale, CA 94086-5301
Tel (408) 523-2100 *Founded/Ownrshp* 1995
Sales 2.1MMM *EMP* 2,978
Accts Pricewaterhousecoopers Llp S
Tkr Sym ISRG *Exch* NGS
SIC 3841 Surgical & medical instruments; Surgical & medical instruments
Pr: Gary S Guthart
**Ch Bd:* Lonnie M Smith
CFO: Marshall L Mohr
Treas: Brian Gawle
Ex VP: Jerome J McNamara
Sr VP: Myriam J Curet
Sr VP: Mark J Meltzer
VP: Dan Karl
VP: Jamie E Samath
VP: Glenn Vavoso
Area Mgr: Josh Dewitt
Board of Directors: Craig H Barratt, Michael A Friedman, Eric H Halvorson, Amal M Johnson, Alan J Levy, Mark J Rubash, George Stalk Jr

D-U-N-S 00-215-0634
▲ INUVO INC
500 President Clinton Ave, Little Rock, AR 72201-1756
Tel (855) 440-8484 *Founded/Ownrshp* 2001
Sales 49.6MM *EMP* 34^E
Accts Mayer Hoffman Mccann Pc Cle
Tkr Sym INUV *Exch* ASE
SIC 7379 7311 ; Advertising agencies; ; Advertising agencies
Ch Bd: Richard K Howe
Pr: Jim Banks
Pr: Brady Whittingham
COO: Don Walker Barrett III
CFO: Wallace D Ruiz
Ofcr: Stephen Lerch
Sr VP: Craig AG Dillon
Board of Directors: F William Conner, Joseph P Durrett, Charles D Morgan, Pat Terrell

D-U-N-S 07-691-6246 IMP/EXP
▲ INVACARE CORP
1 Invacare Way, Elyria, OH 44035-4190
Tel (440) 329-6000 *Founded/Ownrshp* 1971
Sales 1.2MMM *EMP* 5,200
Tkr Sym IVC *Exch* NYS
SIC 3842 2514 2813 Surgical appliances & supplies; Wheelchairs; Personal safety equipment; Beds, including folding & cabinet, household: metal; Industrial gases; Oxygen, compressed or liquefied; Surgical appliances & supplies; Wheelchairs; Personal safety equipment; Beds, including folding & cabinet, household: metal; Industrial gases; Oxygen, compressed or liquefied
Ch Bd: Matthew E Monaghan
CFO: Robert K Gudbranson
CFO: Robert Gudbranson
Ex VP: John M Remmers
Ex VP: John Remmers
Sr VP: Dean Childers
Sr VP: Anthony C Laplaca
Sr VP: Patricia A Stumpp
Sr VP: Gordon Sutherland
VP: Amit Marwah
Comm Dir: Tina Harr
Board of Directors: Michael F Delaney, Marc M Gibeley, C Martin Harris, James L Jones, Dale C Laporte, Michael J Merriman, Clifford D Nastas

D-U-N-S 15-736-4295 IMP/EXP
INVACARE CORP (TW)
39400 Taylor Pkwy, North Ridgeville, OH 44035-6270
Tel (440) 329-6000 *Founded/Ownrshp* 2004
Sales 1.8MMM^E *EMP* 45
SIC 3842 Surgical appliances & supplies; Surgical appliances & supplies
Pr: A Malachi Mixon III

D-U-N-S 03-595-2071 IMP
■ INVACARE FLORIDA CORP
(*Suby of* INVACARE CORP) ★
2101 E Lake Mary Blvd, Sanford, FL 32773-7141
Tel (407) 321-5630 *Founded/Ownrshp* 1996
Sales 45.0MM^E *EMP* 300
SIC 3842 Surgical appliances & supplies; Surgical appliances & supplies
CEO: A Malachi Mixon III
**Pr:* Gerald B Blouch
**VP:* Jerome E Fox

D-U-N-S 80-454-6968
■ INVACARE INTERNATIONAL CORP
(*Suby of* INVACARE CORP) ★
1 Invacare Way, Elyria, OH 44035-4190
Tel (440) 329-6000 *Founded/Ownrshp* 1984
Sales 17.5MM^E *EMP* 313
SIC 3842 2514 3841 Surgical appliances & supplies; Wheelchairs; Personal safety equipment; Beds, including folding & cabinet, household: metal; Inhalation therapy equipment; Surgical appliances & supplies; Wheelchairs; Personal safety equipment; Beds, including folding & cabinet, household: metal; Inhalation therapy equipment
Prin: Sharon Corbett

D-U-N-S 16-510-4469 IMP
INVAGEN PHARMACEUTICALS INC
7 Oser Ave Ste 4, Hauppauge, NY 11788-3811
Tel (631) 231-3233 *Founded/Ownrshp* 2012
Sales 129.0MM *EMP* 370
Accts Christopher E Gargiulo Cpa
SIC 2834 Pharmaceutical preparations; Pharmaceutical preparations
Ch: Sudhakar Vidiyala
**Ch Bd:* Bandi Parthasaradhi Reddy
**VP:* Madhava U Reddy
Dir Lab: Gopichand Inti
QI Cn Mgr: Prashanth Gowreddygari

D-U-N-S 10-797-1306
INVENERGY LLC
1 S Wacker Dr Ste 1900, Chicago, IL 60606-4644
Tel (312) 224-1400 *Founded/Ownrshp* 2001
Sales 93.7MM^E *EMP* 140^E
SIC 8741 Management services
CEO: Michael Polsky
**COO:* James Murphy
**CFO:* Jim Murphy
**Ex VP:* Jim Shield
**Sr VP:* Alex George
**Sr VP:* Bryan Schueler
VP: Dan Ewan
VP: Joel Link
VP: Steve Ryder
VP: Randy Wood
VP: Kris Zadlo
Comm Dir: Alissa Krinsky
Dir Bus: Brett Oakleaf

D-U-N-S 18-793-6138 IMP
▲ INVENSENSE INC
1745 Tech Dr Ste 200, San Jose, CA 95110
Tel (408) 501-2200 *Founded/Ownrshp* 2003
Sales 372.0MM *EMP* 644^E
Accts Deloitte & Touche Llp San Jo
Tkr Sym INVN *Exch* NYS
SIC 3812 Gyroscopes; Gyroscopes
Pr: Behrooz Abdi
**Ch Bd:* Amit Shah
CFO: Mark Dentinger
VP: Daniel Goehl
VP: Adam Tachner
Board of Directors: Jon Olson, Eric Stang

D-U-N-S 07-858-1518
INVENSIS INC
(*Suby of* INVENSIS TECHNOLOGY PRIVATE LIMITED)
1000 N West St Ste 1200, Wilmington, DE 19801-1058
Tel (302) 351-3509 *Founded/Ownrshp* 2010
Sales 20.0MM^E *EMP* 1,200
SIC 7374 Data processing & preparation
Pr: Vara Prasad Rongala

INVENSYS CONTROLS
See CM3 BUILDING SOLUTIONS INC

INVENSYS CONTROLS
See ROBERTSHAW CONTROLS CO

D-U-N-S 14-834-6653 EXP
INVENSYS CONTROLS INC
191 E North Ave, Carol Stream, IL 60188-2064
Tel (630) 260-3400 *Founded/Ownrshp* 1998
Sales NA *EMP* 500
SIC 3822 3823 3492

D-U-N-S 60-582-3194 IMP
INVENSYS ENERGY METERING CORP
(*Suby of* SENSUS USA INC) ★
805 Liberty Blvd, Du Bois, PA 15801-2421
Tel (814) 371-3011 *Founded/Ownrshp* 1989
Sales 47.8MM^E *EMP* 300
SIC 3824 3829 3674 3613 3612 Gas meters, domestic & large capacity: industrial; Measuring & controlling devices; Semiconductors & related devices; Switchgear & switchboard apparatus; Transformers, except electric; Gas meters, domestic & large capacity: industrial; Measuring & controlling devices; Semiconductors & related devices; Switchgear & switchboard apparatus; Transformers, except electric
Pr: Michael Show
VP: Dan Harness
VP Opers: Jim Thomson
Board of Directors: C R Burns, Edgar P De Vylder

INVENSYS ENVIRONMENTAL CONTRLS
See SCHNEIDER ELECTRIC BUILDINGS LLC

INVENSYS PROCESS SYSTEMS
See INVENSYS PROCESSS SYSTEMS INC

D-U-N-S 15-420-9639 IMP
INVENSYS PROCESSS SYSTEMS INC
INVENSYS PROCESS SYSTEMS
(*Suby of* SCHNEIDER ELECTRIC SE)
10900 Equity Dr, Houston, TX 77041-8226
Tel (713) 329-1600 *Founded/Ownrshp* 1965
Sales 1.2MMM^E *EMP* 8,000
SIC 3822 Temperature controls, automatic; Refrigeration controls (pressure); Refrigeration/air-conditioning defrost controls; Humidity controls, air-conditioning types; Temperature controls, automatic; Refrigeration controls (pressure); Refrigeration/air-conditioning defrost controls; Humidity controls, air-conditioning types
Pr: Michael J Caliel
CFO: Jack Spencer
VP: Silji Abraham
VP: James Bachmann
VP: Robert E Cook
VP: Jay S Ehle
VP: Gary Frebjeger
VP: Victoria Jule
VP: Peter Kent
VP: Bruce Larson
VP: Ron Pariseau
Exec: Lisa Delagarza
Dir Risk M: Dennis Kelleher

INVENSYS RAIL
See SIEMENS RAIL AUTOMATION CORP

D-U-N-S 00-101-3994 IMP
INVENSYS SYSTEMS INC (MA)
(*Suby of* INVENSYS LIMITED)
10900 Equity Dr, Houston, TX 77041-8226
Tel (713) 329-1600 *Founded/Ownrshp* 1908, 1914
Sales 365.7MM^E *EMP* 514^E
SIC 3823 8711 8741 Industrial instrmnts msrmnt display/control process variable; Flow instruments, industrial process type; Pressure measurement instruments, industrial; Liquid level instruments, industrial process type; Industrial engineers; Management services
Pr: Gary Freburger
**CFO:* Brian Dibenedetto
**Sr VP:* Karen Hamilton
**Sr VP:* Peter Kent
VP: Mike Caliel
VP: Stephen Halsey
Mng Dir: Harry Song
IT Man: Tony Mann
IT Man: Lynda Paul
IT Man: Terryenz Tan
Sftwr Eng: Michael Atwood

D-U-N-S 60-822-4754
INVENT NOW INC
NATIONAL INVENTORS HALL OF FAM
3701 Highland Park Nw, North Canton, OH 44720-4535
Tel (330) 762-4463 *Founded/Ownrshp* 1987
Sales 20.4MM *EMP* 75^E
Accts Ss&G Inc Akron Oh
SIC 8299 Educational service, nondegree granting: continuing educ.
CEO: David Fink
**CEO:* Michael J Oister
**CFO:* Rhonda Campbell
Ex Dir: Betsy Cuthbertson
Ex Dir: Teresa Legrair

D-U-N-S 07-592-8270
INVENTEC MANUFACTURING (NORTH AMERICA) CORP
6215 W By Northwest Blvd B, Houston, TX 77040-4915
Tel (713) 996-5200 *Founded/Ownrshp* 1997
Sales 25.2MM^E *EMP* 250
SIC 5045 Computer peripheral equipment; Computer peripheral equipment
IT Man: James Wang

D-U-N-S 14-004-3469
INVENTIV CLINICAL LLC
(*Suby of* INVENTIV HEALTH CLINICAL INC) ★
504 Carnegie Ctr, Princeton, NJ 08540-6241
Tel (609) 951-6800 *Founded/Ownrshp* 2003
Sales 24.3MM^E *EMP* 400
SIC 8731 Commercial physical research; Commercial physical research
CFO: John Hamill

D-U-N-S 08-127-8640
INVENTIV COMMUNICATIONS INC (OH)
(*Suby of* INVENTIV HEALTH INC) ★
500 Olde Worthington Rd, Westerville, OH 43082-8913
Tel (614) 848-4848 *Founded/Ownrshp* 1935, 2005
Sales 70.7MM^E *EMP* 615
SIC 7311

D-U-N-S 96-400-0835
INVENTIV GROUP HOLDINGS INC
500 Atrium Dr, Somerset, NJ 08873-4161
Tel (732) 537-4800 *Founded/Ownrshp* 2010
Sales 1.5MMM^E *EMP* 7,112^E
SIC 8742 Marketing consulting services; Marketing consulting services
CEO: R Blane Walter
VP: Jenny Fisher
Dist Mgr: Kreg Ackmann
Natl Sales: Andrew Nelson

D-U-N-S 08-572-6037
INVENTIV HEALTH CLINICAL INC
(*Suby of* INVENTIV HEALTH INC) ★
504 Carnegie Ctr, Princeton, NJ 08540-6241
Tel (609) 514-9400 *Founded/Ownrshp* 2011
Sales 272.9MM^E *EMP* 2,300
SIC 8731 Commercial physical research; Commercial physical research
Pr: Riaz Bandali
CFO: Patricia Coleman
**COO:* Gregg Dearhammer
CFO: George A McMillan
CFO: Thomas J Newman
**CFO:* Richard Shimota
**Chf Mktg O:* Jeffrey Freitag
Ex VP: George Butler
Ex VP: Bengt Danielsson
Sr VP: James P Burns
**Sr VP:* Mj Carino
**Sr VP:* Joseph A Fortunato
Sr VP: Steven Leventer
Sr VP: Valerie Palumbo
VP: St Phane Marin
VP: Roger Taft
VP: Adam Tuckman

D-U-N-S 94-287-1187
INVENTIV HEALTH CLINICAL LP
PHARMASOFT
(*Suby of* INVENTIV HEALTH CLINICAL INC) ★
504 Carnegie Ctr, Princeton, NJ 08540-6241
Tel (609) 951-6800 *Founded/Ownrshp* 2005
Sales 38.6MM[E] *EMP* 458
SIC 8731 8733 Biological research; Commercial research laboratory; Biotechnical research, noncommercial; Biological research; Commercial research laboratory; Biotechnical research, noncommercial
Pr: Jeffrey P McMullen
Pr: Dawn Anderson
**COO:* Thomas J Newman
**CFO:* John Hamill
**CFO:* Richard Shimota
**Chf Mktg O:* Martin Birkhofer
Ex VP: Gregory Skalicky
Ex VP: Jeffrey Trotter
**Sr VP:* James P Burns
**Sr VP:* Pablo Fernandez
**Sr VP:* Jack W Green
**Sr VP:* Gregory Hockel
**Sr VP:* Mary F Johnson
Sr VP: Brian Thorton
VP: Anne Hess
VP: P Marin
VP: Timothy Shull
Assoc Dir: Alla Shargorodskaya

D-U-N-S 07-869-8514
INVENTIV HEALTH CLINICAL SRE LLC
(*Suby of* INVENTIV HEALTH INC) ★
1 Van De Graaff Dr, Burlington, MA 01803-5188
Tel (800) 416-0555 *Founded/Ownrshp* 2004
Sales 221.8MM[E] *EMP* 172[E]
SIC 5122 Pharmaceuticals

D-U-N-S 11-479-4493 IMP
INVENTIV HEALTH INC
(*Suby of* INVENTIV GROUP HOLDINGS INC) ★
1 Van De Graaff Dr, Burlington, MA 01803-5188
Tel (800) 416-0555 *Founded/Ownrshp* 2010
Sales 1.5MMM[E] *EMP* 7,111
SIC 8731 Design, commercial & industrial; Advertising, promotional & trade show services; Commercial physical research
CEO: Michael Bell
Pr: Michael McKelvey
Pr: Paul Mignon
Pr: Tom Sebok
Pr: Eric Sirota
Pr: Jeffrey Thomas
Pr: Jeffrey Wilks
COO: Mike Bell
**COO:* Gregg Dearhammer
**CFO:* Jonathan E Bicknell
CFO: Joe Massaro
CFO: Richard Shimota
Ofcr: Jonathan Bicknell
Ofcr: William L Holden
Ex VP: Rick Finnegan
**Ex VP:* Michael A Griffith
Ex VP: Raymond Hill
Ex VP: Amy Hutnik
**Ex VP:* Michael J McKelvey
Ex VP: Chuck Shea
VP: Mandi Walters

INVENTORY CONTROLLED MDSG
See ICM DISTRIBUTING CO INC

D-U-N-S 14-834-9335 IMP
INVENTORY LIQUIDATORS CORP
REGENT PRODUCTS
8999 Palmer St, River Grove, IL 60171-1928
Tel (708) 453-3143 *Founded/Ownrshp* 1985
Sales 72.6MM[E] *EMP* 108[E]
SIC 5087 5092 5023 Beauty salon & barber shop equipment & supplies; Toys; Home furnishings; Beauty salon & barber shop equipment & supplies; Toys; Home furnishings
Pr: Michael De Paul
**Sec:* William G Bailes
VP: Ray Batkiewicz
VP: John Cherne
Genl Mgr: Andy Andrews
Sls Mgr: Noelle Deville
Sls Mgr: Nicole Laudadio
Sls Mgr: Kevin Neidy
Sales Asso: Kent Davies

D-U-N-S 05-998-4724 IMP
INVENTORY SALES CO
9777 Reavis Rd, Saint Louis, MO 63123-5329
Tel (314) 776-6200 *Founded/Ownrshp* 1972
Sales 67.3MM[E] *EMP* 115
SIC 5072 3441 3469 3452 3356 3272 Nuts (hardware); Bolts; Power handtools; Fabricated structural metal; Metal stampings; Bolts, nuts, rivets & washers; Nonferrous rolling & drawing; Concrete products; Nuts (hardware); Bolts; Power handtools; Fabricated structural metal; Metal stampings; Bolts, nuts, rivets & washers; Nonferrous rolling & drawing; Concrete products
Ch: James Friedmann
**Pr:* Terry Tribout
**Treas:* Jack W Hood
**VP:* Tim Anderson
Dir IT: John Newell
Sales Exec: Brannon Yarber
Sls&Mrk Ex: Cathy Friedmann
Sls Mgr: Bryan Reinisch
Sales Asso: Joe Schenker

D-U-N-S 62-411-7805
▲ INVENTRUST PROPERTIES CORP
2809 Butterfield Rd, Oak Brook, IL 60523-1151
Tel (855) 377-0510 *Founded/Ownrshp* 2004
Sales 1.3MMM *EMP* 287[E]
SIC 6798 Real estate investment trusts; Real estate investment trusts
Pr: Thomas P McGuinness
Ch Bd: J Michael Borden
Pr: Jonathan T Roberts
CFO: Michael E Podboy
Ex VP: David F Collins
Ex VP: Anna Fitzgerald
Ex VP: Scott W Wilton
Sr VP: Lance W Billingsley
Board of Directors: Thomas F Glavin, Paula Saban, William J Wierzbicki

D-U-N-S 83-733-0679 IMP/EXP
▲ INVENTURE FOODS INC
5415 E High St Ste 350, Phoenix, AZ 85054-5484
Tel (623) 932-6200 *Founded/Ownrshp* 1995
Sales 285.6MM *EMP* 785[E]
Tkr Sym SNAK *Exch* NGM
SIC 2096 2037 Potato chips & similar snacks; Fruits, quick frozen & cold pack (frozen); Potato chips & similar snacks; Fruits, quick frozen & cold pack (frozen)
CEO: Terry McDaniel
**Ch Bd:* David L Meyers
CFO: Steve Weinberger
VP: Sandip Parikh
VP: Kirk Roles
VP: Matt Simonian
Off Admin: Whitney Hunsaker
IT Man: Mike Flood
IT Man: Mike Lany
VP Opers: Brian Foster
VP Sls: Russell Law
Board of Directors: Ashton D Asensio, Timothy A Cole, Macon Bryce Edmonson, Harold S Edwards, Paul J Lapadat

INVER GROVE HONDA
See MCROB AUTOMOTIVE INC

INVER GROVE HTS PUB SCHOOLS
See GROVE INVER HEIGHTS COMMUNITY SCHOOLS

INVER GROVE TOYOTA
See MIDWEST MOTORS LLC

D-U-N-S 80-719-7207
INVER HILLS COMMUNITY COLLEGE
IHCC
(*Suby of* BEMIDJI STATE UNIVERSITY) ★
2500 80th St E, Inver Grove Heights, MN 55076-3209
Tel (651) 450-3503 *Founded/Ownrshp* 1970
Sales 48.0MM[E] *EMP* 400
SIC 8222 9411 8221 Community college; Administration of educational programs; ; Colleges universities & professional schools; Community college; Administration of educational programs; ; Colleges universities & professional schools
Pr: Tim Wynes
**VP:* Joan Costello
Assoc Dir: Matt Traxler
**Prin:* Cheyl Frank

D-U-N-S 19-623-2524
INVERNESS HOTEL & CONFERENCE CENTER
(*Suby of* LEI AG SEATTLE) ★
200 Inverness Dr W, Englewood, CO 80112-5200
Tel (303) 799-5800 *Founded/Ownrshp* 1995
Sales 22.9MM[E] *EMP* 335
SIC 7011 7992 5941 5812 Motels; Resort hotel; Public golf courses; Golf goods & equipment; Eating places; Motels; Resort hotel; Public golf courses; Golf goods & equipment; Eating places
Pr: Robert Lowe
**VP:* George Fisher
Natl Sales: Tarah Fowler

D-U-N-S 80-526-7036
INVERNESS MANAGEMENT LLC
21 Locust Ave Ste 1d, New Canaan, CT 06840-4735
Tel (203) 966-4177 *Founded/Ownrshp* 1997
Sales 215.0MM[E] *EMP* 820
SIC 6799 Investors; Investors
Co-Founder: W McComb Dunwoody
Exec: McComb Dunwoody
Mng Dir: Robert Sheehy

D-U-N-S 11-692-3785 IMP
■ INVERNESS MEDICAL LLC
ALERE
(*Suby of* ALERE INC) ★
51 Sawyer Rd Ste 200, Waltham, MA 02453-3482
Tel (781) 314-4000 *Founded/Ownrshp* 2001
Sales 81.4MM[E] *EMP* 120
SIC 5122 Drugs, proprietaries & sundries; Drugs, proprietaries & sundries
Pr: John Yonkin
V Ch: Steve Derullo
VP: Lance Keve
VP: Doug Shaffer
MIS Dir: Kevin Fletchall
QA Dir: Elizabeth Reeve
IT Man: Phil Meeker
VP Opers: Michael Richtmyer
Opers Mgr: Reed Simmons
Ql Cn Mgr: Haim Vilchik
Mktg Dir: Norman Moore

D-U-N-S 82-905-9398
INVESCO AGENCY SECURITIES INC
1360 Peachtree St Ne # 600, Atlanta, GA 30309-3283
Tel (404) 892-0896 *Founded/Ownrshp* 2008
Sales 132.8MM *EMP* 2
SIC 6798 Real estate investment trusts
CFO: Donald Ramon
COO: Robson J Kuster
CFO: Richard Lee Phegley Jr
Chf Inves: John M Anzalone

D-U-N-S 08-149-8818
■ INVESCO AIM ADVISORS INC
AIM BLUE CHIP FUNDS
(*Suby of* INVESCO LTD) ★
11 Greenway Plz Ste 2500, Houston, TX 77046-1188
Tel (713) 626-1919 *Founded/Ownrshp* 1976, 2007
Sales 232.8MM[E] *EMP* 2,000
SIC 6722 Management investment, open-end; Management investment, open-end
Ch: Martin L Flanagan
Pr: Jamie Smith
Pr: Philip A Taylor
Ofcr: Richard Sproll
Ofcr: Shannon Vasquez
Ex VP: Lisa Brinkley
Sr VP: Mary Corcoran
Sr VP: Karen Dunn Kelley
Sr VP: Leslie A Schmidt
VP: Clay King
VP: Jim Russell
Exec: Joe Charpentier
Assoc Dir: Scott Vermilyea

D-U-N-S 07-442-3872
INVESCO CAPITAL MARKETS INC
3500 Lacey Rd Ste 700, Downers Grove, IL 60515-5456
Tel (630) 933-9600 *Founded/Ownrshp* 1974
Sales 141.4MM[E] *EMP* 1,010
Accts Deloitte & Touche Llp Chicago
SIC 6211 Brokers, security; Dealers, security; Underwriters, security; Brokers, security; Dealers, security; Underwriters, security
Pr: John H Zimmermann
Pr: Thomas Bourg
Pr: John Davenport
Pr: Michael Effron
Pr: Lindsey Haglage
Pr: Jeannie Underwood
Sr VP: John Zerr
VP: Paul Baranivsky
VP: Scott Cop
VP: Chris Darragh
VP: Michael Head
VP: Michael Joyce
VP: Kevin Klingert
Exec: Gregory Keck

D-U-N-S 02-448-3476
■ INVESCO GROUP SERVICES INC
AMVESCAP
(*Suby of* INVESCO LTD) ★
1555 Peachtree St Ne, Atlanta, GA 30309-2460
Tel (404) 892-0896 *Founded/Ownrshp* 1992, 1996
Sales 68.6MM[E] *EMP* 165
SIC 6282 6221 Investment advice; Investment advisory service; Commodity contracts brokers, dealers; Investment advice; Investment advisory service; Commodity contracts brokers, dealers
CEO: Martin L Flanagan
**Ch Bd:* Charles W Brady
Pr: Brian Jessen
**CFO:* Robert F McCollough
VP: Aysha Mawani
**Prin:* Loren M Starr
Mktg Dir: Marquette Chester
Counsel: Jonathan Doyle

D-U-N-S 86-937-4405
■ INVESCO INSTITUTIONAL (NA) INC
(*Suby of* INVESCO LTD) ★
1555 Peachtree St Ne, Atlanta, GA 30309-2460
Tel (404) 892-0896 *Founded/Ownrshp* 1986
Sales 75.8MM[E] *EMP* 891
SIC 6282 Investment advisory service; Investment advisory service
Prin: Mark Armour
**CFO:* David Hartley
CFO: Loren Starr

D-U-N-S 78-771-2009
■ INVESCO INVESMENT SERVICES INC
AIM INVESTMENTS
(*Suby of* AIM BLUE CHIP FUNDS) ★
11 Greenway Plz Ste 1000, Houston, TX 77046-1157
Tel (713) 626-1919 *Founded/Ownrshp* 1977
Sales 76.0MM[E] *EMP* 400
SIC 6722 6282 Mutual fund sales, on own account; Investment advice; Mutual fund sales, on own account; Investment advice
Ch: Philip Alexander Taylor
**Pr:* William Joseph Galvin
Pr: David Glabicki
Pr: Clay King
Sr Cor Off: Russell Burk
Ofcr: Bill Canny
Ofcr: Roxanne Farris
Ofcr: Debi Kiemsteadt
Ofcr: Mary Schleinschok
**Sr VP:* Joseph H Charpentier
VP: Krista Coibson
VP: Ruben Franklin
VP: Jeffrey Hemker
VP: Lisa Hultquist
VP: Casi Lahodny
VP: Mary Maloney
VP: John Parker
**VP:* Todd L Spillane
Assoc Dir: Jason Brinkle

D-U-N-S 08-893-3622
▲ INVESCO LTD
1555 Peachtree St Ne 18, Atlanta, GA 30309-2460
Tel (404) 892-0896 *Founded/Ownrshp* 1935
Sales 5.1MMM *EMP* 6,264
Tkr Sym IVZ *Exch* NYS
SIC 6282 Investment advice; Investment advisory service; Investment advice; Investment advisory service
Pr: Martin L Flanagan
Pr: Marissa Cusi
**Pr:* Martin L Flagan
CFO: Loren M Starr
Chf Inves: John Anzalone
Ofcr: Charlie Gehring
Ofcr: David Genova
Ofcr: Lisa Gray
Ofcr: Gary Ho
Ofcr: Colin D Meadows
Ofcr: Mark Mendez
Ofcr: Darci Pearce
Ofcr: Frances Phosarath
Ofcr: Aaron Uhde
Ofcr: Nicky Vague
Assoc Dir: Christopher Lacroix
Comm Man: James Williamson
Board of Directors: Joseph R Canion, C Robert Henrikson, Ben F Johnson III, Denis Kessler, Edward P Lawrence, J Thomas Presby, Nigel Sheinwald, G Richard Wagoner Jr, Phoebe A Wood

D-U-N-S 83-086-2939
INVESCO MORTGAGE CAPITAL INC
1555 Peachtree St Ne, Atlanta, GA 30309-2460
Tel (404) 892-0896 *Founded/Ownrshp* 2008
Sales 103.8MM *EMP* 4
Tkr Sym IVR *Exch* NYS
SIC 6798 Real estate investment trusts; Real estate investment trusts
Pr: Richard J King
COO: Robson J Kuster
CFO: Richard Lee Phegley Jr
CFO: Donald Ramon
Chf Inves: John M Anzalone
Assoc Dir: Alexander Millar
IT Man: Ben Muskett

D-U-N-S 96-369-2442
INVESCO NATIONAL TRUST CO
1555 Peachtree St Ne, Atlanta, GA 30309-2460
Tel (404) 439-4570 *Founded/Ownrshp* 2009
Sales 27.0MM[E] *EMP* 109[E]
SIC 6282 Investment advisory service
Pr: Robert Thomann
CIO: Joshua Rowell

D-U-N-S 07-282-0343
INVEST WEST FINANCIAL CORP
1933 Cliff Dr Ste 1, Santa Barbara, CA 93109-1502
Tel (805) 957-0095 *Founded/Ownrshp* 1970
Sales 140.8MM[E] *EMP* 845
SIC 6726 6513 Investment offices; Apartment hotel operation; Investment offices; Apartment hotel operation
Ch: Dale Marquis
Pr: Matt Marquis
CEO: Dale J Marquis
VP: Thomas Gamble
Brnch Mgr: Michael Vidal
CTO: Jennifer Mertz
IT Man: Helen Mercer

D-U-N-S 05-337-5796
■ INVESTACORP INC
(*Suby of* LADENBURG THALMANN FINANCIAL SERVICES INC) ★
4400 Biscayne Blvd, Miami, FL 33137-3212
Tel (305) 557-3000 *Founded/Ownrshp* 2007
Sales 21.0MM[E] *EMP* 80
SIC 6211 8721 Stock brokers & dealers; Accounting, auditing & bookkeeping
Pr: Bruce Zwigard
Ofcr: Marcus Arneaud
Ofcr: Gil Placensia
Ofcr: Michel Tsaparlis
**Ex VP:* Scott Sherwood
**VP:* Pat Farrell
**VP:* Randy Nestel
VP Admn: Arielle Jaffe
IT Man: Brian Booth

D-U-N-S 78-096-6276
INVESTAR BANK
7244 Perkins Rd, Baton Rouge, LA 70808-4323
Tel (225) 448-5451 *Founded/Ownrshp* 2006
Sales NA *EMP* 21[E]
SIC 6162 Mortgage bankers & correspondents; Mortgage bankers & correspondents
Prin: John Dangelo
Pr: Stephen E Wessel
Ofcr: Dorothy Bellocq
Ofcr: Ana Rupnik
Ofcr: Amanda Yates
Ex VP: Ralph Berni
Ex VP: Charles Chiasson
Ex VP: Travis Lavergne
Sr VP: Ryan Finnan
Sr VP: Robert Lott
VP: Kerry Babin
VP: Sarah Hardy
VP: Keith Short
Exec: Tom Aldrich

D-U-N-S 07-944-7906
INVESTAR HOLDING CORP (LA)
7244 Perkins Rd, Baton Rouge, LA 70808-4323
Tel (225) 227-2222 *Founded/Ownrshp* 2009
Sales NA *EMP* 171[E]
Tkr Sym ISTR *Exch* NGM
SIC 6022 State commercial banks; State commercial banks
Pr: John J D'Angelo
**Ch Bd:* William H Hidalgo Sr
COO: Dane Babin
COO: Ryan P Finnan
CFO: Rachel P Cherco
Chf Cred: Travis M Lavergne
Ex VP: Randolf F Kassmeier
Board of Directors: Andrew C Nelson, James M Baker, Carl R Schneider Jr, Thomas C Besselman Sr, Frank L Walker, James H Boyce III, Robert M Boyce Sr, John Emmerit Brignac Jr, Robert L Freeman, Gordon H Joffrion II, David J Lukinovich, Suzanne O Middleton

D-U-N-S 80-198-0140
INVESTCORP INTERNATIONAL HOLDINGS INC
(*Suby of* INVESTCORP BANK B.S.C)
280 Park Ave Fl 36, New York, NY 10017-1285
Tel (212) 599-4700 *Founded/Ownrshp* 2005
Sales 369.6MM[E] *EMP* 676[E]
SIC 6282 Investment advisory service; Investment advisory service
Pr: Christopher O'Brian
VP: Brian Streko
Mng Dir: Prashant Kolluri
Mng Dir: Herb Myers
CIO: Lionel Erdely
CIO: Deepak Gurnani

D-U-N-S 11-632-3838
INVESTCORP INTERNATIONAL INC
(*Suby of* INVESTCORP SERVICES INC) ★
280 Park Ave Fl 36, New York, NY 10017-1285
Tel (212) 599-4700 *Founded/Ownrshp* 1986
Sales 141.7MM[E] *EMP* 429[E]
SIC 6531 Real estate agents & managers; Real estate agents & managers
CEO: Nemir A Kirdar
Pr: Michael Busacco
**Pr:* Jon P Hedley
Chf Inves: Lionel Erdely
Sr VP: Christine Brohme

VP: Robert Florczak
VP: Sandeep Jain
VP: Jay Jena
VP: Feras Majed
VP: Nirav Shah
VP: Peter Shea
VP: Priya Singh
VP: Gayan Wijesinha
VP: Ali Zainal

D-U-N-S 15-399-0635
INVESTCORP SERVICES INC
(*Suby of* INVESTCORP INTERNATIONAL HOLDINGS INC) ★
280 Park Ave Fl 36, New York, NY 10017-1285
Tel (212) 599-4700 *Founded/Ownrshp* 1982
Sales 302.3MM^E *EMP* 429
SIC 6282 Investment advisory service; Investment advisory service
CEO: Nemir Kirdar
**Pr:* Christopher O'Brian
**Treas:* Mayme Tong
**VP:* Victor Okoth

INVESTMENT BANKERS
See DIRECT INSURANCE CO INC

D-U-N-S 02-030-6304
INVESTMENT CO INSTITUTE
I C I
1401 H St Nw Ste 1200, Washington, DC 20005-2110
Tel (202) 326-5800 *Founded/Ownrshp* 1940
Sales 69.2MM *EMP* 170^E
Accts Pricewaterhousecoopers Llp Wa
SIC 8611 Trade associations; Trade associations
Pr: Paul Schott Stevens
V Ch: Thomas S Schreier Jr
**COO:* Peter Gallary
COO: Jennifer McCain
**Treas:* Mark Delcoco
Ofcr: George Shevlin
VP: Chris Boyland
Mng Dir: Amy Lancellotta
QA Dir: Rong Wang
Dir IT: Paul Camarata
IT Man: Vincent Banfi

D-U-N-S 07-252-8698 IMP
INVESTMENT CONCEPTS INC
1667 E Lincoln Ave, Orange, CA 92865-1929
Tel (714) 283-5800 *Founded/Ownrshp* 1993
Sales 51.5MM^E *EMP* 192
SIC 6552 6531 Subdividers & developers; Real estate managers; Subdividers & developers; Real estate managers
CEO: George A Chami
**COO:* George Mobayed
Sr VP: Russell Khouri
**Sr VP:* Kaye Richey
**VP:* Sam Benz
**VP:* Grace Imamura
VP: Darren Janger
**VP:* Sandra Poiser

D-U-N-S 60-286-0389
INVESTMENT CORP OF AMERICA
700 N Grant Ave Ste 600, Odessa, TX 79761-4554
Tel (432) 334-8881 *Founded/Ownrshp* 1989
Sales 39.6MM^E *EMP* 250
SIC 6719 Personal holding companies, except banks; Personal holding companies, except banks
CEO: John Bushman
**COO:* Ed Lasater
**Ex VP:* John C Nichols

D-U-N-S 08-638-7719
INVESTMENT CORP OF PALM BEACH
PALM BEACH KENNEL CLUB
1111 N Congress Ave, West Palm Beach, FL 33409-6317
Tel (561) 683-2222 *Founded/Ownrshp* 1970
Sales 32.8MM *EMP* 550
Accts Lkd Jupiter Fl
SIC 7948 7999 Dog race track operation; Off-track betting; Dog race track operation; Off-track betting
CEO: Patrick J Rooney Sr
**Pr:* Patrick J Rooney Jr

D-U-N-S 19-694-8488
INVESTMENT FLORIDA REALTY LLC
513 Dodecanese Blvd, Tarpon Springs, FL 34689-3127
Tel (727) 942-6398 *Founded/Ownrshp* 2005
Sales 25.0MM *EMP* 25
SIC 6531 Real estate brokers & agents
Owner: Pantelis Mastrovasilis

D-U-N-S 10-593-7143
■ **INVESTMENT MANAGEMENT & PLANNING LLC**
(*Suby of* L P L FINANCIAL SERVICES) ★
2000 E Lamar Blvd Ste 600, Arlington, TX 76006-7361
Tel (817) 261-3500 *Founded/Ownrshp* 1995
Sales 30.0MM^E *EMP* 45
SIC 6211 6282 Security brokers & dealers; Investment advisory service; Manager of mutual funds, contract or fee basis; Security brokers & dealers; Investment advisory service; Manager of mutual funds, contract or fee basis

D-U-N-S 85-845-0760
INVESTMENT PROFESSIONALS INC
16414 San Pedro Ave # 150, San Antonio, TX 78232-2224
Tel (210) 308-8800 *Founded/Ownrshp* 1992
Sales 29.6MM^E *EMP* 200
SIC 8742 Financial consultant; Financial consultant
Ch Bd: Scott Barnes
Pr: Kristen Pruitt
CEO: Jay McAnelly
CFO: Christine Walters
Sr VP: John Sacchetti
Sr VP: Brian Surovik
Sr VP: Chris Thompson
VP: William Edwards
VP: Adam Eisenhauer
VP: Leslie Gaylord
VP: Jeffrey Jaynes
VP: Brooks McCall
VP: Stephen Mixon

VP: Michael Muns
VP: Steven Ransdell
VP: Bo Rester
Dir Bus: Will Mackey

D-U-N-S 06-654-1442
INVESTMENT RARITIES INC
7850 Metro Pkwy Ste 121, Minneapolis, MN 55425-1530
Tel (952) 853-0700 *Founded/Ownrshp* 1973
Sales 147.9MM *EMP* 60
SIC 5999 Coins; Numismatist shops; Coins; Numismatist shops
Pr: James R Cook
Bd of Dir: Thomas Dillon
Bd of Dir: Harry Meltz

D-U-N-S 79-100-4807
▲ **INVESTMENT TECHNOLOGY GROUP INC**
1 Liberty Plz, New York, NY 10006-1404
Tel (212) 588-4000 *Founded/Ownrshp* 1983
Sales 559.8MM *EMP* 1,001^E
Tkr Sym ITG *Exch* NYS
SIC 6211 Brokers, security; Dealers, security; Brokers, security; Dealers, security
Pr: Francis J Troise
**Ch Bd:* Maureen O'Hara
Pr: Brenda Chiu
Pr: Christopher Ross
Pr: Gunjan Sharma
COO: Alasdair Thomson
CFO: Steven R Vigliotti
Dir Bus: Martin Podeyn
Mng Dir: Savyona Abel
Mng Dir: Sudhanshu Arya
Mng Dir: Robert J Boardman
Board of Directors: Christopher V Dodds, Timothy L Jones, R Jarrett Lilien, T Kelley Millet, Steven S Wood

INVESTMENTS LIMITED
See JAMES BATMASIAN

D-U-N-S 60-744-1172
▲ **INVESTORS BANCORP INC**
101 Jfk Pkwy Ste 3, Short Hills, NJ 07078-2793
Tel (973) 924-5100 *Founded/Ownrshp* 2015
Sales NA *EMP* 1,597
Tkr Sym ISBC *Exch* NGS
SIC 6035 Savings institutions, federally chartered; Savings institutions, federally chartered
Pr: Kevin Cummings
COO: Domenick A Cama
CFO: Sean Burke
Ex VP: Paul Kalamaras
Sr VP: William Cosgrove
VP: Sergio Alonso
VP: Razie Dauti
VP: Richard Demmer
VP: Adriano Duarte
VP: Dan Harris
VP: Deborah Leonard
VP: Brian Turano
VP: Mary Ward
Board of Directors: James H Ward III, Robert C Albanese, Dennis M Bone, Doreen R Byrnes, Domenick A Cama, William V Cosgrove, Brian D Dittenhafer, Brendan J Dugan, James J Garibaldi, Michele N Siekerka

D-U-N-S 60-584-4609
INVESTORS BANCORP MHC
101 Jfk Pkwy Ste 3, Short Hills, NJ 07078-2793
Tel (973) 376-5100 *Founded/Ownrshp* 1997
Sales NA *EMP* 1,942
SIC 6036 Savings institutions, not federally chartered; Savings institutions, not federally chartered
Pr: Robert Cashill

D-U-N-S 07-516-0978
■ **INVESTORS BANK**
(*Suby of* INVESTORS BANCORP INC) ★
101 John F Kennedy Pkwy # 3, Short Hills, NJ 07078-2793
Tel (973) 376-5100 *Founded/Ownrshp* 1997
Sales NA *EMP* 875
SIC 6036 State savings banks, not federally chartered; State savings banks, not federally chartered
Pr: Kevin Cummings
COO: Domenick A Cama
COO: Kevin Cummings
Bd of Dir: Dennis Bone
Bd of Dir: Brendan Dugan
Bd of Dir: Joseph Shepard
Ex VP: Paul Kalamaras
Ex VP: Richard S Spengler
Sr VP: Lois Anderson
Sr VP: Dennis Budinich
Sr VP: Thomas F Splaine
VP: Ana Antunes
VP: Steed Ardanz
VP: Tino Fontes
VP: Luis Francisco
VP: Thomas Hatt
VP: Kim Ickovic
VP: Ron Krauskopf
VP: Ann Lacarrubba
VP: Eric Laurens
VP: Deborah Leonard

D-U-N-S 10-817-1604 IMP
INVESTORS BUSINESS DAILY INC
(*Suby of* DATA ANALYSIS INC) ★
12655 Beatrice St, Los Angeles, CA 90066-7303
Tel (310) 448-6000 *Founded/Ownrshp* 1984
Sales 43.5MM^E *EMP* 250
SIC 2711 Newspapers, publishing & printing; Newspapers, publishing & printing
Pr: William O'Neil
Pr: Ogorzalek Jake
COO: Reinhardt Krause
Ex VP: Karen Anderson
Sr VP: Rajneesh Gupta
VP: John Becker
VP: Doug Fuller
**VP:* Kathy Sherman
Snr Sftwr: Kristine Khachatryan
Opers Mgr: Don Blanchette
Opers Mgr: Adam King

D-U-N-S 92-884-9926
■ **INVESTORS CAPITAL HOLDINGS LLC**
(*Suby of* RCS CAPITAL CORP) ★
6 Kimball Ln Ste 150, Lynnfield, MA 01940-2684
Tel (781) 246-7982 *Founded/Ownrshp* 2014
Sales 93.6MM *EMP* 59^E
SIC 6211 6282 Security brokers & dealers; Investment advisory service
Pr: Timothy B Murphy
COO: James Wallace
CFO: Kathleen L Donnelly
Chf Cred: John G Cataldo
Mng Dir: Brian Woods

D-U-N-S 11-412-2109
INVESTORS CAPITAL MANAGEMENT GROUP
CUISINE PARTNERS USA
10390 Santa Monica Blvd, Los Angeles, CA 90025-5058
Tel (310) 553-5175 *Founded/Ownrshp* 2002
Sales 11.0MM^E *EMP* 277
SIC 8741 Restaurant management; Restaurant management
Pr: Edward Lindor
**CFO:* Manfred Gordon
**VP:* Richere Altport
**VP:* Jason Graham
**VP:* Ray I Ledford II
Prin: Christopher Lindor
**Genl Mgr:* Iman Ghiam

D-U-N-S 17-663-1984
■ **INVESTORS COMMUNITY BANK**
(*Suby of* COUNTY BANCORP INC) ★
860 N Rapids Rd, Manitowoc, WI 54220-3006
Tel (920) 686-9998 *Founded/Ownrshp* 1997
Sales NA *EMP* 46^E
SIC 6022 State commercial banks; State commercial banks
CEO: Tim Schneider
**Ch Bd:* William Censky
**Pr:* Mark Binversie
Pr: Terry Schott
Ofcr: Nicole Bahn
Ofcr: David Diedrich
Ofcr: Jeff Jagodinsky
Ofcr: Paul Kuplic
**VP:* Patricia Schneider

D-U-N-S 08-605-2297
■ **INVESTORS FIDUCIARY TRUST CO**
STATE STREET KANSAS CITY
(*Suby of* STATE STREET CORP) ★
801 Pennsylvania Ave, Kansas City, MO 64105-1307
Tel (816) 871-4100 *Founded/Ownrshp* 1995
Sales 122.5MM^E *EMP* 1,100
SIC 6722 6733 6282 Money market mutual funds; Trusts, except educational, religious, charity: management; Investment advice; Money market mutual funds; Trusts, except educational, religious, charity: management; Investment advice
Pr: W Andrew Fry
**CFO:* Stephen Hilliard
**CFO:* Allen Strain
VP: Kenneth Ducharme
VP: John Granger
**VP:* Robert Novellano
**VP:* Marvin Rau
VP: Rudolf Vanderschoot
**VP:* Michelle Warner
Telecom Mg: Scott McNair
IT Man: John Vanbuskirk

D-U-N-S 05-427-2489
▲ **INVESTORS HERITAGE CAPITAL CORP**
200 Capital Ave, Frankfort, KY 40601-2848
Tel (502) 223-2361 *Founded/Ownrshp* 1963
Sales NA *EMP* 95^E
Accts Mountjoy Chilton Medley Llp L
Tkr Sym IHRC *Exch* OTO
SIC 6311 2752 Life insurance; Commercial printing, lithographic; Life insurance; Commercial printing, lithographic
CEO: Harry Lee Waterfield II
COO: Raymond L Carr
CFO: Larry J Johnson II
Treas: Shane S Mitchell
**Ex VP:* Robert M Hardy Jr
VP: Michael F Dudgeon Jr
VP: Whitney Waterfield
Board of Directors: George R Burgess Jr, Harold G Doran Jr, Michael F Dudgeon Jr, Gordon C Duke, David W Reed, Helen S Wagner

D-U-N-S 05-759-1125
■ **INVESTORS HERITAGE LIFE INSURANCE CO**
(*Suby of* INVESTORS HERITAGE CAPITAL CORP) ★
200 Capital Ave, Frankfort, KY 40601-2848
Tel (502) 223-2361 *Founded/Ownrshp* 1963
Sales NA *EMP* 49^E
SIC 6311 6411 Life insurance; Insurance agents, brokers & service
Ch Bd: Harry Waterfield
**Ch Bd:* Harry Lee Waterfield II
**Treas:* Jimmy R Mc Iver
VP: Debbie Bright
**VP:* Raymond L Carr
VP: Jeff Crippen
**VP:* Michael Dudgeon
**VP:* Robert M Hardy Jr
VP: Julie Hunsinger
**VP:* Don R Philpot
**VP:* Nancy W Walton
**VP:* Jane Wise
Board of Directors: Adron Doran MD, H Glenn Doran, Michael F Dudgeon Jr, Gordon C Duke, Robert M Hardy Jr, Jerry F Howell Sr, Jerry F Howell Jr, Helen Wagner

D-U-N-S 94-773-1311
INVESTORS IN HEARTLAND INC
HEARTLAND CHEVROLET
501 N State Route 291, Liberty, MO 64068-1045
Tel (816) 781-3500 *Founded/Ownrshp* 2011
Sales 20.9MM^E *EMP* 50

SIC 5511 Automobiles, new & used
Pr: Christopher Igoe

D-U-N-S 61-638-4140
INVESTORS LLC
50 Kennedy Plz, Providence, RI 02903-2393
Tel (401) 751-1600 *Founded/Ownrshp* 2007
Sales 228.8MM^E *EMP* 8,100
SIC 3585 3444 3634 3699 2491 2434 Refrigeration & heating equipment; Heating equipment, complete; Air conditioning equipment, complete; Air conditioning units, complete: domestic or industrial; Metal ventilating equipment; Hoods, range: sheet metal; Electric housewares & fans; Fans, exhaust & ventilating, electric: household; Electrical equipment & supplies; Security control equipment & systems; Door opening & closing devices, electrical; Chimes, electric; Wood preserving; Poles, posts & pilings: treated wood; Millwork, treated wood; Wood kitchen cabinets; Vanities, bathroom: wood; Refrigeration & heating equipment; Heating equipment, complete; Air conditioning equipment, complete; Air conditioning units, complete: domestic or industrial; Metal ventilating equipment; Hoods, range: sheet metal; Electric housewares & fans; Fans, exhaust & ventilating, electric: household; Electrical equipment & supplies; Security control equipment & systems; Door opening & closing devices, electrical; Chimes, electric; Wood preserving; Poles, posts & pilings: treated wood; Millwork, treated wood; Wood kitchen cabinets; Vanities, bathroom: wood
**CFO:* Almon C Hall

D-U-N-S 03-402-6112
INVESTORS MANAGEMENT CORP
GOLDEN CORRAL
5151 Glenwood Ave Ste 300, Raleigh, NC 27612-3240
Tel (919) 881-5200 *Founded/Ownrshp* 1971
Sales 656.5MM^E *EMP* 9,000
SIC 8741 Buffet (eating places); Franchises, selling or licensing; Management services
Ch Bd: James H Maynard
**CFO:* Richard A Urquhart III
VP: Ann Perez
VP: Sam Starling
Mng Dir: Jim Hyler

D-U-N-S 15-518-8469
■ **INVESTORS MORTGAGE INSURANCE HOLDING CO**
(*Suby of* OCWEN FINANCIAL CORP) ★
1675 Palm Beach Lakes Blv, West Palm Beach, FL 33401-2122
Tel (561) 681-8500 *Founded/Ownrshp* 1986
Sales NA *EMP* 280
SIC 6361 7011 Title insurance; Hotels; Title insurance; Hotels
Pr: William C Erbey
**CFO:* Christine A Reich

D-U-N-S 07-867-5345
INVESTORS REAL ESTATE TRUST
1400 31st Ave Sw Ste 60, Minot, ND 58701-6965
Tel (701) 837-4738 *Founded/Ownrshp* 1970
Sales 283.1MM *EMP* 445
Accts Grant Thornton Llp Minneapoli
SIC 6798 Real estate investment trusts; Real estate investment trusts
Pr: Timothy P Mihalick
**Ch Bd:* Jeffrey L Miller
**V Ch:* John D Stewart
COO: Diane K Bryantt
CFO: Ted E Holmes
Chf Inves: Mark W Reiling
Ex VP: Michael A Bosh
VP: Nancy Andersen
Creative D: Joshua Gagne
Board of Directors: Jeffrey P Caira, Linda J Hall, Terrance P Maxwell, Pamela J Moret, Stephen L Stenehjem, Jeffrey K Woodbury

D-U-N-S 02-201-1316
▲ **INVESTORS TITLE CO**
121 N Columbia St, Chapel Hill, NC 27514-3502
Tel (919) 968-2200 *Founded/Ownrshp* 1976
Sales NA *EMP* 233^E
Accts Dixon Hughes Goodman Llp High
Tkr Sym ITIC *Exch* NGM
SIC 6361 6351 Real estate title insurance; Surety insurance; Real estate title insurance; Surety insurance
Ch Bd: J Allen Fine
Pr: Lee Brown
**Pr:* James A Fine Jr
Pr: Ruth Smith
Treas: Elizabeth P Bryan
Chf Inves: Carlisle D Whitlock
Ofcr: Michael Aiken
**Ex VP:* W Morris Fine
Ex VP: Carol Hayden
Ex VP: George Snead
Sr VP: Stephen Brown
Sr VP: Bill Collier
VP: John Ferrie
VP: Ben Foreman
VP: Robert Gomez
VP: Holly Simmons
VP: Jane Turner
VP: Elizabeth Wainio
VP: Raymond Wall
VP: Patricia Wolak
Comm Dir: Chris Mcllavary
Board of Directors: David L Francis, Richard M Hutson II, R Horace Johnson, H Joe King Jr, James R Morton, James H Speed Jr

D-U-N-S 07-196-2740
INVESTORS TITLE CO INC
219 S Central Ave, Saint Louis, MO 63105-3505
Tel (314) 721-4001 *Founded/Ownrshp* 1972
Sales NA *EMP* 145
SIC 6361 6541 Real estate title insurance; Title search companies; Real estate title insurance; Title search companies
Pr: John Crutchfield
**CEO:* James Fenberg

D-U-N-S 05-745-2948
■ **INVESTORS TITLE INSURANCE CO**
(*Suby of* INVESTORS TITLE CO) ★
121 N Columbia St, Chapel Hill, NC 27514-3502
Tel (919) 968-2200 *Founded/Ownrshp* 1972
Sales NA *EMP* 200
SIC 6361 Real estate title insurance
Pr: W Morris Fine
CFO: James A Fine Jr
VP: David A Bennington
VP: Jonathan Biggs
VP: Elizabeth P Bryan
VP: Doug Kubel

D-U-N-S 15-115-5041
INVESTORS WARRANTY OF AMERICA INC
(*Suby of* AUSA HOLDING COMPANY)
4333 Edgewood Rd Ne, Cedar Rapids, IA 52499-3830
Tel (319) 398-8511 *Founded/Ownrshp* 1980
Sales 100.7M *EMP* 750
SIC 7011 Hotels & motels; Hotels & motels
Pr: Patrick Baird
**Treas:* Brenda Clancy
**VP:* Craig Bermie
**VP:* Dave Blankenship
IT Man: Vicki Wyatt

D-U-N-S 96-518-7958 IMP/EXP
INVICTA WATCH CO OF AMERICA INC
INVICTA WATCH GROUP
3069 Taft St, Hollywood, FL 33021-4440
Tel (954) 921-2444 *Founded/Ownrshp* 1996
Sales 45.6MM^E *EMP* 125^E
SIC 5094 Watches & parts; Watches & parts
Pr: Eyal Lalo
**Treas:* Gany Cohen
Creative D: Marina Tito
VP Mktg: Gany Lalo
Mktg Dir: Victor Gonzalez

INVICTA WATCH GROUP
See INVICTA WATCH CO OF AMERICA INC

INVISION
See CV FAMILY ENTERPRISES INC

INVISION
See MEDICAL IMAGING OF COLORADO LLC

D-U-N-S 96-157-4790
■ **INVISION AUTOMOTIVE SYSTEMS INC**
(*Suby of* VOXX INTERNATIONAL CORP) ★
2822 Commerce Park Dr # 400, Orlando, FL 32819-8619
Tel (407) 956-5161 *Founded/Ownrshp* 2010
Sales 46.4MM^E *EMP* 265
SIC 3699 Automotive driving simulators (training aids), electronic; Automotive driving simulators (training aids), electronic
Pr: Thomas C Malone
VP: Loriann Shelton
VP: Charles M Stoehr
VP: Catherine Wiginton
Sls Mgr: Chris Holycross

D-U-N-S 55-747-7106
INVISION COMMUNICATIONS INC
1280 Civic Dr Ste 300, Walnut Creek, CA 94596-7244
Tel (925) 944-1211 *Founded/Ownrshp* 1991
Sales 21.0MM^E *EMP* 120
SIC 8742

D-U-N-S 01-783-4652
INVISION CUSTOMIZED SERVICES
160 E Woodford Ave, Pittsburgh, PA 15210-4314
Tel (412) 207-9584 *Founded/Ownrshp* 2011
Sales 24.3MM *EMP* 1^E
SIC 8999 Services; Services

D-U-N-S 06-970-4969
INVISION CUSTOMIZED SERVICES
12450 Perry Hwy Ste 100, Wexford, PA 15090-7387
Tel (724) 933-6100 *Founded/Ownrshp* 2012
Sales 30.4MM *EMP* 2
SIC 8322 Individual & family services
Prin: Ruth Siegfried

D-U-N-S 14-105-7807 IMP
INVISTA CAPITAL MANAGEMENT LLC
(*Suby of* KOCH INDUSTRIES INC) ★
2801 Centerville Rd, Wilmington, DE 19808-1609
Tel (302) 683-3000 *Founded/Ownrshp* 2004
Sales 1.7MMM^E *EMP* 11,000
SIC 2869 Laboratory chemicals, organic; Laboratory chemicals, organic
Pr: Steve R McCracken
**CFO:* William C Pickett
**VP:* Morris L Cranor
Off Mgr: Carla Norwood
IT Man: Lou Shectman

D-U-N-S 07-997-2268
INVISTA SARL
4501 N Access Rd, Chattanooga, TN 37415-3816
Tel (423) 875-7595 *Founded/Ownrshp* 1980
Sales 50.9MM^E *EMP* 350
SIC 2821 2299 Polyethylene resins; Broadwoven fabrics: linen, jute, hemp & ramie
Brnch Mgr: Stephen French
Dir IT: Philip Gaglia

D-U-N-S 00-258-3950
INVITATION HOMES LP
IH
901 Main St Ste 4700, Dallas, TX 75202-3733
Tel (800) 339-7368 *Founded/Ownrshp* 2012
Sales 38.4MM^E *EMP* 230^E
SIC 6531 Real estate agents & managers
Pr: Leslie B Fox
**CFO:* John A Schissel
Chf Mktg O: Andrew Gallina
Chf Inves: Dallas Tanner
Ofcr: Piero Bussani
Mng Dir: Paul McFadyen
Mng Dir: Jonathan Olsen
Off Mgr: Danielle Connolly
Off Mgr: Marlys Thompson
Off Mgr: Linda Zamora
Corp Couns: Joe Pangrac

D-U-N-S 60-179-6084
INVIVA INC
434 Hudson St Apt 2, New York, NY 10014-3937
Tel (212) 741-9322 *Founded/Ownrshp* 2000
Sales NA *EMP* 3,719
SIC 6411 Insurance agents & brokers
Ch Bd: David Smilow
**CFO:* Tim Rogers
CFO: Mark Singleton
CFO: Joe Vap
**V Ch Bd:* Laurence P Greenberg
Off Mgr: John Knox
CIO: Michael Girouard

D-U-N-S 00-923-7140 IMP
INVIVO CORP
(*Suby of* PHILIPS HEALTHCARE) ★
3545 Sw 47th Ave, Gainesville, FL 32608-7691
Tel (407) 275-3220 *Founded/Ownrshp* 1964, 2004
Sales 65.6MM^E *EMP* 600
SIC 3841 3829 Surgical & medical instruments; Diagnostic apparatus, medical; Measuring & controlling devices; Gas detectors; Surgical & medical instruments; Diagnostic apparatus, medical; Measuring & controlling devices; Gas detectors
CEO: Stephen Lorenc
Pr: Brent Berthy
COO: Larry F Young
Treas: Remco Steenbergen
VP: Robert Smith
Dir Surg: Leverda Wallace
Mng Dir: Dellabona Richard
Prgrm Mgr: James Meller
Genl Mgr: Darlene Visher
Snr Sftwr: Scott Thompson
QA Dir: Joe Glascock

INVIVO DIAGNOSTIC IMAGING
See INVIVO INC

D-U-N-S 78-752-0519
INVIVO INC
INVIVO DIAGNOSTIC IMAGING
N27w23676 Paul Rd, Pewaukee, WI 53072-5792
Tel (262) 524-1402 *Founded/Ownrshp* 2004
Sales 42.0MM^E *EMP* 150
SIC 3826 Analytical instruments; Analytical instruments
Pr: Tom Schubert

D-U-N-S 01-190-1963
■ **INVNT LLC**
(*Suby of* TIME INC) ★
295 Lafayette St Ste 700, New York, NY 10012-2722
Tel (212) 334-3415 *Founded/Ownrshp* 2015
Sales 43.0MM *EMP* 70
SIC 8748 7313 7336 Communications consulting; Printed media advertising representatives; Creative services to advertisers, except writers; Graphic arts & related design
CFO: Wolf Karbe

D-U-N-S 00-390-9002
INVOLTA LLC
5055 Rec Dr, Marion, IA 52302-6200
Tel (855) 364-3061 *Founded/Ownrshp* 2007
Sales 24.1MM^E *EMP* 120
SIC 8748 Telecommunications consultant
Ch Bd: Stephen C Gray
Dir Risk M: Gordon Smith
Off Mgr: Michaela Coyle
Netwrk Mgr: Valerie Hiatt
Sls Dir: Dan Jared
Sls Dir: Troy Ward

D-U-N-S 80-915-4156
INVSCO GROUP LTD
182 W Lake St Ste 200, Chicago, IL 60601-1124
Tel (312) 595-4800 *Founded/Ownrshp* 2007
Sales 31.1MM^E *EMP* 250
SIC 1522 Condominium construction; Condominium construction
Pr: Nicholas S Gouletas'
**COO:* Mike Fish
**CFO:* John Cadden
**Treas:* James Schwark
**VP:* Vito Bianco

D-U-N-S 06-173-4067 IMP
INVUE SECURITY PRODUCTS INC
15015 Lancaster Hwy, Charlotte, NC 28277-2010
Tel (704) 752-6513 *Founded/Ownrshp* 1972
Sales 45.8MM^E *EMP* 200
SIC 3089 3429 Cases, plastic; Injection molding of plastics; Locks or lock sets; Cases, plastic; Injection molding of plastics; Locks or lock sets
Pr: James Sankey
Pr: Juergen Lutz
**Ex VP:* Andrew Moock
VP: Cal Shilling
Exec: Michael Stewart
Exec: Lance Weeden
Prgrm Mgr: Andrew Okraski
Off Mgr: Paloma Tovar
Sftwr Eng: Ramu Pulipati
Netwrk Eng: Bobby Dovicsak
QI Cn Mgr: Caine Johnson

INWOOD GOLF COURSE
See JOLIET PARK DISTRICT

D-U-N-S 05-083-7616
INWOOD NATIONAL BANK
(*Suby of* INWOOD BANCSHARES, INC)
7621 Inwood Rd Ste 100, Dallas, TX 75209-4045
Tel (214) 358-5281 *Founded/Ownrshp* 1985
Sales NA *EMP* 226
SIC 6021

D-U-N-S 18-870-5818 IMP/EXP
INX GROUP LTD
(*Suby of* SAKATA INX CORPORATION)
150 N Martingale Rd # 700, Schaumburg, IL 60173-2408
Tel (630) 382-1800 *Founded/Ownrshp* 1988
Sales 247.0MM^E *EMP* 1,275
SIC 2893 Printing ink; Printing ink
Pr: Kotaro Morita
**Ch Bd:* Hiroshi Ota
**Pr:* Richard Clendenning
**COO:* Greg Polasik
**Treas:* Akio Miyata

D-U-N-S 00-510-3528 IMP/EXP
INX INTERNATIONAL INK CO
(*Suby of* INX GROUP LTD) ★
150 N Martingale Rd # 700, Schaumburg, IL 60173-2009
Tel (630) 382-1800 *Founded/Ownrshp* 1992
Sales 247.0MM^E *EMP* 1,100
SIC 2893 Printing ink; Printing ink
Pr: Rick Clendenning
**Ch Bd:* Kotaro Morita
**CFO:* Bryce Kristo
Treas: Jack Knight
Sr VP: Michael J Tennis
VP: Michael Brice
VP: Bill Giczkowski
VP: James Kochanny
**VP:* Matthew Mason
VP Opers: Dan Lombardo
VP Sls: Charles Sagert

D-U-N-S 15-338-6862
INXPO INC
770 N Halsted St Ste 65, Chicago, IL 60642-6940
Tel (312) 226-0782 *Founded/Ownrshp* 1994
Sales 30.3MM^E *EMP* 100
SIC 4813
CEO: Malcolm L Lotzof
Pr: Drew Vanvooren
CFO: Dave Aniol
CFO: Jim Heagney
Ofcr: Scott Kellner
Prgrm Mgr: Whitney Barrett
Mktg Dir: Cece Salomon-Lee

D-U-N-S 83-159-1982 IMP
INZI CONTROLS ALABAMA INC
(*Suby of* INZI CONTROLS CO., LTD.)
375 Alabama Highway 203, Elba, AL 36323-4233
Tel (334) 897-0100 *Founded/Ownrshp* 2009
Sales 26.0MM *EMP* 210
SIC 3089 Injection molding of plastics; Injection molding of plastics
Pr: Jin S Kim
Sls Mgr: Hyeonjin S Lim

D-U-N-S 03-956-4741 IMP
INZI DISPLAY AMERICA INC
(*Suby of* INZI DISPLAY CO., LTD)
7880 Airway Rd Ste B6e, San Diego, CA 92154-8308
Tel (619) 929-3501 *Founded/Ownrshp* 2010
Sales 87.1MM *EMP* 4
SIC 3651 Television receiving sets; Television receiving sets
Pr: Yoonhyoung Cho
**CFO:* Yang Myung Kwon

D-U-N-S 82-985-8070
IO DATA CENTERS LLC
I O
615 N 48th St, Phoenix, AZ 85008-6608
Tel (480) 513-8500 *Founded/Ownrshp* 2008
Sales 121.5MM^E *EMP* 200^E
SIC 7379 Computer related consulting services; Computer related consulting services
CEO: George Slessman
Pr: Anthony Wanger
COO: Ramzi Kheireddine
COO: David Shaw
CFO: Michael Berry
CFO: Jonathan F Mauck
Chf Cred: Bob Olson
Chf Mktg O: Anthony J D'Ambrosi
Ofcr: J Parker Lapp
Ex VP: Jim Kleeman
Ex VP: Brent Wouters
Sr VP: Adil Attlassy
Sr VP: Elizabeth Kubycheck
Sr VP: Alan McIntosh
Sr VP: Aaron Peterson
Sr VP: Anne Wolf
Sr VP: Ronald Yaggi
VP: Bob Butler
VP: Rick Crutchley
VP: Peter Goh
VP: Kathy Kim

D-U-N-S 78-828-9267 IMP
IO METRO LLC
316b Commercial Ave, Lowell, AR 72745-8868
Tel (479) 271-7507 *Founded/Ownrshp* 2006
Sales 21.7MM^E *EMP* 100
SIC 5712 Furniture stores
CEO: Lou Spagna
CFO: Allen Crouch

IQ TEC
See INTEGRATED OFFICE TECHNOLOGY LLC

D-U-N-S 61-651-2570
IOA RE INC
190 W Germantown Pike # 200, Norristown, PA 19401-1385
Tel (610) 277-4139 *Founded/Ownrshp* 1987
Sales NA *EMP* 70
SIC 6321 Accident & health insurance
CEO: John O Parker
Sr VP: Michelle Clark
Sr VP: Walter Dorosz
**VP:* Ben Buhariwalla
VP: Tim Kelly
VP: Constance McClure
VP: Eric Zurbrigen
VP Mktg: Tom McCarthy
VP Sls: Chris Eubank

D-U-N-S 16-049-6449
■ **IOC - BOONVILLE INC**
(*Suby of* ISLE OF CAPRI CASINOS INC) ★
100 Isle Of Capri Blvd, Boonville, MO 65233-1124
Tel (660) 882-1200 *Founded/Ownrshp* 2001
Sales 4.8MM *EMP* 480
SIC 7011 Hotels
Pr: Virginia McDowell

D-U-N-S 87-747-2811
■ **IOC-CARUTHERSVILLE LLC**
CASINO AZTAR
(*Suby of* ISLE OF CAPRI CASINOS INC) ★
777 E 3rd St, Caruthersville, MO 63830-1466
Tel (573) 333-6000 *Founded/Ownrshp* 2007
Sales 7.7MM^E *EMP* 300
SIC 7999 Gambling establishment; Gambling establishment

IOCC
See INTERNATIONAL ORTHODOX CHRISTIAN CHARITIES INC

D-U-N-S 07-841-1372
IOCHPE HOLDINGS LLC
(*Suby of* IOCHPE HOLDINGS AUSTRIA GMBH)
39500 Orchard Hill Pl # 500, Novi, MI 48375-5370
Tel (734) 737-5000 *Founded/Ownrshp* 2000
Sales 2.0MMM^E *EMP* 8,000
SIC 3714 Wheels, motor vehicle; Wheels, motor vehicle
CEO: Dan Ioschpe
**Treas:* Eric Moraw
**VP:* Steve Esau
**VP:* John Salvette

D-U-N-S 79-065-9978
IOD INC
1030 Ontario Rd, Green Bay, WI 54311-8014
Tel (920) 469-5000 *Founded/Ownrshp* 2006
Sales 167.6MM^E *EMP* 1,220^E
SIC 7375 Remote data base information retrieval; On-line data base information retrieval; Remote data base information retrieval; On-line data base information retrieval
Ch Bd: Michael P Wickman
Pr: James Ranck
Pr: Matthew Zastoupil
CEO: George Abatjoglou
CFO: Ben Peters
CFO: Kevin Rukamp
Ofcr: Amy Derlink
Sr VP: Robert Donnelly
Sr VP: Frank Mamone
VP: Tonya Lovelace
VP: Scot Nemchik

D-U-N-S 14-651-9934 IMP
IODITECH INC
951 N Topping Ave, Kansas City, MO 64120-1991
Tel (816) 421-0366 *Founded/Ownrshp* 2003
Sales 20.4MM^E *EMP* 23
SIC 5169 Chemicals & allied products; Chemicals & allied products
Pr: Curtis W Thomas
**VP:* Peter Sunderman
QA Dir: Tracy Doty

D-U-N-S 82-821-7997 IMP
IOFINA CHEMICAL INC
IOFINA TECHNICAL R&D CENTER
(*Suby of* IOFINA PLC)
1025 Mary Laidley Dr, Covington, KY 41017-9528
Tel (859) 356-8000 *Founded/Ownrshp* 2009
Sales 43.8MM^E *EMP* 100
SIC 2869 Industrial organic chemicals; Industrial organic chemicals
CEO: Lance J Baller
**Pr:* Thomas M Becker
**CFO:* Michael Coddington
**CFO:* Kurt Jones
VP Opers: Michael Schneider
Prd Mgr: Dave Ramsey

IOFINA TECHNICAL R&D CENTER
See IOFINA CHEMICAL INC

IOGEAR
See ATEN TECHNOLOGY INC

IOHA TECHNOLOGIES
See IONA TECHNOLOGIES INC

D-U-N-S 02-556-7249
IOLA UNIFIED SCHOOL DISTRICT 257
305 N Washington Ave, Iola, KS 66749-2350
Tel (620) 365-4700 *Founded/Ownrshp* 1872
Sales 16.3MM^E *EMP* 320
SIC 8211 Public elementary & secondary schools; Public elementary & secondary schools
Mktg Dir: Judy Cochran

D-U-N-S 07-766-9950 IMP
IOLANI SCHOOL
563 Kamoku St, Honolulu, HI 96826-5298
Tel (808) 949-5355 *Founded/Ownrshp* 1863
Sales 52.8MM *EMP* 350
Accts Kpmg Llp Honolulu Hi
SIC 8211 Private combined elementary & secondary school; Private combined elementary & secondary school
CFO: Reid Gushiken
Ofcr: Carol Hirashima
VP: Luz Barnard
Exec: Rose Panko
**Prin:* Timothy R Cottrell
Off Admin: Mona Streng
Plnt Mgr: Ricky Key
HC Dir: Patricia Liu
Assoc Ed: Jane Romjue

I.O.M.
See INDEPENDENT OPPORTUNITIES OF MICHIGAN INC

D-U-N-S 06-975-2475
IOM HEALTH SYSTEM LP
LUTHERAN HOSPITAL OF INDIANA
7950 W Jefferson Blvd, Fort Wayne, IN 46804-4140
Tel (260) 435-7001 *Founded/Ownrshp* 1903
Sales 254.7MM^E *EMP* 2,000^E
SIC 8062 General medical & surgical hospitals; Hospital, medical school affiliation; General medical & surgical hospitals; Hospital, medical school affiliation
Pr: William L Anderson
Chf Rad: Randall Phillips
CFO: Mike Makola
**VP:* Jerry Beasley

**VP:* Jan Dax
VP: R T Gray
VP: Annette Johnson
VP: Janice Welch
Dir OR: Tim Amstutz
Dir OR: Joanna Holm
Dir Case M: Linda Pickerman
Dir Lab: Mike Saalfrank
Dir Rx: Kelley Thornton

D-U-N-S 08-839-8891
IOMAX USA INC
133 River Park Rd Ste 202, Mooresville, NC 28117-8934
Tel (704) 489-9200 *Founded/Ownrshp* 2001
Sales 24.9MM^E *EMP* 90
SIC 8711 Consulting engineer
Pr: Ronald E Howard
**CFO:* Robert Brunette
**Treas:* Daniel Garton
Ofcr: Michael George
Ofcr: Clint Hubbard
**Sr VP:* Thomas Dockens
CTO: Jim Toole
IT Man: Matt Kiser
VP Opers: Lee Moritz
Genl Couns: Dottie Hersey

D-U-N-S 02-153-7865 IMP
■ IOMEGA CORP
(*Suby of* EMC CORP) ★
4059 S 1900 W, Roy, UT 84067-4100
Tel (801) 332-1000 *Founded/Ownrshp* 2008
Sales 33.7MM^E *EMP* 300
SIC 3572 7371 Computer storage devices; Disk drives, computer; Tape storage units, computer; Custom computer programming services; Computer storage devices; Disk drives, computer; Tape storage units, computer; Custom computer programming services
Pr: Jonathan S Huberman
V Ch: Jonathan Hurberman
COO: Tom Kemford
CFO: Brooke Beers
CFO: Chandra Williamson
VP: Ryan Johnson
VP: Jamie Wharton
VP: Ron Zolman
Dir IT: Teresa Boyington
Web Dev: Matt Hatch
Software D: David Brenchley

ION
See I/O MARINE SYSTEMS INC

D-U-N-S 07-879-9998 IMP
ION AMERICA LLC
ION CAMERA
513 S Lenola Rd Ste 101, Moorestown, NJ 08057-1550
Tel (856) 439-6473 *Founded/Ownrshp* 2011
Sales 25.0MM *EMP* 25^E
SIC 5043 Cameras & photographic equipment
CEO: Giovanni Tomaselli

D-U-N-S 02-428-3928 IMP/EXP
ION AUDIO LLC
(*Suby of* INMUSIC BRANDS INC) ★
200 Scenic View Dr, Cumberland, RI 02864-1847
Tel (401) 658-3743 *Founded/Ownrshp* 2003
Sales 71.2MM *EMP* 40
SIC 5999 Audio-visual equipment & supplies
CFO: Paul Stansky
Ex VP: Richard Seymour

D-U-N-S 00-691-7629
ION BANK
ION FINANCIAL
(*Suby of* ION FINANCIAL MHC) ★
251 Church St, Naugatuck, CT 06770-4121
Tel (203) 729-5291 *Founded/Ownrshp* 1998
Sales NA *EMP* 250
SIC 6035 Savings institutions, federally chartered; Savings institutions, federally chartered
Pr: Charles Boulier
**Ch Bd:* Mark Yanarella
Pr: Ann Giancarli
Ofcr: Normand Chouinard
VP: Roy A Balkus
**VP:* Ginger Fennell
VP: Sharon Mansfield
Brnch Mgr: Jessica Allen
Brnch Mgr: Lorraine Nemec
Mktg Dir: Craig Porter

ION CAMERA
See ION AMERICA LLC

ION FINANCIAL
See ION BANK

D-U-N-S 07-920-2992
ION FINANCIAL MHC
251 Church St, Naugatuck, CT 06770-4121
Tel (203) 729-5291 *Founded/Ownrshp* 2005
Sales 60.8MM^E *EMP* 250^E
SIC 6719 Investment holding companies, except banks; Investment holding companies, except banks
VP: Ginger Fennell

D-U-N-S 04-908-1441
▲ ION GEOPHYSICAL CORP
2105 Citywest Blvd # 900, Houston, TX 77042-2837
Tel (281) 933-3339 *Founded/Ownrshp* 1968
Sales 509.5MM *EMP* 879
Accts Grant Thornton Llp Houston T
Tkr Sym IO *Exch* NYS
SIC 7372 3829 Application computer software; Geophysical & meteorological testing equipment; Seismographs; Seismometers; Seismoscopes; Application computer software; Geophysical & meteorological testing equipment; Seismographs; Seismometers; Seismoscopes
Pr: R Brian Hanson
**Ch Bd:* James M Lapeyre Jr
COO: Lydia Cannon
COO: Christopher T Usher
COO: Ken Williamson
CFO: Steve Bate
CFO: Brian Hanson
Treas: Davis Maxey
Ex VP: Robbin Adams
Ex VP: Chuck Ledet
Sr VP: Colin Hulme
Sr VP: Jacques Leveille
Sr VP: Robert Maxey
Sr VP: David L Roland
VP: Dale Lambert
VP: Scott Schwausch
Board of Directors: David H Barr, Michael C Jennings, James M Lapeyre Jr, Franklin Myers, S James Nelson Jr, John N Seitz

D-U-N-S 10-649-9791 IMP
ION LABS INC
5355 115th Ave N, Clearwater, FL 33760-4840
Tel (727) 527-1072 *Founded/Ownrshp* 2012
Sales 88.7MM^E *EMP* 116
SIC 5122 2834 Vitamins & minerals; Vitamin, nutrient & hematinic preparations for human use; Vitamins & minerals; Vitamin, nutrient & hematinic preparations for human use
CEO: Clayton Desjardine
Treas: Dawn Carrell
VP: Allan Toole
Exec: Leslie Boggs
Dir Lab: Brett Johns
Sls Dir: Victoria Travers

D-U-N-S 55-687-4980
ION MEDIA NETWORKS INC
601 Clearwater Park Rd, West Palm Beach, FL 33401-6233
Tel (561) 659-4122 *Founded/Ownrshp* 2009
Sales 275.8MM^E *EMP* 508
SIC 4833 Television broadcasting stations; Television broadcasting stations
Pr: R Brandon Burgess
Pr: John Ford
Pr: Steve Friedman
Pr: Douglas Holloway
Pr: John Lawson
**CFO:* Gordon Lavalette
**Chf Cred:* Jeff Quinn
Ex VP: Leslie Glenn Chesloff
Ex VP: Marc Zand
Sr VP: John Heffron
VP: Todd Ackley
VP: Mark Barrington
VP: Kendra Cleary
VP: Cindy Kelly
VP: Kristy Mahlo
VP: Robert Marino
VP: Susan Morgenstein
VP: William O'Shea
VP: Blaine Rominger
VP: Robert Russo
VP: Robin Sheingold

D-U-N-S 80-860-9676
■ ION TORRENT SYSTEMS INC
(*Suby of* LIFE TECHNOLOGIES CORP) ★
246 Goose Ln Ste 100, Guilford, CT 06437-2186
Tel (203) 458-8552 *Founded/Ownrshp* 2010
Sales 14.8MM^E *EMP* 400^E
SIC 8731 Commercial physical research; Commercial physical research
CEO: Jonathan M Rothberg
Pr: Tom Roth
VP: James M Bustillo
**Prin:* Joseph W Secondine Jr
**Prin:* David L Szekeres
Sftwr Eng: Bernard Puc

D-U-N-S 87-622-6655
ION TRADING INC
(*Suby of* ION TRADING UK LIMITED)
200 W Madison St Fl 14, Chicago, IL 60606-3415
Tel (312) 612-7070 *Founded/Ownrshp* 2011
Sales 32.2MM^E *EMP* 260
SIC 7371 5045 7379 7375 Computer software development; Computers, peripherals & software; Computer related consulting services; On-line data base information retrieval; Computer software development; Computers, peripherals & software; Computer related consulting services; On-line data base information retrieval
Pr: Edward Alexander
COO: Gavin Bambury
**VP:* John Munro
Prgrm Mgr: John Blankson
Prgrm Mgr: Riccardo Chiaverini
Genl Mgr: Michael Dienes
Off Mgr: Siobhan Collinson
Snr Sftwr: Andrea Giannini
Snr Sftwr: Massimiliano Mammini
Snr Sftwr: Luca Veraldi
Snr Sftwr: Amit Verma

D-U-N-S 07-870-8914
IONA COLLEGE (INC) (NY)
715 North Ave, New Rochelle, NY 10801-1890
Tel (914) 633-2000 *Founded/Ownrshp* 1940
Sales 151.4MM *EMP* 750
Accts Grant Thornton Llp New York
SIC 8221 College, except junior; College, except junior
Pr: Joseph E Nyre
Assoc VP: Eileen Doyle
VP: Mary Durkin
VP: Justine Erickson
VP: Kristen Mengold
VP: Jeanne Salvatore
VP: Joan Steel
Assoc Dir: Patrick Cin
Creative D: Danielle Mastromarino
Ex Dir: Glenn Horine
Off Mgr: Margaret Bohan
Board of Directors: Matt Rizzetta

D-U-N-S 17-627-7275
IONA TECHNOLOGIES INC
IOHA TECHNOLOGIES
(*Suby of* IONA TECHNOLOGIES LIMITED)
14 Oak Park Dr, Bedford, MA 01730-1414
Tel (800) 672-4948 *Founded/Ownrshp* 1995
Sales 48.6MM^E *EMP* 555
SIC 5045 7371 Computer software; Custom computer programming services; Computer software; Custom computer programming services
Pr: Peter M Zotto
VP: Larry Alston
**VP:* Jim Bridges
**VP:* Martin Delaney
**VP:* Scott Devens
VP: Kevin McCluskey
VP: William B McMurray
VP: Robert Napolitano
**VP:* Andrew O'Sullivan
**VP:* Des Pieri
**VP:* Mark Rogers
**VP:* Joe Weeks

D-U-N-S 87-757-3550 IMP
IONBOND LLC
(*Suby of* IHI IONBOND AG)
1823 E Whitcomb Ave, Madison Heights, MI 48071-1413
Tel (248) 398-9100 *Founded/Ownrshp* 2000
Sales 82.2MM^E *EMP* 500
SIC 3398 3479 Metal heat treating; Bonderizing of metal or metal products; Metal heat treating; Bonderizing of metal or metal products
CEO: Joe Haggerty
**Pr:* Ton Hurkmans
CFO: Gary Elwood
**CFO:* Lukas Haldimann
**CFO:* Antonie Polumba
VP: Walter N Kreil Jr
Genl Mgr: Debbie Degraaf
IT Man: Robert Aharonov
QC Dir: Pat Betz
Opers Mgr: Chip Johnston
Opers Mgr: Rick Zawacki

D-U-N-S 06-157-4208
IONI 2 INC
18325 S 580 W, Remington, IN 47977-8601
Tel (219) 261-2115 *Founded/Ownrshp* 1990
Sales 72.4MM^E *EMP* 156^E
SIC 3462

IONIA COUNTY CLERK OFFICE
See COUNTY OF IONIA

D-U-N-S 07-982-7441
IONIA COUNTY INTERMEDIATE SCHOOL DISTRICT
2191 Harwood Rd, Ionia, MI 48846-9458
Tel (616) 527-4900 *Founded/Ownrshp* 2015
Sales 25.8MM *EMP* 11^E
SIC 8211 Public elementary & secondary schools

D-U-N-S 02-088-8590
IONIA COUNTY MEMORIAL HOSPITAL CORP
SPARROW IONIA HOSPITAL
3565 S State Rd, Ionia, MI 48846-9416
Tel (616) 523-1400 *Founded/Ownrshp* 1951
Sales 32.2MM *EMP* 283
SIC 8062 8082 8071 8011 General medical & surgical hospitals; Home health care services; Medical laboratories; Offices & clinics of medical doctors; General medical & surgical hospitals; Home health care services; Medical laboratories; Offices & clinics of medical doctors
Pr: Evonne Ulmer
**CFO:* Paul Evers
Dir Rad: Blain Pierce
Dir Rx: Michael McDonald
Dir Env Sv: Clare Sutliff
Off Mgr: Melissa Snow
Nurse Mgr: Robbin Glass
Nurse Mgr: Jerry Ritz
QA Dir: Barbara Dora
IT Man: Robert Neal
Mktg Dir: Laurie Tjlasma

D-U-N-S 03-599-3328
IONIA INDEPENDENT SCHOOL DISTRICT
2191 Harwood Rd, Ionia, MI 48846-9458
Tel (616) 527-4900 *Founded/Ownrshp* 1962
Sales 24.6MM *EMP* 330
Accts Roslund Prestage & Company
SIC 8211 Public junior high school; Public senior high school; Public junior high school; Public senior high school
Mktg Dir: Michael Bergman

D-U-N-S 10-030-8303
IONIA PUBLIC SCHOOLS
250 E Tuttle Rd, Ionia, MI 48846-8605
Tel (616) 527-9280 *Founded/Ownrshp* 1870
Sales 18.9MM^E *EMP* 350
SIC 8211 Public elementary & secondary schools; Public elementary & secondary schools
Schl Brd P: Karen Gregory

D-U-N-S 36-194-9092
▲ IONIS PHARMACEUTICALS INC
2855 Gazelle Ct, Carlsbad, CA 92010-6670
Tel (760) 931-9200 *Founded/Ownrshp* 1989
Sales 214.1MM *EMP* 390^E
Tkr Sym IONS *Exch* NGS
SIC 8731 2834 3845 Medical research, commercial; Pharmaceutical preparations; Electromedical equipment; Medical research, commercial; Pharmaceutical preparations; Electromedical equipment
Ch Bd: Stanley T Crooke
Pr: Jennifer Giottonini
CEO: Michael Treble
**COO:* B Lynne Parshall
CFO: Elizabeth L Hougen
Ofcr: Sarah Boyce
Sr VP: Richard S Geary
Sr VP: Brett Monia
Sr VP: Patrick R O'Neil
VP: Sanjay Bhanot
VP: Erin Lettow
VP: Walter Singleton
Exec: Lori Cooper
Assoc Dir: Amy Williford
Board of Directors: Spencer R Berthelsen, Joseph Klein III, Joseph Loscalzo, Frederick T Muto, Joseph H Wender

D-U-N-S 80-230-9922
■ IOS/PCI LLC
INSPECTION OILFIELD SERVICES
(*Suby of* L B FOSTER CO) ★
652 N Sam Houston Pkwy E, Houston, TX 77060-5900
Tel (281) 310-5357 *Founded/Ownrshp* 2015
Sales 158.7MM^E *EMP* 559
SIC 1389 7389 Oil field services; Pipeline & power line inspection service; Safety inspection service; Oil field services; Pipeline & power line inspection service; Safety inspection service
CEO: Dal Miller
COO: Paco McLaughlin
CFO: Jody Arceneaux
VP: Jimmy Clark
VP: Justin Jarski
VP: Bobby Lopez

D-U-N-S 82-832-3647
IOTA ENGINEERING LLC
1361 E Wieding Rd, Tucson, AZ 85706-6028
Tel (520) 294-3292 *Founded/Ownrshp* 1968
Sales 43.8MM^E *EMP* 200^E
SIC 8711 Engineering services; Engineering services
CEO: Stephen W Shell
DP Exec: Daren Hatfield

D-U-N-S 13-837-6103 IMP
IOWA 80 GROUP INC
515 Sterling Dr, Walcott, IA 52773-8573
Tel (563) 468-5500 *Founded/Ownrshp* 1965
Sales 327.8MM^E *EMP* 1,000
SIC 5541 5399 7542 5812 Truck stops; Country general stores; Truck wash; Restaurant, family: independent; Truck stops; Country general stores; Truck wash; Restaurant, family: independent
Pr: William I Moon III
**Ch Bd:* Carolyn Moon
**Pr:* William I Moon III
COO: Kelly Hazen
**CFO:* James L Tillotson
VP: Ron Burmeister
**VP:* Jack Horan
**VP:* Rodney Pugh
Off Mgr: Deb Hartman
Store Mgr: Jim Morris
Netwrk Mgr: Burke Strand

D-U-N-S 02-235-6000
IOWA 80 TRUCKSTOP INC
(*Suby of* IOWA 80 GROUP INC) ★
755 W Iowa 80 Rd I-80, Walcott, IA 52773-8572
Tel (563) 284-6512 *Founded/Ownrshp* 1965
Sales 98.8MM^E *EMP* 300
SIC 5541 5399 7542 5812 Truck stops; Country general stores; Truck wash; Restaurant, family: independent; Truck stops; Country general stores; Truck wash; Restaurant, family: independent
Pr: William I Moon III
**Ch Bd:* Carolyn Moon
**CFO:* James L Tillotson
**VP:* Jack Horan
**VP:* Delia Moon Meier

IOWA ANNUAL CONFERENCE
See IOWA CONFERENCE OF UNITED METHODIST CHURCH

D-U-N-S 96-635-0964
IOWA BANKERS BENEFIT PLAN
8800 Nw 62nd Ave, Johnston, IA 50131-2849
Tel (515) 286-4300 *Founded/Ownrshp* 2011
Sales NA *EMP* 2
Accts Deloitte Tax Lp Minneapolis
SIC 6411 Pension & retirement plan consultants; Pension & retirement plan consultants
Pr: Becki Rogers Neese

D-U-N-S 11-351-9797
IOWA BANKERS INSURANCE AND SERVICES INC
(*Suby of* IOWA BANKERS ASSOCIATION)
8800 Nw 62nd Ave, Johnston, IA 50131-2849
Tel (515) 286-4300 *Founded/Ownrshp* 1971
Sales NA *EMP* 70^E
SIC 6712 Bank holding companies; Bank holding companies
Pr: John Sorenson
VP: Julie Gliha

D-U-N-S 02-205-0959 IMP
IOWA BEER AND BEVERAGE CO
FLECK SALES
1125 Highlife Ct Sw, Cedar Rapids, IA 52404
Tel (319) 848-8275 *Founded/Ownrshp* 1956
Sales 33.9MM^E *EMP* 100
SIC 5181 Beer & other fermented malt liquors; Beer & other fermented malt liquors
Pr: Dudley Fleck
**Pr:* Doris Fleck
**VP:* Jeffrey Fleck
**VP:* Neil Matthias
**VP:* Mike Schulte

D-U-N-S 02-213-1437 IMP
IOWA BEVERAGE SYSTEMS INC
2115 Ne 58th Ave, Des Moines, IA 50313-1633
Tel (515) 266-2274 *Founded/Ownrshp* 1988
Sales 56.2MM^E *EMP* 150
SIC 5181 Beer & other fermented malt liquors; Beer & other fermented malt liquors
Pr: Michael G Brewington

D-U-N-S 05-796-3357
IOWA BRIDGE & CULVERT LC
CONCRETE CUTTING & CORING
409 N Avenue B, Washington, IA 52353-1909
Tel (319) 653-5436 *Founded/Ownrshp* 1954
Sales 21.1MM^E *EMP* 80
SIC 1622 1741 Bridge construction; Concrete block masonry laying
Pr: Kenneth Hanson
**VP:* Burge Hammond
**VP:* Curt Hanson
**VP:* Brian Uitermarket
Mtls Mgr: John Anderson

D-U-N-S 17-165-2795
IOWA CENTRAL COMMUNITY COLLEGE
1 Triton Cir, Fort Dodge, IA 50501-5798
Tel (515) 576-7201 *Founded/Ownrshp* 1966
Sales 34.6MM^E *EMP* 640
Accts Schnurr & Company Llp Fort D
SIC 8244 8221 Business & secretarial schools; Colleges universities & professional schools; Business & secretarial schools; Colleges universities & professional schools
Pr: Eric Pearson
**VP:* Thomas J Beneke
VP: Laurie Hendricks
Dir Lab: Don Heck
CTO: Jessica Kavanaugh

D-U-N-S 11-807-5196
IOWA CHICAGO & EASTERN RAILROAD CORP
I, C & E RAILROAD
(*Suby of* D M & E RAILROAD) ★
140 N Phillips Ave # 300, Sioux Falls, SD 57104-6724
Tel (605) 782-1200 *Founded/Ownrshp* 2002
Sales 25.2MM^E *EMP* 665^E
SIC 4011 Railroads, line-haul operating; Railroads, line-haul operating
Pr: Kevin Schieffer
**VP:* Lynn Anderson
VP: Kurt Feaster

D-U-N-S 08-348-7173
IOWA CITY COMMUNITY SCHOOL DISTRICT FOUNDATION (IA)
1725 N Dodge St, Iowa City, IA 52245-9589
Tel (319) 688-1000 *Founded/Ownrshp* 1900
Sales 94.3MM^E *EMP* 1,600
SIC 8211 Public elementary & secondary schools; Public elementary & secondary schools
**COO:* David Dude
**CFO:* Paul Bobek
**CFO:* Craig Hansel
Treas: Bennett Bork
IT Man: Kelly Nelson
Pr Dir: Chace Ramey
Schl Brd P: Chris Linch

IOWA CLINIC CORPORATE OFFICE
See CENTRAL IOWA HEART CENTER PC

D-U-N-S 79-251-4916
IOWA CLINIC P C
5950 University Ave # 231, West Des Moines, IA 50266-8233
Tel (515) 875-9100 *Founded/Ownrshp* 1994
Sales 48.1MM^E *EMP* 550^E
SIC 8011 Offices & clinics of medical doctors; Offices & clinics of medical doctors
CEO: C Edward Brown
**Pr:* Mark A Reece
**CFO:* David Zielke
**Sec:* Steven J Rosenberg

IOWA COLLEGE ACQUISITION CORP.
See IOWA COLLEGE ACQUISITION LLC

D-U-N-S 04-059-1539
■ **IOWA COLLEGE ACQUISITION LLC**
IOWA COLLEGE ACQUISITION CORP.
(*Suby of* KAPLAN HIGHER EDUCATION LLC) ★
1801 E Kimberly Rd Ste 1, Davenport, IA 52807-2095
Tel (563) 355-3500 *Founded/Ownrshp* 1999
Sales 34.2MM^E *EMP* 160
SIC 8221 Colleges universities & professional schools
Pr: Mart Darland
Pr: Sarah Skelton
**Pr:* Lisa Zerbonia
Pgrm Dir: Grace Keys

D-U-N-S 14-154-1164
IOWA COMPREHENSIVE HEALTH ASSOCIATION
HIP IOWA
700 Walnut St Ste 1600, Des Moines, IA 50309-3800
Tel (515) 283-3172 *Founded/Ownrshp* 2003
Sales 51.7MM *EMP* 15
Accts Leemhuis Group Indianapolis
SIC 8011 Medical insurance associations; Medical insurance associations
Pr: Joseph Day
**VP:* Angela Burke Boston

D-U-N-S 04-058-9681
IOWA CONFERENCE OF UNITED METHODIST CHURCH
IOWA ANNUAL CONFERENCE
2301 Rittenhouse St, Des Moines, IA 50321-3101
Tel (515) 974-8900 *Founded/Ownrshp* 1870
Sales 22.0MM *EMP* 35
SIC 8661 Methodist Church; Methodist Church
IT Man: Roland Minshall

D-U-N-S 87-714-9948
■ **IOWA CONTRACT FABRICATORS INC**
(*Suby of* MCNEILUS COMPANIES INC) ★
12150 Addison Ave, Riceville, IA 50466-7003
Tel (641) 985-2900 *Founded/Ownrshp* 1994
Sales 22.9MM^E *EMP* 152
SIC 3531 3441 Construction machinery attachments; Fabricated structural metal; Construction machinery attachments; Fabricated structural metal
Div Mgr: Joel Losce
Plnt Mgr: James Irvin

D-U-N-S 80-834-6365
IOWA DEPARTMENT OF ADMINISTRATIVE SERVICES
ASSOCIATION OF LABOR RELATIONS
(*Suby of* IOWA DEPARTMENT OF EXECUTIVE OFFICE) ★
1305 E Walnut St, Des Moines, IA 50319-0106
Tel (515) 281-3351 *Founded/Ownrshp* 1986
Sales NA *EMP* 300
SIC 9441 Administration of social & manpower programs; ; Administration of social & manpower programs;

D-U-N-S 80-838-9936
IOWA DEPARTMENT OF AGRICULTURE AND LAND STEWARDSHIP
(*Suby of* IOWA DEPARTMENT OF EXECUTIVE OFFICE) ★
502 E 9th St, Des Moines, IA 50319-5005
Tel (515) 281-5322 *Founded/Ownrshp* 2000
Sales NA *EMP* 400
Accts Richard D Johnson State Audit
SIC 9641 Regulation of agricultural marketing; ; Regulation of agricultural marketing;

D-U-N-S 80-834-8668
IOWA DEPARTMENT OF CORRECTIONS
(*Suby of* IOWA DEPARTMENT OF EXECUTIVE OFFICE) ★
510 E 12th St Rm 4, Des Moines, IA 50319-9025
Tel (515) 725-5701 *Founded/Ownrshp* 1983
Sales NA *EMP* 1,729
SIC 9223 Prison, government; ; Prison, government;
Ofcr: Christian Boyer
Ofcr: Thomas Cooley
Comm Dir: Staci Ballard

D-U-N-S 80-834-8981
IOWA DEPARTMENT OF ECONOMIC DEVELOPMENT
(*Suby of* IOWA DEPARTMENT OF EXECUTIVE OFFICE) ★
200 E Grand Ave Ste 150, Des Moines, IA 50309-1827
Tel (515) 242-4827 *Founded/Ownrshp* 1986
Sales NA *EMP* 320
SIC 9611 Economic development agency, government; ; Economic development agency, government;
VP: Vic Cameruci
Exec: Shawn Rolland
Ex Dir: Maureen Elbert
Ex Dir: Bill Menner
Snr Mgr: Steven Bickford

D-U-N-S 80-834-6555
IOWA DEPARTMENT OF EDUCATION
(*Suby of* IOWA DEPARTMENT OF EXECUTIVE OFFICE) ★
400 E 14th St, Des Moines, IA 50319-0146
Tel (515) 281-5294 *Founded/Ownrshp* 1913
Sales NA *EMP* 300
SIC 9411 Administration of educational programs;
MIS Dir: David Kreiger
MIS Dir: Gary Krob
Pr Dir: Staci Hupp
Teacher Pr: Byron Darnell
HC Dir: Ann Feilmann

D-U-N-S 80-834-1499
IOWA DEPARTMENT OF EXECUTIVE OFFICE
(*Suby of* STATE OF IOWA) ★
State Capital, Des Moines, IA 50319
Tel (515) 281-5211 *Founded/Ownrshp* 1846
Sales NA *EMP* 1,730
SIC 9111 Governors' offices; ; Governors' offices;
Pr: Troy Price
Comm Dir: Phil Roeder

D-U-N-S 80-834-8841
IOWA DEPARTMENT OF HUMAN SERVICES
(*Suby of* IOWA DEPARTMENT OF EXECUTIVE OFFICE) ★
1305 E Walnut St Rm 114, Des Moines, IA 50319-0106
Tel (515) 281-5454 *Founded/Ownrshp* 1978
Sales NA *EMP* 1,730
SIC 9441 Administration of social & manpower programs; ; Administration of social & manpower programs;
CFO: Jan Clausen
Sr VP: Janet Hardenbrook
**Ex Dir:* Eugene I Gessow
Off Mgr: Linda Miller
Snr Mgr: Lorrie Tritch

D-U-N-S 80-834-8866
IOWA DEPARTMENT OF NATURAL RESOURCES
(*Suby of* IOWA DEPARTMENT OF EXECUTIVE OFFICE) ★
502 E 9th St, Des Moines, IA 50319-5005
Tel (515) 281-5876 *Founded/Ownrshp* 1986
Sales NA *EMP* 925
SIC 9512 Land, mineral & wildlife conservation;

D-U-N-S 80-834-9088
IOWA DEPARTMENT OF PUBLIC DEFENSE
(*Suby of* IOWA DEPARTMENT OF EXECUTIVE OFFICE) ★
7105 Nw 70th Ave, Johnston, IA 50131-1824
Tel (515) 252-4211 *Founded/Ownrshp* 1846
Sales NA *EMP* 1,700^E
SIC 9711 National security; ; National security;
Ex Dir: Maj Ron Dardis
Exec: Stefanie Bond

D-U-N-S 80-834-5920
IOWA DEPARTMENT OF PUBLIC HEALTH
(*Suby of* IOWA DEPARTMENT OF EXECUTIVE OFFICE) ★
321 E 12th St Rm 175, Des Moines, IA 50319-0075
Tel (515) 281-7689 *Founded/Ownrshp* 1880
Sales NA *EMP* 450^E
SIC 9431 Administration of public health programs; ; Administration of public health programs;
Treas: Kenneth Choquette
Ofcr: Sarah Brooks
Ofcr: Alex Carfrae

D-U-N-S 80-834-9021
IOWA DEPARTMENT OF PUBLIC SAFETY
(*Suby of* IOWA DEPARTMENT OF EXECUTIVE OFFICE) ★
215 E 7th St Rm 40, Des Moines, IA 50319-1902
Tel (515) 725-6050 *Founded/Ownrshp* 1939
Sales NA *EMP* 930
SIC 9229 Public order & safety statistics centers; ; Public order & safety statistics centers;
CFO: Leon J Frederick

D-U-N-S 80-834-9047
IOWA DEPARTMENT OF TRANSPORTATION
(*Suby of* IOWA DEPARTMENT OF EXECUTIVE OFFICE) ★
800 Lincoln Way, Ames, IA 50010-6915
Tel (515) 239-1111 *Founded/Ownrshp* 1975
Sales NA *EMP* 1,720^E
SIC 9621 Regulation, administration of transportation; ; Regulation, administration of transportation;
CEO: Nancy Richardson

D-U-N-S 07-347-6590
IOWA FARM BUREAU FEDERATION
5400 University Ave, West Des Moines, IA 50266-5950
Tel (515) 225-5400 *Founded/Ownrshp* 1921
Sales 59.8MM *EMP* 1,866^E
Accts Meriwether Wilson And Company
SIC 8699 5154 6311 6321 6411 Farm bureau; Cattle; Life insurance carriers; Health insurance carriers; Insurance agents, brokers & service; Farm bureau; Cattle; Life insurance carriers; Health insurance carriers; Insurance agents, brokers & service
Pr: Craig D Hill
**Sec:* Dennis J Presnall

D-U-N-S 61-482-3722
IOWA FINANCE AUTHORITY
2015 Grand Ave Ste 200, Des Moines, IA 50312-4903
Tel (515) 725-4900 *Founded/Ownrshp* 1975
Sales NA *EMP* 89
Accts Kpmg Llp Des Moines Ia
SIC 6163 Loan brokers; Loan brokers
CEO: David Jamison
**COO:* Steven Harvey
Ofcr: Carolann Jensen
Ofcr: Bob Skelley
Ofcr: Lisa Strait
IT Man: Cindy Harris
Genl Couns: Mark Thompson
Genl Couns: Joanna Wilson

D-U-N-S 00-530-2757
IOWA GLASS DEPOT INC (IA)
4150 C St Sw, Cedar Rapids, IA 52404-7451
Tel (319) 396-2222 *Founded/Ownrshp* 1955
Sales 58.6MM^E *EMP* 400
SIC 5013 5231 Automobile glass; Glass; Automobile glass; Glass
Pr: Steve Dummermuth
**CFO:* John Morrissey
CFO: Randy Vittetoe
Dir IT: Nelson Don
IT Man: Anthony Henderson
IT Man: Doug Martin
Sls&Mrk Ex: Tracy Oster

IOWA HEALTH PHYSICIANS
See IOWA PHYSICIANS CLINIC MEDICAL FOUNDATION

D-U-N-S 83-620-4271
IOWA HEALTH SYSTEM
UNITYPOINT HEALTH
1776 West Lakes Pkwy # 400, West Des Moines, IA 50266-8378
Tel (515) 241-6161 *Founded/Ownrshp* 1994
Sales 2.8MMM *EMP* 18,923
Accts Bkd Llp Kansas City Missouri
SIC 8062 8721 8741 General medical & surgical hospitals; Accounting, auditing & bookkeeping; Hospital management; General medical & surgical hospitals; Accounting, auditing & bookkeeping; Hospital management
Pr: Bill Leaver
Pr: Katherine Pearson
Pr: Scott Whitson
**CFO:* Mark Johnson
**Treas:* Mike Stone
Ofcr: Heidi Goodman
**Ex VP:* Kevin Vermeer
**VP:* Denny Drake
VP: Susan Haider
VP: Joyce McDanel
VP: Jim Mormann
VP: Mark Purtle
VP Bus Dev: Sid Ramsey
Dir Risk M: Barb Earles
Dir Lab: Diana Tank

D-U-N-S 03-530-1535
IOWA HEART CENTER INC
5880 University Ave # 204, West Des Moines, IA 50266-8255
Tel (515) 633-3600 *Founded/Ownrshp* 1970
Sales 29.8MM^E *EMP* 450
SIC 8011 Offices & clinics of medical doctors; Offices & clinics of medical doctors
Pr: Kevin E Crowe MD
**Pr:* Julie Younger
Off Mgr: Margaret Marcouiller
Software D: Brady White
Sls&Mrk Ex: Amy Benz
Surgeon: Jose Borromeo
Surgeon: David Chew
Surgeon: James Ebaugh
Surgeon: Laurie Kuestner

D-U-N-S 11-416-2001
IOWA INTERSTATE RAILROAD LTD
IAIS
(*Suby of* RAILROAD DEVELOPMENT CORP) ★
5900 6th St Sw, Cedar Rapids, IA 52404-4804
Tel (319) 298-5400 *Founded/Ownrshp* 2004
Sales 40.4MM^E *EMP* 215
SIC 4011 Railroads, line-haul operating; Railroads, line-haul operating
Pr: Jerome Lipka
**VP:* Carrie Evans
**VP:* Patrick H Sheldon
**VP:* Cathy Smith

IOWA INTERVIEWING
See PERSONAL MARKETING RESEARCH INC

D-U-N-S 07-984-7830
IOWA KENWORTH INC
(*Suby of* MURPHY-HOFFMAN CO) ★
11120 Tomahawk Creek Pkwy, Leawood, KS 66211-2695
Tel (816) 483-6444 *Founded/Ownrshp* 2015
Sales 20.7MM^E *EMP* 200^E
SIC 5012 7539 Trucks, commercial; Trucks, noncommercial; Automotive repair shops
CEO: Timothy Murphy
Pr: Mike Murphy
CFO: Jeff Johnson

D-U-N-S 87-933-0702
IOWA LAKES COMMUNITY COLLEGE
19 S 7th St, Estherville, IA 51334-2234
Tel (712) 362-2601 *Founded/Ownrshp* 1967
Sales 28.2MM *EMP* 300
Accts Williams & Company Pc Spen
SIC 8222 Community college; Community college
Pr: Jane Lund
CFO: Robert Burqux
Sr VP: Linda Anderson
Sr VP: Heather Bernhard
VP: Robert L'Heureux
VP Admn: Robert Lheureux
Ex Dir: Judith Cook
Dir IT: Jerimiah Depyper
Psych: Jacque Carstens

D-U-N-S 06-522-4362
IOWA LAKES ELECTRIC COOPERATIVE (INC)
702 S 1st St, Estherville, IA 51334-2522
Tel (712) 362-2694 *Founded/Ownrshp* 1938
Sales 66.7MM *EMP* 62
Accts Cliftonlarsonallen Llp Austin
SIC 4911 Electric services; Electric services
Pr: Tresa Hussong
Bd of Dir: Kirby Range
Exec: September Dau
VP Opers: Richard Olesen
Sfty Mgr: Mike Lockwood
Opers Mgr: Rick Olson
Mktg Mgr: Stephanie Green

D-U-N-S 00-527-6738
IOWA LIMESTONE CO (IA)
ILC RESOURCES
3301 106th Cir, Urbandale, IA 50322-3740
Tel (515) 243-3160 *Founded/Ownrshp* 1913
Sales 81.2MM^E *EMP* 101
SIC 1422 5191 Limestones, ground; Phosphate rock, ground
Pr: Franklin Goode
**Pr:* Carl Lamberti
**CEO:* Richard W Witt
**Sec:* Linda E Morris-Dowie
VP: Linda Dowie
**VP:* Mike Tjarks
**VP:* Jim Tompt
IT Man: Ben Caplan
Mktg Dir: Dick Witt

D-U-N-S 09-137-6962
IOWA MACHINE SHED CO INC
THUNDERBAY CAFE
1501 River Dr, Moline, IL 61265-1307
Tel (309) 797-9300 *Founded/Ownrshp* 1978
Sales 14.1MM^E *EMP* 301
SIC 5812 8741 7011 6531 Restaurant, family: independent; Cafe; Management services; Hotels & motels; Real estate agents & managers; Restaurant, family: independent; Cafe; Management services; Hotels & motels; Real estate agents & managers
Pr: Michael Whalen
**Sec:* Mary Kim Whalen
**VP:* Dan A Whalen Jr
Exec: Theresa Chruch

D-U-N-S 00-528-6539 IMP/EXP
■ **IOWA MOLD TOOLING CO INC**
(*Suby of* OSHKOSH CORP) ★
500 W Us Highway 18, Garner, IA 50438-1090
Tel (641) 923-3711 *Founded/Ownrshp* 2006
Sales 91.8MM^E *EMP* 375
SIC 3531 3713 3563 Cranes; Truck bodies (motor vehicles); Air & gas compressors including vacuum pumps; Cranes; Truck bodies (motor vehicles); Air & gas compressors including vacuum pumps
Genl Mgr: Jim Hasty
COO: Richard Long
CFO: John Gerpen
Sfty Mgr: Ken Schaeffer
Plnt Mgr: Jerry Douglas
VP Sls: Eric Neitzke
Manager: John Chester
Manager: Roger Orlandi
Snr Mgr: Glen Ashdown

D-U-N-S 00-694-1488
IOWA MUTUAL INSURANCE CO
509 9th St, De Witt, IA 52742-1333
Tel (563) 659-3231 *Founded/Ownrshp* 1882
Sales NA *EMP* 107
SIC 6331 Property damage insurance; Fire, marine & casualty insurance: mutual; Property damage insurance; Fire, marine & casualty insurance: mutual
Ch Bd: John Bishop
**Pr:* Georgia Puls
**CEO:* David Kaufman
**CFO:* Susan Haack
Sr VP: Drew Bright
VP: John Kessler
VP: Randy Rudowicz
VP: Charles Stapleton
VP: Chuck Wickert
VP Mktg: Sanford Miller
Mktg Dir: Tom Cole
Board of Directors: Michael Wiseman, John Bishop, Thomas Cole, Larry Forrester, Susan Haack, David Kaufman, Robert Lambert, Thomas Ogg, Charles Stapleton, Alan Tubbs

D-U-N-S 18-682-5956 IMP
IOWA NETWORK SERVICES INC
7760 Office Plaza Dr S, West Des Moines, IA 50266-5998
Tel (515) 830-0110 *Founded/Ownrshp* 1984
Sales 657.1MM *EMP* 490
SIC 4813 Long distance telephone communications; Voice telephone communications; Long distance telephone communications; Voice telephone communications
CEO: Richard M Vohs
Pr: Frank Hilton
**VP:* Dennis M Creveling
VP: Howard Juul
Exec: Beth Ellis
IT Man: Mike Czizal
Netwrk Eng: Michael Trembly
Trfc Dir: Sandra Doran
Sales Exec: Rusty Daniels
VP Sls: Thomas Beem
Mktg Mgr: Kristi Petersen

D-U-N-S 02-234-1721
IOWA OFFICE SUPPLY INC
OFFICE ELEMENTS
713 Nebraska St, Sioux City, IA 51101-1103
Tel (712) 258-1213 *Founded/Ownrshp* 1967
Sales 28.2MM^E *EMP* 87
SIC 5044 5943 5021 7699

D-U-N-S 78-600-2766
IOWA ORTHOPAEDIC CENTER PC
450 Laurel St Ste A, Des Moines, IA 50314-3045
Tel (515) 247-8400 *Founded/Ownrshp* 1971
Sales 27.4MM^E *EMP* 250
SIC 8011 Orthopedic physician; Orthopedic physician
CEO: Kevin Ward
**Pr:* Kyle Galles
**Pr:* Joshua Kimelman
**CFO:* Richard Tharp Jr
**Treas:* Cassim Igram
**VP:* Timothy Kenney
Doctor: Lynn M Lindeman

D-U-N-S 10-238-5650
IOWA PACIFIC HOLDINGS LLC
PERMIAN BASIN RAILWAYS
118 S Clinton St Ste 400, Chicago, IL 60661-5772
Tel (312) 466-0900 *Founded/Ownrshp* 2006
Sales 117.0MM^E *EMP* 200
SIC 4011 Railroads, line-haul operating; Railroads, line-haul operating
CEO: Edwin Ellis
**Pr:* H Michael McConville
Chf Mktg O: Steve Schott
Ex VP: Mike McConville
VP: Todd Cecil
VP: Howard W Clark III
**VP:* Tracy Davis
VP: Steve Hill
**Prin:* Clark E Johnson Jr
**VP Opers:* Mike McCondille
VP Mktg: Steve Gregory

D-U-N-S 82-562-6245
IOWA PHYSICIANS CLINIC MEDICAL FOUNDATION
IOWA HEALTH PHYSICIANS
1221 Pleasant St Ste 200, Des Moines, IA 50309-1424
Tel (515) 241-6212 *Founded/Ownrshp* 1993
Sales 304.1MM *EMP* 1,000
SIC 8011 Medical centers; Medical centers
CEO: C Eric Crowell
**CFO:* Robin McNichols
VP: Wayne Schellhammer
IT Man: Jean Duncan

IOWA PRECISION INDUSTRIES
See MESTEK MACHINERY INC

D-U-N-S 04-947-4422
■ **IOWA REALTY CO INC**
(*Suby of* HOMESERVICES OF AMERICA INC) ★
3501 Westown Pkwy, West Des Moines, IA 50266-1007
Tel (515) 224-6222 *Founded/Ownrshp* 1998
Sales 21.5MM^E *EMP* 300
SIC 6531 Real estate brokers & agents; Real estate brokers & agents
Pr: R Michael Knapp
**Pr:* Brennan Buckley
CFO: Kimberly Bakey
**Treas:* Kimberly K Bakey
**VP:* James A Koolhof
Rgnl Mgr: J D Schlotterback
S&M/VP: Mike Stanbrough
Advt Mgr: Terry Manning

D-U-N-S 15-551-1025
IOWA ROTOCAST PLASTICS INC
IRP
1712 Moellers Dr, Decorah, IA 52101-7304
Tel (563) 382-9636 *Founded/Ownrshp* 1986
Sales 20.5MM^E *EMP* 90
SIC 3089 5162 Molding primary plastic; Plastics products
Pr: Floyd E Mount
**Sec:* Jackie Bulman
**VP:* Clark Lewey
Genl Mgr: Greg Lewey
VP Sls: Steve Rolfs
Mktg Dir: Mark Wolf
Sls Dir: Britt Dyke
Sls Dir: Josh Spilde
Mktg Mgr: Chris Shelton

D-U-N-S 80-467-0255
IOWA SELECT FARMS LLP
811 S Oak St, Iowa Falls, IA 50126-9501
Tel (641) 648-4479 *Founded/Ownrshp* 1993
Sales 234.5MM^E *EMP* 850
SIC 0213 Hog feedlot; Hog feedlot
Genl Pt: Jeff Hansen
COO: Clint Hoversten
CFO: William Foley
Ofcr: Keith Kratchmer
Software D: Ryan Grummer
Prd Dir: Tony Thies
Sfty Mgr: Eric Wiechmann

D-U-N-S 60-082-4853
IOWA SOYBEAN ASSOCIATION
1255 Sw Pririe Trail Pkwy, Ankeny, IA 50023
Tel (515) 251-8640 *Founded/Ownrshp* 1964
Sales 35.2MM *EMP* 45
Accts Brooks Lodden Pc West Des Moi
SIC 8611 Business associations
CEO: Kirk Leeds
VP: Dennis Creveling

D-U-N-S 96-822-6469
IOWA SPECIALTY HOSPITAL
WRIGHT MEDICAL CENTER
1316 S Main St, Clarion, IA 50525-2019
Tel (515) 532-3406 *Founded/Ownrshp* 2001
Sales 52.5MM^E *EMP* 375
SIC 8093 8062 Specialty outpatient clinics; Specialty outpatient clinics; General medical & surgical hospitals
CEO: Steve Simonin
**CEO:* Nancy Gabrielson
Nrsg Dir: Tiffini Mericle
HC Dir: Cindy Peterson
Snr Mgr: Alison Angstrom
Snr Mgr: Shreekanth Chutkay

D-U-N-S 08-030-7580
IOWA SPRING MANUFACTURING & SALES CO
2112 Greene St, Adel, IA 50003-1667
Tel (515) 993-4791 *Founded/Ownrshp* 1977
Sales 30.1MM^E *EMP* 88
SIC 3495 3493 Wire springs; Steel springs, except wire
Pr: Timothy J Bianco
**Sec:* Kathleen A Bianco
Genl Mgr: Brian Setchell
Opers Mgr: Tom Quindt
Sls Mgr: Dan Day

D-U-N-S 18-087-0537
IOWA STATE ASSOCIATION OF COUNTIES
5500 Westown Pkwy Ste 190, West Des Moines, IA 50266-8364
Tel (515) 244-7181 *Founded/Ownrshp* 1964
Sales 27.8MM *EMP* 17
SIC 8651 Political organizations; Political organizations
VP: Joan McCalmant
VP: J P White

D-U-N-S 06-224-1401
IOWA STATE BANK
105 Albany Ave Se, Orange City, IA 51041-1790
Tel (712) 737-4818 *Founded/Ownrshp* 1973
Sales NA *EMP* 26
SIC 6022 State commercial banks; State commercial banks
Pr: Leroy Van Kekerix
CFO: Duane Muecke
VP: Clark Pennings
VP: Liz Stowater
Brnch Mgr: Wayne Kooiker

D-U-N-S 60-547-0905
IOWA STATE UNIVERSITY FOUNDATION
ISU FOUNDATION
2505 University Blvd, Ames, IA 50010-8622
Tel (515) 294-4607 *Founded/Ownrshp* 1950
Sales 108.6MM *EMP* 103
Accts Kpmg Llp Omaha Ne
SIC 8399 Fund raising organization, non-fee basis; Fund raising organization, non-fee basis
Pr: Roger Neuhaus
**Pr:* Dan Saftig
**Sr VP:* Lisa Eslinger
VP: Rich Bundy
VP: Mike Persia
Mktg Dir: Jenni Cushman
Mktg Dir: Jodi Odonnell
Snr Mgr: Marena Bitz

D-U-N-S 00-530-9844
IOWA STATE UNIVERSITY OF SCIENCE AND TECHNOLOGY
1350 Beardshear Hall, Ames, IA 50011-2025
Tel (515) 294-6162 *Founded/Ownrshp* 1987
Sales 770.4MM *EMP* 5,800^E
Accts Mary Mosiman Cpa Des Moines
SIC 8221 University; University
Pr: Gregory Geoffroy
Pr: Pam Cain
**Pr:* Elizabeth Hoffman
**Pr:* Steven Leath
Treas: Brad Dye
**VP:* Thomas Hill
VP: Cathann Kress
**VP:* Warren Madden
VP: Sharron Quisenberry
VP: Chitra Rajan
VP: David Trainor
Assoc Dir: Jill Arroyo
Assoc Dir: Corey Williamson
Comm Dir: Rob Schweers

D-U-N-S 05-534-2679
IOWA STUDENT LOAN LIQUIDITY CORP
6775 Vista Dr, West Des Moines, IA 50266-9305
Tel (515) 243-5626 *Founded/Ownrshp* 1979
Sales NA *EMP* 214
Accts Kpmg Llp Des Moines Iowa
SIC 6111 6141 Student Loan Marketing Association; Personal credit institutions; Student Loan Marketing Association; Personal credit institutions
Pr: Steven W McCullough
CFO: Walter Witthoff
**Treas:* Erin Lacey
Ex Dir: Tracy Wilson

D-U-N-S 18-329-8470
IOWA TANKLINES INC
ITL
210 Sw Linden St, Ankeny, IA 50023-2413
Tel (515) 963-8386 *Founded/Ownrshp* 1995
Sales 76.2MM *EMP* 350
Accts Bergan Paulsen & Company Pc
SIC 4212 4213 Liquid haulage, local; Trucking, except local; Liquid haulage, local; Trucking, except local

Pr: Keith Hohensee
**Treas:* Kent Bro
**VP:* Todd Bro
**VP:* Charles C Simmons

D-U-N-S 08-246-9826
IOWA TRIBE OF OKLAHOMA INC
335588 E 750 Rd, Perkins, OK 74059-3268
Tel (405) 547-5552 *Founded/Ownrshp* 2004
Sales 57.3MM^E *EMP* 130
SIC 1542 Commercial & office building, new construction; Commercial & office building, new construction
Pr: Gary Bratt
**Ch:* Janice Rowe Kurak
**Treas:* Lisa Yellowfish
Ofcr: Jeff Bayhylle
**VP:* Perri Ahhaitty
**VP:* Thomas Cox
**VP:* Lydia Renee Prince
**VP:* Eugene Big Soldier
Genl Mgr: David McCullough
MIS Dir: Bob Schults
Dir IT: Michael White

IOWA TURKEY GROWERS COOP
See WEST LIBERTY FOODS LLC

IOWA VALLEY CMNTY COLLEGE DST
See MERGE AREA VI COMMUNITY COLLEGE DISTRICT

D-U-N-S 06-865-9853
IOWA WASTE SYSTEMS INC
2702 Monroe St Ste B, Madison, WI 53711-1897
Tel (608) 277-1070 *Founded/Ownrshp* 1996
Sales 22.3MM^E *EMP* 69
SIC 4953 Sanitary landfill operation
Pr: Robert T Glebs
**VP:* David Kratz

D-U-N-S 08-336-2389
IOWA WEST FOUNDATION
IOWAS WEST RACING ASSOCIATION
25 Main Pl Ste 550, Council Bluffs, IA 51503-0700
Tel (712) 309-3000 *Founded/Ownrshp* 1992
Sales 58.1MM *EMP* 8^E
Accts Kpmg Llp Omaha Ne
SIC 8699 Charitable organization; Charitable organization
Pr: Peter Tulipana
Treas: Suellen Overton
VP: David Harris
**Prin:* Jackie Nix
Ex Dir: Charles Smith

D-U-N-S 00-686-1777
IOWA WESTERN COMMUNITY COLLEGE INC (IA)
2700 College Rd, Council Bluffs, IA 51503-1057
Tel (712) 325-3200 *Founded/Ownrshp* 1966
Sales 28.4MM *EMP* 550
Accts Denman & Company Llp West De
SIC 8222 Junior college; Junior college
Pr: Dan Kinney
**VP:* Tom Johnson
VP: Donald Kohler
Exec: Harvey Wiltsey
Ex Dir: Ann Pross
Genl Mgr: Sophia John
CTO: Jason Hannah
IT Man: Jodi Miller

D-U-N-S 01-412-7737
IOWA WIRELESS SERVICES LLC
4135 Nw Urbandale Dr, Urbandale, IA 50322-7928
Tel (515) 258-7000 *Founded/Ownrshp* 1997
Sales 57.8MM^E *EMP* 120
SIC 4812 Cellular telephone services; Cellular telephone services
**CEO:* Craven Shumaker
CFO: David Frost
VP: Monte Hagge
Genl Mgr: Glenn Clark
IT Man: Ryan Benesch
Netwrk Eng: David Kaus
Netwrk Eng: Joe Sargent
Netwrk Eng: Dave Yerigan
Opers Mgr: Mark Baedky
Opers Mgr: Yavonda Waddell
Mktg Dir: Casey Clement

D-U-N-S 00-694-0795
■ **IOWA-AMERICAN WATER CO INC** (DE)
(*Suby of* AMERICAN WATER WORKS CO INC) ★
5201 Grand Ave, Davenport, IA 52807-1014
Tel (563) 468-9200 *Founded/Ownrshp* 1930
Sales 55.4MM^E *EMP* 160
SIC 4941 Water supply; Water supply
Pr: Terry Gloriod
**Treas:* Fred Ruchman
**VP:* K B Earnhardt Jr
Div Mgr: Robert Gallo
Genl Mgr: Hal Gurkin
IT Man: Greg Davidson
Board of Directors: J J Barr, E H Gemmill, G W Johnstone, G C Smith, J H Ware, P W Ware

IOWAS WEST RACING ASSOCIATION
See IOWA WEST FOUNDATION

IOWH
See INSTITUTE FOR ONEWORLD HEALTH INC

D-U-N-S 82-798-1171
IOXUS INC
18 Stadium Cir, Oneonta, NY 13820-1067
Tel (607) 441-3500 *Founded/Ownrshp* 2011
Sales 35.2MM^E *EMP* 99^E
SIC 8711 Engineering services
Pr: Mark McGough
Pr: Harv Wilkenson
COO: Chad Hall
COO: Philip Meek
CFO: Henry Barber
Ex Ch Bd: Donald Runkle
Sr VP: Van Andrews
Sr VP: Nick Cataldo
VP: Wolfram Krueger
VP: Michael Tentnowski

VP: David Torrey
VP: Harvey Wilkinson
Board of Directors: Jonathan Dokuchitz

IP CASINO RESORT & SPA
See BOYD BILOXI LLC

IPA
See INDEPENDENT PROJECT ANALYSIS INC

D-U-N-S 15-565-9688 IMP
IPA OPERATIONS INC
(*Suby of* INTERNATIONAL POWER AMERICA INC) ★
4601 Brookhollow Dr, Midlothian, TX 76065-5359
Tel (972) 923-7400 *Founded/Ownrshp* 1996
Sales 26.2MM^E *EMP* 46
SIC 4911 Distribution, electric power; Generation, electric power; Transmission, electric power
Pr: Herman Schopman
**Pr:* Bruce Levy
**Genl Mgr:* Ron Reynolds

D-U-N-S 80-754-9472
IPAK HOSPITALITY GROUP INC
IGGY'S SPORTS GRILL
344 N Main St, Layton, UT 84041-7100
Tel (801) 546-2488 *Founded/Ownrshp* 1990
Sales 7.0MM^E *EMP* 400
SIC 5812 American restaurant; American restaurant
Pr: Hersh Ipaktchian
**Treas:* Susan Ipaktchian
**VP:* David Ipaktchian

D-U-N-S 80-738-9770 IMP
IPAK INC
INTERACTIVE PRTG & PACKG CO
301 Grove Rd, West Deptford, NJ 08086-2214
Tel (856) 486-0066 *Founded/Ownrshp* 1993
Sales 23.2MM^E *EMP* 85
SIC 2752 7389 Commercial printing, lithographic; Packaging & labeling services
Ch Bd: Iris Pinsky
**Pr:* Karen Primak
**COO:* Christa Groeller
Ofcr: T J Demarco
Off Mgr: Norma Henson
Prd Mgr: Maryanne Teesdale
Pr Dir: Sheryl Schreiber
Genl Couns: Allan Pinsky

D-U-N-S 10-222-8590
■ **IPALCO ENTERPRISES INC**
(*Suby of* AES CORP) ★
1 Monument Cir, Indianapolis, IN 46204-2901
Tel (317) 261-8261 *Founded/Ownrshp* 1983
Sales 1.3MMM *EMP* 1,401^E
SIC 4911 Electric services; Distribution, electric power; Generation, electric power; Transmission, electric power; Electric services; Distribution, electric power; Generation, electric power; Transmission, electric power
Pr: Kenneth J Zagzebski
**Ch Bd:* Thomas M O'Flynn
**CFO:* Craig L Jackson
Board of Directors: Renaud Faucher, Paul L Freedman, Andrew J Horrocks, Michael S Mizell, Olivier Renault, Richard A Sturges, Margaret E Tigre

IPAP
See INDEPENDENT PROCUREMENT ALLIANCE PROGRAM LLC

D-U-N-S 04-845-8041
■ **IPARTY CORP**
(*Suby of* PARTY CITY HOLDINGS INC) ★
270 Bridge St Ste 301, Dedham, MA 02026-1798
Tel (781) 329-3952 *Founded/Ownrshp* 2013
Sales 48.7MM^E *EMP* 885^E
SIC 5947 5961 Party favors; Catalog & mail-order houses; Party favors; Catalog & mail-order houses
CEO: Sal V Perisano
CFO: David E Robertson
Sr VP: Dorice P Dionne

D-U-N-S 88-424-9876
■ **IPARTY RETAIL STORES CORP**
(*Suby of* IPARTY CORP) ★
270 Bridge St Ste 301, Dedham, MA 02026-1798
Tel (781) 329-3952 *Founded/Ownrshp* 2000
Sales 47.3MM^E *EMP* 850
SIC 5947 Party favors; Party favors
CEO: Sal Perisano
**CFO:* Dave Robertson

D-U-N-S 07-202-6594
IPAS
(*Suby of* IPS)
300 Market St Ste 200, Chapel Hill, NC 27516-4493
Tel (919) 967-7052 *Founded/Ownrshp* 1973
Sales 112.7MM *EMP* 110
Accts Tait Weller & Baker Llp Phila
SIC 8399 3842 Fund raising organization, non-fee basis; Gynecological supplies & appliances; Fund raising organization, non-fee basis; Gynecological supplies & appliances
Pr: John Herrington
**Treas:* Terrence Cominski
Ofcr: Amy Coughlin
**VP:* Barbara Crane
Off Mgr: Susan Eudy
Dir IT: Chris Kesler
IT Man: Eric Jones

D-U-N-S 95-793-0845
▲ **IPASS INC**
3800 Bridge Pkwy, Redwood City, CA 94065-1171
Tel (650) 232-4100 *Founded/Ownrshp* 1996
Sales 69.8MM *EMP* 250^E
Tkr Sym IPAS *Exch* NGS
SIC 4813 7374 ; ; Data processing & preparation; ; ; Data processing & preparation
Pr: Gary A Griffiths
CFO: Darin R Vickery
Chf Cred: Patricia R Hume
Chf Mktg O: June Bower
Ofcr: John Alsop
Sr VP: Christina Tackaberry
Sr VP: Steven Wastie
VP: Christine Braelow

VP: Rajani Kolli
VP: Mehdi Moheimani
VP: Mato Petrusic
VP: David Tauber
Board of Directors: Michael M Chang, Richard A Karp, Brent S Morrison, David E Panos, Damien J Park, Michael J Tedesco

D-U-N-S 92-799-8455
■ IPAY TECHNOLOGIES LLC
(*Suby of* JACK HENRY & ASSOCIATES INC) ★
801 N Black Branch Rd, Elizabethtown, KY 42701-4505
Tel (270) 737-0590 *Founded/Ownrshp* 2010
Sales 54.8MM^E *EMP* 254
SIC 8243 Software training, computer; Software training, computer
CEO: Jack Prim
**Pr:* Bill Ready
CFO: Dana Bowers
Sr VP: Tede Forman
**Sr VP:* Kathy Fripp
**Sr VP:* Alix Hoffman
Sr VP: Steve Hooper
Sr VP: Priya Jakatdar PHD
Sr VP: Jennifer Roth
Sr VP: Guido Schulz
VP: Dave Broyles
VP: J Hynes
VP: Tracy Lopes
VP: Andy Sosnowski
VP: Kelly Vick

D-U-N-S 79-649-1418
IPAYMENT HOLDINGS INC
(*Suby of* IPAYMENT INVESTORS INC) ★
30721 Russell Ranch Rd # 200, Westlake Village, CA 91362-7382
Tel (310) 436-5294 *Founded/Ownrshp* 2001
Sales 666.8MM *EMP* 427^E
SIC 7389 Credit card service
VP: Robert Purcell
Dir Risk M: Julie Braico
Snr Ntwrk: Michael Johnson

D-U-N-S 05-874-7945
IPAYMENT INC
(*Suby of* IPAYMENT HOLDINGS INC) ★
126 E 56th St Fl 33, New York, NY 10022-3685
Tel (212) 802-7200 *Founded/Ownrshp* 2006
Sales 666.8MM *EMP* 422^E
SIC 7389 Credit card service; Credit card service
Ch Bd: Carl A Grimstad
**CFO:* Mark C Monaco
Ofcr: Robert N Purcell
Ex VP: Barnett Sutton
Ex VP: Afshin M Yazdian
Sr VP: Philip J Ragona
VP: Dale Kennedy
VP: Pat Sauder
Dir IT: Kurt Johnson
VP Sls: Christian Murray
VP Sls: Jayanne Nase

D-U-N-S 79-645-2873
IPAYMENT INVESTORS INC
40 Burton Hills Blvd, Nashville, TN 37215-6199
Tel (615) 665-1858 *Founded/Ownrshp* 2001
Sales 666.8MM^E *EMP* 853^E
SIC 7389 Credit card service; Credit card service
Genl Couns: Philip Ragona
CFO: Teresa Sparks
VP: Christa Shook
VP Sls: Aaron Naseh
Sls Dir: Elizabeth Failor

IPBM
See WESTERN SLOPE INDUSTRIES INC

D-U-N-S 14-829-8396
IPC (USA) INC
(*Suby of* ITOCHU CORPORATION)
20 Pacifica Ste 650, Irvine, CA 92618-3391
Tel (949) 648-5600 *Founded/Ownrshp* 2012
Sales 269.0MM^E *EMP* 75
SIC 5172 Aircraft fueling services; Diesel fuel; Gasoline; Aircraft fueling services; Diesel fuel; Gasoline
CEO: Hiroki Okinaga
Ch Bd: Keiji Shigeoka
**CFO:* James Takeuchi
**VP:* Randy Jones
**VP:* Paul Smith

D-U-N-S 96-666-4070
IPC INDUSTRIES INC
64 N Royal St, Mobile, AL 36602-3804
Tel (251) 438-4144 *Founded/Ownrshp* 1993
Sales 20.6MM^E *EMP* 330
SIC 3599 6722 Machine shop, jobbing & repair; Management investment, open-end; Machine shop, jobbing & repair; Management investment, open-end
Ch Bd: Clifton C Inge Jr
Mng Dir: Henry O Connor
Mng Dir: Henry F O'Connor III
Mng Dir: McGowin Patrick
Genl Couns: Kathy Sherman

IPC INFORMATION SYSTEMS
See IPC SYSTEMS INC

D-U-N-S 09-717-6135
IPC INTERNATIONAL CORP
(*Suby of* UNIVERSAL PROTECTION SERVICE LP) ★
10255 W Higgins Rd # 630, Rosemont, IL 60018-5613
Tel (847) 444-2000 *Founded/Ownrshp* 2013
Sales 113.0MM^E *EMP* 5,800
SIC 7381 8742 2389 3199 Security guard service; Industry specialist consultants; Uniforms & vestments; Leather garments; Security guard service; Industry specialist consultants; Uniforms & vestments; Leather garments
Pr: Howard L Kaplan
**CFO:* Scott M Strong
**Treas:* Robert Nutt
**Ex VP:* Michael A Crane
**Ex VP:* Kenneth W Hamilton
**Ex VP:* Donald P Lantz Sr
**Ex VP:* Joseph A Marcello
**Ex VP:* Brian L Neimeyer
Rgnl Mgr: Ben Marth

D-U-N-S 07-886-0993
IPC LYDON LLC
284 Bodwell St Ste 1, Avon, MA 02322-1155
Tel (508) 897-1700 *Founded/Ownrshp* 2013
Sales 30.3MM^E *EMP* 75
SIC 5082 General construction machinery & equipment
IT Man: Lenna Sweeney

IPC PUBLISHING SERVICES
See JOURNAL DISPOSITION CORP

D-U-N-S 83-313-8253 IMP/EXP
IPC SYSTEMS HOLDINGS CORP
HARBORSIDE FINANCIAL CENTER
(*Suby of* SILVER LAKE PARTNERS II LP) ★
1500 Plaza Ten Fl 15, Jersey City, NJ 07311-4050
Tel (201) 253-2000 *Founded/Ownrshp* 2010
Sales 221.8MM^E *EMP* 1,441^E
SIC 5045 4813 Computers, peripherals & software;
Pr: Greg Kenepp
COO: Charles Auster
Sr VP: Michael Speranza
**Prin:* Lance Boxer
Mng Dir: Ritske Clewits
Off Mgr: Donna Palumbo
CIO: Richard Bozzuto
Software D: Sergey Polyakov
Netwrk Eng: Greg Brady
Sales Exec: Andrew Matlak
Sls Dir: Mike Tavares

D-U-N-S 07-844-8961 IMP
IPC SYSTEMS INC
IPC INFORMATION SYSTEMS
Harborside Financial Ctr, Jersey City, NJ 07311
Tel (201) 253-2121 *Founded/Ownrshp* 2015
Sales 591.1MM^E *EMP* 900
SIC 5045 4813 Computers, peripherals & software; ; Computers, peripherals & software;
CEO: Neil Barua
**CFO:* William J McHale Jr
Sr VP: Don C Bell
Sr VP: Pete Simms
VP: Raju Chiluvuri
VP: Gary Everett
VP: Neil Gray
VP: Lois Liebowitz
Off Mgr: Melanie Davis
Sales Exec: Paul Sheehan
VP Sls: Harry Bergen

D-U-N-S 04-341-0554
IPC TECHNOLOGIES INC (VA)
7200 Glen Forest Dr # 100, Richmond, VA 23226-3768
Tel (804) 285-9300 *Founded/Ownrshp* 1981
Sales 21.8MM^E *EMP* 125
SIC 7373 Systems integration services; Systems integration services
Pr: Kenneth G Banks
**Ex VP:* Jeff Andrews
Sr VP: David Brown
**Sr VP:* Bill Southers
**VP:* Eric N Bowling
VP: Curt Island
**VP:* William G Southers
Dir Bus: Bob Baldino
Dir Bus: Kevin Holloway
Dir Bus: Jim Krieger
Dir Bus: Gary Tomlin
Dir Bus: Chris Viverette

D-U-N-S 07-841-2524
IPC/RAZOR LLC
277 Park Ave Fl 39, New York, NY 10172-2901
Tel (212) 551-4500 *Founded/Ownrshp* 2010
Sales 96.5MM^E *EMP* 2,000
SIC 3541 Machine tools, metal cutting type; Machine tools, metal cutting type

I.P.C.C.
See INTERNATIONAL PRECISION COMPONENTS CORP

D-U-N-S 12-834-7361
■ IPCS EQUIPMENT INC
(*Suby of* IPCS, INC.)
1901 N Roselle Rd Ste 500, Schaumburg, IL 60195-3182
Tel (847) 885-7006 *Founded/Ownrshp* 2004
Sales 22.4MM^E *EMP* 229^E
SIC 4812 Radio telephone communication
Pr: Timothy Yager

IPD
See INDUSTRIAL PARTS DEPOT LLC

D-U-N-S 15-762-1830 IMP
IPEG INC
CONAIR
(*Suby of* SEWICKLEY CAPITAL INC) ★
200 W Kensinger Dr # 100, Cranberry Township, PA 16066-3428
Tel (724) 584-5500 *Founded/Ownrshp* 1950
Sales 93.8MM^E *EMP* 631
SIC 3559

D-U-N-S 61-206-8127 IMP/EXP
IPEX USA LLC
(*Suby of* IPEX INC)
10100 Rodney St, Pineville, NC 28134-7538
Tel (704) 889-2431 *Founded/Ownrshp* 2003
Sales 58.6MM^E *EMP* 200
SIC 3084 Plastics pipe; Plastics pipe
CEO: Thomas E Torokvei
**VP:* Katherine Serafino
Genl Mgr: Bessie Yan
IT Man: George Manolakos
Tech Mgr: Detlef Engels
Plnt Mgr: Barry Cline
Manager: Scott Henrich
Sls Mgr: Paul Graddon

IPF
See INDUSTRIAL PIPE FITTINGS LLC

IPFS CORPORATION
See FINANCIAL HOLDING CORP

D-U-N-S 07-682-9084
IPFS CORP
(*Suby of* CAPITAL PAYMENT PLAN) ★
101 Hudson St Fl 33, Jersey City, NJ 07302-3905
Tel (201) 557-4625 *Founded/Ownrshp* 2010
Sales NA *EMP* 300
SIC 6311 Life insurance carriers; Life insurance carriers
Pr: Paul Zarookian
CFO: Jason Stuart
**CFO:* Michael Vogen
Treas: Steven J Bensinger
**Ex VP:* Kevin Olsen
**Ex VP:* James Williamson
**Sr VP:* Claude Graham
VP: James Donaldson
VP: Jamie Renton
Dir IT: Richard Pupello
Sls&Mrk Ex: Polly Mohan

D-U-N-S 09-582-5634
IPFS CORP
CAPITAL PAYMENT PLAN
1055 Broadway Blvd Fl 11, Kansas City, MO 64105-1575
Tel (816) 627-0500 *Founded/Ownrshp* 2005
Sales NA *EMP* 520
SIC 6153 Buying of installment notes; Buying of installment notes
Pr: Mike Gallagher
Pr: Skip Fisher
**COO:* Paul Zarookian
**CFO:* Bryan Andres
**Sr VP:* Jim Bennett
**Sr VP:* Herb Chirico
**Sr VP:* Ted Koeth
**Sr VP:* J Kevin Olsen
IT Man: Dave Bruner
Mktg Mgr: Chad Creamer
Manager: Troy Randolph

D-U-N-S 11-292-7095 IMP/EXP
IPG (US) HOLDINGS INC
INTERTAPE POLYMER GROUP
(*Suby of* INTERTAPE POLYMER GROUP INC.)
100 Paramount Dr Ste 300, Sarasota, FL 34232-6051
Tel (941) 727-5788 *Founded/Ownrshp* 1997
Sales 250.8MM^E *EMP* 2,003
SIC 2672 3953 Tape, pressure sensitive: made from purchased materials; Stencils, painting & marking; Tape, pressure sensitive: made from purchased materials; Stencils, painting & marking
Pr: Greg Yull
Sr VP: Douglas Nalette
**VP:* Jim Bob Carpenter
**VP:* Burgess Hildreth
QA Dir: Dan Philp
VP Sls: Lee Zoller
Sls Dir: Dave Griffith
Sls Mgr: Bob McCarley

D-U-N-S 11-291-9001
IPG (US) INC
(*Suby of* INTERTAPE POLYMER GROUP) ★
100 Paramount Dr Ste 300, Sarasota, FL 34232-6051
Tel (941) 727-5788 *Founded/Ownrshp* 1997
Sales 230.0MM^E *EMP* 1,008
SIC 2672 3953 Tape, pressure sensitive: made from purchased materials; Stencils, painting & marking; Tape, pressure sensitive: made from purchased materials; Stencils, painting & marking
Pr: Dale Mc Sween
**Sec:* Burgess Hildreth

D-U-N-S 04-702-7433 IMP
▲ IPG PHOTONICS CORP
50 Old Webster Rd, Oxford, MA 01540-2706
Tel (508) 373-1100 *Founded/Ownrshp* 1990
Sales 769.8MM *EMP* 3,030^E
Accts Deloitte & Touche Llp Boston
Tkr Sym IPGP *Exch* NGS
SIC 3699 3229 3674 Laser systems & equipment; Fiber optics strands; Semiconductor diodes & rectifiers; Laser systems & equipment; Fiber optics strands; Semiconductor diodes & rectifiers
Ch Bd: Valentin P Gapontsev
CFO: Timothy P V Mammen
Treas: Paolo Sinni
Ofcr: Eugene Shcherbakov
Sr VP: Angelo P Lopresti
Sr VP: Alexander Ovtchinnikov
**Sr VP:* Eugene Scherbakov
Sr VP: Felix Stukalin
Exec: Alexei Markevitch
Prin: Vladlen Ivshin
**CTO:* Igor Samartsev
Board of Directors: Robert A Blair, Michael C Child, Henry E Gauthier, William S Hurley, Eric Meurice, John R Peeler, Thomas J Seifert

D-U-N-S 06-879-5795
■ IPH II LLC
(*Suby of* DYNEGY INC) ★
601 Travis St Ste 1400, Houston, TX 77002-3253
Tel (713) 507-6400 *Founded/Ownrshp* 2013
Sales 658.9MM^E *EMP* 747^E
SIC 4939 Combination utilities
CEO: Robert C Flexon
CFO: Clint C Freeland

IPHD
See INTERNATIONAL PARTNERSHIP FOR HUMAN DEVELOPMENT INC

D-U-N-S 83-032-2991
IPI ACQUISITION LLC
13504 S Point Blvd Ste M, Charlotte, NC 28273-6763
Tel (704) 588-1100 *Founded/Ownrshp* 2008
Sales 44.2MM *EMP* 650
SIC 6719 3599 3569 Sprinkler systems, fire: automatic; Machine shop, jobbing & repair; Investment holding companies, except banks; Machine shop, jobbing & repair; Sprinkler systems, fire: automatic
Pr: Michael L Jones
CFO: Blair A Swogger
Chf Mktg O: Matthew Ryan
Prd Mgr: Billy Stockwell

VP Sls: Frank Durham
Mktg Mgr: Eve Lane

IPIPELINE
See INTERNET PIPELINE INC

D-U-N-S 08-489-9827
IPITEK INC
2461 Impala Dr, Carlsbad, CA 92010-7227
Tel (760) 438-1010 *Founded/Ownrshp* 1998
Sales 20.1MM^E *EMP* 170
SIC 1731 Fiber optic cable installation; Fiber optic cable installation
Ch Bd: Michael M Salour
Sr VP: Bill Moore
Sftwr Eng: Tony Bullock
Sftwr Eng: Truc Nguyen
Sfty Mgr: Robert Huang
Secur Mgr: Carrol Eckmeder
VP Mktg: Rich Loveland

D-U-N-S 06-575-6009 IMP
IPL USA INC
(*Suby of* IPL INC)
401 Se Thompson Dr, Lees Summit, MO 64082-2323
Tel (816) 246-8200 *Founded/Ownrshp* 2011
Sales 85.9MM^E *EMP* 200
SIC 3089 Plastic containers, except foam; Plastic containers, except foam
CEO: Paul Richardson
Ql Cn Mgr: Tim Voskuil

D-U-N-S 10-406-1564
IPLACEMENT INC
SOURCE 2
1245 W Fairbanks Ave # 400, Winter Park, FL 32789-4878
Tel (407) 373-0878 *Founded/Ownrshp* 1999
Sales 21.3MM *EMP* 600
SIC 7361 Employment agencies; Employment agencies
Pr: David Nuxol
CFO: Randy Davis
Ex VP: Robert Backes
Ex VP: Sharon Ball
Ex VP: Cliff Edahl
Dir Sec: Brent Brown
Board of Directors: Bill Cooke, Randy Davis, Mark Hain, John Hillenmeyer, Fred Leonhardt, Craig Polejes

D-U-N-S 00-507-7052 IMP
IPLASTICS LLC (IL)
ILLINOIS VALLEY PLASTICS
300 N Cummings Ln, Washington, IL 61571-2198
Tel (309) 444-8884 *Founded/Ownrshp* 1953, 2010
Sales 23.4MM^E *EMP* 112^E
SIC 3089 3544 Injection molding of plastics; Industrial molds
CEO: Daryl R Lindemann
**Pr:* Tom Williams
VP: Joe Camp
Mfg Mgr: Chris Lamprecht
Sales Exec: Connie Camp
Sls Mgr: Jim Mechowski

D-U-N-S 78-057-0227
IPP USA INC
INTERNATIONAL PIPING PDTS INS
16623 Aldine Westfield Rd, Houston, TX 77032-1351
Tel (713) 895-8400 *Founded/Ownrshp* 2006
Sales 25.0MM *EMP* 15
SIC 5051 Steel
Pr: Paul Haggar

IPPFWHR
See INTERNATIONAL PLANNED PARENTHOOD FEDERATION - WESTERN HEMISPHERE REGION INC

IPPOLITA
See SENO JEWELRY LLC

D-U-N-S 03-960-4530
IPR FRESH
983 E Frontage Rd, Rio Rico, AZ 85648-6234
Tel (520) 377-5710 *Founded/Ownrshp* 2012
Sales 29.0MM *EMP* 2
SIC 5149 Condiments; Condiments
Pr: Jose Luis Obregon
Genl Mgr: Alvaro Obregon
Opers Mgr: Carlos Saavedra

D-U-N-S 79-120-3719
IPREO HOLDINGS LLC
1359 Broadway Fl 2, New York, NY 10018-7123
Tel (212) 849-5000 *Founded/Ownrshp* 2014
Sales 138.2MM^E *EMP* 600^E
SIC 8748 Business consulting; Business consulting
COO: David Miranda
CFO: Brian Dockray
Treas: Anne Montana
Ex VP: Neil Hyman
Ex VP: David Levy
Ex VP: Bill Sherman
Ex VP: Dwight Tierney
Ex VP: Agnies Watson
Ex VP: Ronnie West
Ex VP: Charlie Young
VP: Brooks Adams
VP: Pete Bentson
VP: Denise Conn
VP: Gina Gevinski
VP: Michael Hutto
VP: James Kellum
VP: Michael Lynch
VP: Glenn Randall
VP: Tom Schrule
VP: Amber Seidel
VP: Rukiya Toatley

D-U-N-S 79-957-9623
IPREO LLC
I-DEAL
(*Suby of* IPREO HOLDINGS LLC) ★
1359 Broadway Fl 2, New York, NY 10018-7123
Tel (212) 849-5000 *Founded/Ownrshp* 2001
Sales 110.7MM^E *EMP* 450^E
SIC 8748 Business consulting; Business consulting
CEO: Scott C Ganeles

Pr: Kevin Marcus
**CFO:* Brian Dockray
Ex VP: Joe Maxwell
Ex VP: Bill Sherman
Ex VP: Chris Taylor
Ex VP: Dwight Tierney
Ex VP: Agies Watson
**Ex VP:* Allen Williams
Assoc Dir: Tim Carr
Mng Dir: Brett Suchor

IPRO
See ISLAND PEER REVIEW ORGANIZATION INC

D-U-N-S 07-919-7311
IPRO TECH LLC
1700 N Desert Dr Ste 101, Tempe, AZ 85281-1228
Tel (602) 324-4776 *Founded/Ownrshp* 2013
Sales 20.5MM^E *EMP* 118
SIC 7372 Publishers' computer software
Pr: Jamie Neilon
**Pr:* Kimothy Taylor
**CFO:* Bret Lawson
QA Dir: Graham Parker
Software D: Toni Simon

IPROFESSIONAL
See INDEPENDENT PROFESSIONAL SERVICES INC

D-U-N-S 13-336-2058
IPROMOTEU.COM INC
321 Commonwealth Rd # 101, Wayland, MA 01778-5039
Tel (508) 653-4410 *Founded/Ownrshp* 1999
Sales 21.6MM^E *EMP* 30^E
SIC 8743 Promotion service
CEO: Ross S Silverstein
**Ex VP:* Rick Badiner
**Sr VP:* David Stolper
VP: David Blouin
**VP:* Edward F Burke Jr
Off Admin: Olivia Mello

D-U-N-S 02-757-5242
IPROSPECT.COM INC
1 South Sta Fl 3, Boston, MA 02110-2253
Tel (617) 449-4300 *Founded/Ownrshp* 1998
Sales 32.7MM^E *EMP* 205^E
SIC 8742 Marketing consulting services
Pr: Robert Murray

IPS
See INDUSTRIAL PIPE & STEEL LLC

IPS
See INDIANAPOLIS PUBLIC SCHOOLS

IPS
See INDUSTRIAL PIPING SPECIALISTS INC

D-U-N-S 12-624-7605
IPS ASSOCIATES LLC
INTERNATIONAL PROACTIVE SEC
16-00 State Rt 208 # 301, Fair Lawn, NJ 07410-2506
Tel (201) 967-7800 *Founded/Ownrshp* 2002
Sales 20.1MM^E *EMP* 250
SIC 7382 Protective devices, security; Protective devices, security
CFO: John Snowden

D-U-N-S 00-839-1815 IMP/EXP
IPS CORP
WELD-ON ADHESIVES
(*Suby of* NAUTIC PARTNERS LLC) ★
455 W Victoria St, Compton, CA 90220-6064
Tel (310) 898-3300 *Founded/Ownrshp* 1953, 2015
Sales 196.9MM^E *EMP* 400
SIC 2891 Adhesives, plastic; Cement, except linoleum & tile; Adhesives, plastic; Cement, except linoleum & tile
CEO: Thomas Tracy Bilbrough
**Pr:* Naresh Patel
Bd of Dir: Daniel Smith
VP: Fabio Castellani
VP: Dave Doering
VP: Stephen Gardiner
VP: Edwin Gutierrez
VP: Richard Larson
VP: Greg Paquin
Comm Dir: Elaine De Leon
Mng Dir: Sarah Browning

D-U-N-S 14-244-3881 IMP
IPS GROUP INC
5601 Oberlin Dr Ste 100, San Diego, CA 92121-3747
Tel (858) 404-0607 *Founded/Ownrshp* 2000
Sales 31.9MM^E *EMP* 67^E
SIC 4899 3824 Communication signal enhancement network system; Parking meters
CEO: David W King
**COO:* Chad Randal
**CFO:* Dario Paduano
**VP:* Amir Sedadi
**CTO:* Alexander M Schwarz
IT Man: Brandon Eilerman

D-U-N-S 62-077-9413 IMP/EXP
IPS INDUSTRIES INC
SPECTRUM BAGS
12641 166th St, Cerritos, CA 90703-2101
Tel (562) 623-2555 *Founded/Ownrshp* 1985
Sales 27.5MM^E *EMP* 80
SIC 2673 Cellophane bags, unprinted: made from purchased materials; Plastic bags: made from purchased materials; Food storage & trash bags (plastic); Trash bags (plastic film): made from purchased materials; Cellophane bags, unprinted: made from purchased materials; Plastic bags: made from purchased materials; Food storage & trash bags (plastic); Trash bags (plastic film): made from purchased materials
CEO: Frank Su
**Pr:* David Silva
**Pr:* Ben Tran
**CFO:* Peter Hii
VP: Jack Wilkerson
VP Sls: Mike Sullivan

IPS PACKAGING
See INDUSTRIAL PACKAGING SUPPLIES INC

D-U-N-S 13-694-6998
IPS WORLDWIDE LLC
(*Suby of* CUSCS HOLDINGS LLC) ★
265 Clyde Morris Blvd # 100, Ormond Beach, FL 32174-8137
Tel (386) 672-7727 *Founded/Ownrshp* 1998
Sales 33.9MM^E *EMP* 133
SIC 7389 4731 Financial services; Freight transportation arrangement
Sr VP: Michael Orourke
VP: John Son

D-U-N-S 60-123-5484
IPS-INTEGRATED PROJECT SERVICES LLC
721 Arbor Way Ste 100, Blue Bell, PA 19422-1974
Tel (610) 828-4090 *Founded/Ownrshp* 2015
Sales 203.9MM^E *EMP* 375
SIC 1541 Pharmaceutical manufacturing plant construction; Engineering services; Architectural services; Pharmaceutical manufacturing plant construction
CEO: Dave Goswami
CFO: Brian T Morris
Sr VP: Mark A Butler
Sr VP: Charles W Stock Cxa
Sr VP: John Gilroy
VP: Vince Cebular
Exec: George Tarr
Off Mgr: Karen Katch
Snr PM: Valentin Doering
Snr PM: Richard Werntz

IPSC
See INNER-PARISH SECURITY CORP

IPSCO
See INTERSTATE PAPER SUPPLY CO INC

D-U-N-S 62-041-0613 IMP
IPSCO KOPPEL TUBULARS LLC
TMK-IPSCO
(*Suby of* IPSCO TUBULARS INC) ★
6403 6th Ave, Koppel, PA 16136
Tel (724) 847-6389 *Founded/Ownrshp* 2008
Sales 226.8MM^E *EMP* 950
SIC 3312 Pipes & tubes; Pipes & tubes
Ch: Piotr Galitzine
**Pr:* David Mitch
**Sr VP:* Scott Barnes
**VP:* Prasenjit Adhikari
Genl Mgr: Michaell Penceri

D-U-N-S 80-930-7940
IPSCO TUBULARS (KY) INC
TMK IPSCO
(*Suby of* IPSCO TUBULARS INC) ★
100 Steel Plant Rd, Wilder, KY 41071-2996
Tel (859) 292-6000 *Founded/Ownrshp* 1981
Sales 59.9MM^E *EMP* 180
SIC 3317 Welded pipe & tubes; Tubes, seamless steel; Welded pipe & tubes; Tubes, seamless steel
Pr: Rene J Robichaud
**CFO:* Evgeny Makarov
**Sec:* Thomas J Depenbrock
**VP:* Prasenjit Adhikari
Dir Sec: Joe Frank
QA Dir: Sam Lewis
IT Man: Ronnie Husbands
Sls Mgr: Gary Durbin

D-U-N-S 17-800-8470
IPSCO TUBULARS (OK) INC
(*Suby of* IPSCO TUBULARS INC) ★
5610 Bird Creek Ave, Catoosa, OK 74015-3005
Tel (918) 384-6400 *Founded/Ownrshp* 2008
Sales 24.0MM^E *EMP* 105
SIC 3498 3312 Pipe sections fabricated from purchased pipe; Blast furnaces & steel mills
Ch: Piotr Galitzine
QA Dir: Andrew Fischbach
QA Dir: Rich Hamstra
QA Dir: Michael Tuscana
Plnt Mgr: Richard Alfred
Plnt Mgr: John Desanzo
Plnt Mgr: John Dluhos
Plnt Mgr: Mark Wolber
Prd Mgr: James Montgomery
Ql Cn Mgr: Paul Highberger
Ql Cn Mgr: Philip Huseman

D-U-N-S 80-855-4141
IPSCO TUBULARS INC
TMK IPSCO
(*Suby of* TMK IPSCO INC) ★
10120 Houston Oaks Dr, Houston, TX 77064-3514
Tel (281) 949-1023 *Founded/Ownrshp* 2015
Sales 414.3MM^E *EMP* 1,154
SIC 3498 Fabricated pipe & fittings; Fabricated pipe & fittings
Ch: Piotr Galitzine
Pr: Ryan Chadwick
**Pr:* David Mitch
**COO:* Joel Mastervich
**COO:* Joel C Mastervich
**CFO:* Adrian Cobb
**CFO:* Evgeny Makarov
Sr VP: Dave Mitch
**VP:* Scott Barnes
Comm Dir: Roger Bentley
QA Dir: Michel Beaird

D-U-N-S 11-846-1578
IPSEN BIOPHARMACEUTICALS INC
(*Suby of* IPSEN PHARMA)
106 Allen Rd Ste 301, Basking Ridge, NJ 07920-3851
Tel (908) 275-6300 *Founded/Ownrshp* 2008
Sales 62.0MM^E *EMP* 216
SIC 2833 2834 Endocrine products; Pharmaceutical preparations; Endocrine products; Pharmaceutical preparations
Pr: Cynthia Schwalm
COO: Thomas H Silberg
CFO: Habib Rameani
Sr VP: Thorsten V Stein
VP: Christopher Cozic
VP: Dennis Kim
VP: Lynda Parker
VP: Paul Saatsoglou
VP: Carl H Worrell

Comm Man: Sean McLaughlin
QC Dir: Enona Gopinath

D-U-N-S 14-732-5138 IMP/EXP
IPSEN INC
(*Suby of* IPSEN INTERNATIONAL HOLDING GMBH)
984 Ipsen Rd, Cherry Valley, IL 61016-7706
Tel (815) 332-4941 *Founded/Ownrshp* 1992
Sales 48.1MM^E *EMP* 200
SIC 3567 Industrial furnaces & ovens; Industrial furnaces & ovens
Pr: John Schmitt
Ex VP: Claude Bertrand
Ex VP: Pierre Boulud
Ex VP: Etienne De Blois
Ex VP: Eric Drape
Dir Bus: Jim Perret
Snr Sftwr: Bradley Stewart
CIO: Roger Anderson
IT Man: Ruben Morales
Tech Mgr: Jim Grann
Info Man: Bill Smedburg

D-U-N-S 01-492-5486
IPSOFT INC
17 State St Fl 14, New York, NY 10004-1501
Tel (888) 477-6388 *Founded/Ownrshp* 1999
Sales 141.1MM^E *EMP* 423
SIC 7376 7363 7374 8742 Computer facilities management; Employee leasing service; Data processing service; Management consulting services; Computer facilities management; Employee leasing service; Data processing service; Management consulting services
Pr: Chetan Dube
CEO: Jeya Kumar
COO: Thomas Lindsay
VP: Mike Ghicas
VP: Mike Hicas
VP: David Judge
VP: Pranay Kumar
VP: Peter J Sajewski
VP: Matthew Wrenn
Exec: Dalia Landes
Dir Bus: Susan Ascolese
Dir Bus: Robert Kirk

D-U-N-S 01-985-3592
IPSOS AMERICA INC
(*Suby of* IPSOS)
1271 Ave Of The, New York, NY 10020
Tel (212) 265-3200 *Founded/Ownrshp* 1998
Sales 224.7MM^E *EMP* 3,034^E
SIC 8742 Management consulting services
CEO: James T Smith
**CFO:* Debra S Mason
Sr VP: Jim Douglass
Sr VP: Thomas Aw Miller
VP: Fred Church
VP: David Nemiah
VP: Phil Toner

IPSOS INSIGHT
See IPSOS-INSIGHT CORP

D-U-N-S 04-658-3027
IPSOS PUBLIC AFFAIRS INC
(*Suby of* IPSOS AMERICA INC) ★
222 S Riverside Plz # 350, Chicago, IL 60606-5808
Tel (312) 526-4000 *Founded/Ownrshp* 2011
Sales 99.3MM^E *EMP* 1,500
SIC 8732 8731 Market analysis or research; Market analysis or research; Commercial physical research
Pr: Robert Philpott
V Ch: Sonia Cheng
CFO: Tony Solarz
**Ex VP:* Ignacio Galceran
**Ex VP:* Barbara Goff
**Ex VP:* Lawrence Levin
**Ex VP:* Nan Martin
**Ex VP:* Robert Skolnick
**Ex VP:* Mark Turim
Sr VP: Sheila Baker
Sr VP: Marylou Barney
Sr VP: Marie Brighton
Sr VP: Tom Mularz
Sr VP: Laura Quinn
VP: Stuart Osakada
VP: George Schaumann
Dir Teleco: Christina McCormack
Assoc Dir: Eliza Wong

D-U-N-S 84-019-5676
IPSOS-INSIGHT CORP
IPSOS INSIGHT
(*Suby of* IPSOS AMERICA INC) ★
1700 Broadway Fl 15, New York, NY 10019-5905
Tel (212) 265-3200 *Founded/Ownrshp* 1979
Sales 22.9MM^E *EMP* 400
SIC 8732 Market analysis or research; Market analysis or research
CEO: Didier Truchot
COO: Efrain Ribeiro
CFO: Stoclet Laurence
CFO: Debra Mason
CFO: Peter McDowell
Bd of Dir: Yves-Claude Abescat
Bd of Dir: Wladimir Mollof
Sr VP: Margaret Burns
VP: Marc Beaudoin
VP: Shannon Childs
VP: Cathy Forrest
VP: Colin Seely
Comm Dir: Michelle Crellin

D-U-N-S 01-985-3634
IPSOS-INSIGHT LLC (DE)
(*Suby of* IPSOS AMERICA INC) ★
1600 Stewart Ave Ste 500, Westbury, NY 11590-6663
Tel (516) 507-3000 *Founded/Ownrshp* 2000, 2001
Sales 23.7MM^E *EMP* 250
SIC 8742 Management consulting services; Management consulting services
Ch Bd: Carlos Harding
**Pr:* Didier Truchot
**CFO:* Richard Nachmia
Off Mgr: Nancy Hodes

D-U-N-S 04-943-7528
IPSWICH BAY GLASS CO INC
420 Newburyport Tpke, Rowley, MA 01969-1725
Tel (978) 948-6644 *Founded/Ownrshp* 1969
Sales 35.2MM^E *EMP* 150
SIC 1793 3312 3334 Glass & glazing work; Blast furnaces & steel mills; Primary aluminum; Glass & glazing work; Blast furnaces & steel mills; Primary aluminum
Pr: H A Patrican Jr
**Treas:* Brian J Patrican
Opers Mgr: Clyde Janvrin

D-U-N-S 15-778-0123
IPSWICH MARITIME PRODUCTS CO INC
47 Avery St, Ipswich, MA 01938-1231
Tel (978) 356-9866 *Founded/Ownrshp* 1986
Sales 35.0MM *EMP* 50
SIC 5146

D-U-N-S 07-979-9231
IPSWICH PUBLIC SCHOOLS
1 Lord Sq, Ipswich, MA 01938-1909
Tel (978) 356-2935 *Founded/Ownrshp* 2015
Sales 7.4MM^E *EMP* 350^E
SIC 8211 Public elementary & secondary schools

D-U-N-S 00-142-1478 IMP
IPSWICH SHELLFISH CO INC (MA)
8 Hayward St, Ipswich, MA 01938-2012
Tel (978) 356-6941 *Founded/Ownrshp* 1960
Sales 60.4MM^E *EMP* 90^E
SIC 5146 Seafoods; Seafoods
CEO: Chrissi Pappas
**Pr:* George Pappas
CFO: James Sactson
**CFO:* James Saxonis
Sr VP: Steven Slavin
**VP:* Alexander Pappas
Exec: Robert Cain
Genl Mgr: Michael Trupiano
Dir IT: Kevin O'Donnell
IT Man: Mary Deamario
IT Man: Kevin O Donnell

D-U-N-S 55-737-5391
IPSWITCH INC
WHATSUP GOLD
83 Hartwell Ave, Lexington, MA 02421-3116
Tel (781) 676-5700 *Founded/Ownrshp* 1991
Sales 94.6MM^E *EMP* 300
SIC 5045 Computer software; Computer software
CEO: Joe Krivickas
Pr: Rich Kennelly
Pr: Warren Neuburger
CFO: David Stott
Ofcr: Austin Omalley
Ex VP: Diane Albano
Ex VP: Ennio Carboni
Ex VP: Richard Welch
VP: Lourdes Engel
VP: Greg Faubert
VP: Stephen Hess
VP: Frank Kenney
VP: L Frank Kenney
VP: Maureen Lyons
VP: Mary-Katherine McCarey
Board of Directors: Patrick Melampy, Robert A Steinkrauss

D-U-N-S 10-065-3620
IPT HOLDING INC
751 S Kellogg Ave, Goleta, CA 93117-3832
Tel (805) 683-3414 *Founded/Ownrshp* 2002
Sales 20.9MM^E *EMP* 170^E
Accts Grobstein Horwath & Company L
SIC 3469 Stamping metal for the trade; Stamping metal for the trade
Pr: Stephen Braunheim
**CFO:* Ron Williams

D-U-N-S 12-341-6609
IPT LLC
FM FACILITY MAINTENANCE
10 Columbus Blvd Fl 4, Hartford, CT 06106-1976
Tel (860) 249-2091 *Founded/Ownrshp* 2004
Sales 71.3MM^E *EMP* 238^E
SIC 8741 7349 Management services; Building maintenance services; Management services; Building maintenance services
CEO: Jim Reavey
**Pr:* Trevor Foster
**CFO:* Stephen Park
**Ex VP:* Bryan Hartnett
**Sr VP:* Cheryl Hutchinson
**Sr VP:* John Pavia
VP: David Liguori
**VP:* Keith Nedell
VP Bus Dev: Susan Weber
Prgrm Mgr: Lynn Anderson
Mktg Dir: Janet Zove

IPTAY SCHOLARSHIP FUND
See CLEMSON IPTAY CLUB

IQ COSMETICS
See INTELLIGENT BEAUTY LLC

D-U-N-S 10-812-0551
IQ CREDIT UNION
305 Ne 81st St, Vancouver, WA 98665-8110
Tel (360) 695-3441 *Founded/Ownrshp* 1941
Sales NA *EMP* 160
SIC 6061 6062 Federal credit unions; State credit unions, not federally chartered; Federal credit unions; State credit unions, not federally chartered
Pr: Roger Michaelis
**Ch Bd:* David P Kooken
Bd of Dir: Scott Bieber
Bd of Dir: Sharon Eastman
Bd of Dir: Ed Maxwell
Ofcr: Betsy Arfmann
Ofcr: Ashley Grant
Ofcr: Angela Williams
Sr VP: Dewayne Ledbetter
VP: Chris Anderson
VP: Craig Starkey

D-U-N-S 79-453-0865
IQ HOLDINGS INC
16212 State Highway 249, Houston, TX 77086-1014
Tel (281) 444-6454 Founded/Ownrshp 1991
Sales 51.5MM[E] EMP 150[E]
SIC 7389 5169 Packaging & labeling services; Industrial chemicals
CEO: Yohanne Gupta

D-U-N-S 02-657-5878
IQ PRODUCTS CO
(Suby of IQ HOLDINGS INC) ★
16212 State Highway 249, Houston, TX 77086-1014
Tel (281) 444-6454 Founded/Ownrshp 1992
Sales 51.5MM[E] EMP 150
SIC 5169 7389 Industrial chemicals; Packaging & labeling services; Industrial chemicals; Packaging & labeling services
CEO: Yohanne Gupta
*Pr: Cary Rutland
Sfty Mgr: Marty York
Plnt Mgr: Ray Williamson

D-U-N-S 87-687-5154
IQ SOLUTIONS INC
11300 Rockville Pike # 901, Rockville, MD 20852-3046
Tel (301) 230-2475 Founded/Ownrshp 1993
Sales 31.8MM EMP 250[E]
Accts Rubino & Company Chartered Be
SIC 8742 8748 Management consulting services; Management consulting services; Business consulting
CEO: Ileana Quintas
*Pr: Tom Brackett
*Sr VP: Lisa Swanberg
VP: Stephanie Adams
VP: Stephen Murphy
VP: Curtis Pond
VP: Routh Speir
Creative D: Ody Leonard
*Prin: Jennifer Isenberg
Prgrm Mgr: Sarah Baron
VP Opers: Matt Bowen

D-U-N-S 60-321-4271 IMP
IQE INC
(Suby of IQE PLC)
119 Technology Dr, Bethlehem, PA 18015-1327
Tel (610) 861-6930 Founded/Ownrshp 1999
Sales 35.7MM[E] EMP 100
SIC 3674 Wafers (semiconductor devices); Wafers (semiconductor devices)
Pr: Andrew Nelson
*VP: Stephen Gergar
QC Dir: Timothy Brown
Ql Cn Mgr: John Sousa

D-U-N-S 07-874-4527
IQE KC LLC
200 John Hancock Rd, Taunton, MA 02780-7320
Tel (508) 824-6696 Founded/Ownrshp 2012
Sales 22.8MM[E] EMP 82
SIC 3674 Wafers (semiconductor devices)

D-U-N-S 78-721-1903
IQMS
2231 Wisteria Ln, Paso Robles, CA 93446-9820
Tel (805) 227-1122 Founded/Ownrshp 1989
Sales 37.0MM EMP 230
SIC 7371 Computer software development; Computer software development
Pr: Randall C Flamm
Pr: Karen Sked
VP: Janice Flamm
*VP: Nancy Flamm
VP: Jon Gabelica
VP: Glenn Nowak
Ql Cn Mgr: Tina Jolicoeur
Sales Exec: Alan Goniwich
Sales Exec: John Lutz
Mktg Dir: Perri Cline
Sls Mgr: Dave Conrad

D-U-N-S 15-605-8237
IQNAVIGATOR INC
6465 Greenwood Plaza Blvd, Greenwood Village, CO 80111-4905
Tel (303) 563-1500 Founded/Ownrshp 1999
Sales 147.1MM[E] EMP 320[E]
SIC 7371 7361 Computer software development; Labor contractors (employment agency); Computer software development; Labor contractors (employment agency)
Pr: Joseph Juliano
Pr: Brandy Cline
Pr: Michelle Gates
Pr: Cara Kresge
*CFO: Barry Capoot
Ex VP: Kieran Brady
Ex VP: Graden Gerig
Ex VP: Ed Gould
Ex VP: Jagan Reddy
Ex VP: Eric Riddle
Ex VP: Jeffrey Varon
Sr VP: Jim Golden
Sr VP: Jon Holden
VP: Taylor Allis
VP: Dianna Anderson
VP: Lonnie Byxbe
VP: Christine Calandrella
VP: Victor Chayet
VP: Eric Cohen
VP: Brian Hoffmeyer
VP: Michelle Hudson

IQOR AFTERMAKEFT SERVICES
See JABIL GLOBAL SERVICES LLC

IQOR AFTERMARKET SERVICES
See IQOR GLOBAL SERVICES LLC

D-U-N-S 92-985-0147
IQOR GLOBAL SERVICES LLC
IQOR AFTERMARKET SERVICES
(Suby of IQOR HOLDINGS INC) ★
4600 Pleasant Hill Rd, Memphis, TN 38118-7515
Tel (901) 367-4300 Founded/Ownrshp 2014
Sales NA EMP 19,000
SIC 8748 4731 Computer disk & drum drives & components; Telecommunications consultant; Freight transportation arrangement
Pr: Daniel Montenaro
*Pr: Hartmut Liebel
*COO: Bryan Maguire
*VP: Grant Newmyer

D-U-N-S 96-599-5553
IQOR HOLDINGS INC
1 Progress Plz Ste 170, Saint Petersburg, FL 33701-4335
Tel (866) 657-2057 Founded/Ownrshp 2007
Sales 514.7MM EMP 32,000[E]
Accts Grant Thornton Llp New York
SIC 7374 Data processing service; Data processing service
Pr: Hartmut Liebel
Pr: Matthew Austin
Pr: Sandy Pond
Pr: Ponvel Shanmuganathan
Pr: Nikhil Smotra
COO: Bryan Maguire
COO: Gary Praznik
CFO: Margaret M Cowherd
Ofcr: Mason Argiropoulos
Ofcr: Daniel L Montenaro
Ex VP: Gary Cole
Ex VP: Margaret Cowherd
Ex VP: Dick Eychner
Sr VP: Shane Barlow
Sr VP: Mitch Benveniste
Sr VP: David Mahoney
Sr VP: Richard Temple
VP: Robert Baertlein
VP: Stephanie Buehler
VP: Erik Carlson
VP: Dustin Fleming

D-U-N-S 11-802-5068 IMP
■ **IQOR OF TEXAS LP**
(Suby of JABIL CIRCUIT INC) ★
10560 Dr Martin Luther Ki, Saint Petersburg, FL 33716-3718
Tel (727) 577-9749 Founded/Ownrshp 1999
Sales 38.4MM[E] EMP 100[E]
SIC 3679 Electronic circuits; Electronic circuits
Ch Bd: Timothy L Main
*Pr: William E Peters
*CEO: Mark T Mondello
*CFO: Forbes I J Alexander
*Ex VP: Joseph A McGee

D-U-N-S 14-420-0511
IQOR US INC
1 Prog Plz 200 Central, Saint Petersburg, FL 33701
Tel (866) 657-2057 Founded/Ownrshp 1998
Sales 1.0MMM[E] EMP 17,000
SIC 7322 Adjustment & collection services; Adjustment & collection services
Ch Bd: Randy L Christofferson
Pr: Patrick Burwell
Pr: Mike Frappollo
Pr: Saladin Glanton
Pr: Chris Karounos
Pr: Deb McEldowney
Pr: Norm Merritt
Pr: Prabhjot Singh
Pr: Jamie Welsh
COO: Rajesh Dwivedi
COO: Rakesh Kumar
COO: Bryan Maguire
COO: Gary Praznik
CFO: Margaret M Cowherd
CFO: John Hunts
CFO: Norm Meritt
Chf Cred: Dan Montenaro
Sr VP: Cindy Arnberg
Sr VP: Russ Jakubowski
Sr VP: Sumit Malhotra
Sr VP: David Wright

IQORE
See RECEIVABLE MANAGEMENT SERVICES CORP

D-U-N-S 61-265-5274 IMP/EXP
IQUIQUE US LLC
2320 W Commodore Way # 200, Seattle, WA 98199-1287
Tel (206) 286-1661 Founded/Ownrshp 1988
Sales 98.9MM[E] EMP 200
SIC 0921 Fishing preserves; Fishing preserves
Off Mgr: Michelle Berger

D-U-N-S 01-292-8347
IRA D CONKLIN & SONS INC
94 Stewart Ave, Newburgh, NY 12550-6618
Tel (845) 561-1512 Founded/Ownrshp 1939
Sales 24.6MM[E] EMP 112
Accts Levitan Yegidis & Goldstein Ll
SIC 5084 1629 1799 7538 Pumps & pumping equipment; Tanks, storage; Land preparation construction; Service station equipment installation & maintenance; Gasoline pump installation; Service station equipment installation, maintenance & repair; General automotive repair shops; Pumps & pumping equipment; Tanks, storage; Land preparation construction; Service station equipment installation & maintenance; Gasoline pump installation; Service station equipment installation, maintenance & repair; General automotive repair shops
CEO: James Ludlow
Exec: Pam Hutter

D-U-N-S 07-369-4424
IRA DAVENPORT MEMORIAL HOSPITAL INC
FRED & HARRIET TAYLOR HLTH CTR
(Suby of ARNOT HEALTH INC) ★
7571 State Route 54, Bath, NY 14810-9504
Tel (607) 776-8500 Founded/Ownrshp 1910
Sales 21.0MM EMP 294
SIC 8051 8062 Extended care facility; Hospital, affiliated with AMA residency; Extended care facility; Hospital, affiliated with AMA residency
CEO: Jim Watson
*CFO: Ronald Kintz
VP: Megan Johnson
Dir Soc: Lucas Bay
VP Opers: Linda Donnelly
Nrsg Dir: Diana Phillipson

D-U-N-S 09-894-8144
IRA E CLARK DETECTIVE AGENCY INC
CLARK SECURITY
10 Chestnut St, Evansville, IN 47713-1022
Tel (812) 424-2448 Founded/Ownrshp 1912, 1969
Sales 10.5MM[E] EMP 450
SIC 7381 Security guard service; Security guard service
Pr: Richard P Curby
Treas: Marlene Curby

D-U-N-S 08-243-4028
IRA G STEFFY AND SON INC
460 Wenger Dr, Ephrata, PA 17522-9269
Tel (717) 626-6500 Founded/Ownrshp 2003
Sales 29.6MM[E] EMP 75
Accts Ross Buemler Falk & Company
SIC 3441 7692 1791 3444 Fabricated structural metal; Welding repair; Structural steel erection; Sheet metalwork
Pr: Dennis Rineer
*Pr: Gary R Erb
VP: Patrick F Jeffers

D-U-N-S 00-135-6872 IMP
IRA GREEN INC (RI)
177 Georgia Ave, Providence, RI 02905-4422
Tel (401) 467-4770 Founded/Ownrshp 1945, 1999
Sales 33.3MM[E] EMP 211
SIC 3999 5199 3469 2395 Identification badges & insignia; General merchandise, non-durable; Metal stampings; Pleating & stitching; Identification badges & insignia; General merchandise, non-durable; Metal stampings; Pleating & stitching
Ch Bd: Michael Mc Allister
*Ex VP: Robert D Gilmartin
Store Mgr: Alberto Lavizzari
IT Man: Ed Doyle
Mktg Mgr: Kevin McNelis

D-U-N-S 03-361-0858
IRA HIGDON GROCERY CO
150 Iga Way Ne, Cairo, GA 39828
Tel (229) 377-1272 Founded/Ownrshp 1909
Sales 96.0MM EMP 100
Accts Guy & Johnson Pc Thomasvil
SIC 5141 5147 5142 5143 Groceries, general line; Meats, fresh; Meat, frozen: packaged; Dairy products, except dried or canned; Groceries, general line; Meats, fresh; Meat, frozen: packaged; Dairy products, except dried or canned
CEO: L I Higdon
VP: Matt Higdon
*VP: Nat Higdon
Dir IT: Walt Sellers

IRA LEXUS
See IRA MOTOR GROUP INC

D-U-N-S 78-242-1820
IRA MOTOR GROUP INC
IRA LEXUS
99 Andover St, Danvers, MA 01923-1414
Tel (978) 739-8705 Founded/Ownrshp 1989
Sales 22.1MM[E] EMP 50
SIC 5511 Automobiles, new & used; Automobiles, new & used
Pr: David Rosenberg
*Treas: Judith A Rosenberg
Sys Mgr: Dave Langis
Sls Mgr: Chuck Haddad
Sls Mgr: David Hult
Sales Asso: Andres Damiron
Sales Asso: Elliot Honing
Sales Asso: Jose Silva

D-U-N-S 07-316-6308
■ **IRA PUMP AND SUPPLY CO INC**
(Suby of APPLIED INDUSTRIAL TECHNOLOGIES INC) ★
6120 Ira Pump Rd, Ira, TX 79527
Tel (325) 573-6403 Founded/Ownrshp 2014
Sales 23.3MM[E] EMP 48
SIC 5084 Oil well machinery, equipment & supplies
Pr: Carl Smith
*Sec: Sheila Harless
*VP: Shane Smith
*Prin: Jackie Smith
Store Mgr: Chris Brown
Store Mgr: James Goolsby

D-U-N-S 15-344-5200 IMP
IRACORE INTERNATIONAL INC
INDUSTRIAL RUBBER APPLICATORS
3516 13th Ave E, Hibbing, MN 55746-2338
Tel (218) 263-8831 Founded/Ownrshp 1986
Sales 21.9MM[E] EMP 96[E]
SIC 3069 Linings, vulcanizable rubber
CEO: Daniel O Burkes
COO: Christopher Liesmaki
CFO: Jim Skalski
*VP: Christopher M Liesmaki
MIS Dir: Dave Butterfield
Ql Cn Mgr: Randall Jacobson
Trfc Mgr: Dan Culovich
Sls Mgr: Joe Bugliosi

IRAS MOUNIR ABANNI
See AMERICAN CENTURY INVESTMENT MANAGEMENT INC

D-U-N-S 00-785-1207
■ **IRBY CONSTRUCTION CO** (MS)
(Suby of QUANTA SERVICES INC) ★
318 Old Highway 49 S, Richland, MS 39218-9449
Tel (601) 709-4729 Founded/Ownrshp 1946, 2000
Sales 223.3MM[E] EMP 700
Accts Haddox Reid Eubank Betts Pllc
SIC 1623 1731 Electric power line construction; Transmitting tower (telecommunication) construction; Fiber optic cable installation; Electric power line construction; Transmitting tower (telecommunication) construction; Fiber optic cable installation
Pr: Bill Korlath
*CFO: Robert A Croft Sr
*Sr VP: Mark L Mullen
*VP: Gary Bodam
*VP: David D Brittain
*VP: James H Haddox
*VP: Stuart C Irby
*VP: Pamela L Kunkemoeller
*VP: Mike Leech
*VP: Eddie Moak
*VP: Tana L Pool
VP: Argyle Scott
*VP: Doug Walo
*VP: Mike Wigton

IRBY ELECTRICAL DISTRIBUTORS
See STUART C IRBY CO

IRC AND PARTNERS
See INTERNATIONAL RESCUE COMMITTEE INC

D-U-N-S 61-149-2661
IRC INC
INTERNATIONAL RISK CONSULTANTS
(Suby of NFP ADVISORS) ★
1 Corporation Way Ste 230, Peabody, MA 01960-7925
Tel (781) 581-9800 Founded/Ownrshp 1990
Sales NA EMP 1,450
SIC 6411 Insurance agents & brokers; Insurance agents & brokers
VP: Stephen Bloomberg

IRC INDUSTRIES
See INTERSTATE REHABILITATION CENTER INC

IRD
See INTERNATIONAL RELIEF AND DEVELOPMENT INC

IREA
See INTERMOUNTAIN RURAL ELECTRIC ASSOCIATION

D-U-N-S 94-457-5877 IMP/EXP
IREDALE MINERAL COSMETICS LTD
JANE IREDALE
50 Church St, Great Barrington, MA 01230-1315
Tel (413) 644-9900 Founded/Ownrshp 1994
Sales 65.9MM[E] EMP 167
Accts Kushi & Myers Pc North Adams
SIC 5122 2844 Cosmetics, perfumes & hair products; Cosmetic preparations; Cosmetics, perfumes & hair products; Cosmetic preparations
Pr: Jane Iredale
*COO: Anthony J Patterson
VP: Sharon Gregory
VP: Ann Miller
*VP: Theresa Robison
CTO: Emily Schmidt
Dir IT: Ian Mitchell
Natl Sales: Michele Fenske
Sales Asso: Dana Barr

D-U-N-S 07-450-4507
IREDELL COUNTY
200 S Center St, Statesville, NC 28677-5807
Tel (704) 878-3000 Founded/Ownrshp 1788
Sales NA EMP 900
Accts Martin Starnes & Associates C
SIC 9199 ;
Ofcr: Michael Hooper
IT Man: Susan Robertson
Snr Mgr: Nettie Johnson

IREDELL HEALTH SYSTEM
See IREDELL MEMORIAL HOSPITAL INC

D-U-N-S 07-449-8064
IREDELL MEMORIAL HOSPITAL INC
IREDELL HEALTH SYSTEM
557 Brookdale Dr, Statesville, NC 28677-4100
Tel (704) 873-5661 Founded/Ownrshp 1951
Sales 136.8MM EMP 1,448
SIC 8062 8051 General medical & surgical hospitals; Skilled nursing care facilities; General medical & surgical hospitals; Skilled nursing care facilities
Pr: Ed Rush
Pr: Trishwant Garcha
COO: David Myers
Ofcr: Shelia Watson
VP: Kevin Deter
*VP: Fred Karnap
VP: John Snow
Dir Teleco: Pam Wooten
Dir Lab: Barbara Suddreth
*Prin: Skip Smith
CIO: Andrew Braunstein

D-U-N-S 07-105-7160
IREDELL-STATESVILLE SCHOOLS (NC)
549 N Race St, Statesville, NC 28677-3915
Tel (704) 872-8931 Founded/Ownrshp 1910
Sales 163.0MM EMP 3,300
Accts Mccannon Rogers Driscoll & A
SIC 8211 Public elementary & secondary schools; Public senior high school; Public junior high school; Public elementary school; Public elementary & secondary schools; Public senior high school; Public junior high school; Public elementary school
*CFO: Melissa Wike
Dir IT: Darryll Corpening
Teacher Pr: Bill Long
HC Dir: Kelly Marcy

D-U-N-S 06-667-9754
IRELL & MANELLA LLP
1800 Avenue Of The Stars # 900, Los Angeles, CA 90067-4276
Tel (310) 277-1010 Founded/Ownrshp 1941
Sales 34.6MM EMP 550
SIC 8111 General practice law office; General practice law office
Mng Pt: Elliot Brown
Pt: Gregory Klein
Pt: David Siegel
Mng Pt: Morgan Chu
Mng Pt: Andra Greene
Mng Pt: Richard Sherman
COO: Aaron Cole
Exec: Robert Cramer
Exec: Werner Wolfen

Ex Dir: Mark Hanson
Netwrk Eng: David Moalem

D-U-N-S 16-473-8952
IRENE TRUJILLO
CARE PERSONAL ASSISTANCE
9215 Montana Ave, El Paso, TX 79925-1315
Tel (915) 772-8401 *Founded/Ownrshp* 1999
Sales 4.0MM^E *EMP* 280
SIC 8322 7299 Homemakers' service; Personal appearance services; Homemakers' service; Personal appearance services
Owner: Irene Trujillo

D-U-N-S 09-709-7836
IRET PROPERTIES A NORTH DAKOTA LIMITED PARTNERSHIP
1400 31st Ave Sw Ste 60, Minot, ND 58701-6965
Tel (701) 837-4738 *Founded/Ownrshp* 1997
Sales 20.2MM^E *EMP* 70
Accts Brady Martz & Associates Pc
SIC 6531 Real estate managers
Genl Pt: Thomas A Wentz Sr
Pt: Diane K Bryantt
Sr VP: Andy Martin
VP: Joel Metz
VP: Dave Pankow
Genl Mgr: Tanya Hemphill

IREX
See INTERNATIONAL RESEARCH AND EXCHANGES BOARD INC

D-U-N-S 04-751-2959
IREX CORP
(*Suby of* NORTH LIME HOLDINGS CORP) ★
120 N Lime St, Lancaster, PA 17602-2923
Tel (717) 397-3633 *Founded/Ownrshp* 2006
Sales 246.7MM *EMP* 1,734
Accts Baker Tilly Virchow Krause Llp
SIC 1799 Coating, caulking & weather, water & fireproofing; Asbestos removal & encapsulation; Coating, caulking & weather, water & fireproofing; Asbestos removal & encapsulation
Pr: W K Liddell
**Sec:* Lori Pickell
VP: Gale Blefko
**VP:* James Hipolit
Sfty Dirs: Paul O'Hayre
S&M/VP: John Lamberton

D-U-N-S 10-177-7550
IRG REALTY ADVISORS LLC
4020 Kinross Lakes Pkwy, Richfield, OH 44286-9084
Tel (330) 659-4060 *Founded/Ownrshp* 2013
Sales 49.9MM^E *EMP* 67
SIC 6531 Real estate managers
Pr: Tracy C Green
CFO: Mark Miley
VP: Donald Green
VP: Jessica Hunsinger
Off Admin: Ginny Granc
Dir IT: Suzanne Whitman
Site Mgr: Eric Jackson
Opers Mgr: Gregory Hamrick
Opers Mgr: Tom Markovic
Opers Mgr: Lou Palumbo
Opers Mgr: Joseph Staeuble

IRGENS HLTH CARE FCLTIES GROUP
See IRGENS PARTNERS LLC

D-U-N-S 02-235-2129
IRGENS PARTNERS LLC
IRGENS HLTH CARE FCLTIES GROUP
648 N Plankinton Ave # 200, Milwaukee, WI 53203-2928
Tel (414) 443-0700 *Founded/Ownrshp* 1983
Sales 29.2MM^E *EMP* 74
SIC 6531 6512 8742 6552 Real estate managers; Commercial & industrial building operation; Management consulting services; Subdividers & developers
CEO: Mark F Irgens
**Pr:* Jaclynn C Walsh
CFO: Duane Nolbe
**Ex VP:* David C Arnold
**Ex VP:* Duane H Nolde
Ex VP: Brian Spoerl
VP: Dave Merrick
VP: Rick Nelson
VP: Michael O'Connor
VP: Mike Syman

D-U-N-S 86-123-7670
IRHYTHM TECHNOLOGIES INC
650 Townsend St Ste 380, San Francisco, CA 94103-6248
Tel (415) 632-5700 *Founded/Ownrshp* 2006
Sales 35.6MM^E *EMP* 170
SIC 3841 7699 Diagnostic apparatus, medical; Medical equipment repair, non-electric; Diagnostic apparatus, medical; Medical equipment repair, non-electric
CEO: Kevin King
CFO: Matthew Garrett
Ex VP: Jon Darsee
Ex VP: Marga Ortigas-Wedekind
Ex VP: Derrick Sung
Board of Directors: Sam Brasch, Casper De Clercq, Josh Green, Kevin King, Bill Starling

D-U-N-S 61-292-0785
▲ IRIDEX CORP
1212 Terra Bella Ave, Mountain View, CA 94043-1824
Tel (650) 940-4700 *Founded/Ownrshp* 1989
Sales 42.8MM *EMP* 128^E
Tkr Sym IRIX *Exch* NGM
SIC 3845 Laser systems & equipment, medical; Laser systems & equipment, medical
**Ch Bd:* William M Moore
VP: Ronald Steckel
Board of Directors: Sanford Fitch, George Marcellino, Scott A Shuda

D-U-N-S 82-945-2569
▲ IRIDIUM COMMUNICATIONS INC
1750 Tysons Blvd Ste 1400, Mc Lean, VA 22102-4244
Tel (703) 287-7400 *Founded/Ownrshp* 2000
Sales 408.5MM *EMP* 233^E
Tkr Sym IRDM *Exch* NGS
SIC 4899 Data communication services; Data communication services
CEO: Matthew J Desch
**Ch Bd:* Robert H Niehaus
**COO:* S Scott Smith
**Ofcr:* Thomas J Fitzpatrick
Ex VP: Bryan J Hartin
Ex VP: Scott T Scheimreif
VP: David A Anhalt
VP: Richard P Nyren
Board of Directors: Thomas C Canfield, Jane L Harman, Alvin B Krongard, Eric T Olson, Steven B Pfeiffer, Parker W Rush, Henrik O Schliemann, Barry J West

D-U-N-S 83-086-8407
■ IRIDIUM HOLDINGS LLC
(*Suby of* IRIDIUM COMMUNICATIONS INC) ★
1750 Tysons Blvd Ste 1400, Mc Lean, VA 22102-4244
Tel (703) 287-7400 *Founded/Ownrshp* 2009
Sales 30.5MM^E *EMP* 112
SIC 8748 Communications consulting
CEO: Matthew J Desch

D-U-N-S 07-152-3182 IMP
IRIDIUM INDUSTRIES INC
ARTUBE
147 Forge Rd, East Stroudsburg, PA 18301-2962
Tel (570) 476-8800 *Founded/Ownrshp* 1998
Sales 33.7MM^E *EMP* 200
SIC 3082 Tubes, unsupported plastic; Tubes, unsupported plastic
Ch Bd: Parviz Nazarian
**Pr:* Jacques Sassouni
**CFO:* Charles Lumis
Sls Mgr: Moise Masjedi

D-U-N-S 14-854-9087 IMP
■ IRIDIUM SATELLITE LLC
(*Suby of* IRIDIUM HOLDINGS LLC) ★
1750 Tysons Blvd Ste 1400, Mc Lean, VA 22102-4244
Tel (703) 356-0484 *Founded/Ownrshp* 2000
Sales 30.5MM^E *EMP* 109
SIC 3663 Satellites, communications; Satellites, communications
CEO: Matthew J Desch
**COO:* S Scott Smith
**Ex VP:* Bryan J Hartin
**Ex VP:* Scott T Scheimreif
VP: Jayesh Patel

IRIS
See INC RESEARCH INSTITUTIONS FOR SEISMOLOGY

D-U-N-S 80-147-5810
■ IRIS DATA SERVICES INC
(*Suby of* EPIQ SYSTEMS INC) ★
17795 W 106th St Ste 201, Olathe, KS 66061-3155
Tel (913) 937-0590 *Founded/Ownrshp* 2015
Sales 56.8MM^E *EMP* 200
SIC 7374 7378 4813 Data processing service; Computer & data processing equipment repair/maintenance; ; Data processing service; Computer & data processing equipment repair/maintenance;
Pr: Major Baisden
VP: Brandon Mack
Snr Sftwr: John Morford
IT Man: Adam Moss
IT Man: Ryan Rubert
IT Man: Ryan Rupert
IT Man: Annie Spillman
Prd Mgr: Tamer Mansour
VP Mktg: ADI Elliott
Manager: John Pearson
Sls Mgr: Michael Sneary

D-U-N-S 09-590-5832
IRIS GROUP INC
MODERN POSTCARD
1675 Faraday Ave, Carlsbad, CA 92008-7314
Tel (760) 431-1103 *Founded/Ownrshp* 1977
Sales 73.5MM^E *EMP* 250
SIC 2759 5961 Commercial printing; Mail order house; Commercial printing; Mail order house
CEO: Steve Hoffman
VP: Jim T Brown
VP: Monroe Rifkin
CTO: Kelly Kazeman
Prd Mgr: Waldo Garza
Sls&Mrk Ex: Graham Brown
Sls&Mrk Ex: Allison Orenstein
VP Sls: Robert Malley

D-U-N-S 09-824-0690 IMP/EXP
■ IRIS INTERNATIONAL INC
(*Suby of* BECKMAN COULTER INC) ★
9172 Eton Ave, Chatsworth, CA 91311-5805
Tel (818) 527-7000 *Founded/Ownrshp* 1979
Sales 46.0MM^E *EMP* 387^E
SIC 3841 3845 Surgical & medical instruments; Electromedical equipment; Surgical & medical instruments; Electromedical equipment
Ch Bd: Cesar M Garcia
Pr: Bernard M Alfano
Pr: Robert A Mello
**CFO:* Amin I Khalifa
**Chf Mktg O:* Philip J Ginsburg MD
Ex VP: Sar Garc
VP: Bernard Alfano
VP: Lawrence J Blecka
VP: David W Gates
VP: Alan Koontz
VP: Richard A O Leary
**VP:* Richard Oleary
VP: Thomas E Warekois
**VP:* John U Yi
Board of Directors: Steven M Besbeck, Beth Y Karlan MD, David T Della Penta, Rick Timmins, Edward F Voboril, Stephen E Wasserman

D-U-N-S 94-054-3945
IRIS SOFTWARE INC
(*Suby of* IRIS SOFTWARE PRIVATE LIMITED)
200 Metroplex Dr Ste 300, Edison, NJ 08817-2600
Tel (732) 393-0034 *Founded/Ownrshp* 1996
Sales 37.1MM^E *EMP* 125
SIC 7379 Computer related consulting services; Computer related consulting services
CEO: Sanjiv Khanna
**Pr:* Sunil Puri
VP: Krishna Amirhaligam
VP: Piyush Chandra
Dir Bus: Vijay Tirumala
Snr Sftwr: Varun Mehrotra
IT Man: Edward Raffoul
Info Man: Ravinder Arora
Software D: Rajesh Satauri
Sls Dir: Brett Singer
Sls Mgr: David Gershman

D-U-N-S 78-866-5958 IMP/EXP
IRIS USA INC
(*Suby of* IRIS OHYAMA INC.)
11111 80th Ave, Pleasant Prairie, WI 53158-2910
Tel (262) 612-1000 *Founded/Ownrshp* 1985
Sales 110.7MM^E *EMP* 310
SIC 3089 Cases, plastic; Cases, plastic
CEO: Akihiro Ohyama
**Pr:* Kentaro Ohayama
CFO: Linda Kupper
VP: Bernadette Gaubert
VP: Justin Johnson
VP: Dick Konsinowski
VP: Hideo Ohyama
VP: Tom Thompson
Genl Mgr: Al Muto
CIO: Ingrid Petersen
Dir IT: Thomas Adams

D-U-N-S 17-591-9497 IMP
IRISE
2301 Rosecrans Ave # 4100, El Segundo, CA 90245-4993
Tel (800) 556-0399 *Founded/Ownrshp* 1997
Sales 44.9MM^E *EMP* 150
SIC 7371 Computer software development; Computer software development
CEO: Emmet B Keeffe III
Mng Pt: Martin Brunk
**Pr:* Maurice Martin
**CFO:* Lionel Etrillard
**Chf Mktg O:* Mitch Bishop
Top Exec: Jeff Poon
**Ex VP:* Stephen Brickley
**Ex VP:* Jacques Marine
**Ex VP:* Dean Terry
Mng Dir: Steve Paik
Snr Sftwr: Sahil Mehta
Board of Directors: Dana Stalder

D-U-N-S 14-846-8663
IRISH COMMUNICATION CO INC
(*Suby of* IRISH CONSTRUCTION) ★
2649 Stingle Ave, Rosemead, CA 91770-3326
Tel (626) 288-6170 *Founded/Ownrshp* 1985
Sales 65.3MM^E *EMP* 250
SIC 1623 8748 1731 Telephone & communication line construction; Telecommunications consultant; Communications specialization; Telephone & communication line construction; Telecommunications consultant; Communications specialization
CEO: Gregory C Warde
**Pr:* Dan Mitchell
**Ch:* Pat D Furnare
**VP:* Dennis Brackney
VP: Randy Dale
**VP:* Larry Manke
IT Man: Helen Chen

D-U-N-S 02-953-4070
IRISH CONSTRUCTION (CA)
(*Suby of* MANHATTAN CAPITAL CORP) ★
2641 River Ave, Rosemead, CA 91770-3392
Tel (626) 288-8530 *Founded/Ownrshp* 1947, 1981
Sales 65.3MM^E *EMP* 300
SIC 1623 Water, sewer & utility lines; Water, sewer & utility lines; Communication line & transmission tower construction; Telephone & communication line construction
Ch Bd: Gregory C Warde
**Pr:* Ken West
**Pr:* William E Wilbanks
**Sec:* Randall W Dale
**VP:* Lonnie Gentry
**VP:* Jerry L Olmscheid
VP: Jerry Olmscheid
Board of Directors: Pat Furnare, William E Irish, Matt Stanisich

IRISH DAIRY BOARD INC., THE
See ORNUA FOODS NORTH AMERICA INC

D-U-N-S 86-761-8464 IMP
IRISO USA INC
34405 W 12 Mile Rd # 237, Farmington Hills, MI 48331-5627
Tel (248) 324-9780 *Founded/Ownrshp* 1994
Sales 50.0MM *EMP* 27
SIC 3678 Electronic connectors
CEO: Akihiko Ohira

D-U-N-S 95-920-5568
IRISYS INC
6828 Nncy Rdge Dr Ste 100, San Diego, CA 92121
Tel (858) 623-1520 *Founded/Ownrshp* 1996
Sales 30.5MM^E *EMP* 37
SIC 5122 8748 Pharmaceuticals; Business consulting
Pr: Gina Stack
**CEO:* Robert Ginnini
Ofcr: Robert P Giannini
**VP:* Doug Taylor

IRL
See INTEGRATED REGIONAL LABORATORIES

D-U-N-S 61-984-8711
IRM LLC
INDUSTRIAL RAW MATERIALS
(*Suby of* AUFHAUSER CORP) ★
39 West Mall, Plainview, NY 11803-4209
Tel (212) 688-8080 *Founded/Ownrshp* 2005
Sales 40.0MM^E *EMP* 32
SIC 5172 Petroleum products; Petroleum products

D-U-N-S 80-738-0951 IMP/EXP
▲ IROBOT CORP
8 Crosby Dr, Bedford, MA 01730-1402
Tel (781) 430-3000 *Founded/Ownrshp* 1990
Sales 556.8MM *EMP* 572^E
Accts Pricewaterhousecoopers Llp B
Tkr Sym IRBT *Exch* NGS
SIC 3569 3731 Robots, assembly line: industrial & commercial; Submersible marine robots, manned or unmanned; Robots, assembly line: industrial & commercial; Submersible marine robots, manned or unmanned
Ch Bd: Colin M Angle
COO: Rick Robinson
CFO: Alison Dean
Ex VP: Russell J Campanello
Ex VP: Christian Cerda
Ex VP: Paolo Pirjanian
Sr VP: Tim Saeger
VP: Chun Shih
VP: Michael Tirozzi
Exec: Tom Battistini
Exec: Marie Papas
Exec: Carl Vonnegut
Exec: Rick Vosburgh
Exec: Marcus Williams
Board of Directors: Mohamad Ali, Ronald Chwang, Gail Deegan, Deborah G Ellinger, Andrea Geisser, Paul J Kern, George C McNamee, Paul Sagan, Michelle V Stacy

D-U-N-S 79-683-1217 IMP
IROKO PHARMACEUTICALS LLC
150 Rouse Blvd, Philadelphia, PA 19112-1901
Tel (267) 546-3003 *Founded/Ownrshp* 2007
Sales 43.9MM^E *EMP* 160^E
SIC 2834 Proprietary drug products; Proprietary drug products
Ch Bd: Osagie Imasogie
Pr: John Vavricka
CFO: Fred Krieger
Chf Mktg O: Susan Langer
Ofcr: Clarence L Young
VP: Andrew Bayode
VP: Olalekan Andrew Bayode
VP: Veenita B Bleznak
VP: Humphrey Harte
VP: Paul Hemsley
VP: E O Imasogie MD
VP: Moji James
VP: Steve Jensen
VP: Ariyad Krishnarai
VP: Rohit C Mehta
VP: Jim Moran
Board of Directors: Nathan Burkey, Jeremy Fletcher, Pierre Legault, Bradley T Sheares, Louis Vollmer

D-U-N-S 80-014-6755 IMP
IROL INC
SERV-U-SUCCESS
(*Suby of* MEIJER INC) ★
4695 Helena Dr Sw, Grandville, MI 49418-2514
Tel (616) 249-0025 *Founded/Ownrshp* 1992
Sales 77.2MM^E *EMP* 49
SIC 5141 Food brokers; Food brokers
Pr: Harold Voorhees Jr
**VP:* Paul Gorham

D-U-N-S 03-198-9114 EXP
IRON & METALS INC
5555 Franklin St, Denver, CO 80216-6215
Tel (303) 292-5555 *Founded/Ownrshp* 1961
Sales 26.8MM^E *EMP* 60
SIC 5093 Ferrous metal scrap & waste; Nonferrous metals scrap
Ch: Alan Cohen
**Pr:* Michael Cohen
**VP:* Murray Cohen
**VP:* Michael Yourtz
Store Mgr: Tap Sittiseri

D-U-N-S 00-791-5499 IMP
IRON AGE CORP
(*Suby of* IRON AGE HOLDINGS CORP) ★
200 Friberg Pkwy, Westborough, MA 01581-3991
Tel (508) 768-4100 *Founded/Ownrshp* 1817
Sales 94.7MM^E *EMP* 745
SIC 5139 5661 3143 3144 Shoes; Shoe stores; Men's footwear, except athletic; Women's footwear, except athletic
Pr: William Mills
**Ch Bd:* Dale F Morrison
**Pr:* William J Mills
**CFO:* Bart R Huchel
CFO: Gary Lortie
**VP:* Sean M Cumbie
**VP:* Richard A Kusmer
VP: Jay Sebes
VP: Gary Tousigant
Board of Directors: John Q Anderson, Andrea Geisser

D-U-N-S 61-038-3317
IRON AGE HOLDINGS CORP
(*Suby of* FENWAY PARTNERS LLC) ★
3 Robinson Plz Ste 300, Pittsburgh, PA 15205-1018
Tel (412) 788-0888 *Founded/Ownrshp* 1997
Sales 100.0MM *EMP* 745
SIC 5139 5661 3143 3144 Shoes; Shoe stores; Men's footwear, except athletic; Women's footwear, except athletic; Shoes; Shoe stores; Men's footwear, except athletic; Women's footwear, except athletic
Pr: David Eckert
CFO: Gary Lortye
Bd of Dir: Peter Lamm
Bd of Dir: James McKitrick
VP: Sean M Cubie
VP: Andrea Geisser
VP: William Mills
VP: Willie Taafe
S&M/VP: Richard Kusmer

D-U-N-S 96-841-5781
IRON BOW HOLDINGS INC
4800 Westfields Blvd # 300, Chantilly, VA 20151-4247
Tel (703) 279-3000 *Founded/Ownrshp* 2011
Sales 270.2MM^E *EMP* 310

SIC 7379 7373 Computer related consulting services; Value-added resellers, computer systems; Computer related consulting services; Value-added resellers, computer systems
Pr: Rene B Lavigne
**CFO:* Charles Curran
**Sr VP:* Lance J Lerman
**Sr VP:* Marc Mercilliott
**Sr VP:* Stuart Strang
Board of Directors: Rene Lavigne

D-U-N-S 82-771-4507 IMP
IRON BOW TECHNOLOGIES LLC
(*Suby of* IRON BOW HOLDINGS INC) ★
4800 Westfields Blvd # 300, Chantilly, VA 20151-4247
Tel (703) 279-3000 *Founded/Ownrshp* 1983
Sales 270.2MM^E *EMP* 310
Accts Grant Thornton Mclean Va
SIC 3571 Electronic computers; Electronic computers
Pr: Rene Lavigne
**CFO:* Charles L Curran
Bd of Dir: John Nyland
Ofcr: John Boynton
**Sr VP:* Lance Lerman
Sr VP: Marc Mercilliott
**Sr VP:* Stu Strang
VP: Darryl Korynta
**VP:* Mark Monticelli
Genl Mgr: Andy Sabonis
Genl Mgr: Bill Saltenberger

D-U-N-S 10-007-7544
IRON COUNTY BOARD OF EDUCATION
2077 W Royal Hunte Dr, Cedar City, UT 84720-1883
Tel (435) 586-2804 *Founded/Ownrshp* 1851
Sales 24.4MM^E *EMP* 590
SIC 8211 Public combined elementary & secondary school; School board
Pr: Michelle Jorgenson
IT Man: Corey Stokes

D-U-N-S 02-621-7698
IRON DATA SOLUTIONS INC
MICROPACT
(*Suby of* IRON DATA SOLUTIONS LLC) ★
12901 Worldgate Dr # 800, Herndon, VA 20170-6012
Tel (314) 744-7300 *Founded/Ownrshp* 2010
Sales 796.4M^E *EMP* 400^E
SIC 7371 Custom computer programming services
CEO: Tom Sechler
**Pr:* Kristoffer Collo
CFO: Vicky Moore
**CFO:* Dan Smith
**Ofcr:* Growson Edwards
VP: Chick Barthlow
**VP:* Michael Cerniglia
VP: Brian Combs
VP: Jack Frost
VP: Thomas Lowrey
VP: Todd While

D-U-N-S 11-339-5847
IRON DATA SOLUTIONS LLC
3400 Players Club Pkwy, Memphis, TN 38125-8915
Tel (844) 476-6382 *Founded/Ownrshp* 2005
Sales 85.2MM^E *EMP* 400
SIC 7371 Computer software development & applications; Computer software development & applications
CEO: Thomas Sechler
**CFO:* Dan Smith
Bd of Dir: Michael Lustbader
Bd of Dir: Perry Steiner
VP: Tom Gottlieb
VP: Stephanie Kuhnel

D-U-N-S 02-396-6489 IMP
■ **IRON DYNAMICS INC**
(*Suby of* STEEL DYNAMICS INC) ★
4500 County Road 59, Butler, IN 46721-9747
Tel (260) 868-8402 *Founded/Ownrshp* 1995
Sales 28.0MM^E *EMP* 60
SIC 3312 Primary finished or semifinished shapes; Bar, rod & wire products
Pr: Keith E Busse
Pr: Mark Millett
Ex VP: Gary Heasley
**VP:* Tracy L Shellabarger
Dir IT: Gary Morris
Dir IT: Mark Wilbourn
Sftwr Eng: Mike Eckstein
Manager: Dave Tokos

D-U-N-S 83-985-2725
▲ **IRON EAGLE GROUP INC**
(A DEVELOPMENT STAGE COMPANY)
160 W 66th St Apt 41g, New York, NY 10023-6565
Tel (888) 481-4445 *Founded/Ownrshp* 1995
Sales 20.5MM^E *EMP* 153
Tkr Sym IEAG *Exch* OTO
SIC 1389 Construction, repair & dismantling services
Ch Bd: Joseph E Antonini
Ex VP: Jed M Sabio

D-U-N-S 02-432-5535
IRON ENERGY LLC
KONA ENERGY
(*Suby of* VANTAGE COMMODITIES FINANCIAL SERVICES LLC) ★
901 S Mopac Expwy Barton, Austin, TX 78746
Tel (512) 329-1938 *Founded/Ownrshp* 2015
Sales 80.0MM *EMP* 15^E
SIC 4911 Electric services
Pr: John Edgar

IRON HILL BREWERY & RESTAURANT
See CHESAPEAKE & DELAWARE BREWING CO LLC

D-U-N-S 07-039-7970
IRON HORSE FLOORING LLC
PDL DESIGNS
2545 Golden Bear Dr, Carrollton, TX 75006-2317
Tel (972) 733-3006 *Founded/Ownrshp* 2012
Sales 30.0MM *EMP* 26
SIC 5713 1771 Floor covering stores; Flooring contractor
**Prin:* Rick Butler
**Prin:* Frank Puskarich

D-U-N-S 86-927-1221
■ **IRON HORSE INSURANCE CO**
(*Suby of* TEXACO INC) ★
6001 Bollinger Canyon Rd, San Ramon, CA 94583-2324
Tel (925) 842-1000 *Founded/Ownrshp* 2005
Sales 14.4MM^E *EMP* 900
SIC 1311 Crude petroleum production
CEO: David J O'Riley
**Pr:* James D Lyness
**VP:* M J Barry

D-U-N-S 07-868-9886
IRON HORSE MANAGING SERVICES LLC
421 Eichwurzel Ln, Houston, TX 77009-1880
Tel (713) 426-0513 *Founded/Ownrshp* 2012
Sales 28.0MM *EMP* 60
SIC 7011 Tourist camps, cabins, cottages & courts
CEO: Juan Gutierrez

D-U-N-S 62-709-9070
IRON HORSE SAFETY SPECIALTIES LP
11410 Pagemill Rd, Dallas, TX 75243-5506
Tel (214) 341-9947 *Founded/Ownrshp* 1989
Sales 29.7MM^E *EMP* 60
SIC 5084 2339 2329 5099 Safety equipment; Women's & misses' outerwear; Vests (suede, leatherette, etc.), sport: men's & boys'; Safety equipment & supplies
Pr: Helen Harvey
Pr: David Harvey

IRON MAN TRIATHOLON CHAMP
See WORLD TRIATHLON CORP

D-U-N-S 01-468-5947
IRON MECHANICAL INC
721 N B St Ste 100, Sacramento, CA 95811-0332
Tel (916) 341-3530 *Founded/Ownrshp* 2009
Sales 23.1MM^E *EMP* 97
SIC 1711 Plumbing, heating, air-conditioning contractors
Pr: Terrance Risse
Off Mgr: Judy Gomes
Snr PM: John Emerson
Snr Mgr: Jed Risse

D-U-N-S 62-253-5417 IMP/EXP
▲ **IRON MOUNTAIN INC**
1 Federal St Fl 7, Boston, MA 02110-2003
Tel (617) 535-4766 *Founded/Ownrshp* 1951
Sales 3.1MMM *EMP* 20,000
Accts Deloitte & Touche Llp Boston
Tkr Sym IRM *Exch* NYS
SIC 4226 8741 7375 6798 Document & office records storage; Management services; Information retrieval services; Document & office records storage; Management services; Information retrieval services; Real estate investment trusts
Pr: William L Meaney
**Ch Bd:* Alfred J Verrecchia
COO: Kevin Westerhouse
CFO: Roderick Day
CFO: William Marohn
Ex VP: Ernest W Cloutier
Ex VP: John J Connors
Ex VP: John Tomovcsik
Ex VP: Anastasios Tsolakis
Sr VP: Barry Payne
VP: Bill O'Neill
Dir Bus: John Langol
Dir Bus: Angelique Nasser
Dir Bus: Chad Pulaski
Dir Bus: Eric Rosenberg
Dir Bus: Diana Zanzonico
Board of Directors: Jennifer Allerton, Ted R Antenucci, Pamela M Arway, Clarke H Bailey, Kent P Dauten, Paul F Deninger, Michael W Lamach, Walter C Rakowich

D-U-N-S 62-141-7633
■ **IRON MOUNTAIN INFORMATION MANAGEMENT LLC**
(*Suby of* IRON MOUNTAIN INC) ★
1 Federal St Fl 33, Boston, MA 02110-2005
Tel (617) 357-4455 *Founded/Ownrshp* 1996
Sales 2.6MMM^E *EMP* 17,280
SIC 4226 Document & office records storage; Document & office records storage
Pr: C Richard Reese
**Pr:* William Meaney
**CFO:* Brian McKeon
**Sec:* Garry B Watzke
Opers Mgr: Craig Homenko

D-U-N-S 15-029-1482 IMP
■ **IRON MOUNTAIN RECORDS MANAGEMENT OF OHIO INC**
(*Suby of* IRON MOUNTAIN INC) ★
745 Atlantic Ave Fl 10, Boston, MA 02111-2735
Tel (617) 357-4455 *Founded/Ownrshp* 1997
Sales 28.4MM^E *EMP* 195
SIC 4226 Document & office records storage; Document & office records storage
CEO: William Meaney

D-U-N-S 04-173-3924
■ **IRON MOUNTAIN/NATIONAL UNDERGROUND STORAGE INC**
(*Suby of* IRON MOUNTAIN INC) ★
1137 Branchton Rd, Boyers, PA 16016-0001
Tel (724) 794-7339 *Founded/Ownrshp* 1998
Sales 35.5MM^E *EMP* 140
SIC 4226 Document & office records storage; Document & office records storage
VP: Charles Doughty
Genl Mgr: Tom Somers
DP Exec: Mark Guth
Board of Directors: Arthur O Black, Robert B Filson, Joseph S Leone, Lawrence O Miller, Lawrence E Yont, Lawrence T Zehfuss

D-U-N-S 05-979-7472
■ **IRON MOUNTAIN/PACIFIC RECORDS MANAGEMENT INC**
(*Suby of* IRON MOUNTAIN INFORMATION MANAGEMENT LLC) ★
1 Federal St Fl 33, Boston, MA 02110-2005
Tel (617) 357-4455 *Founded/Ownrshp* 1998
Sales 139.4MM^E *EMP* 9,000
SIC 7382 Protective devices, security; Protective devices, security
Ch Bd: Clark Bailey
**Treas:* Jeff Lawrence

D-U-N-S 05-535-6737
IRON PONY MOTORSPORTS GROUP INC
5436 Westerville Rd, Westerville, OH 43081-8939
Tel (614) 901-7669 *Founded/Ownrshp* 1999
Sales 32.5MM^E *EMP* 65^E
SIC 5571 Motorcycle parts & accessories
Pr: Christopher Jones
**VP:* Tammy Jones
Genl Mgr: Cory Atwood
Genl Mgr: Alan Scahtz
Dir IT: Jon Wieronski
Mktg Dir: Frank Lark

IRON SHOP, THE
See M COHEN AND SONS INC

D-U-N-S 96-962-2497 IMP
IRON SYSTEMS INC
980 Mission Ct, Fremont, CA 94539-8202
Tel (408) 943-8000 *Founded/Ownrshp* 2002
Sales 35.0MM *EMP* 75
SIC 3577 Computer peripheral equipment; Computer peripheral equipment
Pr: Baljit Bath
**Pr:* Billy Bath
**Pr:* Kevin Singh
**CFO:* Garvy Singh
**VP:* Harvey Bath
**VP:* Joe Merrill
**VP:* Bobby Sidhu

IRON WOMAN CONSTRUCTION
See INTEGRATING TECHNOLOGY & STANDARDS INC

D-U-N-S 96-386-2003
IRON WORK 40 361 & 417 HLTH FND
451 Park Ave S, New York, NY 10016-7390
Tel (212) 684-1586 *Founded/Ownrshp* 2011
Sales 101.0MM *EMP* 3^E
SIC 1791 Iron work, structural; Iron work, structural
Prin: Kevin Orourke

D-U-N-S 07-373-3230
IRON WORKERS DISTRICT COUNCIL OF PHILADELPHIA & VICINITY HEALTH BENEFITS & PENSION PLAN
2 International Plz # 125, Philadelphia, PA 19113-1505
Tel (215) 537-0900 *Founded/Ownrshp* 1950
Sales NA *EMP* 12
Accts Fischer Dorwart Pc Audubon N
SIC 6371 Pension funds; Union welfare, benefit & health funds; Pension funds; Union welfare, benefit & health funds

D-U-N-S 05-849-4451
IRON WORKERS DISTRICT COUNCIL OF SOUTHERN OHIO & VICINITY BENEFIT PENSION & ANNUITY TRUST
1470 Worldwide Pl, Vandalia, OH 45377-1156
Tel (937) 454-1744 *Founded/Ownrshp* 1952
Sales NA *EMP* 11
Accts Clark Schaefer Hackett Co Day
SIC 6411 Insurance agents; Insurance agents

D-U-N-S 07-942-7284
IRON WORKERS LOCALS 40 361 & 417 ANNUITY FUND
451 Park Ave S, New York, NY 10016-7390
Tel (212) 684-1586 *Founded/Ownrshp* 2014
Sales 80.4MM *EMP* 2^E
SIC 6722 Money market mutual funds

D-U-N-S 96-727-3868
IRON WORKERS LOCALS 40 AND 361 TOPPING OUT FUND
451 Park Ave S Fl 9, New York, NY 10016-7379
Tel (212) 684-1586 *Founded/Ownrshp* 2011
Sales 36.4MM *EMP* 3
Accts Grassi & Co Cpa S Pc New York
SIC 8631 Labor unions & similar labor organizations; Labor unions & similar labor organizations

D-U-N-S 80-228-1787
IRON WORKERS WELFARE PLAN OF WESTERN PENNSYLVANIA
2201 Liberty Ave, Pittsburgh, PA 15222-4512
Tel (412) 227-6740 *Founded/Ownrshp* 2008
Sales 22.5MM *EMP* 1
Accts Diclaudio & Kramer Llc Bridg
SIC 6732 Trusts: educational, religious, etc.; Trusts: educational, religious, etc.
Prin: Boe Gillespie III

D-U-N-S 13-098-2999
IRON WORLD MANUFACTURING LLC
9390 Davis Ave, Laurel, MD 20723-1958
Tel (301) 776-7448 *Founded/Ownrshp* 2003
Sales 31.3MM^E *EMP* 100^E
SIC 3312 Fence posts, iron & steel
Owner: Richard Stellabuto
Treas: John F Foley
Sls Dir: Kevin Pavuk

D-U-N-S 16-098-7975 IMP
▲ **IRONCLAD PERFORMANCE WEAR CORP**
1920 Hutton Ct Ste 300, Farmers Branch, TX 75234-9004
Tel (972) 996-5664 *Founded/Ownrshp* 1998
Sales 24.2MM *EMP* 29^E
Accts Efp Rotenberg Llp Rochester
Tkr Sym ICPW *Exch* OTO
SIC 2326 2381 Men's & boys' work clothing; Work apparel, except uniforms; Fabric dress & work gloves; Gloves, work: woven or knit, made from purchased materials; Men's & boys' work clothing; Work apparel, except uniforms; Fabric dress & work gloves; Gloves, work: woven or knit, made from purchased materials
CEO: Jeffrey Cordes
**Ch Bd:* Vane Clayton
CFO: William Aisenberg
Sr VP: Tom Felton
VP: Mark R Mackay
VP: Jim McLaughlin
IT Man: Alim Shamji
Board of Directors: Michael A Digregorio, Charles H Giffen, David Jacobs, Patrick O'brien

D-U-N-S 61-523-4796
IRONDALE INDUSTRIAL CONTRACTOR INC
2185 Alton Rd, Birmingham, AL 35210-3772
Tel (205) 956-4509 *Founded/Ownrshp* 1990
Sales 24.6MM *EMP* 120
Accts Frost Cummings Tidwell Group
SIC 1541 1796 Industrial buildings, new construction; Machinery installation; Industrial buildings, new construction; Machinery installation
Pr: John Kosie
CFO: Debra Johnson

D-U-N-S 07-886-9753 IMP
IRONGATE ENERGY SERVICES LLC
ALLIS CHALMERS
19500 State Highway 249 # 600, Houston, TX 77070-3065
Tel (832) 678-8585 *Founded/Ownrshp* 2013
Sales 207.5MM^E *EMP* 276^E
SIC 1389 Servicing oil & gas wells; Servicing oil & gas wells
CEO: Terry Keane
**VP:* Dwight Gross
**VP:* Monty Johnston

D-U-N-S 16-105-7133
IRONHIDE EQUIPMENT INC
3903 Gateway Dr, Grand Forks, ND 58203-0831
Tel (701) 772-5006 *Founded/Ownrshp* 2003
Sales 35.0MM *EMP* 40
SIC 5999 0782 Farm machinery; Farm machinery; Lawn & garden services
Pr: Jason Vasichek
**Prin:* Travis Johnson
Brnch Mgr: Travis Dearinger

IRONMAN PARTS & SERVICE
See AFS INC

D-U-N-S 04-992-9839
IRONMARK INC
9040 Junction Dr Ste 2, Annapolis Junction, MD 20701-1129
Tel (888) 775-3737 *Founded/Ownrshp* 1996
Sales 33.1MM^E *EMP* 105^E
SIC 2752 Commercial printing, lithographic
CEO: Jeff Ostenso
**Pr:* Scott Hargest
VP: Richard Day
**VP:* Chris Marzullo
**VP:* Matt Marzullo
VP: Tom Sears
VP: Jack Thorpe
Creative D: Steve Norwood
VP Opers: Bryan Gunning
VP Opers: Gary Zorn
Sales Exec: Mark Acton

IRONPLANET.
See IRONPLANET INC

D-U-N-S 12-471-5546 IMP/EXP
IRONPLANET INC
IRONPLANET.
3825 Hopyard Rd Ste 250, Pleasanton, CA 94588-2787
Tel (925) 225-8600 *Founded/Ownrshp* 1999
Sales 182.4MM^E *EMP* 316
SIC 7389 Auction, appraisal & exchange services; Auction, appraisal & exchange services
CEO: Gregory J Owens
Pr: James J Jeter
CFO: Debbie Schleicher
Chf Mktg O: Susan Stillings
Sr VP: Randall E Berry
Sr VP: Douglas P Feick
Sr VP: Mike Groves
Sr VP: Michael J O'Donnell
VP: Jeffrey L Barca-Hall
VP: Paul C Blalock
VP: Matthew J Bousky
VP: Jeff Holmes
VP: Randy Johnston
VP: Tim Perkins
VP: H Andrew Pyron

D-U-N-S 00-446-5415
IRONROCK CAPITAL INC
METROPOLITAN CERAMICS DIV
1201 Millerton St Se, Canton, OH 44707-2209
Tel (330) 484-4887 *Founded/Ownrshp* 1866
Sales 20.3MM^E *EMP* 100
SIC 3253 Ceramic wall & floor tile
Pr: Guy F Renkert
Exec: Loraine Godfrey
**Prin:* J G Barbour Et Al
**Prin:* C W Keplinger
**Prin:* H S Renkert
Natl Sales: Randy Wilson
Mktg Dir: Dianne Young
Manager: Lon Turner

D-U-N-S 06-817-0745
■ **IRONSHORE INDEMNITY INC**
(*Suby of* IRONSHORE INC.)
2 Pine Tree Dr, Saint Paul, MN 55112-3754
Tel (651) 631-7000 *Founded/Ownrshp* 1919
Sales NA *EMP* 637
Accts Ernst & Young Llp Chicago Il
SIC 6411 Insurance agents, brokers & service; Insurance agents, brokers & service
Pr: John Blockburn

Treas: Stephen L Rohde
**VP:* Joe Pingatone

D-U-N-S 83-158-0977
■ **IRONSHORE SERVICES INC**
IRONSHORE SPECIALTY INSURANCE
(*Suby of* IRONSHORE INSURANCE LTD)
1 State St Fl 8, New York, NY 10004-1506
Tel (646) 826-6600 *Founded/Ownrshp* 2007
Sales NA *EMP* 319ᴱ
SIC 6411 Property & casualty insurance agent; Property & casualty insurance agent
CEO: Kevin H Kelley
**Ch Bd:* Domenic Serratore
**Pr:* Shaun E Kelly
**CEO:* Kevin Kelley
**COO:* Mitchell E Blaser
COO: Krishnan Ethirajan
Ex VP: Thomas Leahy
Ex VP: Pierre Samson
Sr VP: Andrew Archambault
Sr VP: Alice Johansson
Sr VP: Daniel Owen
Sr VP: Matthew Wasta
VP: Erin Bouren
VP: Alicia Bromfield
VP: Charles Cygal
VP: Tim Delaney
VP: Lisa Freeman
VP: Dawn Krigstin
VP: Jeff Lynn
VP: Elise Millner
VP: Valerie Onderka

IRONSHORE SPECIALTY INSURANCE
See IRONSHORE SERVICES INC

D-U-N-S 03-946-7360
IRONSHORE SPECIALTY INSURANCE CO
(*Suby of* TIG INSURANCE CO) ★
2850 Lake Vista Dr # 150, Lewisville, TX 75067-4228
Tel (646) 826-6600 *Founded/Ownrshp* 1952
Sales NA *EMP* 700
SIC 6331 Automobile insurance; Automobile insurance
CEO: Michael Mitrovic
Pr: Richard Scott Donovan
Treas: Nicolas Arizaga
Treas: Michael Sluka
VP: Cynthia Crandall
VP: Robert Knowles
VP: Ray Roy
CIO: Hank Edmiston

D-U-N-S 00-290-3065
IRONSIDE GROUP INC (MA)
10 Maguire Rd Ste 400, Lexington, MA 02421-3135
Tel (781) 860-8840 *Founded/Ownrshp* 1999
Sales 25.3MMᴱ *EMP* 100
SIC 7379 5734 Computer related consulting services; Computer & software stores; Computer related consulting services; Computer & software stores
CEO: Timothy D Kreytak
**Pr:* Daniel J Hess IV
VP: Gregory Bonnette
VP: Steve Kaplan
VP Sls: Nathan Romanek
Mktg Dir: Michelle Arnold
Sls Mgr: Lynn Archambault

D-U-N-S 03-753-1829
IRONTON AND LAWRENCE COUNTY AREA COMMUNITY ACTION ORGANIZATION
305 N 5th St, Ironton, OH 45638-1578
Tel (740) 532-3534 *Founded/Ownrshp* 1965
Sales 26.0MM *EMP* 300
Accts Clark Schaefer Hackett & Co
SIC 4111 8099 8351 8331 8011 8093 Local & suburban transit; Nutrition services; Preschool center; Job training & vocational rehabilitation services; Primary care medical clinic; Mental health clinic, outpatient; Local & suburban transit; Nutrition services; Preschool center; Job training & vocational rehabilitation services; Primary care medical clinic; Mental health clinic, outpatient
Ex Dir: Donald R Gaussett
**CFO:* Kelly Adkins
Ex Dir: D Gossett
Ex Dir: Donald Ray
Off Mgr: Barb Riley
Dir IT: Matthew Delong

D-U-N-S 05-673-6937
IRONTON PUBLICATIONS INC
IRONTON TRIBUNE THE
(*Suby of* BOONE NEWSPAPERS INC) ★
2903 S 5th St, Ironton, OH 45638-2866
Tel (740) 532-1441 *Founded/Ownrshp* 1979
Sales 23.1MMᴱ *EMP* 508
SIC 2711 Newspapers, publishing & printing; Newspapers, publishing & printing
Board of Directors: John Mathew

IRONTON TRIBUNE THE
See IRONTON PUBLICATIONS INC

D-U-N-S 87-429-5269 IMP
IRONWOOD CANCER & RESEARCH CENTERS PC
6111 E Arbor Ave, Mesa, AZ 85206-6059
Tel (480) 981-1326 *Founded/Ownrshp* 2002
Sales 24.9MMᴱ *EMP* 207ᴱ
SIC 8011 8031 Offices & clinics of medical doctors; Offices & clinics of osteopathic physicians
Pr: Parvinderj S Khanuja MD
Off Mgr: Enid Monaco
Off Mgr: Guldeep Sandhu
Off Admin: Erica Betancourt
Doctor: Roopesh Kantala
Doctor: Michael Musci
Doctor: Joseph Nabong

IRONWOOD CAPITAL
See IRONWOOD CORP

D-U-N-S 05-089-3275
IRONWOOD CORP
IRONWOOD CAPITAL
45 Nod Rd, Avon, CT 06001-3819
Tel (860) 409-2100 *Founded/Ownrshp* 1991
Sales 34.3MMᴱ *EMP* 195
SIC 6211 Investment bankers; Investment bankers
Pr: Marc A Reich
Mng Pt: Pat Johnston
CFO: Zach Luce
Bd of Dir: Alex Leventhal
Mng Dir: James Barra
Mng Dir: John Strahley
Mng Dir: Dickson Suit
Mng Dir: Joshua Tolkoff

D-U-N-S 01-422-3406
IRONWOOD OIL & GAS LLC
16945 Northchase Dr # 1500, Houston, TX 77060-2153
Tel (281) 873-9378 *Founded/Ownrshp* 2009
Sales 25.4MM *EMP* 10ᴱ
SIC 1382 Oil & gas exploration services; Oil & gas exploration services
Pr: C O Bolt
**COO:* R Paul Loveless
**COO:* Jeffrey C Pettit
**Treas:* Kerri D Battaglia
**VP:* Paul C Braun

D-U-N-S 05-445-1401
▲ **IRONWOOD PHARMACEUTICALS INC**
301 Binney St, Cambridge, MA 02142-1030
Tel (617) 621-7722 *Founded/Ownrshp* 1998
Sales 76.4MM *EMP* 464ᴱ
Tkr Sym IRWD *Exch* NGS
SIC 2834 8731 Pharmaceutical preparations; Commercial physical research; Pharmaceutical preparations; Commercial physical research
CEO: Peter M Hecht
**Ch Bd:* Bryan E Roberts
Chf Cred: Thomas A McCourt
Sr VP: Brian M Cali
Sr VP: Mark G Currie
Sr VP: Thomas Graney
Sr VP: Michael Hall
VP: Andrew Chamlin
VP: Gina Consylman
VP: Jason Rickard
Assoc Dir: Gigi Shafai
Board of Directors: George H Conrades, Marsha H Fanucci, Terrance G McGuire, Julie J McHugh, Lawrence S Olanoff, Edward P Owens, Christopher T Walsh, Douglas Williams

D-U-N-S 09-682-8843 IMP
IRONWOOD PLASTICS INC (MI)
1235 Wall St, Ironwood, MI 49938-1764
Tel (906) 932-5025 *Founded/Ownrshp* 1980
Sales 39.5MMᴱ *EMP* 210
Accts Hawkins Ash Baptie & Company
SIC 3089 Injection molded finished plastic products; Injection molded finished plastic products
Pr: Gordon K Stephens
**Pr:* Mark K Stephens
CFO: Thomas Talasca
**VP:* Robert L Stephens
Genl Mgr: John Lorenson
Ql Cn Mgr: Don Jokela
Ql Cn Mgr: Kevin Nasi
Ql Cn Mgr: Jeff Richards
Snr Mgr: Dena Lundin

D-U-N-S 14-889-5308
IRONWOOD PROPERTY GROUP LP
70 Portland Rd, Conshohocken, PA 19428-2717
Tel (610) 941-1164 *Founded/Ownrshp* 2003
Sales 50.0MM *EMP* 3
SIC 6531 Real estate agents & managers; Real estate agents & managers
Pt: Jeremy Fogel
Pt: Ned Kaplin
Pt: Eric Knopping

D-U-N-S 04-073-6761
IRONWORKERS DISTRICT COUNCIL OF NORTHERN NJ
PENSION FUND
12 Edison Pl, Springfield, NJ 07081-1310
Tel (973) 376-7230 *Founded/Ownrshp* 1953
Sales NA *EMP* 20
SIC 6371 Pension funds; Pension funds
Ex Dir: Peter A Sclasani
**Ch:* William Haggerty
**Trst:* Francis Arny
**Trst:* Arthur A Brennan
**Trst:* Walter C Hurley
**Trst:* John Templeton

D-U-N-S 96-639-9193
IRONWORKERS ST LOUIS DISTRICT COUNCIL WELFARE PLAN
13500 Riverport Dr, Maryland Heights, MO 63043-4824
Tel (314) 739-1100 *Founded/Ownrshp* 2011
Sales 32.6MM *EMP* 3ᴱ
Accts Purk & Associates Pc Saint Lo
SIC 8631 Labor unions & similar labor organizations; Labor unions & similar labor organizations
Prin: Daniel Barrett

D-U-N-S 01-063-8349
■ **IRONWORKS CONSULTING LLC**
(*Suby of* ICF CONSULTING GROUP INC) ★
10900 Nuckols Rd Ste 400, Glen Allen, VA 23060-9246
Tel (804) 270-2046 *Founded/Ownrshp* 2012
Sales 56.4MM *EMP* 245
SIC 7379 ;
Pr: John Wasson
**CFO:* James C Morgan
**Treas:* Terrance Mc Govern
**Ex VP:* Ellen Glover
**Sr VP:* Scott Walker

D-U-N-S 04-577-6556
IROQUOIS CENTRAL SCHOOL DISTRICT
2111 Girdle Rd, Elma, NY 14059-9278
Tel (716) 652-3000 *Founded/Ownrshp* 1954
Sales 31.8MMᴱ *EMP* 573
SIC 8211 Public elementary & secondary schools; Public elementary & secondary schools
**Treas:* Barbara Kishel
Schl Brd P: David Lowrey
HC Dir: Robert Erickson

D-U-N-S 05-093-6368
■ **IROQUOIS FEDERAL SAVINGS & LOAN ASSOCIATION**
(*Suby of* IF BANCORP INC) ★
201 E Cherry St, Watseka, IL 60970-1661
Tel (815) 432-2476 *Founded/Ownrshp* 1883
Sales NA *EMP* 40
SIC 6035 6021 Federal savings & loan associations; National commercial banks; Federal savings & loan associations; National commercial banks
Pr: Alan Martin
VP: Terry Acree
VP: Wendy Glass
VP: Walter Hasselbring
VP: Beth Warren
Site Mgr: Dan Goodrum
Snr Mgr: John Anderson

D-U-N-S 60-395-5949 IMP
IROQUOIS GAS TRANSMISSION SYSTEM LP
1 Corporate Dr Ste 600, Shelton, CT 06484-6260
Tel (203) 925-7200 *Founded/Ownrshp* 1989
Sales 199.9MM *EMP* 105
SIC 4922

D-U-N-S 06-648-5911
IROQUOIS LLC
145 N Merchant St, Decatur, IL 62523-1216
Tel (217) 423-9286 *Founded/Ownrshp* 2012
Sales 23.8MM *EMP* 3
SIC 8731 Agricultural research
Pr: Howard Buffet

D-U-N-S 09-257-8129
IROQUOIS MEMORIAL HOSPITAL
IMH SHELDON CLINIC
160 E Grove St, Sheldon, IL 60966-8244
Tel (815) 429-3762 *Founded/Ownrshp* 2001
Sales 38.6MM *EMP* 6
Accts Bkd Llp St Louis Mo
SIC 8011 5912 Offices & clinics of medical doctors; Drug stores; Offices & clinics of medical doctors; Drug stores
Pr: Keith Jenkins DMD

D-U-N-S 06-741-9812
IROQUOIS MEMORIAL HOSPITAL & RESIDENT HOME
200 E Fairman Ave, Watseka, IL 60970-1644
Tel (815) 432-5841 *Founded/Ownrshp* 1914
Sales 37.1MM *EMP* 385
Accts Bkd
SIC 8062 Hospital, affiliated with AMA residency; Hospital, affiliated with AMA residency
CEO: Chuck Bohlmann
Chf Path: Thomas Betlej
Chf Rad: John Tricou
Dir Recs: Joan Yaden
V Ch: Dennis Wittenborn
**COO:* Chris Curry
COO: Susan Freed
CFO: Lori Yelenick
Treas: John Braden
Bd of Dir: Crystal Rabe
Ex VP: G Smith
VP: Linda Berg
VP: Ruth Madawick
VP: Danny Rollins
Exec: Shelly Schoolman
Dir Lab: Jackie Scurlock
Dir Rad: Harry Lah
Dir Rad: Leslie Lindberg
Dir Rx: Bill Nausbaum
Dir Rx: William Nussbum

IRP
See IOWA ROTOCAST PLASTICS INC

IRP
See INTERNATIONAL RUBBER PRODUCTS INC

D-U-N-S 00-289-8443
IRP GROUP INC
726 Trumbull Dr, Pittsburgh, PA 15205-4363
Tel (412) 276-6400 *Founded/Ownrshp* 1954
Sales 43.7MMᴱ *EMP* 70
SIC 5085 3053 Rubber goods, mechanical; Gaskets, packing & sealing devices
Ch Bd: Frank Kelly Jr
**Pr:* Michael Kerestes
Treas: Muriel Laughrey
**Treas:* David W Schnupp
Dir IT: Chuck Ruffing

IRR
See INTEGRA REALTY RESOURCES INC

D-U-N-S 01-373-3613 IMP
IRR SUPPLY CENTERS INC (NY)
NORTHRUP SUPPLY
908 Niagara Falls Blvd # 125, North Tonawanda, NY 14120-2085
Tel (716) 692-1600 *Founded/Ownrshp* 1965
Sales 191.8MMᴱ *EMP* 360
SIC 5074 Plumbing & hydronic heating supplies; Plumbing & hydronic heating supplies
Ch Bd: William R Irr
**Pr:* Michael P Duffy
**Pr:* Michael Stetter
Brnch Mgr: Jim Adamski
Brnch Mgr: Tim Roland
Web Prj Mg: Kevin Saky
Sales Asso: Rich Jordan
Sales Asso: Dave Norris
Sales Asso: Sean Reiss
Sales Asso: Mathew Sanscrainte
Sales Asso: Cliff Silvernail

D-U-N-S 86-107-0878
■ **IRRESISTIBLE INK INC**
(*Suby of* HALLMARK CARDS INC) ★
4444 Haines Rd, Duluth, MN 55811-1524
Tel (218) 336-4200 *Founded/Ownrshp* 1998
Sales 5.9MMᴱ *EMP* 300
SIC 7331 Direct mail advertising services; Direct mail advertising services
COO: David Knoll

D-U-N-S 06-402-7428
■ **IRRIGATION SPECIALISTS INC**
(*Suby of* LINDSAY CORP) ★
2410 N 4th Ave, Pasco, WA 99301-3740
Tel (509) 547-1761 *Founded/Ownrshp* 2002
Sales 22.7MMᴱ *EMP* 50
SIC 5083 5999 Irrigation equipment; Farm equipment & supplies
Pr: Barry Ruffalo
**VP:* Dennis Jordan
**Off Mgr:* Leslie Kroner
CTO: Kim Nelson

D-U-N-S 05-308-2855
IRSIK & DOLL FEED SERVICES INC (KS)
104 W Ave A, Cimarron, KS 67835
Tel (620) 855-3747 *Founded/Ownrshp* 1969
Sales 52.6MMᴱ *EMP* 200
SIC 5153 4221 0211 Grains; Grain elevator, storage only; Beef cattle feedlots; Grains; Grain elevator, storage only; Beef cattle feedlots
Pr: John Petz
**Treas:* Ernie Massoth

IRULU
See USA111 INC

IRUSA
See ISLAMIC RELIEF USA

D-U-N-S 14-912-6752
IRVIN AUTOMOTIVE PRODUCTS INC
(*Suby of* TAKATA) ★
2600 Centerpoint Pkwy, Pontiac, MI 48341-3172
Tel (248) 377-1500 *Founded/Ownrshp* 1995
Sales 270.9MMᴱ *EMP* 1,600
SIC 3429 2396 Manufactured hardware (general); Automotive trimmings, fabric; Manufactured hardware (general); Automotive trimmings, fabric
Pr: Joe Finn

D-U-N-S 02-042-2093 IMP
IRVIN KAHN & SON INC
FLOORS TO YOUR HOME
6555 Guion Rd, Indianapolis, IN 46268-4808
Tel (317) 328-8989 *Founded/Ownrshp* 1921
Sales 21.9MMᴱ *EMP* 20
SIC 5023 5713 Floor coverings; Floor covering stores
Pr: Marshall Kahn
**VP:* Daniel Kahn

D-U-N-S 06-489-7150 IMP
IRVINE ACCESS FLOORS INC
9425 Wa Blvd N Ste Y, Laurel, MD 20723-1378
Tel (301) 617-9333 *Founded/Ownrshp* 1961
Sales 48.5MM *EMP* 88
Accts Bormel Grice & Huyett Pa
SIC 1752 Floor laying & floor work; Floor laying & floor work
Pr: Larry Worthington
**VP:* Chris Irvine
**VP:* James Radtke
VP Sls: Scott Miller

D-U-N-S 82-554-1998
IRVINE APARTMENT COMMUNITIES LP
I A C
(*Suby of* IRVINE CO LLC) ★
110 Innovation Dr, Irvine, CA 92617-3040
Tel (949) 720-5600 *Founded/Ownrshp* 1993
Sales 42.4MMᴱ *EMP* 1,500
SIC 6513 6552 6798 Apartment building operators; Subdividers & developers; Real estate investment trusts; Apartment building operators; Subdividers & developers; Real estate investment trusts
Ex VP: Mike Ellis
VP: Mark Henningan
Mktg Dir: Lisa Cappel

IRVINE B M W
See IRVINE EUROCARS LLC

D-U-N-S 00-496-6313
IRVINE CO LLC
550 Newport Center Dr # 160, Newport Beach, CA 92660-7027
Tel (949) 720-2000 *Founded/Ownrshp* 1977
Sales 1.8MMMᴱ *EMP* 2,000
SIC 6552 6531 0174 0191 4841 Subdividers & developers; Land subdividers & developers, commercial; Land subdividers & developers, residential; Real estate managers; Rental agent, real estate; Citrus fruits; General farms, primarily crop; Cable television services; Subdividers & developers; Land subdividers & developers, commercial; Land subdividers & developers, residential; Real estate managers; Rental agent, real estate; Citrus fruits; General farms, primarily crop; Cable television services
Ch Bd: Donald L Bren
Pr: Doug Holte
CFO: Charles Fedalen Jr
CFO: Mark Lay
Ex VP: Steve Case
Ex VP: Ron Keith
Ex VP: Marc Ley
VP: Brad Engelland
VP: Daniel Hick
VP: Robin Leftwich
VP: Angie Sullivan
VP: Terry Welsh

IRVINE COMPANY OFFICE PROPERTY
See IRVINE EASTGATE OFFICE II LLC

D-U-N-S 36-125-3680
IRVINE EASTGATE OFFICE II LLC
IRVINE COMPANY OFFICE PROPERTY
550 Newport Center Dr, Newport Beach, CA 92660-7011
Tel (949) 720-2000 *Founded/Ownrshp* 2013
Sales 328.1MM^E *EMP* 3,000
SIC 6798 Real estate investment trusts; Real estate investment trusts
VP: Pam Van Nort

D-U-N-S 06-448-1567
IRVINE EUROCARS LLC
IRVINE B M W
9881 Research Dr, Irvine, CA 92618-4304
Tel (949) 380-1200 *Founded/Ownrshp* 1990
Sales 39.2MM^E *EMP* 80
SIC 5511 Automobiles, new & used; Automobiles, new & used
Genl Mgr: Steve Rudkin
Sls Mgr: Brandon Goodemont
Sls Mgr: Franz Hlasny
Sales Asso: Sergik Haftvani

D-U-N-S 02-252-8546
■ **IRVINE IMPORTS INC**
POWER TOYOTA SCION OF IRVINE
(*Suby of* AUTONATION INC) ★
9101 Research Dr, Irvine, CA 92618-4206
Tel (949) 585-6888 *Founded/Ownrshp* 1999
Sales 55.5MM^E *EMP* 182
SIC 5511 Automobiles, new & used; Automobiles, new & used
CEO: Michael Jackson
**COO:* Michael Maroone
Exec: Marc Bell
Opers Mgr: Kevin Olaff

D-U-N-S 13-057-2154
IRVINE LINCOLN INC
(*Suby of* PENDRAGON PLC)
42 Auto Center Dr, Irvine, CA 92618-2802
Tel (888) 260-5291 *Founded/Ownrshp* 2007
Sales 29.0MM^E *EMP* 177^E
SIC 5511 Automobiles, new & used
Pr: Chris Caotter

D-U-N-S 62-708-5608
IRVINE PHARMACEUTICAL SERVICES INC
10 Vanderbilt, Irvine, CA 92618-2010
Tel (949) 951-4425 *Founded/Ownrshp* 1988
Sales 43.8MM^E *EMP* 160^E
SIC 8734 Product testing laboratories; Product testing laboratories
Pr: Assad Kazeminy
Ex VP: Adam Fox
VP: Laura Jones
Dir Bus: Tiffany Murphy
QA Dir: Byron Ayala
Info Man: Mike Trimberger
Mktg Mgr: Katee Fry
Genl Couns: Amir Nikoupour

D-U-N-S 05-927-0884
IRVINE RANCH WATER DISTRICT INC
15600 Sand Canyon Ave, Irvine, CA 92618-3102
Tel (949) 453-5300 *Founded/Ownrshp* 1961
Sales 124.4MM *EMP* 315
SIC 4941 4952 Water supply; Sewerage systems; Water supply; Sewerage systems
Genl Mgr: Paul Jones
**Treas:* Robert Jacobson
Sr VP: Gina Jackson
VP: Lars Oldewage
Rgnl Mgr: Cheryl Kelly
Snr Ntwrk: Jeff Bertsch
Dir IT: Eric Katapati
IT Man: Cheryl Clary
IT Man: Eileen Lin
Sls&Mrk Ex: Beth Beeman
Pr Mgr: Shannon Reed
Board of Directors: Brian Brady, Mary Aileen Matheis, E Darryl Miller, John Withers

D-U-N-S 05-747-5246 IMP
IRVINE SCIENTIFIC SALES CO INC
(*Suby of* JX NIPPON OIL & ENERGY CORPORATION)
1830 E Warner Ave, Santa Ana, CA 92705-5505
Tel (949) 261-7800 *Founded/Ownrshp* 1987
Sales 31.4MM^E *EMP* 150^E
SIC 2836 5047 Blood derivatives; Culture media; Medical laboratory equipment; Blood derivatives; Culture media; Medical laboratory equipment
Pr: Yuichi Nagano
**COO:* Tim Mullane

D-U-N-S 08-493-3709
IRVINE TECHNOLOGY CORP (CA)
17900 Von Karman Ave # 100, Irvine, CA 92614-6249
Tel (714) 445-2624 *Founded/Ownrshp* 2000
Sales 49.1MM^E *EMP* 400
SIC 8742 Management consulting services; Management consulting services
Pr: John Thornby
**Treas:* Mike Rose
VP: Ray Jandga
**VP:* Kevin Orlando

D-U-N-S 80-335-0818
IRVINE UC MEDICAL CENTER
UC IRVINE HEALTH
(*Suby of* REGENTS OF UNIVERSITY OF CALIFORNIA) ★
101 The City Dr S, Orange, CA 92868-3201
Tel (714) 456-7890 *Founded/Ownrshp* 1993
Sales 77.9MM^E *EMP* 4,000
SIC 8322 Crisis intervention center
Owner: Phil Thomas
VP: Theresa Suppanade
Pathlgst: Sherif A Rezk
Surgeon: Jaime Landman
Obsttrcn: Morgan Swank
Ansthlgy: Steven M Suydam

D-U-N-S 06-615-1853
IRVINE UNIFIED SCHOOL DISTICT
IRVINE UNIFIED SCHOOL DISTRICT
5050 Barranca Pkwy, Irvine, CA 92604-4698
Tel (949) 936-5000 *Founded/Ownrshp* 1972
Sales 161.5MM^E *EMP* 2,212
Accts Vavrinek Trine Day & Co Ll
SIC 8211 Public elementary & secondary schools; Public elementary school; Public junior high school; Public senior high school; Public elementary & secondary schools; Public elementary school; Public junior high school; Public senior high school
**CEO:* Michael B Regele
MIS Dir: Brianne Ford
Psych: Susan Rashap

IRVINE UNIFIED SCHOOL DISTRICT
See IRVINE UNIFIED SCHOOL DISTICT

D-U-N-S 02-624-5076
IRVING BRAKEBUSH INC
TRINITY VALLEY FOODS, INC.
(*Suby of* BRAKEBUSH BROTHERS INC) ★
2230 E Union Bower Rd, Irving, TX 75061-8814
Tel (972) 554-0590 *Founded/Ownrshp* 2013
Sales 221.8MM^E *EMP* 375
SIC 5144 Poultry & poultry products; Poultry & poultry products
CEO: Carl Brakebush
VP: Dennis Jameson
Ql Cn Mgr: Reba Woytasczyk

D-U-N-S 07-754-8964
IRVING BURTON ASSOCIATES INC
3150 Fairview Park Dr # 301, Falls Church, VA 22042-4504
Tel (703) 575-8359 *Founded/Ownrshp* 1981
Sales 27.7MM^E *EMP* 225
SIC 8742

D-U-N-S 94-885-1175 IMP
IRVING CONSUMER PRODUCTS INC
IRVING TISSUE DIV
(*Suby of* IRVING CONSUMER PRODUCTS LIMITED)
1 Eddy St, Fort Edward, NY 12828-1711
Tel (518) 747-4151 *Founded/Ownrshp* 1996
Sales 87.6MM^E *EMP* 310
SIC 2621 Towels, tissues & napkins: paper & stock; Towels, tissues & napkins: paper & stock
Prin: J K Irving
**Ch Bd:* Jk Irving
**VP:* Arthur L Irving
VP: Bo B Lam
VP: Rachel Roy
VP: Bernice Wall

IRVING ENERGY DIST & MKTG
See HIGHLANDS FUEL DELIVERY LLC

D-U-N-S 96-701-9600
IRVING HARRIS FOUNDATION
191 N Wacker Dr Ste 1660, Chicago, IL 60606-1890
Tel (312) 621-0590 *Founded/Ownrshp* 2011
Sales 26.3MM *EMP* 9^E
SIC 8699 Charitable organization
Prin: Phyllis Glink
Ofcr: Dell Castillo

D-U-N-S 07-670-0988
IRVING INDEPENDENT SCHOOL DISTRICT INC
IRVING INDEPENDENT SCHOOL DST
2621 W Airport Fwy, Irving, TX 75062-6020
Tel (972) 600-5000 *Founded/Ownrshp* 1946
Sales 211.6MM^E *EMP* 3,934
Accts Weaver And Tidwell Llp Dalla
SIC 8211 Public elementary & secondary schools; Public elementary & secondary schools
**Pr:* Larry Stipes
**CFO:* Gary Micinski
Bd of Dir: Jerry Christian
Bd of Dir: Ronda Huffstetler
Bd of Dir: Steven Jones
Bd of Dir: Jones Valerie
Ofcr: Karen Sturch
**VP:* Randy Randal
Ex Dir: Jan Laden
DP Exec: Diana Jauregui
Dir IT: John Mynatt
Board of Directors: Barbara Cardwell, Rhonda Huffstetler, Mike Junstadt, Terry Waldrun

IRVING INDEPENDENT SCHOOL DST
See IRVING INDEPENDENT SCHOOL DISTRICT INC

D-U-N-S 01-863-8452
IRVING LEVINE AUTOMOTIVE DISTRIBUTORS INC (CT)
118 South St, Danbury, CT 06810-8072
Tel (203) 743-2751 *Founded/Ownrshp* 1955
Sales 40.3MM^E *EMP* 125
SIC 5013 5531

D-U-N-S 00-604-1917
IRVING MATERIALS INC
I M I
8032 N State Road 9, Greenfield, IN 46140-9097
Tel (317) 326-3101 *Founded/Ownrshp* 1967
Sales 785.6MM^E *EMP* 2,200
SIC 3273 3271 5032 2951 Ready-mixed concrete; Concrete block & brick; Sand, construction; Gravel; Stone, crushed or broken; Asphalt paving blocks (not from refineries); Ready-mixed concrete; Concrete block & brick; Sand, construction; Gravel; Stone, crushed or broken; Asphalt paving blocks (not from refineries)
Pr: Earl G Brinker
**Ch:* Pete Irving
VP: Brad Kosiba
Area Mgr: Terry Smith
Dir IT: Billy Carroll
IT Man: Brent Neufelder
Trfc Dir: Tess August
Trfc Dir: Gideon Brown
Trfc Dir: Jeremy Steele
Plnt Mgr: Wayne Carter
Plnt Mgr: Jerry Cyr
Board of Directors: Allen Rosenberg Sr, Tom Thomas

D-U-N-S 02-234-8226
IRVING MCDAVID HONDA LP
MCDAVID, DAVID HONDA
3700 W Airport Fwy, Irving, TX 75062-5903
Tel (972) 790-2000 *Founded/Ownrshp* 1998
Sales 100.0MM *EMP* 120
SIC 5511 Automobiles, new & used; Automobiles, new & used
Pr: B David McDavid Sr

IRVING MICHAELS & COMPANY
See MICHAELS ENTERPRISES INC

D-U-N-S 10-573-5906
IRVING OIL CORP
(*Suby of* HIGHLANDS FUEL DELIVERY LLC) ★
10 Sidney St, Bangor, ME 04401-6229
Tel (207) 582-7000 *Founded/Ownrshp* 1983
Sales 82.8MM^E *EMP* 120
SIC 5172 Fuel oil; Fuel oil
Pr: Arthur L Irving
**VP:* Vernon L Sprague
IT Man: Tim Durling

D-U-N-S 18-999-1701 IMP/EXP
IRVING OIL TERMINALS INC
190 Commerce Way, Portsmouth, NH 03801-3281
Tel (603) 559-8736 *Founded/Ownrshp* 1998
Sales 402.8MM^E *EMP* 99^E
SIC 5171 Petroleum terminals; Petroleum terminals
Pr: Paul Browning
**Pr:* Mike Ashar
**CFO:* Kevin Dumaresque
**Ofcr:* Darren Gillis
Genl Mgr: Kevin Boyle
VP Mktg: Arthur Irving
Mktg Mgr: Leann Wright
Manager: Mike Finnell

D-U-N-S 82-881-2672
IRVING PLACE CAPITAL LLC
745 5th Ave Fl 7, New York, NY 10151-0802
Tel (212) 551-4500 *Founded/Ownrshp* 2002
Sales 1.5MMM^E *EMP* 10,120^E
SIC 3089 Closures, plastic; Closures, plastic
VP: David Grochow
VP: Brad Jacobsen

D-U-N-S 19-994-6054
IRVING S GILMORE FOUNDATION
136 E Michigan Ave Ste 90, Kalamazoo, MI 49007-3947
Tel (269) 342-6411 *Founded/Ownrshp* 1972
Sales 22.4MM *EMP* 6
SIC 8699 8733 Charitable organization; Noncommercial research organizations
Ex Dir: Frederick Freund

IRVING TISSUE DIV
See IRVING CONSUMER PRODUCTS INC

D-U-N-S 04-558-5460
IRVING TOI INC
TOYOTA OF IRVING
1999 W Airport Fwy, Irving, TX 75062-6004
Tel (972) 258-1200 *Founded/Ownrshp* 1968
Sales 68.0MM^E *EMP* 139^E
SIC 5511 Automobiles, new & used; Automobiles, new & used
Pr: Vernon Schoemaker
**Sec:* Barbara Schoemaker
**VP:* David Schoemaker
DP Exec: David Shoemaker
Mktg Mgr: Delilah Carlson
Mktg Mgr: Amanda Giesler
Sls Mgr: Shawn Clift
Sls Mgr: Ivan Funes
Sales Asso: Kirby Jackson
Sales Asso: William Michael

D-U-N-S 06-286-1364
IRVING TOOL & MFG CO INC
2249 Wall St, Garland, TX 75041-4033
Tel (972) 926-4000 *Founded/Ownrshp* 1952
Sales 21.0MM^E *EMP* 100
SIC 3444 3599 Sheet metal specialties, not stamped; Machine shop, jobbing & repair
CEO: Linda C Stringer
**Pr:* Harold E Stringer
**Treas:* Cheryl Pierce
**VP:* Ellen Cain

D-U-N-S 92-697-0849
IRVINGTON HEALTHCARE PROVIDERS LLC
CHANCELOR SPECIALTY CARE CENTE
155 40th St, Irvington, NJ 07111-1184
Tel (718) 567-0400 *Founded/Ownrshp* 1996
Sales 20.4MM *EMP* 100
SIC 8059 8051 Nursing home, except skilled & intermediate care facility; Skilled nursing care facilities

D-U-N-S 03-939-1834
IRVINGTON PUBLIC SCHOOLS
1 University Pl Fl 4, Irvington, NJ 07111-2627
Tel (973) 399-6800 *Founded/Ownrshp* 1898
Sales 67.7MM^E *EMP* 1,250
SIC 8211 Public elementary & secondary schools; Public elementary & secondary schools
Pr: Anthony Vauss
Bd of Dir: Luis Antilus
Bd of Dir: Renee Burgess
Ofcr: Shanequa Ashman
Ofcr: Roger Monel
Ofcr: Cherelle Tolor
**VP:* Romaine Greer
Dir Sec: Harry Little
Dir IT: Eleazar Amores
Web Dev: Carol Coleman
Web Dev: Rochelle Lipsky

D-U-N-S 09-619-0335
IRVINGTON UNION FREE SCHOOL DISTRICT
6 Dows Ln, Irvington, NY 10533-2102
Tel (914) 269-5412 *Founded/Ownrshp* 1800
Sales 57.2MM *EMP* 252
SIC 8211 Public elementary & secondary schools; Public elementary & secondary schools
IT Man: Gwen Carney
IT Man: Ann Tromer

D-U-N-S 01-676-8970
IRVTEX AUTOMOTIVE SALES II LP
WESTWAY FORD
(*Suby of* V.T., INC.)
801 W Airport Fwy, Irving, TX 75062-6314
Tel (972) 256-5551 *Founded/Ownrshp* 1999
Sales 64.4MM^E *EMP* 147
SIC 5511 Automobiles, new & used; Automobiles, new & used
Pr: Cecil Van Tuyl
Prin: Joezel Kennerly
Genl Mgr: Barton Hankins
Store Mgr: Larry Marshall
Netwrk Mgr: Jose Almendarez
Sls Mgr: Ali Benli

D-U-N-S 01-424-2275
IRWIN BUILDERS SUPPLY CORP
I B S
10249 Garnet Ln, Irwin, PA 15642-3874
Tel (724) 863-5200 *Founded/Ownrshp* 1949
Sales 80.7MM^E *EMP* 70^E
SIC 5031 5211 Building materials, exterior; Building materials, interior; Lumber & other building materials; Building materials, exterior; Building materials, interior; Lumber & other building materials
Pr: Daniel J Paulone
**Treas:* Marie Paulone
**VP:* Patrice L Paulone
Opers Mgr: Dave George

IRWIN CONSTRUCTION ACCESSORIES
See IRWIN INDUSTRIAL TOOL CO

D-U-N-S 10-001-3903
IRWIN COUNTY BOARD OF EDUCATION
210 N Apple St, Ocilla, GA 31774-1450
Tel (229) 468-9510 *Founded/Ownrshp* 1930
Sales 12.2MM^E *EMP* 280
Accts Russell W Hinton Atlanta Ge
SIC 8211 Public elementary & secondary schools; Public elementary & secondary schools

D-U-N-S 07-979-9074
IRWIN COUNTY SCHOOL SYSTEM
210 N Apple St, Ocilla, GA 31774-1450
Tel (229) 468-7485 *Founded/Ownrshp* 2015
Sales 5.0MM^E *EMP* 450^E
SIC 8211 Public elementary & secondary schools

D-U-N-S 00-797-7291
IRWIN ELECTRIC MEMBERSHIP CORP (GA)
915 W 4th St, Ocilla, GA 31774-1464
Tel (229) 468-7415 *Founded/Ownrshp* 1935
Sales 28.2MM *EMP* 52
Accts Mcnair Mclemore Middlebrooks
SIC 4911 Distribution, electric power; Distribution, electric power
Ch: Benny Denham
**Pr:* Randy Crenshaw
**CFO:* Karla Bruce
**Treas:* Sandy McClurd

D-U-N-S 15-064-3468 IMP/EXP
■ **IRWIN INDUSTRIAL TOOL CO**
IRWIN CONSTRUCTION ACCESSORIES
(*Suby of* NEWELL RUBBERMAID INC) ★
8935 N Pointe Exec Pk Dr, Huntersville, NC 28078-4857
Tel (704) 987-4555 *Founded/Ownrshp* 2002
Sales 563.9MM^E *EMP* 4,166
SIC 3423 3545 3421 Screw drivers, pliers, chisels, etc. (hand tools); Wrenches, hand tools; Mechanics' hand tools; Drill bits, metalworking; Snips, tinners'; Screw drivers, pliers, chisels, etc. (hand tools); Wrenches, hand tools; Mechanics' hand tools; Drill bits, metalworking; Snips, tinners'
CEO: Mike Polk
**Pr:* Neil R Eibeler
**Pr:* Robert Hudson
**Pr:* Ross Poter
VP: Adam Mack
VP: Christopher Tesmer
Exec: Amanda Busch
CTO: Tom Hamilton
VP Opers: Isaac Read
Plnt Mgr: David Finch
VP Sls: William Shine

D-U-N-S 02-841-7079
IRWIN INDUSTRIES INC
(*Suby of* PARK CORP) ★
1580 W Carson St, Long Beach, CA 90810-1455
Tel (310) 233-3000 *Founded/Ownrshp* 1922
Sales 333.3MM^E *EMP* 710
Accts Meaden & Moore Ltd Cpa S
SIC 1629 1731 1796 7353 1542 Power plant construction; Electric power systems contractors; Power generating equipment installation; Heavy construction equipment rental; Nonresidential construction; Power plant construction; Electric power systems contractors; Power generating equipment installation; Heavy construction equipment rental; Nonresidential construction
CEO: Ricardo B Teamor
CFO: Al Storer
VP: Burt Hong
Genl Mgr: Herman Goedecker
Off Mgr: Rhonda Smith
Site Mgr: John Guagliardo
Opers Mgr: Justin McDonald
Counsel: Carly Drake

D-U-N-S 03-446-2671 EXP
IRWIN INTERNATIONAL INC
AIRCRAFT SPRUCE
225 Airport Cir, Corona, CA 92880-2527
Tel (951) 372-9555 *Founded/Ownrshp* 1980
Sales 97.2MM^E *EMP* 160
SIC 5599 5088 Aircraft instruments, equipment or parts; Aircraft & parts; Aircraft instruments, equipment or parts; Aircraft & parts
Pr: James J Irwin
**VP:* Elizabeth Irwin

Exec: Jerry Aquilar
Sales Asso: Robin McHugh

D-U-N-S 10-594-0121
IRWIN NATURALS
5310 Beethoven St, Los Angeles, CA 90066-7015
Tel (310) 306-3636 *Founded/Ownrshp* 2002
Sales 53.8MM^E *EMP* 80
SIC 5122 Vitamins & minerals; Vitamins & minerals
Pr: Klee Irwin
CFO: Mark Green
Sr VP: Jeff Sugawara
VP: Rebecca Pearman
Genl Mgr: Gary Kleinman
IT Man: Jose Mancilla
IT Man: Jose Mencia
VP Opers: Dan Wing
Mktg Dir: Mike Berg
Mktg Mgr: Jeanene Moenckmeier
Sls Mgr: Steve Farzanfar

D-U-N-S 04-133-9227 IMP/EXP
IRWIN RESEARCH AND DEVELOPMENT INC
2401 W J St Ste B, Yakima, WA 98902-1129
Tel (509) 248-0194 *Founded/Ownrshp* 1965
Sales 68.4MM^E *EMP* 300
SIC 5084

D-U-N-S 00-601-5424 IMP/EXP
IRWIN SEATING CO (MI)
COUNTRY ROADS
(*Suby of* IRWIN SEATING HOLDING CO) ★
3251 Fruit Ridge Ave Nw, Grand Rapids, MI 49544-9748
Tel (616) 784-2621 *Founded/Ownrshp* 1905, 1999
Sales 108.9MM^E *EMP* 600^E
SIC 2531 Public building & related furniture; Public building & related furniture
Pr: Win Irwin
**Pr:* Earle S Irwin
**CFO:* Ray Vander Kooi
Ex VP: Tammy Chartier
**Sr VP:* Bruce J Cohen
**Sr VP:* Dale I Tanis
**Sr VP:* John Eichinger
**Sr VP:* John Fynewever
**Sr VP:* Robert E Weakley
VP: Nancy Edgerle
VP: Chris Hawkins
VP: Rich Provost

D-U-N-S 10-463-4212 IMP/EXP
IRWIN SEATING HOLDING CO
3251 Fruit Ridge Ave Nw, Grand Rapids, MI 49544-9748
Tel (616) 574-7400 *Founded/Ownrshp* 1999
Sales 108.9MM^E *EMP* 725
SIC 2531 7641 Public building & related furniture; School furniture; Stadium seating; Furniture repair & maintenance; Furniture refinishing; Antique furniture repair & restoration; Public building & related furniture; School furniture; Stadium seating; Furniture repair & maintenance; Furniture refinishing; Antique furniture repair & restoration
Pr: Earle S Irwin
**Sr VP:* Dale I Tanis

D-U-N-S 05-383-2697
IRWIN STEEL ERECTORS INC
3824 53rd St, Lubbock, TX 79413-3824
Tel (806) 795-4484 *Founded/Ownrshp* 1966
Sales 22.4MM^E *EMP* 120
SIC 1791 Structural steel erection
Pr: Laughlin F Irwin
**Treas:* David Irwin
**VP:* James C Irwin
Plnt Mgr: Bryan Irwin

D-U-N-S 07-970-5386
IRWIN STEEL LLC
15740 Highway 114, Justin, TX 76247-8511
Tel (817) 636-2508 *Founded/Ownrshp* 2014
Sales 20.0MM^E *EMP* 120
SIC 3441 Fabricated structural metal
Pr: James C Irwin
VP: Bryan Irwin
VP: Lee Irwin

D-U-N-S 62-059-4189 IMP
■ IS ACQUISITION INC
INTEGRITY STAINLESS
(*Suby of* OLYMPIC STEEL INC) ★
3000 Crane Centre Dr, Streetsboro, OH 44241-5035
Tel (440) 287-0150 *Founded/Ownrshp* 2005
Sales 62.7MM^E *EMP* 65
SIC 5051 Steel; Steel
VP: Andy Markowitz
Genl Mgr: Jerry Gideon
QA Dir: Bob Dove
Sls Mgr: Rich Markowitz
Sls Mgr: Richard Ranells

D-U-N-S 07-836-6669
IS ADMINISTRATIVE SERVICES INC
2 Ravinia Dr Ste 270, Atlanta, GA 30346-2104
Tel (678) 262-3200 *Founded/Ownrshp* 2010
Sales 14.9MM^E *EMP* 540
SIC 7361 Employment agencies; Employment agencies
CEO: Eric Stein
**CFO:* Mike Johnson

IS3C
See SELECT SOURCE INTERNATIONAL INC

ISA
See INSERVICE AMERICA INC

D-U-N-S 15-382-1855
ISA CORP
3787 Fairview Indus Dr Se, Salem, OR 97302-1178
Tel (503) 371-7811 *Founded/Ownrshp* 1983
Sales 30.3MM^E *EMP* 215
SIC 3069 8711 Medical & laboratory rubber sundries & related products; Balloons, advertising & toy: rubber; Consulting engineer; Medical & laboratory rubber sundries & related products; Balloons, advertising & toy: rubber; Consulting engineer

Pr: Linda D Feusner
**VP:* Jason Feusner

D-U-N-S 80-230-6316 IMP
ISAAC CONSTRUCTION CO INC
5455 Cameron St, Las Vegas, NV 89118-2248
Tel (702) 364-0398 *Founded/Ownrshp* 1992
Sales 24.1MM^E *EMP* 250
SIC 1542 Nonresidential construction; Nonresidential construction
Pr: Bill Isaac
COO: Robert Welsh
**Treas:* Rory Rowsell
**VP:* Robert C Welch III

ISAAC E CRARY JUNIOR HIGH SCHO
See WATERFORD SCHOOL DISTRICT

D-U-N-S 02-205-1291
■ ISAAC FAIR CORP
(*Suby of* FAIR ISAAC SOFTWARE HOLDINGS LIMITED)
3550 Engrg Dr Ste 200, Norcross, GA 30092
Tel (770) 810-8000 *Founded/Ownrshp* 1996
Sales 63.9MM^E *EMP* 3,000
SIC 7371 Software programming applications; Software programming applications
VP: Chris Anderson
COO: Tom Duvall
VP: Rachel Carawan
VP: Charles M Osborne
Mng Dir: Alan Fish

D-U-N-S 01-311-2883
ISAAC HEATING & AIR CONDITIONING INC (NY)
180 Charlotte St, Rochester, NY 14607-1331
Tel (585) 546-1400 *Founded/Ownrshp* 1945, 1967
Sales 32.3MM^E *EMP* 225
SIC 1711

D-U-N-S 05-536-7239 IMP/EXP
ISAAC INDUSTRIES INC
7330 Nw 36th Ave, Miami, FL 33147-5898
Tel (305) 696-8944 *Founded/Ownrshp* 1970
Sales 60.0MM *EMP* 7
SIC 5169 Polyurethane products; Industrial chemicals
Pr: David Avan
S&M/VP: David Evan
Sales Asso: Eduardo Gutierrez

D-U-N-S 19-731-1723 IMP
ISAAC MORRIS LTD
BUDDY BOYS
20 W 33rd St Fl 9, New York, NY 10001-3305
Tel (646) 827-0000 *Founded/Ownrshp* 1989
Sales 72.4MM^E *EMP* 55
SIC 5136 Men's & boys' clothing
Ch Bd: Isaac Hazen
COO: Steven Tawil
**CFO:* Richard Schaefer
VP: Lawrence Benun
**VP:* Morris Benun
CTO: David Cropper
Snr Mgr: Isaac Hazan

D-U-N-S 09-937-5800
ISAAC SCHOOL DISTRICT
3348 W Mcdowell Rd, Phoenix, AZ 85009-2499
Tel (602) 455-6700 *Founded/Ownrshp* 1878
Sales 51.9MM^E *EMP* 859
Accts Larson Allen Llp
SIC 8211 Public elementary school; Public junior high school; Public elementary school; Public junior high school
Dir Sec: Abedonfinbres Finbres
Dir IT: Rene Castaneda
IT Man: Ryan French
IT Man: Lynn Lang
Trfc Dir: Deanna Engel
Pr Dir: Emily Broome
Pr Dir: Abedn Fimbres

D-U-N-S 12-692-7185
ISAACKS CONTRACTING INC
ISAACKS DIRECTIONAL DRILLING
2710 Fm 1069 N, Aransas Pass, TX 78336
Tel (361) 758-7297 *Founded/Ownrshp* 1980
Sales 27.9MM *EMP* 32
Accts Jennings Hawley & Co Pc Cp
SIC 1623 1794 Underground utilities contractor; Excavation & grading, building construction
Pr: Gary B Isaacks
**VP:* Joann Isaacks

ISAACKS DIRECTIONAL DRILLING
See ISAACKS CONTRACTING INC

D-U-N-S 10-166-4142
ISAACS DELI INC
ISAAC'S RESTAURANT & DELI
354 N Prince St Ste 220, Lancaster, PA 17603-3085
Tel (717) 394-0623 *Founded/Ownrshp* 1983
Sales 29.5MM^E *EMP* 725
SIC 5812 Restaurant, family: independent; Delicatessen (eating places); Restaurant, family: independent; Delicatessen (eating places)
Pr: Philip R Wenger
**VP:* Alan Jacobs
Genl Mgr: Mary Stoltzfus
Art Dir: Steve Myers

D-U-N-S 02-156-1535
ISAACS ENTERPRISES INC
PIONEER PETROLEUM
101 N Fairmont Ave, Morristown, TN 37814-3769
Tel (423) 586-7090 *Founded/Ownrshp* 1978
Sales 50.8MM^E *EMP* 270
SIC 5411 5171 Convenience stores, independent; Petroleum bulk stations; Convenience stores, independent; Petroleum bulk stations
Pr: Steve Isaacs
**VP:* Jerry Isaacs
Opers Mgr: Tony Lamb

ISAAC'S RESTAURANT & DELI
See ISAACS DELI INC

D-U-N-S 11-885-3084
ISAACSON MILLER INC
263 Summer St Fl 7, Boston, MA 02210-1525
Tel (617) 262-6500 *Founded/Ownrshp* 1982
Sales 29.5MM^E *EMP* 117
Accts Mcgladrey & Pullen Llp Boston
SIC 7361 8742 Executive placement; Management consulting services; Executive placement; Management consulting services
Sr VP: Michael A Baer
Pr: Tim McFeeley
COO: Nancy Maull
Chf Mktg O: Lisa Scannell
Ex Dir: Eliot Spitzer
Mng Dir: John Isaacson

D-U-N-S 60-324-3189
▲ ISABELLA BANK CORP
401 N Main St, Mount Pleasant, MI 48858-1649
Tel (989) 772-9471 *Founded/Ownrshp* 1988
Sales NA *EMP* 370
Tkr Sym ISBA *Exch* OTO
SIC 6022 State commercial banks; State commercial banks
CEO: Jae A Evans
Ch Bd: David J Maness
Pr: Dennis P Angner
Ex VP: Jerome Schwind
VP: David Seppala
VP: Aaron Wirsing
Dir IT: Jon Wainwright
Netwrk Eng: Pat Larrance

D-U-N-S 08-896-1180 IMP
ISABELLA GERIATRIC CENTER INC
515 Audubon Ave, New York, NY 10040-3403
Tel (212) 342-9200 *Founded/Ownrshp* 1970
Sales 70.9MM^E *EMP* 1,050
Accts O Connor Davies Llp Harrison
SIC 8051 Skilled nursing care facilities; Skilled nursing care facilities
CEO: Mark J Kator
Dir Vol: Rosa Pascual
**Ch:* Mark Lipton
Bd of Dir: Gregory Fortin
Bd of Dir: John Green
Bd of Dir: Caroline Jacobs
Bd of Dir: Hila Richardson
VP: Ellen Harnett
**VP:* John Zeiss
Dir Soc: Ann McDermott
Dir Sec: Laverne Collins

D-U-N-S 07-381-6829 IMP
ISABELLA STEWART GARDNER MUSEUM INC
25 Evans Way, Boston, MA 02115-5538
Tel (617) 566-1401 *Founded/Ownrshp* 1900
Sales 30.5MM *EMP* 140
Accts Cbiz Tofias Boston Ma
SIC 8412 5812 5947 Museums & art galleries; Cafe; Gift shop; Museums & art galleries; Cafe; Gift shop
Pr: Barbara Hosttetter
**Pr:* Jack Gardner
**COO:* Peter Bryant
CFO: Noah Schneiderman
**Treas:* Gwill York
Ofcr: Erika Gislason
Ofcr: Maureen O'Brien
Exec: Anna Lowi
Dir Sec: Anthony Amore
Genl Mgr: Christopher Mekal
Store Mgr: Kevin Monahan

ISACA
See INFORMATION SYSTEMS AUDIT AND CONTROL ASSOCIATION

D-U-N-S 03-701-8207 IMP
ISACO INTERNATIONAL CORP (FL)
5980 Miami Lakes Dr E, Miami Lakes, FL 33014-2404
Tel (305) 594-4455 *Founded/Ownrshp* 1980
Sales 147.8MM^E *EMP* 250
SIC 5136 Men's & boys' clothing; Men's & boys' clothing
Pr: Isaac Zelcer
Pr: Ruth Zelcer
Sr VP: Richard Alman
VP: Donna Signs
VP: Robert Weaver
VP: Alan Zelcer
IT Man: Maria Rozzen

D-U-N-S 01-344-1720
ISADORE A RAPASADI AND SONS INC
500 N Peterboro St, Canastota, NY 13032-4923
Tel (315) 697-2216 *Founded/Ownrshp* 1960
Sales 27.4MM^E *EMP* 60
SIC 5148 Fresh fruits & vegetables
Ch Bd: Isadore A Rapasadi
**Pr:* Sam S Rapasadi
**CEO:* Robert S Rapasadi

D-U-N-S 14-479-8480 IMP/EXP
ISAGENIX INTERNATIONAL LLC
2225 S Price Rd, Chandler, AZ 85286-7201
Tel (480) 889-5747 *Founded/Ownrshp* 2002
Sales 120.7MM^E *EMP* 350^E
SIC 2834 Vitamin, nutrient & hematinic preparations for human use; Vitamin, nutrient & hematinic preparations for human use
Treas: Jack Spitzer
VP: Kevin Andrus
Exec: Brian Plott
**Prin:* James Pierce
Snr Sftwr: David Rinehart
QA Dir: Kyla Boudreau
QA Dir: Anthony Yeatropoulos
Software D: Kory Masing
Software D: Frank Vella
VP Opers: Patty Raphael

D-U-N-S 11-833-7807
ISAM CORP
CORE BUSINESS TECHNOLOGIES
2224 Pawtucket Ave Unit 6, East Providence, RI 02914-1716
Tel (401) 431-0700 *Founded/Ownrshp* 1983
Sales 29.3MM^E *EMP* 100

SIC 5044 5112 7629 Office equipment; Photocopy machines; Office supplies; Business machine repair, electric
Pr: Mark S Cohen
Admn Mgr: Cindy Gabarra
Admn Mgr: Jon Oneil
Snr Sftwr: Ann Crellin
Snr Sftwr: Michael Okola
Snr Sftwr: Shuang Xiao
Software D: Goldie Hang
Sftwr Eng: Dan Mills
Sftwr Eng: Michael Staley
Sls Mgr: Paul Iemma
Snr Mgr: Michael Desantis

ISBE
See ILLINOIS STATE BOARD OF EDUCATION

D-U-N-S 09-265-5773
ISBERG NOTT CO
4725 1st St Ste 265, Pleasanton, CA 94566-7489
Tel (925) 426-4718 *Founded/Ownrshp* 1986
Sales 35.0MM *EMP* 5
SIC 8742 Sales (including sales management) consultant; Sales (including sales management) consultant
Pr: Steve Kanty
**Prin:* Rep Bryan Herman
**Prin:* Rep Steve McGovern
**Prin:* Rep Karie Spowart

D-U-N-S 96-820-0639
ISC ACQUISITION CORP
ISC BUILDING MATERIALS
2525 Mcallister Rd, Houston, TX 77092-8020
Tel (713) 275-4500 *Founded/Ownrshp* 2011
Sales 129.5MM^E *EMP* 100
SIC 5032 5031 Drywall materials; Wallboard; Enameled tileboard
Pr: Narciso Flores
**CFO:* Russell Pae
**VP:* Michael Flores
Brnch Mgr: Sharon Frank
IT Man: Elizabeth Flores
Opers Supe: Rich Cornwell
Sales Asso: John Berrettini

ISC BUILDING MATERIALS
See ISC ACQUISITION CORP

D-U-N-S 00-621-1270 IMP
ISC COMPANIES INC (MN)
12905 Hwy 55, Plymouth, MN 55441-3841
Tel (763) 559-0033 *Founded/Ownrshp* 1941
Sales 28.0MM *EMP* 130
SIC 5085 3714 3568 Bearings; Power transmission equipment & apparatus; Motor vehicle parts & accessories; Power transmission equipment; Bearings; Power transmission equipment & apparatus; Motor vehicle parts & accessories; Power transmission equipment
CEO: Mark Koch
**COO:* Bill Nelson
**CFO:* Jeff Mattson
CFO: William Nelson
Brnch Mgr: Kenneth Harvey
Brnch Mgr: Mary Holmes
Genl Mgr: Lou Cowart
IT Man: Ken Schmitz
Mktg Dir: Christopher Bursack
Sls Mgr: Dan Dedman
Sls Mgr: Bob Ziegeweid

D-U-N-S 60-948-0686
ISC CONSTRUCTORS LLC
I S C
(*Suby of* ISC GROUP L L C) ★
20480 Highland Rd, Baton Rouge, LA 70817-7347
Tel (225) 756-8001 *Founded/Ownrshp* 1989
Sales 204.2MM^E *EMP* 1,000
SIC 1731 Electrical work; Electrical work
Ch Bd: Edward L Rispone
CFO: Michael Latiolais
VP: Steve Derouen
VP: Craig D Messer
Exec: Lauren Read
Rgnl Mgr: Mike Gremillion
IT Man: Brook Lyon
Sfty Dirs: Ron Campbell
Site Mgr: Bobby Allen
Snr Mgr: Sean Beard
Snr Mgr: James Landry

ISC CONTRACTING
See INTERIOR SYSTEMS CONTRACTING INC

D-U-N-S 11-125-8448
ISC GROUP L L C
20480 Highland Rd, Baton Rouge, LA 70817-7347
Tel (225) 756-8001 *Founded/Ownrshp* 1996
Sales 204.2MM^E *EMP* 1,700
SIC 1731 Electrical work; Electrical work
Pr: Gerard L Rispone
Ex VP: Glen R Redd
Off Mgr: Angela Moore

D-U-N-S 02-122-9702
ISC SERVICES
1271 W Maple Rd, Clawson, MI 48017-1060
Tel (561) 841-8411 *Founded/Ownrshp* 2009
Sales NA *EMP* 64^E
SIC 6311 Life insurance
Prin: Ronald Norman
VP: Russell Frederick
Brnch Mgr: Jan Schroth
Opers Mgr: Joe Muller

ISC SURFACES
See INTERSTATE SUPPLY CO

ISC SURFACES
See INTERSTATE FLOORING LLC

D-U-N-S 05-412-5190 IMP
■ ISCAR METALS INC
(*Suby of* BERKSHIRE HATHAWAY INC) ★
300 Westway Pl, Arlington, TX 76018-1021
Tel (817) 258-3200 *Founded/Ownrshp* 2008
Sales 122.6MM^E *EMP* 395
Accts Pricewaterhousecoopers Llp Ha

SIC 5084 Tools & accessories for machine tools; Tool holders (chucks, turrets)
Pr: Jacob Harpaz
Pr: Bradley Teets
Pr: Sarah Tidwell
Pr: Rick Wallingford
Chf Mktg O: Andrew Benson
*Ex VP: Reggie Lowder
VP: Rod Zimmerman
Rgnl Mgr: Steve Bauers
Rgnl Mgr: Stephan Hardesty
Rgnl Mgr: Steven Lambert
Area Mgr: Ed Karpowicz

D-U-N-S 13-942-7561 IMP/EXP
ISCO HOLDING CO INC
INDEPENDENT STAVE COMPANY
1078 S Jefferson Ave, Lebanon, MO 65536-3601
Tel (417) 588-4151 Founded/Ownrshp 1983
Sales 257.2MM^E EMP 1,150
SIC 2449 Barrels, wood: coopered; Barrels, wood: coopered
Ch Bd: John J Boswell
CFO: Carol McCaghren
S&M/VP: Aime B Dewane

D-U-N-S 00-700-3999 EXP
ISCO INDUSTRIES INC (KY)
I S C O
926 Baxter Ave, Louisville, KY 40204-2066
Tel (502) 318-6626 Founded/Ownrshp 2012
Sales 450.0MM EMP 330
SIC 5085 5083 Valves & fittings; Irrigation equipment; Valves & fittings; Irrigation equipment
CEO: Jimmy Kirchdorfer Jr
*Pr: Mark T Kirchdorfer
COO: Lee Mizell
*CFO: Christopher Feger
Bd of Dir: Brian Zagrodny
Chf Mktg O: Carlos Moreno
VP: Bob Kerr
Dir Bus: Steve Sandstrum
Rgnl Mgr: Cory Wilkinson
Brnch Mgr: Chris Rountree
Genl Mgr: Glen Henderson

ISD 12
See EDMOND PUBLIC SCHOOLS

ISD 15 ST FRANCIS
See INDEPENDENT SCHOOL DISTRICT 15

D-U-N-S 96-352-3076
ISD 535 HEALTH AND DENTAL CARE TRUST
615 7th St Sw, Rochester, MN 55902-2052
Tel (507) 328-4225 Founded/Ownrshp 2010
Sales 23.9MM EMP 3^E
Accts Cliftonlarsonallen Llp Austin
SIC 8699 Charitable organization; Charitable organization

D-U-N-S 82-537-9576
ISD HOLDINGS INC
4715 Frederick Dr Sw, Atlanta, GA 30336-1809
Tel (404) 691-7400 Founded/Ownrshp 1999
Sales 102.1MM^E EMP 400^E
SIC 7389 2542 2759 2752 Design services; Fixtures, store: except wood; Screen printing; Commercial printing, offset; Design services; Fixtures, store: except wood; Screen printing; Commercial printing, offset
CEO: Harmon B Miller III
*CFO: David Seem

D-U-N-S 02-484-1802
ISD PLAINFIELD LLC
PLAINFIELD RENAL CENTER
8110 Network Dr, Plainfield, IN 46168-9024
Tel (317) 838-8089 Founded/Ownrshp 2008
Sales 301.0MM EMP 99
SIC 8092 Kidney dialysis centers; Kidney dialysis centers

D-U-N-S 80-866-8235
■ **ISD RENAL INC**
(Suby of DAVITA HEALTHCARE PARTNERS INC) ★
424 Church St Ste 1900, Nashville, TN 37219-2387
Tel (615) 777-8200 Founded/Ownrshp 2005
Sales 40.3MM^E EMP 2,200^E
SIC 8069 8092 8742 Cancer hospital; Kidney dialysis centers; Management consulting services; Cancer hospital; Kidney dialysis centers; Management consulting services
Pr: Dennis L Kogod
*CFO: James K Hilger
*VP: David R Finn
*VP: Chetan P Mehta
*VP: Javier J Rodriguez
*VP: Steven I Grieger
*VP: Thomas O Usilton

D-U-N-S 01-573-1449
■ **ISD SCHAUMBURG LLC**
ARLINGTON HEIGHTS PD
(Suby of DAVITA HEALTHCARE PARTNERS INC) ★
17 W Golf Rd, Arlington Heights, IL 60005-3905
Tel (847) 437-2188 Founded/Ownrshp 2008
Sales 9.3MM^E EMP 1,525
SIC 8092 Kidney dialysis centers; Kidney dialysis centers

ISD287
See INTERMEDIATE DISTRICT 287

ISD413
See MARSHALL PUBLIC SCHOOL

ISDA
See INTERNATIONAL SWAPS AND DERIVATIVES ASSOCIATION INC

ISE
See INSTITUTE FOR SHIPBOARD EDUCATION

D-U-N-S 00-407-3078 IMP
ISE AMERICA INC
(Suby of ISE INC.)
33335 Galena Sassafras Rd, Golts, MD 21635
Tel (410) 755-6773 Founded/Ownrshp 1980
Sales 71.1MM^E EMP 420^E
SIC 0252 Chicken eggs; Chicken eggs
Ch: Kimio Tabat
Pr: N H ISE
VP: Shuntaro ISE
Plnt Mgr: Barry Griffen
Snr Mgr: Larry Beck

D-U-N-S 15-510-5901
ISE LABS INC
(Suby of ASE TEST LIMITED)
46800 Bayside Pkwy, Fremont, CA 94538-6592
Tel (510) 687-2500 Founded/Ownrshp 1999
Sales 52.4MM^E EMP 500
SIC 8734 3672 Testing laboratories; Printed circuit boards; Testing laboratories; Printed circuit boards
CEO: Tien Wu
*VP: Jeff Thompson

D-U-N-S 05-872-6696 IMP
ISEC INC
6000 Greenwood Plaza Blvd # 200, Greenwood Village, CO 80111-4818
Tel (410) 381-6049 Founded/Ownrshp 1967
Sales 235.5MM EMP 1,150
Accts Martin Vejvoda And Associates
SIC 1751 Cabinet & finish carpentry; Cabinet & finish carpentry
Pr: Dusty Morgan
*CFO: Charles Dietrich
*Ex VP: Joan Norblom
*Ex VP: Mike Polanchyck
*Sr VP: Tim McCoy
*Sr VP: Michael Polanchyck
*VP: David Herzel
*VP: Timothy McCoy
*VP: Brent Paden
*VP: Greg Timmerman
Snr PM: Stacie McConnell

D-U-N-S 15-180-1891
ISEE SYSTEMS INC
31 Old Etna Rd Ste N7, Lebanon, NH 03766-1933
Tel (603) 448-4990 Founded/Ownrshp 2002
Sales 20.3MM EMP 8
SIC 5734 7371 Software, business & non-game; Computer software development
Pr: Katherine Richmond
*VP: Joanne C Egner
IT Man: Robert Eberlein

D-U-N-S 83-275-8960
ISEMAN HOMES INC
4733 N Cliff Ave, Sioux Falls, SD 57104-0451
Tel (605) 336-3270 Founded/Ownrshp 2005
Sales 21.0MM EMP 19^E
Accts David Driver V Pres-Sec By Fa
SIC 5271 Mobile homes; Mobile homes
Pr: Kenneth Ward
*VP: David Driver
*VP: William Krum
Area Mgr: Jonathon Bourne
Sales Asso: Chauncey Anderson
Sales Asso: Brenton Crane

D-U-N-S 00-482-8687
ISEMOTO CONTRACTING CO LTD (HI)
648 Piilani St, Hilo, HI 96720-4691
Tel (808) 935-7194 Founded/Ownrshp 1926
Sales 120.0MM^E EMP 400
Accts Deloitte & Touche Llp Honolul
SIC 1629 1542 1541 Land preparation construction; Commercial & office building contractors; Industrial buildings, new construction; Land preparation construction; Commercial & office building contractors; Industrial buildings, new construction
Pr: Leslie K Isemoto
*Pr: Leslie Isemoto
*VP: Jerry Egami
*VP: Lester Sakamoto
*VP: Bryan Tomiyoshi
IT Man: Loren Tsugawa

D-U-N-S 96-666-6104
ISERVE RESIDENTIAL LENDING LLC
15015 Ave Of Science # 250, San Diego, CA 92128-3436
Tel (858) 486-4169 Founded/Ownrshp 2011
Sales NA EMP 100
SIC 6162 Bond & mortgage companies
Brnch Mgr: Bleu Colquitt
Brnch Mgr: Mohamed Khalil

D-U-N-S 61-144-6345
ISF TRADING INC
390 Commercial St, Portland, ME 04101-4610
Tel (207) 879-1575 Founded/Ownrshp 1989
Sales 29.3MM^E EMP 170
SIC 5146 2092 Seafoods; Fresh or frozen packaged fish
Pr: Atsshi Tamaki

ISG COMPANIES
See INTERNATIONAL FINANCIAL GROUP INC

D-U-N-S 78-330-6327
■ **ISG INFORMATION SERVICES GROUP AMERICAS INC**
T P I
(Suby of INFORMATION SERVICES GROUP INC) ★
25025 N I 45 Ste 225, The Woodlands, TX 77380
Tel (281) 465-5700 Founded/Ownrshp 2007
Sales 81.6MM^E EMP 450
Accts Pricewaterhousecoopers Housto
SIC 7379 Computer related consulting services; Computer related consulting services
Ch Bd: Michael P Connors
*Mng Pt: Mitt Salvaggio
Pr: William Cantor
*CFO: David Berger
Treas: Martha McGuire
*Ex VP: David E Berger
*Ex VP: Harry Somerdyk
VP: Warren Clark
VP: Kathy Welch
VP: Scott Wood
Exec: Tanaka Suzanne

ISG NOVASOFT TECHNOLOGIES
See ISGN CORP

ISG RESOURCES
See HEADWATERS RESOURCES INC

D-U-N-S 06-752-1885
ISG TECHNOLOGY LLC
127 N 7th St, Salina, KS 67401-2603
Tel (785) 823-1555 Founded/Ownrshp 2001
Sales 153.0MM EMP 168
Accts Woods & Durham Chtd Salina
SIC 5734 Computer & software stores; Computer & software stores
Pr: Ben Foster
*CEO: Scott Cissna
CFO: Gary Abbott
VP: Matt Brickey
*VP: Brian Finzen
VP: Martin Lee
VP: Amy Mounts
VP: Doug Zoph
Exec: Jeff Rankin
Dir Bus: Terry Thornsberry
Brnch Mgr: Hal Davey

D-U-N-S 83-571-0641
ISGN CORP
ISG NOVASOFT TECHNOLOGIES
(Suby of CHAMBAL FERTILISERS AND CHEMICALS LIMITED)
31 Inwood Rd, Rocky Hill, CT 06067-3412
Tel (860) 721-0480 Founded/Ownrshp 2003
Sales 31.9MM^E EMP 270
SIC 7379 Computer related consulting services; Computer related consulting services
CEO: Amit Kothiyal
Pr: Niraj Patel
Pr: Reggie Swiney
*COO: Murali Gomatam
*COO: Vishwajit Singh Negi
*CFO: Pradeep Chaudhry
*CFO: Sundararajan Sampath
Sr VP: Matt Kilboy
Sr VP: Eric Taylor
VP: Diane Choquette
VP: Susan Otis

D-U-N-S 80-640-8147
ISGN FULFILLMENT SERVICES INC
(Suby of ISGN SOLUTIONS, INC.)
3220 Tillman Dr Ste 301, Bensalem, PA 19020-2028
Tel (267) 525-9400 Founded/Ownrshp 2009
Sales 13.2MM^E EMP 485^E
SIC 7374 Data processing service
Pr: Chetan Patel
*Pr: Donald A Oneill
*Pr: Niraj Patel
*COO: Murali Gomatam
*COO: Ashok Radhakrishnan
*CFO: Charlie Witzke
Sr VP: Jeanne Rinaldo
VP: Sean Kruuv

IS.GROUP
See INDEPENDENT STATIONERS INC

D-U-N-S 13-525-5417
ISH MOORE INC
ASHLEY FURNITURE HOME STORE
2820 Selwyn Ave Ste 300, Charlotte, NC 28209-1873
Tel (704) 295-8700 Founded/Ownrshp 2002
Sales 33.3MM^E EMP 150
SIC 5712 Furniture stores; Furniture stores
Pr: Jonathan N Ishee
*Pr: Jonathan N Ishe
*VP: Charles Malouf
*Prin: Jackson Moore

D-U-N-S 18-119-9837 IMP
ISHAN INTERNATIONAL INC
TABAN CO
500 Smith St, Farmingdale, NY 11735-1115
Tel (631) 618-3000 Founded/Ownrshp 1983
Sales 106.7MM EMP 6
Accts Marks Paneth Llp New York N
SIC 5065 Electronic parts & equipment; Electronic parts & equipment
Pr: Abdulrahman S Khwaja

ISHARES
See BLACKROCK INSTITUTIONAL TRUST CO NATIONAL ASSOCIATION

D-U-N-S 07-839-8371
ISHARES INC (MD)
400 Howard St, San Francisco, CA 94105-2618
Tel (415) 597-2000 Founded/Ownrshp 1994
Sales 27.2MM^E EMP 75^E
SIC 6722 Management investment, open-end
Ch Bd: Peter Blessing
Mng Dir: Susan Thompson

D-U-N-S 62-024-4264
ISHPI INFORMATION TECHNOLOGIES INC
401 Seacoast Pkwy, Mount Pleasant, SC 29464-8263
Tel (843) 329-4100 Founded/Ownrshp 2006
Sales 37.0MM EMP 217^E
SIC 7379 Computer related maintenance services; Computer related maintenance services
Pr: Noah T Leask
*VP: Lisa Leask
Mktg Dir: Kimberly Fite
Board of Directors: Earl Bowers Mike Beadle Cl

ISI
See IMPACT SALES INC

ISI
See INTEGRATED SERVICES INC

ISI
See INGREDIENTS SOLUTIONS INC

D-U-N-S 87-884-8936
ISI ACQUISITION CORP
5215 Fidelity St, Houston, TX 77029-3566
Tel (281) 233-8000 Founded/Ownrshp 1994
Sales 30.0MM EMP 394
SIC 1611 Highway & street paving contractor; Guardrail construction, highways; Highway & street maintenance; Highway & street paving contractor; Guardrail construction, highways; Highway & street maintenance
Pr: Timothy H Herbert
*CFO: Larry Wagner
Board of Directors: Jack Carter, George Pontikas

I.S.I. AUTOMATION PRODUCTS
See NORGREN AUTOMATION SOLUTIONS LLC

ISI CONNECT
See INFO SYSTEMS LLC

ISI EMERGING MARKETS
See INTERNET SECURITIES INC

ISI ENVIRONMENTAL SERVICES
See INTEGRATED SOLUTIONS INC

D-U-N-S 02-215-3294
ISI HR INC
859 W South Jordan Pkwy # 77, South Jordan, UT 84095-3509
Tel (801) 984-0252 Founded/Ownrshp 2011
Sales 155.0MM EMP 27
SIC 7361 Employment agencies; Employment agencies
Pr: Michelyn Farnsworth

ISI RESEARCHSOFT
See THOMSON REUTERS (SCIENTIFIC) INC

ISI SECURITY GROUP
See ARGYLE SECURITY INC

D-U-N-S 80-856-3142
■ **ISI SECURITY GROUP INC**
ARGYLE SECURITY GROUP
(Suby of ARGYLE SECURITY INC) ★
12903 Delivery, San Antonio, TX 78247-3476
Tel (210) 495-5245 Founded/Ownrshp 2007
Sales 31.7MM^E EMP 350
SIC 1796 Installing building equipment; Installing building equipment
CEO: Buddy Johns
*CFO: Richard Watts
*VP: Matthew Kepke

D-U-N-S 79-131-5021
ISI TELEMANAGEMENT SOLUTIONS INC
1051 Perimeter Dr Ste 200, Schaumburg, IL 60173-5063
Tel (847) 995-0002 Founded/Ownrshp 1992
Sales 31.1MM^E EMP 125
SIC 8748 Telecommunications consultant; Telecommunications consultant
Ch Bd: Irwin Friedman
*Pr: Mark Friedman
*VP: Dan Hoctor
VP: Daneen Reinke
Mng Dir: Dave Whitney
CTO: James Raymer
Opers Mgr: Barbara Furey
Opers Mgr: Royce Schwartz
Mktg Mgr: Amy Williams

D-U-N-S 02-087-4087
ISIDORE NEWMAN SCHOOL (LA)
1903 Jefferson Ave, New Orleans, LA 70115-5699
Tel (504) 899-5641 Founded/Ownrshp 1903
Sales 21.5MM EMP 250
Accts Bourgeois Bennett Llc Metairi
SIC 8211 Private combined elementary & secondary school; Private combined elementary & secondary school
Pr: Ellen Balkin
CFO: Lisa Forsythe
HC Dir: Jennifer Rosen
Snr Mgr: Aaron Malloy

D-U-N-S 80-006-1538
ISIGHT PARTNERS INC
5950 Berkshire Ln # 1600, Dallas, TX 75225-5844
Tel (214) 580-2313 Founded/Ownrshp 2006
Sales 27.6MM^E EMP 300
SIC 8742 Management consulting services
CEO: John P Watters
Pr: Nathan Day
CFO: Matthew Keane
Sr VP: Tiffany O Jones
Sr VP: Jim Timmer
Sr VP: Admiral Patrick M Walsh
Sr VP: Patrick Walsh
VP: Sean Catlett
VP: Paul Dibello
VP: Patrick McBride
VP: Mark Shephard
VP: Madhav Sonthalia
VP: Michael Susong

D-U-N-S 03-320-2479 IMP
■ **ISILON SYSTEMS LLC**
EMC ISILON
(Suby of EMC CORP) ★
505 1st Ave S, Seattle, WA 98104-2803
Tel (206) 315-7500 Founded/Ownrshp 2001, 2010
Sales 90.0MM^E EMP 356
SIC 3572 3674 Computer storage devices; Computer auxiliary storage units; Semiconductors & related devices; Computer storage devices; Computer auxiliary storage units; Semiconductors & related devices
Bd of Dir: Laura Jennings
Sr VP: Steve Fitz
Sr VP: Brett Helsel
VP: Stu Fuhlendorf
VP: Karl Korbus
VP: Thomas Pattigrew
VP: Tony Regier
VP: Mark Schrandt
VP: David Skillern
Exec: Paul Levine
Prgrm Mgr: Andrey Tychkin

ISISLIFE
See INNOVATIVE SOLUTIONS INSURANCE SERVICES LLC

D-U-N-S 09-101-3219 IMP
ISLA LAB PRODUCTS CORP
Amelia Distribution, Guaynabo, PR 00968
Tel (787) 792-2222 Founded/Ownrshp 1976
Sales 34.5MM EMP 45
Accts Jlm & Co Llp San Juan Puer
SIC 5049 Laboratory equipment, except medical or dental; Laboratory equipment, except medical or dental
Pr: Charles Donato
*VP: Joaqyin Bofill

D-U-N-S 87-439-7271
ISLAMIC RELIEF USA
IRUSA
3655 Wheeler Ave, Alexandria, VA 22304-6404
Tel (703) 370-7202 Founded/Ownrshp 2008
Sales 65.2MM EMP 98E
SIC 8399 Antipoverty board; Health & welfare council; Health systems agency; Social change association; Antipoverty board; Health & welfare council; Health systems agency; Social change association
COO: Anwar Khan
V Ch: Khaled Lamada
*Ch: Mohamed AMR Attawia
Creative D: Ridwan Adhami
Pr Dir: Christina Tobias-Nahi

D-U-N-S 78-729-6805
ISLAND ACOUSTICS LLC
518 Johnson Ave, Bohemia, NY 11716-2639
Tel (631) 589-4666 Founded/Ownrshp 1997
Sales 22.5MME EMP 125
SIC 1742 1751 Acoustical & ceiling work; Drywall; Carpentry work
Dir IT: David Bann
Dir IT: Thomas Iacono

D-U-N-S 83-203-8462 EXP
ISLAND APPAREL
135 Renfrew Dr, Athens, GA 30606-3936
Tel (706) 548-3420 Founded/Ownrshp 2001
Sales 53.1MME EMP 1,400
SIC 2325 Men's & boys' trousers & slacks; Men's & boys' trousers & slacks
Pr: Fritz Felchlin

D-U-N-S 87-717-8095
ISLAND ARCHITECTURAL WOODWORK INC
31 Howard Pl Ste 33, Ronkonkoma, NY 11779-7215
Tel (631) 737-0020 Founded/Ownrshp 1993
Sales 22.3MME EMP 125
SIC 1751 8712 5211 Finish & trim carpentry; Architectural services; Millwork & lumber; Finish & trim carpentry; Architectural services; Millwork & lumber
Pr: Edward Rufrano
*Treas: Matthew Stevens
*VP: William Higbie

D-U-N-S 96-121-0838 IMP
ISLAND ASEPTICS LLC
(Suby of ISLAND OASIS FROZEN COCKTAIL CO INC) ★
100 Hope Ave, Byesville, OH 43723-9460
Tel (740) 685-1628 Founded/Ownrshp 2007
Sales 45.4MME EMP 150
SIC 2656 Food containers (liquid tight), including milk cartons; Food containers (liquid tight), including milk cartons
Genl Mgr: John Kasinecz
VP: Jeff Campbell

D-U-N-S 15-506-8950
ISLAND COMPUTER PRODUCTS INC
ICP
20 Clifton Ave, Staten Island, NY 10305-4912
Tel (718) 556-6700 Founded/Ownrshp 1989
Sales 304.3MME EMP 205
Accts Del Rey & Company Llp Cpa S
SIC 5045 7373 7379 7378 Computers, peripherals & software; Computer integrated systems design; Computer related consulting services; Computer maintenance & repair; Computers, peripherals & software; Computer integrated systems design; Computer related consulting services; Computer maintenance & repair
Pr: Michele Fabozzi
COO: Erik Lieberman
COO: Joe Sullivan
CFO: Laura Andersen
*CFO: Annette Fabozzi
CIO: Lou Esposito
*CIO: Paul S Fabozzi
MIS Dir: Beth Hayes
IT Man: German Delgado
IT Man: Anthony Fiore
Sftwr Eng: Bruno Sousa

ISLAND CONSTRUCTION COMPANIES
See ISLAND INTERNATIONAL INDUSTRIES INC

D-U-N-S 00-130-3080
ISLAND CONTAINER CORP (NY)
44 Island Container Plz, Wyandanch, NY 11798-2229
Tel (631) 253-4400 Founded/Ownrshp 1956
Sales 31.9MME EMP 100
SIC 2653 Boxes, corrugated: made from purchased materials; Boxes, corrugated: made from purchased materials
Ch Bd: Edward Berkowitz
*Sec: Rochelle Berkowitz
*VP: Gary Berkowitz
VP: Robert Jeffreys
Sfty Mgr: Terry Olinger

D-U-N-S 07-663-5317
ISLAND ENTERPRISES
KAMILCHE TRADING POST
3591 Se Old Olympic Hwy, Shelton, WA 98584-7733
Tel (360) 426-4933 Founded/Ownrshp 1961
Sales 20.9MME EMP 111
SIC 5921 5411 2091 Liquor stores; Grocery stores; Delicatessens; Oysters: packaged in cans, jars, etc.
CEO: Robert Whitner
Store Mgr: Isaiah Coley

ISLAND ESTATES LC
See KETTLER & SCOTT INC

D-U-N-S 06-805-8494
ISLAND FEDERAL CREDIT UNION
120 Motor Pkwy, Hauppauge, NY 11788-5160
Tel (631) 630-9247 Founded/Ownrshp 1955
Sales NA EMP 50
SIC 6061 Federal credit unions; Federal credit unions
Pr: Robert Dethlefsen
*Ch Bd: Shirley Watson
*V Ch Bd: Edward Doster
VP: Jane Rabben
VP: Joeseph Riccardi
VP: Paul Young
CIO: Bret Sears
IT Man: Brian Barrie
Opers Mgr: Josephine Matus
Mktg Dir: Mary Wyman

D-U-N-S 09-036-4530
■ **ISLAND FINANCE PUERTO RICO INC**
(Suby of WELLS FARGO & CO) ★
1 Calle Hortensia Apt 9j, San Juan, PR 00926-6494
Tel (787) 759-7044 Founded/Ownrshp 2006
Sales NA EMP 700
Accts Kpmg Llp
SIC 6021 National commercial banks
Pr: Oriol Segarra

D-U-N-S 14-331-3208
ISLAND FIRE SPRINKLER INC
(Suby of API GROUP INC) ★
630 Broadway Ave Ste 1, Holbrook, NY 11741-4900
Tel (631) 472-4500 Founded/Ownrshp 2009
Sales 27.1MM EMP 60
Accts Kpmg Llp Minneapolis Mn
SIC 1711 Fire sprinkler system installation; Fire sprinkler system installation
Ch Bd: Brian P McMahon
CFO: Edward B McMahon

D-U-N-S 96-160-2893
ISLAND GRAND RESORT A TRADEWIND RESORT
TRADEWINDS HOTEL
5500 Gulf Blvd, St Pete Beach, FL 33706-2323
Tel (727) 363-2358 Founded/Ownrshp 1992
Sales 9.9MME EMP 600
SIC 7011 5813 5812 Hotels; Drinking places; Eating places; Hotels; Drinking places; Eating places
CEO: Tim Bogott
CFO: Joe Demontiny
Natl Sales: Heather Sill

D-U-N-S 95-741-8890
ISLAND HARVEST LTD
199 2nd St Fl 2, Mineola, NY 11501-4055
Tel (516) 294-8528 Founded/Ownrshp 1992
Sales 26.6MM EMP 14
Accts Weisermazars Llp Woodbury Ny
SIC 8099 Nutrition services
CEO: Randi Shubin Dresner
COO: Joan Flynn
Treas: Daniel Grinberg
VP: Migvalia Otero
VP: Stacy Parsell
VP: Allison Puglia
VP: Lisa Trimarchi
Off Admin: Joann Cannon

D-U-N-S 88-444-3599
ISLAND HOLDINGS INC
NATIONAL MORTGAGE & FINANCE CO
1022 Bethel St Fl 4, Honolulu, HI 96813-4302
Tel (808) 531-1311 Founded/Ownrshp 1990
Sales 227.5MME EMP 450
SIC 6512 Insurance building operation; Insurance building operation
Pr: Colbert M Matsumoto
*CFO: Nolan N Kawano
CFO: Nolan Kawano
VP: Wayne Hikida
VP: Keith Kogachi
VP: Todd Yamanka
VP: Todd Yamanka
Exec: Shirley MA
Snr PM: Sherilyn Kimura

ISLAND HONDA
See KITAGAWA MOTORS INC

ISLAND HOSPITAL
See SKAGIT COUNTY PUBLIC HOSPITAL DISTRICT 2

D-U-N-S 96-342-2550
ISLAND HOSPITAL AUXILIARY
1211 24th St, Anacortes, WA 98221-2562
Tel (360) 299-1300 Founded/Ownrshp 2003
Sales NA EMP 725
Accts Cliftonlarsonallen Llp Bellev
SIC 6324 Hospital & medical service plans; Hospital & medical service plans
Pr: Vince Oliver
Chf Rad: John Burke
*Prin: Shirley Smith
Off Mgr: Donna M Cabe
Doctor: Randolph V Anderson
Doctor: Robert G Billow
Doctor: Pardeep S Brar
Doctor: Gary L Brown
Doctor: Regina L Currier
Doctor: George Hatfield
Doctor: Russell Johnson

ISLAND HOSPITALITY MANAGEMENT
See INNKEEPERS HOSPITALITY INC

D-U-N-S 09-383-1530
ISLAND HOSPITALITY MANAGEMENT LLC
222 Lakeview Ave Ste 200, West Palm Beach, FL 33401-6146
Tel (561) 832-6132 Founded/Ownrshp 2007
Sales 576.8MME EMP 4,000
SIC 8741 Hotel or motel management; Hotel or motel management
Pr: Tim Walker
*CFO: Dennis Craven
*Sr VP: Barbara A Bachman
*Sr VP: Phillip M Cohen
*Sr VP: Michele Mainelli
*Sr VP: Roger Pollak
*Sr VP: Jeffrey Waldt
*VP: Rob Auerbach
VP: Marc Winer
Dir IT: Ron Foster
Dir IT: Dwayne Snyder

D-U-N-S 07-766-4522
ISLAND INSURANCE CO LIMITED
CLAIMS CENTER
(Suby of ISLAND HOLDINGS INC) ★
1022 Bethel St, Honolulu, HI 96813-4302
Tel (808) 564-8200 Founded/Ownrshp 1939
Sales NA EMP 386
SIC 6331 6411 Property damage insurance; Fire, marine & casualty insurance & carriers; Insurance agents, brokers & service; Property damage insurance; Fire, marine & casualty insurance & carriers; Insurance agents, brokers & service
CEO: John Schapperle
Pr: Jim Newberry
Ch: Colbert Matsumoto
Ex VP: Franklin M Tokioka
Sr VP: Beverly Ament
Sr VP: Nolan Kawano
VP: Jeff Fabry
VP: Riki Fujitani
VP: Wayne Hikida
VP: Leila Tamashiro
VP: Gary Watanabe
VP: Pamela Watanabe

D-U-N-S 96-885-5002
ISLAND INTERNATIONAL EXTERIOR FABRICATORS LLC
1101 Scott Ave, Calverton, NY 11933-3056
Tel (631) 208-3500 Founded/Ownrshp 2010
Sales 21.2MME EMP 300
SIC 1542 Commercial & office building contractors; Commercial & office building contractors
Off Mgr: Amanda Vega

D-U-N-S 04-603-8035
ISLAND INTERNATIONAL INDUSTRIES INC
ISLAND CONSTRUCTION COMPANIES
1101 Scott Ave, Calverton, NY 11933-3056
Tel (631) 369-2760 Founded/Ownrshp 1998
Sales 68.4MME EMP 150
SIC 1542 Commercial & office building contractors; Commercial & office building contractors
Pr: Tim Stevens
*VP: Matt Stevens

D-U-N-S 15-196-2628
ISLAND LINCOLN MERCURY INC
1850 E Mrritt Island Cswy, Merritt Island, FL 32952-2665
Tel (321) 452-9220 Founded/Ownrshp 1985
Sales 27.7MME EMP 66
SIC 5511 Automobiles, new & used; Automobiles, new & used
Pr: R Bruce Deardoff
*Sec: Renee Cheney
*VP: Michael G Deardoff

ISLAND MINI MART
See ALOHA PETROLEUM LTD

D-U-N-S 00-945-6427 IMP/EXP
ISLAND MOVERS INC
1004 Makepono St, Honolulu, HI 96819-4335
Tel (808) 832-4000 Founded/Ownrshp 1958
Sales 60.0MME EMP 450
SIC 4731 4212 7389 4215 Freight forwarding; Courier services, except by air; Moving services; Advertising, promotional & trade show services; Freight forwarding; Moving services; Advertising, promotional & trade show services; Courier services, except by air
CEO: Donald M Takaki
*Pr: Donn M Takaki
*COO: Neil Murakami
*Sr VP: Lyle I Okuda
*VP: Richard Olsen
*VP: Patrick Soken
Dir Risk M: Brian Uchima
*Prin: Carl Watanabe
Sfty Mgr: Brandis Mirafuentes
Sfty Mgr: Patrick Nakayama
Opers Mgr: Kenji Saito
Board of Directors: Carl Watanabe

D-U-N-S 78-471-2122
ISLAND OAKS LIVING CENTER LLC
3647 Maybank Hwy, Johns Island, SC 29455-4825
Tel (843) 559-5888 Founded/Ownrshp 2006
Sales 742.7MM EMP 99
SIC 8051 Skilled nursing care facilities
Prin: John Swift

D-U-N-S 15-362-1446 IMP/EXP
ISLAND OASIS FROZEN COCKTAIL CO INC
(Suby of KERRY GROUP PUBLIC LIMITED COMPANY)
141 Norfolk St, Walpole, MA 02081-1703
Tel (508) 660-1177 Founded/Ownrshp 2015
Sales 161.7MME EMP 210
Accts Kpmg Peat Marwick Llp
SIC 5142 Fruit juices, frozen; Fruit juices, frozen
CEO: J Michael Herbert
CFO: Scott A Kumf
Sr VP: Jeff Lombardo
VP: Barry Boehme
VP: Sohail Khan
VP: Phil Marcasciano
Genl Mgr: Joe Keaney
IT Man: Joshua Wexler
Opers Mgr: Randy Mackenzie
Opers Mgr: Thomas Powell
Plnt Mgr: John Kasinecz

D-U-N-S 10-072-7171
ISLAND OF HAWAII SCHOOL DISTRICT
(Suby of EDUCATION BOARD) ★
75 Aupuni St Rm 203, Hilo, HI 96720-4245
Tel (808) 974-6600 Founded/Ownrshp 1959
Sales 43.1MME EMP 1,020
SIC 8211 Public elementary & secondary schools; Public elementary & secondary schools

D-U-N-S 07-323-4056
ISLAND ONE INC
ISLAND ONE RESORTS
7345 Greenbriar Pkwy, Orlando, FL 32819-8935
Tel (407) 859-8900 Founded/Ownrshp 1981
Sales 161.6MME EMP 900
SIC 1522 Residential construction; Residential construction
CEO: Deborah A Linden
Sr VP: Karen S Holbrook
VP: Nancy L Ogden

ISLAND ONE RESORTS
See ISLAND ONE INC

D-U-N-S 17-370-9148
ISLAND OPERATING CO INC
108 Zachary Dr, Scott, LA 70583-5332
Tel (337) 262-0620 Founded/Ownrshp 1986
Sales 352.6MME EMP 1,300
SIC 1389 Oil field services; Oil field services
Pr: Gregg H Falgout
CFO: Kaoen Deen
Ex VP: Kimberly Falgout
VP: Ray Williams
Software D: Roy Miller
Mktg Mgr: Darrel Mouton
Sls Mgr: Sadi Hulin

D-U-N-S 83-196-5087
ISLAND OPERATING CO INC
(Suby of ISLAND OPERATING CO INC) ★
770 S Post Oak Ln Ste 400, Houston, TX 77056-6666
Tel (713) 552-0042 Founded/Ownrshp 2009
Sales 28.8MME EMP 857E
SIC 8741 Management services
Prin: Gregg Falgout
VP Sls: Tim Doyle

ISLAND PACKET YACHTS
See TRADITIONAL WATERCRAFT INC

D-U-N-S 16-824-2068
ISLAND PALM COMMUNITIES LLC
215 Duck Rd Bldg 950, Schofield Barracks, HI 96857
Tel (808) 275-3100 Founded/Ownrshp 2012
Sales 170.0MME EMP 250
SIC 6531 Real estate leasing & rentals; Real estate leasing & rentals

D-U-N-S 14-762-7939
ISLAND PEER REVIEW ORGANIZATION INC
IPRO
1979 Marcus Ave Ste 105, New Hyde Park, NY 11042-1072
Tel (516) 326-7767 Founded/Ownrshp 1983
Sales 67.0MM EMP 400
Accts Bdo Usa Llp New York Ny
SIC 8742 Hospital & health services consultant; Hospital & health services consultant
CEO: Theodore O Will
*Pr: Donald Winikoff
*CFO: Alan King
VP: Erin Maggi
QA Dir: Susan Astor
Opers Mgr: Jas-Michael King
Pharmcst: Anne Myrka
Board of Directors: Laurel Pickering, Charles Stimler

D-U-N-S 55-635-2003 EXP
ISLAND PIZZA INC
DOMINO'S PIZZA
6701 Marginal Biascochea, Carolina, PR 00979-7601
Tel (787) 253-0200 Founded/Ownrshp 1991
Sales 8.2MME EMP 525
SIC 5812 Pizzeria, chain; Pizzeria, chain
Pr: Edward Lieberman
*Treas: Mary Lieberman
*Sec: William Casteline

D-U-N-S 07-631-1539 IMP/EXP
ISLAND PYROCHEMICAL INDUSTRIES CORP (NY)
267 E Jericho Tpke Ste 2, Mineola, NY 11501-2100
Tel (516) 746-2100 Founded/Ownrshp 1982
Sales 24.6MME EMP 215
SIC 3081 2899 5169 Film base, cellulose acetate or nitrocellulose plastic; Pyrotechnic ammunition: flares, signals, rockets, etc.; Chemicals & allied products; Film base, cellulose acetate or nitrocellulose plastic; Pyrotechnic ammunition: flares, signals, rockets, etc.; Chemicals & allied products
Pr: Amnon Parizat
*VP: Anne Parizat
VP: William Solomon
Dir IT: Amnon Wells

D-U-N-S 11-323-0031 EXP
ISLAND RECYCLING INC
91-140 Kaomi Loop, Kapolei, HI 96707-1712
Tel (808) 682-9200 Founded/Ownrshp 1984
Sales 23.3MME EMP 80
SIC 5093 Metal scrap & waste materials; Waste paper; Metal scrap & waste materials; Waste paper
Pr: James Nutter
*VP: Karin Leigh Nutter
Opers Mgr: Kevin Centron
Board of Directors: Betty Morton

D-U-N-S 78-175-6390
ISLAND RESORT & CASINO
CHIP IN CASINO
W399 Hwy 2, Harris, MI 49845
Tel (906) 466-2941 Founded/Ownrshp 1986
Sales 21.2MME EMP 705
SIC 7011 Casino hotel; Casino hotel
Chf Mktg O: Susan Harris
Genl Mgr: Thomas McChesney
Snr Mgr: Joe Stanchina

ISLAND RESORT AND CASINO
See HANNAHVILLE INDIAN COMMUNITY

D-U-N-S 09-045-1477
ISLAND SECURITY SERVICES INC
418 Calle Agueybana Ste 1, San Juan, PR 00918-3316
Tel (787) 274-8286 Founded/Ownrshp 1987
Sales 6.5MM^E EMP 600
SIC 7381 Protective services, guard; Protective services, guard
Pr: Elliott Salgado
*VP: Angel Ortiz Acevedo

D-U-N-S 05-062-4428
■ **ISLAND TELEPHONE CO** (MI)
TDS
(Suby of TDS TELECOMMUNICATIONS CORP) ★
37940 King Hwy, Beaver Island, MI 49782
Tel (608) 831-1000 Founded/Ownrshp 1957, 1991
Sales 867.0MM EMP 2,700
SIC 4813 Local telephone communications; Local telephone communications
Pr: David A Witter

D-U-N-S 60-277-1297
ISLAND TENNIS LP
SPORTIME
275 Old Indianhead Rd, Kings Park, NY 11754-4811
Tel (631) 269-6300 Founded/Ownrshp 1998
Sales 77.8MM^E EMP 600
SIC 5941 7997 Tennis goods & equipment; Tennis club, membership; Tennis goods & equipment; Tennis club, membership
CEO: Claude Okin
Rgnl Mgr: Jodi Krifchin
Genl Mgr: Bea Bielik
Genl Mgr: Rene Bond
Genl Mgr: Sue De Lara
Genl Mgr: Jay Harris
Genl Mgr: Jed Murray

D-U-N-S 00-887-3051
ISLAND TRANSPORTATION CORP
299 Edison Ave Ste 100, West Babylon, NY 11704-1031
Tel (732) 541-8091 Founded/Ownrshp 1959
Sales 41.0MM^E EMP 200
SIC 4213 4212 Trucking, except local; Local trucking, without storage; Trucking, except local; Local trucking, without storage
Pr: Peter Fioretti
VP: Brian Fioretti

D-U-N-S 07-849-4136
ISLAND TREES UNION FREE SCHOOL DISTRICT
74 Farmedge Rd, Levittown, NY 11756-5202
Tel (516) 520-2100 Founded/Ownrshp 2012
Sales 13.3MM^E EMP 447^E
SIC 8211 Elementary & secondary schools
Prin: Nicholas Grande

D-U-N-S 04-718-7737
ISLAND TREES UNION FREE SCHOOL DISTRICT 26
74 Farmedge Rd, Levittown, NY 11756-5202
Tel (516) 520-2111 Founded/Ownrshp 1900
Sales 25.7MM EMP 400
SIC 8211 Public elementary school; Public junior high school; Public senior high school; Public elementary school; Public junior high school; Public senior high school
Treas: Michael Kearns
VP: Daniel Donahue
VP: Kenneth Rochon
Schl Brd P: Oeter Ray
Psych: Amanda Walker

ISLAND VIEW CASINO RESORT
See GULFSIDE CASINO PARTNERSHIP

ISLAND VIEW CASINO RESORT
See GRAND CASINOS INC

ISLANDAIRE
See RE HANSEN INDUSTRIES INC

D-U-N-S 78-963-4391 IMP
ISLANDER GROUP INC
BOOKLINES HAWAII
269 Palii St, Mililani, HI 96789-3964
Tel (808) 676-0116 Founded/Ownrshp 1992
Sales 32.7MM^E EMP 109
SIC 5192 5199 5112

ISLANDS FINE BURGER & DRINKS
See ISLANDS RESTAURANTS LP

D-U-N-S 60-574-4452
ISLANDS MANAGEMENT CO LLC
LEGACY LODGE
7000 Lanier Islands Pkwy, Buford, GA 30518-1442
Tel (770) 945-8787 Founded/Ownrshp 2005
Sales 25.9MM^E EMP 250
SIC 7011 Hotels; Hotels
Genl Mgr: Boyce Grier Todd
*CFO: Rebecca Henderson

D-U-N-S 80-901-3253 IMP
ISLANDS MECHANICAL CONTRACTOR INC
IMC
3070 Blanding Blvd, Middleburg, FL 32068-6337
Tel (904) 406-6100 Founded/Ownrshp 1992
Sales 28.0MM EMP 190
Accts James W Mathews Jacksonville
SIC 1711 1541 1629 Mechanical contractor; Industrial buildings & warehouses; Industrial buildings, new construction; Prefabricated building erection, industrial; Industrial plant construction; Mechanical contractor; Industrial buildings & warehouses; Industrial buildings, new construction; Prefabricated building erection, industrial; Industrial plant construction
CEO: Ronnie E Chason
*Pr: Bob Turnage
*CFO: Robert Turnage
Netwrk Eng: Crisanto Samiano

D-U-N-S 78-688-8305
ISLANDS RESTAURANTS LP
ISLANDS FINE BURGER & DRINKS
5750 Fleet St Ste 120, Carlsbad, CA 92008-4709
Tel (760) 268-1800 Founded/Ownrshp 1982
Sales 112.9MM^E EMP 2,500
SIC 5812 Hamburger stand; Hamburger stand
Sr VP: Ben Schwartz
Pt: Tony Deguazier
COO: Jeff Brackey
CFO: Rob Richards
VP: Lewis Jackson
VP: Tim Perreira
Genl Mgr: Carmen Valentino
Off Mgr: Scott Blakeman
Mktg Mgr: Cara Sprague

ISLE CASINO HOTEL BLACK HAWK
See ISLE OF CAPRI BLACK HAWK LLC

D-U-N-S 01-590-6220
■ **ISLE OF CAPRI BETTENDORF LC**
(Suby of ISLE OF CAPRI CASINOS INC) ★
1800 Isle Pkwy, Bettendorf, IA 52722-4982
Tel (800) 843-4753 Founded/Ownrshp 2000
Sales 28.6MM^E EMP 923
Accts Ernst & Young Des Moines Iow
SIC 7011 5812 Casino hotel; Eating places; Casino hotel; Eating places
VP: MO Hyder

ISLE OF CAPRI BILOXI
See RIVERBOAT CORP OF MISSISSIPPI

D-U-N-S 03-623-3372
■ **ISLE OF CAPRI BLACK HAWK LLC**
ISLE CASINO HOTEL BLACK HAWK
(Suby of ISLE OF CAPRI CASINOS INC) ★
401 Main St, Black Hawk, CO 80422
Tel (303) 998-7777 Founded/Ownrshp 1997
Sales 52.7MM^E EMP 850
SIC 7011 Casino hotel; Casino hotel
CEO: Robert B Sturges
*Ex VP: Allan B Solomon
*VP: Robert S Fiore
VP: Brian Watts
Dir Surg: Greg Kite
Dir Surg: Tood Stefen
Dir Surg: Jeff Towndend
Sales Exec: Kari Johnson

D-U-N-S 04-485-7485
ISLE OF CAPRI CASINO & HOTEL
1118 W Main St, Mc Gregor, IA 52157-8549
Tel (563) 873-3531 Founded/Ownrshp 2004
Sales 7.1MM^E EMP 312
SIC 7011 Casino hotel; Casino hotel
Prin: Pam Coler
Genl Mgr: Darren Fuller

D-U-N-S 60-825-5589
ISLE OF CAPRI CASINO & HOTEL
100 Antimonopoly St, Marquette, IA 52158-7731
Tel (563) 873-3531 Founded/Ownrshp 1999
Sales 4.2MM^E EMP 500
SIC 7011 Casino hotel; Casino hotel
Ch: Dan Becwar
*Pr: John Galloway
*Treas: Rexford Yeisley
Admn Mgr: Tracy Baker

D-U-N-S 79-536-8232
▲ **ISLE OF CAPRI CASINOS INC**
600 Emerson Rd Ste 300, Saint Louis, MO 63141-6762
Tel (314) 813-9200 Founded/Ownrshp 1992
Sales 996.2MM EMP 7,100^E
Accts Ernst & Young Llp St Louis
Tkr Sym ISLE Exch NGS
SIC 7011 7948 Hotels & motels; Racing, including track operation; Hotels & motels; Racing, including track operation
Pr: Virginia M McDowell
COO: Arnold L Block
CFO: Eric L Hausler
Ofcr: Donn R Mitchell II

D-U-N-S 80-961-8978
■ **ISLE OF CAPRI CASINOS INC**
(Suby of ISLE OF CAPRI CASINOS INC) ★
1800 E Front St, Kansas City, MO 64120-1406
Tel (816) 855-7777 Founded/Ownrshp 2005
Sales 27.2MM^E EMP 850
SIC 7999 Gambling & lottery services; Gambling & lottery services
Genl Mgr: Chet Koch
VP: Julia Carcamo
Genl Mgr: Dan Weindruch
MIS Mgr: Bryan Johnson
MIS Mgr: Duncan Mc Kenzie

D-U-N-S 60-768-9833
■ **ISLE OF CAPRI DAVENPORT INC**
RHYTHM CITY CASINO
(Suby of ISLE OF CAPRI CASINOS INC) ★
1777 Isle Pkwy, Bettendorf, IA 52722-4967
Tel (563) 328-8000 Founded/Ownrshp 2000
Sales 19.4MM^E EMP 868
SIC 7999 Gambling establishment; Gambling establishment
Pr: MO Hyder
VP: Nancy Donovan

ISLE OF CAPRI HOTEL
See ISLE OF CAPRI INC

D-U-N-S 80-513-2727
■ **ISLE OF CAPRI INC**
ISLE OF CAPRI HOTEL
(Suby of ISLE OF CAPRI CASINOS INC) ★
600 Emerson Rd Ste 300, Saint Louis, MO 63141-6762
Tel (601) 445-0605 Founded/Ownrshp 1998
Sales 14.1MM^E EMP 464
SIC 7011 Casino hotel; Hotels; Casino hotel; Hotels
Pr: John Gallaway
MIS Mgr: Wallace Duplechain
Mktg Mgr: Colin Spewak

D-U-N-S 08-757-3130
■ **ISLE OF CAPRI LAKE CHARLES**
(Suby of ISLE OF CAPRI CASINOS INC) ★
100 Westlake Ave, Westlake, LA 70669-5716
Tel (337) 430-2400 Founded/Ownrshp 1994
Sales 40.6MM^E EMP 2,021
SIC 7011 Casino hotel; Casino hotel
CEO: Bernard Goldstein
*Pr: John M Gallaway
*Pr: Allan B Solomon
*CFO: Rexford Yeisley

D-U-N-S 03-927-7657
■ **ISLE OF CAPRI OF BOONVILLE**
CAPRI ISLE CASINO
(Suby of ISLE OF CAPRI CASINOS INC) ★
100 Isle Of Capri Blvd, Boonville, MO 65233-1124
Tel (800) 941-4753 Founded/Ownrshp 2001
Sales 80.0MM EMP 400
SIC 7011 Casino hotel
CEO: Virginia McDowell
*VP: Barron Fuller

D-U-N-S 01-006-6769
ISLE OF WIGHT COUNTY
17130 Monument Cir Ste A, Isle of Wight, VA 23397
Tel (757) 357-3191 Founded/Ownrshp 1916
Sales NA EMP 350
Accts Cherry Bekaert Llp Virginia
SIC 9111 Executive offices; ; Executive offices;
Bd of Dir: Kelly Harcum
Dir IT: Lyle Hornbaker

D-U-N-S 07-979-8855
ISLE OF WIGHT COUNTY PUBLIC SCHOOLS
820 W Main St, Smithfield, VA 23430-1034
Tel (757) 357-8841 Founded/Ownrshp 2015
Sales 4.8MM^E EMP 505^E
SIC 8211 Public elementary & secondary schools

D-U-N-S 06-595-3085
ISLIP UNION FREE SCHOOL DISTRICT
215 Main St Unit 2, Islip, NY 11751-3435
Tel (631) 859-2200 Founded/Ownrshp 1875
Sales 28.0MM^E EMP 450
SIC 8211 Public elementary & secondary schools; High school, junior or senior; Public elementary & secondary schools; High school, junior or senior
IT Man: Michael Zeterberg
Schl Brd P: Mary Dennis

ISMG
See INTERNATIONAL SECURITY MANAGEMENT GROUP INC

D-U-N-S 11-368-7164
ISMIE MUTUAL INSURANCE CO
(Suby of ILLINOIS STATE MEDICAL SOCIETY) ★
20 N Michigan Ave Ste 700, Chicago, IL 60602-4822
Tel (312) 782-2749 Founded/Ownrshp 1976
Sales NA EMP 225^E
SIC 6351 Liability insurance; Liability insurance
CEO: Alexander R Lerner
*Pr: Harold L Jersen MD
*Sec: Walter Whisler MD

ISN
See INTEGRATED SUPPLY NETWORK LLC

ISN COMMUNICATIONS
See INTERACTIVE SERVICES NETWORK INC

D-U-N-S 03-737-6907
ISN SOFTWARE CORP
ISNETWORLD
3232 Mckinney Ave # 1500, Dallas, TX 75204-2429
Tel (214) 303-4900 Founded/Ownrshp 2001
Sales 112.0MM^E EMP 233^E
SIC 5045 5734 Computers, peripherals & software; Computer software & accessories; Computers, peripherals & software; Computer software & accessories
CEO: William M Addy
*Pr: Brian Callahan
*Pr: Joseph Eastin
CFO: Rich Fitzpatrick
Ex VP: Joe Eastin
*Sr VP: Saks Ishrat
VP: Dusty Ferrell
Dir IT: Gabe Tijerina
Snr Mgr: Richard Cerenzio
Snr Mgr: Kim Cravens

ISNETWORLD
See ISN SOFTWARE CORP

D-U-N-S 12-984-7310 IMP/EXP
ISO GROUP INC
ISO PARTS
2350 Commerce Park Dr Ne # 2, Palm Bay, FL 32905-7722
Tel (877) 330-1580 Founded/Ownrshp 2003
Sales 64.0MM^E EMP 70
SIC 5088 Transportation equipment & supplies
CFO: Ludovic Sautreuil
Ofcr: Paul Pikel
*VP: Michael Gibson
VP: David Hahn
*VP: Dan Holloway
Mng Dir: Waiel Abukhaled
IT Man: Josh Walker
Opers Mgr: Terry Klassen
VP Sls: Alex Techoueyres
Sls Mgr: Rusty Hammes

ISO MUSIC STAND
See INDIANA SYMPHONY SOCIETY INC

D-U-N-S 78-814-2123
ISO NEW ENGLAND INC
1 Sullivan Rd, Holyoke, MA 01040-2841
Tel (413) 535-4000 Founded/Ownrshp 1997
Sales 163.1MM EMP 560
Accts Kpmg Llp Boston Ma
SIC 8611 Public utility association; Public utility association
Pr: Gordon Van Welie
COO: Vamsi Chadalavada

*CFO: Robert C Ludlow
*V Ch Bd: Kathryn J Jackson
Ofcr: Rhonda Meunier
*VP: Jamshid Afnan
VP: Kevin A Kirby
*VP: David Laplante
Dir IT: Debi Smith
IT Man: Steve Bonasoni
IT Man: Peter Sadloski
Board of Directors: Roberta S Brown, Roberto Denis, Ray Hill, Kathryn J Jackson, Louise McCarren, Barney Rush, Vickie Vanzandt, David Vitale

ISO PARTS
See ISO GROUP INC

D-U-N-S 79-945-3808 IMP
ISO POLY FILMS INC
SIGMA PLASTICS GROUP
(Suby of ALPHA INDUSTRIES MANAGEMENT INC) ★
101 Iso Pkwy, Gray Court, SC 29645-4856
Tel (864) 876-4300 Founded/Ownrshp 1998
Sales 22.2MM^E EMP 120^E
SIC 3081 Polyvinyl film & sheet; Polyvinyl film & sheet
Pr: Jonathan T McClure
VP: Tom Saxon
VP: Beth Scherpenberg

D-U-N-S 10-540-5091
ISO SERVICES INC
I S O
545 Washington Blvd Fl 12, Jersey City, NJ 07310-1613
Tel (201) 469-2000 Founded/Ownrshp 2002
Sales 172.5MM^E EMP 3,000^E
SIC 7375 Data base information retrieval; Data base information retrieval
CEO: Scott G Stephenson
*Ex VP: Mark V Anquillare
*Ex VP: Kenneth E Thompson
*Sr VP: Vince McCarthy
*Sr VP: Perry F Rotella
VP: Rama Duvvuri
VP: Phil Hatfield
VP: Theresa Lea
QA Dir: Bhavna Mukhi
IT Man: Sam Halas
Sftwr Eng: Mark Palczewski

ISOLA GROUP S.A.R.L.
See ISOLA USA CORP

D-U-N-S 19-139-7702 IMP
ISOLA USA CORP
ISOLA GROUP S.A.R.L.
(Suby of TPG GROWTH) ★
3100 W Ray Rd Ste 301, Chandler, AZ 85226-2527
Tel (480) 893-6527 Founded/Ownrshp 2005
Sales 133.9MM^E EMP 500
SIC 3083 Plastic finished products, laminated; Plastic finished products, laminated
CEO: Ray Sharpe
Pr: Robert Chaney
*Pr: Matt Laront
*Pr: Raymond Sharpe
*CFO: Gordon Bitter
*Ex VP: Tarun Amla
VP: Mike Behling
*VP: Lambert Calvert
*VP: Richard Caron
VP: Chuck Englebert
VP: Michael Gastonguay
*VP: Nina Haralambidis
VP: Tim McCloskey
VP: Alan R Potte
VP: Mike Rafford
VP: Saeed Sardar

D-U-N-S 07-877-3296 IMP
ISOLITE INC
1 Brozzini Ct Ste G, Greenville, SC 29615-5363
Tel (864) 332-9782 Founded/Ownrshp 2012
Sales 26.7MM^E EMP 270
SIC 3357 Nonferrous wiredrawing & insulating; Nonferrous wiredrawing & insulating
CFO: Eck Christian
*CEO: Mattias Kroll

D-U-N-S 96-818-5145
ISOLUX CORSAN LLC
ISOLUX CRSAN GRUPO ISLUX CRSAN
(Suby of GRUPO ISOLUX CORSAN SA)
3755 S Capital Of Texas H, Austin, TX 78704-6644
Tel (512) 416-5510 Founded/Ownrshp 2009
Sales 45.2MM^E EMP 180
SIC 8711 8741 Engineering services; Engineering services; Construction management
CEO: Javier Rivera
CFO: Luis Cisnal Fernandez
Prin: Karla Pascarella

ISOLUX CRSAN GRUPO ISLUX CRSAN
See ISOLUX CORSAN LLC

D-U-N-S 78-812-9153
■ **ISOMEDIX OPERATIONS INC**
(Suby of STERIS CORP) ★
5960 Heisley Rd, Mentor, OH 44060-1834
Tel (440) 354-2600 Founded/Ownrshp 1997
Sales 43.1MM^E EMP 1,000^E
SIC 8734 Industrial sterilization service
Pr: Robert E Moss
Treas: Karen L Burton
VP: Michael J Tokich

D-U-N-S 87-670-9619
▲ **ISONICS CORP**
535 8th Ave Fl 3, New York, NY 10018-4305
Tel (212) 356-7400 Founded/Ownrshp 1992
Sales 22.1MM EMP 384
Tkr Sym ISON Exch OTO
SIC 2819 3674 Isotopes, radioactive; Silicon wafers, chemically doped; Isotopes, radioactive; Silicon wafers, chemically doped
Ch Bd: Christopher Toffales
*Pr: John Sakys
*CFO: Gregory A Meadows
VP: Marshall Combs
VP: Daniel J Grady

D-U-N-S 07-451-3235
ISOTHERMAL COMMUNITY COLLEGE
(*Suby of* NORTH CAROLINA COMMUNITY COLLEGE SYSTEM) ★
286 Icc Loop Rd, Spindale, NC 28160
Tel (828) 286-3636 *Founded/Ownrshp* 1965
Sales 16.0MM^E *EMP* 350
Accts Lowdermilk Church & Co Llp Mo
SIC 8222 9411 Community college; Administration of educational programs; ; Community college; Administration of educational programs;
Pr: Dr Myra Johnson
**Ch:* Mr Grady Franklin

D-U-N-S 80-108-9152
ISOTIS ORTHOBIOLOGICS INC
(*Suby of* ISOTIS INTERNATIONAL SARL)
2 Goodyear Ste A, Irvine, CA 92618-2052
Tel (949) 595-8710 *Founded/Ownrshp* 2008
Sales 21.3MM^E *EMP* 150
SIC 8731 5047 Biological research; Surgical equipment & supplies; Biological research; Surgical equipment & supplies
CEO: Keith Valentine
**Pr:* Peter J Arduini
Pr: Bob Seth
**Ex VP:* Christian S Schade
VP: Alan Donze
Prin: Nancy Toledo
IT Man: Fred Tomaseck
IT Man: Long Tran

ISOTOPE PRODUCTS LAB
See ECKERT & ZIEGLER ISOTOPE PRODUCTS INC

D-U-N-S 13-541-2869 IMP/EXP
■ **ISP CHEMICALS INC**
(*Suby of* INTERNATIONAL SPECIALTY HOLDINGS INC) ★
1361 Alps Rd, Wayne, NJ 07470-3700
Tel (973) 628-4000 *Founded/Ownrshp* 2001
Sales 170.2MM^E *EMP* 1,500^E
SIC 2869 Industrial organic chemicals; Industrial organic chemicals
CEO: Sunil Kumar
Genl Mgr: Gorden Miller

D-U-N-S 00-218-8894 IMP
■ **ISP CHEMICALS LLC**
(*Suby of* ISP CHEMICALS INC) ★
455 N Main St, Calvert City, KY 42029-8942
Tel (270) 395-4165 *Founded/Ownrshp* 2001
Sales 110.5MM^E *EMP* 600^E
SIC 2869 Industrial organic chemicals; Industrial organic chemicals
**VP:* Jerry Kimball

D-U-N-S 78-534-5208
■ **ISP MANAGEMENT CO INC**
(*Suby of* ISP CHEMICALS INC) ★
1361 Alps Rd, Wayne, NJ 07470-3688
Tel (973) 628-0770 *Founded/Ownrshp* 1998
Sales 21.0MM^E *EMP* 300
SIC 5999 Fiberglass materials, except insulation; Fiberglass materials, except insulation
Pr: Sunil Kumar
**Treas:* Ed Prosapio
**Ex VP:* Susan Yoss
**VP:* Kenneth McHugh
**CIO:* Kenneth Morris

ISQFT
See CONSTRUCTION SOFTWARE TECHNOLOGIES INC

D-U-N-S 60-449-3304
ISRAEL A ENGLANDER & CO INC
666 5th Ave Ste 1410, New York, NY 10103-1499
Tel (212) 841-4500 *Founded/Ownrshp* 1985
Sales 41.0MM *EMP* 60
SIC 6211 Floor traders, security; Floor traders, security
Pr: Steven Tobias
CFO: Michael Fruchter
**CFO:* Kevin Golden
**Sr VP:* John D Gelbard
**VP:* Israel Englander
Mng Dir: Matthew Shaffer
Snr Mgr: Emily Garber
Snr Mgr: David Gordon

D-U-N-S 01-929-2861 IMP/EXP
ISRAEL ANDLER & SONS INC
ANDLER BOTTLE CO
376 3rd St, Everett, MA 02149-4718
Tel (617) 387-5700 *Founded/Ownrshp* 1915
Sales 49.3MM^E *EMP* 67
SIC 5085 7389 Glass bottles; Plastic bottles; Labeling bottles, cans, cartons, etc.; Glass bottles; Plastic bottles; Labeling bottles, cans, cartons, etc.
Pr: Arnold Andler
CFO: Rick Lewin
**Treas:* Marc Andler
Sales Asso: Mark Goodman

D-U-N-S 02-731-9338
ISRAEL BIRTHRIGHT FOUNDATION
33 E 33rd St Fl 7, New York, NY 10016-5354
Tel (212) 457-0036 *Founded/Ownrshp* 1999
Sales 74.2MM *EMP* 35
Accts Grant Thornton Llp New York
SIC 8641 Civic social & fraternal associations
Pr: Robert Aronson
**COO:* Maxyne Finkelstein
**CFO:* David Shapiro
Ex Dir: Linda Yepoyan

D-U-N-S 07-646-2324
ISRAEL DISCOUNT BANK OF NEW YORK
IDB BANK OF NEW YORK
(*Suby of* ISRAEL DISCOUNT BANK LIMITED)
511 5th Ave, New York, NY 10017-4997
Tel (212) 551-8500 *Founded/Ownrshp* 1949
Sales NA *EMP* 500
SIC 6022 State commercial banks; State commercial banks
Pr: Arie Sheer
**Ch Bd:* Jacob Berman
Pr: Patrick Egan
Pr: Jason Huie
Pr: Golan Kochanovsky
Pr: Lance Reisch
Pr: Ilya Teplitskiy
Pr: Enio Torres
Pr: Li Zhou
**COO:* David Cohen
CFO: Tom Kehrer
Ofcr: Debra Angulo
Ofcr: Lissa Baum
Ofcr: Stephanie Gonzalez
**Ex VP:* Haim Bar-Ziv
Ex VP: Christopher Camuglia
**Ex VP:* Edmond Eskenazi
Ex VP: Deborah Greene
**Ex VP:* Leonard Greer
Ex VP: Moise Hillel
**Ex VP:* Frank J Klein

D-U-N-S 79-789-4735
▲ **ISRAMCO INC**
2425 West Loop S Ste 810, Houston, TX 77027-4214
Tel (713) 621-5946 *Founded/Ownrshp* 1982
Sales 93.9MM *EMP* 263^E
Tkr Sym ISRL *Exch* NAS
SIC 1311 Crude petroleum & natural gas production; Crude petroleum & natural gas production
Ch Bd: Haim Tsuff
CFO: Edy Francis

D-U-N-S 04-328-2870 EXP
ISRINGHAUSEN IMPORTS INC (IL)
MERCEDES BENZ USA
229 E Jefferson St, Springfield, IL 62701-1018
Tel (217) 528-2277 *Founded/Ownrshp* 1977
Sales 35.1MM^E *EMP* 80
SIC 5511 Automobiles, new & used; Automobiles, new & used
Pr: Geoff Isringhausen Sr

D-U-N-S 16-608-4541
ISS ACTION INC
15812 Rockaway Blvd, Jamaica, NY 11434-4840
Tel (718) 978-3000 *Founded/Ownrshp* 1991
Sales 19.5MM^E *EMP* 500^E
SIC 7381 7382 Security guard service; Security systems services; Security guard service; Security systems services
CEO: Pamela Newman
**Pr:* Yehuda Daphna
Mktg Dir: Tom Copowski
Mktg Dir: Bud Heaning

D-U-N-S 10-879-4645
ISS C & S BUILDING MAINTENANCE CORP
1805 Se Hawthorne Rd, Gainesville, FL 32641-7412
Tel (352) 372-8753 *Founded/Ownrshp* 1988
Sales 15.9MM^E *EMP* 475
SIC 7363 7349 0782 Labor resource services; Janitorial service, contract basis; Landscape contractors; Labor resource services; Janitorial service, contract basis; Landscape contractors
Pr: Phyllis Sperring
**Sec:* Tom Sperring

ISS EXPORT
See SALAH SMOUDI

D-U-N-S 11-599-6811
ISS FACILITIES SERVICE INC
2606 Phoenix Dr Ste 200, Greensboro, NC 27406-6353
Tel (336) 855-8480 *Founded/Ownrshp* 1981
Sales 11.3MM^E *EMP* 650
SIC 7349 Janitorial service, contract basis; Janitorial service, contract basis
Pr: Jim Williams
Exec: Maria Path
VP Opers: John Stegall
VP Sls: Bob McLean

D-U-N-S 09-511-1217
ISS FACILITY SERVICES HOLDING INC
(*Suby of* ISS HOLDING INC) ★
1019 Central Pkwy N # 100, San Antonio, TX 78232-5027
Tel (210) 495-6021 *Founded/Ownrshp* 1978
Sales 582.0MM^E *EMP* 15,000
SIC 7349 Building maintenance services; Building maintenance services
CEO: Jennifer Bonilla
Sr VP: Katie Holloway
VP: Arrish Bautista
VP: Billy Tenardhi
VP: Michael Trolley

D-U-N-S 15-296-9077
ISS FACILITY SERVICES INC
4155 N Rancho Dr Ste 150, Las Vegas, NV 89130-3448
Tel (702) 822-1982 *Founded/Ownrshp* 2007
Sales 9.3MM^E *EMP* 500
SIC 7349 7381 Janitorial service, contract basis; Security guard service; Janitorial service, contract basis; Security guard service
Pr: Darrell Glover
**CFO:* Christi Rohmer

D-U-N-S 80-142-6128
ISS FACILITY SERVICES INC
(*Suby of* ISS FACILITY SERVICES HOLDING INC) ★
1019 Central Pkwy N # 100, San Antonio, TX 78232-5078
Tel (210) 495-6021 *Founded/Ownrshp* 2007
Sales 220.4MM^E *EMP* 4,000^E
SIC 7699 Cleaning services; Cleaning services
Pr: Jennifer Bonilla
Sr VP: Katie Holloway
VP: Cornel Sneekes
Site Mgr: Angelo Cracchiolo

D-U-N-S 79-618-1253
ISS GROUNDS CONTROL INC
10822 Chandler Blvd, North Hollywood, CA 91601-2937
Tel (661) 259-9067 *Founded/Ownrshp* 1998
Sales 10.4MM^E *EMP* 330
SIC 0782 5261 Landscape contractors; Nurseries & garden centers; Landscape contractors; Nurseries & garden centers
Pr: James Blumel
**Sr VP:* Daniel Blumel

D-U-N-S 96-346-8454
ISS HOLDING INC
1019 Central Pkwy N # 100, San Antonio, TX 78232-5078
Tel (210) 495-6021 *Founded/Ownrshp* 2007
Sales 582.0MM^E *EMP* 15,000^E
SIC 7349 Building maintenance services
CEO: Jennifer Bonilla
Sr VP: Katie Holloway

D-U-N-S 10-416-9664
ISS MARINE SERVICES INC
INCHCAPE SHIPPING SERVICES
(*Suby of* INCHCAPE SHIPPING SERVICES HOLDINGS LIMITED)
11 N Water St Ste 9290, Mobile, AL 36602-5009
Tel (251) 461-2747 *Founded/Ownrshp* 2001
Sales 58.6MM^E *EMP* 201^E
SIC 4491 Marine cargo handling; Marine cargo handling
CEO: Chris Whiteside
**COO:* Tim Cahill
CFO: Rahul Choudhary
**CFO:* Michael Van Hemert
CFO: Ian Whelan
Ex VP: Charlotte Wills
Sr VP: Ian Tombs
VP: Elaine Dearmon
Exec: Ravi Nathaniel
Exec: Ismail Navrange
Dir Bus: Harish Nair
Dir Bus: Ahmed Selim

D-U-N-S 05-127-3266
ISS TMC SERVICES INC
(*Suby of* ISS FACILITY SERVICES INC) ★
81 Dorsa Ave, Livingston, NJ 07039-1002
Tel (973) 740-0032 *Founded/Ownrshp* 1964
Sales 77.6MM^E *EMP* 2,500
SIC 6512 7349 7699 Nonresidential building operators; Janitorial service, contract basis; Building maintenance, except repairs; Cleaning services; Nonresidential building operators; Janitorial service, contract basis; Building maintenance, except repairs; Cleaning services
CEO: Philip Caprio
**VP:* Joseph C Caprio
**VP:* Philip W Caprio Jr

D-U-N-S 15-423-2920
ISS WORLDWIDE
B G SERVICE SOLUTIONS
1225 E 18th St, Kansas City, MO 64108-1605
Tel (816) 421-8088 *Founded/Ownrshp* 1972
Sales 48.4MM^E *EMP* 3,425
SIC 7349 7381 Building maintenance, except repairs; Janitorial service, contract basis; Security guard service; Building maintenance, except repairs; Janitorial service, contract basis; Security guard service
Ch: Ronald Baker
**Pr:* Sonny Price
**VP:* Judy Brown
VP: Harry Engert

D-U-N-S 80-825-8073
ISSAC MEDICAL INC
2761 Walnut Ave, Tustin, CA 92780-7051
Tel (714) 415-0280 *Founded/Ownrshp* 2001
Sales 65.7MM^E *EMP* 320
SIC 3841 Surgical & medical instruments; Surgical & medical instruments
CEO: William Reising
**Pr:* Ron Fraleigh
VP: Don Borje
**VP:* Tom Mazelin
Sls Mgr: Chris Mazelin

D-U-N-S 07-183-8924
ISSAQUAH SCHOOL DISTRICT 411
565 Nw Holly St, Issaquah, WA 98027-2899
Tel (425) 837-7000 *Founded/Ownrshp* 1889
Sales 284.4MM *EMP* 1,700
SIC 8211 9411 Public elementary school; Public junior high school; Public senior high school; Administration of educational programs; Public elementary school; Public junior high school; Public senior high school; Administration of educational programs
**CFO:* Jacob Kuper
Bd of Dir: Connie Fletcher
Bd of Dir: Alison Meryweather
Web Dev: Brian Ruedi
Teacher Pr: Lisa Heckman
Psych: Kristina Ashby
Psych: Columbare Kristen
Psych: Kirkpatrick Terry

D-U-N-S 10-288-6215 IMP
ISSC INC
SEAPORT STEEL
3660 E Marginal Way S, Seattle, WA 98134-1130
Tel (206) 343-0700 *Founded/Ownrshp* 1983
Sales 102.1MM^E *EMP* 95
SIC 5051 Structural shapes, iron or steel; Plates, metal; Steel; Structural shapes, iron or steel; Plates, metal; Steel
CEO: Lawrence James
**Ch Bd:* Mary McCullough
**Pr:* Rory James
COO: Jim Fetch
**CFO:* Nathaniel Highlander
**Sec:* Joseph Brotherton
Prgrm Mgr: Mike Ridgley
Opers Mgr: Roy Jordan
Board of Directors: Joseph Brotherton, Nancy Pleas Chair Emeritu, Lawrence James, Mary McCullough Chb, Ryan Pleas, Colleen Raymond

ISSD
See PERFORMANCE CONTRACTING INC

ISSI
See INTERNATIONAL STEEL SERVICES INC

ISSI
See INDUSTRIAL SUPPLY SOLUTIONS INC

D-U-N-S 00-902-3292 IMP
ISSPRO INC (OR)
2515 Ne Riverside Way, Portland, OR 97211-1899
Tel (503) 288-4488 *Founded/Ownrshp* 1949, 1979
Sales 25.8MM^E *EMP* 102
SIC 3714 Instrument board assemblies, motor vehicle; Instrument board assemblies, motor vehicle
Pr: Paul Wendlick
**Treas:* Brad Hangartner
**VP:* Donald D Wendlick
Genl Mgr: Peggy Kelly
Natl Sales: Don Gardner

D-U-N-S 18-681-3200
ISSUES & ANSWERS NETWORK INC
5151 Bonney Rd Ste 100, Virginia Beach, VA 23462-4384
Tel (757) 456-1100 *Founded/Ownrshp* 1988
Sales 31.8MM^E *EMP* 550
SIC 8732 Opinion research; Market analysis or research; Opinion research; Market analysis or research
Pr: Peter Mc Guinness
**VP:* Carla Lindemann
IT Man: Scott Gilligan
IT Man: Pam Jenkins
VP Opers: Denise Dodson
Counsel: Williams Mullen

IST
See INDUSTRIAL STEEL TREATING CO

IST
See INTERNATIONAL SPECIALTY TUBE LLC

IST MANAGEMENT SERVICES
See INNOVATIVE SERVICE TECHNOLOGY MANAGEMENT SERVICES INC

IST SOLUCAR
See ABENGOA SOLAR LLC

D-U-N-S 17-640-4820
ISTA NORTH AMERICA INC
401 Congress Ave Ste 2650, Austin, TX 78701-3708
Tel (512) 201-8287 *Founded/Ownrshp* 2012
Sales 24.7MM^E *EMP* 162
SIC 7371 8748 Computer software development & applications; Energy conservation consultant; Computer software development & applications; Energy conservation consultant
Pr: Mark Ianni
**CFO:* Thomas Lemper
Ex VP: Cade Burks
**Ex VP:* Richard Espenhahn
**Sr VP:* Rudiger Neubauer
**VP:* Rachel Bryan
**CIO:* Jim Crysdale
S&M/VP: Lee Helt

D-U-N-S 95-721-2350
ISTA PHARMACEUTICALS INC
50 Technology Dr, Irvine, CA 92618-2301
Tel (949) 788-6000 *Founded/Ownrshp* 2012
Sales NA *EMP* 330
SIC 2834

D-U-N-S 02-811-6122
▲ **ISTAR FINANCIAL INC**
1114 Ave Of The Americas, New York, NY 10036-7703
Tel (212) 930-9400 *Founded/Ownrshp* 1993
Sales 462.0MM *EMP* 175^E
Accts Pricewaterhousecoopers Llp N
Tkr Sym STAR *Exch* NYS
SIC 6798 Real estate investment trusts; Real estate investment trusts
Ch Bd: Jay Sugarman
CFO: David Distaso
Ex VP: Curtis Chase
Ex VP: Chase S Curtis
Ex VP: Barclay G Jones III
Ex VP: Cabot Lodge
Ex VP: Michelle Mackay
Ex VP: Diane Olmstead
Ex VP: Barbara Rubin
Sr VP: Timothy J Doherty
Sr VP: William W Hyatt
Sr VP: Peter K Kofoed
Sr VP: Tom Pacha
Sr VP: Mark E Paparella
Sr VP: Erich J Stiger
Sr VP: Farzad Tabtabai
Sr VP: Cynthia M Tucker
VP: Elisha Blechner
VP: Greg Camia
VP: Anthony Esposito
VP: Alec Nedelman
Board of Directors: Robert W Holman Jr, Robin Josephs, John G McDonald, George P Puskar, Dale A Reiss, Barry W Ridings

ISTATE TRUCK
See INTERSTATE COMPANIES INC

D-U-N-S 16-960-9687
ISTATE TRUCK INC
(*Suby of* INTERSTATE COMPANIES INC) ★
2601 American Blvd E, Minneapolis, MN 55425-1321
Tel (952) 854-2044 *Founded/Ownrshp* 2005
Sales 131.5MM^E *EMP* 320
SIC 5084 Industrial machinery & equipment; Industrial machinery & equipment
CEO: Gordon D Galarneau
**Pr:* Jim Williams
**CEO:* Jeff Caswell
Genl Mgr: Jeff Webber
Mktg Mgr: Carl Brown

ISTC
See INTERNATIONAL SECURITY AND TRADING CORP

ISTI PLANT SERVICES
See INSULATION SPECIALISTS OF TULSA INC

D-U-N-S 78-704-8623
ISTITHMAR HOTELS WASHINGTON LLC
W WASHINGTON DC
515 15th St Nw, Washington, DC 20004-1006
Tel (202) 661-2400 *Founded/Ownrshp* 2006
Sales 40.1MM^E *EMP* 350
SIC 7389 7011 Advertising, promotional & trade show services; Hotels & motels; Advertising, promotional & trade show services; Hotels & motels
Genl Mgr: Julio Melendez
Prin: Nate Nucci
Sales Exec: Summer Abilmona
Sls Dir: Summer Belman
Sls Mgr: Tami Gonzales
Sls Mgr: Barb Vollet

ISU FOUNDATION
See IOWA STATE UNIVERSITY FOUNDATION

D-U-N-S 01-402-9784 IMP
ISU PETASYS CORP
(*Suby of* ISU CHEMICAL CO., LTD.)
12930 Bradley Ave, Sylmar, CA 91342-3829
Tel (818) 833-5800 *Founded/Ownrshp* 1997
Sales 20.6MM^E *EMP* 95
Accts Stephen S Whand & Co Los An
SIC 3672 Printed circuit boards
Pr: Yong Kyoun Kim
Exec: Dave Hwang

ISUZU CITY
See SCHLOSSMANN IMPORTS INC

D-U-N-S 13-194-4709 IMP/EXP
ISUZU COMMERCIAL TRUCK OF AMERICA INC
AMERICAN ISUZU MOTORS
(*Suby of* ISUZU NORTH AMERICA CORP) ★
1400 S Duglaca Rd Ste 100, Anaheim, CA 92806
Tel (714) 935-9300 *Founded/Ownrshp* 2003
Sales 57.5MM^E *EMP* 200^E
SIC 5511 Automobiles, new & used; Automobiles, new & used
CEO: Yoshifumi Komura
**Pr:* Gaku Nitta
Treas: Kimberly J Ruiz
Ex VP: Joe Totaro
VP: Jonathan C Harbaugh
VP: Linda Yamada
Ex Dir: Edward Crawford
Sls Mgr: Ed Fischer

D-U-N-S 03-445-4475 IMP/EXP
ISUZU MOTORS AMERICA LLC
(*Suby of* ISUZU NORTH AMERICA CORP) ★
1400 S Duglaca Rd Ste 100, Anaheim, CA 92806
Tel (734) 455-7595 *Founded/Ownrshp* 2008
Sales 79.9MM^E *EMP* 168^E
SIC 5511 7538 5012 Automobiles, new & used; General automotive repair shops; Automobiles & other motor vehicles; Automobiles, new & used; General automotive repair shops; Automobiles & other motor vehicles
VP: Sherry Woods
Snr Mgr: Dave Adkins
Snr Mgr: Julian Tan

D-U-N-S 07-840-7418 IMP
ISUZU NORTH AMERICA CORP
(*Suby of* ISUZU MOTORS LIMITED)
1400 S Douglass Rd # 100, Anaheim, CA 92806-6906
Tel (714) 935-9300 *Founded/Ownrshp* 1975
Sales 233.5MM^E *EMP* 600
SIC 5511 5084 5013 5015 Automobiles, new & used; Engines & parts, diesel; Automotive supplies & parts; Motor vehicle parts, used; Automobiles, new & used; Engines & parts, diesel; Automotive supplies & parts; Motor vehicle parts, used
CEO: Masayuki Fujimori
**Pr:* Yoshihumi Komura
**CEO:* Makoto Kawahara
VP: Dave Barneich
IT Man: Mike Milton
Opers Mgr: Michael Takemura
Sls Mgr: Jim Holmes
Snr Mgr: Michael Souveroff

ISUZU OF MADISON
See ZIMBRICK INC

ISUZU TRUCK OF COLUMBUS
See CENTER CITY INTERNATIONAL TRUCKS INC

ISUZU TRUCKS OF BIRMINGHAM
See KENWORTH OF BIRMINGHAM INC

D-U-N-S 86-832-1845
ISYS INC
ISYS TECHNOLOGIES
801 W Mineral Ave Ste 105, Littleton, CO 80120-5663
Tel (303) 290-8922 *Founded/Ownrshp* 1990
Sales 22.7MM *EMP* 145^E
SIC 7379 7371 Computer related consulting services; Computer software systems analysis & design, custom; Computer related consulting services; Computer software systems analysis & design, custom
Pr: Teresa Porter
**VP:* Kurt Hotto
Prgrm Mgr: Frank Toney
Prgrm Mgr: Brian Vickers
Genl Mgr: Gary Keller
Info Man: Barbara Holder

ISYS TECHNOLOGIES
See ISYS INC

D-U-N-S 07-691-9211
IT CONVERGENCE
805 Veterans Blvd Ste 105, Redwood City, CA 94063-1750
Tel (415) 675-7935 *Founded/Ownrshp* 1998
Sales 87.2MM^E *EMP* 605
Accts Hood & Strong Llp
SIC 8742 Management consulting services; Management consulting services
Pr: Patrick Krause
**Pt:* Andrew Meinnert
**COO:* Jake Van Der Vort
**CFO:* Joseph Long
**Ex VP:* Dean Welch
VP: Ernesto Espinoza
**VP:* Bryan Koh
Mng Dir: Hazel Pang
Prgrm Mgr: Amanda Obremski
Web Dev: Babajide Okusanya
VP Mktg: Christopher Peterson

D-U-N-S 96-184-7196
IT CREATIONS INC
9142 Independence Ave, Chatsworth, CA 91311-5902
Tel (818) 975-3100 *Founded/Ownrshp* 2010
Sales 45.0MM *EMP* 37
SIC 5734 Computer & software stores
CEO: Alexander Gorban
CFO: Natalie Abramovich
IT Man: Chris Rodinis
Sales Asso: Murad Lalaiev

IT DISTRIBUTORS
See INNOVATIVE TECHNOLOGY DISTRIBUTORS LLC

D-U-N-S 13-451-1810
IT GROUP LLC
MEMBER DRIVEN TECHNOLOGIES
30230 Orchard Lake Rd, Farmington Hills, MI 48334-2267
Tel (586) 795-9135 *Founded/Ownrshp* 2003
Sales 25.5MM *EMP* 140
Accts Plante & Moran Pllc Auburn H
SIC 7379 Computer related consulting services; Computer related consulting services
Ex VP: Scott Johnston
VP: Matt Baaki
VP: Steven McKibben
VP: Dan Schneider
VP: Eric Valla
Off Admin: Eric Felcyn
Netwrk Eng: Anthony White

IT MAKES SCENTS
See SHERALVEN ENTERPRISES LTD

D-U-N-S 83-285-5246
IT MANAGEMENT CORP (CA)
101 VOICE
5201 Great America Pkwy # 320, Santa Clara, CA 95054-1140
Tel (408) 739-1100 *Founded/Ownrshp* 2009
Sales 40.0MM *EMP* 35
SIC 8742

IT SAVVY
See B2B COMPUTER PRODUCTS LLC

IT SOLUTIONS
See INTERNATIONAL TECHNOLOGY SOLUTIONS INC

D-U-N-S 07-039-0641
IT SUPPLIES INC
ATLEX.COM
5100 Newport Dr Ste 6, Rolling Meadows, IL 60008-3825
Tel (847) 213-5928 *Founded/Ownrshp* 1999
Sales 28.0MM *EMP* 42
SIC 5045 Printers, computer; Printers, computer
Pr: Greg Lahart
IT Man: Sean Lahart

D-U-N-S 05-123-3943
IT TRAILBLAZERS LLC
2050 State Route 27 # 203, North Brunswick, NJ 08902-1380
Tel (732) 227-1772 *Founded/Ownrshp* 1999
Sales 37.6MM *EMP* 150
Accts Withum Smith & Brown Pc New
SIC 7361 7373 Employment agencies; Computer integrated systems design; Employment agencies; Computer integrated systems design
COO: Chris Jones
VP: Balaji Nagarajan
IT Man: Santhosh Sagar
IT Man: Suma Sharon
Sls Mgr: Ganesh Jamma

IT WATCHDOGS
See PCE INC

D-U-N-S 11-196-5120
IT WORKS MARKETING INC
908 Riverside Dr, Palmetto, FL 34221-5035
Tel (952) 540-5699 *Founded/Ownrshp* 2001
Sales 510.0MM^E *EMP* 135^E
SIC 5499 8099 Health foods; Blood related health services
Pr: Mark Pentecost
Pr: Janne Heimonen
Pr: Wally Neeson
CFO: Douglas Nooney
**Treas:* Cindy Pentecost
VP Opers: Steve Radius

D-U-N-S 83-484-0860
IT WORX INC
(*Suby of* ITWORX)
20 Batterson Park Rd # 303, Farmington, CT 06032-4500
Tel (860) 656-6336 *Founded/Ownrshp* 2001
Sales 80.6MM^E *EMP* 900
SIC 5045 Computer peripheral equipment; Computer peripheral equipment
Pr: Houssam Amer
Snr Sftwr: Amir Magdy

D-U-N-S 07-968-8704
IT XCHANGE (2013) CORP (NC)
(*Suby of* XTG HOLDINGS 2 (USA) INC) ★
9241 Globe Center Dr # 100, Morrisville, NC 27560-6204
Tel (919) 544-9898 *Founded/Ownrshp* 2013
Sales 45.0MM *EMP* 150^E
SIC 5045 Computer peripheral equipment
CEO: Alan Rupp

D-U-N-S 14-183-3587
IT1 SOURCE LLC
4110 N Scottsdale Rd, Scottsdale, AZ 85251-3919
Tel (480) 777-5995 *Founded/Ownrshp* 2003
Sales 90.0MM *EMP* 85
SIC 5734 Computer & software stores
Sales Exec: Robb Knutson
Sales Exec: Adam Levy
Sales Exec: Richard Parrill

ITA AUDIO VISUAL SOLUTIONS
See T A I INC

D-U-N-S 04-349-0986
ITA GROUP INC (IA)
4600 Westown Pkwy Ste 100, West Des Moines, IA 50266-1042
Tel (515) 326-3400 *Founded/Ownrshp* 1963
Sales 157.5MM^E *EMP* 550
Accts Mcgladrey Llp Des Moines Ia
SIC 8742 4724 Incentive or award program consultant; Travel agencies; Incentive or award program consultant; Travel agencies
CEO: Thomas J Mahoney
**CFO:* Brent V Waal
**Sr VP:* Mary Z Bussone
**Sr VP:* John McCabe
VP: Phil Brewster
**VP:* CJ McKoy
**VP:* John Rose
**VP:* Kent Schlawin
VP: Julie Sherman
Creative D: Adam Clarke
Prgrm Mgr: Anna Boggs

D-U-N-S 12-574-6177
■ **ITA SOFTWARE LLC**
(*Suby of* GOOGLE INC) ★
5 Cambridge Ctr Ste 4, Cambridge, MA 02142-1493
Tel (617) 714-2100 *Founded/Ownrshp* 2011
Sales 36.6MM^E *EMP* 448^E
SIC 7371 Computer software development; Computer software development
Pr: Jeremy Wertheimer
CFO: Milt Alpern
VP: Steve Clarkvp
VP: Daniel Duty
VP: Derek Lewitton
VP: Ed Orciuch
VP: David Sandberg
VP: Eli Sanders
VP: Rujith Silva
Genl Mgr: Nicola Simionato
Snr Sftwr: John Tupper

D-U-N-S 96-175-8344
ITA TRUCK SALES & SERVICE LLC
2835 Nw Evangeline Trwy, Lafayette, LA 70507-3420
Tel (337) 314-0550 *Founded/Ownrshp* 2009
Sales 48.3MM^E *EMP* 63^E
SIC 5511 Trucks, tractors & trailers: new & used
CTO: Cybil Romero
Opers Mgr: Mark Fontenot
VP Sls: Seth Williams

D-U-N-S 96-476-1089
ITA-NOLA LLC
301 Hord St, New Orleans, LA 70123-4117
Tel (504) 733-7711 *Founded/Ownrshp* 2010
Sales 21.3MM^E *EMP* 101
SIC 5511 Trucks, tractors & trailers: new & used

ITAC
See INDUSTRIAL TURNAROUND CORP

ITALCEMENTI GROUP
See ESSROC CEMENT CORP

D-U-N-S 36-060-6362 IMP
ITALEE OPTICS INC
LAB ITALEE
2641 W Olympic Blvd, Los Angeles, CA 90006-2810
Tel (213) 385-8805 *Founded/Ownrshp* 1981
Sales 25.2MM^E *EMP* 120
SIC 5048 Frames, ophthalmic; Frames, ophthalmic
Pr: Jong Young Kim
**VP:* Christopher C Song
Natl Sales: Bart Vandervelde
Mktg Mgr: Amy Hahn

D-U-N-S 09-487-0938 IMP
ITALFOODS INC (CA)
205 Shaw Rd, South San Francisco, CA 94080-6605
Tel (650) 873-2640 *Founded/Ownrshp* 1978
Sales 37.8MM^E *EMP* 80
SIC 5149 Specialty food items
CEO: Walter J Guerra
**Sec:* Georgette Guerra
Chf Mktg O: Aldo Guazzelli
VP: Robin Paniagua
Sls Mgr: Adolfo Calero

D-U-N-S 04-883-8833
ITALGRANI ELEVATOR CO
(*Suby of* ITALGRANI USA INC) ★
7900 Van Buren St, Saint Louis, MO 63111-3611
Tel (314) 638-1447 *Founded/Ownrshp* 1981
Sales 33.4MM^E *EMP* 77
SIC 5153 Grain elevators; Grain elevators
Pr: Roberto Marciano
VP: James Meyer
Sls Dir: Pat Beem

D-U-N-S 09-595-8724
ITALGRANI USA INC
7900 Van Buren St, Saint Louis, MO 63111-3611
Tel (314) 638-1447 *Founded/Ownrshp* 1979
Sales 306.0MM^E *EMP* 95
SIC 2041 5153 Flour & other grain mill products; Grain & field beans; Flour & other grain mill products; Grain & field beans
Pr: James Meyer
**Ex VP:* Hank Thilmony
Genl Mgr: Sharon Connelly
S&M/VP: Patrick Jacoby

ITALIAN AMERICAN CLUB OF NAPLE
See NAPLES ITALIAN AMERICAN CLUB

D-U-N-S 08-070-9918 IMP
ITALIAN AMERICAN CORP
AMERICAN PACKAGING CO
1515 Alvarado St, San Leandro, CA 94577-2640
Tel (510) 877-9000 *Founded/Ownrshp* 1976
Sales 51.6MM^E *EMP* 42
SIC 5085 Industrial supplies
CEO: Kaye Leedham

ITALIAN CONCEPTS
See NAJARIAN FURNITURE CO INC

ITALIAN OVEN, THE
See ARMSTRONG RESTAURANTS LP

D-U-N-S 10-769-0877 IMP
ITALIAN ROSE GARLIC PRODUCTS INC
1380 W 15th St, Riviera Beach, FL 33404-5310
Tel (561) 863-3149 *Founded/Ownrshp* 1983
Sales 32.1MM^E *EMP* 110
SIC 2099 Seasonings & spices; Seasonings & spices
Pr: Ken Berger
**VP:* Arthur Conlan
Opers Mgr: Jose Chavez

D-U-N-S 03-221-8687
ITALIAN TERRAZZO AND TILE CO OF BREVARD INC
ABBEY CARPET
432 S Babcock St, Melbourne, FL 32901-1276
Tel (321) 723-0651 *Founded/Ownrshp* 1970
Sales 26.4MM^E *EMP* 75
SIC 1752 Ceramic floor tile installation; Vinyl floor tile & sheet installation; Carpet laying; Wood floor installation & refinishing
VP: Rodney Noll
**VP:* Jerry Pezzeminti Jr

D-U-N-S 07-909-7066 IMP
ITALMATCH USA CORP
(*Suby of* ITALMATCH CHEMICALS SPA)
660 White Plains Rd # 510, Tarrytown, NY 10591-5187
Tel (732) 383-8309 *Founded/Ownrshp* 2013
Sales 22.0MM *EMP* 12
SIC 2899 Chemical preparations; Chemical preparations
CEO: Foort De Jong

ITAMCO COMPANY
See INDIANA TOOL & MFG CO INC

D-U-N-S 07-058-5393
ITANDT BUSINESS TRAVEL SOLUTIONS
TIME TO TRAVEL,
40 Lloyd Ave Ste 107, Malvern, PA 19355-3091
Tel (610) 647-3100 *Founded/Ownrshp* 1992
Sales 65.0MM *EMP* 64
SIC 4724 Tourist agency arranging transport, lodging & car rental; Tourist agency arranging transport, lodging & car rental
Pr: Eric William Parker
**Ch Bd:* Harry H Parker
**Sec:* Greta Soffa
**Sr VP:* Rachel Klein
VP: Howard Cusick
**VP:* Stephen Stern
**Prin:* Bradley Paul Parker

D-U-N-S 03-001-8741
ITASCA COUNTY OF (INC)
123 Ne 4th St, Grand Rapids, MN 55744-2659
Tel (218) 327-2847 *Founded/Ownrshp* 1887
Sales NA *EMP* 450
Accts Rebecca Otto/Greg Hierlingerc
SIC 9111 Executive offices; ; Executive offices;
Ch: Karen Burthwick
**Treas:* Jeff T Walker

D-U-N-S 96-781-1733
ITASCA-MANTRAP CO-OP ELECTRICAL ASSN TR
16930 County 6, Park Rapids, MN 56470-2883
Tel (218) 732-3377 *Founded/Ownrshp* 2011
Sales 24.3MM^E *EMP* 2
SIC 1731 Electrical work; Electrical work
CEO: Patrick E Obrien
CFO: Charles Andress
CFO: Brenda Keller

D-U-N-S 07-856-5413
ITAWAMBA COMMUNITY COLLEGE FOUNDATION INC
602 W Hill St, Fulton, MS 38843-1022
Tel (662) 862-8000 *Founded/Ownrshp* 1975
Sales 15.9MM^E *EMP* 400
SIC 8222 Community college; Community college
Pr: Mike Eaton
**Pr:* David C Cole
**VP:* Jerry Senter

D-U-N-S 10-003-9858
ITAWAMBA COUNTY SCHOOL DISTRICT
605 S Cummings St, Fulton, MS 38843-1811
Tel (662) 862-2159 *Founded/Ownrshp* 1870
Sales NA *EMP* 400
SIC 9411 ;

ITC
See INTERCONTINENTAL TERMINALS CO LLC

ITC
See INTERNATIONAL TECHNICAL COATINGS INC

D-U-N-S 17-912-0527
ITC ACCEPTANCE CO
I T C
(*Suby of* PACLEASE) ★
2843 S Holt Rd, Indianapolis, IN 46241-6019
Tel (317) 243-1663 *Founded/Ownrshp* 2004
Sales 25.8MM^E *EMP* 165
SIC 5084 Trucks, industrial; Trucks, industrial
Ch Bd: Elden Palmer

ITC DELTA COMMUNICATIONS
See ITC DELTACOM INC

D-U-N-S 10-691-6554
ITC DELTACOM INC
ITC DELTA COMMUNICATIONS
7037 Old Madison Pike Nw, Huntsville, AL 35806-2107
Tel (256) 382-5900 *Founded/Ownrshp* 2010
Sales 440.3MM *EMP* 3,030
SIC 4813 4899

D-U-N-S 12-907-1630
▲ ITC HOLDINGS CORP
27175 Energy Way, Novi, MI 48377-3639
Tel (248) 946-3000 *Founded/Ownrshp* 2002
Sales 1.0MMM *EMP* 539ᴱ
Tkr Sym ITC *Exch* NYS
SIC 4911 Transmission, electric power; Transmission, electric power
Ch Bd: Joseph L Welch
Pr: Diane Coskey
Pr: Brett Leopold
COO: Jon E Jipping
CFO: Rejji P Hayes
Treas: Gretchen Holloway
Treas: Patricia Wenzel
Bd of Dir: Julie Garavaglia
Ofcr: Linda H Blair
Ex VP: Linda Blair
Ex VP: Daniel J Oginsky
Ex VP: Daniel Oginsky
VP: Kevin Burke
VP: Matthew Dills
VP: Joseph Dudak
VP: Terry Harvill
VP: Gregory Ioanidis
VP: Wendy McIntyre-Peard
VP: Hayes Rejji
VP: Kristine Schmidt
VP: Christine Mason Soneral
Board of Directors: Albert Ernst, Christopher H Franklin, Edward G Jepsen, David R Lopez, Hazel R O'leary, Thomas G Stephens, G Bennett Stewart III, Lee C Stewart

D-U-N-S 84-849-1155
ITC INFOTECH (USA) INC
(*Suby of* ITC INFOTECH INDIA LIMITED)
12 N State Rt 17 Ste 303, Paramus, NJ 07652-2644
Tel (201) 336-9431 *Founded/Ownrshp* 2001
Sales 81.6MM *EMP* 70ᴱ
Accts Eisner Amper Llp Iselin Nj
SIC 7379 Computer related consulting services; Computer related consulting services
Pr: L N Balaji
Pr: Alok Verma
CFO: Rakesh Batra
Top Exec: Sanjoy Sen
Sr VP: Khem Aithani
VP: Sunil Ramachandran
VP: Anand Talwar
Exec: Sandeep Stanley
Dir Bus: Bharath Kirumakki
**Prin:* B Sumant
Ex Dir: Sanjiv Puri

D-U-N-S 07-883-5732
■ ITC MIDSOUTH LLC
(*Suby of* ITC HOLDINGS CORP) ★
27175 Energy Way, Novi, MI 48377-3639
Tel (248) 946-3000 *Founded/Ownrshp* 2011
Sales 31.4MMᴱ *EMP* 215ᴱ
SIC 4911 Transmission, electric power
CEO: Joseph L Welch
CFO: Cameron Bready

ITC NEXUS HOLDING COMPANY
See ACCRIVA DIAGNOSTICS INC

D-U-N-S 07-446-5449
ITC SERVICE GROUP INC
I T C
7777 Greenback Ln Ste 201, Citrus Heights, CA 95610-5800
Tel (877) 370-4482 *Founded/Ownrshp* 1999
Sales 31.1MMᴱ *EMP* 700
SIC 8748 Communications consulting; Telecommunications consultant; Communications consulting; Telecommunications consultant
Pr: Timothy S Sauer
**Sr VP:* Christian H Sauer III
Off Mgr: Tara Donaldson
Sfty Dirs: Brett Hoiland
Sfty Dirs: Mike Sauer
Opers Mgr: John Lucas

ITC TRANSMISSION
See INTERNATIONAL TRANSMISSION CO

D-U-N-S 07-598-3499
ITCO SOLUTIONS INC (CA)
1003 Whitehall Ln, Redwood City, CA 94061-3687
Tel (650) 367-0514 *Founded/Ownrshp* 1997
Sales 24.1MMᴱ *EMP* 295
SIC 7379 Computer related consulting services; Computer related consulting services
**VP:* Chris Middleton

ITCOA
See INDEPENDENCE TITLE CO

D-U-N-S 06-261-5174 IMP/EXP
ITD ARIZONA INC
6737 E Washington Blvd, Commerce, CA 90040-1801
Tel (323) 722-8542 *Founded/Ownrshp* 1993
Sales 34.6MM *EMP* 56
SIC 5014 Tires & tubes; Tires & tubes
Pr: John P Farkas
**VP:* Matt Seavers
**VP:* Scott Simpson

ITECH
See INTELLIGENT TECHNOLOGIES LLC

D-U-N-S 14-072-7749
ITECH US INC
20 Kimball Ave Ste 303n, South Burlington, VT 05403-6831
Tel (802) 383-1500 *Founded/Ownrshp* 2001
Sales 56.7MMᴱ *EMP* 371
SIC 7371 Computer software systems analysis & design, custom; Computer software systems analysis & design, custom
Pr: Kishore Khandavalli
Pr: Narasimha Adla
Pr: Richard Bledsoe
CFO: Bill Meckert
VP: Sulekha Banerjee
VP: Tony Beyer
Sftwr Eng: Rakesh Yadav
VP Mktg: Neil Brogan
Sls Mgr: Amit Pandey

D-U-N-S 86-941-3398
ITECH WIRELESS INC
1600 Calebs Path Ext # 201, Hauppauge, NY 11788-5225
Tel (631) 780-7105 *Founded/Ownrshp* 2004
Sales 60.0MM *EMP* 11
SIC 5065 Telephone equipment
Pr: Abhishek Khurana

ITEK ENERGY
See ITEKENERGY LLC

D-U-N-S 02-922-2535 IMP
ITEKENERGY LLC (WA)
ITEK ENERGY
3886 Hammer Dr, Bellingham, WA 98226-7629
Tel (360) 647-9531 *Founded/Ownrshp* 2011
Sales 25.0MM *EMP* 80
SIC 3674 Solar cells
Pr: John Flanagan
**VP:* Kelly Samson
Genl Mgr: Paul Krumrich

D-U-N-S 80-030-7253
ITELLIGENCE INC
(*Suby of* ITELLIGENCE AG)
10856 Reed Hartman Hwy, Cincinnati, OH 45242-2820
Tel (513) 956-2000 *Founded/Ownrshp* 1995
Sales 110.7MMᴱ *EMP* 410ᴱ
SIC 7379 Computer related consulting services; Computer related consulting services
CEO: Herbert Vogel
**Pr:* Steven Niesman
**CFO:* Tim Breen
**CFO:* Norbert Rotter
**Ex VP:* Uwe Bohnhorst
Ex VP: Birgit Wittenbreder
VP: Gene Climer
**VP:* Robert Fiorillo
VP: Ingo Kiesewetter
**VP:* Mark Mueller
VP: Darshan Shah
**VP:* Steve Short
VP: Nathan Weaver

D-U-N-S 00-416-0750 IMP
ITEN INDUSTRIES INC (OH)
PLANT 2
4602 Benefit Ave, Ashtabula, OH 44004-5455
Tel (440) 997-6134 *Founded/Ownrshp* 1922
Sales 39.8MMᴱ *EMP* 190ᴱ
SIC 3089 Laminating of plastic; Injection molded finished plastic products; Laminating of plastic; Injection molded finished plastic products
Pr: Peter D Huggins
CFO: Bill Kane
Exec: Jim Carlson
Off Mgr: Mary Fritz
IT Man: Terry Graeb
IT Man: Kirk Reinhart
Opers Mgr: Mark Dreslinski
Mktg Mgr: Mike Loftus
Board of Directors: Pat Breen, Dallas Droppo, Jim Grenon, Michael Hibberd, Hildegarde D Huggins, Daniel Jucikas, Howard Lichtman, Bradley Thompson, Robert Waters

D-U-N-S 87-821-5474
ITEQ INTEGRATED TECHNOLOGIES INC
3130 Frview Pk Dr Ste 800, Falls Church, VA 22042
Tel (703) 713-4000 *Founded/Ownrshp* 1991
Sales 14.9MMᴱ *EMP* 300
SIC 7373 Computer integrated systems design; Computer integrated systems design
CEO: Todd Stottlemyer
**CFO:* Tom Weston
CTO: Anthony Travaglini

D-U-N-S 04-876-5937 IMP
▲ ITERIS INC
1700 Carnegie Ave Ste 100, Santa Ana, CA 92705-5551
Tel (949) 270-9400 *Founded/Ownrshp* 1969
Sales 72.2MM *EMP* 266
Accts Mcgladrey Llp Irvine Califor
Tkr Sym ITI *Exch* NYS
SIC 3861 8742 3699 Cameras & related equipment; Driers, photographic; Printing equipment, photographic; Densitometers; Transportation consultant; Security control equipment & systems; Cameras & related equipment; Driers, photographic; Printing equipment, photographic; Densitometers; Transportation consultant; Security control equipment & systems
Pr: Joe Bergera
**Ch Bd:* Gregory A Miner
CFO: Andrew Schmidt
Sr VP: Thomas N Blair
Sr VP: Todd Kreter
VP: Scott Carlson
VP: Viggen Davidian
VP: Gary Hamrick
VP: Tiger Harris
VP: Bernard Li
VP: Mark Owens
VP Bus Dev: Ramin Massoumi
Exec: Gary Pena
Board of Directors: Richard Char, Kevin Daly, Gerard M Mooney, Thomas L Thomas, Mikel H Williams

ITESTOUT.COM
See COLLEGE NETWORK INC

D-U-N-S 11-396-2864
ITEX DEVELOPMENT CORP
6633 N Lincoln Ave, Lincolnwood, IL 60712-3605
Tel (847) 674-2383 *Founded/Ownrshp* 1981
Sales 61.9MMᴱ *EMP* 1,500
SIC 8742 Hospital & health services consultant; Hospital & health services consultant
Pt: Jack Raychenbach
**Pt:* Robert Hartman
**Pt:* Bernard Hollander
CFO: Yossi Slusher

D-U-N-S 05-455-4373
■ ITG BRANDS LLC
(*Suby of* IMPERIAL TOBACCO GROUP PLC)
714 Green Valley Rd, Greensboro, NC 27408-7018
Tel (336) 335-7000 *Founded/Ownrshp* 2012
Sales 6.9MMMᴱ *EMP* 2,900ᴱ
Tkr Sym LO *Exch* NYS
SIC 2111

D-U-N-S 14-981-1510 IMP/EXP
■ ITG HOLDINGS INC
IT G
(*Suby of* INTERNATIONAL TEXTILE GROUP INC) ★
804 Green Valley Rd # 300, Greensboro, NC 27408-7039
Tel (336) 379-6220 *Founded/Ownrshp* 2003
Sales 512.2MMᴱ *EMP* 4,000ᴱ
SIC 2211 2231 2221 2273 2262 2261 Denims; Draperies & drapery fabrics, cotton; Upholstery fabrics, cotton; Tickings; Worsted fabrics, broadwoven; Upholstery fabrics, wool; Polyester broadwoven fabrics; Draperies & drapery fabrics, manmade fiber & silk; Upholstery fabrics, manmade fiber & silk; Carpets & rugs; Finishing plants, manmade fiber & silk fabrics; Finishing plants, cotton; Denims; Draperies & drapery fabrics, cotton; Upholstery fabrics, cotton; Tickings; Worsted fabrics, broadwoven; Upholstery fabrics, wool; Polyester broadwoven fabrics; Draperies & drapery fabrics, manmade fiber & silk; Upholstery fabrics, manmade fiber & silk; Carpets & rugs; Finishing plants, manmade fiber & silk fabrics; Finishing plants, cotton
CEO: Joseph L Gorga
Ex VP: Gary Kernaghan
Sr VP: Peter Baumann

D-U-N-S 82-997-2863
■ ITG INC
(*Suby of* INVESTMENT TECHNOLOGY GROUP INC) ★
1 Liberty Plz Fl 4, New York, NY 10006-1426
Tel (212) 588-4000 *Founded/Ownrshp* 1978
Sales 399.2MMᴱ *EMP* 900
SIC 6211 Brokers, security; Brokers, security
Ch Bd: Raymond L Killian Jr
**CEO:* Maureen Ohara
**CFO:* Howard C Naphtali
Bd of Dir: Minder Cheng
Ofcr: Jordan Eshet
Top Exec: David B Drossman
Sr VP: Sujal Bharucha
Sr VP: Stephen Killian
VP: Scott Bauer
VP: Anthony Capriotti
VP: Allison Cassidy
VP: Eugene Choi
VP: Gary Cohen
VP: Anthony Gaglio
VP: Jeff Gamble
VP: Jennifer Goldstein
VP: Anthony Kuehne
VP: Devendra Patel
VP: David Tran
VP: Han Trang
Dir Bus: Will Kennedy

D-U-N-S 61-961-7678
■ ITG SOLUTIONS NETWORK INC
(*Suby of* INVESTMENT TECHNOLOGY GROUP INC) ★
380 Madison Ave Fl 4, New York, NY 10017-2533
Tel (212) 588-4000 *Founded/Ownrshp* 2005
Sales 25.8MMᴱ *EMP* 340
SIC 7379 7372 Computer related consulting services; Prepackaged software; Computer related consulting services; Prepackaged software
CEO: Ian Domowitz
**CFO:* Howard C Naphtali
Mng Dir: David Meitz

ITHACA BAKERY
See COLLEGETOWN BAGELS INC

D-U-N-S 10-005-5789
ITHACA CITY SCHOOL DISTRICT
400 Lake St, Ithaca, NY 14850-2132
Tel (607) 274-2201 *Founded/Ownrshp* 1870
Sales 53.3MMᴱ *EMP* 1,200
SIC 8211 Public elementary school; Public junior high school; Public senior high school; Public elementary school; Public junior high school; Public senior high school
Netwrk Eng: Mary Gottlieb
Netwrk Eng: Les McCormick
Netwrk Eng: Dale Perry
Psych: Gillian Devenpeck
Psych: Jesse Dillon
Psych: Cornelia McCrary
Psych: Jill Tripp
HC Dir: Judy Hoffman
Snr Mgr: Bob Trask

D-U-N-S 04-134-0159
ITHACA COLLEGE
953 Danby Rd, Ithaca, NY 14850-7002
Tel (607) 274-3011 *Founded/Ownrshp* 1892
Sales 330.9MM *EMP* 1,350
SIC 8221

ITHACA PERIPHERALS DIV
See MAGNETEC CORP

D-U-N-S 94-224-3445
ITHAKA HARBORS INC
151 E 61st St, New York, NY 10065-8112
Tel (212) 500-2600 *Founded/Ownrshp* 1995
Sales 85.9MM *EMP* 214
Accts Eisneramper Llp New York Ny
SIC 7379 Computer related maintenance services; Computer related maintenance services
Pr: Kevin Guthrie
Trst: Eugene Lowe
**Ex VP:* Laura Brown
**Ex VP:* Eileen Fenton
**Ex VP:* Michael Spinella
**VP:* Gerard Aurigemma
**VP:* Bruce Heterick
**VP:* Heidi McGregor
VP: Dale Myers
VP: Jabin White
Off Admin: Gigi Grim

ITI
See INDUSTRIAL TECTONICS INC

ITI
See INTERNATIONAL TRADERS INC

ITI
See INDUSTRIAL TOOL INC

ITI & FAC
See FIRST AMERICAN CARRIERS INC

ITL
See IOWA TANKLINES INC

D-U-N-S 00-420-8906 IMP/EXP
ITL CORP (DE)
INDUSTRIAL TIMBER & LUMBER CO
(*Suby of* NORTHWEST HARDWOODS INC) ★
23925 Commerce Park, Cleveland, OH 44122-5821
Tel (216) 831-3140 *Founded/Ownrshp* 1957, 2015
Sales 70.6MMᴱ *EMP* 171
SIC 2421 2426 Kiln drying of lumber; Custom sawmill; Hardwood dimension & flooring mills; Kiln drying of lumber; Custom sawmill; Hardwood dimension & flooring mills
Pr: Larry Evans

D-U-N-S 08-004-0148
ITL LLC
INDUSTRIAL TIMBER AND LBR LLC
(*Suby of* NORTHWEST HARDWOODS INC) ★
23925 Commerce Park, Beachwood, OH 44122-5821
Tel (216) 831-3140 *Founded/Ownrshp* 2015
Sales 6.9MMᴱ *EMP* 325
SIC 2426 Lumber, hardwood dimension

D-U-N-S 11-850-1170
ITN NETWORKS LLC
747 3rd Ave Fl 5, New York, NY 10017-2800
Tel (212) 572-9200 *Founded/Ownrshp* 1983
Sales 21.1MMᴱ *EMP* 115
SIC 8611 Regulatory associations
CEO: Timothy J Connors
Pr: Todd Watson
CFO: Steve Sandler
Ofcr: Dan Costarene
Ex VP: Tim Daly
Ex VP: Stephen Poulin
Ex VP: Alan Walz
VP: Rachel Ammer
VP: Michele Carroll
VP: Meg Danella
Off Mgr: Robin Kenwood

D-U-N-S 05-347-6755 IMP
ITO EN (NORTH AMERICA) INC
KAI RESTRAURANT
(*Suby of* ITO EN, LTD.)
20 Jay St Ste 530, Brooklyn, NY 11201-8324
Tel (718) 250-4000 *Founded/Ownrshp* 2001
Sales 20.6MMᴱ *EMP* 182
SIC 5812 Japanese restaurant; Japanese restaurant
CEO: Yosuke Honjo
**COO:* Jim Hoagland
Sr VP: Brad Angevine
**Sr VP:* Fred Angevine
Sr VP: Kyoichiro Asai
Sr VP: J A Park
**Sr VP:* Rona Tison
**VP:* Masahite Enoki
Mktg Mgr: Rushmi Soni
Sls Mgr: K L Murase
Sales Asso: Bart Jacoby

D-U-N-S 17-362-5310 IMP
ITO INC
KIKKA
431 Isis Ave, Inglewood, CA 90301-2009
Tel (310) 410-4121 *Founded/Ownrshp* 1986
Sales 26.4MMᴱ *EMP* 400
SIC 5812 Caterers; Caterers
Pr: Tonny Soesanto
**Treas:* Fay Sampoerna
**VP:* Ewan Sudarsono

D-U-N-S 05-323-2716 IMP
ITO PACKING CO INC (CA)
1592 11th St Ste H, Reedley, CA 93654-2939
Tel (559) 638-2531 *Founded/Ownrshp* 1940, 1960
Sales 30.2MMᴱ *EMP* 200
SIC 0723 Fruit (fresh) packing services; Fruit (fresh) packing services
Pr: Craig Ito
**Treas:* Yukiko Ito
**VP:* Janet Ito
**VP:* Tracy Ito

D-U-N-S 17-514-4989 IMP/EXP
ITOCHU CHEMICALS AMERICA INC
ICAI
(*Suby of* ITOCHU INTERNATIONAL INC) ★
360 Hamilton Ave Fl 6, White Plains, NY 10601-1811
Tel (914) 333-7800 *Founded/Ownrshp* 1987
Sales 79.6MMᴱ *EMP* 51
SIC 5169 Chemicals & allied products
Pr: Yasuyuki Harada
**Ch Bd:* Hideo Ohori
**Pr:* Hiroaki Yamashita
**CFO:* Mamoru Seki
Sr VP: Alex Tabaco
**Sr VP:* Naohiko Yoshikawa
VP: Yoshikazu Kaho
Opers Mgr: Orit Malev
Mktg Mgr: Satoshi Tojo

Sls Mgr: Brian Everham
Sls Mgr: Jim Lawler

D-U-N-S 00-698-5956 EXP
ITOCHU INTERNATIONAL INC (NY)
(*Suby of* ITOCHU CORPORATION)
335 Madison Ave 22nd, New York, NY 10017-4611
Tel (212) 818-8000 *Founded/Ownrshp* 1952
Sales 4.9MMM^E *EMP* 6,700
Accts Deloitte & Touche Llp New Yor
SIC 5131 5084 5065 5051 5153 5141 Textiles, woven; Industrial machinery & equipment; Electronic parts & equipment; Communication equipment; Ferrous metals; Grains; Groceries, general line; Textiles, woven; Industrial machinery & equipment; Electronic parts & equipment; Communication equipment; Ferrous metals; Grains; Groceries, general line
Ch Bd: Eiichi Yonekura
**CEO:* Yasuyuki Harada
Ex VP: Kotaro Suzuki
**Sr VP:* Shiro Hayashi
Sr VP: Nobuaki Hironaka
Sr VP: Naoyuki Kato
**Sr VP:* Eric Laptook
Sr VP: Michael Mimnaugh
**Sr VP:* Mamoru Seki
Sr VP: Naohiko Yoshikawa
VP: Isamu Akiyama
VP: Thomas Apple
VP: Mounir Rabbat
VP: Jason Rosenberg
VP: Kazunobu Sakai
Dir Risk M: Charles Mead

ITOCHU PIPE & TUBE
See MARUBENI-ITOCHU TUBULARS AMERICA INC

D-U-N-S 78-680-2947 IMP
ITOCHU PROMINENT USA LLC
(*Suby of* ITOCHU INTERNATIONAL INC) ★
1411 Broadway Fl 7, New York, NY 10018-3566
Tel (212) 575-3620 *Founded/Ownrshp* 1993
Sales 61.2MM^E *EMP* 105
SIC 5131 5136 5137 Piece goods & other fabrics; Men's & boys' clothing; Women's & children's clothing
Pr: Yoshihisa Suzuki
VP: Peter Eng
VP: Warren Wendt
Exec: Eileen Jon
Dir IT: Tupper Kinder
IT Man: Mike Lasman
VP Mktg: Katsuma Takei
Snr Mgr: Kishin Datwani

D-U-N-S 60-930-2765 IMP
ITOCHU TECHNO-SOLUTIONS AMERICA INC
(*Suby of* ITOCHU TECHNO-SOLUTIONS CORPORATION)
3945 Freedom Cir Ste 640, Santa Clara, CA 95054-1270
Tel (408) 727-8810 *Founded/Ownrshp* 1990
Sales 65.8MM^E *EMP* 38
SIC 5045 8732 Computers, peripherals & software; Survey service: marketing, location, etc.
Pr: Junshi Maruta
Pr: John Takita
**VP:* Sahinzo Nakano
VP: Kazuyoshi Terui

D-U-N-S 96-872-5668
ITP RAIL ASSOCIATES INC
35 E Main St Ste 415, Avon, CT 06001-3805
Tel (860) 693-6120 *Founded/Ownrshp* 2010
Sales 151.7MM *EMP* 3
SIC 8742 Sales (including sales management) consultant; Sales (including sales management) consultant
CEO: Asa Briggs
Prin: Erik Frenzel

D-U-N-S 11-136-4308
ITPE HEALTH & WELFARE FUND
24 Oglethorpe Blvd, Savannah, GA 31406-3613
Tel (912) 352-7169 *Founded/Ownrshp* 1973
Sales 57.5MM *EMP* 2
Accts Howard Moore & Mcduffie Pc Ma
SIC 8322 Individual & family services

D-U-N-S 04-729-6249 IMP/EXP
ITR AMERICA LLC
HEAVYQUIP
(*Suby of* THE MEYER CRYSTAL FAMILY FOUNDATION)
6301 Northwind Pkwy, Hobart, IN 46342-2495
Tel (601) 939-8821 *Founded/Ownrshp* 2008
Sales 77.7MM^E *EMP* 175
SIC 5082 Construction & mining machinery; General construction machinery & equipment; Excavating machinery & equipment; Construction & mining machinery; General construction machinery & equipment; Excavating machinery & equipment
Pr: Brett Clemens
VP: James Delaney

D-U-N-S 78-036-5487
ITR CONCESSION CO HOLDINGS LLC
8801 S Anthony Ave, Chicago, IL 60617-3056
Tel (312) 552-7100 *Founded/Ownrshp* 2006
Sales 153.0MM *EMP* 500^E
SIC 4785 6719 Toll road operation; Investment holding companies, except banks; Toll road operation; Investment holding companies, except banks
CFO: Gusyeung Yeung

D-U-N-S 78-278-7290
ITR CONCESSION CO LLC
INDIANA TOLL ROAD
(*Suby of* IFM GLOBAL INFRASTRUCTURE FUND) ★
52551 Ash Rd, Granger, IN 46530-7226
Tel (574) 674-8836 *Founded/Ownrshp* 2015
Sales 97.3MM^E *EMP* 390
SIC 1611 Highway & street maintenance; Highway & street maintenance
CEO: Ken Daley
COO: Rick Fedder
CFO: Sally Erhardt
CFO: Ilia Kay
CFO: Gus Yeung
CIO: Juan Ignacio Gomez Lobo
IT Man: Dan Kompare
Sfty Mgr: Ray Hoover
Trfc Mgr: Robert Lapczynski
Pr Mgr: Amber Kettring
Genl Couns: Garrett Phipps

D-U-N-S 15-556-5435 IMP
ITR INDUSTRIES INC
441 Saw Mill River Rd, Yonkers, NY 10701-4913
Tel (914) 964-7063 *Founded/Ownrshp* 2010
Sales 158.1MM^E *EMP* 700
SIC 3431 3429 3446 3088 Shower stalls, metal; Manufactured hardware (general); Architectural metalwork; Shower stalls, fiberglass & plastic; Shower stalls, metal; Manufactured hardware (general); Architectural metalwork; Shower stalls, fiberglass & plastic
Ch Bd: Mario F Rolla
**Pr:* Adrienne Rola
**Pr:* Peter M Rolla

D-U-N-S 62-238-4936 IMP/EXP
ITR NORTH AMERICA LLC
HEAVYQUIP
6301 Northwind Pkwy, Hobart, IN 46342-2495
Tel (219) 947-8230 *Founded/Ownrshp* 2006
Sales 84.9MM^E *EMP* 250
SIC 5084 Industrial machine parts; Industrial machine parts
Pr: Brett Clemens
CFO: Chris Gilleo
VP: Jim Delaney

D-U-N-S 36-302-2620 IMP
ITRENEW INC
8356 Central Ave, Newark, CA 94560-3432
Tel (510) 795-1591 *Founded/Ownrshp* 2002
Sales 40.8MM^E *EMP* 50^E
SIC 4953 7378 Recycling, waste materials; Computer maintenance & repair
CEO: Mostafa Aghamiri
VP: Daniel Niclas
Brnch Mgr: Michael Therrien

D-U-N-S 00-521-5729
ITRIA LLC
333 7th Ave Fl 18, New York, NY 10001-5086
Tel (212) 644-4555 *Founded/Ownrshp* 2007
Sales 221.1MM *EMP* 2^E
SIC 6531 Real estate agent, residential
Prin: Sameer Deshmukh

D-U-N-S 00-129-4651 IMP
■ **ITRON ELECTRICITY METERING INC**
(*Suby of* ITRON INC) ★
313 N Highway 11, West Union, SC 29696-2706
Tel (864) 638-8300 *Founded/Ownrshp* 1892, 2004
Sales 228.8MM^E *EMP* 750
SIC 3825 3823 3824 3679 3829 3612 Watt-hour meters, electrical; Time cycle & program controllers, industrial process type; Speedometers; Mechanical measuring meters; Attenuators; Measuring & controlling devices; Transformers, except electric; Watt-hour meters, electrical; Time cycle & program controllers, industrial process type; Speedometers; Mechanical measuring meters; Attenuators; Measuring & controlling devices; Transformers, except electric
CEO: Malcolm Unsworth
CFO: Ambory Ken
IT Man: Ken Elrod

D-U-N-S 09-364-9895 IMP/EXP
▲ **ITRON INC**
2111 N Molter Rd, Liberty Lake, WA 99019-9469
Tel (509) 924-9900 *Founded/Ownrshp* 1977
Sales 1.9MMM *EMP* 8,000
Accts Ernst & Young Llp Seattle Wa
Tkr Sym ITRI *Exch* NGS
SIC 3829 7371 Measuring & controlling devices; Computer software development & applications; Measuring & controlling devices; Computer software development & applications
Pr: Philip C Mezey
**Ch Bd:* Jon E Eliassen
COO: Tom Deitrich
COO: John W Holleran
CFO: W Mark Schmitz
Bd of Dir: Joan Stephens
Bd of Dir: Jonathan Wanjiru
Ex VP: Julie Carfora
Ex VP: Lara Rossouw
Ex VP: John Shaub
Sr VP: Michel C Cadieux
VP: Mark Champagne
VP: Shannon M Votava
Board of Directors: Kirby A Dyess, Charles H Gaylord Jr, Thomas S Glanville, Jerome Lande, Timothy M Leyden, Sharon L Nelson, Daniel S Pelino, Gary E Pruitt, Lynda L Ziegler

IT'S A "10" HAIRCARE
See ITS A 10 INC

D-U-N-S 80-804-1169
ITS A 10 INC
IT'S A "10" HAIRCARE
153 Nurmi Dr, Fort Lauderdale, FL 33301-1404
Tel (954) 227-7813 *Founded/Ownrshp* 2006
Sales 36.7MM *EMP* 2
Accts Berkowitz Pollack Brant Cpas
SIC 3999 Hair & hair-based products; Hair & hair-based products
CEO: Carolyn Plummer
**Pr:* Scott Scharg
Opers Mgr: Jules Harris

D-U-N-S 96-694-2245 EXP
ITS ENGINEERED SYSTEMS INC
ITS WATER TECHNOLOGY
6818 Fm 2855 Rd, Katy, TX 77493-7503
Tel (281) 371-8026 *Founded/Ownrshp* 1990
Sales 45.0MM^E *EMP* 80
SIC 3589 Sewage & water treatment equipment
Pr: Chet Erwin
Pr: Sam Habash
**Pr:* Robert Welch
**VP:* Larry Hanncock
Sfty Mgr: Clay Kim

D-U-N-S 18-246-0790 IMP
ITS GREEK TO ME INC
G.T.M. SPORTSWEAR
520 Mccall Rd Ste A, Manhattan, KS 66502-7098
Tel (785) 537-8822 *Founded/Ownrshp* 1992
Sales 328.9MM^E *EMP* 900^E
SIC 5136 5699 5137 5947 2759 Sportswear, men's & boys'; Sports apparel; Sportswear, women's & children's; Gift shop; Screen printing; Sportswear, men's & boys'; Sports apparel; Sportswear, women's & children's; Gift shop; Screen printing
CEO: David Dreiling
**Pr:* John Strawn
**CFO:* Rob Berard
VP: Michelle Cromer
Dir IT: Ford Brethour
Web Dev: Nick George
Advt Mgr: Carrie Rich
Mktg Mgr: Katie Vleet
Manager: Cory Cottam
Sales Asso: Tricia Gose

D-U-N-S 04-060-7772
ITS INC
(*Suby of* SHAZAM INC) ★
6700 Pioneer Pkwy, Johnston, IA 50131-1809
Tel (515) 288-2828 *Founded/Ownrshp* 1981
Sales 554.0M *EMP* 400^E
SIC 7374 Data processing service; Data processing service
Pr: Michael K Hollinger
**Pr:* Dale Dooley
**CFO:* Scott Bobesh
Dir IT: Bill Ely

ITS INFINITY TRADING
See INFINITY TRADING & SOLUTIONS LLC

D-U-N-S 00-137-9804
ITS LOGISTICS LLC (NV)
620 Spice Islands Dr, Sparks, NV 89431-6526
Tel (775) 358-5300 *Founded/Ownrshp* 1998
Sales 91.1MM^E *EMP* 375
SIC 4731 4225 4213 Freight forwarding; Brokers, shipping; General warehousing; Trucking, except local; Freight forwarding; Brokers, shipping; General warehousing; Trucking, except local
Pr: Jeffrey Lynch
**Treas:* Darryl Bader
**VP:* Daniel Allen
Plng Mgr: Chad Watnes
Dir IT: David Espinosa
Sfty Dirs: Roxie Holben
Opers Mgr: Robert Heaton
Sls Dir: Mike Crawford
Snr Mgr: Chad Harden
Board of Directors: Daniel Allen, Darryl Bader, Jeffrey Lynch

D-U-N-S 82-473-8863
ITS PARTNERS LLC
4079 Park East Ct Se A, Grand Rapids, MI 49546-8815
Tel (616) 242-5300 *Founded/Ownrshp* 2007
Sales 34.8MM *EMP* 75
SIC 5734 7373 Software, business & non-game; Computer integrated systems design; Software, business & non-game; Computer integrated systems design
Pr: Aaron W Wyant
**COO:* Frederick Byam
CFO: Jeremy Frost
VP: Joshua Bernson
VP: Ben Dixon
VP: Matthew Reid
Rgnl Mgr: Richard Klein
Off Admin: Sandra Conner
Sftwr Eng: Isaiah Tunkara
Sales Asso: Meghan Edgerle

D-U-N-S 78-282-6903
ITS SERVICES INC
APOGEN TECHNOLOGIES
(*Suby of* APOGEN TECHNOLOGIES INC) ★
11091 Sunset Hills Rd # 200, Reston, VA 20190-5378
Tel (703) 644-3862 *Founded/Ownrshp* 1991
Sales 50.8MM^E *EMP* 604
SIC 7379 7371 Computer related consulting services; Custom computer programming services; Computer related consulting services; Custom computer programming services
Pr: Jill Thompson
**Treas:* Thomas Weston
Sr VP: Tom Bailey
IT Man: Judy Dawkins

D-U-N-S 12-756-3984
ITS TECHNOLOGIES & LOGISTICS LLC
(*Suby of* ITS TECHNOLOGIES & LOGISTICS LLC) ★
8200 185th St Ste A, Tinley Park, IL 60487-9244
Tel (708) 225-2400 *Founded/Ownrshp* 2008
Sales 282.8MM^E *EMP* 1,500
SIC 4789 Cargo loading & unloading services; Cargo loading & unloading services

D-U-N-S 96-172-0443
ITS TECHNOLOGIES & LOGISTICS LLC
8200 185th St Ste A, Tinley Park, IL 60487-9244
Tel (708) 225-2400 *Founded/Ownrshp* 2006
Sales 282.8MM^E *EMP* 1,502^E
SIC 4789 Cargo loading & unloading services; Cargo loading & unloading services
CFO: Joseph Brunetti
CFO: Mary Vankoevering

ITS WATER TECHNOLOGY
See ITS ENGINEERED SYSTEMS INC

D-U-N-S 80-054-5845 IMP
ITS-SPRINTURF
SPECIAL T SURFACES
(*Suby of* INTEGRATED TURF SOLUTIONS LLC) ★
900 Circle 75 Pkwy Se, Atlanta, GA 30339-3035
Tel (888) 639-2351 *Founded/Ownrshp* 2010
Sales 33.8MM^E *EMP* 176
SIC 1799 2426 Artificial turf installation; Hardwood dimension & flooring mills; Artificial turf installation; Hardwood dimension & flooring mills
Mng Pt: Rom Reddy

ITSAVVY
See B2B INDUSTRIAL PRODUCTS LLC

ITSC
See INTERMOUNTAIN POWER SERVICE CORP

ITSCO
See INTERNATIONAL TECHNOLOGIES & SYSTEMS CORP

D-U-N-S 82-700-6594
■ **ITSOLUTIONS NET GOVERNMENT SOLUTIONS INC**
(*Suby of* ITSOLUTIONS NET INC) ★
3130 Frview Pk Dr Ste 800, Falls Church, VA 22042
Tel (703) 712-4000 *Founded/Ownrshp* 2006
Sales 30.0MM *EMP* 116
SIC 7379 7373 4813 5045 8731 8711 Computer related maintenance services; Systems engineering, computer related; Systems integration services; Telephone communication, except radio; Computers, peripherals & software; Commercial physical research; Engineering services; Computer related maintenance services; Systems engineering, computer related; Systems integration services; Telephone communication, except radio; Computers, peripherals & software; Commercial physical research; Engineering services
CEO: Todd Stottlemyer
**CFO:* Tom Weston

D-U-N-S 07-537-7395
■ **ITSOLUTIONS NET INC**
(*Suby of* INTERACTIVE TECHNOLOGY SOLUTIONS LLC) ★
3130 Frview Pk Dr Ste 800, Falls Church, VA 22042
Tel (703) 712-4000 *Founded/Ownrshp* 2010
Sales 41.0MM^E *EMP* 650
SIC 8742 Management consulting services; Financial consultant; Management consulting services; Financial consultant
CEO: Todd Stottlemyer
**CFO:* Tom Weston
Ex VP: James Dean
Ex VP: John Wayne
Sr VP: Tricia Iveson
VP: Kathy Dickerson
Prgrm Mgr: Charmaigne Burrell

D-U-N-S 04-483-3126
ITSON INC
ZACT MOBILE
3 Lagoon Dr Ste 230, Redwood City, CA 94065-5152
Tel (650) 517-2780 *Founded/Ownrshp* 2008
Sales 37.1MM^E *EMP* 65
SIC 5065 Mobile telephone equipment
Pr: Gregory G Raleigh
COO: David Johnson
Chf Mktg O: Anna Fieler
Sr VP: Mak Azadi
Sr VP: Thierry Chassaing
Sr VP: Jose Lorenzo
VP: Beau Beck
VP: Richard Borenstein
VP: Justin James
Snr Sftwr: Simon Azriel
Snr Sftwr: Kevin Binkley
Board of Directors: Stewart Gollmer

D-U-N-S 12-653-8649
ITSQUEST INC
4505 82nd St Ste 3, Lubbock, TX 79424-3219
Tel (806) 785-9100 *Founded/Ownrshp* 2003
Sales 7.7MM *EMP* 2,000
SIC 7361 Employment agencies; Employment agencies
Pr: Jeff Reagan
**VP:* Sarah Reagan
Area Mgr: Carol Everly
Area Mgr: Santiago Soto
Brnch Mgr: Jennifer Franklin
Opers Mgr: Joshua Weldy
Mktg Mgr: Nick Merton

ITT AWT F B LEOPOLD
See XYLEM WATER SOLUTIONS ZELIENOPLE LLC

D-U-N-S 05-451-3780
ITT BELL & GOSSETT
8200 Austin Ave, Morton Grove, IL 60053-3283
Tel (847) 966-3700 *Founded/Ownrshp* 2010
Sales 22.9MM^E *EMP* 50^E
SIC 3561 Pumps & pumping equipment
CEO: John Waterfield

D-U-N-S 00-121-6845 IMP/EXP
▲ **ITT CORP**
1133 Westchester Ave N-100, White Plains, NY 10604-3543
Tel (914) 641-2000 *Founded/Ownrshp* 1920
Sales 2.6MMM *EMP* 9,609
Accts Deloitte & Touche Llp Stamfor
Tkr Sym ITT *Exch* NYS
SIC 3594 3625 3823 3812 Fluid power pumps & motors; Control equipment, electric; Fluidic devices, circuits & systems for process control; Radar systems & equipment; Fluid power pumps & motors; Control equipment, electric; Fluidic devices, circuits & systems for process control; Radar systems & equipment
Pr: Denise L Ramos
Pr: Farrokh Batliwala
Pr: Gretchen McClain
Pr: Luca Savi
Pr: William E Taylor
Pr: Neil Yeargin
CFO: Thomas M Scalera
Chf Cred: Mary Beth Gustafsson
Sr VP: Angela Buonocore
Sr VP: Victoria L Creamer
VP: Steven C Giuliano
Board of Directors: Orlando D Ashford, G Peter D'aloia, Donald Defosset Jr, Christina A Gold, Richard P Lavin, Frank T Macinnis, Rebecca A McDonald, Tim-

othy H Powers

D-U-N-S 05-255-4441
■ ITT CORP
EXELIS
(*Suby of* ITT CORP) ★
77 River Rd, Clifton, NJ 07014-2000
Tel (973) 284-0123 *Founded/Ownrshp* 2005
Sales 197.7MM^{E} *EMP* 9,609
SIC 3812 Search & navigation equipment; Search & navigation equipment
Pr: Chris Bernhardt
VP: Mark Bellini
VP: Andrew Dunn
Prgrm Mgr: Arnold Dupont
Prgrm Mgr: Ronald Silbermann
Genl Mgr: Joe Rambala
IT Man: John McGovern
IT Man: Matt Milligan
IT Man: Michael Mugavero
Tech Mgr: Steven Smith
Sftwr Eng: John Janis

D-U-N-S 80-103-9371
■ ITT DEFENSE & ELECTRONICS INC
(*Suby of* ITT CORP) ★
1650 Tysons Blvd Ste 1700, Mc Lean, VA 22102-4827
Tel (703) 790-6300 *Founded/Ownrshp* 1995
Sales 99.0MM^{E} *EMP* 1,148
SIC 3679 3678 3674 3769 3489 Electronic circuits; Electronic connectors; Semiconductors & related devices; Guided missile & space vehicle parts & auxiliary equipment; Ordnance & accessories; Electronic circuits; Electronic connectors; Semiconductors & related devices; Guided missile & space vehicle parts & auxiliary equipment; Ordnance & accessories
Pr: Henry Driese
**CEO:* Marvin R Sambur
CFO: Heidi Kunz
**CFO:* Mark Lang
Bd of Dir: Markos Tambakeras
VP: Kelvin Coppock
VP: Robert Ferrante
**VP:* Jack Murrel
VP: James O Murrell
VP: Ann Reese
VP: Billy Thomas
VP: Edward Williams
VP Bus Dev: Judy Smith

D-U-N-S 05-470-1560
▲ ITT EDUCATIONAL SERVICES INC
13000 N Meridian St, Carmel, IN 46032-1455
Tel (317) 706-9200 *Founded/Ownrshp* 1946
Sales 961.7MM *EMP* 9,500
Tkr Sym ESI *Exch* NYS
SIC 8221 Colleges universities & professional schools; Colleges universities & professional schools
CEO: Kevin M Modany
**Ch Bd:* John E Dean
Pr: Eugene W Feichtner
CFO: Daniel M Fitzpatrick
Treas: Angela K Knowlton
Bd of Dir: Sam Odle
Bd of Dir: Lloyd G Waterhouse
Bd of Dir: John A Yena
Chf Mktg O: Glenn E Tanner
Ex VP: Martin Buren
Ex VP: Clark D Elwood
Ex VP: Gerald T Hope
Ex VP: Cheri Mahoney
Ex VP: Ryan L Roney
Sr VP: Jeffrey R Cooper
Sr VP: Christine G Long
VP: Lola Bennett-Clayton
VP: Jeffrey Cooper
VP: Shawn J Crawford
VP: Shawn Crawford
VP: Donald Feigert
Board of Directors: C David Brown, Jerry M Cohen, John F Cozzi, James D Fowler Jr, Joanna T Lau, Thomas I Morgan, Samuel L Odle, Vin Weber

D-U-N-S 04-983-1704 IMP
■ ITT ENIDINE INC
ENIVATE - AEROSPACE DIVISION
(*Suby of* ITT CORP) ★
7 Centre Dr, Orchard Park, NY 14127-2281
Tel (716) 662-1900 *Founded/Ownrshp* 1995
Sales 120.6MM^{E} *EMP* 650
SIC 3724 3714 3593 Aircraft engines & engine parts; Motor vehicle parts & accessories; Fluid power cylinders & actuators; Aircraft engines & engine parts; Motor vehicle parts & accessories; Fluid power cylinders & actuators
Ch Bd: Munish Nanda
**Pr:* Dennis Schully
**CEO:* Dennise Ramos
VP: Christophe Lee
VP: Mike Semo
IT Man: Chad Fuller
IT Man: Fred Lippert
Plnt Mgr: Dan Claycomb
QI Cn Mgr: Joe Konieczny
Natl Sales: Gregory Herman
Mktg Dir: Marcy Barberio

ITT EXELIS
See IMPACT SCIENCE & TECHNOLOGY INC

D-U-N-S 83-088-5781
■ ITT FEDERAL SERVICES INTERNATIONAL CORP
(*Suby of* ITT CORP) ★
4410 E Fountain Blvd, Colorado Springs, CO 80916-2153
Tel (719) 637-5490 *Founded/Ownrshp* 1991
Sales 20.5MM^{E} *EMP* 700
SIC 8711 Electrical or electronic engineering; Electrical or electronic engineering
Prin: Pete McKinney

D-U-N-S 80-019-8905 IMP/EXP
■ ITT FLUID TECHNOLOGY CORP
(*Suby of* ITT CORP) ★
1133 Westcstr Ave N100 Ste N, White Plains, NY 10604
Tel (914) 641-2000 *Founded/Ownrshp* 1986
Sales 840.9MM^{E} *EMP* 9,000
SIC 3494 3594 3561 Valves & pipe fittings; Fluid power pumps & motors; Pumps & pumping equipment; Valves & pipe fittings; Fluid power pumps & motors; Pumps & pumping equipment
Pr: Henry Driesse
**VP:* Colin Sabol
Mktg Dir: Jennifer Schiavone
Mktg Mgr: Clara Barone

ITT INDUSTRIES SANITAIRE
See SANITAIRE CORP

D-U-N-S 06-697-2670 IMP
■ ITT POWER SOLUTIONS INC
(*Suby of* EXELIS INC) ★
800 Lee Rd, Rochester, NY 14606
Tel (800) 442-4334 *Founded/Ownrshp* 2011
Sales 61.9MM^{E} *EMP* 410
SIC 3679 3674 3676 3812 3829 3823 Power supplies, all types: static; Hybrid integrated circuits; Electronic resistors; Detection apparatus: electronic/magnetic field, light/heat; Measuring & controlling devices; Industrial instrmnts msrmnt display/control process variable; Power supplies, all types: static; Hybrid integrated circuits; Electronic resistors; Detection apparatus: electronic/magnetic field, light/heat; Measuring & controlling devices; Industrial instrmnts msrmnt display/control process variable
VP: Ron Gordon
VP: Kevin F Roberts

D-U-N-S 00-240-6106 IMP
■ ITT WATER & WASTEWATER USA INC
(*Suby of* XYLEM INC) ★
1 Greenwich Pl Ste 2, Shelton, CT 06484-7603
Tel (203) 712-8999 *Founded/Ownrshp* 1957, 2011
Sales 72.8MM^{E} *EMP* 456
SIC 5084 Pumps & pumping equipment; Pumps & pumping equipment
Pr: Ron Port
**VP:* Frank Oliveira
**VP:* Jonny Sandstedt
Rgnl Mgr: Robert Wright
Area Mgr: Christer Helmerius
Plnt Mgr: Tobias Hahn

D-U-N-S 15-369-1725 IMP
■ ITT WATER TECHNOLOGY INC
GOULDS PUMPS
(*Suby of* ITT CORP) ★
2881 E Bayard Street Ext, Seneca Falls, NY 13148-8745
Tel (315) 568-2811 *Founded/Ownrshp* 2004
Sales 74.8MM^{E} *EMP* 350
SIC 3561 Pumps & pumping equipment; Pumps & pumping equipment
Pr: Douglas Bingler
**Treas:* Maria Tzortzatos
**VP:* Robert T Butera
**VP:* Douglas M Lawrence
QA Dir: George Styk
VP Mktg: Robert Kilmer

D-U-N-S 00-178-1186
ITU ABSORBTECH INC (WI)
2700 S 160th St, New Berlin, WI 53151-3602
Tel (262) 782-1950 *Founded/Ownrshp* 1930
Sales 20.2MM^{E} *EMP* 400
SIC 7218 5963

D-U-N-S 03-127-7051
ITV STUDIOS INC
(*Suby of* ITV STUDIOS LIMITED)
15303 Ventura Blvd # 800, Sherman Oaks, CA 91403-3198
Tel (818) 455-4600 *Founded/Ownrshp* 2006
Sales 27.3MM^{E} *EMP* 28
SIC 7812 Television film production
Pr: Paul Buccieri
**COO:* Sam Zoda
**CFO:* Emily Brecher
**VP:* Julie M Johnsen
VP: Henry Marshall
VP: David Wilcox
VP: Claudia Wong
Creative D: Kate Bartlett
Creative D: Francis Hopkinson
Mng Dir: Hans Engholm
Snr Mgr: Jon Ha

ITW
See RANSBURG CORP

ITW
See INTERNATIONAL TRADE WINDS LLC

D-U-N-S 00-102-4355 IMP
■ ITW ARK-LES CORP
(*Suby of* ILLINOIS TOOL WORKS INC) ★
95 Mill St, Stoughton, MA 02072-1422
Tel (781) 297-6000 *Founded/Ownrshp* 1937
Sales 73.9MM^{E} *EMP* 1,295
SIC 3643 3644

D-U-N-S 05-026-4704
■ ITW ARK-LES CORPORATION
(*Suby of* ITW ARK-LES CORP) ★
16955 W Ryerson Rd, New Berlin, WI 53151-3523
Tel (262) 782-7370 *Founded/Ownrshp* 1998
Sales NA *EMP* 300^{E}
SIC 3643 Electric switches

D-U-N-S 04-677-5078 EXP
■ ITW BUILDING COMPONENTS GROUP INC
ALPINE ENGINEERED PRODUCTS
(*Suby of* ILLINOIS TOOL WORKS INC) ★
13723 Riverport Dr # 200, Maryland Heights, MO 63043-4819
Tel (314) 344-9121 *Founded/Ownrshp* 1991
Sales 66.5MM^{E} *EMP* 350
SIC 3446 3443 3444 3441 Architectural metalwork; Truss plates, metal; Sheet metalwork; Fabricated structural metal; Architectural metalwork; Truss plates, metal; Sheet metalwork; Fabricated structural metal
Pr: Brian Borcherds
Sales Asso: Ray Kunze

ITW CHEMTRONICS
See CHEMTRONICS INC

ITW FLTER PDTS TRNSM FLTRATION
See FILTERTEK INC

D-U-N-S 80-789-6261 IMP/EXP
■ ITW FOOD EQUIPMENT GROUP LLC
HOBART SERVICE
(*Suby of* ILLINOIS TOOL WORKS INC) ★
701 S Ridge Ave, Troy, OH 45374-0001
Tel (937) 332-3000 *Founded/Ownrshp* 1995
Sales 405.2MM^{E} *EMP* 1,300
SIC 5046 3556 Restaurant equipment & supplies; Food products machinery; Restaurant equipment & supplies; Food products machinery
**Ex VP:* Chris O Herlihy
CIO: Norm Dykes
Netwrk Eng: Matthew French
Plnt Mgr: Gary Duench
Prd Mgr: Todd Barrett

D-U-N-S 02-444-8007 IMP
ITW GLOBAL BRANDS
6925 Portwest Dr Ste 100, Houston, TX 77024-8056
Tel (855) 888-1990 *Founded/Ownrshp* 2008
Sales 33.5MM^{E} *EMP* 48^{E}
SIC 5013 Automotive supplies
VP: James Stone

D-U-N-S 62-494-7511 IMP/EXP
■ ITW GLOBAL TIRE REPAIR INC
ACCESS MARKETING
(*Suby of* ILLINOIS TOOL WORKS INC) ★
125 Venture Dr Ste 210, San Luis Obispo, CA 93401-9105
Tel (805) 489-0490 *Founded/Ownrshp* 2010
Sales 20.8MM^{E} *EMP* 71
SIC 3011 2891 Tire & inner tube materials & related products; Adhesives & sealants
CEO: David Parry
Ex VP: Rodney Cegelski

D-U-N-S 94-876-1952 IMP
■ ITW GRAPHICS
(*Suby of* ILLINOIS TOOL WORKS INC) ★
375 New State Rd, Manchester, CT 06042-1818
Tel (860) 646-8153 *Founded/Ownrshp* 1997
Sales 41.3MM^{E} *EMP* 51,000
SIC 2759 2821 Commercial printing; Plastics materials & resins; Commercial printing; Plastics materials & resins
Pr: Nicholas W Martino
**Ch Bd:* R Guy Boyle
COO: Joe Tetrault
**Genl Mgr:* Brian Russell
**Genl Mgr:* Brad Wenner
Sls Mgr: Kevin Los

ITW HOBART BROTHERS
See HOBART BROTHERS CO

ITW MILITARY GSE
See GSE HOLDINGS INC

D-U-N-S 18-588-4053 IMP
■ ITW MINIGRIP INC
(*Suby of* ILLINOIS TOOL WORKS INC) ★
1650 N Heideke St, Seguin, TX 78155-2823
Tel (830) 372-4400 *Founded/Ownrshp* 1988
Sales 30.5MM^{E} *EMP* 210
SIC 3089 3083 2673 Plastic kitchenware, tableware & houseware; Laminated plastics plate & sheet; Bags: plastic, laminated & coated; Plastic kitchenware, tableware & houseware; Laminated plastics plate & sheet; Bags: plastic, laminated & coated
Pr: Jim Koho
Genl Mgr: John Stevens
Mktg Mgr: Herb Zivokic

D-U-N-S 00-733-4659 IMP
■ ITW POLYMERS SEALANTS NORTH AMERICA INC
(*Suby of* ILLINOIS TOOL WORKS INC) ★
111 S Nursery Rd, Irving, TX 75060-3153
Tel (972) 438-9111 *Founded/Ownrshp* 2005
Sales 33.3MM^{E} *EMP* 150
SIC 2891 Sealants; Sealants
Pr: Juan Valls
**Treas:* Felix L Rodriguez Jr
**VP:* Mark J Croll
**VP:* Maria C Green
**VP:* Allan C Sutherland
**VP:* James H Wooten Jr
**Genl Mgr:* Bob Seiple
IT Man: Michael Everit

D-U-N-S 78-202-3209 EXP
■ ITW SEXTON INC
(*Suby of* ILLINOIS TOOL WORKS INC) ★
3101 Sexton Rd Se, Decatur, AL 35603-1707
Tel (256) 355-5850 *Founded/Ownrshp* 2006
Sales 48.0MM^{E} *EMP* 230
SIC 3559 Automotive related machinery; Glass making machinery: blowing, molding, forming, etc.; Automotive related machinery; Glass making machinery: blowing, molding, forming, etc.
Pr: Yurij Wowczuk
Plnt Mgr: Jeff Durham

D-U-N-S 92-893-3845
ITXM DIAGNOSTICS INC
(*Suby of* INSTITUTE FOR TRANSFUSION MEDICINE) ★
3636 Blvd Of The Allies, Pittsburgh, PA 15213-4306
Tel (412) 209-7010 *Founded/Ownrshp* 1994
Sales 8.9MM *EMP* 625
Accts Deloitte & Touche Llp
SIC 8071 Testing laboratories; Testing laboratories
Pr: John Davis
VP: Cortese Hassett

ITZAPARTY
See SRG ENTERPRISES INC

D-U-N-S 01-075-3767
IU CANCER CENTER
1030 W Michigan St, Indianapolis, IN 46202-5201
Tel (317) 278-0070 *Founded/Ownrshp* 1996
Sales 19.6MM^{E} *EMP* 500
SIC 8011 Medical centers; Medical centers

IU HEALTH
See INDIANA UNIVERSITY HEALTH PLANS INC

IU HEALTH ALBANY PHARMACY
See INDIANA UNIVERSITY HEALTH BALL MEMORIAL HOSPITAL INC

IU HEALTH BLACKFORD HOSPITAL
See INDIANA UNIVERSITY HEALTH

IU HEALTH BLOOMINGTON HOSPITAL
See INDIANA UNIVERSITY HEALTH BLOOMINGTON INC

D-U-N-S 84-930-1338 EXP
IU HEALTH INC
SIDNEY & LOIS ESKENAZI HOSP
720 Eskenazi Ave Fl 2, Indianapolis, IN 46202-5189
Tel (317) 880-0000 *Founded/Ownrshp* 1986
Sales 35.5MM *EMP* 600
Accts Crowe Horwath Llp Indianapoli
SIC 8011 Physicians' office, including specialists; Physicians' office, including specialists
CEO: John Fitzgerald
**CFO:* Celia Surface-Bruder
**Chf Mktg O:* Gregory Kiray
**Ex Dir:* Kimberley Singleton
Off Mgr: Lisa Underhill
Doctor: Holly Hendrickson
Doctor: Deanna Reinoso
Doctor: Betty Routledge
Doctor: Erin Stephen

D-U-N-S 06-888-5369
IU HEALTH MEDICAL LIBRARY
1701 Senate Blvd, Indianapolis, IN 46202-1239
Tel (317) 962-3204 *Founded/Ownrshp* 2011
Sales 25.2MM^{E} *EMP* 317^{E}
SIC 8099 Health & allied services
Prin: Jay L Hess
Dir Vol: Jennifer Haney
COO: Jonathan Curtright
Exec: Peter Fulgenzi
Dir Risk M: Terri Schmaltz
Chf Nrs Of: Robin Smith
Adm Dir: Carmela Miroff
Ex Dir: Scott Jaggers
Ex Dir: Sid Norton
Ex Dir: Bruce Rush
Dept Mgr: Melissa Finnerty

IU HEALTH STARKE HOSPITAL
See INDIANA UNIVERSITY HEALTH STARKE HOSPITAL LLC

D-U-N-S 07-827-5915
IU HEALTH WHITE MEMORIAL HOSPITAL
720 S 6th St, Monticello, IN 47960-8182
Tel (574) 583-1739 *Founded/Ownrshp* 2010
Sales 26.9MM *EMP* 15
SIC 8062 General medical & surgical hospitals; General medical & surgical hospitals
Bd of Dir: Ronald Gavern

IU HELTH MRGAN HOSP FOUNDATION
See MORGAN COUNTY MEMORIAL HOSPITAL FOUNDATION INC

IUOE
See INTERNATIONAL UNION OF OPERATING ENGINEERS

D-U-N-S 07-912-8826
IUOE LOCAL 138 138A 138B & 138C
137 Gazza Blvd, Farmingdale, NY 11735-1415
Tel (631) 694-2480 *Founded/Ownrshp* 2013
Sales 20.3MM *EMP* 10^{E}
SIC 8631 Labor unions & similar labor organizations
Pr: William Duffy

IUOE LOCAL 30 BENEFIT FUND
See ENGINEERS UNION LOCAL 30 TRUST FUND

D-U-N-S 13-174-3895
IUPAT DISTRICT COUNCIL 78
JATF
1300 Sw 12th Ave, Pompano Beach, FL 33069-4619
Tel (954) 946-9311 *Founded/Ownrshp* 2003
Sales 347.5MM *EMP* 65
SIC 8631 Labor unions & similar labor organizations; Labor unions & similar labor organizations
Sec: Tim Maitland

D-U-N-S 07-877-8467
IUSA WIRE INC
(*Suby of* CAMBRIDGE-LEE HOLDINGS INC) ★
74 Tube Dr, Reading, PA 19605
Tel (610) 926-4141 *Founded/Ownrshp* 1983
Sales 48.3MM^{E} *EMP* 210^{E}
SIC 3351 5051 Tubing, copper & copper alloy; Piling, iron & steel; Tubing, copper & copper alloy; Piling, iron & steel
Pr: Andrea Sunk
Ch: Carlos Peralta

D-U-N-S 18-904-8143
IV HEALTHCORP INC
ILLINOIS VALLEY COMMUNITY HOSP
925 West St, Peru, IL 61354-2757
Tel (815) 223-3300 *Founded/Ownrshp* 1918
Sales 93.4MM^{E} *EMP* 745
SIC 8062 8741 5912 General medical & surgical hospitals; Hospital management; Drug stores & proprietary stores; General medical & surgical hospitals; Hospital management; Drug stores & proprietary stores
Pr: Steven A Hayes

*Pr: Kris Paul
*CFO: Stephen Davis
*Ch: Harry Debo
VP: Mark Fernandez
*VP: James Loveland
VP: Maureen Rebholz
Off Mgr: Dawn Moutray
MIS Dir: Carol Myer
Dir IT: Nancy McDonnell
Pr Dir: Joan Fernandez

D-U-N-S 01-686-3292
IVAN DOVERSPIKE CO
9501 Conner St, Detroit, MI 48213-1241
Tel (313) 579-3000 Founded/Ownrshp 1963
Sales 27.8MM^E EMP 100
SIC 5084 Industrial machinery & equipment; Industrial machinery & equipment
CEO: Ivan Doverspike
*Pr: Craig Neal
*Treas: Judith Rusnak
*VP: Judith Doverspike

D-U-N-S 04-439-1886 EXP
IVAN GANDRUD CHEVROLET INC
GANDRUD NISSAN
919 Auto Plaza Dr, Green Bay, WI 54302-3701
Tel (920) 468-6800 Founded/Ownrshp 1980
Sales 65.8MM^E EMP 142
SIC 5511 5521 7538 7532 5531 Automobiles, new & used; Used car dealers; General automotive repair shops; Top & body repair & paint shops; Automotive & home supply stores; Automobiles, new & used; Used car dealers; General automotive repair shops; Top & body repair & paint shops; Automotive & home supply stores
Pr: Daniel Mangless
Genl Mgr: Steve Arndt
Sls Mgr: Scott Boths
Sls Mgr: Ron Vorhees
Sales Asso: Jared Bartelt
Sales Asso: Dave Bergner
Sales Asso: Richard Bridenhagen
Sales Asso: Jim Koski
Sales Asso: Chris Roberts
Sales Asso: Jon Rodon
Sales Asso: Jared B Sales

D-U-N-S 10-730-4719
IVAN SMITH FURNITURE CO INC
SMITH WAREHOUSE CO
5434 Technology Dr, Shreveport, LA 71129-2682
Tel (318) 688-1335 Founded/Ownrshp 1961
Sales 62.3MM^E EMP 380
SIC 5712 Furniture stores; Furniture stores
Pr: Ivan I Smith Jr
*Sec: Gloria Smith
*VP: Alben Sepulvado

D-U-N-S 83-549-9302 IMP
IVAN SMITH FURNITURE CO LLC
IVAN SMITH FURNITURE WINNFIELD
5434 Technology Dr, Shreveport, LA 71129-2682
Tel (318) 688-1335 Founded/Ownrshp 1995
Sales 129.4MM^E EMP 600
SIC 5712 Furniture stores; Furniture stores
Prin: Ivan I Smith III
IT Man: Debbie Elder
IT Man: Sal Genovese

IVAN SMITH FURNITURE WINNFIELD
See IVAN SMITH FURNITURE CO LLC

D-U-N-S 02-409-1985
IVAN WARE & SON INC
4005 Produce Rd, Louisville, KY 40218-3007
Tel (502) 968-2211 Founded/Ownrshp 1965
Sales 23.7MM^E EMP 73
SIC 1711 7359 5084 Boiler & furnace contractors; Equipment rental & leasing; Industrial machinery & equipment
Ch Bd: Carl Liebert
*CFO: Michael Martin
*VP: Brent Falcone
*VP: Ritchie Ware
Exec: Sharon Determann
Brnch Mgr: Jeff Barto
Off Mgr: Chris Jones

D-U-N-S 55-548-8949
IVANHOE INC
VALUE CENTER MARKET
22700 Ryan Rd, Warren, MI 48091-5708
Tel (586) 754-7899 Founded/Ownrshp 1989
Sales 29.0MM^E EMP 240
SIC 5411 Supermarkets, independent; Supermarkets, independent
Pr: Terry Farida
*Treas: John Farida
*VP: Ron Farida

IVANS INSURANCE SOLUTIONS
See APPLIED SYSTEMS INC

IVAR'S ACRES OF CLAMS
See SEAFOODS INC

D-U-N-S 18-415-0258 IMP
■ **IVAX CORP**
(Suby of TEVA PHARMACEUTICAL INDUSTRIES LIMITED)
4400 Biscayne Blvd, Miami, FL 33137-3212
Tel (305) 329-3795 Founded/Ownrshp 2006
Sales 697.1MM^E EMP 10,100
SIC 2834 Pharmaceutical preparations; Drugs acting on the cardiovascular system, except diagnostic; Drugs acting on the central nervous system & sense organs; Drugs acting on the respiratory system; Pharmaceutical preparations; Drugs acting on the cardiovascular system, except diagnostic; Drugs acting on the central nervous system & sense organs; Drugs acting on the respiratory system
Ch Bd: Phillip Frost MD
V Ch: Jane Hsaio
*Pr: Neil W Flanzraich
*Pr: William Marth
*CFO: Thomas Beier
CFO: Richard Friedman
*V Ch Bd: Jane Hsiao PHD
*Sr VP: Rafick G Henein PHD
*Sr VP: Clifford Montgomery
Sr VP: Steve Rubin
*Sr VP: Ronald Schultz
VP: Michael Fetell
VP: Edmond Fry
*VP: Deborah Griffin
VP: Stephen Sheriff

D-U-N-S 88-407-5235 IMP
■ **IVAX PHARMACEUTICALS LLC**
(Suby of IVAX CORP) ★
74 Nw 176th St, Miami, FL 33169-5043
Tel (305) 575-6000 Founded/Ownrshp 1995
Sales 69.8MM^E EMP 1,500
SIC 2834 Pharmaceutical preparations; Pharmaceutical preparations

IVC
See INTERNATIONAL VITAMIN CORP

IVC HIGH SCHOOL
See ILLINOIS VALLEY CENTRAL HIGH SCHOOL

D-U-N-S 00-642-1820 IMP
■ **IVC INDUSTRIAL COATINGS INC**
(Suby of PPG INDUSTRIES INC) ★
2831 E Industrial Park Dr, Brazil, IN 47834
Tel (812) 442-5080 Founded/Ownrshp 1978
Sales 25.2MM^E EMP 108
SIC 2851 Paints & allied products; Enamels; Varnishes; Lacquer: bases, dopes, thinner; Paints & allied products; Enamels; Varnishes; Lacquer: bases, dopes, thinner
Pr: Michael McCracken
VP: Matt Johnson
VP: Kevin S McCracken
Genl Mgr: Ron Winfrey
Mtls Mgr: Mark Cox
Plnt Mgr: Todd Webster
Ql Cn Mgr: Howard Mitchell
Sls Mgr: Pat Harper
Sls Mgr: Rachelle Minter
Sls Mgr: Rex Savage
Snr Mgr: Larry Zolcienski

D-U-N-S 16-528-6738 IMP/EXP
IVC US INC
(Suby of IVC BVBA)
101 Ivc Dr, Dalton, GA 30721-9711
Tel (706) 529-2600 Founded/Ownrshp 2004
Sales 63.0MM^E EMP 217^E
Accts Morehouse Group Cpa Dalton
SIC 3996 Hard surface floor coverings; Asphalted-felt-base floor coverings: linoleum, carpet; Hard surface floor coverings; Asphalted-felt-base floor coverings: linoleum, carpet
CEO: Xavier Steyaert
*Ch Bd: Filip Balcaen
*CEO: Jan Vergote
*COO: Peter Boschmans
CFO: Heidi De Greve
*CFO: Heidi Degreve
Ofcr: Paul Murfin
Dir IT: Stanton Jones
Natl Sales: Vern Phillips
S&M/VP: Tom Cruys
Mktg Dir: Tammy Horn

D-U-N-S 94-093-1827
IVC USA INC
1551 Montgomery St, South Hill, VA 23970-3920
Tel (434) 447-7100 Founded/Ownrshp 1978
Sales 50.0MM EMP 200
SIC 2435 Veneer stock, hardwood; Veneer stock, hardwood
Pr: Scott Edwards
*Pr: O C Edwards
*Sec: Tyler Howerton
*VP: Lutz Neukirchner
Genl Mgr: Tim Neukirchner
CIO: Jim Cottingham
Sales Asso: Mike Washburn

D-U-N-S 88-453-1112
IVCI LLC
601 Old Willets Path # 100, Hauppauge, NY 11788-4111
Tel (631) 273-5800 Founded/Ownrshp 1995
Sales 65.6MM EMP 180^E
Accts Grassi & Co Cpas Pc Jeri
SIC 5099 Video & audio equipment; Video & audio equipment
CEO: Robert Swing
*Pr: Charles Macli
COO: Felipe Henao
*Sr VP: Chris Bottger
*Sr VP: Curtis Heath
*Sr VP: Tim Hennen
VP: Chris BaTtger
VP: Cliff Frankenberger
VP: David Lemperle
VP: Chris BTtger
Dir Bus: Mark Schwefringhaus

D-U-N-S 96-897-2427
IVD HOLDINGS INC
3130 Gateway Dr, Peachtree Corners, GA 30071-1106
Tel (770) 441-2051 Founded/Ownrshp 2011
Sales 389.3MM^E EMP 1,090^E
SIC 2835 Blood derivative diagnostic agents; In vitro diagnostics; In vivo diagnostics; Blood derivative diagnostic agents

D-U-N-S 07-920-4246 IMP
IVD INTERMEDIATE HOLDINGS B INC
(Suby of IVD HOLDINGS INC) ★
3130 Gateway Dr, Peachtree Corners, GA 30071-1106
Tel (770) 441-2051 Founded/Ownrshp 2011
Sales 389.3MM^E EMP 1,090^E
SIC 2835 In vitro diagnostics; In vivo diagnostics; In vitro diagnostics; In vivo diagnostics

D-U-N-S 09-551-2752
IVEK CORP
10 Fairbanks Rd, North Springfield, VT 05150-9743
Tel (802) 886-2238 Founded/Ownrshp 1978
Sales 25.0MM EMP 75
SIC 3561 Industrial pumps & parts
Pr: Mark N Tanny
*VP: Frank Di Maggio
CIO: Frank Dimaggio
S&M/VP: Frank Maggio

D-U-N-S 78-225-8714
IVERIFYUS INC
150 Iverify Dr, Charlotte, NC 28217-4056
Tel (704) 525-2701 Founded/Ownrshp 2002
Sales 53.3MM^E EMP 405^E
SIC 7382 Confinement surveillance systems maintenance & monitoring
CEO: Mark Spagnolo
*CFO: Mark Simson
*Chf Cred: John McLeod
*Sr VP: Jose Chavarria
Natl Sales: Stanley Sholette

IVERSON'S DRYWALL SUPPLY
See IVERSONS LUMBER CO INC

D-U-N-S 01-712-7341
IVERSONS LUMBER CO INC
IVERSON'S DRYWALL SUPPLY
1664 N Milford Rd, Highland, MI 48357-3806
Tel (248) 889-4910 Founded/Ownrshp 1951
Sales 22.5MM^E EMP 55
SIC 5031 5211 Lumber, plywood & millwork; Lumber & other building materials
VP: Morris Law
Treas: Diana Cook
VP: Patricia Tam

D-U-N-S 00-250-3639 EXP
IVES EQUIPMENT CORP
601 Croton Rd, King of Prussia, PA 19406-3111
Tel (610) 768-1600 Founded/Ownrshp 1954
Sales 34.9MM^E EMP 45
SIC 5085 5074 5049 Valves & fittings; Sanitary ware, metal; Analytical instruments
Pr: Terrence G Ives
*Sec: Donald Courtney
VP: James A Casalenuovo
VP: Neil Jacobs

D-U-N-S 00-531-4547 IMP/EXP
IVESCO HOLDINGS LLC
124 Country Club Rd, Iowa Falls, IA 50126-9534
Tel (641) 648-2529 Founded/Ownrshp 2007
Sales NA EMP 360
SIC 5122 5083 5191

D-U-N-S 12-772-3323
IVEY MECHANICAL CO LLC
514 N Wells St, Kosciusko, MS 39090-3200
Tel (662) 289-8601 Founded/Ownrshp 2003
Sales 125.1MM EMP 790
Accts Carr Riggs & Ingram Llc Rid
SIC 1711 Plumbing, heating, air-conditioning contractors; Plumbing, heating, air-conditioning contractors
Ch Bd: Larry Terrell
*Pr: Denny Terrell
*CFO: Randy Dew
VP: Robert P Arnold
*VP: Bob Cooper
VP: Edward J Lamprecht
VP: Kenny Malone
Div Mgr: Mike Young
Sfty Mgr: Bo Harrel
Opers Mgr: Randy Berry

D-U-N-S 06-482-4436
IVEYS CONSTRUCTION INC
4060 N Courtenay Pkwy, Merritt Island, FL 32953-8111
Tel (321) 453-3812 Founded/Ownrshp 1973
Sales 71.6MM EMP 250
Accts Berman Hopkins Wright & Latham
SIC 1541 1542 1791 Industrial buildings, new construction; Commercial & office building, new construction; Structural steel erection; Industrial buildings, new construction; Commercial & office building, new construction; Structural steel erection
Pr: Kevin W Ivey
*Treas: Kymm Ivey
*VP: Steve Cirges
*VP: Wade A Ivey
*VP: Rocky Johnson
*VP: Johnson L Rocky
VP: Steve Sergis
Trfc Dir: Bob Queen
Board of Directors: Tammie Ivey

D-U-N-S 09-919-0571
IVG HOSPITALS INC
20 Cabot Rd, Woburn, MA 01801-1004
Tel (781) 932-5802 Founded/Ownrshp 1980
Sales 24.7MM^E EMP 150
SIC 0742 Animal hospital services, pets & other animal specialties
CEO: G Ames Prentiss
*Pr: John K Prentiss Dvm
*Treas: Mona Bishlawi
IT Man: Marie Katzen

D-U-N-S 07-874-1355
■ **IVI INTERNATIONAL INC** (NY)
(Suby of CBRE GROUP INC) ★
55 W Red Oak Ln Ste 1, White Plains, NY 10604-3608
Tel (916) 694-1900 Founded/Ownrshp 2002, 2014
Sales 41.0MM^E EMP 200
SIC 8748 Business consulting
Pr: Robert Barone
VP: Jessica Doerner
VP: Tim Hasselbach
VP: Letizia Rubino
VP: Randall Ward
Dir IT: Laurence Goldberg
Snr PM: Craig Brenner
Snr PM: Romeo Fojas
Snr PM: Scott Foster
Snr PM: Gibson Jones
Snr PM: Michael Lafalce

IVI NORTH
See INDUSTRIAL VENTILATION INC

IVIE
See GREENLEAF ADVERTISING & MEDIA INC

D-U-N-S 80-976-6397
IVIE & ASSOCIATES INC
601 Silveron Ste 200, Flower Mound, TX 75028-4030
Tel (972) 899-5000 Founded/Ownrshp 1993
Sales 216.3MM EMP 242
SIC 7311 Advertising agencies; Advertising agencies
Pr: Warren Ivie
*Pr: Brandon Ivie
*Treas: Sharon Renee Rawlings
Ex VP: Kay Ivie
VP: David Bailey
VP: Bob Epping
*VP: Sharon Kay Ivie
VP: Garrison Jim
VP: Gary Long
VP: Osye Pritchett
VP: Renee Rawlings
Creative D: Darrell Basgall
Creative D: Chad Revelle
Creative D: Anthony Woolridge

D-U-N-S 83-910-6267
■ **IVILLAGE INC**
IVILLAGE.COM
(Suby of NBCUNIVERSAL MEDIA LLC) ★
500 Fashion Ave, New York, NY 10018-4502
Tel (212) 600-6000 Founded/Ownrshp 2006
Sales 40.1MM^E EMP 278
SIC 4899 Data communication services; Data communication services
Pr: Elizabeth Comstock
COO: Michael Gutknowski
COO: Ezra Kucharz
CFO: Steven A Elkes
Sr VP: Richard J Kolberg
Sr VP: Steven Lake
Sr VP: Peter R Naylo
Sr VP: Debbie Reichig
VP: Douglas Gottlieb
VP: Kyle Peterson
VP: Michael Rix

IVILLAGE.COM
See IVILLAGE INC

IVINSON MEMORIAL HOSPITAL
See ALBANY COUNTY HOSPITAL DISTRICT

D-U-N-S 17-693-5203
IVOCLAR VIVADENT INC
IVOCLAR WILLIAMS
(Suby of IVOCLAR VIVADENT AKTIENGESELLSCHAFT)
175 Pineview Dr, Amherst, NY 14228-2286
Tel (716) 691-0010 Founded/Ownrshp 1986
Sales 96.1MM^E EMP 233
SIC 5047 8021 Dental equipment & supplies; Dental laboratory equipment; Dentists' professional supplies; Offices & clinics of dentists; Dental equipment & supplies; Dental laboratory equipment; Dentists' professional supplies; Offices & clinics of dentists
Ch Bd: Robert A Ganley
Sr Cor Off: John Stack
VP: Thomas Kingston
VP: Deborah Lamond
VP: Pierre Lamoure
VP: Wayne Ledford
VP: Patrick M Segnere
Creative D: Don Churik
Area Mgr: Jearg Brenn
Genl Mgr: Ulises Merino
CTO: Thomas Hirt

IVOCLAR WILLIAMS
See IVOCLAR VIVADENT INC

D-U-N-S 14-326-7206
IVORY CHEVROLET LLC
4200 Jonesboro Rd, Union City, GA 30291-2266
Tel (770) 969-1001 Founded/Ownrshp 2010
Sales 22.2MM^E EMP 65
SIC 5511 Automobiles, new & used; Automobiles, new & used
Genl Mgr: Jim Long

D-U-N-S 07-298-3265
IVORY HOMES LTD
978 E Woodoak Ln, Salt Lake City, UT 84117-7265
Tel (801) 747-7000 Founded/Ownrshp 1971
Sales 70.1MM^E EMP 120
Accts Hansen Bradshaw Malmrose & Eri
SIC 1521 6552 Single-family housing construction; Subdividers & developers; Single-family housing construction; Subdividers & developers
CEO: Clark Ivory
*Genl Pt: Value Lc
COO: David Broadbent
Area Mgr: John Cahoon
Area Mgr: Dave Zorba
IT Man: Brandon Malan
IT Man: Kasey Medill
Sales Asso: Douglas Babcock
Sales Asso: Ann Hatch
Sales Asso: Clay Heseltine
Sales Asso: Kenneth Hunt

D-U-N-S 96-997-1014
IVOX SOLUTIONS LLC
4485 Sw Port Way, Palm City, FL 34990-5586
Tel (772) 286-8183 Founded/Ownrshp 2007
Sales 132.5MM^E EMP 450
SIC 5065 4812 Mobile telephone equipment; Cellular telephone services; Mobile telephone equipment; Cellular telephone services
CEO: Rob Newton
CFO: Christopher Stapleton

IVP
See INSTITUTIONAL VENTURES PARTNERS

D-U-N-S 09-532-4240
IVS GROUP
1439 1st Ave S, Institute, WV 25112
Tel (304) 768-4307 Founded/Ownrshp 1972
Sales 43.4MM^E EMP 220
SIC 1799 Cleaning building exteriors; Cleaning building exteriors
Pr: Larry Dawson
*Treas: Keith T May
*Sec: Fred Clark

*VP: Jerry L Biehl
Exec: Jeff Becker
Opers Mgr: Dave Griffis
Opers Mgr: Jeremy Johnson

IVY, THE
See LADESSERTS INC

D-U-N-S 01-386-1408
■ IVY H SMITH CO LLC
(Suby of DYCOM INDUSTRIES INC) ★
736 Park North Blvd # 100, Clarkston, GA 30021-1901
Tel (404) 508-5700 Founded/Ownrshp 1946, 2001
Sales 27.7MM^E EMP 171
SIC 1623 Water, sewer & utility lines; Water, sewer & utility lines
Pr: George Summers
*VP: Michael Cassidy
*VP: Michael A Coyle
*VP: Hayden Saling
Board of Directors: Steven Nielsen

D-U-N-S 78-108-2417
IVY INSURANCE GROUP INC
411 E Huntington Dr # 203, Arcadia, CA 91006-3731
Tel (626) 566-2116 Founded/Ownrshp 1988
Sales NA EMP 69
SIC 6331 Fire, marine & casualty insurance: mutual; Automobile insurance
Pr: James V O Donnell
*Ch Bd: William H T Bush

D-U-N-S 06-149-0983
IVY STREET HOTEL LIMITED PARTNERSHIP (GA)
265 Peachtree Ctr Ave Ne, Atlanta, GA 30303-7402
Tel (404) 521-0000 Founded/Ownrshp 1985
Sales 14.6MM^E EMP 800
SIC 5812 5813 5947 5621 6531 Eating places; Caterers; Contract food services; Drinking places; Gift shop; Dress shops; Real estate agents & managers; Eating places; Caterers; Contract food services; Drinking places; Gift shop; Dress shops; Real estate agents & managers
Prin: Erica Qualls

IVY TECH CENTRAL OFFICE
See IVY TECH FOUNDATION INC

D-U-N-S 07-206-6681
IVY TECH FOUNDATION INC
IVY TECH CENTRAL OFFICE
50 W Fall Creek Pkwy N Dr, Indianapolis, IN 46208-5752
Tel (317) 926-0192 Founded/Ownrshp 1963
Sales 318.8MM^E EMP 9,396^E
SIC 8222 Community college; Community college
Pr: Thomas J Snyder
Pr: Janet J Evelyn
Sr VP: Susan W Brooks
Sr VP: Donald S Doucette
Assoc Dir: Connie Swoveland
Adm Dir: Daniel Hunter
Ex Dir: Ray A Vulgan
Prgrm Mgr: Patrick Hulin
Site Mgr: Judy Doppelfeld

D-U-N-S 96-287-3811
IVY TECH FOUNDATION INC
50 W Fall Creek Pkwy N Dr, Indianapolis, IN 46208-5752
Tel (317) 921-4749 Founded/Ownrshp 2010
Sales 36.9MM EMP 2
Accts Ksm Business Services Inc Ind
SIC 8699 Charitable organization; Charitable organization

IVYWOOD INTERIORS
See WOODSIDE GROUP INC

D-U-N-S 62-392-9072
IW GROUP
8687 Melrose Ave Ste G540, West Hollywood, CA 90069-5715
Tel (310) 289-5500 Founded/Ownrshp 1990
Sales 30.0MM EMP 68
SIC 7311 8743 Advertising agencies; Public relations services
CEO: Bill Imada
*Pr: Nita Song
VP: John Author
Creative D: Ting Lin

D-U-N-S 80-585-9493
IWAI METAL (AMERICA) CO LTD
(Suby of NALCOIWAI CO.,LTD.)
2320 Pseo De Ls Amrcs 2 Ste 202, San Diego, CA 92154
Tel (619) 651-1185 Founded/Ownrshp 1991
Sales 42.1MM^E EMP 300^E
SIC 1761 Industrial locomotives & parts; Industrial tools; Sheet metalwork
CEO: Nobuya Nakatani
*Pr: Noritaka Umeda
*Prin: Hideo Mizukoshi
Off Mgr: Ritsuko Seaman
IT Man: Wataru Kamimura
Sls Mgr: Roy Hayashi

D-U-N-S 07-191-0814 IMP
IWATA BOLT USA INC
7131 Orangewood Ave, Garden Grove, CA 92841-1442
Tel (714) 897-0800 Founded/Ownrshp 1971
Sales 38.1MM^E EMP 73
SIC 5072 3452 Miscellaneous fasteners; Bolts; Nuts; Bolts, nuts, rivets & washers
CEO: Shinobu Iwata
*Pr: Kiyotaka Iwata
*CFO: Akira Kayama

D-U-N-S 11-795-1488
IWAY SOFTWARE CO
(Suby of INFORMATION BUILDERS INC) ★
2 Penn Plz Fl 28, New York, NY 10121-2898
Tel (212) 330-1700 Founded/Ownrshp 2003
Sales 46.1MM^E EMP 800
SIC 7373 Systems integration services; Systems integration services
CEO: Gerald Cohen
*Pr: John Senor
*CFO: Harry Lerner
Chf Cred: Michael Corcorcan
VP: Roy Augstino
VP: Frans Deneve
VP: Gregory Dorman
VP: John Knabe
VP: Dennis McLaughlin
VP: Rick Rohde
VP: Monte Roy
VP: David Sandel
VP: David Small
VP: Melissa Treier
VP: Alexey Vorovich
VP: David Watson

IWCO DIRECT
See INSTANT WEB INC

IWCO DIRECT
See INSTANT WEB LLC

D-U-N-S 00-132-6115 IMP
IWG HIGH PERFORMANCE CONDUCTORS INC (NY)
(Suby of BARE WIRE DIVISION) ★
1570 Campton Rd, Inman, SC 29349-8433
Tel (864) 472-9022 Founded/Ownrshp 1902, 2006
Sales 48.0MM^E EMP 300
SIC 3357 3674 Nonferrous wiredrawing & insulating; Semiconductors & related devices; Nonferrous wiredrawing & insulating; Semiconductors & related devices
Pr: Martin G Dew
*CEO: Rodney D Kent
VP: Emilio Cerra
IT Man: Willie Gonzalez
Mfg Dir: Kerry Norman
Mtls Mgr: Kenneth Greene
Plnt Mgr: Emilio L Cerra

IWIF
See CHESAPEAKE EMPLOYERS INSURANCE CO

IWIRELESS CENTER
See ILLINOIS QUAD CITY CIVIC CENTER AUTHORITY

D-U-N-S 16-954-3043 IMP
IWIS DRIVE SYSTEMS LLC
IWIS USA
8266 Zionsville Rd # 100, Indianapolis, IN 46268-1627
Tel (317) 821-3539 Founded/Ownrshp 2004
Sales 40.0MM EMP 36^E
SIC 5083 Agricultural machinery & equipment; Agricultural machinery & equipment
CEO: Glenn Walter
Pr: Daniel P Egenolf
Bd of Dir: Holger Bodenstein
Bd of Dir: Helmut Girg
Bd of Dir: Peter Markowsky
VP: Andy Binford

IWIS USA
See IWIS DRIVE SYSTEMS LLC

D-U-N-S 01-865-1778 IMP
IWKA HOLDING CORP
(Suby of KUKA AG)
6600 Center Dr, Sterling Heights, MI 48312-2666
Tel (586) 795-2000 Founded/Ownrshp 1981, 1998
Sales 82.5MM^E EMP 792
SIC 3549 5084 7371 8711 Assembly machines, including robotic; Industrial machinery & equipment; Computer software development; Engineering services; Assembly machines, including robotic; Industrial machinery & equipment; Computer software development; Engineering services
Ch Bd: Lawrence Drake

D-U-N-S 07-925-6639
IWS ACQUISITION CORP
5901 Broken Sound Pkwy Nw, Boca Raton, FL 33487-2773
Tel (561) 981-7000 Founded/Ownrshp 2012
Sales NA EMP 58
SIC 6399 Deposit insurance; Deposit insurance
CEO: James Hawk
*Sr VP: William Andrew
Dir Bus: Shawn Murphy

IWS-MAHRT
See INDUSTRIAL WAREHOUSE SERVICES INC

IWX MOTOR FREIGHT
See INDIANA WESTERN EXPRESS INC

D-U-N-S 17-941-5773
▲ IXIA
26601 Agoura Rd, Calabasas, CA 91302-1959
Tel (818) 871-1800 Founded/Ownrshp 1997
Sales 464.4MM EMP 1,755^E
Tkr Sym XXIA Exch NGS
SIC 3825 Network analyzers; Network analyzers
Pr: Bethany Mayer
*Ch Bd: Errol Ginsberg
COO: Alexander J Pepe
CFO: Brent T Novak
Sr VP: Matthew S Alexander
Sr VP: Ronald W Buckly
Sr VP: Hans-Peter Klaey
VP: Jim Doherty
VP: Alan Grahame
VP: Fred Kost
VP: Pam Mason
VP: Roark Pollock
Board of Directors: Laurent Asscher, Ilan Daskal, Jonathan Fram, Gail Hamilton

D-U-N-S 14-490-8787 IMP
IXMATION INC
IXMATION NORTH AMERICA
(Suby of IXMATION AG)
31 Presidential Dr, Roselle, IL 60172-3914
Tel (630) 351-3000 Founded/Ownrshp 2005
Sales 39.9MM^E EMP 150
SIC 3599 8711 Custom machinery; Designing: ship, boat, machine & product; Custom machinery; Designing: ship, boat, machine & product
Pr: Michael Macsek
CFO: Marcus Ludwig
Genl Mgr: Dan Gilgen
Snr Mgr: Pradeep Kaura

IXMATION NORTH AMERICA
See IXMATION INC

D-U-N-S 02-036-2635
IXONOS USA LIMITED
(Suby of IXONOS OYJ)
85 2nd St, San Francisco, CA 94105-3459
Tel (949) 278-1354 Founded/Ownrshp 2010
Sales 51.1MM^E EMP 1,000
SIC 7373 8731 Systems software development services; Computer (hardware) development; Systems software development services; Computer (hardware) development
VP: Jo Javier

D-U-N-S 87-426-7370
IXOS SOFTWARE INC
8717 Research Dr, Irvine, CA 92618-4217
Tel (949) 784-8000 Founded/Ownrshp 2012
Sales 39.2MM^E EMP 800
SIC 5045 Computer software; Computer software
CFO: Mark Smith
CFO: Steve Gulley
Off Mgr: Steven Fretz
IT Man: Bob Fiorentino
IT Man: Patrick Lehner
IT Man: Donovan McCulloch
Netwrk Mgr: Patrick Pant

D-U-N-S 11-835-6216
IXP CORP
103 Main St, Princeton, NJ 08540-5754
Tel (609) 759-5100 Founded/Ownrshp 1999
Sales 20.6MM^E EMP 160
SIC 8748 7373 Systems engineering consultant, ex. computer or professional; Computer systems analysis & design; Systems integration services; Computer-aided design (CAD) systems service
CEO: William E Metro
*Pr: Lawrence Consalvos
*Sr VP: Amy Onder
VP: Eldon Wright
VP Sls: Rhona K Wulf
Sales Asso: Benjamin Archer-Clowes
Snr PM: Jack Hart

D-U-N-S 12-134-4027
IXSYSTEMS INC
2490 Kruse Dr, San Jose, CA 95131-1234
Tel (408) 943-4100 Founded/Ownrshp 2002
Sales 50.0MM EMP 60
SIC 7372 Operating systems computer software
CEO: Mike Lauth
COO: Andrew Madrid
CTO: Matt Olander
Dir IT: Josh Paetzel
Mktg Dir: Gary Archer
Pr Dir: Dru Lavigne

D-U-N-S 10-302-7843 IMP
▲ IXYS CORP
1590 Buckeye Dr, Milpitas, CA 95035-7418
Tel (408) 457-9000 Founded/Ownrshp 1983
Sales 338.7MM EMP 1,016^E
Tkr Sym IXYS Exch NGS
SIC 3674 Semiconductors & related devices; Integrated circuits, semiconductor networks, etc.; Modules, solid state; Rectifiers, solid state; Semiconductors & related devices; Integrated circuits, semiconductor networks, etc.; Modules, solid state; Rectifiers, solid state
Ch Bd: Nathan Zommer
Pr: Uzi Sasson
Ofcr: Kent Loose
Sr VP: Dan Schwob
VP: Mark F Heisig
VP: Clifford Knudsen
VP: Kent Paris
Genl Mgr: Thea Kern
Genl Mgr: Elmar Wisotzki
Software D: Patrick Traynor
Mktg Dir: John Williams
Board of Directors: Donald L Feucht, Samuel Kory, S Joon Lee, Timothy A Richardson, James M Thorburn, Kenneth D Wong

D-U-N-S 36-370-0725 IMP/EXP
■ IXYS INTEGRATED CIRCUITS DIVISION INC
(Suby of IXYS CORP) ★
78 Cherry Hill Dr, Beverly, MA 01915-1065
Tel (978) 524-6700 Founded/Ownrshp 2002
Sales 22.5MM^E EMP 100^E
SIC 3625 Industrial electrical relays & switches; Industrial electrical relays & switches
Pr: Nathan Zommer
*Treas: Arnold Agbayani
VP: Bill Boldt
VP: Nestore Polce
Mng Dir: Herve Guerner
IT Man: Steven Froyman
Sfty Mgr: James Chalapatas
Mfg Mgr: Doug Romine
Prd Mgr: David Ambrose
QI Cn Mgr: Marty Brandt
Snr Mgr: Eric Blom

D-U-N-S 96-831-2178
IYPAD INTERNATIONAL INC NFP
419 S East Ave, Oak Park, IL 60302-3969
Tel (773) 654-7141 Founded/Ownrshp 2011
Sales NA EMP 4,000
SIC 9441 Administration of social & manpower programs; Administration of social & manpower programs
Pr: Diane Urban

D-U-N-S 78-949-7500
IZ ON MEDIA LLC
(Suby of TECHNICOLOR)
600 Harrison St Fl 4, San Francisco, CA 94107-1370
Tel (415) 808-3500 Founded/Ownrshp 2005
Sales 43.6MM^E EMP 150^E
SIC 7371 3571 Computer software development & applications; Computers, digital, analog or hybrid; Computer software development & applications; Computers, digital, analog or hybrid
*Pr: Eric Bindelglass
*CFO: Mitch Wortzman
Sr VP: Randy Frank
*Sr VP: Nicholas Marquart
VP: Michael Arkin
VP: Tracy Boyd
VP: Lori Hillman
VP: Gerry Horn
VP Bus Dev: Kevin Carbone
VP Bus Dev: Julie Loder
Exec: Amanda Schwartz

IZONE GROUP
See UV SALES INC

IZZY ORTEGA'S
See MCLINTOCKS

IZZY PLUS
See JSJ FURNITURE CORP

J

D-U-N-S 07-351-1867
J & A MECHANICAL INC
5350 Poplar Ave Ste 500, Memphis, TN 38119-3697
Tel (901) 682-8783 Founded/Ownrshp 1988
Sales 26.1MM^E EMP 650
SIC 1711 Plumbing contractors; Warm air heating & air conditioning contractor
Pr: Edward Nenon
*Treas: John D Lawrence
*VP: Claude J Mc Atee
VP: Claude McAtee
*VP: Martin Waung

D-U-N-S 15-335-6683
J & A SERVICES LLC
3166 Pipe Ct, Grand Junction, CO 81504-6237
Tel (970) 434-9435 Founded/Ownrshp 2004
Sales 39.8MM^E EMP 85^E
SIC 1382 Oil & gas exploration services

J & B CLEANING SERVICE
See MARDONE INC

D-U-N-S 60-815-5347 EXP
J & B FASTENERS LP
NICK'S FASTERNER AND INDUS SUP
6121 Griggs Rd, Houston, TX 77023-6441
Tel (713) 645-3480 Founded/Ownrshp 1989
Sales 39.9MM^E EMP 82
SIC 5085 Industrial supplies; Fasteners & fastening equipment; Fasteners, industrial: nuts, bolts, screws, etc.; Industrial supplies; Fasteners & fastening equipment; Fasteners, industrial: nuts, bolts, screws, etc.
*Genl Pt: Belinda Nichols
*VP: Brad Miedke
Brnch Mgr: Jeannie Scurto
Opers Mgr: Brenda Porter
Sales Asso: Johnny Johnson
Sales Asso: Walter Jones
Sales Asso: Brian Pellegrin
Sales Asso: Billy Reyes
Sales Asso: Dave Schultz
Sales Asso: Louis Speedon

D-U-N-S 94-823-1774
J & B GROUP INC
13200 43rd St Ne, Saint Michael, MN 55376-8420
Tel (763) 497-3913 Founded/Ownrshp 1995
Sales 148.0MM^E EMP 340^E
SIC 6719 Investment holding companies, except banks; Investment holding companies, except banks
Ch Bd: Robert Hageman
*Pr: Michael Hageman
VP: Gary Hageman
Area Mgr: Kevin Regan
CTO: Barb Bartlett
QI Cn Mgr: Lee Jacobs
Manager: Steve Askew
Manager: Rusty Gerrels

D-U-N-S 05-796-7390 IMP/EXP
J & B IMPORTERS INC
J & B NORTHEAST
11925 Sw 128th St, Miami, FL 33186-5209
Tel (305) 238-1866 Founded/Ownrshp 1971
Sales 122.7MM^E EMP 300
SIC 5091 5599 Bicycle parts & accessories; Bicycle parts & accessories; Bicycles; Dunebuggies
Pr: Ben Joannou Sr
*Treas: Ben Joannou Jr
Treas: Barry Silvers
*VP: Jacques Gurdjian
VP: Harreit Margolesky
*VP: Bill Tannen
Exec: Lourdes Barsky
Genl Mgr: Eric Larson
Sales Asso: Liam Fallon
Sales Asso: Michael Kay
Sales Asso: Greg Mixson

J & B MATERIALS, INC.
See PACIFIC GYPSUM SUPPLY INC

J & B NORTHEAST
See J & B IMPORTERS INC

D-U-N-S 93-243-7783
J & B RESTAURANT PARTNERS OF LONG ISLAND INC
FRIENDLY'S
(Suby of J & B RESTAURANT PARTNERS OF LONG ISLAND LLC) ★
3385 Vtrans Mem Hwy Ste A, Ronkonkoma, NY 11779-7660
Tel (631) 218-9067 Founded/Ownrshp 1997

Sales 38.8MM^E *EMP* 1,210
SIC 5812 Restaurant, family: chain
Pr: Joseph Vitrano

D-U-N-S 13-224-5007
J & B RESTAURANT PARTNERS OF LONG ISLAND LLC
4000 Veterans Memorial Hw, Bohemia, NY 11716-1040
Tel (631) 218-9067 *Founded/Ownrshp* 2000
Sales 54.1MM^E *EMP* 1,400^E
SIC 5812 Eating places; Eating places
Pr: Joseph P Vitrano
CFO: Jerry Snearly

D-U-N-S 07-838-6557
J & B RESTAURANT PARTNERS OF NJ LLC
FRIENDLY'S
3385 Vtrans Mem Hwy Ste A, Ronkonkoma, NY 11779-7660
Tel (631) 218-9067 *Founded/Ownrshp* 2012
Sales 8.1MM^E *EMP* 332^E
SIC 5812 Restaurant, family: chain

D-U-N-S 00-812-0750 IMP
J & B SAUSAGE CO INC
J BAR B FOODS
100 Main, Waelder, TX 78959-5329
Tel (830) 788-7661 *Founded/Ownrshp* 1969
Sales 104.1MM^E *EMP* 340
SIC 2011 5147 2013 Sausages from meat slaughtered on site; Meats & meat products; Sausages & other prepared meats; Sausages from meat slaughtered on site; Meats & meat products; Sausages & other prepared meats
CEO: Danny Janecka
**Sec:* Noreen Janecka
Sr VP: Leslie Clifton
**VP:* Lyndell Bisbee
**VP:* Danny Janecka II
Sfty Dirs: Amy Janecka
Ql Cn Mgr: Julie Ohlenbusch
VP Sls: Brian Pirkle
Pr Mgr: Bonnie Hyman
Sls Mgr: Gilbert Velasquez

D-U-N-S 60-544-8083
J & B SOFTWARE INC
(*Suby of* TRANSCENTRA INC) ★
510 Township Line Rd # 100, Blue Bell, PA 19422-2721
Tel (215) 641-1500 *Founded/Ownrshp* 2011
Sales 20.8MM^E *EMP* 165
SIC 7371

D-U-N-S 04-355-5697
J & B SUPPLY INC
4915 S Zero St, Fort Smith, AR 72903-6933
Tel (479) 649-4900 *Founded/Ownrshp* 1968
Sales 47.2MM^E *EMP* 65
SIC 5074 5063 5075 Plumbing & hydronic heating supplies; Electrical supplies; Warm air heating equipment & supplies; Air conditioning & ventilation equipment & supplies; Plumbing & hydronic heating supplies; Electrical supplies; Warm air heating equipment & supplies; Air conditioning & ventilation equipment & supplies
Pr: Barry S Jones
**CFO:* Warren Thompson
VP: Brent Jones
Brnch Mgr: Jeff Francis

D-U-N-S 09-709-6093 IMP/EXP
J & B WHOLESALE DISTRIBUTING INC
(*Suby of* J & B GROUP INC) ★
13200 43rd St Ne, Saint Michael, MN 55376-8420
Tel (763) 497-9431 *Founded/Ownrshp* 1979
Sales 500.0MM *EMP* 340
SIC 5147 5144 5142 5143 5148 Meats, fresh; Meats, cured or smoked; Poultry: live, dressed or frozen (unpackaged); Fish, frozen: packaged; Cheese; Vegetables, fresh; Meats, fresh; Meats, cured or smoked; Poultry: live, dressed or frozen (unpackaged); Fish, frozen: packaged; Cheese; Vegetables, fresh
CEO: Robert Hageman
**Pr:* Michael Hageman
**CFO:* James Chapa
CIO: Chuck Ballard

D-U-N-S 06-914-9920 EXP
J & C ENTERPRISES INC
J & C TROPICALS
17425 Sw 172nd St, Miami, FL 33187-1671
Tel (305) 255-5100 *Founded/Ownrshp* 1967
Sales 35.0MM *EMP* 60
Accts Sanson Kline Jacomino & Compan
SIC 0182 Vegetable crops grown under cover
CEO: Carlos Capote
**Ex VP:* Nibaldo J Capote
Genl Mgr: Pedro Capote
Genl Mgr: David Lopez
Trfc Mgr: Albert Pena

J & C TROPICALS
See J & C ENTERPRISES INC

J & C WHOLESALE CO
See JONES STORES INC

D-U-N-S 04-313-2935
J & D ACQUISITIONS INC (OK)
JIM NORTON TOYOTA
9809 S Memorial Dr, Tulsa, OK 74133-6198
Tel (918) 250-6888 *Founded/Ownrshp* 1989
Sales 71.8MM^E *EMP* 200
SIC 5511

D-U-N-S 60-206-5443 IMP
J & D LABORATORIES INC
2710 Progress St, Vista, CA 92081-8449
Tel (760) 734-6800 *Founded/Ownrshp* 1988
Sales 74.6MM^E *EMP* 300
SIC 2833 2834 Vitamins, natural or synthetic: bulk, uncompounded; Pharmaceutical preparations; Vitamins, natural or synthetic: bulk, uncompounded; Pharmaceutical preparations
CEO: Kiran H Majmudar
CFO: Mike Keefe
**Prin:* Marita Sweeten

J & D MANUFACTURING
See J & D SALES INC OF EAU CLAIRE WISCONSIN

D-U-N-S 08-012-1445
J & D MEAT CO
JD FOOD
4586 E Commerce Ave, Fresno, CA 93725-2203
Tel (559) 445-1123 *Founded/Ownrshp* 1980
Sales 73.4MM *EMP* 72
Accts Kawana & Gong Llp Fresno Ca
SIC 5149 5147 5148 5143 5142 Groceries & related products; Meats & meat products; Fresh fruits & vegetables; Dairy products, except dried or canned; Packaged frozen goods; Groceries & related products; Meats & meat products; Fresh fruits & vegetables; Dairy products, except dried or canned; Packaged frozen goods
Pr: Mark K Ford
**VP:* Robert Maxey
**Prin:* Ken Ford
**Prin:* Jim Maxey
Sls Mgr: Cliff Klein

D-U-N-S 19-517-2531 IMP
J & D PRODUCE INC
7310 N Expressway 281, Edinburg, TX 78542
Tel (956) 380-0353 *Founded/Ownrshp* 1979
Sales 105.7MM *EMP* 420
SIC 5148 Fresh fruits & vegetables; Fresh fruits & vegetables
Pr: James V Bassetti Jr
**VP:* Diane Bassetti
Board of Directors: Shawn M Allen, Yvonne Benavidez

D-U-N-S 02-980-8208
J & D RESTAURANT GROUP LLC
JACK IN THE BOX
7 Village Cir Ste 300, Westlake, TX 76262-5906
Tel (817) 693-5119 *Founded/Ownrshp* 2009
Sales 38.4MM^E *EMP* 1,097^E
SIC 5812 Fast-food restaurant, chain

D-U-N-S 06-360-5372 IMP
J & D SALES INC OF EAU CLAIRE WISCONSIN
J & D MANUFACTURING
6200 Us Highway 12, Eau Claire, WI 54701-8360
Tel (715) 834-1439 *Founded/Ownrshp* 1977
Sales 23.8MM^E *EMP* 70
SIC 3523 3564 3822 3441 3429 Barn, silo, poultry, dairy & livestock machinery; Barn cleaners; Ventilating fans: industrial or commercial; Auto controls regulating residntl & coml environmt & applncs; Fabricated structural metal; Manufactured hardware (general)
CEO: Don Redetzke
**Treas:* Diana Redetzke
Off Mgr: Tripler Scott
VP Sls: Terry Lyons

D-U-N-S 05-761-2145
J & E MANUFACTURING CO
HARMONY ENGINEERING
7925 215th St W, Lakeville, MN 55044-9016
Tel (952) 469-3933 *Founded/Ownrshp* 1996
Sales 35.1MM^E *EMP* 250
SIC 3444 3544 3469 Sheet metal specialties, not stamped; Restaurant sheet metalwork; Die sets for metal stamping (presses); Stamping metal for the trade; Sheet metal specialties, not stamped; Restaurant sheet metalwork; Die sets for metal stamping (presses); Stamping metal for the trade
CEO: Michael Hansen
Sls Mgr: Robert Bearl

D-U-N-S 07-670-4394
J & G ELECTRIC CO INC
512 S Main St, Roswell, NM 88203-5757
Tel (575) 622-0146 *Founded/Ownrshp* 1962
Sales 24.8MM^E *EMP* 56
SIC 5063 1731 5719 Lighting fixtures; General electrical contractor; Lighting fixtures
Pr: Bruce K Gwartney
**Treas:* Geneva Gwartney
**VP:* John E Gwartney

D-U-N-S 10-241-7946 IMP
J & G STEEL CORP
2429 Industrial Rd, Sapulpa, OK 74066-8335
Tel (918) 227-3131 *Founded/Ownrshp* 1982
Sales 29.3MM^E *EMP* 100
SIC 3441 Fabricated structural metal
Pr: Gary Gilliam
Ql Cn Mgr: John Slater

J & H ERECTORS
See J&H REINFORCING AND STRUCTURAL ERECTORS INC

D-U-N-S 15-371-5891
J & H FOREST PRODUCTS INC
3156 S Bown Way, Boise, ID 83706-5400
Tel (208) 343-5988 *Founded/Ownrshp* 1985
Sales 49.5MM *EMP* 12
SIC 5031 Lumber: rough, dressed & finished; Lumber: rough, dressed & finished
Pr: Holly Merritt
CFO: Dave Babb
**VP:* Herb Janson

D-U-N-S 07-259-3692
J & H OIL CO
SERVICE OIL
2696 Chicago Dr Sw, Grand Rapids, MI 49519-1628
Tel (616) 534-2181 *Founded/Ownrshp* 1970
Sales 373.8MM *EMP* 70
Accts Uhy Llp Sterling Heights Mic
SIC 5172 5013 Petroleum products; Automotive supplies & parts; Petroleum products; Automotive supplies & parts
Pr: Jerry Hop
CFO: Joe Albers
**VP:* Sandra Arrasmith
**VP:* Craig Hoppen
Mktg Dir: Abby Albers

Sls Mgr: Dan Dehaan
Sls Mgr: Leonard Kern

J & J BURNING AND FABG CO
See J & J BURNING CO

D-U-N-S 00-534-1128
J & J BURNING CO (MI)
J & J BURNING AND FABG CO
24622 Mound Rd, Warren, MI 48091-2094
Tel (586) 758-7619 *Founded/Ownrshp* 1958, 1974
Sales 20.6MM^E *EMP* 50
SIC 3441 Fabricated structural metal
Pr: Timothy Farrar
**Ex VP:* Gary Farrar
Plnt Mgr: Greg Sieders
Sls Dir: Scott Waple
Sls Mgr: Gary Gron

D-U-N-S 06-104-3337
J & J CARDS INC
HALLMARK
1212 S Air Depot Blvd # 27, Oklahoma City, OK 73110-4870
Tel (405) 733-9480 *Founded/Ownrshp* 1972
Sales 22.8MM^E *EMP* 250
SIC 5947

D-U-N-S 80-824-4466
J & J CHEMICAL AMERICA INC
2100 West Loop S Ste 1220, Houston, TX 77027-3599
Tel (281) 768-5315 *Founded/Ownrshp* 2007
Sales 50.0MM *EMP* 10
SIC 5169 Chemicals, industrial & heavy; Chemicals, industrial & heavy
Pr: Jaihoon Rew
**CFO:* Cesar Purgato

D-U-N-S 08-310-6757 EXP
J & J CHEMICAL CO
1450 Athens Rd, Crawford, GA 30630-2533
Tel (706) 743-1900 *Founded/Ownrshp* 2004
Sales 23.0MM^E *EMP* 45^E
SIC 5169 Chemicals & allied products
Pr: Gerald T Boyd
Mktg Dir: Paolo Lupini
Sls Mgr: Joshua Carmichael

J & J DISTR CO
See ALLIED BEVERAGE GROUP LLC

D-U-N-S 09-905-9289 IMP
J & J DISTRIBUTING CO
653 Rice St, Saint Paul, MN 55103-1849
Tel (651) 221-0560 *Founded/Ownrshp* 1978
Sales 54.9MM *EMP* 140
Accts Babcock Langbein Cpa Minneapo
SIC 5148 Fresh fruits & vegetables; Fresh fruits & vegetables
CEO: James H Hannigan
**CFO:* John Wujek
Ex VP: Stephanie Melstrom
**VP:* Deborah A Hannigan
VP: John Mady
Dir Bus: Chris Nichols
CTO: John Wujack
Dir IT: Tony Lusiba
Opers Mgr: Ron Krantz
Ql Cn Mgr: Jerry Debilzan

D-U-N-S 03-279-5866
J & J DISTRIBUTORS OF FLORIDA INC (DE)
(*Suby of* JJ TAYLOR COMPANIES INC) ★
5102 16th Ave S, Tampa, FL 33619-5336
Tel (813) 247-4000 *Founded/Ownrshp* 1956, 1997
Sales 28.0MM^E *EMP* 120
SIC 5181 Beer & other fermented malt liquors; Beer & other fermented malt liquors
Pr: John J Taylor III

D-U-N-S 00-157-6099 IMP
J & J FARMS CREAMERY INC (NY)
5748 49th St Ste 1, Maspeth, NY 11378-2191
Tel (718) 821-1200 *Founded/Ownrshp* 1968
Sales 95.3MM^E *EMP* 40^E
Accts Schwartz & Company New York
SIC 5143 5149 Dairy products, except dried or canned; Juices
Pr: Simon Friedman
**Treas:* Morris Schlager
VP Sls: Morris Glauber

D-U-N-S 00-333-6971
J & J INDUSTRIES INC (GA)
J&J/INVISION
818 J And J Dr, Dalton, GA 30721-3647
Tel (706) 529-2100 *Founded/Ownrshp* 1957
Sales 207.5MM^E *EMP* 765
SIC 2273 Carpets, hand & machine made; Carpets, hand & machine made
CEO: David Jolly
V Ch: James Bethel
**CFO:* Tom Pendley
VP: Jim Bass
VP: Marc Cormier
**VP:* Bill Crosley
VP: Terry Davis
**VP:* Louis Fordham
VP: Gregg Hayes
VP: Ross Leonard
**VP:* Doug Schneller
**VP:* Brad Townsend

J & J JANITOR SERVICE
See W & J SCHAFER ENTERPRISES INC

D-U-N-S 05-512-4077
J & J MAINTENANCE INC (TX)
J & J WORLDWIDE SERVICES
7710 Rialto Blvd Ste 200, Austin, TX 78735-8563
Tel (254) 532-5603 *Founded/Ownrshp* 1970, 1988
Sales 427.6MM^E *EMP* 1,500
SIC 1799 Post-disaster renovations; Post-disaster renovations
Pr: Mike Voudouris
**Ch Bd:* John L Voudouris
**CFO:* Terry Reynolds
**Sec:* Sharron A Voudouris
Ofcr: Ken Hoffmann

**VP:* Tim Ferry
**VP:* Steve Kelley
**VP:* Duke Malvaney
VP Bus Dev: Steven Kelley
CIO: Jeff Smedley

J & J MARKET AND DELI
See J ENTERPRISES INC

D-U-N-S 11-860-3331 IMP/EXP
J & J PRODUCE INC
J&J FAMILY OF FARMS
(*Suby of* J&J PRODUCE HOLDINGS INC) ★
4003 Seminole Pratt, Loxahatchee, FL 33470-3754
Tel (561) 422-9777 *Founded/Ownrshp* 1981
Sales 100.0MM *EMP* 150
SIC 5148 Fresh fruits & vegetables; Fresh fruits & vegetables
Pr: Chris Erneston III
Recvr: Marco Trejo
**CFO:* Mark Campbell
**VP:* Tj Bauer
**VP:* David Beecher
**VP:* Michael Bentel
**VP:* Brian Rayfield
**VP Sls:* Kohl Brown
Board of Directors: John Leavitt

J & J SALES
See G & C MARKETING CO

D-U-N-S 15-968-0961
J & J SALES INC
14107 Interdrive W, Houston, TX 77032-3326
Tel (361) 242-1300 *Founded/Ownrshp* 2010
Sales 20.7MM^E *EMP* 34
SIC 5082 Oil field equipment; Oil field equipment
Pr: Michael Milam
Genl Mgr: Chad Tidwell
Opers Mgr: Will Vasek

D-U-N-S 93-895-8113
■ **J & J SANITATION INC**
WASTE CONNECTIONS OF NEBRASKA
(*Suby of* WASTE CONNECTIONS INC) ★
87181 494th Ave, Oneill, NE 68763-5388
Tel (402) 336-3011 *Founded/Ownrshp* 1987
Sales 2.0MMM *EMP* 22
SIC 4953 Refuse collection & disposal services; Recycling, waste materials
Pr: Ronald J Mittelstaedt
**Treas:* Michael R Foos
Off Mgr: Amy Strong

D-U-N-S 05-473-2839 IMP/EXP
▲ **J & J SNACK FOODS CORP**
6000 Central Hwy, Pennsauken, NJ 08109-4672
Tel (856) 665-9533 *Founded/Ownrshp* 1971
Sales 976.2MM *EMP* 3,400
Accts Grant Thornton Llp Philadelph
Tkr Sym JJSF *Exch* NGS
SIC 2053 2087 2086 2024 2052 2051 Frozen bakery products, except bread; Doughnuts, frozen; Syrups, drink; Mineral water, carbonated: packaged in cans, bottles, etc.; Ices, flavored (frozen dessert); Juice pops, frozen; Cookies; Bread, cake & related products; Frozen bakery products, except bread; Doughnuts, frozen; Syrups, drink; Mineral water, carbonated: packaged in cans, bottles, etc.; Ices, flavored (frozen dessert); Juice pops, frozen; Cookies; Bread, cake & related products
Ch Bd: Gerald B Shreiber
COO: Robert M Radano
**CFO:* Dennis G Moore
Ex VP: Mark Ferguson
Sr VP: Gerard G Law
VP: T Couzens
VP: Eveline Dootay
VP: William Dougherty
VP: Mimi Ford
VP: Michael Grant
VP: Mary Hartnett
VP: Andres Gonz Lez
VP: John McGuckin
VP: Harry McLaughlin
VP: Robyn Shreiber
VP: Juventino Torres
VP: Kathleen Wong
Board of Directors: Sidney R Brown, Vincent Melchiorre, Peter G Stanley

D-U-N-S 12-088-1974 IMP
■ **J & J SNACK FOODS CORP OF CALIFORNIA**
(*Suby of* J & J SNACK FOODS CORP) ★
5353 S Downey Rd, Vernon, CA 90058-3725
Tel (323) 581-0171 *Founded/Ownrshp* 1978
Sales 121.0MM^E *EMP* 380^E
SIC 2052 5149 Pretzels; Cookies; Pretzels; Cookies
CEO: Gerald B Shreiber
**VP:* Dennis Moore
VP Inf Sys: John Griffith
Trfc Mgr: Sheena Hughes

D-U-N-S 03-138-2467
■ **J & J SNACK FOODS HANDHELDS CORP** (OH)
(*Suby of* J & J SNACK FOODS CORP) ★
312 Sound Rd, Holly Ridge, NC 28445-7812
Tel (910) 329-9061 *Founded/Ownrshp* 2011
Sales 69.4MM^E *EMP* 1^E
SIC 5145 Snack foods
Prin: Carlisle Jennings
Prd Mgr: Doug Jackson

D-U-N-S 78-697-6720
■ **J & J SNACK FOODS SALES CORP**
J&J SNACK FOODS
(*Suby of* J & J SNACK FOODS CORP) ★
6000 Central Hwy, Pennsauken, NJ 08109-4672
Tel (856) 665-9533 *Founded/Ownrshp* 2003
Sales 26.4MM^E *EMP* 42
SIC 5142 Packaged frozen goods
CEO: Gerry Shriber
Sr VP: Robert Pape
Snr Sftwr: Young Son
Sls Dir: Michael Norman
Pr Mgr: John Hartman

J & J STEEL COMPANY
See KEVIN D BALLARD INC

J & J TRUCK BODIES AND TRLRS
See SOMERSET WELDING & STEEL INC

D-U-N-S 83-125-6367
J & J VENTURES INC
PAPA JOHN'S
4527 Tuscarawas St W, Canton, OH 44708-5336
Tel (330) 477-1725 Founded/Ownrshp 1992
Sales 7.4MM^E EMP 325
SIC 5812 Pizzeria, chain; Pizzeria, chain
Pr: David Nickles
*Treas: Kevin O'Connor
*VP: Bob Wagner

J & J WORLDWIDE SERVICES
See J & J MAINTENANCE INC

D-U-N-S 00-279-4691 IMP
J & K PLUMBING AND HEATING CO INC (NY)
24 Thorp St, Binghamton, NY 13905-2897
Tel (607) 772-1666 Founded/Ownrshp 1948
Sales 22.6MM^E EMP 120
SIC 1711 Mechanical contractor; Mechanical contractor
CEO: W Allyn Jones Jr
Treas: Mark J Larson
VP: Louis M Williams

D-U-N-S 61-078-8205
J & K PROJECT MANAGEMENT CONSULTANTS LLC
ACT CONSTRUCTION
350 Mcdonnell St, Lewisville, TX 75057-4808
Tel (972) 436-1144 Founded/Ownrshp 2004
Sales 31.3MM EMP 63
SIC 1522 1542 Residential construction; Nonresidential construction; Residential construction; Nonresidential construction

J & K STAFFING
See CHRISLEX STAFFING LTD

D-U-N-S 05-332-4711 IMP
■ **J & L AMERICA INC**
J & L INDUSTRIAL SUPPLY CO
(Suby of MSC INDUSTRIAL DIRECT CO INC) ★
20921 Lahser Rd, Southfield, MI 48033-4432
Tel (248) 200-4200 Founded/Ownrshp 1997
Sales 22.6MM^E EMP 90
SIC 5084 Machine tools & accessories; Machine tools & accessories
Pr: David Sandler
VP: Kimberly Shacklett
VP Sls: Joe Scime
Sls Mgr: Damon Gustfason

D-U-N-S 00-250-4629
J & L BUILDING MATERIALS INC (PA)
600 Lancaster Ave, Malvern, PA 19355-1846
Tel (610) 644-6311 Founded/Ownrshp 1958, 1961
Sales 69.6MM^E EMP 200
SIC 3089 5072 5031 5033 Window frames & sash, plastic; Hardware; Windows; Roofing, asphalt & sheet metal; Siding, except wood; Window frames & sash, plastic; Hardware; Windows; Roofing, asphalt & sheet metal; Siding, except wood
Pr: David Moretzsohn
*Treas: David A Kraszewski
*VP: David Barnes
VP: Paul Craskey
Brnch Mgr: Tim Bower
Trfc Dir: David Vay
Sls Mgr: John Conte
Sales Asso: Ryan Blain
Sales Asso: Kevin Brittain
Sales Asso: Jon Carter
Sales Asso: R C Creekmur

J & L CONSTRUCTION
See MODERN DOOR AND EQUIPMENT SALES INC

D-U-N-S 09-718-7975
J & L FASTENERS AND GENERAL MAINTENANCE SUPPLIES INC
J&L FASTENERS
6944 Parrish Ave, Hammond, IN 46323-2348
Tel (219) 845-8500 Founded/Ownrshp 1979
Sales 33.5MM^E EMP 68
SIC 5072 5085 Nuts (hardware); Miscellaneous fasteners; Bolts; Industrial supplies
Ch Bd: James R Belford Sr
*Pr: James F Belford Jr

D-U-N-S 79-261-9926 IMP
■ **J & L FIBER SERVICES INC**
(Suby of PCC) ★
809 Philip Dr, Waukesha, WI 53186-5919
Tel (262) 547-0302 Founded/Ownrshp 1997
Sales 21.4MM^E EMP 110^E
SIC 3325 Alloy steel castings, except investment
Pr: Frank Miller
Mtls Mgr: Jim Queisser
VP Mktg: Ola Johansson

D-U-N-S 09-470-0713
J & L HARLEY DAVIDSON INC
J & L HARLEY-DAVIDSON & BUELL
2601 W 60th St N, Sioux Falls, SD 57107-0860
Tel (605) 334-2721 Founded/Ownrshp 1972
Sales 21.3MM EMP 52
Accts Kmwf & Associates Pc Dell Ra
SIC 5571 7699 Motorcycle dealers; Motorcycle repair service; Motorcycle dealers; Motorcycle repair service
Pr: James Lee Entenman
*CFO: Char Roth
*VP: Lonnie J Entenman

J & L HARLEY-DAVIDSON & BUELL
See J & L HARLEY DAVIDSON INC

D-U-N-S 02-707-3195
J & L INC
6506 56th Ave Nw, Gig Harbor, WA 98335-7407
Tel (253) 380-2505 Founded/Ownrshp 2009
Sales 56.0MM EMP 532
SIC 5734 4813 7389 Computer software & accessories; ; Computer software & accessories; ;
Pr: Jonathan Larson
*VP: John Evans

J & L INDUSTRIAL SUPPLY CO
See J & L AMERICA INC

J & L INDUSTRIES
See ALLIANCE MACHINE SYSTEMS INTERNATIONAL LLC

D-U-N-S 01-973-0629
J & L MANAGEMENT CONSULTANTS INC (FL)
1312 Se 2nd Ter, Deerfield Beach, FL 33441-6712
Tel (954) 540-0587 Founded/Ownrshp 2008
Sales 44.0MM EMP 6
SIC 7389 Merchandise liquidators; Merchandise liquidators
Pr: Jennifer Langone
*VP: Louis Melendez

D-U-N-S 13-166-7813
J & L MEDICAL SERVICES LLC
199 Park Road Ext Ste A, Middlebury, CT 06762-1833
Tel (203) 758-2238 Founded/Ownrshp 2002
Sales 43.4MM^E EMP 46
SIC 5047 Medical equipment & supplies
Pr: John Loyer
*COO: Gordon Worley
*CFO: Brian Mitchell
*VP: Lynn Tata

D-U-N-S 08-687-6252
J & L OIL FIELD SERVICES LLC (OK)
2100 S Main St, Shattuck, OK 73858-7009
Tel (580) 938-2205 Founded/Ownrshp 2002
Sales 43.1MM^E EMP 320
SIC 1389 Oil field services; Oil field services
Off Mgr: Jolisa Swanson

D-U-N-S 95-619-0107
J & L STEEL & ELECTRICAL SERVICES
2365 Willis Miller Dr, Hudson, WI 54016-7999
Tel (715) 808-0463 Founded/Ownrshp 2008
Sales 23.6MM^E EMP 60
SIC 5063 Electrical construction materials; Electrical supplies
CEO: Louanne Berg
Off Admin: Chris Williams
Sfty Dirs: Abby Ferri

J & L VENTURES
See GEORGIA NORTH DISTRIBUTING CO

J & M BROWN
See J & M BROWN CO INC

D-U-N-S 00-787-5297
J & M BROWN CO INC (MA)
J & M BROWN
267 Amory St, Jamaica Plain, MA 02130-2337
Tel (617) 971-1400 Founded/Ownrshp 1921
Sales 55.4MM^E EMP 160
SIC 1731 7382 8711 Electronic controls installation; Security systems services; Engineering services; Electronic controls installation; Security systems services; Engineering services
Pr: David Noon
*Treas: Karen Sykes
VP: Brian Greene
IT Man: Steven Feldman
Sales Asso: Heidi Brown
Snr PM: Richard Cucchi
Snr Mgr: Harry Sneider
Board of Directors: Jerome Hart

D-U-N-S 08-032-4486 IMP
J & M DISTRIBUTING CO INC
2500 N America Dr, Buffalo, NY 14224-5316
Tel (716) 827-1133 Founded/Ownrshp 1962
Sales 38.3MM^E EMP 200
SIC 5181 Beer & other fermented malt liquors; Beer & other fermented malt liquors
Pr: Peter Certo

D-U-N-S 09-831-4099
J & M FARMS INC
7001 S 580 Rd, Miami, OK 74354-6501
Tel (918) 540-1567 Founded/Ownrshp 1979
Sales 48.8MM^E EMP 320
SIC 0182 2099 Mushrooms grown under cover; Food preparations; Mushrooms grown under cover; Food preparations
Pr: Curtis Jurgensmeyer
*Ch Bd: Virgil Jurgensmeyer
CFO: Micha Charissa
CFO: Hermila Lamonica
Ofcr: Evelia Debera
*Ex VP: Joseph Jurgensmeyer
VP: Brook Fallon
VP: Otha Frederica
VP: Aurea Jill
*VP: Terry Jurgensmeyer
VP: Hermine Vida

D-U-N-S 84-320-5068
J & M INC
6700 National Dr, Livermore, CA 94550-8804
Tel (925) 724-0300 Founded/Ownrshp 1958
Sales 20.9MM^E EMP 50
SIC 1623 1629 Water, sewer & utility lines; Drainage system construction
CEO: Manuel Marques III
Opers Mgr: John Cooper

D-U-N-S 07-790-4548 IMP
J & M INDUSTRIES INC
300 Ponchatoula Pkwy, Ponchatoula, LA 70454-8311
Tel (985) 386-6000 Founded/Ownrshp 1973
Sales 33.0MM^E EMP 132
SIC 2393 2394 5113 5085 Textile bags; Tarpaulins, fabric: made from purchased materials; Containers, paper & disposable plastic; Corrugated & solid fiber boxes; Industrial supplies
Pr: Maurice G Gaudet III
*CFO: Maurice Gaudet IV
Ex VP: Paul Koenig
*VP: Mark Arnold
IT Man: Steve Gaudet
Plnt Mgr: Lance Power
Sls&Mrk Ex: Aaron Gummer
Manager: Eric Kelley

D-U-N-S 01-802-8407 IMP/EXP
J & M MANUFACTURING CO INC (OH)
284 Railroad St, Fort Recovery, OH 45846
Tel (419) 375-2376 Founded/Ownrshp 1950, 1960
Sales 118.8MM EMP 200
SIC 3523 Farm machinery & equipment; Farm machinery & equipment
Pr: Michael Grieshop
*VP: Jeff Grieshop
Sls Mgr: Shannon Grieshop
Sls Mgr: Mike Van Horn

D-U-N-S 80-113-4032
J & M MOTORS INC
PUTNAM TOYOTA
50 California Dr, Burlingame, CA 94010-4411
Tel (650) 340-6900 Founded/Ownrshp 1992
Sales 30.4MM^E EMP 100
SIC 5511 Automobiles, new & used; Pickups, new & used; Automobiles, new & used; Pickups, new & used
Pr: Joseph Putnam

D-U-N-S 15-513-7458 IMP
J & M PLATING INC
4500 Kishwaukee St, Rockford, IL 61109-2924
Tel (815) 964-4975 Founded/Ownrshp 1986
Sales 27.7MM^E EMP 135
SIC 3471 Electroplating of metals or formed products; Finishing, metals or formed products; Polishing, metals or formed products
Pr: Mark Morris
*VP: Rick Morris
Mfg Mgr: Todd Lindberg
Opers Mgr: Brian Beasley
Ql Cn Mgr: Mike Culverhouse

D-U-N-S 80-998-4409
J & M PREMIER SERVICES INC
12969 N Us Highway 79, Palestine, TX 75801-3926
Tel (903) 584-0152 Founded/Ownrshp 2010
Sales 23.4MM^E EMP 170^E
SIC 4212 Heavy machinery transport, local; Heavy machinery transport, local
Pr: Paul Woodard Jr
*CFO: Melissa Woodard

D-U-N-S 12-464-8697
J & M SALES INC
FALLAS DISCOUNT STORES
15001 S Figueroa St, Gardena, CA 90248-1721
Tel (310) 324-9962 Founded/Ownrshp 1993
Sales 71.8MM^E EMP 2,500
SIC 5651 6531 5311 5611 5621 Unisex clothing stores; Real estate listing services; Department stores, discount; Men's & boys' clothing stores; Women's clothing stores; Unisex clothing stores; Real estate listing services; Department stores, discount; Men's & boys' clothing stores; Women's clothing stores
Pr: Michael Fallas
*VP: Duane Huesers

D-U-N-S 09-930-5807
J & M TANK LINES INC
(Suby of J & M TRUCKING GROUP INC) ★
100 Hwy 19 N, Americus, GA 31719
Tel (229) 924-3663 Founded/Ownrshp 1980
Sales 32.0MM^E EMP 230
SIC 4213

D-U-N-S 96-982-9311
J & M TANK LINES INC
7051 Meadowlark Dr # 102, Birmingham, AL 35242-0304
Tel (205) 876-1900 Founded/Ownrshp 1978
Sales 10.1MM^E EMP 525^E
SIC 4213 Automobiles, transport & delivery
CEO: Harold Sumerford Jr
*Pr: Peter Sumerford
*COO: Jim Pickens
*CFO: Arnold Roberts
*VP: Kyle Gailey

D-U-N-S 16-668-8288
J & M TRUCKING GROUP INC
100 Us Highway 19 N, Americus, GA 31719-8365
Tel (229) 924-3663 Founded/Ownrshp 2000
Sales 44.1MM EMP 231
Accts J Alan Taunton & Company Ll
SIC 4213 4731 Trucking, except local; Contract haulers; Transportation agents & brokers; Trucking, except local; Contract haulers; Transportation agents & brokers
Ch: Harold A Sumerford Sr
*Pr: Peter Sumerford
CFO: Margaret Brown
Sr VP: Jim Pickens
*Sr VP: Arnold Roberts

D-U-N-S 01-764-5706 IMP
J & N AUTO ELECTRIC INC (OH)
10995 Canal Rd, Cincinnati, OH 45241-1886
Tel (513) 771-8000 Founded/Ownrshp 1954
Sales 60.3MM^E EMP 100
SIC 5013 Automotive supplies & parts; Alternators
Pr: Thomas J Kuechly
*Treas: Mary L Kuechly
*VP: David W Blocker
*VP: Nick Kuechly
Sales Asso: Bill Hornung
Sales Asso: Geri Johnson
Sales Asso: Bernie Woermann

D-U-N-S 07-429-7235
J & N STONE INC
905 E Waterford St, Wakarusa, IN 46573-9560
Tel (574) 862-4251 Founded/Ownrshp 1973
Sales 20.2MM^E EMP 115
SIC 3272 Concrete products, precast
Pr: Lengacher Sr Jack W
*CFO: Jamie Lengacher
*Sec: Nadine K Lengacher
*Sr VP: Jack Lengacher Jr
*VP: Jeff Lengacher

D-U-N-S 62-777-4615
J & R ASSOCIATES
WINDSOR CONSTRUCTION
14803 Holland Rd, Brookpark, OH 44142-3065
Tel (440) 250-4080 Founded/Ownrshp 1987
Sales 53.3MM^E EMP 1,000
SIC 1542 8361 6514 Institutional building construction; Home for the aged; Dwelling operators, except apartments; Institutional building construction; Home for the aged; Dwelling operators, except apartments
Pr: John Coury Sr

D-U-N-S 05-667-7438 IMP/EXP
J & R ELECTRONICS INC
J AND R MUSIC STORE
23 Park Row, New York, NY 10038
Tel (212) 238-9000 Founded/Ownrshp 1971
Sales NA EMP 700
SIC 5731 5735

D-U-N-S 02-136-6682
J & R IMPORTS LTD
NISSAN OF QUEENS
9325 Rockaway Blvd, Ozone Park, NY 11417-2446
Tel (718) 835-8300 Founded/Ownrshp 2002
Sales 26.7MM^E EMP 100
SIC 5511 Automobiles, new & used; Automobiles, new & used
Ch: Scott Reback

D-U-N-S 05-790-5044
J & R INVESTMENTS INC (MO)
WOODLEY BUILDING MAINTENANCE
8601 E 63rd St, Kansas City, MO 64133-4702
Tel (816) 358-9444 Founded/Ownrshp 1969
Sales 29.0MM^E EMP 725
SIC 7349 Janitorial service, contract basis; Janitorial service, contract basis
CEO: Robery Woodley
*Pr: Jimmy Woodley
*COO: Terry Woodley
*CFO: Tiffeny Wibley
Opers Mgr: Steve Handley
Opers Mgr: Sarah Harm
Opers Mgr: Amber Lawhon
Opers Mgr: Darrin Sliffe
Opers Mgr: Ken Turley

D-U-N-S 60-401-9653
J & R LUMBER & SUPPLY CO INC
RONALD SEAWRIGHT CONSTRUCTION
9885 County Road 33, Ashville, AL 35953-4116
Tel (205) 594-5994 Founded/Ownrshp 1989
Sales 22.4MM^E EMP 50
SIC 1542 1521 5211

D-U-N-S 82-925-7401
J & R RESTAURANT GROUP INC
OUTBACK STEAKHOUSE
4500 I 55 N Ste 292, Jackson, MS 39211-5966
Tel (601) 982-0568 Founded/Ownrshp 1993
Sales 11.3MM^E EMP 300
SIC 8741 Management services; Management services
Pr: Steve Grantham
*Sec: Dr Faser Triplett
*VP: Robert Grantham

D-U-N-S 00-986-6807
J & R SCHUGEL TRUCKING INC
2026 N Broadway St, New Ulm, MN 56073-1030
Tel (800) 359-2900 Founded/Ownrshp 2012
Sales 117.0MM^E EMP 500
SIC 4213 Trucking, except local; Contract haulers; Trucking, except local; Contract haulers
Pr: Rick Schugel
VP: Mark Shaver
Genl Mgr: Dan Denhof
Genl Mgr: Dan Denhol
DP Dir: Quinton Holmberg
Dir IT: Verna Gebhardt
Dir IT: Bret Thompson
IT Man: Dan Worblowski
VP Opers: Randy Alfred
Opers Mgr: Tim Oneil
Ql Cn Mgr: Kala Hannay

D-U-N-S 03-766-9439
J & R SLAW INC
SLAW PRECAST
438 Riverview Rd, Lehighton, PA 18235-3435
Tel (610) 852-2020 Founded/Ownrshp 1979
Sales 22.3MM^E EMP 90
SIC 3272 Concrete products, precast
Pr: Robert A Slaw Jr
*Treas: Timothy Slaw

D-U-N-S 79-072-8500
J & R SYSTEMS INTEGRATORS LLC
SECURITY 101
1967 Government St Ste D, Mobile, AL 36606-1617
Tel (251) 471-4323 Founded/Ownrshp 2006
Sales 21.3MM^E EMP 38
SIC 5065 5999 7381 Security control equipment & systems; Alarm & safety equipment stores; Detective & armored car services
Owner: John Gibson

J & S AUDIO VISUAL
See PRESENTATION TECHNOLOGIES INC

D-U-N-S 15-469-4384
J & S AUDIO VISUAL COMMUNICATIONS INC
(Suby of J & S AUDIO VISUAL) ★
9150 N Royal Ln, Irving, TX 75063-2420
Tel (972) 241-5444 Founded/Ownrshp 1986
Sales 26.7MM EMP 178
SIC 7359 5999 7812 Audio-visual equipment & supply rental; Audio-visual equipment & supplies; Video production

Pr: Monroe Jost
**VP:* Kevin Jost

D-U-N-S 11-599-6852
J & S CAFETERIAS INC
110 Westover Dr, High Point, NC 27265-2869
Tel (336) 884-0404 *Founded/Ownrshp* 1984
Sales 16.3MM^E *EMP* 450
SIC 5812 Cafeteria; Cafeteria
Pr: F Bernard Nowlan Jr
**Sec:* Anne Nowlan

D-U-N-S 00-441-6855
J & S CONSTRUCTION CO INC (TN)
1843 Foreman Dr, Cookeville, TN 38501-4193
Tel (931) 528-7475 *Founded/Ownrshp* 1957, 1972
Sales 42.0MM *EMP* 115
Accts Cooper Travis & Company Plc
SIC 1541 1542 1623 Industrial buildings, new construction; Commercial & office building, new construction; Sewer line construction; Water main construction; Industrial buildings, new construction; Commercial & office building, new construction; Sewer line construction; Water main construction
CEO: John D Stites II
Pr: Ryan Morris
**Pr:* James Stites
**COO:* Kevin McCaleb
VP: Phil Adams
Mktg Dir: Brittany Key
Snr PM: Andy Tharp

D-U-N-S 19-150-1084 IMP
J & S KIDSWEAR INC
DENNY'S CHILDREN'S WEAR
343b S Oyster Bay Rd, Plainview, NY 11803-3336
Tel (516) 681-4490 *Founded/Ownrshp* 2003
Sales 71.8MM^E *EMP* 400
SIC 5641 Children's & infants' wear stores; Children's & infants' wear stores
Pr: Ronald Klein

D-U-N-S 07-054-8367
J & S MECHANICAL CONTRACTORS INC
194 W 12650 S, Draper, UT 84020-8615
Tel (801) 553-9922 *Founded/Ownrshp* 1976
Sales 42.2MM *EMP* 92
Accts Hj & Associates Llc Salt Lak
SIC 1711 Mechanical contractor; Mechanical contractor
Pr: Jack Jensen
**Sec:* James G Barlow
**VP:* Justin S Barlow
VP: Scott Meyer

D-U-N-S 07-746-7454
J & S OIL CO INC
TEXACO
867 Western Ave, Manchester, ME 04351-3532
Tel (207) 622-1609 *Founded/Ownrshp* 1972
Sales 60.3MM^E *EMP* 150
SIC 5541 5172 7542 7549 Filling stations, gasoline; Marine service station; Gasoline; Carwash, automatic; Carwash, self-service; Lubrication service, automotive; Filling stations, gasoline; Marine service station; Gasoline; Carwash, automatic; Carwash, self-service; Lubrication service, automotive
CEO: John L Babb Jr
**VP:* Kasondra Babb
CIO: Dan Dumais

D-U-N-S 60-936-4091
J & S OPERATIONS LLC
FREMONT FORD
39700 Balentine Dr, Newark, CA 94560-5374
Tel (510) 360-7165 *Founded/Ownrshp* 2005
Sales 42.7MM^E *EMP* 115
SIC 5511 5531 Automobiles, new & used; Trucks, tractors & trailers: new & used; Automotive accessories; Automotive parts; Automotive tires; Automobiles, new & used; Trucks, tractors & trailers: new & used; Automotive accessories; Automotive parts; Automotive tires
VP: Lee Schmidt
Exec: Pauline Greer
Off Mgr: Tiffany Shenave
IT Man: Tim Breedlove
Sls&Mrk Ex: Mike Patel
Sls Mgr: Oliver Abello
Sls Mgr: Shadi Razi

D-U-N-S 01-237-8790
J & S SUPPLY CORP (NY)
5302 37th St, Long Island City, NY 11101-2085
Tel (718) 786-3044 *Founded/Ownrshp* 1951, 1980
Sales 51.2MM^E *EMP* 35
SIC 5033 Roofing & siding materials; Insulation materials
Ch Bd: Michael M Diamond
**VP:* Donald Goebel
Sls Mgr: John Carlovich
Sales Asso: Leo Stern

D-U-N-S 00-699-0204
■ **J & W SELIGMAN & CO INC**
(*Suby of* COLUMBIA MANAGEMENT INVESTMENT ADVISERS LLC) ★
100 Park Ave Fl 7, New York, NY 10017-5598
Tel (212) 850-1864 *Founded/Ownrshp* 1864, 2008
Sales 68.9MM^E *EMP* 417
SIC 6282 6726 6211 Investment advice; Manager of mutual funds, contract or fee basis; Investment offices; Dealers, security; Investment advice; Manager of mutual funds, contract or fee basis; Investment offices; Dealers, security
Ch Bd: William C Morris
**Pr:* Brian Zino
**Sr VP:* Lawrence P Vogel
**Mng Dir:* David F Stein
Mng Dir: Paul Wick

D-U-N-S 10-248-7659 IMP
J & W SERVICES & EQUIPMENT CO
3510 E State Highway 158, Midland, TX 79706-4228
Tel (432) 689-3947 *Founded/Ownrshp* 1999
Sales 73.2MM^E *EMP* 75^E
SIC 5084 Oil well machinery, equipment & supplies; Oil well machinery, equipment & supplies
Pr: Brent Beck
Opers Mgr: James Hendry
Plnt Mgr: Al Moreno

D-U-N-S 06-182-0945
J-TECH
548 Amapola Ave, Torrance, CA 90501-1472
Tel (310) 533-6700 *Founded/Ownrshp* 1987
Sales 32.1MM^E *EMP* 325
SIC 3678 Electronic connectors; Electronic connectors
CEO: Walter Naubauer Jr
CFO: John Vinke
Sls Dir: Rex Aymond

J A A
See JACKSONVILLE AVIATION AUTHORITY

J A B
See JUST A BUCK OF NEW YORK INC

D-U-N-S 17-535-7339
J A CONTRACTING INC
2209 W Tulare Ave, Visalia, CA 93277-2137
Tel (559) 733-4865 *Founded/Ownrshp* 2003
Sales 9.3MM^E *EMP* 300
SIC 0761 Farm labor contractors; Farm labor contractors
Pr: Juan Ayala
Opers Mgr: Javier Diaz

D-U-N-S 79-350-0687
J A FIELDEN CO INC
530 W 5th Ave Ste B, Knoxville, TN 37917-7109
Tel (865) 523-0508 *Founded/Ownrshp* 1992
Sales 69.1MM *EMP* 45
Accts Stanley H Pickering Ii Certi
SIC 1542 Nonresidential construction; Nonresidential construction
Pr: Joe Fielden
CFO: Mark Williamson
VP: David Gardner

D-U-N-S 02-142-8941
J A FRATE INC
J A TRANSPORT SERVICE
7900 Pyott Rd, Crystal Lake, IL 60014-8715
Tel (815) 459-0839 *Founded/Ownrshp* 1971
Sales 25.7MM^E *EMP* 88
SIC 4213 Trucking, except local
Pr: Jill Dinsmore
Pr: Joe Alger
Pr: R Douglas Jennings
VP: Cathy Altenburg
IT Man: Kathy Anderson
Opers Mgr: Tim Gieseke
VP Sls: Mark Peterson
Sales Asso: Lann Tarrant

D-U-N-S 00-780-3117
J A FRITCH & SONS INC
1016 Ne Adams St, Peoria, IL 61603-4097
Tel (309) 671-5353 *Founded/Ownrshp* 1985
Sales 24.3MM *EMP* 75
SIC 1711 Warm air heating & air conditioning contractor; Ventilation & duct work contractor; Warm air heating & air conditioning contractor; Ventilation & duct work contractor
Pr: David Donahue
Treas: Joan Donahue
Sec: Teri Leonard

D-U-N-S 18-473-0067
J A G BLACK GOLD MANAGEMENT CO
2600 London Groveport Rd, Groveport, OH 43125-9401
Tel (614) 409-0290 *Founded/Ownrshp* 1986
Sales 26.7MM^E *EMP* 128
SIC 5541 5411 Filling stations, gasoline; Convenience stores, independent; Filling stations, gasoline; Convenience stores, independent
Pr: Richard M Aumann
**Treas:* Patricia Aumann
**VP:* John Chapan

J A HENCKELS
See J A ZWILLING HENCKELS INC

D-U-N-S 02-459-3717
J A KING AND CO LLC (NC)
6541c Franz Warner Pkwy, Whitsett, NC 27377-9215
Tel (336) 292-0511 *Founded/Ownrshp* 1939
Sales 23.3MM^E *EMP* 138
SIC 7699 5046

D-U-N-S 07-800-0502
J A L ENTERPRISES INC
UNIVERSAL CO'S
10665 Bedford Ave Ste 102, Omaha, NE 68134-3681
Tel (402) 333-9000 *Founded/Ownrshp* 1964
Sales NA *EMP* 181
Accts Peat Marwick Llp
SIC 6411 6311 Loss prevention services, insurance; Life insurance carriers
Ch Bd: John J Micek III
Board of Directors: Reece Micek

D-U-N-S 92-687-5881
J A MACHUCA AND ASSOCIATES INC
1575 Ave Munoz Rivera, Ponce, PR 00717-0211
Tel (787) 848-4381 *Founded/Ownrshp* 1995
Sales 2.0MM *EMP* 500
SIC 8741 Management services; Business management; Management services; Business management
Prin: Jose A Machuca
**Genl Mgr:* Nancy Vega

J A MOODY
See ESI ACQUISITION CORP

D-U-N-S 02-256-5725
J A MOTOR CARS INC
ANTWERPEN TOYOTA-SCION
12420 Auto Dr, Clarksville, MD 21029-2200
Tel (410) 531-5700 *Founded/Ownrshp* 1959
Sales 70.0MM^E *EMP* 200
SIC 5511 Automobiles, new & used; Automobiles, new & used
Pr: Jacob Antwerpen
Sr VP: Stanford Hess
**VP:* David Antwerpen
Advt Dir: Samantha Wheeler
Sls Mgr: Joe Ashkar
Sls Mgr: Paul Tozier
Sales Asso: J C Bermudez

D-U-N-S 01-055-8724
J A MYERS BUILDING AND DEVELOPMENT INC
JA MYERS HOMES
160 Ram Dr, Hanover, PA 17331-8813
Tel (717) 632-9406 *Founded/Ownrshp* 1975
Sales 22.0MM^E *EMP* 110
Accts Beard Miller Company Llp
SIC 1521 1522 6552 1542 Single-family housing construction; Residential construction; Subdividers & developers; Nonresidential construction; Single-family housing construction; Residential construction; Subdividers & developers; Nonresidential construction
Pr: Joseph A Myers
**VP:* Benjamin A Myers

D-U-N-S 79-332-0961
J A O MEAT PACKING CO INC
LONG ISLAND BEEF
565 West St, New York, NY 10014-1407
Tel (212) 243-1121 *Founded/Ownrshp* 1918
Sales 73.0MM^E *EMP* 475
SIC 5147 2013 2011 Meats & meat products; Sausages & other prepared meats; Meat packing plants; Meats & meat products; Sausages & other prepared meats; Meat packing plants
Pr: James A Ortenzio

D-U-N-S 06-795-5500
J A PETERSON ENTERPRISES INC
PETERSON COMPANIES, THE
10000 W 75th St Ste 100, Shawnee Mission, KS 66204-2241
Tel (913) 384-3800 *Founded/Ownrshp* 1959
Sales 9.5MM^E *EMP* 319
SIC 6513 6552 6512 Apartment building operators; Subdividers & developers; Commercial & industrial building operation; Apartment building operators; Subdividers & developers; Commercial & industrial building operation
Ch Bd: Gordon Peterson
Pr: Kenneth Riedemann
Admn Mgr: Pam Engle
Board of Directors: Ruth Peterson

D-U-N-S 04-314-7859
J A R CONCRETE INC (TX)
J.A.R. CONSTRUCTION INC
8000 Escobar Dr, El Paso, TX 79907-1854
Tel (915) 591-3389 *Founded/Ownrshp* 1970
Sales 22.0MM *EMP* 90
SIC 1771 Concrete work
Pr: Joe Rosales Jr
**VP:* Jaime Rosales
**Prin:* Joe Rosales Sr

D-U-N-S 07-365-8510
■ **J A REINHARDT & CO INC**
(*Suby of* B/E AEROSPACE INC) ★
Spruce Cabin Rd, Mountainhome, PA 18342
Tel (570) 595-7491 *Founded/Ownrshp* 2010
Sales 20.7MM^E *EMP* 100
SIC 3728 Aircraft parts & equipment
Genl Mgr: Jeffrey Greco
VP: Mark Reinhardt
IT Man: Robert Snyder

J A S
See JOHNSTON AMBULANCE SERVICE INC

D-U-N-S 09-954-2177
J A SUTHERLAND INC
TACO BELL
228 Main St, Red Bluff, CA 96080-3819
Tel (530) 529-0019 *Founded/Ownrshp* 1978
Sales 19.9MM *EMP* 480
Accts Campbell Taylor & Company Ros
SIC 5812 Fast-food restaurant, chain; Fast-food restaurant, chain
Pr: Janice Sutherland
VP: Guy Mills
**VP:* Kathy Mills

D-U-N-S 09-203-8652
J A T OF FORT WAYNE INC
5031 Industrial Rd, Fort Wayne, IN 46825-5213
Tel (260) 482-8447 *Founded/Ownrshp* 1974
Sales 28.0MM^E *EMP* 120
SIC 4213 Trucking, except local; Trucking, except local
Pr: Jared Thompson
**Sec:* Toni Thompson

J A TRANSPORT SERVICE
See J A FRATE INC

D-U-N-S 00-166-3707 IMP
J A ZWILLING HENCKELS INC
J A HENCKELS
270 Marble Ave, Pleasantville, NY 10570-3464
Tel (914) 749-3440 *Founded/Ownrshp* 1949
Sales 55.8MM^E *EMP* 100^E
SIC 5072 Cutlery; Cutlery
Ch Bd: Claus Holst-Gydesen
**Pr:* Guido Weishaupt
MIS Dir: Jennifer Rigney
VP Mktg: Howard Ammerman
VP Mktg: Joanna Rosenberg
Manager: Amy Schroeder
Sls Mgr: Joel Kauffman
Sls Mgr: Linda Truax

J ALEXANDERS
See J ALEXANDERS RESTAURANTS LLC

D-U-N-S 05-649-6953
■ **J ALEXANDERS LLC** (TN)
(*Suby of* FIDELITY NATIONAL FINANCIAL INC) ★
3401 West End Ave Ste 260, Nashville, TN 37203-6862
Tel (615) 269-1900 *Founded/Ownrshp* 1971, 2012
Sales 378.8MM^E *EMP* 2,720^E
SIC 5812 Fast-food restaurant, chain; Restaurant, family: chain; Fast-food restaurant, chain; Restaurant, family: chain
Pr: Lonnie J Stout II
**CFO:* Gregory Lewis
**CFO:* R Gregory Lewis
**CFO:* Jeffrey Rice
**VP:* Mark A Parkey
Exec: Kelley Richman
Genl Mgr: Jason Benish
Genl Mgr: Kathryn Giannini
Genl Mgr: John Greuling
Genl Mgr: Jeff Heflin
Genl Mgr: Ryan Kavanaugh

D-U-N-S 78-544-4506
■ **J ALEXANDERS RESTAURANTS LLC**
J ALEXANDERS
(*Suby of* J ALEXANDERS LLC) ★
3401 West End Ave Ste 260, Nashville, TN 37203-6862
Tel (615) 269-1900 *Founded/Ownrshp* 1983
Sales 27.1MM^E *EMP* 700
SIC 5812 Fast-food restaurant, chain; Fast-food restaurant, chain
CEO: Lonnie Stout II
**Treas:* R Gregory Lewis
Site Mgr: Rahsaan Stone

D-U-N-S 18-974-8023
J AMBROGI FOOD DISTRIBUTION INC
1400 Metropolitan Ave, Thorofare, NJ 08086
Tel (856) 845-0377 *Founded/Ownrshp* 1987
Sales 115.1MM^E *EMP* 175
SIC 5141 Food brokers; Food brokers
Pr: John G Ambrogi
**Treas:* Kristy K Ambrogi

D-U-N-S 03-481-6873
J AND A MAINTENANCE SERVICES INC
SERVICEMASTER
5913 Linglestown Rd, Harrisburg, PA 17112-1125
Tel (717) 541-0618 *Founded/Ownrshp* 2010
Sales 5.8MM^E *EMP* 290
SIC 7349 7217 Building maintenance services; Janitorial service, contract basis; Floor waxing; Cleaning service, industrial or commercial; Carpet & upholstery cleaning on customer premises; Building maintenance services; Janitorial service, contract basis; Floor waxing; Cleaning service, industrial or commercial; Carpet & upholstery cleaning on customer premises
Pr: Anita Weihbrecht

D-U-N-S 02-274-1284
J AND L ENTERPRISES INC
COOPER'S SUPER VALU FOODS
710 N Walnut St, Chaska, MN 55318-2560
Tel (952) 448-2325 *Founded/Ownrshp* 1949
Sales 64.7MM^E *EMP* 700
SIC 5411 Grocery stores, independent; Grocery stores, independent
Pr: Gary Cooper
**VP:* Sandra Cooper

D-U-N-S 06-639-0951
J AND L HOLDING CO INC
12235 Robin Blvd, Houston, TX 77045-4826
Tel (713) 434-7600 *Founded/Ownrshp* 1990
Sales 138.6MM^E *EMP* 55
SIC 5171 Petroleum bulk stations; Petroleum bulk stations
Pr: L L Leach III

D-U-N-S 15-521-4786 IMP
■ **J AND M LABORATORIES INC**
NORDSON DAWSONVILLE
(*Suby of* NORDSON CORP) ★
11475 Lakefield Dr, Duluth, GA 30097-1511
Tel (770) 497-3400 *Founded/Ownrshp* 2001
Sales 20.1MM^E *EMP* 200^E
SIC 3559 8731 8071 Plastics working machinery; Commercial research laboratory; Medical laboratories; Plastics working machinery; Commercial research laboratory; Medical laboratories
CEO: James E Devries
**CFO:* Raymond L Cushing
**Sr VP:* John Keane
**VP:* Jim Devries
**VP:* Nicholas Pellecchia
Snr Sftwr: Dave Bacco
Plnt Mgr: Jeff Skimel

J AND R MUSIC STORE
See J & R ELECTRONICS INC

D-U-N-S 04-999-6940
J ARTHUR DOSHER MEMORIAL HOSPITAL
924 N Howe St, Southport, NC 28461-3038
Tel (910) 457-3800 *Founded/Ownrshp* 1999
Sales 31.8MM *EMP* 99^E
SIC 8011 General & family practice, physician/surgeon; General & family practice, physician/surgeon
Prin: Margaret Rivera
**CFO:* Dennis Coffey

D-U-N-S 07-200-5499
J ARTHUR DOSHER MEMORIAL HOSPITAL FOUNDATION INC
924 N Howe St, Southport, NC 28461-3038
Tel (910) 457-3800 *Founded/Ownrshp* 1937
Sales 34.1MM^E *EMP* 350^E
Accts Berry Padgett & Chandler Pll
SIC 8062 General medical & surgical hospitals; General medical & surgical hospitals
CEO: Tom Siemers
**Ch Bd:* Sherri Marshall
**CEO:* Edgar Haywood III
**COO:* Lynda Stanley
**CFO:* Dennis Coffey
Ofcr: Audrey Chase
Ofcr: Arlen Copenhaver

CIO: Susan Shomaker
Web Dev: Ava McDonald
Pr Dir: Kirk Singer
Doctor: Ambrose Chazhikattu

D-U-N-S 19-355-5216
J ARTHUR TRUDEAU MEMORIAL CENTER
3445 Post Rd, Warwick, RI 02886-7147
Tel (401) 739-2700 *Founded/Ownrshp* 1964
Sales 25.7MM *EMP* 869
SIC 8361 8351 Home for the mentally retarded; Child day care services; Home for the mentally retarded; Child day care services
CEO: Mary Madden
**CFO:* Robert Teolis
Dir IT: Keith Brutke

J B
See JACKSON - DAWSON COMMUNICATIONS INC

J B
See J B WHOLESALE ROOFING AND BUILDING SUPPLIES INC

J B A
See B JACQUELINE AND ASSOCIATES INC

J B A CHEVROLET
See GLADDING CHEVROLET INC

D-U-N-S 04-875-7025
J B BOSTICK CO INC
2870 E La Cresta Ave, Anaheim, CA 92806-1816
Tel (714) 238-2121 *Founded/Ownrshp* 1969
Sales 36.1MM^E *EMP* 115
SIC 1611 1771 Grading; Highway & street paving contractor; Concrete work; Grading; Highway & street paving contractor; Concrete work
Pr: James B Bostick
CFO: Joyce Stevens
**VP:* Jerry Hamlin
Prd Mgr: Craig Jacob

D-U-N-S 05-727-5935
J B CLARK OIL CO INC
102 Jordan St, Dublin, GA 31027-7581
Tel (478) 272-2276 *Founded/Ownrshp* 1971
Sales 38.6MM^E *EMP* 51
SIC 5171 Petroleum bulk stations; Petroleum bulk stations
Pr: Robert B Clark
**VP:* Billy R McGhee

D-U-N-S 11-924-6320
J B COXWELL CONTRACTING INC
6741 Lloyd Rd W, Jacksonville, FL 32254-1249
Tel (904) 786-1120 *Founded/Ownrshp* 2000
Sales 75.9MM^E *EMP* 200
Accts Charles B Parker Cpa Pa
SIC 1623 1794 Underground utilities contractor; Excavation work; Underground utilities contractor; Excavation work
Ch: John B Coxwell
**Pr:* John D Coxwell
Treas: Wayne Willford
**Sec:* V Wayne Willford
**Ex VP:* Sam E Mousa
**VP:* Christopher C Blank
**VP:* Garland Chick
**VP:* Eddie K Greene
**VP:* Patrick J Knapp
Genl Mgr: Raymond Pace
VP Opers: Christopher Blank

D-U-N-S 02-932-6816
J B DEWAR INC (CA)
75 Prado Rd, San Luis Obispo, CA 93401-7314
Tel (805) 543-0180 *Founded/Ownrshp* 1935, 1955
Sales 31.3MM^E *EMP* 45
SIC 5171 5172 Petroleum bulk stations; Lubricating oils & greases; Petroleum bulk stations; Lubricating oils & greases
Pr: Kenneth L Dewar
CFO: Denise Domingues
Exec: Delieu Brancart
Opers Mgr: Jordan Pickens
Mktg Mgr: Mark Libby
Sls Mgr: Paul Tucker

J B ENTERPRISES
See JOHN BOYD ENTERPRISES INC

J B FRAGANCE
See SHISEIDO COSMETICS (AMERICA) LTD

D-U-N-S 06-626-3799
J B G CORP
1130 N Nimitz Hwy Rm A265, Honolulu, HI 96817-5784
Tel (808) 545-3412 *Founded/Ownrshp* 1971
Sales 20.0MM^E *EMP* 340
SIC 4491 Stevedoring; Stevedoring
Pr: Robert T Guard
**Treas:* John Sims

D-U-N-S 04-181-5630
J B HANAUER & CO
(*Suby of* RBC WEALTH MANAGEMENT) ★
4 Gatehall Dr Ste 3a, Parsippany, NJ 07054-4592
Tel (973) 829-1000 *Founded/Ownrshp* 2007
Sales 24.0MM *EMP* 250
SIC 6211 Security brokers & dealers; Bond dealers & brokers; Mutual funds, selling by independent salesperson; Security brokers & dealers; Bond dealers & brokers; Mutual funds, selling by independent salesperson
Prin: Barry H Zucker
COO: Sarah Mathews
Sr VP: Ronald Maxman
**Prin:* Virginia A Manna
**Prin:* Kenneth M Meiselman
**Prin:* Greg Plifka
Brnch Mgr: Keith Minnigerode
CTO: Charlene Barnes

D-U-N-S 19-855-4107 IMP/EXP
J B HOLDINGS GROUP INC
(*Suby of* JB INDUSTRIES INC) ★
4203 35th St, Long Island City, NY 11101-2301
Tel (718) 729-2020 *Founded/Ownrshp* 1987
Sales 111.7MM^E *EMP* 309^E
SIC 1721 Commercial wallcovering contractor
Ch Bd: Joel Berman
**Pr:* Jan Berman
CFO: Norman Rathfelder

D-U-N-S 06-215-3176
■ **J B HUNT TRANSPORT INC**
(*Suby of* JB HUNT TRANSPORT SERVICES INC) ★
615 J B Hunt Corporate Dr, Lowell, AR 72745-9143
Tel (479) 820-0000 *Founded/Ownrshp* 1969
Sales 2.1MMM^E *EMP* 14,171
SIC 4213 Trucking, except local; Trucking, except local
Ch: Kirk Thompson
**Pt:* John Roberts
**Pr:* John N Roberts III
**CFO:* Jerry W Walton
**Treas:* David N Chelette
Ex VP: Paul R Bergant
Ex VP: Kay J Palmer
Ex VP: Bob D Ralston
**VP:* David G Mee
Genl Mgr: Kenneth Thomas
Plng Mgr: David Martin

D-U-N-S 18-309-9415
J B J ASSOCIATES INC
LIBERTY HONDA
71 W Service Rd, Hartford, CT 06120-1524
Tel (860) 251-6851 *Founded/Ownrshp* 1986
Sales 32.5MM^E *EMP* 100
SIC 5511 Automobiles, new & used; Automobiles, new & used
Pr: John L Orsini
Sls Mgr: Jason Behan
Sales Asso: John Cassidy
Sales Asso: Amnon Udi

D-U-N-S 15-428-0655 IMP/EXP
J B POINDEXTER & CO INC
600 Travis St Ste 200, Houston, TX 77002-2995
Tel (713) 655-9800 *Founded/Ownrshp* 1983
Sales 877.1MM^E *EMP* 3,072
SIC 3713

D-U-N-S 04-139-1822 IMP
J B SULLIVAN INC
SULLIVAN'S FOODS
425 1st St Ste 1, Savanna, IL 61074-1519
Tel (815) 273-4511 *Founded/Ownrshp* 1967
Sales 182.8MM^E *EMP* 1,450
SIC 5411 Grocery stores; Grocery stores
CEO: John B Sullivan
**Pr:* Scott Sullivan
**Sec:* June A Sullivan

D-U-N-S 00-547-7781 IMP
J B TOOL DIE & ENGINEERING CO INC
1509 Dividend Rd, Fort Wayne, IN 46808-1159
Tel (260) 483-9586 *Founded/Ownrshp* 1962
Sales 22.8MM^E *EMP* 115
SIC 3544 3599 Special dies, tools, jigs & fixtures; Machine shop, jobbing & repair
Pr: David Bear
**CFO:* Gregory Beer
**VP:* David Thompson
**VP:* Rick Zorger
Dir IT: Jeff Tinsley
IT Man: Kerry Boggs

J B U
See JOHN BROWN UNIVERSITY

D-U-N-S 02-150-7512
J B VENDING CO INC
JACKSON BROTHERS
31 International Plaza Ct, Saint Ann, MO 63074-1843
Tel (314) 423-1881 *Founded/Ownrshp* 1979
Sales 36.7MM^E *EMP* 180
SIC 5962 5812 5145 Sandwich & hot food vending machines; Caterers; Contract food services; Candy
Pr: Kendall Jackson
Ofcr: Tom Lamm
**VP:* Curtis Campbell
**VP:* Wendell Jackson

D-U-N-S 09-314-7080
J B WEIMAR INC (TN)
7281 Centennial Blvd, Nashville, TN 37209-1019
Tel (615) 350-7050 *Founded/Ownrshp* 1976
Sales 33.1MM^E *EMP* 25
SIC 5172

D-U-N-S 09-562-6040
J B WHOLESALE ROOFING AND BUILDING SUPPLIES INC
J B
21524 Nordhoff St, Chatsworth, CA 91311-5822
Tel (818) 998-0440 *Founded/Ownrshp* 1981
Sales 27.1MM^E *EMP* 111
SIC 5211 5033 Roofing material; Shingles, except wood; Roofing material; Shingles, except wood
Pr: W Keith Jones
CFO: Andre Delagdo

J BAR B FOODS
See J & B SAUSAGE CO INC

D-U-N-S 01-450-1951
J BARBOUR INC
OFFICE SERVICE COMPANY
1009 Tuckerton Ct, Reading, PA 19605-1177
Tel (610) 926-9850 *Founded/Ownrshp* 1988
Sales 23.3MM^E *EMP* 33^E
SIC 5112 5021 Stationery & office supplies; Office & public building furniture
Pr: Jeffrey Barbour
**Sec:* Karen Barbour

D-U-N-S 05-617-9021 IMP/EXP
J BAXTER BRINKMANN INTERNATIONAL CORP
BRIKMANN J BAXTER INTL
4215 Mcewen Rd, Dallas, TX 75244-5202
Tel (972) 387-4939 *Founded/Ownrshp* 1981
Sales 206.8MM^E *EMP* 800
SIC 3648 3631 Spotlights; Barbecues, grills & braziers (outdoor cooking); Spotlights; Barbecues, grills & braziers (outdoor cooking)
Pr: J Baxter Brinkmann

D-U-N-S 17-218-2532 IMP/EXP
J BRAND INC
JBRANDJEANS
(*Suby of* FAST RETAILING CO., LTD.)
1214 E 18th St, Los Angeles, CA 90021-3059
Tel (213) 749-3500 *Founded/Ownrshp* 2012
Sales 24.9MM^E *EMP* 60
SIC 2211 Denims
Pr: Jeffrey Rudes
**CFO:* Efthimios P Sotos
**VP:* Susie Crippen
VP: Stephanie Jungbluth
Art Dir: Laura Pizzarelli

D-U-N-S 06-847-5870
J C ANDERSON INC
834 N Church Rd, Elmhurst, IL 60126-1019
Tel (630) 834-1669 *Founded/Ownrshp* 1976
Sales 28.3MM^E *EMP* 150
SIC 1751 1742 1799 Carpentry work; Drywall; Acoustical & ceiling work; Plastic wall tile installation; Carpentry work; Drywall; Acoustical & ceiling work; Plastic wall tile installation
CEO: Thomas M Schumacher
Pr: Thomas Bean
**Pr:* Kevin M Radoha
**Pr:* Michael L Yazbec
**COO:* Thomas D Bean
**Ch:* James M Schumacher
VP: William Burfeind
Exec: Anthony Dougles
Exec: Seth Erlich
Sfty Dirs: Chris Bowen

D-U-N-S 03-521-8239
J C BILLION INC
BILLION CHRYSLER DODGE KIA
270 Automotive Ave, Bozeman, MT 59718-7797
Tel (866) 224-5895 *Founded/Ownrshp* 1978
Sales 51.0MM^E *EMP* 105
SIC 5511 Automobiles, new & used; Vans, new & used; Pickups, new & used; Automobiles, new & used; Vans, new & used; Pickups, new & used
Pr: Joseph C Billion
**Sec:* Diane Billion
VP: Joshua Deane
**VP:* Dick Frederick
**VP:* Tara Glasgow
VP: Robert Hager
**VP:* Greg Harper
VP: Brian Heidt
VP: Robert Kinna
**VP:* Greg Perrine
VP: David Seminara
VP: Kenneth Swenson

D-U-N-S 07-284-9847
J C BLAIR MEMORIAL HOSPITAL
1225 Warm Springs Ave, Huntingdon, PA 16652-2398
Tel (814) 643-8367 *Founded/Ownrshp* 1909
Sales 44.0MM *EMP* 479^E
Accts Baker Tilly Virchow Krause Llp
SIC 8062 General medical & surgical hospitals; General medical & surgical hospitals
CEO: Lisa Mallon
COO: Joseph Peluso
CFO: Garry Pote
**CFO:* Ed Quinn
**Treas:* Garry L Pote
Bd of Dir: Jim Schall
**VP:* Michael F Hubert
VP: Marlene Kasten
**VP:* Pamela Matthias
VP: Michael McKim
**VP:* Marlene Pierce
Dir OR: Leigh Bizak
Dir Lab: Christina Campbell
Dir Lab: Matthew Lieb
Dir Rad: Larry Garmin
Dir Rx: Jillian Hollen-Archey
Dir Rx: Thomas Marko

J C C
See JEWISH COMMUNITY CENTER OF STATEN ISLAND INC

J C C
See JEWISH COMMUNITY CENTER

J C C CAMPS
See JEWISH COMMUNITY CENTERS OF GREATER PHILADELPHIA

J C FOOD STORES
See KROGER LIMITED PARTNERSHIP I

D-U-N-S 79-514-9004 IMP
J C FORD CO
(*Suby of* RUHE CORP) ★
901 S Leslie St, La Habra, CA 90631-6841
Tel (714) 871-7361 *Founded/Ownrshp* 2004
Sales 39.5MM^E *EMP* 95
SIC 3556 Food products machinery; Food products machinery
CEO: Thomas A Ruhe
IT Man: Terry Kenny
Opers Mgr: Jose Sanchez
VP Sls: Tom McCaleb
VP Sls: Robert Meyer
Sls Mgr: Kyle Armstrong

D-U-N-S 06-529-1783
J C HOWARD FARMS LLC
1373 Davis Mill Rd, Deep Run, NC 28525-9505
Tel (252) 568-4204 *Founded/Ownrshp* 1972
Sales 62.0MM^E *EMP* 100
SIC 5153 Corn; Corn

J C I
See JOHNSON CRUSHERS INTERNATIONAL INC

D-U-N-S 03-385-7566
J C LEWIS FORD LLC (GA)
9505 Abercorn St, Savannah, GA 31406-4595
Tel (912) 925-0234 *Founded/Ownrshp* 1912, 1947
Sales 58.0MM^E *EMP* 135
SIC 5511 5521 7538 7532 7515 5531 Automobiles, new & used; Used car dealers; General automotive repair shops; Top & body repair & paint shops; Passenger car leasing; Automotive & home supply stores; Automobiles, new & used; Used car dealers; General automotive repair shops; Top & body repair & paint shops; Passenger car leasing; Automotive & home supply stores
Genl Mgr: Michael Offer
Sls Mgr: Joe Welch
Sales Asso: Alberto Tapia
Doctor: David Jung
Snr Mgr: Charles Izlar

D-U-N-S 00-797-5535 IMP/EXP
J C NEWMAN CIGAR CO (FL)
2701 N 16th St, Tampa, FL 33605-2616
Tel (813) 248-2124 *Founded/Ownrshp* 1895
Sales 33.8MM^E *EMP* 208
SIC 2121 5194 Cigars; Cigars; Cigars; Cigars
Pr: Eric M Newman
Ch Bd: Stanford J Newman
Treas: Shira D Martin
Ex VP: Robert C Newman
Telecom Ex: Shira Coxbill
Telecom Ex: David Witt
Plnt Mgr: Rich Dolak
Sales Exec: Wally Buechel
Mktg Dir: Shanda Lee
Manager: Alan Goldfarb
Manager: Louis Marshall

D-U-N-S 00-434-8298
J C ORR & SON INC (PA)
438 7th Ave, Altoona, PA 16602-2638
Tel (814) 944-8112 *Founded/Ownrshp* 1882, 1978
Sales 47.4MM^E *EMP* 150
SIC 1542 1541 5211 Commercial & office building, new construction; Institutional building construction; Industrial buildings, new construction; Lumber & other building materials; Commercial & office building, new construction; Institutional building construction; Industrial buildings, new construction; Lumber & other building materials
Pr: Joseph H Orr III
**Pr:* Joseph H Orr Jr
**Sec:* Janet Orr

D-U-N-S 07-317-4310
J C PACE & CO
M SYSTEMS SUPER MARKETS CO.
420 Throckmorton St # 710, Fort Worth, TX 76102-3724
Tel (817) 332-1219 *Founded/Ownrshp* 1963
Sales 41.3MM^E *EMP* 400
SIC 7359 5064 7389 7033 7999 Laundry equipment leasing; Electric household appliances; Flea market; Recreational vehicle parks; Trailer park; Rodeo operation; Laundry equipment leasing; Electric household appliances; Flea market; Recreational vehicle parks; Trailer park; Rodeo operation
Ch Bd: Gary H Pace
**Pr:* Joe K Pace

D-U-N-S 18-759-7646 IMP/EXP
■ **J C PENNEY EUROPE INC**
JC PENNEY
(*Suby of* JC PENNEY) ★
6501 Legacy Dr, Plano, TX 75024-3698
Tel (972) 431-2326 *Founded/Ownrshp* 1969
Sales 450.4MM^E *EMP* 560
SIC 5137 5136 5023 Women's & children's clothing; Men's & boys' clothing; Home furnishings; Women's & children's clothing; Men's & boys' clothing; Home furnishings
CEO: Mike Ullman
Ch Bd: Pat Hampton
**Pr:* Alan Questrom
**Ex VP:* Tony Bartlett
**Ex VP:* Janet Dhillon
**Ex VP:* Brynn Evanson
**Ex VP:* Scott Laverty
**VP:* Vanessa Castagna

D-U-N-S 17-500-2914
J C PENNEY LIFE INSURANCE CO
JC PENNEY
(*Suby of* AEGON DIRECT MARKETING SERVICES INC) ★
2700 W Plano Pkwy, Plano, TX 75075-8205
Tel (972) 881-6000 *Founded/Ownrshp* 1967
Sales NA *EMP* 1,520
Accts Kpmg Peat Marwick Llp
SIC 6311 6321 Life insurance; Health insurance carriers; Life insurance; Health insurance carriers
Ch Bd: Ted L Spurlock
CFO: Donald L Heise
**CFO:* Martha McDonald
Ex VP: George E Suiter
Sr VP: Thomas D McGahey
Sr VP: Joseph A Sartoris
IT Man: Tricia Brown
Sys/Mgr: Gary W Robinson
Genl Couns: Keith Wright

D-U-N-S 87-693-6295
■ **J C PENNEY MEXICO INC**
(*Suby of* JC PENNEY) ★
6501 Legacy Dr, Plano, TX 75024-3698
Tel (972) 431-1000 *Founded/Ownrshp* 1990
Sales 68.1MM^E *EMP* 3,500
SIC 5311 Department stores, non-discount; Department stores, non-discount
Pr: Mike Ullman
**Ch:* Allen Questron
Art Dir: Gus Benevides

J C PENNEY OPTICAL
See US VISION INC

J C PENNEY OPTICAL
See USV OPTICAL INC

D-U-N-S 07-102-6959
■ **J C PENNEY PROPERTIES INC**
JC PENNEY
(*Suby of* JC PENNEY) ★
6501 Legacy Dr, Plano, TX 75024-3698
Tel (972) 431-1000 *Founded/Ownrshp* 2000
Sales 15.4MM^{E} *EMP* 286^{E}
SIC 6512 Commercial & industrial building operation; Commercial & industrial building operation
Pr: N M Lowenkron
**VP:* R J Emma
**VP:* J P Garvey
**VP:* R D Romesberg
Snr Mgr: Lilliana Iannone

D-U-N-S 06-253-3138 IMP/EXP
■ **J C PENNEY PURCHASING CORP**
JCPENNEY
(*Suby of* J C PENNEY EUROPE INC) ★
6501 Legacy Dr, Plano, TX 75024-3698
Tel (972) 431-1000 *Founded/Ownrshp* 1959
Sales 431.7MM^{E} *EMP* 560
SIC 5137 5136 5023 Women's & children's clothing; Men's & boys' clothing; Home furnishings; Women's & children's clothing; Men's & boys' clothing; Home furnishings
CEO: Kenneth Mangone
**COO:* Mike Kramer
**CFO:* Michael P Dastugue
**Ex VP:* Janet L Dhilon
**Ex VP:* Laurie Beja Miller
**Sr VP:* Katheryn Burchett
**Sr VP:* Lorraine Hitch
**Sr VP:* Joan Mudget
**VP:* Adil Raza
**VP:* L C Tucker

D-U-N-S 01-643-8640
J C RIPBERGER CONSTRUCTION CORP
5300 W Old 106th St, Zionsville, IN 46077-9264
Tel (317) 873-3383 *Founded/Ownrshp* 1958, 1993
Sales 21.0MM^{E} *EMP* 75
SIC 1542 Commercial & office building contractors
Pr: William L Ripberger Jr
Sfty Mgr: Reuel Lawburgh

J C S
See JIMENEZ CONTRACT SERVICES LLC

J C S U
See JOHNSON C SMITH UNIVERSITY INC

J C SALES
See SHIMS BARGAIN INC

D-U-N-S 00-893-6650
J C SNAVELY & SONS INC (PA)
150 Main St, Landisville, PA 17538-1295
Tel (717) 394-7277 *Founded/Ownrshp* 1878, 1946
Sales 31.7MM^{E} *EMP* 180
SIC 2439 5211 2431 2452 2435 Trusses, except roof: laminated lumber; Lumber & other building materials; Millwork; Panels & sections, prefabricated, wood; Hardwood veneer & plywood; Trusses, except roof: laminated lumber; Lumber & other building materials; Millwork; Panels & sections, prefabricated, wood; Hardwood veneer & plywood
Pr: Charles B Fessler
**Treas:* James R Snavely
Treas: James Stephen
**VP:* Stephan Snavely
Sls Mgr: Jack Gingrich
Sales Asso: Paul Thoma

D-U-N-S 00-321-6868 IMP/EXP
J C STEELE AND SONS INC (NC)
710 S Mulberry St, Statesville, NC 28677-5714
Tel (704) 872-3681 *Founded/Ownrshp* 1889
Sales 22.0MM^{E} *EMP* 135
SIC 5084 Brick making machinery; Clay working & tempering machines; Industrial machinery & equipment
CEO: David S Steele
**Pr:* John S Steele
**CFO:* Donald J Koepnick
**VP:* Jian Huang
**VP:* Richard B Steele
IT Man: Jim Falter
Plnt Mgr: Dale Potts
Ql Cn Mgr: Wayne York
Sls Mgr: Scott Bass

D-U-N-S 02-748-6554
J C WRIGHT SALES CO
600 Powell Ave Sw, Renton, WA 98057-2247
Tel (253) 395-8799 *Founded/Ownrshp* 1947
Sales 22.4MM^{E} *EMP* 98
SIC 5149 5169 5113 Specialty food items; Natural & organic foods; Detergents & soaps, except specialty cleaning; Industrial & personal service paper; Specialty food items; Natural & organic foods; Detergents & soaps, except specialty cleaning; Industrial & personal service paper
Pr: Jack Wright
**VP:* Kevin Wright

D-U-N-S 01-464-2552
J CALNAN & ASSOCIATES INC (MA)
3 Batterymarch Park Fl 5, Quincy, MA 02169-7541
Tel (617) 801-0200 *Founded/Ownrshp* 1996
Sales 137.6MM *EMP* 65^{E}
Accts Lmhs Pc Norwell Massachusetts
SIC 8741 1542 Management services; Custom builders, non-residential; Management services; Custom builders, non-residential
Pr: James Cahill
COO: Crowther Michael
**VP:* Michael Crowther
Exec: David Ferreira
Mktg Dir: Maureen Rystrom
Snr PM: Rick Borden
Snr PM: Josh Hines
Snr PM: Bill McKenna

D-U-N-S 13-106-4276 IMP
J CHOO USA INC
JIMMY CHOO
750 Lexington Ave Fl 21, New York, NY 10022-9818
Tel (212) 319-9822 *Founded/Ownrshp* 1998
Sales 72.2MM^{E} *EMP* 180^{E}
SIC 5139 Shoes; Shoes
Pr: Tamara Melon
**Ch Bd:* Pierre Denis
COO: Anthony Dimasso
VP: Ayse Jourdan
Store Mgr: Matthew Bonari
Store Mgr: Jessie Mechem
Store Mgr: Lela Sagnelli
Store Mgr: Kim Wilkins
Dir IT: Derrick Lopez
Sls Mgr: Sonja Jimmychoo
Sales Asso: Krysa Di Masso

D-U-N-S 02-650-6485
J CINCO INC
JOHNSON OIL
1113 E Sarah Dewitt Dr, Gonzales, TX 78629-2518
Tel (830) 672-9574 *Founded/Ownrshp* 1958
Sales 339.0MM^{E} *EMP* 480
SIC 5172 5541 Petroleum products; Filling stations, gasoline; Petroleum products; Filling stations, gasoline
Pr: Fletcher Johnson
**Sec:* Jane Johnson
VP: Jeff Loomis
VP: Jim Wilt
Genl Mgr: Jay Tinsley

J CLYDE HOPKINS ELEMENTARY SCH
See SHERWOOD SCHOOL DISTRICT

J COBO & ASSOCIATES
See GREENFIELD WORLD TRADE INC

D-U-N-S 01-890-3542
J COLEMAN ALVIN & SON INC
9 Nh Route 113, Albany, NH 03818-7443
Tel (603) 447-5936 *Founded/Ownrshp* 1942
Sales 41.3MM^{E} *EMP* 80
Accts Melanson Heath & Company Pc
SIC 1542 1794 3273 5032 5211 Commercial & office building, new construction; Excavation work; Ready-mixed concrete; Sand, construction; Gravel; Sand & gravel; Commercial & office building, new construction; Excavation work; Ready-mixed concrete; Sand, construction; Gravel; Sand & gravel
Pr: Calvin J Coleman
**VP:* Curtis Coleman
**VP:* P Noah Coleman

D-U-N-S 07-636-4392
J CRAIG VENTER INSTITUTE INC
9704 Medical Center Dr, Rockville, MD 20850-3343
Tel (301) 838-0200 *Founded/Ownrshp* 1993
Sales 50.7MM *EMP* 325
Accts Ernst & Young Us Llp Greenvil
SIC 8733 8731 Research institute; Biological research; Research institute; Biological research
CEO: J Craig Venter
**Pr:* Karen Nelson
**COO:* Robert Friedman
**CFO:* Harold Davies
CFO: Julie Tune
CFO: Aimee L Turner
Ex VP: Marvin Frazier
VP: Yu Rogers
CTO: Vadim Sapiro
IT Man: Darnell Edwards

D-U-N-S 11-600-4417 IMP
J CREW INC
J CREW WOMEN'S ACCESSORIES
(*Suby of* J CREW OPERATING CORP) ★
770 Broadway Fl 14, New York, NY 10003-9522
Tel (212) 209-8010 *Founded/Ownrshp* 2015
Sales 240.3MM^{E} *EMP* 800
SIC 5961 5621 5611 Women's apparel, mail order; Clothing, mail order (except women's); Women's clothing stores; Men's & boys' clothing stores; Women's apparel, mail order; Clothing, mail order (except women's); Women's clothing stores; Men's & boys' clothing stores
Ch Bd: James Scully
**Pr:* Cornell Stanton
**CEO:* Millard S Drexler
**COO:* Jennifer Smith
Ex VP: Lynda Markoe
**Sr VP:* Darren Chen
VP: Joseph Gaudio
Dir IT: Elizabeth Zulliger
Dir IT: Emil Costache
Dir IT: Allyson Dwyer
Dir IT: John Fech

D-U-N-S 79-953-6271 IMP
J CREW OPERATING CORP
(*Suby of* JCREW GROUP INC) ★
770 Broadway Fl 1112, New York, NY 10003-9522
Tel (212) 209-2500 *Founded/Ownrshp* 1997
Sales 368.6MM^{E} *EMP* 2,500
SIC 5961 5621 5611 5661 5632 6794 Women's apparel, mail order; Clothing, mail order (except women's); Mail order house; Women's clothing stores; Men's & boys' clothing stores; Women's shoes; Men's shoes; Apparel accessories; Franchises, selling or licensing; Women's apparel, mail order; Clothing, mail order (except women's); Mail order house; Women's clothing stores; Men's & boys' clothing stores; Women's shoes; Men's shoes; Apparel accessories; Franchises, selling or licensing
CEO: Millard Drexler
**Ch Bd:* James Scully
**Ex VP:* Ms Tracy Gardner
**VP:* Mr Nicholas Lamberti

J CREW WOMEN'S ACCESSORIES
See J CREW INC

D-U-N-S 05-057-6953
J CROMPTON ELECTRIC INC
1290 N Congress Ave, West Palm Beach, FL 33409-6306
Tel (561) 588-6559 *Founded/Ownrshp* 2000
Sales 21.4MM^{E} *EMP* 70
SIC 1731 General electrical contractor
Pr: Jonathan Crompton
**VP:* Elizabeth Crompton
Off Mgr: Carol Liberman

D-U-N-S 80-268-8325 IMP
J CROWDER CORP
13455 Sunrise Valley Dr # 100, Herndon, VA 20171-3297
Tel (703) 793-1555 *Founded/Ownrshp* 1992
Sales 23.4MM^{E} *EMP* 90
SIC 1731 1711 8741 General electrical contractor; Mechanical contractor; Construction management
Pr: John Crowder
**VP:* Tedd Durden
VP: Dan Miles
Genl Mgr: Kathy Hayes

D-U-N-S 82-839-5454
J CUMBY CONSTRUCTION INC
165 W Broad St, Cookeville, TN 38501-2471
Tel (931) 526-5158 *Founded/Ownrshp* 2008
Sales 25.0MM *EMP* 51
SIC 1623 1541 1521 1542 Pumping station construction; Factory construction; Industrial buildings, new construction; Single-family housing construction; Commercial & office building, new construction; Pumping station construction; Factory construction; Industrial buildings, new construction; Single-family housing construction; Commercial & office building, new construction
Pr: Justin Cumby

D-U-N-S 01-383-3868
J D ECKMAN INC (PA)
4781 Lower Valley Rd, Atglen, PA 19310-1767
Tel (610) 593-5300 *Founded/Ownrshp* 1946, 1977
Sales 135.4MM^{E} *EMP* 400
SIC 1611 Concrete construction: roads, highways, sidewalks, etc.; Concrete construction: roads, highways, sidewalks, etc.
Pr: Mark S Eckman
**CFO:* Dennis Brubaker
VP: Dave Maugle
**Prin:* Michael S Eckman
**Prin:* Virginia L Eckman
Dir IT: Chris Bunting
Opers Mgr: Bob Esposito

D-U-N-S 13-210-3169 IMP/EXP
J D FIELDS & CO INC
55 Waugh Dr Ste 1250, Houston, TX 77007-5840
Tel (281) 558-7199 *Founded/Ownrshp* 1985
Sales 238.5MM^{E} *EMP* 37
SIC 5051 7359 3443 Steel; Equipment rental & leasing; Pipe, standpipe & culverts; Steel; Equipment rental & leasing; Pipe, standpipe & culverts
CEO: Jerry D Fields
**Pr:* Jay D Fields
CFO: Steve Fredrich
**CFO:* Steve Friedrich
**Ex VP:* J Patrick Burk
CIO: Christine Posados
CTO: Brian Ellenberg
IT Man: Todd Fagen
Mktg Dir: Dean Abbondanza
Sls Mgr: Dave Conely

D-U-N-S 00-946-2359
J D HEISKELL HOLDINGS LLC (OR)
J.D. HEISKELL AND COMPANY
1939 Hillman St, Tulare, CA 93274-1601
Tel (559) 685-6100 *Founded/Ownrshp* 2000
Sales 814.8MM^{E} *EMP* 322
SIC 5191 5999 Farm supplies; Feed & farm supply; Farm supplies; Feed & farm supply
Ch Bd: Scot T Hillman
**COO:* Ryan Pellett
Bd of Dir: Tom Caron
Bd of Dir: Duane Fischer
VP: Todd Gearheart
VP: Robert Hodgen
VP: Clark Jeary
VP: Roger Price
VP: Randy W Spiegel
VP: Lori Wilke
VP Bus: Charles Tsatsos

D-U-N-S 02-626-8540 IMP
J D MARTIN CO INC
(*Suby of* J.L. CARR ENTERPRISES, INC.)
1801 Royal Ln Ste 100, Dallas, TX 75229-3192
Tel (972) 277-5600 *Founded/Ownrshp* 2003
Sales 30.7MM^{E} *EMP* 3^{E}
SIC 5063 Electrical fittings & construction materials; Electrical fittings & construction materials
Pr: James L Carr
**Pr:* Greg Baker
**CFO:* Leigh Anne Moore
Manager: Greg Rutch
Sls Mgr: Donny Bordelon
Sls Mgr: Cindy Page
Sales Asso: Doug Johnson
Sales Asso: Shane Ryan

D-U-N-S 00-924-4260
J D OTT CO INC (WA)
2244 6th Ave S, Seattle, WA 98134-2002
Tel (206) 749-0777 *Founded/Ownrshp* 1943
Sales 24.4MM^{E} *EMP* 108
SIC 3728 3441 Aircraft parts & equipment; Fabricated structural metal; Aircraft parts & equipment; Fabricated structural metal
Pr: Rex Ott
**VP:* Bill Cook
VP: Lori Stock
MIS Dir: Matt Mentele
Netwrk Mgr: Rick Sandberg

D-U-N-S 14-460-9427
J D PATRICK PONTIAC INC
4700 W Henrietta Rd, Henrietta, NY 14467-9357
Tel (585) 359-2200 *Founded/Ownrshp* 1984
Sales 33.6MM^{E} *EMP* 125^{E}
SIC 5511 Automobiles, new & used; Pickups, new & used; Vans, new & used; Automobiles, new & used; Pickups, new & used; Vans, new & used
Pr: Patrick M Mulvihill
**VP:* Mark Pennella

J D R F
See JDRF INTERNATIONAL

D-U-N-S 01-665-7413
J D RESTAURANTS INC
DAIRY QUEEN
136 W Jefferson St, Tipton, IN 46072-1801
Tel (765) 675-7531 *Founded/Ownrshp* 1950
Sales 20.4MM^{E} *EMP* 500
SIC 5812 Ice cream stands or dairy bars; Ice cream stands or dairy bars
Pr: David Reasner
**Ch Bd:* Harry E Reasner Jr
**Ex VP:* Brent Reasner

D-U-N-S 10-403-1158
J D RUSSELL CO
4075 N Highway Dr, Tucson, AZ 85705-2911
Tel (520) 742-6194 *Founded/Ownrshp* 1977
Sales 50.2MM^{E} *EMP* 98
SIC 5032 3446 Concrete building products; Architectural metalwork; Concrete building products; Architectural metalwork
Pr: Nicholas H Danna
**Treas:* Robert A Danna
**VP:* Bradley S Danna
Off Mgr: Chris Delarco
Sls Mgr: Gil Romero

D-U-N-S 05-690-3867 IMP
J D STEEL CO INC
2101 W Jackson St, Phoenix, AZ 85009-5262
Tel (602) 254-8833 *Founded/Ownrshp* 1970
Sales 67.8MM^{E} *EMP* 500
Accts Wayne H Clouser Phoenix Ari
SIC 1791 3449 Concrete reinforcement, placing of; Miscellaneous metalwork; Concrete reinforcement, placing of; Miscellaneous metalwork
CEO: Charles Ray Zeek
**Pr:* Cary G Newton
**Treas:* Charles McCurdy
**Ex VP:* Gary Reddin

D-U-N-S 02-151-5200 EXP
J D STREETT & CO INC
144 Weldon Pkwy, Maryland Heights, MO 63043-3100
Tel (314) 432-6600 *Founded/Ownrshp* 1980
Sales 286.3MM *EMP* 240
Accts Bkd Llp St Louis Missouri
SIC 5171 5541 7389 5172 Petroleum bulk stations; Filling stations, gasoline; Packaging & labeling services; Engine fuels & oils; Petroleum bulk stations; Filling stations, gasoline; Packaging & labeling services; Engine fuels & oils
Pr: Newell A Baker Jr
**Ch Bd:* Newell A Baker
**CFO:* James A Schuering
Genl Mgr: Lee Rochnagel
Off Mgr: Dawn Harris
Off Mgr: Dawn Ruhlman
Opers Mgr: Brian Baker
Opers Mgr: Rick Dumey
Opers Mgr: Rick Dumi
Opers Mgr: Don Rogers
Sales Exec: Tom Irwin

D-U-N-S 80-397-0987
J D YOUNG CO INC
116 W 3rd St, Tulsa, OK 74103-3412
Tel (918) 582-9955 *Founded/Ownrshp* 2011
Sales 51.4MM^{E} *EMP* 200
SIC 5999 2752 Photocopy machines; Commercial printing, lithographic; Photocopy machines; Commercial printing, lithographic
Pr: Robert Stuart Jr
**Pr:* Douglas J Stuart
**Prin:* Joe D Young
**Prin:* Lydia S Young

D-U-N-S 09-999-2430 IMP
J DAVID GLADSTONE INSTITUTES
1650 Owens St Fl 2, San Francisco, CA 94158-2337
Tel (415) 734-2000 *Founded/Ownrshp* 1971
Sales 80.1MM *EMP* 370
SIC 8733

D-U-N-S 07-944-9650
J DAVIS AUTOMOTIVE GROUP INC
7250 Gulf Fwy, Houston, TX 77017-1528
Tel (281) 471-6767 *Founded/Ownrshp* 2014
Sales 22.5MM^{E} *EMP* 57^{E}
SIC 7538 General automotive repair shops

D-U-N-S 00-142-2575
J DERENZO CO
338 Howard St, Brockton, MA 02302-1000
Tel (508) 588-2671 *Founded/Ownrshp* 1949
Sales 24.3MM^{E} *EMP* 40
SIC 1794 1623 Excavation & grading, building construction; Pipeline construction
Pr: David Howe
**Treas:* Anthony Loconte
VP: Michael McCarthy
Sfty Dirs: Shawn Dygd
Opers Mgr: Debbie Hamilton

D-U-N-S 88-321-7606
J DIAMOND GROUP INC
6410 Southwest Blvd # 128, Benbrook, TX 76109-6918
Tel (817) 732-2829 *Founded/Ownrshp* 1994
Sales 35.0MM *EMP* 400
SIC 7381 Guard services
CEO: Wilfred Blood
CFO: Griggs Bennett
**VP:* Dennis Roberts

D-U-N-S 00-194-0014
J E & L E MABEE FOUNDATION INC (DE)
401 S Boston Ave Ste 3001, Tulsa, OK 74103-4066
Tel (918) 584-4286 *Founded/Ownrshp* 1948
Sales 72.4MM *EMP* 14
Accts Hogan Taylor Llp Tulsa Ok
SIC 8699 1311 Charitable organization; Crude petroleum production; Charitable organization; Crude petroleum production
Ch: Joe Mabee

D-U-N-S 04-586-8577
J E CORCORAN CO
2 Rutgers Rd Bldg C, Pittsburgh, PA 15205-2566
Tel (412) 921-8900 *Founded/Ownrshp* 1969

Sales 24.4MM EMP 28
SIC 5148 Fruits, fresh; Vegetables, fresh
Pr: Anthony Vivirito Jr
VP: Anthony Vivirito Sr

D-U-N-S 03-409-8942
J E M B REALTY CORP
150 Broadway Rm 800, New York, NY 10038-4396
Tel (212) 608-5100 Founded/Ownrshp 1991
Sales 50.4MM^E EMP 312
SIC 6798 6531 Real estate investment trusts; Real estate agents & managers; Real estate investment trusts; Real estate agents & managers
Pr: Joseph L Gerome

D-U-N-S 03-499-4624
J E MEURET GRAIN CO INC
101 N Franklin St, Brunswick, NE 68720
Tel (402) 842-2515 Founded/Ownrshp 1923
Sales 245.1MM EMP 33^E
Accts Bmg Certified Public Accountan
SIC 5153 Grains; Grains
Pr: John J Meuret
*Sec: James Meuret
*VP: Pat Meuret
*VP: Patrick Meuret

J E ROBERT
See ROBERT CO INC J E

J E SERVICES
See JE REMEDIATION TECHNOLOGIES INC

D-U-N-S 16-253-2352
J E SHEEHAN CONTRACTING CORP
SHEEHAN, J E CONTRACTING
208 Sissonville Rd, Potsdam, NY 13676-3563
Tel (315) 265-8427 Founded/Ownrshp 1981
Sales 26.3MM^E EMP 66
SIC 1542 1521 1794 1741 1711 1629 Commercial & office building contractors; Commercial & office buildings, renovation & repair; New construction, single-family houses; General remodeling, single-family houses; Excavation work; Foundation building; Septic system construction; Land clearing contractor
Pr: James E Sheehan
Off Mgr: Mindy Smith

D-U-N-S 08-077-9226
J EDENS CORP
EDENS TICKETING
115 Chestnut St, Philadelphia, PA 19106-3017
Tel (215) 625-0314 Founded/Ownrshp 1987
Sales 28.7MM^E EMP 200
SIC 0783 7349 4959 Surgery services, ornamental tree; Janitorial service, contract basis; Snowplowing; Surgery services, ornamental tree; Janitorial service, contract basis; Snowplowing
Pr: Janet Edens
*VP: Michele Riegal

D-U-N-S 06-878-5880
J ENTERPRISES INC
J & J MARKET AND DELI
1532 Se Stephens St, Roseburg, OR 97470-4030
Tel (541) 672-8585 Founded/Ownrshp 1996
Sales 30.7MM EMP 6
Accts Daniel A Caccaro Cpa Mark A
SIC 5411 5944 Grocery stores, independent; Jewelry stores; Grocery stores, independent; Jewelry stores
Pr: Mike Bhakta

D-U-N-S 00-896-0122
J F AHERN CO (WI)
855 Morris St, Fond Du Lac, WI 54935-5611
Tel (920) 921-9020 Founded/Ownrshp 1880
Sales 239.3MM EMP 855
SIC 1711

D-U-N-S 00-978-3523
J F BRENNAN CO INC
818 Bainbridge St, La Crosse, WI 54603-1560
Tel (608) 784-7173 Founded/Ownrshp 1959
Sales 72.7MM EMP 240
SIC 1622 1629 8711 Bridge, tunnel & elevated highway; Marine construction; Engineering services; Bridge, tunnel & elevated highway; Marine construction; Engineering services
Pr: Anthony Binsfeld
*COO: Matthew Binsfeld
Exec: Greg Smith
MIS Dir: Brian Jerzak
Mktg Dir: Dianah Colburn
Mktg Dir: David Cullum

D-U-N-S 02-337-6338
J F COOK CO INC
OVERHEAD DOOR GRATER MILWAUKEE
7830 S 10th St, Oak Creek, WI 53154-1916
Tel (414) 762-4000 Founded/Ownrshp 1962
Sales 28.0MM^E EMP 45
SIC 5031 5039 5211 3446 3442 2431

D-U-N-S 00-339-6488
J F DAY AND CO INC (AL)
PELLA WINDOWS & DOORS
12100 Baltimore Ave Ste 1, Beltsville, MD 20705-1374
Tel (301) 957-7000 Founded/Ownrshp 1928
Sales 20.4MM^E EMP 150
SIC 5211 5031 Door & window products; Doors; Windows; Door & window products; Doors; Windows
Ch Bd: J F Day III
*VP: J Frank Day IV
*VP: Thomas Patton
Exec: Alisa Pugh
Genl Mgr: Jim Brewer
IT Man: Byron Chancelor
IT Man: Matin Costa

D-U-N-S 80-845-0449 IMP
J F DUNCAN INDUSTRIES INC
DURAY
9301 Stewart And Gray Rd, Downey, CA 90241-5315
Tel (562) 862-4269 Founded/Ownrshp 1988
Sales 27.6MM^E EMP 100^E
SIC 3589 Cooking equipment, commercial; Cooking equipment, commercial

CEO: Johnny F Wong
COO: Chris Thompson
Snr PM: Dave Jensen

D-U-N-S 02-549-1275
J F EDWARDS CONSTRUCTION CO
(Suby of E.I.P.- ELECTRICIDADE INDUSTRIAL PORTUGUESA, S.A.)
220 S Chicago St, Geneseo, IL 61254-1456
Tel (309) 944-4681 Founded/Ownrshp 1975
Sales 29.4MM^E EMP 50
Accts Mcgladrey Llp Davenport Iow
SIC 1731 Electrical work; Lighting contractor; Electrical work; Lighting contractor
Ch Bd: John F Edwards Jr
*Pr: Ross R Reiling
*Sr VP: Richard H Moburg
*VP: Kate Davis
*VP: Samir Mehic
VP: Richard Moburg

J F F
See JOBS FOR FUTURE INC

D-U-N-S 79-688-1881
J F JOHNSON LUMBER CO LLC
(Suby of JF JOHNSON HOLDINGS INC) ★
8200 Veterans Hwy, Millersville, MD 21108-1444
Tel (410) 987-5200 Founded/Ownrshp 2005
Sales 24.1MM^E EMP 90^E
SIC 5211 Lumber & other building materials
CFO: Bob Foster
Store Mgr: Steve Drumm
IT Man: Brooke Borman
Sales Asso: Russell Thompson

D-U-N-S 79-241-9889
J F K JOHNSON REHABILITATION INSTITUTE
REHABILITATION MEDICINE
65 James St, Edison, NJ 08820-3947
Tel (732) 321-7070 Founded/Ownrshp 1963
Sales 49.8MM^E EMP 5,000
SIC 8093 Rehabilitation center, outpatient treatment; Rehabilitation center, outpatient treatment
Pr: John McGee

D-U-N-S 00-257-0414
J F KIELY CONSTRUCTION CO INC
700 Mcclellan St, Long Branch, NJ 07740-5899
Tel (732) 222-4400 Founded/Ownrshp 1952
Sales 95.0MM^E EMP 225
SIC 1623 7353 Gas main construction; Heavy construction equipment rental; Gas main construction; Heavy construction equipment rental
Pr: John F Kiely Jr
*Pr: John M Kiely
CFO: David Odor
VP: Scott Handel
*VP: Daniel Huber
*VP: Raymond Sexton
VP: Mark Taylor
Dir Risk M: Thomas Beatty
Dir Bus: James Pagano

D-U-N-S 01-601-7183
J F MADDOX FOUNDATION (NM)
220 W Broadway St Ste 200, Hobbs, NM 88240-6038
Tel (575) 393-6338 Founded/Ownrshp 1972
Sales 21.1MM EMP 7
SIC 8322 Individual & family services; Individual & family services
Ex Dir: Robert J Reid
Bd of Dir: Harry Lynch
VP: Kerri Frizzell
VP: Jennifer Grassham
VP: Don Maddox
Ex Dir: Bob Reid

D-U-N-S 07-598-3536
■ **J F MOLLOY & ASSOCIATES INC**
(Suby of PRINCIPAL FINANCIAL GROUP, INC.)
8909 Purdue Rd Ste 100, Indianapolis, IN 46268-3140
Tel (317) 879-4040 Founded/Ownrshp 1966
Sales NA EMP 450
SIC 6411 Insurance information & consulting services; Insurance claim processing, except medical; Insurance information & consulting services; Insurance claim processing, except medical
*CFO: Brian Burkert
*Sec: Monica Earlywine
*Sec: Geraldine Padgett
*Sr VP: Jeff Blake
*Sr VP: Dan Bond
*Sr VP: Paula Chamblin
Sr VP: Aaron Curtis
*Sr VP: Steve Husk
*Sr VP: Ryan Landford
*Sr VP: Chas Lapierre
*VP: L Peter Iverson
*VP: Dwight Klunzinger
VP: Michelle Lucus

D-U-N-S 06-118-5559
J F PALMER AND SONS PRODUCE INC (TX)
900 W Hwy 495, San Juan, TX 78589
Tel (956) 502-5757 Founded/Ownrshp 1973
Sales 15.0MM^E EMP 300
SIC 0161 5148 Onion farm; Vegetables; Onion farm; Vegetables
Pr: Gary Palmer
*Sec: Bennie Palmer
*VP: Mike Palmer

D-U-N-S 00-533-3658 IMP
J F SHEA CO INC (NV)
655 Brea Canyon Rd, Walnut, CA 91789-3078
Tel (909) 594-9500 Founded/Ownrshp 1881, 1981
Sales 1.9MMM^E EMP 2,600
SIC 3273 Ready-mixed concrete; Ready-mixed concrete
CEO: Peter O Shea Jr
*Pr: John Francis Shea
*CFO: James Shontere
*Treas: Robert R O'Dell
Treas: Robert O'Dell
*VP: Andy Roundtree
Dir Risk M: Jackie Huynh
Off Mgr: Lisa Jacobson
CIO: David Miller

Netwrk Eng: Kevin Hayes
Sfty Mgr: Jason Burroughs
Board of Directors: Louise Clark

D-U-N-S 06-345-6370 IMP
J F SHELTON CO
19516 62nd Ave S, Kent, WA 98032-1146
Tel (253) 872-6363 Founded/Ownrshp 1970
Sales 22.4MM^E EMP 25
SIC 5169 5099 Chemicals, industrial & heavy; Containers: glass, metal or plastic
Pr: Daniel Kiefel
*Sec: Rick Strellman
*VP: Bradley Campbell

D-U-N-S 19-861-2210
J F SOBIESKI MECHANICAL CONTRACTORS INC
SOBIESKI J F MECHANICAL CONTRS
14 Hadco Rd, Wilmington, DE 19804-1014
Tel (302) 993-0103 Founded/Ownrshp 1987
Sales 69.8MM^E EMP 300^E
Accts Santora Cpa Group Newark Del
SIC 1711 Mechanical contractor; Fire sprinkler system installation; Mechanical contractor; Fire sprinkler system installation
CEO: John F Sobieski III
*Pr: Richard H Steele
VP: Reggie Braud
*VP: Robert Sobieski
VP: Walter Telford
Div Mgr: Bob Szczepanski
IT Man: Kim Sobieski
VP Opers: Tim Smith

D-U-N-S 11-435-8625
J F TAYLOR INC
21610 S Essex Dr, Lexington Park, MD 20653-4239
Tel (301) 862-4744 Founded/Ownrshp 1983
Sales 100.9MM^E EMP 250
SIC 8711 Consulting engineer; Electrical or electronic engineering; Consulting engineer; Electrical or electronic engineering
Pr: John F Taylor Sr
*Sec: Helen M Taylor
*VP: David M Lowe
*VP: David W Sydnor
*VP: Jeffrey J Taylor
*VP: John F Taylor Jr
*VP: Mark J Taylor
Prgrm Mgr: David Hesse
Prgrm Mgr: Chris Tilghman
Snr Sftwr: Mark Webb
Dir IT: Bill Wahler

D-U-N-S 01-950-5429
J F WHITE CONTRACTING CO (MA)
(Suby of DRAGADOS USA INC) ★
10 Burr St, Framingham, MA 01701-4692
Tel (508) 879-4700 Founded/Ownrshp 1924, 2014
Sales 223.8MM^E EMP 400
SIC 1622 Bridge, tunnel & elevated highway; Bridge construction; Highway construction, elevated; Tunnel construction; Bridge, tunnel & elevated highway; Bridge construction; Highway construction, elevated; Tunnel construction
Pr: Peter T White
COO: Stephen Barlow
CFO: Bob Hoffman
*Ex VP: Kevin Egan
Ex VP: Kevin Pe
*VP: Stephen Cobb
*VP: Michael Delaney
*VP: Robert Hoffman
VP: Bob Murphy
Off Mgr: Julie Perry
CIO: Karen Wuerfl

D-U-N-S 01-126-8927 IMP
J FLETCHER CREAMER & SON INC
101 E Broadway, Hackensack, NJ 07601-6846
Tel (201) 488-9800 Founded/Ownrshp 1923
Sales 428.3MM^E EMP 1,350
SIC 1623 1611 1771 1622 1629

D-U-N-S 02-780-2297
J FRANK SCHMIDT & SON CO
9500 Se 327th Ave, Boring, OR 97009-9710
Tel (503) 663-4128 Founded/Ownrshp 1946
Sales 77.0MM^E EMP 350
SIC 0783 2875 Planting services, ornamental tree; Fertilizers, mixing only; Planting services, ornamental tree; Fertilizers, mixing only
Pr: J Frank Schmidt I
*Ex VP: Jan Schmidt-Barkley

D-U-N-S 00-823-7505 EXP
J G BOSWELL CO (CA)
101 W Walnut St, Pasadena, CA 91103-3836
Tel (626) 356-7492 Founded/Ownrshp 1921
Sales 519.1MM^E EMP 2,000
SIC 0131 6552 Cotton; Subdividers & developers; Cotton; Subdividers & developers
CEO: James W Boswell
*COO: Sherm Railsback
*CFO: Steve Burish
Treas: Cedric Yoshimoto
*Treas: Cedrick Yoshomato
Board of Directors: James Maddox, Blake Quinn

J G C U S A
See JGC AMERICA INC

J G CONSTRUCTION
See JUNE A GROTHE CONSTRUCTION INC

D-U-N-S 87-432-7547
J G ONEIL INC
DELRAY ACCURA
655 Ne 6th Ave, Delray Beach, FL 33483-5611
Tel (561) 265-0000 Founded/Ownrshp 1994
Sales 31.6MM EMP 42
SIC 5511 Automobiles, new & used; Automobiles, new & used
Pr: James G Oneil

D-U-N-S 07-921-9206
▲ **J G WENTWORTH CO**
201 King Of Prussia Rd # 501, Radnor, PA 19087-5148
Tel (484) 434-2300 Founded/Ownrshp 2013
Sales 494.3MM EMP 410^E
Tkr Sym JGW Exch NYS
SIC 7389 6798 Financial services; Mortgage investment trusts; Financial services; Mortgage investment trusts
CEO: Stewart A Stockdale
*Ch Bd: Alexander R Castaldi
Pr: Randy Parker
CFO: Scott Stevens
Ex VP: Stephen Kirkwood
Ex VP: Gregory A Schneider
VP: Lori Borowski
VP: Stephen Butler
Board of Directors: Robert C Griffin, Kevin Hammond, Paul S Levy, William J Morgan, Robert N Pomroy, Francisco J Rodriguez

D-U-N-S 79-805-5620
J G WENTWORTH CO
201 King Of Prussia Rd # 501, Radnor, PA 19087-5148
Tel (215) 567-7660 Founded/Ownrshp 1991
Sales NA EMP 60
SIC 6153 Mercantile financing
Ch Bd: Gary Veloric
*Pr: James D Delaney
*Ex VP: Michael B Goodman
*VP: James J O'Malley
Sls Mgr: John Dougherty
Board of Directors: Gerald E Bisbee Jr, Philip J Kendall, Anthony C Salvo

D-U-N-S 04-856-6947 IMP/EXP
J GIBSON MCILVAIN CO
10701 Philadelphia Rd, White Marsh, MD 21162
Tel (410) 335-9600 Founded/Ownrshp 1798
Sales 38.4MM EMP 73
SIC 5031 Lumber: rough, dressed & finished; Millwork; Lumber: rough, dressed & finished; Millwork
Pr: J Gibson Mc Ilvain III
COO: James Burley
*VP: Scot McAllister
*VP Sls: Larry Cross
Sls Mgr: Norm Moton

D-U-N-S 83-298-9391
J GINGER MASONRY LP
8188 Lincoln Ave Ste 100, Riverside, CA 92504-4329
Tel (951) 688-5050 Founded/Ownrshp 1978
Sales 62.5MM^E EMP 300
SIC 1741 Masonry & other stonework; Masonry & other stonework
Pt: John L Ginger
Pr: Brad Fogg
Opers Mgr: Josh Waite

D-U-N-S 03-895-6306
J GORDON GAINES INC
SHELBY INSURANCE COMPANY
(Suby of VESTA INSURANCE GROUP, INC.)
2 Perimeter Park S 423e, Birmingham, AL 35243-3282
Tel (205) 298-8701 Founded/Ownrshp 1998
Sales NA EMP 400
SIC 6411 Insurance brokers; Insurance agents; Insurance brokers; Insurance agents
CEO: Norman W Gayle
*VP: Hopson Nance

D-U-N-S 00-379-2603
J GRADY RANDOLPH INC
JGR
541 Concord Rd, Gaffney, SC 29341-2905
Tel (864) 488-9030 Founded/Ownrshp 1943, 1988
Sales 34.1MM^E EMP 140
SIC 4213 Heavy hauling; Refrigerated products transport; Heavy hauling; Refrigerated products transport
CEO: Mark S Randolph
*Sec: James J Randolph

D-U-N-S 00-653-0562 IMP
J H BENNETT AND CO INC (MI)
22975 Venture Dr, Novi, MI 48375-4181
Tel (248) 596-5100 Founded/Ownrshp 1958
Sales 36.5MM EMP 65
SIC 3594 5084 Fluid power pumps & motors; Hydraulic systems equipment & supplies; Fluid power pumps & motors; Hydraulic systems equipment & supplies
Pr: Bill Vincent
*Ex VP: David Cassel
Exec: Lisa Albaugh

D-U-N-S 84-968-4394
J H BERRA HOLDING CO INC
BERRA CONSTRUCTION
5091 Baumgartner Rd, Saint Louis, MO 63129-2821
Tel (314) 487-5617 Founded/Ownrshp 1994
Sales 88.3MM^E EMP 800^E
SIC 6552 Subdividers & developers; Subdividers & developers
Pr: John Berra Jr
*Treas: Robert Berra
VP: Joe Nicpon

D-U-N-S 02-338-3656
J H FAGAN CO
1711 Paramount Ct, Waukesha, WI 53186-3967
Tel (262) 409-2150 Founded/Ownrshp 2012
Sales 21.9MM^E EMP 26
SIC 5064 Television sets; High fidelity equipment; Electric household appliances
CEO: Lamon Elrod
*Pr: Judson Just

D-U-N-S 00-610-6520
J H FINDORFF & SON INC
300 S Bedford St, Madison, WI 53703-3622
Tel (608) 257-5321 Founded/Ownrshp 1998
Sales 338.2MM^E EMP 500

SIC 1542 1541 8741 1522 Commercial & office building, new construction; Industrial buildings, new construction; Construction management; Nonresidential construction; Commercial & office building, new construction; Industrial buildings, new construction; Construction management; Residential construction
Ch: Rich Lynch
**Pr:* Richard M Lynch
Pr: Jeff Tubbs
**CFO:* Daniel L Petersen
CFO: Dan Peterson
**Ch:* F Curtis Hastings
VP: Mike Dillis
**VP:* Tim J Stadelman
IT Man: Scott Noles
IT Man: Chuck Wood
Sfty Dirs: Sonny Femal

D-U-N-S 00-578-8740
J H FITZMAURICE INC
2857 Hannah St, Emeryville, CA 94608-4096
Tel (510) 444-7561 *Founded/Ownrshp* 1947
Sales 25.0MM *EMP* 17
SIC 1522 1542 1541 1794 1611 Multi-family dwellings, new construction; Commercial & office building, new construction; Industrial buildings, new construction; Excavation & grading, building construction; Highway & street construction
Pr: Mohammad Hakimi

D-U-N-S 96-867-8128
J H KELLY INVESTMENTS INC
821 3rd Ave, Longview, WA 98632-2105
Tel (360) 423-5510 *Founded/Ownrshp* 1923
Sales 190.0MM *EMP* 5
SIC 1711 Plumbing, heating, air-conditioning contractors; Plumbing, heating, air-conditioning contractors
Pr: Dan Evans

D-U-N-S 00-890-4328
J H LARSON ELECTRICAL CO
10200 51st Ave N Ste B, Plymouth, MN 55442-4506
Tel (763) 545-1717 *Founded/Ownrshp* 1931
Sales 146.5MME *EMP* 186
SIC 5063 5074 5075 Electrical apparatus & equipment; Plumbing & hydronic heating supplies; Warm air heating equipment & supplies; Electrical apparatus & equipment; Plumbing & hydronic heating supplies; Warm air heating equipment & supplies
Pr: Greg Pahl
**Ch Bd:* C E Pahl
**Ch Bd:* Charles E Pahl
**Treas:* Lucas Pahl
VP: Ed Shesen
Brnch Mgr: Charlie Hendrickson
Brnch Mgr: Gregg Miller
IT Man: Margie Westphal
Opers Mgr: Lynda Piel
Sales Exec: Lisa Fox
Sls Mgr: Jane Moelter

D-U-N-S 60-284-6230
J H PROPERTIES INC
(*Suby of* JEWISH HOSPITAL & ST MARYS HEALTHCARE INC) ★
250 E Liberty St Ste 103, Louisville, KY 40202-1534
Tel (502) 568-6655 *Founded/Ownrshp* 1983
Sales 25.8MM *EMP* 2
Accts Ernst & Young Us Llp Chicago
SIC 6512 Nonresidential building operators; Nonresidential building operators
VP: David Laird

D-U-N-S 10-217-2129 IMP/EXP
J H ROBERTS INDUSTRIES INC
6051 Wallace Road Ext, Wexford, PA 15090-7386
Tel (412) 299-7900 *Founded/Ownrshp* 1982
Sales NA *EMP* 800
SIC 3317 3316

D-U-N-S 00-446-1323
J H ROUTH PACKING CO (OH)
4413 W Bogart Rd, Sandusky, OH 44870-9648
Tel (419) 626-2251 *Founded/Ownrshp* 1947, 1942
Sales 160.0MM *EMP* 300
SIC 2011

J H T
See JARDON & HOWARD TECHNOLOGIES INC

J H T
See JOHNSON HEALTH TECH NORTH AMERICA INC

D-U-N-S 85-850-8195
J H TRANSPORTATION INC
1808 Hancock Dr, Bismarck, ND 58501-7903
Tel (701) 222-4518 *Founded/Ownrshp* 1989
Sales 28.2MME *EMP* 81E
SIC 4213 Trucking, except local
Pr: Janel K Helfrich
**VP:* John Helfrich

D-U-N-S 08-496-1754
J H WALKER INC
SUPERIOR DELIVERY SERVICE
11404 Hempstead Rd, Houston, TX 77092-7104
Tel (713) 688-8400 *Founded/Ownrshp* 1978
Sales 36.2MME *EMP* 130
SIC 4213 4214

J H WHITNEY & CO
See WHITNEY & CO LLC

D-U-N-S 07-934-5726
J H WHITNEY CAPITAL PARTNERS LLC
130 Main St, New Canaan, CT 06840-5509
Tel (203) 716-6100 *Founded/Ownrshp* 2004
Sales 629.6MME *EMP* 4,505E
SIC 6799 Investors

J H WILLIAMS OIL CO
See JH WILLIAMS OIL CO INC

D-U-N-S 01-038-7082
J H WRIGHT & ASSOCIATES INC (AL)
27395 Pollard Rd, Daphne, AL 36526-5305
Tel (251) 621-1491 *Founded/Ownrshp* 1962
Sales 22.7MME *EMP* 48
SIC 5084

D-U-N-S 36-227-1686 IMP
J HARRIS INDUSTRIAL WATER TREATMENT INC
PURETEC INDUSTRIAL WATER
3151 Sturgis Rd, Oxnard, CA 93030-8931
Tel (805) 656-4411 *Founded/Ownrshp* 1986
Sales 26.2MME *EMP* 85E
SIC 5999 5074 Water purification equipment; Water purification equipment
CEO: James A Harris
**CFO:* Ben Desantis
Sales Exec: Rachel Eppenger
Sls Mgr: Mike Coniglio

D-U-N-S 00-298-0746
J HENDERSON JOSEPH & SON INC (IL)
J J H
4288 Old Grand Ave, Gurnee, IL 60031-2734
Tel (847) 244-3222 *Founded/Ownrshp* 1928
Sales 27.2MME *EMP* 50E
SIC 1541 1629 1542 Industrial buildings, new construction; Renovation, remodeling & repairs: industrial buildings; Waste water & sewage treatment plant construction; Commercial & office building, new construction; Commercial & office buildings, renovation & repair; Institutional building construction
Pr: David A Henderson
Treas: Robert Bernhardt
Exec: Brenda Sparks

J HENRY HOLLAND
See MAZZELLA JHH CO INC

D-U-N-S 02-725-8865 IMP
J HILBURN INC
12700 Park Central Dr # 106, Dallas, TX 75251-1500
Tel (866) 789-5381 *Founded/Ownrshp* 2008
Sales 23.1MME *EMP* 65
SIC 5651 Family clothing stores
CEO: Veeral Rathod
Mng Pt: Marie Cloutier
Mng Pt: Annette Dresser
Mng Pt: Jennifer Hardock
Mng Pt: Cynthia Johnson
Mng Pt: Kyle Kurtz
Mng Pt: Kay Look
Mng Pt: Cathy Manning
Mng Pt: Carol Massey
Mng Pt: Mary Murphy
Mng Pt: Monica Pappas
Mng Pt: Kim Selby
Mng Pt: Elizabeth Stidham
Mng Pt: Joyce Strimple
Mng Pt: Ginger Williams
**CEO:* Hil Davis
**COO:* Larry Hagenbuch
Chf Mktg O: Kristen Celko

J HILL OIL
See JAMIESON-HILL A GENERAL PARTNERSHIP

J HUNT & CO
See JIMCO LAMP & MANUFACTURING CO

J I S
See JOB INDUSTRIAL SERVICES INC

J IT SUPPLY
See JIT CORP

D-U-N-S 17-765-6464
J IRWIN CO LTD
111 N Hasler Blvd Ste 200, Bastrop, TX 78602-3984
Tel (512) 253-0020 *Founded/Ownrshp* 1999
Sales 49.3MM *EMP* 166
SIC 1623 Natural gas compressor station construction; Natural gas compressor station construction
CEO: Angela Schultz
Pr: Newton Garland Cotton
CFO: Josh Augustine

D-U-N-S 78-958-3700
J IVERSON RIDDLE DEVELOPMENT CENTER
300 Enola Rd, Morganton, NC 28655-4625
Tel (828) 433-2800 *Founded/Ownrshp* 2006
Sales 47.4MME *EMP* 1,000
SIC 8361 Home for the mentally handicapped; Home for the mentally handicapped

D-U-N-S 06-948-7833
J J & H LTD
30 W Monroe St Fl 15, Chicago, IL 60603-2495
Tel (312) 884-0400 *Founded/Ownrshp* 1971
Sales 36.0MME *EMP* 750
SIC 7361 Placement agencies; Placement agencies
Pr: Richard Jacobson
COO: Stephen Siemer
Sr VP: Barbara Schonhofer
**VP:* David N Jacobson
**VP:* Jack J Johnsey
VP: Daron Robertson
VP: Devie Smith
VP: Nicole Stmartin
Genl Mgr: Rosemary Young

D-U-N-S 00-700-8113
J J B HILLIARD W L LYONS LLC
HILLIARD LYONS
(*Suby of* HL FINANCIAL SERVICES LLC) ★
500 W Jefferson St # 700, Louisville, KY 40202-2815
Tel (502) 588-8400 *Founded/Ownrshp* 2008
Sales 258.9MME *EMP* 1,150E
SIC 6211 Dealers, security; Brokers, security; Stock brokers & dealers; Bond dealers & brokers; Dealers, security; Brokers, security; Stock brokers & dealers; Bond dealers & brokers
CEO: James Allen
**COO:* James Rogers
**CFO:* Charles Grimley
Bd of Dir: Lora Norris
Ex VP: James Walters
**Sr VP:* Donald Merrifield
**Sr VP:* George Moorin
Sr VP: Jeannie Oster
**Sr VP:* Kenneth Wagner
VP: John R Bugh
VP: Betsy Bulleit
VP: Joe Cutsinger
VP: Lee Dentinger
VP: Carroll Goslee
VP: David Havens
VP: Lee Leroy
VP: Scott Lobel
VP: John Mascarich
VP: Andy McKay
**VP:* Darryl Metzger
VP: Gary Peters

J. J. COLLINS PRINTERS
See J J COLLINS SONS INC

D-U-N-S 00-524-5865
J J COLLINS SONS INC
J. J. COLLINS PRINTERS
7125 Janes Ave Ste 200, Woodridge, IL 60517-2347
Tel (630) 960-2525 *Founded/Ownrshp* 1991
Sales 30.0MME *EMP* 150
SIC 2752 Business forms, lithographed; Business forms, lithographed
Ch Bd: James F Collins Sr
Pr: James F Collins Jr
Pr: Kevin Rankin
Treas: Robert E Collins
Ex VP: Thomas M Collins
VP: Bob Collins
IT Man: Adam Wisniewski
Snr Mgr: Scott Ellis

D-U-N-S 07-521-8305
J J CREATIONS INC
4742 37th St, Long Island City, NY 11101-1804
Tel (718) 392-2828 *Founded/Ownrshp* 1976
Sales 22.0MM *EMP* 50
SIC 3911 3961 Jewelry, precious metal; Earrings, precious metal; Costume jewelry; Jewelry, precious metal; Earrings, precious metal; Costume jewelry
Pr: John Thor

D-U-N-S 00-380-2501
J J FERGUSON SAND & GRAVEL INC
HOT MIX ASPHALT
4510 Highway 82 E, Greenwood, MS 38930-9404
Tel (662) 453-5451 *Founded/Ownrshp* 1941
Sales 46.2MME *EMP* 160
SIC 1622 1611 1442 3273 2951 Bridge construction; General contractor, highway & street construction; Concrete construction: roads, highways, sidewalks, etc.; Common sand mining; Gravel mining; Ready-mixed concrete; Asphalt & asphaltic paving mixtures (not from refineries); Bridge construction; General contractor, highway & street construction; Concrete construction: roads, highways, sidewalks, etc.; Common sand mining; Gravel mining; Ready-mixed concrete; Asphalt & asphaltic paving mixtures (not from refineries)
Pr: Jerry Steen Jr
Off Mgr: Christy Powell

D-U-N-S 06-633-0309
J J GOUGE & SON OIL CO INC
112 Greenwood Rd, Spruce Pine, NC 28777-2939
Tel (828) 765-4040 *Founded/Ownrshp* 1963
Sales 29.3MME *EMP* 44
SIC 5172 5983 Gasoline; Fuel oil dealers
Pr: J J Gouge Jr
**Sec:* Margaret Gouge
**VP:* Jeffrey S Gouge

J J H
See J HENDERSON JOSEPH & SON INC

D-U-N-S 00-695-0042 IMP
J J HAINES & CO INC (MD)
6950 Aviation Blvd, Glen Burnie, MD 21061-2531
Tel (410) 760-4040 *Founded/Ownrshp* 1874
Sales 229.7MME *EMP* 400
SIC 5023 Floor coverings; Carpets; Resilient floor coverings: tile or sheet; Wood flooring; Floor coverings; Carpets; Resilient floor coverings: tile or sheet; Wood flooring
Pr: Bruce Zwicker
**CFO:* John Coakley
VP: Terry Russell
Rgnl Mgr: Michael McElwaine
Brnch Mgr: Steve Scott
Genl Mgr: Jim Claypool
Snr Ntwrk: Shawn Cannon
Opers Mgr: Tom Hubbard
Opers Mgr: Dustin Waibl
VP Sls: Scott Roy
Mktg Dir: Ken Wells

D-U-N-S 03-371-5095
J J JARDINA CO INC
16 Forest Pkwy Bldg S, Forest Park, GA 30297-2050
Tel (404) 366-6868 *Founded/Ownrshp* 1932
Sales 35.1MM *EMP* 32
Accts Siegel & Siegel Pc Atlanta
SIC 5148 Fresh fruits & vegetables; Fresh fruits & vegetables
CEO: Mike Jardina
**Pr:* Larry Jardina
**VP:* Mark Jadina

D-U-N-S 05-026-4316
J J KELLER & ASSOCIATES INC
3003 Breezewood Ln, Neenah, WI 54956-9611
Tel (920) 722-2848 *Founded/Ownrshp* 1953
Sales 201.4MM *EMP* 1,300
SIC 2741 8742

D-U-N-S 02-879-2682 EXP
J J MOTORCARS INC
ROAD BEAR RV
(*Suby of* TOURISM HOLDINGS LIMITED)
28404 Roadside Dr, Agoura Hills, CA 91301-2606
Tel (818) 865-2925 *Founded/Ownrshp* 2001
Sales 38.6MM *EMP* 50
SIC 7519 5561 Recreational vehicle rental; Recreational vehicle dealers; Recreational vehicle rental; Recreational vehicle dealers
Pr: Daniel P Schneider
**VP:* Horst E Hagner

D-U-N-S 60-890-0296
J J PETROLEUM DISTRIBUTORS INC
Carr 8860 Km 0 7 Bo Las C St Ca, Trujillo Alto, PR 00976
Tel (787) 755-1620 *Founded/Ownrshp* 1982
Sales 67.6MM *EMP* 16
SIC 5172 Diesel fuel; Diesel fuel
Pr: Jose L De Jesus Hernandez

D-U-N-S 00-613-3656 IMP
J J PLANK CORP
SPENCER JOHNSTON CO
728 Watermark Ct, Neenah, WI 54956-1041
Tel (920) 733-4479 *Founded/Ownrshp* 1969
Sales 23.0MME *EMP* 112
SIC 3554 3444 3312 Pulp mill machinery; Sheet metalwork; Blast furnaces & steel mills; Pulp mill machinery; Sheet metalwork; Blast furnaces & steel mills
Pr: David Plank
Mng Pt: Keith Brandt
**VP Opers:* Mark Guckenberger
**Sls&Mrk Ex:* Guy Martinek

D-U-N-S 00-114-9798
J J RYAN CORP (CT)
REX FORGE DIV
355 Atwater St, Plantsville, CT 06479-1653
Tel (860) 628-0393 *Founded/Ownrshp* 1975
Sales 43.0MME *EMP* 170
SIC 3312 3423 3451 3462 Forgings, iron & steel; Mechanics' hand tools; Screw machine products; Iron & steel forgings; Forgings, iron & steel; Mechanics' hand tools; Screw machine products; Iron & steel forgings
Pr: Ronald Fontanella

D-U-N-S 04-499-6051 IMP
J J TAYLOR DISTRIBUTING TAMPA BAY INC
5102 16th Ave S, Tampa, FL 33619-5336
Tel (813) 247-4000 *Founded/Ownrshp* 1997
Sales 74.7MME *EMP* 300
SIC 5181 Beer & ale; Beer & ale
Pr: Manuel Portundo
**Treas:* Henri J Desplaines
VP Opers: Jay Martin

D-U-N-S 01-485-0390 IMP
J J WHITE INC
5500 Bingham St, Philadelphia, PA 19120-2198
Tel (215) 722-1000 *Founded/Ownrshp* 1920
Sales 253.1MME *EMP* 1,500E
SIC 1711 1542 7699 Mechanical contractor; Commercial & office building contractors; Tank repair; Mechanical contractor; Commercial & office building contractors; Tank repair
Pr: James J White IV
CFO: Ed Purdy
**CFO:* Edward W Purdy III
VP: Steve Cant
VP: Mike Depalma
VP: Chip Logue
VP: Larry Pearson
Dir Risk M: Robert Celestino
Off Admin: Inga Hensley
CIO: Jason Morovich
Sfty Mgr: John Paley

D-U-N-S 17-813-8947 IMP
J JILL GROUP INC
4 Batterymarch Park, Quincy, MA 02169-7468
Tel (617) 376-4300 *Founded/Ownrshp* 2015
Sales 440.7MME *EMP* 3,041
SIC 5961 5621 5661 5632 Catalog sales; Women's apparel, mail order; Ready-to-wear apparel, women's; Women's shoes; Apparel accessories; Catalog sales; Women's apparel, mail order; Ready-to-wear apparel, women's; Women's shoes; Apparel accessories
Pr: Paula Bennett
Sr VP: Elaine Clarke
VP: Keith Abbott
VP: Kelly Cooper
VP: Robert Dakin
VP: Chris Dennis
VP: Peter Prandato
VP: Faythe Shortelle
VP: Charlie White
Ex Dir: Alisha Eddy
Dist Mgr: Claire Anderson

D-U-N-S 07-420-3167
J JOHNSON BOB & ASSOCIATES INC
SCALE FREE COMPANY
16420 W Hardy Rd Ste 100, Houston, TX 77060-6227
Tel (512) 989-6586 *Founded/Ownrshp* 2002
Sales 35.6MME *EMP* 48
SIC 5074 Water heaters & purification equipment; Water heaters, except electric; Water softeners
Ch: Neven Hulsey
**Pr:* Belinda Denman
VP: Alan Mercy
**VP:* Alan Murphy
Brnch Mgr: Beth Thomas
Genl Mgr: Len Olavessen
IT Man: Steven Skeels

D-U-N-S 00-130-5176 IMP
J JOSEPHSON INC
(*Suby of* CORONET WALLPAPERS (ONTARIO) LIMITED)
35 Horizon Blvd, South Hackensack, NJ 07606-1804
Tel (201) 440-7000 *Founded/Ownrshp* 1962, 2003
Sales 60.9MME *EMP* 272
SIC 2679 Wallpaper, embossed plastic: made on textile backing; Wallpaper, embossed plastic: made on textile backing
Pr: Mark Goodman
CFO: Estela Martinez
VP: Mario Hroncich
Prd Mgr: Al Lise

Mktg Dir: Lauren Rosa
Mktg Mgr: Julie Landis

J K CHEVROLET ISUZU
See J-K CHEVROLET INC

D-U-N-S 06-112-5159
J K DISTRIBUTORS INC
J.K. AUTO PARTS STORE
3439 Carlin Springs Rd, Falls Church, VA 22041-2802
Tel (703) 845-7040 *Founded/Ownrshp* 1982
Sales 30.4MM^E *EMP* 145
SIC 5013 Motor vehicle supplies & new parts; Motor vehicle supplies & new parts
Ch: Hubert N Hoffman III
**VP:* George R Henard

J K G PRINTING & GRAPHICS
See JKG GROUP INC

D-U-N-S 10-793-4937
J K MOVING & STORAGE INC
JK MOVING SERVICES LOUDOUN CO
44112 Mercure Cir Ste 1, Sterling, VA 20166-2017
Tel (703) 260-4282 *Founded/Ownrshp* 1982
Sales 81.6MM *EMP* 364
SIC 4226 Special warehousing & storage; Special warehousing & storage
Pr: Charles S Kuhn
Pr: Paul Maginnis
CFO: Dave Harris
VP: Rocco Balsamo
VP: Vincent Burruano
VP: Mike Faber
VP: Ted Isaacson
VP: Dave Kordonowy
VP: Matt Logan
VP: David Macpherson
VP: Brian McGuinness
VP: Michael Petersen

D-U-N-S 17-358-2198
J K SCANLAN CO INC
536 Granite St, Braintree, MA 02184-3952
Tel (508) 540-6226 *Founded/Ownrshp* 1984
Sales 50.0MM *EMP* 58
SIC 1542 1541 1522 Commercial & office building, new construction; Renovation, remodeling & repairs: industrial buildings; Industrial buildings, new construction; Residential construction; Commercial & office building, new construction; Renovation, remodeling & repairs: industrial buildings; Industrial buildings, new construction; Residential construction
Pr: John K Scanlan
CFO: Marie A Walker
**VP:* Richard Scanlan

D-U-N-S 07-884-0494
J K SCANLAN CO LLC (MA)
15 Research Rd, East Falmouth, MA 02536-4440
Tel (508) 540-6226 *Founded/Ownrshp* 2012
Sales 20.4MM^E *EMP* 55
SIC 1542 1541 1522 Commercial & office building, new construction; Renovation, remodeling & repairs: industrial buildings; Residential construction; Commercial & office building, new construction; Renovation, remodeling & repairs: industrial buildings; Residential construction
Exec: Seth Adams
**Prin:* Marie Walker
IT Man: Andrew McDonnell
Mktg Dir: Judy Audette
Snr PM: Mitch Barrett

J K-G M C TRUCK
See JK BUICK GMC INC

D-U-N-S 03-916-2771 IMP
J KINGS FOOD SERVICE PROFESSIONALS INC
700 Furrows Rd, Holtsville, NY 11742-2001
Tel (631) 289-8401 *Founded/Ownrshp* 1974
Sales 343.1MM^E *EMP* 350
Accts Biscotti Toback & Company Cp
SIC 5149 5143 5144 5142 5148 Groceries & related products; Dairy products, except dried or canned; Poultry & poultry products; Packaged frozen goods; Fresh fruits & vegetables; Groceries & related products; Dairy products, except dried or canned; Poultry & poultry products; Packaged frozen goods; Fresh fruits & vegetables
Ch Bd: John King
**Pr:* Greg Ferraro
CFO: Bob De Luca
Ex VP: Joel Panagakos
VP: David Gavigan
Exec: Christopher Neary
Genl Mgr: Brian Elliott
Store Mgr: Maria Calhoun
CTO: Ian Obrien
IT Man: Jay Gavigan
Sls Dir: Steve Kass

J KIRK BAREFOOT & ASSOC DIV
See WINFIELD SECURITY CORP

D-U-N-S 17-783-2698
J KNIPPER AND CO INC
1 Healthcare Way, Lakewood, NJ 08701-5400
Tel (732) 905-7878 *Founded/Ownrshp* 1986
Sales 103.5MM^E *EMP* 430^E
SIC 8742 Marketing consulting services; Marketing consulting services
CEO: Jim Knipper
**Pr:* Michael Laferrera
**CFO:* Frank McNicholas
**Sr VP:* Jack Bryndza
**Sr VP:* Linda Hatt JD
**Sr VP:* Linda E Hatt
**Sr VP:* Daniel Horchler
**Sr VP:* Eric Johnson
Sr VP: Nancy Kohler
**Sr VP:* David M Merkel
**Sr VP:* John D Woods
VP: Brad Clayton
VP: Steve Grandsen
VP: Steven Grasden
VP: Jennifer Robin

D-U-N-S 00-970-4180
J KOKOLAKIS CONTRACTING INC
1500 Ocean Ave Ste A, Bohemia, NY 11716-1924
Tel (631) 589-4983 *Founded/Ownrshp* 1972
Sales 49.8MM^E *EMP* 85
SIC 1542 1522 Institutional building construction; Apartment building construction
Pr: Joseph J Kokolakis
**Ch:* John Kokolakis
**Treas:* Pagona Kokolakis
**Ex VP:* Nick Leo
**VP:* Arthur Gureck
**VP:* Rodrick Viogt
Mng Dir: J Walker

D-U-N-S 07-019-7265
J KOSKI CO
J.KOSKI TRUCKING
(*Suby of* API GROUP INC) ★
1502 London Rd, Duluth, MN 55812-1788
Tel (218) 249-1820 *Founded/Ownrshp* 2011
Sales 40.0MM *EMP* 110^E
SIC 1382 4212 Local trucking, without storage; Drilling & production platforms, floating (oil & gas); Aerial geophysical exploration oil & gas; Local trucking, without storage
CEO: John D Koski

D-U-N-S 02-300-6000
J L C FOOD SYSTEMS INC
PERKIN'S FAMILY RESTAURANT
2480 Superior Dr Nw, Rochester, MN 55901-1799
Tel (507) 282-3090 *Founded/Ownrshp* 1997
Sales 9.0MM^E *EMP* 325
SIC 5812 Restaurant, family: chain; Restaurant, family: chain
Pr: Dave Hanson

D-U-N-S 18-818-8577 IMP
J L CLARK INC
(*Suby of* CC INDUSTRIES INC) ★
923 23rd Ave, Rockford, IL 61104-7173
Tel (815) 961-5636 *Founded/Ownrshp* 2015
Sales 77.0MM *EMP* 344
SIC 3411 3499 2752 3089 Plastic containers, except foam; Metal cans; Magnetic shields, metal; Lithographing on metal; Metal cans; Magnetic shields, metal; Lithographing on metal; Plastic containers, except foam
Pr: Phil Baerenwald
**CFO:* Bill Holliday
Exec: Mary Beaver
Ql Cn Mgr: Dave Swenson
Snr Mgr: Ronn Williams

J L COLEBROOK DIVISION
See G-III LEATHER FASHIONS INC

D-U-N-S 02-389-9719
J L CULPEPPER & CO INC
RICHMOND RESTAURANT SERVICE
201 Haley Rd, Ashland, VA 23005-2451
Tel (804) 752-6576 *Founded/Ownrshp* 1939
Sales 103.1MM^E *EMP* 98
SIC 5141 Groceries, general line; Groceries, general line
Pr: S Lynn Townsend
**Ex VP:* Rhett Townsend
**VP:* Patricia C Gibbs
**VP:* Barbara Townsend
Dir IT: Michel Van Laere
Opers Mgr: Pam Leuske
Mktg Mgr: Eileen Duffy
Sls Mgr: Mike Miller
Sales Asso: Kelai Barrett
Sales Asso: Bryan Curry
Sales Asso: Rudy Karkosak

D-U-N-S 18-055-3984
J L DAVIS CO
211 N Colorado St, Midland, TX 79701-4696
Tel (432) 682-6311 *Founded/Ownrshp* 1987
Sales 350.0MM *EMP* 104
SIC 5172 4923 1311 Petroleum products; Gas transmission & distribution; Crude petroleum production; Natural gas production; Petroleum products; Gas transmission & distribution; Crude petroleum production; Natural gas production
Owner: James Lee Davis
MIS Dir: Shirley Weiler

J L F/LONE MEADOW
See J L FURNISHINGS LLC

D-U-N-S 01-430-4786
J L FREED & SONS INC (PA)
685 Bethlehem Pike, Montgomeryville, PA 18936-9702
Tel (215) 368-1840 *Founded/Ownrshp* 1883, 1985
Sales 49.6MM *EMP* 81
SIC 5511 Automobiles, new & used; Automobiles, new & used
Pr: Donald J Franks
**VP:* Suzanne N Franks
Store Mgr: Pete Langen
Sls Mgr: Pete Cozzi
Sales Asso: Randi Cohen
Sales Asso: Ronald Malone
Sales Asso: Daniel Ryan
Sales Asso: Geoffrey Smith

D-U-N-S 11-121-8996 IMP
J L FURNISHINGS LLC
J L F/LONE MEADOW
19007 S Reyes Ave, Compton, CA 90221-5813
Tel (310) 605-6600 *Founded/Ownrshp* 1997
Sales 81.1MM^E *EMP* 300
SIC 2531 2521 Chairs, table & arm; Wood office chairs, benches & stools; Chairs, office: padded, upholstered or plain: wood; Tables, office: wood; Chairs, table & arm; Wood office chairs, benches & stools; Chairs, office: padded, upholstered or plain: wood; Tables, office: wood
Trfc Mgr: Luis Ruiz

J L G
See JLG INDUSTRIES INC

D-U-N-S 03-618-7854
J L GADDY ENTERPRISES INC
WILKERSON SUPPLY CO
6002 Wylie Ave, Hickory Grove, SC 29717-7759
Tel (800) 849-5680 *Founded/Ownrshp* 1917
Sales 37.4MM^E *EMP* 64
SIC 5194 5145 Tobacco & tobacco products; Confectionery; Tobacco & tobacco products; Confectionery
Pr: William S Wilkerson

D-U-N-S 06-781-0200 IMP
J L HALEY ENTERPRISES
3510 Luyung Dr, Rancho Cordova, CA 95742-6872
Tel (916) 631-6375 *Founded/Ownrshp* 1971
Sales 26.4MM^E *EMP* 140
SIC 3599 3312 7692 Machine shop, jobbing & repair; Blast furnaces & steel mills; Welding repair; Machine shop, jobbing & repair; Blast furnaces & steel mills; Welding repair
CEO: James L Haley
Genl Mgr: Steve Butts

J L INDUSTRIES
See SAMSON PRODUCTS INC

D-U-N-S 55-687-3412
J L INTERNATIONAL INC
PFT INDUSTRIES
34364 Goddard Rd, Romulus, MI 48174-3451
Tel (734) 941-0770 *Founded/Ownrshp* 1991
Sales 24.4MM^E *EMP* 250
SIC 3714 5065 Motor vehicle parts & accessories; Telephone equipment; Motor vehicle parts & accessories; Telephone equipment
Pr: Brenda Lewo

J L PRECISION SHEET METAL
See LAPTALO ENTERPRISES INC

D-U-N-S 62-697-7904
J L WAUFORD INC
PRESTIGE PRINTING
536 Myatt Dr, Madison, TN 37115-2452
Tel (615) 847-7600 *Founded/Ownrshp* 1990
Sales 24.1MM^E *EMP* 310
SIC 8741 Management services; Management services
Pr: Jerry L Wauford
**Sec:* V B Wauford

D-U-N-S 00-738-6733
J LEE MILLIGAN INC
9200 Triangle Dr, Amarillo, TX 79108-7531
Tel (806) 373-5352 *Founded/Ownrshp* 1935
Sales 62.6MM^E *EMP* 240
SIC 1611 Highway & street paving contractor; Highway & street paving contractor
Pr: Douglas Walterscheid
**VP:* Swanson Hagerman

D-U-N-S 83-469-2576
J LEVENS BUILDERS INC
125 Jeff Davis Ave, Long Beach, MS 39560-6134
Tel (228) 863-0303 *Founded/Ownrshp* 1992
Sales 26.2MM^E *EMP* 60
Accts Alexander Van Loon Sloan Le
SIC 1542 1521 1611 1771 Nonresidential construction; Single-family housing construction; Concrete construction: roads, highways, sidewalks, etc.; Concrete work
Pr: James Levens III
**Sec:* Lucy R Levens
Off Mgr: Ali Damiens

J. LEWIS COOPER CO.
See GREAT LAKES WINE & SPIRITS LLC

D-U-N-S 17-777-1664
J LEWIS PARTNERS LP
LEWIS COMPANY
13355 Noel Rd Ste 1750, Dallas, TX 75240-6821
Tel (972) 702-7390 *Founded/Ownrshp* 1987
Sales 60.6MM^E *EMP* 556
SIC 6799 2211 2221 5131 4213 5153 Venture capital companies; Apparel & outerwear fabrics, cotton; Upholstery, tapestry & wall coverings: cotton; Manmade & synthetic broadwoven fabrics; Synthetic fabrics; Trucking, except local; Grain elevators; Venture capital companies; Apparel & outerwear fabrics, cotton; Upholstery, tapestry & wall coverings: cotton; Manmade & synthetic broadwoven fabrics; Synthetic fabrics; Trucking, except local; Grain elevators
Mng Pt: John P Lewis

D-U-N-S 01-907-6057
J LODGE ESERVICES LLC (FL)
12298 Matterhorn Rd, Fort Myers, FL 33913-8505
Tel (239) 244-8619 *Founded/Ownrshp* 2007
Sales 23.4MM^E *EMP* 250
SIC 7389 Telephone services; Telephone services
Ex VP: Andy Schrider
VP: Neal Eggers
VP Admn: Kristan Schrider
Dir IT: Chris Kurlinski
Snr Mgr: Amanda Rhine

J LOHR VINEY
See J LOHR WINERY CORP

D-U-N-S 06-912-4824 IMP
J LOHR WINERY CORP
J LOHR VINEY
1000 Lenzen Ave, San Jose, CA 95126-2739
Tel (408) 288-5057 *Founded/Ownrshp* 1974
Sales 23.5MM^E *EMP* 150
SIC 2084 Wines; Wines
CEO: Steven W Lohr
**Pr:* Jerome J Lohr
**VP:* Bruce Arkley
**VP:* James Schuett
Sfty Mgr: Isidro Salas

J M A
See JOHN MORIARTY & ASSOCIATES INC

J M A
See JUDY MADRIGAL & ASSOCIATES INC

D-U-N-S 06-950-3241
J M B REALTY CORP
900 N Michigan Ave # 1850, Chicago, IL 60611-1542
Tel (312) 915-1934 *Founded/Ownrshp* 1970
Sales 67.1MM^E *EMP* 500
SIC 6799 6531 6552 Investors; Real estate agents & managers; Real estate brokers & agents; Subdividers & developers; Investors; Real estate agents & managers; Real estate brokers & agents; Subdividers & developers
Pr: Neil Bluhm
**Ch Bd:* Judd D Malkin
CFO: Ron Godsey

D-U-N-S 00-654-8853
J M BRENNAN INC (WI)
2101 W Saint Paul Ave, Milwaukee, WI 53233-2560
Tel (414) 342-3829 *Founded/Ownrshp* 1932
Sales 54.1MM^E *EMP* 200
SIC 1711 3444

D-U-N-S 96-066-6170
J M C INTERNATIONAL LLC
1470 W Herndon Ave # 100, Fresno, CA 93711-0552
Tel (559) 256-1300 *Founded/Ownrshp* 1996
Sales 22.0MM *EMP* 50
SIC 1542 1522 Commercial & office building contractors; Residential construction; Commercial & office building contractors; Residential construction

J M D
See J M DAVIDSON INC

D-U-N-S 06-237-1331
J M DAVIDSON INC
J M D
2564 County Road 1960, Aransas Pass, TX 78336-8960
Tel (361) 883-0983 *Founded/Ownrshp* 1982
Sales 96.7MM^E *EMP* 250^E
SIC 1541 1731 3441 Industrial buildings, new construction; General electrical contractor; Fabricated structural metal; Industrial buildings, new construction; General electrical contractor; Fabricated structural metal
Pr: John M Davidson
**VP:* Joe R Wallace
**Genl Mgr:* Justin Davidson

D-U-N-S 04-438-6530
J M DAVIS INDUSTRIES INC
HANDY HOUSE CONVENIENCE STORES
812 Arendell St, Morehead City, NC 28557-4235
Tel (252) 726-0974 *Founded/Ownrshp* 1941
Sales 35.5MM^E *EMP* 110
SIC 5541 5171 5411 5983 Filling stations, gasoline; Petroleum bulk stations; Convenience stores, chain; Fuel oil dealers; Filling stations, gasoline; Petroleum bulk stations; Convenience stores, chain; Fuel oil dealers
Pr: Diane B Davis
Genl Mgr: Glenn Lowe

D-U-N-S 15-164-0471
J M ELECTRICAL CO INC
6 Kimball Ln Ste 210, Lynnfield, MA 01940-2684
Tel (781) 581-3328 *Founded/Ownrshp* 1985
Sales 30.5MM *EMP* 68
SIC 1731 General electrical contractor; General electrical contractor
CFO: Shelly Enes
**Pr:* Paul A Guarracino

D-U-N-S 02-868-5782 IMP
J M EQUIPMENT CO INC
JOHN DEERE
321 Spreckels Ave, Manteca, CA 95336-6007
Tel (209) 522-3271 *Founded/Ownrshp* 1999
Sales 31.7MM^E *EMP* 179
SIC 7359 5084 5999 Equipment rental & leasing; Materials handling machinery; Farm equipment & supplies; Farm machinery; Farm tractors; Equipment rental & leasing; Materials handling machinery; Farm equipment & supplies; Farm machinery; Farm tractors
CEO: Ray Azevedo
**Pr:* Dave Baiocchi
**Pr:* Ed Henriquez
**CFO:* Vincent C Victorine
**VP:* Audie Burgan
**VP:* Brian Wagoner
Mktg Dir: Scott Andersen
Sls Mgr: Jerry McAlister
Sls Mgr: Don Myers
Sales Asso: R Days

J M I
See JAMES MARINE INC

J M L APPRAISEL SERVICE
See TOENSMEIER ADJUSTMENT SERVICE INC

J M OIL COMPANY
See JAY MEHTA INC

J M OILFIELD SERVICE
See JM OILFIELD SERVICES INC

D-U-N-S 06-738-4834
J M OLIVER INC
OLIVER HEATING & COOLING
101 Waverly Ave, Morton, PA 19070-1936
Tel (610) 544-4884 *Founded/Ownrshp* 1971
Sales 37.6MM^E *EMP* 153
SIC 1711 Heating & air conditioning contractors; Refrigeration contractor; Heating & air conditioning contractors; Refrigeration contractor
Pr: Rocco Pace
**Treas:* Bernard Sweeney
**VP:* Antoinette Coupe

D-U-N-S 00-586-8245 IMP
J M SMITH CORP
INTEGRAL SOLUTIONS GROUP
101 W Saint John St # 305, Spartanburg, SC 29306-5150
Tel (864) 542-9419 *Founded/Ownrshp* 1944
Sales 2.5MMM *EMP* 1,050

SIC 5122 7374 Drugs, proprietaries & sundries; Data processing service; Drugs, proprietaries & sundries; Data processing service
Ch Bd: William R Cobb
**Pr:* Ken Couch
**CFO:* James C Wilson Jr
Sr VP: Brian Purscell
VP: Linda Campbell
VP: Philip Ryan
VP: Rick Simerly Sr
Dir Risk M: Roy Meidinger
Mktg Dir: Christa Hampton
Mktg Dir: Heidi Jameson
Mktg Mgr: Eddie Huff

D-U-N-S 78-561-8435 EXP
J M SMITH CORP
SMITH DRUG CO
(*Suby of* INTEGRAL SOLUTIONS GROUP) ★
9098 Fairforest Rd, Spartanburg, SC 29301-1134
Tel (864) 582-1216 *Founded/Ownrshp* 1944
Sales 71.8MM^E *EMP* 399^E
SIC 5912 Drug stores
Pr: Jeff Foreman
Treas: Jimmy Wilson
Ofcr: Tracey Burke
**VP:* Jim Benton
**VP:* Isaac Rogers
**VP:* Rick Simerly
Exec: Roger Pritcher
Brnch Mgr: Russ Weber
Genl Mgr: Dave Brown
Dir IT: Charles Bennett
IT Man: Randy McConnell

J M SMUCKER
See INTERNATIONAL MULTIFOODS CORP

D-U-N-S 00-446-1406 IMP/EXP
▲ J M SMUCKER CO (OH)
1 Strawberry Ln, Orrville, OH 44667-1298
Tel (330) 682-3000 *Founded/Ownrshp* 1897
Sales 5.6MMM *EMP* 14,775
Tkr Sym SJM *Exch* NYS
SIC 2099 2033 2023 2087 2035 Syrups; Frosting, ready-to-use; Sandwiches, assembled & packaged: for wholesale market; Peanut butter; Jams, jellies & preserves: packaged in cans, jars, etc.; Jellies, edible, including imitation: in cans, jars, etc.; Vegetable juices: packaged in cans, jars, etc.; Fruit juices: packaged in cans, jars, etc.; Canned milk, whole; Beverage bases, concentrates, syrups, powders & mixes; Pickles, sauces & salad dressings; Syrups; Frosting, ready-to-use; Sandwiches, assembled & packaged: for wholesale market; Peanut butter; Jams, jellies & preserves: packaged in cans, jars, etc.; Jellies, edible, including imitation: in cans, jars, etc.; Vegetable juices: packaged in cans, jars, etc.; Fruit juices: packaged in cans, jars, etc.; Canned milk, whole; Beverage bases, concentrates, syrups, powders & mixes; Pickles, sauces & salad dressings
CEO: Richard K Smucker
**Ch Bd:* Timothy P Smucker
**V Ch:* Vincent C Byrd
CFO: Mark R Belgya
Ofcr: Barry C Dunaway
Sr VP: Barry Dunaway
VP: Jim Brown
VP: John W Denman
VP: Jeannette L Knudsen
VP: Julia Sabin
Dir: Brad Daugherty
Board of Directors: Kathryn W Dindo, Paul J Dolan, Robert B Heisler Jr, Nancy Lopez Knight, Elizabeth Valk Long, Gary A Oatey, Sandra Pianalto, Alex Shumate, Mark T Smucker

D-U-N-S 05-874-1851 IMP
■ J M SMUCKER LLC
CROSS & BLACKWELL
(*Suby of* J M SMUCKER CO) ★
1050 Stanton St, Ripon, WI 54971-1279
Tel (920) 745-6100 *Founded/Ownrshp* 1989
Sales 26.4MM^E *EMP* 160
SIC 2033 2035 Jellies, edible, including imitation: in cans, jars, etc.; Preserves, including imitation: in cans, jars, etc.; Catsup: packaged in cans, jars, etc.; Mustard, prepared (wet); Mayonnaise; Jellies, edible, including imitation: in cans, jars, etc.; Preserves, including imitation: in cans, jars, etc.; Catsup: packaged in cans, jars, etc.; Mustard, prepared (wet); Mayonnaise
Mktg Mgr: Carrie Hogan
Manager: Joel Dominguez
Manager: Gary Hartigan
Snr Mgr: Thomas Strode
Snr Mgr: Ed Sutphin

D-U-N-S 02-220-4598
■ J M SWANK CO INC
(*Suby of* CONAGRA FOODS FOOD INGREDIENTS CO INC) ★
395 Herky St, North Liberty, IA 52317-8523
Tel (319) 626-3683 *Founded/Ownrshp* 1992
Sales 273.8MM^E *EMP* 175
SIC 5149 Groceries & related products; Groceries & related products
Genl Mgr: Taylor Strubell
**VP Sls:* Ron Pardekooper
Mktg Mgr: Millie Feldman

J M T
See JOHNSON MIRMIRAN & THOMPSON INC

D-U-N-S 10-242-7069
J M TEST SYSTEMS INC
7323 Tom Dr, Baton Rouge, LA 70806-2313
Tel (225) 925-2029 *Founded/Ownrshp* 1983
Sales 24.4MM^E *EMP* 199
SIC 7699 3825

D-U-N-S 62-700-9152
■ J M WALLER ASSOCIATES INC
(*Suby of* VERSAR INC) ★
6850 Versar Ctr Ste 201, Springfield, VA 22151-4176
Tel (703) 750-3000 *Founded/Ownrshp* 2014
Sales 23.7MM^E *EMP* 370
SIC 8744 8742 7379 8748

D-U-N-S 05-622-8513
J M WILKERSON CONSTRUCTION CO INC
1734 Sands Pl Se, Marietta, GA 30067-9214
Tel (770) 953-2659 *Founded/Ownrshp* 1982
Sales 69.5MM *EMP* 70^E
Accts Carr Riggs & Ingram Llc Atl
SIC 1542 1541 1522 1622 1629 Commercial & office building, new construction; Industrial buildings & warehouses; Residential construction; Hotel/motel & multi-family home construction; Bridge, tunnel & elevated highway; Dams, waterways, docks & other marine construction; Commercial & office building, new construction; Industrial buildings & warehouses; Residential construction; Hotel/motel & multi-family home construction; Bridge, tunnel & elevated highway; Dams, waterways, docks & other marine construction
Ch Bd: James M Wilkerson
**CFO:* Jason Cureton
**Treas:* Patricia Wilkerson
Sr VP: Matt Bunch
**VP:* Brett K Hawley
**VP:* Darren Sayer
Site Mgr: Ronnie Bixler
Mktg Mgr: Ashlie Prior
Snr PM: Kevin Smith

D-U-N-S 60-659-6013 IMP
J MARCHINI & SON INC
J MARCHINI FARM
8736 Minturn Rd, Le Grand, CA 95333-9711
Tel (559) 665-2944 *Founded/Ownrshp* 1989
Sales 23.2MM^E *EMP* 200
SIC 0161 Rooted vegetable farms; Rooted vegetable farms
Pr: Joe Marchini
**CEO:* Jeff Marchini
**Sec:* Julie Marchini
**VP:* Jenny McAfee
**Prin:* Joseph C Marchini
CIO: Marc Marchini
Opers Mgr: Ector Moreno
Prd Mgr: Nic Marchini
S&M/VP: Jenny Nelson

J MARCHINI FARM
See J MARCHINI & SON INC

J MART
See J&J OIL CO INC

D-U-N-S 09-702-4301
J MCCULLOUGH CORP
1377 Kettering Dr, Ontario, CA 91761-2217
Tel (909) 390-8484 *Founded/Ownrshp* 1973
Sales 61.4MM^E *EMP* 300
SIC 5511 6512 Automobiles, new & used; Commercial & industrial building operation; Automobiles, new & used; Commercial & industrial building operation
Ch Bd: Richard D Romero
**Pr:* Valerie C Romero
**COO:* R J Romero

D-U-N-S 01-931-4483 IMP
J N PHILLIPS CO INC
JN PHILLIPS AUTO GLASS
11 Wheeling Ave, Woburn, MA 01801-2008
Tel (781) 939-3400 *Founded/Ownrshp* 1951
Sales 23.6MM^E *EMP* 300
SIC 7536

D-U-N-S 78-702-7663
J O INC
EXECUTIVE AUTO GROUP
1180 N Colony Rd, Wallingford, CT 06492-1730
Tel (203) 949-7440 *Founded/Ownrshp* 1988
Sales 71.8MM^E *EMP* 400
SIC 5511 Automobiles, new & used; Automobiles, new & used
Pr: John Orsini

D-U-N-S 13-709-8633
J P & D DIGITAL SATELLITE SYSTEMS INC
10916 Spencer Hwy Ste A, La Porte, TX 77571-4537
Tel (281) 471-4400 *Founded/Ownrshp* 2002
Sales 26.0MM^E *EMP* 600
SIC 3663 Satellites, communications; Satellites, communications
Pr: Jerry W Wise
**VP:* Paul Snyder

D-U-N-S 05-889-5442
J P A I MANAGEMENT CO INC
RADISSON HOTEL BOSTON
45 Braintree Hill Park # 402, Braintree, MA 02184-8723
Tel (617) 482-1800 *Founded/Ownrshp* 1969
Sales 6.7MM^E *EMP* 300
SIC 7011 Hotels & motels; Hotels & motels
Pr: Louis N Vinios
**Treas:* Billy Dadasis
Sls Mgr: Thomas Caulfield

D-U-N-S 61-297-0921
J P AUTOMOBILES INC
PFLUEGER HONDA
(*Suby of* PFLUEGER, INC.)
777 Ala Moana Blvd, Honolulu, HI 96813-5503
Tel (808) 528-7200 *Founded/Ownrshp* 1988
Sales 58.2MM^E *EMP* 176
SIC 5511 Automobiles, new & used; Automobiles, new & used
Pr: James Pflueger
**Treas:* Randall Kurata
VP: Kenny Ching
VP: Nolan Hee
**VP:* Allan Pflueger
IT Man: Dan Ke
Sales Exec: Don Brower
Sales Asso: Wes Katekaru
Sales Asso: Sherman Leung
Sales Asso: Hai Nguyen
Sales Asso: Bill Tang

J P CARLTON
See D A F INC

D-U-N-S 07-831-4062
J P CULLEN & SONS INC
(*Suby of* J P CULLEN & SONS INC) ★
J P Cullen & Sons Inc Ns I, Brookfield, WI 53005
Tel (262) 781-4100 *Founded/Ownrshp* 2011
Sales 8.0MM^E *EMP* 468^E
SIC 7389 Telephone services
Pr: David Cullen

D-U-N-S 11-752-4629
J P CULLEN & SONS INC
330 E Delavan Dr, Janesville, WI 53546-2711
Tel (608) 754-6601 *Founded/Ownrshp* 1981
Sales 407.2MM *EMP* 600
Accts Baker Tilly Virchow Krause Ll
SIC 1541 1542 Industrial buildings, new construction; Commercial & office building, new construction; Industrial buildings, new construction; Commercial & office building, new construction
Ch Bd: Mark A Cullen
**Pr:* David J Cullen
**CFO:* Stephen P Wisnefsky
**VP:* Larry D Rocole
**VP:* Daniel A Swanson
Sfty Dirs: Brian Oberle
Sfty Mgr: Tom Gruman
Opers Mgr: Joe Martino

J P DON MOYER
See ONO TRANSPORT SERVICES INC

D-U-N-S 10-785-9134
J P FARLEY CORP
29055 Clemens Rd, Westlake, OH 44145-1135
Tel (440) 250-4300 *Founded/Ownrshp* 1979
Sales NA *EMP* 70
SIC 6311 6321 6324 Life insurance; Accident & health insurance; Hospital & medical service plans
Pr: James P Farley
**VP:* Patricia Hannigan

D-U-N-S 05-814-0877
J P H CONSULTING INC
1101 Crenshaw Blvd, Los Angeles, CA 90019-3112
Tel (323) 934-5660 *Founded/Ownrshp* 1998
Sales 24.8MM^E *EMP* 712
SIC 8051 Skilled nursing care facilities; Skilled nursing care facilities
Pr: Jeoung H Lee
**CFO:* Greda Bernabe

D-U-N-S 02-703-1749
J P HART LUMBER CO
9810 Ball St, San Antonio, TX 78217-3707
Tel (210) 559-7679 *Founded/Ownrshp* 1939
Sales 77.8MM^E *EMP* 105
SIC 5031 Lumber: rough, dressed & finished; Building materials, exterior; Building materials, interior; Lumber: rough, dressed & finished; Building materials, exterior; Building materials, interior
Pr: J P Hart
**VP:* Warren B Hart
VP: Stephanie Szobloski

J P I LEASING
See JPI INVESTMENT CO LP

D-U-N-S 79-363-0849
J P I NATIONAL CONSTRUCTION INC
JPI CONSTRUCTION
600 Las Colinas Blvd E # 1800, Irving, TX 75039-5648
Tel (972) 556-1700 *Founded/Ownrshp* 1998
Sales 876.0M *EMP* 362
Accts Kpmg Llp
SIC 1522 8742 Multi-family dwelling construction; Management consulting services; Multi-family dwelling construction; Management consulting services
Pr: Bobby Page
**CEO:* J Frank Miller III
**CFO:* Frank B Schubert
Ex VP: Joanne Blaylock
Sr VP: Clay Parker

J P L
See J P LAMBORN CO

D-U-N-S 03-785-3140
J P L MANAGEMENT INC
BURGER KING
430 Commerce Dr, Elizabethtown, KY 42701-1293
Tel (270) 769-2248 *Founded/Ownrshp* 1980
Sales 17.5MM^E *EMP* 520
SIC 5812 Fast-food restaurant, chain; Fast-food restaurant, chain
Pr: James Schory

D-U-N-S 05-307-6204 IMP
J P LAMBORN CO (CA)
J P L
3663 E Wawona Ave, Fresno, CA 93725-9236
Tel (559) 650-2120 *Founded/Ownrshp* 1984
Sales 41.9MM^E *EMP* 263^E
SIC 3585 Heating & air conditioning combination units; Heating & air conditioning combination units
CEO: John P Lamborn Jr
Sls Mgr: Kip Davies
Sls Mgr: Brian Queensberry

D-U-N-S 61-528-3363
J P M PRODUCTIONS INC
THE MASTERS OF DISASTERS
582 Etowah Dr Ne, Marietta, GA 30060-1219
Tel (770) 941-0543 *Founded/Ownrshp* 1979
Sales 9.0MM^E *EMP* 400
SIC 8322 Disaster service; Disaster service
CEO: Pete Mitchell
**Sec:* Christine O'Connor
Off Mgr: Christine Oconnor

J P MASCARO & SONS
See SOLID WASTE SERVICES INC

J. P. MCGILLS HOTEL & CASINO
See HOLLAND VENTURES INC

D-U-N-S 79-056-1273
■ J P MORGAN ASSET MANAGEMENT INC
(*Suby of* JPMORGAN CHASE & CO) ★
270 Park Ave Fl 12, New York, NY 10017-7924
Tel (212) 270-6000 *Founded/Ownrshp* 1995
Sales 83.5MM^E *EMP* 136
SIC 6211 6282 Investment firm, general brokerage; Investment advice; Investment firm, general brokerage; Investment advice
CIO: Gary Madich
**Chf Mktg O:* Benji Baer
Chf Inves: Michael Cembalest
Ofcr: Katja Aggas
VP: Megan Goett
Mng Dir: Daniel Hines
Mng Dir: Catherine Keating
Brnch Mgr: Janet Kopel

D-U-N-S 10-836-1002
J P MORGAN CHASE FOUNDATION
270 Park Ave Fl 6, New York, NY 10017-7924
Tel (212) 270-6000 *Founded/Ownrshp* 1969
Sales 48.9MM *EMP* 5
SIC 8699 Charitable organization; Charitable organization
CEO: Bruce McNamer
Owner: Lewis Jones
Pr: Dalila Wilson-Scott
Ch: Jeffrey C Walker
Ofcr: Stan Stanford
VP: Mark Nofziger
VP: Douglas Schwarz
Exec: Michael Alix
Dir IT: Charlie Morgan

D-U-N-S 03-847-4342
■ J P MORGAN SERVICES INC
(*Suby of* JPMORGAN CHASE & CO) ★
500 Stanton Christiana Rd, Newark, DE 19713-2105
Tel (302) 634-1000 *Founded/Ownrshp* 1996
Sales 47.7MM^E *EMP* 1,000
SIC 7374 8741 Data processing service; Management services; Data processing service; Management services
Pr: Rich J Johnson

D-U-N-S 15-185-4585 IMP/EXP
J P ORIGINAL CORP
DOLL HOUSE FOOTWEAR
19101 E Walnut Dr N, City of Industry, CA 91748-1429
Tel (626) 839-4300 *Founded/Ownrshp* 1986
Sales 30.4MM^E *EMP* 60
Accts Hsu Yim Leung & Koo Llp
SIC 5139 Shoes
Ch Bd: C H Hsueh
**Pr:* Si-Tuo Hsu

D-U-N-S 02-975-3555
J P ROSS COTTON CO INC
200 Clay St, Essex, MO 63846
Tel (573) 283-5313 *Founded/Ownrshp* 1938
Sales 21.3MM^E *EMP* 22
SIC 5191 0724 Farm supplies; Fertilizer & fertilizer materials; Seeds & bulbs; Cotton ginning
Pr: Mark Kelley
Sec: Norma Lou Kelly
**VP:* James W Kelley

D-U-N-S 01-196-4539
J P S COMPLETION FLUIDS INC
10380 N Interstate Hwy 37, Mathis, TX 78368-4222
Tel (361) 547-0075 *Founded/Ownrshp* 2008
Sales 30.4MM^E *EMP* 95
SIC 1389 Servicing oil & gas wells
Pr: Pedro Gonzales
**VP:* Sergio R Garza
Opers Mgr: Dennis Vasquez

D-U-N-S 07-880-9784
J P SCHRAMM LLC
TMC 41, STUDIO HOTEL, THE
3753 Howard Hughes Pkwy, Las Vegas, NV 89169-0938
Tel (310) 876-4030 *Founded/Ownrshp* 2013
Sales 7.6MM^E *EMP* 300
SIC 7922 6531 Theatrical producers & services; Real estate agents & managers; Theatrical producers & services; Real estate agents & managers
Sr VP: Neil Schoenblum

J P SPORTSWEAR
See AARON CORP

D-U-N-S 08-248-6820
J P THIBODEAUX LLC
2511 Highway 90 W, New Iberia, LA 70560-9446
Tel (337) 364-4126 *Founded/Ownrshp* 2001
Sales 35.3MM^E *EMP* 84^E
SIC 5511 Automobiles, new & used; Automobiles, new & used
Pr: Joe Bob Thibodeaux
**Treas:* Leona David
**VP:* Ann Thibodeaux
**VP:* Jess Tourne
Genl Mgr: Nathan Hebert
Genl Mgr: Taras Hughes
Opers Mgr: Chris Hawley

D-U-N-S 05-688-1642 EXP
J P THOMAS & CO INC
THOMAS TIRE CO
1191 Us Highway 64 W, Asheboro, NC 27205-2250
Tel (336) 625-3963 *Founded/Ownrshp* 1981
Sales 46.0MM^E *EMP* 86
SIC 5531 5014 Automotive tires; Automobile tires & tubes; Truck tires & tubes
Pr: J Paul Thomas
**Sec:* Sandra Thomas
Genl Mgr: Bryan Thomas

D-U-N-S 19-377-3561
J P WEIGAND AND SONS INC
150 N Market St, Wichita, KS 67202-1985
Tel (316) 262-6400 *Founded/Ownrshp* 1982
Sales 27.6MM^E *EMP* 290
SIC 7389 Brokers, business: buying & selling business enterprises; Brokers, business: buying & selling business enterprises

Pr: Roger Weast
Prin: Nester Weigand
Sales Asso: Cathy Erickson
Sales Asso: Pam Hesse

D-U-N-S 08-985-8989 IMP
J PAUL GETTY TRUST
GETTY PUBLICATIONS
1200 Getty Center Dr 1300v, Los Angeles, CA 90049-1747
Tel (310) 440-7300 *Founded/Ownrshp* 1953
Sales 97.0MM^E *EMP* 1,500
SIC 8412

J PAULEY TOYOTA
See J PAWLEY MOTORS INC

D-U-N-S 03-549-6074
J PAWLEY MOTORS INC
J PAULEY TOYOTA
6200 S 36th St, Fort Smith, AR 72908-7514
Tel (479) 646-7800 *Founded/Ownrshp* 1946
Sales 26.0MM *EMP* 35
SIC 5511 5521 Automobiles, new & used; Used car dealers; Automobiles, new & used; Used car dealers
Pr: Cliff B Peck
**VP:* Ron Pawley

D-U-N-S 78-294-2502
J PETERMAN LEGAL GROUP LTD
BLOMMER LAW OFFICE
165 Bishops Way Ste 100, Brookfield, WI 53005-6215
Tel (262) 790-5719 *Founded/Ownrshp* 1991
Sales 23.0MM^E *EMP* 150
SIC 8111 Real estate law; Real estate law
Pr: James Peterman
**Pt:* Shannon Cummings

D-U-N-S 02-707-4692
J PETERS LLC
202 St Main St, Anderson, SC 29624
Tel (864) 224-0040 *Founded/Ownrshp* 2010
Sales 9.2MM^E *EMP* 296^E
SIC 5812 Grills (eating places); Grills (eating places)
Pr: J Peter Angell

D-U-N-S 79-286-9232 IMP
J PETROCELLI CONTRACTING INC
100 Comac St Ste 3, Ronkonkoma, NY 11779-6937
Tel (631) 981-5200 *Founded/Ownrshp* 1992
Sales 71.1MM *EMP* 40
SIC 1542 Commercial & office building, new construction; Commercial & office building, new construction
Ch Bd: John M Petrocelli Jr
**Treas:* Joseph Petrocelli
**VP:* James Petrocelli

J. POLEP DISTRIBUTION SERVICES
See CONSUMER PRODUCT DISTRIBUTORS INC

D-U-N-S 00-406-9482 IMP
J QUEEN NEW YORK INC (NY)
37 W 20th St Ste 509, New York, NY 10011-3740
Tel (212) 414-1555 *Founded/Ownrshp* 2009
Sales 26.0MM *EMP* 25
SIC 5021 Beds & bedding
CEO: Anthony Cassella
**Pr:* Julie Brady
VP: Pegeen Cooper
VP: Vanessa Piper
**VP:* Kimberley Wright

D-U-N-S 18-373-9374
J R C TRANSPORTATION INC
47 Maple Ave, Thomaston, CT 06787-1901
Tel (860) 283-0207 *Founded/Ownrshp* 1985
Sales 94.4MM^E *EMP* 150
SIC 4213 4212 Trucking, except local; Local trucking, without storage; Trucking, except local; Local trucking, without storage
Pr: Raymond M Cappella

D-U-N-S 04-792-0061 IMP
J R CARLSON LABORATORIES INC
CARLSON LABS
600 W University Dr, Arlington Heights, IL 60004-1818
Tel (847) 255-1600 *Founded/Ownrshp* 1965
Sales 81.3MM^E *EMP* 100
SIC 5122 Vitamins & minerals; Vitamins & minerals
Pr: Carilyn Anderson
**Pr:* John R Carlson
CFO: Trish Lange
**Sec:* Susan Carlson
**Sec:* Kirsten Cecchin
**CIO:* Michael Anderson
CTO: Kelly Wavra
IT Man: Kathryn Bertellotti
IT Man: Toni Edwards
VP Mktg: Carrie Anderson
Snr Mgr: Kimberly Armentrout

D-U-N-S 18-069-2998
J R COLE INDUSTRIES INC
435 Minuet Ln, Charlotte, NC 28217-2718
Tel (704) 523-6622 *Founded/Ownrshp* 1984
Sales 54.7MM^E *EMP* 200
SIC 2752 Commercial printing, lithographic; Commercial printing, lithographic
Ch Bd: Joseph Robert Cole Sr
**CFO:* Donald W Griffin
VP Mfg: Leroy Swope
VP Sls: Joe Richards

J R ENGINEERING
See JR ENGINEERING INC

D-U-N-S 05-731-6242
J R HAYES & SONS INC
22430 Se 231st St, Maple Valley, WA 98038-8272
Tel (425) 392-5722 *Founded/Ownrshp* 1968
Sales 24.3MM^E *EMP* 100
SIC 1794 Excavation work; Excavation work
Pr: Dan Hayes
**COO:* Nick Hayes
CFO: Koll Husemoen
**CFO:* Gary Lasala
VP: Rob Bonnett
**VP:* James R Hayes Jr
Sfty Mgr: Shawna Gilmore
Snr PM: Jeff Rockey

D-U-N-S 06-098-3442
J R HEINEMAN & SONS INC
1224 N Niagara St, Saginaw, MI 48602-4742
Tel (989) 399-0400 *Founded/Ownrshp* 1987
Sales 21.8MM^E *EMP* 60
SIC 1542 Commercial & office building, new construction
Pr: Daniel T Emmenecker
**VP:* Dale Johnson Jr

J R INDUSTRIES
See JRI INC

J R M
See JRM HAULING AND RECYCLING SERVICES II INC

J R METALS
See MISA METALS INC

D-U-N-S 01-292-7187
J R R MANEGEMENT CO INC
WENDY'S
617 S Harris St, Sandersville, GA 31082-2825
Tel (478) 552-0219 *Founded/Ownrshp* 1992
Sales 10.8MM *EMP* 372
SIC 5812 Fast-food restaurant, chain; Fast-food restaurant, chain
Pr: James R Robins
**Pr:* Gene Dickey
Off Mgr: Peggy Smith

D-U-N-S 02-118-1094
J R ROBERTS CORP
(*Suby of* SD DEACON CORP) ★
7745 Greenback Ln Ste 300, Citrus Heights, CA 95610-5866
Tel (916) 729-5600 *Founded/Ownrshp* 1979
Sales 28.2MM^E *EMP* 104
SIC 1542 Commercial & office building, new construction; Commercial & office building, new construction
CEO: Robert Olsen
**Pr:* Robert C Hall Jr
Sr VP: Jim Reilly
**VP:* Mike Vinks

D-U-N-S 00-949-3081
J R SETINA MANUFACTURING CO
2926 Yelm Hwy Se, Olympia, WA 98501-4832
Tel (360) 491-6197 *Founded/Ownrshp* 1962
Sales 30.7MM^E *EMP* 80
SIC 3446 Partitions, ornamental metal
Pr: Terry Setina
**VP:* Judy Setina-Ware
Natl Sales: Brett Ware

D-U-N-S 00-520-2247 IMP
J R SHORT MILLING CO (IL)
1580 Grinnell Rd, Kankakee, IL 60901-8246
Tel (815) 937-2635 *Founded/Ownrshp* 1910
Sales 24.9MM^E *EMP* 125
SIC 2041 5149 Flour; Corn grits & flakes, for brewers' use; Hominy grits (except breakfast food); Baking supplies; Flour; Corn grits & flakes, for brewers' use; Hominy grits (except breakfast food); Baking supplies
CEO: Craig R Petray
**Pr:* Jon E Luikar
**VP:* Richard Cochran
Off Admin: Diane Kempke
VP Opers: Nick Ladin
S&M/VP: Terry Gieseke

D-U-N-S 15-737-0198
J RANCK ELECTRIC INC
JRE
1993 Gover Pkwy, Mount Pleasant, MI 48858-8137
Tel (906) 632-6721 *Founded/Ownrshp* 1986
Sales 59.8MM^E *EMP* 200
SIC 1731 General electrical contractor; General electrical contractor
CEO: James A Ranck
**Pr:* Adam J Ranck
**CFO:* Matt Warren
**VP:* Angela M Wood
Brnch Mgr: Rob Hentkowski
Mtls Mgr: Loren Wilcox
Sls Dir: Bob Caylor

D-U-N-S 94-772-7368
■ **J RAY MCDERMOTT & CO INC**
(*Suby of* MCDERMOTT INTERNATIONAL INC) ★
1340 Poydras St Ste 1200, New Orleans, LA 70112-1232
Tel (504) 587-5000 *Founded/Ownrshp* 1994
Sales 321.0MM^E *EMP* 7,100
Accts Pricewaterhousecoopers Llp
SIC 1629 1389 1623 Marine construction; Industrial plant construction; Power plant construction; Construction, repair & dismantling services; Oil field services; Roustabout service; Servicing oil & gas wells; Pipeline construction; Marine construction; Industrial plant construction; Power plant construction; Construction, repair & dismantling services; Oil field services; Roustabout service; Servicing oil & gas wells; Pipeline construction
CEO: Bruce W Wilkinson
Pr: Robert H Rawle
CFO: Bruce F Longaker Jr
Ex VP: E Allen Womack Jr
Snr PM: Marc Zeringer
Snr Mgr: Michael Campbell

D-U-N-S 18-656-5065
J RAYL TRANSPORT INC
1016 Triplett Blvd 1, Akron, OH 44306-3007
Tel (330) 784-1134 *Founded/Ownrshp* 1977
Sales 37.7MM^E *EMP* 90^E
SIC 4213 4731 4231 Trucking, except local; Truck transportation brokers; Trucking terminal facilities
CEO: Jeremy Rayl
**Pr:* Tim Rayl
**VP:* Dan Rafferty
**VP:* Ryan Richards
**VP:* Jim St John
CIO: Nathan Lambert

D-U-N-S 60-657-3996
J RAYMOND & ASSOCIATES INC
465 W Warren Ave, Longwood, FL 32750-4002
Tel (407) 339-2988 *Founded/Ownrshp* 1988
Sales 109.5MM *EMP* 30
Accts Tschopp Whitcomb & Orr Pa
SIC 1542 Commercial & office building, new construction; Commercial & office buildings, renovation & repair; Commercial & office building, new construction; Commercial & office buildings, renovation & repair
Pr: John R Sofarelli
**VP:* Russ Suddeth
Sfty Mgr: Richard Cooney

D-U-N-S 04-036-4130
J RAYMOND CONSTRUCTION CORP
465 W Warren Ave, Longwood, FL 32750-4002
Tel (407) 862-6966 *Founded/Ownrshp* 2000
Sales 38.6MM^E *EMP* 60
SIC 1542 Nonresidential construction
Pr: John R Sofarelli
Sr VP: V P Russ Sr
**VP:* J Russell Suddeth
Area Mgr: Ken Blevins
Snr PM: Scott Mellen

D-U-N-S 16-789-3619
J RECKNER ASSOCIATES INC
1600 Manor Dr Ste 105, Chalfont, PA 18914-2279
Tel (215) 822-6220 *Founded/Ownrshp* 1991
Sales 26.1MM^E *EMP* 442
SIC 8732 Market analysis or research; Market analysis or research
Pr: Frances Grubb
**Ch:* David Reckner
**Treas:* Peter Reckner
**Sec:* John Reckner
Genl Mgr: Ken Huber
Mktg Mgr: Steve Oliver

D-U-N-S 55-607-2767
J REYNOLDS & CO INC
JR
369 Sansom Blvd, Saginaw, TX 76179-4625
Tel (817) 306-9596 *Founded/Ownrshp* 2002
Sales 56.0MM^E *EMP* 200
SIC 1761 Roofing contractor; Roofing contractor
Pr: Matt Skipper

D-U-N-S 06-623-7983 IMP
J ROBERT SCOTT INC
500 N Oak St, Inglewood, CA 90302-2942
Tel (310) 659-4910 *Founded/Ownrshp* 1972
Sales 52.1MM^E *EMP* 145
SIC 5131 2512 2511 Textiles, woven; Upholstered household furniture; Wood household furniture; Textiles, woven; Upholstered household furniture; Wood household furniture
CEO: Andrew Frumovitz
**Pr:* Sally Lewis
COO: Richard Chilcott

D-U-N-S 87-747-4288
J ROVETA INC
TRACY HONDA
3450 Auto Plaza Way, Tracy, CA 95304-7326
Tel (209) 832-1400 *Founded/Ownrshp* 1994
Sales 22.2MM^E *EMP* 48
SIC 5511 Automobiles, new & used; Automobiles, new & used
Pr: Ken Harvey
Genl Mgr: Brett Allen
**Genl Mgr:* Taz Harvey
Sls Mgr: Frank Esparza
Sls Mgr: James Herren
Sls Mgr: Sonny Singh
Sls Mgr: Russell Ybarra
Sales Asso: Sal Emran

D-U-N-S 00-298-2981 IMP
■ **J RUBIN & CO** (IL)
(*Suby of* METALS USA INC) ★
305 Peoples Ave, Rockford, IL 61104-7034
Tel (815) 964-9471 *Founded/Ownrshp* 1939, 2010
Sales 73.2MM^E *EMP* 110
SIC 5051 Metals service centers & offices; Metals service centers & offices
CEO: Philip E Rubin
**CFO:* Mark Klein
Bd of Dir: Dave Whitmore
**VP:* Gary J Rubin

J S
See JEL SERT CO

D-U-N-S 01-193-2399
J S B INDUSTRIES INC
MUFFIN TOWN
130 Crescent Ave, Chelsea, MA 02150-3030
Tel (617) 884-3251 *Founded/Ownrshp* 1978
Sales 36.3MM^E *EMP* 115
SIC 2053 Frozen bakery products, except bread; Frozen bakery products, except bread
Pr: Jack Anderson
**Pr:* John Anderson
**VP:* Brian Anderson

D-U-N-S 09-397-8419
J S C FEDERAL CREDIT UNION
1330 Gemini St, Houston, TX 77058-2712
Tel (281) 488-7070 *Founded/Ownrshp* 1962
Sales NA *EMP* 100^E
SIC 6061 Federal credit unions; Federal credit unions
Pr: Michael G Brown
**Sr VP:* Becky Lanclos
**VP:* Steven Barnstetter
**VP:* J Stephen Branstetter

J S G
See JOHNSON SERVICE GROUP INC

D-U-N-S 18-827-2330
J S HAREN CO
1175 Highway 11 N, Athens, TN 37303-7541
Tel (423) 745-5000 *Founded/Ownrshp* 1987
Sales 26.5MM^E *EMP* 40
SIC 1542 1623 Commercial & office building, new construction; Water, sewer & utility lines
Pr: J S Haren
Sec: Cassandra Haren

D-U-N-S 19-683-5029
J S LEASING CO INC
SLAY INDUSTRIES
1441 Hampton Ave, Saint Louis, MO 63139-3115
Tel (314) 647-7529 *Founded/Ownrshp* 1979
Sales 163.5MM^E *EMP* 400^E
SIC 7359 Equipment rental & leasing; Equipment rental & leasing
CEO: Eugene Slay
**Pr:* Glen Slay
**Ex VP:* Gary Slay
VP: John Brereton
Dir IT: William Hackel

J S MCCARTHY PRINTING
See LETTER SYSTEMS INC

D-U-N-S 00-520-0589 EXP
J S PALUCH CO INC (IL)
3708 River Rd Ste 400, Franklin Park, IL 60131-2158
Tel (847) 678-9300 *Founded/Ownrshp* 1913
Sales 85.5MM^E *EMP* 200
SIC 2731 2721 7371 2741 Pamphlets: publishing & printing; Periodicals; Computer software development; Miscellaneous publishing; Pamphlets: publishing & printing; Periodicals; Computer software development; Miscellaneous publishing
Pr: William J Rafferty
VP: Everette Locke
VP: Steve Nanai
VP: Margaret A Paluch
CTO: Janice Pacilio
Dir IT: Mark Wozny
Sfty Dirs: Dawn Maitland
Sfty Mgr: Dana Shradder
Plnt Mgr: Dawn Maitland
Plnt Mgr: Dan Shrader
Prd Mgr: Deb Johnston

J S W
See JSW STEEL (USA) INC

D-U-N-S 03-028-5265
J S WEST AND CO
501 9th St, Modesto, CA 95354-3420
Tel (209) 577-3221 *Founded/Ownrshp* 1946
Sales 90.5MM^E *EMP* 300^E
SIC 5172 5211 5251 0723 5499 Gases, liquefied petroleum (propane); Lumber & other building materials; Lumber products; Hardware; Feed milling custom services; Eggs & poultry; Gases, liquefied petroleum (propane); Lumber & other building materials; Lumber products; Hardware; Feed milling custom services; Eggs & poultry
CEO: Eric Benson

J S WEST PROKRANE GAS
See SONORA J S WEST & CO INC

D-U-N-S 00-677-6165 IMP
J SLAGTER & SON CONSTRUCTION CO
SLAGTER CONSTRUCTION
2976 Ivanrest Ave Sw, Grandville, MI 49418-2932
Tel (616) 877-5100 *Founded/Ownrshp* 1954
Sales 35.4MM^E *EMP* 100^E
SIC 1611 1622 Guardrail construction, highways; Bridge construction; Guardrail construction, highways; Bridge construction
Pr: Brian Slagter
CFO: Gina Phillips
**Sec:* Anne Slagter

D-U-N-S 08-608-3193
J SMITH LANIER & CO
300 W 10th St, West Point, GA 31833-1212
Tel (706) 645-2211 *Founded/Ownrshp* 1983
Sales NA *EMP* 560
Accts Warren Averett Llc Atlanta
SIC 6411 Life insurance agents; Property & casualty insurance agent; Fire loss appraisal; Life insurance agents; Property & casualty insurance agent; Fire loss appraisal
Ch Bd: D Gaines Lanier
**Pr:* Gary Ivey
**CFO:* Frank Plan
**Ex VP:* Scott Crawford
Off Mgr: Rob Murphy
Snr Sftwr: Rebecca Stewart
MIS Dir: Mike Milan

D-U-N-S 06-993-6664
J SOLANKI CORP (CA)
BESTWAY SUPERMARKET
1012 W Gardena Blvd, Gardena, CA 90247-4906
Tel (310) 324-9971 *Founded/Ownrshp* 1995
Sales 46.3MM^E *EMP* 300
SIC 5411

D-U-N-S 00-798-5955
J SOLOTKEN & CO INC
6701 English Ave, Indianapolis, IN 46219-7414
Tel (317) 357-5082 *Founded/Ownrshp* 1914, 1965
Sales 28.3MM^E *EMP* 40
Accts Katz Sapper & Miller
SIC 5093 Nonferrous metals scrap; Nonferrous metals scrap
Pr: Joseph M Alpert

D-U-N-S 61-731-3614 IMP/EXP
J SQUARED INC
UNIVERSITY LOFT COMPANY
2588 Jannetides Blvd, Greenfield, IN 46140-9130
Tel (317) 866-5638 *Founded/Ownrshp* 1988
Sales 38.9MM^E *EMP* 175^E
SIC 2511 2521 2531 5021

D-U-N-S 01-086-1201
J STANTON DAVID & ASSOCIATES INC (MI)
WENDY'S
714 W Michigan Ave, Jackson, MI 49201-1909
Tel (517) 784-4094 *Founded/Ownrshp* 1974
Sales 86.4MM^E *EMP* 2,300

SIC 5812 Fast-food restaurant, chain; Fast-food restaurant, chain
Ch Bd: David J Stanton
VP: Alan Lecrone
IT Man: Jim Bunker
Mktg Dir: Dave Wenglekowski

D-U-N-S 09-094-3325
J STELLAR CORP
1363 Down River Dr, Woodland, WA 98674-9546
Tel (360) 225-7996 *Founded/Ownrshp* 1996
Sales 84.5MM^E *EMP* 120
SIC 1542 Nonresidential construction; Nonresidential construction
Pr: Robert E Kinghorn
**Sec:* Anita Kinghorn
**VP:* Jeffrey R Walker

D-U-N-S 03-759-3746
J STERLING MORTON HIGH SCHOOL DISTRICT 201
5041 W 31st St, Cicero, IL 60804-4028
Tel (708) 780-2800 *Founded/Ownrshp* 1903
Sales 72.7MM^E *EMP* 900
Accts Klein Hall & Associates Llc
SIC 8211 Public elementary & secondary schools; Public elementary & secondary schools
Sls Mgr: Cathy Johnson

D-U-N-S 00-702-3112 IMP/EXP
J STRICKLAND AND CO (TN)
J STRICKLAND PRODUCTS
10420 Desoto Rd, Olive Branch, MS 38654-5301
Tel (662) 890-2306 *Founded/Ownrshp* 1936
Sales 23.5MM^E *EMP* 70
SIC 2844 Shampoos, rinses, conditioners: hair
Pr: Linda L Clifton
**VP:* James E McKelroy
VP: Donna Paine
Rgnl Mgr: Michael Jeffreys
Plnt Mgr: Charles Rast

J STRICKLAND PRODUCTS
See J STRICKLAND AND CO

D-U-N-S 04-635-3934
J SUPOR & SON TRUCKING & RIGGING CO INC
433 Bergen Ave, Kearny, NJ 07032-3938
Tel (201) 299-1100 *Founded/Ownrshp* 1965
Sales 20.0MM^E *EMP* 100
SIC 4213 1799 4212 Trucking, except local; Rigging & scaffolding; Local trucking, without storage
Ch: Joseph Supor Jr
Pr: Joseph Supor III
VP: Douglas Filos
VP: Rick Lamantia
VP: Roseann Supor
Genl Mgr: Jeff Gelety
Sfty Dirs: David Becker
Opers Mgr: Rudy Desimone
Opers Mgr: Murphy Triano

D-U-N-S 04-690-5626
J SUPPLY CO
88 Addington Dr Nw, Rome, GA 30165-1297
Tel (706) 235-3321 *Founded/Ownrshp* 2000
Sales 24.6MM^E *EMP* 40
SIC 5085 5063 5084 Industrial supplies; Electrical apparatus & equipment; Compressors, except air conditioning
Ch Bd: Dr Jim Rogers
**Pr:* Freeman Robbins
**Sec:* Allyson Dulaney
**VP:* Rhett Rogers
Opers Mgr: Mark Bohn
Sales Asso: Lance Cleveland
Sales Asso: Jeff Gresham

D-U-N-S 80-086-4670 EXP
J T B AUTOMOTIVE INC
JAMES TOYOTA OUTLET
172 Us Highway 202/31 N, Flemington, NJ 08822-1719
Tel (908) 788-5700 *Founded/Ownrshp* 1993
Sales 21.9MM^E *EMP* 75
SIC 5511 Automobiles, new & used; Automobiles, new & used
Pr: James Botsacos

D-U-N-S 02-479-4711
J T DAVENPORT & SONS INC
1144 Broadway Rd, Sanford, NC 27332-9793
Tel (919) 774-9444 *Founded/Ownrshp* 2012
Sales 108.7MM^E *EMP* 350^E
SIC 5199

D-U-N-S 96-165-6782
J T HARRISON CONSTRUCTION CO INC
5870 Charlie Shirley Rd, Northport, AL 35473-8042
Tel (205) 333-1120 *Founded/Ownrshp* 1993
Sales 38.7MM^E *EMP* 80
SIC 1542 Commercial & office building, new construction
Pr: Tim Harrison
**VP:* Josh Johnson
**VP:* Lance Wyatt

J T PACKARD
See THOMAS & BETTS POWER SOLUTIONS LLC

D-U-N-S 04-648-8896
J T R CO INC
AREA DISTRIBUTING CO
1102 S 3rd St, San Jose, CA 95112-5918
Tel (408) 975-7733 *Founded/Ownrshp* 1960
Sales 73.7MM^E *EMP* 80
SIC 5113 5122 5199 Industrial & personal service paper; Towels, paper; Bags, paper & disposable plastic; Paperboard & products; Toilet articles; Packaging materials; Industrial & personal service paper; Towels, paper; Bags, paper & disposable plastic; Paperboard & products; Toilet articles; Packaging materials
Pr: Josy T Ryan
**Sec:* Louis Ryan
**VP:* Kelly Ryan
**VP:* Gary G Smith
Sls Mgr: Sara Ramsey

D-U-N-S 02-440-5862
J T RUSSELL AND SONS INC
JT RUSSELL ASPHALT
1721 Us Highway 52 N, Albemarle, NC 28001-8503
Tel (704) 982-2225 *Founded/Ownrshp* 1938
Sales 70.0MM *EMP* 170
SIC 1623 1611 Water & sewer line construction; Highway & street construction
Pr: Bob Russell
**Sec:* James T Russell Jr
Sfty Mgr: Julie Plyler
Sales Exec: Dave Normand

D-U-N-S 00-946-6111
J T THORPE & SON INC
(*Suby of* TERRA MILLENNIUM CORP) ★
1060 Hensley St, Richmond, CA 94801-2117
Tel (510) 233-2500 *Founded/Ownrshp* 1985
Sales 127.1MM *EMP* 550
Accts Armanino Llp San Ramon Calif
SIC 1741 8711 Refractory or acid brick masonry; Engineering services; Refractory or acid brick masonry; Engineering services
CEO: Mark C Stutzman
CFO: Michael P Elam
Sr VP: Bryan Young
VP: Gregg Dyakon
VP: Richard Giaramita

D-U-N-S 00-842-4632 IMP
J T THORPE CO (TX)
(*Suby of* THORPE SPECIALTY SERVICES CORP) ★
6833 Kirbyville St, Houston, TX 77033-1194
Tel (713) 644-1247 *Founded/Ownrshp* 1906
Sales 27.5MM^E *EMP* 239^E
SIC 1741 3297 3296 Refractory or acid brick masonry; Nonclay refractories; Mineral wool
Pr: John C Schultz
**CFO:* Sherri W Fruge
Ex VP: John Shultz
**VP:* Richard Nowland
**VP:* Keith West
Brnch Mgr: Heeth Orr

D-U-N-S 08-894-3139
J T TURNER CONSTRUCTION CO INC
2250 E Victory Dr Ste 104, Savannah, GA 31404-3988
Tel (912) 356-5611 *Founded/Ownrshp* 1977
Sales 30.3MM^E *EMP* 45^E
Accts Hancock Askew & Co Savannah
SIC 1542 1521 1522 Commercial & office buildings, renovation & repair; Commercial & office building, new construction; General remodeling, single-family houses; Residential construction
Pr: Jt Turner Jr
COO: Tripp Turner
**CFO:* Gregory Clements
Bd of Dir: Mark Fitzpatrick

D-U-N-S 18-646-1406
J T VAUGHN ENTERPRISES INC
VAUGHN CONSTRUCTION
10355 Westpark Dr, Houston, TX 77042-5312
Tel (713) 243-8300 *Founded/Ownrshp* 1988
Sales 216.4MM^E *EMP* 300
SIC 1542 Commercial & office building, new construction; Hospital construction; Commercial & office building, new construction; Hospital construction
Pr: J T Vaughn Jr
**Pr:* Tom Vaughn
**Treas:* Bob Weeks
**Treas:* Robert Weeks
**VP:* Stephen Skabla
**VP:* Bill Vaughn

D-U-N-S 00-860-0256 IMP/EXP
J T WALKER INDUSTRIES INC
861 N Hercules Ave, Clearwater, FL 33765-2025
Tel (727) 461-0501 *Founded/Ownrshp* 1997
Sales 697.3MM^E *EMP* 5,000
SIC 3442 3089 3585 5193 Screens, window, metal; Window frames & sash, plastic; Parts for heating, cooling & refrigerating equipment; Nursery stock; Screens, window, metal; Window frames & sash, plastic; Parts for heating, cooling & refrigerating equipment; Nursery stock
CEO: Peter Desoto
**Pr:* Jay K Poppleton
CFO: Janet Sasenmyer
**VP:* Janet L Fasenmyer
**VP:* Michael Luther
Genl Mgr: Mark Paul
Off Mgr: Brenda Brannen
MIS Dir: Fred Book
Dir IT: James Beckner
Sfty Dirs: Darlene Moffatt
VP Sls: Grant Tyson

D-U-N-S 00-294-5777 EXP
J TECH SALES LLC (FL)
CITRUS OLEO
6531 Park Of Commerce Blv, Boca Raton, FL 33487-8297
Tel (561) 995-0070 *Founded/Ownrshp* 1997
Sales 43.3MM^E *EMP* 35
SIC 5169 Chemicals & allied products
Pr: Mark Kaszubski
VP: James Coletta
Sls Dir: Ricki Tannenbaum
Sls Mgr: Kathy McVicker

D-U-N-S 15-418-8668
J THOMAS & CO INC
WAFFLE HOUSE
7231 Tylrsvlle Rd Ste 110, Dayton, OH 45424
Tel (937) 235-0021 *Founded/Ownrshp* 1983
Sales 22.5MM^E *EMP* 700
SIC 5812 Restaurant, family: chain; Restaurant, family: chain
Pr: Judith Thomas

D-U-N-S 04-708-1468
J THOMAS ARNOLD & SON INC
THOMAS & SONS DISTRIBUTORS
840 S Front St, Coos Bay, OR 97420-1515
Tel (541) 267-3483 *Founded/Ownrshp* 1992
Sales 30.7MM *EMP* 74
Accts Isler Cpa Llc Eugene Oregon
SIC 4213 Trucking, except local
Pr: Aaron Thomas
COO: Marcia Hart
Sec: Sharon Thomas
Genl Mgr: Rocky Buckles

D-U-N-S 04-700-9147 EXP
J V EQUIPMENT INC
2421 S Expressway 281, Edinburg, TX 78542-1802
Tel (956) 383-0777 *Founded/Ownrshp* 1960
Sales 24.7MM^E *EMP* 72^E
SIC 5084 Lift trucks & parts; Lift trucks & parts
Pr: Valerie Mehis
**VP:* Jim Mehis
Genl Mgr: Lisa Garza
IT Man: Herb Berkley
IT Man: Jim Mehrs

D-U-N-S 15-186-7363
J V LABORATORIES INC
(*Suby of* ST LUKE'S MEMORIAL HOSPITAL INC)
1320 Wisconsin Ave, Racine, WI 53403-1978
Tel (262) 636-2011 *Founded/Ownrshp* 1991
Sales 396.7MM *EMP* 85^E
SIC 8071 Medical laboratories; Medical laboratories
Pr: Kenneth Buser

J V S
See JEWISH VOCATIONAL SERVICES AND COMMUNITY WORKSHOP

J V WINE AND SPIRITS
See VALLERGAS DRIVE-IN MARKETS INC

D-U-N-S 00-309-6666
J VINTON SCHAFER & SONS INC (MD)
(*Suby of* QUANDEL ENTERPRISES INC) ★
1309 Continental Dr Ste A, Abingdon, MD 21009-2336
Tel (410) 335-3000 *Founded/Ownrshp* 1919
Sales 24.1MM^E *EMP* 50
SIC 1541 1542 Industrial buildings, new construction; Commercial & office building, new construction
Pr: Warren Hamilton
CFO: Chris Bushey
VP: H Thomas Gnau
VP: Elmer Hack

J W
See JACKSON WALKER LLP

D-U-N-S 87-744-3648
■ **J W DIDADO ELECTRIC INC**
(*Suby of* QUANTA SERVICES INC) ★
1033 Kelly Ave, Akron, OH 44306-3143
Tel (330) 374-0070 *Founded/Ownrshp* 2013
Sales 47.8MM^E *EMP* 150
SIC 1731 General electrical contractor; General electrical contractor
Pr: Gary Didado
Sec: Rhonda Didado
VP: Tony Didado
CTO: Steve McDevitt

D-U-N-S 62-389-6842
J W EBERT CORP
MCDONALD'S
917 W Main St Ste 201, Bridgeport, WV 26330-1886
Tel (304) 848-2123 *Founded/Ownrshp* 1990
Sales 22.2MM^E *EMP* 750^E
SIC 5812 Fast-food restaurant, chain; Fast-food restaurant, chain
Pr: John Ebert

J W F CO
See JAMES W FOWLER CO

D-U-N-S 10-316-9769
J W FLOOR COVERING INC
9881 Carroll Centre Rd, San Diego, CA 92126-4554
Tel (858) 536-8565 *Founded/Ownrshp* 1983
Sales 44.5MM^E *EMP* 275
SIC 1752 Floor laying & floor work; Floor laying & floor work
Pr: John S Wallace
Sales Exec: Alan Biswick

D-U-N-S 18-657-4471
J W GARLAND WHOLESALE INC
GARLAND WHOLESALE HUNTSVILLE
3502 Highway 43 N, Ethridge, TN 38456-2138
Tel (931) 829-2104 *Founded/Ownrshp* 1981
Sales 41.8MM^E *EMP* 80
SIC 5033 Siding, except wood
Pr: J W Garland
**CFO:* Mike Smith
**VP:* David Herston

D-U-N-S 00-423-3490 IMP/EXP
■ **J W HARRIS CO INC** (OH)
HARRIS PRODUCTS GROUP, THE
(*Suby of* LINCOLN ELECTRIC HOLDINGS INC) ★
4501 Quality Pl, Mason, OH 45040-1971
Tel (513) 754-2000 *Founded/Ownrshp* 1914
Sales 56.9MM^E *EMP* 350
SIC 3356 3548 2899

D-U-N-S 00-896-1823 IMP
J W JUNG SEED CO
MCCLURE AND ZIMMERMAN
335 S High St, Randolph, WI 53957-0002
Tel (920) 326-3121 *Founded/Ownrshp* 1907
Sales 79.4MM^E *EMP* 450
SIC 5261 5961 Garden supplies & tools; Mail order house; Flowers, plants & bulbs: mail order; Garden supplies & tools; Mail order house; Flowers, plants & bulbs: mail order
Pr: Richard Zondag
Manager: Jason Biddick

J W MARRIOTT
See MDM BRICKELL HOTEL GROUP LTD

D-U-N-S 01-764-2837 IMP
J W NUTRITIONAL LLC (OK)
601 Century Pkwy Ste 300, Allen, TX 75013-8037
Tel (214) 221-0404 *Founded/Ownrshp* 2004
Sales 21.0MM *EMP* 70^E
SIC 2023 Dietary supplements, dairy & non-dairy based
Pr: Jesse D Windrix

J W P
See JOHNSON WELDED PRODUCTS INC

D-U-N-S 01-478-3302 IMP
J W PEPPER & SON INC
191 Sheree Blvd Ste 102, Exton, PA 19341-1265
Tel (610) 648-0500 *Founded/Ownrshp* 1945
Sales 49.6MM^E *EMP* 250
SIC 5736 Musical instrument stores; Musical instrument stores
Pr: Glenn D Burtch
Pr: Ron Huisenga
**Treas:* Charles M Slater
**VP:* Lee E Paynter
VP: Steve Rook
VP: Roy Schmidt
IT Man: Niles Jonaitis
Mktg Mgr: Denise Collins

D-U-N-S 04-439-2058
J W PERRY INC
707 S Center Ave, Merrill, WI 54452-3406
Tel (715) 536-9465 *Founded/Ownrshp* 1968
Sales 48.5MM^E *EMP* 170
SIC 5193

J W POWERLINE CONSTRUCTION
See JIM F WEBB INC

D-U-N-S 09-817-3909
J W RICHARDS INC
RICHARDS HONDA
7791 Florida Blvd, Baton Rouge, LA 70806-4707
Tel (225) 928-6100 *Founded/Ownrshp* 1986
Sales 25.2MM^E *EMP* 72
SIC 5511 5521 Automobiles, new & used; Used car dealers; Automobiles, new & used; Used car dealers
Ch: Kent Richards
**Pr:* Polly Lemoine
**VP:* Pamela Richards
Genl Mgr: Con Lemoine
Sales Asso: Ben Woods

D-U-N-S 03-768-2531
J W SANDRI INC
A R SANDRI
400 Chapman St, Greenfield, MA 01301-1736
Tel (413) 772-2121 *Founded/Ownrshp* 2009
Sales 63.2MM^E *EMP* 300
SIC 5541 Gasoline service stations; Gasoline service stations

D-U-N-S 01-582-5458 IMP/EXP
J W T HOLDING CORP
JOHNSTOWN WIRE TECHNOLOGIES
124 Laurel Ave, Johnstown, PA 15906-2246
Tel (814) 532-5600 *Founded/Ownrshp* 1923
Sales 80.3MM^E *EMP* 265
SIC 3312 Bar, rod & wire products; Bar, rod & wire products
Pr: Walt Robertson
**Treas:* Anthony Garcia
**Treas:* Ron Shaffer
**VP:* Jack Leffler
**Prin:* J Thomas Clark
QA Dir: Jason Devan
Sfty Mgr: Jim Griffith
Opers Mgr: Jerry Regan
Ql Cn Mgr: Doug Lohr
Manager: Brian Bonebrake
Board of Directors: Bill Dabney, Ronald N Dubin, Anthony Garcia, William F Mc Cord, Walker Poole

D-U-N-S 02-800-0396
J W WOOD CO INC
3676 Old Hwy 44 Dr, Redding, CA 96003
Tel (530) 894-1325 *Founded/Ownrshp* 1954
Sales 32.4MM^E *EMP* 65
SIC 5074 5051 Plumbing fittings & supplies; Metals service centers & offices; Plumbing fittings & supplies; Metals service centers & offices
Pr: John Alan Wood
**Sec:* Kellie Wood
Brnch Mgr: Art Vasquez
Genl Mgr: Mike Thompson
IT Man: Mike Bloom

J. WALTER INC.
See WALTER SURFACE TECHNOLOGIES INC

D-U-N-S 00-699-1160
J WALTER THOMPSON CO LLC
(*Suby of* WPP GROUP USA INC) ★
466 Lexington Ave Ste 6r, New York, NY 10017-3186
Tel (212) 210-7000 *Founded/Ownrshp* 1864
Sales 495.9MM^E *EMP* 9,000
SIC 7311 Advertising agencies; Advertising agencies
CEO: Bob Jeffrey
Pr: Claire Capeci
Pr: Lynn Power
Pr: Beth Waxman-Arteta
CEO: David Eastman
COO: Gerard Lim
Ofcr: Erin Johnson
Ex VP: Lewis Trencher
VP: Eduardo Harker
Creative D: Joseph Cianciotti
Creative D: Suyin Sleeman

D-U-N-S 10-111-6986
J WALTER THOMPSON USA LLC
JWT DIRECT DIV
(*Suby of* WPP PLC)
466 Lexington Ave Ste 6r, New York, NY 10017-3186
Tel (212) 210-7000 *Founded/Ownrshp* 1991
Sales 56.9MM^E *EMP* 1,390
SIC 7311 Advertising agencies; Advertising agencies
Ch Bd: James B Patterson Jr
Pr: Jeffrey Steir
**CEO:* Ronald S Burns
**Prin:* Robert L Jeffrey
Ex Dir: Josy Paul
CIO: James Hudson
MIS Dir: Ed Brenin

D-U-N-S 11-507-8172 IMP
J&A PRINTING INC
1155 Sherman Rd, Hiawatha, IA 52233-1240
Tel (319) 378-0128 *Founded/Ownrshp* 1988
Sales 40.8MM^E *EMP* 130
SIC 2752 7389 Commercial printing, lithographic; Mailing & messenger services; Commercial printing, lithographic; Mailing & messenger services
Pr: Scott Cadwallader
Natl Sales: Lisa Albrecht
Natl Sales: Janeen Watson

D-U-N-S 11-482-6410
J&B MEDICAL SUPPLY CO INC
ABCO
50496 Pontiac Trl Ste 500, Wixom, MI 48393-2090
Tel (248) 896-6201 *Founded/Ownrshp* 1996
Sales 86.6MM^E *EMP* 172^E
SIC 5047 Medical equipment & supplies; Medical equipment & supplies
CEO: Mary E Shaya
**COO:* Charlene Shaya
**CFO:* Abu Sheikh Bakar

D-U-N-S 96-264-4592
J&D ACQUISITIONS LLC
8096 Excelsior Blvd, Hopkins, MN 55343-3415
Tel (612) 339-9500 *Founded/Ownrshp* 2009
Sales 79.4MM^E *EMP* 409^E
SIC 3732 Boat building & repairing; Boat building & repairing

D-U-N-S 13-451-1612
J&D IMPLEMENT INC
415 Biebel Rd, Caro, MI 48723-9172
Tel (989) 673-8400 *Founded/Ownrshp* 2003
Sales 45.0MM *EMP* 50
SIC 5999 Farm equipment & supplies; Farm equipment & supplies
Pr: Jeffrey Mitchell

J&H FAMILY STORES
See EXIT 76 CORP

D-U-N-S 09-972-5228
J&H REINFORCING AND STRUCTURAL ERECTORS INC
J & H ERECTORS
1406 10th St, Portsmouth, OH 45662-4215
Tel (740) 355-0141 *Founded/Ownrshp* 1983
Sales 40.7MM^E *EMP* 150
SIC 1542 1791 Commercial & office building contractors; Iron work, structural; Commercial & office building contractors; Iron work, structural
Pr: Donald Hadsell
**Sec:* Lisa Hadsell

J&J FAMILY OF FARMS
See J & J PRODUCE INC

D-U-N-S 03-146-3219
J&J OIL CO INC (KS)
J MART
1016 S Cedar St, Stockton, KS 67669-2306
Tel (785) 425-7152 *Founded/Ownrshp* 1937, 1990
Sales 30.6MM *EMP* 40
SIC 5541 Filling stations, gasoline; Filling stations, gasoline
Pr: Eugene Westhausing
**VP:* Patricia Westhusing

J&J PACKAGING
See DEUFOL SUNMAN INC

D-U-N-S 07-922-0481
J&J PRODUCE HOLDINGS INC
4003 Seminle P Whitney Rd, Loxahatchee, FL 33470-3754
Tel (561) 422-9777 *Founded/Ownrshp* 2013
Sales 41.8MM^E *EMP* 150^E
SIC 6719 Investment holding companies, except banks
CEO: John Madden
Recvr: Greg Waldon
**Pr:* Chris Erneston III
Sales Asso: Mike Tetner

J&J SHEET METAL
See APPOLO HEATING INC

J&J SNACK FOODS
See J & J SNACK FOODS SALES CORP

D-U-N-S 07-162-8598
J&J STAFFING RESOURCES INC (NJ)
1814 Marlton Pike E # 210, Cherry Hill, NJ 08003-2058
Tel (856) 751-5050 *Founded/Ownrshp* 1972
Sales 106.4MM^E *EMP* 9,053
SIC 7363 Temporary help service; Temporary help service
Pr: John E Malady
Off Admin: Taylor Golder
Off Admin: Judy Piccione
VP Mktg: Sean Malady

J&J/INVISION
See J & J INDUSTRIES INC

D-U-N-S 04-580-5590 IMP
J&K ELECTRONICS INC
M3 TECHNOLOGY
58 Sawgrass Dr, Bellport, NY 11713-1549
Tel (631) 205-0005 *Founded/Ownrshp* 1998
Sales 33.9MM^E *EMP* 30
SIC 5013 5065 5088 Motor vehicle supplies & new parts; Automotive engines & engine parts; Electronic parts & equipment; Aircraft & parts
Pr: Janine Massa
CFO: Andrew Bach
Genl Mgr: Ken Massa
VP Mktg: Evan Marchese
Sls Dir: Scott Russo

D-U-N-S 95-967-2627
J&K PROPERTIES INC
2016 Riverside Dr, Los Angeles, CA 90039-3707
Tel (323) 669-9090 *Founded/Ownrshp* 1995
Sales 54.2MM^E *EMP* 275
SIC 6799 Real estate investors, except property operators; Real estate investors, except property operators
CEO: Anil Mehta

J&L FASTENERS
See J & L FASTENERS AND GENERAL MAINTENANCE SUPPLIES INC

D-U-N-S 12-674-3249 IMP
J&M SALES OF TEXAS LLC
NATIONAL STORES
15001 S Figueroa St, Gardena, CA 90248-1721
Tel (310) 324-9962 *Founded/Ownrshp* 1962
Sales 79.7MM^E *EMP* 800
SIC 5651 Family clothing stores; Family clothing stores

D-U-N-S 09-872-1509 IMP
J&P CYCLES LLC
(*Suby of* MOTORSPORT AFTERMARKET GROUP INC) ★
13225 Circle Dr, Anamosa, IA 52205-7321
Tel (319) 462-4817 *Founded/Ownrshp* 2010
Sales 140.3MM^E *EMP* 250
SIC 5571 5013 Motorcycle parts & accessories; Motor vehicle supplies & new parts; Motorcycle parts & accessories; Motor vehicle supplies & new parts
Genl Mgr: Zach Parham
**Pr:* John Parham
**Treas:* Michael Moore
**Prin:* Thomas S Collins
IT Man: Colin Gillis
Mktg Dir: Tim Barcz
Mktg Dir: Nicole Ridge
Mktg Mgr: Tom Hines
Mktg Mgr: Rhyde Thomas

D-U-N-S 60-622-1851
J&P FLASH INC
FLASH MARKET
105 W Harrison Ave, West Memphis, AR 72301-4230
Tel (870) 735-3744 *Founded/Ownrshp* 1985
Sales 25.7MM^E *EMP* 150
SIC 5411 Convenience stores, independent
Pr: Myles Stanley Jones
**Pr:* Oscar Patterson
**VP:* Dwayne Jones

D-U-N-S 06-812-4687 IMP
J&P PARK ACQUISITIONS INC
PARK SEED
1 Parkton Ave, Greenwood, SC 29647-0001
Tel (864) 223-8555 *Founded/Ownrshp* 2010
Sales 33.0MM^E *EMP* 200
SIC 0831 Flowers & florists' supplies; Nurseries & garden centers; Forest nurseries
CEO: Richard Pope
**CFO:* Vick Crowley

J&S DEVELOPMENT AND MANAGEMENT
See FIGURE EIGHT PROPERTIES INC

D-U-N-S 03-122-3514
J-A-G CONSTRUCTION CO
11257 109 Rd, Dodge City, KS 67801-6730
Tel (620) 225-0061 *Founded/Ownrshp* 1962
Sales 41.9MM^E *EMP* 140
SIC 1542 3273 Commercial & office building, new construction; Ready-mixed concrete; Commercial & office building, new construction; Ready-mixed concrete
Pr: James A Coffin
**VP:* Mark Green
**VP:* Scott Reiderer
Genl Mgr: Meggan Starks

D-U-N-S 60-271-1129
J-BAR OF NORTH FLORIDA INC
BURGER KING
3657 Regent Blvd Ste 204, Jacksonville, FL 32224-6500
Tel (904) 262-9786 *Founded/Ownrshp* 1988
Sales 5.0MM^E *EMP* 330
SIC 5812 Fast-food restaurant, chain
Pr: Barbara Williams
**VP:* Michael J Williams

D-U-N-S 00-818-0762
J-H-J INC
PIGGLY WIGGLY
5910 Airline Hwy, Baton Rouge, LA 70805-3201
Tel (225) 357-0757 *Founded/Ownrshp* 1984
Sales 23.8MM^E *EMP* 125
SIC 5411 Supermarkets, chain
Pr: Garnett Jones Jr
**VP:* Ted Harvey

D-U-N-S 02-696-0898
J-K CHEVROLET INC
J K CHEVROLET ISUZU
1451 Highway 69 N, Nederland, TX 77627-8017
Tel (409) 527-4142 *Founded/Ownrshp* 2000
Sales 34.1MM^E *EMP* 89
SIC 5511 Automobiles, new & used; Automobiles, new & used
Pr: Robert Turner
Sls Mgr: Sharon Taylor

D-U-N-S 07-857-0306 IMP/EXP
J-LINE PUMP CO (TN)
AMERICAN-MARSH PUMPS
185 Progress Rd, Collierville, TN 38017-2719
Tel (901) 860-2300 *Founded/Ownrshp* 1975
Sales 55.0MM *EMP* 163
SIC 5084 3561 Pumps & pumping equipment; Pumps, domestic: water or sump; Pumps & pumping equipment; Pumps, domestic: water or sump
CEO: David Cheek
**Pr:* Terry Kerbough
VP: Patrick Dickey
VP: Jim Pflugrad
**VP:* Jim REA
Exec: Pat Dickey
MIS Dir: Lindsay Williams
VP Opers: Steven Hitt
Sfty Mgr: Bonnie Allman
Opers Mgr: Sara James
Natl Sales: Russell Brundridge

D-U-N-S 06-248-6238 IMP/EXP
J-M MANUFACTURING CO INC
JM EAGLE
5200 W Century Blvd, Los Angeles, CA 90045-5928
Tel (800) 621-4404 *Founded/Ownrshp* 1983
Sales 1.0MMM^E *EMP* 1,800
SIC 2821 3084 3491 Polyvinyl chloride resins (PVC); Polyvinyl chloride resins (PVC); Plastics pipe; Water works valves
CEO: Walter Wang
CFO: Dick Oxley
Bd of Dir: Richard Perkins
Trst: Kevin Woo
Ofcr: Edward Stanley
VP: Daniel O'Connor
**Prin:* Shirley Wang
Adm Dir: Autumn Carlson
Area Mgr: Beryl Clark
Area Mgr: Brian Lang
Area Mgr: Jerry Liffrig

D-U-N-S 78-484-4060 IMP
■ **J-MAC TOOL INC**
(*Suby of* FORUM ENERGY TECHNOLOGIES INC) ★
8701 Eagle Mountain Cir, Fort Worth, TX 76135-9497
Tel (817) 237-6309 *Founded/Ownrshp* 2015
Sales 23.1MM^E *EMP* 50
SIC 3549 Metalworking machinery
Pr: Jack Coleman
CFO: Jon Urban
VP Opers: Lance Vickers
Plnt Mgr: Randy Macy
Ql Cn Mgr: John Nance
VP Sls: Wayne Wooley

J-MAK INDUSTRIES
See PANACEA PRODUCTS CORP

J-MART FOOD STORES
See CENTRAL ARKANSAS PETROLEUM INC

D-U-N-S 78-748-3960 EXP
J-POWER USA DEVELOPMENT CO LTD
(*Suby of* ELECTRIC POWER DEVELOPMENT CO., LTD.)
1900 E Golf Rd Ste 1030, Schaumburg, IL 60173-5076
Tel (847) 908-2800 *Founded/Ownrshp* 2005
Sales 214.2MM^E *EMP* 578^E
SIC 4911 Generation, electric power
CEO: Mark Condon
Sr VP: Jun Hashimoto
VP: Rick Noble
VP: Paul Peterson
VP: Masaru Sakai
Dir IT: Vincent Torrey

D-U-N-S 80-564-9204
J-TRACK LLC
1445 117th St Ste 1, College Point, NY 11356-1537
Tel (718) 554-2760 *Founded/Ownrshp* 2007
Sales 102.7MM *EMP* 25
SIC 1531 Operative builders; Operative builders
CEO: Tom Iovino
**Pr:* Mitch Levine
**VP:* Scott Sbrocco
**VP:* Christopher Vito
Snr PM: Richard Green
Snr Mgr: Len De Pinto

D-U-N-S 07-840-8341
J-U-B ENGINEERS INC (ID)
250 S Beechwood Dr # 201, Boise, ID 83709-0944
Tel (208) 363-0282 *Founded/Ownrshp* 1954, 1996
Sales 40.1MM *EMP* 330
Accts Ripley Doorn & Company Pll
SIC 8711 8713 Consulting engineer; Surveying services; Consulting engineer; Surveying services
Ch Bd: Kirby D Vickers
**Pr:* Lee E Cammack
**Pr:* George L Wagner
**CFO:* Paul Fisk
Ex VP: Tim Haener
VP: David Day
Area Mgr: Stephen Freiburger
Area Mgr: Alan Giesbrecht
Area Mgr: Kent Gingrich
Area Mgr: Jeff Temple
IT Man: George Wagner

D-U-N-S 96-555-9672
J-W ENERGY CO
15505 Wright Brothers Dr B, Addison, TX 75001-4274
Tel (972) 233-8191 *Founded/Ownrshp* 2006
Sales 557.8MM^E *EMP* 700
SIC 1311 7353 3533 1381 Crude petroleum production; Natural gas production; Oil field equipment, rental or leasing; Oil & gas field machinery; Drilling oil & gas wells; Crude petroleum production; Natural gas production; Oil field equipment, rental or leasing; Oil & gas field machinery; Drilling oil & gas wells
CEO: Howard G Westerman
Pr: Perry A Harris
**Pr:* David A Miller
**Ex VP:* Richard T Clement
VP: Larry Carpenter
**VP:* Richard S Davis
Area Supr: Marc Amick
Dist Mgr: Garrett Lude
Snr Sftwr: Uday Karuppiah
Opers Mgr: John Welge

D-U-N-S 00-677-1356 IMP
J-W OPERATING CO
COHORT ENERGY COMPANY
(*Suby of* J-W ENERGY CO) ★
15505 Wright Brothers Dr B, Addison, TX 75001-4274
Tel (972) 233-8191 *Founded/Ownrshp* 1960
Sales 225.3MM^E *EMP* 700
SIC 3533 1311 7353 1381 Oil & gas field machinery; Crude petroleum production; Oil field equipment, rental or leasing; Drilling oil & gas wells; Oil & gas field machinery; Crude petroleum production; Oil field equipment, rental or leasing; Drilling oil & gas wells
CEO: Howard G Westerman
**Pr:* Tony Meyer
COO: Paul Westerman
CFO: Laura Westerman
**Ex VP:* C D McDaniels
VP: Jeffery Brown
VP: Paul Stephenson
Genl Mgr: Keith Boswell
Off Mgr: Marsha McIntyre
CTO: Todd Stout
Dir IT: Joel Wolfes

D-U-N-S 19-527-5961
J-W POWER CO
(*Suby of* J-W ENERGY CO) ★
15505 Wright Brothers Dr, Addison, TX 75001-4274
Tel (972) 233-8191 *Founded/Ownrshp* 2001
Sales 40.9MM^E *EMP* 160^E
SIC 3585 Compressors for refrigeration & air conditioning equipment; Compressors for refrigeration & air conditioning equipment
Pr: Don Bizzell
**VP:* Lindon Leners

D-U-N-S 04-335-4182 IMP/EXP
J/B INDUSTRIES INC (IL)
601 N Farnsworth Ave, Aurora, IL 60505-3092
Tel (630) 851-9444 *Founded/Ownrshp* 1967, 1973
Sales 32.7MM^E *EMP* 60
SIC 3494 3563 Plumbing & heating valves; Steam fittings & specialties; Vacuum pumps, except laboratory
Pr: Jeff Cherif
CFO: Jim Borja
**Sec:* Ron Hill Jr
Sr Cor Off: Lee Larsen
VP: Oscar Lopez
Off Mgr: Linda Pounds
Mktg Dir: Jennifer Boyajian
Sls Mgr: Sam Roti

D-U-N-S 14-194-8864
J/R HILO ACQUISITION LLC
HONDA
(*Suby of* REED/JONES ACQUISITION HI LLC) ★
124 Wiwoole St, Hilo, HI 96720-5124
Tel (808) 961-6087 *Founded/Ownrshp* 2003
Sales 41.0MM^E *EMP* 260
SIC 5511 Automobiles, new & used; Automobiles, new & used
CEO: Fletcher Jones
Genl Mgr: Jerry Cousin

D-U-N-S 94-622-7774
■ **J2 CLOUD SERVICES INC**
(*Suby of* J2 GLOBAL INC) ★
6922 Hollywood Blvd # 500, Los Angeles, CA 90028-6117
Tel (323) 860-9200 *Founded/Ownrshp* 2014
Sales 599.0MM *EMP* 1,130^E
Tkr Sym JCOM *Exch* NGS
SIC 4822 Telegraph & other communications; Telegraph & other communications
CEO: Nehemia Zucker
**Pr:* R Scott Turicchi
**CFO:* Kathleen M Griggs
CFO: Allen Jones
CFO: Scott R Tuicchi
Sr Cor Off: Susan Park
Sr Cor Off: Jeff Shell
Ex VP: Michael Benevento
Ex VP: Tonia Oconnor
Ex VP: Bedi Singh
**VP:* Jeffrey D Adelman
VP: Andrew Duncan
VP: Kevin Feldman
VP: Ken Ford
VP: Michael W Harris
VP: Timothy Johnson
VP: Paul Kinsella
VP: Ed Patrick
VP: Linda Silva
Exec: Anthony Ghosn
Dir Bus: Charlene Christman
Board of Directors: Douglas Y Bech, Robert J Cresci, W Brian Kretzmer, Richard S Ressler, Stephen Ross, Michael P Schulhof

D-U-N-S 07-954-2179
▲ **J2 GLOBAL INC**
6922 Hollywood Blvd # 500, Los Angeles, CA 90028-6125
Tel (323) 860-9200 *Founded/Ownrshp* 1995
Sales 599.0MM *EMP* 1,410^E
SIC 4822 Telegraph & other communications; Telegraph & other communications
CEO: Nehemia Zucker
Pr: Kamran Izadpanah
Pr: R Scott Turicchi
VP: Alan Alters
VP: Andrew Duncan
VP: Michael Harris
VP: Ed Patrick
VP: Linda Silva
Dir Bus: Joshua Evans
Snr Sftwr: Andrew Weinstein
Sftwr Eng: Emily Hoang
Board of Directors: Douglas Y Bech, Robert J Cresci, W Brian Kretzmer, Jonathan F Miller, Stephen Ross

D-U-N-S 94-515-1590
J3 CO LLC
J3 COMPANIES
6600 State Highway 27, Comfort, TX 78013-3391
Tel (830) 995-5100 *Founded/Ownrshp* 2006
Sales 28.3MM *EMP* 125
Accts Ridout Barrett & Co Pc S
SIC 1794 Excavation work; Excavation work
CEO: H Ritman Jons
Pr: Henry Paris Jons III
CFO: Timothy L Braden
VP: Hugh R Jons Jr

J3 COMPANIES
See J3 CO LLC

D-U-N-S 18-554-5100 IMP/EXP
■ JA APPAREL CORP
JOSEPH ABBOUD
(*Suby of* JA HOLDING INC) ★
6380 Rogerdale Rd, Houston, TX 77072-1624
Tel (281) 776-7964 *Founded/Ownrshp* 2006
Sales 187.2MM^E *EMP* 500
SIC 5136 Men's & boys' clothing; Men's & boys' clothing
Pr: Anthony Sapienza
**Ch Bd:* Bill Watts
Pr: Kenton Selvey
**CFO:* Erick Spiel
Founder: Joseph Abboud
VP: Trudy Larson
VP: Tanja Siburg
Creative D: Bernardo Rojo
VP Sls: Natalie Condon
Board of Directors: Alberto Morabito

D-U-N-S 05-155-2966
JA CO FOODS INC (DE)
SONIC DRIVE-IN
111 Maxwell Ln, Columbus, MS 39702-5243
Tel (662) 328-5009 *Founded/Ownrshp* 1977
Sales 11.1MM *EMP* 500
SIC 5812 Drive-in restaurant; Drive-in restaurant
Pr: Ernie Jacobsen
**VP:* Donna Jacobsen

D-U-N-S 15-366-1009 IMP
JA CROSON LLC
31550 County Road 437, Sorrento, FL 32776-9380
Tel (352) 729-7100 *Founded/Ownrshp* 1959
Sales 42.2MM^E *EMP* 150
SIC 1711 Plumbing contractors; Mechanical contractor; Plumbing contractors; Mechanical contractor
CEO: David A Croson
**Ch Bd:* James A Croson
**Pr:* Paul Croson
CFO: Joe Harvard
**CFO:* Joseph Harvard
**VP:* Taki Spinos
IT Man: Edwin Gonzales

D-U-N-S 07-909-6391
■ JA HOLDING INC
(*Suby of* MENS WEARHOUSE INC) ★
650 5th Ave Fl 20, New York, NY 10019-6108
Tel (212) 586-9140 *Founded/Ownrshp* 2013
Sales 187.2MM^E *EMP* 500
SIC 5136 Men's & boys' clothing; Men's & boys' clothing
Pr: Doug Ewert

D-U-N-S 95-633-8453
JA LEE ELECTRIC INC
115 Bi County Blvd, Farmingdale, NY 11735-3925
Tel (718) 729-7662 *Founded/Ownrshp* 1991
Sales 23.5MM^E *EMP* 70
Accts Monahan & Company Cpas Pc Me
SIC 1731 Fiber optic cable installation
Pr: John A Lee
**VP:* Christopher Lee
**VP:* Thomas Yacopino
Dir IT: Richard Einhorn

J.A. MOMANEY SERVICES
See JAM SERVICES INC

JA MYERS HOMES
See J A MYERS BUILDING AND DEVELOPMENT INC

D-U-N-S 00-690-3512
JA RIGGS TRACTOR CO
9125 Interstate 30, Little Rock, AR 72209-3703
Tel (501) 570-3100 *Founded/Ownrshp* 1927
Sales 196.9MM^E *EMP* 450
SIC 5082 General construction machinery & equipment; General construction machinery & equipment
Pr: John Riggs IV
**Pr:* Rob Riggs
CFO: Denny Upton
**Prin:* Keith Riggs
Manager: Jason Hooper
Sls Mgr: Bree Calley
Sls Mgr: Jason McDonald

D-U-N-S 00-326-2946
JA SCHEIBEL INC (MD)
SCHEIBEL CONSTRUCTION
115 Prospect Dr, Huntingtown, MD 20639-3413
Tel (301) 855-7900 *Founded/Ownrshp* 1946, 1952
Sales 39.5MM^E *EMP* 70
SIC 1542 Commercial & office building, new construction
Pr: John R Bailey
**Sec:* Jerry Bailey
Dir Bus: Kristen Bailey
VP Admn: Sid Moreland
IT Man: Kristen Doty
VP Opers: Richard Mellon
VP Sls: David Weldon
Snr PM: Matt Tessier

D-U-N-S 15-179-7859
JA STREET & ASSOCIATES INC
245 Birch St, Blountville, TN 37617-4758
Tel (423) 323-8017 *Founded/Ownrshp* 1986
Sales 59.6MM^E *EMP* 150
SIC 1542 1541 Commercial & office building, new construction; Commercial & office buildings, renovation & repair; Industrial buildings, new construction; Renovation, remodeling & repairs: industrial buildings; Commercial & office building, new construction; Commercial & office buildings, renovation & repair; Industrial buildings, new construction; Renovation, remodeling & repairs: industrial buildings
Pr: J A Street
**Treas:* Lois A Clarke
VP: Barbara Street
VP: Mark Wininger
Off Mgr: Linda Bridges
Dir IT: Ronald Moore
IT Man: Cloe Collins
Snr Mgr: Brian Poe

D-U-N-S 19-319-4651
JA WEDUM FOUNDATION
2615 University Ave Se, Minneapolis, MN 55414-3207
Tel (612) 789-3363 *Founded/Ownrshp* 1959
Sales 36.7MM *EMP* 2
SIC 8699 Charitable organization
Pr: Jay Portz
Ex Dir: Dale Vesledahl

D-U-N-S 00-177-3399
JA-BAR SILICONE CORP
252 Brighton Rd, Andover, NJ 07821-5032
Tel (973) 786-5000 *Founded/Ownrshp* 1965
Sales 31.5MM^E *EMP* 83
SIC 2822 Silicone rubbers
Pr: Gilbert Jacobs
**Sec:* Myrtle G Jacobs
**Ex VP:* Robert J Lisofski
**VP:* Mark Derr
**VP:* Michael Rovano
Dir Lab: Lansine Sako
Mtls Mgr: Cookie Stephens
Sfty Mgr: Skip Constantine
Sls Mgr: Michael Rabuano

D-U-N-S 02-986-9401
JA-DEL INC
FIORELLA S JACK STACK BARBECUE
7171 W 95th St Ste 500, Overland Park, KS 66212-2254
Tel (816) 942-9141 *Founded/Ownrshp* 1975
Sales 18.0MM^E *EMP* 400
SIC 5812 Barbecue restaurant; Barbecue restaurant
Pr: Jack Fiorella
**Treas:* Case Dorman
**VP:* Delores Fiorella

D-U-N-S 04-239-4395 IMP/EXP
JA-RU INC (FL)
4030 Phillips Hwy, Jacksonville, FL 32207-6835
Tel (904) 733-9311 *Founded/Ownrshp* 1957
Sales 44.2MM^E *EMP* 144
SIC 5092

D-U-N-S 02-116-4384
JAAR INC
MCDONALD'S
1060 W Norton Ave Ste 4, Muskegon, MI 49441-4175
Tel (231) 722-2220 *Founded/Ownrshp* 1994
Sales 8.9MM^E *EMP* 350
SIC 5812 Fast-food restaurant, chain; Fast-food restaurant, chain
Pr: Arthur Scott
Off Mgr: Roonie Reeves

D-U-N-S 07-105-7434
JAARS INC
7601 Radin Rd, Waxhaw, NC 28173-9158
Tel (704) 843-6000 *Founded/Ownrshp* 1963
Sales 5.2MM *EMP* 600
Accts Capin Crouse Llp Lawrenceville
SIC 7389 7812 7363 7371 Translation services; Motion picture & video production; Pilot service, aviation; Custom computer programming services; Translation services; Motion picture & video production; Pilot service, aviation; Custom computer programming services
Ex Dir: Judy Boyd
**Pr:* David Reeves
**CFO:* Tim Staples
Bd of Dir: Marita Eden
Ofcr: Ilene Foote
VP: Chuck Daly
VP: Arthur Lightbody
**VP:* Phil McBride
VP: Craig Whaley

D-U-N-S 06-032-9794
JAB & CO INC
HONDA CITY
3859 Hempstead Tpke, Levittown, NY 11756-1305
Tel (516) 735-8900 *Founded/Ownrshp* 2000
Sales 32.7MM^E *EMP* 90
SIC 5511 Automobiles, new & used; Automobiles, new & used
Pr: John A Burns
Genl Mgr: Dennis Buchanan

D-U-N-S 07-854-9761
JAB BEECH INC
2200 Pennsylvania Ave Nw, Washington, DC 20037-1709
Tel (516) 537-1040 *Founded/Ownrshp* 2012
Sales 1.9MMM^E *EMP* 6,087^E
SIC 6799 Investors; Investors
CEO: Peter Harf

D-U-N-S 01-571-1891
JAB ENERGY SOLUTIONS LLC
262 N Sam Houston Pkwy E, Houston, TX 77060-2027
Tel (281) 260-7500 *Founded/Ownrshp* 2008
Sales 40.0MM *EMP* 19
SIC 1629 Marine construction

JAB WIRELESS BROADBAND
See JAB WIRELESS INC

D-U-N-S 83-558-6095
JAB WIRELESS INC
JAB WIRELESS BROADBAND
400 Inverness Pkwy # 330, Englewood, CO 80112-5830
Tel (303) 705-6522 *Founded/Ownrshp* 2005
Sales 30.2MM^E *EMP* 90^E
SIC 4812 Cellular telephone services
Pr: Jack Koo
Chf Mktg O: John Pitek
Sr VP: Damon Estep
**Sr VP:* Scott Perich
Dir Risk M: Katie Simpson
**Prin:* Jim Vaughn
Genl Mgr: Phil Walsh

D-U-N-S 04-181-0979 IMP/EXP
▲ JABIL CIRCUIT INC
10560 Dr Martin Luther, Saint Petersburg, FL 33716-3718
Tel (727) 577-9749 *Founded/Ownrshp* 1992
Sales 17.9MMM *EMP* 142,000
Tkr Sym JBL *Exch* NYS
SIC 3672 Printed circuit boards; Printed circuit boards
CEO: Mark T Mondello
**Ch Bd:* Timothy L Main
Pr: Dennis Maddock
Pr: William E Peters
COO: William D Muir Jr
CFO: Forbes I J Alexander
Treas: Sergio A Cadavid
Bd of Dir: Armando Ochoa
Ex VP: Joseph A McGee
Sr VP: Scott Brown
Sr VP: Gary L Cantrell
Sr VP: Meheryar Dastoor
Sr VP: Michael Dastoor
VP: Hai Hwai
VP: Alan Myers
VP: Roger Shahnazarian
Exec: Michael Sparksman
Dir Bus: Laurie Banks
Dir Bus: Jeff Broadbent
Dir Bus: Chris Connell
Dir Bus: Jeff Mack
Board of Directors: Martha F Brooks, Mel S Lavitt, Lawrence J Murphy, Frank A Newman, David M Stout, Steven A Raymund,thomas A

D-U-N-S 05-392-7708 IMP
■ JABIL CIRCUIT LLC
(*Suby of* JABIL CIRCUIT INC) ★
10560 Dr Martin, Saint Petersburg, FL 33716
Tel (727) 577-9749 *Founded/Ownrshp* 1992
Sales 282.1MM^E *EMP* 789
SIC 3672 Computer maintenance & repair; Printed circuit boards
CEO: Timothy L Main
Pr: John Foster
Pr: Jerry Pahl
**COO:* Mark T Mondello
**CFO:* Forbes I J Alexander
**Treas:* Sergio A Cadavid
**Ex VP:* Hartmut Liebel
**Sr VP:* Michael K Dastoor
Dir Bus: Molly Jantzen
Dir Bus: Ethan Kline
Dir Bus: Amy Knoth
Dir Bus: Ilkka Pouttu

D-U-N-S 07-379-8337 IMP
■ JABIL DEFENSE AND AEROSPACE SERVICES LLC
(*Suby of* JABIL CIRCUIT INC) ★
10560 Dr M L King Jr St N Martin, Saint Petersburg, FL 33716
Tel (727) 577-9749 *Founded/Ownrshp* 2004
Sales 46.9MM^E *EMP* 75
SIC 3672 Printed circuit boards
CEO: Mark T Mondello
**COO:* William D Muir J
**Ex VP:* Joseph A McGee
**Sr VP:* Sergio A Cadavid
**Sr VP:* Michael Dastoor
Genl Mgr: Santosh Bhagwat
IT Man: Darling James
Netwrk Eng: David Shiver
Opers Mgr: Kristen Widunas

D-U-N-S 06-041-8485 IMP
■ JABIL GLOBAL SERVICES LLC
IQOR AFTERMARKEFT SERVICES
(*Suby of* JABIL CIRCUIT LLC) ★
11201 Electron Dr, Louisville, KY 40299-3827
Tel (502) 240-1000 *Founded/Ownrshp* 2009
Sales 22.3MM^E *EMP* 210
SIC 7629 Electrical equipment repair services; Electrical equipment repair services
Ch: Timothy L Main
**Pr:* William E Peters
**CEO:* Mark T Mondello
**COO:* William D Muir Jr
**CFO:* Forbes I J Alexander
**Treas:* Sergio Alonso Cadavid
VP: Pauline Chambers

D-U-N-S 01-607-6283
JABO SUPPLY CORP
5164 Braley Rd, Huntington, WV 25705-2012
Tel (304) 736-8333 *Founded/Ownrshp* 1964
Sales 35.4MM^E *EMP* 81
SIC 5051 5085 5074

D-U-N-S 18-054-0965
JAC AIRPORT INC
AIRPORT HONDA
3069 Alcoa Hwy, Alcoa, TN 37701-3120
Tel (865) 970-7792 *Founded/Ownrshp* 1991
Sales 27.6MM^E *EMP* 70
SIC 5511 5521 7538 Automobiles, new & used; Automobiles, used cars only; General automotive repair shops; Automobiles, new & used; Automobiles, used cars only; General automotive repair shops
Pr: Jerry L Hodge
**Sec:* Charles Stephens
**VP:* W Allen Lewis
Genl Mgr: Chris Denny
Genl Mgr: Joe Jemley
Dir IT: Scott Wilkins
Sales Exec: Paul McKeever
Sls Mgr: Trustin Hampton
Sales Asso: Tim Bowers
Sales Asso: Gene Charsha
Sales Asso: Kevin Coffman

D-U-N-S 87-826-8432 IMP/EXP
JAC HOLDING CORP
(*Suby of* WYNNCHURCH CAPITAL LTD) ★
3937 Campus Dr, Pontiac, MI 48341-3124
Tel (734) 944-8844 *Founded/Ownrshp* 2009
Sales 267.1MM^E *EMP* 1,505
SIC 3089 Injection molding of plastics; Injection molding of plastics
CEO: Jack Falcon
**COO:* Mike Wood
**CFO:* Mike Vanloon
VP: Bill Elliot
**VP:* Noel Ranka

D-U-N-S 15-473-2572
JAC NISSAN INC
TWIN CITY NISSAN
3247 Alcoa Hwy, Alcoa, TN 37701-3201
Tel (865) 977-6472 *Founded/Ownrshp* 1989
Sales 28.6MM^E *EMP* 54
SIC 5511 Automobiles, new & used; Automobiles, new & used
Pr: Jerry L Hodge
**Sec:* Charles Stephens
Genl Mgr: Eddie Naser
Sls Mgr: Daryl Casteel
Sls Mgr: Jason Russell
Sls Mgr: Darren Scholle

D-U-N-S 05-880-6126 IMP/EXP
JAC PRODUCTS INC
(*Suby of* JAC HOLDING CORP) ★
225 S Industrial Dr, Saline, MI 48176-9183
Tel (734) 944-8844 *Founded/Ownrshp* 2010
Sales 161.3MM^E *EMP* 1,200
SIC 3089 3714

D-U-N-S 01-228-8767 IMP
JAC VANDENBERG INC
100 Corporate Dr, Yonkers, NY 10701-6807
Tel (914) 964-5900 *Founded/Ownrshp* 1947
Sales 173.4MM *EMP* 30
SIC 5148 Fruits, fresh; Fruits, fresh
Pr: David L Schiro
**Treas:* Edward Paap
**VP:* Michael Knatz
**VP:* Fred Vandenberg
VP: Jeffrey Vandenberg
Dir IT: Joseph McEwing
Trfc Mgr: Brian Murphy

D-U-N-S 80-008-1846 IMP
JACADI USA INC
(*Suby of* JACADI)
4 W Red Oak Ln Ste 104, White Plains, NY 10604-3603
Tel (914) 697-7684 *Founded/Ownrshp* 1991
Sales 69.2MM^E *EMP* 500
SIC 5137 5021 5139 Children's goods; Baby goods; Infants' wear; Juvenile furniture; Shoes; Children's goods; Baby goods; Infants' wear; Juvenile furniture; Shoes
Pr: Bruce Pettibone

D-U-N-S 07-882-2339
JACAM CHEMICALS 2013 LLC
205 S Broadway Ave, Sterling, KS 67579-2339
Tel (620) 278-3355 *Founded/Ownrshp* 2013
Sales 57.0MM^E *EMP* 262
SIC 2869 Laboratory chemicals, organic; Laboratory chemicals, organic
Pr: Jason West

JACCUZI GROUP WORLDWIDE
See JACUZZI BRANDS CORP

D-U-N-S 79-642-5853
■ JACINTOPORT INTERNATIONAL LLC
GLOBAL DISTRIBUTION CENTER
(*Suby of* SEABOARD CORP) ★
16398 Jacintoport Blvd, Houston, TX 77015-6586
Tel (281) 457-2415 *Founded/Ownrshp* 2007
Sales 85.1MM^E *EMP* 450
SIC 4491 Marine cargo handling; Marine cargo handling
Ex VP: David Labbe
IT Man: Pete Tinsley
Sfty Mgr: Tracy Portillo
Opers Mgr: Scott Primeaux

JACK & JILL ICE CREAM CO
See SIMCO SALES SERVICE OF PENNSYLVANIA INC

D-U-N-S 01-832-8260
JACK A ALLEN INC
ALLEN OIL
2105 Old State Route 7, Steubenville, OH 43952-4332
Tel (740) 282-4531 *Founded/Ownrshp* 1977
Sales 77.3MM^E *EMP* 65
SIC 5172 5983 5541 5411 Gasoline; Fuel oil dealers; Filling stations, gasoline; Convenience stores, independent; Gasoline; Fuel oil dealers; Filling stations, gasoline; Convenience stores, independent
Pr: Gary Armentrout

D-U-N-S 04-004-0156
JACK A FARRIOR INC
9585 Us Highway 264a, Farmville, NC 27828-9548
Tel (252) 753-2020 *Founded/Ownrshp* 1983
Sales 21.5MM^E *EMP* 60
SIC 3444 7692 3535 1796 3312 Sheet metalwork; Welding repair; Conveyors & conveying equipment; Millwright; Structural shapes & pilings, steel
Pr: Jack A Farrior
**Sec:* Susan Farrior
**VP:* David Baker
Mtls Mgr: Bryan Barrow
Sfty Mgr: Mike Dunbar
Opers Mgr: John Shoemaker

D-U-N-S 00-711-2238
JACK B HENDERSON CONSTRUCTION CO INC (NM)
JB HENDERSON CONSTRUCTION
501 Eubank Blvd Se, Albuquerque, NM 87123-3332
Tel (505) 292-8955 *Founded/Ownrshp* 1959
Sales 61.4MM *EMP* 505
Accts Ricci & Company Llc Albuquerq
SIC 1542 Nonresidential construction; Nonresidential construction
CEO: Mark Henderson
**Pr:* John Stroud
**Sec:* Linda Henderson
**VP:* Bart Davis
**VP:* John Robertson
**VP:* Charles Watson

D-U-N-S 05-223-3020
JACK B KELLEY INC
(*Suby of* KENAN ADVANTAGE GROUP INC) ★
801 S Fillmore St Ste 505, Amarillo, TX 79101-3526
Tel (806) 353-3553 *Founded/Ownrshp* 2011

Sales 30.3MM^E *EMP* 250
SIC 4213

D-U-N-S 03-236-6775 EXP
JACK BECKER DISTRIBUTORS INC
6800 Suemac Pl, Jacksonville, FL 32254-5700
Tel (904) 354-8411 *Founded/Ownrshp* 1956
Sales 26.3MM *EMP* 29
Accts Johnson And Company Pa Jac
SIC 5171 5013 Petroleum bulk stations & terminals; Automotive servicing equipment; Petroleum bulk stations & terminals; Automotive servicing equipment
Pr: David Rowland
**Ch Bd:* Jack Becker
**Ch:* Duane Rowland
**VP:* Ronald Dedicos
**VP:* Don Hudson

D-U-N-S 07-657-9481
JACK CONWAY & CO INC
137 Washington St Ste 1, Norwell, MA 02061-1734
Tel (781) 982-2333 *Founded/Ownrshp* 1955
Sales 9.9MM^E *EMP* 300
SIC 6531 6163 Real estate brokers & agents; Loan brokers; Real estate brokers & agents; Loan brokers
Treas: John E Conway
**Pr:* Richard Cahill
Ex VP: Donna Crowell
VP: Ralph Grassia
Sales Asso: James Donovan
Sales Asso: Anne O'Brien

D-U-N-S 00-696-5537
JACK COOPER TRANSPORT CO INC
1100 Walnut St Ste 2400, Kansas City, MO 64106-2186
Tel (816) 983-4000 *Founded/Ownrshp* 1939
Sales 807.2MM^E *EMP* 3,000
SIC 4213 7389 Automobiles, transport & delivery; Drive-a-way automobile service; Automobiles, transport & delivery; Drive-a-way automobile service
Ch: T Michael Riggs
Pr: Larry Tolstyka
**CEO:* Robert Griffin
Bd of Dir: Samuel Torrence
**Ex VP:* Rudy Bijleveld
**Ex VP:* Theo Ciupitu
Sr VP: David Davis
VP: Wesley Brandon
VP: Stacy Clark
VP: Donald Gallant
VP: Kyle Haulotte
**VP:* Craig Irwin
VP: Mark Kreger
VP: Brian Varano
Dir Risk M: Terry Milford

D-U-N-S 00-404-0325 IMP
■ **JACK DANIEL DISTILLERY LEM MOTLOW PROP INC**
JACK DANIELS WHISKEY
(*Suby of* BROWN-FORMAN CORP) ★
Rr 1, Lynchburg, TN 37352
Tel (931) 759-4221 *Founded/Ownrshp* 1939
Sales 87.4MM^E *EMP* 365
SIC 2085 Bourbon whiskey; Bourbon whiskey
VP: Steve Goodner
**CFO:* Danny Lamb
Exec: Marty Copeland

JACK DANIELS
See DILLS ALTON JACK AND ALICIA F

D-U-N-S 07-334-0619
JACK DANIELS AUDI
(*Suby of* JACK DANIELS MOTORS INC) ★
120 Pleasant Ave, Upper Saddle River, NJ 07458-2304
Tel (201) 368-7300 *Founded/Ownrshp* 1971
Sales 41.6MM^E *EMP* 200
SIC 5511 Automobiles, new & used; Automobiles, new & used
Pr: Jack Daniels
Genl Mgr: Solomon Faizi
Sls Mgr: Minas Papadakis
Sls Mgr: John Zingani

JACK DANIELS CONSTRUCTION
See PHAZE CONCRETE INC

D-U-N-S 83-781-4867 IMP
JACK DANIELS MOTORS INC
16-01 Mcbride Ave, Fair Lawn, NJ 07410-2800
Tel (201) 796-8500 *Founded/Ownrshp* 1972
Sales 96.9MM^E *EMP* 275^E
SIC 5511 Automobiles, new & used; Automobiles, new & used
Genl Mgr: Frank Devita
**Pr:* Michael V Daniels
**COO:* Greg Zulli
**CFO:* Ronald Dubin
Genl Mgr: Tom Baldassare
Genl Mgr: Steven Park
Sls Mgr: Curtis Aldershof
Sls Mgr: Marco Pineros
Sales Asso: Terry Axel
Sales Asso: Angela Bellows
Sales Asso: Jack Daniels

D-U-N-S 06-134-1871
JACK DANIELS PORSCHE INC
DANIELS, JACK PORSCHE
29-09 Broadway, Fair Lawn, NJ 07410-3998
Tel (201) 796-8500 *Founded/Ownrshp* 1972
Sales 27.9MM^E *EMP* 105
SIC 5511 Automobiles, new & used; Automobiles, new & used
Pr: Jack Daniels
Sls Mgr: James Lanzaro
Sls Mgr: George Maloney

JACK DANIELS WHISKEY
See JACK DANIEL DISTILLERY LEM MOTLOW PROP INC

D-U-N-S 04-180-3388
JACK DEMMER FORD INC
37300 Michigan Ave, Wayne, MI 48184-1199
Tel (248) 349-1400 *Founded/Ownrshp* 1957
Sales 53.9MM^E *EMP* 145
SIC 5511 5521 Automobiles, new & used; Used car dealers; Automobiles, new & used; Used car dealers
CEO: John E Demmer
**Pr:* William J Demmer
**CFO:* John Engler
**VP:* James Demmer
Off Mgr: Michelle Nedry
DP Exec: Sue Denomie
Dir IT: Ben Forta
Dir IT: Brad Neilson
Sls&Mrk Ex: Bill Demmer
Sls Mgr: Joe Theis
Sales Asso: Bernard Sakakini

D-U-N-S 06-882-0711
JACK DOHENY COMPANIES INC
T3W
777 Doheny Dr, Northville, MI 48167-1957
Tel (248) 349-0904 *Founded/Ownrshp* 1973
Sales 49.0MM^E *EMP* 100
SIC 5012 7537 Commercial vehicles; Commercial vehicles; Automotive transmission repair shops
CEO: Jack L Doheny
Pr: Dan Weber
CFO: Kathy Nieman
Ex VP: Kay Doheny Snyder
VP: Tom Doheny
VP: Gary Mapes
Brnch Mgr: Dan Coley
Genl Mgr: Brian Bandura
Off Mgr: Teri Barnum
Dir IT: Chris Gravlen
IT Man: Chris Gravlin

JACK ELLIS' GLENDALE DODGE
See GLENDALE DODGE LLC

D-U-N-S 04-405-4302 EXP
JACK ENGLE & CO (CA)
8440 S Alameda St, Los Angeles, CA 90001-4112
Tel (323) 583-6403 *Founded/Ownrshp* 1965
Sales 45.3MM^E *EMP* 55^E
SIC 5093 Metal scrap & waste materials
CEO: Alan M Engle
Genl Mgr: Julius Miller
Off Mgr: Karina Moreno

D-U-N-S 02-359-1605
JACK FORD GRIFFIN INC
LINCOLN MERCURY
1940 E Main St, Waukesha, WI 53186-3906
Tel (262) 542-5781 *Founded/Ownrshp* 1963
Sales 49.6MM^E *EMP* 125^E
SIC 5511 Automobiles, new & used; Automobiles, new & used
Pr: James Griffin
**CFO:* Geoffrey Slomann
**VP:* John Griffin
Off Mgr: Judy Stacey
Netwrk Mgr: Dennis Sullivan
VP Mktg: Brad Braun

JACK FROST BIG BLDER SKI AREAS
See JFBB SKI AREAS INC

JACK FURRIERS WSTN TIRE CTRS
See WESTERN TIRE CENTERS INC

JACK G LEASING CO
See JACK GIAMBALVO MOTOR CO INC

D-U-N-S 03-138-6774
JACK GIAMBALVO MOTOR CO INC
JACK G LEASING CO
1390 Eden Rd, York, PA 17402-1938
Tel (717) 846-1821 *Founded/Ownrshp* 1982
Sales 83.6MM^E *EMP* 200
SIC 5511 7538 Automobiles, new & used; General automotive repair shops; Automobiles, new & used; General automotive repair shops
Pr: John W Giambalvo
**Treas:* Donald J Dusich
**VP:* Michael R Bowman
VP Opers: Thomas Couch
Sls Mgr: Joel Crews
Sales Asso: Bill Gibson
Sales Asso: Bern Little
Sales Asso: Kurt Ziemer

D-U-N-S 02-829-4759
JACK GOSCH FORD INC
GOSCH FORD LINCOLN MERCURY
150 Carriage Cir, Hemet, CA 92545-9610
Tel (951) 658-3181 *Founded/Ownrshp* 1964
Sales 41.2MM^E *EMP* 100
SIC 5511 Automobiles, new & used; Automobiles, new & used
Pr: Jack E Gosch
**CFO:* Richard Rodgers
**VP:* Eric Gosch
Sales Asso: Rami Jawad

D-U-N-S 04-253-4875
JACK GRAY TRANSPORT INC
4600 E 15th Ave, Gary, IN 46403-3699
Tel (219) 938-7020 *Founded/Ownrshp* 1951
Sales 23.6MM^E *EMP* 100
SIC 4213 4491 Contract haulers; Stevedoring
Pr: John S Gray
**VP:* Carmen Mormino

D-U-N-S 09-826-5341
▲ **JACK HENRY & ASSOCIATES INC**
663 W Highway 60, Monett, MO 65708-8215
Tel (417) 235-6652 *Founded/Ownrshp* 1976
Sales 1.2MMM *EMP* 5,822
Accts Deloitte & Touche Llp Kansas
Tkr Sym JKHY *Exch* NGS
SIC 7373 Computer integrated systems design; Computer systems analysis & design; Computer integrated systems design; Computer systems analysis & design
Ch Bd: John F Prim
Pr: David B Foss
COO: Rick Stadel
CFO: Kevin D Williams
**V Ch Bd:* Matthew C Flanigan
**VP:* Mark S Forbis
Corp Couns: John De Lany
Corp Couns: Jeff McCurry
Board of Directors: Jacqueline R Fiegel, Laura G Kelly, Thomas H Wilson Jr, Thomas A Wimsett

D-U-N-S 96-556-1223
JACK HILLIARD DISTRIBUTING CO INC
217 N 12th St, Temple, TX 76501-4358
Tel (254) 778-2748 *Founded/Ownrshp* 1962
Sales 36.5MM^E *EMP* 99
SIC 5181 Beer & ale; Beer & ale
CEO: Jack P Hilliard Jr
Genl Mgr: Jim Schwartz
IT Man: Phyllis Miller

D-U-N-S 15-512-9406
JACK HOOD TRANSPORTATION INC
10827 W County Rd 400 N, Michigan City, IN 46360
Tel (219) 874-2085 *Founded/Ownrshp* 1973
Sales 41.7MM^E *EMP* 250^E
SIC 5963

JACK HUGHSTON MEMORIAL HOSPITA
See RUSSELL COUNTY COMMUNITY HOSPITAL LLC

JACK IN THE BOX
See A 3 H FOODS LP

JACK IN THE BOX
See J & D RESTAURANT GROUP LLC

JACK IN THE BOX
See C R T PARTNERS INC

JACK IN THE BOX
See ODESSA ENTERPRISES INC

JACK IN THE BOX
See EMERALD CASCADE RESTAURANTS SYSTEMS INC

D-U-N-S 04-211-7200 IMP
▲ **JACK IN BOX INC**
9330 Balboa Ave, San Diego, CA 92123-1524
Tel (858) 571-2121 *Founded/Ownrshp* 1951
Sales 1.5MMM *EMP* 19,150
Accts Kpmg Llp San Diego Californi
Tkr Sym JACK *Exch* NGS
SIC 5812 6794 Fast-food restaurant, chain; Franchises, selling or licensing; Fast-food restaurant, chain; Franchises, selling or licensing
Ch Bd: Leonard A Comma
CFO: Jerry P Rebel
Treas: Sean Bogue
Treas: Paul D Melancon
Chf Mktg O: Keith M Guilbault
Ex VP: Mark H Blankenship
Sr VP: Elana M Hobson
Sr VP: Linda A Lang
VP: Patti Caropreso
VP: Lenny Comma
VP: Kathi Corder
VP: Carol Diraimo
VP: Dee Frustaglio
VP: Dan Harbor
VP: Kathy Lama
VP: Brian Luscomb
VP: Daniel Mahaffey
VP: Eddie Nieves
VP: Eric Tunquist
VP: Deborah Williamson
Board of Directors: David L Goebel, Sharon P John, Madeleine A Kleiner, Michael W Murphy, James M Myers, David M Tehle, John T Wyatt

D-U-N-S 03-405-3967
JACK INGRAM MOTORS INC (AL)
227 Eastern Blvd, Montgomery, AL 36117-2084
Tel (334) 277-5700 *Founded/Ownrshp* 1959
Sales 71.8MM^E *EMP* 170
SIC 5511 Automobiles, new & used; Pickups, new & used; General automotive repair shops; Used car dealers; Automobiles, new & used; Pickups, new & used
Pr: C Ray Ingram
**Sec:* Patty Crowell
**VP:* Laurens Pierce
Sls Mgr: Guy Martin
Sales Asso: Melody Acreman
Sales Asso: Joel Flournoy
Sales Asso: Michon Main

D-U-N-S 05-004-7364
JACK KAIN FORD INC
3405 Lexington Rd, Versailles, KY 40383-1842
Tel (859) 873-6666 *Founded/Ownrshp* 1959
Sales 30.8MM *EMP* 46
SIC 5511 Automobiles, new & used; Automobiles, new & used
Pr: Jack A Kain
**VP:* Robert Kain
Genl Mgr: Bob Kain
CTO: James Holt
Sls Mgr: Tom Breeze
Sls Mgr: Eric Thomas

JACK KEY ALAMOGORDO
See JACK KEY MOTOR CO OF ALAMOGORDO LLC

D-U-N-S 03-954-0844 IMP
JACK KEY MOTOR CO OF ALAMOGORDO LLC
JACK KEY ALAMOGORDO
1501 Highway 70 W, Alamogordo, NM 88310-7591
Tel (575) 434-3916 *Founded/Ownrshp* 1985
Sales 45.6MM^E *EMP* 195
SIC 5511 Automobiles, new & used; Pickups, new & used; Automobiles, new & used; Pickups, new & used
Treas: Kevin Key

D-U-N-S 85-904-5999
JACK KLEIN TRUST PARTNERSHIP
KLEIN FAMILY FARMS
3101 W March Ln Ste B, Stockton, CA 95219-2385
Tel (209) 956-8800 *Founded/Ownrshp* 1950
Sales 21.2MM *EMP* 20
SIC 0722 Crop harvesting; Crop harvesting
Pt: Tom Klein
Pt: Jill Corkern
Pt: Kathy Jackson
Pt: Steve Klein
Pt: Jim Renney
Mng Pt: Richard Klein

D-U-N-S 02-341-1622 IMP
JACK L MARCUS INC
MARCUS UNIFORMS
5300 W Fond Du Lac Ave, Milwaukee, WI 53216-1348
Tel (414) 438-4999 *Founded/Ownrshp* 1960
Sales 21.2MM^E *EMP* 100^E
SIC 5961 Catalog & mail-order houses; Catalog & mail-order houses
Pr: Debra Watton
**Sec:* Susan Marcus

D-U-N-S 79-697-7700 IMP
JACK LA LANNE HOLDING CORP
(*Suby of* BALLY TOTAL FITNESS CORP) ★
70 E Sunrise Hwy Ste 412, Valley Stream, NY 11581-1233
Tel (516) 887-7500 *Founded/Ownrshp* 1979
Sales 3.6MM^E *EMP* 875
SIC 7991 Health club; Health club
CEO: Barry Elson

JACK LINK BEEF JERKY
See LINK SNACKS INC

JACK LINK'S BEEF JERKY
See S I L INC

D-U-N-S 01-955-2561
JACK MADDEN FORD SALES INC
825 Bston Providence Tpke, Norwood, MA 02062-4734
Tel (781) 762-4200 *Founded/Ownrshp* 2001
Sales 34.2MM^E *EMP* 90
SIC 5511 7532 7514 Automobiles, new & used; Body shop, automotive; Rent-a-car service; Automobiles, new & used; Body shop, automotive; Rent-a-car service
**Pr:* John P Madden Jr
Genl Mgr: Jason Arruda
Sls Mgr: Lewis Jack

D-U-N-S 04-117-7338
JACK MARSHALL FOODS INC
KFC
113 25th Ave E, Tuscaloosa, AL 35404-2526
Tel (205) 553-8621 *Founded/Ownrshp* 1956
Sales 13.7MM^E *EMP* 380
SIC 5812 Fast-food restaurant, chain; Fast-food restaurant, chain
Pr: Jack Marshall
Opers Mgr: Baha Quraishi

D-U-N-S 01-845-3423 EXP
JACK MAXTON CHEVROLET INC
JACK MAXTON USED CAR
700 E Dublin Granville Rd, Columbus, OH 43229-3210
Tel (614) 885-5301 *Founded/Ownrshp* 1967
Sales 77.7MM^E *EMP* 170
SIC 5511 Automobiles, new & used; Automobiles, new & used
Pr: Jeff Mauk
**VP:* John Nestor
Genl Mgr: Dan Green
Genl Mgr: Amanda Mauk
IT Man: Ed Wilson
Sls Mgr: Doug Lange
Sales Asso: Cliff Boyle
Sales Asso: Brian Connor
Sales Asso: Frank Eliaspour
Sales Asso: Mike Figlestahler
Sales Asso: Duane Floyd

JACK MAXTON USED CAR
See JACK MAXTON CHEVROLET INC

D-U-N-S 96-686-3495
JACK MILLER CENTER FOR TEACHING AMERICAS FOUNDING PRINCIPLES AND HISTOR
3 Bala Plz 401, Bala Cynwyd, PA 19004
Tel (484) 436-2063 *Founded/Ownrshp* 2011
Sales 23.9MM *EMP* 2
Accts Cetrulo & Morgan Group Llc W
SIC 8699 Charitable organization; Charitable organization
Pr: Alfred D Hagen

D-U-N-S 06-928-1350
■ **JACK MORTON WORLDWIDE INC**
INTERPUBLIC GROUP OF COMPANIES
(*Suby of* INTERPUBLIC GROUP OF COMPANIES INC) ★
142 Berkeley St Ste 6, Boston, MA 02116-5143
Tel (617) 585-7000 *Founded/Ownrshp* 1998
Sales 207.4MM^E *EMP* 575
SIC 8748 8742 Communications consulting; Business planning & organizing services; Marketing consulting services; Communications consulting; Business planning & organizing services; Marketing consulting services
Ch Bd: Josh McCall
**Pr:* Tara Back
Pr: Carol Previte
**CFO:* William Davis
Ex VP: William Boris-Schacter
Ex VP: Charlotte Merrell
Sr VP: Alex Apthorpe
Sr VP: Cyndi Davis
Sr VP: Bob Denby
Sr VP: Yvonne Hoffzimmer
Sr VP: David Mervenne
Sr VP: Kevin O'Shea
Sr VP: Ted Przybocki
VP: Amanda Blackman
VP: Theresa Brown
VP: Carley Faircloth
VP: Helen Graney
VP: Marybeth Hall
VP: David Heist
VP: Debbie Melkonian
VP: Kevin Oshea

D-U-N-S 61-947-8738 IMP
■ JACK MORTON WORLDWIDE INC
(*Suby of* INTERPUBLIC GROUP OF COMPANIES INC)
★
800 Connecticut Ave 1e01, Norwalk, CT 06854-1628
Tel (203) 851-7800 *Founded/Ownrshp* 2007
Sales 25.7MM^E *EMP* 75
SIC 7389 8243 Advertising, promotional & trade show services; Software training, computer
Ch: William Morton
**VP:* Julie Nelson
**VP:* Beth Peters
Mng Dir: Cyndi Davis

D-U-N-S 05-387-6504
JACK NADEL INC
JACK NADEL INTERNATIONAL
8701 Bellanca Ave, Los Angeles, CA 90045-4411
Tel (310) 815-2600 *Founded/Ownrshp* 1953
Sales 91.4MM *EMP* 245
Accts Rbz Llp Los Angeles Califor
SIC 8742 5199 Incentive or award program consultant; Gifts & novelties; Incentive or award program consultant; Gifts & novelties
CEO: Craig Nadel
**CFO:* Robert Kritzler
**Ch:* Jack Nadel
**Sr VP:* Debbie Abergel
**Sr VP:* Craig Reese
VP: Mark Hacker
VP: Sheri Holt
VP: Damon Miller
VP: Paul Navabpour
**VP:* Athans Zafiropoulos
**Exec:* Steve Widdicombe
Board of Directors: David Falato, Jeff Jacobs

JACK NADEL INTERNATIONAL
See JACK NADEL INC

D-U-N-S 03-488-7372
JACK PALMER FOOD SERVICE INC
PALMER FOODSERVICE
310 Stanley Blvd, Shelbyville, TN 37160-9163
Tel (931) 684-7011 *Founded/Ownrshp* 1984
Sales 45.1MM^E *EMP* 55
SIC 5141 Groceries, general line
VP: Mary C Palmer
Mktg Dir: Jimmy Hammond

D-U-N-S 01-241-4512
JACK PARKER CONSTRUCTION CORP (NY)
PARKER PROPERTIES
118 W 57th St, New York, NY 10019-3318
Tel (212) 333-3353 *Founded/Ownrshp* 1956
Sales 25.6MM^E *EMP* 400
SIC 1531 1522 Speculative builder, single-family houses; Hotel/motel & multi-family home construction; Speculative builder, single-family houses; Hotel/motel & multi-family home construction
Pr: Adam Glick

D-U-N-S 83-124-4236
JACK PHELAN DODGE LLC
JACK PHELAN DODGE SUZUKI
5859 S La Grange Rd, Countryside, IL 60525-4065
Tel (708) 352-5300 *Founded/Ownrshp* 2009
Sales 25.0MM^E *EMP* 80^E
SIC 5511 Automobiles, new & used; Automobiles, new & used

JACK PHELAN DODGE SUZUKI
See JACK PHELAN DODGE LLC

D-U-N-S 80-265-8922
JACK PITMON
SNAK SHAK
101 N C St, Davis, OK 73030-1721
Tel (580) 369-3135 *Founded/Ownrshp* 1991
Sales 56.6MM *EMP* 85
SIC 5172 5984 5411 5541 Gases, liquefied petroleum (propane); Liquefied petroleum gas dealers; Convenience stores; Gasoline service stations; Gases, liquefied petroleum (propane); Liquefied petroleum gas dealers; Convenience stores; Gasoline service stations
Owner: Jack Pitmon

D-U-N-S 02-814-1729
JACK POWELL CHRYSLER - DODGE INC
JACK POWELL PLYMOUTH
1625 Auto Park Way, Escondido, CA 92029-2008
Tel (760) 745-2880 *Founded/Ownrshp* 1970
Sales 46.7MM^E *EMP* 85
SIC 5511 7538 5531 Automobiles, new & used; General automotive repair shops; Automotive & home supply stores; Automobiles, new & used; General automotive repair shops; Automotive & home supply stores
Pr: Jack Powell Jr
**VP:* Judith Powell

JACK POWELL PLYMOUTH
See JACK POWELL CHRYSLER - DODGE INC

D-U-N-S 60-589-4575
JACK PREWITT HOLDING INC
97 Village Ln Ste 300, Colleyville, TX 76034-2992
Tel (817) 283-2826 *Founded/Ownrshp* 1986
Sales 30.0MM *EMP* 30
Accts David S Crockett & Co
SIC 5599 7359 Aircraft, self-propelled; Aircraft rental
Pr: Jack D Prewitt
**VP:* Rick Pitts

JACK RABBIT FOODS
See PETROLEUM PRODUCT OF SOUTH GEORGIA INC

D-U-N-S 04-368-3424
JACK RESNICK & SONS INC
110 E 59th St Fl 34, New York, NY 10022-1379
Tel (212) 220-3360 *Founded/Ownrshp* 1966
Sales 24.9MM^E *EMP* 120
SIC 6531 Real estate managers
CEO: Burton P Resnick
**Pr:* Jonathan Dresnick
VP: Fran Delgorio
Mng Dir: Jonathan Dean
Mng Dir: C P Forero
Mng Dir: Gary Kossen

D-U-N-S 07-745-9089 IMP
JACK RICHESON & CO INC (WI)
557 Marcella St, Kimberly, WI 54136-1760
Tel (920) 560-3777 *Founded/Ownrshp* 1981
Sales 24.3MM^E *EMP* 70
SIC 5199 Artists' materials
Ch Bd: Jack Richeson
**Pr:* Darren Richeson
**Ex VP:* Shawn Richeson
**VP:* Kelly Ulbrich
Art Dir: Rachelle Hansen

D-U-N-S 04-201-3821
JACK SAFRO TOYOTA INC (WI)
(*Suby of* JRS HOLDING INC) ★
20445 W Capitol Dr, Brookfield, WI 53045-2745
Tel (262) 781-2626 *Founded/Ownrshp* 1962
Sales 57.8MM^E *EMP* 150
SIC 5511 Automobiles, new & used; Automobiles, new & used
Pr: John R Safro
**CFO:* Martin Thomas
**VP:* James Tessmer
Genl Mgr: Steve Recht Jr
Genl Mgr: James Tessemr
Genl Mgr: Henry Tessmer
Off Mgr: Chris Jones
Sls Dir: Jon Merkel
Sls Mgr: Ely Faretta
Sls Mgr: Tom Mahlberg
Sales Asso: Ryan Sayers

D-U-N-S 80-280-0300
JACK SCHMITT CADILLAC OLDSMOBILE INC
915 W Highway 50, O Fallon, IL 62269-1829
Tel (618) 628-7515 *Founded/Ownrshp* 1992
Sales 23.0MM^E *EMP* 48
SIC 5511 Automobiles, new & used
Pr: Jack Schmitt
Sales Asso: Kathy Federico

JACK SCHMITT CHEVROLET OFALLON
See SCHMITT CHEVROLET INC

D-U-N-S 04-637-6463
JACK SCHMITT CHEVROLET OLDS OF COLLINSVILLE INC
1870 E Edwardsville Rd, Wood River, IL 62095-2273
Tel (618) 345-5444 *Founded/Ownrshp* 1991, 1995
Sales 24.2MM^E *EMP* 55
SIC 5511 Automobiles, new & used
Pr: Jack L Schmitt
Off Mgr: Linda Miller
Sls Mgr: Ray Mank
Sales Asso: Ronnie Durbin
Board of Directors: Charles Urban

D-U-N-S 10-802-2880
JACK SCHMITT FORD INC
1820 Vandalia St, Collinsville, IL 62234-4853
Tel (618) 344-5106 *Founded/Ownrshp* 1984
Sales 26.2MM^E *EMP* 60
SIC 5511 Automobiles, new & used; Automobiles, new & used
Pr: Jack L Schmitt
Sales Exec: Scott Riddle

D-U-N-S 00-708-3954
JACK TYLER ENGINEERING INC (AR)
6112 Patterson Rd, Little Rock, AR 72209-2488
Tel (501) 562-2296 *Founded/Ownrshp* 1963, 2000
Sales 26.0MM^E *EMP* 33
SIC 5084 7699 Industrial machinery & equipment; Industrial equipment services
Owner: Sherman Eoff
**Sec:* Cindy Eoff
Genl Mgr: Steve Cooper

D-U-N-S 04-512-8733
JACK WALTERS & SONS CORP
WALTERS BUILDINGS
6600 Midland Ct, Allenton, WI 53002-9579
Tel (262) 629-5521 *Founded/Ownrshp* 2005
Sales 31.9MM^E *EMP* 140
SIC 3448 Buildings, portable: prefabricated metal; Buildings, portable: prefabricated metal
Pr: Scott Walters
**Treas:* William Walters
**VP:* Christoper Walters
Exec: John Kelly
Sfty Mgr: Perry Backhaus

D-U-N-S 02-091-5452
JACK WELCH MANAGEMENT INSTITUTE
(*Suby of* STRAYER UNIV - CNCNNATI CAMPUS) ★
2303 Dulles Station Blvd, Herndon, VA 20171-6353
Tel (703) 561-1646 *Founded/Ownrshp* 2011, 2013
Sales 446.0MM *EMP* 1^E
SIC 8741 Management services
Prin: Matthew Carlson
Pr: Jeff McCullough
Ofcr: Carla Mueller
Sr VP: Andrea Backman
Mktg Mgr: Megan Slatoff-Burke

D-U-N-S 01-427-6430
JACK WILLIAMS TIRE CO INC
JACK WLLAMS TIRE AUTO SVC CTRS
700 Rocky Glen Rd, Avoca, PA 18641-9529
Tel (570) 457-5000 *Founded/Ownrshp* 1969
Sales 237.9MM^E *EMP* 500
SIC 5531 5014 Automotive tires; Automobile tires & tubes; Truck tires & tubes; Automotive tires; Automobile tires & tubes; Truck tires & tubes
Ch Bd: William C Williams
**Pr:* Scott Williams
**CFO:* Frank J Chalk
**Treas:* Caroline Orourke
**Sec:* Sandra Williams
**VP:* Jason Williams
**VP:* Tracey Williams
Div Mgr: Michael Purvin
Sftwr Eng: Tim Franz
Sls Mgr: Dave Matriccino

D-U-N-S 05-311-2876
JACK WILSON CHEVROLET-BUICK INC (FL)
2255 Us Highway 1 S, Saint Augustine, FL 32086-6071
Tel (904) 797-4567 *Founded/Ownrshp* 1971
Sales 38.7MM^E *EMP* 70
SIC 5511

D-U-N-S 05-163-9425
JACK WINEGARDNER CHEVROLET INC
11001 Indian Head Hwy, Fort Washington, MD 20744-4098
Tel (301) 292-6500 *Founded/Ownrshp* 1980
Sales 26.1MM^E *EMP* 61
SIC 5511 7538 5521 5012 Automobiles, new & used; Pickups, new & used; Trucks, tractors & trailers: new & used; General automotive repair shops; Used car dealers; Automobiles & other motor vehicles; Automobiles, new & used; Pickups, new & used; Trucks, tractors & trailers: new & used; General automotive repair shops; Used car dealers; Automobiles & other motor vehicles
Pr: Marlene Winegardner
**Treas:* Thomas J Winegardner
**VP:* Charles Winegardner
Genl Mgr: Kevin Clements
Sls Mgr: Bob Maddox

JACK WLLAMS TIRE AUTO SVC CTRS
See JACK WILLIAMS TIRE CO INC

D-U-N-S 02-495-4067
JACK WOLF PONTIAC-CADILLAC-GMC TRUCK INC (IL)
WOLF, JACK CADILLAC
1855 N State St, Belvidere, IL 61008-2011
Tel (815) 544-3406 *Founded/Ownrshp* 1963
Sales 39.9MM^E *EMP* 90
SIC 5511 Automobiles, new & used; Automobiles, new & used
Pr: John T Wolf
**VP:* Amy J Wolf-Wilcox
Exec: Amy Wilcox
Genl Mgr: John Clark
Opers Mgr: Tony McIntire

JACK YOUNG COMPANY
See CENTRAL AUTOMOTIVE WAREHOUSE CORP

D-U-N-S 00-196-9179 EXP
JACK YOUNG CO INC (MA)
(*Suby of* CONNECTICUT WAREHOUSE DISTRIBUTORS INC) ★
354 Cambridge St, Allston, MA 02134-1725
Tel (617) 782-1250 *Founded/Ownrshp* 1947, 2014
Sales 39.6MM^E *EMP* 75
SIC 5013 Automotive supplies & parts
Pr: John Pluck
VP: Brandon Pluck
Off Mgr: Brian Berkeley

D-U-N-S 05-752-0276
■ JACKALOPE GAS GATHERING SERVICES LLC
(*Suby of* WILLIAMS PARTNERS LP) ★
525 Central Park Dr # 1005, Oklahoma City, OK 73105-1723
Tel (877) 413-1023 *Founded/Ownrshp* 2012
Sales 16.8MM^E *EMP* 692^E
SIC 4922 Natural gas transmission
CEO: J Michael Stice
**COO:* Robert Purgason
**CFO:* David Shiels

JACKIE COOPER BNW
See JACKIE COOPER IMPORTS INC

D-U-N-S 06-542-2156
JACKIE COOPER IMPORTS INC
JACKIE COOPER BNW
14145 Broadway Ext, Edmond, OK 73013-4120
Tel (405) 755-3600 *Founded/Ownrshp* 1950, 1970
Sales 28.1MM^E *EMP* 60
SIC 5511 Automobiles, new & used; Automobiles, new & used
Pr: Jackie R Cooper
**VP:* Joe Cooper

D-U-N-S 09-379-1184
JACKIES INTERNATIONAL INC
LUIGI'S FAMILY RESTAURANT
1554 W Peace St, Canton, MS 39046-5325
Tel (601) 855-0146 *Founded/Ownrshp* 1977
Sales 56.4MM^E *EMP* 1,200
SIC 5812 7011 Pizzeria, chain; Pizza restaurants; Steak restaurant; Family restaurants; Hotels & motels; Pizzeria, chain; Pizza restaurants; Steak restaurant; Family restaurants; Hotels & motels
Pr: S L Sethi
CFO: Jerry Beckwith
Treas: Sethi Raksha
**Sec:* Raksha Sethi
**VP:* Monica Sethi Harrigill
**VP:* John Kirk
**VP:* Dana Moreau
**VP:* Sunny Sethi
Sls Dir: Susan Conerly

D-U-N-S 92-886-7142
JACKMONT HOSPITALITY INC
TGI FRIDAY'S
1760 Peachtree St Nw # 200, Atlanta, GA 30309-2335
Tel (404) 523-5744 *Founded/Ownrshp* 1994
Sales 33.4MM^E *EMP* 600
SIC 5812 Restaurant, family: chain; Restaurant, family: chain
Pr: Daniel J Halpern
**CFO:* Brooke Jackson Edmond
Sr VP: Brooke Jackson
VP: Brenda Branch
Mktg Mgr: Indras Whittaker

D-U-N-S 61-395-1607
JACKPOT JUNCTION CASINO HOTEL
DACOTAH RIDGE GOLF CLUB
39375 County Highway 24, Morton, MN 56270-1273
Tel (507) 697-8000 *Founded/Ownrshp* 1984
Sales 43.1MM^E *EMP* 800
SIC 7011 5813 5812

D-U-N-S 02-978-5110 IMP
JACKRABBIT INC
DAKOTA AG WELDING
471 Industrial Ave, Ripon, CA 95366-2768
Tel (209) 599-6118 *Founded/Ownrshp* 2013
Sales 23.8MM^E *EMP* 82
SIC 3523 Harvesters, fruit, vegetable, tobacco, etc.
Pr: Earl Anderson

JACK'S 99 CENTS STORE
See 32ND STREET 99 CORP

JACK'S FAMILY RESTAURANTS
See BIG JACK ULTIMATE HOLDINGS LP

D-U-N-S 06-560-0843
JACKS FRUIT MARKET INC (MI)
1511 W Center Rd, Essexville, MI 48732-2113
Tel (989) 893-0591 *Founded/Ownrshp* 1949, 1973
Sales 33.0MM *EMP* 220
SIC 5421 5921 5431 5411 Meat markets, including freezer provisioners; Beer (packaged); Wine; Fruit stands or markets; Vegetable stands or markets; Grocery stores, independent; Meat markets, including freezer provisioners; Beer (packaged); Wine; Fruit stands or markets; Vegetable stands or markets; Grocery stores, independent
Pr: Jack W Stehle II
**VP:* Marcia Stehle
Brnch Mgr: Don Horner

D-U-N-S 05-976-4928
JACKS HEAVY EQUIPMENT INC
JACK'S TRUCK AND EQUIPMENT
6100 S Douglas Hwy, Gillette, WY 82718-6906
Tel (307) 686-0608 *Founded/Ownrshp* 1992
Sales 31.2MM *EMP* 46
Accts Todd Hoese Cpa Llc Gillette
SIC 5082 5511 7538 Construction & mining machinery; Mining machinery & equipment, except petroleum; Trucks, tractors & trailers: new & used; General truck repair; Construction & mining machinery; Mining machinery & equipment, except petroleum; Trucks, tractors & trailers: new & used; General truck repair
Pr: Kevin Chafee
Ofcr: George Napoles
**VP:* Gary Chafee
**VP:* Richard Chafee
VP: Mark Clark
Off Mgr: Pam Baumgartner

JACKS RESTAURANT
See MANNA ENTERPRISES INC

JACK'S SUPER IGA
See HAJ SUPERMARKETS

D-U-N-S 03-531-7445
JACKS TIRE & OIL INC
(*Suby of* JACKS TIRE & OIL MANAGEMENT CO INC)
★
1795 N Main St, Logan, UT 84341-1921
Tel (435) 752-7811 *Founded/Ownrshp* 1960
Sales 59.3MM^E *EMP* 142
SIC 5531 7539 7538 Automotive tires; Automotive repair shops; General automotive repair shops; Automotive tires; Automotive repair shops; General automotive repair shops
Pr: J David Bowen
**Pr:* Robert Feldbauer
**CFO:* Doug Swansen
CFO: Doug Swenson
VP: Cory Bowen
**VP:* Rodney Bowen
IT Man: Ray Peterson
Sls Mgr: Steve Michels

D-U-N-S 95-746-8960
JACKS TIRE & OIL MANAGEMENT CO INC
1795 N Main St, Logan, UT 84341-1921
Tel (435) 752-7897 *Founded/Ownrshp* 1995
Sales 81.3MM^E *EMP* 200
SIC 5531 7539 Automotive tires; Automotive repair shops; Automotive tires; Automotive repair shops
Pr: J David Bowen
**Treas:* Jeff Abplanalp
**VP:* Dick Tolotti
Sales Exec: Rod Bowen

JACK'S TRUCK AND EQUIPMENT
See JACKS HEAVY EQUIPMENT INC

JACKSNVLLE CHRYSLER JEEP DODGE
See TT OF JACKSONVILLE INC

JACKSNVLLE UNIV DRMTORY CFTRIA
See JACKSONVILLE UNIVERSITY

D-U-N-S 04-133-0275 IMP
JACKSON & BLANC
7929 Arjons Dr, San Diego, CA 92126-4301
Tel (858) 831-7900 *Founded/Ownrshp* 1997
Sales 48.9MM^E *EMP* 110
Accts Moss Adams Llp San Diego Cal
SIC 1711 Heating & air conditioning contractors; Heating & air conditioning contractors
CEO: Kirk Jackson
**Pr:* John Fusca

D-U-N-S 08-235-0653
JACKSON & CAMPBELL PC
AUSROTAS, RAYMOND P
1120 20th St Nw Ste 300s, Washington, DC 20036-3437
Tel (202) 293-1620 *Founded/Ownrshp* 1895
Sales 24.2MM^E *EMP* 130^E
SIC 8111 General practice law office; General practice law office
Pr: Rick Ryan
Mng Pt: Barry Dirinfeld
Pr: Sherri White
**Treas:* John Brennan III
**VP:* Richard Bryan
VP: Bonnie Gorman
VP: Irina Patiashvil
Info Man: Patrick Lumpkins

Mktg Mgr: Kamaria Salau
Counsel: Michele Dearing

D-U-N-S 03-540-6925
JACKSON - DAWSON COMMUNICATIONS INC
J B
1 Parklane Blvd Ste 1105e, Dearborn, MI 48126-4256
Tel (313) 593-0690 *Founded/Ownrshp* 1980
Sales 30.3MM^E *EMP* 105
SIC 8742 Sales (including sales management) consultant
Pr: Samuel A Dawson
**VP:* Lawrence B Jackson

D-U-N-S 07-091-2100
JACKSON AND TULL CHARTERED ENGINEERS (DC)
2705 Bladensburg Rd Ne, Washington, DC 20018-1424
Tel (202) 333-9100 *Founded/Ownrshp* 1974
Sales 31.9MM^E *EMP* 200
Accts Bert & Smith & Co Cpa Washin
SIC 3441 3663 7376 8711 Fabricated structural metal; Radio & TV communications equipment; Computer facilities management; Engineering services; Fabricated structural metal; Radio & TV communications equipment; Computer facilities management; Engineering services
Pr: Knox W Tull Jr
**COO:* Mossi Tull

D-U-N-S 01-568-1877
JACKSON AWH-BP HOTEL LLC
HILTON JACKSON
1001 E County Line Rd, Jackson, MS 39211-1817
Tel (601) 957-2800 *Founded/Ownrshp* 2007
Sales 20.9MM^E *EMP* 200
SIC 8741 Hotel or motel management; Hotel or motel management
CEO: William Deforrest
**Prin:* Westbrook Skipper
Genl Mgr: Skipper Westbrook
Sls Dir: Cindy Brinson
Sls Mgr: Leigh Lucroy

JACKSON BOARD OF EDUCATION
See JACKSON COUNTY SCHOOL DISTRICT

JACKSON BROTHERS
See J B VENDING CO INC

D-U-N-S 00-593-1860
JACKSON CHEVROLET CO
660 S Main St, Middletown, CT 06457-4258
Tel (860) 346-9655 *Founded/Ownrshp* 1936
Sales 23.7MM *EMP* 49
SIC 5511 5531 Automobiles, new & used; Automobiles, new & used; Automotive parts
Pr: Frederick Jackson
Genl Mgr: Ray Terrible
Off Mgr: T J Jackson

D-U-N-S 07-944-2919
JACKSON CITY SCHOOL DISTRICT
450 Vaughn St, Jackson, OH 45640-1944
Tel (740) 286-6442 *Founded/Ownrshp* 1876
Sales 12.2MM^E *EMP* 280^E
SIC 8211 Public elementary school; Public junior high school; Public senior high school; School board; Public elementary school; Public junior high school; Public senior high school; School board
HC Dir: Lori Moore

D-U-N-S 62-019-9836
JACKSON CLINIC PHARMACY INC
JACKSON CLINIC PROF ASSN INF
(*Suby of* JACKSON CLINIC PROFESSIONAL ASSOCIATION) ★
828 N Parkway, Jackson, TN 38305-3032
Tel (731) 422-0330 *Founded/Ownrshp* 1970
Sales 100.5MM^E *EMP* 800
SIC 5912 Drug stores; Drug stores
Dir Lab: Doris Knott
Ansthlgy: Alan Adams
Ansthlgy: Laura Ermenc
Ansthlgy: Edward Hockaday
Ansthlgy: John Miles
Doctor: Salomon N Asmar MD
Pharmcst: Bruce Hinton

JACKSON CLINIC PROF ASSN INF
See JACKSON CLINIC PHARMACY INC

D-U-N-S 03-466-4938
JACKSON CLINIC PROFESSIONAL ASSOCIATION
828 N Parkway, Jackson, TN 38305-3032
Tel (731) 422-0200 *Founded/Ownrshp* 1970
Sales 125.9MM^E *EMP* 800
SIC 5912 8011 8062 Drug stores; Clinic, operated by physicians; General medical & surgical hospitals; Drug stores; Clinic, operated by physicians; General medical & surgical hospitals
CEO: Carl E Rudd
COO: Mark Allen
Chf Mktg O: Keith Williams
**Exec:* Beverly Waylie
Nurse Mgr: Candy Peterson
Dir IT: Jan Matthews
Doctor: James Crenshaw
Nrsg Dir: Cathy Parrett
Snr Mgr: Rachel Williams

D-U-N-S 80-894-9945
JACKSON CLIP CO INC
(*Suby of* GLASS OPERATING GROUP, L.L.C.)
2 And A Half Mile W, Mazie, OK 74337
Tel (918) 476-8331 *Founded/Ownrshp* 1983
Sales 23.7MM^E *EMP* 196
SIC 3315 Fence gates posts & fittings: steel; Fence gates posts & fittings: steel
Pr: Bill Glass
**VP:* Maxine Glass

D-U-N-S 07-638-3868
JACKSON COLLEGE
2111 Emmons Rd, Jackson, MI 49201-8395
Tel (517) 787-0800 *Founded/Ownrshp* 1928
Sales 29.0MM^E *EMP* 690
Accts Rehman Rohan Jackson Mi
SIC 8222 8221 Community college; Colleges universities & professional schools; Community college; Colleges universities & professional schools
Pr: Daniel Phelen
**Ch Bd:* Samuel Barns
**Ch Bd:* Dr Edward A Mathein
**Treas:* Philip E Hoffman
**Treas:* Donna Lake
**V Ch Bd:* John M Crist
VP: Diane Fenby

D-U-N-S 96-730-3124
JACKSON COMPANIES
1710 Dick Pond Rd, Myrtle Beach, SC 29575-6500
Tel (843) 293-6001 *Founded/Ownrshp* 1973
Sales 47.1MM^E *EMP* 450
SIC 6552 7992 7033 Subdividers & developers; Public golf courses; Trailer parks & campsites; Subdividers & developers; Public golf courses; Trailer parks & campsites
Pr: Dennis Wade
**COO:* David Durant
VP: Steve Alger
Prgrm Mgr: J Domis
**Genl Mgr:* Lance Thompson
**S&M/Dir:* Barb Krumm

D-U-N-S 09-797-9850
JACKSON CONSTRUCTION LTD (TX)
5112 Sun Valley Dr, Fort Worth, TX 76119-6410
Tel (817) 572-3303 *Founded/Ownrshp* 1979
Sales 45.0MM^E *EMP* 185
SIC 1623 Water main construction; Sewer line construction; Water main construction; Sewer line construction
Pr: Larry H Jackson
**Sec:* Linda Jackson
**VP:* Troy Jackson

D-U-N-S 14-464-3079 IMP
JACKSON CORP
JACKSON HANDBAGS
330 5th Ave Fl 11, New York, NY 10001-3101
Tel (212) 239-4530 *Founded/Ownrshp* 1984
Sales 21.8MM^E *EMP* 100
SIC 5137 Handbags
Pr: Jackson Liao
**VP:* Annie Liao
VP: Pat Victory

D-U-N-S 07-313-4868
JACKSON COUNTY
415 E 12th St, Kansas City, MO 64106-2706
Tel (816) 881-3333 *Founded/Ownrshp* 1826
Sales NA *EMP* 2,000
Accts Kpmg Llp Kansas City Missour
SIC 9111 Executive offices; ; Executive offices;
Dir IT: Connie Frey
IT Man: Barbara Casamento
Snr Mgr: Calvin Williford

JACKSON COUNTY BD COMMISSIONER
See COUNTY OF JACKSON

D-U-N-S 03-726-1518
JACKSON COUNTY BOARD OF EDUCATION
4700 Col Vickery Rd, Ocean Springs, MS 39565-6632
Tel (228) 826-1757 *Founded/Ownrshp* 1930
Sales 31.9MM^E *EMP* 1,200
SIC 8211 Public combined elementary & secondary school; School board; School board
Ch Bd: Kenneth Fountain

D-U-N-S 06-175-3844
JACKSON COUNTY BOARD OF EDUCATION
1 School St, Ripley, WV 25271-1538
Tel (304) 372-7300 *Founded/Ownrshp* 1933
Sales 61.9MM^E *EMP* 910
SIC 8211 Public elementary school; Public junior high school; Public senior high school; Public elementary school; Public junior high school; Public senior high school
Pr: Steve Chancey
Brnch Mgr: Joanna McKown
IT Man: Blaine Hess
IT Man: Laura Matheny
Teacher Pr: Jay Carnell
Instr Medi: Debbie Casto

D-U-N-S 10-005-8668
JACKSON COUNTY BOARD OF EDUCATION
JACKSON COUNTY PUBLIC SCHOOLS
398 Hospital Rd, Sylva, NC 28779-5196
Tel (828) 586-5450 *Founded/Ownrshp* 1879
Sales 40.3MM *EMP* 500
Accts Dixon Hughes Goodman Llp Ashe
SIC 8211 Public elementary & secondary schools; Public elementary & secondary schools
Ofcr: Qween Edward
**VP:* Ali Laird-Large
Prin: Alex Bell
Prin: Dr Terry Clark
Prin: Wanda Fernandez
Prin: Nathan Frizzell
Prin: Jay Grisson
Prin: Sue Nations
Prin: Dennis Proffitt
Prin: Carol Rector
HC Dir: Charlotte Cowan

D-U-N-S 15-057-0307
JACKSON COUNTY BOARD OF EDUCATION
1660 Winder Hwy, Jefferson, GA 30549-5458
Tel (706) 367-5151 *Founded/Ownrshp* 1900
Sales 30.7MM^E *EMP* 800
Accts Russell W Hinton Cpa Cgfm
SIC 8211 Public elementary & secondary schools; Public elementary & secondary schools

D-U-N-S 19-306-7030
JACKSON COUNTY BOARD OF EDUCATION
711 School Dr, Gainesboro, TN 38562-9576
Tel (931) 268-6762 *Founded/Ownrshp* 1886
Sales 11.3MM *EMP* 307
SIC 8211 Public elementary & secondary schools; Public elementary & secondary schools

D-U-N-S 19-320-8204
JACKSON COUNTY BOARD OF EDUCATION
16003 Al Highway 35 # 100, Scottsboro, AL 35768-6711
Tel (256) 259-9500 *Founded/Ownrshp* 1900
Sales 38.9MM^E *EMP* 800
SIC 8211 Public elementary & secondary schools; Public elementary & secondary schools
VP: Jerry Jeffery
Exec: Beth Mannon

D-U-N-S 07-764-6537
JACKSON COUNTY HEALTH CARE AUTHORITY
380 Woods Cove Rd, Scottsboro, AL 35768-2428
Tel (256) 259-4444 *Founded/Ownrshp* 1951
Sales 22.2MM^E *EMP* 600
Accts Warren Averett Kimbrough & M
SIC 8051 8062 Skilled nursing care facilities; General medical & surgical hospitals; Skilled nursing care facilities; General medical & surgical hospitals
CEO: Kim Bryant
COO: Melissa Vickers
CFO: Dan B Newell
CTO: Tom Lackey
Cert Phar: Bobbie Chapman
Cert Phar: Elaine Prince

D-U-N-S 09-297-6703
JACKSON COUNTY HOSPITAL DISTRICT
JACKSON HOSPITAL
4250 Hospital Dr, Marianna, FL 32446-1917
Tel (850) 526-2200 *Founded/Ownrshp* 1939
Sales 45.1MM *EMP* 450
SIC 8062 8011 General medical & surgical hospitals; Clinic, operated by physicians; General medical & surgical hospitals; Clinic, operated by physicians
Ch: Holt Floyd
**CFO:* Kevin Rovito
**Treas:* Sarah Clemmons
Ofcr: Ronnie Bowen
CIO: Beth Medlock
MIS Dir: Elizabeth Medlock
IT Man: Martha Carlson
Obsttrcn: Gonzalo Oria
Doctor: David Flick
Pharmcst: Mercedes Young
Phys Thrpy: Nick Kolmetz

D-U-N-S 04-058-5333
JACKSON COUNTY INTERMEDIATE SCHOOL DISTRICT
6700 Browns Lake Rd, Jackson, MI 49201-8379
Tel (517) 768-5200 *Founded/Ownrshp* 1960
Sales 22.5MM^E *EMP* 350
Accts Rehmann Robson Jackson Mi
SIC 8211 Public special education school; School board; Public special education school; School board
CTO: Jon Kopp
Dir IT: Shannon Degan
IT Man: Ben Muscott
IT Man: Lynne Thompson

D-U-N-S 05-311-2996
JACKSON COUNTY MEMORIAL HOSPITAL AUTHORITY
1200 E Pecan St, Altus, OK 73521-6141
Tel (580) 482-4781 *Founded/Ownrshp* 1948
Sales 74.6MM *EMP* 800
Accts Bkd Llp Tulsa Oklahoma
SIC 8062 General medical & surgical hospitals; General medical & surgical hospitals
Pr: Steve Hartgraves
**COO:* Jim King
**CFO:* Nancy Davidson
**VP:* Kay Bolding
**VP:* Michelle Ford
**VP:* Richard Pope

JACKSON COUNTY PUBLIC SCHOOLS
See JACKSON COUNTY BOARD OF EDUCATION

D-U-N-S 10-064-5902
JACKSON COUNTY PUBLIC SCHOOLS
JACKSON COUNTY SCHOOL BOARD
2903 Jefferson St, Marianna, FL 32446-3445
Tel (850) 482-1200 *Founded/Ownrshp* 1900
Sales 58.5MM^E *EMP* 1,099
SIC 8211 Public elementary & secondary schools; Public elementary & secondary schools
Teacher Pr: Mary Skipper
HC Dir: Shirl Williams
Board of Directors: Charlotte Gardner

D-U-N-S 11-910-5641
JACKSON COUNTY PUBLIC SCHOOLS
526 Main St S, Mc Kee, KY 40447-7084
Tel (606) 287-7181 *Founded/Ownrshp* 1940
Sales 18.5MM^E *EMP* 400
Accts Wilson & Company Psc Summerse
SIC 8211 Public elementary school; Public junior high school; Public senior high school; Public elementary school; Public junior high school; Public senior high school
Pr Dir: Brian Thomas

D-U-N-S 00-693-8579
JACKSON COUNTY RURAL ELECTRIC MEMBERSHIP CORP
274 E Base Rd, Brownstown, IN 47220-8500
Tel (812) 358-4458 *Founded/Ownrshp* 1937
Sales 57.6MM *EMP* 63
SIC 4911 Distribution, electric power; Distribution, electric power
Genl Mgr: Jed Wheatley
Off Mgr: Nancy Hawkins
Opers Mgr: Brad Pritchett

D-U-N-S 07-598-0201
JACKSON COUNTY SCHNECK MEMORIAL HOSPITAL
SCHNECK MEDICAL CENTER
411 W Tipton St, Seymour, IN 47274-2363
Tel (812) 522-2349 *Founded/Ownrshp* 1911, 1940
Sales 114.3MM *EMP* 700
SIC 8062 General medical & surgical hospitals; General medical & surgical hospitals
Pr: Gary A Meyer
Chf Rad: Nathan Strabala
COO: Kim Ellerman
**CFO:* Warren Forgey
VP: Robert Coopper
Exec: Lydon Neumann
CTO: Melissa Anderson
Cmptr Lab: Denise Fleenor
IT Man: Charlene Mellencamp
Mktg Mgr: Stephanie Furlow
Obsttrcn: Eric Fish

JACKSON COUNTY SCHOOL BOARD
See JACKSON COUNTY PUBLIC SCHOOLS

D-U-N-S 07-979-9031
JACKSON COUNTY SCHOOL DISTRICT
16003 Al Highway 35, Scottsboro, AL 35768-6706
Tel (256) 259-9500 *Founded/Ownrshp* 2015
Sales 23.0MM^E *EMP* 690^E
SIC 8211 Public elementary & secondary schools
HC Dir: Pam Vernen

D-U-N-S 11-833-1383
JACKSON COUNTY SCHOOL DISTRICT
4700 Colonel Vickrey Rd, Vancleave, MS 39565
Tel (228) 826-1757 *Founded/Ownrshp* 2002
Sales 68.5MM *EMP* 1,403
SIC 8211 School board; Public elementary & secondary schools
Board of Directors: David Sims, Karen Tolbert, Randal Turner, Glen Dickerson J Keith Lee

D-U-N-S 19-331-1362
JACKSON COUNTY SCHOOL DISTRICT
JACKSON BOARD OF EDUCATION
1660 Winder Hwy, Jefferson, GA 30549-5458
Tel (706) 367-5151 *Founded/Ownrshp* 1950
Sales 40.1MM^E *EMP* 1,352
SIC 8211 Public elementary & secondary schools; Public elementary & secondary schools

D-U-N-S 04-879-1859
JACKSON COUNTY SCHOOL DISTRICT 9
EAGLE POINT SCHOOL DISTRICT 9
11 N Royal Ave, Eagle Point, OR 97524-0190
Tel (541) 830-1200 *Founded/Ownrshp* 1855
Sales 37.8MM^E *EMP* 550
SIC 8211 Public combined elementary & secondary school; Public combined elementary & secondary school

D-U-N-S 07-979-2161
JACKSON COUNTY SCHOOLS
1 School St, Ripley, WV 25271-1538
Tel (304) 372-7300 *Founded/Ownrshp* 1933
Sales 8.3MM^E *EMP* 1,148^E
SIC 8211 Public elementary & secondary schools

D-U-N-S 07-979-8784
JACKSON COUNTY SCHOOLS
398 Hospital Rd, Sylva, NC 28779-5196
Tel (828) 586-2311 *Founded/Ownrshp* 2015
Sales 8.4MM^E *EMP* 589^E
SIC 8211 Public elementary & secondary schools
Pr Dir: David Proffitt
HC Dir: Kelly Doppke

D-U-N-S 13-923-3597
JACKSON COUNTY UTILITY AUTHORITY
JCUA
1225 Jackson Ave, Pascagoula, MS 39567-4353
Tel (228) 762-0119 *Founded/Ownrshp* 1980
Sales 46.6MM^E *EMP* 91
Accts Culumber Fletcher Harvey & Ass
SIC 4941 Water supply
**Pr:* L P Bradford Jr
Ex Dir: Tommy Fairfield Jr
Cmptr Lab: Carrie Dennis

D-U-N-S 01-603-4618
JACKSON DEAN CONSTRUCTION INC
3414 S 116th St, Tukwila, WA 98168-1983
Tel (206) 832-2900 *Founded/Ownrshp* 1990
Sales 27.1MM^E *EMP* 75
SIC 1799 1542 Home/office interiors finishing, furnishing & remodeling; Nonresidential construction
Pr: Miles Jackson
Mktg Dir: Ryan McCallen

D-U-N-S 83-278-4776 IMP
JACKSON DIE CASTING LLC
METAL TECH - JACKSON DIE CAST
(*Suby of* KEY 3 CASTING LLC) ★
825 Lower Brownsville Rd, Jackson, TN 38301-9667
Tel (731) 427-9676 *Founded/Ownrshp* 2009
Sales 30.9MM^E *EMP* 109
SIC 3365 3321 Aluminum & aluminum-based alloy castings; Gray iron castings
Sls Mgr: Jimmy Tapp

JACKSON DISHMACHINES
See JACKSON WWS INC

D-U-N-S 07-842-3555
JACKSON ELECTRIC COOPERATIVE INC
8925 State Hwy 111 S, Ganado, TX 77962
Tel (361) 771-4400 *Founded/Ownrshp* 1939
Sales 33.7MM *EMP* 70
SIC 4911 Electric services; Electric services
Pr: Dick Koop
**CFO:* Cindy Bures
**Sec:* David Peterson

D-U-N-S 00-381-3003
JACKSON ELECTRIC MEMBERSHIP CORP (GA)
JACKSON EMC
850 Commerce Rd, Jefferson, GA 30549-3329
Tel (706) 367-5281 *Founded/Ownrshp* 1938
Sales 472.0MM *EMP* 445
Accts Mcnair Mclemore Middlebrooks &
SIC 4911 Distribution, electric power; Distribution, electric power
CEO: Randall Pugh
**CFO:* Greg Keith
Dir IT: Jeff Keen
Dir IT: Joe Pelt
Pr Dir: Mark Owen
Mktg Mgr: Clair Guined
Board of Directors: Steve Blair

JACKSON EMC
See JACKSON ELECTRIC MEMBERSHIP CORP

D-U-N-S 03-838-9347
JACKSON ENERGY AUTHORITY
351 Dr Martin Luther, Jackson, TN 38301
Tel (731) 422-7500 *Founded/Ownrshp* 2001
Sales 245.0MM *EMP* 425
Accts Alexander Thompson Arnold Pllc
SIC 4925 4911 4941 4952 Gas production and/or distribution; Electric services; Water supply; Sewerage systems; Gas production and/or distribution; Electric services; Water supply; Sewerage systems
Ch: Ken Marston
**Pr:* Danny Wheeler
**VP:* Michael Baughn
VP: John Nanney

D-U-N-S 00-877-9159
JACKSON ENERGY COOPERATIVE CORP
115 Jackson Energy Ln, Mc Kee, KY 40447-8847
Tel (606) 364-1000 *Founded/Ownrshp* 1938
Sales 107.9MM *EMP* 130
SIC 4911 Distribution, electric power; Distribution, electric power
Pr: Carol Wright
Ch Bd: Phillip Thompson
Sec: Keith Binder
V Ch Bd: Landis Cornett
Ex VP: Rick Brown
Dist Mgr: Larry Lakes
Dir IT: Karen Combs
Dir IT: Lindsy Russell
IT Man: Patrick Head
IT Man: Roger Truett
IT Man: Ruth Venable

D-U-N-S 03-927-1643
JACKSON ENTERPRISES CORP
2637 Wagner Rd, Waterloo, IA 50703-9602
Tel (319) 235-9537 *Founded/Ownrshp* 1971
Sales 62.2MM *EMP* 150
SIC 1611 6512 Highway & street paving contractor; Nonresidential building operators; Highway & street paving contractor; Nonresidential building operators
CEO: Stephen R Jackson
**VP:* William C Calderwood
**VP:* Jeffery S Rost

D-U-N-S 11-131-3011
JACKSON EXCAVATING & LEASING CO INC
BAKER ENGINEERING
(*Suby of* DEVINEY CO) ★
1059 Deviney Dr, Jackson, MS 39282
Tel (601) 371-7935 *Founded/Ownrshp* 2001
Sales 32.1MM^E^ *EMP* 203
SIC 3629 Electronic generation equipment; Electronic generation equipment
Pr: Jim Baker
**Pr:* W C Deviney Jr

D-U-N-S 01-007-2320
JACKSON FAMILY WINES INC
(*Suby of* JACKSON FAMILY WINES INC) ★
425 Aviation Blvd, Santa Rosa, CA 95403-1069
Tel (707) 544-4000 *Founded/Ownrshp* 1995
Sales 61.4MM^E^ *EMP* 800
SIC 2084 Wines; Wines
Pr: Jess Jackson
CEO: Jill Bartley
**CEO:* Edward Pitlik
COO: Hugh Reimers
**Treas:* Tyler Comstock
Sls Dir: Steve Messinger
Mktg Mgr: Scott Stangeland
Mktg Mgr: Josh Wagner
Corp Couns: Vikki Adams

D-U-N-S 60-511-4644 IMP
JACKSON FAMILY WINES INC
VINEYARDS OF MONTEREY
421 And 425 Aviation Blvd, Santa Rosa, CA 95403
Tel (707) 544-4000 *Founded/Ownrshp* 1987
Sales 355.9MM^E^ *EMP* 1,000
SIC 2084 0172 5813 Wines; Grapes; Wine bar; Wines; Grapes; Wine bar
Prin: Barbara Banke
Ex VP: Brian Hilliard
Ex VP: Rick D Tigner
Sr VP: David K Bowman
VP: Julie Bullock
**VP:* Charles Shea
Board of Directors: Barbara Banke, Larry Kitchen, Harry Wetzel

D-U-N-S 00-384-7233
JACKSON FARMERS INC
5th & Lowell St, Holton, KS 66436
Tel (785) 364-3161 *Founded/Ownrshp* 1916
Sales 41.9MM *EMP* 41
Accts Mayer Hoffman Mccann Pc Wichi
SIC 5153 5191 5541 Grains; Feed; Seeds: field, garden & flower; Fertilizer & fertilizer materials; Filling stations, gasoline; Grains; Feed; Seeds: field, garden & flower; Fertilizer & fertilizer materials; Filling stations, gasoline
Pr: Darla Lanter
Opers Mgr: Gary Amon

JACKSON FIRE DEPARTMENT
See CITY OF JACKSON

D-U-N-S 01-715-8262
JACKSON FORD INC (DE)
SEYMOUR FORD LINCOLN
2600 Seymour Rd, Jackson, MI 49201
Tel (517) 787-9500 *Founded/Ownrshp* 1993
Sales 22.1MM^E^ *EMP* 60
SIC 5511 Automobiles, new & used; Automobiles, new & used
Pr: Cecil L Pryor
**VP:* Randy Kunz

D-U-N-S 07-152-1298 IMP
JACKSON FURNITURE CO OF VIRGINIA
SHAMROCK FURNITURE
239 E 6th St, Front Royal, VA 22630-3409
Tel (540) 635-3187 *Founded/Ownrshp* 1995
Sales 24.0MM^E^ *EMP* 135
SIC 2512 Wood upholstered chairs & couches
Pr: Jackson W Ronald
**VP:* Roger T Jackson
**VP:* Virginia Jackson Matheny
VP: W Kay Stewart
Off Mgr: Betty Owens
Plnt Mgr: Clark Devers
Snr Mgr: Don Puryear

D-U-N-S 00-703-1453 IMP/EXP
JACKSON FURNITURE INDUSTRIES INC (TN)
CATNAPPER
1910 King Edward Ave Se, Cleveland, TN 37311-3076
Tel (423) 476-8544 *Founded/Ownrshp* 1933, 1986
Sales 184.8MM^E^ *EMP* 700
SIC 2512 Chairs: upholstered on wood frames; Living room furniture: upholstered on wood frames; Chairs: upholstered on wood frames; Living room furniture: upholstered on wood frames
Pr: W Ronald Jackson
**VP:* Roger T Jackson
VP: Tom Little
**VP:* Virginia Matheny
VP: W Kay Stewart
Dir IT: Nicholas Townsend
Ql Cn Mgr: Matt Smith
VP Sls: Chuck Catterton

JACKSON GENERAL HOSPITAL
See COMMUNITY HEALTH ASSOCIATION

D-U-N-S 96-533-7996
JACKSON GENERAL HOSPITAL FOUNDATION INC
JGH
122 Pinnell St, Ripley, WV 25271-9101
Tel (304) 372-2731 *Founded/Ownrshp* 1988
Sales 9.7MM^E^ *EMP* 300
SIC 8082 Home health care services; Home health care services
Prin: James J Robins
**CFO:* Angie Frame
Dir Sec: James Payne

D-U-N-S 96-714-0422
■ **JACKSON GROUP INC**
(*Suby of* CONSOLIDATED GRAPHICS INC) ★
5804 Churchman Byp, Indianapolis, IN 46203-6109
Tel (317) 791-9000 *Founded/Ownrshp* 2011
Sales 28.0MM^E^ *EMP* 180
SIC 2752 Commercial printing, lithographic; Commercial printing, lithographic
Pr: Katherine S Jackson
VP: Steve Kramer
Info Man: John Kot
Prd Mgr: Michael McQueary
**VP Sls:* Lee A Miller
VP Sls: Tim Sullivan

JACKSON HANDBAGS
See JACKSON CORP

JACKSON HEALTH SYSTEMS
See PUBLIC HEALTH TRUST OF MIAMI- DADE COUNTY FLORIDA

D-U-N-S 08-768-1537
JACKSON HEALTHCARE LLC
2655 Northwinds Pkwy, Alpharetta, GA 30009-2280
Tel (770) 643-5500 *Founded/Ownrshp* 1989
Sales 546.1MM *EMP* 784
SIC 7361 Labor contractors (employment agency); Labor contractors (employment agency)
Ch Bd: Richard L Jackson
Pr: R Shane Jackson
CFO: Douglas B Kline
Ex VP: Michael Hiffa
Ex VP: Philip Socoloff
VP: Diana D Holmes
VP: Bob Scholtman
VP: Bob Scholtman
Software D: Kusuma Peri
Pr Dir: Billie Wickstrom
Mktg Mgr: Sheryl Sorrell

D-U-N-S 83-068-7286
JACKSON HEIGHTS NH LLC
UNITY HEALTH AND REHABILITATIO
1404 Nw 22nd St, Miami, FL 33142-7742
Tel (305) 325-1050 *Founded/Ownrshp* 2009
Sales 25.2MM *EMP* 99
SIC 8051 Skilled nursing care facilities

D-U-N-S 18-763-1304
JACKSON HEWITT INC
JACKSON HEWITT TAX SERVICE
(*Suby of* JACKSON HEWITT TAX SERVICE INC) ★
3 Sylvan Way Ste 301, Parsippany, NJ 07054-3894
Tel (973) 630-0617 *Founded/Ownrshp* 2004
Sales 34.0MM^E^ *EMP* 305
SIC 7291 6141 6794 Tax return preparation services; Personal finance licensed loan companies, small; Franchises, selling or licensing; Tax return preparation services; Personal finance licensed loan companies, small; Franchises, selling or licensing
Pr: Michael Lister
**CFO:* Mark Heimbouch
Bd of Dir: Nikki Varvatsoulis
Chf Mktg O: Douglas K Foster
Chf Mktg O: Vada Hill
**Ex VP:* Perb Fortner
Ex VP: Forbes Scott
Sr VP: Steven Barnett
Sr VP: Grace Dieterich
Sr VP: Bill Herbert
Sr VP: Peter Karpiac
Sr VP: Angela Sanders
**Sr VP:* William Scavone
VP: Sheila Cort
VP: Mark Dahlke
VP: Justin Di Trolio
VP: Patrick Gleason
VP: Barbara Jordan
VP: Amanda Livingston
VP: Connie Mascioli
**VP:* Martin B Mazer

JACKSON HEWITT TAX SERVICE
See JACKSON HEWITT INC

D-U-N-S 94-499-3211
JACKSON HEWITT TAX SERVICE INC
3 Sylvan Way Ste 301, Parsippany, NJ 07054-3894
Tel (973) 630-1040 *Founded/Ownrshp* 2004
Sales 34.0MM^E^ *EMP* 305
SIC 7291 Tax return preparation services; Tax return preparation services
CFO: Daniel P O'Brien
Pr: Jeffrey Lininger
COO: Michael Yerington
CFO: Daniel N Chicoine
Sr Cor Off: Jessica Kilstrom
Sr Cor Off: Trecie Loyd
Sr Cor Off: John McCormick
Sr Cor Off: Vicky Saari
Sr Cor Off: Shawn Shumble
Bd of Dir: Jackson Hewitt
Chf Mktg O: D Michael Williams
Ofcr: Vada Hill
Ofcr: Lillian Rodriguez
Ex VP: Steven L Barnett
Sr VP: S Matt Botha
Sr VP: Brian Haile
VP: Adel Ali
VP: Kim Belesode
VP: Mark Dahlke
VP: Don Day
VP: Yvonne Duncan
Board of Directors: Ulysses Bridgeman Jr, Harry W Buckley, Rodman L Drake, Margaret Milner Richardson, Louis P Salvatore, James C Spira

D-U-N-S 60-751-7430 IMP
■ **JACKSON HMA LLC**
MERIT HEALTH CENTRAL
(*Suby of* COMMUNITY HEALTH SYSTEMS INC) ★
1850 Chadwick Dr, Jackson, MS 39204-3404
Tel (601) 376-1000 *Founded/Ownrshp* 2014
Sales 109.6MM^E^ *EMP* 850
SIC 8011 Clinic, operated by physicians; Clinic, operated by physicians
Chf Rad: Ralph Wells
Pr: Wanda Aultman
Pr: Carole Newell
Nurse Mgr: Cindy Phillips
Mktg Dir: Jana Fuss
Doctor: Richard Miles MD
Pharmcst: Amanda Labuda
Occ Thrpy: Lisa Davis
HC Dir: Yvonne Sanchez

JACKSON HOLE GOLF & TENNIS
See GRAND TETON LODGE CO

D-U-N-S 08-932-3851
JACKSON HOLE MOUNTAIN RESORT CORP
3395 Cody Ln, Teton Village, WY 83025
Tel (307) 733-2292 *Founded/Ownrshp* 1963
Sales 87.2MM^E^ *EMP* 1,400^E^
SIC 7011 7032 Ski lodge; Sporting & recreational camps; Ski lodge; Sporting & recreational camps
Pr: Jerry Blann
COO: Ned Wonson
Chf Mktg O: Adam Sutner
Ofcr: Scott Horn
VP: Matt Creedy
Exec: Wes Hamilton
Dir Soc: Margaret Brady
Comm Man: Anna Cole
Dir IT: Richard Ray

JACKSON HOSPITAL
See JACKSON COUNTY HOSPITAL DISTRICT

D-U-N-S 03-405-4098
JACKSON HOSPITAL & CLINIC INC
1725 Pine St, Montgomery, AL 36106-1117
Tel (334) 293-8000 *Founded/Ownrshp* 1949
Sales 195.8MM *EMP* 1,400
Accts Dixon Hughes Goodman Llp Ashe
SIC 8062 General medical & surgical hospitals; General medical & surgical hospitals
CEO: Joe B Riley
Pr: Steven Barrington
Pr: Jason Fogg
**COO:* Michael James
**CFO:* Paul Peiffer
Bd of Dir: George Handey
Trst: Glenn Yates
**Ofcr:* Sharon Goodison
**VP:* Janet McQueen
VP: Michael Ritzus
VP: Cindy Walker
Dir Lab: Steve Cartwright
Dir Lab: Patricia Harris
Dir Rad: Henry Batiste
Dir Bus: Cody Butts

D-U-N-S 12-622-2400
■ **JACKSON HOSPITAL CORP**
REGIONAL HOSPITAL OF JACKSON
(*Suby of* COMMUNITY HEALTH SYSTEMS INC) ★
367 Hospital Blvd, Jackson, TN 38305-2080
Tel (731) 661-2000 *Founded/Ownrshp* 1999
Sales 113.0MM *EMP* 643^E^
SIC 8062 General medical & surgical hospitals; General medical & surgical hospitals
CEO: Steve Grubbf
Dir Recs: Judith Mosley
CFO: Roseanen Devault
CFO: Richard Read
Exec: Pat Guy
Dir IT: Matt Snyder
Mtls Mgr: Roslind Richee
Mktg Mgr: Lisa Ragsdale

D-U-N-S 11-907-5666
■ **JACKSON HOSPITAL CORP**
KENTUCKY RIVER MEDICAL CENTER
(*Suby of* COMMUNITY HEALTH SYSTEMS INC) ★
540 Jett Dr, Jackson, KY 41339-9622
Tel (606) 666-6000 *Founded/Ownrshp* 1988
Sales 40.0MM^E^ *EMP* 260
SIC 8062 General medical & surgical hospitals; General medical & surgical hospitals
Pr: Martin G Schweinhart
**CEO:* Donald Rentfro
**CFO:* Mike Ackley
CFO: Mark Actley
**Prin:* Dabbie Linkous
Off Mgr: Denise Trusty
Dir IT: Tess Cantrell
Surgeon: Sreenivasa Alla
Snr Mgr: Christa Botner

JACKSON KEARNEY GROUP, THE
See NEEB KEARNEY & CO LLC

JACKSON KEARNEY GROUP, THE
See COASTAL CARGO CO INC

D-U-N-S 09-655-1403
JACKSON KELLY PLLC
500 Lee St E Ste 1600, Charleston, WV 25301-2189
Tel (304) 340-1000 *Founded/Ownrshp* 1999
Sales 79.3MM^E^ *EMP* 429
SIC 8111 General practice attorney, lawyer; General practice attorney, lawyer
Ch: William A Hoskins III
V Ch: Robert Busse
V Ch: John McClaugherty
V Ch: Robert McLusky
Pr: Mary Browning
Pr: Robin Marion
Pr: Lisa Moore
**CEO:* Michael D Foster
CFO: Karen Nichols
Exec: Clifford Kinney
Admn Mgr: Allen E Etter

JACKSON KITCHEN DESIGN
See JACKSON LUMBER AND MILLWORK CO INC

D-U-N-S 04-214-0483
JACKSON LABORATORY
600 Main St, Bar Harbor, ME 04609-1500
Tel (207) 288-6000 *Founded/Ownrshp* 1929
Sales 274.5MM *EMP* 1,300
Accts Kpmg Llp Boston Ma
SIC 8733 Noncommercial research organizations; Noncommercial research organizations
CEO: Edison T Liu
COO: Tina Hamilton
**COO:* Charles E Hewett
**CFO:* Linda Jensen
CFO: M S Linda
CFO: Janice Vonbrook
CFO: Lee Willur
**Ch:* Brian Wruble
**Treas:* Edward Sameck
Bd of Dir: Alan D Macewan
Sr VP: Yun Wang
**VP:* Robert Braun
**VP:* Michael E Hyde
VP: Kristen Rozansky
VP: Abigail Smith
Exec: Kyuson Yun
Assoc Dir: Ann G Burns
Assoc Dir: Kate Jordan
Assoc Dir: Dianne Pacheco
Assoc Dir: Wenning Qin
Assoc Dir: Robert Taft

JACKSON LEWIS
See LEWIS P C JACKSON

D-U-N-S 14-719-4757
JACKSON LOCAL SCHOOLS DIST
7600 Fulton Dr Nw, Massillon, OH 44646-9393
Tel (330) 830-8000 *Founded/Ownrshp* 1930
Sales 61.0MM^E^ *EMP* 475
Accts Mary Taylor Cpa Auditor Of S
SIC 8211 Public elementary & secondary schools; High school, junior or senior; School board; Public elementary & secondary schools; High school, junior or senior; School board
Pr: Douglas Winkler
Treas: Linda Wrinkler
Bd of Dir: Tim Debevec
DP Exec: Janet Thompson
Dir IT: George Woods
IT Man: Debbie Ciesielczyk
Schl Brd P: Thomas Winkbart
Psych: Marian Beresh
Psych: Monica Buehler
Psych: Julie Prato

D-U-N-S 00-176-9090
JACKSON LUMBER AND MILLWORK CO INC (MA)
JACKSON KITCHEN DESIGN
215 Market St, Lawrence, MA 01843-1616
Tel (978) 686-4141 *Founded/Ownrshp* 1946
Sales 59.0MM *EMP* 135
Accts Mcgladrey Llp Boston Ma
SIC 5211 Lumber & other building materials; Lumber & other building materials
Pr: Mark Thomas Torrisi
**Treas:* Joseph Anthony Torrisi
Sfty Mgr: Ken Pratt

D-U-N-S 01-429-1751
JACKSON MARINE SALES INC
230 Riverside Dr, North East, MD 21901-5314
Tel (410) 287-9400 *Founded/Ownrshp* 1954
Sales 24.7MM^E^ *EMP* 60

SIC 5551 4493 3732 Boat dealers; Motor boat dealers; Marine supplies & equipment; Marinas; Boat building & repairing
VP: Patricia Jackson
**Pr:* Woodlan T Jackson
**VP:* Jean M Jackson
Genl Mgr: Gary Parker

D-U-N-S 83-735-7433
JACKSON MARKETING GROUP INC
2 Task Industrial Ct, Greenville, SC 29607-5709
Tel (864) 272-3000 *Founded/Ownrshp* 1987
Sales 28.9MM^E *EMP* 100
SIC 7311 8743 Advertising agencies; Public relations services; Advertising agencies; Public relations services
Ch Bd: Larry Jackson
**Sec:* David Madson
**Ex VP:* Kevin Johnson
**VP:* Mike Zeller
Exec: Barbara Plotczeyk
Dir Soc: Kristin Decker
Mktg Mgr: Paul Hanna
Board of Directors: David Jones, Mike Zellar

D-U-N-S 07-871-4921
JACKSON NATIONAL LIFE DISTRIBUTORS LLC
JNLD
(*Suby of* JACKSON NATIONAL LIFE INSURANCE CO INC) ★
7601 E Technology Way, Denver, CO 80237-3003
Tel (303) 488-3518 *Founded/Ownrshp* 2003
Sales NA *EMP* 874^E
SIC 6311 Life insurance carriers
Pr: Greg P Cicotte
Pr: Robert Kinsky
Pr: Tate McMillin
Pr: Kiera McNamara
Pr: Dan Pegg
Pr: Christopher Silverstein
Pr: Matt Spurlock
Pr: Todd Stull
Pr: David Thaxter
Pr: Joseph Trahey
Pr: Joshua Travis
Pr: Aron Zierdt
Chf Cred: Daniel Wright
Ofcr: Joseph Oboyle
**Ex VP:* Clifford James Jack
Sr VP: Kevin Grant
**Sr VP:* Alison Reed
VP: Pat Cahill
VP: Chad Gonzalez
**VP:* Doug Mantelli
VP: Matt McGrath

D-U-N-S 00-886-7897
JACKSON NATIONAL LIFE INSURANCE CO INC
(*Suby of* PRUDENTIAL PUBLIC LIMITED COMPANY)
1 Corporate Way, Lansing, MI 48951-1001
Tel (517) 381-5500 *Founded/Ownrshp* 1986
Sales NA *EMP* 3,500
SIC 6311 6282 6211 6411

D-U-N-S 00-402-2689 EXP
JACKSON NORTH MEDICAL CENTER
160 Nw 170th St, North Miami Beach, FL 33169-5576
Tel (305) 651-1100 *Founded/Ownrshp* 2006
Sales 22.9MM^E *EMP* 11,000^E
SIC 8011 8062 Medical centers; General medical & surgical hospitals
Dir Lab: Masoud Ketabchi
Pr: Jose Nunez
VP: Diamela Corrales
Dir Lab: Marianul Pinon
IT Man: Tim Tuohy
Sfty Dirs: Patricia Batchelder
QC Dir: Isis Zambrana
Opers Mgr: Rogelio Borroto
Surgeon: Jaime Rodriguez
Anasthlgy: Sarita Sharma
Doctor: Elliot Silverman

D-U-N-S 79-647-1980
JACKSON NURSE PROFESSIONALS LLC
(*Suby of* JACKSON HEALTHCARE LLC) ★
12124 High Tech Ave # 300, Orlando, FL 32817-8374
Tel (205) 968-7500 *Founded/Ownrshp* 2006
Sales 85.0MM *EMP* 420
SIC 7363 Help supply services; Help supply services
Prin: Brett Doll
IT Man: Patricia Olear

D-U-N-S 07-597-3289
JACKSON OIL & SOLVENTS INC
JOES JUNCTION
1970 Kentucky Ave, Indianapolis, IN 46221-1914
Tel (317) 481-2244 *Founded/Ownrshp* 1979
Sales 109.1MM^E *EMP* 95
SIC 5172 5541 5983 5531 Gasoline; Fuel oil; Filling stations, gasoline; Fuel oil dealers; Automobile & truck equipment & parts; Gasoline; Fuel oil; Filling stations, gasoline; Fuel oil dealers; Automobile & truck equipment & parts
Pr: Monica S Heath
Genl Mgr: Ron Willis
Advt Dir: Diane Poff
Sls Mgr: Mike Williams
Sales Asso: John Rang
Sales Asso: Donneta Thompson

D-U-N-S 04-929-5223
JACKSON PANDROL INC
200 S Jackson Rd, Ludington, MI 49431-2409
Tel (231) 843-3431 *Founded/Ownrshp* 1989
Sales 15.4MM^E *EMP* 300
SIC 4789 3531 Railroad maintenance & repair services; Railroad related equipment; Tampers, powered; Railroad maintenance & repair services; Railroad related equipment; Tampers, powered
CFO: Roy J Orrow
**VP:* Bruce Bradshaw

D-U-N-S 00-820-2137 IMP
JACKSON PAPER CO
NEWELL PAPER CO OF COLUMBUS
4400 Mangum Dr, Flowood, MS 39232-2113
Tel (601) 360-9620 *Founded/Ownrshp* 1978
Sales 107.8MM^E *EMP* 195
Accts Swain Buckalwe & Collins Pa
SIC 5111 5113 5087 Fine paper; Paper & products, wrapping or coarse; Janitors' supplies; Fine paper; Paper & products, wrapping or coarse; Janitors' supplies
Ch: Tommy Galyean
Pr: Noel Machost
Sec: Brenda Bernhard
Netwrk Mgr: Frank Crist

D-U-N-S 83-641-5976 IMP
JACKSON PAPER MANUFACTURING CO
152 W Main St, Sylva, NC 28779-2928
Tel (828) 586-5534 *Founded/Ownrshp* 1995
Sales 58.0MM^E *EMP* 115
SIC 2631 Paperboard mills; Paperboard mills
Pr: Tim Campbell
**VP:* Tammy Francis
**VP:* Jeff Murphy
**VP:* Nicki Slusser
Sfty Mgr: Keisha Bridges
Opers Mgr: Dan Roland
Plnt Mgr: Kenny Rogers
Prd Mgr: Mike Shuler

D-U-N-S 01-783-5869
JACKSON PARISH SCHOOL DISTRICT
315 Pershing Hwy, Jonesboro, LA 71251-2429
Tel (318) 259-4456 *Founded/Ownrshp* 1935
Sales 25.8MM *EMP* 400
Accts Allen Green & Williamson Llp
SIC 8211 Public elementary & secondary schools; Public elementary & secondary schools
Schl Brd P: Wayd McBride
Teacher Pr: Sam Strocier

JACKSON PARK HOSP & MED CTR
See JACKSON PARK HOSPITAL FOUNDATION

D-U-N-S 06-848-3981
JACKSON PARK HOSPITAL FOUNDATION (IL)
JACKSON PARK HOSP & MED CTR
7531 S Stony Island Ave # 1, Chicago, IL 60649-3954
Tel (773) 947-7500 *Founded/Ownrshp* 1960
Sales 108.5MM *EMP* 700
SIC 8062 General medical & surgical hospitals; General medical & surgical hospitals
Pr: Merritt J Hasbrouck
**CFO:* Nelson Vasquez
Chf Mktg O: Lakshmi Dodda
Sr VP: Vernell Williams
VP: Margo Brooks-Pugh
Dir Lab: Jose Ruiz
Dir Rad: Cardell Gentry
Dir Rx: Harold Sias
Chf Nrs Of: Ej Silha
Dir Sec: William Smith
Genl Mgr: Randall Smith

D-U-N-S 80-771-8978
JACKSON PIPE & STEEL
898 Leary Rd, Texarkana, TX 75503-5604
Tel (903) 792-1197 *Founded/Ownrshp* 1993
Sales 27.6MM^E *EMP* 32
SIC 5051 Steel
Owner: Bill Cromer

D-U-N-S 02-620-9296 IMP/EXP
JACKSON POTTERY INC (TX)
JACKSON'S HOME AND GARDEN
2146 Empire Central, Dallas, TX 75235-4306
Tel (214) 357-9819 *Founded/Ownrshp* 1937, 2007
Sales 43.8MM^E *EMP* 120
SIC 5023 5719 5261 Pottery; Pottery; Nurseries & garden centers; Pottery; Pottery; Nurseries & garden centers
Ch Bd: Robert R Jackson
**Pr:* Kent Ferris
**VP:* Marilyn Jackson

D-U-N-S 07-944-7611
JACKSON PUBLIC SCHOOL DISTRICT LEASE CORP INC
JACKSON PUBLIC SCHOOLS
662 S President St, Jackson, MS 39201-5601
Tel (601) 960-8921 *Founded/Ownrshp* 1949
Sales 165.9MM^E *EMP* 4,200
SIC 8211 Public elementary & secondary schools; Public elementary & secondary schools
**CFO:* Michael Thomas
Dir Sec: Gerald Jones
MIS Dir: Stephan George
Pr Dir: Sherwin Johnson
Instr Medi: Larry Keeler

JACKSON PUBLIC SCHOOLS
See JACKSON PUBLIC SCHOOL DISTRICT LEASE CORP INC

D-U-N-S 07-635-1543
JACKSON PUBLIC SCHOOLS
522 Wildwood Ave, Jackson, MI 49201-1013
Tel (517) 841-2200 *Founded/Ownrshp* 1876
Sales 45.5MM^E *EMP* 1,035
Accts Plante & Moran Pllc Portage
SIC 8211 Public combined elementary & secondary school; Public adult education school; Public combined elementary & secondary school; Public adult education school
MIS Dir: Richard Compton
Psych: Eric Baldwin

D-U-N-S 00-694-6099
JACKSON PURCHASE ENERGY CORP
2900 Irvin Cobb Dr, Paducah, KY 42003-0329
Tel (270) 442-7321 *Founded/Ownrshp* 1937
Sales 62.1MM *EMP* 76
Accts Alan M Zumstein Cpa Lexingt
SIC 4911 Electric services; Electric services
Pr: G Kelly Nuckols
VP: Scott Ribble
VP: Richard Sherrill
VP: Izell White
VP: Charles Williamson
Genl Mgr: Kelly Nuckols
IT Man: Gregg Brown

D-U-N-S 03-502-8740
■ **JACKSON PURCHASE MEDICAL CENTER**
(*Suby of* HISTORIC LIFEPOINT HOSPITALS INC) ★
1099 Medical Center Cir, Mayfield, KY 42066-1143
Tel (270) 251-4100 *Founded/Ownrshp* 1993
Sales 58.6MM *EMP* 550
SIC 8062 General medical & surgical hospitals; General medical & surgical hospitals
CEO: David Anderson
**CEO:* Fred Pelle
CFO: Greg Cook
Dir OR: Carolyn Brown
Dir Lab: Joan Harrison
Dir Rad: Bev Walker
Mktg Dir: Tara Straub
Pathlgst: Henry Viles
Surgeon: Puneet Bhatia
Doctor: Surinder Kad
Phys Thrpy: Jay Hardgrove

D-U-N-S 03-249-7794
JACKSON R-2 SCHOOL DISTRICT
BOARD OF EDUCATION
614 E Adams St, Jackson, MO 63755-2150
Tel (573) 243-9501 *Founded/Ownrshp* 1874
Sales 32.2MM^E *EMP* 580
Accts Larson Allen Llp St Louis M
SIC 8211 Elementary & secondary schools; Private senior high school; Private junior high school; Elementary & secondary schools; Private senior high school; Private junior high school

D-U-N-S 80-865-4479
JACKSON RANCHERIA CASINO & HOTEL
JACKSON RNCHERIA CASINO RESORT
12222 New York Ranch Rd, Jackson, CA 95642-9407
Tel (209) 223-1677 *Founded/Ownrshp* 1991
Sales 55.7MM^E *EMP* 1,000
SIC 7999 5812 7011 5813 Bingo hall; Game parlor; Eating places; Hotels & motels; Drinking places; Bingo hall; Game parlor; Eating places; Hotels & motels; Drinking places
Ch Bd: Margaret Dalton
IT Man: Carol Olney

D-U-N-S 18-941-4837
JACKSON READY PAC
148 Riverview Park Rd, Jackson, GA 30233-6132
Tel (770) 504-7100 *Founded/Ownrshp* 1996
Sales 49.0MM^E *EMP* 300
SIC 2099 Salads, fresh or refrigerated; Salads, fresh or refrigerated
Mfg Mgr: Marcos Gutierrez

JACKSON RNCHERIA CASINO RESORT
See JACKSON RANCHERIA CASINO & HOTEL

D-U-N-S 07-353-4620
JACKSON STATE COMMUNITY COLLEGE INC
(*Suby of* UNIVERSITY AND COMMUNITY COLLEGE SYSTEM TENNESSEE STATE) ★
2046 N Parkway, Jackson, TN 38301-3797
Tel (731) 424-3520 *Founded/Ownrshp* 1977
Sales 12.8MM^E *EMP* 326^E
SIC 8222 9411 8221 Junior college; Administration of educational programs; ; Colleges universities & professional schools; Junior college; Administration of educational programs; ; Colleges universities & professional schools
Pr: Bruce Blanding
Pr: Heather Freeman
Ofcr: Brandon Dorris
Ofcr: Shane Young
Ex VP: Judith E Scherer
VP: Larry Bailey
VP: Horse Chase
VP: Bill Seymour
Store Mgr: Chris Jordan

D-U-N-S 04-450-7085
JACKSON STATE UNIVERSITY
JSU
1400 J R Lynch St Ste 206, Jackson, MS 39217-0001
Tel (601) 979-2121 *Founded/Ownrshp* 1877
Sales 166.5MM^E *EMP* 2,000
SIC 8221 College, except junior; College, except junior
Pr: Ronald Mason Jr
Ofcr: Mike Early
**Ex VP:* Willie G Brown
VP: Deborah Dent
VP: Bettye Graves
VP: Felix A Okojie
VP: Idehen Omoregie
VP: James Renick
Assoc Dir: Timothy Abram
Assoc Dir: Donna Antoine-Lavigne
Dir Soc: Brenda Manuel

D-U-N-S 06-874-6254
JACKSON STONEWALL MEMORIAL HOSPITAL CO
230 Hospital Plz, Weston, WV 26452-8558
Tel (304) 269-8000 *Founded/Ownrshp* 1966
Sales 44.2MM *EMP* 400
Accts Arnett Carbis Toothman Llp Ch
SIC 8062 Hospital, AMA approved residency; General medical & surgical hospitals
Pr: John Law
**CFO:* Dodi Arbogast
**Treas:* Denver Turner
**VP:* Joseph Snead
Dir Rx: Dan Walker
Off Mgr: Julie Bush
Dir IT: Cindy Shaver

D-U-N-S 18-456-1611
JACKSON SUPPLY CO
JSC
6655 Roxburgh Dr Ste 100, Houston, TX 77041-5210
Tel (713) 849-5865 *Founded/Ownrshp* 1990
Sales 78.4MM^E *EMP* 85
SIC 5075 Air conditioning & ventilation equipment & supplies; Air conditioning & ventilation equipment & supplies
Pr: Darla D Chakkalakal
**Ch:* James J Durrett
**Sec:* Tina Syzdek
IT Man: Brande Greene

D-U-N-S 12-622-3531
■ **JACKSON TENNESSEE HOSPITAL CO LLC**
(*Suby of* JACKSON HOSPITAL CORP) ★
367 Hospital Blvd, Jackson, TN 38305-2080
Tel (731) 660-6300 *Founded/Ownrshp* 2002
Sales 17.1MM^E *EMP* 600
SIC 8062 General medical & surgical hospitals; General medical & surgical hospitals
Prin: Steve Grubbs

D-U-N-S 01-389-2730
JACKSON THERAPY PARTNERS LLC
(*Suby of* JACKSON HEALTHCARE LLC) ★
12124 High Tech Ave # 300, Orlando, FL 32817-8374
Tel (877) 896-3660 *Founded/Ownrshp* 2006
Sales 37.1MM^E *EMP* 578
SIC 7363 Medical help service; Medical help service
Mktg Mgr: Rochelle Wheeler

JACKSON TOWNSHIP BOARD EDUCATN
See JACKSON TOWNSHIP SCHOOL DISTRICT

D-U-N-S 10-005-2323
JACKSON TOWNSHIP SCHOOL DISTRICT
JACKSON TOWNSHIP BOARD EDUCATN
151 Don Connor Blvd, Jackson, NJ 08527-3407
Tel (732) 833-4600 *Founded/Ownrshp* 1924
Sales 70.5MM^E *EMP* 1,114
Accts Suplee Clooney & Company Wes
SIC 8211 Public elementary school; Public junior high school; Public senior high school; Public elementary school; Public junior high school; Public senior high school
**CFO:* Michelle Richardson
Dir Sec: John Lamela

D-U-N-S 05-839-8165 IMP
JACKSON TUBE SERVICE INC
8210 Industry Park Dr, Piqua, OH 45356-8536
Tel (937) 773-8550 *Founded/Ownrshp* 1972
Sales 36.4MM^E *EMP* 153^E
SIC 3317 Steel pipe & tubes; Steel pipe & tubes
CEO: Robert W Jackson
**VP:* David A Hare
**VP:* Marcus Sergy
Sfty Mgr: Dave Booher
Sls Mgr: Mike Mohr

D-U-N-S 08-073-8628
JACKSON WALKER LLP (TX)
J W
2323 Ross Ave Ste 600, Dallas, TX 75201-2725
Tel (214) 953-6000 *Founded/Ownrshp* 2008
Sales 105.6MM^E *EMP* 650
SIC 8111 General practice law office; General practice law office
Pt: C Wade Cooper
Pt: Howard Baskin
Pt: Carl C Butzer
Pt: Alan N Greenspan
Pt: Phillip R Jones
Pt: David Laney
Pt: Larry Langley
**Pt:* David T Moran
Pt: J S Rose
Mng Pt: Wade Cooper
Pr: Kendra Gradney
Pr: Sharon Stokes
Pr: Diane Watters
**CFO:* Richard A Herlan

D-U-N-S 05-007-1380
JACKSON WHOLESALE CO
129 Armory Dr, Jackson, KY 41339-9256
Tel (606) 666-2495 *Founded/Ownrshp* 1956
Sales 33.2MM *EMP* 38
Accts Dean Dorton & Ford Psc Lexi
SIC 5141 Groceries, general line; Groceries, general line
Pr: Dan C McIntyre

D-U-N-S 09-606-7822
JACKSON WHOLESALE HARDWARE CO
H C I SUPPLY
982 Lower Brownsville Rd, Jackson, TN 38301-5652
Tel (731) 427-7725 *Founded/Ownrshp* 1976
Sales 62.3MM^E *EMP* 100
SIC 5085 5251 5072 5211 Industrial supplies; Builders' hardware; Hardware; Lumber & other building materials; Industrial supplies; Builders' hardware; Hardware; Lumber & other building materials
Pr: Bill Richardson
**CFO:* Tommy Kelly
**Sec:* Mary Ann Richardson
**VP:* Jim Richardson
Exec: Mike Melton
Sales Exec: Allen Richardson

D-U-N-S 62-534-0757 IMP/EXP
JACKSON WWS INC
JACKSON DISHMACHINES
(*Suby of* HOSHIZAKI USA HOLDINGS INC) ★
6209 N Us Highway 25e, Gray, KY 40734-6583
Tel (606) 523-9795 *Founded/Ownrshp* 2013
Sales 83.2MM^E *EMP* 173
SIC 3589 Dishwashing machines, commercial; Dishwashing machines, commercial
Pr: Chris Karssiens
Ofcr: Rhonda Mayne
VP: Chris Adelmann
CTO: Matt Swift
DP Dir: Charlotte Sanders
VP Mfg: John Stern
VP Opers: Carl Stueck
Sfty Dirs: Brad Tonkin
Sfty Mgr: Cheryl Moore
S&M/VP: Jonathan Akin
Mktg Mgr: Karen Huff

JACKSON-HINDS COMPREHENSIVE HE
See CENTRAL MISSISSIPPI CIVIC IMPROVEMENT ASSOCIATION INC

JACKSON-JENNINGS COOP
See JACKSON-JENNINGS FARM BUREAU COOPERATIVE ASSN INC

D-U-N-S 00-693-9698
JACKSON-JENNINGS FARM BUREAU COOPERATIVE ASSN INC
JACKSON-JENNINGS COOP
103 Community Dr, Seymour, IN 47274-1955
Tel (812) 522-4911 *Founded/Ownrshp* 1928
Sales 20.8MM^E *EMP* 130
Accts Blue & Co Llc Seymour In
SIC 5984 5261 5153 Liquefied petroleum gas dealers; Nursery stock, seeds & bulbs; Grain elevators; Liquefied petroleum gas dealers; Nursery stock, seeds & bulbs; Grain elevators
CEO: Ronald Ipert
**CFO:* David Waskom

D-U-N-S 01-629-9943
JACKSON-LEE-PEARSON INC
1002 S Sycamore St, Flora, IN 46929-1506
Tel (574) 967-4164 *Founded/Ownrshp* 1972
Sales 22.0MM *EMP* 41
SIC 5999 Farm equipment & supplies; Farm equipment & supplies
Pr: William Pearson
**VP:* Jason Pearson

D-U-N-S 06-165-4513
JACKSON-MADISON COUNTY GENERAL HOSPITAL DISTRICT
WEST TENNESSEE HEALTH CARE
620 Skyline Dr, Jackson, TN 38301-3923
Tel (731) 541-5000 *Founded/Ownrshp* 1950
Sales 130.2MM^E *EMP* 500^E
Accts Ernst & Young
SIC 8062 General medical & surgical hospitals; General medical & surgical hospitals
Pr: Bobby Arnold
CFO: Brad Ballon
**CFO:* Jeffrey Blankenship
**Ch:* Phil Bryant
Ex Dir: James Brown
CIO: Jeffrey Frieling
IT Man: Bradley Powers
Mtls Dir: Ladonna Ford
Doctor: Rene Hampton
Pharmcst: Nancy Tucker
Phys Thrpy: Jeff Lansdale

D-U-N-S 78-945-8010
JACKSON-MADISON COUNTY SCHOOL SYSTEM
310 N Parkway, Jackson, TN 38305-2712
Tel (731) 664-2500 *Founded/Ownrshp* 2006
Sales 120.1MM^E *EMP* 2,000
SIC 8211 Public elementary & secondary schools; Public elementary & secondary schools
Snr Mgr: Chuck Jones

D-U-N-S 16-153-9903
JACKSONS FOOD STORES INC
3450 E Commercial Ct, Meridian, ID 83642-8915
Tel (208) 888-6061 *Founded/Ownrshp* 1975
Sales 379.8MM^E *EMP* 1,000
SIC 5541 5411 Filling stations, gasoline; Convenience stores; Filling stations, gasoline; Convenience stores
Pr: John D Jackson
**Treas:* Jason Manning
Rgnl Mgr: Brody Kesler-Mauch
Dist Mgr: Jennifer Abrahamson
Dist Mgr: Warren Johnson
Dist Mgr: Toni Smith
Mktg Mgr: Rick Wheldon

D-U-N-S 02-935-4016
JACKSONS HARDWARE INC
MARIN INDUSTRIAL DISTRIBUTORS
62 Woodland Ave, San Rafael, CA 94901-5344
Tel (415) 454-3740 *Founded/Ownrshp* 1998
Sales 27.0MM^E *EMP* 61
SIC 5072 5251 Hardware; Hardware
Pr: Matthew R Olson
**Treas:* Anna Buss
Genl Mgr: Steve Hossfeld

JACKSON'S HOME AND GARDEN
See JACKSON POTTERY INC

D-U-N-S 06-227-3065
JACKSONS OF ENID INC
4405 W Owen K Garriott Rd, Enid, OK 73703-4812
Tel (580) 234-5400 *Founded/Ownrshp* 1993
Sales 25.8MM^E *EMP* 54
SIC 5511 New & used car dealers; New & used car dealers
Pr: Bruce A Jackson
**Sec:* Linda Jackson
Off Mgr: Barbara Hail
Sls Mgr: Gregg Durkee

D-U-N-S 12-323-1776
JACKSONVILLE AVIATION AUTHORITY
J A A
14201 Pecan Park Rd, Jacksonville, FL 32218-9411
Tel (904) 741-2000 *Founded/Ownrshp* 2001
Sales 68.4MM *EMP* 235
Accts Mcgladrey Llp Jacksonville F
SIC 4581 Airport terminal services; Airport terminal services
CEO: Steven Grossman
Dir IT: Steven Schultz

D-U-N-S 11-861-9464
JACKSONVILLE AVIATION AUTHORITY
14201 Pecan Park Rd, Jacksonville, FL 32218-9411
Tel (904) 741-3751 *Founded/Ownrshp* 2001
Sales 20.9MM^E *EMP* 220
SIC 4581 4512 Airport leasing, if operating airport; Air transportation, scheduled; Airport leasing, if operating airport; Air transportation, scheduled
Ex Dir: John Clark
Treas: Sharon Bembry
Off Mgr: Andre Olson

D-U-N-S 03-007-7957 IMP
▲ JACKSONVILLE BANCORP INC
100 N Laura St Ste 1000, Jacksonville, FL 32202-3634
Tel (904) 421-3040 *Founded/Ownrshp* 1997
Sales NA *EMP* 103
Accts Crowe Horwath Llp Fort Lauder
Tkr Sym JAXB *Exch* NGM
SIC 6022 State commercial banks; State commercial banks
Pr: Kendall L Spencer
**Ch Bd:* Donald F Glisson Jr
CFO: Valerie A Kendall
Chf Cred: Joseph W Amy
Ofcr: Scott M Hall
Ofcr: Christine Lombardozzi
Ofcr: Wyndi Partridge
Sr VP: Eric Clemons
VP: Debbie Dennis
Off Mgr: Colleen Keeling
Info Man: Steve Chisholm

D-U-N-S 07-602-1463
■ JACKSONVILLE BANK
(*Suby of* JACKSONVILLE BANCORP INC) ★
100 N Laura St Fl 10, Jacksonville, FL 32202-3669
Tel (904) 288-8933 *Founded/Ownrshp* 1999
Sales NA *EMP* 34^E
SIC 6029 Commercial banks; Commercial banks
Pr: Scott M Hall
CEO: Gilbert J Pomar III
COO: Margaret A Incandela
CFO: Valerie Kendall
VP: Shela Stallings
Board of Directors: John A Delaney, William R Klich, Price W Schwenck, Terrie G Spiro

JACKSONVILLE I SD
See JACKSONVILLE INDEPENDENT SCHOOL DISTRICT

D-U-N-S 80-938-0629
JACKSONVILLE I-10 TRAVEL CENTER INC
ARBY'S
(*Suby of* MORRIS HOLDINGS INC) ★
1024 Us Highway 301 S, Jacksonville, FL 32234-3600
Tel (904) 266-4281 *Founded/Ownrshp* 1993
Sales 23.1MM *EMP* 90
Accts Erwin Fountain & Jackson Pa
SIC 5541 5812 Truck stops; Fast-food restaurant, chain; Truck stops; Fast-food restaurant, chain
Pr: George H Morris
**CFO:* Robert Morris

D-U-N-S 01-046-9641
JACKSONVILLE INDEPENDENT SCHOOL DISTRICT
JACKSONVILLE I SD
800 College Ave, Jacksonville, TX 75766-2930
Tel (903) 586-6511 *Founded/Ownrshp* 1845
Sales 50.1MM *EMP* 900
Accts Robinson & Payne Pllc Cpas
SIC 8211 Public elementary & secondary schools; Public elementary school; Public elementary & secondary schools; Public elementary school
Bd of Dir: Fred Douglass
VP: Jim Tarrant Jr
Pr Dir: Grace Traylor
Schl Brd P: Todd Travis
Teacher Pr: Brad Steward

D-U-N-S 93-139-3250
JACKSONVILLE JAGUARS LLC
1 Everbank Field Dr, Jacksonville, FL 32202-1917
Tel (904) 633-6000 *Founded/Ownrshp* 1991
Sales 28.9MM^E *EMP* 214^E
SIC 7941 Football club; Football club
Owner: Shahid Khan
Pr: Mark Lamping
CFO: Diana Greenstein
Sr VP: Bill Prescott
Sr VP: Paul Vance
VP: Michael Demartino
VP: Curtis J Dvorak
VP: Chad Johnson
Genl Mgr: Gus Bradley
Genl Mgr: Dave Caldwell
Sales Exec: Evans Adonis

D-U-N-S 06-965-6981
JACKSONVILLE KENNEL CLUB INC
1440 Mcduff Ave N, Jacksonville, FL 32254-2035
Tel (904) 646-0001 *Founded/Ownrshp* 1934
Sales 4.9MM^E *EMP* 350
SIC 7948 Dog racing; Dog racing
Pr: Howard I Korman
**Ch Bd:* Charles W Bidwill
CFO: Bob Kuhn
**VP:* William H Johnston
**VP:* Robert J Pitocchelli

D-U-N-S 18-601-0443
JACKSONVILLE ORTHOPAEDIC INSTITUTE INC
1325 San Marco Blvd, Jacksonville, FL 32207-8568
Tel (904) 346-3465 *Founded/Ownrshp* 1987
Sales 52.0MM *EMP* 387
SIC 8011 Orthopedic physician; Orthopedic physician
Pr: Edward H Sim
**VP:* Earl B Mally
**Prin:* Jennifer Manuel
Off Mgr: Carol Larsen
IT Man: Dorothy Hammond

D-U-N-S 09-731-5287
JACKSONVILLE SCHOOL DISTRICT 117
516 Jordan St, Jacksonville, IL 62650-1997
Tel (217) 243-9411 *Founded/Ownrshp* 1954
Sales 34.6MM^E *EMP* 700
SIC 8211 9411 Public elementary school; Public junior high school; Public senior high school; Public special education school; Administration of educational programs; Public elementary school; Public junior high school; Public senior high school; Public special education school; Administration of educational programs
Dir IT: Dan Nash
Dir IT: Bill Poole
Psych: Shannon Folker

JACKSONVILLE SHERIFFS OFFICE
See JACKSONVILLE SHERIFFS OFFICE

D-U-N-S 07-879-9982
JACKSONVILLE SHERIFFS OFFICE
JACKSONVILLE SHERIFFS OFFICE
501 E Bay St, Jacksonville, FL 32202-2927
Tel (904) 630-0500 *Founded/Ownrshp* 1832
Sales NA *EMP* 3,000
SIC 9221 Police protection; Police protection
Ofcr: Guy Barnhart
Ofcr: Ramonda Barrett
Ofcr: Tony Batrous
Ofcr: Samuel Bearden
Ofcr: Mark Bialkoski
Ofcr: David Border
Ofcr: Samara Brazile
Ofcr: Bryan Burnett
Ofcr: April Cobb
Ofcr: Jimmie Collins
Ofcr: Christy Conn
Ofcr: Robert Coyle
Ofcr: Corey Debolt
Ofcr: Larry Dixon
Ofcr: Jeremy Flanigan
Ofcr: Elwin Fuller
Ofcr: David Gaston
Ofcr: Joyce Gay
Ofcr: Bryan Goebel
Ofcr: Raymond Goethe
Ofcr: Gloria Graham

D-U-N-S 07-910-7165
JACKSONVILLE STATE UNIVERSITY (INC)
700 Pelham Rd N, Jacksonville, AL 36265-1623
Tel (256) 782-5781 *Founded/Ownrshp* 1883
Sales 71.1MM *EMP* 850^E
Accts Ronald L Jones Montgomery A
SIC 8221 University; University
Pr: William A Meehan
Ofcr: Buddy Smith
Top Exec: Kingsley O Harbor
Top Exec: Ralph Veasey
Assoc VP: Joe Walsh
VP: Clint Carlson
VP: Gina Glass
VP: Marvin Jenkins
VP: Rebecca Turner
Ex Dir: Delane Hodge
Ex Dir: Alicia Simmons

D-U-N-S 15-020-1689
JACKSONVILLE TRANSPORTATION AUTHORITY (INC)
ENGINEERING DIVISION
100 N Myrtle Ave, Jacksonville, FL 32204-1310
Tel (904) 630-3181 *Founded/Ownrshp* 1955
Sales NA *EMP* 700^E
Accts Berman Hopkins Wright Laham Cp
SIC 9621 Transit system or authority: government, non-operating; ;Transit system or authority: government, non-operating
Pr: Michael Blaylock
**Ch Bd:* Mrs Ave Parker
**CFO:* Blair Fishburn
Ofcr: Ivan Rodriguez
VP: Alice Cannon
VP: Michael Jsloan
VP: Henry Li
VP: Brad Thoburn
CIO: Daniel Gulliver
Snr Mgr: Kevin Badge
Snr Mgr: Janell Damato
Board of Directors: Huey R Hawkins, Carol S Minor, John S Payon

D-U-N-S 07-831-4903
JACKSONVILLE UNIVERSITY
JACKSNVLLE UNIV DRMTORY CFTRIA
2800 University Blvd N, Jacksonville, FL 32211-3394
Tel (904) 256-8000 *Founded/Ownrshp* 1934
Sales 115.6MM *EMP* 450
Accts Crowe Horwath Llp Tampa Fl
SIC 8221 University; University
Pr: Kerry D Romesburg
Ofcr: Emanuel Gwathney
Ofcr: Meg Harmon
Ofcr: Erin McFeely
Ofcr: Shadoe Sullivan
Ofcr: John Trainer
**VP:* Timothy Payne
VP: Gil Pomar Jr
Exec: Brian Bowser
Assoc Dir: Deborah Bridier
Assoc Dir: Donald Horner
Assoc Dir: Mark Willette

D-U-N-S 06-966-5388
JACKSONVILLE URBAN LEAGUE INC
6945 Morse Ave Apt 536, Jacksonville, FL 32244-8011
Tel (904) 723-4007 *Founded/Ownrshp* 1947
Sales 1.1MM *EMP* 370
Accts Harbeson Fletcher & Bateh Llp
SIC 8322 Family service agency; Referral service for personal & social problems; Youth center
Pr: Richard Danford Jr
**VP:* Ernest G Perez
Pr Dir: Linnie Finley

JACKSONVILLE ZOOLOGICAL GARDEN
See JACKSONVILLE ZOOLOGICAL SOCIETY INC

D-U-N-S 05-698-5476
JACKSONVILLE ZOOLOGICAL SOCIETY INC
JACKSONVILLE ZOOLOGICAL GARDEN
370 Zoo Pkwy, Jacksonville, FL 32218-5770
Tel (904) 757-4463 *Founded/Ownrshp* 1920
Sales 20.4MM *EMP* 200
Accts Smoak Davis & Nixon Llp Jacks
SIC 7999 Zoological garden, commercial; Zoological garden, commercial
Treas: Lewis Lee
**CFO:* Holly A Ellis
Bd of Dir: Thomas Burke
**Ex Dir:* Dennis Pate

JACKTHREADS
See THRILLIST ACQUISITION LLC

D-U-N-S 00-716-2782
JACKY JONES FORD LINCOLN MERCURY
714 New Highway 68, Sweetwater, TN 37874-1912
Tel (423) 337-5066 *Founded/Ownrshp* 1999
Sales 26.2MM^E *EMP* 75
SIC 5511 Automobiles, new & used; Automobiles, new & used
Owner: David McMahan
**Co-Ownr:* John McMahan

D-U-N-S 92-818-1387
JACKY W JONES FORD INC
2742 Highway 129 S, Cleveland, GA 30528-7156
Tel (770) 532-0211 *Founded/Ownrshp* 1988
Sales 30.2MM^E *EMP* 90
SIC 5511 Automobiles, new & used; Automobiles, new & used
CEO: Jacky Jones
**CFO:* Dennis Greene
Sls Mgr: John Greene
Sls Mgr: Hal Pardue

D-U-N-S 04-319-0511 IMP
▲ JACLYN INC
197 W Spring Valley Ave # 101, Maywood, NJ 07607-1729
Tel (201) 909-6000 *Founded/Ownrshp* 1968
Sales 28.0MM^E *EMP* 160^E
Tkr Sym JCLY *Exch* OTO
SIC 2335 3111 2824 3172 Women's, juniors' & misses' dresses; Bag leather; Handbag leather; Vinyl fibers; Cosmetic bags; Women's, juniors' & misses' dresses; Bag leather; Handbag leather; Vinyl fibers; Cosmetic bags
Pr: Robert Chestnov
**Ch Bd:* Allan Ginsburg
**CFO:* Anthony Christon
**V Ch Bd:* Howard Ginsburg
VP: Lori Nitzberg
Board of Directors: Norman Axelrod, Richard Chestnov, Abe Ginsburg, Albert Safer

D-U-N-S 06-459-2611
JACMAR COMPANIES
SHAKEY'S PIZZA
300 Baldwin Park Blvd, City of Industry, CA 91746-1405
Tel (626) 281-4296 *Founded/Ownrshp* 1960
Sales 635.7MM^E *EMP* 900
SIC 5141 5812 6552 Fast-food restaurant, chain; Groceries, general line; Land subdividers & developers, commercial; Groceries, general line; Fast-food restaurant, chain; Land subdividers & developers, commercial
Pr: James A Dal Pozzo
Ch Bd: William Tilley
VP: Sonia Barajas
VP: Robert Hill
VP: Victor Santillan
Exec: Julie Bosworth
IT Man: Amy Gehrig
Mktg Dir: Cindy Staats

D-U-N-S 79-352-5903
JACMAR DDC LLC
JACMAR FOOD SERVICE DIST
(*Suby of* JACMAR COMPANIES) ★
3057 Promenade St, West Sacramento, CA 95691-5941
Tel (916) 372-9795 *Founded/Ownrshp* 2004
Sales 22.5MM^E *EMP* 55
SIC 5149 Natural & organic foods
Genl Mgr: Orlando Andrade
Sls Dir: Audrey Lopez

JACMAR FOOD SERVICE DIST
See JACMAR DDC LLC

D-U-N-S 08-689-3815 IMP
JACMEL JEWELRY INC (NY)
1385 Broadway Fl 8, New York, NY 10018-2102
Tel (718) 349-4300 *Founded/Ownrshp* 1977
Sales 26.9MM^E *EMP* 160^E
SIC 3911 Medals, precious or semiprecious metal; Medals, precious or semiprecious metal
Ch Bd: Jack Rahmey
Ex Ofcr: Larry Wang
Ex VP: Nathan Dweck
**VP:* Morris Dweck
VP: Jim Molinari

D-U-N-S 04-585-6879 IMP
▲ JACO ELECTRONICS INC
415 Oser Ave Ste L, Hauppauge, NY 11788-3637
Tel (631) 467-1100 *Founded/Ownrshp* 1961
Sales 72.5MM^E *EMP* 194
Tkr Sym JACO *Exch* OTO
SIC 5065 Electronic parts & equipment; Electronic parts; Capacitors, electronic; Resistors, electronic; Electronic parts & equipment; Electronic parts; Capacitors, electronic; Resistors, electronic
Ch Bd: Joel H Girsky
CFO: Jeffrey D Gash
Ex VP: Gary Giordano
**Ex VP:* Charles B Girsky
VP: Bob Savacchio
VP: Ben Schwartz
Prin: Don Ackley
Prin: Marvin Meiers
Prin: Robert J Waldman
Rgnl Mgr: Mike Lissner Jr
Genl Mgr: Les Girsky
Board of Directors: Don Ackley, Marvin Meirs, Robert J Waldman

D-U-N-S 96-216-4125
JACO ENVIRONMENTAL INC
APPLIANCE RECYCLING OUTLET
18323 Bothell Everett Hwy, Bothell, WA 98012-5246
Tel (425) 398-6200 *Founded/Ownrshp* 1999
Sales 102.7MM^E *EMP* 420
SIC 8748 Environmental consultant

D-U-N-S 06-120-1625
JACO HILL CO
4960 Adobe Rd, Twentynine Palms, CA 92277-1612
Tel (760) 361-1407 *Founded/Ownrshp* 2001
Sales 217.3MM *EMP* 4[E]
Accts Moss Adams Llp Los Angeles C
SIC 5171 Petroleum bulk stations & terminals
Prin: Dan Jaco

D-U-N-S 78-689-0798
JACO HOLDING CO
601 13th St Nw Ste 300n, Washington, DC 20005-3870
Tel (202) 638-3000 *Founded/Ownrshp* 1984
Sales 80.2MM[E] *EMP* 90
SIC 6531 6552 6799 Real estate managers; Subdividers & developers; Real estate investors, except property operators
CEO: John Akridge

D-U-N-S 06-219-5623
JACO INC
140 Constitution Blvd, Franklin, MA 02038-2544
Tel (508) 553-1000 *Founded/Ownrshp* 1972
Sales 27.2MM[E] *EMP* 100
SIC 3674 7692 Integrated circuits, semiconductor networks, etc.; Welding repair; Integrated circuits, semiconductor networks, etc.; Welding repair
Pr: Noreen Rossini
Pr: Len Halio
* *Treas:* Alfred Rossini
VP: Gary Dorn
VP: Umberto Santucci
Exec: Peter Franzosa
IT Man: Rick Bourassa
VP Opers: Bert Santucci
Ql Cn Mgr: Mark Leboeuf
Ql Cn Mgr: Tony Pepicelli
Mktg Dir: Thomas Bagley

JACO OIL
See BASIC PROPERTIES

D-U-N-S 05-642-0318
JACO OIL CO
3101 State Rd, Bakersfield, CA 93308-4931
Tel (661) 393-7000 *Founded/Ownrshp* 1970
Sales 542.2MM *EMP* 350
Accts Moss Adams Llp Loss Angeles
SIC 5541 Filling stations, gasoline; Filling stations, gasoline
CEO: T J Jamieson
* *CFO:* Brian Busacca
* *Sec:* Lee Jamieson
* *VP:* Charles Mc Can
Area Supr: Ron Jonas
MIS Dir: Bill Nguyen
Dir IT: Jessi Moss
Snr Mgr: Jon Stolich

D-U-N-S 18-951-0498
JACO-JAMIESON A GENERAL PARTNERSHIP
FASTRIP
3101 State Rd, Bakersfield, CA 93308-4931
Tel (661) 393-7000 *Founded/Ownrshp* 1983
Sales 23.1MM[E] *EMP* 250
SIC 5411 Convenience stores; Convenience stores
Pt: Thomas J Jamieson
Pt: William Hill
VP: Charles Can
Exec: Alissa Thome
MIS Dir: Bill Nguyen

D-U-N-S 14-830-3506
JACOB GROUP LTD (INC)
EVANS FOOD
4118 S Halsted St, Chicago, IL 60609-2612
Tel (773) 254-7400 *Founded/Ownrshp* 1986
Sales 42.6MM[E] *EMP* 240[E]
SIC 2096 Pork rinds; Pork rinds
Ch: Alex Silva
* *Pr:* Jim Speak
* *Treas:* Jose Garza

D-U-N-S 18-597-6904 IMP
JACOB HOLM INDUSTRIES (AMERICA) INC
(*Suby of* JACOB HOLM & SONNER A/S)
1265 Sand Hill Rd, Candler, NC 28715-6907
Tel (828) 670-0041 *Founded/Ownrshp* 2004
Sales 43.9MM[E] *EMP* 89
SIC 2297 Nonwoven fabrics; Nonwoven fabrics
Ch: Poul M Mikkelsen
* *Pr:* Stephen R Landon
VP: Patricia Higley
* *VP:* Charles Holton
Prd Mgr: Blandine Carton
Ql Cn Mgr: Pascal Buard
Ql Cn Mgr: Michael Heatherly

JACOB K JAVITS CONVENTION CENT
See NEW YORK CONVENTION CENTER OPERATING CORP

D-U-N-S 00-791-4922 IMP/EXP
JACOB STERN & SONS INC (PA)
ACME-HARDESTY CO.
1464 E Valley Rd, Santa Barbara, CA 93108-1241
Tel (805) 565-4532 *Founded/Ownrshp* 1857
Sales 82.2MM[E] *EMP* 100
SIC 5169 5191 5199 Chemicals & allied products; Animal feeds; Greases, animal or vegetable; Chemicals & allied products; Animal feeds; Greases, animal or vegetable
Pr: Phillip L Bernstein
* *CEO:* Doug Shreves
* *CFO:* Chip Hull
VP: Kerry Arnold
* *VP:* Jeff Peeler
Dir IT: Dale Polekoff

D-U-N-S 60-718-0176
JACOB TRANSPORTATION SERVICES LLC
EXECUTIVE LAS VEGAS
3950 W Tompkins Ave, Las Vegas, NV 89103-5524
Tel (702) 949-5379 *Founded/Ownrshp* 2004
Sales 23.2MM[E] *EMP* 500
SIC 4119 Limousine rental, with driver; Limousine rental, with driver
CEO: Carol Jimmerson
Genl Mgr: David Hartson

D-U-N-S 04-429-3819
JACOBES DOWNING HUGHES INC
YUBA CY TOYOTA-LINCOLN-MERCURY
1340 Bridge St, Yuba City, CA 95993-3505
Tel (530) 673-5661 *Founded/Ownrshp* 1995
Sales 21.9MM[E] *EMP* 55
SIC 5511 Automobiles, new & used; Automobiles, new & used
Pr: Roy Jacobs
* *Sec:* Tom Hughes
* *VP:* Steven Downing
Off Mgr: Heather Fanger

D-U-N-S 14-069-0947
JACOBI MEDICAL CENTER
(*Suby of* NEW YORK CITY HEALTH AND HOSPITALS CORP) ★
1400 Pelham Pkwy S, Bronx, NY 10461-1197
Tel (718) 918-5000 *Founded/Ownrshp* 1955
Sales 631.1M *EMP* 4,000
SIC 8062 General medical & surgical hospitals; General medical & surgical hospitals
Ex Dir: William Walsh
CFO: Stuart May
CFO: Jay Weinman
Dir OR: Anna Cassidy
Dir Lab: Alan Jablonsky
Assoc Dir: Janice Amato
Assoc Dir: Juanita Duncan
Assoc Dir: Rafael Fernandez
Assoc Dir: Loren Yellin
Dir Rad: Larry Kassen
Dir Rx: Joseph D'Agostino
Dir Rx: Joe Dagostinoa

D-U-N-S 01-657-2893 IMP
JACOBI SALES INC
KUBOTA
425 Main St Ne, Palmyra, IN 47164-8898
Tel (812) 364-6141 *Founded/Ownrshp* 1928, 1965
Sales 29.5MM[E] *EMP* 105
SIC 5261 5083 Lawn & garden equipment; Agricultural machinery & equipment
CEO: Phillip Jacobi
* *Pr:* Brian M Jacobi
* *Sec:* Uhl G L
* *VP:* Kevin R Book

D-U-N-S 00-336-6135 EXP
■ **JACOBS APPLIED TECHNOLOGY INC**
(*Suby of* JACOBS ENGINEERING GROUP INC) ★
2040 Bushy Park Rd, Goose Creek, SC 29445
Tel (843) 824-1100 *Founded/Ownrshp* 1945, 1990
Sales 147.8MM[E] *EMP* 500
SIC 3559 3443 8711 1629 Petroleum refinery equipment; Vessels, process or storage (from boiler shops): metal plate; Petroleum, mining & chemical engineers; Industrial plant construction; Petroleum refinery equipment; Vessels, process or storage (from boiler shops): metal plate; Petroleum, mining & chemical engineers; Industrial plant construction
Pr: Dan Gaa
Treas: John W Prosser Jr
Site Mgr: Roger Myrick
Board of Directors: W R Kerler, Noel G Watson

JACOBS, BILL BMW
See BILL JACOBS MOTORSPORT HOLDINGS INC

D-U-N-S 05-712-0941
■ **JACOBS CONSTRUCTORS INC**
(*Suby of* JACOBS ENGINEERING GROUP INC) ★
4949 Essen Ln, Baton Rouge, LA 70809-3433
Tel (225) 769-7700 *Founded/Ownrshp* 1977
Sales 83.5MM[E] *EMP* 500
SIC 1629 Industrial plant construction; Industrial plant construction
VP: R Terry Jones
* *Treas:* J W Prosser Jr

JACOBS, DON BMW
See DON JACOBS IMPORTS INC

D-U-N-S 06-382-5236
■ **JACOBS ENGINEERING CO**
(*Suby of* JACOBS ENGINEERING GROUP INC) ★
1111 S Arroyo Pkwy, Pasadena, CA 91105-3254
Tel (626) 449-2171 *Founded/Ownrshp* 1979
Sales 98.4MM[E] *EMP* 4,000
SIC 8711 1629 Engineering services; Chemical plant & refinery construction; Engineering services; Chemical plant & refinery construction
CEO: Noel G Watson
* *Pr:* C L Martin

D-U-N-S 07-410-3508 IMP/EXP
▲ **JACOBS ENGINEERING GROUP INC**
155 N Lake Ave, Pasadena, CA 91101-1849
Tel (626) 578-3500 *Founded/Ownrshp* 1947
Sales 12.7MMM *EMP* 49,945
Accts Ernst & Young Llp Los Angeles
Tkr Sym JEC *Exch* NYS
SIC 8711 1629 1541 8748 Engineering services; Construction & civil engineering; Building construction consultant; Industrial plant construction; Chemical plant & refinery construction; Oil refinery construction; Waste disposal plant construction; Industrial buildings & warehouses; Pharmaceutical manufacturing plant construction; Industrial buildings, new construction; Systems analysis & engineering consulting services; Systems analysis or design; Engineering services; Construction & civil engineering; Building construction consultant; Industrial plant construction; Chemical plant & refinery construction; Oil refinery construction; Waste disposal plant construction; Industrial buildings & warehouses; Pharmaceutical manufacturing plant construction; Industrial buildings, new construction; Systems analysis & engineering consulting services; Systems analysis or design
Pr: Steven J Demetriou
CFO: Kevin C Berryman
Sr VP: Geoffrey P Sanders
Sr VP: Lori S Sundberg
Sr VP: Michael R Tyler
Board of Directors: Christopher Mt Thompson, Joseph R Bronson, Noel G Watson, Juan Jose Suarez Coppel, John F Coyne, Robert C Davidson Jr, Ralph E Eberhart, Edward V Fritzky, Dawne S Hickton, Linda Fayne Levinson, Peter J Robertson

D-U-N-S 96-649-2188
JACOBS ENGINEERING GROUP MEDICAL PLAN TRUST
300 Frank H Ogawa Plz # 10, Oakland, CA 94612-2042
Tel (510) 457-0027 *Founded/Ownrshp* 2011
Sales 144.8MM *EMP* 2
SIC 8711 Engineering services

D-U-N-S 83-175-8359
■ **JACOBS ENGINEERING INC**
(*Suby of* JACOBS ENGINEERING GROUP INC) ★
155 N Lake Ave, Pasadena, CA 91101-1849
Tel (626) 578-3500 *Founded/Ownrshp* 1971
Sales 189.4MM[E] *EMP* 361[E]
SIC 8711 Engineering services
CEO: Craig L Martin
VP: Suzanne Best-Foster
Dir IT: Gregory Gassett
IT Man: Joseph Hernandez
IT Man: Mark Wishart
Netwrk Mgr: John Pratt
Sls Mgr: Jess Elshere

D-U-N-S 10-346-6004
JACOBS ENTERTAINMENT INC
(*Suby of* JACOBS INVESTMENTS INC)
17301 W Colfax Ave # 250, Golden, CO 80401-4891
Tel (303) 215-5196 *Founded/Ownrshp* 2001
Sales 86.4MM[E] *EMP* 1,800[E]
SIC 7993 7948 Coin-operated amusement devices; Horse race track operation; Coin-operated amusement devices; Horse race track operation
Ch Bd: Jeffrey P Jacobs
* *Ch Bd:* Jeffrey Jacobs
* *Pr:* Stephen R Roark
* *COO:* Michael T Shubic
* *CFO:* Brent Kramer
* *Ex VP:* Emanuel J Cotronakis
VP: Stan Guidroz
VP: Michael Shubic
IT Man: Kevin Stewart
Mktg Dir: Meera Rosser

D-U-N-S 13-086-6098
■ **JACOBS FACILITIES INC**
(*Suby of* JACOBS ENGINEERING GROUP INC) ★
707 17th St Ste 2300, Denver, CO 80202-3404
Tel (303) 820-5240 *Founded/Ownrshp* 1994
Sales 19.8MM[E] *EMP* 500
Accts Ernst & Young Llp
SIC 8741 Construction management; Construction management
Pr: Scott Cram
* *Pr:* Rod Cornell
* *Treas:* John Prosser
* *VP:* Patricia Tarnow
Board of Directors: Andy Carlson, Warren Dean, Noel Watson

D-U-N-S 17-336-1601
■ **JACOBS FACILITIES INC**
(*Suby of* JACOBS ENGINEERING GROUP INC) ★
1100 N Glebe Rd Ste 500, Arlington, VA 22201-5785
Tel (571) 218-1000 *Founded/Ownrshp* 1993
Sales 19.9MM[E] *EMP* 395
SIC 8711 Engineering services; Engineering services
VP: Robert Holt
* *VP:* Anne Farmer

D-U-N-S 80-581-7798
■ **JACOBS FACILITIES INC**
(*Suby of* JACOBS ENGINEERING GROUP INC) ★
501 N Broadway, Saint Louis, MO 63102-2131
Tel (314) 335-4000 *Founded/Ownrshp* 1999
Sales 420.7MM *EMP* 2,047
Accts Ernst & Young Llp Los Angeles
SIC 8712 8711 8713 8741 1542 1541 Architectural services; Architectural engineering; Engineering services; Civil engineering; Surveying services; Management services; Nonresidential construction; Industrial buildings & warehouses; Architectural services; Architectural engineering; Engineering services; Civil engineering; Surveying services; Management services; Nonresidential construction; Industrial buildings & warehouses
Pr: Craig Martin
* *VP:* Warren M Dean
* *VP:* H Thomas Mc Duffie
* *VP:* James J Scott
Exec: Audrey Crader
Netwrk Mgr: Kevin V Dickens
Mktg Dir: Stephanie Crouch

D-U-N-S 17-547-3495 IMP
JACOBS FARM/DEL CABO INC
2450 Stage Rd, Pescadero, CA 94060
Tel (650) 879-0580 *Founded/Ownrshp* 1995
Sales 74.4MM *EMP* 300
SIC 0181 0139 0161 Florists' greens & flowers; Herb or spice farm; Snap bean farm (bush & pole); Florists' greens & flowers; Herb or spice farm; Snap bean farm (bush & pole)
Pr: Laurence B Jacobs
CFO: Art Puliafico

D-U-N-S 05-934-5124
■ **JACOBS FIELD SERVICES NORTH AMERICA INC**
(*Suby of* JACOBS ENGINEERING GROUP INC) ★
5995 Rogerdale Rd, Houston, TX 77072-1601
Tel (832) 351-6000 *Founded/Ownrshp* 1978
Sales 362.4MM[E] *EMP* 2,300
SIC 8711 Engineering services; Electrical or electronic engineering; Engineering services; Electrical or electronic engineering
Pr: James E Dixon
* *Treas:* John W Prosser Jr
* *VP:* Walter Lisiewski
Ql Cn Mgr: Allison Zukewich

D-U-N-S 09-277-8182
JACOBS INDUSTRIES INC
JACOBS INTERACTIVE
8096 Excelsior Blvd, Hopkins, MN 55343-3415
Tel (612) 339-9500 *Founded/Ownrshp* 1977
Sales 89.3MM[E] *EMP* 440
SIC 2841 2087 2099 2844 5084 6794 Detergents, synthetic organic or inorganic alkaline; Scouring compounds; Extracts, flavoring; Spices, including grinding; Toilet preparations; Printing trades machinery, equipment & supplies; Franchises, selling or licensing; Detergents, synthetic organic or inorganic alkaline; Scouring compounds; Extracts, flavoring; Spices, including grinding; Toilet preparations; Printing trades machinery, equipment & supplies; Franchises, selling or licensing
Pr: Irwin Jacobs
CFO: David A Mahler

JACOBS INTERACTIVE
See JACOBS INDUSTRIES INC

D-U-N-S 82-541-5359
■ **JACOBS INTERNATIONAL LTD INC**
(*Suby of* JACOBS ENGINEERING GROUP INC) ★
155 N Lake Ave, Pasadena, CA 91101-1849
Tel (626) 578-3500 *Founded/Ownrshp* 2002
Sales 85.0MM *EMP* 300
SIC 8711 Engineering services; Engineering services
Pr: Craig Martin
* *Treas:* John W Prosser Jr
Sr VP: Bruce Mills
* *VP:* Jeff Sanders
Prgrm Mgr: Teresa Buehner
Area Mgr: Eric Hidalgo

D-U-N-S 02-920-2850 IMP
JACOBS MALCOLM & BURTT
18 Crow Canyon Ct Ste 210, San Ramon, CA 94583-1786
Tel (415) 285-0400 *Founded/Ownrshp* 1969
Sales 54.9MM *EMP* 31
Accts Thad Scott & Company Fresno
SIC 5148 Fruits, fresh; Vegetables, fresh; Fruits, fresh; Vegetables, fresh
Pr: Leo M Rolandelli
* *Sec:* Gordon Everet
* *VP:* Roland Acosta
* *VP:* Walter Schivo

D-U-N-S 09-282-2352
JACOBS MECHANICAL CO
4500 W Mitchell Ave, Cincinnati, OH 45232-1912
Tel (513) 681-6800 *Founded/Ownrshp* 1982
Sales 27.2MM[E] *EMP* 125
SIC 1711 3444 Ventilation & duct work contractor; Sheet metalwork; Ventilation & duct work contractor; Sheet metalwork
Pr: John E Mc Donald

D-U-N-S 16-816-3017 IMP
■ **JACOBS P&C US INC**
(*Suby of* JACOBS ENGINEERING GROUP INC) ★
3600 Briarpark Dr, Houston, TX 77042-5206
Tel (713) 988-2002 *Founded/Ownrshp* 2013
Sales 138.5MM[E] *EMP* 1,700[E]
SIC 1629 Power plant construction; Power plant construction
CEO: Inge Hansen
* *Pr:* Craig L Martin
CFO: Dieter Shcheer
Sr VP: Dane Osborn
* *VP:* Andrew Kremer
* *VP:* Keith Vecchini
IT Man: Louis Caplan
IT Man: Jean Chessher
S&M/VP: Donna Rougeaux

D-U-N-S 14-453-3655
JACOBS PRIVATE EQUITY LLC
350 Round Hill Rd, Greenwich, CT 06831-3343
Tel (203) 413-4000 *Founded/Ownrshp* 2003
Sales 91.1MM[E] *EMP* 10,400
SIC 4731 6282 6726 Freight transportation arrangement; Investment advisory service; Investment offices; Freight transportation arrangement; Investment advisory service; Investment offices
Mng Dir: Bradley Jacobs

D-U-N-S 11-263-4480 IMP
■ **JACOBS STRATEGIC SOLUTIONS GROUP INC**
(*Suby of* JACOBS TECHNOLOGY INC) ★
3863 Centerview Dr # 150, Chantilly, VA 20151-3287
Tel (703) 956-8200 *Founded/Ownrshp* 2010
Sales 28.8MM[E] *EMP* 280
SIC 7378 7373 5045 Computer & data processing equipment repair/maintenance; Systems integration services; Local area network (LAN) systems integrator; Computers; Computer & data processing equipment repair/maintenance; Systems integration services; Local area network (LAN) systems integrator; Computers
Pr: Rogers F Starr Jr
Ofcr: Robert Burleson
* *Ex VP:* William J Donahue
* *Sr VP:* Gary Mears
IT Man: Brad Martin

D-U-N-S 00-792-3014
■ **JACOBS TECHNOLOGY INC** (TN)
(*Suby of* JACOBS ENGINEERING GROUP INC) ★
600 William Northern Blvd, Tullahoma, TN 37388-4729
Tel (931) 455-6400 *Founded/Ownrshp* 1980, 1999
Sales 4.0MMM *EMP* 11,000
SIC 8711 Aviation &/or aeronautical engineering; Aviation &/or aeronautical engineering
Pr: Robert Norfleet
Pr: Andrew Allen
Treas: John Prosser Jr
VP: Lon Miller
Snr Sftwr: Karen Adams
Dir IT: Don Kinser
IT Man: Glen Ward

Software D: Cole Hedden
Sftwr Eng: Nadean King
Sftwr Eng: Shawn King

D-U-N-S 17-992-4410 IMP/EXP
■ JACOBS TRADING LLC
(*Suby of* LIQUIDITY SERVICES INC) ★
8090 Excelsior Blvd, Hopkins, MN 55343-3415
Tel (763) 843-2033 *Founded/Ownrshp* 2011
Sales 29.5MM^E *EMP* 360
SIC 7389 5023 5021 Furniture; Home furnishings; Inventory stocking service; Inventory stocking service; Home furnishings; Furniture
Pr: Howard Grodnick
VP: Scott Armstrong
VP: Steve Mocol
Exec: Chris Gerken

D-U-N-S 02-517-2008
JACOBS TWIN BUICK INC
6750 W Grand Ave, Chicago, IL 60707-2212
Tel (773) 889-3030 *Founded/Ownrshp* 1952
Sales 28.2MM^E *EMP* 180
SIC 5511 5013 7538 7532 5521 Automobiles, new & used; Automotive supplies & parts; General automotive repair shops; Top & body repair & paint shops; Used car dealers; Automobiles, new & used; Automotive supplies & parts; General automotive repair shops; Top & body repair & paint shops; Used car dealers
Pr: Kevin McGrath
Sls Mgr: Skip Lanoff

D-U-N-S 00-132-8772 IMP/EXP
■ JACOBS VEHICLE SYSTEMS INC
JAKE BRAKE
(*Suby of* DH HOLDINGS CORP) ★
22 E Dudley Town Rd, Bloomfield, CT 06002-1440
Tel (860) 243-5222 *Founded/Ownrshp* 1903, 1986
Sales 109.1MM^E *EMP* 420
SIC 3519 Engines, diesel & semi-diesel or dual-fuel; Engines, diesel & semi-diesel or dual-fuel
Pr: Sergio Sgarbi
**CFO:* Chris Mulhall
**Treas:* Frank T McFaden
**Treas:* Kevin Potts
**VP:* Joao John Cullen
VP: Gerard Habib
**VP:* Debra Lemay
**VP:* Robert Perkins
QC Dir: Patrick McCotter
Snr Mgr: William Welch

D-U-N-S 00-385-0856
JACOBSEN CONSTRUCTION CO INC
3131 W 2210 S, Salt Lake City, UT 84119-1267
Tel (801) 973-0500 *Founded/Ownrshp* 1998
Sales 237.2MM^E *EMP* 485
SIC 1542 1541 Commercial & office building, new construction; Industrial buildings, new construction; Commercial & office building, new construction; Industrial buildings, new construction
Pr: Douglas C Welling
COO: Jim Cavey
Ex VP: John Fortuna
Ex VP: Terry K Wright
VP: Blake Court
VP: Greg Fix
VP: Gale Mair
VP: Jon Moody
VP: Jack Wixom
Exec: Kirk Dickamore
Creative D: Dustin Smith
Comm Dir: Kareen Openshaw

JACOBSEN HOMES
See JACOBSEN MANUFACTURING INC

D-U-N-S 07-921-2494
JACOBSEN MANUFACTURING INC (FL)
JACOBSEN HOMES
600 Packard Ct, Safety Harbor, FL 34695-3001
Tel (727) 726-1138 *Founded/Ownrshp* 1959
Sales 48.6MM^E *EMP* 215
SIC 2451 3448 2452 Mobile homes, except recreational; Prefabricated metal buildings; Prefabricated wood buildings; Mobile homes, except recreational; Prefabricated metal buildings; Prefabricated wood buildings
CEO: William Robert Jacobsen
**Pr:* Dennis Schrader
CFO: Mike Wnek
**VP:* Sidney Boughton
Genl Mgr: Jon Pierce
Board of Directors: Dusty Rhodes

D-U-N-S 07-930-3359
■ JACOBSEN PROFESSIONAL LAWN CARE INC
(*Suby of* TEXTRON INC) ★
1108 Quality Dr, Charlotte, NC 28273
Tel (704) 504-6600 *Founded/Ownrshp* 2014
Sales 22.9MM^E *EMP* 66^E
SIC 3524 Lawn & garden equipment
Prin: David Withers
Mktg Mgr: Glenn King
Manager: Lee Frie

D-U-N-S 00-698-5964 IMP
JACOBSON & CO INC
1079 E Grand St, Elizabeth, NJ 07201-2655
Tel (908) 355-5200 *Founded/Ownrshp* 1936
Sales 60.0MM^E *EMP* 350
Accts Wiss & Company Llp Livingsto
SIC 1742 Acoustical & ceiling work; Acoustical & ceiling work
Ch: Thomas D Jacobson
**Pr:* David P Norgard
**Ch:* John D Jacobson
**Sec:* Jonathan Burt
**Ex VP:* Patrick Oates

D-U-N-S 00-509-0949 IMP
JACOBSON ACQUISITION HOLDINGS LLC (IL)
S. I. JACOBSON MFG. COMPANY
1414 Jacobson Dr, Waukegan, IL 60085-7601
Tel (847) 623-1414 *Founded/Ownrshp* 1934, 2012
Sales 32.8MM^E *EMP* 225
SIC 2211 2673 3161 2782 3993 Bags & bagging, cotton; Plastic bags: made from purchased materials; Briefcases; Looseleaf binders & devices; Signs & advertising specialties; Bags & bagging, cotton; Plastic bags: made from purchased materials; Briefcases; Looseleaf binders & devices; Signs & advertising specialties
CEO: Charles Gonzalez
VP: Paul G Bryant
Prin: Patricia Stemp

JACOBSON COMPANIES
See JHCI HOLDINGS INC

D-U-N-S 01-921-9815 IMP
JACOBSON FLORAL SUPPLY INC (MA)
500 Albany St, Boston, MA 02118-2582
Tel (617) 426-4200 *Founded/Ownrshp* 1946
Sales 32.1MM^E *EMP* 80
SIC 5193 Florists' supplies
Ch: Alan Jacobson
**Pr:* William Jacobson
COO: Nick Fronduto
**Treas:* Barbara N Jacobson

D-U-N-S 05-873-8431
JACOBSON LOGISTICS CO LC
(*Suby of* JACOBSON TRANSPORTATION CO INC) ★
3811 Dixon St Ste B, Des Moines, IA 50313-3907
Tel (515) 262-1236 *Founded/Ownrshp* 1985
Sales 52.1MM^E *EMP* 99^E
SIC 4731 Freight transportation arrangement
Pr: Kent Jordan
**CFO:* Jack Ingle

D-U-N-S 80-827-6229
JACOBSON MFG - TIFFIN LLC
(*Suby of* CMG CONTMID GROUP) ★
1988 S County Road 593, Tiffin, OH 44883-9275
Tel (419) 447-2221 *Founded/Ownrshp* 2014
Sales 23.2MM^E *EMP* 54
SIC 3452 Bolts, nuts, rivets & washers

D-U-N-S 14-363-0924 IMP
JACOBSON MFG LLC
(*Suby of* CMG CONTMID GROUP) ★
941 Lake Rd 955, Medina, OH 44256-2453
Tel (330) 725-8853 *Founded/Ownrshp* 2004
Sales 47.0MM^E *EMP* 150
SIC 3452 Bolts, nuts, rivets & washers; Bolts, nuts, rivets & washers
CEO: Robert S Kaminski
**COO:* David Kaminski
**CFO:* Jack Woodruff
**Prin:* Matt Kerschner
Store Mgr: Mary Spitzer
Mtls Mgr: William Bartley
Opers Mgr: Michael Kaehler
Plnt Mgr: Pete Nepodal
Prd Mgr: Amro Hassan
Ql Cn Mgr: Ricardo Aspiras
Sales Exec: Stan Rhodes

D-U-N-S 18-853-8255
■ JACOBSON PACKAGING CO LC
(*Suby of* JACOBSON WAREHOUSE CO INC) ★
3811 Dixon St, Des Moines, IA 50313-3907
Tel (515) 265-6171 *Founded/Ownrshp* 1998
Sales 33.3MM^E *EMP* 599
SIC 7389 3089 2899 2844 2099 Packaging & labeling services; Automotive parts, plastic; Chemical preparations; Toothpastes or powders, dentifrices; Mouthwashes; Food preparations; Packaging & labeling services; Automotive parts, plastic; Chemical preparations; Toothpastes or powders, dentifrices; Mouthwashes; Food preparations
CEO: Brian Lutt

D-U-N-S 95-746-4670
JACOBSON TRANSPORTATION CO INC
(*Suby of* JHCI ACQUISITION INC) ★
1275 Nw 128th St, Clive, IA 50325-7426
Tel (515) 262-1236 *Founded/Ownrshp* 1986
Sales 124.5MM^E *EMP* 300^E
SIC 4213 4731 Trucking, except local; Freight transportation arrangement; Trucking, except local; Freight transportation arrangement
Ch Bd: Brian Lutt
**Pr:* Scott Temple
**CFO:* Jack Ingle
Sec: Marty Howard
Board of Directors: Ted Dardani, John Rachwalski

D-U-N-S 04-561-7883
■ JACOBSON WAREHOUSE CO INC
(*Suby of* JHCI ACQUISITION INC) ★
3811 Dixon St, Des Moines, IA 50313-3907
Tel (515) 265-6171 *Founded/Ownrshp* 1968
Sales 552.4MM^E *EMP* 1,500
SIC 4226 4221 4225 8741 6552 4783 Special warehousing & storage; Farm product warehousing & storage; General warehousing & storage; Management services; Subdividers & developers; Packing & crating; Special warehousing & storage; Farm product warehousing & storage; General warehousing & storage; Management services; Subdividers & developers; Packing & crating
Co-Pr: Tony Tegnelia
Ofcr: Marty Howard
Ofcr: Jack Ingle
Ofcr: Gordon Smith
Off Mgr: Carla Rees
CIO: Brian Kautz
Board of Directors: Ted Dardani, John Rachwalski

D-U-N-S 01-311-3352
JACOBSTEIN FOOD SERVICE LLC
(*Suby of* CA CURTZE CO) ★
15 Airline Dr, Rochester, NY 14624-4974
Tel (585) 235-7660 *Founded/Ownrshp* 2001
Sales 33.1MM^E *EMP* 70
SIC 5141 5149 Groceries, general line; Groceries & related products; Groceries, general line; Groceries & related products
IT Man: Barbara Jacques
Opers Mgr: John Parnell
Mktg Dir: John Irish

D-U-N-S 19-845-6980
JACOBUS ENERGY CO
QUICK FUEL
(*Suby of* JACOBUS ENERGY INC) ★
11815 W Bradley Rd, Milwaukee, WI 53224-2532
Tel (414) 359-0700 *Founded/Ownrshp* 1989
Sales 43.2MM^E *EMP* 150
SIC 5171 Petroleum terminals; Petroleum terminals
CEO: Charles D Jacobus Jr

D-U-N-S 02-339-8191
JACOBUS ENERGY INC
QUICK FLASH FUEL
11815 W Bradley Rd, Milwaukee, WI 53224-2532
Tel (414) 577-0217 *Founded/Ownrshp* 1919
Sales 104.9MM^E *EMP* 259
SIC 5983 5172 Fuel oil dealers; Petroleum products; Fuel oil dealers; Petroleum products
Pr: Eugene Jacobus
**CEO:* Chuck Jacobus Jr
**Treas:* Bob Heicher
**Ex VP:* Fred J Regenfuss
Natl Sales: Josh Tippen
Sales Asso: Ramsey Midkiff

JACOBUS ENVIROMENTAL SERVICES
See JACOBUS PETROLEUM PRODUCTS INC

D-U-N-S 55-650-8059
JACOBUS PETROLEUM PRODUCTS INC
JACOBUS ENVIROMENTAL SERVICES
(*Suby of* JACOBUS ENERGY INC) ★
11815 W Bradley Rd, Milwaukee, WI 53224-2532
Tel (414) 359-0700 *Founded/Ownrshp* 1988
Sales 25.0MM^E *EMP* 60
SIC 5172 5541 Gasoline; Fuel oil; Filling stations, gasoline; Gasoline; Fuel oil; Filling stations, gasoline
Pr: Eugene Jacobus
**VP:* Charles Jacobus

D-U-N-S 07-881-5297
JACOBY & MEYERS LLP
39 Broadway Rm 1910, New York, NY 10006-3006
Tel (212) 445-7000 *Founded/Ownrshp* 1995
Sales 18.2MM^E *EMP* 300
SIC 8111 General practice law office; General practice law office
Mng Pt: Gail Koff
Pt: Andrew Finkelstein

D-U-N-S 02-875-2830 IMP
JACON AIRCRAFT SUPPLY CO INC
JACON FASTENERS & ELECTRONICS
9539 Vassar Ave, Chatsworth, CA 91311-4141
Tel (818) 885-3310 *Founded/Ownrshp* 1956
Sales 35.1MM^E *EMP* 39
Accts Stern Kory Sreden & Morgan St
SIC 5085 5065 Fasteners, industrial: nuts, bolts, screws, etc.; Electronic parts
Pr: Don Wientjes
**VP:* Mark Wientjes

JACON FASTENERS & ELECTRONICS
See JACON AIRCRAFT SUPPLY CO INC

D-U-N-S 83-652-0882
■ JACOR BROADCASTING OF COLORADO INC
CLEAR CHANNEL
(*Suby of* IHEARTCOMMUNICATIONS INC) ★
4695 S Monaco St, Denver, CO 80237-3525
Tel (303) 631-2933 *Founded/Ownrshp* 1987
Sales 8.0MMM *EMP* 285
SIC 7313 Radio advertising representative; Radio advertising representative
VP: Lee Larsen
**VP:* Pat Connors
Dir IT: Jeff Archer
Pgrm Dir: Scott Arbough
Snr Mgr: Karl Schipper

D-U-N-S 04-848-4356
■ JACOR COMMUNICATIONS CO
(*Suby of* IHEARTCOMMUNICATIONS INC) ★
200 E Basse Rd, San Antonio, TX 78209-4489
Tel (210) 822-2828 *Founded/Ownrshp* 1999
Sales 21.7MM^E *EMP* 500
SIC 4832 Radio broadcasting stations; Radio broadcasting stations
Ch Bd: L Lowry Mays
**Pr:* Randall Mays
**CEO:* Mark P Mayes
CFO: Thomas Casey
Sr VP: Randy Palmer

D-U-N-S 17-140-8144
JACOR LLC
1011 Lake Rd, Medina, OH 44256-2450
Tel (330) 441-4182 *Founded/Ownrshp* 2003
Sales 16.8MM^E *EMP* 600
SIC 7361 Employment agencies; Employment agencies
CFO: Therese Johnson
CFO: Chester Sipsock

JACQUELINES GOURMET COOKIES
See JACQUELINES WHOLESALE BAKERY INC

D-U-N-S 01-969-6314
JACQUELINES WHOLESALE BAKERY INC (MA)
JACQUELINES GOURMET COOKIES
96 Swampscott Rd Ste 1, Salem, MA 01970-7004
Tel (978) 744-8600 *Founded/Ownrshp* 1997
Sales 24.4MM^E *EMP* 85
SIC 2051 Bread, cake & related products
Pr: Marc Hazel
**CFO:* John A Oneil
CFO: John Oneil
Prd Mgr: Maria Dasilva
VP Sls: Harry Duffin
S&M/VP: Michael Grant
Sls Mgr: Tom Hallman

D-U-N-S 62-295-1788 IMP
JACQUES GOURMET INC
CHAMPAGNE BAKERY
1709 La Costa Meadows Dr, San Marcos, CA 92078-5105
Tel (760) 471-3838 *Founded/Ownrshp* 1987
Sales 68.3MM^E *EMP* 500
SIC 5461 5812 2052 Bakeries; French restaurant; Cookies & crackers; Bakeries; French restaurant; Cookies & crackers
CEO: Roland A De Libran
**Pr:* Roland D'Abel
**Treas:* Jacques Pautrat
IT Man: Daryl Hulten

D-U-N-S 07-770-8618 IMP
JACQUES MORET INC
BOY MEETS GIRL USA
1411 Broadway Fl 8, New York, NY 10018-3565
Tel (212) 354-2400 *Founded/Ownrshp* 2002
Sales 99.7MM^E *EMP* 250^E
SIC 2339 5137 Women's & misses' outerwear; Sportswear, women's & children's; Women's & misses' outerwear; Sportswear, women's & children's
Ch Bd: Ralph Harary
**Pr:* Joey Harary
CFO: Mark A Lopiparo
**Treas:* Jack Beyda
Ex VP: Gary Herwitz
VP: Stuart Morris
**VP:* Allan Sassoon
Web Prj Mg: Elliot Beyda
Manager: Slawomir Dobek
Opers Mgr: Lupe Gonzales
Art Dir: Bill Walker

D-U-N-S 78-944-7476 IMP
JACQUET MID ATLANTIC INC
(*Suby of* JACQUET HOLDING)
191 S Keim St Ste 108, Pottstown, PA 19464-6046
Tel (484) 945-1075 *Founded/Ownrshp* 2006
Sales 39.1MM^E *EMP* 100
SIC 5051

D-U-N-S 15-412-9563 IMP
JACUZZI BRANDS CORP
JACCUZI GROUP WORLDWIDE
13925 City Center Dr # 200, Chino Hills, CA 91709-5437
Tel (909) 606-1416 *Founded/Ownrshp* 1995
Sales 1.4MMM^E *EMP* 4,907
SIC 3842 Whirlpool baths, hydrotherapy equipment; Whirlpool baths, hydrotherapy equipment
CEO: Bob Rowen
**Pr:* Alex P Marini
Pr: Peter Munk
Pr: Robert I Rowan
**CFO:* David Broadbent
CFO: Dave Hellman
**CFO:* Jeffrey B Park
**Sr VP:* Steven C Barre
**Sr VP:* Marie S Dreher
Sr VP: Dorothy E Sander
VP: Todd Adams
VP: Francisco V Pu Al
**VP:* Diana E Burton
VP: Brian Koops
VP: Edmund L Krainski
VP: Howard Lederman
VP: Lillian C Macia
VP: Greg Meisenzahl
VP: Drew Meng
VP: Erica Moir
VP: Patricia Whaley

D-U-N-S 00-634-0798 EXP
JACUZZI INC
JACUZZI OUTDOOR PRODUCTS
(*Suby of* JACCUZI GROUP WORLDWIDE) ★
14525 Monte Vista Ave, Chino, CA 91710-5721
Tel (909) 606-7733 *Founded/Ownrshp* 1979, 1989
Sales 596.7MM^E *EMP* 4,018
SIC 3088 3589 Plastics plumbing fixtures; Hot tubs, plastic or fiberglass; Tubs (bath, shower & laundry), plastic; Shower stalls, fiberglass & plastic; Swimming pool filter & water conditioning systems; Plastics plumbing fixtures; Hot tubs, plastic or fiberglass; Tubs (bath, shower & laundry), plastic; Shower stalls, fiberglass & plastic; Swimming pool filter & water conditioning systems
CEO: Thomas Koos
**Ch Bd:* Roy A Jacuzzi
**Pr:* Donald C Devine
Rgnl Mgr: Thomas Whell
Dir IT: Jeff Castillo
Sls Mgr: Brett Sitton
Corp Couns: Ron Templer

JACUZZI OUTDOOR PRODUCTS
See JACUZZI INC

D-U-N-S 00-914-0005 IMP
JACUZZI WHIRLPOOL BATH INC
(*Suby of* JACUZZI INC) ★
14525 Monte Vista Ave, Chino, CA 91710-5721
Tel (909) 606-1416 *Founded/Ownrshp* 1987
Sales 96.7MM^E *EMP* 800
SIC 3088 Tubs (bath, shower & laundry), plastic; Hot tubs, plastic or fiberglass; Tubs (bath, shower & laundry), plastic; Hot tubs, plastic or fiberglass
CEO: Thomas D Koos
**Pr:* Philip Weeks
Dir IT: Mark Allen
Dir IT: Jeff Castillo
IT Man: Jason Shaw
VP Mktg: Andrew Meng

D-U-N-S 05-641-3974
JAD CORP OF AMERICA
2048 119th St, College Point, NY 11356-2123
Tel (718) 762-8900 *Founded/Ownrshp* 1957
Sales 28.6MM^E *EMP* 50
SIC 2673 5087 5169 Trash bags (plastic film): made from purchased materials; Cleaning & maintenance equipment & supplies; Chemicals & allied products
Pr: Joseph A Dussich Jr
**CFO:* Henry Schaeffer

D-U-N-S 07-934-0300
■ JADAK LLC
(Suby of GSI GROUP INC) ★
7279 William Barry Blvd, North Syracuse, NY 13212-3349
Tel (315) 701-0678 Founded/Ownrshp 2014
Sales 27.7MM[E] EMP 108[E]
SIC 3577 3845 Optical scanning devices; Ultrasonic scanning devices, medical
Pr: Jeffrey Pine
VP: Bill Coleman
Prgrm Mgr: Steve Dolan
Snr Sftwr: Scott Baker
Snr Sftwr: Guodong Ll
Sftwr Eng: John Cairns
Sftwr Eng: Sheri Dunckle
Mktg Mgr: John Prior
Sales Asso: Tom Davis

D-U-N-S 10-630-8653 IMP
JADCO MANUFACTURING INC
167 Evergreen Mill Rd, Harmony, PA 16037-7619
Tel (724) 452-5252 Founded/Ownrshp 1980
Sales 38.3MM[E] EMP 50[E]
SIC 5051 3564 3312 3448 Steel; Blowers & fans; Slabs, steel; Buildings, portable: prefabricated metal
CEO: James A Davison
*Sec: Susan Z Davison
Genl Mgr: Samuel Anderson
Sales Asso: Michael Lewis

D-U-N-S 07-203-9373 IMP
JADCORE LLC
PREMIER COMPOUNDING
300 N Fruitridge Ave A, Terre Haute, IN 47803-1330
Tel (812) 235-9670 Founded/Ownrshp 1974
Sales 71.1MM[E] EMP 200
SIC 3089 4225 5162 4212 2673 Plastic containers, except foam; General warehousing; Plastics materials & basic shapes; Local trucking, without storage; Bags: plastic, laminated & coated; Plastic containers, except foam; General warehousing; Plastics materials & basic shapes; Local trucking, without storage; Bags: plastic, laminated & coated
Pr: David C Doti
COO: Mark Howell
CFO: Jim Hensle
*VP: David Doti
CTO: Benjamin Rothe
Dir IT: Ben Rothe
Trfc Mgr: Bret Steiner
VP Sls: Steven Rife

JADE
See PB HOLDINGS INC

D-U-N-S 04-009-4229 IMP
JADE ENGINEERED PLASTICS INC
121 Broadcommon Rd, Bristol, RI 02809-2714
Tel (401) 253-4440 Founded/Ownrshp 1976
Sales 28.7MM[E] EMP 78
SIC 3053 3089 Gaskets, packing & sealing devices; Molding primary plastic
Pr: Steven M Holland
*VP: Lee Holland
*VP: Mark Holland
Off Mgr: Carol Normandin

D-U-N-S 95-881-4345 IMP
JADE EQUIPMENT CORP
(Suby of JADE) ★
3063 Philmont Ave, Huntingdon Valley, PA 19006-4243
Tel (215) 947-3333 Founded/Ownrshp 1996
Sales 46.5MM[E] EMP 220
SIC 3545 3599 3469 3544 Machine tool accessories; Machine & other job shop work; Metal stampings; Special dies, tools, jigs & fixtures; Machine tool accessories; Machine & other job shop work; Metal stampings; Special dies, tools, jigs & fixtures
Pr: Brian T Manley
Pr: Ric Ross
IT Man: Kenneth Thoman

JADE PRODUCTS
See JADE RANGE LLC

D-U-N-S 95-875-8380 IMP
■ JADE RANGE LLC
JADE PRODUCTS
(Suby of MIDDLEBY CORP) ★
2650 Orbiter St, Brea, CA 92821-6265
Tel (714) 961-2400 Founded/Ownrshp 2007
Sales 31.3MM[E] EMP 120
SIC 3631 3589 Household cooking equipment; Commercial cooking & foodwarming equipment; Household cooking equipment; Commercial cooking & foodwarming equipment
CFO: Selim Bassoul
CFO: Timothy J Fitzgerald
Treas: Martin M Lindsay
VP: Ray Williams
Genl Mgr: Thompson Chris

D-U-N-S 60-627-3837
JADE SYSTEMS CORP
CSJ OF PUTNAM
3377 Route 9, Cold Spring, NY 10516-3848
Tel (718) 392-2908 Founded/Ownrshp 2003
Sales 28.3MM[E] EMP 135
SIC 5045 7378 Disk drives; Keying equipment; Printers, computer; Terminals, computer; Computer maintenance & repair; Disk drives; Keying equipment; Printers, computer; Terminals, computer; Computer maintenance & repair
CFO: David A Carl
Ex VP: Pieter Ruiter
Tech Mgr: David Roman

D-U-N-S 00-452-3726
JADE-STERLING STEEL CO INC
2300 E Aurora Rd, Twinsburg, OH 44087-1987
Tel (330) 425-3141 Founded/Ownrshp 1965, 1970
Sales 48.8MM[E] EMP 59
Accts Cohen & Company Youngstown O
SIC 5051 Steel; Steel
CEO: Mike Manfield
*Pr: Scott Herman
*COO: Howard Fertel
*Ch: Bill Lieberman
Dir Lab: Nate Turner
Genl Mgr: Lisa Krolikowski
Dir IT: A N Luu
Trfc Mgr: Deann Straus
Sales Exec: Bob Alcorn
Sls Dir: Denise Ducca

D-U-N-S 08-610-2316 IMP
JAE ELECTRONICS INC (CA)
(Suby of JAPAN AVIATION ELECTRONICS INDUSTRY, LIMITED)
142 Technology Dr Ste 100, Irvine, CA 92618-2430
Tel (949) 753-2600 Founded/Ownrshp 1977
Sales 175.3MM EMP 180
Accts Kakimoto Nagashima Llc
SIC 5065 5088 3679 3829 3678 Connectors, electronic; Aircraft & space vehicle supplies & parts; Electronic circuits; Measuring & controlling devices; Electronic connectors; Connectors, electronic; Aircraft & space vehicle supplies & parts; Electronic circuits; Measuring & controlling devices; Electronic connectors
CEO: Noboru Norose
*Pr: Shinsuke Takahashi
IT Man: Keith Iwanaga
Opers Mgr: Takaaki Fujita
Sls Dir: Stephanie Jennings
Sls Dir: Shawn O'Callaghan
Sls Mgr: Steve Black
Sales Asso: Mike McFadden

D-U-N-S 60-405-8065 IMP
JAE OREGON INC
(Suby of JAE ELECTRONICS INC) ★
11555 Sw Leveton Dr, Tualatin, OR 97062-6000
Tel (503) 692-1333 Founded/Ownrshp 1988
Sales 33.0MM[E] EMP 180[E]
SIC 3678 Electronic connectors; Electronic connectors
Pr: Takashi Kosaka
VP: Yasu Takagi
Software D: Chuck Linke
Sfty Dirs: Dan Jones
QC Dir: Tom Rutledge

D-U-N-S 95-704-3193
JAEB CENTER FOR HEALTH RESEARCH FOUNDATION INC
15310 Amberly Dr Ste 350, Tampa, FL 33647-1642
Tel (813) 975-8690 Founded/Ownrshp 1993
Sales 24.4MM EMP 15
SIC 8733 Medical research; Medical research
Pr: Roy W Beck MD
Snr Sftwr: Nandan Patibandla
Web Dev: Rosa Pritchard
Software D: Joseph Kaplon

JAECKLE DISTRIBUTORS
See JAECKLE WHOLESALE INC

D-U-N-S 02-332-0419 IMP
JAECKLE WHOLESALE INC
JAECKLE DISTRIBUTORS
4101 Owl Creek Dr, Madison, WI 53718-4407
Tel (608) 838-5400 Founded/Ownrshp 1958
Sales 37.6MM[E] EMP 140
SIC 5023

D-U-N-S 00-256-8681 IMP
JAEGER LUMBER & SUPPLY CO INC
VANNOTE LUMBER DIVISION
2322 Morris Ave, Union, NJ 07083-5704
Tel (908) 686-0073 Founded/Ownrshp 1937
Sales 34.4MM[E] EMP 136
SIC 5211 5251 Lumber & other building materials; Hardware; Lumber & other building materials; Hardware
Pr: Lowell E Jaeger
Sls Mgr: Richard Kohler
Sls Mgr: John Wieboldt

D-U-N-S 96-390-2700 IMP
JAEGER-UNITEK SEALING SOLUTIONS INC
(Suby of ARNOLD JAGER HOLDING GMBH)
115 Koomler Dr, La Porte, IN 46350-2545
Tel (219) 326-1315 Founded/Ownrshp 2010
Sales 20.1MM[E] EMP 60
SIC 3083 Laminated plastics plate & sheet
Ch: Hans Ulrich Von Tippelskirch
*Pr: Mark S Dilley
*CFO: Glenn E Oman Jr
CFO: Glenn Oman
*VP: Raymond A Young
Sales Exec: Roger Brown

D-U-N-S 60-620-3255
JAFCO FOODS INC
890 East St, Tewksbury, MA 01876-1452
Tel (978) 989-0012 Founded/Ownrshp 1985
Sales 21.1MM[E] EMP 22
SIC 5141 Groceries, general line
Ch: John Ferro
*Pr: Matthew Ferro
VP: Mike Chmela
VP: Brian Ganjami
IT Man: Matt Ferro
VP Sls: John Valentine

D-U-N-S 79-039-4113
JAFCO INVESTMENTS INC
ARGUS HAZCO
46400 Continental Dr, Chesterfield, MI 48047-5206
Tel (586) 840-3200 Founded/Ownrshp 2012
Sales 25.8MM[E] EMP 70
Accts The Geary Group Pc Shelby Tow
SIC 5084 Safety equipment
CEO: James Fitzgerald
*Pr: Lawrence Smith
*VP: Brian McEvoy
Genl Mgr: James Tunison
Sales Asso: Kathleen McCann

D-U-N-S 01-939-3420
JAFFARIANS SERVICE INC (MA)
600 River St, Haverhill, MA 01832-5143
Tel (978) 372-8551 Founded/Ownrshp 1941, 1960
Sales 42.5MM[E] EMP 110
SIC 5511 Automobiles, new & used; Automobiles, new & used
Pr: Gary Jaffarian
Genl Mgr: Mike Benoit
Off Mgr: Freddy Lockett
Sls Mgr: Mark Jaffarian
Sls Mgr: Jonathan Russo
Sls Mgr: Joshua Shepard
Sales Asso: Jonathan Mazza
Sales Asso: Louis Monteforte

JAFFE BOOK SOLUTIONS
See GL GROUP INC

D-U-N-S 07-638-6853
JAFFE RAITT HEUER & WEISS PROFESSIONAL CORP
27777 Franklin Rd # 2500, Southfield, MI 48034-2337
Tel (248) 351-3000 Founded/Ownrshp 1969
Sales 52.2MM EMP 187
SIC 8111 Corporate, partnership & business law; Corporate, partnership & business law
Ch: Arthur Weiss
Pr: Donna Burris
Pr: Anne Bye
Pr: Deon Goldberg
Pr: Laura Hunt
Pr: Phyllis Nelson
Pr: Sherel Shand
*Pr: Richard Zussman
*CFO: Ira Jaffe
*Treas: Joel Golden
*VP: Jeffrey Heuer
*VP: Mark Krysinski
*VP: Bill Sider

D-U-N-S 04-024-7751
JAFFREY RINDGE COOPERATIVE SCHOOL DISTRICT
SUPERVISORY UNION #47
81 Fitzgerald Dr Unit 2, Jaffrey, NH 03452-6615
Tel (603) 532-8100 Founded/Ownrshp 1969
Sales 24.9MM EMP 250
SIC 8211 Public elementary school; Public junior high school; Public senior high school; Public elementary school; Public junior high school; Public senior high school

D-U-N-S 06-709-1538
JAFLO INC
JAFLO TREE CARE CENTER
1575 Pond Rd Ste 104, Allentown, PA 18104-2254
Tel (610) 395-3213 Founded/Ownrshp 1965
Sales 43.6MM[E] EMP 175
SIC 0783 0781 Tree trimming services for public utility lines; Landscape services; Tree trimming services for public utility lines; Landscape services
Pr: John A Florio
*Sec: Joyce Florio

JAFLO TREE CARE CENTER
See JAFLO INC

D-U-N-S 04-167-6479 IMP
JAFRA COSMETICS INTERNATIONAL INC
(Suby of VORWERK & CO. KG)
2451 Townsgate Rd, Westlake Village, CA 91361-2506
Tel (805) 449-3000 Founded/Ownrshp 1956
Sales 84.8MM[E] EMP 160[E]
SIC 5122 Cosmetics; Cosmetics
Pr: Mauro Schnaidman
Pr: Connie Tang
*CFO: Hans Ter Pelle
*Treas: Stacy Wolf
Site Mgr: Mary Price
VP Mktg: Beatrice Gutai
Snr Mgr: Jackie Trafk

D-U-N-S 07-916-9169
JAG COMPANIES INC
1433 State Route 34 Ste 5, Wall Township, NJ 07727-1613
Tel (732) 557-6100 Founded/Ownrshp 2010
Sales 178.5MM[E] EMP 452
SIC 1623 1622 1629 1611 Water, sewer & utility lines; Bridge construction; Land clearing contractor; General contractor, highway & street construction; Water, sewer & utility lines; Bridge construction; Land clearing contractor; General contractor, highway & street construction
Owner: Juan A Gutierrez
CFO: Marco Afonso
*Prin: Marco Guttierrez

D-U-N-S 13-726-0399 IMP
JAG FOOTWEAR ACCESSORIES AND RETAIL CORP
180 Rittenhouse Cir, Bristol, PA 19007-1618
Tel (215) 785-4000 Founded/Ownrshp 1983
Sales NA EMP 6,370
SIC 5621

D-U-N-S 78-458-9751
JAG HEALTHCARE INC
220 Buckingham Rd, Rocky River, OH 44116-1623
Tel (440) 385-4370 Founded/Ownrshp 2010
Sales 14.0MM[E] EMP 650
SIC 8082 Home health care services; Home health care services
Pr: James Griffiths
*CFO: David Cooley
*VP: Richard Gebhard
VP: William Soroka
*VP: Miriam Walters

D-U-N-S 05-369-4642
JAGEE HOLDINGS LLP
2918 Wingate St, Fort Worth, TX 76107-1948
Tel (817) 335-5881 Founded/Ownrshp 1988
Sales 26.9MM[E] EMP 111
SIC 6719 Personal holding companies, except banks; Personal holding companies, except banks
Pt: Richard Garvey
Pt: Shirley F Garvey
CFO: Reece Pettigrew

D-U-N-S 00-642-5888
JAGEMANN PLATING CO
1324 S 26th St, Manitowoc, WI 54220-5531
Tel (920) 682-6883 Founded/Ownrshp 1945
Sales 22.7MM[E] EMP 130
SIC 3471 Electroplating of metals or formed products; Finishing, metals or formed products
Ch Bd: Scott E Jagemann
*Sec: David A Jagemann
*Ex VP: Michael J Jagemann
Board of Directors: Barbara Jagemann

D-U-N-S 00-642-5409 IMP
JAGEMANN STAMPING CO
5757 W Custer St, Manitowoc, WI 54220-9790
Tel (920) 682-4633 Founded/Ownrshp 1946
Sales 46.3MM[E] EMP 200[E]
SIC 3469 Stamping metal for the trade; Stamping metal for the trade
Pr: Thomas M Jagemann
*CFO: Debra Berchem
CFO: Martha Vandeleest
Exec: Michael Hillmer
MIS Dir: Craig Pauly
Mfg Dir: Pascal Schroeder
Opers Mgr: Greg Johnsrud
Ql Cn Mgr: James Kuhn
Ql Cn Mgr: Travis Thoreen
Mktg Dir: Jonathan Hintz
Mktg Dir: John Ryan

D-U-N-S 06-007-2857
JAGER MANAGEMENT INC
2000 Maplewood Dr, Maple Shade, NJ 08052-1936
Tel (856) 667-6810 Founded/Ownrshp 1963
Sales 27.9MM[E] EMP 225
SIC 1522 6531 Apartment building construction; Real estate managers; Apartment building construction; Real estate managers
Pr: Joel Gershman
CFO: Marshall Cohen

D-U-N-S 06-349-2701
▲ JAGGED PEAK INC
3000 Bayport Dr Ste 250, Tampa, FL 33607-8413
Tel (813) 637-6900 Founded/Ownrshp 1999
Sales 61.7MM EMP 143[E]
Accts Gregory Sharer & Stuart Pa
Tkr Sym JGPK Exch OTO
SIC 7372 Prepackaged software; Prepackaged software
Ch Bd: Paul Demirdjian
*COO: Daniel Furlong
CFO: Albert Narvades
CFO: Andrew Norstrud
Ofcr: Vincent Fabrizzi
VP: Ron Surfield
Exec: Eric Beckerman
Dir IT: Jeff Stiles
Netwrk Mgr: Justin Williams
Sfty Dirs: Sam Hulme
Opers Mgr: Petrea Hampton
Board of Directors: Primrose Demirdjian

D-U-N-S 00-482-1450
JAGOE-PUBLIC CO
3020 Fort Worth Dr, Denton, TX 76205-8624
Tel (940) 382-2581 Founded/Ownrshp 1926
Sales 48.7MM[E] EMP 100
SIC 5032 1611 Asphalt mixture; General contractor, highway & street construction
Pr: Murray Ricks
*Pr: Doug Walterscheid
*VP: Bill Cheek

D-U-N-S 03-699-9571 IMP
JAGPREET ENTERPRISES INC
QUICK-N-EZEE INDIAN FOODS
25823 Clawiter Rd, Hayward, CA 94545-3217
Tel (510) 336-8376 Founded/Ownrshp 1992
Sales 63.3MM[E] EMP 150
SIC 5149 Groceries & related products; Groceries & related products
CEO: Sukhjeet K Singh
*Pr: Surinder Singh
Ql Cn Mgr: Divya Aggarwal
Sales Asso: Geeta Brara

JAGUAR
See A & L MOTOR SALES LLC

JAGUAR
See NAPLETONS AUTO WERKS INC

JAGUAR AND SAAB OF TROY
See SOMERSET AUTO COLLECTION INC

D-U-N-S 04-633-9081
JAGUAR CARS INC (DE)
(Suby of JAGUAR CARS LIMITED)
555 Macarthur Blvd, Mahwah, NJ 07430-2327
Tel (201) 818-8500 Founded/Ownrshp 1968, 1989
Sales 100.4MM[E] EMP 22
SIC 5012 5013 Automobiles & other motor vehicles; Automotive supplies & parts; Automotive supplies
Ch Bd: Nicholas V Scheele
*Pr: Michael H Dale
VP: Richard N Beattie
VP: John G Crawford
VP: George J Frame
VP: Dale Gambill
Exec: Richard Kelly
Exec: Helen McDonald
IT Man: Ben Weiner
Snr Mgr: John Conrad
Board of Directors: John Edwards

JAGUAR CENTRAL HOUSTON
See MEMORIAL MOTORCARS LTD INC

JAGUAR CLEVELAND
See DAVIS AUTOMOTIVE GROUP INC

JAGUAR COLUMBIA
See COLUMBIA PRESTIGE MOTORCARS LLC

JAGUAR CREDIT
See PRIMUS AUTOMOTIVE FINANCIAL SERVICES INC

D-U-N-S 07-831-5349
JAGUAR ENERGY SERVICES LLC
19171 Hwy 90, Crowley, LA 70526-1803
Tel (337) 250-4030 *Founded/Ownrshp* 2011
Sales 35.7MM *EMP* 145
SIC 1389 Oil field services
COO: Paul Culbreth
VP: Jesse Shaw
Sls Mgr: Dede Terveen

JAGUAR JACKSONVILLE
See MATHENY IMPORTS INC

D-U-N-S 02-290-0815
JAGUAR LAND ROVER MINNEAPOLIS
DOWNTOWN JAGUAR
(*Suby of* LUTHER HOLDING CO) ★
8905 Wayzata Blvd, Golden Valley, MN 55426-1305
Tel (763) 222-2200 *Founded/Ownrshp* 1989
Sales 29.6MM^E *EMP* 78
SIC 5511 Automobiles, new & used; Automobiles, new & used
Ch Bd: David Luther
DP Exec: Jodi Hystead
Sales Exec: Ted Terp
Sls Mgr: Robert Notch
Sales Asso: James Jensen
Sales Asso: Jeremy Schultz

JAGUAR OF PEORIA
See FORD UFTRING INC

JAGUAR OF THOUSAND OAKS
See SILVER STAR A G LTD

JAGUAR SAN DIEGO ASTON MARTIN
See SAN DIEGO EUROPEAN MOTORCARS LTD

JAGUAR VOLVO
See KEMPTHORN AUTOMALL

D-U-N-S 00-409-5378
JAHNA CONCRETE INC (FL)
104 S Railroad Ave, Avon Park, FL 33825-3181
Tel (863) 453-4353 *Founded/Ownrshp* 1925
Sales 28.0MM *EMP* 86
SIC 3271 5032 3273 3272 Blocks, concrete or cinder: standard; Concrete mixtures; Ready-mixed concrete; Concrete products; Blocks, concrete or cinder: standard; Concrete mixtures; Ready-mixed concrete; Concrete products
Pr: Frederick W Jahna Jr
**Sec:* Candis Davis
**VP:* David Jahna
Trfc Dir: Harry Pope
Plnt Mgr: Charlie Lowe

D-U-N-S 07-419-6858
JAHO INC
2003 Wilson Rd, Humble, TX 77396-1540
Tel (281) 446-4781 *Founded/Ownrshp* 1975
Sales 36.7MM^E *EMP* 200
SIC 1623 1611 Underground utilities contractor; Highway & street paving contractor; Underground utilities contractor; Highway & street paving contractor
Pr: Howard T Cardell
**VP:* Andy Cordell
**VP:* Truman Moffett

D-U-N-S 78-409-8977 IMP/EXP
JAIN (AMERICAS) INC
1819 Walcutt Rd Ste 1, Columbus, OH 43228-9149
Tel (614) 850-9400 *Founded/Ownrshp* 1998
Sales 22.0MM *EMP* 81
SIC 2435 2431 4971 Panels, hardwood plywood; Trim, wood; Irrigation systems
CEO: Anil Jain
COO: Nerinder Gupta
CFO: John Donovan
CFO: Narinder Gupta
Ex VP: Murali Ramanathan
Sales Asso: Jenn Greene

D-U-N-S 07-190-6259 IMP
JAIN IRRIGATION INC
(*Suby of* JAIN IRRIGATION SYSTEMS LIMITED)
2060 E Francis St, Ontario, CA 91761-7733
Tel (909) 395-5200 *Founded/Ownrshp* 2007
Sales 46.2MM^E *EMP* 270
SIC 3084 Plastics pipe; Plastics pipe
Pr: Aric Olson
VP: Mike Burch
Off Mgr: Leslie Hongan
IT Man: Tim Jeffus
Pr Mgr: Michelle Verdi
Sls Mgr: Barry Arnold
Sls Mgr: Doug Burt

D-U-N-S 61-951-0662 IMP
JAINCO INTERNATIONAL INC
JAINCOTECH
30405 Solon Rd Ste 9, Solon, OH 44139-3477
Tel (440) 519-0100 *Founded/Ownrshp* 1987
Sales 32.5MM^E *EMP* 250
SIC 5032 Granite building stone; Granite building stone
CEO: Suresh Bafna
**Pr:* Jasvinder Mandair
**CFO:* Vijay Sharma
Mng Dir: Pankaj Jain

JAINCOTECH
See JAINCO INTERNATIONAL INC

D-U-N-S 01-379-8657
JAINDL FARMS LLC
3150 Coffeetown Rd, Orefield, PA 18069-2599
Tel (610) 395-3333 *Founded/Ownrshp* 1965
Sales 26.9MM^E *EMP* 110
SIC 0253 0115 0111 2015 Turkey farm; Corn; Wheat; Poultry slaughtering & processing
Sls Mgr: Alice Brown

D-U-N-S 01-755-1123 IMP/EXP
JAIPUR LIVING INC
2775 Pacific Dr, Norcross, GA 30071-1805
Tel (404) 351-2360 *Founded/Ownrshp* 2005
Sales 27.0MM *EMP* 90
Accts Windham Brannon Atlanta Ga
SIC 5023 2273 5713 Floor coverings; Rugs, hand & machine made; Carpets; Floor coverings; Rugs, hand & machine made; Carpets
Pr: Asha Chaudhary
**COO:* Archana Chaudhary
S&M/VP: Jack Johnson
Sls Mgr: Candace Clarke
Sls Mgr: Norah Medin

D-U-N-S 03-072-4389 IMP
JAJ ENTERPRISES LLC
COACH GLASS
91302 N Coburg Indus Way, Coburg, OR 97408-9330
Tel (541) 684-5690 *Founded/Ownrshp* 1995
Sales 36.6MM^E *EMP* 103
SIC 5013 Automobile glass; Automobile glass

D-U-N-S 12-978-1048
JAK FOODS INC
LONG JOHN SILVER'S
2401 Broad St Ste 201, Chattanooga, TN 37408-2922
Tel (423) 894-3881 *Founded/Ownrshp* 2003
Sales 12.2MM^E *EMP* 300
SIC 5812 Fast-food restaurant, chain; Fast-food restaurant, chain
Pr: John Kleban

JAKE BRAKE
See JACOBS VEHICLE SYSTEMS INC

D-U-N-S 10-141-8536
JAKE MARSHALL LLC
2912 S Hickory St, Chattanooga, TN 37407-1410
Tel (423) 698-3132 *Founded/Ownrshp* 1930
Sales 40.0MM *EMP* 175
SIC 1711 Plumbing, heating, air-conditioning contractors; Plumbing, heating, air-conditioning contractors
Ofcr: Jamie Pollard
Mktg Dir: Duncan Dunn

D-U-N-S 17-344-2633
JAKE MARSHALL SERVICE INC
611 W Manning St Ste A, Chattanooga, TN 37405-3272
Tel (423) 266-7200 *Founded/Ownrshp* 1984
Sales 30.1MM^E *EMP* 100
SIC 1711 Heating & air conditioning contractors
Pr: Marie M Marshall
**VP:* Danny K Daniel
Opers Mgr: Mickey Smith
Sls Mgr: Craig Shann

D-U-N-S 92-721-1326
JAKE SWEENEY AUTOMOTIVE INC
33 W Kemper Rd, Cincinnati, OH 45246-2509
Tel (513) 782-2800 *Founded/Ownrshp* 1970
Sales 23.3MM^E *EMP* 200
SIC 8741 7538 7532 7515 5521 5511 Management services; General automotive repair shops; Top & body repair & paint shops; Passenger car leasing; Used car dealers; New & used car dealers; Management services; General automotive repair shops; Top & body repair & paint shops; Passenger car leasing; Used car dealers; New & used car dealers
Pr: Jake Sweeney Jr
**VP:* Gregory D Sweeney
Sls Mgr: Jo Carter
Sls Mgr: Jonathan Ogden
Sales Asso: Kelly Davis
Sales Asso: Brandon Justes
Sales Asso: Tony Little
Sales Asso: Jon Merk
Sales Asso: Jay Schnieders

D-U-N-S 86-808-0672
JAKE SWEENEY AUTOMOTIVE OF FLORENCE INC
SATURN
5969 Centennial Cir, Florence, KY 41042-1293
Tel (859) 938-2020 *Founded/Ownrshp* 1988
Sales 26.7MM^E *EMP* 70
SIC 5511 Automobiles, new & used; Automobiles, new & used
Pr: Jacob Sweeney III

D-U-N-S 19-651-8120
JAKE SWEENEY CHEVROLET-IMPORTS INC
33 W Kemper Rd, Cincinnati, OH 45246-2536
Tel (513) 782-2800 *Founded/Ownrshp* 1987
Sales 71.8MM^E *EMP* 250
SIC 5511 Automobiles, new & used; Pickups, new & used; Vans, new & used; Automobiles, new & used; Pickups, new & used; Vans, new & used
CEO: Jake Sweeney Jr
**Treas:* Joseph Sweeney
**VP:* Gregory D Sweeney
**Genl Mgr:* Fred Manegold
**Off Mgr:* Jim Daniel
Sls Mgr: Joe Cathey
Sls Mgr: Aaron Pardue

D-U-N-S 09-182-9341
JAKE SWEENEY CHRYSLER-JEEP INC
JAKE SWEENEY JEEP EAGLE
85 W Kemper Rd, Cincinnati, OH 45246-2509
Tel (513) 782-1000 *Founded/Ownrshp* 1978
Sales 26.5MM^E *EMP* 70
SIC 5511 Automobiles, new & used; Pickups, new & used; Vans, new & used; Automobiles, new & used; Pickups, new & used; Vans, new & used
Pr: Jake Sweeney Jr
**VP:* Gregory Sweeney

JAKE SWEENEY JEEP EAGLE
See JAKE SWEENEY CHRYSLER-JEEP INC

JAKES CRAWFISH & SEAFOOD
See PACIFIC SEA FOOD CO INC

JAKE'S DISTRIBUTING COMPANY
See JAKES INC

JAKE'S HOUSE
See GONZALES LABOR SYSTEMS INC

D-U-N-S 00-973-6653 IMP
JAKES INC
JAKE'S DISTRIBUTING COMPANY
13400 Hollister Dr, Houston, TX 77086-1218
Tel (713) 868-1301 *Founded/Ownrshp* 1946
Sales 125.0MM^E *EMP* 140^E
SIC 5144 5142 5141 Eggs; Packaged frozen goods; Food brokers; Eggs; Packaged frozen goods; Food brokers
Pr: Leonard M Bench
**CFO:* Michael C Bench
**Sec:* Patsy Sakowitz
Sr VP: Sam Sakowitz
**VP:* Kevin P Ullrich
IT Man: Ben Nguyen
Opers Mgr: Tony Anthony
Sales Asso: Laura Diaz
Snr Mgr: Kenny Goldstein

D-U-N-S 92-877-9826
▲ **JAKKS PACIFIC INC**
2951 28th St Ste 51, Santa Monica, CA 90405-2961
Tel (424) 268-9444 *Founded/Ownrshp* 1995
Sales 810.0MM *EMP* 783^E
Tkr Sym JAKK *Exch* NGS
SIC 3944 Games, toys & children's vehicles; Games, toys & children's vehicles
Pr: Stephen G Berman
COO: John J McGrath
CFO: Joel M Bennett
VP: Helene Arancon
VP: Michael Dwyer
VP: Nelo Lucich
VP: Shari Mann
VP: Steve Morris
VP: Bill Mote
VP: Adam Stevenson
Creative D: Matt Musselman
Board of Directors: Fergus McGovern, Rex H Poulsen, Peter F Reilly, Michael S Sitrick, Murray L Skala

D-U-N-S 60-502-0130 IMP
JAKOV P DULCICH & SONS
31956 Peterson Rd, Mc Farland, CA 93250-9606
Tel (661) 792-6360 *Founded/Ownrshp* 1963
Sales 25.6MM^E *EMP* 250
SIC 0172 Grapes; Grapes
Owner: Jakov Dulcich
CFO: Jonathan Thomas
VP: Nick Dulcich
Exec: Mayra Contreas

D-U-N-S 12-596-6957
JAKPRINTS INC
3133 Chester Ave, Cleveland, OH 44114-4616
Tel (216) 622-6360 *Founded/Ownrshp* 1994
Sales 23.8MM^E *EMP* 127
SIC 2752 Commercial printing, lithographic; Commercial printing, lithographic
Pr: Jacob Edwards
COO: Bob Collins
**VP:* Dameon Guess
IT Man: Jason Snyder
Mktg Dir: Monica Saylor

D-U-N-S 62-341-7557
JAL AEROPARTS (USA) CORP
(*Suby of* JAPAN AIRLINES CO.,LTD.)
390 N Sepulveda Blvd, El Segundo, CA 90245-4475
Tel (310) 524-2401 *Founded/Ownrshp* 2011
Sales 40.0MM *EMP* 18
Accts Ernst & Young Llp Los Angeles
SIC 7389 Purchasing service
Pr: Hideki Ishii
**Sec:* Keiko Yoshida

D-U-N-S 15-178-4733
JALISCO INTERNATIONAL INC
6663 Colorado Blvd, Commerce City, CO 80022-2219
Tel (303) 287-8905 *Founded/Ownrshp* 1985
Sales 25.2MM^E *EMP* 75
Accts Wojteczko Snyder Group Pc Li
SIC 1611 1622 Highway & street construction; Bridge construction
Pr: Sipriano Ledezma
**Sec:* Margaret Ledezma

D-U-N-S 07-735-9198
JALSON CO INC
GERSON BAKAR & ASSOCIATES
201 Filbert St Ste 700, San Francisco, CA 94133-3242
Tel (415) 391-1313 *Founded/Ownrshp* 1957
Sales 19.1MM^E *EMP* 300
SIC 6531 Real estate agents & managers; Real estate agents & managers
CEO: Linda Zeller
**Pr:* Kathleen McCormick
**CFO:* Tad Scales
**Sr VP:* Steven Lopresti

D-U-N-S 09-545-6406 EXP
JAM DISTRIBUTING CO
7010 Mykawa Rd, Houston, TX 77033-1132
Tel (713) 844-7788 *Founded/Ownrshp* 1978
Sales 179.8MM^E *EMP* 175
SIC 5172 Petroleum products; Lubricating oils & greases; Petroleum products; Lubricating oils & greases
Pr: Jeffrey Kramer
CFO: Richard Vogt
Ex VP: Brian Drake
**VP:* Tim Dillon
**VP:* Betty Maniscalco
VP Opers: Ronald Wittebort
Trfc Dir: Jim Bush
Opers Mgr: Richard Anderson
Opers Mgr: Dan Greenwood
Opers Mgr: Brandon Murphy
Sls Mgr: Tom Chambers

D-U-N-S 87-983-9470
JAM SERVICES INC
J.A. MOMANEY SERVICES
958 E Airway Blvd, Livermore, CA 94551-1618
Tel (925) 455-5267 *Founded/Ownrshp* 1995
Sales 36.9MM^E *EMP* 28
SIC 5065 Electronic parts & equipment
Pr: Jeffrey A Momaney
Sales Asso: Roy Dexter
Sales Asso: Dave Land
Sales Asso: Kelly Momaney

D-U-N-S 15-718-4628
JAM TIRE INC
6202 Fairfield Dr, Northwood, OH 43619-7509
Tel (419) 661-1800 *Founded/Ownrshp* 2003
Sales 42.9MM^E *EMP* 117^E
SIC 5531 Automotive tires
Pr: Jim Jones
VP: Greg Shipley

D-U-N-S 00-187-6895 IMP
JAMAC FROZEN FOOD CORP
570 Grand St, Jersey City, NJ 07302-4115
Tel (201) 333-6200 *Founded/Ownrshp* 1955
Sales 54.2MM^E *EMP* 60
SIC 5142 Packaged frozen goods
Ch Bd: Diane Marbach
**Pr:* Edward Marbach
CFO: John Clary
**CFO:* John Moyer
VP Sls: Marc Greenberg

D-U-N-S 00-182-6627 IMP
JAMAICA BEARINGS CO INC (DE)
1700 Jericho Tpke Ste 1, New Hyde Park, NY 11040-4744
Tel (516) 326-1350 *Founded/Ownrshp* 1932, 1935
Sales 77.5MM^E *EMP* 85
SIC 5085 5088 Bearings; Aircraft & space vehicle supplies & parts; Bearings; Aircraft & space vehicle supplies & parts
Ch Bd: Peter Negri
VP: Scott Carpenter
VP: Dale Swanson
MIS Mgr: Mark Hoffman
QC Dir: Michael Matrazzo
Manager: Wayne Rodriguez
Sales Asso: Dave Hufsmith
Sales Asso: Christopher Kozlowski
Sales Asso: Rick Rusch

JAMAICA HOSPITAL
See FLUSHING HOSPITAL AND MEDICAL CENTER

JAMAICA HOSPITAL
See MEDISYS HEALTH NETWORK INC

D-U-N-S 07-274-0426
JAMAICA HOSPITAL
JAMAICA HOSPITAL MEDICAL CTR
8900 Van Wyck Expy Fl 4n, Jamaica, NY 11418-2897
Tel (718) 206-7642 *Founded/Ownrshp* 1892
Sales 580.7MM^E *EMP* 3,251
SIC 8062 General medical & surgical hospitals; General medical & surgical hospitals
Pr: Bruce Flanz
V Ch: Georges Sylvestre
**COO:* William Lynch
**CFO:* Mounir F Doss
**Ch:* Neil Foster Phillips
Chf Mktg O: Michael Hinck
Ofcr: George Fatoush
Ofcr: Joylene Porter
Ofcr: Ines Rodriguez
VP: Fred Beekman
VP: Teresa Flores
VP: Jacqueline Holley
**VP:* Manzar Sassani
Dir: Ann Corrigan
Dir Rad: Kiran Chawla
Dir Rad: Russell Smith

JAMAICA HOSPITAL MEDICAL CTR
See JAMAICA HOSPITAL

D-U-N-S 07-851-4031
JAMAICA HOSPITAL NURSING HOME CO INC
TRUMP PAVILION FOR NURSING & R
8940 135th St, Jamaica, NY 11418-2828
Tel (718) 206-5000 *Founded/Ownrshp* 1975
Sales 30.0MM *EMP* 270
Accts Jh Cohn Llp New York Ny
SIC 8051 Skilled nursing care facilities; Skilled nursing care facilities
Ex Dir: Gregory Bradley

D-U-N-S 79-649-6594 IMP
JAMAIL & SMITH CONSTRUCTION LP
16875 Diana Ln, Houston, TX 77058-2526
Tel (281) 461-7075 *Founded/Ownrshp* 2005
Sales 41.9MM^E *EMP* 45^E
SIC 1542 Commercial & office building, new construction; Commercial & office building, new construction
CEO: James W Jamail
Pt: Gregory Smith
CFO: Jennifer Trahan
Ex Dir: Rob Reyes
Opers Mgr: Jimmy Jones
Pr Mgr: Lissa Adams

D-U-N-S 15-154-9912 IMP
JAMAK FABRICATION-TEX LLC
(*Suby of* JMK INTERNATIONAL INC) ★
1401 N Bowie Dr, Weatherford, TX 76086-1599
Tel (817) 594-8771 *Founded/Ownrshp* 1971
Sales 49.9MM^E *EMP* 450
SIC 3061 3053 2822

D-U-N-S 04-003-8796
JAMAR CO
ADSCO
(*Suby of* API GROUP INC) ★
4701 Mike Colalillo Dr, Duluth, MN 55807-2762
Tel (218) 628-1027 *Founded/Ownrshp* 1985
Sales 157.0MM *EMP* 80
SIC 1711 1761 1742 5033 7699 3444

D-U-N-S 17-323-1788
JAMAR INDUSTRIES INC
HILLTOP LDSCP ARCHTECTS CONTRS
7909 Edith Blvd Ne, Albuquerque, NM 87113-1407
Tel (505) 898-9690 *Founded/Ownrshp* 1989
Sales 23.2MM^E *EMP* 400

SIC 0782 Landscape contractors; Landscape contractors
Pr: Jim Forrester

D-U-N-S 14-660-1385
▲ JAMBA INC
6475 Christie Ave Ste 150, Emeryville, CA 94608-2259
Tel (510) 596-0100 *Founded/Ownrshp* 1990
Sales 218.0MM *EMP* 4,200
Tkr Sym JMBA *Exch* NGM
SIC 5812 Soft drink stand; Soft drink stand
Ch Bd: James D White
Ofcr: Karen L Luey
Sr VP: Steve Adkins
Sr VP: Dale Goss
Dist Mgr: Georgia Tagliaferri
Board of Directors: Michael A Depatie, Lorna C Donatone, Richard L Federico, Andrew R Heyer, Lesley H Howe, David A Pace, James C Pappas, Glenn W Welling

JAMBA JUICE
See ALAMEDA JUICE LLC

JAMBA JUICE
See ATLANTA DNCTHS

JAMBA JUICE
See JUICE CLUB INC

D-U-N-S 86-892-3442
JAMBOREE HOUSING CORP
17701 Cowan Ste 200, Irvine, CA 92614-6840
Tel (949) 263-8676 *Founded/Ownrshp* 1990
Sales 32.9MM *EMP* 29
Accts Novogradac & Company Llp San
SIC 1522 Residential construction; Residential construction
Pr: Laura Archuleta
**COO:* Mary Jo Goelzer
**CFO:* Marcy Finamore
Ex VP: Mark Hoover
VP: Welton R Smith
Off Mgr: Sue Hansion
Off Mgr: Andrea Hickman
IT Man: Victoria Ramirez

JAMCO
See JOHNSON ARCHITECTURAL METAL CO

D-U-N-S 02-959-4249 IMP
JAMCO AMERICA INC
(*Suby of* JAMCO CORPORATION)
1018 80th St Sw, Everett, WA 98203-6278
Tel (425) 347-4735 *Founded/Ownrshp* 1981
Sales 85.4MM^E *EMP* 350
SIC 3728 Aircraft parts & equipment; Aircraft parts & equipment
Pr: Norikazu Natsume
Pr: Masao Kimura
**VP:* Don Grissitt
**VP:* Masamichi Kato
**VP:* Scott Miller
**VP:* David Nelson
Prgrm Mgr: David Barrat
Prgrm Mgr: Angela Boyd
Prgrm Mgr: Clement Chandrabalan
Prgrm Mgr: Trish Hanrahan
Prgrm Mgr: Taro Kumashiro

D-U-N-S 00-559-9170
JAMCO INTERNATIONAL INC (CA)
8405 Fm 3464 Ste 6, Laredo, TX 78045-1869
Tel (956) 717-3322 *Founded/Ownrshp* 1994
Sales 28.4MM^E *EMP* 120
SIC 4731 Customhouse brokers; Customhouse brokers
Pr: Juan A Menchaca Jr
Manager: Rogelio Fuentes

D-U-N-S 04-836-7275
■ JAMCO PRODUCTS INC
(*Suby of* MYERS INDUSTRIES INC) ★
1 Jamco Ct, South Beloit, IL 61080-2600
Tel (815) 624-0400 *Founded/Ownrshp* 2012
Sales 26.1MM^E *EMP* 120^E
SIC 3312 5084 Blast furnaces & steel mills; Industrial machinery & equipment; Blast furnaces & steel mills; Industrial machinery & equipment
CEO: James Alexander
**Pr:* Dan Johnson
VP: Linda Johnson
**VP:* Dave Tanner
Mktg Mgr: A J Hare

JAME COLEMAN CADILLAC
See BETHESDA INVESTMENT HOLDING CO INC

D-U-N-S 11-595-1543
JAME ROLL FORM PRODUCTS INC
(*Suby of* MARS STEEL CORP) ★
2401 Rose St, Franklin Park, IL 60131-3322
Tel (847) 455-0496 *Founded/Ownrshp* 1978
Sales 23.0MM *EMP* 50
SIC 3325 Rolling mill rolls, cast steel; Rolling mill rolls, cast steel
Pr: Robert P Perkaus
VP: Larry Martin
Off Mgr: Lynn Pikrone
Opers Mgr: Lorena Ramirez

JAMECO ELECTRONICS
See JAMES ELECTRONICS LIMITED

D-U-N-S 12-091-2126
JAMEL CONTAINERS LLC
1859 Polk St, Chattanooga, TN 37408-2319
Tel (256) 845-9775 *Founded/Ownrshp* 1999
Sales 37.7MM^E *EMP* 250
SIC 2653 Boxes, corrugated: made from purchased materials; Boxes, corrugated: made from purchased materials
**Pr:* James Perry Morris

D-U-N-S 02-552-4554
JAMERSON & BAUWENS ELECTRICAL CONTRACTORS INC
3160 Macarthur Blvd, Northbrook, IL 60062-1904
Tel (847) 291-2000 *Founded/Ownrshp* 1974
Sales 63.2MM^E *EMP* 200
Accts Cliftonlarsonallen Llp Oak Br
SIC 1731 General electrical contractor; General electrical contractor
CEO: Richard Jamerson
**COO:* Kenneth Bauwens
Sfty Dirs: James Tancos
Snr PM: Kevin Thompson

D-U-N-S 00-684-8311
JAMERSON & SONS INC J E (VA)
1540 Confederate Blvd B, Appomattox, VA 24522-4103
Tel (434) 352-8227 *Founded/Ownrshp* 1946
Sales 20.3MM^E *EMP* 60
SIC 1542 1522 5211 Commercial & office building contractors; Apartment building construction; Lumber & other building materials
Pr: Philip Jamerson
**Sec:* William Jamerson Sr
**VP:* Brent Harris
VP: William Jackson
**VP:* Bill Jamerson
Off Mgr: Mary Abbitt
Off Mgr: Nolton Blank

D-U-N-S 05-422-9034
■ JAMES A CUMMINGS INC
CUMMINGS GENERAL CONTRACTORS
(*Suby of* TUTOR PERINI CORP) ★
1 E Broward Blvd Ste 1300, Fort Lauderdale, FL 33301-1865
Tel (954) 484-1532 *Founded/Ownrshp* 2003
Sales 122.4MM *EMP* 114
Accts Deloitte & Touche Llp Los Ang
SIC 1542 1541 Commercial & office building, new construction; Industrial buildings, new construction; Commercial & office building, new construction; Industrial buildings, new construction
Pr: William R Derrer
Sr VP: Geoff Bunnell
**VP:* Geoffrey Bunnell
VP: John Church
**VP:* Raymond Feuilliez De La
**VP:* Michael F Lanciault
**VP:* Robert Maphis
**VP:* Scott Pat
VP: Scott Pate
Dir IT: Timothy Parido
IT Man: Jonathan Alexander

D-U-N-S 07-757-7831
JAMES A RHODES STATE COLLEGE
4240 Campus Dr, Lima, OH 45804-3576
Tel (419) 995-8000 *Founded/Ownrshp* 1971
Sales 598.5M *EMP* 385
Accts Es Evans And Company Lima Oh
SIC 8222 8249 8221 Technical institute; Vocational schools; Colleges universities & professional schools; Technical institute; Vocational schools; Colleges universities & professional schools
Pr: Debra L McCurdy
CFO: Cathy L Kohli
VP: Becky Burrell
**VP:* Randall McCullough
VP: Chris Schmidt
Off Admin: Kelvin Bruns
IT Man: Cathi Castro
IT Man: Beverly Rex-Cook

D-U-N-S 03-846-4178 IMP
JAMES AND LUTHER INC
11520 Cedar Oak Dr, El Paso, TX 79936-6027
Tel (915) 591-2429 *Founded/Ownrshp* 1980
Sales 34.5MM^E *EMP* 180
SIC 1541 Industrial buildings, new construction; Renovation, remodeling & repairs: industrial buildings; Industrial buildings, new construction; Renovation, remodeling & repairs: industrial buildings
Pr: Neal Luther
**Sec:* Joseph Boverie
VP: Joseph Berie
**VP:* Richard James

D-U-N-S 14-780-5928
JAMES ARTHUR G CANCER HOSPITAL AND RESEARCH INSTITUTE FOUNDATION
300 W 10th Ave Ste 519, Columbus, OH 43210-1280
Tel (614) 293-4878 *Founded/Ownrshp* 1985
Sales 2.2MM *EMP* 700
SIC 8733 8731 8069 Medical research; Commercial physical research; Specialty hospitals, except psychiatric; Medical research; Commercial physical research; Specialty hospitals, except psychiatric

D-U-N-S 00-434-0923
JAMES AUSTIN CO (PA)
115 Downieville Rd, Mars, PA 16046
Tel (724) 625-1535 *Founded/Ownrshp* 1889
Sales 72.4MM^E *EMP* 215
SIC 2841 2842 Soap: granulated, liquid, cake, flaked or chip; Specialty cleaning, polishes & sanitation goods; Soap: granulated, liquid, cake, flaked or chip; Specialty cleaning, polishes & sanitation goods
CEO: Harry G Austin III
**Ch Bd:* John T Austin Sr
**Ch Bd:* Robert Downie
**VP:* J Douglas Austin
**VP:* John T Austin Jr
MIS Dir: Beverly Ray
IT Man: Doug Austin
Sfty Mgr: Bill Walters

D-U-N-S 00-812-2764 IMP
JAMES AVERY CRAFTSMAN INC (TX)
145 Avery Rd, Kerrville, TX 78028-7603
Tel (830) 895-6800 *Founded/Ownrshp* 1954
Sales 382.1MM^E *EMP* 1,438
SIC 3911 Jewelry, precious metal; Necklaces, precious metal; Earrings, precious metal; Rings, finger: precious metal; Jewelry, precious metal; Necklaces, precious metal; Earrings, precious metal; Rings, finger: precious metal
Pr: Christopher M Avery
CFO: Geroge Lee
Ch: Homer J Avery
Ex VP: Paul Avery
VP: Carol Dollrogers

JAMES B BEAM IMPORT
See JIM BEAM BRANDS CO

D-U-N-S 03-402-1733
JAMES B DONAGHEY INC (AL)
1770 Old Shell Rd, Mobile, AL 36604-1336
Tel (251) 476-6494 *Founded/Ownrshp* 1921, 1987
Sales 33.5MM^E *EMP* 100
SIC 1711 1761 Heating & air conditioning contractors; Plumbing contractors; Sheet metalwork
Ch Bd: J Bradley Donaghey
**Pr:* James Judson Sanders
**Ch:* Maynard J Sanders
**Treas:* Joseph Mark Vallee
**VP:* Robert G Clapper

D-U-N-S 07-787-5086
JAMES B HAGGIN MEMORIAL HOSPITAL INC
464 Linden Ave, Harrodsburg, KY 40330-1882
Tel (859) 734-7045 *Founded/Ownrshp* 1913
Sales 20.4MM *EMP* 245
SIC 8062 General medical & surgical hospitals; General medical & surgical hospitals
CEO: Victoria L Reed
Chf Path: Jill S Ransdell
Chf Rad: David W Hopper
**CFO:* Tony Patterson
Dir OR: Nancy Pike
Dir Risk M: Kathy Parr
Dir Rx: Michelle Pinkston
Ansthlgy: David O Montgomery
Nrsg Dir: Sandra Pelfrey
Pharmcst: Susan Wheeler
Cert Phar: Tyler Short

D-U-N-S 00-717-1564
JAMES B NUTTER & CO
4153 Broadway, Kansas City, MO 64111-2619
Tel (816) 531-2345 *Founded/Ownrshp* 1951
Sales NA *EMP* 170^E
SIC 6163 6162 Loan brokers; Mortgage bankers; Loan brokers; Mortgage bankers
Pr: James B Nutter Jr
**Treas:* Len Kuklenski
VP: Kevin Williams
Ex Dir: Nancy Moore

D-U-N-S 07-452-9520
JAMES B OSWALD CO
OSWALD COMPANIES, THE
1100 Superior Ave E # 1500, Cleveland, OH 44114-2544
Tel (216) 367-8787 *Founded/Ownrshp* 1970
Sales NA *EMP* 260
SIC 6411

D-U-N-S 04-432-1701
JAMES B PIRTLE CONSTRUCTION CO INC
5700 Griffin Rd Ste 200, Davie, FL 33314-4507
Tel (954) 797-0410 *Founded/Ownrshp* 1968
Sales 45.7MM^E *EMP* 80
Accts Moore & Company Cpa Pompano
SIC 1542 Commercial & office building, new construction; Commercial & office buildings, renovation & repair; Commercial & office building, new construction; Commercial & office buildings, renovation & repair
Pr: Mike S Geary
Treas: Suzanne Mannetta
**Sec:* Darrell Lipman
**VP:* Gary Pirtle
VP: Mary Pirtle
VP: Liz Rivera
VP: Joyanne Stephens
Mktg Mgr: Kateryna Brito
Sls Mgr: Ellis Bill
Snr PM: Jeff Miles

D-U-N-S 04-014-3711
JAMES BARRY ROBINSON INSTITUTE
443 Kempsville Rd, Norfolk, VA 23502-4727
Tel (757) 455-6100 *Founded/Ownrshp* 1924
Sales 24.3MM *EMP* 420
Accts Cherry Bekaert & Holland Llp
SIC 8361 Home for the emotionally disturbed; Home for the emotionally disturbed
Ex Dir: Patrick Bateman
Exec: Susan Kent
Ex Dir: Rob McCartney
IT Man: Bobbi Henninger
Psych: Monica Manley
Nrsg Dir: Joanne Lewis

D-U-N-S 08-135-7436
JAMES BATMASIAN
INVESTMENTS LIMITED
215 N Federal Hwy Ste 1, Boca Raton, FL 33432-3928
Tel (561) 392-5890 *Founded/Ownrshp* 1970
Sales 23.2MM^E *EMP* 200
SIC 6514 6512 Residential building, four or fewer units: operation; Shopping center, property operation only; Residential building, four or fewer units: operation; Shopping center, property operation only
Owner: Marta T Batmasian
Ofcr: Travis Niswander
Mktg Mgr: Tim Setterlund

D-U-N-S 07-593-2012
JAMES BROWN CO (GA)
(*Suby of* NCP 2 LP) ★
6908 Chapman Rd, Lithonia, GA 30058-5246
Tel (770) 482-6521 *Founded/Ownrshp* 1970, 2008
Sales 81.9MM^E *EMP* 570
Accts Grant Thornton Llp Atlanta
SIC 4213 Trucking, except local; Trucking, except local
CEO: Brian Kinsey
**Pr:* James W Brown
**CFO:* Barbara Leasure
**Sec:* Patricia A Brown
VP: Richard Jenkins
MIS Dir: Mike Odum
Trfc Dir: Shimone Jones
Trfc Dir: Michael Lepors
Opers Mgr: Rusty Cooper
Opers Mgr: Kevin Slaughter
S&M/VP: Ralph Stanley

JAMES BUILT
See JAMESBUILT LLC

D-U-N-S 07-558-6677
JAMES C GREENE CO INC (NC)
323 W Morgan St, Raleigh, NC 27601-1353
Tel (919) 832-6614 *Founded/Ownrshp* 1932
Sales NA *EMP* 102
SIC 6411 Insurance adjusters
Ch: Sara K Greene
**Pr:* John Hamby
**Ex VP:* James C Greene Jr
VP: James Peck

JAMES C HUDSON CONSTRUCTION CO
See HUDSON CONSTRUCTION CO

D-U-N-S 00-491-7704
JAMES C JENKINS INSURANCE SERVICE INC (CA)
ATHENS INSURANCE
(*Suby of* EDGEWOOD PARTNERS INSURANCE CENTER) ★
1390 Willow Pass Rd # 800, Concord, CA 94520-7924
Tel (925) 798-3334 *Founded/Ownrshp* 1977, 2014
Sales NA *EMP* 125
SIC 6411 Insurance agents, brokers & service; Insurance brokers
CEO: Chris Utterback
**Pr:* James C Jenkins
**CFO:* Jodi Ellington
Ex VP: Vance Root
VP: Jason Del Grande
VP: Fredi Foye-Helms
VP: Dennis Harris
VP: Michael Hogan
VP: Krista O'Rourke
Div Mgr: Julie Simpson
Mktg Mgr: Michael Lynn

D-U-N-S 07-438-7887
JAMES CALVETTI MEATS INC (IL)
INNOVATIVE FOOD CREATIONS
4240 S Morgan St, Chicago, IL 60609-2517
Tel (773) 927-9242 *Founded/Ownrshp* 1974
Sales 25.3MM^E *EMP* 30
SIC 5147 Meats, fresh
Pr: Jamie Calvetti
VP: Carlos Chavez

D-U-N-S 05-389-7187
JAMES CAMPBELL CO LLC
1001 Kamokila Blvd Ofc, Kapolei, HI 96707-2030
Tel (808) 674-6674 *Founded/Ownrshp* 1900
Sales 27.4MM^E *EMP* 75
SIC 6519 Real property lessors
Ch Bd: Richard J Dahl
CFO: Landon Chun
Sr VP: Russell Chinen
VP: D Lloyd
VP: Douglas Morris
Software D: Chuck Hill

D-U-N-S 12-182-7778
JAMES CITY COUNTY ASSOCIATES INC
WILLIAMSBURG HONDA DODGE
7277 Richmond Rd, Williamsburg, VA 23188-7219
Tel (757) 564-0205 *Founded/Ownrshp* 1984
Sales 20.1MM^E *EMP* 50
SIC 5511 5521 Automobiles, new & used; Used car dealers
Pr: John E Dodson
CFO: John Gorbett
**Genl Mgr:* Michael Bowen
**Off Mgr:* Tricia Costa
Sls Mgr: Chris Robinson
Sls Mgr: Mariester Tangney
Sales Asso: Billy Haynes
Sales Asso: Ross Humphreys
Sales Asso: Toby Keller
Sales Asso: Joel Wright

D-U-N-S 08-979-4275
JAMES CONEY ISLAND INC
1750 Stebbins Dr, Houston, TX 77043-2807
Tel (713) 932-1500 *Founded/Ownrshp* 1990
Sales 20.1MM^E *EMP* 450
SIC 5812 Hot dog stand; Hot dog stand
Pr: Darrin Straughan
**Treas:* Edwin Freedman
Genl Mgr: Miguel Zambrano
Dir IT: Paul Dondlinger
Mktg Dir: Michelle Holmes

D-U-N-S 03-733-4179
■ JAMES CONSTRUCTION GROUP LLC
(*Suby of* PRIMORIS SERVICES CORP) ★
18484 E Petroleum Dr, Baton Rouge, LA 70809-6130
Tel (225) 293-0274 *Founded/Ownrshp* 2009
Sales 911.7MM^E *EMP* 1,800^E
SIC 1611 1622 Highway & street construction; Bridge, tunnel & elevated highway; Highway & street construction; Bridge, tunnel & elevated highway
Pr: Danny Hester
**CFO:* Don Bonaventure
CFO: Alfons Theeuwes
**Ex VP:* Mike Killgore
Sfty Dirs: Wayne Gros
Sfty Mgr: Charles Aucoin
Sfty Mgr: Chuck McWhorter
Snr PM: Gerry Tate
Snr PM: Dale Willis
Snr Mgr: Adam Giles

D-U-N-S 05-408-6541
JAMES COOKE & HOBSON INC
JCH
3810 Academy Pkwy S, Albuquerque, NM 87109-4453
Tel (505) 344-7100 *Founded/Ownrshp* 1974
Sales 20.0MM^E *EMP* 20
SIC 5084 Industrial machinery & equipment
Pr: Alfredo M Franco
**Pr:* Richard Hobson

D-U-N-S 03-459-4408
JAMES CORLEW CHEVROLET INC
JAMES CRLEW COLLISION CENTERPO
722 College St, Clarksville, TN 37040-3247
Tel (931) 552-2020 *Founded/Ownrshp* 1985

Sales 67.3MM^E *EMP* 200
SIC 5511 Automobiles, new & used; Automobiles, new & used
Pr: James Corlew
Treas: Jeff Groves
**Sr VP:* Robert M Bennett
**VP:* Agicrobert M Bennett Sr
Genl Mgr: Allen D Groves
Sls Mgr: Elvin Overstreet
Sls Mgr: Ron York
Sales Asso: Kevin Burgess

D-U-N-S 04-181-6000 IMP
JAMES CORRADO INC
CORRADO'S FAMILY AFFAIR
(*Suby of* CARRADOS SPECIALTY GOODS INC) ★
1578 Main Ave, Clifton, NJ 07011-2160
Tel (973) 340-0628 *Founded/Ownrshp* 1957
Sales 63.5MM^E *EMP* 350
SIC 5411 5141 Grocery stores, independent; Groceries, general line; Grocery stores, independent; Groceries, general line
Pr: Gerald Corrado
**VP:* Peter Corrado

JAMES CRLEW COLLISION CENTERPO
See JAMES CORLEW CHEVROLET INC

D-U-N-S 00-486-2017
JAMES D MORRISSEY INC (PA)
9119 Frankford Ave, Philadelphia, PA 19114-2884
Tel (215) 708-8420 *Founded/Ownrshp* 1920
Sales 45.6MM^E *EMP* 135
SIC 1611 General contractor, highway & street construction; General contractor, highway & street construction
Pr: Joseph Morrissey
**Treas:* Scott Barcusky
**VP:* William Greer
VP: Wm Greer

D-U-N-S 05-091-2963
JAMES E BARNES ENTERPRISES INC
MCDONALD'S
6110 Grelot Rd, Mobile, AL 36609-3640
Tel (251) 478-3223 *Founded/Ownrshp* 1993
Sales 20.2MM^E *EMP* 493
SIC 5812 Fast-food restaurant, chain; Fast-food restaurant, chain
Pr: James E Barnes

D-U-N-S 10-301-4833
JAMES E JOHN CONSTRUCTION CO INC
1701 Se Columbia River Dr, Vancouver, WA 98661-8078
Tel (360) 696-0837 *Founded/Ownrshp* 1983
Sales 22.7MM^E *EMP* 50
SIC 1542 Commercial & office building, new construction; Shopping center construction
Ch Bd: James John
**Pr:* Cameron Foroud
**Treas:* Robert Hinnen
VP: Jim Aarhus

D-U-N-S 09-128-2301
JAMES E ROBERTS-OBAYASHI CORP
20 Oak Ct, Danville, CA 94526-4006
Tel (925) 820-0600 *Founded/Ownrshp* 1978
Sales 38.0MM^E *EMP* 110
SIC 1522 1542 Multi-family dwellings, new construction; Commercial & office building, new construction; Multi-family dwellings, new construction; Commercial & office building, new construction
CEO: Larry R Smith
Ofcr: Gina Sakamoto
**Prin:* Obayashi Corporation
Snr PM: Ray Fletcher

D-U-N-S 06-302-3048 IMP
JAMES ELECTRONICS LIMITED
JAMECO ELECTRONICS
1355 Shoreway Rd, Belmont, CA 94002-4105
Tel (650) 592-8097 *Founded/Ownrshp* 1973
Sales 39.3MM^E *EMP* 80
SIC 5961 5065 5063 Electronic kits & parts, mail order; Computers & peripheral equipment, mail order; Electronic parts & equipment; Electrical apparatus & equipment
Ch Bd: Dennis D Farrey
CEO: James Farrey
VP: Greg Harris
Exec: Marianne Sullivan
CTO: Hamid Fard
Mktg Dir: Angela Avazino
Mktg Mgr: Angela Cambre
Sales Asso: Skip Rogers

D-U-N-S 07-975-0028
JAMES FORD OF WILLIAMSON LLC
3923 Route 104, Williamson, NY 14589-9592
Tel (315) 589-4541 *Founded/Ownrshp* 2013
Sales 175.0MM *EMP* 20
SIC 5511 Automobiles, new & used

D-U-N-S 00-326-3167
JAMES G DAVIS CONSTRUCTION CORP
12530 Parklawn Dr Ste 100, Rockville, MD 20852-1762
Tel (301) 881-2990 *Founded/Ownrshp* 1986
Sales 596.3MM *EMP* 350
SIC 1542

D-U-N-S 09-343-5725
JAMES G PARKER INSURANCE ASSOCIATES
BACOME INSURANCE AGENCY
1753 E Fir Ave, Fresno, CA 93720-3840
Tel (559) 222-7722 *Founded/Ownrshp* 1978
Sales NA *EMP* 160
SIC 6411 Insurance agents
Pr: James G Parker
**Treas:* Janice W Parker
**VP:* Leroy Berrett
VP: John Cleveland
VP: Kelly Fiorella
**VP:* Jon Parker
VP: Brad Shannon
**VP:* Gerald Thompson
**VP:* Danny Todd

Exec: Maureen Beashears
Off Mgr: Maureen Beshears

JAMES GROUP INTERNATIONAL
See RENAISSANCE GLOBAL LOGISTICS LLC

D-U-N-S 15-107-0435
JAMES GROUP INTERNATIONAL INC
4335 W Fort St, Detroit, MI 48209-3221
Tel (313) 841-0070 *Founded/Ownrshp* 1971
Sales 75.3MM^E *EMP* 325^E
SIC 4783 4225 Packing goods for shipping; General warehousing & storage; Packing goods for shipping; General warehousing & storage
Pr: John A James
CFO: Ken Banach
**Treas:* Patrick Deeniss
VP: Dan Ford
Dir Bus: Leona Burja
IT Man: Russ Bettridge
IT Man: Jim Herrmann
Opers Mgr: Carla Fitzgerald
Ql Cn Mgr: Antonio Anderson
Mktg Dir: Jeff Green

D-U-N-S 00-503-3410
JAMES H CROSS CO (PA)
QUALITY TOOL SUPPLY
3602 W 23rd St, Erie, PA 16506-2006
Tel (814) 835-8280 *Founded/Ownrshp* 1944
Sales 43.8MM^E *EMP* 58
SIC 5084 Machine tools & accessories
Pr: Jeffrey B Cross
**VP:* William Galla
Site Mgr: Rick Klinect
Site Mgr: Olaf Martinson

D-U-N-S 00-681-1764
JAMES H DREW CORP
(*Suby of* FORTUNE INDUSTRIES INC) ★
8701 Zionsville Rd, Indianapolis, IN 46268-1041
Tel (317) 876-3739 *Founded/Ownrshp* 1932, 2004
Sales 20.0MM^E *EMP* 78
Accts Somerset Cpas Pc Indianapo
SIC 1611 Highway & street sign installation; Guardrail construction, highways
CEO: Gene Lindley
Pr: Harry K Oyler III
Treas: Greg Christoff
VP: Gregory Peck

D-U-N-S 10-266-2111
JAMES H JACKSON INDUSTRIES INC
FORCE CORPORATION
1300 W Adams, La Porte, TX 77571
Tel (713) 470-0550 *Founded/Ownrshp* 1981
Sales 40.0MM *EMP* 400
SIC 1541 1629 Dry cleaning plant construction; Railroad & railway roadbed construction
Pr: James H Jackson
**Treas:* Elinor Jackson
**VP:* Rusty Barnhill
**VP:* Harold Nasse
**VP:* Manuel White

D-U-N-S 00-382-9520
JAMES HAMILTON CONSTRUCTION CO
17 S Ridge Rd, Silver City, NM 88061-6693
Tel (575) 388-1546 *Founded/Ownrshp* 1996
Sales 29.0MM *EMP* 500
SIC 1799 1611 Building site preparation; General contractor, highway & street construction; Building site preparation; General contractor, highway & street construction
CEO: Charles Hamilton
**CFO:* Katie Baldwin
**VP:* Carroll Hamilton
VP: Roy Newman

D-U-N-S 12-533-5674 IMP
JAMES HARDIE BUILDING PRODUCTS INC
17 Unytite Dr, Peru, IL 61354-9710
Tel (815) 220-1243 *Founded/Ownrshp* 2000
Sales 43.7MM^E *EMP* 83^E
SIC 3272 Concrete stuctural support & building material
Prin: Peter McDold
**Pr:* Louis Gries
Sfty Mgr: Tom Salz
Plnt Mgr: Tonny Bonnie
Plnt Mgr: Todd Tyler
Snr PM: Bill Reff

D-U-N-S 18-318-6113 EXP
JAMES HARDIE BUILDING PRODUCTS INC
JAMESHARDIE
(*Suby of* JAMES HARDIE TRANSITION CO INC) ★
26300 La Alameda Ste 400, Mission Viejo, CA 92691-8372
Tel (949) 348-1800 *Founded/Ownrshp* 1986
Sales 431.0MM^E *EMP* 400
SIC 5031 Building materials, exterior; Building materials, interior; Building materials, exterior; Building materials, interior
CEO: Louis Gries
**Treas:* Ginger Lester
**Treas:* Matthew Marsh
Exec: Martin Gonzalez
Dir Lab: Navid Zarinfar
Area Mgr: Andrew Bella
Area Mgr: Scott Hager
Area Mgr: Brian Horstmann
Area Mgr: David Oakley
Tech Mgr: Marcus Kuizenga
Netwrk Eng: Link Cornelius

D-U-N-S 88-425-9524
JAMES HARDIE TRADING CO INC
(*Suby of* JAMES HARDIE TRANSITION CO INC) ★
26300 La Alameda Ste 400, Mission Viejo, CA 92691-8372
Tel (949) 582-2378 *Founded/Ownrshp* 1995
Sales 30.5MM^E *EMP* 160
SIC 2952 Siding materials; Siding materials
Pr: Bryon G Borgardt

D-U-N-S 17-438-5328 IMP/EXP
JAMES HARDIE TRANSITION CO INC
VICTORVILLE INDUSTRIAL MNRL
(*Suby of* JAMES HARDIE HOLDINGS LIMITED)
26300 La Alameda Ste 400, Mission Viejo, CA 92691-8372
Tel (949) 348-1800 *Founded/Ownrshp* 1986
Sales 461.5MM^E *EMP* 1,300
SIC 3275 3523 3494 5072 Wallboard, gypsum; Fertilizing, spraying, dusting & irrigation machinery; Valves & pipe fittings; Hardware; Wallboard, gypsum; Fertilizing, spraying, dusting & irrigation machinery; Valves & pipe fittings; Hardware
Pr: Donald N Manson

D-U-N-S 10-551-9540
JAMES HELWIG & SON INC
5946 Saint Marks Cir, Dallas, TX 75230-4048
Tel (214) 369-3626 *Founded/Ownrshp* 1984
Sales 25.6MM^E *EMP* 300
SIC 4213 4212 Trucking, except local; Local trucking, without storage; Trucking, except local; Local trucking, without storage
Pr: James Helwig
CFO: Gene Zinfer

JAMES HINES ADMINISTRATIVE CTR
See BOARD OF COOPERATIVE EDUCATIONAL SERVICES

D-U-N-S 61-013-2995
JAMES HODGE FORD LINCOLN MERCURY INC
1200 N Main St, Muskogee, OK 74401-4400
Tel (918) 584-0514 *Founded/Ownrshp* 1989
Sales 40.4MM^E *EMP* 80
SIC 5511 Automobiles, new & used; Automobiles, new & used
Pr: James Hodge
**Sec:* Mary Kathryn Hodge

JAMES HOWARD WAYNE ASSOCIATION
See HAYLOR FREYER & COON INC

D-U-N-S 06-162-8905
JAMES HUNT CONSTRUCTION CO
1865 Summit Rd, Cincinnati, OH 45237-2803
Tel (513) 721-0559 *Founded/Ownrshp* 1996
Sales 25.0MM^E *EMP* 30
Accts D Andrea Ebel & Co Cincinna
SIC 1542 Commercial & office buildings, renovation & repair; Commercial & office building, new construction; Commercial & office buildings, renovation & repair; Commercial & office building, new construction
Pr: Veronica Davis
**VP:* Chris Davis

D-U-N-S 08-049-8868
JAMES IMAGING SYSTEMS INC
3375 Intertech Dr, Brookfield, WI 53045-5114
Tel (262) 781-7700 *Founded/Ownrshp* 1977
Sales 24.8MM^E *EMP* 65
SIC 5044 5065 7629 5112 5085 Office equipment; Photocopy machines; Modems, computer; Business machine repair, electric; Laserjet supplies; Office supplies; Ink, printers'
CEO: Lola Tegeder
**Pr:* Tom Tegeder
VP Sls: Bill Coon

D-U-N-S 07-018-6762
JAMES IRVINE FOUNDATION
1 Bush St Fl 8, San Francisco, CA 94104-4414
Tel (415) 777-2244 *Founded/Ownrshp* 1937
Sales 148.3MM *EMP* 36
SIC 6732 Charitable trust management; Charitable trust management
Pr: James Canales
Bd of Dir: Jane W Carney

D-U-N-S 02-365-3827
JAMES J ANDERSON CONSTRUCTION CO INC
6958 Torresdale Ave Ste 3, Philadelphia, PA 19135-1937
Tel (215) 331-7150 *Founded/Ownrshp* 1981
Sales 60.2MM^E *EMP* 125
SIC 1611 General contractor, highway & street construction; General contractor, highway & street construction
Pr: James J Anderson
**Sec:* Martin Griffin
**VP:* Rick Foster
**VP:* George Muller

D-U-N-S 04-400-7433
JAMES J BOYLE & CO
JJ BOYLE
(*Suby of* HITACHI TRANSPORT SYSTEM, LTD.)
400 Oyster Point Blvd # 221, South San Francisco, CA 94080-1952
Tel (650) 871-6334 *Founded/Ownrshp* 2013
Sales 21.9MM^E *EMP* 100
SIC 4731 Customhouse brokers; Foreign freight forwarding
CEO: Greg Kodama
Ex VP: Ray Wang
**VP:* Emylene De Jesus
**VP:* Sandra Nakamura
**Prin:* Edward Inouye
Brnch Mgr: Terry Pilant

D-U-N-S 00-785-1348
JAMES J WELCH & CO INC (MA)
27 Congress St Ste 503, Salem, MA 01970-5577
Tel (978) 744-9300 *Founded/Ownrshp* 1852
Sales 22.1MM^E *EMP* 50
SIC 1542 Commercial & office building, new construction; Commercial & office buildings, renovation & repair; Institutional building construction
Pr: Constance Welch
**Treas:* Michael Welch
Genl Mgr: Maria Holtz

D-U-N-S 19-576-5995
JAMES KOEHLER
COMFORT INN
415 N 4th St, Aberdeen, SD 57401-2770
Tel (605) 229-0760 *Founded/Ownrshp* 1983
Sales 20.5MM^E *EMP* 126
SIC 8741 Hotel or motel management
Pr: James P Koehler

JAMES L MAHER CENTER
See NEWPORT COUNTY CHAPTER R I A R C INC

D-U-N-S 06-928-9218
JAMES L WILEY
OPTION 1 NUTRITION SOLUTIONS
2460 E Germann Rd Ste 18, Chandler, AZ 85286-1573
Tel (480) 883-1188 *Founded/Ownrshp* 2000
Sales 29.1MM *EMP* 15
SIC 5499 Health & dietetic food stores; Dietetic foods
Owner: James L Wiley

D-U-N-S 08-392-5784
JAMES LYNCH
TRIPLE S OIL CO
411 Overland Ave, Burley, ID 83318-1026
Tel (208) 678-9009 *Founded/Ownrshp* 1974
Sales 25.6MM *EMP* 75
Accts Westfall & Westfall Cpas Bur
SIC 5541 5411 7542 Filling stations, gasoline; Convenience stores; Carwashes; Filling stations, gasoline; Convenience stores; Carwashes
Owner: James Lynch

D-U-N-S 07-201-3279
JAMES M PLEASANTS CO INC
JPM
603 Diamond Hill Ct, Greensboro, NC 27406-4617
Tel (336) 275-3152 *Founded/Ownrshp* 1987
Sales 107.8MM^E *EMP* 98
SIC 5075 3585 3561 3494 Warm air heating & air conditioning; Refrigeration & heating equipment; Pumps & pumping equipment; Valves & pipe fittings; Warm air heating & air conditioning; Refrigeration & heating equipment; Pumps & pumping equipment; Valves & pipe fittings
Pr: J Chris Edmonson
**Pr:* Jamie Edmondson
VP: Sam Allred
VP: Pete Conroy
**VP:* G David Pleasants
Genl Mgr: Teresa Turner
IT Man: Joe Claxton
VP Opers: Gerald Edwards
Plnt Mgr: Chris Edmond
Ql Cn Mgr: Shelley Tobin
Mktg Mgr: Chad Edmondson

D-U-N-S 00-817-7495
JAMES MACHINE WORKS LLC
1521 Adams St, Monroe, LA 71201-7078
Tel (318) 322-6104 *Founded/Ownrshp* 1927
Sales 32.3MM *EMP* 176
Accts Robinson Gardner Langston An
SIC 3443 Tanks, standard or custom fabricated: metal plate; Vessels, process or storage (from boiler shops): metal plate; Tanks, standard or custom fabricated: metal plate; Vessels, process or storage (from boiler shops): metal plate
**VP:* Joe K Reljac
Mng Dir: Robert Mason
Netwrk Mgr: Fred Korn
Sfty Mgr: Butch Mason
VP Mktg: John Posey

D-U-N-S 87-932-5355
JAMES MADISON UNIVERSITY INC
800 S Main St, Harrisonburg, VA 22807-0002
Tel (540) 568-6211 *Founded/Ownrshp* 1908
Sales 500.0MM *EMP* 1,700
SIC 8221 Colleges universities & professional schools; Colleges universities & professional schools
Pr: Jonathan R Alger
**CFO:* John Knight
CFO: Robert Reid
**Sr VP:* Charles W King
**VP:* Douglas Brown
VP: Dary Erwin
VP: Weston Hatfield
VP: Nick Langridge
VP: Christopher Pipkins
Dir Lab: Bill Latham
Assoc Dir: Kevin Gibson
Assoc Dir: Jane Hubbell
Assoc Dir: Tisha McCoy
Assoc Dir: Mary Morsch
Assoc Dir: Remy Pangle
Assoc Dir: Maureen Shanahan

D-U-N-S 17-347-4602 IMP
JAMES MARINE INC
J M I
4500 Clarks River Rd, Paducah, KY 42003-0823
Tel (270) 898-7392 *Founded/Ownrshp* 1986
Sales 257.8MM^E *EMP* 1,007
SIC 3731 4492 5541 3732 Barges, building & repairing; Shifting of floating equipment within harbors; Marine towing services; Marine service station; Boat building & repairing; Barges, building & repairing; Shifting of floating equipment within harbors; Marine towing services; Marine service station; Boat building & repairing
CEO: C Ronald James
**Pr:* Phil Crabtree
**CFO:* Brandon Buchanan
Ex VP: Barry Gipson
**Ex VP:* Jeff James
**Sr VP:* Eric Crabtree
VP: Phillip Crabtree
**Genl Mgr:* Brent Gaines

D-U-N-S 07-736-1061
JAMES MC KOANE ENTERPRISES INC
CLAWSON HONDA OF FRESNO
6334 N Blackstone Ave, Fresno, CA 93710-5014
Tel (559) 435-5000 *Founded/Ownrshp* 1990
Sales 71.8MM^E *EMP* 140
SIC 5511 5571

D-U-N-S 00-693-1331 IMP
JAMES MCHUGH CONSTRUCTION CO
(*Suby of* MCHUGH ENTERPRISES INC) ★
1737 S Michigan Ave, Chicago, IL 60616-1211
Tel (312) 986-8000 *Founded/Ownrshp* 1896
Sales 390.8MM^E *EMP* 750
SIC 1542 1522 1622 Hospital construction; Commercial & office building, new construction; Commercial & office buildings, renovation & repair; Hotel/motel & multi-family home construction; Bridge construction; Tunnel construction; Highway construction, elevated; Hospital construction; Commercial & office building, new construction; Commercial & office buildings, renovation & repair; Hotel/motel & multi-family home construction; Bridge construction; Tunnel construction; Highway construction, elevated
Ch Bd: James P McHugh
**Pr:* Bruce E Lake
**CFO:* Patrick Seery
Sr VP: David Alexander
VP: Dale Hendrix
VP: Benjamin Johnston
**VP:* James R Mc Hugh
**VP:* James R McHugh
VP: Richard Mole
VP: Robert Mortimer
**VP:* Daniel Rosenberg
VP: Richard Sheem

JAMES METALS
See HARBOR PIPE AND STEEL INC

D-U-N-S 01-298-1965
JAMES MIRABITO & SONS INC
QUICKWAY
44 Grand St, Sidney, NY 13838-1141
Tel (607) 561-2700 *Founded/Ownrshp* 1927
Sales 44.6MM^E *EMP* 375
SIC 5983 5541 5172 5411 5052 Fuel oil dealers; Gasoline service stations; Fuel oil; Gasoline; Convenience stores, chain; Coal & other minerals & ores; Fuel oil dealers; Gasoline service stations; Fuel oil; Gasoline; Convenience stores, chain; Coal & other minerals & ores
Pr: Joseph Mirabito
**Sec:* Ross Mirabito
**VP:* Arthur Weed
Genl Mgr: Russ Southard
VP Opers: Gene Fuller

D-U-N-S 08-652-5953 IMP
JAMES MONROE WIRE & CABLE CORP
767 Sterling Rd, South Lancaster, MA 01561
Tel (978) 368-0131 *Founded/Ownrshp* 1977
Sales 24.3MM^E *EMP* 80^E
SIC 3315 3357 5063 Cable, steel: insulated or armored; Coaxial cable, nonferrous; Wire & cable; Cable, steel: insulated or armored; Coaxial cable, nonferrous; Wire & cable
Pr: David Fisher
**Genl Mgr:* Robert Leger
Off Mgr: Peggy Hakala
Natl Sales: Jason Thomas
Sls Mgr: Brendan Tally

D-U-N-S 01-501-0908
JAMES MORIEL
IMPERIAL TURF PRODUCTS
25701 Taladro Cir Ste B, Mission Viejo, CA 92691-3122
Tel (949) 240-3340 *Founded/Ownrshp* 1997
Sales 108.2MM *EMP* 7
Accts Haskell & White Llp Irvine C
SIC 5083 Lawn & garden machinery & equipment
Owner: James Moriel

D-U-N-S 00-629-1231
JAMES MULLIGAN PRINTING CO (MO)
1808 Washington Ave Ste 1, Saint Louis, MO 63103-1730
Tel (314) 621-0874 *Founded/Ownrshp* 1865
Sales 23.5MM^E *EMP* 70
SIC 2752 2791 Commercial printing, lithographic; Commercial printing, offset; Typesetting
Pr: Jerome Kiske
CFO: Charlie Schmidlack
**Sec:* James J Kiske
**VP:* Mary Herr
Sls Mgr: Jeff Moss

D-U-N-S 09-411-4295
JAMES MYERS CO INC
12306 Conway Rd, Beltsville, MD 20705-1395
Tel (301) 419-0091 *Founded/Ownrshp* 1978
Sales 22.0MM^E *EMP* 100
SIC 1761 1799 Roofing contractor; Sheet metalwork; Waterproofing
Pr: James Myers
**Treas:* Ellen Myers
**VP:* Richard Myers
Sfty Mgr: Jack Kyle

D-U-N-S 03-424-3162
JAMES P HILL DISTRIBUTOR INC (LA)
HILL OIL
(*Suby of* RELADYNE I LLC) ★
911 Ward Chapel Rd, Farmerville, LA 71241-4976
Tel (318) 345-4302 *Founded/Ownrshp* 1945, 2011
Sales 44.8MM^E *EMP* 62
SIC 5171 5014 5013 Petroleum bulk stations; Tires & tubes; Automotive supplies & parts; Petroleum bulk stations; Tires & tubes; Automotive supplies & parts
Pr: Kerry D Hilll
**VP:* Scott Hill

D-U-N-S 94-735-7539 IMP
JAMES PERSE ENTERPRISES INC
JAMES PERSE LOS ANGELES
7373 Flores St, Downey, CA 90242-4011
Tel (323) 588-2226 *Founded/Ownrshp* 1994
Sales 110.1MM^E *EMP* 70
SIC 5136 5137 Men's & boys' clothing; Women's & children's clothing; Men's & boys' clothing; Women's & children's clothing
CEO: James Perse
COO: Jon Levine
**CFO:* Karen Swanson
VP: David Cappicille
VP: Lisa Lee
VP: Kimberley Smith
Store Mgr: Natasha Exley
CIO: Tom Stevenson
IT Man: Andy Bach
VP Sls: Melissa Dench
Mktg Mgr: Bach Andy

JAMES PERSE LOS ANGELES
See JAMES PERSE ENTERPRISES INC

D-U-N-S 00-658-1987
JAMES PETERSON SONS INC
PETERSON CONCRETE
N2251 Gibson Dr, Medford, WI 54451-9702
Tel (715) 748-3010 *Founded/Ownrshp* 1948
Sales 91.5MM *EMP* 130
Accts Wipfli Llp Eau Claire Wiscon
SIC 1611 General contractor, highway & street construction; General contractor, highway & street construction
Pr: John M Peterson
**Sec:* Timothy Peterson
**VP:* Jeffery Peterson
Off Mgr: John Marshall

D-U-N-S 02-122-8671 IMP
JAMES R GLIDEWELL DENTAL CERAMICS INC (CA)
GLIDEWELL LABORATORIES
4141 Macarthur Blvd, Newport Beach, CA 92660-2015
Tel (949) 440-2600 *Founded/Ownrshp* 1969
Sales 161.7MM^E *EMP* 1,900
SIC 8072 Dental laboratories; Dental laboratories
CEO: James R Glidewell
**COO:* Greg Minzenmayer
**CFO:* Rob Grice
**CFO:* Glenn Sasaki
CFO: Glenn Sasaski
Ofcr: Mike McEachern
Ofcr: Brandon Nelson
VP: David Casper
**VP:* Jim Shuck
Exec: Vince Munoz
Genl Mgr: Darius Raudys

D-U-N-S 03-198-7753
JAMES R HOWELL & CO INC
HOWELL CONSTRUCTION
8085 E Harvard Ave, Denver, CO 80231-3805
Tel (303) 696-5800 *Founded/Ownrshp* 1935
Sales 38.0MM *EMP* 55
SIC 1541 1542 Warehouse construction; Commercial & office building contractors; Commercial & office buildings, renovation & repair
Pr: Joseph L Slavik

D-U-N-S 00-678-0662
JAMES R VANNOY & SONS CONSTRUCTION CO INC (NC)
VANNOY CONSTRUCTION
1608 Us Highway 221 N, Jefferson, NC 28640-9808
Tel (336) 846-7191 *Founded/Ownrshp* 1952
Sales 335.0MM *EMP* 315
Accts Coffey Lovins & Company Pllc
SIC 1542 1541 1799 Commercial & office building, new construction; Institutional building construction; Industrial buildings, new construction; Building site preparation; Commercial & office building, new construction; Institutional building construction; Industrial buildings, new construction; Building site preparation
CEO: W Eddie Vannoy
Pr: J Mark Vannoy
VP: Bill Blank
VP: John J Montgomery
Off Mgr: Sharon Rodriguez
Off Admin: Rhonda Sawyer
IT Man: Neil Asher
Genl Couns: Jim Maloney

D-U-N-S 10-189-3816
JAMES R WORRELL GENERAL AGENT INC
NORTHWESTERN MUTUAL
6235 Morrison Blvd, Charlotte, NC 28211-3508
Tel (704) 365-2014 *Founded/Ownrshp* 1980
Sales NA *EMP* 125^E
SIC 6311 6321 Life insurance; Disability health insurance; Health insurance carriers; Life insurance; Disability health insurance; Health insurance carriers
CEO: James R Worrell
**Pr:* Richard Worrel Jr
COO: John Dunn
Ofcr: Chuck Allison
Ofcr: Eric Andersen
Ofcr: Wm Barton
Ofcr: Michael Bernstein
Ofcr: Pavan Bidani
Ofcr: Sean Bies
Ofcr: James Bishop
Ofcr: Chris Bowen
Ofcr: Mark Bracci
Ofcr: Justin Brown
Ofcr: Bryce Burch
Ofcr: Andrew Capallo
Ofcr: Jon Colton
Ofcr: Frank Coluccio
Ofcr: Jonathan Conrad
Ofcr: John Crane
Ofcr: Darrell Cronan
Ofcr: Spencer Cultra

D-U-N-S 04-334-3151
JAMES RIVER AIR CONDITIONING CO (VA)
1905 Westmoreland St, Richmond, VA 23230-3225
Tel (804) 358-9333 *Founded/Ownrshp* 1967
Sales 54.9MM^E *EMP* 168
SIC 1711 Mechanical contractor; Mechanical contractor
Pr: Hugh Alan Joyce
Pr: Cecil Haskins
**VP:* David Norsworthy

D-U-N-S 78-409-3502
JAMES RIVER COAL CO
901 E Byrd St Ste 1600, Richmond, VA 23219-4529
Tel (804) 780-3000 *Founded/Ownrshp* 1988
Sales 1.1MMM *EMP* 2,124^E
SIC 1221 Bituminous coal & lignite-surface mining; Bituminous coal & lignite-surface mining
Dir Risk M: William B Murphy
Chf Cred: Michael E Weber
VP: Samuel M Hopkins II
Comm Dir: Elizabeth Cook
Genl Mgr: Scott Griffie
Board of Directors: Alan F Crown, Ronald J Florjancic, Leonard J Kujawa, Joseph H Vipperman

D-U-N-S 07-786-3314
JAMES RIVER COAL SERVICE CO
(*Suby of* JAMES RIVER COAL CO) ★
901 E Byrd St Ste 1600, Richmond, VA 23219-4529
Tel (606) 878-7411 *Founded/Ownrshp* 1971
Sales 134.8MM^E *EMP* 1,018
SIC 1222 1221 Underground mining, semibituminous; Strip mining, bituminous; Coal preparation plant, bituminous or lignite; Unit train loading facility, bituminous or lignite; Underground mining, semibituminous; Strip mining, bituminous; Coal preparation plant, bituminous or lignite; Unit train loading facility, bituminous or lignite
CEO: Peter Socha
**Pr:* Talmadge M Mosley
**Pr:* Dexter Brian Patton III
**Treas:* Samuel Hopkins

JAMES RIVER COVALESCENT CENTER
See VIRGINIA HEALTH SERVICES INC

D-U-N-S 05-890-1646 EXP
JAMES RIVER EQUIPMENT INC
11047 Leadbetter Rd, Ashland, VA 23005-3408
Tel (804) 748-9324 *Founded/Ownrshp* 1978
Sales 226.1MM^E *EMP* 550
SIC 5084 5082 Industrial machinery & equipment; General construction machinery & equipment; Industrial machinery & equipment; General construction machinery & equipment
Pr: Mark D Romer
**VP:* Rodger Hargis
VP: John Shearer
Genl Mgr: Will Barbee
Sls Mgr: Ronnie Rathbone
Sales Asso: Blair Hall

D-U-N-S 04-473-5298 EXP
JAMES RIVER EQUIPMENT VIRGINIA LLC
JOHN DEERE
11047 Leadbetter Rd, Ashland, VA 23005-3408
Tel (804) 798-6001 *Founded/Ownrshp* 2000
Sales 78.9MM^E *EMP* 330
SIC 5082 General construction machinery & equipment; General construction machinery & equipment
Pr: Mark Romer
VP: Irvin Marshall
IT Man: John Bussert
Sls Mgr: Steve Newton

D-U-N-S 09-545-6794
JAMES RIVER EQUIPMENT VIRGINIA LLC
JOHN DEERE
9550 Statesville Rd, Charlotte, NC 28269-7644
Tel (704) 597-0211 *Founded/Ownrshp* 2000
Sales 27.0MM^E *EMP* 100
SIC 5211

D-U-N-S 93-922-7351
JAMES RIVER FINANCIAL CORP
58 Broad Street Rd, Manakin Sabot, VA 23103-2213
Tel (804) 578-4500 *Founded/Ownrshp* 1988
Sales 25.1MM^E *EMP* 30
SIC 6221 7997 Commodity contracts brokers, dealers; Tennis club, membership; Commodity contracts brokers, dealers; Tennis club, membership
CEO: Paul H Saunders
**Pr:* Kevin M Brandt
Ofcr: Laura McGrath
Dir IT: John Heitmuller
Sftwr Eng: Michael Sullivan

D-U-N-S 60-324-0644
JAMES RIVER GENCO LLC
9405 Arrowpoint Blvd, Charlotte, NC 28273-8167
Tel (704) 525-3800 *Founded/Ownrshp* 2005
Sales 61.8MM^E *EMP* 120
SIC 4911 Distribution, electric power; Distribution, electric power
Pt: Cogentrix of Virginia
VP: Joseph E Freeman Jr

D-U-N-S 62-621-6295
JAMES RIVER GROUNDS MANAGEMENT INC
11008 Washington Hwy, Glen Allen, VA 23059-1904
Tel (804) 550-3500 *Founded/Ownrshp* 1990
Sales 21.4MM^E *EMP* 400^E
Accts Martin Dolan & Holton Ltd
SIC 0782 Lawn & garden services; Lawn & garden services
Pr: Maria P Candler
**VP:* James B Batterson
**VP:* Jason C Knight
VP: Jason Knight
**VP:* Todd E Pendleton
Brnch Mgr: Trevor Atkins
Brnch Mgr: Matthew Reynal
Brnch Mgr: Jim Tilley
IT Man: Noel Firth
Opers Mgr: Maria Threadgi
Prd Mgr: Matthew Carter

D-U-N-S 12-644-1687
JAMES RIVER GROUP INC
(*Suby of* FRANKLIN HOLDINGS (BERMUDA) LTD)
1414 Raleigh Rd Ste 405, Chapel Hill, NC 27517-8834
Tel (919) 883-4171 *Founded/Ownrshp* 2007
Sales NA *EMP* 197
SIC 6411 Property & casualty insurance agent; Property & casualty insurance agent
CEO: Michael T Oakes
CFO: Gregg T Davis

D-U-N-S 14-700-4634
JAMES RIVER PETROLEUM INC
10487 Lkrdge Pkwy Ste 100, Ashland, VA 23005
Tel (804) 358-9000 *Founded/Ownrshp* 1985
Sales 66.7MM^E *EMP* 21
SIC 5172 Fuel oil; Diesel fuel
Pr: Lloyd Little
**CFO:* Barbara Tainter
**VP:* Tracy Little

D-U-N-S 02-263-0123
JAMES S GRIMES INC
GRIMES TRUCK CENTER
100 Bucheimer Rd Ste D, Frederick, MD 21701-3164
Tel (301) 662-9947 *Founded/Ownrshp* 1961
Sales 21.7MM^E *EMP* 102
SIC 5511 7538 7513 Trucks, tractors & trailers: new & used; Truck engine repair, except industrial; Truck leasing, without drivers; Trucks, tractors & trailers: new & used; Truck engine repair, except industrial; Truck leasing, without drivers
Pr: James S Grimes
**Sec:* Jim Jennelle
**VP:* Melvin Fair Jr

D-U-N-S 01-758-6178
JAMES S MCDONNELL FOUNDATION
1034 S Brentwood Blvd # 1850, Saint Louis, MO 63117-1223
Tel (314) 721-1532 *Founded/Ownrshp* 1950
Sales 20.7MM *EMP* 4
SIC 8733 Medical research; Medical research
Pr: John T Bruer
**VP:* Susan Fitzpatrick

D-U-N-S 00-765-5667
JAMES SAINT HEALTH CARE
1140 N 27th Ave Apt 8, Bozeman, MT 59718-3686
Tel (406) 723-2412 *Founded/Ownrshp* 2008
Sales 77.9MM *EMP* 2^E
Accts Ernst & Young Us Llp Clayton
SIC 8099 Health & allied services; Health & allied services
Prin: Jay Doyle

D-U-N-S 78-646-0006
JAMES SCOTT BARNES INC
BARNES PIPE & STEEL SUPPLY
737 Prairie Dupont Dr, Dupo, IL 62239-1819
Tel (618) 286-8608 *Founded/Ownrshp* 1990
Sales 24.2MM^E *EMP* 23
SIC 5051 Iron & steel (ferrous) products; Iron & steel (ferrous) products
Pr: James S Barnes
**VP:* James C Barnes
Off Mgr: Lisa Bartholic

JAMES SKINNER BAKING CO
See JAMES SKINNER CO

D-U-N-S 10-229-5540
JAMES SKINNER CO
JAMES SKINNER BAKING CO
4651 F St, Omaha, NE 68117-1403
Tel (402) 734-1672 *Founded/Ownrshp* 1983
Sales 20.0MM^E *EMP* 75^E
SIC 2053 Pastries (danish): frozen
CEO: Audie Keaton
**Pr:* James G Skinner
VP: Doug Dinnin
**VP:* Michael Knott
Genl Mgr: Hope Wicken
Sfty Mgr: Jeff Arthur
Sfty Mgr: Scott McKenzie
Plnt Mgr: George Siderewicz
Ql Cn Mgr: Mirela Krueger
Sls&Mrk Ex: Gary Kyle
Mktg Mgr: David Skinner

D-U-N-S 07-555-8833
JAMES SPRUNT COMMUNITY COLLEGE INC
(*Suby of* NORTH CAROLINA COMMUNITY COLLEGE SYSTEM) ★
Hwy 11 St, Kenansville, NC 28349
Tel (910) 296-2400 *Founded/Ownrshp* 1964
Sales 24.2MM^E *EMP* 114
SIC 8222 9411 Community college; Administration of educational programs;
Pr: Lawrence Rouse

JAMES SQ HLTH RHBILITATION CTR
See JAMES SQUARE NURSING HOME INC

D-U-N-S 07-729-6580
JAMES SQUARE NURSING HOME INC
JAMES SQ HLTH RHBILITATION CTR
918 James St, Syracuse, NY 13203-2500
Tel (315) 474-1561 *Founded/Ownrshp* 1983
Sales 45.3MM^E *EMP* 500
SIC 8051 Skilled nursing care facilities; Skilled nursing care facilities
**Ch Bd:* Edward Leffler
**CEO:* Mark Squire
**Sr VP:* Maureen Maroney

D-U-N-S 00-131-6025 IMP
JAMES THOMPSON & CO INC
381 Park Ave S Rm 718, New York, NY 10016-8806
Tel (212) 686-4242 *Founded/Ownrshp* 1860, 1959
Sales 21.7MM^E *EMP* 75
SIC 2299 Burlap, jute; Burlap, jute
Pr: Robert B Judell
Sr VP: Gail Boyle
**VP:* Marc Bieler
MIS Mgr: Sara Loffredo

JAMES TOYOTA OUTLET
See J T B AUTOMOTIVE INC

D-U-N-S 10-041-6437
JAMES VALLEY CAREER & TECHNICAL CENTER
207 2nd Ave Se, Jamestown, ND 58401-4272
Tel (701) 252-1950 *Founded/Ownrshp* 1997
Sales 12.2MM^E *EMP* 355
SIC 8211 Public elementary & secondary schools; Public elementary & secondary schools
IT Man: Lisa Hoffer
IT Man: Michelle Zuther

D-U-N-S 00-677-7189
JAMES W FLETT CO INC
800 Pleasant St, Belmont, MA 02478-1429
Tel (617) 484-8500 *Founded/Ownrshp* 1953

Sales 22.0MM *EMP* 55
Accts Deborah S Eley Cpa Pc We
SIC 1794 Excavation work; Excavation work
Pr: Frank French
**Pr:* Bruce Flett
**VP:* Mark Murphy

D-U-N-S 08-364-9525 IMP/EXP
JAMES W FOWLER CO
J W F CO
12775 Westview Dr, Dallas, OR 97338-9632
Tel (503) 623-5373 *Founded/Ownrshp* 1972
Sales 41.9MM *EMP* 120
Accts Berntson Porter & Co Pllc B
SIC 1623 1629 1711 Water, sewer & utility lines; Dams, waterways, docks & other marine construction; Mechanical contractor; Process piping contractor; Water, sewer & utility lines; Dams, waterways, docks & other marine construction; Mechanical contractor; Process piping contractor
Pr: James W Fowler
**Treas:* Candace Fowler
**VP:* John B Fowler

D-U-N-S 01-405-4571
JAMES W HALTERMAN INC
HALTERMAN AUTO RANCH
1741 Paradise Trl, East Stroudsburg, PA 18301-9190
Tel (570) 421-6930 *Founded/Ownrshp* 1966
Sales 23.9MM^E^ *EMP* 55
SIC 5511 7515 7538 Automobiles, new & used; Passenger car leasing; General automotive repair shops; Automobiles, new & used; Passenger car leasing; General automotive repair shops
Pr: James W Halterman
**VP:* Keith Halterman

D-U-N-S 05-033-2634
JAMES W SEWALL CO
136 Center St, Old Town, ME 04468-1577
Tel (207) 827-4456 *Founded/Ownrshp* 2001
Sales 26.9MM^E^ *EMP* 150
SIC 8711 0851 7335 1382

D-U-N-S 83-027-3111
JAMES W TURNER CONSTRUCTION LTD
14215 Mary Jane Ln, Tomball, TX 77377-6356
Tel (281) 290-9011 *Founded/Ownrshp* 1982
Sales 30.0MM *EMP* 25^E^
SIC 1521 1522 Single-family housing construction; Residential construction; Single-family housing construction; Repairing fire damage, single-family houses; Residential construction; Multi-family dwelling construction
CEO: James W Turner
CFO: Lauren Turner
Genl Mgr: Gene Dinelli

D-U-N-S 15-685-6551
JAMES WEST INC
13344 S Main St Ste B, Los Angeles, CA 90061-1638
Tel (310) 380-1510 *Founded/Ownrshp* 1986
Sales 295.9M *EMP* 850
SIC 2325 2339 7389 Men's & boys' trousers & slacks; Slacks: women's, misses' & juniors'; Sewing contractor; Men's & boys' trousers & slacks; Slacks: women's, misses' & juniors'; Sewing contractor
Pr: James Ahn
**VP:* Bobby Ahn
**VP:* Youn OK Ahn

JAMES WOOD AUTO PARK
See JAMES WOOD AUTOPARK INC

D-U-N-S 55-739-1497 EXP
JAMES WOOD AUTOPARK INC
JAMES WOOD AUTO PARK
3906 S Interstate 35 E, Denton, TX 76210-9321
Tel (940) 591-9663 *Founded/Ownrshp* 1991
Sales 71.8MM^E^ *EMP* 240
SIC 5511 7532 5521 Automobiles, new & used; Body shop, automotive; Automobiles, used cars only; Automobiles, new & used; Body shop, automotive; Automobiles, used cars only
Pr: James Wood
Sales Asso: Erick Knutson

D-U-N-S 05-464-1865
JAMES WOOD MOTORS INC (TX)
2111 S Highway 287, Decatur, TX 76234-2722
Tel (940) 627-2177 *Founded/Ownrshp* 1970, 1978
Sales 92.5MM^E^ *EMP* 215^E^
SIC 5511 Automobiles, new & used; Automobiles, new & used
Pr: James Wood
**CFO:* Thomas J Keenan
Treas: Tom Keenon
**VP:* Shirley Wood
Genl Mgr: Jeff Horn
Genl Mgr: Trynna Roberts
Sls Dir: Amanda Williams
Sls Mgr: Asa Johnson
Sls Mgr: Brandt Wicker
Sls Mgr: Randall Wood
Sales Asso: Joel Bell

JAMES X. MULLEN
See MULLEN ADVERTISING INC

JAMES-MARTIN BUICK
See JAMES-MARTIN CHEVROLET INC

D-U-N-S 06-418-6984
JAMES-MARTIN CHEVROLET INC
JAMES-MARTIN BUICK
6250 Woodward Ave, Detroit, MI 48202-3597
Tel (313) 875-0500 *Founded/Ownrshp* 1973
Sales 26.4MM^E^ *EMP* 70
SIC 5511 5521 Automobiles, new & used; Used car dealers; Automobiles, new & used; Used car dealers
CEO: James P Large Sr
**Pr:* Philip Large
**VP:* James Large Jr

D-U-N-S 02-398-5903
JAMESBUILT LLC (KY)
JAMES BUILT
(*Suby of* J M I) ★
390 Riverside Ln, Calvert City, KY 42029-8928
Tel (270) 898-7392 *Founded/Ownrshp* 2006
Sales 32.0MM^E^ *EMP* 68^E^
SIC 3731 Cargo vessels, building & repairing; Fishing vessels, large: building & repairing; Sailing vessels, commercial: building & repairing

JAMESHARDIE
See JAMES HARDIE BUILDING PRODUCTS INC

D-U-N-S 60-584-9520
JAMESON HEALTH SYSTEM INC
JAMESON HOSPITAL
1211 Wilmington Ave, New Castle, PA 16105-2516
Tel (724) 658-9001 *Founded/Ownrshp* 1986
Sales 1.1MM *EMP* 1,300
SIC 8062 General medical & surgical hospitals; General medical & surgical hospitals
Pr: Thomas White
Chf Rad: Albert Cook
**Ch Bd:* Chris Mitsos
**Pr:* Douglas Danko
COO: Donald Melonio
**CFO:* James Aubel
**Sec:* Steven Warner
Bd of Dir: Robert Bruce
**VP:* Neil Chessin
Dir Lab: Colette Novak
Dir Rx: Ron Shollenberger
Board of Directors: Robert N Chambers, James L Gardner II MD, Walter Higgins, Thomas O'shane, John Sant, R Kay Thompson

JAMESON HOSPITAL
See JAMESON HEALTH SYSTEM INC

JAMESON INN
See PARK MANAGEMENT GROUP LLC

D-U-N-S 36-169-8392
JAMESON INNS INC
ROBERT COMPANY MARYLAND, J. E
(*Suby of* ROBERT COMPANY OF MARYLAND, J. E. (USED IN VA. BY ROBERT COMPANY, J. E.))
41 Perimeter Ctr E # 4100, Atlanta, GA 30346-1910
Tel (770) 512-0462 *Founded/Ownrshp* 2006
Sales 22.7MM^E^ *EMP* 2,100
SIC 7011 1522 Hotels & motels; Hotel/motel, new construction; Hotels & motels; Hotel/motel, new construction
Ch Bd: Thomas W Kitchin
Pr: Craig R Kitchin
Treas: Martin D Brew
VP: Steven A Curlee
VP: William Doug Walker

D-U-N-S 07-498-4758
JAMESON MEMORIAL HOSPITAL
JHS
1211 Wilmington Ave, New Castle, PA 16105-2595
Tel (724) 658-9001 *Founded/Ownrshp* 1986
Sales 304.3MM *EMP* 1,150
SIC 8062 General medical & surgical hospitals; General medical & surgical hospitals
CEO: Douglas Danko
Dir Vol: Cyndee Adamo
**Pr:* Boud Tinko
**CFO:* James Aubel
**Sec:* Steven Warner
**VP:* Neil Chessin
Comm Dir: Chrystie Clarke
CIO: James Vito
Nrsg Dir: Barbara Bernardi
Nrsg Dir: Gina Sodersten
Pharmcst: Terri Natale

D-U-N-S 10-585-1273
JAMESON REALTY GROUP INC
425 W North Ave, Chicago, IL 60610-1186
Tel (312) 751-0300 *Founded/Ownrshp* 1982
Sales 20.8MM^E^ *EMP* 104^E^
SIC 6531 Real estate brokers & agents
Pr: Charles Huzenis
COO: Bob Flannery
Ofcr: Cheri Grossman
Sr VP: Brent Burden
Sr VP: Edward Gerstein
**VP:* Harrison Huzenis
VP: Bruce Johnson-Reid
VP: Tim Salm
VP: Nancy Tassone
Brnch Mgr: Christopher Feurer
Sales Exec: Art Collazo

JAMESTOWN BOARD PUB UTILITIES
See BOARD OF PUBLIC UTILITIES (INC)

D-U-N-S 83-582-4293
JAMESTOWN CITY SCHOOL DISTRICT
MILTON J FLTCHER ELMNTARY SCHL
197 Martin Rd, Jamestown, NY 14701-9224
Tel (716) 483-4350 *Founded/Ownrshp* 1899
Sales 36.3MM^E^ *EMP* 860
SIC 8211 Public elementary school; Public junior high school; Public senior high school; Public elementary school; Public junior high school; Public senior high school
Bd of Dir: Stephen Shulman

JAMESTOWN COLLEGE
See UNIVERSITY OF JAMESTOWN

D-U-N-S 17-590-0281
JAMESTOWN CONTAINER CLEVELAND INC
(*Suby of* JAMESTOWN CONTAINER CORP) ★
4500 Renaissance Pkwy, Cleveland, OH 44128-5702
Tel (216) 831-3700 *Founded/Ownrshp* 1961
Sales 47.0MM^E^ *EMP* 350
SIC 2653 Corrugated boxes, partitions, display items, sheets & pad; Corrugated boxes, partitions, display items, sheets & pad
Ch Bd: Glen Jenowsky
**Treas:* Bruce Janowsky
Plnt Mgr: Jim Reminder
Sales Exec: Larry Hudson

D-U-N-S 00-211-5657 EXP
JAMESTOWN CONTAINER CORP (NY)
14 Deming Dr, Falconer, NY 14733-1697
Tel (716) 665-4623 *Founded/Ownrshp* 1956
Sales 107.2MM^E^ *EMP* 445
SIC 2653 3086 Corrugated & solid fiber boxes; Packaging & shipping materials, foamed plastic; Corrugated & solid fiber boxes; Packaging & shipping materials, foamed plastic
Ch Bd: Bruce Janowsky
**Sec:* Dick Weimer
VP: Richards Emmerick
**VP:* Joseph R Palmeri
Exec: Gary Yager
Genl Mgr: Larry Hudson

D-U-N-S 04-798-3689 IMP/EXP
JAMESTOWN DISTRIBUTORS LLC
17 Peckham Dr, Bristol, RI 02809-2734
Tel (401) 253-3840 *Founded/Ownrshp* 1997
Sales 36.3MM^E^ *EMP* 55
SIC 5088 Marine supplies
Exec: Kristan McClintock
Sales Asso: John Hunt

JAMESTOWN HOSPITAL
See LUTHERAN CHARITY ASSOCIATION

D-U-N-S 78-502-4105 IMP
JAMESTOWN METAL PRODUCTS LLC
(*Suby of* CAMPBELL RHEA) ★
178 Blackstone Ave, Jamestown, NY 14701-2297
Tel (716) 665-5313 *Founded/Ownrshp* 2009
Sales 30.4MM^E^ *EMP* 105
SIC 3821 Laboratory apparatus & furniture; Laboratory equipment: fume hoods, distillation racks, etc.; Laboratory furniture; Laboratory apparatus & furniture; Laboratory equipment: fume hoods, distillation racks, etc.; Laboratory furniture
Pr: Richard McLeod
VP: Mike Cook
Manager: Warren Sieber

D-U-N-S 02-188-5405
JAMESTOWN MOTOR CORP
SIERRA MOTORS
18475 5th Ave, Jamestown, CA 95327-9378
Tel (209) 984-5272 *Founded/Ownrshp* 2001
Sales 20.9MM^E^ *EMP* 45
SIC 5511 7549 Automobiles, new & used; Automotive maintenance services
Pr: John Alexander
Store Mgr: Randy Brooksher
Sls Mgr: Todd Cangiamilla
Sales Asso: Nathan Curran
Sales Asso: Mike Enzi
Sales Asso: Dave Maine

D-U-N-S 83-268-4927
JAMESTOWN PROPERTIES CORP
675 Ponce De Leon Avene, Atlanta, GA 30308
Tel (770) 805-1000 *Founded/Ownrshp* 1999
Sales 45.0MM^E^ *EMP* 140
SIC 8741 Management services
CEO: Matt M Bronfman
**CFO:* D Lee Wright
Sr VP: Alex Chambers
Sr VP: Jim Irwin
Sr VP: Lori Lathem
Sr VP: Heather Stewart
VP: Daniel Cooley
VP: Lorrie Coulson
VP: Annie Evans
VP: Eric Hines
VP: Scott Landsittel
VP: Molly Mackenzie
VP: Chris Martin

D-U-N-S 07-917-0420
JAMESTOWN PUBLIC SCHOOL DISTRICT 1
JAMESTOWN PUBLIC SCHOOLS
207 2nd Ave Se, Jamestown, ND 58401-4272
Tel (701) 252-1950 *Founded/Ownrshp* 1954
Sales 15.0MM^E^ *EMP* 340^E^
SIC 8211 Elementary & secondary schools

JAMESTOWN PUBLIC SCHOOLS
See JAMESTOWN PUBLIC SCHOOL DISTRICT 1

D-U-N-S 05-508-5864
JAMESVILLE-DEWITT CENTRAL SCHOOL DIST (INC)
6845 Edinger Dr, Fayetteville, NY 13066-1768
Tel (315) 445-8300 *Founded/Ownrshp* 1953
Sales 19.1MM^E^ *EMP* 450
SIC 8211 Public combined elementary & secondary school; Public combined elementary & secondary school

D-U-N-S 07-072-6457
JAMEX LLC
2009 Chenault Dr Ste 100, Carrollton, TX 75006-5084
Tel (214) 722-6960 *Founded/Ownrshp* 2013
Sales 40.6MM^E^ *EMP* 70
SIC 4213 7389 4214 Liquid petroleum transport, non-local; Pipeline & power line inspection service; Local trucking with storage
Pr: Julio E Rios II
**COO:* Jeremy H Gamboa
**CFO:* Patrick Kelly
Treas: Dan Giannini
**Ofcr:* James H Ballengee
**Ex VP:* Troy S Lee
Sr VP: Ken Brandes
Sr VP: Randy L Morgan

D-U-N-S 03-270-8463
JAMIES MOTORSPORTS INC
JIM'S HARLEY-DAVIDSON
2805 54th Ave N, Saint Petersburg, FL 33714-2414
Tel (727) 527-9672 *Founded/Ownrshp* 1979
Sales 20.2MM^E^ *EMP* 59
SIC 5571 7699 5699 Motorcycle dealers; Motorcycles; Motorcycle repair service; Customized clothing & apparel

Pr: Jamilou Rosenkrans
Sales Exec: Adam Beattie

JAMIESON FENCE SUPPLY
See JAMIESON MANUFACTURING CO

D-U-N-S 00-734-5259 IMP
JAMIESON MANUFACTURING CO
JAMIESON FENCE SUPPLY
4221 Platinum Way, Dallas, TX 75237-1617
Tel (214) 339-8384 *Founded/Ownrshp* 1965
Sales 87.0MM^E^ *EMP* 124
SIC 5039 2499 Wire fence, gates & accessories; Fencing, docks & other outdoor wood structural products; Wire fence, gates & accessories; Fencing, docks & other outdoor wood structural products
CEO: B J Wallace
**Pr:* Richard Calhoun
**Ex VP:* Len Hoersten
Rgnl Mgr: Justin McMichael
Brnch Mgr: Joel Schumacher
VP Opers: Mike Weaver
Natl Sales: Bill Scudder
Sls Mgr: Edwin Waller
Sales Asso: Jesus Arzate
Sales Asso: Bobbie Duncan

JAMIESON RANCH VINEYARDS
See MADISON VINEYARD HOLDINGS LLC

D-U-N-S 18-951-4284
JAMIESON-HILL A GENERAL PARTNERSHIP
J HILL OIL
3101 State Rd, Bakersfield, CA 93308-4931
Tel (661) 393-7000 *Founded/Ownrshp* 1978
Sales 214.2MM *EMP* 50
Accts Moss Adams Llp Los Angeles C
SIC 5541 6798 Filling stations, gasoline; Real estate investment trusts; Filling stations, gasoline; Real estate investment trusts
Pt: W J Hill
**Pt:* Roy Sanders

D-U-N-S 06-470-9579 IMP
JAMIL PACKAGING CORP
1420 Industrial Dr, Mishawaka, IN 46544-5720
Tel (574) 256-2600 *Founded/Ownrshp* 1994
Sales 25.5MM^E^ *EMP* 106
SIC 2653 5199 Boxes, corrugated: made from purchased materials; Pallets, corrugated: made from purchased materials; Packaging materials; Boxes, corrugated: made from purchased materials; Pallets, corrugated: made from purchased materials; Packaging materials
Pr: David A Diroll
**Sec:* Mary E Diroll
Genl Mgr: Ken Bowers

D-U-N-S 00-404-0879 IMP/EXP
JAMISON BEDDING INC (TN)
381 Mallory Station Rd # 200, Franklin, TN 37067-8264
Tel (615) 794-1883 *Founded/Ownrshp* 1936
Sales 21.5MM^E^ *EMP* 125^E^
SIC 5712 2515 Furniture stores; Mattresses & foundations; Furniture stores; Mattresses & foundations
Pr: Frank C Gorrell III
**COO:* Richard D Maclean

D-U-N-S 00-306-0506 EXP
JAMISON DOOR CO (MD)
55 J V Jamison, Hagerstown, MD 21740
Tel (301) 733-3100 *Founded/Ownrshp* 1906
Sales 27.9MM^E^ *EMP* 133
SIC 3442 Metal doors; Metal doors
Ch Bd: John T Williams
CFO: Grogory R Lloyd
Treas: Richard A Jamison Jr
V Ch Bd: Matthew Wyskieo
Bd of Dir: Chester Hart
VP Sls: Dwight Clark

D-U-N-S 13-098-8223
JAMS INC
1920 Main St Ste 300, Irvine, CA 92614-7279
Tel (949) 224-1810 *Founded/Ownrshp* 1979
Sales 57.8MM^E^ *EMP* 240
SIC 7389 Arbitration & conciliation service; Arbitration & conciliation service
Pr: Chris Poole
Sr Pt: Hughes Hubbard
CFO: Kevin McDonnell
**CFO:* Julie Sager
Ofcr: Raymond Zvetina
VP: Charles G Bakaly
VP: Debbie Masucci
VP: Mark Smalls
VP: Jamie Tran
VP: Maria Walsh
Counsel: Michael Lewis

JAN
See JAPANESE ASSISTANCE NETWORK INC

D-U-N-S 87-927-4736
JAN MARINI SKIN RESEARCH INC
5883 Rue Ferrari, San Jose, CA 95138-1857
Tel (408) 294-4966 *Founded/Ownrshp* 1994
Sales 58.6MM^E^ *EMP* 80
SIC 5122 Drugs, proprietaries & sundries
CEO: Jan Marini
**CFO:* Robert James
**Ex VP:* John Connors
Mktg Mgr: Maile Chock
Manager: Jerry Ginsel
Sls Mgr: Kirby Lantz
Sls Mgr: Mary Poinsignon

D-U-N-S 79-868-8644
JAN SERVICES CORP
GOURMET GARAGE
52 Greene St Fl 3, New York, NY 10013-3096
Tel (212) 965-8144 *Founded/Ownrshp* 1992
Sales 37.0MM^E^ *EMP* 200
SIC 5499 Gourmet food stores; Gourmet food stores
Pr: Andrew Aarons
**VP:* Adam Hartman
Genl Mgr: Angelo Puleo

JAN-CARE AMBLANCE RALEIGH CNTY
See JAN-CARE AMBULANCE OF RALEIGH COUNTY INC

D-U-N-S 07-680-8724
JAN-CARE AMBULANCE OF MCDOWELL COUNTY
117 S Fayette St, Beckley, WV 25801-4606
Tel (304) 255-2931 Founded/Ownrshp 1972
Sales 27.4MM^E EMP 300^E
Accts Richmond Smith & Co Cpa A
SIC 4119 Local passenger transportation; Local passenger transportation
Pr: Richard Cornett II
*CEO: Todd Cornett
*CFO: Debbie Gray
Dir Risk M: Lisa Dennler
IT Man: Dave Richmond
Snr Mgr: Jerry Long

D-U-N-S 14-494-2849
JAN-CARE AMBULANCE OF NORTH CENTRAL WVA INC
8396 Water St, Clarksburg, WV 26301-8005
Tel (304) 624-3719 Founded/Ownrshp 1970
Sales 17.2MM^E EMP 300
SIC 5012 Ambulances; Ambulances
Pr: Richard Cornett II

D-U-N-S 15-529-4536
JAN-CARE AMBULANCE OF RALEIGH COUNTY INC
JAN-CARE AMBLANCE RALEIGH CNTY
1455 4th Ave Apt 1, Huntington, WV 25701-2494
Tel (304) 255-2931 Founded/Ownrshp 1987
Sales 3.2MM^E EMP 300
SIC 4119 Local passenger transportation; Local passenger transportation
CEO: Richard L Cornett

JANAERO
See HARTZELL ENGINE TECHNOLOGIES LLC

JANA'S MINISTRY
See EXXON MOBIL FUELS MARKETING CO

D-U-N-S 96-832-7556
JANCO ENGINEERED PRODUCTS LLC
920 S Logan St, Mishawaka, IN 46544-4828
Tel (574) 255-3169 Founded/Ownrshp 2011
Sales 39.3MM^E EMP 140
SIC 3613 Switchgear & switchboard apparatus; Switchgear & switchboard apparatus
Pr: Peter Giczewski
Treas: Eugene Pucuk
Ex Dir: Becky Harvey
CTO: Joanna Krim

D-U-N-S 83-242-2914 IMP
JANCO FOODS INC
1216 Silber Rd, Houston, TX 77055-7128
Tel (713) 237-8200 Founded/Ownrshp 2007
Sales 23.2MM^E EMP 20
SIC 5141 Food brokers
Pr: Peter Mousoudakis
*VP: James Mousoudakis

D-U-N-S 04-566-6548
JAND INC
WARBY PARKER
161 Avenue Of The, New York, NY 10013
Tel (646) 517-5223 Founded/Ownrshp 2009
Sales 38.6MM^E EMP 56
SIC 5961 5995 Catalog & mail-order houses; Eyeglasses, prescription
Pr: Blumenthal Neil
*CFO: Steve Miller
Sftwr Eng: Ryan Tuck
Pr Dir: Kaki Read
Sls Mgr: Shayna Amato
Sls Mgr: Torie Floyd
Sls Mgr: Sam Marks
Snr Mgr: Neil Blumenthal
Snr Mgr: Dave Gilboa
Snr Mgr: Erick Ruiz

JANDY POOL PRODUCTS
See ZODIAC POOL SYSTEMS INC

D-U-N-S 06-154-8228
JANE GRIPP HOLDING INC
(Suby of ALISAM HOLDINGS LLC) ★
6699 S Fm 1541, Amarillo, TX 79118-6138
Tel (806) 372-9290 Founded/Ownrshp 2011
Sales 37.4MM^E EMP 232
SIC 4213 4231 4212 Trucking, except local; Trucking terminal facilities; Local trucking, without storage; Trucking, except local; Trucking terminal facilities; Local trucking, without storage
Pr: Dorothy Jane Gripp
Sfty Mgr: Lori Epps

JANE IREDALE
See IREDALE MINERAL COSMETICS LTD

D-U-N-S 06-497-9992
JANE PHILLIPS MEDICAL CENTER
3450 E Frank Phllips Blvd, Bartlesville, OK 74006-2406
Tel (918) 338-3730 Founded/Ownrshp 2014
Sales 109.7MM EMP 5^E
SIC 8011 Medical centers

D-U-N-S 12-433-4967
JANE PHILLIPS MEMORIAL MEDICAL CENTER INC
3500 E Frank Phllips Blvd, Bartlesville, OK 74006-2411
Tel (918) 333-7200 Founded/Ownrshp 1952
Sales 117.0MM EMP 900
Accts Tax Llp Bartlesville Ok
SIC 8062 General medical & surgical hospitals; General medical & surgical hospitals
Pr: David Stire
*CFO: Mike Moore
Ofcr: Jennifer Dildine
VP: Sam Guild
*VP: Susan Herron
VP: Sue Parnell
*VP: Scott C Phillips
VP: Scott Smith
Dir Inf Cn: Valerie Vieux
Dir Lab: Dale Kenney
Dir Rad: Jen Wong
Dir Rx: Erin Claiborne
Dir Bus: Brian Lawrence

D-U-N-S 00-570-4601
JANE STREET CAPITAL LLC
1 New York Plz, New York, NY 10004-1901
Tel (212) 651-6070 Founded/Ownrshp 2000
Sales 35.8MM^E EMP 80
SIC 6211 Investment firm, general brokerage
Bd of Dir: Jim Dieterich
Mng Dir: David Proctor
Mng Dir: Orly Sharma
Dir IT: Michael Paluskiewicz
Software D: Isaiah Damron
Software D: Jakob Uecker
Sftwr Eng: Tariq Ansari
Sftwr Eng: Dimas Mero
VP Mktg: Pawan Deedwaniya
VP Sls: R Niu

D-U-N-S 07-923-0585
JANE STREET GROUP LLC
JSG
1 New York Plz Fl 33, New York, NY 10004-1944
Tel (212) 651-6070 Founded/Ownrshp 2013
Sales 19.6MM^E EMP 300^E
SIC 1799 Athletic & recreation facilities construction; Athletic & recreation facilities construction

D-U-N-S 02-040-6740
■ **JANEL GROUP OF NEW YORK INC**
(Suby of JANEL WORLD TRADE LTD) ★
303 Merrick Rd Ste 400, Lynbrook, NY 11563-2521
Tel (516) 593-1390 Founded/Ownrshp 1980
Sales 32.0MM^E EMP 41
SIC 4731 Foreign freight forwarding; Domestic freight forwarding; Customhouse brokers; Foreign freight forwarding; Domestic freight forwarding; Customhouse brokers
CEO: James N Jannelo
*Pr: Stephen P Cesarski

D-U-N-S 04-619-4080
▲ **JANEL WORLD TRADE LTD**
15014 132nd Ave, Jamaica, NY 11434-3500
Tel (718) 527-3800 Founded/Ownrshp 1975
Sales 47.9MM EMP 52
Accts Paritz & Company Pa Hackens
Tkr Sym JLWT Exch OTO
SIC 4731 Freight transportation arrangement; Freight forwarding; Customhouse brokers; Freight transportation arrangement; Freight forwarding; Customhouse brokers
Pr: William J Lally
*COO: Vincent Iacopella
CFO: Brian Aronson
CFO: Philip J Dubato
*VP: Noel J Jannello
Board of Directors: Dominique Schulte, Gerard Van Kesteren

D-U-N-S 07-426-5794
JANEPHILLIPS HEALTH CROP
(Suby of ST JOHN HEALTH SYSTEM INC) ★
1923 S Utica Ave, Tulsa, OK 74104-6520
Tel (918) 273-3102 Founded/Ownrshp 1950
Sales 112.4MM EMP 1,050
SIC 8062 General medical & surgical hospitals; General medical & surgical hospitals
CEO: David Stire

D-U-N-S 01-955-1531
JANESVILLE ACOUSTICS
MICHIGAN SEAT COMPANY
29200 Northwestern Hwy # 400, Southfield, MI 48034-1068
Tel (248) 948-1811 Founded/Ownrshp 2014
Sales NA EMP 867
SIC 3714 Motor vehicle parts & accessories

JANESVILLE GAZETTE
See BLISS COMMUNICATIONS INC

D-U-N-S 10-008-3070
JANESVILLE SCHOOL DISTRICT
527 S Franklin St, Janesville, WI 53548-4779
Tel (608) 743-5000 Founded/Ownrshp 1856
Sales 85.0MM^E EMP 1,395
SIC 8211 Public combined elementary & secondary school; Public combined elementary & secondary school
CFO: Keith Pennington
Bd of Dir: Bill Sodemann
CIO: Bently Turner
MIS Dir: Brandon Keirns
Dir IT: Steve Scholmann
Pr Dir: Bret Berg
Schl Brd P: Greg Ardrey
HC Dir: Christine Wesling
Snr Mgr: Sean Gremminger

D-U-N-S 00-758-4329
JANET L MCNECE
PRODUCTIVE STAFFING
502 Poplar St, Poplar Bluff, MO 63901-7309
Tel (573) 785-4114 Founded/Ownrshp 1996
Sales 18.5MM^E EMP 400
SIC 7361 Employment agencies; Employment agencies
Owner: Janet McNece

JANI-KING
See ENMON ENTERPRISES INC

D-U-N-S 13-102-6239
JANI-KING INC
(Suby of JANI-KING INTERNATIONAL INC) ★
16885 Dallas Pkwy, Addison, TX 75001-5202
Tel (972) 991-0900 Founded/Ownrshp 1983
Sales 40.2MM^E EMP 500
SIC 7349 8721 6794 Janitorial service, contract basis; Billing & bookkeeping service; Franchises, selling or licensing; Janitorial service, contract basis; Billing & bookkeeping service; Franchises, selling or licensing
Pr: Jerry Crawford
CFO: Steve Hawkins
*Ch: James A Cavanaugh Jr
*VP: Donald A Burleson
CTO: Zack Dunnam
Opers Mgr: William Archer
Opers Mgr: Efren Caraveo
Opers Mgr: Franasiak Chester
Opers Mgr: Chris Fernandez
Opers Mgr: Thomas Jenkinson
Opers Mgr: David Kukucka

D-U-N-S 14-712-1024
JANI-KING INTERNATIONAL INC
16885 Dallas Pkwy, Addison, TX 75001-5202
Tel (972) 991-0900 Founded/Ownrshp 1969
Sales 160.5MM EMP 550^E
SIC 7349 Janitorial service, contract basis; Janitorial service, contract basis
Ch: James A Cavanaugh Jr
*Pr: Jerry Crawford
*CFO: Steve Hawkins
*VP: Jill Bean

D-U-N-S 84-744-4445 IMP
JANICKI INDUSTRIES INC
1476 Moore St, Sedro Woolley, WA 98284-7522
Tel (360) 856-5143 Founded/Ownrshp 1994
Sales 88.3MM^E EMP 630^E
SIC 3728

D-U-N-S 60-296-2102
JANITECH INC
60 Pine St Ste D, Methuen, MA 01844-6832
Tel (978) 687-4113 Founded/Ownrshp 1989
Sales 11.7MM^E EMP 325
SIC 7349 Building maintenance services; Building maintenance services
Pr: George J Burke Jr

D-U-N-S 06-408-3827
JANITORIAL SERVICES INC
8555 Sweet Valley Dr H, Cleveland, OH 44125-4210
Tel (216) 341-8601 Founded/Ownrshp 1969
Sales 13.4MM^E EMP 325
SIC 7349 Janitorial service, contract basis; Janitorial service, contract basis
Pr: Ronald J Martinez Sr
*VP: Ronald J Martinez Jr

D-U-N-S 01-408-5336
JANITORS SUPPLY CO INC
540 E 2nd St, Erie, PA 16507-1702
Tel (800) 262-2551 Founded/Ownrshp 1951
Sales 42.0MM^E EMP 71
SIC 5087 Janitors' supplies
Pr: Ed Mascharka III
*VP: Edward P Mascharka Jr
*VP: Thomas E Mascharka
IT Man: Marygrace Cirillo
IT Man: Terry Sova
Sls Mgr: Tim Fitzpatrick

D-U-N-S 01-631-0666
JANITORS SUPPLY CO INC
5005 Speedway Dr, Fort Wayne, IN 46825-5244
Tel (260) 482-8615 Founded/Ownrshp 1956
Sales 21.2MM^E EMP 50
SIC 5087 Janitors' supplies
Pr: Kenneth D Gast
*Sec: Bret Krontz
*VP: James B Gast

D-U-N-S 07-995-0721
JANITRONICS INC (NY)
1988 Central Ave, Albany, NY 12205-4595
Tel (518) 456-8484 Founded/Ownrshp 1972
Sales 30.0MM^E EMP 515
SIC 7349 6794 1521 7217 Building cleaning service; Maid services, contract or fee basis; Window cleaning; Franchises, selling or licensing; Single-family housing construction; Repairing fire damage, single-family houses; Carpet & upholstery cleaning; Building cleaning service; Maid services, contract or fee basis; Window cleaning; Franchises, selling or licensing; Single-family housing construction; Repairing fire damage, single-family houses; Carpet & upholstery cleaning
Ch Bd: James Harris Sr
CFO: George Mahoney
*VP: James Harris Jr
Rgnl Mgr: Patrick Fragomeni
Area Mgr: Mark Nocera
Area Supr: Mike Polino
Site Mgr: Louis Cancilleri
Opers Mgr: Brian Keene

D-U-N-S 10-115-5968
JANITRONICS INC
29 Sawyer Rd Ste 11, Waltham, MA 02453-3400
Tel (781) 647-5570 Founded/Ownrshp 1977
Sales 37.9MM^E EMP 1,187
SIC 7349 Cleaning service, industrial or commercial; Cleaning service, industrial or commercial
Pr: Donald Brecher
*VP: Michael A Halliday
Area Mgr: Luis Franjul
Area Mgr: Richardo Gonzalez

D-U-N-S 00-941-3477
JANJER ENTERPRISES INC
12150 Tech Rd, Silver Spring, MD 20904-1914
Tel (301) 625-5920 Founded/Ownrshp 1981
Sales 52.0MM^E EMP 1,400
SIC 5812 8721 8741 Fast-food restaurant, chain; Accounting, auditing & bookkeeping; Restaurant management; Fast-food restaurant, chain; Accounting, auditing & bookkeeping; Restaurant management
Pr: Jerome Friedlander
*VP: Jan Strompf
Area Mgr: Kenneth Wong

D-U-N-S 82-889-8465 IMP/EXP
JANKEL TACTICAL SYSTEMS LLC
190 Parkway W Ste 100, Duncan, SC 29334-8884
Tel (864) 721-2980 Founded/Ownrshp 2013
Sales 40.2MM^E EMP 89
SIC 3795 Tanks & tank components
Ch Bd: Andrew Jankel
*CEO: Todd Littleton
CFO: James Holloway
Prgrm Mgr: Matt Gleason
Prgrm Mgr: Justin Kingsland
Off Mgr: Cyndi Bailey
IT Man: Patrick Malyszek
Ql Cn Mgr: Teresa Dupuis

D-U-N-S 02-186-2354 IMP
JANKOVICH CO
SAN PEDRO MARINE
14066 Garfield Ave, Paramount, CA 90723-2138
Tel (562) 633-0040 Founded/Ownrshp 1983
Sales 25.0MM^E EMP 82
SIC 5984 5171 2911 5172 Petroleum bulk stations & terminals; Liquefied petroleum gas dealers; Liquefied petroleum gas dealers; Petroleum bulk stations & terminals; Diesel fuels; Diesel fuel
CEO: Thomas J Jankovich
*Sec: Maryann Jankovich
Sls Mgr: Charlie Martinet
Sls Mgr: Denver Miller

JANNELL FORD
See JANNELL MOTORS INC

D-U-N-S 01-963-0540
JANNELL MOTORS INC
JANNELL FORD
2000 Washington St, Hanover, MA 02339-1617
Tel (781) 982-4500 Founded/Ownrshp 1921
Sales 26.5MM^E EMP 55^E
SIC 5511 7532 Automobiles, new & used; Pickups, new & used; Top & body repair & paint shops; Automobiles, new & used; Pickups, new & used; Top & body repair & paint shops
Pr: James H Clapp
*COO: Joseph Clapp
Off Mgr: Katie Deacetis
Mktg Mgr: John Hanson
Sls Mgr: Sean Ternullo
Sales Asso: Vito Umbro
Sales Asso: Charlie Williams

D-U-N-S 05-330-3897
JANNEY MONTGOMERY SCOTT LLC
PARKER HUNTER
(Suby of PENN MUTUAL LIFE INSURANCE CO) ★
1717 Arch St Fl 16, Philadelphia, PA 19103-2772
Tel (215) 665-6000 Founded/Ownrshp 1982
Sales 521.1MM^E EMP 1,200
Accts Pricewaterhousecoopers Llp Ph
SIC 6211 Investment firm, general brokerage; Brokers, security; Investment firm, general brokerage
Ch Bd: Rudolph Sander
*Ch Bd: Norman T Wilde Jr
*Pr: James Wolitarsky
COO: William Hartman
COO: Michael Musson
COO: Stacey Polito
*V Ch Bd: Charles B Cook Jr
Ex Ofcr: Vincent Damasco
Ex Ofcr: Alexander Zorovic
Ex VP: David E Grice
*Ex VP: William Jones
Ex VP: John Kline
Ex VP: Lance McCoy
*Ex VP: Anthony Miller
Ex VP: Kimberly Nickerson
Ex VP: Randall Renneisen
Ex VP: Doug Walters
Ex VP: Christina Wright
*Sr VP: Randall A Carbone
*Sr VP: Gregory B McShea
Sr VP: Kevin Reed

D-U-N-S 15-093-3612
JANNX MEDICAL SYSTEMS INC
30745 Solon Rd Ste 6, Saint Louis, MO 63122
Tel (440) 349-4710 Founded/Ownrshp 1991
Sales 31.1MM EMP 125
SIC 8742 Business consultant; Business consultant
Ch Bd: Robert Forino
*Pr: Rick Devlin
CFO: Mark Speth

D-U-N-S 05-629-2311 IMP/EXP
JANOME AMERICA INC
(Suby of JANOME SEWING MACHINE CO., LTD.)
10 Industrial Ave Ste 2, Mahwah, NJ 07430-3522
Tel (201) 825-3200 Founded/Ownrshp 1922
Sales 22.4MM^E EMP 70
SIC 5064 5949

JANOTTA & HERNER
See 309 MONROE INC

D-U-N-S 01-207-8622 IMP
■ **JANOVIC-PLAZA INC**
(Suby of BENJAMIN MOORE & CO) ★
3035 Thomson Ave, Long Island City, NY 11101-3072
Tel (718) 392-3999 Founded/Ownrshp 1957
Sales 408.2MM^E EMP 270
SIC 5198 5231 5023 5719 Paints; Paint brushes, rollers, sprayers; Wallcoverings; Paint; Paint brushes, rollers, sprayers & other supplies; Wallpaper; Window furnishings; Window furnishings; Paints; Paint brushes, rollers, sprayers; Wallcoverings; Paint; Paint brushes, rollers, sprayers & other supplies; Wallpaper; Window furnishings; Window furnishings
Pr: Paul Renn
VP: Eugene Ollivierre
*Prin: Don Brady
Dist Mgr: John Cholowsky

D-U-N-S 01-601-3500
JANPAK INC
PAPER SUPPLY COMPANY
705 Griffith St Ste 300, Davidson, NC 28036-9308
Tel (704) 892-0219 Founded/Ownrshp 2012
Sales NA EMP 425
SIC 5113 5049 5087 Bags, paper & disposable plastic; Boxes, paperboard & disposable plastic; Paperboard & products; School supplies; Janitors' supplies

D-U-N-S 09-932-2919
JANS LTD
JAN'S MOUNTAIN OUTFITTERS
1600 Park Ave, Park City, UT 84060-5146
Tel (435) 649-1020 *Founded/Ownrshp* 1980
Sales 24.3MM^E *EMP* 200
SIC 5941

JAN'S MOUNTAIN OUTFITTERS
See JANS LTD

D-U-N-S 07-478-3689 IMP
■ JANSPORT INC
(*Suby of* VF CORP) ★
N850 County Road Cb, Appleton, WI 54914-8277
Tel (920) 734-5708 *Founded/Ownrshp* 1967
Sales 115.1MM^E *EMP* 550
SIC 3949 3161 2339 2329 2321 Camping equipment & supplies; Traveling bags; Women's & misses' athletic clothing & sportswear; Men's & boys' sportswear & athletic clothing; Men's & boys' furnishings; Camping equipment & supplies; Traveling bags; Women's & misses' athletic clothing & sportswear; Men's & boys' sportswear & athletic clothing; Men's & boys' furnishings
Pr: Michael Cisler
CFO: Harvey Erickson
VP: Karin Apitz
VP: Richard Hayes
VP: Bill Howard
VP: Jim Koehne
VP: Bill Kramer
VP: Dan Small
VP: Paul Whitener
IT Man: Margaret Fisher
MIS Mgr: Margaret Fietzer
Board of Directors: Mackey McDonald

D-U-N-S 09-909-1753 IMP
■ JANSSEN BIOTECH INC
(*Suby of* JOHNSON & JOHNSON) ★
800 Ridgeview Dr, Horsham, PA 19044-3607
Tel (610) 651-6000 *Founded/Ownrshp* 1999
Sales 825.8MM^E *EMP* 3,000
SIC 2834 2835 Pharmaceutical preparations; Drugs affecting parasitic & infective diseases; Drugs acting on the cardiovascular system, except diagnostic; In vitro diagnostics; Pharmaceutical preparations; Drugs affecting parasitic & infective diseases; Drugs acting on the cardiovascular system, except diagnostic; In vitro diagnostics
Pr: Robert B Bazemore
**Treas:* Jay Fischbein
Chf Mktg O: Samit Shah
Sr VP: Jerome Boscia
VP: Elizabeth Anderson
VP: Wanda Hope
VP: Mark Kreston
**VP:* Bruce Peacock
VP: George Treacy
Assoc Dir: Ibi Fryer
Assoc Dir: Jennifer Lofland

D-U-N-S 55-559-8775
■ JANSSEN DIAGNOSTICS LLC
(*Suby of* JOHNSON & JOHNSON) ★
700 Route 202, Raritan, NJ 08869-1422
Tel (877) 837-4339 *Founded/Ownrshp* 2004
Sales 21.5MM^E *EMP* 100
SIC 8748 Business consulting
VP: Chris Picariello
Sls Mgr: Taryn Depaul

D-U-N-S 06-313-7772 IMP
■ JANSSEN PHARMACEUTICALS INC
(*Suby of* AGILYSYS INC) ★
1125 Trnton Harbourton Rd, Titusville, NJ 08560-1499
Tel (609) 730-2000 *Founded/Ownrshp* 1978
Sales 135.3MM^E *EMP* 1,600
SIC 2833 2834 Anesthetics, in bulk form; Antihistamine preparations; Astringents, medicinal; Anesthetics, in bulk form; Antihistamine preparations; Astringents, medicinal
CEO: William C Weldon
**Pr:* Janet Vergis
**CFO:* Joseph Bondi
CFO: Richard Gatens
**VP:* Steve Bariahtaris
VP: Jim Barr
VP: John Buckingham
VP: Ed Hill
VP: Randall L Morrison
VP: Jose Sotoca
VP: Guy Vercauteren
Exec: Gwenn Brown
Dir Surg: Vic Sipido
Dir Surg: Jim Witt
Assoc Dir: Ibrahim Turkoz
Comm Man: Alex Butler

D-U-N-S 11-923-7597
■ JANSSEN RESEARCH & DEVELOPMENT LLC
(*Suby of* JOHNSON & JOHNSON) ★
920 Route 202, Raritan, NJ 08869-1420
Tel (908) 927-5440 *Founded/Ownrshp* 2000
Sales 442.2MM^E *EMP* 2,513
SIC 2834 8731 Pharmaceutical preparations; Commercial physical research; Pharmaceutical preparations; Commercial physical research
Ch: P A Paterson MD
Ofcr: Paul Stoffels
**VP:* Nicholas C Dracopoli
**VP:* Yusri A Elsayed
**VP:* Joseph Erhardt
VP: Kenneth Leahy
VP: Thomas Manion
Dir Surg: Albert Leung
Assoc Dir: James Buckley
Assoc Dir: Andrew Carmen
Assoc Dir: Lisa Cloutier
Assoc Dir: Wanda Davis
Assoc Dir: Brian Deore
Assoc Dir: Patricia Driver
Assoc Dir: Karen Foster
Assoc Dir: Hui Kimko
Assoc Dir: Anna Klimko
Assoc Dir: Mary Mulligan
Assoc Dir: Ravi Notani
Assoc Dir: Linda Shea

D-U-N-S 96-281-1266
JANSY PACKAGING LLC
2200 Fletcher Ave Ste 514, Fort Lee, NJ 07024-5016
Tel (844) 465-2679 *Founded/Ownrshp* 2010
Sales 23.7MM^E *EMP* 40
SIC 5199 Advertising specialties
CEO: Brad Zaikov
**CFO:* Thomas Calibeo

D-U-N-S 08-954-6691
JANTRAN INC
(*Suby of* BRUCE OAKLEY INC) ★
507 Terminal Rd, Rosedale, MS 38769
Tel (662) 759-6841 *Founded/Ownrshp* 2011
Sales 32.3MM^E *EMP* 255
SIC 4492 Marine towing services; Marine construction; Marine towing services
Pr: Joe W Janoush
**Sec:* Paul Janoush
**VP:* John Janoush

D-U-N-S 60-982-4305
JANTREX BUILDING SERVICES INC
1830 Sw W 2nd St, Pompano Beach, FL 33069
Tel (305) 375-6001 *Founded/Ownrshp* 1988
Sales 2.0MM *EMP* 400
SIC 7349 Janitorial service, contract basis; Janitorial service, contract basis
Mng Pt: Dan Calello
**Pr:* Nicholas J Calello
Treas: Zoila Calello
**VP:* Dan Callello

D-U-N-S 00-181-1251
JANUARY ENVIRONMENTAL SERVICES INC (OK)
2701 S I 35 Service Rd, Oklahoma City, OK 73129-6451
Tel (405) 670-2030 *Founded/Ownrshp* 1994
Sales 38.0MM^E *EMP* 70
SIC 4953 Non-hazardous waste disposal sites
Pr: Cris January
**Sec:* Lorn January
**VP:* Cris January Jr
Off Mgr: Stacy Brimer

D-U-N-S 07-996-1124
■ JANUS CAPITAL CORP
(*Suby of* JANUS CAPITAL GROUP INC) ★
151 Detroit St, Denver, CO 80206-4928
Tel (303) 333-3863 *Founded/Ownrshp* 2000
Sales 338.8MM^E *EMP* 1,113^E
SIC 6282 Manager of mutual funds, contract or fee basis; Investment counselors; Manager of mutual funds, contract or fee basis; Investment counselors
Pr: Gerry Black
Treas: Scott S Grace
**Ex VP:* Darrell Watters
Sr VP: Stephanie Pierce
VP: Gwen E Royl
CIO: Jeff Kautz
Opers Mgr: Corie Carlson
Mktg Dir: Kim Blankenburg

D-U-N-S 02-449-6726
▲ JANUS CAPITAL GROUP INC
151 Detroit St, Denver, CO 80206-4928
Tel (303) 691-3905 *Founded/Ownrshp* 1969
Sales 953.2MM *EMP* 1,209^E
Accts Deloitte & Touche Llp Denver
Tkr Sym JNS *Exch* NYS
SIC 6282 8741 Investment advice; Investment advisory service; Manager of mutual funds, contract or fee basis; Business management; Investment advice; Investment advisory service; Manager of mutual funds, contract or fee basis; Business management
CEO: Richard M Weil
Pr: Bruce L Koepfgen
Pr: Laura Najarian
COO: Gigi Chan
CFO: David R Martin
CFO: Jennifer J McPeek
Treas: Stephen H Belgrad
Bd of Dir: Billie Williamson
Ex VP: Kathy Artaserse
Ex VP: George S Batejan
Ex VP: C M Girard
Ex VP: George Maris
Ex VP: Dominic Martellaro
Sr VP: Andrew B Weisman
VP: Heidi W Hardin
VP: Scott Jones
VP: Mark McGannon
VP: Ron Pratt
Assoc Dir: Tom Vonweise
Assoc Dir: Kevin Worack
Board of Directors: Timothy K Armour, G Andrew Cox, Jeffrey J Diermeier, Eugene Flood Jr, J Richard Fredericks, Deborah R Gatzek, Lawrence E Kochard, Glenn S Schafer, Billie I Williamson

JANUS CAPITAL MANAGEMENT
See JANUS SERVICE CORP

D-U-N-S 60-553-6077
JANUS CORP
1081 Shary Cir, Concord, CA 94518-2407
Tel (925) 969-9200 *Founded/Ownrshp* 1989
Sales 43.0MM^E *EMP* 200
SIC 1799 Decontamination services; Decontamination services
CEO: Mike Ely
**Pr:* Sean Tavernier
VP: Tom Kirkland
**VP:* Craig M Uhle
Opers Mgr: Sandra Kopec
S&M/VP: Paul Chelstowski
Sls Mgr: John Denton

D-U-N-S 08-904-7617 IMP/EXP
JANUS ET CIE
12310 Greenstone Ave, Santa Fe Springs, CA 90670-4737
Tel (310) 601-2958 *Founded/Ownrshp* 1977
Sales 54.8MM^E *EMP* 120
SIC 5021 Outdoor & lawn furniture; Household furniture; Outdoor & lawn furniture; Household furniture; Furniture stores
CEO: Janice K Feldman
COO: Bradley Bransen
**COO:* Paul Warren
**CFO:* Greg Buscher
VP: Robin Love
Genl Mgr: Brian Schwartz
VP Mktg: Alexis Contant
VP Sls: Terry Clayton
Sls Mgr: Jennifer Janian
Sales Asso: Odalys Concepcion
Sales Asso: Jenece Day

JANUS HOTEL AND RESORT
See ELBE PROPERTIES

JANUS HOTELS & RESORTS
See JANUS HOTELS AND RESORTS INC

D-U-N-S 09-182-5125
JANUS HOTELS AND RESORTS INC
JANUS HOTELS & RESORTS
2300 Nw Corp Blvd Ste 232, Boca Raton, FL 33431-7359
Tel (561) 997-2325 *Founded/Ownrshp* 1972
Sales 26.2MM^E *EMP* 271
SIC 7011 8741 Hotels & motels; Hotel or motel management; Hotels & motels; Hotel or motel management
Ch Bd: Louis E Beck
**Pr:* Michael M Nanosky
CFO: Rick Tonges
**V Ch Bd:* Harry G Yeaggy
VP: Deborah Chamberlin
VP: Rick Ziegelmeyer
Genl Mgr: Jim Angelo
Genl Mgr: Dave Clausen
Sls Dir: Dominic Monteleone
Corp Couns: Chuck Thornton

D-U-N-S 05-347-7571 IMP/EXP
JANUS INTERNATIONAL GROUP LLC
135 Janus Intl Blvd, Temple, GA 30179
Tel (770) 562-2850 *Founded/Ownrshp* 2001
Sales 127.2MM^E *EMP* 375
Accts Nichols Cauley & Associates
SIC 3442 Metal doors; Metal doors
Pr: David Curtis
**CFO:* Joe Bricker
VP: Dennis Johnson
**VP:* Vic Nettie
Dir IT: Ken Jorgensen
Opers Mgr: Alan Campbell
VP Sls: Ramey Jackson
Mktg Mgr: Amy Fuhlman
Manager: Scott Garland
Sls Mgr: Dianne Hammond
Sales Asso: Pauline Romero

D-U-N-S 03-445-3097
■ JANUS INTERNATIONAL HOLDING LLC
(*Suby of* JANUS CAPITAL CORP) ★
151 Detroit St, Denver, CO 80206-4805
Tel (303) 333-3863 *Founded/Ownrshp* 2004
Sales 78.3MM^E *EMP* 1,000^E
SIC 6719 Investment holding companies, except banks; Investment holding companies, except banks
Ex VP: Augustus Cheh
Sr VP: Norman Harris
Mktg Mgr: Julie Maguire
Mktg Mgr: Megan McCahill
Counsel: Monica Dawes

D-U-N-S 03-685-7050
JANUS RESEARCH GROUP INC
6504 Reservoir Rd, Appling, GA 30802-3905
Tel (706) 364-9100 *Founded/Ownrshp* 1997
Sales 54.0MM^E *EMP* 336^E
Accts The Cleveland Group Martinez
SIC 8748 3699 3663 4899 7374 Systems analysis & engineering consulting services; Electronic training devices; Space satellite communications equipment; Data communication services; Data processing & preparation; Systems analysis & engineering consulting services; Electronic training devices; Space satellite communications equipment; Data communication services; Data processing & preparation
CEO: Tony Loop
**Ch Bd:* Jeannette Cruz Loop
**Pr:* James Griffith
**CEO:* Thomas Duke
COO: Ron Demeter
**COO:* John Dewey
**CFO:* Jeremy Wagoner
**Ex VP:* David Sales
VP: Carole Wuesthof
Corp Couns: Timothy Hyland

JANUS SECURITY DIV
See NATIONAL BUILDING MAINTENANCE INC OF FLORIDA

D-U-N-S 61-677-1911
■ JANUS SERVICE CORP
JANUS CAPITAL MANAGEMENT
(*Suby of* JANUS CAPITAL CORP) ★
100 Fillmore St Ste 300, Denver, CO 80206-4921
Tel (303) 316-0477 *Founded/Ownrshp* 1987
Sales 24.8MM^E *EMP* 120
SIC 6722 Management investment, open-end; Management investment, open-end
Trst: Thomas Bailey
VP: David Agostine
VP: Steve Goodbarn
Ex Dir: Steven Scheid
Dir IT: Mike Davis
Dir IT: Chris Orr
IT Man: Randy Carmichael
IT Man: Brian Glose
Advt Dir: Jane Ingalls
Board of Directors: Margie G Hurd

D-U-N-S 07-520-7043 IMP
JAPAN PULP & PAPER (USA) CORP
(*Suby of* JAPAN PULP AND PAPER COMPANY LIMITED)
5928 S Malt Ave, Commerce, CA 90040-3504
Tel (323) 838-2680 *Founded/Ownrshp* 1974
Sales 2.2MMM^E *EMP* 537
SIC 5113 5093 5099 Industrial & personal service paper; Waste paper; Pulpwood; Industrial & personal service paper; Waste paper; Pulpwood
CEO: Akihiko Watanabe
**CFO:* Yoshio Takai
CFO: Kazuhiko Yokozawa
**Exec:* Mark Roth

D-U-N-S 17-365-7099
JAPAN TOBACCO INTERNATIONAL USA INC
JT INTERNATIONAL USA
(*Suby of* JAPAN TOBACCO INC.)
500 Frank W Burr Blvd # 24, Teaneck, NJ 07666-6804
Tel (201) 871-1210 *Founded/Ownrshp* 1986
Sales 46.3MM^E *EMP* 130
SIC 5194 Cigarettes; Cigarettes
Pr: Jacqus Coffeng
**CFO:* Michael Mete

D-U-N-S 61-737-5845
JAPANESE ASSISTANCE NETWORK INC
JAN
(*Suby of* RELOCATION INTERNATIONAL,INC.)
11135 Magnolia Blvd # 140, North Hollywood, CA 91601-3183
Tel (818) 505-6080 *Founded/Ownrshp* 1966
Sales 14.0MM^E *EMP* 298
SIC 7389 Translation services; Translation services
Pr: Genichi Kadono

D-U-N-S 00-625-8115 EXP
JAPS-OLSON CO
7500 Excelsior Blvd, St Louis Park, MN 55426-4519
Tel (952) 932-9393 *Founded/Ownrshp* 2006
Sales 169.9MM^E *EMP* 650^E
SIC 2752 7331 2791 2759 Letters, circular or form: lithographed; Calendars, lithographed; Coupons, lithographed; Addressing service; Mailing service; Typesetting; Commercial printing; Letters, circular or form: lithographed; Calendars, lithographed; Coupons, lithographed; Addressing service; Mailing service; Typesetting; Commercial printing
CEO: Michael W Beddor
**Pr:* Michael R Murphy
**CFO:* Gary Petrangelo
**Ch:* Robert E Murphy
Ex VP: Brian Bedder
**Ex VP:* Kevin Beddor
VP: Kevin Bedder
Exec: Rick Gorman
Software D: Jaysen Albright
Software D: Matthew Scott
Prd Mgr: Julie Halverson

J.A.R. CONSTRUCTION INC
See J A R CONCRETE INC

D-U-N-S 00-285-3265 IMP
JARBOE SALES CO
6833 E Reading Pl, Tulsa, OK 74115-4661
Tel (918) 836-2511 *Founded/Ownrshp* 1959
Sales 55.9MM^E *EMP* 135
SIC 5182 Liquor; Wine; Liquor; Wine
Pt: John B Jarboe
Pt: John B Jarboe II
Genl Mgr: Dick Peck
Genl Mgr: Richard W Peck
Sls Mgr: Bud Hill

D-U-N-S 10-826-8723
JARCO STEEL INC
1011 Highway 6 S Ste 314, Houston, TX 77077-1040
Tel (713) 644-4900 *Founded/Ownrshp* 1983
Sales 22.5MM^E *EMP* 54
SIC 3441 Fabricated structural metal
CEO: Joel Ruth
**Ex VP:* Robert Sherman
**Ex VP:* Clifton C Sherrard
**VP:* Faik Ozdogan
VP: Clifton Sherrard
**Prin:* Bob Scheirman
Plnt Mgr: Odorico Ponce

JARDEN BRANDS CONSUMABLES
See HEARTHMARK LLC

D-U-N-S 07-868-0940 IMP
JARDEN CONSUMER SOLUTIONS
555 Theodore Fremd Ave B, Rye, NY 10580-1451
Tel (914) 967-9400 *Founded/Ownrshp* 2012
Sales 72.9MM^E *EMP* 558^E
SIC 5311 Department stores
CEO: James E Lillie
Sr VP: Richard Sansone
Sr VP: David Tolbert
VP: Kyle Kaiser
Prgrm Mgr: George Choy
Mktg Mgr: Kristy Michael
Snr PM: Wilson Poon

D-U-N-S 80-187-5980 IMP/EXP
▲ JARDEN CORP
1800 N Military Trl # 210, Boca Raton, FL 33431-6376
Tel (561) 447-2520 *Founded/Ownrshp* 1991
Sales 8.2MMM *EMP* 33,000
Accts Pricewaterhousecoopers Llp N
Tkr Sym JAH *Exch* NYS
SIC 3089 3634 Plastic containers, except foam; Plastic kitchenware, tableware & houseware; Electric housewares & fans; Electric household cooking appliances; Electric household cooking utensils; Personal electrical appliances; Plastic containers, except foam; Plastic kitchenware, tableware & houseware; Electric housewares & fans; Electric household cooking appliances; Electric household cooking utensils; Personal electrical appliances
CEO: James E Lillie
**Ch Bd:* Martin E Franklin
**Pr:* Ian G H Ashken
CFO: Al Lefevre
CFO: Alan W Lefevre
Ex VP: John E Capps
Ex VP: Richard T Sansone
VP: Dale Sexton
VP: Bill Sterback

D-U-N-S 19-720-1572 IMP/EXP
JARDEN PLASTIC SOLUTION
1303 S Batesville Rd, Greer, SC 29650-4807
Tel (864) 879-8100 *Founded/Ownrshp* 2007
Sales 38.7MM^E *EMP* 90
SIC 2821 Plastics materials & resins; Plastics materials & resins
Owner: Charles Villa Jr
Pr: Kim Carr
Pr: Chris Navratil
CFO: Paul Dilworth
VP: Dewayne Carter
VP: Shirley Milligan
VP: Gareth Moore
VP: Kirk Morrow
Prgrm Mgr: James Casavant
Genl Mgr: Herbert Dankert
Genl Mgr: Bill Torris

JARDEN PROCESS SOLUTIONS
See SHAKESPEARE CO LLC

D-U-N-S 05-398-3862 IMP
■ **JARDEN ZINC PRODUCTS LLC**
(*Suby of* JARDEN CORP) ★
2500 Old Stage Rd, Greeneville, TN 37745-3036
Tel (423) 639-8111 *Founded/Ownrshp* 1997
Sales 50.2MM^E *EMP* 200
SIC 2796 3364 3356 1031 Photoengraving plates, linecuts or halftones; Zinc & zinc-base alloy die-castings; Zinc & zinc alloy bars, plates, sheets, etc.; Lead & zinc ores; Photoengraving plates, linecuts or halftones; Zinc & zinc-base alloy die-castings; Zinc & zinc alloy bars, plates, sheets, etc.; Lead & zinc ores
Pr: Tom Wennogle
**VP:* Christine Mathews

D-U-N-S 96-865-7619 IMP/EXP
■ **JARDEN ZINC PRODUCTS LLC**
(*Suby of* JARDEN CORP) ★
2500 Old Stage Rd, Greeneville, TN 37745-3036
Tel (423) 787-6305 *Founded/Ownrshp* 1997
Sales 70.8MM^E *EMP* 282
SIC 3356 1031 Zinc & zinc alloy bars, plates, sheets, etc.; Lead & zinc ores; Zinc & zinc alloy bars, plates, sheets, etc.; Lead & zinc ores
CEO: Martin Franklin
**Pr:* Tom Wennogle
**Treas:* John Capps
Ofcr: Joan Griffin
VP: Joe Byouk
**VP:* Robert P Totte
Dir IT: David Campbell
Secur Mgr: Eddie Anderson
Sales Exec: Grady Chafin

D-U-N-S 78-567-7451
JARDINE HAWAII MOTOR HOLDINGS LTD
(*Suby of* JARDINE U S MOTOR HOLDINGS LIMITED (DE))
818 Kapiolani Blvd, Honolulu, HI 96813-5210
Tel (808) 592-5600 *Founded/Ownrshp* 1991
Sales 142.3MM *EMP* 88
SIC 5511 New & used car dealers; New & used car dealers
Pr: Fletcher Jones

D-U-N-S 01-287-4871
JARDINE INC (NY)
JOHNSTON'S TOYOTA
5015 Route 17m, New Hampton, NY 10958-4809
Tel (845) 374-8600 *Founded/Ownrshp* 1923, 1994
Sales 62.5MM *EMP* 78
SIC 5511 Automobiles, new & used; Automobiles, new & used
Pr: John Jardine
**VP:* Steven Jardine
Sls Mgr: Drew Lounsbury
Sales Asso: Greg Doremus
Sales Asso: Kelvin Guyadeen
Sales Asso: Kelvin Joseph
Sales Asso: Chris Lee
Sales Asso: Kevin Linton
Sales Asso: Jamie Murcia
Sales Asso: Collin Riley

JARDINE PETROLEUM
See HAYCOCK PETROLEUM CO

D-U-N-S 03-531-6439
JARDINE PETROLEUM CO
1117 N 400 E, North Salt Lake, UT 84054-1933
Tel (801) 298-3252 *Founded/Ownrshp* 1936
Sales 24.1MM^E *EMP* 65
SIC 5172 Petroleum products; Petroleum products
Ch Bd: Sterling J Jardine
Sls&Mrk Ex: Jay Despain

D-U-N-S 62-278-0781
JARDON & HOWARD TECHNOLOGIES INC
J H T
2710 Discovery Dr Ste 600, Orlando, FL 32826-3003
Tel (407) 381-7797 *Founded/Ownrshp* 1990
Sales 33.9MM^E *EMP* 190
SIC 7371 7336 Custom computer programming services; Commercial art & graphic design; Custom computer programming services; Commercial art & graphic design
Pr: James E Jardon II
VP: Larry Anderson
VP: Jay Kullmann
Exec: Sandy Randall
Prgrm Mgr: Ann Skradski
Dir IT: David Alvarado
IT Man: Chris Brewer
IT Man: Joe Nedoroscik
VP Mktg: Tiffany Lamb

JARED - THE GALLERIA JEWELRY
See SHAWS JEWELERS INC (USED IN VA BY STERLING INC)

JARED THE GALLERIA OF JEWELRY
See STERLING JEWELERS INC

JARIT
See INTEGRA LIFESCIENCES CORP

D-U-N-S 15-573-9295
JARO TRANSPORTATION SERVICES INC
975 Post Rd Nw, Warren, OH 44483-2083
Tel (330) 393-5659 *Founded/Ownrshp* 1979
Sales 39.4MM *EMP* 150^E
SIC 4213 Trucking, except local; Trucking, except local
CEO: James S Ffy
**Sec:* Terry Fiorina
**VP:* Rick Pompeo
IT Man: Hyman Olgazar

D-U-N-S 07-329-5396
JAROS BAUM & BOLLES INC
80 Pine St Fl 12, New York, NY 10005-1718
Tel (212) 530-9300 *Founded/Ownrshp* 1915
Sales 35.2MM^E *EMP* 230
SIC 8711 Mechanical engineering; Consulting engineer; Mechanical engineering; Consulting engineer
Prin: Augistine A Digiacomo
**Prin:* Mitchel W Simpler

D-U-N-S 15-464-6103
JAROTH INC
PACIFIC TELEMANAGEMENT SVCS
2001 Crow Canyon Rd # 200, San Ramon, CA 94583-5368
Tel (925) 553-3650 *Founded/Ownrshp* 1986
Sales 35.4MM^E *EMP* 130
SIC 1731 7349 Telephone & telephone equipment installation; Telephone booth cleaning & maintenance; Telephone & telephone equipment installation; Telephone booth cleaning & maintenance
CEO: Thomas R Keane
**Pr:* Michael R Zumbo
**CFO:* Nancy Rossi

D-U-N-S 00-613-6402
JARP INDUSTRIES INC (WI)
1051 Pine St, Schofield, WI 54476-1851
Tel (715) 359-4241 *Founded/Ownrshp* 1949, 1966
Sales 47.6MM^E *EMP* 195
SIC 3593 Fluid power cylinders, hydraulic or pneumatic; Fluid power cylinders, hydraulic or pneumatic
Pr: Kevin Kraft
Exec: Wray Miller
QA Dir: Ron Covelli
IT Man: Hans Heisinger
IT Man: Brad Sherfinski
VP Opers: Robert Stack
Sfty Dirs: Mike Lenzner
Sfty Mgr: Kadem Townsend
VP Sls: Melonie Eternicka
Manager: Les Homeister

JARRELL MECHANICAL CONTRACTORS
See CHARLES E JARRELL CONTRACTING CO INC

JARRETT, DICK FORD
See JARRETT FORD MERCURY LINCOLN INC

D-U-N-S 08-928-3733
JARRETT FORD MERCURY LINCOLN INC
JARRETT, DICK FORD
38300 Dick Jarrett Way, Dade City, FL 33525-5005
Tel (352) 567-6711 *Founded/Ownrshp* 1965
Sales 26.6MM^E *EMP* 73
SIC 5511 Automobiles, new & used; Vans, new & used; Pickups, new & used; Automobiles, new & used; Vans, new & used; Pickups, new & used
Pr: Dick Jarrett
**Pr:* Brian Jarrett
Sales Exec: Mike Kline

JARRETT GRDON FORD WNTER HAVEN
See WINTER HAVEN FORD INC

D-U-N-S 83-989-6441
JARRITOS INC
NOVAMEX
500 W Overland Ave # 300, El Paso, TX 79901-1086
Tel (915) 594-1618 *Founded/Ownrshp* 1997
Sales 126.2MM^E *EMP* 153
SIC 5149 Groceries & related products; Groceries & related products
Pr: Ramon Carrasco
**CFO:* Thomas Deleon
Sales Asso: Lino Guerra

D-U-N-S 16-160-4046 IMP/EXP
JARROW FORMULAS INC
1824 S Robertson Blvd, Los Angeles, CA 90035-4317
Tel (310) 204-6936 *Founded/Ownrshp* 1975
Sales 98.0MM^E *EMP* 90
SIC 5122 Vitamins & minerals; Vitamins & minerals
CEO: Ben Khowong
**Pr:* Jarrow L Rogovin
**Treas:* Clayton Dubose
**Ex VP:* Peilin Guo
**VP:* Michael Jacobs
Dir IT: Charles Fischer
Mktg Mgr: Rory Lipsky

D-U-N-S 06-616-4752 IMP
JARROW INDUSTRIES INC
12246 Hawkins St, Santa Fe Springs, CA 90670-3365
Tel (562) 906-1919 *Founded/Ownrshp* 2000
Sales 31.9MM^E *EMP* 140
SIC 2834 Vitamin, nutrient & hematinic preparations for human use
Ch Bd: Jarrow Rogovin
**Pr:* Mohammed Khalid
**Treas:* Ben Khowong
Opers Mgr: Dwain Chrest

D-U-N-S 10-886-9009
JARVIS CO INC
100 Jarvis Ave, Rochester, NH 03868-8811
Tel (603) 332-9000 *Founded/Ownrshp* 1967
Sales 24.7MM^E *EMP* 220
SIC 3541 5084 Machine tools, metal cutting type; Machine tools & accessories; Machine tools, metal cutting type; Machine tools & accessories
Pr: Marshall N Jarvis II

D-U-N-S 00-434-7365
JARVIS DOWNING & EMCH INC
JD&E
200 G C And P Rd, Wheeling, WV 26003-6133
Tel (304) 232-5000 *Founded/Ownrshp* 1960
Sales 70.0MM^E *EMP* 200^E
SIC 1541 1542 8748 Industrial buildings, new construction; Commercial & office building, new construction; Business consulting; Industrial buildings, new construction; Commercial & office building, new construction; Business consulting
CEO: Kim Carfagna
**CFO:* Rebecca Hood
**CFO:* Mike Leo
VP: John L Reardon
**VP:* Mark R Sampson
Sales Exec: John Reardon

D-U-N-S 96-281-1357
JARVIS ENGINEERED CONSTRUCTION JV LLC
41800 Executive Dr, Harrison Township, MI 48045-1309
Tel (586) 954-4700 *Founded/Ownrshp* 2010
Sales 28.1MM^E *EMP* 150^E
SIC 1542 Commercial & office building contractors; Commercial & office building contractors
Prin: Randy Suciu
Counsel: Jennifer Fitzgibbonz

D-U-N-S 19-644-0317
JARVIS METALS RECYCLING INC
7825 Olive Ave, Lubbock, TX 79404-8912
Tel (806) 744-7091 *Founded/Ownrshp* 1988
Sales 23.0MM^E *EMP* 52^E
SIC 5093 Ferrous metal scrap & waste; Nonferrous metals scrap
CEO: Bob Jarvis
**Pr:* David Bayouth
**Sec:* John Shelby
**VP:* Gene Day II
Plnt Mgr: Shane Quick

D-U-N-S 10-918-9829
JARVIS PAINTING INC
JARVIS PROPERTY RESTORATION
41800 Executive Dr, Harrison Township, MI 48045-1309
Tel (586) 954-4700 *Founded/Ownrshp* 1979
Sales 23.9MM^E *EMP* 80
SIC 1521 Repairing fire damage, single-family houses
Pr: Bill Jarvis
Genl Mgr: Doug Otis
VP Opers: John Ingoglia
Mktg Dir: Don Marks
Counsel: Kelly Braun

D-U-N-S 00-733-4444
■ **JARVIS PRESS INC**
(*Suby of* CONSOLIDATED GRAPHICS INC) ★
9112 Viscount Row, Dallas, TX 75247-5497
Tel (214) 637-2340 *Founded/Ownrshp* 1951
Sales 22.0MM^E *EMP* 90
SIC 2752 Commercial printing, lithographic; Commercial printing, offset
Pr: Steve Zisler
Ex Dir: Scott Wolf
Sys/Mgr: George Duhon
Plnt Mgr: Bubba Reynolds
Snr Mgr: Melissa Pan

D-U-N-S 00-144-3753 IMP
JARVIS PRODUCTS CORP (CT)
(*Suby of* PENCO CORPORATION)
33 Anderson Rd, Middletown, CT 06457-4926
Tel (860) 347-7271 *Founded/Ownrshp* 1956
Sales 25.7MM^E *EMP* 130
SIC 3556 Meat, poultry & seafood processing machinery; Meat, poultry & seafood processing machinery
Pr: Vincent R Volpe
**Treas:* Penfield Jarvis
VP: Peter A Gwyther
Opers Mgr: Michael A Abdul

JARVIS PROPERTY RESTORATION
See JARVIS PAINTING INC

D-U-N-S 00-308-5974
JARVIS STEEL & LUMBER CO INC
1030 E Patapsco Ave, Baltimore, MD 21225-2200
Tel (410) 355-3000 *Founded/Ownrshp* 1959
Sales 29.0MM^E *EMP* 85
Accts Mcgladrey & Pullen Llp
SIC 5031 2439 3441 1791 Lumber: rough, dressed & finished; Millwork; Trusses, wooden roof; Fabricated structural metal; Structural steel erection
Pr: Victor Frenkil Jr
**Treas:* Keith L Straley
**VP:* Patrick M Dorn
Sfty Mgr: Larry Moravec

D-U-N-S 11-417-0330
JAS AMERICA HOLDING INC
(*Suby of* JAS WORLDWIDE SARL)
5424 Glenridge Dr, Atlanta, GA 30342-1342
Tel (770) 688-1240 *Founded/Ownrshp* 1998
Sales 128.6MM^E *EMP* 412
SIC 4731 Customhouse brokers; Domestic freight forwarding; Customhouse brokers; Domestic freight forwarding
Pr: Marco Rebuffi
**CFO:* Tahira Fumo
Mng Dir: Marc Dalais
Mng Dir: Bruno Gerardis
Brnch Mgr: Oliver Hahn
Brnch Mgr: Shirley Macias
**CIO:* Paul Foster
Sls Mgr: Fons De Haan

D-U-N-S 00-952-5098 IMP/EXP
JAS D EASTON INC
5215 W Wiley Post Way # 130, Salt Lake City, UT 84116-3282
Tel (801) 526-6211 *Founded/Ownrshp* 1922
Sales 568.5MM^E *EMP* 1,800
SIC 3949 5091 6552 Baseball equipment & supplies, general; Archery equipment, general; Snow skiing equipment & supplies, except skis; Hockey equipment & supplies, general; Sporting & recreation goods; Subdividers & developers; Baseball equipment & supplies, general; Archery equipment, general; Snow skiing equipment & supplies, except skis; Hockey equipment & supplies, general; Sporting & recreation goods; Subdividers & developers
CEO: Jim Easton
**Pr:* Tony Palma
**Pr:* Eric Watts
**VP:* John Cramer

D-U-N-S 61-464-6172
JAS FORWARDING (USA) INC
JAS FORWARDING WORLDWIDE
(*Suby of* JAS AMERICA HOLDING INC) ★
6165 Barfield Rd, Atlanta, GA 30328-4317
Tel (770) 688-1206 *Founded/Ownrshp* 1998
Sales 104.0MM^E *EMP* 412
SIC 4731 Customhouse brokers; Domestic freight forwarding; Customhouse brokers; Domestic freight forwarding
Pr: Adrian Emmenegger
Ch Bd: Marco Rebuffi
COO: Graeme Robinson
CFO: Kerstin Roche
Brnch Mgr: Ilaria Bertellini
Brnch Mgr: Karla Cardenas
Brnch Mgr: Federico Ceccato
Brnch Mgr: Yassa Fadila
Brnch Mgr: Sergio Gervasi
Brnch Mgr: Oliver Hahn
Brnch Mgr: Cho Kabuto

JAS FORWARDING WORLDWIDE
See JAS FORWARDING (USA) INC

D-U-N-S 00-692-6885
JAS W GLOVER LTD (HI)
248 Sand Island Access Rd, Honolulu, HI 96819-2228
Tel (808) 591-8977 *Founded/Ownrshp* 1935
Sales 58.2MM^E *EMP* 150
SIC 1611 1623 5032 Highway & street construction; Water & sewer line construction; Concrete building products; Aggregate; Paving materials; Highway & street construction; Water & sewer line construction; Concrete building products; Aggregate; Paving materials
Pr: Maile Romanosky
**CFO:* Joni Okuhara
**Treas:* Jennifer Curtis
**Ex VP:* John Romanowski
**VP:* Byron Fujimoto
Plnt Mgr: Dominic Carvalho

JAS WAREHOUSE
See JOHNSTON AUTOMOTIVE & INDUSTRIAL OF SPENCER INC

D-U-N-S 02-641-7950
JAS WORLDWIDE MANAGEMENT INC (GA)
(*Suby of* JAS AMERICA HOLDING INC) ★
6195 Barfield Rd, Atlanta, GA 30328-4336
Tel (404) 705-7600 *Founded/Ownrshp* 2006
Sales 24.5MM^E *EMP* 62
SIC 4731 Freight forwarding
Pr: Marco Rebuffi
**CFO:* Tahira Fumo
Bd of Dir: Jacques Schellekens
**Ex VP:* John O'Connor
**Ex VP:* Graeme Robinson
VP: Sergio Chiccoli
**VP:* Jayne Maser
Mng Dir: Leonardo Baldi
Mng Dir: Claudio Testa
Rgnl Mgr: Gian Allolio
Area Mgr: Paolo Pasetto

D-U-N-S 03-666-9980
JASA
JEWISH ASSOCIATION SERVING THE
247 W 37th St Fl 9, New York, NY 10018-5193
Tel (212) 273-5200 *Founded/Ownrshp* 1968
Sales 40.9MM *EMP* 100^E
Accts Dorfman Abrams Music Llc Sadd
SIC 8082 Home health care services
CEO: Aileen Gitelson
**COO:* Lea Ferster
Pgrm Dir: Florian Edwards

D-U-N-S 03-595-5108
JASAR RECYCLING INC (OH)
183 Edgeworth Ave, East Palestine, OH 44413-1554
Tel (864) 233-5421 *Founded/Ownrshp* 1996
Sales 49.7MM^E *EMP* 70
SIC 5093 Scrap & waste materials
Pr: Ed McNee
Opers Mgr: Robin McClain
Natl Sales: Kelley Lester
Sls Mgr: John Cote

JASCO CUTTING TOOLS
See GRAYWOOD COMPANIES INC

D-U-N-S 08-256-7025 IMP/EXP
JASCO PRODUCTS CO LLC
10 E Memorial Rd Bldg B, Oklahoma City, OK 73114-2205
Tel (405) 752-0710 *Founded/Ownrshp* 1977
Sales 79.1MM^E *EMP* 250
SIC 5065 5064

D-U-N-S 09-292-8071 IMP/EXP
JASON HOLDINGS INC
411 E Wisconsin Ave # 2120, Milwaukee, WI 53202-4467
Tel (414) 277-9300 *Founded/Ownrshp* 2000
Sales NA *EMP* 1,500
SIC 2297 3465 3469 3844 3443 Nonwoven fabrics; Moldings or trim, automobile: stamped metal; Metal stampings; Irradiation equipment; Boilers: industrial, power, or marine

D-U-N-S 07-864-4455
JASON INC
2500 Logistics Dr, Battle Creek, MI 49037-7388
Tel (269) 962-0743 *Founded/Ownrshp* 2012

Sales 12.8MM^E *EMP* 300
SIC 3089 Automotive parts, plastic; Automotive parts, plastic
Pr: David Westgate

D-U-N-S 15-084-8877 IMP/EXP
■ JASON INC
JASON INDUSTRIES
(*Suby of* JPHI HOLDINGS INC) ★
411 E Wisconsin Ave # 2120, Milwaukee, WI 53202-4467
Tel (414) 277-9300 *Founded/Ownrshp* 2014
Sales 700.0MM *EMP* 3,500
SIC 3465 2297 3625 3469 3844 3443 Moldings or trim, automobile: stamped metal; Nonwoven fabrics; Noise control equipment; Metal stampings; Irradiation equipment; Boilers: industrial, power, or marine; Moldings or trim, automobile: stamped metal; Nonwoven fabrics; Noise control equipment; Metal stampings; Irradiation equipment; Boilers: industrial, power, or marine
Pr: David Cataldi
**Pr:* Srivas Prasad
**Pr:* Dr Florestan Von Boxberg
**CFO:* Steve Cripe
**CFO:* Sarah Sutton
Sr VP: Barbara Reilly
VP: Paul Eichenberg
**VP:* John J Hengel
VP: John Hengel
Genl Couns: William P Schultz

D-U-N-S 00-170-7330 IMP/EXP
JASON INDUSTRIAL INC (NJ)
340 Kaplan Dr, Fairfield, NJ 07004-2567
Tel (973) 227-4904 *Founded/Ownrshp* 1965
Sales 77.9MM^E *EMP* 200
SIC 5084 3052 Textile machinery & equipment; Rubber & plastics hose & beltings; Textile machinery & equipment; Rubber & plastics hose & beltings
CEO: Philip Cohenca
**Ch Bd:* Emilia Cohenca
Ex VP: Peter H Batchelar
VP: Edward Menashe
VP: Albert Nacawa
VP: Roy Pyle
Brnch Mgr: Roland Baker
Dir IT: Chuck Depalma
Dir IT: Chuck Ditalma
IT Man: Michael Dame
Sales Exec: Jeff Pence

JASON INDUSTRIES
See JASON INC

D-U-N-S 06-976-7234
JASON INDUSTRIES INC
1500 W Lusher Ave, Elkhart, IN 46517-1422
Tel (574) 294-7595 *Founded/Ownrshp* 1972
Sales 26.7MM^E *EMP* 86
SIC 3792 5013 Pickup covers, canopies or caps; Automotive supplies & parts; Truck parts & accessories
CEO: Lon Franklin
**Sec:* Carol Franklin
Genl Mgr: Jason Franklin
Sls&Mrk Ex: Jim Fike

D-U-N-S 07-888-9261
▲ JASON INDUSTRIES INC
411 E Wisconsin Ave # 2120, Milwaukee, WI 53202-4467
Tel (414) 277-9300 *Founded/Ownrshp* 2014
Sales 1.0MMM^E *EMP* 4,000^E
Tkr Sym JASN *Exch* NAS
SIC 3465 2297 3625 3469 3844 3443 Investors; Automotive stampings; Body parts, automobile: stamped metal; Nonwoven fabrics; Noise control equipment; Metal stampings; Irradiation equipment; Boilers: industrial, power, or marine
Ch Bd: Jeffry N Quinn
Pr: David A Cataldi
Pr: Srivas Prasad
Pr: Florestan Von Boxberg
CFO: Sarah C Sutton
Treas: John J Hengel

JASON MAXWELL
See REGENT-SUTTON LLC

D-U-N-S 82-833-3810
■ JASON PHARMACEUTICALS INC
(*Suby of* MEDIFAST INC) ★
11445 Cronhill Dr, Owings Mills, MD 21117-2263
Tel (410) 581-8042 *Founded/Ownrshp* 1981
Sales 50.6MM^E *EMP* 94^E
SIC 5122 Biologicals & allied products
Pr: Robert M Pugaczewski

D-U-N-S 94-749-6105
JASON ROBERTS LLC
850 Cassatt Rd Ste 100, Berwyn, PA 19312-2701
Tel (484) 615-7000 *Founded/Ownrshp* 2007
Sales 40.0MM *EMP* 147
SIC 8748 7379 Business consulting; Computer related consulting services; Business consulting; Computer related consulting services

JASON'S DELI
See DELI MANAGEMENT INC

JASON'S DELI
See BULLSHARK INC

D-U-N-S 09-242-4886 IMP
JASONS FOODS INC
208 E Helen Rd, Palatine, IL 60067-6955
Tel (847) 358-9901 *Founded/Ownrshp* 1978
Sales 150.0MM^E *EMP* 12
SIC 5144 5147 5142

D-U-N-S 02-987-4232
JASONS SODA CO INC
AL'S BEVERAGE COMPANY
(*Suby of* ALS HOLDING INC) ★
3 Revay Rd, East Windsor, CT 06088-9688
Tel (860) 627-7003 *Founded/Ownrshp* 1998
Sales 22.4MM^E *EMP* 51
SIC 5149 5078 Beverages, except coffee & tea; Refrigerated beverage dispensers

Pr: Marjorie Feldman
VP Sls: Jim Fitzgerald

D-U-N-S 04-047-1997
JASPAN SCHLESINGER LLP
300 Garden City Plz Fl 5, Garden City, NY 11530-3333
Tel (516) 569-6463 *Founded/Ownrshp* 1971
Sales 26.3MM^E *EMP* 130
SIC 8111 General practice attorney, lawyer; General practice attorney, lawyer
Pt: Adam P Wofse
Pr: Patricia Doller
Pr: Irene Weis
CFO: James Leonard
IT Man: Fred Leone
Counsel: Ross Marvin
Counsel: Jeffrey Schwartz

D-U-N-S 00-636-8096
JASPER CHAIR CO INC
534 E 8th St, Jasper, IN 47546-2953
Tel (812) 482-5239 *Founded/Ownrshp* 1921
Sales 20.9MM^E *EMP* 100
SIC 2522 2521 2531 2512 2511 Office furniture, except wood; Chairs, office: padded, upholstered or plain: wood; School furniture; Upholstered household furniture; Wood household furniture
Pr: Jeff S Barth
IT Man: Gene Harpenau
Sls Mgr: Greg Luegers

D-U-N-S 03-952-9938
JASPER CITY SCHOOLS
110 17th St W, Jasper, AL 35501-5365
Tel (205) 384-6880 *Founded/Ownrshp* 1891
Sales 16.9MM^E *EMP* 350
SIC 8211 Public elementary & secondary schools; Public elementary & secondary schools

JASPER CNTY HOSP HOME HLTH CRE
See JASPER COUNTY HOSPITAL FOUNDATION INC

D-U-N-S 15-627-5005
JASPER CONTRACTORS INC
125 N Weinbach Ave 820b, Evansville, IN 47711-6091
Tel (225) 753-6766 *Founded/Ownrshp* 2004
Sales 26.8MM^E *EMP* 140
SIC 1761 1711 Roofing contractor; Heating & air conditioning contractors
Pr: Brian K Wedding
**VP:* Angela Darnell

D-U-N-S 10-001-3929
JASPER COUNTY BOARD OF EDUCATION
JASPER COUNTY SCHOOL DISTRICT
1411 College St, Monticello, GA 31064-2118
Tel (706) 468-6350 *Founded/Ownrshp* 1800
Sales 21.8MM *EMP* 200
Accts Russell W Hinton Atlanta Ga
SIC 8211 Public elementary & secondary schools; Public elementary & secondary schools

D-U-N-S 07-430-2910 IMP
JASPER COUNTY HOSPITAL FOUNDATION INC
JASPER CNTY HOSP HOME HLTH CRE
1104 E Grace St, Rensselaer, IN 47978-3211
Tel (219) 866-5141 *Founded/Ownrshp* 1917
Sales 739.0M *EMP* 500
SIC 8062 8052 General medical & surgical hospitals; Intermediate care facilities; General medical & surgical hospitals; Intermediate care facilities
Pr: James Flickner
Chf Path: James J Dyer
Chf OB: Christopher M Louck
Chf Rad: Steven L Hossler
**Treas:* Jeffrey D Webb
VP: Michael J Bayci
VP: Stacie Klingler
VP: Jeffrey Webb
Dir Inf Cn: Heidi M Leeper
Dir Rad: Cindy Reed
Dir Rx: Susan L Hooker

JASPER COUNTY SCHOOL DISTRICT
See JASPER COUNTY BOARD OF EDUCATION

D-U-N-S 07-979-9077
JASPER COUNTY SCHOOL DISTRICT
1411 College St, Monticello, GA 31064-2118
Tel (706) 468-6350 *Founded/Ownrshp* 2015
Sales 2.6MM^E *EMP* 297^E
SIC 8211 Public elementary & secondary schools
Teacher Pr: Gary Jenkins

D-U-N-S 55-654-9285
JASPER COUNTY SCHOOL DISTRICT
10942 N Jacob Smart Blvd, Ridgeland, SC 29936-2708
Tel (843) 717-1100 *Founded/Ownrshp* 1909
Sales 37.5MM *EMP* 436
Accts Mcgregor & Co Llp Columbia
SIC 8211 Public elementary & secondary schools; Public elementary & secondary schools
Ofcr: Betty Bright
Ofcr: Sheila Martinez
Exec: Antroy Abram
Exec: Shellie Murdaugh
Dir Bus: Sandra Mack Huff
Teacher Pr: Arthur Holmes

JASPER ELEMENTARY
See PICKENS COUNTY BOARD OF EDUCATION

JASPER ENGINE & TRANSM EXCHAGE
See JASPER ENGINE & TRANSMISSION EXCHANGE INC

D-U-N-S 01-645-8473
JASPER ENGINE & TRANSMISSION EXCHANGE INC
JASPER ENGINE & TRANSM EXCHAGE
(*Suby of* INDIANA TOOL & DIE) ★
815 Wernsing Rd, Jasper, IN 47546-8141
Tel (812) 482-1041 *Founded/Ownrshp* 1959
Sales 261.0MM^E *EMP* 1,500
SIC 5013 Automotive engines & engine parts; Automotive engines & engine parts

Ch Bd: Gervase Schwenk
**Pr:* Doug Bawel
**Treas:* Raymond Schwenk
**VP:* Mike Schwenk
Opers Mgr: Kevin Powell

D-U-N-S 01-764-6357 IMP
JASPER ENGINE & TRANSMISSION EXCHANGE INC
(*Suby of* INDIANA TOOL & DIE) ★
815 Wernsing Rd, Jasper, IN 47546-8141
Tel (812) 482-1041 *Founded/Ownrshp* 1958
Sales 171.9MM^E *EMP* 1,500
SIC 5013 Automotive engines & engine parts; Automotive engines & engine parts
CEO: Doug Bawel
**Ch Bd:* Gervase Schwenk
**Pr:* Zach Bawel
**Treas:* Raymond Schwenk
**VP:* Mike Schwenk
Off Mgr: Trenton Smith

D-U-N-S 01-645-8481
JASPER ENGINE & TRANSMISSION EXCHANGE INC (KY)
(*Suby of* INDIANA TOOL & DIE) ★
815 Wernsing Rd, Jasper, IN 47546-8141
Tel (812) 482-1041 *Founded/Ownrshp* 1963
Sales 270.0MM *EMP* 1,500^E
SIC 5013 7537 Automotive engines & engine parts; Automotive transmission repair shops; Automotive engines & engine parts; Automotive transmission repair shops
Pr: Doug Bawel
**Ch Bd:* Gervase Schwenk
**Treas:* Raymond Schwenk
**VP:* Mike Schwenk

D-U-N-S 00-639-8168 IMP/EXP
JASPER ENGINE EXCHANGE INC
INDIANA TOOL & DIE
815 Wernsing Rd, Jasper, IN 47546-8141
Tel (812) 482-1041 *Founded/Ownrshp* 1952
Sales 819.1MM^E *EMP* 1,500
Accts Harding Shymanski & Company
SIC 3714 7538 6512 Rebuilding engines & transmissions, factory basis; Fuel systems & parts, motor vehicle; Gears, motor vehicle; General automotive repair shops; Nonresidential building operators; Rebuilding engines & transmissions, factory basis; Fuel systems & parts, motor vehicle; Gears, motor vehicle; General automotive repair shops; Nonresidential building operators
CEO: Douglas Bawel
**Ch Bd:* Gervase Schwenk
**Pr:* Zachery Bawel
**Treas:* Raymond Schwenk
VP: Darrell Harley
VP: Craig Hessenauer
VP: John Moser
**VP:* Mike Schwenk
Exec: Donald Casper
Exec: Jason Nord
Off Mgr: Trenton Smith

D-U-N-S 02-281-8363 IMP
JASPER ENGINEERING & EQUIPMENT CO INC
3800 5th Ave W Ste 1, Hibbing, MN 55746-3752
Tel (952) 938-6504 *Founded/Ownrshp* 1958
Sales 22.6MM^E *EMP* 44
SIC 5082 5084 Mining machinery & equipment, except petroleum; Forestry equipment; Dairy products manufacturing machinery; Food product manufacturing machinery
Pr: Tom Jamar
**CFO:* Peggy Arthurs
**VP:* Jeff Jamar
Creative D: Denny Potila
Area Mgr: Mike Smith
Sls Mgr: Debbie Elliott
Sls Mgr: Timothy W Rasch
Sales Asso: Zach Fredin
Sales Asso: Jerry Rude
Sales Asso: James Wahlert

JASPER EQUIPMENT CO
See TEXAS TIMBERJACK INC

JASPER GRADING
See GAY CONSTRUCTION CO

JASPER GROUP
See JASPER SEATING CO INC

D-U-N-S 08-085-3849
JASPER INDEPENDENT SCHOOL DISTRICT
128 Park Ln, Jasper, TX 75951-3466
Tel (409) 384-2401 *Founded/Ownrshp* 1932
Sales 30.8MM *EMP* 520
Accts Hereford Lynch Sellars & Kir
SIC 8211 Public elementary school; Public junior high school; Public senior high school; Public elementary school; Public junior high school; Public senior high school
IT Man: Debbie Hollis
Psych: Jennifer Herrington

D-U-N-S 08-217-3485
JASPER JEEP SALES INC
1050 Highway 515 S, Jasper, GA 30143-4883
Tel (404) 525-3500 *Founded/Ownrshp* 1976
Sales 34.3MM^E *EMP* 100
SIC 5511 5521 7538 5531 Automobiles, new & used; Pickups, new & used; Used car dealers; General automotive repair shops; Automotive & home supply stores; Automobiles, new & used; Pickups, new & used; Used car dealers; General automotive repair shops; Automotive & home supply stores
Pr: Riker Lowe

JASPER LAUNDRY & DRY CLEANING
See MICKEYS ENTERPRISES INC

D-U-N-S 17-428-7946
JASPER LUMBER CO INC
2700 Hwy 118 W, Jasper, AL 35501
Tel (205) 384-9088 *Founded/Ownrshp* 1996
Sales 23.8MM^E *EMP* 120

SIC 2421 Lumber: rough, sawed or planed; Lumber: rough, sawed or planed
VP: Al Bracewell
**Sec:* Glen Bracewell
Exec: Jackie Reynolds

D-U-N-S 07-938-1439
JASPER PARENT LLC
9 W 57th St Ste 3100, New York, NY 10019-2701
Tel (212) 796-8500 *Founded/Ownrshp* 2013
Sales 2.0MMM^E *EMP* 10,790^E
SIC 6211 Investment firm, general brokerage; Investment firm, general brokerage

JASPER PLASTICS SOLUTIONS
See JP INC - INDIANA

D-U-N-S 13-244-5201 IMP
JASPER PRODUCTS LLC
(*Suby of* STREMICKS HERITAGE FOODS LLC) ★
3877 E 27th St, Joplin, MO 64804-3306
Tel (417) 206-3333 *Founded/Ownrshp* 2007
Sales 517.7MM^E *EMP* 400
SIC 5149 Health foods; Health foods
Admn Mgr: Judy Rhinehart
Cmptr Lab: Amy Swan
Manager: Gayle Dimaggio
Manager: Jim Walker

D-U-N-S 00-636-7239 IMP
JASPER RUBBER PRODUCTS INC
1010 1st Ave W, Jasper, IN 47546-3201
Tel (812) 482-3242 *Founded/Ownrshp* 1949, 2003
Sales 169.6MM^E *EMP* 750
SIC 3061 Mechanical rubber goods; Mechanical rubber goods
Ch Bd: Jeffrey Geisler
**Pr:* Douglas Mathias
Pr: Laura Mohr
**CFO:* Marcus Oxley
Ex VP: Scott Ferguson
Ex VP: Scott Gehlhausen
**Ex VP:* R Keith Wyatt
VP: Brenda Alles
VP: Kyle Kuczynski
**VP:* Lee Mincey
Dept Mgr: Drew Schmitt
Board of Directors: Dow McCune, G Scott Schwinghammer

D-U-N-S 00-636-7767 IMP
JASPER SEATING CO INC
JASPER GROUP
225 Clay St, Jasper, IN 47546-3306
Tel (812) 482-3204 *Founded/Ownrshp* 1929, 1959
Sales 198.4MM^E *EMP* 840
SIC 2521 2531 2511 2522 Chairs, office: padded, upholstered or plain: wood; School furniture; Wood household furniture; Office furniture, except wood; Chairs, office: padded, upholstered or plain: wood; School furniture; Wood household furniture; Office furniture, except wood
Pr: Elliott Michael
**Ch Bd:* Glen Gramelspacher
CFO: Steve Anderson
Treas: Lisa Brinkman
Chf Mktg O: Jennifer Brockmeyer
**VP:* Ronald Beck
Off Mgr: Betty Braunecker
IT Man: Jeff Brewer
Mfg Dir: Kevin Bieker
Sfty Dirs: Zach Lichlyter
Opers Mgr: Stanley Vollmer

D-U-N-S 12-789-6454
JASPER WATERWORKS AND SEWER BOARD INC
1620 Alabama Ave, Jasper, AL 35501-4720
Tel (205) 221-6031 *Founded/Ownrshp* 1942
Sales 20.5MM^E *EMP* 46
SIC 4952 4941 Sewerage systems; Water supply
IT Man: Dianne Gaddy
IT Man: Jason Langley

D-U-N-S 96-292-5298 IMP
JASPER WELLER LLC
WELLER TRUCK PARTS
(*Suby of* INDIANA TOOL & DIE) ★
1500 Gezon Pkwy Sw, Grand Rapids, MI 49509-9585
Tel (616) 724-2000 *Founded/Ownrshp* 2014
Sales 103.9MM^E *EMP* 850
SIC 7538 5013 Truck engine repair, except industrial; Truck parts & accessories; Truck engine repair, except industrial; Truck parts & accessories
COO: Paul Weller
Prin: John Weller
Dir IT: Mark Huizinga
IT Man: Tim Mayo
Natl Sales: Mike Sipple
Natl Sales: Terry Stranz
Natl Sales: Rick Vanslambrouck
Manager: Mike Kaniecki
Manager: Bill Lewis

D-U-N-S 08-317-5554 IMP/EXP
JASPER WYMAN & SON (ME)
280 Main St, Milbridge, ME 04658
Tel (207) 546-3800 *Founded/Ownrshp* 1874
Sales 24.6MM^E *EMP* 75
SIC 2033 2037 Fruits: packaged in cans, jars, etc.; Fruits, quick frozen & cold pack (frozen)
Pr: Edward Flanagan
**Ch Bd:* Elizabeth Doudoumopoulos

D-U-N-S 00-793-3518
JASPER-NEWTON ELECTRIC COOPERATIVE INC (TX)
812 S Margaret Ave, Kirbyville, TX 75956-2499
Tel (409) 423-2241 *Founded/Ownrshp* 1943
Sales 54.3MM *EMP* 106
Accts Bolinger Segars Gilbert & Mo
SIC 4911 Distribution, electric power; Transmission, electric power; Distribution, electric power; Transmission, electric power
Pr: Hershel Hall
**Sec:* Henry Biscamp
**VP:* Pat Brown
**VP:* Johnie Withers

Genl Mgr: Mark Tamplin
CTO: Kerstin Helm
MIS Dir: Tina Helm
Sfty Dirs: Steve O'Gilbert

D-U-N-S 61-904-6324
JASS & ASSOCIATES INC
2099 Gateway Pl Ste 304, San Jose, CA 95110-1017
Tel (408) 436-1624 *Founded/Ownrshp* 2006
Sales 14.9MM^E *EMP* 325
SIC 7379 Computer related consulting services; Computer related consulting services
Pr: Chakradhar Paturi
COO: Suresh Venna
**CTO:* Jayprasad Vejendla

JAT CREATIVE PDTS DIV LAFRANCE
See LA FRANCE CORP

D-U-N-S 08-120-0719
JAT OIL INC
600 W Main St, Chattanooga, TN 37402-4701
Tel (423) 629-6611 *Founded/Ownrshp* 1976
Sales 99.8MM^E *EMP* 45
SIC 5172 Fuel oil; Fuel oil
CEO: Pat Conroy
**Pr:* William P Conroy Jr
**Sec:* Melinda Hightower
Sales Asso: Kell Harvey

D-U-N-S 06-941-0152
JATA LLC (MN)
11055 Excelsior Blvd, Hopkins, MN 55343-3429
Tel (952) 931-2400 *Founded/Ownrshp* 2000
Sales 46.0MM^E *EMP* 69^E
SIC 5013 5065 3714 5012 Truck parts & accessories; Security control equipment & systems; Motor vehicle parts & accessories; Trucks, commercial
CFO: Gerald Theisen

D-U-N-S 03-096-9646 IMP/EXP
JATCO INC
725 Zwissig Way, Union City, CA 94587-3654
Tel (510) 487-0888 *Founded/Ownrshp* 1976
Sales 21.0MM *EMP* 150
SIC 3089 Injection molding of plastics; Injection molding of plastics
CEO: Paul H Appelblom
**Ex VP:* Steven Jones

JATF
See IUPAT DISTRICT COUNCIL 78

D-U-N-S 80-794-2974
JATH OIL CO
1202 N 10th St, Duncan, OK 73533-3832
Tel (580) 252-5580 *Founded/Ownrshp* 1952
Sales 33.6MM^E *EMP* 130
SIC 1311 1382 Crude petroleum production; Natural gas production; Oil & gas exploration services; Crude petroleum production; Natural gas production; Oil & gas exploration services
Pr: Tom H McCasland III
**Treas:* Noble Means
**VP:* Chris K Fowler
**VP Prd:* Chris F Cain

D-U-N-S 60-304-9685 IMP
JATON CORP
47677 Lakeview Blvd, Fremont, CA 94538-6544
Tel (510) 933-8888 *Founded/Ownrshp* 1982
Sales 28.5MM^E *EMP* 255
SIC 3672 3674 3661 3577 Printed circuit boards; Modules, solid state; Modems; Computer peripheral equipment; Printed circuit boards; Modules, solid state; Modems; Computer peripheral equipment
Pr: Vicky Hong
**CEO:* J S Chiang
CFO: Alex Cheng

D-U-N-S 19-622-1899 IMP
JAV FOOD CORP
AGATA & VALENTINA
414 E 75th St Fl 3, New York, NY 10021-3442
Tel (212) 452-0690 *Founded/Ownrshp* 1991
Sales 31.9MM^E *EMP* 200^E
SIC 5499 Gourmet food stores; Gourmet food stores
Ch: Joseph Musco

D-U-N-S 15-215-3979
JAVA CITY
717 Del Paso Rd, Sacramento, CA 95834-7740
Tel (916) 565-5500 *Founded/Ownrshp* 2000
Sales 16.2MM^E *EMP* 500
SIC 5812 5149 Cafe; Coffee, green or roasted; Cafe; Coffee, green or roasted
CEO: Ross McMahan
**Pr:* Micheal McAdam
CFO: David Carter
**CFO:* Angelie Chuk
VP: Matt Shea
Genl Mgr: Stephanie Wilson
Mktg Mgr: Lucy Montoya

D-U-N-S 78-794-7951 IMP
JAVA TRADING CO LLC
DISTANT LANDS COFFEE
801 Houser Way N, Renton, WA 98057-5506
Tel (425) 917-2920 *Founded/Ownrshp* 2006
Sales 137.8MM^E *EMP* 250
SIC 5149 2095 Coffee, green or roasted; Roasted coffee; Coffee, green or roasted; Roasted coffee
CFO: Jim Ehchweiler
Mktg Mgr: Max Phillips

D-U-N-S 96-235-6668 IMP
JAVAD EMS INC
900 Rock Ave, San Jose, CA 95131-1615
Tel (408) 770-1700 *Founded/Ownrshp* 2009
Sales 20.2MM^E *EMP* 95
SIC 3679 Electronic circuits
Pr: Javad Ashjaee
**VP:* Gary Walker
**Prin:* Linda Bezoni
**Prin:* Pam Walke

JAVELIN BOATS
See STRATOS BOATS INC

D-U-N-S 14-333-1994
■ **JAVELIN DIRECT INC**
JAVELIN MARKETING GROUP
(*Suby of* OMNICOM GROUP INC) ★
7850 N Belt Line Rd, Irving, TX 75063-6062
Tel (972) 443-7000 *Founded/Ownrshp* 2004
Sales 33.1MM^E *EMP* 110
SIC 7311 Advertising agencies; Advertising agencies
Pr: Greg Banks
**Pr:* Michael McCartin
Sr VP: Anne Delorenzo
Sr VP: Tina Posey
Sr VP: David Selwood
**VP:* Don Barlow
VP: Rob Beckley
VP: Joyce Kobilansky
VP: Mia McNiece
VP: Mark Miller
VP: Michael Radigan
VP: Satnam Singh
**VP:* Amy Weaver

D-U-N-S 93-359-4756
JAVELIN LOGISTICS CORP
7447 Morton Ave Ste A, Newark, CA 94560-4208
Tel (510) 795-7287 *Founded/Ownrshp* 1995
Sales 42.7MM^E *EMP* 110
SIC 4214 4731 4225 Local trucking with storage; Freight transportation arrangement; General warehousing & storage
CEO: Malcolm George Winspear
**VP:* Jeff Hoover
Opers Supe: Scott Casto
Opers Supe: Shelly Morales
Opers Supe: Francis Paiso
Opers Mgr: Mike Sacrey
S&M/VP: John Arbuckle
Manager: Ken Rommel

JAVELIN MARKETING GROUP
See JAVELIN DIRECT INC

D-U-N-S 07-863-8332
JAVELIN MORTGAGE INVESTMENT CORP (MD)
3001 Ocean Dr Ste 201, Vero Beach, FL 32963-1992
Tel (772) 617-4340 *Founded/Ownrshp* 2012
Sales 59.4MM *EMP* 19
SIC 6798 Real estate investment trusts; Mortgage investment trusts; Real estate investment trusts; Mortgage investment trusts
Ch Bd: Scott J Ulm
**Ch Bd:* Jeffrey J Zimmer
**COO:* Mark Gruber
**CFO:* James R Mountain

D-U-N-S 08-007-5337
JAVI BUSINESS CENTER CORP
655 W 34th St, New York, NY 10001-1114
Tel (212) 216-2000 *Founded/Ownrshp* 1986
Sales 3.9MM^E *EMP* 500
SIC 7389 Convention & show services
Pr: Alan Steel

JAVIC WHOLESALE DIVISION
See STEIN GARDEN CENTERS INC

D-U-N-S 17-554-5524
JAVID LLC
137 E Baffert Dr, Nogales, AZ 85621-3555
Tel (520) 377-2420 *Founded/Ownrshp* 1983
Sales 20.2MM^E *EMP* 170
SIC 3672 3577 Printed circuit boards; Computer peripheral equipment
Pr: Roberto Klosek

D-U-N-S 07-752-6739 IMP
JAVINE VENTURES INC
CLIMATEC
2851 W Kathleen Rd, Phoenix, AZ 85053-4053
Tel (602) 944-3330 *Founded/Ownrshp* 1988
Sales 185.4MM^E *EMP* 275^E
Accts Cordova & Jones Pc
SIC 5075 1731 Warm air heating equipment & supplies; Air conditioning & ventilation equipment & supplies; Electronic controls installation; Warm air heating equipment & supplies; Air conditioning & ventilation equipment & supplies; Electronic controls installation
Pr: Jack Kucera

D-U-N-S 01-084-6327
JAVITCH BLOCK LLC
1100 Superior Ave E, Cleveland, OH 44114-2530
Tel (216) 623-0000 *Founded/Ownrshp* 1991
Sales 55.1MM^E *EMP* 329
SIC 8111 General practice law office; General practice law office
Pr: Melissa Meserko
Tech Mgr: Mark Cashmere
Ql Cn Mgr: Nicole Emmert
Secur Mgr: Jeffrey Kaput
Snr Mgr: Katrina Davison

D-U-N-S 07-542-5504
JAWONIO INC (NY)
260 N Little Tor Rd, New City, NY 10956-2627
Tel (845) 634-4648 *Founded/Ownrshp* 1947
Sales 39.7MM *EMP* 700
Accts Bdo Usa Lp New York Ny
SIC 8361 Residential care for the handicapped; Residential care for the handicapped
CEO: Jill Warner
**Ch Bd:* Jefferey Keahon
**COO:* Marilyn Astarita
**CFO:* Mark Campione
Sr Cor Off: Estelle Brill
**Ex Dir:* Paul Tendler
IT Man: Anthony Calderone
Prd Mgr: Glen Paonessa
Pgrm Dir: Yves Latouche
Pgrm Dir: Anne Ostroff
Pgrm Dir: Jouliana Petranker

D-U-N-S 60-823-5917
JAWOOD BUSINESS PROCESS SOLUTIONS LLC
JAWOOD MANAGEMENT ASSOCIATES
(*Suby of* GENPACT LIMITED) ★
32270 Telg Rd Ste 200, Bingham Farms, MI 48025
Tel (248) 833-8000 *Founded/Ownrshp* 2013
Sales NA *EMP* 320
SIC 6411 Insurance information & consulting services; Insurance information & consulting services
Exec: Jay Antani

JAWOOD MANAGEMENT ASSOCIATES
See JAWOOD BUSINESS PROCESS SOLUTIONS LLC

JAX BRAND LUBRICANTS
See JAX INC

JAX BROKERAGE
See CYPRESS TRUCK LINES INC

D-U-N-S 02-334-8923 EXP
JAX INC
JAX BRAND LUBRICANTS
W134n5373 Campbell Dr, Menomonee Falls, WI 53051-7023
Tel (262) 781-8850 *Founded/Ownrshp* 1993
Sales 21.1MM^E *EMP* 25
SIC 5172 Lubricating oils & greases
Pr: Eric J Peter
**Sec:* Janet Peter
**VP:* Carl W Peter
Sales Exec: Peter Kerrick
Snr Mgr: Chris Foti

D-U-N-S 11-883-1858
JAX INC
JAX MERCANTILE COMPANY
1200 N College Ave, Fort Collins, CO 80524-1212
Tel (970) 488-3250 *Founded/Ownrshp* 1983
Sales 72.0MM^E *EMP* 380
SIC 5941

JAX MARKET
See MACBER INC

JAX MERCANTILE COMPANY
See JAX INC

D-U-N-S 94-070-8105
JAX REFRIGERATION INC
1680 The Greens Way # 200, Jacksonville Beach, FL 32250-1422
Tel (904) 249-1400 *Founded/Ownrshp* 2010
Sales 27.8MM *EMP* 70
Accts Masters Smith & Wisby Pa J
SIC 1711 Refrigeration contractor; Refrigeration contractor
Pr: Mark Lowery
Sr VP: Ed Trotzke
Rgnl Mgr: Michael Winslow
Off Mgr: Joy Bardin
Natl Sales: Durby Moore
Snr PM: Brian Peterson

D-U-N-S 00-481-2527
JAX TRANSIT MANAGEMENT CORP
100 N Myrtle Ave, Jacksonville, FL 32204-1310
Tel (904) 630-3116 *Founded/Ownrshp* 2008
Sales 950.0M *EMP* 470
SIC 4789 Transportation services; Transportation services
Pr: Charolette Hall
**Prin:* Thomas Jury

JAX UTILITIES & WATERPROOFING
See HASKELL CO INC

JAY AT PLAY
See JAY FRANCO & SONS INC

D-U-N-S 15-057-2774
■ **JAY AUTOMOTIVE GROUP INC**
JAY TOYOTA
(*Suby of* GROUP 1 AUTOMOTIVE INC) ★
1661 Whittlesey Rd, Columbus, GA 31904-3645
Tel (706) 324-1234 *Founded/Ownrshp* 2013
Sales 59.3MM^E *EMP* 290
SIC 7515 5511 6331 6159

JAY BEE OIL & GAS COMPANY
See JAY-BEE OIL & GAS INC

JAY C STORES
See JOHN C GROUB CO INC

D-U-N-S 86-816-0698 EXP
JAY CASHMAN INC
(*Suby of* CGI HOLDING COMPANY)
549 South St, Quincy, MA 02169-7318
Tel (617) 890-0600 *Founded/Ownrshp* 1994
Sales 200.0MM *EMP* 500
SIC 1629 Marine construction; Marine construction
Pr: Dale H Pyatt
Pr: Robert Goodman
Pr: Andrew Timmis
CFO: Christopher C Anderson
**CFO:* Andrew B Goldberg
**Treas:* William Spielvogel
Sr VP: Frank Belesimo
VP: Lew Conley
VP: Michael Empey
VP: Richard Fernandez
Telecom Ex: Quan Pham

D-U-N-S 17-368-5983
JAY CHEVROLET INC
3372 W Highland Rd, Highland, MI 48357-4000
Tel (248) 889-3232 *Founded/Ownrshp* 1987
Sales 46.3MM^E *EMP* 94
SIC 5511 Automobiles, new & used; Automobiles, new & used
Ch Bd: Martin G Feldman
Pr: Jay S Feldman
**CFO:* Valentina Vannote

D-U-N-S 08-704-3105
JAY COUNTY HOSPITAL FOUNDATION INC
SPECIALTY REFERRAL CENTER
500 W Votaw St, Portland, IN 47371-1322
Tel (260) 726-7131 *Founded/Ownrshp* 1916
Sales 36.3MM *EMP* 350
Accts Bollenbacher & Associates Llc
SIC 8062 General medical & surgical hospitals; General medical & surgical hospitals
Ch: Brad Derome
**Pr:* Dave Hyatt
**Treas:* Janet Bantz
Chf Mktg O: Claudia Jones
Dir Rx: Stephanie Robinson

D-U-N-S 04-163-0690 IMP
JAY DEE SERVICE CORP
BEARING & TRANSM SUP CO DIV
1320 Highland Rd E, Macedonia, OH 44056-2310
Tel (330) 425-1546 *Founded/Ownrshp* 1979
Sales 28.0MM *EMP* 8
SIC 5084 Industrial machinery & equipment
CEO: John Zimmerman Sr
**Pr:* Constance A Zimmerman
**VP:* John Zimmerman Jr
**Prin:* Julia Hall
**Prin:* Alfred Palay
**Prin:* Julia Zimmerman
Genl Mgr: Jamin Scibetta

D-U-N-S 00-401-0559
JAY ELECTRIC CO INC (AL)
PRECISION ROTOR SERVICES
5300 E Lake Blvd, Birmingham, AL 35217-3548
Tel (205) 595-3910 *Founded/Ownrshp* 1984
Sales 38.6MM^E *EMP* 211
SIC 3621 Coils, for electric motors or generators; Coils, for electric motors or generators
CEO: Bret Lehr
Pr: William Shiver
CFO: Chad McCowan
Ch: Joel McMahon
VP: Gerald Sartain
VP Sls: Johnny Locklar

D-U-N-S 07-947-4336
JAY ELITE MARKETING & EVENT MANAGEMENT LLC
42 N Athol Ave, Baltimore, MD 21229-2827
Tel (410) 941-9745 *Founded/Ownrshp* 2014
Sales 61.3MM *EMP* 2^E
SIC 7311 8732 8742 8748 Advertising agencies; Survey service: marketing, location, etc.; Management consulting services; Marketing consulting services; Business consulting; Advertising agencies; Survey service: marketing, location, etc.; Management consulting services; Marketing consulting services; Business consulting
Prin: Roberta Johnson

D-U-N-S 94-623-1891
JAY FINN INDUSTRIES INC
57 E Parsonage Way, Manalapan, NJ 07726-7945
Tel (732) 591-8677 *Founded/Ownrshp* 1994
Sales 23.0MM *EMP* 21
SIC 7359 Aircraft & industrial truck rental services
Pr: Jay Finn

D-U-N-S 00-135-6963 IMP
JAY FRANCO & SONS INC (NY)
JAY AT PLAY
295 5th Ave Ste 312, New York, NY 10016-7106
Tel (212) 679-3022 *Founded/Ownrshp* 1958, 1940
Sales 220.0MM *EMP* 60
SIC 2211 5023 Towels & toweling, cotton; Towels; Towels & toweling, cotton; Towels
Ch Bd: Joseph N Franco
CFO: Howard Weinreich
**Treas:* Marc Franco
VP: Maria De Sena
VP: Abraham Franco
**VP:* Joseph A Franco
Natl Sales: Bally Faudar

D-U-N-S 04-568-5831 IMP
JAY GEE WOOD PRODUCTS CO INC
28w206 Commercial Ave, Lake Barrington, IL 60010-2316
Tel (847) 381-7200 *Founded/Ownrshp* 1968
Sales 39.8MM^E *EMP* 250
SIC 2431

JAY GROUP, THE
See JAY GROUP LTD

D-U-N-S 05-676-5233 IMP
JAY GROUP INC
ORIBE
700 Indian Springs Dr, Lancaster, PA 17601-1266
Tel (717) 285-6200 *Founded/Ownrshp* 1970
Sales 92.2MM^E *EMP* 273
SIC 5961 7389 7331 7319 5199 Catalog & mail-order houses; Telemarketing services; Direct mail advertising services; Distribution of advertising material or sample services; Packaging materials; Catalog & mail-order houses; Telemarketing services; Direct mail advertising services; Distribution of advertising material or sample services; Packaging materials
Pr: Dana Chryst
**Ch Bd:* J Freeland Chryst
**Pr:* H Douglas Bushong
**Pr:* Dana A Chryst
COO: Bernard Jay
CFO: Joseph Grabias
**CFO:* Craig Robinson
**Sec:* Michael P Boyer
**Sec:* John J Shields
Bd of Dir: Matt Fitzgerald
VP: Paul Carton
VP: David Durham
VP: Christopher Marett
VP: Dave Wood
**VP:* David E Wood
VP: Tom Woodside

D-U-N-S 78-951-6564 IMP/EXP
JAY GROUP LTD
JAY GROUP, THE
1450 Atlantic Ave, Rocky Mount, NC 27801-2714
Tel (252) 442-2139 *Founded/Ownrshp* 1991
Sales 89.9MM^{E} *EMP* 130
Accts Dixon Hughes Goodman Llp Ral
SIC 5139 Footwear; Footwear
CEO: David Jay
**CFO:* John Kelly
**VP:* Mark Elliott
**VP:* Stephen Parsons

D-U-N-S 04-771-7475
JAY HENGES ENTERPRISES INC (MO)
PORTA KING BUILDING SYSTEMS
4133 Shoreline Dr, Earth City, MO 63045-1211
Tel (314) 291-6600 *Founded/Ownrshp* 1969
Sales 51.1MM^{E} *EMP* 250
SIC 1742 1752 3448 1521

JAY HONDA
See JAY PONTIAC INC

D-U-N-S 00-415-7145 IMP
JAY INDUSTRIES INC
BROSHCO FABRICATED PRODUCTS
150 Longview Ave E, Mansfield, OH 44903-4206
Tel (419) 524-3778 *Founded/Ownrshp* 1946
Sales 230.1MM^{E} *EMP* 930
SIC 2531 3089 Seats, automobile; Injection molding of plastics; Seats, automobile; Injection molding of plastics
Pr: Rick R Taylor
**CFO:* Rodger Loesch
**VP:* Josh Taylor
**Prin:* R G Taylor
Prgrm Mgr: Dan Shell
Div Mgr: Glenn Ertel
Telecom Ex: Mark Amicone
Prd Mgr: Jeffrey Spurlock
Ql Cn Mgr: Dean Wilkinson
Sales Exec: Rodney Earick
VP Mktg: Suha Inal

JAY MARKS MAZDA HYUNDAI SUZUKI
See 10475 PARTNERS LTD

D-U-N-S 01-475-9588 IMP
JAY MEHTA INC (CA)
J M OIL COMPANY
12330 Greenstone Ave, Santa Fe Springs, CA 90670-4737
Tel (562) 941-7772 *Founded/Ownrshp* 1998
Sales 25.0MM *EMP* 8
SIC 5172 Lubricating oils & greases
Pr: Jay Mehta

D-U-N-S 15-235-2733
JAY MID-SOUTH LLC
140 Thomas Dr, Gadsden, AL 35904-8228
Tel (256) 439-6600 *Founded/Ownrshp* 2004
Sales 23.7MM^{E} *EMP* 150
SIC 3499 Automobile seat frames, metal; Automobile seat frames, metal
CFO: Rodger Loesch
Plnt Mgr: Brent Taylor

D-U-N-S 05-091-7111
JAY MILLS CONTRACTING INC
6126 N Hwy 377, Stephenville, TX 76401
Tel (254) 965-6657 *Founded/Ownrshp* 1979
Sales 23.0MM^{E} *EMP* 100
SIC 1629 Earthmoving contractor; Dam construction
Pr: Toby Mills
**Sec:* Debbie Mills
**VP:* Jay Dean Mills
IT Man: Rona Mills

D-U-N-S 09-599-4836
JAY NOLAN COMMUNITY SERVICES INC (CA)
15501 San Fernando Missio, Mission Hills, CA 91345-1385
Tel (818) 361-6400 *Founded/Ownrshp* 1975
Sales 14.9MM *EMP* 525
Accts Green Hasson & Janks Llp Los
SIC 8322 8331 8361 Social services for the handicapped; Job training & vocational rehabilitation services; Residential care; Social services for the handicapped; Job training & vocational rehabilitation services; Residential care
Ex Dir: Jeffrey Strully
Sls Dir: Jorge Preciado

D-U-N-S 01-912-0666
JAY PEAK RESORT INC
JAY PEAK SKI RESORT
830 Jay Peak Rd, Jay Peak, VT 05859-7046
Tel (802) 988-2611 *Founded/Ownrshp* 1970
Sales 49.5MM^{E} *EMP* 411^{E}
SIC 7011 6552 Ski lodge; Subdividers & developers; Ski lodge; Subdividers & developers
Pr: William J Stenger
**CFO:* George Gulisano
Dir Sec: Thomas Howell
QA Dir: Hank Marshall
Dir IT: Craig Russell
IT Man: Diane Dupuis

JAY PEAK SKI RESORT
See JAY PEAK RESORT INC

D-U-N-S 01-658-6075
JAY PETROLEUM INC
PAK-A-SAK
533 S 200 W, Portland, IN 47371-8309
Tel (260) 726-9374 *Founded/Ownrshp* 1959
Sales 153.7MM *EMP* 420
Accts Bkd Llp Fort Wayne In
SIC 5411 5172 Convenience stores, chain; Gasoline; Convenience stores, chain; Gasoline
Pr: Ronald Freeman
**Sec:* Timothy Caster
**VP:* Chris Braun
**VP:* Kevin Huffman

D-U-N-S 01-753-1526
JAY PONTIAC INC
JAY HONDA
18800 Rockside Rd, Bedford, OH 44146-2054
Tel (440) 232-5000 *Founded/Ownrshp* 1957
Sales 46.5MM^{E} *EMP* 133
SIC 5511 Automobiles, new & used; Automobiles, new & used
Pr: Marc Jacobson
**VP:* Michael Mihalic
Sales Asso: Jose Ore
Sales Asso: Tim Schwab
Sales Asso: S Singh
Sales Asso: Matt Stovarksy

JAY PUBLIC SCHOOLS
See JAY SCHOOL DISTRICT 1

JAY R SMITH MFG CO
See SMITH INDUSTRIES INC

D-U-N-S 07-597-7454
JAY SCHOOL CORP
JAY SCHOOL DISTRICT
1976 W Tyson Rd, Portland, IN 47371-7994
Tel (260) 726-9341 *Founded/Ownrshp* 1964
Sales 31.3MM^{E} *EMP* 545
SIC 8211 School board; School board
Treas: Jane Carlin

JAY SCHOOL DISTRICT
See JAY SCHOOL CORP

D-U-N-S 05-658-5128
JAY SCHOOL DISTRICT 1
JAY PUBLIC SCHOOLS
821 N Main St, Jay, OK 74346-2807
Tel (918) 253-4293 *Founded/Ownrshp* 1929
Sales 15.5MM^{E} *EMP* 310
SIC 8211 Public elementary & secondary schools; School board; Public elementary & secondary schools; School board
Treas: Misty Osburn
Cmptr Lab: Sheila Guinn

JAY TOYOTA
See JAY AUTOMOTIVE GROUP INC

D-U-N-S 17-183-6385
JAY W VW LLC
JAY WOLFE VOLKSWAGEN AUDI
10344 Summit St, Kansas City, MO 64114-4522
Tel (816) 941-9500 *Founded/Ownrshp* 2003
Sales 29.0MM *EMP* 50
SIC 5511 Automobiles, new & used; Automobiles, new & used
Mng Pt: Lee Hubbard

D-U-N-S 04-238-6078
JAY WOLFE CHEVROLET INC
7611 State Ave, Kansas City, KS 66112-2817
Tel (913) 334-3300 *Founded/Ownrshp* 1971
Sales 22.3MM^{E} *EMP* 85
SIC 5511 Automobiles, new & used; Pickups, new & used; Vans, new & used; Automobiles, new & used; Pickups, new & used; Vans, new & used
Pr: Jay Wolfe
**CFO:* Bob Priest
**Sec:* Cynthia L Tucci

JAY WOLFE HONDA
See JAY WOLFE IMPORTS L L C

D-U-N-S 03-267-5597
JAY WOLFE IMPORTS L L C
JAY WOLFE HONDA
220 W 103rd St, Kansas City, MO 64114-4739
Tel (816) 942-2200 *Founded/Ownrshp* 1979
Sales 26.3MM^{E} *EMP* 70
SIC 5511 Automobiles, new & used; Automobiles, new & used
Sls Mgr: Jason Brink
Sls Mgr: Charla Eastwood

D-U-N-S 17-562-6266
JAY WOLFE IMPORTS MISSOURI INC
WOLFE, JAY ACURA
1029 W 103rd St, Kansas City, MO 64114-4509
Tel (816) 942-1550 *Founded/Ownrshp* 1986
Sales 34.2MM^{E} *EMP* 97
SIC 5511 Automobiles, new & used; Automobiles, new & used
Ch Bd: Jeff Wolfe

JAY WOLFE TOYOTA
See OAK NORTH AUTOMOTIVE INC

JAY WOLFE TOYOTA WEST COUNTY
See JEFF WOLFE

JAY WOLFE VOLKSWAGEN AUDI
See JAY W VW LLC

D-U-N-S 87-767-2113
JAY-AIMEE DESIGNS INC
99 Railroad Station Plz # 200, Hicksville, NY 11801-2850
Tel (718) 609-0333 *Founded/Ownrshp* 1987
Sales 21.8MM^{E} *EMP* 175
SIC 3911 Jewelry, precious metal; Earrings, precious metal; Bracelets, precious metal; Jewelry, precious metal; Earrings, precious metal; Bracelets, precious metal
CEO: Isaac Matalon
**Pr:* Shlomi Matalon

D-U-N-S 05-441-3935
JAY-BEE OIL & GAS INC
JAY BEE OIL & GAS COMPANY
1720 Us Highway 22 E # 1, Union, NJ 07083-6126
Tel (908) 686-1493 *Founded/Ownrshp* 1989
Sales 52.3MM^{E} *EMP* 75^{E}
SIC 1382 Oil & gas exploration services
Pr: Randy Broda
**VP:* Deborah B Morgan

D-U-N-S 01-293-8122
JAY-K INDEPENDENT LUMBER CORP (NY)
8448 Seneca Tpke, New Hartford, NY 13413-4960
Tel (315) 735-4475 *Founded/Ownrshp* 1937
Sales 32.5MM^{E} *EMP* 65
SIC 5031 5072 5211 5251 2426 2421 Lumber, plywood & millwork; Building materials, exterior; Building materials, interior; Hardware; Lumber & other building materials; Lumber products; Hardware; Hardwood dimension & flooring mills; Sawmills & planing mills, general; Lumber, plywood & millwork; Building materials, exterior; Building materials, interior; Hardware; Lumber & other building materials; Lumber products; Hardware; Hardwood dimension & flooring mills; Sawmills & planing mills, general
Pr: Dean Kelly
**VP:* Jonas Kelly

JAY-MAC
See YOUNG TRUCK SALES INC

D-U-N-S 05-189-2735
JAY-MAR INC (WI)
2130 Jay Mar Rd, Plover, WI 54467-3221
Tel (715) 341-3445 *Founded/Ownrshp* 1970
Sales 31.0MM^{E} *EMP* 35
SIC 5191 5199 Fertilizer & fertilizer materials; Chemicals, agricultural; Feed; Seeds: field, garden & flower; Packaging materials
Pr: Verne Johnson
**VP:* David Warner
IT Man: Bill Spees
Sls Mgr: Clint Hodorff

D-U-N-S 62-316-4506
JAY-REESE CONTRACTORS INC
32780 Ranch Road 12, Dripping Springs, TX 78620-3101
Tel (512) 829-5360 *Founded/Ownrshp* 1989
Sales 27.0MM^{E} *EMP* 55
SIC 1622 1541 8711 Highway construction, elevated; Industrial buildings & warehouses; Construction & civil engineering
Pr: Ron Albee
**Sec:* Chandra Aoueille

D-U-N-S 60-944-6745
JAY-TON CONSTRUCTION CO INC
7000 Highway 59 W, Burlison, TN 38015-7459
Tel (901) 476-1487 *Founded/Ownrshp* 1989
Sales 72.0MM^{E} *EMP* 275
Accts Robert M Wooten Jr Covingt
SIC 1741 Foundation building; Retaining wall construction; Foundation building; Retaining wall construction
Pr: James I Burlison
**Treas:* Kenneth W Holden
Opers Mgr: Shane Bates

D-U-N-S 19-148-3986 IMP
JAYA APPAREL GROUP LLC
5175 S Soto St, Vernon, CA 90058-3620
Tel (323) 584-3500 *Founded/Ownrshp* 2005
Sales 110.0MM *EMP* 170
SIC 2339 Women's & misses' athletic clothing & sportswear; Women's & misses' athletic clothing & sportswear
CEO: Jane Siskin
**CFO:* Don Lewis
VP: Ingrid Saurer
Natl Sales: Katelyn Berberian

D-U-N-S 82-767-4594 IMP
JAYBIRD LLC
1136 S 3600 W Ste 400, Salt Lake City, UT 84104-6527
Tel (801) 803-5700 *Founded/Ownrshp* 2006
Sales 24.6MM^{E} *EMP* 75
SIC 5065 Mobile telephone equipment; Intercommunication equipment, electronic
Chf Mktg O: Rene Oehlerking
Dir Soc: Craig Hansen

JAYC FOOD STORES
See KROGER LIMITED PARTNERSHIP I

D-U-N-S 05-122-1125 EXP
JAYCO INC
BOTTOM LINE RV
903 S Main St, Middlebury, IN 46540-8529
Tel (574) 825-5861 *Founded/Ownrshp* 1968
Sales 435.4MM^{E} *EMP* 1,770
SIC 3792 3716 5013 House trailers, except as permanent dwellings; Campers, for mounting on trucks; Camping trailers & chassis; Motor homes; Recreational van conversion (self-propelled), factory basis; Trailer parts & accessories; House trailers, except as permanent dwellings; Campers, for mounting on trucks; Camping trailers & chassis; Motor homes; Recreational van conversion (self-propelled), factory basis; Trailer parts & accessories
Pr: Derald Bontrager
Ch Bd: Wilbur Bontrager
**Ch Bd:* Bertha Bontrager Rhodes
CFO: John Wolf
CFO: Kent Yoder
VP: David Eash
VP: Paul Geczy
VP: Tadd Jenkins
VP: Chuck Lasley
VP: Joseph Morthorst
Dir IT: Kenneth Jobin

D-U-N-S 07-873-0918
JAYCOR INC
3394 Carmel Mountain Rd, San Diego, CA 92121-1065
Tel (858) 720-4000 *Founded/Ownrshp* 2003
Sales 31.1MM^{E} *EMP* 500
SIC 8733 8711 Scientific research agency; Engineering services; Scientific research agency; Engineering services
CEO: Eric M Demarco

D-U-N-S 02-221-8796
JAYCOX IMPLEMENT INC
403 S Market St, Lake Park, IA 51347-7859
Tel (712) 832-3151 *Founded/Ownrshp* 1956
Sales 87.4MM *EMP* 48
SIC 5083 7699 Agricultural machinery & equipment; Farm machinery repair; Agricultural machinery & equipment; Farm machinery repair
Ch Bd: Raymond L Jaycox
**Pr:* Chad Jaycox
**CFO:* Bonnie Anderson
**VP:* Dennis Puhrman

D-U-N-S 60-507-7031
JAYEN INC
FASTOP FOOD STORES
4102 Us Highway 59 N, Victoria, TX 77905-5592
Tel (361) 575-1981 *Founded/Ownrshp* 1982
Sales 70.4MM *EMP* 43
Accts Ob Furness Cpa
SIC 5411 Convenience stores; Convenience stores
Prin: Jon R New

D-U-N-S 08-742-6136 IMP
JAYHAWK OILFIELD SUPPLY INC (KS)
100 S Main St, Spivey, KS 67142-4202
Tel (620) 532-5175 *Founded/Ownrshp* 1974, 2008
Sales 34.0MM *EMP* 38
SIC 5084 7699 Oil well machinery, equipment & supplies; Industrial machinery & equipment repair
Pr: Frederick L Yoder

D-U-N-S 00-694-4136
■ **JAYHAWK PIPELINE LLC** (KS)
(*Suby of* CHS MCPHERSON REFINERY INC) ★
2000 S Main St, McPherson, KS 67460-9402
Tel (620) 241-9270 *Founded/Ownrshp* 1957
Sales 30.6MM *EMP* 50
SIC 4612 Crude petroleum pipelines; Crude petroleum pipelines
Genl Mgr: Rick Petersen

D-U-N-S 13-047-4971
JAYNES COMPANIES
2906 Broadway Blvd Ne, Albuquerque, NM 87107-1506
Tel (505) 345-8591 *Founded/Ownrshp* 2002
Sales 148.1MM^{E} *EMP* 300^{E}
SIC 1611 General contractor, highway & street construction; General contractor, highway & street construction
VP: Donald Power
IT Man: Berube Mark

D-U-N-S 00-711-2253
JAYNES CORP (NM)
JAYNES STRUCTURES
(*Suby of* JAYNES COMPANIES) ★
2906 Broadway Blvd Ne, Albuquerque, NM 87107-1599
Tel (505) 345-8591 *Founded/Ownrshp* 1965
Sales 148.1MM^{E} *EMP* 250
SIC 1542 1541 Hospital construction; School building construction; Commercial & office building, new construction; Industrial buildings, new construction; Hospital construction; School building construction; Commercial & office building, new construction; Industrial buildings, new construction
CEO: Rick Marquardt
**Pr:* Shad James
**CFO:* Tracy Utterback
Ofcr: Robert McKissick
**Ex VP:* Greg Krause
VP Bus Dev: Douglas Clark
Exec: Del Ameko
IT Man: Berube Mark
IT Man: Brian Oconnell
Sfty Dirs: Bernie Garcia

JAYNES STRUCTURES
See JAYNES CORP

JAYS CATERING
See MASTROIANNI FAMILY ENTERPRISES LTD

D-U-N-S 01-515-0683
JAYS MARKETS INC
CARMACK-JAY'S
575 Maryland Ave, York, PA 17404-2821
Tel (717) 764-1667 *Founded/Ownrshp* 1965
Sales 28.1MM *EMP* 4
Accts Seligman Friedman & Co Cpa S
SIC 5411 Supermarkets, independent
Pr: Joey J Miller
**Ch Bd:* Jay E Miller
Treas: Michael McFatridge
VP: Ken Gotwalt
VP: Tyrone C Miller

D-U-N-S 04-714-3839
JAYS SPORTING GOODS INC
8800 S Clare Ave, Clare, MI 48617-8635
Tel (989) 386-3475 *Founded/Ownrshp* 1967
Sales 27.4MM^{E} *EMP* 245
SIC 5941 Sporting goods & bicycle shops; Sporting goods & bicycle shops
Pr: Jeffery Poet
**Sec:* Arlene Poet
**VP:* John J Poet
Mktg Dir: Matt Poet

D-U-N-S 03-289-3096 IMP
JAYTEC LLC
(*Suby of* L & W INC) ★
17757 Woodland Dr, New Boston, MI 48164-9265
Tel (517) 451-8272 *Founded/Ownrshp* 2001
Sales 31.5MM^{E} *EMP* 150
SIC 3465 Automotive stampings; Automotive stampings
VP: Robert Koss
Genl Mgr: Mark Jones
Opers Mgr: Scott Callow
Plnt Mgr: Johnny Lindeman
Ql Cn Mgr: Alex Garcia

D-U-N-S 01-744-1252
JAZWARES HOLDCO INC
1067 Shotgun Rd, Sunrise, FL 33326-1906
Tel (954) 845-0800 *Founded/Ownrshp* 2014
Sales 75.3MM^{E} *EMP* 101
SIC 5092 Toys & games
CEO: Judd Zebersky

D-U-N-S 85-970-6017 IMP/EXP
JAZWARES LLC
(*Suby of* JAZWARES HOLDCO INC) ★
1069 Shotgun Rd, Sunrise, FL 33326
Tel (954) 845-0800 *Founded/Ownrshp* 1999

Sales 75.3MM^E *EMP* 100
SIC 5092 Toys & games; Toys & games
Pr: Judd Zebersky
Pr: Vincent Yang
COO: David Neustein
COO: Laura Zebersky
CFO: Matt Siesel
VP: Bill Graham
Creative D: Keren Globus
IT Man: Ben May
Sls Mgr: Matt Cohen

D-U-N-S 84-218-3449
JAZZ AT LINCOLN CENTER INC
3 Columbus Cir Fl 12, New York, NY 10019-8716
Tel (212) 258-9800 *Founded/Ownrshp* 1996
Sales 79.8MM *EMP* 120^E
Accts Lutz And Carr Cpas Llp New Yo
SIC 7299 7929 Banquet hall facilities; Entertainers & entertainment groups; Banquet hall facilities; Entertainers & entertainment groups
CEO: Susan Gordon
Pr: Scott Daly
Pr: Lauren Kiel
**COO:* Paul Logan
CFO: Caroline Croen
CFO: Freda Gimpel
**VP:* Gabrielle Armand
**VP:* Dwayne Ashley
**VP:* James E Grooms
VP: Doug Hosney
**VP:* Derek Kwan
**VP:* Todd Stoll

D-U-N-S 05-265-3784
JAZZ CASINO CO L L C
HARRAH'S CASINO
8 Canal St, New Orleans, LA 70130-1601
Tel (504) 525-6260 *Founded/Ownrshp* 2008
Sales 52.5MM^E *EMP* 2,500
SIC 7011 Casino hotel; Casino hotel
MIS Mgr: Desmond Robinson

D-U-N-S 13-592-6363 IMP
■ **JAZZ PHARMACEUTICALS INC**
(*Suby of* JAZZ PHARMACEUTICALS PUBLIC LIMITED COMPANY)
3180 Porter Dr, Palo Alto, CA 94304-1288
Tel (650) 496-3777 *Founded/Ownrshp* 2012
Sales 1.1MMM *EMP* 626^E
Tkr Sym JAZZ *Exch* NGS
SIC 2834 Pharmaceutical preparations; Drugs acting on the central nervous system & sense organs; Pharmaceutical preparations; Drugs acting on the central nervous system & sense organs
Ch Bd: Bruce C Cozadd
**CFO:* Kathryn E Falberg
Bd of Dir: James Momtazee
**Ex VP:* Russell J Cox
**Ex VP:* Suzanne Sawochka Hooper
Ex VP: Jeffrey Tobias
Sr VP: Charles Lapree
Sr VP: Craig Parker
Assoc Dir: Roberta Bongers
Assoc Dir: Wendy Burton
Assoc Dir: Jeff Christensen
Assoc Dir: Anand Hemrajani
Assoc Dir: Yuan Lu
Assoc Dir: Jessica Mendoza
Assoc Dir: Christy Rathjens

D-U-N-S 11-057-3743
JAZZ SEMICONDUCTOR INC
TOWERJAZZ
(*Suby of* JAZZ TECHNOLOGIES INC) ★
4321 Jamboree Rd, Newport Beach, CA 92660-3007
Tel (949) 435-8000 *Founded/Ownrshp* 2007
Sales 208.2MM^E *EMP* 805
SIC 3674 Wafers (semiconductor devices); Wafers (semiconductor devices)
Ch: Amir Elstein
**CEO:* Russell Elwanger
COO: Chang-Ou Lee
**CFO:* Susanna Bennett
CFO: Laryssa Reifel
Ex VP: Karen Wilson
Sr VP: Rafi Mor
VP: Nabil Alali
**VP:* Marco Racanelli
Prgrm Mgr: Clement Ukah
Genl Mgr: Victer Chan
Board of Directors: Donald Beall, Dwight Decker, Patrick R McCarter, Jerry Neal, Todd Newnam, R Douglas Norby, Donald Schrock

D-U-N-S 79-548-7714
JAZZ TECHNOLOGIES INC
(*Suby of* TOWER SEMICONDUCTOR LTD)
4321 Jamboree Rd, Newport Beach, CA 92660-3007
Tel (949) 435-8000 *Founded/Ownrshp* 2008
Sales 221.4MM *EMP* 805
SIC 3674 Wafers (semiconductor devices); Wafers (semiconductor devices)
Pr: Marco Racanelli
CEO: Ronit Vardi
VP: Don Cerney
VP: Andy Chan

D-U-N-S 08-408-6131
JAZZY ELECTRONICS CORP
PYRAMID SOUND
1600 63rd St, Brooklyn, NY 11204-2713
Tel (718) 236-8000 *Founded/Ownrshp* 1977
Sales 104.2MM^E *EMP* 125^E
SIC 6512 5064 3651 Nonresidential building operators; High fidelity equipment; Household audio & video equipment
Pr: Zigmond Brach
**Pr:* Jerry Brach

D-U-N-S 06-773-7718
JB DENTAL SUPPLY CO INC
17000 Kingsview Ave, Carson, CA 90746-1230
Tel (310) 202-8855 *Founded/Ownrshp* 1973
Sales 33.0MM^E *EMP* 450
SIC 5047 Dental equipment & supplies; Dental equipment & supplies
Pr: Joseph Berman
**VP:* Manny Chada
Brnch Mgr: Kip Giro
Sls&Mrk Ex: Ann Westeroff

JB HENDERSON CONSTRUCTION
See JACK B HENDERSON CONSTRUCTION CO INC

D-U-N-S 00-633-8552
▲ **JB HUNT TRANSPORT SERVICES INC**
615 J B Hunt Corporate Dr, Lowell, AR 72745-9143
Tel (479) 820-0000 *Founded/Ownrshp* 1961
Sales 6.1MMM *EMP* 20,158
Accts Ernst & Young Llp Rogers Ar
Tkr Sym JBHT *Exch* NGS
SIC 4213 4731 Trucking, except local; Freight transportation arrangement; Trucking, except local; Freight transportation arrangement
Pr: John N Roberts III
**Ch Bd:* Kirk Thompson
Pr: John McKuin
COO: Craig Harper
CFO: David G Mee
Treas: David N Chelette
Ofcr: Paul R Bergant
Ex VP: John N Roberts III
Sr VP: Greg Breeden
VP: John Kuhlow
Dir Bus: Mark Dewar
Dir Bus: Mark Ferguson
Dir Bus: Jim Krueger
Dir Bus: Barry Leff
Dir Bus: Glenn Meadows
Dir Bus: Bob Miller
Dir Bus: Tim Murphy
Dir Bus: Tony Sica
Dir Bus: Tammy Virgil

D-U-N-S 19-855-4255
JB INDUSTRIES INC
4203 35th St, Long Island City, NY 11101-2301
Tel (718) 729-2020 *Founded/Ownrshp* 1987
Sales 111.7MM^E *EMP* 31
SIC 6512 6531 Nonresidential building operators; Real estate managers
Pr: Joel Berman
**Ex VP:* Jan Berman

D-U-N-S 14-212-4614
JB JAMES CONSTRUCTION LLC
1881 Wooddale Blvd, Baton Rouge, LA 70806-1510
Tel (225) 927-3131 *Founded/Ownrshp* 2001
Sales 85.5MM^E *EMP* 230
SIC 1611 Highway & street construction; Highway & street construction
Off Mgr: Monica Cornette
Mtls Mgr: Mike Tucker
**Sls&Mrk Ex:* Gerald Denley
Snr Mgr: Bill Clark

J.B. KENEHAN, LLC
See JBK SALE LLC

D-U-N-S 96-420-6288
JB MARINE SERVICE INC
4190 Bussen Rd, Saint Louis, MO 63129-4404
Tel (314) 894-3805 *Founded/Ownrshp* 2001
Sales 25.4MM^E *EMP* 109
SIC 3731 Shipbuilding & repairing
Pr: George Foster
**CFO:* Dave Heyl
Exec: Karen Shoot

D-U-N-S 00-121-0368 IMP/EXP
JB MARTIN CO
(*Suby of* MRM)
645 5th Ave Rm 400, New York, NY 10022-5954
Tel (212) 421-2020 *Founded/Ownrshp* 1953, 1989
Sales 23.9MM^E *EMP* 220
SIC 2221

D-U-N-S 00-400-0360 IMP
JB&T HOLDINGS LLC (AL)
10200 Highway 80 E, Montgomery, AL 36117-6060
Tel (334) 834-2210 *Founded/Ownrshp* 1906, 1984
Sales 73.6MM^E *EMP* 315
SIC 5211 3251 Brick; Brick clay: common face, glazed, vitrified or hollow; Brick; Brick clay: common face, glazed, vitrified or hollow
VP: Leon Hawk
VP: Brian Sims
VP: Norris Watson

D-U-N-S 04-167-0183
JBA CONSULTING ENGINEERS INC
5155 W Patrick Ln, Las Vegas, NV 89118-2828
Tel (702) 362-9200 *Founded/Ownrshp* 1966
Sales 26.1MM^E *EMP* 130
SIC 8711 7373

D-U-N-S 11-030-0779 EXP
JBC HOLDING CO
3601 S Banker St, Effingham, IL 62401-2899
Tel (217) 347-7701 *Founded/Ownrshp* 1996
Sales 63.4MM^E *EMP* 190
SIC 2541 2542 2511 2099 Wood partitions & fixtures; Counters or counter display cases: except wood; Wood household furniture; Bread crumbs, not made in bakeries; Wood partitions & fixtures; Counters or counter display cases: except wood; Wood household furniture; Bread crumbs, not made in bakeries
Ch: Louis Kenter
VP: James Gibbons

D-U-N-S 16-614-2083 IMP
JBE INC
512 Hartland Dr, Hartsville, SC 29550-2913
Tel (843) 332-0589 *Founded/Ownrshp* 1984
Sales 30.3MM *EMP* 70
SIC 3711 7521 8741 Automobile assembly, including specialty automobiles; Automobile storage garage; Management services; Automobile assembly, including specialty automobiles; Automobile storage garage; Management services
Pr: Jerry Ellison
**Treas:* Lajuan Ellison Davis
**VP:* Dwayne Ellison
**VP:* Loretta Ellison
**VP:* Ricardo Ellison
Board of Directors: Cleve Ellison

JBF
See NEW JERSEY BUSINESS FORMS MANUFACTURING CORP

JBFCS
See JEWISH BOARD OF FAMILY AND CHILDRENS SERVICES INC

JBG COMPANIES
See JBG PROPERTIES INC

JBG COMPANIES, THE
See JBG COMPANIES L L C

D-U-N-S 07-913-1226
JBG COMPANIES L L C
JBG COMPANIES, THE
4445 Willard Ave, Chevy Chase, MD 20815-3690
Tel (240) 333-3600 *Founded/Ownrshp* 2003
Sales 105.0MM^E *EMP* 251^E
SIC 6799 Investors
VP: Tom Brennan
Pr: Philip Sclafani
Trst: Joseph Gildenhorn
Ex VP: Robin Mosle
Sr VP: Moina Banerjee
Sr VP: Brian Gould
Sr VP: Margaret Klarman
Sr VP: Michael Rogers
VP: Joe Babarsky
VP: Michael Becker
VP: Edward Chaglassian
VP: Kristen Edison
VP: George Hardos
VP: Lauren Jezienicki
VP: Donna McKinnon
VP: Jennifer Michaels
VP: James Nozar
VP: Ashesh Parikh
VP: James Reed
VP: Quinn Rounsaville
VP: Kristi Smith

D-U-N-S 07-679-5207
JBG PROPERTIES INC
JBG COMPANIES
4445 Willard Ave Ste 400, Chevy Chase, MD 20815-4641
Tel (240) 333-3600 *Founded/Ownrshp* 1962
Sales 196.8MM^E *EMP* 500
SIC 6531 6552 Real estate agents & managers; Subdividers & developers; Real estate agents & managers; Subdividers & developers
Ex VP: Robert Schwenger
Sr VP: Brooks A Blake
Sr VP: Krista Di Iaconi
Sr VP: Edward J Kopp
Sr VP: Kai Reynolds
VP: Adam Peters
Genl Mgr: Genny Hardesty
Board of Directors: Brian Coulter, Rob Stewart

D-U-N-S 96-864-5759
JBG/TYSONS HOTEL LLC
SHERATON PRMERE ATTYSONS CRNR
8661 Leesburg Pike, Vienna, VA 22182-2226
Tel (703) 506-2500 *Founded/Ownrshp* 1999
Sales 20.0MM^E *EMP* 206
SIC 7011 Hotels; Hotels
Genl Mgr: Mike Chouri
IT Man: Scarlett Saavedra
Sls Mgr: Cindy Yang

D-U-N-S 60-128-3682
JBI ELECTRICAL SYSTEMS INC
5631 Stratum Dr, Fort Worth, TX 76137-2709
Tel (817) 589-1545 *Founded/Ownrshp* 1989
Sales 33.1MM^E *EMP* 150
Accts Perryman Chaney Russell Llp
SIC 1731 General electrical contractor; General electrical contractor
Pr: Jacky D Martin
CFO: Patrick Olson
**VP:* Pat Olsen
MIS Dir: Dan Carter
Dir IT: Jeff Parish
VP Opers: Pat Olson
Sales Exec: Mike Sapp
Snr Mgr: Gary Dalrymple

D-U-N-S 04-441-2054 IMP/EXP
JBI LLC
2650 E El Presidio St, Long Beach, CA 90810-1142
Tel (310) 886-8034 *Founded/Ownrshp* 1968
Sales 51.0MM^E *EMP* 250
SIC 2599 5046 Restaurant furniture, wood or metal; Restaurant equipment & supplies; Restaurant furniture, wood or metal; Restaurant equipment & supplies
CFO: John Bertoldi
Ex VP: Andy Braddy
Ex VP: Scott Mallory
CIO: William Walser
**CTO:* Gregg Buchbinder
MIS Dir: Sarah Horton
IT Man: William Antun
IT Man: Bill Morris
IT Man: William Parson
VP Sls: Jay Rothman
Sales Asso: Robert Rivas

D-U-N-S 14-474-4224
JBK SALE LLC
J.B. KENEHAN, LLC
(*Suby of* CATCHFIRE MEDIA LLC) ★
W238n1700 Rockwood Dr, Waukesha, WI 53188-1149
Tel (262) 523-8400 *Founded/Ownrshp* 2014
Sales 36.1MM^E *EMP* 200
SIC 2759

D-U-N-S 87-812-7257
JBL ELECTRIC INC
(*Suby of* PHALCON LTD) ★
3001 S Clinton Ave, South Plainfield, NJ 07080-1440
Tel (908) 462-0093 *Founded/Ownrshp* 2006
Sales 79.5MM *EMP* 100
Accts Blumshapiro & Company Pc W
SIC 1731 Electrical work; Electrical work
Pr: James B Leary
**CFO:* John Conroy
**VP:* Terry Craig
**Prin:* Michael O'Donovan
**Prin:* Jerry Reid
Sfty Dirs: Ken Dittmer
Mtls Mgr: Steven Leary

D-U-N-S 09-681-9990
JBL INTERNATIONAL INC
PAGET EQUIPMENT CO
417 E 29th St, Marshfield, WI 54449-5312
Tel (715) 384-3158 *Founded/Ownrshp* 1985
Sales 22.0MM *EMP* 63
Accts Hawkins Ash Baptie & Company
SIC 3443 Industrial vessels, tanks & containers; Heat exchangers, condensers & components; Metal parts; Chutes & troughs; Industrial vessels, tanks & containers; Heat exchangers, condensers & components; Metal parts; Chutes & troughs
CEO: James L Reigel
**Pr:* Paul Hagen
**Sec:* Diane E Reigel
CTO: Aric Strand
Ql Cn Mgr: Steve Desmet
Sls Mgr: Alan Shepard

D-U-N-S 19-688-4175 IMP
JBM INC
2651 Scottish Pike, Knoxville, TN 37920-1946
Tel (865) 573-9800 *Founded/Ownrshp* 1989
Sales 33.2MM^E *EMP* 68
SIC 3444 Sheet metalwork
Pr: Ray Pate
**Treas:* James Stiles
Sales Exec: Cathy Popham

D-U-N-S 94-115-6242
JBM INC
BLUEGRASS SATELLITE AND SEC
33 W 2nd St Ste 504, Maysville, KY 41056-1166
Tel (606) 564-0007 *Founded/Ownrshp* 1977
Sales 21.1MM^E *EMP* 300
SIC 5731 Antennas, satellite dish; Antennas, satellite dish
Pr: John Mattingly
CFO: David Wallingford

JBR GOURMET FOODS
See JBR INC

D-U-N-S 09-706-5510 IMP
JBR INC
JBR GOURMET FOODS
1731 Aviation Blvd, Lincoln, CA 95648-9317
Tel (916) 258-8000 *Founded/Ownrshp* 1979
Sales 170.0MM^E *EMP* 230^E
SIC 2095 2099 Roasted coffee; Coffee roasting (except by wholesale grocers); Tea blending; Roasted coffee; Coffee roasting (except by wholesale grocers); Tea blending
CEO: Jon B Rogers
**VP:* Barbara Rogers
IT Man: Matthew McGinley
S&M/VP: Lisa Smoot
Manager: Bob Giacomelli

D-U-N-S 05-745-7418 IMP
JBR PROPERTIES OF GREENVILLE INC
ROBERTS COMPANY, THE
133 Forlines Rd, Winterville, NC 28590-8508
Tel (252) 355-9353 *Founded/Ownrshp* 1977
Sales 66.4MM^E *EMP* 730
SIC 1541 3443

D-U-N-S 07-843-4126
JBR TECHNOLOGIES LLC
BASE2 SOLUTIONS
400 108th Ave Ne Ste 300, Bellevue, WA 98004-5508
Tel (425) 777-4100 *Founded/Ownrshp* 2011
Sales 21.1MM^E *EMP* 70
SIC 7379
Pr: Ronald Hopkins
CFO: Timothy Graven
VP: Tom McCarthy
Prgrm Mgr: Charlie Barbour
Snr Sftwr: Scot Fordyce
Snr Sftwr: Ernest Kim
Snr Sftwr: Jacob Lambrecht
QA Dir: Steven Walker
IT Man: Dan Gullick
Software D: Paul Charlton
Sftwr Eng: Eric Hicks

JBRANDJEANS
See J BRAND INC

D-U-N-S 07-951-2460
JBRE HOLDINGS LLC
8150 N Central Expy, Dallas, TX 75206-1815
Tel (214) 276-5504 *Founded/Ownrshp* 2014
Sales 106.8MM^E *EMP* 1,001^E
SIC 7539 6719 Brake repair, automotive; Investment holding companies, except banks

D-U-N-S 84-742-2631
JBRE LLC
JUST BRAKES
(*Suby of* JBRE HOLDINGS LLC) ★
8150 N Central Expy M1008, Dallas, TX 75206-1815
Tel (214) 276-5504 *Founded/Ownrshp* 2013
Sales 106.8MM^E *EMP* 850
SIC 7539 Brake repair, automotive; Brake repair, automotive
Ch Bd: Perry Cloud
Pr: Tom Balash
**CFO:* Wil Saqueton
**VP:* Bennet R Cloud
**VP:* Clothilde Cloud
**VP:* Leigh A Cloud
**VP:* Leigh Anne Haugh
**VP:* Stewart Manning
Dir Soc: Sarah Hamp
Dir IT: Jeff Payne
IT Man: Lance Smith

D-U-N-S 00-491-9917
■ **JBS CARRIERS INC**
(*Suby of* JBS USA IMPORTS) ★
2401 2nd Ave, Greeley, CO 80631-7205
Tel (866) 298-4573 *Founded/Ownrshp* 1988

Sales 130.0MM *EMP* 700^E
SIC 4213 Trucking, except local; Trucking, except local
Pr: Rodrigo Horgath
VP: Todd Gooch
Genl Mgr: Jerry Shelton
Sfty Dirs: Mark Respass

D-U-N-S 92-625-1281
JBS CONTRACTING INC
1680 Gover Pkwy, Mount Pleasant, MI 48858-8142
Tel (989) 773-0770 *Founded/Ownrshp* 1993
Sales 20.6MM *EMP* 38
Accts Dedloff Pc Mt Pleasant M
SIC 1541 1542 Industrial buildings, new construction; Commercial & office building, new construction; Industrial buildings, new construction; Commercial & office building, new construction
Pr: James Kremsreiter
**VP:* John Stadtfeld
IT Man: Josh Melnek
Sfty Mgr: Lee Roethlisberger

D-U-N-S 55-647-0651
■ **JBS FIVE RIVERS CATTLE FEEDING LLC**
(*Suby of* JBS USA HOLDINGS INC) ★
1770 Promontory Cir, Greeley, CO 80634-9039
Tel (970) 506-8000 *Founded/Ownrshp* 2008
Sales 106.7MM^E *EMP* 720
SIC 0211 Beef cattle feedlots; Beef cattle feedlots
CEO: Mike Thoren
VP: Tom Brink
Genl Mgr: Nolan Stone
Dir IT: Mike Shafer

D-U-N-S 16-115-7631
JBS INTERNATIONAL INC
5515 Security Ln Ste 800, North Bethesda, MD 20852-5032
Tel (301) 495-1080 *Founded/Ownrshp* 1985
Sales 69.1MM *EMP* 355
SIC 8748 Business consulting; Business consulting
CEO: Jerri Shaw
VP: Susan Gabbard
VP: Latif Khalil
Exec: Cynthia Currin
Creative D: Robert Walter
Creative D: Terrie Young
Telecom Ex: John Reimer
IT Man: Latief Kaleo
IT Man: Matthew Lloyd
Web Dev: Max Handelsman
Software D: Vera Lyalko

D-U-N-S 02-685-9577
■ **JBS LIVE PORK LLC**
(*Suby of* JBS USA IMPORTS) ★
1770 Promontory Cir, Greeley, CO 80634-9039
Tel (970) 506-8000 *Founded/Ownrshp* 2015
Sales 4.9MM^E *EMP* 350^E
SIC 0213 Hogs

D-U-N-S 92-709-2130
JBS MENTAL HEALTH AUTHORITY
940 Montclair Rd Ste 200, Birmingham, AL 35213-1212
Tel (205) 595-4555 *Founded/Ownrshp* 1995
Sales 2.3MM *EMP* 600
SIC 8063 Hospital for the mentally ill; Hospital for the mentally ill
Ex Dir: Richard Craig

D-U-N-S 08-618-6285
■ **JBS PACKERLAND INC**
I-57 SERVICE CENTER
(*Suby of* JBS PACKERLAND INC) ★
1330 Lime Kiln Rd, Green Bay, WI 54311-6044
Tel (920) 468-4000 *Founded/Ownrshp* 1994
Sales 100.9MM^E *EMP* 1,000
SIC 2011 4213 Boxed beef from meat slaughtered on site; Trucking, except local; Boxed beef from meat slaughtered on site; Trucking, except local
Ch Bd: George N Gillett Jr
**Pr:* Richard V Vesta
VP: John Ruby
VP: Jerry Shelton
Genl Mgr: Curt Grimm
Off Mgr: Dave Trimmer
VP Opers: Joe Badoren
Sfty Mgr: Jeremy Klingbeil
Opers Mgr: Rick Deniel

D-U-N-S 94-676-3638
■ **JBS PACKERLAND INC**
(*Suby of* JBS S/A.)
1770 Promontory Cir, Greeley, CO 80634-9039
Tel (970) 506-8000 *Founded/Ownrshp* 2008
Sales 177.0MM^E *EMP* 1,500
SIC 2011 4213 Boxed beef from meat slaughtered on site; Trucking, except local; Boxed beef from meat slaughtered on site; Trucking, except local
Pr: Richard V Vesta
**CFO:* Craig A Liegel
CFO: Fabio Sandri
Bd of Dir: Don Jackson
Bd of Dir: Lonnie Pilgrim
Ex VP: Jeff Johnson
VP: Jerry Shelton
VP: Scott Walker
DP Exec: Curt Vancalster
Sfty Mgr: Jeremy Klingbeil
Sfty Mgr: Eric Plate

D-U-N-S 19-673-7910
JBS PACKING CO INC
101 Houston Ave, Port Arthur, TX 77640-6413
Tel (409) 982-3216 *Founded/Ownrshp* 1988
Sales 41.6MM^E *EMP* 87
SIC 5146 5812 5421 Fish & seafoods; Seafood restaurants; Fish & seafood markets; Fish & seafoods; Seafood restaurants; Fish & seafood markets
Pr: Andrew Blanchard
**Treas:* Mark Leckich
**Sec:* Blake Hemmenway
**Sec:* Scott Young
**VP:* Ryan Hemmenway
**VP:* Jonathan McLendon
**Genl Mgr:* Trey Pearson
**Plnt Mgr:* Jimmy Stringfellow

D-U-N-S 06-435-0234
■ **JBS SOUDERTON INC**
MOPAC
(*Suby of* JBS S/A.)
249 Allentown Rd, Souderton, PA 18964-2207
Tel (215) 723-5555 *Founded/Ownrshp* 2008
Sales 172.3MM^E *EMP* 1,550
SIC 2011 2077 2013 Beef products from beef slaughtered on site; Cured meats from meat slaughtered on site; Luncheon meat from meat slaughtered on site; Meat by-products from meat slaughtered on site; Animal & marine fats & oils; Sausages & other prepared meats; Beef products from beef slaughtered on site; Cured meats from meat slaughtered on site; Luncheon meat from meat slaughtered on site; Meat by-products from meat slaughtered on site; Animal & marine fats & oils; Sausages & other prepared meats
Prin: Keith Fratrick
Prin: Nicholas C Renzi
IT Man: Joshua Duckworth

JBS SWIFT & CO.
See PROTEIN PROVIDERS INC

D-U-N-S 14-836-1249
■ **JBS TOLLESON INC**
SUN LAND BEEF COMPANY
(*Suby of* I-57 SERVICE CENTER) ★
651 S 91st Ave, Tolleson, AZ 85353-9393
Tel (623) 476-4073 *Founded/Ownrshp* 1996
Sales 78.0MM^E *EMP* 475
SIC 2011 Meat packing plants; Meat packing plants
Pr: Andre Nogueira
Genl Mgr: Jerry Brown
IT Man: Allen Kisling
IT Man: Donald Myers

D-U-N-S 01-661-9637 EXP
JBS UNITED INC
4310 W State Road 38, Sheridan, IN 46069-9639
Tel (317) 758-4495 *Founded/Ownrshp* 1956
Sales 145.4MM^E *EMP* 400
SIC 2048 5153 0213 Livestock feeds; Grains; Hog feedlot; Livestock feeds; Grains; Hog feedlot
CEO: John B Swisher
**Pr:* Donald E Orr Jr
COO: Doug Webel
Bd of Dir: Bob Altman
Bd of Dir: Mike Peters
**VP:* John L McGraw
**VP:* Douglas M Webel
**Prin:* John Corbett
Plnt Mgr: Chris Wallace
Nutrtnst: Nathan Horn
Nutrtnst: Xiaojing Li

D-U-N-S 82-796-8640
■ **JBS US HOLDING LLC**
(*Suby of* JBS USA IMPORTS) ★
1770 Promontory Cir, Greeley, CO 80634-9039
Tel (970) 506-8000 *Founded/Ownrshp* 2012
Sales 32.0MM^E *EMP* 72^E
SIC 2011 Boxed beef from meat slaughtered on site
Ch Bd: Wesley Batista

D-U-N-S 12-693-0226 IMP/EXP
■ **JBS USA HOLDINGS INC**
(*Suby of* JBS S/A.)
1770 Promontory Cir, Greeley, CO 80634-9039
Tel (970) 506-8000 *Founded/Ownrshp* 2002
Sales 14.0MMM^E *EMP* 65,570
SIC 2011 5147 Meat packing plants; Beef products from beef slaughtered on site; Pork products from pork slaughtered on site; Lamb products from lamb slaughtered on site; Meats & meat products; Meats, cured or smoked; Meats, fresh; Meat packing plants; Beef products from beef slaughtered on site; Pork products from pork slaughtered on site; Lamb products from lamb slaughtered on site; Meats & meat products; Meats, cured or smoked; Meats, fresh
Pr: Wesley Batista
**CFO:* Andre Nogueira
Top Exec: Steve Snyder
**Sr VP:* Brad Lorenger
VP: Leonard Huskey
Dir IT: Jim Sehi
Plnt Mgr: Keith Strunk
Sls Mgr: Mike McCarthy
Sales Asso: Eric Wallin

JBS USA IMPORTS
See JBS USA LLC

D-U-N-S 04-812-4978 IMP/EXP
■ **JBS USA LLC**
JBS USA IMPORTS
(*Suby of* JBS USA HOLDINGS INC) ★
1770 Promontory Cir, Greeley, CO 80634-9039
Tel (970) 506-7506 *Founded/Ownrshp* 2002
Sales 4.1MMM^E *EMP* 24,800
SIC 2011 Meat packing plants; Boxed beef from meat slaughtered on site; Pork products from pork slaughtered on site; Lamb products from lamb slaughtered on site; Meat packing plants; Boxed beef from meat slaughtered on site; Pork products from pork slaughtered on site; Lamb products from lamb slaughtered on site
CEO: Andre Nogueira
Pr: William Van Solkema
**Ch:* Wesley Batista
Treas: Dennis Roerty
Top Exec: Chad Ferguson
Top Exec: Marco Sampaio
Sr VP: Al Byers
VP: John Bormann
VP: Jimmy Carter
VP: Kiersten Folb
VP: Jim Herlihy
VP: Del Holzer
VP: Dathel Nimmons
VP: Matthew D Wineinger
Exec: Jeffrey Johnson
Dir Risk M: Stephany Rockwell

JBT
See JOHN BEAN TECHNOLOGIES CORP

JBT FOOD TECH
See JBT FOODTECH-CITRUS SYSTEMS

D-U-N-S 82-836-3262
JBT FOODTECH-CITRUS SYSTEMS
JBT FOOD TECH
400 Fairway Ave, Lakeland, FL 33801-2468
Tel (863) 683-5411 *Founded/Ownrshp* 2008
Sales 83.2MM^E *EMP* 93^E
SIC 5169 Food additives & preservatives
CEO: John T Gremp
**Pr:* Thomas W Giacomini
Mktg Dir: Carlos Saavedra

D-U-N-S 17-489-3180
JC & SD INVESTMENTS INC
5901 Broadway, Denver, CO 80216-1026
Tel (303) 292-3025 *Founded/Ownrshp* 1992
Sales 43.9MM^E *EMP* 38
SIC 5075 Warm air heating & air conditioning
Pr: Sal D'Alessandro
**CFO:* Jason Charles

JC B OF AR
See LIFT TRUCK SERVICE CENTER INC

D-U-N-S 83-492-6479
JC BROMAC CORP
EAGLERIDER
11860 S La Cienega Blvd, Hawthorne, CA 90250-3461
Tel (310) 536-6777 *Founded/Ownrshp* 1992
Sales 20.7MM^E *EMP* 200
SIC 7999 6794 4725 Motorcycle rental; Franchises, selling or licensing; Tour operators; Motorcycle rental; Franchises, selling or licensing; Tour operators
CEO: Christopher McIntyre
**VP:* Jeffrey Brown
VP: Tamara Stockstill
**VP:* Peter Wurmer
Genl Mgr: Tambi Lowstan
Sales Asso: Pablo Gonzalez

D-U-N-S 07-546-4107
JC CALHOUN STATE CMTY COLLEGE INC
CALHOUN COMMUNITY COLLEGE
6250 Us Highway 31, Tanner, AL 35671-4028
Tel (256) 306-2500 *Founded/Ownrshp* 1945
Sales 30.6MM *EMP* 565
Accts Byrd Smalley & Adams Pc Decat
SIC 8222 Community college; Community college
Pr: Marilyn Beck
Admn Mgr: Cathy Pope
CTO: Holly Powe
IT Man: Patricia Hughes
IT Man: Jenny Sewell
Pr Dir: Janet Martin
HC Dir: Wayne Tosh

D-U-N-S 01-968-4968
JC CANNISTRARO LLC
80 Rosedale Rd, Watertown, MA 02472-2234
Tel (617) 926-0092 *Founded/Ownrshp* 1963
Sales 158.5MM^E *EMP* 400
Accts Darmody Merlino & Co Llp Bos
SIC 1711 Plumbing contractors; Heating & air conditioning contractors; Fire sprinkler system installation; Plumbing contractors; Heating & air conditioning contractors; Fire sprinkler system installation
Pr: John C Cannistraro Jr
**CEO:* David G Cannistraro
**CFO:* Joseph Ccannistraro
CFO: Joseph Cannistraro
Ex VP: David Cannistraro
MIS Dir: Ken Howington
IT Man: Riccardo Armand
Opers Mgr: Neil Johnson
Snr Mgr: Dick Fish

D-U-N-S 07-866-9215
JC CHRISTENSEN & ASSOCIATES INC
(*Suby of* ARRAY SERVICES GROUP INC) ★
200 14th Ave E, Sartell, MN 56377-4500
Tel (320) 253-7800 *Founded/Ownrshp* 2003
Sales 22.9MM *EMP* 150
SIC 7322

D-U-N-S 15-516-3132
JC COLLINS INC
SPORTS AVENUE
4449 48th Avenue Ct, Rock Island, IL 61201-9213
Tel (309) 793-4980 *Founded/Ownrshp* 1986
Sales 27.5MM^E *EMP* 250
SIC 5699 5947

D-U-N-S 00-389-9655
JC EHRLICH CHEMICAL CO INC
1125 Berkshire Blvd 150, Reading, PA 19610-1211
Tel (610) 372-9700 *Founded/Ownrshp* 1928
Sales 668.0MM^E *EMP* 1,800
SIC 5191 Chemicals, agricultural; Pesticides; Chemicals, agricultural; Pesticides
Pr: John Myers
**CFO:* David Waring
**VP:* John Tercha
Dist Mgr: Eduardo Moncada
Div Mgr: Kim Lewis
Dir IT: Dabney Barker
Tech Mgr: Chad Gore
Opers Mgr: Danny Harper
Mktg Dir: Mary Hart
Manager: Bruce Daeschner
Manager: Sean Landers

D-U-N-S 96-745-1100
JC FODALE ENERGY SERVICES LLC
6003 Fincl Plz Ste 101, Shreveport, LA 71129
Tel (318) 686-4070 *Founded/Ownrshp* 2010
Sales 29.1MM^E *EMP* 50
SIC 4212 Local trucking, without storage
**Ex VP:* James D Pierce
VP: Reynold Leone

D-U-N-S 10-387-7361 IMP/EXP
JC FOODSERVICE INC
ACTION SALES
415 S Atlantic Blvd, Monterey Park, CA 91754-3209
Tel (626) 299-3800 *Founded/Ownrshp* 1997
Sales 45.6MM^E *EMP* 80
SIC 5046 Restaurant equipment & supplies; Restaurant equipment & supplies
Pr: Joel Chang
**VP:* Jack Chang
Sales Asso: Eric Ding
Sales Asso: Vincent Tran
Sales Asso: Johnson Yeh

D-U-N-S 79-307-0889
■ **JC HIGGINS CORP**
(*Suby of* EMCOR GROUP INC) ★
70 Hawes Way, Stoughton, MA 02072-1163
Tel (781) 341-1500 *Founded/Ownrshp* 1990
Sales 101.5MM^E *EMP* 600
SIC 1711 Mechanical contractor; Ventilation & duct work contractor; Heating & air conditioning contractors; Plumbing contractors; Mechanical contractor; Ventilation & duct work contractor; Heating & air conditioning contractors; Plumbing contractors
Pr: Bob Gallagher
**Ch Bd:* Joseph C Higgins
CFO: Ronald Ledeoux
**Sec:* Ron Cherkasly
**VP:* Robert Gallagher
**VP:* R Kevin Matz
**VP:* John W Shaughnessy
**VP:* Kevin Walsh
IT Man: Mukadas Lawal
Sfty Mgr: David Vieira

D-U-N-S 96-325-8348 IMP/EXP
JC HORIZON LTD
LITONG INTERNATIONAL
825 E State St, Ontario, CA 91761-1837
Tel (626) 446-1819 *Founded/Ownrshp* 1996
Sales 21.7MM^E *EMP* 35
SIC 5111 3089 Printing & writing paper; Coloring & finishing of plastic products
Pr: Judy Lee

JC IMPORTS
See HOM FURNITURE INC

JC LICHT EPCO
See JC LICHT LLC

D-U-N-S 02-520-4983
JC LICHT LLC (IL)
JC LICHT EPCO
320 Fullerton Ave Ste 200, Carol Stream, IL 60188-1866
Tel (630) 351-0400 *Founded/Ownrshp* 1907, 2014
Sales 62.2MM^E *EMP* 320
SIC 5231 5198 Paint; Paints; Paint; Paints

D-U-N-S 06-652-0719 IMP
JC PAPER
47422 Kato Rd, Fremont, CA 94538-7319
Tel (510) 413-4700 *Founded/Ownrshp* 1956
Sales 49.0MM *EMP* 115
SIC 5111 5113 5087

JC PENNEY
See JC PENNEY CORP INC

JC PENNEY
See J C PENNEY PROPERTIES INC

JC PENNEY
See J C PENNEY LIFE INSURANCE CO

JC PENNEY
See J C PENNEY EUROPE INC

D-U-N-S 10-206-3521 IMP/EXP
▲ **JC PENNEY CO INC**
6501 Legacy Dr, Plano, TX 75024-3698
Tel (972) 431-1000 *Founded/Ownrshp* 1902
Sales 12.2MMM *EMP* 114,000
Tkr Sym JCP *Exch* NYS
SIC 5311 5961 Department stores, non-discount; Catalog & mail-order houses; Catalog sales; Department stores, non-discount; Catalog & mail-order houses; Catalog sales
CEO: Myron E Ullman III
COO: Rick Kirk
**CFO:* Kenneth H Hannah
Ex VP: Gary Davis
**Ex VP:* Janet L Dhillon
**Ex VP:* Brynn L Evanson
**Ex VP:* D Scott Laverty
Ex VP: Laurie B Miller
Ex VP: Thomas M Nealon
Ex VP: Tim Nichols
Ex VP: Michael T Theilmann
Sr VP: Debra Berman
Sr VP: Vaneet Grover
**Sr VP:* Dennis P Miller
Sr VP: Bob Peterson
Sr VP: Paul Rutenis
Sr VP: Thorsten Weber
Sr VP: Erin Willenberg
VP: Carmen Blanco
VP: Thomas Cassidy
VP: Susan Gerhard
Board of Directors: Colleen C Barrett, Thomas J Engibous, Amanda Ginsberg, B Craig Owens, Leonard H Roberts, Stephen I Sadove, Javier G Teruel, R Gerald Turner, Ronald W Tysoe

D-U-N-S 00-698-8893 IMP/EXP
■ **JC PENNEY CORP INC** (DE)
JC PENNEY
(*Suby of* JC PENNEY CO INC) ★
6501 Legacy Dr, Plano, TX 75024-3698
Tel (972) 431-1000 *Founded/Ownrshp* 1902
Sales 2.3MMM^E *EMP* 15,500^E
SIC 5311 5961 Department stores, non-discount; Catalog & mail-order houses; Catalog sales; Department stores, non-discount; Catalog & mail-order houses; Catalog sales
CEO: Mike Ullman
CFO: Edward J Record

*Ch: Thomas Engibous
*Ex VP: Joanne Bober
*Ex VP: Janet L Dhillon
Ex VP: Ken Mangone
Sr VP: Marie Lacertosa
Sr VP: Timothy M Nichols
*Sr VP: Ed Robben
*VP: Ken Hicks
*VP: E H Sweney

D-U-N-S 94-869-5184
JC RESORTS LLC
533 Coast Blvd S, La Jolla, CA 92037-4641
Tel (858) 605-2700 Founded/Ownrshp 1971
Sales 123.0MM^E EMP 1,200
SIC 8741 7992 7991 Hotel or motel management; Public golf courses; Physical fitness facilities; Hotel or motel management; Public golf courses; Physical fitness facilities
Pr: Paul Reed
CFO: Frank Levett
VP: Blaise Bartell
Genl Mgr: Maureen Carew
Sls Mgr: Heather Ritt

D-U-N-S 06-581-0889
JC RESTORATION INC
3200 Squibb Ave, Rolling Meadows, IL 60008-4020
Tel (800) 956-8844 Founded/Ownrshp 1982
Sales 25.3MM^E EMP 83
SIC 1521 Repairing fire damage, single-family houses
Pr: Warner Cruz
Exec: Michele Fritsch
Genl Mgr: Steven Rost
Off Mgr: Karen Cruz
Prd Mgr: Daniel Boot
Sls Mgr: Lawrence Stephens

D-U-N-S 01-077-0139
JC SMITH INC
345 Peat St, Syracuse, NY 13210-1348
Tel (315) 428-9903 Founded/Ownrshp 1976
Sales 57.8MM^E EMP 58
SIC 5082 7353 General construction machinery & equipment; Heavy construction equipment rental
CEO: Joanne C Reed
*Pr: Jeffrey C Smith
*Treas: Lance Reed
*VP: Mary S Smith

D-U-N-S 79-655-5589
JC TECHNOLOGY INC
ACE COMPUTERS
575 Lively Blvd, Elk Grove Village, IL 60007-2013
Tel (847) 952-6900 Founded/Ownrshp 1983
Sales 20.2MM^E EMP 30
SIC 5734 5045 Personal computers; Computer peripheral equipment; Computers & accessories, personal & home entertainment; Computer peripheral equipment
CEO: John Samborski
*Pr: Marianne Samborski
*VP: Marc Fertik
*VP: Kathy Lacina

D-U-N-S 15-031-4149 IMP
JCA VENTURES INC
DEAL TIRE
11801 Nw 101st Rd Ste 3, Medley, FL 33178-1039
Tel (305) 887-9015 Founded/Ownrshp 2004
Sales 46.8MM^E EMP 50
SIC 5014 Tires & tubes; Tires & tubes
Pr: Patrick Assali
*Treas: James Assali
*Sec: Robert A Douglass
*VP: Armando W Diaz
*VP: Clifford M Martino
*VP: Jeffrey Martino
*VP: Lon C Wadsworth

D-U-N-S 96-679-6174
JCAHO SURVEYOR AND QHR CONSULTANT CORP
1 Renaissance Blvd, Oakbrook Terrace, IL 60181-4294
Tel (801) 364-4800 Founded/Ownrshp 2011
Sales 40.7MM EMP 8^E
Accts Crowe Horwath Llp Chicago Il
SIC 8713 Surveying services; Surveying services
Prin: David Jaimovich

D-U-N-S 05-235-0741 IMP/EXP
JCB INC
(Suby of J.C. BAMFORD EXCAVATORS LIMITED)
2000 Bamford Blvd, Pooler, GA 31322-9504
Tel (912) 447-2000 Founded/Ownrshp 1970
Sales 162.9MM^E EMP 250
SIC 5082 5084 3531 3537 General construction machinery & equipment; Materials handling machinery; Backhoes; Industrial trucks & tractors; General construction machinery & equipment; Materials handling machinery; Backhoes; Industrial trucks & tractors
Ch: John Patterson
*Pr: Graeme Macdonald
CFO: David Miller
VP: Ken Bianco
VP: Liam Brown
VP: Jim Hockaday
VP: Arjin Mirdha
VP: Dan Schmidt
VP: Mike Werner
Comm Man: Karen Guinn
Mng Dir: John Gill
Board of Directors: John J Patterson

D-U-N-S 82-861-2676 IMP
JCB MANUFACTURING INC
2000 Bamford Blvd, Pooler, GA 31322-9504
Tel (912) 447-2000 Founded/Ownrshp 1998
Sales 85.3MM^E EMP 250
SIC 5084 Industrial machinery & equipment; Industrial machinery & equipment
Pr: Arjun Mirdha
*CFO: Nick Weate
*Ch: John Patterson

JCC CAMP KINGSWOOD
See JEWISH COMMUNITY CENTERS OF GREATER BOSTON

JCC CHICAGO
See JEWISH COMMUNITY CENTERS OF CHICAGO

JCC IN MANHATTAN
See JEWISH COMMUNITY CENTER IN MANHATTAN INC

JCC METROWEST
See JEWISH COMMUNITY CENTER OF METROWEST INC

JCC ON THE PALISADES
See JEWISH COMMUNITY CENTER ON PALISADES

JCC THE CENTER
See JEWISH COMMUNITY CENTER OF METROPOLITAN DETROIT

JCCEO
See JEFFERSON COUNTY COMMITTEE FOR ECONOMIC OPPORTUNITY PRIVATE

D-U-N-S 07-851-4041
JCG FOODS OF ALABAMA LLC
764 George Cagle Dr, Collinsville, AL 35961-4296
Tel (256) 524-2147 Founded/Ownrshp 2012
Sales 122.6MM^E EMP 854
SIC 2038 Frozen specialties; Frozen specialties
CEO: Joseph Grendys

D-U-N-S 80-204-2689
JCG INDUSTRIES INC
4404 W Berteau Ave, Chicago, IL 60641-1907
Tel (847) 384-5940 Founded/Ownrshp 1992
Sales 121.3MM^E EMP 201
SIC 5144 Poultry products; Poultry products
Pr: Joseph Grendys
*Sec: Mark J Kaminsky
Off Mgr: Bonnie Diviesti

D-U-N-S 03-380-7756
JCG TECHNOLOGIES INC (FL)
50 S Belcher Rd Ste 104, Clearwater, FL 33765-3949
Tel (727) 461-3776 Founded/Ownrshp 2000
Sales 17.7MM^E EMP 325
SIC 8748 Business consulting; Business consulting
Pr: Srinvas Guthikonda
*Pr: Srinvas Guthyikonda

JCH
See JAMES COOKE & HOBSON INC

JCI
See NORMAN YORK INTERNATIONAL

JCI ASG
See VINTEC CO

D-U-N-S 55-590-4200
JCI GENERAL CONTRACTORS INC
2535 Ga Highway 37 W, Moultrie, GA 31768-2513
Tel (229) 985-4444 Founded/Ownrshp 1991
Sales 20.9MM^E EMP 25
SIC 1542 Commercial & office building, new construction; Commercial & office buildings, renovation & repair; Commercial & office building, new construction; Commercial & office buildings, renovation & repair
Pr: Lynn L Jones Jr
*Sec: Barbara B Jones
*VP: Lynn L Jones Sr

D-U-N-S 09-847-4364
JCI INDUSTRIES INC
1161 Se Hamblen Rd, Lees Summit, MO 64081-2939
Tel (816) 525-3320 Founded/Ownrshp 1987
Sales 79.6MM^E EMP 76^E
SIC 5084 7699 Pumps & pumping equipment; Industrial equipment services; Pumps & pumping equipment; Industrial equipment services
Pr: Robert Kopp
VP: Tom Rogge
*VP: Robert Toth
Brnch Mgr: Gary Edwards
QA Dir: Michael McFetters
Opers Mgr: Derek Boyer
Opers Mgr: Chris Mutzbauer
Sales Asso: Sean Robertson

D-U-N-S 00-221-6091 IMP/EXP
JCI JONES CHEMICALS INC (NY)
1765 Ringling Blvd # 200, Sarasota, FL 34236-6873
Tel (941) 330-1537 Founded/Ownrshp 1930
Sales 109.2MM^E EMP 250
SIC 5169 2842 Chlorine; Swimming pool & spa chemicals; Caustic soda; Ammonia, household; Bleaches, household: dry or liquid; Chlorine; Swimming pool & spa chemicals; Caustic soda; Ammonia, household; Bleaches, household: dry or liquid
CEO: Jeffrey W Jones
*CFO: Dawn Irving
*Ex VP: Tim Gaffney
*Ex VP: Ryan Jones
VP: Wayne Hernandez
Sales Asso: Pat Mulhall

D-U-N-S 82-702-2877 IMP/EXP
JCIM US LLC
(Suby of JOHNSON CONTROLS INTERIORS) ★
45000 Helm St Ste 200, Plymouth, MI 48170-6040
Tel (734) 254-3100 Founded/Ownrshp 2015
Sales 1.3MMM^E EMP 6,700^E
SIC 3089 Injection molding of plastics; Injection molding of plastics
*COO: David Abney
*CFO: Nathan Bowen
*Ex VP: Julie L Bushman
*Sr VP: Natalie A Black

D-U-N-S 78-532-3833
JCK RESTAURANTS INC
CARL'S JR.
875 Country Club Rd, Eugene, OR 97401-6009
Tel (541) 342-6557 Founded/Ownrshp 1989
Sales 15.2MM^E EMP 350
SIC 5812 Fast-food restaurant, chain; Fast-food restaurant, chain
Pr: Joseph C Karcher

D-U-N-S 79-695-2034 IMP
JCM AMERICAN CORP
JCM GLOBAL
(Suby of JAPAN CASH MACHINE CO., LTD.)
925 Pilot Rd, Las Vegas, NV 89119-3728
Tel (702) 651-0000 Founded/Ownrshp 1988
Sales 65.0MM^E EMP 83
SIC 5046 3578 Coin counters; Store machines; Calculating & accounting equipment; Coin counters; Store machines; Calculating & accounting equipment
Pr: Hikaru Izawa
*CFO: John Garner
Sr VP: Tom Nieman
VP: Rob Siemasko
Admn Mgr: Jessica Saruski
IT Man: Joe Jobson
Tech Mgr: Frank Lockwood
Sftwr Eng: Sam Germano
VP Opers: David Kubajak
Mtls Mgr: Jane Sia
Sales Exec: Peter Cummins

D-U-N-S 19-960-1097
JCM ASSOCIATES INC
301 Prince Georges Blvd C, Upper Marlboro, MD 20774-7401
Tel (301) 390-5500 Founded/Ownrshp 1987
Sales 53.5MM^E EMP 185
Accts Deleon & Stang Gaithersburg
SIC 1711 Plumbing contractors; Mechanical contractor; Warm air heating & air conditioning contractor; Plumbing contractors; Mechanical contractor; Warm air heating & air conditioning contractor
Pr: James C McReady III
*Treas: Michael S Wansor
*VP: Thomas Belcher
*VP: Robert L Bryant
Sfty Dirs: Leonardo Delgado

D-U-N-S 04-849-3761
JCM ENGINEERING CORP
2690 E Cedar St, Ontario, CA 91761-8533
Tel (909) 923-3730 Founded/Ownrshp 1979
Sales 45.1MM^E EMP 110
SIC 3812 Defense systems & equipment; Defense systems & equipment
Pr: Carlo A Moyano
Pr: Bill Durante
*CFO: Jay Gross
*VP: Yvonne Moyano
Sls Mgr: Karleen Miller
Board of Directors: Joe McKernan

JCM GLOBAL
See JCM AMERICAN CORP

D-U-N-S 02-061-2768
JCM INDUSTRIES INC
200 Old Boston Rd, Nash, TX 75569-2626
Tel (903) 832-2581 Founded/Ownrshp 1976
Sales 21.9MM^E EMP 135
SIC 3494 3498 3429 Pipe fittings; Fabricated pipe & fittings; Manufactured hardware (general); Pipe fittings; Fabricated pipe & fittings; Manufactured hardware (general)
Pr: Ronald R Collins
Ch Bd: Gladys J Morriss
Sec: Julie Collins
Ex VP: Cynthia Bryan Goerke
Sls&Mrk Ex: Jennifer Williams

D-U-N-S 05-149-9622 EXP
JCM INDUSTRIES INC
ADVANCE STORAGE PRODUCTS
7341 Lincoln Way, Garden Grove, CA 92841-1428
Tel (714) 902-9000 Founded/Ownrshp 1970
Sales 30.6MM^E EMP 150
SIC 3448 2542 Prefabricated metal buildings; Racks, merchandise display or storage: except wood; Prefabricated metal buildings; Racks, merchandise display or storage: except wood
Pr: John Vr Krummell
*Pr: Ken Blankenhorn
*CFO: Charles Kish
Off Mgr: Becky Ogle

JCMUA
See JERSEY CITY MUNICIPAL UTILITIES AUTHORITY

JCP
See ICREST INTERNATIONAL LLC

D-U-N-S 78-648-9554
■ **JCP MEDIA INC**
JCP MEDIA, L.P.
(Suby of JC PENNEY CO INC) ★
6501 Legacy Dr, Plano, TX 75024-3612
Tel (972) 431-1000 Founded/Ownrshp 1999
Sales 98.4MM^E EMP 2,691^E
SIC 8743 Public relations services
Pr: M J Boylson
*VP: Jim Francois

JCP MEDIA, L.P.
See JCP MEDIA INC

D-U-N-S 94-264-7660
■ **JCP PUBLICATIONS CORP**
(Suby of JC PENNEY) ★
6501 Legacy Dr, Plano, TX 75024-3612
Tel (972) 431-1000 Founded/Ownrshp 1996
Sales 71.8MM^E EMP 4,500
SIC 5311 Department stores; Department stores
CEO: Ellen Questrom

D-U-N-S 07-328-6163
■ **JCP REALTY INC**
(Suby of JC PENNEY) ★
6501 Legacy Dr, Plano, TX 75024-3612
Tel (972) 431-1639 Founded/Ownrshp 1971
Sales 28.6MM^E EMP 6^E
SIC 6552 Land subdividers & developers, commercial
Pr: Roy Reed
Pr: Michael Lowenkron
Ex VP: John P Garvey
Snr Mgr: Rick Ivy

D-U-N-S 00-736-8558
JCP SPECIALTY FOODS CO
(Suby of ATLANTIC BEVERAGE CO INC) ★
750 W Lake Cook Rd # 485, Buffalo Grove, IL 60089-2073
Tel (580) 924-2414 Founded/Ownrshp 1952
Sales 73.1MM^E EMP 485
SIC 2011 2013 Meat packing plants; Sausages from meat slaughtered on site; Pork products from pork slaughtered on site; Sausages & other prepared meats; Meat packing plants; Sausages from meat slaughtered on site; Pork products from pork slaughtered on site; Sausages & other prepared meats
VP: Greg Cowin

JCPENNEY
See J C PENNEY PURCHASING CORP

JCPS
See JEFFERSON CITY PUBLIC SCHOOLS

D-U-N-S 60-593-9490
JCR-WESLEY CHAPEL LLC
WESLEY CHAPEL NISSAN
28519 State Road 54, Zephyrhills, FL 33543-3211
Tel (813) 333-9070 Founded/Ownrshp 2003
Sales 23.4MM^E EMP 60
SIC 5511 Automobiles, new & used

D-U-N-S 36-230-8892 IMP
JCREW GROUP INC
(Suby of CHINOS INTERMEDIATE HOLDINGS B INC) ★
770 Broadway Fl 11, New York, NY 10003-9512
Tel (212) 209-2500 Founded/Ownrshp 2011
Sales 2.5MMM EMP 15,600^E
SIC 5961 5621 5611 5632 Catalog & mail-order houses; Women's apparel, mail order; Clothing, mail order (except women's); Mail order house; Women's clothing stores; Men's & boys' clothing stores; Women's accessory & specialty stores; Apparel accessories; Catalog & mail-order houses; Women's apparel, mail order; Clothing, mail order (except women's); Mail order house; Women's clothing stores; Men's & boys' clothing stores; Women's accessory & specialty stores; Apparel accessories
Ch Bd: Millard Drexler
Pr: Jenna Lyons
CFO: Joan Durkin
Ex VP: Sharon Johnston
Ex VP: Lynda Markoe
CIO: Marc Saffer
Board of Directors: James Coulter, John Danhakl, Jonathan Sokoloff, Stephen Squeri, Carrie Wheeler

JC'S 5 STAR OUTLET
See SB CAPITAL ACQUISITIONS LLC

D-U-N-S 60-899-6781
JCS CONTROLS INC
172 Metro Park, Rochester, NY 14623-2610
Tel (585) 227-5910 Founded/Ownrshp 1988
Sales 22.9MM^E EMP 24
SIC 5084 8711 Controlling instruments & accessories; Engineering services
CEO: Philip R Frechette
*Treas: Robert Veitch
*VP: Gregory Frechette
Sftwr Eng: Tom Bertrand
Sftwr Eng: Kevin Mesolella
Sftwr Eng: Randy Straub

D-U-N-S 01-619-8217
JCSD EMERGENCY MEDICAL GROUP INC
MEDICONE MEDICAL RESPONSE
14286 Gillis Rd, Dallas, TX 75244-3722
Tel (972) 554-9300 Founded/Ownrshp 2008
Sales 21.6MM^E EMP 170^E
SIC 4119 Ambulance service; Cable cars, aerial: except amusement & scenic
CEO: James Reeves
*Sr VP: Crystal Reeves
*VP: Kevin Crump

D-U-N-S 18-577-2287
JCT HOLDING CO LLC
19007 W Highway 33, Sapulpa, OK 74066-7545
Tel (918) 227-1600 Founded/Ownrshp 2004
Sales 250.0MM EMP 231
SIC 4213 Refrigerated products transport; Refrigerated products transport
Pr: John M Christner
COO: Daniel L Christner
CFO: Darryl A Christner
VP: Bob Snell

JCUA
See JACKSON COUNTY UTILITY AUTHORITY

J.C.WHITE QUALITY FURNITURE
See BERWIN INC

D-U-N-S 04-614-1537
JD & BILLY HINES TRUCKING INC
407 Hines Blvd, Prescott, AR 71857-9760
Tel (870) 887-6693 Founded/Ownrshp 1936
Sales 34.0MM EMP 250
SIC 4213 Trucking, except local; Trucking, except local
Pr: Billy Hines
COO: Bruce Olney
*Ex VP: Vickie Hines
VP: Wendell Hoover
Dir IT: Danny Steward
Sfty Mgr: Bobby Gravett
Sfty Mgr: Bruce Teutsch

D-U-N-S 00-800-6561
JD ABRAMS LP (TX)
TRANS-MOUNTAIN EQUIPMENT
(Suby of ABRAMS INTERNATIONAL INC) ★
111 Congress Ave Ste 2400, Austin, TX 78701-4298
Tel (512) 243-3317 Founded/Ownrshp 1966
Sales 155.1MM EMP 750
Accts Schmi Broaddus Nugent Gano Pc

SIC 1611 1622 1629 3272 General contractor, highway & street construction; Bridge construction; Dam construction; Prestressed concrete products; General contractor, highway & street construction; Bridge construction; Dam construction; Prestressed concrete products
Ch: Jon F Abrams
**Pt:* James D Abrams Sr
**Pt:* J Kelly Gallagher
**Pt:* Bob Underwood
Bd of Dir: Joe Hernandez
Sr VP: C Worrell
VP: William Burnet
VP: Bill Burnett
**Prin:* Steven Zbranek
Off Mgr: Barbara Bender
IT Man: Dean Jvargin

D-U-N-S 02-648-4373
JD AUTO CORP
MOTORWAY AUTO GROUP
8434 Gateway Blvd E, El Paso, TX 79907-1513
Tel (915) 834-6300 *Founded/Ownrshp* 1994
Sales 28.4MM^E *EMP* 350
SIC 7532 Body shop, automotive; Body shop, automotive
Pr: Jimmy Dick
**Pr:* James A Dice IV
Genl Mgr: Patrick Brown
Mktg Dir: Norma Munoz

D-U-N-S 00-492-9550
■ **JD BANK**
JEFF DAVIS BANK & TRUST CO
(*Suby of* JEFF DAVIS BANCSHARES INC) ★
1611 Elton Rd, Jennings, LA 70546-3613
Tel (337) 824-2074 *Founded/Ownrshp* 1947
Sales NA *EMP* 200
Accts Postlethwaite & Netterville B
SIC 6022 State trust companies accepting deposits, commercial; State trust companies accepting deposits, commercial
Pr: Dan L Donald Jr
**CFO:* Paul Brummett
Ex VP: Jeff Johnson
VP: Linda Beason
VP: Robert Brantley
VP: George Cline
VP: Perry Cormier
**VP:* Judy Duhon
VP: Cynthia Mire
**VP:* Dan Eason Senior
**VP:* Gerald Theunissen

JD BYRIDER
See VENTURCAP INVESTMENT GROUP V INC

J.D. BYRIDER
See BYRIDER SALES OF INDIANA S LLC

D-U-N-S 62-047-4510
JD BYRIDER SYSTEMS LLC
12802 Hmlton Crssing Blvd, Carmel, IN 46032-5424
Tel (317) 249-3000 *Founded/Ownrshp* 1989
Sales 148.4MM^E *EMP* 625
SIC 6794 5734 7538 7515 5521 Franchises, selling or licensing; Computer & software stores; General automotive repair shops; Passenger car leasing; Used car dealers; Franchises, selling or licensing; Computer & software stores; General automotive repair shops; Passenger car leasing; Used car dealers
CEO: Steven E Wedding
Mng Pt: Danielle McPherson
COO: Rob Palmer
CFO: Brian Littleton
CFO: Phillip Ratkovic
VP: Bryan Hohne
VP: Jack Humbert
VP: Thomas L Welter
Off Mgr: Elvia Ysasaga
IT Man: Paul Pavich
Mktg Dir: Emily Frische

D-U-N-S 12-447-5732 EXP
JD EQUIPMENT INC
JOHN DEERE
3979 Parkway Ln, Hilliard, OH 43026-1250
Tel (614) 879-6620 *Founded/Ownrshp* 1983
Sales 250.0MM^E *EMP* 200
SIC 5999 5083 Farm equipment & supplies; Agricultural machinery & equipment; Farm equipment & supplies; Agricultural machinery & equipment
CEO: Jeff Mitchell
**Pr:* Don K Mitchell Jr
**Treas:* Carla Mitchell
**VP:* Maxine Mitchell

D-U-N-S 78-412-1832
JD EVANS OF AUSTIN INC
JIMMY EVANS COMPANY
2222 W North Loop Blvd, Austin, TX 78756-2325
Tel (512) 288-7300 *Founded/Ownrshp* 1991
Sales 22.9MM^E *EMP* 140
SIC 1611 General contractor, highway & street construction; General contractor, highway & street construction
Pr: Jimmy Evans
**VP:* Vince Reinhart

D-U-N-S 03-481-8439
JD FLETCHER AND ASSOCIATES LLC
1718 Peachtree St Nw # 380, Atlanta, GA 30309-2452
Tel (678) 619-1753 *Founded/Ownrshp* 2010
Sales 11.9MM^E *EMP* 350^E
SIC 8721 8741 8748 Accounting services, except auditing; Financial management for business; Business consulting; Accounting services, except auditing; Financial management for business; Business consulting
Pr: Cletonya Lagrand

JD FOOD
See J & D MEAT CO

JD GROUP
See BROKERAGE AND LOGISTICS SOLUTIONS INC

J.D. HEISKELL AND COMPANY
See J D HEISKELL HOLDINGS LLC

D-U-N-S 04-800-8163
JD LUMBER INC
414 Bodie Canyon Rd, Priest River, ID 83856
Tel (208) 448-2671 *Founded/Ownrshp* 1980
Sales 25.5MM^E *EMP* 240
SIC 2421 Sawmills & planing mills, general; Sawmills & planing mills, general
Pr: Jeff Weimer
**Sec:* Dave Slaughter

D-U-N-S 02-772-9299
JD MELLBERG FINANCIAL
3067 W Ina Rd Ste 105, Tucson, AZ 85741-2106
Tel (520) 731-9000 *Founded/Ownrshp* 2011
Sales NA *EMP* 150
SIC 6311 Life insurance
Pr: Josh Mellberg
Sr VP: Brent Matthew
Sr VP: Grace Shirley
IT Man: Eric Thiessen
VP Opers: Rosa Garcia
VP Mktg: Pete Russo

D-U-N-S 00-506-4381 IMP
JD NORMAN INDUSTRIES INC (IL)
787 W Belden Ave, Addison, IL 60101-4942
Tel (630) 458-3700 *Founded/Ownrshp* 1986
Sales 101.2MM^E *EMP* 350
SIC 3469 3496 3495 3452 Metal stampings; Miscellaneous fabricated wire products; Wire springs; Bolts, nuts, rivets & washers; Metal stampings; Miscellaneous fabricated wire products; Wire springs; Bolts, nuts, rivets & washers
Pr: Justin D Norman
Pr: Chey Becker-Varto
Prgrm Mgr: Paul Macduff
Opers Mgr: Timothy M Knight
Plnt Mgr: Alberto Hernandez
Ql Cn Mgr: Dinela Visan
Oper/Mgr: Charles Gibson

D-U-N-S 07-619-6526
■ **JD POWER AND ASSOCIATES**
NADA'S USED CAR GUIDE
(*Suby of* MCGRAW HILL FINANCIAL INC) ★
2625 Townsgate Rd Ste 100, Westlake Village, CA 91361-5737
Tel (805) 418-8000 *Founded/Ownrshp* 2001
Sales 276.7MM^E *EMP* 615
SIC 6282 Investment advisory service; Investment advisory service
Pr: Finbarr O'Neill
COO: Fabien Reille
**Sr VP:* Gary Tucker
**VP:* Frances Caille
VP: Joseph Damour
VP: Greg Hoeg
VP: John Humphrey
VP: David Letson
**VP:* Jonathan Miller
VP: Diane Nott-Kilfoil
VP: Melissa Sauter
VP: Brian Walters

D-U-N-S 82-610-0455
JD RAMMING PAVING MANAGEMENT LLC
RAMMING PAVING COMPANY
(*Suby of* SUMMIT MATERIALS LLC) ★
9020 N Cpitl Of Texas Hwy, Austin, TX 78759-7279
Tel (512) 251-3713 *Founded/Ownrshp* 2011
Sales 77.5MM^E *EMP* 270
SIC 1611 1771 General contractor, highway & street construction; Concrete work; General contractor, highway & street construction; Concrete work
Pt: John D Ramming
Pt: Chuck Fuller
Pt: Dean Lundquist
Pt: Grant Shelton

JD&E
See JARVIS DOWNING & EMCH INC

D-U-N-S 93-973-2673
JD2 INC
450 Nevada St, Auburn, CA 95603-3706
Tel (530) 889-2979 *Founded/Ownrshp* 2014
Sales 43.8MM^E *EMP* 90
SIC 1791 8711 Structural steel erection

D-U-N-S 94-260-3325
JDA SOFTWARE GROUP INC
(*Suby of* RP CROWN PARENT LLC) ★
14400 N 87th St, Scottsdale, AZ 85260-3657
Tel (480) 308-3000 *Founded/Ownrshp* 2012
Sales 1.1MMM^E *EMP* 6,235^E
SIC 7371 Computer software development & applications
CEO: Baljit Dail
Pr: Hamish N J Brewer
CFO: Peter S Hathaway
Ofcr: Brian Boyland
Ofcr: Razat Gaurav
Ofcr: Tod Hogan
Ofcr: Enrique Rodriguez
Ex VP: Brian P Boylan
Ex VP: Thomas Dziersk
Ex VP: David Gai
Ex VP: David Kennedy
Ex VP: David R King
Ex VP: John L Kopcke
Ex VP: Marc Levine
Ex VP: Christopher Moore
VP: Antonio Boccalandro
VP: Bill Kotrba
VP: Randy Masso
VP: John Vrankovich
VP: Charles Wehlage
Exec: Johann Vanderveen

D-U-N-S 18-390-2048
JDA SOFTWARE INC
(*Suby of* JDA SOFTWARE GROUP INC) ★
14400 N 87th St, Scottsdale, AZ 85260-3657
Tel (480) 308-3000 *Founded/Ownrshp* 1985
Sales 1.0MMM *EMP* 794
SIC 7371 7373 Custom computer programming services; Computer integrated systems design; Custom computer programming services; Computer integrated systems design
CEO: Baljit S Dail
**Pr:* Daniel J Maynard
**Ex VP:* Brian Boylan
**Ex VP:* Razat Gaurav
**Ex VP:* Kevin Iaquinto
**Sr VP:* Salil Joshi
Sr VP: Duane Kotsen
Sr VP: David Tidmarsh
VP: Andrew Kirkwood
VP: Aamer Rehman
VP: Oscar Torres

D-U-N-S 06-895-6122
■ **JDAMC INC**
(*Suby of* DEERE & CO) ★
10789 S Ridgeview Rd, Olathe, KS 66061-6448
Tel (913) 310-8100 *Founded/Ownrshp* 1998
Sales 71.4MM^E *EMP* 695
SIC 5083 Farm & garden machinery; Farm & garden machinery
VP: John Lageman
**VP:* John Mockaman
IT Man: Bryn Dolesh

D-U-N-S 02-779-4577 IMP
JDB INC
BRUCE PACKING CO.
380 S Pacific Hwy, Woodburn, OR 97071-5931
Tel (503) 874-3000 *Founded/Ownrshp* 1980
Sales 95.1MM^E *EMP* 475
Accts Perkins & Company Pc Portl
SIC 2015 2013 Poultry slaughtering & processing; Prepared beef products from purchased beef; Poultry slaughtering & processing; Prepared beef products from purchased beef
Pr: Larry Bruce
**Pr:* Glen Golomski
**CFO:* Kristan Hoke
**VP:* Rob Bruce
**VP:* Terry Buford
**Prin:* Don Kelley
IT Man: Deborah Miles
IT Man: Benjamin Waldon
Opers Mgr: Cameron Cooper
Ql Cn Mgr: Monica McLaughlin
Natl Sales: Jennifer Phinisee

J.D.C.
See AMERICAN JEWISH JOINT DISTRIBUTION COMMITTEE INC

D-U-N-S 16-093-1036 IMP
JDC COATINGS INC
206 E Division St, Mount Juliet, TN 37122-3324
Tel (615) 754-9797 *Founded/Ownrshp* 1967
Sales 51.2MM^E *EMP* 65
SIC 5113 Pressure sensitive tape; Pressure sensitive tape
Pr: Mike Frye
**VP:* Wayne Benton
IT Man: Brandon Schultz

D-U-N-S 00-206-3617
JDD INVESTMENT CO (IL)
MCDONALD'S
300 Park Blvd Ste 300, Itasca, IL 60143-2664
Tel (630) 654-9100 *Founded/Ownrshp* 2010, 1990
Sales 18.3MM^E *EMP* 615
SIC 5812 Fast-food restaurant, chain; Fast-food restaurant, chain
Pr: John Dakajos
**CFO:* Herbert Fischer

JDES FARGO
See JOHN DEERE ELECTRONIC SOLUTIONS INC

D-U-N-S 87-843-3606
JDH CONTRACTING INC
8109 Network Dr, Plainfield, IN 46168-9024
Tel (317) 839-0520 *Founded/Ownrshp* 1994
Sales 83.4MM^E *EMP* 150
SIC 1794 1542 1623 1771 7349 Excavation work; Commercial & office building contractors; Water, sewer & utility lines; Telephone & communication line construction; Concrete work; Building maintenance services; Excavation work; Commercial & office building contractors; Water, sewer & utility lines; Telephone & communication line construction; Concrete work; Building maintenance services
Pr: John D Harris
VP: Scott Sontag
VP: Dave Tesmer
IT Man: Jim Lingvai
IT Man: Paul McJuinkin
Sftwr Eng: George Huff

D-U-N-S 14-422-0779 IMP
JDH HOLDINGS INC
8220 Bavaria Dr E, Macedonia, OH 44056-2248
Tel (330) 963-4400 *Founded/Ownrshp* 1985
Sales 35.0MM *EMP* 160
SIC 3089 Injection molded finished plastic products; Injection molded finished plastic products
Pr: Jay Honsaker
**Sec:* Diane Hanson

D-U-N-S 62-515-5403 IMP
JDH PACIFIC INC
15301 Blackburn Ave, Norwalk, CA 90650-6842
Tel (562) 926-8088 *Founded/Ownrshp* 1989
Sales 28.2MM^E *EMP* 180
SIC 3321 3324 3599 Gray iron castings; Commercial investment castings, ferrous; Crankshafts & camshafts, machining; Gray iron castings; Commercial investment castings, ferrous; Crankshafts & camshafts, machining
Pr: Donald Hu
QA Dir: Mark Holman
Ql Cn Mgr: Paula Mann
Ql Cn Mgr: Clementine Matus
Sls Mgr: Jim Dahl

D-U-N-S 11-257-8141
JDK MANAGEMENT CO INC
1388 State Route 487, Bloomsburg, PA 17815-8953
Tel (570) 784-0111 *Founded/Ownrshp* 1982
Sales 58.3MM^E *EMP* 700
SIC 8741 Administrative management; Financial management for business; Administrative management; Financial management for business
Pr: John D Klingerman
Ex VP: Clint Klingerman
**VP:* David Klingerman
VP: Kirk Reichart
**VP:* Carl Womer
Off Mgr: Ann Ramph
IT Man: Drew Lyons
VP Opers: Russ Berner
Snr Mgr: Don Bordner

D-U-N-S 78-730-8485 IMP
■ **JDL TECHNOLOGIES INC**
(*Suby of* COMMUNICATIONS SYSTEMS INC) ★
10900 Red Circle Dr, Hopkins, MN 55343-9106
Tel (952) 946-1810 *Founded/Ownrshp* 1998
Sales 67.9MM^E *EMP* 58
SIC 5045 7379 Computers, peripherals & software; Computer related consulting services
Pr: Thomas J Lapping
**COO:* Michael Skucius
Snr Ntwrk: Dan Gesch
CTO: Skucius Michael
IT Man: Luide Rocha
Netwrk Mgr: Jason Becht
Netwrk Eng: Jeremy Ellison
Netwrk Eng: Dennis Maragh II
Opers Mgr: Virginia Kelly

D-U-N-S 04-895-4572
JDM STEEL SERVICE INC
330 E Joe Orr Rd Unit 3, Chicago Heights, IL 60411-1296
Tel (708) 757-2092 *Founded/Ownrshp* 2005
Sales 100.0MM *EMP* 50^E
SIC 5051 4225 Metals service centers & offices; General warehousing & storage; Metals service centers & offices; General warehousing & storage
Pr: Richard A Merlo
**Pr:* George Cimbala
Pr: Paul Inbody
CFO: Jim Baranthouse
**VP:* Paul Cravens
**VP:* Gene Puk
QA Dir: Ken Ray
Sales Exec: April Allred
VP Sls: Tom Zager

D-U-N-S 07-922-9754
JDM WIGWAM GP LLC
2400 E Ariz Biltmore Cir, Phoenix, AZ 85016-2107
Tel (602) 224-2326 *Founded/Ownrshp* 2009
Sales 8.0MM^E *EMP* 350^E
SIC 7011 Resort hotel; Resort hotel

D-U-N-S 02-358-9166
JDP MECHANICAL INC
2439 44th St, Astoria, NY 11103-2055
Tel (718) 267-6767 *Founded/Ownrshp* 1998
Sales 39.2MM^E *EMP* 150
SIC 1711 Heating & air conditioning contractors; Heating & air conditioning contractors
Pr: Peter A Manos
Ex VP: Charles Medici
Ex VP: Ralph Spinnato

D-U-N-S 82-552-1388 IMP
JDR CABLE SYSTEMS INC
(*Suby of* BI GROUP PLC)
7906 N S Hou Park W 201, Houston, TX 77064
Tel (832) 220-4690 *Founded/Ownrshp* 1998
Sales 25.1MM^E *EMP* 28
SIC 5051 3643 5063 Cable, wire; Power line cable; Wire & cable
CEO: Roger Herbert
Genl Mgr: Oscar Eide

JDR TRUCKING
See SIMONS TRUCKING INC

D-U-N-S 07-772-6172
JDRF INTERNATIONAL
J D R F
26 Broadway, New York, NY 10004-1703
Tel (212) 785-9500 *Founded/Ownrshp* 1970
Sales 205.9MM *EMP* 600^E
Accts Kpmg Llp New York Ny
SIC 8399 8733 Fund raising organization, non-fee basis; Noncommercial research organizations; Fund raising organization, non-fee basis; Noncommercial research organizations
Pr: Derek Rapp
**CFO:* Mark Greene
**Ch:* Robert Wood Johnson IV
**Treas:* David W Nelms
Treas: Peter Wilson
Ex VP: Mania Boyder
**Ex VP:* Richard Insel
Ex VP: David E Wheadon
Sr VP: Pam Gatz
Sr VP: Benita Shobe
VP: Jit Patel
Assoc Dir: Maria Candelore
Dir Soc: Deborah Barge
Dir Soc: Leslie Knudsen

D-U-N-S 02-822-7593 IMP/EXP
JDRUSH CO INC
5900 E Lerdo Hwy, Shafter, CA 93263-4023
Tel (661) 392-1900 *Founded/Ownrshp* 1957
Sales 52.0MM^E *EMP* 80^E
SIC 5051 Pipe & tubing, steel; Pipe & tubing, steel
Pr: James R Varner
**Sec:* Earl L Lindley
**VP:* Craig Clayton
**VP:* J David Guerrerro
**VP:* Darin Sabol
VP: Lisa Tatum

D-U-N-S 62-048-2752 IMP/EXP
JDS INDUSTRIES INC
1800 E 57th St N, Sioux Falls, SD 57104-7115
Tel (605) 339-4010 *Founded/Ownrshp* 1981
Sales 58.4MM^E *EMP* 250
SIC 5094

D-U-N-S 08-174-8766
JDS RESTAURANTS INC
TACO BELL
1520 N Hearne Ave Ste 122, Shreveport, LA 71107-7155
Tel (318) 226-8500 *Founded/Ownrshp* 1996
Sales 10.0MM^E *EMP* 313
SIC 5812 Fast-food restaurant, chain; Fast-food restaurant, chain
Ch Bd: R E Upshaw
**Pr:* Steve Helm
**Sec:* Mary Upshaw
**VP Opers:* Chet Davis

JDS SUPPLY COMPANY
See FORSGREN INC

J.D.S. TRANSPRTN/LOG ADV
See GM FREIGHT INC

JDSU
See ACTERNA LLC

D-U-N-S 14-623-7875
■ **JDSU ACTERNA HOLDINGS LLC**
(*Suby of* VIAVI SOLUTIONS INC) ★
1 Milestone Center Ct, Germantown, MD 20876-7106
Tel (240) 404-1550 *Founded/Ownrshp* 2005
Sales 153.9MM^E *EMP* 1,700
SIC 3825 Instruments to measure electricity; Instruments to measure electricity

JDT HOSPICE INSTITUTE
See CONNECTICUT HOSPICE INC

D-U-N-S 60-909-3257
JDW MANAGEMENT CO
MONTROY SUPPLY
2674 Raymond Ave, Signal Hill, CA 90755-2128
Tel (562) 997-2920 *Founded/Ownrshp* 1989
Sales 38.6MM^E *EMP* 105
SIC 5063 5046 5199 Electrical apparatus & equipment; Store fixtures & display equipment; Art goods & supplies; Electrical apparatus & equipment; Store fixtures & display equipment; Art goods & supplies
Pr: James D Wilson
**CFO:* Wes Buckland
**VP:* Joy Wilson

D-U-N-S 00-228-3125 IMP
JE BERKOWITZ LP
1 Gateway Blvd, Pedricktown, NJ 08067-3629
Tel (856) 456-7800 *Founded/Ownrshp* 1920
Sales 87.3MM^E *EMP* 200
SIC 3231 3211 Insulating glass: made from purchased glass; Tempered glass: made from purchased glass; Laminated glass; Insulating glass: made from purchased glass; Tempered glass: made from purchased glass; Laminated glass
Pt: Arthur M Berkowitz
Pt: David B Byruch
Pr: Chris Lewandowski
CFO: Shawn Smith
Sfty Dirs: Nick Lysik
Opers Mgr: Darrell Cherry
Plnt Mgr: James Mooney
Ql Cn Mgr: James Stinsman
Sls Mgr: Emily Wolanski
Sls Mgr: Stephen Ziegler

D-U-N-S 00-890-6844 IMP
JE DUNN CONSTRUCTION CO
(*Suby of* JE DUNN CONSTRUCTION GROUP INC) ★
1001 Locust St, Kansas City, MO 64106-1904
Tel (816) 474-8600 *Founded/Ownrshp* 1924
Sales 2.2MMM *EMP* 1,635
Accts Kpmg Llp Kansas City Missour
SIC 1542 Commercial & office building, new construction; Commercial & office building, new construction
Ch Bd: Stephen D Dunn
Pr: Bob Jacquinot
Pr: Gordon E Landsford III
CFO: Beth A Soukup
V Ch Bd: William H Dunn Sr
Bd of Dir: Mike Rada
Ofcr: Thomas F Whittaker
Ex VP: William H Dunn Jr
Ex VP: Greg Nook
Sr VP: John Rowlett
VP: Mike Bartlett
VP: Rick Beyer
VP: Randall J Bredar
VP: Bill Dunn Jr
VP: Robert P Dunn
VP: Michael G Householder
VP: Kent Immenschuh
VP: Tom Raney
Exec: Bill Lee

D-U-N-S 00-783-6448
JE DUNN CONSTRUCTION GROUP INC (MO)
1001 Locust St, Kansas City, MO 64106-1904
Tel (816) 474-8600 *Founded/Ownrshp* 1981
Sales 2.2MMM *EMP* 2,080
Accts Kpmg Llp Kansas City Missour
SIC 1542 Commercial & office building, new construction; Commercial & office building, new construction
CEO: Gordon Lansford III
**Ch Bd:* Stephen D Dunn
**V Ch:* William H Dunn Sr
**Pr:* Terrence P Dunn
CFO: Gordon E Lansford
**CFO:* Beth Soukup
Ofcr: Tom Whittaker
**Ex VP:* William H Dunn Jr
Sr VP: Richard Beyer
Sr VP: Tom Raney
**VP:* Robert P Dunn
VP: Chris Sorensen
VP: Melanie Tucker
Board of Directors: Kevin A Dunn, Robert P Dunn, Robert A Long

D-U-N-S 05-884-2410 IMP/EXP
JE GROTE CO INC
1160 Gahanna Pkwy, Columbus, OH 43230-6615
Tel (614) 868-8414 *Founded/Ownrshp* 1971
Sales 29.2MM^E *EMP* 165
SIC 3589 3556 Cooking equipment, commercial; Food products machinery; Cooking equipment, commercial; Food products machinery
Ch Bd: James E Grote
**Pr:* Bob Grote
CFO: Eric Ytterbo
Exec: Karen Artis
Ex Dir: Bob Wacker
Sfty Mgr: John Seifert
Mktg Mgr: Paula Wernet
Sls Mgr: Ray Anklam
Sls Mgr: Jon Hissrich

D-U-N-S 09-801-3493
JE JOHNSON CONTRACTING INC
1550 E Virginia Dr, Midland, MI 48642-7909
Tel (989) 835-6671 *Founded/Ownrshp* 1979
Sales 46.6MM^E *EMP* 260
SIC 1711 Plumbing, heating, air-conditioning contractors; Mechanical contractor; Process piping contractor; Plumbing contractors; Plumbing, heating, air-conditioning contractors; Mechanical contractor; Process piping contractor; Plumbing contractors
Ch Bd: James E Johnson
**Pr:* Richard Johnson
**VP:* John Billinghire
**VP:* Mike Cole
VP: Lee Fitzgerald
**VP:* Greg Younk
Sfty Dirs: Jason Dole

D-U-N-S 00-282-1544
JE KINGHAM CONSTRUCTION CO LTD (TX)
312 Old Tyler Rd, Nacogdoches, TX 75961-4879
Tel (936) 564-3329 *Founded/Ownrshp* 1895, 1948
Sales 43.4MM *EMP* 45
SIC 1542 1541 Nonresidential construction; Commercial & office building contractors; Institutional building construction; Industrial buildings & warehouses; Nonresidential construction; Commercial & office building contractors; Institutional building construction; Industrial buildings & warehouses
Genl Pt: James A Kingham
Pt: John Kingham
Pr: Jim Kingham
Sec: Janie Andress

D-U-N-S 01-752-2913
JE LEVINE BUILDER INC
LEVINE BUILDERS
4209 235th St, Douglaston, NY 11363-1526
Tel (718) 224-7147 *Founded/Ownrshp* 1980
Sales 29.9MM^E *EMP* 125
SIC 1522 8741 Residential construction; Construction management; Residential construction; Construction management
Pr: Jeff Levine
CFO: Cathy Burger
**CFO:* Michael Kessler
**CFO:* Cathy Savino-Berger
VP: Tom Epstein
**VP:* Stuart Morris
Exec: Leonard Jacob
Exec: Marissa Privilegi
IT Man: John Llewellyn
Snr PM: Jack Kestenbaum
Snr Mgr: Fred Goldberg

D-U-N-S 80-018-8617
■ **JE REMEDIATION TECHNOLOGIES INC**
(*Suby of* JACOBS ENGINEERING GROUP INC) ★
4949 Essen Ln, Baton Rouge, LA 70809-3433
Tel (225) 769-7750 *Founded/Ownrshp* 1993
Sales 9.5MM^E *EMP* 301
SIC 8711 Building construction consultant; Building construction consultant

D-U-N-S 87-940-1891
■ **JE REMEDIATION TECHNOLOGIES INC**
J E SERVICES
(*Suby of* JACOBS FIELD SERVICES NORTH AMERICA INC) ★
4848 Loop Central Dr, Houston, TX 77081-2356
Tel (281) 360-3889 *Founded/Ownrshp* 1986
Sales 17.5MM^E *EMP* 295
Accts Ernst & Young Llp Los Angele
SIC 1629 Industrial plant construction; Industrial plant construction
Pr: Donald J Boutwell

D-U-N-S 15-362-9670
JE RICHARDS INC
(*Suby of* PHALCON LTD) ★
10401 Tucker St, Beltsville, MD 20705-2202
Tel (301) 345-1300 *Founded/Ownrshp* 2006
Sales 100.0MM *EMP* 500
SIC 1731

JE SPORT DIV
See JORDACHE LIMITED

D-U-N-S 07-758-0223 IMP
JEA
21 W Church St Fl 1, Jacksonville, FL 32202-3158
Tel (904) 665-6000 *Founded/Ownrshp* 1968
Sales 2.0MMM^E *EMP* 2,356
Accts Ernst & Young Llp Jacksonvill
SIC 4911 1623 Electric services; Electric services; Water, sewer & utility lines
CEO: Paul McElroy
**Pr:* James Chancellor
CFO: Mary Arditti
CFO: Melissa Dykes
Chf Mktg O: Jane McNally
**Ex VP:* James Dickenson
**VP:* Mike Brost
VP: Bill Cutts
**VP:* Brian Roche
Exec: Greg Lynn
Ex Dir: K Para
Board of Directors: John Coxwell, Robert M Harris, Ernest Isaac Jr, Max K Morris, Pamela Quarles, John Schickel, Robert L Stein

D-U-N-S 60-317-0580
JEAN DEVELOPMENT CO LLC
GOLD STRIKE HT & GAMBLING HALL
1 Main St, Jean, NV 89019-1602
Tel (702) 477-5000 *Founded/Ownrshp* 2005
Sales 22.2MM^E *EMP* 820^E
SIC 7011

D-U-N-S 94-950-9160 IMP
JEAN MART INC
6700 Avalon Blvd, Los Angeles, CA 90003-1920
Tel (323) 752-7775 *Founded/Ownrshp* 1995
Sales 50.8MM^E *EMP* 100
SIC 5137 7389 Women's & children's clothing; Sewing contractor; Women's & children's clothing; Sewing contractor
Pr: Helen C Yi

D-U-N-S 03-013-8390 IMP
JEAN NELL ENTERPRISES INC
OUTDOORSMAN, THE
1 Nell Jean Sq 19, Beckley, WV 25801-2200
Tel (304) 253-0200 *Founded/Ownrshp* 1975
Sales 100.6MM *EMP* 9^E
SIC 5941 5082 5091 Archery supplies; Mining machinery & equipment, except petroleum; Sporting & recreation goods; Archery supplies; Mining machinery & equipment, except petroleum; Sporting & recreation goods
Pr: Harry M Hylton
**Sec:* Jerry Acord
**VP:* Tracy W Hylton II
**VP:* Warren Hylton

D-U-N-S 04-781-8505
JEAN PETIT POULTRY INC
1809 Hwy 10 E, Danville, AR 72833
Tel (479) 495-4300 *Founded/Ownrshp* 1982
Sales 75.4MM^E *EMP* 2,100
SIC 2015 Poultry, processed; Poultry, processed
Pr: Rick Millsap
**Sec:* Sharon Carr
Off Mgr: Don Jones

D-U-N-S 78-530-9134 IMP
JEAN SAINT INDUSTRIES INC
(*Suby of* SAINT JEAN INDUSTRIES)
424 Industrial Park Rd, Heber Springs, AR 72543-8520
Tel (501) 362-9500 *Founded/Ownrshp* 2006
Sales 80.8MM^E *EMP* 95
SIC 3714 Motor vehicle parts & accessories; Motor vehicle parts & accessories
Pr: Emile T Di Serio
CFO: Janice Brents
IT Man: Jonathan Richards
Plnt Mgr: Pat Bowens
Plnt Mgr: Patrick Bowens

D-U-N-S 08-165-5029
JEAN SIMPSON PERSONNEL SERVICES INC
JEAN SIMPSON TEMPORARY EMPLOYM
1318 Shreveport Barksdale, Shreveport, LA 71105-2408
Tel (318) 869-3494 *Founded/Ownrshp* 1974
Sales 17.9MM *EMP* 600
SIC 7363 Temporary help service; Temporary help service
Pr: Sandra Braddock
**Sec:* Chester Robert Simpson
**VP:* Jean Simpson
Mktg Mgr: Angel Scott

JEAN SIMPSON TEMPORARY EMPLOYM
See JEAN SIMPSON PERSONNEL SERVICES INC

D-U-N-S 09-486-2190 IMP
JEAN-CLAUDE BOISSET WINES USA INC (CA)
BOISSET FAMILY ESTATES
(*Suby of* GRANDS VINS JEAN CLAUDE BOISSET)
849 Zinfandel Ln, Saint Helena, CA 94574-1645
Tel (800) 878-1123 *Founded/Ownrshp* 1980
Sales 73.1MM *EMP* 180
SIC 5182 Wine; Wine
CEO: Alain Leonnet
Sales Exec: Mark Drake
Mktg Mgr: Stephanie Buiel
Sls Mgr: Tiffany Getten
Sales Asso: Kristyn Park

D-U-N-S 06-901-3605
JEANES HOSPITAL
(*Suby of* TEMPLE UNIVERSITY HEALTH SYSTEM INC) ★
7600 Central Ave, Philadelphia, PA 19111-2499
Tel (215) 728-2000 *Founded/Ownrshp* 1996
Sales 138.1MM^E *EMP* 1,100
SIC 8062 General medical & surgical hospitals; General medical & surgical hospitals
CEO: Dr Marc Hurowitz
**CEO:* Linda J Grass
CFO: Joe Scully
**Treas:* Thomas S Albanesi Jr
Bd of Dir: F P Buckman
Bd of Dir: George C Corson
Bd of Dir: Joseph Evans
Bd of Dir: Joan Randolph
Bd of Dir: Eleanor Reinhardt
Bd of Dir: Thomas Unkefer
Bd of Dir: Roger Wood

D-U-N-S 13-136-0935 IMP
JEANJER LLC
JUST FOR MEN DIV
1400 Broadway Fl 15, New York, NY 10018-5300
Tel (212) 944-1330 *Founded/Ownrshp* 1985
Sales 105.7MM^E *EMP* 3,000
SIC 2331 2337 2339 2369 Blouses, women's & juniors': made from purchased material; Slacks: women's, misses' & juniors'; Suits: women's, misses' & juniors'; Girls' & children's outerwear; Blouses, women's & juniors': made from purchased material; Suits; women's, misses' & juniors'; Slacks: women's, misses' & juniors'; Girls' & children's outerwear
Pr: Joe Nakash
**Treas:* Ralph Nakash
**VP:* AVI Naakash
Sls Mgr: Charles Flores

D-U-N-S 09-745-1785
JEANNE DARC CREDIT UNION
658 Merrimack St, Lowell, MA 01854-3998
Tel (978) 452-5001 *Founded/Ownrshp* 1911
Sales NA *EMP* 124^E
SIC 6062 State credit unions, not federally chartered; State credit unions, not federally chartered
Pr: Paul R Mayotte
**Treas:* David Espindle
Ofcr: Sheila Fortin
Ofcr: Heath Mink
**VP:* Kathy Grieco
**VP:* Elaine Lambert
VP: James Milinazzo
VP: Carolyn Pelletier
VP: Penelope Swallow
**VP:* Suzanne Trudel
Brnch Mgr: Matthew Beaudoin

D-U-N-S 06-490-9492
JEANS EXTRUSIONS INC
201 Jeans Dr, Salem, IN 47167-9200
Tel (812) 883-2581 *Founded/Ownrshp* 1982
Sales 26.3MM^E *EMP* 155
Accts Paul R Rutherford
SIC 3053 Gaskets, all materials; Gaskets, all materials
Pr: Burl Jean
**Sec:* Carmelita Jean
**Genl Mgr:* Vince Lewandowski

JEAN'S RESTAURANT SUPPLY
See TARI INC

D-U-N-S 04-591-7259 IMP
JEANS WAREHOUSE INC
LOCAL FEVER
2612 Waiwai Loop Ste A, Honolulu, HI 96819-5112
Tel (808) 839-2421 *Founded/Ownrshp* 1978
Sales 28.1MM *EMP* 240
Accts Bkd Llp Bowling Green Ky
SIC 5621 2361 Ready-to-wear apparel, women's; Girls' & children's dresses, blouses & shirts; Ready-to-wear apparel, women's; Girls' & children's dresses, blouses & shirts
Pr: William Estill
**CFO:* Phyllis Fujiwara
CFO: Cathy Hankins
VP: Larry Holt

D-U-N-S 61-034-9149
JEB INC
CLEANPAK INTERNATIONAL, INC.
19855 Sw 124th Ave, Tualatin, OR 97062-8007
Tel (503) 639-0113 *Founded/Ownrshp* 2006
Sales NA *EMP* 300
SIC 3564

JEBCO" SCREW" AND SPECIALITY
See AMERICAN/JEBCO CORP

D-U-N-S 06-510-6627 IMP
■ **JEBRO INC**
(*Suby of* KNIFE RIVER COAL MINING) ★
2303 Bridgeport Dr, Sioux City, IA 51111-1096
Tel (712) 234-2800 *Founded/Ownrshp* 2005
Sales 60.9MM^E *EMP* 60
SIC 5032 5172 Paving materials; Petroleum products
**Pr:* Irving Jensen III
**Pr:* Traver Hastings
**CFO:* Keith George
**Treas:* Nancy Christenson
Dir IT: Linda Semple
Trfc Dir: Linda Wilhelmi
Mktg Mgr: Ron Feltz

JEC FOREST & PAPER RELATED CO
See JOHNSON ENERGY CO

JECTO
See JETT AND CO

D-U-N-S 05-833-9417
JEDCO INC
1615 Broadway Ave Nw, Grand Rapids, MI 49504-2026
Tel (616) 459-5161 *Founded/Ownrshp* 1994
Sales 22.0MM^E *EMP* 150
SIC 3724 Aircraft engines & engine parts; Aircraft engines & engine parts
Ch Bd: Daniel Szymanski
COO: Rob Lisk
**CFO:* Michael Taylor
**Treas:* Richard Szymanski J
**VP:* John Boeschenstein
**VP:* Traci Grose
**VP:* Robert Nyquist
Dir Lab: Mary Yoak
IT Man: Raymond Weston
Pr Dir: Barbara Tran

D-U-N-S 92-973-3525
JEDSON ENGINEERING INC
705 Central Ave Ste 300, Cincinnati, OH 45202-1900
Tel (513) 965-5999 *Founded/Ownrshp* 1984
Sales 50.0MM^E *EMP* 125
SIC 8711 Industrial engineers; Electrical or electronic engineering; Consulting engineer; Industrial engineers; Electrical or electronic engineering; Consulting engineer
CEO: Rachid Abdallah
**Pr:* John Vignale
**CFO:* Angela Carroll

JEEP
See SCAP MOTORS INC

D-U-N-S 80-821-1361
JEEP CHRYSLER OF ONTARIO
1202 Auto Center Dr, Ontario, CA 91761-2208
Tel (909) 390-9898 *Founded/Ownrshp* 1993
Sales 30.4MM^E *EMP* 95
SIC 5511 7538 5531 Automobiles, new & used; General automotive repair shops; Automotive & home supply stores; Automobiles, new & used; General automotive repair shops; Automotive & home supply stores
Ch Bd: Richard D Romero
**Pr:* R J Romero
**CFO:* Kathy Brown
**VP:* Valerie Romero

JEEP EAGLE OF WESTCHESTER
See CHRYSLER JEEP OF WHITE PLAINS INC

JEEP EAGLE WEST VOLKSWAGEN W
See HATFIELD JEEP EAGLE INC

JEEP GEAR
See ALCONE MARKETING GROUP INC

JEFF ANDERSON REGIONAL MEDICAL
See ANDERSON REGIONAL MEDICAL CENTER

D-U-N-S 01-410-3287
■ JEFF BANK
FIRST NATIONAL BANK
(*Suby of* JEFFERSONVILLE BANCORP) ★
4866 State Route 52, Jeffersonville, NY 12748-5558
Tel (845) 482-4000 *Founded/Ownrshp* 1914, 1984
Sales NA *EMP* 52
SIC 6021 National commercial banks; National commercial banks
Pr: Raymond L Walter
CEO: Wayne Zanetti
CFO: John Russell
Sr VP: Tatiana Hahn
Sr VP: George Kinne
VP: Florence Horecky
VP: John Veleber
Brnch Mgr: Sharon Deoghean
Mktg Dir: Rhonda Owens
Mktg Mgr: Barbara Hahl
Board of Directors: David W Bodenstein, Philip Coombe III, Fred W Stabbert III

D-U-N-S 02-268-1787
JEFF BARNES CHEVROLET OLDSMOBILE INC
JEFF BARNES OLDSMOBILE
6110 Sykesville Rd, Sykesville, MD 21784-6407
Tel (410) 795-1200 *Founded/Ownrshp* 1983
Sales 25.0MM *EMP* 45
SIC 5511 5531 7538 7515 7513 5521 Automobiles, new & used; Automotive parts; General automotive repair shops; Passenger car leasing; Truck rental & leasing, no drivers; Used car dealers; Automobiles, new & used; Automotive parts; General automotive repair shops; Passenger car leasing; Truck rental & leasing, no drivers; Used car dealers
Pr: Jeffrey Barnes
**VP:* Matthew Barnes

JEFF BARNES OLDSMOBILE
See JEFF BARNES CHEVROLET OLDSMOBILE INC

JEFF BELZER'S CHEVROLET
See JEFF BELZERS TODD CHEVROLET INC

D-U-N-S 05-607-2267
JEFF BELZERS TODD CHEVROLET INC
JEFF BELZER'S CHEVROLET
21111 Cedar Ave, Lakeville, MN 55044-9089
Tel (952) 469-4444 *Founded/Ownrshp* 1980
Sales 47.5MM^E *EMP* 130
SIC 5511 Automobiles, new & used; Automobiles, new & used
Sls Mgr: Jeff Tagtow

D-U-N-S 93-186-3104
▲ JEFF DAVIS BANCSHARES INC
JEFF DAVIS BANK AND TRUST
1611 Elton Rd, Jennings, LA 70546-3613
Tel (337) 824-1422 *Founded/Ownrshp* 1947
Sales NA *EMP* 200
Accts Postlethwaite & Netterville B
Tkr Sym JDVB *Exch* OTO
SIC 6022 State commercial banks; State commercial banks
Pr: Dan L Donald Jr
Chf Mktg O: Carly Person

JEFF DAVIS BANK & TRUST CO
See JD BANK

JEFF DAVIS BANK AND TRUST
See JEFF DAVIS BANCSHARES INC

JEFF DAVIS COUNTY BOARD OF EDU
See JEFF DAVIS COUNTY SCHOOL DISTRICT

D-U-N-S 10-001-3937
JEFF DAVIS COUNTY SCHOOL DISTRICT
JEFF DAVIS COUNTY BOARD OF EDU
44 Charles Rogers Blvd, Hazlehurst, GA 31539-6436
Tel (912) 375-6700 *Founded/Ownrshp* 1900
Sales 27.7MM *EMP* 410
Accts Greg S Griffin Atlanta Geor
SIC 8211 Public elementary & secondary schools; Public elementary & secondary schools
Netwrk Eng: Nathan Miller

D-U-N-S 11-623-5953
JEFF FLORENCE WYLER INC
JEFF WYLER HONDA/MITSUBISHI
949 Burlington Pike, Florence, KY 41042-1233
Tel (859) 283-2727 *Founded/Ownrshp* 1998
Sales 50.0MM *EMP* 51
SIC 5511 5521 New & used car dealers; Used car dealers; New & used car dealers; Used car dealers
Genl Mgr: James R Simon
**Pr:* Jeff Wyler

D-U-N-S 15-345-6025
JEFF FOSTER TRUCKING INC
(*Suby of* FOSTER HOLDING GROUP INC) ★
313 Winter St, Superior, WI 54880-1357
Tel (715) 394-6099 *Founded/Ownrshp* 2000
Sales 59.7MM^E *EMP* 250
SIC 4213 Heavy hauling; Building materials transport; Heavy machinery transport; Heavy hauling; Building materials transport; Heavy machinery transport
CEO: Jeff Foster
**COO:* Leo Naumann
**CFO:* Jim Manion
VP: Jim Jones
VP: Bill Miller
VP: Ryan Stephenson

JEFF GORDON CHEVROLET
See WILMINGTON AUTOMOTIVE INVESTORS CO LLC

D-U-N-S 04-782-9783
JEFF HUNTER MOTORS INC
JEFF HUNTER TOYOTA
1440 W Loop 340, Waco, TX 76712-6836
Tel (254) 662-6644 *Founded/Ownrshp* 1990
Sales 26.6MM^E *EMP* 59
SIC 5511 5521 Automobiles, new & used; Used car dealers; Automobiles, new & used; Used car dealers
Pr: Jeff Hunter
**Sec:* Marilyn Hunter
**VP:* Peter W Mankins
Genl Mgr: Amy Hunter

JEFF HUNTER TOYOTA
See JEFF HUNTER MOTORS INC

D-U-N-S 60-208-3966 IMP
JEFF KERBER POOL PLASTERING INC
10735 Kadota Ave, Montclair, CA 91763-6005
Tel (909) 465-0677 *Founded/Ownrshp* 1989
Sales 22.5MM^E *EMP* 260
SIC 1799 Athletic & recreation facilities construction; Athletic & recreation facilities construction
Pr: Jeff Kerber
COO: Mark Feldstein

D-U-N-S 05-583-4139
JEFF SACHS AUTO PARK
1220 Versailles Rd, Frankfort, KY 40601-9259
Tel (502) 695-1550 *Founded/Ownrshp* 1988
Sales 20.3MM^E *EMP* 85
SIC 5511 7515 5521 Automobiles, new & used; Passenger car leasing; Used car dealers; Automobiles, new & used; Passenger car leasing; Used car dealers
Pr: Jeff Sachs
Genl Mgr: Jeff Ranmey

D-U-N-S 01-801-9034
JEFF SCHMITT AUTO GROUP INC (OH)
1001 N Broad St, Fairborn, OH 45324-5256
Tel (937) 878-3471 *Founded/Ownrshp* 1946, 2000
Sales 81.8MM^E *EMP* 182
SIC 5511 Automobiles, new & used; Pickups, new & used; Automobiles, new & used; Pickups, new & used
Pr: Jeff Schmitt
Sls Mgr: Mark Skiba
Sales Asso: Sean Sandoval

D-U-N-S 12-121-9625
JEFF WOLFE
JAY WOLFE TOYOTA WEST COUNTY
14700 Manchester Rd, Ballwin, MO 63011-3702
Tel (636) 207-3900 *Founded/Ownrshp* 2002
Sales 67.4MM *EMP* 60
SIC 5511 Automobiles, new & used; Automobiles, new & used
Owner: Jeff Wolfe
Genl Mgr: Steve Adams

D-U-N-S 02-845-0570
JEFF WYLER CHEVROLET COLUMBUS
5885 Gender Rd, Canal Winchester, OH 43110-8271
Tel (614) 837-3421 *Founded/Ownrshp* 1965
Sales 43.9MM^E *EMP* 100
SIC 5511 Automobiles, new & used; Automobiles, new & used
Pr: Jeff Wyler
Sls Mgr: Jim Kavanaugh
Sales Asso: Dwayne Carter
Sales Asso: Shandale Johnson
Sales Asso: Selena Laney
Sales Asso: Ryan Rainier
Sales Asso: Matt Wilhelm

D-U-N-S 06-397-1147
JEFF WYLER CHEVROLET INC
JEFF WYLER MAZDA
1117 State Route 32, Batavia, OH 45103-2380
Tel (513) 752-3447 *Founded/Ownrshp* 1959
Sales 71.8MM^E *EMP* 300
SIC 5511 7539 7538 3714 7532 Automobiles, new & used; Automotive repair shops; General automotive repair shops; Motor vehicle parts & accessories; Top & body repair & paint shops; Automobiles, new & used; Automotive repair shops; General automotive repair shops; Motor vehicle parts & accessories; Top & body repair & paint shops
Pr: Jeffrey L Wyler
Chf Mktg O: Jim Simon
**VP:* David Wyler
Store Mgr: Ron Waddle
Dir IT: Francie Kincaid
Sls Mgr: Troy Hammer
Snr Mgr: Bridgett Imhulse

D-U-N-S 11-910-5856
JEFF WYLER CLARKSVILLE INC
GREENTREE TOYOTA
808 Providence Way, Clarksville, IN 47129-1537
Tel (812) 285-1366 *Founded/Ownrshp* 1983
Sales 27.0MM^E *EMP* 75
SIC 5511 Automobiles, new & used
Pr: Jeff Wyler
**CFO:* Terry Davis
Genl Mgr: Rodney Carter
**Genl Mgr:* Tom Josephs

Genl Mgr: Jeff Shaper
IT Man: David Hoover
Sls Mgr: Tim Patillo

D-U-N-S 06-440-3517
JEFF WYLER HONDA OF COLERAIN
8950 Colerain Ave, Cincinnati, OH 45251-2922
Tel (513) 741-3700 *Founded/Ownrshp* 1999
Sales 26.4MM^E *EMP* 80
SIC 5511 Automobiles, new & used; Automobiles, new & used
Pr: Jeff Wyler
Exec: Chuck Burton
Genl Mgr: Paul Bambach
Sls Mgr: Zack Coppage
Sls Mgr: Bob Jordan

JEFF WYLER HONDA/MITSUBISHI
See JEFF FLORENCE WYLER INC

JEFF WYLER MAZDA
See JEFF WYLER CHEVROLET INC

JEFF WYLER OLDSMOBILE CADILLAC
See WYLER CADILLAC

D-U-N-S 11-491-3242 IMP
JEFFBOAT LLC
(*Suby of* COMMERCIAL BARGE LINE CO) ★
1701 E Market St, Jeffersonville, IN 47130
Tel (812) 288-0200 *Founded/Ownrshp* 1915
Sales 62.0MM^E *EMP* 117
SIC 3531 Marine related equipment; Marine related equipment
Pr: Mark K Knoy
**COO:* Paul A Tobin
**CFO:* David J Huls
**Sr VP:* Robert M Blocker

D-U-N-S 05-292-8819 IMP/EXP
JEFFCO FIBRES INC (MA)
12 Park St, Webster, MA 01570-2523
Tel (508) 987-6600 *Founded/Ownrshp* 1971
Sales 29.3MM^E *EMP* 100
SIC 5712 2392 Mattresses; Pillows, bed: made from purchased materials
Pr: Jeffrey H Lonstein
CFO: Hugh Oxnard
**Sec:* Blanche Lonstein
VP: Mark Lorusso
Exec: Rick Wozmack
Dir IT: Pat Elmer
Dir IT: Jonathan Wilson
Tech Mgr: David Bennett
Natl Sales: John Laroche
VP Mktg: Nancy Lonstein
Manager: Gary Kemp

JEFFCO PUBLIC SCHOOLS
See JEFFERSON COUNTY SCHOOL DISTRICT NO R-1

D-U-N-S 12-086-8831
JEFFER MANGELS BUTLER & MITCHELL LLP
JMBM
1900 Avenue Of The Stars, Los Angeles, CA 90067-4301
Tel (310) 203-8080 *Founded/Ownrshp* 1981
Sales 39.9MM^E *EMP* 230
SIC 8111 General practice attorney, lawyer; General practice attorney, lawyer
Mng Pt: Bruce P Jeffer
Pt: Jonathan Bloch
Pt: James R Butler Jr
Pt: Dan E Chambers
Pt: Jennifer A Irrgang
Pt: Robert E Mangels
Pt: Mark Marmaro
Pt: Martin W Taylor
COO: Douglas Kessler
Top Exec: Capps William
Ex VP: Daniel Abrams
Ex VP: Mark Woodworth
Sr VP: Adam Greene
Sr VP: Larry Shupnick
Sr VP: Chris White
VP: Robert Bowers
VP: Jeff Cohen
VP: Jeff Dallas
VP: James Deangelo
VP: Abid Gilani
VP: Irene Hoek

D-U-N-S 00-501-6779 IMP
JEFFERDS CORP (WV)
HOMESTEAD MATERIALS HDLG CO
2070 Winfield Rd, Saint Albans, WV 25177-7802
Tel (304) 755-8111 *Founded/Ownrshp* 1947
Sales 56.5MM *EMP* 230
Accts Gibbons & Kawash Ac Charle
SIC 5084 7353 7699 Materials handling machinery; Cranes & aerial lift equipment, rental or leasing; Industrial machinery & equipment repair; Materials handling machinery; Cranes & aerial lift equipment, rental or leasing; Industrial machinery & equipment repair
Pr: K Richard C Sinclair
**Ch Bd:* Joseph C Jefferds III
**VP:* Kim G Anderson
Brnch Mgr: Arley Eugene Brogan
IT Man: Rick R Pendle
Sales Exec: Faron Kidd
Mktg Dir: David Cronise
Mktg Dir: Amy Martin
Mktg Dir: Wayne Weaver
Mktg Mgr: Debbie Maynard
Sls Mgr: Jason Anderson

D-U-N-S 80-120-2172
■ JEFFERIES BACHE HOLDINGS LLC
(*Suby of* JEFFERIES GROUP LLC) ★
520 Madison Ave, New York, NY 10022-4213
Tel (212) 284-2550 *Founded/Ownrshp* 2011
Sales 59.1MM^E *EMP* 305^E
SIC 6211 Security brokers & dealers; Security brokers & dealers
Pr: Richard Handler
Sr VP: James Lucier
VP: Nancy Bonwit
VP: Jim Gorman
VP: Jack Lerner
VP: Michael Padala

D-U-N-S 78-425-5403
■ JEFFERIES BACHE SECURITIES LLC
(*Suby of* JEFFERIES GROUP LLC) ★
1 New York Plz Fl 13, New York, NY 10004-1928
Tel (800) 643-2902 *Founded/Ownrshp* 2011
Sales 2.9MM *EMP* 300
SIC 6211 Brokers, security; Dealers, security; Brokers, security; Dealers, security
CEO: Patrice Blanc
Pr: Alex Ladouceur
VP: David Collazo
VP: Jim Gorman
VP: Doug Scherer
Mng Dir: Michael Shea
Mng Dir: Richard Shoeniger

D-U-N-S 06-777-8449
■ JEFFERIES GROUP LLC
(*Suby of* LEUCADIA NATIONAL CORP) ★
520 Madison Ave, New York, NY 10022-4213
Tel (212) 284-2550 *Founded/Ownrshp* 2013
Sales 3.8MMM *EMP* 3,804^E
Accts Pricewaterhousecoopers Llp Ne
SIC 6211 Investment bankers; Security brokers & dealers; Investment bankers; Security brokers & dealers
Ch Bd: Richard B Handler
Pr: Peter Laidlaw
Pr: Mark Melvin
Pr: Ernesto Sue
**CFO:* Peregrine C Broadbent
Treas: William H Jennings II
**Treas:* John F Stacconi
Chf Inves: Thomas D Witz
Ex VP: Curis W Schade
**Ex VP:* Michael J Sharp
Sr VP: Robert J Albano
Sr VP: Robert E Enslein
Sr VP: Jeffrey D Farmer
Sr VP: Leon C Green
Sr VP: Geoff M Heyman
Sr VP: Jeffrey Lipton
VP: Daniel A Brierley
VP: Orlando Bustos
Dir Risk M: Rita Di Domenico
Board of Directors: Barry J Alperin, W Patrick Campbell, Ian M Cumming, Richard G Dooley, Brian P Friedman, Maryanne Gilmartin, Robert E Joyal, Michael T O'kane, Joseph S Steinberg

D-U-N-S 04-310-3340
■ JEFFERIES LLC
(*Suby of* JEFFERIES GROUP LLC) ★
520 Madison Ave Fl 10, New York, NY 10022-4213
Tel (212) 284-2300 *Founded/Ownrshp* 1962, 1973
Sales 695.0MM^E *EMP* 1,050
SIC 6211 Brokers, security; Dealers, security; Brokers, security; Dealers, security
Ch Bd: Richard B Handler
Pr: Adam De Chiara
Pr: William F Farmer
Pr: Bradford L Klein
Pr: Michael J Richter
Pr: John Shaw Jr
CFO: Joseph Schenk
Treas: Paul Dolid
Treas: Ronald Johnson
Assoc VP: Tony Cario
Ex VP: Jeffrey Beckmen
Ex VP: Jonathan Cunningham
Ex VP: Lloyd H Feller
Ex VP: Chris Kanoff
Ex VP: Curtis W Schade
Ex VP: Clifford A Siegel
Ex VP: Maxine Syrjamaki
Ex VP: Andrew Whittaker
Sr VP: Kenneth Bann
Sr VP: Adam L Benjamin
Sr VP: Todd Coleman

JEFFERS EQUINE
See JEFFERS INC

D-U-N-S 09-438-5218 IMP/EXP
JEFFERS INC
JEFFERS EQUINE
310 W Saunders Rd, Dothan, AL 36301-8622
Tel (334) 793-6257 *Founded/Ownrshp* 1975
Sales 50.0MM^E *EMP* 130
SIC 5122 5999 Animal medicines; Pet supplies; Animal medicines; Pet supplies
Pr: Dorothy Jeffers
**CFO:* Shane Fundum
CFO: Michael Halke
CFO: Jame Snelgrove
CFO: James Snellgrove
**VP:* Ruth Jeffers
Dir IT: Jacob Hudmon
Snr Mgr: Justin April

JEFFERSON
See JPI PARTNERS LLC

JEFFERSON AND MADISON
See JEFFERSON JOINT SCHOOL DISTRICT 251

D-U-N-S 61-560-2083
JEFFERSON BANCSHARES INC
JEFFERSON BANK
2900 Fredericksburg Rd, San Antonio, TX 78201-4707
Tel (210) 734-4311 *Founded/Ownrshp* 1983
Sales NA *EMP* 230
Accts Harper & Pearson Company Pc
SIC 6712 Bank holding companies; Bank holding companies
CEO: Danny B Butler
**Pr:* Paul E McSween III
**CFO:* Bill Goetz
**VP:* Betsy Baker

D-U-N-S 84-055-3309
JEFFERSON BANCSHARES INC
120 Evans Ave, Morristown, TN 37814-6622
Tel (423) 586-8421 *Founded/Ownrshp* 2003
Sales NA *EMP* 142^E
SIC 6035

JEFFERSON BANK
See JEFFERSON BANCSHARES INC

D-U-N-S 00-895-2848
JEFFERSON BANK (TX)
(*Suby of* JEFFERSON BANCSHARES INC) ★
2900 Fredericksburg Rd, San Antonio, TX 78201-4707
Tel (210) 736-7620 *Founded/Ownrshp* 1946
Sales NA *EMP* 230
SIC 6022 State commercial banks; State commercial banks
Ch: Richard J Petitt
Pr: William J Galbreath
CFO: William J Goetz
Ofcr: Shelley Herring
Ex VP: W Sam Hale
Ex VP: Carroll A Putnam
Ex VP: Michael Rehm
Sr VP: Ted Bowen
Sr VP: Nelson Finch
Sr VP: Joy Leflore
Sr VP: Carlos Pena
VP: Jesse Alonzo
VP: Betsy Baker
VP: Justin Boerner
VP: Danny Butler
VP: Hazel Davis
VP: Hugo Echavarri
VP: Courtney Eisenhauer
VP: Aaron King
VP: Elaine Longmire
VP: Danielle Massey

D-U-N-S 04-012-6401
JEFFERSON BANK OF MISSOURI INC
CENTRAL BANCOMPANY
(*Suby of* CENTRAL BANCOMPANY INC) ★
700 Southwest Blvd, Jefferson City, MO 65109-2600
Tel (573) 634-0800 *Founded/Ownrshp* 1964
Sales NA *EMP* 108
SIC 6022 State commercial banks; State commercial banks
Pr: Harold Westhues
**CFO:* Robert L Bryant Jr
**Ex VP:* Richard T Schutt
**Ex VP:* Richard J Wilson
VP: Chris Wood
Mktg Dir: Jayne Dunkmann

D-U-N-S 82-590-4167 IMP
JEFFERSON BROSE INC
(*Suby of* BROSE NORTH AMERICA INC) ★
25295 Guenther, Warren, MI 48091-6020
Tel (248) 339-4000 *Founded/Ownrshp* 2008
Sales 60.0MM^E *EMP* 130
SIC 5015 5013 Motor vehicle parts, used; Motor vehicle supplies & new parts; Motor vehicle parts, used; Motor vehicle supplies & new parts
VP: John Dunn

D-U-N-S 78-640-5977
JEFFERSON CAPITAL FUND LTD
4148 Old Leeds Rd, Mountain Brk, AL 35213-3210
Tel (205) 967-5786 *Founded/Ownrshp* 1991
Sales 49.9MM^E *EMP* 215
SIC 6211 Investment firm, general brokerage; Investment firm, general brokerage

D-U-N-S 82-534-9652
JEFFERSON CAPITAL SYSTEMS LLC
16 Mcleland Rd Ste 101, Saint Cloud, MN 56303-2160
Tel (320) 229-8540 *Founded/Ownrshp* 2002
Sales 38.2MM^E *EMP* 250
SIC 7322 Collection agency, except real estate; Collection agency, except real estate
CEO: David Burton

D-U-N-S 08-737-2140
JEFFERSON CENTER FOR MENTAL HEALTH INC
4851 Independence St # 100, Wheat Ridge, CO 80033-6711
Tel (303) 425-0300 *Founded/Ownrshp* 1958
Sales 44.7MM *EMP* 500
Accts Bkd Llp Colorado Springs Co
SIC 8093 Mental health clinic, outpatient; Mental health clinic, outpatient
CEO: Harriet Hall PHD
**CFO:* David Goff
VP: Donald Bechtold
Prgrm Mgr: Larry Macro
CIO: Will Walser
QA Dir: Vicki Williams
Dir IT: Tammy Schneidermen
Dir IT: Curtis Sers
IT Man: Curtis Hicks
Psych: Christine W Linville

D-U-N-S 00-653-4598
JEFFERSON CHEVROLET CO
2130 E Jefferson Ave, Detroit, MI 48207-4102
Tel (313) 259-1200 *Founded/Ownrshp* 1953
Sales 30.1MM^E *EMP* 80^E
SIC 5511 5531

D-U-N-S 10-001-3945
JEFFERSON CITY BOARD OF EDUCATION
JEFFERSON CITY SCHOOLS
345 Storey Ln, Jefferson, GA 30549-2126
Tel (706) 367-2880 *Founded/Ownrshp* 1806
Sales 25.3MM *EMP* 350
Accts Russell W Hinton Cpa Cgfm
SIC 8211 Public elementary & secondary schools; Public elementary & secondary schools
CFO: Roy E Stowe
Dir IT: Brian Moore
IT Man: Logan Carter
IT Man: Judith Mahassey

D-U-N-S 10-970-5236
JEFFERSON CITY MEDICAL GROUP PC
FAMILY PRACTICE
1241 W Stadium Blvd, Jefferson City, MO 65109-6023
Tel (573) 556-7700 *Founded/Ownrshp* 1970
Sales 70.4MM^E *EMP* 525
SIC 8011 Physicians' office, including specialists; Physicians' office, including specialists
Pr: Richard B Jennett
COO: John Bisana
CFO: Lyle Rosburg
**Treas:* George Carr
Chf Mktg O: Janet Enloe
**VP:* Reese Thompson
Mng Dir: Stephanie K Hose
Off Mgr: Beverly Cearlock
Off Mgr: Debra Hibdon
Off Mgr: Dinah Jarrett
Off Mgr: Karen Koetting

D-U-N-S 02-980-9282
JEFFERSON CITY OIL CO INC
1601 Christy Dr, Jefferson City, MO 65101-2255
Tel (573) 634-2025 *Founded/Ownrshp* 1959
Sales 21.1MM^E *EMP* 40
SIC 5171 5541 Petroleum bulk stations; Gasoline service stations
Pr: John Kolb
**Sec:* Thomas Kolb
**Prin:* Tom Kolb

D-U-N-S 07-034-2183
JEFFERSON CITY PUBLIC SCHOOLS (MO)
JCPS
315 E Dunklin St, Jefferson City, MO 65101-3197
Tel (573) 659-3000 *Founded/Ownrshp* 1838
Sales 54.0MM^E *EMP* 1,100
SIC 8211 Public elementary & secondary schools; Vocational high school; Elementary school; Public elementary & secondary schools; Vocational high school; Elementary school
CFO: Jason Hoffman
Pr Dir: Amy Berendzen

JEFFERSON CITY SCHOOLS
See JEFFERSON CITY BOARD OF EDUCATION

D-U-N-S 07-979-8777
JEFFERSON CITY SCHOOLS
345 Storey Ln, Jefferson, GA 30549-2126
Tel (706) 367-2880 *Founded/Ownrshp* 2015
Sales 5.7MM^E *EMP* 300^E
SIC 8211 Public elementary & secondary schools
Instr Medi: Adria Witworth

D-U-N-S 02-629-4108
JEFFERSON CO SCHOOL DISTRICT
SUPERINTENDANT OFFICE
575 S Water St, Monticello, FL 32344-1373
Tel (850) 342-0100 *Founded/Ownrshp* 1832
Sales 21.0MM^E *EMP* 420
SIC 8211 Public elementary & secondary schools; Public elementary school; Public junior high school; Public senior high school; Public elementary & secondary schools; Public elementary school; Public junior high school; Public senior high school
IT Man: Debra Lingle
IT Man: Robert Lloyd

JEFFERSON COLLEGE NORTH
See COMMUNITY COLLEGE DISTRICT OF JEFFERSON COUNTY MISSOURI

D-U-N-S 96-919-8402
JEFFERSON COMMUNITY AND TECHNICAL COLLEGE FOUNDATION INC
109 E Broadway, Louisville, KY 40202-2005
Tel (502) 213-5333 *Founded/Ownrshp* 1968
Sales 1.4MM *EMP* 600^E
Accts Blue & Co Llc Louisville Ky
SIC 8249 8222 Vocational schools; Community college; Vocational schools; Community college
Pr: Tony Newberry

D-U-N-S 83-582-5852
JEFFERSON COMMUNITY COLLEGE
(*Suby of* STATE UNIVERSITY OF NEW YORK) ★
1220 Coffeen St, Watertown, NY 13601-1897
Tel (315) 786-2200 *Founded/Ownrshp* 1962
Sales 45.9MM^E *EMP* 325
SIC 8222 9411 Community college; Administration of educational programs; ; Community college; Administration of educational programs;
Pr: Carole McCoy
Ofcr: Joanne Rhubart
VP: Daniel J Dupee II
VP: Thomas Finch
VP: Craig D Johnson
**VP:* Betsy Penrose
Ex Dir: Kerry Young
IT Man: Charlene Moser
Web Dev: Jason Tessier
HC Dir: Rosanne Weir-Laplante

JEFFERSON COUNTY
See COUNTY OF JEFFERSON

D-U-N-S 07-764-9044
JEFFERSON COUNTY ALABAMA
716 Richard Arrington Jr, Birmingham, AL 35203-0114
Tel (205) 731-2880 *Founded/Ownrshp* 1819
Sales NA *EMP* 4,077
SIC 9111 Executive offices; ; Executive offices;
Pr: Bettye Finecollins
Pr: T Furman
Treas: Barry K Stephenson
Ofcr: Patricia Alexander
Ofcr: Brad Dickey
Ofcr: Kenneth McMullen
Ofcr: James Sparks
Ofcr: Adrilisa Steele
CIO: Roosevelt Butler
Sls Mgr: Yolanda Burrells
Sls Mgr: Michele Yarbrough

D-U-N-S 78-177-5663
JEFFERSON COUNTY ATTORNEYS OFFICE
600 W Jefferson St # 2086, Louisville, KY 40202-2740
Tel (502) 574-0903 *Founded/Ownrshp* 2012
Sales 22.8MM^E *EMP* 400
SIC 8111 General practice attorney, lawyer; General practice attorney, lawyer
Prin: Michael J O'Connell
IT Man: Donna Heavrin

JEFFERSON COUNTY BANCSHARES
See EAGLE BANK & TRUST CO OF JEFFERSON COUNTY

JEFFERSON COUNTY BANCSHARES
See EAGLE BANK

JEFFERSON COUNTY BOARD EDUCATN
See JEFFERSON COUNTY SCHOOL DISTRICT

D-U-N-S 06-298-4430
JEFFERSON COUNTY BOARD OF EDUCATION
JEFFERSON COUNTY PUBLIC SCHOOL
3332 Newburg Rd, Louisville, KY 40218-2414
Tel (502) 485-3011 *Founded/Ownrshp* 1884
Sales 1.1MMM *EMP* 14,000^E
Accts Strothman And Company Louisvi
SIC 8211 8741 Public elementary & secondary schools; Specialty education; Management services; Public elementary & secondary schools; Specialty education; Management services
CFO: Cornelia Hardin
Dir Teleco: Gerald Evans

D-U-N-S 07-210-6743
JEFFERSON COUNTY BOARD OF EDUCATION
2100 R Arrington Jr Blvd, Birmingham, AL 35209
Tel (205) 379-2000 *Founded/Ownrshp* 1914
Sales 173.3MM^E *EMP* 5,000
Accts Ronald L Jones
SIC 8211 9111 Public elementary & secondary schools; County supervisors' & executives' offices; Public elementary & secondary schools; County supervisors' & executives' offices
Pr: Jennifer Parsons
Treas: Catherine Brockman
VP: Joe Morris
**VP:* Ronald Rhodes
Dir Sec: Wendell Majors
Pr Dir: Nez Calhoun
Teacher Pr: Brett Kirkham
HC Dir: Ken Storie

D-U-N-S 09-263-6299
JEFFERSON COUNTY BOARD OF EDUCATION
1001 Peachtree St, Louisville, GA 30434-1523
Tel (478) 625-3283 *Founded/Ownrshp* 1900
Sales 24.6MM^E *EMP* 494
Accts Russell W Hinton Cpa Cgfm
SIC 8211 Public elementary & secondary schools; Public elementary & secondary schools
Dir Bus: Rene Week

D-U-N-S 83-976-2739
JEFFERSON COUNTY BOARD OF EDUCATION
110 Mordington Ave, Charles Town, WV 25414-1693
Tel (304) 725-9741 *Founded/Ownrshp* 1801
Sales 54.9MM^E *EMP* 900
SIC 8211 Public elementary & secondary schools; School board
Pr: Scott Sudduth
**VP:* Gary Kable

D-U-N-S 07-895-7867
JEFFERSON COUNTY COMMITTEE FOR ECONOMIC OPPORTUNITY PRIVATE (AL)
JCCEO
300 8th Ave W, Birmingham, AL 35204-3039
Tel (205) 327-7500 *Founded/Ownrshp* 1965
Sales 29.4MM *EMP* 470
Accts Sellers Richardson Holman & We
SIC 8322 Individual & family services; Individual & family services
Ex Dir: Marquita Davis
Treas: Charlie Faulkner

JEFFERSON COUNTY COURT
See COUNTY OF JEFFERSON

D-U-N-S 15-041-1072
JEFFERSON COUNTY DRAINAGE DISTRICT 6
D D 6
6550 Walden Rd, Beaumont, TX 77707-5510
Tel (409) 842-1818 *Founded/Ownrshp* 1920
Sales 24.1MM *EMP* 80
Accts Funchess Mills White & Co
SIC 8641 Environmental protection organization; Environmental protection organization
Genl Mgr: Richard P Leblanc Jr
Board of Directors: Chuck Oakley

JEFFERSON COUNTY HEALTH CENTER
See JEFFERSON COUNTY HOSPITAL

D-U-N-S 07-490-0879
■ **JEFFERSON COUNTY HMA LLC**
(*Suby of* HEALTH MANAGEMENT ASSOCIATES INC) ★
110 Hospital Dr, Jefferson City, TN 37760-5281
Tel (865) 471-2500 *Founded/Ownrshp* 2011
Sales 44.4MM *EMP* 330
SIC 8062 General medical & surgical hospitals; General medical & surgical hospitals
CEO: Colin McRae
Prin: David Bunch
Off Mgr: Jennifer L Bate
Off Mgr: Sharon Kerr
Dir IT: Steve Thompson

D-U-N-S 96-345-4686
JEFFERSON COUNTY HOSPITAL
JEFFERSON COUNTY HEALTH CENTER
2000 S Main St, Fairfield, IA 52556-3793
Tel (641) 472-4111 *Founded/Ownrshp* 1912
Sales 32.7MM^E *EMP* 200
SIC 8011 8062 Offices & clinics of medical doctors; General medical & surgical hospitals; Offices & clinics of medical doctors; General medical & surgical hospitals
Owner: Deb Cardin
Ofcr: Ellen Westhoff
VP: Joneane Parker
Dir Lab: Jim Schwarz
Dir Rx: Carri Pumphrey
Off Mgr: Pat Davis
Dir IT: Carrie Winheim
Software D: Julie Ostby
Surgeon: Gregory Ivins
Phys Thrpy: Lili Wells

D-U-N-S 07-663-5325
JEFFERSON COUNTY PUBLIC HOSPITAL DISTRICT 2
JEFFERSON HEALTHCARE
834 Sheridan St, Port Townsend, WA 98368-2443
Tel (360) 379-8031 *Founded/Ownrshp* 1975
Sales 116.7MM^E *EMP* 500
Accts Dingus Zarecor & Associates P
SIC 8062 General medical & surgical hospitals; General medical & surgical hospitals
CEO: Mike Glenn
**COO:* Paula Dowdle
**CFO:* Hilary Whittington
Ofcr: Terri Camp
Dir Lab: Alice Smith
Dir Rad: Ed Wertz
Chf Nrs Of: Joyce Cardinal
Chf Nrs Of: Elise Raphael
Mng Dir: Rhonda Bowen
Dir Sec: Lorena Sleight
Dir Pat Ac: Kim Bachelor

JEFFERSON COUNTY PUBLIC SCHOOL
See JEFFERSON COUNTY BOARD OF EDUCATION

D-U-N-S 07-846-4998
JEFFERSON COUNTY PUBLIC SCHOOL DISTRICT
3332 Newburg Rd, Louisville, KY 40218-2414
Tel (502) 485-3011 *Founded/Ownrshp* 2012
Sales 13.6MM^E *EMP* 11,166^E
SIC 8211 Elementary & secondary schools
Prin: Shari Morelli
Dir Sec: Stanford Mullen
MIS Dir: Raghu Seshadr
Pr Dir: Helene Kramer
Teacher Pr: Mark Rosen
Instr Medi: Paul Lanata
HC Dir: Bonnie Ciarrocchi

D-U-N-S 15-101-1624
JEFFERSON COUNTY RACING ASSOCIATION INC
BIRMINGHAM RACE COURSE
1000 John Rogers Dr, Irondale, AL 35210-7311
Tel (205) 838-7500 *Founded/Ownrshp* 1992
Sales 16.9MM^E *EMP* 400
SIC 7948 5812 Horse race track operation; Dog race track operation; Eating places; Concessionaire; Horse race track operation; Dog race track operation; Eating places; Concessionaire
Pr: Milton E McGregor
CFO: Lee S Yate
**CFO:* Lee Yates
**VP:* W M Russell
Ex Dir: William Keefer
Pr Mgr: Michelle Morton

D-U-N-S 10-065-3526
JEFFERSON COUNTY SCHOOL DISTRICT
942 Main St, Fayette, MS 39069-5524
Tel (601) 786-8059 *Founded/Ownrshp* 1900
Sales 13.3MM *EMP* 562
SIC 8211 Public elementary & secondary schools; Public elementary & secondary schools
Pr: Roosevelt Anderson

D-U-N-S 10-067-0876
JEFFERSON COUNTY SCHOOL DISTRICT
JEFFERSON COUNTY BOARD EDUCATN
1221 Gay St, Dandridge, TN 37725-4723
Tel (865) 397-3138 *Founded/Ownrshp* 1991
Sales 46.9MM^E *EMP* 1,000
SIC 8211 Public elementary & secondary schools; Public elementary & secondary schools
Dir Sec: Michael Phagan
CIO: Norma Huff
Pr Dir: Ronda Kinnick
Teacher Pr: Carol Baker
Psych: Karen Ramsey

D-U-N-S 03-078-2767
JEFFERSON COUNTY SCHOOL DISTRICT 509-J
445 Se Buff St, Madras, OR 97741-1595
Tel (541) 475-6192 *Founded/Ownrshp* 1957
Sales 28.4MM^E *EMP* 500
Accts Greer Mahr & Associates Llp
SIC 8211 Public elementary & secondary schools; Public junior high school; Public senior high school; Public elementary & secondary schools; Public junior high school; Public senior high school
**CFO:* Martha Bewley
Exec: Simon White
Ex Dir: Patty Jobe
Teacher Pr: Bonnie Dazie

D-U-N-S 01-062-0565
JEFFERSON COUNTY SCHOOL DISTRICT NO R-1
JEFFCO PUBLIC SCHOOLS
1829 Denver West Dr # 27, Golden, CO 80401-3120
Tel (303) 982-6500 *Founded/Ownrshp* 1950
Sales 801.2MM *EMP* 12,000
Accts Cliftonlarsonallen Llp Green
SIC 8211 Public elementary & secondary schools; High school, junior or senior; Public combined elementary & secondary school; Public elementary & secondary schools; High school, junior or senior; Public combined elementary & secondary school
COO: Bob Smith
Comm Man: Marlene Desmond
Ex Dir: Rich Waterman
Dir Sec: John McDonald
Prgrm Mgr: Alvin Tafoya
MIS Dir: Michael Gordon
Dir IT: Brent Heaviland
Telecom Mg: Bill Champman
IT Man: Terry Copper
IT Man: Dawn Miller
Netwrk Mgr: Anne Rosenblum

D-U-N-S 07-953-4552
JEFFERSON COUNTY SCHOOLS
2100 Richard Arrington Jr, Birmingham, AL 35209-1298
Tel (205) 379-2000 *Founded/Ownrshp* 1914
Sales 32.3MM^E *EMP* 4,603^E
SIC 8211 Public elementary & secondary schools

D-U-N-S 07-979-8861
JEFFERSON COUNTY SCHOOLS
110 Mordington Ave, Charles Town, WV 25414-1693
Tel (304) 725-9741 *Founded/Ownrshp* 2015
Sales 8.4MM^E *EMP* 998^E
SIC 8211 Public elementary & secondary schools

D-U-N-S 07-979-9076
JEFFERSON COUNTY SCHOOLS
1001 Peachtree St, Louisville, GA 30434-1523
Tel (478) 625-7626 *Founded/Ownrshp* 2015
Sales 6.1MM^E *EMP* 526^E
SIC 8211 Public elementary & secondary schools
MIS Dir: Cynthia Rabun
Teacher Pr: Shonta Walker

D-U-N-S 78-510-4423
JEFFERSON COUNTY SCHOOLS FILM LIBRARY
(*Suby of* JEFFCO PUBLIC SCHOOLS) ★
809 Quail St, Lakewood, CO 80215-5509
Tel (303) 232-8688 *Founded/Ownrshp* 1991
Sales 37.8MM^E *EMP* 1^E
SIC 8231 Libraries
Prin: Nancy Tucker
Exec: Jessica Wright

D-U-N-S 96-213-4578
JEFFERSON COUNTY SCHOOLS PUBLIC EDUCATION FOUNDATION
2100 Rich Arrington Jr Bl, Birmingham, AL 35203-1102
Tel (205) 379-2216 *Founded/Ownrshp* 1992
Sales 427.4M *EMP* 4,200
Accts Borland Benefield Birmingham
SIC 8699 Animal humane society; Animal humane society
Ex Dir: Sally Price

D-U-N-S 02-087-9243
JEFFERSON DAVIS COUNTY SCHOOL DISTRICT (MS)
909 Leo St, Prentiss, MS 39474
Tel (601) 792-4267 *Founded/Ownrshp* 1950
Sales 19.0MM *EMP* 400
SIC 8211 Public elementary & secondary schools; High school, junior or senior; Public elementary & secondary schools; High school, junior or senior
Pr: Jessie Holloway
Exec: Mary West

D-U-N-S 12-865-9562
JEFFERSON DAVIS PARISH PUBLIC SCHOOLS
203 E Plaquemine St, Jennings, LA 70546-5853
Tel (337) 824-1834 *Founded/Ownrshp* 1900
Sales 38.6MM^E *EMP* 850
SIC 8211 Public elementary & secondary schools; Public elementary & secondary schools
CTO: Steve Thompson

D-U-N-S 95-699-1160 EXP
■ **JEFFERSON ELECTRIC INC**
(*Suby of* PIONEER POWER SOLUTIONS INC) ★
9650 S Franklin Dr, Franklin, WI 53132-8847
Tel (414) 209-1620 *Founded/Ownrshp* 2010
Sales 27.6MM^E *EMP* 100
SIC 3612 Power & distribution transformers; Power & distribution transformers
Pr: Thomas Klink
**COO:* Steve Paul
Natl Sales: Jody Becker
Manager: Ed Armbruster

D-U-N-S 01-417-6135
JEFFERSON ELEMENTARY SCHOOL DISTRICT
101 Lincoln Ave, Daly City, CA 94015-3997
Tel (650) 991-1000 *Founded/Ownrshp* 1958
Sales 29.5MM^E *EMP* 600
SIC 8211 Public elementary & secondary schools; Elementary school; Public elementary & secondary schools; Elementary school
HC Dir: Sandra Linebarger

D-U-N-S 79-307-6795
JEFFERSON ENERGY I LP
3104 Edloe St Ste 205, Houston, TX 77027-6022
Tel (713) 552-0002 *Founded/Ownrshp* 1993
Sales 98.5MM^E *EMP* 4
SIC 1389 5051 Oil field services; Tubing, metal
Pr: Edward T Cotham Jr
**Treas:* John Storms
VP: Robert L Parker

JEFFERSON FERRY
See ACTIVE RETIREMENT COMMUNITY INC

JEFFERSON HEALTHCARE
See JEFFERSON COUNTY PUBLIC HOSPITAL DISTRICT 2

JEFFERSON HOME INFUSION SERVIC
See WALNUT HOME THERAPEUTICS INC

D-U-N-S 05-916-5282
JEFFERSON HOMEBUILDERS INC
CULPEPER WOOD PRESERVERS
501 N Main St, Culpeper, VA 22701-2607
Tel (540) 825-5898 *Founded/Ownrshp* 1972
Sales 74.1MM^E *EMP* 177
SIC 2491 1521 1522 Wood preserving; New construction, single-family houses; Apartment building construction; Wood preserving; New construction, single-family houses; Apartment building construction
Pr: Joseph R Daniel
**Sec:* Doris S Batiste
**VP:* Thomas Powell O Bannon
**VP:* Ronald Daniel
**VP:* B A Kerns

JEFFERSON HOSPITAL
See HOSPITAL AUTHORITY OF JEFFERSON COUNTY AND CITY OF LOUISVILLE GEORGIA

D-U-N-S 06-872-5910
JEFFERSON HOSPITAL
(*Suby of* HIGHMARK BLUE CRSS-BLUE SHIELD) ★
565 Coal Valley Rd, Clairton, PA 15025-3703
Tel (412) 267-6024 *Founded/Ownrshp* 2013
Sales 256.7MM^E *EMP* 2,000
SIC 8062 8063 8069 General medical & surgical hospitals; Psychiatric hospitals; Alcoholism rehabilitation hospital; Drug addiction rehabilitation hospital; General medical & surgical hospitals; Psychiatric hospitals; Alcoholism rehabilitation hospital; Drug addiction rehabilitation hospital
Pr: John J Dempster
**V Ch:* Gary W Deschamps
**COO:* Robert A Frank Sr
CFO: Joanne Hachey
**Treas:* C R Modispacher
VP: Dorothy Bellhouse
VP: Marcie Caplan
VP: Judy M Hall
VP: Mary Kaplan
Netwrk Eng: Maria Salazar
Mtls Mgr: Richard Klosky

D-U-N-S 07-563-9096
JEFFERSON HOSPITAL ASSOCIATION INC
JEFFERSON REGIONAL MEDICAL CTR
1600 W 40th Ave, Pine Bluff, AR 71603-6301
Tel (870) 541-7100 *Founded/Ownrshp* 1966
Sales 180.6MM *EMP* 1,700
Accts Bkd Llp Houston Tx
SIC 8062 General medical & surgical hospitals; General medical & surgical hospitals
Pr: Simpson M Tanya
Chf Rad: Melvin Hedgewood
Pr: Claudia Carberry
CFO: Nathan Van Genderan
**Ex VP:* Tomas Harbuck
Sr VP: Walter Johnson
VP: Brian Thomas
Exec: Sherry Jackson
Dir Inf Cn: Nikki Wallace
Dir Risk M: Dana Bryant
Dir Risk M: Allison Langston
Dir Lab: Michael R Smith
Dir Lab: Jeff Turner

JEFFERSON HOTEL
See HISTORIC HOTELS OF RICHMOND LLC

D-U-N-S 36-152-9373 IMP
JEFFERSON INDUSTRIES CORP
6670 State Route 29, West Jefferson, OH 43162-9677
Tel (614) 879-5300 *Founded/Ownrshp* 1988
Sales 150.8MM^E *EMP* 750^E
SIC 3711 Chassis, motor vehicle; Chassis, motor vehicle
Pr: Shiro Shimokagi
**Sr VP:* Steve Yoder
**VP:* Kazuhiko Hara
**VP:* Hassan Saadat
**Prin:* Curtis A Loveland
Admn Mgr: Sue Waggoner
Sfty Mgr: Larry McDonald

JEFFERSON INSURANCE CO
See AGA SERVICE CO

D-U-N-S 07-279-5784
JEFFERSON INSURANCE CO
(*Suby of* AGA (VIRGINIA) INC) ★
2805 N Parham Rd, Richmond, VA 23294-4401
Tel (804) 285-3300 *Founded/Ownrshp* 2007
Sales NA *EMP* 882^E
SIC 6331 Fire, marine & casualty insurance: mutual
Ch Bd: Johnathan M Ansell
**Treas:* Mark Huntley
**Sec:* Fred Faett
**VP:* David Bloom

D-U-N-S 02-718-2294 IMP/EXP
JEFFERSON IRON AND METAL BROKERAGE INC
3940 Montclair Rd Ste 300, Mountain Brk, AL 35213-2420
Tel (205) 803-5200 *Founded/Ownrshp* 1984
Sales 125.0MM *EMP* 20^E
SIC 5051 Ferrous metals; Miscellaneous nonferrous products
Pr: George Dreher
**Treas:* Alan Dreher
**VP:* Paul Dreher

D-U-N-S 02-973-8903
JEFFERSON JOINT SCHOOL DISTRICT 251
JEFFERSON AND MADISON
3850 E300 N, Rigby, ID 83442
Tel (208) 745-6693 *Founded/Ownrshp* 1949
Sales 30.5MM *EMP* 550
Accts Searle Hart & Associates Pllc
SIC 8211 Public elementary & secondary schools; School board; Public elementary & secondary schools; School board
Teacher Pr: Michele Southwick

JEFFERSON LAB
See THOMAS JEFFERSON NATIONAL ACCELERATOR FACILITY

D-U-N-S 01-833-0928
JEFFERSON LANDMARK INC
1525 State Route 152, Bloomingdale, OH 43910-6903
Tel (740) 944-1971 *Founded/Ownrshp* 1934
Sales 21.0MM *EMP* 27
Accts Harr & Scherer Cpa S Inc
SIC 5984 5999 2875 Liquefied petroleum gas, delivered to customers' premises; Feed & farm supply; Fertilizers, mixing only; Liquefied petroleum gas, delivered to customers' premises; Feed & farm supply; Fertilizers, mixing only
Pr: Joe Rozsa

JEFFERSON LINES
See JEFFERSON PARTNERS LIMITED PARTNERSHIP

JEFFERSON MEDICAL COLLEGE
See THOMAS JEFFERSON UNIVERSITY

D-U-N-S 00-503-3612
JEFFERSON MEMORIAL COMMUNITY FOUNDATION 145
1450 Parkway W, Festus, MO 63028-2385
Tel (636) 638-1400 *Founded/Ownrshp* 2013
Sales 157.1MM *EMP* 3
SIC 8641 Civic social & fraternal associations

JEFFERSON MEMORIAL HOSPITAL
See CHARLES TOWN GENERAL HOSPITAL INC

D-U-N-S 95-982-5993
JEFFERSON PARISH INC SEWERAGE DEPARTMENT
1221 Elmwood Park Blvd # 503, Harahan, LA 70123-2355
Tel (504) 736-6661 *Founded/Ownrshp* 1992
Sales 42.9MM^E *EMP* 200
SIC 4952 Sewerage systems; Sewerage systems

D-U-N-S 05-136-9977
JEFFERSON PARISH PUBLIC SCHOOL SYSTEM
501 Manhattan Blvd, Harvey, LA 70058-4443
Tel (504) 349-7600 *Founded/Ownrshp* 2010
Sales 533.0MM *EMP* 5,919^E
SIC 8211 Elementary & secondary schools; Elementary & secondary schools

D-U-N-S 07-980-2444
JEFFERSON PARISH PUBLIC SCHOOL SYSTEM
JEFFERSON PARISH SCHOOL BOARD
501 Manhattan Blvd, Harvey, LA 70058-4443
Tel (504) 349-7600 *Founded/Ownrshp* 2015
Sales 600.0MM *EMP* 6,000
SIC 8299 Airline training
Dir Sec: James Hufft
Sfty Dirs: Germaine Gilson
Pr Dir: Tina Chong
HC Dir: Alida Wyler

JEFFERSON PARISH SCHOOL BOARD
See JEFFERSON PARISH PUBLIC SCHOOL SYSTEM

D-U-N-S 07-508-4178
JEFFERSON PARISH SCHOOL BOARD INC
501 Manhattan Blvd, Harvey, LA 70058-4443
Tel (504) 349-7600 *Founded/Ownrshp* 1955
Sales 65.7MM *EMP* 7,200
Accts Mike B Gillespie Cpa Jennin
SIC 8211 Public elementary & secondary schools; Public elementary & secondary schools
**COO:* Lale Geer
**CFO:* Robert Fulton
IT Man: Vu Vuong
VP Mktg: Barbara Duplantis

D-U-N-S 07-861-2197
JEFFERSON PARISH SHERIFFS OFFICE
SHERIFF NEWELL NORMAND
1233 Westbank Expy, Harvey, LA 70058-4462
Tel (504) 363-5500 *Founded/Ownrshp* 2007
Sales NA *EMP* 1,450^E
SIC 9221 9223 Sheriffs' offices; ; Sheriffs' offices;
CFO: Paul Rivera
**CEO:* Newell Normand
Ofcr: Michael Cooke
Ofcr: Grace Julia
Snr Mgr: Craig Taffaro

D-U-N-S 79-637-0567
JEFFERSON PARTNERS LIMITED PARTNERSHIP
JEFFERSON LINES
2100 E 26th St, Minneapolis, MN 55404-4101
Tel (612) 359-3400 *Founded/Ownrshp* 1992
Sales 44.2MM^E *EMP* 230
SIC 4131 4142 4141 Interstate bus line; Bus charter service, except local; Local bus charter service; Interstate bus line; Bus charter service, except local; Local bus charter service
Pt: Charles A Zelle
Pt: Fred E Kaiser
Treas: Jeffery D Kruger
Sr VP: Steve Woelfel
VP: Bonnie Buchanan
Trfc Dir: Mike Holliday

D-U-N-S 00-697-2129
■ **JEFFERSON PILOT LIFE AMERICA INSURANCE CO** (NJ)
(*Suby of* LINCOLN NATIONAL CORP) ★
1 Granite Pl, Concord, NH 03301-3258
Tel (603) 226-5000 *Founded/Ownrshp* 1897, 2008
Sales NA *EMP* 462
SIC 6411 6321 Insurance agents, brokers & service; Health insurance carriers; Insurance agents, brokers & service; Health insurance carriers
Ch Bd: David Stonecipher
Pr: Kenneth Mlekush
**COO:* Randell G Craig
Treas: Russel C Simpson
Ofcr: Charles C Cornelio

JEFFERSON PRIMARY SCHOOL
See BROOKE COUNTY SCHOOLS

D-U-N-S 01-017-8275 IMP
JEFFERSON RADIOLOGY PC
111 Founders Plz Ste 400, East Hartford, CT 06108-3240
Tel (860) 289-3375 *Founded/Ownrshp* 1963
Sales 45.4MM^E *EMP* 300
SIC 8011 Radiologist; Radiologist
Pr: Ethan B Foxman MD
**COO:* Jonathan Pine
CFO: Paul Desantis
CFO: Larry Freni
**Treas:* Domenic A Zambuto
**VP:* Doreen Freeman
**VP:* Stuart K Markowitz
VP: Stuart Markowitz
IT Man: Kathy Whalen
Netwrk Eng: Jim Araujo
Site Mgr: Chris Kulman

D-U-N-S 96-940-3026
JEFFERSON REGIONAL MEDICAL CENTER FOUNDATION
565 Coal Valley Rd, Pittsburgh, PA 15236
Tel (412) 469-5000 *Founded/Ownrshp* 2011
Sales 77.0MM *EMP* 45^E
Accts Parentebeard Llc Philadelphia
SIC 8062 General medical & surgical hospitals; General medical & surgical hospitals
Pr: John J Dempster
CFO: Robert Frank
Treas: C Modispacher
VP: Chet Phitayakorn
VP: Albert Ragan
Dir OR: Robert McCoy
Admn Mgr: Marianne Beckman
Dir IT: Toni Fox
Netwrk Eng: Maria Salazar
Obsttrcn: Anthony Gentile
Pharmcst: Lori Shenal

JEFFERSON REGIONAL MEDICAL CTR
See JEFFERSON HOSPITAL ASSOCIATION INC

JEFFERSON REGIONAL MEDICAL CTR
See MERCY HOSPITAL JEFFERSON

D-U-N-S 09-990-3379
JEFFERSON REHABILITATION CENTER INC
AGENCY FOR RETARDED CHILDREN
(*Suby of* NYSARC INC) ★
380 Gaffney Dr, Watertown, NY 13601-1863
Tel (315) 788-2730 *Founded/Ownrshp* 1954
Sales 32.2MM *EMP* 550
Accts Bonadio & Co Llp Cpas Pitt
SIC 8322 8331 2789 2752 Association for the handicapped; Sheltered workshop; Job training services; Skill training center; Bookbinding & related work; Commercial printing, lithographic; Association for the handicapped; Sheltered workshop; Job training services; Skill training center; Bookbinding & related work; Commercial printing, lithographic
Ex Dir: Howard W Ganter
**COO:* Lisa M Jeschawitz

D-U-N-S 01-401-2975
JEFFERSON SCHOOL DISTRICT
101 Lincoln Ave, Daly City, CA 94015-3934
Tel (650) 991-1000 *Founded/Ownrshp* 1895
Sales 21.5MM^E *EMP* 280^E
SIC 8211 Public elementary & secondary schools; School board; Business consulting; Public elementary & secondary schools; School board
IT Man: Colleen Duggan
IT Man: Bruce Erickson
Teacher Pr: Nancy Castro

D-U-N-S 55-718-1422 IMP
JEFFERSON SCIENCE ASSOCIATES LLC
1201 New York Ave Nw # 430, Washington, DC 20005-3917
Tel (202) 408-7872 *Founded/Ownrshp* 2005
Sales 29.0MM^E *EMP* 612
SIC 8733 Noncommercial research organizations; Noncommercial research organizations

D-U-N-S 02-338-4394
JEFFERSON SOUTHERN CORP
1000 Marquette Rd, Rockmart, GA 30153-3656
Tel (770) 684-1228 *Founded/Ownrshp* 2000
Sales 45.0MM^E *EMP* 110
SIC 3711 Chassis, motor vehicle; Chassis, motor vehicle
Pr: Tadashi Kokubo
Plnt Mgr: Ray Wright
Sls Mgr: Yukihisa Kitami

D-U-N-S 07-545-9529
JEFFERSON STATE COMMUNITY COLLEGE FOUNDATION INC
2601 Carson Rd, Birmingham, AL 35215-3007
Tel (205) 853-1200 *Founded/Ownrshp* 1965
Sales 108.2M *EMP* 300
SIC 8222 5942 8221 Community college; College book stores; Colleges universities & professional schools; Community college; College book stores; Colleges universities & professional schools
Pr: Judy M Merritt
**Treas:* Lauren Lentz
VP: Joe Morris

D-U-N-S 06-080-3467
JEFFERSON TOWNSHIP BOARD OF EDUCATION (INC)
31 State Route 181, Lake Hopatcong, NJ 07849-1378
Tel (973) 663-5782 *Founded/Ownrshp* 1956
Sales 24.0MM^E *EMP* 460
SIC 8211 9111 Public elementary & secondary schools; Mayors' offices; Public elementary & secondary schools; Mayors' offices

D-U-N-S 07-983-6274
JEFFERSON UNION HIGH SCHOOL DISTRICT
699 Serramonte Blvd # 100, Daly City, CA 94015-4132
Tel (650) 550-7900 *Founded/Ownrshp* 2015
Sales 11.6MM^E *EMP* 319^E
SIC 8211 Public elementary & secondary schools

D-U-N-S 61-033-9512
JEFFERSON UNIVERSITY HOSPITAL
A M ROSTAMI, MD PHD
1020 Walnut St Ste 1, Philadelphia, PA 19107-5567
Tel (215) 955-8100 *Founded/Ownrshp* 2006
Sales 28.8MM^E *EMP* 500
SIC 8221 University; University
Ch: A M Rostami PHD
Bd of Dir: George Roberson

D-U-N-S 79-004-5665
JEFFERSON UNIVERSITY PHYSICIANS
1020 Walnut St, Philadelphia, PA 19107-5543
Tel (215) 955-6000 Founded/Ownrshp 2007
Sales 410.3MM EMP 4
Accts Pricewaterhousecoopers Llp Ph
SIC 8011 Offices & clinics of medical doctors; Offices & clinics of medical doctors
Prin: John Ogunkeye
Doctor: Barbara A Berko
Doctor: Emmanuel C Besa
Doctor: Richard H Epstein
Doctor: Anna L Rabinowitz
Doctor: Norman G Rosenblum
Doctor: Said Sharifi-Azad

D-U-N-S 01-448-5882
JEFFERSON WHOLESALE GROCERY CO INC (PA)
COMET FOOD WAREHOUSES
47 Anchor Inn Rd, Punxsutawney, PA 15767
Tel (814) 938-8660 Founded/Ownrshp 1947, 1965
Sales 52.8MM^E EMP 265
SIC 5141 5411

D-U-N-S 07-765-3509
JEFFERSON-BLOUNT-ST CLAIR MENTAL HEALTH AUTHORITY
940 Montclair Rd Ste 200, Birmingham, AL 35213-1212
Tel (205) 595-7498 Founded/Ownrshp 1967
Sales 220.0M EMP 290^E
SIC 8361 Residential care; Residential care
Ex Dir: Richard Craig

JEFFERSON-PILOT
See ABE ENTERCOM HOLDINGS LLC

D-U-N-S 14-825-7017
JEFFERSON-RANDOLPH CORP
POLO
805 Curtis Pkwy Se, Calhoun, GA 30701-3688
Tel (706) 602-1700 Founded/Ownrshp 1985
Sales 27.7MM^E EMP 125
SIC 5087 4213 4731 Carpet installation equipment; Trucking, except local; Truck transportation brokers; Carpet installation equipment; Trucking, except local; Truck transportation brokers
Pr: Jefferson Smith

D-U-N-S 78-715-4897
▲ JEFFERSONVILLE BANCORP
4866 State Route 52, Jeffersonville, NY 12748-5558
Tel (845) 482-4000 Founded/Ownrshp 1982
Sales NA EMP 125^E
Tkr Sym JFBC Exch OTO
SIC 6021 National commercial banks; National commercial banks
Pr: Wayne V Zanetti
*Ch Bd: Kenneth C Klein
V Ch: Raymond Walter
Pr: Martha Huebsch
CFO: John A Russell
Bd of Dir: John Galligan
Ofcr: Don Jaroszewski
Ofcr: George Kinne
VP: S Diane
VP: Tatiana Hahn
VP: George W Kinne Jr
Board of Directors: David W Bodenstein, Philip Coombe III, John W Galligan, John K Gempler, Donald L Knack, James F Roche, Fred W Stabbert III, Edward T Sykes, Raymond Walter

JEFFORDS STEEL AND ENGRG CO
See JEFFORDS STEEL AND SPECIALTY CO INC

D-U-N-S 12-275-6083
JEFFORDS STEEL AND SPECIALTY CO INC
JEFFORDS STEEL AND ENGRG CO
4398 Route 22, Plattsburgh, NY 12901-5851
Tel (518) 561-4061 Founded/Ownrshp 1985
Sales 27.9MM EMP 120
SIC 3441 3449 5051

D-U-N-S 09-244-7424
JEFFREY BUICK-NISSAN INC
JEFFREY NISSAN
30800 Gratiot Ave, Roseville, MI 48066-1751
Tel (586) 296-1300 Founded/Ownrshp 1983
Sales 49.8MM^E EMP 110
SIC 5511 Automobiles, new & used; Automobiles, new & used
Pr: Jeffrey L Tamaroff
Div Mgr: Roger Lau
Sales Asso: Donald Vondrak

D-U-N-S 15-554-1063
JEFFREY C STONE INC
SUMMIT BUILDERS
3333 E Camelback Rd # 122, Phoenix, AZ 85018-2323
Tel (602) 508-6775 Founded/Ownrshp 1986
Sales 80.2MM^E EMP 150
Accts Morrison & Associates Cpas Pl
SIC 1542 1522 Commercial & office building contractors; Commercial & office building, new construction; Shopping center construction; School building construction; Residential construction; Commercial & office building contractors; Commercial & office building, new construction; Shopping center construction; School building construction; Residential construction
Pr: Jeffrey C Stone
CFO: Mark Briggs
CFO: Ken Shaw
Sr VP: Kristin Hower
VP: John Mariconda
*Prin: Andy Rabasca
MIS Dir: Kris Feuberling
IT Man: Corey Elias
Sfty Mgr: Dan Horton

D-U-N-S 14-760-9572 IMP
JEFFREY CHAIN LP
RENOLD JEFFREY
(Suby of RENOLD PUBLIC LIMITED COMPANY)
2307 Maden Dr, Morristown, TN 37813-2898
Tel (423) 586-1951 Founded/Ownrshp 1985
Sales 73.3MM^E EMP 270^E
SIC 3568 5072 Chain, power transmission; Chains; Chain, power transmission; Chains
CFO: John Bewley
VP: Bob Deuelt
Dist Mgr: Robert Beattie
VP Mfg: Mick Ingleston
Ql Cn Mgr: Robert Hamilton
Natl Sales: Steve Fleckenstein
VP Sls: Tony Robinson
Manager: Monty Chustz
Manager: Dan Majoy
Sls Mgr: Mark Eggli
Sls Mgr: Jamia Hensley

D-U-N-S 78-053-2164 IMP
JEFFREY COURT INC
620 Parkridge Ave, Norco, CA 92860-3124
Tel (951) 340-3383 Founded/Ownrshp 1991
Sales 30.5MM^E EMP 75
SIC 5032 3253 Tile, clay or other ceramic, excluding refractory; Ceramic wall & floor tile
Pr: James Lawson
*CFO: Janice Lawson
VP Sls: Scott Hassman
Sls Dir: John Beckley
Manager: Ken Davis

D-U-N-S 17-373-4633 IMP
JEFFREY FABRICS INC
261 5th Ave Rm 2001, New York, NY 10016-7700
Tel (212) 447-7333 Founded/Ownrshp 1987
Sales 25.3MM^E EMP 26
SIC 5023 Home furnishings; Home furnishings
Pr: Jeffrey Goldman
*CFO: Paul Galosky
*VP: Jeffrey Erdheim

JEFFREY M PERELMAN MD FACS
See EYE ASSOCIATES OF BOCA RATON

D-U-N-S 08-763-8946 IMP/EXP
JEFFREY MACHINE INC (AL)
3841 Industrial Dr # 151, Birmingham, AL 35217-1375
Tel (205) 841-2009 Founded/Ownrshp 1977
Sales 34.4MM^E EMP 83
SIC 3423 7699 Edge tools for woodworking: augers, bits, gimlets, etc.; Metal reshaping & replating services
CEO: Jeffrey R Sager
*VP: Chris Thompson

JEFFREY NISSAN
See JEFFREY BUICK-NISSAN INC

D-U-N-S 60-218-6967 EXP
JEFFRY KNIGHT INC
KNIGHT ENTERPRISES
6056 Ulmerton Rd, Clearwater, FL 33760-3944
Tel (727) 524-6235 Founded/Ownrshp 1982
Sales 80.4MM^E EMP 200
SIC 1623 1731 Communication line & transmission tower construction; Underground utilities contractor; Electrical work; Communication line & transmission tower construction; Underground utilities contractor; Electrical work
CEO: Jeff Knight
*COO: Bob Halle
*VP: Donna Bentley
*VP: Charles Kwasnicki
Off Mgr: Jill Williams
IT Man: Mark Demerin

D-U-N-S 01-789-9295 IMP/EXP
JEGS AUTOMOTIVE INC
JEG'S HIGH-PERFORMANCE CENTER
101 Jegs Pl, Delaware, OH 43015-9279
Tel (614) 294-5050 Founded/Ownrshp 1989
Sales 494.7M EMP 300
SIC 5013 5961 5531 Automotive supplies & parts; Automotive supplies & equipment, mail order; Automotive parts; Automotive supplies & parts; Automotive supplies & equipment, mail order; Automotive parts
Pr: Edward James Coughlin
*VP: Jeg Coughlin
*VP: John Coughlin

JEG'S HIGH-PERFORMANCE CENTER
See JEGS AUTOMOTIVE INC

D-U-N-S 07-346-4885
JEKYLL ISLAND STATE PARK AUTHORITY
BLACKBEARDS
(Suby of EXECUTIVE OFFICE OF STATE OF GEORGIA) ★
100 James Rd, Jekyll Island, GA 31527-0872
Tel (912) 635-2236 Founded/Ownrshp 1947
Sales NA EMP 450
SIC 9512 Recreational program administration, government; ; Recreational program administration, government;
Ex Dir: C Jones Hooks

D-U-N-S 00-514-1346 IMP/EXP
JEL SERT CO
J S
Conde St Rr 59, West Chicago, IL 60185
Tel (630) 231-7590 Founded/Ownrshp 1929
Sales 186.8MM^E EMP 277^E
SIC 2024 2087 Fruit pops, frozen; Concentrates, flavoring (except drink)
CEO: Gary Ricco
*Ch Bd: Charles T Wegner IV
*Pr: Kenneth E Wegner
CFO: Lori Bottoms
VP: Alex Chimens
VP: Dana Crowley
VP: Larry Hamwey
VP Bus Dev: Matt Ingemi
Dir IT: John Dobrozsi
IT Man: Mike Gomolski
Plnt Mgr: Simon Richards
Board of Directors: Susie Frausto, Joan Wegner, John Wegner

JELD WEN INTERNATIONAL SUPPLY
See JELD-WEN INC

D-U-N-S 00-904-0288 IMP/EXP
JELD-WEN INC
JELD WEN INTERNATIONAL SUPPLY
(Suby of ONEX INVESTMENT CORP) ★
440 S Church St Ste 400, Charlotte, NC 28202-2064
Tel (800) 535-3936 Founded/Ownrshp 1960, 2011
Sales 3.5MMM^E EMP 2,000^E
Accts Pricewaterhousecoopers Llp Ch
SIC 3442 5031 2421 Millwork; Door frames, wood; Window frames, wood; Doors, wood; Sawmills & planing mills, general; Planing mills; Cut stock, softwood; Metal doors, sash & trim; Windows, plastic; Pallets, wood; Land subdividers & developers, commercial; Shutters, door or window: metal; Doors, combination, screen-storm; Building & structural materials, wood
Ch Bd: Kirk Hachigian
*COO: Barry Homrighaus
*COO: Mark Thurman
CFO: Douglas Kintzinger
*CFO: L Brooks Mallard
*Treas: John Linker
Treas: Matt Wendt
*Ex VP: Bob Merrill
*Ex VP: David Sheil
Sr VP: Eric Spence
VP: Bruce Fedio
*VP: Philip S Orsino
Exec: Larry Leitch
Comm Man: Lyndsay Barthel
Comm Man: Suzanna Fierstos

JELENKO
See ARGEN CORP

D-U-N-S 05-190-4720
JELLCO CONTAINER INC
1151 N Tustin Ave, Anaheim, CA 92807-1736
Tel (714) 666-2728 Founded/Ownrshp 1977
Sales 23.0MM^E EMP 72
SIC 2653 Corrugated & solid fiber boxes
Pr: Jeff Erselius
*CFO: Rick Leininger
Trfc Dir: Corey Erselius
Opers Mgr: Jason Wilkerson

D-U-N-S 07-489-4445
JELLICO COMMUNITY HOSPITAL INC
188 Hospital Ln, Jellico, TN 37762-4400
Tel (423) 784-7252 Founded/Ownrshp 1975
Sales 22.9MM EMP 285^E
SIC 8062 Hospital, affiliated with AMA residency; Hospital, affiliated with AMA residency
Pr: Keith Richardson
Chf Rad: Frederick McLean
CFO: Shelle Diehm
VP: Pamela Hodges
Dir Lab: Michael Rose
Dir Rad: Greg Eaton
Dir Rx: Craig Mack
Phys Thrpy: Tawnya Brock
HC Dir: Beth Rowe

D-U-N-S 00-911-8290 IMP
JELLY BELLY CANDY CO (CA)
1 Jelly Belly Ln, Fairfield, CA 94533-6741
Tel (707) 428-2800 Founded/Ownrshp 1900
Sales 212.3MM^E EMP 650
SIC 2064 Candy & other confectionery products; Candy & other confectionery products
CEO: Robert M Simpson Jr
*Ch Bd: Herman G Rowland Sr
Pr: Albert Larson
Pr: Robert Simpson
Sec: Lisa Brasher
V Ch Bd: William Kelley
VP: Dennis Spiller
Plnt Mgr: Danny Williams
Pr Mgr: Jelly Barker
Genl Couns: John Di Giusto

D-U-N-S 60-172-3414 IMP
JEM ELECTRONICS INC
23 National Dr, Franklin, MA 02038-3243
Tel (508) 520-3105 Founded/Ownrshp 1978
Sales 29.0MM^E EMP 125
SIC 3679 Harness assemblies for electronic use: wire or cable; Harness assemblies for electronic use: wire or cable
Pr: John S McDonald
Mtls Mgr: Derik Moore
Sls Dir: Jason Frasca

D-U-N-S 05-915-9579
JEM RESTAURANT GROUP INC
TACO BELL
2 Wharfside St, Charleston, SC 29401-1652
Tel (843) 958-0488 Founded/Ownrshp 1998
Sales 15.9MM^E EMP 350
SIC 5812 Fast-food restaurant, chain; Fast-food restaurant, chain
Pr: John McGrath
VP: Melissa Benson

D-U-N-S 08-211-3366
JEM RESTAURANT MANAGEMENT CORP
312 W Cromwell Ave, Fresno, CA 93711-6113
Tel (559) 435-9648 Founded/Ownrshp 1973
Sales 51.5MM^E EMP 1,200
SIC 5812 Fast-food restaurant, chain; Fast-food restaurant, chain
Ch: Joseph F Desmond
*Pr: Richard Braden
VP: Steve Liles

D-U-N-S 13-924-5237
JEM TECHNICAL MARKETING CO INC
550 N Old Crystal Bay Rd, Long Lake, MN 55356-5612
Tel (952) 473-5012 Founded/Ownrshp 1984
Sales 63.9MM^E EMP 80
SIC 5085 3494 5084 3492 Valves & fittings; Valves & pipe fittings; Industrial machinery & equipment; Fluid power valves & hose fittings; Valves & fittings; Valves & pipe fittings; Industrial machinery & equipment; Fluid power valves & hose fittings
Pr: John E Menge
*VP: Sheryl Menge
*VP: Andrea Tysdal

D-U-N-S 10-322-9084 IMP
JEMBRO VARIETY STORES INC
148 39th St, Brooklyn, NY 11232-2550
Tel (718) 252-5484 Founded/Ownrshp 1983
Sales 21.9MM^E EMP 200
SIC 5331 Variety stores
Pr: Jack Beyda
*Treas: Richard Beyda
*VP: Morris Beyda III

D-U-N-S 03-573-4995
JEMEZ MOUNTAINS ELECTRIC COOPERATIVE INC
19365 Us 84/285, Espanola, NM 87532-2645
Tel (505) 753-2105 Founded/Ownrshp 1948
Sales 79.2MM^E EMP 105
SIC 4911 Distribution, electric power; Transmission, electric power; Distribution, electric power; Transmission, electric power
Pr: John Tapia
Treas: Leroy Ortiz
Bd of Dir: Levi Valdez
*VP: David Salazar
Genl Mgr: Darlene Armijo
*Genl Mgr: Ernesto Gonzales
Opers Mgr: Johnny Lujan
Mktg Mgr: Manuel Vigil

JEMISON DEMSEY METALS
See JEMISON-DEMSEY LLC

D-U-N-S 07-858-5999
JEMISON INC
35 Union Ave Ste 200, Memphis, TN 38103-2417
Tel (901) 544-1705 Founded/Ownrshp 1971
Sales 8.3MM EMP 300^E
Accts Reynolds Bond & Griesbeck Plc
SIC 6531 6513 Real estate managers; Apartment building operators; Real estate managers; Apartment building operators
Pr: Frank Z Jemison Jr
*Ex VP: Michael Johnson

D-U-N-S 09-569-5474 IMP/EXP
JEMISON INVESTMENT CO INC
2001 Park Pl Ste 320, Birmingham, AL 35203-4800
Tel (205) 324-7681 Founded/Ownrshp 1949
Sales 24.6MM^E EMP 90
SIC 6719 5031 Investment holding companies, except banks; Lumber: rough, dressed & finished
CEO: H Corbin Day
*Ch Bd: James D Davis
*Pr: J David Brown III

D-U-N-S 09-885-2890 IMP
JEMISON-DEMSEY LLC (GA)
JEMISON DEMSEY METALS
(Suby of JEMISON INVESTMENT CO INC) ★
3800 Colonnade Pkwy # 250, Birmingham, AL 35243-2351
Tel (205) 986-6600 Founded/Ownrshp 1980, 1988
Sales 72.9MM^E EMP 45
Accts Pearce Bevill Leesburg Moor
SIC 5051 3312 Steel; Sheet or strip, steel, cold-rolled: own hot-rolled; Steel; Sheet or strip, steel, cold-rolled: own hot-rolled
CEO: Peter Heinke
Ex VP: Dave Pratt
Ex VP: Bill Werner
VP: Matt Bradford
VP: J David Brown III
VP: James D Davis
VP: Brant Watts
Plnt Mgr: Mark Clough
Ql Cn Mgr: Rachel White
Sls Mgr: Adam Likowski
Sales Asso: Katherine Heinke

JEN ELECTRIC
See JENCO INC

D-U-N-S 05-799-1820 IMP/EXP
JEN-COAT INC
PROLAMINA
132 N Elm St, Westfield, MA 01085-1644
Tel (413) 562-2315 Founded/Ownrshp 2010
Sales NA EMP 350
SIC 2671 2851 Paper coated or laminated for packaging; Paints & allied products; Paper coated or laminated for packaging; Paints & allied products
CEO: Greg Tucker
CFO: Bob Lapalme
*Treas: Sachin Desai
*Sec: Eric Bradford
VP: Dave Hopkins
VP: William Leavy
Exec: Greg Davidson
Exec: John Marshall
Exec: Jim Tierney
*Prin: Tim French
MIS Dir: Saeed Ghoreshi

D-U-N-S 00-346-5174
JENA CHOCTAW PINES CASINO
149 Chahta Trl, Dry Prong, LA 71423-3576
Tel (318) 648-7773 Founded/Ownrshp 2013
Sales 13.4MM^E EMP 300
SIC 7011 Casino hotel; Casino hotel
Genl Mgr: Norman Runyan
*Genl Mgr: Roy Corby
IT Man: Lee Fine

JENCARE LOUISIANA HOLDING
See PMR LA HOLDING LLC

JENCARE VIRGINIA HOLDING
See VIRGINIA JENCARE HOLDING LLC

D-U-N-S 05-788-6186
JENCAST PRODUCTS INC
(Suby of JENSEN INTERNATIONAL INC) ★
500 W 4th St, S Coffeyville, OK 74072
Tel (918) 255-6500 Founded/Ownrshp 1972
Sales 30.0MM^E EMP 80
SIC 3321 3469 Ductile iron castings; Gray iron castings; Porcelain enameled products & utensils; Ductile iron castings; Gray iron castings; Porcelain enameled products & utensils
Pr: Eric Jensen

*Ch Bd: James B Jensen Sr
*Sec: Diana Nisley
*VP: Donna L Jensen
*VP: Monte Owens

D-U-N-S 96-273-2751
JENCO INC
JEN ELECTRIC
7469 E Monte Cristo Ave, Scottsdale, AZ 85260-1618
Tel (480) 607-9797 Founded/Ownrshp 2010
Sales 32.7MM EMP 200
Accts Pittman & Murdough Pllc Phoe
SIC 1731 1794 8711 General electrical contractor; Excavation work; Construction & civil engineering; General electrical contractor; Excavation work; Construction & civil engineering
CEO: K Kelly Anderson III
*CFO: Joseph Devecchio
*VP Opers: Robert E Kohnen Jr

D-U-N-S 00-819-8710
JENCO PRODUCTIONS INC (CA)
401 S J St, San Bernardino, CA 92410-2605
Tel (909) 381-9453 Founded/Ownrshp 1995
Sales 49.2MM^E EMP 300
SIC 7389 Packaging & labeling services; Packaging & labeling services
Pr: Jennifer Imbriani
CFO: Hazel Walters
Exec: Alicia Garcia
Mktg Dir: Kenn Hughes
Snr Mgr: Mary Wright

D-U-N-S 03-711-4444
JENERIC/PENTRON INC
(Suby of PENTRON CORP) ★
1717 W Collins Ave, Orange, CA 92867-5422
Tel (203) 265-7397 Founded/Ownrshp 1987
Sales 9.2MM^E EMP 280
SIC 3843 Dental equipment; Dental equipment
Pr: Gordon Cohen
CFO: Barry Kosowsky
*Ex VP: Martin Schulman

JENISON HEALTH CENTER
See GRAND VALLEY HEALTH PLAN INC

D-U-N-S 08-034-7412
JENISON PUBLIC SCHOOLS
8375 20th Ave, Jenison, MI 49428-9230
Tel (616) 667-3264 Founded/Ownrshp 1845
Sales 58.9MM EMP 555
Accts Bdo Usa Llp Grand Rapids Mi
SIC 8211 Public elementary & secondary schools; School board; Public elementary & secondary schools; School board
Schl Brd P: William Waalkes

D-U-N-S 60-796-2107
JENISYS ENGINEERED PRODUCTS INC
VICWEST STEEL
404 E Dallas Rd, Grapevine, TX 76051-4110
Tel (817) 481-3521 Founded/Ownrshp 2000
Sales 79.5MM^E EMP 1,116
SIC 3444 Roof deck, sheet metal; Roof deck, sheet metal
Pr: Robert Dryburgh

D-U-N-S 03-459-2840
JENKINS & WYNNE INC
328 College St, Clarksville, TN 37040-3262
Tel (931) 647-3353 Founded/Ownrshp 1959
Sales 65.4MM^E EMP 175
SIC 5511 Automobiles, new & used; Automobiles, new & used
Pr: Don Jenkins
Genl Mgr: Murray Keeter
Telecom Ex: Bobby Smith
IT Man: Cathy Mueller
Sls Mgr: Lisa Dotson
Sls Mgr: Dwight Ladd

D-U-N-S 03-459-2857
JENKINS & WYNNE MOTOR CO INC
JENKINS FORD LINCOLN MERCURY
328 College St, Clarksville, TN 37040-3262
Tel (931) 647-3353 Founded/Ownrshp 1954
Sales 23.4MM^E EMP 200
SIC 5511 Automobiles, new & used; Automobiles, new & used
Pr: Don Jenkins

JENKIN'S ACURA
See DRJ INVESTMENTS INC

D-U-N-S 04-021-9980 IMP
■ **JENKINS BRICK CO 780**
(Suby of ACME BRICK CO) ★
P.O. Box 386 (76101-0386)
Tel (334) 834-2210 Founded/Ownrshp 2011
Sales 58.1MM^E EMP 137^E
SIC 5211 Brick

D-U-N-S 03-113-8258
JENKINS DIESEL POWER INC
1845 E Blaine St, Springfield, MO 65803-4580
Tel (417) 862-7021 Founded/Ownrshp 1967
Sales 38.7MM^E EMP 58
SIC 5511 Automobiles, new & used; Automobiles, new & used
Pr: Jim Jenkins
*Sec: Joe E Jenkins
*VP: Daniel C Jenkins

JENKINS FORD LINCOLN MERCURY
See JENKINS & WYNNE MOTOR CO INC

D-U-N-S 01-601-7121
JENKINS FORD/MERCURY INC
8 Billingsley Dr, Buckhannon, WV 26201-8306
Tel (304) 472-1700 Founded/Ownrshp 1960, 1988
Sales 24.7MM^E EMP 55
SIC 5511 Automobiles, new & used; Automobiles, new & used
Pr: John Jenkins
*VP: Sheila Jenkins
Genl Mgr: Joey Jenkins
Sales Asso: Jason Matthews

JENKINS GAS
See LIBERTY PROPANE OPERATIONS LLC

JENKINS HYUNDAI
See DJ PROPERTY INVESTMENTS INC

D-U-N-S 61-518-7742
JENKINS PLUMBING CO LC
86 Columbia Dr, Pooler, GA 31322-8504
Tel (912) 330-8151 Founded/Ownrshp 2005
Sales 26.3MM^E EMP 124^E
SIC 1711 Plumbing contractors
Pt: Michael L Jenkins

JENKINS RESTORATIONS
See JENKINS SERVICES LLC

D-U-N-S 06-644-5255
JENKINS SERVICES INC
ABC PEST & LAWN SVCS AUSTIN
9475 E Highway 290, Austin, TX 78724-2303
Tel (512) 837-9500 Founded/Ownrshp 1971
Sales 45.4MM^E EMP 600
SIC 7342 Pest control services; Pest control services; Exterminating & fumigating
Pr: Robert W Jenkins Jr
Brnch Mgr: Anthony Sanchez
Genl Mgr: Steve Ambrose
Genl Mgr: Scott Esler
Genl Mgr: Scott Martin
Genl Mgr: Tony Patek
Secur Mgr: Ben Shockley
Mktg Dir: Les Stobart
Sls Mgr: Derek Salazar

D-U-N-S 87-697-5715
JENKINS SERVICES LLC
JENKINS RESTORATIONS
22980 Shaw Rd, Sterling, VA 20166-9446
Tel (703) 450-6580 Founded/Ownrshp 1988
Sales NA EMP 45
SIC 6411 Advisory services, insurance
Pr: Drew Fetterolf
*Pr: Russell W Jenkins III
*CEO: Warren P Jenkins
*CFO: Jeffrey Yoh
VP: Jason Coleman
*VP: Jeremy Jenkins

JENKS INDEPENDENT SCHL DST 5
See JENKS PUBLIC SCHOOLS

D-U-N-S 05-821-0030
JENKS PUBLIC SCHOOLS
JENKS INDEPENDENT SCHL DST 5
205 E B St, Jenks, OK 74037-3906
Tel (918) 299-4415 Founded/Ownrshp 1906
Sales 74.4MM^E EMP 1,400
SIC 8211 Public elementary & secondary schools; Public elementary & secondary schools
Pr: Ron Barber
Bd of Dir: Joe Hidy
Ofcr: Myron Sander
*VP: Chuck Forbes
Comm Dir: Bonnie Rogers
Cmptr Lab: Beth Flusche
Dir IT: Bill Casey
IT Man: Cody Way
Psych: Jennifer Griggs
Psych: Brenda Thomas

D-U-N-S 15-528-3518
JENNE INC
33665 Chester Rd, Avon, OH 44011-1307
Tel (440) 835-0040 Founded/Ownrshp 1986
Sales 54.9MM^E EMP 156
SIC 7371 7382 Telephone equipment; Communication equipment; Software programming applications; Security systems services
CEO: Dave Johnson
*Ch Bd: Rose M Jenne
*Pr: Ray Jenne Jr
CFO: Christopher Anderle
*CFO: Anthony R Grilli
CFO: Tony Grilli
*Ex VP: Dean M Jenne
Sr VP: Rick Coan
VP: William Brennan
IT Man: Joseph Lyons
Natl Sales: Peter Sandrev

D-U-N-S 05-319-7331
JENNER & BLOCK LLP
353 N Clark St Ste 3200, Chicago, IL 60654-5474
Tel (312) 222-9350 Founded/Ownrshp 2003
Sales 164.2MM^E EMP 833
SIC 8111 General practice law office; General practice law office
Pt: Ana R Bugan
Pt: Reena R Bajowala
Pt: Christine L Childers
Pt: Tom Cooke
Pt: Larry P Ellsworth
Pt: Peter M Gaines
Pt: Chris Gair
Pt: Robert Graham
Pt: Mark Heilbrun
Pt: Reginald J Hill
Pt: Eric S Jackson
Pt: Kenneth K Lee
Pt: Bradford P Lyerla
Pt: Kevin P Mullen
Pt: Thomas C Newkirk
Pt: Matt Oppenheim
Pt: Peter B Pope
Pt: Harry Sandick
Pt: Jerold S Solovy
Pt: Terrance Truax
Mng Pt: Michael B Desanctis

D-U-N-S 02-539-2697
JENNER SALES CORP
8990 W Us Rt 36, Harristown, IL 62537
Tel (217) 963-2241 Founded/Ownrshp 1961
Sales 34.0MM^E EMP 33
SIC 5083 7359 Agricultural machinery; Equipment rental & leasing
Pr: Steve Jones
IT Man: Jeremy McCammack

D-U-N-S 07-406-9100
JENNERS POND INC
2000 Greenbriar Ln, West Grove, PA 19390-9485
Tel (610) 869-6800 Founded/Ownrshp 1994
Sales 12.6MM^E EMP 280^E
Accts Larsonallen Llp Blue Bell Pa
SIC 8051 Skilled nursing care facilities; Skilled nursing care facilities
Pr: Toni McClay

JENNERSVILLE REGIONAL HOSPITAL
See WEST GROVE HOSPITAL CO LLC

JENNIE CLRKSON CHILD CARE SVCS
See ST CHRISTOPHERS INC

D-U-N-S 07-133-3157
JENNIE STUART MEDICAL CENTER INC
320 W 18th St, Hopkinsville, KY 42240-1965
Tel (270) 887-0100 Founded/Ownrshp 1913
Sales 122.7MM EMP 750
Accts Bkd Llp Bowling Green Ky
SIC 8062 General medical & surgical hospitals; General medical & surgical hospitals
CEO: Eric Lee
Chf Rad: Michael Clark
*CFO: Greg Moore
Treas: Donna Russell
VP: Beth McCraw
VP: Nancy Raines
Dir Lab: Michael Stokes
Dir Lab: Carla C Wallace
Dir Rad: Patty Gault
Ex Dir: Linda Minton
Dir Sec: Gary Dixon

D-U-N-S 00-616-0766 EXP
■ **JENNIE-O TURKEY STORE INC**
(Suby of HORMEL FOODS CORP) ★
2505 Willmar Ave Sw, Willmar, MN 56201-2711
Tel (320) 235-2622 Founded/Ownrshp 1949
Sales 960.6MM^E EMP 7,000
SIC 2015 0253 Turkey processing & slaughtering; Turkey farm; Turkey processing & slaughtering; Turkey farm
Pr: Glenn Leitch
*CFO: John Court
Sr VP: Robert A Tegt
VP: Steve Atchison
VP: Karen Harris
VP: Mark Nellermore
VP: Petri Papinaho
Dir IT: Robert Merrill
IT Man: James Stark
VP Opers: Donald Cole
VP Opers: Robert Wood

D-U-N-S 07-852-6531
■ **JENNIE-O TURKEY STORE INTERNATIONAL INC**
(Suby of JENNIE-O TURKEY STORE INC) ★
2505 Willmar Ave Sw, Willmar, MN 56201-2711
Tel (320) 235-2622 Founded/Ownrshp 2012
Sales 76.5MM^E EMP 1,581^E
SIC 2015 Poultry slaughtering & processing
Prin: Earl Olson

D-U-N-S 07-852-6553
■ **JENNIE-O TURKEY STORE SALES LLC**
(Suby of JENNIE-O TURKEY STORE INC) ★
2505 Willmar Ave Sw, Willmar, MN 56201-2711
Tel (320) 235-2622 Founded/Ownrshp 2012
Sales 23.3MM^E EMP 719^E
SIC 2015 Poultry slaughtering & processing
Pr: Mike Tolbert
Sr VP: Barry Lynch

D-U-N-S 15-480-6327 IMP
JENNIFER CONVERTIBLES INC
335 Crossways Park Dr, Woodbury, NY 11797-2066
Tel (516) 496-1900 Founded/Ownrshp 1986
Sales 111.9MM^E EMP 417
SIC 5712 6794 5021 Furniture stores; Patent owners & lessors; Furniture stores; Patent owners & lessors; Furniture
Ch Bd: Fred J Love
*Pr: Rami Abada
VP: David Borgen
VP: Nick Carpenter
VP: Teresa Dilone
VP: Thomas Godfrey
VP: Glenn Hillman
VP: Victoria Lombardo
VP: Louis Mazariegos
VP: Philip Rameshwar
VP: Ronald Turin
Exec: Maria Butler
Board of Directors: Mark L Berman, Edward G Bohn, Kevin J Coyle

D-U-N-S 07-418-7329 IMP
JENNINGS AMERICAN LEGION HOSPITAL
1634 Elton Rd, Jennings, LA 70546-3614
Tel (337) 616-7000 Founded/Ownrshp 1930
Sales 36.7MM EMP 450
Accts Lester Miller & Wells Alexand
SIC 8062 General medical & surgical hospitals; General medical & surgical hospitals
Pr: Arthur D Matte
CFO: Chris Kohlenberg
*CFO: Pam Primearu
*VP: Richard Arceneaux
Exec: Ruth Carnes
Dir Inf Cn: Jon Lamb
Dir Lab: Mona Lasher
*Prin: Dana Williams
CIO: Gary Courege
QA Dir: Keith Simpson
Sfty Dirs: Phyllis Theriot

D-U-N-S 05-877-0686
JENNINGS ANDERSON FORD SALES LTD
31480 Interstate 10 W, Boerne, TX 78006-9239
Tel (830) 755-3673 Founded/Ownrshp 1993
Sales 40.3MM^E EMP 110
SIC 5511 Automobiles, new & used; Automobiles, new & used
Pt: Jennings Anderson
Pt: Linda Kay Bowman
Pt: Carol Jean Salkald
Pt: Deeann Wilson
Pt: Scott T Wilson
Sales Asso: David Cruze

D-U-N-S 16-943-6318
JENNINGS CENTER FOR OLDER ADULTS
JENNINGS HALL NURSING FACILITY
10204 Granger Rd, Cleveland, OH 44125-3106
Tel (216) 581-2900 Founded/Ownrshp 1941
Sales 18.9MM EMP 375
Accts Maloney & Novotny Llc Clevel
SIC 8059 8051 8052 Nursing home, except skilled & intermediate care facility; Skilled nursing care facilities; Intermediate care facilities; Nursing home, except skilled & intermediate care facility; Skilled nursing care facilities; Intermediate care facilities
Pr: Martha M Kutik
*COO: Allison Salopeck
*CFO: Richard Zak
IT Man: John Pae
Mktg Dir: Lisa Brazytis
Nrsg Dir: Susan Lodolce

D-U-N-S 02-550-2527
JENNINGS CHEVROLET INC
JENNINGS VOLKSWAGEN
241 Waukegan Rd, Glenview, IL 60025-5190
Tel (847) 729-1000 Founded/Ownrshp 1955
Sales 54.2MM^E EMP 118
SIC 5511 Automobiles, new & used; Pickups, new & used; Vans, new & used; Automobiles, new & used; Pickups, new & used; Vans, new & used
Pr: James Jennings

D-U-N-S 15-213-9697
JENNINGS CHEVROLET OLDSMOBILE CADILLAC INC
JENNING'S VALUE CENTER
916 Norland Ave, Chambersburg, PA 17201-4203
Tel (717) 264-4161 Founded/Ownrshp 1986
Sales 30.5MM EMP 100
SIC 5511 7538 5521 Automobiles, new & used; Pickups, new & used; General automotive repair shops; Used car dealers; Automobiles, new & used; Pickups, new & used; General automotive repair shops; Used car dealers
Pr: Allan E Jennings Jr
*Ch Bd: Allan E Jennings Sr
*VP: Thomas W Jennings

D-U-N-S 07-207-9106
JENNINGS COUNTY SCHOOLS
34 W Main St, North Vernon, IN 47265-1706
Tel (812) 346-4483 Founded/Ownrshp 1963
Sales 31.2MM^E EMP 625
SIC 8211 Public elementary & secondary schools; Public elementary & secondary schools
MIS Dir: Josh Taylor
HC Dir: Roger Williams

JENNINGS DISTRIBUTING
See MARINE VIEW BEVERAGE INC

D-U-N-S 80-659-2023
JENNINGS ELIZA SENIOR CARE NETWORK
14701 Detroit Ave Ste 620, Lakewood, OH 44107-4180
Tel (216) 226-5000 Founded/Ownrshp 1987
Sales 4.4MM EMP 600
SIC 8051 Skilled nursing care facilities; Skilled nursing care facilities
CEO: Deborah Hiller
*COO: Jim Rogerson
Dir IT: Toby Miletta
VP Opers: Greg Storer

JENNINGS GUEST HOUSE
See LOUISIANA GUEST HOUSE LLC

JENNINGS HALL NURSING FACILITY
See JENNINGS CENTER FOR OLDER ADULTS

D-U-N-S 00-347-2081
JENNINGS INC L F (VA)
407 N Washington St # 200, Falls Church, VA 22046-3430
Tel (703) 241-1200 Founded/Ownrshp 1951
Sales 137.2MM^E EMP 300^E
SIC 1542 Commercial & office building, new construction; Commercial & office building, new construction
CEO: Roberta G Jennings
*Pr: Robert R Rucks
*COO: Stanley L Reed
*Sec: Larlyn Jennings
*VP: Jonathan S Jennings
*VP: Michael Killelea
VP: Gregg Monday
Dir IT: David Fitzgerald
Sfty Dirs: Ryan Berry
Sfty Dirs: John Harrison
Sfty Mgr: Ryan Beery

D-U-N-S 02-396-3119
JENNINGS MOTOR CO INC
KAY JNNINGS SPRINGFIELD TOYOTA
7601 Loisdale Rd, Springfield, VA 22150-2103
Tel (703) 451-0300 Founded/Ownrshp 1969
Sales 59.3MM^E EMP 130
SIC 5511 5531 5521 Automobiles, new & used; Automotive & home supply stores; Used car dealers; Automobiles, new & used; Automotive & home supply stores; Used car dealers
Pr: Michael Jennings
*VP: Diane Jennings
VP: Tom Ramey
*VP: Michael Swartz
Sls Dir: Mike Nguyen
Sales Asso: Ricardo Grant
Sales Asso: Josef Puechner
Sales Asso: Earl Stevens
Sales Asso: Milena Taborga

D-U-N-S 03-481-8047
JENNINGS TIRE CO
AMERICAN TIRE
1430 Mark Allen Ln, Murfreesboro, TN 37129-5531
Tel (615) 896-0200 Founded/Ownrshp 1977
Sales 72.7MM^E EMP 160

SIC 5014 5531 7534 Tires & tubes; Automotive tires; Tire recapping; Tires & tubes; Automotive tires; Tire recapping
CEO: Herman B Willis
**Pr:* David Willis
**Treas:* Virginia Willis
Exec: Mary Derryberry

JENNING'S VALUE CENTER
See JENNINGS CHEVROLET OLDSMOBILE CADILLAC INC

JENNINGS VOLKSWAGEN
See JENNINGS CHEVROLET INC

D-U-N-S 07-103-0571
■ **JENNISON ASSOCIATES LLC**
(*Suby of* PRUDENTIAL INSURANCE CO OF AMERICA) ★
466 Lexington Ave Fl 18, New York, NY 10017-3151
Tel (212) 421-1000 *Founded/Ownrshp* 1969, 1985
Sales 40.0MM^E *EMP* 266
SIC 6282

JENNMAR
See CALANDRA FRANK INC

D-U-N-S 04-720-5174 IMP/EXP
JENNMAR CORP
(*Suby of* CALANDRA FRANK INC) ★
258 Kappa Dr, Pittsburgh, PA 15238-2818
Tel (412) 963-9071 *Founded/Ownrshp* 1968
Sales 148.1MM^E *EMP* 560
SIC 3532 Mining machinery; Mining machinery
Pr: Frank Calandra Jr
**COO:* Mark Brandon
COO: Robert Wise
CFO: Tim Maziarz
**Ex VP:* Karl Anthony Calandra
**VP:* Jack Calandra
**VP:* Al Campoli
VP: Hanjie Chen
**VP:* David Hurd
VP: Dan Statler
VP: Gene Zurawsky

D-U-N-S 79-000-6266 IMP
JENNMAR CORP OF UTAH INC
(*Suby of* CALANDRA FRANK INC) ★
155 E 550 S, Clearfield, UT 84015-1770
Tel (801) 728-6100 *Founded/Ownrshp* 1986
Sales 63.6MM^E *EMP* 400
SIC 3532 Mining machinery; Mining machinery
Pr: Frank Calandra Jr
Ex VP: James A Ceresa
VP: Jack Calandra
Plnt Mgr: Bill Henson

D-U-N-S 06-766-8569
JENNMAR MCSWEENEY LLC
(*Suby of* CALANDRA FRANK INC) ★
235 Commerce Dr, South Point, OH 45680-8465
Tel (740) 377-3354 *Founded/Ownrshp* 2013
Sales 26.2MM^E *EMP* 140
SIC 3532 3531 Bits, except oil & gas field tools, rock; Auger mining equipment; Blades for graders, scrapers, dozers & snow plows
CEO: Joe McSweeney
Pr: Frank Calandra
VP: Sandra Blackburn

D-U-N-S 13-051-2221
JENNY CRAIG INC
(*Suby of* NORTH CASTLE PARTNERS LLC) ★
5770 Fleet St, Carlsbad, CA 92008-4700
Tel (760) 696-4000 *Founded/Ownrshp* 2013
Sales 146.3MM^E *EMP* 3,510
SIC 7299 6794 5149 5499 Diet center, without medical staff; Franchises, selling or licensing; Diet foods; Dietetic foods; Diet center, without medical staff; Franchises, selling or licensing; Diet foods; Dietetic foods
CEO: Monty Sharma
**Ch Bd:* Patricia Larchet
CFO: Paul Britton
**CFO:* Jim Kelly
**Chf Mktg O:* Leesa Eichberger
VP: Allen Arvig
VP: Devon Batee
**VP:* Alan V Dobies
**VP:* Doug Fisher
VP: Andy Henton
VP: Corrine Peritano
VP: Corrine Perritano
**VP:* Shoukry Tiab
Exec: Jean Werner
Board of Directors: Richard Laube, Bruce McConnell

D-U-N-S 78-550-9126
JENNY CRAIG WEIGHT LOSS CENTERS INC
(*Suby of* JENNY CRAIG INC) ★
5770 Fleet St, Carlsbad, CA 92008-4700
Tel (760) 696-4000 *Founded/Ownrshp* 2002
Sales 63.4MM^E *EMP* 2,900
SIC 7299 7991 Diet center, without medical staff; Weight reducing clubs; Diet center, without medical staff; Weight reducing clubs
Pr: Dana Fiser
**Ch Bd:* Kent Kreh
**Pr:* Patti Larchet
**CEO:* Jenny Craig
**CFO:* James Kelly

D-U-N-S 05-061-8586 IMP
JENOPTIK INDUSTRIAL METROLOGY NORTH AMERICA LLC
HOMMEL MOVOMATIC
(*Suby of* JENOPTIK NORTH AMERICA INC) ★
1505 W Hamlin Rd, Rochester Hills, MI 48309-3366
Tel (248) 853-5888 *Founded/Ownrshp* 2007
Sales 31.7MM *EMP* 103^E
Accts Bdo Usa Llp Troy Mi

SIC 3829 3823 3545 Measuring & controlling devices; Industrial instrmnts msrmnt display/control process variable; Gauges (machine tool accessories); Measuring tools & machines, machinists' metalworking type; Measuring & controlling devices; Industrial instrmnts msrmnt display/control process variable; Gauges (machine tool accessories); Measuring tools & machines, machinists' metalworking type
Pr: Roland Riechert
CFO: Kurt Andrews
VP: Dave Matynowski
VP: David Matynowski
VP Sls: Roger Blair

D-U-N-S 96-895-1348
JENOPTIK NORTH AMERICA INC
(*Suby of* JENOPTIK AG)
16490 Innovation Dr, Jupiter, FL 33478-6449
Tel (561) 881-7400 *Founded/Ownrshp* 2009
Sales 61.4MM^E *EMP* 1,000
SIC 3827 Optical instruments & lenses
Pr: Albert Miranda
VP: Stephen Hypsh
VP: Paul Safran
**VP:* Susan Wilder

D-U-N-S 00-482-7481
JENSEN CONSTRUCTION CO (IA)
JENSEN CRANE SERVICES
(*Suby of* RASMUSSEN GROUP INC) ★
5550 Ne 22nd St, Des Moines, IA 50313-2530
Tel (515) 266-5173 *Founded/Ownrshp* 1949
Sales 83.2MM^E *EMP* 250
SIC 1622 1629 Bridge construction; Pile driving contractor; Bridge construction; Pile driving contractor
Pr: Kurt Rasmussen
**Treas:* Jeffry Rasmussen
**VP:* Jeff Rasmussen
**VP:* Dan Timmons
Dir IT: Carol Broman
Snr Mgr: Lyle Jobst

D-U-N-S 05-051-2730
JENSEN CORPORATE HOLDINGS INC
1983 Concourse Dr, San Jose, CA 95131-1708
Tel (408) 446-1118 *Founded/Ownrshp* 1969
Sales 116.6MM^E *EMP* 450
SIC 0782 Landscape contractors; Landscape contractors
CEO: John Vlay
**CFO:* Quang Trinh
**Div Pres:* Donald Defever
**VP:* Glenn Berry
**VP:* Kirk Brown
**VP:* Rodney W Morimoto
**Prin:* Scott Mc Gilvray
**Prin:* Duane Wasson

JENSEN CRANE SERVICES
See JENSEN CONSTRUCTION CO

JENSEN DENTAL
See JENSEN INDUSTRIES INC

JENSEN DISTRIBUTION SERVICES
See JENSEN-BYRD CO LLC

D-U-N-S 06-501-8178 IMP
JENSEN ENTERPRISES INC
JENSEN PRECAST
825 Steneri Way, Sparks, NV 89431-6312
Tel (775) 352-2700 *Founded/Ownrshp* 1966
Sales 172.5MM^E *EMP* 450
SIC 3272 Concrete products, precast; Concrete products, precast
Pr: Tony Shanks
**Treas:* Donald L Jensen
Chf Mktg O: Eric Jensen
Ofcr: Paula Dolliver
Sls&Mrk Ex: Mark Voiselle
Mktg Mgr: Marcia Neese
Manager: Josh Bivens
Sales Asso: George McCloe
Genl Couns: Ty Cobb

D-U-N-S 03-504-3744
JENSEN HUGHES INC
3610 Commerce Dr Ste 817, Baltimore, MD 21227-1640
Tel (410) 737-8677 *Founded/Ownrshp* 2015
Sales 94.0MM^E *EMP* 718
SIC 8748 8711 8734 Business consulting; Business consulting; Fire protection engineering; Product testing laboratory, safety or performance
Pr: Phil Rogers
Pr: Dave Boswell
Pr: Mickey Reiss
COO: Paul Sincaglia
CFO: Paula Sidlowski
Chf Mktg O: George Toth
Ofcr: Mary McCarthy
Ex VP: Doug True
Sr VP: Elizabeth Kleinsorg
VP: Jim Antell
VP: Hamid Bahadori
VP: Leonard Belliveau
VP: Jack Brady
VP: Edward Budnick
VP: Joseph Cappuccio
VP: Joe Castellano
VP: Scott Chong
VP: Scott Craig
VP: Mike Crowley
VP: Michael Ferreira
VP: Jeff Harper

D-U-N-S 06-001-8587 IMP
JENSEN INDUSTRIES INC
JENSEN DENTAL
50 Stillman Rd, North Haven, CT 06473-1622
Tel (203) 285-1402 *Founded/Ownrshp* 1976
Sales 36.0MM^E *EMP* 110
SIC 3843 Dental alloys for amalgams; Dental alloys for amalgams
Pr: David J Stine
CFO: Peter Kolakoski
**CFO:* Anthony M Schittina
**VP:* Peter Kouvaris
**VP:* Kevin Mahan
Dir IT: Gina Kupec

Mfg Dir: Ray McTeague
VP Mktg: Joe Carofano
Manager: Jennifer Gaylor
Sls Mgr: Ross Shirer
Sales Asso: Karen Leitner

D-U-N-S 10-359-3158
JENSEN INTERNATIONAL INC
1004 W 14th St, Coffeyville, KS 67337
Tel (620) 251-5700 *Founded/Ownrshp* 1981
Sales 30.0MM^E *EMP* 115
Accts Locke & Associates Pc Tuls
SIC 3321 3561 3713 3533 3444 Gray & ductile iron foundries; Pumps, oil well & field; Pumps, domestic: water or sump; Pump jacks & other pumping equipment; Truck beds; Oil & gas field machinery; Sheet metalwork; Gray & ductile iron foundries; Pumps, oil well & field; Pumps, domestic: water or sump; Pump jacks & other pumping equipment; Truck beds; Oil & gas field machinery; Sheet metalwork
Pr: J Eric Jensen
**Pr:* Mary Nolte

D-U-N-S 02-911-9310
JENSEN MEAT CO INC
2550 Britannia Blvd # 101, San Diego, CA 92154-7408
Tel (619) 754-6450 *Founded/Ownrshp* 1958
Sales 111.2MM^E *EMP* 95
SIC 5147 Meats & meat products; Meats & meat products
CEO: Abel Olivera
**Co-Ownr:* Jeff Hamann
**CFO:* Sam Acuna
VP: Jeff Duran
Exec: Jose Valencia
VP Prd: Anthony Crivello
Prd Mgr: Edmundo Garcia
Prd Mgr: Mundo Garcia
Ql Cn Mgr: Debbie Dardon

JENSEN PRECAST
See JENSEN ENTERPRISES INC

JENSEN, RALPH L JR
See RJR CONSULTING GROUP INC

D-U-N-S 08-173-6691
JENSEN SYSTEM DESIGN
19 Buck Hill Ln, Pound Ridge, NY 10576-1407
Tel (914) 318-0724 *Founded/Ownrshp* 1983
Sales 38.0MM *EMP* 5
SIC 7371 Computer software development; Computer software development
Owner: Susanne Bienenstock

D-U-N-S 06-863-9558
JENSEN TIRE CO
10609 I St, Omaha, NE 68127-1013
Tel (402) 339-2917 *Founded/Ownrshp* 1997
Sales 24.5MM^E *EMP* 200
SIC 7538 5531 General automotive repair shops; Automotive & home supply stores; General automotive repair shops; Automotive & home supply stores
Pr: Matthew D Jensen
**Sec:* Diane L Jensen

D-U-N-S 15-769-2364
JENSEN UNDERGROUND UTILITIES INC
5585 Taylor Rd, Naples, FL 34109-1842
Tel (239) 597-0060 *Founded/Ownrshp* 1987
Sales 30.2MM^E *EMP* 110
SIC 1623 Underground utilities contractor; Underground utilities contractor
Pr: Kevin Jensen

D-U-N-S 04-445-3264 IMP
JENSEN USA INC
99 Aberdeen Loop, Panama City, FL 32405-6463
Tel (850) 271-8464 *Founded/Ownrshp* 1979
Sales 98.3MM^E *EMP* 150
SIC 5087 Laundry equipment & supplies; Laundry equipment & supplies
CEO: Jesper Jensen
**Pr:* Simon Nield
Pr: John Stokes
COO: Scott Jensen
**CFO:* Markus Schalch
**CFO:* Erik Vanderhagen
**VP:* Phyllis Decker
**VP:* Norbert Gittard
VP: Helmut Harfman
**VP:* Helmut Harfmann
VP: Mike McBride
**VP:* James Thorpe
**VP:* Mark Wingrove

D-U-N-S 00-794-3582 IMP
JENSEN-BYRD CO LLC (WA)
JENSEN DISTRIBUTION SERVICES
(*Suby of* ACE HARDWARE CORP) ★
314 W Riverside Ave, Spokane, WA 99201-0272
Tel (509) 624-1321 *Founded/Ownrshp* 1949, 2015
Sales 274.0MM^E *EMP* 230
SIC 5072 Hardware; Hardware
CEO: Michael S Jensen
Pr: Micah Jensen Dunlap
Bd of Dir: Jim Comar
Ex VP: Chris Jensen
Ex VP: Micah C Jensen
Ex VP: P Chris Jensen
VP: Glenn Miller
Prgrm Mgr: Kaylee Paxton
Natl Sales: Chrisanne Evenson
Natl Sales: Robin Hoover
Natl Sales: Frank Trulin

D-U-N-S 02-793-5279
JENSENS COMPLETE SHOPPING INC
JENSEN'S FINEST FOODS
27264 Hwy 189, Blue Jay, CA 92317
Tel (909) 337-8484 *Founded/Ownrshp* 1981
Sales 64.6MM^E *EMP* 450
SIC 5411 Grocery stores, independent; Grocery stores, independent
Pr: Gene A Fulton
**VP:* Adam M Zack

JENSEN'S FINEST FOODS
See JENSENS COMPLETE SHOPPING INC

JENSEN'S FINEST FOODS
See JENSENS OLD COUNTRY BAKERY INC

D-U-N-S 00-797-2052
JENSENS INC (CT)
JENSEN'S RESIDENTIAL COMMUNITI
246 Redstone St, Southington, CT 06489-1133
Tel (860) 793-0281 *Founded/Ownrshp* 1927
Sales 32.7MM *EMP* 125
Accts Cohn Reznick Llp Farmington
SIC 6515 Mobile home site operators; Mobile home site operators
CEO: Kristian Jensen Sr
**CFO:* Alan Krieger
**VP:* Joseph Esposito
**VP:* Tom Flanders
**VP:* Keith Jensen
Off Mgr: Norma Culler
Sales Asso: Joanne Polston

D-U-N-S 04-875-1507
JENSENS OLD COUNTRY BAKERY INC
JENSEN'S FINEST FOODS
(*Suby of* JENSENS COMPLETE SHOPPING INC) ★
2465 E Palm Canyon Dr # 7, Palm Springs, CA 92264-7000
Tel (760) 325-8282 *Founded/Ownrshp* 1947, 1981
Sales 22.8MM^E *EMP* 225
SIC 5411 Grocery stores; Grocery stores
Pr: Gene A Fulton
**Sec:* Lila Fulton

JENSEN'S RESIDENTIAL COMMUNITI
See JENSENS INC

D-U-N-S 04-798-0821
JENZABAR INC
101 Huntington Ave # 2200, Boston, MA 02199-8087
Tel (617) 492-9099 *Founded/Ownrshp* 1998
Sales 80.3MM^E *EMP* 275
SIC 7372 Educational computer software; Educational computer software
Ch Bd: Robert Maginn Jr
**Pr:* Ling Chai
**CFO:* Mimi Jespersen
**VP:* Ben Bassett
**VP:* Christian Hartigan
**VP:* Sashi Parthasarathi
VP: Burt Rubenstein
Mng Dir: Hans Kobler
Rgnl Mgr: Rob Orwat
Off Admin: Julia Mitchell
Off Admin: Jennifer Patrick

D-U-N-S 04-941-0087 IMP
JEOL USA INC
(*Suby of* JEOL LTD.)
11 Dearborn Rd, Peabody, MA 01960-3862
Tel (978) 535-5900 *Founded/Ownrshp* 1962
Sales 102.8MM^E *EMP* 320
Accts Greene Rubin Miller & Pacino
SIC 5049 Scientific instruments; Scientific instruments
Pr: Peter Genovese
Treas: Takashi Takamoto
VP: Masuru Iwatani
VP: Robert Pohorenec
Rgnl Mgr: Craig Koht
Genl Mgr: Patrick McKinley
Tech Mgr: Ryo Funakoshi
Sys/Mgr: Andy Dukehart
Software D: Dan Evans
Sls Mgr: Mini Samuel
Sls Mgr: Yuji Watanabe

JEPPESEN A BOEING COMPANY
See JEPPESEN SANDERSON INC

D-U-N-S 00-706-1062 IMP
■ **JEPPESEN SANDERSON INC**
JEPPESEN A BOEING COMPANY
(*Suby of* BOEING CO) ★
55 Inverness Dr E, Englewood, CO 80112-5412
Tel (303) 799-9090 *Founded/Ownrshp* 1934, 2000
Sales 511.2MM^E *EMP* 3,200
SIC 2741 2731 8748 Miscellaneous publishing; Textbooks: publishing only, not printed on site; Systems analysis or design; Miscellaneous publishing; Textbooks: publishing only, not printed on site; Systems analysis or design
CEO: Mark Van Tine
Ch Bd: Horst A Bergmann
Pr: Judy Mansur
COO: Margarita Kots
COO: Scott Lunda
COO: Brad Thomann
CFO: Jepson Fuller
CFO: Bob Kurtz
Sr VP: Alan Johnson
VP: Bernd Montigny
Exec: Chris Glaser
Dir Bus: David Bree
Dir Bus: Juha Makikalli

D-U-N-S 15-211-1196
JER INVESTORS TRUST INC
1650 Tysons Blvd Ste 1600, Mc Lean, VA 22102-4846
Tel (703) 714-8000 *Founded/Ownrshp* 2004
Sales 108.1MM *EMP* 1^E
SIC 6798 Real estate investment trusts; Real estate investment trusts
CEO: Joseph E Robert Jr
V Ch: Keith W Belcher
**Pr:* Mark S Weiss
VP: John Murray

D-U-N-S 78-665-8380
JER PARTNERS LLC
ROBERT CO INC J E MCLEAN VA
(*Suby of* J E ROBERT) ★
1250 Conn Ave Nw Ste 700, Washington, DC 20036-2657
Tel (703) 714-8000 *Founded/Ownrshp* 2006
Sales 100.1MM^E *EMP* 2,566
SIC 6798 Real estate investment trusts; Real estate investment trusts
VP: Matthew Cady
VP: Aleksandar Obradovic
VP: Kelly Sheehy

Board of Directors: John Haymes, Kevin Nishimura

D-U-N-S 01-413-1481 IMP
JER-JER INC
17361 Armstrong Ave, Irvine, CA 92614-5721
Tel (949) 553-4431 Founded/Ownrshp 1999
Sales 28.2MM^E EMP 35
SIC 5122 Cosmetics
Pr: Jeremy Johnson

D-U-N-S 05-630-0775 IMP
JERACI FOOD DISTRIBUTORS INC
JERACI FOODS
90 Fairview Pk Dr, Elmsford, NY 10523-1520
Tel (914) 250-3520 Founded/Ownrshp 1971
Sales 23.8MM^E EMP 48
SIC 5141 5143 Groceries, general line; Cheese
Pr: Joseph Jeraci Sr
*Treas: Dominic Jeraci

JERACI FOODS
See JERACI FOOD DISTRIBUTORS INC

D-U-N-S 02-973-8341
JERDEN FOODS INC (MO)
PATRICIA'S FOODS
523 S Main St, Concordia, MO 64020-2502
Tel (660) 463-2281 Founded/Ownrshp 1993
Sales 51.8MM^E EMP 367
SIC 5411 Supermarkets, independent; Supermarkets, independent
Pr: Jerry Metcalf
*VP: Janice Baker
*VP: Shelley Brown
*VP: Steve Haney
*VP: Paul Lillard
*VP: Kim Schrag
*VP: Todd White

D-U-N-S 17-627-5725 IMP
JERED LLC
PAR
(Suby of PAR SYSTEMS INC) ★
3000 Sidney Lanier Dr, Brunswick, GA 31525-6813
Tel (912) 262-2000 Founded/Ownrshp 2005
Sales 30.2MM^E EMP 135
SIC 3625 3429 3536 3531 3534 Marine & navy auxiliary controls; Marine hardware; Hoists, cranes & monorails; Ship winches; Elevators & equipment; Marine & navy auxiliary controls; Marine hardware; Hoists, cranes & monorails; Ship winches; Elevators & equipment
CEO: Ian Haley
Pr: Rick J Edger
Genl Mgr: Lamae Parrish
Plnt Mgr: John Benner
Snr Mgr: Warren Percell

JEREMIAH
See CRAFTMADE INTERNATIONAL INC

D-U-N-S 08-523-4388 IMP
JEREMIAHS INTERNATIONAL TRADING CO INC
AMERICA'S AUCTION NETWORK
289 34th St N, Saint Petersburg, FL 33713-8514
Tel (727) 321-5728 Founded/Ownrshp 1983
Sales 45.0MM EMP 170
SIC 5944 6531 Jewelry, precious stones & precious metals; Real estate agents & managers; Jewelry, precious stones & precious metals; Real estate agents & managers
Pr: Jerry Hartman

D-U-N-S 00-418-5641 IMP
JERGENS INC (OH)
TOOLING COMPONENTS DIVISION
15700 S Waterloo Rd, Cleveland, OH 44110-3898
Tel (216) 486-5540 Founded/Ownrshp 1942
Sales 81.9MM^E EMP 307
Accts Ss&G Financial Services Inc
SIC 3544 3443 3452 5084 3545 Special dies, tools, jigs & fixtures; Jigs & fixtures; Fabricated plate work (boiler shop); Bolts, nuts, rivets & washers; Machine tools & accessories; Drill bushings (drilling jig); Precision measuring tools; Special dies, tools, jigs & fixtures; Jigs & fixtures; Fabricated plate work (boiler shop); Bolts, nuts, rivets & washers; Machine tools & accessories; Drill bushings (drilling jig); Precision measuring tools
Pr: Jack H Schron Jr
CFO: Wesley W Hoard
*CFO: W Wesley Howard III
VP: Frank Lebar
Exec: Robert Rubenstahl
Mng Dir: Joseph Killukan
Genl Mgr: Bob Rubenstahl
Genl Mgr: Matt Schron
Genl Mgr: Bryon Shafer
CIO: Micky Morton
CTO: Mark Kish

JERGENS INSULATION
See JERGENS PIPING CORP

D-U-N-S 15-343-0459
JERGENS PIPING CORP
JERGENS INSULATION
21030 M 60, Mendon, MI 49072-8725
Tel (269) 496-7030 Founded/Ownrshp 2003
Sales 26.5MM EMP 105
SIC 1711 Mechanical contractor; Process piping contractor; Mechanical contractor; Process piping contractor
Pr: Timothy Jergens
*VP: Mark Parks

JERGUSON
See CLARK-RELIANCE CORP

JERICH INTERNATIONAL
See JERICH USA INC

D-U-N-S 00-794-1169
JERICH USA INC
JERICH INTERNATIONAL
(Suby of JERICH VERMOGENSVERWALTUNGS GMBH)
1 Industrial Rd Ste 102, Dayton, NJ 08810-3501
Tel (732) 329-4242 Founded/Ownrshp 2000
Sales 32.5MM^E EMP 120
SIC 4225 General warehousing & storage; General warehousing & storage
Pr: Herbert Jerich
*CFO: Stephan Schwarzl
Genl Mgr: Mark Carrga

JERICHO PUBLIC SCHOOLS
See JERICHO UNION FREE SCHOOL DISTRICT

D-U-N-S 07-964-3343
JERICHO RISE WIND FARM LLC
(Suby of EDP RENEWABLES NORTH AMERICA LLC) ★
808 Travis St Ste 700, Houston, TX 77002-5774
Tel (713) 265-0350 Founded/Ownrshp 2014
Sales 45.4MM^E EMP 300
SIC 4911 ;
CEO: Gabriel Alonso Imaz
Sec: Leslie Freiman
VP: Bernardo Goarmon
VP: Brian Hayes
VP: Steve Irvin
VP: Kenneth Ripper
VP: William Whitlock
VP: Andrew Young

D-U-N-S 06-807-5225
JERICHO UNION FREE SCHOOL DISTRICT
JERICHO PUBLIC SCHOOLS
99 Old Cedar Swamp Rd, Jericho, NY 11753-1201
Tel (516) 203-3600 Founded/Ownrshp 1938
Sales 36.9MM^E EMP 600
SIC 8211 Public elementary school; Public junior high school; Public senior high school; Public elementary school; Public junior high school; Public senior high school
IT Man: Diane Castonguay
Schl Brd P: William Ferro
Psych: Laura Hess

D-U-N-S 00-229-1011 EXP
JERITH MANUFACTURING CO INC (PA)
14400 Mcnulty Rd, Philadelphia, PA 19154-1196
Tel (215) 676-4068 Founded/Ownrshp 1953, 1999
Sales 22.9MM^E EMP 90
SIC 3446 3496 Fences or posts, ornamental iron or steel; Miscellaneous fabricated wire products
Pr: Bruce Schwartz
Mktg Dir: Mike Pietrzak

D-U-N-S 60-503-9366
■ **JERNBERG INDUSTRIES LLC**
(Suby of HHI FORGING LLC) ★
328 W 40th Pl, Chicago, IL 60609-2815
Tel (773) 268-3004 Founded/Ownrshp 2006
Sales 110.0MM^E EMP 500^E
SIC 3462 3463 Iron & steel forgings; Nonferrous forgings; Iron & steel forgings; Nonferrous forgings
CEO: George Thanopoulos
Treas: Robert Koscicki
Genl Mgr: Michael Keslar

D-U-N-S 08-088-1865
JERNIGAN NURSING HOME SERVICES INC
HARBOR VIEW HEALTH CARE CENTER
812 Shepard St, Morehead City, NC 28557-4250
Tel (252) 726-6855 Founded/Ownrshp 1979
Sales 469.6MM EMP 85
SIC 8051 8052 Skilled nursing care facilities; Intermediate care facilities; Skilled nursing care facilities; Intermediate care facilities
Pr: Ron Jernigan
*Treas: Jim Jernigan
*VP: Michael Jernigan

D-U-N-S 02-440-2836
JERNIGAN OIL CO INC
DUCK THRU FOOD STORES
415 Main St E, Ahoskie, NC 27910-3421
Tel (252) 332-2131 Founded/Ownrshp 1979
Sales 248.2MM EMP 350
Accts May & Place Pa Louisburg No
SIC 5411 5171 Convenience stores, independent; Petroleum bulk stations; Convenience stores, independent; Petroleum bulk stations
Pr: James M Harrell
*Sec: Jerry Harrell

D-U-N-S 07-603-2119
JEROME GOLDEN CENTER FOR BEHAVIORAL HEALTH INC
1041 45th St, West Palm Beach, FL 33407-2402
Tel (561) 383-8000 Founded/Ownrshp 1966
Sales 22.0MM EMP 350
Accts Kmetz Nuttall Elwell Graham
SIC 8063 Psychiatric hospitals; Psychiatric hospitals
CEO: Linda De Piano
*Ch: Richard H Wilson
*Treas: Terry L Morton
*Treas: Steve Wiesen
Bd of Dir: Terry Morton
CTO: Jamie West
MIS Dir: Emiliano Fernandez
HC Dir: Donna Ackerman

D-U-N-S 80-453-9641
JEROME GROUP INC
RADIATION ONCOLOGY ASSOC PA
6 E Chestnut St, Augusta, ME 04330-5717
Tel (207) 626-1496 Founded/Ownrshp 1982
Sales 13.5MM^E EMP 1,000
SIC 8011 8062 Oncologist; General medical & surgical hospitals; Oncologist; General medical & surgical hospitals
Pr: Scott Bullock

D-U-N-S 96-682-7136
JEROME LEVY FOUNDATION
1 Rockefeller Plz, New York, NY 10020-2003
Tel (212) 455-6228 Founded/Ownrshp 2011
Sales 23.9MM EMP 2
SIC 8699 Charitable organization

D-U-N-S 10-001-5056
JEROME SCHOOL DISTRICT 261
125 4th Ave W, Jerome, ID 83338-1818
Tel (208) 324-2392 Founded/Ownrshp 1918
Sales 18.8MM EMP 350
SIC 8211 Public elementary & secondary schools; Public elementary & secondary schools

D-U-N-S 02-913-8948 IMP
JEROMES FURNITURE WAREHOUSE
16960 Mesamint St, San Diego, CA 92127-2407
Tel (866) 633-4094 Founded/Ownrshp 1954
Sales 129.0MM^E EMP 420
SIC 5712 Furniture stores; Furniture stores
Pr: Lee M Goodman
Pr: Ester Navarra
*CFO: Paul Sanford
VP: Ann Navarra
VP Sls: Dave Brunson
Mktg Dir: Jim Navarra
Mktg Mgr: Glenn Weber

D-U-N-S 01-226-1723
JERR SHOES INC
HARRY'S SHOES
2299 Broadway, New York, NY 10024-4906
Tel (866) 442-7797 Founded/Ownrshp 1975
Sales 23.9MM^E EMP 75
SIC 5661 Shoe stores
Pr: Joseph Goldberg
*Treas: Eleanor Goldberg
*VP: Robert Goldberg

JERR-DAN
See JERRDAN CORP

D-U-N-S 04-751-8014 EXP
■ **JERRDAN CORP**
JERR-DAN
(Suby of OSHKOSH CORP) ★
13224 Fountain Head Plz, Hagerstown, MD 21742-2678
Tel (301) 745-5434 Founded/Ownrshp 2011
Sales 42.4MM^E EMP 300
SIC 3713 Truck bodies (motor vehicles); Automobile wrecker truck bodies; Truck bodies (motor vehicles); Automobile wrecker truck bodies
Pr: Jeffrey L Weller
Pr: Dave Chickowskit
*CFO: Thomas Galas
*VP: Thomas Polnaslek
Genl Mgr: Richard Del Campo
Mktg Mgr: Ashley Soverns
Sls Mgr: David Greenfeld
Sls Mgr: Ronnie Henry
Sls Mgr: Gene McKinney
Sls Mgr: David Noe
Sls Mgr: Joe Osterman
Board of Directors: Jeff Addleman, Bryan Swinehart

D-U-N-S 07-992-3175
JERRITT CANYON GOLD LLC
Rural Route Hc 31 Box 78 (89801)
Tel (775) 738-5600 Founded/Ownrshp 2015
Sales 21.0MM^E EMP 250
SIC 1041 Underground gold mining
CFO: Andres Tinajero

D-U-N-S 02-544-3664
JERRY BIGGERS CHEVROLET INC
BIGGERS CHEVROLET-ISUZU
1385 E Chicago St, Elgin, IL 60120-4715
Tel (847) 742-9000 Founded/Ownrshp 1970
Sales 39.9MM^E EMP 105
SIC 5511 5521 Automobiles, new & used; Used car dealers; Automobiles, new & used; Used car dealers
Pr: James Leichter
Dir Bus: Jennifer Paluch
Off Mgr: Debbie Monteith
Sls Mgr: Dave Arenson
Sls Mgr: Jason Seger
Sls Mgr: Jose Velasquez
Sales Asso: Mike Chobak
Sales Asso: Jeff Purcell

D-U-N-S 02-766-0414
JERRY BROWN CO INC
2690 Prairie Rd, Eugene, OR 97402-9747
Tel (541) 998-2300 Founded/Ownrshp 1997
Sales 29.7MM^E EMP 60
Accts Jones & Roth Pc Eugene Or
SIC 5172 5541 Petroleum products; Filling stations, gasoline; Petroleum products; Filling stations, gasoline
Pr: Troy Likens
*CFO: Helen Wilde

JERRY DAMSON ACURA
See THIRTY THREE INC

D-U-N-S 03-163-5774
JERRY DAMSON INC
DAMSON, JERRY HONDA
2200 Bob Wallace Ave Sw, Huntsville, AL 35805-4737
Tel (256) 533-4105 Founded/Ownrshp 1979
Sales 45.6MM^E EMP 110
SIC 5511 Automobiles, new & used; Pickups, new & used; Automobiles, new & used; Pickups, new & used
Pr: Jerry L Damson
*VP: G K Damson
Genl Mgr: Deke Damson
IT Man: Kerri Floyd
Sales Asso: Lu Izquierdo

D-U-N-S 08-930-5838
JERRY DURANT AUTO GROUP INC
DURANT TOYOTA
3131 Fort Worth Hwy, Hudson Oaks, TX 76087-8774
Tel (817) 597-5000 Founded/Ownrshp 1999
Sales 28.6MM^E EMP 65
SIC 5511 7538 5531 Automobiles, new & used; Vans, new & used; Trucks, tractors & trailers: new & used; General automotive repair shops; Automotive parts; Automobiles, new & used; Vans, new & used; Trucks, tractors & trailers: new & used; General automotive repair shops; Automotive parts
Pr: Jerry Durant
Dir IT: Mark Parker
Sls Mgr: Scotty Stoner
Sales Asso: Chris Hinton
Sales Asso: Steve Webb

D-U-N-S 17-379-4561
JERRY ERWIN ASSOCIATES INC
12115 Ne 99th St Ste 1800, Vancouver, WA 98682-2334
Tel (360) 254-9442 Founded/Ownrshp 1986
Sales 102.3MM^E EMP 650
SIC 6552 6531 Subdividers & developers; Real estate managers; Subdividers & developers; Real estate managers
Pr: Jerry Erwin
*COO: Cody Erwin
*VP: John McNeil

JERRY FERGUSON G M C
See JERRY FERGUSON PONTIAC-GMC INC

D-U-N-S 00-747-1683
JERRY FERGUSON PONTIAC-GMC INC
JERRY FERGUSON G M C
1601 N Elm Pl, Broken Arrow, OK 74012-1704
Tel (918) 258-1800 Founded/Ownrshp 1988
Sales 33.8MM^E EMP 100
SIC 5511 Automobiles, new & used; Automobiles, new & used
Pr: Jerry Ferguson
Sls Mgr: Hugh Bickel

D-U-N-S 02-550-0331
JERRY HAGGERTY CHEVROLET INC
300 Roosevelt Rd, Glen Ellyn, IL 60137-5621
Tel (630) 469-8100 Founded/Ownrshp 1995
Sales 27.3MM^E EMP 65
SIC 5511 7538 5531 Automobiles, new & used; General automotive repair shops; Automotive parts; Automobiles, new & used; General automotive repair shops; Automotive parts
Pr: Gerard S Haggerty Jr
Genl Mgr: Gerard Haggerty
Sls Mgr: Paul Bianchi

D-U-N-S 05-558-0880 EXP
JERRY HAMM CHEVROLET INC
3494 Phillips Hwy, Jacksonville, FL 32207-5610
Tel (904) 398-3036 Founded/Ownrshp 1978
Sales 22.2MM^E EMP 50
Accts Master Amith And Wisby Pa J
SIC 5511 Automobiles, new & used
CEO: Jerry Hamm
*Pr: David Hamm
Treas: Jerry Brewton
Manager: Nathan Hamm
Sls Mgr: Rusty Spears

D-U-N-S 09-819-8971
JERRY KACHEL BUILDER INC
6518 Klein Cemetary Rd, Spring, TX 77379-4246
Tel (281) 370-6049 Founded/Ownrshp 1979
Sales 35.5MM^E EMP 30
SIC 1542

D-U-N-S 02-613-2811
JERRY KIDD OIL CO
KIDD-JONES OIL COMPANY
850 State Highway 31 E, Chandler, TX 75758-9622
Tel (903) 849-6265 Founded/Ownrshp 1965
Sales 28.1MM^E EMP 85
SIC 5541 5411

JERRY LEIGH ENTERTAINMENT AP
See JERRY LEIGH OF CALIFORNIA INC

D-U-N-S 08-718-7944 IMP
JERRY LEIGH OF CALIFORNIA INC (CA)
JERRY LEIGH ENTERTAINMENT AP
7860 Nelson Rd, Van Nuys, CA 91402-6044
Tel (818) 909-6200 Founded/Ownrshp 1977
Sales 372.8MM^E EMP 550^E
SIC 5137 Women's & children's clothing; Women's & children's clothing
CEO: Andrew Leigh
*CFO: Jeff Silver
Ex VP: Jonathan Hirsh
VP: Samira Jammal

D-U-N-S 07-192-6737
JERRY PATE TURF & IRRIGATION INC
301 Schubert Dr, Pensacola, FL 32504-6958
Tel (850) 479-4653 Founded/Ownrshp 1997
Sales 45.1MM^E EMP 110
SIC 5083 Lawn machinery & equipment; Lawn machinery & equipment; Irrigation equipment
Ch Bd: Jerry Pate
*Pr: Brian Masterson
Opers Mgr: Derrick Payne

JERRY SEINER BOUNTIFUL
See JERRY SEINER BUICK PONTIAC GMC TRUCK NISSAN INC

D-U-N-S 03-537-9684
JERRY SEINER BUICK PONTIAC GMC TRUCK NISSAN INC
JERRY SEINER BOUNTIFUL
955 N 400 E, North Salt Lake, UT 84054-1905
Tel (801) 693-7000 Founded/Ownrshp 1964
Sales 26.2MM^E EMP 65
SIC 5511 Automobiles, new & used; Automobiles, new & used
Pr: Jerry Seiner
*Treas: Lorrie Hensley
*VP: Chris Hemmersmeier
Exec: Phillip Finan
MIS Dir: David Killam
Sls Mgr: Glen Hepler
Sls Mgr: Rob Thomas
Sales Asso: Jason Reinke
Sales Asso: David Turner

D-U-N-S 05-243-1988
JERRY SEINER CHEVROLET INC
SEINER, JERRY
730 W 2100 S, Salt Lake City, UT 84119-1576
Tel (801) 972-8411 *Founded/Ownrshp* 1980
Sales 60.6MM^E *EMP* 200
SIC 5511 5531 Automobiles, new & used; Automotive parts; Automotive accessories; Automobiles, new & used; Automotive parts; Automotive accessories
Pr: Jerald Seiner
**Sec:* Mary Ann Moyle
**VP:* Christopher Hemmersmeier
Sls Mgr: Dustin Lawrence
Sls Mgr: Mark McMillan

JERRY SEINER DEALERSHIP
See JERRY SEINER INC

D-U-N-S 80-912-6873
JERRY SEINER INC
JERRY SEINER DEALERSHIP
730 W 2100 S, Salt Lake City, UT 84119-1526
Tel (801) 972-8411 *Founded/Ownrshp* 1986
Sales 31.7MM^E *EMP* 100
SIC 5511 New & used car dealers; New & used car dealers
Pr: Gerald J Seiner
**Sec:* Mary Ann Moyle

D-U-N-S 07-273-3889
JERRY SEINER KIA
955 N 400 E, North Salt Lake, UT 84054-1905
Tel (801) 298-5163 *Founded/Ownrshp* 2001
Sales 23.8MM^E *EMP* 70
SIC 5511 Automobiles, new & used; Automobiles, new & used
Owner: Jerry Seiner
VP: Chris Hemmersmeier
Exec: Merle Zmak
Genl Mgr: Tom Hemmersmeier
Sales Asso: Mark McKay
Sales Asso: Laekin Pascua-Rogers
Sales Asso: Darren Przybyla
Sales Asso: Ian Scott
Sales Asso: James Templin

D-U-N-S 03-276-5901 EXP
JERRY ULM DODGE INC
2966 N Dale Mabry Hwy, Tampa, FL 33607-2415
Tel (813) 872-6645 *Founded/Ownrshp* 1990
Sales 71.8MM^E *EMP* 150
SIC 5511 5521 Automobiles, new & used; Used car dealers; Automobiles, new & used; Used car dealers
Pr: Gerald Ulm Jr
IT Man: Patricia Hasbrouck
VP Sls: David Gonzalez
Sls Mgr: Greig Lundergan
Sls Mgr: Jordy Pratt

D-U-N-S 11-235-9109
JERRYS ARTARAMA NC INC
6104 Maddry Oaks Ct, Raleigh, NC 27616-3156
Tel (919) 878-6782 *Founded/Ownrshp* 1998
Sales 26.8MM^E *EMP* 100^E
SIC 5999 Artists' supplies & materials
Pr: Ira Goldstein
**CEO:* David Goldstein
**CFO:* Bob Marcus
Store Mgr: Laurie Delaprym

D-U-N-S 00-375-1752
JERRYS BUICK PONTIAC G M C INC
3131 Fort Worth Hwy, Hudson Oaks, TX 76087-8774
Tel (817) 596-5581 *Founded/Ownrshp* 1985
Sales 22.3MM^E *EMP* 88
SIC 5511 Automobiles, new & used; Automobiles, new & used
Pr: Don Allen
Exec: Chad Page
Sls Dir: Dick Morgan
Sales Asso: Ines Zak

D-U-N-S 02-763-5747 IMP
JERRYS BUILDING MATERIALS INC
JERRYS HOME IMPROVEMENT CENTER
2600 Highway 99 N, Eugene, OR 97402-9706
Tel (541) 689-1911 *Founded/Ownrshp* 1961
Sales 121.7MM^E *EMP* 450^E
SIC 5211

D-U-N-S 02-244-7395
JERRYS CHEVROLET INC
1940 E Joppa Rd, Baltimore, MD 21234-2798
Tel (410) 661-9100 *Founded/Ownrshp* 1957
Sales 70.6MM^E *EMP* 165
SIC 5511 5521 5012 Automobiles, new & used; Used car dealers; Automobiles & other motor vehicles; Automobiles, new & used; Used car dealers; Automobiles & other motor vehicles
Pr: Gerald J Stautberg
**Sec:* Gail Wallace
Genl Mgr: George Ponko
Dir IT: Bill Bolander
Sales Asso: Stephen Boone
Sales Asso: Carlos Urena

D-U-N-S 04-480-0324
JERRYS ENTERPRISES INC
JERRY'S FOODS
5125 Vernon Ave S, Edina, MN 55436-2104
Tel (952) 929-2685 *Founded/Ownrshp* 1958
Sales 560.0MM^E *EMP* 3,500
SIC 5411 5812 5251 Supermarkets, hypermarket; Restaurant, family: independent; Carry-out only (except pizza) restaurant; Hardware; Supermarkets, hypermarket; Restaurant, family: independent; Carry-out only (except pizza) restaurant; Hardware
CEO: Robert N Shadduck
**VP:* Kent Dixon
**VP:* David Gerdes
**VP:* Mike Jutz
**VP:* Tom Thueson

D-U-N-S 05-760-2401
JERRYS FAMOUS DELI INC
SOLLEY'S
12711 Ventura Blvd # 400, Studio City, CA 91604-2456
Tel (818) 766-8311 *Founded/Ownrshp* 1984
Sales 67.0MM^E *EMP* 1,800
SIC 5812 Restaurant, family: independent; Restaurant, family: independent
Ch Bd: Isaac Starkman
Ch Bd: Guy Starkman
Pr: Jason Starkman
CFO: Christina Sterling
Rgnl Mgr: Billy Friedman

D-U-N-S 06-475-9251
JERRYS FARM MARKET
JERRY'S MARKET
991 115th Ave Ne, Foley, MN 56329-9520
Tel (320) 968-7001 *Founded/Ownrshp* 1974
Sales 1.4MM *EMP* 525
SIC 5431 5148 Fruit & vegetable markets; Fresh fruits & vegetables; Fruit & vegetable markets; Fresh fruits & vegetables
Owner: Shirley Chmielewski

JERRY'S FOODS
See JERRYS ENTERPRISES INC

JERRY'S FORD
See FORD JERRYS SALES INC

D-U-N-S 01-104-7103
JERRYS GM LLC
JERRY'S WEATHERFORD
3118 Fort Worth Hwy, Hudson Oaks, TX 76087-8773
Tel (800) 587-3548 *Founded/Ownrshp* 2004
Sales 71.8MM^E *EMP* 330
SIC 5511 Automobiles; New & used car dealers
Sls Mgr: Lanny Loesch
Sls Mgr: Mike Pedigo

JERRYS HOME IMPROVEMENT CENTER
See JERRYS BUILDING MATERIALS INC

JERRY'S LEESBURG FORD LINCOLN
See FORD JOHNS INC

JERRY'S MARKET
See JERRYS FARM MARKET

D-U-N-S 04-223-4674
JERRYS NUGGET
JERRY'S NUGGET CASINO
1821 Las Vegas Blvd N, North Las Vegas, NV 89030-6999
Tel (702) 399-3000 *Founded/Ownrshp* 1964
Sales 30.2MM^E *EMP* 500
SIC 7993 7999 5813 5812 Gambling establishments operating coin-operated machines; Gambling establishment; Bar (drinking places); Eating places; Gambling establishments operating coin-operated machines; Gambling establishment; Bar (drinking places); Eating places
Pr: Jeremy Stamis
COO: Darlene Ulep
**Treas:* Joseph P Stamis

JERRY'S NUGGET CASINO
See JERRYS NUGGET

D-U-N-S 02-768-0065
JERRYS RESTAURANTS INC
(*Suby of* BLACK BEAR DINER) ★
6360 E Thomas Rd Ste 100, Scottsdale, AZ 85251-7054
Tel (480) 659-1000 *Founded/Ownrshp* 1986
Sales 12.0MM^E *EMP* 850
SIC 5812 Restaurant, family: chain; Family restaurants
CEO: David Doty
**Pr:* Robin Yoshinura
Off Mgr: Gina Watts

D-U-N-S 96-449-9946
JERRYS SPORTS CENTER INC
(*Suby of* ELLETT BROTHERS LLC) ★
100 Capital Rd, Jenkins Township, PA 18640-6146
Tel (570) 883-6800 *Founded/Ownrshp* 2009
Sales 52.1MM^E *EMP* 120^E
SIC 5091 Sporting & recreation goods; Sporting & recreation goods
CEO: Bradd Johnson

D-U-N-S 02-625-6057
JERRYS SUPERMARKETS INC
532 W Jefferson Blvd, Dallas, TX 75208-4722
Tel (214) 948-6243 *Founded/Ownrshp* 1970
Sales 22.5MM *EMP* 130
SIC 5411 Supermarkets, chain
Pr: Myrna K Wages
Sec: Sharron McCaghren
VP: Michael L McCaghren
VP: James R Westmoreland

D-U-N-S 01-718-5398
JERRYS TIRE AND AUTO SERVICE INC
1413 2nd St, Lake Odessa, MI 48849-1121
Tel (269) 651-5707 *Founded/Ownrshp* 1983
Sales 21.2MM^E *EMP* 28
SIC 5014 5531 7538 Automobile tires & tubes; Automotive tires; General automotive repair shops
Pr: Mark Carpenter
Genl Mgr: Curt Wells
Plnt Mgr: Gary Lambert

D-U-N-S 02-244-1943 IMP
JERRYS TOYOTA INC
8001 Belair Rd, Baltimore, MD 21236-3709
Tel (410) 661-5700 *Founded/Ownrshp* 1981
Sales 38.0MM^E *EMP* 85
SIC 5511 5521 Automobiles, new & used; Pickups, new & used; Used car dealers; Automobiles, new & used; Pickups, new & used; Used car dealers
Pr: J A Stautberg
**Sec:* Sherry Price
VP: G Stautber
**VP:* G J Stautberg
IT Man: Susan Pless

JERRY'S WEATHERFORD
See JERRYS GM LLC

D-U-N-S 10-868-6452 IMP/EXP
JERSEN CONSTRUCTION GROUP LLC
6 Industry Dr Ste 2, Waterford, NY 12188-1934
Tel (518) 233-0600 *Founded/Ownrshp* 1983
Sales 45.2MM^E *EMP* 100
SIC 1541 1542 Industrial buildings, new construction; Renovation, remodeling & repairs: industrial buildings; Commercial & office building, new construction; Commercial & office buildings, renovation & repair; Industrial buildings, new construction; Renovation, remodeling & repairs: industrial buildings; Commercial & office building, new construction; Commercial & office buildings, renovation & repair
Pr: John R Jersen
**VP:* Kenneth J Jersen
VP: Galen Pereau
Exec: John Fry
Dir IT: Rose O'Hare
Sfty Dirs: John Keaveney
Sfty Mgr: Sandie Venne

D-U-N-S 00-697-3358 IMP
■ **JERSEY CENTRAL POWER & LIGHT CO** (NJ)
(*Suby of* FIRSTENERGY CORP) ★
76 S Main St, Akron, OH 44308-1812
Tel (800) 736-3402 *Founded/Ownrshp* 1925
Sales 765.5MM^E *EMP* 1,413^E
Accts Pricewaterhousecoopers Llp C
SIC 4911 Electric services; Distribution, electric power; Generation, electric power; Transmission, electric power; Electric services; Distribution, electric power; Generation, electric power; Transmission, electric power
Pr: Donald M Lynch
**CFO:* Marlene A Barwood
CFO: Mark T Clark
Treas: T G Howson
Treas: James F Pearson
Ex VP: Leila L Vespoli
Sr VP: Charles E Jones
Sr VP: David C Luff
VP: C Brooks
VP: William D Byrd
VP: Mark A Jones
VP: Charles D Lasky
VP: C A Mascari
VP: M P O'Flynn
VP: Harvey L Wagner
VP: R S Zechman
Board of Directors: Charles E Jones, Mark A Julian, Jesse T Williams Sr

D-U-N-S 07-754-2942
JERSEY CITY BOARD OF EDUCATION (INC)
JERSEY CITY PUBLIC SCHOOLS
346 Claremont Ave, Jersey City, NJ 07305-1634
Tel (201) 915-6202 *Founded/Ownrshp* 1895
Sales 206.7MM^E *EMP* 2,494
SIC 8211 Public elementary & secondary schools; Public elementary & secondary schools
Bd of Dir: Marilyn Roman
Schl Brd P: Sangeeta Ranade

D-U-N-S 06-750-5990
JERSEY CITY INCINERATOR AUTHORITY
501 State Rt 440, Jersey City, NJ 07305-4823
Tel (201) 432-4645 *Founded/Ownrshp* 1951
Sales 89.1MM^E *EMP* 174^E
SIC 4953 0782 4212 Recycling, waste materials; Lawn & garden services; Local trucking, without storage; Recycling, waste materials; Lawn & garden services; Local trucking, without storage
CEO: Oren K Dabney
**CEO:* Oren K Dadney Sr
CFO: Shirley Marcano
**Ch:* Phillip T Flood
Ofcr: Raj Vasan

D-U-N-S 07-930-8110
JERSEY CITY MEDICAL CENTER INC
LIBERTYHEALTH
(*Suby of* LIBERTY HEALTHCARE SYSTEM INC) ★
355 Grand St, Jersey City, NJ 07302-4321
Tel (201) 915-2000 *Founded/Ownrshp* 1990
Sales 367.1MM *EMP* 1,942
SIC 8062 General medical & surgical hospitals; General medical & surgical hospitals
CEO: Joe Scott
Chf Path: Patricia Tsang
Chf Rad: Andrew Novick
**Ch Bd:* James R Reilly
CFO: Donald Parseghin
Trst: Robert Lahita
Trst: Juan Perez
VP: Richard Bonforte
VP: Brenda Hall
Exec: Fatima Dejesus
Dir Case M: Leigh Baillie
Dir Lab: Rabhia Abdelhady
Dir Lab: Ting Shen
Dir Rad: Linda Saguil
Dir Rad: Anthony Tramontana MD

D-U-N-S 03-025-0484
JERSEY CITY MUNICIPAL UTILITIES AUTHORITY
JCMUA
555 State Rt 440, Jersey City, NJ 07305-4823
Tel (201) 432-1150 *Founded/Ownrshp* 1949
Sales 45.4MM^E *EMP* 102
SIC 4952 Sewerage systems; Sewerage systems
Ex Dir: Daniel F Becht Esq
Bd of Dir: Anthony Cucci
Bd of Dir: William Macchi
IT Man: Dore Carlo
Snr Mgr: Bill Golden
Snr Mgr: P E Prakash

JERSEY CITY PUBLIC SCHOOLS
See JERSEY CITY BOARD OF EDUCATION (INC)

D-U-N-S 07-979-9140
JERSEY CITY PUBLIC SCHOOLS
346 Claremont Ave, Jersey City, NJ 07305-1634
Tel (201) 915-6201 *Founded/Ownrshp* 2015
Sales 80.0MM^E *EMP* 3,601^E
SIC 8211 Public elementary & secondary schools
Dir Sec: Arthur Youmanns
MIS Dir: Debasis Gupta

D-U-N-S 00-780-2911
JERSEY COUNTY GRAIN CO
426 E Exchange St, Jerseyville, IL 62052-1715
Tel (618) 498-2183 *Founded/Ownrshp* 1931
Sales 88.0MM *EMP* 20
SIC 5153 5191 Grain elevators; Feed; Seeds: field, garden & flower; Grain elevators; Feed; Seeds: field, garden & flower
CEO: Mike Welburne
**Pr:* William Kuebrich
**Pr:* Tom Moore
**Sec:* Wayn Fuhler
**VP:* Rich Deverger
Div Mgr: Tom Deurinder
Genl Mgr: Michael Welbourne

JERSEY CY FORD LINCOLN MERCURY
See AAM MOTOR SALES LLC

D-U-N-S 06-384-8386
JERSEY LYNNE FARMS INC (NY)
8801 Foster Ave, Brooklyn, NY 11236-3295
Tel (718) 649-6730 *Founded/Ownrshp* 1959
Sales 48.6MM^E *EMP* 55
Accts Lcs&Z Llp Latham Ny
SIC 5144 5147 5143 Eggs; Meats & meat products; Dairy products, except dried or canned; Eggs; Meats & meat products; Dairy products, except dried or canned
Pr: Michael Loconte
**CFO:* Kenneth Seligson
**VP:* Diane Schmidt
**VP:* Maria Penney Seligson

D-U-N-S 87-704-9148
JERSEY MIKES FRANCHISE SYSTEMS INC
2251 Landmark Pl, Manasquan, NJ 08736-1026
Tel (732) 223-4044 *Founded/Ownrshp* 1994
Sales 24.9MM^E *EMP* 80
Accts Ernst & Young Llp
SIC 6794 Franchises, selling or licensing
Pr: Peter Cancro
**COO:* Michael Manvo
VP: Christopher Daniels
CIO: Scott Scherer

D-U-N-S 80-009-1055
JERSEY NISSAN LLC
NORTH PLAINFIELD NISSAN
545 Us Highway 22 W, North Plainfield, NJ 07060-3724
Tel (908) 755-6400 *Founded/Ownrshp* 2005
Sales 42.9MM^E *EMP* 99^E
SIC 5511 Automobiles, new & used

JERSEY PAPER PLUS
See JPC ENTERPRISES INC

D-U-N-S 18-115-8825
JERSEY PARTNERS INC
1111 Broadhollow Rd Fl 3, Farmingdale, NY 11735-4881
Tel (406) 442-1066 *Founded/Ownrshp* 2000
Sales 59.0MM^E *EMP* 650
Accts Deloitte & Touche Llp New Yor
SIC 6211 Security brokers & dealers; Security brokers & dealers
CEO: Michael Gooch
CFO: Robert Crossan

D-U-N-S 00-217-0975 IMP
JERSEY PLASTIC MOLDERS INC
PRIMO DIVISION
149 Shaw Ave, Irvington, NJ 07111-4779
Tel (973) 926-1800 *Founded/Ownrshp* 1945
Sales 24.6MM^E *EMP* 125
SIC 3089 Molding primary plastic
Pr: Joseph Zazzara
CFO: Kim Nakano
Info Man: Edwin Honrales
Plnt Mgr: Allen Taylor
Sls Mgr: Tony Kaieda

D-U-N-S 03-858-8638 IMP
JERSEY PRECAST CORP INC
853 Nottingham Way, Trenton, NJ 08638-4447
Tel (609) 689-3700 *Founded/Ownrshp* 1997
Sales 45.9MM^E *EMP* 160
SIC 3272 Concrete products, precast; Concrete products, precast
Pr: M Amir Ul Islam
COO: Arshad Afridi
CFO: Gregory A Runion
Genl Mgr: Khwaja Abbas
Snr PM: Paul Dentel

D-U-N-S 06-050-0337
JERSEY SHORE AREA SCHOOL DISTRICT
175 A And P Dr, Jersey Shore, PA 17740-7877
Tel (570) 398-5600 *Founded/Ownrshp* 1876
Sales 36.8MM *EMP* 420
Accts Baker Tilly Virchow Krause Ll
SIC 8211 Public elementary & secondary schools; High school, junior or senior; School board; Public elementary & secondary schools; High school, junior or senior; School board
VP: Harry Brungard
HC Dir: Doreen Eisenauer

D-U-N-S 07-598-7651
JERSEY SHORE HOSPITAL
1020 Thompson St, Jersey Shore, PA 17740-1794
Tel (570) 398-5710 *Founded/Ownrshp* 1929
Sales 28.2MM *EMP* 325
Accts Parentebeard Llc Philadelphia
SIC 8062 General medical & surgical hospitals; General medical & surgical hospitals
Pr: Carey Plummer
Chf Path: Donald Leathers

*CFO: Dean Fleming
CFO: Mark Rice
*Treas: William Camerer III
Dir Rad: Kevin W Kist
Dir Rad: Ed Sowul
Dir Rx: Arleen Kessler
Chf Nrs Of: Paulette Nish
Ex Dir: Linda Yowell
CIO: Kristina Haas

D-U-N-S 00-341-4224
■ JERSEY SHORE STATE BANK
(Suby of PENNS WOODS BANCORP INC) ★
115 S Main St, Jersey Shore, PA 17740-1842
Tel (570) 398-2213 Founded/Ownrshp 1934
Sales NA EMP 100
SIC 6022 State trust companies accepting deposits, commercial; State trust companies accepting deposits, commercial
Pr: Richard A Grafmyre
*Ch Bd: Ronald A Walko
*CFO: Brian L Knepp
*Ex VP: Thomas Donofrio
*Sr VP: Hubert A Valencik
Sr VP: Hubert A Vlencik
VP: John Frey
VP: Misty Mark
Off Mgr: David Palski

D-U-N-S 00-304-3338 IMP
JERSEY SHORE STEEL CO (PA)
70 Maryland Ave, Jersey Shore, PA 17740-7113
Tel (570) 753-3000 Founded/Ownrshp 1938, 1943
Sales 120.5MM^E EMP 400
SIC 3312 Rails, steel or iron; Rails, steel or iron
CEO: John C Schultz
*Treas: Mark Scheffey
*Ex VP: Peter D Schultz
MIS Dir: Bob Kauffman
Dir IT: David Irace
IT Man: Mark Francolino
Sfty Mgr: Ed Robenolt
Ql Cn Mgr: Steve Barto
Ql Cn Mgr: Mike Berry

JERSEY UNIT SCHOOL 100
See COMMUNITY UNIT SCHOOL DISTRICT 100 (INC)

D-U-N-S 07-930-7627
JERUE LOGISTICS SOLUTIONS LLC (FL)
3200 Flightline Dr # 202, Lakeland, FL 33811-2848
Tel (863) 607-5656 Founded/Ownrshp 2012
Sales 24.9MM EMP 9
SIC 4731 Freight forwarding

D-U-N-S 78-928-2167
JERUSALEM BAPTIST CHURCH
150 N Clinton Ave, Trenton, NJ 08609-1010
Tel (609) 393-7042 Founded/Ownrshp 1992
Sales 250.0M EMP 300
SIC 8661 Baptist Church; Baptist Church
VP: T L Steele

D-U-N-S 00-537-8815 IMP
JERVIS B WEBB CO (MI)
(Suby of DAIFUKU CO., LTD.)
34375 W 12 Mile Rd, Farmington Hills, MI 48331-5624
Tel (248) 553-1000 Founded/Ownrshp 1919, 2007
Sales 189.0MM^E EMP 900
SIC 3535 3536 3462 3537 3613 Conveyors & conveying equipment; Overhead conveyor systems; Cranes & monorail systems; Cranes, industrial plant; Monorail systems; Iron & steel forgings; Chains, forged steel; Stacking machines, automatic; Tractors, used in plants, docks, terminals, etc.: industrial; Control panels, electric; Conveyors & conveying equipment; Overhead conveyor systems; Cranes & monorail systems; Cranes, industrial plant; Monorail systems; Iron & steel forgings; Chains, forged steel; Stacking machines, automatic; Tractors, used in plants, docks, terminals, etc.: industrial; Control panels, electric
Pr: Robertus Schmit
CEO: Dina Salehi
CFO: Tetsuya Hibi
VP: George Flintosh
VP: Christopher Murphy
VP: Parker Thomas III
Mng Dir: William Kline
Admn Mgr: Bruce L Redman
Snr Sftwr: Philip Klump
Snr Sftwr: Wayne Ross
CIO: John Jaynes
Board of Directors: Ken Hamel, Lon McAllister, Aki Nishimura

D-U-N-S 82-740-8415 IMP
JES APPAREL LLC
(Suby of AMERICAN FASHION NETWORK LLC) ★
8104 Cazenovia Rd Ste D, Manlius, NY 13104-9667
Tel (315) 682-1677 Founded/Ownrshp 2008
Sales 30.0MM EMP 10
SIC 5137 Women's & children's clothing; Women's & children's clothing
VP: Kevin Stock

D-U-N-S 60-316-6013
JES CONSTRUCTION INC
JES FOUNDATION REPAIR
569 Central Dr Ste 200, Virginia Beach, VA 23454-5281
Tel (757) 558-9909 Founded/Ownrshp 1994
Sales 26.0MM^E EMP 93^E
SIC 1389 Construction, repair & dismantling services
Pr: Jesse Waltz
COO: Adrian Reddington
Treas: Jesse Wattz
VP: Greg Remphrey
Sls Mgr: Nick Feaster
Sls Mgr: Todd Simmons

JES FOUNDATION REPAIR
See JES CONSTRUCTION INC

D-U-N-S 00-480-2112
JESCO INC (MS)
(Suby of YATES COMPANIES INC) ★
2020 Mccullough Blvd, Tupelo, MS 38801-7108
Tel (662) 842-3240 Founded/Ownrshp 1945, 2000
Sales 139.2MM EMP 600
Accts Rea Shaw Giffin & Stuart Ll
SIC 1541 Industrial buildings, new construction; Factory construction; Warehouse construction; Industrial buildings, new construction; Factory construction; Warehouse construction
Pr: Jerry Stubblefield
Ch Bd: William Yates Jr
Sec: Tim Miles
Sr VP: Daniel Steele
VP: Jerry Maxcy
VP Opers: Trey Hard

D-U-N-S 06-317-5509
JESCO INC
JOHN DEERE
118 Saint Nicholas Ave, South Plainfield, NJ 07080-1892
Tel (903) 753-8080 Founded/Ownrshp 1972
Sales 50.9MM^E EMP 115
SIC 5082 5084 5012 Excavating machinery & equipment; Lift trucks & parts; Materials handling machinery; Commercial vehicles; Trucks, commercial; Excavating machinery & equipment; Lift trucks & parts; Materials handling machinery; Commercial vehicles; Trucks, commercial
Pr: Jon Robustelli
*CFO: Greg Blaszka
*Sec: Theresa Robustelli
IT Man: Cris Robustelli
VP Sls: Falzarano Anthony
Sls Mgr: Robert Gamber
Sls Mgr: Anthony Salzarano
Sales Asso: Michael Delia
Sales Asso: Rick England
Sales Asso: Joe Perez
Sales Asso: Steve Rizzi

D-U-N-S 10-584-4976 IMP/EXP
JESCO LIGHTING INC
15 Harbor Park Dr, Port Washington, NY 11050-4604
Tel (718) 366-3211 Founded/Ownrshp 1998
Sales 21.0MM EMP 50^E
SIC 3646 Commercial indusl & institutional electric lighting fixtures
Pr: Richard Kurtz
*Ch: Edward MA
*VP Mktg: Paulin Tham
Mktg Mgr: Andrij Burchak
Sls Mgr: Jeff Sessler
Sales Asso: Mike Wright

D-U-N-S 19-478-0557 IMP
JESON ENTERPRISES INC
CRAFT WAREHOUSE
504 Ne 5th Ave, Camas, WA 98607-2005
Tel (360) 834-7728 Founded/Ownrshp 1980
Sales 30.0MM EMP 400
SIC 5945 Arts & crafts supplies; Arts & crafts supplies
Pr: Jerry Williams
*Sec: Sonya Williams
*VP: Michael Williams

D-U-N-S 08-974-5988 IMP
JESS BRILEY MANUFACTURING CO
1230 Lumpkin Rd, Houston, TX 77043-4102
Tel (713) 932-6995 Founded/Ownrshp 1975
Sales 22.6MM^E EMP 80
SIC 3484 Shotguns or shotgun parts, 30 mm. & below
Pr: Jess Briley
*VP: Cliff Moller
CTO: Claudio Salassa
Dir IT: Stephanie Allen
Opers Mgr: Julio Schmidt
Prd Mgr: Marcos Monzalvo

D-U-N-S 00-286-7331
JESS HOWARD ELECTRIC CO
6630 Taylor Rd, Blacklick, OH 43004-8661
Tel (614) 864-2167 Founded/Ownrshp 1945
Sales 41.4MM^E EMP 140
SIC 1731 General electrical contractor; General electrical contractor
CEO: Jess E Howard
*Pr: John Howard
CFO: Al Bolton
*Ex VP: Bill Walt
*VP: Mel Haywood
*VP: Tim Howard Sr
VP: Bob Kennedy
Sfty Mgr: Chrissy Hudson

D-U-N-S 08-838-7170 IMP/EXP
JESS SMITH & SONS COTTON LLC
BAKERSFIELD COTTON CO
2905 F St, Bakersfield, CA 93301-1819
Tel (661) 325-7231 Founded/Ownrshp 1970
Sales 35.3MM^E EMP 45
SIC 5159 Cotton merchants; Cotton, raw
*CEO: Ernie D Schroeder Jr
COO: Stevem Williams
Dir IT: Larry Bailey
Dir IT: Micky Farley

D-U-N-S 80-050-7993
JESSAMINE CO SCHOOL DISTRICT
871 Wilmore Rd, Nicholasville, KY 40356-9462
Tel (859) 885-4179 Founded/Ownrshp 2007
Sales 77.3MM EMP 9
SIC 8211 Public elementary & secondary schools; Public elementary & secondary schools
Pr: Lu Young

D-U-N-S 07-787-5532
JESSAMINE COUNTY BOARD OF EDUCATION (INC)
871 Wilmore Rd, Nicholasville, KY 40356-9462
Tel (859) 885-4179 Founded/Ownrshp 2003
Sales 77.3MM EMP 1,440
Accts Summers Mccrary & Sparks Psc
SIC 8211 Elementary school; High school, junior or senior; School board
Ch Bd: Eugene Peel

D-U-N-S 96-349-3551
JESSAMINE COUNTY SCHOOLS
871 Wilmore Rd, Nicholasville, KY 40356-9462
Tel (859) 881-4179 Founded/Ownrshp 2010
Sales 38.9MM^E EMP 900^E
SIC 8211 Public elementary & secondary schools
Treas: Holly Wilson

D-U-N-S 07-950-9630
JESSE BAHLKE CORP
2106 33rd St Apt C7, Astoria, NY 11105-2360
Tel (917) 275-4736 Founded/Ownrshp 2014
Sales 250.0M EMP 917
SIC 6531 Real estate brokers & agents; Real estate brokers & agents
Pr: Jesse Bahlke

D-U-N-S 00-328-2842
JESSE CREEK MINING LLC (AL)
1615 Kent Dairy Rd, Alabaster, AL 35007-5271
Tel (205) 358-8826 Founded/Ownrshp 2012, 2013
Sales 29.6MM EMP 113
SIC 1241 Coal mining services; Coal mining services
Pr: John McNab
CFO: David South

D-U-N-S 08-193-1974 EXP
JESSE ENGINEERING CO
1840 Marine View Dr, Tacoma, WA 98422-4106
Tel (253) 552-1500 Founded/Ownrshp 1976
Sales 39.0MM EMP 150
SIC 3441 3542 Fabricated structural metal; Bending machines; Fabricated structural metal; Bending machines
Pr: Marty Diklich
*Pr: Jeff Gellert
*VP: Anne Jesse
*VP: Darrell Jesse
Div Mgr: Philip Jesse
Plnt Mgr: Doug Berg
Sls Mgr: Gust Erickson

D-U-N-S 02-124-5543
JESSE STUTTS INC (AL)
3414 9th Ave Sw, Huntsville, AL 35805-3925
Tel (256) 533-7730 Founded/Ownrshp 1977, 2006
Sales 24.4MM^E EMP 130^E
Accts Anglin Reichmann Snellgrove &
SIC 1731 1521 Electrical work; Single-family housing construction; Electrical work; Single-family housing construction
Pr: Jimmy C Wall
*VP: Jesse Stutts III

D-U-N-S 08-838-1132 IMP
JESSICA COSMETICS INTERNATIONAL INC (CA)
JESSICA'S COSMETICS
13209 Saticoy St, North Hollywood, CA 91605-3405
Tel (818) 759-1050 Founded/Ownrshp 1968
Sales 21.8MM^E EMP 60
SIC 5122 7231 Cosmetics; Beauty shops
Pr: Jessica Vartoughian
Mktg Mgr: Haley Marcus
Snr Mgr: Valentin Safta

D-U-N-S 13-612-1030 EXP
JESSICA LONDON INC
(Suby of BRYLANE HOME) ★
2300 Southeastern Ave, Indianapolis, IN 46201-4001
Tel (317) 266-3300 Founded/Ownrshp 2008
Sales 55.0MM^E EMP 805
SIC 5961 Women's apparel, mail order; Women's apparel, mail order
CEO: Eric Faintrenty
Prin: Amberly Martin

D-U-N-S 05-037-1277 IMP
JESSICA MCCLINTOCK INC
2307 Broadway St, San Francisco, CA 94115-1291
Tel (415) 553-8200 Founded/Ownrshp 1970
Sales 70.5MM^E EMP 600
SIC 2361 2335 2844 Dresses: girls', children's & infants'; Women's, juniors' & misses' dresses; Perfumes, natural or synthetic; Dresses: girls', children's & infants'; Women's, juniors' & misses' dresses; Perfumes, natural or synthetic
Pr: Jessica Mc Clintock
CFO: Dilip K Parekh
CTO: Lambert Dangilan

JESSICA'S BISCUIT
See NEW ENGLAND MOBILE BOOK FAIR INC

D-U-N-S 00-803-7447
JESSICAS BRICK OVEN INC (MA)
1630 Osgood St Ste 1210, North Andover, MA 01845-1000
Tel (978) 655-4455 Founded/Ownrshp 1998, 2008
Sales 27.8MM^E EMP 96
SIC 5149 Bakery products; Bakery products
Pr: Nabil Boghos
*Treas: Farrell Boghos
*VP: Rose Marie Boghous

JESSICA'S COSMETICS
See JESSICA COSMETICS INTERNATIONAL INC

JESSICO OIL
See PETROLEUM SUPPLY CORP

D-U-N-S 14-496-3605 IMP
JESSIE LORD BAKERY LLC
21100 S Western Ave, Torrance, CA 90501-1705
Tel (310) 328-7738 Founded/Ownrshp 2003
Sales 72.5MM^E EMP 40
SIC 5142 Fruit pies, frozen
VP: John Freschi
Genl Mgr: Christine Valley
Plnt Mgr: Timothy Zacharyasz
Manager: Don McNeil

D-U-N-S 02-053-5027 IMP
JESSIE TRICE COMMUNITY HEALTH CENTER INC (FL)
5607 Nw 27th Ave Ste 1, Miami, FL 33142-2826
Tel (305) 805-1700 Founded/Ownrshp 1967
Sales 26.0MM EMP 282
Accts Sharpton Brunson & Company Pa
SIC 8093 Specialty outpatient clinics; Specialty outpatient clinics
Ch: Alvin D Moore
*Pr: Anthony E Munroe
*Pr: Annie Neasman
*CFO: Katrina Bumpers
*Ch: Sherwood Dubose
*Treas: Dr David Ewing Chow
Board of Directors: Gilbert Raiford, Adrian Barr, Jessie Robinson, Elena Becker, Madeline Rodriguez, Elizabeth Boze, Beatrice Louis Saint, Dorothy Edwards, Kathleen A Shea, Joseph S Gay, George A Simpson, Ellen S Heidt, Minnie Smith, J Kenneth Major, Sylvia Unzueta, Nathaniel Miller, Alan S Perera

D-U-N-S 00-432-2343
■ JESSOP STEEL LLC
(Suby of All ACQUISITION LLC) ★
500 Green St, Washington, PA 15301-2398
Tel (724) 222-4000 Founded/Ownrshp 2003
Sales 309.7M^E EMP 2,413^E
SIC 3312 Stainless steel
VP: David R Cate
*Prin: Terry Dunlap
*Prin: JD Walton
Opers Mgr: Dominic Sacco
Opers Mgr: Gary Stitely
Pr Mgr: Dan Mochnaly

JESSUP AUTO PLAZA
See PLAZA MOTORS

D-U-N-S 00-518-9006 IMP
JESSUP MANUFACTURING CO INC (IL)
2815 W Rte 120, Mchenry, IL 60051
Tel (815) 385-6650 Founded/Ownrshp 1956
Sales 21.9MM^E EMP 60
SIC 3089 Battery cases, plastic or plastic combination
Pr: Robert A Jessup
COO: Kiran M Gandhi
VP: Rick Brizek
Prd Mgr: Carl Hansen
Sales Asso: Patty Wiedyk

D-U-N-S 83-042-3344
JESUIT HIGH SCHOOL
9000 Sw Beavrtn Hllsdl Hw, Portland, OR 97225
Tel (503) 292-2663 Founded/Ownrshp 1956
Sales 22.0MM EMP 128
SIC 8211 Secondary school
Pr: John G Gladstone
Pr: Nancy Fausone
CFO: Kenneth Foley
*Treas: Ken Foley
VP: Andrew Asato
VP: Micheal Schwab
Comm Dir: E E Tuenge
Dir IT: Ron Scarcelli

D-U-N-S 09-886-8615
JESUIT HIGH SCHOOL OF SACRAMENTO
1200 Jacob Ln, Carmichael, CA 95608-6099
Tel (916) 482-6060 Founded/Ownrshp 1963
Sales 21.6MM^E EMP 120
SIC 8211 Private senior high school
Pr: David Suwalsky S J
*CFO: Harold Turner
VP: Frank Hernandez
VP: Maureen Longyear
*Prin: Brianna Latko
Dir IT: Jason Sylvester
Psych: Kathy Liefde
HC Dir: Gerry Lane
Art Dir: Ed Trafton

D-U-N-S 09-921-2839
JESUS PEOPLE USA FULL GOSPEL MINISTRIES
LAKE FRONT SUPPLY
2950 N Western Ave, Chicago, IL 60618-8021
Tel (773) 252-1812 Founded/Ownrshp 1973
Sales 20.5MM^E EMP 250
SIC 8661 5211 1731 1751 7336 5699 Religious organizations; Roofing material; Electrical work; Cabinet building & installation; Silk screen design; T-shirts, custom printed; Religious organizations; Roofing material; Electrical work; Cabinet building & installation; Silk screen design; T-shirts, custom printed
Pr: Glenn Kaiser
*Treas: John Herrin
*VP: Dawn Herrin
Genl Mgr: Marsha Spaniel

D-U-N-S 83-287-7521
■ JET AVIATION ENGINEERING MANAGEMENT INC
(Suby of JET AVIATION INTERNATIONAL INC) ★
1515 Perimeter Rd, West Palm Beach, FL 33406-1469
Tel (561) 233-7233 Founded/Ownrshp 2001
Sales 8.0MM^E EMP 318^E
SIC 4581 Airports, flying fields & services
Prin: Kurt Sutterer

D-U-N-S 36-450-4340
■ JET AVIATION HOLDINGS USA INC
(Suby of GENERAL DYNAMICS CORP) ★
112 Chrles A Lindbergh Dr, Teterboro, NJ 07608-1010
Tel (201) 462-4000 Founded/Ownrshp 2008
Sales 33.0MM^E EMP 100
SIC 4581 5599 4522 Aircraft maintenance & repair services; Aircraft servicing & repairing; Airport terminal services; Aircraft instruments, equipment or parts; Flying charter service
Pr: Robert Smith
Pr: Hussain Baqueri
CFO: Bill Beuka
CFO: William Bueka
*CFO: Wim Buesink
*VP: Stefan Benz
VP: William Beversluis
VP: Richard Kunert
VP: Jon Winthrop
Sls Mgr: Peter Kiernan

D-U-N-S 79-066-9857
■ JET AVIATION INTERNATIONAL INC
(Suby of GENERAL DYNAMICS CORP) ★
1515 Perimeter Rd, West Palm Beach, FL 33406-1469
Tel (561) 478-9066 Founded/Ownrshp 2008
Sales 55.7MM^E EMP 800
SIC 4581 5084 Airports, flying fields & services; Machine tools & accessories; Airports, flying fields & services; Machine tools & accessories
VP: John Langevin
*CFO: Michael Gregory
*Treas: Gary Konicki T
Ofcr: Theresa Jardine
*VP: William Beversluis
*VP: David Deitch
Genl Mgr: J S Joiner
Opers Mgr: Masood A Khan
Manager: Bill Dotts

D-U-N-S 04-130-4973
■ JET AVIATION ST LOUIS INC (MO)
(Suby of JET AVIATION INTERNATIONAL INC) ★
6400 Curtiss Steinberg Dr, Cahokia, IL 62206-1458
Tel (618) 337-3981 Founded/Ownrshp 1957, 2006
Sales 34.8MM^E EMP 99^E
SIC 4581 5172 3721 5088 Aircraft servicing & repairing; Aircraft storage at airports; Airport terminal services; Aircraft fueling services; Aircraft; Aircraft & parts
Pr: Robert Smith
*Pr: Kurt Sutterer
*CFO: Jim Bates
*Sr VP: Heinz Aebi
*Sr VP: Stephan Bruhin
*Sr VP: D C Glendinning
*Sr VP: Skip Madsen
*Sr VP: David Paddock
VP: Rodger Renaud
IT Man: Patrick Kasate
Software D: Tim Sumpter

D-U-N-S 19-062-8818 IMP
■ JET AVION CORP
HEICO PARTS GROUP
(Suby of HEICO AEROSPACE HOLDINGS CORP) ★
3000 Taft St, Hollywood, FL 33021-4441
Tel (954) 987-6101 Founded/Ownrshp 1997
Sales 24.3MM^E EMP 70
SIC 3724 Aircraft engines & engine parts; Aircraft engines & engine parts
Pr: Rick Stine
*Treas: Thomas S Irwin
*Treas: Carlos L Macau
*Sr VP: Mike Sego
*VP: Jack Lewis
Sls Dir: Joel Ortiz
Sls Dir: Hongwei Shi

JET CENTER INTERIORS
See AERO TOY STORE LLC

D-U-N-S 02-023-8440
JET CHEVROLET INC
35700 Enchanted Pkwy S, Federal Way, WA 98003-8313
Tel (253) 838-7600 Founded/Ownrshp 1975
Sales 26.3MM^E EMP 56
SIC 5511 Automobiles, new & used; Automobiles, new & used
Pr: Dan Johnson
*Sec: Barbara Johnson
*VP: James Johnson
Sls Mgr: Keith Guinn
Sales Asso: Michael Cady
Sales Asso: Gerry Lee
Board of Directors: Karen Nass

D-U-N-S 00-530-1361
JET CO INC (IA)
1303 13th St N, Humboldt, IA 50548-1198
Tel (515) 332-5001 Founded/Ownrshp 1955
Sales 28.5MM^E EMP 120
SIC 3714 3523 3715 3537 Motor vehicle body components & frame; Trailers & wagons, farm; Truck trailers; Industrial trucks & tractors; Motor vehicle body components & frame; Trailers & wagons, farm; Truck trailers; Industrial trucks & tractors
Pr: Dale Heider
*Treas: Leon Heider
Area Mgr: Chad Hansen
Area Mgr: Jason Paterson

D-U-N-S 15-405-8309
JET CORR
PRATT INDUSTRIES
(Suby of CORRUGATING DIVISION) ★
1800 Sarasot Bus Pkwy Ne B, Conyers, GA 30013-5775
Tel (770) 602-1191 Founded/Ownrshp 1988
Sales 492.2MM^E EMP 3,500
SIC 2653 Boxes, corrugated: made from purchased materials; Sheets, solid fiber: made from purchased materials; Boxes, corrugated: made from purchased materials; Sheets, solid fiber: made from purchased materials
Ch Bd: Richard Pratt
Pr: Anthony Pratt
CEO: Gary B Byrd
COO: Phillip Bulger
COO: Brian McKeely
COO: Brian McPheely
CFO: Troy Faircloth
CFO: David Wiser
Ex VP: Victor Columbus
Ex VP: John Day
Creative D: John Krisko

D-U-N-S 19-460-3478
JET CORR INC
CORRUGATING DIVISION
(Suby of PRATT INDUSTRIES (USA) INC) ★
1800 Sarasot Bus Pkwy Ne B, Conyers, GA 30013-5775
Tel (770) 929-1300 Founded/Ownrshp 1993
Sales 639.9MM^E EMP 3,500
SIC 2653 Boxes, corrugated: made from purchased materials; Boxes, corrugated: made from purchased materials
Pr: Gary B Byrd
*Ch Bd: Richard Pratt
*CEO: Brian McPheely
*COO: Phillip Bulger
*CFO: Aamir Anwar
*Ch: Pratt Anthony
*VP: Douglas Balyeat
*VP: David J Kyles
*VP: David Wiser

D-U-N-S 04-643-2332
JET DELIVERY INC
2169 Wright Ave, La Verne, CA 91750-5835
Tel (800) 716-7177 Founded/Ownrshp 1950
Sales 32.3MM^E EMP 155
SIC 4215 Courier services, except by air; Courier services, except by air
Pr: Michael Barbata
*CIO: Jason Barbata

JET ENGINEERING
See SYMMETRY MEDICAL MANUFACTURING INC

D-U-N-S 10-149-7824
JET EXPRESS INC
4518 Webster St, Dayton, OH 45414-4940
Tel (937) 274-1640 Founded/Ownrshp 1983
Sales 21.7MM^E EMP 134
SIC 4212 4213 Local trucking, without storage; Trucking, except local
Pr: Kevin Burch
*Treas: Amy Hogan
*VP: Greg Atkinson
*VP: Roger Atkinson Jr

D-U-N-S 06-646-0874
JET FOOD STORES OF GEORGIA INC
1106 S Harris St, Sandersville, GA 31082-6904
Tel (478) 552-2588 Founded/Ownrshp 1988
Sales 80.7MM^E EMP 600
SIC 5411 Convenience stores, chain; Convenience stores, chain
Ch Bd: Phillip R Seay
*Pr: Charles E Turner
*CFO: Chuck Hancock
VP: David Usry
Sls&Mrk Ex: Carlene Walden

D-U-N-S 02-280-7122 IMP/EXP
JET INDUSTRIES INC
1372 N Old Laurens Rd, Fountain Inn, SC 29644-7065
Tel (215) 362-1501 Founded/Ownrshp 1997
Sales 34.4MM^E EMP 660
SIC 3089 Injection molding of plastics; Injection molding of plastics
Pr: S James Spierer

D-U-N-S 79-500-9414 IMP/EXP
JET INDUSTRIES INC
OZZ PROPERTIES
1935 Silverton Rd Ne, Salem, OR 97301-0181
Tel (503) 363-2334 Founded/Ownrshp 1977
Sales 141.0MM^E EMP 300
SIC 1711 1731 Heating & air conditioning contractors; Fire sprinkler system installation; Electrical work; Fire detection & burglar alarm systems specialization; Heating & air conditioning contractors; Fire sprinkler system installation; Electrical work; Fire detection & burglar alarm systems specialization
Pr: Hunter Zeeb
*Pr: Oliver Raab
*Pr: Jeff Zeeb
Genl Mgr: Chip Ayers
Snr PM: Will Verboort

D-U-N-S 05-671-2557 EXP
JET LINE PRODUCTS INC
JETLINE
55 Jacobus Ave, Kearny, NJ 07032-4533
Tel (973) 690-2999 Founded/Ownrshp 1999
Sales 30.0MM EMP 40
SIC 5091 Swimming pools, equipment & supplies; Swimming pools, equipment & supplies
Pr: Mark Etstein

JET LITHOCOLOR, INC.
See MPS CHICAGO INC

JET MACHINE & MANUFACTURING
See WULCO INC

D-U-N-S 01-502-0030 IMP
JET MANUFACTURING INC
PRISM AEROSPACE DBA JET MANUFACTURING
13445 Estelle St, Corona, CA 92879-1877
Tel (951) 736-9316 Founded/Ownrshp 1997
Sales 23.4MM^E EMP 105
SIC 3444 3724 Sheet metalwork; Jet assisted takeoff devices (JATO)
CEO: Eric S Cunningham
Prgrm Mgr: Blake Conlin
Prgrm Mgr: Mario Velazquez
Ql Cn Mgr: Mynor Bracamonte

JET PACKAGE PARTS
See STARFISH ENGINEERING ASSOCIATES LLC

D-U-N-S 08-374-8343
JET PEP INC
9481 Highway 278 W, Holly Pond, AL 35083
Tel (256) 796-2237 Founded/Ownrshp 1973
Sales 361.9MM EMP 75
SIC 5541 Petroleum bulk stations; Filling stations, gasoline; Filling stations, gasoline
Pr: Robert G Norris
*CFO: Steve Gaines
*VP: Darlene H Norris
Genl Mgr: Chuck Moore

D-U-N-S 00-237-3041 IMP
JET PLASTICA INDUSTRIES INC
1100 Schwab Rd, Hatfield, PA 19440-3234
Tel (215) 362-1501 Founded/Ownrshp 1997
Sales NA EMP 600
SIC 3089 3421

D-U-N-S 03-994-0655
JET SPECIALTY INC
211 Market Ave, Boerne, TX 78006-3050
Tel (830) 331-9457 Founded/Ownrshp 1991
Sales 202.9MM^E EMP 171
Accts Weaver And Tidwell Llp San A
SIC 5084 5085 Instruments & control equipment; Valves & fittings; Instruments & control equipment; Valves & fittings
Pr: Tom W Darter
*CFO: Ted Williams
*VP: Chad Darter
Genl Mgr: Gary Schroeder
Store Mgr: Matt Marney
Sales Asso: Shadd Bogges
Sales Asso: Britt Poynor

D-U-N-S 10-724-8569
JET STAR INC
10825 Andrade Dr, Zionsville, IN 46077-9232
Tel (317) 873-4222 Founded/Ownrshp 1982
Sales 25.1MM^E EMP 121
SIC 4212 4213 Heavy machinery transport, local; Heavy machinery transport
CEO: Darryl Guiducci
*CFO: Cynthia Bauer
CFO: Brian Guiducci
*VP: Ed Bell
CTO: Evan Tanner
IT Man: Bill Wolfe
Trfc Dir: Jason Norton

D-U-N-S 00-986-5650
JET TRANSPORT CO
1400 6th St Sw, Cedar Rapids, IA 52404-5841
Tel (319) 365-7594 Founded/Ownrshp 1955
Sales 11.6MM^E EMP 350
SIC 4213 Liquid petroleum transport, non-local; Liquid petroleum transport, non-local
Pr: David Nordstrom

D-U-N-S 82-744-7785
JET WAY SECURITY & INVESTIGATIONS LLC
7 Old Rockaway Blvd, Jamaica, NY 11430-1887
Tel (718) 244-0523 Founded/Ownrshp 2008
Sales 5.8MM^E EMP 350
SIC 7381 Security guard service; Security guard service

D-U-N-S 08-900-2799
▲ JETBLUE AIRWAYS CORP
2701 Queens Plz N Ste 1, Long Island City, NY 11101-4021
Tel (718) 286-7900 Founded/Ownrshp 2000
Sales 5.8MMM EMP 15,334
Accts Ernst & Young Llp New York N
Tkr Sym JBLU Exch NGS
SIC 4512 Air passenger carrier, scheduled; Confinement surveillance systems maintenance & monitoring; Air transportation, scheduled; Air passenger carrier, scheduled
Pr: Robin Hayes
*Ch Bd: Joel Peterson
V Ch: Frank V Sica
CFO: Mark D Powers
*V Ch Bd: Frank Sica
Bd of Dir: Bret Anthony
Ex VP: James Hnat
Ex VP: Thomas Lenahan
Ex VP: John Owen
Sr VP: Warren Christie
Sr VP: Mike Elliott
Sr VP: Scott Laurence
Sr VP: Martin St George
Sr VP: Marty St George
VP: Dave Bushy
VP: David Campbell
VP: Alexander Chatkewitz
VP: David Clark
VP: Glenn Cusano
VP: Ian Deason
VP: Donna Draghi-Lemay
Board of Directors: Jens Bischof, Peter Boneparth, David Checketts, Virginia Gambale, Stephan Gemkow, Ellen Jewett, Stanley McChrystal, Ann Rhoades, Thomas Winkelmann

D-U-N-S 06-926-8340
JETCARS INC (VA)
ALEXANDRIA TOYOTA SCION
3750 Jefferson Davis Hwy, Alexandria, VA 22305-3104
Tel (703) 684-0700 Founded/Ownrshp 1973
Sales 56.3MM^E EMP 180
SIC 5511 Automobiles, new & used; Automobiles, new & used
Pr: John E Taylor Jr
*Treas: Jenny Kichinko
*VP: Jeffrey G Falton
Genl Mgr: Jeff Salton
Sls Mgr: Will Boyd
Sls Mgr: Michael Nguyen

D-U-N-S 08-836-4948
JETCO DELIVERY LLC (TX)
3010 Aldine Bender Rd, Houston, TX 77032-3506
Tel (713) 676-1111 Founded/Ownrshp 1976
Sales 33.8MM^E EMP 125
SIC 4214 Local trucking with storage
Pr: Brian Fielkow
*CFO: Kyle Kristynik
*VP: Russell V Mattern
*VP: Steve Zold
Opers Mgr: Matt Sorrentino
Mktg Dir: Lisa Sursavage

D-U-N-S 02-414-8751
JETCORP TECHNICAL SERVICES INC (MO)
657 N Bell Ave Ste 200, Chesterfield, MO 63005-3642
Tel (636) 530-7000 Founded/Ownrshp 1981, 2009
Sales 22.9MM^E EMP 100
SIC 4522 7699 5599 5172 4581 Flying charter service; Aircraft & heavy equipment repair services; Aircraft dealers; Aircraft fueling services; Airport hangar rental
CEO: John Gillespie
*CFO: Sean Gillespie
*Ex VP: Eric Gillespie

VP: Troy Funk
VP: Paul Heaver
QA Dir: Vic Valdes
Dir IT: Gary Peel
IT Man: Mike Machaud
Mktg Dir: Jim McDonough
Sls Dir: Rob Gillen

D-U-N-S 01-110-2926
JETION SOLAR (US) CORP
224 Misty Dawn Ln, Charlotte, NC 28270-0914
Tel (704) 944-1069 Founded/Ownrshp 2010
Sales 50.0MM EMP 3
SIC 5074 Heating equipment & panels, solar; Heating equipment & panels, solar
Pr: Juergen Fehr
Sls Mgr: Pete Page

JETLINE
See JET LINE PRODUCTS INC

D-U-N-S 07-929-0856
JETMORE WIND LLC
15445 Innovation Dr, San Diego, CA 92128-3432
Tel (888) 903-6926 Founded/Ownrshp 2013
Sales 215.2MM^E EMP 826
SIC 4911 Electric services; Electric services
Pr: Tristan Grimbert
VP: Ryan Pfaff

D-U-N-S 12-220-0355
JETOBRA INC
HOFFMAN ENTERPRISES
700 Connecticut Blvd, East Hartford, CT 06108-3222
Tel (860) 528-4811 Founded/Ownrshp 1979
Sales 121.3MM^E EMP 310^E
SIC 5511 New & used car dealers; New & used car dealers
Ch: Jeffrey S Hoffman
COO: Kevin Warriner
CFO: Dennis Zelesky
*Ch: Bradley Hoffman
*Sec: Phyllis B Keyes
*VP: Matthew Hoffman
Off Mgr: Tina Stoddard
Sales Asso: Cherif Diouf
Sales Asso: Charles Hartley
Sales Asso: T J Kudla
Sales Asso: Steve Steller

D-U-N-S 96-738-1547
▲ JETPAY CORP
1175 Lancaster Ave # 200, Berwyn, PA 19312-1297
Tel (484) 324-7980 Founded/Ownrshp 2012
Sales 33.4MM EMP 199^E
Tkr Sym JTPY Exch NAS
SIC 7389 Credit card service; Credit card service
Ch Bd: Bipin C Shah
CFO: Gregory M Krzemien
Ex VP: Jeffrey S Tourek
Sr VP: Jeffry A Beene

JETRO CASH & CARRY
See JETRO CASH AND CARRY ENTERPRISES LLC

JETRO CASH & CARRY
See JETRO CASH AND CARRY ENTERPRISES OF FLORIDA INC

JETRO CASH & CARRY
See JETRO HOLDINGS LLC

D-U-N-S 04-007-5780 IMP/EXP
JETRO CASH AND CARRY ENTERPRISES LLC
JETRO CASH & CARRY
(Suby of JRD HOLDINGS INC) ★
1524 132nd St, College Point, NY 11356-2440
Tel (718) 939-6400 Founded/Ownrshp 1990
Sales 1.8MMM^E EMP 1,000
SIC 5142 5046 5181 5147 5411 Packaged frozen goods; Restaurant equipment & supplies; Beer & other fermented malt liquors; Meats, fresh; Grocery stores; Packaged frozen goods; Restaurant equipment & supplies; Beer & other fermented malt liquors; Meats, fresh; Grocery stores
CEO: Stanley Fleishman
COO: Richard Kirschner
Sr Cor Off: Roger Chavez
VP: Peter Claro
*VP: Richard Kirshner
VP: Clark Pager
Exec: Betty Boyle
Brnch Mgr: Enrique Gallard
Dir IT: Roy Romano
Trfc Dir: Ellen Papakonstantis
Opers Mgr: Gene Casazza

D-U-N-S 08-019-6017 EXP
JETRO CASH AND CARRY ENTERPRISES OF FLORIDA INC
JETRO CASH & CARRY
(Suby of JETRO CASH & CARRY) ★
2041 Nw 12th Ave, Miami, FL 33127-4505
Tel (305) 326-0409 Founded/Ownrshp 1985
Sales 27.7MM^E EMP 110
SIC 5141 5194 5147 5142 Groceries, general line; Tobacco & tobacco products; Meats, fresh; Packaged frozen goods; Groceries, general line; Tobacco & tobacco products; Meats, fresh; Packaged frozen goods
Pr: Stanley Fleishman
*CFO: Brian Emert
CFO: Brian Emmert
*VP: Richard Kirschner
*VP: Morris Lebowitz
*VP: Samuel Rubanenko
IT Man: Omer Dalama

D-U-N-S 96-561-1648 EXP
JETRO HOLDINGS LLC
JETRO CASH & CARRY
1506 132nd St, Flushing, NY 11356-2440
Tel (718) 939-6400 Founded/Ownrshp 1976
Sales 4.3MMM^E EMP 5,000
SIC 5149 5141 5812 Organic & diet foods; Diet foods; Health foods; Groceries, general line; Caterers; Organic & diet foods; Diet foods; Health foods; Groceries, general line; Caterers
*Mng Pt: Glenn Fleischman

CFO: Brian Emmert
Mktg Dir: Jack Sagen

JETS GLOVE MANUFACTURING
See EBINGER MANUFACTURING CO

D-U-N-S 03-010-1682
JETSCAPE INC (FL)
10 S New River Dr E # 200, Fort Lauderdale, FL 33301-2810
Tel (904) 437-4804 *Founded/Ownrshp* 2000, 2008
Sales NA *EMP* 19E
SIC 6159 Equipment & vehicle finance leasing companies; Equipment & vehicle finance leasing companies
Pr: John Evans
CFO: Alan Stanford
VP: Mark Balentine
VP: Stefan K Geman
VP: Ewen Mathieson
VP: Goran Miorner
VP: G Ran Ml Rner
Ex Dir: Mario Sch Ler
Off Mgr: Tracy Skinner
VP Mktg: Michael Davis
VP Legal: Malin P Lsson

JETSON TELEVISION AND APPL CTR
See JETSON TV & APPLIANCE CENTERS INC

D-U-N-S 03-268-0951 EXP
JETSON TV & APPLIANCE CENTERS INC (FL)
JETSON TELEVISION AND APPL CTR
4145 S Us Highway 1, Fort Pierce, FL 34982-6901
Tel (772) 464-7050 *Founded/Ownrshp* 1974
Sales 23.3MME *EMP* 125
SIC 5722 5731

D-U-N-S 13-693-6015
JETSTREAM GROUND SERVICES INC
1070 E Indiantown Rd # 400, Jupiter, FL 33477-5150
Tel (561) 746-3282 *Founded/Ownrshp* 1996
Sales 73.2MME *EMP* 800E
SIC 4581 4111 7349 Airport terminal services; Airfreight loading & unloading services; Airport transportation services, regular route; Janitorial service, contract basis; Airport terminal services; Airfreight loading & unloading services; Airport transportation services, regular route; Janitorial service, contract basis
Pr: Marc J Desnoyers
**CFO:* Georgianne S Graves
**VP:* David M Norris
Comm Man: Teresa Tucker

D-U-N-S 06-418-3608
JETSTREAM XPRESS LLC
Oakhurst Pl Ste 1a, Columbia, SC 29223
Tel (803) 667-4609 *Founded/Ownrshp* 2012
Sales 68.0MM *EMP* 6
SIC 4731 Freight transportation arrangement; Freight transportation arrangement

D-U-N-S 83-068-0521
JETSUITE INC
18952 Macarthur Blvd # 200, Irvine, CA 92612-1401
Tel (949) 892-4300 *Founded/Ownrshp* 2007
Sales 35.7MME *EMP* 170
SIC 4522 Air transportation, nonscheduled; Air transportation, nonscheduled
CEO: Alex Wilcox
**CFO:* Keith Rabin
Ofcr: Daryl Wadsworth
**Sr VP:* Chuck Stumpf
**VP:* Frank Buratti
**VP:* Brian Coulter
VP: Michelle Luedtke
**VP:* Dave Myrick
Area Mgr: Simon Stokes
Sfty Mgr: Robert Hamel
Opers Mgr: Lisa Hastert

D-U-N-S 00-317-9082
JETT AND CO
JECTO
260 Picketts Line, Newport News, VA 23603-1366
Tel (757) 887-0856 *Founded/Ownrshp* 1953
Sales 22.1MME *EMP* 30
SIC 5169 Concrete additives; Industrial gases
CEO: Page Jett
**Ch Bd:* Archie L Jett Jr
**Pr:* Page A Jett
**VP:* Judy Jorgensen

D-U-N-S 96-490-2394
JETT INDUSTRIES INC
(*Suby of* KIEWIT INFRASTRUCTURE CO) ★
121 Willow Ln, Colliersville, NY 13747
Tel (607) 433-2100 *Founded/Ownrshp* 2008
Sales 158.5MME *EMP* 3,773E
SIC 1611 1623 Highway & street construction; Water & sewer line construction
Pr: Matthew P Centofante
**Treas:* Stephen S Thomas
**VP:* Daniel L Dubois
**VP:* Michael J Piechoski
**VP:* Scott A Schmidt
**VP:* Daniel A Shults
Genl Mgr: Brian Vanderwerker
Snr Mgr: Luke Spencer

D-U-N-S 83-012-4330
JETTA OPERATING CO INC
777 Taylor St Ste P1, Fort Worth, TX 76102-4919
Tel (817) 335-1179 *Founded/Ownrshp* 1998
Sales 50.0MME *EMP* 70E
SIC 1382 Oil & gas exploration services
Pr: Gregory A Bird
COO: Carla Koehler
**CFO:* John Jarrett
**VP:* Jeanette Clark
**VP:* Richard Cornelius
VP: Bill Monroe
**VP:* David Patterson
VP: Kurt Pizalate
**VP:* Michael Richardson
IT Man: Teresa Angel
VP Opers: Joe Wynn

JETTY RESTAURANT
See MILT GUGGIA ENTERPRISES INC

JEUNESSE GLOBAL
See JEUNESSE LLC

D-U-N-S 07-839-6625
JEUNESSE GLOBAL HOLDINGS LLC
(*Suby of* JEUNESSE GLOBAL) ★
650 Douglas Ave Ste 1020, Altamonte Springs, FL 32714-2554
Tel (407) 215-7414 *Founded/Ownrshp* 2010
Sales 94.0MME *EMP* 402E
SIC 5999 Toilet preparations

D-U-N-S 02-729-6810
JEUNESSE LLC
JEUNESSE GLOBAL
650 Douglas Ave Ste 1020, Altamonte Springs, FL 32714-2554
Tel (321) 275-7171 *Founded/Ownrshp* 2009
Sales 951.0M *EMP* 407E
Accts Stevenson Smith Cpa S Llc Pro
SIC 5999 Toilet preparations
CEO: Randy Ray
**COO:* Wendy Lewis
CFO: Ryan Ogden
Chf Mktg O: Mark Patterson
Exec: Darren Jensen
Creative D: Vivian Lund
Genl Mgr: Sergio Carrasco
Genl Mgr: Vlad Hadji
Genl Mgr: Lital Shalev
Snr Mgr: Scott Lewis

D-U-N-S 00-285-4370 IMP
JEUNIQUE INTERNATIONAL INC
BY KIMBERLY
(*Suby of* CLEARTREE BRANDS, LLC)
900 Glenneyre St, Laguna Beach, CA 92651-2707
Tel (909) 598-8598 *Founded/Ownrshp* 1960
Sales 16.5MME *EMP* 300
SIC 2833 2342 2844 3961 2834 2339 Vitamins, natural or synthetic: bulk, uncompounded; Foundation garments, women's; Toilet preparations; Costume jewelry; Pharmaceutical preparations; Women's & misses' outerwear; Vitamins, natural or synthetic: bulk, uncompounded; Foundation garments, women's; Toilet preparations; Costume jewelry; Pharmaceutical preparations; Women's & misses' outerwear
Pr: Mulford J Nobbs

D-U-N-S 07-144-9078
JEVIC TRANSPORTATION INC (NJ)
(*Suby of* SUN CAPITAL PARTNERS INC) ★
1540 E Dundee Rd Ste 240, Palatine, IL 60074-8320
Tel (856) 764-1909 *Founded/Ownrshp* 1968, 2006
Sales 51.9MME *EMP* 1,100
SIC 4213 Contract haulers; Contract haulers
Pr: David Gorman
Sr VP: Raymond Conlin
Sr VP: Joe Librizzi
VP: Dennis Ungrady

D-U-N-S 07-376-3450
JEVS HUMAN SERVICES
VOCATIONAL RESEARCH INSTITUTE
1845 Walnut St Ste 700, Philadelphia, PA 19103-4713
Tel (215) 875-7387 *Founded/Ownrshp* 1941
Sales 54.1MM *EMP* 1,000
Accts Grant Thornton Llp Philadelph
SIC 8322 8331 Substance abuse counseling; Vocational rehabilitation agency; Substance abuse counseling; Vocational rehabilitation agency
Pr: Jay Spector
CFO: Bruce Fishberg
VP: Francis Kardos
Exec: Hugh Simmons
QA Dir: Adriana Padilla
IT Man: Debbie Bello
Pgrm Dir: Sharon Rosenberg
Snr Mgr: Jayne Siniari

D-U-N-S 17-078-0444 IMP
■ **JEWEL ACQUISITION LLC**
ATI FLAT ROLLED PRODUCTS
(*Suby of* ALLEGHENY LUDLUM LLC) ★
1000 Six Ppg Pl, Pittsburgh, PA 15222
Tel (412) 394-2800 *Founded/Ownrshp* 2004
Sales 30.8MME *EMP* 436E
SIC 3312 3471 3398 3316 Blast furnaces & steel mills; Plating & polishing; Metal heat treating; Cold finishing of steel shapes
Prin: Terry Dunlap
Bd of Dir: Craig McClelland
Ex VP: Jack Shilling
Prin: JD Walton
Mng Dir: Richard Wright

D-U-N-S 00-119-9157 IMP
JEWEL CASE CORP (RI)
110 Dupont Dr, Providence, RI 02907-3181
Tel (401) 943-1400 *Founded/Ownrshp* 1950, 1987
Sales 44.3MME *EMP* 300
SIC 3499 3172 2631 2671 Boxes for packing & shipping, metal; Cases, jewelry; Cardboard; Packaging paper & plastics film, coated & laminated; Boxes for packing & shipping, metal; Cases, jewelry; Cardboard; Packaging paper & plastics film, coated & laminated
Pr: Therese Eisen
Dir IT: John Tamburro
Opers Mgr: Ed Giglio
Prd Mgr: Sergio Spaziano
Sls Mgr: Frank McKinnon
Sls Mgr: Ken Sabbagh
Board of Directors: John Tamburro

D-U-N-S 00-171-3544
JEWEL ELECTRIC SUPPLY CO (NJ)
455 3rd St, Jersey City, NJ 07302-2223
Tel (201) 653-1613 *Founded/Ownrshp* 1929
Sales 31.2MME *EMP* 35
SIC 5063 Electrical apparatus & equipment
Pr: Herbert Goldman
**VP:* Lawrence Goldman

D-U-N-S 15-424-1116 EXP
JEWEL MARKETING & AGRIBUSINESS LLC
CROWN JWL MKTG & AGRIBUSINESS
423 W Fallbrook Ave Ste 2, Fresno, CA 93711-6138
Tel (559) 438-2335 *Founded/Ownrshp* 1999
Sales 22.2MME *EMP* 33E
SIC 5148 Fresh fruits & vegetables
Genl Mgr: Jesus Gonzales
Sls Mgr: Luis Corella

D-U-N-S 00-506-8630
JEWEL OSCO INC
(*Suby of* ACME) ★
150 E Pierce Rd Ste 200, Itasca, IL 60143-1224
Tel (630) 948-6000 *Founded/Ownrshp* 1899, 2006
Sales 2.1MMME *EMP* 30,000
SIC 5411 2834 Supermarkets, chain; Proprietary drug products; Supermarkets, chain; Proprietary drug products
Pr: Shane Sampson
**Pr:* Mike Withers
Treas: John F Boyd
**Treas:* Thomas P Heneghan
Sr VP: Gerald D Bay
Sr VP: Sherry M Smith
VP: Stephen C Bowater
VP: Gregory E Gullickson
VP: Robert L Hughes
VP: Linda K Massman
VP: Ronald T Mendes
VP: John C Owen
VP: Jeffrey Peszek
VP: Thomas S Rousonelos
VP: Thomas J Walter
VP: Roy C Whitmore
Board of Directors: Jonathan L Scott, Alan D Stewart

D-U-N-S 00-301-1160
JEWEL VALLORBS CO (PA)
(*Suby of* VALCO COMPANIES INC) ★
2599 Old Phladelphia Pike, Bird In Hand, PA 17505-9797
Tel (717) 392-3978 *Founded/Ownrshp* 1934
Sales 22.9MME *EMP* 160
SIC 3451 3568 3541 3471 3366 Screw machine products; Power transmission equipment; Machine tools, metal cutting type; Plating & polishing; Copper foundries; Screw machine products; Power transmission equipment; Machine tools, metal cutting type; Plating & polishing; Copper foundries
Pr: Jeanette Steudler
**VP:* Frederick W Steudler Jr
**VP:* Richard Steudler

JEWEL-OSCO
See NEW ALBERTSONS INC

D-U-N-S 08-302-2012
JEWELERS INC
JEWELERS OF LAS VEGAS, THE
2400 Western Ave, Las Vegas, NV 89102-4880
Tel (702) 382-7411 *Founded/Ownrshp* 1974
Sales 30.4MME *EMP* 200
SIC 5944 3911 Jewelry, precious stones & precious metals; Watches; Jewel settings & mountings, precious metal; Pearl jewelry, natural or cultured; Necklaces, precious metal; Jewelry, precious stones & precious metals; Watches; Jewel settings & mountings, precious metal; Pearl jewelry, natural or cultured; Necklaces, precious metal
Pr: Mordichai Yerushalmi
**Sec:* Victoria Yerushalmi
Dist Mgr: Brenda Gullo
IT Man: Ben Yerushalmi
VP Mktg: Natalie Yerushalmi

D-U-N-S 00-643-6133
JEWELERS MUTUAL INSURANCE CO (WI)
24 Jewelers Park Dr, Neenah, WI 54956-3703
Tel (800) 558-6411 *Founded/Ownrshp* 1913
Sales NA *EMP* 160
SIC 6331 Fire, marine & casualty insurance: mutual; Fire, marine & casualty insurance: mutual
CEO: Darwin Copeman
CFO: Paul Fuhrman
Treas: Kelly Kinas
Sr VP: Tim Riedl
VP: Jared Ashland
VP: Patrick Drummond
VP: Chris Hartrich
Mktg Mgr: Sam Tassoul
Manager: Andy Kretsch
Manager: Tammy Shaffer

JEWELERS OF LAS VEGAS, THE
See JEWELERS INC

JEWELERY MARKETING COMPANY
See DIAMLINK INC

D-U-N-S 04-321-1838 IMP
JEWELL INSTRUMENTS LLC
MODUTEC
850 Perimeter Rd, Manchester, NH 03103-3324
Tel (603) 669-5121 *Founded/Ownrshp* 1938, 2000
Sales 29.7MME *EMP* 220
SIC 3823 Industrial instrmnts msrmnt display/control process variable; Industrial instrmnts msrmnt display/control process variable
**CFO:* Stephen P Morin
VP: Jewell Hires
Dir Bus: Brian Ward
Sftwr Eng: Steve Key
Mfg Dir: Dan Connell

D-U-N-S 18-689-5066
■ **JEWELL RESOURCES CORP**
(*Suby of* SUNCOKE ENERGY INC) ★
1011 Warrenville Rd # 600, Lisle, IL 60532-0903
Tel (276) 935-8810 *Founded/Ownrshp* 1993
Sales 56.7MME *EMP* 610
SIC 1222 Bituminous coal-underground mining; Bituminous coal-underground mining
Pr: Charles Ellis
Treas: Jack Allison

D-U-N-S 06-318-7926
■ **JEWELL SMOKELESS COAL CORP** (VA)
(*Suby of* JEWELL RESOURCES CORP) ★
1029 Miners Rd, Oakwood, VA 24631-8926
Tel (276) 935-8810 *Founded/Ownrshp* 1971, 1979
Sales 37.5MME *EMP* 190
SIC 1222 Bituminous coal-underground mining; Bituminous coal-underground mining
Pr: Denise R Cade
Pr: Michael J Thomson
CFO: Dennis B Taylor
Treas: Earl Humber

D-U-N-S 79-457-3006
JEWELMAK INC
344 E 59th St Fl 1&2, New York, NY 10022-1593
Tel (212) 398-2999 *Founded/Ownrshp* 1992
Sales 35.0MM *EMP* 25
SIC 3911 Jewelry, precious metal; Jewelry, precious metal
Pr: Andy Goetz
**VP:* Vincent Carotenuto

JEWELRY AND HANDBANG WAREHOUSE
See TREES N TRENDS INC

D-U-N-S 79-252-8304 IMP
JEWELRY CHANNEL INC
LIQUIDATION CHANNEL
100 Michael Angelo Way # 400, Austin, TX 78728-1281
Tel (512) 852-7000 *Founded/Ownrshp* 2007
Sales 71.8MME *EMP* 520
SIC 5944 Jewelry stores; Jewelry stores
CEO: Sunil Agrawal
**Pr:* Gerald Tempton
Ofcr: Shannon Becton
**Prin:* Sharon Kincaid
**Prin:* Reeta Sharma
Board of Directors: Suresh Punjabi

JEWELRY EXCHANGE, THE
See DIAMOND GOLDENWEST CORP

JEWELS AND LITTLE SWITZERLAND
See LS HOLDING INC

D-U-N-S 05-434-1391 IMP
JEWELS BY PARK LANE INC (IL)
JEWELS BY PARKLANE
100 Commerce Dr, Schaumburg, IL 60173-5324
Tel (847) 884-9999 *Founded/Ownrshp* 1955
Sales 31.6MME *EMP* 200
SIC 5963 Party-plan merchandising; Party-plan merchandising
Pr: Arthur Levin
**Sec:* Shirley Levin
**VP:* Raymond Levin
**VP:* Donald Rischow
Brnch Mgr: Ellen Levinas
Genl Mgr: Paula Magaw
Natl Sales: Tara Levin

JEWELS BY PARKLANE
See JEWELS BY PARK LANE INC

D-U-N-S 09-891-9079
JEWETT ORTHOPAEDIC CLINIC LLC
1285 Orange Ave, Winter Park, FL 32789-4984
Tel (407) 647-2287 *Founded/Ownrshp* 1970
Sales 20.2MME *EMP* 145
SIC 8011 Orthopedic physician
Pr: John W McCutchen MD
CFO: Martha Harriman
VP: Brenda Harlan
**VP:* Gregory Munson
Dept Mgr: Timothy Black
IT Man: Hugh Morris
Surgeon: Joe Billings
Surgeon: Steven Choung
Surgeon: Kurt Gasner
Doctor: Brian Barnard
Doctor: John Chase

D-U-N-S 11-874-5363 IMP
JEWETT-CAMERON LUMBER CORP
32275 Nw Hillcrest St, North Plains, OR 97133-8167
Tel (503) 647-0110 *Founded/Ownrshp* 1985
Sales 33.0MM *EMP* 45
SIC 5031 5039 Lumber, plywood & millwork; Fencing, wood; Metal guardrails
Pr: Donald M Boone

D-U-N-S 82-681-0173 IMP/EXP
▲ **JEWETT-CAMERON TRADING CO LTD**
32275 Nw Hillcrest St, North Plains, OR 97133-8167
Tel (503) 647-0110 *Founded/Ownrshp* 1987
Sales 42.2MM *EMP* 52E
Accts Davidson & Company Llp Vancou
Tkr Sym JCTCF *Exch* NAS
SIC 5211 5153 5072 Lumber & other building materials; Grain & field beans; Hardware; Lumber & other building materials; Grain & field beans; Hardware
Pr: Donald M Boone

JEWISH AGENCY FOR ISRAEL, THE
See JEWISH AGENCY FOR ISRAEL INC

D-U-N-S 06-120-3865
JEWISH AGENCY FOR ISRAEL INC
JEWISH AGENCY FOR ISRAEL, THE
111 8th Ave Fl 11, New York, NY 10011-5211
Tel (212) 284-6900 *Founded/Ownrshp* 1927
Sales 193.1MM *EMP* 6
Accts Loeb & Troper Llp New York N
SIC 8399 Fund raising organization, non-fee basis; Fund raising organization, non-fee basis
Ch Bd: Jane Sherman
CFO: Didi Latina
**V Ch Bd:* Alan Shulman

JEWISH ASSN SVC THE AGING JASA
See JEWISH ASSOCIATION FOR SERVICES FOR AGED

D-U-N-S 04-007-4445
JEWISH ASSOCIATION FOR SERVICES FOR AGED
JEWISH ASSN SVC THE AGING JASA
247 W 37th St Fl 9, New York, NY 10018-5193
Tel (212) 273-5300 *Founded/Ownrshp* 1968

Sales 40.0MM *EMP* 400
Accts Dorfman Abrams Music Llc Sad
SIC 8322 Senior citizens' center or association; Senior citizens' center or association
CEO: Kathryn Haslanger
CFO: Don Flamm
Bd of Dir: Aileen Hefferren

D-U-N-S 94-034-9418
JEWISH ASSOCIATION ON AGING
200 Jhf Dr, Pittsburgh, PA 15217-2950
Tel (412) 420-4000 *Founded/Ownrshp* 1993
Sales 10.7MM *EMP* 450
Accts Carbis Walker Llp Pittsburgh
SIC 8051 8052 Skilled nursing care facilities; Personal care facility; Skilled nursing care facilities; Personal care facility
CEO: Deborah Winn Horvitz
Dir Vol: Sharyn Rubin
**Ch Bd:* Douglas Ostrow
**COO:* David Gritzer
CFO: Jeff Carraway
**CFO:* Mark Celigoi
**Ch:* Steve Halpern
**Treas:* Mitchell Pakler
Ofcr: Jerry Pannell
Dir IT: Bethann Casar
Dir IT: Norman Keane

JEWISH ASSOCIATION SERVING THE
See JASA

D-U-N-S 07-103-7543
JEWISH BOARD OF FAMILY AND CHILDRENS SERVICES INC (NY)
JBFCS
135 W 50th St Fl 6, New York, NY 10020-1201
Tel (212) 582-9100 *Founded/Ownrshp* 1893
Sales 170.0MM^E *EMP* 2,000
Accts Loeb & Troper Llp New York N
SIC 8361 8322 Home for the emotionally disturbed; Individual & family services; Home for the emotionally disturbed; Individual & family services
CEO: David Rivel
**Ch Bd:* John Herman
**Pr:* Anthony E Mann
CFO: Ronald Ackler
CFO: Helene Stone
**Ch:* Roger A Goldman
**Ch:* Joseph Kaplan
**Ch:* Jean L Troubh
Ex VP: Paul Levine
Ex VP: Leonardo Rodriguez
**VP:* Lynn Korda Korll
Exec: Sarah Ferraro
Assoc Dir: Reginald Fuller

D-U-N-S 07-401-6296
JEWISH CENTER OF GREATER BUFFALO INC
2640 N Forest Rd Ste 400, Getzville, NY 14068-1573
Tel (716) 688-4033 *Founded/Ownrshp* 1893
Sales 7.7MM *EMP* 300
SIC 8322 Social service center; Social service center
Ex Dir: Alan Fredan
Genl Mgr: Ann Vorburger

D-U-N-S 07-686-4891 IMP
JEWISH CHILD AND FAMILY SERVICES
JEWISH CHILDREN'S BUREAU
216 W Jackson Blvd # 800, Chicago, IL 60606-6920
Tel (312) 673-2753 *Founded/Ownrshp* 1893
Sales 29.1MM *EMP* 500
Accts Mcgladrey Llp Chicago Il
SIC 8322 Child related social services; Child related social services
**CFO:* Julia Mellow
CFO: Toni Myckowiak
Off Mgr: Belinda Breytenbach
Opers Supe: Becky Feiler
Opers Supe: Hillery Morris
Opers Supe: Michelle Paris
Mktg Dir: Deanna Shoss
Mktg Dir: Elizabeth Taggart
Snr Mgr: Elizabeth Wyman

D-U-N-S 07-684-9124
JEWISH CHILD CARE ASSOCIATION OF NEW YORK
858 E 29th St, Brooklyn, NY 11210-2927
Tel (917) 808-4800 *Founded/Ownrshp* 1822
Sales 100.0MM *EMP* 950
SIC 8361 8399 Group foster home; Social service information exchange; Group foster home; Social service information exchange
CEO: Ronald E Richter
**Ch Bd:* Barbara Mann
**Pr:* Peter Hauspurg
**COO:* Michael Spindler
**Sr VP:* Mark Edelman
Sr VP: Foster Home
**VP:* Robert Cizma
**VP:* Jeff Dube
VP: Elizabeth Schnur
**VP:* Paul Torres
Brnch Mgr: Peter Gioiella

JEWISH CHILDREN'S BUREAU
See JEWISH CHILD AND FAMILY SERVICES

JEWISH CMNTY RELATIONS COUNCIL
See JEWISH COMMUNITY FEDERATION OF GREATER EAST BAY

JEWISH COM CTR OF GTR PITTSBRG
See YOUNG MEN & WOMENS HEBREW ASSN & IRENE KAUFMANN CENTERS

D-U-N-S 02-127-0905
JEWISH COMMUNAL FUND
575 Madison Ave Ste 703, New York, NY 10022-8591
Tel (212) 752-8277 *Founded/Ownrshp* 1972
Sales 390.1MM *EMP* 14
Accts Eisneramper Llp New York Ny
SIC 6732 Charitable trust management; Charitable trust management
Pr: Harold R Handler
**Sr VP:* Jose Virella
**VP:* Susan F Dickman
VP: Ellen Israelson
VP: Marc Warren
VP Admn: Jane Fraleigh

JEWISH COMMUNITY CARE AT HOME
See JEWISH FAMILY SERVICE ASSOCIATION OF CLEVELAND OHIO

D-U-N-S 07-713-4336
JEWISH COMMUNITY CENTER
J C C
2 Millstone Campus Dr, Saint Louis, MO 63146-5776
Tel (314) 432-5700 *Founded/Ownrshp* 1880
Sales 59.1MM *EMP* 175
Accts Larsonallen Llp St Louis Mo
SIC 8641 Civic social & fraternal associations
Pr: Lynn Wittels
CFO: Steven Rosenzweig
**CFO:* Steven Rosenzweiz
**Ex VP:* Stan Ferdman
Mng Dir: Michelle Almengor
Mktg Mgr: Ben Sandmel
Art Dir: Kathleen Sitzer

D-U-N-S 92-761-6912
JEWISH COMMUNITY CENTER IN MANHATTAN INC
JCC IN MANHATTAN
334 Amsterdam Ave, New York, NY 10023-8205
Tel (646) 505-4497 *Founded/Ownrshp* 1988
Sales 29.8MM *EMP* 170
Accts Baker Tilly Virchow Krause Ll
SIC 8322 Community center; Community center
Pr: Andy Arno
**Ch Bd:* Steven Roppoport
**Pr:* Marti Meyerson
**CFO:* Hillel Hyman
**Treas:* Halle Benett
Assoc Dir: Joan Linder
**Ex Dir:* Joy Levitt
Dir Sec: Eulalio Deleon
CTO: Miriam Leviton
Dir IT: Randi Klein
Dir IT: Sarah Lacks

D-U-N-S 03-082-7752
JEWISH COMMUNITY CENTER OF GREATER BOSTON INC
333 Nahanton St Ste 9, Newton, MA 02459-3213
Tel (617) 558-6000 *Founded/Ownrshp* 1963
Sales 11.1MM^E *EMP* 600
Accts Tonneson & Company Cpas Pc Wa
SIC 8641 Community membership club; Community membership club
Ex Dir: Mark Sokoll
Sr Cor Off: Michael Herman
Sr Cor Off: Larry Kranseler
**Ex Dir:* Mark Slocum

D-U-N-S 07-304-3986
JEWISH COMMUNITY CENTER OF GREATER KANSAS CITY
5801 W 115th St Ste 101, Shawnee Mission, KS 66211-1800
Tel (913) 327-8000 *Founded/Ownrshp* 1935
Sales 9.2MM *EMP* 300
Accts Bkd Llp Kansas City Mo
SIC 8641 8351 8322 7991 Social club, membership; Child day care services; Individual & family services; Physical fitness facilities; Social club, membership; Child day care services; Individual & family services; Physical fitness facilities
Ex Dir: Jacob Shreiber
Dir IT: Adam Safran

D-U-N-S 07-265-9097
JEWISH COMMUNITY CENTER OF GREATER WASHINGTON INC (DC)
6125 Montrose Rd, Rockville, MD 20852-4857
Tel (301) 881-0100 *Founded/Ownrshp* 1923
Sales 13.6MM *EMP* 285
Accts Raffa Pc Washington Dc
SIC 8641 Social club, membership; Social club, membership
Pr: Michael Feinstein
CFO: Ruth Carski

D-U-N-S 07-636-2219
JEWISH COMMUNITY CENTER OF METROPOLITAN DETROIT
JCC THE CENTER
6600 W Maple Rd, West Bloomfield, MI 48322-3003
Tel (248) 661-1000 *Founded/Ownrshp* 1977
Sales 17.4MM *EMP* 350^E
Accts Financial One Accounting Inc
SIC 8322 Community center; Community center
Ch Bd: Brian D Siegel
**Pr:* Florine Mark
**VP:* Ilana Glazier
**VP:* Steve Lefkofsky
**VP:* Eric Lumberg
Ex Dir: James Issner
**Ex Dir:* Mark Lit

D-U-N-S 00-792-2650
JEWISH COMMUNITY CENTER OF METROWEST INC
JCC METROWEST
760 Northfield Ave, West Orange, NJ 07052-1102
Tel (973) 530-3400 *Founded/Ownrshp* 1877, 2007
Sales 23.6MM *EMP* 300
Accts Withumsmithbrown Pc New Bruns
SIC 7991 8211 8351 Health club; Kindergarten; Child day care services; Health club; Kindergarten; Child day care services
CEO: Alan Feldman
**VP:* Jennifer Helprin

D-U-N-S 07-382-7776
JEWISH COMMUNITY CENTER OF NORTH SHORE INC
4 Community Rd Ste 1, Marblehead, MA 01945-2766
Tel (781) 631-8330 *Founded/Ownrshp* 1911
Sales 4.5MM *EMP* 423
Accts O Connor & Drew Pc Braintree
SIC 8322 Community center; Community center
Treas: David Kasoff
Treas: Shepard M Remis
Ex Dir: Perry Frankston

D-U-N-S 07-465-4930
JEWISH COMMUNITY CENTER OF SAN FRANCISCO
3200 California St, San Francisco, CA 94118-1994
Tel (415) 292-1200 *Founded/Ownrshp* 1878
Sales 35.9MM *EMP* 250^E
Accts Hood & Strong Llp San Francis
SIC 8211 7032 8322 Preparatory school; Youth camps; Individual & family services; Preparatory school; Youth camps; Individual & family services
Pr: Barry Finesone
CFO: Diane Walters
Prgrm Mgr: Suman Pangasa
Site Mgr: Kelly Dotson

D-U-N-S 03-031-3092
JEWISH COMMUNITY CENTER OF SOUTHERN NEW JERSEY INC
1301 Springdale Rd, Cherry Hill, NJ 08003-2763
Tel (856) 424-4444 *Founded/Ownrshp* 1960
Sales 7.5MM^E *EMP* 475^E
SIC 8322 8641 8351 7991 Community center; Civic social & fraternal associations; Child day care services; Physical fitness facilities; Community center; Civic social & fraternal associations; Child day care services; Physical fitness facilities
Ex Dir: Les Cohen

D-U-N-S 02-058-4736
JEWISH COMMUNITY CENTER OF STATEN ISLAND INC
J C C
1466 Manor Rd, Staten Island, NY 10314-7027
Tel (718) 475-5290 *Founded/Ownrshp* 1927
Sales 19.8MM *EMP* 325
Accts Potter & Lamarca Llp Staten I
SIC 8322 7999 Community center; Day camp; Community center; Day camp
Ex Dir: David Sorkin
COO: Anita Bruckmeir
Ex Dir: Sheila Lipton

D-U-N-S 07-543-4969
JEWISH COMMUNITY CENTER ON PALISADES
JCC ON THE PALISADES
411 E Clinton Ave, Tenafly, NJ 07670-2319
Tel (201) 569-7900 *Founded/Ownrshp* 1949
Sales 20.0MM *EMP* 500
SIC 8641 8351 8322 Community membership club; Nursery school; Individual & family services; Community membership club; Nursery school; Individual & family services
Ex Dir: AVI Lewinson
**Pr:* Daniel Ruben
Bd of Dir: Mindy Lavin
VP: Tina Guberman
**VP:* Dr Saul Hoffman
**VP:* Nancy I Brown
Creative D: Carol Schulter
Adm Dir: Melissa Peters
Ex Dir: Sharon Kestenbaum
Dir IT: Paul Costa
Mktg Mgr: Larisa Leffel

D-U-N-S 06-948-5787
JEWISH COMMUNITY CENTERS OF CHICAGO
JCC CHICAGO
30 S Wells St Ste 4000, Chicago, IL 60606-5054
Tel (312) 775-1800 *Founded/Ownrshp* 1903
Sales 34.8MM *EMP* 450
Accts Warady & Davis Llp Deerfield
SIC 8322 Community center; Community center
**Pr:* Stuart Hochwert
COO: Todd Braman
CFO: Jerold Wolff
Off Mgr: Charlene Novah

D-U-N-S 04-918-5184
JEWISH COMMUNITY CENTERS OF GREATER BOSTON
JCC CAMP KINGSWOOD
333 Nahanton St Ste 3, Newton, MA 02459-3213
Tel (617) 244-5124 *Founded/Ownrshp* 1955
Sales 23.1MM *EMP* 3
SIC 7032 Recreational camps; Boys' camp; Girls' camp; Recreational camps; Boys' camp; Girls' camp
CEO: Mark Sirkol
**CEO:* Mark Sikol
COO: Betsy Jacobs
**Ch:* Larry Green
**Treas:* Michael Herman
VP: Carol Trager
**Prin:* Linda Brodt
Mktg Mgr: Samantha Levine-Neudel
Pgrm Dir: Lisa Aframe
Pgrm Dir: Sara Kahana

D-U-N-S 07-706-4194
JEWISH COMMUNITY CENTERS OF GREATER PHILADELPHIA
J C C CAMPS
320 S Broad St, Philadelphia, PA 19102-4901
Tel (215) 446-3003 *Founded/Ownrshp* 1875
Sales 1.4MM *EMP* 300
Accts Amper Politziner & Mattia Llp
SIC 8322 Community center; Community center
Pr: Martin J Satinsky
**Treas:* Richard Rosin
**Ex VP:* Edith Kligman
**VP:* Larry Cohan
**VP:* Bernard Glassman
**VP:* Benjamin Goldman
**VP:* Annabel Lindy
**VP:* Gerald Shantzer
MIS Dir: Ron Meltzer

D-U-N-S 07-629-1806
JEWISH COMMUNITY FEDERATION OF GREATER EAST BAY (CA)
JEWISH CMNTY RELATIONS COUNCIL
300 Grand Ave, Oakland, CA 94610-4826
Tel (510) 839-2900 *Founded/Ownrshp* 1910
Sales 3.5MM *EMP* 350
Accts Rina Accountancy Corporation
SIC 8661 Religious organizations; Religious organizations
Ex VP: AMI Nahshon
CFO: Sandra Becker
CFO: Lewis Perryman
Bd of Dir: Howard Kleckner
Assoc Dir: Michelson Abigaail
Ex Dir: Neil Cooper
Off Mgr: Ruth Solom
Pgrm Dir: Loal Isaacs

D-U-N-S 03-098-9701
JEWISH COMMUNITY FEDERATION OF SAN FRANCISCO PENINSULA MARIN & SONOMA COUNTIES
121 Steuart St Fl 7, San Francisco, CA 94105-1280
Tel (415) 777-0411 *Founded/Ownrshp* 1921
Sales 136.0MM *EMP* 110
Accts Rothstein Kass San Francisco
SIC 8399 Fund raising organization, non-fee basis; Fund raising organization, non-fee basis
CEO: Jennifer Gorvitz
**CFO:* Bill Powers
Treas: Nancy Falchuk
VP: Carol Weitz
CIO: Afshin Afshar
IT Man: Kevin Ho
Mktg Dir: Angela Ingel

JEWISH COMMUNITY FOUNDATION
See COMMUNITY FUND OF UNITED JEWISH

D-U-N-S 87-463-0916
JEWISH COMMUNITY FOUNDATION
6505 Wilshire Blvd # 1200, Los Angeles, CA 90048-4906
Tel (323) 761-8700 *Founded/Ownrshp* 1955
Sales 91.3MM *EMP* 26
Accts Ernst & Young Us Llp San Dieg
SIC 8699 Charitable organization; Charitable organization
Pr: Marvin Schotland
COO: Simone Savlov
**CFO:* Steve Shean
Treas: Lorin M Fife
Trst: Bertrand I Gnsberg
Trst: Ronald L Eibow
Trst: Annette Shapiro
Ofcr: Kim Newstadt
Ofcr: Elana Wien
VP: Max Factor III
VP: Elliot Kristal

D-U-N-S 78-944-7534
JEWISH COMMUNITY FOUNDATION OF METROWEST NJ INC
901 State Route 10, Whippany, NJ 07981-1105
Tel (973) 929-3000 *Founded/Ownrshp* 2006
Sales 23.4MM *EMP* 2
Accts Withumsmithbrown Pc New Bruns
SIC 8699 Membership organizations; Membership organizations
CEO: Max L Kleinman

D-U-N-S 01-041-6329
JEWISH COMMUNITY SERVICES OF SOUTH FLORIDA INC
735 Ne 125th St, North Miami, FL 33161-5611
Tel (305) 403-6500 *Founded/Ownrshp* 1958
Sales 14.7MM *EMP* 410
Accts Morrison Brown Argiz & Farra L
SIC 8331 Vocational rehabilitation agency; Vocational rehabilitation agency
Ch: Richard Hoffman
Dir Vol: Barbara Davis
**CEO:* David Saltman
**COO:* Silvia Goldsmith
CFO: Robert Senn
CFO: Martin Weinbaum
**Treas:* Jonathan Raiffe
VP: Ela Goldfarb
Dir IT: Shaikh Ali

D-U-N-S 07-659-7582
JEWISH FAMILY & CHILDRENS SERVICE INC
1430 Main St, Waltham, MA 02451-1623
Tel (617) 227-6641 *Founded/Ownrshp* 1922
Sales 30.4MM *EMP* 400
Accts Rsm Mcgladrey Inc Burlington
SIC 8322 Family (marriage) counseling; Family service agency; General counseling services; Child related social services; Family (marriage) counseling; Family service agency; General counseling services; Child related social services
Ex Dir: Rimma Zelsan
**Pr:* Alan C Dana
**Pr:* John F Levy
CFO: Bruce Haskin
Bd of Dir: Jackie Weinstein
VP: Amy Abrams
Genl Mgr: Judy Engibous
Genl Mgr: Marsha Frankel
Off Mgr: Diana Downey
Off Mgr: Rick Fuchs
CTO: Tom Curtis

D-U-N-S 07-447-3794
JEWISH FAMILY AND CHILDRENS SERVICE INC
JFCS
4747 N 7th St Ste 100, Phoenix, AZ 85014-3654
Tel (602) 279-7655 *Founded/Ownrshp* 1955
Sales 32.4MM *EMP* 390
Accts Cliftonlarsonallen Llp Phoen
SIC 8093 8322 8351 Specialty outpatient clinics; Family (marriage) counseling; Social service center; Child day care services; Specialty outpatient clinics; Family (marriage) counseling; Social service center; Child day care services
Pr: Michael R Zent
**Ch:* Robert Carr
**Ch:* Richard Naimark
**Ch:* Rick Naimark
VP: Linda Scott
VP: Mary Whitfield

Ex Dir: Laura Young
Dir IT: Kevin Rhode
IT Man: Carole Berwald

D-U-N-S 11-386-7873
JEWISH FAMILY AND CHILDRENS SERVICES
CLEANERIFIC
2150 Post St, San Francisco, CA 94115-3508
Tel (415) 449-1200 *Founded/Ownrshp* 1850
Sales 30.5MM *EMP* 500
Accts Good & Fowler Llp South San F
SIC 8322 Family service agency; Family service agency
Ex Dir: Anita Friedman
**CEO:* Michael R Zent
**CFO:* Marga Dusedau
**CFO:* Javier Favela
**VP:* Frank Jacobson
Ex Dir: Gayle Zahler
Off Mgr: Jenni Monnier
Mktg Dir: Christine Coleman

D-U-N-S 14-797-2194
JEWISH FAMILY SERVICE ASSOCIATION OF CLEVELAND OHIO
JEWISH COMMUNITY CARE AT HOME
3659 Green Rd Ste 322, Cleveland, OH 44122-5715
Tel (216) 504-2600 *Founded/Ownrshp* 1907
Sales 21.5MM *EMP* 500
SIC 8322 Family service agency; Family service agency
Pr: Robert Shakno
**CFO:* Patrick Sidley
Prgrm Mgr: Veronica Bellay

D-U-N-S 11-379-9076
JEWISH FAMILY SERVICE OF LOS ANGELES
JEWISH FREE LOAN ASSOCIATION
6505 Wilshire Blvd # 715, Los Angeles, CA 90048-4906
Tel (323) 761-8800 *Founded/Ownrshp* 1919
Sales 36.3MM *EMP* 382
Accts Green Hasson & Janks Llp Los
SIC 8322 Social service center; Social service center
CEO: Paul Castro
COO: Susie Forer-Dehrey
**CFO:* Tran Maggard
Comm Dir: Jennifer Levitt
Ex Dir: Karen Leaf
Ex Dir: Perri Sloane
CTO: Patricia Lynch

JEWISH FEDERATION
See UNITED JEWISH FOUNDATION

D-U-N-S 04-087-6309
JEWISH FEDERATION OF CINCINNATI
8499 Ridge Rd, Cincinnati, OH 45236-1300
Tel (513) 985-1500 *Founded/Ownrshp* 1967
Sales 21.0MM *EMP* 35
Accts Bames Dennig & Co Ltd Cincinn
SIC 8322 Social service center; Social service center
CEO: Shepard Englander
**Pr:* Bret Caller
COO: Dan Fagin
Assoc Dir: Seth Harlan
Assoc Dir: Gal Spinrad
Ex Dir: Sarah Weiss
Mktg Dir: Pam Geller

D-U-N-S 09-328-4578
JEWISH FEDERATION OF CLEVELAND
25701 Science Park Dr, Cleveland, OH 44122-7302
Tel (216) 593-2900 *Founded/Ownrshp* 1903
Sales 69.5MM *EMP* 130
Accts Ss&G Inc Solon Oh
SIC 8399 Fund raising organization, non-fee basis; Fund raising organization, non-fee basis
Pr: Steve Hoffman
**Ex VP:* Joel Fox
Sr VP: Barry Reis
VP: Cathy Weiss
**Prin:* E Joseph
Dir IT: Daniel Strom
Snr Mgr: Jessie Bruder
Snr Mgr: Steven Levine

D-U-N-S 08-009-3578
JEWISH FEDERATION OF GREATER ATLANTA INC (GA)
1440 Spring St Nw, Atlanta, GA 30309-2832
Tel (404) 873-1661 *Founded/Ownrshp* 1936
Sales 41.2MM *EMP* 70
Accts Windham Brannon Pc Atlanta
SIC 8399 8661 Fund raising organization, non-fee basis; Religious organizations; Fund raising organization, non-fee basis; Religious organizations
Ch Bd: Marty Kogon
V Ch: Beth Arogeti
V Ch: Betty Sunshine
**Pr:* Steve Rakitt
COO: Louis Feldstein
CFO: Lisa Steinfeld
CFO: Lisa Steinfeldkatz
VP: Jillian Wagenheim
VP: Stephanie Wyatt
IT Man: Russell Gottschalk
IT Man: David Sarnat

D-U-N-S 07-596-2712
JEWISH FEDERATION OF GREATER INDIANAPOLIS INC
6705 Hoover Rd, Indianapolis, IN 46260-4120
Tel (317) 726-5450 *Founded/Ownrshp* 1948
Sales 10.8MM *EMP* 500
Accts Crowe Horwath Llp
SIC 8399 Fund raising organization, non-fee basis; Fund raising organization, non-fee basis
Pr: Paul Kraft
CFO: Erica Crowell
**Ex VP:* Michael Papo
VP: Marcy Klapper
VP: Melanie Ohlsen
Ex Dir: Ora Leivant
Ex Dir: Judy Sosin
Dir IT: Rob Green
Dir IT: Annette Richard

Info Man: Irina Brodskiy
Mktg Dir: Julia Goodman

D-U-N-S 80-042-8257
JEWISH FEDERATION OF GREATER METROWEST NJ
UJC OF METROWEST NJ
901 State Route 10, Whippany, NJ 07981-1105
Tel (973) 929-3000 *Founded/Ownrshp* 2007
Sales 26.8MM *EMP* 3
Accts Withurnsmithbrown Pc New Brun
SIC 8641 Recreation association; Recreation association
CEO: Max Kleinman
**COO:* Howard Rabner

D-U-N-S 05-716-2059
JEWISH FEDERATION OF GREATER PHILADELPHIA
FEDERATION ALLIED JEWISH APPEA
2100 Arch St, Philadelphia, PA 19103-1300
Tel (215) 832-0500 *Founded/Ownrshp* 1956
Sales 48.6MM *EMP* 110
SIC 8611 Community affairs & services
Pr: Harold Goldman
Ofcr: Sarah Bernstein
Ofcr: Melanie Krutzel
**VP:* Andrea Adelman
Dir Soc: Deby Engelmyer
Snr Ntwrk: Robert Quattro
Mktg Dir: Joshua Hersz

D-U-N-S 07-688-1671
JEWISH FEDERATION OF METROPOLITAN CHICAGO
30 S Wells St, Chicago, IL 60606-5054
Tel (312) 357-4790 *Founded/Ownrshp* 1900
Sales 143.7MM *EMP* 78
Accts Mcgladrey Llp Chicago Illino
SIC 8399 Community development groups; Community development groups
Pr: Steven B Nasatir
VP: Deborah Covington
Comm Dir: Stefanie Bregman
Web Dev: Chris Kranz

D-U-N-S 07-421-0832
JEWISH FEDERATION OF METROPOLITAN DETROIT
6735 Telegraph Rd Ste 30, Bloomfield Hills, MI 48301-3142
Tel (248) 642-4260 *Founded/Ownrshp* 1926
Sales 53.4MM *EMP* 100
Accts Plante & Moran Pllc Auburn Hi
SIC 8399 8661 Fund raising organization, non-fee basis; Regional planning organization; Religious organizations; Fund raising organization, non-fee basis; Regional planning organization; Religious organizations
CEO: Scott Kaufman
**CFO:* Dorothy Benyas
Ofcr: Howard Neistein
VP: Pamela Lippitt
Assoc Dir: Norman Lyle
Assoc Dir: Aliyah Schneider
Ex Dir: Robert Cohen

D-U-N-S 03-944-4252
JEWISH FEDERATION OF PALM BEACH COUNTY INC
4601 Community Dr, West Palm Beach, FL 33417-2716
Tel (561) 478-0700 *Founded/Ownrshp* 1962
Sales 34.9MM *EMP* 95
Accts Morrison Brown Agriz & Farra L
SIC 8699 Charitable organization; Charitable organization
Pr: Michael Hoffman
**Pr:* Arthur Lorting
**COO:* Debbi Roshfeld
**CFO:* Michael Karmelin
Ex VP: Carole-Ann Levine
Sr VP: Joel Breitstein
Sr VP: Hope Dunkel
Exec: Ada Spitzer
Dir Soc: Danielle Liberti
Comm Man: Colin Shalo
Ex Dir: Luis Fleischman

D-U-N-S 11-862-0681
JEWISH FEDERATION OF SOUTH PALM BEACH COUNTY INC
RALES JEWISH FAMILY SERVICE
9901 Donna Klein Blvd, Boca Raton, FL 33428-1756
Tel (561) 852-3100 *Founded/Ownrshp* 1976
Sales 23.6MM *EMP* 250
Accts Cbiz Mhm Llc Boca Raton Fl
SIC 8661 Religious organizations; Religious organizations
Ch Bd: Ellen R Sarnoff
V Ch: Judi Schuman
**Pr:* Bill Branskein
**COO:* Mel R Lowell
**CFO:* Mel Lowell
**Treas:* Stewart Kasen
Bd of Dir: Thomas Kaplan
VP: Jennifer Koenig
VP: Cathrine Schwartz
**Prin:* Wesley E Finch
**Prin:* Anne L Jacobson

D-U-N-S 07-553-9668
JEWISH FEDERATION OF SOUTHERN NEW JERSEY (INC)
1301 Springdale Rd # 200, Cherry Hill, NJ 08003-2763
Tel (856) 424-4444 *Founded/Ownrshp* 1922
Sales 23.1MM *EMP* 400
Accts Bowman & Company Llp Voorhees
SIC 8322 7389 Community center; Fund raising organizations; Community center; Fund raising organizations
CEO: Jennifer Dubrow Weiss
**Pr:* Harriet Schulman
**CFO:* Janet Smith
Exec: Tracy Diamond
Ex Dir: Les Cohen

D-U-N-S 06-499-2076
JEWISH FEDERATIONS OF NORTH AMERICA INC
25 Broadway Fl 17, New York, NY 10004-1015
Tel (212) 284-6500 *Founded/Ownrshp* 1935
Sales 184.7MM *EMP* 150
Accts Loeb & Troper Llp New York N
SIC 8399 Fund raising organization, non-fee basis; Fund raising organization, non-fee basis
Pr: Howard M Rieger
**Ch Bd:* Joseph Kanser
**Ch Bd:* Michael Siegal
CFO: Pamela Zaltsman
**Ch:* Robert Goldberg
Sr VP: Rebecca Caspi
Sr VP: Reuben Romirowsky
VP: Sheldon Zimmerman
Board of Directors: Jerry Silverman

D-U-N-S 15-710-7348
JEWISH FOUNDATION FOR GROUP HOMES INC
JFGH
1500 E Jefferson St, Rockville, MD 20852-1501
Tel (301) 984-3839 *Founded/Ownrshp* 1980
Sales 11.8MM *EMP* 295[E]
Accts Santos Postal & Company Pc R
SIC 8361 Residential care; Residential care
CEO: Vivian Bass
**Pr:* Dennis Speisman
**CFO:* Keith Danos
Prgrm Mgr: Abraham Bility
Pgrm Dir: Denise Gomez

JEWISH FREE LOAN ASSOCIATION
See JEWISH FAMILY SERVICE OF LOS ANGELES

D-U-N-S 06-697-4684
JEWISH GERIATRIC SERVICES INC
770 Converse St, Longmeadow, MA 01106-1719
Tel (413) 567-3949 *Founded/Ownrshp* 1912
Sales 944.1M *EMP* 500
Accts Feeley & Driscoll Pc Boston
SIC 8741 8322 8051 Nursing & personal care facility management; Individual & family services; Skilled nursing care facilities; Nursing & personal care facility management; Individual & family services; Skilled nursing care facilities
Pr: Alan Rosenfeld
**CFO:* Thomas Dybick
**Treas:* David A Kalicka

D-U-N-S 06-496-1600
JEWISH GUILD FOR BLIND
JGB
15 W 65th St, New York, NY 10023-6601
Tel (212) 769-6200 *Founded/Ownrshp* 1916
Sales 691.2MM *EMP* 712
Accts Loeb & Troper Llp New York N
SIC 8399 8331 8322 Council for social agency; Job training services; Individual & family services; Council for social agency; Job training services; Individual & family services
Ch Bd: James M Dubin
**Pr:* Mark Ackermann
**CEO:* Alan R Morse
Treas: Lawrence E Goldschmidt
**V Ch Bd:* Joseph Ripp
Chf Mktg O: Elsa Escalera
Sr VP: Cathleen Wirts
Dir Case M: Nancy Almada
Comm Dir: Peter Williamson
Off Mgr: Bonnie Serrano
Dir IT: Marci Davidow

D-U-N-S 07-952-9483
JEWISH HEALTHCARE CENTER INC
629 Salisbury St, Worcester, MA 01609-1120
Tel (508) 798-8653 *Founded/Ownrshp* 1914, 1915
Sales 21.6MM *EMP* 300
SIC 8051 Convalescent home with continuous nursing care; Convalescent home with continuous nursing care
Pr: Steven Willens
Ex Dir: Carol Halender
Dir IT: Curtis Renner
Snr Mgr: Emily Bomba

JEWISH HOME, THE
See WILLIAM BREMAN JEWISH HOME INC

D-U-N-S 07-383-2685
JEWISH HOME AND CARE CENTER INC
1414 N Prospect Ave, Milwaukee, WI 53202-3018
Tel (414) 276-2627 *Founded/Ownrshp* 1930
Sales 17.0MM *EMP* 314
Accts Wipfli Llp Milwaukee Wi
SIC 8051 Skilled nursing care facilities; Skilled nursing care facilities
Pr: Mina Tetter
Dir Vol: Beth Draper
COO: Randy Crosby
CFO: Gail Boerema
Ofcr: Marge Gehrke
Mktg Dir: Marlene Heller
Nrsg Dir: Cara Hesse
HC Dir: Elisabeth Blischke

JEWISH HOME AND HOSP FOR AGED
See JEWISH HOME LIFECARE HARRY AND JEANETTE WEINBERG CAMPUS BRONX

D-U-N-S 15-558-3883
JEWISH HOME AND HOSPITAL
KITTAY HOUSE
100 W Kingsbridge Rd # 100, Bronx, NY 10468-3962
Tel (718) 579-0420 *Founded/Ownrshp* 1863
Sales 54.4MM[E] *EMP* 1,000
SIC 6513 6531 Apartment building operators; Real estate managers; Apartment building operators; Real estate managers
Pr: Sheldon Goldberg
**Ex Dir:* Arlene Richman
Pharmcst: Sasha Rosado
HC Dir: Christine Schultz

D-U-N-S 96-961-4242
JEWISH HOME AND HOSPITAL FOR AGED
200 Jhf Dr, Pittsburgh, PA 15217-2950
Tel (412) 521-1683 *Founded/Ownrshp* 2011
Sales 21.4MM *EMP* 4
Accts Carbis Walker Llp Pittsburgh
SIC 0742 Animal hospital services, pets & other animal specialties; Animal hospital services, pets & other animal specialties
Prin: David Gritzer

D-U-N-S 18-957-6502 IMP
JEWISH HOME AT ROCKLEIGH INC
10 Link Dr, Rockleigh, NJ 07647-2504
Tel (201) 784-1414 *Founded/Ownrshp* 2000
Sales 26.4MM *EMP* 320
Accts Mercadien Pc Princeton Nj
SIC 8051 Skilled nursing care facilities; Skilled nursing care facilities
CEO: Charles Berkowitz
**Pr:* Angelica Bernie
**Pr:* Myrna Block
**CFO:* Brandy Stefanco
**Treas:* Richard Leventhal
**VP:* Melanie Cohen
**VP:* Carl Epstein
**VP:* Ary Freilich
**VP:* Sandra Gold
**VP:* Margaret Kaplen
**VP:* Robert Lapin
**VP:* Seymour Spirg

D-U-N-S 01-014-8674
JEWISH HOME FOR ELDERLY OF FAIRFIELD COUNTY INC
175 Jefferson St, Fairfield, CT 06825-1078
Tel (203) 365-6400 *Founded/Ownrshp* 1967
Sales 55.0MM[E] *EMP* 600
SIC 8051 8059

JEWISH HOME FOR THE AGED
See HEBREW HOME FOR AGED DISABLED

D-U-N-S 07-772-9606
JEWISH HOME LIFECARE HARRY AND JEANETTE WEINBERG CAMPUS BRONX
JEWISH HOME AND HOSP FOR AGED
120 W 106th St, New York, NY 10025-3923
Tel (212) 870-5000 *Founded/Ownrshp* 1866
Sales 60.1MM[E] *EMP* 1,300[E]
SIC 8051 Skilled nursing care facilities; Skilled nursing care facilities
Pr: Audrey Weiner
Dir Vol: Lorand Ernyey
Pr: Regina Melly
Pr: Donald Worton
**CFO:* Thomas Ruggiero
Ofcr: Thomas Gilmartin
Sr VP: Robert Davis
Sr VP: Bridget Gallagher
Sr VP: Helene Meyers
Sr VP: Bruce Nathanson
Sr VP: Audrey Wathen
VP: Kristine Cerchiara
VP: Gerald Garofalo
VP: Renee Hofman
VP: Richard Nuefeld
**VP:* Kenneth J Sherman
VP: Nancy Stoddard
Dir: Allison Braunstein
Dir Bus: Debbie Bobe

D-U-N-S 07-685-2649
JEWISH HOME LIFECARE MANHATTAN (NY)
GREENWALL PAVILION
120 W 106th St, New York, NY 10025-3923
Tel (212) 870-5000 *Founded/Ownrshp* 1872
Sales 109.8MM *EMP* 2,150
Accts Loeb & Troper Llp New York N
SIC 8361 7521 Home for the aged; Parking garage; Home for the aged; Parking garage
Pr: Audrey Weiner
**CFO:* Thomas Gilmartin
**Sr VP:* Frederic L Bloch
**Sr VP:* Audrey Wathen
**VP:* Lois R Faust
**VP:* Thomas Ruggiero
Off Mgr: Elizabeth Cardamona
Dir IT: Robert Lanfranchi
IT Man: Danesh Singh
Nrsg Dir: Marie Rosenthal
HC Dir: Toyin Savage

D-U-N-S 96-737-8402
JEWISH HOME LIFECARE SARAH NEUMAN CENTER WESTCHESTER
845 Palmer Ave, Mamaroneck, NY 10543-2406
Tel (914) 698-6005 *Founded/Ownrshp* 2011
Sales 42.0MM *EMP* 81
Accts Loeb & Troper Llp New York N
SIC 8051 Skilled nursing care facilities
Mktg Dir: Jeanette Cohen

D-U-N-S 08-093-1199
JEWISH HOME OF CINCINNATI (OH)
CEDAR VILLAGE GIFT SHOPPE
5467 Cedar Village Dr, Mason, OH 45040-8693
Tel (513) 754-3100 *Founded/Ownrshp* 1883
Sales 23.3MM *EMP* 275
Accts Plante & Moran Pllc Columbus
SIC 8051 Skilled nursing care facilities; Skilled nursing care facilities

D-U-N-S 03-244-4094
JEWISH HOME OF ROCHESTER
2021 Winton Rd S, Rochester, NY 14618-3998
Tel (585) 427-7760 *Founded/Ownrshp* 1998
Sales 44.5MM *EMP* 37[E]
SIC 8051 Skilled nursing care facilities
CEO: Daniel Katz
VP: Michele Schirano
VP: Myron Silver
VP: Chris Teumer
**Prin:* Deborah McIlveen
Dir Sec: Mario J Gianforte
Telecom Ex: Robert Ciaccia
QA Dir: Christine V Vessem
Dir IT: Jamie Bennett

Nrsg Dir: Cindy Lovetro
HC Dir: Nancy Scholfield

D-U-N-S 07-368-1140
JEWISH HOME OF ROCHESTER SENIOR HOUSING INC
WOLK MANOR
4000 Summit Circle Dr, Rochester, NY 14618-3965
Tel (585) 442-1950 *Founded/Ownrshp* 1920
Sales 7.8MM *EMP* 665E
Accts Freed Maxick Cpas Pc Buffalo
SIC 8051 Skilled nursing care facilities; Skilled nursing care facilities
CEO: Daniel Ketz
Pr: Travis Masonis
**CFO:* Debbie Mcllveen
CFO: Larry Rabinowitz
Bd of Dir: Rachel Wicks
VP: Mark Plantholt
VP: Jackie Stone
VP: Christine Vanvessem
Dir IT: Jamie Bennett
Mktg Dir: Mary Fazio

JEWISH HOSP ST MRYS HEALTHCARE
See FOUR COURTS INC

JEWISH HOSPITAL
See HEALTH WATCH OF VISITING NURSE INC

D-U-N-S 13-040-1078
JEWISH HOSPITAL & ST MARYS HEALTHCARE INC
(*Suby of* CHI) ★
200 Abraham Flexner Way # 1, Louisville, KY 40202-1886
Tel (502) 587-4011 *Founded/Ownrshp* 2012
Sales NA *EMP* 8,100
SIC 8062 8082 General medical & surgical hospitals; Home health care services; General medical & surgical hospitals; Home health care services
Pr: David Laird
**Pr:* Joseph Gilene
CFO: Ron Farr
**Treas:* Melvin Alexander
Trst: Gary Campbell
Trst: Susan Gatz
**Sr VP:* Kathleen M Haddix
VP: Alice O Bridges
VP: Katie Wood
Dir Lab: Luger Alan
Dir Lab: Mary Frank
Dir Rx: Katie Ruf

D-U-N-S 87-945-4783
JEWISH HOSPITAL CINCINNATI INC
PHYSICAL MEDICINE
3200 Burnet Ave, Cincinnati, OH 45229-3028
Tel (513) 569-2367 *Founded/Ownrshp* 1984
Sales 239.3MM *EMP* 4
Accts Deloitte Tax Llp Cincinnati
SIC 8031 Offices & clinics of osteopathic physicians; Offices & clinics of osteopathic physicians
Owner: William J Bajorek

D-U-N-S 78-222-2991
JEWISH HOSPITAL HEALTHCARE SERVICES INC
200 Abraham Flexner Way # 1, Louisville, KY 40202-2877
Tel (502) 587-4011 *Founded/Ownrshp* 2005
Sales 166.2MME *EMP* 8,125
Accts Ernst & Young Us Llp Chicago
SIC 8062 8082 General medical & surgical hospitals; Home health care services; General medical & surgical hospitals; Home health care services
Pr: Robert L Shircliff
**Ch Bd:* Louis Waterman
Sr VP: Ronald Greenberg
VP: Alice O Bridges
VP: Rick Buono
VP: Michael Collins
VP: Stephan French
VP: Ken Johnson
VP: Jeff Polson
Dir Case M: Bev Beckman
Dir Sec: Steve Collins

D-U-N-S 06-894-7431 IMP
JEWISH HOSPITAL LLC
4777 E Galbraith Rd, Cincinnati, OH 45236-2814
Tel (513) 686-3000 *Founded/Ownrshp* 1941
Sales 185.5MME *EMP* 1,700
SIC 8062 General medical & surgical hospitals; General medical & surgical hospitals
Ex VP: Aurora M Lambert
VP: Julie Clark
VP: Pam Vansant
Exec: Janet Patterson
VP Admn: Janice Falstrom
Adm Dir: Roger Vorherr
CTO: Maria Russo
Pathlgst: Kevin Monroe
Obsttrcn: Michael Schmerler
Ansthlgy: Ernesto Rodriguez
Doctor: Mariana Vardaka

D-U-N-S 11-289-0132 IMP
JEWISH HOSPITAL OF CINCINNATI INC
(*Suby of* MERCY HEALTH PARTNERS) ★
4777 E Galbraith Rd, Cincinnati, OH 45236-2814
Tel (513) 686-3000 *Founded/Ownrshp* 2009
Sales 89.7M *EMP* 2,500
SIC 8062 General medical & surgical hospitals; General medical & surgical hospitals
Pr: Steve Holman
CFO: William Jirgan
**VP:* Donald L D
**VP:* Kathy Smith
Dir Risk M: Julie Clark
Dir Lab: Kevin Monroe
**Prin:* Warren Falberg
QA Dir: Diane Dieckman

JEWISH MEM HOSP & REHABILITAT
See JEWISH MEMORIAL HOSPITAL & REHABILITATION CENTER

D-U-N-S 07-952-3353
JEWISH MEMORIAL HOSPITAL & REHABILITATION CENTER
JEWISH MEM HOSP & REHABILITAT
59 Townsend St, Boston, MA 02119-1318
Tel (617) 989-8315 *Founded/Ownrshp* 1929
Sales 9.1MME *EMP* 300
SIC 8069 Chronic disease hospital; Chronic disease hospital
Ch Bd: Harold Kotler
**CEO:* Kimberly A Smith
CFO: Peter McGrath

D-U-N-S 07-281-2266
JEWISH NATIONAL FUND KEREN KAYEMETH LEISRAEL INC
KEREN KAYEMETH LE ISRAEL
42 E 69th St, New York, NY 10021-5093
Tel (212) 879-9300 *Founded/Ownrshp* 1918
Sales 73.4MM *EMP* 140
Accts Loeb & Troper Llp New York N
SIC 8399 Fund raising organization, non-fee basis; Fund raising organization, non-fee basis
CEO: Russell F Robinson
**Ch Bd:* Ronald Lauder
**CFO:* Harold Cohen
CFO: Mitch Rosenzweig
Bd of Dir: Reuven Avital
Bd of Dir: Stan Baratz
Bd of Dir: Jerome Belson
Bd of Dir: Jerry Berko
Bd of Dir: Daisy Berman
Bd of Dir: Marvin Birger
Bd of Dir: Evelyn Blachor
Bd of Dir: Alan Blumenfeld
Bd of Dir: Elliot Borkson
Bd of Dir: Stephen Breslauer
Bd of Dir: Audrey Brooks
Bd of Dir: Debbie Cohen
Bd of Dir: Ron Cohen
Bd of Dir: Andrew Davids
Bd of Dir: Jack Dweck
Bd of Dir: Narda Forman
Bd of Dir: Susan Fratkin

D-U-N-S 82-676-3435
JEWISH NURSING HOME OF WESTERN MASS INC
770 Converse St, Longmeadow, MA 01106-1719
Tel (413) 567-6211 *Founded/Ownrshp* 1992
Sales 18.9MM *EMP* 350
Accts Feeley & Driscoll Pc Boston
SIC 8051 Skilled nursing care facilities; Skilled nursing care facilities
Pr: Alan S Rosenfeld PHD
CFO: Thomas E Dybvick
**Treas:* Michael Ginsburg
Off Mgr: Judy Tolpa
Phys Thrpy: Sue Guenard

D-U-N-S 80-785-4323
JEWISH PHYSICIAN GROUP INC
539 S 4th St, Louisville, KY 40202-2535
Tel (502) 540-3888 *Founded/Ownrshp* 2011
Sales 61.2MM *EMP* 4E
Accts Bkd Llp Louismille Ky
SIC 8011 General & family practice, physician/surgeon; General & family practice, physician/surgeon
Prin: Debbie Molnar

D-U-N-S 06-496-2145
JEWISH THEOLOGICAL SEMINARY OF AMERICA
CAMP RAMAH
3080 Broadway, New York, NY 10027-4650
Tel (212) 678-8008 *Founded/Ownrshp* 1903
Sales 71.7MME *EMP* 950
Accts Loeb & Troper New York Ny
SIC 8221 Theological seminary; Theological seminary
Pr: Andrew Dorsch
**COO:* Marc Gary
**CFO:* Fred Schnur
Assoc Dir: Deborah Miller
IT Man: Scott Karr
Doctor: Ann Appelbaum
Genl Couns: Martin Oppenheimer

D-U-N-S 07-443-0661
JEWISH UNITED FUND OF METROPOLITAN CHICAGO
30 S Wells St, Chicago, IL 60606-5056
Tel (312) 357-4805 *Founded/Ownrshp* 1949
Sales 98.0MM *EMP* 160
Accts Rsm Mcgladrey Inc Chicago Il
SIC 8399 Fund raising organization, non-fee basis; Fund raising organization, non-fee basis
Pr: Steven B Nasatir
Bd of Dir: Stacy Saltzman
Sr VP: Rachel Sternberg
VP: Tracy More
**VP:* James Pinkston
Pgrm Dir: Sarah Friedman
Pgrm Dir: Ruth Schachter

D-U-N-S 08-747-7964
JEWISH VOCATIONAL SERVICES AND COMMUNITY WORKSHOP
J V S
29699 Southfield Rd, Southfield, MI 48076-2038
Tel (248) 559-5000 *Founded/Ownrshp* 1942
Sales 21.2MM *EMP* 800
Accts Baker Tilly Virchow Krause Llp
SIC 8331 Vocational rehabilitation agency; Vocational rehabilitation agency
CEO: Paul Blatt
**CEO:* Leah Rosenbaum
Bd of Dir: Hamila Kownacki
Trst: Michael Goldberg
**VP:* Nancy Bogdan
**VP:* Susan Earp
**VP:* Teresa Schwartz
Comm Dir: Kim Graziosi
Ex Dir: Leonard Schneider
Prgrm Mgr: Denis Zijadic
CTO: Don Robison

D-U-N-S 07-752-0435 IMP
JEWISH VOICE MINISTRIES INTERNATIONAL (AZ)
10850 N 24th Ave, Phoenix, AZ 85029-4748
Tel (602) 971-8501 *Founded/Ownrshp* 1968
Sales 24.2MM *EMP* 50
Accts Alan Jeff Cpa Pc Tonawanda
SIC 7812 7922 Television film production; Radio producers; Television film production; Radio producers
Pr: Jonathan Bernis
**Ch:* James W Blackburn

D-U-N-S 07-463-7877
JEWS FOR JESUS
60 Haight St, San Francisco, CA 94102-5895
Tel (415) 864-2600 *Founded/Ownrshp* 1973
Sales 21.2MM *EMP* 150
Accts Eckhoff And Company San Rafae
SIC 8661 Non-church religious organizations; Non-church religious organizations
CEO: David Brickner
Trst Ofcr: David Brickmen
Dir IT: Toby Weiss
Software D: Jay Jose

D-U-N-S 07-960-4132
JEYES US HOLDINGS INC
8860 Smiths Mill Rd # 500, New Albany, OH 43054-6653
Tel (614) 984-2896 *Founded/Ownrshp* 2010
Sales 46.9MME *EMP* 500
SIC 2842 Cleaning or polishing preparations; Cleaning or polishing preparations
CFO: Richard Nihei

D-U-N-S 04-997-2870
JEZOWSKI & MARKEL CONTRACTORS INC
749 N Poplar St, Orange, CA 92868-1013
Tel (714) 630-6489 *Founded/Ownrshp* 1996
Sales 27.6MME *EMP* 145
SIC 1771 Concrete work; Concrete work
Pr: Leonard Michael Barth
**VP:* Joseph Dean

D-U-N-S 05-504-4028
JF ACQUISITION LLC
JONES & FRANK
1330 Saint Marys St # 210, Raleigh, NC 27605-1375
Tel (757) 857-5700 *Founded/Ownrshp* 2012
Sales 153.5MME *EMP* 207
SIC 5084 1799 7299 Pumps & pumping equipment; Service station equipment installation, maintenance & repair; Station operation services; Pumps & pumping equipment; Service station equipment installation, maintenance & repair; Station operation services
Pr: Sterling Baker
**CFO:* Jay Trepanier
**Ex VP:* Scott Jones
**VP:* Jeff Badgley
**VP:* Tom Pera
**VP:* Joe Wrightson
Opers Mgr: Roger Ewing
Sls Dir: Ed Perkins
Sls Dir: Bennett Upston
Manager: Rick Holmes
Sls Mgr: Peter Kasputis

D-U-N-S 00-451-2901
JF ALLEN CO INC (WV)
U.S 33 W Red Rock Rd, Buckhannon, WV 26201
Tel (304) 472-8890 *Founded/Ownrshp* 1946
Sales 123.1MME *EMP* 350
SIC 3271 1611 3273 3281 2951 Blocks, concrete or cinder: standard; General contractor, highway & street construction; Ready-mixed concrete; Cut stone & stone products; Asphalt paving mixtures & blocks; Blocks, concrete or cinder: standard; General contractor, highway & street construction; Ready-mixed concrete; Cut stone & stone products; Asphalt paving mixtures & blocks
Pr: John C Allen
CFO: Darren Glover
Treas: Michael Griffith
VP: Delbert Leatherman
Ql Cn Mgr: Ed Phares

D-U-N-S 03-901-0483 IMP
JF DALEY INTERNATIONAL LTD
CANDY & CO
(*Suby of* SWISHER HYGIENE INC) ★
4100 W 76th St Ste Al, Chicago, IL 60652-5600
Tel (800) 222-4566 *Founded/Ownrshp* 1980
Sales 24.2MME *EMP* 150
SIC 2842 2841 Floor waxes; Cleaning or polishing preparations; Soap & other detergents; Floor waxes; Cleaning or polishing preparations; Soap & other detergents
Pr: John F Daley
**Treas:* Fred Meyer
VP: Timothy Daley
**VP:* Cyril Ekkebus
VP: Corrine Kopchik

D-U-N-S 04-773-2136
JF ELECTRIC INC
100 Lake Front Pkwy, Edwardsville, IL 62025-2900
Tel (618) 797-5353 *Founded/Ownrshp* 1925
Sales 162.6MM *EMP* 550
SIC 1731 General electrical contractor; General electrical contractor
Pr: Greg Fowler
**Treas:* Charles Fowler
VP: Larry Noble
VP: Jeff Sherman
Board of Directors: James Fowler

D-U-N-S 16-059-8280 IMP/EXP
JF HILLEBRAND USA INC
(*Suby of* JF HILLEBRAND UK LIMITED)
1600 Saint Georges Ave, Rahway, NJ 07065-2764
Tel (732) 388-0101 *Founded/Ownrshp* 1992
Sales 43.9MME *EMP* 80
SIC 4731 Transportation agents & brokers; Foreign freight forwarding; Transportation agents & brokers; Foreign freight forwarding
Pr: Jean-Jacques Francoulon

**VP:* Allison Greiner
CTO: Laurent Amand
Opers Mgr: Dan Wagner

D-U-N-S 00-695-0927
JF JOHNSON HOLDINGS INC (MD)
8200 Veterans Hwy, Millersville, MD 21108-1444
Tel (410) 987-5200 *Founded/Ownrshp* 1921
Sales 25.0MM *EMP* 65
SIC 5211 6519 Lumber & other building materials; Real property lessors; Lumber & other building materials; Real property lessors
Ch Bd: Robert Johnson
**Treas:* David M Glenn MD
**VP:* Stephen C Rickert

D-U-N-S 16-454-9151
JF LEHMAN & CO INC
110 E 59th St Fl 27, New York, NY 10022-1326
Tel (703) 418-6095 *Founded/Ownrshp* 1990
Sales 154.9MME *EMP* 25E
SIC 6722 Investors; Management investment, open-end
Pr: John Lehman
VP: David Gorton
Admn Mgr: George Sawyer

D-U-N-S 03-024-5575
JF LOMMA INC
JF LOMMA TRUCKING & RIGGING
48 3rd St Ste 1, Kearny, NJ 07032-4588
Tel (973) 589-2000 *Founded/Ownrshp* 1968
Sales 47.1MME *EMP* 135
SIC 4213 Heavy machinery transport; Heavy machinery transport
Pr: James Lomma
CFO: Phil Mascoll
Off Mgr: Jenifer Hansen
IT Man: Art Kistler
Mtls Mgr: Frank Signorelli
Opers Mgr: Jim Beck
Genl Couns: Chris Eriksen

JF LOMMA TRUCKING & RIGGING
See JF LOMMA INC

D-U-N-S 09-119-6246 IMP
JF MONTALVO CASH AND CARRY INC
Amelia Ind Park 46, Guaynabo, PR 00968-8043
Tel (787) 781-2962 *Founded/Ownrshp* 1979
Sales 141.4MME *EMP* 562
SIC 5141 Groceries, general line; Groceries, general line
Pr: Juan F Montalvo

D-U-N-S 00-969-1940 IMP
JF SHEA CONSTRUCTION INC (CA)
SHEA HOMES FOR ACTIVE ADULTS
(*Suby of* J F SHEA CO INC) ★
655 Brea Canyon Rd, Walnut, CA 91789-3078
Tel (909) 595-4397 *Founded/Ownrshp* 1958
Sales 744.3MME *EMP* 2,200
SIC 1521 1622 6512

D-U-N-S 08-968-7334
JF2 LLC
ON TARGET UTILITY SERVICES
617 Water St, Gardiner, ME 04345-2063
Tel (207) 588-3300 *Founded/Ownrshp* 2004
Sales 19.6MM *EMP* 300
Accts Baker Newman & Noyes Portland
SIC 1623 Telephone & communication line construction; Telephone & communication line construction
Rgnl Mgr: Bethaney Wallace

D-U-N-S 78-995-6179
■ **JFBB SKI AREAS INC**
JACK FROST BIG BLDER SKI AREAS
(*Suby of* PEAK RESORTS INC) ★
1 Jack Frost Mountain Rd, Blakeslee, PA 18610
Tel (570) 443-8425 *Founded/Ownrshp* 2005
Sales 14.8MME *EMP* 319E
SIC 7997 Ice sports
Genl Mgr: Mark Daubert
Ofcr: Holy Vanessenvelft

D-U-N-S 16-194-9409
JFC HOLDING CORP
JORGENSEN FORGE PARENT
8531 E Marginal Way S, Tukwila, WA 98108-4018
Tel (206) 762-1100 *Founded/Ownrshp* 1997
Sales 57.2MME *EMP* 276E
SIC 3462 Iron & steel forgings; Iron & steel forgings
Pr: Steven Abelman
**Pr:* Richards E Clemens
**CFO:* Doug James
**Ch:* Joseph Haviv
**Sec:* Juan Lynch
**VP:* Robert O Connor
VP: Dan Drinan
Sales Asso: Bo Hjelmaa

JFC INC.
See JFC LLC

D-U-N-S 00-796-8175 IMP/EXP
JFC INTERNATIONAL INC (CA)
(*Suby of* KIKKOMAN CORPORATION)
7101 E Slauson Ave, Commerce, CA 90040-3622
Tel (323) 721-6100 *Founded/Ownrshp* 1958, 1969
Sales 293.6MME *EMP* 677
SIC 5149 Specialty food items; Specialty food items
Pr: Hiroyuki Enomoto
Brnch Mgr: Ichiro Komatsubara
IT Man: Sonia Benson
S&M/VP: Paul Iiyama
Manager: Jun Semba
Sls Mgr: Masakazu Kaneda
Sls Mgr: Kyung Lee
Sls Mgr: Kohei Matsuda
Sls Mgr: Tomoya Shimada
Sls Mgr: Taka Tanaka
Sls Mgr: Duk Yoon

D-U-N-S 05-108-0653
JFC LLC
JFC INC.
(*Suby of* MASCHHOFFS LLC) ★
4150 2nd St S Ste 200, Saint Cloud, MN 56301-3994
Tel (320) 251-3570 *Founded/Ownrshp* 2013
Sales 175.0MM[E] *EMP* 1,700
SIC 2015 0251 Chicken, processed; Broiling chickens, raising of; Chicken, processed; Broiling chickens, raising of
CEO: Michael Helgeson
Ex VP: Tim Wensman
Exec: Stephen R Jurek
Plnt Mgr: Mandy Korpal

JFCS
See JEWISH FAMILY AND CHILDRENS SERVICE INC

JFGH
See JEWISH FOUNDATION FOR GROUP HOMES INC

JFK HARTWYCK AT OAK TREE
See HARTWYCK AT OAK TREE INC

D-U-N-S 02-690-2705
JFK HEALTH SYSTEM INC
JFK MEDICAL CENTER
80 James St, Edison, NJ 08820-3938
Tel (732) 321-7000 *Founded/Ownrshp* 1990
Sales 527.5MM[E] *EMP* 6,735
Accts Baker Tilly
SIC 8062 General medical & surgical hospitals; General medical & surgical hospitals
Pr: Raymond Fredericks
CFO: Richard Smith
**Ch:* Dr Michael Kleiman
VP: Carole Kolber
Dir Risk M: Norma Bustos
Adm Dir: John Bone
Nurse Mgr: Michelle Siegel
Plnt Mgr: Mark Di Geronimno
Pr Mgr: Jamie Ferlanti
Pathlgst: Hazel H Kim
Pharmcst: Liliya Krasner

D-U-N-S 80-899-7290
JFK INVESTMENT CO LLC
43252 Woodward Ave # 210, Bloomfield Hills, MI 48302-5047
Tel (248) 333-2373 *Founded/Ownrshp* 1993
Sales 27.0MM *EMP* 520
SIC 6552 6512 Land subdividers & developers, commercial; Nonresidential building operators; Land subdividers & developers, commercial; Nonresidential building operators

JFK MEDICAL CENTER
See JFK HEALTH SYSTEM INC

JFK MEDICAL CENTER
See COMMUNITY HOSPITAL GROUP INC

JFK MEDICAL CENTER
See MUHLENBERG REGIONAL MEDICAL CENTER INC

JFK MEDICAL CENTER
See HARTWYCK AT OAK TREE INC

JFM
See JOHNSON FINCH & MCCLURE CONSTRUCTION INC

D-U-N-S 00-818-8880
JFM INC
JR FOOD MARKET
4276 Lakeland Dr, Jackson, MS 39232-8804
Tel (601) 664-7177 *Founded/Ownrshp* 1920
Sales 43.9MM[E] *EMP* 350
SIC 5411 5571 6794

D-U-N-S 02-706-8026
JFMC FACILITIES CORP
30 S Wells St Ste 216-800, Chicago, IL 60606-5056
Tel (312) 346-6700 *Founded/Ownrshp* 2008
Sales 25.4MM *EMP* 2
Accts Mcgladrey Llp Chicago Il
SIC 8699 Charitable organization; Charitable organization
Prin: Michael B Tarnoff

D-U-N-S 60-486-7606
JFMC FACILITIES CORP
216 W Jackson Blvd # 800, Chicago, IL 60606-6909
Tel (312) 357-4790 *Founded/Ownrshp* 1985
Sales 22.3MM *EMP* 26
SIC 6531 Real estate agents & managers; Real estate agents & managers
Pr: Steven B Nasatir
**Ex VP:* Michael B Tarnoff
**VP:* Jeffrey C King
**Ex Dir:* Richard Katz

D-U-N-S 09-814-7580
JFW INDUSTRIES INC
5134 Commerce Square Dr, Indianapolis, IN 46237-9705
Tel (317) 887-1340 *Founded/Ownrshp* 1979
Sales 20.3MM *EMP* 105
Accts Peachin Schwartz & Weingardt
SIC 3825 Radio apparatus analyzers; Radio apparatus analyzers
Pr: Fred D Walker
**VP:* James W Leach

D-U-N-S 05-537-7966
JG BRANDS INC
10530 Nw 26th St Ste F201, Doral, FL 33172-5930
Tel (786) 597-1554 *Founded/Ownrshp* 2011
Sales 120.0MM *EMP* 3
SIC 5999 Mobile telephones & equipment; Mobile telephones & equipment
Pr: Jorbel J Griebeler

D-U-N-S 01-123-3090
JG CONTRACTING CO INC
100 W Main St Ste 200, Carnegie, PA 15106-2481
Tel (412) 446-1701 *Founded/Ownrshp* 1996
Sales 20.4MM[E] *EMP* 44[E]
SIC 1542 Nonresidential construction
Pr: James Gyurina
**Sec:* John Gyurina
Rgnl Mgr: Eric Ronzio
Div Mgr: Fred Tarquinio

D-U-N-S 11-387-9329
JG MANAGEMENT SYSTEMS INC
JGMS
336 Main St Ste 207, Grand Junction, CO 81501-2459
Tel (970) 254-1354 *Founded/Ownrshp* 2001
Sales 20.1MM[E] *EMP* 107
SIC 8711 0851 7336 7389 7371 7373 Consulting engineer; Forest management services; Forest management plans, preparation of; Commercial art & graphic design; Design services; Custom computer programming services; Computer integrated systems design
Pr: Jerome Gonzales
CFO: Jennifer Brown
**VP:* Nicholas R Aranda
Exec: Buddy Garland
IT Man: Frank Szabo
Snr PM: Paul Huber

D-U-N-S 61-898-9123
JG NASCON INC
1400 Industrial Hwy, Eddystone, PA 19022-1522
Tel (610) 872-1200 *Founded/Ownrshp* 1990
Sales 25.0MM *EMP* 10
SIC 1794 1629 1623 1611 Excavation work; Land preparation construction; Sewer line construction; Surfacing & paving; Excavation work; Land preparation construction; Sewer line construction; Surfacing & paving
Pr: Joseph P Nassib
**Treas:* Armen P Nassib
**VP:* Bridget Nassib

JG PRESS
See WORLD PUBLICATIONS GROUP INC

D-U-N-S 00-234-8456
JG TOWNSEND JR & CO INC (DE)
316 N Race St, Georgetown, DE 19947-1166
Tel (302) 856-2525 *Founded/Ownrshp* 1937
Sales 79.0MM *EMP* 80
SIC 6531 6519 5099 5142 2037 Selling agent, real estate; Farm land leasing; Timber products, rough; Packaged frozen goods; Frozen fruits & vegetables; Selling agent, real estate; Farm land leasing; Timber products, rough; Packaged frozen goods; Frozen fruits & vegetables
Pr: Paul G Townsend

D-U-N-S 16-948-6276
■ **JG WENTWORTH HOME LENDING INC**
(*Suby of* J G WENTWORTH CO) ★
3350 Commission Ct, Woodbridge, VA 22192-1784
Tel (888) 349-3773 *Founded/Ownrshp* 2015
Sales NA *EMP* 250
SIC 6163 Mortgage brokers arranging for loans, using money of others; Mortgage brokers arranging for loans, using money of others
Pr: Roger W Jones
CFO: Richard Byrd
Ofcr: Oscar Aizcorbe
Ofcr: Gino Cioffi
Ofcr: Elizabeth Cobb
Ofcr: Paul Diaz
Ofcr: Mark Dugayo
Ofcr: Tim Smith
VP: Christine Moore
Area Mgr: Michelle Nuckols
Brnch Mgr: John Csoka

JGB
See JEWISH GUILD FOR BLIND

JGB
See GUILDNET INC

D-U-N-S 08-517-2005 IMP/EXP
JGB ENTERPRISES INC
115 Metropolitan Dr, Liverpool, NY 13088-5389
Tel (315) 451-2770 *Founded/Ownrshp* 1977
Sales 116.8MM *EMP* 240
SIC 3052 5085 3429

D-U-N-S 06-200-2522
JGB HEALTH FACILITIES CORP
GUILD HOME FOR AGED BLIND
15 W 65th St, New York, NY 10023-6601
Tel (212) 769-6200 *Founded/Ownrshp* 1974
Sales 10.5MM *EMP* 304
Accts Loeb & Troper
SIC 8051 Skilled nursing care facilities; Skilled nursing care facilities
Ch: James M Dubin
**Pr:* Alan R Morse JD PHD
**CFO:* Elliot J Hagler
Sr VP: Larry Carr

D-U-N-S 05-022-5556 EXP
JGC AMERICA INC
J G C U S A
(*Suby of* JGC CORPORATION)
3151 Briarpark Dr Ste 400, Houston, TX 77042-3805
Tel (832) 591-2000 *Founded/Ownrshp* 1983
Sales 22.6MM[E] *EMP* 16
SIC 5084 Oil refining machinery, equipment & supplies
Pr: Eiki Furuta
**VP:* Stephen Gallagher
**VP:* Takehito Hidaka
QA Dir: Max Mountjoy

D-U-N-S 07-909-7248
JGC FOOD CO LLC (WA)
(*Suby of* JOSHUA GREEN CORPORATION)
1425 4th Ave Ste 420, Seattle, WA 98101-2218
Tel (206) 622-0420 *Founded/Ownrshp* 2012
Sales 94.1MM[E] *EMP* 206[E]
SIC 2099 2092 Food preparations; Fresh or frozen fish or seafood chowders, soups & stews
CEO: Joshua Green III
CFO: Claudia Pieropan

JGH
See JACKSON GENERAL HOSPITAL FOUNDATION INC

D-U-N-S 00-179-0898 IMP
JGL HOLDINGS LTD (NY)
MISS GALLERY
463 7th Ave Fl 5, New York, NY 10018-8724
Tel (212) 273-8800 *Founded/Ownrshp* 1965
Sales 26.8MM[E] *EMP* 110
SIC 5137 2337

D-U-N-S 05-714-5745
JGM WELDING & FABRICATING SERVICES INC
1201 Valley Rd, Coatesville, PA 19320-2848
Tel (610) 873-0081 *Founded/Ownrshp* 2001
Sales 22.0MM[E] *EMP* 85
SIC 3441 1541 1542 8711 Fabricated structural metal; Industrial buildings & warehouses; Commercial & office building contractors; Engineering services
Pr: Joseph G Messner Jr
**Ex VP:* Joe Messner Sr
Ex VP: Steve Steingraeber
Sfty Mgr: Bill Thomas
Opers Mgr: Michael Belcher
S&M/VP: Ralph Schockert
Snr PM: Robert Zolinski

JGMS
See JG MANAGEMENT SYSTEMS INC

D-U-N-S 07-976-6905
JGPS HOLDINGS LLC
(*Suby of* BRYNWOOD PARTNERS II LIMITED PARTNERSHIP) ★
8 Sound Shore Dr Ste 265, Greenwich, CT 06830-7272
Tel (203) 622-1790 *Founded/Ownrshp* 2013
Sales 66.7MM[E] *EMP* 306[E]
SIC 6282 4731 Investment advice; Freight forwarding
CEO: Hendrik J Hartong III
Genl Pt: John T Gray
Genl Pt: Joan Y Mc Cabe
Pr: Ian B Mactaggart
CFO: Nicholas Dicarlo
Chf Cred: Guy Einav

JGR
See J GRADY RANDOLPH INC

D-U-N-S 13-583-7560 IMP/EXP
JGR COPA LLC
5611 Dewey St, Hollywood, FL 33023-1915
Tel (954) 966-1196 *Founded/Ownrshp* 2002
Sales 23.3MM *EMP* 11
Accts Cusano & Janvion Pl Plantati
SIC 5091 Surfing equipment & supplies; Surfing equipment & supplies
Pr: Jacob Goldzer
Prd Mgr: Danny Goldszer
Sls Mgr: Rich Bonilla

D-U-N-S 03-101-0077
JH BERRA CONSTRUCTION CO INC
(*Suby of* BERRA CONSTRUCTION) ★
5091 Baumgartner Rd, Saint Louis, MO 63129-2896
Tel (314) 487-5617 *Founded/Ownrshp* 2005
Sales 20.0MM *EMP* 500
SIC 1623 Highway & street construction; Grading; Sewer line construction; Construction sand & gravel; Crushed & broken limestone; Sewer line construction
Ch Bd: John H Berra Jr
**Treas:* Robert Berra
**VP:* Anthony Berra
Plnt Mgr: Andy Craw
Board of Directors: Mike Boston, Al Hicks, Joe Nicpon

D-U-N-S 14-766-3298
JH BRYANT JR INC
17217 S Broadway, Gardena, CA 90248-3117
Tel (310) 532-1840 *Founded/Ownrshp* 1980
Sales 69.0MM[E] *EMP* 180
SIC 1542 1731 1541 Nonresidential construction; Electrical work; Industrial buildings & warehouses; Nonresidential construction; Electrical work; Industrial buildings & warehouses
Pr: John Bryant III
**COO:* David R Bryant
VP: Joseph Perez
Snr PM: Glen Cohen

J.H. COHN
See COHNREZNICK LLP

D-U-N-S 03-381-3395
JH HARVEY CO LLC
HARVEY'S SUPERMARKETS
(*Suby of* BI-LO HOLDING LLC) ★
107 S Davis St, Nashville, GA 31639-2113
Tel (704) 633-8250 *Founded/Ownrshp* 2014
Sales 349.6MM[E] *EMP* 3,500
SIC 5411 Supermarkets, chain; Supermarkets, chain

D-U-N-S 04-630-3963
JH INDUSTRY INC
WOOSHIN USA
(*Suby of* WOSHIN INDUSTRIAL CO., LTD.)
1450 County Road 177, Cusseta, AL 36852-2763
Tel (334) 756-5152 *Founded/Ownrshp* 2011
Sales 47.9MM *EMP* 150
SIC 3465 Body parts, automobile: stamped metal; Body parts, automobile: stamped metal
CEO: Jung Ho Sea
COO: Jae Ik Jang

JH INSTRUMENTS
See FCX PERFORMANCE INC

D-U-N-S 00-283-6070
JH KELLY LLC
(*Suby of* KELLY ELECTRIC GROUP) ★
821 3rd Ave, Longview, WA 98632-2105
Tel (360) 423-5510 *Founded/Ownrshp* 1971
Sales 236.6MM[E] *EMP* 1,000
SIC 1711 Plumbing, heating, air-conditioning contractors; Mechanical contractor; Plumbing, heating, air-conditioning contractors; Mechanical contractor
COO: Mason Evans
DP Exec: Kevin Farley
Dir IT: Craig Harrison
IT Man: Kevin Fleet
IT Man: Meredith Keller
IT Man: Kellie Peterson
IT Man: Eric Smith
Sfty Dirs: Nicole McOmie
Mtls Mgr: Dale King
Opers Mgr: Butch Henry
Mktg Dir: Steve Dahl

D-U-N-S 00-118-9638
JH LYNCH & SONS INC
50 Lynch Pl, Cumberland, RI 02864-5334
Tel (401) 333-4300 *Founded/Ownrshp* 2000
Sales 127.6MM[E] *EMP* 300
SIC 1611 2951 Surfacing & paving; Asphalt & asphaltic paving mixtures (not from refineries); Surfacing & paving; Asphalt & asphaltic paving mixtures (not from refineries)
Pr: Stephen P Lynch Jr
**VP:* Frank Aceto
VP: Francis Foley
**VP:* David C Lynch Sr
**VP:* Harry E Myers III

D-U-N-S 04-932-7026
JH MAXYMILLIAN INC
1801 East St, Pittsfield, MA 01201-3843
Tel (413) 499-3050 *Founded/Ownrshp* 1969
Sales 29.2MM *EMP* 100
Accts Adelson & Company Pc Pittsfie
SIC 1611 1622 1541 General contractor, highway & street construction; Bridge construction; Industrial buildings, new construction; General contractor, highway & street construction; Bridge construction; Industrial buildings, new construction
Pr: Neal A Maxymillian
**Sec:* James H Maxymillian
VP: Vern Palen

D-U-N-S 02-855-4798
JH MCCORMICK INC
MC CORMICK CONSTRUCTION CO
2507 W Empire Ave, Burbank, CA 91504-3320
Tel (818) 843-2010 *Founded/Ownrshp* 1914
Sales 32.0MM[E] *EMP* 100
SIC 1542 1541 1522 Commercial & office building, new construction; Industrial buildings & warehouses; Residential construction; Commercial & office building, new construction; Industrial buildings & warehouses; Residential construction
Ch Bd: Jack Mc Cormick
**Pr:* Michael Mc Cormick
**COO:* Gerald Mc Cormick
CFO: Steven McCormick
Treas: Steven M Corick
**Treas:* Steven Mc Cormick
Ofcr: Michael R Mc Cormick
**VP:* Robert Mc Cormick
VP: Steve McCormick

D-U-N-S 62-388-2367
JH PARTNERS LLC
451 Jackson St Fl 3, San Francisco, CA 94111-1610
Tel (415) 364-0300 *Founded/Ownrshp* 2002
Sales 20.9MM[E] *EMP* 29
SIC 8741 Financial management for business
Pr: John C Hansen

D-U-N-S 01-185-6846 IMP
JH REID GENERAL CONTRACTOR
3230 Hamilton Blvd, South Plainfield, NJ 07080-1204
Tel (732) 752-3373 *Founded/Ownrshp* 1957
Sales 36.4MM[E] *EMP* 100
SIC 1611 1622 General contractor, highway & street construction; Highway construction, elevated; General contractor, highway & street construction; Highway construction, elevated
Ch Bd: James H Reid
**Pr:* Eric Reid
**CFO:* Robert Ginda
**Ex VP:* John Leslie
IT Man: Alex Grebel

D-U-N-S 07-516-1166
JH REID-ONSITE RECYCLING INC
3230 Hamilton Blvd, South Plainfield, NJ 07080-1204
Tel (732) 752-4050 *Founded/Ownrshp* 1974
Sales 26.7MM[E] *EMP* 250
SIC 1611 1622 1623 General contractor, highway & street construction; Bridge construction; Water main construction; General contractor, highway & street construction; Bridge construction; Water main construction
CEO: James H Reid
**Ex VP:* John Leslie

D-U-N-S 07-848-7604
▲ **JH WHITNEY VI LP**
130 Main St, New Canaan, CT 06840-5509
Tel (203) 716-6100 *Founded/Ownrshp* 2005
Sales 1.1MMM[E] *EMP* 10,900[E]
SIC 6726 5812 Management investment funds, closed-end; Seafood restaurants; Management investment funds, closed-end; Seafood restaurants
VP: Daniel T Harknett
**VP:* Ann Kim

D-U-N-S 00-411-4955 EXP
JH WILLIAMS OIL CO INC
J H WILLIAMS OIL CO
1237 E Twiggs St, Tampa, FL 33602-3139
Tel (813) 228-7776 *Founded/Ownrshp* 1942
Sales 58.2MM[E] *EMP* 35[E]
Accts Skoda Minotti Tampa Florida
SIC 5172 5541 5411 Petroleum products; Filling stations, gasoline; Convenience stores; Petroleum products; Filling stations, gasoline; Convenience stores
Pr: J Hulon Williams III
**CFO:* John Ferrell
**VP:* Patricia F Williams
Sls Mgr: Larry McGary

D-U-N-S 11-330-7201
JHC OPERATIONS LLC
JORDAN HEALTH SERVICES
(*Suby of* JORDAN HEALTHCARE HOLDINGS INC) ★
412 Texas Highway 37 S, Mount Vernon, TX 75457-6570
Tel (903) 537-2376 *Founded/Ownrshp* 2010
Sales 20.9MM^E *EMP* 500
SIC 8082 Visiting nurse service; Visiting nurse service
VP: Tim Conroy

D-U-N-S 83-223-4988
JHCI ACQUISITION INC
(*Suby of* JACOBSON COMPANIES) ★
3811 Dixon St, Des Moines, IA 50313-3907
Tel (515) 265-6171 *Founded/Ownrshp* 2007
Sales 734.8MM^E *EMP* 3,500^E
SIC 4225 General warehousing; General warehousing
CEO: Brian Lutt
CFO: Jack Ingle
Treas: John Rachwalski
Sec: John Monsky

D-U-N-S 93-379-9731
■ **JHCI HOLDINGS INC**
JACOBSON COMPANIES
(*Suby of* NORBERT DENTRESSANGLE)
1275 Nw 128th St, Clive, IA 50325-7426
Tel (515) 265-6171 *Founded/Ownrshp* 2014
Sales 670.2MM^E *EMP* 3,500^E
SIC 4226 4221 4225 Special warehousing & storage; Farm product warehousing & storage; General warehousing & storage; Special warehousing & storage; Farm product warehousing & storage; General warehousing & storage
Co-Pr: Tony Tegnelia
Pr: Gordon Smith
Ofcr: Marty Howard
Ofcr: Jack Ingle
Ex VP: Marty Smith
VP: Kraig Enyeart
VP: Brad Jones
VP: Tom Taylor
Dir Bus: James Cord
Brnch Mgr: Justin Andrews
Genl Mgr: Perry Coleman
Board of Directors: Ted Dardani, Denis Nayden, John Thomson

JHCP
See HOPKINS JOHNS COMMUNITY PHYSICIANS INC

JHD
See GRAPHIC SOLUTIONS GROUP INC

D-U-N-S 01-322-0945 EXP
JHF USA EXPORTS INC
9330 W Arprt Blvd Ste 150, Houston, TX 77031
Tel (281) 933-7507 *Founded/Ownrshp* 2007
Sales 31.3MM *EMP* 11
Accts Dr Darshan Wadhwa Houston T
SIC 5149 Groceries & related products; Groceries & related products
Pr: Michael Fernandes

D-U-N-S 02-837-1391
JHH MOTOR CARS INC
43301 12th St W, Lancaster, CA 93534-5861
Tel (661) 948-0731 *Founded/Ownrshp* 1984
Sales 41.6MM^E *EMP* 116
SIC 5511 Automobiles, new & used; Automobiles, new & used
Pr: James Hawse
Sls Mgr: Brett Hawse
Sls Mgr: Bob Zsarko

JHHC
See JOHNS HOPKINS HEALTHCARE LLC

JHIRMACK
See INSPIRED BEAUTY BRANDS INC

JHL CONSTRUCTORS
See JHL ENTERPRISES INC

D-U-N-S 96-787-1141
JHL CORP SERVICES INC
120 W 106th St, New York, NY 10025-3923
Tel (212) 870-5000 *Founded/Ownrshp* 2011
Sales 20.8MM *EMP* 1
Accts Loeb & Troper Llp New York N
SIC 8999 Services; Services
Prin: Thomas Gilmartin

D-U-N-S 15-525-3529
JHL ENTERPRISES INC
JHL CONSTRUCTORS
7076 S Alton Way Ste H, Centennial, CO 80112-2020
Tel (303) 741-6116 *Founded/Ownrshp* 1984
Sales 30.6MM^E *EMP* 40
SIC 1542 1541 1522 8059 Commercial & office building, new construction; Commercial & office buildings, renovation & repair; School building construction; Industrial buildings, new construction; Renovation, remodeling & repairs: industrial buildings; Hotel/motel & multi-family home construction; Personal care home, with health care
CEO: John Hachmeister
**Pr:* Ben Stellor
CFO: Ron Velardi
Ex VP: Patrick D Mershon
**VP:* Timothy Balas
**VP:* Brad Schmahl
**VP:* Brian Townsend
Snr PM: Mike Spallone

D-U-N-S 09-275-0728
JHM ENTERPRISES INC
JHM HOTELS
60 Pointe Cir Ste 300, Greenville, SC 29615-3582
Tel (864) 232-9944 *Founded/Ownrshp* 1974
Sales 65.0MM^E *EMP* 483
SIC 7011 Motel, franchised; Motel, franchised
CEO: Hasmukh P Rama
**Pr:* Jayanti P Rama
COO: Suresh Mathur
**CFO:* Luke Finlay
CFO: John Kennedy
VP: Jay Burnett
VP: Lee Hunter
**VP:* Manhar P Rama
VP: Sid Wall
Exec: Bonnie Franklin
Genl Mgr: Jim Beaty

JHM HOTELS
See JHM ENTERPRISES INC

JHONSON TIMBER
See FUTUREWOOD CORP

D-U-N-S 07-930-9269
■ **JHP GROUP HOLDINGS INC**
(*Suby of* PAR PHARMACEUTICAL COMPANIES INC) ★
1 Upper Pond Rd Ste 4, Parsippany, NJ 07054-1050
Tel (973) 658-3569 *Founded/Ownrshp* 2014
Sales 121.6MM^E *EMP* 957^E
SIC 2834 Pharmaceutical preparations; Druggists' preparations (pharmaceuticals); Tablets, pharmaceutical; Medicines, capsuled or ampuled; Pharmaceutical preparations; Druggists' preparations (pharmaceuticals); Tablets, pharmaceutical; Medicines, capsuled or ampuled
CEO: Paul Campanelli

D-U-N-S 61-802-2149
JHPIEGO CORP
1615 Thames St Ste 310, Baltimore, MD 21231-3492
Tel (410) 537-1800 *Founded/Ownrshp* 1974
Sales 295.6MM *EMP* 1,800
SIC 8299 Educational services; Educational services
Pr: Leslie Mancuso
**Ch Bd:* Joseph Cooper
**COO:* Edwin J Judd
COO: Joe Judd
**CFO:* Ronald Geary
CFO: Ronald Gerair
**V Ch Bd:* Theodore Poehler
Bd of Dir: C C Raffaeli
Ofcr: Amanda Ajulu
Ofcr: Antoinette Allsbrooks
Ofcr: Lee Ann
Ofcr: Manjushree Badlani
Ofcr: Rebecca Fielding
Ofcr: Alishea Galvin
Ofcr: George Hoyah
Ofcr: Stuart Merkel
**Sr VP:* Alain Damiba
VP: Richard Lamporte
**VP:* Harshad Sanghvi

D-U-N-S 05-968-6782
JHR CORP
BODY SHOP
700 N Mcdonald St, McKinney, TX 75069-2138
Tel (975) 547-0811 *Founded/Ownrshp* 1990
Sales 20.0MM^E *EMP* 105
SIC 5999 Perfumes & colognes
Pr: John Rattan
Exec: Debbie Siddall

JHS
See JAMESON MEMORIAL HOSPITAL

D-U-N-S 13-331-1030
JHT HOLDINGS INC
10801 Corporate Dr, Pleasant Prairie, WI 53158-1603
Tel (877) 327-7743 *Founded/Ownrshp* 1999
Sales 246.6MM^E *EMP* 2,891^E
SIC 4213 Trucking, except local; Trucking, except local
CEO: Michael Testman
**Ch Bd:* Dennis M Troha
CFO: Mark Portman
VP: Frank J Pacetti

D-U-N-S 82-870-9969 IMP
JIANGSU ROYAL HOME USA INC
13451 S Point Blvd, Charlotte, NC 28273-2701
Tel (704) 542-2304 *Founded/Ownrshp* 2008
Sales 25.3MM *EMP* 14
SIC 5023 Home furnishings
Pr: Kathy Dayvault

D-U-N-S 06-203-5691
JIC FOOD SOURCE LLC
607 Corinne St Ste C3, Hattiesburg, MS 39401-3852
Tel (601) 544-9442 *Founded/Ownrshp* 1998
Sales 25.0MM *EMP* 4
SIC 5144 Poultry & poultry products; Poultry & poultry products
Off Mgr: Ashley Bass

D-U-N-S 04-070-7366
JICARILLA APACHE NATION
JICARILLA SHOPPING CENTER
Hawks Dr & Hwy 64, Dulce, NM 87528
Tel (575) 759-3242 *Founded/Ownrshp* 1800
Sales 153.4MM^E *EMP* 850
SIC 5251 5541 5921 6512 4911 Hardware; Gasoline service stations; Liquor stores; Shopping center, community (100,000 - 300,000 sq ft); Electric services; Hardware; Gasoline service stations; Liquor stores; Shopping center, community (100,000 - 300,000 sq ft); Electric services
Pr: Levi Pesata
**Treas:* Francine Manwell
**VP:* Ty Vicent

JICARILLA SHOPPING CENTER
See JICARILLA APACHE NATION

D-U-N-S 05-964-7924
JID TRANSPORTATION LLC
158 61st St Apt 2, West New York, NJ 07093-2925
Tel (201) 362-0841 *Founded/Ownrshp* 2014
Sales 85.0MM *EMP* 1
SIC 3713 4212 7363 Truck cabs for motor vehicles; Truck rental with drivers; Truck driver services
Prin: Jaile Luis Diaz

JIFFY FOOD STORES
See HUDSON FOOD STORES INC

JIFFY LUBE
See MFA PETROLEUM CO

JIFFY LUBE
See EMPIRE LUBE INC

JIFFY LUBE
See F L ROBERTS AND CO INC

JIFFY LUBE
See LONE STAR LUBRICATION INC

JIFFY LUBE
See CAROLINA LUBES INC

JIFFY LUBE
See LUBRICAR INC

JIFFY LUBE
See STC MANAGEMENT LLC

JIFFY LUBE
See MC LLC

JIFFY LUBE
See NAJJAR LUBE CENTERS INC

JIFFY LUBE
See LUCOR INC

JIFFY LUBE
See LUBE MANAGEMENT CORP

JIFFY LUBE
See HEARTLAND AUTOMOTIVE SERVICES INC

D-U-N-S 02-172-5379
JIFFY LUBE INTERNATIONAL INC
(*Suby of* PENNZOIL-QUAKER STATE CO) ★
700 Milam St, Houston, TX 77002-2806
Tel (713) 546-4000 *Founded/Ownrshp* 2000
Sales 278.0MM^E *EMP* 6,560^E
SIC 7549 Lubrication service, automotive
Pr: Marc C Graham
**Treas:* David P Alderson II
**VP:* Linda F Condit
**VP:* Thomas M Mc Connell
**VP:* Bradley F Stuebing
Store Mgr: Giancarlo Perez
IT Man: Roque Baecker
IT Man: Linda Johnson

JIGE
See MILLER INDUSTRIES INC

D-U-N-S 15-077-0519
■ **JIL INFORMATION SYSTEMS INC**
(*Suby of* ALLIED TECHNOLOGY GROUP INC) ★
1803 Res Blvd Ste 601, Rockville, MD 20850
Tel (301) 309-1234 *Founded/Ownrshp* 2005
Sales 10.3MM^E *EMP* 290
SIC 7373 Systems engineering, computer related; Systems integration services; Systems engineering, computer related; Systems integration services
CEO: Bailey Walsh

D-U-N-S 83-121-9295 IMP
JILL ACQUISITION LLC
(*Suby of* GOLDEN GATE CAPITAL) ★
4 Batterymarch Park, Quincy, MA 02169-7468
Tel (617) 376-4300 *Founded/Ownrshp* 2009
Sales 419.0MM^E *EMP* 3,200
SIC 5961 5621 Catalog sales; Ready-to-wear apparel, women's; Catalog sales; Ready-to-wear apparel, women's
CEO: Paula Bennett

JILLY, GABOR S MD
See JOSEPH A CAPLAN MD PC

D-U-N-S 06-721-1052 EXP
JIM AND SLIMS TOOL SUPPLY INC
13065 Belcher Rd S, Largo, FL 33773-1697
Tel (727) 535-3363 *Founded/Ownrshp* 1972
Sales 24.9MM^E *EMP* 42
SIC 5082 5251 Contractors' materials; Tools
Pr: James Burczynski
**Sec:* Charmaine Burczynski
Genl Mgr: Kelly Durkin
Sales Asso: Mike Mora

JIM BABBIT LINCOLN-MERCURY
See BABBITT FORD L-M LLC

D-U-N-S 05-423-7482
JIM BAIER INC (IA)
FORD LINCOLN MERCURY
5601 Avenue O, Fort Madison, IA 52627-9426
Tel (319) 372-1012 *Founded/Ownrshp* 1971
Sales 27.8MM^E *EMP* 62
SIC 5511 Automobiles, new & used; Automobiles, new & used
Pr: Jim Baier
**VP:* Linda Baier
MIS Dir: Helen Hoenig
Advt Dir: Roger Anderson
Sls Mgr: Alan Hecht
Sls Mgr: Jeff Rump
Sales Asso: Jay Huffman
Sales Asso: Clayton Varner

D-U-N-S 00-512-1447 IMP/EXP
JIM BEAM BRANDS CO
JAMES B BEAM IMPORT
(*Suby of* BEAM SUNTORY INC) ★
510 Lake Cook Rd Ste 200, Deerfield, IL 60015-4964
Tel (847) 948-8903 *Founded/Ownrshp* 1923, 1997
Sales 203.1MM^E *EMP* 985
SIC 2085 Distilled & blended liquors; Bourbon whiskey; Gin (alcoholic beverage); Vodka (alcoholic beverage); Distilled & blended liquors; Bourbon whiskey; Gin (alcoholic beverage); Vodka (alcoholic beverage)
CEO: Matthew J Shattock
**Pr:* Richard B Reese
**Chf Mktg O:* Rory Finlay
**Ex VP:* Craig M Smith
**Ex VP:* Joseph J Winkler
Sr VP: Beth Bronner
Sr VP: Mike Donohoe
Sr VP: Ed Moser
**Sr VP:* Bob Probst
VP: Thomas J Flocco
VP: Mindy Mackenzie
VP: Florence Pramberger
VP: Marcio Ribeiro

JIM BISHOP BUICK
See JIM BISHOP CHEVROLET-BUICK-PONTIAC-GMC INC

D-U-N-S 13-263-6598
JIM BISHOP CHEVROLET-BUICK-PONTIAC-GMC INC
JIM BISHOP BUICK
221 Beardsley Ct, Muscle Shoals, AL 35661-1075
Tel (256) 383-3731 *Founded/Ownrshp* 1983
Sales 34.5MM^E *EMP* 80
SIC 5511 Automobiles, new & used; Automobiles, new & used
Pr: James E Bishop
COO: Christopher Graham
**Sec:* Gary Kilpatrick
Sls Mgr: Donnie Roden

JIM BISHOP TOYOTA
See BISHOP KILPATRICK INC

D-U-N-S 06-109-4181
JIM BOTTIN ENTERPRISES INC
ABC FINANCIAL
8320 Highway 107, North Little Rock, AR 72120-3825
Tel (501) 835-4569 *Founded/Ownrshp* 1978
Sales 35.0MM^E *EMP* 170
SIC 8721 7322 Billing & bookkeeping service; Collection agency, except real estate; Billing & bookkeeping service; Collection agency, except real estate
Pr: Paul Schaller
**Ch Bd:* Jim Bottin
**CFO:* Bob Whisnant
**Ofcr:* Bill Murray
**Sr VP:* Mike Escobedo
VP: Bob Cassin
VP: Dennis Holcom
VP: Mac Madkins
VP: Nikki Roe
**CIO:* Roger Barnett
**CTO:* Richard Smith

D-U-N-S 09-761-5884
JIM BROWN CHEVROLET INC
6877 Center St, Mentor, OH 44060-4233
Tel (440) 255-5511 *Founded/Ownrshp* 1979
Sales 64.0MM^E *EMP* 225
SIC 5511 7515 Automobiles, new & used; Passenger car leasing; Automobiles, new & used; Passenger car leasing
Pr: James Brown
CFO: Larry Villines
**Sec:* Jeff Fortuna
**VP:* Frank Lakava

D-U-N-S 03-150-5084
JIM BURKE AUTOMOTIVE INC
1409 5th Ave N, Birmingham, AL 35203-1838
Tel (205) 324-3371 *Founded/Ownrshp* 1979
Sales 79.2MM^E *EMP* 200
SIC 5511 7389 Automobiles, new & used; Automobile recovery service; Automobiles, new & used; Automobile recovery service
Pr: Jim Burke Jr
**Sec:* George Taylor III
Opers Mgr: Earl Holley
Sales Exec: Chad Wilson
Sales Asso: J Lynch

JIM BURKE FORD
See FORD HABERFELDE

D-U-N-S 06-368-3759
JIM BURKE MOTORS INC
JIM BURKEH JEEP EAGLE
1301 5th Ave N, Birmingham, AL 35203-1732
Tel (800) 922-4103 *Founded/Ownrshp* 1995
Sales 27.9MM^E *EMP* 109
SIC 5511 5521 Automobiles, new & used; Used car dealers; Automobiles, new & used; Used car dealers
Pr: Jim Burke
Sls Mgr: Mike V Kanel

JIM BURKEH JEEP EAGLE
See JIM BURKE MOTORS INC

D-U-N-S 05-920-3091
JIM BUTLER CHEVROLET INC
BUTLER JIM G M CRTIF U VHICLES
9900 Watson Rd, Saint Louis, MO 63126-1827
Tel (314) 965-6060 *Founded/Ownrshp* 1956
Sales 27.9MM^E *EMP* 75
SIC 5511 Automobiles, new & used; Automobiles, new & used
Pr: James J Butler Jr
**Sec:* Thomas Butler
Sls Mgr: Don Bay
Board of Directors: James J

D-U-N-S 94-123-8144
JIM BUTLER CHEVROLET INC
759 Gravois Bluffs Blvd, Fenton, MO 63026-7719
Tel (314) 966-3311 *Founded/Ownrshp* 1981
Sales 22.8MM^E *EMP* 47^E
SIC 5511 7538 Automobiles, new & used; General automotive repair shops
Pr: James Butler

D-U-N-S 62-299-4507
JIM BUTLER SATURN INC
11157 Lindbergh Bus Ct, Saint Louis, MO 63123-7810
Tel (314) 892-9600 *Founded/Ownrshp* 1990
Sales 36.1MM^E *EMP* 90
SIC 5511 Automobiles, new & used; Automobiles, new & used
Pr: James J Butler Jr

D-U-N-S 08-397-2752
JIM C HAMER CO
901 12th St, Kenova, WV 25530-1734
Tel (304) 453-6381 *Founded/Ownrshp* 1976
Sales 22.9MM^E *EMP* 150
SIC 2421

D-U-N-S 00-786-9555
JIM CAUSLEY BUICK GMC TRUCKS (DE)
CAUSLEY JIM PONTIAC GMC TRCKS
38111 S Gratiot Ave, Clinton Township, MI 48036-3592
Tel (586) 465-1281 *Founded/Ownrshp* 1957
Sales 66.4MM^E *EMP* 125
SIC 5511 Automobiles, new & used; Pickups, new & used; Automobiles, new & used; Pickups, new & used
Pr: Robert Causley
**Sec:* Dan Weis
Sls&Mrk Ex: Mike Elliott
Sls Mgr: Dave Herbert
Sls Mgr: Steve Wiegand
Sales Asso: Jerry BAC
Sales Asso: Eric Dolivo
Sales Asso: Jim Nelson

JIM CLICK AUTOMOTIVE
See JIM CLICK FORD INC

D-U-N-S 03-597-3247
JIM CLICK FORD INC (CA)
JIM CLICK AUTOMOTIVE
6422 E 22nd St, Tucson, AZ 85710-5124
Tel (520) 747-2000 *Founded/Ownrshp* 1969
Sales 71.8MM^E *EMP* 250
SIC 5511 7538 7515 7513 Automobiles, new & used; General automotive repair shops; Passenger car leasing; Truck rental & leasing, no drivers; Automobiles, new & used; General automotive repair shops; Passenger car leasing; Truck rental & leasing, no drivers
Pr: James H Click Jr
Pr: Christoher B Cotter
CFO: Susan Artaz
Sec: Ron Anderson
Sec: Bradley R Wise
VP: Robert Tuttle
Sls Mgr: John Smith
Board of Directors: Robert Tuttle

D-U-N-S 01-775-8996
JIM CLICK INC (CA)
JIM CLICK NISSAN
780 W Competition Rd, Tucson, AZ 85705-6000
Tel (520) 884-4100 *Founded/Ownrshp* 1955
Sales 270.0MM^E *EMP* 750
SIC 5511 Automobiles, new & used; Automobiles, new & used
Pr: Christopher B Cotter
**CFO:* Susan Artaz
**CFO:* Bradley R Wise
**Ch:* James H Click Jr
**VP:* Robert Tuttle
Off Mgr: Eddy Yashar
Sls Mgr: Tim Manzano

JIM CLICK NISSAN
See JIM CLICK INC

D-U-N-S 07-491-2882
JIM COGDILL DODGE CO INC (TN)
COGDILL'S DODGE
8544 Kingston Pike, Knoxville, TN 37919-5373
Tel (865) 690-1611 *Founded/Ownrshp* 1975
Sales 35.6MM^E *EMP* 85
SIC 5511 Automobiles, new & used; Automobiles, new & used
Pr: James T Cogdill
**Treas:* Tom King
**VP:* Edward Allen
**VP:* Claude L Royston
Sls Mgr: Herb Miser
Sls Mgr: Brad Rayfield

JIM COLEMAN AUTOMOTIVE
See COLEMAN CADILLAC CO

D-U-N-S 02-657-7981 IMP/EXP
JIM COLEMAN CO
HANNA
5842 W 34th St, Houston, TX 77092-6402
Tel (713) 683-9878 *Founded/Ownrshp* 1966
Sales 41.1MM^E *EMP* 300^E
SIC 3559 5087 Automotive related machinery; Carwash equipment & supplies; Automotive related machinery; Carwash equipment & supplies
Pr: Russell Coleman
**Ch Bd:* James E Coleman
**Treas:* Wayne Coleman
Ex VP: Jean De Negri
**VP:* Randy Coleman
VP: Ted Winchester
**Ex Dir:* Anette Martin
Ex Dir: Nancy McCall
Mfg Mgr: Jon Graham
Plnt Mgr: Kenneth Macejewski
Mktg Dir: Jamie Ware

D-U-N-S 78-644-9926
JIM COLEMAN TOYOTA INC
(*Suby of* BETHESDA INVESTMENT HOLDING CO INC) ★
10400 Auto Park Ave, Bethesda, MD 20817-1006
Tel (301) 469-7100 *Founded/Ownrshp* 1989
Sales 53.6MM^E *EMP* 212
SIC 5511 7538 5521 Automobiles, new & used; General automotive repair shops; Used car dealers; Automobiles, new & used; General automotive repair shops; Used car dealers
Pr: James R Coleman
**Ch Bd:* William H Coleman Jr
Genl Mgr: Brian Smith
Sls Mgr: Patrick Coleman

D-U-N-S 78-553-5352
JIM COOPER CONSTRUCTION CO INC
5004 5th Ave S, Birmingham, AL 35212-3512
Tel (205) 871-0304 *Founded/Ownrshp* 1991
Sales 24.5MM^E *EMP* 28
Accts Duval & Associates Pc Cpas
SIC 1542 Commercial & office building, new construction
Pr: James L Cooper Jr

D-U-N-S 01-437-7659
JIM CRIVELLI CHEVROLET INC (PA)
108 Mckees Rocks Plz, Mc Kees Rocks, PA 15136-3559
Tel (412) 331-0120 *Founded/Ownrshp* 1940
Sales 22.6MM^E *EMP* 53
SIC 5511 Automobiles, new & used; Automobiles, new & used
Pr: James P Crivelli Sr
**Treas:* Joseph Horgan
Sr VP: Jim Boburka Sr
Mktg Mgr: Lisa Stelmack
Sls Mgr: Brock Baird
S&M/Mgr: James Crivelli Jr

D-U-N-S 06-652-1931 IMP
JIM DONSKEY CORP
NORTHERN BATTERY
1546 Miller St, La Crosse, WI 54601-5242
Tel (608) 785-0044 *Founded/Ownrshp* 1977
Sales 27.0MM *EMP* 51
SIC 5013 5531

JIM EARP PLYMOUTH
See EARP JIM CHRYSLER JEEP LLC

JIM ELLIS DIRECT
See ELLIS ATLANTA JIM INC

D-U-N-S 18-511-7769
JIM ELLIS INC
JIM ELLIS MAZDA OF MARIETTA
1141 Cobb Pkwy S, Marietta, GA 30060-9236
Tel (770) 590-4450 *Founded/Ownrshp* 1988
Sales 27.5MM^E *EMP* 81
SIC 5511 5521 Automobiles, new & used; Used car dealers; Automobiles, new & used; Used car dealers
Pr: James W Ellis Jr
**CFO:* James E Ellis
Genl Mgr: Chuck Wallace
Dir IT: Wayne Ussery
Advt Mgr: Chris Horton

JIM ELLIS MAZDA OF MARIETTA
See JIM ELLIS INC

D-U-N-S 84-516-1983
JIM ELLIS MOTORS INC
JIM ELLIS VLKSWGN/UDI MARIETTA
950 Ernest W Barrett Pkwy, Kennesaw, GA 30144-4530
Tel (770) 955-6565 *Founded/Ownrshp* 1995
Sales 67.0MM *EMP* 103
SIC 5511 Automobiles, new & used; Automobiles, new & used
Pr: Jim Ellis
Sls Mgr: Dane Hulse

JIM ELLIS VLKSWGN/UDI MARIETTA
See JIM ELLIS MOTORS INC

D-U-N-S 07-314-5971
JIM F WEBB INC (TX)
J W POWERLINE CONSTRUCTION
700 S Fairgrounds Rd, Midland, TX 79701-1240
Tel (432) 684-4388 *Founded/Ownrshp* 1974
Sales 342.1MM^E *EMP* 200
SIC 4911 Electric services; Electric services
Pr: Jimmy Webb
**Pr:* Kyle Watkins
**VP:* Linette Webb
Dir IT: Oats Nunez
Board of Directors: Jim F Webb

D-U-N-S 12-131-1195
JIM FALK MOTORS INC
1201 N 2nd St, Clinton, MO 64735-1423
Tel (660) 885-8181 *Founded/Ownrshp* 2000
Sales 26.5MM^E *EMP* 60
SIC 5511 Automobiles, new & used; Pickups, new & used; Vans, new & used
Pr: Jim Falk

D-U-N-S 02-699-4988
JIM FORD BASS INC
LINCOLN MERCURY
4052 W Houston Harte Expy, San Angelo, TX 76901-5049
Tel (325) 949-4621 *Founded/Ownrshp* 1961
Sales 49.2MM^E *EMP* 130
SIC 5511 Automobiles, new & used; Automobiles, new & used
Pr: John A Bass
**Treas:* George M Lomas
**VP:* James M Bass III
IT Man: Gaye Ramsey
Sls&Mrk Ex: Kay Rosser
Mktg Mgr: Laura Sosa
Sls Mgr: Emerald Mica

D-U-N-S 03-153-0546
JIM FORD SKINNER INC
9924 Parkway E, Birmingham, AL 35215-7308
Tel (205) 854-2222 *Founded/Ownrshp* 1958
Sales 47.8MM^E *EMP* 100
SIC 5511 7539 Automobiles, new & used; Pickups, new & used; Automotive repair shops; Automobiles, new & used; Pickups, new & used; Automotive repair shops
VP: James Skinner
**Pr:* Robert Skinner
**CFO:* David Lee
Off Mgr: Rhonda Glover
Store Mgr: Fred Whitworth

D-U-N-S 07-958-6327
JIM FORD SOUTHWORTH INC
SOUTHWRTH FORD LINCOLN MERCURY
1430 N Baldwin Ave, Marion, IN 46952-1929
Tel (765) 662-2561 *Founded/Ownrshp* 1978
Sales 23.4MM^E *EMP* 52
SIC 5511 7538 7532 5521 Automobiles, new & used; General automotive repair shops; Top & body repair & paint shops; Used car dealers
Pr: Jeff Southworth
**VP:* Jacqueline Edwards
Genl Mgr: Denny Aker
Sales Asso: Daryl Yeakle

D-U-N-S 02-553-0023
■ **JIM FORD TIDWELL INC**
JIM TIDWELL'S WORLD FORD
(*Suby of* GROUP 1 AUTOMOTIVE INC) ★
2205 Barrett Lakes Blvd, Kennesaw, GA 30144-4906
Tel (770) 427-5531 *Founded/Ownrshp* 2000
Sales 32.4MM^E *EMP* 85
SIC 5511

D-U-N-S 03-207-6903
JIM FUOCO MOTOR CO
741 N 1st St, Grand Junction, CO 81501-2297
Tel (970) 242-1571 *Founded/Ownrshp* 1956
Sales 48.8MM *EMP* 100
SIC 5511 5012 Automobiles, new & used; Pickups, new & used; Vans, new & used; Automobiles; Automobiles, new & used; Pickups, new & used; Vans, new & used; Automobiles
Pr: Robert Fuoco
**Sec:* Anna Maria Fuoco
Sls&Mrk Ex: Ed Nielsen

JIM GLOVER CHEVROLET
See CLAREMORE AUTOMALL LLC

D-U-N-S 05-299-3672
JIM GLOVER CHEVROLET ISUZU (OK)
RELIABLE GEO
8130 E Skelly Dr, Tulsa, OK 74129-3410
Tel (918) 663-2300 *Founded/Ownrshp* 1957, 1996
Sales 37.5MM^E *EMP* 200
SIC 5511 Automobiles, new & used; Automobiles, new & used
Pr: Cecil Van Tuyl
**Sec:* Robert Holcomb
**VP:* Gary Matern
Store Mgr: Brenda Barricklow
Dir IT: Bruce Gramn
Manager: Randy Christensen
VP Mktg: Steve Barnes
Mktg Dir: Jeff Cooper
Sls Mgr: Rob Melone

D-U-N-S 61-683-3570
JIM HADLEY CHEVROLET CADILLAC INC
CHANDLER CHEVROLET
600 Clifty Dr, Madison, IN 47250-1611
Tel (812) 273-4400 *Founded/Ownrshp* 1990
Sales 24.9MM^E *EMP* 85^E
SIC 5511 5531 7538 7513 5521 5012 Automobiles, new & used; Pickups, new & used; Automotive parts; General automotive repair shops; Truck rental & leasing, no drivers; Used car dealers; Automobiles & other motor vehicles; Automobiles, new & used; Pickups, new & used; Automotive parts; General automotive repair shops; Truck rental & leasing, no drivers; Used car dealers; Automobiles & other motor vehicles
Pr: Jim Hadley
**Sec:* Tom Tepe

JIM HARDMAN BUICK
See HARDMAN JIM PONTIAC-BUICK-GMC TRUCK INC

D-U-N-S 06-865-6628
JIM HAWK TRUCK TRAILER INC
(*Suby of* HAWK JIM GROUP INC) ★
3119 S 9th St, Council Bluffs, IA 51501-7664
Tel (712) 366-2241 *Founded/Ownrshp* 1993
Sales 82.3MM^E *EMP* 275
SIC 5012 Trailers for trucks, new & used; Trailers for trucks, new & used
Pr: James V Hawk
**Pr:* David P Hawk
**CFO:* Gene Dolan
CFO: Eugene Dollen
**Treas:* James V Hawk III
Brnch Mgr: Jack Cory
Genl Mgr: Jack Croy
Genl Mgr: John Minard
Dir IT: Rick Nordman
S&M/VP: Lanny Goetzinger
Sls Mgr: Brent Jensen

D-U-N-S 78-501-8722
JIM HAWK TRUCK-TRAILERS OF ILLINOIS INC
(*Suby of* HAWK JIM GROUP INC) ★
4001 N Main St, East Peoria, IL 61611-1454
Tel (309) 694-6271 *Founded/Ownrshp* 1993
Sales 37.9MM^E *EMP* 275
SIC 5012 Trailers for trucks, new & used; Trailers for trucks, new & used
Pr: James Hawk
**VP:* Dale Young
S&M/VP: Nick Herbst
Sales Asso: Mike Evans

D-U-N-S 06-241-7985
JIM HAYES FORD LINCOLN INC
2130 Us Highway 45 N, Harrisburg, IL 62946-4812
Tel (618) 252-8611 *Founded/Ownrshp* 1976
Sales 21.2MM^E *EMP* 42
SIC 5511 Automobiles, new & used; Pickups, new & used
Pr: Jim Hayes
**Sec:* Stacy L Wasson

D-U-N-S 12-179-5025
JIM HERRICK MOTORS INC
LIBERTY FORD LINCOLN MERCURY
4215 Liberty Ave, Vermilion, OH 44089-2132
Tel (440) 967-6191 *Founded/Ownrshp* 1980
Sales 43.2MM^E *EMP* 280
SIC 5511 Automobiles, new & used; Automobiles, new & used
Pr: James Herrick
IT Man: Ray Warner

D-U-N-S 05-843-5363
JIM HICKS AND CO
565 Mercury Ln, Brea, CA 92821-4831
Tel (714) 671-2153 *Founded/Ownrshp* 1982
Sales 46.0MM^E *EMP* 20
Accts Genske Mulder & Company Llp
SIC 5191 2873 Fertilizer & fertilizer materials; Chemicals, agricultural; Fertilizers: natural (organic), except compost
Pr: James P Hicks

D-U-N-S 02-672-8774
JIM HOFFPAUIR INC
HOFFPAUIR OUTDOOR SUPERSTORE
802 N Key Ave, Lampasas, TX 76550-1123
Tel (512) 556-6285 *Founded/Ownrshp* 1964
Sales 23.9MM^E *EMP* 37
SIC 5511 Automobiles, new & used
Pr: Lee Hoffpauir

D-U-N-S 09-988-4058
JIM HUDSON BUICK GMC CADILLAC INC
4035 Kaiser Hill Rd, Columbia, SC 29203-9356
Tel (803) 783-0110 *Founded/Ownrshp* 1980
Sales 38.5MM^E *EMP* 75^E
SIC 5511 Automobiles, new & used; Pickups, new & used; Automobiles, new & used; Pickups, new & used
Pr: Keith Hudson
**VP:* James E Hudson
Genl Mgr: Robert Yeomans
Sls Mgr: Bobby Maner
Sls Mgr: Steve Matthews
Sales Asso: Scott McLaughlin

D-U-N-S 55-709-7735
JIM HUDSON SUPERSTORE INC
HUDSON, JIM TOYOTA
970 Columbia Ave, Irmo, SC 29063-2854
Tel (803) 407-5678 *Founded/Ownrshp* 1986
Sales 33.2MM^E *EMP* 90
SIC 5511 Automobiles, new & used; Automobiles, new & used
Pr: Jim Hudson

JIM JOHNSON PONTIAC
See JOHNSON JIM PONTIAC NISSAN INC

D-U-N-S 00-892-8731
JIM KEIM FORD
KEIM, JIM FORD SALES
5575 Keim Cir, Columbus, OH 43228-7328
Tel (614) 888-3333 *Founded/Ownrshp* 1996
Sales 45.3MM^E *EMP* 100
SIC 5511 7538 5521 Automobiles, new & used; Pickups, new & used; General automotive repair shops; Used car dealers; Automobiles, new & used; Pickups, new & used; General automotive repair shops; Used car dealers
Pr: James Keim
**Sec:* L D Pellissier III
Ex VP: Carl Mitchell
CIO: Rick Bedard
Sales Exec: Kim Lawrence

JIM KERAS AUTOMOTIVE
See NISSAN JIM KERAS INC

D-U-N-S 03-479-0048
JIM KERAS BUICK CO INC
KERAS, JIM SUBARU
2080 Covington Pike, Memphis, TN 38128-6982
Tel (901) 373-2700 *Founded/Ownrshp* 1972
Sales 25.4MM^E *EMP* 60
SIC 5511 5013 7514 Automobiles, new & used; Pickups, new & used; Vans, new & used; Automotive supplies & parts; Passenger car rental; Automobiles, new & used; Pickups, new & used; Vans, new & used; Automotive supplies & parts; Passenger car rental
Pr: James J Keras
**VP:* Penelli Keras
Genl Mgr: Ben Keras

D-U-N-S 17-519-0339
JIM KOONS MANAGEMENT CO
2000 Chain Bridge Rd, Vienna, VA 22182-2531
Tel (703) 448-7000 *Founded/Ownrshp* 1986
Sales 309.7MM^E *EMP* 165
SIC 8741

D-U-N-S 03-494-4215
JIM L SHETAKIS DISTRIBUTING CO
SHETAKIS WHOLESALERS
3840 Civic Center Dr, North Las Vegas, NV 89030-7534
Tel (702) 940-3663 *Founded/Ownrshp* 1999
Sales 106.2MM^E *EMP* 60
SIC 5141 5046 Groceries, general line; Restaurant equipment & supplies; Groceries, general line; Restaurant equipment & supplies
Pr: Charlie Jackson
**CFO:* Andrew Dannin
VP: John Quinones
**VP:* Michael Winburn

D-U-N-S 96-899-5758
JIM LAR CORP
MCDONALD'S
1325 Buckner Rd Se, Mableton, GA 30126-2710
Tel (770) 948-6558 *Founded/Ownrshp* 1977
Sales 8.9MM^E *EMP* 350
SIC 5812 Fast-food restaurant, chain; Fast-food restaurant, chain
Pr: James Taylor
**VP:* Sandy Taylor

JIM LUPIENT OLDS CO
See LUPIENT OLDSMOBILE CO (INC)

D-U-N-S 80-320-5038
JIM LUPIENT SATURN INC
7911 Lakeland Ave N, Brooklyn Park, MN 55445-2416
Tel (612) 332-7300 *Founded/Ownrshp* 1990
Sales 30.6MM^E *EMP* 88
SIC 5511 Automobiles, new & used; Automobiles, new & used
CEO: Jim Lupient

D-U-N-S 05-765-6506
JIM MC COMB CHEVROLET
3622 N University St, Peoria, IL 61604-1327
Tel (309) 686-2500 *Founded/Ownrshp* 1990
Sales 35.2MM^E *EMP* 106

SIC 5511 5521 Automobiles, new & used; Used car dealers; Automobiles, new & used; Used car dealers
Pr: Mark Weston
**VP:* Gary Uftring
IT Man: Dave Litz
Netwrk Mgr: Rick Nixon

D-U-N-S 00-587-1090 IMP
JIM MCKAY CHEVROLET INC
3509 University Dr, Fairfax, VA 22030-2397
Tel (703) 591-4800 *Founded/Ownrshp* 1956
Sales 35.4MM *EMP* 82
SIC 5511 7699 Automobiles, new & used; Shopping cart repair; Automobiles, new & used; Shopping cart repair
Pr: Kathleen McKay
**VP:* Ruth McKay
Genl Mgr: Patrick Cowan
Sls Mgr: Chris Hahn
Sls Mgr: Rod Kidd

D-U-N-S 02-760-3281
JIM MEIER INC
HERZOG-MEIER AUTO CENTER
4275 Sw 139th Way, Beaverton, OR 97005-2302
Tel (503) 644-9121 *Founded/Ownrshp* 1985
Sales 47.0MME *EMP* 120
SIC 5511 5521 Automobiles, new & used; Used car dealers; Automobiles, new & used; Used car dealers
Pr: Jim Meier
Exec: Tracy Petersen
Genl Mgr: Chris Meier
CTO: Adam Byers
IT Man: Tom Herzog
IT Man: Herzog Tom
Sls Mgr: John Ericksen
Sls Mgr: Scott Green
Sls Mgr: John Kim
Sales Asso: Chelsea Jeffers
Sales Asso: Lucian Slanisot

D-U-N-S 60-758-6641
JIM MELLON GENERAL CONTRACTING INC
MELLON CERTIFIED RESTORATION
436 S Lansdowne Ave Ste 1, Yeadon, PA 19050-2493
Tel (610) 622-5860 *Founded/Ownrshp* 1982
Sales 66.9MME *EMP* 160
SIC 1521 Repairing fire damage, single-family houses; Repairing fire damage, single-family houses
Pr: James A Mellon
**VP:* Elizabeth Mellon
**VP:* Frank Panico
Prd Mgr: Dan Park

D-U-N-S 02-537-7185
JIM MLADY OLDSMOBILE INC
M'LADY, JIM OLDSMOBILE, NISSA
5656 Northwest Hwy, Crystal Lake, IL 60014-8017
Tel (815) 459-2288 *Founded/Ownrshp* 1957
Sales 33.6MME *EMP* 75
SIC 5511 6159 Automobiles, new & used; Automobile finance leasing; Automobiles, new & used; Automobile finance leasing
Pr: James G M Lady
**Pr:* James G M'Lady

JIM MURPHY & ASSOCIATES
See MURPHY-TRUE INC

D-U-N-S 15-478-9853
JIM MURPHY PONTIAC GMC TRUCKS INC
3000 Walden Ave, Depew, NY 14043-2608
Tel (716) 684-8900 *Founded/Ownrshp* 1985
Sales 28.7MME *EMP* 65
SIC 5511 Automobiles, new & used; Pickups, new & used; Automobiles, new & used; Pickups, new & used
Pr: Jim Murphy
Exec: Jim Vavreck
Sales Exec: Michael Murphy
Sls Mgr: Scott Horvatits
Sales Asso: Peter Sabio
Sales Asso: Mary Vella

D-U-N-S 04-615-5339
JIM MYERS & SONS INC
11024 Nations Ford Rd, Pineville, NC 28134-9433
Tel (704) 554-8397 *Founded/Ownrshp* 1962
Sales 21.0MME *EMP* 35
SIC 3589 Water treatment equipment, industrial
Pr: David L Myers
**VP:* James B Myers III

D-U-N-S 83-290-0109
JIM NORTON AUTOMOTIVE
9809 S Memorial Dr, Tulsa, OK 74133-6198
Tel (918) 872-6700 *Founded/Ownrshp* 2009
Sales 23.5MME *EMP* 250
SIC 5511 New & used car dealers; New & used car dealers
Owner: Jim Norton

JIM NORTON TOYOTA
See J & D ACQUISITIONS INC

D-U-N-S 78-625-5005
JIM OLSON MOTORS INC
632 Green Bay Rd, Sturgeon Bay, WI 54235-3039
Tel (920) 743-4461 *Founded/Ownrshp* 2006
Sales 20.7MME *EMP* 45
SIC 5511 5015 Automobiles, new & used; Automotive parts & supplies, used
Pr: Jim Olson
Genl Mgr: Chum Nault
Off Mgr: Lee Bley
Sales Asso: Tom Stephenson

D-U-N-S 01-661-2905 EXP
JIM ONEAL FORD INC
516 S Indiana Ave, Sellersburg, IN 47172-1652
Tel (812) 246-4441 *Founded/Ownrshp* 1961
Sales 30.3MME *EMP* 75
SIC 5511 7515 7513 5521 5012 Automobiles, new & used; Passenger car leasing; Truck rental & leasing, no drivers; Used car dealers; Automobiles & other motor vehicles; Automobiles, new & used; Passenger car leasing; Truck rental & leasing, no drivers; Used car dealers; Automobiles & other motor vehicles
Pr: Chris L O'Neal
**Pr:* James L O'Neal
**VP:* Christopher O'Neal
Off Mgr: Bruce Rager

D-U-N-S 04-521-6900
JIM PALMER TRUCKING
9730 Derby Dr, Missoula, MT 59808-9422
Tel (406) 721-5151 *Founded/Ownrshp* 1967
Sales 72.6MME *EMP* 487
SIC 4213 Trucking, except local; Refrigerated products transport; Trucking, except local; Refrigerated products transport
CEO: Joe Kalafat
**CFO:* Bill Dunn
**Ch:* James V Palmer
**Treas:* Blazo Gjorev

JIM PRICE CHVRLET OLDS HYUNDAI
See PRICE CHEVROLET CO

D-U-N-S 03-221-2508
■ **JIM QUINLAN CHEVROLET CO**
CLEARWATER PARTS CENTER
(*Suby of* AUTONATION INC) ★
15005 Us Highway 19 N, Clearwater, FL 33764-7163
Tel (727) 222-0034 *Founded/Ownrshp* 1997
Sales 71.8MME *EMP* 250
SIC 5511 5013 New & used car dealers; Motor vehicle supplies & new parts; New & used car dealers; Motor vehicle supplies & new parts
Pr: James Bender
Genl Mgr: Chris Bruder

D-U-N-S 03-245-5495
JIM RATHMANN CHEVROLET INC
800 S Harbor City Blvd, Melbourne, FL 32901-1907
Tel (321) 723-3611 *Founded/Ownrshp* 1961
Sales 32.2MME *EMP* 160
SIC 5511 Automobiles, new & used; Pickups, new & used; Automobiles, new & used; Pickups, new & used
Ch Bd: Richard R Jim Rathmann
**Pr:* James T Rathmann
**Treas:* Bernard Shenkman

D-U-N-S 00-792-2776
JIM REED CHEVROLET CO (TN)
1512 Broadway, Nashville, TN 37203-3136
Tel (615) 329-2929 *Founded/Ownrshp* 1914
Sales 36.9MME *EMP* 160
Accts George B Jones
SIC 5511 5012 5521 Automobiles, new & used; Automobiles & other motor vehicles; Used car dealers; Automobiles, new & used; Automobiles & other motor vehicles; Used car dealers
Ch Bd: James H Reed III
**Pr:* James H Reed IV
CFO: T C Staton
**Sec:* Marvis Krantz
Sls Mgr: Allen Vines
Board of Directors: Ed Leroue, J Bradbury Reed, John Clay Reed

D-U-N-S 08-625-4310
JIM RIEHLS FRIENDLY AUTOMOTIVE GROUP INC (MI)
RIEHL'S, JIM FRIENDLY BUICK
18900 Hall Rd, Clinton Township, MI 48038-6909
Tel (586) 412-9600 *Founded/Ownrshp* 2000
Sales 76.7MM *EMP* 64
SIC 5511 Automobiles, new & used; Automobiles, new & used
Pr: James E Riehl Jr
Genl Mgr: Bob Riehl

D-U-N-S 04-180-3446
JIM RIEHLS FRIENDLY CHRYSLER JEEP INC
32899 Van Dyke Ave, Warren, MI 48093-8139
Tel (586) 979-8700 *Founded/Ownrshp* 1987
Sales 50.0MME *EMP* 120
SIC 5511 7538 7532 5531 5521 Automobiles, new & used; General automotive repair shops; Top & body repair & paint shops; Automotive & home supply stores; Used car dealers; Automobiles, new & used; General automotive repair shops; Top & body repair & paint shops; Automotive & home supply stores; Used car dealers
Pr: Jim Riehl Jr
**Sec:* Ida Warner
Exec: Sue Jeleniewski
Sls Mgr: Terry O Mara
Sls Mgr: Patrick Presutti

D-U-N-S 06-654-3265
JIM RYAN CHEVROLET INC
1800 S Broadway, Minot, ND 58701-6506
Tel (701) 852-3571 *Founded/Ownrshp* 1973
Sales 32.6MME *EMP* 80
SIC 5511 5521 Automobiles, new & used; Used car dealers; Automobiles, new & used; Used car dealers
Pr: Kathleen Gaddie
**Pr:* James Ryan
Mktg Dir: Lance Knaup

D-U-N-S 05-689-2482
JIM SCHMIDT CHEVROLET-OLDSMOBILE INC
JIM SCHMIDT OLDSMOBILE
575 W High St, Hicksville, OH 43526-1037
Tel (419) 542-7731 *Founded/Ownrshp* 1984
Sales 35.0MM *EMP* 39
SIC 5511 Automobiles, new & used; Automobiles, new & used
Pr: Jim Schmidt
**Sec:* Tom Meps
**VP:* Karen Schmidt
Off Mgr: Michele Peter
Sls Mgr: Scott Wiling

JIM SCHMIDT OLDSMOBILE
See JIM SCHMIDT CHEVROLET-OLDSMOBILE INC

JIM SIGEL AUTOMOTIVE CENTER
See JIM SIGEL ENTERPRISES INC

D-U-N-S 04-490-4720
JIM SIGEL ENTERPRISES INC
JIM SIGEL AUTOMOTIVE CENTER
1601 Ne 7th St, Grants Pass, OR 97526-1317
Tel (541) 476-0811 *Founded/Ownrshp* 1968
Sales 28.3MME *EMP* 70
SIC 5511 7538 Automobiles, new & used; General automotive repair shops; Automobiles, new & used; General automotive repair shops
Pr: Jeffrey B Sigel
**VP:* James J Sigel
Off Mgr: Debbie McLaughlin
Store Mgr: Brian Malone

D-U-N-S 05-915-5036
JIM SLOAN FORD INC
SLOAN FORD LINCOLN MERCURY
115 S James Campbell Blvd, Columbia, TN 38401-4323
Tel (931) 381-9366 *Founded/Ownrshp* 1971
Sales 28.6MM *EMP* 62
SIC 5511 5531 7539 Automobiles, new & used; Automobile & truck equipment & parts; Automotive repair shops; Automobiles, new & used; Automobile & truck equipment & parts; Automotive repair shops
Pr: James R Sloan
**VP:* Riley D Sloan
Sls Mgr: Doug Smith

D-U-N-S 00-701-2164
JIM SMITH CONTRACTING CO LLC
OHIO VALLEY GRAVEL & SAND CO
1108 Dover Rd, Grand Rivers, KY 42045-9117
Tel (270) 362-8661 *Founded/Ownrshp* 1967
Sales 59.3MME *EMP* 160
SIC 1611 2952 2951 2891 1771 Highway & street construction; Asphalt felts & coatings; Asphalt paving mixtures & blocks; Adhesives & sealants; Concrete work; Highway & street construction; Highway & street paving contractor; Asphalt felts & coatings; Asphalt paving mixtures & blocks; Adhesives & sealants; Concrete work
Pr: Calvin Rex Smith
**CFO:* Cheryl Baugus
Genl Mgr: Randy Armstrong
Prd Mgr: Matt Maxfield
Board of Directors: Cheryl Baugus, Calvin Rex Smith

D-U-N-S 88-313-1401
JIM TAYLOR CHEVROLET LLC
139 Grimshaw St, Rayville, LA 71269-5522
Tel (318) 728-6550 *Founded/Ownrshp* 2002
Sales 57.2MM *EMP* 45
SIC 5511 Automobiles, new & used; Automobiles, new & used
Sales Exec: Jim Taylor
Sls Dir: Buddy Smittherman

JIM TIDWELL'S WORLD FORD
See JIM FORD TIDWELL INC

D-U-N-S 80-994-4812
JIM TRENARY CHEVROLET INC
JIM TRENARY PRE-OWNED CENTER
501 Auto Mall Dr, O Fallon, MO 63368-2204
Tel (636) 946-6300 *Founded/Ownrshp* 1993
Sales 29.8MME *EMP* 71
SIC 5511 Automobiles, new & used; Automobiles, new & used
Pr: James W Trenary
**VP:* Rhonda Trenary
Sls Mgr: Eric Cargill
Sls Mgr: Kent Larkin
Sales Asso: Andrew Chazen

JIM TRENARY PRE-OWNED CENTER
See JIM TRENARY CHEVROLET INC

D-U-N-S 01-706-3108
JIM WERNIG INC
2401 S Otsego Ave, Gaylord, MI 49735-9409
Tel (989) 732-5161 *Founded/Ownrshp* 1977
Sales 21.7MME *EMP* 54
SIC 5511 Automobiles, new & used
Pr: James H Wernig Jr
**VP:* Eugene Skiba
Exec: Lucas Shepherd
Sales Asso: Chris Maxon

D-U-N-S 80-319-9272
JIM WHITE CO INC
LEXUS OF TOLEDO
7505 W Central Ave, Toledo, OH 43617-1523
Tel (419) 841-3500 *Founded/Ownrshp* 1991
Sales 20.7MME *EMP* 60
SIC 5511 Automobiles, new & used; Automobiles, new & used
Pr: Dave White
**VP:* Tim White

D-U-N-S 14-443-7829
JIM WHITEHEAD TIRE SERVICE INC
2514 Deans Bridge Rd, Augusta, GA 30906-2202
Tel (706) 738-5126 *Founded/Ownrshp* 1985
Sales 26.7MM *EMP* 75
Accts The Cleveland Group Martinez
SIC 5014 7534 5531 Truck tires & tubes; Tire recapping; Automotive tires; Truck tires & tubes; Tire recapping; Automotive tires
CEO: James L Whitehead Sr
**CFO:* James L Whitehead Jr
**Sec:* Peggy B Whitehead

D-U-N-S 07-912-3006
JIM WILSON & ASSOCIATES INC
2660 Eastchase Ln Ste 100, Montgomery, AL 36117-7024
Tel (334) 260-2500 *Founded/Ownrshp* 1975
Sales 11.1MME *EMP* 365
SIC 6531 6552 Real estate managers; Land subdividers & developers, commercial; Real estate managers; Land subdividers & developers, commercial
Pr: James Wilson Jr

D-U-N-S 05-334-6649
JIM WINTER BUICK-GMC TRUCK-NISSAN INC
3303 W Michigan Ave, Jackson, MI 49202-1834
Tel (517) 787-5100 *Founded/Ownrshp* 1970
Sales 25.3MME *EMP* 65
SIC 5511 5521 5012 Automobiles, new & used; Used car dealers; Automobiles & other motor vehicles; Automobiles, new & used; Used car dealers; Automobiles & other motor vehicles
Ch: James F Winter
**Pr:* Richard Walicki
Sales Asso: Jeff Braun
Sales Asso: Lynn Hinkley
Sales Asso: Patrick O'Dowd
Sales Asso: Norm Simpson
Sales Asso: John Thomson

D-U-N-S 07-949-2476
JIM WYNN VOLKSWAGEN INC
WYNN GROUP, THE
2049 W Main St, Norristown, PA 19403-3003
Tel (610) 539-1100 *Founded/Ownrshp* 1979
Sales 26.5MME *EMP* 63
SIC 5511 Automobiles, new & used; Automobiles, new & used
Pr: Cynthia J Cook
**Treas:* Warren J Wynn
**VP:* Maxine Kreiner
Genl Mgr: Pat Cook
Mktg Dir: Andy Beittel
Sls Mgr: Rick Strunk
Dietician: Simo Chaoui

D-U-N-S 19-418-8082
JIM-N-I INC
ALLIED STEEL
5415 E Fork Rd, Lewistown, MT 59457-8819
Tel (406) 538-2374 *Founded/Ownrshp* 1980
Sales 25.2MME *EMP* 65
SIC 3441 Fabricated structural metal
CEO: Patrick Southworth
**Pr:* James W Southworth
**Treas:* Julie Walsh
**Sec:* Jeff Southworth

D-U-N-S 14-170-1354
JIMBOS JUMBOS INC
(*Suby of* HAMPTON FARMS) ★
185 Peanut Dr, Edenton, NC 27932-9604
Tel (252) 482-2193 *Founded/Ownrshp* 1946
Sales 136.9MME *EMP* 205
SIC 5159 Peanuts (bulk), unroasted; Peanuts (bulk), unroasted
Pr: Dallas Barnes
**VP:* William E McKeown
VP: Mike Partin
Genl Mgr: Hal Burns
Prd Mgr: Roy Thompson
Trfc Mgr: Eddie McNair

D-U-N-S 11-859-2328
JIMBOS NATURAL FAMILY INC
12853 El Camino Real, San Diego, CA 92130-2010
Tel (858) 793-7755 *Founded/Ownrshp* 1984
Sales 32.3MME *EMP* 250E
SIC 5499 Health foods; Health foods
CEO: James D Someck
Genl Mgr: Eddie Garcia

D-U-N-S 03-153-2526
JIMBURKE AUTOMOTIVES
STEEL CITY OLDS GMC ISUZU
1301 5th Ave N, Birmingham, AL 35203-1732
Tel (205) 324-3371 *Founded/Ownrshp* 1937
Sales 24.6MME *EMP* 71E
SIC 5511 7539 Automobiles, new & used; Pickups, new & used; Automotive repair shops; Automobiles, new & used; Pickups, new & used; Automotive repair shops
Pr: Jim Burke
Sales Exec: Pat Donlevy

D-U-N-S 00-703-7831 IMP
JIMCO LAMP & MANUFACTURING CO (OH)
J HUNT & CO
(*Suby of* HOME DECOR HOLDING CO) ★
11759 Highway 63 N B, Bono, AR 72416-8676
Tel (870) 935-6820 *Founded/Ownrshp* 2005
Sales 28.3MME *EMP* 150E
SIC 3645 3999 Residential lighting fixtures; Table lamps; Floor lamps; Wall lamps; Shades, lamp or candle; Residential lighting fixtures; Table lamps; Floor lamps; Wall lamps; Shades, lamp or candle
Pr: Don Harmon
**CFO:* Dan Shear
**VP:* Ron Lindley
Prin: Greg Tabor
MIS Dir: Dan Dormio

D-U-N-S 15-048-5787
JIMCOR AGENCY INC
60 Craig Rd, Montvale, NJ 07645-1709
Tel (856) 866-8858 *Founded/Ownrshp* 1986
Sales NA *EMP* 89
SIC 6411 Insurance agents
Pr: Francis J Mastowski
**CEO:* Coryn F Thalmann
**Treas:* Ellen Mastowski
**Sr VP:* John J George
**VP:* Alan Dudkiewicz
Brnch Mgr: John George
Brnch Mgr: Christopher Hofmann
Off Mgr: Erika Hasty
CIO: James Mastowski
Sls&Mrk Ex: Andrew Proda

D-U-N-S 82-470-4878
JIMENEZ CONTRACT SERVICES LLC
J C S
1246 Silber Rd, Houston, TX 77055-7100
Tel (713) 681-6407 *Founded/Ownrshp* 1993
Sales 27.1MM *EMP* 70

SIC 5712 1799 4226 7641 Office furniture; Furniture moving, local: without storage; Office furniture installation; Furniture storage, without local trucking; Furniture refinishing; Office furniture; Office furniture installation; Furniture storage, without local trucking; Furniture refinishing

D-U-N-S 05-702-7419
JIMINY PEAK MOUNTAIN RESORT LLC
JIMINY PEAK RESORT
37 Corey Rd, Hancock, MA 01237-9541
Tel (413) 738-5500 *Founded/Ownrshp* 1968
Sales 39.6MM^E *EMP* 750
SIC 7011 7999 Ski lodge; Waterslide operation; Ski lodge; Waterslide operation
Pt: Tyler Fairbank
**Pt:* Joseph Odonnell
**COO:* Paul Maloney
**CFO:* John Filiault
**Ch:* Brian H Fairbank
VP: Jim Van Dyke
Rgnl Mgr: Jim Bronson

JIMINY PEAK RESORT
See JIMINY PEAK MOUNTAIN RESORT LLC

D-U-N-S 01-208-1543 IMP/EXP
JIMLAR CORP
CALVIN KLEIN FOOTWEAR
350 5th Ave Lbby 8, New York, NY 10118-0223
Tel (646) 560-0255 *Founded/Ownrshp* 2010
Sales 85.4MM^E *EMP* 249^E
SIC 5139 Footwear

D-U-N-S 04-709-0014
JIMMIE CROWDER EXCAVATING AND LAND CLEARING INC
901 Geddie Rd, Tallahassee, FL 32304-8671
Tel (850) 576-7176 *Founded/Ownrshp* 1973
Sales 37.5MM^E *EMP* 225
Accts Thomas Howell Ferguson Pa
SIC 1794 1629 1795 1771 1611 Excavation & grading, building construction; Earthmoving contractor; Wrecking & demolition work; Concrete work; Highway & street construction; Excavation & grading, building construction; Earthmoving contractor; Wrecking & demolition work; Concrete work; Highway & street construction
Pr: Tina L Crowder
**Treas:* Robert L Mayo
**VP:* Jason T Crowder

JIMMIE JOHNSON KEARNY
See KEARNY MESA AUTOMOTIVE CO

JIMMY CHOO
See J CHOO USA INC

JIMMY EVANS COMPANY
See JD EVANS OF AUSTIN INC

D-U-N-S 10-219-4339
JIMMY JOHNS ENTERPRISES LLC
JIMMY JOHNS GOURMET
2212 Fox Dr, Champaign, IL 61820-7532
Tel (217) 356-9900 *Founded/Ownrshp* 1983
Sales 21.2MM^E *EMP* 350
SIC 5812 6794 Sandwiches & submarines shop; Franchises, selling or licensing; Sandwiches & submarines shop; Franchises, selling or licensing
Prin: James L Liautaud
**CFO:* Jeff Vaughan
Exec: Giles Brian

JIMMY JOHNS GOURMET
See JIMMY JOHNS ENTERPRISES LLC

D-U-N-S 06-029-9773
JIMMY R LYNCH & SONS INC
307 S Academy St, Pilot Mountain, NC 27041-7604
Tel (336) 368-4047 *Founded/Ownrshp* 1969
Sales 20.7MM^E *EMP* 65
SIC 1623 1611 Water main construction; Sewer line construction; Grading
Pr: Jimmy R Lynch
**VP:* Mark K Lynch
Off Mgr: Cathy Snow

D-U-N-S 55-644-6342
JIMMY RISCKY
RISCKY'S BARBEQUE
2314 Azle Ave, Fort Worth, TX 76164-6740
Tel (817) 624-0765 *Founded/Ownrshp* 1927
Sales 8.0MM^E *EMP* 400
SIC 5812 Barbecue restaurant
Owner: Jimmy Riscky

JIMMY VASSER CHEVROLET TOYOTA
See V S AUTOMOTIVE INC

D-U-N-S 02-358-7264
JIMS CHEESE PANTRY INC
410 Portland Rd, Waterloo, WI 53594-1200
Tel (920) 478-3571 *Founded/Ownrshp* 1970
Sales 25.6MM^E *EMP* 50
SIC 5143 Cheese
Pr: James Peschel
**VP:* Judy Peschel
Sales Exec: Traci Filter

D-U-N-S 18-745-5910
JIMS CONCRETE OF BREVARD INC
6760 Greenland Indus Blvd, Jacksonville, FL 32258-2594
Tel (904) 886-4743 *Founded/Ownrshp* 1990
Sales 26.6MM^E *EMP* 148
SIC 1771 Concrete work; Concrete repair; Concrete work; Concrete repair
Pr: James Jacobson
**VP:* Lisa Jacobson
VP: Bobby R Washington

D-U-N-S 02-588-1145 IMP
JIMS FORMAL WEAR LLC
CRDN OF GREATER ST. LOUIS
804 E Broadway, Trenton, IL 62293-1418
Tel (618) 224-9211 *Founded/Ownrshp* 2012
Sales 20.8MM^E *EMP* 450
SIC 7299 5699

JIM'S HARLEY-DAVIDSON
See JAMIES MOTORSPORTS INC

JIM'S MACHINING
See THIESSEN PRODUCTS INC

D-U-N-S 05-070-6282
JIMS MANAGEMENT CO
MCDONALD'S
5950 N Oak Trfy Ste 204, Kansas City, MO 64118-5164
Tel (816) 455-0800 *Founded/Ownrshp* 1970
Sales 17.9MM^E *EMP* 544
SIC 5812 Fast-food restaurant, chain; Fast-food restaurant, chain
Pr: Jim Wagy

D-U-N-S 04-115-5425 IMP
JIMS SUPPLY CO INC
3530 Buck Owens Blvd, Bakersfield, CA 93308-4920
Tel (661) 324-6514 *Founded/Ownrshp* 1955
Sales 73.4MM^E *EMP* 85
SIC 5051 Steel; Steel
CEO: Doreen M Boylan
**CFO:* Bryan Boylan
**Sec:* Jennifer Drake
**VP:* Greg Boylan
**VP:* Jennice Boylan
**VP:* Dan Drake
Exec: Tim Moreno
Opers Mgr: Jeff Miller
Advt Dir: Daron Hobson
Sales Asso: Kevin Been
Sales Asso: Hillary Boylan

JIM'S TRUCK PLAZA
See WHITE ARROW SERVICE STATIONS INC

D-U-N-S 04-691-6250
JIMS WATER SERVICE INC
205 Newton Rd, Gillette, WY 82716-3226
Tel (307) 682-4051 *Founded/Ownrshp* 1971
Sales 28.5MM^E *EMP* 180
SIC 4212 Liquid haulage, local; Liquid haulage, local
Pr: Jim Rodgers
CFO: Kate Seneca
Sfty Mgr: Teresa Estes

D-U-N-S 11-540-7744 IMP
JIMWAY INC
ALTAIR LIGHTING
20101 S Santa Fe Ave, E Rncho Dmngz, CA 90221-5917
Tel (310) 886-5143 *Founded/Ownrshp* 1982
Sales 22.0MM^E *EMP* 100
SIC 3648 3221 5099 5063 Lighting equipment; Glass containers; Gas lighting fixtures; Brass goods; Containers: glass, metal or plastic; Electrical apparatus & equipment
Pr: James Keng
**VP:* Irene Wang

D-U-N-S 07-916-2113
JINDAL FILMS AMERICAS LLC
(*Suby of* JINDAL POLY FILMS LIMITED)
729 State Route 31, Macedon, NY 14502-9179
Tel (315) 966-1000 *Founded/Ownrshp* 2013
Sales 44.8MM^E *EMP* 100^E
SIC 8732 Research services, except laboratory
Prin: Anand Sundararaman
**CFO:* Corinne Heiter
**Treas:* Greg Zaccardo
**Ex VP:* Paul Griffith
**Ex VP:* Dru Kefalos
**Ex VP:* Dru Kesalos

D-U-N-S 06-162-4453 IMP
JINDAL INTERNATIONAL INC (NY)
INTERNATIONAL TRADING
103 Carnegie Ctr Ste 218, Princeton, NJ 08540-6235
Tel (212) 818-9400 *Founded/Ownrshp* 1996
Sales 21.0MM *EMP* 5
SIC 5169 Essential oils
Pr: Sanjay Jindal

D-U-N-S 82-532-2865 IMP/EXP
JINDAL SAW USA LLC
(*Suby of* JINDAL SAW LIMITED)
1411 S Fm 565 Rd, Baytown, TX 77523-9054
Tel (281) 573-3002 *Founded/Ownrshp* 2007
Sales 35.0MM *EMP* 22
SIC 3317 Steel pipe & tubes; Steel pipe & tubes
Prin: P Jindal
Genl Mgr: Kamaljit Singh
Plnt Mgr: Nitin Kharat

D-U-N-S 07-949-0899
JINHAP US CORP
(*Suby of* JINHAP CO., LTD)
199 W Diversey Ave, Elmhurst, IL 60126-1103
Tel (630) 833-2880 *Founded/Ownrshp* 2013
Sales 70.5MM^E *EMP* 230^E
SIC 3965 Fasteners, buttons, needles & pins; Fasteners, buttons, needles & pins
CEO: Lee Young-Sup

D-U-N-S 12-013-2977 IMP
JINNY BEAUTY SUPPLY CO INC
3587 Oakcliff Rd, Atlanta, GA 30340-3014
Tel (770) 734-9222 *Founded/Ownrshp* 1995
Sales 200.0MM *EMP* 300
SIC 5087 Beauty salon & barber shop equipment & supplies; Beauty salon & barber shop equipment & supplies
Pr: Eddie Jhin
Ofcr: Steven Fischman
Sr VP: Chang Seo
CIO: Craig Wood

D-U-N-S 19-073-2867
JINON CORP
NIJIYA MARKET
2180 W 190th St, Torrance, CA 90504-6103
Tel (310) 787-3305 *Founded/Ownrshp* 1986
Sales 77.6MM^E *EMP* 600
SIC 5411 Grocery stores, independent; Grocery stores, independent
Pr: Saburomaru Tsujino
**Pr:* Alfred Blanckensee
CFO: Akemi Suzuki
IT Man: Geer Frank
Sls Mgr: Yoshito Suzuki

D-U-N-S 62-676-6450 IMP
JINPAN INTERNATIONAL LIMITED
560 Sylvan Ave Ste 104, Englewood Cliffs, NJ 07632-3119
Tel (201) 227-0680 *Founded/Ownrshp* 1997
Sales 18.8MM^E *EMP* 281
Accts Ernst & Young
SIC 3612 Power & distribution transformers; Voltage regulating transformers, electric power

JINX HACKWEAR/JINX.COM
See JINX INC

D-U-N-S 14-937-2117 IMP
JINX INC
JINX HACKWEAR/JINX.COM
13465 Gregg St, Poway, CA 92064-7135
Tel (858) 457-5462 *Founded/Ownrshp* 2004
Sales 23.6MM^E *EMP* 92
SIC 5699 5136 T-shirts, custom printed; Men's & boys' clothing
CEO: Jason Kraus
**Pr:* Tim Norris
**Ch:* Sean Gailey
Creative D: Chris Hope
IT Man: Matthew Gailey
Sales Asso: Samuel Carvalho

D-U-N-S 03-355-6924
JIPC MANAGEMENT INC
JOHN'S INCREDIBLE PIZZA CO
22342 Avenida Empresa # 220, Rcho STA Marg, CA 92688-2161
Tel (949) 916-2000 *Founded/Ownrshp* 1998
Sales 82.3MM^E *EMP* 1,000
SIC 8741 Restaurant management; Restaurant management
Pr: John M Parlet

D-U-N-S 17-379-5360
JIT CORP
J I T SUPPLY
1610 Commerce Way, Paso Robles, CA 93446-3645
Tel (805) 238-5000 *Founded/Ownrshp* 1986
Sales 50.6MM^E *EMP* 60
SIC 5065 Electronic parts
Pr: Brent Smith
**Sec:* Sharon Smith
VP: Ted Hall
Genl Mgr: Mark Whittaker
Netwrk Mgr: Michaele Smith
Mtls Mgr: Eric Eiden
Mtls Mgr: Jon Johnson
Mtls Mgr: Justin Rosemore
Mtls Mgr: Eric Willeford
Ql Cn Mgr: Frank Huggins

D-U-N-S 87-483-6901
JIT PACKAGING INC
PACKAGING WHOLESALERS, THE
1717 Gifford Rd, Elgin, IL 60120-7534
Tel (630) 736-4400 *Founded/Ownrshp* 1994
Sales 48.1MM^E *EMP* 63
SIC 5199 Packaging materials
Pr: Michael E Hrbacek
Sls Mgr: Brenda Marasa

D-U-N-S 18-312-2050 IMP
JIT SERVICES LLC
125 Electronics Blvd Sw A1, Huntsville, AL 35824-2213
Tel (256) 461-7064 *Founded/Ownrshp* 2004
Sales 27.8MM^E *EMP* 135
SIC 4226 3679 4225 Special warehousing & storage; Electronic circuits; General warehousing

D-U-N-S 01-017-9607
JIVE COMMUNICATIONS INC
1275 W 1600 N Ste 102, Orem, UT 84057-2428
Tel (801) 226-4477 *Founded/Ownrshp* 2006
Sales 38.2MM^E *EMP* 27
SIC 5065 4812 4813 Telephone equipment; Radio telephone communication; Local & long distance telephone communications; Wire telephone; Local telephone communications; Long distance telephone communications
Pr: Brent Thomson
**Sec:* Michael Sharp
VP: Brian Moore
Off Admin: Marcie Molnar
CTO: Theo Zourzouvillys
QA Dir: Isaac Aldous
Dir IT: Todd Doyle
IT Man: Dee Jarvis
Software D: Rajasekhar Gadireddy
Software D: Ben Glasser
Software D: Tyler Jones

D-U-N-S 00-802-3181
▲ JIVE SOFTWARE INC
325 Lytton Ave Ste 200, Palo Alto, CA 94301-1431
Tel (650) 319-1920 *Founded/Ownrshp* 2001
Sales 178.6MM *EMP* 658^E
Accts Kpmg Llp Portland Oregon
Tkr Sym JIVE *Exch* NGS
SIC 7372 Prepackaged software; Application computer software; Prepackaged software; Application computer software
Pr: Elisa Steele
**Ch Bd:* Anthony Zingale
CFO: Bryan J Leblanc
Chf Mktg O: John Rizzo
Ofcr: William Pierznik
**Ofcr:* Matthew A Tucker
Ex VP: Oudi Antebi
Ex VP: Ofer Ben-David
VP: Robert Block
VP: Neil Graham
VP: Roberto Lino
VP: Bill Lynch
Comm Dir: Jason Khoury
Board of Directors: Margaret A Breya, James J Goetz, Jonathan G Heiliger, William A Lanfri, Thomas J Reilly, Charles J Robel, Theodore E Schlein, Gabrielle Toledano

JJ BOYLE
See JAMES J BOYLE & CO

D-U-N-S 16-163-1882 IMP
JJ CASSONE BAKERY INC
202 S Regent St, Port Chester, NY 10573-4791
Tel (914) 939-1568 *Founded/Ownrshp* 1984
Sales 61.0MM^E *EMP* 280
SIC 2051 5461 Bread, cake & related products; Bread, all types (white, wheat, rye, etc): fresh or frozen; Bakeries; Bread, cake & related products; Bread, all types (white, wheat, rye, etc): fresh or frozen; Bakeries
Pr: Mary Lou Cassone
COO: Linda Fitzpatrick
**VP:* Dominic Ambrose
**VP:* Tony Crusco
**VP:* Jack Guarcello
**VP:* Greg Mancuso

D-U-N-S 00-450-3686
JJ GUMBERG CO
1051 Brinton Rd Ste 201, Pittsburgh, PA 15221-4571
Tel (412) 262-9339 *Founded/Ownrshp* 1937
Sales 18.6MM^E *EMP* 500
SIC 6512 6513 Shopping center, property operation only; Commercial & industrial building operation; Apartment building operators; Shopping center, property operation only; Commercial & industrial building operation; Apartment building operators
Pr: Ira J Gumberg
**Treas:* Andrew D Gumberg
Ex VP: James D Murphy Jr
Ex VP: Stephen L White
Ex VP: Stephen White
VP: Harvey M Amado
VP: C Ted Donald
VP: David E Kasper
VP: Edward Ponczak
Mktg Dir: Janet Beem
Snr Mgr: Tera Crowe

D-U-N-S 00-310-1466
JJ MCDONNELL & CO INC (MD)
7901 Oceano Ave Ste 26, Jessup, MD 20794-9407
Tel (410) 799-4000 *Founded/Ownrshp* 1941, 1986
Sales 32.1MM^E *EMP* 37
SIC 5146 Fish & seafoods
Owner: George McManus III
Opers Mgr: Kathy Esposito
Sales Asso: Lauren Sackett

D-U-N-S 06-391-4121 IMP
JJ TAYLOR COMPANIES INC
655 N Highway A1a, Jupiter, FL 33477-4579
Tel (813) 247-4000 *Founded/Ownrshp* 1958
Sales 218.2MM^E *EMP* 600
SIC 5181 Ale; Beer & other fermented malt liquors; Ale; Beer & other fermented malt liquors
CEO: John J Taylor Jr
Pr: John J Taylor III
VP: Daniel Daul
Sls Dir: Frank Caputo
Mktg Mgr: Melissa Berger
Mktg Mgr: Lindsey Parra
Mktg Mgr: Jacqueline Santiago
Sls Mgr: Dave Lowery
Sls Mgr: Andy Sielaff

D-U-N-S 82-834-2241 IMP
JJ TAYLOR DISTRIBUTING CO OF MINNESOTA INC
(*Suby of* JJ TAYLOR COMPANIES INC) ★
701 Industrial Blvd Ne, Minneapolis, MN 55413-3019
Tel (651) 482-1133 *Founded/Ownrshp* 1997
Sales 41.1MM^E *EMP* 1^E
SIC 5181 Beer & ale
Pr: Mike Bamonti
VP: Daniel Daul
Mktg Dir: Billy Smith

JJ TEXTILE COMPANY
See JJ WORLD TEXTILE TRADING INC

D-U-N-S 07-913-8028 IMP
JJ WORLD TEXTILE TRADING INC
JJ TEXTILE COMPANY
600 E Wash Blvd Ste 201, Los Angeles, CA 90015-3767
Tel (213) 305-2595 *Founded/Ownrshp* 2011
Sales 24.0MM *EMP* 1
SIC 2282 Beaming yarns, for the trade; Beaming yarns, for the trade
CEO: John Paik

D-U-N-S 80-483-1105
JJB HILLIARD WLLYONS LLC
HILLIARD LYONS
(*Suby of* HOUCHENS INDUSTRIES INC) ★
500 W Jefferson St # 700, Louisville, KY 40202-2815
Tel (502) 588-8400 *Founded/Ownrshp* 2008
Sales 23.0MM^E *EMP* 1,100
SIC 7389 Financial services; Financial services
CEO: James R Allen
**VP:* Chambers Moore

D-U-N-S 06-762-3181 IMP
JJI LIGHTING GROUP INC
ALKCO LIGHTING COMPANY
(*Suby of* KONINKLIJKE PHILIPS N.V.)
11500 Melrose Ave, Franklin Park, IL 60131-1334
Tel (847) 451-3258 *Founded/Ownrshp* 2011
Sales 80.2MM^E *EMP* 650
SIC 3646 3648 3645 Commercial indusl & institutional electric lighting fixtures; Outdoor lighting equipment; Arc lighting fixtures; Floor lamps; Fluorescent lighting fixtures, residential; Table lamps; Wall lamps; Commercial indusl & institutional electric lighting fixtures; Outdoor lighting equipment; Arc lighting fixtures; Floor lamps; Fluorescent lighting fixtures, residential; Table lamps; Wall lamps
Pr: James F Hayworth
**CFO:* Charles J Florio
CFO: John Walsh
**VP Admn:* Peter K Mitchell
Genl Mgr: Bob Haidinger

D-U-N-S 94-395-5849
JJID INC
100 Julian Ln, Bear, DE 19701-2274
Tel (302) 836-0414 *Founded/Ownrshp* 1995
Sales 27.3MM^E *EMP* 50
SIC 1611 1629 Highway & street construction; Waste water & sewage treatment plant construction
Pr: Joseph R Julian
**Pr:* James J Julian
IT Man: Susan Trentham
Sfty Mgr: Doc Conn
Snr Mgr: Thomas Hutt

D-U-N-S 62-461-5345
JJJTB INC
3200 Flightline Dr, Lakeland, FL 33811-2848
Tel (863) 607-5600 *Founded/Ownrshp* 2004
Sales 249.5MM *EMP* 54^E
Accts Harman & Peaslee Pa Plant
SIC 4731 Truck transportation brokers; Truck transportation brokers
Pr: John J Jerue
**Treas:* E Luis Campano

D-U-N-S 80-159-0951
JJO CONSTRUCTION INC
9045 Osborne Dr, Mentor, OH 44060-4326
Tel (440) 255-1515 *Founded/Ownrshp* 1993
Sales 26.1MM *EMP* 20
Accts Martinet Recchia Inc Willough
SIC 1542 Commercial & office building, new construction; Commercial & office buildings, renovation & repair; Commercial & office building, new construction; Commercial & office buildings, renovation & repair
Pr: Joseph J Orel

JJP INVESTMENTS
See PAJCO INC

D-U-N-S 07-610-1112
JJR ENTERPRISES INC
CALTRONICS BUSINESS SYSTEMS
10491 Old Placerville Rd # 150, Sacramento, CA 95827-2533
Tel (916) 363-2666 *Founded/Ownrshp* 1975
Sales 53.7MM *EMP* 225
SIC 7629 5044 Business machine repair, electric; Office equipment; Business machine repair, electric; Office equipment
CEO: Daniel F Reilly
**CFO:* Anne Long
CFO: Shamus McClure
**Ch:* John J Reilly
Dir IT: Dalton Crawford
Manager: Dave Conroy
Sls Mgr: Daryl Sincere
Sls Mgr: Ross Wiffler

JJR PROPERTY MANAGEMENT
See STT INC

JJS
See JOSEPH JINGOLI & SON INC

D-U-N-S 10-897-3157 EXP
JJW CONSTRUCTION INC
1670 W Mcnab Rd, Fort Lauderdale, FL 33309-1001
Tel (954) 970-0211 *Founded/Ownrshp* 1984
Sales 24.1MM^E *EMP* 125
SIC 1542 Commercial & office building, new construction; Commercial & office building, new construction
Pr: Thomas F Walsh
**CFO:* Dennis L Goffar
**Ch:* Joseph J Walsh
Treas: Omar Gonzalez
**Ex VP:* Donald Dollar
VP: Mercedes Kember

D-U-N-S 61-779-5229
JK & T WINGS INC
13405 W Star Dr Ste 2, Shelby Township, MI 48315-2706
Tel (586) 781-0591 *Founded/Ownrshp* 1996
Sales 95.9MM^E *EMP* 1,200
SIC 8741 Administrative management; Administrative management
Pr: Kent Ward

J.K. AUTO PARTS STORE
See J K DISTRIBUTORS INC

D-U-N-S 02-541-3766
JK BUICK GMC INC
J K-G M C TRUCK
2300 Ogden Ave, Downers Grove, IL 60515-1711
Tel (630) 969-0022 *Founded/Ownrshp* 1995
Sales 22.2MM^E *EMP* 50
SIC 5511 7538 Automobiles, new & used; General automotive repair shops; Automobiles, new & used; General automotive repair shops
Pr: Judith K Spellman

D-U-N-S 12-827-9564
JK COMMUNICATIONS & CONSTRUCTION INC
KLEVEN CONSTRUCTION
110 S Priest Dr Ste 101, Tempe, AZ 85281-2493
Tel (480) 736-8400 *Founded/Ownrshp* 2002
Sales 68.8MM^E *EMP* 150
SIC 1623 Underground utilities contractor; Underground utilities contractor
Pr: Jerry A Kleven
**Ex VP:* Douglas N Kimball

D-U-N-S 11-255-1390
JK CONSULTANTS
1257 Sanguinetti Rd, Sonora, CA 95370-6215
Tel (209) 532-7772 *Founded/Ownrshp* 1980
Sales 25.0MM *EMP* 50
SIC 8748 8742 Business consulting; Management consulting services; Business consulting; Management consulting services
Pr: Fred Khachi
**Ex VP:* Elaine Khachi

D-U-N-S 07-075-5354 IMP
JK GROUP USA INC
KIIAN DIGITAL
106 Industrial Park Dr, Soddy Daisy, TN 37379-4224
Tel (423) 486-9378 *Founded/Ownrshp* 2012
Sales 25.0MM^E *EMP* 38^E
SIC 2759 Screen printing
Pr: Dennis Frank Wilby
**VP:* Fabio Festorazzi
Genl Mgr: Alessandro Ratti

D-U-N-S 79-687-7843
JK HILL & ASSOCIATES INC
2680 Prod Rd Ste 101, Virginia Beach, VA 23454
Tel (757) 362-2100 *Founded/Ownrshp* 1992
Sales 23.6MM *EMP* 351
Accts Cherry Bekaert Llp Virginia B
SIC 4581 8744 Airports, flying fields & services; Facilities support services; Airports, flying fields & services; Facilities support services
Prin: Bob Beauchamp
**Pr:* James K Hill
**CEO:* Robert L Beauchamp
**Sec:* Karen E Beauchamp

D-U-N-S 07-872-8635 IMP
JK IMAGING LTD
17239 S Main St, Gardena, CA 90248-3129
Tel (310) 755-6852 *Founded/Ownrshp* 2012
Sales 100.0MM *EMP* 100
SIC 5043 Cameras & photographic equipment; Cameras & photographic equipment
CEO: Joe Atick
**CFO:* Shu-Ping Wu

JK MOVING SERVICES LOUDOUN CO
See J K MOVING & STORAGE INC

D-U-N-S 96-772-2034
JK PETROLEUM INC
4668 Envoy Rd, Staten Island, NY 10312
Tel (718) 984-9551 *Founded/Ownrshp* 1995
Sales 22.6MM^E *EMP* 10
SIC 5172 Gasoline
Pr: Veeru Dhillon

D-U-N-S 87-806-2595
JKC AUTOMOTIVE INC
373 Goodpasture Island Rd, Eugene, OR 97401-2109
Tel (541) 686-8291 *Founded/Ownrshp* 1994
Sales 37.5MM^E *EMP* 120
SIC 5511 Automobiles, new & used; Automobiles, new & used
Pr: John Keifer
**Sec:* Corinne Keifer

D-U-N-S 60-874-7820
JKC TRUCKING INC
5450 S Center Ave, Summit Argo, IL 60501-1025
Tel (708) 496-3901 *Founded/Ownrshp* 1981
Sales 75.0MM *EMP* 370
SIC 4214

D-U-N-S 02-529-9053
JKC WEN LC
WENDY'S
2020 Sw 42nd Pl, Ocala, FL 34471-0159
Tel (352) 408-4627 *Founded/Ownrshp* 1995
Sales 8.8MM^E *EMP* 400
SIC 5812 Fast-food restaurant, chain; Fast-food restaurant, chain
Pr: John J Casey
**VP:* Kevin Casey

D-U-N-S 15-592-4350 IMP
JKG GROUP INC
J K G PRINTING & GRAPHICS
(*Suby of* GITTLIN COMPANIES INC) ★
740 S Powerline Rd, Deerfield Beach, FL 33442-8113
Tel (561) 241-1999 *Founded/Ownrshp* 1993
Sales 36.6MM^E *EMP* 160
SIC 2752 Commercial printing, lithographic; Commercial printing, lithographic
CEO: Bruce D Gittlin
**Pr:* Bob Gittlin
**COO:* Daniel Stansky
COO: Michael Wooldring
Comm Dir: Leon Rubin
Off Mgr: Precious Johnson
Sales Exec: Ed Agnew
Sales Exec: Martin Zenor

D-U-N-S 10-692-5209 IMP/EXP
JKL MANUFACTURING CORP
DISCO AUTOMOTIVE HARDWARE
6300 Highway 177 S, Sulphur, OK 73086-9168
Tel (580) 622-6866 *Founded/Ownrshp* 1986
Sales 25.7MM^E *EMP* 75
SIC 5013 Automotive hardware
Pr: James L Leonard
**VP:* Steven J Leonard
Off Mgr: Tammy Hayes

J.KOSKI TRUCKING
See J KOSKI CO

D-U-N-S 16-318-6059 IMP
JL AUDIO INC
10369 N Commerce Pkwy, Miramar, FL 33025-3962
Tel (954) 443-1100 *Founded/Ownrshp* 1977
Sales 84.3MM^E *EMP* 265
SIC 5065 2519 Sound equipment, electronic; Fiberglass furniture, household: padded or plain; Sound equipment, electronic; Fiberglass furniture, household: padded or plain
CEO: Lucio F Proni
**Pr:* Andy Oxenhorn
**VP:* Clare Gates
**VP:* George Jenkins
**VP:* Carl Kennedy
**VP:* Manville Smith
QA Dir: Oscar Otero
VP Opers: James Clayton
Ql Cn Mgr: George Rodriguez
Sls Dir: Ernie Collado
Sls Dir: Richard Young

D-U-N-S 01-887-4284
JL FRENCH AUTOMOTIVE CASTINGS INC
NEMAK
(*Suby of* NEMAK MEXICO, S.A.)
3101 S Taylor Dr, Sheboygan, WI 53081-9401
Tel (920) 458-7724 *Founded/Ownrshp* 1997
Sales 619.7MM^E *EMP* 3,599
SIC 3341 3363 8711 Aluminum die-castings; Designing: ship, boat, machine & product; Aluminum smelting & refining (secondary); Aluminum smelting & refining (secondary); Aluminum die-castings; Designing: ship, boat, machine & product
Ch Bd: Tom Musgrave
CFO: James A Amodeo
Sr Cor Off: John Falcon
Sr Cor Off: Tim Price
**VP:* Joe Heady
**VP:* Timothy R Kadeabek
Prgrm Mgr: Kirk Nick
CTO: Jerry Palmer
**CTO:* Charles Waldon
VP Opers: Tim Kadarafic
Mfg Mgr: Warren Hacker

D-U-N-S 61-963-2701 IMP
JL FRENCH AUTOMOTIVE LLC
(*Suby of* NEMAK USA INC) ★
3101 S Taylor Dr, Sheboygan, WI 53081-9401
Tel (920) 458-7724 *Founded/Ownrshp* 2004
Sales 128.1MM^E *EMP* 416^E
SIC 3465 Body parts, automobile: stamped metal

D-U-N-S 82-630-5062
JL GONZALEZ PRODUCE INC
2404 S Wolcott Ave Ste 22, Chicago, IL 60608-5343
Tel (312) 433-2335 *Founded/Ownrshp* 1992
Sales 36.7MM^E *EMP* 53^E
SIC 5148 Fresh fruits & vegetables
Pr: Jose Luis Gonzalez
**VP:* Miguel Gonzalez

D-U-N-S 00-679-6155
JL MARSHALL & SONS INC
3 Clara St, Seekonk, MA 02771-3904
Tel (508) 399-8910 *Founded/Ownrshp* 1986
Sales 59.4MM^E *EMP* 200
SIC 1542 1541 1629 Commercial & office building, new construction; Commercial & office buildings, renovation & repair; Institutional building construction; Industrial buildings, new construction; Renovation, remodeling & repairs: industrial buildings; Waste water & sewage treatment plant construction; Commercial & office building, new construction; Commercial & office buildings, renovation & repair; Institutional building construction; Industrial buildings, new construction; Renovation, remodeling & repairs: industrial buildings; Waste water & sewage treatment plant construction
Pr: Leo K Marshall
VP: Jack Conroy
**VP:* Shon McMullen
**VP:* Robert W Niles
**VP:* Kevin A Osborne
Sfty Dirs: Scott Bulger
Snr PM: David D'Angelo
Snr PM: Todd Hayward
Snr Mgr: Brian Cripps

D-U-N-S 03-335-6999
JL ROBERTS MECHANICAL CONTRACTING LLC
150 Linda Jo Dr, Richland, MS 39218-9225
Tel (601) 939-1011 *Founded/Ownrshp* 2003
Sales 28.0MM^E *EMP* 150
SIC 1711 Mechanical contractor; Mechanical contractor
Pr: Leonard Roberts
VP: Stacey Williams
Prin: Richard Sebren
Prin: Missy Shuler
Genl Mgr: Chris Jones
IT Man: Dottie Boylston

JLA HOME
See E & E CO LTD

JLAB AUDIO
See PEAG LLC

D-U-N-S 96-785-5946
JLB BUILDERS LLC
3890 W Northwest Hwy # 700, Dallas, TX 75220-8109
Tel (214) 271-8480 *Founded/Ownrshp* 2008
Sales 21.5MM^E *EMP* 75^E
SIC 1521 Single-family housing construction
COO: Paul Johnston
VP: Scott Sherwood

D-U-N-S 86-948-8333
JLB PARTNERS MANAGEMENT LLC
3890 W Northwest Hwy # 700, Dallas, TX 75220-8108
Tel (214) 271-8480 *Founded/Ownrshp* 2007
Sales 24.0MM^E *EMP* 22^E
SIC 6531 Real estate agents & managers
CEO: Bay Miltenberger
Ex VP: Scott Sherwood
Dir IT: Jon Speegle

D-U-N-S 78-318-9343
JLG HARVESTING INC
1450 S Atlantic Ave, Yuma, AZ 85365-1810
Tel (928) 329-7548 *Founded/Ownrshp* 1991
Sales 23.4MM^E *EMP* 600
SIC 0723 3523 0722 Vegetable packing services; Farm machinery & equipment; Crop harvesting; Vegetable packing services; Farm machinery & equipment; Crop harvesting
Pr: Jose Luis Garcia Sr
**Sec:* Sara Garcia
**VP:* Jose Luis Garcia Jr

D-U-N-S 04-388-7728 IMP/EXP
■ **JLG INDUSTRIES INC**
J L G
(*Suby of* OSHKOSH CORP) ★
1 J L G Dr, Mc Connellsburg, PA 17233-9533
Tel (717) 485-5161 *Founded/Ownrshp* 2006
Sales 780.4MM^E *EMP* 4,993
SIC 3531 Construction machinery; Aerial work platforms: hydraulic/elec. truck/carrier mounted; Cranes; Construction machinery; Aerial work platforms: hydraulic/elec. truck/carrier mounted; Cranes
Pr: Frank Nerenhausen's
COO: Jeff Beechan
**Sr VP:* Timothy Morris
**VP:* Frank Cholewicki
VP: Howard Kaplan
VP: Shawn Kenny
VP: KY Kuehling
VP: Tracey McKenzie
VP: Charles Stoy
**VP:* Andrew Tacelosky
Prgrm Mgr: Brian Blackburn

D-U-N-S 01-970-3807
JLG STRUCTURES INC (TX)
8611 Derrington Rd, Houston, TX 77064-6003
Tel (713) 375-2380 *Founded/Ownrshp* 2008
Sales 30.4MM^E *EMP* 150
Accts Melton & Melton Llp Houst
SIC 1542 Nonresidential construction; Nonresidential construction
Pr: Jesus Lopez
**VP:* Rhonda Shepherd

D-U-N-S 06-598-1441
JLH AUTOMOTIVE INC
JOHN HONDA HINDERER
1515 Hebron Rd, Newark, OH 43056-1037
Tel (740) 522-1106 *Founded/Ownrshp* 1991
Sales 27.3MM^E *EMP* 75^E
SIC 5511 5521 Automobiles, new & used; Used car dealers; Automobiles, new & used; Used car dealers
Pr: John Hinderer
Sls Mgr: John Durbin
Sls Mgr: Dave Kinion

D-U-N-S 55-695-0129
JLH AUTOMOTIVE INC
HAAS, JEFF MAZDA
11222 Katy Fwy, Houston, TX 77043-4611
Tel (713) 932-6004 *Founded/Ownrshp* 1991
Sales 33.7MM^E *EMP* 75
SIC 5511 Automobiles, new & used; Automobiles, new & used
Pr: Jeff Haas
Genl Mgr: Tod Crabtree
Dir IT: Carl Scott

D-U-N-S 87-826-3169
JLH HICKORY LIMITED PARTNERSHIP
HENDRICK HONDA HICKORY
945 Us Highway 70 Se, Hickory, NC 28602-5139
Tel (828) 322-2673 *Founded/Ownrshp* 1995
Sales 33.0MM^E *EMP* 85
SIC 5511 Automobiles, new & used; Automobiles, new & used
Pt: Rick Hendrick
Sls Mgr: Tim Swick
Sales Asso: Jonathan Benfield
Sales Asso: Mark Buchanan
Sales Asso: Zach Cannon
Sales Asso: Andrew Courtney
Sales Asso: JT Dula
Sales Asso: Joey Lankford
Sales Asso: Rick McClure
Sales Asso: Phillip Rosenbalm
Sales Asso: Brian Rutherford

D-U-N-S 01-775-9761
JLJ HOME FURNISHINGS LLC (SC)
SLEEP STYLES
4776 Charlotte Hwy, Lancaster, SC 29720-7769
Tel (704) 239-8630 *Founded/Ownrshp* 2015
Sales 100.0MM^E *EMP* 12^E
SIC 5712 Linen supply; Linen fabrics; Furniture stores

D-U-N-S 96-166-4195
JLL PARTNERS FUND IV LP
450 Lexington Ave Fl 31, New York, NY 10017-3925
Tel (212) 286-8600 *Founded/Ownrshp* 2000
Sales 47.0MM^E *EMP* 1,040
SIC 6722 Money market mutual funds; Money market mutual funds

D-U-N-S 62-707-1103
JLL PARTNERS INC
450 Lexington Ave Fl 31, New York, NY 10017-3925
Tel (212) 286-8600 *Founded/Ownrshp* 1987
Sales 2.2MMM^E *EMP* 13,491
SIC 6799 Investors; Investors
Pr: Paul Levy
**COO:* Michael Schwartz
**VP:* Daniel Agroskin
VP: Andrew Goldfarb
VP: Garret Hall
**VP:* Kevin T Hammond
VP: Stephen H Wise
Mng Dir: Dalia Cohen
Mng Dir: William Miles
IT Man: Ann Meldrum
Mktg Dir: Lauren Nealon

D-U-N-S 83-084-3871
JLL/FCH HOLDINGS I LLC
450 Lexington Ave, New York, NY 10017-3904
Tel (212) 286-8600 *Founded/Ownrshp* 2007
Sales NA *EMP* 224^E
SIC 6712 6029 Bank holding companies; Commercial banks; Bank holding companies; Commercial banks
Prin: Daniel Agroskin

JLM PHARMATECH
See PD PHARMATECH LLC

D-U-N-S 06-754-3871
JLM TITLE LLC
FIRST CENTENNIAL TITLE COMPANY
(*Suby of* ORANGE COAST TITLE CO OF SOUTHERN CALIFORNIA) ★
1450 Ridgeview Dr Ste 100, Reno, NV 89519-6338
Tel (775) 689-8510 *Founded/Ownrshp* 2001
Sales 21.4MM^E *EMP* 118^E
SIC 6541 Title abstract offices
Chf Mktg O: Cindy Cook

Ofcr: Jessica Barr
Ofcr: Kathie Elkins
Ofcr: Yvette Taylor
Exec: Renita Brown
Mktg Mgr: Rose Echezarria

D-U-N-S 00-122-5143 IMP
JLNW INC
3030 47th Ave, Long Island City, NY 11101-3433
Tel (212) 719-4666 *Founded/Ownrshp* 1946
Sales 23.3MM^E *EMP* 99
SIC 2335 2339 5621 Women's, juniors' & misses' dresses; Sportswear, women's; Women's clothing stores
CEO: Norman Wolf
**Sec:* Jeffrey Leff
Sls Mgr: Robert Mann

D-U-N-S 60-317-7176 IMP
JLR RESOURCES INC
154 Hidden Ridge Dr, Syosset, NY 11791-4315
Tel (516) 364-0330 *Founded/Ownrshp* 2001
Sales 25.0MM *EMP* 3
SIC 5141 Groceries, general line; Groceries, general line
Pr: Stefan Unger

D-U-N-S 01-102-0545
JLS CONCEPTS INC
141 S Lake Ave Ste 102, Pasadena, CA 91101-4757
Tel (626) 795-3998 *Founded/Ownrshp* 2004
Sales 6.3MM^E *EMP* 400^E
SIC 5812 American restaurant; American restaurant
Pr: James Luke Strockis

D-U-N-S 62-592-1903
JLS INC
AAA LIMO
908 Spruce St, Texarkana, TX 75501-5124
Tel (903) 793-8944 *Founded/Ownrshp* 1986
Sales 12.1MM^E *EMP* 385
SIC 4119 Limousine rental, with driver; Limousine rental, with driver
Pr: William E Sams
**VP:* Janie Sams

D-U-N-S 93-201-1872
JLT RE (NORTH AMERICA) INC
JLT TOWERS RE
(*Suby of* JARDINE LLOYD THOMPSON GROUP PLC)
300 S Wacker Dr Ste 2424, Chicago, IL 60606-6700
Tel (312) 235-8200 *Founded/Ownrshp* 2006
Sales NA *EMP* 39^E
SIC 6411 Insurance agents, brokers & service
CEO: Craig S Darling
V Ch: Wayne Wignes
Ex VP: Joyce Wignes
VP: Tom McCartney

JLT TOWERS RE
See JLT RE (NORTH AMERICA) INC

JM & A GROUP
See JM FAMILY ENTERPRISES INC

D-U-N-S 03-719-1350 IMP
■ **JM AHLE CO INC**
(*Suby of* MORO CORP) ★
190 William St Ste 2d, South River, NJ 08882-1100
Tel (732) 238-1700 *Founded/Ownrshp* 2000
Sales 26.2MM^E *EMP* 50
SIC 5051 Concrete reinforcing bars
CEO: David Menard
**Pr:* John Ahle
**VP:* Ron Perlman
Div Mgr: Michele Czerpak

D-U-N-S 60-364-0129 EXP
JM AUTO INC
JM LEXUS
(*Suby of* JM & A GROUP) ★
5450 W Sample Rd, Margate, FL 33073-3453
Tel (954) 972-2200 *Founded/Ownrshp* 1988
Sales 71.8MM^E *EMP* 378
SIC 5511 7515 Automobiles, new & used; Passenger car leasing; Automobiles, new & used; Passenger car leasing
CEO: Colin Brown
VP: James P Dunn
VP: John Guerrero
Board of Directors: Colin W Brown

D-U-N-S 95-760-6320
JM BOZEMAN ENTERPRISES INC
166 Seltzer Ln, Malvern, AR 72104-8367
Tel (501) 844-4060 *Founded/Ownrshp* 1992
Sales 33.3MM^E *EMP* 78
SIC 4213 Trucking, except local
Pr: James Bozeman

D-U-N-S 05-701-8376 IMP
JM CONSOLIDATED INDUSTRIES LLC
HUGHES PARKER INDUSTRIES
(*Suby of* JMAC DEVELOPMENT INC) ★
1604 Mahr Ave, Lawrenceburg, TN 38464-2202
Tel (931) 762-9403 *Founded/Ownrshp* 1997
Sales 51.1MM^E *EMP* 350
SIC 3469 3479 3444 Metal stampings; Painting of metal products; Sheet metalwork; Metal stampings; Painting of metal products; Sheet metalwork
Pr: Mike Stigall
**Prin:* Chris Bell
IT Man: Sean O'Connor
Mtls Mgr: Tammie Thomas
Sfty Mgr: Rick McCarty
Plnt Mgr: Mike Stigal

D-U-N-S 00-680-1724
JM COX RESOURCES LP (TX)
400 W Wall St, Midland, TX 79701-4404
Tel (432) 682-9435 *Founded/Ownrshp* 1952
Sales 47.5MM^E *EMP* 90
SIC 1311 Crude petroleum production; Natural gas production; Crude petroleum production; Natural gas production
Genl Mgr: Kelly Cox

JM EAGLE
See J-M MANUFACTURING CO INC

JM EAGLE
See PW EAGLE INC

JM FAMILY ENTERPRISES
See SOUTHEAST TOYOTA DISTRIBUTORS LLC

D-U-N-S 08-242-3435 EXP
JM FAMILY ENTERPRISES INC
JM & A GROUP
100 Jim Moran Blvd, Deerfield Beach, FL 33442-1702
Tel (954) 429-2000 *Founded/Ownrshp* 1969
Sales 1.2MMM^E *EMP* 3,800
SIC 5511 5012 5013 5531 Automobiles & other motor vehicles; Motor vehicle supplies & new parts; Automobile & truck equipment & parts; New & used car dealers; Automobiles & other motor vehicles; Motor vehicle supplies & new parts; Automobile & truck equipment & parts
CEO: Colin Brown
Pr: Rosie Burkman
COO: Paul Rodgers
**CFO:* Brent D Burns
**CFO:* Ron Coombs
Ofcr: Ken Yerves
Sr VP: Dan Chait
VP: Josh Bass
VP: Todd Clarke
**VP:* Ed Sheehy
VP: Michael Stellmach
Dir Risk M: David May
Board of Directors: Arline M Mc Nally, John J Mc Nally, James M Moran Jr, Janice M Moran, Patricia G Moran

D-U-N-S 00-255-4459 IMP/EXP
JM HUBER CORP (NJ)
499 Thornall St Ste 8, Edison, NJ 08837-2267
Tel (732) 603-3630 *Founded/Ownrshp* 1883
Sales 702.1MM^E *EMP* 4,000
Accts Kpmg Llp Short Hills Nj
SIC 1455 2819 2493 1311 0811 Kaolin mining; Industrial inorganic chemicals; Strandboard, oriented; Crude petroleum production; Natural gas production; Timber tracts; Kaolin mining; Industrial inorganic chemicals; Strandboard, oriented; Crude petroleum production; Natural gas production; Timber tracts
Ch Bd: Mike Marberry
**Pr:* William B Goodspeed
Pr: Albert Landers
Pr: Andrew Trott
CFO: Jeffrey Jerome
**CFO:* Michael L Marberry
CFO: Jeff Prosinski
Treas: Lane Silverman
Bd of Dir: Peter Triandafillou
Ofcr: Warren Page
Sr VP: Donald Whaley
VP: Robert L Cornelius
VP: Robert Cornelius
**VP:* Robert Currie
**VP:* Joseph Dunning
VP: Bart Edwards
**VP:* Phyllis A Erikson
VP: William Fricker
VP: Mark Hopkins
VP: B Keidan
VP: Kurt Koch
Board of Directors: Peter S Brock, Martha C Huber, Maria Lilja, W Lee Nutter, Stephen C Tumminello, Richard Wallman, David F Young

JM LEXUS
See JM AUTO INC

D-U-N-S 07-939-6989
JM LOANS INC
SEACLIFF MORTGAGE
9042 Garfield Ave Ste 207, Huntington Beach, CA 92646-2351
Tel (714) 969-2444 *Founded/Ownrshp* 2011
Sales NA *EMP* 1
SIC 6162 Mortgage companies, urban; Mortgage companies, urban
CEO: Jerry A McCormick

D-U-N-S 87-778-4814
JM MECHANICAL LLC
40 W 3800 N, Hyde Park, UT 84318-4114
Tel (435) 563-6267 *Founded/Ownrshp* 2000
Sales 24.1MM^E *EMP* 77^E
SIC 1711 Septic system construction

D-U-N-S 80-118-5435
JM OILFIELD SERVICES INC
J M OILFIELD SERVICE
1006 Saint Paul St, Gonzales, TX 78629-2918
Tel (501) 589-4044 *Founded/Ownrshp* 2015
Sales NA *EMP* 280^E
SIC 4212 Truck rental with drivers

D-U-N-S 04-991-1683
JM STEEL CORP
(*Suby of* CALANDRA FRANK INC) ★
1050 N Steel Cir, Huger, SC 29450-9388
Tel (843) 336-4929 *Founded/Ownrshp* 1998
Sales 34.9MM^E *EMP* 90
SIC 5051 Steel; Steel
Pr: Frank Calandra Jr
**Ex VP:* Tony Calandra
**VP:* John M Calandra
**VP:* James Ceresa
**VP:* Shelly George

D-U-N-S 12-181-3166
JM THOMAS FOREST PRODUCTS CO
2525 N Hwy 89 91, Ogden, UT 84404-2656
Tel (801) 782-8090 *Founded/Ownrshp* 1980
Sales 86.6MM *EMP* 90
Accts Pinnock Robbins Posey & Rich
SIC 5031 Building materials, exterior; Building materials, interior; Building materials, exterior; Building materials, interior
Ch Bd: James Matthew Thomas
**Pr:* Bill Anderson
**CFO:* Carl Daines

JM WILLIAMS CONTRACTORS
See WILLCONSCO INC

D-U-N-S 17-826-5786
JMA ENERGY CO LLC
1021 Nw Grand Blvd, Oklahoma City, OK 73118-6039
Tel (405) 947-4322 *Founded/Ownrshp* 1998
Sales 26.9MM^E *EMP* 50
SIC 1311 Crude petroleum & natural gas
Pr: Jeffrey J McDougall
Ex Dir: Michael Cawley
Opers Mgr: Don Rahmes
Genl Couns: Michael Massad

D-U-N-S 88-449-0830
JMA INFORMATION TECHNOLOGY INC
JMA IT
10551 Barkley St Ste 400, Overland Park, KS 66212-1832
Tel (913) 722-3252 *Founded/Ownrshp* 1994
Sales 58.3MM *EMP* 273^E
SIC 7379 Computer related consulting services; Computer related consulting services
Pr: Joseph Melookaran
Bd of Dir: Dinesh Prakash
**VP:* David Brown
Netwrk Eng: Daniel Hart
Board of Directors: Maria Will,raqibul Huq,mit

JMA IT
See JMA INFORMATION TECHNOLOGY INC

D-U-N-S 60-389-3988
JMA SOLUTIONS LLC
600 Maryland Ave Sw 400e, Washington, DC 20024-2525
Tel (202) 465-8205 *Founded/Ownrshp* 2005
Sales 27.6MM *EMP* 135
SIC 8748 4789 8711 8721 8741 Business consulting; Space flight operations, except government; Engineering services; Accounting services, except auditing; Management services; Business management; Business consulting; Space flight operations, except government; Engineering services; Accounting services, except auditing; Management services; Business management
CEO: Jan Adams
COO: Claudia Angelone
**VP:* Avis Dillard
**VP:* Ronnette Meyers

D-U-N-S 02-532-3247 IMP
JMAC DEVELOPMENT INC
200 W Nationwide Blvd # 1, Columbus, OH 43215-2561
Tel (614) 436-2418 *Founded/Ownrshp* 1980
Sales 87.6MM^E *EMP* 600^E
SIC 3325 5198 7999 5511 8741 Steel foundries; Paints; Ice skating rink operation; Automobiles, new & used; Financial management for business; Steel foundries; Paints; Ice skating rink operation; Automobiles, new & used; Financial management for business
Ch Bd: John P McConnell
**Pr:* Michael A Priest

D-U-N-S 16-346-8932
JMAC LENDING INC
16782 Von Karman Ave # 12, Irvine, CA 92606-2417
Tel (949) 390-2688 *Founded/Ownrshp* 2007
Sales NA *EMP* 60
SIC 6141 Financing: automobiles, furniture, etc., not a deposit bank; Financing: automobiles, furniture, etc., not a deposit bank
Pr: MAI Christina Pham
Bd of Dir: Michael Truong
Ex VP: Travis Pham
VP: Al Crisanty
IT Man: Anthony Pham

D-U-N-S 08-113-3621
JMAC RESOURCES INC
121 48th Ave Sw, Williston, ND 58801-9403
Tel (701) 774-8511 *Founded/Ownrshp* 1970
Sales 24.7MM^E *EMP* 75^E
SIC 1794 Excavation & grading, building construction
Owner: John McCreary
VP: Nathan Hexom
Comm Man: Art Thompson
Off Mgr: Rianna Brunelle
IT Man: Levi Wittmayer

D-U-N-S 78-412-2723 IMP
JMB CONSTRUCTION INC
132 S Maple Ave, South San Francisco, CA 94080-6302
Tel (650) 267-5300 *Founded/Ownrshp* 1976
Sales 39.5MM^E *EMP* 100
SIC 1623 Water & sewer line construction; Water & sewer line construction
Pr: Margaret P Burke
Off Mgr: Pam Burns
IT Man: Colin Larkin
Mtls Mgr: John Dower

D-U-N-S 08-753-1703
JMB INSURANCE AGENCY INC
900 N Michigan Ave # 1500, Chicago, IL 60611-6541
Tel (312) 915-2200 *Founded/Ownrshp* 1971
Sales NA *EMP* 75
SIC 6411 Insurance agents & brokers
Pr: Steven J Topel
**Sr VP:* Barry Gersowsky
VP: Jason Casey
VP: Kimberly Goldstein
VP: Gail Silver
Off Mgr: Hopper Curtissa
Dir IT: Maggie Lyons

D-U-N-S 08-494-5591
JMBL INC
FOODLAND SUPERMARKET
502 N Montgomery Ave, Sheffield, AL 35660-2864
Tel (256) 383-6940 *Founded/Ownrshp* 1984
Sales 27.5MM^E *EMP* 400
SIC 5411 Grocery stores, independent; Grocery stores, independent
Pr: Bob Love
**Sec:* Walter Andrews

JMBM
See JEFFER MANGELS BUTLER & MITCHELL LLP

JMC DESIGN & DEVELOPMENT
See JMC LEASING INC

D-U-N-S 19-677-0437
JMC IMPORTS INC
SAN MARCOS TOYOTA
5101 S Interstate Hwy 35, San Marcos, TX 78666-9597
Tel (512) 805-6529 *Founded/Ownrshp* 1999
Sales 69.0MM *EMP* 110
SIC 5511 5521 Automobiles, new & used; Used car dealers; Automobiles, new & used; Used car dealers
Pr: Michael Chargois
**Genl Mgr:* Jim Stienke
Off Mgr: Cindy Ploch
Sls Mgr: Mike Cartner
Sls Mgr: Jim Stenke
Sls Mgr: Cowen Wilson
Sales Asso: Sam Coffman

D-U-N-S 09-385-8280
JMC LEASING INC (FL)
JMC DESIGN & DEVELOPMENT
2201 4th St N Ste 200, Saint Petersburg, FL 33704-4300
Tel (727) 823-0022 *Founded/Ownrshp* 1972
Sales 42.2MM^E *EMP* 165
SIC 1531 Condominium developers; Condominium developers
CEO: John Michael Cheezem
**Pr:* John Hobach
**Treas:* Robert L Allen
Treas: Dave Maman

D-U-N-S 78-454-0759
JMC RESTAURANT DISTRIBUTION LP
(*Suby of* AWESOME ACQUISITION CO) ★
1080 W Bethel Rd, Coppell, TX 75019-4427
Tel (972) 745-4200 *Founded/Ownrshp* 1990
Sales 30.0MM^E *EMP* 27
SIC 5046 Commercial cooking & food service equipment
Pr: Bob Kulick

JMC STEEL GROUP
See JOHN MANEELY CO

D-U-N-S 82-520-7173
JMC STEEL GROUP INC
ENERGEX TUBE
227 W Monroe St Fl 26, Chicago, IL 60606-5082
Tel (312) 275-1600 *Founded/Ownrshp* 2006
Sales 646.0MM^E *EMP* 1,800
SIC 3317 3644 Pipes, seamless steel; Electric conduits & fittings; Pipes, seamless steel; Electric conduits & fittings
CEO: Barry Zekelman
**Pr:* David W Seeger
**CFO:* John Feenan
CFO: Michael J Graham
Ch: Alan Zekelman
Treas: Bob Campbell
Ofcr: Richard Proszowski
**Ex VP:* John C Higgins
VP: Helen Davis
**VP:* Andrew Klaus
**VP:* Michael McNamara
**VP:* Michael P McNamara Jr
**VP:* Michael E Mechley
VP: Jeff Shulman
Board of Directors: Louis Giuliano, Armand Lauzon, Andrew Marino, Alan Zekelman, Barry Zekelman, Clayton Zekelman

JMD COMPANY
See JOHNSTON-MOREHOUSE-DICKEY CO INC

JME
See JOHNSONS MODERN ELECTRIC CO INC

D-U-N-S 07-318-3436 IMP
JME INC
T M B
527 Prk Ave San Fernando, San Fernando, CA 91340
Tel (201) 896-8600 *Founded/Ownrshp* 1982
Sales 69.0MM^E *EMP* 136
SIC 5063 Lighting fittings & accessories; Lighting fittings & accessories
CEO: Colin R Waters
**Pr:* Thomas M Bissett
CFO: Irene Klebanov
CFO: Don Phillips
VP: Peter Kirkup
Mng Dir: Erhard Lehmann
Mng Dir: Richard Mead
Sales Exec: Lisa Kern

D-U-N-S 93-209-0426
JME INC
MCALISTERS GOURMET DELI
725 Coulter Dr, New Albany, MS 38652-2808
Tel (662) 534-3340 *Founded/Ownrshp* 1994
Sales 9.7MM^E *EMP* 360
SIC 5812 Delicatessen (eating places); Delicatessen (eating places)
Pr: Mark Garrett
**Ch Bd:* John Fullenwider

D-U-N-S 13-046-0657
JMEG LP
EA ELECTRIC
13995 Diplomat Dr Ste 400, Farmers Branch, TX 75234-8804
Tel (972) 590-5555 *Founded/Ownrshp* 2002
Sales 166.5MM^E *EMP* 900
SIC 1731 Electrical work; Electrical work
Pt: Russell Ferraro
Pt: Gary Fraser
Pt: Jerry Mills
Pt: Bill Mitchell
Pt: Ray Naizer
Pt: John Wall
VP: Bill Lerow
Div Mgr: Ron Howard
Sfty Mgr: Becky Flurry

Opers Mgr: Krista Chambers
Opers Mgr: Randy Nichols

D-U-N-S 00-677-3709 IMP
JMF CO
2735 62nd Street Ct, Bettendorf, IA 52722-5599
Tel (563) 332-9200 *Founded/Ownrshp* 1948
Sales 94.2MM^E *EMP* 80
SIC 5074 Plumbing & hydronic heating supplies; Plumbing & hydronic heating supplies
CEO: Max Hansen
**Pr:* Bryan Micheelsem
**CFO:* Dallon Christensen
CFO: Rick Devinney
Software D: Karin Laubhan
Opers Mgr: Roel Hernandez
Opers Mgr: Jaime Mendez
Natl Sales: Justin Rebarcak
VP Sls: Bill Tinker
VP Sls: Bob Wilson
S&M/VP: Bill Tipps

D-U-N-S 02-718-0368
JMG REALTY INC
5605 Glenridge Dr # 1010, Atlanta, GA 30342-1381
Tel (404) 995-1111 *Founded/Ownrshp* 1997
Sales 14.6MM^E *EMP* 550
SIC 6513 Apartment building operators; Apartment building operators
CEO: Karlton T Jackson
Pr: Tim Brock
Pr: Diana Penn
Treas: Thomas Staten
Sr VP: Luanne Acton-Ross
VP: David Glatt
VP: Steve Haskins
VP: Cynthia G Kelley
Board of Directors: Amy Daly, Tammy Harrington, Steve McLaurin

D-U-N-S 17-999-4913
JMH CAPITAL LLC
333 Elm St Ste 215, Dedham, MA 02026-4530
Tel (781) 522-1600 *Founded/Ownrshp* 2003
Sales 27.1MM^E *EMP* 605
SIC 6733 6799 Private estate, personal investment & vacation fund trusts; Investors; Private estate, personal investment & vacation fund trusts; Investors
Mng Dir: Tate Bevis
Mng Dir: John Nies

D-U-N-S 82-884-8437
■ **JMH TRADEMARK INC**
(*Suby of* A&F TRADEMARK INC) ★
6301 Fitch Path, New Albany, OH 43054-9269
Tel (614) 283-6500 *Founded/Ownrshp* 2002
Sales 436.0MM^E *EMP* 350
SIC 5611 Men's & boys' clothing stores; Men's & boys' clothing stores
CEO: Michael S Jeffries

D-U-N-S 07-256-4701
JMHC INC
2816 E Robinson St, Orlando, FL 32803-5828
Tel (407) 865-7600 *Founded/Ownrshp* 1991
Sales 40.5MM^E *EMP* 180
SIC 1623 1611 Underground utilities contractor; General contractor, highway & street construction; Underground utilities contractor; General contractor, highway & street construction
Pr: L Steven Blomeley
**VP:* Candice H Blomeley

D-U-N-S 86-101-1831
JMHS INC
WENDY'S
12 Northgate Dr, Windsor Locks, CT 06096-1205
Tel (860) 627-7960 *Founded/Ownrshp* 1994
Sales 5.3MM^E *EMP* 300
SIC 5812 Fast-food restaurant, chain; Fast-food restaurant, chain
Pr: Brian Maher
**VP:* Stephen J Hinkis

D-U-N-S 07-854-0700
JMJ LLC
WENDY'S
5535 W Glenn Dr, Glendale, AZ 85301-2544
Tel (623) 463-2885 *Founded/Ownrshp* 2000
Sales 16.9MM^E *EMP* 400
SIC 5812 Fast-food restaurant, chain; Fast-food restaurant, chain

D-U-N-S 00-737-1727
JMJ SUPPLY CO
MELETIO ELECTRICAL SUPPLY CO
10930 Harry Hines Blvd, Dallas, TX 75220-1316
Tel (214) 352-3900 *Founded/Ownrshp* 1920
Sales 30.4MM^E *EMP* 61
SIC 5063 5719 Electrical supplies; Lighting fixtures; Lighting, lamps & accessories; Lighting fixtures

D-U-N-S 96-782-0692 IMP
JMJS INC
COE DISTRIBUTING
1020 Franklin Dr Ste 5, Smock, PA 15480-1250
Tel (724) 437-8202 *Founded/Ownrshp* 2009
Sales 33.1MM *EMP* 25
SIC 5021 Office furniture; Office furniture
Pr: James Ewing Jr
**VP:* Stanislaus Idzi
IT Man: Brenda Hoover

D-U-N-S 04-121-9452
JMK AUTO SALES INC
JMK BMW
391 Route 22 399, Springfield, NJ 07081-3599
Tel (973) 379-7744 *Founded/Ownrshp* 1965
Sales 123.0MM *EMP* 145
SIC 7538 5511 General automotive repair shops; Automobiles, new & used; General automotive repair shops; Automobiles, new & used
Pr: Roger J Kosempel
**Pr:* Cathie Maier
**Sec:* Cathryn Maier-Tajkowski
Sls Mgr: Benn Barron
Sls Mgr: Todd Saab
Sls Mgr: Angelo Zito
Corp Couns: Mark Redman

JMK BMW
See JMK AUTO SALES INC

D-U-N-S 15-053-8122 IMP
JMK INTERNATIONAL INC
1401 N Bowie Dr, Weatherford, TX 76086-1503
Tel (817) 737-3703 *Founded/Ownrshp* 1971
Sales 63.2MM^E *EMP* 520^E
SIC 3061 Mechanical rubber goods; Appliance rubber goods (mechanical); Automotive rubber goods (mechanical); Mechanical rubber goods; Appliance rubber goods (mechanical); Automotive rubber goods (mechanical)
Pr: Alfred M Micallef
**CFO:* Patricia Post
Off Mgr: Steve Chase

D-U-N-S 60-638-2919
JML CARE CENTER INC
184 Ter Heun Dr Ste 1, Falmouth, MA 02540-2532
Tel (508) 457-4621 *Founded/Ownrshp* 1990
Sales 15.5MM *EMP* 300
SIC 8051 8322 8093 Skilled nursing care facilities; Adult day care center; Rehabilitation center, outpatient treatment; Skilled nursing care facilities; Adult day care center; Rehabilitation center, outpatient treatment
Pr: Charles Peterman
Ex Dir: Donna Andrade
HC Dir: Helen Martin

JMM INVESTMENTS
See ACCU REFERENCE MEDICAL LAB LIMITED LIABILITY CO

D-U-N-S 03-922-1398
JMM SERVICES INC
TEMPSTAR STAFFING
1431 N George St, York, PA 17404-2014
Tel (717) 848-1100 *Founded/Ownrshp* 2005
Sales 15.5MM^E *EMP* 600
SIC 7361 Employment agencies; Employment agencies
Pr: Michael Rauch
**CFO:* Richard Spaw

JMMC
See JOHNSON MEMORIAL HOSPITAL INC

JMOA ENGINEERING
See SAVIN ENGINEERS PC

D-U-N-S 10-638-1598
▲ **JMP GROUP INC**
600 Montgomery St # 1100, San Francisco, CA 94111-2713
Tel (415) 835-8900 *Founded/Ownrshp* 2015
Sales 206.3MM *EMP* 235^E
Tkr Sym JMP *Exch* NYS
SIC 6211 Investment bankers; Investment bankers
Ch Bd: Joseph A Jolson
Pr: Mark L Lehmann
Pr: Kevin Lynch
**Pr:* Carter D Mack
CFO: Raymond S Jackson
**V Ch Bd:* Craig R Johnson
VP: Andrew Welsh

D-U-N-S 05-829-9327
■ **JMP SECURITIES LLC**
(*Suby of* JMP GROUP INC) ★
600 Montgomery St # 1100, San Francisco, CA 94111-2713
Tel (415) 835-8900 *Founded/Ownrshp* 2001
Sales 55.9MM^E *EMP* 194^E
SIC 6211 Security brokers & dealers; Security brokers & dealers
**Pr:* Carter D Mack
**CFO:* Raymond Jackson
VP: Ryan Abbe
VP: Jason Butler
VP: Brenna Cummings
VP: Laura Fieseler
VP: Laura Hickman
VP: Brenna Kenworthy
VP: Marina Shenderovich
VP: Kyros Shirazi
VP: Tracy Strelow
VP: Jeremy Taylor
VP: Christopher York

JMR GROUP
See FREIGHTLINER OF PORTLAND LLC

D-U-N-S 82-995-4549
JMR GROUP LLC
MCCOY FREIGHTLINER
9622 Ne Vancouver Way, Portland, OR 97211-1224
Tel (503) 283-0345 *Founded/Ownrshp* 2007
Sales 46.8MM^E *EMP* 140
SIC 5012 Truck tractors; Truck tractors
Store Mgr: Jeff Birch

JMS BUILDING SOLUTIONS, LLC
See PARAMOUNT BUILDING SOLUTIONS LLC

D-U-N-S 02-431-8501
JMS BUILDING SOLUTIONS LLC
(*Suby of* JMS BUILDING SOLUTIONS LLC) ★
10235 S 51st St, Phoenix, AZ 85044-5218
Tel (480) 348-1177 *Founded/Ownrshp* 2012
Sales 2.1MM^E *EMP* 947^E
SIC 7832 Motion picture theaters, except drive-in
CEO: Glen Kucera

JMT USA
See JORGENSON MACHINE TOOLS INC

JN AUTOMOTIVE GROUP
See JN GROUP INC

D-U-N-S 10-834-9093
JN FOODS INC
117 Mitch Mcconnell Way, Bowling Green, KY 42101-7519
Tel (270) 843-1121 *Founded/Ownrshp* 1983
Sales 57.1MM^E *EMP* 85
SIC 5142 5141 Packaged frozen goods; Groceries, general line; Packaged frozen goods; Groceries, general line
CEO: Joe Natcher
**Pr:* Doug Polk
**CFO:* Cindy Smith
Ofcr: Lisa Atkins
Dir IT: James Sumpter
Sls Dir: Darrell Logdson
Sls Dir: Matt Malloy
Mktg Mgr: Monica Duvall
Manager: James Supulski

D-U-N-S 03-321-4826 IMP
JN GROUP INC (HI)
JN AUTOMOTIVE GROUP
2999 N Nimitz Hwy, Honolulu, HI 96819-1903
Tel (808) 831-2724 *Founded/Ownrshp* 1961
Sales 71.2MM^E *EMP* 170
SIC 5511 6512 7515 7513 5531 3714 New & used car dealers; Commercial & industrial building operation; Passenger car leasing; Truck rental & leasing, no drivers; Automotive & home supply stores; Motor vehicle parts & accessories; New & used car dealers; Commercial & industrial building operation; Passenger car leasing; Truck rental & leasing, no drivers; Automotive & home supply stores; Motor vehicle parts & accessories
Pr: Joseph P Nicolai
**Treas:* Darrell Toma
**VP:* Kenneth Stanford
Sls Mgr: Jason Hattori

JN PHILLIPS AUTO GLASS
See J N PHILLIPS CO INC

D-U-N-S 14-653-8306
JNET COMMUNICATIONS LLC
25 Independence Blvd # 103, Warren, NJ 07059-2706
Tel (203) 951-6400 *Founded/Ownrshp* 2003
Sales 60.0MM *EMP* 1,500
SIC 4899 1731 Data communication services; Cable television installation; Data communication services; Cable television installation
CEO: David Jefferson
COO: Michael A Dennis
**CFO:* Eugene Caldwell
Dir IT: Dan Kobylanski

D-U-N-S 95-660-1793
JNJ EXPRESS INC
3935 Old Getwell Rd, Memphis, TN 38118-6048
Tel (901) 362-3444 *Founded/Ownrshp* 1993
Sales 82.2MM^E *EMP* 255
SIC 4213 Heavy hauling; Heavy hauling
Pr: John T Ennis Sr
**Sec:* Gail Luna
**VP:* John Ennis Jr
VP: Mike McMillon
Sfty Dirs: Wanda Johnson
Sfty Mgr: Lester Lawson
Opers Mgr: Denis Ennis

JNLD
See JACKSON NATIONAL LIFE DISTRIBUTORS LLC

D-U-N-S 79-113-3023 EXP
JNS FOODS LLC
1401 N University Dr # 602, Coral Springs, FL 33071-8946
Tel (954) 718-7958 *Founded/Ownrshp* 1992
Sales 21.1MM *EMP* 12
Accts Rainey & Rainey Scranton Pen
SIC 5141 Food brokers; Food brokers

D-U-N-S 00-653-8516 IMP
JO GALLOUP CO
SMITH INSTRUMENT
(*Suby of* GREAT LAKES AUTOMATION SUPPLY) ★
130 Helmer Rd N, Battle Creek, MI 49037-4900
Tel (269) 965-2303 *Founded/Ownrshp* 2012
Sales 175.4MM^E *EMP* 233
SIC 5051 5085 5162 Pipe & tubing, steel; Valves & fittings; Industrial fittings; Plastics materials & basic shapes; Pipe & tubing, steel; Valves & fittings; Industrial fittings; Plastics materials & basic shapes
Pr: Martin U Ranly
**Sec:* James L Treadwell
Exec: Sheila Bailey
Genl Mgr: Richard Waters
Sales Exec: Tim Hayes
Sales Exec: Dave Komosinski
Sales Exec: Bob Lund
Sls&Mrk Ex: Scott Hodges
Sls Mgr: Dan Foster
Sls Mgr: Doug Riggs
Sales Asso: Brad Savage

JO JO'S VARIETY STORE
See JOSEPH F BURKE CORP

D-U-N-S 00-884-7097 IMP
JO KING INC
JOK
1265 Old Alpharetta Rd, Alpharetta, GA 30005-3988
Tel (470) 239-3672 *Founded/Ownrshp* 1952
Sales 20.4MM^E *EMP* 25
SIC 5085 5072 3545 3452 Fasteners & fastening equipment; Hardware; Machine tool accessories; Bolts, nuts, rivets & washers
CEO: Russell Sheldon
**Ch Bd:* Herbert Peavy Jr
**VP:* Thomas Morrell
**VP:* Curtis Peace

JO-ANN FABRICS & CRAFTS
See JO-ANN STORES LLC

JO-ANN FABRICS & CRAFTS
See JO-ANN STORES HOLDINGS INC

D-U-N-S 07-946-3509
JO-ANN STORES HOLDINGS INC
JO-ANN FABRICS & CRAFTS
5555 Darrow Rd, Hudson, OH 44236-4054
Tel (888) 739-4120 *Founded/Ownrshp* 2012
Sales 2.3MMM^E *EMP* 19,566^E
SIC 5945 5949 5947 Arts & crafts supplies; Fabric stores piece goods; Notions, including trim; Patterns: sewing, knitting & needlework; Sewing supplies; Gifts & novelties

D-U-N-S 00-294-4684 IMP
JO-ANN STORES LLC
JO-ANN FABRICS & CRAFTS
(*Suby of* JO-ANN FABRICS & CRAFTS) ★
5555 Darrow Rd, Hudson, OH 44236-4054
Tel (330) 656-2600 *Founded/Ownrshp* 2011
Sales 3.1MMM^E *EMP* 22,000
SIC 5945 5949 5947 Arts & crafts supplies; Fabric stores piece goods; Notions, including trim; Patterns: sewing, knitting & needlework; Sewing supplies; Gifts & novelties; Arts & crafts supplies; Fabric stores piece goods; Notions, including trim; Patterns: sewing, knitting & needlework; Sewing supplies; Gifts & novelties
Pr: Jill Soltau
CFO: Brian Carney
**CFO:* Jim Kerr
**Ch:* Darrell Webb
Ex VP: Lee Barnard
Ex VP: Dotty Grexa
**Ex VP:* Kenneth Haverkost
Ex VP: Gerturde Horn
Ex VP: Fred Johnson
Ex VP: Mary Lehman
Ex VP: Mary Marlinski
Ex VP: Bruce Schwallie
Ex VP: Rosalind Thompson
Ex VP: Debra Walker
Ex VP: Alma Zimmerman
Sr VP: Robert R Gerber
**Sr VP:* Riddianne Kline
VP: Jim Bisen
VP: Chad Buscho
VP: Kris Christian
VP: Nelson Clark

D-U-N-S 00-380-5454
JO-CARROLL ENERGY INC (NFP) (IL)
793 Us Highway 20 W, Elizabeth, IL 61028-9304
Tel (800) 858-5522 *Founded/Ownrshp* 1939
Sales 61.3MM *EMP* 60
SIC 4911 4924 Distribution, electric power; Natural gas distribution; Distribution, electric power; Natural gas distribution
Ch: Joe Mattingley
**Pr:* Michael Hastings
COO: Kyle Buros
**CFO:* Tracy Heidenreich
Bd of Dir: Russell Holesinger
Bd of Dir: Thomas Lundy
Bd of Dir: Chris Stadel
VP: John W Cox
VP: John Cox
VP: Patrick Keleher
VP: Jennifer Skien

D-U-N-S 08-414-2785
JO-KELL INC (VA)
1716 Lambert Ct, Chesapeake, VA 23320-8913
Tel (757) 523-2900 *Founded/Ownrshp* 1977
Sales 91.9MM^E *EMP* 64
SIC 5063 8711 Electrical apparatus & equipment; Consulting engineer; Electrical apparatus & equipment; Consulting engineer
CEO: Susan Kelly
**Pr:* Martin Kelly
**COO:* Adrian Marchi
Sr VP: Jim Baur
Exec: Jim Schucker
Creative D: Tara Perrone
Brnch Mgr: Sandy Alterio
Sales Asso: Glenna McLaughlin

D-U-N-S 15-400-2398
JO-LO BUS CO INC
14540 155th St, Jamaica, NY 11434-4217
Tel (718) 276-4038 *Founded/Ownrshp* 1979
Sales 8.5MM^E *EMP* 400
SIC 4151 School buses; School buses

D-U-N-S 15-070-7656
JOAH INC
(*Suby of* JEWEL-OSCO) ★
250 E Parkcenter Blvd, Boise, ID 83706-3940
Tel (208) 395-6200 *Founded/Ownrshp* 1987
Sales 1.4MMM^E *EMP* 18,000
SIC 5411 Supermarkets, chain; Supermarkets, chain
CEO: Lawrence R Johnston

JOAN FENICHEL THERAPEUTIC NURS
See LEAGUE TREATMENT CENTER INC

D-U-N-S 96-239-5484
JOANN.COM LLC
(*Suby of* JO-ANN FABRICS & CRAFTS) ★
5555 Darrow Rd, Hudson, OH 44236-4011
Tel (330) 656-2600 *Founded/Ownrshp* 2007
Sales 30.0MM *EMP* 25
SIC 5945 5949 Arts & crafts supplies; Fabric stores piece goods; Notions, including trim; Arts & crafts supplies; Fabric stores piece goods; Notions, including trim

D-U-N-S 79-101-6991
JOB 1 USA
(*Suby of* JOB1USA) ★
701 Jefferson Ave Ste 202, Toledo, OH 43604-6957
Tel (419) 255-5005 *Founded/Ownrshp* 1951
Sales 30.5MM^E *EMP* 1,012^E
SIC 7381 7363 7361 Security guard service; Protective services, guard; Temporary help service; Medical help service; Employment agencies; Executive placement; Security guard service; Protective services, guard; Temporary help service; Medical help service; Employment agencies; Executive placement
Pr: Bruce F Rumpf
**VP:* Sue Daniels
**VP:* Eloise Huston
VP: Stacie Moss
**VP:* Don Reynolds
Area Mgr: Ken Curry
Area Mgr: Alicia Dodd
Area Mgr: Ray Kasparian
Area Mgr: Rocco RAO

VP Opers: Carol Hayward
Natl Sales: Chris Hammye

D-U-N-S 07-232-2097
JOB AMERICAS NETWORK INC
7979 E Tufts Ave Ste 1400, Denver, CO 80237-2849
Tel (303) 846-2800 *Founded/Ownrshp* 1998
Sales 10.6MM^E *EMP* 300^E
SIC 7361 Executive placement; Executive placement
Pr: Robert J Gerberg Jr
**CFO:* Michael J Egan

D-U-N-S 60-091-1981
JOB INDUSTRIAL SERVICES INC
J I S
1805 S Redwood Rd # 150, Salt Lake City, UT 84104-5151
Tel (801) 433-0901 *Founded/Ownrshp* 2005
Sales 60.7MM *EMP* 35
Accts Tanner Llc Salt Lake City Ut
SIC 8711 Construction & civil engineering; Construction & civil engineering
Pr: Jason Job
**CFO:* Jack Job
**VP:* Eric Schomaker
Dir IT: Ben Rand
Dir IT: Ryan Ranzenberger

JOB JUNCTION
See GOODWILL INDUSTRIES OF NORTH FLORIDA INC

D-U-N-S 82-705-2101 IMP
JOB OPTIONS INC
3465 Camino Dl Rio S 30 Ste 300, San Diego, CA 92108
Tel (619) 688-1784 *Founded/Ownrshp* 1987
Sales 49.0MM *EMP* 900
Accts Hosaka Rotherham & Company S
SIC 8331 Sheltered workshop; Sheltered workshop
CEO: William Mead
COO: Jeff Johnson
**COO:* Jeffrey Johnson
**CFO:* Char Healy
Dir Bus: Brian Priest

D-U-N-S 94-735-2928
JOB READY INC
READY CARE
(*Suby of* RES-CARE INC) ★
610 E 5th Ave, Anchorage, AK 99501-2731
Tel (907) 258-3498 *Founded/Ownrshp* 2010
Sales 10.2MM^E *EMP* 550
SIC 8399 Advocacy group; Advocacy group
Pr: Sandra Heffern
**VP:* Gene Heffern

JOB SERVICE
See MISSISSIPPI DEPARTMENT OF EMPLOYMENT SECURITY

D-U-N-S 80-274-9143
JOB SERVICE NORTH DAKOTA
(*Suby of* EXECUTIVE OFFICE OF STATE OF NORTH DAKOTA) ★
1000 E Divide Ave, Bismarck, ND 58501-1926
Tel (701) 328-2825 *Founded/Ownrshp* 1979
Sales NA *EMP* 400
Accts Brady Martz & Associates Pc
SIC 9441 Administration of social & manpower programs; ; Administration of social & manpower programs;
Ex Dir: Maren L Daley

JOB1USA
See RUMPF CORP

D-U-N-S 02-915-7518
JOBAR INC
TOYOTA WEST
997 Folger Dr, Statesville, NC 28625-6202
Tel (704) 872-2771 *Founded/Ownrshp* 1982
Sales 45.0MM *EMP* 85
SIC 5531 7532 Automotive accessories; Automotive parts; Body shop, automotive; Automotive accessories; Automotive parts; Body shop, automotive
Pr: Joe Bertolami
**VP:* Barbara Bertolami
Sales Asso: Matthew Grooms

D-U-N-S 17-782-5197
JOBAR INC
SHOP N SAVE
995 Wildlife Lodge Rd, Lower Burrell, PA 15068-2750
Tel (724) 339-8275 *Founded/Ownrshp* 1990
Sales 35.6MM^E *EMP* 490
SIC 5411 Supermarkets; Supermarkets
Pr: Joseph J Ferraccio

D-U-N-S 00-285-3497
JOBBERS AUTOMOTIVE WAREHOUSE INC (KS)
AUTO VALUE
801 E Zimmerly St, Wichita, KS 67211-3342
Tel (316) 267-4393 *Founded/Ownrshp* 1954
Sales 82.0MM^E *EMP* 220
SIC 5013 5015 Automotive supplies & parts; Motor vehicle parts, used; Automotive supplies & parts; Motor vehicle parts, used
Pr: Bob Evans
**Pr:* Larry Boehringer
**Pr:* John R Washbish
**VP:* Alfred J Winter
IT Man: Roy Schott

D-U-N-S 19-890-2624
JOBE MATERIALS LP
1150 Southview Dr Ste A, El Paso, TX 79928-5240
Tel (915) 298-9900 *Founded/Ownrshp* 2005
Sales 78.6MM^E *EMP* 430^E
SIC 3272 Concrete products; Concrete products
Genl Pt: Stanley Jobe
Pt: Irene Eperson
IT Man: Victor Salcido
Trfc Dir: Henry Tellez
Opers Mgr: Leo Escobar
Prd Mgr: David Macias
Ql Cn Mgr: Rey Loya

JOBFEST
See SHAKER ADVERTISING AGENCY INC

D-U-N-S 80-261-3984
JOBIN REALTY CO
13890 Braddock Rd Ste 309, Centreville, VA 20121-2438
Tel (703) 272-1000 *Founded/Ownrshp* 1990
Sales 8.9MM^E *EMP* 550
SIC 6531 Real estate brokers & agents; Real estate brokers & agents
Pr: Bob Froehlick

D-U-N-S 00-137-8806
JOBING.COM LLC
1375 N Scottsdale Rd # 300, Scottsdale, AZ 85257-3411
Tel (602) 200-6800 *Founded/Ownrshp* 2001
Sales 58.2MM^E *EMP* 165
SIC 4813 ;
Sr VP: Brian Newkirk
VP: Robert Callaway
VP: Spencer Dettman
VP: Matthew McElrath
Creative D: Kristen Zirkler
Dir Bus: Randy Anderson
Ex Dir: Jason Bartlett
Genl Mgr: Shawna Adams
Genl Mgr: Dave Carns
Genl Mgr: John Chilelli
Genl Mgr: Mike Dean

D-U-N-S 84-960-2032
JOBS FOR FUTURE INC
J F F
88 Broad St Fl 8, Boston, MA 02110-3407
Tel (617) 728-4446 *Founded/Ownrshp* 1984
Sales 20.4MM *EMP* 89
Accts Tonneson & Company Inc Wakefi
SIC 8399 8733 Community development groups; Noncommercial research organizations; Community development groups; Noncommercial research organizations
Pr: Marlene B Seltzer
COO: Lisa Chapnick
**CFO:* Melba Abreu
Assoc VP: Theresa Klebacha
Assoc VP: Donna Rodrigues
VP: Steven Baker
**VP:* Adria Steinberg
VP: Ray Uhalde
**VP:* Joel Vargas
Exec: Ichiro Ashihara
Dir Soc: Grace Ausick
Creative D: Jean Leguillou
Comm Dir: Jessica Howe

JOBS PLUS
See PLUS GROUP INC

JOBS2CAREERS
See INSIDERSREFERRAL.COM INC

D-U-N-S 00-168-3911 IMP
JOBSON MEDICAL INFORMATION LLC
100 Ave Of Amer Fl 9, New York, NY 10013
Tel (212) 274-7000 *Founded/Ownrshp* 1958, 2005
Sales 119.8MM^E *EMP* 403
SIC 2721 2741 Magazines: publishing & printing; Miscellaneous publishing; Magazines: publishing & printing; Miscellaneous publishing
**CEO:* Michael Tansey
**CFO:* John Orr
Sr VP: Michael Lemon
Exec: Robert Amato
Assoc Ed: Patrisha Zabrycki

D-U-N-S 00-179-9191 IMP
■ **JOC GROUP INC**
PIERS
(*Suby of* IHS INC) ★
2 Penn Plz E Fl 12, Newark, NJ 07105-2257
Tel (973) 776-8660 *Founded/Ownrshp* 2014
Sales 20.2MM^E *EMP* 150^E
SIC 2721 Magazines: publishing only, not printed on site; Magazines: publishing only, not printed on site
CEO: Gavin Carter
**CFO:* Ian Blackman
**Ex VP:* Rhiannon James
**Ex VP:* Peter Tirschwell
VP: Matt Cocchiaro
VP: Theresa Harrison
**VP:* Cindy Mevorah
Ql Cn Mgr: Brian Cozzens
Sales Exec: Jany Martinez
Mktg Mgr: Raquel Dinicolas

D-U-N-S 78-328-4656
JOCKEY INTERNATIONAL DOMESTIC INC
JOCKEY STORE
(*Suby of* JOCKEY INTERNATIONAL INC) ★
2300 60th St, Kenosha, WI 53140-3889
Tel (262) 658-8111 *Founded/Ownrshp* 1986
Sales 69.0MM^E *EMP* 700
SIC 5651 5611 Family clothing stores; Men's & boys' clothing stores; Family clothing stores; Men's & boys' clothing stores
Ch Bd: Donna Wolf Steigerwaldt
**Pr:* Edward C Emma
VP: Mark S Jaeger
CIO: Frank Schneider III
Telecom Mg: Tom Ruffalo
Telecom Mg: Bob Schultz
VP Opers: Marion Smith
Plnt Mgr: Danny Hayes
Mktg Mgr: Sara Fuhs

D-U-N-S 79-436-4828
JOCKEY INTERNATIONAL GLOBAL INC
JOCKEY STORE
(*Suby of* JOCKEY INTERNATIONAL DOMESTIC INC) ★
2300 60th St, Kenosha, WI 53140-3889
Tel (262) 658-8111 *Founded/Ownrshp* 1986
Sales 67.4MM^E *EMP* 630
SIC 2211 5611 Underwear fabrics, cotton; Men's & boys' clothing stores; Underwear fabrics, cotton; Men's & boys' clothing stores
Pr: Edward Emma
**Pr:* Frank Sneider
**Treas:* Ron Kwasny

D-U-N-S 04-193-6840 IMP/EXP
JOCKEY INTERNATIONAL INC (WI)
JOCKEY USA
2300 60th St, Kenosha, WI 53140-3889
Tel (262) 658-8111 *Founded/Ownrshp* 1876, 1930
Sales 1.4MMM^E *EMP* 5,000
SIC 2254 2341 2322 Knit underwear mills; Underwear, knit; Women's & children's underwear; Men's & boys' underwear & nightwear; Knit underwear mills; Underwear, knit; Women's & children's underwear; Men's & boys' underwear & nightwear
Ch Bd: Debra Steigerwaldt Waller
**Pr:* Peter J Hannes
**Pr:* Michael S Lapidus
**Pr:* Robert L Nolan
**Pr:* Byron Norsleet
**Pr:* Steven M Tolensky
CFO: Dain Bussewitz
CFO: Frank Schnieder
Sr Cor Off: Conrad Lung
Chf Mktg O: Dustin Cohn
**Sr VP:* F Brad Beal
Sr VP: John Brody
**VP:* Anne T Arbas
VP: Jill Fuerst
VP: Milou Gwyn
**VP:* Mark S Jaeger
**VP:* Ronald E Kwasny
VP: Jamie Lockard
VP: Tomkins Sally
VP: Sally Tomkins
VP: Tracy Williams

JOCKEY STORE
See JOCKEY INTERNATIONAL DOMESTIC INC

JOCKEY STORE
See JOCKEY INTERNATIONAL GLOBAL INC

JOCKEY USA
See JOCKEY INTERNATIONAL INC

D-U-N-S 09-191-2050 IMP
JODHPURI INC
260a Walsh Dr, Parsippany, NJ 07054-5702
Tel (973) 299-7009 *Founded/Ownrshp* 1989
Sales 27.6MM^E *EMP* 100
SIC 5023 5999 Decorative home furnishings & supplies; Toiletries, cosmetics & perfumes; Decorative home furnishings & supplies; Toiletries, cosmetics & perfumes
Pr: Laxmi C Mehta
**COO:* Steven Littman
VP: Rosemary Durkin
**VP:* Sheila Mehta
Mktg Dir: Jim Gregory

D-U-N-S 62-178-6847 IMP
JODI KRISTOPHER INC
CITYTRIANGLES
6015 Bandini Blvd, Commerce, CA 90040-2904
Tel (323) 890-8000 *Founded/Ownrshp* 1990
Sales 52.6MM^E *EMP* 200
Accts Fineman West & Company Llp Lo
SIC 2335 Women's, juniors' & misses' dresses; Women's, juniors' & misses' dresses
Pr: Ira Rosenberg
**CFO:* Ira Fogelman
**VP:* Ellen Delosh-Bacher
**VP Sls:* Jan Smith

D-U-N-S 04-658-8885
JODIKA ENTERPRISES INC
TACO BELL
14978 Sand Canyon Ave A, Irvine, CA 92618-2109
Tel (949) 733-8300 *Founded/Ownrshp* 1974
Sales 10.0MM *EMP* 450
SIC 5812 Fast-food restaurant, chain; Fast-food restaurant, chain
Pr: Richard Armstrong
**VP:* Kerry Bunning

D-U-N-S 13-140-7777
JOE & ROSS INC
5350 W 38th St, Chicago, IL 60804-4459
Tel (708) 656-6869 *Founded/Ownrshp* 1981
Sales 21.4MM^E *EMP* 30
SIC 5143 Dairy products, except dried or canned; Ice cream & ices
Pr: Ross Purpura
Rgnl Mgr: Judy Myers

JOE ANNE
See JOE-ANNE CO INTERNATIONAL INC

D-U-N-S 00-243-1443
JOE BASIL CHEVROLET INC (NY)
5111 Transit Rd, Depew, NY 14043-4466
Tel (716) 683-6800 *Founded/Ownrshp* 1976
Sales 71.8MM^E *EMP* 200
SIC 5511 Automobiles, new & used; Automobiles, new & used
Pr: James Basil
**Treas:* Sandra Petruso
**VP:* Joseph Basil
Off Mgr: Sandy Petruso
DP Exec: Sue Przybyl
Mktg Mgr: Robin Frey
Sls Mgr: Kate Basil
Sales Asso: Tom Barrett

D-U-N-S 94-570-9053
JOE BLAND CONSTRUCTION LP
13111 Dessau Rd, Austin, TX 78754-2039
Tel (512) 821-2808 *Founded/Ownrshp* 1996
Sales 52.7MM *EMP* 300
Accts Brown Graham & Company Pc Ge
SIC 1611 1623 1542 General contractor, highway & street construction; Underground utilities contractor; Nonresidential construction; General contractor, highway & street construction; Underground utilities contractor; Nonresidential construction
Owner: Joe Bland
COO: Gary Pugh
CFO: Steve Pack
CIO: Donald Norris

D-U-N-S 02-376-2982
JOE BOWMAN AUTO PLAZA
2455 E Market St, Harrisonburg, VA 22801-8763
Tel (540) 434-6732 *Founded/Ownrshp* 1958
Sales 26.1MM^E *EMP* 70
SIC 5511 5012 Automobiles, new & used; Automobiles & other motor vehicles; Automobiles, new & used; Automobiles & other motor vehicles
Pr: Joseph B Bowman
**Sec:* Kathryn H Bowman
**VP:* Joseph B Bowman III
Sales Asso: Chad Austin
Sales Asso: Jared Sheets

D-U-N-S 02-673-2503
JOE BRAND INC
5300 San Dario Ave # 2003, Laredo, TX 78041-3052
Tel (956) 722-0771 *Founded/Ownrshp* 1976
Sales 25.0MM^E *EMP* 85
SIC 5611 5621 5661 5999 Clothing, men's & boys': everyday, except suits & sportswear; Ready-to-wear apparel, women's; Men's shoes; Women's shoes; Cosmetics
Pr: Linda Deutsch
**Sec:* Lisa K Deutsch
**VP:* Terri L Deutsch

D-U-N-S 61-118-8327
JOE BULLARD AUTOMOTIVE INC
BULLARD, JOE MITSUBISHI
1017 E I65 Service Rd S, Mobile, AL 36606-3108
Tel (251) 476-2300 *Founded/Ownrshp* 1987
Sales 36.3MM^E *EMP* 100
SIC 5511 Automobiles, new & used; Automobiles, new & used
Pr: Joe Bullard Jr
**CFO:* Dennis Tucker
**Treas:* John Galanos
Exec: Jennifer Wells
Sales Exec: Marc Heiter
Mktg Mgr: Leonard Jeanlouis
Sls Mgr: Ben Jackson
Sls Mgr: Rene Thibodeaux

D-U-N-S 60-298-1409
JOE CAPUTO AND SONS INC
SHOPTOCOOK
959 E Oakton St, Des Plaines, IL 60018-2040
Tel (847) 827-6700 *Founded/Ownrshp* 1999
Sales 62.9MM^E *EMP* 76^E
SIC 5141 5411 Groceries, general line; Delicatessens; Groceries, general line; Delicatessens
Pr: Nat Caputo
**VP:* Vito Caputo

D-U-N-S 00-286-8594
JOE COOPER FORD OF MIDWEST CITY LLC (OK)
6601 Se 29th St, Midwest City, OK 73110-3002
Tel (405) 733-1611 *Founded/Ownrshp* 2005
Sales 70.0MM^E *EMP* 130
SIC 5511 5521 7538 7515 5012 Automobiles, new & used; Used car dealers; General automotive repair shops; Passenger car leasing; Automobiles & other motor vehicles; Automobiles, new & used; Used car dealers; General automotive repair shops; Passenger car leasing; Automobiles & other motor vehicles
Genl Mgr: Charles Davis

D-U-N-S 12-104-1651
JOE CORBIS WHOLESALE PIZZA INC
14100 Darnestown Rd Ste E, Baltimore, MD 21230
Tel (410) 525-8331 *Founded/Ownrshp* 1983
Sales 65.5MM^E *EMP* 224
SIC 2099 Pizza, refrigerated: except frozen; Pizza, refrigerated: except frozen
Pr: Rocco Violi
**VP:* Joan Bell

D-U-N-S 02-405-0254
JOE D CROSS LLC
CROSS CHRYSLER JEEP
1501 Gardiner Ln, Louisville, KY 40218-4550
Tel (502) 459-9900 *Founded/Ownrshp* 1956
Sales 22.0MM^E *EMP* 55
SIC 5511 5521 Automobiles, new & used; Pickups, new & used; Vans, new & used; Used car dealers; Automobiles, new & used; Pickups, new & used; Vans, new & used; Used car dealers
Pr: Joe D Cross
Genl Mgr: Chris Madison
Genl Mgr: David Moser
Sales Asso: Keaton Horvat

D-U-N-S 00-782-1853
JOE DANIELS CONSTRUCTION CO INC
919 Applegate Rd, Madison, WI 53713-3295
Tel (608) 271-4800 *Founded/Ownrshp* 1953
Sales 31.6MM^E *EMP* 100
SIC 1611 1542 1541 General contractor, highway & street construction; Commercial & office building, new construction; Commercial & office buildings, renovation & repair; Industrial buildings, new construction; General contractor, highway & street construction; Commercial & office building, new construction; Commercial & office buildings, renovation & repair; Industrial buildings, new construction
Pr: Joseph Daniels
**VP:* Jerrald Daniels
Genl Mgr: Richard Femrite

D-U-N-S 01-823-9889
JOE DICKEY ELECTRIC INC
180 W South Range Rd, North Lima, OH 44452-9578
Tel (330) 549-3976 *Founded/Ownrshp* 1957
Sales 23.1MM^E *EMP* 80
SIC 1731 General electrical contractor
CEO: Joseph Dickey Jr
**Pr:* David A Dickey
**VP:* Eric Carlson
**VP:* Joseph Dickey III
Sfty Dirs: Shelley Reash

D-U-N-S 55-696-7438
JOE F GRAY
SERVICE GROUP
6907 N Cpitl Of Texas Hwy, Austin, TX 78731-1755
Tel (512) 343-0600 *Founded/Ownrshp* 1951
Sales NA *EMP* 250
SIC 6411 6531 Insurance agents, brokers & service; Real estate agents & managers; Insurance agents, brokers & service; Real estate agents & managers
Prin: Gary Holliday
Sr VP: Sandy Kohl
IT Man: Eric Peabody

D-U-N-S 61-292-4001
JOE FERGUSON PONTIAC
FERGUSON MOTORS
950 S Academy Blvd, Colorado Springs, CO 80910-3965
Tel (719) 596-5005 *Founded/Ownrshp* 1990
Sales 20.6MM[E] *EMP* 100
SIC 5511 7538 Automobiles, new & used; General automotive repair shops; Automobiles, new & used; General automotive repair shops
Pr: Tom Ferguson
**Sec:* Patty Parkey

D-U-N-S 09-915-3074
JOE FISHER
FISHER, JIM VOLVO
2108 W Burnside St, Portland, OR 97210-3520
Tel (503) 295-5571 *Founded/Ownrshp* 1947
Sales 23.4MM[E] *EMP* 61
SIC 5511 Automobiles, new & used; Automobiles, new & used
Pr: Ruth J Fisher
**Sec:* Jane Fisher
**VP:* James D Fisher
Store Mgr: Robert Vingelen
IT Man: Nick Anderson
Netwrk Mgr: Mike O'Connor
Sales Exec: Jim Feltmann
Sls Mgr: Tom Kirby
Sls Mgr: Mike Oconnor
Sales Asso: Wayne Webb

JOE G MALOOF & CO
See MALOOF DISTRIBUTING LLC

D-U-N-S 78-317-9021
JOE GIBBS RACING INC
13415 Reese Blvd W, Huntersville, NC 28078-7933
Tel (704) 944-5000 *Founded/Ownrshp* 1991
Sales 21.6MM[E] *EMP* 130
SIC 7948 Race car owners
Pr: J D Gibbs
**Pr:* Jason Gibbs
Ofcr: Jim Tobias
**Ex VP:* Don Merideth
**Sr VP:* Jimmy Makar
VP: Steve Desouza
**VP:* Todd Merideth
VP Opers: Todd Meredith
Mfg Dir: Kelly Collins
Mtls Mgr: George Skelton
Ql Cn Mgr: Chris Delos

D-U-N-S 01-615-1623
JOE HOLLAND CHEVROLET INC
210 Maccorkle Ave Sw, South Charleston, WV 25303-1599
Tel (304) 744-1561 *Founded/Ownrshp* 1964
Sales 52.7MM[E] *EMP* 140
SIC 5511 Automobiles, new & used; Pickups, new & used; Vans, new & used; Automobiles, new & used; Pickups, new & used; Vans, new & used
Pr: Joe B Holland
**Treas:* J D Dawson

D-U-N-S 84-987-0118
JOE HUDSONS COLLISION CENTER INC
1318 Pike Rd, Pike Road, AL 36064-2264
Tel (334) 386-9076 *Founded/Ownrshp* 1989
Sales 22.0MM[E] *EMP* 300
SIC 7532 Collision shops, automotive; Collision shops, automotive
Co-Ownr: Traweek Dickson
**Co-Ownr:* Joe Hudson

D-U-N-S 13-076-0598 IMP
JOE JURGIELEWICZ & SON LTD
189 Cheese Ln, Hamburg, PA 19526-8057
Tel (610) 562-3825 *Founded/Ownrshp* 1984
Sales 20.6MM[E] *EMP* 20[E]
SIC 5144 2015 Poultry products; Poultry slaughtering & processing
Pr: Joseph Jurgielewicz Jr
COO: Mark Miller
CFO: Janice Loeb
Plnt Mgr: Paul Murphy
Sls&Mrk Ex: John Demchak

JOE KELLEY CONSTRUCTION
See KELLEY CONSTRUCTION INC

D-U-N-S 60-329-3150
JOE KUNZ CO INC
10293 Birtcher Dr, Mira Loma, CA 91752-1827
Tel (714) 541-2442 *Founded/Ownrshp* 1987
Sales 21.3MM[E] *EMP* 40
SIC 5031 Lumber: rough, dressed & finished
CEO: Joseph Kunz

D-U-N-S 00-886-8226
JOE LUNGHAMER CHEVROLET INC
STADIUM CHEVROLET
475 Summit Dr, Waterford, MI 48328-3368
Tel (248) 683-7100 *Founded/Ownrshp* 1972
Sales 41.3MM[E] *EMP* 95
SIC 5511 5521 Automobiles, new & used; Used car dealers; Automobiles, new & used; Used car dealers
Pr: Joseph L Lunghamer
**Prin:* Joe Lunghamer
Sls Mgr: Julie Izzo

D-U-N-S 02-973-3045
JOE MACHENS AUTOMOTIVE GROUP INC
500 Vandiver Dr, Columbia, MO 65202-1507
Tel (573) 875-5000 *Founded/Ownrshp* 1982
Sales 24.4MM[E] *EMP* 55
SIC 5511 Automobiles, new & used; Automobiles, new & used
Pr: William F James Jr
**VP:* Nancy James
Genl Mgr: Mike Zuppardi
Store Mgr: Kevin Bopp
Sls&Mrk Ex: Mary Henry
Sls Mgr: Jake Cohen
Sls Mgr: Jeffrey Holstein
Sales Asso: Michael Atwood
Sales Asso: Perry Cunningham
Sales Asso: Pat Darby
Sales Asso: Jeff Fletcher

D-U-N-S 04-772-3192
JOE MACHENS FORD INC
JOE MACHENS FORD LINCOLN
1911 W Worley St, Columbia, MO 65203-1093
Tel (573) 445-4411 *Founded/Ownrshp* 1969
Sales 141.9MM[E] *EMP* 800
SIC 5511 Automobiles, new & used; Pickups, new & used; Vans, new & used; Automobiles, new & used; Pickups, new & used; Vans, new & used
Pr: Gary R Drewing
**VP:* David Machens
Ex Dir: Mary Jo Henry
Off Mgr: Shirley Cornelison
Mktg Mgr: Sarah Hassemer
Sls Mgr: Ralph Dumas
Sls Mgr: Danny Hammack
Sls Mgr: David Johnson
Sls Mgr: Kerry Thomas
Sls Mgr: Kevin West

JOE MACHENS FORD LINCOLN
See JOE MACHENS FORD INC

D-U-N-S 55-542-1189
JOE MACHENS MOTORS INC
COLUMBIA HYUNDAI
1300 Vandiver Dr, Columbia, MO 65202-1925
Tel (573) 474-7400 *Founded/Ownrshp* 1987
Sales 26.3MM[E] *EMP* 65
SIC 5511 Automobiles, new & used; Automobiles, new & used
Pr: Larry Estes
**VP:* Serina Estes
Genl Mgr: Bob Jacaway
Sls Mgr: Wesley Earl
Sls Mgr: Michael Jacaway
Sls Mgr: Pete Rice
Sales Asso: John Absinthe
Sales Asso: Tim Colton
Sales Asso: Brandon Hall
Sales Asso: Zack Lemen
Sales Asso: James Patrick

D-U-N-S 85-873-2803
■ **JOE MACPHERSON INFINITI**
(*Suby of* AUTONATION INC) ★
33 Auto Center Dr, Tustin, CA 92782-8402
Tel (714) 627-5556 *Founded/Ownrshp* 2001
Sales 22.1MM[E] *EMP* 70
SIC 5511 Automobiles, new & used; Automobiles, new & used
Ch Bd: Joe Mac Pherson
**Treas:* Elizabeth Mac Pherson
**VP:* Reed Chesworth
Brnch Mgr: James Hawthorne

JOE MACPHERSON TOYOTA
See TUSTIN TOYOTA

D-U-N-S 19-636-8245
JOE MCGEE CONSTRUCTION CO INC
6609 Steve Lee Dr, Lake, MS 39092-9088
Tel (601) 775-3754 *Founded/Ownrshp* 1988
Sales 28.2MM[E] *EMP* 96
SIC 1611 1741 General contractor, highway & street construction; Foundation building
Pr: Joe McGee
VP: Patricia Brown
**VP:* Lynn McGee
Sfty Mgr: Kenny Franklin

D-U-N-S 15-474-1177
JOE MYERS AUTOMOTIVE INC
JOE MYERS TOYOTA
(*Suby of* V.T., INC.)
19010 Northwest Fwy, Jersey Village, TX 77065-4713
Tel (281) 890-8700 *Founded/Ownrshp* 2000
Sales 71.8MM[E] *EMP* 205
SIC 5511 Automobiles, new & used; Pickups, new & used; Vans, new & used; Automobiles, new & used; Pickups, new & used; Vans, new & used
Pr: Larry Van Tuyl
**Treas:* Robert J Holcomb
**VP:* Jerome D Rocco
Sls Dir: Mike Grewenig
Sls Mgr: Lance Lewis
Sls Mgr: Alex Weir

D-U-N-S 02-664-1167
JOE MYERS FORD II LP
(*Suby of* V.T., INC.)
16634 Northwest Fwy, Jersey Village, TX 77040-1998
Tel (281) 890-4000 *Founded/Ownrshp* 2000
Sales 71.8MM[E] *EMP* 220
SIC 5511 Automobiles, new & used; Pickups, new & used; Vans, new & used; Automobiles, new & used; Pickups, new & used; Vans, new & used
Genl Mgr: Carolyn Cross
Genl Mgr: Cindy Flores
Genl Mgr: Terry Luker
Genl Mgr: Lonnie Pace
Sales Asso: Nicholas Javurek

JOE MYERS MAZDA
See JOE MYERS MOTORS-THREE INC

JOE MYERS MITSUBISHI
See JOE MYERS MOTORS INC

D-U-N-S 15-407-2318
JOE MYERS MOTORS INC
JOE MYERS MITSUBISHI
(*Suby of* V.T., INC.)
16484 Northwest Fwy, Jersey Village, TX 77040-1918
Tel (713) 937-8080 *Founded/Ownrshp* 2000
Sales 42.9MM *EMP* 60
SIC 5511 Automobiles, new & used; Automobiles, new & used
Pr: Cecil Van Tuyl

D-U-N-S 61-540-5909
JOE MYERS MOTORS-THREE INC
JOE MYERS MAZDA
(*Suby of* V.T., INC.)
16484 Northwest Fwy, Jersey Village, TX 77040-1918
Tel (713) 937-7800 *Founded/Ownrshp* 1988
Sales 20.4MM[E] *EMP* 65
SIC 5511 Automobiles, new & used; Automobiles, new & used
Pr: Larry Van Tuyl
**Treas:* Robert Holcomb
Off Mgr: Walt Sullivan

JOE MYERS TOYOTA
See JOE MYERS AUTOMOTIVE INC

D-U-N-S 04-691-1855
JOE N GUY CO INC
2028 Powers Ferry Rd Se # 280, Atlanta, GA 30339-5013
Tel (770) 955-4224 *Founded/Ownrshp* 1969
Sales 25.4MM[E] *EMP* 50
SIC 1542

D-U-N-S 05-720-8118 EXP
JOE PIPER INC
123 Industrial Dr, Birmingham, AL 35211-4445
Tel (205) 290-2211 *Founded/Ownrshp* 1954
Sales 97.9MM[E] *EMP* 80
SIC 5113 Paperboard & products; Paperboard & products
Pr: Ann Piper Carpenter
CFO: Phillips Crabtree
**Treas:* Richard W Patterson
**VP:* Bill Miller
**VP Opers:* Mims Cooper
Sfty Mgr: Scott Moncrief
Trfc Mgr: Ronnie Smith

JOE PUCCI & SONS SEAFOODS
See BLUE RIVER SEAFOOD INC

D-U-N-S 02-690-7527
JOE R MAY OILFIELD PIPE & SUPPLY LTD
513 Mc Kay At Warren St, Overton, TX 75684
Tel (903) 834-3661 *Founded/Ownrshp* 1953
Sales 30.0MM *EMP* 20
SIC 5084 Oil well machinery, equipment & supplies; Oil well machinery, equipment & supplies
Pr: Richard M May

D-U-N-S 06-417-6993 IMP
JOE RANDAZZOS FRUIT AND VEGETABLE INC
5240 E Outer Dr, Detroit, MI 48234-3445
Tel (313) 892-0093 *Founded/Ownrshp* 1957
Sales 26.8MM[E] *EMP* 200
SIC 5431 5261 Fruit stands or markets; Vegetable stands or markets; Nursery stock, seeds & bulbs; Fruit stands or markets; Vegetable stands or markets; Nursery stock, seeds & bulbs
Pr: Samuel A Randazzo
**Treas:* Patrina Randazzo
**Sec:* Marie Randazzo
**VP:* Peter A Randazzo

D-U-N-S 05-421-9761
JOE RIZZA FORD OF ORLAND PARK INC
8150 W 159th St, Orland Park, IL 60462-4939
Tel (708) 403-0300 *Founded/Ownrshp* 1988
Sales 66.0MM[E] *EMP* 125
SIC 5511 Automobiles, new & used; Automobiles, new & used
Pr: Joseph R Rizza
**CFO:* Dan McMillan
**VP:* Phillip Rizza
IT Man: Dan Talaga
Sls Mgr: Joe Arteaga
Sls Mgr: Jerry Trost
Sls Mgr: Vince Ventrella

D-U-N-S 04-911-1073
JOE SELF CHEVROLET INC
8801 E Kellogg Dr, Wichita, KS 67207-1823
Tel (316) 689-4390 *Founded/Ownrshp* 1977
Sales 48.2MM[E] *EMP* 120
SIC 5511 5531 7538 7515 7532 Automobiles, new & used; Automotive parts; General automotive repair shops; Passenger car leasing; Top & body repair & paint shops; Automobiles, new & used; Automotive parts; General automotive repair shops; Passenger car leasing; Top & body repair & paint shops
Pr: Joe Self
**VP:* John Bell
VP Mktg: Todd Topham

D-U-N-S 15-044-3117
JOE SMITH CO
902 E Jefferson St, Pittsburg, KS 66762-6013
Tel (620) 231-3610 *Founded/Ownrshp* 2002
Sales 24.3MM[E] *EMP* 50
SIC 5194 5145 5113 Tobacco & tobacco products; Candy; Industrial & personal service paper; Tobacco & tobacco products; Candy; Industrial & personal service paper
Pr: Kelly M Kays

D-U-N-S 62-396-8877 IMP
JOE SNOW LLC
305 Veterans Blvd, Carlstadt, NJ 07072-2708
Tel (732) 832-2500 *Founded/Ownrshp* 2004
Sales 46.0MM[E] *EMP* 43
SIC 5083 Lawn & garden machinery & equipment
Pr: Joseph Cohen
**COO:* Stephen Feldschuh
**VP:* Donna Wagner
Off Mgr: Girish Khemchandani
VP Sls: Michael Westermeier

D-U-N-S 02-660-4231
JOE SWARTZ ELECTRIC CO
7200 Roswell St, Houston, TX 77022-3710
Tel (713) 695-5835 *Founded/Ownrshp* 1970
Sales 36.1MM[E] *EMP* 363
SIC 1731 General electrical contractor; General electrical contractor
Pr: Joseph G Swartz
**Treas:* Marguerite Swartz
Dir IT: Gerald Munoz

D-U-N-S 80-807-9284
JOE TORNANTE-MDP HOLDING LLC
233 S Beverly Dr, Beverly Hills, CA 90212-3886
Tel (310) 228-6800 *Founded/Ownrshp* 2007
Sales 321.8MM[E] *EMP* 487[E]
SIC 5145 5092 5112 2064 Confectionery; Candy; Chewing gum; Toys & games; Playing cards; Social stationery & greeting cards; Albums, scrapbooks & binders; Candy & other confectionery products; Lollipops & other hard candy; Confectionery; Candy; Chewing gum; Toys & games; Playing cards; Social stationery & greeting cards; Albums, scrapbooks & binders; Candy & other confectionery products; Lollipops & other hard candy

D-U-N-S 02-349-9650
JOE VAN HORN CHEVROLET INC
3008 Eastern Ave, Plymouth, WI 53073-8608
Tel (920) 893-6361 *Founded/Ownrshp* 1965
Sales 22.6MM *EMP* 40
SIC 5511 7515 Automobiles, new & used; Passenger car leasing; Automobiles, new & used; Passenger car leasing
CEO: Chuck Van Horn
**Owner:* Theresa Van Horn
**Pr:* Dick Strong

D-U-N-S 04-463-0655
JOE W FLY CO INC
FLY, JOE COMPANY
4820 Memphis St, Dallas, TX 75207-5210
Tel (214) 634-2200 *Founded/Ownrshp* 1967
Sales 30.9MM[E] *EMP* 50
SIC 5085 Filters, industrial
Pr: Joe W Fly Jr
**VP:* Hunt Foster
Exec: Boyd Foster
IT Man: Ryan Nehring
IT Man: Nehring Ryan
Mktg Dir: Sarah O'Brien

D-U-N-S 00-690-0898
JOE WHEELER ELECTRIC MEMBERSHIP CORP
25354 Al Highway 24, Trinity, AL 35673-5365
Tel (256) 552-2300 *Founded/Ownrshp* 1937
Sales 148.6MM *EMP* 108
Accts Jackson Thornton & Co Pc Mont
SIC 4911 Distribution, electric power; Distribution, electric power
Pr: Neal Norwood
**Sec:* Rick Knouff

D-U-N-S 78-513-9630
JOE WHEELER EMC
25700 Al Highway 24, Trinity, AL 35673-5395
Tel (256) 552-2300 *Founded/Ownrshp* 2006
Sales NA *EMP* 44[E]
SIC 6111 Rural Electrification Administration; Rural Electrification Administration
CFO: Patrick Holmes
**Genl Mgr:* George Kitchens

D-U-N-S 01-208-2152 IMP/EXP
JOE-ANNE CO INTERNATIONAL INC
JOE ANNE
100 Corporate Plz Ste 103, Islandia, NY 11749-1508
Tel (843) 623-3809 *Founded/Ownrshp* 1987
Sales 40.3MM[E] *EMP* 73
SIC 5131 5136 Trimmings, apparel; Sportswear, men's & boys'
Pr: Neil Morganstern
**VP:* Joey Intoci
Genl Mgr: Aquino Cabrera

JOEL COURT APTS
See MITCHELL CO INC

JOEL OSTEEN MINISTRIES
See LAKEWOOD CHURCH

D-U-N-S 06-890-4390
JOEL POMERENE MEMORIAL HOSPITAL
POMERENE HOSPITAL
981 Wooster Rd, Millersburg, OH 44654-1536
Tel (330) 674-1015 *Founded/Ownrshp* 1937
Sales 28.9MM *EMP* 280
SIC 8062 General medical & surgical hospitals; General medical & surgical hospitals
CEO: P W Smith Jr
Chf Rad: Claudia Rozuk
CFO: Jason Justice
Ofcr: Tony Snyder
VP: Nicole Gemma
VP: Alex Nicolozakes
VP: Mark Smith
Off Mgr: Craig Miller
CIO: Mark Jacobs
Info Man: John Hochstetler
Surgeon: Mark Jaroch

JOEMC
See JONES-ONSLOW ELECTRIC MEMBERSHIP CORP

D-U-N-S 13-763-4309
JOERIS GENERAL CONTRACTORS LTD
823 Arion Pkwy, San Antonio, TX 78216-2922
Tel (210) 286-8696 *Founded/Ownrshp* 1983
Sales 351.0MM *EMP* 200
Accts Padgett Stratermann & Co San
SIC 1542 Commercial & office building, new construction; Commercial & office building, new construction
Genl Pt: Gary Joeris
**Pt:* Michelle Seward
**Pt:* Stephen Walter
Pr: Chris Carruth
CFO: Michelle Davis
Exec: Angela Cardwell
Genl Mgr: Elva Rose
Off Mgr: Vicky Banks
Sfty Mgr: Mark Bakeman

Snr PM: John Casstevens
Snr PM: Blake Larue

D-U-N-S 82-915-0957
JOERNS FURNITURE CO INC
JOERNS HEALTHCARE
2430 Whitehall Park Dr # 100, Charlotte, NC 28273-3422
Tel (800) 826-0270 *Founded/Ownrshp* 2008
Sales 34.0MM^E *EMP* 77^E
SIC 3429 Furniture builders' & other household hardware
CEO: Mark Ludwig

JOERNS HEALTHCARE
See JOERNS FURNITURE CO INC

D-U-N-S 79-093-7150 IMP
JOERNS HEALTHCARE LLC
(*Suby of* QUAD-C JH HOLDINGS INC) ★
2430 Whit Park Dr Ste 100, Charlotte, NC 28273
Tel (800) 826-0270 *Founded/Ownrshp* 2006
Sales NA *EMP* 500
SIC 5047 Hospital furniture; Hospital furniture
CEO: Mark Ludwig
**Ex VP:* Mark Urbania
VP: Gerardo Barrera
VP: Bryan Johnson
**VP:* Stephanie Tucker
QA Dir: Mike Chellson
IT Man: Jeremy Laha

D-U-N-S 12-608-5120
JOERNS LLC
(*Suby of* QUAD-C JH HOLDINGS INC) ★
19748 Dearborn St, Chatsworth, CA 91311-6509
Tel (800) 966-6662 *Founded/Ownrshp* 1998
Sales 54.3MM^E *EMP* 300
SIC 5047 Hospital equipment & furniture; Hospital equipment & furniture
**CFO:* Mark Urbania

JOERNS RECOVERCARE
See RECOVERCARE LLC

JOE'S AUTO MARINE SUPPLY
See FIBERGLASS COATINGS INC

JOE'S CARPET
See WEBER CARPET INC

D-U-N-S 62-644-3204 IMP
▲ JOES JEANS INC
2340 S Eastern Ave, Commerce, CA 90040-1431
Tel (323) 837-3700 *Founded/Ownrshp* 1990
Sales 188.7MM *EMP* 561
Accts Moss Adams Llp Los Angeles
Tkr Sym JOEZ *Exch* NAS
SIC 2337 2339 2311 2325 3111 2387 Women's & misses' suits & coats; Women's & misses' suits & skirts; Women's & misses' capes & jackets; Jeans: women's, misses' & juniors'; Men's & boys' suits & coats; Jeans: men's, youths' & boys'; Accessory products, leather; Handbag leather; Shoe leather; Apparel belts; Women's & misses' suits & coats; Women's & misses' suits & skirts; Women's & misses' capes & jackets; Jeans: women's, misses' & juniors'; Men's & boys' suits & coats; Jeans: men's, youths' & boys'; Accessory products, leather; Handbag leather; Shoe leather; Apparel belts
CEO: Samuel J Furrow
CFO: Hamish Sandhu
VP: Alejandra Dibos
VP: Vicki Eshelman
VP: Katie Hurley
VP: Lori Nembirkow
VP: Elena Pickett
VP: Dolores Rykowski
VP: Shane Whalen
Creative D: Joe Dahan
Store Mgr: Daniela Flynn
Board of Directors: Joanne Calabrese, Kelly Hoffman, Suhail R Rizvi, Kent Savage

JOES JUNCTION
See JACKSON OIL & SOLVENTS INC

D-U-N-S 17-576-1857 IMP
JOES SMOKIN CIGARS LLC
SMOKIN JOE'S
2293 Snders Settlement Rd, Sanborn, NY 14132-9336
Tel (716) 215-2000 *Founded/Ownrshp* 1983
Sales 46.1MM^E *EMP* 200
SIC 5993 5541 Cigarette store; Filling stations, gasoline; Cigarette store; Filling stations, gasoline
Sftwr Eng: Josh Moore

JOE'S SPORTS, OUTDOOR & MORE
See G I JOES INC

JOE'S STONE CRAB RESTAURANT
See JOES STONE CRABS INC

D-U-N-S 03-251-7666
JOES STONE CRABS INC
JOE'S STONE CRAB RESTAURANT
11 Washington Ave, Miami Beach, FL 33139-7395
Tel (305) 673-0365 *Founded/Ownrshp* 1949
Sales 18.2MM^E *EMP* 450
SIC 5812 Seafood restaurants; Seafood restaurants
Pr: Joann S Bass
**CFO:* Marc J Fine
**Treas:* Stephen Sawitz
IT Man: Peggy Evans
IT Man: Louis Vargas

JOEUN CALL TAXI
See GOOD FRIENDS OF NY INC

JOEY GERAD'S
See BARTOLOTTA RESTAURANT GROUP LLC

D-U-N-S 00-636-6116 IMP/EXP
JOFCO INC
JOFCO, INTERNATIONAL
225 Clay St, Jasper, IN 47546-3306
Tel (812) 482-5154 *Founded/Ownrshp* 1922
Sales 49.4MM^E *EMP* 221
SIC 5021 2521 Furniture; Chairs, office: padded, upholstered or plain: wood; Furniture; Chairs, office: padded, upholstered or plain: wood
CEO: William A Rubino
**Pr:* Bill Rubino
**Ch:* Joseph F Steurer
**Treas:* Bernard Messmer
Sr VP: Mike Steurer
VP: Cce Meyer
VP: John Nicholson
**VP:* Gregory Sturm
CTO: Andrea Norris
IT Man: Gene Luebbehusen
Mtls Mgr: Sandra Harder
Board of Directors: Michael Meyer, Joseph Steurar

JOFCO, INTERNATIONAL
See JOFCO INC

D-U-N-S 00-385-5970
JOFFE LUMBER & SUPPLY CO INC (NJ)
18 Burns Ave, Vineland, NJ 08360-7799
Tel (856) 825-1397 *Founded/Ownrshp* 1933
Sales 41.6MM^E *EMP* 75
SIC 5031 2431 Lumber, plywood & millwork; Doors & door parts & trim, wood; Lumber, plywood & millwork; Doors & door parts & trim, wood
Pr: Michael Bergen
Sls Mgr: Joe Phillips

D-U-N-S 13-930-8233
JOFFREYS COFFEE & TEA CO
3803 Corporex Park Dr # 400, Tampa, FL 33619-1187
Tel (813) 250-0404 *Founded/Ownrshp* 1994
Sales 46.8MM^E *EMP* 120
SIC 5149 Coffee, green or roasted; Tea; Spices & seasonings; Coffee, green or roasted; Tea; Spices & seasonings
Ch: Robert Hickey
**Pr:* Ted C Abrams
CFO: Eric Snow
VP: Brian William
Prd Mgr: Randy Erwin

D-U-N-S 08-004-1916 IMP
JOFRAN SALES INC
1 Jofran Way, Norfolk, MA 02056-1671
Tel (508) 384-6019 *Founded/Ownrshp* 1975
Sales 45.4MM^E *EMP* 70
SIC 5021 Furniture
CEO: Robert D Roy
**Pr:* Joffrey Roy
VP: Joff Roy
Opers Mgr: Deniece Fredericks

JOH ATLANTIC PARTNERS
See JOHNSON OHARE CO INC

JOHA
See JOLIET ONCOLOGY-HEMATOLOGY ASSOCIATES LTD

D-U-N-S 03-924-4694 IMP/EXP
JOHANN HALTERMANN LTD
HALTERMANN SOLUTIONS
(*Suby of* MONUMENT CHEMICALS INC) ★
16717 Jacintoport Blvd, Houston, TX 77015-6544
Tel (281) 452-5951 *Founded/Ownrshp* 2010
Sales 47.0MM *EMP* 225
SIC 2824 2869 Organic fibers, noncellulosic; Fuels; Organic fibers, noncellulosic; Fuels
Pr: Wayne Petersen
VP: Ed Guiney
VP: Dr Rainer Potthast
Tech Mgr: Lisa Matthay
Ql Cn Mgr: Blake Saffer
Natl Sales: Josh Petersen
VP Mktg: Donald Power
Manager: Tyler Schneider
Snr Mgr: Maria Gutierrez
Snr Mgr: Wayne Price

D-U-N-S 00-235-0577
JOHANNA FOODS INC
20 Johanna Farms Rd, Flemington, NJ 08822
Tel (908) 788-2200 *Founded/Ownrshp* 1944
Sales 178.8MM^E *EMP* 540^E
SIC 2033 2026 Fruit juices: packaged in cans, jars, etc.; Fruit juices: fresh; Yogurt; Fruit juices: packaged in cans, jars, etc.; Fruit juices: fresh; Yogurt
Pr: Robert A Facchina
Pr: Chris Hirst
**CFO:* Richard Cook
VP: Brasington Beakley
VP: Calvin Reed
VP: Reggie Sanders
VP: Steven Steigerwalt
Dir Risk M: Brad Varney
Mfg Dir: Ramon Lopez
Mfg Dir: Dave Muscatell
Opers Mgr: Walter Fox

D-U-N-S 02-272-0288
JOHANNESONS INC
MARKET PLACE FOODS
2301 Johanneson Dr Nw, Bemidji, MN 56601-4101
Tel (218) 751-9644 *Founded/Ownrshp* 1975
Sales 88.3MM^E *EMP* 650
SIC 5411 Supermarkets, independent; Supermarkets, independent
CEO: Keith Johanneson
CFO: Carmen Nornenberg
**Sec:* Richard Johanneson
Dir IT: Julio Fernandez

JOHANNESSEN STEEL
See JOHANNESSEN TRADING CO

D-U-N-S 04-441-9117
JOHANNESSEN TRADING CO
JOHANNESSEN STEEL
6111 Bandini Blvd, Commerce, CA 90040-3111
Tel (800) 252-7765 *Founded/Ownrshp* 1968
Sales 27.5MM^E *EMP* 23
SIC 5051 Steel
CEO: Holger Lohfeld
**CFO:* Jane Patten
**VP:* Kevin Demarco
CIO: Nassef Tewfik

D-U-N-S 05-643-0820 IMP
JOHANSON DIELECTRICS INC
15191 Bledsoe St, Sylmar, CA 91342-2700
Tel (818) 364-9800 *Founded/Ownrshp* 1965
Sales 39.6MM^E *EMP* 200^E
SIC 3675 Electronic capacitors; Electronic capacitors
CEO: N Eric Johanson
Pr: Sudhir Kulkarni
VP: Kurt Johanson
Dir IT: Paul Binger
IT Man: Larry Williamson
VP Opers: Denis Murphy
Sfty Mgr: Enrique Cianca
Prd Mgr: Richard Besu
Prd Mgr: Renee Dickson
Mktg Dir: David Dupre
Sls Mgr: Scott Muller

D-U-N-S 00-219-3001
JOHANSON MANUFACTURING CORP (NJ)
301 Rockaway Valley Rd, Boonton, NJ 07005-9192
Tel (973) 658-1051 *Founded/Ownrshp* 1945
Sales 38.3MM^E *EMP* 200
SIC 3675 Electronic capacitors; Electronic capacitors
CEO: Nancy Johanson
Pr: C Kim
**Pr:* Rocco Melchione
**Ex VP:* Walter Hutton
**Brnch Mgr:* Jon Krawczyk
Dir IT: Rob Pisapia
Mktg Dir: Tom Anderer
Manager: Jeff Nicoll

D-U-N-S 82-553-2906 IMP
JOHANSON TECHNOLOGY INC
4001 Calle Tecate, Camarillo, CA 93012-5087
Tel (805) 389-1166 *Founded/Ownrshp* 1991
Sales 31.9MM^E *EMP* 159
SIC 3675 5065 3674 Electronic capacitors; Electronic parts & equipment; Semiconductors & related devices; Electronic capacitors; Electronic parts & equipment; Semiconductors & related devices
CEO: N Eric Johanson
**VP:* John Petrinec
VP: John Ricardi
Rgnl Mgr: Dick Eberhart
Rgnl Mgr: Wendell Hautaniemi
Genl Mgr: Tom McKnelly
Plnt Mgr: D Ick Crawford
Plnt Mgr: Como Cusik
Sales Exec: Scott Horton
Manager: Mark Klotka
Sls Mgr: Vivian Nelson

D-U-N-S 02-462-4241
JOHN & DENISE GRAVES FOUNDATION
333 Washington Ave N, Minneapolis, MN 55401-1377
Tel (612) 349-2705 *Founded/Ownrshp* 2014
Sales 47.2MM *EMP* 1
SIC 8641 Civic social & fraternal associations
Pr: Bill Graves

D-U-N-S 00-447-2403
JOHN A BECKER CO
BECKER ELECTRIC SUPPLY
1341 E 4th St, Dayton, OH 45402-2235
Tel (937) 226-1341 *Founded/Ownrshp* 1920
Sales 298.9MM^E *EMP* 231
SIC 5063 Electrical construction materials; Electrical supplies; Lighting fixtures; Motor controls, starters & relays: electric; Electrical construction materials; Electrical supplies; Lighting fixtures; Motor controls, starters & relays: electric
CEO: Thomas J Becker
**Pr:* David Adkinson
**VP:* James Becker
**VP:* Mark Covey
**VP:* James Dichito

D-U-N-S 05-882-1778 IMP
JOHN A BIEWER LUMBER CO (MI)
812 S Riverside Ave, Saint Clair, MI 48079-5393
Tel (810) 329-4789 *Founded/Ownrshp* 1961, 2000
Sales 104.4MM^E *EMP* 300
SIC 2491 Structural lumber & timber, treated wood; Pilings, treated wood; Structural lumber & timber, treated wood; Pilings, treated wood
Pr: Richard Biewer
CFO: Gary Olmstead
**Sec:* Brian B Biewer
**VP:* Timothy Biewer

D-U-N-S 80-018-7494
JOHN A BOUSQUET DR
BAYLER FAMILY MEDICAL CENTER
2460 N Interstate Hwy 35, Waxahachie, TX 75165-5266
Tel (469) 800-9500 *Founded/Ownrshp* 1993
Sales 59.5MM *EMP* 60
SIC 8011 Offices & clinics of medical doctors; Offices & clinics of medical doctors
Owner: John A Bousquet
Off Mgr: Louann Worsham

D-U-N-S 07-105-0512
JOHN A HARTFORD FOUNDATION INC
55 E 59th St Fl 16, New York, NY 10022-1713
Tel (212) 593-4913 *Founded/Ownrshp* 1929
Sales 51.9MM *EMP* 16
SIC 6732 Charitable trust management; Charitable trust management
**V Ch:* Norman H Volk
**Pr:* Terry Fulmer
Bd of Dir: Susan Reinhard
Ofcr: Marcus Escobedo
VP: Martin Learner
**Ex Dir:* Corinne H Rieder

D-U-N-S 08-000-0136
JOHN A LOGAN COLLEGE
700 Logan College Dr, Carterville, IL 62918-2501
Tel (618) 457-7676 *Founded/Ownrshp* 1967
Sales 17.4MM *EMP* 750
Accts Kemper Cpa Group Llp Marion
SIC 8222 Junior college; Junior college
Ch: Mike Hopkins
**Pr:* Robert L Mees PHD
**VP:* Brad McCormick
VP: Jan Otey
VP Admn: Tim Daugherty

D-U-N-S 00-785-6768 EXP
JOHN A MARSHALL CO (KS)
10930 Lackman Rd, Lenexa, KS 66219-1232
Tel (913) 599-4700 *Founded/Ownrshp* 1923
Sales 68.6MM^E *EMP* 101^E
SIC 5021 Office furniture; Office furniture
CEO: John E Marshall
**Pr:* Frank T Stasi
**CFO:* James S Gutschow
**Ch:* Mark J Donnelly
VP: Susan Grisamore
**Prin:* William C Marshall
Area Mgr: Jennifer Drace
CIO: Richard Louvet
IT Man: Chris Harper
IT Man: Stephen Marshall
Natl Sales: Phillip Carson

JOHN A MATA MD
See LSU HEALTH SCIENCE CENTER

D-U-N-S 06-661-7275
JOHN A PENNEY CO INC
270 Sidney St, Cambridge, MA 02139-4833
Tel (617) 547-7744 *Founded/Ownrshp* 1973
Sales 65.0MM *EMP* 200^E
Accts Mcgladrey & Pullen Llp Burli
SIC 1731 General electrical contractor; Fire detection & burglar alarm systems specialization; General electrical contractor; Fire detection & burglar alarm systems specialization
CEO: John A Penney
**Pr:* George Scharfe
**VP:* Alan C Scharfe
Snr PM: Chris Bonanno

D-U-N-S 00-972-0186
JOHN A STEER CO
STEER COMPANY
28 S 2nd St, Philadelphia, PA 19106-2899
Tel (215) 922-6610 *Founded/Ownrshp* 1968
Sales 22.2MM^E *EMP* 65
SIC 4731 Customhouse brokers; Freight forwarding
CEO: Daniel Wackerman
**Ch:* Jack Poole
Treas: Alfred Dutch
**VP:* Denise Allen
**VP:* David J Ferris
VP: Jack Fleischer
**VP:* John K Greenlee
VP Sls: George McGowen

D-U-N-S 01-041-6451 IMP/EXP
JOHN ABELL CORP
10500 Sw 186th St, Cutler Bay, FL 33157-6718
Tel (305) 253-4440 *Founded/Ownrshp* 1975
Sales 23.5MM^E *EMP* 38^E
SIC 5032 Concrete building products
Pr: John W Abell Jr
Sls Mgr: Nick Abell
Sales Asso: Eric Abell

JOHN ADAMS MORTGAGE COMPANY
See GTL INVESTMENTS INC

D-U-N-S 86-716-7017
JOHN AKENS INC
OHARA CHRYSLER DODGE JEEP RAM
1111 W Michigan Ave, Clinton, MI 49236-9686
Tel (517) 456-6555 *Founded/Ownrshp* 1993
Sales 25.3MM^E *EMP* 56
SIC 5511 Automobiles, new & used
Pr: John Akens

D-U-N-S 10-192-9594
JOHN AKRIDGE CO
(*Suby of* JACO HOLDING CO) ★
601 13th St Nw Ste 300n, Washington, DC 20005-4388
Tel (202) 638-3000 *Founded/Ownrshp* 1975
Sales 72.5MM^E *EMP* 90
SIC 6552 6531 6799 Subdividers & developers; Real estate agents & managers; Real estate investors, except property operators
Pr: Matthew Klein
**CFO:* Brian Cass
**Ch:* John E Akridge III
Sr VP: Cathryn Barmes
Sr VP: Stephanie Brown
Sr VP: Brian Connolly
Sr VP: Keita Darling
Sr VP: Rob Kohn
**Sr VP:* Thomas Wilbur
Sr VP: Tae-Sik Yoon
VP: Lavon Butler
VP: Marcela Correa
VP: Sarah Knutson
VP: Mary Lynch
VP: April Mandell
VP: Andrea McCahill
VP: John Otto
VP: Wilbur Pace
VP: Robert E Schofield Jr
VP: Michael Simmons
VP: Gregory Tomasso

D-U-N-S 02-340-4775
JOHN AMATO HYUNDAI MAZDA INC
AMATO MAZDA
8301 N 76th St, Milwaukee, WI 53223-3207
Tel (414) 357-8500 *Founded/Ownrshp* 1980
Sales 27.5MM^E *EMP* 65
SIC 5511 7538 Automobiles, new & used; General automotive repair shops; Automobiles, new & used; General automotive repair shops
Pr: John Amato
**Sec:* Don Morrison
VP: Beth Vanderwal

D-U-N-S 96-705-2254
JOHN AND AMY GRIFFIN FOUNDATION
660 Madison Ave, New York, NY 10065-8405
Tel (212) 446-3327 *Founded/Ownrshp* 2011
Sales 27.0MM^E *EMP* 2
Accts Pricecoopershouse Coopers Llp
SIC 8699 Charitable organization

JOHN ASCUAGA'S NUGGET
See SPARKS NUGGET INC

D-U-N-S 83-883-2657
JOHN B GOODMAN LIMITED PARTNERSHIP
1107 Hazeltine Blvd # 200, Chaska, MN 55318-1070
Tel (952) 361-8000 *Founded/Ownrshp* 1995
Sales 67.4MM^E *EMP* 404
SIC 1542 Design & erection, combined: non-residential; Design & erection, combined: non-residential
Genl Pt: John B Goodman

D-U-N-S 02-529-3481 IMP
▲ JOHN B SANFILIPPO & SON INC
FISCHER NUT COMPANY
1703 N Randall Rd, Elgin, IL 60123-7820
Tel (847) 289-1800 *Founded/Ownrshp* 1979
Sales 887.2MM *EMP* 1,300
Tkr Sym JBSS *Exch* NGM
SIC 2068 2064 2099 2096 2066 Nuts: dried, dehydrated, salted or roasted; Candy & other confectionery products; Peanut butter; Dessert mixes & fillings; Potato chips & similar snacks; Chocolate & cocoa products; Nuts: dried, dehydrated, salted or roasted; Candy & other confectionery products; Peanut butter; Dessert mixes & fillings; Potato chips & similar snacks; Chocolate & cocoa products
Ch Bd: Jeffrey T Sanfilippo
**Pr:* Jasper B Sanfilippo Jr
**Pr:* Michael J Valentine
Sr VP: Frank S Pellegrino
VP: John Accardo
VP: Brenda Cannon
VP: Stephen Chester
VP: Tom Fordonski
VP: Steve Kerr
VP: Robert J Sarlls
Exec: Linda Stockier
Board of Directors: Timothy R Donovan, Jim Edgar, James J Sanfilippo, Ellen C Taaffe, Mathias A Valentine, Daniel M Wright

D-U-N-S 82-705-5869 IMP/EXP
▲ JOHN BEAN TECHNOLOGIES CORP
JBT
70 W Madison St Ste 4400, Chicago, IL 60602-4546
Tel (312) 861-5900 *Founded/Ownrshp* 2008
Sales 984.2MM *EMP* 3,500
Tkr Sym JBT *Exch* NYS
SIC 3556 3585 3537 Food products machinery; Refrigeration & heating equipment; Containers (metal), air cargo; Food products machinery; Refrigeration & heating equipment; Containers (metal), air cargo
Pr: Thomas W Giacomini
COO: Scott Millsap
CFO: Brian A Deck
CFO: Larry Martin
Treas: Donna Iwanski
Ex VP: James L Marvin
Ex VP: Mark K Montague
VP: Brent Ahlstrom
VP: Dave Burdakin
VP: Megan J Rattigan
Telecom Ex: Angela Mas
Board of Directors: C Maury Devine, Edward L Doheny II, Alan D Feldman, James E Goodwin, Polly B Kawalek, James M Ringler

D-U-N-S 04-760-9599
JOHN BLEAKLEY FORD INC
870 Thornton Rd, Lithia Springs, GA 30122-4442
Tel (770) 941-9000 *Founded/Ownrshp* 1965
Sales 66.0MM^E *EMP* 140
SIC 5511 Automobiles, new & used; Automobiles, new & used
Pr: John Bleakley Jr
Treas: Dorothy Bleakley
Sales Asso: Chris Pothoff

JOHN BOMMARITO MAZDA
See JOHN BOMMARITO OLDSMOBILE - CADILLAC INC

D-U-N-S 17-415-4484
JOHN BOMMARITO OLDSMOBILE - CADILLAC INC
JOHN BOMMARITO MAZDA
4190 N Service Rd, Saint Peters, MO 63376-6463
Tel (636) 928-4155 *Founded/Ownrshp* 1992
Sales 22.0MM^E *EMP* 53
SIC 5511 4812 Automobiles, new & used; Radio telephone communication; Automobiles, new & used; Radio telephone communication
Pr: John Bommarito
**Sec:* Janet Duke
VP: Kelly Lagarce
Sales Asso: Joe Biermann

D-U-N-S 00-404-0184
JOHN BOUCHARD & SONS CO (TN)
1024 Harrison St, Nashville, TN 37203-3389
Tel (615) 256-0112 *Founded/Ownrshp* 1900
Sales 34.0MM *EMP* 160
SIC 3321 5085 3599 1711 1799 1731

D-U-N-S 14-862-7383
JOHN BOWMAN CHEVROLET INC
6750 Dixie Hwy, Clarkston, MI 48346-2919
Tel (248) 625-5071 *Founded/Ownrshp* 1984
Sales 31.1MM^E *EMP* 75
SIC 5511 Automobiles, new & used; Automobiles, new & used
Pr: Katie Coleman Bowman
**Pr:* John E Bowman
**Treas:* Julie Bradley
IT Man: Kaity Bowman
Sls Mgr: Joe Jackson

D-U-N-S 11-270-2209
JOHN BOWMAN INC
BOWMAN STEEL
8025 Associate Blvd, Sebring, FL 33876-6616
Tel (239) 303-9739 *Founded/Ownrshp* 2001
Sales 23.1MM^E *EMP* 180
SIC 1791 Structural steel erection; Structural steel erection
Pr: John Bowman
**VP:* Stephen Drager
Sls Mgr: Tom Hayden

D-U-N-S 13-162-3209 IMP
JOHN BOYD ENTERPRISES INC
J B ENTERPRISES
8401 Specialty Cir, Sacramento, CA 95828-2523
Tel (916) 381-4790 *Founded/Ownrshp* 1974
Sales 52.6MM^E *EMP* 259^E
SIC 3714 3433 Radiators & radiator shells & cores, motor vehicle; Heating equipment, except electric; Radiators & radiator shells & cores, motor vehicle; Heating equipment, except electric
Sec: Donna Boyd
Mtls Mgr: Mike Steele
Mfg Mgr: Chris Farasopoulos
Manager: Terrance Duke
Sls Mgr: Tobin Boyd
Sls Mgr: Lance Jenkins
Sls Mgr: Erik Putzrath

D-U-N-S 07-739-4112
JOHN BROWN UNIVERSITY
J B U
2000 W University St, Siloam Springs, AR 72761-2121
Tel (479) 524-9500 *Founded/Ownrshp* 1919
Sales 73.7MM *EMP* 242
Accts Capin Crouse Lp Colorado Spri
SIC 8221 8661 University; Religious organizations; University; Religious organizations
Pr: Charles W Pollard
Top Exec: Marquita Smith
VP: Rodney Arnold
VP: Steve Beers
**VP:* Edward Ericson
VP: Tim Harris
VP: Jim Krall
VP: Shohreh Noorbakhsh
Dir Bus: Chuck Hyde
Ex Dir: Gary Oliver
Off Mgr: Carol Petross

D-U-N-S 00-279-2208
JOHN BUNNING TRANSFER CO INC
1600 Elk St, Rock Springs, WY 82901-4021
Tel (307) 362-3791 *Founded/Ownrshp* 1940
Sales 20.2MM^E *EMP* 105
SIC 4213 4225 Contract haulers; Warehousing, self-storage
Pr: Chris N Bunning
**Treas:* Mark Kurtz
**VP:* Robert Bunning

D-U-N-S 00-797-9206
JOHN BURNS CONSTRUCTION CO (IL)
17601 Southwest Hwy, Orland Park, IL 60467-4200
Tel (708) 326-3500 *Founded/Ownrshp* 1906
Sales 48.7MM^E *EMP* 100
SIC 1611 1623 1629 1731 General contractor, highway & street construction; Sewer line construction; Water main construction; Transmitting tower (telecommunication) construction; Railroad & railway roadbed construction; Power plant construction; General electrical contractor; General contractor, highway & street construction; Sewer line construction; Water main construction; Transmitting tower (telecommunication) construction; Railroad & railway roadbed construction; Power plant construction; General electrical contractor
Pr: William J O'Malley
**CFO:* Dale R Slusarski
**Ch:* John T O'Malley
Ofcr: Kevin Flynn
**VP:* Scott Becker
Off Mgr: Colleen Donahue
Sls&Mrk Ex: Mike Higgins
Snr PM: Eric Probst

D-U-N-S 14-441-9298
JOHN BURNS CONSTRUCTION CO OF TEXAS INC
655 E Main St, Lewisville, TX 75057-4051
Tel (972) 434-6789 *Founded/Ownrshp* 1985
Sales 26.6MM^E *EMP* 100
SIC 1623 Water main construction; Sewer line construction; Underground utilities contractor; Transmitting tower (telecommunication) construction; Water main construction; Sewer line construction; Underground utilities contractor; Transmitting tower (telecommunication) construction
Pr: John T O'Malley
**Pr:* William O'Malley
**VP:* Scott Becker
**VP:* Mike Borstad
**VP:* Driskoll Tubbs
Prgrm Mgr: Andrew Carnegie
Prgrm Mgr: Shane Higgins
Snr Mgr: Kenny Thomas

D-U-N-S 07-199-6839
JOHN BURROUGHS SCHOOL INC
755 S Price Rd, Saint Louis, MO 63124-1899
Tel (314) 993-4040 *Founded/Ownrshp* 1923
Sales 28.1MM *EMP* 150
Accts Rubinbrown Llp
SIC 8211 Preparatory school; Preparatory school
Pr: Judy Grand
Sls&Mrk Ex: Sheri Mines
Psych: Jennifer Jones

D-U-N-S 00-982-7346
JOHN C GRIMBERG CO INC
3200 Tower Oaks Blvd Fl 3, Rockville, MD 20852-4216
Tel (301) 881-5120 *Founded/Ownrshp* 1954
Sales 158.5MM^E *EMP* 215
SIC 1542 Commercial & office building, new construction; Commercial & office buildings, renovation & repair; Commercial & office building, new construction; Commercial & office buildings, renovation & repair
Pr: Peter J Grimberg
**CEO:* John M Grimberg
**VP:* James L Graham
**VP:* Stephen J Grimberg
**VP:* John F Treseler
Exec: John Greenwell
IT Man: Jason Kerlek
QI Cn Mgr: Tom Niederberger

D-U-N-S 00-693-9672
JOHN C GROUB CO INC
JAY C STORES
900 A Ave E, Seymour, IN 47274-3239
Tel (812) 522-1998 *Founded/Ownrshp* 1863
Sales 71.8MM^E *EMP* 2,000
SIC 5411 Grocery stores, chain; Grocery stores, chain
Pr: James T McCoy
**Treas:* Thomas Bollinger
Opers Mgr: Don Belcher
Mktg Mgr: Mark Baker
Mktg Mgr: Tom Bolinger

D-U-N-S 04-301-8480
JOHN C LINCOLN HEALTH NETWORK
JOHN C LINCOLN HOSP - DEER VLY
(*Suby of* SCOTTSDALE HEALTHCARE HOSPITALS) ★
2500 E Dunlap Ave, Phoenix, AZ 85020
Tel (602) 870-6060 *Founded/Ownrshp* 1943, 2015
Sales 584.5MM *EMP* 3,500
SIC 8062 8051 General medical & surgical hospitals; Skilled nursing care facilities; Extended care facility; General medical & surgical hospitals; Skilled nursing care facilities; Extended care facility
CEO: John L Harrington Jr
COO: Heather L Jelonek
Treas: Charez Norris
Bd of Dir: Shirley Goldman
**Sr VP:* Bruce Pearson
VP: MA Anspach
VP: Alaina Chabrier
VP: Jody Chandler
VP: Brian Smit
Dir Lab: Bob Wenham
Dir Rx: Susan Moravec

JOHN C LINCOLN HOSP - DEER VLY
See JOHN C LINCOLN HEALTH NETWORK

D-U-N-S 17-955-8317
JOHN CANNON HOMES INC
6710 Prof Pkwy W Ste 100, Sarasota, FL 34240
Tel (941) 924-5935 *Founded/Ownrshp* 1997
Sales 45.5MM *EMP* 80
Accts Hill Barth & King Llc
SIC 1521 New construction, single-family houses; New construction, single-family houses
Pr: John K Cannon
**CFO:* Mike Finley
**VP:* Phillipa Cannon

D-U-N-S 07-112-4788
JOHN CARROLL UNIVERSITY
1 John Carroll Blvd, University Heights, OH 44118-4581
Tel (216) 397-1886 *Founded/Ownrshp* 1886
Sales 91.4MM *EMP* 2,343^E
Accts Bkd Llp Fort Wayne Indiana
SIC 8221 University; University
Pr: Robert L Niehoff
Treas: Richard F Mausser
Ofcr: Albert Okeefe
VP: John Day
VP: Carol Dietz
VP: Barbara Lovequist
VP: Richard P Salmi
Exec: Duane Dukes
CIO: Michael Bestul
IT Man: William Barker
Sls Dir: Anthony Stone

JOHN CHARLES DESIGNS
See AL LEGACY PARTNERS INC

D-U-N-S 17-411-8190
JOHN CHRISTNER TRUCKING LLC
19007 W Highway 33, Sapulpa, OK 74066-7545
Tel (918) 248-3300 *Founded/Ownrshp* 1986
Sales 107.1MM^E *EMP* 789
SIC 4213 Trucking, except local; Trucking, except local
Pr: John M Christner
COO: Virgil McPherson
**Treas:* Darryl Christner
**VP:* Daniel Christner
VP: Jim Gomez
VP: Greg Gorman
VP: Jim Redwine
**VP:* Bob Snell
VP: David Wilbanks

D-U-N-S 04-041-9616
JOHN CONTI COFFEE CO
4406 Ole Brickyard Cir, Louisville, KY 40218-3066
Tel (502) 499-8600 *Founded/Ownrshp* 1971
Sales 30.4MM^E *EMP* 110
SIC 7389 5499 5149 Coffee service; Coffee; Coffee, green or roasted
CEO: Jack W Wells
Pr: Gary W Schroader
VP: Keith Sharber
Genl Mgr: Walt Meadors

D-U-N-S 60-292-9812
JOHN COOPER SCHOOL
1 John Cooper Dr, The Woodlands, TX 77381-4499
Tel (281) 367-0900 *Founded/Ownrshp* 1988
Sales 26.7MM *EMP* 150
Accts Blazek & Vetterling Houston
SIC 8211 Private elementary school; Private junior high school; Private elementary school; Private junior high school
Exec: Nicky Dempsey
Comm Dir: Deb Spiess
**Prin:* Joe Broccoli
Psych: Linda Donald

D-U-N-S 00-509-4347 IMP/EXP
JOHN CRANE INC
(*Suby of* SMITHS GROUP PLC)
227 W Monroe St Ste 1800, Chicago, IL 60606-5053
Tel (312) 605-7800 *Founded/Ownrshp* 1917, 2000
Sales 1.2MMM^E *EMP* 6,180
SIC 3053 Gaskets & sealing devices; Packing materials; Gaskets & sealing devices; Packing materials
Pr: Duncan Gillis
**CFO:* Eric Evans
**Treas:* Terrance P McNamara
Sr Cor Off: Paul Roberts
VP: Ruben Alvarez
**VP:* John F Donatiello
**VP:* Andrew J Forrest
VP: Joe Haas
**VP:* David Hill
VP: Mike Rizzo
**VP:* David Tallentire
VP: Joseph Trytek

D-U-N-S 85-880-4065 IMP
JOHN CRANE INC
(*Suby of* JOHN CRANE INC) ★
6400 Oakton St, Morton Grove, IL 60053-2725
Tel (847) 967-2400 *Founded/Ownrshp* 1947
Sales 175.2MM^E *EMP* 800
SIC 3317 Steel pipe & tubes; Steel pipe & tubes
Pr: Leb Watsson
**VP:* George Strings

JOHN CRANE ORION
See ORION CORP

D-U-N-S 06-835-3440
JOHN CRANE PRODUCTION SOLUTIONS INC (TX)
(*Suby of* JOHN CRANE INC) ★
114 Jordan Plaza Blvd # 300, Tyler, TX 75704-2056
Tel (903) 595-8600 *Founded/Ownrshp* 1985, 2011
Sales 151.3MM^E *EMP* 238
SIC 5084 Petroleum industry machinery; Petroleum industry machinery
CEO: Ruben Alvarez
**CFO:* John Lutterman

D-U-N-S 00-120-5921
JOHN CRANE SEALOL INC
EAGLE DIV
(*Suby of* JOHN CRANE INC) ★
75 Commerce Dr 101, Warwick, RI 02886-2429
Tel (401) 463-8700 *Founded/Ownrshp* 1998
Sales 30.5MM^E *EMP* 493
SIC 3053 3492 3599 Gaskets, packing & sealing devices; Control valves, aircraft: hydraulic & pneumatic; Bellows, industrial: metal; Gaskets, packing & sealing devices; Control valves, aircraft: hydraulic & pneumatic; Bellows, industrial: metal
Pr: Michael Galluccio

JOHN D
See JOHN H DANIEL CO

D-U-N-S 94-428-6236
JOHN D ADAMS & CO CPA PLLC
1266 Benson Rd, Garner, NC 27529-4648
Tel (919) 779-2020 *Founded/Ownrshp* 1996
Sales 37.9MM *EMP* 2
SIC 8721 7291 Certified public accountant; Tax return preparation services; Certified public accountant; Tax return preparation services
Pr: John D Adams

D-U-N-S 14-831-2481
JOHN D AND CATHERINE T MACARTHUR FOUNDATION
140 S Dearborn St, Chicago, IL 60603-5202
Tel (312) 332-0101 *Founded/Ownrshp* 1970
Sales 430.1MM *EMP* 150^E
SIC 8399 Fund raising organization, non-fee basis
Pr: Julia Stasch
CFO: Marc Pyanchura
Treas: Philip Grace
Bd of Dir: Olga Abalakina
Chf Invés: Su Manske
Ofcr: Marlies Carruth
Ofcr: Allison Clark
Ofcr: Maurice Classen
Ofcr: John Fei
Ofcr: Sean Harder
Ofcr: Alaina Harkness
Ofcr: Christopher Holtz
Ofcr: Jen Humke
Ofcr: Christina Lovely
Ofcr: Tawa Mitchell
Ofcr: Lauren Pabst
Ofcr: Eric Sears
Ofcr: Erin Sines
Ofcr: Jeff Ubois
Ofcr: Mijo Vodopic
VP: Cecilia A Conrad

D-U-N-S 01-010-0899 IMP
JOHN D ARCHBOLD MEMORIAL HOSPITAL (GA)
ARCHBOLD MEDICAL CENTER
915 Gordon Ave, Thomasville, GA 31792-6699
Tel (229) 228-2000 *Founded/Ownrshp* 1925
Sales 233.2MM *EMP* 2,700
Accts Draffin & Tucker Llp Albany
SIC 8062 General medical & surgical hospitals; General medical & surgical hospitals
Pr: Perry Mustian
**Ch Bd:* Daniel Autry
Pr: Jim Bue
COO: Kevin Taylor
**CFO:* Skip Hightower
Trst: James Smith
**Sr VP:* John A Fischer
VP: Debbie Beeson
VP: Ken Brooker
VP: Amy Griffin
VP: J P Mustian
Dir Risk M: Kellie Odom
Dir Rx: Bradley Atherton
Board of Directors: Pryor Cornell, Cindy Parrish, Joy Salter, Zack Wheeler

D-U-N-S 04-582-9330 IMP
JOHN D STEPHENS INC
272 Hrricane Shoals Rd Ne, Lawrenceville, GA 30046-4402
Tel (770) 527-6992 *Founded/Ownrshp* 1964
Sales 23.9MM^E *EMP* 70^E
SIC 1623 Pipeline construction
CEO: Mitchell D Stephens

D-U-N-S 00-697-0115 IMP
JOHN DAY CO (NE)
6263 Abbott Dr, Omaha, NE 68110-2806
Tel (402) 455-8000 *Founded/Ownrshp* 1909
Sales 55.0MM^E *EMP* 110

SIC 5083 5084 Farm & garden machinery; Industrial machinery & equipment; Conveyor systems; Farm & garden machinery; Industrial machinery & equipment; Conveyor systems
Pr: John D Fonda
**CFO:* Nancy J Kurtenbach
**VP:* Duane Chamberlain
**VP:* Steve Reagan
Sls Mgr: Richard Flores

JOHN DEERE
See WESTERN BRANCH DIESEL INC

JOHN DEERE
See W I CLARK CO

JOHN DEERE
See WESTERN DIESEL SERVICES INC

JOHN DEERE
See INLAND POWER GROUP INC

JOHN DEERE
See DOGGETT HEAVY MACHINERY SERVICES LLC

JOHN DEERE
See NEUHAUS & CO INC

JOHN DEERE
See STRIBLING EQUIPMENT LLC

JOHN DEERE
See HERITAGE TRACTOR INC

JOHN DEERE
See WADE INC

JOHN DEERE
See WALLOWA COUNTY GRAIN GROWERS INC

JOHN DEERE
See ROWAND MACHINERY CO

JOHN DEERE
See VALLEY POWER SYSTEMS INC

JOHN DEERE
See COASTAL EQUIPMENT CORP

JOHN DEERE
See MERRYMAN INC SONNY

JOHN DEERE
See WASHINGTON TRACTOR INC

JOHN DEERE
See TRUE NORTH EQUIPMENT CO

JOHN DEERE
See DEER COUNTRY EQUIPMENT LLC

JOHN DEERE
See ELDER SALES AND SERVICE INC

JOHN DEERE
See BOMBERGERS STORE INC

JOHN DEERE
See PLASTERER EQUIPMENT CO INC

JOHN DEERE
See REYNOLDS FARM EQUIPMENT INC

JOHN DEERE
See GODFREY BROS INC

JOHN DEERE
See SCHMIDT EQUIPMENT INC

JOHN DEERE
See BADER & SONS CO

JOHN DEERE
See BODENSTEINER IMPLEMENT CO

JOHN DEERE
See AGRIVISION GROUP LLC

JOHN DEERE
See HULTGREN IMPLEMENT INC

JOHN DEERE
See FARMERS SUPPLY SALES INC

JOHN DEERE
See PUCK IMPLEMENT CO

JOHN DEERE
See BRAKKE IMPLEMENTS INC

JOHN DEERE
See AG POWER ENTERPRISES INC

JOHN DEERE
See MN EQUIPMENT SOLUTIONS INC

JOHN DEERE
See EVERGREEN IMPLEMENT CO OF WARREN MINNESOTA

JOHN DEERE
See RIESTERER & SCHNELL INC

JOHN DEERE
See CENTRAL WISCONSIN COOPERATIVE

JOHN DEERE
See GROSSENBURG IMPLEMENT INC

JOHN DEERE
See REVELS TURF AND TRACTOR LLC

JOHN DEERE
See CENTRAL CAROLINA FARM & MOWER INC

JOHN DEERE
See R W MOORE EQUIPMENT CO

JOHN DEERE
See MCLEAN IMPLEMENT INC

JOHN DEERE
See WM NOBBE AND CO INC

JOHN DEERE
See YELLOWHOUSE MACHINERY CO

JOHN DEERE
See QUALITY IMPLEMENT CO

JOHN DEERE
See RAY LEE EQUIPMENT CO LTD

JOHN DEERE
See COUFAL-PRATER EQUIPMENT LTD

JOHN DEERE
See VUCOVICH INC

JOHN DEERE
See HYDRASERVICE INC

JOHN DEERE
See J M EQUIPMENT CO INC

JOHN DEERE
See BAY CITY EQUIPMENT INDUSTRIES INC

JOHN DEERE
See VALLEY TRUCK AND TRACTOR CO

JOHN DEERE
See ERB EQUIPMENT CO INC

JOHN DEERE
See CARRICO IMPLEMENT CO INC

JOHN DEERE
See BUCKLIN TRACTOR & IMPLEMENT CO INC

JOHN DEERE
See PRAIRIELAND PARTNERS INC

JOHN DEERE
See HONNEN EQUIPMENT CO

JOHN DEERE
See EVERGLADES FARM EQUIPMENT CO INC

JOHN DEERE
See P & K MIDWEST INC

JOHN DEERE
See FIELDS EQUIPMENT CO INC

JOHN DEERE
See P & K EQUIPMENT INC

JOHN DEERE
See COBB COUNTY TRACTOR CO INC

JOHN DEERE
See BLANCHARD EQUIPMENT CO INC

JOHN DEERE
See SAW MCKINNEY AND CYCLE INC

JOHN DEERE
See EFFEM CORP

JOHN DEERE
See W W WILLIAMS SOUTHWEST INC

JOHN DEERE
See LAKELAND EQUIPMENT CORP

JOHN DEERE
See SPARROW & KENNEDY TRACTOR CO INC

JOHN DEERE
See CAROLINE IMPLEMENT CO INC

JOHN DEERE
See GREEN LINE EQUIP INC

JOHN DEERE
See JAMES RIVER EQUIPMENT VIRGINIA LLC

JOHN DEERE
See LESLIE EQUIPMENT CO

JOHN DEERE
See MISSISSIPPI AG CO

JOHN DEERE
See THOMASON TRACTOR CO OF CALIFORNIA

JOHN DEERE
See TRIGREEN EQUIPMENT LLC

JOHN DEERE
See MIDLAND TRACTOR CO

JOHN DEERE
See NOTEBOOM IMPLEMENT LLC

JOHN DEERE
See SOUTH PLAINS IMPLEMENT LTD

JOHN DEERE
See CRAIG TAYLOR EQUIPMENT CO

JOHN DEERE
See LAWRENCE TRACTOR COINC

JOHN DEERE
See AMERICAN IMPLEMENT INC

JOHN DEERE
See BEARD EQUIPMENT CO INC

JOHN DEERE
See SOUTH TEXAS IMPLEMENT CO

JOHN DEERE
See MARTIN EQUIPMENT OF ILLINOIS INC

JOHN DEERE
See SHEARER FARM INC

JOHN DEERE
See 4 RIVERS EQUIPMENT LLC

JOHN DEERE
See HARBOR DIESEL AND EQUIPMENT INC

JOHN DEERE
See BERTHOD MOTORS INC

JOHN DEERE
See HOLLAND & SONS INC

JOHN DEERE
See KIBBLE EQUIPMENT INC

JOHN DEERE
See FRONTIER INC

JOHN DEERE
See MURPHY TRACTOR & EQUIPMENT CO INC

JOHN DEERE
See JESCO INC

JOHN DEERE
See GREAT LAKES POWER PRODUCTS INC

JOHN DEERE
See SMITH IMPLEMENTS INC

JOHN DEERE
See STANDARD EQUIPMENT CO

JOHN DEERE
See FLINT EQUIPMENT CO

JOHN DEERE
See DELTA RIDGE IMPLEMENT INC

JOHN DEERE
See CENTRAL JERSEY EQUIPMENT LLC

JOHN DEERE
See GOOSENECK IMPLEMENT CO

JOHN DEERE
See LONGHORN INTERNATIONAL TRUCKS LTD

JOHN DEERE
See SOUTHEAST FARM EQUIPMENT CO

JOHN DEERE
See BROOKSIDE EQUIPMENT SALES INC

JOHN DEERE
See ARENDS HOGAN WALKER LLC

JOHN DEERE
See GROSSENBURG IMPLEMENT INC

JOHN DEERE
See KIBBLE EQUIPMENT LLC

JOHN DEERE
See GREENMARK EQUIPMENT INC

JOHN DEERE
See XYLEM DEWATERING SOLUTIONS INC

JOHN DEERE
See VAN-WALL EQUIPMENT INC

JOHN DEERE
See WATERS INTERNATIONAL TRUCKS INC

JOHN DEERE
See HIGHLAND TRACTOR CO

JOHN DEERE
See NORTHSTAR POWER LLC

JOHN DEERE
See AGRICULTURAL PRODUCTIVITY COMPANIES

JOHN DEERE
See HARTVILLE HARDWARE INC

JOHN DEERE
See HAMMOND TRACTOR CO

JOHN DEERE
See PAPE MACHINERY INC

JOHN DEERE
See RDO CONSTRUCTION EQUIPMENT CO

JOHN DEERE
See DEER COUNTRY FARM AND LAWN INC

JOHN DEERE
See ENGINES INC

JOHN DEERE
See BRAZOS VALLEY EQUIPMENT CO

JOHN DEERE
See JAMES RIVER EQUIPMENT VIRGINIA LLC

JOHN DEERE
See GREENWAY EQUIPMENT INC

JOHN DEERE
See JD EQUIPMENT INC

JOHN DEERE
See FIVE STAR EQUIPMENT INC

JOHN DEERE
See MINNESOTA AG POWER INC

JOHN DEERE
See GOLDMAN EQUIPMENT LLC

JOHN DEERE
See ATLANTIC TRACTOR LLC

JOHN DEERE
See SHOPPAS FARM SUPPLY INC

JOHN DEERE
See TRIPLE W EQUIPMENT INC

JOHN DEERE
See PETTIT MACHINERY INC

JOHN DEERE
See EAST COAST EQUIPMENT LLC

JOHN DEERE
See DEERE CREDIT INC

JOHN DEERE
See 4 RIVERS EQUIPMENT - AG LLC

JOHN DEERE
See 21ST CENTURY EQUIPMENT LLC

JOHN DEERE
See AG-POWER INC

JOHN DEERE
See COMPLETE COACH WORKS

JOHN DEERE
See SUPERIOR DIESEL INC

JOHN DEERE
See SNEAD AGRICULTURAL SUPPLY & SERVICES INC

JOHN DEERE
See DEERE CREDIT SERVICES INC

JOHN DEERE
See D & G EQUIPMENT INC

JOHN DEERE
See QUALITY EQUIPMENT LLC

JOHN DEERE
See ICON AG SOLUTIONS LLC

JOHN DEERE
See FINCH SERVICES INC

JOHN DEERE
See SLOAN IMPLEMENT CO INC

JOHN DEERE
See SYDENSTRICKER FARM & LAWN INC

JOHN DEERE
See R J REPCO INC

JOHN DEERE
See HENDRENS INC

JOHN DEERE
See SCHUNEMAN EQUIPMENT CO

JOHN DEERE
See PALMER JOHNSON POWER SYSTEMS LLC

JOHN DEERE
See HUTSON INC

D-U-N-S 00-693-4764
■ **JOHN DEERE CAPITAL CORP**
JOHN DEERE FINANCIAL
(*Suby of* JOHN DEERE FINANCIAL SERVICES INC) ★
1 E 1st St Ste 600, Reno, NV 89501-1691
Tel (775) 786-5527 *Founded/Ownrshp* 1958
Sales NA *EMP* 1,713[E]
Accts Deloitte & Touche Llp Chicago
SIC 6153 Short-term business credit; Short-term business credit
Ch Bd: Samuel R Allen
**Pr:* Michael J Mack Jr
**CFO:* Rajesh Kalathur
Board of Directors: James M Field, David C Gilmore, Max A Guinn, Patrick E Mack, John C May, Lawrence W Sidwell

JOHN DEERE CNSTR RET SLS
See JOHN DEERE SHARED SERVICES INC

D-U-N-S 05-423-2962 EXP
■ **JOHN DEERE CO**
(*Suby of* DEERE & CO) ★
1 John Deere Pl, Moline, IL 61265-8010
Tel (309) 765-8000 *Founded/Ownrshp* 1911
Sales 29.5MM[E] *EMP* 10
SIC 5083 Agricultural machinery & equipment; Lawn & garden machinery & equipment
CEO: Samuel R Allen
CEO: Hans Becherer
CFO: Michelle Cross
Treas: Pierre E Leroy
Sr VP: Mary K W Jones
Sr VP: Rajesh Kalathur
**VP:* Neil O Christenson
VP: Joseph W England
VP: Timothy V Haight
**VP:* R W Porter
**VP:* Eugene L Schotanus
**VP:* D H Stowe Jr
VP: James E Temperley

D-U-N-S 60-303-0503 IMP
■ **JOHN DEERE COFFEYVILLE WORKS INC**
(*Suby of* DEERE & CO) ★
2624 N Us Highway 169, Coffeyville, KS 67337-9235
Tel (620) 251-3400 *Founded/Ownrshp* 1989
Sales 119.1MM[E] *EMP* 450
SIC 3714 5531 Power transmission equipment, motor vehicle; Automobile & truck equipment & parts; Power transmission equipment, motor vehicle; Automobile & truck equipment & parts
Genl Mgr: Rob Chopp

D-U-N-S 62-334-6764 IMP
■ **JOHN DEERE COMMERCIAL PRODUCTS INC**
(*Suby of* DEERE & CO) ★
700 Horizon South Pkwy, Grovetown, GA 30813-3000
Tel (706) 868-4040 *Founded/Ownrshp* 1988
Sales 41.0MM[E] *EMP* 200
SIC 3524 Lawn & garden tractors & equipment; Lawn & garden tractors & equipment
VP: John K Lawson
**VP:* Pierre E Leroy
VP: Michael Naylor
VP: Linda Newborn
MIS Dir: Joe Sivertson
Dir IT: Joel Siverton
Sfty Mgr: Kimberly Geary
Sls&Mrk Ex: Tony Thelen
Sls Mgr: Brenda Ourada
Snr Mgr: Jason Combs

D-U-N-S 00-543-3693 EXP
■ **JOHN DEERE CONSTRUCTION & FORESTRY CO** (DE)
JOHN DEERE CONSTRUCTION EQP
(*Suby of* DEERE & CO) ★
1 John Deere Pl, Moline, IL 61265-8010
Tel (309) 765-8000 *Founded/Ownrshp* 1906, 1969
Sales 547.3MM[E] *EMP* 760
SIC 5084 5082 Industrial machinery & equipment; General construction machinery & equipment; Industrial machinery & equipment; General construction machinery & equipment
Pr: Pierre Leroy
CFO: James A Davlin
**Treas:* Michael Mack
VP: Metro Hornbuckle
**VP:* J H Peterson
**VP:* James D White
Prgrm Mgr: John Errthum
Prgrm Mgr: Donna Sickler
Dir IT: Richard Kramer
Ql Cn Mgr: Dennis Barth
Ql Cn Mgr: Andy Lehl

JOHN DEERE CONSTRUCTION EQP
See JOHN DEERE CONSTRUCTION & FORESTRY CO

D-U-N-S 87-797-2109
■ JOHN DEERE CONSUMER PRODUCTS INC
(*Suby of* DEERE & CO) ★
2000 John Deere Run, Cary, NC 27513-2789
Tel (919) 804-2000 *Founded/Ownrshp* 1987
Sales 65.6MM^E *EMP* 374
SIC 3546 8711 3524 Chain saws, portable; Engineering services; Lawn & garden equipment; Chain saws, portable; Engineering services; Lawn & garden equipment
Pr: Curt Hoppestad
Sr VP: Domenic Ruccolo
**VP:* Randy Rulin
MIS Dir: Dale Bogenschnieder
IT Man: Dan Greene
IT Man: Andrew Roman
Sfty Mgr: Ralph Ellingsen
Ql Cn Mgr: Bill Herhold
Mktg Mgr: Matt Guffy
Sls Mgr: Tom Crotty
Snr Mgr: Zachary Kemp

D-U-N-S 18-885-3428 IMP
■ JOHN DEERE ELECTRONIC SOLUTIONS INC
JDES FARGO
(*Suby of* DEERE & CO) ★
1441 44th St N Ste N, Fargo, ND 58102-2854
Tel (701) 451-3600 *Founded/Ownrshp* 1999
Sales 59.7MM^E *EMP* 480
SIC 3829 3643 3823

JOHN DEERE FINANCIAL
See JOHN DEERE CAPITAL CORP

D-U-N-S 55-541-7799
■ JOHN DEERE FINANCIAL SERVICES INC
(*Suby of* DEERE & CO) ★
6400 Nw 86th St, Johnston, IA 50131-2945
Tel (515) 267-3000 *Founded/Ownrshp* 1988
Sales NA *EMP* 1,727
SIC 6141 Personal credit institutions; Personal credit institutions
Ch Bd: Robert Lane
**Pr:* Jon D Volkert
**Treas:* James S Robertson
**VP:* Michael T Feeley
**VP:* Keith R Hanson
**VP:* James R Heseman
**VP:* James A Israel
**VP:* Eugene L Schotanus
**VP:* Steven E Warren
**Prin:* Michael P Orr
IT Man: Beth Ullmark
Board of Directors: Joseph W England, Bernard L Hardiek, Dennis E Hoffmann, Ferdinand F Korndorf, Robert W Lane, Pierre E Leroy

D-U-N-S 80-285-8782
JOHN DEERE FOUNDATION
1 John Deere Pl, Moline, IL 61265-8010
Tel (309) 748-7951 *Founded/Ownrshp* 2007
Sales 24.8MM *EMP* 3
SIC 8641 Civic social & fraternal associations; Civic social & fraternal associations
Pr: James H Collins

JOHN DEERE HEALTH
See UNITEDHEALTHCARE SERVICES CO OF RIVER VALLEY INC

D-U-N-S 96-325-0324
JOHN DEERE INSURANCE CO
(*Suby of* FARMERS MUTUAL HAIL INSURANCE CO OF IOWA) ★
6785 Westown Pkwy, West Des Moines, IA 50266-7732
Tel (515) 282-9104 *Founded/Ownrshp* 2015
Sales NA *EMP* 145
SIC 6331 Agricultural insurance
Pr: Ron Rutledge
CFO: Darin Roggenburg

D-U-N-S 19-427-1771
JOHN DEERE INSURANCE GROUP INC
(*Suby of* SENTRY INSURANCE A MUTUAL CO) ★
3400 80th St, Moline, IL 61265-5884
Tel (309) 765-8000 *Founded/Ownrshp* 1999
Sales NA *EMP* 1,453
SIC 6331 6321 6311 Fire, marine & casualty insurance & carriers; Automobile insurance; Accident & health insurance carriers; Life insurance carriers; Fire, marine & casualty insurance & carriers; Automobile insurance; Accident & health insurance carriers; Life insurance carriers
Pr: Wayne Ashenberg
**Sr VP:* Robert Nixon
Sr VP: Dave Rodger
VP: Robert E Reko
VP: Robert D Schauenberg
Dir Sec: Bradley Howell
Area Mgr: Debbie Fryhling
Dist Mgr: Ken Neal
Dist Mgr: Steven Stelk
Div Mgr: Phil Dowling
Div Mgr: Sam Norwood

D-U-N-S 01-067-8766 IMP
JOHN DEERE REMAN - SPRINGFIELD LLC
4500 E Mustard Way, Springfield, MO 65803-7135
Tel (417) 829-2000 *Founded/Ownrshp* 2008
Sales 55.5MM^E *EMP* 215
SIC 3523 3531 3594 3519 Farm machinery & equipment; Construction machinery; Fluid power pumps & motors; Internal combustion engines

D-U-N-S 14-212-4762
■ JOHN DEERE SHARED SERVICES INC
JOHN DEERE CNSTR RET SLS
(*Suby of* JOHN DEERE CONSTRUCTION & FORESTRY CO) ★
1515 5th Ave Ste 200, Moline, IL 61265-1367
Tel (309) 765-0260 *Founded/Ownrshp* 1985
Sales 391.3MM *EMP* 372^E
SIC 5082 Graders, motor; Graders, motor
VP: Max Guinn
VP Mktg: Paul Knedler

D-U-N-S 00-847-3506 IMP/EXP
■ JOHN DEERE THIBODAUX INC
(*Suby of* DEERE & CO) ★
244 Highway 3266, Thibodaux, LA 70301-1602
Tel (985) 447-7285 *Founded/Ownrshp* 1998
Sales 62.8MM^E *EMP* 600^E
SIC 3523 Planting, haying, harvesting & processing machinery; Planting, haying, harvesting & processing machinery
Pr: Craig Fawcett
**VP:* Francis Richard
Mktg Mgr: Kyle Trosclair

JOHN DEERE WATER
See RIVULIS IRRIGATION INC

D-U-N-S 01-026-1097
JOHN DEERY MOTORS INC (IA)
LINCOLN MERCURY
6823 University Ave, Cedar Falls, IA 50613-5128
Tel (319) 277-6200 *Founded/Ownrshp* 1971, 1975
Sales 21.4MM^E *EMP* 52
SIC 5511 Automobiles, new & used
Pr: John Deery Jr
**Sec:* Marlene Deery
**Genl Mgr:* Scott Grinstead
Sales Exec: Lee Ayers
Sales Exec: Randy Owens
Sales Exec: Bill Powers
Sls Mgr: Terry Johnson
Sales Asso: Tendai Muyengwa

D-U-N-S 00-483-1749
JOHN DEKLEWA & SONS INC (PA)
1273 Washington Pike, Bridgeville, PA 15017-2803
Tel (412) 257-9000 *Founded/Ownrshp* 1920, 1990
Sales 36.4MM^E *EMP* 150
SIC 1542 1541 Commercial & office building, new construction; Industrial buildings, new construction; Commercial & office building, new construction; Industrial buildings, new construction
Pr: David Deklewa
**Sec:* John E Deklewa
**VP:* James R Deklewa

D-U-N-S 07-056-8860
JOHN E ANDRUS MEMORIAL INC
ANDRUS ON HUDSON
185 Old Broadway, Hastings On Hudson, NY 10706-3801
Tel (914) 478-3700 *Founded/Ownrshp* 1954
Sales 40.2MM *EMP* 250
SIC 8361 8052 8051 Rest home, with health care incidental; Intermediate care facilities; Skilled nursing care facilities; Rest home, with health care incidental; Intermediate care facilities; Skilled nursing care facilities
Ex Dir: Betsy Biddle
HC Dir: Patricia Colavito

D-U-N-S 10-163-4954
JOHN E FETZER INSTITUTE INC
9292 W Kl Ave, Kalamazoo, MI 49009-5316
Tel (269) 375-2000 *Founded/Ownrshp* 1962
Sales 30.0MM *EMP* 40
Accts Bdo Usa Llp Grand Rapids Mi
SIC 8733 Noncommercial research organizations; Noncommercial research organizations
Ch: Robert Lehman
**Pr:* Thomas F Beech
**V Ch Bd:* Janis Claflin
Ofcr: Robert L Adams Jr
Ofcr: Jacob Asperger
Ofcr: Sharif Azami
Ofcr: Angela Graham
Ofcr: Linda Grdina
Ofcr: Xiaoan Ll
Ofcr: Mark Nepo
Ofcr: Anne Puente
Ofcr: Michelle Scheidt
Ofcr: Kurian Thomas
Ofcr: Susan Trabucchi
VP: Tina Adams

D-U-N-S 00-695-8193
JOHN E GREEN CO (MI)
220 Victor St, Detroit, MI 48203-3116
Tel (313) 868-2400 *Founded/Ownrshp* 1909
Sales 212.3MM^E *EMP* 600
Accts Plante & Moran Pllc
SIC 1711 Mechanical contractor; Fire sprinkler system installation; Mechanical contractor; Fire sprinkler system installation
Ch Bd: Peter J Green
**Pr:* Michael J Green
**COO:* Rob Martin
**CFO:* John Stelter
**Sec:* John R Green
**Ex VP:* Michael T Brunett
Ex VP: Michael Green
**Ex VP:* Charles Osborne
**VP:* Ed Fici
VP: Gary Fisk
CIO: Kirk Fischer
Board of Directors: Marian R Green, Michael J Green

D-U-N-S 00-718-7362
JOHN E JONES OIL CO INC (KS)
1016 S Cedar St, Stockton, KS 67669-2306
Tel (785) 425-6746 *Founded/Ownrshp* 1941, 1963
Sales 87.5MM *EMP* 15
SIC 4213 5172 Contract haulers; Gases, liquefied petroleum (propane); Gasoline; Diesel fuel; Contract haulers; Gases, liquefied petroleum (propane); Gasoline; Diesel fuel
Pr: Eugene Westhusing
**Sec:* Patrick Lingg
**VP:* Patricia Westhusing
DP Exec: John Falk

D-U-N-S 60-578-3117
JOHN E KELLY & SONS ELECTRICAL CONSTRUCTION INC
KELLY ELECTRIC
8431 Old Marlboro Pike # 200, Upper Marlboro, MD 20772-2614
Tel (301) 736-2250 *Founded/Ownrshp* 1998
Sales 25.9MM^E *EMP* 110
Accts Regan Russell Schickner & Sh
SIC 1731 General electrical contractor; General electrical contractor
Pr: Stephen P Kelly Sr
**Treas:* Bill Sarver
**VP:* Terry P Crouse
**VP:* Mike Farrell
**VP:* Steven Skolnik

D-U-N-S 03-440-8963 IMP
JOHN E KOERNER & CO INC
4820 Jefferson Hwy, Jefferson, LA 70121-3127
Tel (504) 734-1100 *Founded/Ownrshp* 1907
Sales 37.5MM^E *EMP* 57
SIC 5046 Bakery equipment & supplies
CEO: Earl P Koerner Jr
**Pr:* Tim W Koerner
Opers Mgr: Kevin Bradley
Sls Mgr: Mike McClain

D-U-N-S 00-282-5628
JOHN E QUARLES CO
QUARLES LUMBER
1801 Park Place Ave, Fort Worth, TX 76110-1382
Tel (817) 926-1761 *Founded/Ownrshp* 1986
Sales 25.2MM^E *EMP* 49
SIC 5031 5211 Windows; Door & window products
CEO: Nancy Quarles Stuck
**VP:* Bart Graves
**VP:* Paul Reuland

D-U-N-S 03-093-9169
JOHN E RETZNER OIL CO INC
630 S Adams St, Versailles, IN 47042-9003
Tel (812) 609-4178 *Founded/Ownrshp* 2004
Sales 168.4MM *EMP* 5
Accts Brian P Hawkins Kaneohe Haw
SIC 5983 Fuel oil dealers; Fuel oil dealers
Pr: Adam Hanson

JOHN EAGLE HONDA OF HOUSTON
See JOHN EAGLE IMPORTS LLP

D-U-N-S 11-436-9945 IMP
JOHN EAGLE IMPORTS LLP
JOHN EAGLE HONDA OF HOUSTON
18787 Northwest Fwy, Houston, TX 77065-4730
Tel (281) 955-6666 *Founded/Ownrshp* 1983
Sales 45.2MM^E *EMP* 125
SIC 5511 Automobiles, new & used; Automobiles, new & used
Pt: Jre Aquila
**Pr:* Mac Delaup
**CEO:* John Eagle
**Ch:* Robert Eagle
**Sec:* Phyllis Freeman
Sls Mgr: Bobby Amelio
Sls Mgr: Greg Cypher
Sls Mgr: Rashad Jafer
Sls Mgr: Leonte Matthews
Sls Mgr: Bryant Sharp
Sls Mgr: Ammar Sheikh

JOHN ELWAY CADILLAC PK MEADOWS
See EP BULLDOG LLC

JOHN ELWAY CHEVROLET
See CHESROWN CHEVROLET LLC

JOHN ELWAY CROWN TOYOTA
See T ONTARIO INC

D-U-N-S 96-460-6065
JOHN ENTERPRISE LIMITED
SEDONA GROUP, THE
612 Valley View Dr, Moline, IL 61265-6100
Tel (309) 797-8367 *Founded/Ownrshp* 1985
Sales 29.0MM^E *EMP* 520
SIC 8744 8742 7361 Base maintenance (providing personnel on continuing basis); Management consulting services; Employment agencies
Pr: Richard C John
VP: Larry John
**VP:* Timothy M John
Opers Mgr: Paul Rinaldi

D-U-N-S 07-263-3985 IMP/EXP
JOHN F KENNEDY CENTER FOR PERFORMING ARTS
KENNEDY CENTER, THE
2700 F St Nw, Washington, DC 20566-0002
Tel (202) 416-8000 *Founded/Ownrshp* 1958
Sales 211.5MM *EMP* 1,144
Accts Bdo Usa Llp Bethesda Md
SIC 7922 7929 Performing arts center production; Entertainers & entertainment groups; Performing arts center production; Entertainers & entertainment groups
Ex Dir: Michael Kaiser
**CFO:* Lynne Pratt
**Treas:* Roland Betts
Treas: Tony Terronez
Trst: Donald J Hall Jr
VP: John Dow
VP: David Kitto
VP: Kathy Kruse
VP: Roger Mosier
VP: Ann Stock
Assoc Dir: Maria Belikow
Creative D: Scott Bushnell

D-U-N-S 02-550-9071
■ JOHN F KENNEDY MEMORIAL HOSPITAL
JOHN F KNNEDY MEM HOSP EMRGNCY
(*Suby of* DES PERES HOSPITAL INC) ★
47111 Monroe St, Indio, CA 92201-6799
Tel (760) 347-6191 *Founded/Ownrshp* 1966
Sales 695.4M *EMP* 650
SIC 8062 General medical & surgical hospitals; General medical & surgical hospitals
CEO: Gary Honts
CFO: Matt Keating
Ofcr: Dan Bowers
Prgrm Mgr: Joyce Preston
Cmptr Lab: Beverly Bryant
Cmptr Lab: Monica Flores
Phys Thrpy: Isabella Smith

D-U-N-S 03-170-8360
■ JOHN F KENNEDY SPACE CENTER
NASA
(*Suby of* NASA) ★
6225 Vectorspace Blvd, Titusville, FL 32780-8040
Tel (321) 867-5000 *Founded/Ownrshp* 1964
Sales NA *EMP* 16,799
SIC 9661 Space flight operations, government; Space research & development, government; ; Space flight operations, government; Space research & development, government;
CFO: Nap Carroll
VP: Frank Kline
Netwrk Eng: Carla Stodgelwright
Sfty Mgr: Thomas Dwyer
Snr Mgr: Tracy Belford
Snr Mgr: Douglas England
Snr Mgr: Douglas Lindhorst
Snr Mgr: Norman Tokarz

D-U-N-S 07-168-4500
JOHN F KENNEDY UNIVERSITY
100 Ellinwood Way, Pleasant Hill, CA 94523-4817
Tel (925) 969-3300 *Founded/Ownrshp* 1964
Sales 26.3MM *EMP* 487
Accts Jgd & Associates Llp San Dieg
SIC 8221 University; University
CEO: Charles Powell
V Ch: William E Gagn
**Pr:* Steven Stargardter
COO: Anita Korenstein
**CFO:* Alexander Kramer
Treas: Michael McGill
Exec: Robert Valentine
Assoc Dir: Dina Finta
Adm Dir: Charlene Tuckerson
Mktg Dir: John Bowman
HC Dir: Jen Miller-Hogg

JOHN F KNNEDY MEM HOSP EMRGNCY
See JOHN F KENNEDY MEMORIAL HOSPITAL

D-U-N-S 04-388-3081
JOHN F MARTIN & SONS INC
55 Lower Hillside Rd, Stevens, PA 17578-9787
Tel (717) 336-2804 *Founded/Ownrshp* 1945
Sales 94.5MM *EMP* 160
SIC 2013 0212

D-U-N-S 17-815-1874
JOHN F MURPHY HOMES INC
800 Center St, Auburn, ME 04210-6404
Tel (207) 782-2726 *Founded/Ownrshp* 1978
Sales 34.1MM *EMP* 750
Accts Robustelli Soucy Hussey Pa Le
SIC 8361 Home for the mentally retarded; Home for the mentally retarded
Ex Dir: Peter Kowalski
**Pr:* Tom Turmenne
CFO: Andrew Cowan
**Treas:* John Bonneau
**Treas:* Margaret Murphy
QA Dir: Marti Howard
Mktg Dir: Leslie Riehm

D-U-N-S 00-883-4681
JOHN F OTTO INC
OTTO CONSTRUCTION
1717 2nd St, Sacramento, CA 95811-6214
Tel (916) 441-6870 *Founded/Ownrshp* 1958
Sales 112.5MM *EMP* 120
SIC 1542 1541 Commercial & office building, new construction; Industrial buildings, new construction; Commercial & office building, new construction; Industrial buildings, new construction
Pr: Carl Barrett
**Sec:* Carol Otto
**VP:* Rick McVey
**VP:* Allison Otto
**VP:* Elease Terry
Snr PM: Matt Bouquet
Board of Directors: Allison Otto John W Otto C

D-U-N-S 02-409-0474
JOHN F TROMPETER CO (KY)
314 E Burnett Ave, Louisville, KY 40208-2701
Tel (502) 585-5852 *Founded/Ownrshp* 1892, 1958
Sales 24.2MM *EMP* 10
SIC 5145 5194 Candy; Tobacco & tobacco products; Candy; Tobacco & tobacco products
Pr: Mary K Trompeter
VP: Dave Nash

D-U-N-S 03-103-2329 EXP
JOHN FABICK TRACTOR CO
CATERPILLAR
1 Fabick Dr, Fenton, MO 63026-2928
Tel (636) 343-5900 *Founded/Ownrshp* 1917
Sales 277.9MM^E *EMP* 600
SIC 5082 7699 General construction machinery & equipment; Road construction & maintenance machinery; Construction equipment repair; General construction machinery & equipment; Road construction & maintenance machinery; Construction equipment repair
Pr: Harry Fabick
**Treas:* James Jansen
Treas: Mike Jansen
**Ex VP:* Doug Fabick
VP: John Schrader
Genl Mgr: Bob Sydlow
IT Man: Neil Scott
Mtls Mgr: Bob Boedges
Mtls Mgr: Dave Modglin
Mktg Mgr: Jake Callis
Mktg Mgr: Tim Sible

D-U-N-S 01-078-9407
JOHN FAYARD MOVING & WAREHOUSING LLC (MS)
JOHN FAYARD RECORDS MANAGEMENT
10323 Express Dr, Gulfport, MS 39503-4611
Tel (228) 864-2262 *Founded/Ownrshp* 2000
Sales 23.7MM^E *EMP* 137
SIC 4225 4212 General warehousing & storage; Moving services
CFO: Janet Fayard
VP: Steve Bevilaqua

JOHN FAYARD RECORDS MANAGEMENT
See JOHN FAYARD MOVING & WAREHOUSING LLC

D-U-N-S 01-065-8334
JOHN FITZGIBBON MEMORIAL HOSPITAL INC
2305 S Highway 65, Marshall, MO 65340-3702
Tel (660) 886-7431 *Founded/Ownrshp* 1923
Sales 53.8MM *EMP* 600
Accts Bkd Llp Marshall Mo
SIC 8062 General medical & surgical hospitals; General medical & surgical hospitals
Pr: Ron Ott
Chf Rad: Terry Elwing
CFO: Angy Littrell
**VP:* Dennis Sousley
Dir Inf Cn: Dana Sullivan
Dir Rx: Lori Berger
Off Mgr: Kathryn Austin
CIO: Bruce Blalock
CTO: Frances Thatcher
Dir IT: Janet King
Dir IT: Sherry Shannon

D-U-N-S 18-679-4533
JOHN FORD STUCKEY INC
Rr 22 Box W, Hollidaysburg, PA 16648
Tel (814) 695-9862 *Founded/Ownrshp* 1959
Sales 31.7MM^E *EMP* 78
SIC 5511 Automobiles, new & used; Automobiles, new & used
Pr: John Stuckey
**VP:* Matt Stuckey
Store Mgr: Josh Baron

JOHN G SHEDD AQUARIUM
See SHEDD AQUARIUM SOCIETY

D-U-N-S 84-474-4623
JOHN GALT STAFFING INC
77 S Bedford St Ste 325, Burlington, MA 01803-5154
Tel (781) 273-9995 *Founded/Ownrshp* 1997
Sales 29.5MM *EMP* 250
Accts Richardson & Co Pc
SIC 7361 Employment agencies; Employment agencies
Pr: Kirstin Siemering
Treas: Robert Siemering
VP: John Racho
Exec: Bob Siemering
Genl Mgr: Jessica Fallon
Off Mgr: Victoria Chhouy

D-U-N-S 09-456-7062
JOHN GLENN SCHOOL CORP
NORTH LIBERTY ELEM SCHOOL
101 John Glenn Dr, Walkerton, IN 46574-1440
Tel (574) 586-3129 *Founded/Ownrshp* 1965
Sales 27.6MM^E *EMP* 469
SIC 8211 Public elementary school; Public junior high school; Public senior high school; School board; Public elementary school; Public junior high school; Public senior high school; School board
Dir IT: Andy Stegemiller

D-U-N-S 01-890-0936
JOHN GRAPPONE INC (NH)
GRAPPONE FORD
506 Route 3a, Bow, NH 03304-3100
Tel (800) 528-8993 *Founded/Ownrshp* 1936, 1958
Sales 47.0MM *EMP* 80
SIC 5511 Automobiles, new & used; Pickups, new & used; Automobiles, new & used; Pickups, new & used
Pr: Larry Haines
COO: Kathy Kayros
Prin: Robert Grappone

D-U-N-S 00-389-9606 IMP/EXP
JOHN GREENLAND ENTERPRISES INC (PA)
BRADCO SUPPLY COMPANY
80 Old Mills Rd, Towanda, PA 18848-8192
Tel (570) 265-6167 *Founded/Ownrshp* 1949
Sales 20.7MM^E *EMP* 31
SIC 5082 Road construction & maintenance machinery; Front end loaders; Graders, motor; Masonry equipment & supplies
Pr: John Greenland
**VP:* Bill Greenland

JOHN GREENLEAF FURNITURE
See WHITTIER WOOD PRODUCTS CO

D-U-N-S 60-990-9247 IMP
JOHN GRIFFIN CONSTRUCTION INC
244 Jason Ct, Corona, CA 92879-6101
Tel (951) 278-2377 *Founded/Ownrshp* 1983
Sales 28.4MM^E *EMP* 100
SIC 4939 1731 Combination utilities; Cable television installation; Combination utilities; Cable television installation
Pr: John Griffin

D-U-N-S 01-438-6718
JOHN GROSS AND CO INC (PA)
400 Cheryl Ave, Mechanicsburg, PA 17055-3319
Tel (717) 766-2508 *Founded/Ownrshp* 1950, 1995
Sales 32.9MM^E *EMP* 75^E
SIC 5141 5411

D-U-N-S 04-486-4312
JOHN H BURROWS INC
BONANZA PRODUCE CO
1925 Freeport Blvd, Sparks, NV 89431-5565
Tel (775) 358-2442 *Founded/Ownrshp* 1970
Sales 41.5MM^E *EMP* 98^E
SIC 5148

D-U-N-S 00-820-2673 IMP
JOHN H CARTER CO INC (LA)
17630 Perkins Rd Ste West, Baton Rouge, LA 70810-3849
Tel (225) 751-3788 *Founded/Ownrshp* 1957
Sales 327.2MM^E *EMP* 376
SIC 5084 Processing & packaging equipment; Processing & packaging equipment
Pr: Michel E Sansovich III
**Sec:* Robert G Wagnon
**VP:* Danny W Childress
**VP:* Calvin Curtis Douglas
**VP:* Todd E Gilbertson
**VP:* Bruce D Lowrey
**VP:* Michael J Nicaud
Exec: Scott Stein
Opers Mgr: Randy Lambert
Sls Mgr: Jason Fontenot
Sls Mgr: Robby Jones

D-U-N-S 00-337-5334 IMP
JOHN H DANIEL CO
JOHN D
1803 N Central St, Knoxville, TN 37917-5412
Tel (865) 637-6441 *Founded/Ownrshp* 1928
Sales 44.8MM^E *EMP* 300^E
SIC 2311 5611 5621 Suits, men's & boys': made from purchased materials; Tailored dress & sport coats: men's & boys'; Vests: made from purchased materials; Men's & boys' clothing stores; Women's clothing stores; Suits, men's & boys': made from purchased materials; Tailored dress & sport coats: men's & boys'; Vests: made from purchased materials; Men's & boys' clothing stores; Women's clothing stores
Pr: Richard B Bryan
CFO: Coleman Bryan III
CFO: Tennel Robinson
VP: Laura Bryan

D-U-N-S 00-327-4552 IMP/EXP
JOHN H HARLAND CO
2939 Miller Rd, Decatur, GA 30035-4086
Tel (770) 593-5050 *Founded/Ownrshp* 2007
Sales NA *EMP* 5,360
SIC 2782 2752 2761 7371 7379

D-U-N-S 01-777-8333
JOHN H KAPPUS CO
KAPPUS COMPANY
4755 W 150th St, Cleveland, OH 44135-3329
Tel (216) 367-6677 *Founded/Ownrshp* 1965
Sales 23.9MM^E *EMP* 65
SIC 5046 Commercial cooking & food service equipment
Pr: Alfred J Kappus
**CEO:* Fred Kappus
**COO:* John Zalenka
**CFO:* Michael J Marcis
Ex VP: Kevin Ward
VP Admn: Karen Kappus
Dir IT: Bill Cunningham

D-U-N-S 07-846-1235
JOHN H MYERS & SON - US LBM LLC
(*Suby of* US LBM HOLDINGS LLC) ★
2200 Monroe St, York, PA 17404-5556
Tel (717) 792-2500 *Founded/Ownrshp* 2011
Sales 71.5MM^E *EMP* 100
SIC 5031 5211 Lumber: rough, dressed & finished; Millwork & lumber
Pr: Robert L Myers III
Genl Mgr: Rich Runk
Store Mgr: Jared Roomsburg
Info Man: Robert Wood
Sfty Dirs: Rob Miller
Opers Mgr: Dave Orndorff
Sls&Mrk Ex: Amy Green
VP Sls: Kim Craley
Sales Asso: John Griffin
Sales Asso: Brian Seymore

JOHN HANCOCK
See HANCOCK LIFE INSURANCE CO (USA) JOHN

JOHN HANCOCK
See HANCOCK NATURAL RESOURCE GROUP INC

D-U-N-S 95-692-8568
JOHN HANCOCK CORPORATE TAX CREDIT FUND I LP
200 Clarendon St, Boston, MA 02116-5021
Tel (617) 572-6000 *Founded/Ownrshp* 1995
Sales 98.4MM^E *EMP* 8,000
SIC 7389 Personal service agents, brokers & bureaus; Personal service agents, brokers & bureaus
CEO: Dominic D'Aldssandro
V Ch: Michele Van Leer
Sr VP: Deborah H McAneny
Sr VP: Jean Peters
VP: Sam Davis
Mng Dir: John C Anderson
Mng Dir: John Garrison
Mng Dir: Philip Messina

D-U-N-S 96-902-0101
JOHN HANCOCK FINANCIAL CORP
(*Suby of* MANULIFE FINANCIAL CORPORATION)
601 Congress St, Boston, MA 02210-2805
Tel (416) 926-3000 *Founded/Ownrshp* 2012
Sales NA *EMP* 155^E
SIC 6411 Insurance agents & brokers
Pr: Steve Finch
**CFO:* Simonetta Vendittelli
**Treas:* Steven Moore
**VP:* Brian Collins
VP: Donna Wong

D-U-N-S 09-039-5844
JOHN HANCOCK FINANCIAL SERVICES INC
(*Suby of* MANULIFE FINANCIAL CORPORATION)
200 Clarendon St, Boston, MA 02116-5021
Tel (617) 572-6000 *Founded/Ownrshp* 2004
Sales NA *EMP* 7,965
SIC 6311 6351 6411 6371 6321

D-U-N-S 08-001-6937
JOHN HANCOCK LIFE INSURANCE CO
(*Suby of* MANULIFE FINANCIAL CORPORATION)
197 Clarendon St, Boston, MA 02116-5010
Tel (213) 689-0813 *Founded/Ownrshp* 2000
Sales NA *EMP* 24^E
SIC 6411 6351 6371 6321 Insurance agents & brokers; Mortgage guarantee insurance; Pensions; Accident insurance carriers

D-U-N-S 00-695-2410
JOHN HANCOCK LIFE INSURANCE CO (USA)
(*Suby of* JOHN HANCOCK FINANCIAL SERVICES INC) ★
865 S Figueroa St # 3320, Los Angeles, CA 90017-2543
Tel (213) 689-0813 *Founded/Ownrshp* 1862, 2000
Sales NA *EMP* 7,962
SIC 6411 6351 6371 6321 Insurance agents & brokers; Mortgage guarantee insurance; Pensions; Accident insurance carriers; Health insurance carriers; Insurance agents & brokers; Mortgage guarantee insurance; Pensions; Accident insurance carriers; Health insurance carriers
CEO: Emeritus D'Alessandro
**Pr:* David F D'Alessandro
Pr: Ross Fryer
CFO: Steve Finch
**Treas:* Gregory P Winn
Ofcr: Robert F Walters
Ex VP: James Bowhers
Ex VP: Kathleen M Graveline
Ex VP: Harold K Mosher
**Ex VP:* Robert R Reitano
Sr VP: John M Deciccio
Sr VP: John T Farady
Sr VP: Joel V Kamer
Sr VP: Peter M Mawn
VP: Scott Estey
VP: James Logan
VP: Randy Zipse

D-U-N-S 78-959-6327
JOHN HANCOCK MANULIFE
197 Clarendon St Fl 4, Boston, MA 02116-5010
Tel (617) 663-3000 *Founded/Ownrshp* 1991
Sales 308.6MM^E *EMP* 150
SIC 6282 Investment advisory service; Investment advisory service
Pr: Karla Horn
**COO:* John G Vrysen
**CFO:* Charles A Rizzo
Sr VP: Karen A McCafferty
VP: Jerard Beauchamp
VP: Rick Callahan
**VP:* Keith Hartstein
VP: Pierr Johnson
**VP:* Thomas Kinzler
VP: Kristine McManus
VP: Andrea Mercier
VP: Peter Schofield

D-U-N-S 78-959-6228
JOHN HANCOCK SIGNATURE SERVICES INC
101 Huntington Ave Fl 3, Boston, MA 02199-7607
Tel (617) 375-4708 *Founded/Ownrshp* 1990
Sales 87.2MM^E *EMP* 1,000
Accts Ernst & Young Llp
SIC 6289 6282 Security transfer agents; Investment advice; Security transfer agents; Investment advice
VP: Daniel Ouellette
**Treas:* Christopher M Meyer
VP: Dennis Healy
VP: Timothy Malloy
**VP:* Charles McKenney
**VP:* John Morin
VP: Tim Waterworth
Dir IT: Ann Welch
IT Man: Rick Russell
VP Sls: Susan Silkes

D-U-N-S 61-691-4826
JOHN HANCOCK VARIABLE LIFE INSURANCE CO
(*Suby of* JOHN HANCOCK LIFE INSURANCE CO) ★
John Hancock Pl, Boston, MA 02117
Tel (617) 572-6000 *Founded/Ownrshp* 1979
Sales NA *EMP* 1^E
SIC 6311 Life insurance; Life insurance
Pr: Michelle G Van Leer
CFO: Tom Maloney
Sr VP: Jim Brockelman
Sr VP: Joel Kamer
Sr VP: Peter Mawn
Sr VP: Jane Tsai
VP: Brian Benneyworth
VP: Lynne Deinnocentis
VP: Wendy Dickerson
VP: Ramon Gregory
VP: Steve Hope
VP: Larry Loop
VP: Maria Pena
VP: Michele Schneidler

JOHN HARVEY TOYOTA
See HARVEY OF BOSSIER CITY INC

D-U-N-S 96-916-9379
JOHN HEINZ INSTITUTE OF REHABILITATION MEDICINE
100 Abington Executive Pa, Clarks Summit, PA 18411-2260
Tel (570) 348-1300 *Founded/Ownrshp* 2011
Sales 36.4MM *EMP* 4^E
Accts Parentebeard Llc Philadelphia
SIC 8011 Offices & clinics of medical doctors; Offices & clinics of medical doctors

D-U-N-S 12-175-7223
JOHN HENRY FOSTER CO OF ST LOUIS INC
4700 Le Bourget Dr, Saint Louis, MO 63134-3118
Tel (314) 427-0600 *Founded/Ownrshp* 1983
Sales 48.7MM^E *EMP* 100
SIC 5084

D-U-N-S 13-925-1094
JOHN HENRY FOSTER MINNESOTA INC
3103 Mike Collins Dr, Eagan, MN 55121-2220
Tel (651) 452-8452 *Founded/Ownrshp* 1983
Sales 68.7MM^E *EMP* 68
SIC 5084 Industrial machinery & equipment; Compressors, except air conditioning; Pneumatic tools & equipment; Industrial machinery & equipment; Compressors, except air conditioning; Pneumatic tools & equipment
Ch Bd: John Hawkins
Sls&Mrk Ex: Kay Bergstrom
Sales Asso: Dillon Lafaver
Sales Asso: Kris Mickels

D-U-N-S 82-705-3773
JOHN HENRY HOLDINGS INC
MPS HOLDINGS
(*Suby of* MULTI PACKAGING SOLUTIONS INC) ★
5800 W Grand River Ave, Lansing, MI 48906-9111
Tel (517) 886-2526 *Founded/Ownrshp* 2004
Sales 538.8MM^E *EMP* 2,100^E
SIC 6719 Investment holding companies, except banks; Investment holding companies, except banks
CEO: Marc Shore
**Pr:* Dennis Kalpman
**Treas:* Ed Gasper
Sr VP: Tim Schultz
Sr VP: Cindy Smith
VP: Greg Bomers
VP: Ray Wheelan
Creative D: Gary Lenkeit
Off Admin: Maureen Kirrmann
QA Dir: Brian Angell
IT Man: David Diehl

JOHN HINE MAZDA
See JOHN HINE PONTIAC

D-U-N-S 02-911-7744
JOHN HINE PONTIAC
JOHN HINE MAZDA
1545 Camino Del Rio S, San Diego, CA 92108-3575
Tel (619) 297-4251 *Founded/Ownrshp* 1957
Sales 66.1MM^E *EMP* 201^E
SIC 5511 5531 Automobiles, new & used; Pickups, new & used; Vans, new & used; Automotive & home supply stores; Automobiles, new & used; Pickups, new & used; Vans, new & used; Automotive & home supply stores
Pr: John Hine Jr
**Sr VP:* Cindy Hine
**VP:* Suzanne Abraham
**VP:* David Miller Jr
Exec: Jean Fribling
Sls Mgr: Steven Camacho
Sls Mgr: Mel Roberts
Sls Mgr: Michael Watkins

D-U-N-S 03-290-3213
JOHN HOLT AUTO GROUP INC
2501 N Old Highway 81, Chickasha, OK 73018-9304
Tel (405) 224-2132 *Founded/Ownrshp* 1998
Sales 21.5MM^E *EMP* 49
SIC 5511 Automobiles, new & used; Pickups, new & used; Vans, new & used
Owner: John Holt
Sls Mgr: Calvin Bingaman

JOHN HONDA HINDERER
See JLH AUTOMOTIVE INC

JOHN HOWARD MOTORS
See MIDTOWN MOTORS INC

D-U-N-S 08-328-0420
JOHN HUFF ICE CREAM INC (NY)
3 Winkler Rd, Sidney, NY 13838-1057
Tel (607) 563-3999 *Founded/Ownrshp* 1952
Sales 40.7MM^E *EMP* 75
SIC 5143 5812 Ice cream & ices; Ice cream stands or dairy bars
CEO: John P Huff
**Pr:* Paul Huff

D-U-N-S 10-361-8864
JOHN HUMMEL CUSTOM BUILDERS INC
HUMMEL, JOHN CONSTRUCTION
49b Route 114, East Hampton, NY 11937-4902
Tel (631) 324-5644 *Founded/Ownrshp* 1982
Sales 50.0MM *EMP* 25^E
SIC 1521 Single-family housing construction
Pr: John Joseph Hummel

D-U-N-S 00-691-9823 IMP
JOHN I HAAS INC
HAAS HOP PRODUCTS
5185 Mcarthur Blvd Nw # 300, Washington, DC 20016-3341
Tel (202) 777-4800 *Founded/Ownrshp* 1916
Sales 110.6MM^E *EMP* 360
SIC 0139 5159 Hop farm; Hops; Hop farm; Hops
CEO: Henry Von Eichel
**Pr:* Alexander Barth
**CFO:* Thomas Davis
Sls Dir: William Popa

D-U-N-S 96-477-1914
JOHN J BRENNAN CONSTRUCTION CO INC
70 Platt Rd, Shelton, CT 06484-5339
Tel (203) 929-6314 *Founded/Ownrshp* 2005
Sales 25.7MM^E *EMP* 120
Accts Blum Shapiro & Company Pc
SIC 1611 1623 Highway & street construction; Water, sewer & utility lines; Highway & street construction; Water, sewer & utility lines
Pr: David Brennan
**Sec:* Linda Scott
**VP:* Eric T Brennan
Genl Mgr: Nicholas Teodosio
Genl Mgr: Howard Vagt
CTO: Joan Vrosetek
Sfty Mgr: Joseph Keane

D-U-N-S 06-212-8459
JOHN J HEBERT DISTRIBUTOR INC (TX)
CHEVRON
424 Highway 90, Liberty, TX 77575-5516
Tel (936) 336-7311 *Founded/Ownrshp* 1972
Sales 35.2MM^E *EMP* 52
SIC 5172 Gasoline; Gasoline
Pr: John J Hebert Jr
**Pr:* John J Hebertsr
**Treas:* Donna Burk
**Treas:* Donna Ramirez

D-U-N-S 55-595-8651
JOHN J JERUE TRUCK BROKER INC
(*Suby of* JJJTB INC) ★
3200 Flightline Dr # 202, Lakeland, FL 33811-2848
Tel (863) 607-5600 *Founded/Ownrshp* 2005
Sales 24.6MM^E *EMP* 42
SIC 4731 Truck transportation brokers
Pr: John J Jerue
**Treas:* E Luis Campano
**VP:* J Jeff Jerue
**VP:* Laurie Jerue
Genl Mgr: Jeff Jerue

D-U-N-S 12-154-3714
JOHN J KIRLIN INC
JOHN J MECHANICAL SERVICES DIV
515 Dover Rd Ste 2100, Rockville, MD 20850-1290
Tel (301) 424-3410 *Founded/Ownrshp* 1960
Sales 327.1MM^E *EMP* 1,200
SIC 1711 Plumbing contractors; Warm air heating & air conditioning contractor; Plumbing contractors; Warm air heating & air conditioning contractor
Pr: Wayne Day
**CFO:* William Goodrum
**Ex VP:* Michael Mack
Exec: Brian Daly
Exec: David Schanuel
Snr PM: George Case
Snr PM: Matt Yates

D-U-N-S 60-302-4857 IMP
JOHN J KIRLIN INC
515 Dover Rd Ste 2200, Rockville, MD 20850-1290
Tel (301) 424-3410 *Founded/Ownrshp* 1989
Sales 113.2MM *EMP* 1,000
SIC 1711 Mechanical contractor; Mechanical contractor
Pr: Robert Bacon

JOHN J MECHANICAL SERVICES DIV
See JOHN J KIRLIN INC

D-U-N-S 00-629-3260 IMP
JOHN J STEUBY CO (MO)
6002 N Lindbergh Blvd, Hazelwood, MO 63042-2804
Tel (314) 895-1000 *Founded/Ownrshp* 1962
Sales 25.2MM^E *EMP* 110
SIC 3451 Screw machine products; Screw machine products
Pr: John J Steuby Sr
**VP:* Brian Smith
**VP:* John J Steuby Jr
Off Mgr: Tammy Hake

JOHN JACOBS GOLF SCHOOLS
See SCOTTSDALE GOLF GROUP INC

D-U-N-S 05-665-3591
JOHN JAY COLLEGE/UPWARD BOUND
(*Suby of* AFFIRMATIVE ACTION/EEO DEPT) ★
555 W 57th St Ste 600, New York, NY 10019-2925
Tel (212) 237-8900 *Founded/Ownrshp* 2010
Sales 21.4MM^E *EMP* 553^E
SIC 8221 Colleges universities & professional schools
Prin: Karen Texeira

JOHN JONES AUTOMOTIVE GROUP
See JOHN JONES CHEVROLET BUICK CADILLAC OF SALEM INC

D-U-N-S 10-211-9419
JOHN JONES CHEVROLET BUICK CADILLAC OF SALEM INC
JOHN JONES AUTOMOTIVE GROUP
1520 S Jackson St, Salem, IN 47167-9729
Tel (812) 883-3081 *Founded/Ownrshp* 1983
Sales 36.7MM^E *EMP* 84^E
SIC 5511

D-U-N-S 00-695-9449 IMP
JOHN K BURCH CO
BURCH FABRICS
4200 Brockton Dr Se, Grand Rapids, MI 49512-4056
Tel (616) 698-2800 *Founded/Ownrshp* 1897, 1937
Sales 25.6MM^E *EMP* 49
Accts Bredeweg & Zylstra Plc
SIC 5131 5087 Upholstery fabrics, woven; Upholsterers' equipment & supplies
Pr: John B Burch
**VP:* Joseph Governal
Natl Sales: Frank Governal

JOHN KEADY ISUZU
See KEADY JOHN PONTIAC CADILLAC OLDSMOBILE AND ISUZU INC

JOHN KENNEDY FORD
See FEASTERVILLE AUTO CENTER INC

JOHN KENNEDY FORD
See FORD CONSHOHOCKEN INC

D-U-N-S 09-867-1365
JOHN KIRBY PONTIAC INC
RENN KIRBY THURMONT USED CARS
5903 Urbana Pike, Frederick, MD 21704-7206
Tel (301) 663-4185 *Founded/Ownrshp* 1979
Sales 52.9MM^E *EMP* 133
SIC 5511 5521 Automobiles, new & used; Pickups, new & used; Vans, new & used; Used car dealers; Automobiles, new & used; Pickups, new & used; Vans, new & used; Used car dealers
Pr: John Kirby
Treas: Michael Capone
**Sec:* Stephen Capone
**VP:* Sean Kirby
Off Mgr: Becky Strawsburg
Sales Asso: Russell Hewitt

D-U-N-S 07-843-2788
JOHN KIRKSEY ASSOCIATES ARCHITECTS INC (TX)
6909 Portwest Dr, Houston, TX 77024-8010
Tel (713) 850-9600 *Founded/Ownrshp* 1971
Sales 25.8MM^E *EMP* 120
SIC 8712 Architectural services; Architectural engineering; Architectural services; Architectural engineering
Pr: John Kirksey
Ex VP: Terry Greiner
Ex VP: Douglas Hammel
**Ex VP:* Bob Inaba
Ex VP: Randy Thomas
**Ex VP:* Randall Walker
**Ex VP:* Scott Wilkinson
Sr VP: Jim Dietzmann
VP: Steve Durham
VP: Scott Wilkenson
Comm Man: Allie Horne

D-U-N-S 07-307-2316
JOHN KNOX VILLAGE
JOHN KNOX VLG RETIREMENT CMNTY
400 Nw Murray Rd Ofc, Lees Summit, MO 64081-1498
Tel (816) 347-2851 *Founded/Ownrshp* 1970
Sales 66.7MM *EMP* 985
Accts Bkd Llp Kansas City Mo
SIC 8051 8059 8052 Skilled nursing care facilities; Rest home, with health care; Intermediate care facilities; Skilled nursing care facilities; Rest home, with health care; Intermediate care facilities
CEO: Dan Rexroth
**CFO:* Richard Kim Klockenga
**VP:* James Dawson
Genl Mgr: Cindy Stamm
Nurse Mgr: Victoria Wendt
IT Man: Kelli Quinn
IT Man: Teresa Wedel
Netwrk Mgr: Phyllis Woodward
VP Opers: Robert Woody
Mktg Mgr: Beth Webb
Nrsg Dir: Tami Hoversten

D-U-N-S 02-665-1272
JOHN KNOX VILLAGE MEDICAL CENTER
901 Veterans Mem Pkwy, Orange City, FL 32763-6200
Tel (386) 775-2008 *Founded/Ownrshp* 2010
Sales 8.1MM^E *EMP* 400
SIC 8062 General medical & surgical hospitals; General medical & surgical hospitals

D-U-N-S 08-775-9668
JOHN KNOX VILLAGE OF CENTRAL FLORIDA INC
101 Northlake Dr, Orange City, FL 32763-6167
Tel (386) 775-3840 *Founded/Ownrshp* 1978
Sales 37.4MM *EMP* 475
Accts Michael Ray Deland Fl
SIC 8361 Home for the aged; Home for the aged
CEO: Taver Cornett
**Pr:* Lester R Barker
**Sec:* Frank Knight
**VP:* Burl Burgess

D-U-N-S 08-019-5472 IMP
JOHN KNOX VILLAGE OF FLORIDA INC
651 Village Dr, Pompano Beach, FL 33060-3700
Tel (954) 783-4000 *Founded/Ownrshp* 1976
Sales 41.5MM *EMP* 650
Accts Cliftonlarsonallen Llp Orland
SIC 8051 Skilled nursing care facilities; Skilled nursing care facilities
Ex Dir: Robert P Scharman
**Pr:* Frank H Furman
**CFO:* Jean Eccelston
**Treas:* Lester Wheeler
**VP:* William Allison
Ex Dir: Robert Scharmann

D-U-N-S 04-699-1626
JOHN KNOX VILLAGE OF TAMPA BAY INC
ST. JOSEPH'S JOHN KNOX
(*Suby of* BAYCARE EDUCATION SERVICES) ★
4100 E Fletcher Ave, Tampa, FL 33613-4864
Tel (813) 977-4950 *Founded/Ownrshp* 1988
Sales 45.7MM^E *EMP* 425
SIC 8059 8051 Personal care home, with health care; Skilled nursing care facilities; Personal care home, with health care; Skilled nursing care facilities
**Sec:* Diane Yates
Exec: Gary West

JOHN KNOX VLG RETIREMENT CMNTY
See JOHN KNOX VILLAGE

D-U-N-S 00-382-4620
JOHN KORSMO CONSTRUCTION INC
1940 E D St Ste 300, Tacoma, WA 98421-1500
Tel (253) 582-6712 *Founded/Ownrshp* 1951
Sales 21.4MM^E *EMP* 45
SIC 1542 School building construction
Pr: John S Korsmo Jr
**VP:* Greg Primm
Sfty Dirs: Don Coovert

D-U-N-S 07-926-5468
JOHN L SCOTT INC
SCOTT, JOHN L REAL ESTATE
1700 Nw Gilman Blvd # 300, Issaquah, WA 98027-5349
Tel (425) 392-1211 *Founded/Ownrshp* 1931
Sales 4.0MMM *EMP* 155
SIC 6531 Real estate agent, residential; Real estate agent, residential
Ch: J Lennox Scott
**COO:* Phil McBride
VP: Laura Hurme
Genl Mgr: Karen Lindsay
Sales Asso: Jim Albright

D-U-N-S 02-900-9636
JOHN L SULLIVAN CHEVROLET INC
350 Automall Dr, Roseville, CA 95661-3019
Tel (916) 782-1243 *Founded/Ownrshp* 1950
Sales 58.9MM^E *EMP* 150
SIC 5511 7539 7538 5531 5521 Automobiles, new & used; Pickups, new & used; Automotive repair shops; General automotive repair shops; Automotive & home supply stores; Used car dealers; Automobiles, new & used; Pickups, new & used; Automotive repair shops; General automotive repair shops; Automotive & home supply stores; Used car dealers
Pr: John L Sullivan
**Sec:* Steve A Ruckels
**VP:* David Rogers
Sls Mgr: Byron Aguilar
Sls Mgr: Jose Martinez

D-U-N-S 02-117-8702
JOHN L SULLIVAN INVESTMENTS INC (CA)
ROSEVILLE TOYOTA
6200 Northfront Rd, Livermore, CA 94551-9507
Tel (916) 969-5911 *Founded/Ownrshp* 1980, 1992
Sales 126.1MM^E *EMP* 330
SIC 5511 7538 Automobiles, new & used; Pickups, new & used; General automotive repair shops; Automobiles, new & used; Pickups, new & used; General automotive repair shops
Pr: John L Sullivan
**Sec:* Steve Ruckels
**VP:* David Rodgers
Sls Mgr: Thue Lee

D-U-N-S 07-741-7533
JOHN L WORTHAM & SON LP
WORTHAM INSURANCE & RISK MGT
2727 Allen Pkwy, Houston, TX 77019-2115
Tel (713) 526-3366 *Founded/Ownrshp* 1915
Sales NA *EMP* 469
SIC 6411 Insurance agents, brokers & service; Insurance agents, brokers & service
Pt: Fred C Burns
Genl Pt: Stuart Petty
Mng Pt: Robert Crosby
V Ch: Richard Blades
V Ch: Charles Flournoy
CFO: Stephen Bishop
VP: George Adkins
VP: Kevin Daniel
Exec: Debbie Powell
Assoc Dir: Barbara Childers
Assoc Dir: Enrique Gomez
Assoc Dir: Cindy McKinzie
Assoc Dir: Sharon McNease
Assoc Dir: Sharla Ortiz
Assoc Dir: Christine Pace
Assoc Dir: Boyd Parker
Assoc Dir: Missy Simnacher
Assoc Dir: Gail Thompson
Assoc Dir: Elliot Witt
Assoc Dir: Thuy Wong
Assoc Dir: Larry Zajicek

D-U-N-S 00-918-9681
JOHN LAS/ST SPECIALTY CARE CTR
1323 Freedom Rd, Cranberry Township, PA 16066-5001
Tel (724) 776-1100 *Founded/Ownrshp* 2000
Sales 24.1MM^E *EMP* 2
Accts Parantebeard Llc Pittsburgh
SIC 8099 Health & allied services; Health & allied services
Prin: V Hughes

D-U-N-S 01-903-8678
JOHN LUCAS TREE EXPERT CO
12 Northbrook Dr, Falmouth, ME 04105-1318
Tel (207) 797-7294 *Founded/Ownrshp* 1980
Sales 48.5MM *EMP* 400
Accts Baker Newman & Noyes Limited
SIC 0783 Ornamental shrub & tree services; Ornamental shrub & tree services
Pr: Arthur Batson III
**COO:* Peter Marion

D-U-N-S 02-317-2273
JOHN LYNCH CHEVROLET-PONTIAC SALES INC
LYNCH TRUCK CENTER
2300 Browns Lake Dr, Burlington, WI 53105-7105
Tel (262) 763-7500 *Founded/Ownrshp* 1965
Sales 56.3MM^E *EMP* 123
SIC 5511 7538 5521 Automobiles, new & used; Pickups, new & used; General automotive repair shops; Used car dealers; Automobiles, new & used; Pickups, new & used; General automotive repair shops; Used car dealers
Pr: David J Lynch

D-U-N-S 96-308-6017
JOHN M BELK EDUCATIONL ENDOWMENT
4201 Congress St Ste 470, Charlotte, NC 28209-4682
Tel (704) 357-1000 *Founded/Ownrshp* 2010
Sales 244.1MM *EMP* 2
SIC 8699 Charitable organization; Charitable organization
Prin: Morris Katherine Belk

D-U-N-S 09-734-0053 IMP
JOHN M ELLSWORTH CO INC
8700 W Bradley Rd, Milwaukee, WI 53224-2818
Tel (414) 354-1414 *Founded/Ownrshp* 1976
Sales 30.2MM^E *EMP* 33
SIC 5084 Petroleum industry machinery
Pr: John M Ellsworth
COO: Philip Areddia
**COO:* Phil Areddia
**VP:* Matthew Ellsworth
Genl Mgr: Steve Fabiszak
Sls Mgr: Rick Carey
Sales Asso: Don Dellmann

D-U-N-S 11-505-5766
JOHN M FRANK CONSTRUCTION INC
JOHN M FRANK SERVICE GROUP
913 E 4th St, Santa Ana, CA 92701-4748
Tel (714) 210-3600 *Founded/Ownrshp* 1984
Sales 25.5MM^E *EMP* 80
SIC 1542 5411 5812 Commercial & office building, new construction; Commercial & office buildings, renovation & repair; Supermarkets; Family restaurants; Restaurant, lunch counter; Commercial & office building, new construction; Commercial & office buildings, renovation & repair; Supermarkets; Family restaurants; Restaurant, lunch counter
CEO: John M Frank
Exec: Myra Mageo

JOHN M FRANK SERVICE GROUP
See JOHN M FRANK CONSTRUCTION INC

D-U-N-S 09-672-1352
JOHN M QUALY
QUALY INSURANCE AGENCY
701 Market St Ste 1070, Saint Louis, MO 63101-1851
Tel (314) 231-3931 *Founded/Ownrshp* 1992
Sales NA *EMP* 150
SIC 6411 6311 Insurance agents; Life insurance
Ofcr: Sean Babbitt
Ofcr: Matthew Banderman
Ofcr: Justin Hennessey
IT Man: Jennifer Donahue

D-U-N-S 00-791-3981 IMP/EXP
JOHN MANEELY CO
JMC STEEL GROUP
(*Suby of* ENERGEX TUBE) ★
227 W Monroe St Ste 2600, Chicago, IL 60606-5082
Tel (312) 275-1600 *Founded/Ownrshp* 1877, 2006
Sales 118.0MM^E *EMP* 1,300
SIC 3317 3644

D-U-N-S 02-341-4205
JOHN MARSHALL BANK
6601 Little River Tpke, Alexandria, VA 22312-1303
Tel (703) 584-0840 *Founded/Ownrshp* 2008
Sales NA *EMP* 17
SIC 6021 National commercial banks; National commercial banks
Prin: Jim Bowman
Ex VP: Mark Moore
Sr VP: Debbie Boyd
Sr VP: Drew Brown
Sr VP: Jeff Dimeglio
Sr VP: Kerry Donley
Sr VP: Bruce Gemmill
Sr VP: Craig Sacknoff
VP: Jose Castillo
VP: Yvonne Gray
VP: Nadia Itraish

D-U-N-S 05-898-5948
JOHN MARSHALL BANK
1943 Isaac Newton Sq E # 100, Reston, VA 20190-5013
Tel (703) 435-8440 *Founded/Ownrshp* 2011
Sales NA *EMP* 16^E
SIC 6022 State commercial banks
Pr: Bill Ridenour
Pr: Betty Gillen
Ch: John R Maxwell
Ex VP: Carl E Dodson
Ex VP: Mark D Moore
Sr VP: Barry Benishek
Sr VP: Kevin Clarke
Sr VP: Pamela Decandio
Sr VP: David Holden
Sr VP: Robert McCoy
Sr VP: Heather Skigen
Sr VP: Steve Wilson
Sr VP: Chuck Wortman
VP: Shannon Catlett
VP: Susie Kitchin
VP: Matthew Korosi
VP: Christopher Lipscomb

D-U-N-S 07-689-2579
JOHN MARSHALL LAW SCHOOL
315 S Plymouth Ct Fl 1, Chicago, IL 60604-3968
Tel (312) 427-2737 *Founded/Ownrshp* 1899
Sales 60.4MM *EMP* 312
SIC 8221 Professional schools; Professional schools
**Pr:* Leonard F Amari
Assoc Dir: Virginia Russell
Off Mgr: Ibukun Fasoranti
Genl Couns: Trish McGill
Genl Couns: Ashley Rafael

D-U-N-S 02-851-8237
JOHN MASTERS ORGANICS INC
468 Springtown Rd, New Paltz, NY 12561-3032
Tel (844) 324-2244 *Founded/Ownrshp* 2013
Sales 26.0MM *EMP* 28
SIC 5999 Cosmetics; Cleaning equipment & supplies
Ch Bd: Yoshimune Noda

JOHN MEZZALINGUA ASSOC INC
See PPC BROADBAND INC

JOHN MICHAEL MOORETRAUMA CTR
See VIRGINIA WEST UNIVERSITY HOSPITALS INC

D-U-N-S 00-233-0363 IMP/EXP
■ **JOHN MIDDLETON CO** (PA)
(*Suby of* PHILIP MORRIS USA INC) ★
2325 Bells Rd, Richmond, VA 23234-2274
Tel (610) 792-8000 *Founded/Ownrshp* 1856, 2007
Sales 31.2MM^E *EMP* 6
SIC 2131 2121 Smoking tobacco; Cigars
CEO: William Gofford Jr
Mktg Mgr: Christopher Brocco

D-U-N-S 09-079-4611
JOHN MILES CHEVROLET INC
950 Dogwood Dr Se, Conyers, GA 30012-5452
Tel (770) 483-8766 *Founded/Ownrshp* 1996
Sales 27.8MM^E *EMP* 72
SIC 5511 Automobiles, new & used; Automobiles, new & used
Pr: John Miles
Genl Mgr: Lee Lovett
Sales Asso: Jamie Detter

D-U-N-S 09-417-1220
JOHN MILLS DISTRIBUTING CO INC
DELI PEOPLE, THE
3360 N Benzing Rd, Orchard Park, NY 14127-1590
Tel (716) 822-0854 *Founded/Ownrshp* 1976

Sales 28.4MMᴱ *EMP* 53
SIC 5147 5141 5148 Meats & meat products; Groceries, general line; Fresh fruits & vegetables
Ch Bd: John Mills

D-U-N-S 18-554-7556
JOHN MOORE LP
JOHN MOORE SERVICES
10005 W Sam Houston Pkwy, Houston, TX 77064-7510
Tel (281) 949-5353 *Founded/Ownrshp* 2004
Sales 55.5MMᴱ *EMP* 350ᴱ
SIC 7342 1711 Disinfecting & pest control services; Disinfecting & pest control services; Plumbing, heating, air-conditioning contractors
Pt: Don Valentine
VP: Bob Merchant
Secur Mgr: Ken Hrebec

JOHN MOORE SERVICES
See JOHN MOORE LP

D-U-N-S 13-185-4648
JOHN MORIARTY & ASSOCIATES INC
J M A
3 Church St Ste 2, Winchester, MA 01890-1804
Tel (781) 729-3900 *Founded/Ownrshp* 1985
Sales 60.0MMᴱ *EMP* 215
SIC 8741 1542 1522

D-U-N-S 96-786-7461
JOHN MUIR BEHAVIORAL HEALTH
1400 Treat Blvd, Walnut Creek, CA 94597-2142
Tel (925) 939-3000 *Founded/Ownrshp* 2011
Sales 41.9MM *EMP* 2
Accts Deloitte Tax Llp San Francisc
SIC 8099 Health & allied services; Health & allied services
Prin: J K Anderson
Sales Exec: Philip Batchelor

D-U-N-S 07-653-8594
JOHN MUIR HEALTH
1601 Ygnacio Valley Rd, Walnut Creek, CA 94598-3122
Tel (925) 939-3000 *Founded/Ownrshp* 1958
Sales 1.2MMM *EMP* 2,200
Accts Deloitte Tax Llp San Francisc
SIC 8062 General medical & surgical hospitals; General medical & surgical hospitals
CEO: Calvin Knight
Dir Recs: Sue Pena
V Ch: David L Goldsmith
**Pr:* Michael S Thomas
**Pr:* Jane A Willemsen
COO: Lee Huskins
COO: Elizabeth Stallings
Treas: Malcolm J McAuley
Bd of Dir: Burton Baker
Sr VP: Donna Brackley
VP: Mitchell Zack
Exec: Norman Livermore
Dir OR: Karen Herrick

JOHN MUIR MEDICAL CENTER
See JOHN MUIR PHYSICIAN NETWORK

D-U-N-S 80-320-8537
JOHN MUIR MEDICAL PAVILION
MT DIABLO MEDICAL PAVILION
2740 Grant St, Concord, CA 94520-2265
Tel (925) 674-4100 *Founded/Ownrshp* 1997
Sales 21.7MM *EMP* 165
SIC 8063 8051 Psychiatric hospitals; Skilled nursing care facilities; Psychiatric hospitals; Skilled nursing care facilities
COO: Elizabeth Stallings
Doctor: Nagui Achamallah
Doctor: Kiran Koka
Doctor: Peter Tamulevich

D-U-N-S 11-133-8653
JOHN MUIR PHYSICIAN NETWORK
JOHN MUIR MEDICAL CENTER
1450 Treat Blvd, Walnut Creek, CA 94597-2168
Tel (925) 296-9740 *Founded/Ownrshp* 1997
Sales 273.7MMᴱ *EMP* 3,612
SIC 8062 8069 8093 7363 General medical & surgical hospitals; Substance abuse hospitals; Substance abuse clinics (outpatient); Medical help service; General medical & surgical hospitals; Substance abuse hospitals; Substance abuse clinics (outpatient); Medical help service
CEO: Calvin Knightt
Pr: Jackie Schroder
**CEO:* Calvin Knight
VP: Lynn Baskett
VP: Mitchell Zack
Dir IT: Marty Tedlock
Surgeon: Jatinder Dhillon
Surgeon: Tanveer Khan
Surgeon: Ramesh Veeragandham
Board of Directors: Patrick E Kavanaugh, Burton H Baker, Ronald K Mullin, Phillip Batchelor, Thomas Rundall, David A Birdsall, Stuart B Shikora, William F Cronk, Stephen L Davenport, Marilyn M Gardner, Janet E Gaston, William K Hoddick, Steven M Kaplan

D-U-N-S 07-767-8753
JOHN MULLEN & CO INC
677 Ala Moana Blvd # 910, Honolulu, HI 96813-5499
Tel (808) 981-5245 *Founded/Ownrshp* 2004
Sales NA *EMP* 90
SIC 6411 Insurance claim adjusters, not employed by insurance company
Pr: J Terrence Mullen
**VP:* Ernie Seibold

D-U-N-S 01-923-6421 IMP
JOHN NAGLE CO
FISHHOUSE
306 Northern Ave Ste 3, Boston, MA 02210-3213
Tel (617) 542-9418 *Founded/Ownrshp* 1887
Sales 42.2MMᴱ *EMP* 60
SIC 5146 Fish, fresh
Pr: Charles Nagle
**CFO:* Michael Bates
**Treas:* Robert Nagle
VP: Jack Joy
**VP:* John Nagle

Prd Mgr: Tracy Smith
VP Mktg: Tom Spang

D-U-N-S 02-001-4226
JOHN NORTH FORD INC (KS)
JOHN NORTH NISSAN
3002 W Us Highway 50, Emporia, KS 66801-5198
Tel (620) 343-1700 *Founded/Ownrshp* 1963
Sales 26.6MM *EMP* 44
SIC 5511 Automobiles, new & used; Automobiles, new & used
Pr: Timothy North
**Genl Mgr:* Ron Carlson

JOHN NORTH NISSAN
See JOHN NORTH FORD INC

D-U-N-S 01-001-2243
JOHN P PICONE INC
31 Garden Ln, Lawrence, NY 11559-1126
Tel (516) 239-1600 *Founded/Ownrshp* 1980
Sales 201.2MMᴱ *EMP* 400
SIC 1611 1622 1623 1629 Highway & street construction; Bridge construction; Sewer line construction; Waste water & sewage treatment plant construction; Highway & street construction; Bridge construction; Sewer line construction; Waste water & sewage treatment plant construction
Ch Bd: John P Picone
**Pr:* Robert Taikina
**CEO:* Gerald E Rossettie
**Ex VP:* Kenneth Durkin
**VP:* Robert Wessels
Genl Mgr: Michael Germano
Off Mgr: Sara Picone

D-U-N-S 03-422-6951 IMP
JOHN PAC INC (LA)
1860 Hwy 90 W, Crowley, LA 70527
Tel (337) 783-5466 *Founded/Ownrshp* 1953
Sales 22.5MMᴱ *EMP* 30
SIC 5199 Packaging materials
Pr: Peter M John
**CEO:* Mary Ellen Henry
**VP:* David M John
Sls Mgr: James Cannon

D-U-N-S 03-818-5518 IMP/EXP
JOHN PAUL MITCHELL SYSTEMS
26471 Carl Boyer Dr, Santa Clarita, CA 91350-2996
Tel (661) 298-0400 *Founded/Ownrshp* 1980
Sales 132.2MMᴱ *EMP* 174
SIC 5122 Hair preparations; Hair preparations
CEO: John Paul Dejoria
CFO: Rick Battalini
VP: Debbie White
Genl Mgr: Luke Jabellis
Off Mgr: Carin Herman
IT Man: Jim Riely

D-U-N-S 94-512-4246 IMP
JOHN PAUL RICHARD INC
BAG AGE
26800 Agoura Rd, Calabasas, CA 91301-5116
Tel (818) 871-1300 *Founded/Ownrshp* 1996
Sales 60.0MM *EMP* 65
Accts Marcum Llp Los Angeles Ca
SIC 5621 Women's & children's clothing; Women's clothing stores
CEO: John Paul Beltran
**COO:* Robert Hirsh
COO: Natalie Stevenson
**CFO:* Judith Scott
**Co-CEO:* Richard Hirsh
**Co-CEO:* Bertran Kalatchi
Ex VP: Tanias Russell
**Ex VP:* Jack Shilwall
Ex VP: Jack Shiwlall
VP: Brad Whitely
IT Man: Solomon Manansala

JOHN PETER SMITH HOSPITAL
See TARRANT COUNTY HOSPITAL DISTRICT

JOHN Q HAMMONS HOTELS
See ATRIUM HOTELS LP

D-U-N-S 03-178-3806
JOHN Q HAMMONS HOTELS MANAGEMENT LLC
300 S John Q Hammons Pkwy # 900, Springfield, MO 65806-2596
Tel (417) 864-4300 *Founded/Ownrshp* 2005
Sales 249.6MMᴱ *EMP* 5,000
SIC 7011 Hotels & motels; Hotels & motels
CEO: Jacqueline Dowdy
Dir Vol: Pat Martin
**Sr VP:* Greggory Groves
**Sr VP:* Joe Morrissey
**Sr VP:* Christopher Smith
**VP:* Phill Burgess
Prin: Kathy Rutledge
Sls Mgr: Elizabeth Osterhout

JOHN Q HAMMONS HOTELS RESORTS
See JOHN Q HAMMONS RVOC TR 12281989

D-U-N-S 07-831-6201
JOHN Q HAMMONS RVOC TR 12281989
JOHN Q HAMMONS HOTELS RESORTS
300 S John Q Hammons Pkwy # 9, Springfield, MO 65806-2518
Tel (417) 864-4300 *Founded/Ownrshp* 1951
Sales 416.2MMᴱ *EMP* 9,000
SIC 7011 Hotels & motels; Hotels & motels
Owner: Jacquie Dowdy
Co-Ownr: Kathy Rutledge

D-U-N-S 00-623-4173
JOHN R DAILY INC
2900 Mullan Rd, Missoula, MT 59808-5132
Tel (406) 721-7007 *Founded/Ownrshp* 1893, 1968
Sales 46.4MM *EMP* 92
Accts Elmore & Associates Pc
SIC 2013 Sausages & other prepared meats; Prepared pork products from purchased pork; Sausages & other prepared meats; Prepared pork products from purchased pork
CEO: A Warren Wilcox

**Pr:* Mark Wilson
**Sec:* Thomas J Hocevar
**Sr VP:* Sig Skarland
Prd Mgr: Dave Caron

D-U-N-S 03-999-1609
JOHN R HESS & CO INC
400 Station St, Cranston, RI 02910-2932
Tel (401) 785-9300 *Founded/Ownrshp* 1969
Sales 20.4MMᴱ *EMP* 26
SIC 5169 Industrial chemicals
Treas: John R Hess III
**Pr:* PeterY Hess
VP: Roger Blanchette
**VP:* Thomas Anthony Thompson
Dept Mgr: Dawn Carter

D-U-N-S 01-041-2245
JOHN R MCKENZIE JOBBER INC (FL)
MCKENZIE PETROLEUM
210 Tavernier St, Tavernier, FL 33070-2627
Tel (305) 743-7915 *Founded/Ownrshp* 1969
Sales 41.9MM *EMP* 17
Accts Tolley & Hill Pllc Key Largo
SIC 5172 Petroleum products; Petroleum products
Pr: Greg R McKenzie

D-U-N-S 83-130-4865
JOHN R MORREALE INC
216 N Peoria St, Chicago, IL 60607-1706
Tel (312) 421-3664 *Founded/Ownrshp* 2006
Sales 31.7MMᴱ *EMP* 72
SIC 5147 Meats, fresh
Pr: Steven Hurckes
**VP:* Mike Magrini

D-U-N-S 06-435-6967
JOHN R SEIBERLICH INC
SEIBERLICH TRANE
66 Southgate Blvd, New Castle, DE 19720-2068
Tel (302) 356-2400 *Founded/Ownrshp* 1963
Sales 22.7MMᴱ *EMP* 72
Accts Mayer Hoffman Mccann Pc Ply
SIC 5075 Warm air heating & air conditioning; Warm air heating & air conditioning
Pr: John Seiberlich
**Treas:* Ronald Hess
Dist Mgr: John R Seibelich
IT Man: Gerhard R Witteich
Sales Asso: Steve Rendulic
Sales Asso: John Walker

D-U-N-S 07-224-5400
JOHN R WOOD INC
WOOD, JOHN R REALTORS
3255 Tamiami Trl N, Naples, FL 34103-2796
Tel (239) 261-6622 *Founded/Ownrshp* 1958
Sales 21.5MMᴱ *EMP* 470
SIC 6531 Real estate managers; Selling agent, real estate; Real estate managers; Selling agent, real estate
Pr: Phillip Wood
Treas: Nancy Wyckoff
VP Opers: Bonnie Williams
Sales Asso: Betty Kampfer

D-U-N-S 06-601-2626
■ **JOHN RANDOLPH MEDICAL CENTER**
COLUMBIA HCA
(*Suby of* HCA INC) ★
411 W Randolph Rd, Hopewell, VA 23860-2938
Tel (804) 541-7492 *Founded/Ownrshp* 1915
Sales 66.5MMᴱ *EMP* 850
Accts Henry P Harrison Jr Cpa Hope
SIC 8062 General medical & surgical hospitals; General medical & surgical hospitals
CEO: Dia Nichols
**COO:* Ed Littlejohn
CFO: Ron Powell
**CFO:* Tom Steslicki
Dir Rad: Geneva Flexon
Dir Pat Ac: Matt McDearmon
CIO: Kathy Kiaser
Netwrk Mgr: Andy Schrader
Nrsg Dir: Cathy Bailey
Cert Phar: Gregory Newton

D-U-N-S 03-234-0927
JOHN RANDOLPH MEDICAL CENTRE
411 W Randolph Rd, Hopewell, VA 23860-2938
Tel (804) 541-1600 *Founded/Ownrshp* 2011
Sales 66.7MM *EMP* 27ᴱ
SIC 8011 Medical centers
Prin: Marion Williams
Chf Nrs Of: Patsy Coghill
Pharmcst: Zahra Maleki
HC Dir: Cheryl Tucker

D-U-N-S 02-420-5940
JOHN RENFRO SUPPLY INC (KY)
423 S 5th St, Williamsburg, KY 40769-1228
Tel (606) 549-1334 *Founded/Ownrshp* 1922, 2000
Sales 58.8MM *EMP* 36
SIC 5194 5145 5131 Cigarettes; Confectionery; Notions; Cigarettes; Confectionery; Notions
CEO: Rhonda Naumann
**CFO:* Burley McFarland
VP: Lesa Lovitt
**VP:* George Naumann
**VP:* Mike Owens
**VP:* Bernice Renfro
Dir IT: Brad Stephens

D-U-N-S 06-243-1432
JOHN ROBERTS AUSTIN INC
LEXUS OF AUSTIN
9910 Stonelake Blvd, Austin, TX 78759-6530
Tel (512) 343-3400 *Founded/Ownrshp* 1982
Sales 42.9MMᴱ *EMP* 45
SIC 5511 Automobiles, new & used; Pickups, new & used
Pr: John Roberts
COO: George Toreki
**Sec:* Vicki Argo
**VP:* Maxine Roberts
Exec: Linda Dubelbeis
Exec: Dean Royal
Sls Mgr: Curtis Howard
Sls Mgr: R K Johnston

Sls Mgr: Joey Lafave
Sales Asso: Nicco Azari
Sales Asso: Govan Bianchini

D-U-N-S 00-615-9149
JOHN ROBERTS CO
JOHN ROBERTS PRINTING COMPANY
9687 E River Rd Nw, Minneapolis, MN 55433-6018
Tel (763) 755-5500 *Founded/Ownrshp* 1951
Sales 3.8MMᴱ *EMP* 300
SIC 2752

D-U-N-S 15-198-6494
JOHN ROBERTS MANAGEMENT CORP
JR VALENTINES FAMILY REST
438 W Elm St, Bluffton, OH 45817-1122
Tel (419) 358-1010 *Founded/Ownrshp* 1985
Sales 7.5MMᴱ *EMP* 350
SIC 5812 Restaurant, family: independent; Restaurant, family: independent
Pr: Val John Harris
**VP:* John Hedrick

JOHN ROBERTS PRINTING COMPANY
See JOHN ROBERTS CO

D-U-N-S 06-900-0750
JOHN ROCK INC
500 Independence Way, Coatesville, PA 19320-1689
Tel (610) 857-8080 *Founded/Ownrshp* 1997
Sales 20.3MMᴱ *EMP* 90
SIC 2448 Pallets, wood
Pr: Bill Maccauley

JOHN ROGIN BUICK
See JOHN ROGIN LIVONIA INC

D-U-N-S 13-126-9995
JOHN ROGIN LIVONIA INC
JOHN ROGIN BUICK
30500 Plymouth Rd, Livonia, MI 48150-2130
Tel (734) 525-0900 *Founded/Ownrshp* 1985
Sales 21.0MM *EMP* 60ᴱ
SIC 5511 Automobiles, new & used; Automobiles, new & used
Pr: John Rogin
**Sec:* Barbara Kucka

D-U-N-S 11-379-6630
JOHN S AND JAMES L KNIGHT FOUNDATION INC
200 S Biscayne Blvd # 3300, Miami, FL 33131-2349
Tel (305) 358-1061 *Founded/Ownrshp* 1950
Sales 178.5MM *EMP* 50
SIC 8399 Fund raising organization, non-fee basis; Fund raising organization, non-fee basis
Pr: Alberto Ibarguen
**Ch:* Robert W Briggs
Ofcr: Alfredo Cruz
Ofcr: Marie Gilot
**VP:* Paula Ellis
**VP:* Belinda Lawrence
**VP:* Juan Martinez
**VP:* Larry Meyer
**VP:* Eric Newton
VP: Mayur Patel
VP: Dennis Scholl
VP: Andrew Sherry
VP: Trabian Shorters

D-U-N-S 00-342-3001
JOHN S CONNOR INC (MD)
NORTHROP GRMMAN TECHNICAL SVCS
799 Cromwell Park Dr A, Glen Burnie, MD 21061-2578
Tel (410) 863-0211 *Founded/Ownrshp* 1917
Sales 22.7MMᴱ *EMP* 95
SIC 4731 Freight transportation arrangement
Pr: Lee Connor Jr
Pr: Priscilla Royster
**VP:* Butch Connor
Ex Dir: Cleo Conley
Sls Mgr: Robert Cave
Sls Mgr: Bill Settle

D-U-N-S 00-838-2863 IMP
JOHN S FREY ENTERPRISES (CA)
1900 E 64th St, Los Angeles, CA 90001-2104
Tel (323) 583-4061 *Founded/Ownrshp* 1945
Sales 186.5MMᴱ *EMP* 250
Accts Mcgladrey & Pullen Llp Pasad
SIC 3441 3444 6719 Building components, structural steel; Canopies, sheet metal; Investment holding companies, except banks; Building components, structural steel; Canopies, sheet metal; Investment holding companies, except banks
Ch Bd: John S Frey Jr
**Treas:* Grace Lee

D-U-N-S 04-296-7489
JOHN S JAMES CO
6002 Commerce Blvd # 115, Garden City, GA 31408-9760
Tel (912) 963-2964 *Founded/Ownrshp* 1941
Sales 54.0MMᴱ *EMP* 130
SIC 4731 Foreign freight forwarding; Customhouse brokers; Foreign freight forwarding; Customhouse brokers
CEO: Pamela Jill James
**CEO:* Thomas C James
**CFO:* John L James
Dir Bus: David Bryant
Opers Mgr: Larry Thompson

D-U-N-S 94-541-7632
JOHN S MEEK CO INC
14732 S Maple Ave, Gardena, CA 90248-1934
Tel (310) 830-6323 *Founded/Ownrshp* 1995
Sales 20.1MMᴱ *EMP* 60
SIC 1629 Dams, waterways, docks & other marine construction
Pr: John S Meek
Mktg Dir: James Jilk

D-U-N-S 02-563-6903
JOHN SAKASH CO INC (IL)
700 N Walnut St, Elmhurst, IL 60126-1517
Tel (630) 833-3940 *Founded/Ownrshp* 1952
Sales 30.6MMᴱ *EMP* 50

SIC 5082 Construction & mining machinery
Pr: John W Sakash
**VP:* Paul Slavik
Genl Mgr: Harriet Friend

JOHN SCANLON'S VALUE LOT
See FORT MYERS LINCOLN MERCURY NEW & USED CARS INC

D-U-N-S 09-150-0090
JOHN SNOW INC (MA)
44 Farnsworth St Fl 7, Boston, MA 02210-1223
Tel (617) 482-9485 *Founded/Ownrshp* 1975, 1978
Sales 426.0MM *EMP* 297
SIC 8742 Hospital & health services consultant; Hospital & health services consultant
Pr: Joel Lamstein
**COO:* Alexander K Baker
Ofcr: Rebecca Alban
Ofcr: Danielle Cuenoud
Ofcr: Margaret Murphy
Ofcr: Angela Wang
**VP:* Patricia Fairchild
**VP:* Theo Lippeveld
Ex Dir: Penelope Riseborough
Prgrm Mgr: Kirstin Krudwig
Rgnl Mgr: Eric Takang

D-U-N-S 07-969-0284
JOHN SOULES ACQUISITIONS LLC (GA)
PRO VIEW FOODS
(*Suby of* JOHN SOULES FOODS INC) ★
311 Green St Nw Ste 500, Gainesville, GA 30501-3367
Tel (770) 532-3058 *Founded/Ownrshp* 2014
Sales 80.5MM^E *EMP* 750
SIC 2015 Poultry, processed: cooked
CEO: John E Soules Sr
Co-CEO: John Soules Jr
Co-CEO: Mark Soules

D-U-N-S 04-329-5765 IMP
JOHN SOULES FOODS INC
10150 Fm 14, Tyler, TX 75706-7145
Tel (903) 592-9800 *Founded/Ownrshp* 1985
Sales 264.3MM^E *EMP* 1,225^E
SIC 2013 2015 5147 Sausages & other prepared meats; Poultry slaughtering & processing; Meats & meat products; Sausages & other prepared meats; Poultry slaughtering & processing; Meats & meat products
Ch Bd: John E Soules Sr
**CEO:* John E Soules II
**CEO:* Mark D Soules
CFO: Adam Bryant
**Ex VP:* Thomas L Ellis
QA Dir: Tom Miller
Plnt Mgr: Rich McGuire
Prd Mgr: Jose Castaneda
Sls Dir: Doug Aistrup
Manager: Roderick Jones

D-U-N-S 01-201-3363
JOHN SWETT UNIFIED SCHOOL DISTRICT
400 Parker Ave, Rodeo, CA 94572-1400
Tel (510) 245-4300 *Founded/Ownrshp* 1800
Sales 20.7MM *EMP* 200
SIC 8211 Public elementary & secondary schools; Public elementary & secondary schools
Prin: Michael Roth
IT Man: Margaret Sasaki
IT Man: Kathy Taniguchi
Schl Brd P: Brian Colombo

D-U-N-S 01-428-4582
JOHN T HOWE INC
COMFORT INN
1389 Lake Ariel Hwy, Lake Ariel, PA 18436
Tel (570) 698-9232 *Founded/Ownrshp* 1966
Sales 38.1MM^E *EMP* 130
SIC 5172 5411 5541 Gasoline; Convenience stores, independent; Filling stations, gasoline; Gasoline; Convenience stores, independent; Filling stations, gasoline
Pr: Bruce D Howe
**VP:* Thomas B Howe
**VP:* Susan Kwiatek

JOHN T MATHER MEMORIAL HOSPITA
See JOHN T MATHER MEMORIAL HOSPITAL OF PORT JEFFERSON NEW YORK INC

D-U-N-S 06-473-8859
JOHN T MATHER MEMORIAL HOSPITAL OF PORT JEFFERSON NEW YORK INC
JOHN T MATHER MEMORIAL HOSPITA
75 N Country Rd, Port Jefferson, NY 11777-2119
Tel (631) 476-2738 *Founded/Ownrshp* 1928
Sales 292.3MM *EMP* 1,700
Accts Parentebeard Llc New York Ne
SIC 8062 General medical & surgical hospitals; General medical & surgical hospitals
Pr: Kenneth D Roberts
Chf Rad: William Moore
V Ch: Konrad Kuhn
V Ch: Harold Tranchon
COO: Joseph Cirrone
Chf Mktg O: Maryanne Gordon
VP: Mark Borek
**VP:* Barbara Farruggia
VP: Steven Heiman
**VP:* Joseph Josnowsky
**VP:* Frank T Lettera
**VP:* Diane Marotta
VP: Marie Mulligan
**VP:* Kevin Murray
**VP:* Wayne Shattes
VP: Loretta Wagner
VP: Carolyn Williams
Dir Rx: Justin Gaynor

D-U-N-S 92-720-3646
JOHN TEMPLETON FOUNDATION
300 Conshohocken State Rd # 500, Conshohocken, PA 19428-3815
Tel (610) 941-2828 *Founded/Ownrshp* 1987
Sales 135.3MM *EMP* 27
Accts Grant Thornton Llp Philadelp
SIC 8699 Charitable organization; Charitable organization
Pr: John Marks Templeton Jr
COO: Jack Shields
Ofcr: Daniel Darg
VP: Paul Wason
Exec: Felicia Smith
Mng Dir: Jim Pitofsky
Dir IT: Mathew Bernold

JOHN THORNTON MAZDA
See ADZAM INC

JOHN TILLMAN COMPANY
See BLAKE H BROWN INC

JOHN TOLFREE HEALTH SYSTEM
See WEST BRANCH REGIONAL MEDICAL CENTER

D-U-N-S 01-409-3033 IMP
JOHN V SCHULTZ CO
SCHULTZ FURNITURE
7200 Peach St Unit 300, Erie, PA 16509-4759
Tel (814) 868-7125 *Founded/Ownrshp* 1940
Sales 26.7MM^E *EMP* 112
SIC 5712

D-U-N-S 06-545-4993
JOHN VANCE MOTORS INC
5322 S Division St, Guthrie, OK 73044-7021
Tel (888) 758-7382 *Founded/Ownrshp* 1983
Sales 29.6MM^E *EMP* 62
SIC 5511 Automobiles, new & used; Pickups, new & used; Automobiles, new & used; Pickups, new & used
Pr: John T Vance
**Sec:* James E Smith
**VP:* Mike L Vance
Genl Mgr: Megan Ochs
Sls Mgr: Dennis Lynn
Sales Asso: Craig Crafton
Sales Asso: Phil Sites

D-U-N-S 06-441-0637 IMP
JOHN VARVATOS ENTERPRISES INC
26 W 17th St Fl 12, New York, NY 10011-5710
Tel (212) 812-8000 *Founded/Ownrshp* 2012
Sales 274.6MM^E *EMP* 250^E
SIC 5136 Apparel belts, men's & boys'; Apparel belts, men's & boys'
Ch Bd: John Varvatos
Genl Mgr: Ryan Paulo
Genl Mgr: Krista Weissmuller
Off Mgr: Nicole Russo
Sls&Mrk Ex: Faircloth Donna
Sales Asso: Darlon Bush
Sales Asso: Rene Felipe

D-U-N-S 00-629-3724 IMP
JOHN VOLPI & CO INC (MO)
VOLPI ITALIAN FOODS
5263 Northrup Ave, Saint Louis, MO 63110-2033
Tel (314) 772-8550 *Founded/Ownrshp* 1902, 1957
Sales 25.6MM^E *EMP* 115
SIC 2013 Sausages from purchased meat; Cured meats from purchased meat; Sausages from purchased meat; Cured meats from purchased meat
CEO: Lorenza Pasetti
**CFO:* Paul A Gniadek
**VP:* Evelina Pasetti
VP Sls: Peter Hambrecht
Mktg Mgr: Adisa Selmanovic
Board of Directors: Cort Ballard, Adrianna Borojevic

D-U-N-S 05-120-4154
JOHN W CLARK OIL CO INC
101 Wheatley Rd, Ashland, KY 41101-2333
Tel (606) 325-8536 *Founded/Ownrshp* 1970
Sales 30.4MM^E *EMP* 66^E
SIC 5541 5172 Filling stations, gasoline; Petroleum products
Pr: John W Clark
**VP:* Brent Clark
Opers Mgr: Skip Caron

D-U-N-S 00-697-6500
JOHN W DANFORTH CO (NY)
(*Suby of* JWD GROUP INC) ★
300 Colvin Woods Pkwy, Tonawanda, NY 14150-6976
Tel (716) 832-2386 *Founded/Ownrshp* 1884
Sales 45.0MM^E *EMP* 300
Accts Gaines Kriner Elliott Llp Amh
SIC 1629 1711 1623 Waste water & sewage treatment plant construction; Mechanical contractor; Warm air heating & air conditioning contractor; Fire sprinkler system installation; Pipeline construction; Waste water & sewage treatment plant construction; Mechanical contractor; Warm air heating & air conditioning contractor; Fire sprinkler system installation; Pipeline construction
Treas: Kevin G Reilly
**Pr:* Patrick J Reilly

D-U-N-S 80-838-6239
JOHN W DANFORTH CO
(*Suby of* JWD GROUP INC) ★
4770 Bickert Dr, Clarence, NY 14031-2206
Tel (716) 832-1940 *Founded/Ownrshp* 1992
Sales 105.0MM *EMP* 9
SIC 1711 Plumbing, heating, air-conditioning contractors; Plumbing, heating, air-conditioning contractors
Ch Bd: Kevin G Reilly
**Pr:* Emmett L Reilly
**Sr VP:* Patrick J Reilly
**VP:* Nickolas Optis

D-U-N-S 02-768-4042 IMP
JOHN W GASPARINI INC
MARK'S PLUMBING PARTS
3312 Ramona Dr, Fort Worth, TX 76116-6428
Tel (817) 731-6211 *Founded/Ownrshp* 1980
Sales 41.5MM^E *EMP* 135
SIC 5074

D-U-N-S 06-978-3561
JOHN W GLEIM JR INC
GLEIM ENVIRONMENTAL GROUP DIV
625 Hamilton St, Carlisle, PA 17013-1925
Tel (717) 243-7160 *Founded/Ownrshp* 1969
Sales 32.6MM^E *EMP* 103
SIC 1794 Excavation & grading, building construction
Pr: Roger Blain
**CEO:* Jim Gleim
**Treas:* John T Gleim
**VP:* James Gleim
**VP:* Cindy Gleim-Pool

D-U-N-S 00-405-0704
JOHN W MCDOUGALL CO INC
3731 Amy Lynn Dr, Nashville, TN 37218-3813
Tel (615) 321-3900 *Founded/Ownrshp* 1937
Sales 42.7MM^E *EMP* 150
SIC 3444 5039 5031 Sheet metalwork; Architectural metalwork; Windows; Skylights, all materials; Sheet metalwork; Architectural metalwork; Windows; Skylights, all materials
Pr: Alec W McDougall
**CFO:* Tom Newhouse
VP: Mike Beacon
**VP:* Tim Howell
Exec: Joe Green
MIS Dir: Rob Smith
Sfty Dirs: Jorge Bravo
Sales Exec: Larry Farris

D-U-N-S 00-342-7010
JOHN W RITTER TRUCKING INC (MD)
SEMI-EXPRESS
8271 Brock Bridge Rd, Laurel, MD 20724-1412
Tel (410) 880-4333 *Founded/Ownrshp* 1971
Sales 21.7MM^E *EMP* 110^E
SIC 4213 4212 Contract haulers; Local trucking, without storage
Pr: Edmond Ritter
Trfc Dir: Paul Blair
Sfty Mgr: Lorin Turnblacer
Opers Mgr: Mark Oswiecimka

D-U-N-S 05-421-9498
JOHN W ROOKER AND ASSOCIATES INC
445 Bishop St Nw 200, Atlanta, GA 30318-4303
Tel (770) 491-7711 *Founded/Ownrshp* 1955
Sales 25.2MM^E *EMP* 80
SIC 1541 Warehouse construction
CEO: John W Rooker
**Pr:* Jerry Cole
**CFO:* Frank Johnston
VP: Knox Culpepper
VP: Alan N Gray
VP: Alan Gray

D-U-N-S 03-420-0147
JOHN W STONE OIL DISTRIBUTOR LLC
87 1st St, Gretna, LA 70053-4746
Tel (504) 366-3401 *Founded/Ownrshp* 1946
Sales 507.0MM^E *EMP* 300
SIC 5172 Diesel fuel; Fuel oil; Gasoline; Lubricating oils & greases; Diesel fuel; Fuel oil; Gasoline; Lubricating oils & greases
VP Admn: Thoomas Willis
Opers Mgr: John Ledet

D-U-N-S 00-282-3201
JOHN W TIEDER INC
736 Woods Rd, Cambridge, MD 21613-9400
Tel (410) 228-5262 *Founded/Ownrshp* 1978
Sales 32.8MM^E *EMP* 123
SIC 1731 3679 General electrical contractor; Electronic controls installation; Computerized controls installation; Electronic circuits; General electrical contractor; Electronic controls installation; Computerized controls installation; Electronic circuits
CEO: John W Tieder Jr
**VP:* John W Tieder III

D-U-N-S 04-233-5224
JOHN WALTERS CHEVROLET INC
JOHN WALTERS CHEVROLET-GEO
915 E Oak St, Conway, AR 72032-4715
Tel (501) 327-7785 *Founded/Ownrshp* 1977
Sales 24.0MM *EMP* 53
SIC 5511 5521 Automobiles, new & used; Used car dealers; Automobiles, new & used; Used car dealers
Pr: John Walters

JOHN WALTERS CHEVROLET-GEO
See JOHN WALTERS CHEVROLET INC

D-U-N-S 03-532-5232
JOHN WATSON CHEVROLET INC
3535 Wall Ave, Ogden, UT 84401-4012
Tel (801) 394-2611 *Founded/Ownrshp* 1965
Sales 26.3MM^E *EMP* 63
SIC 5511 7538 Automobiles, new & used; General automotive repair shops; Automobiles, new & used; General automotive repair shops
Pr: John L Watson
**Sec:* Jeff Morgan
Exec: Chris Southwick
Sales Exec: Cory Watson

D-U-N-S 05-826-4029
JOHN WIESNER INC
JOHN WSNER BCK-PNTAC-GMC-ISUZU
1645 Interstate 45 N, Conroe, TX 77304-2143
Tel (936) 756-8161 *Founded/Ownrshp* 1972
Sales 63.5MM^E *EMP* 125
SIC 5511 Automobiles, new & used
Pr: John W Wiesner Jr
CFO: Gary Bridge
**Sec:* Cecile Hanus
**VP:* Don Ed Wiesner
**VP:* Ray Howell Wiesner
MIS Dir: Ray Vanryswik
Sales Exec: Terry Hatfield
Sls Mgr: Mark AK
Sls Mgr: Mark Novak
Sls Mgr: Vince Taylor
Sales Asso: Tim Bonvillion

D-U-N-S 00-151-9248 IMP/EXP
▲ **JOHN WILEY & SONS INC** (NY)
111 River St Ste 2000, Hoboken, NJ 07030-5790
Tel (201) 748-6000 *Founded/Ownrshp* 1807
Sales 1.8MMM *EMP* 4,900
Accts Kpmg Llp Short Hills New Jer
Tkr Sym JWA *Exch* NYS
SIC 2731 2721 Textbooks: publishing only, not printed on site; Books: publishing only; Statistical reports (periodicals): publishing only; Trade journals: publishing only, not printed on site; Textbooks: publishing only, not printed on site; Books: publishing only; Statistical reports (periodicals): publishing only; Trade journals: publishing only, not printed on site
Pr: Stephen M Smith
**Ch Bd:* Peter Booth Wiley
**Pr:* Mark Allin
CFO: John A Kritzmacher
Treas: Vincent Marzano
Ex VP: Patrik Dyberg
Ex VP: Gary M Rinck
Sr VP: Edward J Melando
Sr VP: Steven J Miron
VP: Jan Narkiewicz
VP: Clay Stobaugh
Creative D: Jean Morley
Dir Bus: Tom G Blyth
Board of Directors: Jesse C Wiley, Mari J Baker, George Bell, Linda Katehi, Matthew S Kissner, Laurie A Lenshin, Raymond W McDaniel, Eduardo Menasce, William J Pesce, William B Plummer

JOHN WILEY AND SONS
See WILEY PUBLISHING INC

D-U-N-S 07-696-9161
JOHN WOOD COMMUNITY COLLEGE
1301 S 48th St, Quincy, IL 62305-8736
Tel (217) 224-6500 *Founded/Ownrshp* 1974
Sales 5.2MM *EMP* 390
Accts Wipfli Llp Freeport Illinois
SIC 8222 Junior college; Junior college
Pr: Thomas Klincar
**Pr:* Thomas Klincarr
**Pr:* John Letts
**CFO:* Alan Steigelman
Info Man: Josh Brueck
VP Mktg: Dallas Johnson

D-U-N-S 78-501-6481
JOHN WOOD GROUP US HOLDINGS INC
WG
(*Suby of* JOHN WOOD GROUP P.L.C.)
17325 Park Row Ste 500, Houston, TX 77084-4932
Tel (281) 828-3500 *Founded/Ownrshp* 2006
Sales 306.8MM^E *EMP* 420
SIC 4581 Aircraft servicing & repairing; Aircraft servicing & repairing
Ofcr: Rajumon Joseph
VP: Michael Leonard
Dir Bus: Vikas Moharir
Mng Dir: Mark Docherty

JOHN WSNER BCK-PNTAC-GMC-ISUZU
See JOHN WIESNER INC

D-U-N-S 10-152-0716 IMP
JOHN ZIDIAN CO INC
574 Mcclurg Rd, Youngstown, OH 44512-6405
Tel (330) 743-6050 *Founded/Ownrshp* 1983
Sales 37.5MM^E *EMP* 71
SIC 5141 Groceries, general line; Groceries, general line
Pr: Tom Zidian
**CFO:* John Angelilli
**Treas:* Jim Zidian
VP Sls: John Bradley
Sls Mgr: Tiffany Turjonis

D-U-N-S 06-203-6483 IMP/EXP
JOHN ZINK CO LLC
JOHN ZINK HAMWORTHY COMBUSTION
(*Suby of* KOCH CHEMICAL TECHNOLOGY GROUP LLC) ★
11920 E Apache St, Tulsa, OK 74116-1300
Tel (918) 234-1800 *Founded/Ownrshp* 1999
Sales 264.5MM^E *EMP* 1,070
SIC 3823 Combustion control instruments; Combustion control instruments
Pr: Jim Goodman
**CFO:* Casey Chambers
VP: Earl Schnell
Dir Rx: Rick Iwamoto
Dir Rx: Jay Karan
Off Mgr: Fred Moore
Sfty Dirs: Paula Huddleston
QC Dir: Bryan Bohbrink
Plnt Mgr: Brian Edmondson
Plnt Mgr: Gary Goodnight
Ql Cn Mgr: Garry Mayfield

JOHN ZINK HAMWORTHY COMBUSTION
See JOHN ZINK CO LLC

D-U-N-S 12-416-8209 IMP/EXP
JOHNAN AMERICA INC
(*Suby of* JOHNAN MANUFACTURING INC.)
600 Wilson Pkwy, Bardstown, KY 40004-2073
Tel (502) 350-0977 *Founded/Ownrshp* 1998
Sales 32.1MM^E *EMP* 170
SIC 5013

D-U-N-S 00-685-6041 IMP
JOHNNY AND LORENE INC
M3 GLASS TECHNOLOGIES
2924 Rock Island Rd, Irving, TX 75060-2207
Tel (214) 614-9650 *Founded/Ownrshp* 2015
Sales 37.9MM^E *EMP* 80
SIC 5039 1793 5231 Glass construction materials; Glass & glazing work; Glass; Glass construction materials; Glass & glazing work; Glass
Pr: Chris Mammen
Sec: James R Mammen
VP: Jeff Schramm
Exec: Valerie Tribon
Plnt Mgr: Larry Byrd

D-U-N-S 00-102-3639 IMP
■ **JOHNNY APPLESEEDS INC**
(*Suby of* APPLESEEDS BRANDS) ★
30 Tozer Rd, Beverly, MA 01915-5510
Tel (978) 922-2040 *Founded/Ownrshp* 1912
Sales 36.3MM^E *EMP* 400
SIC 2335

JOHNNY CARINOS ITALIAN KITCHEN
See KONA RESTAURANT GROUP INC

D-U-N-S 02-387-4303
JOHNNY CAT INC
670 Powderhorn Dr, Jacksonville, OR 97530-9420
Tel (541) 899-4494 Founded/Ownrshp 1995
Sales 32.7MM^E EMP 140^E
SIC 1623 Water, sewer & utility lines; Water, sewer & utility lines
Pr: John Holmes

D-U-N-S 01-101-1277 IMP
JOHNNY JANOSIK INC
11151 Trussum Pond Rd, Laurel, DE 19956-4522
Tel (302) 875-5955 Founded/Ownrshp 1953
Sales 56.3MM^E EMP 225
Accts Tgm Group Llc Salisbury Mary
SIC 5712 Furniture stores; Furniture stores
CEO: David Koehler
*Pr: Lori J Morrison
COO: Dan Welch
*CFO: Dan Ringer
Brnch Mgr: Adam Stone
Sls Dir: Debi Quillen

D-U-N-S 02-976-4628
JOHNNY LONDOFF CHEVROLET INC
1375 Dunn Rd, Florissant, MO 63031-8199
Tel (314) 837-1800 Founded/Ownrshp 1958
Sales 43.8MM^E EMP 95
SIC 5511 Automobiles, new & used
Ch Bd: John H Londoff Jr
*CFO: Sean Stayton
Exec: Debbie Johns
IT Man: Bill Dalton
Mktg Mgr: Kitty Harrison
Sales Asso: Jeff Bates
Sales Asso: Dave Bell

D-U-N-S 03-105-2467
JOHNNY MACS SPORTING GOODS STORES INC
10100 Watson Rd, Saint Louis, MO 63127-1100
Tel (314) 966-5444 Founded/Ownrshp 1984
Sales 33.0MM^E EMP 250
SIC 5941 Sporting goods & bicycle shops; Sporting goods & bicycle shops
Pr: Robert McArthur
*CFO: Richard D McArthur
CFO: Tammy Robertson
Exec: Chris Blankley
Exec: Rick McArthur
Div Mgr: Brad Jundt
Genl Mgr: Adam Burns
Store Mgr: Jon Kars

D-U-N-S 96-578-8292
JOHNNY ROCKETS GROUP INC
(Suby of FRIENDLYS ICE CREAM LLC) ★
20 Enterprise Ste 300, Aliso Viejo, CA 92656-7107
Tel (949) 643-6100 Founded/Ownrshp 1995
Sales 50.0MM EMP 450
SIC 5812 6794 Eating places; Franchises, selling or licensing
Pr: Charles Bruce
Pr: James Walker
CFO: Chad Hope
CFO: David Kreizinger
Chf Mktg O: Joel Bulger
Sr VP: Jim Hicks
Sr VP: Virgie Pandes
VP: Jim Kensinger
VP: Naresh Vinod Worlikar
Genl Mgr: Lindsay Martin
Mktg Mgr: Janet Gillmore

D-U-N-S 93-830-4680
JOHNNY WALKER HOSPITALITY GROUP
107 Music Cy Cir Ste 100, Nashville, TN 37214
Tel (615) 331-3565 Founded/Ownrshp 1980
Sales 5.8MM^E EMP 450
SIC 7011 Hotels & motels; Hotels & motels
Owner: John D Walker

JOHNNY WALKER RECRTL VEHICLES
See JOHNNY WALKER TRAILERS

D-U-N-S 03-493-8019
JOHNNY WALKER TRAILERS
JOHNNY WALKER RECRTL VEHICLES
3700 Boulder Hwy, Las Vegas, NV 89121-1615
Tel (702) 458-2092 Founded/Ownrshp 1963
Sales 26.6MM^E EMP 75
SIC 5561

D-U-N-S 10-108-8466
JOHNNYS INC
SUNDOWNER MANAGEMENT GROUP
2220 Wo Smith Dr, Lawrenceburg, TN 38464-7373
Tel (931) 762-8134 Founded/Ownrshp 1988
Sales 6.1MM^E EMP 300
SIC 5812 Eating places; Eating places
Pr: Johnny Fleeman
*VP: Bill Osborne

D-U-N-S 03-434-3780
JOHNNYS PIZZA HOUSE INC
100 Arkansas Rd, West Monroe, LA 71291-2302
Tel (318) 323-0518 Founded/Ownrshp 1967
Sales 16.5MM^E EMP 372
SIC 5812 Pizzeria, chain; Pizzeria, chain
Pr: Melvin Delcerda
*Prin: Mely T Fuglaar
IT Man: Bernie Lear
VP Opers: Scott Allen

D-U-N-S 07-747-3080 IMP/EXP
JOHNNYS SELECTED SEEDS
955 Benton Ave, Winslow, ME 04901-2601
Tel (207) 861-3900 Founded/Ownrshp 1973
Sales 49.1MM^E EMP 150
SIC 0181 5191 Mail order house; Garden supplies & tools; Seeds, vegetable: growing of; Seeds: field, garden & flower
Pr: Robert L Johnston Jr
VP: Jeffrey McElroy
CIO: Douglas Grosso
IT Man: Tim Crawford

Sfty Mgr: Joe Nixon
Prd Mgr: Michael Brown
S&M/VP: David Mehlhorn
Mktg Dir: Gretchen Kruysman
Sls Mgr: Nathan Marquis

D-U-N-S 11-823-9458 IMP
JOHNS HOPKINS BAYVIEW MEDICAL CENTER INC
BMC (BAYVIEW MEDICAL CENTER)
(Suby of JOHNS HOPKINS HEALTH SYS CORP) ★
4940 Eastern Ave, Baltimore, MD 21224-2735
Tel (410) 550-0100 Founded/Ownrshp 1986
Sales 541.9MM EMP 3,300
Accts Pricewaterhousecoopers Llp B
SIC 8062 8051 General medical & surgical hospitals; Hospital, medical school affiliated with residency; Hospital, medical school affiliation; Skilled nursing care facilities; Extended care facility; General medical & surgical hospitals; Hospital, medical school affiliated with residency; Hospital, medical school affiliation; Skilled nursing care facilities; Extended care facility
Pr: Steven J Kravet
V Ch: James T Dresher
*Treas: L Kenneth Grabill II
Trst: Robert Harvey
*Ofcr: David Strapelli
*VP: Craig Brodian
VP: Kenneth L Grabill
*VP: Cheryl Koch
VP: Charles Reuland
*VP: Joan H Williams
Dir Risk M: Maggie Miller

JOHNS HOPKINS ENTERPRISE
See JOHNS HOPKINS UNIVERSITY

D-U-N-S 15-534-8113 EXP
JOHNS HOPKINS HEALTH SYS CORP
600 N Wolfe St, Baltimore, MD 21287-0005
Tel (410) 955-5000 Founded/Ownrshp 1986
Sales 3.5MMM^E EMP 13,000
SIC 8062 General medical & surgical hospitals; General medical & surgical hospitals
Pr: Ronald R Peterson
*Ch Bd: C Micheal Armstrong
*CFO: Ronald J Werthman
Sr VP: Bertrand M Emerson II
Sr VP: Steven J Thompson
VP: Kenneth Grant
VP: Dalal J Haldeman
VP: Harry Koffenberger
VP: Joanne E Pollak
VP: Stephanie L Reel
*VP: Beryl Rosenstein

D-U-N-S 78-581-0792
JOHNS HOPKINS HEALTHCARE LLC
JHHC
6704 Curtis Ct, Glen Burnie, MD 21060-6406
Tel (410) 424-4400 Founded/Ownrshp 1994
Sales 35.2MM^E EMP 520
SIC 8082 Home health care services; Home health care services
Prin: Robert Neall
COO: Karen Eskridge
COO: Jeff Joy
CFO: Edward Kumian
Comm Man: Donna Chase
Prgrm Mgr: Regina Richardson
CIO: Charles Andrews
QA Dir: Stephanie McNeil
Secur Mgr: Michael Yirka
Mktg Mgr: Alli Parsons
Snr Mgr: Robert Kritzler

D-U-N-S 80-000-0432 IMP
JOHNS HOPKINS HOME CARE GROUP INC
JOHNS HOPKINS HOME HOSPICE
5901 Holabird Ave Ste A, Baltimore, MD 21224-6015
Tel (410) 288-8000 Founded/Ownrshp 1992
Sales 13.1MM EMP 350
SIC 8082 Home health care services; Home health care services
Pr: Steven A Johnson
MIS Dir: Julio Chavarria
Pharmcst: Nagwa Farrag
Pharmcst: Mark Sugarman

JOHNS HOPKINS HOME HOSPICE
See JOHNS HOPKINS HOME CARE GROUP INC

JOHNS HOPKINS HOSPITAL, THE
See JOHNS HOPKINS MEDICINE INTERNATIONAL LLC

D-U-N-S 02-541-2417 IMP
JOHNS HOPKINS HOSPITAL
(Suby of JOHNS HOPKINS HEALTH SYS CORP) ★
1800 Orleans St, Baltimore, MD 21287-0010
Tel (410) 550-0730 Founded/Ownrshp 1867
Sales 1.9MMM EMP 12,000^E
Accts Pricewaterhousecoopers Llp Ba
SIC 8062 General medical & surgical hospitals; General medical & surgical hospitals
Pr: Ronald Peterson
*CFO: Ronald Werthman
Dir Rx: Rhiannon Fitzsimmons
Adm Dir: Mary Beaudry
Off Mgr: Gail Jackson
Nurse Mgr: Margie Burnett
IT Man: Marc Graff
Mtls Mgr: James Reiter
Mktg Dir: Jenny Lee
Pathlgst: Hua Shan
Pathlgst: Tzyy-Choou Wu

D-U-N-S 00-310-4478 EXP
JOHNS HOPKINS MEDICINE INTERNATIONAL LLC (MD)
JOHNS HOPKINS HOSPITAL, THE
600 N Wolfe St, Baltimore, MD 21287-0005
Tel (410) 955-1725 Founded/Ownrshp 1890
Sales 743.9MM^E EMP 7,000

SIC 8062 8221 Hospital, medical school affiliated with nursing & residency; Colleges universities & professional schools; Hospital, medical school affiliated with nursing & residency; Colleges universities & professional schools
CEO: Harris Benny
*COO: Judy Reitz
CFO: Vinhloc Nguyen
CFO: Ron Werthman
Ofcr: Laura C Mezan
Ofcr: Patricia Toliver
VP: Joanne Pollak
Exec: Charles Rydzy
Dir Lab: Gerard Lutty
Assoc Dir: Barry Zirkin
Adm Dir: Al Valentine

JOHNS HOPKINS REAL ESTATE
See DOME CORP

D-U-N-S 00-191-0777
JOHNS HOPKINS UNIVERSITY (MD)
JOHNS HOPKINS ENTERPRISE
3400 N Charles St, Baltimore, MD 21218-2680
Tel (410) 516-8000 Founded/Ownrshp 1867
Sales 4.3MMM^E EMP 32,000
SIC 8221 University; University
Pr: Ronald J Daniels
Top Exec: Ronald Luman
Sr VP: Daniel G Ennis
Sr VP: Robert Lieberman
VP: Stephen S Dunham
VP: Alan Fish
VP: Fritz Schroeder
Assoc Dir: Holly Benze
Assoc Dir: Barry Meyer
Comm Dir: Mary Maushard
Prgrm Mgr: Sook Chang

D-U-N-S 04-054-9461
JOHNS HOPKINS UNIVERSITY APPLIED PHYSICS LABORATORY LLC
APL
(Suby of JOHNS HOPKINS ENTERPRISE) ★
11100 Johns Hopkins Rd, Laurel, MD 20723-6005
Tel (240) 228-5000 Founded/Ownrshp 2009
Sales 38.3MM^E EMP 99
SIC 8731 Commercial research laboratory
Ofcr: Adam Vanderhook
Div/Sub He: Jon Berry
Comm Man: Margaret Simon
Prgrm Mgr: Catherine Capriolo
Prgrm Mgr: Brian Geesaman
Prgrm Mgr: Mark Lopresto
Prgrm Mgr: John Noble
Prgrm Mgr: Stephen Phillips
Prgrm Mgr: Jeff Thomas
Snr Sftwr: Jeffrey Brush
Snr Sftwr: Constantine Frangos

JOHN'S INCREDIBLE PIZZA CO
See JIPC MANAGEMENT INC

D-U-N-S 13-161-1472
JOHNS INCREDIBLE PIZZA LLC
22342 Avnda Emsa Se 220, Rancho Santa Margari, CA 92688
Tel (949) 916-2000 Founded/Ownrshp 2001
Sales 17.6MM^E EMP 600
SIC 5812 7993 Pizza restaurants; Arcades; Amusement arcade; Video game arcade; Pizza restaurants; Arcades; Amusement arcade; Video game arcade
Store Dir: Alex Rodriguez
Store Dir: Brigena Williams
Dept Mgr: Jeffrey Beckers
Dept Mgr: Arnulfo Reyes
Sftwr Eng: Renato Ciuffo
Sftwr Eng: Chris Oshima
Sftwr Eng: James Vuong
Mktg Mgr: Tara Chapman
Snr Mgr: Chuck Johnson

D-U-N-S 18-114-7463 IMP
JOHNS ISLAND CLUB INC
3 Johns Island Dr, Vero Beach, FL 32963-3234
Tel (772) 231-1700 Founded/Ownrshp 1989
Sales 32.2MM^E EMP 230
Accts Mcgladrey Llp West Palm Beach
SIC 7992 5812 7991 7997 Public golf courses; Eating places; Physical fitness facilities; Country club, membership; Tennis club, membership; Squash club, membership; Public golf courses; Eating places; Physical fitness facilities; Country club, membership; Tennis club, membership; Squash club, membership
Pr: Theodore D Berghorst
*CFO: Cathy Nerfon
*Treas: Fredrick G Taylor
*VP: Dennis C Longwell
*VP: Richard D McDermott
Exec: John Farnsworth
Exec: Kathleen Murgg
Genl Mgr: Brian Kroh
IT Man: Susan Hoover
IT Man: Sean Landon
IT Man: Jim Tall

D-U-N-S 96-797-8594 IMP/EXP
JOHNS LONE STAR DISTRIBUTION GP LLC
11370 Pagemill Rd, Dallas, TX 75243-8306
Tel (214) 340-0718 Founded/Ownrshp 1997
Sales 87.0MM^E EMP 100^E
SIC 5122 5149 Vitamins & minerals; Health foods; Vitamins & minerals; Health foods
Mng Pt: John Hoffmann
*CFO: Chuck Letchman
Ofcr: Lynette Diaz
Sr VP: Angie Glover
*VP: Frank Fenimore
*Genl Mgr: Kelly Crawford
Genl Mgr: Roman Kisz
Natl Sales: Tara Gouleos
Sls Mgr: Mason Stillwell

D-U-N-S 04-542-6558 IMP/EXP
■ **JOHNS MANVILLE CORP**
JOHNS MANVILLE INTERNATIONAL
(Suby of BERKSHIRE HATHAWAY INC) ★
717 17th St Ste 800, Denver, CO 80202-3332
Tel (303) 978-2000 Founded/Ownrshp 1981
Sales 1.6MMM^E EMP 8,000

SIC 2952 1761 1742 Roofing materials; Roofing contractor; Insulation, buildings; Roofing materials; Roofing contractor; Insulation, buildings
Ch Bd: Mary Rhinehart
COO: Thomas E Cook
Treas: W S Bullock
Ofcr: Timothy Swales
Sr VP: William J Ehner
Sr VP: Kenneth L Jensen
Sr VP: Michael P Kane
Sr VP: Michael Lawrence
Sr VP: Cynthia Meyer
Sr VP: Fred Stefan
Sr VP: Robert Wambolt
VP: Lawrence J Blanford
VP: Brien D Hodge
VP: Fred Stephan

JOHNS MANVILLE INTERNATIONAL
See JOHNS MANVILLE CORP

D-U-N-S 00-525-6672
JOHNS-BYRNE CO
6701 W Oakton St, Niles, IL 60714-3917
Tel (847) 583-3100 Founded/Ownrshp 1959
Sales 27.2MM^E EMP 100^E
SIC 2752 2791 2789 Commercial printing, lithographic; Typesetting; Bookbinding & related work; Commercial printing, lithographic; Typesetting; Bookbinding & related work
Pr: Corey Gustafson
*COO: John Gustafson Jr
CFO: Tim Uchwat
*Ex VP: James Pate Gustafson
*Ex VP: Michael J Gustafson
Dir Bus: Harriet Kessler
Prd Mgr: Paul Fabis
VP Mktg: Michael Difranco

D-U-N-S 09-728-3394
JOHNSBURG COMMUNITY UNIT SCHOOL DISTRICT 12
2222 Church St, Johnsburg, IL 60051-5910
Tel (815) 385-6916 Founded/Ownrshp 1950
Sales 17.7MM^E EMP 375
SIC 8211 Public combined elementary & secondary school; Public junior high school; Public senior high school; Public combined elementary & secondary school; Public junior high school; Public senior high school
Bd of Dir: Karen Baird
Bd of Dir: Michelle Martin
Bd of Dir: Steve Rooney
VP: Thomas Low

D-U-N-S 01-030-1455
JOHNSON & BELL LTD (IL)
33 W Monroe St Ste 2700, Chicago, IL 60603-5404
Tel (312) 372-0770 Founded/Ownrshp 1997
Sales 39.2MM^E EMP 250
SIC 8111 General practice law office; General practice law office
Pr: William V Johnson
Pr: Deborah Burger
*CFO: Laura Johnson
CFO: John Vandenburgh
*Treas: Brian C Fetzer
*VP: John W Bell
*VP: John A Childers
Opers Mgr: Marsha Lade

JOHNSON & GALYON CONTRACTORS
See JOHNSON & GALYON INC

D-U-N-S 00-982-3808
JOHNSON & GALYON INC (TN)
JOHNSON & GALYON CONTRACTORS
1130 Atlantic Ave, Knoxville, TN 37917-3798
Tel (865) 688-1111 Founded/Ownrshp 1955, 1984
Sales 64.0MM EMP 100
SIC 1542 1541

D-U-N-S 00-130-7081 IMP/EXP
▲ **JOHNSON & JOHNSON** (NJ)
1 Johnson And Johnson Plz, New Brunswick, NJ 08933-0002
Tel (732) 524-0400 Founded/Ownrshp 1886
Sales 74.3MMM EMP 126,500
Accts Pricewaterhousecoopers Llp Fl
Tkr Sym JNJ Exch NYS
SIC 2676 2844 3841 3842 2834 Feminine hygiene paper products; Napkins, sanitary: made from purchased paper; Panty liners: made from purchased paper; Infant & baby paper products; Toilet preparations; Oral preparations; Toilet preparations; Powder: baby, face, talcum or toilet; Surgical & medical instruments; Surgical instruments & apparatus; Diagnostic apparatus, medical; Ophthalmic instruments & apparatus; Surgical appliances & supplies; Ligatures, medical; Sutures, absorbable & non-absorbable; Dressings, surgical; Pharmaceutical preparations; Drugs acting on the central nervous system & sense organs; Dermatologicals; Drugs affecting parasitic & infective diseases; Feminine hygiene paper products; Napkins, sanitary: made from purchased paper; Panty liners: made from purchased paper; Infant & baby paper products; Toilet preparations; Oral preparations; Toilet preparations; Powder: baby, face, talcum or toilet; Surgical & medical instruments; Surgical instruments & apparatus; Diagnostic apparatus, medical; Ophthalmic instruments & apparatus; Surgical appliances & supplies; Ligatures, medical; Sutures, absorbable & non-absorbable; Dressings, surgical; Pharmaceutical preparations; Drugs acting on the central nervous system & sense organs; Dermatologicals; Drugs affecting parasitic & infective diseases
Ch Bd: Alex Gorsky
CFO: Dominic J Caruso
VP: Peter M Fasolo
VP: Michael H Ullmann
Assoc Dir: Greet Beets
Assoc Dir: Kevin Bradley
Assoc Dir: Carlo Crisostomo
Assoc Dir: Betty Delise
Assoc Dir: Dominique Devogel
Assoc Dir: Ping Hu
Assoc Dir: Debbie Lettani

Assoc Dir: Benjamin Lundgren
Assoc Dir: Michele Neeter
Assoc Dir: Nicholas Pemble
Assoc Dir: Genevieve Pissart
Assoc Dir: Ilham Smyej
Assoc Dir: Kristien Van Nimmen
Assoc Dir: Hilde Vanaken
Assoc Dir: Peter Willems
Board of Directors: Charles Prince, Mary Beckerle, A Eugene Washingtonm, Mary Sue Coleman, Ronald A Williams, James G Cullen, D Scott Davis, Ian E L Davis, Susan L Lindquist, Mark B McClellan, Anne M Mulcahy, William D Perez

D-U-N-S 00-234-7102 EXP
■ JOHNSON & JOHNSON CONSUMER INC
MCNEIL-PPC, INC.
(*Suby of* JOHNSON & JOHNSON) ★
199 Grandview Rd, Skillman, NJ 08558-1303
Tel (908) 874-1000 *Founded/Ownrshp* 1879, 1959
Sales 266.7MM^E *EMP* 977
SIC 2834 Pharmaceutical preparations; Pharmaceutical preparations
Pr: William McComb
Pr: Rebecca Tillet
VP: Mike Gowen
VP: Jerry B Hansen
VP: Ed Hemwall
VP: Vicki Walker
Exec: Maria Schinella
Div/Sub He: Colin Watts
Assoc Dir: Euen Gunn
Assoc Dir: Stephen Pitt
Assoc Dir: John Rytel
Assoc Dir: Nancy Sommer
Assoc Dir: Ying Wan
Board of Directors: Gerald Ostrov

D-U-N-S 78-205-3516 EXP
■ JOHNSON & JOHNSON HEALTH CARE SYSTEMS INC
(*Suby of* JOHNSON & JOHNSON) ★
425 Hoes Ln, Piscataway, NJ 08854-4103
Tel (732) 562-0177 *Founded/Ownrshp* 1976
Sales 62.2MM^E *EMP* 100
SIC 5047 Hospital equipment & supplies; Hospital equipment & supplies
Pr: Doug Michels
Ex VP: Mel Campbell
Prgrm Mgr: William Stevens
IT Man: Scotty Ayers
IT Man: Chris Brehm
IT Man: Douglas Cole
IT Man: Joanne Coles
IT Man: Domenick Colotti
IT Man: George Gee
IT Man: Bill Hoernlein
IT Man: Songling Huang

D-U-N-S 03-244-7047
JOHNSON & JOHNSON INC
FUEL DELIVERY
1607 E Us Highway 90, Madison, FL 32340-4280
Tel (850) 973-2277 *Founded/Ownrshp* 1976
Sales 47.4MM^E *EMP* 250
SIC 5411 5171 5541 5531 5812 Convenience stores, chain; Petroleum bulk stations & terminals; Truck stops; Automotive tires; Fast-food restaurant, chain; Convenience stores, chain; Petroleum bulk stations & terminals; Truck stops; Automotive tires; Fast-food restaurant, chain
Pr: Jacob K Johnson Jr
**Treas:* Elizabeth Waring

D-U-N-S 04-837-2544
JOHNSON & JOHNSON INC
200 Wingo Way Ste 200, Mount Pleasant, SC 29464-1816
Tel (843) 577-0800 *Founded/Ownrshp* 1934
Sales NA *EMP* 135
SIC 6411 Insurance agents
CEO: Robert C Johnson Jr
**Pr:* Francis G Johnson

D-U-N-S 04-750-8247
■ JOHNSON & JOHNSON INTERNATIONAL
(*Suby of* JOHNSON & JOHNSON) ★
1 Johnson And Johnson Plz, New Brunswick, NJ 08901-1241
Tel (732) 524-0400 *Founded/Ownrshp* 1956
Sales 48.6MM^E *EMP* 40^E
SIC 5047 5122 Medical equipment & supplies; Drugs, proprietaries & sundries
Pr: Michelle R Ryan
**V Ch:* Stephen J Cosgrove
VP: Francisco J Aponte-Santa
VP: Antonio J Ferreira
VP: Randy E Godard

D-U-N-S 12-215-2379 EXP
■ JOHNSON & JOHNSON INTERNATIONAL
(*Suby of* JOHNSON & JOHNSON) ★
475 Calle C Ste 200, Guaynabo, PR 00969-4293
Tel (787) 272-1905 *Founded/Ownrshp* 2004
Sales 146.0MM^E *EMP* 300
SIC 5122 Drugs, proprietaries & sundries; Drugs, proprietaries & sundries
VP: Francis Boero

D-U-N-S 00-801-3583
■ JOHNSON & JOHNSON MEDICAL INC
(*Suby of* ETHICON INC) ★
Us Rt 22, Somerville, NJ 08876
Tel (908) 218-0707 *Founded/Ownrshp* 1949
Sales 127.7MM^E *EMP* 3,128
SIC 3842 Surgical appliances & supplies; Drapes, surgical (cotton); Surgical appliances & supplies; Drapes, surgical (cotton)
Pr: William Clarke

D-U-N-S 96-563-0150
JOHNSON & JOHNSON PATIENT ASSISTANCE FOUNDATION INC
1 Johnson And Johnson Plz, New Brunswick, NJ 08933-0001
Tel (732) 524-1394 *Founded/Ownrshp* 2010
Sales 741.6MM *EMP* 16^E
SIC 8699 Charitable organization; Charitable organization
Prin: Nancy Moyer

D-U-N-S 96-982-9147
■ JOHNSON & JOHNSON PHARMACEUTICAL RESEARCH & DEVELOPMET LLC
(*Suby of* JOHNSON & JOHNSON) ★
1125 Trnton Harbourton Rd, Titusville, NJ 08560-1504
Tel (732) 524-0400 *Founded/Ownrshp* 2011
Sales 70.5MM^E *EMP* 443^E
SIC 8731 Medical research, commercial
Ofcr: Gina Giordano
Ofcr: Sue Seferian
VP: Catherine Piech
Assoc Dir: David Aizenman
Assoc Dir: Ying Li
Assoc Dir: Jane Nowicki
Assoc Dir: Deborah Santicerma
Assoc Dir: Hong Zhou
IT Man: Tracey Colonna
Snr Mgr: Sherry Meeh

D-U-N-S 09-045-1824 IMP
■ JOHNSON & JOHNSON PROFESSIONAL CO (PR) INC
(*Suby of* JOHNSON & JOHNSON) ★
Carr 183 Km 8 3 St Ca, San Lorenzo, PR 00754
Tel (787) 736-7070 *Founded/Ownrshp* 1974
Sales 58.0MM^E *EMP* 600
SIC 3842 2844 Surgical appliances & supplies; Sutures, absorbable & non-absorbable; Bandages: plastic, muslin, plaster of paris, etc.; Gauze, surgical; Denture cleaners; Surgical appliances & supplies; Sutures, absorbable & non-absorbable; Bandages: plastic, muslin, plaster of paris, etc.; Gauze, surgical; Denture cleaners
Pr: John Nugents

D-U-N-S 00-406-0273 EXP
■ JOHNSON & JOHNSON VISION CARE INC (FL)
VISTAKON
(*Suby of* JOHNSON & JOHNSON) ★
7500 Centurion Pkwy, Jacksonville, FL 32256-0517
Tel (904) 443-1000 *Founded/Ownrshp* 1962
Sales 753.3MM^E *EMP* 3,500
SIC 3851 Contact lenses; Eyes, glass & plastic; Contact lenses; Eyes, glass & plastic
Pr: Fran Mirmina
**Pr:* J Hogan
**Pr:* P R Keefer
COO: Tim Newton
**CFO:* James Buschmeier
**CFO:* Steve Tremmel
Div/Sub He: D Keefer
Brnch Mgr: Bernard Walsh
Genl Mgr: Tim Ryan
Dir IT: Judy Nathan
Dir IT: Dave Parkinson

D-U-N-S 78-553-7614
JOHNSON & JORDAN INC
18 Mussey Rd, Scarborough, ME 04074-9553
Tel (207) 883-8345 *Founded/Ownrshp* 1991
Sales 33.0MM^E *EMP* 180
SIC 1711 Mechanical contractor; Mechanical contractor
CEO: Christopher Jordan

D-U-N-S 00-508-7366
JOHNSON & QUIN INC (IL)
7460 N Lehigh Ave, Niles, IL 60714-4099
Tel (847) 588-4800 *Founded/Ownrshp* 1953
Sales 29.6MM^E *EMP* 310
SIC 7331 2752 2759 2789

D-U-N-S 00-230-0051 IMP
JOHNSON & TOWERS INC (PA)
2021 Briggs Rd, Mount Laurel, NJ 08054-4618
Tel (856) 234-6990 *Founded/Ownrshp* 1926
Sales 72.7MM^E *EMP* 210
SIC 5084 5013 7699 7538 5085 Engines & parts, diesel; Automotive supplies & parts; Marine engine repair; General automotive repair shops; Diesel engine repair: automotive; Industrial supplies; Engines & parts, diesel; Automotive supplies & parts; Marine engine repair; General automotive repair shops; Diesel engine repair: automotive; Industrial supplies
CEO: Walter F Johnson
**CFO:* Thomas Hogan
**Sec:* Thomas M Dutterer
Sr VP: Robert Shomo
**VP:* David P Johnson
Exec: Walter Johnson
Genl Mgr: Bob Shomo
CIO: Patty Findeisen
Sls Mgr: Vincent Devlin
Sls Mgr: Bob Price

D-U-N-S 05-518-1036
JOHNSON & WALES UNIVERSITY INC
8 Abbott Park Pl, Providence, RI 02903-3775
Tel (401) 598-1000 *Founded/Ownrshp* 1947
Sales 529.2MM *EMP* 1,400
Accts Mcgladrey Llp Boston Massach
SIC 8221 College, except junior; College, except junior
**Pr:* John A Yena
CFO: Joseph J Greene
**Treas:* Christopher Del Sesto
Treas: Christopher D Sesto
Trst: Dana Gaebe
Trst: Edward P Grace
Trst: Robert Taylor
Ofcr: Keri Adams
Ofcr: Eryn Jennings
Ofcr: Sandra Lawrence
Ofcr: Robert Purfurst
Ofcr: Debra Vieira
Top Exec: Paul J Colbert
**Ex VP:* John Bowen
Sr VP: Merlin A Deconti
Sr VP: Manuel Pimentel
**VP:* Thomas Dwyer
**VP:* Arthur J Gallagher
Comm Dir: Lisa Pelosi
Mng Ofcr: Toni Green
Adv Bd Mbr: Kellie Mieremet

D-U-N-S 08-162-9479
JOHNSON - DAVIS INC
604 Hillbrath Dr, Lantana, FL 33462-1694
Tel (561) 588-1170 *Founded/Ownrshp* 1977
Sales 56.5MM^E *EMP* 165
SIC 1623 Underground utilities contractor; Underground utilities contractor
Pr: Scott Johnson
**Sec:* Christopher Johnson
**VP:* Robert Hopler

JOHNSON AIR PRODUCTS
See AIR SUPPLY INC

JOHNSON APARTMENTS
See PATH FINDER SCHOOLS INC

D-U-N-S 05-804-9339 IMP
JOHNSON ARCHITECTURAL METAL CO
JAMCO
2160 Kingston Ct Se Ste I, Marietta, GA 30067-8951
Tel (770) 980-9380 *Founded/Ownrshp* 1981
Sales 26.2MM^E *EMP* 100
SIC 1793 Glass & glazing work
CEO: George F Johnson Jr
**Treas:* George F Johnson Sr
VP: Van Nguyen
Plnt Mgr: John House
Snr PM: Robert Machol

JOHNSON BANK
See JOHNSON FINANCIAL GROUP INC

D-U-N-S 00-896-0288
JOHNSON BANK NA
(*Suby of* JOHNSON BANK) ★
1 S Main St Ste 100, Janesville, WI 53545-3977
Tel (262) 639-6010 *Founded/Ownrshp* 1855, 1990
Sales NA *EMP* 75
SIC 6021 National commercial banks; National commercial banks
Pr: Scott K Kelly
**Chf Cred:* Dan Defnet
VP: Joel Bailey
**VP:* Carolyn Beretta
VP: Loren Fellows
VP: Karen Reilly
**VP:* Larry Squire

D-U-N-S 00-609-1813
JOHNSON BRASS & MACHINE FOUNDRY INC
JOHNSON CENTRIFUGAL TECHNOLOGY
270 N Mill St, Saukville, WI 53080-1940
Tel (262) 377-9440 *Founded/Ownrshp* 1995
Sales 33.4MM^E *EMP* 110
Accts Wipfli Llp Milwaukee Wi
SIC 3366 3365 Castings (except die): brass; Castings (except die): bronze; Aluminum & aluminum-based alloy castings
Pr: Lance F Johnson
**VP:* Tim Devine
**VP:* Thomas Pheister
Sfty Mgr: Jamy Levesque
Mfg Mgr: Thomas Kempke
Plnt Mgr: Dennis Golbach
Pr Dir: Stephen Stollberg

D-U-N-S 86-744-6551 IMP
JOHNSON BROS BAKERY SUPPLY INC
10731 N Interstate 35, San Antonio, TX 78233-6639
Tel (210) 590-2575 *Founded/Ownrshp* 1994
Sales 88.9MM^E *EMP* 74
SIC 5149 5046 Baking supplies; Bakery equipment & supplies
Pr: Kevin G Johnson
**CFO:* Lorrena Paz
Genl Mgr: Randy Andres
Sls Mgr: Kevin Mayfield
Sales Asso: Ron Turner

D-U-N-S 02-284-7354
JOHNSON BROS CORP
(*Suby of* SOUTHLAND HOLDINGS LLC) ★
608 Henrietta Creek Rd, Roanoke, TX 76262-6339
Tel (813) 685-5101 *Founded/Ownrshp* 1959
Sales 124.2MM^E *EMP* 225
SIC 1623 1629 1622 Underground utilities contractor; Industrial plant construction; Earthmoving contractor; Bridge, tunnel & elevated highway; Underground utilities contractor; Industrial plant construction; Earthmoving contractor; Bridge, tunnel & elevated highway
CEO: Walter D Johnson
**Treas:* Benita Rueckert
**Ex VP:* John A Hogan Jr
**Ex VP:* Paul E Johnson
Sr VP: Joseph Michaels
**VP:* Roberto Elbo
**VP:* Zvonko Juric
**VP:* Jimmy W Kirkman
**VP:* David D Kofstad
**VP:* Joseph Michels
**VP:* Michael Swanson
**Exec:* Charlie L Humphries

D-U-N-S 17-999-6756 IMP
JOHNSON BROS OF HAWAII INC
(*Suby of* JOHNSON BROTHERS LIQUOR CO) ★
1011 Munu St, Kapolei, HI 96707-1874
Tel (808) 487-5355 *Founded/Ownrshp* 1988
Sales 40.8MM^E *EMP* 100^E
SIC 5182 5149 5181 Wine; Neutral spirits; Juices; Beverage concentrates; Beer & other fermented malt liquors; Wine; Neutral spirits; Juices; Beverage concentrates; Beer & other fermented malt liquors
Pr: Robert Johnson
IT Man: Steve Kohoutek
Sales Exec: Sean Shapiro

D-U-N-S 00-422-6015 IMP
JOHNSON BROS RUBBER CO INC (OH)
42 W Buckeye St, West Salem, OH 44287-9747
Tel (419) 853-4122 *Founded/Ownrshp* 1947, 1995
Sales 54.9MM^E *EMP* 130
SIC 5199 3061 Foams & rubber; Mechanical rubber goods; Foams & rubber; Mechanical rubber goods
Pr: Lawrence G Cooke
COO: Joyce Porter
CFO: Marji Daugherty
**VP:* Eric Vail
Plnt Mgr: Jim Sloan

D-U-N-S 02-452-1155 IMP/EXP
JOHNSON BROTHERS CAROLINA DISTRIBUTING CO INC
(*Suby of* JOHNSON BROTHERS LIQUOR CO) ★
712 Ellis Rd, Durham, NC 27703-6017
Tel (919) 596-1144 *Founded/Ownrshp* 1975
Sales 23.2MM^E *EMP* 73
SIC 5182 5149 Wine & distilled beverages; Juices; Wine & distilled beverages; Juices
Pr: Lex Grey
**Ch Bd:* Lynn Johnson
**Treas:* Mitchell Johnson
Exec: Kim Carnell
Dist Mgr: Amanda Bussey
Sales Exec: Jason Lemansky
Mktg Mgr: Morgan Klein

D-U-N-S 04-704-4755 IMP
JOHNSON BROTHERS FAMOUS BRANDS INC
(*Suby of* JOHNSON BROTHERS LIQUOR CO) ★
300 E 50th St N, Sioux Falls, SD 57104-0627
Tel (414) 963-9932 *Founded/Ownrshp* 1980
Sales 22.9MM^E *EMP* 80
SIC 5182 Bottling wines & liquors
Pr: Paul West
Sls Mgr: Justin Albrecht
Sls Mgr: Tim Starr

D-U-N-S 11-098-5517
JOHNSON BROTHERS FORD II LTD
7455 S General Bruce Dr, Temple, TX 76502-5833
Tel (254) 773-5257 *Founded/Ownrshp* 1985
Sales 28.0MM^E *EMP* 80
SIC 5521 5511 Automobiles, new & used; Used car dealers; Used car dealers; Automobiles, new & used
Pt: Harry Adams
Genl Pt: Johnson Bros Ford-NV I
Store Mgr: Scott Schoppe
Sls Mgr: Amy Carranza
Sales Asso: Jack Anderson
Sales Asso: Gene Barnes
Sales Asso: Dennis Green
Sales Asso: Michael Moneyhun

D-U-N-S 00-886-7921 IMP/EXP
JOHNSON BROTHERS LIQUOR CO (MN)
1999 Shepard Rd, Saint Paul, MN 55116-3210
Tel (651) 649-5800 *Founded/Ownrshp* 1954
Sales 585.2MM^E *EMP* 2,000
SIC 5182 5149

D-U-N-S 80-985-0043 IMP
JOHNSON BROTHERS LIQUOR CO OF FLORIDA
(*Suby of* JOHNSON BROTHERS LIQUOR CO) ★
4520 S Church Ave, Tampa, FL 33611-2201
Tel (813) 832-4477 *Founded/Ownrshp* 1993
Sales 100.2MM^E *EMP* 223
SIC 5182 5149 Wine; Liquor; Juices; Wine; Liquor; Juices
Pr: Frank Galante
**Ch:* Lynn Johnson
**VP:* Michael Johnson
Exec: Cindy Clement
Area Mgr: Shon Grace
Genl Mgr: Keith Miranda
Sls Mgr: John Ampe
Sls Mgr: Samantha Paluch
Sls Mgr: Cullen Sullivan

D-U-N-S 05-274-2103 IMP
JOHNSON BROTHERS OF IOWA INC (MN)
(*Suby of* JOHNSON BROTHERS LIQUOR CO) ★
2515 Dean Ave Ste B, Des Moines, IA 50317-7956
Tel (515) 262-1199 *Founded/Ownrshp* 1970
Sales 39.7MM^E *EMP* 128
SIC 5182 5149 5181 Liquor; Wine; Juices; Beer & ale; Liquor; Wine; Juices; Beer & ale
Pr: Michael Johnson
**Ex VP:* Lynn Johnson
VP: Bill Anderson
Dist Mgr: Tina Blunt
Off Mgr: Debbie Kemp
IT Man: Lyle Stutzman
VP Sls: Gene Spaldang
Sales Asso: Timothy Hutchins

D-U-N-S 03-285-7869 IMP
JOHNSON BROTHERS OF NEVADA INC
ALTERNATIVE BEVERAGE DISTRS
4701 Mitchell St, North Las Vegas, NV 89081-2728
Tel (702) 643-2963 *Founded/Ownrshp* 2001
Sales 26.7MM^E *EMP* 65
SIC 5182 Wine
Pr: Gary Charmel
**Treas:* Todd Johnson

D-U-N-S 06-350-7768 IMP
JOHNSON BROTHERS WINCONSIN INC
WINE MERCHANTS
(*Suby of* JOHNSON BROTHERS LIQUOR CO) ★
301 E Vienna Ave, Milwaukee, WI 53212-1600
Tel (414) 963-9932 *Founded/Ownrshp* 1973
Sales 68.1MM^E *EMP* 135
SIC 5182 5149 Wine & distilled beverages; Juices; Wine & distilled beverages; Juices
Pr: Gary M De George
**Treas:* Michael Johnson
**VP:* Todd Breske
Exec: Mark Bedore
Exec: Jeff Hudson
Exec: Mark Law
Brnch Mgr: Tom Little
Opers Mgr: James Phernetton

JOHNSON C EMORY JR MD
See ORTHOGEORGIA

D-U-N-S 07-105-7806
JOHNSON C SMITH UNIVERSITY INC
J C S U
100 Beatties Ford Rd, Charlotte, NC 28216-5302
Tel (704) 378-1000 *Founded/Ownrshp* 1866
Sales 45.6MM *EMP* 280
Accts Grant Thornton Llp Charlotte
SIC 8221 University; University
Pr: Ronald L Carter
**CFO:* Greg Petzke
VP: Diane Bowles
VP: Joy Paige
Off Admin: Janelle Martin
Dir IT: John Norris

D-U-N-S 80-295-5856
JOHNSON CAPITAL GROUP INC
18400 Von Karman Ave # 340, Irvine, CA 92612-0532
Tel (949) 660-1999 *Founded/Ownrshp* 1987
Sales 32.9MM^E^ *EMP* 115
SIC 6282 6162 6531 6141
Pr: Cliff Carnes
CFO: Guy Johnson
Ex VP: Patrick Kinlan
Sr VP: Donald W Burnes Jr
Sr VP: Brent Lister
Sr VP: Scott Meseck
Sr VP: Craig Mueller
Sr VP: Eric Salveson
Sr VP: Amos Smith
Sr VP: Greg West
Sr VP: Bob Williams
VP: Geoff Arrobio
VP: Kevin Burkhalter
VP: Richard Caterina
VP: Ryan Chapman
VP: Ron Davi
VP: Jeff Kearns
VP: Brent Kenefick
VP: George Pappas
VP: Andrew Port
VP: Robert Staniforth

D-U-N-S 00-583-0732
JOHNSON CARLIER INC
738 S 52nd St, Tempe, AZ 85281-7211
Tel (602) 275-2222 *Founded/Ownrshp* 1921
Sales 26.5MM^E^ *EMP* 50
SIC 1542 Commercial & office building, new construction
Ch Bd: Christopher Johnson
**Pr:* Carol Warner
**CFO:* Helen Spencer
**VP:* Rick Capernick
VP: Brock Huttenmeyer
**VP:* Rick Weiss
Snr PM: Rick Zapernick

JOHNSON CENTRIFUGAL TECHNOLOGY
See JOHNSON BRASS & MACHINE FOUNDRY INC

JOHNSON CITY ALT SCHOOL
See JOHNSON CITY CENTRAL SCHOOL DISTRICT

D-U-N-S 96-782-0564
JOHNSON CITY CENTRAL SCHOOL DISTRICT
JOHNSON CITY ALT SCHOOL
5 Cenacle Plz, Johnson City, NY 13790-2735
Tel (607) 763-1292 *Founded/Ownrshp* 1995
Sales 49.1MM *EMP* 10^E^
Accts Ciaschi Dietershagen Little
SIC 8211 Public combined elementary & secondary school; Public combined elementary & secondary school
Prin: Michael Morane

D-U-N-S 05-567-9864
JOHNSON CITY CENTRAL SCHOOLS
666 Reynolds Rd, Johnson City, NY 13790-1398
Tel (607) 763-1200 *Founded/Ownrshp* 1929
Sales 48.2MM *EMP* 582
Accts Ciaschi Dietershagen Little
SIC 8211 Public combined elementary & secondary school; Public combined elementary & secondary school
Bd of Dir: Susan Capone
Bd of Dir: Ronald Zarzycki
CIO: Cliff Butler
IT Man: Deborah Comstock
HC Dir: Eric Race

JOHNSON CITY MEDICAL CENTER
See MOUNTAIN STATES HEALTH ALLIANCE

JOHNSON CITY PRESS
See PRESS HOLDING CORP

D-U-N-S 07-979-8735
JOHNSON CITY SCHOOLS
100 E Maple St, Johnson City, TN 37601-6816
Tel (423) 434-5200 *Founded/Ownrshp* 2015
Sales 21.9MM^E^ *EMP* 628^E^
SIC 8211 Public elementary & secondary schools

D-U-N-S 19-308-1551
JOHNSON CO SCH DISTRICT 1
601 W Lott St, Buffalo, WY 82834-1629
Tel (307) 684-9571 *Founded/Ownrshp* 1970
Sales 0.0 *EMP* 395
SIC 8211 Public elementary & secondary schools; Public elementary & secondary schools

D-U-N-S 00-527-3974
JOHNSON CONTRACTING CO INC (IA)
JOHNSON HEATING VENT & AC
2750 Morton Dr, East Moline, IL 61244-1886
Tel (309) 755-0601 *Founded/Ownrshp* 1918
Sales 30.8MM^E^ *EMP* 150
SIC 1761 1711 1721 Sheet metalwork; Architectural sheet metal work; Warm air heating & air conditioning contractor; Ventilation & duct work contractor; Interior commercial painting contractor; Exterior commercial painting contractor; Sheet metalwork; Architectural sheet metal work; Warm air heating & air conditioning contractor; Ventilation & duct work contractor; Interior commercial painting contractor; Exterior commercial painting contractor
Pr: C Douglas Johnson
**Sec:* Calvin K Askeland
VP: Mike Burke
**VP:* Karry Cox
Genl Mgr: Katie Salz
IT Man: Lauri Graham
Prd Mgr: Jim Schaubroeck

D-U-N-S 07-546-3562
JOHNSON CONTRACTORS INC
3635 2nd St, Muscle Shoals, AL 35661-1275
Tel (256) 383-0313 *Founded/Ownrshp* 1973
Sales 66.9MM^E^ *EMP* 166
Accts Norvell & Associates Pc Cpas
SIC 1541 1711 1731 1771 Industrial buildings, new construction; Mechanical contractor; Refrigeration contractor; Electrical work; Gunite contractor; Industrial buildings, new construction; Mechanical contractor; Refrigeration contractor; Electrical work; Gunite contractor
Ch Bd: Clyde H Roberts
**Pr:* Thomas Counts
VP: Ed Quigley
**VP:* Bill Strickland
Off Mgr: Billy Scoggins
Sfty Dirs: Keith McPeters
Snr PM: Russ Lambert
Snr Mgr: Billy Davis

JOHNSON CONTROLS
See GUSTAVE A LARSON CO

JOHNSON CONTROLS
See STANDARD AIR & LITE CORP

JOHNSON CONTROLS
See SID HARVEY INDUSTRIES INC

JOHNSON CONTROLS
See MEIER SUPPLY CO INC

JOHNSON CONTROLS
See SOUTHERN REFRIGERATION CORP

JOHNSON CONTROLS
See DRILLERS SERVICE INC

JOHNSON CONTROLS
See ALLIED SUPPLY CO INC

JOHNSON CONTROLS
See DWYER INSTRUMENTS INC

JOHNSON CONTROLS
See DUNCAN SUPPLY CO INC

JOHNSON CONTROLS
See CRESCENT PARTS & EQUIPMENT CO INC

JOHNSON CONTROLS
See YOUNG SUPPLY CO

JOHNSON CONTROLS
See BARSCO INC

JOHNSON CONTROLS
See STANDARD SUPPLY AND DISTRIBUTING CO INC

JOHNSON CONTROLS
See CHARLES D JONES AND CO INC

JOHNSON CONTROLS
See MORRISON SUPPLY CO

JOHNSON CONTROLS
See G W BERKHEIMER CO INC

JOHNSON CONTROLS
See BROCK-MCVEY CO

JOHNSON CONTROLS
See JOHNSON SUPPLY AND EQUIPMENT CORP

JOHNSON CONTROLS
See BEHLER-YOUNG CO

JOHNSON CONTROLS
See FAMOUS INDUSTRIES INC

JOHNSON CONTROLS
See UNIVERSAL SUPPLY GROUP INC

JOHNSON CONTROLS
See RAL SUPPLY GROUP INC

JOHNSON CONTROLS
See CAPP USA INC

JOHNSON CONTROLS
See SOUTH CENTRAL GWB CO INC

JOHNSON CONTROLS
See APCO INC

JOHNSON CONTROLS
See HABEGGER CORP

JOHNSON CONTROLS
See BELL PUMP SERVICE CO

JOHNSON CONTROLS
See DENNIS SUPPLY CO

JOHNSON CONTROLS
See S W H SUPPLY CO

JOHNSON CONTROLS
See ROGERS SUPPLY CO INC

JOHNSON CONTROLS
See HATFIELD AND CO INC

JOHNSON CONTROLS
See INSCO DISTRIBUTING INC

JOHNSON CONTROLS
See TEMPERATURE CONTROL SYSTEMS INC

JOHNSON CONTROLS
See WASHER SPECIALTIES CO

JOHNSON CONTROLS
See MINGLEDORFFS INC

JOHNSON CONTROLS
See KBC INC

JOHNSON CONTROLS
See CONTROLCO

JOHNSON CONTROLS
See CONTROLS CENTER INC

JOHNSON CONTROLS
See CFM DISTRIBUTORS INC

JOHNSON CONTROLS
See GEMAIRE DISTRIBUTORS LLC

JOHNSON CONTROLS
See WITTICHEN SUPPLY CO

JOHNSON CONTROLS
See G-A-P SUPPLY CORP

JOHNSON CONTROLS
See REFRICENTER OF MIAMI INC

JOHNSON CONTROLS
See UNITED PRODUCTS DISTRIBUTORS INC

JOHNSON CONTROLS
See TROPIC SUPPLY INC

JOHNSON CONTROLS
See KELE INC

JOHNSON CONTROLS
See COASTAL SUPPLY CO INC

JOHNSON CONTROLS
See CENTURY AIRCONDITIONING SUPPLY LP

JOHNSON CONTROLS
See INDUSTRIAL CONTROLS DISTRIBUTORS LLC

JOHNSON CONTROLS
See COMFORT CONTROL SUPPLY CO INC

JOHNSON CONTROLS
See SOUTHERN REFRIGERATION CORP

JOHNSON CONTROLS
See CONSOLIDATED COMMERCIAL CONTROLS INC

JOHNSON CONTROLS
See AMERICAN GRANBY INC

JOHNSON CONTROLS
See Z & Z SUPPLY INC

JOHNSON CONTROLS
See ENE SYSTEMS INC

JOHNSON CONTROLS
See RFC CO

JOHNSON CONTROLS
See BOYS LLC

JOHNSON CONTROLS
See PITTSBURGH PLUMBING & HEATING SUPPLY CORP

JOHNSON CONTROLS
See WSI MANUFACTURING INC

D-U-N-S 62-358-7263
■ **JOHNSON CONTROLS ADVANCED POWER SOLUTIONS LLC**
(*Suby of* JOHNSON CONTROLS INC) ★
5757 N Green Bay Ave, Milwaukee, WI 53209-4408
Tel (414) 524-1200 *Founded/Ownrshp* 2006
Sales 34.9MM^E^ *EMP* 200^E^
SIC 3691 Storage batteries; Storage batteries
VP: Steven Gibbs

D-U-N-S 84-065-2580 IMP
■ **JOHNSON CONTROLS BATTERY GROUP INC**
(*Suby of* JOHNSON CONTROLS INC) ★
5757 N Green Bay Ave, Milwaukee, WI 53209-4408
Tel (414) 524-1200 *Founded/Ownrshp* 1990
Sales 3.3MM^E^ *EMP* 4,000
SIC 3691 Storage batteries; Storage batteries
CEO: Alex A Molinaroli
**Pr:* Stephen A Roell
Mng Dir: Jason Searl

D-U-N-S 12-565-8950 IMP
■ **JOHNSON CONTROLS CLANTON INC**
(*Suby of* JOHNSON CONTROLS INC) ★
2541 7th St S, Clanton, AL 35046-6304
Tel (205) 755-0976 *Founded/Ownrshp* 2011
Sales 194.2MM^E^ *EMP* 550
SIC 2531 Vehicle furniture; Vehicle furniture
Pr: Robert Houston
**CEO:* Dean Lenane
CFO: Gian Deligios
Treas: Colin Ogroman
VP: John Hay
VP: Tim Tow
Dir IT: Phillip Anglin
Dir IT: Joseph Lavis
Dir IT: Mike Maynard
IT Man: Robert Power
QC Dir: Kevin Cloch

D-U-N-S 14-456-1003
■ **JOHNSON CONTROLS FEDERAL SYSTEMS INC**
(*Suby of* JOHNSON CONTROLS INC) ★
50 W Watkins Mill Rd B, Gaithersburg, MD 20878-4023
Tel (240) 683-7600 *Founded/Ownrshp* 2004
Sales 55.3MM^E^ *EMP* 350
SIC 7382 Security systems services; Security systems services
CEO: Mark Elliot
**Ch:* Dennis Archer
**VP:* Mark Duszynski
VP: Doug Knight

D-U-N-S 18-204-5752
■ **JOHNSON CONTROLS HOLDING CO INC**
(*Suby of* JOHNSON CONTROLS INC) ★
5757 N Green Bay Ave, Milwaukee, WI 53209-4408
Tel (414) 524-1200 *Founded/Ownrshp* 1992
Sales 669.8MM^E^ *EMP* 10,500
SIC 6719 Personal holding companies, except banks; Personal holding companies, except banks

D-U-N-S 00-609-2860 IMP/EXP
▲ **JOHNSON CONTROLS INC** (WI)
5757 N Green Bay Ave, Milwaukee, WI 53209-4408
Tel (414) 524-1200 *Founded/Ownrshp* 1885
Sales 37.1MMM *EMP* 139,000
Accts Pricewaterhousecoopers Llp Mi
Tkr Sym JCI *Exch* NYS
SIC 2531 3714 3691 3822 8744 Seats, automobile; Motor vehicle body components & frame; Instrument board assemblies, motor vehicle; Lead acid batteries (storage batteries); Building services monitoring controls, automatic; Facilities support services; Seats, automobile; Motor vehicle body components & frame; Instrument board assemblies, motor vehicle; Lead acid batteries (storage batteries); Building services monitoring controls, automatic; Facilities support services
Ch Bd: Alex A Molinaroli
Pr: Brian Kesseler
Pr: John Murphy
Pr: Brian J Stark
CFO: Brian J Stief
**V Ch Bd:* R Bruce McDonald
Ex VP: Bill Jackson
Ex VP: William C Jackson
Ex VP: Bruce McDonald
VP: Brian J Cadwallader
VP: Simon Davis
VP: Catherine Mulvey
VP: Suzanne M Vincent
Exec: Phil Cramer
Exec: Michael Su
Board of Directors: Mark P Vergnano, David P Abney, Natalie A Black, Julie L Bushman, Raymond L Conner, Richard Goodman, Jeffrey A Joerres, William H Lacy, Juan Pablo Del Valle Peroc, Eugenio Clariond Reyes-Ret

JOHNSON CONTROLS INTERIORS
See YANFENG US AUTOMOTIVE INTERIOR SYSTEMS I LLC

JOHNSON CONTROLS INTERIORS
See YANFENG US AUTOMOTIVE INTERIOR SYSTEMS II LLC

D-U-N-S 00-654-5438 IMP/EXP
JOHNSON CONTROLS INTERIORS LLC
1 Prince Ctr, Holland, MI 49423-5486
Tel (616) 392-5151 *Founded/Ownrshp* 1964
Sales NA *EMP* 20,500
SIC 3714 Motor vehicle parts & accessories

JOHNSON CONTROLS-BATTLE CREEK
See HOOVER UNIVERSAL INC

D-U-N-S 00-694-3039
JOHNSON COOPERATIVE GRAIN CO INC
304 E Highland Ave, Johnson, KS 67855
Tel (620) 492-6210 *Founded/Ownrshp* 1930
Sales 83.9MM *EMP* 68
SIC 5153 5191 5172 Grain elevators; Farm supplies; Feed; Fertilizer & fertilizer materials; Seeds: field, garden & flower; Petroleum products; Grain elevators; Farm supplies; Feed; Fertilizer & fertilizer materials; Seeds: field, garden & flower; Petroleum products
CEO: David Corn
**Pr:* Martie Floyd
**CFO:* Rodney Friesen

D-U-N-S 10-214-7803
JOHNSON COUNTY BOARD OF EDUCATION
211 N Church St, Mountain City, TN 37683-1325
Tel (423) 727-2640 *Founded/Ownrshp* 2000
Sales 12.4MM^E^ *EMP* 420
SIC 8211 Public elementary & secondary schools; Public elementary & secondary schools

D-U-N-S 10-002-7440
JOHNSON COUNTY BOARD OF EDUCATION
JOHNSON COUNTY SCHOOLS
253 N Mayo Trl, Paintsville, KY 41240-1803
Tel (606) 789-2530 *Founded/Ownrshp* 1913
Sales 38.4MM *EMP* 620
Accts Wells & Company Psc Paint
SIC 8211 Public elementary & secondary schools; Public elementary & secondary schools
Pr Dir: Tim Adams

D-U-N-S 07-307-3546
JOHNSON COUNTY COMMUNITY COLLEGE
12345 College Blvd, Overland Park, KS 66210-1283
Tel (913) 469-8500 *Founded/Ownrshp* 1968
Sales 53.4MM *EMP* 2,004
Accts Mcgladrey Llp Davenport Iowa
SIC 8222 8221 Community college; Colleges universities & professional schools; Community college; Colleges universities & professional schools
Pr: Terry Calaway
Ofcr: Chuck Northcott
Ofcr: Dwight Rhodes
Ofcr: Dan Robles
Ofcr: Christopher Sager
Ofcr: Ed Vesey
VP: Denise Moore
Exec: Ellen Fisher
Exec: Dian Jauregui-Smith
Exec: John Nicholson
Ex Dir: Kate Allen

D-U-N-S 17-352-3569
JOHNSON COUNTY PIPE INC
800 County Road 209, Alvarado, TX 76009-8028
Tel (817) 783-3444 *Founded/Ownrshp* 2003
Sales 35.3MM^E^ *EMP* 100
SIC 3498 Fabricated pipe & fittings
Pr: Kevin Thompson

JOHNSON COUNTY SCHOOLS
See JOHNSON COUNTY BOARD OF EDUCATION

D-U-N-S 07-988-0563
JOHNSON COUNTY UNIFIED WASTEWATER DISTRICTS (KS)
11811 S Sunset Dr # 2500, Olathe, KS 66061-2793
Tel (913) 715-8500 *Founded/Ownrshp* 1947
Sales 50.2MM^E *EMP* 229
SIC 4952 Sewerage systems; Sewerage systems
Bd of Dir: Ed Peterson

D-U-N-S 00-622-7094
JOHNSON CRANE CO INC (ND)
CRANE JOHNSON LUMBER COMPANY
3320 Main Ave, Fargo, ND 58103-1227
Tel (701) 237-0612 *Founded/Ownrshp* 1883
Sales 31.0MM *EMP* 80
SIC 2439 5211 Trusses, wooden roof; Lumber & other building materials; Trusses, wooden roof; Lumber & other building materials
Pr: Wayne Briggs
**Ch:* Wylie N Briggs

D-U-N-S 92-693-8598 IMP/EXP
■ **JOHNSON CRUSHERS INTERNATIONAL INC**
J C I
(*Suby of* ASTEC INDUSTRIES INC) ★
86470 Franklin Blvd, Eugene, OR 97405-9642
Tel (541) 736-1400 *Founded/Ownrshp* 1998
Sales 72.0MM *EMP* 270^E
SIC 3532 Crushers, stationary; Crushers, stationary
Pr: Jeff Schwarz
Exec: Andrea Paola
Genl Mgr: Jeff Lininger
IT Man: Steve Allard
Prd Mgr: Chris Rolfe
Sls Dir: Danny Miller
Manager: Dave Bibby
Manager: David Mael
Manager: Don Mueller

D-U-N-S 14-484-0766
JOHNSON DEVELOPMENT ASSOCIATES INC
100 Dunbar St Ste 400, Spartanburg, SC 29306-5189
Tel (864) 585-2000 *Founded/Ownrshp* 1986
Sales 22.6MM^E *EMP* 50
SIC 6552 6531 Subdividers & developers; Real estate agents & managers
CEO: Foster Chapman
**Ch Bd:* George D Johnson Jr
**Pr:* Garrett Scott
**COO:* Jim White
**CFO:* Dan Breeden
CFO: Dan Breeden
**CFO:* Sloan Evans
Ex VP: Kimberley Thompson
VP: Dan Rountree
Opers Mgr: Randall Chambers
Mktg Mgr: Roger Johnson

JOHNSON ELECTRIC
See SAIA-BURGESS AUTOMOTIVE ACTUATORS LLC

D-U-N-S 09-507-0251 IMP
JOHNSON ELECTRIC AUTOMOTIVE INC
(*Suby of* JOHNSON ELECTRIC HOLDINGS LIMITED)
47660 Halyard Dr, Plymouth, MI 48170-2453
Tel (734) 392-1022 *Founded/Ownrshp* 1976
Sales 139.9MM^E *EMP* 550^E
SIC 5013 8731 8742 Automotive supplies; Commercial physical research; Management consulting services; Automotive supplies; Commercial physical research; Management consulting services
Pr: Patrick Wang
Sr VP: Yue Ll
**VP:* Winnie Wang
Dir Lab: Adam Hall
Admn Mgr: Eduardo Catta-Preta

D-U-N-S 08-438-0807
JOHNSON ELECTRIC NORTH AMERICA INC (CT)
(*Suby of* JOHNSON ELECTRIC HOLDINGS LIMITED)
47660 Halyard Dr, Plymouth, MI 48170-2453
Tel (734) 392-5300 *Founded/Ownrshp* 1976
Sales 500.0MM^E *EMP* 40,000
SIC 5063 3625 3674 8711 Motors, electric; Testing laboratories; Noncommercial research organizations; Engineering services; Motors, electric; Solenoid switches (industrial controls); Microcircuits, integrated (semiconductor); Engineering services
Ch: Patrick Shui-Chung Wang
VP: Thomas Roschke
Dir Bus: James McMillan
Ql Cn Mgr: Darwin Thankaswamy
Sales Exec: Doug Eberle
Sls Mgr: Chad Reed

D-U-N-S 08-970-9471
JOHNSON ENERGY CO
JEC FOREST & PAPER RELATED CO
1 Prestige Pl Ste 270, Miamisburg, OH 45342-6146
Tel (937) 435-5401 *Founded/Ownrshp* 1978
Sales 42.5MM *EMP* 3
SIC 5052 2671 Coal & other minerals & ores; Plastic film, coated or laminated for packaging; Coal & other minerals & ores; Plastic film, coated or laminated for packaging
Pr: Michael D Johnson
**VP:* Frank V Surico

D-U-N-S 04-817-7489
JOHNSON ENGINEERING INC
2122 Johnson St, Fort Myers, FL 33901-3408
Tel (239) 334-0046 *Founded/Ownrshp* 1967
Sales 24.8MM^E *EMP* 150
SIC 8711 8713 0781 Civil engineering; Surveying services; Landscape architects; Civil engineering; Surveying services; Landscape architects
Pr: Lonnie Howard
**VP:* Andrew D Tilton
Mktg Mgr: Lindsay Puig

D-U-N-S 00-289-5100 EXP
JOHNSON EQUIPMENT CO
4674 Olin Rd, Dallas, TX 75244-4615
Tel (713) 856-6000 *Founded/Ownrshp* 1959
Sales 62.8MM^E *EMP* 125
SIC 5084 Materials handling machinery; Materials handling machinery
Pr: Randy L Johnson
**Sec:* Elaine Johnson
**VP:* Chris Hammons
VP: Justin Johnson
**VP:* Lawrence Rapp
Rgnl Mgr: Jeremy Benson
Area Mgr: Dane Ferguson
Off Mgr: Leslie Schwarz
Dir IT: Paul Ludovicy
Dir IT: Ed Roch
Opers Mgr: Tom Jones

D-U-N-S 12-426-0212
JOHNSON FARMS
JOHNSON SOD & NURSERY
1633 State Hwy No 77, Deerfield Street, NJ 08313
Tel (856) 358-1123 *Founded/Ownrshp* 1940
Sales 21.0MM^E *EMP* 150
SIC 5193 Flowers & nursery stock; Flowers & nursery stock
Pr: Donald Johnson Sr

D-U-N-S 02-432-1119
JOHNSON FEED INC (SD)
305 W Industrial Rd, Canton, SD 57013-5801
Tel (605) 987-4201 *Founded/Ownrshp* 1949, 1954
Sales 89.8MM *EMP* 190
SIC 4213 5153

D-U-N-S 61-922-2060
JOHNSON FINANCIAL GROUP INC
JOHNSON BANK
555 Main St Ste 400, Racine, WI 53403-4615
Tel (262) 619-2700 *Founded/Ownrshp* 1988
Sales NA *EMP* 1,233
SIC 6022 6021 6712 6733 6311 State commercial banks; National commercial banks; Bank holding companies; Trusts, except educational, religious, charity: management; Life insurance; State commercial banks; National commercial banks; Bank holding companies; Trusts, except educational, religious, charity: management; Life insurance
Ch: Helen Johnson-Liepold
Pr: Kristin Braska
Pr: Louis Burg
Pr: Gretchen Choynacki
Pr: Christine Erdman
Pr: Joseph Guerin
Pr: Greg Hanson
Pr: Brent Hess
Pr: Sue Hullin
Pr: Susan Kutz
Pr: Larry Lukasavage
Pr: Claire Nemec
Pr: Kristine Opatz
Pr: Bob Reinders
Pr: Jennifer Rombak
Pr: Mike Ryan
Pr: Paula Scanlon
Pr: Jeanine Stadler
Pr: Russ Weyers
Pr: Tracey Zapata
CEO: Thomas M Bolger
Board of Directors: Jane M Hutterly, S Curtis Johnson, John Jeffrey Louis III, Winifred J Marquart, Neal R Nottleson, Richard D Pauls, Alan J Ruud, John M Schroeder, Carol Scornicka

D-U-N-S 08-973-1533
JOHNSON FINCH & MCCLURE CONSTRUCTION INC (CA)
JFM
9749 Cactus St, Lakeside, CA 92040-4117
Tel (619) 938-9727 *Founded/Ownrshp* 1977
Sales 28.5MM^E *EMP* 200^E
SIC 1799 1742 Demountable partition installation; Acoustical & ceiling work; Demountable partition installation; Acoustical & ceiling work
CEO: Mark Finch
**Pr:* Scott McClure
**Ch:* Jim Johnson
VP Opers: Jerry Delgadillo
Sfty Dirs: Daniel Lopez

JOHNSON FLORIEST & GARDEN CTRS
See RAYMOND T JOHNSON INC

D-U-N-S 01-282-6991
JOHNSON FOOD SERVICES LLC
Forney Smter St Bldg 3290, Columbia, SC 29207
Tel (803) 782-1461 *Founded/Ownrshp* 2000
Sales 14.8MM^E *EMP* 1,200
SIC 5812 Eating places; Eating places
Owner: Donald Johnson

D-U-N-S 02-758-6395 EXP
JOHNSON FOODS INC
336 Blaine Ave, Sunnyside, WA 98944
Tel (509) 837-4214 *Founded/Ownrshp* 1945
Sales 44.8MM^E *EMP* 100
SIC 5148 4222 Vegetables, fresh; Fruits, fresh; Warehousing, cold storage or refrigerated; Vegetables, fresh; Fruits, fresh; Warehousing, cold storage or refrigerated
CEO: George E Johnson
**Pr:* Gary E Johnson
**VP:* Evelyn Johnson

D-U-N-S 02-837-1003
JOHNSON FORD
ANTELOPE VALLEY LINCOLN
1155 Auto Mall Dr, Lancaster, CA 93534-5867
Tel (661) 949-3586 *Founded/Ownrshp* 1979
Sales 64.5MM^E *EMP* 170
SIC 5511 7538 5561 Automobiles, new & used; General automotive repair shops; Camper & travel trailer dealers; Automobiles, new & used; General automotive repair shops; Camper & travel trailer dealers
Pr: Michael H Johnson
**VP:* Judith Sirmons
Sls Mgr: Doug Killebrew

D-U-N-S 01-956-7296
JOHNSON FORD-LINCOLN-MERCURY INC
JOHNSON LINCOLN
694 East St, Pittsfield, MA 01201-5325
Tel (413) 443-6431 *Founded/Ownrshp* 1964
Sales 24.6MM^E *EMP* 61
SIC 5511 Automobiles, new & used; Automobiles, new & used
Pr: Gary A Johnson

D-U-N-S 00-528-0607 IMP
JOHNSON GAS APPLIANCE CO (IA)
MENDOTA HEARTH
520 E Ave Nw, Cedar Rapids, IA 52405-3855
Tel (319) 365-5267 *Founded/Ownrshp* 1901
Sales 27.6MM^E *EMP* 120
SIC 3567 3531 3433 3429 Industrial furnaces & ovens; Driers & redriers, industrial process; Construction machinery; Burners, furnaces, boilers & stokers; Manufactured hardware (general); Industrial furnaces & ovens; Driers & redriers, industrial process; Construction machinery; Burners, furnaces, boilers & stokers; Manufactured hardware (general)
Pr: Stephen B O'Donnell Jr
Pr: Raj Thapa
CFO: Amy Woodward
**Sec:* William O'Donnell
Plnt Mgr: Richard Schmerbach
Sls Mgr: Bill Odonnell

D-U-N-S 19-439-9259 IMP
JOHNSON GUNNEBO CORP
(*Suby of* GUNNEBO INDUSTRIER AB)
1240 N Harvard Ave, Tulsa, OK 74115-6103
Tel (918) 832-8933 *Founded/Ownrshp* 1989
Sales 39.8MM^E *EMP* 190
SIC 3531 Crane carriers; Crane carriers
CEO: Maurice Boukelif
Pr: Ken Sellers
**CEO:* Nicke Astermo
VP: Guy Minnix
VP: Bob Myers
**VP:* Sylvia Walton
VP: John Wilson
Plng Mgr: Camille Bagley
VP Opers: Bob Henry
Natl Sales: Quin Lloyd
Snr PM: Brad Beall

JOHNSON HARDWARE
See L E JOHNSON PRODUCTS INC

D-U-N-S 03-512-5673
JOHNSON HARDWARE CO
1201 Pacific St, Omaha, NE 68108-3235
Tel (402) 444-1650 *Founded/Ownrshp* 1855
Sales 25.9MM^E *EMP* 74
SIC 5072 Hardware; Hardware
Ch: Rich Nicoll
**Pr:* Bill Stock
Ofcr: Lori Wood
**Sr VP:* David Sullivan
Genl Mgr: Anthony Nicholas
Sales Asso: Jolene Krabbenhoft

D-U-N-S 82-848-0165
JOHNSON HEALTH TECH NORTH AMERICA INC
J H T
(*Suby of* JOHNSON HEALTH TECH CO., LTD.)
1600 Landmark Dr, Cottage Grove, WI 53527-8967
Tel (608) 839-1240 *Founded/Ownrshp* 1975
Sales 186.0MM *EMP* 350
SIC 5091 5941 Engineering services; Fitness equipment & supplies; Exercise equipment
Pr: Nathan Pyles
**COO:* Robert Zande
**Ex VP:* Stewart Kent Stevens
VP: Mike Olson
VP: Andy Richters
**VP:* Mark Zabel
IT Man: Eric Chow
IT Man: Howard Launstein
QC Dir: Kyle Schweitzer
Natl Sales: Todd Boerboom
Sales Asso: Matthew Johnson

JOHNSON HEATER
See ARIZON COMPANIES INC

JOHNSON HEATING VENT & AC
See JOHNSON CONTRACTING CO INC

D-U-N-S 03-353-9693
JOHNSON INDUSTRIES INC
PARTS EXPRESS
5944 Peachtree Cors E, Norcross, GA 30071-1336
Tel (770) 441-1128 *Founded/Ownrshp* 2008
Sales NA *EMP* 300
SIC 5013

D-U-N-S 07-097-4928 IMP/EXP
JOHNSON INTERNATIONAL INDUSTRIES INC
CONTINENTAL HARDWOOD CO
20205 59th Pl S, Kent, WA 98032-2128
Tel (253) 479-9900 *Founded/Ownrshp* 1976
Sales 33.8MM^E *EMP* 105
SIC 5031 Lumber, plywood & millwork; Plywood; Lumber: rough, dressed & finished; Lumber, plywood & millwork; Plywood; Lumber: rough, dressed & finished
CEO: Lisa Johnson
**Pr:* Matthew Deines
**CFO:* Larry Nelson
**Prin:* William L Johnson
Sls Mgr: James Sommers
Sales Asso: Sam Eischen
Sales Asso: Willy Schlitt
Sales Asso: Kevin Winkler

JOHNSON J B CAREER DEV CTR
See ALTON COMMUNITY UNIT SCHOOL DISTRICT 11 INC

D-U-N-S 06-156-1981
JOHNSON JIM PONTIAC NISSAN INC
JIM JOHNSON PONTIAC
2200 Scottsville Rd, Bowling Green, KY 42104-4106
Tel (270) 781-6770 *Founded/Ownrshp* 1972
Sales 29.0MM *EMP* 70
SIC 5511 Automobiles, new & used; Pickups, new & used; Automobiles, new & used; Pickups, new & used
Pr: Jim Johnson
CFO: David Keinger
**Sec:* Darlene Johnson
Exec: Amy Schneider
Genl Mgr: Lynda Broderick
Sls Mgr: David Kurtz
Sls Mgr: Linda Pawley
Sls Mgr: Alex Sizemore

D-U-N-S 00-506-8382 IMP/EXP
■ **JOHNSON KADANT INC** (MI)
(*Suby of* KADANT INC) ★
805 Wood St, Three Rivers, MI 49093-1053
Tel (269) 278-1715 *Founded/Ownrshp* 1930, 2005
Sales 166.9MM^E *EMP* 1,600
Accts Ernst & Young Llp Boston Ma
SIC 3494 Steam fittings & specialties; Steam fittings & specialties
Pr: Greg Wedel
Netwrk Mgr: Bill Covell
Mfg Dir: Dan Snyder
Manager: Kristina Estavillo
Sales Asso: Bill Hasbrouck

JOHNSON L L DISTRIBUTING CO
See PATTLEN ENTERPRISES INC

D-U-N-S 04-742-9147
JOHNSON LAMINATING AND COATING INC
20701 Annalee Ave, Carson, CA 90746-3503
Tel (310) 635-4929 *Founded/Ownrshp* 1960
Sales 34.5MM^E *EMP* 75
SIC 3083 3081 2891 Laminated plastic sheets; Window sheeting, plastic; Unsupported plastics film & sheet; Adhesives & sealants
Pr: Scott Davidson
Sfty Mgr: Ed Zovski
Opers Mgr: James Costere

D-U-N-S 00-607-5386 IMP/EXP
JOHNSON LEVEL & TOOL MFG CO INC (WI)
6333 W Donges Bay Rd, Mequon, WI 53092-4456
Tel (262) 242-1161 *Founded/Ownrshp* 1965, 1970
Sales 24.5MM^E *EMP* 200
SIC 3423 3829 3699 Carpenters' hand tools, except saws: levels, chisels, etc.; Rules or rulers, metal; Measuring & controlling devices; Laser systems & equipment; Carpenters' hand tools, except saws: levels, chisels, etc.; Rules or rulers, metal; Measuring & controlling devices; Laser systems & equipment
Pr: William G Johnson
**COO:* Robert A Johnson
COO: Gar Luckmann
CFO: Dan Patzer
VP: Paul H Buzzell
IT Man: Steven Joy
VP Opers: Dee Kellner
Opers Mgr: Ken Krogmann
Ql Cn Mgr: Tim Wojciechowski
VP Sls: Jeff Johnson
Manager: Mark Morgan

JOHNSON LEXUS OF RALEIGH
See HOL-DAV INC

JOHNSON LINCOLN
See JOHNSON FORD-LINCOLN-MERCURY INC

D-U-N-S 00-691-0855 IMP/EXP
JOHNSON MACHINERY CO (CA)
CATERPILLAR
800 E La Cadena Dr, Riverside, CA 92507-8715
Tel (951) 686-4560 *Founded/Ownrshp* 1940
Sales 199.7MM^E *EMP* 385
SIC 5082 General construction machinery & equipment; General construction machinery & equipment
Pr: William Johnson Jr
Pr: Harold Wondolleck
CFO: Jeff Solem
**Ex VP:* Kevin Kelly
**Ex VP:* Matt Merickel
Sr VP: Wayne Denton
VP: David OHM
VP: Albert Sanchez
Exec: Bryn Glover
Brnch Mgr: Wilma Cox
Genl Mgr: Chris Johnson

D-U-N-S 05-269-5509
JOHNSON MANLEY LUMBER CO
1501 N 15th Ave, Tucson, AZ 85705-6498
Tel (520) 882-0885 *Founded/Ownrshp* 1970
Sales 36.5MM^E *EMP* 300
SIC 1751 5031 Framing contractor; Lumber: rough, dressed & finished; Framing contractor; Lumber: rough, dressed & finished
Pr: Paul Patrick Manley Jr
**Prin:* PA Pat Manley Jr Rev Tr

JOHNSON MATTHEY CHEMICAL
See MATTHEY JOHNSON INC

JOHNSON MEMORIAL HEALTH SVCS
See DAWSON AREA HOSPITAL DISTRICT

D-U-N-S 07-597-7348
JOHNSON MEMORIAL HOSPITAL GUILD INC
TODD-AIKENS HEALTH CARE CENTER
1125 W Jefferson St, Franklin, IN 46131-2140
Tel (317) 736-3300 *Founded/Ownrshp* 1947
Sales 21.7M *EMP* 600^E

SIC 8052 8062 8051 8351 6512 Intermediate care facilities; General medical & surgical hospitals; Convalescent home with continuous nursing care; Child day care services; Nonresidential building operators; Intermediate care facilities; General medical & surgical hospitals; Convalescent home with continuous nursing care; Child day care services; Nonresidential building operators
Pr: Larry R Heydon
**COO:* Elizabeth A Hedden
**COO:* Steve Wohlford
**CFO:* Katherine Johnson
Chf Nrs Of: Anita Keller
**Prin:* Gregg Bechtold
Ex Dir: Pennie Rogers
CTO: Shari Little
CTO: Steve Louwagie
CTO: Keith Neuman
CTO: Mark Rivard

D-U-N-S 07-731-0985
JOHNSON MEMORIAL HOSPITAL INC
JMMC
201 Chestnut Hill Rd, Stafford Springs, CT 06076-4005
Tel (860) 684-4251 *Founded/Ownrshp* 1984
Sales 64.2MM *EMP* 750
SIC 8062 General medical & surgical hospitals; General medical & surgical hospitals
CEO: David R Morgan
Chf Rad: Anal Patel
Dir Vol: Amy Kearns
Dir Vol: Cathy Truehart
Pr: Peter Betts
Pr: Stuart E Rosenberg
CFO: Frank Shiffer
Ch: Patrick Mahon
Ofcr: Lisa Lemire
VP: Herbert Dimeola
VP: Jim Fidanza
VP: Ian S Tucker
VP: Michele Urban
Dir Lab: Mingfu Yu

D-U-N-S 08-119-6099
JOHNSON MENTAL HEALTH CENTER
420 W Bell Ave, Chattanooga, TN 37405-3404
Tel (423) 634-8884 *Founded/Ownrshp* 1974
Sales 12.3MM^E *EMP* 600
SIC 8093 8063 Mental health clinic, outpatient; Hospital for the mentally ill; Mental health clinic, outpatient; Hospital for the mentally ill
Pr: Bobby Freeman
Ex Dir: Donald Fontana
Ex Dir: Robert L Freeman
MIS Mgr: Jim Collins

D-U-N-S 05-627-8633
JOHNSON MIRMIRAN & THOMPSON INC
J M T
72 Loveton Cir, Sparks, MD 21152-9202
Tel (410) 329-3100 *Founded/Ownrshp* 1971
Sales 124.8MM *EMP* 1,000
Accts Mister Burton & French Llc
SIC 8711 Civil engineering; Civil engineering
Ch Bd: Fred F Mirmiran
**Pr:* Jack Moeller
Pr: Jonathan Ryan
**CFO:* Rick Smulovitz
**Sr VP:* Daniel Cheng
Sr VP: Douglas Rose
Sr VP: Brian Stickles
VP: James Blake
VP: Frederick Braerman
VP: Jeffrey Cerquetti
VP: Gerald Fry
VP: Mike Hild
VP: Jerry Jurick
VP: Mike Luning
VP: Gary Miller
VP: Bill Schaub
VP: William Smith
VP: Mark Tiger
Dir Bus: Jeanne Ruthloff

D-U-N-S 00-331-4978
JOHNSON MOTOR CO OF GEORGIA INC
1122 Walton Way, Augusta, GA 30901-2144
Tel (706) 724-0111 *Founded/Ownrshp* 1945
Sales 25.9MM^E *EMP* 60
SIC 5511 Automobiles, new & used; Automobiles, new & used
Pr: Duncan N Johnson
Off Mgr: Nancy Kruger

D-U-N-S 02-347-2525
JOHNSON MOTOR SALES INC
620 Deere Dr, New Richmond, WI 54017-1254
Tel (715) 246-2261 *Founded/Ownrshp* 1925
Sales 33.9MM^E *EMP* 85
SIC 5511 5013 Automobiles, new & used; Automotive supplies & parts; Automobiles, new & used: Automotive supplies & parts
Pr: Mick Anderson
**CFO:* Sandy Bollam
CFO: Sandy Bollom
**VP:* Curtis Anderson
Sls Mgr: Dick Donatelle
Sls Mgr: Chris Wheeler

D-U-N-S 01-403-2817
JOHNSON MOTORS INC
1891 Blinker Pkwy, Du Bois, PA 15801-5238
Tel (814) 371-4444 *Founded/Ownrshp* 1958
Sales 26.8MM^E *EMP* 68
SIC 5511 Automobiles, new & used; Pickups, new & used; Automobiles, new & used; Pickups, new & used
Pr: Robert G Johnson
Treas: Laura Johnson
Sales Asso: Stacia Calliari
Sales Asso: Bruce Dickey
Sales Asso: Dan Knapp
Sales Asso: James Nunley
Sales Asso: Gene Pendolino
Sales Asso: Matt Reed
Sales Asso: Darin Strishock
Sales Asso: John Westen
Sales Asso: Don Williams

D-U-N-S 09-628-7990
JOHNSON OHARE CO INC
JOH ATLANTIC PARTNERS
1 Progress Rd, Billerica, MA 01821-5731
Tel (978) 663-9000 *Founded/Ownrshp* 1956
Sales 150.0MM^E *EMP* 580
SIC 5141 Food brokers; Food brokers
Ch: Harry O'Hare Sr
**Pr:* John Saidnawey
Ex VP: Tom Casey
Ex VP: Brian Gasuik
Ex VP: Terri Lowden
Ex VP: Jim Oettinger
Ex VP: Art Papazian
Ex VP: Gary Rosenthal
Ex VP: Kevin Shea
Ex VP: Kevin Tassinari
**Sr VP:* Carl Annese
**Sr VP:* Will Martinez
VP: Phillip Allin
VP: Richard Davis
VP: Peter Kenyon
VP: William Martins
VP: Ron McLean
VP: Bob Monroe
VP: Bobbie Ohare
VP: Dave Parker
VP: Donna St Louis

JOHNSON OIL
See J CINCO INC

D-U-N-S 02-578-5965
JOHNSON OIL CO
1305 12th Ave, Rock Falls, IL 61071-2799
Tel (815) 625-6380 *Founded/Ownrshp* 1959
Sales 33.0MM^E *EMP* 53
SIC 5172 5541 Petroleum products; Gasoline service stations; Petroleum products; Gasoline service stations
Pr: Arthur J Johnson

D-U-N-S 01-706-2621
JOHNSON OIL CO OF GAYLORD
JOHNSONS OIL & PROPANE COMPANY
507 S Otsego Ave, Gaylord, MI 49735-1718
Tel (989) 732-6014 *Founded/Ownrshp* 1954
Sales 97.7MM^E *EMP* 120
SIC 5171 5541 5983 Petroleum bulk stations; Filling stations, gasoline; Fuel oil dealers; Petroleum bulk stations; Filling stations, gasoline; Fuel oil dealers
Pr: Kevin Johnson
**Pr:* Dale E Johnson
**VP:* Steven Johnson

D-U-N-S 07-135-2595
JOHNSON OIL CO OF HALLOCK INC
1215 Atlantic Ave S, Hallock, MN 56728-4217
Tel (218) 843-2681 *Founded/Ownrshp* 1969
Sales 21.1MM^E *EMP* 59
SIC 5172 5541 Petroleum products; Gasoline service stations
Pr: Ronald W Johnson
**Sec:* Kathryn Johnson
**VP:* Brian R Johnson

D-U-N-S 14-474-2129 IMP/EXP
▲ JOHNSON OUTDOORS INC
555 Main St, Racine, WI 53403-1000
Tel (262) 631-6600 *Founded/Ownrshp* 1987
Sales 430.4MM *EMP* 1,100
Accts Mcgladrey Llp Milwaukee Wisc
Tkr Sym JOUT *Exch* NGM
SIC 3949 3732 3812 Sporting & athletic goods; Skin diving equipment, scuba type; Camping equipment & supplies; Canoes, building & repairing; Kayaks, building & repairing; Sailboats, building & repairing; Navigational systems & instruments; Compasses & accessories; Sporting & athletic goods; Skin diving equipment, scuba type; Camping equipment & supplies; Canoes, building & repairing; Kayaks, building & repairing; Sailboats, building & repairing; Navigational systems & instruments; Compasses & accessories
Ch Bd: H P Johnson-Leipold
**Ch Bd:* Helen P Johnson-Leipold
CFO: David W Johnson
**V Ch Bd:* Thomas F Pyle Jr
VP: Jim Culp
VP: Bill Kelly
VP: William S Kelly
VP: Patricia G Penman
VP: Holley Stacy
VP: Joseph B Stella
Mng Dir: Andrew Dron
Board of Directors: Katherine Button Bell, John M Fahey Jr, Edward F Lang III, Terry E London, W Lee McCollum, Casey Sheahan

D-U-N-S 05-590-6002 IMP/EXP
■ JOHNSON OUTDOORS MARINE ELECTRONICS INC
HUMMINBIRD
(*Suby of* JOHNSON OUTDOORS INC) ★
678 Humminbird Ln, Eufaula, AL 36027-3366
Tel (334) 687-6613 *Founded/Ownrshp* 2004
Sales 54.4MM^E *EMP* 235
SIC 3679 3812 3663 Liquid crystal displays (LCD); Sonar systems & equipment; Marine radio communications equipment; Receiver-transmitter units (transceiver); Liquid crystal displays (LCD); Sonar systems & equipment; Marine radio communications equipment; Receiver-transmitter units (transceiver)
CEO: Helen Johnson-Leipold
Genl Mgr: Craig Packard
Snr Sftwr: Shawn Zhu
CTO: Eugene Roman
Sftwr Eng: Jeffrey Cole

D-U-N-S 00-110-6517 EXP
■ JOHNSON OUTDOORS WATERCRAFT INC
OLD TOWN CANOE
(*Suby of* JOHNSON OUTDOORS INC) ★
125 Gilman Falls Ave B, Old Town, ME 04468-1325
Tel (207) 827-5513 *Founded/Ownrshp* 1974
Sales 21.2MM^E *EMP* 138
SIC 3732 Canoes, building & repairing; Canoes, building & repairing
CEO: Helen P Johnson-Leipold
Treas: Wade Neuharth
**VP:* Del McAlpine
Exec: Chris Jacobs
Genl Mgr: Jeremy Smith
QA Dir: Rob Neill
Sftwr Eng: William Bates

D-U-N-S 08-437-2168
■ JOHNSON PRODUCTS LLC
(*Suby of* SERVICE PARTNERS LLC) ★
490 S Cherry St, Florence, AL 35630-5747
Tel (256) 718-2345 *Founded/Ownrshp* 1992
Sales 51.3MM^E *EMP* 49
SIC 5033 Insulation, thermal

JOHNSON PROPERTIES
See JOHNSON STORAGE & MOVING CO HOLDINGS LLC

D-U-N-S 00-506-8259 EXP
JOHNSON PUBLISHING CO INC (IL)
FASHION FAIR COSMETICS DIV
200 S Michigan Ave Fl 21, Chicago, IL 60604-2473
Tel (312) 322-9200 *Founded/Ownrshp* 1942
Sales 89.6MM^E *EMP* 300
SIC 2721 2731 2844 Periodicals: publishing only; Books: publishing only; Cosmetic preparations; Hair preparations, including shampoos; Periodicals: publishing only; Books: publishing only; Cosmetic preparations; Hair preparations, including shampoos
Ch: Linda Johnson Rice
Pr: Clarisa Wilson
**COO:* Cheryl Mayberry McKissack
**CFO:* Ronald E Denard
**CFO:* Rich Magid
**CFO:* Desiree Rogers
VP: James Btucker
VP: Kierna Mayo
VP: Arlene Noel
VP: Anu Pillai
VP: Tammy E Roll
VP: Tammy Rolley
Creative D: Ian Robinson

D-U-N-S 15-283-7068
JOHNSON RA INC
JOHNSON RICK AUTO & TIRE SVC
4499 Corporate Sq Ste A, Naples, FL 34104-4774
Tel (239) 643-4415 *Founded/Ownrshp* 1997
Sales 24.8MM^E *EMP* 55
SIC 5531 7538 Automotive tires; General automotive repair shops
CEO: Richard A Johnson
**Treas:* Rosie Johnson

D-U-N-S 10-385-8981
JOHNSON REAL ESTATE INVESTORS
380 Union St Ste 300, West Springfield, MA 01089-4128
Tel (413) 781-0712 *Founded/Ownrshp* 2010
Sales 11.9MM^E *EMP* 350
SIC 6531 Real estate brokers & agents; Real estate brokers & agents
Prin: Nancy Kosakowski

D-U-N-S 01-032-5744
JOHNSON REGIONAL MEDICAL CENTER
1100 E Poplar St, Clarksville, AR 72830-4419
Tel (479) 754-5396 *Founded/Ownrshp* 1952
Sales 77.3MM^E *EMP* 380
SIC 8062 General medical & surgical hospitals; General medical & surgical hospitals
Ch Bd: Kanna Lou Phillips
Chf Rad: Doug Kerin
**CEO:* Larry Morse
CFO: Edward Anderson
Ofcr: Jane Tumbleson
Sr VP: Kanna Philips
Dir OR: Lynne Yarbrough
Dir Lab: Kelli Kist
Dir Rad: Becky Keith
Dir Rad: Clint Ratliff
Dir Sec: Leland Nordin

JOHNSON RICK AUTO & TIRE SVC
See JOHNSON RA INC

D-U-N-S 11-743-7228
JOHNSON ROOFING INC
574 Youngblood Rd, Robinson, TX 76706-7162
Tel (817) 375-0789 *Founded/Ownrshp* 1974
Sales 52.8MM^E *EMP* 250^E
SIC 1761 Roofing contractor; Sheet metalwork; Roofing contractor; Sheet metalwork
Ch Bd: Bill Johnson
**CFO:* Shawn Brown
VP: Johnson B E

D-U-N-S 00-782-2588
JOHNSON SCHOOL BUS SERVICE INC
2151 W Washington St, West Bend, WI 53095-2205
Tel (262) 334-3146 *Founded/Ownrshp* 1942
Sales 54.9MM^E *EMP* 430
SIC 4151 School buses; School buses
Ch Bd: Charles Johnson
**Pr:* Steve Johnson
**VP:* Judy Holzman
**VP:* Diane Johnson

JOHNSON SCREENS
See BILFINGER WATER TECHNOLOGIES INC

D-U-N-S 11-147-5070 EXP
JOHNSON SCREENS
11939 Aldine Westfield Rd, Houston, TX 77093-1001
Tel (713) 661-9483 *Founded/Ownrshp* 2002
Sales 71.8MM^E *EMP* 800
SIC 3442 Screens, window, metal; Screen doors, metal; Screens, window, metal; Screen doors, metal
Pr: Bill Rose
**Pr:* Richard Grifno

D-U-N-S 83-082-0119 IMP/EXP
JOHNSON SCREENS INC
(*Suby of* BILFINGER WATER TECHNOLOGIES GMBH)
1950 Old Highway 8 Nw, New Brighton, MN 55112-1827
Tel (651) 636-3900 *Founded/Ownrshp* 2013
Sales 27.0MM^E *EMP* 550
SIC 3533 3312 8711 Oil & gas field machinery; Rods, iron & steel: made in steel mills; Bar, rod & wire products; Engineering services
Pr: Bill Rouse
**VP:* David Colley
**VP:* James Hudgins
**VP:* Keith Morley
**VP:* Kenneth Springob
Software D: Sean Epping
Ql Cn Mgr: Steve Danelius
Sls Mgr: Gene Eberhardt
Sales Asso: Penny Ulmaniec

D-U-N-S 17-788-5548
JOHNSON SERVICE GROUP INC
J S G
1 E Oakhill Dr Ste 200, Westmont, IL 60559-5540
Tel (630) 655-3500 *Founded/Ownrshp* 1975
Sales 92.8MM^E *EMP* 5,600
SIC 7363 8711 Temporary help service; Engineering services; Temporary help service; Engineering services
Pr: Louis Bertone
**VP:* Dale Slater
VP: April Weston
Brnch Mgr: Lethea Davis
Brnch Mgr: Ben Shirley
IT Man: Stu Shipinski
Manager: Jamie Tran

D-U-N-S 01-690-2488 IMP/EXP
JOHNSON SMITH CO (FL)
4514 19th Street Ct E, Bradenton, FL 34203-3799
Tel (941) 747-5566 *Founded/Ownrshp* 1914
Sales 27.2MM^E *EMP* 120^E
SIC 5961

JOHNSON SOD & NURSERY
See JOHNSON FARMS

JOHNSON STATE COLLEGE
See VERMONT STATE COLLEGES

D-U-N-S 00-579-7675
JOHNSON STORAGE & MOVING CO (130) LLC
UNITED VAN LINES
(*Suby of* JOHNSON PROPERTIES) ★
7009 S Jordan Rd, Centennial, CO 80112-4219
Tel (303) 785-4300 *Founded/Ownrshp* 1900, 1995
Sales 45.3MM^E *EMP* 800
SIC 4213 4214

D-U-N-S 03-052-8020
JOHNSON STORAGE & MOVING CO HOLDINGS LLC
JOHNSON PROPERTIES
7009 S Jordan Rd, Centennial, CO 80112-4219
Tel (303) 785-4300 *Founded/Ownrshp* 1995
Sales 148.2MM^E *EMP* 800
SIC 4213 4214 Household goods transport; Household goods moving & storage, local; Household goods transport; Household goods moving & storage, local

D-U-N-S 00-842-4459
JOHNSON SUPPLY AND EQUIPMENT CORP
JOHNSON CONTROLS
10151 Stella Link Rd, Houston, TX 77025-5398
Tel (713) 830-2300 *Founded/Ownrshp* 1977
Sales 157.9MM^E *EMP* 270
Accts Bkd
SIC 5075 Warm air heating equipment & supplies; Air conditioning & ventilation equipment & supplies; Warm air heating equipment & supplies; Air conditioning & ventilation equipment & supplies
CEO: Carl I Johnson
**Pr:* Richard W Cook
COO: Thomas Goble
**CFO:* Donald K Wile
**VP:* James B Cook
**VP:* Douglas Domgard
**VP:* Sonia Mendiola
**VP:* Darrell J Simoneaux
Rgnl Mgr: Jimmy Dwyer
Brnch Mgr: John Klier
Brnch Mgr: Thomas Valdez

D-U-N-S 02-318-6232
JOHNSON TRACTOR INC
KUBOTA
1110 N Us Highway 14, Janesville, WI 53546-8641
Tel (608) 756-1257 *Founded/Ownrshp* 1980
Sales 26.1MM^E *EMP* 68
SIC 5083 Farm implements; Farm implements
Pr: Sue Johnson
**VP:* Eric Johnson

D-U-N-S 00-615-7598 IMP/EXP
JOHNSON TRUCK BODIES LLC
(*Suby of* CC INDUSTRIES) ★
215 E Allen St, Rice Lake, WI 54868-2203
Tel (715) 234-7071 *Founded/Ownrshp* 1931, 2004
Sales 47.9MM^E *EMP* 330
SIC 3713 3715 3585 Truck bodies (motor vehicles); Truck trailers; Refrigeration & heating equipment; Truck bodies (motor vehicles); Truck trailers; Refrigeration & heating equipment
Pr: Ron Ricci
CFO: Kirsten Olson
**Chf Mktg O:* Mayo Rude
CTO: Jason Humphrey
Mtls Mgr: Don Breault
Sales Exec: Shelly Casey
**Sales Exec:* Tim Griffin
Sales Exec: Dana Nielsen
Sls Dir: Kyle Howard

D-U-N-S 01-396-3099
JOHNSON TRUCK CENTER LLC
3801 Ironwood Pl, Landover, MD 20785-2312
Tel (301) 832-9100 *Founded/Ownrshp* 2004
Sales 25.2MM^E *EMP* 65
SIC 5511 Trucks, tractors & trailers: new & used; Trucks, tractors & trailers: new & used
Genl Mgr: Mark L Riddle
Sls Mgr: Michael Liberto

D-U-N-S 07-490-9417
JOHNSON UNIVERSITY
7900 Johnson Dr, Knoxville, TN 37998-0001
Tel (865) 573-4517 *Founded/Ownrshp* 1901
Sales 21.0MM^E *EMP* 160^E
SIC 8221 College, except junior; College, except junior
Pr: Gary E Weedman
**Treas:* Chris Rolph
Off Admin: Debbie Stclair
CIO: Cliff McCartney
IT Man: Cynthia Barnard
HC Dir: Tim Wingfield
Snr Mgr: Roger Brady

D-U-N-S 05-402-5895 EXP
JOHNSON WELDED PRODUCTS INC
J W P
625 S Edgewood Ave, Urbana, OH 43078-8600
Tel (937) 652-1242 *Founded/Ownrshp* 1970
Sales 66.1MM^E *EMP* 210
SIC 3714 Air brakes, motor vehicle; Air brakes, motor vehicle
Prin: Clayton W Rose Jr
**Pr:* Lilli A Johnson
Sfty Mgr: Burt Bowen
Prd Mgr: Truman Johnson

D-U-N-S 03-353-6814 IMP
JOHNSON WHOLESALE FLOORS INC
1874 Defoor Ave Nw, Atlanta, GA 30318-3039
Tel (404) 352-2700 *Founded/Ownrshp* 1963
Sales 33.0MM^E *EMP* 107
SIC 5023 Floor coverings; Floor coverings
Ch Bd: Donald J Johnson
Pr: Melinda McChesney
VP Sls: Emory A Deaton Jr
Sls Mgr: Terry Feimster
Sls Mgr: Bill Scoggins
Sls Mgr: Les Sizemore

JOHNSON WILSHIRE
See AUSTIN PANG GLOVES MFG (USA) CORP

D-U-N-S 02-744-1856
JOHNSON-BARROW INC
FLUIDTEK
2203 23rd Ave S, Seattle, WA 98144-4636
Tel (206) 284-1476 *Founded/Ownrshp* 1984
Sales 24.9MM^E *EMP* 40
SIC 5075 Warm air heating equipment & supplies; Ventilating equipment & supplies; Air conditioning equipment, except room units
Pr: Patrick Hollister
Ofcr: Stacey Koebin
**VP:* Gary Bodenstab
Off Mgr: Stacey Koeven
CTO: Larry Bonwell
IT Man: Rebbecca Ripperger
VP Opers: Charlotte Blackwell
Sales Exec: Tyler Hillenbrand

D-U-N-S 03-782-8258
JOHNSON-LANCASTER AND ASSOCIATES INC
13031 Us Highway 19 N, Clearwater, FL 33764-7224
Tel (727) 796-5622 *Founded/Ownrshp* 1980
Sales 61.1MM^E *EMP* 55
Accts Elizabeth Wadsworth Pa Cle
SIC 5046 Restaurant equipment & supplies; Restaurant equipment & supplies
CEO: Gerald Lancaster
**Pr:* Bradford W Lancaster
**Sec:* Donna Lancaster
VP: Brad Lancaster

D-U-N-S 12-254-2413
JOHNSON-LAUX CONSTRUCTION LLC
8100 Chancellor Dr # 165, Orlando, FL 32809-7664
Tel (407) 770-2180 *Founded/Ownrshp* 2000
Sales 23.7MM *EMP* 38
Accts Berman Hopkins Wright & Laham
SIC 1542 Nonresidential construction; Nonresidential construction
Pr: Gina Johnson
**VP:* Kevin Johnson

D-U-N-S 08-152-8150
JOHNSON-MELLOH INC
5925 Stockberger Pl Ste 1, Indianapolis, IN 46241-5420
Tel (317) 244-5993 *Founded/Ownrshp* 1976
Sales 27.2MM^E *EMP* 67^E
SIC 8711 1711 Engineering services; Plumbing, heating, air-conditioning contractors
Pr: Nick Melloh
**Treas:* Robert Melloh

D-U-N-S 02-611-8174
JOHNSON-SEWELL FORD LINCOLN MERCURY INC
JOHNSON-SEWELL IMPORTS
3301 N Us Highway 281, Marble Falls, TX 78654-3822
Tel (830) 798-9828 *Founded/Ownrshp* 1979
Sales 48.0MM^E *EMP* 120
SIC 5511 Automobiles, new & used; Pickups, new & used; Automobiles, new & used; Pickups, new & used
Pr: Thomas Kindall
**Sec:* Alice Johnson
Sales Asso: Trent Lockwood

JOHNSON-SEWELL IMPORTS
See JOHNSON-SEWELL FORD LINCOLN MERCURY INC

D-U-N-S 19-959-3679 IMP
JOHNSONITE INC
JOHNSONITE RUBBER FLOORING
(*Suby of* TARKETT)
16035 Industrial Pkwy, Middlefield, OH 44062-9386
Tel (440) 632-3441 *Founded/Ownrshp* 1895
Sales 77.5MM^E *EMP* 500
SIC 3086 Carpet & rug cushions, foamed plastic; Carpet & rug cushions, foamed plastic
Pr: Jeff Buttitta
**CFO:* Tom Dowling

D-U-N-S 62-107-2656 IMP
JOHNSONITE INC
TARKETT USA
30000 Aurora Rd, Solon, OH 44139-2728
Tel (440) 543-8916 *Founded/Ownrshp* 1895
Sales 111.5MM^E *EMP* 450^E
SIC 3069 3089 Floor coverings, rubber; Floor coverings, plastic; Floor coverings, rubber; Floor coverings, plastic
Pr: Louis J Buttitta
**CFO:* Tom Dowling
CFO: Christopher Webb
**Treas:* Geary C Cochran
Sr VP: George Morris
VP: Chuck Diftulo
**VP:* Carmen Pastore
**VP:* Guy Williams
Tech Mgr: Joe Nogosek
Mktg Dir: Jeff Krejsa
Snr Mgr: Bob Kellar

JOHNSONITE RUBBER FLOORING
See JOHNSONITE INC

JOHNSON'S AUTO PLAZA
See JOHNSONS AUTO SALES INC

D-U-N-S 03-190-8247
JOHNSONS AUTO SALES INC
JOHNSON'S AUTO PLAZA
12410 E 136th Ave, Brighton, CO 80601-7300
Tel (303) 654-1940 *Founded/Ownrshp* 1992
Sales 34.1MM^E *EMP* 60
SIC 5511 Automobiles, new & used; Automobiles, new & used
Pr: Richard Johnson
**Sec:* Marylou Johnson

D-U-N-S 02-465-5516
JOHNSONS MODERN ELECTRIC CO INC
JME
6629 E Old Us 421 Hwy, East Bend, NC 27018-8733
Tel (336) 699-3957 *Founded/Ownrshp* 1966, 1968
Sales 52.8MM^E *EMP* 175
Accts Edwards Falls Renegar Pllc W
SIC 1731 General electrical contractor; General electrical contractor
Pr: Steven Johnson
**CFO:* Duane A Danner
**VP:* Zachery Johnson
VP: Keith Marshall
VP: Leonard Simpson

JOHNSONS OIL & PROPANE COMPANY
See JOHNSON OIL CO OF GAYLORD

D-U-N-S 01-967-9364
JOHNSONS TIRE SERVICE INC
JOHNSONS TIRE SVC PRO-WASH EX
3330 Denali St, Anchorage, AK 99503-4033
Tel (907) 561-1414 *Founded/Ownrshp* 1982
Sales 34.3MM^E *EMP* 95
SIC 5531 7538 Automotive tires; General automotive repair shops
Pr: Kelly Geade
**Owner:* James Johnson
**VP:* Michelle Hogan
Genl Mgr: Rich Lamar
Sales Exec: Mike Fox

JOHNSONS TIRE SVC PRO-WASH EX
See JOHNSONS TIRE SERVICE INC

D-U-N-S 04-261-9932 IMP/EXP
JOHNSONVILLE SAUSAGE LLC
N6928 Johnsonville Way, Sheboygan Falls, WI 53085
Tel (920) 453-6900 *Founded/Ownrshp* 1945
Sales 423.9MM^E *EMP* 1,356
SIC 2013 Sausages from purchased meat; Sausages from purchased meat
CEO: Ralph Stayer
**Pr:* William Morgan
**CFO:* Kristine Dirkse
VP: Michelle Folz
VP: Jena Goosen
VP: Lisa Lieffring
VP: Fabian Pereira
**VP:* Alice Stayer
**VP:* Launa Stayer
Dir: Brian Harlin
Creative D: Tony Rammer
Dir Bus: Gene Rech

D-U-N-S 62-776-7296
JOHNSTON AMBULANCE SERVICE INC
J A S
2803 Us Highway 70 W, Goldsboro, NC 27530-9559
Tel (919) 736-2735 *Founded/Ownrshp* 1979
Sales 21.7MM^E *EMP* 170
SIC 4119 Ambulance service
Sec: D McKinley Price
**Pr:* Maynard E Price
**VP:* Jerry L Price
IT Man: Jeffrey White

D-U-N-S 09-467-8521
JOHNSTON AUTOMOTIVE & INDUSTRIAL OF SPENCER INC
JAS WAREHOUSE
500 37th Ave W, Spencer, IA 51301-7631
Tel (712) 262-2605 *Founded/Ownrshp* 1978
Sales 24.3MM^E *EMP* 105
SIC 5013 5531 Automotive supplies & parts; Automotive & home supply stores
Pr: Mark Lykke
**VP:* Tim Beachem

JOHNSTON CMMNCTIONS VOICE DATA
See G P JOHNSTON INC

JOHNSTON CNTY BD COMMISSIONERS
See COUNTY OF JOHNSTON

D-U-N-S 07-556-2363
JOHNSTON COMMUNITY COLLEGE
(*Suby of* NORTH CAROLINA COMMUNITY COLLEGE SYSTEM) ★
245 College Rd, Smithfield, NC 27577-6055
Tel (919) 209-2094 *Founded/Ownrshp* 1969
Sales 17.7MM^E *EMP* 500
SIC 8222 9411 Community college; Administration of educational programs; ; Community college; Administration of educational programs;
Pr: Dr David Johnson
Pr: Jeanne Whisnant
Exec: Bernadette Dove
Assoc Dir: Debbie Dunn
IT Man: Lisa McLaurin
Psych: Michael Ammons
Psych: Thomas Dean
Psych: Tamara Lamassa
Pgrm Dir: Lynn Hurt

D-U-N-S 04-550-6318
JOHNSTON COMMUNITY SCHOOL DISTRICT
5608 Merle Hay Rd, Johnston, IA 50131-1213
Tel (515) 278-0470 *Founded/Ownrshp* 1990
Sales 75.1M *EMP* 700
SIC 8211 Public elementary & secondary schools; School board; Public elementary & secondary schools; School board
Bd of Dir: Nancy Upton
Ex Dir: Jan Miller-Hook
Dir IT: Tony Sparks
Pr Dir: Nancy Buryanek
Teacher Pr: Laura Kacer

D-U-N-S 08-188-1088
JOHNSTON CONSTRUCTION CO
INDUSTRIAL SERVICES DIVISION
4331 Fox Run Rd, Dover, PA 17315-2737
Tel (717) 292-3606 *Founded/Ownrshp* 2002
Sales 33.3MM^E *EMP* 87^E
SIC 1629 Waste water & sewage treatment plant construction
Pr: George K Johnston III
**Treas:* Dayna A Gross
VP: Tom Courtney
**VP:* Karl Rice

D-U-N-S 10-005-8676
JOHNSTON COUNTY SCHOOLS
2320 Us Highway 70 Bus E, Smithfield, NC 27577-7790
Tel (919) 934-6031 *Founded/Ownrshp* 1955
Sales 124.3MM^E *EMP* 3,500
SIC 8211 Public elementary & secondary schools; Public elementary & secondary schools
IT Man: Wanda Mourer
IT Man: Larkin Wallace
Pr Dir: Tracey Peedin-Jones
Teacher Pr: Kay Gardner
Teacher Pr: Brian Vetrano
HC Dir: Oliver Johnson

D-U-N-S 08-058-9716
JOHNSTON ENTERPRISES INC
WB JOHNSTON GRAIN COMPANY
411 W Chestnut Ave, Enid, OK 73701-2057
Tel (580) 233-5800 *Founded/Ownrshp* 1971
Sales 334.2MM *EMP* 280
SIC 5153 5191 Grains; Fertilizer & fertilizer materials; Seeds: field, garden & flower; Grains; Fertilizer & fertilizer materials; Seeds: field, garden & flower
Ch Bd: Lew Meibergen
**Pr:* Butch Meibergen
**CFO:* Gary Tucker
**VP:* Roger Henneke
VP: Glenn Richards
VP: Steve Taylor
Rgnl Mgr: Van Scheurmann
Dir IT: Abraham Guerrero

JOHNSTON FABRICS & FINISHING
See JOHNSTON TEXTILES INC

JOHNSTON HEALTH
See JOHNSTON MEMORIAL HOSPITAL CORP

D-U-N-S 96-699-3578
JOHNSTON INDUSTRIES INC
217 Gembler Rd, Marion, TX 78124-5042
Tel (830) 914-4658 *Founded/Ownrshp* 1997
Sales 24.1MM *EMP* 75
SIC 1771 1794 Concrete work; Excavation work
Pr: Ben Johnston
**CEO:* Shelia Johnston

JOHNSTON MCLAMB
See CRGT INC

D-U-N-S 07-201-0713
JOHNSTON MEMORIAL HOSPITAL CORP
JOHNSTON HEALTH
509 N Brightleaf Blvd, Smithfield, NC 27577-4407
Tel (919) 934-8171 *Founded/Ownrshp* 2006
Sales 152.6MM *EMP* 1,200
SIC 8062 General medical & surgical hospitals; General medical & surgical hospitals
CEO: Chuck Elliott
Chf Rad: Kerry Chandler
Chf Rad: Joseph Cornett
V Ch: David Mills
**COO:* Ruth Marler
**COO:* Jackie Ring
**CFO:* Eddie Klein
CFO: Eddie Kline
**VP:* April Culver
VP: Joyce Lassiter
**VP:* Donald Pocock MD
Dir Lab: Daniel Rogers
Dir Rx: Greg Garris

D-U-N-S 07-902-0087
JOHNSTON MEMORIAL HOSPITAL INC
351 Court St, Abingdon, VA 24210-2921
Tel (423) 328-7548 *Founded/Ownrshp* 1919
Sales 143.2MM^E *EMP* 2,500
Accts Pershing Yoakley & Associates
SIC 8062 8011 General medical & surgical hospitals; Offices & clinics of medical doctors; General medical & surgical hospitals; Offices & clinics of medical doctors
CEO: Sean Mc Murray
Chf OB: Brett A Manthey
COO: Sean McMurray
**Treas:* Fleming Ann
**Treas:* Donald Jeanes
Ofcr: Haynes Melton
**Prin:* Joanne Gilmer
**Prin:* Jackie Phipps
**Prin:* Michael Spiegler
Pharmcst: Leslie Hart
Dir Health: Kim Ratliss

D-U-N-S 01-362-9928
JOHNSTON PAPER CO INC
2 Eagle Dr, Auburn, NY 13021-8696
Tel (315) 253-8435 *Founded/Ownrshp* 1976
Sales 147.1MM^E *EMP* 97
Accts Dermody Burke & Brown Cpas
SIC 5113 5084 Industrial & personal service paper; Towels, paper; Cups, disposable plastic & paper; Napkins, paper; Packaging machinery & equipment; Industrial & personal service paper; Towels, paper; Cups, disposable plastic & paper; Napkins, paper; Packaging machinery & equipment
Pr: Michael D May
**Treas:* Thomas E Lewis
VP: Shelly Hoffman
**VP:* David Kristin May
MIS Dir: David Colbert
Dir IT: David Wallace
Sls Mgr: Carter Lucas
Sales Asso: Mike Festa
Sales Asso: Justin Rafferty

D-U-N-S 07-979-9249
JOHNSTON PUBLIC SCHOOLS
10 Memorial Ave, Johnston, RI 02919-3222
Tel (401) 233-1900 *Founded/Ownrshp* 2015
Sales 4.9MM^E *EMP* 325^E
SIC 8211 Public elementary & secondary schools
MIS Dir: George Paquette

D-U-N-S 14-298-4405
JOHNSTON TEXTILES INC
JOHNSTON FABRICS & FINISHING
300 Colin Powell Pkwy, Phenix City, AL 36869-6953
Tel (334) 298-9351 *Founded/Ownrshp* 2003
Sales NA *EMP* 500
SIC 2221 3552 Polyester broadwoven fabrics

D-U-N-S 00-439-2916 IMP
JOHNSTON-MOREHOUSE-DICKEY CO INC (PA)
JMD COMPANY
5401 Progress Blvd, Bethel Park, PA 15102-2517
Tel (412) 833-7100 *Founded/Ownrshp* 1902, 1967
Sales 34.4MM^E *EMP* 65
SIC 2299 3089 5039 Narrow woven fabrics: linen, jute, hemp & ramie; Plastic hardware & building products; Netting, plastic; Soil erosion control fabrics; Narrow woven fabrics: linen, jute, hemp & ramie; Plastic hardware & building products; Netting, plastic; Soil erosion control fabrics
Ch Bd: Herbert E Forse Jr
**Pr:* Mark Forse
CFO: Patti Fagan
**VP:* Scot Forse
Brnch Mgr: Tony Blatnik
Brnch Mgr: Glenn Dupilka
Genl Mgr: Mary Westerman
Off Mgr: Lori Jackson
Info Man: Denny Long
Sales Asso: Adam Filipowicz

D-U-N-S 00-401-8834
JOHNSTON-TOMBIGBEE FURNITURE MANUFACTURING CO (MS)
JTB
(*Suby of* LOUNORA INDUSTRIES INC) ★
1402 Waterworks Rd, Columbus, MS 39701-2757
Tel (662) 328-1685 *Founded/Ownrshp* 1942
Sales 38.1MM^E *EMP* 200
Accts Frost Pllc Little Rock Ar
SIC 2511 Wood household furniture; Wood household furniture
Pr: J Reau Berry
**COO:* Duke Berry
COO: Tommy Word
**CFO:* Judy P Griffith
**VP:* Kelli Caldwell Berry

D-U-N-S 05-720-4187
JOHNSTON-WILLIS HOSPITAL NURSES ALUMNAE ASSOCIATION
1401 Johnston Willis Dr, North Chesterfield, VA 23235-4730
Tel (804) 560-5800 *Founded/Ownrshp* 1931
Sales 169.1MM^E *EMP* 3,000
SIC 8062 Hospital, AMA approved residency; Hospital, AMA approved residency
CEO: Peter Marmerstein
CFO: Lynn Strader
Off Mgr: Ruth Michaud

D-U-N-S 06-589-0998
JOHNSTONE FOODS INC
MCDONALD'S
2101 Northside Dr # 202, Panama City, FL 32405-3686
Tel (850) 769-1397 *Founded/Ownrshp* 1965
Sales 15.9MM^E *EMP* 450
SIC 5812 8742 Fast-food restaurant, chain; Restaurant & food services consultants; Fast-food restaurant, chain; Restaurant & food services consultants
Pr: Thomas T Johnstone
**Treas:* Tracy Johnstone
Genl Mgr: Jan Smaw

JOHNSTONE SUP S JACKSONVILLE
See WARE GROUP INC

JOHNSTONE SUPPLY
See ATWATER SUPPLY

JOHNSTONE SUPPLY
See WARE GROUP LLC

D-U-N-S 06-343-8675 IMP/EXP
JOHNSTONE SUPPLY INC
11632 Ne Ainsworth Cir, Portland, OR 97220-9016
Tel (503) 256-3663 Founded/Ownrshp 1981
Sales 949.4MM EMP 299
SIC 5075 5085 5063 5064

JOHNSTON'S TOYOTA
See JARDINE INC

D-U-N-S 55-657-0968 IMP/EXP
■ JOHNSTOWN AMERICA CORP
FREIGHT CAR DIVISION
(Suby of FREIGHTCAR AMERICA INC) ★
17 Johns St, Johnstown, PA 15901-1531
Tel (814) 533-5000 Founded/Ownrshp 1991
Sales 97.7MM^E EMP 288^E
SIC 3743 Freight cars & equipment
Pr: Jim Hart
Treas: Joseph E McNeely
VP: Kelly Bodway
VP: Glen Karan
VP: Gary Somesn
Prd Mgr: Dave Lohr

D-U-N-S 60-969-9504
JOHNSTOWN SPECIALTY CASTINGS INC
(Suby of WHEMCO INC) ★
545 Central Ave, Johnstown, PA 15902-2600
Tel (814) 535-9002 Founded/Ownrshp 2006
Sales 51.8MM^E EMP 260
SIC 3312 Blast furnaces & steel mills; Blast furnaces & steel mills
Pr: Charles R Novelli
*Treas: Carl Maskiewicz
*Genl Mgr: Ken Hall

JOHNSTOWN TRIBUNE DEMOCRAT
See NEWSPAPER HOLDING INC

D-U-N-S 10-889-5798 IMP
JOHNSTOWN WELDING AND FABRICATION INC
JWF INDUSTRIES
84 Iron St, Johnstown, PA 15906-2618
Tel (800) 225-9353 Founded/Ownrshp 1987
Sales 89.4MM^E EMP 275
SIC 3441 7692 3479 Fabricated structural metal; Welding repair; Etching & engraving; Fabricated structural metal; Welding repair; Etching & engraving
Pr: William C Polacek
Pr: Mark Sotosky
*Sec: Shari Polacek
VP: Tim Vranich
Prgrm Mgr: Graham Crowe
CTO: Butch Getz
IT Man: Patrick McClain
Sftwr Eng: Joshua McCloskey
VP Opers: Joe Boyle
Sfty Dirs: Alex Polacek
Opers Mgr: James Loncella

JOHNSTOWN WIRE TECHNOLOGIES
See J W T HOLDING CORP

D-U-N-S 79-731-9662
JOHNSTOWN WIRE TECHNOLOGIES INC
(Suby of J W T HOLDING CORP) ★
124 Laurel Ave, Johnstown, PA 15906-2246
Tel (814) 532-5600 Founded/Ownrshp 2014
Sales 50.6MM^E EMP 260
SIC 3312 Bar, rod & wire products; Bar, rod & wire products
Pr: Gregg Sherrill
*Treas: Joseph E McNeely
*VP: Jack Leffler

D-U-N-S 09-400-6855 IMP
JOICO LABORATORIES INC
488 E Santa Clara St # 301, Arcadia, CA 91006-7229
Tel (626) 321-4100 Founded/Ownrshp 1976
Sales 29.8MM^E EMP 200
SIC 2844 Hair preparations, including shampoos; Cosmetic preparations; Hair preparations, including shampoos; Cosmetic preparations
Pr: Sara Jones
*Ex VP: Akira Mochizuki

JOIE
See DUTCH LLC

D-U-N-S 04-853-1060
JOIE DE VIVRE HOSPITALITY LLC
530 Bush St Ste 501, San Francisco, CA 94108-3633
Tel (415) 835-0300 Founded/Ownrshp 1987
Sales 231.8MM^E EMP 2,000
SIC 8741 Hotel or motel management; Hotel or motel management
CEO: Niki Leondakis
*CEO: Stephen T Conley Jr
COO: Ingrid Summerfield
CFO: Michael J Wisner
Ofcr: Linda Palermo
Ex VP: Rick Colangelo
Ex VP: Greg Smith
Ex VP: Jorge Trevino
VP: Brett Blass
VP: Jennifer Jordan
VP: Dan Korn
VP: Morgan Plant
VP: Gregory Weiss
Exec: Eddie Blyden
Exec: Oliver Ridgeway
Exec: Sarah Shay
Dir Soc: Marjorie Dowdy
Dir Soc: Nadiya Mazurczak

D-U-N-S 14-024-0008
JOINED ALLOYS LLC
2350 W Shangri La Rd, Phoenix, AZ 85029-4724
Tel (602) 870-5600 Founded/Ownrshp 1959
Sales 24.4MM^E EMP 65
SIC 3398 Metal heat treating
CEO: Rich McManus
CEO: Joe Yockey
COO: Bill Pesch
CFO: Keith Kranzow
VP: Jim Bowen
VP: Jordan Geotas
VP: Tom Kenrick
VP: Swaminathan Subramanian

D-U-N-S 87-738-5492
JOINER FIRE SPRINKLER CO INC
3408 Messer Airport Hwy, Birmingham, AL 35222-1264
Tel (205) 716-1317 Founded/Ownrshp 1994
Sales 21.2MM^E EMP 50
SIC 3569 1711 Sprinkler systems, fire: automatic; Fire sprinkler system installation
Pr: Robert E Joiner
*Sec: Andrea Joiner

D-U-N-S 07-248-2375
JOINT & ORTHOPEDIC CENTER AT HOUSTON HEALTHCARE
1601 Watson Blvd, Warner Robins, GA 31093-3431
Tel (478) 922-4281 Founded/Ownrshp 2008
Sales 276.6MM^E EMP 2,000
SIC 8062 General medical & surgical hospitals; General medical & surgical hospitals
CEO: Cary Martin
Chf Rad: Ali Shaikh
Dir Vol: Melissa Phagan
V Ch: Kent McBride
*CFO: Mike Fowler
*CFO: Sean Whilden
Bd of Dir: Ed Dyson
Bd of Dir: Fred Graham
Bd of Dir: Jack Ragland
Bd of Dir: Tommy Stalnaker
Bd of Dir: Sonny Watson
Ofcr: Audra Cabiness
Ofcr: Stephen Machen
Ofcr: Heather Stewart
*Sr VP: Skip Philips
VP: Mike Ohara
Dir OR: Diane Taylor
Dir Lab: Britt Pilcher
Dir Rad: Steve Smith

D-U-N-S 14-621-3637
JOINT ACTIVE SYSTEMS INC
2600 S Raney St, Effingham, IL 62401-4219
Tel (217) 342-3412 Founded/Ownrshp 1995
Sales 20.8MM^E EMP 110
SIC 7352 Medical equipment rental
Pr: Peter Bonutti
*COO: Boris Bonutti
VP: Peggy Sullivan
Genl Mgr: Lori Workman
VP Sls: Ed Coffin
Manager: Kyle Landrum
Sls Mgr: Sherry Goeckner

D-U-N-S 07-838-9817
JOINT AID MANAGEMENT USA
726 7th St Se, Washington, DC 20003-2739
Tel (202) 706-5333 Founded/Ownrshp 2012
Sales 20.6MM EMP 2
SIC 8322 Child related social services; Child related social services
Prin: Peter Pretorius
IT Man: Rebecca Bratter

JOINT BOARD OF FAMILY PRACTICE
See GEORGIA REGENTS UNIVERSITY

D-U-N-S 03-317-7242
■ JOINT CHIEFS OF STAFF
(Suby of UNITED STATES DEPARTMENT OF DEFENSE) ★
The Pentagon, Washington, DC 20301-0001
Tel (703) 545-6700 Founded/Ownrshp 1998
Sales NA EMP 494^E
SIC 9711 National security;
Ch: Gen Martin E Dempsey

JOINT COMMISSION, THE
See JOINT COMMISSION ON ACCREDITATION OF HEALTHCARE ORGANIZATIONS

D-U-N-S 06-847-5391
JOINT COMMISSION ON ACCREDITATION OF HEALTHCARE ORGANIZATIONS
JOINT COMMISSION, THE
1 Renaissance Blvd, Oakbrook Terrace, IL 60181-4813
Tel (630) 792-5000 Founded/Ownrshp 1951
Sales 102.9MM^E EMP 936
Accts Kpmg Llp Chicago Il
SIC 8621 Medical field-related associations; Medical field-related associations
Pr: Mark Chassin MD
*Pr: Dennis S O Leary MD
COO: Mark G Pelletier
*Ex VP: Anne Marie Benedicto
Ex VP: Ana Pujols McKee
VP: Erin S Dupree
VP: Anne Rooney
VP: Robert Wise
Assoc Dir: Steve Misenko
Ex Dir: M Hampel
Prgrm Mgr: Susan Murray

D-U-N-S 19-377-1029
JOINT COMMISSION RESOURCES INC
1515 W 22nd St Ste 1300, Oak Brook, IL 60523-2000
Tel (630) 268-7400 Founded/Ownrshp 1986
Sales 56.3MM EMP 241
Accts Crowe Horwath Llp Chicago Il
SIC 8748 Business consulting; Business consulting
CEO: Paula Wilson
*CFO: Jean E Courtney
*Sr VP: Paul M Schyve
VP: Marwa Zohdy
*Prin: Karen Timmons
Genl Mgr: Mary Furumoto
Dir IT: Mike Degraff

D-U-N-S 18-291-2493
JOINT FINANCE OFFICE
SHOSHONE
15 N Fork Rd, Fort Washakie, WY 82514
Tel (307) 332-5402 Founded/Ownrshp 1868
Sales NA EMP 300
SIC 9131 Indian reservation; ; Indian reservation;
Prin: Caroline Hill

D-U-N-S 62-755-4983
JOINT HOLDINGS/BASIC METAL INDUSTRIES INC
11921 Fm 529 Rd, Houston, TX 77041-3017
Tel (713) 937-7474 Founded/Ownrshp 1988
Sales 50.6MM^E EMP 65
SIC 5051 3441 Steel; Fabricated structural metal
Pr: Gerald Hodge
*Sec: Thomas Viele

JOINT IMPLANT SURGEONS
See EAST OHIO REGIONAL HOSPITAL

D-U-N-S 80-735-1585
JOINT INDUSTRY BOARD OF ELECTRICAL INDUSTRY
15811 Jewel Ave, Flushing, NY 11365-3085
Tel (718) 591-2000 Founded/Ownrshp 1945
Sales NA EMP 114^E
SIC 6371 Pension, health & welfare funds; Pension, health & welfare funds
Prin: Gerald Finkle

D-U-N-S 07-744-5096
JOINT INDUSTRY BOARD OF ILLUMINATION PRODUCTS INDUSTRY
15811 Jewel Ave Ste 2, Fresh Meadows, NY 11365-3067
Tel (718) 591-2000 Founded/Ownrshp 1943
Sales 45.4MM EMP 26
SIC 8611 Industrial Standards Committee; Industrial Standards Committee
Treas: Thomas Van Arsdale
VP: Randy Alamo
VP: Diana Clark
Mng Dir: Nicholas Papapietro
DP Dir: Ron Weiss
Dir IT: Stephen Butman
Dir IT: Steve Buttman
Genl Couns: Christina Sessa

D-U-N-S 96-453-6291
JOINT ISRAEL
711 3rd Ave, New York, NY 10017-4014
Tel (212) 687-6200 Founded/Ownrshp 2010
Sales 80.3MM EMP 2
Accts Grant Thornton Lp New York N
SIC 8699 Charitable organization; Charitable organization
Pr: Penny Blumenstein

JOINT JUICE
See PREMIER NUTRITION CORP

D-U-N-S 15-116-5610
JOINT LABOR MANAGEMENT RETIREMENT TRUST
ATPA
7600 Sw Mohawk St, Tualatin, OR 97062-8121
Tel (503) 454-3800 Founded/Ownrshp 1985
Sales NA EMP 50
Accts Miller Kaplan Arase Llp North
SIC 6321 Accident & health insurance; Accident & health insurance
Prin: Peter Harrling

D-U-N-S 06-582-2165
JOINT MEETING OF ESSEX & UNION COUNTY
SEWAGE DISPOSAL COMMISSION
500 S 1st St, Elizabeth, NJ 07202-3093
Tel (908) 353-1313 Founded/Ownrshp 1898
Sales 44.1MM^E EMP 118
SIC 4953

JOINT PENSION TRUST OF CHICAGO
See ELECTRICAL INSURANCE TRUSTEES

JOINT POWERS AGENCY
See SAN JOAQUIN HILLS TRANSPORTATION CORRIDOR AGENCY

D-U-N-S 79-139-1233
JOINT RESTORATION FOUNDATION INC
(Suby of ALLOSOURCE) ★
6278 S Troy Cir, Centennial, CO 80111-6422
Tel (209) 832-4373 Founded/Ownrshp 2007
Sales 25.9MM EMP 2
Accts Rsm Mcgladrey Inc Davenport
SIC 8621 Health association; Health association
Ex Dir: Pete Jenkins
Rgnl Mgr: Keith Byers

JOINT SCHOOL DIST 128
See MACKAY JOINT SCHOOL DIST 182

D-U-N-S 03-423-9678
JOINT SCHOOL DISTRICT
1303 E Central Dr, Meridian, ID 83642-7991
Tel (208) 350-5093 Founded/Ownrshp 2001
Sales 244.7MM EMP 99
SIC 8211 Public elementary & secondary schools; Public elementary & secondary schools

D-U-N-S 02-960-4402
JOINT SCHOOL DISTRICT 2
WEST ADA SCHOOL DISTRICT
1303 E Central Dr, Meridian, ID 83642-7991
Tel (208) 855-4500 Founded/Ownrshp 1950
Sales 231.8MM EMP 4,000
Accts Eide Bailly Llp Boise Id
SIC 8211 Public elementary & secondary schools; Public elementary & secondary schools
Admn Mgr: Jason Leforgee
Admn Mgr: Marilyn Renolds
IT Man: Ken Smith
Pr Dir: Eric Exline
Teacher Pr: Barbara Leeds
Instr Medi: Troy Stephens

D-U-N-S 06-027-9304
JOINT SCHOOL DISTRICT 2
ALBERTON SCHOOLS
306 Railroad Ave, Alberton, MT 59820-9499
Tel (406) 722-3381 Founded/Ownrshp 1919
Sales 237.6MM EMP 63
SIC 8211 Public combined elementary & secondary school; School board; Public combined elementary & secondary school; School board
Instr Medi: Linda Gardner

D-U-N-S 09-311-1615
JOINT SCHOOL DISTRICT 60
545 Seminary Ave, Shelley, ID 83274-1461
Tel (208) 357-3411 Founded/Ownrshp 1900
Sales 8.6MM^E EMP 300
SIC 8211 Public elementary & secondary schools; Public elementary & secondary schools
Schl Brd P: Ken Kearsley

JOINT TEST TACTICS & TRAINING
See JT3 LLC

D-U-N-S 06-371-5007
JOINT TOWNSHIP DISTRICT MEMORIAL HOSPITAL
GRAND LAKE HEALTH SYSTEM
200 Saint Clair Ave, Saint Marys, OH 45885-2494
Tel (419) 394-3335 Founded/Ownrshp 1989
Sales 72.7MM EMP 600
Accts Plante & Moran Pllc Columbus
SIC 8062 8051 General medical & surgical hospitals; Skilled nursing care facilities; General medical & surgical hospitals; Skilled nursing care facilities
CEO: Kevin W Harlan
CFO: Jeffrey Vassler
Treas: Jeff Vossler
Dir Risk M: Kate Hartwig
Dir Lab: Gabriel Factora
Dir Rx: Brett Randolph
CTO: Dewayne Marce
Orthpdst: Lori Atha
Pharmcst: Kari Houser

JOINT VENT THE CARLYLE GRP
See PHILADELPHIA ENERGY SOLUTIONS REFINING AND MARKETING LLC

D-U-N-S 05-384-6812
JOJOS CALIFORNIA (CA)
COCO'S
120 Chula Vis, San Antonio, TX 78232-2234
Tel (877) 225-4160 Founded/Ownrshp 1948, 1996
Sales 145.0MM^E EMP 9,000
SIC 5812 Fast-food restaurant, chain; Fast-food restaurant, chain
Pr: David Devoy

JOK
See JO KING INC

D-U-N-S 10-859-1256
JOKAKE CONSTRUCTION SERVICES
5013 E Washington St # 100, Phoenix, AZ 85034-2029
Tel (602) 224-4500 Founded/Ownrshp 1983
Sales 26.0MM^E EMP 61
SIC 1542 Nonresidential construction
CEO: Rozlyn Lipsey
*Pr: Casey Cartier
*CFO: David Miller
*VP: Dave Alben
*VP: Mike Keller
Dir Bus: Jenna Borcherding
Dir IT: Ron Cadman
Sfty Mgr: Terry Scott

D-U-N-S 83-058-2297
JOKAKE CONSTRUCTION SERVICES INC
5013 E Washington St # 100, Phoenix, AZ 85034-2029
Tel (602) 224-4500 Founded/Ownrshp 2009
Sales 38.1MM EMP 58
SIC 1542 Nonresidential construction
Pr: Rozlyn Lipsey

D-U-N-S 13-070-3465
JOLAR CORP
FINISH LINE FRD-LNCOLN-MERCURY
1011 Folger Dr, Statesville, NC 28625-6274
Tel (704) 873-3673 Founded/Ownrshp 1992
Sales 25.4MM^E EMP 80
SIC 5511 7539 5531 Automobiles, new & used; Automotive repair shops; Automotive parts; Automobiles, new & used; Automotive repair shops; Automotive parts
Pr: Joe Bertolami
Opers Mgr: Bobby Merryman
Sls Mgr: Terri Barricello
Sls Mgr: Travis Chatham
Sls Mgr: Andy Hedrick

D-U-N-S 05-192-6145
JOLIET AVIONICS INC (IL)
GPS WORLD SUPPLY COMPANY
43w730 Us Highway 30 A, Sugar Grove, IL 60554-9837
Tel (630) 584-3200 Founded/Ownrshp 1965, 1971
Sales 23.4MM^E EMP 95
SIC 4581 5088 1731 Aircraft servicing & repairing; Aircraft & parts; Communications specialization
Pr: Brad Zeman
VP: Ron Jennings
Sls Mgr: Scott Fank
Snr Mgr: Ken Dalton

JOLIET CENTRAL HIGH SCHOOL
See JOLIET TOWNSHIP HIGH SCHOOL DISTRICT 204

JOLIET JUNIOR COLLEGE BKSTR
See JOLIET JUNIOR COLLEGE DISTRICT 525

D-U-N-S 06-995-9013
JOLIET JUNIOR COLLEGE DISTRICT 525
JOLIET JUNIOR COLLEGE BKSTR
1215 Houbolt Rd, Joliet, IL 60431-8800
Tel (815) 280-6767 Founded/Ownrshp 1901
Sales 22.4MM^E EMP 1,296
SIC 8222 Junior college; Junior college
Pr: Debra S Daniels

VP: Judy Mitchell
**Prin:* Kat Boehle
**Prin:* Eric Monahan
**Prin:* Frank Zeller

D-U-N-S 10-938-0659
JOLIET ONCOLOGY-HEMATOLOGY ASSOCIATES LTD
JOHA
2614 W Jefferson St, Joliet, IL 60435-6433
Tel (815) 725-1355 *Founded/Ownrshp* 1995
Sales 24.3MM^E *EMP* 182^E
SIC 8011 Oncologist
Pr: Sarode K Pundaleeka MD
**Prin:* Nafisa Burhani MD
**Prin:* Sanjiv Modi
**Prin:* Kulumani M Sivarajan MD
Off Mgr: P Cidhu
Info Man: Jennifer Crocker

D-U-N-S 07-001-4113
JOLIET PARK DISTRICT
INWOOD GOLF COURSE
3000 W Jefferson St, Joliet, IL 60435-5246
Tel (815) 741-7275 *Founded/Ownrshp* 1922
Sales NA *EMP* 600
SIC 9512 Recreational program administration, government; ; Recreational program administration, government;
Ex Dir: Dominic Egizio
**Ex Dir:* Ronald Dodd

D-U-N-S 07-975-1194
JOLIET PUBLIC SCHOOLS DISTRICT 86
420 N Raynor Ave, Joliet, IL 60435-6065
Tel (815) 740-3196 *Founded/Ownrshp* 1857
Sales 132.0MM *EMP* 1,000
SIC 8211 Public elementary school; Public elementary school
MIS Dir: John Armstrong
Schl Brd P: Jeffery Pritz
Schl Brd P: Deborah Zeich

D-U-N-S 07-974-9388
JOLIET TOWNSHIP HIGH SCHOOL DISTRICT 204 (IL)
JOLIET CENTRAL HIGH SCHOOL
300 Caterpillar Dr, Joliet, IL 60436-1047
Tel (815) 727-6890 *Founded/Ownrshp* 1880
Sales 36.3MM^E *EMP* 640
Accts Wermer Rogers Doran & Ruzon
SIC 8211 Public elementary & secondary schools; Public senior high school; Public elementary & secondary schools; Public senior high school
Psych: Yvette Jacquet
Board of Directors: Arlene Albert, John Allen, Tana Gray, Richard Johnson, Chet June, Patrick McGuire, Joann Tomosieski, V Pres

D-U-N-S 09-325-1882
JOLLEY ASSOCIATES
SHORT STOP STORES
54 Lower Welden St, Saint Albans, VT 05478-2359
Tel (802) 527-3272 *Founded/Ownrshp* 1978
Sales 24.6MM^E *EMP* 180
SIC 5411 5541 Convenience stores; Filling stations, gasoline; Convenience stores; Filling stations, gasoline
CEO: Bruce Charley
Pt: Bruce Jolley
Dist Mgr: Larry Rohm

D-U-N-S 15-031-6313
JOLLY ROOFING AND CONTRACTING CO INC
711 Chaney Cv, Collierville, TN 38017-2993
Tel (901) 854-5393 *Founded/Ownrshp* 1968
Sales 32.9MM *EMP* 140
Accts Berry & Caccamisi Pc Memph
SIC 1761 Roofing, siding & sheet metal work; Roofing, siding & sheet metal work
Pr: John H Jolly Sr
**Sec:* John Jolly Jr
Genl Mgr: Brent Alexander
Genl Mgr: Burk Berry

JOLLY TIME POP CORN
See AMERICAN POP CORN CO

D-U-N-S 96-250-8458 EXP
JOM PHARMACEUTICAL SERVICES INC
1 Cottontail Ln, Somerset, NJ 08873-1135
Tel (908) 218-7653 *Founded/Ownrshp* 2006
Sales 23.1MM^E *EMP* 125
SIC 5122 Pharmaceuticals
Pr: Rebecca Lyons

D-U-N-S 12-655-8340
JOMAR CONTRACTORS INC
JOMAR ELECTRICAL CONTRACTORS
8515 E North Belt, Humble, TX 77396-2930
Tel (281) 441-2299 *Founded/Ownrshp* 1993
Sales 23.6MM^E *EMP* 100
SIC 1731 Electrical work
Pr: Mark Lapaglia
Snr PM: Gregg Clark

JOMAR ELECTRICAL CONTRACTORS
See JOMAR CONTRACTORS INC

D-U-N-S 05-704-4927 IMP
JOMAR INVESTMENTS INC
NEW LIFE TRANSPORT PARTS CTR
400 Gordon Indus Ct Sw, Byron Center, MI 49315-8354
Tel (616) 878-3633 *Founded/Ownrshp* 1972
Sales 146.3MM^E *EMP* 300
SIC 5013 Trailer parts & accessories; Trailer parts & accessories
Pr: Robert L Hinton
Chf Mktg O: Scott Hammon
**VP:* Michael J Hinton
**VP:* Larry Yeager
CIO: Tom Chandler
VP Opers: Robert Lindley
Opers Mgr: Raymond Peterson
**VP Sls:* David P Broyles
VP Sls: Al Stabler

Manager: Patrick Bailey
Manager: Don Dattilo

D-U-N-S 80-031-6861
JOMAR INVESTMENTS LC
15 Lakeside Dr Ste B, Lake Saint Louis, MO 63367-1378
Tel (636) 561-1885 *Founded/Ownrshp* 1989
Sales 25.5MM^E *EMP* 850
SIC 5812 Restaurant, family: chain; Restaurant, family: chain
Off Mgr: Pat Smith

D-U-N-S 96-757-2041
JOMARSHE INVESTMENT GROUP INC
KELLER WILLIAMS REALTORS
1617 Nc Highway 66 S # 201, Kernersville, NC 27284-3828
Tel (336) 992-0200 *Founded/Ownrshp* 1999
Sales 89.0MM *EMP* 7
SIC 6531 Real estate agent, residential; Real estate agent, residential
Pr: Sam Rogers
**Pr:* Samuel Wrogers
**Treas:* Richard Woolridge
**Ex VP:* Carol K Whicker
**VP:* Shirley Ramsey
Mktg Dir: Marie White

D-U-N-S 00-748-0809
JOMAX CONSTRUCTION CO INC (KS)
(*Suby of* API GROUP INC) ★
238 Se 10 Ave, Great Bend, KS 67530-9624
Tel (620) 792-3686 *Founded/Ownrshp* 1974, 2012
Sales 249.0MM *EMP* 350
Accts Kpmg Llp Minneapolis Mn
SIC 1623 Oil & gas pipeline construction; Oil & gas pipeline construction
Pr: M E Nichols
Sec: Bill Duryee
Sfty Mgr: Rick Wilenzick

D-U-N-S 03-223-7281 EXP
JON HALL CHEVROLET INC
HALL, JON JEEP EAGLE
551 N Nova Rd, Daytona Beach, FL 32114-1701
Tel (386) 255-4444 *Founded/Ownrshp* 1991
Sales 85.2MM^E *EMP* 210
SIC 5511 7538 Automobiles, new & used; General automotive repair shops; Automobiles, new & used; General automotive repair shops
Genl Mgr: Pat Turner

D-U-N-S 85-886-2337
JON K TAKATA CORP
RESTORATION MANAGEMENT COMPANY
4142 Point Eden Way, Hayward, CA 94545-3703
Tel (510) 315-5400 *Founded/Ownrshp* 1985
Sales 34.9MM^E *EMP* 300
SIC 8322 1799 4959 Disaster service; Asbestos removal & encapsulation; Environmental cleanup services; Disaster service; Asbestos removal & encapsulation; Environmental cleanup services
Pr: Jon Takata
Rgnl Mgr: Robert Sandoval
Div Mgr: Rick Arias
Div Mgr: Dave Sailer

JON LANCASTER TOYOTA
See PAG MADISON T1 LLC

D-U-N-S 62-365-4217
JON M HALL CO
1920 Boothe Cir Ste 230, Longwood, FL 32750-6700
Tel (407) 215-0410 *Founded/Ownrshp* 1974
Sales 27.5MM^E *EMP* 100
SIC 1629 6512 Land clearing contractor; Commercial & industrial building operation; Land clearing contractor; Commercial & industrial building operation
Pr: Keith Carson
**VP:* Jon M Hall Jr

D-U-N-S 15-970-1833 EXP
JON MILLIKEN
EMERSON
1612 S 17th Ave, Marshalltown, IA 50158
Tel (641) 754-2340 *Founded/Ownrshp* 1987
Sales 50.0MM *EMP* 65
SIC 3571 Electronic computers; Electronic computers
Pr: Jon Milliken

JON WAYNE CONSTRUCTION
See JWC CONSTRUCTION INC

D-U-N-S 09-177-3820 IMP
JON-DON INC
400 Medinah Rd, Roselle, IL 60172-2329
Tel (630) 872-5401 *Founded/Ownrshp* 1978
Sales 90.2MM^E *EMP* 100
SIC 5087 Carpet & rug cleaning equipment & supplies, commercial; Janitors' supplies; Carpet & rug cleaning equipment & supplies, commercial; Janitors' supplies
Pr: John T Paolella
VP: Ellis Cohn
Brnch Mgr: Tim Wessels
Div Mgr: Shawn Erickson
IT Man: Bill Piet
Natl Sales: Derek Zimmermann
Mktg Dir: Mike Cushing
Mktg Mgr: Michael Tolkson
Manager: Rick Jensen
Manager: Ryan Meier
Sls Mgr: Sherry Essany

JON-LIN FOODS
See JON-LIN FROZEN FOODS

D-U-N-S 10-311-1969
JON-LIN FROZEN FOODS
JON-LIN FOODS
1620 N 8th St, Colton, CA 92324-1302
Tel (909) 825-8542 *Founded/Ownrshp* 1962
Sales 20.4MM^E *EMP* 160^E
SIC 5142 Packaged frozen goods; Packaged frozen goods
Pr: Russell H Burch

**Treas:* Jan Burch
**VP:* Joseph Burch

D-U-N-S 06-283-3496 IMP
JONACO MACHINE LLC
3990 Peavey Rd, Chaska, MN 55318-2385
Tel (952) 448-5544 *Founded/Ownrshp* 2005
Sales 25.6MM^E *EMP* 110
SIC 3599 Machine shop, jobbing & repair
CFO: Mark Schroeder
Dir Bus: Greg Dietrich

D-U-N-S 04-358-1626 IMP
JONAH BROOKLYN INC (CA)
YOGA SAK
9673 Topanga Canyon Pl, Chatsworth, CA 91311-4118
Tel (877) 964-2725 *Founded/Ownrshp* 2011
Sales 500.0MM *EMP* 5
SIC 2673 Wardrobe bags (closet accessories): from purchased materials
Pr: Daniel Meyers

D-U-N-S 07-938-0282
JONAH ENERGY LLC
(*Suby of* TEXAS PACIFIC GROUP) ★
707 17th St Ste 2700, Denver, CO 80202-3429
Tel (720) 577-1000 *Founded/Ownrshp* 2014
Sales 111.5MM^E *EMP* 137^E
SIC 1382 Oil & gas exploration services
CEO: Thomas M Hart III
**Pr:* L Craig Manaugh
**VP:* C Mark Brannum
**VP:* David W Honeyfield
**VP:* Rory Obyrne

D-U-N-S 01-018-2376
JONAS SERVICE & SUPPLY INC
700 Coronis Cir, Green Bay, WI 54304-5747
Tel (920) 336-2400 *Founded/Ownrshp* 2007
Sales 27.8MM^E *EMP* 27
SIC 5085 Industrial supplies; Tools; Abrasives
CEO: Jim Jansen
**VP:* Dan Shanley
Off Mgr: Gregg Sausen
Sls Mgr: Craig Shaver

D-U-N-S 07-834-5288
JONAS SOFTWARE USA LLC
330 S Warminster Rd # 360, Hatboro, PA 19040-3433
Tel (800) 352-6647 *Founded/Ownrshp* 2003, 2012
Sales 48.8MM *EMP* 124
SIC 7371 Computer software development & applications; Computer software development & applications
CEO: Barry Symons
Pr: James Fedigan
Treas: Jeff Mackinnon

D-U-N-S 16-048-5194 IMP
JONATHAN ADLER ENTERPRISES LLC
333 Hudson St Fl 7, New York, NY 10013-1031
Tel (212) 645-2802 *Founded/Ownrshp* 2004
Sales 91.0MM^E *EMP* 150
SIC 5023 Decorative home furnishings & supplies; Decorative home furnishings & supplies
Store Mgr: Dwight Culver
Pr Mgr: Ryan Dziadul
Snr Mgr: Pilar Campos
Snr Mgr: Scott Jacobson
Snr Mgr: Danna Kaufman

D-U-N-S 00-690-7695
JONATHAN CLUB
545 S Figueroa St, Los Angeles, CA 90071-1793
Tel (213) 624-0881 *Founded/Ownrshp* 1935
Sales 38.0MM^E *EMP* 300
SIC 8641 Social club, membership; Social club, membership
Pr: Gregory J Dumas
**CEO:* Randolph P Sinnott
CFO: Plato Skouras
Ofcr: Anne Benedicto
Ofcr: Harold Bressler
Ofcr: Jerod Loeb
Ofcr: Charles Mowll
Ofcr: Paige Rodgers
Ofcr: Paul Schyve
Ofcr: Robert Wise
VP: Hollis Cheek
Comm Dir: Tico Baloyan

D-U-N-S 00-848-7209 IMP
JONATHAN ENGINEERED SOLUTIONS CORP
410 Exchange Ste 200, Irvine, CA 92602-1328
Tel (714) 665-4400 *Founded/Ownrshp* 1977
Sales 86.3MM^E *EMP* 370
SIC 3429 3562 Manufactured hardware (general); Ball bearings & parts; Manufactured hardware (general); Ball bearings & parts
CEO: Paul Salazar
**Pr:* Michael Berneth
Rgnl Mgr: Joe Meitch
Ql Cn Mgr: Hector Anchondo
Ql Cn Mgr: Marco Jimenez
Sls&Mrk Ex: Marie Christopher

D-U-N-S 01-137-0731 IMP
JONATHAN GREEN & SONS INC
48 Sqankum Yellowbrook Rd, Farmingdale, NJ 07727-3734
Tel (732) 938-7007 *Founded/Ownrshp* 1957
Sales 24.4MM^E *EMP* 45
SIC 5191 Farm supplies; Seeds: field, garden & flower; Fertilizer & fertilizer materials; Limestone, agricultural
CEO: Barry K Green Sr
**Pr:* Barry K Green II
**VP:* Todd Pretz
Plnt Mgr: Mike Burk
Natl Sales: John Niciewski

D-U-N-S 12-203-4978 IMP
JONATHAN LOUIS INTERNATIONAL LTD
544 W 130th St, Gardena, CA 90248-1502
Tel (323) 770-3330 *Founded/Ownrshp* 1985
Sales 222.3MM^E *EMP* 610

SIC 2512 Upholstered household furniture; Upholstered household furniture
CEO: Juan Valle
Pt: Javier Sanchez
VP: Abel Herrera
IT Man: Jose Sandoval
VP Sls: Mary Bowling

JONATHAN M WAINRIGHT MEM V A M
See VETERANS ADMINISTRATION OF MEDICAL CENTER

D-U-N-S 83-503-1675 IMP
JONATHAN METAL & GLASS LTD
17818 107th Ave, Jamaica, NY 11433-1802
Tel (718) 846-8000 *Founded/Ownrshp* 1993
Sales 36.1MM *EMP* 70
SIC 3446 Bank fixtures, ornamental metal; Brasswork, ornamental: structural; Grillwork, ornamental metal; Bank fixtures, ornamental metal; Brasswork, ornamental: structural; Grillwork, ornamental metal
Pr: Wilfred Smith

D-U-N-S 61-527-2713
JONDY CHEMICALS INC
ULTRA SHIELD
4432 W Highway 80, Somerset, KY 42503-4785
Tel (606) 679-1483 *Founded/Ownrshp* 1987
Sales 24.4MM^E *EMP* 80
SIC 5085 Industrial supplies
Pr: Randy Wahlman PHD
**VP:* Deanna Wahlman
Dir IT: Scott Gleason
VP Opers: Rhonda Miller

D-U-N-S 18-160-0859 EXP
JONELL FILTRATION PRODUCTS INC
900 Industrial Pkwy, Breckenridge, TX 76424-2369
Tel (254) 559-7591 *Founded/Ownrshp* 1987
Sales 21.8MM^E *EMP* 85
SIC 3677 Filtration devices, electronic
Pr: William Elliott
**Pr:* John W Clarke
**VP:* Alan Clarke
**VP:* George Clarke
**VP:* John W Clarke Jr
Rgnl Mgr: Timothy Cacchione
IT Man: Daryl Chisholm
VP Sls: John W Clarkenb
Mktg Dir: Mike Click
Manager: Darrell Kisselburgh
Board of Directors: Bruce Galloway, Donald G Green, David Richards

D-U-N-S 10-115-6362 IMP
JONES & BARTLETT LEARNING LLC
FESHE SOLUTIONS
5 Wall St, Burlington, MA 01803-4770
Tel (978) 443-5000 *Founded/Ownrshp* 1983
Sales 34.3MM^E *EMP* 167
SIC 2731 Textbooks: publishing only, not printed on site; Textbooks: publishing only, not printed on site
CEO: Ty Field
Pr: Rick Willett
COO: Donald W Jones
Ex VP: Larry Newell
VP: Elvis Cabral
VP: Larry Jones
VP: Lisa Papa
VP Bus Dev: Tim Spurlock
Prin: James Homer
Ex Dir: Eileen Ward
VP Mfg: Therese Connell

D-U-N-S 09-396-8394
JONES & CARTER INC
COTTON SURVEYING COMPANY
6335 Gulfton St Ste 100, Houston, TX 77081-1112
Tel (713) 981-0275 *Founded/Ownrshp* 1976
Sales 63.0MM^E *EMP* 310
SIC 8711 Civil engineering; Civil engineering
Pr: J R Jones
**Pr:* J Bryan Jordan
Pr: John Pledger
**COO:* Carlos P Cotton
**Sr VP:* Bobby Jones
**Sr VP:* Thomas Stroh
VP: Cindy Fields
**VP:* John E Pledger
**VP:* Robert E Ybaez
VP: Robert Ybanez
Dept Mgr: Clayton Chabannes

JONES & COOK OFFICE SUPPLY
See GATEWAY PRINTING & OFFICE SUPPLY INC

JONES & FRANK
See JF ACQUISITION LLC

D-U-N-S 04-297-5151
JONES & JONES INC
110 9th St E, Tifton, GA 31794-4822
Tel (229) 382-6300 *Founded/Ownrshp* 1946
Sales 21.8MM *EMP* 90^E
SIC 1611 3272

D-U-N-S 09-739-7442
JONES & LANIER ELECTRIC INC
WEST GEORGIA ELECTRIC
108 Parkwood Cir, Carrollton, GA 30117-8353
Tel (770) 537-2335 *Founded/Ownrshp* 1979
Sales 32.0MM *EMP* 2
Accts Garrett Thomas & Fazio Pc
SIC 1731 General electrical contractor; General electrical contractor
CEO: Clarence Dennis Jones
**Sec:* Anette H Jones
**VP:* Clyde West
**VP:* Kin White

D-U-N-S 00-106-4914 IMP
JONES & VINING INC (DE)
1115 W Chestnut St Ste 2, Brockton, MA 02301-7501
Tel (508) 232-7470 *Founded/Ownrshp* 1930
Sales 78.7MM^E *EMP* 413
SIC 2499 3131 Lasts, boot & shoe; Boot & shoe accessories; Lasts, boot & shoe; Boot & shoe accessories
Ch Bd: Mark A Krentzman
**Pr:* Lars Vaule

**COO:* Scott Krentzman
**CFO:* Patricia Moretti
Mng Dir: Sonny Bibb

JONES AND COONTZ
See DEKALB FEEDS INC

JONES, ANDY MAZDA
See GERALD JONES VOLKSWAGEN INC

JONES AUTO CENTERS
See TJF 1979 INC

D-U-N-S 07-314-0170
JONES BROS DIRT & PAVING CONTRACTORS INC
1401 S Grandview Ave, Odessa, TX 79761-7144
Tel (432) 332-0721 *Founded/Ownrshp* 1982
Sales 43.5MM^E *EMP* 100^E
SIC 1611 Highway & street construction; Highway & street construction
Pr: R E Jones
**CFO:* Brandy Hines
**VP:* Terry Bryant
Exec: Gary McCorle
IT Man: Shayne Barrios

D-U-N-S 00-484-0864
JONES BROS INC
JONES BROTHERS CONSTRUCTION CO
(*Suby of* JONES INVESTMENT HOLDING INC) ★
5760 Old Lebanon Dirt Rd, Mount Juliet, TN 37122-3393
Tel (615) 754-4710 *Founded/Ownrshp* 1964
Sales 96.7MM^E *EMP* 200
SIC 1622 1771 1794 1629 1611 Bridge construction; Driveway, parking lot & blacktop contractors; Excavation & grading, building construction; Land leveling; General contractor, highway & street construction; Bridge construction; Driveway, parking lot & blacktop contractors; Excavation & grading, building construction; Land leveling; General contractor, highway & street construction
Ch Bd: Robert A Jones
**Pr:* M Dale Mc Cullough
VP: Eugene M Hubbard
**VP:* M Eugene Hubbard
**VP:* Robert S Mc Culloch
VP: James McCulloch
**VP:* Mann R P Pendleton

JONES BROTHERS CONSTRUCTION CO
See JONES BROS INC

D-U-N-S 95-913-2879
JONES BROTHERS TRUCKING LLC
2438 Highway 98 E, Columbia, MS 39429-8056
Tel (601) 736-1151 *Founded/Ownrshp* 1996
Sales 30.4MM^E *EMP* 75^E
SIC 4212 Local trucking, without storage
Mng Pt: Jonathan Jones
Dir IT: Chris Bullock

D-U-N-S 02-612-8520
JONES CASSITY INC
HOME PLUS
306 Pine Tree Rd, Longview, TX 75604-4106
Tel (903) 759-0736 *Founded/Ownrshp* 1958
Sales 47.0MM^E *EMP* 200
SIC 5211 Home centers; Home centers
Ch Bd: John Jones
COO: Jeb Jones
Genl Mgr: J D Ferguson
Sfty Mgr: Yale Swatzell

JONES CHEVROLET
See LEXINGTON CHEVROLET INC

D-U-N-S 03-627-3829
JONES CHEVROLET CO INC (SC)
1230 Broad St, Sumter, SC 29150-1910
Tel (803) 469-2515 *Founded/Ownrshp* 1966, 1995
Sales 28.7MM^E *EMP* 61
SIC 5511 5521 5012

JONES CHRYSLER
See JONES GMC TRUCKS

D-U-N-S 12-094-0721
JONES CO
215 Pendleton St Ste A, Waycross, GA 31501-2330
Tel (912) 285-4011 *Founded/Ownrshp* 1982
Sales 528.9MM^E *EMP* 1,800
Accts Moore Colson And Company Pc
SIC 5541 5411 5172 Gasoline service stations; Grocery stores; Petroleum products; Gasoline service stations; Grocery stores; Petroleum products
CEO: James C Jones III
**CFO:* James A Walker Jr
VP: Patrick C Jones

D-U-N-S 78-515-6527
■ **JONES CO HOMES LLC**
(*Suby of* CENTEX HOMES INC) ★
16640 Chesterfiel Ste 200, Chesterfield, MO 63005
Tel (636) 537-7000 *Founded/Ownrshp* 2002
Sales 14.6MM^E *EMP* 738
SIC 1522 Condominium construction; Condominium construction

JONES COUNTY BOARD EDUCATION
See JONES COUNTY SCHOOL DISTRICT

D-U-N-S 07-508-5761
JONES COUNTY JUNIOR COLLEGE
900 S Court St, Ellisville, MS 39437-3999
Tel (601) 477-4000 *Founded/Ownrshp* 1988
Sales 64.7MM^E *EMP* 425
SIC 8222 Community college; Community college
Pr: Jesse Smith
**CFO:* Rick Youngblood
VP: Charlie Garretson
Store Mgr: Kevin Kuhn
IT Man: Daphne Yeager
Mktg Dir: Bryan Rowell
Psych: Crystal Nail

D-U-N-S 03-678-1466
JONES COUNTY PUBLIC SCHOOLS
JONES COUNTY SCHOOL DISTRICT
320 W Jones St, Trenton, NC 28585-7571
Tel (252) 448-2531 *Founded/Ownrshp* 1900
Sales NA *EMP* 350
Accts David W Martin Cpa Tallahas
SIC 9411 ;
V Ch: Charlie Gray
V Ch: Billy Griffin
Schl Brd P: Barry Jones

JONES COUNTY SCHOOL DISTRICT
See JONES COUNTY PUBLIC SCHOOLS

D-U-N-S 07-193-2693
JONES COUNTY SCHOOL DISTRICT
JONES COUNTY SCHOOLS
5204 Highway 11 N, Ellisville, MS 39437-5072
Tel (601) 649-5201 *Founded/Ownrshp* 1900
Sales 47.2MM^E *EMP* 1,100
SIC 8211 9411 Public elementary & secondary schools; High school, junior or senior; Administration of educational programs; Public elementary & secondary schools; High school, junior or senior; Administration of educational programs
**CFO:* Scott Lewis
Schl Brd P: Lester Boyles
Psych: Barbara Odom

D-U-N-S 10-001-3986
JONES COUNTY SCHOOL DISTRICT
JONES COUNTY BOARD EDUCATION
125 Stewart Ave, Gray, GA 31032-5201
Tel (478) 986-6580 *Founded/Ownrshp* 1800
Sales 32.9MM^E *EMP* 500
Accts Russell W Hinton Cpa Cgfm
SIC 8211 Public elementary & secondary schools; Public elementary & secondary schools

JONES COUNTY SCHOOLS
See JONES COUNTY SCHOOL DISTRICT

D-U-N-S 17-726-4819
JONES DAIDONE JA ELECTRIC
FIBRE OPTIC DATA DIVISION
200 Raymond Blvd, Newark, NJ 07105-4608
Tel (973) 344-6124 *Founded/Ownrshp* 1986
Sales 7.2MM^E *EMP* 300
Accts Huler & Company Point Pleasan
SIC 1731 General electrical contractor; General electrical contractor
Mng Pt: John Daidone

D-U-N-S 00-606-0941
JONES DAIRY FARM (WI)
800 Jones Ave, Fort Atkinson, WI 53538-2169
Tel (920) 563-2432 *Founded/Ownrshp* 1843, 1889
Sales 60.8MM^E *EMP* 350
SIC 2013 Sausages from purchased meat; Prepared pork products from purchased pork; Scrapple from purchased meat; Sausages from purchased meat; Prepared pork products from purchased pork; Scrapple from purchased meat
Pr: Philip Jones
Rgnl Mgr: Olin Newberry
QA Dir: Shellie Siegel
VP Opers: Roger Borchardt
Plnt Mgr: Jeff Theder
Manager: Liz Blackwell
Manager: Jim Glynn
Manager: Peter Riddlebarger
Sls Mgr: Joseph Moore

D-U-N-S 07-674-4234
JONES DAY LIMITED PARTNERSHIP
901 Lakeside Ave E Ste 2, Cleveland, OH 44114-1190
Tel (216) 586-3939 *Founded/Ownrshp* 1893
Sales 899.2MM^E *EMP* 4,600
SIC 8111 General practice law office; General practice law office
Pt: Jones Day
Pt: Dennis Barsky
Pt: Patrick Belville
Pt: Erin L Burke
Pt: James A Cox
Pt: Harry I Johnson III
Pt: Robert F Kennedy
Pt: Bruce McDonald
Pt: Jason C Murray
Pt: Warren L Nachlis
Pt: Eric S Namrow
Pt: Deborah Saxe
Pt: Frank E Sheeder III
Pt: Brent D Sokol
Pt: Michael A Tomasulo
Pt: Louis Touton
Pt: Paula Batt Wilson

D-U-N-S 07-254-1576
JONES EDMUNDS & ASSOCIATES INC
730 Ne Waldo Rd Ste 700, Gainesville, FL 32641-3604
Tel (352) 377-5821 *Founded/Ownrshp* 1974
Sales 39.0MM^E *EMP* 180
Accts James Moore & Co Pl Gaine
SIC 8711 Consulting engineer; Consulting engineer
CEO: Rick Ferreira
Pr: Richard H Jones
COO: Stanley F Ferreira Jr
Ex VP: Robert C Edmunds
Sr VP: Ken Vogel
Sr VP: James Williamson
VP: Dennis Davis
VP: Thomas Friedrich
VP: Mark Nelson
VP: Wallace Schroeder
VP: Douglas M Toth
VP: Steven Yeats

D-U-N-S 02-460-0673
JONES ELKINS INSURANCE AGENCY INC (CA)
12100 Wilshire Blvd # 300, Los Angeles, CA 90025-7136
Tel (310) 207-9796 *Founded/Ownrshp* 1995
Sales NA *EMP* 35^E
SIC 6411 Insurance agents, brokers & service; Insurance agents, brokers & service
Pr: Janet C Jones
**Ch:* John Anderson
**Sr VP:* Jeffrey Shibata
VP: Suzanne Matheson

D-U-N-S 19-617-2639
■ **JONES ENERGY HOLDINGS LLC**
JONES ENERGY LIMITED
(*Suby of* JONES ENERGY INC) ★
807 Las Cimas Pkwy # 350, Austin, TX 78746-6191
Tel (512) 328-2953 *Founded/Ownrshp* 1988
Sales 119.7MM^E *EMP* 65^E
SIC 1311 1382 Crude petroleum production; Natural gas production; Oil & gas exploration services; Crude petroleum production; Natural gas production; Oil & gas exploration services
Genl Pt: Jonny Jones
CFO: Craig M Fleming
Ex VP: Robert J Brooks
Sr VP: Jody Crook
Sr VP: Hal Hawthorne
VP: Todd Wehner
Mng Dir: Robin Picard
IT Man: Ryan O'Dea
VP Prd: Dennis Corkran

D-U-N-S 07-909-0501
▲ **JONES ENERGY INC**
807 Las Cimas Pkwy # 350, Austin, TX 78746-6191
Tel (512) 328-2953 *Founded/Ownrshp* 1988
Sales 380.6MM *EMP* 104
Tkr Sym JONE *Exch* NYS
SIC 1311 Crude petroleum & natural gas; Crude petroleum & natural gas production; Natural gas production; Crude petroleum & natural gas; Crude petroleum & natural gas production; Natural gas production
Ch Bd: Jonny Jones
**Pr:* Mike S McConnell
COO: Eric Niccum
CFO: Robert J Brooks
Sr VP: Jeff Tanner
VP: David Cape
Snr Mgr: Denise Percival
Board of Directors: Alan D Bell, Howard I Hoffen, Gregory D Myers, Robb L Voyles, Halbert S Washburn

JONES ENERGY LIMITED
See JONES ENERGY HOLDINGS LLC

D-U-N-S 05-965-1638 IMP/EXP
JONES FIBER PRODUCTS INC
312 S 14th Ave, Humboldt, TN 38343-3312
Tel (731) 784-2832 *Founded/Ownrshp* 2000
Sales 21.7MM^E *EMP* 100
SIC 2515 2511 Mattresses & foundations; Wood bedroom furniture
Ch: W Ralph Jones Jr
**Pr:* Kenneth R Oliver
**Ofcr:* Alan Posner
**VP:* Stephen Wolf
VP Opers: Steve Wolf
Plnt Mgr: Jeremy Raines
Plnt Mgr: Dale Strand

D-U-N-S 18-592-3232
JONES FINANCIAL COMPANIES LLLP
12555 Manchester Rd, Saint Louis, MO 63131-3710
Tel (314) 515-2000 *Founded/Ownrshp* 1987
Sales 6.3MMM *EMP* 40,000
Accts Pricewaterhousecoopers Llp S
SIC 6211 6411 6163 Stock brokers & dealers; Investment firm, general brokerage; Advisory services, insurance; Loan brokers; Stock brokers & dealers; Investment firm, general brokerage; Advisory services, insurance; Loan brokers
CEO: James D Weddle
Genl Pt: Kevin D Bastien
Genl Pt: Kenneth R Cella Jr
Genl Pt: Penny Pennington
Genl Pt: Daniel J Timm
Genl Pt: James Tricarico
CFO: Kevin Bastien
Prin: Mary Burnes
Prin: Brett A Campbell
Prin: Vinny Ferrari
Prin: David Lane

D-U-N-S 03-609-3359
JONES FORD INC
5757 Rivers Ave, North Charleston, SC 29406-6028
Tel (843) 744-3311 *Founded/Ownrshp* 1967
Sales 50.9MM *EMP* 120
SIC 5511 5521 5012 Automobiles, new & used; Used car dealers; Automobiles & other motor vehicles; Automobiles, new & used; Used car dealers; Automobiles & other motor vehicles
Pr: David M Walters Sr
Treas: David M Walters Jr
VP: Richard G Cooper
IT Man: Kevin Whitt
Sls Mgr: John Richardson

D-U-N-S 93-905-1892
JONES GMC TRUCKS
JONES CHRYSLER
1510 Bel Air Rd, Bel Air, MD 21014-5112
Tel (410) 879-6400 *Founded/Ownrshp* 1946
Sales 29.0MM^E *EMP* 130
SIC 5511 5521 7538 7513 Automobiles, new & used; Used car dealers; General automotive repair shops; Truck rental & leasing, no drivers; Automobiles, new & used; Used car dealers; General automotive repair shops; Truck rental & leasing, no drivers
Pr: Danny Jones
Sales Exec: Tom Caminiti
VP Mktg: Sean Ohara

D-U-N-S 04-006-2168 IMP/EXP
JONES GROUP INC
1411 Broadway Fl 15, New York, NY 10018-3410
Tel (212) 642-3860 *Founded/Ownrshp* 2014
Sales NA *EMP* 10,790
SIC 5632 5137 5139 5661 5641

D-U-N-S 00-975-0247
JONES HENDERSON ACQUISITION LLC
MERCEDES BENZ OF HENDERSON
925 Auto Show Dr, Henderson, NV 89014-6714
Tel (702) 485-3000 *Founded/Ownrshp* 2008
Sales 26.5MM^E *EMP* 83
SIC 5511 Automobiles, new & used; Automobiles, new & used

D-U-N-S 07-950-3552
JONES HOLDINGS LLC
1411 Brdwy, New York, NY 10018
Tel (215) 785-4000 *Founded/Ownrshp* 2013
Sales 296.1MM^E *EMP* 400^E
SIC 5137 Women's & children's clothing; Women's & children's clothing
VP: Karen Curione
**CFO:* Joseph T Donnalley

JONES HONDA
See JONES PONTIAC-GMC TRUCK CO

D-U-N-S 00-424-2561
JONES INDUSTRIAL HOLDINGS INC (TX)
806 Seaco Ct, Deer Park, TX 77536-3176
Tel (281) 479-6000 *Founded/Ownrshp* 1998
Sales 132.6MM^E *EMP* 450
SIC 3564 Air purification equipment; Air purification equipment
CEO: Bradley T Jones
**Pr:* Stewart H Jones
**COO:* Reagan Busbee

D-U-N-S 07-340-9864 EXP
JONES INTERNATIONAL LTD
JONES.COM
9697 E Mineral Ave, Centennial, CO 80112-3446
Tel (303) 792-3111 *Founded/Ownrshp* 1969
Sales 121.4MM^E *EMP* 330
SIC 4832 4841 7371 7372 Radio broadcasting stations, music format; Cable television services; Custom computer programming services; Prepackaged software; Radio broadcasting stations, music format; Cable television services; Custom computer programming services; Prepackaged software
Ch Bd: Glenn R Jones
**VP:* Vincent Dibiase
VP: Jim Ginsburg
**Prin:* John Jennings

D-U-N-S 05-397-6747
JONES INVESTMENT HOLDING INC
5760 Old Lebanon Dirt Rd, Mount Juliet, TN 37122-3393
Tel (615) 754-4710 *Founded/Ownrshp* 1999
Sales 96.7MM^E *EMP* 200
SIC 1622 1771 1794 1611 Bridge, tunnel & elevated highway; Concrete work; Excavation work; Highway & street construction; Bridge, tunnel & elevated highway; Concrete work; Excavation work; Highway & street construction
Pr: Dan McCullch
Treas: Michael Randolph
VP: Robert S McCulloch
VP: William R Slinkard

D-U-N-S 15-453-7807 IMP
■ **JONES LANG LASALLE AMERICAS INC**
HOTELS & HOSPITALITY GROUP
(*Suby of* JONES LANG LASALLE INC) ★
200 E Randolph St # 4300, Chicago, IL 60601-6519
Tel (312) 782-5800 *Founded/Ownrshp* 1988
Sales 0.7 *EMP* 15,000
SIC 6282 1542 Investment advisory service; Commercial & office building contractors; Investment advisory service; Commercial & office building contractors
CEO: Greg O'Brian
**Ch Bd:* Sheila A Penrose
**Pr:* Colin Dyer
**Pr:* Peter Roberts
**Ex VP:* Louis Breeding
**Ex VP:* David Calverley
**Ex VP:* Lauralee E Martin
Sr VP: Douglas Neye
**VP:* Vendetta Blowe
VP: Peter Bulgarelli
VP: Beth Hayden
VP: Ann Montilla
VP: Stephen Pollard

D-U-N-S 94-922-0032
JONES LANG LASALLE AT BEAUMONT HOSPITALS LLC
BSC
3601 W 13 Mile Rd, Royal Oak, MI 48073-6712
Tel (248) 551-5000 *Founded/Ownrshp* 1997
Sales 49.8MM^E *EMP* 350
SIC 7389 8741 Design services; Management services; Design services; Management services
Pr: Patricia S Stoller
**CFO:* Mark Smith
Ofcr: Mary D'Onofrio
CTO: Fragomeni John
Dir IT: Pamela Muller
Mktg Dir: Tom McGannon
Pr Dir: Colette Stimmell
Mktg Mgr: Lori Manos
Doctor: Steven Priest
Doctor: Ali Shirkhoda
Snr PM: Jared Kopydlowski

D-U-N-S 05-600-6935
■ **JONES LANG LASALLE CONSTRUCTION CO INC**
(*Suby of* JONES LANG LASALLE INC) ★
1 Post Office Sq Ste 2600, Boston, MA 02109-2197
Tel (617) 523-8000 *Founded/Ownrshp* 2007
Sales 41.7MM^E *EMP* 110^E
SIC 1542 Commercial & office building, new construction; Commercial & office building, new construction
Pr: Todd Burns
**Pr:* Mark David
**Sr VP:* Gary M Hodlin
**VP:* David McGarry
**VP:* James Murty
**VP:* Joseph J Romenesko

*VP: Daniel Ryan
*VP: David Slye
*VP: Peter Stankiewicz
*VP: Steve Wassersug
Genl Mgr: Dermot Roe

D-U-N-S 02-878-1060
▲ JONES LANG LASALLE INC
200 E Randolph St # 4300, Chicago, IL 60601-6537
Tel (312) 782-5800 Founded/Ownrshp 1997
Sales 5.4MMM EMP 58,100E
Accts Kpmg Llp Chicago Illinois
Tkr Sym JLL Exch NYS
SIC 6512 6531 Commercial & industrial building operation; Real estate agents & managers; Commercial & industrial building operation; Real estate agents & managers
Pr: Colin Dyer
Pr: Naveen Jaggi
CEO: Greg O'Brien
CFO: Christie B Kelly
Treas: Bryan Duncan
Treas: Joseph J Romenesko
Chf Mktg O: Charles J Doyle
Chf Mktg O: Jill Kouri
Ex VP: Lawrence Deans
Ex VP: Ron Gantner
Ex VP: Shawn McDonald
Ex VP: Mark J Ohringer
Ex VP: Jay Schliesman
Sr VP: Jeff Fyffe
Sr VP: Cary Krier
Sr VP: Nicholas J Willmott
Exec: Joe Ryan
Board of Directors: Hugo Bague, Dame Deanne Julius, Ming Lu, Martin H Nesbitt, Sheila A Penrose, Ann Marie Petach, David B Rickard, Roger T Staubach, Samuel A Di Piazza Jr

D-U-N-S 01-282-6975
■ JONES LANG LASALLE SECURITIES LLC (IL)
(Suby of JONES LANG LASALLE INC) ★
200 E Randolph St # 4600, Chicago, IL 60601-6436
Tel (312) 782-7288 Founded/Ownrshp 1997
Sales 10.9MME EMP 500
SIC 6531 Real estate agent, commercial; Real estate agent, commercial
CEO: Peter Roberts
*Prin: Earl Webb

D-U-N-S 08-163-0576 EXP
JONES LUMBER - US LBM LLC
(Suby of US LBM HOLDINGS LLC) ★
4500 Oak Cir, Boca Raton, FL 33431-4212
Tel (561) 391-3995 Founded/Ownrshp 2014
Sales 25.8MME EMP 22E
SIC 5031 Lumber, plywood & millwork; Plywood
Pr: Mark Randall Jones
Off Mgr: Geala Zech
Sales Exec: Howard Olsen

JONES LUMBER COMPANY
See JONES LUMBER CO INC

D-U-N-S 02-864-2098
JONES LUMBER CO INC
10711 Alameda St, Lynwood, CA 90262-1753
Tel (323) 564-6656 Founded/Ownrshp 1923
Sales 35.6MM EMP 71
SIC 5211 Lumber & other building materials; Lumber & other building materials
CEO: Roderick M Jones
*Pr: John M Cencak
VP: Bob Jones
*VP: Rick H Jones
IT Man: Rick Jones
Board of Directors: John M Cencak, Rick H Jones, Robert H Jones, Roderick M Jones

D-U-N-S 95-738-1155
JONES LUMBER CO INC
JONES LUMBER COMPANY
2438 Highway 98 E, Columbia, MS 39429-8056
Tel (601) 876-2427 Founded/Ownrshp 1973
Sales 64.7MME EMP 150
SIC 5031 Lumber: rough, dressed & finished; Lumber: rough, dressed & finished
Pr: Jonathan Jones
*VP: Brett Jones
Sales Exec: Scott Ervin

D-U-N-S 12-064-6471
JONES MEDIA NETWORKS LTD
(Suby of JONES INTERNATIONAL LTD) ★
9697 E Mineral Ave, Centennial, CO 80112-3408
Tel (303) 792-3111 Founded/Ownrshp 1998
Sales 9.9MME EMP 330
SIC 7822 Television & video tape distribution; Television & video tape distribution
Pr: Jeffrey C Wayne
CFO: Tim Oswald
CFO: Stacy Slaughter
VP: Oswaldo H Le N
CTO: Oswaldo Le N

D-U-N-S 16-977-7062
JONES MEDIAAMERICA INC
(Suby of TRITON MEDIA GROUP LLC) ★
11399 Overseas Hwy 5sw, Marathon, FL 33050-3403
Tel (305) 289-4524 Founded/Ownrshp 2008
Sales 23.9MME EMP 560E
SIC 3825 Network analyzers
Pr: Gwen Jones
*Treas: Lorri Ellis
*VP: Robert W Hampton
*VP: Gary Schonfeld
Off Mgr: Shari Levy

JONES MEMORIAL HOSPITAL
See MEMORIAL HOSPITAL OF WILLIAM F AND GERTRUDE F JONES INC

D-U-N-S 11-879-5384
JONES MEMORIAL HOSPITAL AUXILIARY
191 N Main St, Wellsville, NY 14895-1150
Tel (585) 593-1100 Founded/Ownrshp 1951
Sales 64.0M EMP 350
SIC 8062 General medical & surgical hospitals; General medical & surgical hospitals
Pr: Ann Gilpin
*Pr: Marty Fuller
*Treas: Virginia Hogan
*VP: Peg Bennett

D-U-N-S 00-428-0897
JONES METAL PRODUCTS CO (OH)
JONES ZYLON COMPANY
200 N Center St, West Lafayette, OH 43845-1270
Tel (740) 545-6381 Founded/Ownrshp 1923, 1968
Sales 21.1MME EMP 124
SIC 3842 3444 3469 Surgical appliances & supplies; Forming machine work, sheet metal; Metal stampings
Pr: Daniel P Erb III
*Ch Bd: Marion M Sutton
*Treas: Michael G Baker
VP: Harold R Howell
*VP: Carole M Loos
Mtls Mgr: Steve Loos

D-U-N-S 00-620-8235
JONES METAL PRODUCTS INC (MN)
3201 3rd Ave, Mankato, MN 56001-2725
Tel (507) 625-4436 Founded/Ownrshp 1942
Sales 46.0MME EMP 125
SIC 3444 3449 3443 3441 Sheet metalwork; Miscellaneous metalwork; Fabricated plate work (boiler shop); Fabricated structural metal
Ch Bd: John Finke
*CEO: Sarah Richards
*Sec: Lynn P Swartz
*Prin: Peter Jones
Dir IT: Chuck Mook
Mktg Mgr: Doug Fredickson

D-U-N-S 00-791-7354
JONES MOTOR CO INC (NY)
654 Enterprise Dr, Limerick, PA 19468-1290
Tel (610) 948-7900 Founded/Ownrshp 1898
Sales 62.6MME EMP 100
SIC 4213 Trucking, except local
Pr: Donald R Sheehy
*Pr: James J Koegel
*Treas: Daniel E Nelson
*VP: Judith A Civitello

D-U-N-S 03-488-1193
JONES MOTOR CO INC
545 Florence Rd, Savannah, TN 38372-3137
Tel (731) 925-4923 Founded/Ownrshp 1962
Sales 22.6MME EMP 52
SIC 5511 7515 7513 Automobiles, new & used; Passenger car leasing; Truck rental & leasing, no drivers; Automobiles, new & used; Passenger car leasing; Truck rental & leasing, no drivers
Pr: Charles Jones
Treas: Clark J Ones
*Sec: J Clark Jones

D-U-N-S 10-142-4497
JONES MOTOR GROUP INC
654 Enterprise Dr, Limerick, PA 19468-1290
Tel (484) 932-8869 Founded/Ownrshp 1982
Sales 22.7MME EMP 120
SIC 8741 4731 4213 Administrative management; Financial management for business; Freight transportation arrangement; Trucking, except local
Ch Bd: Donald R Sheehy
*Pr: James J Koegel
*Treas: Daniel Nelson
*VP: Judith A Civitello
VP: Ken Lacey
Dir IT: Deb Risco
Trfc Dir: Annette Granahan
Sfty Mgr: Marisa Swiderski

JONES NEWYORK
See NINE WEST HOLDINGS INC

JONES NEWYORK
See AMEREX GROUP LLC

JONES NEWYORK
See AUTHENTIC BRANDS GROUP LLC

D-U-N-S 02-457-7553
JONES NISSAN DEACON INC (NC)
1220 W Grantham St, Goldsboro, NC 27530-1112
Tel (919) 734-2411 Founded/Ownrshp 1944, 2004
Sales 27.3MME EMP 80
SIC 5511 Automobiles, new & used; Automobiles, new & used
Genl Mgr: Gordon Barnes
Genl Mgr: Joe Maus
Sls Mgr: Michael Cherry
Sls Mgr: Steve Marsh
Sales Asso: Mondi Applewhite

D-U-N-S 01-662-0239
JONES OIL CO INC
PHILLIPS 66 SERVICE STATION
314 4th St Hwy 50, Shoals, IN 47581
Tel (812) 247-3183 Founded/Ownrshp 1946, 1970
Sales 35.6MME EMP 125
SIC 5171 5541 5411

D-U-N-S 07-679-8198 IMP
JONES OIL CO INC
67 Lonesome Cedar Ln, Pikeville, KY 41501-6012
Tel (606) 432-5724 Founded/Ownrshp 1978
Sales 32.4MME EMP 40E
SIC 5171 Petroleum bulk stations & terminals
Pr: Earl J Jones
*Sec: Linda Jones

D-U-N-S 05-101-7820
JONES OIL DISTRIBUTOR INC
184 Old Federal Rd, Jasper, GA 30143-1117
Tel (706) 692-2449 Founded/Ownrshp 1971
Sales 44.1MM EMP 11
Accts Bell Rugh & Logan Llc Jasper
SIC 5172 Fuel oil; Engine fuels & oils; Lubricating oils & greases; Service station supplies, petroleum; Fuel oil; Engine fuels & oils; Lubricating oils & greases; Service station supplies, petroleum
Pr: Virginia Jones
*Sec: Angie Walker
*VP: Greg Jones

D-U-N-S 03-534-0231
JONES PAINT & GLASS INC
1250 W 100 N, Provo, UT 84601-2402
Tel (801) 373-3131 Founded/Ownrshp 1938
Sales 22.8MM EMP 175
SIC 3442 5198 5231 5013 1793 3089 Louvers, shutters, jalousies & similar items; Paints; Paint; Automobile glass; Body repair or paint shop supplies, automotive; Glass & glazing work; Windows, plastic; Louvers, shutters, jalousies & similar items; Paints; Paint; Automobile glass; Body repair or paint shop supplies, automotive; Glass & glazing work; Windows, plastic
Pr: David K Jones
COO: Dave Stemmons
Sec: Mark D Butler
VP: Mark Butler
VP: Jeffery M Jones
Exec: Kendra Jones
Exec: Brenda Warner
Store Mgr: Dave Koch
Plnt Mgr: Scott Lybbert
Sales Asso: Michael Garlick
Sales Asso: Joe Macias

D-U-N-S 84-926-6572
JONES PETROLEUM CO INC
STARK PROPERTIES
846 E 3rd St, Jackson, GA 30233-2148
Tel (678) 752-0212 Founded/Ownrshp 1988
Sales 29.0MME EMP 54
SIC 5171 5541 5411 Petroleum bulk stations & terminals; Filling stations, gasoline; Convenience stores, chain; Petroleum bulk stations & terminals; Filling stations, gasoline; Convenience stores, chain
Pr: William Jones
Pr: Bill Jones
*VP: Henry Anderson
VP: Joseph Humphries
Dir IT: Lauren Potts

D-U-N-S 00-637-3633 IMP
JONES PLASTIC AND ENGINEERING CO LLC
2410 Plantside Dr, Louisville, KY 40299-2528
Tel (502) 491-3785 Founded/Ownrshp 1961
Sales 360.1MME EMP 1,310
SIC 3089 Injection molded finished plastic products; Injection molded finished plastic products
Genl Mgr: Chuck Flaherty

D-U-N-S 01-429-1942
JONES PONTIAC-GMC TRUCK CO
JONES HONDA
1335 Manheim Pike, Lancaster, PA 17601-3123
Tel (717) 394-0711 Founded/Ownrshp 1960
Sales 64.4MME EMP 180
SIC 5511 Automobiles, new & used; Pickups, new & used; Automobiles, new & used; Pickups, new & used
Pr: Steven G Jones
*Treas: James A Jones
*VP: Mark R Jones
Genl Mgr: Don Slavin
Store Mgr: Howie Musser
Sls Mgr: Adam Barbour
Sls Mgr: J Kirkessner
Sls Mgr: Jeremy Lookenbill
Sls Mgr: Nick Skidmore
Sls Mgr: Nick Zachery
Sales Asso: Matt Heinaman

JONES POULTRY
See JPI WHOLESALERS INC

D-U-N-S 04-843-7347
JONES PRODUCE INC
831 A St Se, Quincy, WA 98848-1587
Tel (509) 787-3537 Founded/Ownrshp 1967
Sales 31.0MME EMP 70
SIC 5148 Fresh fruits & vegetables; Potatoes, fresh; Fresh fruits & vegetables; Potatoes, fresh
Pr: Mike Jones
COO: Al Lopez
CFO: Debbie Hassan

D-U-N-S 17-706-2366
JONES REGIONAL MEDICAL CENTER
1795 Highway 64 E, Anamosa, IA 52205-2112
Tel (319) 462-6131 Founded/Ownrshp 1962
Sales 20.8MM EMP 60E
SIC 8062 General medical & surgical hospitals
CEO: Sean Williams
Treas: Victor Hamre
Dir Rx: Tom Devaney

D-U-N-S 80-585-4130
JONES SCHOOL BUS SERVICE INC
511 S Lincoln St Stop 1, Elkhorn, WI 53121-1863
Tel (262) 723-4309 Founded/Ownrshp 1992
Sales 12,3MME EMP 400
SIC 4151 School buses; School buses
Pr: Scott Jones
*VP: Eric Jones

D-U-N-S 02-324-7984 IMP
JONES SIGN CO INC
1711 Scheuring Rd, De Pere, WI 54115-9414
Tel (920) 983-6700 Founded/Ownrshp 1982
Sales 67.9MME EMP 350
SIC 1799 Sign installation & maintenance; Sign installation & maintenance
Pr: John Mortensen
Pr: Michael Bjorklund
Sr VP: Thomas Cummings
*Sr VP: Tom Cummings
VP: Steve Berryman
VP: Jeff Jarvis
*VP: Mimi Olson
*VP: Todd Patrickus
IT Man: Neil Oelklaus
Sftwr Eng: Dennis Wolfgram
Sales Exec: James Starkes

D-U-N-S 11-131-6790
JONES SKELTON & HOCHULI PLC
2901 N Central Ave # 800, Phoenix, AZ 85012-2798
Tel (602) 263-1700 Founded/Ownrshp 1983
Sales 29.6MME EMP 160
SIC 8111 Legal services; Legal services
Pt: Edward G Hochuli
Pt: William R Jones
Pt: J Russell Skelton
Pt: Russ Skelton
Pt: Mance Carroll
VP: Sean Moore
Exec: John Sticht

D-U-N-S 80-763-9273 IMP
JONES STEPHENS CORP
PLUMBEST
(Suby of PLUMBING HOLDINGS CORP) ★
3249 Moody Pkwy, Moody, AL 35004-2622
Tel (800) 355-6637 Founded/Ownrshp 2006
Sales 87.9MME EMP 220E
SIC 5074 Plumbing & hydronic heating supplies; Plumbing fittings & supplies; Plumbing & hydronic heating supplies; Plumbing fittings & supplies
CEO: Butch Jones
CFO: Blue Akers
Sr VP: Byron Shaw
*VP: Garry L Taylor
Sfty Dirs: Terry Shaw
Opers Mgr: Brian Owens
Manager: Brett Hicks
Manager: Mark Hipps
Manager: Dmitriy Mintsin
Sales Asso: Brent Wyatt

D-U-N-S 02-482-9087
JONES STORES INC (NC)
J & C WHOLESALE CO
250 N Us Highway 701 Byp, Tabor City, NC 28463-8378
Tel (910) 653-4001 Founded/Ownrshp 1961
Sales 29.9MME EMP 600
SIC 5331 5199 Variety stores; Variety store merchandise; Variety stores; Variety store merchandise
Pr: Michael K Jones
*VP: Dennis D Jones
*VP: James R Jones
Board of Directors: James A Cartrette, James P Jones

D-U-N-S 02-254-5495
JONES TOYOTA GMC TRUCKS INC (MD)
1510 Bel Air Rd, Bel Air, MD 21014-6112
Tel (410) 879-6400 Founded/Ownrshp 1965
Sales 40.4MME EMP 155
SIC 5511 Automobiles, new & used; Automobiles, new & used
Pr: Danny Jones
*VP: Vernon J Jones

D-U-N-S 04-784-9117
JONES UTILITIES CONSTRUCTION INC
436 Tv Dr, Fredericksburg, VA 22408-4158
Tel (540) 891-5545 Founded/Ownrshp 1997
Sales 82.0MM EMP 32
SIC 1623 Underground utilities contractor; Underground utilities contractor
Pr: Robert Jones

D-U-N-S 01-039-7404
JONES WALKER LLP
201 Saint Charles Ave # 5200, New Orleans, LA 70170-5000
Tel (504) 582-8000 Founded/Ownrshp 1982
Sales 180.0MM EMP 800
SIC 8111 General practice law office; General practice law office
Mng Pt: William H Hines
Pt: Jesse R Adams
Pt: Arnold I Havens
Pt: Matthew T Brown
Pt: Andre Burvant
Pt: Susan Chambers
Pt: Scott D Chenevert
Pt: Glen G Goodier
Pt: Curtis R Hearn
Pt: William Joyce
Pt: Robin McGuire
Pt: Marshall J Page III
Pt: John Reynolds
Pt: Coleman D Ridley
Pt: M Richard Schroeder
Pt: R Patrick Vance
Pr: Jacquelyn Stephenson
COO: Jeffrey Bash
CFO: Andrew Bruns
Chf Mktg O: Carol Todd Thomas
Trst Ofcr: Erin Allemand
Board of Directors: Robert S Lazarus, Gary J Russo

D-U-N-S 04-795-4102
JONES WELDING & INDUSTRIAL SUPPLIES INC
1359 Schley Ave, Albany, GA 31707-1848
Tel (229) 888-3917 Founded/Ownrshp 1984
Sales 26.7MME EMP 55
SIC 5085 5084

D-U-N-S 05-135-8323
JONES WHITE HARDWARE & SPORTING GOODS INC (SC)
128 E Shockley Ferry Rd, Anderson, SC 29624-3730
Tel (864) 225-1406 Founded/Ownrshp 1965
Sales 36.0MME EMP 112
SIC 5531 5719 5941 5251 5261 5072 Automotive & home supply stores; Housewares; Sporting goods & bicycle shops; Hardware; Nurseries & garden centers; Hardware
Pr: Walter F Jones
*VP: B D Davis
*VP: Lynn Mullikin

D-U-N-S 09-307-0670
JONES WHOLESALE LUMBER CO INC
10761 Alameda St, Lynwood, CA 90262-1751
Tel (323) 567-1301 Founded/Ownrshp 1977
Sales 110.1MM EMP 45

SIC 5031 Lumber: rough, dressed & finished; Lumber: rough, dressed & finished
CEO: Roderick M Jones
**Pr:* John M Cencak
**Sec:* Robert H Jones
**VP:* Rick Jones
Exec: Stephanie Jones
CIO: Terry Dunlap
Sales Exec: John Pasqualetto
Sls Mgr: Craig Evans
Board of Directors: John M Cencak, Rick H Jones, Robert H Jones, Roderick M Jones

JONES ZYLON COMPANY
See JONES METAL PRODUCTS CO

D-U-N-S 00-732-7364 IMP/EXP
JONES-BLAIR CO LLC
NEOGARD DIVISION
(*Suby of* HEMPEL (USA) INC) ★
2728 Empire Central, Dallas, TX 75235-4409
Tel (214) 353-1600 *Founded/Ownrshp* 1928, 2015
Sales 46.8MM^E *EMP* 160
SIC 2851 5198 2821 1799 5231 Paints & allied products; Undercoatings, paint; Wallcoverings; Plastics materials & resins; Waterproofing; Paints & allied products; Undercoatings, paint; Wallcoverings; Plastics materials & resins; Waterproofing; Paint
Pr: Jeff Powell
CFO: Gary Hauseman
**CFO:* Mark Jarvis
VP: Dan Hamlin
VP: Richard Nayes
Exec: Paul Dague
Exec: Ramona Reich
Exec: Dan Trythall
Exec: Daniel Vazquez
Dir Lab: Rushikesh Amin
Dir Lab: Jasmine Solis

D-U-N-S 00-916-6349 IMP/EXP
JONES-HAMILTON CO
30354 Tracy Rd, Walbridge, OH 43465-9792
Tel (419) 666-9838 *Founded/Ownrshp* 1950
Sales 87.0MM^E *EMP* 90^E
Accts Cliftonlarsonallen Llp Toledo
SIC 2819 Hydrochloric acid; Sodium sulfate, glauber's salt, salt cake; Sulfuric acid, oleum
Pr: Robert L James
**Ch Bd:* J Kern Hamilton
CFO: Brian Brooks
Div Mgr: Ken Jones
IT Man: Dave Moore
Mfg Dir: Chris Obrien
Sfty Mgr: Sam Perras
Plnt Mgr: Chuck Almroth
Plnt Mgr: William Gist
Plnt Mgr: Steve Markovic
Sls Mgr: David Busch

D-U-N-S 00-779-4191
JONES-ONSLOW ELECTRIC MEMBERSHIP CORP
JOEMC
259 Western Blvd, Jacksonville, NC 28546-5736
Tel (910) 353-1940 *Founded/Ownrshp* 1939
Sales 128.1MM *EMP* 151
Accts Adams Jenkins And Cheatham R
SIC 4911 Distribution, electric power; Distribution, electric power
CEO: J Ronald McElheney
**CFO:* Jeff Clark
**Treas:* Thomas Waller
VP: Danny Parker
**Prin:* Horace Phillips
Genl Mgr: Ron McElheney
CIO: Carrie Peters
Sftwr Eng: Querida Butler

D-U-N-S 03-495-2648
JONES-WEST FORD
3600 Kietzke Ln, Reno, NV 89502-4738
Tel (775) 329-8800 *Founded/Ownrshp* 1977
Sales 64.0MM^E *EMP* 185
SIC 5511 7515 Automobiles, new & used; Pickups, new & used; Vans, new & used; Passenger car leasing; Automobiles, new & used; Pickups, new & used; Vans, new & used; Passenger car leasing
Pr: Richard West
**Ch Bd:* Fletcher Jones Jr
**CFO:* Will Klaus
Off Mgr: Dawn Intihar
Store Mgr: Tim Ruff
IT Man: Kathy Griffin

JONES.COM
See JONES INTERNATIONAL LTD

D-U-N-S 07-937-5527
JONES/BLUMENTHAL TEMECULA LLC
MERCEDES-BENZ OF TEMECULA
(*Suby of* FLETCHER JONES MOTOR CARS INC) ★
40910 Temecula Center Dr, Temecula, CA 92591-6007
Tel (877) 800-2654 *Founded/Ownrshp* 2006
Sales 38.6MM^E *EMP* 187^E
SIC 5511 Automobiles, new & used

D-U-N-S 04-159-5997
JONESBORO PUBLIC SCHOOLS
2506 Southwest Sq, Jonesboro, AR 72401-5982
Tel (870) 933-5800 *Founded/Ownrshp* 1998
Sales 52.0MM *EMP* 700
SIC 8211 Public elementary & secondary schools; Public elementary & secondary schools
CFO: Ben Barylske
Dir Sec: Leon Brown
Dir IT: Michael Summers
IT Man: Timothy L Tayor
Sales Asso: Chad R Oldham
Psych: Linda Whiteside

JONESBORO REHABILITATION
See PETERSEN HEALTH PROPERTIES LLC

JONESBURG GRAIN CO
See RHINELAND GRAIN INC

D-U-N-S 03-966-7597
JONI AND FRIENDS
30009 Ladyface Ct, Agoura, CA 91301-2583
Tel (818) 707-5664 *Founded/Ownrshp* 1979
Sales 21.2MM *EMP* 135
Accts Capin Crouse Llp Brea Ca
SIC 8322 Association for the handicapped; Association for the handicapped
CEO: Joni E Tada
Bd of Dir: Chuck Musfeldt
Bd of Dir: Colin Reeves
Bd of Dir: Terry Winkler
**Ex VP:* Billy Burnett
**Ex VP:* Douglas Mazza
Mng Dir: Steve Bundy
Prgrm Mgr: Cheryl Birmingham
Mktg Dir: Lorraine Mazza
Pgrm Dir: Katy Thuleen

JON'S MARKETPLACE
See BERBERIAN ENTERPRISES INC

D-U-N-S 02-203-0118 IMP
JONTI-CRAFT INC
171 State Highway 68, Wabasso, MN 56293-1400
Tel (507) 342-5169 *Founded/Ownrshp* 1979
Sales 25.6MM^E *EMP* 150
SIC 3999 3944 2531 Education aids, devices & supplies; Games, toys & children's vehicles; Public building & related furniture; Education aids, devices & supplies; Games, toys & children's vehicles; Public building & related furniture
CEO: Donald F Schwarz
COO: Neil Dolan
**Sec:* Catherine Schwarz
**VP:* Thomas J Franta
VP: Nick Schwarz
Natl Sales: Kayleb Lassche

D-U-N-S 83-068-0422 IMP
JOON LLC
AJIN USA
(*Suby of* AJIN INDUSTRIAL CO., LTD.)
1500 County Road 177, Cusseta, AL 36852-2764
Tel (334) 756-8601 *Founded/Ownrshp* 2008
Sales 191.3MM *EMP* 500
Accts Choi Kim & Park Llp Montgome
SIC 3465 4214 Automotive stampings; Local trucking with storage; Automotive stampings; Local trucking with storage
CEO: Jung Ho Sea
**COO:* Taechul Kim
Genl Mgr: Hyun Yun
Ql Cn Mgr: Young Park

D-U-N-S 04-034-4277 IMP
JOONG-ANG DAILY NEWS CALIFORNIA INC
KOREA DAILY
(*Suby of* JOONGANG ILBO)
690 Wilshire Pl, Los Angeles, CA 90005-3930
Tel (213) 368-2500 *Founded/Ownrshp* 1988
Sales 60.8MM^E *EMP* 500
SIC 2711 Newspapers, publishing & printing; Newspapers, publishing & printing
CFO: Kae Hong Ko
**Pr:* In Taek Park
Genl Mgr: Yoonsoo Kim
Genl Mgr: Jung Lee
IT Man: Jumi Cho
IT Man: You Jun
Sales Exec: Song Kim
Sls&Mrk Ex: Dong Park
Mktg Dir: Sam Lee
Mktg Mgr: Jin Hong
Mktg Mgr: Brian Kim

D-U-N-S 19-497-2162
JOONGANG USA
KOREA CENTRAL DAILY NEWS
22727 Highway 99 Ste 204, Edmonds, WA 98026-8381
Tel (206) 365-4000 *Founded/Ownrshp* 1985
Sales 15.9MM^E *EMP* 400
SIC 2711 Newspapers; Newspapers
Pr: Tae Won Kang
Sls&Mrk Ex: Justin Kim

D-U-N-S 06-054-1901
JOPAL LLC
BARNWELL NRSING RHBLTATION CTR
3230 Church St, Valatie, NY 12184-2303
Tel (518) 758-1864 *Founded/Ownrshp* 2003
Sales 24.9MM^E *EMP* 330
SIC 8051 Convalescent home with continuous nursing care; Convalescent home with continuous nursing care
Pr: Pasqual De Benedictis
**VP:* Joseph Carillo
**VP:* Alex Solovney
HC Dir: Betty Engel

JOPLIN 44
See TRUCKSTOP DISTRIBUTORS INC

D-U-N-S 06-795-6102
JOPLIN SCHOOL
310 W 8th St, Joplin, MO 64801-4302
Tel (417) 625-5200 *Founded/Ownrshp* 1874
Sales 88.9MM *EMP* 1,260
Accts Mense Churchwell & Mense Pc
SIC 8211 Public elementary school; Public junior high school; Public senior high school; Public vocational/technical school; Public elementary school; Public junior high school; Public senior high school; Public vocational/technical school
**CFO:* Paul Barr
Bd of Dir: Rhonda Randall
IT Man: Ross Lauck
Pr Dir: Kelli Price

D-U-N-S 04-334-7285
JOPO INC (WA)
A&W RESTAURANT
16124 E Marietta Ln, Spokane Valley, WA 99216-1812
Tel (509) 535-7701 *Founded/Ownrshp* 1968, 1988
Sales 57.1MM^E *EMP* 240
Accts Schoedel & Schoedel Cpas Spo
SIC 5541 5411 Filling stations, gasoline; Convenience stores, independent; Filling stations, gasoline; Convenience stores, independent
Pr: Ronald Armacost
**Sec:* Rick Bates
**VP:* Ian Johnstone

D-U-N-S 00-609-4585
JOR-MAC CO INC (WI)
155 Main St, Lomira, WI 53048-9544
Tel (920) 269-8500 *Founded/Ownrshp* 2000
Sales 22.7MM^E *EMP* 110
SIC 3291 3444 3599 Abrasive metal & steel products; Sheet metalwork; Machine shop, jobbing & repair
Pr: Kelly Sayles
Plnt Mgr: Chris Binder

D-U-N-S 08-896-7005
JORDACHE ENTERPRISES INC
1400 Broadway Rm 1404b, New York, NY 10018-5336
Tel (212) 643-8400 *Founded/Ownrshp* 1978
Sales 1.4MMM^E *EMP* 8,000
SIC 2339 2325 2369 2331 2321 2361 Slacks: women's, misses' & juniors'; Men's & boys' trousers & slacks; Slacks: girls' & children's; Jackets: girls', children's & infants'; Shirts, women's & juniors': made from purchased materials; Men's & boys' furnishings; Shirts: girls', children's & infants'; Slacks: women's, misses' & juniors'; Men's & boys' trousers & slacks; Slacks: girls' & children's; Jackets: girls', children's & infants'; Shirts, women's & juniors': made from purchased materials; Men's & boys' furnishings; Shirts: girls', children's & infants'
CEO: Joe Nakash
**Sec:* Ralph Nakash
Ofcr: Channie Laniado
Ex VP: Eddie Benaderet
VP: Shaul Cohen
VP: Charles Flores
**VP:* AVI Nakash
Mng Dir: Jonathan Bennett
Off Mgr: Bruce Byriel
Off Mgr: Miriam Pinillo
Off Mgr: Guy Watson

D-U-N-S 11-060-0678
JORDACHE LIMITED
JE SPORT DIV
(*Suby of* JORDACHE ENTERPRISES INC) ★
1400 Broadway Rm 1404b, New York, NY 10018-5336
Tel (212) 944-1330 *Founded/Ownrshp* 1991
Sales 105.6MM^E *EMP* 200
SIC 5137 5136 6153 Women's & children's clothing; Men's & boys' clothing; Factoring services; Women's & children's clothing; Men's & boys' clothing; Factoring services
Pr: Joseph Nakash
CFO: Joe Taylor
**Sec:* Ralph Nakash
Ofcr: Jamee Jordache
Ex VP: Eddie Aderet
Ex VP: Suzanne Stromfeld
VP: Shaul Cohen
VP: Matt Debnar
**VP:* AVI Nakash
VP: Ricky Ramnani
VP: Ezri Silver

D-U-N-S 17-011-1509
JORDAN & SKALA ENGINEERS INC
4275 Shackleford Rd # 200, Norcross, GA 30093-2997
Tel (770) 447-5547 *Founded/Ownrshp* 2000
Sales 21.0MM^E *EMP* 80^E
SIC 8711 Engineering services
CEO: Charles Jordan
**Ex VP:* Charles C Jordan
**VP:* James Haefeli
VP: Chuck J Pe
**Prin:* W Ross Bush
VP Sls: Christopher McDaniel
Snr Mgr: Regina Young

D-U-N-S 80-852-3229
JORDAN CARRIERS INC
170 Highway 61 S, Natchez, MS 39120-5279
Tel (601) 446-8899 *Founded/Ownrshp* 1992
Sales 77.4MM^E *EMP* 248
SIC 4213 Contract haulers; Contract haulers
Pr: Kenneth Jordan
CFO: Doug Jordan
VP: Charles Jordan

D-U-N-S 19-686-4607
JORDAN CF CONSTRUCTION LLC
(*Suby of* JORDAN CF INVESTMENTS LLP) ★
7700 Cf Jordan Dr Ste 200, El Paso, TX 79912-8807
Tel (915) 877-3333 *Founded/Ownrshp* 1993
Sales 299.9MM *EMP* 500
Accts Schmid Broaddus Nugent Gano Pc
SIC 1542 1541 1522 Nonresidential construction; Industrial buildings & warehouses; Residential construction; Nonresidential construction; Industrial buildings & warehouses; Residential construction
Ch Bd: C F Jordan III
**Pr:* Darren G Woody
**CFO:* Cynthia Rogers
Off Mgr: Kelly Riley
IT Man: Reyna Jamis
Sfty Dirs: Jesus Miranda

D-U-N-S 83-612-7183
JORDAN CF INVESTMENTS LLP
7700 Cf Jordan Dr, El Paso, TX 79912-8808
Tel (915) 877-3333 *Founded/Ownrshp* 1993
Sales 301.9MM^E *EMP* 500
Accts Schmid Broaddus Nugent Gano Pc
SIC 1542 1541 1522 1611 Nonresidential construction; Industrial buildings & warehouses; Residential construction; Highway & street paving contractor; Grading; Nonresidential construction; Industrial buildings & warehouses; Residential construction; Highway & street paving contractor; Grading
Ch: CF Paco Jordan
Pt: C F Jordan III
Ex VP: Paul Bauer
Sfty Dirs: Crystal Stewart
Snr Mgr: Ryan Lack

D-U-N-S 05-038-1243
JORDAN CO L P
399 Park Ave Fl 30, New York, NY 10022-4871
Tel (212) 572-0800 *Founded/Ownrshp* 1982
Sales 441.1MM^E *EMP* 290
SIC 6726

D-U-N-S 86-830-1243
JORDAN CO LC W M
BASS STEEL BUILDINGS COMPANY
(*Suby of* WMJORDAN CO INC) ★
708 Bainbridge St, Richmond, VA 23224-2320
Tel (804) 233-3039 *Founded/Ownrshp* 1994
Sales 26.2MM^E *EMP* 80
SIC 1542 1541 1761 School building construction; Hospital construction; Warehouse construction; Roofing contractor
CEO: John R Lawson
**Treas:* Thomas M Shelton
**Ex VP:* Kenneth Taylor
**VP:* James M Collins
**VP:* Michael Daniels

D-U-N-S 09-558-4439
JORDAN ELBRIDGE CENTRAL SCHOOL DISTRICT
9 N Chappell St, Jordan, NY 13080-4511
Tel (315) 689-8500 *Founded/Ownrshp* 1961
Sales 13.6MM^E *EMP* 300
SIC 8211 Public elementary school; Public junior high school; Public senior high school; Public elementary school; Public junior high school; Public senior high school
Treas: Isabell Montague
Dir IT: Steve Mendrek

JORDAN FORD
See JORDAN MOTORS INC

D-U-N-S 00-895-2855
JORDAN FORD LTD
13010 N Interstate 35, Live Oak, TX 78233-2644
Tel (210) 653-3673 *Founded/Ownrshp* 1946
Sales 84.1MM^E *EMP* 220
SIC 5511 Automobiles, new & used; Automobiles, new & used
Genl Mgr: Tom Murray
**Pt:* Charles Jordan
**Pt:* William A Jordan Jr
CFO: Mike Trompeter
Genl Mgr: Marc Cross
Sls Mgr: Mack Dodd
Sls Mgr: Chuck Perry
Sls Mgr: Don Smith
Sales Asso: Jacob Elizondo
Sales Asso: Rowdy Huff
Sales Asso: Cody Robinson

D-U-N-S 07-909-9262
JORDAN FOSTER CONSTRUCTION LLC (TX)
7700 Cf Jordan Dr Ste 200, El Paso, TX 79912-8807
Tel (915) 877-3333 *Founded/Ownrshp* 2013
Sales 9.1MM *EMP* 1,000
Accts Bkd Llp San Antonio Texas
SIC 1542 Commercial & office building, new construction; Commercial & office building, new construction
Ex VP: Paul Bauer
Ex VP: Roger Pavlovich
Ex VP: Leland Rocchio
VP: John Goodrich
Exec: Roy Allen
Dir Bus: Joe Gomez
Dir IT: John Buraczyk
VP Opers: Roy Raines
Sfty Dirs: Crystal Stewart
Snr PM: Clint Henson

D-U-N-S 94-639-4111
JORDAN HEALTH CARE INC
JORDAN HEALTH SERVICES
(*Suby of* JORDAN HEALTHCARE HOLDINGS INC) ★
412 Texas Highway 37 S, Mount Vernon, TX 75457-6570
Tel (903) 537-3600 *Founded/Ownrshp* 1996
Sales 202.7MM^E *EMP* 13,000^E
SIC 8082 Home health care services; Home health care services
CEO: Dean Anthony Holland
**Pr:* Gregg Cannady
**CFO:* Lance Cornell
**Sr VP:* Chad Wooten
**VP:* Tim Conroy
VP: George Hutto
**VP:* Kathy Poland
Off Admin: Antonio Alvarado
QA Dir: Leigh Claire
Dir IT: Patrick Egan
Dir IT: Craig Miller

JORDAN HEALTH SERVICES
See JHC OPERATIONS LLC

JORDAN HEALTH SERVICES
See JORDAN HEALTH CARE INC

D-U-N-S 17-576-0164
JORDAN HEALTH SYSTEMS INC
JORDAN HOSPITAL
275 Sandwich St, Plymouth, MA 02360-2183
Tel (508) 830-2388 *Founded/Ownrshp* 1901
Sales 194.4MM *EMP* 1,600
Accts Kpmg Llp Boston Massachusett
SIC 8741 8062 Hospital management; General medical & surgical hospitals; Hospital management; General medical & surgical hospitals
CEO: Peter J Holden
CFO: Jack Patricio
CFO: Jason Radzevich
**Ch:* Wilfred Sheehan
**Treas:* Joseph Iannoni
**Sr VP:* James Fanale
**VP:* Donna Doherty
**VP:* Andrea Holleran
Exec: Bill McCarthy
Dir Rad: Ronald Goldberg
Ex Dir: Vivian Divaia

D-U-N-S 96-769-5904
JORDAN HEALTHCARE HOLDINGS INC
SKILLED CARE
412 Texas Highway 37 S, Mount Vernon, TX 75457-5570
Tel (903) 537-2445 *Founded/Ownrshp* 2010
Sales 1.2MMᴱ *EMP* 13,000ᴱ
SIC 6719 8082 Investment holding companies, except banks; Home health care services; Investment holding companies, except banks; Home health care services
CEO: Dean Holland

JORDAN HOSPITAL
See JORDAN HEALTH SYSTEMS INC

D-U-N-S 07-952-3668
JORDAN HOSPITAL CLUB INC
275 Sandwich St, Plymouth, MA 02360-2196
Tel (508) 830-2391 *Founded/Ownrshp* 1901
Sales 197.0MM *EMP* 1,600
SIC 8062 General medical & surgical hospitals; General medical & surgical hospitals
Pr: Peter Holden
**CFO:* Elliot Schwartz
CIO: Cheryl Crowley
Nrsg Dir: Christine Klucznik

D-U-N-S 86-743-8061
JORDAN HOSPITAL INC
275 Sandwich St, Plymouth, MA 02360-2196
Tel (508) 746-2000 *Founded/Ownrshp* 1901
Sales 187.1MM *EMP* 3ᴱ
SIC 8082 Home health care services; Home health care services
VP: Russell Averna
CFO: Jason Radzevich
Treas: Kevin Feeney
**Treas:* Elliot L Schwartz
Chf Mktg O: Bernard Durante
Ofcr: Peter Holden
VP: James Canavan
VP: Lisa L Mennonna
Dir Lab: Bob Hardy
Dir Rad: Justino Fernandes
Dir Rad: James Galvin
Dir Rad: Kenneth Kelly
Dir Rx: John Leone

D-U-N-S 02-794-0683
JORDAN IMPLEMENT CO
BIG HEART SEED A CALIFORNIA
1280 Main St, Brawley, CA 92227-9404
Tel (760) 344-3322 *Founded/Ownrshp* 1950
Sales 22.2MMᴱ *EMP* 75
SIC 5999 5083 Farm equipment & supplies; Farm equipment parts & supplies
Pr: Steven Ellison
IT Man: Luis Felix
IT Man: David Hoskins

D-U-N-S 18-915-8736 IMP/EXP
JORDAN INDUSTRIES INC
1751 Lake Cook Rd Ste 550, Deerfield, IL 60015-5658
Tel (847) 945-5591 *Founded/Ownrshp* 1988
Sales 578.9MMᴱ *EMP* 3,973
SIC 3621 3625 3714 3089 2759 5999 Motors, electric; Electric motor & generator auxiliary parts; Motor starters & controllers, electric; Motor vehicle engines & parts; Rebuilding engines & transmissions, factory basis; Gears, motor vehicle; Thermoformed finished plastic products; Labels & seals: printing; Art, picture frames & decorations; Picture frames, ready made; Motors, electric; Electric motor & generator auxiliary parts; Motor starters & controllers, electric; Motor vehicle engines & parts; Rebuilding engines & transmissions, factory basis; Gears, motor vehicle; Thermoformed finished plastic products; Labels & seals: printing; Art, picture frames & decorations; Picture frames, ready made
Ch Bd: John W Jordan II
Pr: Thomas H Quinn
CFO: Dan Drury
CFO: Michael Elia
CFO: Lisa M Ondrula
Treas: Gordon L Nelson
Sr VP: Joseph C Linen
VP: Edward F Lilly
VP: Pam Ross
Dir Rx: Pal Hayer
Snr Mgr: Reagan Hogerty

JORDAN KITT'S MUSIC
See JORDAN-KITT GROUP

JORDAN LINCOLN MERCURY
See JORDAN TOYOTA INC

D-U-N-S 00-316-5958
JORDAN LUMBER & SUPPLY INC (NC)
1939 Nc Highway 109 S, Mount Gilead, NC 27306-8455
Tel (910) 439-6121 *Founded/Ownrshp* 1939
Sales 72.7MMᴱ *EMP* 400
SIC 2421 Lumber: rough, sawed or planed; Lumber: rough, sawed or planed
Pr: Bob Jordan
COO: Dan Mosley
**Ex VP:* Jack P Jordan
**VP:* Robert B Jordan IV
IT Man: Nick Huneycutt
IT Man: Roy Little
Sls Mgr: Ellen Thompson

D-U-N-S 06-086-9450 EXP
JORDAN MANUFACTURING CO INC
1200 S 6th St, Monticello, IN 47960-8200
Tel (574) 583-6008 *Founded/Ownrshp* 1986
Sales 125.1MMᴱ *EMP* 500ᴱ
SIC 2392 5021 Cushions & pillows; Outdoor & lawn furniture; Cushions & pillows; Outdoor & lawn furniture
Pr: David N Jordan
Ofcr: Gwen Rodenberger
VP: David Wolfe
Exec: Ashley Medley
Telecom Ex: Charles Harvey
CIO: Paul Suhr
Dir IT: Tara Bailey
Dir IT: Oliver Cox
Sfty Mgr: Keith Lehocky
VP Mktg: BJ Mursener

D-U-N-S 01-652-5206 EXP
JORDAN MOTORS INC
JORDAN FORD
609 E Jefferson Blvd, Mishawaka, IN 46545-6524
Tel (574) 259-1981 *Founded/Ownrshp* 1947
Sales 61.6MMᴱ *EMP* 175
SIC 5511 7539 Automobiles, new & used; Pickups, new & used; Vans, new & used; Automotive repair shops; Automobiles, new & used; Pickups, new & used; Vans, new & used; Automotive repair shops
Pr: Craig Kapson
VP: Robert Hayden
MIS Dir: Linda Hazen
Sls Mgr: Kelly Rakowski

D-U-N-S 10-863-5129
JORDAN OUTDOOR ENTERPRISES LTD
1390 Box Cir, Columbus, GA 31907-3200
Tel (706) 569-9101 *Founded/Ownrshp* 1982
Sales 25.7MMᴱ *EMP* 65
SIC 6794 Copyright buying & licensing
CEO: William R Jordan
COO: Rod Hinton
**CFO:* Bill Ross

D-U-N-S 06-506-0717
JORDAN PROPERTIES INC
1451 Fernwood Glendale Rd, Spartanburg, SC 29307-3044
Tel (864) 585-2784 *Founded/Ownrshp* 1985
Sales 22.3MMᴱ *EMP* 655
SIC 7011 Resort hotel; Resort hotel
Pr: Robert L Jordan
**CEO:* William Crosby

D-U-N-S 07-298-3406
JORDAN SCHOOL DISTRICT
7387 S Campus View Dr, West Jordan, UT 84084-5500
Tel (801) 280-3689 *Founded/Ownrshp* 1913
Sales 391.8MM *EMP* 5,900
Accts Squire & Company Pc Orem Ut
SIC 8211 Public elementary & secondary schools; Elementary school; Specialty education; Public elementary & secondary schools; Elementary school; Specialty education
**VP:* Leah Voorhies
**Prin:* Richard S Osborn
**Prin:* Susan Pulsipher
Dir Sec: Jeff Beesley
Off Admin: Wendy Johnson
MIS Dir: Cindy Nagasawa-Cruz
IT Man: Denice Brown
Pr Dir: Sandra Riesgraf
Teacher Pr: June Lemaster
Cert Phar: Kathy Richins
Occ Thrpy: Melinda Stevens

D-U-N-S 62-408-3684
JORDAN SPECIALTY PLASTICS INC
(*Suby of* JORDAN INDUSTRIES INC) ★
1751 Lake Cook Rd Ste 550, Deerfield, IL 60015-5624
Tel (847) 945-5591 *Founded/Ownrshp* 2006
Sales 138.6MMᴱ *EMP* 701ᴱ
SIC 3089 3081 Plastic containers, except foam; Unsupported plastics film & sheet
Prin: Lisa Ondrula

D-U-N-S 94-851-4328 IMP/EXP
JORDAN TECHNOLOGIES LLC
(*Suby of* AEREON) ★
5051 Cmmerce Crossings Dr, Louisville, KY 40229-2101
Tel (502) 267-8344 *Founded/Ownrshp* 2013
Sales 21.5MMᴱ *EMP* 63ᴱ
SIC 3671 Gas or vapor tubes
Pr: Mark A Jordan
**VP:* John F Jordan
**VP:* Paul D Jordan
Sls Mgr: Mike Abner

D-U-N-S 62-538-3419
JORDAN TOYOTA INC
JORDAN LINCOLN MERCURY
609 E Jefferson Blvd, Mishawaka, IN 46545-6524
Tel (574) 259-1981 *Founded/Ownrshp* 1981
Sales 22.7MMᴱ *EMP* 60
SIC 5511 New & used car dealers; Automobiles, new & used
Ch Bd: Jordan H Kapson
Sls Mgr: Todd Elgas
Sls Mgr: Deb Starkweather

D-U-N-S 16-939-5691
JORDAN TRANSFORMER LLC
1000 Syndicate St, Jordan, MN 55352-1110
Tel (952) 492-2720 *Founded/Ownrshp* 2004
Sales 26.1MMᴱ *EMP* 67
SIC 3612 7629 Feeder voltage boosters (electric transformers); Feeder voltage regulators (electric transformers); Electrical equipment repair services; Electrical equipment repair, high voltage
IT Man: Cinda Smith
Sls Mgr: John Progar

D-U-N-S 01-111-6019
JORDAN TRANSPORTATION INC
(*Suby of* STUDENT TRANSPORTATION OF AMERICA INC) ★
284 Main St Ste A, Butler, NJ 07405-1099
Tel (973) 838-1284 *Founded/Ownrshp* 1962
Sales 12.5MMᴱ *EMP* 310ᴱ
SIC 4151 School buses; School buses
Pr: Mark Jordan
**Treas:* Arthur Jordan
Trfc Dir: Gayle Stager

D-U-N-S 19-439-3781
JORDAN TRUCK SALES INC
1460 Bankhead Hwy, Carrollton, GA 30116-8586
Tel (770) 836-1700 *Founded/Ownrshp* 1987
Sales 28.0MM *EMP* 42
SIC 5511

D-U-N-S 96-376-3719
JORDAN VALLEY MEDICAL CENTER LP
(*Suby of* IASIS HEALTHCARE CORP) ★
3580 W 9000 S, West Jordan, UT 84088-8812
Tel (801) 561-8888 *Founded/Ownrshp* 1996
Sales 61.4MMᴱ *EMP* 1,300
SIC 8062 General medical & surgical hospitals; General medical & surgical hospitals
CEO: Steven M Anderson
CFO: Jerry Panter
Dir Inf Cn: Mary Jordan
Dir Inf Cn: Robyn Rollins-Root
Chf Nrs Of: Jolisa Catmull
Off Mgr: Laurie Madsen
Doctor: Patrick Vandenhazel

D-U-N-S 06-677-6048 IMP
JORDAN-KITT GROUP
JORDAN KITT'S MUSIC
9520 Baltimore Ave, College Park, MD 20740-1322
Tel (301) 474-9500 *Founded/Ownrshp* 1912, 1983
Sales 23.4MMᴱ *EMP* 180
Accts Beers & Culer Pllc Vienna Vi
SIC 5736 Pianos; Keyboard instruments; Organs; Pianos; Keyboard instruments; Organs
CEO: William J McCormick Jr
**Pr:* Richard G Grant
**Ex VP:* Christoph Syllaba
Sls&Mrk Ex: J Ottenritter

D-U-N-S 15-272-5248 IMP/EXP
JORDANA COSMETICS CORP
2035 E 49th St, Vernon, CA 90058-2801
Tel (323) 585-4859 *Founded/Ownrshp* 1986
Sales 39.5MMᴱ *EMP* 65
SIC 5122 Cosmetics
Pr: Laurie Minc
Ex VP: Bob Wallner
Exec: Haskel Hoseph
**Prin:* Ralph Bijou
Dir IT: Jenny Ponce
Opers Mgr: John Papa
S&M/VP: Robert Wallner

JORDANO'S FOOD SERVICE
See JORDANOS INC

D-U-N-S 02-937-9088 IMP
JORDANOS INC
JORDANO'S FOOD SERVICE
550 S Patterson Ave, Santa Barbara, CA 93111-2498
Tel (805) 964-0611 *Founded/Ownrshp* 1915
Sales 441.7MMᴱ *EMP* 500
SIC 5181 5182 5149 5141 5142 5148 Beer & other fermented malt liquors; Wine; Soft drinks; Groceries, general line; Packaged frozen goods; Fresh fruits & vegetables; Beer & other fermented malt liquors; Wine; Soft drinks; Groceries, general line; Packaged frozen goods; Fresh fruits & vegetables
CEO: Peter Jordano
CFO: Michael F Sieckowski
Ex VP: Jeffrey S Jordano
Manager: Dave Lynn

D-U-N-S 01-967-8168 IMP
■ **JORDANS FURNITURE INC**
(*Suby of* BERKSHIRE HATHAWAY INC) ★
450 Revolutionary Dr, East Taunton, MA 02718-1369
Tel (508) 828-4000 *Founded/Ownrshp* 1999
Sales 245.7MMᴱ *EMP* 1,200
SIC 5712 Furniture stores; Furniture stores
CEO: Barry Tatelman
**COO:* Peter Bolton
**CFO:* David Stavros
**Sec:* Steve Wholley
**VP:* Joshua Tatelman
VP: Michael Tatelman
Exec: Ethan Peterson
Dir Risk M: Denise Deslauriers
Dir IT: Peter Clark
Software D: Andrew Hanson
Opers Mgr: Tom Jensen

D-U-N-S 11-680-5917 IMP
JORE CORP
(*Suby of* WESTERN MORTGAGE & REALTY CO) ★
34837 Innovation, Ronan, MT 59864-8796
Tel (406) 528-4350 *Founded/Ownrshp* 2002
Sales 45.2MMᴱ *EMP* 138
SIC 3423 Hand & edge tools; Hand & edge tools
Pr: Frank Tiegs
**Treas:* Tim Tippett
**VP:* Mick Cheff
VP: Jeffrey M Heutaker
VP: Jeffrey Heutmaker
VP Opers: Mick Scheff

D-U-N-S 06-629-9397 IMP
JORGE M PEREZ ART MUSEUM OF MIAMI-DADE COUNTY INC
101 W Flagler St Ste B, Miami, FL 33130-1541
Tel (305) 375-3000 *Founded/Ownrshp* 1980
Sales 55.3MM *EMP* 40ᴱ
Accts Marcum Llp Miami Fl
SIC 8412 7389 Museums & art galleries; Fund raising organizations; Museums & art galleries; Fund raising organizations
**Pr:* Jeff Krinsky
Treas: Luke Palacio
**VP:* Gregory C Ferrero
**VP:* Walid G Wahab

JORGENSEN & CO
See JORGENSEN & SONS INC

D-U-N-S 02-819-3191
JORGENSEN & SONS INC
JORGENSEN & CO
2691 S East Ave, Fresno, CA 93706-5409
Tel (559) 268-6241 *Founded/Ownrshp* 1937
Sales 42.3MMᴱ *EMP* 111
SIC 5099 1731 Safety equipment & supplies; Fire detection & burglar alarm systems specialization; Safety equipment & supplies; Fire detection & burglar alarm systems specialization
CEO: Darrell Hefley
Ch Bd: Donald Jorgensen
Pr: Leon Young
Treas: Jack Jorgensen
Treas: Jim Rushing
V Ch Bd: Al V Jorgensen
IT Man: Stephen Hughes
Mktg Dir: Ken McCollum
Sls Mgr: Jeff Young

D-U-N-S 95-896-8117
JORGENSEN CONTRACT SERVICES LLC
(*Suby of* ROY JORGENSEN ASSOCIATES INC) ★
17400 East St, North Fort Myers, FL 33917-2102
Tel (239) 567-2043 *Founded/Ownrshp* 2002
Sales 16.6MMᴱ *EMP* 300
SIC 8711 Engineering services; Engineering services
Pr: Douglas W Selby

JORGENSEN FORD
See FORD JORGENSEN SALES INC

D-U-N-S 79-088-5842 IMP/EXP
JORGENSEN FORGE CORP
(*Suby of* JFC HOLDING CORP) ★
8531 E Marginal Way S, Tukwila, WA 98108-4018
Tel (206) 762-1100 *Founded/Ownrshp* 1997
Sales 57.2MMᴱ *EMP* 180
SIC 3462 Iron & steel forgings; Gear & chain forgings
Pr: Steve Abelman
CFO: Jon Wagoner
**VP:* Robert O'Connor
IT Man: Cindy Brown
IT Man: David Carlisle
VP Opers: Dennis Martin
Sfty Mgr: Chris Duke
VP Sls: Mark Twete
Sls Mgr: Joe Nelson

JORGENSEN FORGE PARENT
See JFC HOLDING CORP

JORGENSEN STEEL AND ALUMINUM
See EARLE M JORGENSEN CO

D-U-N-S 07-923-7427 IMP
JORGENSON MACHINE TOOLS INC
JMT USA
2895 S 300 W, Salt Lake City, UT 84115-3435
Tel (801) 493-0151 *Founded/Ownrshp* 1967
Sales 20.8MMᴱ *EMP* 38
SIC 5084 Machine tools & metalworking machinery
Pr: Kyle Jorgenson
**VP:* Bryan Jorgenson
Opers Mgr: Jared Peterson
Manager: Lance Lamberton
Manager: Shane Reynolds
Sales Asso: Beau Moore

D-U-N-S 95-708-3954
JORMAC AEROSPACE
11221 69th St, Largo, FL 33773-5504
Tel (727) 549-9600 *Founded/Ownrshp* 1995
Sales 23.2MMᴱ *EMP* 85
SIC 3728 Aircraft parts & equipment
Pr: Steve Jourdenais
Exec: Patricia Hollingsworth
IT Man: Andrew Kates
VP Sls: Tom Cutchall

D-U-N-S 04-777-4633
JORY JOHN CORP
1894 N Main St, Orange, CA 92865-4117
Tel (714) 279-7901 *Founded/Ownrshp* 1965
Sales 64.9MMᴱ *EMP* 500
SIC 1742 Drywall; Drywall
CEO: Kenneth Johnson
VP: Tim Harrison
VP: Greg Petersen
Snr PM: Rodney Kline

D-U-N-S 06-490-0079 IMP
■ **JOS A BANK CLOTHIERS INC**
(*Suby of* MENS WEARHOUSE INC) ★
500 Hanover Pike, Hampstead, MD 21074-2002
Tel (410) 239-2700 *Founded/Ownrshp* 2014
Sales 697.7MMᴱ *EMP* 6,342
SIC 5611 5961 Men's & boys' clothing stores; Clothing accessories: men's & boys'; Clothing, mail order (except women's); Men's & boys' clothing stores; Clothing accessories: men's & boys'; Clothing, mail order (except women's)
Pr: R Neal Black
CEO: Robert Wildrick
CFO: David E Ullman
Treas: Richard Pitt
Treas: Richard E Pitts
Chf Mktg O: James Singh
Chf Mktg O: James W Thorne
Ex VP: Neal Black
Ex VP: Robert B Hensley
Ex VP: Gary M Merry
VP: Andrea Boling
VP: Gary Cejka
VP: Carol Moore
VP: Nick Rizzi
VP: Brent Thompson

D-U-N-S 06-829-6839 IMP/EXP
JOS H LOWENSTEIN AND SONS INC (NY)
420 Morgan Ave, Brooklyn, NY 11222-5705
Tel (718) 218-8013 *Founded/Ownrshp* 1897
Sales 31.5MMᴱ *EMP* 85
SIC 2869 2865 Industrial organic chemicals; Dyes, synthetic organic; Industrial organic chemicals; Dyes, synthetic organic
Ch Bd: Stephen J Lowenstein
**Pr:* David Lowenstein
**Ex VP:* Sue Papish
VP: Richard Cahayla-Wynne
**VP:* Thomas Sowpel
VP: Chao Zheng
Plnt Mgr: John Rotter
Plnt Mgr: Armando Thapellquen

D-U-N-S 00-980-5813
JOS SCHMITT & SONS CONST CO INC
KIRBY STEEL BUILDINGS
2104 Union Ave, Sheboygan, WI 53081-5560
Tel (920) 457-4426 *Founded/Ownrshp* 1986
Sales 36.7MM *EMP* 80
Accts Schenck Sc Sheboygan Wiscons

SIC 1542 1541 Commercial & office building, new construction; Commercial & office buildings, renovation & repair; Industrial buildings, new construction; Renovation, remodeling & repairs: industrial buildings; Commercial & office building, new construction; Commercial & office buildings, renovation & repair; Industrial buildings, new construction; Renovation, remodeling & repairs: industrial buildings
Pr: Steven J Schmitt
**Treas:* Reed Schmitt
**VP:* Roy E Ten Pas

D-U-N-S 07-911-6847
JOSE MASSUH REVOCABLE TRUST
825 Brickell Bay Dr, Miami, FL 33131-2936
Tel (305) 358-1900 *Founded/Ownrshp* 1982
Sales 85.0MM *EMP* 48
SIC 5162 Plastics resins; Plastics resins
Pr: Jose M Massuh

D-U-N-S 09-006-7786 IMP/EXP
JOSE SANTIAGO INC
Marginal Carr 5 Km 4 4 St Marginal Ca, Bayamon, PR 00959
Tel (787) 288-8835 *Founded/Ownrshp* 1902
Sales 221.8MM[E] *EMP* 300
SIC 5142 5149 Meat, frozen: packaged; Canned goods: fruit, vegetables, seafood, meats, etc.; Meat, frozen: packaged; Canned goods: fruit, vegetables, seafood, meats, etc.
Pr: Jose Santiago
**Treas:* Eduardo Santiago
**VP:* Eduardo S Gonzalez
**VP:* Julio Julia

D-U-N-S 79-170-1063
JOSEPH A CAPLAN MD PC
JILLY, GABOR S MD
13128 N 94th Dr Ste 100, Peoria, AZ 85381-4252
Tel (623) 876-8816 *Founded/Ownrshp* 1989
Sales 21.8MM[E] *EMP* 85
SIC 8011 Cardiologist & cardio-vascular specialist
Pr: Joseph A Caplan MD
**VP:* Gabor S Jilly
Prac Mgr: Lori Duval
Off Mgr: Josie Chapman
Doctor: Jeffery Greenberg
Doctor: Fredric Klopf
Doctor: George Wong

JOSEPH ABBOUD
See JA APPAREL CORP

D-U-N-S 04-008-4469 IMP
■ **JOSEPH ABBOUD MANUFACTURING CORP**
(*Suby of* MENS WEARHOUSE INC) ★
689 Belleville Ave, New Bedford, MA 02745-6011
Tel (508) 999-1301 *Founded/Ownrshp* 2007
Sales 52.1MM[E] *EMP* 500
SIC 2311 Suits, men's & boys': made from purchased materials; Jackets, tailored suit-type: men's & boys'; Suits, men's & boys': made from purchased materials; Jackets, tailored suit-type: men's & boys'
Pr: Anthony Sapienza
CFO: Kim Raphael
**CFO:* Eric Spiel
Exec: Marisol Fernandez

JOSEPH AIRPORT TOYOTA
See JOSEPH T OF D CO

D-U-N-S 03-859-2572
JOSEPH AND WILLIAM STAVOLA INC
460 River Rd, Kingston, NJ 08528
Tel (609) 924-0300 *Founded/Ownrshp* 1966
Sales 15.7MM[E] *EMP* 350
SIC 3273 2951 1429 1611 Ready-mixed concrete; Concrete, bituminous; Trap rock, crushed & broken-quarrying; Highway & street paving contractor; Ready-mixed concrete; Concrete, bituminous; Trap rock, crushed & broken-quarrying; Highway & street paving contractor
Pr: Joseph W Stavola
**Sec:* William Stavola

D-U-N-S 00-581-2011
JOSEPH B FAY CO
100 Sky Ln, Tarentum, PA 15084-2807
Tel (412) 963-1870 *Founded/Ownrshp* 2009
Sales 60.6MM[E] *EMP* 100[E]
SIC 1611 1622 1623 Highway & street construction; Bridge, tunnel & elevated highway; Water, sewer & utility lines; Highway & street construction; Bridge, tunnel & elevated highway; Water, sewer & utility lines
Pr: Lester C Snyder
**Treas:* Chad M Vittone
VP: John P Greene
**VP:* James P McNelis
VP: James McNelis
**Prin:* Shawn M Fay
IT Man: John Thompson
Sfty Dirs: Braedon Foreman
Sfty Dirs: Dave Maloney
Mtls Mgr: Carter Dicken
Mtls Mgr: Sean Schoedel

D-U-N-S 02-947-9169
JOSEPH B WHITEHEAD FOUNDATION
ROBERT WOODRUSS FOUNDATION
191 Peachtree St Ne # 3540, Atlanta, GA 30303-1799
Tel (404) 522-6755 *Founded/Ownrshp* 1937
Sales 36.5MM *EMP* 12
SIC 6732 8733 Charitable trust management; Noncommercial research organizations; Charitable trust management; Noncommercial research organizations
Pr: P Russell Hardin
V Ch: James M Sibley
**Treas:* Lee Trible
Ofcr: Elizabeth A Smith

D-U-N-S 00-693-5571
JOSEPH BEHR & SONS INC (IL)
BEHR IRON & METAL
1100 Seminary St, Rockford, IL 61104-4644
Tel (815) 987-2600 *Founded/Ownrshp* 1906
Sales 174.1MM[E] *EMP* 412
Accts Mc Gladrey & Pullen Cpas Roc
SIC 5093 Ferrous metal scrap & waste
CEO: Richard Behr
**CFO:* Leland R Foecking
VP: Michael Schwebke
MIS Dir: Dave Steneck
IT Man: David Lai

D-U-N-S 08-510-7522
JOSEPH BETHANY-ST CORP
BETHANY-ST JOSEPH HEALTH CARE
2501 Shelby Rd, La Crosse, WI 54601-8037
Tel (608) 788-5700 *Founded/Ownrshp* 1977
Sales 22.2MM *EMP* 525
Accts Hawkins Ash Baptie And Co Llp
SIC 8051 Convalescent home with continuous nursing care; Convalescent home with continuous nursing care
Ex Dir: Craig Ubbelohde
Ex Dir: Kim Scholze
Nrsg Dir: Nancy Johnson

D-U-N-S 02-337-2113 IMP
JOSEPH CAMPIONE INC
2201 W South Branch Blvd, Oak Creek, WI 53154-4906
Tel (414) 761-8944 *Founded/Ownrshp* 1963
Sales 24.4MM[E] *EMP* 75
SIC 2051 Bread, cake & related products
Pr: Angelina Campione
**Treas:* Gena Campione
**VP:* Ann Campione
**VP:* Salvatore Campione

D-U-N-S 01-764-7488
JOSEPH CHEVROLET OLDSMOBILE CO INC (OH)
8733 Colerain Ave, Cincinnati, OH 45251-2992
Tel (513) 741-6700 *Founded/Ownrshp* 1965
Sales 37.4MM[E] *EMP* 110
SIC 5511 5521 7538 7532 Automobiles, new & used; Trucks, tractors & trailers: new & used; Used car dealers; General automotive repair shops; Top & body repair & paint shops; Automobiles, new & used; Trucks, tractors & trailers: new & used; Used car dealers; General automotive repair shops; Top & body repair & paint shops
Ch Bd: Ronald Joseph
**Sec:* Louis Rouse
Ex VP: Ben Bishop

D-U-N-S 06-671-0732
JOSEPH CONSTRUCTION CO INC
203 Letterman Rd, Knoxville, TN 37919-6300
Tel (865) 584-3945 *Founded/Ownrshp* 1972
Sales 45.9MM[E] *EMP* 93
SIC 1542 1541 Commercial & office building, new construction; Industrial buildings, new construction; Commercial & office building, new construction; Industrial buildings, new construction
Pr: Gerry Eastman
**VP:* Michael Nichols
**Prin:* Joseph R Zappa
Dir IT: Tony Parton

JOSEPH CORY COMPANIES
See CORY JOSEPH HOLDING LLC

D-U-N-S 00-891-5167
JOSEPH DAVIS INC
DAVIS JOSEPH MECHANICAL SVCS
120 W Tupper St, Buffalo, NY 14201-2170
Tel (716) 842-1500 *Founded/Ownrshp* 1932
Sales 22.7MM[E] *EMP* 350
SIC 1711 1629 1623 3498 3443 2448 Plumbing contractors; Ventilation & duct work contractor; Warm air heating & air conditioning contractor; Refrigeration contractor; Power plant construction; Water, sewer & utility lines; Fabricated pipe & fittings; Fabricated plate work (boiler shop); Wood pallets & skids; Plumbing contractors; Ventilation & duct work contractor; Warm air heating & air conditioning contractor; Refrigeration contractor; Power plant construction; Water, sewer & utility lines; Fabricated pipe & fittings; Fabricated plate work (boiler shop); Wood pallets & skids
Pr: Jeffrey J Davis
**CFO:* Jean G Gaulin Jr
**Ex VP:* Steven G Shahin
**Sr VP:* James Davis
**VP:* Donald Hills
**VP:* Mark Jarnot
**VP:* Joseph Kuczkowski
**VP:* Peter Orendorf
**VP:* Paul M Price

D-U-N-S 80-820-0328
JOSEPH EDMUNDS
COASTAL MILLING WORKS
58 Swan St, Medford, MA 02155-4644
Tel (781) 560-2855 *Founded/Ownrshp* 2007
Sales 80.0MM[E] *EMP* 1
SIC 3356 3339 3364 3369 Titanium; Titanium metal, sponge & granules; Titanium die-castings; Titanium castings, except die-casting; Titanium; Titanium metal, sponge & granules; Titanium die-castings; Titanium castings, except die-casting
Owner: Joseph Edmunds
Off Mgr: Kelly Edmunds

D-U-N-S 00-786-7252
JOSEPH ELETTO TRANSFER INC (NY)
CIRCLE E LEASEWAYS
575 Underhill Blvd # 222, Syosset, NY 11791-3416
Tel (516) 937-3950 *Founded/Ownrshp* 1950
Sales 43.0MM[E] *EMP* 192
SIC 4213 Trucking, except local; Trucking, except local
CEO: John Eletto

D-U-N-S 03-895-5837
JOSEPH F BURKE CORP
JO JO'S VARIETY STORE
6965 Truck World Blvd, Hubbard, OH 44425-3258
Tel (330) 534-8700 *Founded/Ownrshp* 1980
Sales 51.1MM[E] *EMP* 220
SIC 5541 5812 5531 Truck stops; Eating places; Automotive accessories; Truck equipment & parts; Truck stops; Eating places; Automotive accessories; Truck equipment & parts
Pr: Joseph F Burke

JOSEPH FARMS CHEESE
See GALLO CATTLE CO A LIMITED PARTNERSHIP

D-U-N-S 01-964-0044
JOSEPH FREEDMAN CO INC (MA)
115 Stevens St, Springfield, MA 01104-3120
Tel (203) 887-1463 *Founded/Ownrshp* 1891, 1971
Sales 21.0MM[E] *EMP* 86
SIC 3355 Aluminum wire & cable; Aluminum wire & cable
Pr: John Freedman
**CFO:* Don George
**VP:* Michael Freedman
**VP:* Ernest Gagnon Jr
Trfc Dir: Bill Nichols
Sls Mgr: Ernie Gagnon

JOSEPH GILENE, PRESIDENT
See LOUISVILLE HOSPITAL

D-U-N-S 02-938-5994
JOSEPH J ALBANESE INC
851 Martin Ave, Santa Clara, CA 95050-2903
Tel (408) 727-5700 *Founded/Ownrshp* 1974
Sales 158.5MM[E] *EMP* 700
SIC 1771 Concrete work; Concrete work
CEO: John L Albanese
VP: Leslie Cusimano
VP: Nick Dalis
Exec: Stephanie Nguyen
Off Mgr: Melissa Delgado
CTO: John Formoso
VP Opers: Filemon Calderon
Sfty Mgr: Gary Thomas
VP Sls: Phil Roby
S&M/VP: Jeff Jacobs
Sls Mgr: Ronald Vega

D-U-N-S 02-425-7826
JOSEPH J MAGNOLIA INC (MD)
600 Gallatin St Ne, Washington, DC 20017-2359
Tel (202) 829-8510 *Founded/Ownrshp* 1954
Sales 34.4MM[E] *EMP* 130
SIC 1711

D-U-N-S 01-178-9237
JOSEPH JINGOLI & SON INC
JJS
100 Lenox Dr Ste 100, Lawrenceville, NJ 08648-2332
Tel (609) 896-3111 *Founded/Ownrshp* 1922
Sales 169.4MM[E] *EMP* 350
SIC 1541 Industrial buildings & warehouses; Industrial buildings & warehouses
CEO: Joseph R Jingoli Jr
**Pr:* Robert E Reager
**CFO:* Michael D Jingoli
VP: Frank Kark
VP: Andy Why
Exec: Stella Jones
IT Man: Nick Tzanavaris
Sfty Dirs: Edward Kuhn
Genl Couns: Glenn Clouser
Snr PM: Richard Basso
Snr PM: Steve Burke

D-U-N-S 05-100-5601 IMP
JOSEPH L ERTL INC
SCALE MODELS
502 5th St Nw, Dyersville, IA 52040-1026
Tel (563) 875-2436 *Founded/Ownrshp* 1970
Sales 21.1MM[E] *EMP* 125
SIC 3089 3363 3999 3944 3369 3365 Injection molded finished plastic products; Aluminum die-castings; Miniatures; Games, toys & children's vehicles; Nonferrous foundries; Aluminum foundries; Injection molded finished plastic products; Aluminum die-castings; Miniatures; Games, toys & children's vehicles; Nonferrous foundries; Aluminum foundries
Pr: Joseph L Ertl
**Treas:* Helen R Ertl
Treas: Julie Jensen
Mng Dir: Bob Willits
Genl Mgr: Robert Willits
QA Dir: Linda Fangmann
IT Man: Mary Clostermann
Opers Mgr: Bill Sauser
Ql Cn Mgr: Dean Johnson
Ql Cn Mgr: Dean Schmidt
Mktg Dir: Randy Fendell

D-U-N-S 10-198-2957
JOSEPH L MORSE GERIATRIC CENTER INC
4847 Fred Gladstone Dr, West Palm Beach, FL 33417-8023
Tel (561) 471-5111 *Founded/Ownrshp* 1980
Sales 40.1MM *EMP* 711
Accts Moore Stephens Lovelace Pa Cl
SIC 8051 Skilled nursing care facilities; Skilled nursing care facilities
CEO: Keith A Myers
**COO:* Morrif Funk
**CFO:* Hong Chae
**CFO:* Janet McCullum
**Treas:* Carol Cohen
**Sr VP:* Mary Alice Pappas
**Sr VP:* Alan Sadowsky
VP: Mary Pappas
Dir Soc: Paola Wierzbicki
**Ex Dir:* E Drew Gackenheimer
Ex Dir: Drew E Gackenhimr

D-U-N-S 03-569-4926
JOSEPH M ZIMMER INC
2225 Northwood Dr, Salisbury, MD 21801-7806
Tel (410) 546-5700 *Founded/Ownrshp* 1982
Sales 20.5MM[E] *EMP* 75
SIC 1711 Mechanical contractor
CEO: Mark Rinker
**Pr:* Joseph Zimmer III
VP: Dwayne Austin
VP: Richard Forrest

D-U-N-S 01-869-0214
JOSEPH MERRITT & CO INC
650 Franklin Ave Ste 3, Hartford, CT 06114-3091
Tel (860) 296-2500 *Founded/Ownrshp* 1908
Sales 31.3MM[E] *EMP* 73
SIC 8748 2752 7331 7374 7389 Communications consulting; Commercial printing, offset; Direct mail advertising services; Computer graphics service; Document & office record destruction
Pr: Edward W Perry
**CFO:* Carla Francalangia
**VP:* Patrick Freer
**VP:* Craig Perry
Exec: Tom Kalinski
Mktg Mgr: Jessica Grant

JOSEPH P. ADDABBO FAMILY HEALT
See JOSEPH P ADDABBO FAMILY HEALTH CENTER INC

D-U-N-S 17-513-5524
JOSEPH P ADDABBO FAMILY HEALTH CENTER INC
JOSEPH P. ADDABBO FAMILY HEALT
6200 Beach Channel Dr, Arverne, NY 11692-1409
Tel (718) 945-7150 *Founded/Ownrshp* 1986
Sales 38.1MM *EMP* 125
SIC 8011 Medical centers
Ch: Beverly Tate
CFO: Yolinda Berrosa
Treas: Sam Awasolu
Ex Dir: J R Peter Nelson

D-U-N-S 79-692-0929
JOSEPH PRINCE MINISTRIES INC
1075 Maxwell Mill Rd, Fort Mill, SC 29708-8198
Tel (866) 909-9673 *Founded/Ownrshp* 2007
Sales 27.6MM *EMP* 3
SIC 8661 Religious organizations; Religious organizations
Pr: Joseph Prince
**Ch Bd:* An Tian Fiew

JOSEPH SIMON & SONS
See SIMON METALS LLC

D-U-N-S 06-927-2292
JOSEPH SMITH & SONS INC (DE)
(*Suby of* SMITH INDUSTRIES INC) ★
2001 Kenilworth Ave, Capitol Heights, MD 20743-6711
Tel (301) 773-1266 *Founded/Ownrshp* 1923, 1985
Sales 66.6MM[E] *EMP* 188[E]
SIC 5093

D-U-N-S 01-107-2469
JOSEPH SOLTZ PAINT STORE INC
2517 Atlantic Ave 19, Atlantic City, NJ 08401-6521
Tel (609) 344-2177 *Founded/Ownrshp* 1973
Sales 22.2MM[E] *EMP* 28
SIC 5198 5231 Paints; Paint
Pr: Lawrence Gash

D-U-N-S 87-430-1013
JOSEPH STEVENS & CO INC
4 Windham Ct, Glen Head, NY 11545-3200
Tel (212) 361-3000 *Founded/Ownrshp* 1993
Sales 20.5MM[E] *EMP* 260
SIC 6282 6211 Investment advice; Investment bankers; Investment advice; Investment bankers
CEO: Joseph Sorbaro
**Pr:* Steven Markowitz
CFO: Maria Tingoli

D-U-N-S 01-796-8223
JOSEPH T OF D CO
JOSEPH AIRPORT TOYOTA
1180 W National Rd, Vandalia, OH 45377-1027
Tel (937) 898-8060 *Founded/Ownrshp* 1981
Sales 45.7MM[E] *EMP* 65
SIC 5511 Automobiles, new & used; Automobiles, new & used
Pr: Ron Joseph
**Treas:* Lou Rouse
IT Man: Christian Hahn
Sls Mgr: Paul Mayo
Sls Mgr: Dan Zappia
Sales Asso: Eddy Galera

D-U-N-S 00-693-2446 IMP
■ **JOSEPH T RYERSON & SON INC**
(*Suby of* RYERSON HOLDING CORP) ★
227 W Monroe St Fl 27, Chicago, IL 60606-5081
Tel (773) 762-2121 *Founded/Ownrshp* 1999
Sales 2.7MMM[E] *EMP* 3,200
SIC 5051 5162 Metals service centers & offices; Steel; Aluminum bars, rods, ingots, sheets, pipes, plates, etc.; Miscellaneous nonferrous products; Plastics materials & basic shapes; Metals service centers & offices; Steel; Aluminum bars, rods, ingots, sheets, pipes, plates, etc.; Miscellaneous nonferrous products; Plastics materials & basic shapes
CEO: Michael C Arnold
Pr: Tom Endres
**Pr:* Kevin Richardson
**CEO:* Edward J Lehner
CFO: Jay M Grapz
**CFO:* Terence Rogers
**CFO:* Erich Schnaufer
Treas: Terrance R Oges
Ex VP: Gary Niederpruem
VP: Leslie M Norgren
**VP:* Mary Ann Sigler CPA

JOSEPH TOYOTA
See TOYOTA OF CINCINNATI

D-U-N-S 05-496-1701
JOSEPHINE COUNTY
500 Nw 6th St, Grants Pass, OR 97526-2037
Tel (541) 474-5221 *Founded/Ownrshp* 1856
Sales NA *EMP* 641
Accts Pauly Rogers And Co PcT
SIC 9131
Ch Bd: Jim Riddle
**V Ch:* Dwight Ellis
Treas: Jim Harelson

JOSEPHINE SUNSET HOME DAYCARE
See JOSEPHINE SUNSET HOME INC

D-U-N-S 07-818-9842
JOSEPHINE SUNSET HOME INC (WA)
JOSEPHINE SUNSET HOME DAYCARE
9901 272nd Pl Nw, Stanwood, WA 98292-7449
Tel (360) 629-2126 *Founded/Ownrshp* 1908
Sales 14.2MM *EMP* 285
Accts Moss Adams Llp Tacoma Wa
SIC 8051 8059 8322 8052 8351 Skilled nursing care facilities; Personal care home, with health care; Adult day care center; Intermediate care facilities; Child day care services; Skilled nursing care facilities; Personal care home, with health care; Adult day care center; Intermediate care facilities; Child day care services
Nrsg Dir: Karen Jacobson

D-U-N-S 15-501-8708
JOSEPHS FOOD PRODUCTS CO INC
2759 S 25th Ave, Broadview, IL 60155-4533
Tel (708) 338-4090 *Founded/Ownrshp* 1985
Sales 29.2MM^E *EMP* 240
SIC 2099 Spices, including grinding; Spices, including grinding
Pr: Reginald Van Eekeren

D-U-N-S 78-655-0645 EXP
JOSEPHS GOURMET PASTA CO
(*Suby of* JGPS HOLDINGS LLC) ★
262 Primrose St, Haverhill, MA 01830-3930
Tel (978) 521-1718 *Founded/Ownrshp* 2013
Sales 66.7MM^E *EMP* 300
SIC 2099 Pasta, uncooked: packaged with other ingredients; Pasta, uncooked: packaged with other ingredients
CEO: David Zwartendijk
CFO: John Birch
VP: Kevin Hartnett
Opers Mgr: Dave Wojtowicz
S&M/VP: David Robinson
Mktg Dir: Tim Beam

JOSEPH'S ONLINE BAKERY
See MIDDLE EAST BAKERY INC

D-U-N-S 09-259-8820
JOSEPHSON MANAGEMENT CO
JS FOODS
4250 Executive Sq Ste 500, La Jolla, CA 92037-9105
Tel (858) 642-0064 *Founded/Ownrshp* 1978
Sales 11.6MM^E *EMP* 400
SIC 5812 Fast-food restaurant, chain; Fast-food restaurant, chain
Pr: Julian Josephson
**VP:* Stanley Smiedt

D-U-N-S 00-776-9783
JOSH BIRT LLC
JOSHBIRT
2 Fordham Ave, Pittsburgh, PA 15229-1546
Tel (412) 719-7182 *Founded/Ownrshp* 2009
Sales 170.0MM *EMP* 4
SIC 7812 Motion picture & video production; Motion picture & video production
Owner: Josh Birt

D-U-N-S 01-529-3232
JOSH MCDOWELL MINISTRY
(*Suby of* CAMPUS CRUSADE FOR CHRIST INC) ★
2001 W Plano Pkwy # 2400, Plano, TX 75075-8637
Tel (972) 907-1000 *Founded/Ownrshp* 2010
Sales 7.5MM^E *EMP* 778^E
SIC 8661 Religious organizations
Prin: Josh McDowell

JOSHBIRT
See JOSH BIRT LLC

D-U-N-S 18-827-6596 IMP/EXP
JOSHEN PAPER & PACKAGING CO
5800 Grant Ave, Cleveland, OH 44105-5608
Tel (216) 441-5600 *Founded/Ownrshp* 1988
Sales 290.4MM^E *EMP* 325
SIC 5113 5169 Bags, paper & disposable plastic; Cups, disposable plastic & paper; Boxes & containers; Sanitation preparations; Bags, paper & disposable plastic; Cups, disposable plastic & paper; Boxes & containers; Sanitation preparations
CEO: Michelle Reiner
**Pr:* Bob Reiner
COO: Candice Brown
**CFO:* Joe Monroe
**VP:* John Caldwell
VP: Terry Coyne
**VP:* Don Morgenroth
**Prin:* Elliot M Kaufman

D-U-N-S 83-623-7065
JOSHUA INC
WENDY'S
1701 Woodland Ter, Lake Oswego, OR 97034-5838
Tel (503) 699-0462 *Founded/Ownrshp* 1996
Sales 2.0MM^E *EMP* 433^E
SIC 5812 Fast-food restaurant, chain
Pr: John Kibler

D-U-N-S 02-878-9808
JOSHUA INDEPENDENT SCHOOL DISTRICT
JOSHUA ISD
310 E 18th St, Joshua, TX 76058-3117
Tel (817) 202-2500 *Founded/Ownrshp* 1909
Sales 29.6MM^E *EMP* 500
Accts Snow Garnett & Company Weath
SIC 8211 Public elementary school; Public junior high school; Public senior high school; Public elementary school; Public junior high school; Public senior high school
**Pr:* Ray Dane
**CFO:* Jeff Rowland
Psych: Dale Sturgeon
HC Dir: Linda Warren

JOSHUA ISD
See JOSHUA INDEPENDENT SCHOOL DISTRICT

JOSHUA TREE CENTER FOR CHANGE
See MENTAL HEALTH SYSTEMS INC

D-U-N-S 05-462-2097 IMP
JOSIE ACCESSORIES INC (NY)
ELRENE HOME FASHIONS
261 5th Ave Rm 501, New York, NY 10016-0036
Tel (212) 889-6376 *Founded/Ownrshp* 1945
Sales 23.3MM^E *EMP* 175
SIC 2392 Tablecloths: made from purchased materials; Placemats, plastic or textile; Tablecloths: made from purchased materials; Placemats, plastic or textile
Pr: Mark Siegel
**Ch Bd:* Bryan Siegel
CFO: Frank Giacomini
**CFO:* Richard Orent
**VP:* Craig Siegel
Board of Directors: Larry Wernick

JOSLIN CLINIC
See JOSLIN DIABETES CENTER INC

D-U-N-S 80-843-3163
JOSLIN CONSTRUCTION CO INC
21518 W Wallis Dr, Porter, TX 77365-4658
Tel (281) 354-5840 *Founded/Ownrshp* 1985
Sales 48.0MM^E *EMP* 140
SIC 1623 Water, sewer & utility lines; Water, sewer & utility lines
Pr: Curtis Ray Joslin
**CEO:* Curtis Ray Joslin Sr
**CFO:* Shaun Dean
**VP:* Philip Deliganis

D-U-N-S 07-172-3084
JOSLIN DIABETES CENTER INC (MA)
JOSLIN CLINIC
1 Joslin Pl, Boston, MA 02215-5394
Tel (617) 732-2400 *Founded/Ownrshp* 1953
Sales 85.2MM *EMP* 600
Accts Kpmg Llp Boston Ma
SIC 8011 Medical centers; Medical centers
CEO: John L Brooks III
**Pr:* C R Kahn MD
**CFO:* Rick Markello
**Treas:* C Richard Carlson
Ofcr: Steve Fiander
Ofcr: Christi Gabbay
**Ex VP:* Rajni Aneja
Sr VP: Martin Abrahamson
Sr VP: Alan Jacobson
Sr VP: Paul O'Brien
VP: Cathy Carver
VP: Nandan Padukone
VP: Bridget Stewart
VP: Michael Sullivan
Exec: Beth Peterson
Exec: Wesley Straub
Dir Lab: Dan Jamieson
Dir Lab: Jennifer Lock
Assoc Dir: Melinda Maryniuk

JOSLOFF GLASS COMPANY
See JOSLOFF INDUSTRIES LLC

D-U-N-S 60-100-0560
JOSLOFF INDUSTRIES LLC
JOSLOFF GLASS COMPANY
169 Meeker Ave, Newark, NJ 07114-1329
Tel (973) 622-2200 *Founded/Ownrshp* 2002
Sales 30.4MM *EMP* 70
Accts Alperin Nebbia & Associates
SIC 1793 Glass & glazing work; Glass & glazing work
CEO: Lawrence Josloff
**Pr:* Alberta Josloff
**VP:* Ian Josloff

D-U-N-S 00-954-5658
■ **JOSLYN SUNBANK CO LLC**
(*Suby of* ESTERLINE TECHNOLOGIES CORP) ★
1740 Commerce Way, Paso Robles, CA 93446-3620
Tel (805) 238-2840 *Founded/Ownrshp* 2013
Sales 154.2MM^E *EMP* 500
SIC 3678 3643 5065 Electronic connectors; Electronic connectors; Connectors & terminals for electrical devices; Connectors, electronic
Prin: Angel Cruz
Exec: Paul Winkler
Mfg Mgr: Nick Bogdan
Ql Cn Mgr: Gordon Krueger
S&M/VP: William Flaherty

D-U-N-S 05-454-4355
JOSS & MAIN
4 Copley Pl Ste 700, Boston, MA 02116-6513
Tel (800) 632-8158 *Founded/Ownrshp* 2011
Sales 985.1M^E *EMP* 800
SIC 7319 Shopping news, advertising & distributing service
CEO: Steve Conin
Mktg Dir: Andrea Black

D-U-N-S 14-788-2294 IMP/EXP
JOST CHEMICAL CO
8150 Lackland Rd, Saint Louis, MO 63114-4524
Tel (314) 428-3992 *Founded/Ownrshp* 1985
Sales 105.1MM^E *EMP* 200
SIC 2834 2819 Pharmaceutical preparations; Industrial inorganic chemicals; Pharmaceutical preparations; Industrial inorganic chemicals
Pr: Jerry L Jost
IT Man: Howard Ashley
Manager: Jerry Lynch
Sls Mgr: Dayna Cooper

D-U-N-S 01-774-6207 IMP/EXP
JOST INTERNATIONAL CORP
(*Suby of* JOST-WERKE INTERNATIONAL BETEILIGUNGSVERWALTUNG GMBH)
1770 Hayes St, Grand Haven, MI 49417-9428
Tel (616) 223-3333 *Founded/Ownrshp* 2013
Sales 39.7MM^E *EMP* 180
SIC 3714 3715 Motor vehicle parts & accessories; Truck trailers; Motor vehicle parts & accessories; Truck trailers
Pr: Lee Brace
Pr: Van Eizenga
**Pr:* Greg Laarman
**VP:* Rich Carroll
**VP:* Jens Polte
Dir IT: Linda Vaneizenga
IT Man: Scott Dyk
IT Man: Linda Van Eizenga
Plnt Mgr: Dan Athey
Prd Mgr: Brett Johnson
Natl Sales: Rob Marsh

D-U-N-S 04-834-1556 IMP/EXP
JOSTENS INC
(*Suby of* VISANT CORP) ★
3601 Minnesota Dr Ste 400, Minneapolis, MN 55435-6008
Tel (952) 830-3300 *Founded/Ownrshp* 2004
Sales 1.1MMM^E *EMP* 4,755^E
SIC 3911 2759 2741 Rings, finger: precious metal; Commercial printing; Invitation & stationery printing & engraving; Announcements: engraved; Yearbooks: publishing & printing
VP: Rick Cochran
Bd of Dir: Tagar C Olson
Sr VP: Marjorie Brown
Sr VP: John Larsen
VP: Vickie Broxterman
VP: Paul Carousso
**VP:* Keith Kugler
**VP:* Patrick Lambert
**VP:* Eric Loring
VP: Gary Nelson
VP: Albert Nuness

D-U-N-S 03-349-0640 IMP
■ **JOTALY INC**
(*Suby of* RICHLINE GROUP INC) ★
1385 Broadway Fl 12, New York, NY 10018-6118
Tel (212) 886-6000 *Founded/Ownrshp* 1981
Sales 101.2MM^E *EMP* 750
SIC 3911 Jewelry, precious metal
Ch Bd: Ofer Azrielant
**VP:* John C Esposito
Dir IT: Fred Poluhovich
MIS Mgr: Marvin Pincus
VP Sls: Scott Lyle
VP Sls: Martha McGrath
VP Sls: John Peters
VP Sls: Marilyn Williams
Snr Mgr: Michael Milgrom

D-U-N-S 03-771-6750 IMP
JOTUL NORTH AMERICA INC
(*Suby of* JOTUL AS)
55 Hutcherson Dr, Gorham, ME 04038-2644
Tel (207) 797-5912 *Founded/Ownrshp* 2008
Sales 24.6MM^E *EMP* 85
SIC 3433 Heating equipment, except electric
Pr: Bret Watson
**VP Sls:* Jim Merkel

D-U-N-S 01-331-2740
JOULE UNLIMITED TECHNOLOGIES INC
18 Crosby Dr, Bedford, MA 01730-1402
Tel (781) 533-9100 *Founded/Ownrshp* 2007
Sales 31.6MM^E *EMP* 100
SIC 2869 8731 Ethyl alcohol, ethanol; Biotechnical research, commercial; Ethyl alcohol, ethanol; Biotechnical research, commercial
Pr: Paul Snaith
**Ch Bd:* Noubar Afeyan
**Pr:* Tom Jensen
**Treas:* Eric D Esparbes
Ex VP: Peter Erich
Sr VP: Troy J Campione
Sr VP: Dan Robertson
**Sr VP:* Mark Solakian
**Sr VP:* David St Angelo
**Sr VP:* John Ward
**VP:* David A Berry
VP: Frank Hillery
VP: Chang Hong
Comm Dir: Felicia Spagnoli
Board of Directors: Caroline Dorsa, William J Sims, Serge Tchuruk

D-U-N-S 19-206-2164
■ **JOURDANTON HOSPITAL CORP**
SOUTH TEXAS REGIONAL MED CTR
(*Suby of* COMMUNITY HEALTH SYSTEMS INC) ★
1905 Highway 97 E, Jourdanton, TX 78026-1504
Tel (830) 769-3515 *Founded/Ownrshp* 2001
Sales 53.0MM^E *EMP* 300
SIC 8062 General medical & surgical hospitals; General medical & surgical hospitals
Pr: Martin G Schweinhart
Pr: Desiree Schorp
**Ex VP:* Larry W Cash
**Sr VP:* Rachel A Seifert
**VP:* T Mark Buford
**VP:* James W Doucette
Dir Rx: Claudette Leiker
Chf Nrs Of: Shelly Farrow

JOURNAGAN CNSTR & AGGREGATES
See LEO JOURNAGAN CONSTRUCTION CO INC

JOURNAL
See SMALL NEWSPAPER GROUP

D-U-N-S 06-351-1216 IMP
JOURNAL BROADCAST GROUP INC
WSYM-TV
(*Suby of* DESK BC MERGER LLC) ★
720 E Capitol Dr, Milwaukee, WI 53212-1308
Tel (414) 332-9611 *Founded/Ownrshp* 1973
Sales 204.4MM^E *EMP* 1,000
SIC 4833 Television broadcasting stations; Television broadcasting stations
CEO: Steve Smith
Pt: Bob Uecker
CFO: Ronald G Kurtis
Ex VP: Jim Prather
Ex VP: Debbie Turner
Ex VP: Steve Wexler
VP: Bill Berra
VP: Beverlee Brannigan
VP: David Bruce
VP: Kim Buchanan
VP: Dianne Downey
VP: Dominic Fails
VP: Bill Lutzen
VP: Brian McHale
VP: Bob Rosenthal
VP: Andrew Stewart
VP: Jim Thomas
Dir Soc: Molly Fay
Creative D: Doak Breen
Creative D: Walker Foard

D-U-N-S 00-607-7101 IMP/EXP
JOURNAL COMMUNICATIONS INC
333 W State St, Milwaukee, WI 53203-1305
Tel (414) 224-2000 *Founded/Ownrshp* 1882
Sales 428.4MM *EMP* 2,700^E
SIC 4832 4833 2711 2759 4813 Radio broadcasting stations; Television broadcasting stations; Newspapers, publishing & printing; Commercial printing; Data telephone communications; Voice telephone communications

D-U-N-S 07-614-3643
JOURNAL COMMUNITY PUBLISHING GROUP INC
(*Suby of* DESK BC MERGER LLC) ★
600 Industrial Dr, Waupaca, WI 54981-8814
Tel (715) 258-8450 *Founded/Ownrshp* 1971
Sales 104.5MM^E *EMP* 1,156
SIC 2741 2711 Shopping news: publishing & printing; Commercial printing & newspaper publishing combined; Shopping news: publishing & printing; Commercial printing & newspaper publishing combined
CEO: Elizabeth Brenner
Pr: David Honan
Bd of Dir: Mark Rosenau
Off Mgr: Sandy Ebner

D-U-N-S 00-547-7047 EXP
JOURNAL DISPOSITION CORP
IPC PUBLISHING SERVICES
(*Suby of* WALSWORTH PUBLISHING CO INC) ★
2180 Maiden Ln, Saint Joseph, MI 49085-9596
Tel (888) 563-3220 *Founded/Ownrshp* 1947, 2010
Sales 27.4MM^E *EMP* 350
SIC 2752 7389

D-U-N-S 02-715-8067
JOURNAL ENTERPRISES INC
7777 Jefferson St Ne, Albuquerque, NM 87109-4343
Tel (505) 823-7777 *Founded/Ownrshp* 1906
Sales 43.6MM^E *EMP* 400
SIC 2711 Newspapers; Newspapers
Pr: William P Lang
**VP:* William P Lang
Dir IT: Bill Maes

D-U-N-S 00-902-6105
JOURNAL GRAPHICS INC
2840 Nw 35th Ave Ste B, Portland, OR 97210-1604
Tel (503) 572-6549 *Founded/Ownrshp* 1936
Sales 25.3MM^E *EMP* 160
SIC 2711 2789 2759 2752 Commercial printing & newspaper publishing combined; Bookbinding & related work; Commercial printing; Commercial printing, lithographic; Commercial printing & newspaper publishing combined; Bookbinding & related work; Commercial printing; Commercial printing, lithographic
Pr: Phillip C Bridge
COO: Theresa Spada
CFO: Ed Chess
**Sec:* Suzanne Smith
**VP:* Dorothy M Smith
Exec: Joan Schok
VP Opers: Dianne Bullas

JOURNAL INQUIRER
See GREEN MANOR CORP

JOURNAL INQUIRER
See JOURNAL PUBLISHING CO INC

D-U-N-S 07-954-1886
▲ **JOURNAL MEDIA GROUP INC** (WI)
333 W State St, Milwaukee, WI 53203-1305
Tel (414) 224-2000 *Founded/Ownrshp* 2015
Sales 767.8MM^E *EMP* 3,000^E
Tkr Sym JMG *Exch* NYS
SIC 2711 Newspapers; Newspapers, publishing & printing
Pr: Timothy E Stautberg
CFO: Jason R Graham
VP: Marty V Ozolins
Board of Directors: Steven J Smith

JOURNAL OF BUSINESS
See COWLES PUBLISHING CO

JOURNAL OF CHEMICAL & ENGINEER
See AMERICAN CHEMICAL SOCIETY

D-U-N-S 14-463-4367
JOURNAL OF COMMERCE INC
PIERS
(*Suby of* ECONOMIST NEWSPAPER LIMITED(THE))
2 Penn Plz E 12, Newark, NJ 07105-2257
Tel (973) 776-8660 *Founded/Ownrshp* 1995
Sales 46.9MM^E *EMP* 681
SIC 7375 2711 2721 Data base information retrieval; Newspapers: publishing only, not printed on site; Magazines: publishing only, not printed on site; Data base information retrieval; Newspapers: publishing only, not printed on site; Magazines: publishing only, not printed on site
CFO: Mark Harabedian
Pr: Bill Ralph
**Pr:* William Ralph
Sr VP: Steven Brennen
**Sr VP:* Doug Weber
VP: Lenny Corallo
**VP:* Marcia Holland
VP: Brian Neuhart
VP: James Roe
**VP:* Nancy Schlake
Div Mgr: Don Holt

JOURNAL OF THE AMERICAN ACADEM
See AMERICAN ACADEMY OF DERMATOLOGY INC

D-U-N-S 00-710-9028
JOURNAL PUBLISHING CO
ALBUQUERQUE JOURNAL
(*Suby of* JOURNAL ENTERPRISES INC) ★
7777 Jefferson St Ne, Albuquerque, NM 87109-4343
Tel (505) 823-3800 *Founded/Ownrshp* 1906
Sales 25.6MM^E *EMP* 400
SIC 2711 6512 Newspapers, publishing & printing; Nonresidential building operators; Newspapers, publishing & printing; Nonresidential building operators
Pr: Thompson H Lang
**VP:* William P Lang

D-U-N-S 05-254-5704
JOURNAL PUBLISHING CO INC
JOURNAL INQUIRER
(*Suby of* GREEN MANOR CORP) ★
306 Progress Dr, Manchester, CT 06042-9011
Tel (860) 646-0500 *Founded/Ownrshp* 1970
Sales 34.1MM^E *EMP* 560
SIC 2711 Newspapers, publishing & printing; Newspapers, publishing & printing
Pr: Elizabeth Ellis

JOURNAL REGISTER COMPANY
See 21ST CENTURY MEDIA NEWSPAPER LLC

D-U-N-S 15-411-8400
JOURNAL REGISTER CO
5 Hanover Sq Fl 25, New York, NY 10004-4008
Tel (212) 257-7212 *Founded/Ownrshp* 2013
Sales 894.1MM^E *EMP* 4,500
SIC 2711 Newspapers, publishing & printing; Newspapers, publishing & printing
CEO: John Paton
Ch Bd: James W Hall
Pr: Paul Provost
CFO: Jeff Bairstow
Ex VP: Guy Gilmore
Ex VP: Michael Kuritzkes
Sr VP: William J Higginson
Sr VP: Allen J Mailman
Sr VP: Jeannie Parent
Sr VP: Edward J Yocum Jr
VP: Jerry Bammel
VP: Jared Bean
VP: Eric Lamont Mayberry
VP: Brian McNamara

D-U-N-S 06-351-1224
JOURNAL SENTINEL INC
MILWAUKEE JOURNAL/SENTINEL
(*Suby of* DESK BC MERGER LLC) ★
333 W State St, Milwaukee, WI 53203-1305
Tel (414) 224-2000 *Founded/Ownrshp* 2015
Sales 320.1MM^E *EMP* 1,820
SIC 2711 Commercial printing & newspaper publishing combined; Commercial printing & newspaper publishing combined
Ch Bd: Steve J Smith
Pr: Elizabeth Brenner
CFO: Ken McNamee
Sr VP: Casey Hester
Sr VP: Marty Kaiser
VP: Christopher Apel
VP: Michael Gay
VP: Jeff Goelz
VP: Jason Graham
VP: Rhonda Graham
VP: Daryl Hively
VP: Dani Longoria
VP: Lori McGarry
VP: Faith Perkins
VP: Clay Perry
Board of Directors: Paul Bonaiuto, Gerry Hinkley, W Martin Kaiser, Douglas Kiel, Thomas Massopust, David Meissner, George Stanley

D-U-N-S 00-726-4336
■ **JOURNAL-STAR PRINTING CO**
OAK CREEK PRINTING
(*Suby of* LEE ENTERPRISES INC) ★
926 P St, Lincoln, NE 68508-3668
Tel (402) 473-2695 *Founded/Ownrshp* 1995
Sales 36.6MM^E *EMP* 465
SIC 2711 Newspapers, publishing & printing; Newspapers, publishing & printing
CEO: Mary Junck
**Pr:* Greg R Veon
**Treas:* Jayne Hermiston
Brnch Mgr: Don Walton
Dist Mgr: Dianne Witmer
Web Dev: Justin Parks
Advt Dir: Ava Obst
Advt Dir: Ava Thomas
Advt Dir: Natalia Wiita
Sls Mgr: Jennifer Witherby
Snr Mgr: Ted Kirk

D-U-N-S 07-199-3568
JOURNEY CHURCH COLORADO
8237 S Holly St Ste C, Centennial, CO 80122-4027
Tel (303) 921-5595 *Founded/Ownrshp* 2004
Sales 90.0MM *EMP* 9
SIC 8661 Churches, temples & shrines; Churches, temples & shrines

D-U-N-S 00-482-5691 IMP
JOURNEY GROUP COMPAINES (SD)
SIOUX FALLS CONSTRUCTION
800 S 7th Ave, Sioux Falls, SD 57104-5123
Tel (605) 336-1640 *Founded/Ownrshp* 1910, 1999
Sales 79.6MM^E *EMP* 150
SIC 1542 1622 1771 Commercial & office building, new construction; Commercial & office buildings, renovation & repair; Bridge construction; Blacktop (asphalt) work; Commercial & office building, new construction; Commercial & office buildings, renovation & repair; Bridge construction; Blacktop (asphalt) work
Pr: Randy R Knecht
**Ch Bd:* David F Fleck
Ch Bd: David Fleck
**Sec:* Becky Dockter
**VP:* Marlyn Bergeson
**VP:* Jared J Gusso
**VP:* Darin W Hage
**VP:* Jay Rasmussen

D-U-N-S 07-617-2543
JOURNEY MENTAL HEALTH CENTER INC
625 W Washington Ave, Madison, WI 53703-2637
Tel (608) 280-2700 *Founded/Ownrshp* 1948
Sales 20.4MM *EMP* 350^E
Accts Wipfli Llp Madison Wisconsi
SIC 8093 Mental health clinic, outpatient; Mental health clinic, outpatient
Pr: William Greer
CFO: Gerry Brew
Treas: Greg Blum
CTO: Jay Otto
IT Man: Penny Holum
Web Prj Mg: Chris Bjork
Netwrk Eng: Paul Czerniak
Psych: Roger Garms
Psych: Rebecca Ramirez

JOURNEYCARE FOUNDATION
See JOURNEYCARE INC

D-U-N-S 62-206-3832
JOURNEYCARE INC
JOURNEYCARE FOUNDATION
405 Lake Zurich Rd, Barrington, IL 60010-3141
Tel (847) 381-5599 *Founded/Ownrshp* 1984
Sales 31.3MM *EMP* 300
Accts Sikich Llp Naperville Il
SIC 8082 Visiting nurse service; Visiting nurse service
CEO: Sarah Bealles
Dir Vol: Janice Farrell
Pr: Syed Haque
COO: Kelly Fischer
Sr VP: Martha Twaddle
VP: Beth Raseman
Dir Soc: Kristin Frazier
Dir Bus: Mary Scoltock
HC Dir: Leslie Horwitz
Snr Mgr: Kathy Erickson

D-U-N-S 11-777-5606
JOURNEYMAN CONSTRUCTION INC
7701 N Lamar Blvd Ste 100, Austin, TX 78752-1012
Tel (512) 247-7000 *Founded/Ownrshp* 2000
Sales 134.8MM *EMP* 55^E
Accts Kemp & Stich Pc San Antonio
SIC 1542 Commercial & office building contractors; Commercial & office building contractors
Pr: Sam Kumar
Ex VP: Michael Kiehnau
Off Admin: Stephanie Sanchez
Snr PM: Tim Bentley

D-U-N-S 07-958-9944
JOURNYX INC
7600 Burnet Rd Ste 300, Austin, TX 78757-1280
Tel (512) 834-8888 *Founded/Ownrshp* 1999
Sales 50.0MM *EMP* 3
SIC 7371 Computer software development & applications; Computer software development & applications
Pr: Curtis L Finch
Sr VP: Bill Balcezak
VP: Kathleen Hall
**VP:* John Maddalozzo
VP: Bob Ramsdell
IT Man: Whitney Scott
Software D: Christine Chun
Mktg Dir: Whitney Otstott

D-U-N-S 60-795-2587
JOVAN INC
MCDONALD'S
7510 Highway 107, North Little Rock, AR 72120-4645
Tel (501) 834-6121 *Founded/Ownrshp* 1979
Sales 6.1MM^E *EMP* 350
SIC 5812 Fast-food restaurant, chain; Fast-food restaurant, chain
Pr: Hendrick Van Rossum
**VP:* Bobby Roetvel

JOWAT ADHESIVES
See JOWAT CORP

D-U-N-S 04-079-3106 IMP/EXP
JOWAT CORP
JOWAT ADHESIVES
(*Suby of* JOWAT SE)
6058 Lois Ln, High Point, NC 27263-8588
Tel (336) 434-9000 *Founded/Ownrshp* 1979
Sales 22.8MM^E *EMP* 95^E
SIC 2891 5169 Adhesives; Adhesives, chemical; Adhesives; Adhesives, chemical
Pr: Rainhard Kramme
**VP:* Jerry Crouse
**VP:* Gerhard Haas
Plnt Mgr: Mark Gommenginger
Plnt Mgr: Martin Lamberg
Prd Mgr: Jack McMorrow
Ql Cn Mgr: Frank T Linton
Ql Cn Mgr: Frank Linton
VP Sls: Marco Kubitza
Mktg Dir: Michael Ermel
Sls Mgr: Eddy Credico

D-U-N-S 06-566-6059 EXP
JOWDY INDUSTRIES INC
INDEPENDENT SEAFOOD
5300 Georgia Ave, West Palm Beach, FL 33405-3520
Tel (954) 427-1234 *Founded/Ownrshp* 1987
Sales 29.2MM^E *EMP* 45
SIC 5146 Fish, fresh; Seafoods
Pr: Joseph Molina
**VP:* Miguel E Molina

D-U-N-S 00-433-9537 IMP/EXP
JOY CONE CO
SCOOPY'S CONE CO
3435 Lamor Rd, Hermitage, PA 16148-3097
Tel (724) 962-5747 *Founded/Ownrshp* 1964
Sales 99.0MM *EMP* 500
SIC 2052 2099 Cones, ice cream; Food preparations; Cones, ice cream; Food preparations
Ch Bd: Joseph George
**Pr:* David George
**CFO:* Scott Kalmanek
QA Dir: Gary Provencher
QA Dir: Stacey Wickland

IT Man: Mark Hiler
Opers Mgr: Brent Fisher
Ql Cn Mgr: Sharon George
Sls Dir: Sue Pippin

D-U-N-S 79-878-5473 IMP
JOY CONSTRUCTION CORP
40 Fulton St Rm 2100, New York, NY 10038-5079
Tel (212) 766-9651 *Founded/Ownrshp* 1995
Sales 46.1MM^E *EMP* 130
SIC 1542 1521 Commercial & office building, new construction; Commercial & office buildings, renovation & repair; New construction, single-family houses; General remodeling, single-family houses; Commercial & office building, new construction; Commercial & office buildings, renovation & repair; New construction, single-family houses; General remodeling, single-family houses
Pr: Amnon Shalhov

D-U-N-S 94-283-2247
JOY DARR & ASSOC INC
RE/MAX
1425 Gross Rd Ste 108, Mesquite, TX 75149-1365
Tel (972) 222-3867 *Founded/Ownrshp* 1996
Sales 30.0MM *EMP* 14
SIC 6531 Real estate agent, residential; Real estate agent, residential
Pr: Joy Darr

D-U-N-S 02-171-4520
JOY FOR OURYOUTH
1805 Swarthmore Ave, Lakewood, NJ 08701-4540
Tel (877) 527-7454 *Founded/Ownrshp* 2012
Sales 28.1MM *EMP* 2^E
Accts Roth & Company Llp Brooklyn
SIC 8699 Charitable organization

D-U-N-S 00-401-5822 IMP
■ **JOY GLOBAL CONVEYORS INC**
JOY MINING MACHINERY
(*Suby of* JOY GLOBAL INC) ★
438 Industrial Dr 4513, Winfield, AL 35594-4503
Tel (205) 487-6492 *Founded/Ownrshp* 1959, 2008
Sales 135.7MM^E *EMP* 537
SIC 3535 Conveyors & conveying equipment; Conveyors & conveying equipment
Pr: Michael W Sutherlin
CFO: Mickey Earrey
MIS Dir: Dennis Davidson
Site Mgr: Cy Christian
Mktg Dir: Mike Rigsby
Sls Mgr: Doug Markham

D-U-N-S 15-355-0793 IMP/EXP
▲ **JOY GLOBAL INC**
100 E Wisconsin Ave # 2780, Milwaukee, WI 53202-4127
Tel (414) 319-8500 *Founded/Ownrshp* 1884
Sales 3.1MMM *EMP* 15,400
Tkr Sym JOY *Exch* NYS
SIC 3532 Mining machinery; Drills & drilling equipment, mining (except oil & gas); Feeders, ore & aggregate; Mining machinery; Drills & drilling equipment, mining (except oil & gas); Feeders, ore & aggregate
Pr: Edward L Doheny II
**Ch Bd:* John Nils Hanson
Pr: Michael W Sutherlin
COO: Randal W Baker
COO: Chuck Bruskin
CFO: James M Sullivan
Chf Mktg O: Doug Blom
Ex VP: James A Chokey
Ex VP: John Fons
Ex VP: Sean D Major
Ex VP: Johannes S Maritz
VP: Matthew S Kulasa
VP: Greg Ladzinski
VP: Neil Massey
VP: Scott Weber
VP: Andre Williams
Exec: Val Lahti
Exec: Todd Parks

D-U-N-S 19-521-0443 IMP
JOY GLOBAL INC
JOY MINING
120 Liberty St, Franklin, PA 16323-1066
Tel (814) 432-1202 *Founded/Ownrshp* 2001
Sales 40.0M *EMP* 278^E
Accts Baker Tilly Virchow Krause Llp
SIC 3532 Mining machinery
CEO: Michael W Sutherlin
**COO:* Randal W Baker
**CFO:* Michael S Olsen
Ofcr: Dale Oliver
**Ex VP:* Sean D Major
**Ex VP:* Eric A Nielsen
**Ex VP:* James M Sullivan
**Ex VP:* Dennis R Winkleman
VP: Keith Richardson
VP: Randy White
Rgnl Mgr: Leon Burant

D-U-N-S 00-731-7480 IMP
■ **JOY GLOBAL LONGVIEW OPERATIONS LLC**
(*Suby of* JOY GLOBAL INC) ★
2400 S Macarthur Dr, Longview, TX 75602
Tel (903) 237-7000 *Founded/Ownrshp* 2011
Sales 494.6MM^E *EMP* 2,500
SIC 3532 3533 3312 3531 Trucks (dollies), mining; Loading machines, underground: mobile; Well logging equipment; Drill rigs; Plate, steel; Plate, sheet & strip, except coated products; Construction machinery; Trucks (dollies), mining; Loading machines, underground: mobile; Well logging equipment; Drill rigs; Plate, steel; Plate, sheet & strip, except coated products; Construction machinery
Pr: Randal W Baker
Pr: Thomas Burke
CFO: Gordie Beittenmiller
Sr VP: Brad C Rogers
Sr VP: N Pharr Smith
VP: Blazek Dave
VP: Anniken Hoelsaeter

Tech Mgr: Jason Gahan
Mfg Mgr: Gavin Stahl

D-U-N-S 00-608-2275 IMP/EXP
■ **JOY GLOBAL SURFACE MINING INC**
(*Suby of* JOY GLOBAL INC) ★
4400 W National Ave, Milwaukee, WI 53214-3639
Tel (414) 671-4400 *Founded/Ownrshp* 1972
Sales 573.1MM^E *EMP* 2,700
SIC 3462 Construction or mining equipment forgings, ferrous; Construction or mining equipment forgings, ferrous
Pr: Mark Readinger
CFO: Donald C Roof
**Treas:* Ken Stark
Ex VP: Michael S Olsen
**VP:* John Diclemente
**VP:* Wayne Feasby
**VP:* Eugene Fuhrmann
**VP:* Mark Verdova
MIS Dir: Mark Shaver
IT Man: Robin Pearsick
IT Man: Mark Schmidt

D-U-N-S 17-292-0225 IMP
■ **JOY GLOBAL UNDERGROUND MINING LLC**
MINING JOY MACHINERY
(*Suby of* JOY GLOBAL INC) ★
177 Thorn Hill Rd, Warrendale, PA 15086-7527
Tel (724) 779-4500 *Founded/Ownrshp* 1994
Sales 1.1MMM^E *EMP* 5,200
SIC 3535 3532 Conveyors & conveying equipment; Drills, bits & similar equipment; Conveyors & conveying equipment; Drills, bits & similar equipment
Pr: Wayne Hunnell
**Pr:* Michael Sutherlin
CFO: James M Sullivan
VP: Rachael Baldwin
VP: Jennifer Guyton
VP: Karina Livshin
VP: Johan Maritz
**VP:* Michael S Olsen
VP: Robert Richens
Mng Dir: Mark Finlay
Telecom Ex: Kevin Rushton

JOY MINING
See JOY GLOBAL INC

JOY MINING MACHINERY
See JOY GLOBAL CONVEYORS INC

D-U-N-S 80-953-0889 IMP
JOY MINING MACHINERY
BEDFORD GEAR
6160 Cochran Rd, Solon, OH 44139-3306
Tel (440) 248-7970 *Founded/Ownrshp* 1996
Sales 60.1MM^E *EMP* 140
SIC 3532 Mining machinery; Mining machinery
Pr: Ed Doheny
**Pr:* Edward L Doheny II
Plnt Mgr: Mike Thomas

D-U-N-S 62-062-1094
JOY PARIS INC
RE/MAX LAKE GRANBURY
4810 E Hwy 377, Granbury, TX 76049
Tel (817) 579-1504 *Founded/Ownrshp* 1987
Sales 37.1MM *EMP* 3
SIC 6531 Real estate brokers & agents
Pr: Lesley Joyce Paris
VP: Steven W Cook

D-U-N-S 83-885-8298 IMP
JOY PIPE USA LP
39850 Interstate 10 W, Boerne, TX 78006-8805
Tel (830) 249-7400 *Founded/Ownrshp* 2005
Sales 26.3MM^E *EMP* 48
SIC 5051 Structural shapes, iron or steel
Pt: William F Thomas
**Pt:* Thomas W Bibb

D-U-N-S 10-284-1397 IMP/EXP
JOY SYSTEMS INC
101 Cottontail Ln, Somerset, NJ 08873-1147
Tel (732) 907-1590 *Founded/Ownrshp* 2001
Sales 64.1MM *EMP* 48
Accts Bruno Dibello & Co Llc
SIC 5045 Computer peripheral equipment; Computer peripheral equipment
Pr: Jimmy Lee
**VP:* Myeungjouh Woo
Genl Mgr: Jay Han
IT Man: Alex Bae
Mktg Dir: Sam Yaari

D-U-N-S 80-339-3086
JOYCE CO
3 Mill Rd, Wilmington, DE 19806-2146
Tel (302) 353-4011 *Founded/Ownrshp* 2007
Sales 50.0MM *EMP* 50
SIC 6799 Venture capital companies

D-U-N-S 02-467-3253
JOYCE FARMS INC
4787 Kinnamon Rd, Winston Salem, NC 27103-9605
Tel (336) 766-9900 *Founded/Ownrshp* 1981
Sales 41.7MM^E *EMP* 75
SIC 5144 5146 Poultry & poultry products; Seafoods; Poultry & poultry products; Seafoods
Pr: Ron Joyce
Opers Mgr: Eric Ivey
Ql Cn Mgr: Jimmy Mitchell

D-U-N-S 06-745-5758
JOYCE FOUNDATION
321 N Clark St Ste 1500, Chicago, IL 60654-4740
Tel (312) 782-2464 *Founded/Ownrshp* 1948
Sales 58.5MM *EMP* 28
SIC 6732 Charitable trust management; Charitable trust management
VP: Larry Hansen
Pr: Jessica McElroy
CFO: Deborah Gillespie
CFO: Jenny Patterson
Ofcr: George Cheung
Ofcr: Matthew Muench
Ofcr: Angelique Power

Ofcr: Jason Quiara
Ofcr: Nina Vinik
VP: Gretchen Crosby Sims
VP: Beth Swanson
Exec: John Luczak
Board of Directors: Tracey L Meares, Margot M Rogers

JOYCE HONDA
See JOYCE MOTORS CORP

JOYCE KOONS HONDA
See KOONS OF MANASSAS INC

D-U-N-S 00-891-6736 IMP
JOYCE LESLIE INC
170 W Commercial Ave, Moonachie, NJ 07074-1706
Tel (201) 804-7800 *Founded/Ownrshp* 1947
Sales 122.5MM^E *EMP* 900
Accts Citrin Cooperman & Company Ll
SIC 5621 Ready-to-wear apparel, women's; Ready-to-wear apparel, women's
CEO: Celia Clancy
**Sec:* Hermine Gewirtz
Board of Directors: Joyce Segal, Nancy Shapiro

D-U-N-S 16-136-1613 IMP
JOYCE MEYER MINISTRIES INC
LIFE IN THE WORD
700 Grace Pkwy, Fenton, MO 63026-5390
Tel (636) 349-0303 *Founded/Ownrshp* 1985
Sales 110.5MM *EMP* 537
Accts Stanfield & O Dell Pc Tulsa
SIC 8661 Non-church religious organizations; Non-church religious organizations
Pr: Joyce Meyer
CFO: Delanie Truty
Bd of Dir: Paul O Steen
**VP:* David Meyer
Exec: Jonathan Smith
Snr Sftwr: Bhaskar Mohanraj

D-U-N-S 06-203-9573
JOYCE MOTORS CORP
JOYCE HONDA
3166 State Route 10, Denville, NJ 07834-3429
Tel (973) 361-3000 *Founded/Ownrshp* 1972
Sales 44.4MM^E *EMP* 100
SIC 5511 Automobiles, new & used; Automobiles, new & used
Pr: James Grecco
**Sec:* Joyce Grecco
VP: Tom Stark
Sales Exec: Joe Sanroman

D-U-N-S 94-633-5721
JOYENT INC
655 Montgomery St # 1600, San Francisco, CA 94111-2635
Tel (415) 291-2480 *Founded/Ownrshp* 2005
Sales 39.0MM^E *EMP* 88
SIC 4813
CEO: Scott Hammond
**CFO:* Brett Newsome
Ex VP: Brian Brown
VP: Bryan Cantrill
Off Mgr: Lisa Claybaugh
Snr Sftwr: Jerry Jelinek
Sftwr Eng: Mark Cavage
Sftwr Eng: Trent Mick
Sftwr Eng: Robert Mustacchi
Sftwr Eng: David Pacheco
Sales Asso: David Masciorini
Board of Directors: Charles Beeler, Khaled Bichara, Don Listwin, Hanan Abdel-Meguid, Rob Rueckert, Henry Wasik, David Young

D-U-N-S 00-648-1287
JOYNER DIE CASTING & PLATING INC (MN)
JOYNERS
7801 Xylon Ave N, Brooklyn Park, MN 55445-2306
Tel (763) 425-2104 *Founded/Ownrshp* 1944, 1995
Sales 22.8MM^E *EMP* 120
SIC 3364 3471 Zinc & zinc-base alloy die-castings; Finishing, metals or formed products; Decorative plating & finishing of formed products; Zinc & zinc-base alloy die-castings; Finishing, metals or formed products; Decorative plating & finishing of formed products
Pr: Orlyn D Joyner
**VP:* Dwight Joyner
Sfty Mgr: John Kosina
Plnt Mgr: Janet Carlson
Sls Mgr: Carla Anderson
Sls Mgr: Claudine Marick

JOYNERS
See JOYNER DIE CASTING & PLATING INC

D-U-N-S 11-090-3317
JP CONSTRUCTION GROUP INC
14721 Industry Ct, Woodbridge, VA 22191-3125
Tel (703) 492-2220 *Founded/Ownrshp* 1995
Sales 26.1MM^E *EMP* 120
SIC 1542 Commercial & office buildings, renovation & repair; Commercial & office buildings, renovation & repair
CEO: Joe Parada

D-U-N-S 00-484-4627
JP DONMOYER INC (PA)
(*Suby of* J P DON MOYER) ★
10603 Allentown Blvd, Ono, PA 17077
Tel (717) 865-2148 *Founded/Ownrshp* 1934
Sales 28.4MM^E *EMP* 155
SIC 4213 4212

D-U-N-S 96-882-1400
▲ **JP ENERGY PARTNERS LP**
600 Las Colinas Blvd E, Irving, TX 75039-5616
Tel (972) 444-0300 *Founded/Ownrshp* 2011
Sales 1.6MMM *EMP* 100^E
Tkr Sym JPEP *Exch* NYS
SIC 1321 Propane (natural) production
CEO: J Patrick Barley
COO: Jeremiah J Ashcroft III
**CFO:* Patrick Welch

D-U-N-S 17-991-2605
JP FLOORING SYSTEMS INC
9097 Union Centre Blvd, West Chester, OH 45069-4861
Tel (513) 346-4300 *Founded/Ownrshp* 1988
Sales 36.6MM^E *EMP* 50
SIC 5023 5713 Wood flooring; Resilient floor coverings: tile or sheet; Carpets; Floor tile; Carpets
Pr: Phil Shrimper
VP: John Dickhaus
**Prin:* Scott M Slovin
**Prin:* Kenneth Robert Thompson II
**Prin:* Linda B Woodrow

D-U-N-S 15-096-9363
JP HOLDING CO INC
4020 W 73rd St, Anderson, IN 46011-9609
Tel (765) 778-6960 *Founded/Ownrshp* 2002
Sales 359.0MM^E *EMP* 800
SIC 4213 Trucking, except local; Trucking, except local
Pr: John Paugh

D-U-N-S 62-669-5477
JP INC - INDIANA
JASPER PLASTICS SOLUTIONS
501 W Railroad Ave, Syracuse, IN 46567-1568
Tel (574) 457-2062 *Founded/Ownrshp* 2005
Sales 65.3MM^E *EMP* 300
SIC 3081 Film base, cellulose acetate or nitrocellulose plastic; Film base, cellulose acetate or nitrocellulose plastic
CEO: Roger Korenstra
**Pr:* Sam Korenstra
**Sec:* Bruce Korenstra

JP MORGAN
See JP MORGAN INVESTMENT MANAGEMENT INC

D-U-N-S 79-489-8841
■ **JP MORGAN CLEARING CORP**
(*Suby of* JP MORGAN SECURITIES LLC) ★
1 Metrotech Ctr N Lbby 4, Brooklyn, NY 11201-3878
Tel (212) 272-1000 *Founded/Ownrshp* 1991
Sales 148.3MM^E *EMP* 2,000
SIC 6289 6211 Exchange clearinghouses, security; Traders, security; Brokers, security; Exchange clearinghouses, security; Traders, security; Brokers, security
CEO: Michael Minikes
**Ch Bd:* James E Cayne
**COO:* Samuel L Molinaro
**Treas:* John Stacconi
**Ex VP:* Ronald M Hersch
VP: Robert Steinberg
**VP:* Colleen Sullivan
VP: Paul Tarantino
Assoc Dir: Joe Weinberg
Genl Mgr: Mark Gianchetti
CTO: Paul Brock

D-U-N-S 96-631-8255
■ **JP MORGAN H&Q PRINCIPALS LP**
(*Suby of* JPMORGAN CHASE & CO) ★
560 Mission St Fl 2, San Francisco, CA 94105-2915
Tel (415) 315-5000 *Founded/Ownrshp* 1999
Sales 113.4MM^E *EMP* 827
SIC 6211 6799 6282 7389 Security brokers & dealers; Underwriters, security; Investment bankers; Venture capital companies; Investment advisory service; Telephone services; Security brokers & dealers; Underwriters, security; Investment bankers; Venture capital companies; Investment advisory service; Telephone services
Pt: William R Timken
Pt: Patrick J Allen
Pt: Steven M Machtinger
Pt: David M McAuliffe
Prin: Rupen Dolasia
Prin: Gene Eidenberg
Prin: Chris Hollenbeck

D-U-N-S 14-975-9912
■ **JP MORGAN INVESTMENT MANAGEMENT INC**
JP MORGAN
(*Suby of* JPMORGAN CHASE & CO) ★
270 Park Ave Fl 12, New York, NY 10017-7924
Tel (212) 483-2323 *Founded/Ownrshp* 1984
Sales 1.1MMM^E *EMP* 2,000
SIC 6722 Management investment, open-end; Management investment, open-end
CEO: Eve Guernsey
Ofcr: Jacquie Peluso
Ofcr: Alexeev Taboas
Sr VP: Patrick Chase
Sr VP: Ron Digiacomo
Sr VP: Sharon Harris
VP: Kevin Abato
VP: Timothy Bauer
VP: Richard Berg
VP: Anne Berry
VP: Andres Blanco
VP: Nicola Boone
VP: Brian Bunker
VP: Bill Cardwell
VP: Lisa Carpitella
VP: Brent Chandaria
VP: J Cima
VP: Lenny Daich
VP: Sait Dogru
VP: Gaurav Hariani
VP: Andrew Hoffman

D-U-N-S 14-464-7393
■ **JP MORGAN SECURITIES LLC**
(*Suby of* JPMORGAN CHASE & CO) ★
383 Madison Ave Fl 9, New York, NY 10179-0001
Tel (212) 272-2000 *Founded/Ownrshp* 2010
Sales 1.0MMM^E *EMP* 6,000
SIC 6211 6282 6289 Security brokers & dealers; Underwriters, security; Traders, security; Brokers, security; Investment advisory service; Investment research; Exchange clearinghouses, security; Security brokers & dealers; Underwriters, security; Traders, security; Brokers, security; Investment advisory service; Investment research; Exchange clearinghouses, security

CEO: James Edward Staley
**Pr:* Carlos Hernandez
Pr: Randy Howell
Pr: Yvonne Yeung
COO: Jeffrey Bernstein
CFO: James Collins
CFO: Marianne Lake
**Treas:* Lisa Fitzgerald
VP: Jerome Altschul
VP: Anthony Bonfig
VP: Cory Braunstein
VP: Brian Browne
VP: James Campbell
VP: Louis Flores
VP: Jaime Garza
VP: Frank Geiger
VP: Enrique Gonzalez
VP: Ricardo Hunt
VP: Joan Jia
VP: Brendan Kelly
VP: Peter Landgraff

D-U-N-S 01-928-0288
JP NOONAN TRANSPORTATION INC
415 West St, West Bridgewater, MA 02379-1030
Tel (508) 588-8026 *Founded/Ownrshp* 1959
Sales 43.3MM^E *EMP* 400
SIC 4213 4212 Trucking, except local; Liquid petroleum transport, non-local; Local trucking, without storage; Trucking, except local; Liquid petroleum transport, non-local; Local trucking, without storage
CEO: J Peter Noonan Sr
Treas: Laurence Noonan Jr
**VP:* Jay Timothy Noonan
Off Mgr: William Vieno
MIS Dir: Matt Cole
Sales Exec: Terry Chamberlain

D-U-N-S 03-348-3744
JP OIL CO LLC
JP OIL HOLDINGS
1604 W Pinhook Rd Ste 300, Lafayette, LA 70508-3729
Tel (337) 234-1170 *Founded/Ownrshp* 1975
Sales 1.5MMM^E *EMP* 100
SIC 1311

JP OIL HOLDINGS
See JP OIL CO LLC

D-U-N-S 80-659-6615
■ **JP TURNER & CO LLC**
(*Suby of* RCS CAPITAL CORP) ★
1 Buckhead Plaza 3060, Atlanta, GA 30305
Tel (404) 479-8300 *Founded/Ownrshp* 2014
Sales 109.3MM^E *EMP* 550
SIC 6211 Investment bankers; Investment bankers
Pt: Tim McAfee
**Pt:* Bill Mello
**COO:* Dean Vernoia
Chf Mktg O: Angela Gilmore
**Ofcr:* Ed Woll
Ex VP: Mike Bresner
Sr VP: Richard Boatright
Sr VP: Reed Lengel
Sr VP: Robert Omohundro
VP: Lois Cohen
VP: Daniel Forbes
VP: Jack Leniart
VP: Herman Mannings
VP: Chip Owens

D-U-N-S 16-663-6691
JPAY INC
12864 Biscayne Blvd # 243, North Miami, FL 33181-2007
Tel (866) 333-5729 *Founded/Ownrshp* 2002
Sales NA *EMP* 25
Accts Daszkal Bolton Llp Boca Raton
SIC 6099 Electronic funds transfer network, including switching
CEO: Ryan Shapiro
**COO:* Daniel Shapiro
**CFO:* Mark Silverman
**Genl Couns:* Errol Feldman

D-U-N-S 06-428-2988
JPB FOUNDATION
9 W 57th St Ste 3800, New York, NY 10019-2701
Tel (212) 364-6266 *Founded/Ownrshp* 2011
Sales 1.2MMM *EMP* 3
SIC 8641 Civic social & fraternal associations; Civic social & fraternal associations
Prin: April C Freilich
VP: Dana Bourland

D-U-N-S 12-999-1584
JPB PARTNERS
8820 Columbia 100 Pkwy # 400, Columbia, MD 21045-2175
Tel (410) 884-1960 *Founded/Ownrshp* 1994
Sales 4.3M *EMP* 510
SIC 6282 Investment advisory service; Investment advisory service
CEO: J P Boulduc
Pr: James Bolduc
CEO: Mark Rohde
Sr VP: Sam Beritela
Sr VP: Richard Story
VP: Gayle Horn
VP: Mark Regal
VP: Gayle A Van Horn

D-U-N-S 05-350-6002
JPC ENTERPRISES INC
JERSEY PAPER PLUS
47 Brunswick Ave, Edison, NJ 08817-2576
Tel (732) 750-1900 *Founded/Ownrshp* 1993
Sales 88.3MM^E *EMP* 95
SIC 5113 Industrial & personal service paper; Bags, paper & disposable plastic; Boxes, paperboard & disposable plastic; Towels, paper; Industrial & personal service paper; Bags, paper & disposable plastic; Boxes, paperboard & disposable plastic; Towels, paper
CEO: Steven Tabak
**Ch:* Joseph Tabak
VP: Steve Halper
Sales Exec: Steve Bilawsky

D-U-N-S 03-875-3088
JPC GROUP INC
1309 S Harmony St, Philadelphia, PA 19146-3211
Tel (215) 243-9660 *Founded/Ownrshp* 2001
Sales 73.9MM^E *EMP* 200
Accts Gold Gerstein Group Llc Moore
SIC 1611 1623 General contractor, highway & street construction; Water, sewer & utility lines; General contractor, highway & street construction; Water, sewer & utility lines
Pr: Joseph Petrongolo Jr
**Treas:* Jeffrey Petrongolo
**VP:* James Petrongolo

D-U-N-S 07-947-8422
■ **JPHI HOLDINGS INC**
(*Suby of* JASON INDUSTRIES INC) ★
411 E Wisconsin Ave, Milwaukee, WI 53202-4461
Tel (414) 277-9445 *Founded/Ownrshp* 2014
Sales 700.0MM^E *EMP* 3,500^E
SIC 3465 2297 3625 3469 3844 3443 Personal holding companies, except banks; Moldings or trim, automobile: stamped metal; Nonwoven fabrics; Noise control equipment; Metal stampings; Irradiation equipment; Boilers: industrial, power, or marine

D-U-N-S 02-233-6130
JPI APARTMENT CONSTRUCTION LP
600 Las Colinas Blvd E # 1800, Irving, TX 75039-5648
Tel (972) 556-1700 *Founded/Ownrshp* 1997
Sales 139.5MM^E *EMP* 1,170
SIC 1522 Apartment building construction; Apartment building construction
Pt: J Frank Miller III
CIO: Tom Bumpass

JPI CONSTRUCTION
See J P I NATIONAL CONSTRUCTION INC

D-U-N-S 95-839-5410
JPI INVESTMENT CO LP
J P I LEASING
600 Las Colinas Blvd E # 1800, Irving, TX 75039-5648
Tel (972) 556-1700 *Founded/Ownrshp* 1991
Sales 181.8MM^E *EMP* 1,200
SIC 6552 Subdividers & developers; Subdividers & developers
Prin: Bobby Page
CEO: J Frank Miller III
Sr VP: Ben Montgomery
VP: Heidi Mather

D-U-N-S 01-947-3763
JPI LIFESTYLE APARTMENT COMMUNITIES LP
600 Las Colinas Blvd E, Irving, TX 75039-5648
Tel (972) 556-1700 *Founded/Ownrshp* 1997
Sales 33.1MM^E *EMP* 1,200
SIC 6513 6552 Apartment building operators; Land subdividers & developers, residential; Apartment building operators; Land subdividers & developers, residential
Mng Pt: J Frank Miller III
Genl Pt: Jpi I LP
Pt: GE Capital
Mng Pt: Scott Matthews

D-U-N-S 13-186-8841
JPI MANAGEMENT LLC
JPI MANAGEMENT SERVICES
600 Las Colinas Blvd E, Irving, TX 75039-5648
Tel (972) 556-1700 *Founded/Ownrshp* 2009
Sales 30.4MM^E *EMP* 1,150
SIC 8741 Management services; Management services

JPI MANAGEMENT SERVICES
See JPI MANAGEMENT LLC

D-U-N-S 62-066-8830
JPI PARTNERS LLC
JEFFERSON
600 Las Colinas Blvd E # 1800, Irving, TX 75039-5648
Tel (972) 556-1700 *Founded/Ownrshp* 1989
Sales 46.3MM^E *EMP* 133
SIC 1522 6531 Multi-family dwellings, new construction; Real estate agents & managers; Multi-family dwellings, new construction; Real estate agents & managers
Genl Mgr: Kim Self

D-U-N-S 09-439-5696
JPI WHOLESALERS INC
JONES POULTRY
1 Rooster Way, Barry, IL 62312-9749
Tel (217) 335-3113 *Founded/Ownrshp* 1996
Sales 25.0MM^E *EMP* 35
SIC 5144 5147 Poultry: live, dressed or frozen (unpackaged); Meats & meat products; Poultry: live, dressed or frozen (unpackaged); Meats & meat products
Pr: Duane Venvertloh
Genl Mgr: Todd Degitz

D-U-N-S 14-115-8746 IMP
■ **JPJC ENTERPRISES INC**
(*Suby of* VALMONT INDUSTRIES INC) ★
15 Oser Ave, Hauppauge, NY 11788-3808
Tel (631) 231-7660 *Founded/Ownrshp* 2008
Sales 27.1MM^E *EMP* 50
SIC 5065 Communication equipment
Ch Bd: Joseph P Catapano
Manager: Vanessa Carr
Manager: Joshua Tawwater
Manager: Monica Vink
Manager: Daniel Zamora

JPM
See JAMES M PLEASANTS CO INC

D-U-N-S 96-459-6865
JPM CHASE VEBA TRUST FOR ACTIVE EMPLO
1 Chase Pla, New York, NY 10005
Tel (212) 552-2992 *Founded/Ownrshp* 2010
Sales 553.4MM *EMP* 2^E
Accts Wtas Madison Nj

SIC 6733 Trusts; Trusts

JPMC CARD SERVICES
See JPMORGAN CHASE & CO

D-U-N-S 79-691-2785
■ JPMORGAN ASSET MANAGEMENT HOLDINGS INC
(Suby of JPMORGAN CHASE & CO) ★
245 Park Ave Fl 33, New York, NY 10167-4299
Tel (212) 648-2355 Founded/Ownrshp 2000
Sales 27.4MM^E EMP 45^E
SIC 6282 Investment advice
Prin: France Bastien
COO: James Gearin
VP: Preston Meyer

D-U-N-S 78-734-9021
■ JPMORGAN CAPITAL CORP
(Suby of BANC ONE FINANCIAL LLC) ★
55 W Monroe St, Chicago, IL 60603-5001
Tel (614) 248-5800 Founded/Ownrshp 1996
Sales 59.5MM^E EMP 2,368^E
SIC 8748 6726 Business consulting; Investment offices
Prin: Kristie McNab

D-U-N-S 04-767-5947
▲ JPMORGAN CHASE & CO
270 Park Ave, New York, NY 10017-2014
Tel (212) 270-6000 Founded/Ownrshp 1968
Sales NA EMP 241,359^E
Tkr Sym JPM Exch NYS
SIC 6021 6211 6162 6141 National commercial banks; Security brokers & dealers; Mortgage bankers & correspondents; Automobile loans, including insurance; Financing: automobiles, furniture, etc., not a deposit bank; National commercial banks; Security brokers & dealers; Mortgage bankers & correspondents; Automobile loans, including insurance; Financing: automobiles, furniture, etc., not a deposit bank
Ch Bd: James Dimon
CEO: Mary Callahan Erdoes
CEO: Douglas B Petno
CEO: Daniel E Pinto
CEO: Gordon A Smith
COO: Matthew E Zames
CFO: Marianne Lake
Dir Risk M: Ashley Bacon
Adm Dir: Nicole Arnold
Advt Mgr: Sethu Warrier
Genl Couns: Stephen M Cutler
Board of Directors: William C Weldon, Linda B Bammann, James A Bell, Crandall C Bowles, Stephen B Burke, James S Crown, Timothy P Flynn, Laban P Jackson Jr, Michael A Neal, Lee R Raymond

D-U-N-S 12-255-7143
■ JPMORGAN CHASE & CO
JPMC CARD SERVICES
(Suby of JPMORGAN CHASE & CO) ★
201 N Walnut St Fl 2, Wilmington, DE 19801-2901
Tel (302) 282-4000 Founded/Ownrshp 1997
Sales NA EMP 10,410
SIC 6021 National commercial banks; National commercial banks
Ch Bd: William Campbell
Top Exec: Michael Cleary
Assoc VP: Omar Amin
Sr VP: Joan Bassett
Sr VP: Sangeeta Prasad
VP: Terrance Bowman
VP: Katie Brobst
VP: Anil Jacob
VP: Jim Kane
VP: Darren Leeman
VP: Bill Loughery
VP: Reza Nemat
VP: Satish Patel
VP: Keith Pulsifer
VP: Donald Radacosky
VP: William Telkowski

D-U-N-S 00-698-1831 IMP/EXP
■ JPMORGAN CHASE BANK NATIONAL ASSOCIATION
(Suby of JPMORGAN CHASE & CO) ★
1111 Polaris Pkwy, Columbus, OH 43240-2050
Tel (614) 436-3055 Founded/Ownrshp 1824
Sales NA EMP 170,538
SIC 6022 6099 6799 6211 6162 7389 State commercial banks; Travelers' checks issuance; Safe deposit companies; Real estate investors, except property operators; Investment bankers; Mortgage bankers; Credit card service; State commercial banks; Travelers' checks issuance; Safe deposit companies; Real estate investors, except property operators; Investment bankers; Mortgage bankers; Credit card service
Ch Bd: James Dimon
*Pr: Sean Friedman
Pr: Randy Howell
Ofcr: Mercy Borjas
Assoc VP: Ed Eppick
Assoc VP: Megan Franzen
Assoc VP: Joe Gutman
Sr VP: Mark Gamble
Sr VP: Bradly Isbell
Sr VP: Michael Lancaster
Sr VP: David Nolan
Sr VP: Larry Reccoppa
Sr VP: Cheri Thompson
VP: Daniel Anton
VP: Adam Barck
VP: Kristy Blue
VP: Lisa Cecil
VP: Mukund Chandrasekar
VP: Soundar Chinnadurai
VP: Vicki Cole
VP: Brian Elliott

JPMORGAN CHASE VASTERA INC.
See LIVINGSTON INTERNATIONAL TECHNOLOGY SERVICES CORP

D-U-N-S 79-871-8367
■ JPMORGAN INVESTMENT ADVISORS INC
(Suby of JPMORGAN CHASE & CO) ★
1111 Polaris Pkwy, Columbus, OH 43240-2031
Tel (614) 248-5800 Founded/Ownrshp 2005
Sales 116.1MM^E EMP 650
SIC 6282 Investment advisory service; Investment advisory service
Pr: David J Kundert

D-U-N-S 13-123-4148 IMP
JPR SYSTEMS INC
305 N Berry St, Brea, CA 92821-3140
Tel (714) 674-9520 Founded/Ownrshp 2002
Sales 20.1MM^E EMP 30
SIC 5084 5085 3823 Industrial machinery & equipment; Valves & fittings; Industrial instrmnts msrmnt display/control process variable
Pr: Jeff Radcliff
*Prin: Scott Boley
*Prin: Bob Goulette
*Prin: Ralf Oelschlager
*Prin: Steve Schenker
Off Admin: Nancy Watts
Sales Asso: Leo Stemler

JP'S COFFEE
See FERRIS COFFEE AND NUT CO

D-U-N-S 18-974-0608 IMP/EXP
■ JPS COMPOSITE MATERIALS CORP
JPS GLASS
(Suby of JPS INDUSTRIES INC) ★
2200 S Murray Ave, Anderson, SC 29624-3139
Tel (864) 836-8011 Founded/Ownrshp 1988
Sales 114.9MM^E EMP 325^E
SIC 3231 Products of purchased glass; Products of purchased glass
Pr: M Gary Wallace
*VP: Donald R Burnette
*VP: Dieter R Wachter
IT Man: Keith Bendyk
IT Man: Brian Green
Tech Mgr: Mark A Anderson
Sfty Mgr: Donnie Richey
Plnt Mgr: Donald Gunter

D-U-N-S 05-560-2607
JPS EQUIPMENT RENTAL LLC
6301 Highway 165 Byp, Monroe, LA 71202-7263
Tel (318) 651-9640 Founded/Ownrshp 2013
Sales 34.6MM^E EMP 36^E
SIC 5084 Industrial machinery & equipment

JPS GLASS
See JPS COMPOSITE MATERIALS CORP

D-U-N-S 18-724-2797 IMP/EXP
■ JPS INDUSTRIES INC
(Suby of HANDY & HARMAN GROUP LTD) ★
2200 S Murray Ave, Anderson, SC 29624-3139
Tel (864) 239-3900 Founded/Ownrshp 2015
Sales 114.9MM^E EMP 900
Tkr Sym JPST Exch OTO
SIC 2221 3081 Fiberglass fabrics; Unsupported plastics film & sheet; Fiberglass fabrics; Unsupported plastics film & sheet
Pr: Mikel H Williams
CFO: Charles R Tutterow
VP: Monnie L Broome
VP: William Jackson
Mfg Mgr: Dale Jordan
Plnt Mgr: Gary M Wallace

D-U-N-S 93-214-9144
JPS PHYSICIAN GROUP INC
1500 S Main St, Fort Worth, TX 76104-4917
Tel (817) 921-3431 Founded/Ownrshp 2008
Sales 49.7MM EMP 35^E
Accts Bkd Llp Houston Tx
SIC 8011 General & family practice, physician/surgeon; General & family practice, physician/surgeon
Prin: Gale Pileggi

D-U-N-S 00-948-2621 IMP
JPW INDUSTRIES INC (WA)
427 New Sanford Rd, La Vergne, TN 37086-4184
Tel (615) 793-8900 Founded/Ownrshp 1960, 2013
Sales 28.3MM^E EMP 120^E
SIC 3423 5084 5085 Hand & edge tools; Industrial machinery & equipment; Machine tools & accessories; Materials handling machinery; Woodworking machinery; Industrial supplies; Hand & edge tools; Industrial machinery & equipment; Machine tools & accessories; Materials handling machinery; Woodworking machinery; Industrial supplies
Pr: Robert Romano
*Treas: Jochen Nutz
VP: Cliff Rickmers
VP: Mark Smith
*VP: Bob Varzino
*VP: Ivan Wehrli
Prgrm Mgr: Steven Myers
IT Man: Travis Gleaves
IT Man: Scott Howell
Web Dev: Rob Ackerman
Natl Sales: Jared Connor

JR
See J REYNOLDS & CO INC

D-U-N-S 10-289-8335
JR ABBOTT CONSTRUCTION INC
3408 1st Ave S Ste 101, Seattle, WA 98134-1805
Tel (206) 467-8500 Founded/Ownrshp 1983
Sales 87.1MM^E EMP 144
Accts Berntson Porter And Co Pllc
SIC 1542 Commercial & office building, new construction; Commercial & office buildings, renovation & repair; Commercial & office building, new construction; Commercial & office buildings, renovation & repair
Pr: John P McGowan
*CFO: Mark C Seaman
*VP: Doug J Klein
*VP: Wendy P Newman
*VP: Robert M Robertson
VP: Troy Stedman
CTO: Pete Ophoven
IT Man: Joel Hagemeyer
IT Man: Christine Mayes
Sfty Mgr: Mark Knudson
Sfty Mgr: Ron Nelson

D-U-N-S 02-103-9607 IMP
JR AUTOMATION TECHNOLOGIES LLC
EPOCH ROBOTICS
(Suby of JR TECHNOLOGY GROUP LLC) ★
13365 Tyler St, Holland, MI 49424-9421
Tel (616) 399-2168 Founded/Ownrshp 2015
Sales 214.0MM^E EMP 451
SIC 3549 Assembly machines, including robotic; Assembly machines, including robotic
Co-CEO: Bryan Jones
CFO: Randy Bethke
*CFO: Barry Kohn
*Co-CEO: Scot Lindemann
Prgrm Mgr: Scott Williamson
Genl Mgr: Bill Yeck
Software D: Kyle Smith
Sftwr Eng: Tim Kelch
Opers Mgr: Harry Leeuw
Sls Mgr: Darren Stark
Snr Mgr: Jeff Seaberg

D-U-N-S 07-398-9357 IMP
JR CAPITAL CORP
ATLAS LOX
1660 Nw 19th Ave, Pompano Beach, FL 33069-1648
Tel (954) 543-9800 Founded/Ownrshp 1999
Sales 20.4MM^E EMP 145
SIC 4953 Recycling, waste materials; Recycling, waste materials
Pr: Angelo Marzano
*VP: Patrick Marzano

D-U-N-S 03-063-2566
JR CUSTOM METAL PRODUCTS INC
2237 S West Street Ct, Wichita, KS 67213-1100
Tel (316) 263-1318 Founded/Ownrshp 1974
Sales 42.6MM^E EMP 150
SIC 3535 3537 3531 3444 Conveyors & conveying equipment; Platforms, stands, tables, pallets & similar equipment; Construction machinery; Sheet metalwork; Conveyors & conveying equipment; Platforms, stands, tables, pallets & similar equipment; Construction machinery; Sheet metalwork
Pr: Patricia Koehler
*Treas: Jorge Martinez
*VP: Jesus Raul Martinez Jr
Sls Mgr: Scott Kailer

D-U-N-S 15-270-8244
JR DAVIS CONSTRUCTION CO INC
210 S Hoagland Blvd, Kissimmee, FL 34741-4534
Tel (407) 870-0066 Founded/Ownrshp 1985
Sales 115.9MM^E EMP 400
SIC 1629 6552 1521 Land preparation construction; Land clearing contractor; Subdividers & developers; Single-family housing construction; Land preparation construction; Land clearing contractor; Subdividers & developers; Single-family housing construction
Pr: James B J Davis
*Treas: Kimberly Buccellato
*Sec: Tama Davis
Genl Mgr: Glenn Kelley

D-U-N-S 03-809-7010 IMP
JR ENGINEERING INC
J R ENGINEERING
5208 Wooster Rd W, Norton, OH 44203-6267
Tel (330) 825-1565 Founded/Ownrshp 1979
Sales 76.4MM^E EMP 500
SIC 3714 Motor vehicle parts & accessories; Motor vehicle parts & accessories
Pr: Louis Bilinovich Jr
*Sec: Louis Bilinovich Sr
VP: Dave Blankenship
IT Man: Darin Nist
Ql Cn Mgr: John Callan

D-U-N-S 00-683-7165
JR FILANC CONSTRUCTION CO INC (CA)
740 N Andreasen Dr, Escondido, CA 92029-1414
Tel (760) 941-7130 Founded/Ownrshp 1952
Sales 152.4MM^E EMP 200
SIC 1623 1629 Pumping station construction; Waste water & sewage treatment plant construction; Pumping station construction; Waste water & sewage treatment plant construction
CEO: Mark E Filanc
*Pr: Harry S Cosmos
*CFO: Kevin Elliotts
*VP: Vincent L Diaz

JR FOOD MARKET
See JFM INC

JR FOOD MARKET
See ANDERSON OIL CO INC

JR FOOD MARKET
See JR FOOD STORES INC

D-U-N-S 18-553-2090
JR FOOD STORES INC
JR FOOD MARKET
(Suby of HOUCHENS FOOD GROUP INC) ★
700 Church St, Bowling Green, KY 42101-1816
Tel (270) 843-3252 Founded/Ownrshp 1998
Sales 38.7MM^E EMP 365
SIC 5411 5541 Convenience stores, chain; Filling stations, gasoline; Convenience stores, chain; Filling stations, gasoline
Pr: Jimmie Gipson

D-U-N-S 03-741-6757 IMP
JR FOUR LTD
TECHNICAL GLASS PRODUCTS
8107 Bracken Pl Se, Snoqualmie, WA 98065-9258
Tel (425) 396-8200 Founded/Ownrshp 1980
Sales 65.2MM^E EMP 100
SIC 5039 Glass construction materials; Glass construction materials
Pr: Jeff R Razwick
Genl Mgr: Tim Anderson
Off Mgr: Janet Grimsby
Plnt Mgr: Mike Colvin
Natl Sales: Devin Bowman
Sls Mgr: William Evans
Sls Mgr: Jack Watson

D-U-N-S 60-319-7278
JR GETTIER & ASSOCIATES INC
GETTIER SECURITY
2 Centerville Rd, Wilmington, DE 19808-4708
Tel (302) 478-0911 Founded/Ownrshp 1987
Sales 12.2MM^E EMP 500
SIC 7381 8748 Detective services; Guard services; Business consulting; Detective services; Guard services; Business consulting
CEO: Jim Gettier
*Pr: Lou Manerchia
CTO: Charles Williams

D-U-N-S 05-620-5735
JR HOBBS CO - ATLANTA LLC
2021 Cedars Rd Ste 100, Lawrenceville, GA 30043-7589
Tel (678) 495-0394 Founded/Ownrshp 1971
Sales 42.9MM^E EMP 120
SIC 1711 Warm air heating & air conditioning contractor; Warm air heating & air conditioning contractor
Pr: Barry G Camp
Pr: David Woodall
VP: Ron Oudi
CTO: Kmckenzie Parker
Opers Mgr: Alex Lemeshko

D-U-N-S 15-148-3922
JR INSULATION SALES & SERVICE INC
Km 2 Hm 9 Rr 385, Penuelas, PR 00624
Tel (787) 836-1756 Founded/Ownrshp 1984
Sales 4.8MM EMP 500
Accts Bolivar Barreto Pagan
SIC 1742 1799 1741 Acoustical & insulation work; Asbestos removal & encapsulation; Lead burning; Scaffolding construction; Refractory or acid brick masonry; Acoustical & insulation work; Asbestos removal & encapsulation; Lead burning; Scaffolding construction; Refractory or acid brick masonry
Pr: Jose Ruiz Vasquez
CFO: Bolivar Barreto

D-U-N-S 07-065-2339 IMP
JR MANUFACTURING INC
900 Industrial Dr, Fort Recovery, OH 45846
Tel (419) 375-8021 Founded/Ownrshp 1998
Sales 29.8MM^E EMP 150
SIC 3315 3441 Steel wire & related products; Fabricated structural metal; Steel wire & related products; Fabricated structural metal
CFO: Chad Guggenbiller
*Pr: Jeff Roessner
*Pr: Tomo Yamamoto
CFO: Rich Wood
*VP: Greg Lefevre
DP Exec: John Zehringer
Plnt Mgr: Dave Lamm

D-U-N-S 04-931-1673
JR MC DADE CO INC
J.R. MCDADE
1102 N 21st Ave, Phoenix, AZ 85009-3723
Tel (602) 258-7134 Founded/Ownrshp 1959
Sales 82.3MM^E EMP 170
SIC 5023 1752 Carpets; Carpet laying; Carpets; Carpet laying
Pr: John R McDade II

J.R. MCDADE
See JR MC DADE CO INC

D-U-N-S 05-391-3877
JR PIERCE PLUMBING CO INC OF SACRAMENTO (CA)
3610 Cincinnati Ave, Rocklin, CA 95765-1203
Tel (916) 434-9554 Founded/Ownrshp 1927
Sales 35.6MM^E EMP 150
SIC 1711 Plumbing contractors; Plumbing contractors
Pr: Dennis Pierce

D-U-N-S 15-984-3531 IMP/EXP
JR PLASTICS CORP
5111 S Pine Ave Ste G, Ocala, FL 34480-7176
Tel (352) 401-0880 Founded/Ownrshp 1997
Sales 49.3MM^E EMP 100
SIC 2671 2673 Plastic film, coated or laminated for packaging; Plastic & pliofilm bags; Plastic film, coated or laminated for packaging; Plastic & pliofilm bags
Ch: Robert Ruwitch
*Pr: Rick Diamond
CFO: Warren Steffey
*VP: James Wear
Off Mgr: Carol Stewart

D-U-N-S 10-361-7176 IMP
JR RODRIGUEZ INTERNATIONAL CORP
INTERCON PAPER
4545 Leston St, Dallas, TX 75247-5709
Tel (214) 905-5086 Founded/Ownrshp 1999
Sales 34.4MM^E EMP 25
SIC 5111 Printing & writing paper
Pr: Roy Rodriguez
*CFO: Cristina Rodriguez
*VP: Jose R Rodriguez
Sls Mgr: Christian Trevino
Sls Mgr: Russ Woodlief
Snr Mgr: Tony Ramirez

D-U-N-S 00-907-3503 IMP/EXP
JR SIMPLOT CO
SIMPLOT WESTERN STOCKMEN'S
999 W Main St Ste 1300, Boise, ID 83702-9009
Tel (208) 336-2110 Founded/Ownrshp 1923
Sales 4.9MMM^E EMP 9,970

SIC 0211 2879 2037 2874 2873 Beef cattle feedlots; Agricultural chemicals; Potato products, quick frozen & cold pack; Vegetables, quick frozen & cold pack, excl. potato products; Fruits, quick frozen & cold pack (frozen); Phosphatic fertilizers; Ammonium phosphate; Nitrogenous fertilizers; Beef cattle feedlots; Agricultural chemicals; Potato products, quick frozen & cold pack; Vegetables, quick frozen & cold pack, excl. potato products; Fruits, quick frozen & cold pack (frozen); Phosphatic fertilizers; Ammonium phosphate; Nitrogenous fertilizers
Ch: Scott Simplot
Pr: Roger Park
**Pr:* William Whitacre
**CFO:* Annette Elg
CFO: Dennis Mogensen
**Treas:* Amber Post
Sr Cor Off: Steve Deirs
Sr Cor Off: Maureen Duffy
Sr Cor Off: Lori Otter
Bd of Dir: David McDermott
Ex VP: Janss Franden
Sr VP: Alan Kahn
**Sr VP:* Garrett Lofto
**Sr VP:* Mark McKellar
Sr VP: Blaine McKinney
**Sr VP:* Terry T Uhling
VP: James Crawford
VP: Mark Dunn
VP: Jeff Lehn
VP: Roger Parks
VP: Ted Roper
Board of Directors: Stephen A Beebe, A Dale Dunn, Richard M Hormaechea, Robert J Lane, Joseph Marshall, Debbie McDonald, Gay C Simplot, J E Simplot, Scott R Simplot

D-U-N-S 07-978-3699
JR TECHNOLOGY GROUP LLC
13365 Tyler St, Holland, MI 49424-9421
Tel (616) 399-2168 *Founded/Ownrshp* 2015
Sales 241.9MM^E *EMP* 521^E
SIC 3549 Assembly machines, including robotic
Co-CEO: Bryan Jones
CFO: Barry Kohn
Co-CEO: Scot Lindemann

JR VALENTINES FAMILY REST
See JOHN ROBERTS MANAGEMENT CORP

D-U-N-S 12-820-1709
JR VINAGRO CORP
2208 Plainfield Pike, Johnston, RI 02919-5717
Tel (401) 647-3176 *Founded/Ownrshp* 1998
Sales 44.3MM^E *EMP* 90
SIC 1795 4953 Wrecking & demolition work; Recycling, waste materials
Pr: Joseph R Vinagro
IT Man: Donna Davis
IT Man: David Dimaio
Sfty Dirs: Matt Leonard

D-U-N-S 82-519-0205
JR WHOLESALER INC
1304 Zaragoza St Ste D, Laredo, TX 78040-5968
Tel (956) 723-7379 *Founded/Ownrshp* 2007
Sales 30.0MM *EMP* 2
SIC 5092 Video games; Video games

D-U-N-S 03-040-6755 IMP
JRB ATTACHMENTS LLC
(*Suby of* PALADIN ATTACHMENTS) ★
820 Glaser Pkwy, Akron, OH 44306-4133
Tel (330) 734-3000 *Founded/Ownrshp* 2004
Sales 32.8MM^E *EMP* 176
SIC 3531 Construction machinery attachments; Construction machinery attachments
CEO: Steve Andrews
**CFO:* Steve Klyn
**VP:* Paul Burton
VP: Gale Dilday
**VP:* Michael Flannery
**VP:* Wendell Moss
**VP:* John Thomas
VP Mfg: Jeff Dore
Sfty Mgr: John Lech
Sfty Mgr: Tim Mulhollen
Plnt Mgr: Pat Ford

D-U-N-S 17-446-4883
JRC LAKESIDE INC
401 N Michigan Ave # 1300, Chicago, IL 60611-4255
Tel (312) 642-6000 *Founded/Ownrshp* 1986
Sales 48.0MM^E *EMP* 301
SIC 6552 Subdividers & developers; Subdividers & developers
CEO: Donald A Smith
**Pr:* E Michael Pompizzi
**Ex VP:* Jerry Ong

D-U-N-S 04-007-5723 IMP/EXP
JRD HOLDINGS INC
(*Suby of* JETRO CASH & CARRY) ★
1524 132nd St, College Point, NY 11356-2440
Tel (718) 762-8700 *Founded/Ownrshp* 1990
Sales 2.2MMM^E *EMP* 1,500
SIC 5141 5142 5147 5181 5194 Groceries, general line; Packaged frozen goods; Meats, fresh; Beer & other fermented malt liquors; Tobacco & tobacco products; Groceries, general line; Packaged frozen goods; Meats, fresh; Beer & other fermented malt liquors; Tobacco & tobacco products
Pr: Stanley Fleishman
**CFO:* Brian Emmert
**VP:* Richard Kirshner
CIO: Richard Grossman
Netwrk Mgr: Ravi Sahni
Opers Mgr: Russell Depaolis

D-U-N-S 07-543-4621
JRD MANAGEMENT CORP
MAXX PROPERTIES
600 Mamaroneck Ave Fl 5, Harrison, NY 10528-1613
Tel (914) 899-8000 *Founded/Ownrshp* 1999
Sales 66.1MM^E *EMP* 350
SIC 6513 Apartment building operators; Apartment building operators
Pr: Eric Wiener
**COO:* Gerald Haak
**CFO:* Marc L Samplin
Sr VP: Suzi Randolph
**VP:* Thomas Discioscia
VP: Andrew Wiener
Rgnl Mgr: Michele Bravo
**VP Opers:* Maria Valente

JRE
See J RANCK ELECTRIC INC

D-U-N-S 18-610-2356 IMP
JRI INC
J R INDUSTRIES
31280 La Baya Dr, Westlake Village, CA 91362-4005
Tel (818) 706-2424 *Founded/Ownrshp* 1987
Sales 21.6MM^E *EMP* 50
SIC 5065 Electronic parts & equipment
Pr: Kathy Becker
**Sec:* Gary Becker

D-U-N-S 78-291-3169
JRJ ENERGY SERVICES LLC
7302 Northland Dr, Stanwood, MI 49346-8742
Tel (231) 823-2171 *Founded/Ownrshp* 2006
Sales 29.3MM *EMP* 120
SIC 1389 Construction, repair & dismantling services; Construction, repair & dismantling services
Genl Mgr: John R Johnson

D-U-N-S 07-043-4188
JRL VENTURES INC
2443 Sw Pine Island Rd, Cape Coral, FL 33991-1282
Tel (239) 283-0800 *Founded/Ownrshp* 1994
Sales 21.3MM^E *EMP* 90
SIC 3429 Marine hardware
Pr: Robert Long

D-U-N-S 05-438-5935 IMP
JRLON INC
4344 Fox Rd, Palmyra, NY 14522-9423
Tel (315) 597-4067 *Founded/Ownrshp* 1981
Sales 21.2MM^E *EMP* 80
SIC 2821 3566 3479 3462 2851 Molding compounds, plastics; Gears, power transmission, except automotive; Painting, coating & hot dipping; Iron & steel forgings; Paints & allied products
Pr: James F Redmond
**Sec:* Lindsey Redmond
Mktg Mgr: Brandon Redmond

D-U-N-S 85-944-3025
JRM CONSTRUCTION MANAGEMENT LLC
242 W 36th St Rm 901, New York, NY 10018-8957
Tel (212) 545-0500 *Founded/Ownrshp* 2007
Sales 140.9MM^E *EMP* 200
SIC 1542 Commercial & office building, new construction; Commercial & office building, new construction

D-U-N-S 01-938-0807
JRM HAULING AND RECYCLING SERVICES II INC
J R M
265 Newbury St, Peabody, MA 01960-1315
Tel (978) 536-2500 *Founded/Ownrshp* 1995
Sales 54.6MM^E *EMP* 100
SIC 4953 Recycling, waste materials; Garbage: collecting, destroying & processing
Pr: James R Motzkin

D-U-N-S 05-427-7298
JRN INC (TN)
KFC
209 W 7th St, Columbia, TN 38401-3233
Tel (931) 381-3000 *Founded/Ownrshp* 1971
Sales 148.4MM^E *EMP* 4,000
SIC 5812

D-U-N-S 12-236-7795 IMP
JRNA INC
UNCLAIMED FREIGHT
2260 Industrial Dr, Bethlehem, PA 18017-2138
Tel (610) 974-8194 *Founded/Ownrshp* 2002
Sales 23.7MM^E *EMP* 120
SIC 5712 Furniture stores
CEO: Andy Eskow
**Pr:* Joseph Colabella

D-U-N-S 94-811-3899 IMP
JRS DISTRIBUTION CO
1333 Grandview Pkwy, Sturtevant, WI 53177-1261
Tel (262) 884-9828 *Founded/Ownrshp* 1993
Sales 43.5MM^E *EMP* 90
SIC 5192 Books
CEO: Louis Webber
**Pr:* J Robert Stanik
**CFO:* Jeff Coyle

D-U-N-S 79-110-0944
JRS HOLDING INC
20445 W Capitol Dr, Brookfield, WI 53045-2745
Tel (262) 781-2626 *Founded/Ownrshp* 1985
Sales 116.1MM^E *EMP* 250
SIC 5511 Automobiles, new & used; Automobiles, new & used
Pr: John R Safro
**Pr:* Martin Thomas
**VP:* James Tessmer
Genl Mgr: Steve Recht

D-U-N-S 08-746-0218
JS & LC CO
(*Suby of* BENESYS INC) ★
1220 Sw Morrison St # 300, Portland, OR 97205-2235
Tel (503) 224-0048 *Founded/Ownrshp* 2015
Sales NA *EMP* 60
SIC 6371 Union welfare, benefit & health funds
Pr: Jennifer L Schmidt
CFO: David Corbelli
Sr VP: Lee Centrone
VP: Liz Cowles
IT Man: Craig Stallcup

D-U-N-S 14-982-3663
JS AUTOWORLD INC
PLANET NISSAN
5850 Centennial Ctr Blvd, Las Vegas, NV 89149-4570
Tel (702) 876-8000 *Founded/Ownrshp* 1999
Sales 48.4MM^E *EMP* 91
SIC 5511 7549 Automobiles, new & used; Automotive maintenance services; Automobiles, new & used; Automotive maintenance services
CEO: John Staluppi Jr
CFO: Christina Ribaudo
Sls Mgr: Jesse Quintero

JS FOODS
See JOSEPHSON MANAGEMENT CO

D-U-N-S 93-124-1371
JS FOODS INC
PAPA JOHN'S
605 German St, Fayetteville, NC 28301-5419
Tel (910) 321-7373 *Founded/Ownrshp* 2000
Sales 8.2MM^E *EMP* 350
SIC 6531 Real estate agents & managers; Real estate agents & managers
Pr: Marrof Jahangir

D-U-N-S 00-213-7561
JS HELWIG & SON LLC (TX)
222 Metro Dr, Terrell, TX 75160-9169
Tel (214) 771-3464 *Founded/Ownrshp* 2005
Sales 40.1MM^E *EMP* 200
Accts Bland Garvey Pc Richardson T
SIC 4731 Freight transportation arrangement; Freight transportation arrangement
Mng Pt: James S Helwig
Sr VP: Kurt Antkiewicz
VP: Terry Fabian
Sfty Mgr: John Whiteside

D-U-N-S 15-380-2277
JS INTERNATIONAL SHIPPING CORP
JSI SHIPPING
1535 Rollins Rd Ste B, Burlingame, CA 94010-2305
Tel (650) 697-3963 *Founded/Ownrshp* 1986
Sales 195.4MM^E *EMP* 1,500
SIC 4731 Freight forwarding; Customhouse brokers; Freight forwarding; Customhouse brokers
CEO: James G Cullen
VP: Scott French
Dir Bus: Gabby Ang
Brnch Mgr: Yvonne Angelo
Brnch Mgr: Ramesh Raman
Genl Mgr: Chris Chung
Genl Mgr: Jayson Gispan
Genl Mgr: James Lin
Snr Sftwr: Victoria Santos
IT Man: Izhar Burica
IT Man: Izhar Saharuddin

D-U-N-S 00-110-1187
JS MCCARTHY CO INC (ME)
SAWYER PRINTING
(*Suby of* J S MCCARTHY PRINTING) ★
15 Darin Dr, Augusta, ME 04330-7815
Tel (207) 622-6241 *Founded/Ownrshp* 1947, 2000
Sales 35.0MM *EMP* 207
SIC 2791 2752 2789 2759 Commercial printing, offset; Typesetting; Bookbinding & related work; Commercial printing; Typesetting, computer controlled; Commercial printing, offset; Beveling of cards; Business forms: printing
Pr: Richard Tardiff
**COO:* Bill White
**CFO:* Conrad Ayott
**VP:* Jon Tardiff
Comm Dir: Michael Tardiff
CIO: Judi Hansen
Sfty Mgr: Lee Richardson

D-U-N-S 15-281-4646 IMP
JS PRODUCTS INC
STEELMAN
6445 Montessouri St # 100, Las Vegas, NV 89113-1188
Tel (702) 362-7011 *Founded/Ownrshp* 1986
Sales 60.3MM^E *EMP* 80
SIC 5013 3423 Tools & equipment, automotive; Screw drivers, pliers, chisels, etc. (hand tools)
Pr: Juan F Mora
CFO: Roger Weineman
**Sec:* Roger Wiesenauer
IT Man: Nicholas Ruggiero
Web Dev: T J Helton
Ql Cn Mgr: David Ogilvie
S&M/VP: Seth Holliday
Sls Mgr: Ronnie Castillo

D-U-N-S 06-840-9747 IMP
JS REDPATH CORP
(*Suby of* J.S. REDPATH HOLDINGS INC)
1410 Greg St Ste 404, Sparks, NV 89431-5947
Tel (705) 474-2461 *Founded/Ownrshp* 1987
Sales 55.0MM^E *EMP* 330
SIC 1081 Mine development, metal; Mine development, metal
Pr: George B Flumerfelt
**Treas:* David Brokaski
**VP:* David C Hansman
**VP:* Mark Immonen
**Prin:* Chris C Hickey
**Prin:* Clyde Hunter
IT Man: Mark Imnonen

D-U-N-S 60-924-4793
JS VENTURES INC
APPLEBEE'S
2400 N Woodlawn Blvd # 230, Wichita, KS 67220-3989
Tel (316) 683-7799 *Founded/Ownrshp* 1989
Sales 54.7MM^E *EMP* 2,000
SIC 5812 Restaurant, family: chain; Restaurant, family: chain
Pr: James Stevens
Dir IT: Dave Hosbein

D-U-N-S 13-736-3966
■ **JSA HEALTHCARE CORP**
JSA MEDICAL GROUP
(*Suby of* HEALTHCARE PARTNERS LLC) ★
10051 5th St N Ste 200, Saint Petersburg, FL 33702-2211
Tel (727) 824-0780 *Founded/Ownrshp* 2006
Sales 67.3MM^E *EMP* 450
SIC 8011 Medical centers; Ambulatory surgical center; Clinic, operated by physicians; Primary care medical clinic; Medical centers; Ambulatory surgical center; Clinic, operated by physicians; Primary care medical clinic
Pr: Lorie B Glisson
Pr: John Jaufmann
**COO:* Sidney Morgan
COO: Oraida Roman
**Chf Mktg O:* Barbara Allen
Ofcr: Kathleen Premo
**Sr VP:* Robert Warden
VP: Marty Keyes-Goodemote
Dir Case M: Laurene Dougherty
**Prin:* Gary L Damkoehler
MIS Dir: Bob Clark

JSA INTERNATIONAL
See MECCA ENTERPRISES INC

JSA MEDICAL GROUP
See JSA HEALTHCARE CORP

JSC
See JACKSON SUPPLY CO

D-U-N-S 06-891-5206
JSC EMPLOYEE LEASING CORP
1560 Firestone Pkwy, Akron, OH 44301-1626
Tel (330) 773-8971 *Founded/Ownrshp* 1971
Sales 25.0MM^E *EMP* 173^E
SIC 2522 5021 Office cabinets & filing drawers: except wood; Filing units; Office cabinets & filing drawers: except wood; Filing units
Pr: Jack Jeter
**Ex VP:* Pam Love
DP Exec: Nancy Woerther
Sales Exec: Brian McCann

D-U-N-S 04-709-2150
JSC SYSTEMS INC
5021 Stepp Ave, Jacksonville, FL 32216-6085
Tel (352) 378-9777 *Founded/Ownrshp* 1969
Sales 28.6MM^E *EMP* 130
SIC 1731 Sound equipment specialization; Fire detection & burglar alarm systems specialization; Telephone & telephone equipment installation; Sound equipment specialization; Fire detection & burglar alarm systems specialization; Telephone & telephone equipment installation
Treas: Wilson W Sick Jr
**Pr:* Robert E Begley Jr
Ofcr: Holly Eichhooz
VP: Hilda Castillo
**VP:* Thomas L Milhon
**VP:* Mickey C Rudd
Brnch Mgr: Brad Magee
IT Man: Kathie Adams

D-U-N-S 15-452-8640
JSC TERMINAL LLC
MID WESTTERMINAL
725 N 5th St, Paducah, KY 42001-1085
Tel (270) 442-0362 *Founded/Ownrshp* 1986
Sales 38.7MM^E *EMP* 30
SIC 5172 Diesel fuel; Gasoline; Fuel oil; Lubricating oils & greases
VP: Don Kirby
IT Man: Michael Smith

JSG
See JANE STREET GROUP LLC

D-U-N-S 83-234-1338 IMP
JSI CONSTRUCTION GROUP LLC
(*Suby of* JUWI INC) ★
1710 29th St Unit 1068, Boulder, CO 80301-1051
Tel (303) 440-7430 *Founded/Ownrshp* 2008
Sales 37.0MM *EMP* 50
SIC 1711 Solar energy contractor
Pr: Michael Martin
Treas: Stephen Ihnot

D-U-N-S 14-572-9117
JSI RESEARCH AND TRAINING INSTITUTE INC
44 Farnsworth St Fl 7, Boston, MA 02210-1206
Tel (617) 482-9485 *Founded/Ownrshp* 1979
Sales 196.5MM *EMP* 135^E
Accts Norman R Fougere Jr Cpa Du
SIC 8742 Management consulting services; Management consulting services
Pr: Joel H Lamstein
**COO:* Alexander K Baker
VP: Pat Fairchild
**VP:* Theo Lippeveld
Genl Mgr: Robert Schlink
IT Man: Lori Kiel
Tech Mgr: Wayne Zafft

JSI SHIPPING
See JS INTERNATIONAL SHIPPING CORP

D-U-N-S 85-845-2147 IMP
JSI STORE FIXTURES INC
140 Park St, Milo, ME 04463-1740
Tel (207) 943-5203 *Founded/Ownrshp* 2012
Sales 59.7MM^E *EMP* 190^E
SIC 2541 2499 5046 2542 Display fixtures, wood; Bakers' equipment, wood; Store fixtures; Partitions & fixtures, except wood; Display fixtures, wood; Bakers' equipment, wood; Store fixtures; Partitions & fixtures, except wood
CEO: Terry Awalt
**Ex VP:* Mark Awalt
Sfty Mgr: Gordon Smith
Opers Mgr: Kevin Robbins
Sales Exec: Gretel Seeley
Natl Sales: Sam Civiello
Sls Mgr: Emily Genest
Snr PM: Norma Salmon

D-U-N-S 05-366-8729 IMP/EXP
JSJ CORP
700 Robbins Rd, Grand Haven, MI 49417-2603
Tel (616) 847-8474 *Founded/Ownrshp* 1970
Sales 528.0MM^E *EMP* 2,568

SIC 3465 3469 3366 3089 3086 2522 Automotive stampings; Metal stampings; Stamping metal for the trade; Castings (except die): brass; Castings (except die): bronze; Injection molded finished plastic products; Plastics foam products; Chairs, office: padded or plain, except wood; Desks, office: except wood; Automotive stampings; Metal stampings; Stamping metal for the trade; Castings (except die): brass; Castings (except die): bronze; Injection molded finished plastic products; Plastics foam products; Chairs, office: padded or plain, except wood; Desks, office: except wood
CEO: Nelson Jacobson
**COO:* Barry Lemay
**CFO:* Michael D Metzger
**VP:* Nelson C Jacobson
**VP:* Timothy Liang
**VP:* Edward L Ozark
Mng Dir: Bruce Olmsted
Dir IT: Todd Brower
IT Man: Jim Nutt
Netwrk Eng: Troy Putnam
S&M/VP: Hazen Sills

D-U-N-S 10-107-0709 EXP
JSJ FURNITURE CORP
IZZY PLUS
(*Suby of* JSJ CORP) ★
17237 Van Wagoner Rd, Spring Lake, MI 49456-9702
Tel (616) 847-6534 *Founded/Ownrshp* 2000
Sales 120.4MM^E *EMP* 710^E
SIC 2521 Wood office furniture; Wood office furniture
Pr: Chuck Saylor
**Pr:* Rick Glasser
**Pr:* Gregg Masenthin
**COO:* Joan Hill
COO: Todd Robart
**CFO:* Eric Jorgensen
**VP:* Dan Vukcevich
Opers Mgr: Michael Sheridan
S&M/VP: Scott Reus
Snr Mgr: Jeff Askew

D-U-N-S 80-474-6212
JSK CO INC
I K ELECTRIC COMPANY
214 Dr Mrtn Lther King Dr, Little Rock, AR 72201-1824
Tel (501) 376-2081 *Founded/Ownrshp* 1919
Sales 22.0MM^E *EMP* 120
SIC 1731 General electrical contractor; Fiber optic cable installation; General electrical contractor; Fiber optic cable installation
Pr: Scott Korenblat
IT Man: Mike Seitz
Netwrk Eng: Robert Horn

D-U-N-S 62-188-1564 IMP
JSL FOODS INC
3550 Pasadena Ave, Los Angeles, CA 90031-1946
Tel (323) 223-2484 *Founded/Ownrshp* 1990
Sales 26.4MM^E *EMP* 120^E
SIC 2099 5142 2052 Pasta, uncooked: packaged with other ingredients; Packaged frozen goods; Cookies; Pasta, uncooked: packaged with other ingredients; Packaged frozen goods; Cookies
Pr: Teiji Kawana
**Ex VP:* Koji Kawana
VP: Wayne Nelson
QA Dir: Rhaun Turner
IT Man: Edwardo Rivas
VP Opers: Jerry Kobayashi
Sfty Mgr: Marco Melgar
Prd Mgr: Gustavo Cardona
Sls Mgr: Wayne Nielsen

D-U-N-S 14-783-9422
JSMN INTERNATIONAL INC
591 Summit Ave Ste 522, Jersey City, NJ 07306-2703
Tel (201) 792-6800 *Founded/Ownrshp* 1998
Sales 32.2MM^E *EMP* 260
SIC 7371 Computer software systems analysis & design, custom; Computer software systems analysis & design, custom
Pr: Ravinder Kumar

D-U-N-S 11-505-1674
JSN INDUSTRIES INC
9700 Jeronimo Rd, Irvine, CA 92618-2019
Tel (949) 458-0050 *Founded/Ownrshp* 1984
Sales 20.8MM^E *EMP* 70
SIC 3089 Injection molded finished plastic products
CEO: James H Nagel Jr
**VP:* Sandra Nagel
Genl Mgr: Jay Nagel
Sfty Mgr: Casey Nagel
Snr Mgr: Amy Nagel

D-U-N-S 80-847-2455
JSP INTERNATIONAL GROUP LTD
(*Suby of* JSP CORPORATION)
1285 Drummers Ln Ste 301, Wayne, PA 19087-1572
Tel (610) 651-8600 *Founded/Ownrshp* 1985
Sales 74.4MM^E *EMP* 335
SIC 2821 Polypropylene resins; Polypropylene resins
Pr: Rokurou Inoue
**CFO:* Daniel W Doyle
**Sec:* Zachary R Estrin
**VP:* Carl W Moyer

D-U-N-S 62-358-7912 IMP
JSP INTERNATIONAL LLC
SPECIALITY FIRMS
(*Suby of* JSP INTERNATIONAL GROUP LTD) ★
1285 Drummers Ln Ste 301, Wayne, PA 19087-1572
Tel (610) 651-8600 *Founded/Ownrshp* 1985
Sales 80.3MM^E *EMP* 327
SIC 2821 Polypropylene resins; Polypropylene resins
Pr: Carl W Moyer
**VP:* Richard C Alloway
**VP:* Zachary R Estrin
Off Mgr: Helen Hooalnd
Dir IT: Joe Landy

D-U-N-S 13-330-8283
JSR INC
8835 Greaves Ln, Schertz, TX 78154-6220
Tel (210) 653-7772 *Founded/Ownrshp* 2003
Sales 30.0MM^E *EMP* 150
Accts Stratemann & Associates Selma
SIC 1542 3499 1541 Commercial & office building, new construction; Aerosol valves, metal; Industrial buildings & warehouses; Commercial & office building, new construction; Aerosol valves, metal; Industrial buildings & warehouses
Pr: Nancy A Greaves
**Sec:* Rita Jordan
**VP:* Bobby D Greaves
Genl Mgr: Jennifer Greaves

JSR MERCHANDISING
See JUST SAY ROCK INC

D-U-N-S 62-161-2431 IMP
JSR MICRO INC
MATERIALS INNOVATION
(*Suby of* JSR CORPORATION)
1280 N Mathilda Ave, Sunnyvale, CA 94089-1213
Tel (408) 543-8800 *Founded/Ownrshp* 1990
Sales 32.2MM^E *EMP* 150
SIC 2869 2899 Industrial organic chemicals; Chemical preparations; Industrial organic chemicals; Chemical preparations
Pr: Eric R Johnson
**Treas:* Hitoshi Inoue
Treas: Yasuhiko Sawada
VP: Jim Mulready
Exec: Norbert Fronczak
Dir Bus: Maria Peterson
Prgrm Mgr: Jeff Myron
QA Dir: Arlene Canlas
IT Man: Tuan Than
Plnt Mgr: Ray Hung
Sls Mgr: Tim Lowery

D-U-N-S 02-945-8197 IMP
JST CORP
(*Suby of* J.S.T. MFG. CO.,LTD.)
1957 S Lakeside Dr, Waukegan, IL 60085-8331
Tel (847) 473-1957 *Founded/Ownrshp* 1981
Sales 78.8MM^E *EMP* 500
SIC 5065 Connectors, electronic; Connectors, electronic
Ch Bd: Atsuhiro Takahashi
Prgrm Mgr: Brianna Porter
Sls&Mrk Ex: Rick Nunemacher

D-U-N-S 19-287-4592
JST ENTERPRISES
5120 Summerhill Rd, Texarkana, TX 75503-1824
Tel (903) 794-3743 *Founded/Ownrshp* 1990
Sales 25.0MM *EMP* 1,000^E
SIC 8741 Management services; Management services
Pr: Joe Thomson
Treas: Gwen Dean

D-U-N-S 78-622-8580 IMP
JST PERFORMANCE INC
RIGID INDUSTRIES
779 N Colorado St, Gilbert, AZ 85233-3402
Tel (480) 655-0100 *Founded/Ownrshp* 2007
Sales 68.4MM^E *EMP* 152
SIC 3648 Lighting equipment; Lighting equipment
Pr: Jason Christiansen
**Sr VP:* Seth Anderson
**VP:* Steve Adams
Off Mgr: Elizabeth Haws
QA Dir: Bradley Seymoure
Prd Mgr: Brad Lamarche
Prd Mgr: Daniel Piluga
**VP Sls:* Taylor Anderson
VP Sls: Dave Davis
Mktg Dir: Miranda Fuller
Mktg Mgr: Sean Jennings

D-U-N-S 87-635-1243
JST SALES AMERICA INC
(*Suby of* JST CORP) ★
1957 S Lakeside Dr, Waukegan, IL 60085-8331
Tel (847) 473-1957 *Founded/Ownrshp* 1999
Sales 36.1MM^E *EMP* 133^E
SIC 5065 Connectors, electronic; Connectors, electronic
Ch Bd: Masao Yoshimura

JSU
See JACKSON STATE UNIVERSITY

D-U-N-S 17-597-3163 IMP/EXP
JSW STEEL (USA) INC
J S W
(*Suby of* JSW STEEL LIMITED)
5200 E Mckinney Rd # 110, Baytown, TX 77523-8291
Tel (281) 383-2525 *Founded/Ownrshp* 2007
Sales 365.6MM *EMP* 696
Accts Braj Aggarwal Cpa Pc Hicksv
SIC 3317 3312 Steel pipe & tubes; Blast furnaces & steel mills; Tubes, steel & iron; Steel pipe & tubes; Blast furnaces & steel mills; Tubes, steel & iron
Pr: Michael Fitch
**Sec:* Krishnamurty Karra
Ofcr: Rocky Crain
VP: Charles Bartholomew
VP: Jason Jamieson
**VP:* Daniel E Meinzen
QA Dir: Jude Lemelle
Sfty Dirs: Jimmie Worley
Plnt Mgr: Digvijay Shinde
Manager: Joseph Dagro
Sales Asso: Terry Matney

D-U-N-S 79-693-5856
■ **JT CO INC**
(*Suby of* TOOTSIE ROLL INDUSTRIES INC) ★
7401 S Cicero Ave, Chicago, IL 60629-5818
Tel (773) 838-3400 *Founded/Ownrshp* 2013
Sales 16.4MM^E *EMP* 1,000
SIC 7389 Personal service agents, brokers & bureaus; Personal service agents, brokers & bureaus
Pr: Ellen R Gordon

D-U-N-S 00-526-2803
JT CULLEN CO INC (IL)
901 31st Ave, Fulton, IL 61252-9609
Tel (815) 589-2412 *Founded/Ownrshp* 1900, 1957
Sales 25.8MM^E *EMP* 70
SIC 3443 5051 3444 Fabricated plate work (boiler shop); Iron or steel flat products; Sheet metalwork
Pr: Eric N Johnson
Pr: Roger Johnson
Dir IT: Jennifer Dean

JT INTERNATIONAL USA
See JAPAN TOBACCO INTERNATIONAL USA INC

D-U-N-S 87-289-4886
JT MAGEN & CO INC
44 W 28th St Fl 11, New York, NY 10001-4212
Tel (212) 790-4200 *Founded/Ownrshp* 1992
Sales 171.5MM^E *EMP* 150
SIC 1542 Nonresidential construction; Nonresidential construction
Pr: Maurice Regan
**CFO:* Steven M Mount
Ex VP: Kevin Powers
Exec: Jeffrey Smith
IT Man: Betty Chang
Snr PM: Nick Parisi

D-U-N-S 07-838-1037
JT PACKARD LLC
275 Investment Ct, Verona, WI 53593-8787
Tel (800) 972-9778 *Founded/Ownrshp* 2002
Sales 322.8MM^E *EMP* 230
SIC 4911 Distribution, electric power; Distribution, electric power
Exec: Kevin Mengelt

D-U-N-S 00-850-3294 IMP
JT POSEY CO
5635 Peck Rd, Arcadia, CA 91006-5897
Tel (626) 443-3143 *Founded/Ownrshp* 1937
Sales 32.2MM^E *EMP* 150
SIC 3842 5047 Surgical appliances & supplies; Belts: surgical, sanitary & corrective; Fracture appliances, surgical; Medical & hospital equipment; Surgical appliances & supplies; Belts: surgical, sanitary & corrective; Fracture appliances, surgical; Medical & hospital equipment
Pr: Ernest M Posey
Sr VP: Robert Kelleher
VP: Bonnie Bishop
VP: Laurie Lawton
VP: Edwin Neas
Dist Mgr: John Crocetti
Dist Mgr: Pat Devaney
Dist Mgr: Bob Dickens
Dist Mgr: Janet Douthit
Dist Mgr: Dave Forrest
Dist Mgr: Bill Kennedy

JT RUSSELL ASPHALT
See JT RUSSELL AND SONS INC

D-U-N-S 10-180-3963 IMP/EXP
JT SHANNON LUMBER CO INC
SHAMROCK PLANK FLOORING
2200 Cole Rd, Horn Lake, MS 38637-2300
Tel (662) 393-3765 *Founded/Ownrshp* 1982
Sales 105.3MM^E *EMP* 270
SIC 5031 3559 2421 Lumber: rough, dressed & finished; Kilns, lumber; Planing mills; Lumber: rough, dressed & finished; Kilns, lumber; Planing mills
CEO: Jack T Shannon Jr

D-U-N-S 83-242-1114
JT VAUGHN CONSTRUCTION LLC
10355 Westpark Dr, Houston, TX 77042-5312
Tel (713) 243-8300 *Founded/Ownrshp* 2008
Sales 45.8MM^E *EMP* 99^E
SIC 1542 Nonresidential construction; Nonresidential construction
CFO: Robert Weeks
Off Mgr: Lillie Lewis
CIO: Rahul Deshmukh
Sfty Dirs: Eloy Silva
Ql Cn Mgr: Pedro Gutierrez
Mktg Dir: Christine Sellew
Snr PM: Brett Fairman
Snr Mgr: Micah Hovda

D-U-N-S 82-766-3576
JT WIMSATT CONTRACTING CO INC
28064 Avenue Stanford B, Valencia, CA 91355-1159
Tel (661) 775-8090 *Founded/Ownrshp* 1992
Sales 30.4MM^E *EMP* 275^E
SIC 1771 Concrete work; Concrete work
Pr: John E Wimsatt III
CFO: Steven Moscrop
**VP:* Tricia Wimsatt
Snr PM: Joseph Antonio

D-U-N-S 15-809-1848
JT3 LLC
JOINT TEST TACTICS & TRAINING
821 Grier Dr, Las Vegas, NV 89119-3717
Tel (702) 492-2100 *Founded/Ownrshp* 2001
Sales 395.5MM^E *EMP* 2,000
SIC 8711 Engineering services; Engineering services
Sr VP: Jarrett Jordan
VP: Ralph Decker
VP: Matt Densmore
VP: Reynaldo Garza
VP: Paul Krause
Prgrm Mgr: Michael Adams
Dept Mgr: Angel Guilloty
Dept Mgr: Dan Painter
Brnch Mgr: Lorraine Kinney
Snr Sftwr: Dan Laforce
Web Dev: Brian Simmons

JTB
See JOHNSTON-TOMBIGBEE FURNITURE MANUFACTURING CO

D-U-N-S 07-282-3693
JTB AMERICAS LTD
(*Suby of* JTB CORP.)
19700 Mariner Ave, Torrance, CA 90503-1648
Tel (310) 303-3750 *Founded/Ownrshp* 1991
Sales 95.8MM^E *EMP* 1,356
SIC 4724 Travel agencies; Travel agencies
Pr: Tsuneo Irita

D-U-N-S 79-046-5751
JTB HAWAII INC
(*Suby of* JTB AMERICAS LTD) ★
818 Pine St, Honolulu, HI 96817-5072
Tel (808) 922-0200 *Founded/Ownrshp* 2009
Sales 30.6MM^E *EMP* 400
SIC 4725 Tour operators; Tour operators
Pr: Keiichi Tsujino
**Treas:* Ko Yanagida
Genl Mgr: Masakazu Miyakoshi
Genl Mgr: Tatsuo Watanabe
CIO: Herbert Lee

D-U-N-S 07-968-1882
JTB HAWAII TRAVEL LLC
(*Suby of* JTB HAWAII INC) ★
2155 Kalakaua Ave Fl 9, Honolulu, HI 96815-2335
Tel (808) 922-0200 *Founded/Ownrshp* 1999
Sales 20.0MM^E *EMP* 135^E
SIC 4724 4725 Travel agencies; Tour operators
Pr: Masato Tezuka

D-U-N-S 78-199-7150
JTB INTERNATIONAL INC
(*Suby of* JTB AMERICAS LTD) ★
19700 Mariner Ave, Torrance, CA 90503-1648
Tel (310) 303-3750 *Founded/Ownrshp* 1991
Sales 39.6MM^E *EMP* 258
SIC 4724 Travel agencies; Travel agencies
CEO: Yoshinori Himeno
**Treas:* Tsuneo Tadachi
IT Man: Teruko Tanaka

D-U-N-S 62-664-1815
JTD HEALTH SYSTEMS INC
SPEECH CENTER
200 Saint Clair Ave, Saint Marys, OH 45885-2400
Tel (419) 394-3335 *Founded/Ownrshp* 1953
Sales 90.0MM *EMP* 600
Accts Ernst & Young Llp Dayton Oh
SIC 8741 Hospital management; Hospital management
**Treas:* Jeff Vossler

D-U-N-S 04-069-7265 IMP
JTEKT AUTOMOTIVE SOUTH CAROLINA INC
(*Suby of* JTEKT AUTOMOTIVE TENNESSEE-MORRISTOWN INC) ★
1866 Old Grove Rd, Piedmont, SC 29673-9661
Tel (864) 277-0400 *Founded/Ownrshp* 2012
Sales 26.7MM^E *EMP* 100
SIC 3714 Transmission housings or parts, motor vehicle; Transmission housings or parts, motor vehicle
Pr: Keith Kamiki

D-U-N-S 61-531-0216 IMP/EXP
JTEKT AUTOMOTIVE TENNESSEE-MORRISTOWN INC
(*Suby of* JTEKT NORTH AMERICA INC) ★
5932 Commerce Blvd, Morristown, TN 37814-1051
Tel (423) 585-2544 *Founded/Ownrshp* 1989
Sales 102.6MM^E *EMP* 545^E
SIC 3714 Power steering equipment, motor vehicle; Power steering equipment, motor vehicle
Ch Bd: Ike Funahashi
**Pr:* Max Biery
CIO: Sandra Graves

D-U-N-S 80-827-6328 IMP/EXP
JTEKT AUTOMOTIVE TEXAS LP
(*Suby of* JTEKT NORTH AMERICA INC) ★
4400 Sterilite Dr, Ennis, TX 75119-7816
Tel (972) 878-1800 *Founded/Ownrshp* 2004
Sales 96.6MM^E *EMP* 405^E
SIC 3714 Motor vehicle steering systems & parts
Pr: Murray Durham
Prgrm Mgr: Rich McCurry
VP Sls: Gary Bourque

D-U-N-S 07-372-3868 IMP
JTEKT NORTH AMERICA CORP
KOYO BEARINGS
(*Suby of* JTEKT CORPORATION)
29570 Clemens Rd, Westlake, OH 44145-1007
Tel (440) 835-1000 *Founded/Ownrshp* 1973
Sales 910.9MM^E *EMP* 1,907
SIC 5085 3562 Industrial supplies; Ball & roller bearings; Industrial supplies; Ball & roller bearings
CEO: Hirouki Kaijima
**COO:* Mike Davidson
COO: Sam Holt
**COO:* Ken Hopkins
**Sr VP:* Gary Bourque
**Sr VP:* James Gregory
**Sr VP:* Christelle Orzan
Sls Mgr: Dale Neumann

D-U-N-S 07-272-0399
JTEKT NORTH AMERICA INC
(*Suby of* JTEKT CORPORATION)
47771 Halyard Dr, Plymouth, MI 48170-2479
Tel (734) 454-1500 *Founded/Ownrshp* 1988
Sales 258.5MM^E *EMP* 1,000
SIC 5013 Motor vehicle supplies & new parts; Motor vehicle supplies & new parts
Pr: Yoshio Tsuji
**VP:* Charles Brandt
Ex Dir: Graham Fullerton
Genl Mgr: Tomohiro Ishii
Plnt Mgr: Craig Woodford
Ql Cn Mgr: Andrea Jamieson

D-U-N-S 01-556-5401
■ **JTH TAX INC**
LIBERTY TAX SERVICE
(*Suby of* LIBERTY TAX INC) ★
1716 Corp Landing Pkwy, Virginia Beach, VA 23454-5681
Tel (757) 493-8855 *Founded/Ownrshp* 1997
Sales 29.0MM^E *EMP* 450
SIC 7291 Tax return preparation services; Tax return preparation services
CEO: John T Hewitt
Pr: Mark Jackson
COO: Mike Trainor
**CFO:* Mark F Baumgartner

VP: Kathleen Curry
VP: Tiffany W Dodson
VP: Raymond Dunn
**VP:* Wheaton James
VP: Charles Lovelace
**VP:* Martha O'Gorman
VP: Mike Piper
**VP:* Sandy Stow
**VP:* T Rufe Vanderpool
**VP:* Jim Wheaton
Board of Directors: George T Robson

D-U-N-S 82-777-4225
■ **JTL GROUP INC**
KNIFE RIVER-BILLINGS
(*Suby of* KNIFE RIVER COAL MINING) ★
4014 Hesper Rd, Billings, MT 59106-3352
Tel (406) 655-2010 *Founded/Ownrshp* 1999
Sales 276.3MM^E *EMP* 2,200
SIC 1611 Highway & street construction; Highway & street construction
Pr: David K Zinke
**Treas:* Nancy K Christenson
**VP:* Terry Haven
Genl Mgr: Dave Resch
Plnt Mgr: Clint Satrom

JTM FOOD GROUP
See JTM PROVISIONS CO INC

D-U-N-S 14-818-1449 IMP
JTM FOODS LLC
2126 E 33rd St, Erie, PA 16510-2554
Tel (814) 899-0886 *Founded/Ownrshp* 2011
Sales 22.5MM^E *EMP* 90
SIC 2051 Cakes, pies & pastries
Ch: Angelo Fraggos
CFO: Joe Heid
VP: Beverly Braley
VP: Shirley Kelley
Off Mgr: Kelly Boswitc
Dir IT: Jeff Jung
Ql Cn Mgr: Keith Burke
VP Sls: Byard Ebling
Mktg Mgr: Paul Jordan
Sls Mgr: Brian Cancilla

D-U-N-S 01-762-5856
JTM PROVISIONS CO INC (OH)
JTM FOOD GROUP
200 Sales Ave, Harrison, OH 45030-1485
Tel (513) 367-4900 *Founded/Ownrshp* 1963
Sales 143.4MM^E *EMP* 350
SIC 2013 2051 Frozen meats from purchased meat; Buns, bread type: fresh or frozen; Frozen meats from purchased meat; Buns, bread type: fresh or frozen
Pr: Anthony A Maas
CFO: Bill Meier
VP: Jamie Cronen
VP: Jeff Jung
VP: Tim Kern
**VP:* Jerome Maas
**VP:* John Maas Jr
**VP:* Joseph Maas
VP: Candace Walker
Dir IT: Kurt Loy
IT Man: Ray Littelmann

D-U-N-S 96-610-8755
JTP LIQUIDATION INC
(*Suby of* THOMAS & BETTS CORP) ★
275 Investment Ct, Verona, WI 53593-8787
Tel (608) 845-9900 *Founded/Ownrshp* 2010
Sales 26.9MM^E *EMP* 250
SIC 1731 3699 Electric power systems contractors; Appliance cords for household electrical equipment; Electric power systems contractors; Appliance cords for household electrical equipment
Pr: Steve Bray
Sec: Steve Cady
VP Bus Dev: Jim Nolden
Manager: Andrew Borchardt

D-U-N-S 04-049-0765
JTS COMMUNITIES INC
11249 Gold Country Blvd # 180, Gold River, CA 95670-3006
Tel (916) 487-3434 *Founded/Ownrshp* 1973
Sales 67.4MM^E *EMP* 400
SIC 1521 Single-family housing construction; Single-family housing construction
CEO: Jack T Sweigart
**CFO:* Tim Weir
Treas: Vikki Holt
VP: Corinne Mostad
VP Prd: Randy Sweigart
Sls Mgr: Ray Melville

D-U-N-S 19-043-2570
JTS DIRECT LLC
DOODAD
1180 Walnut Ridge Dr, Hartland, WI 53029-8319
Tel (262) 369-9500 *Founded/Ownrshp* 1998
Sales 21.8MM^E *EMP* 86^E
SIC 2759 Publication printing
Pr: John T Shinners
VP: John Collins
VP: Sharon Poulos
VP Opers: Mark Wiskirchen

D-U-N-S 05-436-4476 IMP
JTS ENTERPRISES OF TAMPA LIMITED
MCDONALD'S
4908 W Nassau St, Tampa, FL 33607-3827
Tel (813) 287-2231 *Founded/Ownrshp* 2005
Sales 149.7MM^E *EMP* 3,500
SIC 5812 Fast-food restaurant, chain; Fast-food restaurant, chain
Genl Pt: Blake Casper
Pt: Allison Casper Adams
VP: Brian Wishnek
Area Supr: Donna Peters

D-U-N-S 04-670-6565
JTW ENTERPRISES INC
CHESTERFIELD DODGE
11701 Midlothian Tpke, Midlothian, VA 23113-2646
Tel (804) 794-0300 *Founded/Ownrshp* 1983
Sales 20.5MM^E *EMP* 85

SIC 5511 Automobiles, new & used; Automobiles, new & used
Pr: Max Pearson
Genl Mgr: Dennis Ramey
Sls Mgr: John Beasley

D-U-N-S 16-524-1720
JUAN POLLO INC
1398 N E St, San Bernardino, CA 92405-4529
Tel (909) 885-6324 *Founded/Ownrshp* 1984
Sales 12.9MM^E *EMP* 350
SIC 5812 Mexican restaurant; Mexican restaurant
Pr: Al Okura
Ofcr: Lilia Ramos
**VP:* Robert Komatsu

D-U-N-S 00-827-3401
JUANITAS FOODS (CA)
PICO PICA FOODS
645 Eubank Ave, Wilmington, CA 90744-6055
Tel (310) 834-5339 *Founded/Ownrshp* 1946
Sales 37.8MM^E *EMP* 125
SIC 2032 Mexican foods: packaged in cans, jars, etc.; Mexican foods: packaged in cans, jars, etc.
CEO: Aaron De La Torre
**CFO:* James Steveson
**Ch:* Mark De La Torre
VP: Kimberly Mederos
VP: Roberto Orci
VP: John Thompson
Sls Mgr: Lorraine Aguilera

JUAREZ SALONS & SPAS
See GJS HOLDING LLC

D-U-N-S 80-957-4627
JUBA ALUMINUM PRODUCTS CO
8000 Poplar Tent Rd Ste A, Concord, NC 28027-9540
Tel (704) 262-4460 *Founded/Ownrshp* 1993
Sales 22.7MM *EMP* 60
Accts Dixon Hughes Goodman Llp Wins
SIC 1793 Glass & glazing work
CEO: John Juba
**Pr:* Janna Juba Riley
CFO: Phil Campolo
VP Opers: Kim Dockery
Sfty Mgr: Michele Juba King

D-U-N-S 02-249-0515 IMP
JUBILANT CADISTA PHARMACEUTICALS INC
(*Suby of* JUBILANT LIFE SCIENCES LIMITED)
207 Kiley Dr, Salisbury, MD 21801-2249
Tel (410) 860-8500 *Founded/Ownrshp* 2005
Sales 52.1MM^E *EMP* 200
SIC 2834 Pharmaceutical preparations; Pharmaceutical preparations
CEO: Scott B Delaney
**COO:* Ward Barney
**CFO:* Kamal Mandan
**VP:* Travis Roberts
Plng Mgr: Karen Cooper
CTO: Rajeev Nair
IT Man: Peggy Briggs
IT Man: Neal Miller
IT Man: Tejvir Singh
VP Opers: Mark Celeste
Mfg Dir: Richard Adkins

D-U-N-S 93-331-5194
JUBILANT CLINSYS INC
1 Crossroads Dr Ste 201a, Bedminster, NJ 07921-1569
Tel (908) 947-7777 *Founded/Ownrshp* 2005
Sales 42.3MM^E *EMP* 350
SIC 8731 Biotechnical research, commercial; Biotechnical research, commercial
CEO: Nayan Nanavati
**COO:* Ashish K Dasgupta
CFO: Rahul Devani
**Sr VP:* Rahul Devnani
**Sr VP:* Hartmut Schmied
**VP:* Daniele De Leo
VP: Karen Lewis
VP: Linda Miller
Dir Bus: Maura Laverty
Ex Dir: Georgia Grant
Ex Dir: Jeffrey Page

D-U-N-S 06-926-3643 IMP
JUBILANT HOLLISTERSTIER LLC
HOLLISTER-STIER LABORATORIES
(*Suby of* JUBILANT LIFE SCIENCES LIMITED)
3525 N Regal St, Spokane, WA 99207-5788
Tel (509) 482-4945 *Founded/Ownrshp* 1999, 2007
Sales 158.5MM^E *EMP* 265
SIC 2834 Pharmaceutical preparations; Pharmaceutical preparations
CFO: Richard Freeman
Pr: Rajeev Nair
**CEO:* Marcelo Morales
COO: Alice Sanders
Sr VP: Bradley Larson
**VP:* Curtis L Gingles
VP: Jason Keene
VP: Craig Mastenbaum
**VP:* Jeffrey K Milligan
**VP:* Rabindra Sahoo
Telecom Ex: Dennis Hunter

D-U-N-S 08-567-2652
JUBILEE ACADEMIC CENTER INC
4434 Roland Rd, San Antonio, TX 78222-2830
Tel (210) 333-6227 *Founded/Ownrshp* 2000
Sales 26.2MM *EMP* 160
Accts Johnm Sabatino Cpa Pc San Ant
SIC 8299 Educational services; Educational services
Dir IT: Carlos Muniz

D-U-N-S 84-499-6637
JUBILEE CENTER
SAINT VINCENT'S
10330 N Meridian St, Indianapolis, IN 46290-1024
Tel (317) 415-5300 *Founded/Ownrshp* 1985
Sales 210.5MM *EMP* 15
SIC 8748 Educational consultant; Educational consultant
Ex Dir: Izera McAfee-Day

JUBILEE FOODS
See TEDS & FREDS INC

D-U-N-S 02-772-3097
JUBITZ CORP
PORTLANDER INN MARKETPLACE
33 Ne Middlefield Rd, Portland, OR 97211-1277
Tel (503) 283-1111 *Founded/Ownrshp* 1952
Sales 199.0MM *EMP* 230^E
Accts Fordham Goodfellow Llp Hills
SIC 5541 4789 5014 7011 Filling stations, gasoline; Truck stops; Cargo loading & unloading services; Automobile tires & tubes; Hotels; Filling stations, gasoline; Truck stops; Cargo loading & unloading services; Automobile tires & tubes; Hotels
Pr: Frederick D Jubitz
**CFO:* Rich Jansen
**VP:* Mark G Gram
**VP:* Victor D Stibolt

D-U-N-S 07-303-5214
JUCKETTE MANAGEMENT SERVICES INC (MO)
13858 Liv 247, Chillicothe, MO 64601
Tel (660) 646-5385 *Founded/Ownrshp* 1967
Sales 24.2MM^E *EMP* 380
SIC 8741 Business management; Business management
Pr: Hal F Juckette
**Treas:* Thomas Juckette

D-U-N-S 04-819-8105
JUDCO INC (PA)
1 Armstrong Pl, Butler, PA 16001-1951
Tel (724) 283-0925 *Founded/Ownrshp* 1961
Sales 33.2MM^E *EMP* 100^E
SIC 5063 1623 Power transmission equipment, electric; Cable conduit; Cable television line construction; Power transmission equipment, electric; Cable conduit; Cable television line construction
Ch Bd: Jay L Sedwick
**Pr:* Dru A Sedwick
**CFO:* Bryan Cipoletti
VP: Edward Hassler
**VP:* William C Stewart

D-U-N-S 03-037-8194 IMP
JUDCO MANUFACTURING INC
1429 240th St, Harbor City, CA 90710-1306
Tel (310) 534-0959 *Founded/Ownrshp* 1980
Sales 30.1MM^E *EMP* 250
SIC 3643

D-U-N-S 19-571-2542 IMP
JUDD WIRE INC
(*Suby of* SUMITOMO ELECTRIC USA INC) ★
124 Turnpike Rd, Turners Falls, MA 01376-2699
Tel (413) 863-4357 *Founded/Ownrshp* 1988
Sales 43.3MM^E *EMP* 229
SIC 3357 Nonferrous wiredrawing & insulating; Nonferrous wiredrawing & insulating
Pr: Hidetoshi Kinuta
CFO: Ed Werenski
Opers Mgr: Jim Koulgeorge
Plnt Mgr: Maurice Cloutier
Ql Cn Mgr: Vijay Mistry
Ql Cn Mgr: Bill Shaw
Sls&Mrk Ex: Bill Brown

D-U-N-S 08-001-4780
JUDEVINE CENTER FOR AUTISM (MO)
9355 Olive Blvd, Saint Louis, MO 63132-3212
Tel (314) 432-6200 *Founded/Ownrshp* 1970
Sales 14.6MM *EMP* 500
SIC 8211 Specialty education; Specialty education
Ex Dir: Rebecca Blackwell

JUDGE & DOLPH
See WIRTZ CORP

D-U-N-S 07-551-3853
JUDGE GROUP INC
300 Conshohocken State Rd # 300, Conshohocken, PA 19428-3820
Tel (610) 667-7700 *Founded/Ownrshp* 1970
Sales 273.9MM *EMP* 2,050
Accts Grant Thornton Llp Philadelph
SIC 7373 7379 7361 Computer integrated systems design; Computer related consulting services; Executive placement; Computer integrated systems design; Computer related consulting services; Executive placement
Pr: Michael A Dunn
Pr: Brian T Anderson
Pr: Bryan Anderson
Pr: Edward Carmody
Pr: Gary R Morris
Pr: Khang Nguyen
Pr: Richard W Schnell
Pr: Sanjay Shah
Pr: Raj Singh
COO: Jack Shields
COO: Katharine A Wiercinski
CFO: Robert G Alessandrini
CFO: Frank Barrett
Bd of Dir: Randolph Angermann
Bd of Dir: James Hahn
Assoc VP: Keith Elliott
Ex VP: Peter Fong
Ex VP: Dennis F Judge Jr
Ex VP: Jared Rakes
Ex VP: Michael Tedesco
Sr VP: Stephen Spaeder
Board of Directors: Steve Marzuke

D-U-N-S 08-935-0201
JUDGE ROTENBERG EDUCATIONAL CENTER INC
250 Turnpike St, Canton, MA 02021-2359
Tel (781) 828-0401 *Founded/Ownrshp* 1971
Sales 64.9MM *EMP* 850
Accts Mullen Scorpio Cerilli Provid
SIC 8361 Home for the mentally handicapped; Home for the mentally handicapped
Pr: Glenda P Crookes
**VP:* Ann-Maire Iasimone
Ex Dir: Glenda Crooks

Dir IT: Jeremy Busey
Dir IT: Doug Leahy

JUDGE'S OFFICE
See COUNTY OF CAMERON

JUDICIAL BRANCH OF STATE ARIZ
See JUDICIARY COURTS OF STATE OF ARIZONA

D-U-N-S 36-070-7004
JUDICIAL BRANCH STATE OF CONNECTICUT
(*Suby of* STATE OF CONNECTICUT) ★
231 Capitol Ave, Hartford, CT 06106-1548
Tel (860) 706-5146 *Founded/Ownrshp* 1818
Sales NA *EMP* 2,381
SIC 9211 State courts; ; State courts;
Admn Mgr: Donna Anderson
Admn Mgr: Judith Borman
Admn Mgr: Mark Burgess
Admn Mgr: Kelly Case
Admn Mgr: Matthew Emond
Admn Mgr: Patricia Gargiulo
Admn Mgr: Elizabeth Inkster
Admn Mgr: Denise Kupstis
Admn Mgr: Peter Palmer
Admn Mgr: Benjamin Redding
Admn Mgr: Patricia Sabol

D-U-N-S 36-070-9414
JUDICIAL COUNCIL OF CALIFORNIA
(*Suby of* STATE OF CALIFORNIA) ★
455 Golden Gate Ave Fl 7, San Francisco, CA 94102-7016
Tel (415) 865-4200 *Founded/Ownrshp* 1850
Sales NA *EMP* 19,000
SIC 9211 State courts; State courts
Prin: Victoria Henley

D-U-N-S 36-070-8275
JUDICIAL COURTS OF STATE OF ILLINOIS
(*Suby of* STATE OF ILLINOIS) ★
Clerk Supreme Court Bldg, Springfield, IL 62704
Tel (217) 782-2035 *Founded/Ownrshp* 1818
Sales NA *EMP* 2,012
SIC 9111 9211 Governors' offices; Courts; Governors' offices; Courts

JUDICIAL RETIREMENT FUND
See RETIREMENT SYSTEMS OF ALABAMA

D-U-N-S 16-020-7361
JUDICIAL WATCH INC
425 3rd St Sw Ste 800, Washington, DC 20024-3232
Tel (202) 646-5172 *Founded/Ownrshp* 1994
Sales 20.2MM^E *EMP* 50
Accts Calibre Cpa Group Pllc Washin
SIC 8111 General practice attorney, lawyer; General practice attorney, lawyer
Pr: Thomas Fitton
Mktg Dir: Steve Andersen
Pr Dir: Jill Farrell
Snr Mgr: Dave Messics

D-U-N-S 36-070-5610
JUDICIARY COURTS OF COMMONWEALTH OF KENTUCKY
(*Suby of* COMMONWEALTH OF KENTUCKY) ★
700 Capital Ave Rm 231, Frankfort, KY 40601-3410
Tel (502) 564-6753 *Founded/Ownrshp* 1975
Sales NA *EMP* 2,700
SIC 9211 State courts; ; State courts;
VP: Susan Clary
Prgrm Mgr: Nila Meeks

D-U-N-S 36-070-6345 EXP
JUDICIARY COURTS OF COMMONWEALTH OF VIRGINIA
EXECUTIVE SECRETARY
(*Suby of* COMMONWEALTH OF VIRGINIA) ★
100 N 9th St, Richmond, VA 23219-2335
Tel (804) 786-6455 *Founded/Ownrshp* 1788
Sales NA *EMP* 2,485
SIC 9211 State courts; ; State courts;
**Prin:* Rebecca Schmidt

D-U-N-S 36-070-5321
JUDICIARY COURTS OF STATE OF ARIZONA
JUDICIAL BRANCH OF STATE ARIZ
(*Suby of* GOVERNORS OFFICE) ★
1501 W Washington St, Phoenix, AZ 85007-3225
Tel (602) 452-3300 *Founded/Ownrshp* 1863
Sales NA *EMP* 1,500
SIC 9211 State courts; ; State courts;
Bd of Dir: Priscilla Pina
Ofcr: Don Barks
Web Dev: Rand Rosenbaum

D-U-N-S 36-070-9893
JUDICIARY COURTS OF STATE OF ARKANSAS
SUPREME COURT CLERK OFFICE
(*Suby of* STATE OF ARKANSAS) ★
625 Marshall St Ste 1100, Little Rock, AR 72201-1021
Tel (501) 682-6849 *Founded/Ownrshp* 1836
Sales NA *EMP* 1,200
SIC 9211 State courts; ; State courts;
Admn Mgr: Cherilyn Beeler
Admn Mgr: Cynthia Betters
Admn Mgr: Don Betts
Admn Mgr: Debbie Blevins
Admn Mgr: Sheila Brewer
Admn Mgr: Lisa Bridges
Admn Mgr: Daniel Brightwell
Admn Mgr: Danielle Brown
Admn Mgr: Elizabeth Byers
Admn Mgr: Amy Byrd
Admn Mgr: Margaraet Carnes

D-U-N-S 36-070-9505
JUDICIARY COURTS OF STATE OF COLORADO
COLORADO JUDICIAL DEPARTMENT
(*Suby of* STATE OF COLORADO) ★
1300 N Broadway Ste 1200, Denver, CO 80203-2104
Tel (303) 837-3741 *Founded/Ownrshp* 1876
Sales NA *EMP* 3,500

SIC 9211 State courts; State courts;
CEO: Nancy E Rice
Ofcr: Elisabeth Dickinson
Netwrk Eng: Reaha Dahlke II

D-U-N-S 36-070-6212
JUDICIARY COURTS OF STATE OF FLORIDA
FLORIDA STATE COURT SYSTEM
(Suby of STATE OF FLORIDA) ★
500 S Duval St, Tallahassee, FL 32399-6556
Tel (850) 922-5081 Founded/Ownrshp 1845
Sales NA EMP 2,288
Accts Johnson & Cate Rockport Texa
SIC 9211 State courts; ; State courts;
Snr Mgr: Gregory Youchock

D-U-N-S 36-070-5149
JUDICIARY COURTS OF STATE OF HAWAII
(Suby of STATE OF HAWAII) ★
417 S King St, Honolulu, HI 96813-2943
Tel (808) 539-4700 Founded/Ownrshp 1895
Sales NA EMP 1,200
SIC 9211 State courts; ; State courts;
Brnch Mgr: Thomas R Kelle

D-U-N-S 36-070-4456
JUDICIARY COURTS OF STATE OF INDIANA
(Suby of STATE OF INDIANA) ★
200 W Washington St # 217, Indianapolis, IN 46204-2728
Tel (317) 232-1930 Founded/Ownrshp 1816
Sales NA EMP 3,201
SIC 9211 State courts; ; State courts;
*CEO: Brent Dickson
Sls Dir: Gardner Kim

D-U-N-S 36-070-6329
JUDICIARY COURTS OF STATE OF IOWA
(Suby of STATE OF IOWA) ★
1111 E Court Ave, Des Moines, IA 50319-5003
Tel (515) 281-5911 Founded/Ownrshp 1846
Sales NA EMP 1,000
SIC 9211 State courts; ; State courts;
Prin: Lewis Lavorato Chf Jus
Ofcr: Shawn Moss

D-U-N-S 36-070-5487
JUDICIARY COURTS OF STATE OF KANSAS
(Suby of STATE OF KANSAS) ★
301 Sw 10th Ave, Topeka, KS 66612-1500
Tel (785) 296-4873 Founded/Ownrshp 1891
Sales NA EMP 2,350
SIC 9211 ;
Ex VP: Marla Luckert
Snr Mgr: Wanda Backstrom

D-U-N-S 36-070-6618
JUDICIARY COURTS OF STATE OF LOUISIANA
(Suby of STATE OF LOUISIANA) ★
400 Royal St Ste 4200, New Orleans, LA 70130-8102
Tel (504) 310-2300 Founded/Ownrshp 1812
Sales NA EMP 1,000
SIC 9211 State courts; ; State courts;
Ch: Pascal F Calogero Jr
*Brnch Mgr: John T Olivier
IT Man: Dejon Stewart
IT Man: Paul Tumminello

D-U-N-S 36-070-6824
JUDICIARY COURTS OF STATE OF MAINE
(Suby of STATE OF MAINE) ★
205 Newbury St, Portland, ME 04101-4125
Tel (207) 822-4146 Founded/Ownrshp 1820
Sales NA EMP 379
SIC 9211 State courts;

D-U-N-S 36-070-9356
JUDICIARY COURTS OF STATE OF MICHIGAN
(Suby of STATE OF MICHIGAN) ★
925 W Ottawa St, Lansing, MI 48915-1741
Tel (517) 373-0120 Founded/Ownrshp 1805
Sales NA EMP 1,150E
SIC 9211 State courts; ; State courts;
Prin: Robert P Young Jr
Ofcr: Michael Benedict
Dir Sec: Robert Bertee
MIS Dir: Marcus Dobek
Dir IT: Mark Wing
IT Man: Joy Owen

D-U-N-S 36-070-6907
JUDICIARY COURTS OF STATE OF MINNESOTA
(Suby of STATE OF MINNESOTA) ★
25 Rev Dr Mlk Jr Blvd, Saint Paul, MN 55155-1500
Tel (651) 297-7650 Founded/Ownrshp 1857
Sales NA EMP 3,700
SIC 9211 State courts; State courts;

D-U-N-S 36-070-9547
JUDICIARY COURTS OF STATE OF MISSOURI
MISSOURI OFFC OF STATE CRT ADM
(Suby of STATE OF MISSOURI) ★
207 High St, Jefferson City, MO 65101
Tel (573) 751-4144 Founded/Ownrshp 1821
Sales NA EMP 1,400
SIC 9211 State courts; State courts;

D-U-N-S 36-070-6626
JUDICIARY COURTS OF STATE OF NEVADA
(Suby of STATE OF NEVADA) ★
201 S Carson St Ste 201, Carson City, NV 89701-4780
Tel (775) 684-1700 Founded/Ownrshp 1861
Sales NA EMP 1,051
SIC 9211 State courts; ; State courts;
Bd of Dir: Evie Lancaster

D-U-N-S 36-070-6915
JUDICIARY COURTS OF STATE OF NEW HAMPSHIRE
ADMINSTRATIVE OFFICE OF COURTS
(Suby of STATE OF NEW HAMPSHIRE) ★
Supreme Ct Bldg 1 Noble D, Concord, NH 03301
Tel (603) 271-2646 Founded/Ownrshp 1788
Sales NA EMP 600
SIC 9211 State courts; ; State courts;
Prin: David A Brock
Ofcr: John Dube
Ofcr: Michael Golding
Ofcr: Thomas Powers
*Comm Dir: Laura Kiernan

D-U-N-S 36-070-8283
JUDICIARY COURTS OF STATE OF NEW JERSEY
MANAGEMENT SERVICES DIVISION
(Suby of STATE OF NEW JERSEY) ★
25 Market St, Trenton, NJ 08611-2148
Tel (609) 984-0627 Founded/Ownrshp 1787
Sales NA EMP 1,699
SIC 9211 State courts; ; State courts;
Ofcr: Iris Gonzalez
Ofcr: Jenna Kennett
Ofcr: William Nicoletta
Ofcr: Jan Palmer
IT Man: Cheryl Dubin

D-U-N-S 36-070-4332
JUDICIARY COURTS OF STATE OF NORTH CAROLINA
ADMINSTRATIVE OFFICE OF COURTS
(Suby of STATE OF NORTH CAROLINA) ★
2 E Morgan St, Raleigh, NC 27601-1568
Tel (919) 733-3723 Founded/Ownrshp 1789
Sales NA EMP 7,234E
SIC 9211 State courts;

D-U-N-S 36-070-5339
JUDICIARY COURTS OF STATE OF OKLAHOMA
(Suby of STATE OF OKLAHOMA) ★
1915 N Stiles Ave Ste 305, Oklahoma City, OK 73105-4914
Tel (405) 521-2450 Founded/Ownrshp 1907
Sales NA EMP 800
SIC 9211 State courts;
Prin: Jo Watt
CFO: Lin Buchanan
Exec: Michael Harkey
Adm Dir: Mike Evans
Adm Dir: Michael Smith
IT Man: Robin Frank
IT Man: Bud Webster
Genl Couns: Joyce Green
Snr Mgr: Keith Aycock

D-U-N-S 36-070-5735
JUDICIARY COURTS OF STATE OF OREGON
(Suby of STATE OF OREGON) ★
1163 State St, Salem, OR 97301-2562
Tel (503) 986-5555 Founded/Ownrshp 1859
Sales NA EMP 1,715
SIC 9211 State courts; State courts
Prin: Wallace P Carson

D-U-N-S 36-070-9331
JUDICIARY COURTS OF STATE OF SOUTH CAROLINA
(Suby of STATE OF SOUTH CAROLINA) ★
1231 Gervais St, Columbia, SC 29201-3206
Tel (803) 734-1080 Founded/Ownrshp 1776
Sales NA EMP 450
SIC 9211 State courts; ; State courts;

D-U-N-S 36-070-5040
JUDICIARY COURTS OF STATE OF TEXAS
SUPREME COURT OF TEXAS
(Suby of STATE OF TEXAS) ★
205 W 14th St Ste 600, Austin, TX 78701
Tel (512) 463-1312 Founded/Ownrshp 1845
Sales NA EMP 1,049
SIC 9211 State courts; ; State courts;
Ofcr: Osler McCarthy
IT Man: Drew Sartin

D-U-N-S 36-070-5388
JUDICIARY COURTS OF STATE OF UTAH
(Suby of GOVERNORS OFFICE) ★
450 S State St, Salt Lake City, UT 84111-3101
Tel (801) 538-3000 Founded/Ownrshp 1851
Sales NA EMP 772
SIC 9211 State courts; ; State courts;
Prin: Zimmerman Chief Justice
Ofcr: Johnny Caine
Ofcr: Eileen Deelstra
Ofcr: Laura Emery
Ofcr: Andrea Fielding
Ofcr: Cary Freeman
Ofcr: Samantha Heath
Ofcr: Philip Martinez
Ofcr: Dustin Rich
Ofcr: David Sengprasent
Ofcr: Jacquie Thompson
Ofcr: Susana Tonga
Ofcr: Gina Trujillo
Ofcr: David Visser
Ofcr: Juanita Washington
Exec: Nancy Volmer

D-U-N-S 36-070-5925
JUDICIARY COURTS OF STATE OF VERMONT
(Suby of STATE OF VERMONT) ★
109 State St, Montpelier, VT 05609-0002
Tel (802) 828-3278 Founded/Ownrshp 1791
Sales NA EMP 310
SIC 9211 State courts; ; State courts;
Prin: Jeffrey Amestoy
Ofcr: Brenda Ball
Ofcr: Deanna Goodrich
Ofcr: Elaine Lamell
Ofcr: Donald Vasseur

D-U-N-S 36-070-6857
JUDICIARY COURTS OF STATE OF WASHINGTON
(Suby of GOVERNORS OFFICE) ★
Temple Of Justice, Olympia, WA 98504-0001
Tel (360) 357-2077 Founded/Ownrshp 1889
Sales NA EMP 1,586
SIC 9211 State courts; ; State courts;

D-U-N-S 36-070-9091
JUDICIARY COURTS OF STATE OF WEST VIRGINIA
WV SUPREME COURT OF APPEALS
(Suby of STATE OF WEST VIRGINIA) ★
State Capital Bldg E100, Charleston, WV 25305
Tel (304) 558-0145 Founded/Ownrshp 1863
Sales NA EMP 1,172
SIC 9211 State courts; ; State courts;
Board of Directors: Steve Canterbury, Melissa Crawford, Angela Saunders

D-U-N-S 36-070-8713
JUDICIARY COURTS OF STATE OF WISCONSIN
WISCONSIN SUPREME COURT
(Suby of STATE OF WISCONSIN) ★
16 E Capital, Madison, WI 53701
Tel (608) 266-1883 Founded/Ownrshp 1848
Sales NA EMP 800
SIC 9211 State courts; ; State courts;
Prin: Shirley S Abrahamson

D-U-N-S 36-070-6469
JUDICIARY OF STATE OF RHODE ISLAND AND PROVIDENCE PLANTATIONS
(Suby of STATE OF RHODE ISLAND AND PROVIDENCE PLANTATIONS) ★
250 Benefit St, Providence, RI 02903-2719
Tel (401) 222-8654 Founded/Ownrshp 1636
Sales NA EMP 729
SIC 9211 State courts; ; State courts;

D-U-N-S 01-046-5693
JUDITH RIPKA COMPANIES INC (NY)
JUDITH RIPKA JEWELRY
475 10th Ave Fl 4l, New York, NY 10018-9723
Tel (212) 244-1230 Founded/Ownrshp 1995
Sales 30.8MME EMP 120
SIC 5094 Jewelry; Jewelry
Ch: Ron Berk
*Pr: Charles Jayson
*COO: David Ripka
VP: Heide Binstock
VP: Jessica Stark

JUDITH RIPKA JEWELRY
See JUDITH RIPKA COMPANIES INC

D-U-N-S 06-725-7329
JUDLAU CONTRACTING INC (NY)
(Suby of OHL USA INC) ★
2615 Ulmer St, Flushing, NY 11354-1144
Tel (718) 554-2320 Founded/Ownrshp 1981, 2010
Sales 313.4MM EMP 140
SIC 1611 1623 Highway & street paving contractor; Sewer line construction; Water main construction; Highway & street paving contractor; Sewer line construction; Water main construction
CEO: Tom Iovino
Sr VP: Neville Bugwadia
VP: Arnav Amin
Exec: John Ventimiglia
Exec: Michael Williams
Ex Dir: Gustavo Monne
QC Dir: Todd Mace
Sfty Mgr: Richard Longenecker
Opers Mgr: Vincent Sefershayan
Opers Mgr: Jorge Silva
Ql Cn Mgr: Rajan Mathew

D-U-N-S 07-675-7327
JUDSON
JUDSON UNIVERSITY CIRCLE
2181 Ambleside Dr Apt 411, Cleveland, OH 44106-7604
Tel (216) 791-2004 Founded/Ownrshp 1906
Sales 30.4MM EMP 500
Accts Hw&Co Cleveland Oh
SIC 8059 6513 8052 Domiciliary care; Personal care home, with health care; Retirement hotel operation; Intermediate care facilities; Domiciliary care; Personal care home, with health care; Retirement hotel operation; Intermediate care facilities
CEO: Hong Chae
*Pr: Cynthia Dunn
Ofcr: Sheri Sax
Sr VP: James Carnovale
VP: Roy Call
VP: Daniel Selby
VP: Kendra Urdzik
Off Mgr: Benjamin Wcislo
VP Mktg: Kristina Kuprevicius
Nutrtnst: Mary Schellhammer
Nrsg Dir: Debbie Willcox

D-U-N-S 14-740-7068 IMP
JUDSON A SMITH CO
(Suby of ATW COMPANIES INC) ★
857 Sweinhart Rd, Boyertown, PA 19512
Tel (610) 367-2021 Founded/Ownrshp 1960
Sales 55.3MME EMP 125
SIC 3498 Tube fabricating (contract bending & shaping); Tube fabricating (contract bending & shaping)
CEO: Peter Frost
*Pr: Duane Ottolini
*CFO: Caryn Mitchell
IT Man: Dave Johnson

D-U-N-S 09-540-7110
JUDSON CENTER INC
CHILDREN'S HOME JUDSON CENTER
4410 W 13 Mile Rd, Royal Oak, MI 48073-6515
Tel (248) 549-4339 Founded/Ownrshp 1924
Sales 17.0MM EMP 400
Accts Uhy Llp Farmington Hills Mic
SIC 8322 8361 Child related social services; Adoption services; Family counseling services; Home for the emotionally disturbed; Home for the mentally handicapped; Child related social services; Adoption services; Family counseling services; Home for the emotionally disturbed; Home for the mentally handicapped
Pr: Marn Myers
*Ch Bd: Curtis D Bolden
*CEO: Cameron Hosner
*CEO: Carl Smith
COO: Sean De Four
*COO: Janet Flanegin
Treas: Richard Dibartolomeao
Ofcr: Erika Jones
Ofcr: Peggy Kerr
VP: Kelli Dobner
VP: Laura Huot
VP: Kristine Schultz

D-U-N-S 02-649-2686 IMP
JUDSON ENTERPRISES INC
K-DESIGNERS
2440 Gold River Rd # 100, Rancho Cordova, CA 95670-6390
Tel (916) 631-9300 Founded/Ownrshp 1978
Sales 108.0MME EMP 650
SIC 2431 5031 Windows, wood; Windows; Windows, wood; Windows
Pr: Larry D Judson
*CFO: Tony Tobia
*VP: Michael Burgess
*VP: Brian Vidlock
Brnch Mgr: Jeff Plant
Off Admin: Lane Black
IT Man: Jason Powell
Prd Mgr: John French
VP Sls: Mike Ferguson
Mktg Dir: Caroline Bengtson
Mktg Dir: Mike Kane

D-U-N-S 01-054-2637
JUDSON INDEPENDENT SCHOOL DISTRICT
8012 Shin Oak Dr, Live Oak, TX 78233-2413
Tel (210) 945-5100 Founded/Ownrshp 1959, 2007
Sales 169.6MME EMP 3,500
Accts Abip Pc San Antonio Texas
SIC 8211 Public elementary & secondary schools; High school, junior or senior; Public special education school; Public elementary & secondary schools; High school, junior or senior; Public special education school
CFO: Karen Robb
VP: Arnoldo Salinas
Ex Dir: Irma Hernandez
Ex Dir: Yvette Reyna
Dir Sec: Teresa Ramon
Netwrk Mgr: Jesse Hernandez
Pr Dir: Steve Linscomb

JUDSON PARK RETIREMENT
See AMERICAN BAPTIST HOMES OF WASHINGTON INC

D-U-N-S 06-800-7384
JUDSON UNIVERSITY - A BAPTIST INSTITUTION
1151 N State St, Elgin, IL 60123-1404
Tel (847) 628-2500 Founded/Ownrshp 1963
Sales 29.4MM EMP 837
Accts Capin Crouse Llp Wheaton Ill
SIC 8221 College, except junior; College, except junior
Pr: Gene Crume Jr
VP: Stephanie Grunenfelder
*VP: Laine Malmquist
*VP: Leann Paulieheard
*VP: John Potter
*VP: Dale Simmons
*Ex Dir: Nancy Binger
Off Mgr: Jan Andresen

JUDSON UNIVERSITY CIRCLE
See JUDSON

D-U-N-S 07-128-3642
JUDY CONSTRUCTION CO
103 S Church St, Cynthiana, KY 41031-1509
Tel (859) 234-6900 Founded/Ownrshp 1974
Sales 62.7MM EMP 185
SIC 1629 1622 1542 1541

D-U-N-S 83-730-6943
JUDY FENWICK CORP
TACO BELL
7409 Woodmont Dr, Amarillo, TX 79119-6411
Tel (806) 352-5468 Founded/Ownrshp 1988
Sales 4.1MME EMP 280
SIC 5812 8741 Fast-food restaurant, chain; Restaurant management; Fast-food restaurant, chain; Restaurant management
Pr: Judy Fenwick
*VP: William Fenwick

D-U-N-S 78-946-3833
JUDY MADRIGAL & ASSOCIATES INC
J M A
2000 Alameda De Las Pulga, San Mateo, CA 94403-1289
Tel (650) 873-3444 Founded/Ownrshp 1991
Sales 29.9MME EMP 550
SIC 8011 8742 Offices & clinics of medical doctors; Management consulting services; Offices & clinics of medical doctors; Management consulting services
Pr: Judy Madrigal
*VP: Tammy Attard
VP: Allison Martinez

JUERGENS LAWN CARE SERVICE
See JUERGENS PRODUCE & FEED CO

D-U-N-S 02-204-1164
JUERGENS PRODUCE & FEED CO
JUERGENS LAWN CARE SERVICE
620 W 3rd St, Carroll, IA 51401-2173
Tel (712) 792-3506 Founded/Ownrshp 1945
Sales 36.9MME EMP 100

SIC 5153 5191 Grain elevators; Feed; Chemicals, agricultural; Grain elevators; Feed; Chemicals, agricultural
Pr: Linda Kueper

D-U-N-S 02-270-3193
JUETTNER MOTORS INC
FORD LINCOLN MERCURY
1900 Broadway St, Alexandria, MN 56308-2745
Tel (320) 763-3126 Founded/Ownrshp 1977
Sales 30.0MM EMP 38
SIC 5511 Automobiles, new & used; Pickups, new & used; Automobiles, new & used; Pickups, new & used
Pr: Mark Juettner
*Ch Bd: John Juettner
*Treas: Bruce Wiitanen
Off Mgr: Carol Blowers
Off Mgr: Brad Hanson
Mktg Mgr: Cathy Juettner
Sales Asso: Dean Solem

D-U-N-S 07-960-9021
JUGGERNAUT MACHINERY LLC (TX)
7475 W Fm 140, Jourdanton, TX 78026-4930
Tel (210) 399-3374 Founded/Ownrshp 2014
Sales 22.0MM EMP 17
SIC 3599 Machine & other job shop work; Machine & other job shop work
Pr: David Stainthorpe

D-U-N-S 04-247-3496 IMP/EXP
JUICE BOWL PRODUCTS INC
(Suby of WHITLOCK PACKAGING CORP) ★
2090 Bartow Rd, Lakeland, FL 33801-6557
Tel (863) 665-5515 Founded/Ownrshp 2008
Sales 57.2MM^E EMP 180
SIC 2033 2086 Fruit juices: packaged in cans, jars, etc.;Tea, iced: packaged in cans, bottles, etc.; Fruit juices: packaged in cans, jars, etc.;Tea, iced: packaged in cans, bottles, etc.
Pr: David Moller
*COO: Terry Simmers
*Ch: John P Grady
*VP: Keith Bishop
*VP: Ted Smith
*Prin: J Michael Grady

D-U-N-S 80-101-1578
■ **JUICE CLUB INC**
JAMBA JUICE
(Suby of JAMBA INC) ★
6475 Christie Ave Ste 150, Emeryville, CA 94608-2259
Tel (510) 596-0100 Founded/Ownrshp 1991
Sales 181.4MM^E EMP 4,000
SIC 5812 6794 Soft drink stand; Franchises, selling or licensing; Soft drink stand; Franchises, selling or licensing
CEO: James D White
*CFO: Donald D Breen
Treas: Erik Mattias
*Chf Mktg O: Susan Shields
Sr VP: Steve Adkins
*Sr VP: Paul Coletta
*Sr VP: Karen Kelley
VP: Arnaud Joliff
VP: Tom Madsen
VP: Greg Schwartz
VP: Malia Spaulding
Comm Dir: Mike Fuccillo

D-U-N-S 12-646-9092
JUICE PHARMA WORLDWIDE LLC
322 8th Ave Fl 10, New York, NY 10001-6781
Tel (212) 647-1595 Founded/Ownrshp 2002
Sales 28.4MM^E EMP 100
SIC 7311 Advertising agencies; Advertising agencies
CEO: Forrest King
Ex VP: Robert Palmer
VP: Ben Putman
Art Dir: Taylor Moore

D-U-N-S 06-166-1641
JUICE PLUS CO LLC
140 Crescent Dr, Collierville, TN 38017-3374
Tel (901) 850-3000 Founded/Ownrshp 1969
Sales 96.3MM^E EMP 220
SIC 5149 Health foods; Health foods
COO: Paulo Teixeira
Sec: Stan Turk
Bd of Dir: Steve Wyatt
VP: John Blair
VP: Marvin Orr
VP: Ron Watkins
CIO: Dennis Wilson
Dir IT: Terry Freeze
IT Man: Floyd Gibbs
IT Man: Debbie Miller

D-U-N-S 15-730-7547 IMP/EXP
JUICETYME INC
BEVOLUTION GROUP
4401 S Oakley Ave, Chicago, IL 60609-3020
Tel (773) 579-1291 Founded/Ownrshp 2013
Sales 91.0MM^E EMP 73
SIC 2033 2037 Canned fruits & specialties; Frozen fruits & vegetables
CEO: Sam Lteif
*Pr: Philip L Scott
COO: Matt Marten
*CFO: Kimberly Frank
*CFO: David Prill
Ex VP: Jerry Desmond
*VP: Jim Crauchy
*VP Opers: Matt Martens
Plnt Mgr: Bill Conti
*VP Mktg: Lynn Mayers
VP Sls: Kevin Loiselle

JUICECO
See UNITED JUICE COMPANIES OF AMERICA INC

D-U-N-S 01-973-1985
JUICYS LLC (AZ)
2851 Nw 9th St Ste C, Corvallis, OR 97330-3897
Tel (888) 909-9991 Founded/Ownrshp 2004
Sales 10.6MM^E EMP 403
SIC 5812 Contract food services; Contract food services

CFO: William Witt

D-U-N-S 07-860-1903
JUILLIARD SCHOOL
60 Lincoln Center Plz, New York, NY 10023-6588
Tel (212) 799-5000 Founded/Ownrshp 1905
Sales 131.1MM EMP 550
Accts Grant Thornton Llp New York
SIC 8299 7911 5942 8221 Music school; Dramatic school; Professional dancing school; Book stores; Colleges universities & professional schools; Music school; Dramatic school; Professional dancing school; Book stores; Colleges universities & professional schools
Pr: Joseph W Polisi
Trst: Sidney Knafel
*VP: Karen Wagner
Netwrk Mgr: Jeremy Pinquist
Prd Mgr: J B Barricklo

D-U-N-S 06-101-4379
JUJAMCYN THEATERS CORP
ST JAMES THEATRE
246 W 44th St Lbby, New York, NY 10036-3910
Tel (212) 840-8181 Founded/Ownrshp 1937
Sales 35.3MM^E EMP 473
SIC 6512 Theater building, ownership & operation; Theater building, ownership & operation
Ch: James Binger
*Pr: Rocco Landisin
*VP: Virginia Binger
VP: Micah Hollingworth
Sls Dir: Karen Freidus

D-U-N-S 07-945-8111
JULE MANAGEMENT GROUP LLC
80 Kingsbridge Rd, Piscataway, NJ 08854-3953
Tel (732) 980-1900 Founded/Ownrshp 2013
Sales 9.0MM EMP 420^E
SIC 8351 Child day care services; Child day care services

JULIA ANN SINGER CENTER
See VISTA DEL MAR CHILD AND FAMILY SERVICES

D-U-N-S 07-667-7723
JULIA DYCKMAN ANDRUS MEMORIAL INC
ANDRUS CHILDREN CENTER
1156 N Broadway, Yonkers, NY 10701-1108
Tel (914) 965-3700 Founded/Ownrshp 1928
Sales 35.8MM EMP 250
Accts Bdo Usa Llp New York Ny
SIC 8211 8361 Specialty education; Children's home; Specialty education; Children's home
Pr: Nancy Woodruff Ment
*COO: Brian Farragher
*CFO: Derek Kolleeny
*Ch: John P McLaughlin
*Treas: Steven J Friedman

D-U-N-S 07-561-8892
JULIA RACKLEY PERRY MEMORIAL HOSPITAL
530 Park Ave E, Princeton, IL 61356-3901
Tel (815) 875-2811 Founded/Ownrshp 1916
Sales 33.8MM EMP 360^E
SIC 8062 General medical & surgical hospitals; General medical & surgical hospitals
Ch Bd: Thomas Tester
Dir Vol: Alecia Weber
*Ch Bd: Greg Davis MD
*Pr: Robert Senneff
*CEO: Fache Rex Conger
CFO: Patricia Ellison
*CFO: Lynn Luloff
*Ch: Rick Clary
VP: Denise Jackson
*VP: Shelly Stouffer
*VP: Cindy Tilson
Dir Risk M: Luanne Behrens
Dir Rx: Jim Burke

D-U-N-S 00-519-8809
JULIAN ELECTRICAL SERVICE AND ENGINEERING INC
406 Plaza Dr, Westmont, IL 60559-5525
Tel (630) 920-8951 Founded/Ownrshp 1958
Sales 22.7MM^E EMP 160
SIC 3694 3679 3714 3625 3357

D-U-N-S 02-702-9149
JULIAN GOLD LTD
4109 Mccullough Ave, San Antonio, TX 78212-1999
Tel (210) 824-2601 Founded/Ownrshp 1945
Sales 29.6MM EMP 175
SIC 5621 5632 Bridal shops; Dress shops; Apparel accessories; Bridal shops; Dress shops; Apparel accessories
Pr: Robert E Gurwitz
CFO: Kelley Keeth
Treas: James Glover

D-U-N-S 03-353-9792
JULIAN LECRAW AND CO LLC
1575 Northside Dr Nw 100-200, Atlanta, GA 30318-4243
Tel (404) 351-8434 Founded/Ownrshp 1990
Sales 63.4MM^E EMP 400
SIC 6799 6552 Real estate investors, except property operators; Land subdividers & developers, commercial; Real estate investors, except property operators; Land subdividers & developers, commercial
Ex VP: Anna Swann
VP: Robert L Walker
IT Man: Dan Magill

D-U-N-S 05-463-6182
JULIE VILLA COLLEGE
1525 Greenspring Vly Rd, Stevenson, MD 21153-0641
Tel (410) 486-7000 Founded/Ownrshp 2010
Sales 124.9MM EMP 28^E
SIC 8221 Colleges universities & professional schools; Colleges universities & professional schools
Prin: Kevin J Manning
VP: Glenda Legendre

D-U-N-S 88-387-7602
JULIMAR TRADING LLC
8211 S Delaware Pl, Tulsa, OK 74137-1309
Tel (918) 630-2760 Founded/Ownrshp 2008
Sales 42.0MM EMP 4
SIC 5051 7389 Ferroalloys; ; Ferroalloys;

D-U-N-S 12-001-7277
JULIO & SONS CO
1101 N Union Bower Rd # 160, Irving, TX 75061-5850
Tel (972) 554-6886 Founded/Ownrshp 1999
Sales 14.8MM^E EMP 500
SIC 5812 Eating places; Eating places
Pr: Todd Conger
*Sec: Steve Bratton
Dir IT: Charles Banks
Mktg Mgr: Valerie Voges

D-U-N-S 60-625-3516 IMP
JULIOS UNCLE CORP
RIO GRANDE CAFE
1101 N Union Bower Rd # 160, Irving, TX 75061-5850
Tel (972) 554-6886 Founded/Ownrshp 1988
Sales 40.5MM^E EMP 900
SIC 5812 Mexican restaurant; Mexican restaurant
CEO: Todd Conger
*Pr: Abdo J Shashy
*CFO: Steve Bratton
CFO: Steven Bratton
VP: Chuck Register
Genl Mgr: Robert Clark
Genl Mgr: Jake Guevara
Genl Mgr: Orio Lodal
Genl Mgr: Brien Terhune
Off Mgr: Ashley Hoover
MIS Dir: Paul Davis

JULISKA
See PENSHURST TRADING INC

D-U-N-S 00-259-8951 IMP
JULIUS SILVERT INC (PA)
231 E Luzerne St, Philadelphia, PA 19124-4219
Tel (215) 455-1600 Founded/Ownrshp 1915
Sales 48.8MM^E EMP 35
SIC 5143 5144 Butter; Eggs
Pr: Stephen Sorkin
*Treas: Edward Sorkin
*Sec: Jim Sorkin
*VP: Myron B Finer
*VP: James Sorkin
Sales Asso: Eric Gonzalez
Snr Mgr: Amy Marotta
Board of Directors: Charles Bachert, Charles Lewis

D-U-N-S 12-319-7535 IMP
JULIUS ZORN INC
JUZO
3690 Zorn Dr, Cuyahoga Falls, OH 44223-3580
Tel (330) 923-4999 Founded/Ownrshp 1980
Sales 28.6MM^E EMP 75
SIC 5047 3842 Medical & hospital equipment; Hosiery, support; Supports: abdominal, ankle, arch, kneecap, etc.; Socks, stump
Pr: Anne Rose Zorn
COO: Walter Zorn
*Treas: Uwe Schettler
Natl Sales: Tom Gross
Natl Sales: Liz Shields
Mktg Dir: Tom Musone
Sls Dir: Greg Biddulph

D-U-N-S 79-145-7547
JUMA TECHNOLOGY CORP
154 Toledo St, Farmingdale, NY 11735-6619
Tel (631) 300-1000 Founded/Ownrshp 2003
Sales 23.3MM^E EMP 57
Accts Seligson & Giannattasio Llp
Tkr Sym JUMT Exch OTO
SIC 5065 7622 Communication equipment; Communication equipment repair
Ch Bd: Anthony M Servidio
Pr: Joseph Fuccillo
Pr: David Giangano
CFO: Anthony Fernandez
Sr Cor Off: Robert Rubin
Ex VP: Joseph Cassano
Ex VP: Frances Vinci
Sls Dir: Heath Saminsky
Board of Directors: Kenneth Archer, Robert Rubin, Robert H Thomson

JUMBO FOODS
See P AND J LLC

D-U-N-S 04-302-6160
JUMBO FOODS INC (WA)
EMERALD HILLS COFFEE
11502 Cyrus Way, Mukilteo, WA 98275-5404
Tel (425) 355-1103 Founded/Ownrshp 1967
Sales 36.0MM^E EMP 200
SIC 2099 5145 5149 Sandwiches, assembled & packaged: for wholesale market; Snack foods; Coffee, green or roasted; Sandwiches, assembled & packaged: for wholesale market; Snack foods; Coffee, green or roasted
CEO: William Mynar
*Pr: Stephen Giles
COO: Margaret Ostervold
*Sec: Susan Oliver
Board of Directors: William L Eisenhart

JUMER'S CASINO
See RIB HOLDING CO

JUMER'S CASINO & HOTEL
See ROCK ISLAND BOATWORKS INC

JUMP APPAREL GROUP, THE
See JUMP DESIGN GROUP INC

D-U-N-S 78-161-4870 IMP
JUMP DESIGN GROUP INC
JUMP APPAREL GROUP, THE
1400 Brdwy F 2 2 F, New York, NY 10018
Tel (212) 869-3300 Founded/Ownrshp 1991
Sales 65.0MM EMP 140
Accts Citrin Cooperman & Company Llp
SIC 2335 Women's, juniors' & misses' dresses; Women's, juniors' & misses' dresses

Ch Bd: Glenn Schlossberg
*Pr: Terry Friedman
*Pr: Peter Gabbe
*CFO: Patrick M Corrigan

D-U-N-S 04-181-9801
JUMP HIGHER LLC
225 E Aurora St, Waterbury, CT 06708-2015
Tel (203) 597-0400 Founded/Ownrshp 1997
Sales 26.5MM^E EMP 250
SIC 6719 Investment holding companies, except banks; Investment holding companies, except banks
Pr: Michael Jordan
CFO: Timo Makkonen

JUMP INC
D-U-N-S 03-109-6899
CODEWELL BANKER LEGACY
6725 Academy Rd Ne Ste A, Albuquerque, NM 87109-3345
Tel (505) 857-2276 Founded/Ownrshp 1998
Sales 17.8MM^E EMP 412
SIC 6531 Real estate agent, residential; Real estate agent, residential
CEO: Joe Gilmore
*Pr: Peter Parmagg
CEO: Brenda Jenkins
COO: Laura Haman
CFO: Homer Greer
*VP: Michael Carter
Genl Mgr: Dennis Fish
Off Mgr: Lucy Gonzales
Mktg Dir: Tila Hoffman
Mktg Dir: Shuree Sandin
Sls Dir: Alicia Feil

JUMP OIL & PROPANE
See MILTENBERGER OIL CO INC

D-U-N-S 82-687-3197
JUMP OPERATIONS LLC
600 W Chicago Ave Ste 825, Chicago, IL 60654-2528
Tel (312) 205-8900 Founded/Ownrshp 2006
Sales 37.8MM^E EMP 200
SIC 8748 Business consulting; Business consulting

D-U-N-S 01-418-0058
JUMP TRADING LLC
600 W Chicago Ave Ste 825, Chicago, IL 60654-2528
Tel (312) 205-8900 Founded/Ownrshp 2000
Sales 51.6MM^E EMP 115
SIC 6211 Stock brokers & dealers; Stock brokers & dealers
Mng Pt: Paul Gurinas
COO: Bob Kirkland
*CFO: Carey Harrold
Dir Risk M: Timothy Jensen
Mng Dir: Ken Terao
Off Admin: Eric Abbe
Off Admin: Kathryn Cerny
Off Admin: Adrian Gonzalez
Off Admin: Constance Moore
Snr Sftwr: Darius Buntinas
Snr Sftwr: Mike Doubek

D-U-N-S 09-004-5972
JUNCO STEEL CORP
155 Calle A, Bayamon, PR 00959-1900
Tel (787) 798-1000 Founded/Ownrshp 1966
Sales 21.3MM^E EMP 55
SIC 5051 Steel; Tubing, metal
Pr: Ana M Junco

D-U-N-S 01-759-7261
JUNCTION AUTO SALES INC (OH)
12423 Mayfield Rd, Chardon, OH 44024-9476
Tel (440) 286-6161 Founded/Ownrshp 1927
Sales 35.0MM^E EMP 82
SIC 5511 Automobiles, new & used; Automobiles, new & used
Pr: Edward Babcock

D-U-N-S 14-125-6177
JUNCTION SOLUTIONS INC
4643 S Ulster St Ste 400, Denver, CO 80237-2897
Tel (303) 327-8800 Founded/Ownrshp 2002
Sales 48.6MM^E EMP 200
SIC 5045 Computer software; Computer software
Pr: Jeff Grell
COO: Nick Bova
Sr VP: John Bonati
VP: Jeff Allen
CIO: Hillary McCrea
CTO: George C Casey Jr
Sls Dir: Jonathan Nye

D-U-N-S 15-981-5919
JUNE A GROTHE CONSTRUCTION INC
J G CONSTRUCTION
15632 El Prado Rd, Chino, CA 91710-9108
Tel (909) 993-9400 Founded/Ownrshp 1993
Sales 32.9MM EMP 65
Accts Glenn M Gelman & Associates
SIC 1542 Shopping center construction; Shopping center construction
CEO: June A Grothe
*VP: Wally Clark
*VP: Michael Crawford
Dir Bus: Stacy Peterson
Genl Mgr: Bret Freeman
Dir IT: Kristin Freeman
Mktg Dir: Gwenn Norton-Perry
Mktg Dir: Nan Richardson
Snr PM: Dennis Beswick

D-U-N-S 05-956-4856
JUNE SHELTON SCHOOL AND EVALUATION CENTER
15720 Hillcrest Rd, Dallas, TX 75248-4161
Tel (972) 774-1772 Founded/Ownrshp 1976
Sales 22.9MM EMP 225
Accts Weaver And Tidwell Llp Dallas
SIC 8299 Educational services; Educational services
Ch Bd: Gary Webb
*Treas: Robert Pickering
Treas: Darcy Preheim
Ex Dir: Blair King
*Ex Dir: Joyce Pickering

*Ex Dir: Susan Spell
Dir IT: Donny Campbell
Board of Directors: Dr Robert Pickering

D-U-N-S 96-825-8822
JUNEAU CONSTRUCTION CO LLC
3715 Northside Pkwy Nw, Atlanta, GA 30327-2882
Tel (404) 287-6000 Founded/Ownrshp 1997
Sales 35.1MM[E] EMP 60
SIC 1542 Commercial & office building contractors
CEO: Nancy Juneau
Pr: Leston J Juneau
COO: Royce Elliott
Chf Mktg O: Jenifer Andrews
Ofcr: Jeff Potts
Sr VP: Eric Kerley
Sr VP: Todd Weldon
VP: Marc Levin

D-U-N-S 10-064-2040
JUNEAU SCHOOL DISTRICT CITY AND BOROUGH OF JUNEAU
10014 Crazy Horse Dr, Juneau, AK 99801-8529
Tel (907) 523-1701 Founded/Ownrshp 1964
Sales 89.8MM EMP 620
Accts Elgee Rehfeld Mertz Llc June
SIC 8211 Public elementary school; Public elementary & secondary schools; Public senior high school; Public elementary school; Public elementary & secondary schools; Public senior high school

D-U-N-S 11-274-7100 IMP/EXP
JUNELL CORP
ADVANCED LUBRICATION SPC
420 Imperial Ct, Bensalem, PA 19020-7327
Tel (215) 244-2114 Founded/Ownrshp 1984
Sales 95.6MM[E] EMP 52
SIC 5172 2899 2992 5531 Lubricating oils & greases; Chemical preparations; Lubricating oils & greases; Lubricating oils; Cutting oils, blending: made from purchased materials; Transmission fluid: made from purchased materials; Automotive & home supply stores; Lubricating oils & greases; Chemical preparations; Lubricating oils & greases; Lubricating oils; Cutting oils, blending: made from purchased materials; Transmission fluid: made from purchased materials; Automotive & home supply stores
Pr: Greg T Julian
Pr: Joe Fitzmier
Pr: Glenn Krasley
*CFO: Bob Devenney
*Ch: Gary Julian
Treas: Robert Powers
*VP: Bob Mack
VP: Robert Mack
VP: Marc Tachev
Plnt Mgr: Mike Cimino
Prd Mgr: Ron Koenig

D-U-N-S 83-114-9922
JUNGLE CONCEPTS LLC
PITAJUNGLE
1850 W Southern Ave, Mesa, AZ 85202-4823
Tel (480) 615-7482 Founded/Ownrshp 2008
Sales 8.3MM[E] EMP 500
SIC 5812 Sandwiches & submarines shop; Sandwiches & submarines shop

JUNGLE JIMS INTERNATIONAL MKT
See JUNGLE JIMS MARKET INC

D-U-N-S 07-677-8745
JUNGLE JIMS MARKET INC
JUNGLE JIMS INTERNATIONAL MKT
5440 Dixie Hwy Frnt, Fairfield, OH 45014-7426
Tel (513) 674-6000 Founded/Ownrshp 1972
Sales 89.3MM[E] EMP 320[E]
SIC 5411 Supermarkets, hypermarket; Supermarkets, hypermarket
Pr: James O Bonaminio
CFO: George Wissing
Genl Mgr: Ed Carroll
Off Mgr: Terry Barton
Off Mgr: Marion Stricker
Store Mgr: Debbie Burt
Manager: Allison Beel
Prd Mgr: James Nye

D-U-N-S 07-284-5035
JUNIATA COLLEGE
1700 Moore St, Huntingdon, PA 16652-2196
Tel (814) 641-3000 Founded/Ownrshp 1876
Sales 50.5MM EMP 500
Accts Baker Tilly Virchow Krause Llp
SIC 8221 College, except junior; College, except junior
Pr: James A Troha
*Pr: Thomas R Kepple Jr
CFO: Andrea M Denkovich
Trst: Judith Kimmel
Ex VP: John Hille
Ex VP: James Lakso
VP: Nicholas Casabona
VP: Fumio Sugihara
Brnch Mgr: Brandon Hillegas

D-U-N-S 11-513-9834
JUNIATA COUNTY SCHOOL DISTRICT
75 S 7th St, Mifflintown, PA 17059-8099
Tel (717) 436-2111 Founded/Ownrshp 1991
Sales 21.0MM[E] EMP 350
SIC 8211 Public elementary & secondary schools; High school, junior or senior; Public elementary & secondary schools; High school, junior or senior

JUNIATA PACKING CO
See CCK INC

D-U-N-S 01-516-9170
■ **JUNIATA VALLEY BANK**
(Suby of JUNIATA VALLEY FINANCIAL CORP) ★
2 S Main St, Mifflintown, PA 17059-1313
Tel (717) 436-8211 Founded/Ownrshp 1983
Sales NA EMP 144
SIC 6022 State commercial banks; State commercial banks
Pr: Francis Evanitsky
*Sr VP: Judy Aumiller
Sr VP: Patricia Yearick
VP: Kathy Hutchinson
VP: Steve Kramm
Ex Dir: Judy Robinson

D-U-N-S 11-258-0204
▲ **JUNIATA VALLEY FINANCIAL CORP**
218 Bridge St, Mifflintown, PA 17059-1305
Tel (717) 436-8211 Founded/Ownrshp 1983
Sales NA EMP 153[E]
Tkr Sym JUVF Exch OTC
SIC 6022 State commercial banks; State commercial banks
Pr: Marcie A Barber
CFO: Joann N McMinn
Ts Inv Off: Paul Grego
Trst Ofcr: William L Barnett
VP: Jon Yarger
IT Man: S Hubler

D-U-N-S 06-825-8060
JUNIOR ACHIEVEMENT USA (CO)
1 Education Way, Colorado Springs, CO 80906-4477
Tel (719) 540-8000 Founded/Ownrshp 1919, 1993
Sales 28.4MM EMP 78
Accts Bkd Llp Colorado Springs Co
SIC 8299 Arts & crafts schools
Pr: Jack Kosakowski
Dir Vol: Mitzi Sokolowski
*CFO: Timothy Armijo
*Ex VP: Buzzy Thibodeaux
Sr VP: Cynthia Hofmann
Sr VP: Tom Inscho
Sr VP: Cherlyn Linden
Sr VP: Linda Rimer
VP: Jackie Dant
VP: Joni Dietsch
VP: Ed Grocholski
VP: Mary Johnson
VP: Susan Luu
VP: Leslie Pierce
VP: Kris Ponciroli
VP: Dawn Schwartz
VP: Joe Thomas
Dir Soc: Jennifer McAllen
Dir: Melissa Belkin

D-U-N-S 07-575-9324
JUNIOR AIMS COLLEGE DISTRICT INC
AIMS COMMUNITY COLLEGE
5401 W 20th St, Greeley, CO 80634-3002
Tel (970) 339-6213 Founded/Ownrshp 1967
Sales 18.2MM EMP 856
Accts Bkd Llp Denver Colorado
SIC 8222 8221 5942 Junior college; Colleges universities & professional schools; College book stores; Junior college; Colleges universities & professional schools; College book stores
Pr: Marilynn Liddell PHD
*Pr: Walt Richter
CFO: Leslie Dale
Treas: Larry Wood
Exec: Andria Brabo
CTO: Arvon Engel
Dir IT: Jack Heidrick
Dir IT: Andria Rogers
IT Man: Cindy Cook
Netwrk Mgr: Bill Waggner
Pgrm Dir: John Dixon

D-U-N-S 07-307-2266
JUNIOR COLLEGE DISTRICT OF METROPOLITAN KANSAS CITY MISSOURI
METROPOLITAN COMMUNITY COLLEGE
3200 Broadway Blvd, Kansas City, MO 64111-2408
Tel (816) 604-1000 Founded/Ownrshp 1964
Sales 77.3MM EMP 1,450
Accts Cliftonlarsonallen Llp St Lo
SIC 8222 Community college; Community college
IT Man: Kendra Edwards
Mktg Dir: Roger Banbury
Psych: Jim McGraw
Nrsg Dir: Marjorie Thomason
Snr Mgr: Alex Frogge
Snr Mgr: Kathy Walter-Mack

D-U-N-S 03-069-5530
JUNIOR COLLEGE DISTRICT OF NEWTON AND MCDONALD COUNTIES
CROWDER COLLEGE
601 Laclede Ave, Neosho, MO 64850-9165
Tel (417) 451-3223 Founded/Ownrshp 1963
Sales 35.9MM EMP 272
SIC 8222

D-U-N-S 07-199-5963
JUNIOR COLLEGE DISTRICT OF ST LOUIS
ST LOUIS COMMUNITY COLLEGE
300 S Broadway, Saint Louis, MO 63102-2800
Tel (314) 206-2150 Founded/Ownrshp 1962
Sales 125.8MM[E] EMP 3,900
SIC 8222 Community college; Community college
CFO: Carla Chance
CFO: Laverne Gee
Ofcr: Daphne Walker-Thoth
VP: Ashok Agrawal
VP: Carolyn Jackson
VP: Jason McClelland
VP: Thomas Walker
Comm Dir: Dan Kimack
Ex Dir: Jeff Allen
Off Mgr: Teresa Huether
CIO: John Klimczak

D-U-N-S 87-684-3249
JUNIOR DRAUGHON COLLEGE INC
TN DAYMAR INSTITUTE
(Suby of DAYMAR HOLDINGS INC) ★
2401 New Hartford Rd, Owensboro, KY 42303-1312
Tel (270) 926-1188 Founded/Ownrshp 2001
Sales 7.6MM[E] EMP 289
SIC 8222 Junior college; Junior college
Pr: Terrie Gabis

D-U-N-S 15-447-9166
■ **JUNIOR FOOD STORES OF WEST FLORIDA INC**
TOM THUMB
(Suby of DILLON COMPANIES INC) ★
619 8th Ave, Crestview, FL 32536-2101
Tel (850) 244-5447 Founded/Ownrshp 1984
Sales 302.3MM[E] EMP 1,250
SIC 5541 5411 Filling stations, gasoline; Convenience stores, chain; Filling stations, gasoline; Convenience stores, chain
Pr: Mark W Salisbury
*Treas: Scott M Henderson
*VP: David Daigle
*VP: William Mullen
VP: Trey Powell

D-U-N-S 07-509-6487
JUNIOR HILL COLLEGE
112 Lamar Dr, Hillsboro, TX 76645-2711
Tel (254) 659-7500 Founded/Ownrshp 1923
Sales 6.7MM EMP 500
Accts Lott Verdon & Company Pc
SIC 8222 Junior college; Junior college
Pr: William Auvenshine
VP: Pam Boehm
*VP: Billy Don Curbo

D-U-N-S 11-782-1806
JUNIOR LEAGUE OF JACKSON INC
805 Riverside Dr, Jackson, MS 39202-1138
Tel (601) 948-2357 Founded/Ownrshp 1941
Sales 1.4MM EMP 900[E]
Accts Tann Brown & Russ Co Pllc
SIC 8322 Youth center; Youth center
Pr: Mary Purbis
*Treas: Lisa Leste
*VP: Elaina Jackson
*VP: Missye Martin
Ex Dir: Cynthia Till
Off Mgr: Joi Fitzgerald
IT Man: John Kroeze

D-U-N-S 12-373-8523
JUNIOR SENIOR INC
IHOP
601 E Slaton Rd, Lubbock, TX 79404-5821
Tel (806) 748-7827 Founded/Ownrshp 1999
Sales 9.0MM[E] EMP 300
SIC 5812 Restaurant, family: chain; Restaurant, family: chain
Pr: Bill Butler
VP: Colleen Butler

JUNIORS SUPERMARKET
See FE-MA ENTERPRISES INC

D-U-N-S 00-121-0996 IMP
JUNIPER ELBOW CO INC (NY)
JUNIPER INDUSTRIES
7215 Metropolitan Ave, Middle Village, NY 11379-2198
Tel (718) 326-2546 Founded/Ownrshp 1929
Sales 29.3MM[E] EMP 200
SIC 3444 3498 3433 3312 Elbows, for air ducts, stovepipes, etc.: sheet metal; Ventilators, sheet metal; Metal ventilating equipment; Fabricated pipe & fittings; Heating equipment, except electric; Blast furnaces & steel mills; Elbows, for air ducts, stovepipes, etc.: sheet metal; Ventilators, sheet metal; Metal ventilating equipment; Fabricated pipe & fittings; Heating equipment, except electric; Blast furnaces & steel mills
CEO: Jesse L Wiener
*VP: Celia Wiener
*VP: Elliot Wiener
Genl Mgr: Marvin Jacobs

D-U-N-S 01-357-6633
JUNIPER HOLDINGS INC
555 Madison Ave Fl 24, New York, NY 10022-3315
Tel (212) 339-8500 Founded/Ownrshp 2013
Sales 75.9MM[E] EMP 534[E]
SIC 6719 Investment holding companies, except banks

JUNIPER INDUSTRIES
See JUNIPER ELBOW CO INC

D-U-N-S 02-978-1774
JUNIPER INVESTMENT CO LLC
555 Madison Ave Fl 24, New York, NY 10022-3315
Tel (212) 339-8500 Founded/Ownrshp 2012
Sales 20.0MM[E] EMP 534
SIC 6799 Investors; Investors
Pt: Bradley J Hoecker

D-U-N-S 60-423-2343
JUNIPER NETWORKS (US) INC
1133 Innovation Way, Sunnyvale, CA 94089-1228
Tel (408) 745-2000 Founded/Ownrshp 2015
Sales 104.4MM[E] EMP 9,000
SIC 3577 Computer peripheral equipment
CEO: Mitchell Lee Gaynor
*Ch Bd: Scott Kriens
CFO: Robyn Denholm
CFO: Kenneth Niven
VP: Sue Oliva
Snr Ntwrk: Joe Stankus
Sftwr Eng: Dwann Hall

D-U-N-S 94-679-2355 IMP
▲ **JUNIPER NETWORKS INC**
1133 Innovation Way, Sunnyvale, CA 94089-1228
Tel (408) 745-2000 Founded/Ownrshp 1996
Sales 4.6MMM EMP 8,846
Accts Ernst & Young Llp San Jose C
Tkr Sym JNPR Exch NYS
SIC 3577 7372 Computer peripheral equipment; Computer peripheral equipment; Prepackaged software
CEO: Rami Rahim
*Ch Bd: Scott Kriens
COO: Robyn M Denholm
*V Ch Bd: Pradeep Sindhu
Chf Cred: Vince Molinaro
Ofcr: Gerri Elliott
Ex VP: Mark Bauhaus
Ex VP: Jonathan Davidson
Ex VP: Mitchell Gaynor
Ex VP: Robert Muglia
Ex VP: David Yen
Sr VP: Martin J Garvin
Sr VP: Robert Worrall
VP: Carlos Brito
VP: Joe Carson
VP: Kathleen Conroy
VP: Harish Devanagondi
VP: Robert Dix
VP: Jeff Green
VP: Courtney Harrison
VP: Dan Muly
Board of Directors: Robert M Calderoni, Mary B Cranston, Gary Daichendt, Kevin Denuccio, Jim Dolce, Mercedes Johnson, Rahul Merchant, David Schlotterbeck, William R Stensrud

D-U-N-S 17-762-1224
▲ **JUNIPER PHARMACEUTICALS INC**
4 Liberty Sq Fl 4, Boston, MA 02109-4811
Tel (617) 639-1500 Founded/Ownrshp 1986
Sales 32.4MM EMP 77[E]
Tkr Sym JNP Exch NAS
SIC 2834 Pharmaceutical preparations; Pharmaceutical preparations
Pr: Frank C Condella Jr
Ch Bd: James A Geraghty
*COO: Nikin Patel
CFO: George O Elston
CFO: James A Meer
Treas: James Meer
Chf Mktg O: Bridget Martell
Ex Dir: Paul B Schwartz
Board of Directors: Valerie L Andrews, Frank M Armstrong, Cristina Csimma, James A Geraghty, Donald H Hunter, Ann Merrifield

D-U-N-S 04-173-8340
JUNIPER SYSTEMS INC
HARVEST MASTER
(Suby of CAMPBELL SCIENTIFIC INC) ★
1132 W 1700 N, Logan, UT 84321-1723
Tel (435) 753-1881 Founded/Ownrshp 1993
Sales 46.8MM[E] EMP 94
SIC 3571 7371 3829 3523 Minicomputers; Custom computer programming services; Measuring & controlling devices; Farm machinery & equipment; Minicomputers; Custom computer programming services; Measuring & controlling devices; Farm machinery & equipment
Pr: Robert Campbell
*Pr: Ryan Harris
*CFO: Ignacio Birkner
*VP: Ronald Campbell
*VP: Devon Labrum
*VP: Janice Saalfeld
*VP: Gary Spence
Prgrm Mgr: Nathan Holman
Snr Sftwr: John McKell
CIO: C W Daniels
Dir IT: Dan Parchman

D-U-N-S 96-948-9447
JUNIPERO SERRA CATHOLIC HIGH SCHOOL
26351 Junipero Serra Rd, San Juan Capistrano, CA 92675-1635
Tel (949) 474-7368 Founded/Ownrshp 2011
Sales 21.4MM EMP 28
Accts Wertz & Company Llp Irvine C
SIC 8211 Elementary & secondary schools; Elementary & secondary schools
Psych: Tim Egan

D-U-N-S 80-152-9186
JUNO INVESTMENTS LLC
950 3rd Ave Ste 2300, New York, NY 10022-2705
Tel (212) 688-2700 Founded/Ownrshp 2002
Sales NA EMP 227[E]
SIC 6159 Small business investment companies
CFO: John Huber

JUNO LIGHTING GROUP
See JUNO LIGHTING LLC

D-U-N-S 06-036-1276 IMP
JUNO LIGHTING LLC
JUNO LIGHTING GROUP
(Suby of SCHNEIDER ELECTRIC USA INC) ★
1300 S Wolf Rd, Des Plaines, IL 60018-1300
Tel (847) 827-9880 Founded/Ownrshp 2005
Sales 199.4MM[E] EMP 1,000
SIC 3646 3645 Commercial indusl & institutional electric lighting fixtures; Fluorescent lighting fixtures, commercial; Residential lighting fixtures; Fluorescent lighting fixtures, residential; Commercial indusl & institutional electric lighting fixtures; Fluorescent lighting fixtures, commercial; Residential lighting fixtures; Fluorescent lighting fixtures, residential
Pr: Amelia Huntington
*COO: Glenn R Bordfeld
*Ex VP: W Allen Fromm
*Sr VP: Charles F Huber
VP: Kevin Grayson
VP: Patrick Murphy
VP: Scott Roos
VP: Chris Walsch
Off Mgr: Joanne Terra
Tech Mgr: John Donato
Tech Mgr: Cyndi Stahlke

D-U-N-S 94-538-4915
■ **JUNO ONLINE SERVICES INC**
(Suby of UNITED ONLINE INC) ★
75 9th Ave Fl 4, New York, NY 10011-7025
Tel (212) 597-9000 Founded/Ownrshp 2001
Sales 41.1MM[E] EMP 397
SIC 4813 ;
Pr: Mark Goldston
COO: Art Robinson
CFO: Rick Eaton
CFO: Charles Hilliard
Sr VP: David E Baade
Sr VP: Richard D Buchban
Sr VP: Richard D Buchband
Sr VP: V S Mani
Sr VP: C S Murali
Sr VP: Wendy Rosenberg

Sr VP: Alex C Sarafian
Sr VP: Peter D Skopp
Sr VP: Clark D Swain
Sr VP: Edward Weber
VP: Rick Lundy

D-U-N-S 07-929-0042
▲ JUNO THERAPEUTICS INC
307 Westlake Ave N # 300, Seattle, WA 98109-5235
Tel (206) 582-1600 *Founded/Ownrshp* 2013
Sales 23.7MM^E *EMP* 33
Tkr Sym JUNO *Exch* NGS
SIC 8731 Biotechnical research, commercial
CEO: Hans Bishop
Chf Cred: Robert Azelby
Ex VP: Mark W Frohlich
Ex VP: Hyam I Levitsky
Genl Couns: Barney Cassidy

D-U-N-S 00-626-1820 EXP
JUNOPACIFIC INC
(*Suby of* CRETEX COMPANIES INC) ★
1040 Lund Blvd, Anoka, MN 55303-1089
Tel (763) 703-5000 *Founded/Ownrshp* 1984
Sales 40.0MM^E *EMP* 180
SIC 3841 Surgical & medical instruments; Surgical & medical instruments
CEO: Kern Bhugra
Genl Mgr: Brian Esch
Sfty Mgr: Garry Olson
Opers Mgr: Jon Johnson
Prd Mgr: Jim Scott
Sls Mgr: Mark McCourntey

JUNTA DE CALIDAD AMBIENTAL
See ENVIRONMENTAL QUALITY BOARD

JUNTA DE PLANIFICACION
See PLANNING BOARD

D-U-N-S 78-679-4099 IMP
JUPITER ALUMINUM CORP
1745 165th St Ste 6, Hammond, IN 46320-2800
Tel (219) 932-3322 *Founded/Ownrshp* 1992
Sales 63.3MM^E *EMP* 200
SIC 3353 3354 Aluminum sheet, plate & foil; Coils, rod, extruded, aluminum; Aluminum sheet, plate & foil; Coils, rod, extruded, aluminum
CEO: Dietrich M Gross
**CFO:* Loren Jahn
VP: Paul Obrien
VP: Lawrence Rowe
Genl Mgr: Ron Nuckles
Dir IT: Mike Schmidt
Dir IT: Mike Smith
Sftwr Eng: Ichitaro Yamazaki
Plnt Mgr: Bill Altgilbers
Plnt Mgr: William Altgilderf
Plnt Mgr: William Altilders

D-U-N-S 02-649-2496
JUPITER CHEVROLET LP
11611 Lbj Fwy, Garland, TX 75041-3803
Tel (972) 271-9900 *Founded/Ownrshp* 1993
Sales 37.5MM^E *EMP* 96^E
SIC 5511 5531 7532 7538 Automobiles, new & used; Vans, new & used; Pickups, new & used; Automotive parts; Body shop, automotive; Body shop, trucks; General automotive repair shops; General truck repair; Automobiles, new & used; Vans, new & used; Pickups, new & used; Automotive parts; Body shop, automotive; Body shop, trucks; General automotive repair shops; General truck repair
Pt: Mike Matetich
Genl Mgr: Berry Wooten
Sales Asso: Eli Martinez

D-U-N-S 96-811-0531 IMP
JUPITER COMPOSITES INC
3301 Bill Metzger Ln, Pensacola, FL 32514-7078
Tel (850) 476-6304 *Founded/Ownrshp* 2006
Sales 33.2MM^E *EMP* 110
SIC 3511 Turbines & turbine generator set units, complete; Turbines & turbine generator set units, complete
CEO: Jens Kristensen
**CFO:* Kenneth Nilsson
**VP:* Preben Almind

D-U-N-S 87-804-5558
■ JUPITER HOLDINGS INC
(*Suby of* NORTHLAND CO) ★
1285 Northland Dr, Saint Paul, MN 55120-1374
Tel (952) 681-3005 *Founded/Ownrshp* 1993
Sales NA *EMP* 249^E
SIC 6331 Fire, marine & casualty insurance & carriers; Fire, marine & casualty insurance & carriers
Ch Bd: Gene G Gopon

D-U-N-S 79-748-0332
JUPITER I LLC
OFFICESCAPES
9900 E 51st Ave, Denver, CO 80238-2430
Tel (303) 574-1115 *Founded/Ownrshp* 1998
Sales 125.3MM^E *EMP* 160
SIC 5021 Furniture; Furniture
CFO: Joel Bolgrien
Opers Mgr: Al Mitze
Sales Exec: Sharie Grant
Sales Exec: Robert Sobota
Sls&Mrk Ex: Mary Bloomer
Mktg Mgr: Linda Rumbarger
Sls Mgr: Dan Moreton
Sls Mgr: Danna Squires

D-U-N-S 13-150-6958
JUPITER MEDICAL CENTER INC
1210 S Old Dixie Hwy, Jupiter, FL 33458-7205
Tel (561) 747-2234 *Founded/Ownrshp* 1979
Sales 182.9MM *EMP* 1,500
SIC 8062 8051 General medical & surgical hospitals; Skilled nursing care facilities; General medical & surgical hospitals; Skilled nursing care facilities
Ch Bd: Barrie Godown
**Pr:* Seldon Taub MD
**COO:* Terri Wentz
CFO: Jan Grigsby
**Treas:* Robert E Grogan MD
**VP:* Thomas Murray MD
**VP:* Cathy Thomson MD
Exec: Ray Beane
Exec: John Wolf
Dir Inf Cn: Linda Wilson
Dir Risk M: Terri Freeman
Dir Lab: Cathy Rogers
Dir Rx: Alan Davis

D-U-N-S 06-547-8877
■ JUPITER STREET INC (MS)
TOWER LOAN
(*Suby of* PROSPECT CAPITAL CORP) ★
1505 Airport Rd N, Flowood, MS 39232-2219
Tel (601) 664-1000 *Founded/Ownrshp* 1937, 2012
Sales NA *EMP* 38^E
SIC 6141 6411 6311 Personal credit institutions; Insurance agents, brokers & service; Life insurance
Ch Bd: Jack R Lee
**Pr:* Frank Lee
Treas: Leland Martin
VP: Jody Macon
Brnch Mgr: Ryan Cartier
Brnch Mgr: Trevor Cassard
Brnch Mgr: Christopher Jones
Brnch Mgr: Matthew Vrbenec
QA Dir: Jason Poole

D-U-N-S 03-389-6077 IMP
JUPITER SYSTEMS
31015 Huntwood Ave, Hayward, CA 94544-7007
Tel (510) 675-1000 *Founded/Ownrshp* 1981
Sales 30.0MM^E *EMP* 65^E
SIC 3575 Computer terminals

D-U-N-S 05-240-1049 IMP
JUPITOR CORP USA
(*Suby of* JUPITOR CORPORATION)
55 Fairbanks, Irvine, CA 92618-1603
Tel (949) 588-0505 *Founded/Ownrshp* 1971
Sales 35.7MM^E *EMP* 36
SIC 5088 Aircraft equipment & supplies
CEO: Rick Oishi
**VP:* Becky Papas

D-U-N-S 86-717-8725 IMP
JURA INC
CAPRESSO
(*Suby of* JURA ELEKTROAPPARATE AG)
20 Craig Rd, Montvale, NJ 07645-1709
Tel (800) 220-5701 *Founded/Ownrshp* 1994
Sales 25.5MM^E *EMP* 39
SIC 5046 Coffee brewing equipment & supplies
Pr: Richard Boynton
**Prin:* Judith Schwartz
Admn Mgr: Roseann Colonna
Opers Mgr: Stephen Cracchiolo
Mktg Mgr: Becky Sawicki
Snr Mgr: Ernest Rodriguez

D-U-N-S 06-040-1796
JURISOLUTIONS INC
JURISTAFF
1600 Market St Fl 38, Philadelphia, PA 19103-7244
Tel (800) 972-9103 *Founded/Ownrshp* 1997
Sales 11.4MM^E *EMP* 300
SIC 8111 Legal services
Pr: Cynthia Towers
Pr: James Larosa
VP: Rachel O'Hara
Ex Dir: Stella Fleming

JURISTAFF
See JURISOLUTIONS INC

D-U-N-S 82-690-2566
JURLIQUE HOLISTIC SKIN CARE INC
2425 Colo Ave Ste B250, Santa Monica, CA 90404
Tel (914) 998-8800 *Founded/Ownrshp* 2005
Sales 8.0MM^E *EMP* 500
SIC 7231 Beauty shops; Beauty shops
CEO: Sam McKay

D-U-N-S 05-927-6832
JURUPA COMMUNITY SERVICES DISTRICT
11201 Harrel St, Jurupa Valley, CA 91752-1443
Tel (951) 360-5770 *Founded/Ownrshp* 1956
Sales 69.9MM^E *EMP* 101
SIC 4941 4952 Water supply; Sewerage systems; Water supply; Sewerage systems
Pr: Robert Craig
**Pr:* Ken J McLaughlin
Ofcr: Aileen Flores
**VP:* Betty Anderson
**VP:* Kathryn Bogart
Genl Mgr: Alden Horst
Genl Mgr: Carol McGreevy
Sfty Dirs: Dave Smith
Opers Mgr: Todd Minten
Opers Mgr: Charlie Smith

D-U-N-S 07-814-3286
JURUPA UNIFIED SCHOOL DISTRICT
4850 Pedley Rd, Jurupa Valley, CA 92509-3966
Tel (951) 360-4100 *Founded/Ownrshp* 1963
Sales 102.9MM^E *EMP* 2,000
Accts Nigro & Nigro Pc Merrietta
SIC 8211 Public elementary school; Public junior high school; Public senior high school; Public elementary school; Public junior high school; Public senior high school
**Pr:* Sheryl Schmidt
Treas: Rolanda Cavasos
Treas: Heather Larsen
MIS Dir: Joshua Lewis
Schl Brd P: Sheryl Schmitt
Psych: Laura Beal

D-U-N-S 62-185-0007
JUST A BUCK OF NEW YORK INC
J A B
563 Temple Hill Rd, New Windsor, NY 12553-5534
Tel (518) 966-4934 *Founded/Ownrshp* 2002
Sales 25.9MM^E *EMP* 160
SIC 6794 5331 Franchises, selling or licensing; Variety stores; Franchises, selling or licensing; Variety stores
Ch Bd: Steve Bakst

D-U-N-S 96-593-5778 EXP
JUST BAGELS MANUFACTURING INC
527 Casanova St, Bronx, NY 10474-6711
Tel (718) 328-9700 *Founded/Ownrshp* 1996
Sales 29.5MM^E *EMP* 83
SIC 5149 2051 Bakery products; Bread, cake & related products
Pr: Clifford R Nordquist
**CEO:* Charles E Contreras
VP: James Connell
**VP:* James O'Connell
Ql Cn Mgr: Abel Mendez
S&M/VP: Andrew Russo

D-U-N-S 00-239-7982 IMP/EXP
JUST BORN INC (PA)
1300 Stefko Blvd, Bethlehem, PA 18017-6672
Tel (610) 867-7568 *Founded/Ownrshp* 1923
Sales 168.4MM^E *EMP* 550
SIC 2064 Candy & other confectionery products; Candy & other confectionery products
CEO: David N Shaffer
Pr: Kevin McElvain
**Pr:* David Yale
**CEO:* Ross J Born
**Treas:* Jack M Shaffer
VP: Ron Arnold
VP: George Cinquegrana
VP: Ronald Izewski
VP: Norman G Jungmann
VP: Richard Milker
VP: Dave Stephens
VP: Rob Sweatman

JUST BRAKES
See JBRE LLC

JUST CABINETS
See RTA FURNITURE DISTRIBUTORS INC

JUST DESSERTS
See NEW DESSERTS INC

D-U-N-S 07-945-0483
JUST ENERGY (US) CORP
(*Suby of* JUST ENERGY GROUP INC)
5251 Westheimr Rd # 1000, Houston, TX 77056-5414
Tel (713) 850-6784 *Founded/Ownrshp* 2001
Sales 80.5MM^E *EMP* 495
SIC 3621 4924 Power generators; Natural gas distribution; Power generators; Natural gas distribution
Pr: Deborah Merril
Pr: James Lewis
CFO: Beth Summers
Ex VP: Jonah Davids
Snr Mgr: Vanessa Anesetti-Parra

D-U-N-S 07-948-1509
JUST FAB INC
FABLETICS
800 Apollo St, El Segundo, CA 90245-4701
Tel (310) 683-0940 *Founded/Ownrshp* 2011
Sales 23.2MM^E *EMP* 122^E
SIC 3171 3144 Women's handbags & purses; Dress shoes, women's
CEO: Carrie Tsupin Chien
Mktg Mgr: Carly Dahlen
Mktg Mgr: Ryan Heller

D-U-N-S 05-275-8501 IMP
JUST FABULOUS INC
FABKIDS
800 Apollo St, El Segundo, CA 90245-4701
Tel (310) 683-0940 *Founded/Ownrshp* 2009
Sales 108.6MM^E *EMP* 257^E
SIC 5961 5661 5632 5651 Catalog & mail-order houses; Catalog sales; Jewelry, mail order; Women's shoes; Handbags; Jeans stores
CEO: Adam Goldenberg
**Pr:* Kimora Lee Simmons
**Co-CEO:* Don Ressler
Sr VP: Sandra Diaz
VP: Tom Dean
VP: Traci Milholend
VP: Gita Rebbapragada
CIO: Dane Pescaia
CTO: Tim Collins
Mktg Dir: Lesley Holmes
Mktg Mgr: Ryan Heller
Board of Directors: Mark Leschly

JUST FOODS
See HASTINGS FOODS LLC

JUST FOR MEN DIV
See JEANJER LLC

D-U-N-S 08-173-5367 IMP
JUST FOR WRAPS INC
A-LIST
5815 Smithway St, Commerce, CA 90040-1605
Tel (213) 239-0503 *Founded/Ownrshp* 1980
Sales 30.3MM^E *EMP* 145
SIC 2339 2335 2337 Sportswear, women's; Women's, juniors' & misses' dresses; Women's & misses' suits & coats; Sportswear, women's; Women's, juniors' & misses' dresses; Women's & misses' suits & coats
CEO: Vrajesh Lal
**VP:* Rakesh Lal
VP: Roger Tonin
CIO: Ric Baksh

D-U-N-S 78-523-0793
JUST IN TIME STAFFING INC
8130 Tyler Blvd, Mentor, OH 44060-4852
Tel (440) 205-2002 *Founded/Ownrshp* 2003
Sales 13.4MM^E *EMP* 350
SIC 7361 Employment agencies; Employment agencies
Pr: Michael J Donato
VP: Marco Dinovo
Area Mgr: Adam Kastning
Off Admin: Holly Armstrong

D-U-N-S 15-918-9278 IMP/EXP
JUST LIKE SUGAR INC
2020 Pama Ln, Las Vegas, NV 89119-4678
Tel (702) 483-6777 *Founded/Ownrshp* 2003
Sales 192.9MM^E *EMP* 1,300
SIC 2869 Sweeteners, synthetic; Sweeteners, synthetic
CEO: Mike Silver
**Pr:* Randall W Robirds
**Sec:* Gary L Silver

D-U-N-S 00-510-0466 IMP
JUST MANUFACTURING CO INC (IL)
9233 King St, Franklin Park, IL 60131-2189
Tel (847) 671-7161 *Founded/Ownrshp* 1933
Sales 29.7MM^E *EMP* 160
SIC 3431 Sinks: enameled iron, cast iron or pressed metal; Plumbing fixtures: enameled iron cast iron or pressed metal; Sinks: enameled iron, cast iron or pressed metal; Plumbing fixtures: enameled iron cast iron or pressed metal
Pr: Paul Just
**Treas:* Matthew E Just

D-U-N-S 82-519-7572 IMP
JUST ONE LLC
SECRET LACE
1450 Broadway Fl 21, New York, NY 10018-2221
Tel (212) 302-2336 *Founded/Ownrshp* 2007
Sales 33.0MM^E *EMP* 43
SIC 5137 5621 Women's & children's clothing; Women's clothing stores
Off Mgr: Jeannine Galliani

D-U-N-S 01-208-5403
JUST ONE MORE RESTAURANT CORP
1730 Rhode Island Ave Nw # 900, Washington, DC 20036-3101
Tel (202) 775-7256 *Founded/Ownrshp* 1945
Sales 21.1MM^E *EMP* 1,000
SIC 5812 5813 Steak restaurant; Bar (drinking places); Steak restaurant; Bar (drinking places)
VP: Louise Bozzi
**Pr:* James Longo
**Treas:* Bruce Bozzi

JUST RITE RENTAL
See CCS CONTRACTOR EQUIPMENT & SUPPLY INC

JUST SAVE
See LOWES FOOD STORES INC

D-U-N-S 62-310-4197 IMP
JUST SAY ROCK INC
JSR MERCHANDISING
1 Washington St Ste 530, Dover, NH 03820-3854
Tel (603) 742-4377 *Founded/Ownrshp* 1989
Sales 22.8MM^E *EMP* 87
Accts Rodman & Rodman Pc Newton
SIC 5136 5137 5199 Men's & boys' clothing; Women's & children's clothing; Novelties, paper; Men's & boys' clothing; Women's & children's clothing; Novelties, paper
Pr: Wes Bockley
**VP:* Brad Hudson

JUST STRINGZ
See BELLE BOEAU LTD INC

JUST TEMPS & PERSONNEL PLUS
See PERSONNEL PLUS OF DC INC

JUST WIRELESS
See CASE BEST AND ACCESSORIES INC

D-U-N-S 13-857-0390 IMP
JUSTCOM TECH INC
2283 Paragon Dr, San Jose, CA 95131-1307
Tel (408) 392-9998 *Founded/Ownrshp* 2003
Sales 10.0MM *EMP* 300
SIC 3613 Switches, electric power except snap, push button, etc.; Switches, electric power except snap, push button, etc.
Pr: Genny Wu
**Ex VP:* Chris Finotti

D-U-N-S 05-427-5518
JUSTFAB INC
MAELI ROSE
134 145 Aa E Duarte Rd, Arcadia, CA 91006
Tel (626) 701-7575 *Founded/Ownrshp* 2011
Sales 24.8MM^E *EMP* 300
SIC 5651 5661 Family clothing stores; Shoes, custom
CEO: Carrie Tsupin Chien

D-U-N-S 85-860-9873
JUSTGIVE
312 Sutter St Ste 410, San Francisco, CA 94108-4317
Tel (415) 982-5700 *Founded/Ownrshp* 2007
Sales 40.3MM *EMP* 2
Accts Benson & Neff Cpa S A Prof Co
SIC 4724 Travel agencies; Travel agencies
Prin: Donald Kendall
Bd of Dir: William E McGlashan Jr
Dir IT: Roxanne Gentile
Sftwr Eng: Curtis Keuker

D-U-N-S 92-735-0215
JUSTICE CABINET KENTUCKY
(*Suby of* EXECUTIVE OFFICE OF COMMONWEALTH OF KENTUCKY) ★
125 Holmes St Fl 2, Frankfort, KY 40601-2108
Tel (502) 564-7554 *Founded/Ownrshp* 1792
Sales NA *EMP* 4,400
SIC 9229 ;
IT Man: Penny Quatman

D-U-N-S 00-410-4061
JUSTICE FAMILY GROUP LLC
300 W Main St, Wht Sphr Spgs, WV 24986-2414
Tel (304) 252-1074 *Founded/Ownrshp* 2009
Sales 100.2MM^E *EMP* 1,000^E
SIC 8741 Management services; Management services

D-U-N-S 96-370-9436
JUSTICE FCU
5175 Parkstone Dr Ste 200, Chantilly, VA 20151-3816
Tel (703) 480-5300 *Founded/Ownrshp* 2010
Sales NA *EMP* 4
SIC 6061 Federal credit unions
Prin: Peter Sainato

JUSTICE HOLDCO
See BURGER KING HOLDCO LLC

D-U-N-S 78-771-5051 IMP
■ JUSTIN BRANDS INC
JUSTIN ORIGINAL WORK BOOT
(Suby of ACME BRICK) ★
610 W Daggett Ave, Fort Worth, TX 76104-1103
Tel (817) 332-4385 Founded/Ownrshp 1991
Sales 72.9MM^E EMP 1,035
SIC 3144 3143 3149 Boots, canvas or leather: women's; Boots, dress or casual: men's; Work shoes, men's; Children's footwear, except athletic; Boots, canvas or leather: women's; Boots, dress or casual: men's; Work shoes, men's; Children's footwear, except athletic
Ch Bd: Randy Watson
*Pr: Jaime Morgan
*CFO: Herbert Beckwith Jr
*Sr VP: Larry Nelson
VP: John Darnold
*VP: Lisa Lankes
VP: Scott C Milden
*VP: Chuck Smallbach
Genl Mgr: Louis Russo
IT Man: Gene Martinez
IT Man: Fernie Moure

D-U-N-S 07-020-7878
JUSTIN DAVIS ENTERPRISES INC
7201 E Dr Martin Martin Luther, Tampa, FL 33619
Tel (850) 929-4584 Founded/Ownrshp 1998
Sales 38.7MM^E EMP 79^E
SIC 4213 Trucking, except local; Liquid petroleum transport, non-local
CEO: James B Davis
*Pr: Andy Young
Treas: Martha Davis

D-U-N-S 00-801-8772 IMP
■ JUSTIN INDUSTRIES INC (TX)
ACME BRICK
(Suby of BERKSHIRE HATHAWAY INC) ★
2821 Crockett St, Fort Worth, TX 76107-2907
Tel (817) 332-4101 Founded/Ownrshp 1891
Sales 384.7MM^E EMP 4,111
SIC 3251 3271 5211 5032 Brick clay: common face, glazed, vitrified or hollow; Concrete block & brick; Blocks, concrete or cinder: standard; Brick; Tile, ceramic; Brick, except refractory; Brick clay: common face, glazed, vitrified or hollow; Concrete block & brick; Blocks, concrete or cinder: standard; Brick; Tile, ceramic; Brick, except refractory
Pr: Dennis D Knautz
*Pr: Edward L Stout Jr
*Ch: Warren Buffett
*CEO: Warren Buffett
*Sec: Judy B Hunter
VP: JT Dickenson
*VP: J Randy Watson

JUSTIN ORIGINAL WORK BOOT
See JUSTIN BRANDS INC

D-U-N-S 05-703-0104
JUSTINTV INC
225 Bush St Fl 6, San Francisco, CA 94104-4222
Tel (415) 684-7494 Founded/Ownrshp 2006
Sales 29.9MM^E EMP 120
SIC 5734 Software, computer games
COO: Kevin Lin
Sr VP: Kym Nelson
VP: Scott Newton
Dir Bus: Brooke Van Dusen
Netwrk Eng: Jon Shipman

D-U-N-S 00-694-6875 IMP/EXP
JUSTISS OIL CO INC
BAKER TANK CO DIVISION
1120 E Oak St, Jena, LA 71342-5448
Tel (318) 992-4111 Founded/Ownrshp 1946
Sales 68.6MM EMP 350
SIC 1381 3443 1389 1311

D-U-N-S 19-947-0261 IMP
JUSTMAN PACKAGING & DISPLAY
5819 Telegraph Rd, Commerce, CA 90040-1515
Tel (323) 728-8888 Founded/Ownrshp 1989
Sales 72.7MM^E EMP 70
SIC 5113 5046 Corrugated & solid fiber boxes; Display equipment, except refrigerated; Corrugated & solid fiber boxes; Display equipment, except refrigerated
Pr: Morley Justman
*CFO: Barbara Cabaret
*VP: Russell Justman
Sales Exec: Josh Justman
Sales Exec: Mike Widdoss
Natl Sales: Jimmy Metzidis
VP Sls: John Burnstine
Mktg Dir: Mark Bagan
Sls Mgr: Tammy Castro

D-U-N-S 00-510-6018 IMP/EXP
JUSTRITE MANUFACTURING CO LLC
EX, LUBERITE
2454 E Dempster St # 300, Des Plaines, IL 60016-5319
Tel (847) 298-9250 Founded/Ownrshp 2015
Sales 49.2MM^E EMP 240
SIC 3411

D-U-N-S 02-969-3723
JUUT HOLDINGS INC
JUUT SALOON SPA
310 Groveland Ave, Minneapolis, MN 55403-3598
Tel (612) 676-2250 Founded/Ownrshp 2000
Sales 13.5MM^E EMP 410
SIC 7231 Hairdressers; Hairdressers
Pr: David Wagner
CFO: Mike Herron
CTO: Kate Hendershott

D-U-N-S 78-278-4318
JUUT MIDWEST INC
JUUT SALONS
(Suby of JUUT HOLDINGS INC) ★
201 Se Main St Ste 324, Minneapolis, MN 55414-7050
Tel (612) 676-2250 Founded/Ownrshp 2000
Sales 6.2MM^E EMP 400
SIC 7231 Cosmetology & personal hygiene salons; Cosmetology & personal hygiene salons
Ch Bd: David Wagner
*Pr: Thomas Kuhn

JUUT SALONS
See JUUT MIDWEST INC

JUUT SALOON SPA
See JUUT HOLDINGS INC

JUVENILE DETENTION CENTER
See COUNTY OF WEBB

D-U-N-S 80-748-7533
JUVENILE JUSTICE DIVISION CALIFORNIA
(Suby of CALIFORNIA DEPARTMENT OF CORRECTIONS & REHABILITATION) ★
1515 S St Ste 502s, Sacramento, CA 95811-7243
Tel (916) 323-2848 Founded/Ownrshp 1980
Sales NA EMP 42,000
SIC 9223 Prison, government; ; Prison, government;

JUVENILE JUSTICE SERVICES
See PHILADELPHIA CITY OF DEPARTMENT OF HUMAN SERVICES

JUVENILE PROBATION OFFICE
See COUNTY OF BLAIR

D-U-N-S 01-877-5366
JUVENILE REHABILITATION ADMINISTRATION WASHINGTON STATE
(Suby of DSHS) ★
14th Jefferson St, Olympia, WA 98504-0001
Tel (360) 902-7804 Founded/Ownrshp 2001
Sales NA EMP 378
SIC 9431 ;
IT Man: Jan Smith

D-U-N-S 80-881-7014
JUWI INC
(Suby of JUWI AG)
1710 29th St Unit 1068, Boulder, CO 80301-1051
Tel (303) 440-7430 Founded/Ownrshp 2008
Sales 37.1MM^E EMP 50^E
SIC 4911

JUZO
See JULIUS ZORN INC

D-U-N-S 79-119-7296 IMP
JV ASSOCIATES INC
FOUR SEASONS RESORT PALM BEACH
2800 S Ocean Blvd, Palm Beach, FL 33480-6234
Tel (561) 582-2800 Founded/Ownrshp 1983
Sales 29.5MM^E EMP 320
SIC 7011 5813 5812 Resort hotel; Drinking places; Eating places; Resort hotel; Drinking places; Eating places
Pt: S Lyon Sachs
Genl Mgr: Collin Clerk

D-U-N-S 01-663-8384 IMP
JV INDUSTRIAL COMPANIES LTD (TX)
JV PIPING
4040 Red Bluff Rd, Pasadena, TX 77503-3606
Tel (713) 568-2600 Founded/Ownrshp 1998, 2012
Sales 358.3MM^E EMP 2,500
SIC 7692 3441 8711 Welding repair; Building components, structural steel; Construction & civil engineering; Welding repair; Building components, structural steel; Construction & civil engineering
Pt: Joe Vardell
Pt: John Durham
CFO: Steve Gillioz
VP: David Herzog

D-U-N-S 07-496-8710 IMP
JV MANUFACTURING CO INC
1603 Burtner Rd, Natrona Heights, PA 15065-1541
Tel (724) 224-9914 Founded/Ownrshp 1974
Sales 35.8MM^E EMP 90
SIC 3545 3544 Precision measuring tools; Special dies & tools
VP: Sam Gruber
*Pr: Alan M Vecchi
Pr: Ryan Vecchi
*Sec: Richard C Celecki
Sr VP: Georgia Grant
QA Dir: James Smith
IT Man: Walt Hill

D-U-N-S 09-168-0603
JV MANUFACTURING INC
CRAM-A-LOT
701 Butterfield Coach Rd, Springdale, AR 72764-0224
Tel (479) 751-7320 Founded/Ownrshp 1978
Sales 40.6MM^E EMP 200
SIC 3589 3569 7692 Garbage disposers & compactors, commercial; Baling machines, for scrap metal, paper or similar material; Welding repair; Garbage disposers & compactors, commercial; Baling machines, for scrap metal, paper or similar material; Welding repair
Pr: Chris Weiser
*Ch: Jack D Perry
VP: James Stuckey
Off Mgr: Amber Ewton
IT Man: Shaun Swearingen
Sfty Mgr: Charles Hester
Plnt Mgr: Tom Hickman
Mktg Dir: Sharon Wright
Manager: Robert Gleich
Manager: Doug Hardman
Manager: Ernie Horton

D-U-N-S 12-153-5157
JV NORTHWEST INC
JVNW
390 S Redwood St, Canby, OR 97013-2459
Tel (503) 263-2858 Founded/Ownrshp 1981
Sales 27.6MM^E EMP 125^E
SIC 2834 3795 Pills, pharmaceutical; Tanks & tank components; Pills, pharmaceutical; Tanks & tank components
Ch Bd: Donald F Jones
*CEO: David C Jones
*COO: Kyle Sawyer
CFO: Rich Shawen
*VP: Phil Loen
Mktg Dir: Jeri Riha

JV PIPING
See JV INDUSTRIAL COMPANIES LTD

D-U-N-S 83-632-0288
JVAC INC
KELLER LINCOLN FORD
1073 Cadillac Ln, Hanford, CA 93230-4966
Tel (559) 584-5531 Founded/Ownrshp 2008
Sales 26.5MM^E EMP 70
SIC 5511 Automobiles, new & used; Automobiles, new & used
Pr: Jon Keller
*VP: Valerie Keller
Genl Mgr: Patrick Ryan

D-U-N-S 04-470-1126 IMP/EXP
JVC AMERICAS CORP
1700 Valley Rd Ste 1, Wayne, NJ 07470-2045
Tel (973) 317-5000 Founded/Ownrshp 1968
Sales NA EMP 350
SIC 3651

D-U-N-S 62-726-1535
JVC HENDRICKS BOX CO INC
H B C
2245 Killion Ave, Seymour, IN 47274-4308
Tel (812) 523-6600 Founded/Ownrshp 1999
Sales 49.3MM^E EMP 50
SIC 5113 4789 Corrugated & solid fiber boxes; Car loading
Pr: Brad Albright
VP Sls: Kimberly Brown

D-U-N-S 00-598-7268 IMP
JVCKENWOOD USA CORP (CA)
(Suby of JVC KENWOOD CORPORATION)
2201 E Dominguez St, Long Beach, CA 90810-1009
Tel (310) 639-9000 Founded/Ownrshp 1961, 2008
Sales 119.9MM^E EMP 170
Accts Deloitte & Touche Llp
SIC 5064 High fidelity equipment; High fidelity equipment
Pr: Kuhiro Aigami
*CEO: Joseph Glassett
*CFO: Dilip Patki
Treas: Michael McConnell
*Ex VP: Craig Geiger
*Ex VP: Mark Jasin
Ex VP: Osamu Yonahara
VP: Joe Glassit
VP: Dave Hoag
VP: Keith Lehman
*VP: Harvey D Mitnick
VP: Chris Montanez
VP: Bill Neel
VP: Keith Wakefield
VP: Tom Wineland
Board of Directors: Mark Jasin, Keith Lehmann

JVIS - USA
See JVIS INTERNATIONAL LLC

JVIS CRYSTAL AVENUE
See JVIS MANUFACTURING LLC

D-U-N-S 79-645-4655 IMP
JVIS INTERNATIONAL LLC
JVIS - USA
(Suby of JVIS USA LLC) ★
52048 Shelby Pkwy, Shelby Township, MI 48315-1787
Tel (586) 739-9542 Founded/Ownrshp 2015
Sales 324.0MM^E EMP 800^E
SIC 3089 Automotive parts, plastic; Automotive parts, plastic
CEO: Jason Murar

D-U-N-S 96-468-0990 IMP
JVIS MANUFACTURING LLC
JVIS CRYSTAL AVENUE
(Suby of JVIS - USA) ★
1285 N Crystal Ave, Benton Harbor, MI 49022-9215
Tel (269) 927-8200 Founded/Ownrshp 2010
Sales 234.6MM^E EMP 300^E
SIC 5015 Automotive supplies, used; Automotive supplies, used
QI Cn Mgr: Jason Hoose

D-U-N-S 04-494-0093
JVIS USA LLC
52048 Shelby Pkwy, Shelby Township, MI 48315-1787
Tel (586) 884-5700 Founded/Ownrshp 2006
Sales 324.0MM^E EMP 1,000^E
SIC 3089 Automotive parts, plastic
Ofcr: Lisa Tava

D-U-N-S 96-960-4503 IMP
JVL LABORATORIES INC
3784 Opelika Rd, Phenix City, AL 36870-2311
Tel (334) 448-1568 Founded/Ownrshp 1997
Sales 40.3MM^E EMP 50
SIC 5122 Cosmetics
Pr: Jesse Tovar
*CFO: Maria C Tovar

D-U-N-S 96-776-7646
JVL VENTURES LLC
SOFTCARD
230 Park Ave Rm 2829, New York, NY 10169-2801
Tel (212) 365-7555 Founded/Ownrshp 2010
Sales 20.2MM^E EMP 100
SIC 7372 Application computer software; Application computer software
CEO: Michael Abbott
CFO: Tony Lauro
Dir Bus: Brian Buckley
Mktg Mgr: Lynn Panattoni

D-U-N-S 02-931-6296
JVM REALTY CORP
903 Commerce Dr Ste 100, Oak Brook, IL 60523-1957
Tel (630) 242-1000 Founded/Ownrshp 1975
Sales 26.6MM^E EMP 200
SIC 6513 6531 Apartment building operators; Real estate managers; Apartment building operators; Real estate managers
Pr: James V Madary II
COO: Dan Nauert
*VP: John Mc Cloud
VP Opers: Angela Fielder

D-U-N-S 08-045-3483
JVM SALES CORP
3401a Tremley Point Rd, Linden, NJ 07036
Tel (908) 862-4866 Founded/Ownrshp 1983
Sales 40.0MM EMP 100
SIC 2022 Cheese, natural & processed; Cheese, natural & processed
Pr: Mary Beth Tomasino
VP: Anthony Caliendo

JVNW
See JV NORTHWEST INC

D-U-N-S 79-707-6796
JVS CONTRACTING INC
1608 N 43rd St, Tampa, FL 33605-5938
Tel (813) 514-8229 Founded/Ownrshp 2005
Sales 23.6MM^E EMP 145
SIC 1623 Water, sewer & utility lines; Water, sewer & utility lines
Pr: John V Simon Jr
Genl Mgr: April Heyder

D-U-N-S 18-917-0715 IMP/EXP
JW ALUMINUM CO
(Suby of WELLSPRING CAPITAL MANAGEMENT LLC) ★
435 Old Mount Holly Rd, Goose Creek, SC 29445-2805
Tel (843) 572-1100 Founded/Ownrshp 2008
Sales 295.1MM^E EMP 809
SIC 3353 3497 Coils, sheet aluminum; Foil, aluminum; Metal foil & leaf; Coils, sheet aluminum; Foil, aluminum; Metal foil & leaf
CEO: Lee McCarter
*Pr: Don Kassing
Pr: Rick Vance
*COO: Stan Brant
*CFO: Andrew Burrett
*CFO: Barry G Peake
Ofcr: Chester Roush
VP: Kevin Monroe
*VP: Blair H Stewart
Dir Rx: John Mucci
Dir IT: Tim Monahan

D-U-N-S 92-698-3834
JW CHILDS ASSOCIATES LIMITED PARTNERSHIP
1000 Winter St Ste 4300, Waltham, MA 02451-1446
Tel (617) 753-1100 Founded/Ownrshp 1995
Sales 1.8MMM^E EMP 21,380
SIC 6211 Investment firm, general brokerage; Investment firm, general brokerage
Pt: Arthur Byrne
Pt: John Childs
Pt: Philip Damiano
Pt: Alan Dowds
Pt: Dr Mitchell Eisenberg
Pt: David Fiorentino
CFO: Todd Fitzpatrick
VP: Jeffrey Miller
VP: Hemanshu Patel
Dir IT: Gerry Polman
Dir IT: Gerry Tolman

D-U-N-S 78-322-6475 IMP
JW DIRECT SOURCE INC
1200 Lkeside Pkwy Ste 400, Flower Mound, TX 75028
Tel (972) 243-5254 Founded/Ownrshp 1989
Sales 20.5MM^E EMP 32
SIC 5112 Business forms
Pr: Jay Earley
*Treas: Wendy Earley
IT Man: Brent Allen
Opers Mgr: David Whitener

D-U-N-S 03-447-5553
JW HUGHES EXCAVATION INC
790 S State Highway 220, Hico, TX 76457-6183
Tel (254) 796-4799 Founded/Ownrshp 1999
Sales 23.3MM^E EMP 100^E
SIC 1794 Excavation work
Pr: John W Hughes

D-U-N-S 00-313-1224 EXP
JW JONES LUMBER CO INC (NC)
1443 Northside Rd, Elizabeth City, NC 27909-8531
Tel (252) 771-2497 Founded/Ownrshp 1941
Sales 31.9MM^E EMP 150
SIC 2421

D-U-N-S 01-812-6594
JW MARRIOT HOTEL
221 N Rampart Blvd, Las Vegas, NV 89145-5722
Tel (702) 869-7500 Founded/Ownrshp 2001
Sales 51.2MM^E EMP 750
SIC 6552 7011 Land subdividers & developers, commercial; Resort hotel; Casino hotel; Land subdividers & developers, commercial; Resort hotel; Casino hotel
Pr: Thad Alston
CFO: Louis Capone

JW MARRIOTT HOTEL
See 806 MAIN HOTEL LLC

JW MARRIOTT HOUSTON
See 806 MAIN MASTERTENANT LLC

D-U-N-S 07-861-8059
JW MARRIOTT INDIANAPOLIS
10 W Market St Ste 801, Indianapolis, IN 46204-5906
Tel (317) 860-5800 Founded/Ownrshp 2011
Sales 8.5MM^E EMP 800
SIC 7011 Hotels; Hotels
CEO: Scott Blabock

D-U-N-S 83-179-9114
JW MARRIOTT INDIANAPOLIS
10 S West St, Indianapolis, IN 46204-2709
Tel (317) 860-5800 Founded/Ownrshp 2008
Sales 29.9MM^E EMP 750
SIC 7011 Hotels & motels; Hotels & motels
Genl Mgr: Scott Blalock

D-U-N-S 96-675-6202 IMP
JW MARRIOTT RESORT & SPA
74855 Country Club Dr, Palm Desert, CA 92260-1961
Tel (760) 341-2211 *Founded/Ownrshp* 2010
Sales 24.0MM^E *EMP* 1,500
SIC 7991 Spas; Spas
Prin: Richard Marriott
Genl Mgr: Susan Belleville
Genl Mgr: Ken Schwatz
QA Dir: Stephen Kowalski

D-U-N-S 62-735-2573 IMP
JW MILLWORK LLC
(*Suby of* JIM WHITE GROUP, INC.)
1701 Porter St Sw Ste 1c, Wyoming, MI 49519-1770
Tel (616) 252-1332 *Founded/Ownrshp* 2005
Sales 70.0MM *EMP* 16
SIC 2431 Millwork; Millwork

D-U-N-S 00-538-4756
JW POWERLINE
(*Suby of* ENERGY SERVICES HOLDINGS LLC) ★
700 S Fairgrounds Rd, Midland, TX 79701-1240
Tel (432) 684-4388 *Founded/Ownrshp* 2013
Sales 60.0MM *EMP* 250
SIC 7539 Electrical services
Pr: Jimmy Webb
Pr: Kyle Watkins
VP: Justin Burris

D-U-N-S 83-099-1886 IMP
JW SIEG & CO INC
1180 Seminole Trl Ste 290, Charlottesville, VA 22901-5713
Tel (434) 244-5300 *Founded/Ownrshp* 2007
Sales 32.5MM *EMP* 25
SIC 5921 Wine; Wine
CEO: Terry Sieg
**Pr:* Walter Smith Williams

J.W. TERRILL
See BRADY I INC

JW TERRILL
See BRADY BS INC

D-U-N-S 04-716-9503 IMP
■ **JW WILLIAMS INC**
(*Suby of* FLINT ENERGY SERVICES INC) ★
2139 W Renauna Ave, Casper, WY 82601
Tel (281) 304-5600 *Founded/Ownrshp* 2013
Sales 100.0MM^E *EMP* 350
SIC 3533 3443 3547 1761 3291 Gas field machinery & equipment; Oil field machinery & equipment; Vessels, process or storage (from boiler shops): metal plate; Heat exchangers, plate type; Structural mills (rolling mill equipment); Sheet metalwork; Abrasive metal & steel products; Gas field machinery & equipment; Oil field machinery & equipment; Vessels, process or storage (from boiler shops): metal plate; Heat exchangers, plate type; Structural mills (rolling mill equipment); Sheet metalwork; Abrasive metal & steel products
Pr: Steve Russom
**CFO:* Paul Boechler
**Treas:* Lynn Warden
Sls Mgr: Pat Keefe
Sales Asso: Brendon Lusk

D-U-N-S 12-632-0324
JWC CONSTRUCTION INC
JON WAYNE CONSTRUCTION
2580 Fortune Way, Vista, CA 92081-8441
Tel (760) 727-2494 *Founded/Ownrshp* 1982
Sales 23.4MM^E *EMP* 100
SIC 1522 1521 Residential construction; New construction, single-family houses
CEO: Jon Wayne

D-U-N-S 61-059-2388 IMP
JWC ENVIRONMENTAL LLC
DISPOSABLE WASTE SYSTEMS
(*Suby of* WESTWIND EQUITY INVESTORS) ★
290 Paularino Ave, Costa Mesa, CA 92626-3314
Tel (949) 833-3888 *Founded/Ownrshp* 2011
Sales 62.8MM^E *EMP* 150
SIC 5084 Industrial machinery & equipment; Industrial machinery & equipment
CEO: Ronald Duecker
VP: Greg Queen
**Prin:* Steve Glomb
**Prin:* Marsha Robinson
Software D: Andrew Maxie
Sfty Mgr: Vincent Quintana
Sales Exec: Pete Garcia
Mktg Dir: Dave Barkey

D-U-N-S 09-305-9533
JWCH INSTITUTE INC
5650 Jillson St, Commerce, CA 90040-1482
Tel (323) 477-1171 *Founded/Ownrshp* 1960
Sales 25.1MM^E *EMP* 240
Accts Simpson Cpas Los Angeles Ca
SIC 8621 8733 Health association; Medical research; Health association; Medical research
CEO: Alvaro Ballesteros
COO: Eduardo Gonzalez
CFO: Jeanni Lam
Sr VP: Jerry Santo
Chf Nrs Of: Jeny Argame
QA Dir: Daniel Rocha
Pgrm Dir: Jill Rotenberg

D-U-N-S 16-114-7608 IMP
JWD GROUP INC
300 Colvin Woods Pkwy, Tonawanda, NY 14150-6976
Tel (716) 832-1940 *Founded/Ownrshp* 1985
Sales 172.6MM *EMP* 450
SIC 1711 1629 1623 Mechanical contractor; Warm air heating & air conditioning contractor; Fire sprinkler system installation; Waste water & sewage treatment plant construction; Pipeline construction; Mechanical contractor; Warm air heating & air conditioning contractor; Fire sprinkler system installation; Waste water & sewage treatment plant construction; Pipeline construction
Ch Bd: Kevin Reilly
Sec: Mary Everhart
**Ex VP:* Nickolas Optis
**Ex VP:* Patrick Reilly
**VP:* Patrick Mc Parlane
**VP:* John Samar
**VP:* Gerald Wilson

JWF INDUSTRIES
See JOHNSTOWN WELDING AND FABRICATION INC

D-U-N-S 02-627-8992
JWH EQUIPMENT LLC (MS)
1101 Highway 80 W, Jackson, MS 39204-3919
Tel (601) 974-8090 *Founded/Ownrshp* 2011
Sales 25.0MM *EMP* 15
SIC 5084 Industrial machinery & equipment; Industrial machinery & equipment
Mng Pt: Justin Loftin
**Owner:* Joey Hayles

D-U-N-S 18-797-4431
JWK ENTERPRISES INC
KELLEY'S COUNTRY COOKIN'
4604 Gulf Fwy, La Marque, TX 77568-3508
Tel (409) 935-3131 *Founded/Ownrshp* 1983
Sales 8.1MM^E *EMP* 300
SIC 5812 American restaurant; American restaurant
Pr: Robby K Kelley Sr
**CEO:* Betty Kelley

D-U-N-S 60-557-3740
JWMCC LIMITED PARTNERSHIP
HYATT HOTEL
2151 Avenue Of The Stars, Los Angeles, CA 90067-5004
Tel (310) 277-1234 *Founded/Ownrshp* 1987
Sales 5.6MM^E *EMP* 353
SIC 7011 5812 Hotels & motels; Eating places; Hotels & motels; Eating places
Genl Mgr: Ulrich Samietz
Dir Soc: Jay Cosico
Pr Dir: Adrienne Vore

D-U-N-S 19-743-2276
JWS DISTRIBUTING LLC
155 Brozzini Ct, Greenville, SC 29615-5340
Tel (864) 213-5494 *Founded/Ownrshp* 2012
Sales 51.1MM *EMP* 11
Accts Dixon Hughes Goodman Llp Gre
SIC 5031 Building materials, exterior; Building materials, exterior

JWT DIRECT DIV
See J WALTER THOMPSON USA LLC

D-U-N-S 19-357-7418
JX ENTERPRISES INC
1320 Walnut Ridge Dr, Hartland, WI 53029-8311
Tel (800) 810-3410 *Founded/Ownrshp* 2000
Sales 178.8MM^E *EMP* 500^E
SIC 5012 5511 7538 6159 7513 Trucks, commercial; Trucks, tractors & trailers: new & used; General truck repair; Truck finance leasing; Truck leasing, without drivers; Trucks, commercial; Trucks, tractors & trailers: new & used; General truck repair; Truck finance leasing; Truck leasing, without drivers
Pr: Eric K Jorgensen
**CFO:* Mark Muskevitsch
Bd of Dir: Kevin Whitehill
VP: John Bidochka
**VP:* Kurt Jorgensen
**Prin:* Kenton H Kuhlman
Genl Mgr: Larry Raspor
Off Mgr: Pam Vopravil
VP Opers: Randy Buening
Opers Mgr: Alan Purath
Sales Exec: James Ambrosius

D-U-N-S 62-514-1825 IMP/EXP
JX NIPPON CHEMICAL TEXAS INC
NCTI
(*Suby of* JX NIPPON OIL & ENERGY CORPORATION)
10500 Bay Area Blvd, Pasadena, TX 77507-1722
Tel (713) 754-1000 *Founded/Ownrshp* 2009
Sales 77.2MM^E *EMP* 94
SIC 2911 2899 Petroleum refining; Solvents; Chemical preparations
Ch Bd: Haruo Nakano
**CEO:* Hajime Kado
**CFO:* Shin Matsumoto
**VP:* Aubrey Cannon
**VP:* Webster Draughan
IT Man: D Johnson
Opers Mgr: Dave Burch
Sls Mgr: Brad Costello

D-U-N-S 04-360-0840 IMP
JX NIPPON OIL & ENERGY USA INC
ENEOS
(*Suby of* JX NIPPON OIL & ENERGY CORPORATION)
20 N Martingale Rd # 300, Schaumburg, IL 60173-2425
Tel (847) 413-2188 *Founded/Ownrshp* 1960
Sales 126.0MM *EMP* 70
SIC 5172 Petroleum products
Pr: Satoru Uchida
**Treas:* Shinichi Nakaya
VP: Gary Steele
**VP:* Thomas Takahashi
**Prin:* Motoshi Sunami

D-U-N-S 10-094-7618
JYCO INTERNATIONAL INC
JYCO SEALING TECHNOLOGIES
955 W Eisenhower Cir G, Ann Arbor, MI 48103-5868
Tel (734) 663-9000 *Founded/Ownrshp* 2001
Sales NA *EMP* 350
SIC 5531

JYCO SEALING TECHNOLOGIES
See JYCO INTERNATIONAL INC

K

D-U-N-S 13-328-1303
K & C LLC
HEAVENER NURSING CENTER
204 W 1st St, Heavener, OK 74937-2062
Tel (918) 653-2464 *Founded/Ownrshp* 1997
Sales 142.8MM *EMP* 30
SIC 8059 Nursing home, except skilled & intermediate care facility; Nursing home, except skilled & intermediate care facility

D-U-N-S 05-477-3895
K & E EXCAVATING INC (OR)
3871 Langley St Se, Salem, OR 97317-9322
Tel (503) 399-4833 *Founded/Ownrshp* 1998
Sales 71.2MM^E *EMP* 200
SIC 1794 Excavation work; Excavation work
Pr: Kerry Kuenzi
**VP:* Eric Kuenzi
Snr Mgr: John Kuenzi

K & G CONOCO
See K & G STORES INC

D-U-N-S 01-334-5095
K & G ELECTRIC MOTOR & PUMP CORP
KG POWER SYSTEMS
150 Laser Ct, Hauppauge, NY 11788-3912
Tel (631) 342-1171 *Founded/Ownrshp* 1949
Sales 46.2MM^E *EMP* 28
Accts Gabriel & Sciacca Syosset Ny
SIC 5063 5084 5999 5251 5722 7629 Motors, electric; Compressors, except air conditioning; Pumps & pumping equipment; Fans, industrial; Motors, electric; Pumps & pumping equipment; Fans, electric; Electrical repair shops
Ch Bd: John Gandolfo
Area Mgr: Angelo Lambros
Area Mgr: Gene McKenna

D-U-N-S 61-157-1485
K & G PETROLEUM LLC
10459 Park Meadows Dr # 101, Lone Tree, CO 80124-5305
Tel (303) 792-9467 *Founded/Ownrshp* 2002
Sales 94.6MM^E *EMP* 300^E
SIC 5541 Gasoline service stations; Gasoline service stations
Snr Mgr: Bob Claar

D-U-N-S 83-902-0674
K & G STORES INC
K & G CONOCO
9777 S Yosemite St # 120, Littleton, CO 80124-3191
Tel (303) 792-9467 *Founded/Ownrshp* 1995
Sales 22.9MM^E *EMP* 220
SIC 5411 Convenience stores, chain; Convenience stores, chain
Pr: Baljit Nanda
**VP:* Preet Singh
Dist Mgr: Ravi Singh
VP Mktg: Michael Haynes

K & H CO-OP OIL CO
See K & H COOPERATIVE OIL CO INC

K & H CONTAINERS DIV
See K&H GROUP INC

D-U-N-S 02-237-4813
K & H COOPERATIVE OIL CO INC
K & H CO-OP OIL CO
302 Main St W, Wesley, IA 50483-7759
Tel (515) 679-4212 *Founded/Ownrshp* 1930
Sales 23.6MM *EMP* 48
SIC 5172 5541 5984 Petroleum products; Gasoline service stations; Liquefied petroleum gas dealers; Petroleum products; Gasoline service stations; Liquefied petroleum gas dealers
Pr: Reuben Skow

K & I LUMBER CO
See KENTUCKY-INDIANA LUMBER CO INC

K & K
See KK ENTERPRISES INC

K & K CONSTRUCTION
See KENYON CONSTRUCTION INC

K & K DISTRIBUTORS
See KOMATSU ENTERPRISES INC

D-U-N-S 17-441-5810 IMP/EXP
K & K EXPRESS LLC
K2 LOGISTICS
2980 Commers Dr Ste 100, Eagan, MN 55121-2370
Tel (651) 209-8771 *Founded/Ownrshp* 2000
Sales 28.0MM^E *EMP* 45
SIC 4731 4212 4213

D-U-N-S 87-306-4745
K & K FAST FOODS INC
CHECKERS DRIVE-IN RESTAURANT
15434 New Hampshire Ave, Silver Spring, MD 20905-4163
Tel (301) 325-2759 *Founded/Ownrshp* 1992
Sales 8.7MM^E *EMP* 400
SIC 5812 Drive-in restaurant; Drive-in restaurant
Pr: Dana Keith
**Ch:* Stefan Keuhnert

D-U-N-S 07-357-7350
K & K FRAMERS LLC
5795 Rogers St Ste A, Las Vegas, NV 89118-3017
Tel (702) 873-6238 *Founded/Ownrshp* 1995
Sales 11.9MM^E *EMP* 300
SIC 1521 Single-family housing construction; Single-family housing construction
Sr VP: Matthew Pallotta
Prgrm Mgr: Kenneth Ochs

D-U-N-S 05-250-5914 EXP
K & K INDUSTRIES INC
8518 E 550 N, Montgomery, IN 47558-5073
Tel (812) 486-3281 *Founded/Ownrshp* 1972
Sales 30.4MM^E *EMP* 100
SIC 2439 Trusses, wooden roof
VP: Jerry Stoll
**Sec:* Bonnita Knepp

D-U-N-S 07-429-9512
K & K INSURANCE GROUP INC
(*Suby of* K & K INSURANCE SPECIALTIES INC) ★
1712 Magnavox Way, Fort Wayne, IN 46804-1557
Tel (260) 459-5000 *Founded/Ownrshp* 1984
Sales NA *EMP* 325
SIC 6411 6331 Property & casualty insurance agent; Fire, marine & casualty insurance; Property & casualty insurance agent; Fire, marine & casualty insurance
Pr: Stephen L Lunsford
**COO:* Todd Bixler
COO: Lisa Stephens
**CFO:* Jerry Montero
**Treas:* Paul A Hagy
Sr VP: Matthew Sackett
**VP:* Ram Padmanabhan
VP: Mike Woodward
Site Mgr: Joe Dowling
Sls Dir: Sheila Morton
Counsel: Kate Brogan

D-U-N-S 36-185-3302
K & K INSURANCE SPECIALTIES INC
(*Suby of* A O N) ★
1712 Magnavox Way, Fort Wayne, IN 46804-1557
Tel (260) 459-5000 *Founded/Ownrshp* 1993
Sales NA *EMP* 651
SIC 6331 6411 Fire, marine & casualty insurance; Insurance agents; Fire, marine & casualty insurance; Insurance agents
Pr: Stephan Lunsford
CFO: Jerry Montaro
**VP:* Todd Bixler
**VP:* Jerry Tegan

D-U-N-S 00-619-5965 IMP/EXP
K & K INTERIORS INC (OH)
2230 Superior St, Sandusky, OH 44870-1843
Tel (419) 627-0039 *Founded/Ownrshp* 1996
Sales 25.4MM^E *EMP* 53
SIC 5092 Arts & crafts equipment & supplies
Pr: Kyle Camp
**VP:* Mark Wall
Natl Sales: Angela Roberts

D-U-N-S 08-906-8829
K & K IRON WORKS LLC
5100 Lawndale Ave Ste 7, Mc Cook, IL 60525-3311
Tel (708) 924-0000 *Founded/Ownrshp* 2011
Sales 24.9MM^E *EMP* 90^E
SIC 3441 3446 Fabricated structural metal; Stairs, staircases, stair treads: prefabricated metal; Railings, prefabricated metal; Fabricated structural metal; Stairs, staircases, stair treads: prefabricated metal; Railings, prefabricated metal
Pr: Bob Sullivan
CFO: Clark Roemmich

K & K METAL RECYCLING
See KIRSCHBAUM-KRUPP METAL RECYCLING LLC

D-U-N-S 18-700-7372 IMP
K & K VETERINARY SUPPLY INC
675 Laura Ln, Tontitown, AR 72770
Tel (479) 361-1516 *Founded/Ownrshp* 1987
Sales 54.4MM^E *EMP* 96
SIC 5199 5191 5072 Pet supplies; Farm supplies; Seeds & bulbs; Power tools & accessories; Pet supplies; Farm supplies; Seeds & bulbs; Power tools & accessories
Pr: John K Lipsmeyer
**VP:* Melissa S Lipsmeyer
Dir Bus: Duke Hrabe

K & L
See K&L FREIGHT MANAGMENT INC

K & L BEVERAGE CO
See K AND L DISTRIBUTORS INC

D-U-N-S 02-214-5601
K & L ELECTRICAL INC
2300 Kerper Blvd, Dubuque, IA 52001-2220
Tel (563) 588-1469 *Founded/Ownrshp* 1992
Sales 21.6MM^E *EMP* 27
SIC 5063 Electrical supplies
Pr: Kevin Oyen
VP: Bruce Hallahan
**VP:* Lynn Oyen
VP: Dean Tucker
Brnch Mgr: Bud Mielkey
IT Man: Patty Kirschbaum
Sls Mgr: Mike Martin
Sales Asso: Mike Rabbett

D-U-N-S 80-695-1091
K & L FIELD MARKETING LLC
22 W 19th St Lbby, New York, NY 10011-4204
Tel (212) 627-4101 *Founded/Ownrshp* 2005
Sales 24.3MM^E *EMP* 725
SIC 8732 Market analysis or research; Market analysis or research

D-U-N-S 06-792-2831
K & M DISTRIBUTING CO INC (MO)
PREMIUM BEVERAGE SALES
2855 S Austin Ave, Springfield, MO 65807-4164
Tel (417) 887-0454 *Founded/Ownrshp* 1966, 1973
Sales 32.0MM^E *EMP* 55
SIC 5181 5149 Beer & other fermented malt liquors; Soft drinks
Pr: Richard E Gelner
**VP:* Brian Gelner
VP: Mark Gelner
Genl Mgr: Marc Kiser

D-U-N-S 05-854-7746 EXP
K & M ELECTRIC SUPPLY INC
7641 Central Indus Dr, Riviera Beach, FL 33404-3487
Tel (561) 842-4911 *Founded/Ownrshp* 1972
Sales 59.1MM^E *EMP* 60
SIC 5063 Wire & cable; Wire & cable
Pr: William K Mooney

*Pr: Derrick E Hoskins
*CFO: Jeff Galler
VP: John Bryant
*VP: Philip McCracken
*VP: Ronald Stewart

D-U-N-S 08-925-0799 IMP
K & M INTERNATIONAL INC
WILD REPUBLIC
1955 Midway Dr Ste A, Twinsburg, OH 44087-1961
Tel (330) 425-2550 Founded/Ownrshp 1979
Sales 26.9MM^E EMP 100^E
SIC 5092 3944 5199 Toys & games; Games, toys & children's vehicles; Gifts & novelties; Bags, baskets & cases; Art goods;Toys & games; Games, toys & children's vehicles; Gifts & novelties; Bags, baskets & cases; Art goods
Pr: Gopala B Pillai
COO: Joe Onderko
CFO: Dan Davies
*CFO: Daniel Davis
*VP: Kamala Pillai
Mktg Dir: Craig Hopp
Manager: Bob Lutz
Sls Mgr: Steven Harper
Sls Mgr: Sharon Spores

D-U-N-S 00-516-7754 IMP
K & M MACHINE-FABRICATING INC (MI)
20745 M 60, Cassopolis, MI 49031-9431
Tel (269) 445-2495 Founded/Ownrshp 1951, 1984
Sales 48.6MM^E EMP 250
SIC 3599 Custom machinery; Custom machinery
Pr: Michael Mc Loughlin
VP: Kevin McLoughlin
IT Man: Charles Hooper
Sfty Mgr: Emily McLoughlin
Opers Mgr: Carl Thomas
Plnt Mgr: Justin Moore

K & M MANUFACTURING CO.
See GREAT NORTHERN EQUIPMENT DISTRIBUTING INC

K & M MEAT CO
See K & M PACKING CO INC

D-U-N-S 06-586-8903
K & M NORTHFIELD DODGE INC (MI)
4100 Plainfield Ave Ne, Grand Rapids, MI 49525-1682
Tel (616) 365-3303 Founded/Ownrshp 1960, 1974
Sales 56.2MM^E EMP 130
SIC 5511 7538 7532 5531 Automobiles, new & used; Pickups, new & used; Vans, new & used; General automotive repair shops; Top & body repair & paint shops; Automotive & home supply stores; Automobiles, new & used; Pickups, new & used; Vans, new & used; General automotive repair shops; Top & body repair & paint shops; Automotive & home supply stores
Pr: Henry Makarewicz
Exec: Kim Lamagoon
Store Mgr: Darin Johnson
Store Mgr: Sam Kaltak
Store Mgr: Chris Pitts
IT Man: Drew Dykstra
Mktg Mgr: Beckie Orszula
Sls Mgr: Jim Fouts
Sls Mgr: Paul Vredevelt

D-U-N-S 09-899-6242
K & M PACKING CO INC
K & M MEAT CO
2443 E 27th St, Vernon, CA 90058-1219
Tel (323) 585-5318 Founded/Ownrshp 1977
Sales 20.9MM^E EMP 150
SIC 2011 Meat packing plants; Meat packing plants
Pr: Felix Goldberg

D-U-N-S 06-862-3214
K & M PRINTING CO INC
SPOTLIGHT GRAPHICS
1410 N Meacham Rd Frnt, Schaumburg, IL 60173-4845
Tel (847) 884-1100 Founded/Ownrshp 1976
Sales 24.6MM^E EMP 95
SIC 2752 2791 2789 Commercial printing, offset; Typesetting; Bookbinding & related work; Commercial printing, offset; Typesetting; Bookbinding & related work
Pr: Ken J Stobart
*VP: Michael Stobart
Prd Mgr: Chris Kelly
Prd Mgr: Gary Kinsman

K & M TIRE COMPANY
See TRI-JAY TIRE DISTRIBUTORS INC

D-U-N-S 05-162-9467 IMP
K & M TIRE INC
965 Spencerville Rd, Delphos, OH 45833-2351
Tel (419) 695-1061 Founded/Ownrshp 1977
Sales 308.0MM EMP 500
Accts Hellman Nomina Cpa Delphos O
SIC 5014 7538 5531 Tires & tubes; General automotive repair shops; Automotive tires; Tires & tubes; General automotive repair shops; Automotive tires
Pr: Ken Langhals
*VP: Cheryl Gossard
*VP: Paul Zurcher
Dir IT: Jason Baker
Opers Mgr: Jennifer Erhart
Manager: Jay Goring
Sls Mgr: Mark Knippen
Sales Asso: Ryan Walden

D-U-N-S 03-047-6894
K & M TRUCKING INC
1201 E 40th St, Lubbock, TX 79404-3015
Tel (806) 747-7071 Founded/Ownrshp 1998
Sales 28.8MM^E EMP 200
SIC 4213 Trucking, except local; Trucking, except local
CEO: James C Shankle
*Owner: Terri Shankle
*Pr: Joe G Heath

D-U-N-S 02-750-8670 IMP
K & N ELECTRIC MOTORS INC
415 N Fancher Rd, Spokane Valley, WA 99212-1059
Tel (509) 838-8000 Founded/Ownrshp 1975
Sales 49.9MM^E EMP 70^E
SIC 5063 7694 5999 3621 Electrical apparatus & equipment; Electric motor repair; Motors, electric; Motors & generators; Electrical apparatus & equipment; Electric motor repair; Motors, electric; Motors & generators
Pr: Gerald Schmidlkofer
*Pr: Janet Schmidlkofer
*Treas: Bob Schmidlkofer
*Sec: Robert J Schmidlkofer
Ofcr: Ross Parrish
*VP: John Schmidlkofer
IT Man: Alex Raske
Ql Cn Mgr: Jeff Williams

D-U-N-S 04-659-2424 IMP
K & N ENGINEERING INC
1455 Citrus St, Riverside, CA 92507-1603
Tel (951) 826-4000 Founded/Ownrshp 2011
Sales 128.5MM^E EMP 580
SIC 3751 3599 3714 Handle bars, motorcycle & bicycle; Air intake filters, internal combustion engine, except auto; Filters: oil, fuel & air, motor vehicle; Handle bars, motorcycle & bicycle; Air intake filters, internal combustion engine, except auto; Filters: oil, fuel & air, motor vehicle
Ch: Jerry E Mall
*CEO: Steven J Rogers
Prd Mgr: Jere Wall
Natl Sales: Tim Inglee
Sls&Mrk Ex: Bob Donovan
Mktg Mgr: Lucio Tapia
Snr PM: Kevin McClelland
Snr Mgr: Dave Martis

D-U-N-S 87-713-5632
K & N MANAGEMENT INC
RUDY'S COUNTRY STR & BAR-B-QUE
11570 Research Blvd, Austin, TX 78759-4036
Tel (512) 418-0444 Founded/Ownrshp 1993
Sales 70.1MM^E EMP 450
SIC 5411 5812 Convenience stores, independent; Barbecue restaurant; Convenience stores, independent; Barbecue restaurant
Pr: Thomas K Schiller
Mng Pt: Dan Peabody
*VP: Brian K Nolan

K & R EXCAVATING
See KAMMINGA & ROODVOETS INC

D-U-N-S 01-907-0283
■ **K & R HOLDINGS INC**
PARADIGM SOLUTIONS
(Suby of BEACON ROOFING SUPPLY INC) ★
400 Warren Ave, Portland, ME 04103-1109
Tel (207) 797-7950 Founded/Ownrshp 2014
Sales 95.4MM^E EMP 135
SIC 5033 3089 Siding, except wood; Insulation, thermal; Roofing, asphalt & sheet metal; Doors, folding: plastic or plastic coated fabric; Windows, plastic; Siding, except wood; Insulation, thermal; Roofing, asphalt & sheet metal; Doors, folding: plastic or plastic coated fabric; Windows, plastic
Pr: Scott Koocher
*Sec: Richard Robinov
*Prin: Jerry Robinov
Brnch Mgr: Tom Leighton
IT Man: Denise Dube
Opers Mgr: Todd Cray
Mktg Dir: Tony Eldridge
Mktg Dir: Brian Mills
Sales Asso: Aaron Frigon

K & R TRUCK SALES AND SERVICE
See K & R TRUCK SALES INC

D-U-N-S 80-802-5332
K & R TRUCK SALES INC
K & R TRUCK SALES AND SERVICE
840 Interchange Dr, Holland, MI 49423-8513
Tel (616) 546-2487 Founded/Ownrshp 1992
Sales 27.2MM^E EMP 50
SIC 5599 7538 5521 7549 5511 Utility trailers; General truck repair; Trucks, tractors & trailers: used; Towing services; Pickups, new & used
Pr: Edwin Rietman
Genl Mgr: Brian Arens
Advt Dir: Robb Lubbers
Snr Mgr: Bob Razenberg

D-U-N-S 02-964-7427
K & S AIR CONDITIONING INC
K&S
143 E Meats Ave, Orange, CA 92865-3309
Tel (714) 685-0077 Founded/Ownrshp 1976
Sales 23.5MM EMP 140
Accts Ernest G Vining Cpa Rancho
SIC 1711 Warm air heating & air conditioning contractor; Warm air heating & air conditioning contractor
Pr: Steven Patz
*VP: Renee Patz
Genl Mgr: Kevin Patz

D-U-N-S 55-623-2382
K & S GROUP INC
18601 Lyndn B Jhnsn 420, Mesquite, TX 75150-6439
Tel (214) 234-8871 Founded/Ownrshp 2005
Sales NA EMP 5
SIC 6411 Insurance agents, brokers & service; Insurance agents, brokers & service
Pr: Richard Daiker
Div Mgr: Peggy Hogan
Div Mgr: Steve Rickenbacher
S&M/VP: Sophie Kheang

D-U-N-S 05-700-7502
K & S PROPERTY INC
CUMMINS BRIDGEWAY
21810 Clessie Ct, New Hudson, MI 48165-8573
Tel (248) 573-1600 Founded/Ownrshp 1971
Sales 110.0MM EMP 630
SIC 5084 Engines & parts, diesel; Engines & parts, diesel
Pr: Gregory Boll
CFO: Ken Clark

D-U-N-S 01-737-7136
K & W CAFETERIAS INC
1391 Plaza West Dr, Winston Salem, NC 27103-1440
Tel (336) 852-1661 Founded/Ownrshp 1981
Sales 112.7MM^E EMP 2,940
SIC 5812 Cafeteria; Cafeteria
CEO: Donald C Allred
*Pr: Dax Allred
Pr: Jeffrey Loken
*Pr: Jimmy Sizemore
*Treas: R Leo Sasaki
*Ex VP: Todd Smith
Exec: Robert Walker
Genl Mgr: Richard Corbett
Genl Mgr: Bobby Eaton
Dir IT: Tom Hutchen
Sls Dir: Russell Sizemore

D-U-N-S 80-362-7710
K & W MOTORS INC
BROWN'S TOYOTA-CHRYSLER
1357 Richmond Rd, Charlottesville, VA 22911-3517
Tel (434) 977-3380 Founded/Ownrshp 1993
Sales 29.2MM^E EMP 100
SIC 5511 Automobiles, new & used; Automobiles, new & used
Pr: Kenneth Brown

D-U-N-S 00-340-2229 IMP
K & W TIRE CO INC (PA)
735 N Prince St, Lancaster, PA 17603-2793
Tel (717) 397-3596 Founded/Ownrshp 1951, 1969
Sales 92.0MM^E EMP 180
SIC 5014 5531 Automobile tires & tubes; Truck tires & tubes; Automotive tires; Automobile tires & tubes; Truck tires & tubes; Automotive tires
Pr: Kenneth E Kline
*Ch Bd: Richard J Kline
*Treas: Robert T Nave
*VP: Jeffrey A Hood
Brnch Mgr: Gordon Knapp
Dir IT: Tim Krauter

D-U-N-S 07-545-5717
K + S SERVICES INC
15677 Noecker Way, Southgate, MI 48195-2272
Tel (734) 374-0400 Founded/Ownrshp 1993
Sales 53.0MM EMP 250
SIC 7699 Professional instrument repair services; Professional instrument repair services
Pr: Kenneth W Kirchner
*VP: Joseph Didomenico
Rgnl Mgr: Jason Ballard
Rgnl Mgr: Wes Faistenhammer
Rgnl Mgr: John Fogarty
Rgnl Mgr: Cathy Kunak
Rgnl Mgr: Charles Miller
Rgnl Mgr: Ashley Mills
Area Mgr: Rick Niesyto
Div Mgr: Brian Roe
Tech Mgr: Jerry Guido

D-U-N-S 04-160-2160 IMP
K - O - I WAREHOUSE INC
K O I AUTO PARTS
(Suby of K O I) ★
2701 Spring Grove Ave, Cincinnati, OH 45225-2221
Tel (513) 357-2400 Founded/Ownrshp 1966
Sales 71.2MM^E EMP 147
SIC 5013 Automotive supplies & parts; Automotive supplies & parts
Pr: David Wesselman
*CFO: Tom Frank
*Sec: Mary Riesenbeck

K A
See KRAUS-ANDERSON CONSTRUCTION CO

K A P C O
See KENT ADHESIVE PRODUCTS CO

K AND K OIL COMPANY
See PAHWA POOMAN

D-U-N-S 02-744-3043 IMP/EXP
K AND L DISTRIBUTORS INC (WA)
K & L BEVERAGE CO
3215 Lind Ave Sw, Renton, WA 98057-3320
Tel (206) 454-8800 Founded/Ownrshp 1942
Sales 112.6MM^E EMP 400
SIC 5182

D-U-N-S 04-121-1934
K AND S OWL INC
OWL HOMECARE PHARMACY
13851 Garvey Ave Ste A, Baldwin Park, CA 91706-4914
Tel (626) 960-0646 Founded/Ownrshp 1998
Sales 24.0MM EMP 140
SIC 5912 Drug stores; Drug stores
CEO: Peter Kaldas
*Pr: Maher Kaldas
*CFO: Albert Soliman

K B
See KNOCHEL BROS INC

D-U-N-S 10-732-9484 IMP/EXP
K B & ASSOCIATES INC
11060 Winfield Rd, Winfield, WV 25213-7934
Tel (304) 586-2863 Founded/Ownrshp 1983
Sales 35.6MM^E EMP 285
SIC 5712 Mattresses; Beds & accessories; Mattresses; Beds & accessories
Pr: Kimberly A Brown-Knopf
CFO: Nathan McBrayer

D-U-N-S 05-779-7896
K B DAVIS INC
DAVIS CADILLAC
5433 Poplar Ave, Memphis, TN 38119-3634
Tel (901) 761-1900 Founded/Ownrshp 1970
Sales 26.8MM^E EMP 200
SIC 5511 Automobiles, new & used; Automobiles, new & used
Pr: Kindle B Davis
*Sec: Gary Davis

K B H CONSTRUCTION
See POWER AND CONSTRUCTION GROUP INC

D-U-N-S 15-366-4255
K B H INC
SOUTHWEST INDUSTRIAL RIGGING
2802 W Palm Ln, Phoenix, AZ 85009-2507
Tel (602) 256-7161 Founded/Ownrshp 1985
Sales 31.8MM EMP 200
SIC 7353 4213 7299 Cranes & aerial lift equipment, rental or leasing; Heavy machinery transport; Personal item care & storage services; Cranes & aerial lift equipment, rental or leasing; Heavy machinery transport; Personal item care & storage services
Pr: Harry K Baker
*Treas: Jim Wilson
*VP: Scott Miller

K B I
See KINSBURSKY BROS SUPPLY INC

K B I
See KENS BEVERAGE INC

K B I
See KYKLOS BEARING INTERNATIONAL LLC

K B I BIOPHARMA
See KBI BIOPHARMA INC

D-U-N-S 02-929-3172 IMP/EXP
K B M OFFICE EQUIPMENT INC
K B M WORKSPACE
160 W Santa Clara St, San Jose, CA 95113-1701
Tel (408) 351-7100 Founded/Ownrshp 2007
Sales 22.8MM^E EMP 25
SIC 5021 7389 Office & public building furniture; Interior design services
Pr: Stan Vuckovich
*VP: Mark Dailey
*VP: Anne Johnson
Genl Mgr: Shanna Dollarhide

K B M WORKSPACE
See K B M OFFICE EQUIPMENT INC

D-U-N-S 07-492-5967
K B OF BALTIMORE INC
BURGER KING
1937 Greenspring Dr, Lutherville Timonium, MD 21093-4113
Tel (410) 561-3100 Founded/Ownrshp 1975
Sales 21.9MM^E EMP 600
SIC 5812 Fast-food restaurant, chain; Fast-food restaurant, chain
Pr: Philip Hoag
*Treas: Robert Windsor

K B OIL
See KEN BETTRIDGE DISTRIBUTING INC

K B R
See KBR HOLDINGS LLC

K B R
See KELLOGG BROWN & ROOT SERVICES INC

K B R SERVICES
See KELLOGG BROWN & ROOT LLC

D-U-N-S 07-773-0034
K B RECYCLING INC
1600 Se 4th Ave Ste C, Canby, OR 97013-4365
Tel (503) 266-7903 Founded/Ownrshp 1979
Sales 35.2MM^E EMP 150
SIC 4953 Recycling, waste materials; Recycling, waste materials
Pr: Fred A Kahut

K B S
See KBS CONSTRUCTION INC

K B S
See PLUMBERS SUPPLY CO OF ST LOUIS

D-U-N-S 08-498-8906
K BANK
11407 Cronhill Dr Ste N, Owings Mills, MD 21117-6218
Tel (443) 271-6491 Founded/Ownrshp 1992
Sales NA EMP 217
SIC 6029 Commercial banks
Pr: David H Wells Jr
COO: W Benton Knight
CFO: David Berman
Ofcr: Sara Gilgenbach
Ofcr: Quinten McCorvey
Assoc VP: Eli Akel
Assoc VP: Mark Fowler
Assoc VP: Charlie Shoop
Sr VP: Kirk Albert
Sr VP: Mark Delucca
Sr VP: Rich Foley
Sr VP: Randy Foster
Sr VP: Curtis Hollis
Sr VP: Kevin McDonald
Sr VP: Mitch Robinson
Sr VP: Jack Slocum
Sr VP: Pat Tamblyn
Sr VP: George Wachter
VP: Henry Alonso
VP: Janet Beach
VP: Tom Borzell

D-U-N-S 04-813-4241
K BARNETT & SONS INC
2405 W 7th St, Clovis, NM 88101-9691
Tel (575) 762-4407 Founded/Ownrshp 1959
Sales 21.8MM^E EMP 100
SIC 1611 Highway & street paving contractor
Pr: Kenneth Barnett
*VP: Jereme Barnett
*VP: Jackie Freeman

K C A
See KCA ELECTRONICS INC

D-U-N-S 11-595-9116
K C A CORP
1831 Peartree Ln, Hopkinsville, KY 42240-4460
Tel (270) 886-5551 *Founded/Ownrshp* 1983
Sales 9.0MM *EMP* 480
SIC 5812 Contract food services; Contract food services
Pr: Kyong Cha Anderson
**VP:* Frederick Anderson
Genl Mgr: Thomas Neville

K C C
See CARSON KURTZMAN CONSULTANTS LLC

K C D C
See KNOXVILLES COMMUNITY DEVELOPMENT CORP

D-U-N-S 00-279-3131
K C ELECTRIC ASSOCIATION
422 3rd Ave, Hugo, CO 80821
Tel (719) 743-2431 *Founded/Ownrshp* 1946
Sales 24.8MM *EMP* 29
SIC 4911 Distribution, electric power; Distribution, electric power
Pr: Kevin Penny
VP: Robert Bledsoe
Genl Mgr: Timothy Power
Opers Mgr: J Huppert

K C FOOD
See KWIK CHEK FOOD STORES INC

K C G
See KNOWLEDGE CONSULTING GROUP INC

K C I
See KCI TECHNOLOGIES INC

K C I
See KCI USA INC

K C I
See KCI HOLDINGS INC

D-U-N-S 18-182-9615
K C OIL INC
TRI STAR MEPERTON GAS CO
230 Us Highway 130, Bordentown, NJ 08505-2112
Tel (609) 298-0200 *Founded/Ownrshp* 1986
Sales 30.0MM *EMP* 25
SIC 5983 5541 Fuel oil dealers; Filling stations, gasoline
Pr: Jan Creighton

K C P
See KIRTLAND CAPITAL PARTNERS LP

D-U-N-S 17-445-0460 IMP
K C PHARMACEUTICALS INC
3201 Producer Way, Pomona, CA 91768-3916
Tel (909) 598-9499 *Founded/Ownrshp* 1987
Sales 25.5MM^E *EMP* 93^E
SIC 2834 Solutions, pharmaceutical; Cough medicines; Cold remedies; Antacids; Solutions, pharmaceutical; Cough medicines; Cold remedies; Antacids
Ch Bd: L T Khouw
**Pr:* Joseph Sutedjo
**CEO:* Dr Pramuditya Oen
VP: Raja Mamidi
Ql Cn Mgr: Warren Cheung
Sls Mgr: Simon Cherdy

K C SUMMERS TOYOTA
See SUMMERS K C BUICK TOYOTA GMC INC

D-U-N-S 18-065-5797
K C TRANSPORTATION INC
888 Will Carleton Rd, Carleton, MI 48117-9704
Tel (734) 654-0010 *Founded/Ownrshp* 1986
Sales 46.9MM^E *EMP* 250
SIC 4212 4213 Local trucking, without storage; Trucking, except local; Local trucking, without storage; Trucking, except local
CEO: Kenyon Calender
**Pr:* Dale Tanner
CFO: Phillip Masserant
**CFO:* William Vandenberghe
**VP:* Michael Hanschu

D-U-N-S 07-676-5254
K CO INC
2234 S Arlington Rd, Akron, OH 44319-1929
Tel (330) 773-5125 *Founded/Ownrshp* 1972
Sales 35.0MM *EMP* 110
Accts Meaden & Moore Ltd Akron O
SIC 1711 Warm air heating & air conditioning contractor; Warm air heating & air conditioning contractor
CEO: Thomas Bauer
Pr: Christopher Martin
Treas: Carmen Dempsey
VP: Daniel Bauer
Prin: Thomas G Bauer
Prin: Jerry L Kriebel
Sls Mgr: Karl Frye

D-U-N-S 05-394-9967
K CORP LEE INC
KFC
13180 N Cleveland Ave # 316, Fort Myers, FL 33903-6232
Tel (239) 997-1992 *Founded/Ownrshp* 1990
Sales 5.6MM^E *EMP* 400
SIC 5812 Fast-food restaurant, chain; Fast-food restaurant, chain
VP: Bonnie Polverari

K D C
See KENNEDY-DONOVAN CENTER INC

K D C
See KONIAG DEVELOPMENT CORP

K D C
See KONIAG TECHNOLOGY SOLUTIONS INC

K D C
See TRI-TECH LABORATORIES INC

D-U-N-S 61-279-1988
K D CONSTRUCTION OF FLORIDA INC
1831 Sw 7th Ave, Pompano Beach, FL 33060-9027
Tel (954) 943-4241 *Founded/Ownrshp* 1990
Sales 27.7MM^E *EMP* 150
SIC 1522 Apartment building construction
CEO: Karl Davis
**Pr:* Oliver Von Troll

D-U-N-S 61-894-6771
K D E ENTERPRISES LLC
ROLLING HILSS NISSAN
3801 Sherman Ave, Saint Joseph, MO 64506-3677
Tel (816) 279-2711 *Founded/Ownrshp* 2006
Sales 80.0MM *EMP* 57
SIC 5511 Automobiles, new & used; Automobiles, new & used
Genl Mgr: Todd R Hill
Sales Exec: Mark Thomas

D-U-N-S 08-074-1705
K DIAMOND CORP
2305 County Road 3210, Mount Pleasant, TX 75455-7949
Tel (903) 572-9804 *Founded/Ownrshp* 1970
Sales 21.9MM^E *EMP* 150
SIC 1541 1542 Industrial buildings, new construction; Commercial & office building, new construction; Industrial buildings, new construction; Commercial & office building, new construction
Pr: Tommy King
Off Admin: Kay King

D-U-N-S 80-841-9902
K E & G CONSTRUCTION INC
1601 Paseo Sn Luis 202, Sierra Vista, AZ 85635
Tel (520) 748-0188 *Founded/Ownrshp* 2006
Sales 21.3MM^E *EMP* 99
SIC 1542 Nonresidential construction
Pr: Karol E George
**VP:* Chris Albright
**VP:* Christopher W Albright
**VP:* Ed Anderson
**VP:* Nancy George
IT Man: Chris Weinell

K E A
See KODIAK ELECTRIC ASSOCIATION INC

D-U-N-S 05-852-7193
K E AUSTIN CORP
GOGAS
3301 Burnt Mill Dr, Wilmington, NC 28403-2699
Tel (910) 762-4700 *Founded/Ownrshp* 1945
Sales 36.7MM^E *EMP* 109
SIC 5541

D-U-N-S 02-761-7794
K E MCKAYS MARKET OF COOS BAY INC
PRICE'N PRIDE FOOD CENTER
226 Hull St, Coos Bay, OR 97420-3038
Tel (541) 269-5921 *Founded/Ownrshp* 1960
Sales 39.2MM^E *EMP* 350
SIC 5411 Supermarkets, independent; Supermarkets, independent
Pr: Charles P McKay

D-U-N-S 15-095-4779
K ELEMENT DELAWARE INC
500 Canal View Blvd, Rochester, NY 14623-2800
Tel (585) 240-7500 *Founded/Ownrshp* 2001
Sales 4.3MM^E *EMP* 700
SIC 8243 Software training, computer; Software training, computer
CEO: Steve Hoffman

D-U-N-S 05-682-2653
■ **K F C NATIONAL MANAGEMENT CO**
KFC
(*Suby of* KFC CORP (DE)) ★
1441 Gardiner Ln, Louisville, KY 40213-1957
Tel (502) 874-8300 *Founded/Ownrshp* 1969
Sales 431.3MM^E *EMP* 20,000
SIC 5812 Fast-food restaurant, chain; Fast-food restaurant, chain
Ch: Anne P Byerlein
**Pr:* Cheryl A Bachelder
**Pr:* Chuck Rawley
COO: Mark Cosby
**Treas:* Kathleen Corsi
**Treas:* Debbie Medley
Sr VP: Rob Saxton
VP: Amy Sherwood
VP: Michael Tierney
**VP:* R Scott Toop
VP: Nikki Weis
Dir Surg: Niel Bronzo

K G E
See KANSAS GAS AND ELECTRIC CO

K G S ELECTRONICS
See GAR ENTERPRISES

D-U-N-S 08-467-8148
K GIRDHARLAL INC
(*Suby of* K. GIRDHARLAL INTERNATIONAL LIMITED)
10 W 46th St Fl 10, New York, NY 10036-4515
Tel (212) 944-4500 *Founded/Ownrshp* 1998
Sales 27.0MM *EMP* 15
SIC 5094 Diamonds (gems); Diamonds (gems)
Pr: Pranav Shah

D-U-N-S 80-689-9746 IMP/EXP
K GRIMMER INDUSTRIES INC
HURRICANE COMPRESSOR COMPANY
17301 Juniper Ln, Leo, IN 46765-9340
Tel (317) 736-3800 *Founded/Ownrshp* 1995
Sales 54.7MM^E *EMP* 160
SIC 3563 4924 Air & gas compressors including vacuum pumps; Natural gas distribution; Air & gas compressors including vacuum pumps; Natural gas distribution
Pr: Kenneth Grimmer
**Ch Bd:* John E Grimmer
Plnt Mgr: John E Grimmr

K H
See KELLY-HILL CO LLC

K H A M
See KAISER HOSPITAL ASSET MANAGEMENT INC

D-U-N-S 78-375-3465
K H F HOLDINGS LLC
11521 Bluegrass Pkwy, Louisville, KY 40299-2351
Tel (502) 238-2347 *Founded/Ownrshp* 2003
Sales NA *EMP* 375
SIC 6719 Investment holding companies, except banks; Investment holding companies, except banks
Pr: Miachel L McCord
CFO: Lisa Burden

D-U-N-S 00-794-3590
K H Q INC (WA)
Q-6 TV
(*Suby of* COWLES PUBLISHING CO) ★
1201 W Sprague Ave, Spokane, WA 99201-4102
Tel (509) 448-6000 *Founded/Ownrshp* 1922
Sales 44.6MM^E *EMP* 205
SIC 4833 Television translator station; Television translator station
Pr: Lon Lee
**Ch:* Elizabeth Cowles
**Sec:* Steven Rector
Exec: Jeff Hite
Genl Mgr: Patricia McRay
CTO: Robert Wyatt
IT Man: Patrick Cleary
Sls Mgr: Bill Storms

D-U-N-S 01-379-5505
K HEEPS INC
FRESH CUT
5239 Tilghman St, Allentown, PA 18104-9378
Tel (610) 530-1950 *Founded/Ownrshp* 1948
Sales 60.4MM^E *EMP* 100^E
SIC 5147 Meats, fresh; Meats, fresh
Pr: Beau J Heeps
Sec: Deborah Heeps
Sec: Theodore L Heeps
VP: James W Heeps
Genl Mgr: John Meyers
Sales Asso: Ken Eck

K HOVNANIAN
See HOVNANIAN ENTERPRISES INC

K HOVNANIAN
See K HOVNANIAN DEVELOPMENTS OF PENNSYLVANIA INC

K HOVNANIAN
See K HOVNANIAN ENTERPRISES INC

K HOVNANIAN
See K HOVNANIAN COMPANIES OF CALIFORNIA INC

D-U-N-S 86-781-0525
K HOVNANIAN COMPANIES OF CALIFORNIA INC
K HOVNANIAN
400 Exchange Ste 200, Irvine, CA 92602-1340
Tel (949) 222-7700 *Founded/Ownrshp* 1994
Sales 94.0MM^E *EMP* 150
SIC 1521 Single-family housing construction; Single-family housing construction
Pr: Nicholas Pappas

D-U-N-S 16-161-7170
■ **K HOVNANIAN COMPANIES OF NEW YORK INC**
(*Suby of* K HOVNANIAN DEVELOPMENTS OF NEW YORK INC) ★
10 Rte 35, Red Bank, NJ 07701-5902
Tel (732) 747-7800 *Founded/Ownrshp* 1985
Sales 187.4MM^E *EMP* 2,900^E
SIC 6531 Real estate agents & managers; Real estate agents & managers
Pr: ARA Hovnanian
**Ch Bd:* Kevork Hovnanian
**Treas:* Kevin Hake
**Sr VP:* Peter Reinhart
**VP:* Paul Buchanan
**VP:* Larry Sorsby
CTO: John E Uln
IT Man: Rex Rexford

D-U-N-S 61-714-5073
■ **K HOVNANIAN DEVELOPMENTS OF NEW JERSEY INC**
(*Suby of* HOVNANIAN ENTERPRISES INC) ★
10 State Route 35, Red Bank, NJ 07701-5902
Tel (732) 747-7800 *Founded/Ownrshp* 1985
Sales 183.1MM^E *EMP* 500
SIC 1531 Operative builders; Operative builders
Prin: A Hovnanian
Ex Dir: Robert Jackson

D-U-N-S 79-180-1947
■ **K HOVNANIAN DEVELOPMENTS OF NEW YORK INC**
(*Suby of* HOVNANIAN ENTERPRISES INC) ★
10 State Route 35, Red Bank, NJ 07701-5902
Tel (732) 747-7800 *Founded/Ownrshp* 1985
Sales 254.2MM^E *EMP* 1,565
SIC 1531 Operative builders; Operative builders
Ch Bd: ARA K Hovanian
**Pr:* James Corbett

D-U-N-S 61-107-8122
■ **K HOVNANIAN DEVELOPMENTS OF PENNSYLVANIA INC**
K HOVNANIAN
(*Suby of* HOVNANIAN ENTERPRISES INC) ★
110 Fieldcrest Ave Ste 39, Edison, NJ 08837-3631
Tel (732) 225-4001 *Founded/Ownrshp* 1959
Sales 37.1MM^E *EMP* 136
SIC 1531 Operative builders; Condominium developer; Speculative builder, single-family houses; Townhouse developers; Operative builders; Condominium developers; Speculative builder, single-family houses; Townhouse developers
Ch Bd: Kevork Hovnanian
**Pr:* ARA Hovnanian
**Sr VP:* Peter Reinhart
**VP:* Timothy Mason
Sales Asso: Glen Husband
Counsel: Michael Macaninch

D-U-N-S 82-557-0302
■ **K HOVNANIAN ENTERPRISES INC**
K HOVNANIAN
(*Suby of* HOVNANIAN ENTERPRISES INC) ★
110 W Front St, Red Bank, NJ 07701-1139
Tel (732) 747-7800 *Founded/Ownrshp* 1982
Sales 55.4MM^E *EMP* 200
SIC 1531 Condominium developers; Townhouse developers; Speculative builder, single-family houses; Condominium developers; Townhouse developers; Speculative builder, single-family houses
Ch: Kevork S Hovnanian
Pr: ARA K Hovnanian
CFO: Larry Sorsby

D-U-N-S 12-929-5965
■ **K HOVNANIAN HOLDINGS NJ LLC**
(*Suby of* K HOVNANIAN DEVELOPMENTS OF NEW JERSEY INC) ★
110 W Front St, Red Bank, NJ 07701-1139
Tel (732) 747-7800 *Founded/Ownrshp* 2002
Sales 133.8MM *EMP* 3
SIC 6552 Subdividers & developers; Subdividers & developers
Pr: ARA Hovnanian
CFO: Larry Sorsby

K HOVNANIAN HOMES
See K HOVNANIAN HOMES AT FAIRWOOD LLC

D-U-N-S 02-268-6208
■ **K HOVNANIAN HOMES AT FAIRWOOD LLC**
K HOVNANIAN HOMES
(*Suby of* HOVNANIAN ENTERPRISES INC) ★
1802 Brightseat Rd # 500, Landover, MD 20785-4232
Tel (301) 772-8900 *Founded/Ownrshp* 2002
Sales 159.5MM^E *EMP* 500
SIC 1531 1522 1521 Speculative builder, single-family houses; Townhouse developers; Condominium developers; Residential construction; Single-family housing construction; Speculative builder, single-family houses; Townhouse developers; Condominium developers; Residential construction; Single-family housing construction
CTO: Joe Grecski
CTO: Mary Phelan
Dir IT: Brian Patterson
Dir IT: Christopher Spendley
VP Opers: Steve Snyder
Sls Mgr: Angela Hawkins
Sales Asso: Alison Osborne

D-U-N-S 86-832-1191
K HOVNANIAN HOMES INC
(*Suby of* K HOVNANIAN DEVELOPMENTS OF CALIFORNIA, INC)
400 Exchange Ste 200, Irvine, CA 92602-1340
Tel (909) 483-7340 *Founded/Ownrshp* 2002
Sales 23.5MM^E *EMP* 50
SIC 1531 Speculative builder, single-family houses
Pr: Lou Smith
**Pr:* James Rex
**CFO:* John Hadley

D-U-N-S 60-384-1255
■ **K HOVNANIAN SUMMIT HOMES LLC**
(*Suby of* HOVNANIAN ENTERPRISES INC) ★
2000 10th St Ne, Canton, OH 44705-1414
Tel (330) 454-4048 *Founded/Ownrshp* 1985
Sales 52.8MM^E *EMP* 160
SIC 1521 New construction, single-family houses; New construction, single-family houses

D-U-N-S 13-971-3863
■ **K HOVNANIAN T&C HOMES AT ILLINOIS LLC**
TOWN & COUNTRY HOMES
(*Suby of* HOVNANIAN ENTERPRISES INC) ★
1804 N Naper Blvd Ste 200, Naperville, IL 60563-8833
Tel (630) 517-8057 *Founded/Ownrshp* 2005
Sales 45.7MM^E *EMP* 120
SIC 1521 6531 Single-family housing construction; New construction, single-family houses; Townhouse construction; Real estate agents & managers; Single-family housing construction; New construction, single-family houses; Townhouse construction; Real estate agents & managers
VP Opers: Brian Murphy

K I D S
See KIDS IN DISTRESSED SITUATIONS INC

D-U-N-S 79-611-9857
K I INVESTMENTS INC
Ave 65 De Infntria St1179, San Juan, PR 00924
Tel (787) 622-0600 *Founded/Ownrshp* 1991
Sales 214.0MM *EMP* 230
SIC 6519 5012 5511 Sub-lessors of real estate; Automobiles; Automobiles, new & used; Sub-lessors of real estate; Automobiles; Automobiles, new & used
Pr: Kyffin D Simpson
CFO: Roberto Cabello
**VP:* Garry D Clarke
Genl Mgr: John Bowen

K I K
See KIK-SOCAL INC

K I X
See KUTZLER EXPRESS INC

D-U-N-S 03-774-3622 IMP
K INTERNATIONAL INC
3333 N Oak Grove Ave, Waukegan, IL 60087-1828
Tel (847) 623-2304 *Founded/Ownrshp* 1980
Sales 24.4MM^E *EMP* 29
SIC 5085 Fasteners, industrial: nuts, bolts, screws, etc.
Pr: John D White
**Sec:* Barbara White
Genl Mgr: Pam White
Off Mgr: Tony Clesceri

D-U-N-S 02-730-5700
K INVESTMENTS LIMITED PARTNERSHIP
PERKINS FAMILY RESTAURANT
1500 Sycamore Rd Ste 10, Montoursville, PA 17754-9303
Tel (570) 327-0111 *Founded/Ownrshp* 1996
Sales 48.8MM^E *EMP* 3,400
SIC 7011 5712 5521 Hotels & motels; Furniture stores; Used car dealers; Hotels & motels; Furniture stores; Used car dealers
Pt: Dan Klingerman

K J ELECTRIC
See KJDE CORP

D-U-N-S 12-833-9699 IMP
K J S INDUSTRIES INC
KJS GREETINGS/BURGOYNE
4245 International Blvd, Norcross, GA 30093-3222
Tel (770) 638-3434 *Founded/Ownrshp* 1991
Sales 39.1MM^E *EMP* 380
SIC 5947 Greeting cards; Greeting cards
CEO: Karen Ipek
**Pr:* Cumhur Ipek
Art Dir: Jennifer Ipek

K K DISTRIBUTORS
See KITCHEN KAPERS INC

D-U-N-S 17-554-5706
K K MECHANICAL INC
1858 W 5150 S Ste 504, Roy, UT 84067-3064
Tel (801) 820-2500 *Founded/Ownrshp* 1987
Sales 28.1MM^E *EMP* 120
SIC 1711

D-U-N-S 04-441-2302
K K W TRUCKING INC
3100 Pomona Blvd, Pomona, CA 91768-3230
Tel (909) 869-1200 *Founded/Ownrshp* 1967
Sales 82.9MM^E *EMP* 350
Accts Hoag & Robi Cpa S Los Angeles
SIC 4213 4231 4226 4214 Trucking, except local; Trucking terminal facilities; Special warehousing & storage; Local trucking with storage; Trucking, except local; Trucking terminal facilities; Special warehousing & storage; Local trucking with storage
CEO: Dennis W Firestone
COO: Steve Benninghoss
**CFO:* Lynnette Brown
VP: Steve Benninghoff
Off Mgr: Susan Dancel
IT Man: Alex Solario
Sfty Mgr: Sara Sherman
Sfty Mgr: Susan Zellmann
Opers Mgr: Martin Campos
Opers Mgr: Mark Knickerbocker
Sales Exec: Doug Lawson

D-U-N-S 09-362-7099 EXP
K L JACK & CO
RELIABLE FASTNERS
145 Warren Ave, Portland, ME 04103-1190
Tel (207) 878-3600 *Founded/Ownrshp* 1987
Sales 20.3MM^E *EMP* 53
SIC 5085 5088 Industrial supplies; Marine supplies
Pr: Kenneth L Jack
**VP:* Gus Jack
Brnch Mgr: Alan Lucier
IT Man: Julia Goulia
Opers Mgr: Jerry Bumford
Sls Dir: Peter Wiers
Sales Asso: Matthew Szklarz
Sales Asso: Kevin Violet

D-U-N-S 62-161-0344
K LINE AMERICA INC
(*Suby of* KAWASAKI KISEN KAISHA, LTD.)
8730 Stony Point Pkwy # 400, Richmond, VA 23235-1952
Tel (804) 560-3600 *Founded/Ownrshp* 1998
Sales 123.2MM^E *EMP* 489
SIC 4412 4491 Deep sea foreign transportation of freight; Marine loading & unloading services
CEO: Shio Suzuki
Sr VP: Nobuo Ishida
**Sr VP:* David N Mills
**Sr VP:* Ishida Nubuo
VP: Tom Aldridge
VP: Maria Bodnar
**VP:* A Chai
VP: Ty Cheng
VP: David Daly
VP: Tetsuya Gyotoku
VP: Jim Harris
VP: Akihiko Ichie
VP: Shingo Kogure
VP: Masaru Nakahara
VP: Konosuke Suzuki
VP: Takafumi Tomaru
VP: David Xiao
VP: Noriaki Yamaga

K LINE METALS
See KRAMARS IRON & METAL INC

K M C
See KAUAI MEDICAL CLINIC

D-U-N-S 09-155-2018
K M C CORP (OH)
2670 Commercial Ave, Mingo Junction, OH 43938-1613
Tel (740) 598-4171 *Founded/Ownrshp* 1975
Sales 20.6MM^E *EMP* 50
SIC 5181 5182 5194 Beer & other fermented malt liquors; Wine; Tobacco & tobacco products
Pr: Michael C Bellas
**Sec:* Dianne Bellas Terezis
**Sr VP:* Robert M Chapman
**VP:* Albert Bellas

K M C P I
See ALLIANCE PHYSICIANS INC

D-U-N-S 80-268-5586
K M INVESTMENT CORP
475 Steamboat Rd, Greenwich, CT 06830-7144
Tel (203) 625-9200 *Founded/Ownrshp* 1987
Sales 28.0MM^E *EMP* 278
SIC 5052 Coal; Coal
CEO: Fritz Kundrun
**Pr:* Hans J Mende

D-U-N-S 02-295-6551
K M J CONVENIENCE CO
FOOD-N-FUEL
1319 Grove Ave Ste 2, Montevideo, MN 56265-1726
Tel (320) 269-6424 *Founded/Ownrshp* 2004
Sales 22.6MM^E *EMP* 100
SIC 5171 5541 5411 Petroleum bulk stations; Gasoline service stations; Convenience stores, independent; Petroleum bulk stations; Gasoline service stations; Convenience stores, independent
Pr: Mark Jaspersen

D-U-N-S 19-290-5219
K M M P INC
3003 Marvin Rd Ne, Olympia, WA 98516
Tel (360) 491-2236 *Founded/Ownrshp* 2005
Sales 25.0MM *EMP* 99
SIC 7373 Computer integrated systems design; Computer integrated systems design
CEO: Mark P Pallotta

D-U-N-S 02-914-0712
K MOTORS INC
TOYOTA OF EL CAJON
965 Arnele Ave, El Cajon, CA 92020-3001
Tel (619) 270-3000 *Founded/Ownrshp* 1990
Sales 158.2MM^E *EMP* 186
SIC 5521 5013 5511 Used car dealers; Automotive supplies & parts; Automobiles, new & used; Used car dealers; Automotive supplies & parts; Automobiles, new & used
Pr: Robert Kaminsky
**Sec:* Kim Kaminsky
**VP:* Gary Kaminsky
Dir Bus: Khang Nguyen
Sls Mgr: Tan Nguyen
Sls Mgr: Paul Sphabmixay

K N G BUILDERS
See EAGLE CONSTRUCTION OF VIRGINIA INC

K N INTEGER
See KRAGIE/NEWELL ADVERTISING INC

D-U-N-S 19-711-5116
■ **K N NATURAL GAS INC**
(*Suby of* KINDER MORGAN KANSAS INC) ★
370 Van Gordon St, Lakewood, CO 80228-1519
Tel (303) 243-3400 *Founded/Ownrshp* 1938
Sales 18.3MM^E *EMP* 475
SIC 4924 Natural gas distribution; Natural gas distribution
CEO: Richard Kinder
Snr Ntwrk: Randy Baus
IT Man: Troy Bower
IT Man: Diedre O'Callaghan

D-U-N-S 79-976-3396
■ **K N TRANSCOLORADO INC**
(*Suby of* KINDER MORGAN KANSAS INC) ★
1001 Louisiana St, Houston, TX 77002-5089
Tel (713) 369-9000 *Founded/Ownrshp* 1997
Sales 9.9MM^E *EMP* 396
SIC 4613 Refined petroleum pipelines; Refined petroleum pipelines
CEO: Richard Kinder

D-U-N-S 36-360-5606
K NEAL HOLDINGS INC
4902 Sharon Rd, Temple Hills, MD 20748-2236
Tel (301) 772-5100 *Founded/Ownrshp* 2005
Sales 63.6MM^E *EMP* 125^E
SIC 5511 5531 7513 7538 Trucks, tractors & trailers: new & used; Truck equipment & parts; Truck leasing, without drivers; General truck repair; Trucks, tractors & trailers: new & used; Truck equipment & parts; Truck leasing, without drivers; General truck repair
Pr: Stephen Neal
**CFO:* Sharon Calomese

D-U-N-S 08-107-1920
K NEAL INTERNATIONAL TRUCKS INC
(*Suby of* K NEAL HOLDINGS INC) ★
5000 Tuxedo Rd, Hyattsville, MD 20781-1213
Tel (301) 772-5100 *Founded/Ownrshp* 2006
Sales 63.4MM^E *EMP* 120
SIC 5511 5531 7513 7538

D-U-N-S 05-322-4379
K NEAL PATRICK & ASSOCIATES INC
8210 Lakewood Ranch Blvd, Lakewood Ranch, FL 34202-5157
Tel (941) 328-1111 *Founded/Ownrshp* 1972
Sales 150.0MM^E *EMP* 100
SIC 6531 Real estate managers; Real estate managers
Pr: Patrick Neal
**VP:* James R Schier
**VP:* Mark Sochar

K O
See OXFORD KINGSWOOD SCHOOL INC

K O I
See KOI ENTERPRISES INC

K O I AUTO PARTS
See K - O - I WAREHOUSE INC

K P
See KING PAR LLC

K P I
See KPI ULTRASOUND INC

K P S
See KENT PLACE SCHOOL INC

D-U-N-S 14-297-5841
K POST CO
1841 W Northwest Hwy, Dallas, TX 75220-7017
Tel (214) 448-7675 *Founded/Ownrshp* 2003
Sales 38.3MM^E *EMP* 290
Accts Blackburn May & Co Llp D
SIC 1761 1799 Roofing contractor; Waterproofing; Roofing contractor; Waterproofing
CEO: Keith Post
**Pr:* Stephen G Little
**CFO:* Jayne Williams
Ofcr: Renae Bales
**VP:* Kelly Lea
**VP:* Brent McFarlin
Dir Bus: Scott Bredehoeft
Dir IT: Wayne Hardin

D-U-N-S 00-634-1120
K PREET CORP
SUBWAY
210 S Cobb Prwy, Marietta, GA 30060
Tel (404) 667-2595 *Founded/Ownrshp* 2006
Sales 45.0MM *EMP* 10
SIC 5812 Sandwiches & submarines shop; Sandwiches & submarines shop
CEO: Kalpit A Patel
**VP:* Hari Patel

D-U-N-S 04-487-4592 IMP
K R ANDERSON INC
KRAYDEN
18330 Sutter Blvd, Morgan Hill, CA 95037-2841
Tel (408) 825-1800 *Founded/Ownrshp* 1974
Sales 48.6MM^E *EMP* 60^E
SIC 5169 Chemicals & allied products; Synthetic resins, rubber & plastic materials; Adhesives, chemical; Chemicals & allied products; Synthetic resins, rubber & plastic materials; Adhesives, chemical
CEO: Dennis Wagner
**Treas:* Jim Caviglia
Dir: Mark Silliman
Sales Asso: Chris Christianson

D-U-N-S 79-837-1233
K R DRENTH TRUCKING INC
KRD TRUCKING
20340 Stoney Island Ave, Chicago Heights, IL 60411-8657
Tel (708) 757-3333 *Founded/Ownrshp* 1987
Sales 86.6MM^E *EMP* 325^E
SIC 4212 Garbage collection & transport, no disposal; Garbage collection & transport, no disposal
Pr: Thomas J Manzke
CFO: Ken Andresen
**Sec:* Kenneth S Drenth
Genl Mgr: Steven Ruckert

K R G
See KRG TECHNOLOGIES INC

K S & R
See KNOWLEDGE SYSTEMS & RESEARCH INC

D-U-N-S 83-253-3108
K S FABRICATION & MACHINE INC
KS FABRICATION & MACHINE
6205 District Blvd, Bakersfield, CA 93313-2141
Tel (661) 617-1700 *Founded/Ownrshp* 2009
Sales 44.0MM^E *EMP* 150
SIC 1623 Water, sewer & utility lines; Water, sewer & utility lines
CEO: Kevin S Small
CFO: Becky Scott

K S I
See KS INDUSTRIES LP

K S L
See BONNEVILLE INTERNATIONAL CORP

K S M
See KELLY SCOTT AND MADISON INC

K S S
See KEY SAFETY RESTRAINT SYSTEMS INC

K S S
See KEY SAFETY SYSTEMS INC

K T A
See KTA-TATOR INC

D-U-N-S 96-966-6106
K T I INC
10301 Wayzata Blvd # 100, Minnetonka, MN 55305-1656
Tel (612) 378-9731 *Founded/Ownrshp* 1997
Sales 25.0MM *EMP* 36
SIC 4789 Pipeline terminal facilities, independently operated
CEO: Alan Weiner
Pr: Michael Kroul

K T P
See KLEEN TEST PRODUCTS CORP

K T R K T V
See KTRK TELEVISION INC

K T T V-FOX 11
See FOX TELEVISION STATIONS INC

D-U-N-S 12-456-2054
K T W PRODUCTIONS INC
6303 E Cedarbrooks Rd, Orange, CA 92867-2491
Tel (714) 685-0428 *Founded/Ownrshp* 1989
Sales 64.7MM^E *EMP* 800
SIC 5023 Home furnishings; Home furnishings
Pr: Lola Wang
**VP:* Rex Wang

K TUBE TECHNOLOGIES
See K-TUBE CORP

D-U-N-S 02-256-9187
K U ANESTHESIOLOGY FOUNDATION
3901 Rainbow Blvd # 1034, Kansas City, KS 66160-8500
Tel (913) 588-3304 *Founded/Ownrshp* 2009
Sales 26.1MM *EMP* 4
Accts Cornerstone Cpa Group Llc Sha
SIC 8011 Anesthesiologist; Anesthesiologist
Prin: James Kindscher

K U B
See KNOXVILLE UTILITIES BOARD

K U CREDIT UNION
See TRUITY CREDIT UNION

K V B W
See SINCLAIR MEDIA II INC

D-U-N-S 02-954-5878 IMP
K V MART CO
AMR RANCH MARKET
522 E Vermont Ave, Anaheim, CA 92805-5621
Tel (310) 816-0200 *Founded/Ownrshp* 1977
Sales 102.0M *EMP* 600
Accts White Nelson Diehl Evans Llp
SIC 5411 Supermarkets, chain; Supermarkets, chain
Ch Bd: Darioush Khaledi
**Pr:* Paul Vazin
Sr VP: Miguel Alarcon
**Sr VP:* Greg Sproul
VP: Miguel Alercon
VP: Miguel Arroyo
VP: Bruce Brandlin
VP: Murray Marks
VP: Thad Smith
Dir IT: Jeff Huggins
IT Man: Sam King

K W
See K-W CONSTRUCTION INC

D-U-N-S 07-180-8880
K W ASSOCIATES LLC
BUDWEISER OF COLUMBIA
825 Bluff Rd, Columbia, SC 29201-4709
Tel (803) 799-5490 *Founded/Ownrshp* 2000
Sales 83.1MM^E *EMP* 215^E
SIC 5181 Beer & ale; Beer & other fermented malt liquors; Beer & ale; Beer & other fermented malt liquors
Pr: Gene E Williams
**COO:* Jim Kirkham
VP: Jesse Bazemore
**VP:* Jesse Dazemore
Dir Sec: Mike Terry
Dir IT: Mark Lee
Opers Mgr: Robert Batson

D-U-N-S 03-071-4869
K W BROCK DIRECTORIES INC
NAMES AND NUMBERS
1225 E Centennial Dr, Pittsburg, KS 66762-6623
Tel (620) 231-4000 *Founded/Ownrshp* 1974
Sales 29.9MM^E *EMP* 200
SIC 2741 Directories, telephone: publishing only, not printed on site; Directories, telephone: publishing only, not printed on site
Pr: Ken W Brock
COO: Ken Martin
**VP:* Debra Brock
Sales Exec: Tim East
Sales Exec: Elmer Thorn
Sls Mgr: Joe Encinias
Sls Mgr: Brian Wallace
Snr Mgr: Kathy Swezey

D-U-N-S 61-437-4379
K W FUELS INC
PEARSON OIL
717 W Sanger St, Hobbs, NM 88240-3823
Tel (575) 393-5135 *Founded/Ownrshp* 1978
Sales 20.0MM^E *EMP* 13
SIC 5172 Petroleum products
Pr: Keith W Pearson

K W INTERNATIONAL
See KW INTERNATIONAL LLC

K W MANAGEMENT
See WILLIAMS KELLER REALTY

D-U-N-S 07-737-2399
K W P H ENTERPRISES
AMERICAN AMBULANCE
2911 E Tulare St, Fresno, CA 93721-1502
Tel (559) 443-5900 *Founded/Ownrshp* 1975
Sales 29.0MM^E *EMP* 500
SIC 4119 Ambulance service; Ambulance service
Pr: James Kaufman
**CEO:* Todd R Valeri
Dir Bus: Edgar Escobedo
IT Man: Donna Hankins
Opers Mgr: Casey Jenkins
Ql Cn Mgr: Cindy Schueler

D-U-N-S 00-428-5904
K WM BEACH MFG CO INC (OH)
4655 Urbana Rd, Springfield, OH 45502-9503
Tel (937) 390-2421 *Founded/Ownrshp* 1945
Sales 32.2MM^E *EMP* 200
SIC 3053 3714 Gaskets, all materials; Motor vehicle parts & accessories; Gaskets, all materials; Motor vehicle parts & accessories
CEO: William R Beach
**COO:* Bret L Beach
CTO: Chris Cox

K X T V CHANNEL 10
See KXTV INC

K YAMADA DISTRIBUTORS
See KYD INC

D-U-N-S 79-568-8717
K&B ENGINEERING
290 Corporate Terrace Cir, Corona, CA 92879-6033
Tel (951) 808-9501 *Founded/Ownrshp* 2007
Sales 25.5MM^E *EMP* 200
SIC 8711 Engineering services; Engineering services
Owner: Trey Gibbs
Snr PM: John Manning

D-U-N-S 06-809-8804
K&B MACHINE
KB INDUSTRIES
8500 Miller Road 2, Houston, TX 77049-1951
Tel (281) 456-0293 *Founded/Ownrshp* 2011
Sales 41.4MM^E *EMP* 260
SIC 3561 Pumps, oil well & field; Pumps, oil well & field
Pr: Kenny Wood
**Pr:* Terry Yawn

D-U-N-S 07-261-0025 IMP
K&B MACHINE WORKS LLC
208 Rebeccas Pond Rd, Schriever, LA 70395-3307
Tel (985) 868-6730 Founded/Ownrshp 1974
Sales 133.4MM EMP 500
Accts K&B Machine Works Llc Hou
SIC 3599 Machine shop, jobbing & repair; Machine shop, jobbing & repair
Pr: Kenneth Wood Jr
COO: Terry Yawn
Sec: Cathleen Wood
VP: Craig Cenac
Dir Risk M: Scott Hebert
QA Dir: Jeremy Griffin
IT Man: Eugene Templet
Opers Mgr: Gregg Babin
Ql Cn Mgr: Paul Porche
Sales Exec: Steve Williams
Mktg Mgr: Chantal Haynes

D-U-N-S 06-405-3234
K&C RV CENTERS LLC
(Suby of BLAINE JENSEN RV CENTERS LLC) ★
14504 E I25 Frontage Rd, Longmont, CO 80504-9626
Tel (303) 776-1309 Founded/Ownrshp 2004
Sales 23.8MM^E EMP 100
SIC 5561

D-U-N-S 05-471-7319 IMP
K&D FUTURE INC (PA)
MEALEY'S FURNITURE WARMINSTER
(Suby of PARALLEL INVESTMENT PARTNERS LLC) ★
908 W Street Rd, Warminster, PA 18974-3124
Tel (215) 674-3555 Founded/Ownrshp 1970, 2006
Sales 104.9MM^E EMP 165
SIC 5021 Beds & bedding; Mattresses; Beds & bedding; Mattresses
Pr: Dan Mealey
*Pr: Kevin Mealey
VP: Bill Levine
Genl Mgr: Kim Gibialante
Sales Exec: Dan Fedena
Sales Exec: Joe Pietrowski
Sls Mgr: Una Eitzen
Sales Asso: Alison Dinstel
Sales Asso: Carol Malinowski

D-U-N-S 08-549-1566
K&D GROUP INC
4420 Sherwin Rd Ste 1, Willoughby, OH 44094-7995
Tel (440) 946-3600 Founded/Ownrshp 1984
Sales 32.4MM^E EMP 287
SIC 6513 Apartment building operators; Apartment building operators
CEO: Douglas E Price III
*Pr: Karen M Harrison
Mktg Dir: Kathy Fanger
Sales Asso: Kim Stakley
Genl Couns: Mark Schildhouse

K&D PLASTICS
See RELIANT WORLDWIDE PLASTICS LLC

D-U-N-S 55-688-3627 IMP
■ **K&G MENS CO INC**
K&G MEN'S SUPERSTORE
(Suby of MENS WEARHOUSE INC) ★
6380 Rogerdale Rd, Houston, TX 77072-1624
Tel (281) 776-7000 Founded/Ownrshp 1999
Sales 139.4MM^E EMP 1,500
SIC 5611 5621 Men's & boys' clothing stores; Women's clothing stores; Men's & boys' clothing stores; Women's clothing stores
CEO: Douglas S Ewert
*CFO: Jon W Kimmins
*Ex VP: Carole L Souvenir
*Sr VP: Kelly M Dilts
*Sr VP: William Evans Jr
VP: Scott R Saban

K&G MEN'S SUPERSTORE
See K&G MENS CO INC

D-U-N-S 00-139-9534 IMP
K&H GROUP INC
K & H CONTAINERS DIV
(Suby of CONNECTICUT CONTAINER CORP) ★
330 Lake Osiris Rd, Walden, NY 12586-2605
Tel (845) 778-3555 Founded/Ownrshp 1956, 1999
Sales 26.3MM^E EMP 290
SIC 2653 2675

D-U-N-S 03-201-3690
■ **K&H LLC**
(Suby of OMNICOM GROUP INC) ★
685 S Broadway, Denver, CO 80209-4003
Tel (303) 296-8400 Founded/Ownrshp 1999
Sales 24.1MM^E EMP 76
SIC 7311 8743 Advertising agencies; Public relations & publicity
VP: Meg Milligan
VP: David Stewart
Creative D: Darren Brickel
Creative D: Becky Ferguson
Creative D: Jason Kusmanoff
Sls&Mrk Ex: Tracy Broderick
Art Dir: Kelsey Wittenberg
Art Dir: Chris Woodruff

D-U-N-S 10-960-2750
K&L FREIGHT MANAGMENT INC
K & L
745 S Rohlwing Rd, Addison, IL 60101-4215
Tel (630) 607-1491 Founded/Ownrshp 1999
Sales 21.5MM^E EMP 60
SIC 4731 Brokers, shipping
Pr: Russell S Gallemore
COO: Faby Leal
Trfc Dir: Tony Martinek
Opers Mgr: Adriana Sandoval
Natl Sales: Tom Marino

D-U-N-S 01-044-1459
K&L GATES LLP
210 6th Ave Ste 1100, Pittsburgh, PA 15222-2602
Tel (412) 355-6500 Founded/Ownrshp 1946
Sales 461.2MM^E EMP 1,917
SIC 8111

D-U-N-S 08-507-6214
K&L GATES LLP
214 N Tryon St Ste 4700, Charlotte, NC 28202-2367
Tel (704) 331-7400 Founded/Ownrshp 2008
Sales 27.6MM^E EMP 350
SIC 8111 General practice attorney, lawyer; General practice attorney, lawyer
Pt: Gene Pridgen
Pt: Stacy G Ackermann
Pt: James Earle
Pt: David Franchina
Pt: William Harris
Pt: Clifford Jarrett
Pt: Sean Jones
Pt: Warren Kean
Pt: Scott Schattenfield
Pt: Carol Jones Van Buren
Mng Pt: Eugene Pridgen
Pr: Barbara Camacho
Pr: Felicia Ellis
Pr: Carol Ridgeway
COO: Lee Movius

D-U-N-S 05-393-7421 IMP/EXP
■ **K&L MICROWAVE INC**
(Suby of DOVER CORP) ★
2250 Northwood Dr, Salisbury, MD 21801-8811
Tel (410) 749-2424 Founded/Ownrshp 1983
Sales 54.2MM^E EMP 290
SIC 3679 Oscillators, audio & radio frequency (instrument types); Microwave components; Filtration devices, electronic; Microwave components
Pr: David Howett
Pr: Timothy Dolan
*Treas: Joseph Smith
Sr Cor Off: Dave Witheman
VP: Al Adomavicius
VP: Manfred Funke
*VP: Michelle Garigliano
VP: Louis Gentile
VP: Rafi Hershtig
Exec: Robin Hall
Prgrm Mgr: Stewart Wallace
Board of Directors: Carrie Anderson, C Anderson Fincher

D-U-N-S 01-236-5961 IMP
■ **K&M ASSOCIATES LP**
(Suby of AMERICAN BILTRITE INC) ★
425 Dexter St, Providence, RI 02907-2814
Tel (401) 461-4300 Founded/Ownrshp 1995
Sales 43.5MM^E EMP 200
SIC 5094 Jewelry; Jewelry
Pr: Richard G Marcus
CFO: Kathy Bush
Ex Dir: Nelson Williams
IT Man: Stephen Masse
Opers Mgr: James Heagney

D-U-N-S 11-139-1715
K&M ENERGY SERVICES INC
3805 S Douglas Hwy Unit 3, Gillette, WY 82718-6557
Tel (307) 670-9038 Founded/Ownrshp 2002
Sales 41.7MM^E EMP 37
SIC 1389 Gas field services
Pr: Brian Mensing
*Co-Ownr: Loretta Mensing
Off Mgr: Lorraine Smelser

D-U-N-S 07-882-4004 IMP
K&M INDIANA LLC
MITCHELL PLASTICS
301 Pike St, Charlestown, IN 47111-8608
Tel (812) 256-3351 Founded/Ownrshp 2012
Sales 43.8MM^E EMP 160
SIC 3089 Automotive parts, plastic; Automotive parts, plastic
Pr: Joe D'Angelo

K&M TECHNOLOGY GROUP
See SCHLUMBERGER TECHNOLOGY CORP

D-U-N-S 96-847-4184
K&R ENTERPRISES OF ILLINOIS LLC
DRAGONS DEN
610 E Kelly Ave, Westville, IL 61883-1026
Tel (217) 274-9812 Founded/Ownrshp 2011
Sales 12.9MM EMP 463
SIC 8011 7381 7382 8742 Offices & clinics of medical doctors; Detective & armored car services; Security systems services; Management consulting services; Offices & clinics of medical doctors; Detective & armored car services; Security systems services; Management consulting services
Trst: Helon Demarest

K&S
See K & S AIR CONDITIONING INC

D-U-N-S 08-289-3751
■ **K&S INTERCONNECT INC**
(Suby of KULICKE AND SOFFA INDUSTRIES INC) ★
1005 Virginia Dr, Fort Washington, PA 19034-3101
Tel (267) 256-1725 Founded/Ownrshp 2000
Sales 31.1MM^E EMP 787
SIC 3825 5065 Test equipment for electronic & electrical circuits; Electronic parts & equipment; Test equipment for electronic & electrical circuits; Electronic parts & equipment
Pr: Carl Zane Close
*Ch Bd: Ross W Mangano
*COO: Daniel J Hill
*CFO: Randal L Buness
*Sr VP: Michael K Bonham
*VP: Henry P Scutoski
*VP: Mike Sykes
*VP Opers: Kevin M Kurtz
VP Mktg: Karen Lynch

K&W TRANSPORTATION
See CARLILE TRANSPORTATION SYSTEMS INC

D-U-N-S 96-887-1348
K+S MONTANA HOLDINGS LLC
(Suby of K+S FINANCE BELGIUM BVBA)
123 N Wacker Dr, Chicago, IL 60606-1743
Tel (312) 807-2000 Founded/Ownrshp 2009
Sales 835.6MM^E EMP 2,911^E
SIC 2899 Salt

D-U-N-S 83-243-6005
K+S SALT LLC
(Suby of K+S MONTANA HOLDINGS LLC) ★
123 N Wacker Dr Fl 6, Chicago, IL 60606-1743
Tel (312) 807-2000 Founded/Ownrshp 2009
Sales 835.6MM^E EMP 2,901
SIC 2899 5149 5169 Salt; Salt, edible; Salts, industrial; Salt; Salt, edible; Salts, industrial
Ch: Norbert Steiner

D-U-N-S 82-906-9731 IMP
K-1 PACKAGING GROUP
17989 Arenth Ave, City of Industry, CA 91748-1126
Tel (626) 964-9384 Founded/Ownrshp 1992
Sales 25.1MM^E EMP 120
SIC 2752 Offset & photolithographic printing; Offset & photolithographic printing
Pr: Mike Tsai
Ofcr: Angela Hsu
VP: Fred Liu
IT Man: Nancy Tzeng
Prd Mgr: Tommy Duong
Sls Mgr: Jimmy Tsai

K-12 PUBLIC EDUCATION
See LA CANADA UNIFIED SCHOOL DISTRICT

D-U-N-S 15-588-1394
K-3 RESOURCES LP
K3 BMI
850 County Road 149, Alvin, TX 77511-1316
Tel (281) 585-2817 Founded/Ownrshp 2005
Sales 124.8MM^E EMP 100^E
SIC 1389 Oil field services
Genl Pt: Karlis Ercums III
Ofcr: Scott Haney

D-U-N-S 18-338-6911
K-B TRANSPORT INC
WESTERN LIVESTOCK EXPRESS
4700 Dakota Ave, South Sioux City, NE 68776-3677
Tel (402) 494-3459 Founded/Ownrshp 1986
Sales 75.4MM^E EMP 600
SIC 4213

D-U-N-S 60-473-5191
K-BO INC
BOJANGLE'S
212 S Tryon St Ste 1700, Charlotte, NC 28281-0005
Tel (704) 872-0070 Founded/Ownrshp 1988
Sales 13.8MM^E EMP 436
SIC 5812 Fast-food restaurant, chain; Fast-food restaurant, chain
Pr: Kevin C Archer
*VP: Leslie K Archer

D-U-N-S 01-472-6256 EXP
K-C INTERNATIONAL LLC
EKMAN RECYCLING
(Suby of EKMAN & CO INC) ★
1800 Rte 34 Ste 401, Wall Township, NJ 07719-9167
Tel (732) 202-9500 Founded/Ownrshp 2002
Sales 230.0MM^E EMP 30^E
SIC 5093 Scrap & waste materials
CEO: Frank Crowley
*Ch Bd: Matts Ekman
*Ex VP: Phil Epstein

K-CUP
See KAUAI COFFEE CO LLC

K-DESIGNERS
See JUDSON ENTERPRISES INC

D-U-N-S 05-091-9570 IMP
K-FAB INC
1408 N Vine St, Berwick, PA 18603-1218
Tel (570) 759-8411 Founded/Ownrshp 1972
Sales 27.4MM^E EMP 85
SIC 3544 3599 Special dies & tools; Machine shop, jobbing & repair
Pr: Martin F Koch
*Treas: Martin N Koch
*VP: Doreen A Koch
Dir IT: Craig Barroll
Mfg Dir: Denny Vought
Sfty Mgr: Charlie Kersey
Plnt Mgr: Duane Coch
Manager: Mark Welsh
Sls Mgr: Michael Kedell

D-U-N-S 08-982-0161
K-FIVE CONSTRUCTION CORP (IL)
13769 Main St, Lemont, IL 60439-9371
Tel (630) 257-5600 Founded/Ownrshp 1977
Sales 100.0MM^E EMP 80
SIC 1611 Highway & street construction; Highway & street construction
Pr: George Krug
*CFO: Mark Asniegowski
*Treas: Josephine M Krug
*VP: Dennis Devitto
*VP: Jennifer Krug
*VP: Robert G Krug
VP: Scott Pirkins
*VP: Rick Sniegowski
Dir IT: Steve Murphy
Sfty Dirs: Mark Banaszak
Sfty Dirs: David Sode

D-U-N-S 11-801-3221 IMP
K-FLEX USA LLC
(Suby of L'ISOLANTE KFLEX SPA)
100 Nomaco Dr, Youngsville, NC 27596-9133
Tel (919) 556-3475 Founded/Ownrshp 2008
Sales 60.9MM^E EMP 175
SIC 3069 Hard rubber & molded rubber products; Hard rubber & molded rubber products
Pr: Giuseppe Guarino
Top Exec: Brooke Chase
*Dir IT: Kristin Wolfe
Sfty Dirs: Naha Amin
Ql Cn Mgr: Kirat Bakshi
Ql Cn Mgr: Eric Fisher
Natl Sales: Byron Bassett
Sls Dir: Frank Baur
Manager: Steven Brown
Manager: Phil Donovan

D-U-N-S 17-862-6966
K-LIMITED CARRIER LTD
131 Matzinger Rd, Toledo, OH 43612-2623
Tel (419) 269-0002 Founded/Ownrshp 1997
Sales 24.9MM EMP 110
SIC 4213 Trucking, except local; Trucking, except local
CEO: Dean Kaplan
*Pr: Kim Kaplan
*CFO: Dennis Perna
Bd of Dir: Paul Gray
Ex VP: Dean Wilson
*VP: John Spurling

D-U-N-S 00-601-5630
K-LINE INDUSTRIES INC (MI)
315 Garden Ave, Holland, MI 49424-8967
Tel (616) 396-3564 Founded/Ownrshp 1958
Sales 21.6MM^E EMP 90
Accts Ferris Busscher & Zwiers Pc
SIC 8711 Engineering services
Ch Bd: Thomas W Knowles II
*CFO: Caleb Doezema
*VP: Kevin Kammeraad
*VP: Chris Rosich
Plnt Mgr: Ben Laarman
Ql Cn Mgr: Bob Koning

D-U-N-S 12-232-2316
K-LOG INC
VAST MARKET
1224 27th St, Zion, IL 60099-2673
Tel (847) 731-5000 Founded/Ownrshp 1984
Sales 23.4MM^E EMP 30
SIC 5021 5045 Office furniture; Computer peripheral equipment
Pr: Timothy C Klebe
COO: John Murphy
Genl Mgr: Jackie Voss

K-LOVE RADIO NETWORK
See EDUCATIONAL MEDIA FOUNDATION

D-U-N-S 03-113-3044
K-MAC ENTERPRISES INC
KFC
1820 S Zero St, Fort Smith, AR 72901-8400
Tel (479) 646-2053 Founded/Ownrshp 1964
Sales 135.4MM^E EMP 3,000
SIC 5812 Fast-food restaurant, chain; Fast-food restaurant, chain
Pr: Virgil S Fiori
*Ex VP: Jon A Dyer
*Ex VP: Sam Fiori
VP: Brent McGruder

K-R AUTOMATION
See APPLIED MANUFACTURING TECHNOLOGY LLC

D-U-N-S 04-470-8352
■ **K-SEA TRANSPORTATION CORP**
(Suby of KIRBY OFFSHORE MARINE LLC) ★
3245 Richmond Ter, Staten Island, NY 10303-1309
Tel (718) 720-7207 Founded/Ownrshp 1987
Sales 32.3MM^E EMP 370
SIC 4449 River transportation, except on the St. Lawrence Seaway; Canal barge operations; River transportation, except on the St. Lawrence Seaway; Canal barge operations
Pr: Timothy Casey
*VP: Richard Falcinelli
Dir IT: Chong Caro
VP Sls: Carl Ekloft

D-U-N-S 05-447-4890 IMP
K-SOLV LP
9660 Katy Fwy, Houston, TX 77055-6322
Tel (713) 468-5768 Founded/Ownrshp 2002
Sales 72.7MM^E EMP 30
SIC 5169 Chemicals, industrial & heavy
Owner: Russ Allen
*Pt: Larry Jamieson
*Pr: David Hovde
*COO: Pamela Cox
*CFO: Steve Lombardo
*CFO: Randy Orr
*Plnt Mgr: Gary Weatherly
Manager: Andrea Orr

K-STATE
See KANSAS STATE UNIVERSITY

K-STATE UNIVERSITY FERDERAL CR
See KANSAS STATE UNIVERSITY FEDERAL CREDIT

D-U-N-S 04-443-6335 IMP
K-SWISS INC
(Suby of E.LANDWORLD LTD.)
31248 Oak Crest Dr, Westlake Village, CA 91361-4692
Tel (818) 706-5100 Founded/Ownrshp 2013
Sales 492.0MM^E EMP 609^E
Accts Grant Thornton Llp Los Angele
SIC 3021 3911 Rubber & plastics footwear; Jewelry apparel; Rubber & plastics footwear; Jewelry apparel
Pr: Larry Remington
Pr: Mark Miller
*COO: Edward Flora
*CFO: George Powlick
*Chf Mktg O: Barney Waters
VP: Hugh Henley
VP: Eric Sarin
Mng Dir: John Militano
Genl Mgr: Masaki Saito
CIO: Galen Uptgrant
IT Man: Joseph Wen

D-U-N-S 06-644-8726
K-SWISS SALES CORP
(Suby of K-SWISS INC) ★
31248 Oak Crest Dr # 150, Westlake Village, CA 91361-4692
Tel (818) 706-5100 Founded/Ownrshp 1999
Sales 484.0MM EMP 242
SIC 3021 Rubber & plastics footwear; Rubber & plastics footwear
Pr: Cheryl Kuchinka

D-U-N-S 78-714-9681
K-TECH MACHINE INC
1377 Armorlite Dr, San Marcos, CA 92069-1341
Tel (760) 471-9262 Founded/Ownrshp 1990
Sales 31.7MM^E EMP 134
SIC 3599 3444 Machine & other job shop work; Sheet metalwork; Machine & other job shop work; Sheet metalwork
Pr: Kenneth Russell
*CFO: Stuart John Russell
Ql Cn Mgr: Ray Baker

D-U-N-S 09-867-9632 IMP
K-TOOL CORP OF MICHIGAN
PREFERRED TOOL & EQUIPMENT
31111 Old Wixom Rd, Wixom, MI 48393-2425
Tel (863) 603-0777 Founded/Ownrshp 1979
Sales 28.8MM^E EMP 100
SIC 5013 5072 3545 3544 3541 Tools & equipment, automotive; Hardware; Machine tool accessories; Special dies, tools, jigs & fixtures; Machine tools, metal cutting type; Tools & equipment, automotive; Hardware; Machine tool accessories; Special dies, tools, jigs & fixtures; Machine tools, metal cutting type
Pr: Robert E Geisinger
*Sec: Bill Driscoll
Sr VP: Steve Loveless
Sales Asso: Larry Clarkson
Sales Asso: Scott Gignac

D-U-N-S 04-327-9504 IMP/EXP
■ **K-TRON INTERNATIONAL INC**
PENNSYLVANIA CRUSHER
(Suby of HILLENBRAND INC) ★
590 Woodbury Glassboro Rd, Sewell, NJ 08080-4558
Tel (856) 589-0500 Founded/Ownrshp 1997, 2010
Sales 95.7MM^E EMP 727^E
SIC 3532 3535 Feeders, ore & aggregate; Conveyors & conveying equipment; Feeders, ore & aggregate; Conveyors & conveying equipment
Ch Bd: Edward B Cloues II
*CFO: Robert E Wisniewski
*Sr VP: Kevin C Bowen
*Sr VP: Lukas Guenthardt
*Sr VP: Donald W Melchiorre
Sr VP: Ronald Remick
VP: Robert Barnett
VP: Mike Sullivan
Dir Lab: Shaun Kibbe
Admn Mgr: Mary Vaccara
Genl Mgr: John Collins

D-U-N-S 78-107-1642 EXP
■ **K-TRON INVESTMENT CO**
(Suby of K-TRON INTERNATIONAL INC) ★
300 Delaware Ave Ste 900, Wilmington, DE 19801-1671
Tel (856) 589-0500 Founded/Ownrshp 1990
Sales 89.9MM^E EMP 190
SIC 3823 Industrial process control instruments; Industrial process control instruments
Pr: Kenneth Camp
CFO: Jacky McMorris
*Treas: Dorit Bannett
Board of Directors: Andrew Byod, Amanda D Foster

D-U-N-S 07-336-5546
K-TUBE CORP
K TUBE TECHNOLOGIES
(Suby of COOK GROUP INC) ★
13400 Kirkham Way Frnt, Poway, CA 92064-7167
Tel (858) 513-9229 Founded/Ownrshp 1982
Sales 33.4MM^E EMP 100
SIC 3317 Tubing, mechanical or hypodermic sizes: cold drawn stainless; Tubing, mechanical or hypodermic sizes: cold drawn stainless
CEO: Greg May
IT Man: Carl Lindberg
Ql Cn Mgr: Lori Tysdal

D-U-N-S 14-823-0691
K-VA-T FOOD STORES INC
FOOD CITY
201 Trigg St, Abingdon, VA 24210-3435
Tel (800) 826-8451 Founded/Ownrshp 1955
Sales 1.8MMM^E EMP 10,500
SIC 5411 5141 6512 Grocery stores, chain; Groceries, general line; Commercial & industrial building operation; Grocery stores, chain; Groceries, general line; Commercial & industrial building operation
Pr: Steven C Smith
*Pr: Robert L Neeley
COO: Jesse A Lewis
*CFO: Michael T Lockard
Ofcr: Trina Robertson
Ex VP: Jody Helms
Ex VP: John Jones
*Sr VP: Thomas Hembree
VP: Phil Gass
VP: Robert Neelay
VP: Louis Scudere
VP: Don Smith
*VP: Bob Sutherland
*VP: Steve Trout
Exec: John Flint
Exec: Pamela Murray
Exec: Pat Osborne
Creative D: Tim Rhea

D-U-N-S 07-860-2414
K-W CONSTRUCTION INC
K W
320 Barnes Dr Ste 109, San Marcos, TX 78666-6173
Tel (512) 353-5900 Founded/Ownrshp 1982
Sales 21.7MM^E EMP 21
SIC 1542

D-U-N-S 19-450-8149
K/E ELECTRIC SUPPLY CORP
146 N Groesbeck Hwy, Mount Clemens, MI 48043-1529
Tel (586) 469-3005 Founded/Ownrshp 1988
Sales 45.2MM EMP 67
Accts Cusmano & Co Pc
SIC 5063 Electrical construction materials; Electrical construction materials
Pr: Rock W Kuchenmeister
*Treas: Rhandi W Kuchenmeister
*Trst: Cheryl A Kuchenmeister
*VP: Rock C Kuchenmeister
IT Man: Nancy Healy
Sls Mgr: John Heitchue
Sales Asso: Mark Bettinger
Sales Asso: Brian Lipscomb
Board of Directors: Cheryl A Kuchenmeister, Rock W Kuchenmeister, Rock C Kuchenmeister, Ryan C Kuchenmeister

D-U-N-S 07-921-3728
K1 INVESTMENT MANAGEMENT LLC
2141 Rosecrans Ave # 5110, El Segundo, CA 90245-4747
Tel (800) 310-2870 Founded/Ownrshp 2011
Sales 46.7MM^E EMP 70
SIC 6726 Investment offices
Mng Pt: R Neil Malik
Mng Pt: Taylor Beaupain
Mng Pt: Dan Ghammachi

D-U-N-S 78-927-5091
K1 SPEED INC
17221 Von Karman Ave, Irvine, CA 92614-6201
Tel (949) 250-0242 Founded/Ownrshp 2003
Sales 22.2MM^E EMP 153
SIC 7999 Go-cart raceway operation & rentals
CEO: David Danglard
Genl Mgr: Ryan Teague

D-U-N-S 19-007-8621
▲ **K12 INC**
2300 Corporate Park Dr, Herndon, VA 20171-4838
Tel (703) 483-7000 Founded/Ownrshp 2000
Sales 948.2MM EMP 4,800
Accts Bdo Usa Llp Bethesda Maryla
Tkr Sym LRN Exch NYS
SIC 8211 8299 Elementary & secondary schools; Educational services; Elementary & secondary schools; Educational services
Ch Bd: Nathaniel A Davis
Pr: Timothy L Murray
CFO: James J Rhyu
Ex VP: Allison Cleveland
Ex VP: Bruce Davis
Ex VP: George Hughes
Ex VP: Tim McEwen
Ex VP: Howard D Polsky
Ex VP: Chuck Sullivan
Sr VP: James Donley
VP: Aaron Hall
VP: John Holdren
VP: Todd McAnally
VP: Steve Watson
VP Bus Dev: Randall Greenway
VP Bus Dev: Cliff Meyers
Board of Directors: Craig R Barrett, Guillermo Bron, Fredda J Cassell, Adam L Cohn, John M Engler, Steven B Fink, Mary H Futrell, Jon Q Reynolds, Andrew H Tisch

K2
See SOURCECODE TECHNOLOGY HOLDINGS INC

K2 ADVISORS
See K2 LLC

D-U-N-S 04-600-0747
K2 CAPITAL GROUP LLC
6500 City West Pkwy # 401, Eden Prairie, MN 55344-7732
Tel (952) 224-2450 Founded/Ownrshp 2010
Sales 26.5MM^E EMP 32^E
SIC 6799 Investors
Pr: Scott H Anderson
Chf Mktg O: Bill Kelly

D-U-N-S 78-360-0146 IMP
K2 ENERGY SOLUTIONS INC
7461 Eastgate Rd, Henderson, NV 89011-4058
Tel (702) 478-3590 Founded/Ownrshp 2006
Sales 23.6MM^E EMP 60
SIC 3691 Storage batteries
Pr: Johnnie M Stoker
*CFO: Richard Gordon
CFO: Gary Stoker
CTO: Jim Hodge
Sls&Mrk Ex: James Hoganson
Mktg Mgr: Lysle Oliveros

D-U-N-S 13-164-5215
K2 INDUSTRIAL SERVICES INC
7820 Graphic Dr Ste 105, Tinley Park, IL 60477-6275
Tel (708) 928-4765 Founded/Ownrshp 2003
Sales 155.0MM EMP 1,500
SIC 2842 1799 Fireproofing buildings; Cleaning service, industrial or commercial; Specialty cleaning preparations; Coating, caulking & weather, water & fireproofing
CEO: Ted L Mansfield
*COO: Rick Napier
*CFO: Rich Bartell
*Prin: Frank Davenport
*Prin: David Johnson
Sls Mgr: Liz Beison

D-U-N-S 07-844-9326
K2 INSURANCE SERVICES LLC
514 Via De La Valle Ste 3, Solana Beach, CA 92075-2750
Tel (858) 866-8966 Founded/Ownrshp 2011
Sales NA EMP 97
SIC 6411 Insurance agents, brokers & service
CEO: Pat Kilkenny
*Pr: Bob Kimmel
*COO: Matt Lubien
*CFO: Nathan Hunter

D-U-N-S 07-876-0536
K2 INTELLIGENCE LLC
845 3rd Ave Fl 4, New York, NY 10022-6647
Tel (212) 694-7000 Founded/Ownrshp 2010
Sales NA EMP 120^E
SIC 6411 Inspection & investigation services, insurance
Ch Bd: Jeremy M Kroll
*CEO: James W Crystal
CFO: Phil Sherman
Mng Dir: Matteo Bigazzi
Mng Dir: Thomas Bock
Mng Dir: Brian Cairl
Mng Dir: Charles Carr
Mng Dir: Max Cawdron
Mng Dir: Bruce Goslin
Mng Dir: Jason Lewis
Mng Dir: David Robertson
Board of Directors: Thomas Glocer

D-U-N-S 07-024-0499
K2 LLC
K2 ADVISORS
300 Atlantic St Fl 12, Stamford, CT 06901-3514
Tel (203) 348-5252 Founded/Ownrshp 2003
Sales NA EMP 100
SIC 6371 Pension, health & welfare funds

K2 LOGISTICS
See K & K EXPRESS LLC

D-U-N-S 19-084-1168 IMP
K2 NETWORK INC
GAMERSFIRST
17011 Beach Blvd Ste 320, Huntington Beach, CA 92647-7420
Tel (949) 870-3126 Founded/Ownrshp 2001
Sales 28.5MM^E EMP 200^E
SIC 5734 Software, computer games; Software, computer games
CEO: Bjorn Book Larsson
Pr: Haesung Hwang
CEO: Joshua Hong
COO: Bjorn Book-Larsson

D-U-N-S 12-970-8587
K2 SOLUTIONS INC
5735 Us Hwy 1 N, Southern Pines, NC 28387
Tel (910) 692-6898 Founded/Ownrshp 2003
Sales 36.9MM^E EMP 275
SIC 8742 General management consultant; General management consultant
Pr: Lane Kjellsen
*Treas: Robert Spivey
*VP: James A Lynch
VP Opers: Nancy Mills-Smith
Mktg Mgr: Kate Anderson
Mktg Mgr: Heather Ybarra

D-U-N-S 03-587-5504 EXP
K2D INC
COLORADO PREMIUM FOOD
2035 2nd Ave, Greeley, CO 80631-7201
Tel (970) 313-4400 Founded/Ownrshp 1998
Sales 269.6MM^E EMP 300^E
SIC 5147 Meats & meat products; Meats & meat products
Pr: Kevin Lafleur
*CFO: Michael Rodgers
VP: Catie Beauchamp
VP: Rob Streight
Genl Mgr: Dan Lafleur
QA Dir: Dolores Casillas
Ql Cn Mgr: Paul Lange
S&M/VP: Zack Henderson

D-U-N-S 07-933-2204
K2M GROUP HOLDINGS INC
751 Miller Dr Se, Leesburg, VA 20175-8993
Tel (703) 777-3155 Founded/Ownrshp 2010
Sales 186.6MM EMP 448
Tkr Sym KTWO Exch NGS
SIC 3842 Surgical appliances & supplies; Surgical appliances & supplies
Pr: Eric D Major
*Ch Bd: Daniel A Pelak
CFO: Gregory S Cole
*Chf Mktg O: John P Kostuik
Ex VP: Gianluca Iasci
Sr VP: Dave Macdonald
Board of Directors: Brett P Brodnax, Carlos A Ferrer, Paul B Queally, Raymond A Ranelli, Sean M Traynor, Michael A Turpin

D-U-N-S 14-606-0863
K2M INC
(Suby of WELSH CARSON ANDERSON & STOWE) ★
751 Miller Dr Se Ste F1, Leesburg, VA 20175-8993
Tel (703) 777-3155 Founded/Ownrshp 2010
Sales 23.7MM^E EMP 135^E
SIC 3841 Surgical & medical instruments; Surgical & medical instruments
Pr: Eric Majors
CFO: Gregory Cole
Chf Mktg O: John Kostuik
Ex VP: Gianluca Iasci
Sr VP: Joe Chaudoin
Sr VP: Larry W Found
Sr VP: Dave Macdonald
Sr VP: Lane Major
VP: Don O'Hearn
VP: Vicki Phillos
VP: Carol Pinto
VP: Richard W Woods

K3 BMI
See K-3 RESOURCES LP

D-U-N-S 02-849-6672
K4 SOLUTIONS INC
8300 Boone Blvd Ste 200, Vienna, VA 22182-2626
Tel (703) 448-4860 Founded/Ownrshp 2001
Sales 25.3MM^E EMP 220
SIC 7379 Computer related maintenance services
Pr: Sumi Krishnan
*VP: Natarajan Krishnan

D-U-N-S 04-524-6238
KA BERGQUIST INC
1100 King Rd, Toledo, OH 43617-2002
Tel (419) 865-4196 Founded/Ownrshp 1986
Sales 44.7MM^E EMP 60
SIC 5084 1711 Propane conversion equipment; Plumbing, heating, air-conditioning contractors; Propane conversion equipment; Plumbing, heating, air-conditioning contractors
Pr: Robert Barry
*Ch: Larry Hinkley
Sr VP: Bruce Montroy
*VP: Donald Heller
*Prin: Hilda C Bergquist
*Prin: Karl Bergquist
*Prin: Charles E Ide Jr
Area Mgr: Alan Cook
Area Mgr: Ken Dubay
Area Mgr: Terry Gadberry
Area Mgr: Brian Larson

D-U-N-S 04-335-2269 IMP
■ **KA STEEL CHEMICALS INC** (DE)
KASC
(Suby of OLIN CORP) ★
15185 Main St, Lemont, IL 60439-2722
Tel (630) 257-3900 Founded/Ownrshp 1953, 2012
Sales 73.4MM^E EMP 87
SIC 5169 Caustic soda; Chlorine; Industrial chemicals; Caustic soda; Chlorine; Industrial chemicals
Pr: Robert Steel
*CFO: Bernard Ludwig
Ex VP: Michael Hurley
*Ex VP: Kenneth A Steel Jr
VP: Mike Jakovich

KAANAPALI BEACH HOTEL
See KBHL LLC

KAAP
See KOBE ALUMINUM AUTOMOTIVE PRODUCTS LLC

D-U-N-S 04-790-7084 IMP
KABA ILCO CORP
(Suby of DORMA+KABA HOLDING AG)
400 Jeffreys Rd, Rocky Mount, NC 27804-6624
Tel (252) 446-3321 Founded/Ownrshp 2005
Sales 173.0MM^E EMP 1,250
Accts Pricewater House Coopers Llp
SIC 3429 Keys, locks & related hardware; Keys & key blanks; Locks or lock sets; Keys, locks & related hardware; Keys & key blanks; Locks or lock sets
Pr: Frank Belflower
Pr: Barb Cummings
CFO: Jack Miller
VP: Amerique Du Nord
VP: Giovanni Iacovino
VP: Rich Lang
Genl Mgr: Charles Murray
Opers Mgr: Noel Baltzell
Ql Cn Mgr: Glenn Davis
Natl Sales: Harry Schneider
Mktg Dir: Alastair Cush

D-U-N-S 62-083-4820 IMP
KABA MAS LLC
(Suby of KABA AG)
749 W Short St, Lexington, KY 40508-1200
Tel (859) 253-4744 Founded/Ownrshp 2005
Sales 27.4MM^E EMP 100
SIC 3429 Locks or lock sets; Locks or lock sets
Pr: Ashley Prall
*Pr: Frank Belflower
Pr: Stephen Lim
*Pr: Carl Sideranko
CFO: Mark Duncan
Sr VP: Michael Kincaid
*VP: Larry Stokes
VP: URS Winkelmann
Dir Bus: Desmond Loh
Comm Man: Saskia Hengartner
Rgnl Mgr: Jon Nevison

D-U-N-S 00-977-6683
KABACK ENTERPRISES INC
45 W 25th St Fl 10, New York, NY 10010-2083
Tel (212) 645-5100 Founded/Ownrshp 1981
Sales 36.6MM EMP 51
Accts Marks Pareth Llp New York Ny
SIC 1711 Warm air heating & air conditioning contractor
Pr: John J Murphy
VP: Donald M Murphy
VP: Vance F Schipani
VP: Jennifer Widay
Off Mgr: Tara Strazzulla

D-U-N-S 00-417-5862
KABAM INC (DE)
795 Folsom St Fl 6, San Francisco, CA 94107-4226
Tel (415) 391-0817 Founded/Ownrshp 2006
Sales 87.1MM^E EMP 200^E
SIC 7371 Computer software development & applications; Computer software development; Computer software development & applications; Computer software development
Pr: Kevin Chou
Pr: Nick Earl
Pr: Peter Jackson
*COO: Chris Carvalho
*CFO: Steve Klei
Ofcr: Scott Thomas
*Ex VP: Kent Wakeford
Sr VP: Paxton R Cooper
Sr VP: Mike Delaet
Sr VP: Doug Inamine
Sr VP: Aaron Loeb
VP: Jordan Edelstein
VP: Andy Riedel
VP: Mike Termezy
Dir Bus: Daniel Wiggins
Board of Directors: Joe Kraus

D-U-N-S 09-452-0178 IMP
KABANA INC
616 Indian School Rd Nw, Albuquerque, NM 87102-1231
Tel (505) 843-9330 Founded/Ownrshp 1975
Sales 50.0MM^E EMP 300
SIC 3911 5944 Jewelry, precious metal; Jewelry, precious stones & precious metals; Jewelry, precious metal; Jewelry, precious stones & precious metals
Pr: Stavros Eleftheriou
CFO: Chris Preston
*Treas: Heidi Eleftheriou
VP: Susanne Bragg
VP: Nick Eleftheriou
*VP: William R Thompson
Store Mgr: Krystin Apodaca

D-U-N-S 02-563-3120
KABBAGE INC
730 Peachtree St Ne # 350, Atlanta, GA 30308-1226
Tel (855) 278-7084 *Founded/Ownrshp* 2009
Sales NA *EMP* 90
SIC 6153 Short-term business credit
Ch Bd: Marc Gorlin
CEO: Robert Frohwein
COO: Kathryn T Petralia
CFO: Simon Yoo
Chf Mktg O: Victoria Treyger
CIO: Kevin Phillips

D-U-N-S 07-992-1155
KABBLER LLC
3435 Wilshire Blvd, Los Angeles, CA 90010-1901
Tel (310) 710-7474 *Founded/Ownrshp* 2015
Sales 30.0MM *EMP* 10
SIC 7371 Computer software development
CEO: David Kwon

D-U-N-S 13-093-7035
KABCO BUILDERS INC
1300 Industrial Blvd, Boaz, AL 35957-1040
Tel (256) 593-1941 *Founded/Ownrshp* 2003
Sales 36.9MM *EMP* 180
Accts Mda Professional Group Pc
SIC 1521 General remodeling, single-family houses; General remodeling, single-family houses
Pr: Keith Bennett
**VP:* Mike Thompson
IT Man: Jason Lockmiller

KABINART
See UNITED CABINET CO LLC

D-U-N-S 92-983-0107
KABLE FULFILLMENT SERVICES INC
(*Suby of* KABLE NEWS CO INC) ★
308 E Hitt St, Mount Morris, IL 61054-1210
Tel (815) 734-4151 *Founded/Ownrshp* 1995
Sales 30.7MM^E *EMP* 800
SIC 7389 Subscription fulfillment services: magazine, newspaper, etc.; Subscription fulfillment services: magazine, newspaper, etc.
Pr: Mike Duloc
**Treas:* David Bakener
**Ex VP:* Bruce Obendorf
IT Man: Dennis Dotson

D-U-N-S 79-316-6799
KABLE MEDIA SERVICES INC
(*Suby of* DFI HOLDINGS, LLC)
14 Wall St Ste 4c, New York, NY 10005-2143
Tel (212) 705-4600 *Founded/Ownrshp* 2015
Sales 126.3MM^E *EMP* 29^E
SIC 5192 7389 Books, periodicals & newspapers; Books, periodicals & newspapers; Building scale models
CEO: Michael P Duloc
VP: Doug Knodle
CTO: Sue McCanse
IT Man: Kent Welling
Opers Mgr: Carl Arnold
Sls Dir: Mark Earley
Sls Mgr: Yasandra Botello

D-U-N-S 00-385-3405 IMP
KABLE NEWS CO INC
(*Suby of* KABLE MEDIA SERVICES INC) ★
16 S Wesley Ave, Mount Morris, IL 61054-1473
Tel (815) 734-4151 *Founded/Ownrshp* 1969
Sales 30.7MM^E *EMP* 29^E
SIC 5192 7389 Magazines; Subscription fulfillment services: magazine, newspaper, etc.; Magazines; Subscription fulfillment services: magazine, newspaper, etc.
Pr: Michael P Duloc
CFO: Tim Hough
**Sr VP:* Bruce Obendorf
VP: Richard Noser
Dir IT: Todd McMillion
IT Man: Jim Tourtillott
Info Man: William Knipp

D-U-N-S 95-636-4954
KABOOM INC
4301 Conn Ave Nw Ste M1, Washington, DC 20008-2364
Tel (202) 659-0215 *Founded/Ownrshp* 1996
Sales 29.1MM *EMP* 85
Accts Lane & Company Washington Dc
SIC 8322 Individual & family services; Individual & family services
CEO: Darell Hammond
**CFO:* Gerry Megas
VP: Scott Anderson
VP: Kate Becker
VP: James Hunn
Ex Dir: Abdoo Richard
Netwrk Mgr: Mila Liachenko
Mktg Mgr: Kate Asaturyan

KACA
See COMMUNITY ACTION KENTUCKY INC

D-U-N-S 93-151-3261
KACE LOGISTICS LLC
862 Will Carleton Rd, Carleton, MI 48117-9704
Tel (734) 946-8600 *Founded/Ownrshp* 1986
Sales 21.1MM^E *EMP* 60
SIC 4731 3577 Truck transportation brokers; Bar code (magnetic ink) printers
CEO: Kenyon S Calender
**Pr:* Joseph Parin
**VP:* Jeff Carroll
**VP:* Paul Pavelich
Opers Mgr: Tom Brown

KACHINA CADILLAC HUMMER & SAAB
See KACHINA CADILLAC HUMMER SAAB

D-U-N-S 04-805-9120
KACHINA CADILLAC HUMMER SAAB
KACHINA CADILLAC HUMMER & SAAB
1200 N Scottsdale Rd, Scottsdale, AZ 85257-3409
Tel (480) 945-1200 *Founded/Ownrshp* 1998
Sales 30.4MM^E *EMP* 150
SIC 5511 Automobiles, new & used; Automobiles, new & used
Sls Mgr: Chase Gibbs

D-U-N-S 05-363-6577
KACHINA INVESTMENTS INC
CULLIVER CADILLAC
1200 N Scottsdale Rd, Scottsdale, AZ 85257-3409
Tel (480) 945-1200 *Founded/Ownrshp* 1988
Sales 81.3MM *EMP* 110
SIC 5511 Automobiles, new & used; Automobiles, new & used
Pr: Wayne L Culiver
**Sec:* Pencie Culiver
Genl Mgr: Dan Hoggatt
Off Mgr: Peggy Rissi
Sls Dir: John Wacker
Sls Mgr: Carl Gwinn

KACHWA FOOD GROUP
See CHARLEY & SONS INC

KACI
See KATAYAMA AMERICAN CO INC

D-U-N-S 62-162-8259 IMP
KACO USA INC
(*Suby of* KACO GMBH + CO. KG)
1001 Lincoln County Pkwy, Lincolnton, NC 28092-6134
Tel (828) 428-2550 *Founded/Ownrshp* 1999
Sales 30.8MM^E *EMP* 128^E
SIC 5013 Motor vehicle supplies & new parts
CEO: Marcio Lima
**Treas:* Amy Hargett

D-U-N-S 16-202-6231 IMP
■ **KADANT BLACK CLAWSON INC**
(*Suby of* KADANT INC) ★
7312 Central Parke Blvd, Mason, OH 45040-6802
Tel (513) 229-8100 *Founded/Ownrshp* 1893
Sales 35.1MM^E *EMP* 186
SIC 3554 Paper industries machinery; Paper industries machinery
Pr: Jonathan W Painter
**Pr:* Thomas M Obrie
Ex VP: Thomas Brien
VP: Michael McKenney
Exec: Kathy Murphy
Exec: Nancy Myles
Genl Mgr: Arnold Skidmore
Dir IT: Christopher Demler
Dir IT: Ron Shryock
VP Mktg: Woody Tyler
Sls Dir: Paul Powers

D-U-N-S 61-734-9139 IMP/EXP
▲ **KADANT INC**
1 Technology Park Dr # 210, Westford, MA 01886-3139
Tel (978) 776-2000 *Founded/Ownrshp* 1991
Sales 402.1MM *EMP* 1,800^E
Tkr Sym KAI *Exch* NYS
SIC 3554 3321 2621 Paper industries machinery; Ductile iron castings; Pressed & molded pulp & fiber products; Paper industries machinery; Ductile iron castings; Pressed & molded pulp & fiber products
Pr: Jonathan W Painter
COO: Eric T Langevin
CFO: Michael J McKenney
Ofcr: Sue Pierce
Ex VP: Jeffrey L Powell
VP: Sandra L Lambert
VP: Deborah S Selwood
IT Man: Bill Giguere
IT Man: John Huang
Sls Dir: John Lefkowitz
Mktg Mgr: Vicki Hunsberger
Board of Directors: John M Albertine, Scott P Brown, Thomas C Leonard, William A Rainville, William P Tully

D-U-N-S 82-915-2029
KADELS AUTO BODY LLC
9350 Sw Tigard St, Tigard, OR 97223-5238
Tel (503) 598-1159 *Founded/Ownrshp* 2007
Sales 24.2MM^E *EMP* 350
SIC 7532 Top & body repair & paint shops; Top & body repair & paint shops
IT Man: Van Truong

D-U-N-S 62-380-0401
KADENT CORP
645 Penn St Ste 400, Reading, PA 19601-3559
Tel (800) 364-0735 *Founded/Ownrshp* 2005
Sales 25.9MM^E *EMP* 245^E
SIC 7374 7322 Data processing service; Collection agency, except real estate
Prin: John P Fiumano
Sr VP: John M Kunysz Jr
Software D: Suzanne Miller
Ql Cn Mgr: Joanne Koehler

D-U-N-S 94-617-6401
KADES CORP
MCDONALD'S
5621 Red Bluff Rd, Pasadena, TX 77505-2638
Tel (281) 479-4700 *Founded/Ownrshp* 1992
Sales 30.0MM^E *EMP* 850
SIC 5812 Fast-food restaurant, chain; Fast-food restaurant, chain
Pr: Ken Kades

D-U-N-S 09-648-9539
KADLEC MOTORS INC
TOM'S CADILLAC-HONDA
3333 Wilder Rd Nw, Rochester, MN 55901-5401
Tel (507) 281-2500 *Founded/Ownrshp* 1979
Sales 25.3MM^E *EMP* 50
SIC 5511 Automobiles, new & used
Pr: Thomas Kadlec
Sls Dir: Andy Gostomczik

D-U-N-S 07-666-0513
KADLEC REGIONAL MEDICAL CENTER
888 Swift Blvd, Richland, WA 99352-3514
Tel (509) 946-4611 *Founded/Ownrshp* 1984
Sales 417.4MM *EMP* 2,668
Accts Moss-Adams Llp Yakima Washin
SIC 8062 General medical & surgical hospitals; General medical & surgical hospitals
CEO: Lane Savitch
**Pr:* Rand Wortman
COO: Jason Paslean
**CFO:* Julie Meek
Bd of Dir: Edward Temple
**VP:* Larry Christensen
**VP:* Jeffrey Clark
**VP:* Dale Hoekema
**VP:* Bill Wingo
Dir Rx: Dave Pearson
Genl Mgr: Flash Fiegel

D-U-N-S 96-292-3947
KADMON CORP LLC
450 E 29th St Fl 5, New York, NY 10016-8367
Tel (212) 308-6000 *Founded/Ownrshp* 2006
Sales 31.3MM^E *EMP* 99^E
SIC 2834 Pharmaceutical preparations; Pharmaceutical preparations
Ch: Samuel D Waksal
**CEO:* Harlan Waksal
**CFO:* Konstantin Poukalov
Ex VP: Steve Gordon
**Ex VP:* John Ryan
**Ex VP:* Zhenping Zhu
Sr VP: Ronda Bixon
**Sr VP:* Michael Boxer
**Sr VP:* Lawrence K Cohen
Sr VP: Ellen Lubman
VP: Cameron Durrant
VP: James Tonra
VP: Sara Weiss
**Dir Surg:* Kevin Llu
**Dir Surg:* Jacinta Nagler
Assoc Dir: Bryson Bennett
Assoc Dir: Aaron Enke
Assoc Dir: Dan Lu

D-U-N-S 84-391-3216 IMP
KADMON PHARMACEUTICALS LLC
(*Suby of* KADMON CORP LLC) ★
119 Commonwealth Dr, Warrendale, PA 15086-7503
Tel (724) 778-6100 *Founded/Ownrshp* 2010
Sales 26.1MM^E *EMP* 95
SIC 2834 Pharmaceutical preparations; Pharmaceutical preparations
**Ex VP:* Steven N Gordon
**Ex VP:* Adriann Sax
**Ex VP:* Zhenping Zhu
**Sr VP:* Lawrence K Cohen
Sr VP: Thomas Gallagher
Sr VP: Louis Lombardo
Sr VP: David Munno
VP: Hamm Gary Conte
VP: Jonathan Ieyoub
VP: Jean Kim
VP: Gregory Moss
VP: Doug Williams

D-U-N-S 06-400-6398
KADON PRECISION MACHINING INC
3744 Publishers Dr, Rockford, IL 61109-6316
Tel (779) 368-0294 *Founded/Ownrshp* 1973
Sales 22.1MM^E *EMP* 100
SIC 3451 Screw machine products; Screw machine products
Pr: Jeffrey Franklin
**Sec:* Cheryl L Spencer
Prd Mgr: Justin Franklin

D-U-N-S 04-677-8718
KADRMAS LEE & JACKSON INC
(*Suby of* KLJ SOLUTIONS CO) ★
1463 I94 Business Loop E, Dickinson, ND 58601-6434
Tel (701) 355-8400 *Founded/Ownrshp* 2001
Sales 85.2MM^E *EMP* 780
Accts Dickinson Nd
SIC 8711 8713 Engineering services; Civil engineering; Structural engineering; Electrical or electronic engineering; Surveying services; Engineering services; Civil engineering; Structural engineering; Electrical or electronic engineering; Surveying services
CEO: Niles Hushka
**Treas:* Dean Anagnost
**VP:* Barry Schuchard
Off Mgr: Sherry Kulish
IT Man: Jon Artz
Sfty Mgr: Troy Clark
Sfty Mgr: Darin Rathjen
Snr PM: Tracy Haag
Snr Mgr: Colin Moran
Snr Mgr: Ron Williams

D-U-N-S 07-988-8620
KADRMAS LEE & JACKSON INC (ND)
12510 World Plaza Ln # 1, Fort Myers, FL 33907-3924
Tel (239) 208-9527 *Founded/Ownrshp* 1971
Sales 8.3MM^E *EMP* 593
SIC 8711 Engineering services
CEO: Niles Hushka

KAEC
See KENTUCKY ASSOCIATION OF ELECTRIC CO-OPERATIVES INC

D-U-N-S 05-826-2346 IMP
KAEMARK INC
KAEMARK SALON FURNISHINGS
1338 County Road 208, Giddings, TX 78942-4742
Tel (979) 542-3651 *Founded/Ownrshp* 2000
Sales 24.0MM^E *EMP* 75
SIC 5251 Hardware
Pr: Howard H Owen
VP: Owen Karen
**VP:* Karen Owen
Sfty Mgr: Daniel Krause
VP Mktg: Owen Jeff
Manager: Jeff Coit
Art Dir: Jehan Medina

KAEMARK SALON FURNISHINGS
See KAEMARK INC

D-U-N-S 00-649-0064
KAEMMERLEN ELECTRIC CO
2728 Locust St, Saint Louis, MO 63103-1479
Tel (314) 535-2226 *Founded/Ownrshp* 1924
Sales 28.4MM^E *EMP* 130
Accts Rubin Brown
SIC 1731 General electrical contractor; General electrical contractor
Pr: Robert M Kaemmerlen Jr
**CFO:* Brian J Trembath
**VP:* Tracey K Trembath
VP: Bob Woestendiek
Genl Mgr: Jim Withers
CIO: Ron Bacheller

KAEMPF & HARRIS CUSTOM SHTMTL
See R W WARNER INC

D-U-N-S 83-792-2959
KAERCHER CAMPBELL ASSOCIATE IN
1800 Century Park E # 400, Los Angeles, CA 90067-1507
Tel (310) 556-1900 *Founded/Ownrshp* 2008
Sales NA *EMP* 119
SIC 6411 Insurance agents, brokers & service
Ch Bd: David Putman
Pr: Rod Austria
**Pr:* Allan Kaercher
**CEO:* Penni Campbell
VP: Maureen Bernstein
VP: Rick Krause
VP: Tia Porter
VP: Joan Sormanti

D-U-N-S 00-423-1783 IMP
KAESER AND BLAIR INC
4236 Grissom Dr, Batavia, OH 45103-1696
Tel (513) 732-6400 *Founded/Ownrshp* 1894
Sales 72.6MM *EMP* 117
SIC 5199

D-U-N-S 09-960-4217 IMP/EXP
KAESER COMPRESSORS INC
(*Suby of* SIGMA-TEC GMBH)
511 Sigma Dr, Fredericksburg, VA 22408-7330
Tel (540) 898-5500 *Founded/Ownrshp* 2008
Sales 126.8MM^E *EMP* 371
Accts Rodl Langford De Kock Llp Atl
SIC 5084 Compressors, except air conditioning; Compressors, except air conditioning
Pr: Frank R Mueller
**VP:* Laurie L Pouliot
VP: Roy A Stuhlman
Area Mgr: Gabriel Atodiresei
Brnch Mgr: Kevin Gates
Dist Mgr: Joe D'Orazio
Dist Mgr: Mark Olson
IT Man: Jennifer Bareford
IT Man: Cheryl Garland
QC Dir: Tim Fitch
Opers Mgr: Chris Erickson

D-U-N-S 00-449-0470
KAFFENBARGER TRUCK EQUIPMENT CO INC (OH)
10100 Ballentine Pike, New Carlisle, OH 45344-9534
Tel (937) 845-3804 *Founded/Ownrshp* 1961, 1965
Sales 28.1MM^E *EMP* 180
SIC 3713 5013 Truck bodies (motor vehicles); Truck parts & accessories; Truck bodies (motor vehicles); Truck parts & accessories
Pr: Larry Kaffenbarger
**Prin:* Edward W Dunn
**Prin:* Everett L Kaffenbarger

D-U-N-S 16-776-6658
KAFKA GRANITE LLC
550 State Highway 153, Mosinee, WI 54455-1741
Tel (715) 687-2423 *Founded/Ownrshp* 1979
Sales 21.8MM^E *EMP* 60
SIC 1411 Granite, dimension-quarrying

KAFP
See KAISER ALUMINUM FABRICATED PRODUCTS LLC

D-U-N-S 17-254-7130
KAG LOGISTICS INC
4366 Mount Pleasant St Nw, North Canton, OH 44720-5446
Tel (877) 999-2524 *Founded/Ownrshp* 2004
Sales 22.0MM^E *EMP* 132^E
SIC 4613 Gasoline pipelines (common carriers)
Pr: Dennis A Nash Predir
**Ex VP:* Bill Downey
**Ex VP:* Patty Harcourt
**Ex VP:* Becky Perlaky
VP: Mike Forbes
**VP:* Stan Tedder
Opers Mgr: Greg Kemp

D-U-N-S 79-825-1109
KAGOME FOODS INC
(*Suby of* KAGOME INC) ★
710 N Pearl St, Osceola, AR 72370-2038
Tel (870) 563-2601 *Founded/Ownrshp* 2007
Sales 62.6MM^E *EMP* 230
SIC 2079 1541 Edible fats & oils; Food products manufacturing or packing plant construction; Edible fats & oils; Food products manufacturing or packing plant construction
CEO: Luis Deoliveira
**Pr:* Hiroshi Mori
CFO: Jason Collard
**Treas:* Yoshikazu Watanabe
**VP:* James McGinnis
Genl Mgr: John Allen
Dir IT: David Virts
Plnt Mgr: Jerry Hughey

D-U-N-S 02-756-4058 IMP/EXP
KAGOME INC
(*Suby of* KAGOME CO.,LTD.)
333 Johnson Rd, Los Banos, CA 93635-9768
Tel (209) 826-8850 *Founded/Ownrshp* 1998
Sales 66.1MM^E *EMP* 230^E
SIC 2033 Tomato products: packaged in cans, jars, etc.; Tomato products: packaged in cans, jars, etc.
Pr: Luis De Oliviera
CFO: Pete Watanabe
VP: Tresa Chapman
**VP:* Ann Hall
Opers Mgr: Dennis Brazil
Opers Mgr: Brazil Dennis

Prd Mgr: Jaime Sandoval
Ql Cn Mgr: Elaine Betanio
Sls Mgr: Jeff Bickle
Snr Mgr: Luis De Oliveira

D-U-N-S 87-813-9513
KAHALA BRANDS LTD
BLIMPIE
9311 E Via De Ventura, Scottsdale, AZ 85258-3423
Tel (480) 362-4800 *Founded/Ownrshp* 1997
Sales 39.3MM^E *EMP* 702
SIC 5812 6794 Fast-food restaurant, chain; Franchises, selling or licensing; Fast-food restaurant, chain; Franchises, selling or licensing
CEO: Michael Serruya
Ex VP: Chris Henry
Sr VP: Tony Crosby
VP: John Brunn
VP: Kevin Burnett
VP: Tom Ciomek
VP: Eddy Jimenez
VP: Walter Mejia
VP: Renee Mitchell
VP: Tom O'Dear
VP: Sherin Sakr
VP: Ronald Stilwell

KAHALA HOTEL AND RESORT, THE
See RESORTTRUST HAWAII LLC

D-U-N-S 92-987-5748
KAHALA HOTEL ASSOCIATES LIMITED LIABILITY LIMITED PARTNERSHIP
KAHALA MNDRIN ORIENTAL HAWA HT
5000 Kahala Ave, Honolulu, HI 96816-5498
Tel (808) 739-8888 *Founded/Ownrshp* 1993
Sales 15.0MM^E *EMP* 450
SIC 7011 Resort hotel; Resort hotel
Mng Pt: Charles M Sweeney
Genl Mgr: Fify Shyanguya

D-U-N-S 61-473-6754
KAHALA HOTEL INVESTORS LLC
5000 Kahala Ave, Honolulu, HI 96816-5498
Tel (808) 739-8739 *Founded/Ownrshp* 1987
Sales 39.7MM^E *EMP* 500
SIC 7011 6799 Resort hotel; Investors; Resort hotel; Investors
Prin: Stefa Bascon
IT Man: Adam Schroder
MIS Mgr: Velma Kam

KAHALA MNDRIN ORIENTAL HAWA HT
See KAHALA HOTEL ASSOCIATES LIMITED LIABILITY LIMITED PARTNERSHIP

KAHALA NUI
See SENIOR KAHALA LIVING COMMUNITY INC

D-U-N-S 15-916-7993
KAHANE & ASSOCIATES PA
FLORIDA PREMIER TITLE & ESCROW
8201 Peters Rd Ste 3000, Plantation, FL 33324-3292
Tel (954) 382-3486 *Founded/Ownrshp* 2004
Sales 40.6MM^E *EMP* 300
SIC 8111 General practice law office; General practice law office
Pr: Robert S Kahane

D-U-N-S 11-735-7608
KAHIKI FOODS INC
(*Suby of* ABARTA INC) ★
1100 Morrison Rd, Gahanna, OH 43230-6645
Tel (614) 322-3180 *Founded/Ownrshp* 2007
Sales 48.3MM^E *EMP* 160
SIC 2038 Frozen specialties; Frozen specialties
Pr: Alan L Hoover
CFO: Frederick A Niebauer
VP: Tim Tsao
VP: Gil Wilson
Area Mgr: Jonathan Velderrain
Prd Mgr: Henry Liu
Prd Mgr: Mike Williams
Mktg Dir: Scott Corey

KAHIMHALA BHVORAL HLTH SYSTEMS
See SUTTER HEALTH PACIFIC

D-U-N-S 02-687-5302
KAHLIG ENTERPRISES INC
BLUEBONNET MOTORS
351 S Interstate 35, New Braunfels, TX 78130-4894
Tel (830) 606-8011 *Founded/Ownrshp* 1984
Sales 99.1MM^E *EMP* 230
SIC 5511 Automobiles, new & used; Trucks, tractors & trailers: new & used; Automobiles, new & used; Trucks, tractors & trailers: new & used
Pr: Clarence J Kahlig II
Pt: Wes Studdard
VP: Gary Kahlig
Exec: Jeff Nolan
Genl Mgr: William F Vaughn Jr
Dir IT: Jeremy Echols
Sls Mgr: Ed Donaho
Sls Mgr: Alan Gullet
Sls Mgr: Bob Hasbrook
Sls Mgr: Donna Kneese
Sales Asso: Neil Bligh

D-U-N-S 61-511-7744
KAHLIG MOTOR CO
NORTH PARK LEXUS
611 Lockhill Selma Rd, San Antonio, TX 78216-5041
Tel (210) 308-8900 *Founded/Ownrshp* 1994
Sales 167.2MM *EMP* 140
Accts Morrison Brown Argiz & Farra
SIC 5511 7515 Automobiles, new & used; Passenger car leasing; Automobiles, new & used; Passenger car leasing
Pr: Clarence J Kahlig
VP: William F Vaughn Jr
VP: Lee Willis
Sls Dir: Toma Murders
Sls Mgr: Tripp Bridges
Sls Mgr: Tom Murgers
Sales Asso: Leslie Hernandez
Sales Asso: Erik Joseph
Sales Asso: Erika Joseph
Sales Asso: Jose Karam
Sales Asso: Jamesa Pelayo

D-U-N-S 60-685-8132
KAHLO CHRYSLER JEEP DODGE INC
9900 Pleasant St, Noblesville, IN 46060-3940
Tel (317) 773-6363 *Founded/Ownrshp* 1987
Sales 34.3MM^E *EMP* 75
SIC 5511 Automobiles, new & used; Automobiles, new & used
Pr: Peter Kahlo
Sec: Donna Kahlo
VP: Kevin Kahlo
Genl Mgr: Salli Brown
Sls Mgr: Tom Porter
Sales Asso: Maria Hedge
Sales Asso: Stan Ignas

KAHN LUCAS
See KAHN-LUCAS-LANCASTER INC

D-U-N-S 00-155-1522 IMP/EXP
KAHN-LUCAS-LANCASTER INC (PA)
KAHN LUCAS
805 Estelle Dr Ste 101, Lancaster, PA 17601-2131
Tel (717) 396-7859 *Founded/Ownrshp* 1889, 1964
Sales 48.7MM^E *EMP* 185
SIC 2369 2361 Girls' & children's outerwear; Dresses: girls', children's & infants'; Girls' & children's outerwear; Dresses: girls', children's & infants'
Pr: Howard Kahn
Ch Bd: Andrew L Kahn
CFO: John Zander
Treas: Donald E McKonly
VP: Paul R Beshler
Site Mgr: Lucas Kahn

D-U-N-S 18-107-2547 IMP
KAHRS INTERNATIONAL INC
(*Suby of* AB GUSTAF KAHR)
940 Centre Cir Ste 1000, Altamonte Springs, FL 32714-7242
Tel (407) 260-9910 *Founded/Ownrshp* 1986
Sales 34.2MM^E *EMP* 30
SIC 5031 Lumber: rough, dressed & finished; Lumber: rough, dressed & finished
Pr: Sean Swanson
Pr: Carsten Sventesson
VP: Chuck Antonucci
VP: Sean Brennan
VP: Tim Colgan
VP: Peter Svanberg
VP: Bruce Uhler
Rgnl Mgr: Rusty Lawson
Genl Mgr: Sverre Severinsen
IT Man: Shane Smartt
Sls Mgr: Dave Barnard

D-U-N-S 88-395-9079
KAHUNA VENTURES LLC
11400 Westmoor Cir # 325, Broomfield, CO 80021-2740
Tel (303) 451-7374 *Founded/Ownrshp* 1999
Sales 25.1MM^E *EMP* 72^E
SIC 2911 Gasoline
Mng Pt: Gary Davis

KAI
See KURARAY AMERICA INC

KAI RESTAURANT
See ITO EN (NORTH AMERICA) INC

KAI TOTAL PAVEMENT MANAGEMENT
See KANSAS ASPHALT INC

D-U-N-S 08-442-4043 IMP/EXP
KAI USA LTD
KERSHAW KNIVES
(*Suby of* SANSUI SHOJI K.K.)
18600 Sw Teton Ave, Tualatin, OR 97062-8841
Tel (503) 682-1966 *Founded/Ownrshp* 1974
Sales 102.4MM *EMP* 150^E
Accts Maginnis & Carey Llp Portlan
SIC 3421 Carving sets; Carving sets
Ch Bd: Koji Endo
Ex VP: Hiroshi Igarashi
Exec: Les Shields
Prd Mgr: David Lyman
Natl Sales: Thomas Welk
S&M/VP: Steve Grutbo
Mktg Dir: Jeff Goddard

KAIBAB ADVENTURE OUTFITTERS
See KAIBAB TRAILS INC

D-U-N-S 78-298-0569
KAIBAB TRAILS INC
KAIBAB ADVENTURE OUTFITTERS
391 S Main St, Moab, UT 84532-2540
Tel (435) 259-7423 *Founded/Ownrshp* 1990
Sales 800.0M *EMP* 296
SIC 4725 5699 7999 Tour operators; Sports apparel; Bicycle & motorcycle rental services; Tour operators; Sports apparel; Bicycle & motorcycle rental services
Pr: Jessica Stabrylla
Treas: Brett Taylor

KAIC
See KAISER ALUMINUM INVESTMENTS CO

KAILYANUL
See ORMSBY TRUCKING INC

D-U-N-S 17-828-4105
■ **KAIRAK INC**
KAIRAK INNOVATIONS
(*Suby of* ILLINOIS TOOL WORKS INC) ★
4401 Blue Mound Rd, Fort Worth, TX 76106-1928
Tel (714) 870-8661 *Founded/Ownrshp* 2006
Sales 20.7MM^E *EMP* 150
SIC 3585 5078 Refrigeration equipment, complete; Refrigeration equipment & supplies; Refrigeration equipment, complete; Refrigeration equipment & supplies
CEO: Craig S Kushen

KAIRAK INNOVATIONS
See KAIRAK INC

D-U-N-S 00-921-3570
KAISER AEROSPACE & ELECTRONICS CORP
2701 Orchard Pkwy Ste 100, San Jose, CA 95134-2008
Tel (949) 250-1015 *Founded/Ownrshp* 2000
Sales NA *EMP* 3,580
SIC 3728

KAISER ALUMINUM & CHEMICAL
See KAISER BELLWOOD CORP

D-U-N-S 17-776-2192
▲ **KAISER ALUMINUM CORP**
27422 Portola Pkwy # 200, Foothill Ranch, CA 92610-2836
Tel (949) 614-1740 *Founded/Ownrshp* 1946
Sales 1.3MMM *EMP* 2,650
Tkr Sym KALU *Exch* NGS
SIC 3334 3353 3354 3355 Primary aluminum; Aluminum sheet, plate & foil; Aluminum rod & bar; Bars, extruded, aluminum; Rods, extruded, aluminum; Wire, aluminum: made in rolling mills; Cable, aluminum: made in rolling mills; Primary aluminum; Aluminum sheet, plate & foil; Aluminum rod & bar; Bars, extruded, aluminum; Rods, extruded, aluminum; Wire, aluminum: made in rolling mills; Cable, aluminum: made in rolling mills
Ch Bd: Jack A Hockema
V Ch: Carolyn Bartholomew
Pr: Ted Diguiseppe
COO: Jen Ryu
COO: Malcolm Wright
CFO: Daniel J Rinkenberger
Treas: Melinda C Ellsworth
Ex VP: Peter S Bunin
Ex VP: John M Donnan
Ex VP: Keith A Harvey
Ex VP: Keith Harvey
Sr VP: Peter Bunn
VP: Holly Duckworth
VP: Mark Krouse
VP: W S Lamb
VP: Barton McMillin
VP: Del Miller
VP: Neal E West
VP: Michael Zerga
Board of Directors: Carolyn Bartholomew, David Foster, L Patrick Hassey, Teresa A Hopp, Alfred E Osborne Jr, Jack Quinn, Thomas M Van Leeuwen, Brett E Wilcox

D-U-N-S 78-383-9652 IMP/EXP
■ **KAISER ALUMINUM FABRICATED PRODUCTS LLC**
(*Suby of* KAISER ALUMINUM CORP) ★
600 Kaiser Dr, Heath, OH 43056-1088
Tel (740) 522-1151 *Founded/Ownrshp* 2006
Sales 27.9MM^E *EMP* 245
SIC 1099 Aluminum ore mining; Aluminum ore mining
Genl Mgr: Dragos Ungurean
Sls Mgr: Karen Miller

D-U-N-S 78-704-3715 IMP
■ **KAISER ALUMINUM FABRICATED PRODUCTS LLC**
KAFP
(*Suby of* KAISER ALUMINUM CORP) ★
27422 Portola Pkwy # 200, Foothill Ranch, CA 92610-2831
Tel (949) 614-1740 *Founded/Ownrshp* 2006
Sales 721.5MM^E *EMP* 2,400
SIC 3353 3334 3354 3355 Aluminum sheet, plate & foil; Primary aluminum; Aluminum rod & bar; Wire, aluminum: made in rolling mills; Aluminum sheet, plate & foil; Primary aluminum; Aluminum rod & bar; Wire, aluminum: made in rolling mills
Pr: Jack A Hockema
CFO: Joseph P Bellino
VP: John M Donnan
Dir IT: Jerry Tessim

D-U-N-S 62-404-0619
■ **KAISER ALUMINUM INVESTMENTS CO**
KAIC
(*Suby of* KAISER ALUMINUM CORP) ★
27422 Portola Pkwy # 200, Foothill Ranch, CA 92610-2831
Tel (949) 614-1740 *Founded/Ownrshp* 2006
Sales 161.5MM^E *EMP* 2,400
SIC 3353 3334 3354 3355 Aluminum sheet, plate & foil; Primary aluminum; Aluminum rod & bar; Wire, aluminum: made in rolling mills; Aluminum sheet, plate & foil; Primary aluminum; Aluminum rod & bar; Wire, aluminum: made in rolling mills
Pr: Jack A Hockema
CFO: Joseph P Bellino
Treas: Daniel J Rinkenberger
VP: John M Donnan

D-U-N-S 11-549-5434
KAISER ASSOCIATES INC
1615 L St Nw Ste 1300, Washington, DC 20036-5677
Tel (202) 454-9000 *Founded/Ownrshp* 1982
Sales 22.7MM^E *EMP* 105
SIC 8742 8748 Business planning & organizing services; Business consulting
CEO: Kevin Slayden
Sr Pt: Jose Netto
Pr: Lisa Pizzarelo
Sr VP: Kathy Ebner
VP: Ali Cumber
VP: John Rodgers
Mng Dir: Rupert Barnard
Mktg Dir: Robert Fifer
Mktg Dir: Mary Redding
Snr Mgr: Aimee Martin

D-U-N-S 09-063-3314
■ **KAISER BELLWOOD CORP**
KAISER ALUMINUM & CHEMICAL
(*Suby of* KAFP) ★
1901 Reymet Rd, North Chesterfield, VA 23237-3723
Tel (804) 743-6300 *Founded/Ownrshp* 1997
Sales 20.8MM^E *EMP* 100
SIC 3354 Pipe, extruded, aluminum; Pipe, extruded, aluminum
Pr: Jack A Hockema
VP: Peter Bunin
Genl Mgr: Stephen Rogers
IT Man: Teno Bratton

KAISER BUICK
See KAISER PONTIAC BUICK GMCTRUCK INC

KAISER CNTRACT CLG SPCLSTS INC
See KAISER CONTRACT CLEANING SPECIALISTS LLC

D-U-N-S 96-743-0745
KAISER CONTRACT CLEANING SPECIALISTS LLC
KAISER CNTRACT CLG SPCLSTS INC
(*Suby of* PACKERS HOLDINGS LLC) ★
3691 Prism Ln, Kieler, WI 53812
Tel (608) 568-3413 *Founded/Ownrshp* 2010
Sales 32.5MM^E *EMP* 3,000^E
SIC 7349 Building maintenance services; Building maintenance services
CEO: Jeff Kaiser
VP: Anne Kaiser
Prin: Kevin Mc Donnell

D-U-N-S 00-685-1513
KAISER ELECTRIC INC (MO)
1552 Fencorp Dr, Fenton, MO 63026-2942
Tel (636) 305-1515 *Founded/Ownrshp* 1949, 1962
Sales 30.6MM *EMP* 180
Accts Maher & Co St Louis Missou
SIC 1731 General electrical contractor; General electrical contractor
Pr: Kenneth Naumann
Ex VP: Mike Compton
VP: Ed Casey
VP: Michael C Compton
VP: James W Kaiser
VP: Michael J Lundry
VP: Roger Messmer
VP: Michael Murphy
VP: Jason Russell
Snr PM: Steven Elfrink

D-U-N-S 96-783-5690
KAISER FDN HEALTH PLAN OF COLORADO
1 Kaiser Plz Ste 15l, Oakland, CA 94612-3610
Tel (510) 271-6611 *Founded/Ownrshp* 2011
Sales 3.2MMM *EMP* 15^E
Accts Pricewaterhousecoopers Llp Ph
SIC 8099 Childbirth preparation clinic; Childbirth preparation clinic
VP: Justin Chang
Pharmcst: Monica Yoshinaga

D-U-N-S 07-169-5183
KAISER FOUNDATION HEALTH PLAN INC (CA)
1 Kaiser Plz, Oakland, CA 94612-3610
Tel (510) 271-5800 *Founded/Ownrshp* 1955
Sales NA *EMP* 13,651
Accts Kpmg Llp San Francisco Ca
SIC 6324 Hospital & medical service plans; Health maintenance organization (HMO), insurance only; Dental insurance; Group hospitalization plans; Hospital & medical service plans; Health maintenance organization (HMO), insurance only; Dental insurance; Group hospitalization plans
Ch Bd: Bernard J Tyson
COO: Harold F Wolf III
CFO: Kathy Lancaster
Chf Mktg O: Patrick Courneya
Ofcr: David Strickland
Ex VP: Richard Daniels
Sr VP: Raymond J Baxter PHD
Sr VP: Robert M Crane
Sr VP: J Clifford Dodd
Sr VP: Philip Fasano
Sr VP: Louise Liang MD
Sr VP: Louise L Liang MD
Sr VP: Laurence G O Neil
Sr VP: Paul B Records
Sr VP: Arthur M Southam MD
Sr VP: Bernard Tyson
Sr VP: Steve Zatkin
VP: Diane Comer
VP: Hovannes Daniels
VP: Carol Davis-Smith
VP: Lisa Koltun
Board of Directors: Regina Benjamin, Judith A Johansen, Jenny J Ming, Edward Pei, Meg Porfido, Richard Shannon, Sandra P Thompkins

D-U-N-S 04-070-7275
KAISER FOUNDATION HEALTH PLAN OF COLORADO
(*Suby of* KAISER FOUNDATION HEALTH PLAN INC) ★
10350 E Dakota Ave, Denver, CO 80247-1314
Tel (866) 239-1677 *Founded/Ownrshp* 1969
Sales NA *EMP* 7,000
SIC 6324 Hospital & medical service plans; Hospital & medical service plans
Pr: Donna Lynne
Adm Dir: Shelly Dodd
IT Man: Gwyn Saylor

D-U-N-S 15-522-2102
KAISER FOUNDATION HEALTH PLAN OF GEORGIA INC
(*Suby of* KAISER FOUNDATION HEALTH PLAN INC) ★
3495 Piedmont Rd Ne # 9, Atlanta, GA 30305-1717
Tel (404) 364-7000 *Founded/Ownrshp* 1984
Sales NA *EMP* 1,111
SIC 6324 Hospital & medical service plans; Hospital & medical service plans
CEO: George C Halvorson
Pr: Julie Miller-Phipps
CFO: Kathy Lancaster
Ofcr: Larry Panatera
Ex VP: Donna Lynne
VP: Tammy Jones
VP: Jonna Kirkwood
VP: James Linnane
VP: Gene No
VP: Dawn Rock
VP: Michael Wathen

Dir Lab: Tom Addington
Dir Rx: Gary Beals

D-U-N-S 07-266-1143
KAISER FOUNDATION HEALTH PLAN OF MID-ATLANTIC STATES INC
(*Suby of* KAISER FOUNDATION HEALTH PLAN INC) ★
2101 E Jefferson St, Rockville, MD 20852-4908
Tel (301) 816-2424 *Founded/Ownrshp* 1995
Sales NA *EMP* 950
SIC 6324 Hospital & medical service plans; Hospital & medical service plans
CEO: Bernard J Tyson
**Pr:* Kim Horn
**CEO:* George C Halvorson
**CEO:* Robert M Pearl
CFO: Michael Wise
**Treas:* Thomas R Meier
Ofcr: Ken Hunter
**Sr VP:* Mitch Goodstein
**Sr VP:* Kathy Lancaster
**VP:* Gregory A Adams
VP: Sherri Locke
VP: Heather Wilson

D-U-N-S 04-491-0461
KAISER FOUNDATION HEALTH PLAN OF NORTHWEST (OR)
(*Suby of* KAISER FOUNDATION HEALTH PLAN INC) ★
500 Ne Multnomah St # 100, Portland, OR 97232-2023
Tel (503) 813-2440 *Founded/Ownrshp* 1942
Sales NA *EMP* 1,495
SIC 6324 Hospital & medical service plans; Hospital & medical service plans
Pr: Bernard J Tyson
**CEO:* Andrew McCulloch
Sr VP: Robert Crane
IT Man: Merry Maese

D-U-N-S 05-305-2619 IMP
KAISER FOUNDATION HOSPITALS INC
KAISER PERMANENTE
1 Kaiser Plz, Oakland, CA 94612-3610
Tel (510) 271-6611 *Founded/Ownrshp* 1948
Sales NA *EMP* 175,668
SIC 8062 8011 General medical & surgical hospitals; General medical & surgical hospitals; Medical centers
Pr: Bernard J Tyson
Pr: Janet Liang
CFO: Kathy Lancaster
Ex VP: Patrick Courneya
Sr VP: Daniel P Garcia
VP: Richard Daniels
VP: Tammy Fisher
Assoc Dir: Yan Chow
Assoc Dir: Rod Dayley
Comm Man: Anne Little
Ex Dir: Sas Mukherjee

KAISER FRANCES OIL CO
See TILCO INC

D-U-N-S 01-411-5088
KAISER GRAND AVE DENTAL
(*Suby of* KAISER FOUNDATION HOSPITALS INC) ★
1314 Ne Grand Ave, Portland, OR 97232-1127
Tel (503) 280-2877 *Founded/Ownrshp* 1990
Sales 7.2MM^E *EMP* 530
SIC 8021 Dental clinics & offices; Dental clinics & offices
Pr: Barbara A West
**CFO:* Rolfe Norman

D-U-N-S 18-638-2701
▲ **KAISER GROUP HOLDINGS INC**
9300 Lee Hwy, Fairfax, VA 22031-6050
Tel (703) 934-3000 *Founded/Ownrshp* 2000
Sales 578.9MM^E *EMP* 915
Tkr Sym KGHI *Exch* OTO
SIC 4953 Non-hazardous waste disposal sites
Pr: Douglas W McMinn
**Ch Bd:* Frank E Williams Jr
CFO: Allen Stewart
VP: Paul Jackson
VP: Courtney Partlow
VP: Matthew Perry

D-U-N-S 13-372-5262
KAISER HEALTH PLAN ASSET MANAGEMENT INC
KAISER PERMANENTE
(*Suby of* KAISER FOUNDATION HEALTH PLAN INC) ★
1 Kaiser Plz Ste 1333, Oakland, CA 94612-3604
Tel (510) 271-5910 *Founded/Ownrshp* 1998
Sales 31.6MM *EMP* 50
Accts Kpmg Llp San Francisco Ca
SIC 8741 Hospital management; Hospital management
Pr: Thomas R Meier

D-U-N-S 11-099-2307
KAISER HOSPITAL ASSET MANAGEMENT INC
K H A M
(*Suby of* KAISER FOUNDATION HOSPITALS INC) ★
1 Kaiser Plz 19l, Oakland, CA 94612-3610
Tel (510) 271-5910 *Founded/Ownrshp* 2003
Sales 170.4MM *EMP* 25
SIC 5047 Hospital equipment & supplies
Pr: Thoams R Meir
**Pr:* Thomas R Meier
Snr Mgr: Jennifer Loh

D-U-N-S 15-278-9280
KAISER MIDWEST INC
808 Highway 34 W, Marble Hill, MO 63764-4302
Tel (573) 238-2675 *Founded/Ownrshp* 1990
Sales 136.4MM *EMP* 86^E
Accts Van De Ven Llc Cape Girardeau
SIC 5083 5084 Lawn machinery & equipment; Chainsaws; Lawn machinery & equipment; Chainsaws
Pr: Stanley Crader
**Ch Bd:* Don Crader
**Sec:* Val Crader
**VP:* Becky Hurst

KAISER PERMANENTE
See KAISER FOUNDATION HOSPITALS INC

KAISER PERMANENTE
See SOUTHERN CALIFORNIA PERMANENTE MEDICAL GROUP

KAISER PERMANENTE
See HAWAII PERMANENTE MEDICAL GROUP INC

KAISER PERMANENTE
See P C NORTHWEST PERMANENTE

KAISER PERMANENTE
See KAISER HEALTH PLAN ASSET MANAGEMENT INC

D-U-N-S 00-288-7466
KAISER PERMANENTE
NUEROLOGY DEPT
401 Bicentennial Way, Santa Rosa, CA 95403-2149
Tel (707) 393-4000 *Founded/Ownrshp* 2012
Sales 62.8MM^E *EMP* 278^E
SIC 8011 General & family practice, physician/surgeon
Owner: John F Cassidy MD
Chf Rad: Al Duffis
Dir OR: Brian Erickson
Dir Risk M: Patricia Carini
Dir Risk M: Monica Minguillon
Dir Lab: John Drew
Dir Lab: Scott Montros
Sfty Mgr: Judi Goodin
Pathlgst: Lena Berena
Pathlgst: John Kunkel
Obsttrcn: Denise Hoover

D-U-N-S 05-107-3185
KAISER PERMANENTE FONTANA MEDICAL CENTER
9961 Sierra Ave, Fontana, CA 92335-6720
Tel (909) 427-5000 *Founded/Ownrshp* 2010
Sales 42.8MM^E *EMP* 145^E
SIC 8062 General medical & surgical hospitals
Prin: Patricia Trantham
Dir Rad: Jeff Jobe
Surgeon: Jun Yamanishi
Nrsg Dir: Toni Andersen
Pharmcst: Julie Chae
Pharmcst: Lloyd Senzaki

D-U-N-S 83-279-6432
KAISER PERMANENTE INTERNATIONAL
1 Kaiser Plz, Oakland, CA 94612-3610
Tel (510) 271-5910 *Founded/Ownrshp* 2009
Sales 206.1MM^E *EMP* 2,564^E
SIC 8062 General medical & surgical hospitals
CEO: Bernard J Tyson
**CEO:* Raymond J Baxter
**CFO:* Kathy Lancaster
Bd of Dir: Glenn Weinraub
Admn Mgr: Cheryl Cooper
Admn Mgr: Gretchen Fritz
Opthamlgy: John Chong

D-U-N-S 60-557-6305
KAISER PERMANENTE PHARMACY
KAISER PERMANENTE PHARMACY 364
(*Suby of* KAISER FOUNDATION HOSPITALS INC) ★
23781 Maquina, Mission Viejo, CA 92691-2765
Tel (949) 837-7100 *Founded/Ownrshp* 2005
Sales 71.8MM^E *EMP* 769^E
SIC 5912 Drug stores & proprietary stores
Prin: Dori Finigan
Mng Dir: Suzie Characky
Pharmcst: Kelly Wan

KAISER PERMANENTE PHARMACY 364
See KAISER PERMANENTE PHARMACY

D-U-N-S 08-418-6337
KAISER PONTIAC BUICK GMC TRUCK INC
KAISER BUICK
1590 S Woodland Blvd, Deland, FL 32720-7709
Tel (386) 734-6882 *Founded/Ownrshp* 1967
Sales 21.2MM^E *EMP* 52
SIC 5511 Automobiles, new & used
VP: Frederick H Kaiser
**VP:* Helen J Kaiser

D-U-N-S 00-537-1356
■ **KAISER STEMCO INC** (MI)
(*Suby of* ENPRO INDUSTRIES INC) ★
4641 Industrial Dr, Millington, MI 48746-9300
Tel (989) 871-4541 *Founded/Ownrshp* 1962, 2008
Sales 26.7MM^E *EMP* 85
SIC 3713 Truck bodies & parts
Pr: Jon Cox
VP: Todd Anderson
**VP:* Drake Piper
Snr Mgr: Jason Trato

KAISER SUPPLY
See ACME REFRIGERATION OF BATON ROUGE LLC

D-U-N-S 80-830-8030
KAISER TRADING LLC
6733 S Yale Ave, Tulsa, OK 74136-3302
Tel (918) 491-4440 *Founded/Ownrshp* 2007
Sales 50.0MM *EMP* 4
SIC 5172 Gases; Gases

KAISER-FRANCIS OIL COMPANY
See GBK CORP

D-U-N-S 07-241-7900 IMP
KAISER-FRANCIS OIL CO
PILGRIM DRILLING CO
(*Suby of* GBK CORP) ★
6733 S Yale Ave, Tulsa, OK 74136-3330
Tel (918) 494-0000 *Founded/Ownrshp* 1976
Sales 8.1MM *EMP* 2,067
Accts Hogantaylor Llp Tulsa Ok
SIC 1382 1311 Oil & gas exploration services; Crude petroleum & natural gas; Oil & gas exploration services; Crude petroleum & natural gas
Pr: George B Kaiser
Pr: Kelly Shuck
CFO: Steve Berlin
**CFO:* Don Millican
Ex VP: Robert Waldo
**Ex VP:* Jim Willis
VP: Chaitanya Jagarlapudi
VP: Genevive Pinto
Exec: Dee Cooper
Genl Mgr: Brian Jobe
CIO: Kirk Walker

D-U-N-S 88-436-6527
KAISER-HILL CO LLC
11025 Dover St Unit 1000, Broomfield, CO 80021-5573
Tel (303) 966-7000 *Founded/Ownrshp* 1994
Sales 118.4MM^E *EMP* 1,500
Accts Kpmg Llp
SIC 4953 Radioactive waste materials, disposal; Radioactive waste materials, disposal
CEO: Alan M Parker
**COO:* Nancy Tuor
**CFO:* Leonard A Martinez
Prin: E Chandler Jr
Prin: Robert K Merkins

D-U-N-S 09-799-6672
KAISERAIR INC
8735 Earhart Rd, Oakland, CA 94621-4547
Tel (510) 569-9622 *Founded/Ownrshp* 1980
Sales 33.0MM^E *EMP* 185
SIC 5172 4522 7359 4581 Aircraft fueling services; Air transportation, nonscheduled; Aircraft rental; Aircraft maintenance & repair services; Aircraft fueling services; Air transportation, nonscheduled; Aircraft rental; Aircraft maintenance & repair services
Pr: Ronald J Guerra
**CFO:* Jim Strickland
**Sr VP:* Rob Guerra
**VP:* Glenn Barrett
**VP:* David Campbell
**VP:* Sandy Waters
IT Man: Neil Stevens
Opers Mgr: Bart Amond

D-U-N-S 00-660-0472
KAISERKANE INC
6802 Paragon Pl Ste 410, Richmond, VA 23230-1655
Tel (850) 567-2425 *Founded/Ownrshp* 2005
Sales 21.8MM^E *EMP* 23
Accts J Randall Graham Cpa Tallah
SIC 1542 Commercial & office building, new construction; Commercial & office building, new construction
Pr: Melissa Oglesy
**VP:* Richard Trey Gardner
Mktg Dir: Benjamin Baer

KAIWAH ISLAND CLUB
See KIAWAH RESORT ASSOCIATES LP

D-U-N-S 01-035-3745
KAIZEN EDUCATION FOUNDATION
SUMMIT HIGH SCHOOL
7878 N 16th St Ste 150, Phoenix, AZ 85020-4470
Tel (602) 953-2933 *Founded/Ownrshp* 2008
Sales 30.6MM *EMP* 5^E
Accts Sarvas Coleman Edgell & Tobi
SIC 8641 Civic social & fraternal associations
Pr: Theodore C Frederick
**CFO:* Patrick Lawrence

D-U-N-S 17-190-3342
KAIZEN RESTAURANTS INC
16500 Nw Bethany Ct # 150, Beaverton, OR 97006-6013
Tel (214) 221-7599 *Founded/Ownrshp* 2003
Sales 26.9MM^E *EMP* 1,000
SIC 5812 Fast-food restaurant, chain; Fast-food restaurant, chain
Pr: Syed J Ahmad

D-U-N-S 94-132-4324
KAJIMA BUILDING & DESIGN GROUP INC
KBD GROUP
(*Suby of* KAJIMA INTERNATIONAL INC) ★
3490 Piedmont Rd Ne # 900, Atlanta, GA 30305-4804
Tel (404) 812-8600 *Founded/Ownrshp* 2006
Sales 22.2MM^E *EMP* 76^E
SIC 7389 Design services
Pr: Shinya Urano
COO: Jeff Stiner
**CFO:* Bona Allen
Dir Bus: Mike Rhinehart
IT Man: Neil Lovelace
IT Man: Ray Punzalan

D-U-N-S 78-809-4225 IMP
KAJIMA CONSTRUCTION SERVICES INC
(*Suby of* KAJIMA INTERNATIONAL INC) ★
3475 Piedmont Rd Ne Ste 1, Atlanta, GA 30305-2954
Tel (404) 564-3900 *Founded/Ownrshp* 1991
Sales 62.5MM^E *EMP* 200
SIC 1541 1542 Industrial buildings, new construction; Renovation, remodeling & repairs: industrial buildings; Commercial & office building, new construction; Commercial & office buildings, renovation & repair; Institutional building construction; Religious building construction; Industrial buildings, new construction; Renovation, remodeling & repairs: industrial buildings; Commercial & office building, new construction; Commercial & office buildings, renovation & repair; Institutional building construction; Religious building construction
Ch Bd: Marvin J Suomi
**Pr:* Wells Jeffrey
**Pr:* Shinya Urano
**CEO:* Richard Nigro
CFO: Walt Antonenko
**Treas:* Takeshi Sasaki
Exec: Susan Ledford
Mktg Mgr: Takayuki Oto

D-U-N-S 02-472-6700 IMP
KAJIMA INTERNATIONAL INC
(*Suby of* KAJIMA USA INC) ★
3475 Piedmont Rd Ne # 1600, Atlanta, GA 30305-2954
Tel (404) 564-3900 *Founded/Ownrshp* 1998
Sales 675.0MM^E *EMP* 1,003
Accts Deloitte & Touche Llp
SIC 1541 3446 1542 Industrial buildings & warehouses; Architectural metalwork; Nonresidential construction; Industrial buildings & warehouses; Architectural metalwork; Nonresidential construction
CEO: Shinya Urano
**Treas:* Katsushi Norihama

D-U-N-S 07-228-6933
KAJIMA REAL ESTATE DEVELOPMENT INC
(*Suby of* KAJIMA USA INC) ★
3475 Pdmn Rd Ne Ste 1600, Atlanta, GA 30305-2993
Tel (404) 564-3900 *Founded/Ownrshp* 1964
Sales 287.2MM *EMP* 480
Accts Deloitte & Touche Llp New Yor
SIC 6552 Land subdividers & developers, commercial; Land subdividers & developers, commercial
Pr: Keisuke Koshijima
**CFO:* Hiroshi Unno
**VP:* Yoichi Tsuchiyama

D-U-N-S 18-942-6257 IMP
KAJIMA USA INC
(*Suby of* KAJIMA CORPORATION)
3475 Piedmont Rd Ne, Atlanta, GA 30305-2954
Tel (404) 564-3900 *Founded/Ownrshp* 1986
Sales 1.1MMM *EMP* 9,000
Accts Deloitte & Touche Llp Atlanta
SIC 1542 1541 6531 1522 6552 1622 Commercial & office building, new construction; Commercial & office buildings, renovation & repair; Factory construction; Industrial buildings, new construction; Renovation, remodeling & repairs: industrial buildings; Real estate agents & managers; Hotel/motel, new construction; Hotel/motel & multi-family home renovation & remodeling; Subdividers & developers; Bridge construction; Commercial & office building, new construction; Commercial & office buildings, renovation & repair; Factory construction; Industrial buildings, new construction; Renovation, remodeling & repairs: industrial buildings; Real estate agents & managers; Hotel/motel, new construction; Hotel/motel & multi-family home renovation & remodeling; Subdividers & developers; Bridge construction
CEO: Noriaki Ohashi
**CFO:* Mitsuyoshi Tamura
Treas: Yoshitaka Mizunaka
IT Man: Ray Punzalan
VP Mktg: Noriyuki Sato

D-U-N-S 12-715-9911
KAKTOVIK INUPIAT CORP
KIKKITAK STORE
4089 Hula Hula Ave, Kaktovik, AK 99747
Tel (907) 640-6120 *Founded/Ownrshp* 1973
Sales 63.0MM^E *EMP* 172
SIC 5541 1542 Gasoline service stations; Nonresidential construction; Gasoline service stations; Nonresidential construction
Pr: Philip Tikluk Jr
**Ch:* Eve Ahlers
**VP:* Alford Lynn Jr

D-U-N-S 06-772-4781 IMP
KAKUICHI AMERICA INC
(*Suby of* KAKUICHI CO.,LTD.)
23540 Telo Ave, Torrance, CA 90505-4013
Tel (310) 539-1590 *Founded/Ownrshp* 1973
Sales 32.0MM^E *EMP* 100
SIC 3084 Plastics pipe; Plastics pipe
CEO: Yasuo Ogami
**Prin:* Kenichi Tanaka

D-U-N-S 00-814-9551
KAL SERVICES INC
MIDWEST SANITATION SERVICE
906 W 9th St, Pella, IA 50219-2305
Tel (641) 628-2610 *Founded/Ownrshp* 1970
Sales 21.5MM^E *EMP* 60
SIC 4953 Garbage: collecting, destroying & processing; Recycling, waste materials
Pr: Lyle Vander Meiden
**Sec:* Kathy Vander Meiden

D-U-N-S 12-337-8049 IMP
KALAHARI DEVELOPMENT LLC
KALAHARI RESORTS
1305 Kalahari Dr, Wisconsin Dells, WI 53965
Tel (608) 254-5466 *Founded/Ownrshp* 1998
Sales 97.5MM^E *EMP* 1,800
SIC 7011 5812 5813 Hotels; Eating places; Drinking places; Hotels; Eating places; Drinking places
COO: Josef Haas
CFO: Mary Bonte-Stath
**CFO:* Mary Spath
**Ex VP:* William Otto
VP: Kelby Lainneken
**VP:* Shari Nelson
CTO: Matthew Roux
IT Man: Greg Gogola

KALAHARI RESORTS
See KALAHARI DEVELOPMENT LLC

KALAHARI WATERPARK RESORT
See LMN DEVELOPMENT LLC

D-U-N-S 18-223-8121 IMP/EXP
KALALOU INC
COUNTRY ORIGINAL
3844 W Northside Dr, Jackson, MS 39209-2559
Tel (601) 366-4229 *Founded/Ownrshp* 1984
Sales 24.1MM^E *EMP* 39
SIC 5023 Decorative home furnishings & supplies
Pr: John D Williams
**VP:* Susan F Williams
Creative D: Bradley Adair

D-U-N-S 04-059-7424 EXP
KALAMA EXPORT CO LLC
PACIFICOR
(*Suby of* GAVILON GROUP LLC) ★
1300 Sw 5th Ave Ste 2705, Portland, OR 97201-5634
Tel (503) 820-7460 *Founded/Ownrshp* 1998
Sales 53.5MM^E *EMP* 108
SIC 5153 Grains; Wheat
Pr: Patrick Bryan
**VP:* Sean Tingey

KALAMAZOO BOARD OF EDUCATION
See KALAMAZOO PUBLIC SCHOOL DISTRICT

D-U-N-S 18-517-1204
KALAMAZOO CO
HAMMOUND ROTO-FINISH
1600 Douglas Ave, Kalamazoo, MI 49007-1630
Tel (269) 345-7151 *Founded/Ownrshp* 1987
Sales 27.3MM^E *EMP* 176
SIC 3541 5085 3291 Deburring machines; Grinding machines, metalworking; Buffing & polishing machines; Robots for drilling, cutting, grinding, polishing, etc.; Abrasives; Abrasive products; Deburring machines; Grinding machines, metalworking; Buffing & polishing machines; Robots for drilling, cutting, grinding, polishing, etc.; Abrasives; Abrasive products
Pr: Robert E Hammond
Ex Dir: Veronne Williams
IT Man: Mike Gray
Sfty Mgr: Susan Sweerin
Sls Mgr: Philip Hammond

D-U-N-S 06-222-3532
KALAMAZOO COLLEGE
1200 Academy St, Kalamazoo, MI 49006-3295
Tel (269) 337-7000 *Founded/Ownrshp* 1833
Sales 82.7MM *EMP* 297
SIC 8221

D-U-N-S 15-582-0194
KALAMAZOO COMMUNITY FOUNDATION
KALAMAZOO FOUNDATION
402 E Michigan Ave, Kalamazoo, MI 49007-3888
Tel (269) 381-4416 *Founded/Ownrshp* 1925
Sales 67.8MM *EMP* 27
Accts Plante & Moran Pllc Portage
SIC 6732 Charitable trust management; Educational trust management; Religious trust management
CEO: Carrie Pickett-Erway
**CFO:* Susan Springgate
Ofcr: Coby Chalmers
Ofcr: Jeanne Grubb
Ofcr: Sam Lealofi
VP: Suprotik Stotz-Ghosh
VP: Ronda Stryker
CTO: Nancy Timmons
Dir IT: Rob Sursely
Mktg Dir: Tom Vance

KALAMAZOO FOUNDATION
See KALAMAZOO COMMUNITY FOUNDATION

D-U-N-S 02-103-8799 IMP/EXP
KALAMAZOO HOLDINGS INC
KALAZACK
3713 W Main St, Kalamazoo, MI 49006-2842
Tel (269) 349-9711 *Founded/Ownrshp* 1979
Sales 63.1MM^E *EMP* 257
SIC 2099 Spices, including grinding; Spices, including grinding
Pr: George Todd
**Ch:* Paul Todd
**Treas:* Donn Baird
**VP:* Gary Hainrihar

D-U-N-S 15-443-3085
KALAMAZOO MANUFACTURING CORP GLOBAL
PRAB
5944 E N Ave, Kalamazoo, MI 49048-9776
Tel (269) 382-8200 *Founded/Ownrshp* 2003
Sales 40.7MM^E *EMP* 130
SIC 3535 5084 Conveyors & conveying equipment; Industrial machinery & equipment; Conveyors & conveying equipment; Industrial machinery & equipment
Pr: Edward Thompson
**CFO:* Robert W Klinge

D-U-N-S 14-869-6156 IMP/EXP
KALAMAZOO METAL RECYCLERS INC
1525 King Hwy, Kalamazoo, MI 49001-3151
Tel (269) 381-1315 *Founded/Ownrshp* 1985
Sales 24.1MM^E *EMP* 44
SIC 5093 Metal scrap & waste materials
Pr: Patrick Farrell
**Sec:* Kay Farrell

D-U-N-S 07-259-0433
KALAMAZOO PUBLIC SCHOOL DISTRICT
KALAMAZOO BOARD OF EDUCATION
1220 Howard St, Kalamazoo, MI 49008-1871
Tel (269) 337-0113 *Founded/Ownrshp* 1924
Sales 157.8MM *EMP* 2,000
Accts Plante & Moran Pllc Portage
SIC 8211 Public elementary & secondary schools; Public elementary school; Public junior high school; Public senior high school; Public elementary & secondary schools; Public elementary school; Public junior high school; Public senior high school
Netwrk Mgr: Carol Patrick
HC Dir: Jill Reynolds

D-U-N-S 07-929-2330
KALAMAZOO REGIONAL EDUCATIONAL SERVICE AGENCY
KRESA
1819 E Milham Ave, Portage, MI 49002-3035
Tel (269) 250-9200 *Founded/Ownrshp* 1961
Sales 66.7MM *EMP* 500
Accts Plante & Moran Pllc Portage
SIC 8211 Public elementary & secondary schools; Public elementary & secondary schools
Pr: James Harrington
**VP:* Skip Knowles
Ex Dir: Barbara Payne
Admn Mgr: Lyn Lenox
Admn Mgr: Angela Telfer
Pr Dir: Christine Finger
Pr Dir: Kelly Kuhlmann

D-U-N-S 07-846-3792
KALAMAZOO REGIONAL EDUCATIONAL SERVICE AGENCY FOUNDATION
1819 E Milham Ave, Portage, MI 49002-3035
Tel (269) 385-1500 *Founded/Ownrshp* 1961
Sales 81.3MM *EMP* 100
SIC 8211 Elementary & secondary schools
Treas: Holly Norman

D-U-N-S 06-018-3498
KALAMAZOO VALLEY COMMUNITY COLLEGE
KVCC
6767 W O Ave, Kalamazoo, MI 49009-9606
Tel (269) 488-4400 *Founded/Ownrshp* 1966
Sales 40.4MM^E *EMP* 1,000
Accts Plante & Moran Pllc Portage
SIC 8222 Community college; Community college
Pr: Marilyn J Schlack
VP: Jack Taylor
Netwrk Mgr: Ryan Cummings
Netwrk Mgr: David Lynch

D-U-N-S 00-300-4389 IMP
KALAS MFG INC
167 Greenfield Rd, Lancaster, PA 17601-5814
Tel (717) 335-2360 *Founded/Ownrshp* 1958
Sales 84.2MM^E *EMP* 300
SIC 3357 3694 Nonferrous wiredrawing & insulating; Engine electrical equipment; Nonferrous wiredrawing & insulating; Engine electrical equipment
Pr: Richard P Witwer
**CFO:* Dennis M Melnyk
VP: Tim Gaalswyk
VP: Steven W Heisey
**VP:* Jon J Wiig
CIO: Lauren Winslow
Dir IT: Richard Hause
IT Man: Wagaman Fred
Mfg Mgr: Lance Moyer
Plnt Mgr: Joseph Carr
Prd Mgr: Rick Kile

KALAZACK
See KALAMAZOO HOLDINGS INC

D-U-N-S 84-078-4032
KALDI MANAGEMENT INC
4824 Winterset Dr Ste 100, Las Vegas, NV 89130-3612
Tel (702) 340-7283 *Founded/Ownrshp* 1979
Sales NA *EMP* 22
SIC 6099 Check cashing agencies; Check cashing agencies
Pr: Steven R Kaldi

D-U-N-S 01-846-9429
KALEEL BROS INC
KALEEL BROTHERS
761 Bev Rd, Youngstown, OH 44512-6423
Tel (330) 758-0861 *Founded/Ownrshp* 1956
Sales 41.8MM^E *EMP* 75
SIC 5148 5142 5149 5113 5087

KALEEL BROTHERS
See KALEEL BROS INC

D-U-N-S 01-085-7238
KALEIDA HEALTH
726 Exchange St, Buffalo, NY 14210-1484
Tel (716) 859-8000 *Founded/Ownrshp* 1996
Sales 1.1MMM *EMP* 9,000
SIC 8062 General medical & surgical hospitals; General medical & surgical hospitals
Pr: James R Kaskie
CFO: Jonathan T Swiatkowski
**Ex VP:* Toni L Booker
Ex VP: David P Hughes
**Ex VP:* Margaret Paroski
**Sr VP:* Donald Boyd
VP: Lynne Ferraro
Dir Rad: John Mycek
Nurse Mgr: Barbara Kuppel
Mtls Dir: Diane Artieri
QC Dir: Buckley Lisa

D-U-N-S 15-698-5186
■ **KALIBURN INC**
(*Suby of* LINCOLN ELECTRIC CO) ★
4130 Crlina Commerce Pkwy, Ladson, SC 29456-6707
Tel (800) 252-2850 *Founded/Ownrshp* 2012
Sales 26.9MM^E *EMP* 114
SIC 3548 Welding & cutting apparatus & accessories; Welding & cutting apparatus & accessories
Pr: Steven F Hardwick
**Sec:* Carolyn J Hardwick
**VP:* James Travis Hardwick
**Genl Mgr:* Kenneth Skyles

D-U-N-S 03-677-1558 IMP
KALIDA MANUFACTURING INC
(*Suby of* KTH PARTS INDUSTRIES INC) ★
801 Ottawa St, Kalida, OH 45853
Tel (419) 532-2026 *Founded/Ownrshp* 1996
Sales 76.0MM^E *EMP* 250
SIC 3714 Motor vehicle parts & accessories; Motor vehicle parts & accessories
Pr: Bruce R Henke
**Pr:* Tim Inoue
**VP:* Sho Akimoto

KALIHI PALAMA HEALTH CENTER
See HALE HOOLA HOU INC

D-U-N-S 04-434-9389 EXP
KALIKOW H J & CO LLC
101 Park Ave Rm 2500, New York, NY 10178-2500
Tel (212) 808-7000 *Founded/Ownrshp* 1965
Sales 76.2MM^E *EMP* 400
SIC 1542 6552 6512 6513 Commercial & office building, new construction; Subdividers & developers; Nonresidential building operators; Apartment building operators; Commercial & office building, new construction; Subdividers & developers; Nonresidential building operators; Apartment building operators
CFO: Richard T Nasit
Sec: Dorothy Vermeer

D-U-N-S 00-900-1132
KALIL BOTTLING CO (AZ)
931 S Highland Ave, Tucson, AZ 85719-6796
Tel (520) 624-1788 *Founded/Ownrshp* 1946
Sales 248.8MM^E *EMP* 800
SIC 2086 7359 Soft drinks: packaged in cans, bottles, etc.; Vending machine rental; Soft drinks: packaged in cans, bottles, etc.; Vending machine rental
Pr: George Kalil
**Sec:* William Ourand
**VP:* John P Kalil
VP Sls: Paul Durbin

D-U-N-S 07-183-6951
KALISPEL INDIAN COMMUNITY OF KALISPEL RESERVATION
KALISPEL TRIBE OF INDIANS
1981 Leclerc Rd N, Cusick, WA 99119-9682
Tel (509) 445-1147 *Founded/Ownrshp* 1934
Sales 14.0MM *EMP* 400
Accts Egghart Llc Cpa Reno Nevad
SIC 8611 3441 Business associations; Fabricated structural metal
Ch: Glen Nenema
V Ch: Curt Holmes
**V Ch:* Raymond Pierre III
COO: Albert Prudente
Genl Mgr: Terry Napton
Plng Mgr: Angelena Campobasso
Plng Mgr: Kevin Freibott
IT Man: Nick Brown

KALISPEL TRIBE OF INDIANS
See KALISPEL INDIAN COMMUNITY OF KALISPEL RESERVATION

D-U-N-S 08-000-1958
KALISPELL MOTOR CO (MT)
KALISPELL TOYOTA SCION
2845 Us Highway 93 S, Kalispell, MT 59901-8601
Tel (406) 755-6060 *Founded/Ownrshp* 2007
Sales 58.0MM *EMP* 90
SIC 7538 5511 Recreational vehicle repairs; Automobiles, new & used
Pr: Gerrid M Gandrud
**Sec:* Ivan O Gandrud

KALISPELL PUBLIC SCHOOLS
See KALISPELL SCHOOL DISTRICT 5

D-U-N-S 10-657-8826
KALISPELL REGIONAL HEALTHCARE SYSTEM
310 Sunnyview Ln, Kalispell, MT 59901-3129
Tel (406) 752-8991 *Founded/Ownrshp* 1982
Sales 2.9MM *EMP* 1,300
Accts Jordahl & Sliter Pllc Kalispe
SIC 8051 8011 4522 7352 Skilled nursing care facilities; Health maintenance organization; Physicians' office, including specialists; Ambulance services, air; Medical equipment rental; Skilled nursing care facilities; Health maintenance organization; Physicians' office, including specialists; Ambulance services, air; Medical equipment rental
Pr: Velinda Stevens
**Ch Bd:* Doug Nelson
Treas: William Freeman
**Treas:* Charles T Pearce
VP: Tate Kreitenger
VP: Tate Kreitinger
QA Dir: Sandra Swanson
Snr Mgr: Rebecca Manna
Snr Mgr: Randy Nightengale

D-U-N-S 01-036-7506
KALISPELL REGIONAL MEDICAL CENTER INC
PATHWAYS TREATMENT CENTER
310 Sunnyview Ln, Kalispell, MT 59901-3199
Tel (406) 752-5111 *Founded/Ownrshp* 1982
Sales 273.5MM *EMP* 1,800^E
SIC 8062

D-U-N-S 08-371-0590
KALISPELL SCHOOL DISTRICT 5
KALISPELL PUBLIC SCHOOLS
233 1st Ave E, Kalispell, MT 59901-4560
Tel (406) 751-3433 *Founded/Ownrshp* 1957
Sales 28.9MM^E *EMP* 510
SIC 8211 Public elementary & secondary schools; Public elementary & secondary schools
IT Man: Kevin Clark
HC Dir: Tracy Scott

KALISPELL TOYOTA SCION
See KALISPELL MOTOR CO

D-U-N-S 00-462-5435
KALITTA AIR LLC
818 Willow Run Airport, Ypsilanti, MI 48198-0899
Tel (734) 484-0088 *Founded/Ownrshp* 1999
Sales 203.1MM^E *EMP* 1,100^E
Accts Wright Griffen Davis Ann Arbo
SIC 4513 Air courier services; Air courier services
Owner: Conrad Kalitta
CFO: Greg Strzynski
QC Dir: Zoltan Kocis
Sfty Mgr: Jim Malzone
Opers Mgr: Tina Dewitt
Ql Cn Mgr: Rich Stone

D-U-N-S 10-267-0879
KALITTA CHARTERS LLC
KALLITA MEDFLIGHT
843 Willow Run Airport, Ypsilanti, MI 48198-0899
Tel (734) 544-3400 *Founded/Ownrshp* 2002
Sales 38.0MM^E *EMP* 200
SIC 4522 Flying charter service; Flying charter service
Owner: Doug Kalitta
CFO: Berry Birurakis
Dir IT: Chad Rider
IT Man: Michael Barnocki
Sfty Dirs: Carl Barnes
Opers Mgr: Sheri Ryan
Opers Mgr: Ryan Sniegowski
Mktg Dir: Steven Greene
Snr Mgr: John Horn
Board of Directors: Steve Greene, Dawn A Messer

D-U-N-S 07-258-1309
KALKASKA COUNTY HOSPITAL AUTHORITY
KALKASKA MEMORIAL HEALTH CTR
419 S Coral St Ste A, Kalkaska, MI 49646-2503
Tel (231) 258-7500 *Founded/Ownrshp* 1950
Sales 28.5MM *EMP* 300
Accts Ernst & Young Llp Grand Rapid
SIC 8062 8093 8011 General medical & surgical hospitals; Specialty outpatient clinics; Offices & clinics of medical doctors; General medical & surgical hospitals; Specialty outpatient clinics; Offices & clinics of medical doctors
**Ch Bd:* John Siddall
**Treas:* Betty Dunham
Dir OR: Danielle Grant
Dir Soc: Jillian Snyder
Doctor: John Beattie
HC Dir: Patti Mathis

KALKASKA MEMORIAL HEALTH CTR
See KALKASKA COUNTY HOSPITAL AUTHORITY

D-U-N-S 12-168-0458
KALKREUTH ROOFING & SHEET METAL INC
53 14th St Ste 100, Wheeling, WV 26003-3433
Tel (304) 232-8540 *Founded/Ownrshp* 1984
Sales 117.9MM^E *EMP* 330
SIC 1761 3446 3444 3441 Roofing contractor; Sheet metalwork; Architectural metalwork; Sheet metalwork; Fabricated structural metal; Roofing contractor; Sheet metalwork; Architectural metalwork; Sheet metalwork; Fabricated structural metal
Pr: John Kalkreuth
COO: Andrew Vanlandingham
Treas: John Bailey
Div VP: Dave Hesse
Div VP: Pat Hurley
**Ex VP:* Jim Hurley
**VP:* Chad McLeish
Div Mgr: Jeff Piazza
Genl Mgr: John Trifonoff
Sfty Dirs: Jeremy Dvorcek
Sfty Mgr: Kevin Barnhart

KALLITA MEDFLIGHT
See KALITTA CHARTERS LLC

D-U-N-S 00-891-9243 IMP
KALMAN FLOOR CO
1202 Bergen Pkwy Ste 110, Evergreen, CO 80439-9559
Tel (303) 674-2290 *Founded/Ownrshp* 1922
Sales 21.0MM^E *EMP* 150
SIC 1771 Flooring contractor; Flooring contractor
CEO: Carl N Ytterberg
**VP:* Scott Vogeler

D-U-N-S 12-334-3027 IMP/EXP
KALMAR RT CENTER LLC
(*Suby of* CARGOTEC OYJ)
103 Guadalupe Dr, Cibolo, TX 78108-3144
Tel (210) 599-6541 *Founded/Ownrshp* 1999
Sales 25.0MM^E *EMP* 160
SIC 3537 6399 5531 Industrial trucks & tractors; Warranty insurance, automobile; Truck equipment & parts
Pr: Steven Speakes
CFO: Bob Wills
Ex VP: David Peacock
VP: Michael Loch
VP: Cynthia Marsden
VP: Graeme McWilliams
VP: Ron Price
VP: Esteban Smith
CTO: Jerry Crosby
Dir IT: Bart Morrison
Ql Cn Mgr: George Vollrath

D-U-N-S 03-307-3862 IMP/EXP
KALMAR SOLUTIONS LLC
CARGOTEC SOLUTIONS LLC
(*Suby of* CARGOTEC HOLDING INC) ★
415 E Dundee St, Ottawa, KS 66067-1543
Tel (785) 242-2200 *Founded/Ownrshp* 2011
Sales 114.2MM^E *EMP* 375
SIC 3537 3714 3713 3643 Industrial trucks & tractors; Fifth wheel, motor vehicle; Truck & bus bodies; Current-carrying wiring devices; Industrial trucks & tractors; Fifth wheel, motor vehicle; Truck & bus bodies; Current-carrying wiring devices
Pr: Ton Case
Pr: Jorma Tirkkonen
CFO: Mike Manning
Treas: Bob Wills
VP: Tom Kay
Genl Mgr: Merlin Halverson
IT Man: Jenie Montgomery
Ql Cn Mgr: Predrag Gagic

D-U-N-S 04-107-3701 IMP
KALMBACH FEEDS INC
7148 State Highway 199, Upper Sandusky, OH 43351-9359
Tel (419) 294-3838 *Founded/Ownrshp* 1963
Sales 27.6MM^E *EMP* 110^E
SIC 2048 Livestock feeds; Poultry feeds; Livestock feeds; Poultry feeds
Pr: Paul M Kalmbach
**CFO:* Dick Regnier
VP: Todd Stickley
Plnt Mgr: Dave Moyers
Sls Mgr: Pat Bryan
Sls Mgr: Todd Ricker

Sls Mgr: Jim Wilson
Nutrtnst: Kyle Nickles

D-U-N-S 00-608-0758 IMP
KALMBACH PUBLISHING CO (WI)
21027 Crossroads Cir, Waukesha, WI 53186-4055
Tel (262) 796-8776 *Founded/Ownrshp* 1933
Sales 56.0MM^E *EMP* 300
Accts Deloitte & Touche Llp Milwauk
SIC 2721 2731 5192 Magazines: publishing only, not printed on site; Books: publishing only; Magazines; Books; Magazines: publishing only, not printed on site; Books: publishing only; Magazines; Books
Pr: Gerald Boettcher
**VP:* Connie S Bradley
**VP:* Charles Croft
VP: Robert Hayden
**VP:* Kevin P Keefe
**VP:* Daniel R Lance
**VP:* James Schweder
**VP:* Scott Stollberg
Genl Mgr: Bonnie Markwiese
CIO: Keith Bauer
Prd Mgr: Helene Tsigistras

D-U-N-S 14-794-4870
KALMIA MOTORS INC
FORD LINCOLN MERCURY
1850 Jefferson Davis Hwy, Graniteville, SC 29829-4032
Tel (803) 593-3700 *Founded/Ownrshp* 1985
Sales 20.2MM *EMP* 52
SIC 5511 5521 5012 Automobiles, new & used; Used car dealers; Automobiles & other motor vehicles; Automobiles, new & used; Used car dealers; Automobiles & other motor vehicles
Pr: Richard Heath
Board of Directors: Jackie Cushman

KALONA CHEESE
See TWIN COUNTY DAIRY INC

D-U-N-S 78-372-7555 IMP
KALOT INDUSTRIES INC
STAMPEDE PRODUCTS
1924 S Washington Blvd, Camanche, IA 52730-1717
Tel (563) 259-4083 *Founded/Ownrshp* 1996
Sales 22.8MM^E *EMP* 100
SIC 3714 Motor vehicle parts & accessories; Motor vehicle parts & accessories
Pr: Loyal Tullius
**VP:* Karen Tullius
Genl Mgr: Rick Metro

D-U-N-S 18-929-0752
KALOTI WHOLESALE INC
BEST VALUE FOODS
5475 S Westridge Ct, New Berlin, WI 53151-7951
Tel (262) 754-3870 *Founded/Ownrshp* 1988
Sales 33.0MM^E *EMP* 35
SIC 5141 5411 Groceries, general line; Grocery stores, independent
Pr: Russ A Kaloti
**CFO:* Don Kressin
**VP:* Ronald Delong
**VP:* Issac Kaloti

D-U-N-S 62-079-3018
KALOUTAS & CO INC
KALOUTAS PAINTING
11 Railroad Ave, Peabody, MA 01960-4311
Tel (978) 532-1414 *Founded/Ownrshp* 1984
Sales 25.1MM^E *EMP* 120
SIC 1721 Interior commercial painting contractor; Interior residential painting contractor; Exterior commercial painting contractor; Exterior residential painting contractor
Pr: Jim Kaloutas
**VP:* Bruce Durkee
Opers Mgr: Phil Gabriele
Opers Mgr: John Lydon
VP Sls: Judith Martine

KALOUTAS PAINTING
See KALOUTAS & CO INC

D-U-N-S 17-359-0860 IMP
KALOW TECHNOLOGIES LLC
238 Innovation Dr, North Clarendon, VT 05759-9387
Tel (802) 775-4633 *Founded/Ownrshp* 1986
Sales 20.0MM^E *EMP* 58
Accts O Brien Shortle Reynolds & Sab
SIC 3569 Assembly machines, non-metalworking
Pr: Paul Van Huis
VP: Jeff Bartell
Exec: Paul Huis
Off Mgr: Erin Allen

D-U-N-S 06-369-9172
KALPANA LLC
620 Newport Center Dr # 14, Newport Beach, CA 92660-6420
Tel (949) 610-8200 *Founded/Ownrshp* 1995
Sales 7.0MM^E *EMP* 300^E
SIC 7011 Hotels; Hotels
Prin: Mayur Patel

D-U-N-S 02-090-7341 IMP/EXP
KALSEC INC (MI)
(*Suby of* KALAMAZOO HOLDINGS INC) ★
3713 W Main St, Kalamazoo, MI 49006-2842
Tel (269) 349-9711 *Founded/Ownrshp* 1950, 1979
Sales 63.2MM^E *EMP* 257
SIC 2099 2087 2834 Spices, including grinding; Flavoring extracts & syrups; Spices, including grinding; Flavoring extracts & syrups; Pharmaceutical preparations
Pr: George Todd
**CFO:* Robert Monk
CFO: John Weaver
**Ex VP:* Gary Hainrihar
VP: Thomas Barry
VP: Howard Haley
Exec: Jill McKeague
Mng Dir: Paul Filby
Mng Dir: Phil Schlein
QA Dir: Erik Knedgen
Software D: Melinda Murphy

D-U-N-S 07-976-9729
KALTEX AMERICA INC (NY)
(*Suby of* KALTEX NORTH AMERICA INC) ★
350 5th Ave Ste 7100, New York, NY 10118-0110
Tel (212) 971-0575 *Founded/Ownrshp* 1987, 2002
Sales 161.0MM *EMP* 18
SIC 2339 2325 Jeans: women's, misses' & juniors'; Jeans: men's, youths' & boys'
Ch Bd: Rafael M Kalach
Pr: Bradford Fritts
CEO: Hebe Schecter

D-U-N-S 14-114-7525 IMP
KALTEX NORTH AMERICA INC
(*Suby of* KALTEX TEXTILES, S.A. DE C.V.)
350 5th Ave Ste 7100, New York, NY 10118-0110
Tel (212) 894-3200 *Founded/Ownrshp* 2002
Sales 192.7MM^E *EMP* 120
SIC 2392 Comforters & quilts: made from purchased materials
Ch Bd: Rafael Kalach
VP: Tom McGrath

D-U-N-S 09-806-7192
KALTHOFF FABRICATORS INC
(*Suby of* SHOFFNER ACQUISITION CORP) ★
3600 Papermill Dr, Knoxville, TN 37909-1518
Tel (865) 525-5122 *Founded/Ownrshp* 1984
Sales 21.1MM^E *EMP* 135
SIC 3444 1711 Sheet metal specialties, not stamped; Plumbing, heating, air-conditioning contractors
Ch Bd: Jan Dugger
**Pr:* David Dugger
COO: Kenny Smith
**CFO:* Todd Wolf
**Treas:* Joyce Griffin
**VP:* Janet Dugger
VP: Richard Whillock
IT Man: David McConnell

D-U-N-S 83-108-7726
KALTURA INC
250 Park Ave S Fl 10, New York, NY 10003-1402
Tel (646) 560-5514 *Founded/Ownrshp* 2006
Sales 38.0MM *EMP* 387
SIC 7371 Computer software development
CEO: Ron Yekutiel
**COO:* Leah Belsky
**CFO:* Naama Halevi-Davidov
**Chf Mktg O:* Michal Tsur
VP: Juan C Santamaria
**Dir Risk M:* Shay David
**CTO:* Eran Etam
QA Dir: Russell Rahman
Sls Mgr: Michael Kummer

D-U-N-S 01-208-7284 IMP
KALUSTYAN CORP
855 Rahway Ave, Union, NJ 07083-6633
Tel (908) 688-0853 *Founded/Ownrshp* 1948
Sales 32.5MM^E *EMP* 80
SIC 2099 5149 5159 5153 Seasonings & spices; Spices, including grinding; Spices & seasonings; Fruits, dried; Nuts & nut by-products; Beans, dry: bulk
CEO: Errol Karakash
**Pr:* John Bas
VP: Sarkis Agopcaen
VP: M J Bas
VP: Abdul Basit
VP: Aury Cumpa
VP: Nancy Gumaz
VP: Michelle Hill-Taylor
VP: Nora Ortiz
VP: Gorken Perincek
Sls Mgr: Kerri Goad-Berrios

D-U-N-S 00-108-6198 IMP/EXP
KALWALL CORP (NH)
1111 Candia Rd, Manchester, NH 03109-5211
Tel (603) 627-3861 *Founded/Ownrshp* 1955
Sales 92.9MM^E *EMP* 450
Accts Katherine K Garfield Manches
SIC 3089 3083 Panels, building: plastic; Thermoplastic laminates: rods, tubes, plates & sheet; Panels, building: plastic; Thermoplastic laminates: rods, tubes, plates & sheet
Pr: Richard Keller
CFO: Kathy Garfield
Treas: Richard Severance
**Sec:* Katherine Garfield
VP: Amy Keller
**VP:* Bruce M Keller
IT Man: Dan Cronin
IT Man: Elanchard Mathew
Netwrk Mgr: Doug Deland
Info Man: Paul Fisher
Opers Mgr: Allan Fiore

D-U-N-S 05-667-2009 IMP
KAM MAN FOOD PRODUCTS INC
200 Canal St, New York, NY 10013-4584
Tel (212) 571-0330 *Founded/Ownrshp* 1972
Sales 21.0MM^E *EMP* 49
Accts Kafitin & Negrin Cpa
SIC 5411 5141 Grocery stores; Groceries, general line
Pr: Chung HEI Wong
**VP:* Wellmen Wu

D-U-N-S 09-601-5664
KAM SANG CO INC
NEW AGE LA MIRADA INN
411 E Huntington Dr # 305, Arcadia, CA 91006-3731
Tel (626) 446-2988 *Founded/Ownrshp* 1977
Sales 23.6MM^E *EMP* 82
SIC 6799 Real estate investors, except property operators
CEO: Ronnie Lam
Web Prj Mg: Joanne Web

KAMA-AINA KIDS
See KAMAAINA CARE INC

D-U-N-S 62-099-8575
KAMAAINA CARE INC
KAMA-AINA KIDS
156 Hamakua Dr Ste C, Kailua, HI 96734-2834
Tel (808) 262-4538 *Founded/Ownrshp* 1988
Sales 20.8MM *EMP* 750
SIC 8351 Child day care services; Child day care services
Pr: Ray Sanborn
Treas: Charlene Yamasaki
VP: Kathy Hew
VP: Mark Nishiyama
Comm Man: Jeff Subee
Off Mgr: Sheryl Winterbottom

D-U-N-S 15-054-7578
KAMAL CORP
TRADE FAIR 1
3012 30th Ave Ste 210, Astoria, NY 11102-2121
Tel (718) 721-2437 *Founded/Ownrshp* 1982
Sales 27.5MM^E *EMP* 125
SIC 5411 5141 5921 Supermarkets, independent; Food brokers; Beer (packaged); Supermarkets, independent; Food brokers; Beer (packaged)
Pr: Farid Jaber

D-U-N-S 05-254-3188 IMP
■ **KAMAN AEROSPACE CORP**
(*Suby of* KAMAN AEROSPACE GROUP INC) ★
30 Old Windsor Rd, Bloomfield, CT 06002-1414
Tel (860) 242-4461 *Founded/Ownrshp* 1969
Sales 214.4MM^E *EMP* 1,326
SIC 3721 3728 Aircraft; Aircraft parts & equipment; Aircraft; Aircraft parts & equipment
Pr: Gregory Steiner
Treas: Russ Jones
**Treas:* Robert D Starr
Div Pres: Alphonse J Lariviere Jr
Div Pres: James C Larwood Jr
Div Pres: Gerald C Ricketts
Ofcr: Mark Stevens
VP: Jairaj Chetnani
VP: Clarence Close
VP: Janna L Drake
VP: Richard C Forsberg
VP: Philip A Goodrich
VP: Michael Lafleur
VP: Jeffrey Leeper
VP: James B Melvin
VP: Robert Renz
VP: Christopher Simmons
VP: Darlene R Smith
VP: John K Stockman
VP: Patrick Wheeler
VP: William H Zmyndak
Board of Directors: Neal J Keating

D-U-N-S 78-279-7583 IMP/EXP
■ **KAMAN AEROSPACE GROUP INC**
(*Suby of* KAMAN CORP) ★
1332 Blue Hills Ave, Bloomfield, CT 06002-5302
Tel (860) 243-7100 *Founded/Ownrshp* 1945
Sales 428.9MM^E *EMP* 1,678
SIC 3721 3724 3728 3769 Aircraft; Aircraft engines & engine parts; Aircraft parts & equipment; Guided missile & space vehicle parts & auxiliary equipment; Aircraft; Aircraft engines & engine parts; Aircraft parts & equipment; Guided missile & space vehicle parts & auxiliary equipment
Pr: Gregory L Steiner
Treas: William Denninger Jr
**Treas:* Robert D Starr
Div Pres: James C Larwood Jr
Sr VP: Patrick Owens
Sr VP: Patrick Renehan
VP: Richard C Forsberg
VP: Philip A Goodrich
VP: Nancy A L'Esperance
VP: Michael Lafleur
VP: Christopher Simmons
VP: Gary V Tenison
VP: Gary Tenison
VP: Pat Wheeler
VP: Patrick J Wheeler

D-U-N-S 09-524-9397 EXP
■ **KAMAN COMPOSITES - VERMONT INC**
(*Suby of* KAMAN AEROSPACE GROUP INC) ★
25 Performance Dr, Bennington, VT 05201-1947
Tel (802) 442-9964 *Founded/Ownrshp* 2011
Sales 37.4MM^E *EMP* 188
SIC 3083 Laminated plastics plate & sheet; Laminated plastics plate & sheet
Pr: James C Larwood Jr
**Treas:* Robert D Starr
Div Pres: Alphonse J Lariviere Jr
VP: Michael Lafleur
VP: Mark Schmitz
VP: James Sharkey
VP: Christopher Simmons
IT Man: Denise Mekita
Board of Directors: Neal J Keating, Gregory L Steiner

D-U-N-S 00-723-3257
■ **KAMAN COMPOSITES - WICHITA INC**
(*Suby of* KAMAN AEROSPACE GROUP INC) ★
1650 S Mccomas St, Wichita, KS 67213-1239
Tel (316) 942-1241 *Founded/Ownrshp* 2002
Sales 28.4MM^E *EMP* 140
SIC 3082 Unsupported plastics profile shapes; Unsupported plastics profile shapes
Pr: James C Larwood Jr
**Treas:* Robert D Starr
Div Pres: Alphonse J Lariviere Jr
VP: Michael L Lafluer
VP: Christopher Simmons
IT Man: John Reeves
Board of Directors: Neal J Keating, Gregory L Steiner

D-U-N-S 00-115-5225 IMP/EXP
▲ **KAMAN CORP**
1332 Blue Hills Ave, Bloomfield, CT 06002-5302
Tel (860) 243-7100 *Founded/Ownrshp* 1945
Sales 1.8MMM *EMP* 4,743
Accts Pricewaterhousecoopers Llp Ha
Tkr Sym KAMN *Exch* NYS
SIC 5085 3721 3728 Industrial supplies; Bearings; Power transmission equipment & apparatus; Pistons & valves; Helicopters; Aircraft parts & equipment; Roto-blades for helicopters; Flaps, aircraft wing; Wing assemblies & parts, aircraft; Industrial supplies; Bearings; Power transmission equipment & apparatus; Pistons & valves; Helicopters; Aircraft parts & equipment; Roto-blades for helicopters; Flaps, aircraft wing; Wing assemblies & parts, aircraft
Ch Bd: Neal J Keating
Mng Pt: Mike Star
CFO: Robert D Starr
Ex VP: William C Denninger Jr
Sr VP: Ronald M Galla
Sr VP: Shawn G Lisle
Sr VP: Gregory T Troy
Sr VP: Tribby Warfield
VP: Al Lariviere
VP: Michael J Lyon
VP: Eric Remington
VP: Ed Smith
VP: Pat Sullivan
VP: John Tedone
VP: Clifford A Ward
VP: Pat Wheeler
VP: William H Zmyndak
Dir Bus: Ken Kelly
Board of Directors: Richard J Swift, Brian E Barents, E Reeves Callaway III, Karen M Garrison, A William Higgins, Eileen S Kraus, Scott E Kuechle, George E Minnich, Jennifer M Pollino, Thomas W Rabaut

D-U-N-S 07-731-6412 IMP
■ **KAMAN INDUSTRIAL TECHNOLOGIES CORP**
(*Suby of* KAMAN CORP) ★
1 Vision Way, Bloomfield, CT 06002-5321
Tel (860) 687-5000 *Founded/Ownrshp* 1974
Sales 618.8MM^E *EMP* 2,141
SIC 3491 5085 Industrial valves; Industrial supplies; Industrial valves; Industrial supplies
CEO: Neal J Keating
**Pr:* Steven J Smidler
**Treas:* Robert D Starr
**Sr VP:* Ronald M Galla
**Sr VP:* Gary J Haseley
**Sr VP:* Roger S Jorgensen
**Sr VP:* Thomas A Weihsmann
**VP:* Kyle Ahlinger
**VP:* Jeffrey M Brown
**VP:* Thomas M Caputo
**VP:* Anthony L Clark
VP: Robert F Go
**VP:* Philip A Goodrich
**VP:* Tom R Holtry
**VP:* Michael J Kelly
**VP:* David H Mayer
**VP:* Michael J Pastore
**VP:* Donald O Roland
**VP:* Abraham D Samaro
VP: Steve Smidler
VP: Thomas Weihsmann
Board of Directors: Neal J Keating

D-U-N-S 11-831-2680 EXP
■ **KAMAN PRECISION PRODUCTS INC**
(*Suby of* KAMAN AEROSPACE GROUP INC) ★
6655 E Colonial Dr, Orlando, FL 32807-5200
Tel (407) 282-1000 *Founded/Ownrshp* 2002
Sales 53.3MM^E *EMP* 300
SIC 3483 3489 Ammunition, except for small arms; Ordnance & accessories; Ammunition, except for small arms; Ordnance & accessories
Pr: Gerald C Ricketts
**Treas:* Robert D Starr
VP: Clarence Close
VP: Jeffrey Leeper
VP: Robert Renz
QA Dir: Michelle Wilson
IT Man: Sandra Kirk
Board of Directors: Neal J Keating, Gregory L Steiner

D-U-N-S 06-220-4573 IMP
■ **KAMATICS CORP**
(*Suby of* KAMAN AEROSPACE GROUP INC) ★
1330 Blue Hills Ave, Bloomfield, CT 06002-5303
Tel (860) 243-9704 *Founded/Ownrshp* 1971
Sales 79.1MM^E *EMP* 425
SIC 3451 3562 3724 3728 Screw machine products; Ball & roller bearings; Aircraft engines & engine parts; Aircraft parts & equipment; Screw machine products; Ball & roller bearings; Aircraft engines & engine parts; Aircraft parts & equipment
CEO: Neal J Keating
Pr: Robert G Paterson
**Treas:* Robert D Starr
Ex VP: Steven J Smidler
Ex VP: Gregory L Steiner
Sr VP: Ronald M Galla
Sr VP: Philip A Goodrich
VP: Mathew Mormino
VP: Jeff Post
VP: Patrick C Sullivan
Dist Mgr: Tony Clark
Board of Directors: Neal J Keating, Gregory L Steiner

D-U-N-S 00-535-4899 IMP/EXP
KAMAX LP
(*Suby of* KAMAX HOLDING GMBH & CO. KG)
500 W Long Lake Rd, Troy, MI 48098-4540
Tel (248) 879-0200 *Founded/Ownrshp* 1995, 2011
Sales 123.1MM^E *EMP* 400
SIC 3452 Bolts, nuts, rivets & washers; Bolts, metal; Rivets, metal; Bolts, nuts, rivets & washers; Bolts, metal; Rivets, metal
VP: David Winn
COO: Wolfgang Ruoff
Mng Dir: Herman Van Maaren
IT Man: Rick Johnson
Ql Cn Mgr: Christopher Pierik
Ql Cn Mgr: Michelle Pillion
Sales Asso: Barbara Lewis
Snr Mgr: Wayne Powell

D-U-N-S 15-138-9954
KAMCO BUILDING SUPPLY CORP OF PENNSYLVANIA
(*Suby of* KAMCO SUPPLY CORP) ★
1100 Township Line Rd, Chester, PA 19013-1446
Tel (610) 364-1356 *Founded/Ownrshp* 1986
Sales 78.1MM^E *EMP* 57
SIC 5031 Building materials, exterior; Building materials, interior
Pr: Charles Dougherty
**Treas:* Carl Ingram
**VP:* John W Sheehy
Genl Mgr: Glenn Reilly
Genl Mgr: John Rymiszewski

D-U-N-S 18-303-8314 IMP
KAMCO INDUSTRIES INC
(*Suby of* KUMI KASEI CO.,LTD.)
1001 E Jackson St, West Unity, OH 43570-9414
Tel (419) 924-5511 *Founded/Ownrshp* 1987
Sales 70.2MM^E *EMP* 464
SIC 3089 Injection molded finished plastic products; Thermoformed finished plastic products; Injection molded finished plastic products; Thermoformed finished plastic products
VP: Joe Tubbs
IT Man: Tony Brown
IT Man: Chad Walls
Prd Mgr: Ian Macdonald
Snr Mgr: Mohammed Ali
Snr Mgr: John Carlsen
Snr Mgr: Gary Delenardo
Snr Mgr: Keith Motoyama
Snr Mgr: Ai Phomphakdy
Snr Mgr: Melissa Scott

D-U-N-S 01-257-0651 IMP
KAMCO SUPPLY CORP
80 21st St, Brooklyn, NY 11232-1138
Tel (718) 840-1700 *Founded/Ownrshp* 1969
Sales 158.7MM^E *EMP* 150
SIC 5031 5033 Lumber: rough, dressed & finished; Plywood; Building materials, interior; Building materials, exterior; Roofing & siding materials; Lumber: rough, dressed & finished; Plywood; Building materials, interior; Building materials, exterior; Roofing & siding materials
Pr: Allan B Swerdlick
**CFO:* Raymond Barter
Sr VP: Faisal Sarkhou
VP: Steve Cangialosi
VP: Dave Kovacs
VP: Durga Prasad
Brnch Mgr: Cesar Chavez
MIS Dir: Sandi Haddad
Dir IT: Seth Mayers
Mktg Dir: Evan Meyers
Sales Asso: Adam Blackwell

D-U-N-S 05-518-2042
KAMCO SUPPLY CORP OF BOSTON
181 New Boston St, Woburn, MA 01801-6203
Tel (508) 587-1500 *Founded/Ownrshp* 1981
Sales 165.4MM^E *EMP* 200
SIC 5032 5031 5039 5023 5033 Brick, stone & related material; Building materials, exterior; Building materials, interior; Doors, garage; Ceiling systems & products; Floor coverings; Insulation materials; Brick, stone & related material; Building materials, exterior; Building materials, interior; Doors, garage; Ceiling systems & products; Floor coverings; Insulation materials
Pr: James F Scaia
VP: David Kovacs
Brnch Mgr: Mark Cell
Off Mgr: Judy Stauffer
Mktg Dir: Tom Estona
Sls Mgr: Mike Williams
Sales Asso: Joe Dimaria
Sales Asso: Heather Dodge
Sales Asso: Ted Jennings
Sales Asso: Mark Plouffe
Sales Asso: Chris Sheppard

D-U-N-S 09-721-2336
KAMCO SUPPLY CORP OF NEW ENGLAND
(*Suby of* KAMCO SUPPLY CORP) ★
780 N Colony Rd, Wallingford, CT 06492-2475
Tel (203) 284-1968 *Founded/Ownrshp* 1979
Sales 74.7MM^E *EMP* 100
SIC 5031 5039 5051 5072 5023 5084 Building materials, exterior; Building materials, interior; Ceiling systems & products; Nails; Screws; Carpets; Drilling equipment, excluding bits; Building materials, exterior; Building materials, interior; Ceiling systems & products; Nails; Screws; Carpets; Drilling equipment, excluding bits
Pr: Paul Taylor
**Ex VP:* Leon Slomkowski
**VP:* Jay Sheehy
**VP:* Alan Swerdlick

KAMEHAMEHA SCHOOLS
See TRUSTEES OF ESTATE OF BERNICE PAUAHI BISHOP

D-U-N-S 01-892-7306 IMP
KAMEI NORTH AMERICA CO LTD
(*Suby of* KAMEI CORPORATION)
1815 W 213th St Ste 235, Torrance, CA 90501-2825
Tel (310) 782-1900 *Founded/Ownrshp* 2012
Sales 35.9MM^E *EMP* 658
SIC 5411 5311 Grocery stores, chain; Department stores, non-discount; Grocery stores, chain; Department stores, non-discount
Pr: Yoshiya Watanabe

D-U-N-S 13-601-5781 IMP
KAMILCHE CO
1301 5th Ave Ste 2800, Seattle, WA 98101-2675
Tel (206) 224-5800 *Founded/Ownrshp* 1961
Sales 485.3MM^E *EMP* 2,870
SIC 2621 2611 2421 2435 2431 Paper mills; Pulp mills; Lumber: rough, sawed or planed; Plywood, hardwood or hardwood faced; Doors, wood; Paper mills; Pulp mills; Lumber: rough, sawed or planed; Plywood, hardwood or hardwood faced; Doors, wood
Pr: Colin Moseley
**Treas:* Colley Nancy L
**VP:* Reed Jr Wm G

KAMILCHE TRADING POST
See ISLAND ENTERPRISES

D-U-N-S 82-463-9822 IMP/EXP
KAMIN LLC
KAMIN PERFORMANCE MINERALS
822 Huber Rd, Macon, GA 31217-9208
Tel (478) 750-5410 *Founded/Ownrshp* 2008
Sales 145.2MM^E *EMP* 350^E
SIC 3295 Earths, ground or otherwise treated; Earths, ground or otherwise treated
CEO: Rankin Hobbs
**Pr:* Harlan Archer
CFO: Roddy Wells
VP: Doug Carter
VP: Warren McPhillips
IT Man: Britt Cicerchi
IT Man: Lou Gatti
Opers Mgr: Mike Sheppard
Plnt Mgr: George Lee
Ql Cn Mgr: Randy Moritz

KAMIN PERFORMANCE MINERALS
See KAMIN LLC

KAMINO INTERNATIONAL TRANSPORT
See TIGERS (USA) GLOBAL LOGISTICS INC

KAMMCO
See KANSAS MEDICAL MUTUAL INSURANCE CO INC

D-U-N-S 00-677-6041
KAMMINGA & ROODVOETS INC
K & R EXCAVATING
3435 Broadmoor Ave Se, Grand Rapids, MI 49512-2899
Tel (616) 949-0800 *Founded/Ownrshp* 1951
Sales 65.4MM *EMP* 280
SIC 1794 Excavation work; Excavation work
Pr: Richard Steigenga
**Treas:* Kraig Klynstra
**VP:* Kurt Poll
**VP:* Marcus Tidey

D-U-N-S 00-781-9709
KAMO ELECTRIC COOPERATIVE INC
KAMO POWER
500 S Kamo Dr, Vinita, OK 74301-4613
Tel (918) 256-5551 *Founded/Ownrshp* 1941
Sales 372.1MM *EMP* 154
Accts Bkd Llp Oklahoma City Oklah
SIC 4911 Transmission, electric power; Transmission, electric power
CEO: J Chris Cariker
COO: Cindy Allen
COO: Ted Hilmes
CFO: Ann Hartne
**CFO:* Ann Hartness
Bd of Dir: David Cupps
Exec: Terry Brown
**Prin:* Howard E Freeman
**Prin:* W S Warner
**Prin:* J G Williams
CIO: Tim McCracken

KAMO POWER
See KAMO ELECTRIC COOPERATIVE INC

KAMP OIL CO., INC. OF LANSING
See KAMP OIL INC

D-U-N-S 04-192-6056
KAMP OIL INC (MI)
KAMP OIL CO., INC. OF LANSING
3650 Eastern Ave Se, Grand Rapids, MI 49508-2483
Tel (616) 241-5481 *Founded/Ownrshp* 1964, 1996
Sales 23.3MM^E *EMP* 26
SIC 5172 5531 Lubricating oils & greases; Automotive accessories
Pr: Rosalyn Mulder
**Treas:* Merle Mulder
Manager: Sam Pantelleria

D-U-N-S 00-229-1581
KAMPACK INC (PA)
100 Frontage Rd, Newark, NJ 07114-3718
Tel (973) 589-7400 *Founded/Ownrshp* 1959, 1993
Sales 82.0MM^E *EMP* 206
SIC 2653 Sheets, corrugated: made from purchased materials; Boxes, corrugated: made from purchased materials; Display items, corrugated: made from purchased materials; Sheets, corrugated: made from purchased materials; Boxes, corrugated: made from purchased materials; Display items, corrugated: made from purchased materials
CEO: Karen Mehiel
**Pr:* Karen Aguerosmehiel
**Treas:* Randy Poisson
**VP:* Randy Baer
**VP:* Irving Levine
IT Man: Robert Bonds
Sfty Mgr: Stephen Berney
Opers Mgr: Ingrid Santiago
Prd Mgr: Raymond Street
Ql Cn Mgr: Jobeth Rivera
Board of Directors: Jeff Corke, Dennis Mehiel, Dennis D Mehiel, Michael Mehiel

D-U-N-S 01-402-0036
KAMPEL ENTERPRISES INC
MYERS SHEET METAL DIVISION
8930 Carlisle Rd, Wellsville, PA 17365-9660
Tel (717) 432-9452 *Founded/Ownrshp* 1954
Sales 26.1MM^E *EMP* 49
SIC 5162 3444 Plastics materials; Sheet metalwork
Pr: Thomas E Kampel
Div Mgr: Barry Yoder
IT Man: Lynn Grasmick
IT Man: Mary Maccluskie

D-U-N-S 04-691-5948
KAMPGROUNDS OF AMERICA INC
550 N 31st St Ste 400, Billings, MT 59101-1123
Tel (406) 248-8135 *Founded/Ownrshp* 2006
Sales 196.0MM^E *EMP* 830
SIC 6794 7033 Franchises, selling or licensing; Campgrounds; Franchises, selling or licensing; Campgrounds
CEO: Jim Rogers
Pr: Erik Gothberg
**Pr:* Patrick C Hittmeier
Pr: Michael Zimmerman
**CFO:* John J Burke
VP: Robert Bouse
VP: Mike Bresnahan
VP: Lora Burrowes
**VP:* Michael E Zimmerman
Comm Man: Susan Austin
Rgnl Mgr: Greg Taylor

D-U-N-S 12-267-9228 IMP
KAMPI COMPONENTS CO INC
88 Canal Rd, Fairless Hills, PA 19030-4302
Tel (215) 736-2000 *Founded/Ownrshp* 1984
Sales 88.9MM^E *EMP* 65
SIC 5088 Aircraft & space vehicle supplies & parts
Pr: Don Chandler
**Pr:* Allan Goodman
**Treas:* Geraldine Gerguson
**Treas:* Dorothy Walker
QA Dir: John Carroll
Sls Mgr: Sabrina David
Sales Asso: Melissa Rivera

D-U-N-S 03-862-6149
KAMPS INC
KAMPS WOOD RESOURCES
2900 Peach Ridge Ave Nw, Grand Rapids, MI 49534-1333
Tel (616) 453-9676 *Founded/Ownrshp* 1973
Sales 169.1MM^E *EMP* 650
SIC 2448 2499 Pallets, wood; Mulch, wood & bark; Pallets, wood; Mulch, wood & bark
Pr: Bernard Kamps
COO: Bill Viveen
**CFO:* Ken Haines
Mng Dir: Jaap Schalken
Dir IT: Pat Carey
Sfty Dirs: Tommy Jones
Plnt Mgr: Frank Swartz
VP Mktg: Tom Bodbyl
Sls Mgr: Steve Kromdyk

KAMPS PROPANE
See SERVICES GROUP INC

D-U-N-S 05-170-2298
KAMPS PROPANE INC
(*Suby of* KAMPS PROPANE) ★
1929 Moffat Blvd, Manteca, CA 95336-8945
Tel (209) 823-8924 *Founded/Ownrshp* 1969
Sales 42.6MM^E *EMP* 170
SIC 5984

KAMPS WOOD RESOURCES
See KAMPS INC

D-U-N-S 19-496-5489 EXP
KAMRAN AND CO INC
411 E Montecito St, Santa Barbara, CA 93101-1718
Tel (805) 963-3016 *Founded/Ownrshp* 1988
Sales 27.3MM^E *EMP* 48^E
Accts Keith O Felton Cpa Moorpark
SIC 5046 1799 Restaurant equipment & supplies; Home/office interiors finishing, furnishing & remodeling
CEO: Firouzeh Amiri
VP: Gary Siegel
Board of Directors: Louis Agamie

D-U-N-S 80-824-6461 IMP
KAMTEK INC
(*Suby of* COSMA ENGINEERING) ★
1595 Sterilite Dr, Birmingham, AL 35215-4189
Tel (205) 327-7000 *Founded/Ownrshp* 2008
Sales 228.8MM^E *EMP* 600
SIC 3714 Motor vehicle parts & accessories; Motor vehicle parts & accessories
Genl Mgr: Bill Jones
Snr Mgr: Tammy Simmons

D-U-N-S 07-413-9007
KAN-DI-KI LLC
DIAGNOSTIC LABS & RDLGY
2820 N Ontario St, Burbank, CA 91504-2015
Tel (818) 549-1880 *Founded/Ownrshp* 2008
Sales 82.7MM^E *EMP* 1,500
SIC 8071 Testing laboratories; X-ray laboratory, including dental; Testing laboratories; X-ray laboratory, including dental
VP: Brian Tees
Area Mgr: Nedd Sherbanee
Opers Supe: Vanessa Zamora
Pathlgst: Toni Leggs

KANA
See KODIAK AREA NATIVE ASSOCIATION

KANA
See KAYTECHNOLOGY HOLDINGS INC

D-U-N-S 18-125-1513
KANA PIPELINE INC
1639 E Miraloma Ave, Placentia, CA 92870-6623
Tel (714) 986-1400 *Founded/Ownrshp* 1984
Sales 36.7MM^E *EMP* 100
SIC 1623 1629 Water main construction; Sewer line construction; Drainage system construction; Water main construction; Sewer line construction; Drainage system construction
Pr: Dan Locke
Genl Mgr: Helen Troy

D-U-N-S 19-519-1650
■ **KANA SOFTWARE INC**
(*Suby of* VERINT SYSTEMS INC) ★
840 W California Ave # 100, Sunnyvale, CA 94086-4828
Tel (650) 614-8300 *Founded/Ownrshp* 2014
Sales 135.0MM^E *EMP* 790
SIC 7372 Prepackaged software; Prepackaged software
CEO: Mark Duffell
Pr: William A Bose
Pr: Brett White
CFO: Brian Allen
**CFO:* Jeff Wylie
Bd of Dir: Robert Frick
Bd of Dir: Tom Galvin
**Chf Mktg O:* James Norwood
Ofcr: Jay A Jones
Ex VP: Mark A Angel
Ex VP: David Milam
**Sr VP:* Jim Bureau
**Sr VP:* Amy Mosher
VP: Joseph Ansanelli
VP: Brian Donn
VP: John Montgomery
VP: Peter Morton
VP: John Murray
VP: Arleigh Taylor
VP: Michael Wolfe

D-U-N-S 18-057-8288
KANAAK CORP
(*Suby of* SEALASKA CORP) ★
1 Sealaska Plz Ste 400, Juneau, AK 99801-1245
Tel (907) 586-1512 *Founded/Ownrshp* 2001
Sales 56.4MM *EMP* 445
SIC 6719 Injection molding of plastics; Investment holding companies, except banks
CEO: Chris McNeil
**CFO:* Doug Morris

D-U-N-S 07-290-2307
KANABEC COUNTY HOSPITAL
FIRSTLIGHT HEALTH SYSTEM
301 Highway 65 S, Mora, MN 55051-1899
Tel (320) 679-1212 *Founded/Ownrshp* 1945
Sales 52.5MM^E *EMP* 300
SIC 8062 General medical & surgical hospitals; General medical & surgical hospitals
CEO: Randy Ulseth
**CFO:* Gordon Forbort
Dir QC: Ellen Ryan
IT Man: Cathy Bergren
IT Man: Becky Gallik
IT Man: Ella Stenstrom
Surgeon: Scott Lagaard
Pharmcst: Kati Devorak
Pharmcst: Nick Giller
Pharmcst: Jenny Hoglum
Pharmcst: Jenny Houglum

D-U-N-S 92-825-6825 IMP
KANAFLEX CORP
(*Suby of* KANAFLEX CORPORATION CO., LTD.)
800 Woodlands Pkwy, Vernon Hills, IL 60061-3170
Tel (847) 634-6100 *Founded/Ownrshp* 1991
Sales 23.2MM^E *EMP* 32^E
SIC 5085 Rubber goods, mechanical
Pr: Shigeki Kanao
**VP:* Tokiyoshi Kosaka
Manager: Peter Bishop
Manager: Kevin Cornell
Manager: Ron Darling

D-U-N-S 14-605-6762
KANAKUK MINISTRIES
1353 Lake Shore Dr, Branson, MO 65616-9470
Tel (417) 266-3000 *Founded/Ownrshp* 1999
Sales 20.9MM *EMP* 3
Accts Capin Crouse Llp Greenwood I
SIC 8322 Social service center
Pr: Doug Goodone
CFO: Don Frank

D-U-N-S 00-418-0683 IMP/EXP
KANAN ENTERPRISES INC (OH)
KING NUT COMPANIES
31900 Solon Rd, Solon, OH 44139-3536
Tel (440) 248-8484 *Founded/Ownrshp* 1927
Sales 77.4MM^E *EMP* 300^E
SIC 2068 2034 Nuts: dried, dehydrated, salted or roasted; Fruits, dried or dehydrated, except freeze-dried; Nuts: dried, dehydrated, salted or roasted; Fruits, dried or dehydrated, except freeze-dried
Pr: Martin Kanan
**Ch:* Michael Kanan
**VP:* Matthew Kanan
Comm Dir: Diane Radatz
Sales Exec: Lynn Gordon

D-U-N-S 06-894-5844
KANAWAY SEAFOODS INC
ALASKA GENERAL SEAFOODS
(*Suby of* JIM PATTISON INDUSTRIES LTD)
6425 Ne 175th St, Kenmore, WA 98028-4808
Tel (425) 485-7755 *Founded/Ownrshp* 1986
Sales 77.0MM^E *EMP* 352^E
SIC 2091 Canned & cured fish & seafoods; Canned & cured fish & seafoods
Pr: Gordon Lindquist
Off Mgr: Jessica Hgester

D-U-N-S 05-160-8412
KANAWHA COUNTY BOARD OF EDUCATION
200 Elizabeth St, Charleston, WV 25311-2197
Tel (304) 348-7770 *Founded/Ownrshp* 1863
Sales 206.1MM^E *EMP* 3,770
SIC 8211 Public elementary & secondary schools; School board
Pr: Robin Rector
COO: Margaret Buttrick
VP: Ron Canestraro

D-U-N-S 12-375-3493
KANAWHA COUNTY SCHOOLS
200 Elizabeth St, Charleston, WV 25311-2197
Tel (304) 348-7770 *Founded/Ownrshp* 1863
Sales 51.7MM^E *EMP* 3,638^E
SIC 8211 Public elementary & secondary schools
Psych: Jennifer Jackfert
Psych: Janice Standish

D-U-N-S 17-384-7294
KANAWHA HOSPICE CARE INC
HOSPICECARE
1606 Kanawha Blvd W, Charleston, WV 25387-2536
Tel (304) 768-8523 *Founded/Ownrshp* 1980
Sales 22.0MM *EMP* 225
Accts Gibbons & Kawash Cpa S Charle
SIC 8322 8082 Individual & family services; Home health care services; Individual & family services; Home health care services
Ex Dir: Larry Robertson
**CFO:* Michael Morris
Dir Soc: Richie Hills
Mktg Dir: Jeff Sikorovsky
Mktg Dir: James Wilkerson

D-U-N-S 06-632-4195
■ **KANAWHA INSURANCE CO** (SC)
KMG AMERICA
(*Suby of* KMG AMERICA CORP) ★
210 S White St, Lancaster, SC 29720-2560
Tel (803) 283-5300 *Founded/Ownrshp* 1958, 2007
Sales NA *EMP* 400
SIC 6321 6311 Accident insurance carriers; Health insurance carriers; Life insurance carriers; Accident insurance carriers; Health insurance carriers; Life insurance carriers
Pr: Dale Vaughn
VP: George Bauernfeind
VP: Bob Sweeney
Dir Risk M: Alvin Heggie

D-U-N-S 01-604-7565 IMP
KANAWHA SCALES & SYSTEMS INC
111 Jacobson Dr, Poca, WV 25159-7501
Tel (304) 755-8321 *Founded/Ownrshp* 1969
Sales 51.1MM *EMP* 202
Accts Arnett Foster Toothman Pllc C
SIC 5046 7699 3822 3596 Scales, except laboratory; Scale repair service; Auto controls regulating residntl & coml environmt & applncs; Scales & balances, except laboratory; Scales, except laboratory; Scale repair service; Auto controls regulating residntl & coml environmt & applncs; Scales & balances, except laboratory
Pr: James A Bradbury
**COO:* James Freeman
**Treas:* Robert Foy
**Sec:* Judith L Bradbury
**VP:* William McHale
Brnch Mgr: Ken Welsh
IT Man: Heidi Keeton

D-U-N-S 06-348-0081
KANAWHA STONE CO INC
409 Jacobson Dr, Poca, WV 25159-9691
Tel (304) 755-8271 *Founded/Ownrshp* 1973
Sales 59.1MM^E *EMP* 100
SIC 1611 1794 1629 General contractor, highway & street construction; Excavation work; Land reclamation; Earthmoving contractor; General contractor, highway & street construction; Excavation work; Land reclamation; Earthmoving contractor
Sr VP: David W Lawman
**VP:* Rock Brogan
**VP:* Virginia L King
**Prin:* Tom Kittredge
Ex Dir: Peggy Winters
Off Mgr: Angel Lake
Netwrk Mgr: Kevin Verhaalen
Opers Mgr: Brian Randolph

D-U-N-S 07-710-3054
KANDERS & CO INC
2 Sound View Dr Ste 3, Greenwich, CT 06830-6471
Tel (203) 552-9600 *Founded/Ownrshp* 1999
Sales NA *EMP* 1,805
SIC 6159 Small business investment companies; Small business investment companies
Pr: Warren B Kanders

D-U-N-S 84-748-7600
KANDI KOUNTRY EXPRESS LTD
TOWMASTER TRAILERS
61381 Us Highway 12, Litchfield, MN 55355-5228
Tel (320) 693-7900 *Founded/Ownrshp* 1988
Sales 56.1MM^E *EMP* 140
SIC 3537 3715 Industrial trucks & tractors; Truck trailers; Industrial trucks & tractors; Truck trailers
Pr: Leonard Stulc
**CFO:* Janelle Johnson
Plnt Mgr: Jamie Lemke
Natl Sales: Chris Pokornowski
Manager: Bob Pace
Manager: Russ Woelke

KANDIYOHI COUNTY ADMIN
See COUNTY OF KANDIYOHI

D-U-N-S 06-586-1007
KANDU INC
4190 Sunnyside Dr, Holland, MI 49424-8716
Tel (616) 396-3585 *Founded/Ownrshp* 1953
Sales 7.7MM *EMP* 301
Accts Rehmann Robson Llc Grand Rapi
SIC 8331 Sheltered workshop; Sheltered workshop
CEO: Tom Vreeman
**Mktg Mgr:* Tami Elhart

D-U-N-S 07-722-8468 IMP
KANDY KISS OF CALIFORNIA INC
14761 Califa St, Van Nuys, CA 91411-3107
Tel (818) 833-6360 *Founded/Ownrshp* 1975
Sales 20.9MM^E *EMP* 132
SIC 2339 Women's & misses' outerwear; Women's & misses' outerwear
Ch: David Friedland
**CEO:* Thomas Akin
**CEO:* Robert M Friedland

KANE CARPET
See ART FLOCK & SCREEN INC

D-U-N-S 00-781-3140
KANE CO
6500 Kane Way, Elkridge, MD 21075-6000
Tel (410) 799-3200 *Founded/Ownrshp* 1945
Sales 58.2MM *EMP* 1,500
SIC 4212 Local trucking, without storage; Furniture moving, local: without storage; Local trucking, without storage; Furniture moving, local: without storage
Ch Bd: John M Kane
**COO:* Ronald H Meliker
**CFO:* David J Korotkin
VP: Jim Durfee
VP: Steve Gilbert
VP: Joy Grubb
VP: Brad Jones
Admn Mgr: Lolita Williams
Off Mgr: Tina Chism
Dir IT: Rich Santers
Dir IT: Cindy Willams

D-U-N-S 08-032-2712
KANE COMMUNITY HOSPITAL
4372 Route 6, Kane, PA 16735-3099
Tel (814) 837-8585 *Founded/Ownrshp* 1987
Sales 22.1MM *EMP* 190
Accts Parentebeard Llc Philadelphia
SIC 8062 General medical & surgical hospitals; General medical & surgical hospitals
CEO: James Armstrong
**CEO:* J Gary Rhodes
Dir Rad: Janet Brunner
CTO: Julie Laughner
IT Man: Dino Cherry
IT Man: Margaret Twidale
Nrsg Dir: Val Boni
Nrsg Dir: Pam Bray
Phys Thrpy: Kellie Ely
Snr Mgr: Gary Rhodes
Snr Mgr: Jamil Sarfraz

KANE COUNT HUMAN RESOU SPECI S
See KANE COUNTY HOSPITAL

D-U-N-S 78-723-5373
KANE COUNTY COUGARS
1 Cougar Trl, Geneva, IL 60134
Tel (630) 232-8811 *Founded/Ownrshp* 1990
Sales 15.0MM^E *EMP* 300
SIC 7941 7997 Baseball club, professional & semi-professional; Baseball club, except professional & semi-professional; Baseball club, professional & semi-professional; Baseball club, except professional & semi-professional
Pr: Mike Woleben
VP: Mike Murtaugh
Dir Sec: Dan Klinkhamer
IT Man: Douglas Czurylo

D-U-N-S 18-932-7166
KANE COUNTY HOSPITAL
KANE COUNT HUMAN RESOU SPECI S
355 N Main St, Kanab, UT 84741-3260
Tel (435) 644-5811 *Founded/Ownrshp* 1962
Sales 24.2MM^E *EMP* 170
SIC 8062 General medical & surgical hospitals
Ch: Chad Szymanski
**CEO:* Sherrie Pandya
CFO: Stephen Howells
Phys Thrpy: Shawn Adams
HC Dir: Kelly Jackson

KANE DETENTION PRODUCTS
See KANE INNOVATIONS INC

D-U-N-S 00-686-9242
KANE FREIGHT LINES INC
(*Suby of* KANE IS ABLE INC) ★
3 Stauffer Industrial Par, Taylor, PA 18517-9630
Tel (570) 344-9801 *Founded/Ownrshp* 1930
Sales 24.5MM^E *EMP* 155
SIC 4214 4213 4212 Local trucking with storage; Trucking, except local; Local trucking, without storage; Local trucking with storage; Trucking, except local; Local trucking, without storage
CEO: Richard P Kane
**Pr:* Eugene J Kane Sr
**CFO:* Eugene J Kane Jr
**VP:* Christopher Kane

D-U-N-S 03-271-3497 IMP/EXP
KANE FURNITURE CORP
KANE'S FURNITURE
5700 70th Ave N, Pinellas Park, FL 33781-4238
Tel (727) 545-9555 *Founded/Ownrshp* 1948
Sales 199.7MM^E *EMP* 900
SIC 5712

D-U-N-S 00-210-2986 IMP
KANE INNOVATIONS INC (PA)
KANE DETENTION PRODUCTS
2250 Powell Ave, Erie, PA 16506-1842
Tel (814) 838-7731 *Founded/Ownrshp* 1959, 2001
Sales 44.3MM^E *EMP* 125
SIC 3442 3211 3496 3446 Metal doors, sash & trim; Screen & storm doors & windows; Screens, window, metal; Screen doors, metal; Strengthened or reinforced glass; Miscellaneous fabricated wire products; Architectural metalwork; Metal doors, sash & trim; Screen & storm doors & windows; Screens, window, metal; Screen doors, metal; Strengthened or reinforced glass; Miscellaneous fabricated wire products; Architectural metalwork
Pr: Dean Campbell
**Pr:* Todd Frederick
**Treas:* Nancy Henry
**VP:* Michael D Show
Exec: Sheryl Shannon
IT Man: Michael Demmick
Sfty Mgr: Brenda Morrison
Plnt Mgr: Roy Hayes
VP Sls: Thomas Hemdal
VP Sls: Harry Taylor
Sls Dir: Vince Tutino

D-U-N-S 11-257-0551
KANE IS ABLE INC
3 Stauffer Industrial Par, Taylor, PA 18517-9628
Tel (570) 344-9801 *Founded/Ownrshp* 1995
Sales 132.4MM^E *EMP* 500
SIC 4213 4222 4225 4214 Trucking, except local; Warehousing, cold storage or refrigerated; Storage, frozen or refrigerated goods; General warehousing; Local trucking with storage; Trucking, except local; Warehousing, cold storage or refrigerated; Storage, frozen or refrigerated goods; General warehousing; Local trucking with storage
Pr: Michael J Gardner
**Ch Bd:* Lee Stucky
**CFO:* Eugene J Kane Jr
Sr VP: John W Hurst
Sr VP: Satu Mehta
VP: Mike Albert
**VP:* Christopher Kane
CIO: Gerry Smith
Opers Supe: Bill Bagg
Opers Mgr: Bill Tigue

D-U-N-S 80-597-0308
KANE RUSSELL COLEMAN & LOGAN PC
1601 Elm St Ste 3700, Dallas, TX 75201-7207
Tel (214) 777-4200 *Founded/Ownrshp* 1992
Sales 22.0MM^E *EMP* 105
SIC 8111 General practice law office
Pr: Raymond J Kane
Pr: Mary Jabin
**VP:* Kenneth W Biermacher
**VP:* Joseph M Coleman
**VP:* Michael A Logan
**VP:* Gordon B Russell
Genl Mgr: William Pilat
Dir IT: Brian Clark

D-U-N-S 00-595-5513
KANE WAREHOUSING INC
(*Suby of* KANE IS ABLE INC) ★
3 Stauffer Industrial Par, Scranton, PA 18517-9628
Tel (570) 344-9801 *Founded/Ownrshp* 1985
Sales 70.6MM^E *EMP* 290
SIC 4222 4225 4214 Warehousing, cold storage or refrigerated; Storage, frozen or refrigerated goods; General warehousing; Local trucking with storage; Warehousing, cold storage or refrigerated; Storage, frozen or refrigerated goods; General warehousing; Local trucking with storage
Pr: Richard P Kane
**Ch:* Eugene J Kane Sr
**Sec:* Joan Kane
**Sr VP:* Veronica Donchez
**VP:* Christopher Kane
Snr Mgr: Jim Lahey

D-U-N-S 04-525-6831
KANE-MILLER CORP
1 S School Ave Ste 401, Sarasota, FL 34237-6052
Tel (941) 346-2003 *Founded/Ownrshp* 1920
Sales 27.0MM^E *EMP* 300
SIC 2077 Tallow rendering, inedible; Tallow rendering, inedible
CEO: Stanley B Kane
**Pr:* Harold Oelbaum
**CFO:* Robert Wininger

D-U-N-S 03-105-8824
■ **KANEB INFORMATION SERVICES INC**
(*Suby of* FURMANITE CORP) ★
2435 N Central Expy, Richardson, TX 75080-2753
Tel (972) 699-4000 *Founded/Ownrshp* 1991
Sales 15.6MM^E *EMP* 365
SIC 7374 Data processing service; Data processing service
CEO: John Barnes
**VP:* Howard Watsworth

D-U-N-S 01-088-9418 IMP
KANEBRIDGE CORP
250 Pehle Ave Ste 303, Saddle Brook, NJ 07663-5832
Tel (201) 337-3200 *Founded/Ownrshp* 1975
Sales 23.2MM^E *EMP* 70
SIC 5072 Hardware; Miscellaneous fasteners
Pr: Joseph McGrath
**Sec:* Robert Williams
Ofcr: Jennifer Hyman
Genl Mgr: Kellie Nirmaier
Sales Exec: Edward Desouza

D-U-N-S 06-809-3483 IMP
KANEKA AMERICAS HOLDING INC
(*Suby of* KANEKA CORPORATION)
6250 Underwood Rd, Pasadena, TX 77507-1061
Tel (281) 474-7084 *Founded/Ownrshp* 1982
Sales 125.8MM^E *EMP* 300
SIC 2023

D-U-N-S 07-844-7033 IMP/EXP
KANEKA NORTH AMERICA LLC
(*Suby of* KANEKA AMERICAS HOLDING INC) ★
6161 Underwood Rd, Pasadena, TX 77507-1096
Tel (281) 474-7084 *Founded/Ownrshp* 2012
Sales 126.4MM^E *EMP* 300
SIC 2821 3081 2023 Plastics materials & resins; Unsupported plastics film & sheet; Dry, condensed, evaporated dairy products; Plastics materials & resins; Unsupported plastics film & sheet; Dry, condensed, evaporated dairy products
Pr: Kazuhiko Fujii
**Sec:* Masatoshi Yoshimatsu
Ex VP: Katsunobu Doro
**Ex VP:* Steven C Skarke
**VP:* Bruce Duerringer
VP: Masaharu Inoue
**VP:* Alvin Proctor
**VP:* William Renaud
Natl Sales: Greg Clements
Mktg Mgr: John Jarmul
Sls Mgr: Tina Daily

D-U-N-S 00-193-1344 IMP/EXP
KANEMATSU USA INC (NY)
(*Suby of* KANEMATSU CORPORATION)
500 5th Ave Fl 29, New York, NY 10110-2999
Tel (212) 704-9400 *Founded/Ownrshp* 1951
Sales 433.0MM *EMP* 100
Accts Pricewaterhousecoopers Llp N
SIC 5084 5051 5065 5153 Industrial machinery & equipment; Steel; Ferrous metals; Nonferrous metal sheets, bars, rods, etc.; Electronic parts & equipment; Electronic parts; Grains; Industrial machinery & equipment; Steel; Ferrous metals; Nonferrous metal sheets, bars, rods, etc.; Electronic parts & equipment; Electronic parts; Grains
CEO: Katsumi Morita
**Treas:* Taro Unno
Div/Sub He: Sigehiro Yamanaka
Div Mgr: Kenji Ogiso
Genl Mgr: K Koshiyama
Genl Mgr: Hiroshi Uemura

D-U-N-S 05-457-8716
KANEQUIP INC
KUBOTA
(*Suby of* KANEQUIP INC) ★
1152 Pony Express Hwy, Marysville, KS 66508-8647
Tel (785) 562-2377 *Founded/Ownrshp* 1999
Sales 117.0MM *EMP* 167
SIC 5046 Commercial equipment; Commercial equipment
**CEO:* James Meinhardt
Sales Asso: Greg Schultejans

D-U-N-S 07-635-6562
KANEQUIP INC
KUBOTA
18035 E Us Highway 24, Wamego, KS 66547-9790
Tel (785) 456-2041 *Founded/Ownrshp* 1966
Sales 117.0MM^E *EMP* 167
SIC 5999 Farm machinery; Farm machinery
Pr: James Meinhardt
**VP:* Jim Burke
Off Mgr: April Goff
Store Mgr: Randy Auer
IT Man: Jason Baity

KANE'S ELECTRICAL CONTRACTING
See R W MERCER CO

KANE'S FURNITURE
See KANE FURNITURE CORP

KANEY FOODS
See AMK FOODSERVICES INC

D-U-N-S 07-920-2867
KANG & ASSOCIATES MDS PA (FL)
FLORIDA EMERGENCY PHYSICIANS
500 Winderley Pl Ste 115, Maitland, FL 32751-7406
Tel (407) 875-0555 *Founded/Ownrshp* 1970
Sales 21.9MM^E *EMP* 100
SIC 8011 Freestanding emergency medical center
Pr: Rodney C Kang MD
Sr VP: Kim Fauskee
VP: Jesse Caron
Doctor: Omayra Marrero MD

D-U-N-S 14-830-0358 IMP
KANGADIS FOOD INC
GOURMET FACTORY
55 Corporate Dr, Hauppauge, NY 11788-2021
Tel (800) 715-8441 *Founded/Ownrshp* 2003
Sales 47.7MM^E *EMP* 65
SIC 5149 Specialty food items; Specialty food items
Ch Bd: Themis Kangadis
**CFO:* Dennis Detore
**Prin:* Aristidis Kangadis
Sales Exec: Andrew Lax

KANGAROO EXPRESS
See PANTRY INC

D-U-N-S 06-741-7923
KANKAKEE COMMUNITY COLLEGE DISTRICT 520
100 College Dr, Kankakee, IL 60901-6505
Tel (815) 802-8100 *Founded/Ownrshp* 1966
Sales 27.5MM *EMP* 515
Accts Groskreutz Schmidt Abraham
SIC 8222 Community college; Community college
Pr: John Avendano
Bd of Dir: Sharon Hoogstraat
Chf Mktg O: Kari Sargeant
VP: Judith Marwick
VP: Paul O'Connor
Ex Dir: Gina Walter
Admn Mgr: Bill Yohnka
Off Mgr: Imani Cobb
MIS Dir: Shannon James
IT Man: Kathy French
Opers Mgr: John Martin

D-U-N-S 07-143-1290
KANKAKEE COUNTY TRAINING CENTER FOR DISABLED INC
333 S Schuyler Ave, Bradley, IL 60915-2341
Tel (815) 939-9980 *Founded/Ownrshp* 1966
Sales 37.8M *EMP* 366
SIC 8331 8322 Job training & vocational rehabilitation services; Individual & family services; Job training & vocational rehabilitation services; Individual & family services
Pr: Stephen D Mitchell

D-U-N-S 02-556-4436
KANKAKEE DAILY JOURNAL CO LLC
DAILY JOURNAL, THE
(*Suby of* JOURNAL) ★
8 Dearborn Sq, Kankakee, IL 60901-3945
Tel (815) 937-3300 *Founded/Ownrshp* 1853, 1983
Sales 21.9MM^E *EMP* 250
SIC 2711 Newspapers, publishing & printing; Newspapers, publishing & printing
Genl Mgr: Mario Sebastiani

KANKAKEE INDUSTRIAL TECHNOLOGY
See DECATUR INDUSTRIAL ELECTRIC INC

D-U-N-S 09-258-5173
KANKAKEE SCHOOL DISTRICT 111
240 Warren Ave, Kankakee, IL 60901-4319
Tel (815) 933-0700 *Founded/Ownrshp* 1865
Sales 75.6MM *EMP* 978
Accts Smith Koelling Dykstra & Ohm

SIC 8211 Public elementary school; Private vocational/technical school; Public senior high school; Public elementary school; Private vocational/technical school; Public senior high school
**VP:* Amelia A Davis
Pr Dir: Nina Epstein
Teacher Pr: John Thomas

D-U-N-S 14-291-4428
KANKAKEE VALLEY CONSTRUCTION CO INC
4356 W State Route 17, Kankakee, IL 60901-7974
Tel (815) 937-8700 *Founded/Ownrshp* 2002
Sales 27.3MM^E *EMP* 150
Accts Wadley & Associates Bourbonna
SIC 1611 Highway & street construction; Highway & street construction
Pr: Leonard Tobey
VP: John Azzarelli
**VP:* Jimmy Joines
VP: Mark Kraetzer
Sfty Mgr: Phil Czernik

D-U-N-S 62-175-3300
KANKAKEE VALLEY SCHOOL CORP
12021 N 550 W, Wheatfield, IN 46392
Tel (219) 987-4711 *Founded/Ownrshp* 1965
Sales 27.0MM *EMP* 475
SIC 8211 Public elementary & secondary schools; Public elementary & secondary schools
Dir Rx: William Orsburn
Dir Bus: Bill Orsburn
Dir IT: Bob Heid

D-U-N-S 00-527-7033 EXP
KANN MANUFACTURING CORP
210 Regent St, Guttenberg, IA 52052-4701
Tel (563) 252-2035 *Founded/Ownrshp* 1963
Sales 27.1MM^E *EMP* 85
SIC 3713 Truck bodies (motor vehicles)
Pr: Rose Kann
COO: Ken Goedken
**Treas:* William Kann
IT Man: Tim Andregg
IT Man: Randy Heller
Plnt Mgr: Steve Friedlein
Sales Asso: Becky Kelly

KANNAPLIS CY SCHOLS BD EDUCATN
See KANNAPOLIS CITY SCHOOL SYSTEM

D-U-N-S 04-554-2180
KANNAPOLIS CITY SCHOOL SYSTEM
KANNAPLIS CY SCHOLS BD EDUCATN
100 Denver St, Kannapolis, NC 28083-3609
Tel (704) 932-2999 *Founded/Ownrshp* 1928
Sales 40.6MM^E *EMP* 750
SIC 8211 Public elementary & secondary schools; Public elementary & secondary schools
VP: Camilla Buckwell
Pr Dir: Ellen Boyd
Schl Brd P: Todd Adams
Teacher Pr: Kim Harn

KANNEGIESSER USA
See PASSAT LAUNDRY SYSTEMS INC

KANO FOODS
See LEMON GROVE ULTRA MART INC

D-U-N-S 78-090-1216
KANSAS ASPHALT INC
KAI TOTAL PAVEMENT MANAGEMENT
7000 W 206th St, Bucyrus, KS 66013-9610
Tel (913) 384-1010 *Founded/Ownrshp* 2003
Sales 30.2MM *EMP* 75
Accts Dh Scott & Company Redding
SIC 1611 8744 8741 Surfacing & paving; Grading; Base maintenance (providing personnel on continuing basis); Construction management
Pr: Jane Jeffries
**COO:* Charles Jeffries
**CFO:* Candi Eckert
Bd of Dir: Jennifer Mick
**VP:* Jenna Beckett
VP: Rose Olesen
**VP:* Jeanne Pollard
**VP:* Tya Smith
VP Sls: Charlie Schulz

D-U-N-S 08-410-2870
KANSAS ATHLETICS INC
(*Suby of* UNIVERSITY OF KANSAS) ★
1651 Naismith Dr, Lawrence, KS 66045-4069
Tel (785) 864-7050 *Founded/Ownrshp* 1925
Sales 103.7MM *EMP* 434
Accts Bkd Llp Kansas City Missour
SIC 8699 Athletic organizations; Athletic organizations

D-U-N-S 60-711-6233
KANSAS BUILDING SUPPLY CO INC
7600 Wedd St, Overland Park, KS 66204-2227
Tel (913) 962-5227 *Founded/Ownrshp* 1989
Sales 50.3MM^E *EMP* 80
SIC 5031 Building materials, exterior; Building materials, interior; Building materials, exterior; Building materials, interior
Pr: Dennis Donelly
Div Mgr: Jay Waldenmeyer

D-U-N-S 03-142-8261
KANSAS CANDY & TOBACCO INC
4430 W 29th Cir S, Wichita, KS 67215-1018
Tel (316) 942-9081 *Founded/Ownrshp* 2000
Sales 25.0MM *EMP* 14
SIC 5145 5194 Candy; Cigarettes; Candy; Cigarettes
Pr: Scott Larkin
**Sec:* Julie Daugherty

D-U-N-S 07-304-6773
KANSAS CITY AREA TRANSPORTATION AUTHORITY
KCATA
1200 E 18th St, Kansas City, MO 64108-1606
Tel (816) 221-0660 *Founded/Ownrshp* 1965
Sales 12.9MM *EMP* 866
Accts Mcgladrey Llp Kansas City Mi
SIC 4111 Bus transportation; Bus transportation
Genl Mgr: Mark Huffer
Dir Risk M: Lawrence Baker
Dir IT: Bryan Beck
IT Man: Deborah Dotson
Netwrk Mgr: Laura Reeves
Sfty Mgr: Garcia Robert
Mktg Dir: Cindy Baker
Mktg Mgr: Bridget Moss

D-U-N-S 06-795-4735
KANSAS CITY ART INSTITUTE (MO)
4415 Warwick Blvd, Kansas City, MO 64111-1820
Tel (816) 472-4852 *Founded/Ownrshp* 1885
Sales 29.9MM *EMP* 240^E
Accts Bkd Llp Kansas City Mo
SIC 8221 College, except junior; College, except junior
Pr: Jacqueline Chanda
Bd of Dir: John Hoffman
**VP:* Anne Canfiled
VP: Nicolle Ratliff
**VP:* Richard Rieder
**VP:* Pam Sibert
**VP:* Larry Stone
Comm Man: Brian Spano
Off Mgr: Beverly Ahern
CIO: Crystal Denson
IT Man: Sharon Autry

D-U-N-S 00-716-9584 IMP
KANSAS CITY BOARD OF PUBLIC UTILITIES
BPU
540 Minnesota Ave, Kansas City, KS 66101-2930
Tel (913) 573-9000 *Founded/Ownrshp* 1909
Sales 143.5MM *EMP* 1,772
SIC 4931 4941 Electric & other services combined; Water supply; Electric & other services combined; Water supply
Pr: David Alvey
CFO: Lori Austin
Bd of Dir: Thomas Groneman
Ofcr: Kristina Daggett
**Prin:* Don L Gray
Adm Dir: Laurie Cassidy
CIO: Spurlynn Byers
Cmptr Lab: Frank Liu
Telecom Mg: Joe Sachen
Sfty Dirs: Teresa Grimes
Trfc Dir: Lisa Sarras

D-U-N-S 07-303-8523
KANSAS CITY CHIEFS FOOTBALL CLUB INC
1 Arrowhead Dr, Kansas City, MO 64129-1651
Tel (816) 861-5437 *Founded/Ownrshp* 1960
Sales 32.2MM^E *EMP* 190
SIC 7941 Football club; Football club
CEO: Daniel L Crumb
**Pr:* Mark Donovan
Sr VP: Bill Chaplin
VP: Rob Alberino
VP: Tyler Epp
VP: Bill Kuharich
VP: Andrew Smitka
Exec: Kirsten Krug
Genl Mgr: John Dorsey
S&M/VP: Tammy Fruits
Pr Dir: Bob Moore

D-U-N-S 19-671-6591
KANSAS CITY DOWNTOWN HOTEL GROUP LLC
MARRIOTT
200 W 12th St, Kansas City, MO 64105-1638
Tel (816) 421-6800 *Founded/Ownrshp* 1995
Sales 37.6MM^E *EMP* 500
SIC 7011 7389 5812 Hotels & motels; Convention & show services; Caterers; Hotels & motels; Convention & show services; Caterers
Sr VP: Phil Algrim
VP: Michael Lally
VP: Jamie McGrail
Genl Mgr: Carol Peckoraro
Sls Mgr: Farhonda Cullum
Sls Mgr: Leticia Hickman

D-U-N-S 00-785-6602
KANSAS CITY ELECTRICAL SUPPLY CO INC (MO)
KCES
14851 W 99th St, Lenexa, KS 66215-1110
Tel (913) 541-1717 *Founded/Ownrshp* 1927
Sales 24.0MM *EMP* 40
SIC 5063 Electrical supplies; Electrical supplies
Pr: Joyce Jones
**Treas:* John Owens
**VP:* James Jones

D-U-N-S 08-777-4386
KANSAS CITY FREIGHTLINER SALES INC
7800 Ne 38th St, Kansas City, MO 64161-9454
Tel (816) 453-4400 *Founded/Ownrshp* 1982
Sales 62.5MM^E *EMP* 257
SIC 5012 5013 7538 Truck tractors; Truck parts & accessories; Truck engine repair, except industrial; Truck tractors; Truck parts & accessories; Truck engine repair, except industrial
Pr: Janie O'Dell
**Ex VP:* Mark O'Dell
**Ex VP:* William P Westfall
Mktg Mgr: Mike Westfall
Sales Asso: Dierk Hamilton
Sales Asso: Ryan Huff
Sales Asso: Greg Koelling
Sales Asso: Bren Rose

D-U-N-S 62-442-4040
KANSAS CITY HOSPICE INC
1500 Meadow Lake Pkwy # 200, Kansas City, MO 64114-1615
Tel (816) 276-2657 *Founded/Ownrshp* 1979
Sales 22.6MM *EMP* 275^E
Accts Dixon Hughes Goodman Llp Cha
SIC 8082 Home health care services; Home health care services
Pr: Elaine McIntosh
Off Mgr: Lisa Ray
Doctor: Kristen C Sladek MD

D-U-N-S 08-069-0597
KANSAS CITY KANSAS COMMUNITY COLLEGE ENDOWMENT (KS)
7250 State Ave, Kansas City, KS 66112-3003
Tel (913) 334-1100 *Founded/Ownrshp* 1923
Sales 25.3MM^E *EMP* 500
Accts Leon Logan Cpa Pa Kansas
SIC 8222 Community college; Community college
Pr: Doris Givens
**Pr:* Tom Burke
**CFO:* Brian Bode
Ofcr: Scott Bailie
Ofcr: Scott Breshears
Ofcr: Mel Casson
Ofcr: John Davis
Ofcr: Mike Golden
Ofcr: Henry Horn
Ofcr: Alan Jaskinia
Ofcr: Evelyn McConnell
Ofcr: Richard Peters
Ofcr: Ken Swearingen
Ofcr: Robert Tesch
**VP:* Tamara Agha
Exec: Grant Von Lunen

D-U-N-S 00-696-5834
▲ KANSAS CITY LIFE INSURANCE CO
3520 Broadway Blvd, Kansas City, MO 64111-2565
Tel (816) 753-7000 *Founded/Ownrshp* 1895
Sales NA *EMP* 446^E
Accts Kpmg Llp Kansas City Missour
Tkr Sym KCLI *Exch* NAS
SIC 6311 6411 Life insurance; Life insurance carriers; Life insurance agents; Life insurance; Life insurance carriers; Life insurance agents
Ch Bd: R Philip Bixby
Pr: Brenna Gardino
Pr: Anne Snoddy
**CFO:* Tracy W Knapp
**V Ch Bd:* Walter E Bixby
Ofcr: Daniel Harber
Ofcr: Kelly Ullom
Sr VP: Charles R Duffy
Sr VP: Donald E Krebs
Sr VP: A Craig Mason Jr
Sr VP: Craig Mason
Sr VP: Mark A Milton
VP: Ryan Beasley
VP: Bill Browning
VP: Kathryn Church
VP: Susanna Denney
VP: Rob Fisher
VP: Timothy Knott
VP: David A Laird
VP: Francis P Lemery
VP: Tom Morgan
Board of Directors: Kevin G Barth, William R Blessing, Michael Braude, John C Cozad, Richard L Finn, Cecil R Miller, Mark A Milton, William A Schalekamp

KANSAS CITY MILLWORK
See MOEHL MILLWORK INC

D-U-N-S 07-988-3096
KANSAS CITY PETERBILT INC
8915 Woodend Rd, Kansas City, KS 66111-1717
Tel (913) 441-2888 *Founded/Ownrshp* 1986
Sales 43.7MM^E *EMP* 125
SIC 5012 Trucks, commercial; Trucks, commercial
Pr: Leon C Geis
Genl Mgr: Clyde Bates
Opers Mgr: Mark Thomas
Advt Dir: Cody Hoffman
Sales Asso: Big Mike

D-U-N-S 00-696-5842 IMP
■ KANSAS CITY POWER & LIGHT CO
(*Suby of* GREAT PLAINS ENERGY INC) ★
1200 Main St, Kansas City, MO 64105-2122
Tel (816) 556-2200 *Founded/Ownrshp* 2001
Sales 1.7MMM *EMP* 2,935^E
Accts Deloitte & Touche Llp Kansas
SIC 4911 Generation, electric power; Transmission, electric power; Distribution, electric power; Generation, electric power; Transmission, electric power; Distribution, electric power
Ch Bd: Terry Bassham
COO: Scott H Heidtbrink
CFO: James C Shay
Treas: Michael W Cline
Chf Cred: Ellen E Fairchild
Sr VP: Heather A Humphrey
VP: Duane Anstaett
VP: Steven P Busser
VP: Chuck Caisley
Dir IT: Mitch Krysa
Sfty Dirs: Rita Sandstrom
Board of Directors: David L Bodde, Randall C Ferguson Jr, Gary D Forsee, Scott D Grimes, Thomas D Hyde, James A Mitchell, Ann D Murtlow, John J Sherman, Linda H Talbott

D-U-N-S 04-366-7385
KANSAS CITY PUBLIC SCHOOLS (MO)
KCPS
1211 Mcgee St, Kansas City, MO 64106-2416
Tel (816) 418-7000 *Founded/Ownrshp* 1867
Sales 216.0MM^E *EMP* 4,700
Accts Mcgladrey Llp Kansas City Mi
SIC 8211 Public elementary & secondary schools; Public elementary & secondary schools
**CFO:* Rebecca Lee Gwin
**Chf Cred:* Eileen Houston Stewart
Bd of Dir: Duane Kelly

D-U-N-S 10-709-7446
KANSAS CITY REPERTORY THEATRE INC
REP, THE
4949 Cherry St Ste 307, Kansas City, MO 64110-2214
Tel (816) 235-2700 *Founded/Ownrshp* 1964
Sales 10.1MM *EMP* 330
Accts Cbiz Mhm Llc Leawood Ks
SIC 7922 Repertory, road or stock companies: theatrical; Repertory, road or stock companies: theatrical
Ex Dir: Eric Rosen
Comm Dir: Laura Muir
**Genl Mgr:* Laurie Jarrett
Sls Mgr: Brendan Martin

D-U-N-S 00-194-2218
▲ KANSAS CITY SOUTHERN
427 W 12th St, Kansas City, MO 64105-1403
Tel (816) 983-1303 *Founded/Ownrshp* 1962
Sales 2.5MMM *EMP* 6,490^E
Accts Kpmg Llp Kansas City Missou
Tkr Sym KSU *Exch* NYS
SIC 4011 Railroads, line-haul operating; Railroads, line-haul operating
Pr: David L Starling
**Ch Bd:* Robert J Druten
Pr: Steve Evans
Pr: Darin Selby
CFO: Michael W Upchurch
Chf Mktg O: Brian D Hancock
Ofcr: William J Wochner
Ex VP: Daniel Avramovich
Ex VP: Warren K Erdman
Sr VP: Brian H Bowers
Sr VP: Lora Cheatum
Sr VP: John S Jacobsen
Sr VP: Michael J Naatz
Sr VP: Mary K Stadler
Sr VP: Mary Stadler
Sr VP: Robert B Terry
Sr VP: Richard M Zuza
VP: Doniele Carlson
VP: William Galligan
VP: Erik B Hansen
VP: Gary W Jarboe
Board of Directors: Lu M Cordova, Henry R Davis, Terrence P Dunn, Antonio O Garza Jr, Michael R Haverty, Thomas A McDonnell, Rodney E Slater

D-U-N-S 00-696-5859
■ KANSAS CITY SOUTHERN RAILWAY CO INC
(*Suby of* KANSAS CITY SOUTHERN) ★
427 W 12th St, Kansas City, MO 64105-1403
Tel (816) 983-1303 *Founded/Ownrshp* 2008
Sales 138.9MM^E *EMP* 880^E
SIC 4011 4213 Railroads, line-haul operating; Trucking, except local; Railroads, line-haul operating; Trucking, except local
Ch Bd: Landon H Rowland
COO: David R Ebbrecht
Sr VP: Mike Naatz
Sr VP: Jeff Songer
Sr VP: Robert B Terry
VP: Wayne Godlewski
VP: D Morris Godwin
VP: Mark A Redd
VP: Michael Smith
VP: T Scot Stottlemyre
VP: Steve Truitt

KANSAS CITY STAR, THE
See CYPRESS MEDIA LLC

D-U-N-S 06-145-2343
KANSAS CITY STRUCTURAL STEEL INC
3801 Raytown Rd, Kansas City, MO 64129-2270
Tel (816) 924-0977 *Founded/Ownrshp* 1998
Sales 43.3MM *EMP* 35
Accts Mayer Hoffman Mccann Pc Kan
SIC 3441 Fabricated structural metal; Fabricated structural metal
Pr: Timothy J Olah
**Sec:* Chris Olah
VP: Mike Bennett
IT Man: Tab White

D-U-N-S 61-829-6982
KANSAS CITY SYMPHONY
1703 Wyandotte St Ste 200, Kansas City, MO 64108-1207
Tel (816) 471-1100 *Founded/Ownrshp* 1982
Sales 31.9MM *EMP* 108
Accts Bkd Llp Kansas City Mo
SIC 7929 Symphony orchestras; Symphony orchestras
Ch Bd: Shirley Bush Helzberg
**VP:* Robert A Kipp
**Ex Dir:* Frank Byrne
Ex Dir: Gail Rohman
Mktg Mgr: Megan Felling

D-U-N-S 06-795-2572
KANSAS CITY UNIVERSITY OF MEDICINE AND BIOSCIENCES
COLLEGE OSTEOPATHIC MEDICINE
1750 Independence Ave, Kansas City, MO 64106-1453
Tel (816) 283-2000 *Founded/Ownrshp* 1916
Sales 48.6MM^E *EMP* 160^E
Accts Bkd Llp Kansas City Mo
SIC 8221 8031 Professional schools; Offices & clinics of osteopathic physicians; Professional schools; Offices & clinics of osteopathic physicians
Pr: Marc B Hahn
V Ch: Shawn Moulder
Ofcr: Stacy Jackson
**Ex VP:* Joe Massman
**VP:* Doug Dalzell Douglas
VP: Jeffrey Joyce
VP: Jane Lampo
**VP:* James Park
Dir Lab: Linda Adkison
Dir Lab: Abdulbaki Agbas
Web Dev: Curt Douglas

KANSAS CITY ZOO
See FRIENDS OF ZOO INC OF KANSAS CITY MISSOURI

D-U-N-S 17-593-7804
KANSAS DEPARTMENT FOR CHILDREN AND FAMILIES
(*Suby of* EXECUTIVE OFFICE OF STATE OF KANSAS) ★
915 Sw Harrison St, Topeka, KS 66612-1505
Tel (785) 368-6358 *Founded/Ownrshp* 1861
Sales NA *EMP* 6,256
SIC 9441 9431 Administration of social & manpower programs; ; Administration of public health programs; ; Administration of social & manpower programs; ; Administration of public health programs;

D-U-N-S 87-804-5608
KANSAS DEPARTMENT OF ADMINISTRATION
(*Suby of* EXECUTIVE OFFICE OF STATE OF KANSAS) ★
1000 Sw Jackson St # 500, Topeka, KS 66612-1300
Tel (785) 296-3011 *Founded/Ownrshp* 1861
Sales NA *EMP* 450
SIC 9111 Executive offices; ; Executive offices;
CTO: Bradley Williams
IT Man: Lindsey Cooper
IT Man: Larry Zeller
Snr Mgr: Philip Michael

D-U-N-S 00-252-2832
KANSAS DEPARTMENT OF CORRECTIONS
(*Suby of* EXECUTIVE OFFICE OF STATE OF KANSAS) ★
714 Sw Jackson St Fl 3, Topeka, KS 66603-3721
Tel (785) 296-3317 *Founded/Ownrshp* 1861
Sales NA *EMP* 3,100
SIC 9223 Prison, government; ; Prison, government;
Pr: Dennis Williams
VP: Karen Rohling
Mktg Mgr: Brad Sowter
Sls Mgr: Kelly Potter
Sls Mgr: Ray Roberts

D-U-N-S 17-594-1483
KANSAS DEPARTMENT OF HEALTH AND ENVIRONMENT
(*Suby of* EXECUTIVE OFFICE OF STATE OF KANSAS) ★
1000 Sw Jackson St, Topeka, KS 66612-1300
Tel (785) 296-1500 *Founded/Ownrshp* 1861
Sales NA *EMP* 975
SIC 9431 Administration of public health programs; ; Administration of public health programs;
Ch: Ed Eilert
Ofcr: Cory Sheedy
Dir IT: Glen Yancey
IT Man: Maria Scherich
IT Man: Pam Tierce
Genl Couns: Yvonne Anderson

D-U-N-S 87-994-1482
KANSAS DEPARTMENT OF LABOR
(*Suby of* ROYAL LONDON MUTUAL INSURANCE SOCIETY,LIMITED(THE))
401 Sw Topeka Blvd, Topeka, KS 66603-3182
Tel (785) 296-1800 *Founded/Ownrshp* 1868
Sales NA *EMP* 350
SIC 9651 Labor-management negotiations board, government; ; Labor-management negotiations board, government;
Sr Cor Off: Don Cunningham
Ofcr: Debbie Gassert
IT Man: Joyce Leblanc
IT Man: Dawn Palmberg

D-U-N-S 17-607-8103
KANSAS DEPARTMENT OF TRANSPORTATION
EXECUTIVE OFFCE OF THE STATE
(*Suby of* EXECUTIVE OFFICE OF STATE OF KANSAS) ★
700 Sw Harrison St # 500, Topeka, KS 66603-3964
Tel (785) 296-3501 *Founded/Ownrshp* 1868
Sales NA *EMP* 3,000ᴱ
Accts Cliftonlarsonallen Llp Broom
SIC 9621 ;
Ofcr: Salih Petzold
Ofcr: Ashla Prockish
Adm Dir: Brenda Abney-Gonzalez
Prgrm Mgr: Sondra Clark
Prgrm Mgr: David Schwartz
Prgrm Mgr: Joel Skelley
IT Man: Roger Moore
Sfty Dirs: Kelly Gaer
Pr Mgr: Kirk Hutchinson
Counsel: Kate Gellatly
Snr Mgr: Kent Anschutz
Board of Directors: Mike Crow, Marcia Ferrill, Lon Ingram, Dale Jost, Julie Lorenz, Ben Nelson, Dan Scherschligt, Bob Stacks, Ed Young

D-U-N-S 87-807-2883
KANSAS DEPARTMENT OF WILDLIFE PARKS AND TOURISM
(*Suby of* EXECUTIVE OFFICE OF STATE OF KANSAS) ★
1020 S Kansas Ave Rm 200, Topeka, KS 66612-1326
Tel (785) 296-2281 *Founded/Ownrshp* 1987
Sales NA *EMP* 406
SIC 9512 ;
IT Man: Jason Dickson
IT Man: Carl Magnuson

D-U-N-S 09-582-9693
KANSAS ELECTRIC POWER COOPERATIVE INC
KEPCO
600 Sw Corporate Vw, Topeka, KS 66615-1233
Tel (785) 273-7010 *Founded/Ownrshp* 1975
Sales 174.1MM *EMP* 24
Accts Bkd Llp Tulsa Ok
SIC 4911 Distribution, electric power; Distribution, electric power
CEO: Thuck Terrill
Trst: KS Altamont
Trst: KS Mankato
Trst: KS Meade
Trst: KS Pratt
Trst: KS Wellington
Ex VP: Stephen Parr
VP: William Riggins

D-U-N-S 05-658-0053
KANSAS ELKS TRAINING CENTER FOR HANDICAPPED INC
KETCH
1006 E Waterman St, Wichita, KS 67211-1525
Tel (316) 383-8700 *Founded/Ownrshp* 1962
Sales 12.6MM *EMP* 300
Accts Mayer Hoffman Mccann Pc Wic
SIC 8331 Vocational rehabilitation agency; Vocational rehabilitation agency
Pr: Ron Pasmore
**Treas:* Dan Krug
**Sr VP:* Sheila Brown
VP: Laura Roberds
IT Man: Tina Cumley

KANSAS EQUIPMENT LEASING,
See CLARKSON CONSTRUCTION CO

D-U-N-S 10-407-4604
KANSAS FEEDS INC
1110 E Trail St, Dodge City, KS 67801-9062
Tel (620) 225-3500 *Founded/Ownrshp* 2000
Sales 31.0MMᴱ *EMP* 34
SIC 5149 Molasses, industrial; Shortening, vegetable
Pr: John Synar
Genl Mgr: Brad Smith
Off Mgr: Kim Hudson

D-U-N-S 00-694-4151
■ **KANSAS GAS AND ELECTRIC CO**
K G E
(*Suby of* WESTAR ENERGY INC) ★
120 E 1st St N, Wichita, KS 67202-2001
Tel (316) 721-1899 *Founded/Ownrshp* 1909
Sales 304.7MMᴱ *EMP* 1,900
SIC 4911 Generation, electric power; Transmission, electric power; Distribution, electric power; Generation, electric power; Transmission, electric power; Distribution, electric power
Pr: William B Moore
VP: Caroline Williams

D-U-N-S 02-671-3284
KANSAS HEART HOSPITAL LLC
3601 N Webb Rd, Wichita, KS 67226-8129
Tel (800) 574-3278 *Founded/Ownrshp* 1999
Sales 43.7MMᴱ *EMP* 235
SIC 8069 8062 Cardiologist & cardio-vascular specialist; Specialty hospitals, except psychiatric; General medical & surgical hospitals
Ofcr: Thomas Ashcom
**Pr:* Gregory F Duick
**COO:* Joyce Heismeyer
**CFO:* Steve Smith BBA
CFO: Steve Smith
VP: Stephanie Costello
Dir Lab: Nancy Bacon
Dir Rad: Deanna Boso
Dir Rx: Terry Bontraeger
CIO: Jim Derry
Opers Mgr: Carla Nelson

KANSAS LUMBER COMPANY
See KANSAS LUMBER HOMESTORE INC

D-U-N-S 00-890-6471
KANSAS LUMBER HOMESTORE INC
KANSAS LUMBER COMPANY
217 S 4th St, Manhattan, KS 66502-6111
Tel (785) 776-5353 *Founded/Ownrshp* 1967
Sales 21.4MMᴱ *EMP* 80
SIC 5031 5211 Lumber: rough, dressed & finished; Building materials, exterior; Building materials, interior; Lumber & other building materials
Pr: Kenton Glasscock
**CFO:* Amy Abitz
**Sec:* Terrence L Glasscock
**VP:* Todd Fulmer

D-U-N-S 15-281-9454
KANSAS MEDICAL CENTER LLC
1124 W 21st St, Andover, KS 67002-5500
Tel (316) 300-4000 *Founded/Ownrshp* 2003
Sales 60.0MM *EMP* 2
SIC 8011 Medical centers
Chf Rad: Eddy Lucas
**COO:* Daryl Thornton
CFO: Steven Hadley
CFO: Badr Idbeis
Dir Lab: Dixie Matson
Dir Rad: Lex Johnson
IT Man: Bill Young
Sfty Dirs: Belal Seyam
Mktg Dir: Malik Idbeis
Doctor: Shilpa Kshatriya
Nrsg Dir: Janet Kaiser

D-U-N-S 82-465-9551
KANSAS MEDICAL MUTUAL INSURANCE CO INC
KAMMCO
623 Sw 10th Ave Fl 2, Topeka, KS 66612-1679
Tel (785) 232-2224 *Founded/Ownrshp* 1989
Sales NA *EMP* 61
SIC 6321 8111 Accident & health insurance; Legal services
Pr: Jimmy Gleason MD
CFO: Randy Shideler
**Treas:* Kurt Scott
**VP:* Jerry Slaughter
Genl Couns: Kasey Rogg

D-U-N-S 12-622-9707
KANSAS NEUROLOGICAL INSTITUTE
3107 Sw 21st St, Topeka, KS 66604-3298
Tel (785) 296-5301 *Founded/Ownrshp* 1959
Sales 23.0MM *EMP* 486
SIC 8059 Nursing home, except skilled & intermediate care facility; Nursing home, except skilled & intermediate care facility
CFO: Sara Watson

KANSAS SAMPLER
See SAMPLER STORES INC

KANSAS SIDING SUPPLY
See SOUTHARD CORP

D-U-N-S 13-714-5608
KANSAS SPINE & SPECIALTY HOSPITAL LLC
3333 N Webb Rd, Wichita, KS 67226-8123
Tel (316) 462-5000 *Founded/Ownrshp* 2003
Sales 150.0MM *EMP* 125
Accts Bkd Llp Wichita Ks
SIC 8062 8071 General medical & surgical hospitals; Neurological laboratory
CEO: Thomas M Schmitt
CFO: Kevin Vaughn
Dir Lab: Watie McGlothlin
Dir Rad: Kim Nelson
Chf Nrs Of: Barbara Beugelsdyk
Sfty Dirs: Sam Blanton
Nrsg Dir: John Coslett

D-U-N-S 96-879-0712
■ **KANSAS STAR CASINO LLC**
(*Suby of* BOYD GAMING CORP) ★
777 Kansas Star Dr, Mulvane, KS 67110
Tel (316) 719-5000 *Founded/Ownrshp* 2010
Sales 40.9MMᴱ *EMP* 1ᴱ
SIC 7011 Casino hotel
Prin: Scott Cooper
Genl Mgr: Dan Ihm
Dir IT: David Johnson

KANSAS STATE BANK
See MANHATTAN BANKING CORP

D-U-N-S 04-826-2653
KANSAS STATE BANK OF MANHATTAN
(*Suby of* KANSAS STATE BANK) ★
1010 Westloop Pl, Manhattan, KS 66502-2836
Tel (785) 587-4000 *Founded/Ownrshp* 1986
Sales NA *EMP* 112
SIC 6022 State commercial banks; State commercial banks
CEO: Mike H Daniels
Ex VP: Rhett Johnston
Sr VP: Jim Ashcraft
Sr VP: Mike Babich
Sr VP: Steven Burr
Sr VP: Graham Foust
Sr VP: Corrine Kanode
VP: Penny Alonso
VP: Debbie Bylkas
VP: Tami Camamo
VP: Marsha Jarvis
VP: Curtis Loub
VP: Gregg Masterson
**VP:* John F Musselman III

D-U-N-S 04-114-6432
KANSAS STATE UNIVERSITY
K-STATE
110 Anderson Hall, Manhattan, KS 66506-0100
Tel (785) 532-6210 *Founded/Ownrshp* 1863
Sales 552.7MM *EMP* 5,168
SIC 8221 University; University
Pr: Kirk Schulz
Ex VP: Paul Harris
Sr VP: Shane Giese
**Sr VP:* April Mason
VP: Amy Auch
VP: Tatiana Nzinkeu
VP: Elizabeth A Unger
Dir Risk M: Theo Brooks
Adm Dir: Janette Jensen
Opers Mgr: Richard Mistler

D-U-N-S 00-740-8476
KANSAS STATE UNIVERSITY FEDERAL CREDIT
K-STATE UNIVERSITY FERDERAL CR
2600 Anderson Ave, Manhattan, KS 66502-2802
Tel (785) 776-3003 *Founded/Ownrshp* 2007
Sales NA *EMP* 18ᴱ
SIC 6062 State credit unions, not federally chartered; State credit unions, not federally chartered
CEO: Larae J Kraemer
Brnch Mgr: Stacy Tallent

D-U-N-S 07-628-2235
KANSAS STATE UNIVERSITY FOUNDATION INC
KSU FOUNDATION
1800 Kimball Ave Ste 200, Manhattan, KS 66502-3373
Tel (785) 532-6266 *Founded/Ownrshp* 1944
Sales 228.2MM *EMP* 100
Accts Bkd Llp Kansas City Mo
SIC 7389 Fund raising organizations; Fund raising organizations
CEO: Gary Hellebust
**CEO:* Fred Scholick
**CFO:* Greg Lohrentz
IT Man: Josh Gfeller
IT Man: Chuck Gould

D-U-N-S 87-875-8721
KANSAS SURGERY & RECOVERY CENTER LLC
(*Suby of* VIA CHRISTI HEALTH PARTNERS INC) ★
2770 N Webb Rd, Wichita, KS 67226-8112
Tel (316) 634-0090 *Founded/Ownrshp* 1993
Sales 36.4MMᴱ *EMP* 150
SIC 8069 Orthopedic hospital
Orthpdst: Ely Bartal
Genl Mgr: Ashley Simon
Sfty Dirs: Richard Davidson
Sfty Dirs: John Fiebich
Doctor: Jacob Amrani
Doctor: Thomas Ashcom
Doctor: Michael Lloyd
Doctor: Layne Reusser
Doctor: Roger Roberts
Doctor: Erik Severud
Doctor: Richard Steckley

KANSAS TRANE SALES COMPANY
See KNIPP EQUIPMENT INC

D-U-N-S 06-794-2904
KANSAS TURNPIKE AUTHORITY
9401 E Kellogg Dr, Wichita, KS 67207-1804
Tel (316) 682-4537 *Founded/Ownrshp* 1953
Sales 106.7MM *EMP* 500
Accts Allen Gibbs & Houlik Lc W
SIC 4785 Toll road operation; Toll road operation
Pr: Michael L Johnston
**V Ch:* Gary Hayzlett
**COO:* Alan Bakaitis
**Sec:* Les Donovan
Telecom Ex: John Dye
MIS Dir: Bruce Meisch
Sfty Dirs: Merlin Eck
Genl Couns: Alan Streit
Counsel: Eldon Shields
Snr Mgr: Reesa Wiltse

D-U-N-S 07-625-7427
KANSAS UNIVERSITY ENDOWMENT ASSOCIATION
KU ENDOWMENT
1891 Constant Ave, Lawrence, KS 66047-3743
Tel (785) 832-7400 *Founded/Ownrshp* 1891
Sales 403.1MM *EMP* 163
SIC 6732

D-U-N-S 92-922-8021
KANSAS UNIVERSITY PHYSICIANS INC
UNIVERSITY OF KANSAS
3901 Rainbow Blvd, Kansas City, KS 66160-8500
Tel (913) 362-2128 *Founded/Ownrshp* 1995
Sales 136.0MMᴱ *EMP* 480
Accts Bkd Llp Kansas City Mo
SIC 8011 Clinic, operated by physicians; Clinic, operated by physicians
CEO: Jim Albertson
Dir Case M: Jill Hagel
Dir IT: Sean Roberts
Surgeon: Joseph Noland
Surgeon: Wojciech Przylecki
Nutrtnst: Kelsey Dean
Doctor: Zaid Alirhayim
Doctor: Christa Balanoff MD
Doctor: Christopher Kafka
Doctor: Russell McCulloh
Pharmcst: Eric Finkbiner
Board of Directors: Keith Baskin

D-U-N-S 10-637-9282
KANSAS VENTURE CAPITAL INC
10601 Mission Rd Ste 250, Leawood, KS 66206-2463
Tel (913) 262-7117 *Founded/Ownrshp* 1976
Sales NA *EMP* 350
SIC 6159 6211 Small business investment companies; Security brokers & dealers; Small business investment companies; Security brokers & dealers
Pr: Thomas Blackbur
**Pr:* Marshall Parker

D-U-N-S 96-333-4540
KANSAS WESLEYAN UNIVERSITY
100 E Claflin Ave, Salina, KS 67401-6196
Tel (785) 827-5541 *Founded/Ownrshp* 2010
Sales 22.5MM *EMP* 7
SIC 8221 University; University
VP: Glenna Alexander
VP: Jay Krob
VP: Robert Scott
Ex Dir: Nancy Klostermeyer
Off Mgr: Jessica Allen
Off Mgr: Linda Baumberger
Off Mgr: Jenny Lawson
Store Mgr: Steve Carrier
Mktg Dir: John Elmore
Nrsg Dir: Debra Logan
HC Dir: Steve Berry

D-U-N-S 06-844-4140
KANSAS WESLEYAN UNIVERSITY AID ASSOCIATION
100 E Claflin Ave Ste 1, Salina, KS 67401-6196
Tel (785) 827-5541 *Founded/Ownrshp* 1886
Sales 20.5MM *EMP* 150
SIC 8221 8661 University; Religious organizations; University; Religious organizations
Pr: Philip P Kerstetter
**CFO:* Wayne Schneider

D-U-N-S 14-854-0896
KANSAS-SMITH FARMS LLC
23179 5 Rd, Plains, KS 67869-9162
Tel (620) 563-7226 *Founded/Ownrshp* 2003
Sales 40.7MM *EMP* 85
Accts Black Chestnutt & Johnson Pa
SIC 0213 Hogs; Hogs

D-U-N-S 11-326-9864 IMP
KANSASLAND TIRE INC
(*Suby of* NEBRASKALAND TIRE CO OF NORTH) ★
2904 S Spruce St, Wichita, KS 67216-2434
Tel (316) 522-5434 *Founded/Ownrshp* 1984
Sales 87.3MMᴱ *EMP* 193
SIC 5531 7538 Automotive tires; General automotive repair shops; Automotive tires; General automotive repair shops
Pr: Gary K Wright
**CFO:* Scott Samway
**Sec:* Nancy Wright
Ofcr: Travis Wright
IT Man: Brian Ewing

D-U-N-S 01-908-9746
KANTAR GROUP
(*Suby of* WPP 2008 LIMITED)
401 Merritt 7 Ste 4, Norwalk, CT 06851-1069
Tel (203) 330-5200 *Founded/Ownrshp* 2011
Sales 21.5MMᴱ *EMP* 130ᴱ
SIC 7311 Advertising consultant
CFO: Robert Bowtell
**CFO:* Charles Mason
**Ch:* Jonathan Shingleton
VP Mktg: Heather Stern
Snr Mgr: Ella Calcote
Snr Mgr: Tim Kelsall
Snr Mgr: Dave Patten

D-U-N-S 17-329-9827
KANTAR MEDIA INTELLIGENCES INC
TNS MEDIA INTELLIGENCE
(*Suby of* TNS GROUP HOLDINGS LIMITED)
11 Madison Ave Fl 12, New York, NY 10010-3643
Tel (212) 991-6000 *Founded/Ownrshp* 2010
Sales 71.3MMᴱ *EMP* 677
SIC 7313 Newspaper advertising representative; Magazine advertising representative; Radio advertising representative; Newspaper advertising representative; Magazine advertising representative; Radio advertising representative
CEO: Terry Kent
**Pr:* George Carens
Pr: Ron Mulliken
**CFO:* Amy Silverstein

Ex VP: Paul Fiolek
Sr VP: Leslie Darling
Sr VP: Carl Dickens
Sr VP: Mike Jaffe
**Sr VP:* Diane Laura
Sr VP: Dan Lewis
Sr VP: Libby Macdonald
Sr VP: Lori Madeloff
**Sr VP:* Joel Pacheco
Sr VP: Anita Watkins
Sr VP: Kirsten Zapiec
VP: Maria Abadia
VP: Rumpelt Andrew
VP: Denise Bercovitch
VP: Scott Bernberg
VP: Elaine Chen
VP: Pete Davis

D-U-N-S 62-361-1188
KANTAR OPERATIONS
(*Suby of* WPP GROUP USA INC) ★
3333 Warrenville Rd # 400, Lisle, IL 60532-1157
Tel (630) 505-0066 *Founded/Ownrshp* 2006
Sales 97.5MM^E *EMP* 1,000
SIC 8732 Market analysis or research; Market analysis or research
Pr: Beth Teehan
**CFO:* Lee Larocuqe
IT Man: Cook Jim

KANTER AUTO PRODUCTS
See PACKARD MOTOR CAR CO INC

D-U-N-S 86-866-8211 IMP/EXP
KANTO CORP
(*Suby of* KANTO KAGAKU HOLDINGS K.K.)
13424 N Woodrush Way, Portland, OR 97203-6417
Tel (503) 283-0405 *Founded/Ownrshp* 1990
Sales 39.5MM^E *EMP* 62^E
SIC 5169 Chemicals & allied products; Chemicals & allied products
Pr: Norihide Ampo
Dir Lab: Rey Castino
Sls Mgr: Shawn Sahbari

D-U-N-S 13-104-9041 IMP
KANTUS CORP
(*Suby of* CALSONICKANSEI NORTH AMERICA INC) ★
201 Garrett Pkwy, Lewisburg, TN 37091-3552
Tel (931) 359-4001 *Founded/Ownrshp* 2001
Sales 74.4MM^E *EMP* 650
SIC 3714 Radiators & radiator shells & cores, motor vehicle; Instrument board assemblies, motor vehicle; Radiators & radiator shells & cores, motor vehicle; Instrument board assemblies, motor vehicle
Pr: Masaharu Sato
Prin: Ted Lovett

D-U-N-S 03-127-9367
KANZA COOPERATIVE ASSOCIATION
102 N Main St, Iuka, KS 67066-9401
Tel (620) 546-2231 *Founded/Ownrshp* 1915
Sales 300.0MM *EMP* 150
SIC 5153 5191 5541 4221 Grains; Farm supplies; Fertilizer & fertilizer materials; Chemicals, agricultural; Filling stations, gasoline; Grain elevator, storage only; Grains; Farm supplies; Fertilizer & fertilizer materials; Chemicals, agricultural; Filling stations, gasoline; Grain elevator, storage only
CEO: Bruce Krehbiel
COO: Jeff Bolen
CFO: Brad Riley
IT Man: Anthony Holmes
IT Man: Keith Rose
Sls Mgr: Mickaela Bonnewell

D-U-N-S 15-518-4435 IMP/EXP
KANZAKI SPECIALTY PAPERS INC
(*Suby of* OJI IMAGING MEDIA CO.,LTD.)
20 Cummings St, Ware, MA 01082-1716
Tel (413) 967-6204 *Founded/Ownrshp* 1993
Sales 78.2MM^E *EMP* 233
SIC 2672 Coated & laminated paper; Coated & laminated paper
Pr: Stephen P Hefner
**VP:* David Gonsalves
**VP:* Stephen Hefner
**VP:* Joshua Polak
**VP:* Peter Sawosi
Sls Dir: Frank Neffinger
Sls Mgr: Frank Messemger

D-U-N-S 12-511-8872 IMP/EXP
KAO SPECIALTIES AMERICAS LLC
(*Suby of* KAO CORPORATION)
243 Woodbine St, High Point, NC 27260-8339
Tel (336) 878-4230 *Founded/Ownrshp* 1999
Sales 222.3MM^E *EMP* 152^E
SIC 5169 Chemicals & allied products; Chemicals & allied products
**Ofcr:* Gerald Sykes
VP: Kikumi Hirai
Dir Lab: Steve Williams
Cmptr Lab: Gwen Glover
IT Man: Jahaziel Mata
Opers Mgr: Keisha Barrett
Prd Mgr: Robert Lechner
VP Sls: Kenji Omori
Mktg Mgr: Warren Kotacska
Sls Mgr: Harriet Gayle
Sls Mgr: Sid Outlaw

D-U-N-S 00-425-1617 IMP/EXP
KAO USA INC (DE)
(*Suby of* KAO CORPORATION)
2535 Spring Grove Ave, Cincinnati, OH 45214-1729
Tel (513) 421-1400 *Founded/Ownrshp* 1882, 1988
Sales 453.1MM^E *EMP* 1,100
SIC 2844 2841 Cosmetic preparations; Face creams or lotions; Soap: granulated, liquid, cake, flaked or chip; Cosmetic preparations; Face creams or lotions; Soap: granulated, liquid, cake, flaked or chip
Pr: Bill Gentner
**Pr:* John Nosek
Pr: Satoshi Onitsuka
CFO: Joe Workman
VP: Judy Beaudry
VP: Jayson Zoller
Assoc Dir: Cindy Wengert

CIO: Bob G Rriot
CTO: Teri Barrigar
QA Dir: Allison Kidd
IT Man: Carolyn Calkins

D-U-N-S 04-454-1019 IMP
KAOLIN MUSHROOM FARMS INC
649 W South St, Kennett Square, PA 19348-3417
Tel (610) 444-4800 *Founded/Ownrshp* 1985
Sales 124.4MM^E *EMP* 491
SIC 0182 Mushroom spawn, production of; Mushroom spawn, production of
Pr: Michael Pia
**VP:* John Pia
IT Man: Randall Prewitt
Sfty Mgr: Richard Rush
Sales Asso: Marie Brackin

KAOLINA WASTE REMOVAL
See ORANGE RECYCLING SERVICES INC

D-U-N-S 94-592-5329 IMP
KAPALUA FUEL & MARINE SERVICES INC
SOUTHWEST SERVICES
341 44th St, Corpus Christi, TX 78405-3305
Tel (361) 887-9898 *Founded/Ownrshp* 1995
Sales 36.0MM *EMP* 10
SIC 5172 4499 4953 Gasoline; Engine fuels & oils; Ship cleaning; Recycling, waste materials; Gasoline; Engine fuels & oils; Ship cleaning; Recycling, waste materials
Pr: Leslie L Shook

KAPCO GLOBAL
See KIRKHILL AIRCRAFT PARTS CO

D-U-N-S 05-997-8957
KAPCO INC
1000 Badger Cir, Grafton, WI 53024-9487
Tel (262) 377-6500 *Founded/Ownrshp* 1972
Sales 35.4MM^E *EMP* 210
SIC 3469 3499

D-U-N-S 96-954-1155
KAPIOLANI MEDICAL CENTER AT PALI MOMI
55 Merchant St, Honolulu, HI 96813-4306
Tel (808) 486-6000 *Founded/Ownrshp* 2011
Sales 151.4MM^E *EMP* 2
Accts Ernst & Young Us Llp Honolulu
SIC 8322 Emergency shelters
Prin: Arnobit

D-U-N-S 06-628-1080
KAPIOLANI MEDICAL CENTER FOR WOMEN AND CHILDREN
(*Suby of* HAWAI I PACIFIC HEALTH) ★
1319 Punahou St, Honolulu, HI 96826-1001
Tel (808) 535-7401 *Founded/Ownrshp* 1890
Sales 37.0MM^E *EMP* 1,378
SIC 8069 Maternity hospital; Children's hospital; Maternity hospital; Children's hospital
CEO: Martha Smith
VP: Dew-Anne Langcaon
Dir Rx: Dawn Tsuha-Scarlett
Dir Rx: Len Yonemura
Off Mgr: Tina Chong
Mktg Dir: Kelly Holden
Surgeon: Devin Puapong
Obsttrcn: Leticia Diniega
Obsttrcn: Angela Pratt
Doctor: Jaime Harrington
Doctor: Kent Kumashiro

D-U-N-S 04-835-2244
KAPIOLANI MEDICAL SPECIALISTS (HI)
1319 Punahou St Ste 600, Honolulu, HI 96826-1044
Tel (808) 983-6000 *Founded/Ownrshp* 1995
Sales 20.3MM *EMP* 100
SIC 8099 8062 8011 Medical services organization; General medical & surgical hospitals; Offices & clinics of medical doctors; Medical services organization; General medical & surgical hospitals; Offices & clinics of medical doctors
Pr: Charles Sted

D-U-N-S 96-961-5165
KAPIOLANI MEDICAL SPECIALISTS
55 Merchant St Fl 24, Honolulu, HI 96813-4333
Tel (808) 983-8986 *Founded/Ownrshp* 2011
Sales 24.8MM *EMP* 4^E
Accts Ernst & Young Us Llp Honolulu
SIC 8011 Offices & clinics of medical doctors; Offices & clinics of medical doctors
Prin: Warren Chaiko

D-U-N-S 87-805-7330
KAPL INC
KNOLLS ATOMIC POWER LABORATORY
2401 River Rd, Schenectady, NY 12309-1103
Tel (518) 395-4000 *Founded/Ownrshp* 2009
Sales 287.2MM^E *EMP* 2,600
SIC 8731 Energy research; Energy research
Ch Bd: Michael F Quinn
**Treas:* Janet L McGregor
Exec: Len Yanazzo
Mng Dir: Emmanuel Seiz
Brnch Mgr: John Freeh

KAPLAN & CRAWFORD DODGE WORLD
See DAR CARS DODGE INC

D-U-N-S 78-738-9337
KAPLAN AT OLD BRIDGE INC
KAPLAN COMPANIES
433 River Rd, Highland Park, NJ 08904-1918
Tel (732) 846-5900 *Founded/Ownrshp* 1983
Sales 200.0MM *EMP* 180
SIC 6552 Land subdividers & developers, residential; Land subdividers & developers, residential
CEO: Michael Kaplan
**Pr:* Jason Kaplan
CFO: Stevenz Sprauss
CFO: Steven Strauss
**VP:* Morris Kaplan
Sales Exec: Rose Kramer
Mktg Dir: Christina Santowasso

KAPLAN COLLEGE
See KAPLAN HIGHER EDUCATION LLC

KAPLAN COMPANIES
See KAPLAN AT OLD BRIDGE INC

D-U-N-S 14-565-6752
KAPLAN DEVELOPMENT GROUP LLC
30 Jericho Executive Plz 400e, Jericho, NY 11753-1081
Tel (516) 496-1505 *Founded/Ownrshp* 1999
Sales 39.3MM^E *EMP* 250^E
SIC 6531 7997 Real estate agents & managers; Country club, membership; Real estate agents & managers; Country club, membership

KAPLAN EDUCATIONAL CENTERS
See KAPLAN INC

D-U-N-S 05-246-7201
■ **KAPLAN HIGHER EDUCATION LLC**
(*Suby of* KAPLAN EDUCATIONAL CENTERS) ★
900 North Point Pkwy, Alpharetta, GA 30005-4134
Tel (770) 360-6100 *Founded/Ownrshp* 1988
Sales 250.1MM^E *EMP* 5,141
SIC 8221 8244 Colleges universities & professional schools; Business & secretarial schools; Colleges universities & professional schools; Business & secretarial schools
Pr: Jefffrey Conlon
COO: Andrew Rosen
CFO: Lionel Lenz
Sr VP: Elaine Neely
Sr VP: Matthew Seelye
VP: Kevin L Corser

D-U-N-S 08-179-7110
■ **KAPLAN HIGHER EDUCATION LLC**
KAPLAN COLLEGE
(*Suby of* KAPLAN HIGHER EDUCATION LLC) ★
9055 Balboa Ave, San Diego, CA 92123-1509
Tel (858) 279-4500 *Founded/Ownrshp* 1989
Sales 39.8MM^E *EMP* 2,000
SIC 8249 Medical training services; Medical training services
Pr: Mike Seifert
Prin: Vickie Davis
HC Dir: Renee Codner
Pgrm Dir: Joe Twohig

D-U-N-S 06-607-6837
■ **KAPLAN INC**
KAPLAN EDUCATIONAL CENTERS
(*Suby of* GRAHAM HOLDINGS CO) ★
6301 Kaplan Univ Ave, Fort Lauderdale, FL 33309-1905
Tel (212) 492-5800 *Founded/Ownrshp* 1984
Sales 306.6MM^E *EMP* 6,388
SIC 8299 7361 7372 2731 Educational services; Tutoring school; Reading school, including speed reading; Employment agencies; Prepackaged software; Book publishing; Educational services; Tutoring school; Reading school, including speed reading; Employment agencies; Prepackaged software; Book publishing
Ch: Andrew S Rosen
Mng Pt: David Kaplan
Pr: Howard Benson
**Pr:* Eric Cantor
Pr: Maria Closs
Pr: Hal Jones
**Pr:* Thomas C Leppert
Pr: Donna Skibbe
**CEO:* Jonathan N Grayer
COO: Prodeep Ghosh
CFO: Scott August
**CFO:* Robert L Lane
CFO: David Munns
**CFO:* Matthew Seelye
Chf Mktg O: Eric Plath
Ofcr: M J Miller
Ofcr: Sharon Miller
**Ex VP:* Veronica Dillon
**Ex VP:* Vince Pisano
**Ex VP:* Darrell Splithoff
Sr VP: Wade Dyke

D-U-N-S 07-852-8400
■ **KAPLAN K12 LEARNING SERVICES LLC**
(*Suby of* KAPLAN EDUCATIONAL CENTERS) ★
395 Hudson St Fl 3, New York, NY 10014-3991
Tel (888) 527-5268 *Founded/Ownrshp* 2012
Sales 16.4MM^E *EMP* 7,383
SIC 8299 Educational services; Educational services
CEO: John Polstein
**Treas:* Matthew Seelye
**VP:* Janice Block
VP: Jeffery Elie
**VP:* Mark Freidberg

D-U-N-S 11-249-5882
■ **KAPLAN PROFESSIONALS**
INSURANCE SYSTEMS OF TENNESSEE
(*Suby of* KAPLAN EDUCATIONAL CENTERS) ★
332 Front St S Fl 5, La Crosse, WI 54601-4031
Tel (608) 779-5599 *Founded/Ownrshp* 1989
Sales 10.1MM^E *EMP* 400
SIC 8249 Books: publishing only; Business training services; Business training services; Real estate & insurance school
Pr: Andy Temte
Pr: Anderia Menali
CFO: Michael Peyer
Treas: Ross Hamachek
VP: Michael Casey
VP: Veronica Dillon
VP: Joseph Keyes
VP: Denise Probert
Ex Dir: Steve Lee
Div Mgr: Andrew Temte
Dir IT: Tim Smaby

D-U-N-S 17-674-1932
KAPLAN THALER GROUP LTD
(*Suby of* PUBLICIS GROUPE S A) ★
1675 Broadway, New York, NY 10019-5820
Tel (212) 474-5000 *Founded/Ownrshp* 2005
Sales 24.7MM^E *EMP* 90
SIC 7311 Advertising agencies; Advertising agencies

Ch: Linda Kaplan-Thaler
**Pr:* Rob Feakins
**CEO:* Andrew Bruce
Ex VP: Mandy Antoniacci
Ex VP: Don Blashford
Ex VP: Laurie Garnier
VP: Frank Bele
VP: Jason Graff
VP: Paul Jones
VP: Kaitlyn Nolan
VP: Madhu Pai
VP: Courtney Russell
VP: Patrick Trainor
Creative D: Susan Achey
Creative D: Alex Avsharian
Creative D: Jack Cardone
Creative D: Andrew Landorf
Creative D: Whitney Pillsbury
Creative D: Mike Towell

D-U-N-S 00-790-0806
KAPLAN TRUCKING CO (OH)
6600 Bessemer Ave, Cleveland, OH 44127-1897
Tel (216) 341-3322 *Founded/Ownrshp* 1934, 1983
Sales 53.8MM^E *EMP* 100
SIC 4213 Trucking, except local
Pr: David Ferrante
**Ch:* Anthony Ferrante
Ofcr: Jeff Ries
VP: Dave Feronite
**VP:* James B Gifford
**VP:* John Wynne
IT Man: Brian Drab
Software D: Adam Skinner
Sfty Dirs: Linda Chluda
Trfc Dir: Aaron Gurgon
Opers Mgr: Eric Hoffman

D-U-N-S 05-169-3901
KAPLAN/MCLAUGHLIN/DIAZ INC
KMD
222 Vallejo St, San Francisco, CA 94111-1512
Tel (415) 398-5191 *Founded/Ownrshp* 1963
Sales 31.4MM^E *EMP* 225
SIC 8712 Architectural services; Architectural services
Ch: Herbert P McLaughlin
**Pr:* Roy Latka
Mktg Mgr: Annie Wilson

D-U-N-S 07-756-0480
KAPNICK & CO INC
KAPNICK INSURANCE GROUP
333 Industrial Dr, Adrian, MI 49221-8780
Tel (517) 263-4600 *Founded/Ownrshp* 2007
Sales NA *EMP* 116
SIC 6411 Insurance agents, brokers & service
CEO: James D Kapnick
**CFO:* Michael Kapnick
**Ex VP:* Stephen J Peck
**Ex VP:* Robert V Weiland
**Sr VP:* Samuel Engardio
**Sr VP:* Phillip Morley
Sr VP: Bill Rauser
VP: Linda Aiken
VP: Angela Dean
**VP:* Richard Donner
**VP:* Guldan Doug
VP: Michael L Eckert
**VP:* Scott McDonald
**VP:* John Seiser
VP: Jay Vanburen

KAPNICK INSURANCE GROUP
See KAPNICK & CO INC

D-U-N-S 92-748-7983 IMP
KAPPA GRAPHICS L P
50 Rock St, Hughestown, PA 18640-3028
Tel (570) 655-9681 *Founded/Ownrshp* 1994
Sales 53.6MM^E *EMP* 198
SIC 2759 2789 2752 2721 Magazines: printing; Bookbinding & related work; Commercial printing, lithographic; Periodicals; Magazines: printing; Bookbinding & related work; Commercial printing, lithographic; Periodicals
Pt: Nick G Karabots
Pt: Tom Brisbon
Pt: Andrea Duloc

D-U-N-S 83-703-9700 IMP
KAPPA GRAPHICS LP
50 Rock St, Hughestown, PA 18640-3028
Tel (570) 655-9681 *Founded/Ownrshp* 1991
Sales 31.1MM^E *EMP* 200
SIC 2732 Books: printing only; Books: printing only
Pt: Nick Karabots

D-U-N-S 96-987-9654
KAPPA KAPPA GAMMA FRATERNITY GROUP
530 E Town St, Columbus, OH 43215-4820
Tel (614) 228-6515 *Founded/Ownrshp* 2011
Sales 50.7MM *EMP* 3^E
Accts Crowe Norwatii Llp Columbus
SIC 8641 University club; University club

D-U-N-S 04-797-5966
KAPPA KAPPA GAMMA FRATERNITY INC
530 E Town St, Columbus, OH 43215-4820
Tel (614) 228-6515 *Founded/Ownrshp* 1870
Sales 7.1MM *EMP* 1,000
Accts Crowe Horwath Llp Columbus O
SIC 8641 Fraternal associations; Fraternal associations
Mktg Dir: Ashley Moyer

D-U-N-S 07-926-2711
KAPPA SIGMA FRATERNITY
7150 Montview Blvd, Denver, CO 80220-1800
Tel (720) 263-1075 *Founded/Ownrshp* 2013
Sales 10.3MM^E *EMP* 500
SIC 8641 University club; Social club, membership; Fraternal associations; University club; Social club, membership; Fraternal associations
CEO: James Leamon
**Treas:* Tobias Pinney
**Ofcr:* Steven Bayes

Ofcr: Jesse Haslip
**VP:* Cameron Murdzia

D-U-N-S 07-050-9468 IMP
KAPPLER USA INC
(*Suby of* KAPPLER, INC.)
55 Grimes Dr, Guntersville, AL 35976-9381
Tel (256) 505-4005 *Founded/Ownrshp* 1986
Sales 20.3M^E *EMP* 668
SIC 2326 Men's & boys' work clothing; Men's & boys' work clothing
Pr: George P Kappler
VP Sls: Jung Chang

KAPPUS COMPANY
See JOHN H KAPPUS CO

D-U-N-S 82-828-6281
KAPSCH TRAFFICCOM US CORP
(*Suby of* KAPSCH TRAFFICCOM AG)
8201 Greensboro Dr # 1002, Mc Lean, VA 22102-3840
Tel (703) 885-1976 *Founded/Ownrshp* 2008
Sales 54.1MM^E *EMP* 132^E
SIC 7382 Security systems services
Pr: Erwin Toplak
**CFO:* Peter Schuchlenz
Sr VP: Janet Eichers
Sr VP: John Freund
VP: Sabina Berloffa
VP: Verena Bibaritsch
VP: Jutta Hanle
VP: Dan Toohey
Mng Dir: Sharon Kindleysides
Mng Dir: Soren Tellegen
Genl Mgr: Liviu Bozga

D-U-N-S 06-967-7094
KAPSCH TRAFFICCOM USA INC
(*Suby of* KAPSCH TRAFFICCOM US CORP) ★
2855 Premiere Pkwy Ste F, Duluth, GA 30097-5201
Tel (678) 473-6400 *Founded/Ownrshp* 2003
Sales 54.1MM^E *EMP* 125
SIC 7373 8711 3625 Computer integrated systems design; Electrical or electronic engineering; Relays & industrial controls; Computer integrated systems design; Electrical or electronic engineering; Relays & industrial controls
Pr: Gerald Marcus Thompson Jr
**VP:* Dr Thomas P McPharlin
Off Mgr: Sharon Velasquez
IT Man: Mike Orth
Sftwr Eng: Ruchira Agarwal

KAPSTONE
See LONGVIEW FIBRE PAPER AND PACKAGING INC

D-U-N-S 82-865-1799 IMP/EXP
■ KAPSTONE CHARLESTON KRAFT LLC
(*Suby of* KAPSTONE PAPER AND PACKAGING CORP) ★
5600 Virginia Ave, North Charleston, SC 29406-3612
Tel (843) 745-3000 *Founded/Ownrshp* 2008
Sales 178.9MM^E *EMP* 1,088
SIC 2621 Bag paper

D-U-N-S 17-443-2070
■ KAPSTONE CONTAINER CORP
(*Suby of* KAPSTONE PAPER AND PACKAGING CORP) ★
1601 Blairs Ferry Rd Ne, Cedar Rapids, IA 52402-5805
Tel (319) 393-3610 *Founded/Ownrshp* 2011
Sales 202.6MM^E *EMP* 135^E
SIC 2653 Sheets, corrugated: made from purchased materials; Sheets, corrugated: made from purchased materials
CEO: Roger Stone
**Pr:* Matthew Kaplan
**Pr:* Timothy P Keneally
**Pr:* Randy J Nebel
Pr: Ingrid Santiago
**VP:* Andrea K Tarboxm
Genl Mgr: Guy Robertshaw
IT Man: Stephen Weeks

D-U-N-S 79-092-8936
■ KAPSTONE KRAFT PAPER CORP
(*Suby of* KAPSTONE PAPER AND PACKAGING CORP) ★
1101 Skokie Blvd Ste 300, Northbrook, IL 60062-4124
Tel (252) 533-6000 *Founded/Ownrshp* 2006
Sales 347.5MM^E *EMP* 453
SIC 2621 Packaging paper; Packaging paper
Pr: Timothy Keneally
Bd of Dir: Earl Shapiro
VP: Tim Keneally

D-U-N-S 60-714-1442 EXP
▲ KAPSTONE PAPER AND PACKAGING CORP
1101 Skokie Blvd Ste 300, Northbrook, IL 60062-4124
Tel (847) 239-8800 *Founded/Ownrshp* 2005
Sales 2.3MMM *EMP* 4,628
Tkr Sym KS *Exch* NYS
SIC 2621 Paper mills; Paper mills
Ch Bd: Roger W Stone
Pr: Tim Davisson
Pr: Matthew Kaplan
CFO: Andrea K Tarbox
VP: Timothy P Davisson
VP: Mark A Niehus
Netwrk Eng: Brian Burns
Plnt Mgr: David Hunt
Plnt Mgr: Scott Sumner
Board of Directors: Robert J Bahash, John M Chapman, Jonathan R Furer, David G Gabriel, Brian R Gamache, Ronald J Gidwitz, Matthew H Paull, Maurice Reznik, David P Storch

D-U-N-S 06-210-2975
KAPUR & ASSOCIATES INC
7711 N Port Washington Rd, Milwaukee, WI 53217-3130
Tel (414) 351-6668 *Founded/Ownrshp* 1981
Sales 24.2MM^E *EMP* 175
SIC 8711 Consulting engineer; Consulting engineer
Pr: Ramesh C Kapur
**VP:* Timothy Anheuser

**VP:* Dennis Fleischfresser
**VP:* Prasad Narayan

D-U-N-S 80-056-7534
■ KAR AUCTION SERVICES INC
(*Suby of* KAR HOLDINGS II LLC) ★
13085 Hmlton Crssing Blvd, Carmel, IN 46032-1412
Tel (800) 923-3725 *Founded/Ownrshp* 2007
Sales 2.3MMM *EMP* 12,600^E
Accts Kpmg Llp Indianapolis Indian
Tkr Sym KAR *Exch* NYS
SIC 5012 6153 5521 Automobiles & other motor vehicles; Automotive brokers; Financing of dealers by motor vehicle manufacturers organ.; Used car dealers; Automobiles & other motor vehicles; Automotive brokers; Financing of dealers by motor vehicle manufacturers organ.; Used car dealers
CEO: James P Hallett
COO: Donald S Gottwald
CFO: Eric M Loughmiller
Chf Cred: Thomas J Caruso
Ex VP: John R Nordin
Ex VP: Becca Polak
Ex VP: Rebecca C Polak
Sr VP: Jason Ferreri
VP: Christopher Anderson
VP: Huey Antley
VP: Matthew Effland
VP: John Rogers
VP: Tim Wardlow
Board of Directors: Ryan M Birtwell, Donna R Ecton, Peter R Formanek, Mark E Hill, J Mark Howell, Lynn Jolliffe, Michael T Kestner, John P Larson, Stephen E Smith

D-U-N-S 80-055-0019
▲ KAR HOLDINGS II LLC
13085 Hamil Cross Blvd St Ste 500, Carmel, IN 46032
Tel (317) 815-1100 *Founded/Ownrshp* 2006
Sales 2.3MMM^E *EMP* 13,253
SIC 5012 6153 Automobiles & other motor vehicles; Automotive brokers; Commercial vehicles; Short-term business credit; Financing of dealers by motor vehicle manufacturers organ.; Automobiles & other motor vehicles; Automotive brokers; Commercial vehicles; Short-term business credit; Financing of dealers by motor vehicle manufacturers organ.
VP: James Money

D-U-N-S 04-242-8037
KAR NUT PRODUCTS CO
KAR'S NUTS
1200 E 14 Mile Rd Ste A, Madison Heights, MI 48071-1421
Tel (248) 588-1903 *Founded/Ownrshp* 1967
Sales 165.7MM^E *EMP* 140
SIC 5145 2068 Confectionery; Nuts: dried, dehydrated, salted or roasted; Confectionery; Nuts: dried, dehydrated, salted or roasted
Pr: Ernest L Nicolay III
**VP:* William P Elam
Exec: Lisa Brace
Exec: Nick Nicolay
Dist Mgr: Clayton Ross
Prd Mgr: Bill Leva
Natl Sales: John Peters
Mktg Mgr: John Koskovich
Mktg Mgr: Scott McKinnon
Manager: Tim Callahan
Sls Mgr: Bill Dennis

D-U-N-S 12-947-9924
■ KAR PRODUCTS
(*Suby of* BARNES GROUP INC) ★
1301 E 9th St Ste 700, Cleveland, OH 44114-1800
Tel (216) 416-7200 *Founded/Ownrshp* 2005
Sales 100.5MM^E *EMP* 1,200
SIC 5013 5084 5072 Automotive supplies & parts; Automobile glass; Hydraulic systems equipment & supplies; Pneumatic tools & equipment; Screws; Nuts (hardware); Bolts; Washers (hardware); Automotive supplies & parts; Automobile glass; Hydraulic systems equipment & supplies; Pneumatic tools & equipment; Screws; Nuts (hardware); Bolts; Washers (hardware)
Prin: Ronald Koskela

D-U-N-S 00-799-7406 IMP
KARAS & KARAS GLASS CO INC (MA)
455 Dorchester Ave, Boston, MA 02127-2797
Tel (617) 268-8800 *Founded/Ownrshp* 1924
Sales 34.8MM^E *EMP* 175
SIC 1751 5039 Window & door (prefabricated) installation; Exterior flat glass: plate or window; Window & door (prefabricated) installation; Exterior flat glass: plate or window
Ch: Barbara Karas
**Pr:* Joseph Karas
**Treas:* Leo Karas
**VP:* Joseph Argus
**VP:* Richard Scaven
Off Mgr: Kathy Scherer
Opers Mgr: Michael Dempsey
Mktg Dir: Dick Skavin
Snr Mgr: Tom Mayo

D-U-N-S 01-885-4943
KARAS MOTORS INC
19 Coolidge Ave, Waterbury, CT 06708-2283
Tel (203) 597-8899 *Founded/Ownrshp* 1993
Sales 25.0MM^E *EMP* 35
SIC 7538 7549 5521 5511 General automotive repair shops; Towing service, automotive; Automobiles, used cars only; New & used car dealers; General automotive repair shops; Towing service, automotive; Automobiles, used cars only; New & used car dealers
Pr: Joe Karas
VP: Carl Karas Jr

D-U-N-S 15-419-8196 EXP
KARAVAN TRAILERS INC
100 Karavan Dr, Fox Lake, WI 53933-9561
Tel (920) 928-6200 *Founded/Ownrshp* 2008
Sales 53.3MM^E *EMP* 210
SIC 3799 Trailers & trailer equipment; Boat trailers; Trailers & trailer equipment; Boat trailers

Pr: Scott A Boyd
VP: Ed De Tuncq
VP: Edward E Detuncq
Prin: Dave Meilahn
VP Mfg: Michael Boyd

KARCHER NORTH AMERICA
See C-TECH INDUSTRIES INC

D-U-N-S 07-703-0773 IMP/EXP
KARCHER NORTH AMERICA INC
(*Suby of* ALFRED KARCHER GMBH & CO. KG)
4555 Airport Way Fl 4, Denver, CO 80239-5801
Tel (303) 783-5143 *Founded/Ownrshp* 2006
Sales 240.0MM^E *EMP* 1,018
SIC 3635 5084 Household vacuum cleaners; Cleaning equipment, high pressure, sand or steam; Household vacuum cleaners; Cleaning equipment, high pressure, sand or steam
CEO: Hannes Subert
V Ch: Markus Asch
**CFO:* Peter Lynch
Treas: Roland Deibler
Mktg Mgr: David Hults
Sls Mgr: Brian Herreman

D-U-N-S 00-255-5654 IMP/EXP
KARDEX REMSTAR LLC
(*Suby of* KARDEX AG)
41 Eisenhower Dr, Westbrook, ME 04092-2032
Tel (207) 854-1861 *Founded/Ownrshp* 1982
Sales 50.7MM^E *EMP* 113
SIC 5084 3496 2542 Materials handling machinery; Miscellaneous fabricated wire products; Partitions & fixtures, except wood; Materials handling machinery; Miscellaneous fabricated wire products; Partitions & fixtures, except wood
VP: Patrick Mulligan
Brnch Mgr: Gary Gould
Genl Mgr: Tony Arsenault
CTO: Donald Gonzales
Dir IT: Henri Brady
Web Dev: David Marquis
VP Sls: Mark Dunaway
Mktg Mgr: Christina Hilligoss
Mktg Mgr: Chelsea Rondeau
Mktg Mgr: Bonnie Sawyer
Sls Mgr: Rachelle Cashman

KAREL MANUFACTURING
See LORENZ INC

D-U-N-S 02-106-4480 IMP
KAREN KANE INC
2275 E 37th St, Vernon, CA 90058-1435
Tel (323) 588-0000 *Founded/Ownrshp* 1981
Sales 56.9MM^E *EMP* 200
Accts Kaufman & Kabani Los Angeles
SIC 2339 Sportswear, women's; Women's & misses' jackets & coats, except sportswear; Sportswear, women's; Women's & misses' jackets & coats, except sportswear
Pr: Lonnie Kane
**Treas:* Cecelia Jenkins
**VP:* Karen Kane
Store Mgr: Elaine Bush
Store Mgr: Karen Pazdorski
Dir IT: Duane Putnam
Mktg Dir: Michael Kane
Sales Asso: Shonneia Rose

KAREN RADLEY ACURA VOLKSWAGEN
See RADLEY KAREN CORREIA INC

D-U-N-S 62-488-1459
KAREO INC
KAREO PM
3353 Michelson Dr Ste 400, Irvine, CA 92612-5611
Tel (888) 775-2736 *Founded/Ownrshp* 2004
Sales 23.2MM^E *EMP* 21^E
SIC 7371 Computer software development & applications
CEO: Daniel Rodrigues
CFO: Jason Gardner
CFO: Tom Patterson
Bd of Dir: Bill Conroy
Bd of Dir: Adam Marcus
Chf Mktg O: Tom Giannulli
VP: James Armijo
VP: Jason Leu
VP: James Mathews
VP: David Mitzenmacher
Dir Bus: Tom Nicholas

KAREO PM
See KAREO INC

D-U-N-S 06-388-1353
KARETAS FOODS INC
1012 Tuckerton Ct, Reading, PA 19605-1177
Tel (610) 926-3663 *Founded/Ownrshp* 1972
Sales 36.0MM *EMP* 46
SIC 5142 5148 5149 5147 5146

D-U-N-S 79-953-4271
KARGO GLOBAL INC
826 Broadway Fl 5, New York, NY 10003-4826
Tel (212) 979-9000 *Founded/Ownrshp* 2003
Sales 50.0MM^E *EMP* 150
SIC 7313 7372 7374 Electronic media advertising representatives; Application computer software; Computer graphics service; Electronic media advertising representatives; Application computer software; Computer graphics service
Pr: Harry Kargman
**COO:* Ryan McConville
**Chf Mktg O:* Terri Walter
Ex VP: Jill Labert
**VP:* Alexis Berger
**VP:* Kevin Canty
VP: Theresa Gaffney
**VP:* Neal Modi
**VP:* Jeremy Sadwith
Off Mgr: Laura Pintado
**CTO:* Kartal Goksel

D-U-N-S 03-568-5320
KARL A MALONE CORP ALBUQUERQUE
10401 Copper Ave Ne, Albuquerque, NM 87123-1155
Tel (505) 294-8800 *Founded/Ownrshp* 1960

Sales 35.9MM^E *EMP* 95
SIC 5511 Automobiles, new & used; Automobiles, new & used
Pr: Larry Miller
**VP:* Karen G Miller
Genl Mgr: Wade Nelson
Sls Mgr: Randy Martin

D-U-N-S 07-867-3538 IMP
KARL BISSINGER LLC
1600 N Broadway, Saint Louis, MO 63102-1226
Tel (314) 615-2407 *Founded/Ownrshp* 2012
Sales 26.0MM^E *EMP* 117^E
SIC 2066 Chocolate & cocoa products
CEO: Timothy R Fogerty
COO: Bill Bremer
**COO:* Steve Scaff
**CFO:* Kent Bock

KARL CHEVROLET AUTO PARTS
See KARL CHEVROLET INC

KARL CHEVROLET COMPANY, THE
See LEO E KARL INC

D-U-N-S 06-521-2904
KARL CHEVROLET INC
KARL CHEVROLET AUTO PARTS
1101 Se Oralabor Rd, Ankeny, IA 50021-4022
Tel (515) 964-4255 *Founded/Ownrshp* 1977
Sales 71.8MM^E *EMP* 400
SIC 5511 5521

D-U-N-S 04-247-2134
KARL FLAMMER FORD INC
41975 Us Highway 19 N, Tarpon Springs, FL 34689-4196
Tel (727) 937-5131 *Founded/Ownrshp* 1965
Sales 37.9MM^E *EMP* 94
SIC 5511 Automobiles, new & used; Automobiles, new & used
Pr: Karl Flammer
Genl Mgr: Jim Flammer
Sls Mgr: Tom Sfero

D-U-N-S 12-131-6827
KARL HC LLC
VILLA ANGELA CARE CENTER
5700 Karl Rd, Columbus, OH 43229-3602
Tel (614) 846-5420 *Founded/Ownrshp* 2001
Sales 16.4MM *EMP* 350
SIC 8051 Skilled nursing care facilities; Skilled nursing care facilities
Off Mgr: Rick Raynard
Nrsg Dir: Kayla Jenkins
Phys Thrpy: Kevin Martin
HC Dir: Erin Hoffman

KARL KLEMENT
See KK FORD LP

D-U-N-S 02-557-8170
KARL KNAUZ MOTORS INC
775 Rockland Rd, Lake Bluff, IL 60044-2208
Tel (847) 615-3670 *Founded/Ownrshp* 1961
Sales 96.2MM^E *EMP* 280
SIC 5511 Automobiles, new & used; Automobiles, new & used
Pr: William R Madden
**Owner:* H William Knauz
**Sec:* Ingeborg Knauz
Genl Mgr: James Astuno
Telecom Ex: Jeff Lefevbre
IT Man: Ann Morocco
Sales Asso: Al Wagener

KARL MALONE TOYOTA
See M & M AUTOMOTIVE INC

KARL MAYER NORTH AMERICA
See MAYER TEXTILE MACHINE CORP

KARL SCHMIDT UNISIA
See KSUS INTERNATIONAL LLC

D-U-N-S 07-529-3423 IMP
KARL STORZ ENDOSCOPY-AMERICA INC
(*Suby of* KARL STORZ GMBH & CO. KG)
2151 E Grand Ave, El Segundo, CA 90245-5017
Tel (424) 218-8100 *Founded/Ownrshp* 1971
Sales 248.2MM^E *EMP* 900^E
SIC 3841 5047 Surgical & medical instruments; Medical equipment & supplies; Surgical & medical instruments; Medical equipment & supplies
CEO: Charles Wilhelm
**CFO:* Dean Ditto
**VP:* Mark Green
Assoc Dir: Monica Botwinski
Assoc Dir: Crit Fisher
Brnch Mgr: Marsha Hunter
Brnch Mgr: Robert Sapp
Genl Mgr: Cory Alcala
Genl Mgr: Ramon Luna
VP Opers: Cristina Lee
Sales Exec: Daniel Dandridge

D-U-N-S 78-091-3190
KARL STORZ ENDOVISION INC
(*Suby of* KARL STORZ GMBH & CO. KG)
91 Carpenter Hill Rd, Charlton, MA 01507-5274
Tel (508) 248-9011 *Founded/Ownrshp* 1989
Sales 130.2MM^E *EMP* 400
SIC 3841 Surgical & medical instruments; Surgical & medical instruments
Pr: Gary Macker
**Owner:* Sybill Storz
Genl Mgr: Bruce Watkins
Off Mgr: Kelli Banas
QA Dir: Jason Johnson
QA Dir: Jodi Peck
Mfg Dir: Thomas Caron
QC Dir: Tina Seifert
Opers Mgr: Frank Vecchio
Prd Mgr: Rich Santora
Ql Cn Mgr: Devon Masse

D-U-N-S 83-253-7976 IMP
KARL STORZ IMAGING INC
(*Suby of* KARL STORZ GMBH & CO. KG)
175 Cremona Dr, Goleta, CA 93117-5502
Tel (800) 964-5563 *Founded/Ownrshp* 1984

Sales 102.4MM[E] *EMP* 350
SIC 3841 Optometers
Pr: Thomas Caron
Mng Dir: Jerry Xu
CTO: Karl Storz
Dir IT: David Chatenever
Dir IT: Craig Pannett
IT Man: Yesenia Vasquez
Sftwr Eng: Phil Johnson
Ql Cn Mgr: Dan Korkut
Sales Exec: Michael Hendershot
Sls Dir: Anna Fritz
Mktg Mgr: Pauline Bedard

KARL STRAUSS BREWERY GARDEN
See ASSOCIATED MICROBREWERIES INC

D-U-N-S 08-074-6654
KARLEE CO
701 S International Rd, Garland, TX 75042-7817
Tel (972) 543-3051 *Founded/Ownrshp* 1977
Sales 128.9MM[E] *EMP* 300
SIC 3599 3444 Custom machinery; Machine shop, jobbing & repair; Sheet metalwork; Custom machinery; Machine shop, jobbing & repair; Sheet metalwork
CEO: Jo Ann Brumit
**Pr:* Rick Cherry
**COO:* Lee Brumit
**VP:* Chad Brumit
Ql Cn Mgr: David Walker
Board of Directors: Frank Driska

D-U-N-S 08-473-8566 EXP
KARLIN FOODS CORP (IL)
1845 Oak St Ste 19, Northfield, IL 60093-3022
Tel (847) 441-8330 *Founded/Ownrshp* 1977
Sales 128.9MM *EMP* 17
SIC 2034 Dehydrated fruits, vegetables, soups
Pr: Mitchell Karlin
**Treas:* Donna Hastings
Dir IT: Michelle Kavanagh
Opers Mgr: Pat Marquardt
Ql Cn Mgr: Kris Guenther
Manager: Keith Creel
Sls Mgr: Michael Frick

D-U-N-S 09-841-3177
KARLS EVENT RENTAL INC
KARL'S EVENT SERVICES
(*Suby of* ARENA GROUP LIMITED)
7000 S 10th St, Oak Creek, WI 53154-1421
Tel (414) 831-7000 *Founded/Ownrshp* 2013
Sales 26.0MM[E] *EMP* 305
SIC 7359 Party supplies rental services; Party supplies rental services
CEO: Christopher Doerr
**Pr:* Ronald Creten
**CEO:* John Haener
**CFO:* Kevin Zwirchowski

KARL'S EVENT SERVICES
See ARENA EVENT SERVICES INC

KARL'S EVENT SERVICES
See KARLS EVENT RENTAL INC

D-U-N-S 17-788-0945
KARLSTRANSPORT INC
975 Amron Ave, Antigo, WI 54409-2908
Tel (715) 623-2791 *Founded/Ownrshp* 1986
Sales 24.7MM[E] *EMP* 70
SIC 4213 Contract haulers; Refrigerated products transport
Pr: Karl A Schulz
**VP:* Jill Schulz
Sfty Dirs: Sarah Sanden

D-U-N-S 02-432-6092
KARLSTV & APPLIANCE INC
605 Main St, Gregory, SD 57533-1434
Tel (605) 835-8711 *Founded/Ownrshp* 1969
Sales 47.6MM[E] *EMP* 260
SIC 5722 5731 5712 Household appliance stores; Gas household appliances; Radio, television & electronic stores; Radios, two-way, citizens' band, weather, short-wave, etc.; Furniture stores; Household appliance stores; Gas household appliances; Radio, television & electronic stores; Radios, two-way, citizens' band, weather, short-wave, etc.; Furniture stores
Pr: Elmer Karl
**Treas:* Kay J Karl
**VP:* Mike Karl
Dir Soc: Jerri Kenzy

D-U-N-S 07-952-3495
KARMA AUTOMOTIVE LLC
(*Suby of* WANXIANG AMERICA CORP) ★
3080 Airway Ave, Costa Mesa, CA 92626-6034
Tel (714) 723-3247 *Founded/Ownrshp* 2014
Sales 26.0MM[E] *EMP* 300
SIC 3711 Motor vehicles & car bodies
Pr: Tom Corcoran
VP: Ronald Samaco

D-U-N-S 10-321-0167 EXP
KARMAK INC
1 Karmak, Carlinville, IL 62626-4088
Tel (217) 854-4721 *Founded/Ownrshp* 1981
Sales 47.8MM[E] *EMP* 235
SIC 7373 Turnkey vendors, computer systems; Turnkey vendors, computer systems
Pr: Billy J Healy
**CFO:* Scott Simpson
**Ch:* Richard Schien
**VP:* Jeff Eudy
**VP:* Mike Kirk
**VP:* John Lebel
**VP:* Chuck Scahill
Rgnl Mgr: Price Jones
Rgnl Mgr: Todd Robertson
QA Dir: Dave Barr
QA Dir: Beth Leach
Board of Directors: Joseph Pereles Richard Wal

D-U-N-S 16-525-9727
KARMALOOP INC
KARMALOOP.COM
334 Boylston St Fl 4, Boston, MA 02116-3899
Tel (617) 695-0117 *Founded/Ownrshp* 2008
Sales 51.0MM[E] *EMP* 65
SIC 5611 5621

KARMALOOP.COM
See KARMALOOP INC

D-U-N-S 00-244-3752 IMP
KARNAK CORP
330 Central Ave, Clark, NJ 07066-1199
Tel (732) 388-0300 *Founded/Ownrshp* 1933
Sales 20.5MM[E] *EMP* 75[E]
SIC 2952 Roofing materials; Roof cement: asphalt, fibrous or plastic
V Ch: James D Hannah
**Pr:* Sarah J Jelin
COO: Mike Brehm
**COO:* Chris Salazar
CFO: Bob Andrews
**CFO:* David Gritz
Ex VP: Sarah Jelin
**VP:* John McDermott
Dir Lab: Scott Gregory
CTO: Andrew Ortiz
IT Man: Lucy Wright
Board of Directors: James D Hannah, Abraham Jelin, Sarah J Jelin

D-U-N-S 80-457-8487
KARNAVATI HOLDINGS INC
(*Suby of* NIRMA LIMITED)
9401 Indian Creek Pkwy # 1000, Overland Park, KS 66210-2007
Tel (913) 344-9500 *Founded/Ownrshp* 2008
Sales 416.4MM[E] *EMP* 649
SIC 1479 Salt & sulfur mining; Salt & sulfur mining

KARNDEAN DESIGNFLOORING
See KARNDEAN INTERNATIONAL LLC

D-U-N-S 02-257-6719 IMP/EXP
KARNDEAN INTERNATIONAL LLC
KARNDEAN DESIGNFLOORING
1100 Pontiac Ct, Export, PA 15632-9067
Tel (724) 387-2056 *Founded/Ownrshp* 1998
Sales 73.0MM[E] *EMP* 125
SIC 5023 Floor coverings; Floor coverings
**Pr:* Ed Perrin
**CEO:* Mark Sefton
**Treas:* Rosanne Daniels
Mng Dir: Martin Bell
Rgnl Mgr: Thomas Hellberg
Off Mgr: Andrea Klement
IT Man: Jennifer Geibel
VP Opers: Bill Anderson
VP Mktg: Emil Mello
VP Sls: Todd Gates
Mktg Mgr: Michael Lang

D-U-N-S 07-461-9586
KARNES COUNTY HOSPITAL DISTRICT
OTTO KAISER MEMORIAL HOSPITAL
3349 S Highway 181, Kenedy, TX 78119-5247
Tel (830) 583-3401 *Founded/Ownrshp* 1975
Sales 23.6MM[E] *EMP* 140
SIC 8062 General medical & surgical hospitals
Pr: Ray Rossett
Chf Rad: Granville Coggs
**Treas:* Rita Jordan
**VP:* David Purser
Mktg Dir: Barbara James
Psych: Christina Benavides
Psych: Dennis Mika

KARNES EC. NET
See KARNES ELECTRIC COOPERATIVE INC

D-U-N-S 00-682-4106 IMP
KARNES ELECTRIC COOPERATIVE INC (TX)
KARNES EC. NET
1007 N Hwy 123, Karnes City, TX 78118-1929
Tel (830) 780-3952 *Founded/Ownrshp* 1938
Sales 67.8MM *EMP* 62
SIC 4911 Distribution, electric power; Distribution, electric power
Pr: Arlon Retzloff
**Treas:* Alfred Moczygemba
**Sec:* Larry Schendel
**VP:* Martin R Harris Jr
DP Dir: Tammy Labus
Opers Mgr: Daphne Bianchi

KARNS FOOD
See KARNS PRIME AND FANCY FOOD LTD

D-U-N-S 06-977-5781
KARNS PRIME AND FANCY FOOD LTD (PA)
KARNS FOOD
675 Silver Spring Rd, Mechanicsburg, PA 17050-2846
Tel (717) 766-6477 *Founded/Ownrshp* 1959
Sales 124.9MM[E] *EMP* 800
SIC 5411

D-U-N-S 78-438-0792 IMP
KAROUN DAIRIES INC
13023 Arroyo St, San Fernando, CA 91340-1540
Tel (818) 767-7000 *Founded/Ownrshp* 1991
Sales 62.5MM[E] *EMP* 70
SIC 2022 5143 Cheese, natural & processed; Cheese
Pr: Anto Baghdassarian
**COO:* Rostom Baghdassarian
**CFO:* Tsolak Khatcherian
**VP:* Ohan Baghdassarian
Off Mgr: Lynette Baghdassarian
VP Sls: Andre Mesropian
Sls Dir: George Koshkaryan
Sls Mgr: Luis Gutierrez
Sls Mgr: Simon Sislyan
Sales Asso: Susana Cabrera

D-U-N-S 00-135-7102
KARP ASSOCIATES INC (NY)
ADJUSTABLE SHELVING
260 Spagnoli Rd, Melville, NY 11747-3505
Tel (631) 768-8300 *Founded/Ownrshp* 1956, 2005
Sales 22.9MM[E] *EMP* 95[E]
SIC 3442 2541 Metal doors; Shelving, office & store, wood
Ch: Adam Gold
IT Man: Seth Kwitko
Sfty Mgr: Augustine Lopez
Plnt Mgr: Ziggy Midura
Sales Exec: Mitch Salerno
Sls&Mrk Ex: Chantale Laraque
VP Sls: Lawrence Mass

D-U-N-S 93-860-1176
KARP AUTOMOTIVE INC
KARP BUICK & SAAB
400 Sunrise Hwy, Rockville Centre, NY 11570-4910
Tel (516) 764-0200 *Founded/Ownrshp* 1996
Sales 31.9MM[E] *EMP* 100
SIC 5511 5531 7538 7532 Automobiles, new & used; Automotive parts; General automotive repair shops; Body shop, automotive
Pr: David Karp
Off Mgr: Debbie Russo

KARP BUICK & SAAB
See KARP AUTOMOTIVE INC

D-U-N-S 80-863-1084
KARPREILLY LLC
104 Field Point Rd Ste 2, Greenwich, CT 06830-6481
Tel (203) 504-9900 *Founded/Ownrshp* 2007
Sales 23.4MM[E] *EMP* 105[E]
SIC 6726 5812 Investors syndicates; Pizza restaurants
Mng Dir: Allan Karp
CFO: Lillian Cooke

D-U-N-S 11-876-5478
KARRIERS INC
809 S 48th St, Grand Forks, ND 58201-3831
Tel (701) 746-8307 *Founded/Ownrshp* 1982
Sales 31.1MM *EMP* 15[E]
Accts Curtis Wischer Cpa Grand For
SIC 4213 Trucking, except local; Refrigerated products transport
Pr: Brooky Anderson
**Sec:* Sandee Anderson
**VP:* Wayne Anderson

D-U-N-S 95-681-7332
■ **KARRINGTON OPERATING CO INC**
(*Suby of* SUNRISE SENIOR LIVING INC) ★
919 Old Henderson Rd, Columbus, OH 43220-3722
Tel (614) 324-5951 *Founded/Ownrshp* 1999
Sales 10.8MM[E] *EMP* 900
SIC 8059 Personal care home, with health care
Ch Bd: Richard R Slager
Pr: Pete Klisares
COO: Richard J Clark
CFO: Thomas J Klimback
Treas: Mark N Mace
Ex VP: Robin Holderman
Sr VP: Stephen Lewis
Board of Directors: John S Christie, Bernadine P Healy, David H Hoag, John H McConnell, James V Pickett, Harold A Poling, Michael H Thomas, Robert D Walter

KARS 4 KIDS
See CARS FOR KIDS INC

KAR'S NUTS
See KAR NUT PRODUCTS CO

D-U-N-S 94-227-1115
KARSON FOOD SERVICE INC
3409 Rose Ave, Ocean, NJ 07712-3923
Tel (732) 922-1900 *Founded/Ownrshp* 1995
Sales 27.9MM[E] *EMP* 49
SIC 5141 Groceries, general line
Pr: Robert Kardane

D-U-N-S 06-275-6908
■ **KARSTEN HOMES LLC**
KARSTENCO.COM
(*Suby of* CLAYTON HOMES INC) ★
2700 Karsten Ct Se, Albuquerque, NM 87102-5082
Tel (505) 242-8751 *Founded/Ownrshp* 1997
Sales 23.1MM[E] *EMP* 160
SIC 2452 Prefabricated buildings, wood; Prefabricated buildings, wood
CFO: Joel Durante
Exec: Rejane A Jansen
Genl Mgr: Buck Wooten

D-U-N-S 04-201-8184 IMP
KARSTEN MANUFACTURING CORP
PING
2201 W Desert Cove Ave, Phoenix, AZ 85029-4912
Tel (602) 870-5000 *Founded/Ownrshp* 1959
Sales 332.5MM[E] *EMP* 1,400
SIC 3949 3398 3363 3325 8711 7997 Golf equipment; Metal heat treating; Aluminum die-castings; Steel foundries; Civil engineering; Country club, membership; Golf equipment; Metal heat treating; Aluminum die-castings; Steel foundries; Civil engineering; Country club, membership
CEO: John A Solheim
CFO: George Drewry
Treas: Dawn M Grove
**Treas:* Michael T Trueblood
**Ex VP:* K Louis Solheim
**Ex VP:* Louise Solheim
**VP:* Rawleigh Grove
**VP:* Stacey S Pauwels
CTO: Stacey Solheim
Plnt Mgr: Pat Patrick
Snr Mgr: Jolana Dyson

KARSTENCO.COM
See KARSTEN HOMES LLC

D-U-N-S 15-456-4306
■ **KARTA TECHNOLOGIES INC**
(*Suby of* NCI INFORMATION SYSTEMS INC) ★
5710 W Hausman Rd Ste 112, San Antonio, TX 78249-1646
Tel (210) 582-3000 *Founded/Ownrshp* 2007
Sales 23.4MM[E] *EMP* 450
SIC 7379 8711 Computer related consulting services; Engineering services; Computer related consulting services; Engineering services
CEO: Chander K Narang
**Pr:* Terry W Glasgow
CFO: Judy Bjornaas
CFO: Nick Gray
**CFO:* Jim McDermott
Sr VP: G P Sinh
VP: Marco De Vito
VP: Thomas E Downey
VP: Stephen Hoech
VP: Hoverman Phillip
CTO: Patrick Asher

D-U-N-S 80-032-4027
KARTOS HOLDINGS LP
2055 Burton Rd, Mount Pleasant, TX 75455-2208
Tel (903) 572-4371 *Founded/Ownrshp* 2005
Sales 55.0MM *EMP* 1
SIC 5511 Automobiles, new & used; Automobiles, new & used
Genl Pt: Christopher B Elliott

KARWOSKI & COURAGE DIV
See MARTIN-WILLIAMS INC

D-U-N-S 00-276-4605
KAS DIRECT LLC
BABYGANICS
1600 Stewart Ave Ste 411, Westbury, NY 11590-6654
Tel (516) 934-0544 *Founded/Ownrshp* 2008
Sales 34.5MM[E] *EMP* 37
SIC 5199 Pet supplies
**COO:* Keith Garber
CFO: Helen Junda
Mktg Dir: Lindsay Joyce

KAS-KEL
See KASSON & KELLER INC

D-U-N-S 01-868-0798
KASA ASSOCIATES INC (CA)
OAK TREE MAZDA
4250 Stevens Creek Blvd, San Jose, CA 95129-1336
Tel (408) 553-6300 *Founded/Ownrshp* 1998
Sales 22.4MM[E] *EMP* 55
SIC 5511 Automobiles, new & used; Automobiles, new & used
Pr: Kevan Del Grande
Genl Mgr: Jeff Velisek
Sls Mgr: Eddie Pourshahbazi
Sales Asso: Ignacio Carrilo

D-U-N-S 06-843-8753 EXP
KASA COMPANIES INC
KASA FAB
418 E Avenue B, Salina, KS 67401-8960
Tel (785) 825-7181 *Founded/Ownrshp* 1974
Sales 31.8MM *EMP* 150
Accts Mayer Hoffman Mccann Pc Wic
SIC 3613 3714 3625 Control panels, electric; Panel & distribution boards & other related apparatus; Motor vehicle parts & accessories; Relays & industrial controls; Control panels, electric; Panel & distribution boards & other related apparatus; Motor vehicle parts & accessories; Relays & industrial controls
CEO: Mike Haug
**Pr:* Dan Stutterheim
**CFO:* Brad Strathe
Mktg Dir: Laura Munsch

KASA FAB
See KASA COMPANIES INC

KASC
See KA STEEL CHEMICALS INC

D-U-N-S 83-632-5670 IMP/EXP
KASC INC
270 Samuel Barnet Blvd, New Bedford, MA 02745-1219
Tel (508) 985-9898 *Founded/Ownrshp* 1994
Sales NA *EMP* 303
SIC 2395 Embroidery & art needlework

D-U-N-S 36-127-9334
KASCO INC
226 E Hudson Ave, Royal Oak, MI 48067-3700
Tel (248) 547-1210 *Founded/Ownrshp* 1989
Sales 47.9MM[E] *EMP* 82
SIC 1542 1541 Commercial & office building, new construction; Commercial & office buildings, renovation & repair; Institutional building construction; Industrial buildings, new construction; Renovation, remodeling & repairs: industrial buildings; Commercial & office building, new construction; Commercial & office buildings, renovation & repair; Institutional building construction; Industrial buildings, new construction; Renovation, remodeling & repairs: industrial buildings
Pr: Stephen J Kassab
**CFO:* David Kassab
**VP:* Mike Engle
**VP:* Geoff Hutchison

D-U-N-S 16-109-1996
■ **KASCO LLC**
KASCO SHARPTECH
(*Suby of* BAIRNCO CORP) ★
1569 Tower Grove Ave, Saint Louis, MO 63110-2215
Tel (314) 771-1550 *Founded/Ownrshp* 1986
Sales 41.0MM *EMP* 200
SIC 5084 3421 Food industry machinery; Knives: butchers', hunting, pocket, etc.; Food industry machinery; Knives: butchers', hunting, pocket, etc.
Ch: Luke E Fichthorn III
**Pr:* Ryan Turner
Treas: Lawrence C Maingot
VP: James McCabe
Sls Dir: Mark Dobson

KASCO SHARPTECH
See KASCO LLC

D-U-N-S 04-409-0637 IMP/EXP
KASE EQUIPMENT CORP
7400 Hub Pkwy, Cleveland, OH 44125-5735
Tel (216) 642-9040 *Founded/Ownrshp* 1962

Sales 22.2MM^E *EMP* 100
SIC 3555 Printing trades machinery; Printing trades machinery
Ch Bd: Edward Hawkins
**Pr:* Partick Hawkins
**VP:* Dave Hodgson

D-U-N-S 19-839-1195 IMP
KASEL ASSOCIATES INDUSTRIES INC
3315 Walnut St, Denver, CO 80205-2429
Tel (303) 296-4417 *Founded/Ownrshp* 1986
Sales 24.3MM^E *EMP* 135
SIC 2047 Dog & cat food; Dog & cat food
Pr: Raymond J Kasel
Sls Mgr: Galina Kasel

KASEMAN
See MICHAEL BAKER GLOBAL SERVICES LLC

D-U-N-S 07-832-4946 IMP
KASH APPAREL LLC
1929 Hooper Ave, Los Angeles, CA 90011-1332
Tel (213) 747-8885 *Founded/Ownrshp* 2011
Sales 20.8MM *EMP* 68
SIC 5137 Women's & children's accessories; Women's & children's accessories

D-U-N-S 02-111-7635 IMP
KASH N KARRY FOOD STORES INC
SWEETBAY SUPERMARKET
(*Suby of* DELHAIZE AMERICA LLC) ★
2110 Executive Dr, Salisbury, NC 28147-9007
Tel (813) 620-1139 *Founded/Ownrshp* 2000
Sales 558.3MM^E *EMP* 9,046
SIC 5411 2051 5912 5921 Supermarkets, chain; Supermarkets, 66,000-99,000 square feet; Bread, cake & related products; Drug stores & proprietary stores; Liquor stores; Supermarkets, chain; Supermarkets, 66,000-99,000 square feet; Bread, cake & related products; Drug stores & proprietary stores; Liquor stores
Pr: Mike Vail
**Sr VP:* Karen Farnald
**Sr VP:* Geoff Waldou
**VP:* Eddie Garcia
**VP:* Amy Standard
Dist Mgr: Mike Hall
Dist Mgr: Gary Stephens
Store Mgr: Tony Brown
Pharmcst: James Baudin

D-U-N-S 19-592-0793 IMP
KASH N KARRY FOOD STORES INC
SWEETBAY SUPERMARKET
1802 Jim Johnson Rd, Plant City, FL 33566-8735
Tel (813) 707-2700 *Founded/Ownrshp* 1988
Sales 28.3MM^E *EMP* 400
SIC 5411 Grocery stores; Grocery stores
Pr: Jerry Greenleaf

D-U-N-S 07-198-2409
KASKASKIA COLLEGE
27210 College Rd, Centralia, IL 62801-7878
Tel (618) 532-0701 *Founded/Ownrshp* 1966
Sales 9.2MM *EMP* 450
Accts Mcgladrey Llp Springfield Il
SIC 8222 Community college; Community college
Pr: Dr James Underwood
Ofcr: Steve Donoho
VP: Sedgwick Harris
Exec: Robert Rhymes
Store Mgr: Cheryl Johnson
Dir IT: Gina Schuetz
Mktg Dir: Travis Hinson
Snr Mgr: Deana Belcher

KASMIR FABRICS
See FRANK KASMIR ASSOCIATES INC

D-U-N-S 09-129-1856 IMP/EXP
KASO PLASTICS INC
5720 Ne 121st Ave C, Vancouver, WA 98682-6480
Tel (360) 254-3980 *Founded/Ownrshp* 1962
Sales 25.1MM^E *EMP* 96
SIC 3089 Injection molded finished plastic products
Ch Bd: Ralph Miller
**Pr:* Darin King
**Treas:* Ned Buhler
**VP:* Craig Ausmus
**VP:* Timothy Bailey
**VP:* Linda Clark
**Prin:* Norm Webb
DP Exec: Mark Copeland
Prd Mgr: Tom Smith
VP Sls: Dean Christensen
Sales Asso: Tamra Parton

D-U-N-S 00-121-0749 IMP/EXP
KASON INDUSTRIES INC
KASON MID-WEST
57 Amlajack Blvd, Newnan, GA 30265-1093
Tel (770) 251-1422 *Founded/Ownrshp* 1928
Sales 76.9MM^E *EMP* 360
SIC 3589

KASON MID-WEST
See KASON INDUSTRIES INC

D-U-N-S 80-718-0815
KASOWITZ BENSON TORRES & FRIEDMAN LLP
1633 Broadway Fl 21, New York, NY 10019-6708
Tel (212) 506-1700 *Founded/Ownrshp* 1995
Sales 72.2MM^E *EMP* 400
SIC 8111 Specialized law offices, attorneys; Specialized law offices, attorneys
Pt: Marc Kasowitz
Pt: Daniel R Benson
Pt: David M Friedman
Pt: Hector Torres
Snr Ntwrk: Alfie Woods
IT Man: Lloyanda J Ruchit
Opers Mgr: Victor Emma
Counsel: David Mark
Counsel: David Max
Snr Mgr: Linda Kornfeld

D-U-N-S 79-207-2469
KASPAR RANCH HAND EQUIPMENT LP
RANCH HAND TRUCK ACCESSORIES
961 N Us Highway 95 E, Shiner, TX 77984-5883
Tel (361) 594-4608 *Founded/Ownrshp* 2000
Sales 41.9MM^E *EMP* 150
SIC 5013 3714 Truck parts & accessories; Motor vehicle parts & accessories; Truck parts & accessories; Motor vehicle parts & accessories
Pt: Dan Kaspar
Genl Mgr: Jill Matula
CTO: Celia Glass

D-U-N-S 00-809-2983
KASPAR WIRE WORKS INC
959 N Us Highway 95 E, Shiner, TX 77984-5883
Tel (361) 594-3327 *Founded/Ownrshp* 1898
Sales 103.6MM^E *EMP* 650
SIC 3496 Miscellaneous fabricated wire products; Miscellaneous fabricated wire products
Pr: Dan A Kaspar
COO: Greg Chumchal
**Treas:* Douglas D Kaspar
Treas: Lori Malina
**VP:* David C Kaspar
VP: John Valis
CIO: Sylvia Glass

D-U-N-S 96-928-1120
KASPER ASL LTD
180 Rittenhouse Cir, Bristol, PA 19007-1618
Tel (215) 785-4000 *Founded/Ownrshp* 2003
Sales NA *EMP* 2,240
SIC 2337

D-U-N-S 94-216-9343
KASPER GROUP LLC
1412 Broadway Fl 5, New York, NY 10018-3330
Tel (212) 354-4311 *Founded/Ownrshp* 2008
Sales 350.0MM *EMP* 250
SIC 2335 2337 Women's & children's dresses, suits, skirts & blouses; Women's, juniors' & misses' dresses; Women's & misses' suits & coats
Pr: Gregg Marks
**CFO:* Daniel Fishman
Board of Directors: Arthur Levine, Lester Schreiber, Meredith Warz

D-U-N-S 17-304-5688
KASPERSKY LAB INC
500 Unicorn Park Dr # 302, Woburn, MA 01801-3345
Tel (781) 503-1800 *Founded/Ownrshp* 2004
Sales 35.9MM^E *EMP* 75^E
SIC 5045 5961 5734 Computer software; Computer software, mail order; Software, business & non-game
Pr: Chris Doggett
**CFO:* Angelo Gentile
Top Exec: Elke Woessner
Sr VP: Nancy Reynolds
VP: Marina Alekseeva
VP: David P Aucoin
VP: Dan Burke
VP: William Cunningham
VP: Stephanie Edwards
VP: John Malatesta
VP: John Murdock
VP: Patricia Sanders
Dir Bus: Brett Matesen

D-U-N-S 87-499-7943 IMP
KASSBOHRER ALL TERRAIN VEHICLES INC
(*Suby of* KASSBOHRER GELANDEFAHRZEUG AG)
8850 Double Diamond Pkwy, Reno, NV 89521-5908
Tel (775) 857-5000 *Founded/Ownrshp* 1994
Sales 21.5MM^E *EMP* 53
SIC 5012 Recreation vehicles, all-terrain
Pr: John C Gilbert
**CFO:* Brian Pomerleau
Ofcr: Andy Thomas
Rgnl Mgr: Colin Hales
Snr Mgr: Darren Cameron

D-U-N-S 00-209-2948
KASSELMAN ELECTRIC CO INC (NY)
29 Broad St, Albany, NY 12202-1812
Tel (518) 465-4795 *Founded/Ownrshp* 1948, 1967
Sales 22.6MM *EMP* 200
Accts Saxbst Llp Albany New York
SIC 1731 General electrical contractor; General electrical contractor
CEO: Paul G Kasselman
**Pr:* Becky L Kasselman
**VP:* Thomas J Henchey
**VP:* Steve Kasselman
Board of Directors: Kevin Heelan

D-U-N-S 00-207-7196 IMP
KASSON & KELLER INC (NY)
KAS-KEL
60 School St, Fonda, NY 12068-4809
Tel (518) 853-3421 *Founded/Ownrshp* 1946
Sales 162.1MM^E *EMP* 900
SIC 3442 3089 1521 3231 Window & door frames; Windows, plastic; Single-family housing construction; Products of purchased glass; Window & door frames; Windows, plastic; Single-family housing construction; Products of purchased glass
Ch Bd: William Keller III
**Ex VP:* James P Keller
Genl Mgr: Matthew Sullivan
CIO: Greg Spencer
Sls Mgr: Mark Empie

D-U-N-S 62-079-9382
KAST CONSTRUCTION CO LLC
701 Nrthpint Pkwy Ste 400, West Palm Beach, FL 33407
Tel (561) 689-2910 *Founded/Ownrshp* 2005
Sales 203.5MM *EMP* 125
Accts E F Alvarez & Company Pa
SIC 1531 Operative builders
Pr: Michael Neal
Dir Bus: Ashlee Figg
Snr PM: Peter Supple
Snr PM: Daniel Zorrilla

D-U-N-S 10-391-7357 IMP
KAST MARKETING INC
10435 Seymour Ave, Franklin Park, IL 60131-1209
Tel (630) 227-0600 *Founded/Ownrshp* 1983
Sales 22.0MM *EMP* 14
Accts Steinberg Silverman & Company
SIC 5074 Plumbing fittings & supplies; Pipes & fittings, plastic; Plumbing fittings & supplies; Pipes & fittings, plastic
Pr: Daniel Bellezzo
Sales Asso: Sara Sexton

D-U-N-S 00-427-6085
KASTLE ELECTRIC CO (OH)
4501 Kettering Blvd, Moraine, OH 45439-2137
Tel (937) 254-2681 *Founded/Ownrshp* 1925
Sales 22.7MM^E *EMP* 120
SIC 1731 General electrical contractor; General electrical contractor
CEO: K Andrew Stuhlmiller
**Pr:* Gregory P Brush
**CFO:* William S Page
Admn Mgr: Andy Stuhlmiller

D-U-N-S 80-978-9618
KASTLE SYSTEMS INTERNATIONAL LLC
6402 Arlington Blvd Lobby, Falls Church, VA 22042-2333
Tel (703) 528-8800 *Founded/Ownrshp* 1970
Sales 52.6MM^E *EMP* 200
SIC 7382 Protective devices, security; Protective devices, security
CEO: Piyush Sodha
**CFO:* Steve Yevich
Treas: Jennifer L Roberts
Ex VP: Steve Bacica
**Ex VP:* Brian Eckert
**Ex VP:* Mohammad Soleimani
VP: Nik Gagvani
VP: Stephen Harrup
VP: Rafael Molinari
VP: Jim Mustard
Dir IT: Todd Scalzott

D-U-N-S 08-687-7917
KATAHDIN TRUST CO
11 Main St, Patten, ME 04765-3100
Tel (207) 528-2211 *Founded/Ownrshp* 1917
Sales NA *EMP* 72
SIC 6022 State commercial banks; State commercial banks
Pr: Jon J Prescott
**Ch Bd:* Steven Richardson
**VP:* Paul Adams
**VP:* Robert Porter
VP: Sherry Roberts
Brnch Mgr: Tori Barber
Brnch Mgr: Sunny Flannery
Brnch Mgr: Janet Jandreau

D-U-N-S 02-966-2154
KATALYST TECHNOLOGIES INC
500 Davis St Ste 801, Evanston, IL 60201-4623
Tel (847) 425-4312 *Founded/Ownrshp* 2011
Sales 46.6MM^E *EMP* 296
SIC 7371 Computer software development & applications; Computer software development & applications
Pr: Rahul Shah
Board of Directors: Rahul Shah

D-U-N-S 80-791-1011 IMP/EXP
KATAMAN METALS OF MISSOURI LLC
7733 Forsyth Blvd Ste 300, Saint Louis, MO 63105-1833
Tel (314) 863-6699 *Founded/Ownrshp* 2007
Sales 34.0MM^E *EMP* 29
SIC 5051 5093 Copper; Zinc; Steel; Nonferrous metals scrap
Pr: Joseph P Reinmann
**CFO:* Trevor Hansen
**VP:* Alan Courtois
VP: Sharon Heien
**VP:* David Kramer
Mng Dir: Jeffrey Allman
Trfc Mgr: Michelle Dugger
VP Mktg: Kristy Hammond
Board of Directors: David Blue, Doug Smith

D-U-N-S 01-739-6172 IMP
KATANA RACING INC
KATANA RACING WHL & TIRE DISTR
14407 Alondra Blvd, La Mirada, CA 90638-5504
Tel (562) 977-8565 *Founded/Ownrshp* 1998
Sales 102.0MM *EMP* 105^E
Accts Agoplan & Baboghli Torrance
SIC 5013 Wheels, motor vehicle; Tires & tubes; Wheels, motor vehicle
CEO: ARA Tcgaghlassian
Genl Mgr: Joe Garcia

KATANA RACING WHL & TIRE DISTR
See KATANA RACING INC

D-U-N-S 60-319-8847 IMP
KATAYAMA AMERICAN CO INC
KACI
(*Suby of* KATAYAMA KOGYO CO.,LTD.)
6901 Midland Indus Dr, Shelbyville, KY 40065-9717
Tel (502) 633-7280 *Founded/Ownrshp* 1989
Sales 75.0MM^E *EMP* 350
SIC 3465 3714 3442 3429 3231 Moldings or trim, automobile: stamped metal; Body parts, automobile: stamped metal; Motor vehicle parts & accessories; Metal doors, sash & trim; Manufactured hardware (general); Products of purchased glass; Moldings or trim, automobile: stamped metal; Body parts, automobile: stamped metal; Motor vehicle parts & accessories; Metal doors, sash & trim; Manufactured hardware (general); Products of purchased glass
Pr: Masayuki Katayama
**VP:* Naoki Katayama
Mtls Mgr: Tom Cox
Opers Mgr: Patrick Burnett
Ql Cn Mgr: David Krauss
Sls Mgr: Yugo Ogawa

D-U-N-S 02-239-0025 IMP
KATCEF BROS INC
2404 A And Eagle Blvd, Annapolis, MD 21401-8905
Tel (410) 224-2391 *Founded/Ownrshp* 1933
Sales 31.7MM^E *EMP* 80
SIC 5181 Beer & other fermented malt liquors; Beer & other fermented malt liquors
Pr: Sylvia Katcef
**Treas:* Neal B Katcef ★
**VP:* Janice Cohen
VP: Zack Cohen
Off Mgr: Murray Snider
IT Man: Penny Fowler

D-U-N-S 16-280-4855
KATCH
2381 Rosecrans Ave # 400, El Segundo, CA 90245-4917
Tel (310) 219-6200 *Founded/Ownrshp* 2002
Sales 140.0MM *EMP* 70
SIC 7311 Advertising agencies; Advertising agencies
CEO: Patrick Quigley
Pr: Darren Wiebe
VP: Greg Isaacs
VP: Christopher Yip
Dir Bus: Jeff Sweetser
Snr Sftwr: Hovanes Gambaryan
CTO: Sergio Vela
VP Sls: Michael Foster
Mktg Dir: Jason Barlow
Snr Mgr: Patrick Copeland
Board of Directors: Jamie Montgomery, Rory O'driscoll

D-U-N-S 61-515-5533 IMP
KATE SOMERVILLE SKINCARE LLC
(*Suby of* UNILEVER PLC)
144 S Beverly Dr Ste 500, Beverly Hills, CA 90212-3023
Tel (323) 655-7546 *Founded/Ownrshp* 2015
Sales 46.5MM^E *EMP* 102
SIC 5122 Toiletries; Cosmetics; Perfumes
VP: Shellie Gainer
Mktg Mgr: Victoria Ripa

D-U-N-S 04-005-9230 IMP
▲ KATE SPADE & CO
2 Park Ave Fl 8, New York, NY 10016-5613
Tel (212) 354-4900 *Founded/Ownrshp* 1976
Sales 1.1MMM *EMP* 3,500
Accts Deloitte & Touche Llp New Yor
Tkr Sym KATE *Exch* NYS
SIC 2331 5651 5136 5137 5961 Women's & misses' blouses & shirts; Family clothing stores; Unisex clothing stores; Men's & boys' clothing; Women's & children's clothing; Catalog & mail-order houses; Women's & misses' blouses & shirts; Family clothing stores; Unisex clothing stores; Men's & boys' clothing; Women's & children's clothing; Catalog & mail-order houses
CEO: Craig A Leavitt
Pr: George M Carrara
Pr: Ned Goepp
CFO: Thomas Linko
**Chf Cred:* Deborah J Lloyd
Ex VP: Edgar Huber
Sr VP: Mary Beech
Sr VP: Christopher Di Nardo
Sr VP: William Higley
Sr VP: Linda Yanussi
VP: Kerry Fogarty
VP: Michael Rinaldo
VP: Theresa Zast
Board of Directors: Lawrence S Benjamin, Raul J Fernandez, Kenneth B Gilman, Nancy J Karch, Kenneth P Kopelman, Douglas Mack, Doreen A Toben

D-U-N-S 00-592-6030 EXP
■ KATE SPADE LLC
(*Suby of* KATE SPADE & CO) ★
2 Park Ave Fl 8, New York, NY 10016-5613
Tel (201) 295-6000 *Founded/Ownrshp* 2006
Sales 225.5MM^E *EMP* 190
SIC 5137 5632 Handbags; Handbags; Handbags; Handbags
CEO: Craig A Leavitt
**Pr:* George M Carrara
**Sr VP:* Mary Beech
**Sr VP:* Christopher Di Nardo
**Sr VP:* Bill Higley
VP: Donna Chiffriller
VP: John Cullina
Ex Dir: Al Mateo

D-U-N-S 13-979-1743 IMP
KATECHO INC
4020 Gannett Ave, Des Moines, IA 50321-2951
Tel (515) 244-1212 *Founded/Ownrshp* 1984
Sales 85.4MM^E *EMP* 250
SIC 3841 Surgical & medical instruments; Surgical & medical instruments
Pr: Mark Scharnberg
CFO: Cathy Scharnberg
**Treas:* Lorne C Scharnberg
**VP:* Warren Walters
CIO: Chad Whiting
Netwrk Mgr: Michael Galvin
Mfg Dir: James Wolff
Mfg Dir: Drew Woodworth
QC Dir: David Livingston
Sfty Mgr: John Hold
Mktg Mgr: Brian Farrell

D-U-N-S 05-463-3839
KATERI RESIDENCE (NY)
205 Lexington Ave Fl 2, New York, NY 10016-6053
Tel (646) 505-3500 *Founded/Ownrshp* 1981
Sales 23.5MM^E *EMP* 650
Accts O Connor Davies Llp Harrison
SIC 8051 Skilled nursing care facilities; Skilled nursing care facilities

D-U-N-S 02-304-0546
KATH MANAGEMENT CO
KATH'S AUTO SUPPLY
3096 Rice St, Saint Paul, MN 55113-2204
Tel (651) 484-3325 *Founded/Ownrshp* 1946
Sales 77.0MM^E *EMP* 255

SIC 5541 5411 5983 5172 5531 5013 Gasoline service stations; Convenience stores, independent; Fuel oil dealers; Petroleum products; Fuel oil; Automotive parts; Automotive supplies & parts; Gasoline service stations; Convenience stores, independent; Fuel oil dealers; Petroleum products; Fuel oil; Automotive parts; Automotive supplies & parts
Pr: Bruce Kath
**Sec:* Jeff Larson
**VP:* Steve Dahl

D-U-N-S 16-735-2780
KATHERINE BIRD TRUST
CENTENIAL APPARTMENTS
2677 Willakenzie Rd Ste 3, Eugene, OR 97401-4873
Tel (541) 344-0028 *Founded/Ownrshp* 1986
Sales 22.0MM^E *EMP* 125
SIC 6799 6531 Real estate investors, except property operators; Real estate investors, except property operators; Real estate leasing & rentals
Trst: David C Mc Culloch

D-U-N-S 96-326-0638
KATHERINE LUTHER RESIDENTIAL HEALTH CARE & REHABILITATION CENTER INC
LUTHERAN CARE
110 Utica Rd, Clinton, NY 13323-1548
Tel (315) 853-5515 *Founded/Ownrshp* 2010
Sales 21.1MM *EMP* 99
SIC 8082 Home health care services; Home health care services
Pr: Andrew Peterson
**CFO:* Robert Beach
CIO: William Preuss
HC Dir: Roxanne Barrett

D-U-N-S 06-401-2008
KATHERINE SHAW BETHEA HOSPITAL
KSB HOSPITAL
403 E 1st St, Dixon, IL 61021-3187
Tel (815) 288-5531 *Founded/Ownrshp* 1893
Sales 129.6MM *EMP* 1,000
SIC 8062

KATH'S AUTO SUPPLY
See KATH MANAGEMENT CO

D-U-N-S 01-516-0045
KATHY KAYE FOODS LLC
695 W 1700 S Bldg 30, Logan, UT 84321-6297
Tel (435) 563-0204 *Founded/Ownrshp* 2006
Sales 20.5MM^E *EMP* 30
SIC 5145 Snack foods

D-U-N-S 82-550-0791
KATMAI GOVERNMENT SERVICES LLC
(*Suby of* OUZINKIE NATIVE CORP) ★
11001 Omalley Centre Dr # 204, Anchorage, AK 99515-3096
Tel (907) 333-7000 *Founded/Ownrshp* 2007
Sales 114.7MM^E *EMP* 812^E
SIC 6719 Personal holding companies, except banks; Personal holding companies, except banks
CEO: R David Stephens
**Pr:* Shane Harvey
**CFO:* Thomas Clements
**Ex VP:* Cynthia Vanden Berg
Dir IT: Jeff Hall

D-U-N-S 04-816-5146
KATO DISTRIBUTING INC
PUNP AND MUNCH & PETROL PUMPER
2109 S Broadway, Rochester, MN 55904-5526
Tel (507) 289-7456 *Founded/Ownrshp* 1958
Sales 40.3MM^E *EMP* 276
SIC 5541 5411 5013 5531 Gasoline service stations; Convenience stores; Motor vehicle supplies & new parts; Automobile & truck equipment & parts; Gasoline service stations; Convenience stores; Motor vehicle supplies & new parts; Automobile & truck equipment & parts
Pr: John J Jensen
**CFO:* Jack Briggs
VP: Raymond Colbert

D-U-N-S 04-182-7986 IMP/EXP
■ **KATO ENGINEERING INC**
EMERSON INDUSTRIAL AUTOMATION
(*Suby of* EMERSON ELECTRIC CO) ★
2075 Howard Dr W, North Mankato, MN 56003-9921
Tel (507) 345-2716 *Founded/Ownrshp* 1998
Sales 154.5MM^E *EMP* 350
SIC 3621 3643 3625 Motors & generators; Current-carrying wiring devices; Relays & industrial controls; Motors & generators; Current-carrying wiring devices; Relays & industrial controls
CEO: David Farr
Exec: Valerie Lilliander
Genl Mgr: Gary Burandt
Dir IT: Will Bauman
Advt Dir: Richard Rohlfing

D-U-N-S 83-872-2361
KATO KAGAKU CO LTD
HYATT REGENCY CHICAGO
151 E Wacker Dr, Chicago, IL 60601-3764
Tel (312) 565-1234 *Founded/Ownrshp* 1989
Sales 130.6MM^E *EMP* 1,300
SIC 6512 7011 Nonresidential building operators; Hotels & motels; Nonresidential building operators; Hotels & motels
Pr: Eiichi Kato
Sr VP: Peter Norman
**VP:* Shoji Kato
Ex Dir: Erica Korpi
Genl Mgr: Randy Thompson
Sls Mgr: Lisa Kirk
Sls Mgr: Sarah Lane

KATO RADIATOR
See WESTMAN FREIGHTLINER INC

KATO TOOL
See NORTHERN STATES SUPPLY INC

D-U-N-S 03-723-0265 IMP
KATOEN NATIE GULF COAST INC
(*Suby of* KATOEN NATIE USA INC) ★
10925 Sh 225, La Porte, TX 77571
Tel (281) 941-1011 *Founded/Ownrshp* 1854
Sales 54.5MM^E *EMP* 151
SIC 4225 4783 General warehousing & storage; Packing & crating; General warehousing & storage; Packing & crating
CEO: Fernand Huts
**Pr:* Frank Vingerhoets
**VP:* Ray Stavinoha
Off Mgr: Jennifer Anderson

D-U-N-S 15-984-8530
KATOEN NATIE USA INC
(*Suby of* KATOEN NATIE NV)
10925 Sh 225, La Porte, TX 77571
Tel (281) 941-1001 *Founded/Ownrshp* 1854
Sales 73.3MM^E *EMP* 500
SIC 7389 4225 Packaging & labeling services; General warehousing & storage; Packaging & labeling services; General warehousing & storage
Pr: Frank Vingerhoets
**CFO:* Dan Faber
Snr Mgr: Joachim Westerlinck

KATOM RESTURANT SUPPLY
See B & B EQUIPMENT & SUPPLY INC

D-U-N-S 01-396-7591
KATONAH FIRE DISTRICT INC (NY)
65 Bedford Rd, Katonah, NY 10536-2118
Tel (914) 232-4570 *Founded/Ownrshp* 1874
Sales NA *EMP* 300
SIC 9224 Fire department, volunteer; Fire department, volunteer
**Pr:* Chris Maranarow
Snr Mgr: Jose Corsino

D-U-N-S 10-139-5655
KATONAH-LEWISBORO SCHOOL DISTRICT
Shady Ln Rr 123, South Salem, NY 10590
Tel (914) 763-7000 *Founded/Ownrshp* 1952
Sales 32.7MM^E *EMP* 800
SIC 8211 Public elementary & secondary schools; Public elementary & secondary schools

KATSIROUBAS BROS
See THEODORE J KATSIROUBAS AND SONS INC

KATSURAGAWA ELECTRIC
See KIP AMERICA INC

D-U-N-S 02-003-4351
KATTEN MUCHIN ROSENMAN LLP
525 W Monroe St Ste 1900, Chicago, IL 60661-3718
Tel (312) 902-5200 *Founded/Ownrshp* 1974
Sales 232.9MM^E *EMP* 1,731
SIC 8111

D-U-N-S 09-391-6377 IMP/EXP
KATUN CORP
BLMGTN
(*Suby of* MONOMOY CAPITAL PARTNERS LP) ★
10951 Bush Lake Rd # 100, Minneapolis, MN 55438-2391
Tel (952) 941-9505 *Founded/Ownrshp* 2008
Sales 394.5MM^E *EMP* 1,060
SIC 5112 Photocopying supplies; Photocopying supplies
Pr: Carlyle Singer
Pr: Jan Bolin
**Pr:* Todd Mavis
Treas: Tom Wallace
Sr VP: Russell S John
VP: Bob Moore
Exec: Gordon Cavanagh
IT Man: Mark Lother
Tech Mgr: Leo Kooistra
Sls&Mrk Ex: Mauricio Gonzalez
Mktg Mgr: Matthew Oconnor

D-U-N-S 02-081-4232
KATY INDEPENDENT SCHOOL DISTRICT
6301 S Stadium Ln, Katy, TX 77494-1057
Tel (281) 396-6000 *Founded/Ownrshp* 1919
Sales 443.4MM^E *EMP* 6,631
SIC 8211 Elementary & secondary schools; High school, junior or senior; Elementary & secondary schools; High school, junior or senior
Pr: Bryan Michalsky
**Pr:* Rebecca Fox
**CFO:* William L Moore
**Treas:* Charles Griffin
Bd of Dir: Neal Howard
Bd of Dir: Tom Law
**VP:* Joe M Adams
**VP:* Henry Dibrell
Ex Dir: Ron Pleasant
Dir Sec: Peggy Caruso
Dir Sec: Mark Hopkins

D-U-N-S 14-557-9491
KATY INDEPENDENT SCHOOL DISTRICT DARE ADVISORY BOARD INC
20380 Franz Rd, Katy, TX 77449-5600
Tel (281) 396-2500 *Founded/Ownrshp* 1999
Sales 45.4MM^E *EMP* 7,000^E
Accts Null-Lairson Pc Cpas Houst
SIC 8211 Public elementary & secondary schools; Public elementary & secondary schools

D-U-N-S 04-463-8369 IMP/EXP
▲ **KATY INDUSTRIES INC**
305 Rock Industrial Pk Dr, Bridgeton, MO 63044-1214
Tel (314) 656-4321 *Founded/Ownrshp* 1967
Sales 99.6MM *EMP* 263^E
Tkr Sym KATY *Exch* OTO
SIC 3589 2673 Commercial cleaning equipment; Food storage & trash bags (plastic); Commercial cleaning equipment; Food storage & trash bags (plastic)
Pr: David J Feldman
**Ch Bd:* Richard A Mark
CFO: Curt Kroll
CFO: James W Shaffer
VP: R Mills
VP: Brian G Nichols
VP: Brian Nichols
VP: D Redmond
S&M/VP: Timothy C Haeffner
Board of Directors: Christopher W Anderson, Daniel B Carroll, Pamela Carrol Crigler, Samuel P Frieder

KATZ COMMUNICATIONS
See KATZ MEDIA GROUP INC

D-U-N-S 88-354-1302
■ **KATZ MEDIA GROUP INC**
KATZ COMMUNICATIONS
(*Suby of* IHEARTCOMMUNICATIONS INC) ★
125 W 55th St Fl 11, New York, NY 10019-5385
Tel (212) 315-0956 *Founded/Ownrshp* 1997
Sales 25.0MM^E *EMP* 1,300
SIC 7313 Radio, television, publisher representatives; Radio, television, publisher representatives
CEO: Stuart O Olds
Pr: Mark Rivera
CEO: Mark Rosenthal
**CFO:* Robert Damon
Bd of Dir: Pamela Peterson
Ex VP: Stacey Lynn Schulman
Ex VP: Jay Zeitchik
Sr VP: Sari Shaw
**VP:* James E Beloyianis
**VP:* Joe Brewer
VP: Jim Chittick
VP: Mike Donnelly
VP: Tammy Greenberg
VP: Peter Kakoyiannis
VP: Robert Mahoney
VP: Patrick McGee
VP: Vic McGill
VP: Peggy O'Neill
VP: Dominick Patrone
VP: Klein Paul
VP: Janine Quintana

D-U-N-S 80-887-4408
■ **KATZ MILLENNIUM SALES & MARKETING INC**
(*Suby of* KATZ COMMUNICATIONS) ★
125 W 55th St Frnt 3, New York, NY 10019-5936
Tel (212) 424-6000 *Founded/Ownrshp* 1990
Sales 17.6MM^E *EMP* 1,300
SIC 7313 Radio, television, publisher representatives; Radio, television, publisher representatives
Pr: James E Beloyianis
CEO: Stuart O Olds

D-U-N-S 07-070-6734
KATZ SAPPER & MILLER LLP
KSM BUSINESS SERVICES
800 E 96th St Ste 500, Indianapolis, IN 46240-3771
Tel (317) 580-2000 *Founded/Ownrshp* 1942
Sales 34.9MM^E *EMP* 160^E
SIC 8721 Certified public accountant; Certified public accountant
Pt: David Resnick
Pt: Timothy Almack
Pt: Rosanne Ammirati
Pt: Andy Belser
Pt: Jay Benjamin
Pt: Mark Bernstein
Pt: Patrick Brauer
Pt: Scott Brown
Pt: David B Charles
Pt: Mark Flinchum
Pt: Keith Gambrel
Pt: Steven Gaylord
Pt: Bruce Jacobsen
Pt: William Leach
Pt: Ron Lenz
Pt: Kent Manuel
Pt: Karen Mersereau
Pt: Curtis Miller
Pt: Scott Read
Pt: Scott Schuster
Pt: Kevin Sullivan

D-U-N-S 17-510-1401 IMP
KATZKIN LEATHER INC
6868 W Acco St, Montebello, CA 90640-5441
Tel (323) 725-1243 *Founded/Ownrshp* 1998
Sales 102.1MM^E *EMP* 265
SIC 5199 2531 Leather & cut stock; Seats, automobile; Leather & cut stock; Seats, automobile
Pr: Brook Mayberry
Pr: Jim Roberson
VP Mfg: Mario Peregrina
Prd Mgr: Alicia Garcia
Mktg Dir: Miles Hubbard
Mktg Mgr: Dara Ward
Sls Mgr: Omer Aslam
Sls Mgr: Rae Fox
Snr Mgr: Dave O'Connell

KAUAI COFFEE CO
See MASSIMO ZANETTI BEVERAGE USA INC

D-U-N-S 00-913-0832 IMP/EXP
KAUAI COFFEE CO LLC
K-CUP
(*Suby of* KAUAI COFFEE CO) ★
1 Numila Rd, Eleele, HI 96705
Tel (808) 335-3237 *Founded/Ownrshp* 2010
Sales 28.2MM^E *EMP* 75
SIC 5149 5499 2095 Coffee & tea; Coffee; Roasted coffee
VP: Mark Majors
VP: Donn A Soares
VP: Lyle Wilkison
Snr Mgr: Marlene Tomon

D-U-N-S 12-272-1587
KAUAI ISLAND UTILITY COOPERATIVE
4463 Pahee St Ste 1, Lihue, HI 96766-2000
Tel (808) 246-4300 *Founded/Ownrshp* 2002
Sales 179.3MM *EMP* 159^E
Accts Moss Adams Llp Portland Oreg
SIC 4911 Generation, electric power; Generation, electric power
Pr: Dennis Esaki
**Ch Bd:* Allan Smith
**CEO:* David J Bissell
**CFO:* Karissa Jonas
**Treas:* Peter Yukimura
**V Ch Bd:* Jan Tenbruggencate
Comm Man: Jim Kelly
**Prin:* Carol Bain
**Prin:* Karen Baldwin
**Prin:* Patrick Gegen
**Prin:* Calvin Murashige

D-U-N-S 09-769-2644
KAUAI MEDICAL CLINIC
K M C
(*Suby of* HAWAII PACIFIC HEALTH) ★
3-3420b Kuhio Hwy, Lihue, HI 96766-1096
Tel (808) 245-1500 *Founded/Ownrshp* 2008
Sales 7.9MM^E *EMP* 295
SIC 8011 Clinic, operated by physicians; Clinic, operated by physicians
Pr: Kenneth Pierce
**COO:* Lynne Joseph
**VP:* Hilton Raethel

D-U-N-S 19-331-5272
KAUAI SCHOOL DISTRICT
(*Suby of* EDUCATION BOARD) ★
3060 Eiwa St Ste 305, Lihue, HI 96766-1876
Tel (808) 274-3502 *Founded/Ownrshp* 2002
Sales 27.4MM^E *EMP* 645^E
SIC 8211 9411 Public elementary & secondary schools; Administration of educational programs

D-U-N-S 18-278-0569 IMP
KAUAI VETERANS MEMORIAL HOSPITAL
WEST KAUAI MEDICAL CENTER
(*Suby of* HAWAII HEALTH SYSTEMS CORP) ★
4643 Waimea Canyon Dr, Waimea, HI 96796
Tel (808) 338-9431 *Founded/Ownrshp* 1957
Sales 55.5MM^E *EMP* 300
SIC 8062 General medical & surgical hospitals; General medical & surgical hospitals
CEO: Jerry Walker
**CFO:* Mike Perel
Off Mgr: Donnalee Smith
QC Dir: Rebecca Obrien
Psych: Dudley McDaniel
Surgeon: Teresa Sakai
Ansthlgy: Michael Clark
Nrsg Dir: Emma Padilla
HC Dir: Danna Oneil

D-U-N-S 86-898-2583
KAUFFMAN CENTER FOR PERFORMING ARTS
1601 Broadway Blvd, Kansas City, MO 64108-1229
Tel (816) 994-7200 *Founded/Ownrshp* 2008
Sales 27.2MM *EMP* 43
Accts Mayer Hoffman Mccann Pc Leawo
SIC 8412 Arts or science center; Arts or science center
Pr: Paul J Schofer
VP: Amy McAnarney
Mktg Mgr: Jo Keatley
Sls Mgr: Lisa Voss

D-U-N-S 06-280-4737 IMP
KAUFFMAN ENGINEERING INC
701 Ransdell Rd, Lebanon, IN 46052-2385
Tel (765) 483-4919 *Founded/Ownrshp* 1999
Sales 54.3MM^E *EMP* 250
SIC 3679 Harness assemblies for electronic use: wire or cable; Harness assemblies for electronic use: wire or cable
Pr: Michael W Buis
**Treas:* Otto N Frenzel IV
Prd Mgr: Brandon Scobell

D-U-N-S 18-611-6802 IMP
KAUFFMAN TIRE INC
2832 Anvil Block Rd, Ellenwood, GA 30294-2301
Tel (404) 762-4944 *Founded/Ownrshp* 1978
Sales 315.8MM^E *EMP* 600
SIC 5014 5531 Automobile tires & tubes; Automotive tires; Automobile tires & tubes; Automotive tires
Pr: John Kauffman
**CFO:* Susan Reeves
CFO: Reeves Susan
**Ex VP:* Tom Money
Sales Asso: Brian Massey

KAUFMAN & BROAD
See KAUFMAN AND BROAD OF TEXAS INC

D-U-N-S 94-058-0954
■ **KAUFMAN AND BROAD OF TEXAS INC**
KAUFMAN & BROAD
(*Suby of* KB HOME) ★
4800 Fredericksburg Rd, San Antonio, TX 78229-3628
Tel (210) 349-1111 *Founded/Ownrshp* 1995
Sales 34.4MM^E *EMP* 258
SIC 1531 Speculative builder, single-family houses; Speculative builder, single-family houses
Pt: John E Goodwin Jr
VP: Michael Moore
VP: Herb Quiroga

D-U-N-S 06-341-6606
KAUFMAN AND CANOLES PC (INC)
150 W Main St Ste 1800, Norfolk, VA 23510-1681
Tel (757) 624-3000 *Founded/Ownrshp* 1951
Sales 39.5MM^E *EMP* 235
SIC 8111 General practice law office; General practice law office
Pr: Gus J James
Pr: Carrie Moore
**Sec:* John A Lynn
Bd of Dir: Kristan Burch
Bd of Dir: Laura Geringer Gross
Trst: Alvin Anderson
**VP:* Vincent J Mastracco Jr
VP: Virginia B Vernon
CIO: Sandra Stovall
Genl Couns: Alfred Randolph Jr
Counsel: Michael E Barney

D-U-N-S 00-385-6143 IMP
KAUFMAN CO INC (MA)
19 Walkhill Rd, Norwood, MA 02062-3522
Tel (781) 255-1000 *Founded/Ownrshp* 1929
Sales 33.7MM^E *EMP* 50
SIC 5085 5072 Industrial tools; Hardware
Pr: Norman B Kaufman

**Treas:* Daniel Kaufman
VP: Howard Kaufman
**VP:* Jeffrey Kaufman
IT Man: Louis Kaufman
Sls Mgr: Doug Crowe
Sales Asso: Michael Dowling
Sales Asso: Jack Houston

D-U-N-S 00-452-3288 IMP
KAUFMAN CONTAINER CO (OH)
1000 Keystone Pkwy # 100, Cleveland, OH 44135-5119
Tel (216) 898-2000 *Founded/Ownrshp* 1910, 1963
Sales 60.7MM^E *EMP* 128
SIC 5085 2759 Industrial supplies; Plastic bottles; Glass bottles; Screen printing; Labels & seals: printing; Industrial supplies; Plastic bottles; Glass bottles; Screen printing; Labels & seals: printing
CEO: Roger Seid
**Pr:* Ken Slater
**Treas:* Anita Seid
**VP:* Charles Borowiak
**VP:* Roderick Cywinski
**VP:* Jeffery Gross
**VP:* Karen D Melton
MIS Mgr: Larry Keilin
Prd Mgr: Gwen Chrulski

D-U-N-S 17-724-7905
KAUFMAN DOLOWICH VOLUCK & GONZO LLP
KDVG LAW
135 Crossways Park Dr D, Woodbury, NY 11797-2008
Tel (516) 364-1935 *Founded/Ownrshp* 1986
Sales 29.0MM^E *EMP* 140^E
SIC 8111 General practice attorney, lawyer; General practice attorney, lawyer
Genl Pt: Arthur Kaufman
**Pt:* Michael A Kaufman
Mng Pt: Ivan Dolowich
Mng Pt: Kevin Mattessich
V Ch: Mark Mao
CFO: Jeffrey Knee
Mktg Dir: Tricia McCoy
Mktg Dir: Amy Selich
Counsel: Jeffery Meyer

D-U-N-S 00-504-4169
KAUFMAN ENGINEERED SYSTEMS INC (OH)
1260 Wtrville Monclova Rd, Waterville, OH 43566-1066
Tel (419) 878-9727 *Founded/Ownrshp* 1957
Sales 28.0MM^E *EMP* 72
SIC 3567 3565 Industrial furnaces & ovens; Packaging machinery
Pr: Andrew J Quinn
**Pr:* Charles R Kaufman
Pr: Ted Kaufman
**VP:* Robert J Kaufman
Sfty Mgr: Robert Johnson
Natl Sales: Zac Boehm
Natl Sales: Scott Stiverson
Natl Sales: James Walsh
VP Sls: Nick Kaufman

D-U-N-S 02-930-7782
KAUFMAN INDEPENDENT SCHOOL DISTRICT
1000 S Houston St, Kaufman, TX 75142-2214
Tel (972) 932-2622 *Founded/Ownrshp* 1936
Sales 27.7MM^E *EMP* 500
Accts Hankins Eastup Deaton Tonn
SIC 8211 Public elementary & secondary schools; Public elementary & secondary schools
IT Man: Kathy Chambers
Sls Mgr: Dan Clark

D-U-N-S 60-738-1878
KAUFMAN LYNN CONSTRUCTION INC
4850T Rex Ave Ste 300, Boca Raton, FL 33431-4496
Tel (561) 361-6700 *Founded/Ownrshp* 1989
Sales 69.8MM *EMP* 99^E
Accts Dglf Orlando Florida
SIC 1542 Commercial & office building, new construction; Commercial & office building, new construction
Pr: Michael I Kaufman
**COO:* Christopher Long
**CFO:* Douglas Simms
Ex VP: Sam Doggart
**Sr VP:* Frank White
**VP:* Timothy Bonczek
**VP:* Garret Southern
Mng Dir: Neil Carson
Dir IT: Seon Johnson
VP Opers: Ben Baffer

D-U-N-S 07-600-5545
KAUFMAN ROSSIN & CO A PROFESSIONAL ASSOCIATION
2699 S Byshr Dr Ste 500, Miami, FL 33133-5486
Tel (305) 858-5600 *Founded/Ownrshp* 1962
Sales 53.0MM^E *EMP* 380
SIC 8699 Athletic organizations; Athletic organizations
Pr: James R Kaufman
CEO: James R Kaufman
COO: Skip Shearman
**Trst Ofcr:* John R Anzivino
Trst Ofcr: Deborah L Frishman
Trst Ofcr: Scott L Goldberger
Trst Ofcr: Mark Scott
**VP:* Steven M Berwick
**VP:* Steven M Demar
**VP:* Kenneth S Dubow
**VP:* Miguel G Farra
**VP:* Patrick Gannon
**VP:* Blain Heckaman
**VP:* Greg Levy
**VP:* Gerald A Michelson
**VP:* Manuel Murga
**VP:* Jay H Rossin
**VP:* Henry W Schade
**VP:* Keith S Scharkey
**VP:* Robert A Stone
Dir Bus: Christine Egan
Board of Directors: Jorge Decardenas

D-U-N-S 92-903-8610 EXP
KAUFMAN TRAILERS INC
702 N Silver St, Lexington, NC 27292-6192
Tel (336) 790-6800 *Founded/Ownrshp* 1995
Sales 27.8MM^E *EMP* 30
SIC 5599 5084 3799 3537 Utility trailers; Trailers, industrial; Trailers & trailer equipment; Industrial trucks & tractors
Pr: Robb Kaufman
**VP:* Tim Carter
Mktg Mgr: Chad Blackman
Sales Asso: Sandra Hardwick

D-U-N-S 17-274-6083
KAUKAUNA AREA SCHOOL DISTRICT
1701 County Road Ce, Kaukauna, WI 54130-3916
Tel (920) 766-6100 *Founded/Ownrshp* 1886
Sales 26.5MM^E *EMP* 400
Accts Kerber Rose & Associates S
SIC 8211 Public elementary & secondary schools; School board; Public elementary & secondary schools; School board

D-U-N-S 14-425-7933
KAUKAUNA UTILITIES
777 Island St, Kaukauna, WI 54130-2559
Tel (920) 766-5721 *Founded/Ownrshp* 2004
Sales 68.0MM^E *EMP* 82^E
SIC 4911 Electric services
Pr: Pete Prast

D-U-N-S 00-533-5906
KAUL GLOVE AND MFG CO
CHOCTAW-KAUL DISTRIBUTION CO
3540 Vinewood St, Detroit, MI 48208-2363
Tel (313) 894-9494 *Founded/Ownrshp* 1972
Sales 41.5MM^E *EMP* 125
SIC 2381 3151 5136 Fabric dress & work gloves; Gloves, leather: work; Work clothing, men's & boys'; Fabric dress & work gloves; Gloves, leather: work; Work clothing, men's & boys'
CEO: Kenny Tubby
**CFO:* Michael G Conniff Jr
**VP:* Anthony C Naso
**Exec:* David Shall
Dir IT: Richard Noel
IT Man: Rick Breckenridge
Natl Sales: Jeff Klemish
VP Sls: David W Shall

D-U-N-S 09-997-2465
KAUP PHARMACY INC
HEALTH MART
110 E Butler St, Fort Recovery, OH 45846
Tel (419) 375-2323 *Founded/Ownrshp* 1980
Sales 23.0MM^E *EMP* 105
SIC 5912 5999 8082 Drug stores; Hospital equipment & supplies; Visiting nurse service
Pr: Lorraine M Kaup
**Sec:* Gerald M Kaup
Opers Mgr: Greg Schmitz

D-U-N-S 10-140-5397 IMP
■ **KAUTEX INC**
(*Suby of* TEXTRON INC) ★
750 Stephenson Hwy, Troy, MI 48083-1103
Tel (248) 616-5100 *Founded/Ownrshp* 1996
Sales 2.6MMM^E *EMP* 16,000
SIC 3714 Motor vehicle parts & accessories; Instrument board assemblies, motor vehicle; Bumpers & bumperettes, motor vehicle; Motor vehicle parts & accessories; Instrument board assemblies, motor vehicle; Bumpers & bumperettes, motor vehicle
Pr: Vicente Perez-Lucerga
COO: Hanno Neizer
Treas: Mary F Lovejoy
Ex VP: Edward Certisimo
Ex VP: Klaus Konig
Sr VP: Janes Heffner
VP: Rob Abfall
VP: Mark Ankenbauer
**VP:* John H Bracken
VP: Mira Eigler
VP: Klaus Esser
VP: Arnold M Friedman
VP: Greg Fuller
VP: James M Heethuis
VP: Paul Luft
VP: Andrew Quibell
VP: Norman B Richter
VP: Paul Sullivan
VP: Ann T Willamson

D-U-N-S 06-583-3001
KAVLI FOUNDATION
1801 Solar Dr Ste 250, Oxnard, CA 93030-8297
Tel (805) 983-6000 *Founded/Ownrshp* 2000
Sales 22.9MM *EMP* 1
SIC 8299 Educational services; Educational services
Pr: Fred Kavli
Comm Dir: James Cohen

D-U-N-S 00-826-7262 EXP
KAVLICO CORP
(*Suby of* SENSATA TECHNOLOGIES INC) ★
1461 Lawrence Dr, Thousand Oaks, CA 91320-1311
Tel (805) 523-2000 *Founded/Ownrshp* 2015
Sales 287.5MM^E *EMP* 1,400
SIC 3679 3829 3823 Transducers, electrical; Measuring & controlling devices; Industrial instrmnts msrmnt display/control process variable; Transducers, electrical; Measuring & controlling devices; Industrial instrmnts msrmnt display/control process variable
CEO: Eric Pilaud
COO: Carmine Villani
CFO: John Laboskey
VP: William Estes
VP: Rick Hubbard
VP: Deanna Luna
VP: Kassie Parker
Exec: Jason Thorpe
Prgrm Mgr: Lawrence Hutton
Prgrm Mgr: Phil Roessler
Genl Mgr: Bob Ciurczak

D-U-N-S 03-759-1419 IMP
■ **KAVO DENTAL TECHNOLOGIES LLC**
PELTON & CRANE
(*Suby of* DANAHER CORP) ★
11729 Fruehauf Dr, Charlotte, NC 28273-6507
Tel (888) 275-5286 *Founded/Ownrshp* 1980
Sales 106.4MM^E *EMP* 465
SIC 5047 Dental equipment & supplies; Dental equipment & supplies
Pr: Ronie Seaford
Bd of Dir: Scott Fraser
VP: Jeff Thibadeau
VP: Robert Winter
Exec: Steve Kelly
Exec: Jason Spencer
Mng Dir: Henner Witte
Genl Mgr: Mike Rock
Snr Sftwr: Nathan Hemmer
Dir IT: Mike Sherman
IT Man: Jamie Allen

KAW VALLEY CENTER
See KVC BEHAVIORAL HEALTHCARE INC

D-U-N-S 04-213-8532
KAW VALLEY COMPANIES INC
KAW VALLEY SAND & GRAVEL
5600 Kansas Ave, Kansas City, KS 66106-1147
Tel (913) 281-9950 *Founded/Ownrshp* 1998
Sales 33.6MM^E *EMP* 69
SIC 5032 1611 Sand, construction; Highway & street construction
Pr: Benjamin Kates
VP Opers: Jason Jacobson

D-U-N-S 00-883-6934
KAW VALLEY ELECTRIC COOPERATIVE INC
1100 Sw Auburn Rd, Topeka, KS 66615-1426
Tel (785) 478-3444 *Founded/Ownrshp* 1937
Sales 21.3MM *EMP* 32^E
Accts Schmidt & Company Llc Lee S
SIC 4911 Distribution, electric power; Distribution, electric power
Pr: Daniel O'Brien
Genl Mgr: Jerry Manning

D-U-N-S 10-854-1236
KAW VALLEY ENGINEERING INC
2319 N Jackson St, Junction City, KS 66441-4724
Tel (785) 762-5040 *Founded/Ownrshp* 1982
Sales 20.4MM^E *EMP* 100
SIC 8711 8713 0711 7389 Civil engineering; Surveying services; Soil testing services; Inspection & testing services
Pr: Leon Osbourn
**Treas:* Michael Osborne
Dir Bus: Jennifer Elliott
Off Mgr: Gary Leeds
Board of Directors: Steve Gabay

KAW VALLEY SAND & GRAVEL
See KAW VALLEY COMPANIES INC

D-U-N-S 11-893-4710
KAW VALLEY SAND AND GRAVEL INC
(*Suby of* KAW VALLEY COMPANIES INC) ★
5600 Kansas Ave, Kansas City, KS 66106-1147
Tel (913) 281-9950 *Founded/Ownrshp* 1984
Sales 23.5MM^E *EMP* 69
SIC 5032 Sand, construction; Gravel
Pr: Ben Kates
Sls Mgr: Dan Hays

D-U-N-S 02-358-2303
KAWA CAPITAL MANAGEMENT INC
21500 Biscayne Blvd # 700, Aventura, FL 33180-1256
Tel (305) 560-5200 *Founded/Ownrshp* 2007
Sales 35.3MM^E *EMP* 82
SIC 8741 Financial management for business
Mng Pt: Daniel Ades
**Pt:* Felipe Lemos
Software D: Jordan Fishman

D-U-N-S 00-958-4871 IMP/EXP
KAWAI AMERICA CORP
(*Suby of* KAWAI MUSICAL INSTRUMENTS MANUFACTURING CO., LTD.)
2055 E University Dr, Compton, CA 90220-6411
Tel (310) 631-1771 *Founded/Ownrshp* 1963
Sales 25.0MM^E *EMP* 100
SIC 5099 Musical instruments; Pianos; Musical instruments; Pianos
Pr: Hirotaka Kawai
**Pr:* Naoki Mori
Ofcr: Mark Wisner

D-U-N-S 62-096-0732
KAWAILOA DEVELOPMENT LLP
POIPU BAY RESORT
1571 Poipu Rd Ste 3063, Koloa, HI 96756-9402
Tel (808) 742-1234 *Founded/Ownrshp* 1987
Sales 47.7MM^E *EMP* 1,000
SIC 7011 7992 Hotels & motels; Public golf courses; Hotels & motels; Public golf courses
Pt: Jun Fukada
Chf Mktg O: Katy Britzmann
Exec: Mike Borsdorf
IT Man: Lydia Villanueva
Sls Dir: Ann Takechi
Sls Mgr: Sherrie Holl

D-U-N-S 04-660-3379 IMP/EXP
KAWASAKI MOTORS CORP USA
(*Suby of* KAWASAKI HEAVY INDUSTRIES, LTD.)
9950 Jeronimo Rd, Irvine, CA 92618-2084
Tel (949) 837-4683 *Founded/Ownrshp* 1967
Sales 234.9MM^E *EMP* 530
SIC 5012 5013 5084 5091 Motorcycles; Motorcycle parts; Engines, gasoline; Boats, canoes, watercrafts & equipment; Motorcycles; Motorcycle parts; Engines, gasoline; Boats, canoes, watercrafts & equipment
Pr: Masatoshi Tsurutani
**Ofcr:* Richard N Beattie
VP: Gary Bozych
**Exec:* Terunori Kitajima
Dist Mgr: Russell Corey
Dist Mgr: Chip Dongara
Dist Mgr: John Kochanek
Dist Mgr: Scott Lincourt
Dist Mgr: David Pelt
Dist Mgr: John Rathyen
Dist Mgr: Michael Webster

D-U-N-S 17-556-6215 IMP
KAWASAKI MOTORS MANUFACTURING CORP USA
(*Suby of* KAWASAKI HEAVY INDUSTRIES, LTD.)
6600 Nw 27th St, Lincoln, NE 68524-8904
Tel (402) 476-6600 *Founded/Ownrshp* 1981
Sales 318.2MM^E *EMP* 2,000
SIC 3732 3799 All terrain vehicles (ATV); Fishing boats: lobster, crab, oyster, etc.: small; Motorcycles & related parts; Jet skis; Recreational vehicles; All terrain vehicles (ATV)
Pr: Matt Kurushima
VP: Richard Grundman
**Genl Mgr:* Naoshi Kato
Prd Mgr: Nick Hatfield
Prd Mgr: Brad Nelson
Prd Mgr: Jason Niemann
Snr Mgr: Yoshinori Tsumiyama

D-U-N-S 18-577-5335 IMP
KAWASAKI RAIL CAR INC
(*Suby of* KAWASAKI MOTORS MANUFACTURING CORP USA) ★
29 Wells Ave Bldg 4, Yonkers, NY 10701-8815
Tel (914) 376-4700 *Founded/Ownrshp* 2004
Sales 57.3MM^E *EMP* 230^E
SIC 3743 Railroad equipment, except locomotives; Railway motor cars; Train cars & equipment, freight or passenger; Railroad equipment, except locomotives; Railway motor cars; Train cars & equipment, freight or passenger
CEO: Hiroji Iwasaki
**Pr:* Yuichi Yamamoto
COO: Michael Doyle
**Ex VP:* Yoshinori Kanehana
Ex VP: Koyo Kondo
VP: Akira Matsufuji
Genl Mgr: Steven Vangellow
Snr Sftwr: Peter Marcato
Snr Ntwrk: Tirso Laygan
QA Dir: Peter Gilberg
QA Dir: Ed Parkerson

KAWASAKI RBTICS N A TRNING CTR
See KAWASAKI ROBOTICS (USA) INC

D-U-N-S 62-339-9748 IMP
KAWASAKI ROBOTICS (USA) INC
KAWASAKI RBTICS N A TRNING CTR
(*Suby of* KAWASAKI MOTORS CORP USA) ★
28140 Lakeview Dr, Wixom, MI 48393-3157
Tel (855) 855-1414 *Founded/Ownrshp* 1989
Sales 49.9MM^E *EMP* 72
SIC 5571 7699 Motorcycle dealers; Industrial machinery & equipment repair
Pr: Yafuo Chihara
**Treas:* Tomohiro Otsuki
VP: Sudhir Jain
QI Cn Mgr: Simon Jeyapalan
Sales Exec: Troy Krueger
Snr Mgr: Robert Caulkins
Snr Mgr: Tetsuya Yoshida

D-U-N-S 07-463-4593
KAWEAH DELTA HEALTH CARE DISTRICT GUILD
KAWEAH DELTA MEDICAL CENTER
400 W Mineral King Ave, Visalia, CA 93291-6237
Tel (559) 624-2000 *Founded/Ownrshp* 1961
Sales 452.4MM^E *EMP* 3,200
SIC 8062 Hospital, AMA approved residency; Hospital, AMA approved residency
CEO: Donna Archer
Pr: Harry Lively
**CEO:* Lindsay K Mann
COO: Thomas Rayner
**CFO:* Gary Herbst
Ofcr: Chadwick Gonsalves
Ofcr: Sherri Shannon
VP: Janet Danielson
Exec: Debbie Wood
Dir Inf Cn: Katherine Wittman
Dir Risk M: Barbara Maxwell
Dir Lab: David Peterson
Dir Rad: Gordon Tye

KAWEAH DELTA MEDICAL CENTER
See KAWEAH DELTA HEALTH CARE DISTRICT GUILD

D-U-N-S 18-386-5278
KAWERAK INC
500 Seppala Dr, Nome, AK 99762
Tel (907) 443-5231 *Founded/Ownrshp* 1973
Sales 29.1MM *EMP* 200
Accts Kohler Schmitt & Hutchison P
SIC 8322 8331 8351 8742 8641 Aid to families with dependent children (AFDC); Job training & vocational rehabilitation services; Head start center, except in conjunction with school; Management consulting services; Civic social & fraternal associations; Aid to families with dependent children (AFDC); Job training & vocational rehabilitation services; Head start center, except in conjunction with school; Management consulting services; Civic social & fraternal associations
Pr: Loretta Bullard
**Treas:* Merlin Koonooka
**VP:* Melanie Bahnko
**VP:* Melanie Edwards
VP: Pearl Mikulski
VP: Dawn Salesky
IT Man: William Gemar
IT Man: Donna Ray
Sls Mgr: Kenneth Kingeekuk
Sls Mgr: Patrick Omiak

D-U-N-S 00-175-8333 IMP/EXP
■ **KAWNEER CO INC**
(*Suby of* ALCOA INC) ★
555 Guthridge Ct, Norcross, GA 30092-3503
Tel (770) 449-5555 *Founded/Ownrshp* 1906, 1998
Sales 406.1MM^E *EMP* 2,900

SIC 3442 3446 Metal doors; Architectural metalwork; Metal doors; Architectural metalwork
Pr: Glen Morrison
**CFO:* Peter Hong
**VP:* Bob Leylend
**VP:* Leslie McDole
VP: Henry Taylor
Exec: Jane Ashley
Area Mgr: Matthew McIntyre
Dir IT: Roger Rainey
VP Opers: Tim Cunningham
Prd Mgr: Brian Porbeck
Manager: Gerry Portelli

D-U-N-S 06-744-8076
KAY AND ASSOCIATES INC
165 N Arlington Hts 150, Buffalo Grove, IL 60089-1783
Tel (847) 255-8444 *Founded/Ownrshp* 1960
Sales 72.5MM^E *EMP* 700
SIC 8711 Consulting engineer; Consulting engineer
Ch Bd: Donald J Kay
**Pr:* Gregory Kay
**Ex VP:* Brad Kayv
**VP:* Rick Bell
**VP:* Steve Perille
**VP:* Jim Scroggs
Exec: Robert Wilcox
Adm Dir: Louise Huff
Adm Dir: Josh Kay
Prgrm Mgr: Jim Pinder
Dir IT: Jay Fenneman

D-U-N-S 08-839-7021
KAY AUTOMOTIVE DISTRIBUTORS INC
14650 Calvert St, Van Nuys, CA 91411-2807
Tel (818) 781-6850 *Founded/Ownrshp* 1980
Sales 23.9MM^E *EMP* 95
SIC 5013 Automotive supplies & parts; Automotive supplies & parts
Pr: Jona Kardish
**Pr:* Jona Karadish
**Sec:* Annette Karadish

KAY AUTOMOTIVE GRAPHICS
See KAY SCREEN PRINTING INC

D-U-N-S 05-189-2677 IMP
KAY BEER DISTRIBUTING INC
1881 Commerce Dr, De Pere, WI 54115-9227
Tel (920) 336-2267 *Founded/Ownrshp* 1970
Sales 28.3MM^E *EMP* 65
SIC 5181 5149 Beer & other fermented malt liquors; Water, distilled; Tea; Soft drinks
Pr: Thomas Kolocheski II
**VP:* Donna Kolocheski
Exec: Paul De Grave
Sls Mgr: Todd Pennings

D-U-N-S 00-446-5696
■ KAY CAPITAL CO
ADVANCED VEHICLES
(*Suby of* PARK-OHIO INDUSTRIES INC) ★
1441 Chardon Rd, Cleveland, OH 44117-1510
Tel (216) 531-1010 *Founded/Ownrshp* 1995
Sales 20.5MM^E *EMP* 75
SIC 3542 3537 3549 3541 Machine tools, metal forming type; Lift trucks, industrial: fork, platform, straddle, etc.; Metalworking machinery; Machine tools, metal cutting type
Ch Bd: Edward Crawford
**Pr:* Tim Dunagan
**V Ch Bd:* Felix Tarorick

D-U-N-S 00-323-7021 IMP/EXP
■ KAY CHEMICAL CO (NC)
(*Suby of* ECOLAB INC) ★
8300 Capital Dr, Greensboro, NC 27409-9790
Tel (336) 668-7290 *Founded/Ownrshp* 1963
Sales 136.8MM^E *EMP* 620
SIC 2842 Specialty cleaning preparations; Specialty cleaning preparations
Pr: Ching-Meng Chew
**CFO:* George G Harris
Bd of Dir: Douglas Baker
Bd of Dir: Barbara Beck
Bd of Dir: Leslie Biller
Bd of Dir: Jerry Grundhofer
Bd of Dir: Joel Johnson
Bd of Dir: Jerry Levin
Bd of Dir: Robert Lumpkins
Bd of Dir: Richard D Schutter
Bd of Dir: John Zillmer
**Sr VP:* Bob Sherwwod
VP: Doug Douthitt
**VP:* Michael A Hickey
**VP:* Robert Inchaustegui
**VP:* Judy M McNamara

D-U-N-S 07-733-0710
KAY COUNTY OKLAHOMA HOSPITAL CO LLC
PONCA CITY MEDICAL CENTER
1900 N 14th St, Ponca City, OK 74601-2035
Tel (580) 765-3321 *Founded/Ownrshp* 2005
Sales 55.3MM^E *EMP* 400^E
SIC 8062 Pediatrician; General medical & surgical hospitals
CEO: Andy Wachtel
Chf Rad: Amy Kirby
CEO: Nikia Beene
Dir OR: Marci Langston
Dir Risk M: Beth Moore
Dir Lab: Charles Snow
Dir Rad: Gary Jernigan
Dir Rx: Rick McCumber
Dir Env Sv: J Wyatt
Prin: Ahmad S Agha
Prin: Michael Walker

D-U-N-S 00-778-0166
KAY ELECTRIC COOPERATIVE
300 W Doolin Ave, Blackwell, OK 74631-1648
Tel (580) 363-1260 *Founded/Ownrshp* 1937
Sales 35.8MM *EMP* 53^E
SIC 4911 Distribution, electric power; Distribution, electric power
CEO: Timothy Rodriguez
**Pr:* Max Hohmann
**COO:* JD Soulek
**VP:* Verl Brorsen
VP: Steve Harden
Ex Dir: Kent McAninch

D-U-N-S 01-109-7409 IMP
KAY HONDA
D C H KAY HONDA
(*Suby of* DCH NORTH AMERICA INC.)
200 State Route 36, Eatontown, NJ 07724-2512
Tel (732) 542-5900 *Founded/Ownrshp* 1944
Sales 22.0MM^E *EMP* 60
SIC 5511 Automobiles, new & used; Automobiles, new & used
Pr: Shau-Wai Lam
**Sec:* Billy Wong
**VP:* Barney Ghaw
Sls Mgr: Michael Lyttle
Sls Mgr: Anthony Paparella
Sales Asso: Justin Amorin
Sales Asso: Nader Awad
Sales Asso: Ray Furslew
Sales Asso: Ed Garrigal
Sales Asso: Dave Radice
Sales Asso: Steve Simon

KAY JEWELLERS
See STERLING INC

KAY JNNINGS SPRINGFIELD TOYOTA
See JENNINGS MOTOR CO INC

D-U-N-S 00-517-7506
KAY MANUFACTURING CO (IL)
602 State St, Calumet City, IL 60409-2041
Tel (708) 862-6800 *Founded/Ownrshp* 1946, 1987
Sales 25.3MM^E *EMP* 150
SIC 3714 Transmission housings or parts, motor vehicle; Transmission housings or parts, motor vehicle
Pr: Brian Pelke
**COO:* Steven C Pelke
**VP:* Scott Dekker
Admn Mgr: John Petro
QA Dir: Roger Bratcher
QA Dir: Kevin Grover
Plnt Mgr: Jeff Bond
Plnt Mgr: Julio Martinez
Prd Mgr: Michael Groos
Ql Cn Mgr: David Jenkins

D-U-N-S 04-243-8176 IMP
KAY SCREEN PRINTING INC
KAY AUTOMOTIVE GRAPHICS
57 Kay Industrial Dr, Lake Orion, MI 48359-1832
Tel (248) 377-4999 *Founded/Ownrshp* 1968
Sales 54.4MM^E *EMP* 300^E
SIC 2752 2396 Commercial printing, lithographic; Automotive & apparel trimmings; General automotive repair shops; Commercial printing, lithographic; Automotive & apparel trimmings
Pr: Joseph Kowalczyk
**CFO:* David Duggan
CFO: Joe Kay
**Ex VP:* Alfred H Bonnell
VP: Lynn Strayer
Sfty Mgr: Joshua Flood
Plnt Mgr: Jim Ruddy
S&M/VP: William Farnen

D-U-N-S 83-305-7073
■ KAY TECHNOLOGY HOLDINGS INC
KANA
(*Suby of* VERINT ACQUISITION LLC) ★
2500 Sand Hill Rd Ste 300, Menlo Park, CA 94025-7063
Tel (650) 289-2481 *Founded/Ownrshp* 2014
Sales 138.6MM *EMP* 11^E
SIC 7372 Prepackaged software; Prepackaged software
Pr: Jason Klein
Exec: Justine Herman
Prin: Thomas Barnds

D-U-N-S 13-104-3189
KAYA ASSOCIATES INC
101 Quality Cir Nw # 120, Huntsville, AL 35806-4534
Tel (256) 382-8084 *Founded/Ownrshp* 2003
Sales 34.2MM^E *EMP* 195^E
SIC 8742 Management consulting services; Management consulting services
Pr: John H Prince
**COO:* Robert Dunn
Brnch Mgr: Steve Scott
Software D: Joshua Etress
Software D: Renia Glover
Genl Couns: Brendan Prince
Snr Mgr: Thomas Knight

D-U-N-S 17-530-8845
■ KAYAK SOFTWARE CORP
KAYAK.COM
(*Suby of* PRICELINE GROUP INC) ★
7 Market St, Stamford, CT 06902-5810
Tel (203) 899-3100 *Founded/Ownrshp* 2012
Sales 87.1MM^E *EMP* 185
SIC 4813 ;
CEO: D Stephen Hafner
Pr: Brett Cochran
**Pr:* Paul English
**CFO:* Melissa H Reiter
**Chf Mktg O:* Robert M Birge
VP: Ian Akehurst
VP: Mike Bernardo
**Prin:* Joel E Cutler
**Prin:* Terrell B Jones
**Prin:* Michael Moritz
**Prin:* Hendrik W Nelis

KAYAK.COM
See KAYAK SOFTWARE CORP

D-U-N-S 61-299-9961 EXP
KAYCAN LTD
(*Suby of* KAYCAN LTEE)
402 Boyer Cir, Williston, VT 05495-8924
Tel (802) 865-0114 *Founded/Ownrshp* 1990
Sales 45.0MM *EMP* 250
SIC 5033 Roofing, siding & insulation; Roofing, siding & insulation
Pr: Lionel Dubrofsky
Manager: Joe Conohan

KAYCO
See KENOVER MARKETING CORP

D-U-N-S 94-305-8698
KAYDEN INDUSTRIES (USA) INC
(*Suby of* KAYDEN INDUSTRIES INC)
9400 Grogans Mill Rd # 305, Spring, TX 77380-3642
Tel (607) 739-2565 *Founded/Ownrshp* 2007
Sales 41.9MM^E *EMP* 80
SIC 5082 Oil field equipment
CEO: Russ Fisher
**Pr:* Anthony Foscolos
**COO:* Darcy Smith
VP: David Van Dvliert

D-U-N-S 10-163-3782 IMP/EXP
KAYDON CORP
(*Suby of* ATLAS MANAGEMENT INC) ★
2723 S State St Ste 300, Ann Arbor, MI 48104-6188
Tel (734) 747-7025 *Founded/Ownrshp* 2013
Sales 566.0MM^E *EMP* 2,187^E
SIC 3562 3569 3592 3053 3621 3679 Ball & roller bearings; Ball bearings & parts; Roller bearings & parts; Filters, general line: industrial; Pistons & piston rings; Gaskets & sealing devices; Sliprings, for motors or generators; Electronic circuits; Ball & roller bearings; Ball bearings & parts; Roller bearings & parts; Filters, general line: industrial; Pistons & piston rings; Gaskets & sealing devices; Sliprings, for motors or generators; Electronic circuits
Pr: James O'Leary
COO: Pierre Demandolx
**CFO:* Timothy J Heasley
**Sr VP:* Peter C Dechants
**VP:* Debra K Crane
VP: Tracy Crosson
VP: John Genova
**VP:* Laura Kowalchik
VP: Kevin Lechene
VP: Les Miller
CIO: Greg Billingsley

D-U-N-S 80-115-9013
KAYE GROCERY HOLDINGS INC
KAYE'S FOOD MARKET
2900 Kirby Rd Ste 6, Memphis, TN 38119-8205
Tel (901) 737-5055 *Founded/Ownrshp* 1992
Sales 53.3MM^E *EMP* 474
SIC 5411 Grocery stores, independent; Grocery stores, independent
Pr: Joel Marshall Kaye
**Pr:* Matthew Kaye
**Prin:* Matthew Houston Kaye

D-U-N-S 07-329-5230
KAYE SCHOLER LLP
250 W 55th St Fl 4, New York, NY 10019-7649
Tel (212) 836-8000 *Founded/Ownrshp* 2007
Sales 273.0MM^E *EMP* 1,200
SIC 8111 General practice law office; General practice law office
Mng Pt: Barry Willner
Pt: James Blank
Pt: Gary Gartner
Pt: Andrew B Harris
Pt: Peter L Haviland
Pt: Jeffrey Scheine
Pt: Gary R Silverman
Pt: Rhonda R Trotter
Pt: William E Wallace Jr
Mng Pt: Michael B Solow
Ch Bd: Stanley Pierre-Louis
Ch Bd: David J Stoll
CFO: Rod Dolan
Ofcr: Cliff Hook
Dir Bus: Josette Winograd

D-U-N-S 14-424-7558
KAYE-SMITH ENTERPRISES INC
700 112th Ave Ne Ste 302, Bellevue, WA 98004-5106
Tel (425) 455-0923 *Founded/Ownrshp* 1964
Sales 32.8MM^E *EMP* 162^E
SIC 2761 Manifold business forms; Manifold business forms
Pr: Alexander M Smith
**Treas:* Lester M Smith
**VP:* Bernice R Smith
Dir IT: Steve Kawaski

D-U-N-S 00-104-6432 IMP
KAYEM FOODS INC (MA)
75 Arlington St, Chelsea, MA 02150-2365
Tel (781) 933-3115 *Founded/Ownrshp* 1909
Sales 132.1MM^E *EMP* 490
SIC 2011 2013 Meat packing plants; Smoked meats from purchased meat; Sausages from purchased meat; Meat packing plants; Smoked meats from purchased meat; Sausages from purchased meat
Pr: Ralph O Smith
COO: Carl Colson
**Treas:* Stephan Monkiewicz
**VP:* Peter Monkiewicz
IT Man: Glenn Bolvin
IT Man: Bob Kufferman
IT Man: Mark Whitney
Plnt Mgr: Steve Tapley
Prd Mgr: Ernesto Barrezueta
Sales Exec: Joellen West
VP Sls: Chris Reisner
Board of Directors: Michael Mulrain, Lawrence Siff

D-U-N-S 07-445-6948
KAYENTA UNIFIED SCHOOL
Us Hwy 163 Mp395, Kayenta, AZ 86033
Tel (928) 697-2499 *Founded/Ownrshp* 1957
Sales 19.6MM^E *EMP* 380
SIC 8211 Public elementary & secondary schools; Public elementary & secondary schools
HC Dir: Paulson Brontson

KAYE'S FOOD MARKET
See KAYE GROCERY HOLDINGS INC

D-U-N-S 07-182-2978
KAYLA SOSSIN
1446 Newton St Nw, Washington, DC 20010-3117
Tel (631) 560-8463 *Founded/Ownrshp* 2011
Sales 26.5MM^E *EMP* 248^E
SIC 8011 Medical centers
Owner: Kayla Sossin

D-U-N-S 78-998-5467
KAYNE ANDERSON CAPITAL ADVISORS LP
1800 Avenue Of The Stars 2nd, Los Angeles, CA 90067-4201
Tel (800) 231-7414 *Founded/Ownrshp* 1994
Sales 3.0MM *EMP* 300
SIC 6282 Investment advice
Ch: Richard Kayne
Mng Pt: Edward Cerny
CEO: Robert Sinnott
Ofcr: Judy Ridder
VP: Gifford Wilkerson
Mng Dir: Frank Arentowicz Jr

D-U-N-S 11-540-2315
KAYNE ANDERSON INVESTMENT MANAGEMENT INC
1800 Avenue Of The Stars # 200, Los Angeles, CA 90067-4204
Tel (310) 556-2721 *Founded/Ownrshp* 1984
Sales 20.6MM^E *EMP* 67
SIC 8742 6211 6726 6282 Financial consultant; Investment firm, general brokerage; Investment offices; Investment advice
Ch Bd: Richard Kayne
**CEO:* John Anderson
CFO: John Daley
**Treas:* Paul Stapleton
**CIO:* Bob Sinnott

KAYO CLOTHING COMPANY
See KAYO OF CALIFORNIA INC

D-U-N-S 05-225-3291
KAYO OF CALIFORNIA INC (CA)
KAYO CLOTHING COMPANY
161 W 39th St, Los Angeles, CA 90037-1080
Tel (323) 233-6107 *Founded/Ownrshp* 1968
Sales 22.5MM^E *EMP* 50
SIC 2337 2339 Skirts, separate: women's, misses' & juniors'; Sportswear, women's; Shorts (outerwear): women's, misses' & juniors'; Slacks: women's, misses' & juniors'; Skirts, separate: women's, misses' & juniors'; Sportswear, women's; Shorts (outerwear): women's, misses' & juniors'; Slacks: women's, misses' & juniors'
CEO: Jeff Michaels
**Ch Bd:* Jack Ostrovsky
**Pr:* Jeffrey Michaels
**CFO:* Annabelle Wall
**VP:* Jonathan Kaye

D-U-N-S 00-792-0796 IMP
■ KAYO OIL CO
CONOCO
(*Suby of* PHILLIPS PETROLEUM CO) ★
600 N Dairy Ashford Rd, Houston, TX 77079-1100
Tel (281) 293-1000 *Founded/Ownrshp* 1940, 1959
Sales 367.9MM^E *EMP* 3,450
SIC 5541 5411 Gasoline service stations; Convenience stores, independent; Gasoline service stations; Convenience stores, independent
Pr: Archie Dunham
**Treas:* M W Espinosa
**VP:* J S Hill

KAYSER AUTOMOTIVE GROUP
See FORD KAYSER INC

D-U-N-S 00-148-2033 IMP
KAYSER-ROTH CORP
NO NONSENSE
(*Suby of* GOLDEN LADY COMPANY SPA)
102 Corporate Center Blvd, Greensboro, NC 27408-3172
Tel (336) 852-2030 *Founded/Ownrshp* 1999
Sales 427.8MM^E *EMP* 2,200^E
SIC 2252 2251 5961 8741 3842 Men's, boys' & girls' hosiery; Socks; Women's hosiery, except socks; Women's apparel, mail order; Management services; Surgical appliances & supplies; Men's, boys' & girls' hosiery; Socks; Women's hosiery, except socks; Women's apparel, mail order; Management services; Surgical appliances & supplies
Pr: Kevin Toomey
Ex VP: Julia Townsend
VP: Gianni Orsini
Exec: Joey Schmissrauter
MIS Dir: Kevin Aliff
QA Dir: Donna Lerner
Dir IT: Dave Douglas
IT Man: Denise Washington
Tech Mgr: Stacy Chadwell
Plnt Mgr: Belva Smith
Trfc Mgr: Nancy Davenport

D-U-N-S 09-378-2563
KAYSER-ROTH HOSIERY INC
102 Corporate Center Blvd, Greensboro, NC 27408-3172
Tel (336) 852-2030 *Founded/Ownrshp* 2009
Sales 20.8MM^E *EMP* 150
SIC 2389 2252 Men's miscellaneous accessories; Socks; Men's miscellaneous accessories; Socks
Pr: Kevin Toomey
**CFO:* Todd Howard
**Ex VP:* Julia Townsend
**VP:* Gianni Orsini

D-U-N-S 00-642-4220 IMP
KAYSUN CORP (WI)
5500 West Dr, Manitowoc, WI 54220-8306
Tel (920) 686-5814 *Founded/Ownrshp* 1974, 1975
Sales 48.5MM^E *EMP* 200^E
SIC 3089 3544 Injection molding of plastics; Forms (molds), for foundry & plastics working machinery; Industrial molds; Injection molding of plastics; Forms (molds), for foundry & plastics working machinery; Industrial molds
CEO: Benjamin G Harrison

Ch Bd: Richard W Robinson
**Pr:* Bruce Wendt
**Treas:* David Turiff
**VP:* David Robinson
Exec: Jim Bauer
VP Mfg: Keith Bridgford
Ql Cn Mgr: Betty Ackerman
Ql Cn Mgr: Jeffrey Bath
Sls Mgr: Allen Elger

D-U-N-S 00-606-9496 IMP
■ **KAYTEE PRODUCTS INC** (WI)
(*Suby of* BREEDERS CHOICE) ★
521 Clay St, Chilton, WI 53014-1477
Tel (920) 849-2321 *Founded/Ownrshp* 1866
Sales 91.8MM^E *EMP* 500
SIC 0723 2048 Crop preparation services for market; Bird food, prepared; Feeds, specialty: mice, guinea pig, etc.; Crop preparation services for market; Bird food, prepared; Feeds, specialty: mice, guinea pig, etc.
CEO: William E Brown
VP: Jim Glassford
VP: Lori Pethan
Exec: Cindy Cherney
Dir Lab: Cindy Pederson
Dir IT: Sherry Satler
IT Man: Mark Doss
Software D: Richard Best
Sfty Mgr: Rita Balemy
Sfty Mgr: Rita Bollini
Sfty Mgr: Fernando Yebra

KAYU
See MOUNTAIN BROADCASTING LLC

D-U-N-S 00-148-3890 IMP
KAZ INC (NY)
(*Suby of* HELEN OF TROY LIMITED)
400 Donald Lynch Blvd # 300, Marlborough, MA 01752-4733
Tel (508) 490-7000 *Founded/Ownrshp* 1936, 2011
Sales 113.6MM^E *EMP* 2,500
SIC 8082 2834 5047 Home health care services; Pharmaceutical preparations; Medical & hospital equipment; Home health care services; Pharmaceutical preparations; Medical & hospital equipment
Pr: Julien Mininberg
**Ch Bd:* Jon Kosheff
V Ch: Ramesh Ghodasara
**COO:* Tim Simmone
Treas: Amanda Wilson
**Chf Mktg O:* Christophe Coudray
Sr VP: Mark Simon
Sr VP: Roelof Zeijpveld
VP: Marcus Allemann
VP: Ric Arenas
VP: Alfredo Mayne-Nicholls
Creative D: Jennifer Petersen

D-U-N-S 05-363-7893
KAZI FOODS CORP OF HAWAII
KFC
560 N Nimitz Hwy Ste 214, Honolulu, HI 96817-5380
Tel (808) 550-4100 *Founded/Ownrshp* 1998
Sales 33.8MM^E *EMP* 1,175
SIC 5812 Fast-food restaurant, chain; Fast-food restaurant, chain
Pr: Zubair Kazi
**CFO:* Shambhu Acharya
**VP:* Brian Burr
Genl Mgr: Steve Johnson

D-U-N-S 82-751-9711
KAZI FOODS INC
KFC
3671 Sunswept Dr, Studio City, CA 91604-2325
Tel (818) 980-1185 *Founded/Ownrshp* 1993
Sales 21.5MM^E *EMP* 292
SIC 5812 Fast-food restaurant, chain; Fast-food restaurant, chain
Pr: Zubair Kazi

D-U-N-S 14-743-5700
KAZTRONIX LLC
8260 Greensboro Dr # 150, Mc Lean, VA 22102-3806
Tel (703) 356-5440 *Founded/Ownrshp* 2001
Sales 34.4MM *EMP* 250^E
Accts Cohn Reznick Llp Vienna Virg
SIC 7361 7371 7379 7376 8999 Employment agencies; Custom computer programming services; Computer related maintenance services; Computer facilities management; Scientific consulting; Employment agencies; Custom computer programming services; Computer related maintenance services; Computer facilities management; Scientific consulting
CFO: Daniel Hallihan
Natl Sales: Richie Brown

D-U-N-S 02-861-8499 IMP
KB & R TRADING CORP
33 Newman Springs Rd B, Tinton Falls, NJ 07724-2644
Tel (732) 842-0746 *Founded/Ownrshp* 1997
Sales 35.1MM^E *EMP* 6^E
SIC 5148 Fresh fruits & vegetables; Fresh fruits & vegetables
Pr: Steve Goodman
Snr Mgr: Matthew Andras

KB CREATIVE NETWORK
See KIRSHENBAUM BOND SENECAL & PARTNERS LLC

D-U-N-S 04-317-8441 IMP
KB ELECTRONICS INC (FL)
(*Suby of* NIDEC AMERICAS HOLDING CORP) ★
12095 Nw 39th St, Coral Springs, FL 33065-2516
Tel (954) 346-4900 *Founded/Ownrshp* 2015
Sales 26.2MM^E *EMP* 195
SIC 3621 Motors & generators; Motors & generators
Pr: Gilbert Knauer
Owner: Tim McBride
Pr: Sid Ambort
Pr: Michael Nedier
CFO: Jeff Connor
Ex VP: Greg Levine
Natl Sales: Richard Fritts
Manager: Ron Blank

D-U-N-S 08-661-9223
KB FRAMERS LLC
5795 Rogers St, Las Vegas, NV 89118-3017
Tel (702) 873-9451 *Founded/Ownrshp* 1998
Sales 17.6MM^E *EMP* 1,000
SIC 1751 1521 Framing contractor; Single-family housing construction; Framing contractor; Single-family housing construction

D-U-N-S 17-772-3061
▲ **KB HOME**
10990 Wilshire Blvd Fl 5, Los Angeles, CA 90024-3902
Tel (310) 231-4000 *Founded/Ownrshp* 1957
Sales 2.4MMM *EMP* 1,590
Tkr Sym KBH *Exch* NYS
SIC 1531 6351 6162 Operative builders; Speculative builder, single-family houses; Condominium developers; Speculative builder, multi-family dwellings; Surety insurance; Mortgage guarantee insurance; Credit & other financial responsibility insurance; Operative builders; Speculative builder, single-family houses; Condominium developers; Speculative builder, multi-family dwellings; Surety insurance; Mortgage guarantee insurance; Credit & other financial responsibility insurance; Mortgage bankers & correspondents
Pr: Jeffrey T Mezger
Pr: Jon Adler
Pr: Tom Dunn
Pr: Ken Hilligoss
Pr: Todd Holder
Pr: George Schulmeyer
Pr: Tom Sewitsky
CFO: Jeff J Kaminski
Ex VP: Jon Doherty
Ex VP: Nick Franklin
Ex VP: Elaine Namba
Ex VP: Albert Z Praw
Ex VP: Brian J Woram
Sr VP: John Fenn
Sr VP: John E Goodwin Jr
Sr VP: William R Hollinger
Sr VP: Thomas F Norton
Sr VP: Tom Silk
Dir Bus: Kevin Bond
Board of Directors: Stephen F Bollenbach, Timothy W Finchem, Thomas W Gilligan, Kenneth M Jastrow II, Robert L Johnson, Melissa Lora, Robert L Patton Jr, Michael M Wood

D-U-N-S 00-640-2103
■ **KB HOME COLORADO INC**
(*Suby of* KB HOME) ★
7807 E Pkview Ave Ste 300, Centennial, CO 80111
Tel (303) 323-1100 *Founded/Ownrshp* 1994
Sales 100.0MM *EMP* 60
SIC 1522 Residential construction; Residential construction
Pr: Rusty Crandall
VP: Micheal Dee

D-U-N-S 06-446-4621
■ **KB HOME GREATER LOS ANGELES INC**
(*Suby of* KB HOME) ★
10990 Wilshire Blvd # 700, Los Angeles, CA 90024-3913
Tel (310) 231-4000 *Founded/Ownrshp* 1988
Sales 54.3MM^E *EMP* 400
SIC 1521 1522 Single-family home remodeling, additions & repairs; Multi-family dwelling construction; Single-family home remodeling, additions & repairs; Multi-family dwelling construction
CEO: Bruce Karatz
VP: Leonard Leichnitz
IT Man: Jacqueline Sargent

D-U-N-S 80-076-5992
■ **KB HOME NEVADA INC**
(*Suby of* KB HOME) ★
5655 Badura Ave, Las Vegas, NV 89118-4713
Tel (702) 266-8400 *Founded/Ownrshp* 1992
Sales 29.3MM^E *EMP* 350
SIC 1522 Residential construction; Residential construction
Pr: Don Delgiorno
VP: Tim Sprague
**Rgnl Mgr:* Jim Widener
Genl Couns: Matt Stark

D-U-N-S 87-769-1592
■ **KB HOME ORLANDO LLC**
(*Suby of* KB HOME) ★
9102 Southpark Center Loo, Orlando, FL 32819-8626
Tel (407) 587-3400 *Founded/Ownrshp* 2002
Sales 40.6MM^E *EMP* 163
SIC 1531 1522 Speculative builder, single-family houses; Residential construction; Speculative builder, single-family houses; Residential construction
Sr VP: George O Glance
Ofcr: Jay Arvin
**Sr VP:* Darren Dulice
VP Opers: Chad Burlingame

KB INDUSTRIES
See K&B MACHINE

D-U-N-S 85-850-1492
KBA DOCUSYS INC
32900 Alvarado Niles Rd # 100, Union City, CA 94587-3106
Tel (510) 214-4040 *Founded/Ownrshp* 2007
Sales 21.0MM^E *EMP* 47^E
SIC 5084 5044 7371 Printing trades machinery, equipment & supplies; Photocopy machines; Computer software systems analysis & design, custom; Computer software writers, freelance
Pr: James E Graf
CFO: Todd Court
**Treas:* Todd Moody
Dir IT: George Fidentzis
IT Man: Gloria Lontoc
Site Mgr: Brooke Cowger
Sls Mgr: Artie Atencio
Sales Asso: Jeff Chang

D-U-N-S 01-224-3510
KBA ENGINEERING LLC (CA)
2157 Mohawk St, Bakersfield, CA 93308-6020
Tel (661) 323-0487 *Founded/Ownrshp* 1997, 1998
Sales 23.1MM^E *EMP* 95
SIC 3533 3462 Oil & gas field machinery; Gear & chain forgings; Oil & gas field machinery; Gear & chain forgings
Sfty Mgr: Ryan Fergon
Opers Mgr: Robert Collins
Sls&Mrk Ex: Rick Jones

D-U-N-S 00-166-9472 IMP
KBA NORTH AMERICA INC
SHEETFED DIVISION
(*Suby of* KOENIG & BAUER AG)
2555 Regent Blvd, Dallas, TX 75261
Tel (800) 522-7521 *Founded/Ownrshp* 1990
Sales 37.0MM^E *EMP* 45
SIC 5084 Printing trades machinery, equipment & supplies
Pr: Claus Bolza Schnemann
Pr: Sascha Fischer
**Pr:* Ralf Sammeck
**COO:* Gerrit Zwergel
**CFO:* Axel Kaufmann
Sr VP: Soren Larsen
VP: Walter Chmura
**VP:* Timothy Mc Keon
IT Man: Michael Sodolak
Mktg Dir: Jerry Crowder
Sls Mgr: Mark Hischar

D-U-N-S 09-649-0573
KBACE TECHNOLOGIES INC
6 Trafalgar Sq, Nashua, NH 03063-1988
Tel (603) 821-7000 *Founded/Ownrshp* 1998
Sales 28.1MM^E *EMP* 306
SIC 8742 7371 Management consulting services; Custom computer programming services; Management consulting services; Custom computer programming services
CEO: Ed Lazzari
**Pr:* Michael Peterson
**CFO:* Darla Cauley
Sr VP: Jeff Johnson
Sr VP: Ed Kirwin
Sr VP: Don Kisiday
VP: Andy Constable
VP: Bill Keenan
VP: Patrick Lazzari
**VP:* Ravishankar Mamgaim
VP: Brian Testa

D-U-N-S 15-076-0262 IMP/EXP
KBC ADVANCED TECHNOLOGIES INC
(*Suby of* KBC ADVANCED TECHNOLOGIES PLC)
15021 Katy Fwy Ste 600, Houston, TX 77094-1900
Tel (281) 293-8200 *Founded/Ownrshp* 1983
Sales 24.8MM^E *EMP* 176
SIC 8711 Professional engineer; Professional engineer
CEO: Michael Kirk
**Pr:* W George Bright
Ex VP: Paul Eisman
Ex VP: Edward Kleinguetl
**Ex VP:* Ramon C Loureiro
Sr VP: Mike Aylott
Sr VP: Jason Durst
**VP:* T Coombs
**VP:* Ralph F Goodrich
**VP:* Richard A Manner
VP: Michael Rutkowski

D-U-N-S 10-975-5855
KBC FINANCIAL HOLDING INC
(*Suby of* KBC BANK SA)
1177 Ave Of The Americas, New York, NY 10036-2714
Tel (212) 845-2000 *Founded/Ownrshp* 1999
Sales 41.3MM^E *EMP* 600
SIC 6726 Investment offices; Investment offices
Mng Dir: Art Muscio
VP: Diane Gioseffi
VP: Joe Yang
**Mng Dir:* Thomas Krorossy
**Mng Dir:* Anthony Zissel

D-U-N-S 80-915-7068 IMP
KBC GROUP INC
3400 109th St, Des Moines, IA 50322-8104
Tel (515) 270-2417 *Founded/Ownrshp* 1993
Sales 103.0MM^E *EMP* 100
SIC 1542 5083 Agricultural building contractors; Agricultural machinery & equipment; Agricultural building contractors; Agricultural machinery & equipment
Pr: Peter Bratney
CFO: Obrasio Brawn
IT Man: Matt Bettis

D-U-N-S 03-512-5897
KBC INC
JOHNSON CONTROLS
4444 S 108th St, Omaha, NE 68137-1203
Tel (402) 339-2342 *Founded/Ownrshp* 1981
Sales 23.7MM^E *EMP* 65
SIC 5075 Air conditioning & ventilation equipment & supplies; Warm air heating equipment & supplies; Air conditioning & ventilation equipment & supplies; Warm air heating equipment & supplies
Pr: Kim B Cafferty
**VP:* Mary Ann Cafferty

KBC MACHINERY
See KBC TOOLS INC

D-U-N-S 04-376-8209 IMP
KBC TOOLS INC
KBC MACHINERY
6300 18 Mile Rd, Sterling Heights, MI 48314-4208
Tel (586) 264-6600 *Founded/Ownrshp* 1964
Sales 48.4MM^E *EMP* 150
SIC 5084 Machine tools & accessories; Machine tools & accessories
CEO: Sheila Bass
**Pr:* Paula Bass
Ex VP: Gregg Smith
**VP:* Elaina Cavataio
**VP:* John Earles
IT Man: Nate Stone
Advt Mgr: Charlie Yankee

KBD GROUP
See KAJIMA BUILDING & DESIGN GROUP INC

D-U-N-S 04-918-4633
KBE BUILDING CORP
76 Batterson Park Rd # 1, Farmington, CT 06032-2571
Tel (860) 284-7424 *Founded/Ownrshp* 1966
Sales 96.1MM^E *EMP* 155
SIC 1542 1541 Shopping center construction; Commercial & office building, new construction; Renovation, remodeling & repairs: industrial buildings; Shopping center construction; Commercial & office building, new construction; Renovation, remodeling & repairs: industrial buildings
Pr: Michael Kolakowski
**CFO:* Tim O'Brien
**Sr VP:* Eric Brown
**Sr VP:* Simon Etzel
**VP:* Robert G Dunn
**VP:* Dan Hannon
**VP:* Gary Sherman
Dir Risk M: Lori Bonini
VP Admn: Allan Kleban
Netwrk Mgr: Paul Hallaway
Mktg Dir: Jonelle Lawhorn

D-U-N-S 13-183-0135
KBEW L P
VICTORIA NISSAN
6003 N Navarro St, Victoria, TX 77904-1766
Tel (361) 578-5000 *Founded/Ownrshp* 2005
Sales 29.0MM *EMP* 30
SIC 5511 Automobiles, new & used; Automobiles, new & used

D-U-N-S 13-723-6456
KBF AMSTERDAM PARTNERS
SAGAMORE APARTMENTS
189 W 89th St, New York, NY 10024-1959
Tel (212) 712-2661 *Founded/Ownrshp* 2006
Sales 30.4MM^E *EMP* 1,828
SIC 6531 Real estate agents & managers; Real estate agents & managers
Prin: Larry Lipton
Prin: Michael Herrington

D-U-N-S 15-397-9935
KBF ASSOCIATES LP
MORGAN PROPERTIES
160 Clubhouse Rd, King of Prussia, PA 19406-3300
Tel (610) 265-2800 *Founded/Ownrshp* 1985
Sales 21.2MM^E *EMP* 39
SIC 6513 Apartment building operators
Pr: Mitchell Morgan
Pr: Carol Jackson
CFO: J Patrick O'Grady
Sr VP: Jeffrey Weissman
VP: Karen McAlonen
VP: Jonathan Morgan
VP: Steve Waters
Rgnl Mgr: Annemarie Hobson
Genl Mgr: Lethra Holmes
IT Man: Jim Alder
IT Man: Steve Fox

KBFUS
See KING BAUDOUIN FOUNDATION UNITED STATES I

D-U-N-S 17-638-6519
KBG COMMERCIAL INC
KBG LOGISTICS
50 Inez Dr, Bay Shore, NY 11706-2204
Tel (631) 231-1022 *Founded/Ownrshp* 2004
Sales 30.0MM^E *EMP* 40
SIC 4213 Trucking, except local; Trucking, except local
Prin: Sameal Gutierrez

KBG LOGISTICS
See KBG COMMERCIAL INC

D-U-N-S 00-703-2444 IMP
KBH CORP (MS)
395 Anderson Blvd, Clarksdale, MS 38614-4701
Tel (662) 624-5471 *Founded/Ownrshp* 1951
Sales 51.7MM^E *EMP* 150
SIC 3523 Fertilizing machinery, farm; Trailers & wagons, farm; Sprayers & spraying machines, agricultural; Harvesters, fruit, vegetable, tobacco, etc.; Fertilizing machinery, farm; Trailers & wagons, farm; Sprayers & spraying machines, agricultural; Harvesters, fruit, vegetable, tobacco, etc.
Pr: Buddy Bass Sr
**Pr:* M H Bass
**Sec:* Ann Bass

D-U-N-S 84-901-4360
KBHL LLC
KAANAPALI BEACH HOTEL
2525 Kaanapali Pkwy, Lahaina, HI 96761-2936
Tel (808) 661-0011 *Founded/Ownrshp* 1988
Sales 22.3MM^E *EMP* 300
SIC 7011 5812 7299 Resort hotel; Eating places; Banquet hall facilities; Resort hotel; Eating places; Banquet hall facilities
Exec: Nora Rabago
IT Man: Brylian Soronda
Sls Dir: Roy Butteling
Sls Mgr: Susan Haigh-Bishop

D-U-N-S 03-424-8380
KBI BIOPHARMA INC
K B I BIOPHARMA
1101 Hamlin Rd, Durham, NC 27704-9658
Tel (919) 479-9898 *Founded/Ownrshp* 2001
Sales 49.8MM^E *EMP* 66
SIC 2834 8733 Pharmaceutical preparations; Biotechnical research, noncommercial
Pr: Joseph T McMahon
Pr: Andrew Cohen
Pr: Thomas Milici
**CFO:* Nicholas J Leb
**VP:* Michael J Cavanaugh
**VP:* James Chopas
VP: Mary Gibson
**VP:* Timothy M Kelly

VP: Dirk Lange
VP: Firoz Mistry
*VP: Abhinav Shukla
VP: Abhinav A Shukla
VP: Brandon Vail
Assoc Dir: Greg Chrimes
Assoc Dir: Victoria Dowling
Assoc Dir: Larry Herbst
Assoc Dir: Ying Huang
Assoc Dir: Michael Landau
Assoc Dir: Carnley Norman
Assoc Dir: Micah Shagoury
Assoc Dir: Bill Upright

KBIC
See LEADING INSURANCE SERVICES INC

D-U-N-S 00-180-2453 IMP
KBK INC (NY)
(Suby of KYOKUTO BOEKI KAISHA, LTD.)
420 Lexington Ave Rm 2853, New York, NY 10170-2800
Tel (212) 687-8564 Founded/Ownrshp 1956
Sales 43.0MM EMP 6E
SIC 5162 5198 5084 Resins; Paints; Industrial machinery & equipment
Pr: Tadashi Yoshikawa
*VP: Yuji Takagi

D-U-N-S 07-330-9726
KBK INDUSTRIES LLC
2537 Highway 96, Rush Center, KS 67575-7634
Tel (785) 372-4331 Founded/Ownrshp 2006
Sales 29.5MME EMP 125
SIC 3443 7699 3088 Tanks, lined: metal plate; Tank repair; Plastics plumbing fixtures
Ch: Bill Baalmann
Pr: William G Baalman
CFO: James Clements
VP: Scott Case
Genl Mgr: Brain Baalmann
Prd Mgr: Trevor Steinert
VP Sls: Steven White
Sls Mgr: Kevin Baalman
Sls Mgr: Jesse Muller

D-U-N-S 13-136-0075 IMP
KBL GROUP INTERNATIONAL LTD
CRYSTAL SPORT
1407 Broadway Rm 610, New York, NY 10018-3380
Tel (212) 391-1551 Founded/Ownrshp 1985
Sales 47.1MME EMP 133
SIC 5137 Sportswear, women's & children's; Sportswear, women's & children's
Ch Bd: Steven Begleiter
*Pr: Michael Begleiter
*VP: Danny Tsung
Off Mgr: Latisha Elmes

D-U-N-S 08-000-0561
KBLB-KEN LTD
SAN MARCOS AUTO OUTLET
2990 S Ih 35, San Marcos, TX 78666-6185
Tel (512) 831-7625 Founded/Ownrshp 1999
Sales 45.1MM EMP 71
SIC 5511 Automobiles, new & used
Pr: Kevin Blewett
*Co-Ownr: Kenneth Blewitt

KBM BUILDING SERVICES
See KBM FACILITY SOLUTIONS HOLDINGS LLC

D-U-N-S 10-315-2021
KBM FACILITY SOLUTIONS HOLDINGS LLC
KBM BUILDING SERVICES
(Suby of PRISTINE ENVIRONMENTS INC) ★
7976 Engineer Rd Ste 200, San Diego, CA 92111-1935
Tel (858) 467-0202 Founded/Ownrshp 2013
Sales 26.2MME EMP 500
Accts Cea Llp Carlsbad California
SIC 7349 Janitorial service, contract basis; Janitorial service, contract basis
CEO: Brian Snow
*CFO: Susan Cologna
*VP: Rene Tuthscher

D-U-N-S 79-986-0499 IMP
KBM GROUP LLC
(Suby of YOUNG & RUBICAM GROUP) ★
2050 N Greenville Ave, Richardson, TX 75082-4322
Tel (972) 664-3600 Founded/Ownrshp 1997
Sales 48.3MME EMP 200
SIC 7331 7374 8742 Direct mail advertising services; Data processing & preparation; Marketing consulting services; Direct mail advertising services; Data processing & preparation; Marketing consulting services
Pr: Gary Laben
*Pr: William Burkart
Pr: Kevin Wells
COO: Bret Harper
*COO: Dennis Kooker
*CFO: Jim Pike
Ofcr: Brooks Dobbs
Ex VP: Joe Brehm
Ex VP: Mike Burns
Ex VP: Tom Young
Ex VP: Andy Ziegler
Sr VP: Peter Rodes
VP: Renee Besel
VP: Diane Brussow
VP: Pat Chuffo
VP: Mark Fiddes
VP: Randy Herzog
VP: Jennifer Hickman
VP: Dan Kummer
VP: Sandy McCray
VP: Barbara Palmer

KBP FOODS
See FQSR LLC

KBR BUILDING GROUP, LLC
See BE&K BUILDING GROUP LLC

D-U-N-S 60-829-9801
KBR BUILDING GROUP LLC
201 E Mcbee Ave Ste 400, Greenville, SC 29601-2894
Tel (615) 742-6620 Founded/Ownrshp 2004
Sales 22.8MME EMP 75
SIC 1542 Commercial & office building contractors
Pr: Luther Cochran
Opers Mgr: Tim Parker

D-U-N-S 03-231-1284 IMP
■ **KBR CONSTRUCTION CO LLC**
(Suby of B E & K INC) ★
2000 International Pk Dr, Birmingham, AL 35243-4221
Tel (205) 972-6538 Founded/Ownrshp 1980
Sales 1.2MMME EMP 6,000E
SIC 1541 1796 1711 1629 1799 1521 Industrial buildings, new construction; Paper/pulp mill construction; Machinery installation; Mechanical contractor; Industrial plant construction; Athletic & recreation facilities construction; Single-family housing construction; Industrial buildings, new construction; Paper/pulp mill construction; Machinery installation; Mechanical contractor; Industrial plant construction; Athletic & recreation facilities construction; Single-family housing construction

D-U-N-S 62-155-9876
■ **KBR HOLDINGS LLC**
K B R
(Suby of KBR INC) ★
601 Jefferson St Ste 7911, Houston, TX 77002-4003
Tel (713) 753-4176 Founded/Ownrshp 2006
Sales 2.1MMME EMP 20,010
Accts Kpmg Llp
SIC 1629 8711 8741 Industrial plant construction; Dams, waterways, docks & other marine construction; Engineering services; Construction management; Industrial plant construction; Dams, waterways, docks & other marine construction; Engineering services; Construction management
Pr: William P Utt
*CFO: Cedric Burgher
*Treas: Charles E Schneider

D-U-N-S 78-407-2626 IMP
▲ **KBR INC**
601 Jefferson St Ste 3400, Houston, TX 77002-7901
Tel (713) 753-3011 Founded/Ownrshp 2006
Sales 6.3MMM EMP 25,000
Tkr Sym KBR Exch NYS
SIC 1629 8711 8741 Land preparation construction; Industrial plant construction; Dams, waterways, docks & other marine construction; Engineering services; Petroleum, mining & chemical engineers; Construction & civil engineering; Management services; Business management; Construction management; Land preparation construction; Industrial plant construction; Dams, waterways, docks & other marine construction; Engineering services; Petroleum, mining & chemical engineers; Construction & civil engineering; Management services; Business management; Construction management
Pr: Stuart Bradie
CFO: Brian K Ferraioli
Ex VP: Eileen G Akerson
VP: Kenneth Allen
VP: Brian Pettersen
VP: Nelson E Rowe
VP: Martin W Siddle

KBS
See KOCH BUSINESS SOLUTIONS LP

D-U-N-S 13-340-9495
KBS BUILDING SYSTEMS INC
KBS HOMES
300 Park St, South Paris, ME 04281-6417
Tel (207) 739-2400 Founded/Ownrshp 2002
Sales 73.3MME EMP 203
SIC 2452 Modular homes, prefabricated, wood; Modular homes, prefabricated, wood
Pr: Ray Atkinsson
Pr: Kathi Haley
Genl Mgr: Ray Atkisson
Plnt Mgr: Jay Atkisson

D-U-N-S 02-036-4449
KBS CONSTRUCTION INC (WI)
K B S
3841 Kipp St, Madison, WI 53718-6878
Tel (608) 838-6100 Founded/Ownrshp 2000
Sales 55.9MME EMP 200
SIC 1542 Commercial & office building, new construction; Commercial & office building, new construction
Pr: Tom Schuchardt
*CFO: Douglas Carlson
*VP: Pat Babe
*VP: Larry Breneman

D-U-N-S 10-682-6290
KBS ELECTRICAL DISTRIBUTORS INC
7554 E State Highway 21, Bryan, TX 77808-8658
Tel (979) 778-3200 Founded/Ownrshp 1984
Sales 70.0MME EMP 18
SIC 5063 Electrical construction materials; Electrical supplies; Electrical construction materials; Electrical supplies
Pr: Ronnie Gidley
*Sec: Rhonda Gidley
*VP: Bobby Bauch
*VP: Marvin Oldham
IT Man: Brian Gidley

KBS HOMES
See KBS BUILDING SYSTEMS INC

D-U-N-S 01-006-3048
KBS INC (VA)
8050 Kimway Dr, Richmond, VA 23228-2831
Tel (804) 262-0100 Founded/Ownrshp 1975
Sales 137.1MM EMP 130
Accts Lewis & Company Pc Chesapeak
SIC 1542 Commercial & office building, new construction; Industrial buildings, new construction; Commercial & office building, new construction
Pr: Bill Paulette
*CFO: James Lipscombe
*Ex VP: Dennis Lynch
*VP: John Gillenwater
*VP: Steve Satterfield
*VP: Sam Stocks
Sales Exec: Matthew S Gass

D-U-N-S 83-305-2850
KBS LEGACY PARTNERS APARTMENT REIT INC
620 Newport Center Dr, Newport Beach, CA 92660-6420
Tel (949) 417-6500 Founded/Ownrshp 2009
Sales 42.2MM EMP 2
Accts Ernst & Young Llp Irvine Cal
SIC 6798 Real estate investment trusts; Real estate investment trusts
Pr: Randall Plischke

D-U-N-S 96-342-6734
KBS REAL ESTATE INVESTMENT TRUST II INC
KBS SOR WESTMOOR CENTER
800 Nwport Ctr Dr Ste 700, Newport Beach, CA 92660
Tel (949) 417-6500 Founded/Ownrshp 2008
Sales 279.4MM EMP 2E
SIC 6799 Investors; Investors
CEO: Charles Schreiber Jr
CFO: David E Snyder

D-U-N-S 96-210-4944
KBS REAL ESTATE INVESTMENT TRUST III INC
620 Newport Center Dr # 1300, Newport Beach, CA 92660-8013
Tel (949) 417-6500 Founded/Ownrshp 2010
Sales 188.9MM EMP 2
SIC 6798 Real estate investment trusts; Real estate investment trusts
CEO: Charles J Schreiber Jr

D-U-N-S 01-259-4946
KBS REALTY ADVISORS LLC
KOLL BREN SCHRBER RLTY ADVSORS
800 Nwport Ctr Dr Ste 700, Newport Beach, CA 92660
Tel (949) 417-6500 Founded/Ownrshp 1998
Sales 34.2MME EMP 60
SIC 6512

KBS SOR WESTMOOR CENTER
See KBS REAL ESTATE INVESTMENT TRUST II INC

D-U-N-S 83-069-8333
KBS STRATEGIC OPPORTUNITY REIT INC
620 Newport Center Dr, Newport Beach, CA 92660-6420
Tel (949) 417-6500 Founded/Ownrshp 2008
Sales 106.1MM EMP 2
SIC 6798 Real estate investment trusts; Real estate investment trusts
CEO: Keith D Hall
*Pr: Peter B McMillan
*CFO: David E Snyder

D-U-N-S 15-158-2855
KBT INC
SANTA MONICA ACURA
1717 Santa Monica Blvd, Santa Monica, CA 90404-1906
Tel (310) 829-1113 Founded/Ownrshp 1986
Sales 26.8MME EMP 62
SIC 5511 Automobiles, new & used; Automobiles, new & used
Pr: Tom Kasra
Genl Mgr: Amir Kasra

D-U-N-S 79-034-5107
■ **KBW LLC**
(Suby of STIFEL FINANCIAL CORP) ★
787 7th Ave Fl 4, New York, NY 10019-6018
Tel (212) 887-7777 Founded/Ownrshp 2013
Sales 110.4MME EMP 537E
SIC 6211 Security brokers & dealers; Investment bankers; Security brokers & dealers; Security brokers & dealers; Investment bankers; Security brokers & dealers
VP: Dan Frascone
Ex VP: Will Allen
Ex VP: Ben Plotkin
VP: Sharad Daswani
VP: Paula Mars
Mng Dir: Victor Sack

KC
See KERNODLE CLINIC INC

D-U-N-S 01-318-1743
KC AUTO HOLDING INC
9400 W 65th St, Shawnee Mission, KS 66203-3662
Tel (913) 677-3300 Founded/Ownrshp 1999
Sales 60.7MME EMP 150
SIC 5511 Automobiles, new & used; Automobiles, new & used
Pr: Marion Battaglia

D-U-N-S 02-785-7569
KC BELL INC
TACO BELL
8100 E 22nd St N 300-100, Wichita, KS 67226-2343
Tel (316) 684-8100 Founded/Ownrshp 1998
Sales 22.4MME EMP 500
SIC 5812 Fast-food restaurant, chain; Fast-food restaurant, chain
Pr: Paul R Hoover
*Sec: David Murfin

D-U-N-S 00-325-4000
KC CO INC (MD)
12100 Baltimore Ave Ste 1, Beltsville, MD 20705-1399
Tel (301) 957-7000 Founded/Ownrshp 1931, 1958
Sales 45.2MME EMP 150
SIC 5031 5211 1751 Lumber, plywood & millwork; Building materials, exterior; Building materials, interior; Doors & windows; Windows, storm: wood or metal; Doors, storm: wood or metal; Doors, wood or metal, except storm; Carpentry work; Lumber, plywood & millwork; Building materials, exterior; Building materials, interior; Doors & windows; Windows, storm: wood or metal; Doors, storm: wood or metal; Doors, wood or metal, except storm; Carpentry work
Pr: Stan Stokes
*Ch Bd: Kevin Cassidy
COO: Stanley Stokes
VP: James Cassidy
*VP: Terrence M Sheehan
VP: Brad Yourkavitch
Genl Mgr: Ed Gorey
Sls Mgr: David Lebowitz
Sls Mgr: Ken Weckesser
Sales Asso: Kent Guillot
Snr Mgr: Danny Kalmus

D-U-N-S 06-442-1410
■ **KC DISTANCE LEARNING INC**
(Suby of K12 INC) ★
830 Ne Holladay St # 150, Portland, OR 97232-5104
Tel (503) 731-5427 Founded/Ownrshp 2010
Sales 29.5MME EMP 2,996E
SIC 8299 Educational services
Pr: Caprice Young
VP: Gregg Levin
*VP: Kathi Littmann
Dir Surg: Rebecca Tomasini
Dir Bus: Anton Leof
VP Mktg: Janet Johnson

D-U-N-S 10-900-6353
KC ELECTRONIC DISTRIBUTORS INC
186 N Belle Mead Rd, Setauket, NY 11733-3455
Tel (631) 689-2200 Founded/Ownrshp 1982
Sales 44.0MME EMP 53E
SIC 5065 Electronic parts
Pr: Rocco Rotunno
Sls Mgr: Kevjn Rotunno

D-U-N-S 86-726-2214 IMP
KC FIXTURE & DISPLAY INC
K.C STORE FIXTURES
7400 E 12th St Ste 4, Kansas City, MO 64126-2367
Tel (816) 842-8866 Founded/Ownrshp 1994
Sales 24.2MME EMP 40
SIC 5046 3999 2542 Store equipment; Store fixtures; Mannequins; Shelving, commercial & industrial; Artificial trees & flowers; Partitions & fixtures, except wood
Pr: Leo Galey
CFO: Chris Kramer
Opers Mgr: Shane Wright

K.C STORE FIXTURES
See KC FIXTURE & DISPLAY INC

D-U-N-S 05-017-5371
KC WINDUSTRIAL CO
(Suby of WINSUPPLY INC) ★
4400 E 12th St, Kansas City, MO 64127-1619
Tel (816) 842-9466 Founded/Ownrshp 1981
Sales 27.9MME EMP 51E
SIC 5085 5074 Industrial fittings; Plumbing fittings & supplies
Pr: Daniel Cline
*Treas: Greg Shelby
*VP: Larry Eklund
Genl Mgr: Dennis Murphy
Off Mgr: Jennifer Bowen
Sls Mgr: Bob Wilcox
Sales Asso: Jim Bates
Sales Asso: Monty Betterton
Sales Asso: Joe Higbee
Sales Asso: Kevin Jones
Sales Asso: Kevin Latham

D-U-N-S 79-625-9166 IMP
KCA ELECTRONICS INC
K C A
(Suby of DY U INC) ★
223 N Crescent Way, Anaheim, CA 92801-6704
Tel (714) 239-2433 Founded/Ownrshp 2004
Sales 27.6MM EMP 160
SIC 3672 5999 Printed circuit boards; Electronic parts & equipment; Printed circuit boards; Electronic parts & equipment
CEO: Tae Myoung Kim
COO: Bob Oesterle
CFO: Binh Tran
VP: Mike Busby
VP: Dan Dang
Exec: Amie Wolfe
Prgrm Mgr: Dennis Curran
IT Man: Kashif Tahir
Ql Cn Mgr: Mark Alexander
Ql Cn Mgr: Jeff Frost

D-U-N-S 07-846-4201 EXP
KCA SOLAR POWER GENERATING LTD LIABILITY CO
6209 Nw 18th Ave, Miami, FL 33147-7801
Tel (954) 369-5547 Founded/Ownrshp 2012
Sales 40.5MME EMP 3
SIC 4911 6799 Generation, electric power; Commodity contract trading companies

D-U-N-S 79-043-0388
▲ **KCAP FINANCIAL INC**
295 Madison Ave Fl 6, New York, NY 10017-7731
Tel (212) 455-8300 Founded/Ownrshp 2006
Sales 41.2MM EMP 27
Tkr Sym KCAP Exch NGS
SIC 6726 Management investment funds, closed-end; Management investment funds, closed-end
Pr: Dayl W Pearson
CFO: Edward U Gilpin
CFO: Edward Gilpin
Chf Inves: R Jon Corless
Ofcr: Michael Wirth
Top Exec: Denise Rodriguez
VP: Daniel P Gilligan
CIO: Jon Corless
Genl Couns: Jill Simeone

KCATA
See KANSAS CITY AREA TRANSPORTATION AUTHORITY

D-U-N-S 10-922-3198
KCB TOWERS INC
27260 Meines St, Highland, CA 92346-4223
Tel (909) 862-0322 Founded/Ownrshp 1983
Sales 20.1MME EMP 100
SIC 1791 3441 Structural steel erection; Fabricated structural metal
CEO: S Lynn Bogh
*Sec: Sharon Bogh

*VP: Miles Bogh
Off Mgr: Lynne Behunin
Off Mgr: Lonnie Gallaher

KCC
See BLITZ USA INC

D-U-N-S 18-108-8337
KCC TRANSPORT SYSTEMS INC
KOREAN CARGO CONSOLIDATED USA
311 W Artesia Blvd, Compton, CA 90220-5525
Tel (310) 764-5933 Founded/Ownrshp 1987
Sales 26.2MM^E EMP 50
SIC 4731 4231 Freight forwarding; Customhouse brokers; Trucking terminal facilities
CEO: Arthur Lee
*VP: Jin Kim

D-U-N-S 62-160-7191 IMP
KCE AMERICA INC
KCE ELECTRONICS PUBLIC COMPANY
954 San Rafael Ave, Mountain View, CA 94043-1926
Tel (650) 390-8000 Founded/Ownrshp 1990
Sales 61.6MM EMP 20
SIC 5065 Electronic parts & equipment; Electronic parts & equipment
Pr: Frederick R Rhodes
*VP: Kraig Belisle
VP Sls: Joe Yeo

KCE ELECTRONICS PUBLIC COMPANY
See KCE AMERICA INC

KCES
See KANSAS CITY ELECTRICAL SUPPLY CO INC

D-U-N-S 00-678-1348
KCETLINK (CA)
COMMUNITY TELEVISION OF SOUTHE
2900 W Alameda Ave # 600, Burbank, CA 91505-4267
Tel (747) 201-5000 Founded/Ownrshp 1960
Sales 22.7MM EMP 150^E
Accts Singerlewak Llp Los Angeles
SIC 4833 Television broadcasting stations; Television broadcasting stations
Pr: Al Jerome
*Ch Bd: Richard Cook
Assoc Dir: Bernie Roscetti
Snr Mgr: Paul Mason

KCG
See KNIGHT CAPITAL AMERICAS LP

D-U-N-S 07-881-4681
▲ **KCG HOLDINGS INC**
545 Washington Blvd Fl 1, Jersey City, NJ 07310-2608
Tel (201) 222-9400 Founded/Ownrshp 2012
Sales 1.3MMM EMP 1,093^E
Tkr Sym KCG Exch NYS
SIC 6211 6282 Security brokers & dealers; Investment advice; Management investment, open-end; Security brokers & dealers; Investment advice
CEO: Daniel Coleman
COO: Nick Ogurtsov
CFO: Steffen Parratt
VP: Doug Grossfeld
VP: Vincent Robertini
VP: James P Smyth
VP: Erica Snell
VP: Yuriy Vasilyev
CTO: Jonathan Ross
Board of Directors: Charles S Haldeman Jr, Rene Kern, James T Milde, John C Morris, Daniel F Schmitt, Stephen Schuler, Laurie M Shahon, Daniel Tierney

D-U-N-S 03-981-5410 IMP
KCG INC
REW MATERIALS
15720 W 108th St Ste 100, Lenexa, KS 66219-1338
Tel (913) 438-4142 Founded/Ownrshp 1993
Sales 326.9MM^E EMP 250
SIC 5032 2992 Drywall materials; Lubricating oils & greases; Drywall materials; Lubricating oils & greases
Pr: Rick J Rew
*Pr: James W Bedsworth Sr
COO: Kim Gray
*CFO: James W Bedsworth Jr
*VP: Jeff Butts
CTO: Kenneth Greenwell
IT Man: Todd Thielbar

KCHA
See HOUSING AUTHORITY OF COUNTY OF KING

KCI
See KINETIC CONCEPTS INC

D-U-N-S 03-105-6690
KCI CONSTRUCTION CO (MO)
10315 Lake Bluff Dr, Saint Louis, MO 63123-7245
Tel (314) 894-8888 Founded/Ownrshp 1940, 2005
Sales 129.5MM^E EMP 215
SIC 1542 1611 1629 Specialized public building contractors; Highway & street construction; Industrial plant construction; Specialized public building contractors; Highway & street construction; Industrial plant construction
Pr: Doug Jones
*VP: Tom Huster
*VP: Ron Webel Huth
*VP: Brent Krueger

D-U-N-S 84-703-1770 IMP
KCI HOLDING USA INC
(Suby of KONECRANES FINANCE OY)
4401 Gateway Blvd, Springfield, OH 45502-9339
Tel (937) 525-5533 Founded/Ownrshp 1993
Sales 213.1MM^E EMP 2,500
SIC 3536 Cranes, industrial plant; Cranes, industrial plant
Sr VP: Bernie D'Ambrosi
CFO: Guy Shoumaker
*Treas: Amy Corbisier
*Treas: Steve Mayes
*VP: Guy Shumaker
Board of Directors: Teo Ottola, Tom Sothard

D-U-N-S 60-510-8141
KCI HOLDINGS INC
K C I
936 Ridgebrook Rd, Sparks Glencoe, MD 21152-9390
Tel (410) 316-7800 Founded/Ownrshp 1988
Sales 160.6MM EMP 1,001
Accts Grant Thornton Llp Baltimore
SIC 8711 1799 Consulting engineer; Petroleum storage tank installation, underground; Consulting engineer; Petroleum storage tank installation, underground
CEO: Terry F Neimeyer
*CFO: Christine Koski
Ex VP: Judd Carothers
*Ex VP: William Franswick
VP: Joe Bell
VP: David Colclough
VP: Kien Nguyen
VP: John Scott
Area Mgr: Maya Katkoria
Off Mgr: Michael Ebner
Dir IT: Jim Lofft

D-U-N-S 79-026-5672
KCI INTERNATIONAL INC
(Suby of KCI) ★
12930 W Interstate 10, San Antonio, TX 78249-2248
Tel (210) 524-9000 Founded/Ownrshp 1991
Sales 46.1MM^E EMP 430^E
SIC 2599 7352 Beds, not household use; Medical equipment rental; Beds, not household use; Medical equipment rental
Pr: Martin J Landon
*VP: Stephen D Seidel
CIO: David H Ramsey

D-U-N-S 08-499-3344
KCI TECHNOLOGIES INC
K C I
(Suby of K C I) ★
936 Ridgebrook Rd, Sparks, MD 21152-9390
Tel (410) 316-7800 Founded/Ownrshp 1955, 1988
Sales 123.5MM EMP 1,000
Accts Grant Thornton Llp Baltimore
SIC 8711 Consulting engineer; Consulting engineer
CEO: Terry F Neimeyer
*Pr: Harvey Floyd
*CFO: Donald A McConnell
*Ex VP: Nathan J Beil
Ex VP: William Franswick
Sr VP: Scott Lang
*Sr VP: Charles A Phillips Jr
*VP: Edward D Berger
VP: Stephen Drumm
*VP: Christopher Griffith
VP: Ken Harmel
VP: Stephen Redding
*VP: Kenneth H Trout
VP: Tim Wolfe
Assoc Dir: Heidi Hammel

D-U-N-S 10-272-6734
KCI USA INC
K C I
(Suby of ACELITY LP INC) ★
12930 W Interstate 10, San Antonio, TX 78249-2248
Tel (210) 255-6027 Founded/Ownrshp 1991
Sales 61.1MM^E EMP 1,071
SIC 7352 3842 5047 Medical equipment rental; Surgical appliances & supplies; Medical & hospital equipment
Pr: Joseph F Woody
*Ex VP: Robert P Hureau
*VP: Peter Arnold
*VP: David Ball
*VP: John T Bibb
*VP: Jim Cunniff
*VP: Butch Hulse
*VP: Rohit Kashyap
*VP: David Lillback
*VP: Mike Matthews
*VP: Ron Silverman
VP: Eric Smith

KCI WIRELESS
See KEY-COMM INTERNATIONAL INC

KCLS
See KING COUNTY LIBRARY SYSTEM

D-U-N-S 14-790-8966 EXP
KCM MARKETING INC
MK BATTERY
(Suby of DEKA BATTERIES & CABLES) ★
1631 S Sinclair St, Anaheim, CA 92806-5929
Tel (714) 937-1033 Founded/Ownrshp 1995
Sales 25.4MM^E EMP 70
SIC 5063 Batteries; Batteries
Pr: Mark G Wels
*Treas: Christopher Pruitt
*VP: Mark Kettler
*VP: Daniel Langdon
Sls&Mrk Ex: Wayne Merdinger
VP Sls: David Brunelle
Sls Mgr: David Kettler

D-U-N-S 01-646-0917 IMP
KCMA CORP (GA)
(Suby of KAWASAKI HEAVY INDUSTRIES, LTD.)
2140 Barrett Park Dr Nw # 101, Kennesaw, GA 30144-3614
Tel (770) 499-7000 Founded/Ownrshp 1978, 1994
Sales 37.0MM^E EMP 105
SIC 5082 5013

KCMC HOME HEALTH & HOSPICE
See KERSHAW HEALTH MEDICAL CENTER

D-U-N-S 00-696-6055 IMP/EXP
■ **KCP&L GREATER MISSOURI OPERATIONS CO** (KS)
(Suby of GREAT PLAINS ENERGY INC) ★
1200 Main St Fl 30, Kansas City, MO 64105-2122
Tel (816) 556-2200 Founded/Ownrshp 1987
Sales 220.8M EMP 2,213
SIC 4911 Generation, electric power; Transmission, electric power; Distribution, electric power; Generation, electric power; Transmission, electric power; Distribution, electric power

CEO: Terry Bassham
*Pr: William H Downey
*CEO: Michael J Chesser
*Treas: Michael W Cline
*Ex VP: John R Marshall
*Sr VP: Michael L Deggendorf
Sr VP: Norma F Dunn
*Sr VP: Stephen T Easley
*Sr VP: Scott Heidtbrink
*VP: Jim Alberts
*VP: Kevin E Bryant
*VP: Lora C Cheatman
*VP: Carl Churchman
*VP: F Dana Crawford
*VP: Ellen Fairchild
*VP: Chris B Giles
*VP: William P Herdegen
*VP: Todd Kobayashi
*VP: Marvin L Rollison
*VP: Richard A Spring
*VP: Charles H Tickles
Board of Directors: Dr David L Bodde, Michael J Chesser, William H Downey, Mark A Ernst, Randall C Ferguson Jr, Luis A Jimenez, James A Mitchell, William C Nelson, Dr Linda H Talbott

D-U-N-S 80-034-3878
■ **KCPC HOLDINGS INC**
(Suby of SP PLUS CORP) ★
2401 21st Ave S Ste 200, Nashville, TN 37212-5309
Tel (615) 297-4255 Founded/Ownrshp 2012
Sales 112.7MM^E EMP 18,940^E
SIC 7521 Automobile parking; Automobile parking
CEO: Monroe Carell Jr
*VP: Seth H Hollander

KCPS
See KANSAS CITY PUBLIC SCHOOLS

KCPS
See KENT COUNTY PUBLIC SCHOOLS

D-U-N-S 05-333-6145
KCR INTERNATIONAL TRUCKS INC
(Suby of ROBERTS ISUZU) ★
7700 Ne 38th St, Kansas City, MO 64161-9410
Tel (816) 455-1833 Founded/Ownrshp 1999
Sales 68.6MM^E EMP 199
SIC 5511 5531 7538 7513 Trucks, tractors & trailers: new & used; Truck equipment & parts; Truck engine repair, except industrial; Truck leasing, without drivers; Trucks, tractors & trailers: new & used; Truck equipment & parts; Truck engine repair, except industrial; Truck leasing, without drivers
CEO: Richard Sweebe
COO: Rocky Zinser
CFO: Scott Gill
CFO: Lisa Key

D-U-N-S 07-932-5091
KCS HOLDINGS LLC (MO)
8001 Nw 106th St, Kansas City, MO 64153-2379
Tel (515) 266-4100 Founded/Ownrshp 2013
Sales 200.0MM EMP 1
SIC 6719 Personal holding companies, except banks

D-U-N-S 80-181-6091 EXP
KCS INTERNATIONAL INC
CRUISER YACHTS
804 Pecor St, Oconto, WI 54153-1761
Tel (920) 834-2211 Founded/Ownrshp 1993
Sales 213.6MM^E EMP 1,000
SIC 3732 Boats, fiberglass: building & repairing; Boats, fiberglass: building & repairing
Pr: Mark Pedersen
CFO: Pedersen Mark
*Ch: Kenneth C Stock
MIS Dir: Sue Hoffman
Dir IT: Jim Schuh
Plnt Mgr: Bruce Allen
Manager: Mike McGarity

KCTCS
See KENTUCKY COMMUNITY AND TECHNICAL COLLEGE SYSTEM

KCTCS-BLUEGRASS DISTRICT
See LEXINGTON COMMUNITY COLLEGE

KCUSD
See KING CITY UNION ELEMENTARY SCHOOL DISTRICT

KD
See KRIZ-DAVIS CO

D-U-N-S 78-024-6398
KD ACQUISITION I LLC
KINGS DELIGHT
2063 Memorial Park Dr, Gainesville, GA 30504-5801
Tel (770) 536-5177 Founded/Ownrshp 2001
Sales 75.7MM^E EMP 837
SIC 2037 2013 Frozen fruits & vegetables; Frozen meats from purchased meat; Frozen fruits & vegetables; Frozen meats from purchased meat
CFO: Lee Turner
Treas: Sally Jones
Sr VP: Stan Hayman
VP: Barry J Cooley
IT Man: Larry Miller
Sfty Mgr: George Osborne
Ql Cn Mgr: Phil Bradberry
Ql Cn Mgr: Howard Mobley
VP Mktg: Michael Farmer

KD DISTRIBUTORS
See LA MINA DE ORO INC

KD PAINT
See KLEIN-DICKERT CO INC

D-U-N-S 00-392-2321
KD RESOURCE GROUP LLC (GA)
6400 Powers Ferry Rd # 250, Atlanta, GA 30339-4729
Tel (678) 247-2008 Founded/Ownrshp 2008
Sales 40.0MM EMP 6
SIC 8742 Business planning & organizing services; Business planning & organizing services
VP: Fred Cox

KDC CONSTRUCTION
See CIRKS CONSTRUCTION INC

D-U-N-S 07-841-7834
KDC HOLDINGS LLC
KDC REAL ESTATE DEV INVSTMENTS
8115 Preston Rd Ste 700, Dallas, TX 75225-6344
Tel (214) 696-1700 Founded/Ownrshp 1998
Sales 46.6MM^E EMP 43
SIC 6552 Land subdividers & developers, commercial
Pr: Lawrence Wilson
Ex VP: Walt Mountford
Ex VP: Scott Ozymy
Sr VP: Randy Doran
Sr VP: Nathan Golik
Sr VP: William Guthrey
Sr VP: Jake Ragusa
VP: Michael Alost
VP: Bob Browning
VP: Bret Creel
VP: Jeff Innmon
VP: Kurt Petersen
VP: James Williams

D-U-N-S 62-514-8101
KDC INC
KDC SYSTEMS
4462 Corporate Center Dr, Los Alamitos, CA 90720-2539
Tel (714) 828-7000 Founded/Ownrshp 1976
Sales 77.5MM^E EMP 348^E
SIC 1731 1611 3823 General electrical contractor; General contractor, highway & street construction; Industrial instrmnts msrmnt display/control process variable; General electrical contractor; General contractor, highway & street construction; Industrial instrmnts msrmnt display/control process variable
Pr: Johnny Menninga
Pr: Curt Reese
*CFO: William B Davenport
VP: Nancy Hickman
VP: Rick Pham
VP: Greg Thornton
Exec: Juan Herrera
Genl Mgr: Todd York
Sfty Dirs: John Vergo
Sfty Mgr: Billy Baskin
Mktg Dir: Tom Bykoski

KDC LYNCHBURG
See TRI-TECH LABORATORIES INC

KDC REAL ESTATE DEV INVSTMENTS
See KDC HOLDINGS LLC

KDC SYSTEMS
See KDC INC

D-U-N-S 78-783-6758 IMP
KDDI AMERICA INC
KDDI MOBILE
(Suby of KDDI CORPORATION)
825 3rd Ave Fl 3, New York, NY 10022-9526
Tel (212) 295-1200 Founded/Ownrshp 2003
Sales 86.6MM^E EMP 164
SIC 4813 7375 7374 8743 Long distance telephone communications; On-line data base information retrieval; Data processing & preparation; Sales promotion; Long distance telephone communications; On-line data base information retrieval; Data processing & preparation; Sales promotion
Pr: Satoru Manabe
Pr: Yoichi Iwaki
*CFO: Masato Takei
Ex VP: Masahiro Yamamoto
VP: Kiyoshi Goto
VP: Hiromu Naratani
*VP: Takami Teshigawara
VP: Hiroshi Uchida
Ex Dir: Shin Shinohara
Off Mgr: Takashi Sugiyama
Netwrk Eng: Shigeki Kawazoe

KDDI MOBILE
See KDDI AMERICA INC

D-U-N-S 14-735-3916
KDE INC
MCDONALD'S
3060 Commerce Dr Ste 2, Fort Gratiot, MI 48059-3878
Tel (810) 987-3374 Founded/Ownrshp 1982
Sales 13.5MM^E EMP 500
SIC 5812 8741 Fast-food restaurant, chain; Business management; Fast-food restaurant, chain; Business management
Pr: Markus Schulz
Software D: Jerri Deb

KDFW FOX 4
See NW COMMUNICATIONS OF TEXAS INC

D-U-N-S 14-298-4124
KDH DEFENSE SYSTEMS INC
750a W Fieldcrest Rd, Eden, NC 27288-3631
Tel (336) 635-4158 Founded/Ownrshp 2003
Sales 34.6MM^E EMP 140
SIC 3812 Defense systems & equipment; Defense systems & equipment
CEO: David E Herbener
Pr: Daniel Walsh
S&M/VP: Steve Phillips
Snr Mgr: Lane Graden

KDH PRIMARY CARE
See BAPTIST MEDICAL CENTER - YAZOO INC

D-U-N-S 83-082-7999
KDI ELEMENTS
79431 Country Club Dr, Bermuda Dunes, CA 92203-1200
Tel (760) 345-9933 Founded/Ownrshp 1990
Sales 25.7MM^E EMP 250
SIC 1743 5999 1741 Terrazzo, tile, marble, mosaic work; Monuments & tombstones; Masonry & other stonework; Terrazzo, tile, marble, mosaic work; Monuments & tombstones; Masonry & other stonework
CEO: Paul Klein
CFO: Lew Piper
Dir IT: Mike Castro

D-U-N-S 04-089-2317 IMP
■ **KDI TRANSITION CO INC**
KERR HEALTH CARE CENTERS
(*Suby of* WALGREEN CO) ★
3220 Spring Forest Rd, Raleigh, NC 27616-2822
Tel (412) 828-1884 *Founded/Ownrshp* 2013
Sales 389.1MM^E *EMP* 2,400
SIC 5912 Drug stores; Drug stores
CEO: Anthony N Civello
Pr: Kathy Kennedy
Ex VP: Chris Labbe
VP: Mark Gregory
Pharmcst: Steve Gluck
Pharmcst: Kim Hoang
Pharmcst: Billy Womack
Snr Mgr: Angelia Hayes

KDIC FM RADIO
See TRUSTEES OF GRINNELL COLLEGE

D-U-N-S 12-264-2820
KDK TRANSPORT INC
R & R EXPRESS
3 Crafton Sq, Pittsburgh, PA 15205-2831
Tel (412) 920-1336 *Founded/Ownrshp* 1985
Sales 46.5MM *EMP* 63
Accts Alpern Rosenthal Pittsburgh
SIC 4213 Contract haulers; Contract haulers
CEO: Ronald Reinerth
**Pr:* Richard S Francis
Brnch Mgr: Tom Ruff
Dir IT: David Brooking
Dir IT: Michelle Liang
Opers Mgr: Scott Troxell

KDKF
See KDRV CHANNEL 12

KDL
See KEYSTONE DEDICATED LOGISTICS CO LLC

KDLAMP COMPANY
See ATC LIGHTING & PLASTICS INC

D-U-N-S 00-120-2477 IMP
KDM ENTERPRISES LLC (IL)
820 Commerce Pkwy, Carpentersville, IL 60110-1721
Tel (847) 783-0333 *Founded/Ownrshp* 2000
Sales 29.0MM^E *EMP* 43
SIC 2621 4731 Paper mills; Freight transportation arrangement
CFO: Joseph Marzullo

KDM SCREEN PRINTING
See KDM SIGNS INC

D-U-N-S 05-510-4525
KDM SIGNS INC
KDM SCREEN PRINTING
10450 Medallion Dr, Cincinnati, OH 45241-3199
Tel (513) 769-1932 *Founded/Ownrshp* 1984
Sales 99.9MM^E *EMP* 337
SIC 2759 3993 Screen printing; Signs & advertising specialties; Screen printing; Signs & advertising specialties
Pr: Robert J Kissel
CFO: William Holbrook
Sec: Kathy McQueen
Prd Dir: Wesley Clark
Plnt Mgr: Bonnie Kissel
Prd Mgr: Dan Bergman
Sales Exec: Dominick Cuocci
Sales Exec: Charlie Leavitt
Natl Sales: Jon Kowal
Natl Sales: Jim Miller
Natl Sales: Jack Moran

D-U-N-S 01-917-3921 IMP
KDN HOLDINGS INC
AGAR SUPPLY CO.
225 John Hancock Rd, Taunton, MA 02780-7318
Tel (508) 821-2060 *Founded/Ownrshp* 1946
Sales NA *EMP* 375
SIC 5149

D-U-N-S 07-988-0509
KDR HOLDING INC
47448 Fremont Blvd, Fremont, CA 94538-6503
Tel (510) 230-2777 *Founded/Ownrshp* 2015
Sales 75.4MM^E *EMP* 204^E
SIC 6799 7372 Investors; Application computer software
Pr: James F Brear

D-U-N-S 07-775-6112
KDRV CHANNEL 12
KDKF
(*Suby of* KEZI INC) ★
1090 Knutson Ave, Medford, OR 97504-4164
Tel (541) 773-1212 *Founded/Ownrshp* 1993
Sales 34.9MM^E *EMP* 250
SIC 4833 8611 Television broadcasting stations; Business associations; Television broadcasting stations; Business associations
Genl Mgr: Mark Hatfield

KDS
See KOMAN DIVERSIFIED SERVICES LLC

D-U-N-S 07-116-1624
KDV LABEL CO INC
431 W Newhall Ave, Waukesha, WI 53186-6017
Tel (262) 544-5891 *Founded/Ownrshp* 1974
Sales 35.9MM *EMP* 112
Accts Vrakas/Blum Sc Brookfield
SIC 2672 Labels (unprinted), gummed: made from purchased materials; Labels (unprinted), gummed: made from purchased materials
CEO: Richard L Vaughn
**Pr:* Shane M Vaughn
**CFO:* Andrew Hulen
VP: Keith Seidel
**VP:* Karen D Vaughn
IT Man: Steve McBride

KDVG LAW
See KAUFMAN DOLOWICH VOLUCK & GONZO LLP

D-U-N-S 07-472-4626
KEADY JOHN PONTIAC CADILLAC OLDSMOBILE AND ISUZU INC (DE)
JOHN KEADY ISUZU
3210 E Kimberly Rd, Davenport, IA 52807-2500
Tel (563) 359-3611 *Founded/Ownrshp* 1982
Sales 27.5MM^E *EMP* 125
SIC 5511 7539 5531 7538 7532 5521 Automobiles, new & used; Pickups, new & used; Automotive repair shops; Automotive parts; Truck equipment & parts; General automotive repair shops; Top & body repair & paint shops; Used car dealers; Automobiles, new & used; Pickups, new & used; Automotive repair shops; Automotive parts; Truck equipment & parts; General automotive repair shops; Top & body repair & paint shops; Used car dealers
Pr: John Keady
**Treas:* Ted Smith
**VP:* Catherine Keady
Exec: Eric Dresing
**Genl Mgr:* Dennis Hendry

D-U-N-S 10-245-7967
KEAN MILLER LLP
400 Convention St Ste 700, Baton Rouge, LA 70802-5628
Tel (225) 387-0999 *Founded/Ownrshp* 1983
Sales 33.3MM^E *EMP* 230
SIC 8111 General practice law office; General practice law office
Pt: Ben R Miller Jr
**Pt:* Gary A Bezet
Pt: James R Chastain Jr
**Pt:* G Blane Clark Jr
**Pt:* William R D'Armond
**Pt:* Michael C Garrard
**Pt:* Vance A Gibbs
**Pt:* Isaac A Gregorie Jr
**Pt:* Maureen N Harbourt
Pt: Jay M Jalenak Jr
**Pt:* G William Jarman
**Pt:* M Dwayne Johnson
**Pt:* Leonard L Kilgore III
**Pt:* James R Lackie
**Pt:* Charles S McCowan Jr
CFO: Don Champagne

D-U-N-S 01-744-9260
KEAN UNIVERSITY
1000 Morris Ave Ste 1, Union, NJ 07083-7131
Tel (908) 737-5326 *Founded/Ownrshp* 2001
Sales 183.2MM *EMP* 8
Accts Wiss & Company Llp Iselin N
SIC 8221 Colleges universities & professional schools; Colleges universities & professional schools
Pr: Dawood Farahi
Pr: Marsha McCarthy
VP: Susan Kayne
Sales Asso: Myriam Charles

D-U-N-S 15-594-3111
KEAN UNIVERSITY REALTY FOUNDATION INC
RAPE SURVIVAL CENTER
1000 Morris Ave Ste 1, Union, NJ 07083-7133
Tel (908) 527-2000 *Founded/Ownrshp* 1855
Sales 123.8MM^E *EMP* 1,900
SIC 8221 College, except junior; College, except junior
Pr: Dawood Farahi
Bd of Dir: Maria Luciano
Ofcr: James Gurland
Ex VP: Johan Villegas
Genl Mgr: Ted Glynn
Dir IT: Joe Marinello

KEANE
See VENIO LLC

D-U-N-S 83-295-3959
KEANE FRAC LP
ULTRA TECH FRAC SERVICES
14235 Route 6, Mansfield, PA 16933-8828
Tel (570) 302-4050 *Founded/Ownrshp* 2009
Sales 37.7MM^E *EMP* 20
SIC 1381 Drilling oil & gas wells
CEO: James Stewart

D-U-N-S 07-951-2488
KEANE GROUP HOLDINGS LLC
11200 Westheimer Rd # 900, Houston, TX 77042-3229
Tel (713) 960-0381 *Founded/Ownrshp* 2011
Sales 314.5MM^E *EMP* 650^E
SIC 1381 7353 4212 Drilling oil & gas wells; Oil well drilling equipment, rental or leasing; Petroleum haulage, local; Drilling oil & gas wells; Oil well drilling equipment, rental or leasing; Petroleum haulage, local
CEO: James Stewart
CFO: Gregory Powell
Opers Mgr: John Soenen

KEANY PRODUCE COMPANY
See P J K FOOD SERVICE CORP

D-U-N-S 09-787-8680
KEARES INC
DOC HOLLIDAY'S STEAKHOUSE
300 W James St, Lancaster, PA 17603-2912
Tel (717) 396-8634 *Founded/Ownrshp* 1990
Sales 14.5MM^E *EMP* 425
SIC 5812 5813 American restaurant; Cocktail lounge; American restaurant; Cocktail lounge
**Pr:* Peter H Keares
**Ch:* Nicholas H Keares

D-U-N-S 19-515-6500
KEARFOTT CORP
(*Suby of* ASTRONAUTICS CORP OF AMERICA) ★
1150 Mcbride Ave Ste 1, Woodland Park, NJ 07424-2564
Tel (973) 785-6000 *Founded/Ownrshp* 1988
Sales 148.3MM^E *EMP* 1,050
Accts Bdo Seidman Llp Milwaukee W
SIC 3812 Search & navigation equipment; Search & navigation equipment
Pr: Ronald E Zelazo
COO: Jane Owen
CFO: Stephen G Givant
Prgrm Mgr: Dominic Pascucci
Prgrm Mgr: Marcos Simon
Genl Mgr: Middleton John
Plng Mgr: Rich Reidinger
QA Dir: Greg Gerard
QA Dir: Robin Robinson
IT Man: Vincent Giammona
IT Man: Natasha McLucas

D-U-N-S 01-851-0714
KEARN ALTERNATIVE CARE INC
2029 21st St, Bakersfield, CA 93301-4219
Tel (661) 631-2036 *Founded/Ownrshp* 1998
Sales 5.5MM^E *EMP* 305
SIC 8082 Home health care services; Home health care services
Pr: Jean Schamblin

D-U-N-S 18-657-6310
KEARNEY & CO PC
1701 Duke St Ste 500, Alexandria, VA 22314-3492
Tel (703) 931-5600 *Founded/Ownrshp* 1985
Sales 7.6MM^E *EMP* 380
SIC 8721

D-U-N-S 04-219-4456
KEARNEY CLINIC PC (NE)
211 W 33rd St Ste 1, Kearney, NE 68845-3485
Tel (308) 865-2141 *Founded/Ownrshp* 1952
Sales 36.2MM^E *EMP* 179
SIC 8011 8062 Offices & clinics of medical doctors; General medical & surgical hospitals
Pr: Feeth Ernst MD
**Sec:* M J Hanich MD
Genl Mgr: Josette McCenivelle
Off Mgr: Deb Jensen
Surgeon: Larry Bragg
Surgeon: Brent Steffen

D-U-N-S 96-122-4144
KEARNEY COMPANIES INC
4000 France Road Pkwy, New Orleans, LA 70126
Tel (504) 831-0266 *Founded/Ownrshp* 1996
Sales 20.2MM^E *EMP* 55
SIC 4225 4731 4449 General warehousing & storage; Customhouse brokers; Transportation (freight) on bays & sounds of the ocean
Pr: Michael W Kearney
**Sec:* Suzanne Kearney
**VP:* David W Kearney

D-U-N-S 05-350-4858
KEARNEY R-1 BOARD OF EDUCATION
KEARNEY SCHOOL DISTRICT
1002 S Jefferson St, Kearney, MO 64060-8770
Tel (816) 628-4116 *Founded/Ownrshp* 1800
Sales 38.5MM *EMP* 400
Accts Westbrook & Co Pc Cpas Ric
SIC 8211 Public elementary & secondary schools; Public elementary & secondary schools
**Pr:* Mike Miller
Treas: Jill Chaloupka
CTO: Daryl Rinne
Cmptr Lab: Connie Seuell

KEARNEY SCHOOL DISTRICT
See KEARNEY R-1 BOARD OF EDUCATION

D-U-N-S 10-004-8388
KEARNEY WEST HIGH SCHOOL
310 W 24th St, Kearney, NE 68845-5331
Tel (308) 698-8000 *Founded/Ownrshp* 1988
Sales 26.7MM^E *EMP* 461
Accts Mcdermott & Miller Pc Kearney
SIC 8211 Public elementary & secondary schools; Public elementary & secondary schools
Dir IT: Troy Dehaven
Teacher Pr: Lance Fuller
Psych: Lynette Womeldorf

D-U-N-S 04-319-0198 IMP
KEARNEY-NATIONAL INC
COTO TECHNOLOGY
(*Suby of* DYSON-KISSNER-MORAN CORP) ★
565 5th Ave Fl 4, New York, NY 10017-2424
Tel (212) 661-4600 *Founded/Ownrshp* 1988
Sales 178.8MM^E *EMP* 1,780
SIC 3679 3694 3714 3625 Electronic switches; Engine electrical equipment; Fuel systems & parts, motor vehicle; Relays & industrial controls; Electronic switches; Engine electrical equipment; Fuel systems & parts, motor vehicle; Relays & industrial controls
Ch Bd: Robert R Dyson
**VP:* Marc Feldman
VP: Sue Frazier

D-U-N-S 17-677-3216 IMP
KEARNEYS METALS INC
2660 S Dearing Ave, Fresno, CA 93725-2104
Tel (559) 233-2591 *Founded/Ownrshp* 1965
Sales 20.6MM^E *EMP* 41
SIC 3363 Aluminum die-castings
Pr: Michael T Kearney
**Sec:* Gary Kearney

D-U-N-S 09-222-6356
■ **KEARNY BANK**
(*Suby of* KEARNY FINANCIAL CORP) ★
120 Passaic Ave, Fairfield, NJ 07004-3523
Tel (973) 244-4500 *Founded/Ownrshp* 2001
Sales NA *EMP* 255
SIC 6035 Federal savings banks; Federal savings banks
Ch Bd: John Mazur
CFO: William Ledgerwood
Treas: Albert E Gossweiler
VP: Coronato Frank
VP: Timothy Swanson
Board of Directors: Raymond E Chandonnet, Christopher D Petermann

D-U-N-S 10-500-7967
KEARNY BOARD OF EDUCATION
100 Davis Ave Ste 2, Kearny, NJ 07032-3398
Tel (201) 955-5021 *Founded/Ownrshp* 1800
Sales 46.7MM^E *EMP* 1,087
SIC 8211 Public elementary & secondary schools; Public elementary & secondary schools
Pr Dir: Kelly Lindenfelser
HC Dir: Donna Dyl

D-U-N-S 08-742-2333
KEARNY COUNTY HOSPITAL
500 E Thorpe St, Lakin, KS 67860-9625
Tel (620) 355-1365 *Founded/Ownrshp* 1952
Sales 25.7MM^E *EMP* 202^E
SIC 8062 General medical & surgical hospitals; General medical & surgical hospitals
COO: Arlo Reimer
Dir Lab: Keith Pothuisje
IT Man: James Bemis
IT Man: Lisa Kay-Garcia
S&M/VP: Jennifer Davenport
Doctor: Julie Munson
Nrsg Dir: Pam Twilleger
Phys Thrpy: Kimmie Lennington
HC Dir: Kimberely Meyer
Snr Mgr: Kelly Speckman

KEARNY FEDERAL SAVINGS BANK
See KEARNY MHC

D-U-N-S 07-544-5866
■ **KEARNY FEDERAL SAVINGS BANK** (NJ)
(*Suby of* KEARNY BANK) ★
120 Passaic Ave, Fairfield, NJ 07004-3523
Tel (973) 439-0927 *Founded/Ownrshp* 1943
Sales NA *EMP* 135
SIC 6022 State commercial banks; State commercial banks
CEO: Craig L Montanaro
**CFO:* Albert Gossweiler
Ofcr: Donna Portuesi
**Sr VP:* Sharon Jones
VP: Margaret Sanchez
VP: Nancy Slingland
VP: Robert Slowikowski
VP: Keith Suchodolski
Brnch Mgr: Casandra Degutis
Board of Directors: Kathleen Fisher, John Hopkins, Bernard Leung M D, Richard Masch, James Mason, Robert Miller

D-U-N-S 16-982-0748
■ **KEARNY FINANCIAL CORP**
(*Suby of* KEARNY FEDERAL SAVINGS BANK) ★
120 Passaic Ave, Fairfield, NJ 07004-3523
Tel (973) 244-4500 *Founded/Ownrshp* 2001
Sales NA *EMP* 491^E
Accts Bdo Usa Llp New York New Yo
Tkr Sym KRNY *Exch* NGS
SIC 6035 Savings institutions, federally chartered; Savings institutions, federally chartered
Pr: Craig L Montanaro
**Ch Bd:* John J Mazur Jr
COO: William C Ledgerwood
CFO: Eric B Heyer
Ofcr: Patrick M Joyce
Ex VP: Sharon Jones
Ex VP: Erika K Parisi
Sr VP: Khanh B Vuong

D-U-N-S 02-835-3506
KEARNY MESA AUTOMOTIVE CO
JIMMIE JOHNSON KEARNY
7978 Balboa Ave, San Diego, CA 92111-2415
Tel (858) 560-9008 *Founded/Ownrshp* 2005
Sales 38.6MM^E *EMP* 111
SIC 5511 Automobiles, new & used; Pickups, new & used; Vans, new & used; Automobiles, new & used; Pickups, new & used; Vans, new & used
Pr: Jim Perkins

D-U-N-S 12-080-8915
■ **KEARNY MESA TOYOTA INC**
(*Suby of* PENSKE AUTOMOTIVE GROUP INC) ★
4910 Kearny Mesa Rd, San Diego, CA 92111-2407
Tel (858) 279-8151 *Founded/Ownrshp* 1970
Sales 64.6MM^E *EMP* 52^E
SIC 5511 Automobiles, new & used
Pr: George Brochick
Genl Mgr: Francois Chaker
Genl Mgr: Scotty McBean
Sls Mgr: Ali Asad
Sls Mgr: Paul Bunning
Sls Mgr: Case Culiver
Sls Mgr: Steven Rogers
Sls Mgr: Honore Vernon
Sales Asso: Cyrus Ghahremani

D-U-N-S 16-960-1841
▲ **KEARNY MHC**
KEARNY FEDERAL SAVINGS BANK
120 Passaic Ave, Fairfield, NJ 07004-3523
Tel (973) 244-4500 *Founded/Ownrshp* 2001
Sales NA *EMP* 556
SIC 6035 Savings institutions, federally chartered; Savings institutions, federally chartered
**Ch Bd:* John J Mazur
COO: Erika Sacher
Treas: William Ledgerwood
Sr VP: Patrick Joyce
VP: Allan Cronheim
VP: Grace Cruz-Beyer
VP: Cheryl Lyons
VP: Donna Porcaro
VP: Marry Webb
Dir IT: Tim Swanson
Site Mgr: Anna Wright

KEARNY PEARSON FORD
See SUNROAD AUTO LLC

D-U-N-S 80-972-0860
KEARNY PUBLIC SCHOOLS
100 Davis Ave, Kearny, NJ 07032-3328
Tel (201) 955-5000 *Founded/Ownrshp* 2008
Sales 22.5MM^E *EMP* 582^E
SIC 8211 Public elementary & secondary schools
Pr: George King
Bd of Dir: Barbara Cifelli
Bd of Dir: Mercedes Davidson
Bd of Dir: James Hill
**VP:* Paul Castelli
Dir IT: Neil Brohm

Dir IT: Kimberly Kyak
Pr Dir: Kelly Lindenfelser
Schl Brd P: Bernadette McDonald
Psych: Frank Armenio
Psych: Alexandra Garcia

D-U-N-S 01-137-1267
KEARNY SHOP RITE INC
KEARNY SHOP-RITE PHARMACY DEPT
100 Passaic Ave, Kearny, NJ 07032-1140
Tel (201) 991-3568 *Founded/Ownrshp* 1957
Sales 31.4MM^E *EMP* 350
SIC 5411 5912 Supermarkets; Drug stores & proprietary stores; Supermarkets; Drug stores & proprietary stores
Pr: Richard Tully

KEARNY SHOP-RITE PHARMACY DEPT
See KEARNY SHOP RITE INC

D-U-N-S 00-244-7993
KEARNY STEEL CONTAINER CORP
401 South St, Newark, NJ 07105-1976
Tel (973) 589-2070 *Founded/Ownrshp* 1950
Sales 32.0MM^E *EMP* 60
SIC 5085 Barrels, new or reconditioned; Drums, new or reconditioned
Pr: Michael Verzaleno

D-U-N-S 07-633-4986
KEARSLEY COMMUNITY SCHOOLS (INC)
4396 Underhill Dr, Flint, MI 48506-1534
Tel (810) 591-9816 *Founded/Ownrshp* 1937
Sales 23.9MM^E *EMP* 500
SIC 8211 Public elementary school; Public senior high school; Public elementary school; Public senior high school
Instr Medi: Derrita Manningham

KEATING BUILDING COMPANY
See DANIEL J KEATING CONSTRUCTION CO LLC

D-U-N-S 07-287-2534
KEATING MUETHING & KLEKAMP PLL
KMK
1 E 4th St Ste 1400, Cincinnati, OH 45202-3752
Tel (513) 579-6400 *Founded/Ownrshp* 1955
Sales 55.5MM^E *EMP* 400
SIC 8111 General practice law office; General practice law office
Sr Pt: Donald P Klekamp
Sr Pt: Stephen Goodson
Pt: Jody T Klekamp
Pt: Mary Ellen Malas
Pt: Paul V Muething
Pt: Christy M Nageleisen
Mng Pt: Paul Muething
Exec: Randall Ayers
Counsel: J Hurst
Counsel: Timothy Matthews
Counsel: Linda Schaffer

D-U-N-S 05-784-0761 IMP
KEATING OF CHICAGO INC
8901 W 50th St, Mc Cook, IL 60525-6001
Tel (708) 246-3000 *Founded/Ownrshp* 1939
Sales 28.9MM^E *EMP* 80
SIC 5046 Cooking equipment, commercial; Cooking equipment, commercial
Pr: Eliza Keating
IT Man: Dave Adams

D-U-N-S 00-509-7464 IMP
KEATS MANUFACTURING CO
350 Holbrook Dr, Wheeling, IL 60090-5812
Tel (847) 520-1133 *Founded/Ownrshp* 1958
Sales 31.7MM^E *EMP* 100
SIC 3496 3312 Clips & fasteners, made from purchased wire; Tool & die steel
CEO: Wade Keats
**COO:* Matt Eggemeyer
**CFO:* Ron McConville
**VP:* Matthew Keats
Plnt Mgr: Herb Fink
Ql Cn Mgr: Matt Bujak

D-U-N-S 83-728-2201
KEC ENGINEERING
200 N Sherman Ave, Corona, CA 92882-7162
Tel (951) 734-3010 *Founded/Ownrshp* 1953
Sales 23.2MM^E *EMP* 110
SIC 1611 Highway & street construction; Highway & street construction
Pr: James Elfring
**VP:* Les Card
VP: Matthew Card
**VP:* Scott Pfeiffer
Sfty Mgr: Steve Urban

D-U-N-S 01-111-6907
KECK GRADUATE INSTITUTE (CA)
KGI
535 Watson Dr, Claremont, CA 91711-4817
Tel (909) 621-8000 *Founded/Ownrshp* 1997
Sales 22.5MM *EMP* 65^E
Accts Moss Adams Llp Stockton Ca
SIC 8733 Research institute
Pr: Sheldon M Schuster
**Pr:* T Gregory Dewey
**CFO:* Robert W Caragher
CFO: Andy Davenport
Sr VP: Larry Couture
**VP:* Kerry Howell
**VP:* Michael Jones
VP: Brian Kelley
VP: Jim Osborne
**VP:* Matthew T Reed
VP: Karen Schneider
VP: James Sterling
VP: Chas Syndergaard
VP: Buff Wright

D-U-N-S 07-933-9971 IMP
KECK HOSPITAL OF USC
1500 San Pablo St, Los Angeles, CA 90033-5313
Tel (800) 872-2273 *Founded/Ownrshp* 2013
Sales 685.0MM *EMP* 86^E
SIC 8011 Health maintenance organization
CFO: Kamyar Afshar

Exec: Karen Chapman
HC Dir: Mike Fong
Snr Mgr: Gus Lowery

D-U-N-S 01-431-4959
KECKS FOOD SERVICE INC
2796 Route 328, Millerton, PA 16936-9644
Tel (570) 537-2515 *Founded/Ownrshp* 1964
Sales 63.0MM^E *EMP* 83
SIC 5142 5147 5461 5141 5148 Packaged frozen goods; Meats, fresh; Bakeries; Groceries, general line; Fresh fruits & vegetables; Packaged frozen goods; Meats, fresh; Bakeries; Groceries, general line; Fresh fruits & vegetables
Pr: Brian Keck
**Ch Bd:* Ronald W Keck
**VP:* Greg Gleason

KEDREN ACUTE PSYCHIA HOSPIT AN
See KEDREN COMMUNITY HEALTH CENTER INC

D-U-N-S 07-531-9616
KEDREN COMMUNITY HEALTH CENTER INC
KEDREN ACUTE PSYCHIA HOSPIT AN
4211 Avalon Blvd, Los Angeles, CA 90011-5622
Tel (323) 233-0425 *Founded/Ownrshp* 1965
Sales 55.3MM *EMP* 800
Accts Qiu Accountancy Corporation L
SIC 8063 8093 Hospital for the mentally ill; Specialty outpatient clinics; Hospital for the mentally ill; Specialty outpatient clinics
Ofcr: John Griffith
**Treas:* Robert Lawson
Psych: Billie Ivra

D-U-N-S 09-918-5076
■ **KEDS LLC**
(*Suby of* STRIDE RITE CORP) ★
191 Spring St, Lexington, MA 02421-8045
Tel (617) 824-6000 *Founded/Ownrshp* 1979
Sales 100.8MM^E *EMP* 500
SIC 5139 5661 Footwear, athletic; Shoes; Shoe stores; Footwear, athletic; Shoes; Shoe stores
Pr: Pamela Salkovitz
CFO: Frank Karuso
Treas: Gordon W Johnson
VP: John J Nannicelli
Genl Mgr: Peter Charles
Genl Mgr: Julie Forsyth
VP Mktg: Sue Dooley

D-U-N-S 83-314-8476
KEE ACTION SPORTS HOLDINGS INC
(*Suby of* G.I SPORTZ INC)
570 Mantua Blvd, Sewell, NJ 08080-1022
Tel (856) 464-1068 *Founded/Ownrshp* 2015
Sales 91.3MM^E *EMP* 386
SIC 5091 6719 Sporting & recreation goods; Personal holding companies, except banks; Sporting & recreation goods; Personal holding companies, except banks
CEO: George Eurick
CFO: Frank J Rizzo

D-U-N-S 78-820-1924 IMP/EXP
KEE ACTION SPORTS LLC
(*Suby of* KEE ACTION SPORTS HOLDINGS INC) ★
570 Mantua Blvd, Sewell, NJ 08080-1022
Tel (856) 464-1068 *Founded/Ownrshp* 2006
Sales 91.3MM^E *EMP* 275
Accts Pricewaterhousecoopers Llp Ph
SIC 5091 3949 Sporting & recreation goods; Sporting & athletic goods; Sporting & recreation goods; Sporting & athletic goods
Pr: John Robinson
CFO: Mark Malone
VP: Billy Ceranski
VP: Chris York
Exec: Carole Taylor
IT Man: Jeff Frye
Genl Couns: Jeffrey Horowitz
Snr Mgr: Louis Spicer

KEEBLER
See KELLOGG CARIBBEAN SERVICES CO INC

D-U-N-S 00-132-6065 EXP
■ **KEEBLER CO**
(*Suby of* KELLOGG CO) ★
1 Kellogg Sq, Battle Creek, MI 49017-3534
Tel (630) 956-9887 *Founded/Ownrshp* 1927, 2001
Sales 1.1MMM^E *EMP* 12,000
SIC 2052 2051 Cookies; Crackers, dry; Cones, ice cream; Pretzels; Bread, cake & related products; Cookies; Crackers, dry; Cones, ice cream; Pretzels; Bread, cake & related products
Pr: David McKay

D-U-N-S 80-587-8340
■ **KEEBLER FOODS CO**
(*Suby of* KELLOGG CO) ★
677 N Larch Ave, Elmhurst, IL 60126-1521
Tel (630) 833-2900 *Founded/Ownrshp* 2001
Sales 71.4MM^E *EMP* 146^E
SIC 2052 Cookies & crackers
CFO: E Nichol McCully
VP: Jeff Boser
VP: James T Willard
VP Mktg: Roger Kalinowski
Mktg Mgr: Frank Schade
Mktg Mgr: Scott Sundheim
Board of Directors: Amos R McMullian Jimmy M

D-U-N-S 03-946-1777 IMP/EXP
KEECO LLC
30736 Wiegman Rd, Hayward, CA 94544-7819
Tel (510) 324-8800 *Founded/Ownrshp* 1977
Sales 69.8MM^E *EMP* 209
SIC 5023 2392 Linens & towels; Linens, table; Household furnishings; Linens & towels; Linens, table; Household furnishings
**Pr:* Ben Steingl
Ex VP: Bruce Garfinkel

D-U-N-S 01-209-1427
■ **KEEFE BRUYETTE & WOODS INC**
(*Suby of* KBW LLC) ★
787 7th Ave Fl 4, New York, NY 10019-6080
Tel (212) 887-7777 *Founded/Ownrshp* 1962
Sales 110.4MM^E *EMP* 450
Accts Ernst & Young Llp New York N
SIC 6211 Brokers, security; Dealers, security; Investment bankers; Brokers, security; Dealers, security; Investment bankers
Pr: Andrew M Senchak
CEO: Thomas Michaud
CFO: Jeff Fox
CFO: Robert Giambrone
Ex VP: Rick Maples
Ex VP: Dennis O'Rourke
Ex VP: James B Penny
Ex VP: Peter J Wirth
Sr VP: Nikolei Bjorkedal
Sr VP: Bernard Caffrey
Sr VP: Charles Crowley
Sr VP: Thomas M Ekert
Sr VP: Tim Guba
Sr VP: Philip Haggard
Sr VP: Rick Jeffrey
Sr VP: Mary Johnstone
Sr VP: Edward Kreppein
Sr VP: Bryce Nucera
Sr VP: Roger Puccio-Johnson
Sr VP: Patrick Ryan
Sr VP: Arthur Sarzen

D-U-N-S 55-666-2851
KEEFE GROUP LLC
KEEFE SUPPLY COMPANY
(*Suby of* CENTRIC GROUP LLC) ★
10880 Linpage Pl, Saint Louis, MO 63132-1008
Tel (314) 963-8700 *Founded/Ownrshp* 2003
Sales 98.4MM^E *EMP* 1,099^E
SIC 7389 Packaging & labeling services
CEO: James Theiss
Pr: Ken Dubinsky
Pr: Tim Nichols
Pr: Dean Pollnow
**CEO:* John Spesia
VP: Dana Dierdorf
VP: Darren Drexler
VP: Paul Eifert
**VP:* Paul Scherer
Exec: Carla Knysak
Off Mgr: Katie Schneider

KEEFE PLUMBING SERVICES
See H L MOE CO INC

KEEFE SUPPLY COMPANY
See KEEFE GROUP LLC

KEELER HONDA, BMW
See KEELER MOTOR CAR CO LIMITED PARTNERSHIP

D-U-N-S 01-281-8183
KEELER MOTOR CAR CO LIMITED PARTNERSHIP
KEELER HONDA, BMW
1111 Troy Schenectady Rd, Latham, NY 12110-1094
Tel (518) 785-4197 *Founded/Ownrshp* 1966
Sales 50.3MM^E *EMP* 125
SIC 5511 5521 7538 7532 7515 5531 Automobiles, new & used; Used car dealers; General automotive repair shops; Top & body repair & paint shops; Passenger car leasing; Automotive & home supply stores; New & used car dealers; Used car dealers; General automotive repair shops; Top & body repair & paint shops; Passenger car leasing; Automotive & home supply stores
Mng Pt: Alexander Keeler
Treas: Charles W Whelan
Dir Bus: Maria Dunning
Genl Mgr: Joseph Messner
Genl Mgr: Kevin Oneill
Genl Mgr: Luis Pabon
Genl Mgr: Heath Walajtys
Genl Mgr: Henry Wolford
IT Man: Seth Trowbridge
Trfc Dir: June Benya
Trfc Dir: Steve Delorme

D-U-N-S 00-649-2417
KEELEY & SONS INC
6303 Collinsville Rd, East Saint Louis, IL 62201-2523
Tel (618) 271-7470 *Founded/Ownrshp* 1947
Sales 21.7MM^E *EMP* 80
SIC 1611 1622 General contractor, highway & street construction; Bridge construction
Pr: Eugene T Keeley
**Treas:* Henry E Keeley
**VP:* Mark E Keeley
Off Mgr: Dinese Mathews
Off Mgr: Denise M Matthews

KEELEY COMPANIES, THE
See L KEELEY CONSTRUCTION CO

D-U-N-S 04-143-0414 IMP
KEELING CO
4227 E 43rd St, North Little Rock, AR 72117-2536
Tel (501) 945-4511 *Founded/Ownrshp* 1965
Sales 60.4MM^E *EMP* 120^E
Accts Bkd Llp
SIC 5074 5084 Plumbing & hydronic heating supplies; Engines, gasoline; Engines & parts, diesel
Pr: Joe E Keeling Jr
Treas: Helen Keeling
**Sec:* Melissa K Lorg
**VP:* James Keeling

D-U-N-S 07-156-1328
KEEN BATTLE MEAD & CO
7850 Nw 146th St Ste 200, Miami Lakes, FL 33016-1586
Tel (305) 558-1101 *Founded/Ownrshp* 1972
Sales NA *EMP* 60
SIC 6331 6321 6311 Automobile insurance; Property damage insurance; Accident & health insurance; Life insurance
Co-Ownr: Michael Battle
CFO: Naomi Dominick

Dir IT: Edward Knox
Mktg Dir: Dungan Cari

D-U-N-S 00-248-4723
KEEN COMPRESSED GAS CO
101 Rogers Rd Ste 200, Wilmington, DE 19801-5797
Tel (302) 594-4545 *Founded/Ownrshp* 1987
Sales 28.4MM *EMP* 92
Accts Gunnip & Company Llp Wilmingt
SIC 5085 5169 Welding supplies; Gases, compressed & liquefied; Welding supplies; Gases, compressed & liquefied
Pr: Bryan Keen
**CEO:* J Merrill Keen
**CFO:* David Haas
**VP:* Jon Keen
Sls Mgr: Steven Culver
Sales Asso: Jack Corbett

KEEN FOOTWEAR
See KEEN INC

D-U-N-S 14-159-0559 IMP
KEEN INC
KEEN FOOTWEAR
515 Nw 13th Ave, Portland, OR 97209-3000
Tel (503) 402-1520 *Founded/Ownrshp* 2006
Sales 176.2MM^E *EMP* 125^E
SIC 5139 5661 Footwear; Footwear, athletic; Footwear; Footwear, athletic
CEO: Rory Fuerst
**CFO:* John Barron
Sr VP: Francisco Garbayo
CTO: Jim Velden
IT Man: Jason Parrish
IT Man: Steve Schantin
Tech Mgr: Johnny Madsen
Ql Cn Mgr: Derek Newell
Mktg Dir: David Munk
Mktg Mgr: Kirsten Blackburn
Mktg Mgr: Becky Chambers
Board of Directors: Robin Smith

D-U-N-S 00-986-9801
KEEN TRANSPORT INC
(*Suby of* PLATINUM EQUITY LLC) ★
1951 Harrisburg Pike, Carlisle, PA 17015-7304
Tel (717) 243-6885 *Founded/Ownrshp* 2012
Sales 156.7MM^E *EMP* 550
SIC 4213 Heavy machinery transport; Heavy machinery transport
CEO: Christopher R Easter
**Treas:* Kenneth Sheibley
Ex VP: Betsy Keen
**Ex VP:* Elizabeth Keen
VP: Carol Barrett
**VP:* Dan Higgins
VP: Jesse Keen
**VP:* Alan Shilvock
Rgnl Mgr: Tom Sheedy
Off Mgr: Linda Kulp
Off Admin: Melissa Nelson

D-U-N-S 18-874-4916
KEENA STAFF INC
KEENA STAFFING SERVICES
2 Progress Blvd, Queensbury, NY 12804-3202
Tel (518) 793-9825 *Founded/Ownrshp* 1985
Sales 73.6MM^E *EMP* 1,800
SIC 7361 7363 Employment agencies; Temporary help service; Employment agencies; Temporary help service
Owner: Connie Gerarde
VP Opers: Michael Niles

KEENA STAFFING SERVICES
See KEENA STAFF INC

D-U-N-S 06-668-8441
KEENAN & ASSOCIATES
2355 Crenshaw Blvd # 200, Torrance, CA 90501-3395
Tel (310) 212-3344 *Founded/Ownrshp* 1972
Sales NA *EMP* 675
SIC 6411 Insurance brokers; Insurance brokers
Ch Bd: John Keenan
**CEO:* Sean Smith
**COO:* Davis Seres
Ex VP: Dave Dewenter
**Sr VP:* Henry Loubet
VP: Toni Hendel
VP: Robert Herrmann
VP: Tim Keenan
VP: James C Krieg
VP: Rick McHale
**VP:* Keith Pippard
VP: Bharat Saoji

D-U-N-S 03-611-5822
KEENAN ENERGY CO
3923 W Beltline Blvd, Columbia, SC 29204-1503
Tel (803) 256-0667 *Founded/Ownrshp* 1920
Sales 70.2MM^E *EMP* 115^E
SIC 5171 Petroleum bulk stations; Petroleum bulk stations
Pr: William J Keenan II

D-U-N-S 03-097-5106 IMP/EXP
KEENAN FARMS INC
31510 Plymouth Ave, Kettleman City, CA 93239-9721
Tel (559) 945-1400 *Founded/Ownrshp* 1974
Sales 28.4MM^E *EMP* 100
SIC 0173 2068 Pistachio grove; Nuts: dried, dehydrated, salted or roasted
CEO: Robert M Keenan
VP: Manny Guerrero
**VP:* Charles J Keenan III
Off Mgr: Catherine Underwood
IT Man: Bob Keenan
IT Man: Teresa Keenan

D-U-N-S 13-195-7722 EXP
KEENAN HOPKINS SCHMIDT AND STOWELL CONTRACTORS INC
KHS&S CONTRACTORS
5422 Bay Center Dr # 200, Tampa, FL 33609-3437
Tel (813) 628-9330 *Founded/Ownrshp* 1984
Sales 110.9MM *EMP* 350
Accts B2d Semago Tampa Florida

SIC 1542 1742 Commercial & office building, new construction; Plastering, drywall & insulation; Commercial & office building, new construction; Plastering, drywall & insulation
Pr: Michael R Cannon
**Ch Bd:* Mark Keenan
**CFO:* Lynda Licht
CFO: David Williams
**Sr VP:* Michael Carrigan
**Sr VP:* Daniel F Casey Jr
**Sr VP:* Thomas J Gibbons
**Sr VP:* Neal W Harris Jr
**Sr VP:* Tony L Hemgesberg
**Sr VP:* Robert C Luker
**Sr VP:* Robert J McCarthy
**Sr VP:* Erik S Santiago
**VP:* Robert Evans
VP: Mark Gill
**VP:* Ted Malone
**VP:* Thomas Pickford
**VP:* Matthew Pollard
**VP:* Richard Pollicino
**VP:* Jess Robinson
**VP:* Angela Sechrest
VP: Derek Stevens

D-U-N-S 00-929-0032 IMP
KEENAN HOPKINS SUDER & STOWELL CONTRACTORS INC
KHS & S CONTRACTORS
5109 E La Palma Ave Ste A, Anaheim, CA 92807-2066
Tel (714) 695-3670 *Founded/Ownrshp* 1996
Sales 264.6MM^E^ *EMP* 2,000
Accts Moore Stephens Wurth Frazer An
SIC 1742 1751 1743 1741 1721 Plastering, plain or ornamental; Carpentry work; Terrazzo, tile, marble, mosaic work; Masonry & other stonework; Painting & paper hanging; Plastering, plain or ornamental; Carpentry work; Terrazzo, tile, marble, mosaic work; Masonry & other stonework; Painting & paper hanging
Pr: David Suder
Pr: Jeff Castagnola
**COO:* Philip Cherne
**Treas:* Dennis Norman
Sr VP: Mark Gill
**Sr VP:* John Platon
Sr VP: Jim Stafford
VP: Rod Lee
VP: Jeff Miller
VP: Amberly Sacalas
VP: Kelly Sell
VP: Keith Volesky

D-U-N-S 14-732-1236 IMP
KEENAN MOTORS LTD
856 N Easton Rd, Doylestown, PA 18902-1007
Tel (215) 348-0800 *Founded/Ownrshp* 1984
Sales 34.9MM^E^ *EMP* 100
SIC 5511 Automobiles, new & used; Automobiles, new & used
Pr: James Peruto
IT Man: Steve Makowski
Sls Mgr: Erwin Bieber
Sales Asso: Bob Johnson
Sales Asso: Mike Ventresca

D-U-N-S 05-633-3529
KEENE CHRYSLER INC
410 Winchester St, Keene, NH 03431-3912
Tel (603) 357-0808 *Founded/Ownrshp* 1971
Sales 22.1MM^E^ *EMP* 50
SIC 5511 Automobiles, new & used
Pr: Michael Korpi
Sales Exec: Paul Blanchette

D-U-N-S 04-023-0302
KEENE DARTMOUTH HITCHCOCK
590 Court St, Keene, NH 03431-1719
Tel (603) 357-3411 *Founded/Ownrshp* 1948
Sales 16.9MM^E^ *EMP* 350
SIC 8011 Clinic, operated by physicians; Clinic, operated by physicians
Doctor: Geraldine Rubin

D-U-N-S 02-145-9839
KEENE DODGE CO INC
3707 Norrisville Rd, Jarrettsville, MD 21084-1418
Tel (410) 692-5111 *Founded/Ownrshp* 1980
Sales 33.0MM *EMP* 66
SIC 5511

D-U-N-S 07-397-6409
KEENE MEDICAL PRODUCTS INC
5 Landing Rd, Enfield, NH 03748-3545
Tel (603) 448-5290 *Founded/Ownrshp* 1975
Sales 21.4MM^E^ *EMP* 110
SIC 7352 5999

KEENE MITSUBISHI
See FAIRFIELDS CADILLAC BUICK GMC INC

D-U-N-S 55-588-6324
KEENE SCHOOL DISTRICT
193 Maple Ave, Keene, NH 03431-3392
Tel (603) 357-9002 *Founded/Ownrshp* 1865
Sales 27.9MM^E^ *EMP* 600
SIC 8211 Public elementary & secondary schools; Public elementary & secondary schools
Prin: Victor Sokul

D-U-N-S 11-124-9061
KEENE STATE COLLEGE CHEERLEADERS
(*Suby of* U N H) ★
229 Main St Student Ctr, Keene, NH 03435-0001
Tel (603) 358-2476 *Founded/Ownrshp* 1981
Sales 17.2MM^E^ *EMP* 323^E^
SIC 8221 Colleges universities & professional schools
Prin: Chris Fecteau
VP: Maryann Lindberg
Sls Mgr: Samer Aly

D-U-N-S 07-133-6465 IMP
KEENELAND ASSOCIATION INC
4201 Versailles Rd, Lexington, KY 40510-9662
Tel (859) 288-4236 *Founded/Ownrshp* 1936
Sales 121.0MM^E^ *EMP* 100
SIC 5154 7948 0751 Auctioning livestock; Thoroughbred horse racing; Livestock services, except veterinary; Auctioning livestock; Thoroughbred horse racing; Livestock services, except veterinary
CEO: Bill Thomason
**Ch Bd:* James E Bassett III
**Treas:* Stanley H Jones
**VP:* Vince Gabbert

D-U-N-S 07-204-7053 IMP
KEENER CORP
5300 Western Ave, Connersville, IN 47331-9703
Tel (765) 825-4193 *Founded/Ownrshp* 1974
Sales 32.5MM^E^ *EMP* 125
SIC 3535 Conveyors & conveying equipment; Conveyors & conveying equipment
Pr: Gary Keener Sr

D-U-N-S 80-722-6840
KEENER MANAGEMENT INC
1746 N St Nw, Washington, DC 20036-2907
Tel (202) 833-3050 *Founded/Ownrshp* 1985
Sales 40.0MM *EMP* 65^E^
SIC 6513 Apartment building operators; Apartment building operators
Pr: Claude Keener Jr
**VP:* Gary I Squire

D-U-N-S 00-115-5159 IMP
KEENEY MANUFACTURING CO
PLUMB PAK MEDICAL
1170 Main St, Newington, CT 06111-3098
Tel (603) 239-6371 *Founded/Ownrshp* 1923
Sales 124.7MM *EMP* 500
SIC 3432 5074 Plumbers' brass goods: drain cocks, faucets, spigots, etc.; Plumbing fittings & supplies; Plumbers' brass goods: drain cocks, faucets, spigots, etc.; Plumbing fittings & supplies
CEO: Robert S Holden
Ch: Jean Hanna Holden
Treas: Kenneth L Collett
Ex VP: James H Holden
VP: Edwin F Atkins
VP: Ken Colete
VP: Stephen Cook
VP: Stephen A Cooke
VP: Rachel Garate
VP: Chris Jeffers
VP: Wayne Moore
Board of Directors: Virginia Holden Atkins, Jessica Holden

KEENSBURG SCHOOL DISTRICT RE-3
See WELD COUNTY SCHOOL DISTRICT RE-3J

D-U-N-S 09-811-2790 IMP/EXP
KEEPER CORP
(*Suby of* HAMPTON PRODUCTS INTERNATIONAL CORP) ★
322 Main St Ste 9, Willimantic, CT 06226-3152
Tel (860) 456-4151 *Founded/Ownrshp* 2006
Sales 21.0MM^E^ *EMP* 170
SIC 5131 Narrow fabrics; Narrow fabrics
Pr: Kenneth L Porter III
**CFO:* Ray Hunt
Sls Mgr: Gary Schenck

KEEPSIE NISSAN
See NISSAN POUGHKEEPSIE INC

D-U-N-S 82-519-7585
KEES KAR INC
1499 E Camelback Rd, Phoenix, AZ 85014-3333
Tel (602) 265-6600 *Founded/Ownrshp* 1998
Sales 21.3MM^E^ *EMP* 124
SIC 5511 Automobiles, new & used; Automobiles, new & used
Pr: William C Epperson

D-U-N-S 01-038-9609
KEESLER FEDERAL CREDIT UNION
KFCU
2602 Pass Rd, Biloxi, MS 39531-2728
Tel (228) 385-5500 *Founded/Ownrshp* 1947
Sales NA *EMP* 432
SIC 6061 Federal credit unions; Federal credit unions
Pr: John R Goff
**Pr:* Jerry Caldwell
Ofcr: Joel Gregory
Ofcr: Carol Robinson
Sr VP: Mel Valenzuela
**VP:* Cindy Childers
VP: Delma Powell
VP: Ann Selvage
**VP:* Richard Tolar
**Ex Dir:* D S Broome
Brnch Mgr: Vicki Bush

KEETER FORD LINCOLNS & MERCURY
See KEETER MOTORS INC

D-U-N-S 02-480-4072
KEETER MOTORS INC (NC)
KEETER FORD LINCOLNS & MERCURY
1775 E Dixon Blvd, Shelby, NC 28152-6946
Tel (704) 482-6791 *Founded/Ownrshp* 1936
Sales 24.1MM^E^ *EMP* 65
SIC 5511 Automobiles, new & used; Pickups, new & used; Automobiles, new & used; Pickups, new & used
Pr: H S Keeter Jr
**VP:* Sandra Keeter

D-U-N-S 11-848-4190
KEETON INTERNATIONAL LLC
1209 Nandina Cir, North Little Rock, AR 72116-5115
Tel (501) 771-1771 *Founded/Ownrshp* 2001
Sales 70.0MM *EMP* 3
SIC 5421 5144 Meat markets, including freezer provisioners; Freezer provisioners, meat; Poultry & poultry products

D-U-N-S 07-101-6893
KEEVILY SPERO WHITELAW INC
500 Mmaroneck Ave Ste 405, Harrison, NY 10528
Tel (914) 381-5511 *Founded/Ownrshp* 1983
Sales NA *EMP* 50
SIC 6411 Insurance agents, brokers & service
Ch Bd: Thomas F Mc Evily Jr
**Pr:* Thomas Mc Evily III
COO: Ellen Teenan
**Ch:* William Kaufman
**Sec:* Michael Mc Evily
**VP:* Kenneth W Kaufman
Exec: Paul Moskowitz
CTO: Rebecca Walkley
IT Man: Pawel Ochman
S&M/VP: Tony Caggiano
Sls Dir: Dina Bonifacio

D-U-N-S 07-843-4632
KEFFER AUTOMOTIVE GROUP LLC (NC)
13651 Statesville Rd, Huntersville, NC 28078-9013
Tel (704) 766-2121 *Founded/Ownrshp* 2007
Sales 30.6MM^E^ *EMP* 150
SIC 5511 New & used car dealers
Owner: Jim Keffer
Sls Mgr: Josh McNichol

D-U-N-S 19-761-5974
KEFFER INC
KEFFER JEEP CHRYSLER DODGE
8110 E Independence Blvd, Charlotte, NC 28227-7775
Tel (704) 532-1050 *Founded/Ownrshp* 1988
Sales 21.2MM^E^ *EMP* 60
SIC 5511 7538 5531

KEFFER JEEP CHRYSLER DODGE
See KEFFER INC

D-U-N-S 02-685-2798
KEG 1 ONEAL LLC
O'NEAL DISTRIBUTING COMPANY
213 Patriot Dr, Weatherford, TX 76087-1603
Tel (940) 325-6971 *Founded/Ownrshp* 2008
Sales 71.0MM^E^ *EMP* 225
SIC 5181 5182 Beer & other fermented malt liquors; Wine; Beer & other fermented malt liquors; Wine
CEO: Bruce Leetz
Sls Mgr: Jeff Gillespie

KEGELS PRODUCE
See KEGELS PRODUCE INC

D-U-N-S 07-945-7768
KEGELS PRODUCE INC (PA)
KEGELS PRODUCE
2851 Old Tree Dr, Lancaster, PA 17603-7301
Tel (717) 392-6612 *Founded/Ownrshp* 1958
Sales 71.2MM^E^ *EMP* 85
SIC 5148 Fruits, fresh; Fruits, fresh
VP: Kenneth G Myers
**Treas:* Mary L Myers

D-U-N-S 05-837-7276
KEGLER BROWN HILL & RITTER CO LPA
65 E State St Ste 1800, Columbus, OH 43215-4294
Tel (614) 462-5400 *Founded/Ownrshp* 1964
Sales 25.1MM^E^ *EMP* 142
SIC 8111 General practice attorney, lawyer; General practice attorney, lawyer
Mng Pt: Michael E Zatezalo
Pr: Elise Elman
Pr: Allison Post
Pr: Wendy Schmidt
CFO: Michelle Kondas
Chf Mktg O: Jeff Dennis
Counsel: Luis M Alcalde
Counsel: Richard Brahmof
Counsel: Robert D Marotta
Counsel: Michael S Miller
Counsel: Aneezal H Mohamed

D-U-N-S 07-918-1985 IMP/EXP
KEHE DISTRIBUTORS HOLDINGS LLC
900 N Schmidt Rd, Romeoville, IL 60446-4056
Tel (630) 343-0000 *Founded/Ownrshp* 2010
Sales 6.4MM^E^ *EMP* 8,200^E^
SIC 5149 Groceries & related products; Specialty food items; Pickles, preserves, jellies & jams; Spices & seasonings; Groceries & related products; Specialty food items; Pickles, preserves, jellies & jams; Spices & seasonings
Pr: Brandon Barnholt
CFO: Chris Meyers
Sr VP: Ted Beilman
Sr VP: Scott Leannais
Sr VP: Jack Porter
VP: Michelle Dufresne
VP: Gary Messmore
VP: Barry Sheldrick
VP: Ronald Turner
VP: Mike Weger
Dir IT: Eddie Addis

D-U-N-S 00-543-7033 IMP/EXP
KEHE DISTRIBUTORS LLC
KEHE SOLUTIONS
(*Suby of* KEHE DISTRIBUTORS HOLDINGS LLC) ★
1245 E Diehl Rd Ste 200, Naperville, IL 60563-4816
Tel (630) 343-0000 *Founded/Ownrshp* 1952
Sales 4.8MM^E^ *EMP* 3,400
SIC 5149 Groceries & related products; Specialty food items; Pickles, preserves, jellies & jams; Spices & seasonings; Groceries & related products; Specialty food items; Pickles, preserves, jellies & jams; Spices & seasonings
Pr: Brandon Barnholt
**COO:* Gene Carter
**CFO:* Christopher Meyers
**Chf Cred:* Mike Leone
**Sr VP:* Annette Roder
VP: David Klein
VP: Joe Shannon
Exec: Melanie Onyett
**CIO:* Scott Cousins
Mktg Dir: Jim Kavanagh
Sales Asso: Melinda Rukstela

KEHE SOLUTIONS
See KEHE DISTRIBUTORS LLC

D-U-N-S 01-489-3432
KEHM OIL CO (PA)
T. J.'S DELI MART
1600 Oakdale Rd, Oakdale, PA 15071
Tel (724) 693-9800 *Founded/Ownrshp* 1960
Sales 54.0MM *EMP* 37
Accts Alpern Rosenthal Pittsburgh
SIC 5983 5171 5411 5541 Fuel oil dealers; Petroleum bulk stations; Convenience stores, independent; Filling stations, gasoline; Fuel oil dealers; Petroleum bulk stations; Convenience stores, independent; Filling stations, gasoline
Pr: George M Kehm
**VP:* Terriann Conoschuito

KEHOE DESIGNS EVENT STYLE
See KEHOE DESIGNS INC

D-U-N-S 05-281-7892
KEHOE DESIGNS INC (IL)
KEHOE DESIGNS EVENT STYLE
2555 S Leavitt St, Chicago, IL 60608-5202
Tel (312) 421-0030 *Founded/Ownrshp* 1996
Sales 21.5MM^E^ *EMP* 150
SIC 7389 1521 Decoration service for special events; Single-family home remodeling, additions & repairs
Pr: Thomas G Kehoe
**CFO:* Christopher Lee Nordhoff
VP: Kevin Kehoe
Dir Soc: Ryan Wille
Creative D: Bridget Johnson
Genl Mgr: Wendy Miller
IT Man: Renee Barricklow
IT Man: John Beran

D-U-N-S 15-289-8888
KEICHCO PETROLEUM
2330 Highway 43 S, Picayune, MS 39466-8277
Tel (601) 798-6800 *Founded/Ownrshp* 1996
Sales 31.1MM^E^ *EMP* 200
SIC 5172 Gasoline; Gasoline
Pr: Keith Saucier

D-U-N-S 00-447-3898
KEIDEL SUPPLY CO INC (OH)
1150 Tennessee Ave, Cincinnati, OH 45229-1010
Tel (513) 351-1600 *Founded/Ownrshp* 1954, 2009
Sales 34.8MM^E^ *EMP* 49
SIC 5074 5031 5064 5099 Plumbing & hydronic heating supplies; Kitchen cabinets; Electrical appliances, television & radio; Firearms & ammunition, except sporting
Ch Bd: Michael Barton
**Pr:* Barry Keidel
Ex VP: John Robinson
Store Mgr: Gordon Hemsink
Sls Mgr: Glenn Williams
Sales Asso: Jon Sechkar
Sales Asso: Jerry Siemer

D-U-N-S 12-544-1043 IMP
KEIHIN AIRCON NORTH AMERICA INC
(*Suby of* KEIHIN NORTH AMERICA INC) ★
4400 N Superior Dr, Muncie, IN 47303-6436
Tel (765) 213-4915 *Founded/Ownrshp* 2000
Sales 36.4MM^E^ *EMP* 175
SIC 3714 Air conditioner parts, motor vehicle; Air conditioner parts, motor vehicle
Pr: Nobuaki Suzuki
**Sr VP:* Taka Mori
VP: Nobu Nishimaki
**VP:* Robert Riddle
VP: Shiro Saito
Exec: Annette Lapradd
IT Man: Susan Conrad
Sfty Dirs: Ken Vandevender
Mtls Mgr: Todd Furniss
Ql Cn Mgr: Jeff Hiatt
Ql Cn Mgr: Tony White

D-U-N-S 01-611-0509 IMP
KEIHIN CAROLINA SYSTEM TECHNOLOGY LLC
(*Suby of* KEIHIN NORTH AMERICA INC) ★
4047 Mcnair Rd, Tarboro, NC 27886-9055
Tel (252) 641-6750 *Founded/Ownrshp* 1997
Sales 218.9MM^E^ *EMP* 468
SIC 3694 3625 3714 Automotive electrical equipment; Actuators, industrial; Motor vehicle parts & accessories; Automotive electrical equipment; Actuators, industrial; Motor vehicle parts & accessories
Pr: Shigeo Umesaki
Pr: Nobuaki Suzuki
Pr: Mamoru Tanaka
Pr: Masahiro Wakaki
Pr: Gregory S Young
VP: Roy Furo
Genl Mgr: Dave Thomas
Dir IT: Chris Sandlin
IT Man: Dave Naessens
VP Mfg: Shoji Ujie
Mfg Mgr: Beverly Crawford

D-U-N-S 16-688-6429 IMP
KEIHIN IPT MFG LLC
(*Suby of* KEIHIN NORTH AMERICA INC) ★
400 W New Rd, Greenfield, IN 46140-3001
Tel (317) 462-3015 *Founded/Ownrshp* 2001
Sales 228.8MM^E^ *EMP* 2,000
SIC 3714 Fuel systems & parts, motor vehicle
Pr: Koki Onuma
**Treas:* Mamoru Tanaka
VP: Chugo Sato
**VP:* Gregory S Young
Admn Mgr: Mary Richard
VP Opers: Larry Phillipho
Ql Cn Mgr: Dan Kenkel
Sales Asso: Michelle Wells

D-U-N-S 80-849-9441 IMP
KEIHIN MICHIGAN MANUFACTURING LLC
(*Suby of* KEIHIN NORTH AMERICA INC) ★
14898 Koehn Rd, Mussey, MI 48014-4310
Tel (317) 462-3015 *Founded/Ownrshp* 2007
Sales 35.6MM^E^ *EMP* 160
SIC 3089 Automotive parts, plastic; Automotive parts, plastic
CEO: Yasufhi Takahashi
VP: Kevin Mitchell
VP: Dave Thomas

D-U-N-S 19-243-8042 IMP
KEIHIN NORTH AMERICA INC
(*Suby of* KEIHIN CORPORATION)
2701 Enterprise Dr # 100, Anderson, IN 46013-6101
Tel (765) 298-6030 *Founded/Ownrshp* 1988
Sales 1.0MMM *EMP* 4,591
Accts Ernst & Young Llp Columbus O
SIC 3714 Fuel systems & parts, motor vehicle; Manifolds, motor vehicle; Motor vehicle engines & parts; Fuel systems & parts, motor vehicle; Manifolds, motor vehicle; Motor vehicle engines & parts
Pr: Koki Onuma
COO: Todd Kimball
**Treas:* Toru Sugihara
VP: Greg Trusty
**VP:* Greg York
**VP:* Gregory S Young
**Prin:* Sosuke Sese
**Prin:* Masami Watanabe
Genl Mgr: Dave Hanks
Genl Mgr: Satoshi Noda
Plng Mgr: Tom Mann

D-U-N-S 96-931-7143 IMP/EXP
KEIHIN THERMAL TECHNOLOGY OF AMERICA INC
10500 Oday Harrison Rd, Mount Sterling, OH 43143-9474
Tel (740) 869-3000 *Founded/Ownrshp* 2011
Sales 100.0MM^E *EMP* 475
SIC 5013 3714 Automotive engines & engine parts; Motor vehicle engines & parts; Automotive engines & engine parts; Motor vehicle engines & parts
Pr: Tatsuhiko Arai
VP: Tatsuya Harada
**VP:* Scott Amortimer
Sfty Mgr: Robert Feltz

KEIM, JIM FORD SALES
See JIM KEIM FORD

D-U-N-S 01-759-7899 IMP
KEIM LUMBER CO
4465 St Rte 557, Charm, OH 44617
Tel (330) 893-2251 *Founded/Ownrshp* 1968
Sales 41.4MM^E *EMP* 150^E
SIC 5211 5031

KEIM T S
See T S KEIM INC

D-U-N-S 96-735-4457 IMP
■ **KEIPER LLC**
(*Suby of* KEIPER ENTERPRISES, INC.)
2600 Bellingham Dr # 100, Troy, MI 48083-2014
Tel (248) 655-5100 *Founded/Ownrshp* 2011
Sales 29.6MM^E *EMP* 200
SIC 3089 Automotive parts, plastic; Automotive parts, plastic
CEO: Andrew Ason
IT Man: Frank Gora
Ql Cn Mgr: Leta Corwin

KEIRO SENIOR HEALTH CARE
See KEIRO SERVICES

D-U-N-S 15-282-2292
KEIRO SERVICES
KEIRO SENIOR HEALTH CARE
325 S Boyle Ave, Los Angeles, CA 90033-3812
Tel (323) 263-1007 *Founded/Ownrshp* 1984
Sales 5.1MM *EMP* 500
SIC 8741 Nursing & personal care facility management; Nursing & personal care facility management
CEO: Shawn Miyake
Ofcr: Beverly Ito
Ofcr: Dianne Kujububelli
Ofcr: Shelley Kwan
Exec: Susan Lara

KEISER UNIVERSITY
See EVERGLADES COLLEGE INC

D-U-N-S 09-670-0265
KEITER STEPHENS HURST GARY & SHREAVES A PROFESSIONAL CORP
4401 Dominion Blvd # 300, Glen Allen, VA 23060-3379
Tel (804) 747-0000 *Founded/Ownrshp* 1978
Sales 20.9MM *EMP* 84
SIC 8721 Certified public accountant; Certified public accountant
Pr: Lewis O Hall
**VP:* Robert Gary IV
**VP:* Robert H Keiter
Snr Mgr: Kay Gotshall
Board of Directors: Carroll D Hurst, Robert H Keiter, Carl A Loden, Debra G Snodgress, J Michael Todd, Barry Yaffe

D-U-N-S 07-222-7762
KEITH AND SCHNARS PA
6500 N Andrews Ave, Fort Lauderdale, FL 33309-2126
Tel (954) 776-1616 *Founded/Ownrshp* 1999
Sales 25.0MM *EMP* 100
SIC 8711 8713 Civil engineering; Surveying services; Civil engineering; Surveying services
Pr: Tanzer H Kalayci
**COO:* Errol Kalayci
**VP:* Jack N Breed
Dir: John Abbott
Off Mgr: Kathleen Gunn
IT Man: Dewey Oliver
Sls Dir: Kim Giles
Snr PM: Barry Ehrlich

D-U-N-S 13-920-4619
KEITH CAMPBELL FOUNDATION FOR ENVIRONMENT
410 Severn Ave Ste 210, Annapolis, MD 21403-2540
Tel (410) 990-0900 *Founded/Ownrshp* 2003
Sales 30.8MM *EMP* 4
SIC 8641 Environmental protection organization
CEO: Keith Campbell
Ex Dir: Verna Harrison

D-U-N-S 07-928-1153
KEITH DAVIS
DAVIS TRUCKING SERVICES
3574 Boxtown Rd, Memphis, TN 38109-3300
Tel (901) 496-6477 *Founded/Ownrshp* 2010
Sales 386.4MM *EMP* 5
SIC 4213 Contract haulers; Contract haulers
Owner: Keith Davis
Co-Ownr: Rochelle Davis

KEITH HAWTHORNE FORD
See DIXON FORD INC

D-U-N-S 05-827-9399
KEITH LAWSON CO INC
LAWSON KEITH MECHANICAL CONTRS
4557 Capital Cir Nw, Tallahassee, FL 32303-7216
Tel (850) 562-7711 *Founded/Ownrshp* 1980
Sales 34.3MM^E *EMP* 80
SIC 1711 Mechanical contractor; Warm air heating & air conditioning contractor
Ch Bd: Keith Lawson Sr
**Pr:* Keith Lawson II
VP: Tim Harrell
Genl Mgr: Thomas M Phelps

D-U-N-S 13-709-7838
KEITH MANUFACTURING CO
LOCKING FLOORS
401 Nw Adler St, Madras, OR 97741-9491
Tel (541) 475-3802 *Founded/Ownrshp* 1950
Sales 30.2MM^E *EMP* 150
SIC 8731 3535 Commercial physical research; Conveyors & conveying equipment; Commercial physical research; Conveyors & conveying equipment
Pr: R Mark Foster
CTO: Dan Jackson

D-U-N-S 02-726-7384
KEITH OIL CO
1440 Admiral Pl, Ferndale, WA 98248-8965
Tel (360) 312-1100 *Founded/Ownrshp* 1980
Sales 39.0MM *EMP* 15
SIC 5171 5194 Petroleum bulk stations; Cigarettes; Petroleum bulk stations; Cigarettes
Pr: Mahmoud Sam Boulos
Sales Asso: Victor Boulos

KEITH PEARSON TOYOTA
See ORANGE PARK TOYOTA

D-U-N-S 10-832-0516
KEITH PROPERTIES INC
KEITH'S HARDWARE
201 S Frontage Rd, Lorena, TX 76655-9601
Tel (254) 857-8667 *Founded/Ownrshp* 1984
Sales 24.2MM^E *EMP* 100
SIC 5251 Hardware
CEO: John Keith
Store Mgr: Jeremy Harris
VP Opers: Beau Nickel

D-U-N-S 00-634-8858
KEITH SMITH CO INC
130 K Tech Ln, Hot Springs, AR 71913-9140
Tel (501) 760-0100 *Founded/Ownrshp* 1958
Sales 27.1MM^E *EMP* 90
SIC 5144 0252 2015

D-U-N-S 09-196-7299
KEITH TITUS CORP
2758 Trombley Rd, Weedsport, NY 13166-9510
Tel (315) 834-6681 *Founded/Ownrshp* 1975
Sales 31.0MM^E *EMP* 95
Accts Grossman St Amour Cpas Syrac
SIC 4213 Trucking, except local
Ch Bd: Piper Titus
**Pr:* Daniel K Titus
**CEO:* Debra L Titus
**VP:* Chris R Jorolemon

D-U-N-S 00-750-5751
KEITH WHITE FORD LINCOLN
2102 Veterans Blvd, McComb, MS 39648-6124
Tel (601) 684-3970 *Founded/Ownrshp* 2008
Sales 43.0MM *EMP* 49
SIC 5511 Automobiles, new & used
Owner: Keith White

D-U-N-S 13-756-6360
KEITH ZARS POOLS LTD
17427 San Pedro Ave, San Antonio, TX 78232-1407
Tel (210) 494-0800 *Founded/Ownrshp* 1985
Sales 68.3MM^E *EMP* 250
SIC 1799 Swimming pool construction; Swimming pool construction
Pr: Keith Zars
**Sec:* Mary Cunningham
**VP:* Parker Smith
**VP:* Barbara Zars
Ex Dir: Laurie Deavers
Sls Mgr: Curt Collier

D-U-N-S 00-419-0419 IMP
■ **KEITHLEY INSTRUMENTS INC**
(*Suby of* TEKTRONIX INC) ★
28775 Aurora Rd, Solon, OH 44139-1891
Tel (440) 248-0400 *Founded/Ownrshp* 2010
Sales 68.8MM^E *EMP* 490^E
SIC 3825 3823 7371 Instruments to measure electricity; Test equipment for electronic & electric measurement; Multimeters; Semiconductor test equipment; Computer interface equipment for industrial process control; Computer software development; Instruments to measure electricity; Test equipment for electronic & electric measurement; Multimeters; Semiconductor test equipment; Computer interface equipment for industrial process control; Computer software development
Pr: Joseph P Keithley
**COO:* Linda C Rae
**CFO:* Mark J Plush
**VP:* Philip R Etsler
VP: Alan S Gaffney
**VP:* Mark A Hoersten
VP: Mark Hoersten
**VP:* Larry L Pendergrass
QA Dir: Tom Gallagher
Sls&Mrk Ex: Earl Cook
**VP Sls:* Daniel A Faia

D-U-N-S 62-331-5793
■ **KEITHLEY INSTRUMENTS INTERNATIONAL CORP**
(*Suby of* KEITHLEY INSTRUMENTS INC) ★
28775 Aurora Rd, Cleveland, OH 44139-1891
Tel (440) 248-0400 *Founded/Ownrshp* 1984
Sales 57.4MM^E *EMP* 450
SIC 5065 3825 Electronic parts & equipment; Test equipment for electronic & electric measurement; Electronic parts & equipment; Test equipment for electronic & electric measurement
Pr: Joseph P Keithley
**Treas:* Ron Molder

D-U-N-S 05-663-1328 IMP
KEITHLY-WILLIAMS SEEDS INC
420 Palm Ave, Holtville, CA 92250-1156
Tel (760) 356-5533 *Founded/Ownrshp* 1981
Sales 90.9MM^E *EMP* 75
Accts Swain & Kennerson
SIC 5191 0721 0181 Seeds: field, garden & flower; Seeds: field, garden & flower; Crop seeding services; Seeds, vegetable: growing of
CEO: Kelly G Kiehtly
CFO: Walt Williams
VP: Mary Bornt
VP: Pat Cooley
Dir IT: Gerald Juettner
IT Man: Greg Estrada
Netwrk Eng: Wendy Vega
Opers Mgr: Neil Lewi
Ql Cn Mgr: Kevin Ford
Sls Mgr: Jose Gudino
Snr Mgr: Matt Dicori

KEITH'S HARDWARE
See KEITH PROPERTIES INC

D-U-N-S 16-708-0837 IMP
KEJR INC
GEOPROBE SYSTEMS
1835 Wall St, Salina, KS 67401-1736
Tel (785) 825-1842 *Founded/Ownrshp* 1986
Sales 26.4MM^E *EMP* 118^E
SIC 3523 Soil sampling machines; Soil sampling machines
Pr: Melvin Kejr
**VP:* Tom Christy
Dir IT: Jeremy Friesen

D-U-N-S 02-758-3533
KEKER AND VAN NEST LLP
633 Battery St Bsmt 91, San Francisco, CA 94111-1899
Tel (415) 391-5400 *Founded/Ownrshp* 1978
Sales 20.7MM^E *EMP* 100
SIC 8111 Criminal law; Specialized law offices, attorneys
Pr: Laure Mandin
Pr: Maureen Stone
Netwrk Eng: Eric Portenier
Snr Mgr: Joy Scharton

KEL-SAN PRODUCTS
See KELSAN INC

D-U-N-S 62-422-7013
KEL-TECH CONSTRUCTION INC
1211 Redfern Ave, Far Rockaway, NY 11691-3817
Tel (718) 383-3353 *Founded/Ownrshp* 1990
Sales 24.5MM^E *EMP* 180
SIC 1742 Drywall; Drywall
Pr: Philip Kelleher
**VP:* Vincent Kelleher

D-U-N-S 07-652-0261
KELBER CATERING INC
CONVENTION CENTER FOOD SERVICE
1301 2nd Ave S Ste B, Minneapolis, MN 55403-2600
Tel (612) 335-6045 *Founded/Ownrshp* 1964
Sales 14.1MM^E *EMP* 400
SIC 5812 Caterers; Concessionaire; Caterers; Concessionaire
Pr: Max Kurnow
**CFO:* Robert Kelber
**VP:* Jeanette Kurnow

D-U-N-S 14-068-4213
KELBRO INC
PROCESS SOLUTIONS INTL
7519 Prairie Oak Dr, Houston, TX 77086-1775
Tel (281) 893-4774 *Founded/Ownrshp* 1993
Sales 24.9MM *EMP* 6
SIC 3533 Oil field machinery & equipment; Oil field machinery & equipment
Pr: John D Keliehor
**VP:* Stacie Keliehor

D-U-N-S 00-678-3765
KELCHNER INC
50 Advanced Dr, Springboro, OH 45066-1805
Tel (937) 704-9890 *Founded/Ownrshp* 1982
Sales 79.4MM^E *EMP* 200^E
SIC 1794 1389 Excavation work; Mud service, oil field drilling; Bailing wells; Excavation work; Mud service, oil field drilling; Bailing wells
CEO: Todd Kelchner
**Pr:* Troy Norvell
**VP:* Jeff Kelchner
**VP:* Kevin Weckel

D-U-N-S 04-419-9636
KELCO LIMITED
STOP N SAVE FOOD MARTS
114 Joy St, Sevierville, TN 37862-3425
Tel (865) 453-4666 *Founded/Ownrshp* 1986
Sales 30.1MM *EMP* 75
SIC 5172 5541 5411 Petroleum products; Filling stations, gasoline; Grocery stores; Petroleum products; Filling stations, gasoline; Grocery stores
Pt: Kenneth R Wade
Pt: Tasha Wade

D-U-N-S 06-658-3506
KELDANERI CORP
MARINA SQUARE AUTO CENTER
1152 Marina Blvd, San Leandro, CA 94577-3359
Tel (510) 347-4000 *Founded/Ownrshp* 2000
Sales 33.7MM^E *EMP* 88
SIC 5511 Automobiles, new & used; Automobiles, new & used
Pr: George Assoun

D-U-N-S 06-614-5236 IMP
KELE INC
JOHNSON CONTROLS
3300 Brother Blvd, Memphis, TN 38133-8950
Tel (901) 382-6084 *Founded/Ownrshp* 2006
Sales 96.7MM^E *EMP* 230
SIC 5075 3822 3829 Air conditioning & ventilation equipment & supplies; Auto controls regulating residntl & coml environmt & applncs; Measuring & controlling devices; Air conditioning & ventilation equipment & supplies; Auto controls regulating residntl & coml environmt & applncs; Measuring & controlling devices
CEO: Tim Vargo
**CFO:* Keith Mayer
CFO: Keith Mayor
CFO: Mike Phillips
VP: Dean Mueller
VP: Anton Schneider
Exec: Johnny Enoch
Genl Mgr: Janet Flickinger
IT Man: Tom Ovidio
Natl Sales: Jason Campbell
VP Sls: Tom Benson

D-U-N-S 04-852-4719
KELL WEST REGIONAL HOSPITAL LLC
5420 Kell Blvd, Wichita Falls, TX 76310-1610
Tel (940) 692-5888 *Founded/Ownrshp* 1998
Sales 31.9MM *EMP* 340
SIC 8062 General medical & surgical hospitals; General medical & surgical hospitals
COO: Charlaine Vardeman
**CFO:* Fran Lindemann
**Sec:* Adam Alpert
Dir OR: Bonnie Beavers
Dir Lab: Rich Kirkland
Dir Rad: Sondra Paul
Dir Rx: Caleb Adams
Dir Rx: Greg McHugh
Off Mgr: Vicki Benson
CIO: Bill O'Brien
HC Dir: B Jackson

D-U-N-S 03-289-0501 IMP
KELLE OIL CO
102 N Broadway St, Braman, OK 74632
Tel (580) 385-2131 *Founded/Ownrshp* 1959
Sales 20.9MM *EMP* 20
SIC 5984 5171 5541 5531 5172 Propane gas, bottled; Petroleum bulk stations; Filling stations, gasoline; Automotive tires; Petroleum products; Propane gas, bottled; Petroleum bulk stations; Filling stations, gasoline; Automotive tires; Petroleum products
Pr: Steve Kelle
**Sec:* Kristi Kelle
**VP:* Aubrey F Kelle
Opers Mgr: John Kelle

D-U-N-S 05-035-5460 IMP
KELLEHER CORP (CA)
KELLEHER LUMBER COMPANY
1543 5th Ave, San Rafael, CA 94901-1806
Tel (415) 454-8861 *Founded/Ownrshp* 1972
Sales 99.6MM^E *EMP* 200
SIC 5031 Lumber: rough, dressed & finished; Millwork; Molding, all materials; Lumber: rough, dressed & finished; Millwork; Molding, all materials
CEO: Donald J Kelleher
**CFO:* Brett Merner
**Sec:* Donna Kelleher
**VP:* Jeffrey Barnes
VP: Sean Williams
Dir IT: Paul Herzog
IT Man: Shawn Maloney
Sales Exec: Dave Westlake

KELLEHER LUMBER COMPANY
See KELLEHER CORP

D-U-N-S 04-067-7494
KELLEN CO INC
1100 Jhsn Frry Rd Ste 300, Atlanta, GA 30342
Tel (404) 836-5050 *Founded/Ownrshp* 1964
Sales 32.2MM^E *EMP* 210
SIC 8611 Trade associations; Trade associations
CEO: Peter Rush
**Pr:* Richard E Cristol
**CFO:* Mike Brooks
Ex VP: Reed Hitchcock
Ex VP: Mardi Mountford
VP: Eric Allen
**VP:* Debra Berliner
**VP:* Joan R Cear
VP: Peter Dicks
**VP:* Jim Fowler
**VP:* Carol Freysinger
**VP:* Tor Holtan
VP: Holly Koenig
VP: Jeannie Milewski
VP: Lyn Nabors
VP: Maria T Scardigli
VP: Lydia Caffery Wilbanks
Assoc Dir: Tara Wagner
Creative D: June Price
Comm Man: Ryan Foster
Comm Man: Danielle Griffin

D-U-N-S 02-030-0158
KELLER AND HECKMAN LLP (DC)
1001 G St Nw Ste 500w, Washington, DC 20001-4564
Tel (202) 434-4100 *Founded/Ownrshp* 1962
Sales 26.0MM^E *EMP* 153
SIC 8111 General practice law office; General practice law office
Prin: Wayne V Black
Exec: Colleen Evale
Exec: Tracy Marshall
**Prin:* John B Dubeck

**Prin:* John S Eldred
**Prin:* Jerome Heckman
**Prin:* C Douglas Jarrett
**Prin:* Tracy P Marshall
**Prin:* Ralph A Simmons
Off Admin: Lester Borodinsky
Counsel: Albert Catalano

D-U-N-S 01-434-2596
KELLER BROS AUTO CO (PA)
KELLER BROS FORD
730 S Broad St, Lititz, PA 17543-2807
Tel (717) 626-2000 *Founded/Ownrshp* 1932, 1950
Sales 21.2MM^E *EMP* 45
SIC 5511 Automobiles, new & used
Pr: Dan Keller
Off Mgr: Kirsti Wright
Sales Asso: Tim Hoover
Sales Asso: Frank Kowalski

KELLER BROS FORD
See KELLER BROS AUTO CO

KELLER BROS KUBOTA
See KELLER BROS MOTOR CO

D-U-N-S 01-431-8158
KELLER BROS MOTOR CO
KELLER BROS KUBOTA
1030 Schaeffer Rd, Lebanon, PA 17042-9609
Tel (717) 949-2000 *Founded/Ownrshp* 1968
Sales 31.1MM^E *EMP* 71
SIC 5511 5083 Automobiles, new & used; Agricultural machinery & equipment; Automobiles, new & used; Agricultural machinery & equipment
Pr: Dan Keller
**VP:* Nathan Keller
IT Man: Travis Stuber
Sls Mgr: Rich Weiss
Sales Asso: Tom Buch
Sales Asso: Mike Esseff
Sales Asso: Rose Lapp

KELLER CRESCENT CO
See CLONDALKIN PHARMA & HEALTHCARE INC

D-U-N-S 02-522-1771 IMP/EXP
KELLER ELECTRICAL INDUSTRIES INC
1881 E University Dr, Phoenix, AZ 85034-4082
Tel (602) 437-3015 *Founded/Ownrshp* 2007
Sales 79.4MM^E *EMP* 88
SIC 5063 1731 7629 Electrical apparatus & equipment; General electrical contractor; Electrical equipment repair services; Electrical apparatus & equipment; General electrical contractor; Electrical equipment repair services
Pr: Don Anderson
**CFO:* Jim Everson
**VP:* Cody Eslick

D-U-N-S 04-995-8036
KELLER ENTERPRISES INC
1202 N Keller Dr, Effingham, IL 62401-4523
Tel (217) 347-7777 *Founded/Ownrshp* 1981
Sales 33.3MM^E *EMP* 276
SIC 7011 5411 Hotels & motels; Convenience stores, independent; Hotels & motels; Convenience stores, independent
CEO: Charles F Keller

D-U-N-S 03-129-2154
KELLER FIRE & SAFETY INC (KS)
(*Suby of* FIKE CORP) ★
1138 Kansas Ave, Kansas City, KS 66105-1226
Tel (913) 371-8494 *Founded/Ownrshp* 1951, 2004
Sales 23.9MM^E *EMP* 60
SIC 5087 5099 Sprinkler systems; Fire extinguishers
Pr: Maxwell Jewel
**Sec:* Logan J Wilson
Genl Mgr: Craig Schraad
IT Man: Stef Pearce
Sls Mgr: Diane Bayer

D-U-N-S 61-675-8074 IMP/EXP
KELLER FOUNDATION
(*Suby of* KELLER GROUP PLC)
7550 Teague Rd Ste 300, Hanover, MD 21076-1807
Tel (410) 551-8200 *Founded/Ownrshp* 1991
Sales 645.9MM^E *EMP* 3,000
SIC 1799 8711 Building site preparation; Engineering services; Building site preparation; Engineering services
Pr: Robert M Rubright
CFO: Dan Jor
**CFO:* Dan Jordan
Ex VP: George Grisham
VP: George Burke
VP: Robin Johnson
**VP:* Richard N Yale
Dir Risk M: Kim Smith
Off Mgr: Rose Brown
IT Man: Andy Balto
Sls Mgr: Rebecca Miller

D-U-N-S 05-905-9949
KELLER GROUP INC
1 Northfield Plz Ste 510, Northfield, IL 60093-1216
Tel (847) 446-7550 *Founded/Ownrshp* 1945
Sales 88.1MM^E *EMP* 700
SIC 3462 1221 1222 Iron & steel forgings; Bituminous coal & lignite-surface mining; Bituminous coal-underground mining; Iron & steel forgings; Bituminous coal & lignite-surface mining; Bituminous coal-underground mining
Ch Bd: John P Keller
VP: David Spada
IT Man: Kenneth Dachman
IT Man: Jon Schepke
Board of Directors: Judith K Keller

D-U-N-S 00-614-2566
KELLER INC
KELLER PLNNRS/RCHTCTS/BUILDERS
N216 State Highway 55, Kaukauna, WI 54130-8401
Tel (920) 766-5795 *Founded/Ownrshp* 1960
Sales 101.9MM^E *EMP* 185
Accts Schenck Sc - Appleton Wi
SIC 1542 1541 7336 Commercial & office building contractors; Industrial buildings & warehouses; Commercial art & graphic design; Commercial & office building contractors; Industrial buildings & warehouses; Commercial art & graphic design
Pr: Wayne Stellmacher
**VP:* Gerald Cohen
**VP:* Steven Klessig
**VP:* Douglas Stecker
VP Opers: Jerry Cohen
Opers Mgr: Tom Fricke

D-U-N-S 03-903-3337
KELLER INDEPENDENT SCHOOL DISTRICT
KELLER ISD
350 Keller Pkwy, Keller, TX 76248-2249
Tel (817) 744-1000 *Founded/Ownrshp* 1911
Sales 310.7MM *EMP* 3,400
Accts Weaver And Tidwell Llp Fort
SIC 8211 Public elementary & secondary schools; Public elementary school; Public junior high school; Public senior high school; Public elementary & secondary schools; Public elementary school; Public junior high school; Public senior high school
Pr: Steve Dunmore
Psych: Michelle Mayfield

KELLER ISD
See KELLER INDEPENDENT SCHOOL DISTRICT

KELLER, JACK FORD
See FORD KELLER INC

KELLER LINCOLN FORD
See JVAC INC

D-U-N-S 82-892-3065
KELLER LOGISTICS GROUP INC
24862 Elliott Rd Ste 101, Defiance, OH 43512-9237
Tel (800) 245-7557 *Founded/Ownrshp* 2002
Sales 58.0MM^E *EMP* 152^E
SIC 4731 Freight transportation arrangement
Pr: Bryan Keller
**CFO:* Scott Galbraith
**VP:* Aaron Keller
Dir IT: Dan Ferris
Dir IT: Randy Schad
Mktg Dir: Julie Wanstedt

KELLER MARINE & RV
See KELLER MARINE SERVICE INC

D-U-N-S 00-302-7919
KELLER MARINE SERVICE INC (PA)
KELLER MARINE & RV
2712 Main St, Port Trevorton, PA 17864-9493
Tel (570) 374-8169 *Founded/Ownrshp* 1958
Sales 33.1MM^E *EMP* 75
SIC 5091 Camping equipment & supplies; Boat accessories & parts
Pr: G Michael Keller
**Sec:* Lori Morrow
Sales Asso: Marge Reichenbach

D-U-N-S 02-802-6169
KELLER MOTORS INC
700 Cadillac Ln, Hanford, CA 93230-4964
Tel (559) 582-1000 *Founded/Ownrshp* 1965
Sales 34.3MM^E *EMP* 75
SIC 5511 Automobiles, new & used; Pickups, new & used; Automobiles, new & used; Pickups, new & used
Pr: Jon M Keller
**VP:* Valerie Keller
Exec: Lori Dodd

KELLER OIL CO
See L KELLER OIL PROPERTIES INC

KELLER PLNNRS/RCHTCTS/BUILDERS
See KELLER INC

D-U-N-S 07-112-9027
KELLER RIGGING & CONSTRUCTION INC (OH)
1247 Eastwood Ave, Tallmadge, OH 44278-2645
Tel (330) 633-6160 *Founded/Ownrshp* 1956, 1974
Sales 23.8MM^E *EMP* 125
SIC 1796 1541

D-U-N-S 19-702-0738
KELLER SCHROEDER & ASSOCIATES INC
4920 Carriage Dr, Evansville, IN 47715-2578
Tel (812) 474-6825 *Founded/Ownrshp* 1982
Sales 20.1MM^E *EMP* 80
SIC 7379 Computer related consulting services
Pr: Larry May
Netwrk Eng: Brent Edwards
Board of Directors: James H Keller

D-U-N-S 00-948-2837 IMP
KELLER SUPPLY CO (WA)
LEISURE SUPPLY
3209 17th Ave W, Seattle, WA 98119-1792
Tel (206) 285-3300 *Founded/Ownrshp* 1952
Sales 324.4MM^E *EMP* 410
SIC 5074 Plumbing & hydronic heating supplies; Plumbing & hydronic heating supplies
CEO: Neil Keller
**Pr:* Michael P Murphy
**CFO:* George W Debell
VP: Patrick Murphy
**VP:* Stuart Sulman
Brnch Mgr: Bridgette Jackson
Brnch Mgr: Dean Logstrom
Brnch Mgr: Ryan Mahoney
Brnch Mgr: Louis Strahler
Dist Mgr: Dan Page
Genl Mgr: Mitchell King

D-U-N-S 00-211-1615 IMP
KELLER TECHNOLOGY CORP (NY)
2320 Military Rd, Tonawanda, NY 14150-6005
Tel (716) 693-3840 *Founded/Ownrshp* 1918
Sales 60.6MM^E *EMP* 250
SIC 3599 Custom machinery; Custom machinery
CEO: Michael A Keller
**Ch Bd:* Arthur Keller Jr
CFO: Dan Dirrigel
**CFO:* Daniel Dirrigl
**Treas:* Kathie Ann Keller
**VP:* Peter Keller
Admn Mgr: J Arthur
Prd Mgr: Chris Sansone

D-U-N-S 17-415-5119
KELLER TRUCK SERVICES INC
614 State Highway H, Sikeston, MO 63801-5352
Tel (573) 471-9555 *Founded/Ownrshp* 2004
Sales 27.2MM^E *EMP* 30
SIC 5172 Fuel oil
Pr: Joseph King

KELLER WILLIAMS REALTORS
See KELLER WILLIAMS REALTY

KELLER WILLIAMS REALTORS
See KELLER WILLIAMS REALTY INC

KELLER WILLIAMS REALTORS
See JOMARSHE INVESTMENT GROUP INC

D-U-N-S 14-807-3815
KELLER WILLIAMS REALTY
KELLER WILLIAMS REALTORS
23670 Hawthorne Blvd # 100, Torrance, CA 90505-5968
Tel (310) 375-3511 *Founded/Ownrshp* 2004
Sales 10.1MM^E *EMP* 300
SIC 6531 Real estate agent, residential; Real estate agent, residential

D-U-N-S 19-858-6807
KELLER WILLIAMS REALTY INC
KELLER WILLIAMS REALTORS
1221 S Mo Pac Expy # 400, Austin, TX 78746-7650
Tel (512) 327-3070 *Founded/Ownrshp* 1983
Sales 157.0MM^E *EMP* 170
SIC 6531 Real estate agent, residential
CEO: Mark Willis
**Pr:* Mary Tennant
**COO:* Jim Talbot
**CFO:* Ann Yett
**Ch:* Gary Keller
Ofcr: Byron Ellington
Exec: Brandy Egan
Ex Dir: Jason Tang
Dir IT: Kyle Johnson
Sales Exec: Valerie Murphy
Sales Exec: Ron Thorne

D-U-N-S 02-536-6477
KELLER-HEARTT CO INC
4411 S Tripp Ave, Chicago, IL 60632-4320
Tel (773) 247-7606 *Founded/Ownrshp* 1977
Sales 21.9MM^E *EMP* 30^E
SIC 5172 Lubricating oils & greases; Gasoline; Diesel fuel
Pr: Brian P McGrath
Off Mgr: Flo Zedak

D-U-N-S 18-141-7143
KELLERMEYER BERGENSONS SERVICES LLC
1575 Henthorne Dr, Maumee, OH 43537-1372
Tel (419) 867-4300 *Founded/Ownrshp* 2001
Sales 486.4MM^E *EMP* 12,000
SIC 7349 Building & office cleaning services; Building & office cleaning services
CEO: Mark Minasian
**COO:* Paul Jones
**CFO:* Brett Himes
VP: Chris Bean
VP: Chris Bomtempo
VP: Robert Crampton
VP: Terry Dru
VP: Mike Mese
VP: Mike Somes
VP: Mike Sunderland
VP: John Torres

D-U-N-S 62-283-1857
KELLERS CREAMERY LLC
(*Suby of* DAIRY FARMERS OF AMERICA INC) ★
855 Maple Ave, Harleysville, PA 19438-1031
Tel (215) 256-8871 *Founded/Ownrshp* 2000
Sales 27.5MM^E *EMP* 210
SIC 2021 2023 Creamery butter; Dry, condensed, evaporated dairy products; Condensed, concentrated & evaporated milk products; Creamery butter; Dry, condensed, evaporated dairy products; Condensed, concentrated & evaporated milk products
Sr Cor Off: Jim Coleman
Ex VP: Glenn Millar

D-U-N-S 87-920-3776 IMP
KELLEX CORP
33390 Liberty Pkwy, North Ridgeville, OH 44039-2600
Tel (440) 327-4428 *Founded/Ownrshp* 2007
Sales 77.7MM^E *EMP* 149
SIC 5021 Office & public building furniture; Office & public building furniture
Pr: Chris Rice
CFO: Bryan Beam
**CFO:* Quez Little
VP: Vicki Elliott
VP: Lew English
**VP:* Doug Fawcett
QA Dir: Chris Blackburn

D-U-N-S 01-631-1185
KELLEY AUTOMOTIVE GROUP INC
TOM KELLEY GMC PONTIAC
633 Avenue Of Autos, Fort Wayne, IN 46804-1184
Tel (260) 434-4884 *Founded/Ownrshp* 1985
Sales 57.3MM^E *EMP* 136^E
SIC 5511 Automobiles, new & used; Automobiles, new & used
Pr: Thomas W Kelley
COO: John McCormick
**CFO:* Gary Thelen
Genl Mgr: Trent Waybright
Dir IT: Jill Stroud
IT Man: Thomas Bissett
S&M/VP: Justin Depasquale
Sls Mgr: Jim Scarbeary
Sls Mgr: Gary Shepherd

D-U-N-S 00-696-9893 EXP
KELLEY BEAN CO INC (NE)
2407 Circle Dr, Scottsbluff, NE 69361-1791
Tel (308) 635-6438 *Founded/Ownrshp* 1927, 1961
Sales 84.6MM^E *EMP* 225
SIC 5153 2034 Beans, dry: bulk; Grain elevators; Dehydrated fruits, vegetables, soups; Beans, dry: bulk; Grain elevators; Dehydrated fruits, vegetables, soups
Pr: Kevin L Kelley
**CFO:* Lee Glenn
Off Mgr: Kim Fertufon
IT Man: Dustin Church
Opers Mgr: Juan Carrizales
Plnt Mgr: Brian Kaman

D-U-N-S 13-928-1513
■ **KELLEY BLUE BOOK CO INC**
(*Suby of* AUTOTRADER.COM INC) ★
195 Technology Dr, Irvine, CA 92618-2402
Tel (949) 770-7704 *Founded/Ownrshp* 2010
Sales 76.5MM^E *EMP* 500
SIC 2721 Trade journals: publishing only, not printed on site; Trade journals: publishing only, not printed on site
CEO: Jared Rowe
CFO: John Morrison
VP: Scott Ehlers
Snr Sftwr: Erin Blackbourn
Snr Sftwr: Brian Ward
CIO: Dave Templeton
CTO: Jeff McCombs
Web Dev: Kay Souksamlane
Sftwr Eng: Eugene Ngo
Sftwr Eng: Anh Vu
Sftwr Eng: Valentyna Yurtyn

D-U-N-S 00-820-5213
KELLEY BROTHERS CONTRACTORS INC (MS)
401 County Farm Rd, Waynesboro, MS 39367-8772
Tel (601) 735-2541 *Founded/Ownrshp* 1955
Sales 107.3MM^E *EMP* 115
SIC 1389 1382 1381 Oil field services; Oil & gas exploration services; Drilling oil & gas wells
Pr: Jerry Kelley
**Treas:* Bessie Kelley
**VP:* Thomas O Kelley Jr

D-U-N-S 00-225-6188
KELLEY BROTHERS LLC
317 E Brighton Ave, Syracuse, NY 13210-4141
Tel (315) 478-2151 *Founded/Ownrshp* 1886
Sales 40.2MM^E *EMP* 105
SIC 5072 Builders' hardware; Builders' hardware
Brnch Mgr: Fred Yakush
Off Mgr: Kristen Barnett
Off Mgr: Helen Fleming
IT Man: Craig Parker
Opers Mgr: Stuart Curtis
VP Sls: Jim Tartre

D-U-N-S 10-659-9426
KELLEY CONSTRUCTION INC
2454 N 27th St, Decatur, IL 62526-5262
Tel (217) 422-1800 *Founded/Ownrshp* 1983
Sales 41.0MM^E *EMP* 300
SIC 1541 3444 Industrial buildings, new construction; Sheet metalwork; Industrial buildings, new construction; Sheet metalwork
Pr: I Dean Benson
**Treas:* Virginia A Foster
**VP:* Gary Cooper
IT Man: Perry Crowe
Sfty Mgr: Steve Morse

D-U-N-S 09-419-7613
KELLEY CONSTRUCTION INC (KY)
JOE KELLEY CONSTRUCTION
12550 Lake Station Pl, Louisville, KY 40299-6394
Tel (502) 239-2848 *Founded/Ownrshp* 2000
Sales 112.3MM^E *EMP* 120^E
SIC 1542 Commercial & office building, new construction; Commercial & office building, new construction
Pr: Joseph T Kelley Jr
**VP:* Mark Kelley
IT Man: Tom Buchanan

D-U-N-S 07-861-0094
KELLEY DRYE & WARREN LLP
101 Park Ave Fl 30, New York, NY 10178-3099
Tel (212) 808-7800 *Founded/Ownrshp* 1835, 1836
Sales 142.8MM^E *EMP* 1,100
SIC 8111 General practice law office; General practice law office
Mng Pt: James J Kirk
Pt: John Callagy
Pt: Merrill B Stone
Mng Pt: Kathleen Cannon
Mng Pt: Richard S Chargar
Mng Pt: David E Fink
Mng Pt: Michael S Insel
Mng Pt: Henry T Kelly
Mng Pt: Lauri A Mazzuchetti
Mng Pt: Robert I Steiner
Mng Pt: Lewis Rose
Mng Pt: Andrew M White
Dir Soc: John Bergin

D-U-N-S 06-814-8964
KELLEY FUELS INC (MN)
250 Sarazin St, Shakopee, MN 55379-3941
Tel (952) 884-4100 *Founded/Ownrshp* 1940, 1972
Sales 21.2MM^E *EMP* 9
Accts Michael A Johnson Ltd
SIC 5172 Petroleum products
Pr: Vernon R Kelley

D-U-N-S 05-931-8248
KELLEY IMAGING SYSTEMS INC
SEATTLE DATA SYSTEMS
22710 72nd Ave S, Kent, WA 98032-1926
Tel (206) 284-9100 *Founded/Ownrshp* 2007
Sales 43.4MM^E *EMP* 84^E
SIC 5044 7629 Office equipment; Copying equipment; Business machine repair, electric; Office equipment; Copying equipment; Business machine repair, electric

Pr: Aric Manion
Dir IT: Shane Vanhulle
Sfty Dirs: John Pfingsten
Natl Sales: Ryan Franklin

D-U-N-S 11-138-9144
KELLEY KRONENBERG PA
8201 Peters Rd Ste 4000, Plantation, FL 33324-3267
Tel (954) 370-9970 Founded/Ownrshp 1980
Sales 29.8MM^E EMP 100
SIC 8111 General practice law office
Pr: Michael J Fichtel
*Pt: Michael Fichtel
Mng Pt: Jorge Cruz
COO: Angelo Filippi
*Treas: Howard L Wander
*VP: Karen M Gilmartin
Off Mgr: Liss Haris
Dir IT: David Depillis

D-U-N-S 00-349-1651 IMP/EXP
KELLEY MANUFACTURING CO
80 Vernon Dr, Tifton, GA 31794-8821
Tel (229) 382-9393 Founded/Ownrshp 1982
Sales 45.5MM EMP 185
Accts Herring Cpa Group Pc Tifto
SIC 3523 Harrows: disc, spring, tine, etc.; Harrows: disc, spring, tine, etc.
CEO: E L Carson
*Pr: Bennie Branch
*CFO: Jimmy Tomberlin

D-U-N-S 01-753-1633
KELLEY STEEL ERECTORS INC
7220 Division St, Cleveland, OH 44146-5406
Tel (440) 232-1573 Founded/Ownrshp 1990
Sales 38.8MM^E EMP 200^E
SIC 1791 7353 Structural steel erection; Cranes & aerial lift equipment, rental or leasing; Structural steel erection; Cranes & aerial lift equipment, rental or leasing
CEO: Dan Gold
*Pr: Michael Kelley
*COO: Bob Hurley
COO: Robert Hurley

D-U-N-S 02-312-4712 IMP
KELLEY SUPPLY INC
704 Industrial Dr, Colby, WI 54421-9778
Tel (715) 223-3614 Founded/Ownrshp 1981
Sales 32.6MM^E EMP 42
SIC 5143 Dairy products, except dried or canned
Pr: Bernard J Alberts
*Sec: Kay Alberts
VP: Van Werken
Mktg Dir: Craig Netzer
Manager: Larry Heacock
Sales Asso: Jill Schaefer
Sales Asso: Rachel Wolfe

D-U-N-S 10-254-1679
KELLEY TRUCKING INC
6201 Mcintyre St, Golden, CO 80403-7446
Tel (303) 279-4150 Founded/Ownrshp 1973
Sales 30.1MM^E EMP 120
SIC 1794 4212 1611 Excavation & grading, building construction; Local trucking, without storage; Highway & street construction; Excavation & grading, building construction; Local trucking, without storage; Highway & street construction
CEO: John Kelley
Ex VP: Kendra Aguilar
*VP: Dorothy Kelley
Snr Mgr: Mike Easley

D-U-N-S 00-693-5654
KELLEY WILLIAMSON CO (IL)
KW LUBES
1132 Harrison Ave, Rockford, IL 61104-7290
Tel (815) 397-9410 Founded/Ownrshp 1924, 1975
Sales 196.5MM^E EMP 480
SIC 5541 5411 5171 Filling stations, gasoline; Convenience stores, independent; Petroleum bulk stations; Filling stations, gasoline; Convenience stores, independent; Petroleum bulk stations
Pr: John Griffin
CFO: Kim Schmidt
VP: Mark Long
Exec: Bob Sanders

D-U-N-S 12-424-1402
KELLEY-CLARKE LLC
(Suby of ACOSTA INC) ★
6600 Corporate Ctr Pkwy, Jacksonville, FL 32216-0973
Tel (904) 281-9800 Founded/Ownrshp 1982
Sales 111.9MM^E EMP 2,200
SIC 5141 Food brokers; Food brokers
Ch Bd: Gary Chartrand

KELLEYAMERIT FLEET SERVICES
See KELLEYAMERIT HOLDINGS INC

D-U-N-S 07-834-8854
KELLEYAMERIT FLEET SERVICES INC (CA)
AMERIT FLEET SOLUTIONS
1331 N Calif Blvd Ste 150, Walnut Creek, CA 94596-4535
Tel (877) 512-6374 Founded/Ownrshp 2012
Sales 30.5MM^E EMP 255^E
SIC 7549 Inspection & diagnostic service, automotive
CEO: Gary Herbold
*Pr: Bob Brauer
*COO: Amein Punjani
*COO: Dan Williams
*Ch: Don Kelly
Sr VP: Heather Sager
*VP: Angelina Grossi
Sls Dir: Rebecca Lacey

D-U-N-S 83-317-2468
KELLEYAMERIT HOLDINGS INC
KELLEYAMERIT FLEET SERVICES
1331 N Calif Blvd Ste 150, Walnut Creek, CA 94596-4535
Tel (877) 512-6374 Founded/Ownrshp 2010
Sales 98.4MM^E EMP 1,300
SIC 8741 Management services; Management services
CEO: Gary Herbold
*Pr: Robert Brauer
*COO: Amein Punjani
*CFO: Dan Williams
VP: Lorraine Brady
Dir IT: Marlene Welsh
Board of Directors: Gary Herbold, Dan Williams

KELLEY'S COUNTRY COOKIN'
See JWK ENTERPRISES INC

D-U-N-S 61-241-2742
KELLINGTON CONSTRUCTION INC
807 Broadway St Ne, Minneapolis, MN 55413-2332
Tel (612) 455-7300 Founded/Ownrshp 1992
Sales 21.0MM^E EMP 75
SIC 1542 1541 Commercial & office building contractors; Industrial buildings & warehouses
CEO: Reed Lewis
*VP: Dan Guider

D-U-N-S 07-164-6894
KELLINGTON PROTECTION SERVICE LLC
1100 Washington Ave # 203, Carnegie, PA 15106-3614
Tel (412) 339-0010 Founded/Ownrshp 2010
Sales 14.0MM EMP 500^E
SIC 7381 Guard services

KELLI'S GIFT SHOP SUPPLIERS
See LAMACAR INC

D-U-N-S 18-125-7510
KELLOGG & KIMSEY INC
6077 Clark Center Ave, Sarasota, FL 34238-2718
Tel (941) 927-7700 Founded/Ownrshp 1986
Sales 80.0MM EMP 60^E
SIC 1542 Commercial & office building contractors
Pr: Philip A Kellogg
Pr: Brent Bobo
*CFO: Ed Doughty
*Ex VP: Charles Kimsey
*VP: David Pfeil

D-U-N-S 06-129-1951 IMP/EXP
■ **KELLOGG BROWN & ROOT INTERNATIONAL INC**
(Suby of K B R SERVICES) ★
601 Jefferson St Ste 7911, Houston, TX 77002-7915
Tel (713) 676-3011 Founded/Ownrshp 1986
Sales 53.5MM^E EMP 165
SIC 1389 3441 8711 1629 Oil & gas wells: building, repairing & dismantling; Fabricated structural metal; Oil & gas wells: building, repairing & dismantling; Fabricated structural metal; Professional engineer; Blasting contractor, except building demolition
CEO: Mary Hawk
*Ch Bd: Glenn Wong
*Pr: Robert R Harl
*CFO: Bruce A Stanski
*Treas: M S Bender
*Treas: Robert Telschow
*VP: Peter W Arbour
*VP: J Robert Taylor

D-U-N-S 01-081-0893
■ **KELLOGG BROWN & ROOT LLC**
K B R SERVICES
(Suby of K B R) ★
601 Jefferson St Ste 100, Houston, TX 77002-7911
Tel (713) 753-2000 Founded/Ownrshp 2005
Sales 1.7MMM^E EMP 20,010
SIC 8711 1629 Engineering services; Industrial plant construction; Engineering services; Industrial plant construction
CEO: Stuart Bradie
CFO: Sue Carter
*CFO: Brian Ferraioli
*Ex VP: Andrew D Farley
*Ex VP: Farhan Mujib
Comm Dir: Susan Wasley
CTO: Van Sickels

D-U-N-S 92-966-6709
■ **KELLOGG BROWN & ROOT SERVICES INC**
K B R
(Suby of K B R) ★
2451 Crystal Dr Ste 1124, Arlington, VA 22202-4804
Tel (703) 526-7500 Founded/Ownrshp 1996
Sales 297.8MM^E EMP 20,010
SIC 8741 Construction management; Construction management
Pr: John Derbyshire
*Pr: William P Utt
VP: David Swindle

D-U-N-S 92-614-2233 IMP/EXP
■ **KELLOGG CARIBBEAN SERVICES CO INC**
KEEBLER
(Suby of KELLOGG CO) ★
305 Carr 5, Bayamon, PR 00961-7422
Tel (787) 273-8888 Founded/Ownrshp 2008
Sales 34.9MM^E EMP 88
SIC 5149 5145 Breakfast cereals; Snack foods
Pr: David Mackay
Genl Mgr: Eric Gripentrog

KELLOGG CMNTY COLLEGE BK STR
See KELLOGG COMMUNITY COLLEGE FOUNDATION

D-U-N-S 00-535-6209 IMP/EXP
▲ **KELLOGG CO**
1 Kellogg Sq, Battle Creek, MI 49017-3534
Tel (269) 961-2000 Founded/Ownrshp 1906
Sales 14.5MMM EMP 29,790
Accts Pricewaterhousecoopers Llp De
Tkr Sym K Exch NYS
SIC 2043 2041 2052 2051 2038 Cereal breakfast foods; Corn flakes: prepared as cereal breakfast food; Rice: prepared as cereal breakfast food; Wheat flakes: prepared as cereal breakfast food; Cookies; Crackers, dry; Pastries, e.g. danish: except frozen; Waffles, frozen; Cereal breakfast foods; Corn flakes: prepared as cereal breakfast food; Rice: prepared as cereal breakfast food; Wheat flakes: prepared as cereal breakfast food; Flour & other grain mill products; Cookies; Crackers, dry; Pastries, e.g. danish: except frozen; Waffles, frozen
Ch Bd: John A Bryant
Pr: Paul Norman
CFO: Ronald L Dissinger
Treas: Mel Wickremasinghe
Sr VP: Margaret R Bath
Sr VP: George Chumakov
Sr VP: Alistair Hirst
Sr VP: Samantha J Long
Sr VP: Paul T Norman
Sr VP: Gary H Pilnick
Sr VP: Brian S Rice
VP: Jeffery W Arnold
VP: Celeste Clark
VP: Mark Clise
VP: Richard Coe
VP: Kimberly Crewsgoode
VP: Maribeth A Dangel
VP: Maribeth Dangel
VP: Rick Davis
VP: Lisa Favia
VP: Erin Herbstreith
Board of Directors: Rogelio M Rebolledo, Stephanie A Burns, Carolyn Tastad, John T Dillon, Noel Wallace, G Zachary Gund, Gordon Gund, James M Jennes, Donald R Knauss, Ann McLaughlin Korologos, Mary A Laschinger, Cynthia Hardin Milligan

D-U-N-S 79-802-7512 EXP
■ **KELLOGG CO**
(Suby of KELLOGG CO) ★
1 Kellogg Sq, Battle Creek, MI 49017-3534
Tel (269) 961-2000 Founded/Ownrshp 1906
Sales 828.4MM^E EMP 5,882
SIC 2043 Cereal breakfast foods; Cereal breakfast foods
Pr: John Bryant
Bd of Dir: Dorothy A Johnson
Ex VP: Jonathan Wilson
*Prin: David Pfanzelter

D-U-N-S 07-929-3312
KELLOGG COMMUNITY COLLEGE FOUNDATION (MI)
KELLOGG CMNTY COLLEGE BK STR
450 North Ave, Battle Creek, MI 49017-3306
Tel (269) 965-4142 Founded/Ownrshp 1957
Sales 20.9MM EMP 1,000
Accts Plante & Moran Pllc Portage
SIC 8222 Community college; Community college
Ch: Jonathan D Byrd
*Pr: Dennis Bona
*Treas: Matthew A Davis
*VP: Jill Booth
Exec: Bob Reynolds
VP Admn: Robert Rimkus
CIO: Robert Reynolds
MIS Dir: Kelli Cowell
Nrsg Dir: Cynthia Sublett

D-U-N-S 00-532-3704
KELLOGG CRANKSHAFT CO
3524 Wayland Dr, Jackson, MI 49202-1294
Tel (517) 788-9200 Founded/Ownrshp 1956
Sales 20.4MM^E EMP 89
SIC 3714 Crankshaft assemblies, motor vehicle
Pr: Allen E Spiess Jr
*Treas: Allen E Spiess Sr
Sfty Mgr: Amy Butler
Plnt Mgr: Brad Parrott

D-U-N-S 11-980-5930
KELLOGG HUBER HANSEN TODD EVANS & FIGEL PLLC
1615 M St Nw Ste 400, Washington, DC 20036-3215
Tel (202) 326-7900 Founded/Ownrshp 1993
Sales 22.4MM^E EMP 150
SIC 8111 Legal services; Legal services
Counsel: William J Conyngham Jr

D-U-N-S 07-971-1967
■ **KELLOGG NORTH AMERICA CO**
(Suby of KEEBLER CO) ★
1 Kellogg Sq, Battle Creek, MI 49017-3517
Tel (269) 961-2000 Founded/Ownrshp 1997
Sales 227.7MM^E EMP 5,046^E
SIC 2052 Cookies
Pr: David McKay

D-U-N-S 06-951-8371 EXP
■ **KELLOGG SALES CO**
(Suby of KELLOGG CO) ★
1 Kellogg Sq, Battle Creek, MI 49017-3534
Tel (269) 961-2000 Founded/Ownrshp 1923
Sales 554.3MM^E EMP 1,000
SIC 5149 Breakfast cereals; Breakfast cereals
Pr: Carlos Gutierrez
*Pr: Jim Jenneff
CFO: Raymond Held

KELLOGG SNACKS
See AUSTIN QUALITY FOODS INC

D-U-N-S 07-848-2311 IMP
KELLOGG SUPPLY CO
405 N 75th Ave Bldg 2, Phoenix, AZ 85043-2103
Tel (310) 830-2200 Founded/Ownrshp 1977
Sales 29.6MM^E EMP 27
SIC 5141 Food brokers
CEO: Doug Mahoney
*VP: Don Fisk

D-U-N-S 00-838-6450 IMP
KELLOGG SUPPLY INC (CA)
CASCADE FOREST PRODUCTS
350 W Sepulveda Blvd, Carson, CA 90745-6389
Tel (310) 830-2200 Founded/Ownrshp 1925, 1959
Sales 41.8MM^E EMP 180
SIC 2873

D-U-N-S 11-412-5490 IMP
KELLSTROM AEROSPACE LLC
14400 Nw 77th Ct Ste 306, Miami Lakes, FL 33016-1592
Tel (847) 233-5800 Founded/Ownrshp 2002
Sales 135.6MM^E EMP 83
SIC 5088 Aircraft engines & engine parts; Aircraft engines & engine parts
Ofcr: Duane Wilson
VP: Mario Arcacha
VP: Scott Campbell
VP: Scott Lescher
VP: Dixie Newton
S&M/VP: Elmer Davis
Sales Asso: Robert Scotland

D-U-N-S 11-412-5698
KELLSTROM COMMERCIAL AEROSPACE INC
KELLSTROM MATERIALS
450 Medinah Rd, Roselle, IL 60172-2329
Tel (630) 351-8813 Founded/Ownrshp 2015
Sales 89.8MM^E EMP 79^E
SIC 5088 Aircraft engines & engine parts; Transportation equipment & supplies
CEO: Roscoe Musselwhite
CEO: Jeff Lund
CFO: Oscar Torres
IT Man: Vince Colgan
IT Man: Frank Slawinski
Sls Dir: Morayma Carpio
Sls Dir: Pauline Esty
Manager: Harold Ballou
Manager: Ryan Gengler
Sls Mgr: Kathy Morales

D-U-N-S 11-412-5862 IMP
KELLSTROM DEFENSE AEROSPACE INC
(Suby of MEREX HOLDING CORPORATION)
15501 Sw 29th St Ste 101, Miramar, FL 33027-5261
Tel (954) 538-2189 Founded/Ownrshp 2014
Sales 98.0MM^E EMP 150
SIC 5088 Aircraft engines & engine parts
Pr: Christopher R Celtruda
*Pr: David Faulkner
*CFO: Jikun Kim
*Ex VP: Nathan A Skop
*VP: Stuart Reid
Manager: Tony Ramirez

KELLSTROM MATERIALS
See KELLSTROM COMMERCIAL AEROSPACE INC

D-U-N-S 07-986-6134
KELLTON TECH SOLUTIONS LTD
3 Independence Way # 209, Princeton, NJ 08540-6626
Tel (844) 469-8900 Founded/Ownrshp 2015
Sales 71.8MM^E EMP 282^E
SIC 7373 Systems software development services
CEO: Srinivas Raghavan
*CEO: Karanjit Singh
Sr VP: Abhishek Vinod Singh
Sr VP: Nitin Verma
VP: Akash Agrawal
VP: Jim Burton
VP: Julius Garcia

D-U-N-S 00-512-0431 IMP
KELLWOOD CO LLC
(Suby of SUN CAPITAL PARTNERS INC) ★
600 Kellwood Pkwy Ste 200, Chesterfield, MO 63017-5809
Tel (314) 576-3100 Founded/Ownrshp 1961, 2008
Sales 687.6MM^E EMP 1,132
SIC 5136 5137 Men's & boys' clothing; Women's & children's clothing; Men's & boys' clothing; Women's & children's clothing
CEO: Lynn Shanahan
Pr: Marc Babins
Pr: Janice Sullivan
*CFO: Joe Lombardi
Treas: Roger D Joseph
Sr Cor Off: Phil Iosca
Ex VP: David Falwell
Ex VP: Mary P Hinson
Sr VP: Linda Kinder
VP: Stephen R Beluk Jr
VP: Elton Graham
VP: J David Larocca
VP: Donald E Riley
VP: Stephen Walmsley
Exec: Joe Rutz
Dir Risk M: Ellen Mundel

D-U-N-S 08-260-5106
KELLY & ASSOCIATES INSURANCE GROUP INC (GA)
1 Kelly Way, Sparks Glencoe, MD 21152-9484
Tel (410) 527-3400 Founded/Ownrshp 1976
Sales NA EMP 350
SIC 6411 Insurance brokers; Insurance brokers
Pr: Francis X Kelly III
*Ch Bd: Francis X Kelly Jr
*CFO: Craig Horner
Bd of Dir: Rebecca Pellegrini
Ofcr: Susan Storrer
Ex VP: Bryan Kelly
*Ex VP: Joan Kelly
VP: Kitty Bollinger
VP: Jason Danner
*VP: Bryan Keely
*VP: David Kelly
VP: Michele Sargent
Exec: Tara Gaskins

D-U-N-S 01-854-6572
KELLY & PICERNE INC
(Suby of PICERNE INVESTMENT CORP) ★
75 Lambert Lind Hwy # 300, Warwick, RI 02886-1190
Tel (401) 732-3700 Founded/Ownrshp 1944
Sales 23.6MM^E EMP 650
Accts Ernst & Young Llp
SIC 6531 Real estate brokers & agents; Real estate managers; Real estate brokers & agents; Real estate managers
Ch Bd: Ronald R S Picerne Jr
*CEO: David R Picerne

*COO: Robert M Picerne
*VP: Raymond Urieescu

D-U-N-S 00-894-2385
KELLY AUTO GROUP INC
KELLY CADILLAC-SAAB AND SUBARU
900 Riverfront Pkwy, Chattanooga, TN 37402-2101
Tel (423) 490-0181 Founded/Ownrshp 1947, 1966
Sales 21.7MM[E] EMP 45
SIC 5511 Automobiles, new & used
Pr: Patrick W Kelly
*VP: Timothy Kelly
Exec: Robin Setzer
Sls Mgr: Tyson Lafferty
Sales Asso: Randall Curtis

KELLY BMW
See MID-OHIO IMPORTED CAR CO

D-U-N-S 04-136-3003
KELLY BUICK INC
KELLY CAR & TRUCK CENTER
(Suby of KELLY MANAGEMENT CORP) ★
501-23 State Ave, Emmaus, PA 18049-3051
Tel (610) 967-2101 Founded/Ownrshp 1967
Sales 65.4MM[E] EMP 200
SIC 5511 Automobiles, new & used; Automobiles, new & used
VP: Robert P Kelly
*Pr: Gregory Kelly

KELLY CADILLAC-SAAB AND SUBARU
See KELLY AUTO GROUP INC

D-U-N-S 80-095-6323
KELLY CAPITAL GROUP INC
12730 High Bluff Dr # 250, San Diego, CA 92130-3023
Tel (619) 687-5000 Founded/Ownrshp 1994
Sales 105.8MM[E] EMP 845[E]
SIC 6733 Personal investment trust management; Personal investment trust management
CEO: Michael Kelly
*Pr: Kenneth R Satterlee
VP: Sean Murphy
Counsel: Luke Kosters
Snr Mgr: Michael Kellychairman

KELLY CAR & TRUCK CENTER
See KELLY BUICK INC

KELLY CAR/TRUCK CENTER
See KELLY JEEP-EAGLE INC

KELLY CHEVROLET CADILLAC
See KELLY CHEVROLET-CADILLAC INC

D-U-N-S 01-391-5277
KELLY CHEVROLET-CADILLAC INC
KELLY CHEVROLET CADILLAC
252 Pittsburgh Rd, Butler, PA 16002-3996
Tel (724) 287-2701 Founded/Ownrshp 2012
Sales 28.5MM EMP 100
SIC 5511 7538 7532 7537 Automobiles, new & used; General automotive repair shops; Top & body repair & paint shops; Automotive transmission repair shops; Automobiles, new & used; General automotive repair shops; Top & body repair & paint shops; Automotive transmission repair shops
Pr: George J Kelly Jr
Sec: Steffany L McCafferty
VP: Brendan Kelly
Store Mgr: Jason Sholes
Sales Exec: Joe Zupancic

D-U-N-S 83-278-3224
KELLY CHEVROLET-CADILLAC INC
252 Pittsburgh Rd, Butler, PA 16002-3996
Tel (724) 287-2701 Founded/Ownrshp 1953
Sales 28.9MM[E] EMP 99
SIC 5511 Automobiles, new & used; Automobiles, new & used
Pr: George J Kelly Jr
*Sec: Stefany L McAfferty
*VP: Brendan P Kelly

D-U-N-S 06-485-8509
KELLY COMPANIES
1701 Cabin Branch Dr, Cheverly, MD 20785-3820
Tel (301) 386-2800 Founded/Ownrshp 1973
Sales 88.4MM[E] EMP 250
SIC 2752 2791 2789 Commercial printing, offset; Typesetting; Bookbinding & related work; Commercial printing, offset; Typesetting; Bookbinding & related work
Pr: Michael Kelly
*Treas: Paul Kelly
*VP: Kathleen Kelly
Dir Soc: Erin Kelly
Plnt Mgr: Brian Dunn
Plnt Mgr: Mike Meredith

D-U-N-S 83-621-6689 IMP
KELLY CONSTRUCTION OF INDIANA INC
KELLY GROUP, THE
3310 Concord Rd, Lafayette, IN 47909-5128
Tel (765) 474-1800 Founded/Ownrshp 1994
Sales 43.0MM EMP 400
Accts Bkd Llp Decatur Illinois
SIC 1541 Industrial buildings & warehouses; Food products manufacturing or packing plant construction; Renovation, remodeling & repairs: industrial buildings; Industrial buildings & warehouses; Food products manufacturing or packing plant construction; Renovation, remodeling & repairs: industrial buildings
Pr: David L Daugherty
*VP: Mary Clouser
Sfty Dirs: Kimm Wheeler
Sfty Mgr: Howard David
Opers Mgr: Jason Voight
Prd Mgr: Mike Doty

KELLY CONVENIENCE STORES
See CLINARD OIL CO INC

D-U-N-S 06-442-0656 EXP
KELLY CORNED BEEF CO OF CHICAGO
KELLY EISENBERG
3531 N Elston Ave, Chicago, IL 60618-5631
Tel (773) 588-2882 Founded/Ownrshp 1929
Sales 43.7MM[E] EMP 61[E]
SIC 5147 2011 Meats, fresh; Meats, cured or smoked; Meat packing plants
Pr: Howard Eisenberg
Sales Asso: Mark Hopper

KELLY EISENBERG
See KELLY CORNED BEEF CO OF CHICAGO

KELLY ELECTRIC
See JOHN E KELLY & SONS ELECTRICAL CONSTRUCTION INC

KELLY ELECTRIC COMPANY
See TOWNSEND CORP

KELLY ELECTRIC GROUP
See KELLY JH HOLDING LLC

KELLY FOODS
See KELLYS FOODS INC

D-U-N-S 03-225-3486
KELLY FORD INC
(Suby of KELLY MANAGEMENT CORP) ★
776 Magnolia Ave, Melbourne, FL 32935-6498
Tel (321) 254-4283 Founded/Ownrshp 1975
Sales 45.2MM[E] EMP 100
SIC 5511 5521 Automobiles, new & used; Used car dealers; Automobiles, new & used; Used car dealers
Pr: Robert P Kelly
*Treas: Gregory W Kelly
*VP: Edward J Kelly Jr
Genl Mgr: Glenn Wood
Sls Mgr: Jim Ahlquist
Sls Mgr: Jim Barndt

KELLY FRADET LUMBER
See ENFIELD LUMBER CO INC

D-U-N-S 80-947-8274
KELLY FUELS INC
2030 4th St, Jackson, MI 49203-4516
Tel (517) 787-1210 Founded/Ownrshp 1993
Sales 81.4MM[E] EMP 150
SIC 5172 5983 Engine fuels & oils; Fuel oil dealers; Engine fuels & oils; Fuel oil dealers
Pr: Bob Preider
*Sec: Thomas C Evanson
VP: Rich Tallman

KELLY GENERAL CNSTR CO DECATUR
See KELLY GENERAL CONSTRUCTION CO OF DECATUR

D-U-N-S 61-456-9627
KELLY GENERAL CONSTRUCTION CO OF DECATUR
KELLY GENERAL CNSTR CO DECATUR
2454 N 27th St, Decatur, IL 62526-5262
Tel (217) 422-1800 Founded/Ownrshp 1998
Sales 73.3MM[E] EMP 275
Accts Bkd Llp Decatur Il
SIC 1542 1521 Nonresidential construction; Single-family housing construction; Nonresidential construction; Single-family housing construction
Pr: Dean Benson
*CFO: Virginia A Foster
*VP: David W Rathje
*Prin: I Dean Benson
Plnt Mgr: Robert Foley

D-U-N-S 16-667-6200
KELLY GLOBAL LOGISTICS INC
KGL
701 W 20th St, Hialeah, FL 33010-2429
Tel (305) 591-7321 Founded/Ownrshp 1989
Sales 20.5MM[E] EMP 60
SIC 4731 Foreign freight forwarding
Pr: Humberto De Lara
*VP: Tomas Burcet
Genl Mgr: Alex Comesana

KELLY GROUP, THE
See KELLY CONSTRUCTION OF INDIANA INC

D-U-N-S 02-659-7906
KELLY HART & HALLMAN LLP (TX)
201 Main St Ste 2500, Fort Worth, TX 76102-3129
Tel (817) 332-2500 Founded/Ownrshp 1979
Sales 23.8MM[E] EMP 173
SIC 8111 General practice law office; General practice law office
Pr: Dee J Kelly
Pr: Diane Hellwig
Pr: Lancia Hoover
Pr: Gloria McGowan
Pr: Karen Moore
COO: Sharon Millians
Bd of Dir: J Arnette
*VP: William P Hallman
*VP: Mark L Hart Jr
Exec: Sherry Broyles
Dir IT: Mike Reece

D-U-N-S 15-446-0034
KELLY INNS LTD
3205 W Sencore Dr, Sioux Falls, SD 57107-0728
Tel (605) 965-1440 Founded/Ownrshp 2009
Sales 10.6MM[E] EMP 500[E]
SIC 7011 Hotels; Hotels
Pt: Brenda Jefferson

KELLY JEEP CHRYSLER
See KELLY JEEP EAGLE INC

D-U-N-S 78-681-1620
KELLY JEEP EAGLE INC
KELLY JEEP CHRYSLER
353 Broadway, Lynnfield, MA 01940-2315
Tel (781) 581-6000 Founded/Ownrshp 1991
Sales 22.0MM[E] EMP 65
Accts O Connor & Drew Pc/Kevin Carne
SIC 5511 Automobiles, new & used; Automobiles, new & used
Pr: Brian D Kelly
*Treas: Roland D Kelly
Genl Mgr: Andrew Turransky
Sls Mgr: Lucas Stecker
Sales Asso: Scott Lassiter

D-U-N-S 79-830-4721
KELLY JEEP-EAGLE INC
KELLY CAR/TRUCK CENTER
(Suby of KELLY MANAGEMENT CORP) ★
501 State Ave 23, Emmaus, PA 18049-3027
Tel (610) 776-0100 Founded/Ownrshp 1967
Sales 24.9MM[E] EMP 100[E]
SIC 5511 5521 Automobiles, new & used; Used car dealers; Automobiles, new & used; Used car dealers
Pr: Robert Kelly
*VP: Gregory Kelly

D-U-N-S 01-728-3156
KELLY JH HOLDING LLC
KELLY ELECTRIC GROUP
821 3rd Ave, Longview, WA 98632-2105
Tel (360) 423-5510 Founded/Ownrshp 1998
Sales 236.6MM[E] EMP 1,000
Accts Pricewaterhousecoopers Llp Po
SIC 1711 1542 1731 Plumbing, heating, air-conditioning contractors; Nonresidential construction; Electrical work; Plumbing, heating, air-conditioning contractors; Nonresidential construction; Electrical work
CFO: Paul Furth

D-U-N-S 02-098-1965
KELLY MANAGEMENT CORP
KELLY PONTIAC
2415 S Babcock St Ste C, Melbourne, FL 32901-5369
Tel (321) 768-2424 Founded/Ownrshp 1973
Sales 210.7MM[E] EMP 425
SIC 5511 Automobiles, new & used; Automobiles, new & used
Ch Bd: Edward J Kelly Jr
*Pr: Robert P Kelly
Board of Directors: Gregory W Kelly, Robert T Kelly

D-U-N-S 83-083-3716
KELLY MIDWEST VENTURES LIMITED PARTNERSHIP
3205 W Sencore Dr, Sioux Falls, SD 57107-0728
Tel (605) 965-1440 Founded/Ownrshp 2008
Sales 21.3MM[E] EMP 408
SIC 7011 Hotels; Hotels
Pt: Brenda Schmidt
Sls Mgr: Carol Broer

D-U-N-S 04-288-4580
KELLY MITCHELL GROUP INC (MO)
8229 Maryland Ave, Saint Louis, MO 63105-3643
Tel (314) 727-1700 Founded/Ownrshp 1998
Sales 137.2MM[E] EMP 1,200
SIC 7371 7373 Custom computer programming services; Computer integrated systems design; Custom computer programming services; Computer integrated systems design
CEO: Cassandra Sanford
*Pr: Mark Locigno
*CFO: Rebecca Boyer
Mng Dir: Jason Heilman
Mng Dir: Shannon Hernandez
Brnch Mgr: Brittney Hargraves
Brnch Mgr: Sara Kirby

D-U-N-S 83-085-2575
KELLY MWG LLC
(Suby of KELLY INNS LTD) ★
3205 W Sencore Dr, Sioux Falls, SD 57107-0728
Tel (605) 965-1440 Founded/Ownrshp 2008
Sales 2.2MM[E] EMP 466[E]
SIC 7011 Hotels

D-U-N-S 06-121-5844
KELLY NISSAN OF LYNNFIELD INC
275 Broadway, Lynnfield, MA 01940-2313
Tel (781) 598-1234 Founded/Ownrshp 1996
Sales 45.6MM EMP 65
Accts O Connor & Drew Pc/Kevin Carn
SIC 5511 Automobiles, new & used; Automobiles, new & used
Pr: Brian D Kelly
*Treas: Roland D Kelly
Sales Asso: Brett Desrosier

D-U-N-S 07-952-2164
KELLY OCG
999 W Big Beaver Rd, Troy, MI 48084-4716
Tel (248) 362-4444 Founded/Ownrshp 2014
Sales 32.3MM[E] EMP 101[E]
SIC 8742 8748 Human resource consulting services; Business consulting
CEO: Carl T Camden
*VP: Anthony Raja Devadoss
VP: Mike Dobbertin
VP: Tim Meehan
VP: Anthony Raja
Dir Lab: Bob Hardy
CTO: John Dipietro
Opers Mgr: Brad Jones
Opers Mgr: Debra Kowalski

D-U-N-S 00-796-5619 IMP
KELLY PAPER CO (CA)
(Suby of CENTRAL NATIONAL-GOTTESMAN INC) ★
288 Brea Canyon Rd, Walnut, CA 91789-3087
Tel (909) 859-8200 Founded/Ownrshp 1936, 2012
Sales 231.6MM[E] EMP 315
SIC 5111 5943 Printing paper; Office forms & supplies; Printing paper; Office forms & supplies
Pr: Janice Gottesman
COO: Rod Schaar
VP: Donald Hellon
Dist Mgr: Rorie Johnston
Dist Mgr: Robert Soto
Store Mgr: Tom Barcello
Store Mgr: Luis Barreda
Store Mgr: Patrick Linares
Store Mgr: Ernesto Navarro
Store Mgr: John Olmos
Info Man: Arthur Guerrero

D-U-N-S 12-834-5381 IMP/EXP
KELLY PIPE CO LLC
LINE PIPE INTERNATIONAL
(Suby of SHOJI JFETRADE AMERICA INC) ★
11680 Bloomfield Ave, Santa Fe Springs, CA 90670-4608
Tel (562) 868-0456 Founded/Ownrshp 2014
Sales 245.3MM[E] EMP 285
SIC 5051 Pipe & tubing, steel; Pipe & tubing, steel
Ch: Eddy Ogawa
*CEO: Leonard Gross
*CFO: Leo Mann
*CFO: Hideki Matsumoto
VP: Rick Boily
*VP: Mark Brozek
*VP: Cullen King
*VP: Steve Livingston
*VP: John N Wolfson

KELLY PONTIAC
See KELLY MANAGEMENT CORP

KELLY PRODUCTS
See CONTRACT PACKAGING INC

D-U-N-S 16-156-9652
KELLY RENTALS INC
AARON'S SALES & LEASED OWNERSH
201 Eastwood Dr Ste A, Danville, VA 24540-4962
Tel (434) 799-0884 Founded/Ownrshp 1984
Sales 24.9MM EMP 165
SIC 7359 Furniture rental; Appliance rental; Television rental; Rental store, general; Furniture rental; Appliance rental; Television rental; Rental store, general
Pr: Bobbie M Floyd
*Sec: Jo Ann Grainger
*VP: Derek L Mitchell
Off Mgr: Joanne Cassell

D-U-N-S 00-728-2429
KELLY RYAN EQUIPMENT CO
900 Kelly Ryan Dr, Blair, NE 68008
Tel (402) 426-2151 Founded/Ownrshp 1986
Sales 23.3MM[E] EMP 60
SIC 3523 3535 3531 Cattle feeding, handling & watering equipment; Spreaders, fertilizer; Conveyors & conveying equipment; Construction machinery
Pr: Steven Cook
*Treas: Kathleen Cook
Sfty Dirs: Kelly L Ryan
Sls Mgr: Tom Wachter

D-U-N-S 06-850-3648
KELLY SCOTT AND MADISON INC
K S M
303 E Wacker Dr Lowr 8, Chicago, IL 60601-5211
Tel (312) 977-0772 Founded/Ownrshp 1965
Sales 25.6MM[E] EMP 80[E]
SIC 7319 7311 Media buying service; Advertising agencies
Pr: Joni Williams
*CFO: Jerome Shneider
*Treas: David Warso
*Ex VP: Herb Isaac
*Sr VP: Elizabeth Amstutz
VP: Patty Brick
VP: Darrell Drake
*VP: Elizabeth Kalmbach
*VP: Donna Kleinman
VP: Kay Wesolowski
QA Dir: Breanne Doherty

D-U-N-S 00-695-8318
▲ **KELLY SERVICES INC**
999 W Big Beaver Rd, Troy, MI 48084-4716
Tel (248) 362-4444 Founded/Ownrshp 1946
Sales 5.5MMM EMP 8,300
Accts Pricewaterhousecoopers Llp De
Tkr Sym KELYA Exch NGS
SIC 7363 Temporary help service; Temporary help service
Pr: Carl T Camden
*Ch Bd: Terence E Adderley
COO: George S Corona
CFO: Patricia Little
Treas: Sandra Galac
Bd of Dir: Jane Dutton
Ofcr: Joe Campa
Ofcr: Campa Joe
Ofcr: Timothy Keating
Ofcr: Peter Quigley
Sr VP: Greg Barker
Sr VP: Teresa Carroll
Sr VP: Teresa S Carroll
Sr VP: George Corona
Sr VP: Myke Hawkins
Sr VP: Peter W Quigley
Sr VP: Larry Seyfarth
Sr VP: Olivier G Thirot
Sr VP: Leif Agn US
Sr VP: Andrew W Watt
Sr VP: Michael Webster
Board of Directors: Carol M Adderley, Robert S Cubbin, Jane E Dutton, Terrence B Larkin, Conrad L Mallett Jr, Leslie A Murphy, Donald R Parfet, B Joseph White

D-U-N-S 00-749-7688 IMP
KELLY SUPPLY CO
1004 W Oklahoma Ave, Grand Island, NE 68801-6649
Tel (308) 382-5670 Founded/Ownrshp 1903
Sales 56.6MM[E] EMP 94
SIC 5085 5074 5063 Industrial supplies; Plumbing fittings & supplies; Electrical supplies; Industrial supplies; Plumbing fittings & supplies; Electrical supplies
CEO: Luke P Kelly
*CEO: Luke P Kelley
COO: Tanya Broawell
*Treas: John V Kelly
IT Man: Terry Falkena

KELLY TOY
See KELLYTOY (USA) INC

D-U-N-S 00-692-2553 IMP/EXP
KELLY TRACTOR CO
8255 Nw 58th St, Doral, FL 33166-3493
Tel (305) 592-5360 Founded/Ownrshp 1933
Sales 178.8MM[E] EMP 415

SIC 5082 5083 7359 7353 5084 7699 Construction & mining machinery; Farm & garden machinery; Equipment rental & leasing; Heavy construction equipment rental; Industrial machinery & equipment; Industrial machinery & equipment repair; Agricultural equipment repair services; Construction & mining machinery; Farm & garden machinery; Equipment rental & leasing; Heavy construction equipment rental; Industrial machinery & equipment; Industrial machinery & equipment repair; Agricultural equipment repair services
Pr: Patrick L Kelly
**Treas:* Bridget G Duncan
**Sr VP:* David K Julian
**Sr VP:* Nicholas D Kelly
VP: Dan Christofferson
**VP:* K David Julian
Genl Mgr: Juan Alvarez
Genl Mgr: John Socol
Software D: Ernesto Leon
VP Sls: David Erkelens
Advt Mgr: Nelda Figueiredo
Board of Directors: Eileen Kelly, Marjorie Kelly, Evelyn J Shelley

D-U-N-S 00-486-1878
KELLY-HILL CO LLC
K H
4100 Nw Van Depopulier St, Riverside, MO 64150-9457
Tel (816) 741-7727 *Founded/Ownrshp* 1955, 1987
Sales 37.9MM^E *EMP* 125^E
SIC 1629 Railroad & railway roadbed construction
Pr: Alice Houser
**Sec:* Kathy Wright
**VP:* Neal D Houser
**VP:* Greg Wright

D-U-N-S 00-912-5303 EXP
KELLY-MOORE PAINT CO INC
KELLY-MOORE PAINTS
987 Commercial St, San Carlos, CA 94070-4018
Tel (650) 592-8337 *Founded/Ownrshp* 1946
Sales 732.1MM^E *EMP* 1,500
SIC 2851 Paints: oil or alkyd vehicle or water thinned; Lacquers, varnishes, enamels & other coatings; Removers & cleaners; Paints: oil or alkyd vehicle or water thinned; Lacquers, varnishes, enamels & other coatings; Removers & cleaners
Ch Bd: Steve De Voe
CFO: Barbara Barboza
**CFO:* Roy George
CFO: Dan Stritmatter
Treas: Russell Jones
VP: James Alberts
VP: Michael Black
VP: Daniel Englert
VP: Rusty Martindale
**VP:* James Maul
VP: Athanasios Pantazis
VP: Ivy Reite
VP: Carl Sweetland
**VP:* Mark A Zielinski
Dir Risk M: Robert Stetson
Board of Directors: L Dale Crandall, Steve Devoe, Christine McCall, Bill Moore Jr

KELLY-MOORE PAINTS
See KELLY-MOORE PAINT CO INC

D-U-N-S 09-642-4866
KELLY/BRADY ADVERTISING INC (WA)
9921 N Nevada St Ste 200, Spokane, WA 99218-1145
Tel (509) 323-9666 *Founded/Ownrshp* 1976
Sales 21.9MM^E *EMP* 74
SIC 7311 Advertising agencies
CEO: Carol Santantonio
**Pr:* Darren Case
Dir Bus: Tyler Harris
Board of Directors: Alicia Day

KELLY'S
See SALEM BUILDING SPECIALTIES INC

D-U-N-S 02-429-4875
KELLYS FOODS INC
KELLY FOODS
650 Carter Rd, Winter Garden, FL 34787-4100
Tel (407) 654-0500 *Founded/Ownrshp* 1981
Sales 19.2MM^E *EMP* 300
SIC 2099 Food preparations; Food preparations
CEO: Kenneth M Kelly
**Pr:* Richard Robertson
**VP:* Dale Kelly
**VP:* Kenny Kelly Jr
**VP:* Pat Kenney

D-U-N-S 04-424-1511 EXP
KELLYS FOODS INC
650 Carter Rd, Winter Garden, FL 34787-4100
Tel (407) 654-0500 *Founded/Ownrshp* 1981
Sales 58.5MM^E *EMP* 90^E
SIC 5144 5113 5142

KELLY'S PIPE & SUPPLY CO
See BRADLEY S SHOEN INC

D-U-N-S 01-959-2294
KELLYS ROAST BEEF INC
605 Broadway Ste 300, Saugus, MA 01906-3200
Tel (781) 284-9129 *Founded/Ownrshp* 1962
Sales 11.8MM^E *EMP* 400
SIC 5812 Fast food restaurants & stands; Fast food restaurants & stands
CFO: Steve Scali

D-U-N-S 15-767-2197 IMP
KELLYTOY (USA) INC
KELLYTOY
4811 S Alameda St, Vernon, CA 90058-2805
Tel (323) 923-1300 *Founded/Ownrshp* 1986
Sales 25.3MM^E *EMP* 47
SIC 5092 Toys
Pr: Hannie Kelly
CFO: Rami Hajeb
VP: Jonathan Kelly
Board of Directors: Jonathan Kelly

D-U-N-S 36-225-1332 IMP/EXP
KELMAR INDUSTRIES INC
(*Suby of* WACKER CHEMIE AG)
310 Spartangreen Blvd, Duncan, SC 29334-9220
Tel (864) 439-0324 *Founded/Ownrshp* 1989
Sales 50.0MM *EMP* 65
SIC 2819 Industrial inorganic chemicals; Industrial inorganic chemicals
Prin: Marvin Anderson
**VP:* Dennis D Lowery

D-U-N-S 17-660-6432 IMP
■ **KELMSCOTT COMMUNICATIONS LLC**
(*Suby of* CONSOLIDATED GRAPHICS INC) ★
5858 Westheimer Rd # 200, Houston, TX 77057-5650
Tel (713) 787-0977 *Founded/Ownrshp* 2005
Sales 76.0MM^E *EMP* 700
SIC 2752 Commercial printing, lithographic; Commercial printing, lithographic
Mktg Mgr: Gary Krattenmaker

KELNARD REFRIGERATION DIVISION
See ARISTA AIR CONDITIONING CORP

KELO-LAND
See YOUNG BROADCASTING OF SIOUX FALLS INC

D-U-N-S 06-993-9544 IMP
KELPAC MEDICAL
1000 Calle Recodo, San Clemente, CA 92673-6225
Tel (949) 361-0774 *Founded/Ownrshp* 1982
Sales 20.0MM^E *EMP* 98
SIC 3082 Tubes, unsupported plastic; Tubes, unsupported plastic
Pr: Patrick C Mickle
**Sec:* Robert Roper
CIO: Jeff Homan
CTO: Jeff Hunter
Plnt Mgr: Patrick C Mikle
Doctor: Ruediger Roessler

D-U-N-S 10-834-9937
KELSAN INC
KEL-SAN PRODUCTS
5109 N National Dr, Knoxville, TN 37914-6512
Tel (865) 525-7132 *Founded/Ownrshp* 1983
Sales 97.9MM^E *EMP* 125
SIC 5087 5169 7699 Cleaning & maintenance equipment & supplies; Janitors' supplies; Specialty cleaning & sanitation preparations; Industrial equipment services; Cleaning & maintenance equipment & supplies; Janitors' supplies; Specialty cleaning & sanitation preparations; Industrial equipment services
Ch Bd: Tillman J Keller III
Pr: J Ken Bodie
CEO: Vincent Keller
COO: Todd Allen
CFO: Kyle Kirchhofer
Prgrm Mgr: Connie Carr
Brnch Mgr: Deonna Shipley
Genl Mgr: Andy Smith
Dir IT: P M Stover
IT Man: Robert Bergquist
Mktg Dir: Monty Kilburn

D-U-N-S 01-710-4563
KELSER CORP
111 Roberts St Ste D, East Hartford, CT 06108-3666
Tel (860) 610-2200 *Founded/Ownrshp* 1981
Sales 88.4MM *EMP* 53
SIC 5045 Computers; Computer peripheral equipment; Computer software; Computers; Computer peripheral equipment; Computer software
Pr: Barry Kelly

D-U-N-S 14-473-5433 IMP
KELSEY-HAYES CO
(*Suby of* LUCASVARITY AUTOMOTIVE HOLDING CO) ★
12001 Tech Center Dr, Livonia, MI 48150-2122
Tel (734) 812-6979 *Founded/Ownrshp* 2010
Sales 77.7MM^E *EMP* 250
SIC 3714 Motor vehicle parts & accessories; Motor vehicle engines & parts; Motor vehicle body components & frame; Motor vehicle electrical equipment; Motor vehicle parts & accessories; Motor vehicle engines & parts; Motor vehicle body components & frame; Motor vehicle electrical equipment
Pr: John C Plant
Treas: R P Vargo
VP: William A Warren

KELSEY-SEYBOLD CLINIC
See KELSEY-SEYBOLD MEDICAL GROUP PLLC

D-U-N-S 62-468-0559
KELSEY-SEYBOLD MEDICAL GROUP PLLC
KELSEY-SEYBOLD CLINIC
11511 Shadow Creek Pkwy, Pearland, TX 77584-7298
Tel (713) 442-0000 *Founded/Ownrshp* 1992
Sales 256.0MM^E *EMP* 2,800
SIC 8011 5912 Offices & clinics of medical doctors; Physicians' office, including specialists; Drug stores; Offices & clinics of medical doctors; Physicians' office, including specialists; Drug stores
Ch Bd: Spencer Berthelsen
**CFO:* John Sperry
**Sec:* Tejash Patel
**V Ch Bd:* Azam Kundi
Ofcr: Nick Row
VP: Kenneth Janis
Off Mgr: Cathy Alan
Off Mgr: Vera Griggs
Off Mgr: Jennifer Todd
Snr Ntwrk: Roshy Kuruvilla
CTO: Michael Burns
Board of Directors: Herbert Ashe MD, James Boland MD, P K Champion MD, Michael Condit MD Chb, John Hughes MD, Donald Owens MD Sec-Treas, Marilyn Rice MD, Julie Toll MD

D-U-N-S 94-310-5122
KELSINGTON GROUP OF COMPANIES
228 W Us Highway 30, Schererville, IN 46375-1854
Tel (219) 791-4819 *Founded/Ownrshp* 1977
Sales 58.4MM^E *EMP* 6,600
SIC 8748 Agricultural consultant; Agricultural consultant
CEO: Robert W Kelsey
**CFO:* Edward Johnson

D-U-N-S 03-821-8939
KELSO & CO LP
320 Park Ave Fl 24, New York, NY 10022-6834
Tel (212) 751-3939 *Founded/Ownrshp* 1980
Sales 0.0 *EMP* 905^E
SIC 6211 Investment bankers; Investment bankers
Mng Pt: Frank Nickell
Mng Pt: George E Matelich
Mng Pt: Thomas R Wall IV
Bd of Dir: H Thelliyankal
VP: Irvin K Culpepper
VP: Shane Tiemann
Mng Dir: John Kim
Mng Dir: Stanley Osborne
Plnt Mgr: Ed Lemke
Genl Couns: James J Connors
Snr Mgr: Holly Billeris

D-U-N-S 83-861-0277
KELSO INVESTMENT ASSOCIATES VI LP
320 Park Ave Fl 24, New York, NY 10022-6834
Tel (212) 751-3939 *Founded/Ownrshp* 1993
Sales 46.7MM^E *EMP* 822
SIC 6211 Investment bankers; Investment bankers
CEO: Frank T Nickell
Mng Dir: George E Matelich

D-U-N-S 08-118-0994
KELSO SCHOOL DISTRICT
601 Crawford St, Kelso, WA 98626-4315
Tel (360) 501-1900 *Founded/Ownrshp* 1903
Sales 32.1MM^E *EMP* 525
SIC 8211 Public elementary school; Public junior high school; Public senior high school; Public elementary school; Public junior high school; Public senior high school
IT Man: Sandra McVey
IT Man: Scott Westlund

D-U-N-S 00-543-9070
KELSO-BURNETT CO
5200 Newport Dr, Rolling Meadows, IL 60008-3806
Tel (847) 259-0720 *Founded/Ownrshp* 1908, 1959
Sales 104.7MM^E *EMP* 400
SIC 1731 General electrical contractor; General electrical contractor
Pr: Stefan Lopata
**CFO:* Allen Bondi
**VP:* Paul Brown
VP: Mike Cultra
VP: Jim Diderrich
VP: Kathleen Eaves
**VP:* Carl Ehr
VP: John Paik
**VP:* David Raasch
VP: Paul Raymond
Div Mgr: Louis Cerone

D-U-N-S 16-855-3332 IMP
KELTA INC
141 Rodeo Dr, Edgewood, NY 11717-8378
Tel (631) 789-5000 *Founded/Ownrshp* 2003
Sales 99.2MM^E *EMP* 1,000^E
SIC 3089 3643 3661 Plastic hardware & building products; Current-carrying wiring devices; Telephone & telegraph apparatus; Plastic hardware & building products; Current-carrying wiring devices; Telephone & telegraph apparatus
Pr: Parag Mehta

D-U-N-S 10-710-2519 IMP/EXP
KELTEC INC
KELTEC-TECHNOLAB
2300 E Enterprise Pkwy, Twinsburg, OH 44087-2349
Tel (330) 425-3100 *Founded/Ownrshp* 1983
Sales 24.0MM^E *EMP* 75
SIC 3569 Separators for steam, gas, vapor or air (machinery); Gas separators (machinery)
Pr: Edward Kaiser
COO: Paul Kaiser
**VP:* Dolores Kaiser
**Prin:* Ed Kaiser Sr

KELTEC-TECHNOLAB
See KELTEC INC

D-U-N-S 05-192-2060
KELVYN PRESS INC
FINANCIAL GRAPHIC SERVICE
2910 S 18th Ave, Broadview, IL 60155-4733
Tel (708) 343-0448 *Founded/Ownrshp* 1976
Sales 32.5MM^E *EMP* 200
SIC 2752 Commercial printing, lithographic; Commercial printing, lithographic
Pr: Richard J Malacina
**CFO:* Nancy Overholt
**VP:* Richard Malacina Jr
Genl Mgr: Gary Malacine
Sfty Mgr: Lynn Suchecki

D-U-N-S 07-890-4901 IMP
KEM KREST CORP
3221 Magnum Dr, Elkhart, IN 46516-9021
Tel (574) 295-0000 *Founded/Ownrshp* 2008
Sales 96.2MM^E *EMP* 90
SIC 5169 5013 5085 4783 4225 Chemicals & allied products; Motor vehicle supplies & new parts; Industrial supplies; Packing & crating; General warehousing & storage; Chemicals & allied products; Motor vehicle supplies & new parts; Industrial supplies; Packing & crating; General warehousing & storage
CEO: Amish Shah
**CFO:* David Weaver
Adv Bd Mbr: Gary Andrews
Opers Mgr: Jeff Rawn
Mktg Mgr: Tamara Adame
Mktg Mgr: Mindy Brooks

D-U-N-S 09-239-5219
KEMA INC
DNV GL
(*Suby of* DNV GL) ★
67 S Bedford St Ste 201e, Burlington, MA 01803-6803
Tel (781) 273-5700 *Founded/Ownrshp* 1994
Sales 14.5MM^E *EMP* 365
SIC 8742 8748 Management consulting services; Energy conservation consultant; Management consulting services; Energy conservation consultant
Pr: Carole Barbeau
Treas: Xander Van Der Meijden
Sr VP: Joseph Moran
Sr VP: Gregory Reed
Sr VP: Kevin Sullivan
VP: Marty Rana
Dir IT: Michael Marrow
Software D: Michael Frank
Sftwr Eng: Aaron Reicher
Ql Cn Mgr: Leo Vissers
Mktg Mgr: Julia Vetromile

KEMA SERVICES INC.
See DNV GL ENERGY SERVICES USA INC

D-U-N-S 61-889-4273
KEMA USA INC
DNV GL
(*Suby of* KEMA INTERNATIONAL B.V.)
67 S Bedford St Ste 201e, Burlington, MA 01803-6803
Tel (781) 273-5700 *Founded/Ownrshp* 1990
Sales 59.5MM^E *EMP* 902
SIC 8748 8742 8734 7379 Energy conservation consultant; Management consulting services; Testing laboratories; Computer related consulting services; Energy conservation consultant; Management consulting services; Testing laboratories; Computer related consulting services
Pr: Hugo Van Nispen
Pr: Jos Huijbregts
Treas: Xander Van Der Meijden
Sr VP: Pierre Bartholomeus
VP: Richard S Barnes
VP: Paul Leufkens
Software D: Dave Smelser
Snr Mgr: Raymond Hudson
Board of Directors: Jos Huijbregts, Hans Van Haarst

D-U-N-S 08-273-3551
KEMBA FINANCIAL CREDIT UNION INC
555 Officenter Pl Ste 100, Gahanna, OH 43230-5333
Tel (614) 235-2395 *Founded/Ownrshp* 1933
Sales NA *EMP* 145
SIC 6062 State credit unions, not federally chartered; State credit unions, not federally chartered
CEO: Gerald Guy
**CFO:* Phil Hunt
Chf Mktg O: Marco Capalino
Dir Risk M: Adrian Higgins
Brnch Mgr: Ryan Ambrose
Dir IT: Frank Broering

D-U-N-S 09-216-5042
KEMBA FINANCIAL CREDIT UNION INC (OH)
55 Office Centre Pl, Columbus, OH 43228
Tel (614) 853-9774 *Founded/Ownrshp* 1935
Sales NA *EMP* 125
SIC 6062 State credit unions, not federally chartered; State credit unions, not federally chartered
Pr: Gerald D Guy

KEMCO
See KRUEGER ENGINEERING & MANUFACTURING CO INC

KEMCO AEROSPACE MANUFACTURING
See KEMCO TOOL AND MACHINE CO INC

D-U-N-S 05-082-5827
KEMCO SYSTEMS INC
11500 47th St N, Clearwater, FL 33762-4955
Tel (727) 573-2323 *Founded/Ownrshp* 2005
Sales 23.6MM^E *EMP* 70
SIC 3582 Commercial laundry equipment
Pr: Carroll D Gorrell
**CFO:* Richard T Ruffi
Rgnl Mgr: Bill Gallagher
Sls Mgr: John Ohehir

D-U-N-S 00-627-7529
KEMCO TOOL AND MACHINE CO INC (MO)
KEMCO AEROSPACE MANUFACTURING
3616 Scarlet Oak Blvd, Saint Louis, MO 63122-6606
Tel (636) 343-1168 *Founded/Ownrshp* 1955, 2007
Sales 33.9MM^E *EMP* 80
SIC 3545 Precision tools, machinists'
CEO: Rick Zimmerman
**Pr:* Dan Ladenberger
Pr: Robyn Oleary
**CFO:* Chris Foulk
CTO: Henry Todd
VP Opers: Dan Ammons
Mfg Dir: Alan Hurt
Snr Mgr: Greg Abbass

D-U-N-S 78-842-1808 IMP
▲ **KEMET CORP**
2835 Kemet Way, Simpsonville, SC 29681-6298
Tel (864) 963-6300 *Founded/Ownrshp* 1919
Sales 823.1MM *EMP* 9,225^E
Accts Ernst & Young Llp Greenville
Tkr Sym KEM *Exch* NYS
SIC 3675 Electronic capacitors; Electronic capacitors
CEO: Per-Olof Loof
**Ch Bd:* Frank G Brandenberg
CFO: William M Lowe Jr
Ofcr: Susan B Barkal
Ofcr: Roberto Natalini
Ofcr: John C Powers
Ofcr: Stefano Vetralla
Ex VP: Charles C Meeks Jr
Sr VP: R James Assaf
Sr VP: Phillip M Lessner
Sr VP: Claudio Lollini
Sr VP: Robert S Willoughby
VP: Brian W Burch
VP: Philip M Lessner
VP: Michael L Raynor
Board of Directors: Wilfried Backes, Joseph V Borruso, Jacob T Kozubei, E Erwin Maddrey II, Robert G Paul

D-U-N-S 15-750-2634 IMP
■ KEMET ELECTRONICS CORP
(*Suby of* KEMET CORP) ★
2835 Kemet Way, Simpsonville, SC 29681-6298
Tel (864) 963-6700 *Founded/Ownrshp* 1987
Sales 858.8MM^E *EMP* 9,225
SIC 3675 Electronic capacitors; Electronic capacitors
CEO: Per Olaf Loof
**CFO:* William M Lawe Jr
**Ex VP:* Chuck Meeks Jr
**Sr VP:* Susan B Barkal
VP: John Boan
VP: William Johnson
CIO: Brian Burch
Netwrk Mgr: Kurt Baumwart
Sfty Dirs: Carolyn Cox
Opers Mgr: Janice Oberg
Prd Mgr: Gary Rhoden

KEMI
See KENTUCKY EMPLOYERS MUTUAL INSURANCE AUTHORITY

KEMIN FOODS
See KEMIN INDUSTRIES INC

D-U-N-S 00-527-4287 IMP/EXP
KEMIN INDUSTRIES INC
KEMIN FOODS
2100 Maury St, Des Moines, IA 50317-1100
Tel (515) 559-5100 *Founded/Ownrshp* 1961
Sales 216.4MM^E *EMP* 919
SIC 2834 2879

D-U-N-S 03-387-0585 IMP
KEMIRA CHEMICALS INC
KEMIRA SPECIALITY CHEMICALS
(*Suby of* KEMIRA OYJ)
1000 Parkwood Cir Se # 500, Atlanta, GA 30339-2131
Tel (863) 533-5990 *Founded/Ownrshp* 2002
Sales 149.4MM^E *EMP* 350
SIC 2869 2819 Industrial organic chemicals; Industrial inorganic chemicals; Industrial organic chemicals; Industrial inorganic chemicals
CEO: Carolina Den Brok-Perez
**Pr:* Hannu Melarti
**CFO:* Belinda Rosario
**CFO:* Suzanne G Smith
Ex VP: Heidi Fagerholm
**Ex VP:* Harri Kerminen
Ex VP: Antti Salminen
VP: Raisa Jyrkinen
VP: Pedro Materan
Exec: Susan Wynne
**Prin:* Randy T Owens

KEMIRA SPECIALITY CHEMICALS
See KEMIRA CHEMICALS INC

D-U-N-S 62-794-5702
KEMIRA WATER SOLUTIONS INC
(*Suby of* KEMIRA OYJ)
1000 Parkwood Cir Se # 500, Atlanta, GA 30339-2130
Tel (770) 436-1542 *Founded/Ownrshp* 1988
Sales 202.2MM^E *EMP* 750
SIC 2899 Water treating compounds; Water treating compounds
**CFO:* Belinda Rosario
**Treas:* Daniel Britt

D-U-N-S 00-810-7815
KEMLON PRODUCTS & DEVELOPMENT CO INC
1424 N Main St, Pearland, TX 77581-2215
Tel (281) 997-3300 *Founded/Ownrshp* 1963
Sales 33.8MM^E *EMP* 265
SIC 3643 3561 Connectors & terminals for electrical devices; Pumps & pumping equipment; Connectors & terminals for electrical devices; Pumps & pumping equipment
Pr: Russell K Ring
**VP:* William S Ring
Exec: Sherry Washburn
Sfty Mgr: Mark Ring
Mktg Mgr: William Watts

D-U-N-S 92-715-2194
KEMOSABE MOTORS LP
HONDA CARS OF KATY
21001 Katy Fwy, Katy, TX 77450-1818
Tel (281) 994-0055 *Founded/Ownrshp* 2007
Sales 28.2MM^E *EMP* 78^E
SIC 5511 New & used car dealers
Mng Pt: Rene R Isip Jr
Genl Mgr: Chris Morrison
Sales Asso: Rene Valdez

KEMP
See FLAIRE CORP

KEMP
See SPX FLOW TECHNOLOGY USA INC

D-U-N-S 02-933-2061
KEMP FORD
3810 E Thousand Oaks Blvd, Westlake Village, CA 91362-3608
Tel (805) 522-8474 *Founded/Ownrshp* 1975
Sales 30.2MM *EMP* 92
SIC 5511 Automobiles, new & used; Pickups, new & used; Automobiles, new & used; Pickups, new & used
Pr: John J Kemp
**Treas:* Cynthia Kemp
Sls Mgr: Jon Butterworth

D-U-N-S 07-488-4800
KEMP INDUSTRIES INC
TEXAS PAINT
4410 Ross Ave, Dallas, TX 75204-5003
Tel (214) 824-4574 *Founded/Ownrshp* 1992
Sales 52.5MM^E *EMP* 85
SIC 5231 Paint; Wallpaper
Pr: Kathy Harvey

KEMPER
See RESERVE NATIONAL INSURANCE CO

D-U-N-S 06-678-0219
KEMPER & ETHEL MARLEY FOUNDATION
2001 E Colter St, Phoenix, AZ 85016-3403
Tel (602) 269-6081 *Founded/Ownrshp* 1990
Sales 46.7MM *EMP* 2
SIC 6733 Trusts, except educational, religious, charity: management; Trusts, except educational, religious, charity: management
CFO: Nancy Ball

KEMPER A UNITRIN BUSINESS
See KEMPER INDEPENDENCE INSURANCE CO

D-U-N-S 14-472-5855
KEMPER CO
10307 Detroit Ave # 101, Cleveland, OH 44102-1605
Tel (216) 472-4200 *Founded/Ownrshp* 1994
Sales 26.7MM^E *EMP* 200
SIC 8748 Business consulting; Business consulting
Pr: Betty J Kemper
**Ex VP:* Kristin West
VP: Frances Saxton
**Prin:* Chris Hulten
Mktg Dir: Jennifer Nance

D-U-N-S 61-193-5909
▲ KEMPER CORP
1 E Wacker Dr, Chicago, IL 60601-1474
Tel (312) 661-4600 *Founded/Ownrshp* 1990
Sales NA *EMP* 6,100^E
Accts Deloitte & Touche Llp Chicago
Tkr Sym KMPR *Exch* NYS
SIC 6331 6321 6311 6141 Property damage insurance; Fire, marine & casualty insurance: stock; Accident & health insurance; Life insurance carriers; Automobile loans, including insurance; Fire, marine & casualty insurance; Property damage insurance; Fire, marine & casualty insurance: stock; Accident & health insurance; Life insurance; Life insurance carriers; Automobile loans, including insurance
CEO: Joseph P Lacher Jr
Ch Bd: Robert J Joyce
Pr: Pete Braitsch
Pr: Andrea James
Pr: Lisa Love
Pr: Kirk Triance
CFO: Frank J Sodaro
Ex VP: Timothy D Bruns
Ex VP: Fcas Elkins
Sr VP: John M Boschelli
Sr VP: J W Burkett
Sr VP: David Elkins
Sr VP: Judy Hecker
Sr VP: Keith Sievers
VP: Brad Andrekus
VP: David Bengston
VP: Diana J Hickert-Hill
VP: Dorothy Langley
VP: Elizabeth Lupetini
VP: Stephen Marsden
VP: Thom McDaniel
Board of Directors: George N Cochran, Kathleen M Cronin, Douglas G Geoga, Robert J Joyce, Christopher B Sarofim, David P Storch

D-U-N-S 03-355-5822 IMP
KEMPER EQUIPMENT INC
5051 Horseshoe Pike # 200, Honey Brook, PA 19344-1365
Tel (610) 273-2066 *Founded/Ownrshp* 1981
Sales 26.2MM^E *EMP* 50
SIC 5084 5082 Materials handling machinery; Mining machinery & equipment, except petroleum
CEO: H Lyn Kemper
**Pr:* Gregory R Donecker
**CFO:* Thomas Mc Donald
VP: Ray Melleady
**Prin:* Beverly L Kemper

D-U-N-S 11-486-8818
■ KEMPER INDEPENDENCE INSURANCE CO
KEMPER A UNITRIN BUSINESS
(*Suby of* KEMPER CORP) ★
12926 Gran Bay Pkwy W, Jacksonville, FL 32258-4469
Tel (904) 245-5600 *Founded/Ownrshp* 1998
Sales NA *EMP* 900
SIC 6411 Insurance agents, brokers & service; Patrol services, insurance; Insurance agents, brokers & service; Patrol services, insurance
Pr: Denise I Lynch
Pr: Chuck Esola
Pr: Jennifer Fredenberg
Pr: Ken Holderbaum
Pr: Tony Prete
**Treas:* Edwin P Schultz
Ex VP: Thomas McDaniel
**Sr VP:* Steven S Andrews
Sr VP: Gabriel Carrillo
Sr VP: Sharon Shofner-Meyer
VP: Mark Asel
VP: David Backs
VP: Daniel Ignarski

KEMPER INSURANCE
See UNIVERSITY FEDERAL CREDIT UNION

KEMPER INSURANCE
See VENBROOK INSURANCE SERVICES LLC

KEMPER INSURANCE
See RISK STRATEGIES CO

KEMPER INSURANCE
See ANSAY & ASSOCIATES LLC

KEMPER INSURANCE
See MITCHELL BUCKMAN INC

KEMPER INSURANCE
See BB&T INSURANCE SERVICES INC

KEMPER INSURANCE
See LONG & FOSTER INSTITUTE OF REAL ESTATE INC

KEMPER INSURANCE
See AAA MINNEAPOLIS

KEMPER INSURANCE
See R W TROXELL & CO

KEMPER INSURANCE
See DIVERSIFIED INSURANCE INDUSTRIES INC

KEMPER INSURANCE
See ENGLE-HAMBRIGHT & DAVIES INC

KEMPER INSURANCE
See VAN BEURDEN INSURANCE SERVICES INC

KEMPER INSURANCE
See RYAN ROBERTSON AND ASSOCIATES INC

KEMPER INSURANCE
See ROCKWOOD CO

KEMPER INSURANCE
See GROSSLIGHT INSURANCE INC

KEMPER INSURANCE
See ZANDER INSURANCE GROUP LLC

KEMPER INSURANCE
See CONOVER INSURANCE INC

KEMPER INSURANCE
See HENDERSON BROTHERS INC

KEMPER INSURANCE
See UNITED AGENCIES INC

KEMPER INSURANCE
See PARIS-KIRWAN ASSOCIATES INC

KEMPER INSURANCE
See INTERWEST INSURANCE SERVICES INC

KEMPER INSURANCE
See HICKOK & BOARDMAN INC

KEMPER INSURANCE
See U S I SOUTH WEST

KEMPER INSURANCE
See ARISON INSURANCE SERVICES INC

KEMPER INSURANCE
See CHERNOFF DIAMOND & CO LLC

KEMPER INSURANCE
See TOM JONES INSURANCE INC

KEMPER INSURANCE
See UNIVERSAL BUSINESS INSURANCE INC

KEMPER INSURANCE
See ANCO INSURANCE SERVICES OF BRYAN COLLEGE STATION INC

KEMPER INSURANCE
See SINCLAIR INSURANCE GROUP INC

KEMPER INSURANCE
See TEXCAP-CONCORD INSURANCE SERVICES LP

KEMPER INSURANCE
See HMS INSURANCE ASSOCIATES INC

KEMPER LESNIK ORGANIZATION
See KEMPER SPORTS INC

D-U-N-S 07-911-5823
KEMPER NORTHWEST INC (ID)
223 Roedel Ave, Caldwell, ID 83605-6716
Tel (208) 482-7811 *Founded/Ownrshp* 2013
Sales 20.7MM^E *EMP* 61^E
SIC 3585 Refrigeration & heating equipment
Pr: Matthew Medeiros

D-U-N-S 09-253-3959
KEMPER SPORTS INC
KEMPER LESNIK ORGANIZATION
500 Skokie Blvd Ste 444, Northbrook, IL 60062-2844
Tel (847) 850-1818 *Founded/Ownrshp* 1989
Sales 229.0MM^E *EMP* 4,250
SIC 8743 7941 7992 Public relations services; Promotion service; Sports clubs, managers & promoters; Basketball club; Public golf courses; Public relations services; Promotion service; Sports clubs, managers & promoters; Basketball club; Public golf courses
CEO: Steven K Skinner
**Pr:* Josh W Lesnik
**CFO:* Brian Milligan
**Treas:* Robert L Wallace
**Ex VP:* Gary S Binder
**Ex VP:* Ben Blake
**Sr VP:* Amy Littleton
**VP:* Steve Argo

D-U-N-S 85-855-8166
KEMPER SPORTS MANAGEMENT INC
(*Suby of* KEMPER LESNIK ORGANIZATION) ★
500 Skokie Blvd Ste 444, Northbrook, IL 60062-2844
Tel (847) 850-1818 *Founded/Ownrshp* 1978
Sales 93.9MM^E *EMP* 2,000
SIC 7999 Public golf courses; Golf professionals
Ch: Steven H Lesnik
**Owner:* Jim Stegall
**Pr:* Josh W Lesnik
**CEO:* Stephen K Skinner
**CFO:* Brian Milligan
**Ex VP:* Gary S Binder
**Ex VP:* Ben Blake
Ex VP: James R Seeley
Sr VP: Barrett Eiselman
**Sr VP:* Andrew Fleming
Sr VP: Douglas Hellman
Sr VP: Eric Jonke
Sr VP: Tom Valdiserri
VP: John C Clark
VP: Andy Crosson
VP: Daniel F Cunningham
VP: Barnaby Dinges
VP: David Goltz
VP: Keith Hanley
VP: Hank Hickox
VP: Jeff Kline

D-U-N-S 00-542-4338 IMP/EXP
KEMPER VALVE & FITTINGS CORP (IL)
3001 Darrell Rd, Island Lake, IL 60042-9157
Tel (847) 526-2166 *Founded/Ownrshp* 1963
Sales 32.4MM^E *EMP* 180
SIC 3494

D-U-N-S 00-774-5578
KEMPERSPORTS CO
ALLGOLF
500 Skokie Blvd Ste 444, Northbrook, IL 60062-2867
Tel (847) 480-4705 *Founded/Ownrshp* 2000
Sales 13.3MM^E *EMP* 425
SIC 7992 Public golf courses; Public golf courses
V Ch: Robert Wallace
CFO: Brian Milligan
Treas: Robert Waace
Ex VP: Jim Stegall
Sr VP: Andrew Fleming
VP: Daniel Cunningham
VP: Dave Goltz
Div Mgr: Pete Busch
Genl Mgr: Dean Lytton
Genl Mgr: Andy Perez
Genl Mgr: Brett Plymell

D-U-N-S 07-026-1995
KEMPF PAPER CORP (MN)
3145 Columbia Ave Ne, Minneapolis, MN 55418-1811
Tel (612) 781-9225 *Founded/Ownrshp* 1976
Sales 45.4MM^E *EMP* 58
SIC 5111 Printing paper
CEO: Jeff Kempf
**Pr:* Gust Kempf Jr
VP: Bill Forehlith
VP: Bill Froehlich
**VP:* Michael Kempf
Sales Asso: Christine Sweeney

D-U-N-S 78-312-0889
KEMPLER & CO INC
1450 Brickell Ave # 2110, Miami, FL 33131-3478
Tel (786) 235-8434 *Founded/Ownrshp* 2006
Sales 43.8MM^E *EMP* 20
SIC 5172 Fuel oil
CEO: ARI Kempler
**VP:* Peter Ryan
Dir Bus: Daniel Kempler

D-U-N-S 00-625-9501 IMP
KEMPS LLC
(*Suby of* DAIRY FARMERS OF AMERICA INC) ★
1270 Energy Ln, Saint Paul, MN 55108-5225
Tel (651) 379-6500 *Founded/Ownrshp* 2011
Sales 155.5MM^E *EMP* 1,060
SIC 2026 2024

D-U-N-S 00-317-5783
KEMPSVILLE BUILDING MATERIALS INC
(*Suby of* CARTER LUMBER) ★
3300 Business Center Dr, Chesapeake, VA 23323-2638
Tel (757) 485-0782 *Founded/Ownrshp* 1955, 2009
Sales 21.1MM^E *EMP* 215
SIC 2439 5211 2431 Trusses, wooden roof; Trusses, except roof: laminated lumber; Lumber & other building materials; Millwork; Trusses, wooden roof; Trusses, except roof: laminated lumber; Lumber & other building materials; Millwork
Pr: Scott M Gandy
**VP:* Bobby G Johnson
**VP:* Brenda C Onley
IT Man: Don McGee
Opers Mgr: Joseph Maez
Sales Asso: Shawn Jennings
Sales Asso: Andrew Schule

D-U-N-S 01-757-9616
KEMPTHORN AUTOMALL
JAGUAR VOLVO
1449 Cleveland Ave Nw, Canton, OH 44703-3138
Tel (800) 451-3877 *Founded/Ownrshp* 1930
Sales 29.0MM^E *EMP* 105
SIC 5511 5521 7538 7515 7513 Automobiles, new & used; Vans, new & used; Pickups, new & used; Used car dealers; General automotive repair shops; Passenger car leasing; Truck rental & leasing, no drivers; Automobiles, new & used; Vans, new & used; Pickups, new & used; Used car dealers; General automotive repair shops; Passenger car leasing; Truck rental & leasing, no drivers
Pr: Richard Kempthorn
**VP:* Marilyn Kempthorn

D-U-N-S 02-826-9491
KEMPTHORN MOTORS INC (OH)
1449 Cleveland Ave Nw, Canton, OH 44703-3181
Tel (330) 452-6511 *Founded/Ownrshp* 1938, 1965
Sales NA *EMP* 100
SIC 6159 Automobile finance leasing; Automobile finance leasing
Pr: Richard Kempthorn
Exec: Fran Mastroine
Exec: Tom Quinn
Telecom Ex: Mike Hedrick
Sls Mgr: Ian Franz
Sls Mgr: Dwayne Holbrook
Sls Mgr: Mike Lyons

D-U-N-S 08-278-5585
KEMRON ENVIRONMENTAL SERVICES INC
1359a Ellswrth Indus Blvd, Atlanta, GA 30318
Tel (404) 636-0928 *Founded/Ownrshp* 1983
Sales 39.4MM^E *EMP* 150
SIC 8711 Consulting engineer; Consulting engineer
CEO: Juan J Gutierrez
CFO: Ralph Vaccaro
**VP:* Tracy Bergquist
**VP:* John M Dwyer
VP: David Vandnbrg
**Prin:* Sandy Carlson
Rgnl Mgr: Thomas Ohara
Off Mgr: Cindy Papousek

D-U-N-S 61-203-0924
KEMTAH GROUP INC
7601 Jefferson St Ne # 120, Albuquerque, NM 87109-4496
Tel (505) 346-4923 *Founded/Ownrshp* 1987
Sales 27.9MM *EMP* 450

SIC 7379 7373 7376 Computer related maintenance services; Computer related consulting services; Computer hardware requirements analysis; Computer integrated systems design; Systems engineering, computer related; Computer facilities management; Computer related maintenance services; Computer related consulting services; Computer hardware requirements analysis; Computer integrated systems design; Systems engineering, computer related; Computer facilities management
CEO: Keith Harris
**Pr:* Steve Wade
IT Man: Jennifer Malone
MIS Mgr: David Luft
Sftwr Eng: Garrett Speck
Opers Mgr: Garridon Grady
Snr Mgr: Tom Seals

KEMTRON TECHNOLOGIES, INC.
See KEMTRON TECHNOLOGIES LLC

D-U-N-S 83-802-7787 IMP
KEMTRON TECHNOLOGIES LLC
KEMTRON TECHNOLOGIES, INC.
(*Suby of* ELGIN EQUIPMENT GROUP LLC) ★
10050 Cash Rd, Stafford, TX 77477-4407
Tel (281) 261-5778 *Founded/Ownrshp* 2014
Sales 26.6MM^E *EMP* 95^E
SIC 3533 Oil & gas drilling rigs & equipment; Oil & gas drilling rigs & equipment
Pr: Michael Anderson
CFO: Nadeem Abdullah
VP: Arun Chhaya
QA Dir: David Nassif
Mfg Dir: Ilene Millan
S&M/VP: John Rabon
Mktg Mgr: Ray Pietramale
Sls Mgr: Chuck Skillman

KEN - API SUPPLY
See KEN BUILDERS SUPPLY INC

D-U-N-S 03-942-4254 EXP
KEN BATCHELOR CADILLAC CO INC
SEWELL MOTOR COMPANY
11001 W Ih 10, San Antonio, TX 78230-1099
Tel (210) 690-0700 *Founded/Ownrshp* 1979
Sales 71.8MM^E *EMP* 250
SIC 5511 5521

D-U-N-S 07-309-4948
KEN BETTRIDGE DISTRIBUTING INC (UT)
K B OIL
386 N 100 W, Cedar City, UT 84721-3520
Tel (435) 586-2411 *Founded/Ownrshp* 1925, 2007
Sales 26.9MM^E *EMP* 95
SIC 5171 5541 5411

KEN BLANCHARD COMPANIES, THE
See BLANCHARD TRAINING AND DEVELOPMENT INC

D-U-N-S 04-348-5218 IMP
KEN BRATNEY CO (IA)
(*Suby of* KBC GROUP INC) ★
3400 109th St, Des Moines, IA 50322-8104
Tel (515) 270-2417 *Founded/Ownrshp* 1964, 1994
Sales 45.6MM^E *EMP* 100
SIC 1541 Industrial buildings & warehouses; Industrial buildings & warehouses
Pr: J Paul Bratney
**Treas:* Peter K Bratney
VP: Bruce Bratney
VP: Darin Stutler
VP: Jack Teagarden
Dir Bus: Curt Davis
Off Mgr: Christine Mikkelson
Off Mgr: Ann Stutler
Info Man: Andrew Beltrame
Info Man: Travis Tweed
Sfty Mgr: Scott Buchanan

D-U-N-S 05-002-9347
KEN BUILDERS SUPPLY INC
KEN - API SUPPLY
2048 Rolling Hills Dr, Covington, KY 41017-9418
Tel (859) 431-0626 *Founded/Ownrshp* 1948
Sales 77.5MM^E *EMP* 90
SIC 5031 Lumber, plywood & millwork; Wallboard; Lumber, plywood & millwork; Wallboard
Pr: Jonathan Votel
**VP:* Ruth Votel
Genl Mgr: Dan Guess
Sls Mgr: Greg Davis

D-U-N-S 07-095-5604
KEN CAL MAINTENANCE CORP
399 Knollwood Rd Ste 116, White Plains, NY 10603-1916
Tel (914) 761-5900 *Founded/Ownrshp* 1975
Sales 9.0MM *EMP* 450
SIC 7349 Building maintenance services; Office cleaning or charring; Building maintenance services; Office cleaning or charring
Pr: Kenneth M Hirschberg
**Treas:* Gertie Hirschberg
VP: Robin Hirschberg
Opers Mgr: Mauricio Carranza

D-U-N-S 12-141-0450 IMP
KEN CARYL GLASS INC
12450 Mead Way, Littleton, CO 80125-9757
Tel (303) 791-3122 *Founded/Ownrshp* 1984
Sales 25.8MM^E *EMP* 160
SIC 1793 Glass & glazing work; Glass & glazing work
Pr: Kevin Cavanaugh
**VP:* Bruce Linder
Mktg Dir: Josh Cavanaugh
Snr PM: Steve Akin

KEN DIXON AUTOMOTIVE
See KEN DIXON CHEVROLET-BUICK INC

D-U-N-S 02-268-5598
KEN DIXON CHEVROLET-BUICK INC
KEN DIXON AUTOMOTIVE
2298 Crain Hwy, Waldorf, MD 20601-3145
Tel (301) 645-7000 *Founded/Ownrshp* 1961
Sales 43.0MM^E *EMP* 150
SIC 5511 Automobiles, new & used; Automobiles, new & used
Pr: Andrew Dixon
**VP:* Daniel Tayman
Sls Mgr: Dan Shepherd

D-U-N-S 80-512-9038
KEN ELLEGARD - PEORIA INC
ARROWHEAD HONDA
8380 W Bell Rd, Peoria, AZ 85382-3702
Tel (623) 974-9700 *Founded/Ownrshp* 1992
Sales 43.9MM^E *EMP* 100^E
SIC 5511 Automobiles, new & used; Automobiles, new & used
Pr: Kenneth E Ellegard
**Sec:* Cheryl O Ellegard
Genl Mgr: Thad Zorn
Dir IT: Dan Lowe

D-U-N-S 05-466-1632
KEN FORGING INC (OH)
1049 Griggs Rd, Jefferson, OH 44047-8772
Tel (440) 993-8091 *Founded/Ownrshp* 1970
Sales 36.5MM^E *EMP* 115
SIC 3462 3544 Iron & steel forgings; Special dies & tools; Iron & steel forgings; Special dies & tools
Pr: Richard Kovach
**VP:* Ken Kovach
IT Man: Steve Tarbet
Sfty Mgr: Wes Alanen
Plnt Mgr: Tony Pasanen
Sales Asso: Senthia Fleischer
Sales Asso: Marc Loveland
Sales Asso: Mike Siemers

KEN GAFF NISSAN
See GARFF WARNER AUTOMOTIVE GROUP INC

KEN GARFF AUTOMOTIVE GROUP
See GARFF-UC LLC

KEN GARFF AUTOMOTIVE GROUP
See GARFF ENTERPRISES INC

D-U-N-S 07-479-6707
KEN GRAHAM TRUCKING INC
5018 W M 28, Brimley, MI 49715-9232
Tel (906) 635-0629 *Founded/Ownrshp* 1965
Sales 25.4MM^E *EMP* 75
SIC 7513 4213 Truck leasing, without drivers; Refrigerated products transport; Truck leasing, without drivers; Refrigerated products transport
Pr: Kenneth E Graham
Treas: Jeff Graham
**VP:* Marlene Graham
Exec: Kris Haller

KEN GRODY FORD
See TED JONES FORD INC

D-U-N-S 08-886-5019
KEN LUNEACK CONSTRUCTION INC
BEAR TRUSS & COMPONENTS
721 E Washington St, Saint Louis, MI 48880-1986
Tel (989) 681-5774 *Founded/Ownrshp* 1973
Sales 43.7MM^E *EMP* 200
SIC 2439 Trusses, wooden roof; Trusses, except roof: laminated lumber; Trusses, wooden roof; Trusses, except roof: laminated lumber
Pr: Paul B Luneack
**CFO:* Pam Luneack
**VP:* Philip Luneack
Exec: Marilyn Fenby

D-U-N-S 01-845-0718 IMP
KEN MILLER SUPPLY INC (OH)
1537 Blachleyville Rd, Wooster, OH 44691-9752
Tel (330) 263-7890 *Founded/Ownrshp* 1959
Sales 106.8MM^E *EMP* 70
SIC 5084 Oil field tool joints; Oil field tool joints
CEO: Kirk Miller
**CEO:* Lindy Chandler
**CFO:* Joseph Zehnder
Sls Mgr: Doug Dye
Sls Mgr: Troy Poling
Sls Mgr: Dave Tracey
Sales Asso: Gary Jarrell
Board of Directors: Jack Miller

D-U-N-S 17-353-5840
KEN NELSON AUTO MALL INC
KEN NELSON NISSAN
1100 N Galena Ave, Dixon, IL 61021-1016
Tel (815) 616-9367 *Founded/Ownrshp* 1984
Sales 80.0MM *EMP* 150
SIC 5511 Automobiles, new & used; Automobiles, new & used
VP: Richard Curia

D-U-N-S 96-107-5421
KEN NELSON AUTO PLAZA INC
1100 N Galena Ave, Dixon, IL 61021-1016
Tel (815) 288-4455 *Founded/Ownrshp* 1966
Sales 26.9MM^E *EMP* 75
SIC 5511 Automobiles, new & used; Automobiles, new & used
Pr: Ken Nelson
IT Man: Tony Winstead
Sls Mgr: Craig Buchanan
Sls Mgr: Warren Gridley
Sales Asso: Mike Baker
Sales Asso: Tony Penick

KEN NELSON NISSAN
See KEN NELSON AUTO MALL INC

D-U-N-S 05-911-0445
KEN NEYER PLUMBING INC
4895 State Route 128, Cleves, OH 45002-9752
Tel (513) 353-3311 *Founded/Ownrshp* 1972
Sales 35.0MM^E *EMP* 150
SIC 1711 Plumbing contractors
Pr: James Neyer
**Treas:* Janet Neyer
**VP:* Ken Neyer Jr

KEN NICHOLS FORD
See FORD NICHOLS LTD

D-U-N-S 08-382-0639
KEN SMALL CONSTRUCTION INC (CA)
6205 District Blvd, Bakersfield, CA 93313-2141
Tel (661) 617-1700 *Founded/Ownrshp* 1968
Sales 147.3MM^E *EMP* 2,000
SIC 1623

D-U-N-S 03-458-5711
KEN SMITH AUTO PARTS INC
ROCK BOTTOM AUTO PARTS
4140 Jersey Pike, Chattanooga, TN 37421-2201
Tel (423) 756-5418 *Founded/Ownrshp* 1991
Sales 39.1MM^E *EMP* 107^E
SIC 5013 5531 Automotive supplies & parts; Automotive parts; Automotive supplies & parts; Automotive parts
CEO: Raun Smith
**CFO:* Richard Spurling
**VP:* Robert Smith
Sales Asso: Don Harper
Sales Asso: Cliff Miller

D-U-N-S 08-101-1587
KEN TOWERYS AUTO CARE OF KENTUCKY INC
AMERICA'S BEST TIRES
(*Suby of* TOWERYS MANAGEMENT SERVICES INC) ★
2103 Production Dr, Louisville, KY 40299-2113
Tel (502) 499-2600 *Founded/Ownrshp* 1976
Sales 46.9MM^E *EMP* 200
SIC 5531 7538 Automotive tires; Automotive accessories; General automotive repair shops; Automotive tires; Automotive accessories; General automotive repair shops
Pr: Kenneth W Towery

KEN VANCE HYUNDAI
See KEN VANCE MOTORS INC

D-U-N-S 05-273-6642
KEN VANCE MOTORS INC (WI)
KEN VANCE HYUNDAI
5252 State Road 93, Eau Claire, WI 54701-9678
Tel (715) 834-4162 *Founded/Ownrshp* 1970, 1981
Sales 29.2MM^E *EMP* 75
SIC 5511

D-U-N-S 02-278-2783
KEN WASCHKE AUTO PLAZA INC
501 9th St N, Virginia, MN 55792-2301
Tel (218) 741-6000 *Founded/Ownrshp* 1983
Sales 27.4MM^E *EMP* 74
SIC 5511 Automobiles, new & used; Automobiles, new & used
Pr: Ken Waschke
**Sec:* Mary Waschke
**Genl Mgr:* Kerri Waschke-Collie
Sls Mgr: Aric Venne

D-U-N-S 09-874-1630
KEN WEAVER MEATS INC
WEAVER'S OF WELLSVILLE
47 North St, Wellsville, PA 17365-9636
Tel (717) 502-0118 *Founded/Ownrshp* 1889
Sales 45.8MM *EMP* 24
Accts Boreman & Babb Cpas New Cumb
SIC 2013 5147 5143 5421 5451 Sausages from purchased meat; Bologna from purchased meat; Prepared pork products from purchased pork; Meats, fresh; Cheese; Meat markets, including freezer provisioners; Cheese; Sausages from purchased meat; Bologna from purchased meat; Prepared pork products from purchased pork; Meats, fresh; Cheese; Meat markets, including freezer provisioners; Cheese
Pr: Craig Weaver

D-U-N-S 02-445-3805
KEN WILSON FORD INC
769 Champion Dr, Canton, NC 28716-3027
Tel (828) 648-2313 *Founded/Ownrshp* 1980
Sales 47.7MM^E *EMP* 100^E
SIC 5511 Automobiles, new & used; Automobiles, new & used
Pr: Kenneth Wilson
**CFO:* Lisa Haynes
Genl Mgr: Rodney Lunsford
IT Man: Debbie Wilson
Info Man: Lisa Ledford
Mktg Dir: Cecil Queen
Sls Mgr: Bill Gourley
Sales Asso: Daniel Andreotta
Sales Asso: Ronnie Brown
Sales Asso: Joey Davis
Sales Asso: Robbie Dorsey

KEN-CREST SERVICES
See KENCREST SERVICES

D-U-N-S 06-605-3455 IMP
KEN-MAC METALS INC
(*Suby of* THYSSENKRUPP MATERIALS NA INC) ★
17901 Englewood Dr, Cleveland, OH 44130-3454
Tel (440) 891-1480 *Founded/Ownrshp* 1994
Sales 275.0MM^E *EMP* 230
SIC 5051 Nonferrous metal sheets, bars, rods, etc.; Aluminum bars, rods, ingots, sheets, pipes, plates, etc.; Nonferrous metal sheets, bars, rods, etc.; Aluminum bars, rods, ingots, sheets, pipes, plates, etc.
Pr: Larry Parsons
Sr VP: Tim Yost
VP: Scott H Seabeck

D-U-N-S 60-634-9025
KENAI DRILLING LIMITED
6430 Cat Canyon Rd, Santa Maria, CA 93454
Tel (805) 937-7871 *Founded/Ownrshp* 1978
Sales 279.9MM^E *EMP* 271
SIC 1381 Drilling oil & gas wells; Drilling oil & gas wells
Pr: Tim Crist
**COO:* David Arias
**CFO:* David Uhler
VP: Hank Crist
**VP:* Rex Northern
Opers Mgr: Gene Kramer

D-U-N-S 10-064-2099
KENAI PENINSULA BOROUGH SCHOOL DISTRICT
148 N Binkley St, Soldotna, AK 99669-7520
Tel (907) 714-8888 *Founded/Ownrshp* 1964
Sales 168.0MM *EMP* 1,104
Accts Bdo Usa Llp Anchorage Alask
SIC 8211 Public elementary & secondary schools; Public elementary & secondary schools
Info Man: Bob Jones

D-U-N-S 86-132-1826
KENAMERICAN RESOURCES INC
(*Suby of* MURRAY ENERGY CORP) ★
46226 National Rd W, Saint Clairsville, OH 43950-8742
Tel (740) 338-3100 *Founded/Ownrshp* 2007
Sales 44.3MM^E *EMP* 165
SIC 1222 Bituminous coal-underground mining
Pr: Bob Sandidge
**Treas:* James R Turner
**VP:* Randy L Wiles

D-U-N-S 02-053-4637
KENAN ADVANTAGE GROUP INC
4366 Mount Pleasant St Nw, North Canton, OH 44720-5446
Tel (877) 999-2524 *Founded/Ownrshp* 2010
Sales 898.2MM^E *EMP* 4,923
SIC 4213 4212 Trucking, except local; Liquid petroleum transport, non-local; Local trucking, without storage; Petroleum haulage, local; Trucking, except local; Liquid petroleum transport, non-local; Local trucking, without storage; Petroleum haulage, local
CEO: Dennis Nash
Ch Bd: Lee Shaffer
Pr: Bruce Blaise
Pr: Jacqueline Musacchia
COO: Douglas Allen
CFO: Carl H Young
Treas: Kimberly Conley
Treas: Jerry Hoover
Ex VP: Doug Allen
Ex VP: Bill Downey
Ex VP: Rex Molder
Ex VP: Kevin Spencer
VP: Richard Cole
VP: Charlie Delacey
VP: Patricia Harcourt
VP: Justin Jeffers
VP: William Prevost
VP: John Rakoczy
VP: Ron Ritchie
VP: Steve Welty

D-U-N-S 00-346-1233
KENAN TRANSPORT LLC
(*Suby of* KENAN ADVANTAGE GROUP INC) ★
100 Europa Dr Ste 170, Chapel Hill, NC 27517-2310
Tel (919) 967-8221 *Founded/Ownrshp* 2001
Sales 106.9MM^E *EMP* 1,674
SIC 4212 4213 Local trucking, without storage; Trucking, except local; Liquid petroleum transport, non-local; Local trucking, without storage; Trucking, except local; Liquid petroleum transport, non-local
Pr: Lee P Shaffer
**Treas:* William L Boone
Treas: Carl H Young
**VP:* John Krovic
**VP:* Dennis Waller
**VP Mktg:* Gary Knutson

D-U-N-S 96-487-0450
KENAN-FLAGLER BUSINESS SCHOOL FOUNDATION
300 Kenan Ste 3411, Chapel Hill, NC 27599-0001
Tel (919) 962-7158 *Founded/Ownrshp* 2010
Sales 37.8MM *EMP* 12
Accts Bernard Robinson & Company Llp
SIC 8299 Educational services; Educational services
Ch Bd: John P Evans
Ex Dir: Shannon McKeen

KENBY OIL COMPANY
See FUEL MANAGERS INC

D-U-N-S 07-153-1586
KENCO GROUP INC
KENCO LOGISTIC SERVICES
2001 Riverside Dr # 3000, Chattanooga, TN 37406-4303
Tel (423) 622-1113 *Founded/Ownrshp* 1968
Sales 1.6MMM^E *EMP* 4,000
SIC 4225 6512 General warehousing; Nonresidential building operators; General warehousing; Nonresidential building operators
CEO: Jane Kennedy Greene
Ch Bd: James D Kennedy Jr
Pr: Sheila Crane
CEO: Gerald Perritt
COO: David Caines
CFO: Dwight Crawley
VP: Jimmy Glascock
Genl Mgr: Kevin Charles
Genl Mgr: Kal Dawson
Genl Mgr: Grant Denton
Genl Mgr: Kendall Foss

D-U-N-S 10-647-2145 EXP
KENCO INC
COUNTRY MARKET
1821 Spring Arbor Rd, Jackson, MI 49203-2703
Tel (517) 787-6081 *Founded/Ownrshp* 1983
Sales 42.8MM^E *EMP* 400
SIC 5411 Supermarkets, chain; Supermarkets, chain
Pr: Kim Kennedy
**VP:* Sean Kennedy

KENCO LOGISTIC SERVICES
See KENCO GROUP INC

D-U-N-S 08-239-6024
KENCO LOGISTIC SERVICES INC
520 W 31st St, Chattanooga, TN 37410-1115
Tel (423) 756-5552 *Founded/Ownrshp* 1950
Sales 91.1MM^E *EMP* 2,500

SIC 4225 4783 Warehousing, self-storage; Crating goods for shipping; Warehousing, self-storage; Crating goods for shipping
Ch Bd: James D Kennedy III
**Pr:* Gary Mayfield

D-U-N-S 82-520-8676
KENCO MATERIAL HANDLING SOLUTIONS LLC
KENKO
(*Suby of* KENCO GROUP INC) ★
2001 Riverside Dr, Chattanooga, TN 37406-4303
Tel (800) 758-3289 *Founded/Ownrshp* 2008
Sales 58.7MM^E *EMP* 140
SIC 5084 Materials handling machinery; Materials handling machinery
Pr: Jeff Burns

D-U-N-S 06-503-9562
KENCOIL INC (LA)
2805 Engineers Rd, Belle Chasse, LA 70037-3211
Tel (504) 394-4010 *Founded/Ownrshp* 1982
Sales 34.5MM^E *EMP* 130
SIC 3621 Coils, for electric motors or generators; Coils, for electric motors or generators
Pr: J Scott Key
COO: Eran Rosenzweig
Ex VP: Rocky Gremillion
Genl Mgr: Denise Guidry
Genl Mgr: Daryl Lallande
Opers Mgr: Fred Brooks
Ql Cn Mgr: Frank Divincenti
Sales Exec: Darren Houillon
Mktg Dir: Darren Houillon
Snr Mgr: Mike Kreller

D-U-N-S 78-446-4489
KENCREST SERVICES
KEN-CREST SERVICES
960 Harvest Dr, Blue Bell, PA 19422-1900
Tel (610) 825-9360 *Founded/Ownrshp* 1984
Sales 103.4MM *EMP* 1,200
Accts Bbd Llp Philadelphia Pa
SIC 8361 8322 8351 Residential care for the handicapped; Individual & family services; Child day care services; Residential care for the handicapped; Individual & family services; Child day care services
Pr: Herta Clements
**CFO:* Tonia McNeal
**Ex Dir:* Jim McFalls
**Ex Dir:* W James McFalls
**Ex Dir:* Bill Nolan
Off Mgr: Sheila Fehrenbach
Netwrk Mgr: Margaret Rothenberger
Mktg Mgr: Mik Gregoire
Nrsg Dir: Rosemarie Kehoe
Pgrm Dir: Gary Clofine
Pgrm Dir: Denise Lamlin

KENDA USA
See AMERICAN KENDA RUBBER INDUSTRIAL CO LTD

D-U-N-S 84-846-5738
KENDAL AT HANOVER
80 Lyme Rd Ofc, Hanover, NH 03755-1218
Tel (603) 643-8900 *Founded/Ownrshp* 1988
Sales 24.8MM *EMP* 250
SIC 6513 Retirement hotel operation; Retirement hotel operation
CEO: Rebecca A Smith
Off Mgr: Sheryl Buckman
IT Man: Jennifer Anderson
HC Dir: Lisa Stone

D-U-N-S 96-153-0818
KENDAL CORP
1107 E Baltimore Pike, Kennett Square, PA 19348-2366
Tel (610) 335-1200 *Founded/Ownrshp* 1991
Sales 9.5MM *EMP* 500
Accts Cliftonlarsonallen Llp Plymou
SIC 6513 Apartment building operators; Apartment building operators
CEO: John A Diffey
**CFO:* Timothy L Myers
CFO: Timothy Myers
Treas: Mark Myers
**Treas:* James Wood
VP: Crystal Baker
Ex Dir: Robert Woolrich
Telecom Ex: Steve Cooper
CTO: Jennifer Anderson
Info Man: Ted Kirkpatrick
Sls&Mrk Ex: Nancy Regano

D-U-N-S 07-607-2321 IMP
KENDAL FLORAL SUPPLY LLC
KENDAL NORTH BOUQUET CO
1960 Kellogg Ave, Carlsbad, CA 92008-6581
Tel (760) 431-4910 *Founded/Ownrshp* 1973
Sales 74.3MM^E *EMP* 119
SIC 5193 Flowers, fresh; Flowers, fresh
Pr: Kenneth X Baca

KENDAL NORTH BOUQUET CO
See KENDAL FLORAL SUPPLY LLC

D-U-N-S 02-195-6602
KENDAL-CROSSLANDS COMMUNITIES
CARTMEL
1109 E Baltimore Pike, Kennett Square, PA 19348-2366
Tel (610) 388-7001 *Founded/Ownrshp* 1980
Sales 50.4MM *EMP* 572
Accts Cliftonlarsonallen Llp Plymou
SIC 8051 6513 Convalescent home with continuous nursing care; Retirement hotel operation; Convalescent home with continuous nursing care; Retirement hotel operation
CEO: Richard J Kirk Clerk
**Treas:* Mark Myers
**VP:* Roland Woodward
**Ex Dir:* Philip Debaun
**Ex Dir:* Richard D Lysle
Off Mgr: Ann Devine
DP Exec: Dan Hoffman
QC Dir: John Yost
Nrsg Dir: Pamela A Henderson
HC Dir: Julie Porter
HC Dir: Nancy Regeye
Board of Directors: Joanna Savery, Marjorie Barnard, Joseph Stratton, Jo Bewley, Susan Temple, Robert Bodine Jr, Philip Vail, Emily Fulton, Sarah Worth, Anne Harrington, Beverly Hess, Richard Kirk, Christian Mc Quail, Gerald Risser

D-U-N-S 06-831-9388
KENDALL AUTOMOTIVE GROUP INC (OR)
1400 Executive Pkwy # 400, Eugene, OR 97401-6712
Tel (541) 335-4000 *Founded/Ownrshp* 1963
Sales 197.8MM^E *EMP* 675
SIC 5511

KENDALL COUNTY MENTAL HEALTH
See HILL COUNTRY COMMUNITY MHMR CENTER

D-U-N-S 88-329-6428
KENDALL DUHADWAY & ASSOCIATES INC
DK SECURITY
5160 Falcon View Ave Se, Grand Rapids, MI 49512-5450
Tel (616) 656-0123 *Founded/Ownrshp* 1994
Sales 15.2MM *EMP* 750^E
SIC 7381 7389 Security guard service; Detective agency; Personal investigation service; Security guard service; Detective agency; Personal investigation service
Pr: John R Kendall
**CFO:* Terry Reese
**Ch:* Robert Duhadway
Treas: Alicia Despres
Ofcr: Jeremy Kleinjan
VP: Steve Pekrul
VP Opers: Mindy Putney
Opers Mgr: Heather Block
Opers Mgr: Ed Moore
Opers Mgr: Dave Pekrul

D-U-N-S 06-584-9168
KENDALL ELECTRIC INC
GREAT LAKES AUTOMATION SUPPLY
5101 S Sprinkle Rd, Portage, MI 49002-2049
Tel (269) 978-3838 *Founded/Ownrshp* 1973
Sales 291.3MM^E *EMP* 950
SIC 5063 7629 5084

D-U-N-S 02-763-8444
KENDALL ENTERPRISES INC
KENDALL HONDA
(*Suby of* KENDALL AUTOMOTIVE GROUP INC) ★
20 Coburg Rd, Eugene, OR 97401-2435
Tel (541) 485-6111 *Founded/Ownrshp* 1990
Sales 24.1MM^E *EMP* 81
SIC 5511 Automobiles, new & used; Automobiles, new & used
Pr: Paul Skilleran
**Sec:* Dana De Martini-Skillern

D-U-N-S 02-763-6166
KENDALL FORD INC (OR)
(*Suby of* KENDALL AUTOMOTIVE GROUP INC) ★
1700 Valley River Dr # 200, Eugene, OR 97401-6713
Tel (541) 335-4000 *Founded/Ownrshp* 1937, 1963
Sales 70.1MM^E *EMP* 261
SIC 5511 7515 7513 Automobiles, new & used; Passenger car leasing; Truck leasing, without drivers; Automobiles, new & used; Passenger car leasing; Truck leasing, without drivers
VP: Paul Skillern
**CFO:* Dave Blewett
**Sec:* Dana Skillern

D-U-N-S 03-397-7653
KENDALL FORD OF MERIDIAN LLC
MERIDIAN FORD SALES, INC
(*Suby of* KENDALL AUTOMOTIVE GROUP INC) ★
250 E Overland Rd, Meridian, ID 83642-3046
Tel (208) 888-4403 *Founded/Ownrshp* 2012
Sales 23.2MM^E *EMP* 75
SIC 5511 Automobiles, new & used; Pickups, new & used; Vans, new & used; Automobiles, new & used; Pickups, new & used; Vans, new & used
Pr: Lawrence H Chetwood
VP: Bill Robertson
Genl Mgr: David Shears
Off Mgr: Rebecca Reesman
Sales Asso: Larry Ensminger

D-U-N-S 62-683-9211
■ **KENDALL HEALTHCARE GROUP LTD**
KENDALL REGIONAL MEDICAL CTR
(*Suby of* HCA INC) ★
11750 Sw 40th St, Miami, FL 33175-3530
Tel (305) 227-5500 *Founded/Ownrshp* 1991
Sales 89.5MM^E *EMP* 1,700
SIC 8062 General medical & surgical hospitals; General medical & surgical hospitals
CEO: Scott A Cihak
CFO: Mauricio E Sirvent
Pathlgst: Miguel M Gonzalez
HC Dir: Mayra Muntaner
Snr Mgr: Michael Houston

KENDALL HONDA
See KENDALL ENTERPRISES INC

D-U-N-S 01-816-8872
KENDALL HOUSE INC
KFC
1207 Lincoln Way E, Massillon, OH 44646-6991
Tel (330) 837-5041 *Founded/Ownrshp* 1960
Sales 14.8MM^E *EMP* 359
SIC 5812 Fast-food restaurant, chain; Fast-food restaurant, chain
Pr: Ernest A Lambos
**Owner:* Mark Lambos
**VP:* George Lambos

D-U-N-S 04-886-5851 EXP
KENDALL IMPORTS LLC
KENDALL TOYOTA
10943 S Dixie Hwy, Miami, FL 33156-3752
Tel (305) 666-1784 *Founded/Ownrshp* 1998
Sales 217.5MM^E *EMP* 425
SIC 5511 5521 Automobiles, new & used; Used car dealers; Automobiles, new & used; Used car dealers
IT Man: Luis Garcia
Prd Mgr: Michael Menchero
Sls Dir: Frank Marsala
Sls Mgr: Ruben Diaz
Sales Asso: Delfin Espinal
Sales Asso: Davi Pea

D-U-N-S 18-482-1270
KENDALL PACKAGING CORP
10335 N Pt Washington Rd # 200, Mequon, WI 53092-5763
Tel (262) 404-1200 *Founded/Ownrshp* 1970
Sales 21.3MM^E *EMP* 120
SIC 2671 Packaging paper & plastics film, coated & laminated; Packaging paper & plastics film, coated & laminated
Pr: Eric G Erickson III
**CFO:* Michael Sallmann
Ofcr: Luana Merriman
**VP:* Russ Schneider
**VP:* Stuart Zeisse
Area Mgr: Randy Mjelde
Area Mgr: Dave Weber
Off Admin: Joey Ross
IT Man: Jim Town
Info Man: Sean Eaton
Mfg Dir: Nate Freidl

KENDALL REGIONAL MEDICAL CTR
See KENDALL HEALTHCARE GROUP LTD

KENDALL TOYOTA
See KENDALL IMPORTS LLC

D-U-N-S 61-942-6211
KENDALL TOYOTA SCION
(*Suby of* KENDALL AUTOMOTIVE GROUP INC) ★
373 Goodpasture Island Rd, Eugene, OR 97401-2109
Tel (541) 344-5566 *Founded/Ownrshp* 2004
Sales 31.7MM^E *EMP* 120
SIC 5511 7538 Automobiles, new & used; General automotive repair shops; Automobiles, new & used; General automotive repair shops
Owner: Paul Skillern
Sls Mgr: Steve Harris

D-U-N-S 96-630-9135
KENDALL WEST BAPTIST HOSPITAL INC
(*Suby of* BAPTIST HEALTH SOUTH FLORIDA INC) ★
9555 Sw 162nd Ave, Miami, FL 33196-6408
Tel (786) 467-2000 *Founded/Ownrshp* 2003
Sales 182.0MM *EMP* 138
Accts Deloitte & Touche Llp
SIC 8062 General medical & surgical hospitals; General medical & surgical hospitals
CEO: Javier Hernandez Lichtl

D-U-N-S 03-723-1800
KENDALL/HEATON/ASSOCIATES INC (TX)
3050 Post Oak Blvd # 1000, Houston, TX 77056-6508
Tel (713) 877-1192 *Founded/Ownrshp* 1978
Sales 29.6MM *EMP* 63
Accts Howard W Acton Cpa
SIC 8712 Architectural services; Architectural services
Pr: William D Kendall
**VP:* Wayne M Shull
**VP:* Rex H Wooldridge
Prin: Rollie D Childers
Prin: Michael R Desguin

D-U-N-S 10-394-7214
KENDALL/HUNT PUBLISHING CO
4050 Westmark Dr, Dubuque, IA 52002-2624
Tel (563) 589-1000 *Founded/Ownrshp* 1944
Sales 53.2MM *EMP* 230^E
SIC 2731 Textbooks: publishing only, not printed on site; Textbooks: publishing only, not printed on site
Ch Bd: Mark C Falb
**Pr:* Chad Chandlee
CFO: Karen Mahe
**Treas:* Ron Cavanagh
Sr VP: Amy Wagner
**VP:* Tim Beitzel
IT Man: Brittni Imhof
Plnt Mgr: David Mattaliano
Sales Exec: Tom Gantz
Sls&Mrk Ex: Ryan Brown

D-U-N-S 82-951-7143
KENDELL DOORS & HARDWARE INC
222 E 2nd St, Winona, MN 55987-6316
Tel (507) 454-1723 *Founded/Ownrshp* 1981
Sales 24.4MM^E *EMP* 75
SIC 5072 5031 1751 Hardware; Doors & windows; Door frames, all materials; Metal doors, sash & trim; Carpentry work
CEO: John Katter
**Pr:* John Catter
**CEO:* Jack Cornwell
CTO: Katherine Blasko

D-U-N-S 19-732-2886
KENDLE DELAWARE INC
(*Suby of* KENDLE GOVERNMENT SERVICES) ★
4024 Stirrup Creek Dr, Durham, NC 27703-9464
Tel (919) 257-6500 *Founded/Ownrshp* 2006
Sales 15.3MM^E *EMP* 900
SIC 8731 Medical research, commercial; Medical research, commercial
Genl Mgr: Tom Connolly

KENDLE GOVERNMENT SERVICES
See KENDLE INTERNATIONAL LLC

D-U-N-S 01-696-8919
KENDLE INTERNATIONAL LLC (OH)
KENDLE GOVERNMENT SERVICES
(*Suby of* INC RESEARCH LLC) ★
3201 Beechleaf Ct, Durham, NC 27703
Tel (919) 876-9300 *Founded/Ownrshp* 1989, 2011
Sales 125.1MM^E *EMP* 3,105^E
SIC 8731 Medical research, commercial; Medical research, commercial
CEO: James T Ogle
Treas: Anthony L Forcellini
Chf Mktg O: Thomas E Stilgenbauer
VP: Sarah Beeby
VP: James P Burns Jr
VP: Sylva H Collins
VP: Karen L Crone
VP: Philip J W Davies
VP: Gregg Dearhammer
VP: Michael J Gallagher
VP: Pierre Geoffroy
VP: Ross J Horsburgh
VP: Dennis Hurley
VP: J Michael Sprafka
VP: Patricia A Steigerwald
VP: Satish Tripathi
Exec: Michael Gallagher

D-U-N-S 12-884-6800
KENDRA SCOTT DESIGN INC
4401 West Gate Blvd # 300, Austin, TX 78745-1494
Tel (512) 499-8400 *Founded/Ownrshp* 2003
Sales 21.9MM^E *EMP* 23^E
SIC 5094 Jewelers' findings
Pr: Kendra Scott
COO: Lon Weingart
Dist Mgr: Leslie Fearka
Sales Asso: Kelsey Kelcher
Sales Asso: Kara Robinson

D-U-N-S 07-204-1130
KENDRICK MEMORIAL HOSPITAL INC
1201 Hadley Rd, Mooresville, IN 46158-1737
Tel (317) 831-1160 *Founded/Ownrshp* 1966
Sales 25.9MM *EMP* 319
SIC 8062 General medical & surgical hospitals; General medical & surgical hospitals
Pr: Charles Swisher
**Ch Bd:* Michael Berks
**CFO:* Jeff Buchanan
**V Ch Bd:* Richard V Newcomer

D-U-N-S 02-647-6754
KENDRICK OIL CO
FAST STOP
801 Main St, Friona, TX 79035-2039
Tel (806) 250-3991 *Founded/Ownrshp* 1982
Sales 68.1MM^E *EMP* 200
SIC 5172 5541

D-U-N-S 09-687-3666
KENECO INC
123 N 8th St, Kenilworth, NJ 07033-1108
Tel (908) 241-3700 *Founded/Ownrshp* 2000
Sales 350.0MM *EMP* 3
SIC 3535 Conveyors & conveying equipment; Conveyors & conveying equipment
Pr: William Van Loan III
**VP:* Thomas Hoefenkrieg

D-U-N-S 08-623-0542
KENERGY CORP
6402 Old Corydon Rd, Henderson, KY 42420-9392
Tel (270) 926-4141 *Founded/Ownrshp* 1999
Sales 474.7MM *EMP* 155
SIC 4911 Distribution, electric power; Distribution, electric power
Pr: Stanford Noveick
**Ch:* Robert White
Bd of Dir: William H Reid
**VP:* William Reid
**VP:* Steve Thompson
Comm Man: Renee Jones
Dist Mgr: Tim Miller
Dir IT: Ted Crabtree
Tech Mgr: Scott Gentry
VP Opers: Gerald Ford
VP Opers: Ken Stock

D-U-N-S 10-822-8151
■ **KENEXA COMPENSATION INC**
(*Suby of* IBM) ★
160 Gould St, Needham, MA 02494-2313
Tel (877) 971-9171 *Founded/Ownrshp* 2010
Sales 52.0MM^E *EMP* 528^E
SIC 7372 Business oriented computer software; Business oriented computer software
Pr: Donald F Volk
Pr: Cooper Moo
Sr VP: Tim Driver
Sr VP: Bill Lucky
VP: Douglas Finke
VP: Alison French
VP: Archie L Jones
VP: Stephen Schoonover
VP: Larry Schumer
VP: Roger C Sturtevant
VP Bus: James McIntyer
Exec: Devon Murphy

D-U-N-S 60-264-3827
■ **KENEXA CORP**
IBM
(*Suby of* IBM) ★
650 E Swedesford Rd # 200, Wayne, PA 19087-1628
Tel (877) 971-9171 *Founded/Ownrshp* 2012
Sales 155.2MM^E *EMP* 2,744
SIC 7361 7371 Placement agencies; Computer software systems analysis & design, custom; Placement agencies; Computer software systems analysis & design, custom
Ch Bd: Nooruddin S Karsan
Genl Pt: John Rutherford
Pr: Addison Grimes
Pr: Kevin Horigan
**Pr:* Troy A Kanter
Pr: Zahir Ladhani
**CFO:* Donald F Volk
Ex VP: Keith Bradley
Ex VP: Bill Erickson
VP: Bill Anstine
VP: Trevor Brown
VP: Zach Canaday
VP: Andrew Jackson
**VP:* Archie L Jones Jr
VP Bus Dev: Tim Dawkins
Exec: Lori Bowman
Board of Directors: Barry M Abelson, Joseph A Konen, Rebecca J Maddox, John A Nies, Richard J Pinola

KENISON LIBRARY
See BREWSTER ACADEMY

KENKO
See KENCO MATERIAL HANDLING SOLUTIONS LLC

KENLAKE FOODS
See INTER AMERICAN PRODUCTS INC

KENLAKE FOODS
See KROGER LIMITED PARTNERSHIP II

KENLY 95 TA TRUCKSTOP
See CORBITT PARTNERS LLC

KENMARK OPTICAL COMPANY
See KENMARK OPTICAL INC

D-U-N-S 06-295-2593 IMP
KENMARK OPTICAL INC
KENMARK OPTICAL COMPANY
11851 Plantside Dr, Louisville, KY 40299-6329
Tel (502) 267-4486 *Founded/Ownrshp* 1972
Sales 59.1MM^E *EMP* 300
SIC 5049

D-U-N-S 00-523-8266 IMP
KENMODE TOOL AND ENGINEERING INC
820 W Algonquin Rd, Algonquin, IL 60102-2482
Tel (847) 658-5041 *Founded/Ownrshp* 1960
Sales 50.7MM^E *EMP* 150
SIC 3469 3544 Metal stampings; Special dies & tools
CEO: Werner Moders
**Pr:* Kurt Moders
COO: Rolf Riebe
**CFO:* Kurt Gascho
**Treas:* Christa Moders
VP: Bob Lackowski
VP: Tim Lynch
**VP:* Petra Schindler

D-U-N-S 08-596-4591
KENMOR ELECTRIC CO LP (TX)
(*Suby of* HEICO COMPANIES L L C) ★
8330 Hansen Rd, Houston, TX 77075-1004
Tel (713) 869-0171 *Founded/Ownrshp* 1976, 1997
Sales 89.1MM^E *EMP* 400
SIC 1731 General electrical contractor; General electrical contractor
Pr: John C Quebe
**Ex VP:* Joe Martin
VP: Kip Farrington
**VP:* Jeff Hinton
**VP:* Steve Parris
VP: Pete Rosser
Exec: Jim Landing
Snr PM: Stu Jardine

D-U-N-S 08-568-7937
KENMORE BOARD OF EDUCATION (INC)
1500 Colvin Blvd, Buffalo, NY 14223-1118
Tel (716) 871-3070 *Founded/Ownrshp* 1930
Sales 58.9MM^E *EMP* 706
SIC 8211 Public senior high school; Public junior high school; Public elementary school; School board
Pr: Jill O'Malley
Prin: Barbara Bateguillia

D-U-N-S 01-748-1797 IMP
KENMORE CONSTRUCTION CO INC
700 Home Ave, Akron, OH 44310-4190
Tel (330) 762-8936 *Founded/Ownrshp* 1956
Sales 93.9MM^E *EMP* 200^E
SIC 1611 5032 General contractor, highway & street construction; Sand, construction; General contractor, highway & street construction; Sand, construction
Pr: William A Scala
Ofcr: Doug Staubs
**VP:* Terrence M Costigan
VP: Matt Moravec
VP: Thomas Postak
**VP:* Paul Scala

D-U-N-S 04-014-5070
KENMORE ENVELOPE CO INC
4641 Intl Trade Ct, Richmond, VA 23231
Tel (804) 271-2100 *Founded/Ownrshp* 1975
Sales 28.8MM^E *EMP* 69
SIC 2677 2759 2752 Envelopes; Envelopes: printing; Commercial printing, lithographic
Ch Bd: Dennis R Riddle Sr
**Pr:* D Rhett Riddle Jr
CFO: Derek Zbyszinski
**Sec:* Carolyn M Riddle
**VP:* Wayne A Riddle
Exec: Jennifer Wash
Ex Dir: Alice Fletcher
VP Mfg: Dennis Campbell

D-U-N-S 03-022-8522
KENMORE MERCY HOSPITAL
(*Suby of* CATHOLIC HEALTH SYSTEM INC) ★
2950 Elmwood Ave Fl 6, Kenmore, NY 14217-1390
Tel (716) 447-6100 *Founded/Ownrshp* 1997
Sales 13.8MM^E *EMP* 1,000
SIC 8062 8059 8011 General medical & surgical hospitals; Nursing home, except skilled & intermediate care facility; Medical centers; General medical & surgical hospitals; Nursing home, except skilled & intermediate care facility; Medical centers
CEO: Mary Hoffman
Pr: Patricia Marcus
Dir Rx: Frank Heinrich
QA Dir: Kathy Coughlin
Pr Mgr: Dawn Cwierley
Snr Mgr: Chris Walker
Snr Mgr: Lisa Zacher

D-U-N-S 07-979-9142
KENMORE-TONAWANDA UNION FREE SCHOOL DISTRICT
1500 Colvin Blvd, Buffalo, NY 14223-1118
Tel (716) 874-8400 *Founded/Ownrshp* 2015
Sales 10.2MM^E *EMP* 1,591^E
SIC 8211 Public elementary & secondary schools
Pr Dir: Christine Ljungberg

D-U-N-S 84-583-5896
KENN-FELD GROUP LLC
5228 State Route 118, Coldwater, OH 45828-9702
Tel (419) 678-2375 *Founded/Ownrshp* 2005
Sales 25.9MM^E *EMP* 100^E
SIC 5999 Farm equipment & supplies
Mng Pt: Tom Burenga

D-U-N-S 01-841-2283
■ **KENNAMETAL HOLDINGS EUROPE INC**
(*Suby of* KENNAMETAL INC) ★
1600 Technology Way, Latrobe, PA 15650-4647
Tel (724) 539-5000 *Founded/Ownrshp* 2000
Sales 90.6MM^E *EMP* 900^E
SIC 6719 Investment holding companies, except banks; Investment holding companies, except banks
Pr: John R Tucker
**Treas:* Brian E Kelly

D-U-N-S 00-439-7659 IMP
▲ **KENNAMETAL INC** (PA)
1600 Technology Way, Latrobe, PA 15650-4647
Tel (724) 539-5000 *Founded/Ownrshp* 1938
Sales 2.6MMM *EMP* 12,700
Accts Pricewaterhousecoopers Llp Pi
Tkr Sym KMT *Exch* NYS
SIC 3545 3532 3531 3313 3399 Machine tool accessories; Cutting tools for machine tools; Bits for use on lathes, planers, shapers, etc.; Tool holders; Mining machinery; Bits, except oil & gas field tools, rock; Auger mining equipment; Construction machinery attachments; Blades for graders, scrapers, dozers & snow plows; Snow plow attachments; Screeds & screeding machines; Electrometallurgical products; Tungsten carbide powder; Metal powders, pastes & flakes; Machine tool accessories; Cutting tools for machine tools; Bits for use on lathes, planers, shapers, etc.; Tool holders; Mining machinery; Bits, except oil & gas field tools, rock; Auger mining equipment; Construction machinery attachments; Blades for graders, scrapers, dozers & snow plows; Snow plow attachments; Screeds & screeding machines; Electrometallurgical products; Tungsten carbide powder; Metal powders, pastes & flakes
Pr: Donald A Nolan
**Ch Bd:* Lawrence W Stranghoener
CFO: Jan Kees Van Gaalen
CFO: Jan K Van Gaalen
Treas: Deb Mullen
Chf Mktg O: John H Jacko Jr
Ofcr: Judith L Bacchus
Ex VP: Jeswant Gill
VP: James R Breisinger
VP: Robert J Clemens
VP: Peter Dragich
VP: Michael Enste
VP: Martha Fusco
VP: Steven R Hanna
VP: Kevin G Nowe
Exec: Jennifer McDonough
Board of Directors: Cindy L Davis, Ronald M Defeo, Philip A Dur, William J Harvey, Timothy R McLevish, Steven H Wunning

D-U-N-S 04-647-4912 EXP
KENNAMETAL TRICON METALS & SERVICES INC
(*Suby of* MADISON INDUSTRIES HOLDINGS LLC)
2700 5th Ave S, Irondale, AL 35210-1236
Tel (205) 956-2567 *Founded/Ownrshp* 1968, 2015
Sales 66.7MM^E *EMP* 220^E
SIC 5051 3443 3316 Steel; Fabricated plate work (boiler shop); Cold finishing of steel shapes; Steel; Fabricated plate work (boiler shop); Cold finishing of steel shapes
Pr: Joseph Richard Cashio
CFO: Larry E Thomas
CFO: Ricky W Thomas
Treas: Lawrence J Lanza
Sr VP: Greg Boggis
VP: Robert Gross
VP: Larry Thomas
Sls Mgr: Rick Vogis

KENNEBEC CRANE
See HALLAMORE CORP

D-U-N-S 04-146-0445
KENNEBEC SAVINGS BANK
150 State St Ste 1, Augusta, ME 04330-7418
Tel (207) 622-5801 *Founded/Ownrshp* 1870
Sales NA *EMP* 81
SIC 6022 State commercial banks; State commercial banks
Pr: Mark L Johnston
V Ch: Harry Jose
V Ch: William W Sprague Jr
V Ch: Sprague William
Pr: Bill Dawson
Pr: William Hill
Ofcr: Brent Hall
Ofcr: Mary Hammond
Ofcr: Tamara Hillman-Tardiff
Ofcr: Nicolas Patenaude
Ofcr: Katie Vickers
Assoc VP: Cheryl A Holmes
Sr VP: James Chase
Sr VP: Sandra Goodwin
VP: Marie Charest
VP: George W Diplock Jr
VP: George Diplock
VP: Cheryl Dow
VP: James Lagasse
VP: Gary Lapierre
VP: David Roy

D-U-N-S 96-938-0471
KENNEBEC VALLEY MENTAL HEALTH CENTER
67 Eustis Pkwy, Waterville, ME 04901-5173
Tel (207) 873-2136 *Founded/Ownrshp* 2011
Sales 24.4MM *EMP* 2
Accts Gibson Leclair Llc Augusta
SIC 8049 Psychologist, psychotherapist & hypnotist; Psychologist, psychotherapist & hypnotist
Prin: Thomas McAdam

D-U-N-S 04-146-0502
KENNEBUNK SAVINGS BANK
104 Main St, Kennebunk, ME 04043-7023
Tel (207) 985-4903 *Founded/Ownrshp* 1871
Sales NA *EMP* 300
SIC 6036 State savings banks, not federally chartered; State savings banks, not federally chartered
Pr: Bradford C Paige
Pr: Mary Berry
CFO: Stephen Soubble
**Treas:* Pamela Drew
Ofcr: Kelly Goodwin
Ofcr: Bryanna Thibault
Sr VP: Peg Stansfield
VP: Michael Arndt
VP: Peggy Boyle
VP: Alan Brown
VP: James Carrigan
VP: Danny Edgecomb
VP: Rich Goodenough
VP: Jill Knight
VP: Andrew Lederer
VP: Michelle Nappi
VP: Lisa Randall
VP: Mark Ross
VP: Mary Weickert
VP: Kimberly Whitmore

D-U-N-S 15-595-9463
KENNECOTT CORP
(*Suby of* RIO TINTO AMERICA INC) ★
8315 W 3595 S, Magna, UT 84044-3406
Tel (801) 913-8335 *Founded/Ownrshp* 1979
Sales 19.3MMM^E *EMP* 3,065
SIC 1041 1021 1044 1061 1221 Gold ores; Copper ore mining & preparation; Silver ores; Molybdenum ores mining; Surface mining, bituminous; Gold ores; Copper ore mining & preparation; Silver ores; Molybdenum ores mining; Surface mining, bituminous
Ch Bd: Oscar L Groeneveld
Pr: Jonathon Leslie
CFO: Roger Johnson
Ofcr: James Elegante
Sr VP: Bruce Farmer
Sr VP: William Orchow
Sr VP: Richard Pierce
Dir IT: Richard Landinghan
Sls Mgr: Jim Cowley

D-U-N-S 61-996-8779 EXP
KENNECOTT UTAH COPPER LLC
RIO TINTO REGIONAL CENTER
(*Suby of* KENNECOTT CORP) ★
4700 W Daybreak Pkwy, South Jordan, UT 84009-5120
Tel (801) 204-2000 *Founded/Ownrshp* 1982
Sales 19.3MMM^E *EMP* 2,400
SIC 1021 1041 1044 1061

D-U-N-S 03-789-2569
KENNEDALE INDEPENDENT SCHOOL DISTRICT
120 W Kennedale Pkwy, Kennedale, TX 76060-2416
Tel (817) 563-8000 *Founded/Ownrshp* 1907
Sales 19.2MM^E *EMP* 350
Accts Kirk Richardson & Poole Pc
SIC 8211 Public elementary school; Public junior high school; Public senior high school; Public elementary school; Public junior high school; Public senior high school
Bd of Dir: Scott Roland
Prin: James F Delaney

D-U-N-S 12-303-2732
KENNEDY AUTOMOTIVE GROUP INC
620 Bustleton Pike, Feasterville Trevose, PA 19053-6054
Tel (215) 357-6600 *Founded/Ownrshp* 1955
Sales 189.8MM^E *EMP* 341
SIC 5511 Automobiles, new & used; Automobiles, new & used
Prin: J Michael Kennedy
**Treas:* Kurt Kennedy

D-U-N-S 03-889-8375
KENNEDY CAPITAL MANAGEMENT INC
10829 Olive Blvd Fl 1, Saint Louis, MO 63141-7768
Tel (314) 432-0400 *Founded/Ownrshp* 1980
Sales 24.0MM^E *EMP* 60
SIC 6282 Investment advisory service
Pr: Randall Kirkland
**COO:* Stephen Mace
**CFO:* Richard E Oliver
**Ex VP:* Richard Sinise
**VP:* Frank Latuda Jr
CTO: Niraj Shah
Mktg Mgr: Charles Bryant

KENNEDY CENTER, THE
See JOHN F KENNEDY CENTER FOR PERFORMING ARTS

D-U-N-S 01-014-8211
KENNEDY CENTER INC
SOUPS & SUCH
2440 Reservoir Ave Ste 1, Trumbull, CT 06611-4757
Tel (203) 332-4535 *Founded/Ownrshp* 1951
Sales 32.2MM *EMP* 450
Accts Blum Shapiro & Company Pc Wes
SIC 8361 8331 Home for the mentally retarded; Vocational training agency; Home for the mentally retarded; Vocational training agency
Pr: Martin D Schwartz
**Treas:* Anthony Milano
Treas: Anne Vantine
**VP:* Stuart Gordon
VP: Lynn McCrystal
VP: Roger Mosier
**VP:* Lynn Pellegrino
CIO: Steven Marra
Prd Mgr: Owen Burke
Prd Mgr: William Foster
Pgrm Dir: Stephanie Litvak

KENNEDY COMPANIES, THE
See KENNEDY CULVERT & SUPPLY INC

D-U-N-S 06-569-5751
KENNEDY CULVERT & SUPPLY INC
KENNEDY COMPANIES, THE
125 6th Ave Ste 100, Mount Laurel, NJ 08054-1801
Tel (856) 813-5000 *Founded/Ownrshp* 1973
Sales 83.0MM^E *EMP* 130
SIC 5085 Industrial supplies; Industrial supplies
Pr: Robert A Kennedy Sr
**Pr:* Robert A Kennedy Jr
IT Man: Joe Flaherty
Sales Asso: Michael Gaughan

D-U-N-S 15-876-7111
KENNEDY FABRICATING INC
25370 Fm 2090 Rd, Splendora, TX 77372-3721
Tel (281) 399-3008 *Founded/Ownrshp* 1984
Sales 52.4MM^E *EMP* 135
SIC 3441 Fabricated structural metal; Fabricated structural metal
CEO: Jeremy Want
**Pr:* Kevin Kenndy
**COO:* John Coleman
**CFO:* Jason Watson
**VP:* Joe Hnatek
QA Dir: Kenneth Kennedy

D-U-N-S 07-110-9110 IMP
KENNEDY GROUP INC
38601 Kennedy Pkwy, Willoughby, OH 44094-7395
Tel (440) 951-7660 *Founded/Ownrshp* 1974
Sales 34.8MM^E *EMP* 140
SIC 2679 2673 3089 3565 2441 Tags & labels, paper; Bags: plastic, laminated & coated; Garment bags (plastic film): made from purchased materials; Plastic containers, except foam; Boxes, plastic; Cases, plastic; Packaging machinery; Nailed wood boxes & shook; Tags & labels, paper; Bags: plastic, laminated & coated; Garment bags (plastic film): made from purchased materials; Plastic containers, except foam; Boxes, plastic; Cases, plastic; Packaging machinery; Nailed wood boxes & shook
CEO: Bertram Kennedy
**Pr:* Michael R Kennedy
**COO:* Todd Kennedy
**CFO:* Jerry Kish
**VP:* Mary Lou Kennedy
**VP:* Patrick Kennedy

D-U-N-S 11-433-6910
KENNEDY HEALTH CARE FOUNDATION INC
18 E Laurel Rd, Stratford, NJ 08084-1327
Tel (856) 661-5100 *Founded/Ownrshp* 1983
Sales 165.2MM^E *EMP* 2,800^E
SIC 6733 4119 8051 6531 7361 8721 Trusts; Ambulance service; Extended care facility; Real estate managers; Nurses' registry; Accounting services, except auditing; Trusts; Ambulance service; Extended care facility; Real estate managers; Nurses' registry; Accounting services, except auditing
Ch Bd: Joseph Maressa
Pr: A R Pirolli
VP: Joseph M Lario

KENNEDY HEALTH SYSTEM
See KENNEDY UNIVERSITY HOSPITAL INC

D-U-N-S 07-696-1481
KENNEDY HEALTH SYSTEM INC
1099 White Horse Rd, Voorhees, NJ 08043-4405
Tel (856) 566-5200 *Founded/Ownrshp* 1982
Sales 458.3MM^E *EMP* 4,000
SIC 8062 Hospital, medical school affiliated with residency; Hospital, medical school affiliated with residency
CEO: Martin A Bieber
**Pr:* Richard E Murray
**CEO:* Joseph W Devine
**COO:* Joseph Hummel
**CFO:* Gary Perrinoni
Sr VP: Carman Ciervo
**Sr VP:* Joseph Lario
VP: Thomas J Balcavage
VP: Christopher J Barone
VP: Kevin J Caracciolo
VP: Michael P Dennis
VP: Daniel L Herriman
VP: Richard Koss
VP: Suzette Martella
VP: Gary Terrinoni

KENNEDY HOME
See BAPTIST CHILDREN S HOMES OF NORTH CAROLINA INC

KENNEDY HOUSE SYSTEM
See KENNEDY MEMORIAL HOSPITAL UNIVERSITY MEDICAL CENTER INC

D-U-N-S 01-745-3473
KENNEDY INDUSTRIES INC
4925 Holtz Dr, Wixom, MI 48393
Tel (248) 684-1200 *Founded/Ownrshp* 1994
Sales 30.0MM *EMP* 70^E
SIC 7699 5085 3594 Pumps & pumping equipment repair; Industrial machinery & equipment repair; Valves & fittings; Valves, pistons & fittings; Fluid power pumps
Pr: Jeffrey Nachtweih
**Sec:* Shirley Schmitz
**VP:* Marcus Hemeyer
VP: Michael Kennedy
**Prin:* Mark Hemeyer

D-U-N-S 11-377-7606 IMP/EXP
KENNEDY INTERNATIONAL INC
25 Stults Rd, Dayton, NJ 08810-1541
Tel (609) 409-4515 *Founded/Ownrshp* 1996
Sales 32.8MM^E *EMP* 60
SIC 5064 Fans, household: electric; Fans, household: electric
Pr: Henry Guindi

D-U-N-S 06-487-2518
KENNEDY KRIEGER CHILDRENS HOSPITAL INC (MD)
707 N Broadway, Baltimore, MD 21205-1832
Tel (443) 923-9400 *Founded/Ownrshp* 1937

Sales 138.2MM *EMP* 1,200
Accts Sc&H Tax & Advisory Services L
SIC 8069 Children's hospital; Children's hospital
Pr: Dr Gary Goldstein
**COO:* James M Anders Jr
**CFO:* Michael Neuman
VP: James Christensen

D-U-N-S 15-534-2371
KENNEDY KRIEGER INSTITUTE INC
707 N Broadway, Baltimore, MD 21205-1888
Tel (443) 923-9200 *Founded/Ownrshp* 1986
Sales 217.8MM *EMP* 2,500
Accts Pricewaterhousecoopers Llp B
SIC 8069 Children's hospital; Children's hospital
Pr: Gary W Goldstein
**COO:* James M Anders Jr
**CFO:* Michael Neuman
Bd of Dir: Gove Allen
VP: Robert L Findling
Comm Man: Elise Welker
Doctor: Qun Ll MD
Occ Thrpy: Gina Covi
Board of Directors: Dorothy Hamill, William J Toomey II

KENNEDY LOGISTICS
See LOUIS J KENNEDY TRUCKING CO

D-U-N-S 04-127-6718
KENNEDY LT JOSEPH P INSTITUTE
801 Buchanan St Ne, Washington, DC 20017-3924
Tel (202) 281-2700 *Founded/Ownrshp* 1959
Sales 14.7MM *EMP* 300
SIC 8361 8331 7361 Home for the physically handicapped; Job training & vocational rehabilitation services; Placement agencies; Home for the physically handicapped; Job training & vocational rehabilitation services; Placement agencies
CEO: John Enzler

KENNEDY MANUFACTURING CO.
See KMC HOLDINGS LLC

D-U-N-S 80-387-8396
KENNEDY MECHANICAL PLUMBING AND HEATING INC
11 Comfort St, Rochester, NY 14620-1003
Tel (585) 232-2800 *Founded/Ownrshp* 1990
Sales 27.7MM^E^ *EMP* 98
Accts Davie Kaplan Cpa Pc Roche
SIC 1711 Plumbing contractors; Warm air heating & air conditioning contractor
Pr: Stephen Cassidy
**CFO:* Wayne Gould
**VP:* Darren Englert
**VP:* Guy Slack

D-U-N-S 11-337-9890
KENNEDY MEMORIAL HOSPITAL UNIVERSITY MEDICAL CENTER INC
KENNEDY HOUSE SYSTEM
(*Suby of* KENNEDY HEALTH SYSTEM INC) ★
1099 White Horse Rd Fl 3, Voorhees, NJ 08043-4405
Tel (856) 566-2000 *Founded/Ownrshp* 2002
Sales 455.1MM *EMP* 2
SIC 8062 General medical & surgical hospitals; General medical & surgical hospitals

D-U-N-S 02-475-2271
KENNEDY OFFICE SUPPLY CO INC (NC)
4211 Atlantic Ave Ste A, Raleigh, NC 27604-1797
Tel (919) 878-5400 *Founded/Ownrshp* 1960
Sales 65.1MM^E^ *EMP* 63
SIC 5112 Stationery & office supplies
Pr: Mary Kennedy
**VP:* Charlie Kennedy
Sales Exec: Johnnie Barefoot
Sales Exec: Susan Hudson
Manager: Andy Riddle
Sls Mgr: Don Hill

D-U-N-S 84-332-6273
KENNEDY RESTAURANT & BAR MANAGEMENT INC
VINE TAVERN & EATERY
801 E Apache Blvd, Tempe, AZ 85281-6809
Tel (480) 894-2662 *Founded/Ownrshp* 1991
Sales 11.6MM^E^ *EMP* 500
SIC 8741 Restaurant management; Restaurant management
Pr: Joseph Kennedy
**VP:* Peggy Kennedy
Genl Mgr: Dan Wilkerson

KENNEDY SPACE CTR VSTOR CMPLEX
See DNC PARKS & RESORTS AT KSC INC

D-U-N-S 00-641-2928
KENNEDY TANK & MANUFACTURING CO INC
833 E Sumner Ave, Indianapolis, IN 46227-1345
Tel (317) 787-1311 *Founded/Ownrshp* 1898
Sales 30.0MM *EMP* 130
SIC 3443 Industrial vessels, tanks & containers; Industrial vessels, tanks & containers
Pr: Patrick W Kennedy
**VP:* Paul K Bolin
**VP:* Paul Bolin
**VP:* John Cochran
**VP:* Scot W Evans
Trfc Mgr: Danny Kemper

D-U-N-S 11-969-2619
KENNEDY TRANSPORTATION INC
8 Greenwood Ave, Lockport, IL 60446-1341
Tel (815) 372-9898 *Founded/Ownrshp* 1985
Sales 71.8MM^E^ *EMP* 300
SIC 5511 4212 New & used car dealers; Local trucking, without storage; New & used car dealers; Local trucking, without storage
Pr: Frank Galman
Natl Sales: Andruskiewicz Becky

D-U-N-S 07-838-4413
KENNEDY UNIVERSITY HOSPITAL INC
KENNEDY HEALTH SYSTEM
435 Hurffvl Cross Keys Rd, Turnersville, NJ 08012-2453
Tel (856) 582-2500 *Founded/Ownrshp* 1965
Sales 182.0MM^E^ *EMP* 4,000
SIC 8221 Colleges universities & professional schools
CEO: Joe Devine
**Ch:* John P Silvestri
**Treas:* Michele A Fletcher
**Sec:* Bruce J Paparone
**Prin:* Marty Bieber

D-U-N-S 04-493-3943
KENNEDY WIEDEN INC
224 Nw 13th Ave, Portland, OR 97209-2920
Tel (503) 937-7000 *Founded/Ownrshp* 1983
Sales 145.2MM^E^ *EMP* 928
SIC 7311 Advertising agencies; Advertising agencies
Pr: Dave W Luhr
**Pr:* Dan G Wieden
VP: Keith McLellan
Dir: Paul Colman
Dir: David Terry
Creative D: Aaron Allen
Creative D: Johan Arlig
Creative D: Eric Baldwin
Creative D: Stuart Brown
Creative D: Chuck Carlson
Creative D: Oonie Chase
Creative D: Mark Fitzloff
Creative D: Stuart Jennings
Creative D: Jason Kreher
Creative D: Karl Lieberman
Creative D: Sean McLaughlin
Creative D: Matt Moore
Creative D: Matt O'Rourke
Creative D: Micah Walker
Creative D: Chris Whalley
Dir Rx: Elena Cartasegna

D-U-N-S 09-509-9016
KENNEDY WIRE ROPE & SLING CO INC
302 Flato Rd, Corpus Christi, TX 78405-4205
Tel (361) 289-1444 *Founded/Ownrshp* 1979
Sales 58.9MM *EMP* 160
SIC 5072 Chains; Chains
CEO: Jacqueline Kennedy
**Pr:* Garland M Kennedy Sr
**Treas:* Walter Schwamb
**VP:* Garland M Kennedy Jr
Brnch Mgr: Chip Schwamb
Genl Mgr: Walter G Schwamb
Manager: Mark Jackson
Sales Asso: Jarrett Penter

D-U-N-S 09-218-0793
KENNEDY-DONOVAN CENTER INC
K D C
1 Commercial St, Foxboro, MA 02035-2530
Tel (508) 543-2542 *Founded/Ownrshp* 1973
Sales 30.1MM *EMP* 370
SIC 8322 Social service center; Social service center
Pr: Kevin Rodman Conare
**CFO:* Rick Bornstein
**VP:* Ann Buono
**VP:* Dan Couet
**VP:* Mike Hyland

D-U-N-S 82-535-0007
▲ KENNEDY-WILSON HOLDINGS INC
9701 Wilshire Blvd # 700, Beverly Hills, CA 90212-2007
Tel (310) 887-6400 *Founded/Ownrshp* 2007
Sales 398.6MM *EMP* 451^E^
Tkr Sym KW *Exch* NYS
SIC 6531 6799 Real estate agent, commercial; Real estate agent, residential; Investors; Real estate agent, commercial; Real estate agent, residential; Investors
Ch Bd: William J McMorrow
CFO: Justin Enbody
Treas: James J Cahill
Ofcr: Barry S Schlesinger
Ex VP: Matt Windisch
Sr VP: In Ku Lee
VP: Louis Gauthier
Genl Couns: Kent Mouton

D-U-N-S 79-521-0228
KENNEDY-WILSON INC
9701 Wilshire Blvd # 700, Beverly Hills, CA 90212-2007
Tel (310) 887-6400 *Founded/Ownrshp* 1977
Sales 35.5MM^E^ *EMP* 530
SIC 6531 6799 Auction, real estate; Real estate investors, except property operators; Auction, real estate; Real estate investors, except property operators
Ch Bd: William Mc Morrow
**Pr:* Freeman A Lyle
**CEO:* Donald J Herrema
CFO: Philip Wintner
Ex VP: Gregory Dumas
**Sr VP:* Bill Cerone
**Sr VP:* Stephen Collias
**Sr VP:* Clifford R Smith
**VP:* Teri A Anodide
**VP:* Cynthia Giordano
**VP:* Ken Kuropatkin
Board of Directors: Cathy Allen, Norm Creighton, Jeff Hudson, Gary Kasper, Kent Y Mouton, Jerry R Solomon

D-U-N-S 04-652-4260
KENNEDY/JENKS CONSULTANTS INC
303 2nd St Ste 300, San Francisco, CA 94107-1366
Tel (415) 243-2150 *Founded/Ownrshp* 1919
Sales 125.4MM^E^ *EMP* 450
Accts Hood & Strong Llp San Francis
SIC 8711 Consulting engineer; Consulting engineer
CEO: Keith A London
**CFO:* Patrick J Courtney
CFO: Stacey Ho
**Ch:* Lynn Takaichi
VP: Michael Greenspan
VP: Eric Hinzel
VP: Patrick Huston
VP: Craig W Lichty
VP: John Rayner
VP: Kim Tanner
Off Admin: Caroline Toy

D-U-N-S 02-606-0145
KENNEL VACCINE VET SUPPLY CO
KV VET SUPPLY COMPANY
3190 N Rd, David City, NE 68632
Tel (402) 367-6047 *Founded/Ownrshp* 1988
Sales 22.2MM^E^ *EMP* 100
SIC 5961 0742 Mail order house; Veterinary services, specialties; Mail order house; Veterinary services, specialties
Pr: Raymond Metzner
**Sec:* Karen Fendrich
**Sec:* Barb Stabbe
Genl Mgr: Tracie Lloyd
Dir IT: Lee Mysenburg
Sales Exec: Boden Cassie
Mktg Dir: Dan Metzner

KENNELWOOD PET RESORTS
See KENNELWOOD VILLAGE INC

D-U-N-S 06-465-0898
KENNELWOOD VILLAGE INC
KENNELWOOD PET RESORTS
1875 Lackland Hill Pkwy, Saint Louis, MO 63146-3555
Tel (314) 446-1000 *Founded/Ownrshp* 1973
Sales 20.7MM^E^ *EMP* 151
SIC 0752 5999 6794 Boarding services, kennels; Grooming services, pet & animal specialties; Pet supplies; Franchises, selling or licensing; Boarding services, kennels; Grooming services, pet & animal specialties; Pet supplies; Franchises, selling or licensing
Pr: Alan D Jones
**Ch Bd:* Donald Danforth Jr
**VP:* Josiah Robertson

D-U-N-S 15-739-5641
KENNER & CO INC
437 Madison Ave Ste 3601, New York, NY 10022-7019
Tel (212) 319-2300 *Founded/Ownrshp* 1986
Sales 547.8MM^E^ *EMP* 2,800
SIC 6211 Investment firm, general brokerage; Investment firm, general brokerage
Pr: Jeffrey Kenner
**Mng Dir:* Thomas Wolf

KENNER FINISH LINE
See FINISH LINE MANAGEMENT CORP

D-U-N-S 10-291-9388 IMP
KENNERLEY-SPRATLING INC
2116 Farallon Dr, San Leandro, CA 94577-6604
Tel (510) 351-8230 *Founded/Ownrshp* 1982
Sales 122.1MM^E^ *EMP* 400
SIC 3089 3082 Injection molding of plastics; Unsupported plastics profile shapes; Injection molding of plastics; Unsupported plastics profile shapes
CEO: Richard Spratling
**CFO:* Bill Roure
VP: Ed Lopez
**Prin:* Paul Hoefler
Plnt Mgr: Tim Arambula
**VP Sls:* Jeffrey Cranor

D-U-N-S 78-494-6444
KENNESAW MOTOR SALES INC
COBB COUNTY TOYOTA
2111 Brett Lakes Blvd Nw, Kennesaw, GA 30144-4904
Tel (770) 422-8555 *Founded/Ownrshp* 1991
Sales 53.1MM^E^ *EMP* 130^E^
SIC 5511 7538 7532 5531 5012 Automobiles, new & used; General automotive repair shops; Top & body repair & paint shops; Automotive & home supply stores; Automobiles & other motor vehicles; Automobiles, new & used; General automotive repair shops; Top & body repair & paint shops; Automotive & home supply stores; Automobiles & other motor vehicles
Pr: Michael Perrin
**CFO:* Barbara W Evans
**VP:* James O Perrin
Genl Mgr: Chuck Perrin
IT Man: Dion Glass
Prd Mgr: Russell Morris
Sls Mgr: Jim Pyron
Sls Mgr: George Rollins
Sales Asso: Tony Cloud
Sales Asso: Kapleton Forrest
Sales Asso: Grant Guzowski

D-U-N-S 62-775-8923
KENNESAW STATE UNIVERSITY
BOARD OF RGNTS OF THE UNVRSTY
(*Suby of* BOARD OF REGENTS OF UNIVERSITY SYSTEM OF GEORGIA) ★
1000 Chastain Rd Nw, Kennesaw, GA 30144-5591
Tel (770) 423-6000 *Founded/Ownrshp* 1966
Sales 265.8MM^E^ *EMP* 3,000
Accts Russell W Hinton-State Audito
SIC 8221 Colleges universities & professional schools; Colleges universities & professional schools
Pr: Daniel S Papp
COO: Debbie Chimeno
COO: Richard Corhen
**COO:* Randy Hinds
CFO: Paula Campbell
Bd of Dir: Richard W Whiteside
Assoc Dir: Donald Brookshire
Assoc Dir: Michael Dutcher
Assoc Dir: McCree Lake
Assoc Dir: Carolyn E Lliottfarino
Assoc Dir: Kristi S McMillan
Assoc Dir: Ruth A Middleton
Assoc Dir: Karen S Ohlsson
Assoc Dir: Vincenzo A Patone
Assoc Dir: Christine L Storey
Assoc Dir: Caryn Young

D-U-N-S 06-920-4659
KENNESAW STATE UNIVERSITY FOUNDATION INC (GA)
1000 Chastain Rd Nw, Kennesaw, GA 30144-5588
Tel (770) 423-6675 *Founded/Ownrshp* 1966, 1969
Sales 42.6MM *EMP* 6
SIC 6732 Educational trust management; Educational trust management
**Pr:* Ron H Francis
Genl Mgr: Emily Jacobson

D-U-N-S 05-620-6311
KENNESAW TRANSPORTATION INC
3794 Highway 411 Ne, Rydal, GA 30171-1501
Tel (770) 382-3748 *Founded/Ownrshp* 1981
Sales 39.9MM *EMP* 350
Accts Smith & Howard
SIC 4213 Contract haulers; Contract haulers
Pr: Pat Patrick
**CEO:* C W Patrick
**CFO:* Bryan Ishmel
**CFO:* Donald A Rutledge
**VP:* Charles Patrick
IT Man: Victor Velasquez
Sls Dir: Tony Page

D-U-N-S 03-721-7064
KENNESTONE HOSPITAL AT WINDY HILL INC
WELL STAR
(*Suby of* WELLSTAR HEALTH SYSTEM INC) ★
677 Church St Ne, Marietta, GA 30060-1101
Tel (770) 793-5000 *Founded/Ownrshp* 1972
Sales 38.6M *EMP* 2,950
SIC 8062 General medical & surgical hospitals; General medical & surgical hospitals
CEO: Thomas E Hill
Chf Rad: Ashutosh RAO
Dir Recs: Allison Adams
**CFO:* Dick Stovall
Ofcr: Andre Hayden
VP: Michael Paul
Exec: Cecelia Byers
Dir Rx: Chris Saboura
Chf Nrs Of: Melissa Box
Ex Dir: Don Burton
Ex Dir: Edward J Peterson
Board of Directors: James Coffey, Richard Hammonds

D-U-N-S 96-960-9390
KENNESTONE HOSPITAL INC
805 Sandy Plains Rd, Marietta, GA 30066-6340
Tel (770) 792-5023 *Founded/Ownrshp* 2011
Sales 836.4MM *EMP* 17^E^
Accts Pricewaterhousecoopers Llp Ph
SIC 8062 General medical & surgical hospitals; General medical & surgical hospitals
CEO: Reynold J Jennings

D-U-N-S 07-644-8257 IMP
KENNETH COLE PRODUCTIONS INC
(*Suby of* KCP HOLDCO, INC.)
603 W 50th St, New York, NY 10019-7051
Tel (212) 265-1500 *Founded/Ownrshp* 2012
Sales 403.9MM^E^ *EMP* 1,600^E^
SIC 3143 3144 3171 5661 5632 5611 Men's footwear, except athletic; Women's footwear, except athletic; Handbags, women's; Purses, women's; Shoe stores; Women's boots; Men's shoes; Women's accessory & specialty stores; Apparel accessories; Costume jewelry; Handbags; Men's & boys' clothing stores; Men's footwear, except athletic; Women's footwear, except athletic; Handbags, women's; Purses, women's; Shoe stores; Women's boots; Men's shoes; Women's accessory & specialty stores; Apparel accessories; Costume jewelry; Handbags; Men's & boys' clothing stores
CEO: Marc Schneider
Pr: Mia Dellosso-Caputo
Pr: Chris Nakatani
Pr: Joshua Schulman
COO: David Edelman
CFO: David P Edelman
Ch: Kenneth Cole
Ex VP: Michael Devirgilio
Ex VP: Richard Olicker
Sr VP: David Bressman
Sr VP: Regina Gorinshteyn
Sr VP: Henrik Madsen
Sr VP: Lori Wagner
VP: Derek Benson
VP: Prama Bhatt
VP: Amy Choyne
VP: Bruce Cohen
VP: Robert Genovese
VP: Orital Karelic
VP: Gayle Kasuba
VP: Stephen Policano

KENNETH COPELAND MINISTRIES
See EAGLE MOUNTAIN INTERNATIONAL CHURCH INC

D-U-N-S 10-336-4068
KENNETH CORP
GARDEN GROVE HOSPITAL
12601 Garden Grove Blvd, Garden Grove, CA 92843-1908
Tel (714) 537-5160 *Founded/Ownrshp* 1951
Sales 63.4MM^E^ *EMP* 615
SIC 8011 Medical centers; Medical centers
CEO: Edward Mirzabegian
**Ch Bd:* Hassan Alkhouli
CFO: Mary B Formy
VP: Carla Glaze
Dir Risk M: Jacinto Panes
Dir Lab: Susan David
Dir Rx: Leslie Wolder
CIO: Debbie Horgan
Dir QC: Ahmad Imran
Ansthlgy: Christopher Lui
Dir Health: Liz Alvarez

D-U-N-S 02-681-8955 IMP/EXP
KENNETH FOX SUPPLY CO
SAN ANTONIO BAG & BURLAP
2200 Fox Dr, McAllen, TX 78504-4150
Tel (956) 682-6176 *Founded/Ownrshp* 1965
Sales 25.2MM^E^ *EMP* 150^E^
SIC 2393 5113 Bags & containers, except sleeping bags: textile; Shipping supplies
Pr: Kenneth Fox
VP: Gabriel Cuellar
Plnt Mgr: Pedro Sanchez

KENNETH NORRIS CANCER HOSPITAL
See TENET HEALTH SYSTEMS NORRIS INC

D-U-N-S 03-472-0631 IMP
■ KENNETH O LESTER CO INC
PFG CUSTOMIZED DISTRIBUTION
(*Suby of* P F G) ★
245 N Castle Heights Ave, Lebanon, TN 37087-2741
Tel (615) 444-2995 *Founded/Ownrshp* 1988
Sales 2.8MMM^E *EMP* 1,700
SIC 5141 5142 5148 Groceries, general line; Packaged frozen goods; Fruits, fresh; Groceries, general line; Packaged frozen goods; Fruits, fresh
CEO: Thomas Hoffman
VP: Kevin Lester
**VP:* Robert Provalenko
**VP:* Jeff Ray
Genl Mgr: Chris Flynn
Genl Mgr: Tom Hoeffel
Software D: Alan Combs
Natl Sales: Jackie Finley
VP Sls: John Hogan

D-U-N-S 06-133-6231
KENNETH RAININ FOUNDATION
155 Grand Ave Ste 1000, Oakland, CA 94612-3779
Tel (510) 625-5200 *Founded/Ownrshp* 1997
Sales 135.3MM *EMP* 17^E
SIC 8999 Scientific consulting; Scientific consulting
Pr: Jennifer A Rainin
Comm Dir: Amanda Witte

KENNETH'S DESIGN GROUP
See KENNETHS HAIR SALONS & DAY SPAS INC

D-U-N-S 08-942-5573
KENNETHS HAIR SALONS & DAY SPAS INC (OH)
KENNETH'S DESIGN GROUP
5151 Reed Rd Ste 250b, Columbus, OH 43220-2594
Tel (614) 457-7712 *Founded/Ownrshp* 1977
Sales 9.1MM^E *EMP* 310
SIC 7231 5999 Beauty shops; Hair dressing school; Facial salons; Beauty culture school; Toiletries, cosmetics & perfumes; Beauty shops; Hair dressing school; Facial salons; Beauty culture school; Toiletries, cosmetics & perfumes
Pr: Kenneth Anders
CFO: John McElheny
Info Man: John Hale

D-U-N-S 07-550-5560
KENNETT CONSOLIDATED SCHOOL DISTRICT
300 E South St, Kennett Square, PA 19348-3655
Tel (610) 444-6600 *Founded/Ownrshp* 1932
Sales 29.5MM^E *EMP* 410
Accts Umbreit Korengel & Associates
SIC 8211 Public elementary & secondary schools; Public elementary & secondary schools
Bd of Dir: Rudy Alfonso
Bd of Dir: Kendra Lacosta
Bd of Dir: Joseph Meola
Bd of Dir: Dominic Perigo
Bd of Dir: Tessa Pulli
Bd of Dir: Janis Reynolds
Bd of Dir: Heather Schaen
Exec: Jason Cordova
Exec: Michael Kelly
Exec: Michael King
IT Man: Steve Mancini

D-U-N-S 07-588-9667
■ KENNETT HMA INC
(*Suby of* HEALTH MANAGEMENT ASSOCIATES INC) ★
1301 1st St, Kennett, MO 63857-2525
Tel (573) 888-4522 *Founded/Ownrshp* 2003
Sales 64.7MM *EMP* 400
SIC 8062 Hospital, medical school affiliation; Hospital, medical school affiliation
CEO: Ken James
**Pr:* John M Clellan
**CFO:* Curtis Herrin
**Ch:* Terry Berry
Dir Lab: Kelly Jordan
Dir IT: Gail Tucker
Pathlgst: Terry Green
Nrsg Dir: Shawn Waugh

D-U-N-S 17-719-8595
KENNETT SQUARE SPECIALTIES LLC
KENNETT STEAK AND MUSHROOM
546 Creek Rd, Kennett Square, PA 19348-2620
Tel (610) 444-8122 *Founded/Ownrshp* 1992
Sales 20.9MM^E *EMP* 90
SIC 2499 Mulch or sawdust products, wood
Ex Dir: Mary Hutchins

KENNETT STEAK AND MUSHROOM
See KENNETT SQUARE SPECIALTIES LLC

KENNEWICK GENERAL HOSPITAL
See KENNEWICK PUBLIC HOSPITAL DISTRICT

D-U-N-S 02-733-1461
KENNEWICK INDUSTRIAL & ELECTRICAL SUPPLY INC
KIE SUPPLY
113 E Columbia Dr, Kennewick, WA 99336-3718
Tel (509) 582-5156 *Founded/Ownrshp* 1955
Sales 21.0MM *EMP* 85
Accts Baker & Giles Ps Pasco Wash
SIC 5999 5063 5074 5719 5722 Plumbing & heating supplies; Electrical supplies; Plumbing fittings & supplies; Lighting, lamps & accessories; Electric household appliances, major
Pr: Augustan Kittson
**VP:* George C Peterson
Sls Mgr: Richard Cox

D-U-N-S 18-617-7408
KENNEWICK INVESTORS LLC
ROYAL COLUMBIAN RETIREMENT INN
5101 Ne 82nd Ave Ste 200, Vancouver, WA 98662-6343
Tel (360) 254-9442 *Founded/Ownrshp* 1986
Sales 12.5MM^E *EMP* 715
SIC 7011 8361 Inns; Residential care; Inns; Residential care

D-U-N-S 07-183-9781
KENNEWICK PUBLIC HOSPITAL DISTRICT
KENNEWICK GENERAL HOSPITAL
900 S Auburn St, Kennewick, WA 99336-5621
Tel (509) 586-6111 *Founded/Ownrshp* 1952
Sales 144.7MM *EMP* 540
Accts Eide Bailly Llp Fargo North
SIC 8062 General medical & surgical hospitals; General medical & surgical hospitals
CEO: Glenn Marshal
**Owner:* Darren Szendre
**CFO:* Jerry Paule
**VP:* Vik Johnson
IT Man: Tony Sudduth

D-U-N-S 07-096-8151
KENNEWICK SCHOOL DISTRICT 17
1000 W 4th Ave, Kennewick, WA 99336-5533
Tel (509) 222-5000 *Founded/Ownrshp* 1884
Sales 74.9MM^E *EMP* 2,600
SIC 8211 9411

D-U-N-S 00-604-9670
KENNEY MACHINERY CORP
EN-COM
8420 Zionsville Rd, Indianapolis, IN 46268-1565
Tel (317) 870-2619 *Founded/Ownrshp* 1898
Sales 28.9MM^E *EMP* 60
SIC 5083 Lawn & garden machinery & equipment; Irrigation equipment; Lawn & garden machinery & equipment; Irrigation equipment
Pr: Mike Kenney
**Pr:* James E Kenney
Dir IT: Kristin Kenney

D-U-N-S 00-145-7845 IMP/EXP
KENNEY MANUFACTURING CO (RI)
1000 Jefferson Blvd, Warwick, RI 02886-2200
Tel (401) 739-2200 *Founded/Ownrshp* 1914
Sales 120.2MM^E *EMP* 600
SIC 2591 3261 2511 3699 3499 2541 Drapery hardware & blinds & shades; Mini blinds; Window shades; Bathroom accessories/fittings, vitreous china or earthenware; Storage chests, household: wood; Security devices; Magnetic shields, metal; Display fixtures, wood; Drapery hardware & blinds & shades; Mini blinds; Window shades; Bathroom accessories/fittings, vitreous china or earthenware; Storage chests, household: wood; Security devices; Magnetic shields, metal; Display fixtures, wood
Pr: Leslie M Kenney
**Ch Bd:* G D Kenney
CFO: Joseph Desouse
Bd of Dir: Harry Schult
MIS Dir: Ann Tortolano
Dir IT: Tony Richards
Mtls Mgr: Jim McDonald
Natl Sales: Paul Grimes
Sls&Mrk Ex: Sally Voas
Sls Dir: Steve Brayer
Sls Mgr: Karen Wirta

D-U-N-S 02-518-5455
KENNICOTT BROS CO
AMC FLORAL INTERNATIONAL
1638 W Hubbard St, Chicago, IL 60622-6681
Tel (312) 492-8200 *Founded/Ownrshp* 1881, 2000
Sales 99.2MM^E *EMP* 229
SIC 5193 Flowers, fresh; Artificial flowers; Florists' supplies; Planters & flower pots; Flowers, fresh; Artificial flowers; Florists' supplies; Planters & flower pots
CEO: Red Kennicott
**Pr:* Gary Doran
**Pr:* Gustavo Gilchrist
**CEO:* Harrison Kennicott
**CFO:* Randy Smestad
IT Man: Lucy Tolentino

D-U-N-S 01-413-9778
KENNIES MARKET INC
217-W Middle St, Gettysburg, PA 17325-2127
Tel (717) 334-2179 *Founded/Ownrshp* 1978
Sales 21.3MM^E *EMP* 200
SIC 5411 Grocery stores, independent; Grocery stores, independent
Pr: Paul Hoover Jr
**VP:* William Coston III

D-U-N-S 02-583-7287 EXP
■ KENNY CONSTRUCTION A GRANITE CO (IL)
(*Suby of* KENNY INDUSTRIES INC) ★
2215 Sanders Rd Ste 400, Northbrook, IL 60062-6114
Tel (847) 919-8200 *Founded/Ownrshp* 1927, 1985
Sales 133.8MM^E *EMP* 500^E
SIC 1622 1611 1629 1623 1541 Bridge construction; Tunnel construction; General contractor, highway & street construction; Subway construction; Power plant construction; Water, sewer & utility lines; Industrial buildings & warehouses; Bridge construction; Tunnel construction; General contractor, highway & street construction; Subway construction; Power plant construction; Water, sewer & utility lines; Industrial buildings & warehouses
Pr: John E Kenny Jr
**CFO:* Gene Huebner
CFO: Robert Strong
**Treas:* Joan Rose
**Ex VP:* Patrick B Kenny
Board of Directors: Michael Africk, Michael Futch

D-U-N-S 17-787-6745
■ KENNY INDUSTRIES INC
(*Suby of* GRANITE CONSTRUCTION INC) ★
2215 Sanders Rd Ste 400, Northbrook, IL 60062-6114
Tel (847) 919-8200 *Founded/Ownrshp* 1985
Sales 337.6MM^E *EMP* 1,000^E
SIC 1611 1622 1629 1623 1541 6552 Highway & street construction; Highway construction, elevated; Bridge construction; Tunnel construction; Subway construction; Sewer line construction; Industrial buildings & warehouses; Subdividers & developers; Highway & street construction; Highway construction, elevated; Bridge construction; Tunnel construction; Subway construction; Sewer line construction; Industrial buildings & warehouses; Subdividers & developers
Pr: John E Kenny Jr
**Treas:* Joan E Rose
**Ex VP:* Patrick Kenny
VP: Theodore Budd
VP: Dan Zarletti
Dir Risk M: John Tuisl
MIS Dir: David Jean
Mktg Dir: Samantha Allen
Mktg Dir: Larry Dunlap

D-U-N-S 01-628-7013
KENNY KENT CHEVROLET CO INC
KENNY KENT SUPER USED CAR CENT
4600 E Division St, Evansville, IN 47715-8614
Tel (812) 477-4600 *Founded/Ownrshp* 1999
Sales 54.6MM *EMP* 155
SIC 5511 Automobiles, new & used; Pickups, new & used; Vans, new & used; Automobiles, new & used; Pickups, new & used; Vans, new & used
Pr: Cecil Van Tuyl
**Sec:* Robert Holcomb
**VP:* John Morford

KENNY KENT SUPER USED CAR CENT
See KENNY KENT CHEVROLET CO INC

KENNY KENT TOYOTA
See ROBERT KENT MOTOR CO INC

KENNY KENT TOYOTA
See EVANSVILLE AUTOMOTIVE INC

D-U-N-S 78-786-0501
KENNY PIPE & SUPPLY INC
811 Cowan St, Nashville, TN 37207-5623
Tel (615) 242-5909 *Founded/Ownrshp* 1992
Sales 105.0MM^E *EMP* 190
SIC 5074 Plumbing fittings & supplies
Pr: William H Kenny Jr
**Treas:* Thomas J Guzik Jr
VP: David Gordon
**VP:* Howard Hodges
**VP:* Randy McKnight
Brnch Mgr: Harry Allman
Brnch Mgr: Hudson Cole
Brnch Mgr: Chris Finley
Brnch Mgr: Britt Norris
Off Mgr: Kathy Duer
Opers Mgr: Ryan Thomas

KENNY ROSS CHEVROLET CADILLAC
See KENNY ROSS CHEVROLET GEO OLDSMOBILE & CADILLAC INC

D-U-N-S 01-458-6325
KENNY ROSS CHEVROLET GEO OLDSMOBILE & CADILLAC INC
KENNY ROSS CHEVROLET CADILLAC
2006 N Center Ave, Somerset, PA 15501-7436
Tel (814) 445-4113 *Founded/Ownrshp* 1996
Sales 23.2MM^E *EMP* 60
SIC 5511 Automobiles, new & used; Automobiles, new & used
Pr: James Ross
**Ch Bd:* Kenny Ross
Genl Mgr: Jeff Hess
Genl Mgr: Gary Spangler
Opers Mgr: Robert Fetty
Sales Asso: John Heiple

D-U-N-S 05-554-2617
KENNY ROSS CHEVROLET INC
11250 State Route 30, Irwin, PA 15642-2081
Tel (724) 863-9000 *Founded/Ownrshp* 1951
Sales 70.8MM^E *EMP* 133
SIC 5511 7538 7532 5531 5521 Automobiles, new & used; Engine repair; Top & body repair & paint shops; Automotive & home supply stores; Used car dealers
Pr: Dennis Kral
**Ch Bd:* James Ross
Sales Exec: John Shannon
Sls Mgr: Kevin Clay
Sls Mgr: Michael Naretto
Sales Asso: Chuck Durbiano

D-U-N-S 01-424-6946
KENNY ROSS FORD INC
Blackhill Rd Rr 30, Adamsburg, PA 15611
Tel (724) 864-3601 *Founded/Ownrshp* 1954
Sales 46.9MM^E *EMP* 125
SIC 5511 5521 7538 7532 Automobiles, new & used; Used car dealers; General automotive repair shops; Top & body repair & paint shops; Automobiles, new & used; Used car dealers; General automotive repair shops; Top & body repair & paint shops
Ch: Kenneth Ross
**Pr:* James Ross

D-U-N-S 14-803-5504
KENNY SENG CONSTRUCTION INC
250 N Orem Blvd, Orem, UT 84057-6601
Tel (801) 226-4125 *Founded/Ownrshp* 1985
Sales 23.1MM^E *EMP* 90
SIC 1794 1611 1623 1771 Excavation work; Highway & street construction; Water, sewer & utility lines; Concrete work
CEO: Kenny Seng
**Pr:* Dallan Carter
**Sec:* Lena Seng
**VP:* Travis Price

D-U-N-S 10-314-8078
KENNY STRICKLAND INC
UNION 76
50021 Harrison St, Coachella, CA 92236-1474
Tel (760) 398-2031 *Founded/Ownrshp* 1981
Sales 25.6MM^E *EMP* 14
SIC 5172 5541 Gasoline; Filling stations, gasoline
CEO: Kenny Strickland Jr
**Prin:* Kenneth E Strickland

D-U-N-S 92-603-6427 EXP
KENNY THOMAS ENTERPRISES INC
OLATHE TOYOTA
685 N Rawhide Dr, Olathe, KS 66061-3688
Tel (913) 780-9919 *Founded/Ownrshp* 1994
Sales 62.2MM^E *EMP* 125
SIC 5511 5531 Automobiles, new & used; Automotive parts; Automobiles, new & used; Automotive parts
Pr: Kenny Thomas
**VP:* Kelly Thomas
Off Mgr: Tracy Davis
Sls Mgr: Aubri Plantz

D-U-N-S 16-102-5333 IMP
KENNYS CANDY CO INC
(*Suby of* KLN ENTERPRISES INC) ★
609 Pinewood Ln, Perham, MN 56573
Tel (218) 346-2340 *Founded/Ownrshp* 1986
Sales 38.9MM^E *EMP* 190
SIC 2064 Licorice candy; Licorice candy
CEO: Kenneth Nelson
**CFO:* Wayne Caughey
Ex Dir: Nancy Belka

D-U-N-S 02-328-4516
KENOSHA BEEF INTERNATIONAL LTD
BIRCHWOOD TRANSPORT
3111 152nd Ave, Kenosha, WI 53144-7630
Tel (262) 859-2272 *Founded/Ownrshp* 1960
Sales 183.9MM^E *EMP* 755
SIC 2011 Trucking, except local; Meats, fresh; Meat packing plants
CEO: Charles Vignieri
**Pr:* Dennis Vignieri
**CFO:* Jerome D King
VP: Matt Fischer
IT Man: Jim Capps
Secur Mgr: Natalie Murray
S&M/VP: Dave Vankampen

KENOSHA MEDICAL CENTER
See UNITED HOSPITAL SYSTEM INC

KENOSHA NEWS
See UNITED COMMUNICATIONS CORP

D-U-N-S 09-634-4197
KENOSHA UNIFIED SCHOOL DISTRICT 1
3600 52nd St, Kenosha, WI 53144-2664
Tel (262) 359-6300 *Founded/Ownrshp* 1967
Sales 168.5MM^E *EMP* 2,093
SIC 8211 Public elementary school; Secondary school; Public elementary school; Secondary school
Pr: Rebecca Stevens
**CFO:* Tina Schmitz
**Treas:* Carl Bryan
**VP:* Jo Ann Taube
**Ex Dir:* Ms Sheronda Glass
MIS Dir: Daniel J Honor
IT Man: Kristine Stibb
Pr Dir: Tanya Ruder
Pr Dir: Gary Vaillancourt
Schl Brd P: Tamarra Coleman
Teacher Pr: Radovan Dimitrijevic

D-U-N-S 94-817-7175 IMP/EXP
KENOVER MARKETING CORP
KAYCO
72 Hook Rd, Bayonne, NJ 07002-5007
Tel (718) 369-4600 *Founded/Ownrshp* 1996
Sales 86.2MM^E *EMP* 180^E
Accts Goldstein Golub Kessler Llp
SIC 5141 Groceries, general line
Pr: Ilan Ron
VP: Moshe Doppelt
VP: Effe Landsberg

KENOWA HILLS PUBLIC SCHOOL
See KENOWA HILLS SCHOOL DISTRICT

D-U-N-S 02-090-2144
KENOWA HILLS SCHOOL DISTRICT
KENOWA HILLS PUBLIC SCHOOL
2325 4 Mile Rd Nw, Grand Rapids, MI 49544-9703
Tel (616) 784-2511 *Founded/Ownrshp* 1961
Sales 35.9MM *EMP* 403
SIC 8211 9411 Public junior high school; Public senior high school; Administration of educational programs; Public junior high school; Public senior high school; Administration of educational programs
VP: Matt Rettig
Sls Mgr: Cindy Heinbeck
HC Dir: Michael Burde

D-U-N-S 13-700-6446
KENPAT USA LLC
516 Cooper Commerce Dr, Apopka, FL 32703-6223
Tel (407) 464-7070 *Founded/Ownrshp* 2003
Sales 25.3MM^E *EMP* 90
SIC 1742 Plaster & drywall work
CFO: Al Anderson
**VP:* Phil Klote
VP: Phil Kote
Div Mgr: David Cockrum
Snr PM: Jeremy Welbourn

D-U-N-S 60-702-3835
KENS BEVERAGE INC
K B I
10015 S Mandel St, Plainfield, IL 60585-7598
Tel (630) 904-1555 *Founded/Ownrshp* 1989
Sales 38.7MM *EMP* 256
Accts Mueller & Co Llp Elgin Ill
SIC 8742 Food & beverage consultant; Food & beverage consultant
Pr: Kenneth T Reimer
Brnch Mgr: Tom Norrie
VP Opers: Dan Reimer
Sls&Mrk Ex: Lex Fogg
Manager: Gary Prince

D-U-N-S 00-106-3114
KENS FOODS INC (MA)
1 Dangelo Dr, Marlborough, MA 01752-3066
Tel (508) 229-1100 *Founded/Ownrshp* 1958

Sales 275.4MM^E *EMP* 920
Accts Mayer Hoffman Mccann Pc Cam
SIC 2033 Barbecue sauce: packaged in cans, jars, etc.; Barbecue sauce: packaged in cans, jars, etc.
Pr: Frank A Crowley III
COO: Bob Merchant
**CFO:* James Sutherby
**VP:* Brian L Crowley
VP: Mark Holbrook
VP: John Pritchard
**VP:* Joseph Shay
VP: Al Slingluff
VP: Bob Wynne
Mng Dir: Mark Shaye
Off Admin: Sarah Lemay

KEN'S NEWMARKET
See TECHAUS INC

D-U-N-S 07-293-7741
■ **KENS SPRAY EQUIPMENT INC**
ALLOY PROCESSING
(*Suby of* PCC) ★
1900 W Walnut St, Compton, CA 90220-5019
Tel (310) 635-9995 *Founded/Ownrshp* 2014
Sales 23.4MM^E *EMP* 133^E
SIC 3479 Painting, coating & hot dipping
Pr: Brian Leibl
**Sec:* Sandra Jeglum
VP: Vanessa Avila
Genl Mgr: Daniel Gear
Opers Mgr: David De Leon
Plnt Mgr: Kenneth L Jegum
Plnt Mgr: Jason Liebl

D-U-N-S 05-491-2951 IMP
KENSEAL CONSTRUCTION PRODUCTS OF NEW JERSEY INC
799 Edwards Rd, Parsippany, NJ 07054-4201
Tel (973) 325-6330 *Founded/Ownrshp* 1982
Sales 30.9MM^E *EMP* 40
SIC 5031 Building materials, exterior
Pr: Paul McKinnell
**Treas:* Chris Lippmann
**VP:* Ken Lippmann Jr
VP: John P McKinnell
CTO: Mark Debinski
Sales Asso: Harry Burbank
Sales Asso: Michael Thomas

D-U-N-S 05-631-2667
KENSHOO INC
(*Suby of* KENSHOO LTD)
22 4th St Fl 7, San Francisco, CA 94103-3141
Tel (877) 536-7462 *Founded/Ownrshp* 2008
Sales 25.1MM^E *EMP* 110
SIC 8742 Management consulting services
CEO: Yoav Izhar-Prato
COO: Shirley Grill-Rachman
CFO: Sarit Firon
CFO: Igal Shany
Sr VP: Israel David
Sr VP: Ted Krantz
Sr VP: William Martin-Gill
VP: Sushil Goel
VP: Hila Hubsch
VP: Brian Quinn
VP: Ben Sand
VP: Paul Vallez
VP: Sharon Witzrabin
Dir Bus: Tiffany Miller
Board of Directors: Grady Burnett

D-U-N-S 07-543-4886
KENSICO CEMETERY INC (NY)
SHARON GARDENS
273 Lakeview Ave, Valhalla, NY 10595-1617
Tel (914) 949-0347 *Founded/Ownrshp* 1889
Sales 21.7MM *EMP* 80
SIC 6553 Cemetery association; Cemetery association
Pr: Chester Day
Pr: Chester S Day
Sr VP: George Lawrence
Board of Directors: William Frank, George H C Lawrence, David Malane, Allan Stevens

KENSINGTON , THE
See EPISCOPAL COMMUNITIES & SERVICES FOR SENIORS

KENSINGTON CARE CENTER
See ANNA MARIA OF AURORA INC

D-U-N-S 14-777-1117
KENSINGTON PLUMBING AND HEATING INC
6804 Pineway, University Park, MD 20782-1157
Tel (301) 864-1117 *Founded/Ownrshp* 1985
Sales 40.0MM *EMP* 1
SIC 1711 Plumbing contractors; Warm air heating & air conditioning contractor; Plumbing contractors; Warm air heating & air conditioning contractor
Owner: Frederick M Werth

D-U-N-S 07-979-4178
KENSTON LOCAL SCHOOL DISTRICT
17419 Snyder Rd, Chagrin Falls, OH 44023-2765
Tel (440) 543-9722 *Founded/Ownrshp* 1953
Sales 28.0MM^E *EMP* 500
Accts Charles E Harris And Associat
SIC 8211 Public elementary school; Public junior high school; Public senior high school; Public elementary school; Public junior high school; Public senior high school
Pr: Anne Randall
**Treas:* Linda Hein
VP: Andy Kenen
**VP:* Bill Timmons
Pr Dir: Katy McGrath
Psych: Sara Frank
Psych: Eileen Kubas

D-U-N-S 06-936-6151
KENT & QUEEN ANNES HOSPITAL INC
UMMS
(*Suby of* UMMS) ★
100 Brown St, Chestertown, MD 21620-1499
Tel (410) 778-3300 *Founded/Ownrshp* 1930
Sales 100.8M *EMP* 350
SIC 8062 General medical & surgical hospitals; General medical & surgical hospitals
Pr: William R Kirk Jr

D-U-N-S 07-112-9290 EXP
KENT ADHESIVE PRODUCTS CO
KAPCO
1000 Cherry St, Kent, OH 44240-7501
Tel (330) 678-1626 *Founded/Ownrshp* 1974
Sales 36.7MM^E *EMP* 80
SIC 2679 2672 2675 7389 Paper products, converted; Adhesive papers, labels or tapes: from purchased material; Tape, pressure sensitive: made from purchased materials; Die-cut paper & board; Laminating service; Tape slitting
Pr: Edward Small
Pr: Mike Boone
**VP:* Jenifer Codrea
**VP:* Philip M Zavracky
MIS Dir: Ron Pickings
Plnt Mgr: Larry Davis
Plnt Mgr: Joyce McCauley
VP Mktg: Brenda Shick
Manager: Joy Dunning
Manager: Chuck Lazor

D-U-N-S 10-356-4902
KENT AUTOMOTIVE INC
KENT LINCOLN-MERCURY SALES
1080 W Main St, Kent, OH 44240-2006
Tel (330) 678-5520 *Founded/Ownrshp* 1985
Sales 32.9MM *EMP* 40
SIC 5511 5521 7538 7515 5531 Automobiles, new & used; Used car dealers; General automotive repair shops; Passenger car leasing; Automotive & home supply stores; Automobiles, new & used; Used car dealers; General automotive repair shops; Passenger car leasing; Automotive & home supply stores
Pr: Bruce A Caudill
**Sec:* Heather Knapp
**VP:* Janet Caudill

KENT BEVERAGE
See BEVCO INC

D-U-N-S 94-538-0244
KENT CENTER INC
215 Scheeler Rd, Chestertown, MD 21620-1020
Tel (410) 778-7303 *Founded/Ownrshp* 1970
Sales 3.2MM *EMP* 300^E
SIC 8361 Home for the mentally handicapped; Home for the physically handicapped
Pr: Lou Anne Usilton
**Pr:* Cheerey D Jones
**CFO:* Randall Cooper

D-U-N-S 02-744-3761
KENT CHAPLINS ENTERPRISES INC
CHAPLINS BLLVUE SBARU VLKSWGEN
15000 Se Eastgate Way, Bellevue, WA 98007-6530
Tel (425) 641-2002 *Founded/Ownrshp* 1972
Sales 44.8MM^E *EMP* 150
SIC 5511 Automobiles, new & used; Automobiles, new & used
Pr: Kent P Chaplin
**Sec:* Barbara Chaplin
Sales Asso: Karl Buelow
Sales Asso: Roger Dever
Sales Asso: Tim Hunley
Sales Asso: Kalvin Langford
Sales Asso: Andy Nelson
Sales Asso: Sonny Roberson
Sales Asso: Matt Sanglier

D-U-N-S 06-042-9495
KENT CITY SCHOOL DISTRICT
321 N Depeyster St, Kent, OH 44240-2514
Tel (330) 673-6515 *Founded/Ownrshp* 1887, 1920
Sales 50.7MM *EMP* 650
SIC 8211 Public elementary school; Public junior high school; Public senior high school; Public elementary school; Public junior high school; Public senior high school
**Treas:* Deborah Krutz
Pr Dir: Karen Rumley
Schl Brd P: Rebekah Wrightkuus

KENT COMMONS, RESOURCE CENTER
See CITY OF KENT

D-U-N-S 01-708-9269
KENT COMPANIES INC
KENT CONCRETE
130 60th St Sw, Grand Rapids, MI 49548-5703
Tel (616) 534-4909 *Founded/Ownrshp* 2008
Sales 44.6MM *EMP* 200
Accts Beenegarter Llp Grand Rapids
SIC 1771 Concrete work; Concrete work
CEO: Jeffrey Vanderlaan
COO: Jeff Laan
CFO: Randall Brink
VP: Christopher Fennema
VP: Mark Tromp
Rgnl Mgr: Roger Bilton
Div Mgr: Duane Andrus
Div Mgr: Phil Bouma
Div Mgr: Jeff French
Sls Mgr: Mike Wegman
Snr Mgr: David Fordon

KENT CONCRETE
See KENT COMPANIES INC

D-U-N-S 00-339-6637
KENT CORP (AL)
4446 Pinson Valley Pkwy, Birmingham, AL 35215-2940
Tel (205) 853-3420 *Founded/Ownrshp* 1958
Sales 49.5MM^E *EMP* 220
Accts Carr Riggs & Ingram Cpas
SIC 2542 2541 Shelving, office & store: except wood; Store fixtures, wood; Shelving, office & store: except wood; Store fixtures, wood
Pr: M A Oztekin
Sec: Sharron Harbison
VP: V J Albano
VP: Aykut Mentes
VP: A Yaman
Dir IT: Shane Wilson

D-U-N-S 00-526-9923 IMP/EXP
KENT CORP (IA)
2905 N Highway 61, Muscatine, IA 52761-5809
Tel (563) 264-4211 *Founded/Ownrshp* 1943
Sales 649.7MM^E *EMP* 1,800
SIC 2869 2085 2046 2048 Alcohols, industrial: denatured (non-beverage); Grain alcohol for beverage purposes; Corn starch; Corn oil, refined; Livestock feeds; Poultry feeds; Alcohols, industrial: denatured (non-beverage); Grain alcohol for beverage purposes; Corn starch; Corn oil, refined; Livestock feeds; Poultry feeds
COO: G A Kent
**CFO:* D A Jones
Treas: Mark Dunsmore
Ex VP: Kevin Fields
VP: Douglas M Dermid
VP: John Randolph
Dir Risk M: Hal Larson
Rgnl Mgr: Meyer Lieberman
Mktg Mgr: Renee Lloyd
Board of Directors: Jeff Underwood

D-U-N-S 82-899-1323
KENT CORP
HARVEST PRIDE
1224 Ne Walnut St Ste 252, Roseburg, OR 97470-2026
Tel (541) 672-4765 *Founded/Ownrshp* 1993
Sales 23.0MM *EMP* 15
SIC 5141 Food brokers; Food brokers
Pr: Dennis Yeo
CFO: Jones Dave
**Treas:* Lori Yeo
Sr VP: Rich Dwyer
Dir Risk M: Hal Larson

D-U-N-S 83-261-2415
KENT COUNTY CMH AUTHORITY
NETWORK 180
790 Fuller Ave Ne, Grand Rapids, MI 49503-1918
Tel (616) 336-3765 *Founded/Ownrshp* 2008
Sales 23.0MM^E *EMP* 120
Accts Bdo Usa Llp Grand Rapids Mi
SIC 8069 Drug addiction rehabilitation hospital
Ex Dir: Paul Ippel
Bd of Dir: Tom Dooley
Ex Dir: Bonnie Huntley

D-U-N-S 06-985-5195
KENT COUNTY MEMORIAL HOSPITAL
HOSPITALITY SHOP
455 Toll Gate Rd, Warwick, RI 02886-2770
Tel (401) 737-7000 *Founded/Ownrshp* 1946
Sales 323.6MM *EMP* 1,850
SIC 8062 General medical & surgical hospitals; General medical & surgical hospitals
Pr: Michael Dacey
Chf OB: Maural Colavitta
Chf Rad: Julie Armada
Treas: Polly E Leonard Do
Trst: James R Hagety
Trst: Daniel B Reardon
Ofcr: Caren Santos
VP: Dan Callahan
VP: Alicia Condon
Dir Risk M: Ruth Denehy
Dir Rad: Stevens L Bruce
Dir Rad: Rogovitz M David
Dir Rad: Williams C Mihael
Dir Rad: Silva Rafael

D-U-N-S 16-953-8543
KENT COUNTY MOTOR SALES CO
2181 S Dupont Hwy, Dover, DE 19901-5556
Tel (302) 697-3000 *Founded/Ownrshp* 1953
Sales 21.1MM^E *EMP* 50
SIC 5511 5521 New & used car dealers; Used car dealers; New & used car dealers; Used car dealers
Pr: John Whitby
**VP:* Audrey Whitby
Store Mgr: Andrew Best

D-U-N-S 02-088-5463
KENT COUNTY OF (INC)
NETWORK 180
300 Monroe Ave Nw Unit 1, Grand Rapids, MI 49503-2206
Tel (616) 632-7580 *Founded/Ownrshp* 1836
Sales NA *EMP* 2,000
Accts Bdo Seidman Llp Grand Rapids
SIC 9111 Executive offices; ; Executive offices;

D-U-N-S 78-019-1321
KENT COUNTY PUBLIC SCHOOLS
KCPS
5608 Boundary Ave, Rock Hall, MD 21661-1604
Tel (410) 778-1595 *Founded/Ownrshp* 2006
Sales 18.5MM^E *EMP* 356^E
SIC 8211 Public elementary & secondary schools
Teacher Pr: Ed Silver
HC Dir: Darlene Spurrier .

D-U-N-S 06-061-5267
KENT DENVER SCHOOL
4000 E Quincy Ave, Englewood, CO 80113-4916
Tel (303) 770-7660 *Founded/Ownrshp* 1974
Sales 21.8MM *EMP* 110
Accts Eide Bailly Llp Golden Co
SIC 8211 Preparatory school; Preparatory school
Pr: Todd Horn
Trst: Krista Sahrbeck
Ex Dir: Christine Capeless
IT Man: Denise Wylde

D-U-N-S 08-671-3299
KENT DESIGN BUILD INC
1875 Highway 59, Mandeville, LA 70448-1905
Tel (985) 626-9964 *Founded/Ownrshp* 1999
Sales 25.7MM^E *EMP* 33
SIC 1542 Commercial & office building contractors; Commercial & office building contractors
Pr: Kyle Lee Kent

D-U-N-S 80-268-8457 IMP
KENT DISPLAYS INC
IMPROV ELECTRONICS
343 Portage Blvd, Kent, OH 44240-9200
Tel (330) 673-8784 *Founded/Ownrshp* 1996
Sales 21.2MM^E *EMP* 105^E
SIC 3679 Liquid crystal displays (LCD)
CEO: Albert M Green PHD
**Pr:* Joel Domino
**Pr:* Asad Khan
**VP:* Taesun Cha
**VP:* J W Doane
**Comm Dir:* Kevin Oswald
Dir Bus: Al Davis
CIO: Mark Ferrel
IT Man: Mike Nicoletti
Mfg Mgr: Bill Emanuele
Mktg Dir: Billy Chapnick

D-U-N-S 04-788-1750
KENT DISTRIBUTORS INC
KENT OIL
3314 W Loop 250 N, Midland, TX 79707-3420
Tel (432) 699-7124 *Founded/Ownrshp* 1984
Sales 50.7MM^E *EMP* 250
SIC 5411 5172 Convenience stores; Gasoline; Convenience stores; Gasoline; Diesel fuel
Pr: William B Kent
VP: Julie Kent
**VP:* Bennett Robb

D-U-N-S 17-052-2007
KENT DISTRICT LIBRARY
814 W River Center Dr Ne, Comstock Park, MI 49321-8955
Tel (616) 784-2007 *Founded/Ownrshp* 1994
Sales 16.5MM *EMP* 300
SIC 8231 Libraries; Libraries
Comm Man: Eric Dehaan
Comm Man: Heidi Nagel
Brnch Mgr: Nancy Mulder

D-U-N-S 15-197-3732 IMP
KENT ELASTOMER PRODUCTS INC
(*Suby of* MERIDIAN INDUSTRIES INC) ★
1500 Saint Clair Ave, Kent, OH 44240-4364
Tel (330) 673-1011 *Founded/Ownrshp* 2001
Sales 28.4MM^E *EMP* 150
SIC 3052 Rubber & plastics hose & beltings; Rubber & plastics hose & beltings
Pr: Bob Oborn

KENT F PAUL, MD, PHD
See DEPARTMENT OF NEUROLOGY MEDICAL SERVICE GROUP

D-U-N-S 07-706-5928
KENT GENERAL HOSPITAL INC
MILFORD MEMORIAL HOSPITAL
(*Suby of* BAYHEALTH MEDICAL CENTER INC) ★
640 S State St, Dover, DE 19901-3599
Tel (302) 674-4700 *Founded/Ownrshp* 1921
Sales 537.3MM *EMP* 2,600^E
SIC 8062 General medical & surgical hospitals; General medical & surgical hospitals
Pr: Terry M Murphy
**CEO:* Dennis Klima
Exec: Kia Evans
Doctor: Richard Dushuttle
HC Dir: Courtney Breasure

D-U-N-S 05-931-1944
KENT GYPSUM SUPPLY INC
10720 26th Ave S, Lakewood, WA 98499-8719
Tel (253) 722-1234 *Founded/Ownrshp* 1982
Sales 25.8MM^E *EMP* 45
SIC 5031 Wallboard
Pr: Matthew Klein
**Pr:* Jon Horner

KENT H LANDSBERG CO
See APOLLO PAPER CO OF DALLAS

D-U-N-S 07-258-4329
KENT INTERMEDIATE SCHOOL DISTRICT
KENT ISD
2930 Knapp St Ne, Grand Rapids, MI 49525-7006
Tel (616) 364-1333 *Founded/Ownrshp* 1903
Sales 243.5MM *EMP* 1,000
Accts Maner Costerisan Pc Lansing
SIC 8211 Public elementary & secondary schools; Public elementary & secondary schools
**Pr:* Andrea Haidle
CFO: James McLian
**Treas:* Steve Zinger
**VP:* Claudia Bajema
Prin: Gail Persons
Doctor: Frank Schwartz

D-U-N-S 00-257-3780 IMP/EXP
KENT INTERNATIONAL INC
60 E Halsey Rd, Parsippany, NJ 07054-3705
Tel (973) 434-8180 *Founded/Ownrshp* 1958
Sales 35.5MM^E *EMP* 70
SIC 5091

KENT ISD
See KENT INTERMEDIATE SCHOOL DISTRICT

KENT LINCOLN-MERCURY SALES
See KENT AUTOMOTIVE INC

D-U-N-S 00-602-0002
KENT MANUFACTURING CO
2200 Oak Industrial Dr Ne, Grand Rapids, MI 49505-6016
Tel (616) 942-0500 *Founded/Ownrshp* 1940
Sales 32.7MM^E *EMP* 60
SIC 2672 3053 3069 2891 3086 3083 Tape, pressure sensitive: made from purchased materials; Adhesive papers, labels or tapes: from purchased material; Gaskets & sealing devices; Gasket materials; Medical & laboratory rubber sundries & related products; Tape, pressure sensitive: rubber; Foam rubber; Adhesives; Plastics foam products; Laminated plastics plate & sheet
Pr: Kenneth Muraski
**Treas:* Edie Muraski
**VP:* Camille Cebelak

**VP:* Michael Muraski
**VP:* Thomas Muraski
**VP:* Mary Rott
QI Cn Mgr: Bob Glowacki
Natl Sales: Peter Woods
Sls Mgr: Michael Hagan
Sls Mgr: George Supri

D-U-N-S 08-355-7173
KENT MOORE CABINETS LTD (TX)
501 Industrial Blvd, Bryan, TX 77803-2012
Tel (979) 775-2906 *Founded/Ownrshp* 1971
Sales 96.7MM[E] *EMP* 400
SIC 2434 Wood kitchen cabinets; Vanities, bathroom: wood; Wood kitchen cabinets; Vanities, bathroom: wood
Pr: R Kent Moore
**CFO:* Eric Carter
VP: Casey Moore
VP: Dale Tolmsoff
VP: John Trclek
CIO: Teresa Galliher
IT Man: Lucinda Orr
Manager: Gary Belt

D-U-N-S 06-180-8754 EXP
KENT MOTORCAR CO INC
HONDA OF PRINCETON
987 State Rd, Princeton, NJ 08540-1417
Tel (609) 683-0840 *Founded/Ownrshp* 2000
Sales 24.5MM[E] *EMP* 55
SIC 5511 Automobiles, new & used; Automobiles, new & used
Pr: Robert Burt
Exec: Sue Powers
Sls Mgr: Jonathan Dorf

D-U-N-S 03-517-2907
KENT NEWS CO LLC
100511 Airport Rd, Scottsbluff, NE 69361-7619
Tel (308) 632-4180 *Founded/Ownrshp* 1997
Sales 62.9MM[E] *EMP* 150
SIC 5192 Periodicals; Magazines; Books; Periodicals; Magazines; Books
Pr: Dave Knoles

D-U-N-S 00-694-1926 EXP
KENT NUTRITION GROUP INC (IA)
EVERGREEN MILLS DIVISION
(*Suby of* KENT CORP) ★
1600 Oregon St, Muscatine, IA 52761-1404
Tel (563) 264-4211 *Founded/Ownrshp* 1927, 1946
Sales 112.6MM[E] *EMP* 400
SIC 2048 Livestock feeds; Poultry feeds; Livestock feeds; Poultry feeds
Pr: D T Tubandt
**Pr:* Rich Dwyer
**Treas:* M R Dunsmore
**Treas:* Larry Schaapveld
**Treas:* D B Tinio
Rgnl VP: D R Beck
VP: R J Dennis
VP: J M Dougherty
VP: Gary L Mercer
VP: Dan Paca
VP: Bruce Read
VP: Tony Woods
**VP:* Kevin Zeimet

KENT OIL
See KENT DISTRIBUTORS INC

D-U-N-S 08-061-9661
KENT PLACE SCHOOL INC
K P S
42 Norwood Ave, Summit, NJ 07901-1900
Tel (908) 273-0900 *Founded/Ownrshp* 1894
Sales 25.6MM *EMP* 155
Accts Eisner Amper Llp Iselin New
SIC 8211 Private combined elementary & secondary school; Private combined elementary & secondary school
CEO: Susan C Bosland
**Pr:* Beverly B Mills
CFO: Karen Jones
CFO: Rita Oconnor
**Treas:* James A Hislop
**VP:* Kimberly E Taylor
DP Exec: Sandy Ozkaya
Snr Mgr: Kate Hunzinger

D-U-N-S 00-285-4933
KENT QUALITY FOODS INC
703 Leonard St Nw, Grand Rapids, MI 49504-4236
Tel (616) 459-4595 *Founded/Ownrshp* 1980
Sales 49.5MM[E] *EMP* 145
SIC 2011 2013 Meat packing plants; Sausages & other prepared meats; Meat packing plants; Sausages & other prepared meats
Pr: Charles M Soet
**VP:* Karl Soet
Rgnl Mgr: Joe Biondo
Plnt Mgr: Rick Anderson
VP Sls: Jim Zubkus

D-U-N-S 07-540-9250
KENT SCHOOL CORP
1 Macedonia Rd, Kent, CT 06757-1304
Tel (860) 927-3501 *Founded/Ownrshp* 1906
Sales 39.0MM *EMP* 195
Accts Blum Shapiro & Company Pc Cpa
SIC 8211 Private elementary & secondary schools; Private elementary & secondary schools
**Pr:* Benjamin Waring Partridge IV
CFO: Thomas B Sides
**Treas:* Robert S Anderson
Treas: Thomas Craig
**VP:* David C Clapp
Dir Sec: Bill Kasbarian
DP Exec: Adam Fischer
HC Dir: Kathryn Sullivan

D-U-N-S 01-317-8363
KENT SCHOOL DISTRICT
12033 Se 256th St, Kent, WA 98030-6643
Tel (253) 373-7000 *Founded/Ownrshp* 1942
Sales 292.3MM *EMP* 3,505
Accts Troy Kelley Olympia Washingt
SIC 8211 Public elementary & secondary schools; Public senior high school; Public junior high school; Public elementary school; Public elementary & secondary schools; Public senior high school; Public junior high school; Public elementary school
COO: Jeffrey Barth
Bd of Dir: Kristina McCormick
Exec: Charles Lind
Dir Soc: Grant Hayden
Dir Sec: Tim Kovich
Off Mgr: Marylyn Yoder
CTO: Thuan Nguyen
MIS Dir: Danni Phiffer
IT Man: Donald Hauck
IT Man: Karla Huston
Netwrk Eng: James Keele II

D-U-N-S 10-197-2362 IMP
KENT SECURITY SERVICES INC
14600 Biscayne Blvd, North Miami, FL 33181-1212
Tel (305) 919-9400 *Founded/Ownrshp* 1982
Sales 48.8MM[E] *EMP* 1,000[E]
SIC 7381 7299 Protective services, guard; Security guard service; Valet parking; Protective services, guard; Security guard service; Valet parking
CEO: Gil Neuman
**Ch Bd:* Shlomi Alexander
**Pr:* Shelly Tygielski
**CFO:* Orly Alexander
Sr VP: Michael Freeman
VP: Ovadiya Aharonoff
Exec: Newman Gil
**Prin:* Alon Alexander
Off Mgr: Rosemary Curillo
Off Mgr: John Montgomery

D-U-N-S 06-154-0704 IMP
KENT SPORTING GOODS CO INC
433 Park Ave, New London, OH 44851-1314
Tel (419) 929-7021 *Founded/Ownrshp* 1961
Sales 139.1MM[E] *EMP* 575
SIC 3949 Water sports equipment; Water sports equipment
CEO: Robert Archer
Pr: Lisa Rankine
**Pr:* J Robert Tipton
CFO: John Archer
**CFO:* John A Clark
**VP:* Marlene Sipp
VP: Wayne Walters
**VP:* Brian C Zaletel
VP Sls: Bev White
Board of Directors: Dennis Campbell

D-U-N-S 04-107-1101
KENT STATE UNIVERSITY
1500 Horning Rd, Kent, OH 44242-0001
Tel (330) 672-3000 *Founded/Ownrshp* 1910
Sales 474.6MM *EMP* 5,466
Accts Dave Yost Columbus Ohio
SIC 8221 University; University
Pr: Lester A Lefton
Trst: Sandra W Harbrecht
Trst: Gina C Spencer
Ofcr: Anthony Davis
Ofcr: John Ditrick
Ofcr: Alice Ickes
Ofcr: Richard O'Neill
Ofcr: Wayne Parker
Ofcr: Nancy Shefchuk
Ofcr: Trisha Synder
Ofcr: Miguel Witt
Assoc VP: Cynthia Crimmins
Sr VP: Todd A Diacon
Sr VP: Robert G Frank
VP: Alvin Evans
VP: Iris E Harvey
VP: Gregory Jarvie
VP: Thomas R Neumann
Exec: Zouheir N Kahwaji
Assoc Dir: Scott McKinney
Assoc Dir: Roberto Uribe

D-U-N-S 07-548-0228
KENT-SUSSEX INDUSTRIES INC
KSI CARTRIDGE SERVICE
301 N Rehoboth Blvd, Milford, DE 19963-1305
Tel (302) 422-4014 *Founded/Ownrshp* 1962
Sales 8.1MM *EMP* 313
Accts Rowland Johnson & Company Pa
SIC 3955 Print cartridges for laser & other computer printers; Print cartridges for laser & other computer printers
CEO: B Craig Crouch
VP: Jim Greenwell
Prgrm Mgr: Rudee Taylor
Telecom Ex: Shawn Bowman
VP Opers: Jayson Crouch

D-U-N-S 03-355-7752 IMP
KENTEC INC
AOK RENTALS
3250 Centerville Hwy, Snellville, GA 30039-3102
Tel (770) 985-1907 *Founded/Ownrshp* 1993
Sales 34.1MM[E] *EMP* 58
SIC 5085 5211 5084 5072 Staplers & tackers; Tools; Lumber & other building materials; Industrial machinery & equipment; Hardware
Pr: George W Morgan III
COO: Mark Kennedy
**CFO:* Charles O Rawlins
Sales Asso: Ron Decatur

KENTFIELD REHABILATION HOSP
See 1125 SIR FRANCIS DRAKE BOULEVARD OPERATING CO LLC

D-U-N-S 00-827-1553 IMP
KENTMASTER MFG CO INC (CA)
1801 S Mountain Ave, Monrovia, CA 91016-4270
Tel (626) 359-8888 *Founded/Ownrshp* 1948, 1967
Sales 24.8MM[E] *EMP* 60
SIC 5084 Pneumatic tools & equipment
CEO: Ralph Karubian

D-U-N-S 00-184-5643
KENTON COUNTY AIRPORT BOARD (KY)
CINCINNATI/NORTHERN KENTUCKY I
2939 Terminal Dr, Hebron, KY 41048
Tel (859) 767-3151 *Founded/Ownrshp* 1947
Sales 9.0MM *EMP* 340[E]
Accts Blue & Co Llc Lexington Ky
SIC 4581 Airport; Airport
CEO: Candace S McGraw
**COO:* Tim Zeis
**CFO:* Sheila R Hammons
Ofcr: Candace McGraw
Ofcr: Chris McGreevy
VP: Robert Barker
VP: Shannon Oldfield
Secur Mgr: Jon Unruh
Snr Mgr: Debbie Conrad
Snr Mgr: Gene Cossey
Snr Mgr: Paul Griffith

D-U-N-S 08-002-0877
KENTON COUNTY SCHOOL DISTRICT
1055 Eaton Dr, Ft Wright, KY 41017-9655
Tel (859) 344-8888 *Founded/Ownrshp* 1884
Sales 1.9MM[E] *EMP* 1,750
SIC 8211 Public elementary & secondary schools; Public senior high school; Public junior high school; Public elementary school

D-U-N-S 06-091-5824
KENTON COUNTY SCHOOL DISTRICT EDUCATIONAL FOUNDATION INC
1055 Eaton Dr, Ft Wright, KY 41017-9655
Tel (859) 344-8888 *Founded/Ownrshp* 1938
Sales 118.3MM[E] *EMP* 1,750
Accts Bertke & Spaks Inc Crestvie
SIC 8399 Public elementary & secondary schools; Public senior high school; Public junior high school; Public elementary school; Fund raising organization, non-fee basis
Pr: Karen Collins
Genl Mgr: Steve Jablonowski
Board of Directors: Robert Lape

D-U-N-S 08-091-1944 IMP
KENTS BROMELIAD NURSERY INC
1266 Ridge Rd, Vista, CA 92081-6514
Tel (760) 758-1661 *Founded/Ownrshp* 1975
Sales 42.2MM[E] *EMP* 49[E]
SIC 5193 Flowers & nursery stock
Pr: Jeffrey Craig Kent
**Sec:* Larry Kent
**VP:* Michael Kent

KENT'S KORNER
See GARVIN OIL CO INC

D-U-N-S 14-124-3522
KENTUCKIANA HOME FURNISHINGS LLC
ASHLEY FURNITURE HOME STORE
11521 Bluegrass Pkwy, Louisville, KY 40299-2351
Tel (502) 238-2350 *Founded/Ownrshp* 2003
Sales 60.0MM *EMP* 450
SIC 5023 Decorative home furnishings & supplies; Decorative home furnishings & supplies
IT Man: Bill Buckler

D-U-N-S 00-639-8416 IMP
KENTUCKY ASSOCIATION OF ELECTRIC COOPERATIVES INC
KAEC
4515 Bishop Ln, Louisville, KY 40218-4507
Tel (502) 451-2430 *Founded/Ownrshp* 1943
Sales 88.2MM *EMP* 186
SIC 3612 2721 7629 5063 Power transformers, electric; Periodicals: publishing only; Electrical equipment repair, high voltage; Power transmission equipment, electric; Power transformers, electric; Periodicals: publishing only; Electrical equipment repair, high voltage; Power transmission equipment, electric
Pr: J William Corum
**Pr:* Ron Sheets
CFO: Tim Hargrove
VP: Dennis Cannon
VP: Julie Mayton
**Prin:* Carol Hall Fraley
Sls&Mrk Ex: Gary Burnett
Snr Mgr: Mike McHargue

D-U-N-S 10-856-2919
▲ **KENTUCKY BANCSHARES INC**
339 Main St, Paris, KY 40361-2031
Tel (859) 987-1795 *Founded/Ownrshp* 1981
Sales NA *EMP* 208[E]
Tkr Sym KTYB *Exch* OTO
SIC 6022 State commercial banks; State commercial banks
Pr: Louis Prichard
**Ch Bd:* Buckner Woodford IV
CFO: Gregory J Dawson
Chf Cred: Norman J Fryman
Ofcr: James B Braden
Ofcr: Lydia Sosby
Sr VP: Carol Caskey

D-U-N-S 00-799-3280
■ **KENTUCKY BANK** (KY)
(*Suby of* KENTUCKY BANCSHARES INC) ★
1500 Flemingsburg Rd, Morehead, KY 40351-9767
Tel (859) 987-1795 *Founded/Ownrshp* 1851
Sales NA *EMP* 130
SIC 6022 6163 State commercial banks; Loan brokers; State commercial banks; Loan brokers
Pr: Louis Prichard
**Ch:* Buckner Woodford
Bd of Dir: Jonah Mitchell
**Sr VP:* Norman J Fryman
VP: Hugh M Crombie
**VP:* Gregory J Dawson
VP: Shane Foley
Exec: John Hamilton
Opers Mgr: Clarky Orpauto

D-U-N-S 96-671-3807
KENTUCKY BANKERS ASSOCIATION HEALTH AND WELFARE BENEFIT TRUST
600 W Main St Ste 400, Louisville, KY 40202-2998
Tel (502) 582-2453 *Founded/Ownrshp* 2011
Sales 31.3MM *EMP* 1
SIC 7389 Financial services; Financial services
Pr: Ben Keeton

D-U-N-S 07-409-9904
KENTUCKY BLOOD CENTER INC
3121 Beaumont Centre Cir, Lexington, KY 40513-1709
Tel (859) 276-2534 *Founded/Ownrshp* 1968
Sales 28.3MM *EMP* 230[E]
Accts Dean Dorton Allen Ford Pllc L
SIC 8099 Blood bank; Blood donor station; Blood bank; Blood donor station
CEO: William Reed
**CFO:* Shelley Vish
**Prin:* Susan Berry Buckley
CTO: Pamela Sutton
Dir IT: Gary Burchfield
IT Man: Jill Ball
IT Man: John Maune

D-U-N-S 92-753-4594
KENTUCKY CABINET OF FINANCE AND ADMINISTRATION
(*Suby of* EXECUTIVE OFFICE OF COMMONWEALTH OF KENTUCKY) ★
702 Capital Ave Rm 383, Frankfort, KY 40601-3448
Tel (502) 564-4240 *Founded/Ownrshp* 1900
Sales NA *EMP* 400
SIC 9311 Finance, taxation & monetary policy; ; Finance, taxation & monetary policy;
Ex Dir: Tom Howard

D-U-N-S 05-011-2098
KENTUCKY COMMUNITY AND TECHNICAL COLLEGE SYSTEM
KCTCS
300 N Main St, Versailles, KY 40383-1245
Tel (859) 256-3100 *Founded/Ownrshp* 1999
Sales 334.2M *EMP* 9,000
Accts Dean Dorton Allen Ford Pllc L
SIC 8222 Community college; Community college
Ch: F Lee Hess
**Pr:* Michael B McCall
Ofcr: Kathie Stamper
**VP:* Kenneth Walker
Off Admin: Laura Bates
Off Admin: Darlene West
Dir IT: Null G Gabbar
Netwrk Mgr: Robert Tucker
Pr Mgr: Heather Baber
HC Dir: Shelble Hugle

KENTUCKY CONNECT
See LEXINGTON H-L SERVICES INC

KENTUCKY CRM VCTMS CMPNSTS BRD
See PUBLIC PROTECTION & REGULATION CABINET KENTUCKY

D-U-N-S 10-259-4426
KENTUCKY DEPARTMENT OF EDUCATION
500 Mero St Ste 2200, Frankfort, KY 40601-1957
Tel (502) 564-2351 *Founded/Ownrshp* 1994
Sales NA *EMP* 600[E]
SIC 9411 Administration of educational programs; Administration of educational programs

D-U-N-S 83-276-3283
KENTUCKY DEPARTMENT OF FISH & WILDLIFE RESOURCES
(*Suby of* EXECUTIVE OFFICE OF COMMONWEALTH OF KENTUCKY) ★
1 Sportsmans Ln, Frankfort, KY 40601-3951
Tel (502) 564-2468 *Founded/Ownrshp* 2009
Sales NA *EMP* 303[E]
SIC 9512 Land, mineral & wildlife conservation;
Counsel: David Hise

D-U-N-S 92-725-8731
KENTUCKY DEPARTMENT OF MILITARY AFFAIRS
OFFICE MANAGEMENT ADM
(*Suby of* EXECUTIVE OFFICE OF COMMONWEALTH OF KENTUCKY) ★
100 Minuteman Pkwy # 100, Frankfort, KY 40601-6120
Tel (502) 607-1545 *Founded/Ownrshp* 1996
Sales NA *EMP* 600
SIC 9711

D-U-N-S 92-735-0090
KENTUCKY DEPARTMENT OF PARKS
(*Suby of* TOURISM ARTS AND HERITAGE CABINET) ★
500 Mero St Ste 2200, Frankfort, KY 40601-1957
Tel (502) 564-2172 *Founded/Ownrshp* 1924
Sales NA *EMP* 1,300
SIC 9512 Land, mineral & wildlife conservation; ; Land, mineral & wildlife conservation;

D-U-N-S 13-971-8717
KENTUCKY DEPARTMENT OF VETERANS AFFAIRS
1111 Louisville Rd Ste B, Frankfort, KY 40601-6123
Tel (502) 564-9203 *Founded/Ownrshp* 2003
Sales NA *EMP* 500
SIC 9451
Ofcr: Lisa Aug

D-U-N-S 92-748-5862
KENTUCKY DEPARTMENT OF VOCATIONAL REHABILITATION
(*Suby of* KENTUCKY EDUCATION AND WORK FORCE DEVELOPMENT CABINET) ★
209 Saint Clair St, Frankfort, KY 40601-1817
Tel (502) 564-5841 *Founded/Ownrshp* 1949
Sales NA *EMP* 500
SIC 9411 9441 ; Income maintenance programs; ; ; Income maintenance programs;
Prgrm Mgr: Teresa Brandenburg

D-U-N-S 92-748-5847
KENTUCKY DEPT OF TECHNICAL EDUCATION
(*Suby of* KENTUCKY EDUCATION AND WORK FORCE DEVELOPMENT CABINET) ★
500 Mero St Fl 20, Frankfort, KY 40601-1987
Tel (502) 564-4286 *Founded/Ownrshp* 1792
Sales NA *EMP* 1,100

SIC 9411 9441 State education department; ; Income maintenance programs; ; State education department; ; Income maintenance programs;
**Ex Dir:* John Marks
Pgrm Dir: Kara Burkett

D-U-N-S 01-521-5502
KENTUCKY DEPARTMENT OF JUVENILE JUSTICE
(*Suby of* EXECUTIVE OFFICE OF COMMONWEALTH OF KENTUCKY) ★
1025 Capital Center Dr # 300, Frankfort, KY 40601-8205
Tel (502) 573-2738 *Founded/Ownrshp* 1996
Sales 11.9MM^E *EMP* 293
SIC 8322 9441 Child related social services; Administration of social & manpower programs; ; Child related social services; Administration of social & manpower programs;
Brnch Mgr: Pam Jarvis
IT Man: Bill May
IT Man: Patrick Whitaker

D-U-N-S 09-466-7735
KENTUCKY DIVISION OF MINE RECLAMATION & ENFORCEMENT
MANNING PERMIT
(*Suby of* ENERGY AND ENVIRONMENT CABINET) ★
2 Hudson Hollow Rd, Frankfort, KY 40601-4311
Tel (502) 564-6940 *Founded/Ownrshp* 1977
Sales NA *EMP* 296
SIC 9511 Environmental protection agency, government; Environmental protection agency, government

KENTUCKY EAGLE BEER
See KENTUCKY EAGLE INC

D-U-N-S 02-402-9282
KENTUCKY EAGLE INC (KY)
KENTUCKY EAGLE BEER
2440 Innovation Dr, Lexington, KY 40511-8515
Tel (859) 280-2171 *Founded/Ownrshp* 1948
Sales 70.6MM^E *EMP* 172^E
SIC 5181 Beer & other fermented malt liquors; Beer & other fermented malt liquors
Pr: Ann McBrayer
CFO: Jeff Baltzer
**Sec:* Wanda Murphy
**VP:* Rusty Dyer
**VP:* Jim Gann
VP: David Stubblefield
**VP:* David Stubblesield
IT Man: Alan Ritchie

D-U-N-S 07-132-4842
KENTUCKY EASTER SEAL SOCIETY INC
2050 Versailles Rd, Lexington, KY 40504-1405
Tel (859) 254-5701 *Founded/Ownrshp* 1923
Sales 60.8MM *EMP* 660
Accts Dean Dorton Allen Ford Pllc L
SIC 8399 8069 Health systems agency; Specialty hospitals, except psychiatric; Health systems agency; Specialty hospitals, except psychiatric
Ch: Jimmy Nash
**CFO:* Marty Alutner

D-U-N-S 92-741-0555
KENTUCKY EDUCATION AND WORK FORCE DEVELOPMENT CABINET
(*Suby of* EXECUTIVE OFFICE OF COMMONWEALTH OF KENTUCKY) ★
500 Mero St Ste 3, Frankfort, KY 40601-1957
Tel (502) 564-6606 *Founded/Ownrshp* 1990
Sales NA *EMP* 1,179^E
SIC 9441 9111 Income maintenance programs; ; Executive offices; ; Income maintenance programs; ; Executive offices;
**Pr:* Gerry Don Crump
**VP:* James Spencer

D-U-N-S 92-753-4313
KENTUCKY EDUCATION AND WORKFORCE DEVELOPMENT CABINET
500 Mero St Ste 3, Frankfort, KY 40601-1957
Tel (502) 564-0372 *Founded/Ownrshp* 1994
Sales NA *EMP* 2,500
SIC 9411 Administration of educational programs; ; Administration of educational programs;
Ofcr: Charles L Harman
Dir Soc: Bruce Brooks
Ex Dir: Sarah Milligan
Store Mgr: Nina Elmore
IT Man: Sandie Sachwald

D-U-N-S 06-956-1324
KENTUCKY ELECTRONICS INC
222 Riggs Ave, Portland, TN 37148-1500
Tel (615) 325-4127 *Founded/Ownrshp* 1970
Sales 27.1MM^E *EMP* 140^E
SIC 3469 3599 3555 Metal stampings; Machine shop, jobbing & repair; Printing trade parts & attachments
Pr: Kenneth J Best Jr
**VP:* Vince Haynes
CTO: Kenneth Best

D-U-N-S 92-605-2622
KENTUCKY EMPLOYERS MUTUAL INSURANCE AUTHORITY
KEMI
250 W Main St Ste 900, Lexington, KY 40507-1724
Tel (859) 425-7800 *Founded/Ownrshp* 1994
Sales NA *EMP* 210
SIC 6331 Workers' compensation insurance; Workers' compensation insurance
Pr: Roger Fries
**Ex VP:* Jon Stewart
**VP:* Michelle Landers
Dir IT: Nancy Maglothin
Dir IT: Jason Montgomery
Dir IT: Kathy Phelps
Software D: Adam Dickison
Software D: Jesse Smith
Mktg Dir: Brian Worthen
Corp Couns: Amy Griffin

D-U-N-S 80-169-9422
KENTUCKY FARM BUREAU INSURANCE AGENCY INC
(*Suby of* FB INSURANCE CO) ★
9201 Bunsen Pkwy, Louisville, KY 40220-3792
Tel (502) 495-5000 *Founded/Ownrshp* 1962
Sales NA *EMP* 138
SIC 6411 Insurance agents, brokers & service
CEO: Bradley R Smith
Treas: Paula Kessler
Sls Mgr: Robin Thompson

D-U-N-S 00-694-5380
KENTUCKY FARM BUREAU MUTUAL INSURANCE CO
FB INSURANCE COMPANY
9201 Bunsen Pkwy, Louisville, KY 40220-3792
Tel (502) 495-5000 *Founded/Ownrshp* 1943
Sales NA *EMP* 680
SIC 6411 Property & casualty insurance agent; Property & casualty insurance agent
CEO: Bradley R Smith
**Pr:* Mark Haney
**Treas:* Nathan C Anguiano
VP: Janet Cox
VP: Paul Diersing
VP: Melissa Laroche
VP: John Sparrow
Exec: Harmony Brenner
Exec: Suzanne Dewitt
Exec: Treasa Jenkins
Exec: Roger Simpson
Exec: Ryan Wood

D-U-N-S 14-779-3632
■ **KENTUCKY FRIED CHICKEN CORP DE**
KFC
(*Suby of* KFC ENTERPRISES INC)
1441 Gardiner Ln, Louisville, KY 40213-1914
Tel (502) 874-8300 *Founded/Ownrshp* 1997
Sales 492.5MM^E *EMP* 25,000
SIC 5812 6794 Fast-food restaurant, chain; Franchises, selling or licensing; Fast-food restaurant, chain; Franchises, selling or licensing
Pr: David C Novak

D-U-N-S 79-868-0989 IMP/EXP
■ **KENTUCKY FRIED CHICKEN OF LOUISVILLE INC**
KFC
(*Suby of* YUM BRANDS INC) ★
1441 Gardiner Ln, Louisville, KY 40213-1914
Tel (502) 874-8300 *Founded/Ownrshp* 1997
Sales 25.9MM^E *EMP* 1,000
SIC 5812 Fast-food restaurant, chain; Fast-food restaurant, chain
Pr: Gregg Dedrick

D-U-N-S 04-613-7998
KENTUCKY FRIED CHICKEN OF NORTH LITTLE ROCK
KFC
600 Edgewood Dr, North Little Rock, AR 72113-6269
Tel (501) 851-1411 *Founded/Ownrshp* 1968
Sales 7.4MM^E *EMP* 300
SIC 5812 Fast-food restaurant, chain; Fast-food restaurant, chain
Pr: Jerry N Haynie
**Sec:* Betty Haynie

D-U-N-S 07-247-1683
KENTUCKY FRIED CHICKEN OF STATESBORO GEORGIA INC
KFC
7 N Main St, Statesboro, GA 30458-5750
Tel (912) 764-9991 *Founded/Ownrshp* 1972
Sales 10.2MM^E *EMP* 500
SIC 5812 Fast-food restaurant, chain; Fast-food restaurant, chain
Pr: L Inman Hodges
**Sec:* Mary Sue Hodges

D-U-N-S 05-447-4646
KENTUCKY HEART INSTITUTE INC
1709 Ky Route 321 Ste 2, Prestonsburg, KY 41653-9097
Tel (606) 886-0892 *Founded/Ownrshp* 2009
Sales 20.3MM *EMP* 3
Accts Bkd Llp Bowling Green Ky
SIC 8733 Noncommercial research organizations; Noncommercial research organizations
Prin: Richard E Paulus

D-U-N-S 03-800-9150
KENTUCKY HIGHER EDUCATION ASSISTANCE AUTHORITY
KHEAA
100 Airport Rd, Frankfort, KY 40601-6161
Tel (502) 696-7200 *Founded/Ownrshp* 2001
Sales 36.6MM *EMP* 90
Accts Strothman & Company Psc Louis
SIC 8299 Student exchange program; Student exchange program
Ex Dir: Edward Cunningham
Ex VP: James Ackinson
Genl Mgr: Wendie Beswick
IT Man: April Johnson
Netwrk Eng: Chris Bailey
Genl Couns: Diana Barber
Snr Mgr: Ted Franzeim

D-U-N-S 09-420-3031
KENTUCKY LABORERS DISTRICT COUNCIL
KLDC
1994 Bypass S, Lawrenceburg, KY 40342-9755
Tel (502) 839-8280 *Founded/Ownrshp* 1960
Sales 20.2MM *EMP* 4
SIC 8631 Labor unions & similar labor organizations
Pr: Mitchell Oney

D-U-N-S 96-676-5484
KENTUCKY LABORERS DISTRICT COUNCIL HEALTH AND WELFARE FUND
1996 Bypass S, Lawrenceburg, KY 40342-9755
Tel (502) 839-8166 *Founded/Ownrshp* 2012
Sales 24.2MM *EMP* 14^E
Accts Mountjoy Chilton Medley Llp L
SIC 8631 Labor unions & similar labor organizations; Labor unions & similar labor organizations
Prin: James Gerescher

D-U-N-S 02-412-3473
KENTUCKY LAKE OIL CO INC (KY)
POCKETS CONVENIENCE STORE
620 S 4th St, Murray, KY 42071-2680
Tel (270) 753-1323 *Founded/Ownrshp* 1932, 1973
Sales 111.8MM *EMP* 170
Accts Alexander Thompson Arnold Pllc
SIC 5541 5571 5171 5411 Filling stations, gasoline; Motorcycles; Petroleum terminals; Convenience stores, independent; Filling stations, gasoline; Motorcycles; Petroleum terminals; Convenience stores, independent
CEO: Chuck Baker
**Sec:* Vicki Baker
VP: Steve Weathereford

D-U-N-S 05-956-9350
KENTUCKY MACHINE & ENGINEERING INC (KY)
590 Glenwood Mill Rd, Cadiz, KY 42211-9344
Tel (270) 522-6061 *Founded/Ownrshp* 1968, 1971
Sales 26.0MM^E *EMP* 71
SIC 3599 3444 7692 Machine shop, jobbing & repair; Sheet metalwork; Welding repair
Pr: Gregory B Allen
**CEO:* Chappel B Allen
**Sec:* Stephen B Allen
Off Mgr: Amy Vaughan Kuberski

D-U-N-S 09-538-5068
KENTUCKY MEDICAL SERVICES FOUNDATION INC
2333 Alumni Park Plz # 200, Lexington, KY 40517-4012
Tel (859) 257-7910 *Founded/Ownrshp* 1978
Sales 225.1MM^E *EMP* 150
Accts Dean Dorton Allen Ford Pllc L
SIC 8721 Billing & bookkeeping service; Billing & bookkeeping service
Pr: Marc Randall
**VP:* Raleigh Jones
**Ex Dir:* Darrell Griffith
CIO: Bill Merritt
IT Man: John Tripure
Mktg Dir: Dawn Wilson

D-U-N-S 92-741-1611
KENTUCKY OFFICE OF ATTORNEY GENERAL
(*Suby of* EXECUTIVE OFFICE OF COMMONWEALTH OF KENTUCKY) ★
Capitol Building Rm 100, Frankfort, KY 40601
Tel (502) 696-5615 *Founded/Ownrshp* 1792
Sales NA *EMP* 2,428^E
SIC 9199 General government administration;

D-U-N-S 00-500-3934
KENTUCKY OIL AND REFINING CO (KY)
156 Ky Oil Vlg, Betsy Layne, KY 41605
Tel (606) 478-2303 *Founded/Ownrshp* 1956
Sales 130.0MM^E *EMP* 150
SIC 5171 5541 Petroleum bulk stations & terminals; Filling stations, gasoline; Petroleum bulk stations & terminals; Filling stations, gasoline
Pr: Dale Tomlinson
**Sec:* Jessie Tomlinson
VP: Thomas S Stanley III
**VP:* Chris Tomlinson
Sales Exec: Coby Johnson

D-U-N-S 00-698-6277
■ **KENTUCKY POWER CO**
(*Suby of* AMERICAN ELECTRIC POWER CO INC) ★
1 Riverside Plz, Columbus, OH 43215-2355
Tel (614) 716-2654 *Founded/Ownrshp* 1919
Sales 67.5MM^E *EMP* 466
SIC 4911 Generation, electric power; Transmission, electric power; Distribution, electric power; Generation, electric power; Transmission, electric power; Distribution, electric power
Ch Bd: Michael G Morris
**CFO:* Holly K Koeppel

D-U-N-S 09-655-3300
KENTUCKY RIVER COMMUNITY CARE INC (KY)
178 Community Way, Jackson, KY 41339-6153
Tel (606) 666-8001 *Founded/Ownrshp* 1979
Sales 34.4MM *EMP* 380
SIC 8093 Mental health clinic, outpatient; Mental health clinic, outpatient
Ex Dir: Nici Gaines
Ex Dir: Christa Frances
IT Man: Glenna Lesondak

D-U-N-S 07-131-6657
KENTUCKY RIVER FOOTHILLS DEVELOPMENT COUNCIL INC
KY RIVER FOOTHILLS HEAD START
309 Spangler Dr, Richmond, KY 40475-2457
Tel (859) 624-2046 *Founded/Ownrshp* 1962
Sales 17.4MM *EMP* 300
Accts Mountjoy Chilton Medley Llp L
SIC 8399 Community action agency; Community action agency
Ex Dir: Vicki Jozefowicz
**Ch Bd:* Linda Ginter
**V Ch:* Jamie Crabtree
**Treas:* Marci Martin
Board of Directors: Adriel Woodman

KENTUCKY RIVER MEDICAL CENTER
See JACKSON HOSPITAL CORP

KENTUCKY STATE DIST COUNCL OF
See KENTUCKY STATE DISTRICT COUNCIL OF CARPENTERS HEALTH & WELFARE & PENSION TRUST FUND

D-U-N-S 78-394-7542
KENTUCKY STATE DISTRICT COUNCIL OF CARPENTERS HEALTH & WELFARE & PENSION TRUST FUND
KENTUCKY STATE DIST COUNCIL OF
3608 Dixie Hwy, Louisville, KY 40216-4106
Tel (502) 448-6644 *Founded/Ownrshp* 1987
Sales NA *EMP* 10
SIC 6371 Pension, health & welfare funds; Pension, health & welfare funds

D-U-N-S 07-133-5434
KENTUCKY STATE PIPE TRADES ASSOC
PIPEFITTERS LOCAL 522
1317 Berry Blvd, Louisville, KY 40215-1950
Tel (606) 325-2544 *Founded/Ownrshp* 1911
Sales 20.0MM *EMP* 11
SIC 8631 Labor unions & similar labor organizations; Labor unions & similar labor organizations
VP: Del Melcher
Off Admin: Lorri Campbell

D-U-N-S 07-131-7788
KENTUCKY STATE UNIVERSITY
400 E Main St, Frankfort, KY 40601-2355
Tel (502) 597-6000 *Founded/Ownrshp* 1850
Sales 38.7MM *EMP* 500^E
Accts Dean Dorton Allen Ford Pllc
SIC 8221 University; University
Pr: Mary Evans Sias
**Pr:* Paul Bibbins
COO: Gary Meiseles
Exec: Harold Fenderson
**Int Pr:* William Turner
HC Dir: Jimmy Arrington

D-U-N-S 95-880-3025 IMP
KENTUCKY STEEL CENTER INC
1101 Mayde Rd, Berea, KY 40403-8676
Tel (859) 986-0572 *Founded/Ownrshp* 1996
Sales 27.3MM^E *EMP* 70
SIC 5051 Metals service centers & offices; Metals service centers & offices
Pr: Seiji Motoni

D-U-N-S 05-304-2354
KENTUCKY TEXTILES INC (KY)
MAGIC IMAGE
1800 Main St, Paris, KY 40361-1109
Tel (859) 987-5228 *Founded/Ownrshp* 1981, 1987
Sales 31.5MM^E *EMP* 557
SIC 2339 2329 2322 2253 Bathing suits: women's, misses' & juniors'; Athletic clothing: women's, misses' & juniors'; Jogging & warmup suits: women's, misses' & juniors'; Men's & boys' sportswear & athletic clothing; Athletic (warmup, sweat & jogging) suits: men's & boys'; Underwear, men's & boys': made from purchased materials; Knit outerwear mills; Bathing suits: women's, misses' & juniors'; Athletic clothing: women's, misses' & juniors'; Jogging & warmup suits: women's, misses' & juniors'; Men's & boys' sportswear & athletic clothing; Athletic (warmup, sweat & jogging) suits: men's & boys'; Underwear, men's & boys': made from purchased materials; Knit outerwear mills
Ch Bd: Wayne Shumate
**Pr:* Cliff Shumate
**Treas:* Ricky Hicks
**VP:* Dan Short
Plnt Mgr: Inez Hines

D-U-N-S 04-378-0667
KENTUCKY TRUCK SALES INC
1403 Truckers Blvd, Jeffersonville, IN 47130-9654
Tel (812) 283-7172 *Founded/Ownrshp* 1989
Sales 23.6MM^E *EMP* 55
SIC 5012 5013 Trucks, commercial; Truck parts & accessories
Pr: Donald M Ashby
CFO: Deborah Jones
Sls Mgr: Chris McDonogh

D-U-N-S 00-694-4938 IMP
■ **KENTUCKY UTILITIES CO INC** (KY)
(*Suby of* LG&E AND KU ENERGY LLC) ★
1 Quality St, Lexington, KY 40507-1462
Tel (502) 627-2000 *Founded/Ownrshp* 1912
Sales 1.7MMM *EMP* 945^E
Accts Ernst & Young Llp
SIC 4911 Electric services; Distribution, electric power; Generation, electric power; Transmission, electric power; Electric services; Distribution, electric power; Generation, electric power; Transmission, electric power
Ch Bd: Victor A Staffieri
CFO: Kent W Blake
VP: Gary E Blake
VP: Roger Smith
VP: David Vogel
CTO: Dave Collett
Board of Directors: S Bradford Rives, Vincent Sorgi, William H Spence, Paul A Thompson

D-U-N-S 00-791-5929
■ **KENTUCKY WEST VIRGINIA GAS CO**
(*Suby of* EQT CORP) ★
748 N Lake Dr, Prestonsburg, KY 41653-1283
Tel (606) 886-2311 *Founded/Ownrshp* 1927
Sales 120.3MM^E *EMP* 240
SIC 1311 1389 4922 Natural gas production; Servicing oil & gas wells; Natural gas transmission; Natural gas production; Servicing oil & gas wells; Natural gas transmission

D-U-N-S 00-694-4946
■ **KENTUCKY-AMERICAN WATER CO**
(*Suby of* AMERICAN WATER WORKS CO INC) ★
2300 Richmond Rd, Lexington, KY 40502-1390
Tel (859) 269-2386 *Founded/Ownrshp* 1882
Sales 53.7MM^E *EMP* 155
SIC 4941 Water supply; Water supply
Pr: Nick O Rowe
**Treas:* Coleman Bush
Prd Mgr: Cheryl Taylor

D-U-N-S 02-406-7175 IMP
KENTUCKY-INDIANA LUMBER CO INC
K & I LUMBER CO
(*Suby of* US LBM HOLDINGS LLC) ★
4010 Collins Ln, Louisville, KY 40245-1644
Tel (502) 637-1401 *Founded/Ownrshp* 1959, 2014
Sales 184.4MM^E *EMP* 220
SIC 5031 2439 2431 Lumber, plywood & millwork; Plywood; Millwork; Pallets, wood; Trusses, wooden roof; Millwork; Lumber, plywood & millwork; Plywood; Millwork; Pallets, wood; Trusses, wooden roof; Millwork
Pr: Bob Deferraro

D-U-N-S 94-301-0475
KENTUCKYONE HEALTH INC
CHI
(*Suby of* CATHOLIC HEALTH INITIATIVES) ★
200 Abraham Flexner Way, Louisville, KY 40202-2877
Tel (502) 587-4011 *Founded/Ownrshp* 1982
Sales 107.1MM *EMP* 9,709^E
Accts Catholic Health Initiatives E
SIC 8099 Medical services organization; Medical services organization
Ch: Robert M Hewett
**Pr:* Ruth W Brinkley
**Pr:* David Laird
**Treas:* Melvin Alexander
**VP:* Ronald J Farr
Doctor: Morris Weiss

KENTUCKYONE HEALTH SOURCE
See SAINT JOSEPH HEALTH SYSTEM INC

D-U-N-S 07-970-7055
KENTWOOD DTC LLC
5690 Dtc Blvd Ste 600w, Greenwood Village, CO 80111-3224
Tel (303) 773-3399 *Founded/Ownrshp* 1981, 2007
Sales 1.9MMM *EMP* 68
SIC 6531 7389 Real estate brokers & agents; Relocation service
CEO: Peter Niederman

D-U-N-S 08-589-0762
KENTWOOD OFFICE FURNITURE LLC
3063 Breton Rd Se, Grand Rapids, MI 49512-1747
Tel (616) 957-2320 *Founded/Ownrshp* 1976, 2001
Sales 53.7MM^E *EMP* 81
SIC 5021 Office & public building furniture; Office & public building furniture
Pr: Art Hasse
**VP:* Laura Hopson
**VP:* James Porter
Genl Mgr: Don Edema
Genl Mgr: Joyce Nyenhuis
Sys Mgr: Geoff Rozich
Sls Mgr: Bob Ellis
Sls Mgr: Tom Lear

D-U-N-S 08-467-6832 IMP
KENTWOOD PACKAGING CORP
KPC
2102 Avastar Pkwy Nw, Walker, MI 49544-1928
Tel (616) 698-9000 *Founded/Ownrshp* 1977
Sales 27.4MM^E *EMP* 60
SIC 2653 3496 2821 2631 Boxes, corrugated: made from purchased materials; Miscellaneous fabricated wire products; Plastics materials & resins; Paperboard mills
Pr: Thomas A Boluyt
VP: Jack Skoog
**Prin:* Leonard R Vining
Plnt Mgr: Dave Welker
VP Sls: Bill Marsh

D-U-N-S 07-927-8230
KENTWOOD PUBLIC SCHOOLS
5820 Eastern Ave Se, Grand Rapids, MI 49508-6200
Tel (616) 455-4400 *Founded/Ownrshp* 1959
Sales 46.2M *EMP* 1,161
Accts Bdo Usa Llp Kalamazoo Michi
SIC 8211 Public combined elementary & secondary school; Public combined elementary & secondary school
IT Man: Karen Slaby
Opers Mgr: Ellen Rankin
Psych: Jennifer Galloway
Psych: Nikki Stilson

D-U-N-S 80-690-6595
KENTZ USA INC
(*Suby of* KENTZ CORPORATION LIMITED)
1800 West Loop S Ste 1800, Houston, TX 77027-3240
Tel (713) 862-4066 *Founded/Ownrshp* 1997
Sales 23.6MM^E *EMP* 77^E
SIC 1521 8711 1731 Single-family housing construction; Engineering services; General electrical contractor
CEO: Hugh O'Donnell
COO: Eamonn O Hanln
**COO:* James Moore
**CFO:* Ed Power
Ofcr: Mark Payton
Dir Bus: Darrell Breaux
Mng Dir: Chris Warlow
Genl Mgr: Michael Costello

D-U-N-S 00-695-8326 IMP
KENWAL STEEL CORP (MI)
KENWEL STEEL BURNS HARBOR
8223 W Warren Ave, Dearborn, MI 48126-1615
Tel (313) 739-1000 *Founded/Ownrshp* 1947
Sales 99.3MM^E *EMP* 230
SIC 5051 Steel; Steel
Ch Bd: Kenneth Eisenberg
**COO:* David Bazzy
**CFO:* Frank Jerneycic
**VP:* Larry Bogner
**VP:* Jon Davidson
VP: Trevor Ryals
VP: Paul Wolf
Netwrk Eng: Hadi Hannon
Plnt Mgr: Ron Mackinnon
Plnt Mgr: Wes Steffey

D-U-N-S 00-110-2003 IMP/EXP
KENWAY CORP (ME)
681 Riverside Dr, Augusta, ME 04330-8300
Tel (207) 622-6229 *Founded/Ownrshp* 1947, 1977
Sales 21.2MM^E *EMP* 118
SIC 3089 Laminating of plastic
CEO: Kenneth G Priest II
**Pr:* Ian D Kopp
Treas: Gregg W Kenyon
**VP:* Michael Priest
CTO: Scott Cole
Ql Cn Mgr: Robert Oneil

KENWEL STEEL BURNS HARBOR
See KENWAL STEEL CORP

D-U-N-S 55-544-1179
KENWOOD DEALER GROUP INC
4780 Scialville Foster Rd, Mason, OH 45040-8265
Tel (513) 683-5484 *Founded/Ownrshp* 1987
Sales 4.5MM *EMP* 800
SIC 8741 7532 Management services; Body shop, automotive
Pr: Robert Reichert
**CFO:* Louis K Galbraith
**VP:* Gerald M Carmichael
**VP:* Gerry Carmichael
**VP:* Lawrence W Feldhaus
**VP:* Mark Pittman

D-U-N-S 15-175-5741
KENWOOD PAINTED METALS INC
20200 Governors Dr # 202, Olympia Fields, IL 60461-1056
Tel (708) 957-4443 *Founded/Ownrshp* 1986
Sales 25.3MM^E *EMP* 16^E
SIC 5051 Metals service centers & offices
Pr: Gregory Underwood
CFO: Rick Zeller
Genl Mgr: Lonnie Taylor
Ql Cn Mgr: Kevin Hamlin
Ql Cn Mgr: Dennis Timm
Sls Mgr: Keith Goggans
Sls Mgr: Will Nguyen
Sls Mgr: Michael Polansky
Sales Asso: Shane Goode

KENWORTH MID-IOWA
See RL FRENCH CORP

KENWORTH NORTHWEST
See MARSHALLS HOLDING CO

D-U-N-S 04-669-3305
KENWORTH NORTHWEST INC (WA)
(*Suby of* KENWORTH NORTHWEST) ★
20220 International Blvd, Seatac, WA 98198-5703
Tel (206) 433-5911 *Founded/Ownrshp* 1967, 1997
Sales 49.7MM^E *EMP* 150
Accts Moss-Adams Llp Everett Washi
SIC 5012 5013 7538 5511 Trucks, commercial; Truck parts & accessories; General truck repair; New & used car dealers; Trucks, commercial; Truck parts & accessories; General truck repair; New & used car dealers
Pr: Marshall Cymbaluk
COO: Ken Mason
CFO: Paul Heneghan
**VP:* Jeff Cymbaluk
Admn Mgr: Mark Case
IT Man: John Morgus
Sls Mgr: Tom Merritt

D-U-N-S 08-654-6652
KENWORTH OF BIRMINGHAM INC
ISUZU TRUCKS OF BIRMINGHAM
2220 Finley Blvd, Birmingham, AL 35234-1121
Tel (205) 326-6170 *Founded/Ownrshp* 1978
Sales 72.7MM^E *EMP* 125^E
SIC 5511 Automobiles, new & used; Automobiles, new & used
Pr: Robert L Mitchell
**VP:* William T Mitchell
Exec: Tony Quesenberry
MIS Mgr: Clifton Hartin
Sales Asso: Thomas Burdett
Sales Asso: Heather Moore

D-U-N-S 61-993-3471
KENWORTH OF BUFFALO NY INC
100 Commerce Dr, Buffalo, NY 14218-1041
Tel (716) 852-0143 *Founded/Ownrshp* 2005
Sales 47.8MM^E *EMP* 109^E
SIC 5531 Truck equipment & parts
Pr: Dennis Dintino
**CFO:* Eric Hoxsie
**VP:* Daniel Penksa

D-U-N-S 06-349-3159 EXP
KENWORTH OF CENTRAL FLORIDA INC
1800 N Orange Blossom Trl, Orlando, FL 32804-5605
Tel (407) 425-3170 *Founded/Ownrshp* 1982
Sales 55.1MM^E *EMP* 118
SIC 5511 5531 5012 Pickups, new & used; Truck equipment & parts; Automobiles & other motor vehicles; Pickups, new & used; Truck equipment & parts; Automobiles & other motor vehicles
Pr: Robert E Sutton Jr
**VP:* Barry J Haslett
Store Mgr: Robert Phillips

D-U-N-S 08-743-5681
KENWORTH OF CINCINNATI INC
PACLEASE
65 Partnership Way, Cincinnati, OH 45241-1570
Tel (513) 771-5831 *Founded/Ownrshp* 1979
Sales 33.4MM^E *EMP* 90
SIC 5012 5013 7538 7513 Trucks, commercial; Truck parts & accessories; General automotive repair shops; Truck leasing, without drivers; Trucks, commercial; Truck parts & accessories; General automotive repair shops; Truck leasing, without drivers
Ch: Eldon Palmer
**Pr:* John Nichols
**Treas:* Jeffrey Gauger
**VP:* Jeffrey Curry
Store Mgr: Steve Hedger
Sales Exec: Daniel Curry

D-U-N-S 11-275-7158 IMP/EXP
KENWORTH OF JACKSONVILLE INC
833 Pickettville Rd, Jacksonville, FL 32220-2733
Tel (904) 739-2296 *Founded/Ownrshp* 2003
Sales 24.3MM^E *EMP* 66^E
SIC 5013 5531 7538 Truck parts & accessories; Truck equipment & parts; General truck repair
Pr: Denis Ross
**CFO:* David Butler
Store Mgr: Gary Tittle
IT Man: Daniel Johnson
Sales Exec: Ed Costello
Sls Mgr: Mike Grande
Sales Asso: Randall Smith

KENWORTH OF PENNSYLVANIA
See MOTOR TRUCK EQUIPMENT CO INC

KENWORTH OF RITCHFIELD
See HISSONG-KENWORTH INC

D-U-N-S 79-899-8428
KENWORTH OF SOUTH LOUISIANA LLC
3699 W Park Ave, Gray, LA 70359-3407
Tel (985) 876-0000 *Founded/Ownrshp* 2004
Sales 44.3MM^E *EMP* 100^E
Accts Martin And Pellegrin
SIC 5511 Trucks, tractors & trailers: new & used; Trucks, tractors & trailers: new & used
Pr: Scott Oliphant
VP: Chris Carlos
Sales Asso: Willie Duncan
Sales Asso: Rhett Fulton

D-U-N-S 00-895-4687 IMP
KENWORTH SALES CO (UT)
TRANSPORT FINANCE
2125 S Constitution Blvd, West Valley City, UT 84119-1219
Tel (801) 487-4161 *Founded/Ownrshp* 1945
Sales 243.2MM^E *EMP* 700
Accts Poston Denney & Killpack Pllc
SIC 5012 5013 7538 3519 Trucks, commercial; Truck parts & accessories; General truck repair; Trucks, commercial; Truck parts & accessories; General truck repair; Diesel engine repair: automotive; Engines, diesel & semi-diesel or dual-fuel
Pr: R Kyle Treadway
**CFO:* Lance Jorgensen
Exec: Harry Dahl
Exec: Jim Dreher
Off Admin: Bonita Latimer
Telecom Ex: Dave Rasmussen
Sls Mgr: Chuck Knorr

KENWORTH TRCK RENTON MFG FCTRY
See KENWORTH TRUCK CO RENTON MANUFACTURING FACTORY

KENWORTH TRUCK CO
See RUMPKE/KENWORTH CONTRACT

D-U-N-S 96-954-5545 IMP
KENWORTH TRUCK CO RENTON MANUFACTURING FACTORY
KENWORTH TRCK RENTON MFG FCTRY
1601 N 8th St, Renton, WA 98057-5507
Tel (425) 227-5800 *Founded/Ownrshp* 2011
Sales 33.9MM^E *EMP* 100^E
SIC 5012 Trucks, commercial
Sfty Mgr: Pat Bauer
Prd Mgr: Doug Baugh

D-U-N-S 02-302-0027
KENYAN ENTERPRISES INC
PIGGLY WIGGLY
543 S Main St, Springhill, LA 71075-4027
Tel (318) 539-9116 *Founded/Ownrshp* 1982
Sales 29.0MM^E *EMP* 152
SIC 5411 Supermarkets, chain
Pr: Edwin Kenyan
**Treas:* Susan Kenyan
**VP:* Theodore M Bennett

D-U-N-S 07-326-8153
KENYON & KENYON LLP
1 Broadway Fl 1, New York, NY 10004-1055
Tel (212) 425-7200 *Founded/Ownrshp* 1879
Sales 66.3MM^E *EMP* 500
SIC 8111 Patent, trademark & copyright law; Patent, trademark & copyright law
Pt: George E Badenoch
Sr Pt: Michael J Lennon
Pt: Patrick J Birde
Pt: Jerry Canada
Pt: Robert V Cerwinski
**Pt:* Edward Colbert
**Pt:* Richard L Delucia
**Pt:* John Flock
Pt: Elizabeth Gardner
Pt: Jeffrey S Gerchick
**Pt:* Walter E Hanley Jr
**Pt:* Elizabeth J Holland
Pt: Ms Azeen Roohi James
Pt: Linda Shudy Lecomte
**Pt:* Steve J Lee
Pt: Michelle Mancino
Pt: Neil M McCarthy
Pt: Brian Mudge
Pt: Joseph Nicholson
Pt: Maria Luisa Palmese
Pt: Mr A Antony Pfeffer

D-U-N-S 06-358-0369
KENYON COLLEGE
1 Kenyon College, Gambier, OH 43022-9623
Tel (740) 427-5000 *Founded/Ownrshp* 1824
Sales 42.9MM^E *EMP* 450^E
SIC 8221 Colleges universities & professional schools; Colleges universities & professional schools
Pr: Shawne Decator
Pr: Cathy Lake
Trst: Cornelia Hallinan
Trst: Julia Johnson
VP: Ronald K Griggs
VP: Barbara Hamm
VP: Sarah H Kahrl
Mktg Dir: Megan Monaghan

D-U-N-S 96-959-0442
KENYON COLLEGE
Eaton Ctr, Gambier, OH 43022
Tel (740) 427-5181 *Founded/Ownrshp* 2011
Sales 145.6MM *EMP* 24^E
Accts Maloney Novotny Llc Cleveland
SIC 8221 Colleges universities & professional schools; Colleges universities & professional schools
Pr: Sean Decatur

D-U-N-S 93-160-4235
KENYON COMPANIES
2602 N 35th Ave, Phoenix, AZ 85009-1311
Tel (602) 233-1191 *Founded/Ownrshp* 1992
Sales 63.0MM^E *EMP* 1,400
SIC 1742 2819 Stucco work, interior; Industrial inorganic chemicals; Stucco work, interior; Industrial inorganic chemicals
Ch Bd: John W Kenyon III
**CFO:* Daniel Bang

D-U-N-S 11-512-0123
KENYON CONSTRUCTION INC
K & K CONSTRUCTION
4001 W Indian School Rd, Phoenix, AZ 85019-3314
Tel (602) 484-0080 *Founded/Ownrshp* 1978
Sales 171.9MM^E *EMP* 1,500
SIC 1742 Stucco work, interior; Stucco work, interior
Ch Bd: John W Kenyon III
**CFO:* Daniel Bang
**VP:* Bonnie Mason
Genl Mgr: Anthony Kenyon

D-U-N-S 03-221-4280 IMP
■ **KENYON DODGE INC**
AUTOWAY DODGE
(*Suby of* AUTONATION INC) ★
27547 Us Highway 19 N, Clearwater, FL 33761-2973
Tel (727) 533-4000 *Founded/Ownrshp* 1997
Sales 22.6MM^E *EMP* 114
SIC 5511 5521 Automobiles, new & used; Trucks, tractors & trailers: new & used; Used car dealers; Automobiles, new & used; Trucks, tractors & trailers: new & used; Used car dealers
Pr: Scott Wilkerson
**Treas:* Kathleen W Hyle
Genl Mgr: Corvin Morris

D-U-N-S 17-994-4194 EXP
KENYON INDUSTRIES INC
(*Suby of* BROOKWOOD COMPANIES INC) ★
36 Sherman Ave, Kenyon, RI 02836-1012
Tel (401) 364-7761 *Founded/Ownrshp* 1989
Sales 72.9MM^E *EMP* 300
SIC 2262 2269 2295 Dyeing: manmade fiber & silk broadwoven fabrics; Finishing plants; Coated fabrics, not rubberized; Dyeing: manmade fiber & silk broadwoven fabrics; Finishing plants; Coated fabrics, not rubberized
Pr: Joanne Bagley
**Treas:* Joseph Trumpetto
Dir Lab: Susan McHugh
Snr Mgr: Joe Trumpetto

D-U-N-S 07-593-1662
KENYON PLASTERING INC
(*Suby of* K & K CONSTRUCTION) ★
4001 W Indian School Rd, Phoenix, AZ 85019-3314
Tel (602) 233-1191 *Founded/Ownrshp* 1995
Sales 76.3MM^E *EMP* 800
SIC 1742 Stucco work, interior; Stucco work, interior
Pr: John W Kenyon III
**Treas:* Daniel Bang
**Prin:* Brian Chien
Sfty Mgr: Robert Garcia
Sfty Mgr: Luis Murillo

D-U-N-S 03-521-8783 IMP
KENYON-NOBLE LUMBER CO
DO IT BEST
1243 Oak St, Bozeman, MT 59715-8798
Tel (406) 586-2371 *Founded/Ownrshp* 1889
Sales 83.6MM^E *EMP* 350
SIC 5211 5251 3273 Lumber & other building materials; Millwork & lumber; Roofing material; Wallboard (composition) & paneling; Hardware; Builders' hardware; Tools, hand; Tools, power; Ready-mixed concrete; Lumber & other building materials; Millwork & lumber; Roofing material; Wallboard (composition) & paneling; Hardware; Builders' hardware; Tools, hand; Tools, power; Ready-mixed concrete
Pr: Richard J Ogle
**VP:* William A Ogle
Dept Mgr: Scott McCauley
Opers Mgr: Court Huff
Sales Exec: Mike Thompson
Sls Mgr: Carl Donaldson

D-U-N-S 05-502-2810
KENZAN MEDIA LLC
858 State Route 203, Spencertown, NY 12165
Tel (212) 239-1010 *Founded/Ownrshp* 2010
Sales 25.0MM *EMP* 40
SIC 7373 Systems software development services
CEO: Christopher Kilmer
Pr: Larry Samuels
CFO: Eric Spiegel
VP: Ming-Lien Linsley

D-U-N-S 13-861-6433
KENZIE AND CO LLC
MCINTYRE GROUP
63 Glover Ave, Norwalk, CT 06850-1203
Tel (203) 750-1111 *Founded/Ownrshp* 2002
Sales 14.0MM *EMP* 300^E
SIC 7361 Employment agencies; Employment agencies
Dir IT: Jason Berman

D-U-N-S 07-809-1212
KEOKUK AREA HOSPITAL (IA)
1600 Morgan St, Keokuk, IA 52632-3497
Tel (319) 526-8684 *Founded/Ownrshp* 1900, 1901
Sales 22.9MM *EMP* 350^E
SIC 8062 General medical & surgical hospitals; General medical & surgical hospitals
Pr: Walt Stephens

**CEO:* Joseph Whiting
**Ex Dir:* Allan W Zastrow
Mktg Dir: Amy Conlee

D-U-N-S 07-807-5991
KEOKUK COMMUNITY SCHOOL DISTRICT
BOARD OF EDUCATION
1721 Franklin St, Keokuk, IA 52632
Tel (319) 524-1402 *Founded/Ownrshp* 1851
Sales 17.4MM^E *EMP* 308
SIC 8211 9411 Public elementary & secondary schools; School board; Administration of educational programs; Public elementary & secondary schools; School board; Administration of educational programs
**Pr:* Dr Wilson Davis
**Bd of Dir:* Mary Jo Hendrickson
**Bd of Dir:* Fred Karre
**Bd of Dir:* Bill Richards
**Bd of Dir:* Sandy Stark
Dir IT: Brent Haage

D-U-N-S 10-737-9372
KEOKUK HEALTH SYSTEMS INC
1600 Morgan St, Keokuk, IA 52632-3456
Tel (319) 524-7150 *Founded/Ownrshp* 1985
Sales 0.0 *EMP* 450^E
SIC 8741 8011 Hospital management; Offices & clinics of medical doctors; Hospital management; Offices & clinics of medical doctors
CEO: Allan W Zastrow
**COO:* Richard Thomason
**CFO:* Wally Winkler
CIO: Linda Schaffner

KEOKUK STEEL CASTINGS CO
See MATRIX METALS LLC

D-U-N-S 00-630-4766
KEOLIS AMERICA INC
(*Suby of* GROUPE KEOLIS SAS)
3003 Washington Blvd, Arlington, VA 22201-2194
Tel (301) 251-5612 *Founded/Ownrshp* 2008
Sales 304.9MM^E *EMP* 1,875^E
SIC 4111 Passenger rail transportation; Passenger rail transportation
CEO: Steve Townsend
Ex VP: Eric Asselin
Mng Dir: Michel Masson

D-U-N-S 78-901-4847
KEOLIS TRANSIT AMERICA INC
(*Suby of* KEOLIS AMERICA INC) ★
6053 W Century Blvd # 900, Los Angeles, CA 90045-6400
Tel (310) 981-9500 *Founded/Ownrshp* 2006
Sales 175.4MM^E *EMP* 1,205
Accts Windes & Mcclaughry Cpas Lon
SIC 4119 7699 Local passenger transportation; Customizing services; Local passenger transportation; Customizing services
Pr: Michael Griffus
COO: Stephen Shaw
**CFO:* Joseph Cardoso
**CFO:* Francis Homan
Ex VP: Kevin Adams
**Ex VP:* Dwight D Brashear
Sr VP: Vasti Amaro
Sr VP: Stephen Helriegel
Sr VP: Sandi Hill
Sr VP: Drew Jones
Sr VP: Barbara Perry
**Sr VP:* Cindi Ritter
**Sr VP:* Larry Slagle
**Sr VP:* Brian Sullivan
**Sr VP:* Scott Williams
VP: Ryan Adams

KEP AMERICAS
See CELANESE AMERICAS CORP

KEPB
See OREGON PUBLIC BROADCASTING

KEPCO
See KANSAS ELECTRIC POWER COOPERATIVE INC

D-U-N-S 00-151-9750
KEPCO INC
13138 Sanford Ave, Flushing, NY 11355-4245
Tel (718) 461-7000 *Founded/Ownrshp* 1946
Sales 21.8MM^E *EMP* 150
SIC 3612 Power & distribution transformers; Power & distribution transformers
Pr: Martin Kupferberg
**Ch:* Max Kupferberg
**VP:* Saul Kupferberg
**VP:* Seth Kupferberg
**VP Mfg:* Mark Kupferberg
Sls Dir: Kim Schonmann

D-U-N-S 06-987-5813
KEPNER-TREGOE INC
KT
116 Village Blvd Ste 300, Princeton, NJ 08540-5700
Tel (609) 921-2806 *Founded/Ownrshp* 1996
Sales 34.4MM^E *EMP* 175
SIC 8742 Business consultant; Business consultant
CEO: Chris Geraghty
**CFO:* William B Baldwin
VP: Nancy Debake
Dir Bus: Josh Hill
Mng Dir: Anthony Friedli
Netwrk Mgr: David Nikithser
Pr Dir: Petra Rademaker
Mktg Mgr: David Kossoff
Snr Mgr: Paul Johnson

D-U-N-S 18-476-8547 IMP
KEPPEL AMFELS LLC
(*Suby of* KEPPEL FELS LIMITED)
20000 State Highway 48, Brownsville, TX 78521-8910
Tel (956) 831-8220 *Founded/Ownrshp* 1998
Sales 554.5MM^E *EMP* 1,532
Accts Burton Mccumber & Cortez Ll
SIC 1629 3731 1389 3449 3546 3443 Oil refinery construction; Shipbuilding & repairing; Oil & gas wells: building, repairing & dismantling; Miscellaneous metalwork; Power-driven handtools; Fabricated plate work (boiler shop); Oil refinery construction; Shipbuilding & repairing; Oil & gas wells: building, repairing & dismantling; Miscellaneous metalwork; Power-driven handtools; Fabricated plate work (boiler shop)
CEO: Ho Yuen
**COO:* G S Tan
**CFO:* Tim Lin
CFO: Wong Ngiam
**VP:* Gilberto Elisonto
**VP:* Thomas Mc Coy
**VP:* Eric Phua
Ex Dir: Aziz Merchant
QA Dir: Mario Jauregui
QI Cn Mgr: Pablo Alaniz

D-U-N-S 10-000-6543
KEPPEL UNION SCHOOL DISTRICT
34004 128th St E, Pearblossom, CA 93553
Tel (661) 944-2155 *Founded/Ownrshp* 1930
Sales 27.6MM *EMP* 400
Accts Moss Levy & Hartzheim Llp S
SIC 8211 Public elementary school; School board; Public elementary school; School board
Bd of Dir: Christine Smith
Schl Brd P: Mathew Gaines
Teacher Pr: Stacy Nestlerode

KEPRO
See KEYSTONE PEER REVIEW ORGANIZATION INC

KERA
See NORTH TEXAS PUBLIC BROADCASTING INC

KERAS, JIM SUBARU
See JIM KERAS BUICK CO INC

D-U-N-S 78-617-5786
■ **KERASOTES SHOWPLACE THEATRES LLC**
(*Suby of* AMC ENTERTAINMENT INC) ★
224 N Des Plns Ste 200, Chicago, IL 60661
Tel (312) 756-3360 *Founded/Ownrshp* 2010
Sales 61.3MM^E *EMP* 2,200
SIC 7832 Motion picture theaters, except drive-in; Motion picture theaters, except drive-in
CEO: Anthony Kerasotes
**Pr:* Dean Kerasotes
**CFO:* James Debruzzi
Dir IT: Fred Walraven
Software D: Bill Scott

D-U-N-S 04-964-3372
KERBECK CADILLAC PONTIAC CHEVROLET INC
KERBECK PONTIAC
430 N Albany Ave, Atlantic City, NJ 08401-1334
Tel (609) 345-2100 *Founded/Ownrshp* 1977
Sales 34.2MM^E *EMP* 92
SIC 5511 5521 7538 5012 Automobiles, new & used; Used car dealers; General automotive repair shops; Automobiles & other motor vehicles; Automobiles, new & used; Used car dealers; General automotive repair shops; Automobiles & other motor vehicles
Pr: Charles Kerbeck
**Sec:* Frank Kerbeck
**VP:* George Kerbeck
VP Mktg: Chris Smith

KERBECK PONTIAC
See KERBECK CADILLAC PONTIAC CHEVROLET INC

D-U-N-S 00-527-5227
KERBER MILLING CO
1817 Main St, Emmetsburg, IA 50536-1655
Tel (712) 852-2712 *Founded/Ownrshp* 2009
Sales 58.0MM^E *EMP* 250^E
SIC 2048 Livestock feeds; Livestock feeds
Pr: Jeff Kerber
**VP:* Jill Kerber-Aldous
Sfty Mgr: Kyle Caven

KEREN KAYEMETH LE ISRAEL
See JEWISH NATIONAL FUND KEREN KAYEMETH LEISRAEL INC

D-U-N-S 80-018-4673
KERINS ASSOCIATES INC
13821 Mills Ave, Silver Spring, MD 20904-1053
Tel (301) 236-4556 *Founded/Ownrshp* 1987
Sales NA *EMP* 3
SIC 6162 Mortgage bankers; Mortgage bankers
Pr: Kathleen Kerins

D-U-N-S 11-126-8566 IMP
KERIO TECHNOLOGIES INC
111 N Market St Fl 6, San Jose, CA 95113-1100
Tel (408) 496-4500 *Founded/Ownrshp* 2001
Sales 28.4MM^E *EMP* 107
SIC 7372 Prepackaged software; Prepackaged software
CEO: Mirek Kren
**Pr:* Scott Schrieman
**CEO:* Martin Viktora
**CFO:* Alan Hughes
Chf Mktg O: Des Cahill
VP: Michal Jezek
VP: Heather Paunet
VP: Pavel Suk
VP: Dusan Vitek
Software D: Stanislav Kolar
VP Mktg: Richard Gooding

KERK MOTION PRODUCTS
See HAYDON KERK MOTION SOLUTIONS INC

KERKAU MANUFACTURING COMPANY
See BALDAUF ENTERPRISES INC

D-U-N-S 02-104-2478 IMP
KERKSTRA PRECAST INC
SPANCRETE GREAT LAKES
3373 Busch Dr Sw, Grandville, MI 49418-1341
Tel (616) 457-4920 *Founded/Ownrshp* 1971
Sales 27.0MM^E *EMP* 150
SIC 3432 3272 Plumbing fixture fittings & trim; Septic tanks, concrete; Plumbing fixture fittings & trim; Septic tanks, concrete
CEO: Greg Kerkstra
**Pr:* Derek Hunderman
CFO: Phil Holtrop
**CFO:* Andy Odehnal
**VP:* Steve Haskill
IT Man: Scott Woltjer
Sys Mgr: Scott Bosscher
QC Dir: Susan Rollins
Sls Mgr: Scott Woodard
Snr PM: Lynn Zylman

D-U-N-S 06-909-7256
KERLEY BIOKIMICA INC
33707 Prairieview Ln, Oconomowoc, WI 53066
Tel (262) 567-8840 *Founded/Ownrshp* 1997
Sales 23.6MM^E *EMP* 1,082
SIC 7389 Artists' agents & brokers; Artists' agents & brokers
Pr: Abbas A Fadel
**VP:* Micheal Green

D-U-N-S 01-210-9153
KERMAN UNIFIED SCHOOL DISTRICT
151 S 1st St, Kerman, CA 93630-1000
Tel (559) 842-2121 *Founded/Ownrshp* 1983
Sales 30.4MM^E *EMP* 400
SIC 8211 Public elementary school; Public elementary & secondary schools; Public elementary school; Public elementary & secondary schools
**CFO:* James Foley
MIS Dir: Scott Castillo

D-U-N-S 02-016-7425
KERN COMMUNITY COLLEGE DISTRICT (CA)
CERRO COSO COMM COLLEGE
2100 Chester Ave, Bakersfield, CA 93301-4014
Tel (661) 336-5100 *Founded/Ownrshp* 1961
Sales 32.5MM *EMP* 1,269
Accts Matson And Isom Redding Cali
SIC 8222 Community college; Community college
CEO: Sandra Serrano
Netwrk Mgr: Mike Arnold
Netwrk Mgr: Ron Wilson
Web Dev: Richard Robinson
Netwrk Eng: Juan Lucero
Sfty Dirs: Sheila Shearer

D-U-N-S 96-952-0100
KERN COMMUNITY COLLEGE DISTRICT PUBLIC FACILITIES CORP
2100 Chester Ave, Bakersfield, CA 93301-4099
Tel (661) 336-5100 *Founded/Ownrshp* 2011
Sales 49.1MM *EMP* 4^E
Accts Matson And Isom Redding Ca
SIC 8222 Community college

D-U-N-S 11-880-5860
KERN COUNTY SUPERINTENDENT OF SCHOOLS EDUCATIONAL SERVICES FOUNDATION
1300 17th St, Bakersfield, CA 93301-4504
Tel (661) 636-4000 *Founded/Ownrshp* 1900
Sales 465.8M *EMP* 1,400
Accts Brown Armstrong Ac Bakersfie
SIC 8211 Public elementary & secondary schools; Public elementary & secondary schools
**Pr:* Chris Hall
Prin: Janice Barricklow
Prin: Denis Desmond
Ex Dir: Gregory Rhoten
IT Man: Alan Wells
Schl Brd P: Ronald G Froelick
Pgrm Dir: Desiree Von Flue

D-U-N-S 08-302-1097
KERN COUNTY WATER AGENCY
3200 Rio Mirada Dr, Bakersfield, CA 93308-4944
Tel (661) 634-1400 *Founded/Ownrshp* 1961
Sales 41.7MM^E *EMP* 70
SIC 4941

KERN DIRECT MARKETING
See KERN ORGANIZATION INC

KERN FAMILY HELATHCARE
See KERN HEALTH SYSTEMS INC

D-U-N-S 82-968-2400
KERN FOOD DISTRIBUTING INC
2711 Wagel Rd, Brooksville, KY 41004-7005
Tel (606) 756-2255 *Founded/Ownrshp* 1993
Sales 23.5MM *EMP* 34
Accts Grelle Jump & Company Llc C
SIC 5147 5144 5142 Meats & meat products; Poultry & poultry products; Packaged frozen goods; Meats & meat products; Poultry & poultry products; Packaged frozen goods
Pr: Edward B Kern
**VP:* Mary Kern

D-U-N-S 79-645-7679
KERN HEALTH SYSTEMS INC
KERN FAMILY HELATHCARE
9700 Stockdale Hwy, Bakersfield, CA 93311-3617
Tel (661) 664-5000 *Founded/Ownrshp* 1995
Sales 22.0MM^E *EMP* 98
SIC 8011 Offices & clinics of medical doctors
Ch Bd: Paul Hensler

D-U-N-S 01-071-6280
KERN HIGH SCHOOL DST
5801 Sundale Ave, Bakersfield, CA 93309-7908
Tel (661) 827-3100 *Founded/Ownrshp* 1893
Sales 409.5MM *EMP* 2,000
Accts Mayer Hoffman Mccann Pc Bak
SIC 8211 Public elementary & secondary schools; Public elementary & secondary schools
Prin: Jim Caswell
Prin: Robert Schneider
Web Dev: Seven Bates
Instr Medi: Debra Thorson

D-U-N-S 06-102-4899 IMP
KERN MANUFACTURING INC
24050 Commerce Park, Cleveland, OH 44122-5833
Tel (216) 464-5490 *Founded/Ownrshp* 1970
Sales 20.7MM^E *EMP* 350
SIC 2342 2389 Maternity bras & corsets; Garter belts; Maternity bras & corsets; Garter belts
Pr: Alfred G Corrado

D-U-N-S 11-504-1477
■ **KERN ORGANIZATION INC**
KERN DIRECT MARKETING
(*Suby of* OMNICOM GROUP INC) ★
20955 Warner Center Ln, Woodland Hills, CA 91367-6511
Tel (818) 703-8775 *Founded/Ownrshp* 2008
Sales 29.2MM^E *EMP* 80
SIC 7311 Advertising agencies; Advertising agencies
Pr: Russell Kern
**COO:* Zeke Ibarbia
CFO: Ezequiel Ibarbia
**CFO:* Steven Orenstein
**Sr VP:* David Azulay
**VP:* Tom Mackendrick
VP: Jim Rosen
Creative D: Jeannine Darretta
Art Dir: Sharon Yamamoto

D-U-N-S 08-838-7469
KERN REGIONAL CENTER (CA)
3200 N Sillect Ave, Bakersfield, CA 93308-6333
Tel (661) 327-8531 *Founded/Ownrshp* 1971
Sales 147.9MM *EMP* 178
SIC 8322 Association for the handicapped; Association for the handicapped
Ex Dir: Michal Clark
**CEO:* Duane Law
**CFO:* Jerry Bowman

D-U-N-S 06-460-2592
KERN RIDGE GROWERS LLC
25429 Barbara St, Arvin, CA 93203-9748
Tel (661) 854-3141 *Founded/Ownrshp* 1996
Sales 44.5MM *EMP* 500
Accts Mayer Hoffman Mccann Pc Los
SIC 0723 5148 Vegetable packing services; Vegetables, fresh; Vegetable packing services; Vegetables, fresh
Opers Mgr: Zak Karlan

D-U-N-S 17-357-0292
■ **KERN RIVER CO GENERATION CO**
(*Suby of* SOUTHERN SIERRA ENERGY CO) ★
Sw China Grade Loop, Bakersfield, CA 93308
Tel (661) 392-2663 *Founded/Ownrshp* 1984
Sales 36.5MM^E *EMP* 65
SIC 4911 4961 ; Steam supply systems, including geothermal
Ex Dir: Neil Bridges
**Treas:* Gaylord Edward
Ex Dir: Gordon Thomson

D-U-N-S 62-161-7372
■ **KERN RIVER GAS SUPPLY CORP**
KERN RIVER GAS TRANSMISSION
(*Suby of* BERKSHIRE HATHAWAY ENERGY CO) ★
2755 E Cottonwood Pkwy # 300, Salt Lake City, UT 84121-6946
Tel (801) 937-6000 *Founded/Ownrshp* 2002
Sales 125.0MM^E *EMP* 160
SIC 4922 Pipelines, natural gas; Pipelines, natural gas
Pr: Gary W Hoogeveen
**VP:* Robert S Checketts
VP: Laura Demman
**VP:* Micheal Dunn
**VP:* John T Dushinske
VP: Patricia M French
**VP:* Mary Kay Miller
**VP:* J Gregory Porter
**VP:* Bret W Reich
**VP:* Richard Stapler
IT Man: Stan Child

KERN RIVER GAS TRANSMISSION
See KERN RIVER GAS SUPPLY CORP

KERN RIVER HEALTH CENTER
See CLINICA SIERRA VISTA

D-U-N-S 08-540-3111
KERN SCHOOLS FEDERAL CREDIT UNION
KSFCU
11500 Bolthouse Dr, Bakersfield, CA 93311-8822
Tel (661) 833-7900 *Founded/Ownrshp* 1940
Sales NA *EMP* 420
SIC 6061 Federal credit unions; Federal credit unions
Pr: Stephen P Renock IV
**CFO:* Neil Marshall
Bd of Dir: Scott Begin
Sr VP: Penny Fulton
Sr VP: Rudy Tafoya
VP: Hilary Appleby
VP: Tim Spencer
Brnch Mgr: Chei Brown
Brnch Mgr: Erin Hodson
Snr Ntwrk: Lee Jacobs
IT Man: Martin Olivas

D-U-N-S 00-965-6216
KERN STEEL FABRICATION INC
627 Williams St, Bakersfield, CA 93305-5445
Tel (661) 327-9588 *Founded/Ownrshp* 1959
Sales 22.1MM^E *EMP* 80^E
Accts Mayer Hoffman Mccann Pc Bak
SIC 1791 3441 3721 3728 3449 Structural steel erection; Fabricated structural metal; Aircraft; Aircraft parts & equipment; Miscellaneous metalwork
Pr: Tom Champness
**VP:* Gene Panelli
VP: Blair Pruett
Prgrm Mgr: Bruce Alton
Prgrm Mgr: Tennyson Kwok
CTO: Al Champness
QA Dir: Carlos Rios
IT Man: Dan Champness

KERN STUDIOS
See BLAINE KERN ARTISTS INC

D-U-N-S 96-337-7549
KERN VALLEY HEALTHCARE DISTRICT
6412 Laurel Ave, Lake Isabella, CA 93240-9529
Tel (760) 379-2681 *Founded/Ownrshp* 1964
Sales 21.1MM *EMP* 2
Accts Tca Partners Llp Fresno Cal
SIC 5047 Beds, hospital; Beds, hospital
Ch: David Derr
CFO: Chester Beedle
Dir Inf Cn: Mary Completo
Dir Risk M: Lori Leonardi
Dir Risk M: Heidi Sage
CIO: Brenda Pettijohn
Dir QC: Sharon Brucker
Mktg Dir: Anna Leon

D-U-N-S 07-621-3545
KERN VALLEY HOSPITAL FOUNDATION
6412 Laurel Ave, Lake Isabella, CA 93240-9529
Tel (760) 379-2681 *Founded/Ownrshp* 1964
Sales 37.7MM^E *EMP* 310
SIC 8062 8051 General medical & surgical hospitals; Extended care facility; General medical & surgical hospitals; Extended care facility
Pr: Clarence Semonious
Chf Path: Bruce Swinyer
**CEO:* Rick Carter
CFO: Chet Beadle
**CFO:* Chet Beedle
**Ch:* Victoria Alwin
Dir Lab: Adam Summers
Dir Rad: Jesse Alvarez
Dir Rad: Bhatty Shah
Nrsg Dir: George Adams

D-U-N-S 02-026-6417 IMP
KERN-LIEBERS USA INC (NC)
(*Suby of* HUGO KERN UND LIEBERS GMBH & CO. KG PLATINEN- UND FEDERNFABRIK)
1510 Albon Rd, Holland, OH 43528-9159
Tel (419) 865-2437 *Founded/Ownrshp* 1977
Sales 20.2MM^E *EMP* 125
SIC 3495 3493 Mechanical springs, precision; Steel springs, except wire; Mechanical springs, precision; Steel springs, except wire
Pr: Lothar Bauerle
**Ch Bd:* Hans Jocheim Steim
**Treas:* Gert Wagner
Bd of Dir: Jaroslav Kopp
Prgrm Mgr: John Bosnali
S&M/VP: Todd Stender

D-U-N-S 00-506-9467
KERNERSVILLE CHRYSLER DODGE LLC (NC)
KERNERSVLLE CHRYSLER DDGE JEEP
950 Nc Highway 66 S, Kernersville, NC 27284-3133
Tel (336) 996-4111 *Founded/Ownrshp* 2007
Sales 71.8MM^E *EMP* 175
SIC 5511 Automobiles, new & used
**CFO:* Scott Clements
Mktg Dir: April Mabe
Sls Mgr: Blake Mitchell
Sls Mgr: Jeff Sedlacek

KERNERSVLLE CHRYSLER DDGE JEEP
See KERNERSVILLE CHRYSLER DODGE LLC

D-U-N-S 07-158-1854
KERNODLE CLINIC INC
KC
1234 Huffman Mill Rd, Burlington, NC 27215-8777
Tel (336) 538-1234 *Founded/Ownrshp* 1949
Sales 24.8MM *EMP* 300
Accts Thomas Chandler Thomas & Hinsh
SIC 8011 Clinic, operated by physicians; Clinic, operated by physicians
Pr: Mark F Miller
Dir Lab: Stephanie Swanson
Doctor: Michael Menz

D-U-N-S 00-128-8810 IMP
KERNS MANUFACTURING CORP
3714 29th St, Long Island City, NY 11101-2690
Tel (718) 784-4044 *Founded/Ownrshp* 1950
Sales 24.6MM^E *EMP* 128
SIC 3469 3724 3812 3714 Electronic enclosures, stamped or pressed metal; Aircraft engines & engine parts; Search & navigation equipment; Motor vehicle parts & accessories; Electronic enclosures, stamped or pressed metal; Aircraft engines & engine parts; Search & navigation equipment; Motor vehicle parts & accessories
Ch Bd: Simon Srybnik
**Pr:* Louis Srybnik
Dir IT: Ciro Ruggiero
IT Man: Avrom Fattakhov

D-U-N-S 05-301-3306
KERNS TRUCKING INC (NC)
703 S Battleground Ave, Grover, NC 28073-9542
Tel (704) 739-4747 *Founded/Ownrshp* 1970, 2007
Sales 25.0MM^E *EMP* 85
SIC 4213 4212 Contract haulers; Dump truck haulage; Animal & farm product transportation services
Pr: Clyde C Kerns
**VP:* Doug Prestwood

D-U-N-S 19-935-4556 IMP/EXP
■ **KERR CORP**
(*Suby of* ANALYTIC ENDODONTICS) ★
1717 W Collins Ave, Orange, CA 92867-5422
Tel (714) 516-7400 *Founded/Ownrshp* 1987
Sales 236.1MM^E *EMP* 1,431
SIC 3843 Dental materials; Dental laboratory equipment; Impression material, dental; Dental hand instruments; Dental materials; Dental laboratory equipment; Impression material, dental; Dental hand instruments
CEO: Damien McDonald
**Pr:* Steve Semmelmayer
**Treas:* Steve Dunkerken
VP: Lars Gehlbach
**VP:* Leo Pranitis
VP: Dr Edward Shellard
Rgnl Mgr: Brian Kolb
Rgnl Mgr: Chris Ozanne
IT Man: Trish Tazelaar
VP Opers: Lawrence J Girling
VP Mktg: Phil Prentice

D-U-N-S 04-166-8047 IMP/EXP
■ **KERR GROUP LLC**
(*Suby of* BERRY PLASTICS CORP) ★
1846 Charter Ln Ste 209, Lancaster, PA 17601-6773
Tel (812) 424-2904 *Founded/Ownrshp* 2008
Sales 90.6MM^E *EMP* 780
SIC 3089 Closures, plastic; Jars, plastic; Tubs, plastic (containers); Plastic containers, except foam; Closures, plastic; Jars, plastic; Tubs, plastic (containers); Plastic containers, except foam
Pr: Richard D Hofmann
Pr: Steven Rafter
**COO:* Peter A Siebert
**CFO:* Robert C Rathsam
**Ex VP:* Lawrence C Caldwell
VP: Bruce T Cleevely
VP: Kathy Cruse
VP: James T Farley
VP: James A Foy
VP: Mark R Fricke
**VP:* Timothy E Guhl
VP: Robert J Kiely
VP: Megan Petry
VP: John W Rogers
VP: Thomas G Ryan
VP: Thomas E Sweeney

KERR HEALTH CARE CENTERS
See KDI TRANSITION CO INC

KERR NORTON STRACHAN AGENCY
See NORTON LILLY INTERNATIONAL INC

D-U-N-S 00-638-5751
KERR OFFICE GROUP INC
BEAN EVERYTHING FOR THE OFFICE
117 N Main St, Elizabethtown, KY 42701-1481
Tel (270) 765-6171 *Founded/Ownrshp* 2006
Sales 20.1MM^E *EMP* 29
SIC 5112 5044 5021 7699 Stationery & office supplies; Office equipment; Furniture; Cash register repair; Photocopy machine repair; Typewriter repair, including electric
Pr: Brian K Kerr
**VP:* Tabitha Kerr
Genl Mgr: Tom Hamilton
Dir IT: Dennis Smith
S&M/VP: Ed McCoy

D-U-N-S 00-902-8598 IMP/EXP
KERR PACIFIC CORP
PENDLETON FLOUR MILLS
1211 Sw 6th Ave, Portland, OR 97204-1001
Tel (503) 221-1301 *Founded/Ownrshp* 1986
Sales 204.1MM^E *EMP* 200
SIC 5141 2041 2051 5153 5149 Food brokers; Flour; Doughs & batters; Bread, cake & related products; Grains; Bakery products; Food brokers; Flour; Doughs & batters; Bread, cake & related products; Grains; Bakery products
Pr: Christopher W Labbe
VP: Timothy Kerr

KERR YOUTH & FAMILY SERVICES
See ALBERTINA KERR CENTERS

D-U-N-S 01-732-6877
KERR-ALBERT OFFICE SUPPLY INC
1121 Military St, Port Huron, MI 48060-5495
Tel (810) 984-4129 *Founded/Ownrshp* 1990
Sales 26.8MM^E *EMP* 32
Accts Schlaupitz & Associates Plc
SIC 5112 5943 Stationery & office supplies; Office supplies; Stationery stores; Office forms & supplies
Pr: Ernest Albert
COO: Rick Neumeyar
Trfc Dir: Shannon Bass

D-U-N-S 93-869-2902
■ **KERR-MCGEE (NEVADA) LLC**
(*Suby of* KERR-MCGEE CORP) ★
1201 Lake Robbins Dr, The Woodlands, TX 77380-1181
Tel (303) 321-0683 *Founded/Ownrshp* 2004
Sales 48.7MM^E *EMP* 372
SIC 1311 1382 Crude petroleum & natural gas; Oil & gas exploration services; Crude petroleum & natural gas; Oil & gas exploration services
Pr: Karl F Kurz
**Pr:* Barth E Whitham
**CFO:* Lon McCain
**Ex VP:* Grant W Henderson
**VP:* Howard L Boigon
VP: Allan D Keel

D-U-N-S 11-072-1003 IMP/EXP
■ **KERR-MCGEE CORP**
(*Suby of* ANADARKO PETROLEUM CORP) ★
1201 Lake Robbins Dr, Spring, TX 77380-1181
Tel (832) 636-1000 *Founded/Ownrshp* 2006
Sales 225.5MM^E *EMP* 3,200
SIC 2816 2819 1311 1221 1222 Titanium dioxide, anatase or rutile (pigments); Boron compounds, not from mines; Crude petroleum production; Natural gas production; Bituminous coal & lignite-surface mining; Bituminous coal-underground mining; Titanium dioxide, anatase or rutile (pigments); Boron compounds, not from mines; Crude petroleum production; Natural gas production; Bituminous coal & lignite-surface mining; Bituminous coal-underground mining
Pr: Karl F Kurz
Sr VP: David A Hger
VP: Tom Adams
VP: Richard C Buterbaugh
VP: Darrell E Hollek
VP: Mary Mikkelson
Exec: Charles A Meloy
Exec: Frank Patterson

KERRVILLE BUS COMPANY
See CUSA KBC LLC

D-U-N-S 00-793-3443
KERRVILLE BUS CO INC (TX)
GRAY LINE OF DALLAS
1430 E Houston St, San Antonio, TX 78202-2791
Tel (800) 474-3352 *Founded/Ownrshp* 1929
Sales 15.1MM^E *EMP* 550
SIC 4142 4131 4141 Bus charter service, except local; Interstate bus line; Local bus charter service; Bus charter service, except local; Interstate bus line; Local bus charter service
Pr: Richard Funke
**VP:* William Budds

D-U-N-S 08-628-1722
KERRVILLE INDEPENDENT SCHOOL DISTRICT
KERRVILLE ISD
1009 Barnett St, Kerrville, TX 78028-4614
Tel (830) 257-2200 *Founded/Ownrshp* 1890
Sales 35.9MM^E *EMP* 700
Accts Pressler Thompson And Company
SIC 8211 Public elementary school; Public junior high school; Public senior high school; Kindergarten; Public elementary school; Public junior high school; Public senior high school; Kindergarten
Mng Pt: Holley Weaver
Ex Dir: Everautumn Whatley
Brnch Mgr: Lyn Gold
Opers Mgr: Hillarie Swanner
Teacher Pr: Wade Ivy
Psych: Kate Allen
Psych: Jackie Swinney
Psych: Keely Vanacker
Psych: Amy Waiser

KERRVILLE ISD
See KERRVILLE INDEPENDENT SCHOOL DISTRICT

D-U-N-S 96-830-8184 EXP
KERRY FLAVOR SYSTEMS US LLC
KERRY INGREDIENTS & FLAVOURS
10261 Chester Rd, Cincinnati, OH 45215
Tel (513) 387-1742 *Founded/Ownrshp* 2012
Sales 15.8MM^E *EMP* 417^E
SIC 5499 Health foods
VP: Gerry Ferrara

D-U-N-S 04-106-4536
KERRY FORD INC
KERRY MITSUBISHI
155 W Kemper Rd, Cincinnati, OH 45246-2590
Tel (513) 671-6400 *Founded/Ownrshp* 1967
Sales 50.1MM^E *EMP* 103
SIC 5511 7538 7532 7515 5531 Automobiles, new & used; Pickups, new & used; Vans, new & used; General automotive repair shops; Top & body repair & paint shops; Passenger car leasing; Automotive & home supply stores; Automobiles, new & used; Pickups, new & used; Vans, new & used; General automotive repair shops; Top & body repair & paint shops; Passenger car leasing; Automotive & home supply stores
Pr: Patrick De Castro
**Sec:* Daniel J Brady
**Prin:* Paul W Krone
Genl Mgr: Jim Bloebaum
Off Mgr: Sharon Johnson
Sls Mgr: James Ashurst
Sls Mgr: Bev Mills

D-U-N-S 10-192-3303 IMP/EXP
KERRY HOLDING CO
KERRY INGREDIENTS & FLAVOURS
(*Suby of* KERRY GROUP PUBLIC LIMITED COMPANY)
3330 Millington Rd, Beloit, WI 53511-9542
Tel (608) 363-1200 *Founded/Ownrshp* 1998
Sales 908.6MM^E *EMP* 2,313
SIC 2099 2079 2023 2022 2087 Food preparations; Seasonings: dry mixes; Edible fats & oils; Dry, condensed, evaporated dairy products; Natural cheese; Beverage bases, concentrates, syrups, powders & mixes; Food preparations; Seasonings: dry mixes; Edible fats & oils; Dry, condensed, evaporated dairy products; Natural cheese; Beverage bases, concentrates, syrups, powders & mixes
CEO: Gerry Behan
VP: Kevin Andreson
VP: Dennis Fechhelm
VP: Melissa Kuehl

KERRY HYUNDAI OF FLORENCE
See KERRY NISSAN INC

D-U-N-S 10-751-7591 IMP/EXP
KERRY INC
KERRY INGREDIENTS & FLAVOURS
(*Suby of* KERRY HOLDING CO) ★
3330 Millington Rd, Beloit, WI 53511-9542
Tel (608) 363-1200 *Founded/Ownrshp* 1983
Sales 680.0MM^E *EMP* 1,800
SIC 2099 Food preparations; Food preparations
Pr: Gerry Behan
Pr: Alan Barrett
**CFO:* Olivia Nelligan
**Sr VP:* Mike Gransee
**VP:* William R Coole
**VP:* Anita Loch
VP: Gordon Pincaerd
Dir Lab: Joni Rogers
IT Man: Matt Beschta
Plnt Mgr: Mike Iannuzzelli
Plnt Mgr: Dale Olmstead

KERRY INGREDIENTS & FLAVOURS
See KERRY HOLDING CO

KERRY INGREDIENTS & FLAVOURS
See KERRY INC

KERRY INGREDIENTS & FLAVOURS
See KERRY FLAVOR SYSTEMS US LLC

D-U-N-S 17-795-1563 IMP
KERRY INGREDIENTS & FLAVOURS
(*Suby of* KERRY INC) ★
1640 W 1st St, Blue Earth, MN 56013-1176
Tel (507) 526-7575 *Founded/Ownrshp* 1992
Sales 42.8MM^E *EMP* 230
SIC 2043 2096 2099 Cereal breakfast foods; Potato chips & similar snacks; Food preparations; Cereal breakfast foods; Potato chips & similar snacks; Food preparations
Pr: Gerry Behan
Ex VP: David Duffy

KERRY INGREDIENTS AND FLAVOURS
See MASTERTASTE INC

KERRY MITSUBISHI
See KERRY FORD INC

D-U-N-S 03-667-6351
KERRY NISSAN INC (OH)
KERRY HYUNDAI OF FLORENCE
8053 Burlington Pike, Florence, KY 41042-1247
Tel (859) 371-8191 *Founded/Ownrshp* 1997
Sales 48.1MM^E *EMP* 130
SIC 5511 Automobiles, new & used; Automobiles, new & used
Pr: Doy Baker
Exec: Steve Hall

KERRY SMITH CONTRACTORS
See SMITH CONTRACTORS INC

KERRY TOYOTA
See TOYOTA TOWNE INC

D-U-N-S 09-763-7144
KERSHAW COUNTY SCHOOL DISTRICT
2029 W Dekalb St, Camden, SC 29020-2093
Tel (803) 432-8416 *Founded/Ownrshp* 1970
Sales 70.0MM *EMP* 1,400
SIC 8211 Public combined elementary & secondary school; Public combined elementary & secondary school
**CFO:* Donnie Wilson
**Ch:* Mr Ron Blackmon
Ex Dir: John Thompson
Pr Dir: Mariane Byrd
Pr Dir: Maryanne A Byrd
Teacher Pr: Claire Champion
HC Dir: Tarry McGovern

D-U-N-S 03-009-8404
KERSHAW HEALTH MEDICAL CENTER
KCMC HOME HEALTH & HOSPICE
1315 Roberts St, Camden, SC 29020-3737
Tel (803) 432-4311 *Founded/Ownrshp* 1958
Sales 100.0MM *EMP* 575
Accts Dixon Hughes Goodman Llp Ashe
SIC 8062 8051 8082 General medical & surgical hospitals; Skilled nursing care facilities; Home health care services; General medical & surgical hospitals; Skilled nursing care facilities; Home health care services
CEO: Email Terry Gunn
**Ch Bd:* Jay Green
**Pr:* Donnie J Weeks
**COO:* Susan Outen
CFO: Richard Humphrey
**CFO:* Rick Humphrey
**Ex VP:* Mike Bunch
VP: Joseph Bruce
**VP:* Angie Johnson
**VP:* Gloria Keeffe
**VP:* Angela Nettles
Dir Rx: Doug Murray

KERSHAW KNIVES
See KAI USA LTD

D-U-N-S 00-401-7968 IMP
■ **KERSHAW MANUFACTURING CO INC** (AL)
(*Suby of* PROGRESS RAIL SERVICES CORP) ★
10650 Highway 80 E, Montgomery, AL 36117-6038
Tel (334) 387-9100 *Founded/Ownrshp* 1944
Sales 47.1MM^E *EMP* 120
SIC 3531 Railway track equipment; Railway track equipment
Pr: Royce Kershaw Jr
VP: Don Bates
Exec: Seele Shea

D-U-N-S 78-478-7160 IMP
KERUSSO ACTIVEWEAR INC
402 Highway 62 Spur, Berryville, AR 72616-4516
Tel (870) 423-6242 *Founded/Ownrshp* 1990
Sales 21.5MM^E *EMP* 95
SIC 2759 2395 Screen printing; Pleating & stitching
CEO: Victor Kennett
COO: Gene Arnold
**COO:* Terry Bowen
CFO: Roger Filizetti
Genl Mgr: Rusty Dycus
Prd Mgr: Lorri Carter
Mktg Mgr: Valerie Drane
Mktg Mgr: Chris Rainey
Mktg Mgr: Jeremy Richards

D-U-N-S 80-815-5233
KERZNER INTERNATIONAL LIMITED
1000 S Pine Island Rd, Plantation, FL 33324-3906
Tel (954) 809-2000 *Founded/Ownrshp* 2008
Sales 36.9MM^E *EMP* 420
SIC 7011 Resort hotel; Resort hotel
Prin: Kathy Thomas
VP: Errol Cohen

D-U-N-S 00-409-0387
KERZNER INTERNATIONAL NORTH AMERICA INC
INTERNATIONAL SUPPLIERS
1000 S Pine Island Rd, Plantation, FL 33324-3906
Tel (954) 809-2000 *Founded/Ownrshp* 1958, 1996
Sales 143.6MM^E *EMP* 3,220
SIC 7011 Casino hotel; Resort hotel; Casino hotel; Resort hotel
Ex VP: Bonnie Biumi
**Sr VP:* Jones Catherine
Ex Dir: Joe Savino

D-U-N-S 87-272-7078 IMP/EXP
■ KERZNER INTERNATIONAL RESORTS INC
(*Suby of* ATLANTIS PARADISE ISLAND RESORT)
1000 S Pine Island Rd # 800, Plantation, FL 33324-3907
Tel (954) 809-2000 *Founded/Ownrshp* 1993
Sales 15.8MM^E *EMP* 300^E
SIC 5812 7011 Casino hotel; Eating places; Eating places; Casino hotel
Pr: Alan Leibman
Pr: Howard Kerzner
Pr: George Markantonis
Pr: Serge Zaalof
CFO: Michael Manocchio
CFO: Ali Tabbal
Ch: Solomon Kerzner
Ex VP: John Allison
Ex VP: Monica Lee
VP: Howerd C Karawan
VP: David Tessier

D-U-N-S 80-267-2691
KES TRUCKING INC
3608 Tindall Ct, Fayetteville, NC 28311-2431
Tel (910) 822-5364 *Founded/Ownrshp* 1992
Sales 80.9MM *EMP* 15
SIC 4212 Local trucking, without storage; Local trucking, without storage
Pr: Edward L Johnson

KESCO I
See KUBAT EQUIPMENT & SERVICE CO

KESER NURSING & REHABILITATION
See KESER NURSING AND REHABILITATION CENTER INC

D-U-N-S 96-632-4555
KESER NURSING AND REHABILITATION CENTER INC
KESER NURSING & REHABILITATION
40 Heyward St, Brooklyn, NY 11249-7823
Tel (718) 858-6200 *Founded/Ownrshp* 2005
Sales 20.7MM *EMP* 55^E
Accts Martin Friedman Cpa Pc Brookl
SIC 8051 Skilled nursing care facilities
Prin: Rachel Binet
**Ex Dir:* Israel Framovitz

D-U-N-S 04-852-6909
KESLER-SCHAEFER AUTO AUCTION INC
5333 W 46th St, Indianapolis, IN 46254-2014
Tel (317) 297-2300 *Founded/Ownrshp* 1943
Sales 28.1MM^E *EMP* 165
SIC 5012 Automobile auction; Automobile auction
Pr: Steve Kesler
**Ch:* Jack A Kesler
**Treas:* Jacqueline Kesler
Off Mgr: Mary Kesler
VP Sls: Ann Kuh

D-U-N-S 93-136-2722
KESSEL ENTERPRISES LLC
PET SUPPLIES PLUS
7550 S Saginaw St Ste 5, Grand Blanc, MI 48439-1875
Tel (810) 953-0772 *Founded/Ownrshp* 1999
Sales 78.9MM^E *EMP* 286^E
SIC 5199 Pet supplies; Pet supplies
VP: Ed Ayotte

D-U-N-S 02-371-5629
KESSLER ASHEVILLE LLC
GRAND BOHEMIAN HOTEL ASHEVILLE
11 Boston Way, Asheville, NC 28803-2656
Tel (828) 505-2949 *Founded/Ownrshp* 2009
Sales 30.0MM^E *EMP* 120
Accts Vestal & Wiler Cpas Orladon
SIC 7011 Hotels; Hotels
Genl Mgr: Haley Batsel
Genl Mgr: John Luckett

KESSLER COLLECTION THE
See KESSLER HOTELS LTD

KESSLER COLLECTION
See KESSLER ENTERPRISE INC

D-U-N-S 15-098-5661 IMP
KESSLER ENTERPRISE INC
KESSLER COLLECTION
4901 Vineland Rd Ste 650, Orlando, FL 32811-7195
Tel (407) 996-9999 *Founded/Ownrshp* 1984
Sales 188.0MM^E *EMP* 1,200
SIC 8741 7011 Administrative management; Hotels; Administrative management; Hotels
Ch: Richard C Kessler
COO: Rob Buffaloe
CFO: Day Dantzler
**VP:* Dantzler Day B
VP: Deb Golding
VP: Michael Havener
Ex Dir: Walter Deppe
Area Mgr: Seth Richardson
Genl Mgr: Joseph Kelley
Off Mgr: Wayne Stokes
CTO: Kerri McKenzie

D-U-N-S 80-655-5376
KESSLER FAMILY LLC
FRIENDLY'S
410 White Spruce Blvd, Rochester, NY 14623-1608
Tel (585) 424-5277 *Founded/Ownrshp* 1999
Sales 47.8MM^E *EMP* 1,500
SIC 5812 Restaurant, family: chain; Restaurant, family: chain

D-U-N-S 07-967-9924
KESSLER GROUP INC (NY)
BURGER KING
410 White Spruce Blvd, Rochester, NY 14623-1656
Tel (585) 424-5277 *Founded/Ownrshp* 1975
Sales 28.4MM^E *EMP* 700
SIC 5812 Fast-food restaurant, chain; Fast-food restaurant, chain
CEO: Laurence Kessler
Sr VP: Mike Manno
VP: Gregg Hoffman
**VP:* Dennis Kessler
VP: Greg Murphy

D-U-N-S 07-883-8164
KESSLER HOTELS LTD
KESSLER COLLECTION THE
4901 Vineland Rd Ste 650, Orlando, FL 32811-7195
Tel (407) 996-9999 *Founded/Ownrshp* 1999
Sales 53.0MM^E *EMP* 50
Accts Vestal & Wiler Cpas Orladon
SIC 7011 5621 Hostels; Boutiques
Pr: Richard C Kessler

D-U-N-S 01-162-0333 IMP
KESSLER INDUSTRIES INC
KESSLER SALES AND DISTRIBUTION
500 Green St, Woodbridge, NJ 07095-2023
Tel (732) 634-4404 *Founded/Ownrshp* 1993
Sales 104.6MM^E *EMP* 105
SIC 5074 Plumbing & hydronic heating supplies; Plumbing & hydronic heating supplies
Pr: Neil Kessler
**VP:* John Brower
VP: Douglas Hanke
VP: Roland Sauer
Plnt Mgr: James Santangelo
Natl Sales: Patrick Patton
VP Sls: Brower John
Sls Mgr: Steve Goodwyn
Sales Asso: Audrey Donovan
Sales Asso: Gary Roberti
Sales Asso: Joseph Sadlock

D-U-N-S 07-932-9579
■ KESSLER INSTITUTE FOR REHABILITATION INC
(*Suby of* SELECT MEDICAL CORP) ★
1199 Pleasant Valley Way, West Orange, NJ 07052-1424
Tel (973) 731-3600 *Founded/Ownrshp* 2003
Sales 63.8MM^E *EMP* 1,706
SIC 8069 8093 Specialty hospitals, except psychiatric; Specialty hospitals, except psychiatric; Rehabilitation center, outpatient treatment
Pr: Robert Brehm
Pr: Robin Hedeman
COO: Sue Kida
Chf Mktg O: Bruce M Gans
VP: Lonnie L Busby
VP: Michael Glickert
VP: Barry Kirschbaum
VP: Ron Logue
VP: Judd Patricia
VP: Gail Solomon
Exec: Karen Dresher
Exec: Steve Koltenuk
Dir Rx: Neil Schulman
Dir Bus: Rich Romano

D-U-N-S 78-962-2677
■ KESSLER REHABILITATION CORP
(*Suby of* SELECT MEDICAL CORP) ★
1199 Pleasant Valley Way, West Orange, NJ 07052-1424
Tel (973) 731-3600 *Founded/Ownrshp* 2003
Sales 226.2MM *EMP* 1,363
SIC 8062 General medical & surgical hospitals; General medical & surgical hospitals
Pr: Kenneth W Aitchison
VP: William Rosa
Exec: Ken Coulden
Dir Pat Ca: Karen Liszner
Dir Inf Cn: Rita Guellnitz
Dir Rx: Neil Schuman
VP Admn: Sue Kida
Off Admin: Sheila Dixon
Telecom Ex: Bonnie Evans
Dir IT: Donna Nadeau
Sfty Dirs: Cliff Lassiter

KESSLER SALES AND DISTRIBUTION
See KESSLER INDUSTRIES INC

D-U-N-S 02-429-7376
KESSLERS INC
KESSLER'S PHARMACY
621 6th Ave Se, Aberdeen, SD 57401-4538
Tel (605) 225-1692 *Founded/Ownrshp* 1959
Sales 49.7MM^E *EMP* 260
SIC 5921 5411 5912 5812 2052 2051 Liquor stores; Grocery stores, independent; Drug stores & proprietary stores; Eating places; Cookies & crackers; Bread, cake & related products; Liquor stores; Grocery stores, independent; Drug stores & proprietary stores; Eating places; Cookies & crackers; Bread, cake & related products
Pr: Tim Kessler
**Treas:* Thomas Kessler
**VP:* George Kessler
Store Dir: Kelly Comstock
Dept Mgr: Ron Lindner
Pharmcst: Kirby Hay
Pharmcst: Joe Stoebner

KESSLER'S PHARMACY
See KESSLERS INC

D-U-N-S 79-899-9061
KESTE LLC
6100 W Plano Pkwy # 1800, Plano, TX 75093-8230
Tel (214) 778-2100 *Founded/Ownrshp* 2004
Sales 22.9MM^E *EMP* 90
SIC 7379 Computer related consulting services
VP: Srirama K Ayyeppen
Snr Sftwr: Sriram Venkata
IT Man: Sirisha Gorantala
Art Dir: Sylvia McCrory

D-U-N-S 14-722-2785 IMP/EXP
■ KESTER INC
(*Suby of* ILLINOIS TOOL WORKS INC) ★
800 W Thorndale Ave, Itasca, IL 60143-1341
Tel (630) 616-4000 *Founded/Ownrshp* 2004
Sales 78.6MM^E *EMP* 500
SIC 3356 Solder: wire, bar, acid core, & rosin core; Solder: wire, bar, acid core, & rosin core
Pr: Steven L Martindale
**Pr:* Roger Savage
Mktg Mgr: Mike Gonzalez

D-U-N-S 12-754-6732 IMP/EXP
KESTREL LINER AGENCIES LLP
TROPICAL GLOBAL LOGISTICS
16320 Nw 59th Ave, Miami Lakes, FL 33014-5601
Tel (786) 220-1650 *Founded/Ownrshp* 2002
Sales 28.0MM *EMP* 25
SIC 4731 Freight forwarding
CEO: Andrew Thorne
VP: Steven Keats
Snr Mgr: Karen Davies

D-U-N-S 08-614-4433
KESWICK MULTI-CARE CENTER INC
700 W 40th St, Baltimore, MD 21211-2140
Tel (410) 554-0180 *Founded/Ownrshp* 1883
Sales 36.1MM *EMP* 400
Accts Gross Mendelsohn & Associates
SIC 8069 8361 8322 Chronic disease hospital; Residential care; Adult day care center; Chronic disease hospital; Residential care; Adult day care center
CFO: Mary Jean Herron
CFO: Mary Herron
CFO: Pat Supik
Dir Bus: Lynn Gordon
QC Dir: Jayne Haynes
Mktg Dir: Michelle Larcey
Nrsg Dir: Terry Smith

D-U-N-S 80-013-2735
KET INDUSTRIES INC
3660 Burkholm Rd, Mims, FL 32754-5111
Tel (321) 264-1021 *Founded/Ownrshp* 1988
Sales 25.0MM^E *EMP* 7
SIC 8741 Management services; Management services
Pr: Jeffery Cotton
**VP:* Kenneth Greenslade

KETCH
See KANSAS ELKS TRAINING CENTER FOR HANDICAPPED INC

D-U-N-S 79-729-2794
KETCHIKAN GATEWAY BOROUGH SCHOOL DISTRICT
333 Schoenbar Rd, Ketchikan, AK 99901-6278
Tel (907) 225-2118 *Founded/Ownrshp* 1963
Sales 41.2MM *EMP* 152
Accts Mikunda Cottrell & Co Ancho
SIC 8211 Public elementary & secondary schools; Public elementary & secondary schools
Treas: David Timmerman
IT Man: Jurgen Johannsen

D-U-N-S 80-651-5347
KETCHIKAN GENERAL HOSPITAL FOUNDATION
3100 Tongass Ave, Ketchikan, AK 99901-5746
Tel (907) 228-8300 *Founded/Ownrshp* 2004
Sales 31.0MM^E *EMP* 700
SIC 8062 General medical & surgical hospitals; General medical & surgical hospitals
CEO: Patrick Blanco
Bd of Dir: Barb Lander
Sr VP: Marty West
Doctor: Peter Rice
Pharmcst: Sally Hansen

D-U-N-S 09-368-1401
KETCHIKAN INDIAN COMMUNITY
KETCHIKAN INDIAN CORPORATE
2960 Tongass Ave, Ketchikan, AK 99901-5742
Tel (907) 228-4945 *Founded/Ownrshp* 2002
Sales 33.3MM *EMP* 200^E
Accts Stauffer & Associates Pllc Li
SIC 8099 Child guidance agency; Blood related health services
Pr: Richard Jackson
**CFO:* Norman Arriola
**CFO:* Tom Gubatayao
**CFO:* Nina Nathan
**Treas:* Merle N Hawkins
Genl Mgr: Karen Carter
Genl Mgr: Debra Patton

KETCHIKAN INDIAN CORPORATE
See KETCHIKAN INDIAN COMMUNITY

KETCHIKAN NORTHERN SALES
See NORTHERN SALES CO INC

D-U-N-S 00-791-5937
■ KETCHUM COMMUNICATIONS HOLDINGS INC
(*Suby of* OMNICOM GROUP INC) ★
6 Ppg Pl Fl 12, Pittsburgh, PA 15222-5442
Tel (412) 316-8000 *Founded/Ownrshp* 1923, 2007
Sales 40.6MM^E *EMP* 240
SIC 8743 Public relations & publicity; Public relations & publicity
Pr: Rob Lorfink
Sr VP: Mike Finn
**VP:* Judith Martin
VP: Nancy Martira
VP: Geralyn Perrotti
IT Man: Ronald Brandon
IT Man: Kathryn Wholey
Snr Mgr: Bob Wooley

D-U-N-S 01-057-4247
■ KETCHUM INC
(*Suby of* OMNICOM GROUP INC) ★
1285 Avenue Of The Americ, New York, NY 10019-6029
Tel (646) 935-3900 *Founded/Ownrshp* 1996
Sales 115.7MM^E *EMP* 1,348^E
SIC 8743 Public relations services; Public relations & publicity
CEO: Raymond L Kotcher
Pr: Tyler Durham
Pr: Debra Forman
Ofcr: Paul M Rand
Ofcr: Stephen Waddington
Ex VP: Matthew Afflixio
Ex VP: Lori Beecher
Ex VP: Joseph Kelliher
Ex VP: R P Kumar
Ex VP: Marcus Peterzell
Sr VP: Jon Chin
Sr VP: Cheryl Damian
Sr VP: Kim Essex
Sr VP: Genevieve Hilton
Sr VP: Sandy Hu
Sr VP: Juliet Johnson
Sr VP: Stacey Kerans
Sr VP: Jill Bratina Kermes
Sr VP: Becca Leish
Sr VP: Dean McBeth
Sr VP: Tamara Norman

D-U-N-S 02-496-0551
KETONE AUTOMOTIVE INC (IL)
2535 S 25th Ave, Broadview, IL 60155-3856
Tel (708) 344-9998 *Founded/Ownrshp* 1946
Sales 33.8MM^E *EMP* 80
SIC 5013 5085 5198 Automotive supplies; Abrasives; Enamels; Lacquers; Automotive supplies; Abrasives; Enamels; Lacquers
Pr: Richard A Graf
**VP:* Janet Ralph

D-U-N-S 04-115-7801
KETT ENGINEERING CORP
15500 Erwin St Ste 1029, Van Nuys, CA 91411-1028
Tel (818) 908-5388 *Founded/Ownrshp* 1973
Sales 22.6MM *EMP* 525
SIC 8734 Product testing laboratory, safety or performance; Automobile proving & testing ground; Product testing laboratory, safety or performance; Automobile proving & testing ground
CEO: Eric Stromsborg
**CFO:* Brett Bergman
**Ex VP:* Dan Jones
IT Man: Clive Param
IT Man: Benitzhak Ron
Info Man: Jerry Giacento
Doctor: Vic Estrada

D-U-N-S 80-018-7999
KETTCOR INC
COLLABORATIVE PHARMACY SVCS
(*Suby of* GRANDVIEW HOSPITAL & MED CTR) ★
4301 Lyons Rd, Miamisburg, OH 45342-6446
Tel (937) 458-4949 *Founded/Ownrshp* 1983
Sales 10.5MM^E *EMP* 303
SIC 8741 Nursing & personal care facility management
VP: Russ Weatherall

D-U-N-S 12-327-7923
KETTERING ADVENTIST HEALTHCARE
KETTERING MEDICAL CENTER
3535 Southern Blvd, Dayton, OH 45429-1221
Tel (937) 298-4331 *Founded/Ownrshp* 1982
Sales 524.9MM^E *EMP* 6,800^E
SIC 8741 Hospital management; Hospital management
Pr: Roy Chew
**Pr:* Frank Perez
**VP:* Russ Wethell
Dir IT: Henrietta Sadler
Pharmcst: Barb Groff

D-U-N-S 12-254-4455
KETTERING AFFILIATED HEALTH SERVICES INC
APOTHECARY
(*Suby of* CHARLES F KETTERING MEM HOSP) ★
3535 Southern Blvd, Dayton, OH 45429-1221
Tel (937) 298-4331 *Founded/Ownrshp* 1993
Sales 20.5MM^E *EMP* 115
SIC 8742 Hospital & health services consultant
Prin: Susan Bal
CFO: Peter King
Dir Lab: Diane Strickling
Dir Rx: Jeff Post
Dir Sec: Pat Bernard
CIO: John Russell
Mktg Dir: Frank Engler
Plas Surg: Robert G Chami

D-U-N-S 07-127-2843
KETTERING CITY SCHOOL DISTRICT
3750 Far Hills Ave, Dayton, OH 45429-2506
Tel (937) 499-1400 *Founded/Ownrshp* 1841
Sales 96.5MM *EMP* 782
Accts Mary Taylor Cpa Dayton Oh
SIC 8211 Public elementary school; Public junior high school; Public senior high school; Public elementary school; Public junior high school; Public senior high school
**Treas:* Steven G Clark

D-U-N-S 06-897-0786
KETTERING HEALTH NETWORK
SOIN MEDICAL CENTER
3535 Pentagon Park Blvd, Beavercreek, OH 45431
Tel (937) 702-4000 *Founded/Ownrshp* 2011
Sales 99.0MM *EMP* 49^E
SIC 8062 General medical & surgical hospitals
Brnch Mgr: Terry Burns
VP: Ronald Connovich
HC Dir: Sheyla Harris

KETTERING MEDICAL CENTER
See KETTERING ADVENTIST HEALTHCARE

D-U-N-S 07-128-8450
KETTERING MEDICAL CENTER (OH)
CHARLES F KETTERING MEM HOSP
(*Suby of* KETTERING ADVENTIST HEALTHCARE) ★
3535 Southern Blvd, Kettering, OH 45429-1298
Tel (937) 298-4331 *Founded/Ownrshp* 1959
Sales 494.2MM^E *EMP* 3,100^E
Accts Clark Schaefer Hackett & Co D
SIC 8062 Hospital, professional nursing school; Hospital, medical school affiliated with nursing & residency; Hospital, professional nursing school; Hospital, medical school affiliated with nursing & residency
CEO: Frank J Perez
Chf Rad: J Bidell
**Pr:* Roy Chew
**Pr:* Terri Day
**Pr:* Fred Manchur
**CFO:* Russell Wetherell

Treas: Ed Mann
Ofcr: Bill White
VP: Tom Gross
VP: Jarrod McNaughton
VP: Beverly Morris
Exec: Darlene Fannin
Dir Lab: Tom Foster

D-U-N-S 07-468-2931
KETTERING MEDICAL CENTER
GRANDVIEW HOSPITAL & MED CTR
3535 Southern Blvd, Dayton, OH 45429-1298
Tel (937) 298-4331 *Founded/Ownrshp* 1999
Sales 101.0MME *EMP* 1,800
Accts Ernst & Young Llp
SIC 8062 General medical & surgical hospitals; General medical & surgical hospitals
Pr: Fred Manchur
**Pr:* Roy Chew
**Pr:* Richard Haas
**Pr:* Frank J Perez
**CFO:* Russell J Wetherell
**Treas:* Edward Mann
Dir IT: Shannon McMorris
Surgeon: Marilyn Borst
Snr Mgr: Charles Watson

D-U-N-S 06-418-1076
KETTERING UNIVERSITY
1700 University Ave, Flint, MI 48504-4898
Tel (810) 762-9925 *Founded/Ownrshp* 1919
Sales 57.3MM *EMP* 425
Accts Plante & Moran Pllc Ann Arbo
SIC 8221 Professional schools; Professional schools
Pr: Robert McMahan
Pr: Tabitha Bourassa
Pr: Jim Hamilton
**Treas:* Thomas Ayers
Bd of Dir: Brent Triplett
Ofcr: Bonnie McArthur
Ofcr: Rachel Tithof
Sr VP: Robert L Simpson
Sr VP: James Zhang
VP: Susan L Davies
VP: John Lorenz
VP: Viola Sprague
VP: Christine Wallace
Dir Lab: Jennifer Rivet

KETTERING UNIVERSITY ARCHIVES
See RICHARD P SCHARCHBURG ARCHIVES

D-U-N-S 07-848-6031
KETTLE CUISINE HOLDINGS LLC
330 Lynnway Ste 405, Lynn, MA 01901-1713
Tel (617) 409-1100 *Founded/Ownrshp* 2011
Sales 33.4MME *EMP* 125E
SIC 6719 Investment holding companies, except banks

D-U-N-S 18-350-0131 IMP
KETTLE CUISINE LLC
(*Suby of* KETTLE CUISINE HOLDINGS LLC) ★
330 Lynnway Ste 405, Lynn, MA 01901-1713
Tel (617) 884-1219 *Founded/Ownrshp* 1986
Sales 45.5MME *EMP* 125
SIC 2032 2038 2035 Soups, except seafood: packaged in cans, jars, etc.; Soups & broths: canned, jarred, etc.; Soups, frozen; Seasonings & sauces, except tomato & dry; Soups, except seafood: packaged in cans, jars, etc.; Soups & broths: canned, jarred, etc.; Soups, frozen; Seasonings & sauces, except tomato & dry
Prin: Jeremiah A Shafir
COO: Nick Murphy
VP: Julie Bonney
VP: Ken Murray
Exec: Joseph Ascoli
Exec: Volker Frick
Rgnl Mgr: Gerrie Schenk
QA Dir: Karen Bishop-Carbone
IT Man: Anthony Fusco
VP Sls: Lorie Donnelly
Mktg Dir: Dennis Flynn

D-U-N-S 09-699-5642 EXP
■ **KETTLE FOODS INC**
(*Suby of* DIAMOND FOODS INC) ★
3125 Kettle Ct Se, Salem, OR 97301-5572
Tel (503) 364-0399 *Founded/Ownrshp* 1981
Sales 111.8MME *EMP* 550
SIC 2096 Potato chips & similar snacks; Potato chips & similar snacks
Pr: Richard Wolford
**Pr:* Brian Driscoll
VP: Howard Allred
VP: Mark Cramer
VP: Bays Michael
Netwrk Mgr: Ruth Ann
Sls Dir: Ed Charbonneau
Sls Dir: Joelle Simmons

KETTLE RESTAURANT
See DIRLYNN CO INC

D-U-N-S 84-891-0857
KETTLE-LAKES COOPERATIVE
430 1st St, Random Lake, WI 53075-1772
Tel (920) 668-8561 *Founded/Ownrshp* 1994
Sales 36.9MM *EMP* 45
Accts Clifton Gunderson Llp Marshfi
SIC 5999 5251 Feed & farm supply; Hardware; Feed & farm supply; Hardware
Genl Mgr: Mark Mentink

D-U-N-S 09-534-9643
KETTLER & SCOTT INC
ISLAND ESTATES LC
8081 Wolftrap Rd Ste 300, Vienna, VA 22182-5182
Tel (703) 556-0012 *Founded/Ownrshp* 1978
Sales 26.9MME *EMP* 300
SIC 6552 Land subdividers & developers, residential; Land subdividers & developers, residential
Ch: Robert Charles Kettler
**Sec:* Susan Brunkow
Chf Mktg O: Jamie Kowinsky
Sr VP: Richard Hausler
VP: Knapp Richard
VP: James Turner

D-U-N-S 00-687-8193
KETTLER MANAGEMENT INC (VA)
KSI MANAGEMENT ALEXANDRIA CI
1751 Pinnacle Dr Ste 700, Mc Lean, VA 22102-4003
Tel (703) 641-9000 *Founded/Ownrshp* 1992
Sales 28.8MME *EMP* 275
SIC 6531 Real estate agents & managers; Real estate agents & managers
CEO: Robert C Kettler
**Pr:* Andrew W Buchanan
**Sr VP:* Leslie Furst
Sr VP: Pamela Tyrrell
VP: Joseph Ades

D-U-N-S 00-246-4212
KEUKA COLLEGE
141 Central Ave, Keuka Park, NY 14478-9764
Tel (315) 279-5000 *Founded/Ownrshp* 1890
Sales 40.3MM *EMP* 253
Accts Efp Rotenberg Llp Canandaigu
SIC 8221 Colleges universities & professional schools; Colleges universities & professional schools
Pr: Dr Jorge L Daz-Herrera
**CFO:* Jerry Hiller
Treas: Robert Schick
Ofcr: Charles Angelo
**VP:* James Blackburn
VP: Larry Lehner
VP: Timothy Sellers
**VP:* Dr Gary Smith
**VP:* Dr Anne K Weed
VP: Anne K Weed
Assoc Dir: Sally Daggett

D-U-N-S 03-770-4855 IMP/EXP
▲ **KEURIG GREEN MOUNTAIN INC**
33 Coffee Ln, Waterbury, VT 05676-8900
Tel (802) 244-5621 *Founded/Ownrshp* 1993
Sales 4.5MMM *EMP* 6,000
Accts Pricewaterhousecoopers Llp Bo
Tkr Sym GMCR *Exch* NGS
SIC 2095 3634 Roasted coffee; Coffee makers, electric: household; Roasted coffee; Coffee makers, electric: household
Pr: Brian P Kelley
**Ch Bd:* Norman H Wesley
CFO: Peter G Leemputte
CFO: Frances G Rathke
Bd of Dir: Ben Frost
Bd of Dir: Gordie Garvey
Bd of Dir: Bruce Grant
Bd of Dir: Pat Kelly
Chf Mktg O: Mark Baynes
Ofcr: Michael J Degnan
Ofcr: Michael Degnan
Ofcr: Robert P Ostryniec
VP: Sonia G Cudd
VP: Stephen L Gibbs
VP: Daniel R Martin
Exec: Donna Deak
Exec: Jacklyn Spence
Creative D: Rick Slade
Dir Bus: Bill McCauley
Board of Directors: Barbara D Carlini, John D Hayes, Susan Saltzbart Kilsby, Jose Octavio Reyes Lagunes, A D David Mackay, Michael J Mardy, Hinda Miller, David E Moran, Robert A Steele

D-U-N-S 18-106-9733
KEVCON CORP
MISTY HARBOR
228 Kenyon Rd W, Fort Dodge, IA 50501-5762
Tel (515) 573-1093 *Founded/Ownrshp* 1990
Sales 20.4MME *EMP* 60
SIC 3732 Pontoons, except aircraft & inflatable
Pr: Dave Wilson
**VP:* Lisa Wilson
Snr PM: Chris Young

D-U-N-S 60-350-2220
KEVCON INC
295 Trade St, San Marcos, CA 92078-4373
Tel (760) 432-0307 *Founded/Ownrshp* 1992
Sales 28.3MME *EMP* 38
SIC 1541 1542 8741 Industrial buildings & warehouses; Commercial & office building contractors; Management services; Industrial buildings & warehouses; Commercial & office building contractors; Management services
Pr: Kevin Kutina
CFO: Angie Howard

D-U-N-S 08-839-7851
KEVIN D BALLARD INC (TX)
J & J STEEL COMPANY
2300 Andrews Hwy, Odessa, TX 79761-1121
Tel (432) 332-4351 *Founded/Ownrshp* 1971, 2002
Sales 23.6MME *EMP* 24
SIC 5051 Metals service centers & offices
Pr: Kevin Ballard

D-U-N-S 80-136-7033
KEVIN GROS OFFSHORE LLC
13080 W Main St, Larose, LA 70373-2301
Tel (985) 798-7607 *Founded/Ownrshp* 2003
Sales 22.0MM *EMP* 180
SIC 4213 Trucking, except local; Trucking, except local

D-U-N-S 01-902-3522
KEVIN INC
KITTERY TRADING POST
301 Us Route 1, Kittery, ME 03904-5510
Tel (207) 439-2700 *Founded/Ownrshp* 1938
Sales 71.8MME *EMP* 350
SIC 5941 5699 5661

D-U-N-S 13-145-9489
KEVIN WHITAKER CHEVROLET INC
2320 Laurens Rd, Greenville, SC 29607-3247
Tel (864) 297-0011 *Founded/Ownrshp* 1989
Sales 35.0MME *EMP* 85
SIC 5511 Automobiles, new & used; Automobiles, new & used
Pr: Kevin Whitaker
**Sec:* Kathy Fasco

D-U-N-S 79-784-4743 IMP
KEVINS WHOLESALE LLC
710 Capouse Ave, Scranton, PA 18509-3120
Tel (570) 344-9055 *Founded/Ownrshp* 1994
Sales 27.1MME *EMP* 40
Accts Jacob & O Boyle Llp Kingston
SIC 5136 7389 Men's & boys' clothing; Shirts, men's & boys'; Advertising, promotional & trade show services
Pr: Kevin Tinkelman
**Ch Bd:* Larry Tinkelman
**Ex VP:* Scott Tinkelman
Exec: Josh Kaufer
VP Sls: Ron Parkinson
S&M/VP: Scott Vogelmeier
Sls Mgr: Debbie Boedeker

D-U-N-S 01-707-1107
KEVITA INC
2220 Celsius Ave Ste A, Oxnard, CA 93030-5181
Tel (805) 200-2250 *Founded/Ownrshp* 2009
Sales 28.0MM *EMP* 60
SIC 2086 Bottled & canned soft drinks
CEO: William Moses
CFO: James Linesch
VP Opers: Nate Patena
Opers Mgr: Carlos Quinones
VP Sls: Robert Adams
Sls Dir: Marc Hoopingarner
Board of Directors: Elliot Karathanasis

D-U-N-S 87-446-7764
KEW CORP
DODGE CHRYSLER PLYMOUTH JEEP E
671 Orange Dr, Vacaville, CA 95687-3100
Tel (707) 455-4500 *Founded/Ownrshp* 1993
Sales 58.7MME *EMP* 150
SIC 5511 5521 Automobiles, new & used; Used car dealers; Automobiles, new & used; Used car dealers
Pr: Clarence A Williams Jr
Sls Dir: Rebecca Anderson
Sls Mgr: Chun Chin
Sls Mgr: Dave Lewis
Sls Mgr: Armando Ramirez

D-U-N-S 80-698-9380 IMP
KEW INC
KING ESTATE
80854 Territorial Hwy, Eugene, OR 97405-9715
Tel (541) 942-9874 *Founded/Ownrshp* 1992
Sales 20.2MME *EMP* 100
SIC 2084 5812 Wines; Wine cellars, bonded: engaged in blending wines; Eating places; Wines; Wine cellars, bonded: engaged in blending wines; Eating places
CEO: Edward J King Jr
Chf Mktg O: Mark Feinberg
Ofcr: Lisa Frasieur
VP: Rick Durette
VP: Grant Hughes
Dir Lab: Brent Stone
Ex Dir: Gladys Sandlin
IT Man: Ed Marcotte
Prd Mgr: John Albin
Ql Cn Mgr: Lindsay Boudreaux
Sls Mgr: Doug Frost

KEWANEE HOMECARE
See KEWANEE HOSPITAL

D-U-N-S 05-423-5593
KEWANEE HOSPITAL
KEWANEE HOMECARE
1051 W South St, Kewanee, IL 61443-8354
Tel (309) 852-7500 *Founded/Ownrshp* 1998
Sales 27.6MM *EMP* 321
SIC 8062 5912 5947

D-U-N-S 00-613-0132
■ **KEWAUNEE FABRICATIONS LLC** (WI)
(*Suby of* OSHKOSH CORP) ★
520 N Main St, Kewaunee, WI 54216-1044
Tel (920) 388-2000 *Founded/Ownrshp* 1941, 1999
Sales 81.4MME *EMP* 241
SIC 3441 3444 Fabricated structural metal; Sheet metalwork; Fabricated structural metal; Sheet metalwork
Ex VP: Bryan Blankfield
Exec: Helen Lacrosse
Mfg Mgr: Michael Trakel
Plnt Mgr: Phil Gomoluch

D-U-N-S 00-503-6330 IMP/EXP
▲ **KEWAUNEE SCIENTIFIC CORP**
2700 W Front St, Statesville, NC 28677-2894
Tel (704) 873-7202 *Founded/Ownrshp* 1906
Sales 118.8MM *EMP* 645
Accts Cherry Bekaert Llp Charlotte
Tkr Sym KEQU *Exch* NGM
SIC 3821 2599 Laboratory furniture; Worktables, laboratory; Laboratory apparatus, except heating & measuring; Laboratory equipment: fume hoods, distillation racks, etc.; Factory furniture & fixtures; Work benches, factory; Laboratory furniture; Worktables, laboratory; Laboratory apparatus, except heating & measuring; Laboratory equipment: fume hoods, distillation racks, etc.; Factory furniture & fixtures; Work benches, factory
Pr: David M Rausch
CFO: Thomas D Hull III
VP: Bain K Black
IT Man: David Foote
VP Mfg: Keith D Smith
Sfty Mgr: Randy Winston
Manager: Pete Caudle
Board of Directors: John C Campbell Jr, Keith M Gehl, Margaret B Pyle, David S Rhind, John D Russell, Donald F Shaw, William A Shumaker

D-U-N-S 07-996-4623
KEWEENAW BAY INDIAN COMMUNITY (INC)
OJIBWA LANES & LOUNGE
16429 Bear Town Rd, Baraga, MI 49908-9210
Tel (906) 353-6623 *Founded/Ownrshp* 1837
Sales 48.3MME *EMP* 700
SIC 7999 7011 7933 Gambling establishment; Bingo hall; Motels; Bowling centers; Gambling establishment; Bingo hall; Motels; Bowling centers
CFO: Gerald Hays
IT Man: Tom Chosa

D-U-N-S 80-024-2211
KEWEENAW FINANCIAL CORP
235 Quincy St, Hancock, MI 49930-1816
Tel (906) 482-0404 *Founded/Ownrshp* 2007
Sales NA *EMP* 79E
SIC 6712 Bank holding companies
Pr: Willis J Fontaine

D-U-N-S 83-112-4065
KEWEENAW MEMORIAL MEDICAL CENT
205 Osceola St, Laurium, MI 49913-2134
Tel (906) 337-6500 *Founded/Ownrshp* 2009
Sales 38.8MM *EMP* 23E
SIC 8011 Medical centers; Medical centers
CEO: Chuck Nelson
**COO:* Mike Hauswirth
**CFO:* Shane Jaques
Dir Lab: Nicole Frantti
Chf Nrs Of: Grace Tousignant
Off Admin: Cathy Taskila
CIO: Mark Bresky
Sfty Mgr: John Cander
Mktg Dir: Matthew Vertin
Mktg Mgr: Carol Carr
Surgeon: Elizabeth Benyi

D-U-N-S 62-421-5075
KEWILL INC
(*Suby of* KEWILL LIMITED)
1 Executive Dr Ste 201, Chelmsford, MA 01824-2564
Tel (978) 482-2500 *Founded/Ownrshp* 1998
Sales 25.5MME *EMP* 120
SIC 7372 7371 7373 Business oriented computer software; Custom computer programming services; Systems integration services; Business oriented computer software; Custom computer programming services; Systems integration services
CEO: Doug Braun
COO: Patrick Chua
CFO: Kim Dodge
**CFO:* Andrew Hicks
**Sr VP:* Greg Carter
**Sr VP:* Matt Gaywood
**Sr VP:* Sin Hopwood
Ex Dir: Ken Sourback
Dir IT: Kevin Remde
VP Opers: Robert De Rooij
Sales Exec: John Webb
Board of Directors: Paul Ilse, Bill Larson

D-U-N-S 83-277-5410 IMP/EXP
KEY 3 CASTING LLC
(*Suby of* METAL TECHNOLOGIES OF INDIANA INC) ★
301 Commerce St Ste 3200, Fort Worth, TX 76102-4150
Tel (817) 332-9500 *Founded/Ownrshp* 2013
Sales 87.8MME *EMP* 338
SIC 3365 3321 Aluminum & aluminum-based alloy castings; Gray iron castings; Aluminum & aluminum-based alloy castings; Gray iron castings
**Sec:* Tanya McClanahan

KEY AMERICA
See KEYSTONE GROUP HOLDINGS INC

D-U-N-S 06-104-4186
KEY AUTO MALL INC
3700 16th St, Moline, IL 61265-7207
Tel (309) 762-5397 *Founded/Ownrshp* 1979
Sales 25.0MME *EMP* 67
SIC 5511 Automobiles, new & used; Automobiles, new & used
Pr: Dave Kehoe
**VP:* Dan Kehoe
Genl Mgr: Randy Allison
IT Man: Connie McKean
Sales Asso: Evgeny Kokshin
Sales Asso: Ryan Peterson

D-U-N-S 87-445-2311 IMP
KEY AUTOMOTIVE OF FLORIDA INC
(*Suby of* K S S) ★
5300 Allen K Breed Hwy, Lakeland, FL 33811-1130
Tel (863) 668-6000 *Founded/Ownrshp* 1990
Sales 41.3MME *EMP* 350
SIC 3714 Motor vehicle parts & accessories; Motor vehicle parts & accessories
Pr: William G Koerber
Pr: Robert M Rapone
**Treas:* Robert J Saltarelli

KEY BANK
See KEYBANK NATIONAL ASSOCIATION

D-U-N-S 04-354-8049
KEY BENEFIT ADMINISTRATORS INC
E-ZBENEFITS
8330 Allison Pointe Trl, Indianapolis, IN 46250-1682
Tel (317) 284-7100 *Founded/Ownrshp* 1979, 1992
Sales NA *EMP* 275
SIC 6371 Pension, health & welfare funds; Pension, health & welfare funds
Pr: Larry R Dust
COO: Tom Remlinger
**CFO:* Bradley Ray
Sr VP: John Toledano
VP: Tiffany Alsabrook
VP: Kris Cardell
VP: Patrick Cohen
VP: Anita Dust
**VP:* Wally T Gray
VP: Dale Kaliser
VP: Jan Macy

D-U-N-S 04-231-4633 IMP
KEY BLUE PRINTS INC
KEY COLOR
195 E Livingston Ave, Columbus, OH 43215-5793
Tel (614) 228-3285 *Founded/Ownrshp* 1966
Sales 21.1MME *EMP* 73
SIC 5049 7334 Drafting supplies; Blueprinting service
Pr: David M Key III

Assoc VP: Jill McAuley
Sr VP: William Nottage
VP: Daniel Brown
VP: Robert Levy
VP: T J Monico
VP: Nicholas Stuart
VP: Chuck Tacoronte
Mng Dir: Scott Berman
Mng Dir: Mark Koster
Mng Dir: Mark Lasek

D-U-N-S 01-949-9520
KEY BRAND ENTERTAINMENT INC
BROADWAY ACROSS AMERICA
1619 Broadway Fl 9, New York, NY 10019-7412
Tel (917) 421-5400 *Founded/Ownrshp* 2004
Sales 473.0M *EMP* 1,843ᴱ
SIC 7922 Entertainment promotion
Ch Bd: John Gore
**CFO:* Paul Dietz
**Ch:* Peter Schneider
Treas: Stephen Conroy
Ex VP: Seth Popper
VP: Glenn Hill
VP: Felix Sebacious

D-U-N-S 04-940-3132
KEY BROTHERS & ASSOCIATES ENGINEERING CO
1626 S George Nigh Expy, McAlester, OK 74501-7411
Tel (918) 423-1047 *Founded/Ownrshp* 1967
Sales 29.7MM *EMP* 12
SIC 8711 Consulting engineer; Consulting engineer
Pt: Walter E Key
Pt: Kimberly Key

D-U-N-S 03-238-2020 EXP
KEY BUICK CO
KEY HYUNDAI
4660-100 Southside Blvd, Jacksonville, FL 32216-6358
Tel (904) 642-6060 *Founded/Ownrshp* 1960
Sales 42.7MMᴱ *EMP* 95
SIC 5511 7538 Automobiles, new & used; General automotive repair shops; Automobiles, new & used; General automotive repair shops
Pr: Maureen Perry Burnett
Off Mgr: Mary Braddock
Store Mgr: Dave Lowe
Sls Dir: Karl Graves
Sls Mgr: Steve Barranco

D-U-N-S 06-654-6094
KEY CADILLAC INC
KEY CADILLAC OLDSMOBILE
6825 York Ave S, Minneapolis, MN 55435-2534
Tel (952) 920-4300 *Founded/Ownrshp* 1973
Sales 29.2MMᴱ *EMP* 82
SIC 5511 Automobiles, new & used; Automobiles, new & used
CEO: Adam Stanzak
**Pr:* Michael Stanzak
Exec: Lisa Jensen
**Genl Mgr:* Dennis Burg
Opers Mgr: Tom Fridgen
Sales Asso: Brian Thoresen

KEY CADILLAC OLDSMOBILE
See KEY CADILLAC INC

D-U-N-S 18-856-6439
KEY CLUB ASSOCIATES LIMITED PARTNERSHIP
LONGBOAT KEY CLUB
442 Gulf Of Mexico Dr, Longboat Key, FL 34228-4010
Tel (941) 383-0292 *Founded/Ownrshp* 1980
Sales 27.2MMᴱ *EMP* 500ᴱ
SIC 7011 Resort hotel; Resort hotel
Pt: Michael Welly
Comm Dir: Sandra Rios
Genl Mgr: Jeff Mayers
Sls Mgr: Maria Cruz
Snr Mgr: Juliette Valin

D-U-N-S 05-049-5345
KEY CODE MEDIA INC
270 S Flower St, Burbank, CA 91502-2101
Tel (818) 303-3900 *Founded/Ownrshp* 2001
Sales 22.7MMᴱ *EMP* 102
SIC 5734 Computer & software stores
CEO: Michael Cavanagh
**CFO:* Karman Chan
Sales Exec: James Biro
Sls Mgr: Pat Howley
Sales Asso: Corey Todd

KEY COLOR
See KEY BLUE PRINTS INC

KEY COMMERCIAL MORTGAGE
See KEY EQUIPMENT FINANCE INC

D-U-N-S 10-407-5551
KEY CONSTRUCTION INC
741 W 2nd St N, Wichita, KS 67203-6004
Tel (816) 221-7171 *Founded/Ownrshp* 1978
Sales 191.2MM *EMP* 210
SIC 1542 1541 Commercial & office building, new construction; Industrial buildings, new construction; Commercial & office building, new construction; Industrial buildings, new construction
Pr: David E Wells
Pr: Troy Heckart
**CEO:* Kenneth A Wells
**Ex VP:* Larry Gourley
**Ex VP:* Richard McCafferty
VP: Tim Sortore
VP: Phil Wells
Exec: John Hoffman
**Exec:* John Walker
VP Opers: Eric Scott
Sls&Mrk Ex: Shane Faurot

D-U-N-S 82-848-4365
KEY CONSTRUCTION TEXAS LLC
3960 Sandshell Dr, Fort Worth, TX 76137-2403
Tel (817) 306-7979 *Founded/Ownrshp* 2006
Sales 77.7MM *EMP* 47
SIC 1542 Commercial & office building contractors; Commercial & office building contractors

D-U-N-S 05-801-5264 IMP
KEY CONTAINER CO
4224 Santa Ana St, South Gate, CA 90280-2557
Tel (323) 564-4211 *Founded/Ownrshp* 1981
Sales 35.0MMᴱ *EMP* 110
SIC 2653 Corrugated & solid fiber boxes; Corrugated & solid fiber boxes
Pr: Robert J Watts
**VP:* William J Watts

D-U-N-S 00-119-7482 IMP
KEY CONTAINER CORP
21 Campbell St, Pawtucket, RI 02861-4005
Tel (401) 723-2000 *Founded/Ownrshp* 1985
Sales 43.3MMᴱ *EMP* 185
SIC 2653 Boxes, corrugated: made from purchased materials; Boxes, corrugated: made from purchased materials
Pr: David Strauss
VP: Telmo Dasilva

D-U-N-S 11-867-0124 EXP
KEY CONTROLS OF TAMPA INC
5030 Gateway Blvd Ste 14, Lakeland, FL 33811-2708
Tel (863) 583-0071 *Founded/Ownrshp* 2003
Sales 24.9MMᴱ *EMP* 28
SIC 5084 Controlling instruments & accessories
Pr: Robert Munday
**Sr VP:* Lama Munday
Off Mgr: Bonnie McKeon
Sales Asso: Italo Batista
Sales Asso: Mike Brennan

D-U-N-S 00-798-9262
KEY COOPERATIVE
SCE
13585 620th Ave, Roland, IA 50236-8061
Tel (515) 388-4341 *Founded/Ownrshp* 1936
Sales 371.5MM *EMP* 180
SIC 5153 5541 2048 5191 Grains; Filling stations, gasoline; Livestock feeds; Fertilizers & agricultural chemicals; Grains; Filling stations, gasoline; Livestock feeds; Fertilizers & agricultural chemicals
Pr: Bob Finch
**Treas:* Dave Vander Pol
**VP:* Rick Fopma
Genl Mgr: Jim Magnuson
Sfty Dirs: Mark Gaunt
Opers Mgr: Boyd Brodie
Opers Mgr: Marv Freeborn

D-U-N-S 03-055-8080
KEY DISTRIBUTORS LLC
14740 W 107th St, Lenexa, KS 66215-4024
Tel (913) 213-6090 *Founded/Ownrshp* 2012
Sales 65.0MM *EMP* 2
SIC 7319 Shopping news, advertising & distributing service; Shopping news, advertising & distributing service
Owner: Jeff Zeller

D-U-N-S 17-221-8799 IMP
KEY ELECTRONICS INC
2533 Centennial Blvd, Jeffersonville, IN 47130-8535
Tel (812) 206-2500 *Founded/Ownrshp* 2004
Sales 79.1MMᴱ *EMP* 185
SIC 3679 Printed circuit boards; Electronic circuits
Pr: A Thomas Hardy
**COO:* Larry Porter
**CFO:* David Meece
Prgrm Mgr: Cepm Carter
Prgrm Mgr: Melissa Long
Prgrm Mgr: Steve Schumaker
Off Mgr: Marty Branch
Trfc Dir: Russell Payton
Ql Cn Mgr: Tim Ground
Ql Cn Mgr: Jack Leonard
Snr Mgr: Matthew Stone

D-U-N-S 93-191-7546 IMP
■ **KEY ENERGY DRILLING INC**
(*Suby of* KEY ENERGY SERVICES INC) ★
1301 Mckinney St Ste 1800, Houston, TX 77010-3057
Tel (432) 620-0300 *Founded/Ownrshp* 1995
Sales 138.0MMᴱ *EMP* 283
SIC 1381 Drilling oil & gas wells; Drilling oil & gas wells
Pr: Newton W Wilson III
V Ch: James Byerlotzer
COO: Dick Alario
**VP:* J Marshall Dodson
VP: J Dodson
**VP:* Kimberly R Frye
Dist Mgr: Roger Henderson
Div Mgr: REO Brownlee

D-U-N-S 03-768-0964 EXP
▲ **KEY ENERGY SERVICES INC**
1301 Mckinney St Ste 1800, Houston, TX 77010-3057
Tel (713) 651-4300 *Founded/Ownrshp* 1978
Sales 1.4MMM *EMP* 8,100
Accts Grant Thornton Llp Houston T
Tkr Sym KEG *Exch* NYS
SIC 1389 1381 1311 Servicing oil & gas wells; Drilling oil & gas wells; Crude petroleum production; Natural gas production; Servicing oil & gas wells; Drilling oil & gas wells; Crude petroleum production; Natural gas production
Ch Bd: Richard J Alario
**Pr:* Robert Drummond
CFO: J Marshall Dodson
Ofcr: Marshall Dodson
Sr VP: Kim B Clarke
Sr VP: Jim Flynt
Sr VP: Kimberly R Frye
Sr VP: Jeffrey S Skelly
VP: Guillermo Capacho
VP: Mark A Cox
VP: Boris Cura
VP: Mike Furrow
VP: Joe Halsey
VP: Ike Smith
Board of Directors: Arlene M Yocum, Lynn R Coleman, Kevin P Collins, Robert Drummond, William D Fertig, W Phillip Marcum, Ralph S Michael III, William F Owens, Robert K Reeves, Mark H Rosenberg

D-U-N-S 03-052-1988
■ **KEY EQUIPMENT FINANCE INC**
(*Suby of* KEYCORP) ★
127 Public Sq, Cleveland, OH 44114-1217
Tel (216) 689-3000 *Founded/Ownrshp* 1973
Sales NA *EMP* 400
SIC 6159 Equipment & vehicle finance leasing companies; Equipment & vehicle finance leasing companies
Pr: Paul A Larkins
**COO:* Karen Lawson
**CFO:* John R Pfeiffenberger
VP: Arindam Basu
VP: Thomas B Brigham Jr
VP: Beau Conway
VP: Bryan Powell
Mng Dir: Jamie Johns

D-U-N-S 03-106-2883 IMP
■ **KEY EQUIPMENT FINANCE INC**
KEY COMMERCIAL MORTGAGE
(*Suby of* KEYBANK NATIONAL ASSOCIATION) ★
1000 S Mccaslin Blvd, Superior, CO 80027-9437
Tel (800) 539-2968 *Founded/Ownrshp* 2007
Sales 175.3MMᴱ *EMP* 400
SIC 7359 Equipment rental & leasing; Equipment rental & leasing
Pr: Linda A Grandstaff
Ofcr: Cynthia George
Sr VP: Deborah Brady
Sr VP: Brian Deponte
Sr VP: Amy Gross
Sr VP: Mark Hoffman
Sr VP: Brian Madison
Sr VP: Mike O'Hern
Sr VP: Scott Sullivan
Sr VP: Michelle Worster
VP: Kaileen Almond
VP: Shawn Arnone
VP: Julie Babcock
VP: Mark Brandt
VP: Gale Burket
VP: Mark Casel
VP: Colleen Daly
VP: Scott Daugherty
VP: Douglas Dupy
VP: Jim Epstein
VP: Jonathan Fales

KEY FOOD
See DANS SUPREME SUPER MARKETS INC

KEY FOOD
See PICK QUICK FOODS INC

KEY FOOD SERVICES
See KEY FOODS CO

D-U-N-S 01-257-3358
KEY FOOD STORES CO-OPERATIVE INC
1200 South Ave, Staten Island, NY 10314-3413
Tel (718) 370-4200 *Founded/Ownrshp* 1937
Sales 893.2MM *EMP* 84ᴱ
Accts Anchin Block & Anchin Llp Ne
SIC 5141 Groceries, general line; Groceries, general line
CEO: Dean Janeway
**Ch Bd:* Lawrence Mandel
Pr: Richard Grobman
CFO: Chet Koby
Treas: Anthony Bileddo
VP: Salvatore Bonavita
VP: George Knobloch
Mktg Mgr: Paul Gelardi

D-U-N-S 10-545-4206 IMP
KEY FOODS CO
KEY FOOD SERVICES
620 W 24th Pl, Chicago, IL 60609
Tel (312) 225-0225 *Founded/Ownrshp* 2001
Sales 31.3MMᴱ *EMP* 38
SIC 5141 Food brokers
Pr: D W Tseung
**CEO:* Henry Gee
VP: Keith Gee
VP: Gino Palummo
**VP:* Rick Pseung

KEY FORD
See WORLD FORD PENSACOLA

D-U-N-S 61-180-2786
KEY HUMAN SERVICES INC
1290 Silas Deane Hwy 1a, Wethersfield, CT 06109-4337
Tel (860) 409-7350 *Founded/Ownrshp* 1989
Sales 16.0MM *EMP* 320
Accts Key Human Services Inc Farm
SIC 8361 Home for the mentally handicapped; Home for the mentally handicapped
Pr: Mary Beth O'Neil
**Pr:* Dennis Felty
**CFO:* Roger Burns
**CFO:* Mark E Kovitch
VP: Robyn Joppy
**Ex Dir:* Mark Ritter

KEY HYUNDAI
See KEY BUICK CO

D-U-N-S 02-412-0867
KEY IMPACT SALES & SYSTEMS INC
1701 Crossroads Dr, Odenton, MD 21113-1110
Tel (410) 381-1239 *Founded/Ownrshp* 1981
Sales 79.3MMᴱ *EMP* 500
SIC 8742 Marketing consulting services; New products & services consultants; Marketing consulting services; New products & services consultants
CEO: Daniel Cassidy
**Pr:* Randy Wieland
**COO:* Eric Frost
**CFO:* Kathleen Mooy
**Ex VP:* Rob Monroe
**Sr VP:* Butch Cassidy
Sr VP: Joe Hargadon
VP: Cass Ahern
**VP:* Eric Garvin
VP: Lane Gordon
VP: Clay Marcum
**VP:* Tony Odorissio
**VP:* Gary Vonck
VP: Peter Voss
Exec: Denise Low

D-U-N-S 00-714-0106 IMP
KEY INDUSTRIES INC
400 Marble Rd, Fort Scott, KS 66701-8639
Tel (620) 223-2000 *Founded/Ownrshp* 1938
Sales 35.9MMᴱ *EMP* 45
SIC 5136 Men's & boys' outerwear
Ch: William K Pollock
**Pr:* Chris Barnes
Sr VP: Mike Johnson

D-U-N-S 01-940-3935
KEY INFORMATION SYSTEMS INC
30077 Agoura Rd Fl 1, Agoura Hills, CA 91301-2499
Tel (818) 992-8950 *Founded/Ownrshp* 1999
Sales 28.3MMᴱ *EMP* 50
SIC 7373

D-U-N-S 01-098-2812
KEY INGREDIENTS INC
1115 Vicksburg Ln N # 19, Minneapolis, MN 55447-3219
Tel (763) 476-5957 *Founded/Ownrshp* 1998
Sales 36.4MM *EMP* 3
Accts Terry Nelson Cpa Pc Wausa
SIC 6221 Commodity traders, contracts; Commodity traders, contracts
Pr: Randall C Betcher

KEY LIME COVE WATER RESORT
See GURNEE WATER PARK LLC

D-U-N-S 10-206-8368
KEY MACHINERY CO INC
3755 Industrial Pkwy, Birmingham, AL 35217-5316
Tel (205) 849-8298 *Founded/Ownrshp* 1980
Sales 35.0MMᴱ *EMP* 40
SIC 5082 7359 General construction machinery & equipment; Equipment rental & leasing; General construction machinery & equipment; Equipment rental & leasing
Pr: Gilbert J Key Jr
**VP:* Jim Key
Genl Mgr: Larry Broadley

D-U-N-S 08-149-1805
KEY MECHANICAL CO OF WASHINGTON
19430 68th Ave S Ste B, Kent, WA 98032-1193
Tel (253) 872-7392 *Founded/Ownrshp* 1995
Sales 25.6MMᴱ *EMP* 130
SIC 1711 Heating & air conditioning contractors; Refrigeration contractor; Heating & air conditioning contractors; Refrigeration contractor
Pr: Frank W Leonard
**Sec:* Mary H Leonard
**VP:* Robert L Heisler

KEY OIL CO
See KEYSTOPS LLC

D-U-N-S 09-942-3043 IMP
KEY PLASTICS LLC
19575 Victor Pkwy Ste 400, Livonia, MI 48152-7026
Tel (248) 449-6100 *Founded/Ownrshp* 2009
Sales 1.0MMMᴱ *EMP* 3,600
SIC 3089 7389 Automotive parts, plastic; Design services; Automotive parts, plastic; Design services
Ch Bd: Eugene Davis
CEO: Terry Gohl
CFO: Jonathan Ball
CFO: Rex Carlile
VP: Calvin Saur
VP: Adrian Stull
VP: Joseph White
Prgrm Mgr: Derek Fisher
Prgrm Mgr: Karl Kowalyk
Prgrm Mgr: Misael Menezo
Dir IT: Lisa Pidun

KEY PRINCIPAL INVESTING
See KEY PRINCIPAL PARTNERS CORP

D-U-N-S 02-683-0518
■ **KEY PRINCIPAL PARTNERS CORP**
KEY PRINCIPAL INVESTING
(*Suby of* KEYCORP) ★
800 Superior Ave E # 1000, Cleveland, OH 44114-2613
Tel (888) 539-3322 *Founded/Ownrshp* 2000
Sales 64.3MMᴱ *EMP* 900
SIC 6799 8741 3825 6726 3399 Investors; Management services; Test equipment for electronic & electrical circuits; Investment offices; Powder, metal; Investors; Management services; Test equipment for electronic & electrical circuits; Investment offices; Powder, metal
Pr: John Sinnenberg
**CFO:* Dennis Wagner
**VP:* Cindy Babitt
**VP:* Samir Desai
**VP:* Patrick Rond

D-U-N-S 36-228-6817
■ **KEY PRODUCTION CO INC**
(*Suby of* CIMAREX ENERGY CO) ★
1700 N Lincoln St # 1800, Denver, CO 80203-4518
Tel (303) 295-3995 *Founded/Ownrshp* 2002
Sales 35.2MMᴱ *EMP* 66
SIC 1311 Crude petroleum production; Natural gas production; Crude petroleum production; Natural gas production
Ch Bd: Francis H Merelli
CFO: Paul Korus
Sr VP: Stephen P Bell
VP: Joseph R Albi
Exec: Thomas E Jorden

D-U-N-S 03-080-9974
KEY PROGRAM INC
670 Old Connecticut Path, Framingham, MA 01701-4548
Tel (508) 877-1631 *Founded/Ownrshp* 1974
Sales 32.1MM *EMP* 450
Accts Kahn Litwin Renza & Co Ltd Pr
SIC 8322 Social service center; Social service center
Ch Bd: Edward D Feldstein Esq
**Pr:* William Lyttle

CFO: Jack Araujo
**Treas:* Michael Kan
Exec: Pat Forkis

D-U-N-S 84-151-2416
KEY QUEST WHOLESALE INC
8401 Claude Thomas Rd # 18, Franklin, OH 45005-2195
Tel (937) 704-0520 *Founded/Ownrshp* 2004
Sales 28.0MM *EMP* 16
SIC 5141 Food brokers; Food brokers
Pr: Robert M Pitman
**VP:* Debra Pitman

D-U-N-S 05-090-6655
KEY REHABILITATION INC
1335 Nw Broad St Ste B, Murfreesboro, TN 37129-4428
Tel (615) 896-6400 *Founded/Ownrshp* 1999
Sales 22.0MM[E] *EMP* 305
SIC 8049 Occupational therapist; Occupational therapist
CEO: Janet S Irwin
CFO: Randy Schertz
**Ex VP:* Randy K Schertz
VP: Jodi Foster
VP: Laura Pfeifer
VP: Shayla Thomas

D-U-N-S 09-032-6765 IMP/EXP
KEY SAFETY RESTRAINT SYSTEMS INC
K S S
(*Suby of* K S S) ★
7000 19 Mile Rd, Sterling Heights, MI 48314-3210
Tel (586) 726-3800 *Founded/Ownrshp* 1997
Sales 193.7MM[E] *EMP* 1,264
SIC 3714 3674 3679 Motor vehicle steering systems & parts; Bumpers & bumperettes, motor vehicle; Instrument board assemblies, motor vehicle; Radiation sensors; Resonant reed devices, electronic; Motor vehicle steering systems & parts; Bumpers & bumperettes, motor vehicle; Instrument board assemblies, motor vehicle; Radiation sensors; Resonant reed devices, electronic
Pr: William G Koerber
**Treas:* Robert J Salterelli

D-U-N-S 18-065-6753 IMP
KEY SAFETY SYSTEMS INC
K S S
(*Suby of* FOUNTAINVEST PARTNERS (ASIA) LIMITED)
7000 19 Mile Rd, Sterling Heights, MI 48314-3210
Tel (586) 726-3800 *Founded/Ownrshp* 2014
Sales 2.0MMM[E] *EMP* 6,000
SIC 2399 3714 Seat belts, automobile & aircraft; Motor vehicle steering systems & parts; Seat belts, automobile & aircraft; Motor vehicle steering systems & parts
Pr: Jason Luo
Treas: Natalia Zaryckyj

D-U-N-S 02-569-5727
KEY SCALES FORD INC (FL)
1719 Citrus Blvd, Leesburg, FL 34748-3497
Tel (352) 787-3511 *Founded/Ownrshp* 1938
Sales 20.5MM[E] *EMP* 48
SIC 5511 Automobiles, new & used; Pickups, new & used
Pr: Key Scales III
Exec: Dan Marshall
Div/Sub He: Don Lukich
Genl Mgr: Bruce Johnson
Sls Mgr: Dave Ainsworth
Sls Mgr: Wayne Cassell
Sls Mgr: Blake Kelly
Sls Mgr: Jeff Wagner
Sales Asso: Fred Almonte
Sales Asso: Rod Berger
Sales Asso: Don Garrett

D-U-N-S 07-782-9695 IMP/EXP
▲ KEY TECHNOLOGY INC
150 Avery St, Walla Walla, WA 99362-4703
Tel (509) 529-2161 *Founded/Ownrshp* 1948
Sales 102.9MM *EMP* 547[E]
Tkr Sym KTEC *Exch* NGM
SIC 3556 2834 Food products machinery; Pharmaceutical preparations; Food products machinery; Pharmaceutical preparations
Pr: John J Ehren
COO: Jonathan Marley
CFO: Jack Ehren
CFO: Jeffrey T Siegal
Ofcr: Roxann Forkan
Sr VP: Stephen M Pellegrino
Sr VP: Louis C Vintro
VP: Michael Nichols
Exec: Grace Bender
Exec: James Ruff
Prgrm Mgr: John Kadinger
Board of Directors: Richard Lawrence, John E Pelo, Michael L Shannon, Charles H Stonecipher, Donald A Washburn, Paul J Wolf, Frank L A Zwerts

D-U-N-S 04-844-0424 IMP
▲ KEY TRONIC CORP
KEYTRONICEMS
4424 N Sullivan Rd, Spokane Valley, WA 99216-1593
Tel (509) 928-8000 *Founded/Ownrshp* 1969
Sales 434.0MM *EMP* 4,866
Accts Bdo Usa Llp Spokane Washingt
Tkr Sym KTCC *Exch* NGM
SIC 3577 Computer peripheral equipment; Computer peripheral equipment
Pr: Craig D Gates
Ch Bd: Patrick Sweeney
CFO: Brett R Larsen
Ex VP: Douglas G Burkhardt
Ex VP: Philip S Hochberg
VP: Frank Crispigna III
VP: Brett Larson
VP: Dave Manky
Prgrm Mgr: Dave Allert
Prgrm Mgr: Carla Cpim
Prgrm Mgr: Mark Glynn
Board of Directors: James R Bean, Ronald F Klawitter

D-U-N-S 18-827-6927
KEY WEST BOATS INC
593 Ridgeville Rd, Ridgeville, SC 29472-8049
Tel (843) 873-0112 *Founded/Ownrshp* 1986
Sales 36.6MM[E] *EMP* 160
SIC 3732 Boats, fiberglass: building & repairing; Boats, fiberglass: building & repairing
Pr: William Holseberg
Exec: Amy Murray
Off Mgr: Boogie Westebury
Mktg Mgr: Tom Marlowe
Sls Mgr: Dale John

KEY WEST TOYOTA
See DUNCANS AUTO SALES INC

D-U-N-S 84-864-8846 IMP
KEY-COMM INTERNATIONAL INC
KCI WIRELESS
3007 S Dairy Ashford Rd # 8, Houston, TX 77082-2794
Tel (713) 524-2727 *Founded/Ownrshp* 1992
Sales 30.0MM[E] *EMP* 20
SIC 5999 Communication equipment; Communication equipment
Pr: Liem T Phan
**Treas:* Chien M Phan
**VP:* Hieu T Phan
Exec: Francisco Garza
Exec: North Houston

D-U-N-S 18-787-1702
■ KEYBANC CAPITAL MARKETS INC
MCDONALD FINANACIAL GROUP
(*Suby of* KEYCORP) ★
800 Superior Ave E # 1400, Cleveland, OH 44114-2613
Tel (800) 553-2240 *Founded/Ownrshp* 1999
Sales NA *EMP* 2,200
SIC 6021 6211 National commercial banks; Security brokers & dealers; National commercial banks; Security brokers & dealers
Pr: Randy Paine
**CEO:* Douglas Preiser
**CFO:* Robert D Moran Jr
Chf Cred: William Hayden
Ofcr: Lillian Faust
Assoc VP: Boris Goldsteyn
Assoc VP: Joseph Sabol
Sr VP: John Conner
Sr VP: Mitch Miller
VP: Joseph Angeloro
VP: Jason Black
VP: Jim Boyle
VP: Tod Burkert
VP: Greg Caso
VP: Alejandro Cola
VP: Laura Conway
VP: Marylee Gotch
VP: Neill Heins
VP: Stephen Holler
VP: Christian Lan
VP: Larsen Mettler

D-U-N-S 83-001-1057
■ KEYBANK EB MANAGED GUARANTEED INVESTMENT CONTRACT FUND
MAGIC FUND
(*Suby of* KEYBANK NATIONAL ASSOCIATION) ★
127 Public Sq, Cleveland, OH 44114-1217
Tel (216) 689-3000 *Founded/Ownrshp* 2009
Sales 326.9MM[E] *EMP* 1,848[E]
SIC 6722 Money market mutual funds
Prin: Joseph Dedek
Sr VP: Kathleen Foley
Sr VP: Stephen Holler
Sr VP: Poppie Parish
VP: Thompson Guy
VP: Suzi Redlin
Mng Dir: Steve Hughes
Mng Dir: Mark Koster
Brnch Mgr: Sue Bentz
Brnch Mgr: Dana Leon
Brnch Mgr: Joe Voytik

D-U-N-S 03-632-0174
■ KEYBANK NATIONAL ASSOCIATION (OR)
KEY BANK
(*Suby of* KEYCORP) ★
1211 Sw 5th Ave Ste 300, Portland, OR 97204-3713
Tel (503) 790-7500 *Founded/Ownrshp* 1907, 1985
Sales NA *EMP* 97
SIC 6022 State trust companies accepting deposits, commercial; State trust companies accepting deposits, commercial
Pr: James J Atkinson
CFO: Albert V Legge
**Ofcr:* Thomas A Elmer
Ofcr: Linda Lozano
**Ex VP:* Doug Leeding
VP: Larry Baker
VP: Amanda Hall
**VP:* Malcom K Mathes
VP: Jerald Robinson
VP: Christa Short
Off Mgr: Karin Jacobs

D-U-N-S 06-603-5056
■ KEYBANK NATIONAL ASSOCIATION
(*Suby of* KEYCORP) ★
127 Public Sq Ste 5600, Cleveland, OH 44114-1226
Tel (800) 539-2968 *Founded/Ownrshp* 1958
Sales NA *EMP* 13,500
SIC 6021 6022 6159 National commercial banks; State commercial banks; Automobile finance leasing; National commercial banks; State commercial banks; Automobile finance leasing
CEO: R B Heisler
Pr: Patrick Auletta
Pr: Mark R Danahy
Ofcr: David Opatrny
Ofcr: Thomas C Stevens
Ofcr: Cheryl Voigt
Ex VP: Alfred Carpetto
Ex VP: Norman Nichols
Ex VP: Kevin Ryan
Ex VP: Tom Tulodzieski
Sr VP: Michael Bellardine
Sr VP: Dave Brown
Sr VP: Robin Cottingham
Sr VP: Eric Peiffer
Sr VP: Babette Schubert
Sr VP: Matthew Wyner
VP: Jeffrey Eades
VP: Sally Gesouras
VP: Albert B Holding
VP: Dan Koszczewski
VP: Aneta Kuzma

D-U-N-S 12-594-4442
KEYBRIDGE TECHNOLOGIES INC
4415 Highline Blvd, Oklahoma City, OK 73108-1895
Tel (405) 488-0800 *Founded/Ownrshp* 2002
Sales 29.5MM[E] *EMP* 150[E]
SIC 7379 Computer data escrow service
Pr: Yunsheng Simon Hsu
Prgrm Mgr: Thomas Dale
Prgrm Mgr: Charles Gregg
Snr Sftwr: Jim Tang
Ql Cn Mgr: Kelly Lynch
Ql Cn Mgr: Kelly Zachgo

D-U-N-S 01-443-8881
KEYCO DISTRIBUTORS INC
625 New Commerce Blvd, Hanover Township, PA 18706-1433
Tel (570) 825-9445 *Founded/Ownrshp* 1949
Sales 32.8MM *EMP* 70
Accts Kupstas & Kupstas Llc Annapo
SIC 5141 5142 5194 5113 Groceries, general line; Packaged frozen goods; Cigarettes; Cigars; Cups, disposable plastic & paper; Containers, paper & disposable plastic; Groceries, general line; Packaged frozen goods; Cigarettes; Cigars; Cups, disposable plastic & paper; Containers, paper & disposable plastic
Pr: Frank X Kowalski Jr
**Treas:* Francis X Kowalski
**VP:* Sophie T Kowalski

D-U-N-S 00-294-5293 IMP/EXP
▲ KEYCORP (OH)
127 Public Sq, Cleveland, OH 44114-1306
Tel (216) 689-3000 *Founded/Ownrshp* 1958
Sales NA *EMP* 13,853
Accts Ernst & Young Llp Cleveland
Tkr Sym KEY *Exch* NYS
SIC 6021 6141 6211 National commercial banks; Personal credit institutions; Automobile & consumer finance companies; Consumer finance companies; Financing: automobiles, furniture, etc., not a deposit bank; Investment bankers; Brokers, security; National commercial banks; Personal credit institutions; Automobile & consumer finance companies; Consumer finance companies; Financing: automobiles, furniture, etc., not a deposit bank; Investment bankers; Brokers, security
Ch Bd: Beth E Mooney
Pr: Daniel Jacques
Pr: Terry Jenkins
Pr: Michael Rowland
COO: David Brown
COO: Douglas Preiser
CFO: Donald R Kimble
CFO: Christopher Manderfield
Treas: Denise Almeida
Treas: Carolina Mathis
Treas: Peter D Wheeler
Ofcr: Craig A Buffie
Ofcr: Tricia Husser
Ex VP: Kevin M Blakely
Ex VP: Craig Brooks
Ex VP: Cindy P Crotty
Ex VP: Renee R Csuhan
Ex VP: George E Emmons
Ex VP: Paul N Harris
Ex VP: Dean Kontul
Ex VP: Richard M Kulbieda

D-U-N-S 83-045-8290
KEYCORP REAL ESTATE CAPITAL MARKETS INC
11501 Outlook St Ste 300, Overland Park, KS 66211-1807
Tel (913) 317-4558 *Founded/Ownrshp* 1995
Sales NA *EMP* 280
SIC 6021 National commercial banks; National commercial banks
VP: Brenda Harmon
**Ex VP:* Marty O'Connor
**Sr VP:* Bryan Nitcher

D-U-N-S 88-482-1679
■ KEYCORP REAL ESTATE CAPITAL MARKETS INC
(*Suby of* KEYBANK NATIONAL ASSOCIATION) ★
127 Public Sq, Cleveland, OH 44114-1306
Tel (216) 689-3000 *Founded/Ownrshp* 1995
Sales NA *EMP* 160
SIC 6162 Mortgage bankers & correspondents; Mortgage bankers & correspondents
Pr: Henry Mayor III
**Ofcr:* Barbara Bredenberg
**Ofcr:* Sheila Darrow
**Ofcr:* Mary Holevinski
**Sr VP:* Todd A Rodenberg
Sr VP: John Scott
**Sr VP:* Jerry A Wheeler
**Sr VP:* Calvin Zeringue
**VP:* Molly Barton
**VP:* Patrick J Bianca
VP: Dale Brem
**VP:* Daniel Freeman
**VP:* Penny Newton
**VP:* Jon P Reible
**VP:* Linda C Rochin

D-U-N-S 14-718-0418 IMP
KEYENCE CORP OF AMERICA
(*Suby of* KEYENCE CORPORATION)
669 River Dr Ste 403, Elmwood Park, NJ 07407-1361
Tel (201) 930-0100 *Founded/Ownrshp* 1985
Sales 173.7MM[E] *EMP* 300
SIC 3825 5084 3674 Electronic parts & equipment; Measuring & testing equipment, electrical; Semiconductors & related devices; Instruments to measure electricity; Measuring & testing equipment, electrical; Semiconductors & related devices
Prin: Katsuhiro Yoshii
Area Mgr: Tony Ocampo
IT Man: Michael Yip
Tech Mgr: Hideki Nishikawa
Sales Exec: Billy Evers
Sls&Mrk Ex: Patrick Chu
Sls Mgr: Gary Nolan
Sls Mgr: Kyle Simpson
Sales Asso: Tim Calie
Sales Asso: Tim Westbrook
Snr Mgr: Nathan Kufel

KEYES EUROPEAN
See HAK INC

D-U-N-S 03-444-9871 IMP
KEYES FIBRE CORP
3715 State Highway 97a, Wenatchee, WA 98801-9624
Tel (509) 663-8537 *Founded/Ownrshp* 1903
Sales 30.0MM[E] *EMP* 65[E]
SIC 5031 Molding, all materials; Molding, all materials
Pr: Ted Kozikowski
**Pr:* Ted Smith
CFO: Robert Mazzacavallo
**CFO:* Josh Weldy
Manager: Michael Wold
Board of Directors: Rebecca Kalis

KEYES LEXUS
See KEYLEX INC

D-U-N-S 02-958-6732
KEYES MOTORS INC
TOYOTA-KEYES MOTORS
5855 Van Nuys Blvd, Van Nuys, CA 91401-4219
Tel (818) 782-0122 *Founded/Ownrshp* 1968
Sales 79.4MM[E] *EMP* 175
SIC 5511 7538 7515 5012 Automobiles, new & used; General automotive repair shops; Passenger car leasing; Automobiles & other motor vehicles; Automobiles, new & used; General automotive repair shops; Passenger car leasing; Automobiles & other motor vehicles
Pr: Howard Keyes
**VP:* Lawrence Abramson
IT Man: Frank Barkley
Sls Mgr: Brian Sobel

D-U-N-S 14-702-4087
KEYIMPACT SALES SYSTEMS
95 Connecticut Dr, Burlington, NJ 08016-4180
Tel (609) 265-8300 *Founded/Ownrshp* 1984
Sales 39.9MM[E] *EMP* 140
SIC 5141 Food brokers; Food brokers
Pr: Dan Cassidy
**VP:* Keith Dwyer
**VP:* Tony Odorisio
Dir IT: Doug Ml

KEYKERT USA, INC.
See KIEKERT USA INC

D-U-N-S 61-040-5748
KEYLEX INC
KEYES LEXUS
5905 Van Nuys Blvd, Van Nuys, CA 91401-3624
Tel (818) 379-4000 *Founded/Ownrshp* 1990
Sales 36.4MM[E] *EMP* 100
SIC 5511 7538 7515 5531 Automobiles, new & used; General automotive repair shops; Passenger car leasing; Automotive & home supply stores; Automobiles, new & used; General automotive repair shops; Passenger car leasing; Automotive & home supply stores
Pr: Howard Keyes
Genl Mgr: Ryan Gallante
Sales Exec: George Morales
Mktg Dir: Howard Tenenbaum
Sls Mgr: Charlie Nicgorski
Sales Asso: Ellie Shafiee
Sales Asso: Jose Zetina

D-U-N-S 05-430-3180
KEYLOGIC SYSTEMS INC (WV)
3168 Collins Ferry Rd, Morgantown, WV 26505-3352
Tel (304) 296-9100 *Founded/Ownrshp* 1998
Sales 27.0MM *EMP* 175
SIC 7379 7373 Computer related consulting services; Computer integrated systems design; Computer related consulting services; Computer integrated systems design
Pr: Jon Hammock
**CFO:* Ken Bissett
**VP:* Glenn Copen
**VP:* Jim Dieterle
VP: Scott Theaing
**Ex Dir:* Carey Butler

D-U-N-S 00-395-9251 IMP
KEYMARK CORP (NY)
1188 Cayadutta St, Fonda, NY 12068
Tel (518) 853-3421 *Founded/Ownrshp* 1964, 1988
Sales 228.8MM[E] *EMP* 600
SIC 3354 3479 3471 Aluminum extruded products; Painting of metal products; Anodizing (plating) of metals or formed products; Aluminum extruded products; Painting of metal products; Anodizing (plating) of metals or formed products
Ch Bd: William L Keller III
**COO:* Tony Maiolo
**CFO:* Brad Harring
**Ex VP:* James P Keller
Genl Mgr: Kelly Fernet
VP Opers: Bob Channell
Plnt Mgr: Shawn Gavin
Plnt Mgr: Leo Slecton
Ql Cn Mgr: Robert Dubois
Ql Cn Mgr: Jeff Thompson
Trfc Mgr: Joseph Rachon

D-U-N-S 01-951-7999
KEYMARK CORP OF FLORIDA
2540 Knights Station Rd, Lakeland, FL 33810-2505
Tel (863) 858-5500 *Founded/Ownrshp* 1997
Sales 79.8MM[E] *EMP* 115
SIC 3354 Aluminum extruded products; Aluminum extruded products
Pr: William L Keller III
Pr: Gus Brotsis
**COO:* Tony Maiolo

*CFO: Bradley Harring
VP: Bob Channell
*VP: Joe Crenna
*VP: James Keller
QA Dir: Michelle Barone
Sfty Mgr: Mike Jackman
Ql Cn Mgr: Michael Drindak
Mktg Dir: Michael Durkin

D-U-N-S 88-459-7287
KEYMARK INC
105 Tech Ln, Liberty, SC 29657-4313
Tel (864) 343-0500 Founded/Ownrshp 1990
Sales 35.0MM^E EMP 110^E
SIC 7373 Computer integrated systems design
CEO: Jim Wanner
Pr: Gus Brotsis
COO: Ken Furie
CFO: Bradley Harring
*VP: Cameron Boland
VP: Jami Mullikin
VP: Victoria Pruitt
Sftwr Eng: Robert King
Sftwr Eng: Hugh Kinsey
Sales Exec: Alls Mike
VP Sls: Ed M McQuiston

D-U-N-S 87-743-4217
KEYMEL TECHNOLOGIES LLC
10941 Roger Dr Apt D, New Orleans, LA 70127-2836
Tel (504) 570-6037 Founded/Ownrshp 1992
Sales 60.0MM EMP 2
SIC 1542 7363 3564 3399 4952 Brads: aluminum, brass or other nonferrous metal or wire; Greenhouse construction; Help supply services; Greenhouse construction; Help supply services; Blowers & fans; Brads: aluminum, brass or other nonferrous metal or wire; Sewerage systems

KEYNOTE SYSTEMS, INC.
See SIGOS LLC

D-U-N-S 94-081-6069
KEYPATH EDUCATION
15500 W 113th St Ste 200, Lenexa, KS 66219-5106
Tel (913) 254-6000 Founded/Ownrshp 2013
Sales 68.0MM^E EMP 225^E
SIC 7311 Advertising consultant; Advertising consultant
CEO: Dave Admire
Pt: Sonya Larson
Pr: Vince Giambalvo
*Pr: Mike McHugh
*Pr: Michael Platt
Pr: Lori Turec
*CEO: Steve Fireng
*CFO: Patrick Donoghue
CFO: Ed Henee
*Chf Cred: Steve Booth
*Chf Mktg O: Tracy Kreikemeier
Ofcr: Greg Lindsey
Ofcr: Mallory Ragon
Ex VP: Lyle Kraft
Sr VP: Sean Nicholson
VP: Brian Hubbard
VP: Jessica John
*VP: Tami Platt
VP: Nate Rowe
VP: Jeremy Schoen
*VP: John Vanfleet

D-U-N-S 10-209-9728
KEYPOINT CREDIT UNION
2805 Bowers Ave Ste 105, Santa Clara, CA 95051-0972
Tel (408) 731-4100 Founded/Ownrshp 1979
Sales NA EMP 184
SIC 6062 State credit unions; State credit unions
CEO: T Bradford Canfield
*Pr: Timothy M Kramer
*CFO: John Herrick
Ex VP: Timothy Green
Sr VP: Leeanne Giblin
Sr VP: Helen Grays
Sr VP: Helen Jones
Sr VP: Steven Weiler
VP: Suzanne Carlisle
VP: Doug Schrock
VP: Larry Scofield
VP: Victor Smilgys

D-U-N-S 15-286-7235
KEYPOINT GOVERNMENT SOLUTIONS INC
1750 Foxtrail Dr, Loveland, CO 80538-4424
Tel (866) 667-3635 Founded/Ownrshp 2000
Sales 33.7MM^E EMP 500
SIC 7381 Private investigator; Private investigator
CEO: Eric A Hess
*CFO: Michael Chao
CFO: Carolyn Symsack
VP: Susan Ordakowski
Mng Dir: John Lenoir
*Dir Sec: David Kervin
CIO: Rory Job
IT Man: Bridget Vurgich
Sftwr Eng: Brant Gajda
Sftwr Eng: Anthony Spencer
Board of Directors: Michael Chertoff, Jeffrey Schlanger

D-U-N-S 00-843-3469
KEYPOINT PARTNERS LLC
1 Burlington Woods Dr # 1, Burlington, MA 01803-4503
Tel (781) 273-5555 Founded/Ownrshp 2008
Sales 22.2MM^E EMP 90
SIC 8741 Management services
VP: Alicia Bouthillette
VP: Robert Hayes
VP: Robert Sheehan
Sales Exec: Robert Lemons
Mktg Mgr: Christopher Cardoni
Snr PM: Loran Macumber

D-U-N-S 10-215-0919 IMP
KEYPORT LLC
5309 Shilshole Ave Nw # 210, Seattle, WA 98107-5343
Tel (206) 284-1947 Founded/Ownrshp 1997
Sales 32.0MM EMP 10
SIC 5411 5399 5146 Grocery stores; Warehouse club stores; Fish & seafoods
Off Mgr: Jane Pedersen

KEYS ENERGY SERVICE
See UTILITY BOARD OF CITY OF KEY WEST

KEYS GATE CHARTER SCHOOL
See HOMESTEAD CHARTER FOUNDATION INC

D-U-N-S 07-936-5688
KEYS HOTEL OPERATOR INC
HAWKS CAY RESORT
61 Hawks Cay Blvd, Marathon, FL 33050
Tel (305) 743-7000 Founded/Ownrshp 2014
Sales 4.0MM^E EMP 400
SIC 7011 Resort hotel
Mng Dir: Sheldon Suga
*Treas: Sandra Wilson

KEYSER ENERGY
See HOP ENERGY LLC

D-U-N-S 07-929-7662
▲ KEYSIGHT TECHNOLOGIES INC
KEYSIGHT TECHNOLOGIES WORLD
1400 Fountaingrove Pkwy, Santa Rosa, CA 95403-1738
Tel (707) 577-5000 Founded/Ownrshp 2013
Sales 2.8MMM EMP 9,600^E
Tkr Sym KEYS Exch NYS
SIC 3825 Instruments to measure electricity; Instruments to measure electricity; Microwave test equipment; Oscillators, audio & radio frequency (instrument types)
Pr: Ronald S Nersesian
CFO: Neil Dougherty
Sr VP: Jay Alexander
Sr VP: Ingrid Estrada
VP: Hamish Gray
VP: Guy Sene
VP: Bob Witte
Exec: Carmina Stremlau
Board of Directors: Paul N Clark, James G Cullen, Charles J Dockendorff, Jean M Halloran, Richard Hamada, Mark Templeton

KEYSIGHT TECHNOLOGIES WORLD
See KEYSIGHT TECHNOLOGIES INC

D-U-N-S 83-032-6448
KEYSPAN CORP
(Suby of NATIONAL GRID USA) ★
1 Metrotech Ctr Fl 1, Brooklyn, NY 11201-3949
Tel (718) 403-1000 Founded/Ownrshp 1998
Sales 7.2MMM^E EMP 9,595
SIC 4924 Natural gas distribution; Natural gas distribution
CEO: Robert B Catell
CFO: Fred Yam
VP: Thomas Caronna
VP: Victor Courtien
VP: Cathy Gamble
VP: Marilyn Lennon
Prgrm Mgr: Diane Blankenhorn
IT Man: Bonnie Burkhardt
IT Man: Valerie Debono
IT Man: Mark Kuperman
Sfty Dirs: Bernie Alvarez

KEYSPAN ENERGY
See ENERGYNORTH INC

KEYSPAN ENERGY
See NATIONAL GRID CORPORATE SERVICES LLC

D-U-N-S 12-507-7136 IMP
KEYSPAN ENERGY DELIVERY
(Suby of NATIONAL GRID USA) ★
1 One Metrotech Ctr Fl 1, Brooklyn, NY 11201
Tel (718) 403-1000 Founded/Ownrshp 2007
Sales 33.8MM^E EMP 67^E
SIC 4924 Natural gas distribution
CEO: Robert Catell
*Pr: Robert Fani
VP: Joe Pradas
Exec: Philip Clark
Genl Mgr: Ruth Sullivan
Software D: Shivankur Goel
Sftwr Eng: Constance Madeo
Genl Couns: Frederick Lowther

D-U-N-S 05-310-6352
KEYSPAN GAS EAST CORP
NATIONAL GRID
(Suby of KEYSPAN CORP) ★
175 Old Country Rd, Hicksville, NY 11801
Tel (718) 403-1000 Founded/Ownrshp 1998
Sales 295.0MM^E EMP 1,500
SIC 4924 Natural gas distribution; Natural gas distribution
Pr: William J Akley
*CFO: David B Doxsee
VP: Ronald Boches
*VP: Robert Teetz
*VP: Martin Wheatcroft
Genl Mgr: Arthur Olsen
Opers Mgr: Aaron Choo
Counsel: Cynthia Clark
Board of Directors: Nickolas Stavropoulus

D-U-N-S 83-040-7966
KEYSPAN INTERNATIONAL CORP
(Suby of NATIONAL GRID DEVELOPMENT HOLDINGS CORP) ★
1 Metrotech Ctr, Brooklyn, NY 11201-3948
Tel (718) 403-2000 Founded/Ownrshp 1996
Sales 33.9MM^E EMP 100
SIC 4911 Electric services; Electric services
Treas: Michael J Nilsen
Ex Dir: Irene Rivera

D-U-N-S 13-714-2613
KEYSTEEL CORP
KEYSTEEL WIRE
(Suby of ACEROS Y LAMINADOS LEAL, S.A. DE C.V.)
18900 W Industrial Pkwy, New Caney, TX 77357-3503
Tel (281) 572-2536 Founded/Ownrshp 2004
Sales 29.1MM^E EMP 30
SIC 5051 Steel
Pr: Nicolas A Leal
*Owner: Nicolas Leal

KEYSTEEL WIRE
See KEYSTEEL CORP

D-U-N-S 00-916-4914 IMP
KEYSTON BROS (INC) (CA)
(Subsy of KUDZU FABRICS, INC)
1000 Holcomb Wds Pkwy # 111, Roswell, GA 30076-2588
Tel (770) 587-2555 Founded/Ownrshp 1868, 2001
Sales 110.2MM^E EMP 210
SIC 5199 5131 5191 Automobile fabrics; Upholstery fabrics, woven; Saddlery; Automobile fabrics; Upholstery fabrics, woven; Saddlery
CEO: Dan Duncan Jr
*COO: Ron Crumbley
*CFO: Dennis Alieksaites
*Ex VP: Jeff Gower
*Sr VP: Heather H Breedlove
*Sr VP: Joel Brook
Sr VP: Keyston Bros
*Sr VP: Ann Duncan
*Sr VP: Paul Radke
*Sr VP: Ron Steik
VP: Dennis Bueker
*VP: Greg Chaffee

KEYSTONE
See IMPACT SYSTEMS INC

D-U-N-S 05-254-8492
■ KEYSTONE AMERICA INC
SERIVCE CORP INTERNATIONAL
(Suby of SCI) ★
2685 Henderson Dr, Jacksonville, NC 28546-5239
Tel (910) 347-2595 Founded/Ownrshp 1955
Sales 93.5MM^E EMP 10
SIC 7261 Funeral home; Funeral home
Genl Mgr: Johnny Thompson
*Off Mgr: Christina Wagoner
IT Man: Tina Wagoner

D-U-N-S 78-243-8928
■ KEYSTONE AMERICA INC
(Suby of SCI CERBERUS LLC) ★
400 N Ashley Dr Ste 1900, Tampa, FL 33602-4311
Tel (813) 225-4650 Founded/Ownrshp 1996
Sales 10.2MM^E EMP 800
SIC 7261 Funeral service & crematories; Funeral service & crematories
Pr: Robert G Horn
*Pr: Steven A Tidwell
*COO: James D Price
CFO: Stephen Shaffer

D-U-N-S 00-518-2019
KEYSTONE ANILINE CORP (IL)
KEYSTONE ANILINE PACIFIC DIV
2501 W Fulton St, Chicago, IL 60612-2103
Tel (312) 666-2015 Founded/Ownrshp 1920
Sales 23.5MM^E EMP 65
SIC 2819 Industrial inorganic chemicals; Industrial inorganic chemicals
Pr: George A Andrews
*VP: Steven Maiolo
*VP: Charle Wilkinson
MIS Dir: Osvaldo Velasquez
Opers Mgr: Bruce Worley
Plnt Mgr: Mark Mesenbrink
S&M/VP: Steve Maiolo
Sls Mgr: Nick Vertucci
Sales Asso: Douglas Morgan
Sales Asso: Van Peet
Sales Asso: Robin Roberts

KEYSTONE ANILINE PACIFIC DIV
See KEYSTONE ANILINE CORP

D-U-N-S 04-059-8443
KEYSTONE AREA EDUCATION AGENCY
1400 2nd St Nw, Elkader, IA 52043-9564
Tel (563) 245-1480 Founded/Ownrshp 1975
Sales 12.3MM^E EMP 280
SIC 8211 Public special education school; Private special education school; Public special education school; Private special education school
Psych: Cynthia Ehrlich
Psych: Honora Swift

D-U-N-S 80-075-3498 IMP/EXP
■ KEYSTONE AUTOMOTIVE HOLDINGS INC
(Suby of LKQ CORP) ★
44 Tunkhannock Ave, Exeter, PA 18643-1221
Tel (570) 655-4514 Founded/Ownrshp 2014
Sales 510.0MM^E EMP 1,896
SIC 5013 5531 Automotive supplies & parts; Automotive supplies; Tools & equipment, automotive; Automotive parts; Automotive supplies & parts; Automotive supplies; Tools & equipment, automotive; Automotive parts
Pr: Edward H Orzetti
*CFO: Richard S Paradise
VP: Bill Rogers
VP: Ralph Ruzzi
Sls Mgr: John Ruch

D-U-N-S 10-198-8988 IMP
■ KEYSTONE AUTOMOTIVE INDUSTRIES FL INC
NORTH STAR NECO SERVICE CENTER
(Suby of KEYSTONE AUTOMOTIVE INDUSTRIES INC) ★
11701 Nw 101st Rd Ste 1, Medley, FL 33178-1021
Tel (305) 885-6500 Founded/Ownrshp 1998
Sales 48.4MM^E EMP 146
SIC 5013 Automotive supplies & parts; Automotive supplies & parts
Pr: Charles Hogarty
Genl Mgr: Ralph Viera
Sls Mgr: Mike Rodriquez

D-U-N-S 05-923-0151 IMP/EXP
■ KEYSTONE AUTOMOTIVE INDUSTRIES INC
(Suby of LKQ CORP) ★
655 Grassmere Park, Nashville, TN 37211-3659
Tel (615) 781-5200 Founded/Ownrshp 2007
Sales 994.4MM^E EMP 5,000
SIC 5013 5531 3714 Automotive supplies & parts; Motor vehicle parts & accessories; Automotive parts; Automotive supplies & parts; Automotive parts; Motor vehicle parts & accessories
CEO: Robert L Wagman
Treas: Frank Erlain
Ex VP: Al Ronco
VP: Barnett L Gershen
VP: Dwain K Lanier
VP: John M Palumbo
VP: Kim D Wood
Comm Man: Elier Rodriguez
*Prin: John S Quinn
Genl Mgr: Sean Bickers
Genl Mgr: Ralph Hairsine

D-U-N-S 04-671-1743 IMP
■ KEYSTONE AUTOMOTIVE INDUSTRIES MN INC
NORTH STAR BUMPER
(Suby of KEYSTONE AUTOMOTIVE INDUSTRIES INC) ★
3615 Marshall St Ne, Minneapolis, MN 55418-1005
Tel (612) 789-1919 Founded/Ownrshp 1997
Sales 120.6MM^E EMP 800
SIC 5013 3312 3465 Automotive supplies & parts; Wheels; Body parts, automobile: stamped metal; Automotive supplies & parts; Wheels; Body parts, automobile: stamped metal
Pr: Joseph Hlosten
*VP: Rob Wagman
Genl Mgr: Joe Hernandez
Mktg Dir: Barry Harris

D-U-N-S 16-094-2363 IMP
■ KEYSTONE AUTOMOTIVE INDUSTRIES TN INC
(Suby of KEYSTONE AUTOMOTIVE INDUSTRIES INC) ★
655 Grassmere Park, Nashville, TN 37211-3659
Tel (615) 781-5200 Founded/Ownrshp 2007
Sales 162.9MM^E EMP 500
SIC 5013 Automotive supplies & parts; Automotive supplies & parts
Pr: Joseph M Holsten
CTO: Mike Marlo
VP Sls: Joe Turner

D-U-N-S 01-167-8799 IMP/EXP
■ KEYSTONE AUTOMOTIVE OPERATIONS INC
(Suby of LKQ CORP) ★
44 Tunkhannock Ave, Exeter, PA 18643-1221
Tel (570) 654-1232 Founded/Ownrshp 2014
Sales 790.1MM^E EMP 1,724
SIC 5531 5013 Automotive parts; Automotive supplies & parts; Automotive parts; Automotive supplies & parts
Pr: Edward Orzetti
CFO: Bryant P Bynum
CFO: Richard Paradise
VP: Kevin Canavan
VP: Rudy Esteves
VP: Murthy Sathya
Dir Soc: Melissa Holland
Rgnl Mgr: Bill Johnson
Dir IT: Robert Lewis
Opers Mgr: Rob Ford
Opers Mgr: Greg Phillips

D-U-N-S 05-671-9883 IMP
■ KEYSTONE AUTOMOTIVE WAREHOUSE
(Suby of KEYSTONE AUTOMOTIVE HOLDINGS INC) ★
44 Tunkhannock Ave, Exeter, PA 18643-1221
Tel (570) 655-4514 Founded/Ownrshp 1972
Sales 173.9MM^E EMP 750
SIC 5013 Automotive supplies & parts; Automotive supplies; Tools & equipment, automotive; Automotive supplies & parts; Automotive supplies; Tools & equipment, automotive
Prin: Joseph Amato
*Prin: James Chebalo
*Prin: Leonard Ross

D-U-N-S 06-798-0508
KEYSTONE AVIATION LLC (UT)
TAC AIR
(Suby of TAC) ★
303 N 2370 W, Salt Lake City, UT 84116-2948
Tel (801) 933-7500 Founded/Ownrshp 1954, 2012
Sales 20.7MM^E EMP 210
SIC 4581 5172 7359 Airports, flying fields & services; Petroleum products; Aircraft rental; Airports, flying fields & services; Petroleum products; Aircraft rental
COO: Kim Page
Exec: Bill Haberstock
CTO: Kimberly Rasmussen
Dir IT: Kenneth Loder
IT Man: Corey Rose
Sls Mgr: Arnie Richins

D-U-N-S 83-217-8177 IMP
KEYSTONE BAKERY HOLDINGS LLC
(Suby of MAPLEHURST BAKERIES LLC) ★
520 Lake Cook Rd, Deerfield, IL 60015-5611
Tel (603) 792-3113 Founded/Ownrshp 2010
Sales 81.1MM^E EMP 360
SIC 2053 2051 Doughnuts, frozen; Bread, cake & related products; Doughnuts, frozen; Bread, cake & related products
Pr: Kevin McDonough
VP: John Brennan
VP: Phil Streeter
VP Sls: Ed Cassidy

KEYSTONE BREWERS
See PITTSBURGH BREWING CO

D-U-N-S 83-939-1810
KEYSTONE CAPITAL INC
155 N Wacker Dr Ste 4150, Chicago, IL 60606-1788
Tel (312) 219-7900 *Founded/Ownrshp* 1994
Sales 46.4MM^E *EMP* 35^E
SIC 6799 Venture capital companies
Pr: Kent P Dauten
**CFO:* Brian C Chung
CFO: Brian C Hung
**VP:* Dennis J Howe
VP: Bill Sommerschield
**Prin:* Megan C Anderson
Mng Dir: David Greer
Mng Dir: Scott L Gwiiam

D-U-N-S 00-229-0948 IMP
KEYSTONE CEMENT CO (PA)
(*Suby of* GIANT CEMENT HOLDING INC) ★
Rr 329, Bath, PA 18014
Tel (610) 837-1881 *Founded/Ownrshp* 1926, 1994
Sales 33.6MM^E *EMP* 121
SIC 3241 Portland cement; Masonry cement; Portland cement; Masonry cement
VP: Robert K Aichele
**Pr:* Jose A Llontop
**VP:* William Biddix
**VP:* Gerry Geier
VP: Michael J Luybli
**VP:* John Von Tress
Rgnl Mgr: Gretchen Scipio
QA Dir: Mechella Saba
Plnt Mgr: Steve Hayden
Ql Cn Mgr: Jonathan Graham
Sls Mgr: Dominic Jampo

D-U-N-S 12-625-1201
KEYSTONE CEMENT INC
(*Suby of* GIANT CEMENT HOLDING INC) ★
320 Midland Pkwy Ste D, Summerville, SC 29485-8113
Tel (843) 851-9898 *Founded/Ownrshp* 2003
Sales 25.9MM^E *EMP* 190
SIC 3241 Masonry cement; Masonry cement
CEO: Terry L Kinder

D-U-N-S 05-139-6042
■ **KEYSTONE CENTERS INC** (PA)
(*Suby of* RITE AID CORP) ★
30 Hunter Ln, Camp Hill, PA 17011-2400
Tel (717) 761-2633 *Founded/Ownrshp* 1958, 1976
Sales 27.5MM^E *EMP* 530
SIC 5912 Drug stores; Drug stores
Ch Bd: Alex Grass
**Pr:* Martin Grass
**Treas:* Frank Bergonzi
**VP:* Franklin Brown

D-U-N-S 09-304-0731
KEYSTONE CENTRAL CAREER & TECHNICAL CENTER
KEYSTONE CENTRAL SCHOOL DST
86 Administration Dr, Mill Hall, PA 17751-8462
Tel (570) 726-4223 *Founded/Ownrshp* 1970
Sales 41.6MM^E *EMP* 700
SIC 8211 Public elementary & secondary schools; Public elementary & secondary schools
**CFO:* Paul Larocque
Dir Sec: Brandon Coleman
MIS Dir: Rolanda Austin
Dir IT: Blake Bergey
Dir IT: Ralonda Pote
Schl Brd P: Jack Peters
Teacher Pr: Mona Calhoun

KEYSTONE CENTRAL SCHOOL DST
See KEYSTONE CENTRAL CAREER & TECHNICAL CENTER

D-U-N-S 80-996-7557
KEYSTONE CHEVROLET INC
8700 Charles Page Blvd, Sand Springs, OK 74063-8504
Tel (918) 245-2201 *Founded/Ownrshp* 1993
Sales 57.8MM^E *EMP* 150
SIC 5511 Automobiles, new & used; Automobiles, new & used
Pr: Michael Henry
**Sec:* Michael Farley
Genl Mgr: Mike Frizell
Sls Mgr: Mike Bohning
Sls Mgr: Danny Henderson
Sls Mgr: Wayne Jackson
Sls Mgr: Eric Wells
Sales Asso: Tony Barnes
Sales Asso: Brian Braden
Sales Asso: Marte Christian
Sales Asso: Jody Dalton

KEYSTONE CLEARWATER SOLUTIONS
See WATER SOLUTIONS HOLDINGS LLC

D-U-N-S 04-813-1478
KEYSTONE COAL MINING CORP
(*Suby of* MURRAY ENERGY CORP) ★
1000 Consol Energy Dr, Canonsburg, PA 15317-6506
Tel (740) 338-3100 *Founded/Ownrshp* 2013
Sales 15.9MM^E *EMP* 425
SIC 1221 Bituminous coal surface mining; Bituminous coal surface mining
Pr: Bart Hyita
Treas: Daniel S Cangilla
VP: Alexander Reyes

D-U-N-S 07-599-9417
KEYSTONE COLLEGE
1 College Grn, La Plume, PA 18440-1099
Tel (570) 945-5141 *Founded/Ownrshp* 1868
Sales 39.3MM *EMP* 405
Accts Parentebeard Llc Wilkes Barre
SIC 8221 College, except junior; College, except junior
Pr: Edward G Boehm Jr
**Pr:* David Poppola
Treas: Lorrie Roberts
VP: Kevin Wilson
Exec: Tom Chapka
Genl Mgr: Michael Lusk
HC Dir: Sarah Keating

D-U-N-S 06-959-4729
KEYSTONE COMMUNITY RESOURCES INC
100 Abington Executive Pa, Clarks Summit, PA 18411-2260
Tel (570) 702-8000 *Founded/Ownrshp* 2006
Sales 22.1MM^E *EMP* 500^E
SIC 8361 8052 Home for the mentally handicapped; Intermediate care facilities; Home for the mentally handicapped; Intermediate care facilities
Pr: Robert Fleese
**Treas:* Henri Deutsch
**VP:* Raymond Fantuzzi

KEYSTONE CONCRETE PLACEMENT
See STEWART BUILDERS INC

D-U-N-S 00-512-9309 IMP
■ **KEYSTONE CONSOLIDATED INDUSTRIES INC**
(*Suby of* CONTRAN CORP) ★
5430 Lyndon B Johnson Fwy # 1740, Dallas, TX 75240-2601
Tel (972) 458-0028 *Founded/Ownrshp* 1889
Sales 201.7MM^E *EMP* 1,087
SIC 3312 3315 Bar, rod & wire products; Rods, iron & steel: made in steel mills; Wire products, steel or iron; Wire & fabricated wire products; Fencing made in wiredrawing plants; Barbed & twisted wire; Welded steel wire fabric; Bar, rod & wire products; Rods, iron & steel: made in steel mills; Wire products, steel or iron; Wire & fabricated wire products; Fencing made in wiredrawing plants; Barbed & twisted wire; Welded steel wire fabric
CEO: David L Cheek
**Ch Bd:* Glenn R Simmons
Pr: C Vic Stirnaman
CFO: Bert E Downing Jr
VP: Mark S Brachbill
VP: Kelly D Luttmer
CTO: Saundra Hess

D-U-N-S 07-976-9785
KEYSTONE CONSOLIDATED INDUSTRIES INC
7000 S Adams St, Peoria, IL 61641-0002
Tel (800) 447-6444 *Founded/Ownrshp* 2015
Sales 32.9MM^E *EMP* 38^E
SIC 5051 Rods, wire (not insulated)
CEO: Chris Armstrong

D-U-N-S 13-202-1762
KEYSTONE CONSTRUCTORS INC
121 Sarratt School Rd, Gaffney, SC 29341-3132
Tel (864) 488-2505 *Founded/Ownrshp* 2002
Sales 41.0MM^E *EMP* 120
SIC 1711 1731 3443 Mechanical contractor; Process piping contractor; Electric power systems contractors; Industrial vessels, tanks & containers; Mechanical contractor; Process piping contractor; Electric power systems contractors; Industrial vessels, tanks & containers
Pr: James Penn
**VP:* David B Shehan
Off Mgr: Joan Penn
MIS Dir: Ross Gossett

D-U-N-S 08-650-4417
KEYSTONE DEDICATED LOGISTICS CO LLC
KDL
800 N Bell Ave Ste 100, Carnegie, PA 15106-4316
Tel (412) 227-5148 *Founded/Ownrshp* 1999
Sales 30.3MM^E *EMP* 39
Accts Schneider Downs & Co Inc P
SIC 4731 Freight transportation arrangement
Trfc Dir: Dan Resanovich
Sls Dir: Tom Cannizzo
Sls Mgr: Jim Page

D-U-N-S 82-583-8907
KEYSTONE DIGITAL IMAGING INC
200 Racoosin Dr Ste 101, Aston, PA 19014-1572
Tel (610) 604-0300 *Founded/Ownrshp* 2000
Sales 40.4MM^E *EMP* 135^E
SIC 7373 Local area network (LAN) systems integrator; Local area network (LAN) systems integrator
Pr: Ricardo Salcedo
**Pr:* Ed Peach
Ofcr: Greg Bryan
Ofcr: Jeffery France
VP Sls: Don Schatzman
Mktg Dir: Lisa Richards
Sls Dir: Bob Earley
Sls Dir: Larry Emerson
Sls Dir: Jim Pucci

D-U-N-S 06-856-7171
KEYSTONE DODGE INC
VALLEY VEHICLE LEASING
2350 Lehigh St, Allentown, PA 18103-4786
Tel (610) 791-1900 *Founded/Ownrshp* 1984
Sales 20.8MM^E *EMP* 50
SIC 5511 Automobiles, new & used; Pickups, new & used; Vans, new & used
Pr: Charles E Merrill III
**VP:* Charles E Merrill IV

D-U-N-S 62-806-2754
KEYSTONE DRILL SERVICES LLC (DE)
184 Alisa St, Somerset, PA 15501-7742
Tel (814) 443-2670 *Founded/Ownrshp* 2008
Sales 41.2MM^E *EMP* 100
SIC 5084 7359 Drilling bits; Drilling equipment, excluding bits; Tool rental
Pr: Tom Walker
CFO: Stephanie Verna

D-U-N-S 14-702-3449
■ **KEYSTONE EDUCATION AND YOUTH SERVICES LLC**
(*Suby of* UNIVERSAL HEALTH SERVICES INC) ★
3401 West End Ave Ste 400, Nashville, TN 37203-6847
Tel (615) 250-0000 *Founded/Ownrshp* 2000
Sales 15.4MM^E *EMP* 2,200^E
SIC 8299 8322 Educational services; Child related social services; Educational services; Child related social services
VP: Buddy Turner

D-U-N-S 00-530-4332
KEYSTONE ELECTRICAL MANUFACTURING CO (IA)
2511 Bell Ave, Des Moines, IA 50321-1118
Tel (515) 283-2567 *Founded/Ownrshp* 1964
Sales 26.0MM *EMP* 70
SIC 3625 3613 Switchgear & switchboard apparatus; Relays & industrial controls; Relays & industrial controls; Switchgear & switchboard apparatus
Pr: Frederick V Buie
**VP:* Valdeska Buie
Mktg Dir: Jessy Rombou

D-U-N-S 10-719-0969
KEYSTONE FAMILY HEALTH PLAN
KEYSTONE FIRST
200 Stevens Dr, Philadelphia, PA 19113-1520
Tel (215) 937-8000 *Founded/Ownrshp* 1996
Sales NA *EMP* 1,500
SIC 6324 Hospital & medical service plans; Hospital & medical service plans
CEO: Michael Rashid
Pt: Independence Blue Cross
Pt: Mercy Health Plan
Pr: Jay Feldstein
Sr VP: Maria Pajil Battle
Sr VP: Christopher Drumm
Sr VP: William Morsell
Sr VP: Carol Muldoon
VP: Scott Bass
VP: Amy Knapp
Ex Dir: Russell Gianforcaro

KEYSTONE FIRST
See KEYSTONE FAMILY HEALTH PLAN

D-U-N-S 00-214-5571
KEYSTONE FOLDING BOX CO (NJ)
367 Verona Ave, Newark, NJ 07104-1713
Tel (973) 483-1054 *Founded/Ownrshp* 1890
Sales 34.7MM^E *EMP* 75
SIC 2657 Folding paperboard boxes
Pr: Wade E Hartman
Ex VP: Harold E Hartman II
Ex VP: Harold Hartman
**VP:* William Hartman
Ql Cn Mgr: Richard Rossbach

D-U-N-S 00-238-8130 IMP
KEYSTONE FOOD PRODUCTS INC (PA)
3767 Hecktown Rd, Easton, PA 18045-2350
Tel (610) 258-2706 *Founded/Ownrshp* 1946
Sales 45.1MM^E *EMP* 150
SIC 2096 Potato chips & similar snacks; Pork rinds; Cheese curls & puffs; Popcorn, already popped (except candy covered); Potato chips & similar snacks; Pork rinds; Cheese curls & puffs; Popcorn, already popped (except candy covered)
Ch Bd: William Corriere Sr
**Pr:* William Corriere
**CEO:* William Corriere Jr
**VP:* Ford Corriere
Plnt Mgr: Robert Fosburg
VP Sls: Eduardo Gonzalez
S&M/VP: Chris Busse
Manager: Chuck Curtis
Manager: Ron Tappan

KEYSTONE FOODS
See EQUITY GROUP EUFAULA DIVISION LLC

D-U-N-S 06-988-8717
KEYSTONE FOODS LLC
M & M RESTAURANT SUPPLY
(*Suby of* MARFRIG GLOBAL FOODS S/A.)
300 Barr Harbor Dr # 850, Conshohocken, PA 19428-3809
Tel (610) 667-6700 *Founded/Ownrshp* 2010
Sales 532.2MM^E *EMP* 3,753
SIC 2013 2015 5087

KEYSTONE FORD
See MAR-ECO INC

D-U-N-S 04-405-3353
KEYSTONE FORD INC
12000 Firestone Blvd, Norwalk, CA 90650-2907
Tel (562) 868-0825 *Founded/Ownrshp* 1977
Sales 30.5MM *EMP* 150
SIC 5511 5531 7514 Automobiles, new & used; Pickups, new & used; Vans, new & used; Automotive parts; Rent-a-car service; Automobiles, new & used; Pickups, new & used; Vans, new & used; Automotive parts; Rent-a-car service
Pr: Norman P Stutzke
**Treas:* Paul Stutzke
**VP:* Lamberto Colon

D-U-N-S 00-304-5085 IMP
KEYSTONE FORGING CO (PA)
215 Duke St, Northumberland, PA 17857-1838
Tel (570) 473-3524 *Founded/Ownrshp* 1895
Sales 34.4MM^E *EMP* 105
SIC 3462 3463 Iron & steel forgings; Nonferrous forgings; Iron & steel forgings; Nonferrous forgings
Pr: Joseph Cipriani
**Ch Bd:* Fred Schluter Jr
VP: Michael Kratzer
Ql Cn Mgr: Roger Snook

D-U-N-S 15-433-1227
KEYSTONE FREIGHT CORP
(*Suby of* N R S) ★
2820 16th St, North Bergen, NJ 07047-1541
Tel (201) 330-1900 *Founded/Ownrshp* 1985
Sales 50.7MM^E *EMP* 300
SIC 4213 4212 Trucking, except local; Local trucking, without storage; Trucking, except local; Local trucking, without storage
CEO: Donna Walsh
**Pr:* Raymond Wisniewski

D-U-N-S 00-303-5763 IMP
KEYSTONE FRICTION HINGE CO (PA)
520 Matthews Blvd, Williamsport, PA 17702-7243
Tel (570) 321-0693 *Founded/Ownrshp* 1905, 1965
Sales 20.6MM^E *EMP* 110
Accts Eberhart Flanigan & Rogers I
SIC 3469 3429 Metal stampings; Furniture hardware
Pr: Edward J Hannan
**Treas:* Creighton Mac Gill

D-U-N-S 01-589-6806
KEYSTONE GROUP HOLDINGS INC
KEY AMERICA
4901 Vineland Rd Ste 350, Orlando, FL 32811-7192
Tel (813) 225-4650 *Founded/Ownrshp* 1996
Sales 41.7MM^E *EMP* 1,375
SIC 7389 7261 Brokers' services; Funeral home; Brokers' services; Funeral home
CEO: Steven Tidwell
**Pr:* Steve Tidwell
**COO:* Jim Price
**CFO:* Steve Shaffer
**VP:* Gary Baker
**VP:* Richard Wood
Sales Exec: Mark Burley

KEYSTONE HEALTH
See KEYSTONE RURAL HEALTH CENTER

D-U-N-S 62-532-3969
KEYSTONE HEALTH PLAN CENTRAL INC
(*Suby of* CAPITAL BLUE CROSS) ★
2500 Elmerton Ave Ste 110, Harrisburg, PA 17177-9764
Tel (717) 541-7000 *Founded/Ownrshp* 1985
Sales NA *EMP* 450
SIC 6324 Health maintenance organization (HMO), insurance only; Health maintenance organization (HMO), insurance only
Ch Bd: Anita Smith
Ofcr: Deborah Ziegler
Sls Mgr: Tom Dunaway

D-U-N-S 16-166-6771
KEYSTONE HEALTH PLAN EAST INC
(*Suby of* BLUE CROSS) ★
1901 Market St Ste 1000, Philadelphia, PA 19103-1475
Tel (215) 241-2001 *Founded/Ownrshp* 1991
Sales NA *EMP* 696
Accts Deloitte & Touche Llp Philade
SIC 6324 8011 Health maintenance organization (HMO), insurance only; Health maintenance organization; Health maintenance organization (HMO), insurance only; Health maintenance organization
CEO: Joseph Frick
**Pr:* G Fred Dibona Jr
**COO:* John A Daddis
**CFO:* Thomas F Pappalardo
Sr VP: Stephen Udvarhelyi I

D-U-N-S 92-949-4789 IMP
KEYSTONE HOLDINGS INC
COLUMBIA
(*Suby of* DATWYLER HOLDING AG)
875 Center Dr, Vandalia, OH 45377-3129
Tel (937) 890-7464 *Founded/Ownrshp* 2014
Sales 22.4MM^E *EMP* 36
SIC 5085 Seals, industrial; Gaskets
Pr: William Shannon

D-U-N-S 12-967-3443 IMP/EXP
KEYSTONE HOLDINGS LLC
10 Nw 42nd Ave Ste 700, Miami, FL 33126-5473
Tel (305) 567-1577 *Founded/Ownrshp* 2002
Sales 688.6MM^E *EMP* 6,102
SIC 8711 3053 3081 3082 3545 Porcelain electrical supplies; Gaskets, packing & sealing devices; Unsupported plastics film & sheet; Unsupported plastics profile shapes; Machine tool accessories; Construction & civil engineering; Gaskets, packing & sealing devices; Unsupported plastics film & sheet; Unsupported plastics profile shapes; Machine tool accessories
CFO: Steve Rasa

D-U-N-S 79-806-2204
KEYSTONE HOME HEALTH SERVICES INC
8765 Stenton Ave, Philadelphia, PA 19188-0001
Tel (215) 836-2440 *Founded/Ownrshp* 1992
Sales 7.5MM *EMP* 300
Accts Carpenter & Onorato Pc
SIC 8082 Home health care services; Home health care services
Pr: Joan Reese

D-U-N-S 01-205-9553
KEYSTONE HUMAN SERVICES
124 Pine St, Harrisburg, PA 17101-1208
Tel (717) 232-7509 *Founded/Ownrshp* 1999
Sales 11.5MM *EMP* 500
SIC 8322 Individual & family services; Individual & family services
Pr: Dennis W Felty
COO: Norman Whitman
CFO: Charles Sweeder
**Sr VP:* Charles J Hooker III
VP: Lora Ball
VP: Christina Diehl
VP: Fatima Dumbuya
VP: John Ferdinand
VP: Eileen Scott
Ex Dir: Carol A Amy
Ex Dir: Robert Bausinger

KEYSTONE INSURANCE CO
See CSAA AFFINITY INSURANCE CO

D-U-N-S 06-340-7365
KEYSTONE LANDFILL INC
(*Suby of* DENAPLES AUTO PARTS INC) ★
249 Dunham Dr, Dunmore, PA 18512-2686
Tel (570) 343-5782 *Founded/Ownrshp* 1973
Sales 47.9MM^E *EMP* 90
SIC 4953 Sanitary landfill operation
Pr: Louis A Denaples
Sec: Savario Denaples
VP: Dominick Denaples

D-U-N-S 00-433-1278
KEYSTONE LIME CO (PA)
1156 Christner Hollow Rd, Springs, PA 15562
Tel (814) 662-2025 *Founded/Ownrshp* 1928, 1974
Sales 25.8MM^E *EMP* 95

SIC 1611 1422 3274 Highway & street construction; Crushed & broken limestone; Agricultural lime; Highway & street construction; Crushed & broken limestone; Agricultural lime
Pr: Melinda F Gibson
**VP:* Melinda Walker
**Treas:* Kendra K Geiger
**VP:* Lura M Folk

KEYSTONE MANAGEMENT GROUP
See KMG PRESTIGE INC

KEYSTONE MERCY HEALTH PLAN
See MERCY HEALTH PLAN INC

D-U-N-S 17-766-6604
KEYSTONE MILLS LLC
1975 State Route 336, Romulus, NY 14541-9744
Tel (315) 549-8226 *Founded/Ownrshp* 1996
Sales 30.3MM^E *EMP* 40
SIC 5191 Feed
CFO: Jamie Mesmer

KEYSTONE MOTORS
See ALFRED STEIN INC

KEYSTONE MUNICIPAL COLLECTIONS
See KRATZENBERG & ASSOCIATES INC

D-U-N-S 17-451-9017
■ **KEYSTONE NPS LLC**
KEYSTONE SCHOOLS-RAMONA
(*Suby of* CHILDRENS COMPREHENSIVE SERVICES INC) ★
11980 Mount Vernon Ave, Grand Terrace, CA 92313-5172
Tel (909) 633-6354 *Founded/Ownrshp* 1988
Sales 18.3MM^E *EMP* 750
SIC 8399 Advocacy group; Advocacy group
Prin: Alfredo Alvarado
**CFO:* Don Whitfield
**Ex VP:* Martha Petrey
Off Mgr: Donna Estrada

KEYSTONE OILFIELD FABRICATION
See KEYSTONE SYNERGY LLC

D-U-N-S 06-995-1135
KEYSTONE PACIFIC PROPERTY MANAGEMENT INC
REFLECTIONS AND ENCLAVE HOA
16775 Von Karman Ave # 100, Irvine, CA 92606-4966
Tel (949) 833-2600 *Founded/Ownrshp* 1982
Sales 20.3MM^E *EMP* 56
SIC 6531 Real estate managers
Pr: Cary Treff
**COO:* Denise Bergstrom
**CFO:* Gerry Kay
**VP:* Jaime Chandler
VP: Sarah Miller
VP: Mike Smith
**VP:* Tim Taylor
VP Mktg: Joseph Winkler

D-U-N-S 01-884-7061
KEYSTONE PAPER & BOX CO INC
31 Edwin Rd, South Windsor, CT 06074-2413
Tel (860) 291-0027 *Founded/Ownrshp* 1944
Sales 23.8MM^E *EMP* 52
SIC 2657 2631 Folding paperboard boxes; Container, packaging & boxboard
Pr: James Rutt
VP: Mike Hryzak
QA Dir: Kathy Caron

D-U-N-S 15-542-1159
KEYSTONE PEER REVIEW ORGANIZATION INC
KEPRO
777 E Park Dr, Harrisburg, PA 17111-2754
Tel (717) 564-8288 *Founded/Ownrshp* 2014
Sales 40.2MM^E *EMP* 1,000
SIC 8099

D-U-N-S 01-101-9110
KEYSTONE PIZZA PARTNERS LLC
PIZZA HUT
1338 Pawnee Ln, Leawood, KS 66209
Tel (913) 948-8350 *Founded/Ownrshp* 2008
Sales 20.0MM *EMP* 600
SIC 5812 Pizzeria, chain; Pizzeria, chain

D-U-N-S 00-210-3174 IMP
KEYSTONE POWDERED METAL CO (PA)
251 State St, Saint Marys, PA 15857-1658
Tel (814) 781-1591 *Founded/Ownrshp* 1927
Sales 127.1MM^E *EMP* 770
SIC 3399 3568 Powder, metal; Power transmission equipment; Powder, metal; Power transmission equipment
Pr: Conrad I Kogovsek III
Pr: Gary Anderson
**Treas:* Douglas I Thomas
VP: John Cerroni
**VP:* Michael G Stauffer
**VP:* Michael Werner
Genl Mgr: Pete Imbrogno
CIO: John Cerrome
QA Dir: Denny Piccirillo
Plnt Mgr: Randy Dacanal
Plnt Mgr: Paul Orr

D-U-N-S 13-447-5636 IMP
KEYSTONE PROFILES LTD
220 7th Ave, Beaver Falls, PA 15010-3274
Tel (724) 846-0823 *Founded/Ownrshp* 2003
Sales 31.3MM^E *EMP* 63
SIC 3316 Cold finishing of steel shapes
Pr: Mark H Breedlove
Sls Mgr: Jeff Strum
Sales Asso: Phyllis Grubb
Sales Asso: Kay Murphy

D-U-N-S 94-723-3797
KEYSTONE QUALITY TRANSPORT CO
1260 E Wdlnd Ave Ste 220, Springfield, PA 19064
Tel (215) 492-5880 *Founded/Ownrshp* 1993
Sales 25.0MM^E *EMP* 240
SIC 4119 7363 Local passenger transportation; Medical help service; Local passenger transportation; Medical help service
Pr: Stephen Barr
**Ex VP:* Neil Brady
**VP:* Barb Lamanna
IT Man: Kevin Smith

KEYSTONE RESORT
See VAIL SUMMIT RESORTS INC

D-U-N-S 79-623-5653
KEYSTONE RURAL HEALTH CENTER
KEYSTONE HEALTH
755 Norland Ave Ste 200, Chambersburg, PA 17201-4223
Tel (717) 709-7900 *Founded/Ownrshp* 1987
Sales 31.4MM *EMP* 330
Accts Smith Elliott Kearns & Company
SIC 8011 Clinic, operated by physicians; Clinic, operated by physicians
Pr: Joanne Cochran
**Ch:* Sam King
CIO: Daryl Rock
Doctor: Stephen Flack
Doctor: Stephen Henderson
Doctor: Michael Patti
Doctor: Mary Varkey

D-U-N-S 92-781-1950
■ **KEYSTONE RV CO**
(*Suby of* THOR INDUSTRIES INC) ★
2642 Hackberry Dr, Goshen, IN 46526-6811
Tel (574) 534-9430 *Founded/Ownrshp* 2001
Sales 393.0MM^E *EMP* 1,851
SIC 3792 Travel trailers & campers; Travel trailer chassis; Campers, for mounting on trucks; Travel trailers & campers; Travel trailer chassis; Campers, for mounting on trucks
Pr: H Coleman Davis III
Pr: Bullock Mark
**COO:* David Chupp
**CFO:* Tonya Lucchese
**Treas:* Lon Franklin
Ex VP: Doug Rheinheimer
VP: Jeff Runels
Exec: Bill Wilson
Genl Mgr: Bren Lauck
CTO: Kevin Silcox
Dir IT: Steve Sausman

KEYSTONE SCHOOLS-RAMONA
See KEYSTONE NPS LLC

KEYSTONE SENIOR CAPITAL
See KEYSTONE SENIOR LLC

D-U-N-S 17-591-6584
KEYSTONE SENIOR LLC
KEYSTONE SENIOR CAPITAL
3965 Airport Dr, Indianapolis, IN 46254-5845
Tel (317) 280-8455 *Founded/Ownrshp* 1997
Sales 27.4MM^E *EMP* 165
SIC 6552 1522 Land subdividers & developers, residential; Multi-family dwellings, new construction
Sr VP: Bradley Wood
Ex Dir: Kent Mulkey

D-U-N-S 01-505-8670
KEYSTONE SERVICE CENTER INC
7108 W Chester Pike, Upper Darby, PA 19082-2202
Tel (610) 352-4474 *Founded/Ownrshp* 1986
Sales 89.6MM *EMP* 2
SIC 7538 General automotive repair shops; General automotive repair shops
Pr: Ki Kim

D-U-N-S 05-608-2233
KEYSTONE SERVICE SYSTEMS INC
124 Pine St, Harrisburg, PA 17101-1208
Tel (717) 232-7509 *Founded/Ownrshp* 1972
Sales 121.6MM *EMP* 3,000
Accts Kpmg Llp Harrisburg Pennsylv
SIC 8361 Home for the mentally handicapped; Home for the mentally handicapped
CEO: Robert J Baker
**Pr:* Dennis W Felty
**CFO:* Charles J Hooker III
**Treas:* Roger W Burns

D-U-N-S 00-893-7922
KEYSTONE SHIPPING CO
(*Suby of* CHAS KURZ & CO INC)
1 Bala Plz Ste 600, Bala Cynwyd, PA 19004-1496
Tel (610) 617-6800 *Founded/Ownrshp* 1941
Sales 87.0MM^E *EMP* 1,000
SIC 4731 4412 4424 Agents, shipping; Deep sea foreign transportation of freight; Coastwide transportation, freight; Agents, shipping; Deep sea foreign transportation of freight; Coastwide transportation, freight
Pr: Robert K Kurz
**Treas:* J A Wassel
Treas: J A Wssel
**VP:* Mitchell K Koslow
**VP:* Donald R Kurz
CIO: Louis Cavaliere
IT Man: Mary Specht
IT Man: Mike Westergom
VP Opers: Bruce Fernie
Sfty Mgr: Tim O'Conner
Snr Mgr: Bruce Bonnecarrere
Board of Directors: J F Fricko

D-U-N-S 02-089-9657
KEYSTONE SYNERGY LLC (TX)
KEYSTONE OILFIELD FABRICATION
1870 Illinois St, Rhome, TX 76078-4280
Tel (817) 636-3300 *Founded/Ownrshp* 2009
Sales 25.1MM^E *EMP* 80
SIC 3533 5051 Oil field machinery & equipment; Steel

D-U-N-S 82-914-4588 IMP
KEYSTONE TEXTILE INC
1201 Mateo St, Los Angeles, CA 90021-1737
Tel (213) 622-7755 *Founded/Ownrshp* 2008
Sales 21.0MM *EMP* 15
SIC 2241 Manmade fiber narrow woven fabrics; Manmade fiber narrow woven fabrics
Pr: Jason Cho
**VP:* Kenny Hwang

D-U-N-S 62-532-4470
KEYSTONE TURF CLUB INC
PHILADELPHIA PARK
(*Suby of* GREENWOOD RACING INC) ★
3001 Street Rd, Bensalem, PA 19020-2006
Tel (215) 639-9000 *Founded/Ownrshp* 1989
Sales NA *EMP* 800
SIC 6719 Investment holding companies, except banks; Investment holding companies, except banks
CEO: Robert W Green
**COO:* William Hogwood
CFO: Tony Ricci
**Sec:* Anthony Ricci
Sr VP: Andy Green
VP: Bill Fleck
VP: Mike Jaffe
VP: Dave Norcutt
Exec: Susan Eckert
Mng Ofcr: Ron Davis
MIS Dir: Gary Prestage

D-U-N-S 09-089-0922
KEYSTONE WEST INC
3749 N Cloverdale Rd, Boise, ID 83713-3610
Tel (208) 376-7298 *Founded/Ownrshp* 1996
Sales 12.0MM *EMP* 600
SIC 8051 Skilled nursing care facilities; Skilled nursing care facilities
Pr: Keith Flecther
**Treas:* Jason Fletcher
**VP:* Roger Malm

D-U-N-S 05-758-9384
KEYSTOPS LLC
KEY OIL CO
376 Reasonover Ave, Franklin, KY 42134-4003
Tel (270) 586-8283 *Founded/Ownrshp* 1999
Sales 900.1MM *EMP* 200
Accts Bkd Llp Bowling Green Ky
SIC 5541 5171 Truck stops; Petroleum bulk stations; Truck stops; Petroleum bulk stations

D-U-N-S 12-668-7891
KEYSTROKES TRANSCRIPTION SERVICE INC
220 Garden St, Yorkville, IL 60560-8921
Tel (630) 553-3680 *Founded/Ownrshp* 2002
Sales 31.9MM^E *EMP* 602
SIC 8099 Medical services organization; Medical services organization
Pr: Lee Tkachuk

D-U-N-S 88-481-2330
KEYSTRUCT CONSTRUCTION INC
30 Marianne Dr, York, PA 17406-8406
Tel (717) 764-1326 *Founded/Ownrshp* 1995
Sales 30.3MM^E *EMP* 50
SIC 1542 1541 Commercial & office building, new construction; Industrial buildings, new construction
Pr: Jerry L Watson
**Treas:* Deanna Copp
**VP:* Douglas M Leister
Snr Mgr: Bill Loy

KEYTRONICEMS
See KEYTRONIC CORP

D-U-N-S 07-879-1834
■ **KEYW CORP**
(*Suby of* KEYW HOLDING CORP) ★
250 Clark St, North Andover, MA 01845-1018
Tel (978) 682-7767 *Founded/Ownrshp* 2012
Sales 290.5MM^E *EMP* 1,100^E
SIC 7371 8713 7389 Computer software systems analysis & design, custom; Photogrammetric engineering; Photogrammatic mapping; Computer software systems analysis & design, custom; Photogrammetric engineering; Photogrammatic mapping

D-U-N-S 82-711-0136
■ **KEYW CORP**
(*Suby of* KEYW HOLDING CORP) ★
7740 Milestone Pkwy # 400, Hanover, MD 21076-1754
Tel (443) 733-1600 *Founded/Ownrshp* 2008
Sales 290.5MM^E *EMP* 1,100
Accts Grant Thornton Llp Baltimore
SIC 8711 8748 Engineering services; Engineering services; Testing services
Pr: William J Weber
CEO: John G Hannon
COO: Mark Willard
CFO: Philip Calamia
CFO: John Krobath
CFO: Caroline S Pisano
Sr VP: Greg Dixon
VP: Jack Russell
Prgrm Mgr: Russ Barnes
Prgrm Mgr: Judson Bennett
Prgrm Mgr: Peter Buckingham
Board of Directors: Pierre Chao

D-U-N-S 96-166-5820
▲ **KEYW HOLDING CORP**
7740 Milestone Pkwy # 400, Hanover, MD 21076-1754
Tel (443) 733-1600 *Founded/Ownrshp* 2008
Sales 290.5MM *EMP* 1,100^E
Tkr Sym KEYW *Exch* NGS
SIC 7373 7372 8731 7375 Computer integrated systems design; Prepackaged software; Computer (hardware) development; Information retrieval services; Computer integrated systems design; Prepackaged software; Computer (hardware) development; Information retrieval services
Pr: Mark A Willard
**Ch Bd:* Caroline S Pisano
CFO: Philip L Calamia
Ofcr: Kimberly J Dechello
Ex VP: Chris Fedde
CTO: Bruce Potter
Board of Directors: Deborah A Bonanni, William I Campbell, Pierre A Chao, John G Hannon, Kenneth A Minihan, Arthur L Money

D-U-N-S 07-924-5811
KEYWELL METALS LLC
(*Suby of* PROPHET EQUITY LP) ★
7808 W College Dr Ste 3ne, Palos Heights, IL 60463-1377
Tel (773) 660-2060 *Founded/Ownrshp* 2013
Sales 46.1MM^E *EMP* 80^E
SIC 5093 Metal scrap & waste materials
Pr: J Mark Lozier

D-U-N-S 10-795-8845
KEZI INC
KEZI TV 9
2975 Chad Dr, Eugene, OR 97408-7427
Tel (541) 485-5611 *Founded/Ownrshp* 1983
Sales 85.1MM^E *EMP* 250
SIC 4841 4833 6512 4813 Cable television services; Television broadcasting stations; Commercial & industrial building operation; ; Cable television services; Television broadcasting stations; Commercial & industrial building operation;
Ch Bd: Carolyn S Chambers
**Pr:* Scott Chambers
IT Man: Jim Plummer
Sls Mgr: Mike Boring
Sls Mgr: Gregory Hasser

KEZI TV 9
See KEZI INC

D-U-N-S 83-829-4445
KEZJMAN ENTERPRISES LTD
RAMADA INN
2216 W Landis Ave, Vineland, NJ 08360-3431
Tel (856) 696-3800 *Founded/Ownrshp* 1956
Sales 9.8MM^E *EMP* 500
SIC 7011 5812 Hotels & motels; Caterers; Hotels & motels; Caterers
Owner: Helen Kejzman

D-U-N-S 18-756-8977
KF FOODS INC
KITCHEN FRESH FOODS
1375 Gruber Rd, Green Bay, WI 54313-8938
Tel (920) 434-8874 *Founded/Ownrshp* 1988
Sales 28.1MM^E *EMP* 150
SIC 2099 5149 Sandwiches, assembled & packaged: for wholesale market; Sandwiches; Sandwiches, assembled & packaged: for wholesale market; Sandwiches
Pr: Timothy Neerdaels
**VP:* Steven Neerdaels

K.F. INDUSTRIES
See CIRCOR ENERGY PRODUCTS INC

KFC
See KENDALL HOUSE INC

KFC
See H & K PARTNERS LLC

KFC
See LUIHN FOOD SYSTEMS INC

KFC
See RAHEEL

KFC
See B & G DIVERSIFIED CONCEPTS LLC

KFC
See K-MAC ENTERPRISES INC

KFC
See HANNONS KENTUCKY FRIED CHICKEN OF JACKSON MISSISSIPPI

KFC
See PRYORS INC

KFC
See JACK MARSHALL FOODS INC

KFC
See LARIOT CORP

KFC
See TEM-KIL CO INC

KFC
See KENTUCKY FRIED CHICKEN OF NORTH LITTLE ROCK

KFC
See GGG FOODS INC

KFC
See KAZI FOODS CORP OF HAWAII

KFC
See K CORP LEE INC

KFC
See JRN INC

KFC
See HOMETOWN ENTERPRISES INC

KFC
See K F C NATIONAL MANAGEMENT CO

KFC
See WEST QUALITY FOOD SERVICE INC

KFC
See DOW SHERWOOD CORP

KFC
See FULENWIDER ENTERPRISES INC

KFC
See DAY ENTERPRISES INC

KFC
See SJ RESTAURANTS LLC

KFC
See PARIS & POTTER MANAGEMENT CORP

KFC
See KENTUCKY FRIED CHICKEN OF STATESBORO GEORGIA INC

KFC
See MORGANS RESTAURANT OF PENNSYLVANIA INC

KFC
See T R FOODS INC

KFC
See NATIONAL RESTAURANT DEVELOPMENT INC

KFC
See POLLYS INC

KFC
See NORTHWEST RESTAURANTS INC

KFC
See KENTUCKY FRIED CHICKEN CORP DE

KFC
See BARTLETT MANAGEMENT SERVICES INC

KFC
See WMCR CO

KFC
See FIELDS FAST FOODS FAMILY LIMITED PARTNERSHIP

KFC
See SOUTH SHORE RESTAURANT MANAGEMENT INC

KFC
See KENTUCKY FRIED CHICKEN OF LOUISVILLE INC

KFC
See TABLE ROCK RESTAURANTS LLC

KFC
See SUMMERWOOD CORP

KFC
See KAZI FOODS INC

KFC
See SOUTHWEST K F C INC

KFC
See S AND H INC

KFC
See SHAMROCK CO

D-U-N-S 04-143-4838
■ KFC CORP (DE)
(Suby of KENTUCKY FRIED CHICKEN CORP DE) ★
1900 Colonel Sanders Ln, Louisville, KY 40213-1970
Tel (502) 874-8300 Founded/Ownrshp 1997
Sales 492.5MM^E EMP 24,000
SIC 5812 6794 Fast-food restaurant, chain; Franchises, selling or licensing; Fast-food restaurant, chain; Franchises, selling or licensing
CEO: David Novak
*Pr: Chuck Rawley
COO: Tony Mastropaolo
CFO: Kathy Corsi
*Chf Cred: Terry Davenport
Ofcr: Joanne Towery
VP: Matt Kelly
VP: Jerry Merritt
VP: Jeff Rager
VP: Allan Scott
Genl Mgr: Melinda Rafuse

KFCU
See KEESLER FEDERAL CREDIT UNION

D-U-N-S 78-504-5720 IMP
KFH INDUSTRIES INC
2926 Columbia Hwy, Dothan, AL 36303-5406
Tel (334) 671-5532 Founded/Ownrshp 2006
Sales 30.0MM EMP 135
SIC 3569 Firehose, except rubber; Firehose, except rubber
Pr: Charles Genthner
*CFO: Larry Donegan
*VP: Robert Gourlay

KFMB 760 AM
See MIDWEST TELEVISION INC

D-U-N-S 00-467-0829
■ KFORCE GOVERNMENT HOLDINGS INC
(Suby of KFORCE INC) ★
1001 E Palm Ave, Tampa, FL 33605-3551
Tel (813) 552-5000 Founded/Ownrshp 2000
Sales 77.8MM^E EMP 1,095
SIC 6719 Investment holding companies, except banks; Investment holding companies, except banks
CEO: Patrick Moneymaker
*Ofcr: William Turner

D-U-N-S 06-570-3209
■ KFORCE GOVERNMENT SOLUTIONS INC
(Suby of KFORCE GOVERNMENT HOLDINGS INC) ★
2677 Prosperity Ave # 100, Fairfax, VA 22031-4928
Tel (703) 245-7350 Founded/Ownrshp 2006
Sales 90.7MM^E EMP 948
SIC 7379 Computer related consulting services; Computer related consulting services
CEO: Patrick D Moneymaker
V Ch: Richard M Cocchiaro
CFO: Marc M Herman
Treas: Judy M Genshino
Ofcr: Mike Ettore
Ofcr: Randy Marmon
Ofcr: Richard Orpin
*Sr VP: Karen L Bell
Sr VP: Michael R Blackman
Sr VP: Jill Carney
Sr VP: Andrew Thomas
VP: Anton T Hartman
VP: Paul Hull
VP: David Kelly
VP: Alyssa Krisko
VP: Kathleen Massie
VP: Virg Palumbo
VP: Joseph Rhodes
VP Bus Dev: Keith Griffin
VP Bus: Graham M Palmer

D-U-N-S 05-828-7814
▲ KFORCE INC
1001 E Palm Ave, Tampa, FL 33605-3551
Tel (813) 552-5000 Founded/Ownrshp 1962
Sales 1.2MMM EMP 2,600
Tkr Sym KFRC Exch NGS
SIC 7363 7361 Help supply services; Employment agencies; Help supply services; Employment agencies
Ch Bd: David L Dunkel
Pr: Randy Kehrmeyer
Pr: Joseph J Liberatore
COO: Kye Mitchell
CFO: David M Kelly
Ofcr: Graig Paglieri
Sr VP: Larry Huffman
VP: Michael Follin
Exec: Roxanne Bowser
Exec: Nichole Cutler
Exec: Matt Duvall
Exec: Michael Garassino
Exec: James Irvin
Exec: Chris Isaac
Exec: Casey Jacox
Exec: Helen Pendleton
Exec: Jim Pierrakos
Exec: Richard Raniere
Exec: John Vagie
Exec: Paul Williams
Dir Bus: Jennifer Carswell
Board of Directors: John N Allred, Richard M Cocchiaro, Mark F Furlong, Elaine D Rosen, N John Simmons, Ralph E Struzziero, Howard W Sutter, A Gordon Tunstall

D-U-N-S 07-937-8967
KFORCE SERVICES CORP
1001 E Palm Ave, Tampa, FL 33605-3551
Tel (813) 552-3734 Founded/Ownrshp 2014
Sales 24.0MM^E EMP 1,000
SIC 7361 Employment agencies
CEO: David Dunkel

D-U-N-S 60-303-9454 IMP/EXP
KFS INC
186 Intermodal Pkwy, Fort Worth, TX 76177-4514
Tel (682) 831-0001 Founded/Ownrshp 1989
Sales 27.6MM^E EMP 53
SIC 4214 4212 4581 4731 Local trucking with storage; Local trucking, without storage; Air freight handling at airports; Freight transportation arrangement
Pr: James F Keller
*Ch: Sam Dimiao
*Treas: James Wirth
*VP: Alec Gizzi
*VP: Matt Keller
Opers Mgr: Tony Rubalcava

KG POWER SYSTEMS
See K & G ELECTRIC MOTOR & PUMP CORP

D-U-N-S 17-669-0378
KGBO HOLDINGS INC
4289 Ivy Pointe Blvd, Cincinnati, OH 45245-0002
Tel (513) 831-2600 Founded/Ownrshp 2006
Sales 2.1MMM EMP 2,150^E
Accts Barnes Dennig & Co Ltd Ci
SIC 4731 Truck transportation brokers; Truck transportation brokers
Pr: Kenneth Oaks
Sr Cor Off: Ryan Legg
Ex VP: Kerry Byrne
Sls&Mrk Ex: Destiny Palcic

D-U-N-S 16-927-5489
■ KGEN HOT SPRING LLC
(Suby of ENTERGY ARKANSAS INC) ★
696 Black Branch Rd, Malvern, AR 72104-6897
Tel (501) 609-4600 Founded/Ownrshp 2012
Sales 1.8MMM^E EMP 2^E
SIC 4911 Electric services

KGI
See KECK GRADUATE INSTITUTE

KGL
See KELLY GLOBAL LOGISTICS INC

D-U-N-S 11-287-8061
KGM CONTRACTORS INC
9211 Highway 53, Angora, MN 55703-8239
Tel (218) 666-5698 Founded/Ownrshp 1979
Sales 45.0MM^E EMP 30
SIC 1611 Grading; Grading
Pr: Karla Abramson
*Sec: Mark Abramson
*VP: Gary Abramson

D-U-N-S 61-726-4478
■ KGO TELEVISION INC
ABC7 BROADCAST CENTER
(Suby of ABC HOLDING CO INC) ★
900 Front St, San Francisco, CA 94111-1413
Tel (415) 954-7777 Founded/Ownrshp 1949
Sales 25.7MM^E EMP 230
SIC 4833 Television broadcasting stations; Television broadcasting stations
Pr: Bill Burton
VP: Todd Farber
VP: David Rosati
Prd Dir: Mike Amatori

KGON
See ENTERCOM PORTLAND LLC

D-U-N-S 04-760-9094
KGP GROUP INC
SPEQTRUM
1404 Everman Pkwy, Fort Worth, TX 76140-5006
Tel (817) 354-0766 Founded/Ownrshp 2002
Sales 20.6MM^E EMP 100
SIC 3423 3555 3069 Cutting dies, except metal cutting; Printing plates; Sponge rubber & sponge rubber products
Ch: Steven R Purvis
*Pr: Kelly G Vaughn
*CEO: Gregory D Burger
IT Man: Steve Chastain

KGP LOGISTICS
See KGP TELECOMMUNICATIONS INC

D-U-N-S 11-336-4301
KGP PRODUCTS INC
PREMIER
(Suby of KGP LOGISTICS) ★
600 New Century Pkwy, New Century, KS 66031-1101
Tel (800) 755-1950 Founded/Ownrshp 2006
Sales 112.9MM^E EMP 192^E
SIC 3661 Telephones & telephone apparatus; Facsimile equipment
CEO: Kathleen G Putrah
VP: Tim Texley
Exec: Randy Aldridge
Dir Bus: Richard Snyder
Prgrm Mgr: Bradly Griggs
Netwrk Eng: Charles Holoman
VP Opers: Richard Summers
Opers Mgr: Larry Liles
Sls Mgr: Skip Miller

D-U-N-S 14-850-4814
KGP TELECOMMUNICATIONS INC
KGP LOGISTICS
3305 Highway 60 W, Faribault, MN 55021-4869
Tel (507) 334-2268 Founded/Ownrshp 1975
Sales 1.0MMM^E EMP 1,248
SIC 5065 Telephone equipment; Telephone equipment
CEO: Kathleen G Putrah
COO: Trevor Putrah
CFO: Stuart Romenesko
CFO: Don Shaffer
VP: Steven Locke
VP: Ken Marcotte
VP: Tim Putrah
VP: Cheryl Riggle
VP: Hal Wooden
Dir IT: Jim Smith
Netwrk Eng: Floyd Nunn

KGS ELECTRIC
See DON KRUEGER CONSTRUCTION CO

D-U-N-S 60-315-7512
KGS STEEL INC
3725 Pine Ln Se, Bessemer, AL 35022-5642
Tel (205) 425-0800 Founded/Ownrshp 1986
Sales 32.0MM^E EMP 60
SIC 5051 Iron & steel (ferrous) products; Iron & steel (ferrous) products
Pr: Gaston Stein
Mng Pt: Mark Lawrence
*VP: Kerry Stein
*VP: Scott Stein
IT Man: Al Boohaker
Opers Mgr: Jeff Hubbard
Plnt Mgr: Jeff Hubbert
Sales Asso: Thomas Hager

D-U-N-S 00-309-0742
KH PHILADELPHIA-HAVERTOWN
4510 KH HAVERTON
2000 Old W Chester Pike, Havertown, PA 19083-2712
Tel (610) 853-2572 Founded/Ownrshp 2010
Sales NA EMP 189
SIC 6324 Hospital & medical service plans; Hospital & medical service plans
Ex Dir: Margaret Murphy
*CEO: Elizabeth Younkins

D-U-N-S 18-432-1479
KHA HOLDINGS INC
5202 Old Orchard Rd N700, Skokie, IL 60077-4407
Tel (847) 965-3273 Founded/Ownrshp 1985
Sales 26.6MM^E EMP 75
SIC 8742 Financial consultant; Hospital & health services consultant
CEO: Kenneth Kaufman
*CFO: Andrew Majka
*CFO: Sandra Nuccio
CFO: Sandy Nuccio
Sr VP: Brian Fuller
Sr VP: Jason Hahn
Sr VP: Steven Hollis
Sr VP: Matthew Lambert
Sr VP: Glenn Wagner
VP: Jeff Asik
VP: Andrew Cohen
VP: Scott Engel
VP: Kevin Neuman
VP: Jason Oriordan
VP: David Ratliff
VP: Debra Ryan
*VP: Jason Sussman
VP: Robert Turner
*VP: Therese Wareham

D-U-N-S 96-287-4025 EXP
KHANNA PAPER INC
(Suby of KHANNA PAPER MILLS LIMITED)
50 Harrison St Ste 118, Hoboken, NJ 07030-8843
Tel (201) 850-1707 Founded/Ownrshp 2010
Sales 60.0MM EMP 7
SIC 5093 Scrap & waste materials
Ex Dir: Saurbh Khanna
Genl Mgr: Mike Diplacido

D-U-N-S 01-714-2444
■ KHANTY MANSIYSK OIL CORP
(Suby of MARATHON OIL CORP) ★
5555 San Felipe St, Houston, TX 77056-2701
Tel (713) 629-6600 Founded/Ownrshp 2003
Sales 17.8MM^E EMP 900
Accts Pricewaterhousecoopers
SIC 1382 Oil & gas exploration services; Oil & gas exploration services
Pr: John Fitzgibbons
*Ch Bd: Gerard De Geer
*V Ch: Nikolai V Bogatchev
*COO: Mark C Bilsland
*CFO: Gail Coleman
*Ex VP: Alexander Y Pankov
*Ex VP: Elena K Shevchenko
*Ex VP: Sergey Shibakin
*Ex VP: Henry Wolski
IT Man: Jerry Lowery
Board of Directors: Adolf Lundin, James T Rodgers, Robert F Semmens, William Wallace, Kevin P Watts

KHEAA
See KENTUCKY HIGHER EDUCATION ASSISTANCE AUTHORITY

D-U-N-S 01-790-0820
KHEMPCO BUILDING SUPPLY CO LIMITED PARTNERSHIP
ARLINGTON-BLAINE LUMBER CO
130 Johnson Dr, Delaware, OH 43015-8699
Tel (740) 549-0465 Founded/Ownrshp 1992
Sales 25.0MM^E EMP 300
SIC 5031 5211 2439 2431 5072 Lumber: rough, dressed & finished; Building materials, exterior; Building materials, interior; Lumber & other building materials; Trusses, except roof: laminated lumber; Trusses, wooden roof; Doors, wood; Hardware; Lumber: rough, dressed & finished; Building materials, exterior; Building materials, interior; Lumber & other building materials; Trusses, except roof: laminated lumber; Trusses, wooden roof; Doors, wood; Hardware
Genl Pt: James D Klingbeil Jr
Pt: Donny Bowman
Pt: Richard Robinson

D-U-N-S 00-597-8507 IMP
KHORPORATE HOLDINGS INC
CR MAGNETICS
P.O. Box 217 (46750)
Tel (260) 357-3365 Founded/Ownrshp 1950
Sales 24.2MM^E EMP 194
SIC 3496 3676 3089 5084 Cable, uninsulated wire: made from purchased wire; Wire winding; Electronic resistors; Injection molding of plastics; Tool & die makers' equipment; Cable, uninsulated wire: made from purchased wire; Wire winding; Electronic resistors; Injection molding of plastics; Tool & die makers' equipment
Pr: Michael Khorshid
Opers Mgr: Greg Baker

D-U-N-S 00-516-5282
KHOTOL SERVICES CORP
(Suby of GANA-AYOO LIMITED) ★
100 Front St, Galena, AK 99741
Tel (907) 656-1606 Founded/Ownrshp 1998
Sales 7.2MM^E EMP 353
Accts Newhouse & Vogler Anchorage
SIC 6531 7513 5812 8744 7349 4212 Real estate managers; Truck rental, without drivers; Eating places; Lunchrooms & cafeterias; Box lunch stand; Carry-out only (except pizza) restaurant; Facilities support services; Janitorial service, contract basis; Cleaning service, industrial or commercial; Draying, local: without storage; Real estate managers; Truck rental, without drivers; Eating places; Lunchrooms & cafeterias; Box lunch stand; Carry-out only (except pizza) restaurant; Facilities support services; Janitorial service, contract basis; Cleaning service, industrial or commercial; Draying, local: without storage
Pr: Betty Huntington
*CEO: Dominica F Quitevis

KHOU-TV CHANNEL 11
See KHOU-TV INC

D-U-N-S 10-267-2284
■ KHOU-TV INC
KHOU-TV CHANNEL 11
(Suby of BELO CORP) ★
1945 Allen Pkwy, Houston, TX 77019-2596
Tel (713) 284-1011 Founded/Ownrshp 1984
Sales 22.5MM^E EMP 220
SIC 4833 Television broadcasting stations; Television broadcasting stations
Pr: Susan Mc Eldoon
*Treas: Carey P Hendrickson
*Treas: Guy H Kerr
IT Man: Linda Deprado

D-U-N-S 83-248-3718 IMP
KHQ INVESTMENT LLC
(Suby of GBG USA INC) ★
1359 Brdwy Fl 21, New York, NY 10018
Tel (212) 615-3400 Founded/Ownrshp 2009
Sales 123.2MM^E EMP 300^E
SIC 5136 2321 Men's & boys' clothing; Men's & boys' clothing; Men's & boys' furnishings
Pr: Kelly Grant
CFO: Jon Kimmins

KHS & S CONTRACTORS
See KEENAN HOPKINS SUDER & STOWELL CONTRACTORS INC

KHS DIVISION
See KHS USA INC

D-U-N-S 09-739-4241 IMP
KHS USA INC
KHS DIVISION
(Suby of KHS GMBH)
880 Bahcall Ct, Waukesha, WI 53186-1801
Tel (262) 797-7200 Founded/Ownrshp 2011
Sales 106.4MM^E EMP 400
SIC 3556 Beverage machinery; Pasteurizing equipment, dairy machinery; Beverage machinery; Pasteurizing equipment, dairy machinery
Pr: Michael Brancato
Pr: Jeff Camargo
COO: Johann Grabenweger
COO: Marc Hartmann
*CFO: Jim Elliott
CFO: Anke Fischer
VP: Darrell Landry
VP: Les Matson
VP: Bob Peace
VP: Kay Seybold
Exec: Joyce Narr

KHS&S CONTRACTORS
See KEENAN HOPKINS SCHMIDT AND STOWELL CONTRACTORS INC

KHUBANI ENTERPRISES
See AZAD INTERNATIONAL INC

KHUDAIRI GROUP
See AZKU INC

KI
See KRUEGER INTERNATIONAL INC

D-U-N-S 55-548-6190 IMP
KI (USA) CORP
(*Suby of* KEIAISHA CO.,LTD.)
501 Mayde Rd, Berea, KY 40403-8730
Tel (859) 986-1420 *Founded/Ownrshp* 2012
Sales 67.5MM^E *EMP* 240
SIC 3465 7692 3714 3469 Body parts, automobile: stamped metal; Welding repair; Motor vehicle parts & accessories; Metal stampings; Body parts, automobile: stamped metal; Welding repair; Motor vehicle parts & accessories; Metal stampings
Pr: Gary Robinson
**Prin:* H Kanno
Genl Mgr: Dan Jeffries
Dir IT: Allen Kinscer
Opers Mgr: Beverly Chambers
Plnt Mgr: Troy Williams
Ql Cn Mgr: Chriss Niceley
**VP Sls:* P Kato

D-U-N-S 11-976-5923
KI BOIS COMMUNITY ACTION FOUNDATION INC
200 Se A St, Stigler, OK 74462-2418
Tel (918) 967-9992 *Founded/Ownrshp* 1968
Sales 38.8MM *EMP* 975
Accts Gibson Reynolds & Blakemore Pc
SIC 8322 1542 1521 Individual & family services; Commercial & office building, new construction; New construction, single-family houses; Individual & family services; Commercial & office building, new construction; New construction, single-family houses
Ex Dir: R Carroll Huggins
**Pr:* Gene Bass
**Sec:* Kenneth Monroe
MIS Dir: Stephen Wotring
Pgrm Dir: Claudia Jeffrey

D-U-N-S 13-776-8482
KI HO MILITARY ACQUISITION CONSULTING INC
KIHOMAC
5501 Backlick Rd Ste 200, Springfield, VA 22151-3940
Tel (703) 960-5450 *Founded/Ownrshp* 2003
Sales 24.2MM^E *EMP* 100^E
SIC 8711 Consulting engineer
Pr: Ki Ho Kang
**Treas:* Madelline Kang
**VP:* Frank Griffo
VP: Adam Grimm
**VP:* Scot Merrihew
**VP:* Mark Muellerv
Snr Sftwr: Brian Hendershot

D-U-N-S 82-971-5049
KI LLC
(*Suby of* AKIMA LLC) ★
10807 New Allegiance Dr # 350, Colorado Springs, CO 80921-3797
Tel (719) 264-0909 *Founded/Ownrshp* 2009
Sales 24.7MM^E *EMP* 600
Accts Ernst & Young Llp
SIC 7373 7389 Computer integrated systems design; Brokers, business: buying & selling business enterprises; Computer integrated systems design; Brokers, business: buying & selling business enterprises
Treas: Eric Woller

D-U-N-S 07-851-6488
KIA AUTOSPORT OF PENSACOLA INC
6637 Pensacola Blvd, Pensacola, FL 32505-1705
Tel (850) 457-7772 *Founded/Ownrshp* 1999
Sales 28.2MM^E *EMP* 150
SIC 5511 Automobiles, new & used; Automobiles, new & used
Pr: Jessica Lee

D-U-N-S 02-344-3146
KIA DARROW RUSS
DARROW RUSS PNTC-SZ-KIA-NISSAN
W133n8569 Executive Pkwy, Menomonee Falls, WI 53051-3344
Tel (262) 250-9600 *Founded/Ownrshp* 1955
Sales 38.5MM^E *EMP* 123
SIC 5511 5521 Automobiles, new & used; Used car dealers; Automobiles, new & used; Used car dealers
Pr: Russ Darrow Jr

KIA GROUP
See KIA INC

D-U-N-S 80-383-8176 IMP
KIA INC
KIA GROUP
16516 Via Esprillo # 100, San Diego, CA 92127-1728
Tel (858) 824-2999 *Founded/Ownrshp* 1992
Sales 21.5MM *EMP* 30^E
SIC 3149 Athletic shoes, except rubber or plastic; Athletic shoes, except rubber or plastic
CEO: Reza Mohseni
**CFO:* Tannaz Mohseni
**VP:* Bano Mohseni
VP Sls: Hamed Mosheni

D-U-N-S 80-267-0687 IMP
KIA MOTORS AMERICA INC
(*Suby of* KIA MOTORS CORPORATION)
111 Peters Canyon Rd, Irvine, CA 92606-1790
Tel (949) 468-4800 *Founded/Ownrshp* 1992
Sales 1.3MMM^E *EMP* 3,000
SIC 5511 5013 8741 Automobiles, new & used; Automotive supplies & parts; Management services; Automobiles, new & used; Automotive supplies & parts; Management services
CEO: Byung M Ahn
COO: Peter Nochar
**COO:* Michael Sprague
CFO: Ahn Hee-Bong
CFO: Byeong-Wook Kim
**Ex VP:* Tom Loveless
**Ex VP:* John Yoon
VP: John Crowe
Ex Dir: Bob Kuntze
Dist Mgr: Michelle Hurney
Dir IT: Richard Lin

D-U-N-S 87-725-6862 IMP/EXP
KIA MOTORS MANUFACTURING GEORGIA INC
KMMG
(*Suby of* KIA MOTORS AMERICA INC) ★
7777 Kia Pkwy, West Point, GA 31833-4897
Tel (706) 902-7777 *Founded/Ownrshp* 2006
Sales 1.0MMM^E *EMP* 3,000^E
SIC 5511 Automobiles, new & used; Automobiles, new & used
CEO: Byung MO Ahn
CFO: Kang In
**CFO:* Jae Cheon Jeong
**CFO:* In Ho Kang
Sr VP: Randy Jackson
Sr VP: Hee Mok
IT Man: Regina Farmer
IT Man: James OH
Sfty Mgr: Austin Starr
Opers Mgr: Narae Cho
Ql Cn Mgr: Chris Tarver

KIA OF BATON ROUGE
See ALL STAR CHEVROLET INC

D-U-N-S 12-346-0631
KIA OF BATON ROUGE
ALL STAR KIA
5740 Siegen Ln, Baton Rouge, LA 70809-4147
Tel (225) 490-8000 *Founded/Ownrshp* 2001
Sales 71.8MM^E *EMP* 600
SIC 5511 Automobiles, new & used; Automobiles, new & used
Pr: Matt McKay

KIA OF LAGRANGE
See PLANT CITY AUTOMOTIVE INC

KIA SOUTH
See BICKERSTAFF IMPORTS INC

D-U-N-S 00-287-2091
KIAMICHI ELECTRIC COOPERATIVE INC
966 Sw Highway 2, Wilburton, OK 74578-7657
Tel (918) 465-2338 *Founded/Ownrshp* 1945
Sales 39.8MM *EMP* 45
SIC 4911 Distribution, electric power; Distribution, electric power
CEO: Jim Jackson
**Pr:* Robert Williams
VP: Larry Culwell
**VP:* Dan Murphy
Info Man: William Robertson
Opers Mgr: Bob Owens

D-U-N-S 07-428-3110
KIAMICHI TECHNOLOGY CENTERS
KTC
1004 Highway 2 N, Wilburton, OK 74578-3607
Tel (918) 465-2323 *Founded/Ownrshp* 1974
Sales 18.0MM *EMP* 550
SIC 8222 Technical institute; Technical institute
Pr: Larry Culwell
**CFO:* Lois Welch
**Treas:* Bulena Oller
**VP:* Phil Chitwood
Psych: Mary J Pruitt

D-U-N-S 80-103-8951
KIARA
(*Suby of* HOSPITAL SISTERS HEALTH SYSTEM) ★
4936 Laverna Rd, Springfield, IL 62707-9797
Tel (217) 523-4747 *Founded/Ownrshp* 1984
Sales 39.3MM^E *EMP* 60
SIC 8741 Management services
Pr: Ken Butler
Treas: Lisa Rusciolelli

KIAWAH ISLAND GOLF TNNIS RSORT
See KIAWAH ISLAND INN CO

D-U-N-S 82-462-9836
KIAWAH ISLAND INN CO
KIAWAH ISLAND GOLF TNNIS RSORT
1 Sanctuary Beach Dr, Johns Island, SC 29455-5434
Tel (843) 768-6000 *Founded/Ownrshp* 1993
Sales 105.0MM^E *EMP* 1,200
SIC 7011 Resort hotel; Resort hotel
Pr: Roger Warren
Mng Pt: Pat McKinney
VP: Greg Vanderwerker
Exec: Terri Hall
Dir Soc: Jabari Murdock
**Prin:* Tom Bewley
**Prin:* Dan Dipmars
**Prin:* Brian Gerard
**Prin:* Mike Vegis
Mng Dir: Prem Devadas
Genl Mgr: Alex Berentzen

D-U-N-S 18-956-8694
KIAWAH RESORT ASSOCIATES LP
KAIWAH ISLAND CLUB
245 Gardners Cir, Johns Island, SC 29455-5471
Tel (843) 768-3400 *Founded/Ownrshp* 1988
Sales 104.9MM^E *EMP* 250
SIC 6552 Subdividers & developers; Subdividers & developers
Pt: Charles P Darby III
Pr Dir: Mike Touhill

D-U-N-S 80-311-5521
KIBBI LLC
RENEGADE
52216 State Road 15, Bristol, IN 46507-9524
Tel (574) 848-1126 *Founded/Ownrshp* 2004
Sales 44.1MM^E *EMP* 78^E
SIC 5012 5561 Recreational vehicles, motor homes & trailers; Recreational vehicle dealers
CEO: Michael Lanciotti
Mktg Mgr: Danny Lagunas
Sls Mgr: Bryan Hilbert

D-U-N-S 78-797-0524
KIBBLE & PRENTICE HOLDING CO INC
(*Suby of* USI HOLDINGS CORP) ★
601 Union St Ste 1000, Seattle, WA 98101-4064
Tel (206) 441-6300 *Founded/Ownrshp* 2006
Sales NA *EMP* 575
SIC 6411 Insurance agents, brokers & service; Insurance agents, brokers & service
CEO: Arlen L Prentice
Sr VP: Rex Lund
VP: Brian Orton
VP: David Prentice
VP: Dave Ross
VP: Ron Sheron
IT Man: Jesse Dykshoorn

D-U-N-S 07-666-1032
KIBBLE & PRENTICE INC
USI
(*Suby of* KIBBLE & PRENTICE HOLDING CO INC) ★
601 Union St Ste 1000, Seattle, WA 98101-4064
Tel (206) 441-6300 *Founded/Ownrshp* 1962
Sales 27.0MM^E *EMP* 300
SIC 8741 Financial management for business
Ch Bd: Edward B Kibble
**Pr:* Mike Gano
**COO:* Ellen Boyer
Ex VP: Ed Fugo
Ex VP: Dudley Johnson
Ex VP: Kristin Kenefick
Ex VP: Steve Palmer
Sr VP: Cliff Axelson
Sr VP: Doug Darlington
Sr VP: Phil Dyer
Sr VP: Jamie Frits
Sr VP: Dinny Hansen
Sr VP: Pamm Jardine
Sr VP: Dallas Otter
Sr VP: Joe Strecker
Sr VP: Scott Summers
Sr VP: Bill Whitaker
**Sr VP:* Kenneth Wiltse
VP: Jim Anderson
VP: Marty Andrews
**VP:* Dale Cowles

D-U-N-S 06-047-8260
KIBBLE EQUIPMENT INC
JOHN DEERE
3099 Highway 7 Sw, Montevideo, MN 56265-4095
Tel (320) 269-6466 *Founded/Ownrshp* 1976
Sales 24.0MM^E *EMP* 90
SIC 5083 7699 Farm implements; Farm equipment parts & supplies; Farm machinery repair; Farm implements; Farm equipment parts & supplies; Farm machinery repair
CEO: Ace A Brandt
**Pr:* William Kibble
Bd of Dir: Gary Lensing
QA Dir: Jeff Kodet
Site Mgr: Butch Kibble
Snr Mgr: Bob Raveling

D-U-N-S 07-868-4628
KIBBLE EQUIPMENT LLC
JOHN DEERE
1150 S Victory Dr, Mankato, MN 56001-5307
Tel (507) 387-8201 *Founded/Ownrshp* 1974
Sales 30.7MM^E *EMP* 115
SIC 5999 5261 Farm equipment & supplies; Lawn & garden equipment
**CEO:* Steve Kibble
Store Mgr: Dave Goebel
Site Mgr: Gary Hoffmann
Sls Mgr: Pat Bruggeman

D-U-N-S 00-724-1433 EXP
KICE INDUSTRIES INC
5500 N Mill Heights Dr, Park City, KS 67219-2358
Tel (316) 744-7148 *Founded/Ownrshp* 1946
Sales 33.4MM^E *EMP* 190
SIC 3444 3564 3494 3556 3321 3441 Sheet metalwork; Air cleaning systems; Valves & pipe fittings; Food products machinery; Gray & ductile iron foundries; Fabricated structural metal; Sheet metalwork; Air cleaning systems; Valves & pipe fittings; Food products machinery; Gray & ductile iron foundries; Fabricated structural metal
Ch Bd: Edward M Kice
**Pr:* Thomas F Kice
VP: Jerrod Hanson
**VP:* James D Kice
Exec: Dan Davis
Exec: Kurt Meyers
Rgnl Mgr: Robert Williams
Dir IT: Doyle Hamilton
Dir IT: Nick Marsh
IT Man: Joe Holt
Sls Mgr: Katy Lamb

KICHLER LIGHTING
See L D KICHLER CO

D-U-N-S 16-797-5965
KICKAPOO LUCKY EAGLE CASINO HOTEL
(*Suby of* KICKAPOO TRADITIONAL TRIBE OF TEXAS) ★
794 Lucky Eagle Dr, Eagle Pass, TX 78852-2430
Tel (830) 758-1936 *Founded/Ownrshp* 2001
Sales 23.8MM^E *EMP* 640
SIC 7011 Hotels & motels; Casino hotel
CFO: Rolando Benavides
Genl Mgr: Robin Miller

D-U-N-S 62-105-6100
KICKAPOO TRADITIONAL TRIBE OF TEXAS
2212 Rosita Valley Rd, Eagle Pass, TX 78852-2503
Tel (830) 773-2105 *Founded/Ownrshp* 1989
Sales 92.2MM^E *EMP* 1,300
SIC 7011 Casino hotel; Casino hotel
**CFO:* Robert F Kuhnemund
**Genl Couns:* Gloria Hernandez

D-U-N-S 08-618-4660
KICKAPOO VALLEY CHEESE CORP
9285 3rd St, Milladore, WI 54454-9733
Tel (715) 652-2173 *Founded/Ownrshp* 1995
Sales 43.3MM *EMP* 125
SIC 5143

KICKER
See STILLWATER DESIGNS AND AUDIO INC

D-U-N-S 11-997-5902
KICKERILLO BUILDING CO
KICKERILLO COMPANIES
1306 S Fry Rd, Katy, TX 77450-4372
Tel (713) 951-0666 *Founded/Ownrshp* 1958
Sales 49.0MM *EMP* 26
SIC 1521 Single-family housing construction; Single-family housing construction
Ch Bd: Vincent D Kickerillo
**V Ch:* Mary Kay Kickerillo
**Pr:* Jim A Miller
**CFO:* Thomas H McQuilling
Chf Mktg O: Kelli Kickerillo
**VP:* Sara Kelli Kickerillo

KICKERILLO COMPANIES
See KICKERILLO BUILDING CO

D-U-N-S 01-158-6153 IMP/EXP
KID BRANDS INC
1 Meadowlands Plz Ste 803, East Rutherford, NJ 07073-2152
Tel (201) 405-2400 *Founded/Ownrshp* 1963
Sales 188.1MM *EMP* 201^E
SIC 2399 3944 Infant carriers; Games, toys & children's vehicles

D-U-N-S 05-128-8132
KIDANGO INC
44000 Old Warm Sprng Blvd, Fremont, CA 94538-6145
Tel (510) 897-6900 *Founded/Ownrshp* 1979
Sales 26.0MM *EMP* 475
Accts Randolp Scott & Company Cpas I
SIC 8351 Preschool center; Group day care center; Preschool center; Group day care center
Ex Dir: Paul Miller
Genl Mgr: Minoo Vasseghi
IT Man: Matt Lovell
Opers Supe: Tena Sloan
Pgrm Dir: Jennifer Pare

KIDD ROOFING
See DR KIDD CO INC

KIDD-JONES OIL COMPANY
See JERRY KIDD OIL CO

KIDDE FIRE FIGHTING
See KIDDE FIRE PROTECTION INC

D-U-N-S 15-729-5361 IMP
■ **KIDDE FIRE FIGHTING INC**
(*Suby of* KIDDE FIRE FIGHTING) ★
180 Sheree Blvd Ste 3900, Exton, PA 19341-1272
Tel (610) 363-1400 *Founded/Ownrshp* 1987
Sales 90.4MM^E *EMP* 550
SIC 3569 2899 Firefighting apparatus & related equipment; Fire retardant chemicals; Firefighting apparatus & related equipment; Fire retardant chemicals
Pr: John Hittson
CFO: Cary Brinker
**CFO:* Larry E Mansfield
Natl Sales: John Vieweger

D-U-N-S 62-757-8016 IMP/EXP
■ **KIDDE FIRE PROTECTION INC**
KIDDE FIRE FIGHTING
(*Suby of* UNITED TECHNOLOGIES CORP) ★
350 E Union St, West Chester, PA 19382-3450
Tel (610) 363-1400 *Founded/Ownrshp* 2009
Sales 285.0MM^E *EMP* 2,450^E
SIC 3669 3999 3823 Fire detection systems, electric; Fire extinguishers, portable; Temperature instruments: industrial process type; Fire detection systems, electric; Fire extinguishers, portable; Temperature instruments: industrial process type
Pr: John Hargreaves
Treas: Bill Langan
Sr VP: Holly O Paz
VP: Dean Byrne
VP: John Dowling
IT Man: Richard Schulman
Mktg Dir: Dennis Jackson
Mktg Dir: Chick Labounty
Manager: Benjamin Waterman
Manager: Woody Woodson
Sls Mgr: Bobby Nelson

KIDDE FIRE SYSTEM
See KIDDE-FENWAL INC

KIDDE SAFETY
See WALTER KIDDE PORTABLE EQUIPMENT INC

D-U-N-S 60-695-5318 EXP
■ **KIDDE TECHNOLOGIES INC**
FENWAL SAFETY SYSTEMS
(*Suby of* KIDDE FIRE FIGHTING) ★
4200 Airport Dr Nw, Wilson, NC 27896-8630
Tel (252) 237-7004 *Founded/Ownrshp* 1989
Sales 92.0MM^E *EMP* 730
SIC 3728 Aircraft parts & equipment; Aircraft parts & equipment
Pr: Terry Hayden
**Pr:* Brent Ehmke
**CFO:* W Thomas Ramsey
VP: John J Shea
Genl Mgr: Dennis Bissonnette
Genl Mgr: Vincent Rowe
IT Man: Vicki Lewis
Sfty Dirs: Brent Ehmeke
Mtls Mgr: Lee Gardner
Sls Dir: Martin Sturla
Sls Mgr: Jeanette Cousin
Board of Directors: Ronald V Daggon, J Michael Harper, Alton D Slay, James W Stansberry, John E Sullivan, Lewis B Sykes, Douglas J Vaday

D-U-N-S 19-974-4715 IMP/EXP
■ **KIDDE-FENWAL INC**
KIDDE FIRE SYSTEM
(*Suby of* UNITED TECHNOLOGIES CORP) ★
400 Main St, Ashland, MA 01721-2150
Tel (508) 881-2000 *Founded/Ownrshp* 2010

Sales 190.4MM^E *EMP* 650
SIC 3669 3823 3825 3822 3643 3625 Fire detection systems, electric; Temperature instruments: industrial process type; Instruments to measure electricity; Auto controls regulating residntl & coml environmt & applncs; Current-carrying wiring devices; Relays & industrial controls; Fire detection systems, electric; Temperature instruments: industrial process type; Instruments to measure electricity; Auto controls regulating residntl & coml environmt & applncs; Current-carrying wiring devices; Relays & industrial controls
Pr: Michael C Burcham
**Treas:* Martin Fernandez
VP: David Olchowski
Exec: Jennifer Miller
**Prin:* John Vernon
Genl Mgr: Jerry Connolly
Snr Sftwr: Walter Greene
CIO: Bob Coleman
QA Dir: Larry Rodkey
IT Man: Mauro Ciccarelli
Netwrk Mgr: William Sawyer

D-U-N-S 07-925-3801
KIDDER MATHEWS LLC (WA)
601 Union St Ste 4720, Seattle, WA 98101-1356
Tel (206) 296-9600 *Founded/Ownrshp* 2009
Sales 97.0MM *EMP* 450
SIC 6531 Real estate agents & managers; Real estate agent, commercial
CEO: Jeffrey S Lyon
COO: Gordon K Buchan
Ex VP: Brian Hatcher
Ex VP: D Keith Kaiser
Ex VP: Reed W Payne
Ex VP: Peter K Shorett
Sr VP: Todd Battison
Sr VP: Karen Benoit
Sr VP: Christopher Corr
Sr VP: Joe Dejager
Sr VP: Gregg Domanico
Sr VP: Vanessa Herzog
Sr VP: Ron King
Sr VP: Steven Klein
Sr VP: James Klinger
Sr VP: James Lees
Sr VP: Tim Mason
Sr VP: Joe McDermott
Sr VP: Christopher Moe
Sr VP: Benjamin Pollock
Sr VP: Jason Rosauer

D-U-N-S 61-056-8222 IMP/EXP
KIDKRAFT INC
4630 Olin Rd, Dallas, TX 75244-4615
Tel (972) 385-0100 *Founded/Ownrshp* 2015
Sales 58.7MM^E *EMP* 300
SIC 2511

D-U-N-S 00-415-4696
KIDRON INC
13442 Emerson Rd, Kidron, OH 44636
Tel (330) 857-3011 *Founded/Ownrshp* 1994
Sales NA *EMP* 500
SIC 3713 3715 3444 Truck bodies (motor vehicles); Trailer bodies; Sheet metalwork

D-U-N-S 92-947-3353
KIDS 1 INC
3071 Bordentown Ave 1, Parlin, NJ 08859-1168
Tel (732) 390-0303 *Founded/Ownrshp* 1993
Sales 18.9MM^E *EMP* 400
SIC 8741 Management services; Management services
CEO: David Winikur
**Pr:* Ellyn Lerner
CFO: Antoinette Crudo

D-U-N-S 01-390-2301
KIDS BEHAVIORAL HEALTH OF HAWAII INC
ACADIA HEALTHCARE
6100 Tower Cir Ste 1000, Franklin, TN 37067-1509
Tel (615) 861-6000 *Founded/Ownrshp* 2005
Sales 18.0MM^E *EMP* 971^E
SIC 8093 Mental health clinic, outpatient
Ch Bd: Rod Laughlin
**Pr:* Trey Carter
**Treas:* Robert Swinson

D-U-N-S 04-982-4183
KIDS BEHAVIORAL HEALTH OF MONTANA
55 Basin Creek Rd, Butte, MT 59701-9704
Tel (406) 496-6300 *Founded/Ownrshp* 2006
Sales 14.1MM^E *EMP* 630
SIC 8062 8361 8322 General medical & surgical hospitals; Residential care; Individual & family services; General medical & surgical hospitals; Residential care; Individual & family services
Exec: Kristine Carpenter
CFO: Cindy Fuell
Mktg Dir: Jim McVeigh
Nrsg Dir: Lana Schaffer
HC Dir: Cricket Peach

D-U-N-S 00-205-3571
KIDS CENTRAL
3304 Sw 34th Cir, Ocala, FL 34474-3358
Tel (352) 291-1134 *Founded/Ownrshp* 2008
Sales 46.8MM *EMP* 2
SIC 8351 Child day care services; Child day care services
CEO: John Cooper

D-U-N-S 08-214-1677
KIDS CENTRAL INC
2117 Sw Highway 484, Ocala, FL 34473-7949
Tel (352) 873-6332 *Founded/Ownrshp* 2003
Sales 47.8MM *EMP* 150^E
Accts Purvis Gray And Company Ltd
SIC 8322 Child related social services; Child related social services
CEO: John Cooper
**CFO:* John Aitken
**Prin:* Cynthia Schuler
QA Dir: Chrissy Vickers
IT Man: Brian Bolduc

Pr Dir: Danielle Doty
Snr Mgr: Shalonda Sims

D-U-N-S 06-353-6098 IMP/EXP
KIDS II INC
3333 Piedmont Rd Ne # 1800, Atlanta, GA 30305-1712
Tel (770) 751-0442 *Founded/Ownrshp* 1999
Sales 47.3MM^E *EMP* 175
SIC 3944 5092 Games, toys & children's vehicles; Toys & games; Games, toys & children's vehicles; Toys & games
Pr: Ryan Gunnigle
**COO:* Dwaine Clarke
VP: Jeffrey Cornelison
VP: Scott Dale
VP: Shannon Delaney
VP: Chris Dixon
VP: David Manning
VP: Tim Martin
VP: Doug Miller
**VP:* Carl Watry
Exec: Juanita Biasini
Exec: James Rex
Exec: Maryann Riggins

D-U-N-S 16-323-7159
KIDS IN DISTRESS FOUNDATION INC
819 Ne 26th St, Wilton Manors, FL 33305-1239
Tel (954) 390-7654 *Founded/Ownrshp* 1981
Sales 1.1MM *EMP* 290^E
Accts Falkins & Company Cpa S Pa
SIC 8322 Individual & family services; Individual & family services
Ex Dir: Thomas Tomczyk
**CFO:* Jeff Byrd
**Ex VP:* Ellyen Okrent

D-U-N-S 96-239-2312
KIDS IN DISTRESSED SITUATIONS INC
K I D S
112 W 34th St Ste 1133, New York, NY 10120-1133
Tel (212) 279-5493 *Founded/Ownrshp* 1985
Sales 125.9MM *EMP* 5
Accts Fry & Allen Pc Rockville
SIC 8322 Social service center
Pr: Janice Weinman
Treas: Alice Beckman
Chf Mktg O: Laura Belvedere

D-U-N-S 82-726-8249
KIDS IN NEED FOUNDATION
3055 Kettering Blvd # 119, Moraine, OH 45439-1989
Tel (937) 296-1230 *Founded/Ownrshp* 2008
Sales 71.9MM *EMP* 23^E
Accts Brady Ware & Schoenfeld Inc D
SIC 8641 Civic social & fraternal associations; Civic social & fraternal associations
Ex Dir: David Smith

KIDS OUTLET
See W & W WHOLESALE INC

D-U-N-S 96-834-3256
KIDS PREFERRED INC
IN-TOYS
81 Twin Rivers Dr, East Windsor, NJ 08520-5212
Tel (732) 274-1144 *Founded/Ownrshp* 1984
Sales 44.2MM^E *EMP* 70
SIC 5092 Toys & hobby goods & supplies
CEO: Louis Premselaar

KIDS WITH CHARACTER
See MYSTIC APPAREL LLC

KIDSLINE
See TG VALENTINE LLC

D-U-N-S 96-571-8997
KIDSPEACE CORP
WILEY HOUSE
5300 Kidspeace Dr, Orefield, PA 18069-2098
Tel (610) 799-8000 *Founded/Ownrshp* 1886
Sales 42.4MM *EMP* 3^E
SIC 8699 Charitable organization
Pr: William R Isemann

D-U-N-S 86-081-8152
KIDSPEACE NATIONAL CENTERS OF NEW YORK INC
5300 Kidspeace Dr, Orefield, PA 18069-2098
Tel (800) 992-9543 *Founded/Ownrshp* 1991
Sales 47.4MM *EMP* 3,601
SIC 8322 Child guidance agency; Child guidance agency
Pr: CT O'Donnell
CFO: James Horan
**VP:* Richard A Boyer
VP: Gerard Gleeson
VP: Michael Slack
Ex Dir: Paige Keeter
Ex Dir: Scott Merritt
Prgrm Mgr: Marcus Gamble
Prgrm Mgr: Jodi Reinke
Genl Mgr: Denise Card
Genl Mgr: Nora Culley

D-U-N-S 07-365-1143
KIDSPEACE NATIONAL CENTERS OF NORTH AMERICA INC
4085 Independence Dr, Schnecksville, PA 18078-2574
Tel (610) 799-8353 *Founded/Ownrshp* 1886
Sales 16.4MM *EMP* 2,070
SIC 8322

KIDWELL ELECTRIC
See KIDWELL INC

D-U-N-S 03-506-9129
KIDWELL INC
KIDWELL ELECTRIC
3333 Folkways Cir, Lincoln, NE 68504-4762
Tel (402) 475-8737 *Founded/Ownrshp* 1973
Sales 29.2MM^E *EMP* 105
SIC 1731 General electrical contractor
Pr: Christopher A Kidwell
**Treas:* Andrew Davenport
VP: Joel Rourke
**VP:* Ryan Theil

KIE SUPPLY
See KENNEWICK INDUSTRIAL & ELECTRICAL SUPPLY INC

D-U-N-S 96-347-3371
KIE-CON INC
(*Subsy of* KIEWIT CORP) ★
3551 Wilbur Ave, Antioch, CA 94509-8530
Tel (925) 754-9494 *Founded/Ownrshp* 2010
Sales 43.8MM^E *EMP* 90
Accts Kpmg Llp Omaha Nebraska
SIC 1542 Commercial & office building contractors; Commercial & office building contractors
Pr: Allen Kung
Mktg Mgr: Joe Hernandez

KIEFER MANUFACTURING
See STELLAR HOLDINGS INC

D-U-N-S 04-729-2602 IMP
KIEFER SPECIALTY FLOORING INC
KIEFER USA
2910 Falling Waters Blvd, Lindenhurst, IL 60046-6799
Tel (847) 245-8450 *Founded/Ownrshp* 2003
Sales 27.1MM *EMP* 50
Accts Weltman Bernfield Llc Buffalo
SIC 5023 Floor coverings; Floor coverings
Pr: Brion Rittenberry
CFO: Dean Heidloff
**VP:* Dan Kiefer
Manager: Dave Dillon
Manager: Chris Nelms
Manager: Phil Waters

KIEFER USA
See KIEFER SPECIALTY FLOORING INC

D-U-N-S 00-610-4376
KIEFFER & CO INC (WI)
(*Subsy of* KIEFFER HOLDING CO) ★
3322 Washington Ave, Sheboygan, WI 53081-6404
Tel (920) 458-4394 *Founded/Ownrshp* 1959, 2008
Sales 28.0MM *EMP* 105
SIC 3993 1799 Electric signs; Signs, not made in custom sign painting shops; Sign installation & maintenance; Electric signs; Signs, not made in custom sign painting shops; Sign installation & maintenance
Pr: John Troy
**VP:* Larry Caracciolo
**VP:* Jeffrey Fuhrmann
**VP:* Kevin Hofert
IT Man: Estela Chavez
VP Mfg: Jeff Furmann
Prd Mgr: Tim Zastrow
Mktg Dir: Dennis Smith
Board of Directors: John Troy

D-U-N-S 82-860-5191
KIEFFER HOLDING CO
585 Bond St, Lincolnshire, IL 60069-4226
Tel (847) 520-1255 *Founded/Ownrshp* 2008
Sales 28.0MM^E *EMP* 112
SIC 3993 Electric signs; Signs, not made in custom sign painting shops
Pr: Matthew Mele
**Treas:* Mark Steffen
**VP Mfg:* Jeffrey Fuhrmann
**VP Sls:* Larry Caracciolo

D-U-N-S 00-683-0335
KIEFNER BROTHERS INC (MO)
1459 N Kingshighway St, Cape Girardeau, MO 63701-2116
Tel (573) 334-0707 *Founded/Ownrshp* 1946
Sales 38.1MM *EMP* 60
Accts Kerber Eck & Braeckel Llp Ca
SIC 1542 Commercial & office buildings, prefabricated erection; Hospital construction; School building construction; Commercial & office buildings, prefabricated erection; Hospital construction; School building construction
Pr: Thomas Kiefner
**Treas:* Kent B Kiefner
Treas: Matthew Kiefner

D-U-N-S 61-416-1115 IMP
KIEKERT USA INC
KEYKERT USA, INC.
(*Subsy of* KIEKERT AG)
46941 Liberty Dr, Wixom, MI 48393-3603
Tel (248) 960-4100 *Founded/Ownrshp* 1987
Sales 73.4MM^E *EMP* 500
SIC 3714 Motor vehicle body components & frame; Motor vehicle body components & frame
CEO: Karl Krause
Bd of Dir: John Dey
**Ex VP:* Matthias Berg
**Ex VP:* Guido Hanel
Ex VP: Diana Korner
**Ex VP:* Andrea Kusemann
Ex VP: Ulrich Nass
**Ex VP:* Jrgen Peulen
Prgrm Mgr: Scott Bills
Prgrm Mgr: Brian Couture
Cmptr Lab: Jianguang Sun

D-U-N-S 79-718-1625
KIEL CENTER PARTNERS LP
SCOTTRADE CENTER
1401 Clark Ave, Saint Louis, MO 63103-2700
Tel (314) 622-5400 *Founded/Ownrshp* 1992
Sales 40.8MM^E *EMP* 994
SIC 7941 Sports clubs, managers & promoters; Sports clubs, managers & promoters
Pt: Peter McLoughlin
VP: Fred Corsi
VP: Jerome Jasiek
VP: Scott Siebers
Exec: Jeffrey Seaborn
Mktg Mgr: Renah Rushing
Snr Mgr: Rick Pipkins

KIENLEN CONSTRUCTORS
See ALBERICI CORP

D-U-N-S 15-397-3581
KIER CONSTRUCTION CORP
3710 Quincy Ave, Ogden, UT 84403-1934
Tel (801) 627-1414 *Founded/Ownrshp* 1986
Sales 85.3MM *EMP* 57
Accts Haynie & Co Ogden Utah
SIC 1522 1542 1541 Multi-family dwelling construction; Nonresidential construction; Industrial buildings, new construction; Multi-family dwelling construction; Nonresidential construction; Industrial buildings, new construction
Pr: Stephen J Kier
**Treas:* Brent Openshaw
**VP:* Scott J Kier
Exec: Tom Hart
Snr PM: Chris Comish

D-U-N-S 04-130-1086
KIESEL CO
4801 Fyler Ave, Saint Louis, MO 63116-2005
Tel (314) 351-5500 *Founded/Ownrshp* 1976
Sales 49.1MM^E *EMP* 50
SIC 5172 Fuel oil; Fuel oil
Pr: Lorraine Kiesel
Genl Mgr: Larry Gooden
IT Man: Stephen Daues

D-U-N-S 05-781-3396
KIESSLING TRANSIT INC
206 Dedham St Ste 1, Norfolk, MA 02056-1667
Tel (508) 384-5701 *Founded/Ownrshp* 1970
Sales 17.0MM^E *EMP* 300
SIC 4119 Local passenger transportation; Local passenger transportation
CEO: Lars Kiessling
**Pr:* Paula D Kiessling

D-U-N-S 18-965-7138
KIEWIT BUILDING GROUP INC
(*Subsy of* KIEWIT CORP) ★
302 S 36th St Ste 500, Omaha, NE 68131-3894
Tel (402) 977-4500 *Founded/Ownrshp* 2005
Sales 844.1MM *EMP* 1,047^E
Accts Kpmg Llp Omaha Ne
SIC 1521 General remodeling, single-family houses; General remodeling, single-family houses
Pr: Joseph R Lempka
**Treas:* Stephen S Thomas
**Sr VP:* Michael J Colpack
**Sr VP:* Ronald C Duce
**Sr VP:* J D Vetter
**Sr VP:* Kevin P Welker
**Sr VP:* Lance K Wilhelm
**VP:* Becky S Golden
**VP:* Raymond D Hallquist
**VP:* Michael J Piechoski
**VP:* Herb J Reuss
**VP:* Tobin A Schropp
**VP:* William L Schwarten
**VP:* Don E Sloane
**VP:* Terry L White
**VP:* Randall D Zuke
Exec: John Sibley
Exec: Andy Stine
Board of Directors: Scott L Cassels

D-U-N-S 04-917-1630
KIEWIT CONSTRUCTORS INC
(*Subsy of* KIEWIT INFRASTRUCTURE CO) ★
Kiewit Plaza No 1103, Omaha, NE 68131
Tel (402) 342-2052 *Founded/Ownrshp* 1988, 1995
Sales 63.0MM^E *EMP* 189
SIC 1622 Tunnel construction; Tunnel construction
Pr: H E Adams
**Pr:* Bruce Grewcock
**Treas:* Stephen S Thomas
**Ex VP:* Kenneth R Ouellette
Sr VP: Bruce A Tresslr
**VP:* David A Flickinger
**VP:* Jeffrey P Petersen
**VP:* Michael J Piechoski

D-U-N-S 15-454-9877 IMP
KIEWIT CORP
(*Subsy of* PETER KIEWIT SONS INC) ★
3555 Farnam St Ste 1000, Omaha, NE 68131-3302
Tel (402) 342-2052 *Founded/Ownrshp* 1985
Sales 11.8MMM *EMP* 10,441
Accts Kpmg Llp Omaha Ne
SIC 1542 1541 1611 1622 1629 Commercial & office building contractors; Industrial buildings & warehouses; Highway & street paving contractor; Bridge construction; Tunnel construction; Highway construction, elevated; Marine construction; Commercial & office building contractors; Industrial buildings & warehouses; Highway & street paving contractor; Bridge construction; Tunnel construction; Highway construction, elevated; Marine construction
CEO: Bruce E Grewcock
Treas: Stephen S Thomas
Ex VP: Doug Legursky
Sr VP: Scott L Cassels
Sr VP: Steven Hansen
Sr VP: Tobin Schropp
Sr VP: Lance Wilhelm
VP: Robert Alder
VP: Phil Berthelot
VP: Larry Cochran
VP: Richard W Colf
VP: Mike Colpack
VP: Jeff Gordon
VP: Donald Lemoine
VP: Douglas E Patterson
VP: Andy Peplow
VP: Frank Ratajski
VP: Anthony Ritter
VP: P E Rowings
VP: Terry White
Exec: Mary Brown

D-U-N-S 06-365-5096
KIEWIT ENGINEERING & DESIGN CO
(*Subsy of* KIEWIT CORP) ★
9401 Renner Blvd, Lenexa, KS 66219-9707
Tel (913) 227-3600 *Founded/Ownrshp* 1998
Sales 128.1MM^E *EMP* 263
SIC 8712 8711 Architectural services; Consulting engineer; Architectural services; Consulting engineer

CEO: Bruce Grewcock
**Pr:* James K Needham
**CFO:* Trent M Demulling
**Treas:* Stephen S Thomas
**Ex VP:* David A Flickinger
**Ex VP:* Thomas S Shelby
**VP:* John R Burns
VP: Doug Duplisea
**VP:* Dave L Freeman
**VP:* Robert R Rausch
VP: James Rowings
Exec: Marty Barreca

D-U-N-S 18-766-6461
KIEWIT FEDERAL GROUP INC
(*Suby of* KIEWIT CORP) ★
1775 Greensboro Station P, Mc Lean, VA 22102-3849
Tel (703) 415-2689 *Founded/Ownrshp* 2004
Sales 34.1MM^E *EMP* 70
SIC 1541 Industrial buildings & warehouses
Pr: Joseph R Lempka
**VP:* H E Adams
**VP:* Micheal J Piechoski
Snr PM: Ron Tanner

D-U-N-S 96-336-7920
KIEWIT INDUSTRIAL GROUP INC
(*Suby of* KIEWIT CORP) ★
3555 Farnam St, Omaha, NE 68131-3311
Tel (402) 342-2052 *Founded/Ownrshp* 2005
Sales 3.4MMM *EMP* 20^E
Accts Kpmg Llp Omaha Ne
SIC 1629 Power plant construction; Power plant construction
Pr: Douglas E Patterson
Ex VP: Richard A Lanoha

D-U-N-S 05-882-2412 IMP
KIEWIT INFRASTRUCTURE CO (DE)
(*Suby of* KIEWIT CORP) ★
Kiewit Plz, Omaha, NE 68131
Tel (402) 342-2052 *Founded/Ownrshp* 1981
Sales NA *EMP* 9,000
Accts Kpmg Llp Lincoln Nebraska
SIC 1541 1542 1629 1622 1522 Industrial buildings & warehouses; Warehouse construction; Nonresidential construction; Commercial & office building contractors; Institutional building construction; Stadium construction; Subway construction; Tunnel construction; Residential construction; Industrial buildings & warehouses; Warehouse construction; Nonresidential construction; Commercial & office building contractors; Institutional building construction; Stadium construction; Subway construction; Tunnel construction; Residential construction
Pr: Bruce Grewcock
**CFO:* Michael J Piechoski
**Treas:* Stephen S Thomas
**Ex VP:* H E Adams
**Ex VP:* David J Miles
**VP:* Stephen P Allen
**VP:* Parke D Ball
**VP:* Michael K Breyer
**VP:* Craig A Briggs
**Prin:* Scott L Cassels

D-U-N-S 96-336-8050
KIEWIT INFRASTRUCTURE GROUP INC
(*Suby of* KIEWIT CORP) ★
3555 Farnam St, Omaha, NE 68131-3311
Tel (402) 342-2052 *Founded/Ownrshp* 2014
Sales 24.3MM^E *EMP* 50^E
SIC 1611 1622 Highway & street construction; Bridge, tunnel & elevated highway; Highway & street construction; Bridge, tunnel & elevated highway
Pr: Scott L Cassels
Ex VP: R Michael Phelps

D-U-N-S 05-507-6616
KIEWIT INFRASTRUCTURE SOUTH CO
(*Suby of* KIEWIT CORP) ★
Kiewit Plz No 1044, Omaha, NE 68131
Tel (402) 342-2052 *Founded/Ownrshp* 1969
Sales 603.0MM *EMP* 333
Accts Kpmg Llp Omaha Nebraska
SIC 1622 1611 Bridge, tunnel & elevated highway; Highway & street construction; Bridge, tunnel & elevated highway; Highway & street construction
Pr: David J Miles
**CFO:* Connie Lanoha
**Treas:* Stephen S Thomas
**VP:* Howard L Barton Jr
**VP:* Stephen Paul Carter Jr
**VP:* Timothy J Cleary
**VP:* Ricardo Cummings
**VP:* William D Glaser
**VP:* Mark D Langford
**VP:* Jeffrey P Petersen
**VP:* Michael J Piechoski
**VP:* John D Proskovec
**VP:* Joseph Richard
**VP:* Randall P Sanman
**VP:* Keith N Sasich
**VP:* Tobin A Schropp
**VP:* S Van Groves

D-U-N-S 07-423-2216 IMP
KIEWIT INFRASTRUCTURE WEST CO
(*Suby of* KIEWIT CORP) ★
3555 Farnam St, Omaha, NE 68131-3311
Tel (402) 342-2052 *Founded/Ownrshp* 1982
Sales 1.6MMM *EMP* 2,625
Accts Kpmg Llpomaha Nebraska
SIC 1611 1629 1541 1622 1623 Highway & street construction; Highway & street paving contractor; Grading; Land preparation construction; Dam construction; Industrial plant construction; Marine construction; Industrial buildings & warehouses; Bridge, tunnel & elevated highway; Water, sewer & utility lines; Highway & street construction; Highway & street paving contractor; Grading; Land preparation construction; Dam construction; Industrial plant construction; Marine construction; Industrial buildings & warehouses; Bridge, tunnel & elevated highway; Water, sewer & utility lines
Pr: Scott L Cassels
**CFO:* Trent M Demulling
Treas: Stephen S Thomas
**Ex VP:* H E Adams
**Ex VP:* David J Miles
**Ex VP:* Alfredo E Sori
**Sr VP:* Jeffrey P Petersen
**Sr VP:* Eric M Scott
**Sr VP:* AT Skoro
**Sr VP:* Matt L Swinton
**Sr VP:* Eugene D Van Wagner III
**Sr VP:* J D Vetter
**Sr VP:* Jamie D Wisenbaker
**VP:* Jeffrey C Arviso
**VP:* Kent A Boden
**VP:* Steven J Caniglia
**VP:* Jeffrey Ellis
**VP:* Paul H Giuntini
**VP:* Erik A Nelson
**VP:* Andrew J Peplow
**VP:* Terrence L Robinson

D-U-N-S 79-329-0354
KIEWIT MINING GROUP INC
Q BUILDING
(*Suby of* KIEWIT INFRASTRUCTURE CO) ★
Kiewit Plz, Omaha, NE 68131
Tel (402) 342-2052 *Founded/Ownrshp* 1991
Sales 121.5MM^E *EMP* 150
SIC 1241 Coal mining services; Coal mining services
Pr: Christopher J Murphy
**Treas:* Michael J Whetstine
**Sec:* Michael F Norton
**VP:* Michael J Piechoski
**VP:* Anthony A Ritter

D-U-N-S 17-596-9427 IMP
KIEWIT NEW MEXICO CO
(*Suby of* KIEWIT SOUTHWEST CO) ★
Kiewit Plaza No 1144, Omaha, NE 68131
Tel (402) 342-2052 *Founded/Ownrshp* 2006
Sales 47.2MM^E *EMP* 255
Accts Kpmg Llc
SIC 1611 1622 1629 Highway & street construction; Bridge, tunnel & elevated highway; Dams, waterways, docks & other marine construction; Highway & street construction; Bridge, tunnel & elevated highway; Dams, waterways, docks & other marine construction
Pr: Craig A Briggs
Treas: Stephen S Thomas
Sec: Michael F Norton
Sr VP: Gray D Kite
VP: Michael J Piechoski

D-U-N-S 01-553-9344 IMP/EXP
KIEWIT OFFSHORE SERVICES LTD
(*Suby of* PETER KIEWIT SONS INC) ★
2440 Kiewit Rd, Ingleside, TX 78362-5101
Tel (361) 775-4300 *Founded/Ownrshp* 2001
Sales 201.5MM^E *EMP* 500
SIC 1623 Oil & gas line & compressor station construction; Oil & gas line & compressor station construction
CEO: Bruce Grewcock
**Pr:* Myron Rodrigue
**Pr:* Fuat Sezer
**VP:* Jeffrey J Gordon
**VP:* Michael J Piechoski
**VP:* Tobin A Schropp
Exec: John Hardin
Sfty Dirs: Rand Magee

D-U-N-S 84-067-0470
KIEWIT OFFSHORE SERVICES LTD
(*Suby of* PETER KIEWIT SONS INC) ★
Kiewit Plz, Omaha, NE 68131
Tel (402) 342-2052 *Founded/Ownrshp* 2001
Sales 216.4MM^E *EMP* 2,368
SIC 3441 Fabricated structural metal; Fabricated structural metal
Pr: Fuat Sezer
**Treas:* Stephen S Thomas
**VP:* Michael J Piechoski
**VP:* Tobin A Schropp

D-U-N-S 07-431-5557
KIEWIT POWER CONSTRUCTORS CO
(*Suby of* KIEWIT CORP) ★
9401 Renner Blvd, Lenexa, KS 66219-9707
Tel (913) 928-7800 *Founded/Ownrshp* 2006
Sales 82.3MM^E *EMP* 169
SIC 1731 Electrical work; Electrical work
Pr: Howard L Barton
**Pr:* Dave Flickinger
**Treas:* Stephen S Thomas
**VP:* Bruce W Ballai
VP: Robert Farrell
**VP:* Dennis J Grenier
**VP:* Mark D Langford
**VP:* Joseph W Miller
VP: Glenn Miltenberger
**VP:* Michael J Piechoski
Prin: Kristie Petersen

D-U-N-S 05-144-4164
KIEWIT SOUTHWEST CO
(*Suby of* KIEWIT CORP) ★
Kiewit Plaza No 1025, Omaha, NE 68131
Tel (402) 342-2052 *Founded/Ownrshp* 1980
Sales 64.9MM *EMP* 933
Accts Kpmg Llp Omaha Nebraska
SIC 1611 1622 1629 Highway & street construction; Bridge, tunnel & elevated highway; Dams, waterways, docks & other marine construction; Highway & street construction; Bridge, tunnel & elevated highway; Dams, waterways, docks & other marine construction
Pr: Douglas C Duplisea
**Treas:* Stephen S Thomas
**VP:* Michael J Piechoski
**VP:* Rodney K Rosenthal
**VP:* Mark W Ruml
**VP:* Randall P Sanman
**VP:* Tobin A Schropp

D-U-N-S 61-320-1029 IMP
KIEWIT TEXAS CONSTRUCTION LP
GILBERT TEXAS CONSTRUCTION
(*Suby of* KIEWIT FRONTIER INC)
13119 Old Denton Rd, Fort Worth, TX 76177-2403
Tel (817) 337-7000 *Founded/Ownrshp* 1989
Sales 110.5MM^E *EMP* 559
Accts Kpmg Llp
SIC 1611 Airport runway construction; Airport runway construction
CEO: Bruce Grewcock
Pt: Kiewit Frontier
Prin: William D Glaser
Prin: Wh Murphy
Prin: Michael F Norton
Prin: Jeffrey P Petersen
Prin: Michael J Piechoski
Prin: John D Proskovec
Prin: Timothy S Riley
Prin: Keith N Sasich
Prin: Tobin A Schropp

D-U-N-S 10-229-1812
KIEWIT WESTERN CO
(*Suby of* KIEWIT CORP) ★
3888 E Broadway Rd, Phoenix, AZ 85040-2924
Tel (602) 437-7878 *Founded/Ownrshp* 1981
Sales 143.6MM *EMP* 1,672
Accts Kpmg Llp Omaha Ne
SIC 1622 1623 1629 1611 1794 Bridge, tunnel & elevated highway; Land preparation construction; Excavation & grading, building construction; General contractor, highway & street construction; Water main construction; Pipeline construction; Bridge, tunnel & elevated highway; Water main construction; Pipeline construction; Land preparation construction; General contractor, highway & street construction; Excavation & grading, building construction
CEO: Bruce Grewcock
**Pr:* H John Jansen
**Ex VP:* H E Adams
**Ex VP:* Scott L Cassels
**Ex VP:* Ken E Riley
**Ex VP:* Randall P Sanman
**Sr VP:* Craig A Briggs
**Sr VP:* Stan M Driver
**Sr VP:* Gregory A Hill
**Sr VP:* Richard H Raine
**VP:* Michaek K Breyer
**VP:* Kenneth W Hanna
**VP:* Troy L Heckmaster
**VP:* Thomas R Howell
**VP:* Gray D Kite
**VP:* Dwight Metcalf
**VP:* Michael J Piechoski
**VP:* Tobin A Schropp
**VP:* Wayne D Thomas

D-U-N-S 12-722-9438 IMP
KIEWIT/FCI/MANSON JOINT VENTURE
2200 Columbia House Blvd, Vancouver, WA 98661-7753
Tel (360) 693-1478 *Founded/Ownrshp* 2002
Sales 64.2MM^E *EMP* 550
SIC 1622 Bridge construction; Bridge construction
Prin: Steve Hansen
Dist Mgr: Keith Rasmussen

D-U-N-S 60-773-8028 IMP
KIFUKI USA CO INC
(*Suby of* KEWPIE CORPORATION)
15547 1st St, Irwindale, CA 91706-6201
Tel (626) 334-8090 *Founded/Ownrshp* 1989
Sales 65.3MM^E *EMP* 320
SIC 2015 2013 2035 Eggs, processed: dehydrated; Poultry, processed; Beef, dried: from purchased meat; Seasonings & sauces, except tomato & dry; Dressings, salad: raw & cooked (except dry mixes); Mayonnaise; Eggs, processed: dehydrated; Poultry, processed; Beef, dried: from purchased meat; Seasonings & sauces, except tomato & dry; Dressings, salad: raw & cooked (except dry mixes); Mayonnaise
Pr: Kuniaki Ishikaiwa

KIHOMAC
See KI HO MILITARY ACQUISITION CONSULTING INC

KIIAN DIGITAL
See JK GROUP USA INC

KIK COSTUM PRODUCTS
See HOUSTON KIK INC

KIK CUSTOM PRODUCTS
See KIK PIEDMONT LLC

KIK CUSTOM PRODUCTS
See VIRGINIA KIK INC

KIK CUSTOM PRODUCTS
See KIK INTERNATIONAL LLC

D-U-N-S 84-864-7657
KIK CUSTOM PRODUCTS INC
KIK DANVILLE
(*Suby of* KIK CUSTOM PRODUCTS INC)
1 W Hegeler Ln, Danville, IL 61832-8341
Tel (217) 442-1400 *Founded/Ownrshp* 1989
Sales 716.3MM^E *EMP* 2,500
SIC 2841 2842 2843 2844 Soap & other detergents; Specialty cleaning, polishes & sanitation goods; Surface active agents; Toilet preparations; Soap & other detergents; Specialty cleaning, polishes & sanitation goods; Surface active agents; Toilet preparations
Pr: William Smith
VP: Sheila Wankewycz
**Prin:* Bill Smith

KIK DANVILLE
See KIK CUSTOM PRODUCTS INC

KIK FLORIDA
See SEWELL PRODUCTS OF FLORIDA INC

D-U-N-S 11-785-4153
KIK INTERNATIONAL HOUSTON INC
(*Suby of* KIK HOLDCO COMPANY)
2921 Corder St, Houston, TX 77054-3401
Tel (713) 747-8710 *Founded/Ownrshp* 1996
Sales 440.0MM^E *EMP* 3,000
SIC 5999 Cleaning equipment & supplies; Cleaning equipment & supplies
CEO: David Cynamon
VP Sls: Christopher Benning

D-U-N-S 80-346-0950
KIK INTERNATIONAL LLC
KIK CUSTOM PRODUCTS
909 Magnolia Ave, Auburndale, FL 33823-4007
Tel (863) 967-4463 *Founded/Ownrshp* 1996
Sales 33.6MM^E *EMP* 150
SIC 5999 Cleaning equipment & supplies; Cleaning equipment & supplies
QA Dir: David Burnam

D-U-N-S 07-848-2780 IMP
KIK PIEDMONT LLC
KIK CUSTOM PRODUCTS
(*Suby of* KIK CUSTOM PRODUCTS INC)
2030 Old Candler Rd, Gainesville, GA 30507-7262
Tel (770) 534-0300 *Founded/Ownrshp* 2007
Sales 32.6MM^E *EMP* 500
SIC 2819 Bleaching powder, lime bleaching compounds
**Pr:* Jeffrey M Nodland

D-U-N-S 00-830-2895 IMP
KIK POOL ADDITIVES INC (CA)
5160 E Airport Dr, Ontario, CA 91761-7824
Tel (909) 390-9912 *Founded/Ownrshp* 1958
Sales 58.6MM^E *EMP* 140
SIC 2899 3089 7389 5169 Chemical preparations; Plastic hardware & building products; Packaging & labeling services; Swimming pool & spa chemicals; Chemical preparations; Plastic hardware & building products; Packaging & labeling services; Swimming pool & spa chemicals
Pr: John A Christensen
CFO: Brian Patterson
VP: David M Christensen
VP: Debra Schonk
VP: Chet Yoakum
IT Man: Matt Statler
Opers Mgr: Alejandro Santiago
Prd Mgr: Humberto Gomez

D-U-N-S 05-148-2784
KIK-SOCAL INC
K I K
(*Suby of* KIK INTERNATIONAL HOUSTON INC) ★
9028 Dice Rd, Santa Fe Springs, CA 90670-2520
Tel (562) 946-6427 *Founded/Ownrshp* 1999
Sales NA *EMP* 3,000
SIC 2842 Bleaches, household: dry or liquid; Fabric softeners; Ammonia, household; Cleaning or polishing preparations; Bleaches, household: dry or liquid; Fabric softeners; Ammonia, household; Cleaning or polishing preparations
CEO: Jeffrey M Nodland
**Pr:* Stratis Katsiris
**Pr:* William Smith
**CFO:* Ben W Kaak
Genl Mgr: Greg Wiese

KIKKA
See ITO INC

KIKKITAK STORE
See KAKTOVIK INUPIAT CORP

D-U-N-S 06-173-9058 IMP/EXP
KIKKOMAN FOODS INC
(*Suby of* KIKKOMAN CORPORATION)
N1365 Six Corners Rd, Walworth, WI 53184-5702
Tel (262) 275-6181 *Founded/Ownrshp* 1972
Sales 52.5MM^E *EMP* 190
SIC 2035 Soy sauce; Seasonings, meat sauces (except tomato & dry); Seasonings & sauces, except tomato & dry; Soy sauce; Seasonings, meat sauces (except tomato & dry); Seasonings & sauces, except tomato & dry
Ch Bd: Yubaburo Mogi
**Pr:* Kazuo Shimizu
**CFO:* Karl Keane
Dir: Helen Roberts
Sfty Mgr: Ann Slavin
Ql Cn Mgr: Makoto Kurose
Manager: Sarah Holmes
Sls Mgr: Jordan Greene
Sls Mgr: Yasuhiro Yamazaki
Snr Mgr: Mary Andrich
Board of Directors: Dr Kaaduya Hayashi, Dr Nadasawa, Dr Robert Spitzer

D-U-N-S 02-920-6547 IMP
KIKKOMAN SALES USA INC
(*Suby of* KIKKOMAN CORPORATION)
50 California St Ste 3600, San Francisco, CA 94111-4760
Tel (415) 956-7750 *Founded/Ownrshp* 1957
Sales 86.2MM^E *EMP* 60
SIC 5149 2035 Specialty food items; Pickles, sauces & salad dressings
CEO: Yuzaburo Mogi
**Treas:* Nakamura Mitsunodu
VP: Yuichi Nakagawa
Mng Dir: Annie Isobe
Mktg Dir: Deborah Carpenter
Manager: Helen Robert
Mktg Mgr: Jane Foreman
Sls Mgr: Masahiro Kobayashi
Sls Mgr: B E Reese
Snr Mgr: Yoshinori Masuda

D-U-N-S 01-812-4115
KILBARGER CONSTRUCTION INC
C & L SUPPLY
450 Gallagher Ave, Logan, OH 43138-1893
Tel (740) 385-5531 *Founded/Ownrshp* 1958
Sales 25.8MM^E *EMP* 120
SIC 1381 Drilling oil & gas wells; Drilling oil & gas wells
CEO: Edward Kilbarger
**VP:* Anthony Kilbarger
Opers Mgr: Daniel Stohs
Snr Mgr: Jan Tom

D-U-N-S 10-019-9884
KILDEER COUNTRYSIDE CCSD 96 PTO COORDINATING COUNCIL
1050 Ivy Hall Ln, Buffalo Grove, IL 60089-1333
Tel (847) 459-4260 *Founded/Ownrshp* 1953
Sales 20.8M *EMP* 375

Accts Eder Casella & Co Mchenry
SIC 8211 Public elementary school; Public junior high school; Public elementary school; Public junior high school
Sls&Mrk Ex: Michelle Whitlow

D-U-N-S 82-979-4440 IMP/EXP
KILFROST INC
(*Suby of* CLARIANT CORP) ★
1801 N Military Trl # 201, Boca Raton, FL 33431-1810
Tel (954) 282-5050 *Founded/Ownrshp* 2015
Sales 26.0MM *EMP* 16
SIC 2899 Deicing or defrosting fluid; Deicing or defrosting fluid
CEO: Gary Lydiate
VP: Hortencia Barton
Rgnl Mgr: Nick Patel
VP Opers: Frank Galasso
Opers Mgr: Brian Anderson
Ql Cn Mgr: Susan Baum
Sls&Mrk Ex: Sarah Minto
Sls Mgr: Andrew Murray

KILGORE COLLEGE
See KILGORE JUNIOUR COLLEGE DISTRICT

D-U-N-S 86-807-3888
KILGORE COMPANIES LLC
KILGORE PAVING & MAINTANCE
(*Suby of* SUMMIT MATERIALS LLC) ★
7057 W 2100 S, Salt Lake City, UT 84128-6430
Tel (801) 250-0132 *Founded/Ownrshp* 2010
Sales 108.8MM^E *EMP* 379
SIC 1721 Pavement marking contractor
Genl Mgr: Jason Kilgore
VP: Joe Johnson
IT Man: Brian Hall
Sfty Dirs: Rich Kauss
Sfty Mgr: Jamie Rentmeister

D-U-N-S 01-824-3985 IMP
KILGORE FLARES CO LLC
(*Suby of* CHG GROUP INC) ★
155 Kilgore Rd, Toone, TN 38381-7850
Tel (731) 658-5231 *Founded/Ownrshp* 2001
Sales 116.4MM^E *EMP* 91
SIC 2899 3728 Chemical preparations; Countermeasure dispensers, aircraft; Chemical preparations; Countermeasure dispensers, aircraft
Pr: Chuck Stout
COO: Nick Vlahakis
CFO: Eric Rangen
VP: Ron Kunkle
VP: Tom Plummer
CTO: Jeremy Glenn
QA Dir: Mike Johnson
Dir IT: Alan Phillips
IT Man: Dave Herbage
IT Man: Melissa McPhearson
Opers Mgr: Aric Allen

D-U-N-S 09-136-1923
KILGORE FORD INC
1615 Us Highway 259 N, Kilgore, TX 75662-5503
Tel (903) 984-2006 *Founded/Ownrshp* 2001
Sales 23.0MM *EMP* 42
SIC 5511 Automobiles, new & used; Trucks, tractors & trailers: new & used; Automobiles, new & used; Trucks, tractors & trailers: new & used
Pr: Fernando Varela
**VP:* Gibert Lopez
Sls Mgr: Mike Allums

D-U-N-S 08-388-5947
KILGORE INDEPENDENT SCHOOL DISTRICT (INC)
301 N Kilgore St, Kilgore, TX 75662-5825
Tel (903) 984-2073 *Founded/Ownrshp* 1911
Sales 22.5MM^E *EMP* 530
Accts Brown Bronstad Habenicht & R
SIC 8211 Public elementary & secondary schools; Public elementary & secondary schools
VP: Dereck Borders
Prin: Joe Allen
Prin: Charlotte Austin
Prin: Duane Deen
Prin: Randy Gaddis
Prin: Pete Hillin
Prin: David Smith
Psych: Amon H Horton

KILGORE INDUSTRIES
See KILGORE MECHANICAL LLC

D-U-N-S 78-649-5858
KILGORE INDUSTRIES LP
KILGORE MECHANICAL
10050 Houston Ox Dr, Houston, TX 77064
Tel (713) 924-4900 *Founded/Ownrshp* 2000
Sales 56.5MM^E *EMP* 180
SIC 1711 Plumbing, heating, air-conditioning contractors; Plumbing, heating, air-conditioning contractors

D-U-N-S 07-838-5101
KILGORE JUNIOUR COLLEGE DISTRICT
KILGORE COLLEGE
1100 Broadway Blvd, Kilgore, TX 75662-3204
Tel (903) 983-8105 *Founded/Ownrshp* 1935
Sales 16.2MM *EMP* 350
Accts Henry & Peters Pc Tyler Texa
SIC 8221 College, except junior; College, except junior
Pr: Dr William Holda
**CFO:* Duane J McNaney
Trst: Brian Nutt
Ofcr: Lawrence Kenealy
VP: Gerald Stanglin
VP: Michael Turpin
Dir Lab: Helen Boston
Psych: Virgil Conner
Pgrm Dir: Bill Anderson

KILGORE MECHANICAL
See KILGORE INDUSTRIES LP

D-U-N-S 03-390-5246
KILGORE MECHANICAL LLC
KILGORE INDUSTRIES
15814 Champion Dr, Spring, TX 77379-6820
Tel (713) 924-4900 *Founded/Ownrshp* 2000
Sales 35.5MM^E *EMP* 200
SIC 1711 Mechanical contractor; Mechanical contractor
Genl Mgr: Dion Spafford
Snr PM: Ray Dupree

KILGORE PAVING & MAINTANCE
See KILGORE COMPANIES LLC

D-U-N-S 78-933-2368 IMP
KILIAN MANAGEMENT SERVICES INC
MCDONALD'S
1722 Clarence Ct, West Bend, WI 53095-8543
Tel (262) 338-6111 *Founded/Ownrshp* 1976
Sales 23.6MM^E *EMP* 550
SIC 5812 8742 Fast-food restaurant, chain; Management consulting services; Fast-food restaurant, chain; Management consulting services
Pr: Steve Kilian
**Treas:* Christopher Kilian

D-U-N-S 00-222-5167 IMP
■ **KILIAN MANUFACTURING CORP** (DE)
(*Suby of* ALTRA INDUSTRIAL MOTION CORP) ★
1728 Burnet Ave, Syracuse, NY 13206-3340
Tel (315) 432-0700 *Founded/Ownrshp* 1921, 2005
Sales 77.3MM^E *EMP* 400^E
SIC 3562 3429 Ball bearings & parts; Manufactured hardware (general); Ball bearings & parts; Manufactured hardware (general)
Ch Bd: Michael L Hurt
**Pr:* Christopher H Lake
**Treas:* Joseph Manzelli
Ofcr: John Ellis
Genl Mgr: William Duff
IT Man: Janice Burke
Plnt Mgr: Lorenzo Spinelli
Ql Cn Mgr: David Sheridan
S&M/VP: Donald Wierbinski

KILLAM ASSOC CNSLTING ENGINEERS
See ELSON T KILLAM ASSOCIATES INC

D-U-N-S 00-627-8261 IMP
■ **KILLARK ELECTRIC MANUFACTURING CO INC**
HUBBEL KILLARK
(*Suby of* HUBBELL INC) ★
3940 Mrtin Luther King Dr, Saint Louis, MO 63113
Tel (314) 531-0460 *Founded/Ownrshp* 1985
Sales 68.8MM^E *EMP* 330
SIC 3644 Electric conduits & fittings; Electric conduits & fittings
Pr: John Cower
**COO:* Mac Chriswell
**VP:* Travis Criswell
**VP:* V Petrecca
Ql Cn Mgr: Ken Hubble

D-U-N-S 19-631-5675
KILLDEER MOUNTAIN MANUFACTURING INC
233 Rodeo Dr, Killdeer, ND 58640
Tel (701) 764-5651 *Founded/Ownrshp* 1987
Sales 57.9MM^E *EMP* 275
SIC 3643 3672 Current-carrying wiring devices; Printed circuit boards; Current-carrying wiring devices; Printed circuit boards
Pr: Don Hedger
CFO: Doug Fettig
**CFO:* Doug Fettig
**VP:* Patricia Hedger
Dir IT: Erika Bauer
IT Man: Connie Sailer
Mfg Mgr: Bryan Hanstad
Mktg Mgr: Jerry Fischer

KILLEBREW CHRYSLER JEEP DODGE
See KILLEBREW INC

D-U-N-S 02-718-0173
KILLEBREW INC
KILLEBREW CHRYSLER JEEP DODGE
2203 Houston Hwy, Victoria, TX 77901
Tel (877) 219-9081 *Founded/Ownrshp* 1921
Sales 57.3MM^E *EMP* 47
SIC 5511 5521 Automobiles, new & used; Used car dealers
Pr: Milton A Killebrew
**Sec:* Pam Hill
**VP:* David W Killebrew

D-U-N-S 18-542-6269
KILLEEN IMPORTS INC
DENNIS EAKIN MAZDA
5200 E Central Texas Expy, Killeen, TX 76543-5527
Tel (254) 953-2401 *Founded/Ownrshp* 1987
Sales 28.7MM^E *EMP* 90
SIC 5511 Automobiles, new & used; Automobiles, new & used
Pr: Dennis Eakin
**Sec:* Candice Eakin
Off Mgr: Heather Courtney

D-U-N-S 08-330-7348
KILLEEN INDEPENDENT SCHOOL DISTRICT
200 N W S Young Dr, Killeen, TX 76543-4025
Tel (254) 336-0000 *Founded/Ownrshp* 1882
Sales 392.0MM *EMP* 6,200^E
Accts Lott Vernon & Company Pc
SIC 8211 Public elementary & secondary schools; Public elementary & secondary schools
**Pr:* Carlos Cole Jr
**CFO:* Megan Bradley
Bd of Dir: Mike Helm
Bd of Dir: Ronald Rainosek
**VP:* Joshua Ayers
Brnch Mgr: Don Webster
Dir IT: Michelle Greene
Telecom Mg: Russ Jarret
IT Man: Melissa Lafferty
Netwrk Mgr: John Hocking
Pr Dir: J J Johnson

D-U-N-S 00-718-5085
KILLIAN CONSTRUCTION CO (MO)
(*Suby of* KILLIAN GROUP LLC) ★
2664 E Kearney St, Springfield, MO 65803-4913
Tel (417) 883-1204 *Founded/Ownrshp* 1947, 2005
Sales 46.8MM^E *EMP* 80
SIC 1542 1541 Commercial & office building, new construction; Industrial buildings, new construction; Commercial & office building, new construction; Industrial buildings, new construction
Pr: William F Killian
**CFO:* Benny Nale
**CFO:* Luther Salonen
Ex VP: Kevin Hardy
Sr VP: Stan Hammack
**VP:* Duane Prewitt
Exec: Michael Barbee
CTO: Michael Trush

D-U-N-S 62-347-8208
KILLIAN GROUP LLC
3107 E Chestnut Expy N, Springfield, MO 65802-2548
Tel (417) 883-1204 *Founded/Ownrshp* 2005
Sales 50.9MM^E *EMP* 87
SIC 1542 Nonresidential construction; Commercial & office building contractors; Commercial & office buildings, prefabricated erection; Shopping center construction
CEO: William F Killian
**CFO:* Benny Nale
**VP:* Stan M Hammack
**VP:* Kevin Hardy
Dir IT: Michael Mihalevich
Sfty Mgr: Steve Ratliff

KILLINGLY BOARD OF EDUCATION
See KILLINGLY PUBLIC SCHOOLS

D-U-N-S 80-886-0530
KILLINGLY PUBLIC SCHOOLS
KILLINGLY BOARD OF EDUCATION
79 Westfield Ave, Danielson, CT 06239-2133
Tel (860) 779-6600 *Founded/Ownrshp* 1924
Sales 32.6MM^E *EMP* 500
SIC 8211 Public elementary & secondary schools; Public elementary & secondary schools
CTO: Thomas Milne
Dir IT: Anthony Tomah

D-U-N-S 00-242-1121
KILLINGTON/PICO SKI RESORT PARTNERS LLC
(*Suby of* POWDR CORP) ★
4763 Killington Rd, Killington, VT 05751-9746
Tel (802) 422-3333 *Founded/Ownrshp* 2008
Sales 19.1MM^E *EMP* 1,500^E
SIC 7011 Ski lodge
Pr: Mike Solimano
**Sr VP:* Herwig Demschar
VP: Jeff Temple
IT Man: Vince Wynn

D-U-N-S 08-497-9640 IMP
KILLION INDUSTRIES INC
1380 Poinsettia Ave, Vista, CA 92081-8504
Tel (760) 727-5102 *Founded/Ownrshp* 1981
Sales 33.0MM^E *EMP* 175
SIC 2541 Store & office display cases & fixtures; Display fixtures, wood; Counters or counter display cases, wood; Store & office display cases & fixtures; Display fixtures, wood; Counters or counter display cases, wood
Pr: Richard W Killion
**VP:* Larry Edward
Sls Dir: Lance Block

D-U-N-S 02-298-1419
KILLMER ELECTRIC CO INC
5141 Lakeland Ave N, Minneapolis, MN 55429-3556
Tel (763) 425-2525 *Founded/Ownrshp* 1920
Sales 25.2MM *EMP* 75
Accts Smith Schafer & Associates Lt
SIC 1731 Electrical work; Electrical work
Pr: Brian Palmer
**CFO:* Brian Bakk
**VP:* Gordon Johnson
**VP:* Ray Palmer
**VP:* Scott Palmer

D-U-N-S 04-741-7456
KILOHANA CORP
2024 N King St Ste 200, Honolulu, HI 96819-3494
Tel (808) 842-1133 *Founded/Ownrshp* 2001
Sales 25.5MM^E *EMP* 169
SIC 8711 8713 Engineering services; Surveying services
Pr: Greg H Hiyakumoto
**Treas:* Nancy Matsuno
**VP:* Leighton W K Lum

D-U-N-S 06-973-2881
KILPATRICK LIFE INSURANCE CO OF LOUISIANA INC (LA)
1818 Marshall St, Shreveport, LA 71101-4109
Tel (318) 222-0555 *Founded/Ownrshp* 1932, 1971
Sales NA *EMP* 201
SIC 6311 Life insurance carriers; Life insurance carriers
Pr: Virginia K Shehee
CFO: Dona Wilson
Treas: W P Shehee Jr
**Sec:* Jacqulyn Wine
VP: Margaret Shehee
Dist Mgr: Ken Evans
Dist Mgr: Linda Thiels
Off Admin: Anne Fontenot
Dir IT: Autry Brown
Sales Asso: Vera Lee
Sales Asso: Dana Patterson

D-U-N-S 07-587-5500
KILPATRICK TOWNSEND & STOCKTON LLP
HYDREL
1100 Peachtree St Ne, Atlanta, GA 30309-4501
Tel (404) 815-6500 *Founded/Ownrshp* 1874
Sales 229.2MM^E *EMP* 1,165
SIC 8111 General practice attorney, lawyer; General practice attorney, lawyer
Mng Pt: Susan M Spaeth
Pt: Bill Dorris
Pt: William E Dorris
Pt: Thomas J Dougherty
Pt: Keith Harper
Pt: Gerald A Jeutter
Pt: Wyck A Knox
Pt: Nils Sk Ld
Pt: Diane Prucino
Pt: Hayden J Silver
Pt: David B Whelpley
Mng Pt: Susan Mspaeth
Mng Pt: Susan M Spaeth
CFO: John B Murphy

D-U-N-S 01-843-8259
KILROY CO
TRUST TECHNOLOGIES
34929 Curtis Blvd Ste 104, Eastlake, OH 44095-4053
Tel (440) 951-8700 *Founded/Ownrshp* 1967
Sales 27.7MM^E *EMP* 80
SIC 3544 3549 3545 3541 3444 3356 Jigs & fixtures; Metalworking machinery; Machine tool accessories; Machine tools, metal cutting type; Sheet metalwork; Nonferrous rolling & drawing
Ch Bd: William S Kilroy II
**Pr:* Mike Campbell
**Pr:* Paul Cardinale
**CFO:* Mark Plush
Ql Cn Mgr: Dave Fox
Snr Mgr: Sandy Laforce

D-U-N-S 00-161-2381
KILROY METAL PRODUCTS INC
283 Greene Ave, Brooklyn, NY 11238-1394
Tel (718) 638-2503 *Founded/Ownrshp* 1946
Sales 24.0MM^E *EMP* 60
SIC 5031 5211 1751 Window frames, all materials; Windows, storm: wood or metal; Window & door (prefabricated) installation
Pr: Charles Krobot Jr
**VP:* Charles Krobot III
Sales Exec: Bill Kennedy

D-U-N-S 05-239-0192
▲ **KILROY REALTY CORP**
12200 W Olympic Blvd # 200, Los Angeles, CA 90064-1044
Tel (310) 481-8400 *Founded/Ownrshp* 1997
Sales 521.7MM *EMP* 219^E
Accts Deloitte & Touche Llp Los Ang
Tkr Sym KRC *Exch* NYS
SIC 6798 Real estate investment trusts; Real estate investment trusts
Ch Bd: John B Kilroy Jr
COO: Jeffrey C Hawken
CFO: Richard E Moran
CFO: Tyler H Rose
Ex VP: Eli Khouri
Ex VP: Marcum David Eli Khouri
Ex VP: A Robert Paratte
Ex VP: Justin Smart
Sr VP: Glenn Cohen
Sr VP: Heidi R Roth
VP: Rich Ambidge
VP: Joe Bruna
VP: Rick Buziak
VP: Jamas Gwilliam
VP: Joe Hanen
VP: Randy Jackson
VP: Bob Little
VP: Joseph Magri
VP: Marshall Mc Daniel
VP: Susan Moss
VP: Richard Mount
Board of Directors: Edward F Brennan, Jolie Hunt, Scott S Ingraham, Dale F Kinsella, Gary R Stevenson, Peter B Stoneberg

D-U-N-S 10-557-0084
KILROY REALTY LP
12200 W Olympic Blvd # 200, Los Angeles, CA 90064-1044
Tel (310) 481-8400 *Founded/Ownrshp* 1996
Sales 521.7MM^E *EMP* 226^E
SIC 6798 Real estate investment trusts; Real estate investment trusts
Pr: John B Kilroy Jr
Genl Pt: Kilroy Realty Corporation
CFO: Tyler H Rose
CIO: Lance Coffey
Dir IT: Campbell Greenup

KIM LIGHTING & MFG
See KIM LIGHTING INC

D-U-N-S 19-388-8377 IMP
KIM LIGHTING INC
KIM LIGHTING & MFG
16555 Gale Ave, City of Industry, CA 91745-1788
Tel (626) 968-5666 *Founded/Ownrshp* 2002
Sales NA *EMP* 550
SIC 3648 3646 3317

KIMAL LUMBER & HARDWARE
See KIMAL LUMBER CO

D-U-N-S 04-862-2435
KIMAL LUMBER CO
KIMAL LUMBER & HARDWARE
400 Riverview Dr S, Nokomis, FL 34275-2776
Tel (941) 484-9721 *Founded/Ownrshp* 1981
Sales 22.3MM^E *EMP* 65
SIC 5211 5031 Lumber & other building materials; Lumber, plywood & millwork
Pr: Al Bavry Sr
**VP:* Kim Pavkovich
DP Exec: Kim Pavakovich
Opers Mgr: Jeff Koerbel
Mktg Mgr: Ann Walke

D-U-N-S 17-735-3844
KIMASTLE CORP
DAGER SYSTEMS
28291 Kehrig St, Chesterfield, MI 48047-5248
Tel (586) 949-2355 *Founded/Ownrshp* 1980

Sales 24.5MM^E *EMP* 75
SIC 3559 3544 Degreasing machines, automotive & industrial; Special dies, tools, jigs & fixtures
Pr: Kirk Gilewski
VP: Steve Gilewski
**VP:* Rob Houston
Prgrm Mgr: Ryan Verbeke
Plnt Mgr: Ray Kujawa

KIMBALL BAKERY FEEDS
See PHOENIX FEEDS AND NUTRITION INC

KIMBALL CORPORATE, THE
See KIMBALL ELECTRONICS GROUP LLC

KIMBALL DISTRIBUTIONS
See KIMBALL ELECTRONICS INC

D-U-N-S 94-560-3392 IMP
■ KIMBALL ELECTRONICS GROUP LLC
KIMBALL CORPORATE, THE
(*Suby of* KIMBALL ELECTRONICS INC) ★
1205 Kimball Blvd, Jasper, IN 47546-0017
Tel (812) 634-4000 *Founded/Ownrshp* 2015
Sales 1.4MMM^E *EMP* 3,510
SIC 3571 Electronic computers; Electronic computers
Pr: Donald D Charron
**Pr:* James C Thyen
**CFO:* Michael K Sergesketter
**Ch:* Douglas A Habig
**Treas:* Adam Smith
VP: Steve Korn
**VP:* Gary W Schwartz
**VP:* Kevin R Smith
VP: Spiro Vamvakas
Exec: Marla Haas
Prgrm Mgr: Noe Marquez
Board of Directors: Greg Bannick, Dennis Gradler

D-U-N-S 00-909-3311 IMP
KIMBALL ELECTRONICS INC (UT)
KIMBALL DISTRIBUTIONS
2233 S 300 E, Salt Lake City, UT 84115-2803
Tel (801) 464-0113 *Founded/Ownrshp* 1921, 1951
Sales 80.1MM^E *EMP* 200
SIC 5065 5063 Electronic parts & equipment; Electrical apparatus & equipment; Electronic parts & equipment; Electrical apparatus & equipment
Pr: Richard A Kimball Jr
**Ch:* Richard Kimball Sr
**Treas:* Ray M Schenk
Sales Asso: Jeff Richman

D-U-N-S 13-152-2401
▲ KIMBALL ELECTRONICS INC
1205 Kimball Blvd, Jasper, IN 47546-0017
Tel (812) 634-4200 *Founded/Ownrshp* 2015
Sales 819.3MM *EMP* 1,934^E
Tkr Sym KE *Exch* NGS
SIC 3672 Printed circuit boards
Pr: Donald D Charron
CFO: Charles L Pope
CFO: Robert F Schneider
**CFO:* Michael K Sergesketter
VP: Randall Catt
VP: Roger Chang
VP: Charles J Crep
VP: Steven A Johnson
**VP:* R Gregory Kincer
VP: Steve Korn
**VP:* Michelle R Schroeder
VP: Sandy Smith
VP: Spiro Vamvakas
Board of Directors: Gregory J Lampert

D-U-N-S 13-920-4783
■ KIMBALL ELECTRONICS MANUFACTURING INC
(*Suby of* KIMBALL INTERNATIONAL INC) ★
1600 Royal St, Jasper, IN 47549-1022
Tel (812) 482-1600 *Founded/Ownrshp* 1999
Sales 780.0MM *EMP* 825
SIC 3679 Electronic circuits; Electronic circuits
Ch Bd: Douglas Habig
**Pr:* Don Charron

D-U-N-S 08-875-3710 IMP
■ KIMBALL ELECTRONICS TAMPA INC
(*Suby of* KIMBALL CORPORATE) ★
13750 Reptron Blvd, Tampa, FL 33626-3040
Tel (813) 854-2000 *Founded/Ownrshp* 2007
Sales 228.8MM^E *EMP* 952
SIC 3679 3672 Electronic circuits; Printed circuit boards; Electronic circuits; Printed circuit boards
**CFO:* Michael K Sergesketter
**Treas:* Gregory R Kincer
**Treas:* R G Kincer
**VP:* Michelle R Schroeder
Dir: Marilyn Cooper
Dir IT: Brad Schulz
Opers Mgr: Jerry Anderson
Opers Mgr: Mahmod Zand
Prd Mgr: Shawn Woods

D-U-N-S 79-473-2313 IMP
■ KIMBALL FURNITURE GROUP INC
ARTEC MANUFACTURING
(*Suby of* KIMBALL INTERNATIONAL INC) ★
1600 Royal St, Jasper, IN 47549-1022
Tel (317) 873-8100 *Founded/Ownrshp* 1988
Sales 71.8MM^E *EMP* 6,295
SIC 2521 2522 Wood office furniture; Office furniture, except wood; Wood office furniture; Office furniture, except wood
Pr: Donald W Van Winkle
**Treas:* R Gregory Kincer
**VP:* Michelle R Schroeder
**VP:* James C Thyen
Board of Directors: Brian K Habig, Polly Kawalek, Christina M Vujovich, Jack R Wentworth, John Hagig Alan B Graf Jr

KIMBALL HILL HOMES
See KIMBALL HILL INC

D-U-N-S 02-492-3799
KIMBALL HILL INC
KIMBALL HILL HOMES
5999 New Wilke Rd Ste 306, Rolling Meadows, IL 60008-4503
Tel (847) 364-7300 *Founded/Ownrshp* 1969
Sales 153.7MM^E *EMP* 900
SIC 1521 1531 New construction, single-family houses; Operative builders; New construction, single-family houses; Operative builders; Condominium developers; Cooperative apartment developers; Speculative builder, multi-family dwellings
CEO: David K Hill
**Ch Bd:* Ken Love
Pr: Isaac Heimbinder
CFO: Gene Rowehl
Sr VP: Hal Barber
Sr VP: Robert J Bob Ryan
Board of Directors: Diane Hill

D-U-N-S 88-300-5738 IMP/EXP
■ KIMBALL HOSPITALITY INC
(*Suby of* KIMBALL OFFICE INC) ★
1600 Royal St, Jasper, IN 47549-1022
Tel (812) 482-8090 *Founded/Ownrshp* 1986
Sales 49.3MM^E *EMP* 385^E
SIC 2599 Hospital furniture, except beds; Hospital furniture, except beds
Pr: Kourtney Smith
**Ch:* Douglas A Habig
**VP:* Robert W Bomholt
VP: Stanley Sapp
**VP:* Robert F Schneider
**VP:* Chris Thyen
**Exec:* Gary P Critser
**Exec:* John T Thyen
Dist Mgr: Danielle King
Opers Mgr: Andy McKeough
Sls Mgr: Patrick Oubre

D-U-N-S 00-636-5803 IMP
▲ KIMBALL INTERNATIONAL INC
1600 Royal St, Jasper, IN 47549-1022
Tel (812) 482-1600 *Founded/Ownrshp* 1939
Sales 600.8MM *EMP* 2,894^E
Accts Deloitte & Touche Llp Indiana
Tkr Sym KBAL *Exch* NGS
SIC 2511 2512 2521 2522 2517 Printed circuit boards; Wood household furniture; Upholstered household furniture; Wood office furniture; Office furniture, except wood; Stereo cabinets, wood; Television cabinets, wood; Wood household furniture; Upholstered household furniture; Wood office furniture; Office furniture, except wood; Stereo cabinets, wood; Television cabinets, wood
Ch Bd: Robert F Schneider
Pr: Kourtney Smith
Pr: Donald W Van Winkle
CFO: Michelle R Schroeder
Ofcr: Rhonda Elliott
Ofcr: Lonnie P Nicholson
VP: Julia E Heitz Cassidy
VP: Richard C Farr
VP: Jeff Fenwick
VP: Allen Parker
VP: Mike Wagner
Dir Bus: Patrick Prondzinski
Board of Directors: Patrick E Connolly, Timothy J Jahnke, Kimberly K Ryan, Geoffrey L Stringer, Thomas J Tischhauser, Christine M Vujovich

D-U-N-S 07-827-2713
KIMBALL MEDICAL CENTER INC
BARNABAS HEALTH
600 River Ave, Lakewood, NJ 08701-5281
Tel (732) 363-1900 *Founded/Ownrshp* 1911
Sales 131.1MM *EMP* 1,500^E
Accts Withumsmithbrown Pc Morristow
SIC 8062 General medical & surgical hospitals; General medical & surgical hospitals
Pr: Michael Mimoso
**CFO:* Paul Rouvell
**VP:* Judy Colorado
VP: Elizabeth Deblock
**VP:* Caryl Russo
Dir Risk M: Cathy Johnson
Dir Case M: Anne White
Dir IT: Kim Good
Mtls Mgr: Jonohan Ango
Surgeon: John Parron
Ansthlgy: Menelio Bolante

KIMBALL MIDWEST
See MIDWEST MOTOR SUPPLY CO

D-U-N-S 79-731-2147
■ KIMBALL OFFICE INC
(*Suby of* KIMBALL INTERNATIONAL INC) ★
1600 Royal St, Jasper, IN 47549-1022
Tel (812) 482-1600 *Founded/Ownrshp* 1988
Sales 519.0MM^E *EMP* 2,500
Accts Deloitte & Touche Llp Indiana
SIC 2522 Office desks & tables: except wood; Office desks & tables: except wood
Ch Bd: Douglas A Habig
**Pr:* James C Thyen
**Treas:* R Gregory Kincer
**V Ch Bd:* Thomas L Habig
Ex VP: Randall L Catt
**VP:* C Allen Parker
**Exec:* John T Thyen
Dir Bus: Denise Meagles
Prgrm Mgr: Bruce Nitteberg
Rgnl Mgr: Janet Shannon
Dist Mgr: Michael Bradley

D-U-N-S 03-536-9255 IMP
KIMBALL RENTALS LLC
CRUSHER WEAR PARTS
2839 W California Ave, Salt Lake City, UT 84104-4566
Tel (801) 972-2121 *Founded/Ownrshp* 1956
Sales 32.4MM^E *EMP* 60
SIC 5082 8711 3496

D-U-N-S 15-866-0209
KIMBALL TIREY & ST JOHN LLP
7676 Hazard Center Dr # 900, San Diego, CA 92108-4515
Tel (619) 234-1690 *Founded/Ownrshp* 1977
Sales 23.8MM^E *EMP* 140
SIC 8111 General practice attorney, lawyer; General practice attorney, lawyer
Pt: Theodore C Kimball
Mng Pt: Steven Mehlman
VP: Machelle Lozano
Prin: Leslie Mason
Off Admin: Angela Bhalla
Dir IT: Peter Stevenson
IT Man: Brenda Eiden
IT Man: Jocelyn Fernandez
Sls Dir: Cristina Anderson

D-U-N-S 09-550-6275
KIMBALL UNION ACADEMY
7 Campus Center Rd, Meriden, NH 03770-5402
Tel (603) 469-2000 *Founded/Ownrshp* 1813
Sales 22.1MM *EMP* 95
Accts Tyler Simms & Stsauveur Cpas P
SIC 8211 Boarding school; Preparatory school
COO: Hunter Ulf
CFO: Bob Blake
Ofcr: Gayle Schafer
Assoc Dir: Sarah Moore
Board of Directors: Jason Bourne, Julia Brennan

D-U-N-S 05-115-6706
KIMBEL MECHANICAL SYSTEMS INC
9310 E Wagon Wheel Rd, Springdale, AR 72762-9769
Tel (479) 756-1099 *Founded/Ownrshp* 2001
Sales 40.4MM^E *EMP* 75
SIC 1711 Plumbing contractors
CEO: Brad Smith
**COO:* Dustin Hughes
**CFO:* Ken Childress
**CFO:* Tim Ewalt
**VP:* Miles Kimbel

D-U-N-S 08-108-0558 IMP
KIMBELL ART FOUNDATION
KIMBELL ART MUSEUM
3333 Camp Bowie Blvd, Fort Worth, TX 76107-2744
Tel (817) 336-6100 *Founded/Ownrshp* 1936
Sales 44.6MM *EMP* 110
SIC 8412 Museum
Pr: Kay Carter Fortson
**Sec:* Brenda Cline

KIMBELL ART MUSEUM
See KIMBELL ART FOUNDATION

D-U-N-S 00-792-9789
KIMBELL INC
420 Throckmorton St # 710, Fort Worth, TX 76102-3724
Tel (817) 332-6104 *Founded/Ownrshp* 1962
Sales 26.1MM^E *EMP* 120
SIC 6512 Commercial & industrial building operation
Ch Bd: J C Pace Jr

D-U-N-S 08-708-2491 IMP
KIMBER MFG INC
1 Lawton St, Yonkers, NY 10705-2617
Tel (914) 964-0771 *Founded/Ownrshp* 1996
Sales 95.2MM^E *EMP* 330
SIC 3599 Machine shop, jobbing & repair; Machine shop, jobbing & repair
Ch Bd: Leslie Edelmen
VP: Boaz Hayik
VP: Benny Kokia
VP: Doron Segal
Mng Dir: Abdool Jamal
Dir IT: Gerry Keho
Mfg Dir: Robert Nemergut
Mfg Mgr: Kieran Kelly
Manager: David Richardson
Ql Cn Mgr: Robert Wydro
VP Sls: Ryan Busse

D-U-N-S 00-403-9053 IMP/EXP
■ KIMBERLAND SWAN HOLDINGS INC
(*Suby of* PERRIGO CO) ★
1 Swan Dr, Smyrna, TN 37167-2099
Tel (615) 459-8900 *Founded/Ownrshp* 1898, 1992
Sales 275.0MM *EMP* 825
SIC 2844 Toilet preparations; Toilet preparations
VP: All Goia
VP Sls: Greg Plummer

D-U-N-S 09-343-2680
KIMBERLY AREA SCHOOL DISTRICT
425 S Washington St, Combined Locks, WI 54113-1049
Tel (920) 687-3024 *Founded/Ownrshp* 1910
Sales 30.4MM^E *EMP* 500
Accts Erickson & Associates Sc A
SIC 8211 Public elementary & secondary schools; School board; Public elementary & secondary schools; School board
Dir Sec: Herculas Nikolaou
Teacher Pr: Dawn Thomas
Instr Medi: Laura Brigman
HC Dir: Cindy Vanderberg

D-U-N-S 11-877-3282
KIMBERLY BRYAN INVESTMENT CORP
WHATCHAMACALLIT FASHIONS
17174 Preston Rd, Dallas, TX 75248-1216
Tel (972) 380-1313 *Founded/Ownrshp* 1984
Sales 17.4MM^E *EMP* 401
SIC 5621 5632 Dress shops; Women's sportswear; Women's accessory & specialty stores; Dress shops; Women's sportswear; Women's accessory & specialty stores
Pr: William Danches

D-U-N-S 05-086-0506
KIMBERLY CAR CITY INC
625 W Kimberly Rd, Davenport, IA 52806-5705
Tel (563) 391-8300 *Founded/Ownrshp* 1975
Sales 40.0MM^E *EMP* 54
SIC 5511 Automobiles, new & used; Automobiles, new & used
Pr: David Kehoe

D-U-N-S 00-607-2136 IMP
▲ KIMBERLY-CLARK CORP
351 Phelps Dr, Irving, TX 75038-6540
Tel (972) 281-1200 *Founded/Ownrshp* 1872
Sales 19.7MMM *EMP* 43,000^E
Accts Deloitte & Touche Llp Dallas
Tkr Sym KMB *Exch* NYS
SIC 2621 2676 Paper mills; Facial tissue stock; Toilet tissue stock; Sanitary tissue paper; Surgical & medical instruments; Surgical instruments & apparatus; Surgical appliances & supplies; Sanitary paper products; Towels, napkins & tissue paper products; Feminine hygiene paper products; Infant & baby paper products; Paper mills; Facial tissue stock; Toilet tissue stock; Sanitary tissue paper; Sanitary paper products; Towels, napkins & tissue paper products; Feminine hygiene paper products; Infant & baby paper products
Ch Bd: Thomas J Falk
Pr: Robert Abernathy
COO: Timothy Painter
CFO: Mark A Buthman
CFO: Maria Henry
CFO: Martha Richey
CFO: Kelly Tilooh
Ofcr: Lizanne C Gottung
Sr VP: Sandra Macquillan
Sr VP: Thomas J Mielke
Assoc Dir: Christine Johanski
Comm Man: Wayne Pirman
Comm Man: Pia Tyagi
Board of Directors: Linda Johnson Rice, John R Alm, Marc J Shapiro, John F Bergstrom, Abelardo E Bru, Robert W Decherd, Fabian T Garcia, Mae C Jemison, James M Jenness, Nancy J Karch, Ian C Read

D-U-N-S 07-975-9020
KIMBERLY-CLARK PROFESSIONAL
1400 Holcomb Bridge Rd, Roswell, GA 30076-2190
Tel (800) 241-3146 *Founded/Ownrshp* 2015
Sales 101.2MM^E *EMP* 481^E
SIC 3589 Commercial cleaning equipment
VP: Aaron Powell

D-U-N-S 09-053-1526 IMP/EXP
■ KIMBERLY-CLARK PUERTO RICO INC
(*Suby of* KIMBERLY-CLARK CORP) ★
Pueblo Viejo Ste 165, Guaynabo, PR 00970
Tel (787) 785-3625 *Founded/Ownrshp* 1964
Sales 29.2MM^E *EMP* 135
SIC 2676 5137 5113 Diapers, paper (disposable): made from purchased paper; Diapers; Industrial & personal service paper
Pr: Gustavo Schmidt
**VP:* Ailsa Valledor

D-U-N-S 92-849-6335
KIMBIA INC
1050 E 11th St Ste 200, Austin, TX 78702-1934
Tel (512) 961-7817 *Founded/Ownrshp* 2007
Sales 25.8MM^E *EMP* 52^E
SIC 5045 Computer software
CEO: Daniel Gillett
Chf Mktg O: Christine Lowry
VP: Dom Granato
VP: Phil Murray
CTO: Conleth Oconnell
Web Dev: Cole Latimer
Web Dev: Craig Sanders
Mktg Mgr: Beth Bond
Board of Directors: Daniel Gillett, dan Meyer, Brian Smith

KIMBLE CHASE
See CHASE SCIENTIFIC GLASS INC

D-U-N-S 02-800-1528
KIMBLE CHASE
234 Cardiff Valley Rd, Rockwood, TN 37854-4135
Tel (865) 717-2682 *Founded/Ownrshp* 2009
Sales 35.4MM^E *EMP* 860
SIC 8741 Management services; Management services
Pr: Klaus Walber

D-U-N-S 00-250-1211 IMP/EXP
KIMBLE CHASE LIFE SCIENCE AND RESEARCH PRODUCTS LLC (NJ)
KONTES OF CALIFORNIA
1022 Spruce St, Vineland, NJ 08360-2841
Tel (865) 717-2600 *Founded/Ownrshp* 1934, 2007
Sales 190.8MM^E *EMP* 1,200
SIC 3231 Medical & laboratory glassware: made from purchased glass; Medical & laboratory glassware: made from purchased glass
CEO: Klaus Walber
CFO: Randy Baughman
VP: Ken Falkowi
VP: Bradley Hogg
S&M/VP: Ken Falkowitz
Board of Directors: Axel Herberg, Gerhard Schulze

KIMBLE CLAY & LIMESTONE
See KIMBLE CO

D-U-N-S 04-106-7869
KIMBLE CO
KIMBLE CLAY & LIMESTONE
3596 State Route 39 Nw, Dover, OH 44622-7232
Tel (330) 343-1226 *Founded/Ownrshp* 1952
Sales 1.5MMM^E *EMP* 185
SIC 1221

D-U-N-S 83-467-4566
KIMBLE COMPANIES INC
ACE DISPOSAL
3596 State Route 39 Nw, Dover, OH 44622-7232
Tel (330) 343-5665 *Founded/Ownrshp* 1994
Sales 146.7MM^E *EMP* 191
SIC 4953 Refuse collection & disposal services; Refuse collection & disposal services
Pr: Keith Kimble
**Sec:* Rick Kimble
VP: Eric Kimble
**VP:* Greg Kimble
Genl Mgr: Scott Walter
Genl Mgr: Don Zaucha
Sfty Mgr: Kris Lowdermilk

Sls Mgr: Gerry Helline
Sales Asso: Tom Morris
Sales Asso: Lisa Plantner
Genl Couns: Nathan Vaughan

D-U-N-S 62-735-5733 IMP
KIMBLE CUSTOM CHASSIS CO
KIMBLE MANUFACTURING COMPANY
(*Suby of* HINES CORP) ★
1951 Reiser Ave Se, New Philadelphia, OH 44663-3348
Tel (877) 546-2537 *Founded/Ownrshp* 2006
Sales 34.3MM^E *EMP* 100
SIC 3713 Truck bodies & parts
Pr: James C Cahill
**CFO:* Amie Guy
**VP:* Philip Keegan
**VP:* Jim Moberg
**VP:* Gregory Stohler

KIMBLE MANUFACTURING COMPANY
See KIMBLE CUSTOM CHASSIS CO

D-U-N-S 92-796-1722 IMP
KIMBLE MIXER CO
1951 Reiser Ave Se, New Philadelphia, OH 44663-3348
Tel (330) 308-6700 *Founded/Ownrshp* 2006
Sales 31.0MM^E *EMP* 75
SIC 3713 Cement mixer bodies
Pr: James C Cahill
Pr: Philip Keegan
CFO: Scott Johnston
**CFO:* Chuck Loveless
VP: Jim Moberg
Sls Dir: Derek Leggett

KIMBRELL'S FURNITURE
See FURNITURE DISTRIBUTORS INC

D-U-N-S 03-811-7081
KIMC INVESTMENTS INC
FORTIS INSTITUTE
(*Suby of* EDUCATION AFFILIATES INC) ★
1025 Highway 111, Cookeville, TN 38501-4305
Tel (713) 266-6594 *Founded/Ownrshp* 2000
Sales 4.0MM^E *EMP* 400
SIC 8249 Medical & dental assistant school
CEO: John Hopkins
CFO: Bill Denham
**VP:* Bob Reese

D-U-N-S 96-643-5997
KIMC INVESTMENTS INC
(*Suby of* EDUCATION AFFILIATES INC) ★
5026d Campbell Blvd, Baltimore, MD 21236-4966
Tel (410) 633-2929 *Founded/Ownrshp* 2003
Sales 1.6MM^E *EMP* 1,845^E
SIC 8221 Colleges universities & professional schools
Pr: Duncan M Anderson
**Sec:* Stephen J Budosh

D-U-N-S 96-839-5694
KIMC LOUISIANA HOLDING LLC
(*Suby of* KIMC INVESTMENTS INC) ★
5026d Campbell Blvd, Baltimore, MD 21236-4966
Tel (410) 633-2929 *Founded/Ownrshp* 2003
Sales 529.7M^E *EMP* 1,846^E
SIC 8221 Colleges universities & professional schools
Pr: Duncan M Anderson
Sec: Stephen J Budosh

D-U-N-S 82-543-7028
KIMC PORT LUCIE LLC
FORTIS INSTITUTE
(*Suby of* KIMC LOUISIANA HOLDING LLC) ★
9022 S Us Highway 1 Us-1, Port Saint Lucie, FL 34952-3417
Tel (410) 633-2929 *Founded/Ownrshp* 2003
Sales 328.0M^E *EMP* 1,199^E
SIC 8221 Colleges universities & professional schools
Pr: Duncan Anderson
Sec: Stephen J Budosh

D-U-N-S 00-183-8101
KIMCHUK INC (CT)
1 Corporate Dr Ste 1, Danbury, CT 06810-4139
Tel (203) 790-7800 *Founded/Ownrshp* 1957
Sales 36.2MM^E *EMP* 150
SIC 3625 7389 3312 7371 7373 Control equipment, electric; Design, commercial & industrial; Sheet or strip, steel, cold-rolled: own hot-rolled; Custom computer programming services; Computer integrated systems design; Control equipment, electric; Design, commercial & industrial; Sheet or strip, steel, cold-rolled: own hot-rolled; Custom computer programming services; Computer integrated systems design
Pr: Jim Marquis
**Pr:* William Kimbell
COO: Mike Moeller
CFO: Manny Cipriano
**VP:* James A Marquis
Mng Dir: Dick Cardillo
CIO: Steve Sconzo
IT Man: Vincent Rodriguez
Ql Cn Mgr: Standish Jim
Ql Cn Mgr: Jim Standish
Manager: Jim Mackenzie

D-U-N-S 07-943-2815
KIMCO FACILITY SERVICES LLC
KIMCO SERVICES
6055 Lakeside Commons Dr, Macon, GA 31210-5790
Tel (478) 752-7000 *Founded/Ownrshp* 2014
Sales 200.0MM *EMP* 3,000
SIC 7349 Janitorial service, contract basis; Janitorial service, contract basis
CFO: James Fritze

KIMCO GOVERNMENT SERVICES
See KIMCO STAFFING SERVICES INC

D-U-N-S 06-803-3117 IMP
▲ KIMCO REALTY CORP
3333 New Hyde Park Rd # 100, New Hyde Park, NY 11042-1205
Tel (516) 869-9000 *Founded/Ownrshp* 1966
Sales 993.9MM *EMP* 580
Tkr Sym KIM *Exch* NYS
SIC 6798 Real estate investment trusts; Real estate investment trusts
Pr: David B Henry
**Ch Bd:* Milton Cooper
Pr: Conor C Flynn
CFO: Glenn G Cohen
Ofcr: Michael V Pappagallo
VP: Scott G Onufrey
Board of Directors: Philip E Coviello, Richard G Dooley, Frank Lourenso, Richard B Saltzman, Joe Grills

KIMCO SERVICES
See KIMCO FACILITY SERVICES LLC

D-U-N-S 16-126-7430
KIMCO STAFFING SERVICES INC
KIMCO GOVERNMENT SERVICES
17872 Cowan, Irvine, CA 92614-6010
Tel (949) 331-1199 *Founded/Ownrshp* 1986
Sales 187.4MM^E *EMP* 4,000
SIC 7361 Employment agencies; Employment agencies
CEO: Kim I Megonigal
**Pr:* Lisa Pierson
**VP:* Steven Bradley
VP: Eric Coe
Exec: Leticia Kelch
Brnch Mgr: Peggy Best
Brnch Mgr: Serena Gray
Brnch Mgr: Rachael McGarvey
Brnch Mgr: Louise Ruiz
Off Mgr: Windy McNay
Dir IT: Barbara Heeger

D-U-N-S 00-379-0276
KIMES & STONE CONSTRUCTION CO INC
484 Highway 145 S, Booneville, MS 38829-7539
Tel (662) 728-3501 *Founded/Ownrshp* 1986
Sales 24.1MM *EMP* 50
Accts Alexander Thompson Arnold Pllc
SIC 1611 General contractor, highway & street construction; General contractor, highway & street construction
Pr: William E Stone
Treas: Gloria Copeland
**Sec:* Duane Newman
**VP:* Murray Cook

D-U-N-S 06-109-9131
KIMLEY-HORN AND ASSOCIATES INC
(*Suby of* KIMLEY-HORN GROUP INC) ★
3001 Weston Pkwy, Cary, NC 27513-2301
Tel (919) 677-2000 *Founded/Ownrshp* 2008
Sales 372.1MM^E *EMP* 2,177
SIC 8711 Engineering services; Engineering services
Pr: John C Atz
**Ch Bd:* Brooks Peed
**CFO:* Mark Wilson
**Treas:* David McEntee
Sr VP: John Benditz
Sr VP: Steve Daugherty
Sr VP: Mike Kiefer
Sr VP: Pierre Pretorius
Sr VP: Mark Tabor
Sr VP: Roy Wilshire
Sr VP: Jon Wilson
VP: Jeff Allen
VP: Roscoe Biby
VP: Johnathan Dorman
VP: Dave Leistiko
VP: Marwan Mufleh
VP: Vicki Purtle
VP: Kevin Roberson
VP: Kurt Schulte
Board of Directors: Brooks Peed

D-U-N-S 19-156-3824
KIMLEY-HORN GROUP INC
3001 Weston Pkwy, Cary, NC 27513-2301
Tel (919) 677-2000 *Founded/Ownrshp* 2008
Sales 380.7MM^E *EMP* 2,300
SIC 8711 Consulting engineer; Consulting engineer
Pr: Mark S Wilson
**Pr:* John C Atz
**VP:* Nicholas L Ellis

D-U-N-S 04-843-4138 IMP
KIMMEL ATHLETIC SUPPLY CO INC (WA)
RB SPORTING GOODS
202 E Mission Ave, Spokane, WA 99202-1819
Tel (509) 241-1979 *Founded/Ownrshp* 1969, 1980
Sales 29.0MM^E *EMP* 85
SIC 5091 5941 Athletic goods; Team sports equipment; Athletic goods; Team sports equipment
CEO: William D Davis
**VP:* James R Kimmel
Exec: Cindy Weston
Sls Mgr: Art Thunell
Sls Mgr: Pat Welch
Sales Asso: Brent Leifer

D-U-N-S 00-309-8753
■ KIMMEL AUTOMOTIVE INC (MD)
KIMMEL TIRE
(*Suby of* MONRO MUFFLER BRAKE INC) ★
200 Holleder Pkwy, Rochester, NY 14615-3808
Tel (800) 876-6676 *Founded/Ownrshp* 1938, 2002
Sales 40.1MM^E *EMP* 280
Accts Black Reilly & Associates
SIC 5531 7538 5014 7534 Automotive tires; General automotive repair shops; Truck tires & tubes; Tire recapping; Tire repair shop; Automotive tires; General automotive repair shops; Truck tires & tubes; Tire recapping; Tire repair shop
Pr: James Hartman
**VP:* Allen L Benoit
**VP:* Robert M Ignozzi
**VP:* Ronald H Rhodes
VP: T Sudano

KIMMEL CENTER FOR PRFRMG ARTS
See KIMMEL CENTER INC

D-U-N-S 05-360-1733
KIMMEL CENTER INC
KIMMEL CENTER FOR PRFRMG ARTS
1500 Walnut St Ste 1700, Philadelphia, PA 19102-3525
Tel (215) 670-2300 *Founded/Ownrshp* 1996
Sales 26.3MM^E *EMP* 654
Accts Grant Thornton Llp Philadelph
SIC 8641 7922 Theatrical producers & services; Civic associations; Civic associations; Theatrical producers & services
Pr: Anne C Eyers
COO: Natalie Paquin
**CFO:* Rick Perkins
VP: Matt Wolf
Genl Mgr: Jason S Bray
IT Man: Stan Applegate
Opers Mgr: Daniel Palmieri
Prd Mgr: Amy Kurzban
Prd Mgr: Nicole Thornton
S&M/VP: Crystal Brewe
Pr Mgr: Dafni Comerota

KIMMEL TIRE
See KIMMEL AUTOMOTIVE INC

D-U-N-S 12-172-5634 EXP
KIMMELS COAL AND PACKAGING INC
401 Machamer Ave, Wiconisco, PA 17097
Tel (717) 453-7151 *Founded/Ownrshp* 2000
Sales 33.0MM^E *EMP* 65^E
SIC 5052 5032 1422 1241 Coal; Stone, crushed or broken; Crushed & broken limestone; Coal mining services
Pr: Scott B Kimmel
**Treas:* Tamela E Kimmel
Opers Mgr: Scott Cecco

D-U-N-S 09-074-5522
KIMMINS ASSOCIATES INC
(*Suby of* KIMMINS CORP) ★
1501 E 2nd Ave, Tampa, FL 33605-5005
Tel (813) 248-3878 *Founded/Ownrshp* 1996
Sales 56.2MM *EMP* 327
SIC 8741 Management services; Management services
Pr: Francis Williams
**Sec:* Joe Williams
**VP:* Norm Dominiak

D-U-N-S 19-647-3557
KIMMINS CONTRACTING CORP
(*Suby of* KIMMINS CORP) ★
1501 E 2nd Ave, Tampa, FL 33605-5005
Tel (813) 248-3878 *Founded/Ownrshp* 1983
Sales 86.4MM^E *EMP* 320
SIC 1623 Water, sewer & utility lines; Water, sewer & utility lines
Pr: Joseph Williams
CFO: Ray Rowland
**Sec:* Norm Dominiak
**VP:* Candice Agosto
**VP:* Mike O Brien
VP: Mike O'Brien
**VP:* John Zemina
Area Mgr: Mike Wabuda
Genl Mgr: Buz Molennor
Off Mgr: Winnie Jackson
Sfty Mgr: Domenic Deamicis

D-U-N-S 17-568-4018 IMP
KIMMINS CORP
1501 E 2nd Ave, Tampa, FL 33605-5005
Tel (813) 248-3878 *Founded/Ownrshp* 1985
Sales 143.4MM^E *EMP* 327
SIC 1799 1795 1522 Decontamination services; Asbestos removal & encapsulation; Demolition, buildings & other structures; Apartment building construction; Multi-family dwelling construction; Decontamination services; Asbestos removal & encapsulation; Demolition, buildings & other structures; Apartment building construction; Multi-family dwelling construction
Pr: Francis M Williams
**Sec:* Joseph M Williams
VP: Candice Agosto
**VP:* Karl Burgin

D-U-N-S 10-346-6231
KIMPTON HOTEL & RESTAURANT GROUP LLC
(*Suby of* INTERCONTINENTAL HOTELS GROUP PLC)
222 Kearny St Ste 200, San Francisco, CA 94108-4537
Tel (415) 397-5572 *Founded/Ownrshp* 2015
Sales 1.0MMM^E *EMP* 7,500
SIC 8741 Hotel or motel management; Hotel or motel management
CEO: Mike Depatie
COO: Mike Defrino
COO: Niki Leondakis
CFO: Ben Rowe
Ex VP: Joe Long
Ex VP: Nir Margarlit
Ex VP: Judy Miles
Ex VP: Gregory Wolkom
Sr VP: Troy Furbay
Sr VP: John Inserra
Sr VP: Greg Smith
VP: Chris Bybee
VP: Jin Lee
VP: Andrea Mue
VP: Greg Taylor
Comm Dir: Jessica Madrigal

D-U-N-S 19-434-2510
KIMRAD TRANSPORT LP
371 W Loop 335 S, Amarillo, TX 79118-6137
Tel (806) 359-3882 *Founded/Ownrshp* 2004
Sales 50.8MM^E *EMP* 95
SIC 4731 Freight transportation arrangement; Freight transportation arrangement
Pr: Brad Pohlmeier
Pt: Kimlia Pohlmeier
Genl Mgr: Curt Pohlmeier
IT Man: Michael Patton
Opers Mgr: Jason Smith

D-U-N-S 00-719-4475
KIMRAY INC (OK)
52 Nw 42nd St, Oklahoma City, OK 73118-8590
Tel (405) 507-5214 *Founded/Ownrshp* 1948
Sales 87.7MM^E *EMP* 300
SIC 3829 3533 3822 3612 3561 3491 Measuring & controlling devices; Oil field machinery & equipment; Auto controls regulating residntl & coml environmt & applncs; Transformers, except electric; Pumps & pumping equipment; Industrial valves; Measuring & controlling devices; Oil field machinery & equipment; Auto controls regulating residntl & coml environmt & applncs; Transformers, except electric; Pumps & pumping equipment; Industrial valves
Pr: Garman Kimmell
Dist Mgr: Steve Copeland
**Genl Mgr:* Thomas A Hill
Sfty Dirs: Paul Turner

D-U-N-S 07-387-1998 IMP/EXP
KIMRE INC
744 Sw 1st St, Homestead, FL 33030-6902
Tel (786) 243-1479 *Founded/Ownrshp* 1973
Sales 21.8MM^E *EMP* 40
SIC 1389 Gas field services
Ch Bd: George C Pedersen
**Pr:* Mary R Keenan
**VP:* Marrietta Pedersen
Plnt Mgr: Jackie Silva
Prd Mgr: Maria Leon
Sales Exec: Roy Dibiney
Sales Exec: Edward Fowler

D-U-N-S 12-467-8744 IMP
KIMURA INC
(*Suby of* KIMURA UNITY CO.,LTD.)
102 Cherry Blossom Dr, Laurens, SC 29360-5206
Tel (864) 682-8700 *Founded/Ownrshp* 2002
Sales 26.7MM^E *EMP* 100
SIC 3444 Metal housings, enclosures, casings & other containers
Pr: Takashi Yamauchi
**Pr:* Kenji Kanatani
Sales Exec: Justin Lane

D-U-N-S 04-812-5227
KIMZEY CASING SERVICE LLC
3400 Quebec St Ste 3200, Denver, CO 80207
Tel (303) 248-3425 *Founded/Ownrshp* 2007
Sales 47.9MM^E *EMP* 70
SIC 1389 Cementing oil & gas well casings
VP: Trisha Kimzey
Pr: David Howard

KINARD
See BDB EQUITIES INC

KINCAID FURNITURE
See LA-Z-BOY CASEGOODS INC

D-U-N-S 05-132-4093 IMP
■ KINCAID FURNITURE CO INC
(*Suby of* LA-Z-BOY INC) ★
240 Pleasant Hill Rd, Hudson, NC 28638-2244
Tel (828) 728-3261 *Founded/Ownrshp* 1988
Sales 91.9MM^E *EMP* 550
SIC 2511 2512 Wood household furniture; Upholstered household furniture; Wood household furniture; Upholstered household furniture
Pr: Steven M Kincaid
Pr: Tim Annas
Sr VP: Ryan Allen
Sr VP: Bob Lemons
VP: David Pollpeter
VP: Reggie Probst
Creative D: Seth Olsen
Brnch Mgr: Clarence Gilbert
Snr Sftwr: Reba Baldwin
Snr Sftwr: Daren Wilz
Snr Sftwr: Jason Winkler

D-U-N-S 04-247-8961
■ KINCAID GENERATION LLC
(*Suby of* DOMINION ENERGY INC) ★
4 Miles W Of Kincaid, Kincaid, IL 62540
Tel (217) 237-4311 *Founded/Ownrshp* 1996
Sales 111.8MM *EMP* 144
Accts Deloitte & Touche Llp Richmo
SIC 4911 Generation, electric power; Generation, electric power
Owner: Dan Helms
CFO: Douglas Black

KINCAID'S
See RESTAURANTS UNLIMITED INC

KINCO CONSTRUCTION
See KINCO CONSTRUCTORS LLC

D-U-N-S 07-567-1289
KINCO CONSTRUCTORS LLC
KINCO CONSTRUCTION
12600 Lawson Rd, Little Rock, AR 72210-2711
Tel (501) 225-7606 *Founded/Ownrshp* 2001
Sales 78.9MM^E *EMP* 185
SIC 1542 1541 Nonresidential construction; Industrial buildings & warehouses; Nonresidential construction; Industrial buildings & warehouses
CEO: Doug Wasson
VP: Brian Carney
**VP:* Marc Dillard
**VP:* William Fletcher
**VP:* Keith Jacks

D-U-N-S 05-311-2074
KINCO LTD
(*Suby of* ATRIUM WINDOWS AND DOORS INC) ★
5245 Old Kings Rd, Jacksonville, FL 32254-1191
Tel (904) 355-1476 *Founded/Ownrshp* 1971
Sales 21.6MM^E *EMP* 425
SIC 3442 Metal doors, sash & trim; Metal doors, sash & trim

KIND FOODS
See KIND LLC

D-U-N-S 87-940-8680 IMP
KIND LLC
KIND FOODS
1372 Broadway, New York, NY 10018-6107
Tel (212) 616-3006 *Founded/Ownrshp* 1994
Sales 221.8MM^E *EMP* 125
SIC 5141 Groceries, general line; Groceries, general line
CEO: Daniel Lubetzky
CFO: Neal Cravens
Ex VP: Jaques Antebi
Comm Dir: Erin Pineda
Comm Man: Meghan Kelleher
Comm Man: Amanda Sirianni
Rgnl Mgr: Jason Wood
CTO: Khaled Schubert
QA Dir: Tom Marchisello
Dir IT: Khaled Arden
IT Man: Jbeily Joe

KINDE CO-OP
See FARMERS CO-OPERATIVE GRAIN CO OF KINDE

D-U-N-S 06-018-4314
KINDEL FURNITURE CO
4047 Eastern Ave Se, Grand Rapids, MI 49508-3401
Tel (616) 243-3676 *Founded/Ownrshp* 1968
Sales 39.5MM^E *EMP* 175
SIC 2511 7641 Dining room furniture: wood; Tables, household: wood; Chairs, household, except upholstered: wood; Reupholstery & furniture repair; Dining room furniture: wood; Tables, household: wood; Chairs, household, except upholstered: wood; Reupholstery & furniture repair
Ch Bd: Robert S Fogarty
Sr VP: Moore Councill
**VP:* John Fisher
**VP:* Paul Hebert
**VP:* Dennis Patterson

D-U-N-S 60-649-3666
■ **KINDER MORGAN (DELAWARE) INC**
(*Suby of* KINDER MORGAN INC) ★
Rr 2, Muleshoe, TX 79347
Tel (806) 272-3309 *Founded/Ownrshp* 1997
Sales 57.8MM^E *EMP* 200
SIC 4923 4922 1311 1382 Gas transmission & distribution; Natural gas transmission; Crude petroleum & natural gas; Oil & gas exploration services; Gas transmission & distribution; Natural gas transmission; Crude petroleum & natural gas; Oil & gas exploration services
Ch Bd: Richard D Kinder
**Pr:* Paul Steinway
**CFO:* Kimberly A Dang
CFO: Park C Shaper
**Treas:* David D Kinder
**Ex VP:* Steve Kean
**VP:* Richard Bullock
**VP:* Joseph Listengart
**VP:* Michael Morgan
CIO: Laurel Tippin
Dir IT: Darine Davis

D-U-N-S 07-507-9822
■ **KINDER MORGAN BULK TERMINALS INC**
(*Suby of* KINDER MORGAN ENERGY PARTNERS LP) ★
1001 Louisiana St # 1000, Houston, TX 77002-5089
Tel (713) 369-9000 *Founded/Ownrshp* 1998
Sales 166.7MM^E *EMP* 767
SIC 4491 Marine terminals; Stevedoring; Marine terminals; Stevedoring
Pr: Steven J Kean
**CEO:* Richard D Kinder
**CFO:* Kimberly Allen Dang
**Sr VP:* Steve Daigle

D-U-N-S 03-512-3850 IMP/EXP
■ **KINDER MORGAN ENERGY PARTNERS LP**
(*Suby of* KINDER MORGAN INC) ★
1001 La St Ste 1000, Houston, TX 77002
Tel (713) 369-9000 *Founded/Ownrshp* 2014
Sales 12.5MMM *EMP* 11,075
SIC 4613 4925 4922 4226 4619 5171 Refined petroleum pipelines; Gasoline pipelines (common carriers); Gas production and/or distribution; Liquefied petroleum gas, distribution through mains; Natural gas transmission; Pipelines, natural gas; Storage, natural gas; Petroleum & chemical bulk stations & terminals for hire; Coal pipeline operation; Petroleum terminals; Refined petroleum pipelines; Gasoline pipelines (common carriers); Gas production and/or distribution; Liquefied petroleum gas, distribution through mains; Natural gas transmission; Pipelines, natural gas; Storage, natural gas; Petroleum & chemical bulk stations & terminals for hire; Coal pipeline operation; Petroleum terminals
CEO: Richard D Kinder
Pr: Duane Kokinda
Pr: Tom Martin
CFO: Kimberly A Dang
VP: Bill Henderson
VP: Mark Huse

D-U-N-S 80-040-8192
▲ **KINDER MORGAN INC**
1001 La St Ste 1000, Houston, TX 77002
Tel (713) 369-9000 *Founded/Ownrshp* 2006
Sales 16.2MMM *EMP* 11,535
Tkr Sym KMI *Exch* NYS
SIC 4922 Natural gas transmission; Pipelines, natural gas; Storage, natural gas; Natural gas transmission; Pipelines, natural gas; Storage, natural gas
Ch Bd: Richard D Kinder
Pr: Ian D Anderson
Pr: Jesse Arenivas
**Pr:* Steven J Kean
Pr: Thomas A Martin
Pr: Ronald G McClain
Pr: John W Schlosser
CFO: Kimberly A Dang
Ofcr: Kimberly Allen
VP: John Chapman
VP: David R Deveau
VP: Randy Ramsey
VP: Dax A Sanders
VP: Debra Witges
VP: Terry Woolfe
Board of Directors: William A Smith, Ted A Gardner, Joel V Staff, Anthony W Hall Jr, Robert F Vagt, Gary L Hultquist, Perry M Waughtal, Ronald L Kuehn Jr, Deborah A Macdonald, Michael J Miller, Michael C Morgan, Arthur C Reichstetter, C Park Shaper

D-U-N-S 00-694-3500 IMP/EXP
■ **KINDER MORGAN KANSAS INC**
(*Suby of* KINDER MORGAN INC) ★
1001 La St Ste 1000, Houston, TX 77002
Tel (713) 369-9000 *Founded/Ownrshp* 2007
Sales 2.2MMM^E *EMP* 7,931
SIC 4922 4924 Natural gas transmission; Pipelines, natural gas; Natural gas distribution; Natural gas transmission; Pipelines, natural gas; Natural gas distribution
CEO: Richard D Kinder
Pr: Tom Martin
**Pr:* C Park Shaper
**COO:* Steven J Kean
CFO: Kimberly A Dang
Ex VP: Steve Kean
VP: Joseph Listengart
Prin: Henry Cornell
Prin: Deborah A Macdonald
Prin: Michael Miller
Prin: Michael C Morgan
Board of Directors: Henry Cornell, Deborah A Macdonald, Michael Miller, Michael C Morgan, Kenneth A Pontarelli, Joel V Staff, John Stokes, R Baran Tekkora, Glenn A Youngkin

D-U-N-S 13-988-7975 IMP/EXP
■ **KINDER MORGAN LIQUIDS TERMINALS LLC**
(*Suby of* KINDER MORGAN ENERGY PARTNERS LP) ★
500 Dallas St Ste 1000, Houston, TX 77002-4718
Tel (713) 369-8758 *Founded/Ownrshp* 1975
Sales 212.3MM^E *EMP* 1,000^E
SIC 4226 Oil & gasoline storage caverns for hire; Oil & gasoline storage caverns for hire
CEO: Richard D Kinder
**Pr:* John Schlosser
**CFO:* Kimberly Dang
**Treas:* David D Kinder
**Ex VP:* Steven J Kean
**VP:* Joseph Listengart
**Prin:* Jeff Armstrong

D-U-N-S 02-918-8021
■ **KINDER MORGAN MATERIALS SERVICES LLC**
(*Suby of* KINDER MORGAN ENERGY PARTNERS LP) ★
333 Rouser Rd Ste 4601, Moon Township, PA 15108-2773
Tel (412) 264-6068 *Founded/Ownrshp* 2002
Sales 163.7MM^E *EMP* 5,485
SIC 4011 Railroads, line-haul operating; Railroads, line-haul operating
VP: Arthur Rudolph
VP: Michael Chutz
**Genl Mgr:* Brian Seaman

D-U-N-S 14-359-8048
■ **KINDER MORGAN PRODUCTION CO LP**
(*Suby of* KINDER MORGAN ENERGY PARTNERS LP) ★
1001 La St Ste 1000, Houston, TX 77002
Tel (800) 525-3752 *Founded/Ownrshp* 2007
Sales 221.8MM^E *EMP* 435^E
SIC 5172 Crude oil
CEO: Richard Kinder
Dir Bus: Pamela Baden
IT Man: Robert Arnold
Counsel: Jim Seitz

KINDERCARE
See MULBERRY CHILDCARE CENTERS INC

D-U-N-S 60-366-9052
KINDERCARE LEARNING CENTERS LLC
(*Suby of* C D C) ★
650 Ne Holladay St # 1400, Portland, OR 97232-2096
Tel (503) 872-1300 *Founded/Ownrshp* 2005
Sales 427.4MM^E *EMP* 24,000
SIC 8351 Group day care center; Group day care center
CEO: Thomas A Heymann
**CFO:* Dan R Jackson
**Sr VP:* Edward L Brewington
**Sr VP:* S Wray Hutchinson
**Sr VP:* Eva M Kripalani
**Sr VP:* Bruce Walters
Ex Dir: Jacquie Ciccia
Ex Dir: Casey Crest
Ex Dir: Michelle Grubb
Ex Dir: Melonie Hilstad
Ex Dir: Michelle Moser
Board of Directors: Richard J Goldstein, Henry R Kravis, Michael W Michelson, Scott C Nuttall, George R Roberts

D-U-N-S 09-525-0544
KINDERHOOK CENTRAL SCHOOL DISTRICT
ICHABOD CRANE CENTRAL SCHOOL
Rr 9, Valatie, NY 12184
Tel (518) 758-7575 *Founded/Ownrshp* 1955
Sales 37.0MM *EMP* 400
Accts West & Company Cpas Pc Sarato
SIC 8211 Public elementary school; Public junior high school; Public senior high school; Public elementary school; Public junior high school; Public senior high school
Psych: Steve Leader
Psych: Joan White

D-U-N-S 16-276-4414
KINDERHOOK INDUSTRIES LLC
521 5th Ave Fl 34, New York, NY 10175-3301
Tel (212) 201-6780 *Founded/Ownrshp* 2003
Sales 141.6MM^E *EMP* 520
SIC 6799 Investors; Investors
CFO: Lisa Clarke
**CFO:* Lisa Schmidt
VP: Louis Aurelio
VP: Michael Zoch

KINDLE DODGE
See KINDLE FORD-MERCURY-LINCOLN- DODGE INC

D-U-N-S 00-799-1866
KINDLE FORD LINCOLN MERCURY INC
525 Stone Harbor Blvd, Cape May Court House, NJ 08210-2474
Tel (609) 465-5000 *Founded/Ownrshp* 2007
Sales 53.0MM *EMP* 40
SIC 5511 Automobiles, new & used; Automobiles, new & used
Genl Mgr: Dave Sharp
Sls Mgr: Fran Adelizzi
Sales Asso: Roger Bergeron
Sales Asso: Tom McAteer

D-U-N-S 01-186-7710
KINDLE FORD-MERCURY-LINCOLN- DODGE INC
KINDLE DODGE
525 Stone Harbor Blvd, Cape May Court House, NJ 08210-2417
Tel (609) 465-5100 *Founded/Ownrshp* 1957
Sales 30.2MM^E *EMP* 87
SIC 5511 Automobiles, new & used; Automobiles, new & used
Pr: William J Kindle
**Ch Bd:* Robert G Kindle
**Sec:* Steven Kindle
**VP:* James T Falzlein
Genl Mgr: Dave Sharp
Sls Mgr: Kevin Perry
Sls Mgr: Bonnie Vitola
Sales Asso: Bobby Lind
Sales Asso: Albert Thalheimer
Sales Asso: Rob Walker

D-U-N-S 62-607-4355
KINDLON ENTERPRISES INC
2300 Raddant Rd Ste B, Aurora, IL 60502-9108
Tel (708) 367-4000 *Founded/Ownrshp* 1997
Sales 25.1MM^E *EMP* 250
SIC 2653 Boxes, corrugated: made from purchased materials; Pads, corrugated: made from purchased materials; Partitions, corrugated: made from purchased materials; Boxes, corrugated: made from purchased materials; Pads, corrugated: made from purchased materials; Partitions, corrugated: made from purchased materials
Pr: Randall C Mohler

D-U-N-S 10-904-1835
KINDNESS GENERAL CONTRACTORS INC
12891 Nelson St, Garden Grove, CA 92840-5018
Tel (714) 636-4542 *Founded/Ownrshp* 2000
Sales 27.2MM^E *EMP* 40
SIC 1541 Industrial buildings, new construction
Pr: Jeff Kindness
CFO: Veronica Kilanda
Off Mgr: Karen Penwarden

D-U-N-S 62-318-8203
KINDRED CARE LLC
1918 E 23rd St Ste A, Lawrence, KS 66046-5008
Tel (913) 782-3055 *Founded/Ownrshp* 2008
Sales 25.0MM *EMP* 50
SIC 5961 5912 Pharmaceuticals, mail order; Drug stores; Pharmaceuticals, mail order; Drug stores
COO: Gordon Roll
CFO: Steve Jalowlec

D-U-N-S 79-905-5608
KINDRED CARE LLC
196 Highway Cc, Linn, MO 65051-3500
Tel (573) 897-0246 *Founded/Ownrshp* 2006
Sales 22.0MM *EMP* 102
SIC 6282 Manager of mutual funds, contract or fee basis
Prin: Rayanne C Strubberg

D-U-N-S 13-153-0511
▲ **KINDRED HEALTHCARE INC**
680 S 4th St, Louisville, KY 40202-2412
Tel (502) 596-6806 *Founded/Ownrshp* 1998
Sales 5.0MMM *EMP* 63,300
Tkr Sym KND *Exch* NYS
SIC 8062 8051 8322 8082 General medical & surgical hospitals; Skilled nursing care facilities; Rehabilitation services; Home health care services; General medical & surgical hospitals; Skilled nursing care facilities; Rehabilitation services; Home health care services
Pr: Benjamin A Breier
**Ch Bd:* Phyllis R Yale
Pr: Benjamin A Breier
CFO: Rosa Bennett
CFO: Stephen D Farber
CFO: Michael Franks
Chf Cred: Noris Aleman
Chf Mktg O: Marc Rothman
Sr VP: William M Altman
Sr VP: Barbara L Baylis
Sr VP: Vincent S Hambright
Sr VP: Sandra Long
Sr VP: David Mikula
Sr VP: Brian L Pugh
Sr VP: Hank Robinson
Sr VP: Robert Schmidt
Board of Directors: Joel Ackerman, Jonathan D Blum, Thomas P Cooper, Heyward R Donigan, Richard Goodman, Christopher T Hjelm, Frederick J Kleisner, John H Shor

D-U-N-S 08-966-6478
■ **KINDRED HEALTHCARE OPERATING INC**
(*Suby of* KINDRED HEALTHCARE INC) ★
680 S 4th St, Louisville, KY 40202-2412
Tel (502) 596-7300 *Founded/Ownrshp* 1998
Sales 616.2MM^E *EMP* 7,800
SIC 8051 Extended care facility; Extended care facility
CFO: Chris Porter
Treas: Steven L Monaghan
Sr VP: William M Altman
Sr VP: Barbara L Baylis
Sr VP: Michael W Beal
Sr VP: Peter D Corless
Sr VP: Anthony Disser
Sr VP: Dennis J Hansen
Sr VP: David G Henderson
Sr VP: Donna G Kelsey
Sr VP: Joseph L Landenwich
Sr VP: Ruth A Lusk
Sr VP: Gregory C Miller
Sr VP: James J Novak
Sr VP: Russel D Ragland
Sr VP: M S Riedman
Sr VP: Donald H Robinson
Sr VP: Traci K Shelton
Sr VP: Richard H Starke
Sr VP: T S Turner
Sr VP: Anthony P Whitehead

KINDRED HOSPITAL
See SCCI HOSPITALS OF AMERICA INC

KINDRED HOSPITAL - RANCHO
See KND DEVELOPMENT 55 LLC

KINDRED HOSPITAL LA MIRATA
See SOUTHERN CALIFORNIA SPECIALTY CARE INC

KINDRED HOSPITAL-MID WEST DST
See KINDRED HOSPITALS LIMITED PARTNERSHIP

D-U-N-S 07-252-4168
■ **KINDRED HOSPITAL-WESTMINSTER**
(*Suby of* KINDRED HEALTHCARE INC) ★
200 Hospital Cir, Westminster, CA 92683-3910
Tel (714) 372-3014 *Founded/Ownrshp* 1992
Sales 46.7MM^E *EMP* 400
SIC 8062 General medical & surgical hospitals; General medical & surgical hospitals
CEO: Virg Narbutas
**COO:* Jack Boggess
VP: Adam Darvish
Dir Rad: Jeanie Carpio
Dir QC: David McConnell
Nutrtnst: Danielle Armstrong
Nrsg Dir: Jackie Donaldson
Pharmcst: Connie Le
Pharmcst: Dang Le
HC Dir: Eun Kim
HC Dir: Mary Walker

D-U-N-S 94-567-0289
■ **KINDRED HOSPITALS LIMITED PARTNERSHIP**
KINDRED HOSPITAL-MID WEST DST
(*Suby of* KINDRED HEALTHCARE INC) ★
1313 Saint Anthony Pl, Louisville, KY 40204-1740
Tel (502) 587-7001 *Founded/Ownrshp* 1994
Sales 84.1MM^E *EMP* 650
SIC 8069 Specialty hospitals, except psychiatric; Specialty hospitals, except psychiatric
CFO: Debra Michaelek
VP: Rich Chatman
VP: Pete Kalmey
Dir Lab: Lisa Brown
Dir Lab: Michelle Hall
Dir Soc: Maureen Chambers
Dir Rad: Sharon Scott
IT Man: Catherine Gooch
IT Man: Sue Revlett
IT Man: James Rogers
IT Man: Leslie Wright

D-U-N-S 07-840-6637
■ **KINDRED NURSING CENTERS EAST LLC**
(*Suby of* KINDRED HEALTHCARE OPERATING INC) ★
680 S 4th St, Louisville, KY 40202-2412
Tel (502) 596-7300 *Founded/Ownrshp* 1998
Sales 82.5MM^E *EMP* 5,500
SIC 8051 Skilled nursing care facilities
Dir Surg: Rose Michels

D-U-N-S 14-558-1141
■ **KINDRED NURSING CENTERS LIMITED PARTNERSHIP**
ROYAL OAKS HEALTH CARE & REHAB
(*Suby of* KINDRED HEALTHCARE OPERATING INC) ★
3500 Maple Ave, Terre Haute, IN 47804-1732
Tel (502) 596-7300 *Founded/Ownrshp* 1998
Sales 63.5MM^E *EMP* 6,165^E
SIC 8051 Skilled nursing care facilities
Sr VP: Arthur L Rothgerber
Off Mgr: Heather Dickerson
Nrsg Dir: Vanessa Atkinson Rn
HC Dir: Bre Fox

D-U-N-S 04-646-1950
KINECTA ALTERNATIVE FINANCIAL SOLUTIONS INC
NIX CHECK CASHING SERVICE
1440 Rosecrans Ave, Manhattan Beach, CA 90266-3702
Tel (310) 538-2242 *Founded/Ownrshp* 1966
Sales NA *EMP* 400
SIC 6099 Check cashing agencies; Check cashing agencies
Pr: Thomas E Nix Jr
**VP:* Darlene Gavin

D-U-N-S 09-270-5375
KINECTA FEDERAL CREDIT UNION
1440 Rosecrans Ave, Manhattan Beach, CA 90266-3702
Tel (310) 643-5400 *Founded/Ownrshp* 1994
Sales NA *EMP* 450
SIC 6061 Federal credit unions; Federal credit unions
CEO: Keith Sultemeier
**Pr:* Randall G Dotemoto
**Pr:* Douglas C Wicks
**CEO:* Steve Lumm
**COO:* Joseph E Whitaker
**CFO:* Gregory C Talbott
Ofcr: Randy Dotemoto
Ofcr: Maricela Pineda-Gonzalez
Ex VP: Luis Peralta
Sr VP: Brian Ctti

Sr VP: Mark Steiman
VP: Bruce Bingham
VP: Curt Byers
**VP:* Steven J Glouberman
VP: Karen Introcaso
VP: Robert Lane
**VP:* Sharon Moseley
VP: Ali Sadri

D-U-N-S 84-131-2569
KINECTA FINANCIAL & INSURANCE SERVICES LLC
(*Suby of* KINECTA FEDERAL CREDIT UNION) ★
1440 Rosecrans Ave, Manhattan Beach, CA 90266-3702
Tel (310) 643-5400 *Founded/Ownrshp* 2009
Sales NA *EMP* 23ᴱ
SIC 6061 Federal credit unions; Federal credit unions

D-U-N-S 06-748-5664 EXP
KINEDYNE LLC
(*Suby of* HEICO COMPANIES L L C) ★
151 Industrial Pkwy, Branchburg, NJ 08876-3451
Tel (908) 231-1800 *Founded/Ownrshp* 1981
Sales 77.7MMᴱ *EMP* 400
SIC 3714 Motor vehicle parts & accessories; Motor vehicle parts & accessories
Pr: James M Klausmann
CFO: Dan Schlotterbeck
Ex VP: Robert L Chamberlin
Ex VP: James M Klausmann II
IT Man: Judy Tharp

KINEFLOW DIVISION
See CUMMINS-WAGNER-SIEWERT LLC

D-U-N-S 94-306-5722 IMP
KINEMATICS MANUFACTURING INC
KINEMATICSMFG
21410 N 15th Ln Ste 104, Phoenix, AZ 85027-2740
Tel (623) 780-8944 *Founded/Ownrshp* 1995
Sales 35.0MMᴱ *EMP* 12
SIC 3531 Construction machinery; Construction machinery
Pr: David Pope
**COO:* Mark Henderson
**Founder:* Brent Morgan
**Chf Cred:* Kyle Zech
Mng Dir: Ray Lin

KINEMATICSMFG
See KINEMATICS MANUFACTURING INC

D-U-N-S 05-010-4330
KINEMETRICS INC (CA)
(*Suby of* OYO CORP USA) ★
222 Vista Ave, Pasadena, CA 91107-3295
Tel (626) 795-2220 *Founded/Ownrshp* 1969, 1991
Sales 22.7MMᴱ *EMP* 75
Accts Pricewaterhousecoopers
SIC 8711 3829 Engineering services; Seismographs
CEO: Tadashi Jimbo
**Treas:* Michelle Harrington
**Ex VP:* Melvin Lund
**VP:* Ogie Kuraica
**VP:* Ian Standley
Exec: Robert Swain
IT Man: Mark Potter
Snr Mgr: Sting Lai
Board of Directors: Ken Morita

D-U-N-S 09-327-1591
KINERGY CORP
7310 Grade Ln, Louisville, KY 40219-3437
Tel (502) 366-5685 *Founded/Ownrshp* 1978
Sales 23.8MMᴱ *EMP* 45
SIC 3535 Conveyors & conveying equipment
Pr: George D Dumbaugh

D-U-N-S 05-636-2628
KINESTRAL TECHNOLOGIES INC
400 E Jamie Ct Ste 201, South San Francisco, CA 94080-6230
Tel (650) 416-5200 *Founded/Ownrshp* 2011
Sales 22.4MMᴱ *EMP* 105ᴱ
SIC 3231 Products of purchased glass
CEO: Suk Bae Cha
**COO:* Sam Bergh
CFO: Geoffrey Richardson
Off Mgr: Susan Alejandrino
CTO: Howard Turner
Snr Mgr: Mark Bailey
Snr Mgr: John Bass

D-U-N-S 96-955-7008 IMP/EXP
KINETEK INC
(*Suby of* NIDEC AMERICAS HOLDING CORP) ★
25 Northwest Point Blvd # 900, Elk Grove Village, IL 60007-1044
Tel (224) 265-1290 *Founded/Ownrshp* 2012
Sales 223.7MMᴱ *EMP* 2,578ᴱ
SIC 3621 3566 3613 Motors & generators; Motors, electric; Generators & sets, electric; Speed changers, drives & gears; Control panels, electric; Motors & generators; Motors, electric; Generators & sets, electric; Speed changers, drives & gears; Control panels, electric
Ch Bd: Thomas H Quinn
**Pr:* D Randall Bays
**CFO:* Daniel D Drury
Board of Directors: John W Jordan II

D-U-N-S 62-368-8608
KINETEK INDUSTRIES INC
(*Suby of* KINETEK INC) ★
25 Northwest Point Blvd # 900, Elk Grove Village, IL 60007-1044
Tel (224) 265-1290 *Founded/Ownrshp* 2006
Sales 122.3MMᴱ *EMP* 400ᴱ
SIC 3613 3621 3625 Control panels, electric; Motors, electric; Industrial electrical relays & switches; Control panels, electric; Motors, electric; Industrial electrical relays & switches
Ch Bd: Thomas H Quinn

D-U-N-S 08-313-9394 IMP
KINETIC CONCEPTS INC
KCI
(*Suby of* CHIRON HOLDINGS INC) ★
12930 W Interstate 10, San Antonio, TX 78249-2248
Tel (800) 531-5346 *Founded/Ownrshp* 2011
Sales 1.1MMMᴱ *EMP* 5,500
SIC 3842 Surgical appliances & supplies; Surgical appliances & supplies
Pr: Joseph F Woody
**Ch Bd:* Ronald A Matricaria
**Pr:* Catherine M Burzik
**Pr:* Stephen D Seidel
Pr: Joseph Woody
**CFO:* William Brown
**CFO:* Robert Hureau
**CFO:* Martin J Landon
CFO: Sam Peace
Ex VP: Cameron McKennit
Ex VP: Debbie Mitchell
Ex VP: Margie Morales
Ex VP: Mike Schaeffer
Sr VP: Peter Arnold
**Sr VP:* R James Cravens
Sr VP: James Cunniff
Sr VP: Michael Delvacchio
Sr VP: Mike Mathews
**VP:* John T Bibb
**VP:* Mike Helbock
**VP:* Theresa McCutcheon

D-U-N-S 06-355-2194
KINETIC SYSTEMS INC
(*Suby of* KINETICS HOLDING GMBH)
48400 Fremont Blvd, Fremont, CA 94538-6505
Tel (510) 683-6000 *Founded/Ownrshp* 2012
Sales 148.4MMᴱ *EMP* 500
SIC 1711 Mechanical contractor; Mechanical contractor
CEO: Peter Maris
COO: Norm Escover
CFO: Martin Kaus
Treas: Seth Cuni
VP: Jose Bre A
VP: Joachim Biggen
VP: Rajesh Gupte
VP: Abby Heskett
Exec: Loni Roberts
Genl Mgr: J Rgen Schr Der
Genl Mgr: Jnrgen Schr Der

D-U-N-S 06-888-9344 IMP
KINETICO INC
WATER ONE QUALITY WTR SYSTEMS
(*Suby of* AXEL JOHNSON INC) ★
10845 Kinsman Rd, Newbury, OH 44065-9787
Tel (440) 564-9111 *Founded/Ownrshp* 2005
Sales 60.1MMᴱ *EMP* 427
SIC 3589 5074

D-U-N-S 15-101-9796
KINETICOM INC
701 B St Ste 1350, San Diego, CA 92101-8170
Tel (619) 330-3100 *Founded/Ownrshp* 1999
Sales 32.0MMᴱ *EMP* 400ᴱ
SIC 7361 Employment agencies; Employment agencies
CEO: Michael Wager
**CFO:* Casey Marquand
**VP:* Blair Bode
**VP:* William Coyman
**VP:* Michael Steadman

D-U-N-S 55-602-9523
■ **KINETICS CLIMAX INC**
(*Suby of* FM) ★
10085 Sw Commerce Cir, Wilsonville, OR 97070-8600
Tel (503) 404-1200 *Founded/Ownrshp* 2005
Sales 25.9MMᴱ *EMP* 120ᴱ
SIC 3089 Injection molding of plastics
Pr: David H Thornton
Genl Mgr: Fred Robinson

D-U-N-S 00-428-4089 IMP/EXP
KINETICS NOISE CONTROL INC (OH)
HAMMOND KINETICS
6300 Irelan Pl, Dublin, OH 43016-1278
Tel (614) 889-0480 *Founded/Ownrshp* 1958, 1990
Sales 30.5MMᴱ *EMP* 200
SIC 3829 3625 3446 5084 3296 1711

D-U-N-S 96-451-9362
KINETIX INTERNATIONAL LOGISTICS LLC
5301 Shawnee Rd Ste 402, Alexandria, VA 22312-2335
Tel (703) 564-9500 *Founded/Ownrshp* 2010
Sales 25.0MM *EMP* 20
SIC 4731 Freight transportation arrangement
Off Mgr: Greg Sims
Dir Opers: Brooks Isoldi

KING & GROVE
See CHELSEA HOTELS MANAGEMENT LLC

D-U-N-S 02-984-9205
KING & KING ENTERPRISES INC
KING OIL CO
7925 N Lane Ave, Kansas City, MO 64158-7601
Tel (816) 781-9574 *Founded/Ownrshp* 1959
Sales 47.1MMᴱ *EMP* 325
SIC 5541 5172 Gasoline service stations; Petroleum products; Gasoline service stations; Petroleum products
Pr: Carl R King
**VP:* Charles Pack

D-U-N-S 00-407-4431 IMP/EXP
KING & PRINCE SEAFOOD CORP (GA)
MRS. FRIDAY'S
(*Suby of* GORTONS) ★
1 King And Prince Blvd, Brunswick, GA 31520-8668
Tel (912) 265-5155 *Founded/Ownrshp* 1933, 2005
Sales 62.4MMᴱ *EMP* 500
SIC 2092

D-U-N-S 06-454-1881
KING & SPALDING LLP
1180 Peachtree St, Atlanta, GA 30309
Tel (404) 572-4600 *Founded/Ownrshp* 1885
Sales 352.0MMᴱ *EMP* 1,927
SIC 8111 General practice law office; General practice law office
Ch Bd: Robert Hays
Pt: Juan M Alcal
Pt: Raymond E Baltz
Pt: Eleanor Banister
Pt: Patricia T Barmeyer
Pt: W Randall Bassett
Pt: Crayton L Bell
Pt: Paul R Bessette
Pt: Michael J Biles
Pt: James F Bowe
Pt: Gregory N Etzel
Pt: John S Herbert
Pt: Abraham NM Shashy
Pt: Geoffrey R Unger
Mng Pt: Robert E Meadows
Mng Pt: Donald F Zimmer Jr
COO: Derek J Hardesty
Ofcr: Kevin A Cavanaugh

D-U-N-S 79-652-0807
KING AEROSPACE INC
(*Suby of* FAITH ENTERPRISES INC) ★
4444 Westgrove Dr, Addison, TX 75001-5317
Tel (972) 248-4886 *Founded/Ownrshp* 1994
Sales 29.7MMᴱ *EMP* 125
SIC 4581 Aircraft servicing & repairing; Aircraft servicing & repairing
Pr: Jerry A King
Pr: Gary Simpson
**VP:* Pat Brooks
**VP:* Keith Weaver
Opers Mgr: Humberto Ramos
Snr Mgr: Keith Snyder

D-U-N-S 09-791-9794 EXP
KING AMERICA FINISHING INC
1351 Scarboro Hwy, Sylvania, GA 30467-7607
Tel (912) 863-4511 *Founded/Ownrshp* 2001
Sales 105.7MMᴱ *EMP* 450
SIC 2211 2261 Broadwoven fabric mills, cotton; Dyeing cotton broadwoven fabrics; Broadwoven fabric mills, cotton; Dyeing cotton broadwoven fabrics
CEO: George Renaldi III
**Pr:* Mike Beasley
VP: Joshua Moody
Plnt Mgr: Billy Parrish

KING ARCHITECTURAL METALS
See KING SUPPLY CO LLC

D-U-N-S 00-799-7935
KING ARTHUR FLOUR CO INC (VT)
BAKER'S STORE, THE
135 Us Route 5 S, Norwich, VT 05055-9430
Tel (802) 649-3881 *Founded/Ownrshp* 1984
Sales 100.0MM *EMP* 350
SIC 5149 5961 5461 8299 Flour; Bakery products; Catalog & mail-order houses; Bakeries; Educational service, nondegree granting: continuing educ.; Flour; Bakery products; Catalog & mail-order houses; Bakeries; Educational service, nondegree granting: continuing educ.
Pr: Steve Voigt
IT Man: Ray Coffin

D-U-N-S 06-549-6387
KING ARTHUR FLOUR CO INC
(*Suby of* BAKERS STORE) ★
62 Fogg Farm Rd, White River Junction, VT 05001-9485
Tel (802) 649-3881 *Founded/Ownrshp* 1790
Sales 80.9MMᴱ *EMP* 270
SIC 5149 Flour; Flour
Ch Bd: Frank E Sands II
**Pr:* Steven P Voigt
**VP:* Brinna Sands
VP Sls: Beth Kluge

D-U-N-S 03-975-2530 IMP
KING ASSOCIATES LTD
KORD KING COMPANY
62 Industrial Cir, Lancaster, PA 17601-5928
Tel (717) 556-5673 *Founded/Ownrshp* 1975
Sales 30.0MMᴱ *EMP* 100
SIC 3643 Connectors, electric cord; Connectors, electric cord
Pr: Tom King
**Sec:* Carol E King
**VP:* Thomas King

D-U-N-S 95-847-5261
KING AUTO CENTER INC
KING CHRYSLER DODGE JEEP
4330 Kukui Grove St, Lihue, HI 96766-1674
Tel (808) 245-5977 *Founded/Ownrshp* 1995
Sales 22.0MMᴱ *EMP* 55
Accts Kobayashi & Company Pasadena
SIC 5511 5012 Automobiles, new & used; Automobiles; Automobiles, new & used; Automobiles
Pr: Charlie King
**COO:* Ronald R Hansen
**Sec:* Mary Bea King
CIO: Gary Goldberg
Sls Mgr: Joy Kagawa
Sls Mgr: Roy Yamashita

D-U-N-S 60-169-6334
KING BAUDOUIN FOUNDATION UNITED STATES I
KBFUS
10 Rockefeller Plz, New York, NY 10020-1903
Tel (212) 713-7660 *Founded/Ownrshp* 2005
Sales 20.5MM *EMP* 1
Accts Tait Weller & Baker Llp Phil
SIC 7389 Fund raising organizations
Ex Dir: Jean Paul Warmoes

D-U-N-S 02-749-6538
KING BEVERAGE INC
6715 E Mission Ave, Spokane Valley, WA 99212-1141
Tel (509) 444-3700 *Founded/Ownrshp* 2011
Sales 42.2MMᴱ *EMP* 100
SIC 5181 5149 Beer & other fermented malt liquors; Soft drinks; Beer & other fermented malt liquors; Soft drinks

Pr: Theodore Rusnak
**VP:* Peter Rusnak
Opers Supe: Robyn Sciuchetti
Opers Mgr: Mike Nye
Mktg Dir: Steve Stockton

D-U-N-S 61-790-1350
KING BIO INC
SAFE CARE RX
3 Westside Dr, Asheville, NC 28806-2846
Tel (828) 255-0201 *Founded/Ownrshp* 1989
Sales 30.8MMᴱ *EMP* 100
SIC 5912 2834 5122 Proprietary (non-prescription medicine) stores; Pharmaceutical preparations; Pharmaceuticals
Pr: Frank J King Jr
CFO: Frank Richardson
**VP:* Suzie King
Creative D: Andrea Dedman
Rgnl Mgr: Neil Collie
Prd Mgr: Neil Spence
Sls Mgr: Karen Hardie

D-U-N-S 04-251-6646
■ **KING BROADCASTING CO**
KING TV
(*Suby of* BELO CORP) ★
333 Dexter Ave N, Seattle, WA 98109-5107
Tel (206) 448-2999 *Founded/Ownrshp* 1997
Sales 31.4MMᴱ *EMP* 300
SIC 4833 Television broadcasting stations; Television broadcasting stations
Ch: Dunia A Shive
**Pr:* Racine B Heacox

D-U-N-S 07-867-7022
KING BUICK GMC LLC
16200 Frederick Rd, Gaithersburg, MD 20877-4023
Tel (301) 948-9111 *Founded/Ownrshp* 2010
Sales 23.6MMᴱ *EMP* 88
SIC 5511 Automobiles, new & used; Automobiles, new & used
VP: William Aschenbach
Sls Mgr: Paul Bayhurst
Sls Mgr: Bob Benson
Board of Directors: William H Aschenbach

KING BUICK PONTIAC GMC
See KING-FOGLE INC

D-U-N-S 04-451-7980
KING BUSINESS INTERIORS INC
6155 Huntley Rd Ste D, Columbus, OH 43229-1096
Tel (614) 430-0020 *Founded/Ownrshp* 1998
Sales 36.8MMᴱ *EMP* 36
Accts Clark Schaefer Hackett Columb
SIC 5021 1799 Furniture; Home/office interiors finishing, furnishing & remodeling
Pr: Darla J King
**VP:* David R King
IT Man: Heather Malloy
IT Man: Corey Richardson
Opers Mgr: Ernie Haggerty
VP Sls: Dick James
Sales Asso: Bo Comer
Sales Asso: Matt Gorman
Sales Asso: Kim Hart
Sales Asso: Gary Jones
Sales Asso: Nicole Lanier

D-U-N-S 03-614-3907
KING CADILLAC BUICK PONTIAC GMC INC
1700 W Evans St, Florence, SC 29501-3332
Tel (843) 662-3296 *Founded/Ownrshp* 1980
Sales 55.0MM *EMP* 84
SIC 5511 Automobiles, new & used; Automobiles, new & used
Pr: Reamer B King
Sales Asso: Pete Dover
Sales Asso: Ron Locklair

D-U-N-S 04-030-2395
KING CANNON INC
FUDDRUCKERS
60 River St, Beverly, MA 01915-4223
Tel (978) 921-7438 *Founded/Ownrshp* 1998
Sales 38.6MMᴱ *EMP* 2,075
SIC 5812 Restaurant, family: chain; Restaurant, family: chain
Pr: Bryce L King
Genl Mgr: Karen Delguerico

D-U-N-S 10-625-7744
KING CHRIS CO INC
MCDONALD'S
880 S Pleasantburg Dr 2g, Greenville, SC 29607-2422
Tel (864) 675-0921 *Founded/Ownrshp* 1981
Sales 11.3MMᴱ *EMP* 500
SIC 5812 Fast-food restaurant, chain; Fast-food restaurant, chain
Pr: Frank Landgraff

KING CHRYSLER DODGE JEEP
See KING AUTO CENTER INC

D-U-N-S 01-314-7566
KING CITY JOINT UNION HIGH SCHOOL DISTRICT (CA)
800 Broadway St, King City, CA 93930-3326
Tel (831) 385-0606 *Founded/Ownrshp* 1977
Sales NA *EMP* 400
SIC 9411 8211 County supervisor of education, except school board; Public elementary & secondary schools; County supervisor of education, except school board; Public elementary & secondary schools

D-U-N-S 01-312-8434
KING CITY UNION ELEMENTARY SCHOOL DISTRICT
KCUSD
435 Pearl St Rm 15, King City, CA 93930-2919
Tel (831) 385-1144 *Founded/Ownrshp* 2007
Sales 22.3MM *EMP* 200
SIC 8211 Public elementary school; Public elementary school
Prin: Richard Presten
Dir IT: Shawn Angulo

Schl Brd P: Vina Paramo-Alanzo
Psych: Michelle Horgan
Psych: Alice Jones

D-U-N-S 06-524-7657
KING CO LIMITED PARTNERSHIP
KING COMPANY OF LOUISIANA
639 N Dupre St, New Orleans, LA 70119-4106
Tel (504) 486-9195 *Founded/Ownrshp* 2002
Sales 30.9MM^E *EMP* 251
SIC 1742 Plaster & drywall work; Acoustical & insulation work; Plaster & drywall work; Acoustical & insulation work
Pt: Cyril Geary III
Pt: Jeffery L Geary
Pt: Warren Jaubert

KING COMPANY OF LOUISIANA
See KING CO LIMITED PARTNERSHIP

KING COAL MINE
See GCC ENERGY LLC

KING COLLEGE BOOK STORE
See KING UNIVERSITY

D-U-N-S 93-005-7807
KING COUNTY HOUSING AUTHORITY
TALL CEDARS MOBILE COURT
401 37th St Se, Auburn, WA 98002-8006
Tel (206) 205-8837 *Founded/Ownrshp* 1994
Sales 103.0MM *EMP* 14^E
SIC 6515 Mobile home site operators; Mobile home site operators
Prin: Liz Hlavaty
Ex Dir: Stephen Norman

D-U-N-S 80-837-4248
KING COUNTY LIBRARY SYSTEM
KCLS
960 Newport Way Nw, Issaquah, WA 98027-2702
Tel (425) 369-3200 *Founded/Ownrshp* 1942
Sales 110.0MM *EMP* 1,364
SIC 8231 Libraries; Libraries
Bd of Dir: Kathryn Brown
Bd of Dir: William Ptacek
Bd of Dir: Julia Shaw
VP: Dan Featherkile
VP: Imelda Garcia
VP: Mark Whitaker
Assoc Dir: Kay Johnson
Ex Dir: Elizabeth Castleberry
IT Man: SRI Mylavarapu

D-U-N-S 07-184-0789
KING COUNTY PUBLIC HOSPITAL DISTRICT 2
EVERGREEN HOSPITAL MEDICAL CTR
12040 Ne 128th St, Kirkland, WA 98034-3013
Tel (425) 899-2769 *Founded/Ownrshp* 1967
Sales 263.7MM^E *EMP* 2,400
SIC 8062 General medical & surgical hospitals; General medical & surgical hospitals
CEO: Bob Malte
CFO: Chrissy Yamada
* *Sr VP:* Neil Johnson
* *VP:* Jack Handley
VP: Kay Taylor
Exec: Mark Rubenstein
CIO: Jamie Trigg
CIO: Jamie Tripp
Dir QC: Beverly Hodge
QC Dir: Kathy Schoenrock
Opers Mgr: Chuck Davis

D-U-N-S 01-288-7738
KING COUNTY PUBLIC HOSPITAL DISTRICT NO 2
EVERGREEN HEALTHCARE
12040 Ne 128th St, Kirkland, WA 98034-3013
Tel (425) 899-1000 *Founded/Ownrshp* 1971
Sales 301.2MM *EMP* 2,800
Accts Kpmg Llp Seattle Wa
SIC 8742 Hospital & health services consultant; Hospital & health services consultant
CEO: Steve Brown
COO: Neil Johnson
Sr VP: Chrissy Ymada
VP: Robert Geise
Chf Nrs Of: Nancee Hofmeister
QA Dir: Kathy Schoenrock
Dir IT: Benjamin Trigg
IT Man: Jessica Granger
Doctor: Terry Pheifer
Dir Health: Sheila Greenshook

D-U-N-S 80-844-4553
KING COUNTY PUBLILC HOSPITAL DISTRICT 2
EVERGREENHEALTH
12040 Ne 128th St, Kirkland, WA 98034-3013
Tel (425) 899-2646 *Founded/Ownrshp* 1972
Sales 511.8MM *EMP* 4,000^E
SIC 8062 General medical & surgical hospitals; General medical & surgical hospitals
CEO: Robert Malte
* *CFO:* Chrissy Yamada
Ofcr: Christie Elliott
* *Ofcr:* Nancee R Hofmeister
Sr VP: Tom Martin
Sr VP: Bob Sampson
VP: Kay Taylor
Off Mgr: Patricia Tsybulnik
Nurse Mgr: Linda Surace
IT Man: Lance Traicoff
Surgeon: Dodie Roberson

D-U-N-S 08-742-5674
KING CRUSTBUSTER/SPEED INC (KS)
2300 E Trail St, Dodge City, KS 67801
Tel (620) 385-2651 *Founded/Ownrshp* 1960
Sales 38.1MM^E *EMP* 100
SIC 5083 Agricultural machinery & equipment; Agricultural machinery & equipment
Pr: Donald Hornung
* *Treas:* Walter Ludt
* *VP:* Wayne Daubert
Sales Asso: Lloyd Derowitsch

D-U-N-S 00-924-1183 IMP
KING ELECTRICAL MANUFACTURING CO (WA)
9131 10th Ave S, Seattle, WA 98108-4612
Tel (206) 762-0400 *Founded/Ownrshp* 1958
Sales 27.0MM^E *EMP* 100
SIC 3634 3585 3567 Heating units, electric (radiant heat): baseboard or wall; Heating equipment, complete; Heating & air conditioning combination units; Industrial furnaces & ovens; Heating units, electric (radiant heat): baseboard or wall; Heating equipment, complete; Heating & air conditioning combination units; Industrial furnaces & ovens
Pr: Robert E Wilson
* *Treas:* Robert Wilson II
* *VP:* Brad Wilson
IT Man: Sara Killham
Manager: Doug Kaer
Sls Mgr: Ben Bouchard

KING EMPLOYER SERVICES
See OASIS OUTSOURCING II INC

D-U-N-S 09-298-1521
KING ENGINEERING ASSOCIATES INC
4921 Memorial Hwy Ste 300, Tampa, FL 33634-7507
Tel (813) 880-8881 *Founded/Ownrshp* 1977
Sales 24.6MM^E *EMP* 133
SIC 8711 Consulting engineer; Consulting engineer
Ch Bd: Keith A Appenzeller
* *Pr:* Thomas M O'Connor
* *CFO:* James A Orchard
* *Sr VP:* Christopher F Kuzler
* *Sr VP:* Michael E Ross
* *Sr VP:* Scott D Sheridan
VP: Charles M Courtney
* *VP:* James E Godfrey
* *VP:* Aaron Googins
* *VP:* O Denise Greer
* *VP:* Agustin E Maristany
VP: Bill Moriarty
* *VP:* William Moriarty

D-U-N-S 80-803-8298
KING EQUIPMENT LLC
1080 Ontario Blvd, Ontario, CA 91761-2026
Tel (909) 986-5300 *Founded/Ownrshp* 2007
Sales 32.0MM *EMP* 73
SIC 7359 Business machine & electronic equipment rental services
Sfty Dirs: Tim Quijada

KING ESTATE
See KEW INC

D-U-N-S 83-220-4044
KING FABRICATION LLC
19300 W Hardy Rd, Houston, TX 77073-3500
Tel (281) 209-0811 *Founded/Ownrshp* 1997
Sales 34.5MM^E *EMP* 95
SIC 3441 Building components, structural steel; Building components, structural steel
Exec: Charlotte Ward
Prin: Vince Rossitto
Sfty Dirs: Anthony Garcia
Prd Mgr: Skip Vandervegte

D-U-N-S 00-813-3084
KING FISHER MARINE SERVICE LP
159 Hwy 316, Port Lavaca, TX 77979
Tel (361) 552-6751 *Founded/Ownrshp* 1998
Sales 102.6MM *EMP* 350^E
SIC 1629

D-U-N-S 84-483-4614
KING FOOD ENTERPRISES
EL CHICO RESTAURANT
12200 N Stemmons Fwy, Dallas, TX 75234-5888
Tel (972) 406-0370 *Founded/Ownrshp* 1996
Sales 10.3MM^E *EMP* 600
SIC 5812 Mexican restaurant; Mexican restaurant
Owner: C C Theophiene Chamakala

KING FRESH MARKETING
See KING FRESH PRODUCE LLC

D-U-N-S 86-754-7382 IMP/EXP
KING FRESH PRODUCE LLC
KING FRESH MARKETING
4731 Avenue 400, Dinuba, CA 93618-9029
Tel (559) 596-2040 *Founded/Ownrshp* 1992
Sales 48.4MM *EMP* 40
SIC 5141

D-U-N-S 94-900-5706
KING FUELS INC
C & S INTERNATIONAL
14825 Willis St, Houston, TX 77039-1025
Tel (281) 449-9975 *Founded/Ownrshp* 1992
Sales 39.4MM^E *EMP* 25^E
SIC 5172 Engine fuels & oils
Pr: Zaki Niazi
* *VP:* Wazim Niazi

KING G M C TRUCK
See KING PONTIAC G M C TRUCK INC

D-U-N-S 96-920-7331
KING GEORGE COUNTY PUBLIC SCHOOL PUBLIC DISTRICT
KING GEORGE SCHOOL BOARD OFF
9100 Saint Anthonys Rd, King George, VA 22485-3413
Tel (540) 775-5833 *Founded/Ownrshp* 1994
Sales 33.2MM^E *EMP* 548
SIC 8211 Public elementary & secondary schools; Public elementary & secondary schools
Teacher Pr: Bill Wishard
HC Dir: Gayle Hock

KING GEORGE SCHOOL BOARD OFF
See KING GEORGE COUNTY PUBLIC SCHOOL PUBLIC DISTRICT

D-U-N-S 96-661-6799
KING HAGERSTOWN MOTORS LLC
HAGERSTOWN FORD
1714 Massey Blvd, Hagerstown, MD 21740-6962
Tel (301) 733-3673 *Founded/Ownrshp* 1995
Sales 46.7MM^E *EMP* 110
SIC 5511 Automobiles, new & used; Automobiles, new & used
Genl Mgr: Jimmy Bussard
Genl Mgr: Doug Massey
Store Mgr: Dwayne Demory
Store Mgr: Robert Gartner
Store Mgr: Rob Wenk
Telecom Ex: Judy Sterlang
Sls Mgr: Eric Carper
Sls Mgr: Sherry Kennedy
Sls Mgr: Chris Mason
Sls Mgr: John Smith
Sls Mgr: Mike Stimmel

D-U-N-S 05-132-6122 IMP/EXP
KING HICKORY FURNITURE CO
1820 Main Ave Se, Hickory, NC 28602-1340
Tel (828) 322-6025 *Founded/Ownrshp* 1969
Sales 30.6MM *EMP* 210
Accts Phillip J Rink Cpa Pllc Hic
SIC 2512 Couches, sofas & davenports: upholstered on wood frames; Couches, sofas & davenports: upholstered on wood frames
Ch: Robert E Palmer
CIO: Karen Sherrill
Sales Exec: Keith Hart

D-U-N-S 79-120-0947
KING HOLDING CORP
360 N Crescent Dr, Beverly Hills, CA 90210-4874
Tel (586) 254-3900 *Founded/Ownrshp* 2006
Sales NA *EMP* 7,970
SIC 3452 3465 3469 3089 5072

D-U-N-S 04-227-9513 IMP/EXP
KING INDUSTRIES INC
1 Science Rd, Norwalk, CT 06852
Tel (203) 866-5551 *Founded/Ownrshp* 1932
Sales 31.4MM^E *EMP* 170^E
SIC 2899 2819

D-U-N-S 19-210-0691
KING INDUSTRIES INC
KING MECHANICAL CONTRACTORS
3945 Cromwell Rd, Chattanooga, TN 37421-2133
Tel (423) 622-4500 *Founded/Ownrshp* 1987
Sales 22.9MM^E *EMP* 100
SIC 1711 Mechanical contractor; Mechanical contractor
Pr: Bill King
* *CFO:* Krista Marter
* *Sec:* Deborah Marie King
* *VP:* Bart Bledsoe
Off Mgr: Gayle Williams

D-U-N-S 96-819-5599
KING JD
289 Us Highway 385 S, Seminole, TX 79360-6167
Tel (800) 805-6302 *Founded/Ownrshp* 2011
Sales 26.0MM *EMP* 130
SIC 1794 4959 Excavation work; Environmental cleanup services
Owner: Chad King

KING KOIL
See DIXIE BEDDING CORP

KING KOIL NORTHEAST
See BLUE BELL MATTRESS CO LLC

D-U-N-S 00-699-5443
KING KULLEN GROCERY CO INC (NY)
185 Central Ave, Bethpage, NY 11714-3929
Tel (516) 733-7100 *Founded/Ownrshp* 1930
Sales 707.7MM^E *EMP* 4,500
SIC 5411 Supermarkets, chain; Supermarkets, chain
Ch Bd: Ronald Conklin
* *Ch Bd:* Brian C Cullen
* *Ch Bd:* Bernard Kennedy
* *Pr:* J Donald Kennedy
* *Sr VP:* James Flynn
* *VP:* Joseph Brown
* *VP:* James Carey
* *VP:* Thomas K Cullen
* *VP:* Joseph E Eck
* *VP:* Anthony Femminella
VP: Stanley Mitchell
Exec: John Santoro

D-U-N-S 06-114-5918 IMP
KING KUTTER INC
305 Commerce Dr, Winfield, AL 35594-9016
Tel (205) 487-3202 *Founded/Ownrshp* 1978
Sales 22.2MM^E *EMP* 92
SIC 3523 Farm machinery & equipment; Cutters & blowers, ensilage; Harrows: disc, spring, tine, etc.; Plows, agricultural: disc, moldboard, chisel, listers, etc.
Pr: James Fraley
* *VP:* Phillip Fraley
Off Mgr: Judy Lowery

D-U-N-S 12-268-0366
KING LIMOUSINE SERVICE INC
DELAWARE COUNTY TRNSP SVC
370 Crooked Ln, King of Prussia, PA 19406-2545
Tel (610) 431-3210 *Founded/Ownrshp* 1983
Sales 21.5MM^E *EMP* 83
SIC 4119 Automobile rental, with driver
Pr: Robert Euler

D-U-N-S 06-192-0260
KING LOAD MANUFACTURING CO
LK INDUSTRIES
1357 W Beaver St, Jacksonville, FL 32209-7694
Tel (904) 354-8882 *Founded/Ownrshp* 1972
Sales 41.9MM^E *EMP* 200^E
SIC 2542 2541 3569 3496 2599 Counters or counter display cases: except wood; Racks, merchandise display or storage: except wood; Store fixtures, wood; Baling machines, for scrap metal, paper or similar material; Grocery carts, made from purchased wire; Carts, restaurant equipment; Counters or counter display cases: except wood; Racks, merchandise display or storage: except wood; Store fixtures, wood; Baling machines, for scrap metal, paper or similar material; Grocery carts, made from purchased wire; Carts, restaurant equipment
Pr: Charles O Chupp
* *Treas:* Carrie Chupp
Founder: James M Chupp Sr
IT Man: Josh Buono
IT Man: Rob Dendtler
MIS Mgr: Faith Carlson
Plnt Mgr: Bill Cromity

D-U-N-S 06-000-9321
KING LOW HEYWOOD THOMAS SCHOOL INC
1450 Newfield Ave, Stamford, CT 06905-1501
Tel (203) 322-3496 *Founded/Ownrshp* 1875
Sales 31.2MM *EMP* 125
Accts Blum Shapiro & Company Pc Wes
SIC 8211 Preparatory school; Preparatory school
Pr: Louis Paglia
* *Pr:* Peter Reinemann
* *CFO:* Kim Leeker
* *Treas:* Fred Sivert
* *Treas:* Timothy Tully
* *VP:* Edward Cesare
* *VP:* Thomas Conheeney
CTO: Jerry Rodriguez
Board of Directors: Richard M Goldman

D-U-N-S 92-836-4850
KING MACHINE OF NORTH CAROLINA INC
3900 Westinghouse Blvd, Charlotte, NC 28273-4517
Tel (704) 583-0486 *Founded/Ownrshp* 1994
Sales 56.2MM^E *EMP* 50
SIC 5014 Tires & tubes
Pr: Michael Wells
* *VP:* Justin Roberts
Off Mgr: Belinda Crosby
Sls Mgr: Kevin Cooper

D-U-N-S 08-007-3125 IMP
KING MEAT INC (CA)
(*Suby of* BICARA LTD) ★
1611 S Catalina Ave # 205, Redondo Beach, CA 90277-5255
Tel (323) 582-7401 *Founded/Ownrshp* 1975
Sales 96.6MM^E *EMP* 10
SIC 5147 5142 Meats & meat products; Packaged frozen goods; Meats & meat products; Packaged frozen goods
Pr: Raymond Rosenthal
CFO: Gene Matsuda

KING MECHANICAL CONTRACTORS
See KING INDUSTRIES INC

D-U-N-S 00-603-1553 IMP
KING MILLING CO (MI)
115 S Broadway St, Lowell, MI 49331-1666
Tel (616) 897-9264 *Founded/Ownrshp* 1890
Sales 67.6MM *EMP* 40
SIC 2041 Wheat flour; Wheat flour
Pr: Brian Doyle
* *Sr VP:* James M Doyle
* *VP:* Stephen Doyle

D-U-N-S 05-217-1337
KING MOTOR CENTER ET AL
KING TOYOTA
1345 S Federal Hwy, Deerfield Beach, FL 33441-7248
Tel (877) 546-7480 *Founded/Ownrshp* 1969
Sales 79.8MM^E *EMP* 330
SIC 5511 Automobiles, new & used; Vans, new & used; Pickups, new & used; Automobiles, new & used; Vans, new & used; Pickups, new & used
Pr: Jeff Gale
* *CFO:* Mark Montgomery
* *VP:* A Edward Appleby
* *VP:* Norman Rohan

D-U-N-S 03-147-7029
KING MOTOR CO INC
SUNNY KING FORD
1507 S Quintard Ave, Anniston, AL 36201-8250
Tel (256) 831-5300 *Founded/Ownrshp* 1922
Sales 25.4MM^E *EMP* 50
SIC 5511

D-U-N-S 01-674-0792
KING MOTOR CO OF COCONUT CREEK LTD
COCONUT CREEK MITSUBISHI
(*Suby of* KING MOTOR CENTER ET AL) ★
4950 N State Road 7, Coconut Creek, FL 33073-3302
Tel (954) 283-1000 *Founded/Ownrshp* 1998
Sales 24.9MM^E *EMP* 100
SIC 5511 Automobiles, new & used; Automobiles, new & used
Pt: Edward Applebee
Pt: Linda Applebee
VP: Mark Montgomery
Sls Mgr: Bill Key

D-U-N-S 14-858-6183
KING MOTOR CO OF SOUTH FLORIDA INC
KING OLDSMOBILE DEERFIELD BCH
1399 S Federal Hwy, Deerfield Beach, FL 33441-7248
Tel (954) 421-3330 *Founded/Ownrshp* 1989
Sales 20.6MM^E *EMP* 50
SIC 5511 7538 New & used car dealers; General automotive repair shops; New & used car dealers; General automotive repair shops
Pr: W Clay King
* *Treas:* Kirk Francis
* *VP:* Jeffrey Gale
* *VP:* Louis King

KING NUT COMPANIES
See KANAN ENTERPRISES INC

D-U-N-S 14-489-1587
KING OF TEXAS ROOFING CO LP
307 Gilbert Cir, Grand Prairie, TX 75050-6579
Tel (972) 399-0003 *Founded/Ownrshp* 1983
Sales 21.2MM^E *EMP* 100
Accts Namanny & Co North Richland H
SIC 1761 Roofing contractor
Genl Pt: Nelson R Braddy Jr
Pt: Jaclyn Braddy
VP: James Hammel
Off Mgr: Iris Bonneau
Opers Mgr: Thomas Grimm
Sales Exec: Jim Hammel

KING OIL CO
See KING & KING ENTERPRISES INC

KING OLDSMOBILE DEERFIELD BCH
See KING MOTOR CO OF SOUTH FLORIDA INC

D-U-N-S 10-547-0467 IMP
KING PAR LLC
K P
5140 Flushing Rd, Flushing, MI 48433-2522
Tel (810) 732-2470 Founded/Ownrshp 2009
Sales 39.2MMᴱ EMP 54
Accts R D Franchi Pllc Waterford
SIC 5091 3949 Golf & skiing equipment & supplies; Golf equipment; Golf & skiing equipment & supplies; Golf equipment
CEO: John Runyon
CFO: Ryan Coffell
Exec: Elisabeth Rohl
IT Man: Rob Harris
Mktg Mgr: David Pillsbury
Sls Mgr: James Hirschfield
Sales Asso: Brad Davis

KING PAVING
See KING ROAD MATERIALS INC

D-U-N-S 80-958-7413 IMP
■ KING PHARMACEUTICALS LLC
PFIZER
(Suby of PFIZER INC) ★
501 5th St, Bristol, TN 37620-2304
Tel (423) 989-8000 Founded/Ownrshp 2011
Sales 345.1MMᴱ EMP 2,637
SIC 2834 Pharmaceutical preparations; Pharmaceutical preparations
Pr: Brian A Markison
Pr: Tim Leonard
Pr: Brian A Markison
*CFO: Joseph Squicciarino
Ofcr: Eric G Carter
Ex VP: Michael Davis
Ex VP: Sarah Faust
Ex VP: Dennis O'Brien
Ex VP: Dennis Obrien
Ex VP: Henry Richards
Ex VP: David Robinson
Ex VP: Janet Tuffy
Sr VP: Richard Pascoe
VP: Ray Feagins
VP: John J Howarth
VP: Charles L Pamplin
VP: Dean Slack
*VP: Bryan Supran
VP: Jeff Taylor
VP: Linda Wase
Dir Rx: Sajani Mehta

D-U-N-S 00-201-8356
KING PIPELINE AND UTILITY CO INC (LA)
520 Lester Ave, Nashville, TN 37210-4260
Tel (615) 256-6363 Founded/Ownrshp 1970
Sales 22.5MMᴱ EMP 120
SIC 1623 Underground utilities contractor; Underground utilities contractor
Pr: Forrest H King Jr
*Treas: Alane McCormick
*Sec: G Kevin King

D-U-N-S 05-156-4433
KING PLASTIC CORP
1100 N Toledo Blade Blvd, North Port, FL 34288-8694
Tel (941) 423-8666 Founded/Ownrshp 1968
Sales 70.1MMᴱ EMP 120
SIC 3081 3082 Plastic film & sheet; Rods, unsupported plastic; Plastic film & sheet; Rods, unsupported plastic
CEO: Jeff King
*Ch: Thomas M King
*Treas: Judith King
Exec: Bruce Fleming
Genl Mgr: Linda Amato
IT Man: Jim Cassidy
IT Man: Michael Fabbri
IT Man: Karen Navas

D-U-N-S 02-259-5755
KING PONTIAC G M C TRUCK INC
KING G M C TRUCK
16200 Frederick Rd, Gaithersburg, MD 20877-4023
Tel (301) 948-9111 Founded/Ownrshp 1957
Sales 50.0MM EMP 90
SIC 5511 Automobiles, new & used; Automobiles, new & used
Pr: Conrad V Aschenbach
*Treas: Lois Aschenbach
*VP: William H Aschenbach
Sls Dir: Charlie Benson
Sls Mgr: Gary Barber
Sls Mgr: Kevin Gaynor
Sls Mgr: Pete Holman
Sales Asso: Jim McGarry

D-U-N-S 04-634-0006 IMP
KING PRINTING CO INC
181 Industrial Ave E, Lowell, MA 01852-5147
Tel (978) 458-2345 Founded/Ownrshp 1981
Sales 31.8MMᴱ EMP 80
SIC 2732 Book printing
Pr: Aditya Chinai
*Treas: Siddharth Chinai
VP: Thomas Campbell
VP: Edmund Leone
VP: Brenda Struck
Software D: Bob Anderson

D-U-N-S 78-467-0820
KING RANCH HOLDINGS INC
(Suby of KING RANCH INC) ★
3 Riverway Ste 1600, Houston, TX 77056-1967
Tel (832) 681-5700 Founded/Ownrshp 1853
Sales 51.6MMᴱ EMP 682
SIC 1311 3199 5211 5083 Crude petroleum production; Natural gas production; Saddles or parts; Corners, luggage: leather; Lumber & other building materials; Agricultural machinery; Crude petroleum production; Natural gas production; Saddles or parts; Corners, luggage: leather; Lumber & other building materials; Agricultural machinery
Pr: Jack Hunt

D-U-N-S 00-793-3492 EXP
KING RANCH INC
3 Riverway Ste 1600, Houston, TX 77056-1967
Tel (832) 681-5700 Founded/Ownrshp 1853
Sales 217.3MMᴱ EMP 776
SIC 0212 2711 5083 5948 Beef cattle except feedlots; Newspapers, publishing & printing; Agricultural machinery; Leather goods, except luggage & shoes; Beef cattle except feedlots; Newspapers, publishing & printing; Agricultural machinery; Leather goods, except luggage & shoes
Pr: Robert Underbrink
*CFO: Bill Gardiner
*CFO: William J Gardiner
*Ch: James H Clement Jr
Treas: Tracy Janik
*VP: Michael Z Rhyne
Oper/Dir: Stephen J Kleberg

KING RANCH MARKET 1
See E & T FOODS INC

D-U-N-S 80-803-2622
KING RANCH TURFGRASS LP
(Suby of KING RANCH HOLDINGS INC) ★
106 N Dennis St, Wharton, TX 77488-5227
Tel (713) 287-2700 Founded/Ownrshp 2007
Sales 43.6MMᴱ EMP 220ᴱ
SIC 0181 0782 Sod farms; Lawn & garden services; Sod farms; Lawn & garden services
Mng Pt: Robert Under
Pt: Jack Hunt
IT Man: Melissa Hooker

D-U-N-S 07-574-2841
KING RETAIL SOLUTIONS INC
(Suby of L D V INVESTMENTS INC) ★
3850 W 1st Ave, Eugene, OR 97402-5367
Tel (541) 686-2848 Founded/Ownrshp 1993
Sales 24.6MMᴱ EMP 130ᴱ
SIC 3993 7389 Signs & advertising specialties; Design, commercial & industrial; Signs & advertising specialties; Design, commercial & industrial
Pr: Shaun Londahl
*CEO: Kris Londahl
*Ex VP: Farrah Potter
Ex VP: James Sundstad
*Ex VP: Andrew Swedenborg
Genl Mgr: Blake Holton

D-U-N-S 00-206-5274
KING ROAD MATERIALS INC
KING PAVING
(Suby of OLDCASTLE MATERIALS GROUP) ★
1245 Kings Rd, Schenectady, NY 12303-2831
Tel (518) 381-9995 Founded/Ownrshp 1959
Sales 20.4MMᴱ EMP 205
SIC 2951 Asphalt & asphaltic paving mixtures (not from refineries); Asphalt & asphaltic paving mixtures (not from refineries)
Pr: Donald E Fane

D-U-N-S 11-272-3861
KING SECURITY SERVICES INC
428 13th St Fl 2, Oakland, CA 94612-2614
Tel (415) 556-5464 Founded/Ownrshp 1980
Sales 14.5MMᴱ EMP 528
SIC 7381 Security guard service; Private investigator; Security guard service; Private investigator
Pr: Kimberly King
*CFO: Jolanta King
*VP: Louis Siracusa
Off Admin: James Mahoney

D-U-N-S 12-892-6701
KING SOLUTIONS INC
11011 Holly Ln N, Maple Grove, MN 55369-9203
Tel (763) 428-5464 Founded/Ownrshp 2000
Sales 57.8MMᴱ EMP 188
SIC 4731 4213 Freight forwarding; Freight consolidation; Trucking, except local; Freight forwarding; Freight consolidation; Trucking, except local
CEO: Michael Patterson
Pr: Tom Sellin
*VP: Meyer Bolnick
Dir Bus: Peter Tulisaari
CIO: Ryan Neuharth
Opers Mgr: Chris Wherland
Trfc Mgr: Tom Larson

D-U-N-S 09-480-5793 IMP
KING STEEL CORP
AMERICAN ROD CONSUMERS
5225 E Cook Rd Ste K, Grand Blanc, MI 48439-8388
Tel (810) 953-7637 Founded/Ownrshp 2010
Sales 20.5MMᴱ EMP 20ᴱ
SIC 5051 3312 Steel; Bar, rod & wire products
CEO: Doug King
CFO: Don Johnson
VP: Dave Scribner
Off Mgr: Kathy Addington

D-U-N-S 61-858-8206 IMP/EXP
KING SUPPLY CO LLC
KING ARCHITECTURAL METALS
9611 E R L Thornton Fwy, Dallas, TX 75228-5618
Tel (214) 388-9834 Founded/Ownrshp 1990
Sales 117.5MMᴱ EMP 320
SIC 5039 5051 Architectural metalwork; Metals service centers & offices; Architectural metalwork; Metals service centers & offices
Pr: Stewart E King
*VP: Kathy King
*VP: Kathy Walker
CIO: Jeff Payn
Dir IT: Senecca Miller
IT Man: Zipper Leo
IT Man: Alex Rodriguez
Mktg Dir: Larry Robertson

KING SYSTEMS
See AMBU INC

D-U-N-S 01-070-5390
KING TACO RESTAURANT INC
3421 E 14th St, Los Angeles, CA 90023-3837
Tel (323) 266-3585 Founded/Ownrshp 1974
Sales 19.1MMᴱ EMP 430
SIC 5812 Fast-food restaurant, chain; Fast-food restaurant, chain
CEO: Raul D Martinez
Pr: Raul O Martinez Sr

D-U-N-S 07-650-9660
KING TECHNOLOGY INC
530 11th Ave S, Hopkins, MN 55343-7842
Tel (952) 933-6118 Founded/Ownrshp 1956
Sales 23.4MMᴱ EMP 50
SIC 5091 Swimming pools, equipment & supplies
Pr: Joseph A King

D-U-N-S 96-101-2978
KING TELESERVICES LLC
48 Wall St Fl 23, New York, NY 10005-2922
Tel (718) 238-7924 Founded/Ownrshp 1996
Sales 43.7MMᴱ EMP 1,500
SIC 7389 Brokers' services; Brokers' services

D-U-N-S 92-692-5439
KING TORTILLA INC
MAMA LUPE'S TORTILLA PRODUCTS
249 23rd Ave, Moundridge, KS 67107-7417
Tel (620) 345-2674 Founded/Ownrshp 1996
Sales 40.4MMᴱ EMP 140
SIC 2099 Tortillas, fresh or refrigerated; Tortillas, fresh or refrigerated
Pr: Juan Guardiola
QA Dir: Megan Leonard
Plnt Mgr: Brian Smith

KING TOYOTA
See KING MOTOR CENTER ET AL

KING TV
See KING BROADCASTING CO

D-U-N-S 07-490-8989
KING UNIVERSITY
KING COLLEGE BOOK STORE
1350 King College Rd, Bristol, TN 37620-2632
Tel (423) 968-1187 Founded/Ownrshp 1867
Sales 48.1MM EMP 130ᴱ
Accts Blackburn Childers & Steagall
SIC 8221 College, except junior; College, except junior
Pr: Gregory Jordan PHD
*CFO: James P Donohue
Assoc VP: Gloria Oster
VP: Jim Wood
Info Man: Daniel Harris
Mktg Dir: Sarah Clevinger

D-U-N-S 17-847-5638
KING VENTURE INC
BURGER KING
17800 N Laurel Park Dr, Livonia, MI 48152-3985
Tel (248) 357-6182 Founded/Ownrshp 1981
Sales 131.4MMᴱ EMP 3,200
SIC 5812 Fast-food restaurant, chain; Fast-food restaurant, chain
Pr: Mark S Schostak
*Ch: Alexandre Behring
VP: Paula Goldman-Spinner
VP: Mark London
VP: J M McFee
VP: Lori Schechter
*VP: David W Schostak

D-U-N-S 17-268-7261
KING WILLIAM SCHOOL DISTRICT
18450 King William Rd, King William, VA 23086-2908
Tel (804) 769-3434 Founded/Ownrshp 1900
Sales 15.3MMᴱ EMP 300
SIC 8211 Public elementary & secondary schools; School board; Public elementary & secondary schools; School board
Dir IT: David Rorick
Dir IT: Gerrit Vanvoorhees
Schl Brd P: Steven Tupponce
HC Dir: Shelia Carr

D-U-N-S 09-464-1024
KING WINDWARD NISSAN LLC
45-568 Kamehameha Hwy, Kaneohe, HI 96744-1944
Tel (808) 235-6433 Founded/Ownrshp 1999
Sales 21.6MMᴱ EMP 69
SIC 5511

D-U-N-S 01-089-6264
■ KING WORLD PRODUCTIONS INC
(Suby of CBS BROADCASTING INC) ★
825 8th Ave Fl 30, New York, NY 10019-7650
Tel (212) 315-4000 Founded/Ownrshp 1999
Sales 31.5MMᴱ EMP 440
SIC 6794 7313 7822 Franchises, selling or licensing; Television & radio time sales; Distribution for television: motion picture; Franchises, selling or licensing; Television & radio time sales; Distribution for television: motion picture
CEO: Roger King
CFO: Steven A Locascio
VP: Ralph Goldberg

D-U-N-S 05-493-1654
KING-FOGLE INC
KING BUICK PONTIAC GMC
4175 Byrd Dr, Loveland, CO 80538-7100
Tel (303) 893-1306 Founded/Ownrshp 1971, 1998
Sales 22.5MMᴱ EMP 50
SIC 5511 Automobiles, new & used
Pr: Rex King
*Sec: Yale King
Genl Mgr: Jerad King
Sls Mgr: Keith Cater
Sls Mgr: Michael Sealander

D-U-N-S 00-479-1919
KING-LAR CO
2020 E Olive St, Decatur, IL 62526-5137
Tel (217) 429-2323 Founded/Ownrshp 1994
Sales 23.4MMᴱ EMP 70
SIC 1711 Warm air heating & air conditioning contractor; Ventilation & duct work contractor
Ch Bd: Robert Lamb
*Pr: Scott Lamb
VP: Brian Lamb

D-U-N-S 09-145-9925
KING-OROURKE CADILLAC INC
756 Smithtown Byp, Smithtown, NY 11787-5023
Tel (631) 982-4447 Founded/Ownrshp 1981
Sales 28.4MMᴱ EMP 90
SIC 5511 Automobiles, new & used; Automobiles, new & used
Pr: Stephen King
Genl Mgr: Sean King
Store Mgr: Terry Pyres
Sls Dir: Ben Signorelli
Sales Asso: William Albano
Sales Asso: Anthony Digirolamo
Sales Asso: Joe Honeycutt
Sales Asso: Bill Reale

KINGAIRE
See EAST COAST METAL DISTRIBUTORS LLC

D-U-N-S 78-804-0657 IMP
KINGBRIGHT CORP
225 Brea Canyon Rd, City of Industry, CA 91789-3077
Tel (909) 468-0506 Founded/Ownrshp 1989
Sales 30.0MMᴱ EMP 30
SIC 5065 Diodes; Diodes
CEO: Wen Yu Sung
Manager: Tony Chen
Manager: Eva Cheung
Manager: Michael Tsao

D-U-N-S 14-740-5732 IMP/EXP
KINGDOM INC
KINGDOM TAPES CDS & ELEC
719 Lambs Creek Rd, Mansfield, PA 16933-9001
Tel (570) 662-7515 Founded/Ownrshp 1994
Sales 27.4MMᴱ EMP 120
SIC 5065

KINGDOM TAPES CDS & ELEC
See KINGDOM INC

D-U-N-S 07-852-8423
KINGDOM TECHNOLOGIES WORLDWIDE LLC
27603 E Benders Lndg, Spring, TX 77386-2804
Tel (281) 658-6056 Founded/Ownrshp 2012
Sales 40.0MM EMP 25
SIC 8711 8748 Petroleum, mining & chemical engineers; Systems analysis & engineering consulting services; Petroleum, mining & chemical engineers; Systems analysis & engineering consulting services

D-U-N-S 14-464-4986
KINGDON CAPITAL MANAGEMENT LLC
152 W 57th St Fl 50, New York, NY 10019-3308
Tel (212) 333-0100 Founded/Ownrshp 1983
Sales 21.2MMᴱ EMP 80
SIC 6282 Investment advisory service
Pr: Mark Kingdon
Pt: Peter Cobos
*COO: Alan Winters
CFO: Sely Dinc
*CFO: Bill Walsh
Ofcr: Brad Odom
CTO: Bryant Morse
Dir IT: Norma Berrios
Dir IT: Danny Christov
Dir IT: Karen Lamensdorf

D-U-N-S 04-884-4781
KINGERY PRINTING CO
M & D PRINTING DIV
3012 S Banker St, Effingham, IL 62401-2900
Tel (217) 347-5151 Founded/Ownrshp 1979
Sales 31.0MM EMP 200
SIC 2752 Commercial printing, offset; Commercial printing, offset
Pr: Michael C Kingery
*Ch Bd: John Kingery
*Treas: Terry Probst
Dir IT: Lynn Koester
IT Man: Kurt Jansen
MIS Mgr: Mike Flack
Sls Mgr: Steven Shedelbower

D-U-N-S 05-500-1499
KINGFISH INC
KINGFISH RESTAURANT
7400 New La Grange Rd # 405, Louisville, KY 40222-8821
Tel (502) 339-0194 Founded/Ownrshp 1989
Sales 12.4MMᴱ EMP 350
SIC 5812 5813 Seafood restaurants; Bar (drinking places); Seafood restaurants; Bar (drinking places)
Pr: Charles A Brown Jr
*VP: Norman V Noltemeyer

KINGFISH RESTAURANT
See KINGFISH INC

D-U-N-S 18-001-1459
KINGFISHER SYSTEMS INC
3110 Fairview Park Dr # 1150, Falls Church, VA 22042-4536
Tel (703) 635-2952 Founded/Ownrshp 2005
Sales 35.6MM EMP 193
Accts Berman Goldman & Ribakow Llp
SIC 8731 7373 7379 Systems engineering, computer related; Computer related consulting services; Computer (hardware) development; Computer (hardware) development; Systems engineering, computer related; Computer related consulting services
CEO: Harry M Howton
*Pr: Roy L Reed Jr
CFO: Damon Hecker
Ofcr: Thomas Harley
VP: Lydia Bosnos
VP: Rob Jobrack
VP: Dennis Karambelas
*CIO: Chris Harris
IT Man: Sonya Ford

D-U-N-S 01-011-6239
KINGLAND COMPANIES LTD
KINGLAND SYSTEMS
1401 6th Ave S Ste 1, Clear Lake, IA 50428-2632
Tel (641) 355-1000 *Founded/Ownrshp* 1998
Sales 35.6MM^E *EMP* 100
SIC 7372 7374 5045 Application computer software; Data entry service; Computers, peripherals & software
Pr: David J Kingland
**CEO:* Todd A Rognes

KINGLAND SYSTEMS
See KINGLAND COMPANIES LTD

D-U-N-S 80-470-2629
KINGLAND SYSTEMS CORP
(*Suby of* KINGLAND COMPANIES LTD) ★
1401 6th Ave S Ste 1, Clear Lake, IA 50428-2632
Tel (641) 355-1000 *Founded/Ownrshp* 1998
Sales 35.6MM^E *EMP* 70
SIC 5045 7379 Computers, peripherals & software; Computer related consulting services
Pr: David Kingland
Pr: Kevin Dear
COO: Peter L Streit
**CFO:* Todd Rognes
Sftwr Eng: Jordan Petersen
Sftwr Eng: Gaye Sletten

D-U-N-S 96-574-8325
KINGMAN COUNTY ECONOMIC DEVELOPMENT COUNCIL INC
324 N Main St, Kingman, KS 67068-1303
Tel (620) 532-3694 *Founded/Ownrshp* 1997
Sales 104.2M *EMP* 521
SIC 8732 7389 Economic research; Brokers, business: buying & selling business enterprises; Economic research; Brokers, business: buying & selling business enterprises
CEO: Daniel Shea

KINGMAN DAILY MINER
See MOHAVE COUNTY MINER INC

D-U-N-S 11-511-4654 IMP
KINGMAN HOSPITAL INC
KINGMAN REGIONAL MEDICAL CENTE
3269 Stockton Hill Rd, Kingman, AZ 86409-3619
Tel (928) 757-2101 *Founded/Ownrshp* 1980
Sales 254.7MM *EMP* 1,300
Accts Bkd Llp Colorado Springs Co
SIC 8062 General medical & surgical hospitals; General medical & surgical hospitals
CEO: Brian Turney
**Pr:* Pat Shook
COO: Eileen Pressler
CFO: Larry Lewis
Bd of Dir: Barbara Merritt
**VP:* Judy Stahl
Dir OR: Pauline Coakley
Dir Risk M: Karol Collison
Dir Lab: Michael Oursler
Dir Lab: Roger Rasmussen
Dir Rad: Greg Phillips

KINGMAN REGIONAL MEDICAL CENTE
See KINGMAN HOSPITAL INC

D-U-N-S 12-396-8794
KINGMAN UNIFIED SCHOOL DISTRICT 20
3033 Mcdonald Ave, Kingman, AZ 86401-4235
Tel (928) 753-5678 *Founded/Ownrshp* 1960
Sales 49.0MM^E *EMP* 950
SIC 8211 Public elementary & secondary schools; Public elementary & secondary schools

D-U-N-S 17-184-7270
KINGOLD JEWELRY INC
888c 8th Ave, New York, NY 10019-8511
Tel (212) 509-1700 *Founded/Ownrshp* 1995
Sales 28.3MM^E *EMP* 532^E
SIC 6799 3911 Investors; Jewel settings & mountings, precious metal
Ch Bd: Zhihong Jia
**CFO:* Bin Liu

D-U-N-S 14-473-2554 IMP/EXP
KINGPIN HOLDINGS LLC
10 S Wacker Dr Ste 3175, Chicago, IL 60606-7407
Tel (312) 876-1275 *Founded/Ownrshp* 2003
Sales 920.3MM^E *EMP* 8,841
SIC 7933 Duck pin center; Duck pin center

D-U-N-S 61-929-9709
KINGPIN INTERMEDIATE CORP
(*Suby of* KINGPIN HOLDINGS LLC) ★
10 S Wacker Dr, Chicago, IL 60606-7453
Tel (312) 876-1275 *Founded/Ownrshp* 2004
Sales 920.3MM^E *EMP* 8,841
SIC 7933 Duck pin center; Duck pin center
Pr: Thomas J Formolo
CFO: Stephen D Satterwhite
VP: Richard A Lobo

KINGREY PRICE & DUYCK INSUR
See KPD INSURANCE INC

KINGS AIRE
See KINGSAIRE INC

D-U-N-S 96-615-4887
KINGS BAY SERVICES GROUP LLC
3755 S Cptl Of Tx Hwy # 35, Austin, TX 78704-8810
Tel (931) 241-1183 *Founded/Ownrshp* 2011
Sales 950.0M *EMP* 1,100
SIC 7349 Janitorial service, contract basis; Janitorial service, contract basis

D-U-N-S 08-155-3901
KINGS CANYON UNIFIED SCHOOL DISTRICT
675 W Manning Ave, Reedley, CA 93654-2427
Tel (559) 637-1250 *Founded/Ownrshp* 1965
Sales 33.1MM^E *EMP* 500
Accts Vavrinek Trine Day & Co Ll
SIC 8211 Public elementary & secondary schools; Public elementary school; Public elementary & secondary schools; Public elementary school
Bd of Dir: Noel Remick
Ofcr: Janie Chiasson
Ofcr: Eleni March
Prin: James Blide

KING'S CAPS
See H & C HEADWEAR INC

D-U-N-S 02-481-6521
KINGS CASINO MANAGEMENT CORP (CA)
6510 Antelope Rd, Citrus Heights, CA 95621-1077
Tel (916) 560-4405 *Founded/Ownrshp* 2013
Sales 8.4MM^E *EMP* 350
SIC 7999 Card & game services
CEO: Ryan Stone

D-U-N-S 04-566-9223
KINGS COLLEGE
56 Broadway, New York, NY 10004-1613
Tel (212) 659-7200 *Founded/Ownrshp* 2015
Sales 27.8MM *EMP* 20
SIC 8221 College, except junior; College, except junior
Pr: Gregory Alan Thornbury
Treas: Roger Craft
VP: Eric Bennett
VP: Kimberly Thornbury
Dir Soc: Catherine Corbin
**Prin:* Dinesh D'Souza
Off Mgr: Tonnie Ng
Dir IT: Louis Tullo
Psych: Stacey Chen
Snr Mgr: Duanne Moeller

D-U-N-S 06-959-4687
KINGS COLLEGE
133 N River St, Wilkes Barre, PA 18711-0801
Tel (570) 208-5900 *Founded/Ownrshp* 1946
Sales 83.8MM *EMP* 500^E
Accts Parentebeard Llc Wilkes Barre
SIC 8221 College, except junior; College, except junior
Ch: Thomas R Smith
**Pr:* Lisa Marie McCauley
VP: Joseph Evans
**VP:* Nicholas Holodick
**VP:* Janet Mercincavage
VP: Steven Seitchik
**Prin:* Lou Mazza
**Prin:* Eric Shotto
Ex Dir: Paul Moram
**Genl Mgr:* Mary Wood
CIO: Keith Hermansader

D-U-N-S 06-851-2796
KINGS COMMAND FOODS LLC
(*Suby of* AMERICAN FOODS GROUP LLC) ★
7622 S 188th St, Kent, WA 98032-1021
Tel (425) 251-6788 *Founded/Ownrshp* 1966
Sales 74.0MM^E *EMP* 270
SIC 2013 Sausages & other prepared meats; Sausages & other prepared meats
Pr: Ron T Baer
VP: Kay Sohjia
Dir Bus: Jim Rash
Opers Mgr: Tim Beardsley
Ql Cn Mgr: Jerry Clark
VP Mktg: Tom Butler
Manager: Darrin Hinck
Sls Mgr: Justin Baas

D-U-N-S 04-173-4625
KINGS COUNTRY SHOPPES INC
KING'S FAMILY RESTAURANTS
1180 Long Run Rd Ste 2, White Oak, PA 15131-2096
Tel (412) 751-0700 *Founded/Ownrshp* 1967
Sales 123.1MM^E *EMP* 3,200
SIC 5812 Restaurant, family: chain; Restaurant, family: chain
CEO: Hartley C King
Treas: Joseph Amorose
Ex VP: Nick Hrehovchak
VP: Chris Whalen
Rgnl Mgr: Tony Karam
Mktg Dir: Barbara Dunlay

D-U-N-S 07-937-9671
KINGS COUNTY HOSPITAL CENTER
(*Suby of* NEW YORK CITY HEALTH AND HOSPITALS CORP) ★
451 Clarkson Ave, Brooklyn, NY 11203-2054
Tel (718) 245-3131 *Founded/Ownrshp* 2014
Sales 175.6MM^E *EMP* 442^E
SIC 8062 General medical & surgical hospitals
Dir Teleco: Ken Deer
Dir Lab: Imelda Johnson
Assoc Dir: Nihad Makaryus
Dir Rad: Sajjad Ahmed
Psych: Cheryl Blonstein
Psych: Stephanie Erickson
Psych: Darnaliah Gibson
Psych: Jean Kaluk
Psych: Elizabeth Owen
Psych: Alan Perry
Psych: Moses Preiser

D-U-N-S 19-353-7008
KINGS COUNTY OFFICE OF EDUCATION
1144 W Lacey Blvd, Hanford, CA 93230-5956
Tel (559) 589-7026 *Founded/Ownrshp* 1942
Sales NA *EMP* 1,468
Accts Borchardt Corona & Faeth Fre
SIC 9411 County supervisor of education, except school board; County supervisor of education, except school board
**Bd of Dir:* John Boogaard
**Bd of Dir:* William Gundaker
**Bd of Dir:* Joe Hammond
**Bd of Dir:* Larella Howe
**Bd of Dir:* Jim Kilner
IT Man: Jamie Dial
IT Man: Corryne Montgomery
IT Man: Kim Spicer
IT Man: Natalie Wilson

KINGS COUNTY SCHOOLS
See LEMOORE UNION HIGH SCHOOL DISTRICT

D-U-N-S 00-796-9272
KINGS COUNTY TRUCK LINES
(*Suby of* RUAN TRANSPORTATION MANAGEMENT SYSTEMS INC) ★
754 S Blackstone St, Tulare, CA 93274-5757
Tel (559) 686-2857 *Founded/Ownrshp* 1940, 2005
Sales 12.5MM^E *EMP* 325
SIC 4213 Trucking, except local; Refrigerated products transport; Contract haulers; Trucking, except local; Refrigerated products transport; Contract haulers
VP: Mark Tisdale
Mktg Mgr: Rosemary Gomes

D-U-N-S 10-690-0330
KINGS COVE AUTOMOTIVE LLC
PERFORMANCE LEXUS
5726 Dixie Hwy, Fairfield, OH 45014-4204
Tel (513) 677-0177 *Founded/Ownrshp* 2001
Sales 20.2MM^E *EMP* 60
SIC 5511 6159 7539 Automobiles, new & used; Automobile finance leasing; Automotive repair shops
Genl Mgr: Dan Kommeth
Genl Mgr: Phil Von Hagel
Sales Asso: Jay Holbrook

D-U-N-S 01-396-1193
KINGS CREEK PLANTATION LLC (VA)
191 Cottage Cove Ln, Williamsburg, VA 23185-5811
Tel (757) 221-6760 *Founded/Ownrshp* 1997
Sales 25.7MM^E *EMP* 175
SIC 6531 Time-sharing real estate sales, leasing & rentals
Sls&Mrk Ex: Willie Byles

D-U-N-S 02-097-3830
■ **KINGS CROWN FORD INC**
MIKE SHAD FORD AT THE AVENUES
(*Suby of* AUTONATION INC) ★
10720 Philips Hwy, Jacksonville, FL 32256-1555
Tel (904) 292-3325 *Founded/Ownrshp* 1999
Sales 39.6MM^E *EMP* 128
SIC 5511 Automobiles, new & used; Automobiles, new & used
CEO: Michael Jackson
Off Mgr: Kathrine Smith
VP Mktg: Doug Sovich

D-U-N-S 08-752-8287
KINGS CUSTOM BUILDERS INC
1608 Us Highway 19 S, Ellaville, GA 31806-9276
Tel (229) 937-2150 *Founded/Ownrshp* 1978
Sales 33.5MM^E *EMP* 150
SIC 2451 Mobile buildings: for commercial use
Pr: Russell J Taylor Jr
**Treas:* Mary Taylor

D-U-N-S 07-865-1559
KINGS DAUGHTER COMMUNITY HEALTH & REHAB
(*Suby of* CONSULATE HEALTH CARE LLC) ★
1410 N Augusta St, Staunton, VA 24401-2401
Tel (540) 886-6233 *Founded/Ownrshp* 2011
Sales 52.5MM^E *EMP* 4,873^E
SIC 8059 Nursing home, except skilled & intermediate care facility
Pr: Joseph D Conte

D-U-N-S 15-617-4831
KINGS DAUGHTERS CLINIC
1905 Sw H K Dodgen Loop, Temple, TX 76502-1814
Tel (254) 298-2400 *Founded/Ownrshp* 1928
Sales 39.0MM^E *EMP* 285
SIC 8011 Clinic, operated by physicians; Clinic, operated by physicians
Pr: Edward McCaffrey
**Ch Bd:* James Callas
Bd of Dir: Richard Tay
**VP:* Herman Poteet
Off Mgr: Ryan Fowler

KINGS DAUGHTERS HEALTH
See BETHANY CIRCLE OF KINGS DAUGHTERS HEALTH OF MADISON INDIANA INC

D-U-N-S 07-930-2762
KINGS DAUGHTERS HEALTH SYSTEM INC
2201 Lexington Ave, Ashland, KY 41101-2843
Tel (606) 408-4000 *Founded/Ownrshp* 2010
Sales 465.2MM^E *EMP* 4,200^E
SIC 8062 General medical & surgical hospitals; General medical & surgical hospitals
CEO: Fred Jackson
COO: Kristie Whitlatch
**Treas:* Jeff Treasure
Dir Risk M: Travis Sanders

D-U-N-S 07-508-9391
KINGS DAUGHTERS HOSPITAL ASSOCIATION
1901 Sw H K Dodgen Loop, Temple, TX 76502-1814
Tel (254) 771-8600 *Founded/Ownrshp* 1899
Sales 18.0MM^E *EMP* 400
SIC 8062 General medical & surgical hospitals; General medical & surgical hospitals
Pr: Tucker Bonner
CFO: Joe Fojtasek
Bd of Dir: Jerry Bawcom
Bd of Dir: Joseph Bray
Bd of Dir: Lydia Santibanez
Bd of Dir: Mike Thompson
VP Mktg: Lydia Higgins
Pharmcst: Becky Harvey

D-U-N-S 07-506-8189
KINGS DAUGHTERS MEDICAL CENTER
427 Highway 51 N, Brookhaven, MS 39601-2350
Tel (601) 833-6011 *Founded/Ownrshp* 1913
Sales 76.9MM *EMP* 490
Accts Horne Llp Ridgeland Mississi
SIC 8062 General medical & surgical hospitals; General medical & surgical hospitals
CEO: Alvin Hoover
**COO:* Tom Hood
**CFO:* Randy Pirtle
**CFO:* Dean Snider
Ex VP: Freddie Tillitson
Exec: Peggy King
Dir Rad: Kelly Smith
CIO: Cathy Cooper-Weidner
Tech Mgr: Emma Coleman
Sls Mgr: Jo A Sproles
HC Dir: Cathy Davis

D-U-N-S 11-038-5262
KINGS DAUGHTERS MEDICAL CENTER
2201 Lexington Ave, Ashland, KY 41101-2843
Tel (606) 408-4000 *Founded/Ownrshp* 2002
Sales 368.5MM *EMP* 1,306^E
SIC 8062 General medical & surgical hospitals
Pr: Fred Jackson
VP: Philip Fioret
VP: Rob Walters
Exec: Lisa Reynolds
Dir Lab: Donna Flocker
Dir IT: Chad Phipps
Doctor: Linda Eskew

KING'S DAUGHTERS MEDICAL CTR
See ASHLAND HOSPITAL CORP

D-U-N-S 96-634-8976
KINGS DAUGHTERS MEDICAL SPECIALTIES INC
2201 Lexington Ave, Ashland, KY 41101-2843
Tel (606) 408-4000 *Founded/Ownrshp* 2011
Sales 41.1MM *EMP* 5
SIC 8099 Health & allied services; Health & allied services
Pr: Fred Jackson

KINGS DELIGHT
See KD ACQUISITION I LLC

D-U-N-S 18-422-9094
KINGS DODGE INC
4486 Kings Water Dr, Cincinnati, OH 45249-8312
Tel (513) 683-3000 *Founded/Ownrshp* 1988
Sales 31.6MM^E *EMP* 100
SIC 5511 Automobiles, new & used; Pickups, new & used; Automobiles, new & used; Pickups, new & used
Pr: Robert Reichert
**Sec:* Louis K Galbraith
**VP:* Gerald M Carmichael
**VP:* Mark Pittman

KINGS ELECTRONICS
See WINCHESTER ELECTRONICS CORP

KING'S FAMILY RESTAURANTS
See KINGS COUNTRY SHOPPES INC

KING'S FISH HOUSE
See UNIVERSITY RESTAURANT GROUP INC

D-U-N-S 01-813-7539
KINGS FORD INC
9555 Kings Auto Mall Rd, Cincinnati, OH 45249-8309
Tel (513) 683-0220 *Founded/Ownrshp* 1979
Sales 90.0MM *EMP* 75
SIC 5511

KINGS HARBOR MULTICARE CENTER
See BRONX HARBOR HEALTH CARE COMPLEX INC

D-U-N-S 06-110-7745
KINGS HAWAIIAN HOLDING CO INC
19161 Harborgate Way, Torrance, CA 90501-1316
Tel (310) 755-7100 *Founded/Ownrshp* 1996
Sales 152.6MM^E *EMP* 278
SIC 2051 5812 Bread, all types (white, wheat, rye, etc): fresh or frozen; Restaurant, family: independent; Bread, all types (white, wheat, rye, etc): fresh or frozen; Restaurant, family: independent
Pr: Mark Taira
**Sec:* Leatrice Taira
VP: Rich Fitzgerald
**VP:* Curtis Taira

D-U-N-S 06-828-8315
KINGS HIGHWAY HOSPITAL CENTER INC (NY)
3201 Kings Hwy, Brooklyn, NY 11234-2625
Tel (718) 252-3000 *Founded/Ownrshp* 1955
Sales 43.8MM^E *EMP* 600
SIC 8062 General medical & surgical hospitals; General medical & surgical hospitals
Pr: Dr Samuel L Berson
**Treas:* Bonnie Stern
**VP:* Iolabee Berson
HC Dir: Sandy Ceballos

D-U-N-S 61-179-8828 IMP
■ **KINGS ISLAND CO**
(*Suby of* CEDAR FAIR LP) ★
6300 Kings Island Dr, Kings Mills, OH 45034
Tel (513) 754-5700 *Founded/Ownrshp* 1984
Sales 24.7MM^E *EMP* 220
SIC 7996 Amusement parks; Amusement parks
Pr: Carl Lindner
VP: Jamie Gaffney
Genl Mgr: Greg Scheid
Mktg Dir: Matt Shafer

D-U-N-S 08-185-7237
KINGS LOCAL SCHOOL DISTRICT
1797 King Ave, Kings Mills, OH 45034-1721
Tel (513) 398-8050 *Founded/Ownrshp* 1890
Sales 41.9MM *EMP* 446
SIC 8211 Public elementary & secondary schools; High school, junior or senior; School board; Public elementary & secondary schools; High school, junior or senior; School board
Pr Dir: Dawn Gould
Schl Brd P: Toby Darkins
Schl Brd P: Becky Holloway
Schl Brd P: William Russell

KINGS MAZDA KIA
See AUTO CENTER USA INC

D-U-N-S 04-905-4430
KINGS MEDICAL GROUP INC
1920 Georgetown Rd A, Hudson, OH 44236-4060
Tel (330) 528-1802 *Founded/Ownrshp* 1981
Sales 62.5MM^E *EMP* 251

SIC 5047 8099 Medical & hospital equipment; Medical services organization; Medical & hospital equipment; Medical services organization
CEO: William Newton
**COO:* Kimberly Jacobs
CIO: Bill Beattie
Sales Exec: Jon Dinardo
Podiatrist: Gail Davis

D-U-N-S 07-451-2377
KINGS MOUNTAIN HOSPITAL INC
706 W King St, Kings Mountain, NC 28086-2708
Tel (980) 487-5000 *Founded/Ownrshp* 1951
Sales 52.2MM^E *EMP* 300
SIC 8062 8051 8063 General medical & surgical hospitals; Skilled nursing care facilities; Psychiatric hospitals; General medical & surgical hospitals; Skilled nursing care facilities; Psychiatric hospitals
CEO: Brian Gwyn
Ofcr: Gail McKillop
Dir Env Sv: Harold Rogers
Off Mgr: Brenda Lowery

D-U-N-S 05-356-2153
KINGS NISSAN INC
2758 Coney Island Ave, Brooklyn, NY 11235-5016
Tel (718) 934-3300 *Founded/Ownrshp* 1985
Sales 22.3MM^E *EMP* 75
SIC 5511 Automobiles, new & used; Automobiles, new & used
Pr: Salvatore Trantino
Sls Mgr: Nick Scalici

D-U-N-S 05-592-2413
KINGS PARK CENTRAL SCHOOL DISTRICT (INC)
KINGS PARK CSD
180 Lawrence Rd Rm 208, Kings Park, NY 11754-2802
Tel (631) 269-3310 *Founded/Ownrshp* 1929
Sales 33.6MM^E *EMP* 539^E
SIC 8211 Public elementary & secondary schools; Kindergarten; Public combined elementary & secondary school; Public elementary & secondary schools; Kindergarten; Public combined elementary & secondary school
Pr: Marie Goldstein
Dir Sec: Steven Weisse
Snr Mgr: Tom Stevenson

KINGS PARK CSD
See KINGS PARK CENTRAL SCHOOL DISTRICT (INC)

D-U-N-S 00-316-8945 IMP
KINGS PLUSH INC
STI
515 Marie St, Kings Mountain, NC 28086-3147
Tel (704) 739-9931 *Founded/Ownrshp* 1989
Sales 54.6MM^E *EMP* 200
SIC 2221 Nylon broadwoven fabrics; Upholstery, tapestry & wall covering fabrics; Nylon broadwoven fabrics; Upholstery, tapestry & wall covering fabrics
Pr: John Kay
**CEO:* Sean D Gibbons
**COO:* Mark Hovis
CFO: John Wine
CTO: Moses Neuman
VP Mfg: Rick Hahn
Sales Exec: Diane Jenkins

D-U-N-S 60-423-0263 IMP
KINGS SEAFOOD CO LLC
555 EAST
3185 Airway Ave Ste J, Costa Mesa, CA 92626-4601
Tel (310) 451-4595 *Founded/Ownrshp* 2005
Sales 73.6MM^E *EMP* 1,500^E
SIC 5812 Seafood restaurants; Seafood restaurants
Pr: A Samuel King
**COO:* Rj Thomas
**CFO:* Roger Doan
Dir Soc: Sarah Lipnik
Genl Mgr: Robert Benson
Genl Mgr: Joseph Bowman
Genl Mgr: Dede Commans
Genl Mgr: Michelle Corley
Genl Mgr: Jose Covarrubias
Genl Mgr: Justin Dickens
Genl Mgr: Kristal Evans

D-U-N-S 00-787-5354 IMP
KINGS SUPER MARKETS INC (NJ)
(*Suby of* AG SUPERMARKET HOLDINGS LLC) ★
700 Lanidex Plz Ste 2, Parsippany, NJ 07054-2705
Tel (973) 463-6300 *Founded/Ownrshp* 1936, 2006
Sales 404.3MM^E *EMP* 2,500
SIC 5411 Supermarkets, chain; Supermarkets, chain
Pr: Alan Levitan
Ofcr: Calvin Thomas
**Sr VP:* Sherrie Bliwise
**Sr VP:* Fred Brohm
VP: Jeffrey Binder
VP: Richard Durante
VP: Craig Frank
VP: Arthur Goncalves
VP: Ed Quintana
VP: Scott Zoeller
Exec: Jennifer Keane
Dir Bus: Rick Michener

D-U-N-S 06-348-5510
KINGS TIRE SERVICE INC
6242 Airport Rd, Bluefield, WV 24701
Tel (304) 589-3756 *Founded/Ownrshp* 1973
Sales 27.0MM^E *EMP* 24^E
SIC 5014 5531 Automobile tires & tubes; Automotive tires
Pr: Sam King
**Sec:* Ed King
**VP:* Matt King Jr

D-U-N-S 02-845-0620
KINGS TOYOTA INC
KINGS TOYOTA SCION
4700 Fields Ertel Rd, Cincinnati, OH 45249-8200
Tel (513) 583-4333 *Founded/Ownrshp* 1988
Sales 37.3MM^E *EMP* 95
SIC 5511 7515 5521 7538 Automobiles, new & used; Passenger car leasing; Used car dealers; General automotive repair shops; Automobiles, new & used; Passenger car leasing; Used car dealers; General automotive repair shops
Pr: Gerald Carmichael
Dir IT: Tim Rodriguez
Dir IT: Tim Shockley
Mktg Dir: Mike Rutherford
Sls Mgr: Dennis Collins
Sales Asso: Terrell Davis
Sales Asso: Abid Khan

KINGS TOYOTA SCION
See KINGS TOYOTA INC

D-U-N-S 06-887-2167
KINGS VIEW
7170 N Fincl Dr Ste 110, Fresno, CA 93720
Tel (559) 256-0100 *Founded/Ownrshp* 1948
Sales 23.7MM^E *EMP* 269
Accts Tca Partners Llp Fresno Ca
SIC 8093 8361 8331 Alcohol clinic, outpatient; Drug clinic, outpatient; Mental health clinic, outpatient; Home for the emotionally disturbed; Work experience center; Alcohol clinic, outpatient; Drug clinic, outpatient; Mental health clinic, outpatient; Home for the emotionally disturbed; Work experience center
CEO: Leon Hoover
Dir Bus: Jeffrey Gorski
Dir IT: John Kasdorf
Opers Supe: Douglas Rolly

D-U-N-S 01-752-4747
KINGS VIEW CORP
7170 N Fincl Dr Ste 110, Fresno, CA 93720
Tel (559) 256-0100 *Founded/Ownrshp* 2011
Sales 27.4MM *EMP* 6^E
SIC 8093 Mental health clinic, outpatient; Mental health clinic, outpatient
CEO: Leon Hoover
**Prin:* Bill Dollar

D-U-N-S 02-162-0125
KINGSAIRE INC
KINGS AIRE
1035 Kessler Dr, El Paso, TX 79907-1840
Tel (915) 592-2997 *Founded/Ownrshp* 1980
Sales 30.7MM^E *EMP* 200
SIC 1711 1731 Heating & air conditioning contractors; Electrical work; Heating & air conditioning contractors; Electrical work
Pr: Armando Reyes
**VP:* Elena Reyes

D-U-N-S 96-477-6913
KINGSBOROUGH COMMUNITY COLLEGE
2001 Oriental Blvd, Brooklyn, NY 11235-2333
Tel (718) 368-5125 *Founded/Ownrshp* 2010
Sales 20.3MM^E *EMP* 95^E
SIC 8222 Community college
Prin: Regina Peruggi
COO: Doron Glazer
CFO: Amy Haas
Ofcr: Colleen Maeder
Ofcr: Audrey Phillips
VP: Elizabeth Basile
VP: Peter Cohen
Ex Dir: Anna Becker
CTO: Ryan Hubbard
IT Man: Marc Wiskoff
IT Man: Aleksey Zhulenev

D-U-N-S 07-884-6508
KINGSBRIDGE HEIGHTS NURSING HOME
3400 Cannon Pl, Bronx, NY 10463-4302
Tel (718) 796-8100 *Founded/Ownrshp* 1971
Sales 16.6MM^E *EMP* 400
SIC 8051 Skilled nursing care facilities; Skilled nursing care facilities
Pt: Albert Schwartzberg
Pt: Helen Seizer

D-U-N-S 84-467-0216
KINGSBRIDGE HEIGHTS REHABILITATION CARE CENTER INC
3400-26 Cannon Pl, Bronx, NY 10463
Tel (718) 549-9025 *Founded/Ownrshp* 1995
Sales 42.9MM *EMP* 400
SIC 8059 Nursing home, except skilled & intermediate care facility; Nursing home, except skilled & intermediate care facility
Pr: Helen Sieger
QC Dir: Fidelma Dolan

D-U-N-S 96-777-5607
KINGSBROOK HEALTHCARE SYSTEM INC
(*Suby of* KINGSBROOK HOSPITAL) ★
585 Schenectady Ave, Brooklyn, NY 11203-1822
Tel (718) 604-5532 *Founded/Ownrshp* 2011
Sales 12.0MM^E *EMP* 362^E
SIC 8062 General medical & surgical hospitals
Prin: Linda Brady

D-U-N-S 79-044-5386
KINGSBROOK HOSPITAL
KINGSBROOK JEWISH MEDICAL CTR
585 Schenectady Ave Ste 3, Brooklyn, NY 11203-1809
Tel (718) 604-5000 *Founded/Ownrshp* 1925
Sales 182.8MM *EMP* 1,501
Accts Mcgladrey Llp New York Ny
SIC 8011 Psychiatric clinic; Psychiatric clinic
Prin: Yuliya Feygis
COO: Harold McDonald
CFO: John Schmitt
Sr VP: Sibte Burney
Sr VP: Robert Dubicki
VP: Christine Kay
VP: Kevin Molloy
Exec: Richard Moeller
Exec: Nia Prendergast
Dir Risk M: Karol Murov
Dir Rx: Darko Todorov

D-U-N-S 06-829-8306
KINGSBROOK JEWISH MEDICAL CENTER INC (NY)
585 Schenectady Ave Ste 2, Brooklyn, NY 11203-1809
Tel (718) 604-5000 *Founded/Ownrshp* 1926
Sales 57.7MM^E *EMP* 2,100
SIC 8062 General medical & surgical hospitals; General medical & surgical hospitals
CEO: Linda Brady
**COO:* Harold McDonald
**CFO:* John Schmitt
S&M/VP: Clare Small

KINGSBROOK JEWISH MEDICAL CTR
See KINGSBROOK HOSPITAL

D-U-N-S 15-370-7620 IMP/EXP
KINGSBURG APPLE PACKERS INC
KINGSBURG ORCHARDS
10363 Davis Ave, Kingsburg, CA 93631-9539
Tel (559) 897-5132 *Founded/Ownrshp* 1984
Sales 124.8MM^E *EMP* 450
SIC 5148 Fruits, fresh; Fruits, fresh
Pr: George H Jackson
**Treas:* Colleen Jackson

KINGSBURG ORCHARDS
See KINGSBURG APPLE PACKERS INC

D-U-N-S 00-283-0065
KINGSBURY ELEVATOR INC
5621 S Us Hwy 35, Kingsbury, IN 46345
Tel (219) 393-5581 *Founded/Ownrshp* 1870, 1978
Sales 26.7MM *EMP* 20
Accts Applegate & Company Pc Michig
SIC 5153 5191 4213 Grain elevators; Farm supplies; Trucking, except local; Grain elevators; Farm supplies; Trucking, except local
Pr: Edgar K Lindborg
**VP:* Yvonne Lindborg
**Prin:* Paul Lindborg

D-U-N-S 00-227-5535 IMP
KINGSBURY INC
MESSINGER BEARINGS
10385 Drummond Rd, Philadelphia, PA 19154-3884
Tel (215) 824-4000 *Founded/Ownrshp* 1912
Sales 36.6MM^E *EMP* 140
SIC 3568 Bearings, bushings & blocks; Bearings, bushings & blocks
Ch Bd: Joseph C Hill
**Pr:* William R Strecker
**CFO:* Sean O'Hara
**VP:* Michael Brawley
**VP:* Mick McCann
**VP:* Jerry W Powers
**VP:* Mike Wilkes
CIO: Brad Hermansky
IT Man: Harry Geiger
Sls Mgr: Patricia Comitale
Sls Mgr: Don McGinnis
Board of Directors: Andrew K Chase, Evelyn K Clulow, Jeffrey K De Mers, Joseph C Hill

D-U-N-S 00-321-8294 IMP
KINGSDOWN INC
126 W Holt St, Mebane, NC 27302-2622
Tel (919) 563-3531 *Founded/Ownrshp* 1904
Sales 103.9MM^E *EMP* 330
SIC 2515 Mattresses, innerspring or box spring; Box springs, assembled; Mattresses, innerspring or box spring; Box springs, assembled
Pr: Frank Hood
Ex VP: Damewood Kevin
**Sr VP:* Joe Schmoeller
VP: David Kresser
VP: Lance McElreath
VP: Craig Wilson
VP Mfg: John Farnham
VP Mfg: Abdul Majid
Plnt Mgr: Jason Niles

D-U-N-S 06-464-1798
■ **KINGSFORD PRODUCTS CO LLC**
(*Suby of* CLOROX CO) ★
1221 Broadway Ste 1300, Oakland, CA 94612-2072
Tel (510) 271-7000 *Founded/Ownrshp* 1973
Sales 133.8MM^E *EMP* 684
SIC 2861 2099 2035 2033 2879 Charcoal, except activated; Dressings, salad: dry mixes; Dressings, salad: raw & cooked (except dry mixes); Barbecue sauce: packaged in cans, jars, etc.; Insecticides, agricultural or household; Charcoal, except activated; Dressings, salad: dry mixes; Dressings, salad: raw & cooked (except dry mixes); Barbecue sauce: packaged in cans, jars, etc.; Insecticides, agricultural or household
Pr: Richard T Conti
**Pr:* A W Biebl
**CFO:* Karen Rose
**Treas:* L L Hoover
**VP:* B C Blewett

D-U-N-S 01-611-2349
KINGSLAND DEVELOPMENT CO L P (GA)
CAMDON WAY SHOPPING CENTER
1805 Us Highway 82 W, Tifton, GA 31793-8165
Tel (229) 386-0552 *Founded/Ownrshp* 1992
Sales 37.8MM^E *EMP* 750
SIC 7011 Hotels & motels

D-U-N-S 06-808-6529
KINGSLEY CONSTRUCTORS INC
25250 Borough Park Dr # 106, Spring, TX 77380-3565
Tel (281) 363-1979 *Founded/Ownrshp* 1976
Sales 80.3MM^E *EMP* 220^E
SIC 1623 1611 Underground utilities contractor; General contractor, highway & street construction; Underground utilities contractor; General contractor, highway & street construction
Pr: J D Kingsley Sr
**Sec:* Tawna H Kingsley
VP: Brad Kingssley

KINGSLEY FINANCIAL SERVICES
See WOODBURY FINANCIAL SERVICES INC

D-U-N-S 12-035-1940 IMP
■ **KINGSLEY TOOLS LLC**
(*Suby of* DANAHER CORP) ★
3000 W Kingsley Rd, Garland, TX 75041-2313
Tel (972) 278-2387 *Founded/Ownrshp* 1997
Sales 58.0MM^E *EMP* 270
SIC 3423 5085 Wrenches, hand tools; Tools; Wrenches, hand tools; Tools
Pr: Jason Shzu

KINGSMILL RESORT
See XANTERRA KINGSMILL LLC

D-U-N-S 07-919-1278
KINGSOFT OFFICE SOFTWARE INC
530 Lytton Ave Fl 2, Palo Alto, CA 94301-1541
Tel (408) 806-0998 *Founded/Ownrshp* 2013
Sales 28.8MM^E *EMP* 800
SIC 7371 Computer software development; Computer software development
Pr: Frank Fu
CTO: Sun Shaw

KINGSPAN - ASI
See KINGSPAN INSULATED PANELS INC

D-U-N-S 06-785-6211 IMP/EXP
KINGSPAN INSULATED PANELS INC
KINGSPAN - ASI
(*Suby of* KINGSPAN INSULATED PANELS LTD)
726 Summerhill Dr, Deland, FL 32724-2021
Tel (386) 626-6789 *Founded/Ownrshp* 1987
Sales 129.3MM^E *EMP* 440^E
SIC 3448 Prefabricated metal buildings; Prefabricated metal buildings
Pr: Russell Shiels
**VP:* Ilhan Eser
VP: Fergal Murphy
**VP:* Carlo Vezza
Opers Mgr: Gabor Nagy

D-U-N-S 07-980-3723
KINGSPAN INSULATION LLC
GREENGUARD
(*Suby of* KINGSPAN GROUP PUBLIC LIMITED COMPANY)
2100 Riveredge Pkwy # 175, Atlanta, GA 30328-4693
Tel (678) 589-7331 *Founded/Ownrshp* 2014
Sales 22.2MM^E *EMP* 135^E
SIC 2493 5033 Insulation & roofing material, reconstituted wood; Roofing, siding & insulation
Mng Dir: Aiswinn Kieboom

D-U-N-S 60-709-4992 EXP
KINGSPAN-MEDUSA INC
(*Suby of* KINGSPAN GROUP PUBLIC LIMITED COMPANY)
726 Summerhill Dr, Deland, FL 32724-2021
Tel (386) 626-6789 *Founded/Ownrshp* 2008
Sales 66.9MM^E *EMP* 442^E
SIC 3448 Prefabricated metal buildings; Prefabricated metal buildings
Pr: Russell Shiels
**CFO:* V Balakrishnan
**CFO:* Carlo Vezza
Genl Mgr: Ralph Mannion
Ql Cn Mgr: Terry Jones
VP Sls: Allen Rockafellow
Mktg Dir: Andrea Peters
Manager: Robert Busby
Manager: Brad Kirkland
Manager: Tim Marzolf
Manager: Joe Moore
Board of Directors: A Forte, H Furrer, M Morandi

D-U-N-S 00-339-0192
KINGSPORT ARMATURE & ELECTRIC CO INC (TN)
323 E Market St 325, Kingsport, TN 37660-4825
Tel (423) 247-7189 *Founded/Ownrshp* 1951
Sales 21.8MM^E *EMP* 120
SIC 1731 7694 General electrical contractor; Armature rewinding shops; General electrical contractor; Armature rewinding shops
CEO: Jim Haun
**Sec:* Barbara E Haun
Plnt Mgr: Edward Harris

D-U-N-S 10-007-3030
KINGSPORT CITY SCHOOLS
400 Clinchfield St # 200, Kingsport, TN 37660-3687
Tel (423) 378-2100 *Founded/Ownrshp* 1927
Sales 49.5MM^E *EMP* 900
SIC 8211 Public elementary & secondary schools; School board; Public elementary & secondary schools; School board
**Pr:* Dr Randall Montgomery
**VP:* Carrie Upshaw
Off Admin: Debbie Murray
Dir IT: John Payne
IT Man: Julie Thompson-Trent
Pr Dir: Andy True
Teacher Pr: Jennifer Guthrie
Psych: Beth Calvert
Psych: Paulette Cathey

D-U-N-S 00-337-6514
KINGSPORT FOUNDRY & MANUFACTURING CORP (VA)
141 Unicoi St, Kingsport, TN 37660-4837
Tel (423) 224-1100 *Founded/Ownrshp* 1927
Sales 21.0MM^E *EMP* 180
SIC 3321 3599 3369 3322 Gray iron castings; Gray iron ingot molds, cast; Machine shop, jobbing & repair; Nonferrous foundries; Malleable iron foundries; Gray iron castings; Gray iron ingot molds, cast; Machine shop, jobbing & repair; Nonferrous foundries; Malleable iron foundries
Pr: W Everett Ring III
**CFO:* K Gardner Hammond
Sls Mgr: J O Bud
Board of Directors: Don Ring, Sara Ring, Vic Ring

D-U-N-S 00-338-4385
KINGSPORT PUBLISHING CORP (OH)
KINGSPORT TIMES-NEWS
(*Suby of* SANDUSKY NEWSPAPERS INC) ★
701 Lynn Garden Dr, Kingsport, TN 37660-5607
Tel (423) 246-8121 *Founded/Ownrshp* 1962
Sales 22.3MM^E *EMP* 225
SIC 2711 Newspapers, publishing & printing; Newspapers, publishing & printing
Pr: David A Rau
**Treas:* Susan White Smith
**VP:* Keith Wilson

KINGSPORT TIMES-NEWS
See KINGSPORT PUBLISHING CORP

D-U-N-S 01-621-1760 IMP/EXP
KINGSTON & ASSOCIATES MARKETING LLC
KINGSTON COMPANIES
477 Shoup Ave Ste 207, Idaho Falls, ID 83402-3658
Tel (208) 522-7070 *Founded/Ownrshp* 1999
Sales 28.2MM^E *EMP* 25
SIC 5148 Fresh fruits & vegetables
CEO: Dave Kingston
**Pr:* Mike Kingston
**CFO:* Richard Reece
**VP:* Jodi Boline
**VP:* Richard Connelly
Exec: Bill Tanner
IT Man: Ryan Cheney

KINGSTON CITY SCHOOLS CNSLD
See CITY SCHOOL DISTRICT KINGSTON NY

KINGSTON COMPANIES
See KINGSTON & ASSOCIATES MARKETING LLC

D-U-N-S 61-175-6065
KINGSTON HEALTHCARE CO
KINGSTON RESIDENCE
1 Seagate Ste 1960, Toledo, OH 43604-1592
Tel (419) 247-2880 *Founded/Ownrshp* 1989
Sales 95.5MM *EMP* 565
Accts William Vaughan Company Maume
SIC 8059 8741 Nursing home, except skilled & intermediate care facility; Personal care home, with health care; Nursing & personal care facility management; Nursing home, except skilled & intermediate care facility; Personal care home, with health care; Nursing & personal care facility management
Pr: M George Rumman
**Treas:* Larry A Nirschl
**VP:* Kent Libbe
Rgnl Mgr: Becky Housman
QA Dir: Travis Grasley
Dir IT: Darrin Posta
Mktg Dir: Heather Moore
Mktg Mgr: Amy Peters
Nrsg Dir: Rachel Mamere
Board of Directors: Bruce Dukeman, Bruce G Thompson, F D Wolfe

D-U-N-S 01-280-0173
KINGSTON OIL SUPPLY CORP (NY)
STARKTATOR
(*Suby of* GETTY PETROLEUM MARKETING INC.)
2926 Route 32, Saugerties, NY 12477-5120
Tel (518) 943-3500 *Founded/Ownrshp* 1957, 1987
Sales 25.5MM^E *EMP* 140
SIC 5983 5541 5984 5172 5074 Fuel oil dealers; Filling stations, gasoline; Propane gas, bottled; Fuel oil; Plumbing & hydronic heating supplies; Fuel oil dealers; Filling stations, gasoline; Propane gas, bottled; Fuel oil; Plumbing & hydronic heating supplies
Ch Bd: Robert Ferluga
**VP:* Barry Motzkin

D-U-N-S 11-833-0252
KINGSTON REGIONAL HEALTH CARE SYSTEM
741 Grant Ave, Lake Katrine, NY 12449-5350
Tel (845) 943-6019 *Founded/Ownrshp* 1986
Sales 85.0M *EMP* 850
SIC 8062 General medical & surgical hospitals; General medical & surgical hospitals
CEO: Michael Kaminski
Pr: Lorraine Salmon
**CFO:* Wah-Chung Hsu

KINGSTON RESIDENCE
See KINGSTON HEALTHCARE CO

D-U-N-S 17-958-8280
KINGSTON RESOURCES INC
(*Suby of* RIVERTON COAL PRODUCTION INC)
400 Patterson Ln, Charleston, WV 25311-1570
Tel (304) 252-4726 *Founded/Ownrshp* 1997
Sales 16.1MM^E *EMP* 350
SIC 1221 1222 Bituminous coal & lignite-surface mining; Bituminous coal-underground mining
Pr: Dale Birchfield

D-U-N-S 00-341-5635 IMP
KINGSTON SALES INC
PULVERMAN
1170 Lower Demunds Rd, Dallas, PA 18612-9033
Tel (570) 255-5000 *Founded/Ownrshp* 1972
Sales 38.2MM^E *EMP* 140
SIC 1761 3443 3444 Sheet metalwork; Fabricated plate work (boiler shop); Sheet metalwork; Sheet metalwork; Fabricated plate work (boiler shop); Sheet metalwork
Pr: Randy Mark
VP: Bill Race
**VP:* Scott Stephenson
**VP:* Jennifer Williams
Dir IT: Jim King
Ql Cn Mgr: Joe Milazzo
Ql Cn Mgr: Michael Polachek

D-U-N-S 14-704-5699
KINGSTON TEACHERS FEDERATION
KINGSTON TRUST FUND
307 Wall St Ste 6, Kingston, NY 12401-8001
Tel (845) 338-5422 *Founded/Ownrshp* 2004
Sales 21.3MM *EMP* 1
SIC 8631 Labor union; Labor union

Prin: Hugh Spoljaric

D-U-N-S 19-781-9683 IMP/EXP
KINGSTON TECHNOLOGY CO INC
(*Suby of* KINGSTON TECHNOLOGY CORP) ★
17600 Newhope St, Fountain Valley, CA 92708-4220
Tel (714) 435-2600 *Founded/Ownrshp* 1987
Sales 507.1MM^E *EMP* 4,000
SIC 3577

D-U-N-S 80-122-2238 IMP
KINGSTON TECHNOLOGY CORP
17600 Newhope St, Fountain Valley, CA 92708-4298
Tel (714) 445-3495 *Founded/Ownrshp* 1987
Sales 831.9MM^E *EMP* 4,150
SIC 3674 Semiconductors & related devices; Semiconductors & related devices
CEO: John Tu
VP: Samson Gong
**Prin:* David Leong
**Prin:* David Sun
Dist Mgr: Daniel Reilly
QA Dir: Diep MAI
Software D: Karen O'Bryan
Software D: Jenny Tseng
Sftwr Eng: Kwong Sam
Ql Cn Mgr: Kim Elliott

KINGSTON TRUST FUND
See KINGSTON TEACHERS FEDERATION

D-U-N-S 61-420-4253
▲ KINGSTONE COMPANIES INC
15 Joys Ln, Kingston, NY 12401-3705
Tel (845) 802-7900 *Founded/Ownrshp* 1961
Sales NA *EMP* 66
Tkr Sym KINS *Exch* NAS
SIC 6411 Insurance agents, brokers & service; Insurance agents, brokers & service
Ch Bd: Barry B Goldstein
CFO: Victor J Brodsky
Board of Directors: Jay M Haft, Jack D Seibald

D-U-N-S 11-922-6827
KINGSTONE INSURANCE CO
15 Joys Ln, Kingston, NY 12401-3705
Tel (845) 331-3288 *Founded/Ownrshp* 2006
Sales NA *EMP* 32
SIC 6331 Property damage insurance; Fire, marine & casualty insurance: mutual; Property damage insurance; Fire, marine & casualty insurance: mutual
Pr: John Reiersen
CFO: Victor Brodsky
**CFO:* Karl Houseknecht
VP: William Muller
VP: David Smith
**VP:* Benjamin Walden
Mktg Dir: Shannon Matty
Mktg Dir: Nancy Reiersen
Board of Directors: Benjamin Walden

D-U-N-S 04-540-2190
KINGSTREE GROUP INC
900 W Valley Rd Ste 300, Wayne, PA 19087-1852
Tel (610) 254-9050 *Founded/Ownrshp* 1998
Sales NA *EMP* 50
SIC 6321 Disability health insurance
CEO: Mary Anne Hawrylak
Sls&Mrk Ex: Anne Rivers

D-U-N-S 01-054-5770
KINGSVILLE INDEPENDENT SCHOOL DISTRICT
207 N 3rd St, Kingsville, TX 78363-4401
Tel (361) 592-3387 *Founded/Ownrshp* 1903
Sales 43.0MM *EMP* 643
SIC 8211 Public elementary school; Public junior high school; Public senior high school; Public elementary school; Public junior high school; Public senior high school
Dir Sec: Jose Mendietta
IT Man: Sharon Michalk
Teacher Pr: Dolores Hernandez
Psych: Cindie Garza

D-U-N-S 08-048-4025
KINGSWAY ARMS NURSING CENTER INC
KINGSWAY COMMUNITY
323 Kings Rd, Schenectady, NY 12304-3645
Tel (518) 393-8800 *Founded/Ownrshp* 1975
Sales 17.8MM *EMP* 325
SIC 8051 Skilled nursing care facilities; Skilled nursing care facilities
Ch Bd: J Peter Mc Partlon
CFO: Terry Mariano
Exec: Paul Canale
Ex Dir: Gina Cook
Mktg Dir: Jean Barnoski
Mktg Dir: Ann McCabe
Mktg Dir: Pat Wiwchar
Nrsg Dir: Carol Thompson
Phys Thrpy: Amy Green
HC Dir: Kathy Campbell

D-U-N-S 01-146-4133
KINGSWAY CHARITIES INC (VA)
1119 Commonwealth Ave, Bristol, VA 24201-2629
Tel (276) 466-3014 *Founded/Ownrshp* 1993
Sales 120.9MM *EMP* 9
Accts Brown Edwards & Company Ll
SIC 8699 Charitable organization; Charitable organization
Ch Bd: John Gregory

KINGSWAY COMMUNITY
See KINGSWAY ARMS NURSING CENTER INC

D-U-N-S 10-761-5791
KINGSWOOD CHRYSLER PLYMOUTH INSURANCE AGENCY INC
KINGSWOOD PLYMOUTH
(*Suby of* FCA US LLC) ★
4486 Kings Water Dr, Cincinnati, OH 45249-8317
Tel (513) 677-5790 *Founded/Ownrshp* 2011
Sales 25.4MM^E *EMP* 120
SIC 5511 Automobiles, new & used; Automobiles, new & used
Pr: Robert Rdichert
Exec: Vickie Powell

Sls Mgr: John Gholz
Sls Mgr: Y Charles Shamblee Jr

KINGSWOOD PLYMOUTH
See KINGSWOOD CHRYSLER PLYMOUTH INSURANCE AGENCY INC

KINGWOOD COUNTRY CLUB GOLF SP
See KINGWOOD COUNTRY CLUB INC

D-U-N-S 07-419-7377
■ KINGWOOD COUNTRY CLUB INC
KINGWOOD COUNTRY CLUB GOLF SP
(*Suby of* CLUBCORP USA INC) ★
1700 Lake Kingwood Trl, Kingwood, TX 77339-3796
Tel (281) 358-2171 *Founded/Ownrshp* 1972
Sales 17.2MM^E *EMP* 350
SIC 7997 5941 5813 5812 Country club, membership; Sporting goods & bicycle shops; Drinking places; Eating places; Country club, membership; Sporting goods & bicycle shops; Drinking places; Eating places
Pr: Eric Affeldt
CFO: Linda Miller
VP: Judy Price

D-U-N-S 10-651-8280
KINGWOOD HYUNDAI LLC
NORTH FREEWAY HYUNDAI
20440 Interstate 45, Spring, TX 77373-2916
Tel (832) 446-4000 *Founded/Ownrshp* 1998
Sales 24.2MM^E *EMP* 50
SIC 5511 Automobiles, new & used

D-U-N-S 03-758-1167
KINGWOOD MEDICAL CENTER
22999 Highway 59 N # 100, Kingwood, TX 77339-4439
Tel (281) 348-8000 *Founded/Ownrshp* 1996
Sales 236.4MM *EMP* 1,200
SIC 8011 Medical centers; Medical centers
CEO: Melinda Stephenson
Dir Lab: Leslie Wentworth
Prac Mgr: Lacey Buford
Podiatrist: Travis Bodeker
Podiatrist: Bailey Griffin
Doctor: Dai Lu

D-U-N-S 03-757-6076
KINGWOOD MINING CO LLC
208 Business St, Beckley, WV 25801-5904
Tel (304) 568-2460 *Founded/Ownrshp* 2000
Sales 25.8MM^E *EMP* 400
SIC 5052 Coal; Coal
IT Man: Saul Hernandez

KINGWOOD PINES HOSPITAL
See SHC-KPH LP

D-U-N-S 62-385-5918
KINGWOOD PIPE INC
3 N Main St, Kingwood, TX 77339-3710
Tel (281) 359-7473 *Founded/Ownrshp* 2004
Sales 24.0MM *EMP* 5
SIC 5051 Structural shapes, iron or steel; Structural shapes, iron or steel
Genl Pt: Raymond Vetters
**Pt:* Ricki Vetters
**CFO:* James R Vetters

D-U-N-S 07-392-5059
KINKAID SCHOOL INC
201 Kinkaid School Dr, Houston, TX 77024-7599
Tel (713) 785-7688 *Founded/Ownrshp* 1906
Sales 40.0MM *EMP* 200
Accts Blazek & Vetterling Houston
SIC 8211 Preparatory school; Preparatory school
Ch: Frances Hopper Jeter
Dir Vol: Tiffany Smith
**Pr:* Donald North
**Treas:* Eugene Werlin Jr
Trst: Andrew Martire
Ofcr: Kris Marron
**Prin:* E Staman Ogilvie
Mng Dir: Jane Murdock
Sales Exec: Mary Greer

D-U-N-S 61-495-4345
KINKOSHA INC
TARACA PACIFIC
660 Sacramento St Ste 302, San Francisco, CA 94111-2525
Tel (415) 765-0475 *Founded/Ownrshp* 1986
Sales 58.0MM *EMP* 19^E
SIC 5031 6512 Lumber, plywood & millwork; Commercial & industrial building operation; Lumber, plywood & millwork; Commercial & industrial building operation
Ch: W Murdaya
**Pr:* Hartati Murdaya

D-U-N-S 15-782-1919
KINLEY CONSTRUCTION CO
KINLEY CONSTRUCTION GROUP
7301 Commercial Blvd E, Arlington, TX 76001-7149
Tel (817) 461-2100 *Founded/Ownrshp* 1900
Sales 42.9MM^E *EMP* 109
SIC 1796 1623 Installing building equipment; Water, sewer & utility lines; Installing building equipment; Water, sewer & utility lines
Ch: Jim H Kinley
**Pr:* Jason Crisafulli
**Pr:* J L Kinley
**CFO:* Shelly Kenney
CFO: Mark McGuire
**Sr VP:* Mike Giardini
IT Man: Thomas Hansen

KINLEY CONSTRUCTION GROUP
See KINLEY CONSTRUCTION CO

KINNAIRD & FRANCKE
See FLOORING GALLERY LLC

D-U-N-S 03-848-2923
KINNELON BOARD OF EDUCATION
109 Kiel Ave, Butler, NJ 07405-1619
Tel (973) 838-1418 *Founded/Ownrshp* 1880
Sales 36.6MM *EMP* 250
Accts Nisivoccia Llp Mount Arlingto

SIC 8211 9411 Public elementary & secondary schools; Administration of educational programs; Public elementary & secondary schools; Administration of educational programs

KINNEY
See FOOT LOCKER RETAIL INC

KINNEY DRUGS
See KPH HEALTHCARE SERVICES INC

D-U-N-S 00-514-2492
KINNEY ELECTRICAL MANUFACTURING CO (IL)
678 Buckeye St, Elgin, IL 60123-2827
Tel (847) 742-9600 *Founded/Ownrshp* 1937
Sales 40.4MM^E *EMP* 80
SIC 3613 Panelboards & distribution boards, electric; Switchboard apparatus, except instruments; Panelboards & distribution boards, electric; Switchboard apparatus, except instruments
Pr: Lowell D Naber
**Sec:* Nancy Naber

KINNEY PARKING
See KINNEY SYSTEM INC

D-U-N-S 07-523-1852
■ KINNEY SYSTEM INC
KINNEY PARKING
(*Suby of* CENTRAL PARKING CORP) ★
60 Madison Ave Fl 7, New York, NY 10010-1600
Tel (212) 889-2056 *Founded/Ownrshp* 1998
Sales 23.9MM^E *EMP* 1,800
SIC 7521 8742 Parking lots; Parking garage; Industry specialist consultants; Parking lots; Parking garage; Industry specialist consultants
Pr: James H Bond
**CFO:* Stephen A Tisdell
Ex VP: Daniel Stark
MIS Dir: Anna Guidone
**MIS Dir:* Lewis Katz
MIS Dir: Charles Monteleone

D-U-N-S 01-389-5841
KINNSER SOFTWARE INC
ADLWARE
2600 Via Fortuna Ste 150, Austin, TX 78746-7982
Tel (512) 879-3135 *Founded/Ownrshp* 2003
Sales 36.0MM *EMP* 200^E
SIC 7372 Prepackaged software
Pr: Christopher Hester
CFO: Brian Thomson
VP: Shirley Fritsch
VP: Scott Hester
VP: Michael McAlpin
VP: Carla Ray
VP: George D Santillan
CTO: Mark Johnson
QA Dir: Stephanie Black
QA Dir: Deepika Dasari
QA Dir: Stephanie Engel

KINO PACKAGING CO
See TUCSON CONTAINER CORP

D-U-N-S 13-088-9033 IMP
KINPLEX CORP
200 Heartland Blvd, Edgewood, NY 11717-8380
Tel (631) 242-4800 *Founded/Ownrshp* 1984
Sales 94.1MM^E *EMP* 353
SIC 3589 Commercial cooking & foodwarming equipment; Commercial cooking & foodwarming equipment
Pr: Penny Hunter
**VP:* Daniel Schwartz

D-U-N-S 01-257-4513
■ KINRAY INC
(*Suby of* CARDINAL HEALTH INC) ★
15235 10th Ave, Whitestone, NY 11357-1233
Tel (718) 767-1234 *Founded/Ownrshp* 2010
Sales 221.8MM^E *EMP* 1,000
SIC 5122 Drugs & drug proprietaries; Druggists' sundries; Drugs & drug proprietaries; Druggists' sundries
Ch Bd: Michael C Kaufmann
**Pr:* Stewart Rahr
Manager: Joe Caccavale
Opers Mgr: Anthony Halpin
Manager: Craig Bakalac
Art Dir: Jason Callori

D-U-N-S 14-420-5770
■ KINRO COMPOSITES
(*Suby of* KINRO MANUFACTURING INC) ★
101 Mushroom Rd, Waxahachie, TX 75165-6103
Tel (972) 937-2002 *Founded/Ownrshp* 2002
Sales 20.4MM^E *EMP* 105
SIC 3088 3211 Tubs (bath, shower & laundry), plastic; Window glass, clear & colored
CEO: Fredric M Zinn
**Pr:* William Mitchell

D-U-N-S 03-875-5232 IMP
■ KINRO MANUFACTURING INC
(*Suby of* KINRO MANUFACTURING INC) ★
200 Mmaroneck Ave Ste 301, White Plains, NY 10601
Tel (817) 483-7791 *Founded/Ownrshp* 1997
Sales 118.2MM^E *EMP* 1,250
SIC 3442 Metal doors, sash & trim; Metal doors, sash & trim
Pr: Jason Lippert
**CFO:* Gary McPhail
**VP:* Scott Mereness

D-U-N-S 10-246-8360 IMP
■ KINRO MANUFACTURING INC
STARQUEST PRODUCTS
(*Suby of* DREW INDUSTRIES INC) ★
3501 County Road 6 E, Elkhart, IN 46514-7663
Tel (574) 535-1125 *Founded/Ownrshp* 1982
Sales 466.1MM^E *EMP* 2,000
SIC 3442 Screen doors, metal; Screens, window, metal; Storm doors or windows, metal; Screen doors, metal; Screens, window, metal; Storm doors or windows, metal
Pr: Jason Lippert

VP: Tom Beasley
*VP: Dominic Gattuso
VP: Tom Gattuso
*Prin: Scott Mereness
Off Mgr: Jenith Kele
MIS Dir: Howard Grainger
Plnt Mgr: John Becker

D-U-N-S 03-875-5646
KINRO TEXAS LIMITED PARTNERSHIP
4381 W Green Oaks Blvd # 200, Arlington, TX 76016-4477
Tel (817) 483-7791 Founded/Ownrshp 1982
Sales 29.7MM^E EMP 304
SIC 3442 Metal doors, sash & trim
Pt: David L Webster

D-U-N-S 80-754-5777 EXP
KINROSS GOLD USA INC
(Suby of KINROSS GOLD CORPORATION)
5075 S Syracuse St, Denver, CO 80237-2712
Tel (775) 829-1666 Founded/Ownrshp 1993
Sales 596.8MM^E EMP 1,573
Accts Deloitte & Touche Llp
SIC 1041 1044 Gold ores; Silver ores; Gold ores; Silver ores
Pr: James Fowler
*Treas: Brian Penny
*Treas: P Kristopher Sims
*VP: Richard Dye
Off Mgr: Ron Law
Cmptr Lab: Cherie Mondragon

D-U-N-S 19-882-2293
KINSALE HOLDINGS INC
VALIDANT
475 Sansome St Ste 700, San Francisco, CA 94111-3129
Tel (415) 400-2600 Founded/Ownrshp 2005
Sales 114.4MM^E EMP 250
SIC 5122 Pharmaceuticals; Pharmaceuticals
CEO: Brian Healy
*Pr: Michael Beatrice
CFO: Tom Anderson
VP: Maya Kraft
VP: Helm Siegel

D-U-N-S 08-850-4881 IMP
KINSBURSKY BROS SUPPLY INC
K B I
125 E Commercial St Ste A, Anaheim, CA 92801-1214
Tel (714) 738-8516 Founded/Ownrshp 1976
Sales 50.7MM^E EMP 75^E
SIC 5093 Metal scrap & waste materials; Metal scrap & waste materials
Pr: Steven Kinsbursky
CFO: Aaron Zisman
VP: Scott Kinsbursky
Dir IT: Shaun Nieves

D-U-N-S 05-642-3148
KINSETH HOTEL CORP
2 Quail Creek Cir, North Liberty, IA 52317-9571
Tel (319) 626-5600 Founded/Ownrshp 1977
Sales 38.5MM^E EMP 350
SIC 7011 8741 Hotels & motels; Hotel or motel management; Hotels & motels; Hotel or motel management
Pr: Leslie B Kinseth
*Pr: Linda Skinner
*VP: Bruce Kinseth

D-U-N-S 11-419-2347
KINSEY FARMS
5330 Independence Rd, Sunnyside, WA 98944-9797
Tel (509) 837-7554 Founded/Ownrshp 1980
Sales 30.5MM^E EMP 200
SIC 5148 Vegetables, fresh; Vegetables, fresh
Pt: Lyle Kinsey

D-U-N-S 00-301-2689 IMP
KINSEYS ARCHERY PRODUCTS INC (PA)
1660 Steel Way, Mount Joy, PA 17552-9515
Tel (717) 653-5524 Founded/Ownrshp 1967
Sales 48.5MM EMP 35
SIC 5091 3949 Archery equipment; Arrows, archery
Pr: James Kinsey
*Treas: Helen Kinsey
*VP: Sherri Gorman
*VP: Rick Kinsey
Store Mgr: Doug Williams
Netwrk Mgr: Matt Ealy
Sales Asso: Nate McFadden

D-U-N-S 01-515-1186 IMP
KINSLEY CONSTRUCTION INC
KINSLEY MANUFACTURING
2700 Water St, York, PA 17403-9306
Tel (717) 741-3841 Founded/Ownrshp 1960
Sales 947.4MM^E EMP 1,284
SIC 1541 1542 1611 Industrial buildings, new construction; Warehouse construction; Commercial & office building, new construction; Shopping center construction; Highway & street paving contractor; Industrial buildings, new construction; Warehouse construction; Commercial & office building, new construction; Shopping center construction; Highway & street paving contractor
Ch Bd: Robert A Kinsley
Pr: Jonathan R Kinsley
Treas: Jerry L Caslow
Ex VP: Daniel M Driver
VP: Dennis J Falvey
VP: Patrick A Kinsley
VP: Timothy J Kinsley
Rgnl Mgr: Ken Stoutzenberger
Genl Mgr: Bobby Chenault
CTO: Russ Witmer
Dir IT: Sheridan Palmer

D-U-N-S 01-970-6365
KINSLEY GROUP INC
KINSLEY POWER SYSTEMS
14 Connecticut South Dr, East Granby, CT 06026-9738
Tel (860) 844-6100 Founded/Ownrshp 1964
Sales 20.0MM^E EMP 50
SIC 5063 7629

KINSLEY MANUFACTURING
See KINSLEY CONSTRUCTION INC

KINSLEY POWER SYSTEMS ★
See KINSLEY GROUP INC

D-U-N-S 17-704-1993 IMP
KINSTON NEUSE CORP
(Suby of CROWN EQUIPMENT CORP) ★
2000 Dobbs Farm Rd, Kinston, NC 28504-8907
Tel (252) 522-3088 Founded/Ownrshp 1987
Sales 116.1MM^E EMP 250
SIC 3537 Pallet loaders & unloaders; Pallet loaders & unloaders
Pr: James F Dicke III
*Ch Bd: James Dicke II
*VP: Bradley Smith
*VP: Kent W Spille
Plnt Mgr: Mike Sperati
Snr Mgr: Beverly Andrews

D-U-N-S 13-553-0751
■ **KINTERA INC**
BLACKBAUD INTERNET SOLUTIONS
(Suby of BLACKBAUD INC) ★
9605 Scranton Rd Ste 200, San Diego, CA 92121-1768
Tel (858) 795-3000 Founded/Ownrshp 2008
Sales 34.5MM^E EMP 281^E
SIC 7372 Prepackaged software; Prepackaged software
CEO: Marc E Chardon
Ch Bd: Alfred R Berkeley III
Pr: Steve Klein
Pr: Richard Labarbera
CFO: Richard Davidson
CFO: James A Rotherham
Sr VP: Alexander A Fitzpatrick
Sr VP: Greg Kostello
VP: Harry Chiu
VP: Greg Hammill
VP: S Kelly Herrick
VP: Stephen Kerwick
VP: Andy Lavagnino
VP: David Lawson
VP: John Murphy
VP: Andrew Pan
VP: Scott Sandell
VP: Jim Schenck
VP: Andrew Scofield
VP: Stryder Thompkins
Assoc Dir: Tuvinh Vuong

D-U-N-S 04-862-7020
KINTETSU INTERNATIONAL EXPRESS (USA) INC
KINTETSU INTL TRVL CONS CO
879 W 190th St Ste 720, Gardena, CA 90248-4205
Tel (310) 525-1800 Founded/Ownrshp 1999
Sales 41.4MM^E EMP 190
SIC 4724

KINTETSU INTL TRVL CONS CO
See KINTETSU INTERNATIONAL EXPRESS (USA) INC

D-U-N-S 06-193-1689
KINTETSU WORLD EXPRESS (USA) INC
(Suby of KINTETSU WORLD EXPRESS, INC.)
1 Jericho Plz Ste 100, Jericho, NY 11753-1635
Tel (516) 933-7100 Founded/Ownrshp 1969
Sales 165.3MM^E EMP 703
SIC 4731 Freight forwarding; Customhouse brokers; Freight forwarding; Customhouse brokers
CEO: Takashi Chris Bamba
Treas: Nobukazu Tani
*VP: Luke Nakano
VP: Edward Palleschi
*VP: Hideto Tazura
*Prin: Joji Tomiyama
Opers Mgr: Tinh Ly
Sales Exec: Christophe Lenaertz
Sls Mgr: Rod Noche

KINTIGH MLKEN GOUDEY GREENIDGE
See AES EASTERN ENERGY LP

D-U-N-S 18-673-6690
KINTOCK GROUP INC
580 Virginia Dr Ste 250, Fort Washington, PA 19034-2715
Tel (610) 687-1336 Founded/Ownrshp 1987
Sales 9.0MM EMP 473
Accts O Hara Ward & Associates Feas
SIC 8331 8361 Vocational rehabilitation agency; Residential care; Vocational rehabilitation agency; Residential care
Pr: Diane Debarri
*CFO: Catherine Farley
CFO: Priya Raja

D-U-N-S 94-005-8175
KINTOCK GROUP OF NEW JERSEY INC
20142 Valley Forge Cir, King of Prussia, PA 19406-1112
Tel (610) 687-1336 Founded/Ownrshp 1994
Sales 24.1MM EMP 470
Accts O Hara Ward & Associates Fea
SIC 8322 Individual & family services; Individual & family services
Ch Bd: David Fawkner
*Pr: Diane Di Barri

D-U-N-S 07-867-3558
KINTZEL CONSTRUCTION
3233 120th St, Amana, IA 52203-8042
Tel (319) 533-7545 Founded/Ownrshp 2002
Sales 40.0MM EMP 1
SIC 1771 1389 Concrete work; Construction, repair & dismantling services; Concrete work; Construction, repair & dismantling services
Owner: Ryan Kintzel

D-U-N-S 08-031-1384
KINZE MANUFACTURING INC
2172 M Ave, Williamsburg, IA 52361-8563
Tel (319) 668-1300 Founded/Ownrshp 1965
Sales 31.4MM^E EMP 500^E
SIC 3523

D-U-N-S 80-072-1193
KINZLER CONSTRUCTION SERVICES INC
2335 230th St, Ames, IA 50014-6303
Tel (515) 292-5714 Founded/Ownrshp 1983
Sales 24.2MM^E EMP 55
SIC 1742 5033 Plaster & drywall work; Insulation materials
Pr: Tanner J Kinzler
*Pr: Kevin Kinzler
*Sec: Yvonne Kinzler
*Sec: Mae D Saunders
VP Opers: Winn Galyean
Opers Mgr: Glen Hartz
S&M/VP: Brian Schwartze

D-U-N-S 02-703-7894
KIOLBASSA PROVISION CO (TX)
1325 S Brazos St, San Antonio, TX 78207-6931
Tel (210) 226-8127 Founded/Ownrshp 1949
Sales 47.5MM EMP 115
Accts Boehm And Boehm Cpa S San An
SIC 2013 Sausages from purchased meat; Frankfurters from purchased meat; Sausages from purchased meat; Frankfurters from purchased meat
CEO: Robert A Kiolbassa
*Pr: Michael R Kiolbassa
COO: David Rosenbusch
*Sec: Barbara K Britton
*VP: Charles Harris
*VP: Sandra K Kiolbassa
VP Opers: Ismail Jaber
Prd Mgr: John Canales

D-U-N-S 05-350-5991 IMP/EXP
KION NORTH AMERICA CORP
(Suby of LINDE MATERIAL HANDLING GMBH)
2450 W 5th North St, Summerville, SC 29483-9621
Tel (843) 875-8000 Founded/Ownrshp 2008
Sales 46.3MM^E EMP 140
SIC 3537 Forklift trucks; Forklift trucks
Pr: Vincent Halma
*CFO: Gregory Stein
VP: Paul Antor
VP: John Pizarro
VP Sls: Skip Sumers

D-U-N-S 02-849-1996 IMP
KIONIX INC
(Suby of ROHM COMPANY LIMITED)
36 Thornwood Dr, Ithaca, NY 14850-1263
Tel (607) 257-1080 Founded/Ownrshp 2000
Sales 80.0MM^E EMP 185
SIC 3676 Electronic resistors; Electronic resistors
Pr: Nader Sadrzadeh
*CFO: Steve Hughes
Bd of Dir: Frederick Flynn
*Ex VP: Paul Bryan
*Ex VP: Timothy J Davis
*Ex VP: Kenneth N Salky
*VP: Kenneth Hager
VP: Michael J Maia
VP: Drake Margiotta

D-U-N-S 04-383-9222
KIOSK CO - DOMINICAN REPUBLIC LLC
869 N La Salle Dr, Chicago, IL 60610-3219
Tel (312) 532-1019 Founded/Ownrshp 2011
Sales 39.0MM EMP 15
SIC 5599 Golf cart, powered; Golf cart, powered

D-U-N-S 84-705-7023
KIOSK INFORMATION SYSTEMS INC
346 S Arthur Ave, Louisville, CO 80027-3010
Tel (303) 466-5471 Founded/Ownrshp 1993
Sales 42.2MM^E EMP 135^E
Accts Richey May & Co Llp Englew
SIC 3577 Computer peripheral equipment; Computer integrated systems design; Computer peripheral equipment
CEO: Tom Weaver
*Pr: Rick Malone
*COO: Dan Houck
CFO: Anthony Cirocco
*VP: Don Stark
Genl Mgr: Matt Karnicki
Snr Sftwr: Kevin Heitland
QA Dir: Luke Bonner
QA Dir: Bryan Cahow
QA Dir: Karen Looney
Dir IT: Charley Newsom
Board of Directors: Rick Malone

KIOTI TRACTOR DIVISION
See DAEDONG-USA INC

D-U-N-S 62-126-3628
KIOWA CASINO OPERATING AUTHORITY
KIOWA RED RIVER CASINO
Rr 1 Box 26x, Devol, OK 73531-9712
Tel (580) 299-3333 Founded/Ownrshp 2006
Sales 14.3MM^E EMP 500
SIC 7011 Casino hotel; Casino hotel
Genl Mgr: Tom Carr
*CFO: Scott Cannaday

KIOWA RED RIVER CASINO
See KIOWA CASINO OPERATING AUTHORITY

D-U-N-S 10-155-2495 IMP/EXP
KIP AMERICA INC
KATSURAGAWA ELECTRIC
(Suby of KATSURAGAWA ELECTRIC CO., LTD.)
39575 W 13 Mile Rd, Novi, MI 48377-2303
Tel (800) 252-6793 Founded/Ownrshp 1997
Sales 31.5MM^E EMP 80
SIC 5044 7699 Photocopy machines; Photocopy machine repair
Pr: Sherman Sawtelle
CFO: Thomas Houdek
VP Opers: Larry Cappetto
Manager: Scott Sarel
Manager: Guy Spencer
Manager: Justin Stowe
Board of Directors: Michael R Mc Cord

D-U-N-S 00-324-8002
KIPLINGER WASHINGTON EDITORS INC
KIPLINGER WASHINGTON LETTER
1100 13th St Nw Ste 750, Washington, DC 20005-4364
Tel (202) 887-6400 Founded/Ownrshp 1925, 1956
Sales 21.8MM^E EMP 109^E
SIC 2721 2752 6552 6282

KIPLINGER WASHINGTON LETTER
See KIPLINGER WASHINGTON EDITORS INC

D-U-N-S 06-344-3382
KIPP BAY AREA SCHOOLS
1404 Franklin St Ste 500, Oakland, CA 94612-3208
Tel (510) 465-5477 Founded/Ownrshp 2012
Sales 41.6MM EMP 2
SIC 8699 Charitable organization; Charitable organization
Prin: Chloe Bellows
IT Man: Nora Reikosky
Snr Mgr: Kendra Ferguson

D-U-N-S 13-572-1921
KIPP DC
2600 Virginia Ave Nw # 900, Washington, DC 20037-1905
Tel (202) 223-4505 Founded/Ownrshp 2000
Sales 87.5MM EMP 750
Accts Mcgladrey Llp Gaithersburg M
SIC 8211 Elementary & secondary schools;
Ex Dir: Susan Schaeffler
*Pr: Allison Fansler
*CFO: Jane Hoffman

D-U-N-S 02-924-6977
KIPP FOUNDATION
135 Main St Ste 1700, San Francisco, CA 94105-1850
Tel (415) 399-1556 Founded/Ownrshp 2000
Sales 64.8MM EMP 110
Accts Hood & Strong Llp San Francis
SIC 8399 Public elementary & secondary schools; Elementary school; Fund raising organization, non-fee basis
CEO: Richard Barth
*CFO: Tarun Bhatia
*CFO: Jack Chorowsky
*CFO: Tina Sachs
Ex Dir: Anne Patterson
Off Mgr: Theresa Key

KIPP HOUSTON PUBLIC SCHOOLS
See KIPP INC

D-U-N-S 94-795-0879 IMP
KIPP INC
KIPP HOUSTON PUBLIC SCHOOLS
10711 Kipp Way Dr, Houston, TX 77099-2675
Tel (832) 328-1051 Founded/Ownrshp 1995
Sales 111.0MM EMP 100^E
Accts Blazek & Vetterling Houston
SIC 8211 Public elementary & secondary schools;
Pr: Brian McCabe
*CFO: John Murphy
Dir Soc: Deanna Sheaffer
Off Mgr: Glenda Castillo
IT Man: Colleen Dippel
Snr Mgr: Denise Rodriguez

D-U-N-S 00-603-8089
KIPP LA SCHOOLS (CA)
3601 E 1st St, Los Angeles, CA 90063-2325
Tel (213) 489-4461 Founded/Ownrshp 2008
Sales 49.3MM EMP 250
Accts Vicenti Lloyd & Stutzman Glen
SIC 8211 Elementary & secondary schools; Elementary & secondary schools
Ex Dir: Marcia Aaron
*Ch Bd: Frank Reddick
Bd of Dir: Zac Guevara
Bd of Dir: Allen Narcisse
Off Mgr: Nayyely Alfaro
Opers Mgr: Melissa Benson
Mktg Mgr: Jess Joswick
Snr Mgr: Alma Cibrian
Snr Mgr: Sara Gibson
Snr Mgr: Orpheus Williams

D-U-N-S 84-556-0395
KIPP MEMPHIS INC
KIPP MMPHIS COLLEGIATE SCHOOLS
2670 Union Avenue Ext # 1100, Memphis, TN 38112-4426
Tel (901) 452-2682 Founded/Ownrshp 2002
Sales 20.0MM EMP 175
Accts Zoccola Kaplan Pllc Germantow
SIC 8211
Ex Dir: Kelly Wright
*CFO: Ann Fite
*CFO: Mike Touchet
Exec: Ashley Williamson
Dir IT: Christopher Williams

KIPP MMPHIS COLLEGIATE SCHOOLS
See KIPP MEMPHIS INC

D-U-N-S 80-025-7136
KIPP NEW ORLEANS INC
KIPP NEW ORLEANS SCHOOLS
1307 Oretha Castle Haley, New Orleans, LA 70113-1256
Tel (504) 373-6269 Founded/Ownrshp 2005
Sales 57.7MM EMP 361^E
Accts Postlethwaite & Netterville M
SIC 8211 Public elementary school;
Pr: Joseph Giarrusso III

KIPP NEW ORLEANS SCHOOLS
See KIPP NEW ORLEANS INC

D-U-N-S 83-083-5776
KIPP NEW YORK INC
625 W 133rd St, New York, NY 10027-7303
Tel (212) 991-2600 Founded/Ownrshp 2008
Sales 28.1MM^E EMP 14^E
Accts Cliftonlarsonallen Llp Plymout
SIC 8211 Private junior high school; Private junior high school
Prin: Joseph Negron
Mng Dir: Vicki Zubovic

D-U-N-S 07-951-9379
KIPPAX PLACE APARTMENTS LLC
100 S Kippax St, Hopewell, VA 23860-7802
Tel (540) 382-2002 *Founded/Ownrshp* 2014
Sales 3.8MM^E *EMP* 300
SIC 6513 Apartment building operators; Apartment building operators
Pr: Janaka Casper
Treas: Jeffrey Reed
Ex VP: Orlando Artz

D-U-N-S 82-895-3166 IMP/EXP
KIPPERTOOL CO
2375 Murphy Blvd, Gainesville, GA 30504-6001
Tel (770) 532-3232 *Founded/Ownrshp* 1992
Sales 48.3MM *EMP* 55^E
Accts Hudson Carter & Company Pc
SIC 5085 Industrial supplies; Industrial supplies
Pr: Jerome Kipper
**CFO:* Nancy Kipper
VP: Bill Deringer
IT Man: Errick Crawford
VP Opers: Darrin Lee
Sfty Mgr: Jim O'Dell
Prd Mgr: Chris Traylor
Natl Sales: Trey Sears
Mktg Dir: Charmayne Scruggs
Board of Directors: Mary J Kipper

D-U-N-S 60-979-0944
KIRA INC
2595 Canyon Blvd Ste 240, Boulder, CO 80302-6737
Tel (303) 402-1526 *Founded/Ownrshp* 1987
Sales 64.3MM^E *EMP* 400
SIC 8744 Facilities support services; Base maintenance (providing personnel on continuing basis); Facilities support services; Base maintenance (providing personnel on continuing basis)
Pr: Carlos Garcia
Sr VP: Constance O'Brien
Assoc Dir: Jennifer Winston

D-U-N-S 79-651-8558 IMP
KIRAN JEWELS INC
(*Suby of* KIRAN JEWELS)
521 5th Ave Rm 820, New York, NY 10175-0800
Tel (212) 819-0215 *Founded/Ownrshp* 2003
Sales 50.9MM^E *EMP* 25^E
Accts Prajapati Associates Llp New
SIC 5094 Jewelry; Jewelry
CEO: Tejas Shah
**CFO:* Deepak RAO

KIRBERG COMPANY
See KIRBERG ROOFING INC

D-U-N-S 06-852-3430
KIRBERG ROOFING INC
KIRBERG COMPANY
1400 S 3rd St, Saint Louis, MO 63104-4430
Tel (314) 534-4444 *Founded/Ownrshp* 1920
Sales 32.0MM *EMP* 157
SIC 1761 Roofing contractor; Roofing contractor
Ch: Douglas O Kirberg
**Pr:* Eric G Kirberg
**VP:* Charles Kirberg
CTO: Mike Bock
IT Man: Brian Donahue
Sfty Dirs: C Gilmore
Opers Mgr: Jim Schriefer
Sales Exec: Jim King

D-U-N-S 10-588-9752
KIRBY - SMITH MACHINERY INC
6715 W Reno Ave, Oklahoma City, OK 73127-6590
Tel (817) 378-0600 *Founded/Ownrshp* 1983
Sales 353.9MM *EMP* 385
Accts Eidebailly Llp Oklahoma City
SIC 7353 5082 7692 Heavy construction equipment rental; Road construction equipment; General construction machinery & equipment; Welding repair; Heavy construction equipment rental; Road construction equipment; General construction machinery & equipment; Welding repair
Pr: Ed Kirby
Brnch Mgr: Bruce Taylor
Div Mgr: Kevin D Phillips
S&M/Mgr: Glen Townsend

D-U-N-S 09-873-6887
KIRBY AGRI INC
MARGRO
500 Running Pump Rd, Lancaster, PA 17601-2241
Tel (717) 299-2541 *Founded/Ownrshp* 1992
Sales 21.5MM^E *EMP* 53
SIC 2875 5191 Fertilizers, mixing only; Chemicals, agricultural; Fertilizer & fertilizer materials
Pr: Carroll Kirby Jr
**Treas:* Thomas Calcaterra
**Sr VP:* Carroll Kirby III
**Sr VP:* Rick Kirby
Ql Cn Mgr: Michele Smith
Sls Dir: Kevin Neyer

D-U-N-S 00-592-7744 EXP
■ KIRBY BUILDING SYSTEMS INC (TN)
(*Suby of* MAGNATRAX CORP) ★
124 Kirby Dr, Portland, TN 37148-2003
Tel (615) 325-4165 *Founded/Ownrshp* 1957, 1995
Sales 100.8MM^E *EMP* 293
SIC 3448 Prefabricated metal buildings; Prefabricated metal buildings
Pr: Thomas Mc Cann
COO: Robert Marinella
Dist Mgr: Jay Evans
IT Man: Monte Olson
Sftwr Eng: Jeffery Clark
Sfty Dirs: Larry Tennant
**Prd Mgr:* Mike Newton
Sls&Mrk Ex: Sam Thompson
Mktg Mgr: Tina Dickerson
Sls Mgr: Jon Amann
Sls Mgr: Mike Cockrell

D-U-N-S 02-079-7296
▲ KIRBY CORP
55 Waugh Dr Ste 1000, Houston, TX 77007-5834
Tel (713) 435-1000 *Founded/Ownrshp* 1969
Sales 2.5MMM *EMP* 4,175^E
Accts Kpmg Llp Houston Texas
Tkr Sym KEX *Exch* NYS
SIC 4449 7699 Intracoastal (freight) transportation; River transportation, except on the St. Lawrence Seaway; Marine engine repair; Intracoastal (freight) transportation; River transportation, except on the St. Lawrence Seaway; Marine engine repair
Pr: David W Grzebinski
**Ch Bd:* Joseph H Pyne
CFO: Norman W Nolen
CFO: C Andrew Smith
Ofcr: Steven Valerius
Ex VP: Mel Jodeit
Ex VP: Michael McQuillan
Sr VP: John Russell
VP: Ronald A Dragg
VP: Amy D Husted
VP: Patrick Kelly
VP: David R Mosley
VP: Lester Parker
Board of Directors: Richard J Alario, C Sean Day, William M Lamont Jr, Monte J Miller, Richard R Stewart, William M Waterman

D-U-N-S 01-497-4935
KIRBY ELECTRIC INC
KIRBY ELECTRIC SERVICE
415 Northgate Dr, Warrendale, PA 15086-7574
Tel (724) 772-1800 *Founded/Ownrshp* 1978
Sales 27.8MM^E *EMP* 120
Accts Beckwith Daprile & Co Polan
SIC 1731 General electrical contractor; General electrical contractor
Pr: John Kirby
**CEO:* Pat Kirby
**CFO:* Randall S McMillan
**VP:* James P Kirby Jr
**VP:* Randy McMillan
**VP:* Vince Zakowski
Genl Mgr: Cory Drusbasky
IT Man: Mary Buriak

D-U-N-S 80-932-9410
KIRBY ELECTRIC INC
4826 B St Nw Ste 101, Auburn, WA 98001-1752
Tel (253) 859-2000 *Founded/Ownrshp* 1990
Sales 22.1MM^E *EMP* 70
SIC 1542 Commercial & office building contractors
Pr: Doug Kirby
**Sec:* Shanon Kirby

KIRBY ELECTRIC SERVICE
See KIRBY ELECTRIC INC

D-U-N-S 02-538-5568
KIRBY FOODS INC
IGA
4104 Fieldstone Rd, Champaign, IL 61822-8801
Tel (217) 352-2600 *Founded/Ownrshp* 2001
Sales 128.9MM^E *EMP* 950
SIC 5411

KIRBY HOSPITAL
See KIRBY MEDICAL CENTER

D-U-N-S 00-793-1223
■ KIRBY INLAND MARINE LP
(*Suby of* KIRBY CORP) ★
55 Waugh Dr Ste 1000, Houston, TX 77007-5834
Tel (713) 435-1000 *Founded/Ownrshp* 1948, 1969
Sales 141.0MM^E *EMP* 1,950
SIC 4449 Intracoastal (freight) transportation; Intracoastal (freight) transportation
Mng Pt: William Ivey
Mng Pt: Joseph H Pyne
Mng Pt: Carl Whitlach
Ex VP: James C Guidry
Ex VP: Mel R Jodeit
VP: Ronald C Dansby

KIRBY JEEP-EAGLE SUZUKI
See KIRBY OLDSMOBILE

D-U-N-S 11-618-4789 IMP
KIRBY LESTER LLC
(*Suby of* CAPSA SOLUTIONS LLC) ★
13700 W Irma Lee Ct, Lake Forest, IL 60045-5123
Tel (847) 984-3377 *Founded/Ownrshp* 2014
Sales 22.8MM^E *EMP* 70
SIC 3559 Pharmaceutical machinery
Pr: Gary Zage
**COO:* Karen Bergendorf
**VP:* Dave Johnson
VP: Kirby Lester
**VP:* Christopher Thomsen
Off Mgr: Kay Benedict
**CTO:* Dave Schultz
Opers Mgr: Russell Wilford
Mktg Dir: Tom Rudolph

D-U-N-S 07-561-3364
KIRBY MEDICAL CENTER
KIRBY HOSPITAL
1000 Medical Center Dr, Monticello, IL 61856-2116
Tel (217) 762-6241 *Founded/Ownrshp* 1939
Sales 29.8MM *EMP* 180
Accts Bkd Llp Decatur Il
SIC 8062 General medical & surgical hospitals; General medical & surgical hospitals
CEO: Steven Tenhouse
Pr: Joseph Lamb
CFO: Dave Hains
Dir Risk M: Andrew Buffenbarger
Off Mgr: Cathy Manint
Dir IT: Kyle Williams
Snr Mgr: Gayla Hisplope
Snr Mgr: Jennifer Moss

D-U-N-S 17-380-3149
KIRBY NAGELHOUT CONSTRUCTION CO
20635 Brinson Blvd, Bend, OR 97701-8506
Tel (541) 389-7119 *Founded/Ownrshp* 1986
Sales 28.3MM^E *EMP* 60
SIC 1542 Commercial & office building, new construction
Pr: Jeff Deswert
Sfty Mgr: Shay Perry

D-U-N-S 62-142-3987
■ KIRBY OFFSHORE MARINE LLC
(*Suby of* KIRBY CORP) ★
55 Waugh Dr Ste 1000, Houston, TX 77007-5834
Tel (713) 435-1000 *Founded/Ownrshp* 2011
Sales 785.0MM^E *EMP* 992^E
SIC 5172 4212 4213 Petroleum products; Petroleum haulage, local; Liquid petroleum transport, non-local; Petroleum products; Petroleum haulage, local; Liquid petroleum transport, non-local
Genl Pt: Timothy J Casey
Pt: Richard P Falcinelli
Pt: Terrence P Gill
Pt: Gregory J Haslinsky
Pt: Thomas M Sullivan
VP: William Oppenheimer
Dir IT: John Carl

D-U-N-S 02-960-2331
KIRBY OLDSMOBILE
KIRBY JEEP-EAGLE SUZUKI
6424 Auto Center Dr, Ventura, CA 93003-7289
Tel (805) 485-8841 *Founded/Ownrshp* 1966
Sales 29.8MM^E *EMP* 55
SIC 5511 Automobiles, new & used; Automobiles, new & used
Pr: John W Kirby
CFO: Juan Rizo
**VP:* Jeffrey Sukay
Store Mgr: Bert Rodriguez
Sls Mgr: Robert Papandrea
Sls Mgr: David Rykowski

KIRBY PINES ESTATES
See PSALMS INC

D-U-N-S 00-175-3755 IMP
KIRBY RISK CORP
KIRBY RISK ELECTRICAL SUPPLY
1815 Sagamore Pkwy N, Lafayette, IN 47904-1765
Tel (765) 448-4567 *Founded/Ownrshp* 1926
Sales 401.3MM *EMP* 950
Accts Bkd Llp Indianapolis In
SIC 5063 7694 3599 3679 3629 Electrical supplies; Electric motor repair; Machine shop, jobbing & repair; Harness assemblies for electronic use: wire or cable; Capacitors, fixed or variable; Electrical supplies; Electric motor repair; Machine shop, jobbing & repair; Harness assemblies for electronic use: wire or cable; Capacitors, fixed or variable
Pr: James K Risk III
**CFO:* Jason J Bricker
VP: Doug Gutridge
VP Bus Dev: Steve Ward
Area Mgr: Jon Davis
Board of Directors: Robert B Truitt

KIRBY RISK ELECTRICAL SUPPLY
See KIRBY RISK CORP

D-U-N-S 80-968-1369 IMP/EXP
KIRBY SALES CO INC
1920 W 114th St, Cleveland, OH 44102-2344
Tel (216) 228-2400 *Founded/Ownrshp* 1923
Sales 103.3MM^E *EMP* 500
SIC 3635 Household vacuum cleaners; Household vacuum cleaners
Pr: Mike Nichols
Pr: Bill Bell
COO: Jim Ramey
Top Exec: Greg Ball
**VP:* H K Bell
VP: William Bell
**Prin:* Bud Miley
Dept Mgr: Tom Tibbits
MIS Dir: Anthony Morris
Sales Exec: Kevin Reitmeier

D-U-N-S 01-030-2198
KIRBY SCHOOL DISTRICT 140
16931 Grissom Dr, Tinley Park, IL 60477-2698
Tel (708) 532-6462 *Founded/Ownrshp* 1851
Sales 49.8MM *EMP* 647
Accts Mulcahy Pauritsch Salvador &
SIC 8211 Public elementary & secondary schools; School board; Public elementary & secondary schools; School board
IT Man: Brian Nemeth

KIRBY STEEL BUILDINGS
See JOS SCHMITT & SONS CONST CO INC

KIRBY VACUUM CLEANER
See SCOTT FETZER CO

D-U-N-S 79-171-8307
KIRCHHOFF-CONSIGLI CONSTRUCTION MANAGEMENT LLC
(*Suby of* CONSIGLI BUILDING GROUP INC) ★
199 West Rd Ste 100, Pleasant Valley, NY 12569-7975
Tel (845) 635-1121 *Founded/Ownrshp* 2009
Sales 85.3MM^E *EMP* 160
SIC 1542 Nonresidential construction; Nonresidential construction
CEO: Joseph Kirchhoff
**Pr:* Greg Burns

KIRCHMAN BROTHERS
See STAFFORD-SMITH INC

D-U-N-S 01-755-5129
KIRILA CONTRACTORS INC (OH)
505 Bedford Rd Se, Brookfield, OH 44403-9750
Tel (330) 448-4055 *Founded/Ownrshp* 1956
Sales 21.0MM *EMP* 70
Accts Black Bashor & Porsch Llp S
SIC 1611 1542 1623 Highway & street paving contractor; Commercial & office building contractors; Water, sewer & utility lines; Highway & street paving contractor; Commercial & office building contractors; Water, sewer & utility lines
Pr: Ronald Kirila Jr
Sr VP: Frank Obhof
**VP:* Paul Kirila
**VP:* William Kirila Jr

D-U-N-S 11-148-3488 IMP
KIRIU USA CORP
(*Suby of* KIRIU CORPORATION)
359 Mitch Mcconnell Way, Bowling Green, KY 42101-7520
Tel (270) 843-4160 *Founded/Ownrshp* 2001
Sales 42.4MM^E *EMP* 120
SIC 3714 Motor vehicle parts & accessories; Motor vehicle parts & accessories
Pr: Makoto Kimura
IT Man: Ryan Penrose
Ql Cn Mgr: David Rucker

D-U-N-S 00-424-9447
■ KIRK & BLUM MANUFACTURING CO (OH)
(*Suby of* CECO GROUP INC) ★
4625 Red Bank Rd Ste 200, Cincinnati, OH 45227-1552
Tel (513) 458-2600 *Founded/Ownrshp* 1907, 1999
Sales 71.8MM^E *EMP* 400
SIC 1761 3444 3443 Sheet metalwork; Sheet metal specialties, not stamped; Fabricated plate work (boiler shop); Sheet metalwork; Sheet metal specialties, not stamped; Fabricated plate work (boiler shop)
CEO: Jeff Lang
CFO: D W Blazer
VP: L Bertoli
Off Mgr: Jeanie Cook
CIO: Mike Purvis
IT Man: Hal Menz

D-U-N-S 01-866-4896
KIRK BROS CO INC (OH)
11942 Us Highway 224, Alvada, OH 44802-9609
Tel (419) 595-4020 *Founded/Ownrshp* 1969
Sales 23.0MM^E *EMP* 65
SIC 1629 1623 Waste water & sewage treatment plant construction; Water & sewer line construction
Pr: Richard C Kirk
**Treas:* Robert Kirk
Sfty Mgr: Robert Fruth

D-U-N-S 13-841-8434
KIRK BROTHERS CHEVROLET OLDS INC
3000 Gateway St, Grenada, MS 38901-2840
Tel (662) 226-5596 *Founded/Ownrshp* 2001
Sales 20.3MM^E *EMP* 48
SIC 5511 Automobiles, new & used
CEO: J S Kirk
Treas: Wayne Williams
VP: Bruce Kirk
Genl Mgr: Kristi Snyder

KIRK CONTAINERS
See ARTHURMADE PLASTICS INC

D-U-N-S 05-918-8763
KIRK GROSS CO
4015 Alexandra Dr, Waterloo, IA 50702-6119
Tel (319) 234-6641 *Founded/Ownrshp* 1987
Sales 21.1MM^E *EMP* 49
SIC 1542 5712 7389 Bank building construction; Office furniture; Interior designer
Pr: Robert Buckley
**CFO:* Julie K Hayes
**Treas:* Julie Hayes
**VP:* Jackie Buckley
VP: Roger Clayton
Mktg Dir: Chuck Yagla
Snr PM: Chris Griess

D-U-N-S 00-184-6880
KIRK NATIONALEASE CO (OH)
3885 Michigan St, Sidney, OH 45365-8623
Tel (937) 498-1151 *Founded/Ownrshp* 1920, 2008
Sales 45.7MM^E *EMP* 280
SIC 7513 7538 Truck leasing, without drivers; Truck rental, without drivers; Truck engine repair, except industrial; Truck leasing, without drivers; Truck rental, without drivers; Truck engine repair, except industrial
Pr: Jeff Phlitot
COO: Jeff Phlipot
**CFO:* Tom Menker
**VP:* James R Harvey
**VP:* Deb Hovestreybt
Exec: Deb Hovestreydt
Sls&Mrk Ex: Jim Hoying

D-U-N-S 05-489-6881
KIRK PATRICK BANK
(*Suby of* AMERICAN BANCORP OF OKLAHOMA INC) ★
15 E 15th St, Edmond, OK 73013-4302
Tel (405) 341-8222 *Founded/Ownrshp* 1985
Sales NA *EMP* 104
SIC 6021 National commercial banks; National commercial banks
Pr: George Drew
**Ch Bd:* Christian K Keesee
COO: Dana Rogers
Ofcr: Carly Freeman
Assoc VP: Ryan Miller
**Ex VP:* Robert R Kirby
Sr VP: Mark Benes
**Sr VP:* Carolyn Daniels
Sr VP: Bill Koch
VP: Michael Boecking
**VP:* Georgia Fulmer
**VP:* Jay Morrey
**VP:* Kathleen Ogle
Exec: Sarah Brown

D-U-N-S 00-387-1084
KIRK WILLIAMS CO INC
2734 Home Rd, Grove City, OH 43123-1701
Tel (614) 875-9023 *Founded/Ownrshp* 1949
Sales 39.8MM^E *EMP* 80
SIC 1711 3444 3564 Mechanical contractor; Warm air heating & air conditioning contractor; Ventilation & duct work contractor; Sheet metalwork; Blowers & fans
Pr: James K Williams Jr
**Sec:* James K Williams III
CIO: Mike Oryan
IT Man: David Ubbing
Sales Asso: Stephen Miller

D-U-N-S 08-697-3187 IMP
KIRK-RUDY INC
125 Lorraine Pkwy, Woodstock, GA 30188-2487
Tel (770) 427-4203 *Founded/Ownrshp* 1967
Sales 44.1MM^E *EMP* 100
SIC 3554 Paper industries machinery; Paper industries machinery
CEO: Harry V Kirk
**Pr:* Rick Marshall
CFO: Mitch Crowe
**VP:* Andrea Blaesing
**VP:* Wolfgang Fraint
Genl Mgr: Robert Millls
Genl Mgr: Robert H Mills
Plnt Mgr: Mike Grisham

D-U-N-S 04-527-7308
KIRKHAM-MICHAEL INC
12700 W Dodge Rd, Omaha, NE 68154-2154
Tel (402) 393-5630 *Founded/Ownrshp* 1986
Sales 24.4MM^E *EMP* 345
SIC 8712 8711 8713 Architectural engineering; Civil engineering; Photogrammetric engineering; Architectural engineering; Civil engineering; Photogrammetric engineering
Pr: Roger M Helgoth
**COO:* Michael S Olson
Sr VP: John L Ader

KIRKHILL
See KMC ACQUISITION CORP

D-U-N-S 06-311-1405
KIRKHILL AIRCRAFT PARTS CO
KAPCO GLOBAL
3120 Enterprise St, Brea, CA 92821-6236
Tel (714) 223-5400 *Founded/Ownrshp* 1972
Sales 232.5MM^E *EMP* 300
SIC 5088 3728 Aircraft & parts; Aircraft parts & equipment; Aircraft & parts; Aircraft parts & equipment
Pr: Andrew Todhunter
Pr: Joseph Gullion
Pr: John Valentine
Sr VP: Russ Bucklin
VP: Ron Basbas
VP: Pete Curti
VP: John Valantine
Dir Bus: Jim Kuwik
Mng Dir: Paul Ferri
Prgrm Mgr: Marian Ryan
Prgrm Mgr: Stephen Scott

D-U-N-S 00-825-5168
■ **KIRKHILL-TA CO**
(*Suby of* ESTERLINE TECHNOLOGIES CORP) ★
300 E Cypress St, Brea, CA 92821-4007
Tel (714) 529-4901 *Founded/Ownrshp* 1919
Sales 201.0MM^E *EMP* 1,100
SIC 3069 Reclaimed rubber & specialty rubber compounds; Reclaimed rubber & specialty rubber compounds
Pr: Richard B Lawrence
**CEO:* Michael R Johnson
**VP:* Rick Gentle
**VP:* Steve Lautenschlager
VP: Larry Pierce
**VP:* Jim Sweeney
Dir IT: Lester Fountain
Dir IT: Ali Sarhangpour
IT Man: Alan Young
Mtls Mgr: Ron Hagen
Ql Cn Mgr: Kenneth Kaler

D-U-N-S 06-861-3447
KIRKLAND & ELLIS LLP
300 N La Salle Dr # 2400, Chicago, IL 60654-5412
Tel (312) 862-2000 *Founded/Ownrshp* 1920, 1968
Sales 491.2MM^E *EMP* 2,400
SIC 8111 General practice attorney, lawyer; General practice law office; General practice attorney, lawyer; General practice law office
Pt: Robert B Ellis
Pt: Greg S Arovas
Pt: Eugene F Assaf
Pt: David A Breach
Pt: Richard M Cieri
Pt: Mark Filip
Pt: Michael P Foradas
Pt: David Fox
Pt: Richard C Godfrey
Pt: Jay P Lefkowitz
Pt: Linda K Myers
Pt: Stephen L Richie
**Pt:* James H M Sprayregen
Pt: Matthew E Steinmetz
Pt: Graham White
CFO: Christian Cooley
CFO: Neil Freeman
**CFO:* Nicholas J Willmott
**Ch:* Jeffrey C Hammes

D-U-N-S 04-812-4598 IMP/EXP
KIRKLAND CONSTRUCTION RLLP
2101 Main St, Rye, CO 81069
Tel (719) 489-3385 *Founded/Ownrshp* 1964
Sales 34.8MM^E *EMP* 100
Accts Hughes Wedgwood & Company Llc
SIC 1611 1794 General contractor, highway & street construction; Excavation work; General contractor, highway & street construction; Excavation work
Genl Pt: James H Kirkland

D-U-N-S 08-364-0722
KIRKLAND INC
4140 Mendenhall Oaks Pkwy, High Point, NC 27265-8347
Tel (336) 882-6909 *Founded/Ownrshp* 1977
Sales 42.5MM^E *EMP* 70
SIC 1542 1521 Commercial & office building contractors; New construction, single-family houses
Pr: Milton Kirkland
**Pr:* Scott Kirkland
**Sec:* Janice Kirkland
VP: Jim Downing
VP: Tracy Parker
Sales Exec: Doug Dreyer
Snr PM: Frank Havens

D-U-N-S 03-042-5250 IMP
▲ **KIRKLANDS INC**
5310 Maryland Way, Brentwood, TN 37027-5091
Tel (615) 872-4800 *Founded/Ownrshp* 1966
Sales 507.6MM *EMP* 6,312^E
Accts Ernst & Young Llp Nashville
Tkr Sym KIRK *Exch* NGS
SIC 5999 5947 Art, picture frames & decorations; Gift shop; Art, picture frames & decorations; Gift shop
Pr: W Michael Madden
**Ch Bd:* R Wilson Orr III
Treas: Ashley Deffenbaugh
Ofcr: Adam C Holland
Ex VP: Michelle R Graul
VP: Karla Q Calderon
VP: Michael Clem
VP: Anthony J Debruno
VP: James W Harris
VP: Al Oliver
VP: Philip H Rogers
Exec: Kelli Jarrell
Exec: Richard Johnson
Exec: Jeremy Salazar
Board of Directors: Robert E Alderson, Steven J Collins, Carl T Kirkland, Miles T Kirkland, Jeffery C Owen, Ralph T Parks, Murray M Spain

KIRKLIN CLINIC
See UNIVERSITY OF ALABAMA HEALTH SERVICES FOUNDATION PC

D-U-N-S 62-154-3792
KIRKPATRICK CONCRETE INC
(*Suby of* NATIONAL CEMENT CO INC) ★
2909 3rd Ave N, Birmingham, AL 35203-3996
Tel (205) 323-8394 *Founded/Ownrshp* 1989
Sales 26.3MM^E *EMP* 265
SIC 3273 5211 Ready-mixed concrete; Lumber & other building materials; Ready-mixed concrete; Lumber & other building materials
Pr: Bart Moore
Brnch Mgr: Tom Levin

D-U-N-S 03-944-8618
KIRKSVILLE R-III SCHOOL DISTRICT (MO)
1901 E Hamilton St, Kirksville, MO 63501-3904
Tel (660) 665-7774 *Founded/Ownrshp* 1950
Sales 27.6MM *EMP* 400
Accts Gerding Korte & Chitwood Boo
SIC 8211 Public elementary & secondary schools; Public elementary & secondary schools
IT Man: Maria Bradshaw
IT Man: Pam Sykes
Psych: Laurie Ward

D-U-N-S 02-036-0103
KIRKWOOD CITY OF (INC)
139 S Kirkwood Rd, Saint Louis, MO 63122-4303
Tel (314) 822-5833 *Founded/Ownrshp* 1853
Sales NA *EMP* 288
Accts Hochschild Bloom & Company Ll
SIC 9111 Mayors' offices; ; Mayors' offices;

D-U-N-S 87-804-7943
KIRKWOOD COMMUNITY COLLEGE FOUNDATION
6301 Kirkwood Blvd Sw, Cedar Rapids, IA 52404-5260
Tel (319) 398-5411 *Founded/Ownrshp* 1966
Sales 4.9MM *EMP* 1,750
Accts Mcgladrey Llp Cedar Rapids I
SIC 8222 Community college; Community college
Pr: Steve Caves
**Treas:* George Grask
**Treas:* Lois Nanke
Assoc VP: Dale Simon
VP: Kim Becicka
**VP:* John Bloomhall
VP: Jim Choate
VP: Kristie Fisher
Exec: Darryl Borcherding
Exec: Melanie Ewalt
**Ex Dir:* Rick Anderson

KIRKWOOD DIRECT
See KIRKWOOD HOLDINGS INC

D-U-N-S 60-621-8811
KIRKWOOD HOLDING INC
1239 Rockside Rd, Cleveland, OH 44134-2772
Tel (216) 362-3800 *Founded/Ownrshp* 2004
Sales 25.7MM^E *EMP* 200
SIC 3621 Commutators, electric motor; Collector rings, for electric motors or generators; Commutators, electric motor; Collector rings, for electric motors or generators
CEO: L Thomas Koechley
**CFO:* Donna Ross
**VP:* Paul Hensen

D-U-N-S 07-662-4998 IMP
KIRKWOOD HOLDINGS INC
KIRKWOOD DIRECT
904 Main St, Wilmington, MA 01887-3319
Tel (978) 658-4200 *Founded/Ownrshp* 2004
Sales 62.6MM^E *EMP* 200^E
SIC 2752 2791 2789 2759 Commercial printing, lithographic; Typesetting; Bookbinding & related work; Commercial printing; Commercial printing, lithographic; Typesetting; Bookbinding & related work; Commercial printing
Pr: Robert Coppinger
**Treas:* William Winship IV
Ex VP: Chuck Colvin
**VP:* Edward Kelley
VP: Ed Mitchell
Exec: Julianne Burr
VP Admn: Andy Brennan
IT Man: Stan Monfette
VP Opers: Steven Kuczwara
Prd Mgr: Scott Morse
Sales Exec: Ralph Dellatto

D-U-N-S 08-678-6738
KIRKWOOD R-VII SCHOOL DISTRICT
11289 Manchester Rd, Saint Louis, MO 63122-1122
Tel (314) 213-6100 *Founded/Ownrshp* 1863
Sales 78.8MM *EMP* 683
Accts Schowalter & Jabouri Pc St
SIC 8211 Public elementary & secondary schools; Public elementary & secondary schools
Off Admin: Mary Hart
Schl Brd P: Matt Cottler

KIRLIN
See NATIONAL FIRE PROTECTION LLC

D-U-N-S 78-954-1625
KIRLIN MID-ATLANTIC LLC
515 Dover Rd Ste 2200, Rockville, MD 20850-1290
Tel (301) 424-3410 *Founded/Ownrshp* 2006
Sales 28.4MM^E *EMP* 160
SIC 1711 Plumbing, heating, air-conditioning contractors; Plumbing, heating, air-conditioning contractors
Pr: Robert W Bacon

KIRLIN'S HALLMARK
See KIRLINS INC

D-U-N-S 02-577-0199 IMP
KIRLINS INC
KIRLIN'S HALLMARK
532 Maine St, Quincy, IL 62301-3932
Tel (217) 222-0813 *Founded/Ownrshp* 1948
Sales 59.0MM *EMP* 1,600
SIC 5947 Greeting cards; Greeting cards
Ch Bd: Dale Kirlin Jr
**Pr:* Gary Kirlin
COO: Kelly Otte
Site Mgr: Mary Durbin
Site Mgr: Jim Lubbring

D-U-N-S 02-415-5809
KIRMANI GROUP LLC
3042 Steinway St, Astoria, NY 11103-3802
Tel (718) 721-2500 *Founded/Ownrshp* 2011
Sales 24.4MM^E *EMP* 350
SIC 6794 Franchises, selling or licensing; Franchises, selling or licensing

D-U-N-S 82-708-0347 EXP
KIRSCHBAUM-KRUPP METAL RECYCLING LLC
K & K METAL RECYCLING
1728 N 2nd St, Minneapolis, MN 55411-3408
Tel (612) 521-9212 *Founded/Ownrshp* 2006
Sales 20.4MM^E *EMP* 45
Accts Drees Riskey & Vallager Ltd
SIC 5093 Metal scrap & waste materials
CFO: Linda Hull

D-U-N-S 96-804-2361
KIRSCHENMAN ENTERPRISES SALES LP
12826 Edison Hwy, Edison, CA 93220
Tel (661) 366-5736 *Founded/Ownrshp* 2009
Sales 100.0MM *EMP* 300
SIC 7389 Brokers, business: buying & selling business enterprises; Brokers, business: buying & selling business enterprises
Genl Pt: Wayde Kirschenman

D-U-N-S 00-610-2925
KIRSH FOUNDRY INC (WI)
125 Rowell St, Beaver Dam, WI 53916-2317
Tel (920) 887-0395 *Founded/Ownrshp* 1937
Sales 29.5MM^E *EMP* 115
SIC 3321 3322 Gray iron castings; Ductile iron castings; Malleable iron foundries
Pr: James T Kirsh
CFO: Richard Hiley
**Ex VP:* Steve Kirsh
VP: Roger Budde
VP: John Cernick
VP Opers: Kevin Paul

D-U-N-S 18-181-5424
KIRSHENBAUM BOND SENECAL & PARTNERS LLC
KB CREATIVE NETWORK
160 Varick St Fl 4, New York, NY 10013-1273
Tel (646) 336-9400 *Founded/Ownrshp* 2013
Sales 88.1MM^E *EMP* 350
Accts Stephen M Smith & Company Llc
SIC 7311 Advertising agencies; Advertising agencies
CEO: Lori Senecal
Pr: Robin D Hafitz
COO: Stephen Fick
**Ch:* Richard Kirshenbaum
Chf Mktg O: Bill Grogan
Sr VP: Eileen Matthews
VP: Julie Paciulli
VP: Lisa Zakarin
Assoc Dir: Sean Galligan
Assoc Dir: Ludmila Palasin
Creative D: Mike Abell
Creative D: Ed Brojerdi
Creative D: Michael Craven
Creative D: Isidoro Debellis
Creative D: Kevin Gentile
Creative D: Jon Goldberg
Creative D: Kathi Stark

D-U-N-S 94-337-6277 IMP/EXP
KIRTLAND CAPITAL PARTNERS LP
K C P
3201 Entp Pkwy Ste 200, Beachwood, OH 44122
Tel (216) 593-0100 *Founded/Ownrshp* 1992
Sales 252.4MM^E *EMP* 998^E
SIC 5051 3312 3498 3494 3492 3317 Metals service centers & offices; Tubes, steel & iron; Fabricated pipe & fittings; Valves & pipe fittings; Fluid power valves & hose fittings; Steel pipe & tubes; Metals service centers & offices; Tubes, steel & iron; Fabricated pipe & fittings; Valves & pipe fittings; Fluid power valves & hose fittings; Steel pipe & tubes
Sr Pt: Tom Littman
Sr Pt: John G Nestor
Pt: Bob Fines
Pt: Jim Foley
Pt: Corrie Menary
Mng Pt: Robert Fines
Board of Directors: Kirtland Capital Corporati, Gen Partner

D-U-N-S 79-376-5397
KIRTLAND FEDERAL CREDIT UNION
6440 Gibson Blvd Se, Albuquerque, NM 87108-4971
Tel (505) 254-4369 *Founded/Ownrshp* 1958
Sales NA *EMP* 120
SIC 6061 Federal credit unions; Federal credit unions
Pr: David Seely
**Ch:* Michael Chase
**Ex VP:* Vince Setnar
VP: Sharon Foreman
VP: Linda Herrera
**VP:* Sharlene Howell
VP: Kris Jones
CTO: George Walker
IT Man: William McClellan
VP Mktg: Judy Ruiz
VP Mktg: Stacy Sacco

D-U-N-S 08-950-2157
KIRTON & MCCONKIE PC
60 E South Temple # 1800, Salt Lake City, UT 84111-1032
Tel (801) 328-3600 *Founded/Ownrshp* 1964
Sales 20.1MM^E *EMP* 87^E
SIC 8111 General practice law office
Ch Bd: Oscar W McConkie
CFO: Brent Glad
**Sec:* Raeburn G Kennard
Bd of Dir: Christian S Collins
Prin: Mark Hall
**Prin:* David M McConkie
Dir IT: David Clark
IT Man: Alex Lutz
IT Man: David Margers
Mktg Dir: Deb Kirby
Counsel: Robert McKinley

D-U-N-S 83-142-0059
KIRYAS JOEL POULTRY PROCESSING PLANT INC
7 Dinev Ct, Monroe, NY 10950-6449
Tel (845) 783-8085 *Founded/Ownrshp* 2004
Sales 14.2MM^E *EMP* 350
SIC 7299 Butcher service, processing only; Butcher service, processing only
Pr: Mayer Hirsch

D-U-N-S 09-268-0222
KISATCHIE CORP
9258 Highway 84, Winnfield, LA 71483-7560
Tel (318) 628-4116 *Founded/Ownrshp* 1978
Sales 29.4MM^E *EMP* 1,100
SIC 8741 Nursing & personal care facility management; Nursing & personal care facility management
Pr: Teddy R Price

D-U-N-S 05-432-8562
KISER CONTROLS CO
7045 High Grove Blvd, Burr Ridge, IL 60527-7593
Tel (630) 920-9171 *Founded/Ownrshp* 1966
Sales 27.5MM^E *EMP* 28
SIC 5084 Pneumatic tools & equipment
Pr: Kerry A Kiser
Sales Asso: Judy Gil

D-U-N-S 18-883-6506
▲ **KISH BANCORP INC**
KISH VALLY NATIONAL BANK
4255 E Main St, Belleville, PA 17004-9291
Tel (717) 935-2191 *Founded/Ownrshp* 1986
Sales NA *EMP* 71
Accts Sr Snodgrass Sc Wexford
Tkr Sym KISB *Exch* OTO
SIC 6021 National commercial banks; National commercial banks
Ch: William P Hayes
Pr: John Massie
**Pr:* Brad Scovill
**CFO:* Sangeeta Kishore
**Ex VP:* Peter Collins
**Ex VP:* Robert McMinn
VP: Steven Jefferis
VP: Denise Quinn
VP: Gary Royer
VP: Julie Snare
VP: Lynn Thompson
VP: Lana Walker
Board of Directors: Donald Baggus, Raymond M Byler, Richard Calkins, Karl J Westover, James Xanthopolis

D-U-N-S 09-536-6035
■ **KISH BANK**
KISHACOQUILLAS VALLEY NAT BNK INC.
(*Suby of* KISH BANCORP INC) ★
4255 E Main St, Belleville, PA 17004-9291
Tel (717) 935-2191 *Founded/Ownrshp* 1986
Sales NA *EMP* 13
SIC 6021 National commercial banks; National commercial banks
Pr: William P Hayes
**Sr VP:* Donald L Smith
VP: John Cook
VP: Scott Reigle
VP: Lynn Thompson

D-U-N-S 16-108-4355 IMP
KISH CO INC
8020 Tyler Blvd Ste 100, Mentor, OH 44060-4825
Tel (440) 205-9970 *Founded/Ownrshp* 1986
Sales 30.8MM^E *EMP* 51
SIC 5052 Coal & other minerals & ores
Pr: John R Kish
**VP:* Brian Richards
Off Mgr: Kathy Jackson
Manager: Laura Copeland
Manager: Shannon Everett
Manager: Mike Lynn
Manager: John Yafanaro

KISH HEALTH SYSTEMS
See KISHWAUKEE COMMUNITY HOSPITAL

KISH VALLY NATIONAL BANK
See KISH BANCORP INC

KISHACOQUILLAS VALLEY NAT BNK INC.
See KISH BANK

D-U-N-S 02-163-8653
KISHHEALTH SYSTEM
(*Suby of* NORTHWESTERN MEMORIAL HEALTHCARE) ★
1 Kish Hospital Dr, Dekalb, IL 60115-9602
Tel (815) 756-1521 *Founded/Ownrshp* 2008
Sales 20.7MM *EMP* 1E
Accts Cliftonlarsonallen Llp Dixon
SIC 8062 Business services; General medical & surgical hospitals
Prin: Loren Foelske

D-U-N-S 06-800-6584
KISHWAUKEE COLLEGE
ILLINOIS CMNTY COLLEGE DST 523
(*Suby of* ILLINOIS COMMUNITY COLLEGE BD) ★
21193 Malta Rd, Malta, IL 60150-9699
Tel (815) 825-2086 *Founded/Ownrshp* 1967
Sales 74.3MME *EMP* 500
Accts Wipfli Llp Rockford Illinois
SIC 8222 8221 9411 Community college; Colleges universities & professional schools; Administration of educational programs; Community college; Colleges universities & professional schools; Administration of educational programs
Pr: Thomas Choice
Exec: Melissa Blake
Exec: Patricia Mitchell
Exec: Janis Ormond
Exec: Beth Young
Off Mgr: Beathy Ann
Cmptr Lab: Rita Jacisin
Dir IT: Scott Arm
Web Dev: Lindsay Barron
Mktg Dir: Kayte Hamel

D-U-N-S 07-458-5795
KISHWAUKEE COMMUNITY HOSPITAL
KISH HEALTH SYSTEMS
(*Suby of* KISHWAUKEE HEALTH SYSTEM INC) ★
1 Kish Hospital Dr, Dekalb, IL 60115-9602
Tel (815) 756-1521 *Founded/Ownrshp* 1975
Sales 180.1MM *EMP* 1,600
SIC 8062 General medical & surgical hospitals; General medical & surgical hospitals
**CFO:* Loren Foelske
Trst: Ann West
Mktg Mgr: Jennifer Fairbanks
Pharmcst: Daryl Burtzos
Pharmcst: Marlo Larson
Snr Mgr: Paul Dubrick

D-U-N-S 19-622-6179
KISHWAUKEE HEALTH SYSTEM INC
1 Kish Hospital Dr, Dekalb, IL 60115-9602
Tel (815) 756-1521 *Founded/Ownrshp* 1988
Sales 1.1MM *EMP* 2,878
Accts Clifton Gunderson Llp Dixon
SIC 8062 General medical & surgical hospitals; General medical & surgical hospitals
Pr: Kevin Poorten
**CFO:* Loren Foelske
VP: Michele McClelland
Dir Case M: Beth Gale
MIS Dir: R Shurson
QA Dir: Christine Cain
Web Dev: Tatum Glas

D-U-N-S 08-508-9126
KISINGER CAMPO & ASSOCIATES CORP
201 N Franklin St Ste 400, Tampa, FL 33602-5132
Tel (813) 871-5331 *Founded/Ownrshp* 1976
Sales 38.7MME *EMP* 215
SIC 8711 Consulting engineer; Consulting engineer
CEO: Joaquin M Campo
**Sr Pt:* Stephen McGucken
**Pr:* Paul Foley
**CFO:* Ronald Gott
**Ex VP:* Edward Burkett
Area Mgr: Gerald Hilton
Sfty Mgr: Tom Locicero
Mktg Mgr: Donna Douglas

D-U-N-S 62-720-1270 IMP
KISKA CONSTRUCTION CORP-USA
(*Suby of* KISKA DEVELOPERS INC) ★
4310 11th St, Long Island City, NY 11101-6802
Tel (718) 943-0400 *Founded/Ownrshp* 1989
Sales 62.4MME *EMP* 69
Accts Grassi & Co Cpa Pc Lake S
SIC 1622 1611 Tunnel construction; Highway & street construction
VP: Alp Baysal
IT Man: Kadir Ozbek

D-U-N-S 14-555-8941
KISKA CONSTRUCTION INC
(*Suby of* KISKA CONSTRUCTION CORP-USA) ★
4310 11th St, Long Island City, NY 11101-6802
Tel (718) 943-0400 *Founded/Ownrshp* 2007
Sales 62.4MM *EMP* 50
Accts Grassi & Co Cpas Pc Jeri
SIC 1622 1611 Tunnel construction; Highway & street construction;Tunnel construction; Highway & street construction
Ch Bd: Alp Baysal
S&M/VP: Ahmet Kefsli

D-U-N-S 18-307-0127 IMP
KISKA DEVELOPERS INC
4310 11th St, Long Island City, NY 11101-6802
Tel (718) 943-0400 *Founded/Ownrshp* 2013
Sales 71.8MM *EMP* 120
Accts Grassi & Co Cpas Pc Jeri
SIC 1622 1611 Tunnel construction; Highway & street construction;Tunnel construction; Highway & street construction
CEO: Alp Baysal

D-U-N-S 03-724-7822
KISKI AREA SCHOOL DISTRICT
200 Poplar St, Vandergrift, PA 15690-1466
Tel (724) 845-2022 *Founded/Ownrshp* 1964
Sales 25.5MME *EMP* 400
SIC 8211 9411 Public elementary & secondary schools; Public junior high school; Public senior high school; Administration of educational programs; Public elementary & secondary schools; Public junior high school; Public senior high school; Administration of educational programs
Bd of Dir: Gary Haag

D-U-N-S 62-689-2020
KISS NAIL PRODUCTS INC
57 Seaview Blvd, Port Washington, NY 11050-4660
Tel (516) 625-9292 *Founded/Ownrshp* 1989
Sales 28.6MME *EMP* 300E
SIC 7231 Manicurist, pedicurist; Manicurist, pedicurist
Ch Bd: Won S Kang
**CEO:* John Chang
**CFO:* Richard K Kim
Genl Mgr: Sung Y Chang

D-U-N-S 83-271-3692 IMP/EXP
KISS PRODUCTS INC
57 Seaview Blvd, Port Washington, NY 11050-4660
Tel (516) 625-9292 *Founded/Ownrshp* 1987
Sales 25.2MME *EMP* 54E
SIC 5087 Beauty parlor equipment & supplies
Ch Bd: Richard Altieri Jr
**CEO:* John Chang
COO: Rick Price
Sr VP: Grace Tallon
IT Man: Yong Chang
Mktg Dir: Deanna Mannion
Sls Dir: Rick McQuarrie
Mktg Mgr: Carrie Connell
Snr Mgr: Steven Shin

D-U-N-S 86-738-3606
KISSICK CONSTRUCTION CO INC
8131 Indiana Ave, Kansas City, MO 64132-2507
Tel (816) 363-5530 *Founded/Ownrshp* 1994
Sales 98.3MME *EMP* 200
SIC 1541 1623 1771 1794 Industrial buildings, new construction; Water, sewer & utility lines; Concrete work; Excavation & grading, building construction; Industrial buildings, new construction; Water, sewer & utility lines; Concrete work; Excavation & grading, building construction
Pr: Jim Kissick
**VP:* Pete Browne
Mtls Mgr: Rick White
Site Mgr: Chris Magner
Plnt Mgr: Dennis Richardson

D-U-N-S 18-739-8797
KISSIMMEE UTILITY AUTHORITY (INC)
1701 W Carroll St, Kissimmee, FL 34741-6804
Tel (407) 933-7777 *Founded/Ownrshp* 1985
Sales 272.5MME *EMP* 300
Accts Purvis Gray & Company Gainesv
SIC 4911 Electric services; Electric services
Pr: James C Welsh
Pr: Cindy Herrera
Treas: Michelle Daboin
**VP:* Kenneth L Davis
**VP:* Chris Gent
**VP:* Jeffery S Gray
**VP:* Wilbur Hill
**VP:* Joseph Hostetlar
VP Opers: Greg Woessner
Sfty Dirs: Michelle Scharfenberg

D-U-N-S 60-253-9962
KISSITO HEALTH CARE INC
5228 Valleypointe Pkwy, Roanoke, VA 24019-3074
Tel (540) 265-0322 *Founded/Ownrshp* 2005
Sales 56.1MME *EMP* 600
SIC 8051 Skilled nursing care facilities; Skilled nursing care facilities
CEO: Lynn Hodge
**Pr:* Tom Clarke
**COO:* Sean Pressman
CFO: Cherie Hidcs
CFO: Lori Hoffman
**Ch:* Wayne Fuquay
Treas: Gail Glass
Ofcr: Bob Bell
Ofcr: Gary Watson
VP: Andy Dameron
VP: Josh McGuillard
Exec: Carlan Myers

KISTLER-OBRIEN FIRE PROTECTION
See GEO W KISTLER INC

D-U-N-S 08-165-3599 IMP
KISWIRE INC
(*Suby of* KISWIRE LTD.)
257 Mawsons Way, Newberry, SC 29108-6362
Tel (803) 321-0940 *Founded/Ownrshp* 1999
Sales 65.9MM *EMP* 99E
SIC 3312 3315 Wire products, steel or iron; Steel wire & related products; Wire products, steel or iron; Steel wire & related products
Ch: Y C Hong
**Pr:* David Minnick
COO: David Vanderkaay
VP: Steve Yoon
Mng Dir: Yin Baek
Mng Dir: Bert De Ruijter
Snr Mgr: Park Chang-Hee

D-U-N-S 60-438-4164 IMP
KISWIRE PINE BLUFF INC
(*Suby of* KISWIRE LTD.)
5100 Industrial Dr S, Pine Bluff, AR 71602-3109
Tel (870) 247-2444 *Founded/Ownrshp* 2014
Sales 110.7MME *EMP* 300
SIC 3312 2296 Wire products, steel or iron; Steel tire cords & tire cord fabrics; Wire products, steel or iron; Steel tire cords & tire cord fabrics
CEO: Mike Morris
**Pr:* David Minnick
**Sec:* Beverly Barrett
Plnt Mgr: Nicholas Boyan
Plnt Mgr: Charley Chen
Ql Cn Mgr: Joe Gieringer

D-U-N-S 96-752-1027
KIT CARSON ELECTRIC COOPERATIVE INC
118 Cruz Alta Rd, Taos, NM 87571-6490
Tel (575) 751-9064 *Founded/Ownrshp* 1939
Sales 42.2MM *EMP* 64E
Accts Eide Bailly Llp Phoenix Az
SIC 4911 Electric services
Prin: Robert Iko
Trst: Ambrose Mascareas
Exec: Andrea Chavez
Exec: Steve Fuhlendorf
Sfty Mgr: Richard Garcia

D-U-N-S 15-373-8570
■ **KIT FIT INC**
POWER TOYOTA OF BUENA PARK
(*Suby of* AUTONATION INC) ★
6400 Beach Blvd, Buena Park, CA 90621-2813
Tel (714) 627-5562 *Founded/Ownrshp* 1998
Sales 29.9MME *EMP* 90
SIC 5511 Automobiles, new & used; Automobiles, new & used
Pr: Jerry Heuer
Genl Mgr: Shawn Davidson

D-U-N-S 13-120-5127
KIT HOMEBUILDERS WEST LLC
1124 Garber St, Caldwell, ID 83605-6727
Tel (208) 454-5000 *Founded/Ownrshp* 2003
Sales 36.0MME *EMP* 201
Accts Eide Baillyboiseidaho
SIC 2451 Mobile homes; Mobile homes
Mng Dir: Mike Wolf
Sls&Mrk Ex: Shane Hansen

KIT PAK
See PACKAGING UNLIMITED LLC

D-U-N-S 07-883-0302
■ **KIT ZELLER INC**
(*Suby of* KAMAN INDUSTRIAL TECHNOLOGIES CORP) ★
1000 University Ave # 800, Rochester, NY 14607-1286
Tel (585) 254-8840 *Founded/Ownrshp* 1999, 2012
Sales 216.1MME *EMP* 200
SIC 5063 Electrical apparatus & equipment; Electrical apparatus & equipment
Pr: Steve Snidler
**Sr VP:* Dary Haseley
VP: D J Mosher
VP Opers: Joe Bertalli
Sales Asso: Dwight Roth

D-U-N-S 03-321-7183
KITAGAWA MOTORS INC
ISLAND HONDA
110 Hana Hwy, Kahului, HI 96732-2303
Tel (808) 873-8081 *Founded/Ownrshp* 1959
Sales 32.7MME *EMP* 105
SIC 5511 Automobiles, new & used; Automobiles, new & used
Pr: Roy Kitagawa
**Treas:* Ronald Furukawa
**VP:* John Kitagawa
**VP:* Anne Oishi
Sls Mgr: Doug Fujiwara

D-U-N-S 04-059-9750
KITAHARA PONTIAC GMC BUICK INC
KITIHARA PONTIAC, BUICK, GMC
5515 N Blackstone Ave, Fresno, CA 93710-5017
Tel (559) 431-2020 *Founded/Ownrshp* 1998
Sales 21.9MME *EMP* 47
SIC 5511 Automobiles, new & used
Pr: Larry Kitahara

D-U-N-S 80-623-5268
■ **KITARA MEDIA CORP**
(*Suby of* PROPEL MEDIA INC) ★
525 Washington Blvd, Jersey City, NJ 07310-1606
Tel (201) 539-2200 *Founded/Ownrshp* 2015
Sales 25.3MM *EMP* 64E
Tkr Sym KITM *Exch* OTC
SIC 7311 7372 Advertising agencies; Prepackaged software
CEO: Robert Regular
**Pr:* Joshua Silberstein
**COO:* Limor Regular
**CFO:* Lisa Vanpatten
Ex VP: Randy Orndorf
VP Bus Dev: Lizz Cramm
CTO: Chris Magdelinskas
Snr Mgr: Howard Yeaton

D-U-N-S 07-276-9151
KITCH DRUTCHAS WAGNER VALITUTTI & SHERBROOK PC
1 Woodward Ave Ste 2400, Detroit, MI 48226-5485
Tel (248) 645-9468 *Founded/Ownrshp* 1969
Sales 27.2MME *EMP* 225
SIC 8111 General practice law office; General practice law office
Pr: Richard A Kitch
**Treas:* Harry J Sherbrook
Chf Mktg O: Elaine Samuelson
**Ex VP:* Ronald E Wagner
Prin: Susan Beutel
Prin: Paul O Hinshaw
Counsel: Carrie Fuca
Counsel: Michael Shpiece
Snr Mgr: Terri Archer

D-U-N-S 18-112-7358
KITCHELL CONTRACTORS INC OF ARIZONA
(*Suby of* KITCHELL CORP) ★
1707 E Highland Ave Ste 2, Phoenix, AZ 85016-4657
Tel (602) 264-4411 *Founded/Ownrshp* 1985
Sales 93.3MME *EMP* 472
SIC 1541 1542 1521 Industrial buildings, new construction; Commercial & office building, new construction; Specialized public building contractors; Single-family housing construction; Industrial buildings, new construction; Commercial & office building, new construction; Specialized public building contractors; Single-family housing construction
CEO: Jim Swanson
**Pr:* Daniel D Pierce
CFO: Misty Tonstad
Exec: Paul Oconnell

D-U-N-S 00-901-0984
KITCHELL CORP (AZ)
1707 E Highland Ave # 100, Phoenix, AZ 85016-4668
Tel (602) 264-4411 *Founded/Ownrshp* 1962
Sales 796.9MME *EMP* 946
Accts Mayer Hoffman Mccann Pc Ph
SIC 1542 1541 1521 8711 5078 6552 Commercial & office building, new construction; Specialized public building contractors; Industrial buildings, new construction; Single-family housing construction; Engineering services; Refrigeration equipment & supplies; Subdividers & developers; Commercial & office building, new construction; Specialized public building contractors; Industrial buildings, new construction; Single-family housing construction; Engineering services; Refrigeration equipment & supplies; Subdividers & developers
Pr: Jim Swanson
**Ch:* William C Schubert
Treas: Dick Crowley
**Treas:* William J Judge
**VP:* Jeffrey W Allen
**VP:* Russell A Fox
VP: James B Hoyne
**VP:* Mark J Pendelton
Genl Mgr: Tom Millman
QA Dir: Bill Vandrovec
Dir IT: Damon Stephens

D-U-N-S 13-356-6385
KITCHELL FLEET SERVICES INC
3752 E Anne St, Phoenix, AZ 85040-1818
Tel (602) 426-8109 *Founded/Ownrshp* 2003
Sales 9.0MME *EMP* 300
SIC 7538 General automotive repair shops; General automotive repair shops

KITCHEN AND BATH
See CARHART LUMBER CO

KITCHEN AND BATH GALLERY
See SUPPLY NEW ENGLAND INC

D-U-N-S 08-153-7912 IMP
■ **KITCHEN COLLECTION LLC**
LE GOURMET CHEF
(*Suby of* NACCO INDUSTRIES INC) ★
71 E Water St, Chillicothe, OH 45601-2577
Tel (740) 773-9150 *Founded/Ownrshp* 2011
Sales 920.3MME *EMP* 2,487
Accts Mcgladrey & Pullen
SIC 5719 Kitchenware; Kitchenware
CEO: Greg Trepp
Treas: L J Kennedy
VP: Joe Gawelek
VP: Roger Metzger
VP: Randy Sklenar
VP: Robert Strenski
Dir IT: Conrad Dana

KITCHEN FACTOR , THE
See EAST HAVEN BUILDERS SUPPLY - US LBM LLC

KITCHEN FRESH FOODS
See KF FOODS INC

D-U-N-S 01-719-1008
KITCHEN INVESTMENT GROUP INC
COUNTRY KITCHEN INTERNATIONAL
1289 Deming Way Ste 212, Madison, WI 53717-2097
Tel (608) 833-9633 *Founded/Ownrshp* 1994
Sales 5.0MM *EMP* 518
Accts Smith & Gesteland Llp
SIC 6794 8741 Franchises, selling or licensing; Restaurant management; Franchises, selling or licensing; Restaurant management
Pr: Charles M Myers
Site Mgr: Gillanne McGuiver

D-U-N-S 07-706-6017
KITCHEN KAPERS INC
K K DISTRIBUTORS
1250 Marlkress Rd, Cherry Hill, NJ 08003-2624
Tel (856) 424-3400 *Founded/Ownrshp* 1975
Sales 26.3MME *EMP* 150
SIC 5719 Housewares; Housewares
Pr: Robert Kratchman
Sec: Pearl Kratchman
VP: Richard Kratchman
Sls Mgr: Pete Murray

D-U-N-S 00-637-4813
KITCHEN KOMPACT INC
911 E 11th St, Jeffersonville, IN 47130-4172
Tel (812) 282-6681 *Founded/Ownrshp* 1937
Sales 42.5MME *EMP* 200
SIC 2434 Wood kitchen cabinets; Vanities, bathroom: wood; Wood kitchen cabinets; Vanities, bathroom: wood
Ch Bd: Walter Dwight Gahm
**Pr:* Walter Dwight Gahm Jr
**Treas:* Gordon Gahm
**VP:* Robert G Wilson
Exec: John Gahm
Sls Mgr: David R Duke

KITCHEN MAGIC
See GREENELL CORP

D-U-N-S 78-475-1067
■ **KITCHENAID INC**
(*Suby of* MAYTAG APPLIANCES) ★
101 E Maple St, Canton, OH 44720
Tel (330) 499-9200 *Founded/Ownrshp* 1989
Sales 570.7MME *EMP* 16,700E
SIC 5064 Electric household appliances; Electric household appliances
Ch Bd: Leonard A Hadley
VP: R J Elsaesser
VP: Gregory Puplin
VP Sls: Marty Armstrong

KITCHENS & BATHS
See DALLAS PLUMBING CO

D-U-N-S 00-817-0995 IMP/EXP
KITCHENS BROTHERS MANUFACTURING CO
4854 Reed Town Rd, Utica, MS 39175
Tel (601) 885-6001 *Founded/Ownrshp* 1946
Sales 35.3MM^E *EMP* 250
SIC 2421 Furniture dimension stock, softwood; Furniture dimension stock, softwood
Pr: D Greg Kitchens
Sls Mgr: John Clark

KITCHEN'S SEAFOOD
See TAMPA BAY FISHERIES INC

KITCO DEFENSE
See KITCO INC

D-U-N-S 05-242-3506
KITCO INC
KITCO DEFENSE
1625 N 1100 W, Springville, UT 84663-3184
Tel (801) 489-2000 *Founded/Ownrshp* 1970
Sales 33.0MM^E *EMP* 50
SIC 5088 3724 Aircraft engines & engine parts; Aircraft engines & engine parts
CEO: Greg Beason
**Pr:* Richard L Ballantyne
**Treas:* Dennis R Larsen
VP: Jim Prewitt
Mfg Mgr: Carl James
Opers Mgr: Harry Smith
Mktg Dir: Doug Newcomb

D-U-N-S 05-847-9072
KITE INC
3745 N Kitley Ave, Indianapolis, IN 46226-5633
Tel (317) 591-7741 *Founded/Ownrshp* 1972
Sales 16.7MM^E *EMP* 430
SIC 1742 1721 1799 Drywall; Acoustical & ceiling work; Plastering, plain or ornamental; Commercial painting; Sandblasting of building exteriors; Fireproofing buildings; Drywall; Acoustical & ceiling work; Plastering, plain or ornamental; Commercial painting; Sandblasting of building exteriors; Fireproofing buildings
Ch: Alvin E Kite Jr
**Pr:* John A Kite
**Sec:* Daniel Sink
Trst: Darell E Zink Jr
**VP:* Mark Bryant
**VP:* Pete Kupperbusch
**VP:* John Schelling

D-U-N-S 82-756-3631
KITE REALTY GROUP TRUST
30 S Meridian St Ste 1100, Indianapolis, IN 46204-3565
Tel (317) 577-5600 *Founded/Ownrshp* 2004
Sales 259.5MM *EMP* 141^E
SIC 6798 Real estate investment trusts; Real estate investment trusts
Ch Bd: John A Kite
Pr: Thomas K McGowan
CFO: Daniel R Sink
CFO: Michael L Smith
Ex VP: Scott E Murray
VP: Brad Bisser
VP: Mitch Rippe
VP: Jason P Samreny
VP: Jeff Schroeder
Exec: Adam Chavers
Off Mgr: Kim Holland
Board of Directors: William E Bindley, Victor J Coleman, Lee A Daniels, Gerald W Grupe, Christie B Kelly, David R O'reilly, Barton R Peterson, Charles H Wurtzebach

KITIHARA PONTIAC, BUICK, GMC
See KITAHARA PONTIAC GMC BUICK INC

D-U-N-S 00-895-7664
KITSAP BANK (WA)
OLYMPIC BANK
619 Bay St, Port Orchard, WA 98366-5307
Tel (360) 876-7800 *Founded/Ownrshp* 1908
Sales NA *EMP* 220
SIC 6022 6021 State trust companies accepting deposits, commercial; National commercial banks; State trust companies accepting deposits, commercial; National commercial banks
Pr: James E Carmichael
CFO: Anthony M George
Ofcr: Steve Maxwell
Ex VP: Steve Politakis
Sr VP: Shannon Childs
Sr VP: Larry Krueger
Sr VP: Linda Smith
Sr VP: Joyce Taylor
VP: Jerry Christensen
VP: Dave Jeffco
Opers Mgr: Valerie Borland

D-U-N-S 80-385-7184
KITSAP COUNTY PUBLIC TRANSPORTATION BENEFIT AREA AUTHORITY
KITSAP TRANSIT
60 Washington Ave Ste 200, Bremerton, WA 98337-1888
Tel (360) 479-6962 *Founded/Ownrshp* 1982
Sales 26.3MM^E *EMP* 450
Accts Brian Sonntag Cgfm
SIC 4111 Bus line operations; Bus line operations
Ex Dir: Richard Hayes
**Ex Dir:* John Clauson
IT Man: Donald Orton
IT Man: Scott Rider

D-U-N-S 08-336-2871
KITSAP CREDIT UNION
155 Washington Ave, Bremerton, WA 98337-5606
Tel (360) 662-2000 *Founded/Ownrshp* 1934
Sales NA *EMP* 275
SIC 6061 Federal credit unions; Federal credit unions
CEO: Elliott Gregg
**CFO:* Scott Henderson
Treas: Terry Thomas
Ofcr: Dawn Martin
**Sr VP:* Colin Morrison
VP: Jeanette Hughes
VP: Dave Willis
Brnch Mgr: Randy Guidinger
Brnch Mgr: Wanda Norman
Dir IT: Jay Bell
IT Man: Timothy Jones

D-U-N-S 02-131-2129
KITSAP MENTAL HEALTH SERVICES
5455 Almira Dr Ne, Bremerton, WA 98311-8331
Tel (360) 373-5031 *Founded/Ownrshp* 1978
Sales 25.3MM *EMP* 300
Accts Ball And Treger Llp Bremerto
SIC 8093 8361 Mental health clinic, outpatient; Home for the mentally handicapped; Mental health clinic, outpatient; Home for the mentally handicapped
Ex Dir: Joe Roszak
VP: Donna Poole
Assoc Dir: Elena Argomaniz
Assoc Dir: Beth Darner
VP Mktg: Glen Johnson
Psych: Lisa Cruz
Orthpdst: Larry Keller
Nrsg Dir: Jennifer Drake
Snr Mgr: Stacey Devenney

KITSAP TRANSIT
See KITSAP COUNTY PUBLIC TRANSPORTATION BENEFIT AREA AUTHORITY

KITSON MEN ON ROBERTSON
See A-LIST INC

D-U-N-S 00-101-3069
KITTATINNY BOARD OF EDUCATION (NJ)
KITTATINNY REGIONAL SCHOOL DIS
77 Halsey Rd, Newton, NJ 07860-7046
Tel (973) 383-1800 *Founded/Ownrshp* 1972, 1976
Sales 23.0MM *EMP* 219
Accts Dickinson Vrabel & Cassells
SIC 8211 8748 Public elementary & secondary schools; School board; Business consulting; Public elementary & secondary schools; School board; Business consulting
Admn Mgr: Susan Kappler

KITTATINNY REGIONAL SCHOOL DIS
See KITTATINNY BOARD OF EDUCATION

KITTAY HOUSE
See JEWISH HOME AND HOSPITAL

D-U-N-S 19-483-5088
KITTELSON & ASSOCIATES INC
610 Sw Alder St Ste 700, Portland, OR 97205-3608
Tel (503) 228-5230 *Founded/Ownrshp* 1985
Sales 33.4MM^E *EMP* 168
SIC 8711 7375 Consulting engineer; Information retrieval services; Consulting engineer; Information retrieval services
CEO: Mark Vandehey
**Pr:* Mark A Vandehey
**CFO:* Larry Van Dyke
Bd of Dir: Ivan Mutabazi
VP: Thuha Lyew
Genl Mgr: Dave Mills
Plng Mgr: Matt Hughart
Plng Mgr: Kamala Parks
Off Admin: Geni Butterfield
Off Admin: Jackie Olsommer
CIO: Paul White

KITTERY TRADING POST
See KEVIN INC

D-U-N-S 04-019-0621
KITTITAS COUNTY PUBLIC HOSPITAL DISTRICT NO 1
KITTITAS VALLEY HEALTHCARE
603 S Chestnut St, Ellensburg, WA 98926-3875
Tel (509) 933-7593 *Founded/Ownrshp* 1964
Sales 68.7MM *EMP* 420
Accts Dingus Zarecor & Associates P
SIC 8062 General medical & surgical hospitals; General medical & surgical hospitals
CEO: Paul Nurick
COO: Catherine Bambrick
**CFO:* Libby Allgood
Bd of Dir: Brian Cullinane
Bd of Dir: Mary Seubert
VP: Joan Glover
Dir Lab: Debbie Sonntag
Brnch Mgr: Terry Clark
CIO: James Roberts
Mtls Mgr: Patty Doolin
Pharmcst: Michael Porter

KITTITAS VALLEY HEALTHCARE
See KITTITAS COUNTY PUBLIC HOSPITAL DISTRICT NO 1

D-U-N-S 01-642-2016 IMP
KITTLES HOME FURNISHINGS CENTER INC
ETHAN ALLEN GALLERY
8600 Allisonville Rd, Indianapolis, IN 46250-1583
Tel (317) 849-5300 *Founded/Ownrshp* 1969
Sales 179.3MM^E *EMP* 750
SIC 5712 5719 Furniture stores; Bedding & bedsprings; Lighting, lamps & accessories; Pictures & mirrors; Furniture stores; Bedding & bedsprings; Lighting, lamps & accessories; Pictures & mirrors
Ch Bd: James L Kittle Jr
**Pr:* John F Durkott
**CEO:* Eric Easter
CFO: Lisa Hudak
Off Mgr: Eve Teeters
Dir IT: Thomas Wirt
Site Mgr: Brian Helmerick
Sales Exec: Beth Eckert
Sls Mgr: Jason Craft
Sls Mgr: Honor Lothamer
Sls Mgr: Mike Schmersal

D-U-N-S 18-648-5579
KITTREDGE AND ASSOCIATES INC
63 Grand Ave Ste 220, River Edge, NJ 07661-1930
Tel (201) 342-8300 *Founded/Ownrshp* 1978
Sales 50.0MM *EMP* 20
SIC 5139 5136 5137 Footwear, athletic; Caps, men's & boys'; Men's & boys' outerwear; Women's & children's outerwear; Footwear, athletic; Caps, men's & boys'; Men's & boys' outerwear; Women's & children's outerwear
Pr: Brian Kittredge
CFO: Cathy Kittredge
**VP:* Bill Kittredge
Comm Dir: Brian Way
Off Mgr: Allyson Watson
Counsel: Scott Hosey

D-U-N-S 01-964-3345
KITTREDGE EQUIPMENT CO INC (MA)
100 Bowles Rd, Agawam, MA 01001-2901
Tel (413) 788-6101 *Founded/Ownrshp* 1934, 1962
Sales 38.5MM^E *EMP* 66^E
Accts Meyers Brothers Kalicka Pc
SIC 5046 Restaurant equipment & supplies; Hotel equipment & supplies; Restaurant equipment & supplies; Hotel equipment & supplies
Pr: Wendy Webber
**COO:* James Scott
**CFO:* Kevin J Campion
**Ex VP:* Arthur Grodd
**VP:* Jeff Mackey
Genl Mgr: Bob Beattie

D-U-N-S 09-253-1409 IMP/EXP
KITTRICH CORP
1585 W Mission Blvd, Pomona, CA 91766-1233
Tel (714) 736-1000 *Founded/Ownrshp* 1978
Sales 172.4MM^E *EMP* 500
SIC 2591 2392 2381 Blinds vertical; Household furnishings; Fabric dress & work gloves; Blinds vertical; Household furnishings; Fabric dress & work gloves
CEO: Robert Friedland
Pr: Robert Silverman
CFO: Jesse Macias
VP: Kelly Gambina
VP: Tony Zazzu
Exec: Lynette Jennings
Mng Ofcr: Marissa Delasalas
MIS Dir: Walter Kampschuur
Sfty Mgr: James Briscoe
Opers Mgr: Richard Hoehn
Sales Exec: Lazara Morales

D-U-N-S 08-074-5813
KITTY HAWK INC
1515 W 20th St, Dallas, TX 75261
Tel (214) 456-6000 *Founded/Ownrshp* 1994
Sales 45.5MM^E *EMP* 849
SIC 4731 4512 4215 Freight transportation arrangement; Air cargo carrier, scheduled; Package delivery, vehicular; Parcel delivery, vehicular; Freight transportation arrangement; Air cargo carrier, scheduled; Package delivery, vehicular; Parcel delivery, vehicular
Ch Bd: Melvin Keating
CFO: James R Kupferschmid
Treas: Jessica L Wilson
VP: Danny K Clifton
VP: Kim Wiemuth
Mng Dir: Donald A Premel
Mng Dir: Randy P Smith
CTO: Jessica Wilson
IT Man: Chris Manzo
Pr Dir: Erin Hitchcock
Mktg Dir: Mike Males
Board of Directors: Alan Howe, Bryant R Riley, Joseph D Ruffolo, Robert W Zoller Jr

KITTYHAWK MANOR APARTMENTS
See BURNAM HOLDING COMPANIES CO INC

KITV-TV
See HEARST STATIONS INC

D-U-N-S 13-754-3369 IMP/EXP
KITZ CORP OF AMERICA
(Suby of KITZ CORPORATION*)*
10750 Corporate Dr, Stafford, TX 77477-4008
Tel (281) 491-7333 *Founded/Ownrshp* 1984
Sales 85.0MM *EMP* 38
Accts Hein & Associates Llp Housto
SIC 5085 Valves & fittings; Valves & fittings
Pr: James Walther
**Ch:* Hirofumi Fujhara
VP: Darrell Lueckemeyer
Ex Dir: Hideki Ozawa
Div Mgr: Eric Olson
Genl Mgr: Doug Smith
Off Mgr: Cristina Rubio

D-U-N-S 07-930-8536
KIUC RENEWABLE SOLUTIONS TWO LLC
(Suby of KAUAI ISLAND UTILITY COOPERATIVE*)* ★
4463 Pahee St Ste 1, Lihue, HI 96766-2000
Tel (808) 246-4300 *Founded/Ownrshp* 2012
Sales 36.3MM^E *EMP* 150
SIC 4911 Electric services; Electric services

D-U-N-S 96-281-4786
KIVA ENERGY INC
(Suby of KAMPS PROPANE*)* ★
1262 Dupont Ct, Manteca, CA 95336-6003
Tel (209) 823-8924 *Founded/Ownrshp* 1996
Sales 26.5MM^E *EMP* 26
SIC 5171 Petroleum bulk stations
Pr: John Paul
**CEO:* Mark Harris
**VP:* Jack Penzes
**VP:* Jan Peterson
Opers Mgr: Dwight Frey

KIVA, KITCHEN AND BATH
See CHAMP INDUSTRIES INC

D-U-N-S 84-955-8569
KIVA MICROFUNDS
875 Howard St Ste 340, San Francisco, CA 94103-3027
Tel (415) 369-9414 *Founded/Ownrshp* 2005
Sales 20.7MM *EMP* 8
Accts Singerlewak Llp Los Angeles
SIC 8399 Fund raising organization, non-fee basis
Pr: Premal Shah
**CEO:* Matthew Flannery
Prgrm Mgr: Akash Trivedi

KIVA STONE APPLIANCES
See STONE APPLIANCES INC

D-U-N-S 15-292-1388
■ **KIVA SYSTEMS INC**
(Suby of AMAZON.COM INC*)* ★
300 Riverpark Dr, North Reading, MA 01864-2622
Tel (781) 221-4640 *Founded/Ownrshp* 2012
Sales 66.0MM^E *EMP* 105^E
SIC 7373 Computer integrated systems design; Computer integrated systems design
CEO: Michael Mountz
Pr: Amy Villeneuve
CFO: Keith Seidman
VP: Benge Ambrogi
VP: Bob Doucette
VP: Robert Doucette
VP: Joe Quinlivan
VP: Rob Stevens
VP: Kevin Willis
Prgrm Mgr: Pallavi Chaube
Prgrm Mgr: Gregory Mongeau
Board of Directors: Stephen Kaufman, Patrick J Scannell Jr

D-U-N-S 02-482-2355
KIVETT OIL CO (NC)
FAST PHILS
132 N Elm St Ste C, Statesville, NC 28677-5337
Tel (704) 872-3601 *Founded/Ownrshp* 1965, 1981
Sales 21.3MM *EMP* 90
Accts Norris Stewart & Ralston Pa
SIC 5411 5172 5983 Convenience stores, independent; Petroleum products; Fuel oil dealers; Convenience stores, independent; Petroleum products; Fuel oil dealers
Pr: Wayne K Martin
**VP:* Herbert Lawton
VP: Dick Raymer
Off Mgr: Annie Sanders

D-U-N-S 01-334-7729
KIVORT STEEL INC (NY)
380 Hudson River Rd, Waterford, NY 12188-1914
Tel (518) 590-7233 *Founded/Ownrshp* 1935, 1965
Sales 35.3MM^E *EMP* 26
SIC 5051 5211 5093 Steel; Lumber & other building materials; Ferrous metal scrap & waste
Ch Bd: Stanley Kivort
**Pr:* Robert Kivort
**Sec:* Josephine Kivort

D-U-N-S 83-320-8486
KIWI ENERGY NY LLC
240 Kent Ave, Brooklyn, NY 11249-4121
Tel (832) 397-6937 *Founded/Ownrshp* 2008
Sales 63.0MM *EMP* 30
SIC 4911 Electric services
Pr: Kitty Bromhead
Ex VP: Nikki Clark

D-U-N-S 03-137-6609
KIXEYE INC
333 Bush St Fl 19, San Francisco, CA 94104-2860
Tel (415) 400-8280 *Founded/Ownrshp* 2008
Sales 29.8MM^E *EMP* 99^E
SIC 5092 Video games
CEO: Will Harbin
CFO: Hera Chen
Sr VP: Danielle Deibler
VP: Mark Braatz
VP: John Getze
VP: Neil Shepherd
Genl Mgr: Rade Stojsavljevic
Snr Sftwr: John Northwood
QA Dir: Che Bajandas
QA Dir: Andrew Bangel
QA Dir: Addison Bierman

D-U-N-S 05-958-7824 IMP
KIZAN INTERNATIONAL INC
LOUIS RAPHAEL
100 W Hill Dr, Brisbane, CA 94005-1213
Tel (415) 657-2241 *Founded/Ownrshp* 1972
Sales 67.4MM *EMP* 98
Accts Pricewaterhousecoopers Llp Sa
SIC 5136 Men's & boys' clothing; Men's & boys' clothing
CEO: Bill S Kim
**Pr:* Edward Srsic
**CFO:* Kathy Liu
**Treas:* Aaron E Kim
Ex VP: John Berg
VP: Joe Koontz
Exec: Cheryl Wilson
IT Man: Steven Lock
IT Man: Peter Ong

D-U-N-S 60-449-1480 IMP
KJB SUPPLY CO INC
BIG D FLOORCOVERING SUPPLIES
2802 W Virginia Ave, Phoenix, AZ 85009-1716
Tel (602) 442-2200 *Founded/Ownrshp* 1989
Sales 24.4MM^E *EMP* 55
SIC 5023 Floor coverings
CEO: Stephen Kleinhans
**Sec:* Jeff Brugman
**VP:* Wade Jackson
Genl Mgr: Scott Keniston
Store Mgr: Tom Puchta
Mktg Dir: Steve Clinkingbeard
Sls Dir: Raul Mateus

D-U-N-S 07-835-8854
KJC AUTO TITLE LOAN CORP
8509 Western Hills Blvd # 100, Fort Worth, TX 76108-3410
Tel (915) 544-1109 *Founded/Ownrshp* 2009
Sales NA *EMP* 160^E
SIC 6141 Personal credit institutions
Prin: Clifton H Morris III

D-U-N-S 78-588-2085
KJC OPERATING CO
41100 Us Highway 395, Boron, CA 93516-2109
Tel (760) 762-5562 *Founded/Ownrshp* 2007
Sales 30.9MM^E *EMP* 117
SIC 4911 Electric services; Electric services

Ch: Chris Kelleher
**Pr:* Janet Doyle
**COO:* Scott Frier

D-U-N-S 04-483-6492
KJDE CORP
K J ELECTRIC
5894 E Molloy Rd, Syracuse, NY 13211-2108
Tel (315) 454-5535 *Founded/Ownrshp* 1981
Sales 56.7MM^E *EMP* 126
SIC 5063 7629 Motors, electric; Motor controls, starters & relays: electric; Transformers, electric; Electrical repair shops; Motors, electric; Motor controls, starters & relays: electric; Transformers, electric; Electrical repair shops
Ch Bd: Ken Jacobs
**VP:* Jeff Lawrence
**VP:* Benjamin Nordmark
IT Man: Pam Guyder
IT Man: John Mulligan
Opers Mgr: John Piedmonte
Mktg Dir: Bill Flowers
Sales Asso: Mike Digiacomo
Sales Asso: Elizabeth Kosarovich
Sales Asso: Chuck McCarthy
Sales Asso: John Preston

D-U-N-S 00-979-7333
KJELLSTROM AND LEE INC
1607 Ownby Ln, Richmond, VA 23220-1318
Tel (804) 288-0082 *Founded/Ownrshp* 1999
Sales 100.0MM *EMP* 200^E
SIC 1541 1542 Industrial buildings, new construction; Renovation, remodeling & repairs: industrial buildings; Commercial & office building, new construction; Commercial & office buildings, renovation & repair; Industrial buildings, new construction; Renovation, remodeling & repairs: industrial buildings; Commercial & office building, new construction; Commercial & office buildings, renovation & repair
Pr: Peter S Alcorn
**Ch Bd:* Donald B Garber
**Sr VP:* H Fulton Sensabaugh
VP: Richard Britt
**VP:* Roger D Young
Exec: Rick Berrey
Exec: Ben Smyth
**Prin:* N David Kjellstrom
**Prin:* Harry G Lee
Snr PM: David Turner

D-U-N-S 14-440-9695
■ KJR 950 AM
OLDIES 95.7
(*Suby of* IHEARTMEDIA INC) ★
645 Elliott Ave W Ste 400, Seattle, WA 98119-3960
Tel (206) 285-2295 *Founded/Ownrshp* 2007
Sales 41.1MM^E *EMP* 125
SIC 4832 Radio broadcasting stations
Genl Mgr: Lynn O'Dele
VP: Jen O'Twomney
VP: Mark Thompson
Exec: Wendy Krumroy
Genl Mgr: Michele Grosenick
Pgrm Dir: Rich Moore
Snr Mgr: Anthony Mora

KJS GREETINGS/BURGOYNE
See K J S INDUSTRIES INC

D-U-N-S 06-324-8736
KJWW CORP
KJWW ENGINEERING CONSULTANTS
623 26th Ave, Rock Island, IL 61201-5263
Tel (309) 788-0673 *Founded/Ownrshp* 2003
Sales 69.1MM^E *EMP* 425
SIC 8711

KJWW ENGINEERING CONSULTANTS
See KJWW CORP

D-U-N-S 13-015-0113
KK ENTERPRISES INC
K & K
258 King George Rd Ste 4, Warren, NJ 07059-5179
Tel (908) 542-9401 *Founded/Ownrshp* 1976
Sales 64.1MM^E *EMP* 30
Accts Connolly & Company Pc Warr
SIC 5051 Pipe & tubing, steel; Iron or steel semifinished products; Pipe & tubing, steel; Iron or steel semifinished products
Pr: John Kapoor
**VP:* Neeru Kapoor

D-U-N-S 10-705-7861
KK FORD LP
KARL KLEMENT
2670 S Highway 287, Decatur, TX 76234-4301
Tel (940) 627-1101 *Founded/Ownrshp* 1999
Sales 35.0MM^E *EMP* 70
SIC 5511 Automobiles, new & used; Automobiles, new & used
Pr: Allen Mitchell

D-U-N-S 80-625-6132
▲ KKR & CO LP
9 W 57th St Ste 4200, New York, NY 10019-2707
Tel (212) 750-8300 *Founded/Ownrshp* 2007
Sales 1.1MMM *EMP* 1,209^E
Tkr Sym KKR *Exch* NYS
SIC 6282 6799 Investment advice; Manager of mutual funds, contract or fee basis; Venture capital companies; Investment advice; Manager of mutual funds, contract or fee basis; Venture capital companies
Ch Bd: Henry R Kravis
Genl Pt: KKR M LLC
Ch Bd: George R Roberts
CFO: Peter Liu
Ofcr: Todd A Fisher
Ofcr: Jessica Gold
Ex VP: Jeffrey Van Horn
VP: Sid Ballurkar
VP: Susan Murphy
VP: Neerav Nayyar
Dir Risk M: Jerry Sullivan

D-U-N-S 80-031-8599
■ KKR FINANCIAL HOLDINGS LLC
(*Suby of* KKR FUND HOLDINGS LP) ★
555 California St Fl 50, San Francisco, CA 94104-1701
Tel (415) 315-3620 *Founded/Ownrshp* 2014
Sales 211.7MM^E *EMP* 4^E
SIC 6798 6282 Mortgage investment trusts; Manager of mutual funds, contract or fee basis
Pr: William J Janetschek
**COO:* Jeffrey B Van Horn
CFO: Thomas N Murphy
VP: Jenny Farrelly

D-U-N-S 08-005-4916
■ KKR FUND HOLDINGS LP
(*Suby of* KKR & CO LP) ★
9 W 57th St Fl 41, New York, NY 10019-2701
Tel (212) 230-9742 *Founded/Ownrshp* 2014
Sales 211.7MM^E *EMP* 4^E
SIC 6798 Real estate investment trusts

D-U-N-S 82-632-9364
KKR MILLENNIUM GP LLC
9 W 57th St Ste 4150, New York, NY 10019-2701
Tel (212) 750-8300 *Founded/Ownrshp* 2001
Sales 160.4MM^E *EMP* 4,850
SIC 2515 Mattresses, innerspring or box spring; Mattresses, innerspring or box spring
Pr: Lawrence J Rogers

D-U-N-S 04-791-2928 IMP
KKSP PRECISION MACHINING LLC
1688 Glen Ellyn Rd, Glendale Heights, IL 60139-2504
Tel (630) 260-1735 *Founded/Ownrshp* 2009
Sales 60.0MM *EMP* 200
SIC 3451 Screw machine products; Screw machine products
CEO: Dave Dolan
CFO: Mark Murray
CFO: Mark Ollinger
Software D: George Semenov
VP Opers: Chris Hafke
Ql Cn Mgr: Phillip Yowell
Sales Exec: Barb De Larosa
Sales Exec: Tim Gibson

D-U-N-S 06-983-4349
KL MCCOY AND ASSOCIATES INC
13200 Levan Rd, Livonia, MI 48150-1256
Tel (734) 452-8230 *Founded/Ownrshp* 1920
Sales 52.6MM^E *EMP* 203
SIC 5075 5074 Warm air heating & air conditioning; Plumbing & hydronic heating supplies; Warm air heating & air conditioning; Plumbing & hydronic heating supplies
Pr: John Coy
**VP:* Michael Lowe
**VP:* Todd Mc Coy

D-U-N-S 01-690-3932
KLA LABORATORIES INC
6800 Chase Rd, Dearborn, MI 48126-1793
Tel (313) 846-3800 *Founded/Ownrshp* 1952
Sales 25.8MM *EMP* 140
Accts Plante & Moran Pllc Ann Arbo
SIC 8748 7373 Communications consulting; Communications consulting; Telecommunications consultant; Local area network (LAN) systems integrator
CEO: Matthew J Obryan
**CEO:* Norma L Obryan
**VP:* Thomas J Cataldo III

D-U-N-S 01-093-6193 IMP
▲ KLA-TENCOR CORP
1 Technology Dr, Milpitas, CA 95035-7916
Tel (408) 875-3000 *Founded/Ownrshp* 1975
Sales 2.8MMM *EMP* 5,820
Accts Pricewaterhousecoopers Llp Sa
Tkr Sym KLAC *Exch* NGS
SIC 3827 3825 7699 7629 Optical instruments & lenses; Optical test & inspection equipment; Semiconductor test equipment; Optical instrument repair; Electronic equipment repair; Optical instruments & lenses; Optical test & inspection equipment; Semiconductor test equipment; Optical instrument repair; Electronic equipment repair
Pr: Richard P Wallace
CFO: Bren D Higgins
CFO: Bren Higgins
Chf Mktg O: Brian Trafas
Ex VP: Bobby R Bell
Ex VP: Lance Glasser
Ex VP: Michael D Kirk
Ex VP: Brian M Martin
Ex VP: Neil Richardson
Ex VP: Arthur P Schnitzer
Ex VP: Bin-Ming B Tsai
Sr VP: Samuel A Harrell
Sr VP: Virendra A Kirloskar
VP: Frank Brienzo
VP: Jim Cordoba
VP: David Fisher
VP: John Greene
VP: Brian Haas
VP: Ahmad Khan
VP: Maureen L Lamb
VP: Mehdi Vaez-Iravani
Board of Directors: Edward W Barnholt, Robert T Bond, Robert M Calderoni, John T Dickson, Kevin J Kennedy, David C Wang

D-U-N-S 06-766-7055
KLAASMEYER CONSTRUCTION CO INC (AR)
35 Middle Rd, Conway, AR 72032-9017
Tel (501) 327-7860 *Founded/Ownrshp* 1972
Sales 25.3MM *EMP* 100
Accts Michelle M Phillips Cpa Pa
SIC 1623 Telephone & communication line construction; Telephone & communication line construction
Pr: Eugene Klaasmeyer
**Prin:* Jim Bartlett
**Prin:* Gary Fielder

KLABEN AUTO GROUP
See KLABEN FORD LINCOLN INC

D-U-N-S 04-874-2514
KLABEN FORD LINCOLN INC
KLABEN AUTO GROUP
1089 W Main St, Kent, OH 44240-2005
Tel (330) 673-3139 *Founded/Ownrshp* 1981
Sales 57.2MM^E *EMP* 145^E
SIC 5511 7515 5012 Automobiles, new & used; Pickups, new & used; Passenger car leasing; Automobiles & other motor vehicles; Automobiles, new & used; Pickups, new & used; Passenger car leasing; Automobiles & other motor vehicles
Pr: Albert Klaben
**VP:* Richard Klaben
Sales Exec: Tim Casto
Sls Mgr: Jim Bills

D-U-N-S 11-929-2746
KLABEN FORD LINCOLN OF WARREN INC
KLABEN'S CROWN FORD
3853 Youngstown Rd Se, Warren, OH 44484-2836
Tel (330) 369-4444 *Founded/Ownrshp* 1984
Sales 31.0MM *EMP* 49
SIC 5511 Automobiles, new & used; Automobiles, new & used
Pr: Albert Klaben
**Sec:* Vicki S Basista
**VP:* Michael G Klaben
Sls Mgr: James Valesky

KLABEN'S CROWN FORD
See KLABEN FORD LINCOLN OF WARREN INC

D-U-N-S 01-877-8795 IMP
KLAFFS INC
165 Water St, Norwalk, CT 06854-3738
Tel (203) 642-7000 *Founded/Ownrshp* 1934
Sales 36.9MM^E *EMP* 150
SIC 5719 5211 5722 5074 Lighting fixtures; Lamps & lamp shades; Cabinets, kitchen; Electric household appliances, major; Plumbing fittings & supplies; Lighting fixtures; Lamps & lamp shades; Cabinets, kitchen; Electric household appliances, major; Plumbing fittings & supplies
Ch Bd: Joseph K Passero
**Pr:* Mollie K Passero
**COO:* John Petito
**Sec:* Debbie K Katz

D-U-N-S 01-445-5760
KLAFTERS INC
CIGARETTE EXPRESS
216 N Beaver St, New Castle, PA 16101-2298
Tel (724) 856-3249 *Founded/Ownrshp* 1963
Sales 32.9MM *EMP* 106
Accts Philip Weiner And Company Ltd
SIC 5993 5194 5145 Tobacco stores & stands; Tobacco & tobacco products; Candy; Tobacco stores & stands; Tobacco & tobacco products; Candy; Chewing gum; Snack foods
VP: Lee Silverman
**Treas:* Randy D Silverman
**VP:* Judy Silverman

D-U-N-S 08-859-1177
KLAMATH COUNTY SCHOOL DISTRICT
10501 Washburn Way, Klamath Falls, OR 97603-8626
Tel (541) 883-5000 *Founded/Ownrshp* 1930
Sales 44.7MM^E *EMP* 872
SIC 8211 Public elementary school; Public junior high school; Public senior high school; Kindergarten; Public elementary school; Public junior high school; Public senior high school; Kindergarten
Psych: Erin Schuhmacher

D-U-N-S 03-080-4538
KLAMATH FALLS CITY SCHOOLS
1336 Avalon St, Klamath Falls, OR 97603-4423
Tel (541) 883-4700 *Founded/Ownrshp* 1919
Sales 29.5MM^E *EMP* 650
SIC 8211 Public elementary school; Public senior high school; Public junior high school; Public elementary school; Public senior high school; Public junior high school
Dir Sec: Shawn Fern
Teacher Pr: Bill Feusahrens

D-U-N-S 80-813-1262
KLAMATH FALLS INTERCOMMUNITY HOSPITAL AUTHORITY
SKYLAKES MEDICAL CENTER
2865 Daggett Ave, Klamath Falls, OR 97601-1106
Tel (541) 883-6150 *Founded/Ownrshp* 1967
Sales NA *EMP* 9
SIC 6162 Bond & mortgage companies; Bond & mortgage companies
Pr: Paul Stewart
**VP:* Joe Chamberland
**VP:* Leslie Flick
**VP:* Sarah Whities
**VP:* Don York
Anesthlgy: Charles T Gonsowski
Anesthlgy: Vincent D Herr
Anesthlgy: Stefan J Jodko
Anesthlgy: Todd J Kirschenmann
Anesthlgy: John R Pattee
Anesthlgy: Eric B Swetland

D-U-N-S 00-947-7902
KLAMATH PUBLISHING CO
HERALD & NEWS
(*Suby of* PIONEER NEWSPAPERS INC)
2701 Foothills Blvd, Klamath Falls, OR 97603-3785
Tel (541) 885-4410 *Founded/Ownrshp* 1988
Sales 39.3MM^E *EMP* 785
SIC 2711 Commercial printing & newspaper publishing combined; Commercial printing & newspaper publishing combined
Pr: David Lord
**Sec:* De Lancey Lewis
Advt Dir: Kendal Daiger
Sls Mgr: Lamont Debarbieri

D-U-N-S 02-141-1467
KLARQUIST SPARKMAN LLP
121 Sw Salmon St Ste 1600, Portland, OR 97204-2988
Tel (503) 595-5300 *Founded/Ownrshp* 1941
Sales 25.5MM^E *EMP* 145
SIC 8111 General practice attorney, lawyer; Patent solicitor; General practice attorney, lawyer; Patent solicitor
Mng Pt: Patrick M Bible
Sr Pt: James Leigh
Pt: Karri Kuenzli Bradley
Pt: Lisa Caldwell
Pt: James Geringer
Pt: Joseph Jakubek
Pt: Michael D Jones
Pt: Ramon Klitzke II
Pt: William Noonan MD
Pt: David Petersen
Pt: Richard Polley
Pt: Robert Scotti
Pt: Stacey Slater
Pt: Donald Stephens Jr
Pt: John Stuart
Pt: John Vandenberg
Pt: Arthur Whinston
Pt: Stephen Wight
Pt: Garth Winn

D-U-N-S 09-399-6692
KLASSEN DEVELOPMENT INC
2021 Westwind Dr, Bakersfield, CA 93301-3015
Tel (661) 327-0875 *Founded/Ownrshp* 1977
Sales 30.5MM^E *EMP* 70^E
SIC 1542 Commercial & office building contractors
Pr: Jerry D Klassen
COO: Bob Klassen
CFO: Troy Fringer
VP: Robert Blair
**VP:* Ed Childres
**VP:* Mark Delmarter
Exec: Jayson Bryan
Dir Bus: Robbie Smith
Sys Mgr: Luis Alvarez
VP Opers: Rod Paine
Snr PM: Ryan Inglehart

D-U-N-S 00-514-5081
KLAUER MANUFACTURING CO INC (IA)
1185 Roosevelt St Ext, Dubuque, IA 52001-1477
Tel (563) 582-7201 *Founded/Ownrshp* 1870
Sales 40.8MM^E *EMP* 180
SIC 3444 Siding, sheet metal; Gutters, sheet metal; Downspouts, sheet metal; Ventilators, sheet metal; Siding, sheet metal; Gutters, sheet metal; Downspouts, sheet metal; Ventilators, sheet metal
Pr: William R Klauer
**COO:* Michael Igo
**CFO:* Michael Klauer
**VP:* James F Klauer
**VP:* Robert E Klauer

D-U-N-S 09-615-5098 IMP
KLAUSSNER CORP (NC)
KLAUSSNER HOME FURNISHINGS
405 Lewallen Rd, Asheboro, NC 27205-6111
Tel (888) 732-5948 *Founded/Ownrshp* 1979
Sales 491.6MM^E *EMP* 2,100
SIC 2512 Upholstered household furniture; Upholstered household furniture
Ch Bd: Hans Klaussner
CFO: David O Bryant
Sec: Scott Kauffman
Ex VP: J B Davis
VP: Darren York
VP Mfg: Rick Kite

D-U-N-S 00-347-1463 IMP/EXP
KLAUSSNER FURNITURE INDUSTRIES INC (NC)
KLAUSSNER HOME FURNISHINGS
(*Suby of* KLAUSSNER CORP) ★
405 Lewallen Rd, Asheboro, NC 27205-6111
Tel (336) 625-6174 *Founded/Ownrshp* 1964, 2013
Sales 287.9MM^E *EMP* 1,200^E
SIC 2512 Upholstered household furniture; Upholstered household furniture
CEO: Bill Wittenberg
**Pr:* Claud William Wittenber
**CFO:* David O Bryant
**Treas:* Scott Kauffman
VP: Chuck Welch
VP Merchng: Bruce Sinning

KLAUSSNER HOME FURNISHINGS
See KLAUSSNER FURNITURE INDUSTRIES INC

KLAUSSNER HOME FURNISHINGS
See KLAUSSNER CORP

D-U-N-S 15-691-3998
KLB CONSTRUCTION INC
3405 121st St Sw, Lynnwood, WA 98087-1549
Tel (425) 355-7335 *Founded/Ownrshp* 1984
Sales 94.5MM^E *EMP* 250
SIC 1623 1611 General contractor, highway & street construction; Underground utilities contractor; Underground utilities contractor; General contractor, highway & street construction
Pr: Kelly Bosa
**CFO:* Corey Christenson

KLBJ-AM
See EMMIS AUSTIN RADIO BROADCASTING CO LP

D-U-N-S 88-385-3459
KLC HOLDINGS LTD
QUICK LOK
2712 S 16th Ave, Yakima, WA 98903-9530
Tel (509) 248-4770 *Founded/Ownrshp* 1989
Sales 32.5MM^E *EMP* 250^E
SIC 3556 3565 Closures, plastic; Plastics working machinery; Food products machinery; Packaging machinery
Pr: John K Rothenbueler
**Pr:* Lorne House
**Pr:* Jerre Paxton
**Treas:* Hal Miller

KLDC
See KENTUCKY LABORERS DISTRICT COUNCIL

KLEAN-STRIP
See WM BARR & CO INC

D-U-N-S 79-692-8567
KLEBERG AND CO BANKERS INC
100 E Kleberg Ave, Kingsville, TX 78363-4581
Tel (361) 592-8501 *Founded/Ownrshp* 1979
Sales NA *EMP* 109ᴱ
SIC 6712 Bank holding companies; Bank holding companies
Ch Bd: Stewart L Armstrong
CFO: Fred Wollmann
**Treas:* Velma Delgado
Ofcr: Frank Benvenuto
Ofcr: Gina Ulisse
Ex VP: Chad Stary
Sr VP: Chip Collins
VP: Wilma Allen
VP: George Livas
Off Mgr: Liza Benitez
Off Mgr: Susan Geissel

KLEBERG BANK, N.A.
See KLEBERG BANK NATIONAL ASSOCIATION

D-U-N-S 00-793-3500
KLEBERG BANK NATIONAL ASSOCIATION
KLEBERG BANK, N.A.
(*Suby of* KLEBERG AND CO BANKERS INC) ★
100 E Kleberg Ave, Kingsville, TX 78363-4581
Tel (361) 592-8501 *Founded/Ownrshp* 2013
Sales NA *EMP* 109
SIC 6021 6163 National commercial banks; Loan brokers; National commercial banks; Loan brokers
Pr: Joe Henkle
Pr: Gaurav Sethi
CFO: Albert Jordan
**CFO:* Sharon Michalk
**Ch:* Stewart Armstrong
Ofcr: Liz Garcia
Ofcr: Hanes Segler
Ex VP: Bill Cone
Sr VP: Pete Mitchell
Sr VP: Frank Urbanek
VP: Louann Arangio
VP: Kerry Barnes
VP: Debbie Dodson
VP: Connie Gallardo
VP: Joe Gutierrez
VP: Janice Lawrence
VP: John McColgan
VP: Sylvia Olivarez
VP: Lynda Richter

D-U-N-S 05-160-1631
KLEEBERG SHEET METAL INC
65 Westover Rd, Ludlow, MA 01056-1298
Tel (413) 589-1854 *Founded/Ownrshp* 1969
Sales 40.9MMᴱ *EMP* 100
Accts Meyers Brothers Kalicka Pc H
SIC 3444 1711 Sheet metalwork; Plumbing, heating, air-conditioning contractors; Sheet metalwork; Plumbing, heating, air-conditioning contractors
Pr: Dan Kleeberg
VP: Ed Buckley
**VP:* Todd Davis
Exec: Scott Demers
Exec: Maureen Sullivan
Genl Mgr: Scott Cushman
Off Mgr: Mike Denis
Mktg Mgr: Maureen Kelly

KLEEN BLAST
See CANAM MINERALS INC

D-U-N-S 05-291-4595
KLEEN RITE CORP (PA)
257 S 9th St, Columbia, PA 17512-1505
Tel (717) 684-6721 *Founded/Ownrshp* 1969
Sales 23.2MMᴱ *EMP* 30ᴱ
SIC 5087 Carwash equipment & supplies
Pr: Michael L McKonly
**Sec:* Keith Lutz

D-U-N-S 16-816-5814 IMP/EXP
KLEEN TEST PRODUCTS CORP
K T P
(*Suby of* MERIDIAN INDUSTRIES INC) ★
1611 S Sunset Rd, Port Washington, WI 53074-9673
Tel (262) 284-6600 *Founded/Ownrshp* 1943
Sales 129.7MMᴱ *EMP* 500ᴱ
SIC 2842 2675 Cleaning or polishing preparations; Paper die-cutting; Cleaning or polishing preparations; Paper die-cutting
Pr: Bill Ahlborn
Admn Mgr: Nicole Kenehan
IT Man: Foga Zellermayer
Plnt Mgr: Rob Hercreg
Plnt Mgr: Ed Kosobucki
Prd Mgr: Patrick Bichler
Natl Sales: Robert Boyer
Natl Sales: Daniel Thomas

KLEEN-IT SERVICE CO
See EASTERN JANITORIAL SERVICES INC

D-U-N-S 82-468-4864
KLEEN-TECH SERVICES CORP
(*Suby of* HB MANAGEMENT GROUP INC) ★
7100 Broadway Ste 6I, Denver, CO 80221-2925
Tel (303) 468-6313 *Founded/Ownrshp* 1993
Sales 29.8MMᴱ *EMP* 950
SIC 7349 Janitorial service, contract basis; Janitorial service, contract basis
Pr: Brad Brandt
**Ch Bd:* Kathy Hughes
**COO:* Patrick Hughes

D-U-N-S 05-104-3313 EXP
KLEEN-TEX INDUSTRIES INC
101 N Greenwood St Ste C, Lagrange, GA 30240-2632
Tel (706) 882-0111 *Founded/Ownrshp* 1967
Sales 83.5MMᴱ *EMP* 550
SIC 3069 2273 2392 Sheeting, rubber or rubberized fabric; Mats & matting; Mops, floor & dust; Sheeting, rubber or rubberized fabric; Mats & matting; Mops, floor & dust
CEO: Bruce Howard
**Sr VP:* Duncan Allen
Sls Mgr: Lee Fox

D-U-N-S 05-577-2172
KLEENCO CORP
3015 Koapaka St Ste A, Honolulu, HI 96819-1936
Tel (808) 831-7600 *Founded/Ownrshp* 1990
Sales 9.2MMᴱ *EMP* 350
SIC 7349 Janitorial service, contract basis; Janitorial service, contract basis
Pr: Danny C Perry
**Pr:* Paul Scott B
**COO:* Reeves Michael
**VP:* Miller Diane
Admn Mgr: Diane Miller

D-U-N-S 61-670-3059
KLEENCO MAINTENANCE & CONSTRUCTION INC
8239 N State Road 9, Alexandria, IN 46001-8649
Tel (765) 724-3554 *Founded/Ownrshp* 1998
Sales 24.7MMᴱ *EMP* 180
SIC 7349 Building maintenance services
Pr: Kurt Tatman
**VP:* Donald Vanhooser
Div Mgr: Tony Thompson
Sls Mgr: Todd Stone

D-U-N-S 02-046-4210
KLEENMARK SERVICES CORP (WI)
1210 Ann St, Madison, WI 53713-2410
Tel (608) 258-3131 *Founded/Ownrshp* 1961, 2000
Sales 24.0MMᴱ *EMP* 600ᴱ
SIC 7349 Janitorial service, contract basis; Janitorial service, contract basis
Pr: Scott Stevenson
COO: Tim Waldsmith
**Treas:* John W Stevenson
**Ex VP:* Thomas Fischer
S&M/VP: Susan Enlow
Mktg Mgr: Josh Haroldson
Manager: Kevin Odle

D-U-N-S 06-806-3528 EXP
KLEER-FAX INC
750 New Horizons Blvd, Amityville, NY 11701-1191
Tel (631) 225-1100 *Founded/Ownrshp* 1973
Sales 24.4MMᴱ *EMP* 97
SIC 2678 2677 3089 5943 2675 Stationery products; Envelopes; Extruded finished plastic products; Office forms & supplies; Die-cut paper & board
Pr: Louis Nigro
**CEO:* Elias Cruz
IT Man: Christopher Pascale
Sfty Mgr: Dan Smith
Opers Mgr: Larry Campbell

D-U-N-S 01-275-3299
KLEET LUMBER CO INC
777 Park Ave, Huntington, NY 11743-3993
Tel (631) 427-7060 *Founded/Ownrshp* 1946
Sales 99.6MMᴱ *EMP* 89
SIC 5031 Lumber, plywood & millwork; Lumber, plywood & millwork
Pr: Howard Kleet
Pr: Gene Wolff
**Treas:* Warren Kleet
**VP:* Linda Nussbaum
Store Mgr: Ray Nurnberger
IT Man: William Shultz
Opers Mgr: Butch Diantonio
Sales Asso: Christine Dugan
Sales Asso: Louis Kleet
Sales Asso: Glenn Landberg
Sales Asso: Tom Legere

D-U-N-S 08-186-9943
KLEHR HARRISON HARVEY BRANZBURG LLP
1835 Market St Ste 1400, Philadelphia, PA 19103-2945
Tel (215) 568-6060 *Founded/Ownrshp* 1985
Sales 23.6MMᴱ *EMP* 200
SIC 8111 General practice attorney, lawyer; General practice attorney, lawyer
Pt: Leonard M Klehr
Pt: Lawrence Arem
Pt: Stuart Askot
Pt: Morton R Branzburg
Pt: David L Braverman
Pt: Steven Burdumy
Pt: Edward S Ellers
Pt: Ronald L Glick
Pt: William A Harvey
Pt: William T Hill
Pt: Rosetta B Packer
Pt: Richard S Roisman
Pt: Alan M Rosen
Pt: Rona J Rosen
Pt: Robert C Seiger Jr
Pt: Joan R Sheak
Pt: John H Spelman

KLEIN DENATALE GOLDNER COOPER
See KLEIN DENATALE GOLDNER ET AL

D-U-N-S 09-514-0364
KLEIN DENATALE GOLDNER ET AL
KLEIN DENATALE GOLDNER COOPER
4550 California Ave Fl 2, Bakersfield, CA 93309-7012
Tel (661) 395-1000 *Founded/Ownrshp* 2007
Sales 24.6MMᴱ *EMP* 110ᴱ
SIC 8111 General practice law office
Pt: Anthony J Klein
Pt: Jennifer A Adams
Pt: Hagop T Bedoyan
Pt: David J Cooper
Pt: Thomas V Denatale Jr
Pt: Barry L Goldner
Pt: Jay L Rosenlieb
COO: Lisa Baldridge
Counsel: Bruce F Bunker

KLEIN FAMILY FARMS
See JACK KLEIN TRUST PARTNERSHIP

D-U-N-S 07-026-1300
KLEIN FINANCIAL INC
1550 Audubon Rd Ste 200, Chaska, MN 55318-4547
Tel (952) 448-2484 *Founded/Ownrshp* 1975
Sales NA *EMP* 559
SIC 6021 6022 6311 National commercial banks; State commercial banks; Life reinsurance; National commercial banks; State commercial banks; Life reinsurance
Pr: Daniel Klein
CFO: Roger Wichelman
**Ex VP:* Alan C Klein
**Ex VP:* James C Klein
**Sr VP:* Robert Perutka
**Sr VP:* Gerald Wenande
**VP:* Fred Whitney

D-U-N-S 60-795-1597 IMP
KLEIN FOODS INC
RODNEY STRONG VINEYARDS
11455 Old Redwood Hwy, Healdsburg, CA 95448-9523
Tel (707) 431-1533 *Founded/Ownrshp* 1988
Sales 25.6MMᴱ *EMP* 100
SIC 0172 2084 5182 Grapes; Wines; Wine & distilled beverages
Pr: Thomas B Klein
**CFO:* Tobin Ginter
Dist Mgr: Damien Correia
CTO: Jean Brennan

KLEIN HONDA
See STEVEN KLEIN INC

D-U-N-S 07-392-2270
KLEIN INDEPENDENT SCHOOL DISTRICT
KLEIN ISD
7200 Spring Cypress Rd, Spring, TX 77379-3215
Tel (832) 249-4000 *Founded/Ownrshp* 1988
Sales 474.0MM *EMP* 5,691
Accts Hereford Lynch Sellars & Kir
SIC 8211 Public elementary school; Public junior high school; Public senior high school; Public elementary school; Public junior high school; Public senior high school
Pr: Ronnie K Anderson
Ofcr: Susan Green
VP: Paul Lanham
VP: Lorraine R Pratt
VP: Steven Smith
Comm Man: Denise McLean
Dir Sec: David Kimberly
Dir IT: Judy Schwietzer
Dir IT: Candace Threadgill
IT Man: Amanda Boles
IT Man: Karen Fuller

KLEIN ISD
See KLEIN INDEPENDENT SCHOOL DISTRICT

KLEIN, JUDY
See KLEINS NATURALS LTD

D-U-N-S 04-777-9301 EXP
KLEIN PRODUCTS OF TEXAS INC
16576 Highway 79 E, Jacksonville, TX 75766
Tel (903) 589-4546 *Founded/Ownrshp* 2008
Sales 27.4MMᴱ *EMP* 45
SIC 3531 3443 Construction machinery; Tanks, lined: metal plate
Pr: Barry K McManus

D-U-N-S 15-149-0463 IMP
KLEIN STEEL SERVICE INC
105 Vanguard Pkwy, Rochester, NY 14606-3100
Tel (585) 328-4000 *Founded/Ownrshp* 1986
Sales 182.0MMᴱ *EMP* 211ᴱ
SIC 5051 Metals service centers & offices; Iron & steel (ferrous) products; Bars, metal; Aluminum bars, rods, ingots, sheets, pipes, plates, etc.; Metals service centers & offices; Iron & steel (ferrous) products; Bars, metal; Aluminum bars, rods, ingots, sheets, pipes, plates, etc.
Pr: Todd Zyra
**Owner:* Joseph Klein
CFO: Dave Feinstein
**CFO:* Michelle Westrich
Ofcr: Patrick Dilaura
Genl Mgr: Heather Pimm
IT Man: Jenell Cassano
Opers Supe: Stacy Dipasquale
Sfty Mgr: David Donaldson
Sls&Mrk Ex: Jane Elliot
VP Mktg: Laura Ribas

D-U-N-S 00-514-9141 IMP/EXP
KLEIN TOOLS INC
450 Bond St, Lincolnshire, IL 60069-4225
Tel (847) 821-5500 *Founded/Ownrshp* 1958
Sales 326.0MMᴱ *EMP* 1,000
SIC 3423 3199 Hand & edge tools; Belting for machinery: solid, twisted, flat, etc.: leather; Safety belts, leather; Hand & edge tools; Belting for machinery: solid, twisted, flat, etc.: leather; Safety belts, leather
Pr: Thomas R Klein Jr
**Pr:* Mark Klein
**CFO:* Verne Tuite
VP: James Finneman
VP: Ron Smetana
VP: Jim Van Hius
Dist Mgr: Jerred Henderson
Dist Mgr: Dan Pierce
Dist Mgr: Vince Waldvogel
Mfg Mgr: James Thompson
VP Mktg: Greg Palese

D-U-N-S 08-004-7836
KLEIN TOOLS INC
7200 Mccormick Blvd, Skokie, IL 60076-4038
Tel (847) 821-5500 *Founded/Ownrshp* 2015
Sales 9.4MMᴱ *EMP* 983
SIC 5072 Power tools & accessories; Hand tools
CEO: Richard T Klein Jr
**Pr:* Mat Klein III
**VP:* Thomas R Klein
**VP:* John F Phelan

D-U-N-S 00-381-9844
KLEIN-DICKERT CO INC (WI)
KD PAINT
1406 Emil St Ste B, Madison, WI 53713-2326
Tel (608) 258-3315 *Founded/Ownrshp* 1919, 1947
Sales 23.7MMᴱ *EMP* 120
SIC 1721 7699 Residential painting; Picture framing, custom
CEO: Francis X Dickert
**Pr:* M Susan Dickert
**CFO:* Amy Olson

D-U-N-S 06-801-7896
KLEIN/KAUFMAN CORP (NY)
MCDONALD'S
134 W Hills Rd, Huntington Station, NY 11746-3140
Tel (631) 271-8055 *Founded/Ownrshp* 1960, 1985
Sales 19.9MMᴱ *EMP* 900
SIC 5812 Fast-food restaurant, chain; Fast-food restaurant, chain
CEO: Irving Klein
**Pr:* Jonah Kauffman

D-U-N-S 08-780-9026
KLEINBANK
(*Suby of* KLEIN FINANCIAL INC) ★
19943 County Road 43 Nw, Big Lake, MN 55309-9158
Tel (763) 263-2100 *Founded/Ownrshp* 1925
Sales NA *EMP* 400
SIC 6036 6022 State savings banks, not federally chartered; State commercial banks; State savings banks, not federally chartered; State commercial banks
Pr: Mark Ethen
Pr: Charles Arndt
VP: Jim Jeffrey
VP: Chuck Peterson
VP: David Schwalbe
VP: Stephen Spears
VP: Fred Whitney
Exec: Greg Monson
VP Mktg: Kathy Gilkey

D-U-N-S 09-750-5044
KLEINBERG ELECTRIC INC
174 Hudson St Fl 2, New York, NY 10013-2161
Tel (212) 206-1140 *Founded/Ownrshp* 1979
Sales 24.8MMᴱ *EMP* 150
SIC 1731 General electrical contractor; General electrical contractor
Pr: Carol Kleinberg
**VP:* Paul Kleinberg

D-U-N-S 06-884-1576
KLEINER PERKINS CAUFIELD & BYERS LLC
KPCB
2750 Sand Hill Rd, Menlo Park, CA 94025-7020
Tel (650) 233-2750 *Founded/Ownrshp* 1984
Sales 60.9MMᴱ *EMP* 163
SIC 6799 3691 Venture capital companies; Storage batteries; Venture capital companies; Storage batteries
Pt: Frank Caufield
**Genl Pt:* John Doerr
**Genl Pt:* William Hearst III
**Genl Pt:* Tom Jermoluk
**Genl Pt:* Bill Joy
**Genl Pt:* Joseph Lacob
**Genl Pt:* Bernard Lacroute
**Genl Pt:* James Lally
**Genl Pt:* Raymond Lane
**Genl Pt:* Thomas J Perkins
**Genl Pt:* Ted Schlein
**Genl Pt:* Russell Siegelman
**Pt:* Mike Abbott
**Pt:* Mark Allen
**Pt:* Susan Biglieri
**Pt:* Ray Bradford
**Pt:* Brook Byers
Pt: Isaac Ciechanover
**Pt:* Juliet De Baubigny
**Pt:* Eugene Kleiner
**Pt:* Randy Komisar

D-U-N-S 18-295-9882
KLEINERT KUTZ AND ASSOCIATES HAND CARE CENTER PLLC
225 Abraham Flexner Way # 700, Louisville, KY 40202-3806
Tel (502) 561-4263 *Founded/Ownrshp* 1962
Sales 20.8MMᴱ *EMP* 200
SIC 8011 Physical medicine, physician/surgeon; Surgeon; Physical medicine, physician/surgeon; Surgeon
CFO: Rob Slawinski
**CFO:* Sharon Wall
Prac Mgr: Margie Stotts
Surgeon: Elkin Leon
Doctor: Rodrigo Banegas
Doctor: Warren Breidenbach
Doctor: Rodrigo Garcia MD
Doctor: Michelle Palazzo
Doctor: Moreno Rodrigo
**Doctor:* Luis Scheker MD

D-U-N-S 60-621-7524
KLEINFELDER ASSOCIATES
(*Suby of* KLEINFELDER GROUP INC) ★
550 W C St Ste 1200, San Diego, CA 92101-3532
Tel (619) 831-4600 *Founded/Ownrshp* 1985
Sales 51.0MMᴱ *EMP* 1,500
SIC 8748 Environmental consultant; Environmental consultant
CEO: William Siegel
**COO:* Bart Patton
**CFO:* John Pilkington
**Sr VP:* Larry Peterson
**VP:* Russ Carey
VP: Simon Wong
**CTO:* Russ Erbes
Board of Directors: Craig Vaughn, Rich Young

D-U-N-S 14-470-8682
KLEINFELDER GROUP INC
550 W C St Ste 1200, San Diego, CA 92101-3532
Tel (619) 831-4600 *Founded/Ownrshp* 1985
Sales 258.9MM *EMP* 1,522ᴱ
Accts Grant Thornton Llp San Diego
SIC 8711 Consulting engineer; Consulting engineer
Pr: William Siegel
Pr: Sharon Province
VP: Gary Higashi
VP: Carl D Lowman
VP: P E Ng
Dir Lab: Uly Panuncialman
Prgrm Mgr: Steven Carty

Prgrm Mgr: Paul Lucuski
Prgrm Mgr: Brent Neece
Rgnl Mgr: Joel G Carson
Rgnl Mgr: Richard McCain

D-U-N-S 04-600-7506
KLEINFELDER INC (CA)
(*Suby of* KLEINFELDER GROUP INC) ★
550 W C St Ste 1200, San Diego, CA 92101-3532
Tel (619) 831-4617 *Founded/Ownrshp* 1962, 1985
Sales 207.2MM *EMP* 200
SIC 8711 Consulting engineer; Consulting engineer
Pr: William C Siegel
**COO:* Michael P Kesler
**CFO:* John Holgrenn
CFO: Jon Holmgren
**CFO:* David Johnson
**Sr VP:* Russ Carey
**Sr VP:* Larry Peterson
**Sr VP:* Donald L Pomeroy
**VP:* Terry Reynolds
VP: James Schaefer
**Prin:* Bart Patton

D-U-N-S 01-105-8175
KLEINPARTNERS CAPITAL CORP
400 Continental Blvd # 600, El Segundo, CA 90245-5076
Tel (310) 426-2055 *Founded/Ownrshp* 2009
Sales 13.5MM^E *EMP* 405
SIC 6799 Investors; Investors
Pr: Edward McMahon
**Ch:* Greg Klein

D-U-N-S 03-418-3905
KLEINPETER FARMS DAIRY LLC
14444 Airline Hwy, Baton Rouge, LA 70817-6899
Tel (225) 753-2121 *Founded/Ownrshp* 2002
Sales 61.9MM^E *EMP* 210
SIC 2026 2024 Milk processing (pasteurizing, homogenizing, bottling); Ice cream & frozen desserts; Milk processing (pasteurizing, homogenizing, bottling); Ice cream & frozen desserts
VP: Stephen Kleinpeter
CIO: Sue Ann
Dir IT: Kris Braud
Sfty Dirs: Branden Bennett
Sfty Mgr: Bruce Boulton

D-U-N-S 78-999-4068 IMP
KLEINS NATURALS LTD
KLEIN, JUDY
4702 2nd Ave, Brooklyn, NY 11232-4219
Tel (718) 499-4299 *Founded/Ownrshp* 1992
Sales 33.4MM^E *EMP* 50
SIC 5159 5149 2068 Nuts & nut by-products; Fruits, dried; Salted & roasted nuts & seeds; Seeds: dried, dehydrated, salted or roasted
Pr: Judy Klein

KLEIN'S SUPERMARKET
See KLEINS TOWER PLAZA INC

D-U-N-S 02-258-8719
KLEINS TOWER PLAZA INC
KLEIN'S SUPERMARKET
(*Suby of* WAKEFERN FOOD CORP) ★
2011 Klein Plaza Dr 2c, Forest Hill, MD 21050-2603
Tel (410) 593-8000 *Founded/Ownrshp* 1948
Sales 26.2MM^E *EMP* 140
SIC 5411 Supermarkets, independent
Pr: Ralph L Klein
Sec: Shirley Klein
VP: Andrew P Klein
Dir Rx: Cindy Glos

D-U-N-S 00-609-3975 IMP
KLEMENT SAUSAGE CO INC (WI)
(*Suby of* BLUE RIBBON) ★
207 E Lincoln Ave, Milwaukee, WI 53207-1593
Tel (414) 744-2330 *Founded/Ownrshp* 1927, 2014
Sales 80.5MM^E *EMP* 355
SIC 2013 Sausages from purchased meat; Sausages from purchased meat
CEO: Ray Booth
**Pr:* George Lampros
**CFO:* Tom Klement
**Sec:* James W Gustafson
Ex VP: Jack Belke
VP: Steve Feye
VP: Dan Sotski
Rgnl Mgr: Don Treichel
Area Mgr: Don Gordon
Sfty Mgr: Dennis Rousseau
S&M/VP: Dan Lipke

KLEMM TANK LINES
See CARL KLEMM INC

D-U-N-S 83-127-8077
KLEO COMMUNITY FAMILY LIFE CENTER
119 E Garfield Blvd, Chicago, IL 60637-1008
Tel (773) 363-6941 *Founded/Ownrshp* 2008
Sales NA *EMP* 318
Accts Tax Accounting Headquarters I
SIC 9229 ;
CEO: Torrey L Barrett Sr
**Pr:* Brandon Johnson

D-U-N-S 08-918-0954
KLEPPE & NASH MORGAN
MKNI
600 W Acequia Ave, Visalia, CA 93291-6130
Tel (559) 732-3436 *Founded/Ownrshp* 1943
Sales NA *EMP* 58
SIC 6411 Insurance agents, brokers & service; Insurance agents, brokers & service
Pt: Keith Kleppe
Pt: Gerry Folmer
Off Admin: Stewart Crain

KLEVEN CONSTRUCTION
See JK COMMUNICATIONS & CONSTRUCTION INC

D-U-N-S 08-312-3542
KLEWIN BUILDING CO INC
40 Connecticut Ave Ste 1, Norwich, CT 06360-1565
Tel (860) 886-5545 *Founded/Ownrshp* 1982
Sales 26.2MM^E *EMP* 140
SIC 1541 1542 Industrial buildings, new construction; Renovation, remodeling & repairs: industrial buildings; Commercial & office building, new construction; Commercial & office buildings, renovation & repair; Hospital construction
Ch Bd: Charles Klewin
**Pr:* Michael D'Amato
Sr VP: Keith Kabeary

KLG
See KUECKER LOGISTICS GROUP INC

KLICK LEWIS MOTORS CO
See KLICK-LEWIS INC

D-U-N-S 01-490-8222
KLICK-LEWIS INC
KLICK LEWIS MOTORS CO
720 E Main St, Palmyra, PA 17078-1909
Tel (717) 838-7779 *Founded/Ownrshp* 1960
Sales 52.1MM *EMP* 85
SIC 5511 Automobiles, new & used; Automobiles, new & used
Pr: Warren L Lewis Jr
**Treas:* Steve Malaro
**VP:* Don Risser
Off Mgr: Sharon Brown
Sales Asso: Carl Deiner
Sales Asso: Jon Heberling
Sales Asso: Chris Nordai

D-U-N-S 08-662-0481
KLICKITAT COUNTY PUBLIC HOSPITAL DISTRICT 2
SKYLINE HOSPITAL
211 Ne Skyline Dr, White Salmon, WA 98672-1948
Tel (509) 493-1101 *Founded/Ownrshp* 1952
Sales 31.6MM^E *EMP* 129
SIC 8062 General medical & surgical hospitals; General medical & surgical hospitals
CEO: Robb Kimmes
Dir OR: Kathleen Funk
QA Dir: Beth Robison
Mktg Dir: Renee Warner
Surgeon: Gianna Scannell
Doctor: Chad Foster
Doctor: Forrest Hoffer
Nrsg Dir: Stehainie Boen

D-U-N-S 18-948-3027
KLIGER-WEISS INFOSYSTEMS INC
KWI
2200 Nthrn Blvd Ste 102, Greenvale, NY 11548
Tel (516) 621-2400 *Founded/Ownrshp* 1985
Sales 26.4MM^E *EMP* 110
SIC 7371 Custom computer programming services
CEO: Sam Kliger
**Pr:* Gary Brill
**Pr:* Stuart Levine
**CFO:* Robert Schildkraut
VP: James Barbas
**VP:* Daniel Markowitz
VP: Krishna Mukherjee
**VP:* Evan Rubin
Dir Bus: Chris Jannuzzi
CTO: Michael Ruvolo
Software D: Silvio Delpercio

KLIKLOK - WOODMAN
See KLIKWOOD CORP

D-U-N-S 00-325-7383 IMP/EXP
KLIKWOOD CORP (GA)
KLIKLOK - WOODMAN
5224 Snapfinger Woods Dr, Decatur, GA 30035-4023
Tel (770) 776-3120 *Founded/Ownrshp* 1948
Sales 66.4MM^E *EMP* 180
SIC 3565 Packaging machinery; Packaging machinery
CEO: William Crist
**Pr:* Peter Black
**CEO:* William L Crist
Ofcr: Kevin Hauck
VP: Alan Staples
Mtls Mgr: Bob Martin
S&M/VP: Ross Long
Manager: Michael Gilbertson

KLINE AUTOWORLD
See KLINE VOLVO INC

D-U-N-S 05-310-7512
KLINE CHEVROLET SALES CORP (VA)
PRIORITY CHEVROLET
1495 S Military Hwy, Chesapeake, VA 23320-2603
Tel (757) 424-1811 *Founded/Ownrshp* 1926, 1999
Sales 47.4MM^E *EMP* 130
SIC 5511 Automobiles, new & used; Automobiles, new & used
Pr: Dennis Ellmer
**Treas:* Stacy Cummings
**VP:* William Fink
Sls Mgr: Wib Davenport
Sales Asso: Ed Williamson

D-U-N-S 78-821-7693
KLINE IMPORTS CHESAPEAKE INC
KLINE TOYOTA GREENBRIER
1499 S Military Hwy, Chesapeake, VA 23320-2603
Tel (757) 366-5000 *Founded/Ownrshp* 1990
Sales 35.1MM^E *EMP* 100^E
SIC 5511 Automobiles, new & used; Automobiles, new & used
Pr: Dennis Ellmer
**VP:* George Mumejian

KLINE TOYOTA GREENBRIER
See KLINE IMPORTS CHESAPEAKE INC

D-U-N-S 06-677-5750
KLINE TYSONS IMPORTS INC
KOONS TYSONS TOYOTA
(*Suby of* JIM KOONS MANAGEMENT CO) ★
8610 Leesburg Pike, Vienna, VA 22182-2225
Tel (888) 886-8159 *Founded/Ownrshp* 1989
Sales 34.5MM^E *EMP* 105^E
SIC 5511 Automobiles, new & used; Automobiles, new & used
Store Mgr: Chad Danielski
Sls Mgr: Patrick Prendergast
Sls Mgr: Dave Slebodnick
Sales Asso: Barrod Jones
Sales Asso: Earl Jones

D-U-N-S 06-285-6422
KLINE VOLVO INC (MN)
KLINE AUTOWORLD
3040 Maplewood Dr, Saint Paul, MN 55109-1081
Tel (866) 730-0629 *Founded/Ownrshp* 1956, 1972
Sales 27.5MM^E *EMP* 85
SIC 5511 7538 Automobiles, new & used; General automotive repair shops; Automobiles, new & used; General automotive repair shops
Pr: Rick Kline
Sls Mgr: Teresa Williams
Sales Asso: Charlie Mankowski
Sales Asso: Johnny Rogers

D-U-N-S 96-731-5297
KLINGBEIL CAPITAL MANAGEMENT LLC
500 W Wilson Bridge Rd # 145, Worthington, OH 43085-2238
Tel (614) 396-4919 *Founded/Ownrshp* 2000
Sales 159.6MM^E *EMP* 300
SIC 6799 8741 Real estate investors, except property operators; Management services
CEO: James D Klingbeil Jr
VP: Kasey Stevens

D-U-N-S 08-506-1604
KLINGBERG FAMILY CENTERS INC
370 Linwood St, New Britain, CT 06052-1998
Tel (860) 224-9113 *Founded/Ownrshp* 1904
Sales 18.5MM *EMP* 300
Accts Blumshapiro & Company Pc W
SIC 8361 Home for destitute men & women; Home for destitute men & women
CEO: Steven A Girelli
**Ch Bd:* Cathline Sullivan
COO: Lynne Roe
**V Ch Bd:* Peter H Goldfarb
**VP:* Mark Johnson
VP: David Lawrence-Hawley
**VP:* Joseph Milke
VP: Mark MA
VP: David Tompkins
**VP:* David Tompkinsv
**VP:* Patricia Wilcox

D-U-N-S 00-991-4032 IMP
KLINGELNBERG AMERICA INC
118 E Mi Ave Ste 200, Saline, MI 48176-1729
Tel (734) 470-6278 *Founded/Ownrshp* 1999
Sales 25.0MM *EMP* 14
SIC 5084 7699 Machinists' precision measuring tools; Industrial machinery & equipment repair; Machinists' precision measuring tools; Industrial machinery & equipment repair
CEO: Hastings Wyman

D-U-N-S 00-694-2148
KLINGER COMPANIES INC (IA)
2015 7th St, Sioux City, IA 51101-2003
Tel (712) 277-3900 *Founded/Ownrshp* 1919
Sales 256.1MM^E *EMP* 600
Accts Henjes Conner & Williams Pc
SIC 1542 1541 Commercial & office building contractors; Industrial buildings, new construction; Commercial & office building contractors; Industrial buildings, new construction
CEO: John W Gleeson
**CFO:* Robert J Desmidt
CFO: Robert Desmidt
VP: Larry Claeys
IT Man: Shelley Shell
Pharmcst: Elliot Paige

D-U-N-S 05-816-1977
KLINGER CONSTRUCTORS LLC
(*Suby of* KLINGER COMPANIES INC) ★
8701 Washington St Ne, Albuquerque, NM 87113-1680
Tel (505) 856-8200 *Founded/Ownrshp* 1982
Sales 74.8MM^E *EMP* 300
SIC 1541 1542 Industrial buildings, new construction; Commercial & office building, new construction; Institutional building construction; Industrial buildings, new construction; Commercial & office building, new construction; Institutional building construction
Pr: Ray Smith
CFO: Robert Desmidt
Ch: John W Gleeson
Sr VP: Dave Larson
VP: Matt Thompson
VP: James Werkmeister

D-U-N-S 09-876-5001 IMP
KLINGSPOR ABRASIVES INC
(*Suby of* KLINGSPOR AG)
2555 Tate Blvd Se, Hickory, NC 28602-1445
Tel (828) 322-3030 *Founded/Ownrshp* 1979
Sales 50.0MM *EMP* 321
SIC 3291 Abrasive products; Coated abrasive products; Abrasive products; Coated abrasive products
Pr: Christoph Klingspor
Pr: Olga Abramova
**VP:* Berthold Spatz
Rgnl Mgr: Jack Nowak
Rgnl Mgr: Bob Stephenson
Opers Mgr: Brian Matteson
Manager: Marcus Cram
Manager: Brandon Storie
Manager: Jeff Weiland
Sls Mgr: Zach Pease
Sales Asso: Melissa Church

D-U-N-S 00-173-7949
■ **KLINGSTUBBINS INC** (NC)
(*Suby of* JACOBS ENGINEERING GROUP INC) ★
2301 Chestnut St, Philadelphia, PA 19103-3035
Tel (215) 569-2900 *Founded/Ownrshp* 1926, 2011
Sales 37.0MM^E *EMP* 500
SIC 8712 8711 Architectural services; Civil engineering; Structural engineering; Mechanical engineering; Electrical or electronic engineering; Architectural services; Civil engineering; Structural engineering; Mechanical engineering; Electrical or electronic engineering
Pr: Michael R Lorenz
CFO: James Yadavaia
Sec: Robert T Hsu
Sr VP: Bradford Fiske
VP: Alan Sloan
Prgrm Mgr: Christina Neumann
Dir IT: Mark Svehlik
IT Man: Robert Defeo
Snr PM: Joanne Barrera
Snr Mgr: Frank Klusek
Snr Mgr: Todd Lambert

D-U-N-S 02-833-2088
KLINK CITRUS ASSOCIATION
KLINK CITRUS EXCHANGE
32921 Road 159, Ivanhoe, CA 93235-1455
Tel (559) 798-1881 *Founded/Ownrshp* 1917
Sales 20.2MM^E *EMP* 170
SIC 0723 Fruit (fresh) packing services; Fruit (fresh) packing services
CEO: Eric Meling

KLINK CITRUS EXCHANGE
See KLINK CITRUS ASSOCIATION

D-U-N-S 00-634-2505 IMP/EXP
■ **KLIPSCH GROUP INC**
(*Suby of* VOXX INTERNATIONAL CORP) ★
3502 Woodview Trce # 200, Indianapolis, IN 46268-3182
Tel (317) 860-8100 *Founded/Ownrshp* 1946
Sales 50.3MM^E *EMP* 180
SIC 3651 Loudspeakers, electrodynamic or magnetic; Loudspeakers, electrodynamic or magnetic
Ch Bd: Fred S Klipsch
Pr: Mark Casavant
Pr: Lawrence Coan
**Pr:* Paul Jacobs
Pr: Rick Santiago
**CFO:* Frederick L Farrar
Ex VP: Fred Farra
VP: Oscar Bernardo
VP: Sal Cannatella
VP: Dwight Clarke
VP: Jim Hunter
VP: Caroline Jones
VP: Anthony Ostrom
VP: Rob Standley
Dir Bus: Thomas Handrup

D-U-N-S 10-652-2225
KLJ SOLUTIONS CO
4585 Coleman St, Bismarck, ND 58503-0431
Tel (701) 355-8400 *Founded/Ownrshp* 2001
Sales 77.4MM^E *EMP* 780
SIC 8711 8713 Engineering services; Civil engineering; Structural engineering; Electrical or electronic engineering; Surveying services; Engineering services; Civil engineering; Structural engineering; Electrical or electronic engineering; Surveying services
CEO: Niles Hushka
**Pr:* Gene Jackson
**CFO:* Dean Anagnost
**Sr VP:* Mark Anderson
**Sr VP:* Lanny Harris
**Prin:* Barry Schuchard

D-U-N-S 13-619-5570
KLJM
LEE JOFA PORTFOLIO TEXTILES
225 Central Ave S, Bethpage, NY 11714-4940
Tel (516) 293-2000 *Founded/Ownrshp* 2003
Sales 39.2MM^E *EMP* 400
SIC 5131 Textiles, woven; Textiles, woven
CEO: Cary Kravet
**CFO:* Mike Wilbur
Mktg Dir: Ann Feldstein

D-U-N-S 00-977-9083
KLLM INC
KLLM TRANSPORT SERVICES
(*Suby of* KLLM TRANSPORT SERVICES LLC) ★
135 Riverview Dr, Richland, MS 39218-4401
Tel (800) 925-1000 *Founded/Ownrshp* 1975
Sales 237.9MM^E *EMP* 1,500
SIC 4213 Refrigerated products transport; Trailer or container on flat car (TOFC/COFC); Refrigerated products transport; Trailer or container on flat car (TOFC/COFC)
Pr: James M Richards Jr
**VP:* Kirk Blankenship
**VP:* Greg Carpenter
VP: Irene Howard
VP: Andy Morris
**VP:* Wilson Risinger
VP: Vince Shotts
**VP:* Milton Tallant Jr
Sfty Mgr: Clarence Woodard
Opers Mgr: Dale Prax
Opers Mgr: Warren Swindle

KLLM TRANSPORT SERVICES
See KLLM INC

D-U-N-S 04-532-1841
KLLM TRANSPORT SERVICES LLC
135 Riverview Dr, Jackson, MS 39218-4401
Tel (601) 939-2545 *Founded/Ownrshp* 2000
Sales 311.8MM^E *EMP* 1,650
SIC 4213 Trucking, except local; Refrigerated products transport; Trailer or container on flat car (TOFC/COFC); Trucking, except local; Refrigerated products transport; Trailer or container on flat car (TOFC/COFC)
CEO: James M Richards Jr
Ch Bd: William Liles III
Pr: David Carter
CEO: Jim Richards
COO: Richards James
CFO: Kevin Adams
CFO: John P Hammonds
VP: Greg Carpenter
VP: Joe Stianche

VP: Milton Tallant Jr
Area Mgr: Melinda Tinsley

D-U-N-S 80-033-6906
KLM ACQUISITION CORP
ALUMA
101 E Seneca Rd, Bancroft, IA 50517-8150
Tel (515) 885-2398 *Founded/Ownrshp* 2000
Sales 41.1MM *EMP* 150
Accts Eide Bailly Llp Mankato Miss
SIC 3334 Primary aluminum; Primary aluminum
Pr: Lloyd Michael D
**Treas:* Kollasch Lori J

D-U-N-S 04-442-9678 EXP
KLM MANAGEMENT CO
AMCOM FOOD SERVICE
14120 Valley Blvd, City of Industry, CA 91746-2802
Tel (626) 330-3479 *Founded/Ownrshp* 1993
Sales 45.8MM[E] *EMP* 70
SIC 5143 Dairy products, except dried or canned; Dairy products, except dried or canned
Pr: Ted Degroot
**Sec:* Curtis Degroot
VP: Kurt Degroot

D-U-N-S 09-946-0404
KLM ORTHOTIC LABORATORIES INC
28280 Alta Vista Ave, Valencia, CA 91355-0958
Tel (661) 295-2600 *Founded/Ownrshp* 1974
Sales 24.5MM[E] *EMP* 100
SIC 5047 3842 Medical laboratory equipment; Foot appliances, orthopedic
Pr: Kirk Marshall
**Sec:* Scott Marshall
**VP:* Kent Marshall

D-U-N-S 95-985-5081 IMP/EXP
KLN ENTERPRISES INC
400 Lakeside Dr, Perham, MN 56573-2202
Tel (218) 346-7000 *Founded/Ownrshp* 1995
Sales 299.5MM[E] *EMP* 500[E]
SIC 2096 2064 Potato chips & other potato-based snacks; Candy & other confectionery products; Potato chips & other potato-based snacks; Candy & other confectionery products
CEO: Kenneth Nelson
**COO:* Kurt Nelson
**CFO:* Wayne Caughey
VP: Justus Lisa
CTO: Robert Kinlund
Natl Sales: Katherine Bridgeman
Sls Mgr: Brian Smith

D-U-N-S 07-855-5379 IMP
KLN MANUFACTURING LLC
2 Winnco Dr, San Antonio, TX 78218-5201
Tel (210) 227-5580 *Founded/Ownrshp* 2012
Sales 26.1MM[E] *EMP* 130
SIC 2514 5021 Metal household furniture; Furniture
CFO: Dave Fyffe
Opers Mgr: Daniel Lee
Plnt Mgr: Jeff Gonzales

D-U-N-S 00-813-1955 IMP
KLN STEEL PRODUCTS CO LLC
(*Suby of* AVTEQ INC) ★
4342 N Interstate 35, San Antonio, TX 78218-5225
Tel (210) 227-4747 *Founded/Ownrshp* 2012
Sales 38.9MM[E] *EMP* 180
SIC 2514 Metal household furniture; Metal household furniture
Pr: Edward Herman
CTO: Gilbert Benavides
Dir IT: Ernie Miller
IT Man: Leah Peene
IT Man: Leah Tran
VP Sls: Kris Benson
Mktg Mgr: Thor Augustus

D-U-N-S 06-984-2789 IMP/EXP
KLOCKNER NAMASCO HOLDING CORP
(*Suby of* KLOECKNER & CO USA BETEILIGUNGS GMBH)
500 Colonial Center Pkwy # 500, Roswell, GA 30076-8853
Tel (678) 259-8800 *Founded/Ownrshp* 2011
Sales 1.7MMM[E] *EMP* 1,473
SIC 5051 Steel; Aluminum bars, rods, ingots, sheets, pipes, plates, etc.; Steel; Aluminum bars, rods, ingots, sheets, pipes, plates, etc.
CEO: Bill Partalis
CFO: Kirk Johnson

D-U-N-S 06-033-6104 IMP/EXP
KLOCKNER PENTAPLAST OF AMERICA INC
(*Suby of* KP INTERNATIONAL HOLDING GMBH)
3585 Kloeckner Rd, Gordonsville, VA 22942-6148
Tel (540) 661-3350 *Founded/Ownrshp* 1982
Sales 362.4MM[E] *EMP* 1,284
SIC 3081 4213 Plastic film & sheet; Trucking, except local; Plastic film & sheet; Trucking, except local
Pr: Michael P Ryan
V Ch: Gordon Von Bretten
Pr: David Veasey
Treas: Eric Sigler
VP: Stefan Brandt
VP: Rainer Greilmeier
VP: Markus Hoelzl
VP: Tracy Scott
CIO: Markus Fichtinger
Netwrk Mgr: Lisa Walton
Tech Mgr: Frank Bria
Board of Directors: Robert Kramer

D-U-N-S 10-172-9374 IMP/EXP
KLOCKNER PENTAPLAST PARTICIPATION LLC
3585 Kloeckner Rd, Gordonsville, VA 22942-6148
Tel (540) 832-3600 *Founded/Ownrshp* 2001
Sales NA *EMP* 1,284[E]
SIC 3081 4213

D-U-N-S 60-527-1803
KLOCKNER USA HOLDING INC
(*Suby of* KLOCKNER & CO SE)
500 Colonial Center Pkwy # 500, Roswell, GA 30076-8853
Tel (678) 259-8800 *Founded/Ownrshp* 2004
Sales 141.7MM[E] *EMP* 1,329
SIC 6799 5051 Investors; Steel; Investors; Steel
Prin: Bill Partalis

KLODE AUTO
See KLODE SALVAGE DISTRIBUTION CENTER INC

D-U-N-S 00-625-2670
KLODE SALVAGE DISTRIBUTION CENTER INC
KLODE AUTO
8300 Blakeland Dr # 200, Littleton, CO 80125-9742
Tel (303) 470-5511 *Founded/Ownrshp* 1964
Sales 48.0MM *EMP* 100
SIC 5012 7389 Automobiles & other motor vehicles; Auction, appraisal & exchange services; Automobiles & other motor vehicles; Auction, appraisal & exchange services
Pr: Ron Dendorfer
**Sec:* Brian Dendorfer
**VP:* Eric Dendorfer
Brnch Mgr: Matt Rot

D-U-N-S 79-997-3094 IMP/EXP
KLOECKNER METALS CORP
(*Suby of* KLOCKNER NAMASCO HOLDING CORP) ★
500 Colonial Center Pkwy, Roswell, GA 30076-8856
Tel (918) 831-1933 *Founded/Ownrshp* 1997
Sales 1.7MMM[E] *EMP* 1,473
SIC 5051 Ferrous metals; Nonferrous metal sheets, bars, rods, etc.; Metal wires, ties, cables & screening; Ferrous metals; Nonferrous metal sheets, bars, rods, etc.; Metal wires, ties, cables & screening
Pr: Bill Partalis
**CFO:* Kirk Johnson
CFO: Kirk Johson
**VP:* John Ganem
Exec: Annette Jansen
Brnch Mgr: James Boedeker
Genl Mgr: Darryl Grinstead
Genl Mgr: Larry Hatlestad
Genl Mgr: Bill Loveland
Genl Mgr: David Mueller
Genl Mgr: Travis Nishi

D-U-N-S 13-053-2005
KLOKE ENTERPRISES INC
KLOKE TRANSFER
10 E Belt Blvd, Richmond, VA 23224-1202
Tel (804) 353-0212 *Founded/Ownrshp* 1981
Sales 21.2MM[E] *EMP* 125
SIC 4213 4214 Contract haulers; Local trucking with storage
Pr: Gregory K Herceg
**Ch Bd:* John G Kloke
**Sec:* Daniel S Short
**VP:* Greg Calvert
VP: Dan Hayes
**VP:* Beth L Kloke
Opers Mgr: Mark Haynes

KLOKE TRANSFER
See KLOKE ENTERPRISES INC

D-U-N-S 00-608-4792 IMP
KLONDIKE CHEESE CO (WI)
W7839 State Road 81, Monroe, WI 53566-9179
Tel (608) 325-3021 *Founded/Ownrshp* 1925
Sales 82.9MM *EMP* 95
Accts Boeke & Associates Ltd Rock
SIC 2022 Natural cheese; Natural cheese
Pr: Ronald A Buholzer
Pr: Matt Erdley
**Treas:* David Buholzer
Treas: Dave Bulholzer
**Ex VP:* Steve Buholzer
**VP:* Luke Buholzer
Opers Mgr: Adam Buholzer
Prd Mgr: Jon Brunner
Sls Mgr: Larry Schwartz

KLONDIKE MANOR CARE
See KLONDIKE MANOR LLC

D-U-N-S 96-632-6519
KLONDIKE MANOR LLC
KLONDIKE MANOR CARE
(*Suby of* HBR KENTUCKY LLC) ★
3802 Klondike Ln, Louisville, KY 40218-1796
Tel (502) 452-1579 *Founded/Ownrshp* 2011
Sales 346.8M[E] *EMP* 308[E]
SIC 8051 Skilled nursing care facilities
Nrsg Dir: Bonnie Langley

D-U-N-S 80-963-5886
KLONDYKE CONSTRUCTION LLC
(*Suby of* PIKE CORP) ★
2640 W Lone Cactus Dr, Phoenix, AZ 85027-2411
Tel (623) 869-6969 *Founded/Ownrshp* 2010
Sales 70.0MM *EMP* 195
SIC 8741 1629 Construction management; Power plant construction
Pr: Howard Varner
**Sr VP:* Larry Knight
**VP:* Steve McClain
**VP:* Bruce Thornton

D-U-N-S 06-401-0861 IMP
KLOSS DISTRIBUTING CO INC
1333 Northwestern Ave, Gurnee, IL 60031-2347
Tel (847) 336-5610 *Founded/Ownrshp* 1973
Sales 23.6MM[E] *EMP* 60
SIC 5181 Beer & other fermented malt liquors; Beer & other fermented malt liquors
Pr: Eugene Kloss
**VP:* Larry Guthrie

D-U-N-S 08-000-9020 IMP
KLOSS FURNITURE INTERIORS INC
THOMASVILLE HOME FURNISHINGS
135 Poplar St, Highland, IL 62249-1279
Tel (618) 654-9801 *Founded/Ownrshp* 1976
Sales 20.8MM[E] *EMP* 120
SIC 5712 Furniture stores; Bedding & bedsprings; Office furniture; Juvenile furniture
CEO: Steve Kloss
**Pr:* Dan Kennedy
**CFO:* Don Simcons

D-U-N-S 00-424-8837
KLOSTERMAN BAKING CO (OH)
4760 Paddock Rd, Cincinnati, OH 45229-1004
Tel (513) 242-5667 *Founded/Ownrshp* 1900
Sales 182.6MM[E] *EMP* 630
SIC 2051 Bread, cake & related products; Bread, cake & related products; Bread, all types (white, wheat, rye, etc): fresh or frozen; Cakes, bakery: except frozen; Yeast goods, sweet: except frozen
Pr: Kenneth Klosterman
**COO:* Dennis Wiltshire
VP: Trent Doak
**VP:* Ed Piasecki
VP: Jerry Prues
Exec: Jeff Zorman
QA Dir: Kevin Stevens
Plnt Mgr: Lawrence Moore
Prd Mgr: Chad Gorrell
Mktg Dir: Amy Ott
Mktg Mgr: Mike Howlett

D-U-N-S 13-762-8228
KLOTZ ASSOCIATES INC
(*Suby of* RPS GROUP INC) ★
1160 Dairy Ashford Rd # 500, Houston, TX 77079-3098
Tel (281) 589-7257 *Founded/Ownrshp* 2015
Sales 23.0MM[E] *EMP* 116
SIC 8711 Consulting engineer; Consulting engineer
Pr: D Wayne Klotz
Treas: Richard Lewis
Ex VP: Billy M Cooke
Sr VP: Bill Abbott
Sr VP: Lesliet Pittman
Sr VP: Tom S Ramsey
VP: Brad Brown
VP: Delvin Dennis
VP: Scott Dukette
VP: Mike Ogten
VP: Gary Struzick
VP: Ricardo Zamarripa
VP: Joe Zimmerman

D-U-N-S 00-704-8395
KLQ ENTERPRISES INC
QUALITY RENTALS
15003 Meridian E, Puyallup, WA 98375-6634
Tel (253) 848-6644 *Founded/Ownrshp* 1986
Sales 60.1MM *EMP* 5[E]
SIC 7359 Furniture rental; Furniture rental
**CFO:* Bill Quin

D-U-N-S 17-038-4031 IMP/EXP
KLS AIR EXPRESS INC
FREIGHT SOLUTION PROVIDERS
2851 Gold Tailings Ct, Rancho Cordova, CA 95670-6189
Tel (916) 373-3353 *Founded/Ownrshp* 1992
Sales 30.1MM[E] *EMP* 100
Accts Don W Mckaughan Cpa Sacramen
SIC 4731 Freight transportation arrangement; Freight transportation arrangement
CEO: Lielanie Steers
**Pr:* Kenneth Steers
**VP:* Jeff Adams
Sales Asso: Alecia Soriano

D-U-N-S 82-649-9238 IMP
KLS-MARTIN LP
(*Suby of* KARL LEIBINGER GMBH & CO. KG)
11201 St Johns Industrial, Jacksonville, FL 32246
Tel (904) 996-0649 *Founded/Ownrshp* 1993
Sales 39.6MM[E] *EMP* 120
SIC 5047 Orthopedic equipment & supplies; Medical laboratory equipment; Orthopedic equipment & supplies; Medical laboratory equipment
Genl Pt: Mike Teague
Pt: Jeff Ashby
Pt: Brian Carney
Pt: Mike Greene
Pt: Karl Leibinger
Genl Mgr: Jill Johnson
Genl Mgr: Chantel Turner
Dir IT: Clay Hudgins
Sls Mgr: Matthew Long
Sls Mgr: Gabe Pennone
Sales Asso: Bryce Classen

D-U-N-S 15-930-0636
KLT INDUSTRIES INC
33 Boston Post Rd W # 501, Marlborough, MA 01752-1853
Tel (508) 305-2214 *Founded/Ownrshp* 2002
Sales 32.0MM[E] *EMP* 50
SIC 4953 Recycling, waste materials
Pr: Kyle Trayner
**Treas:* Sheryl Caterino-Klosowski
**VP:* Mark Francis

D-U-N-S 02-182-8652
KLUKWAN INC
425 Sawmill Rd, Haines, AK 99827
Tel (907) 766-2211 *Founded/Ownrshp* 1973
Sales 24.1MM[E] *EMP* 200
Accts Peterson Sullivan Pllc
SIC 1611 2411 2421 Highway & street construction; Airport runway construction; Logging camps & contractors; Sawmills & planing mills, general; Highway & street construction; Airport runway construction; Logging camps & contractors; Sawmills & planing mills, general
Ch: Johanna Hotch
**Pr:* Thomas Crandall
**V Ch Bd:* Les Katzek

D-U-N-S 00-819-8186 IMP
KLUMB LUMBER CO (MS)
KLUMB SOUTHERN DIVISION
1080 River Oaks Dr A200, Flowood, MS 39232-9779
Tel (601) 932-6070 *Founded/Ownrshp* 1945
Sales 160.2MM *EMP* 140
Accts May & Company Vicksburg Ms
SIC 5031 Lumber: rough, dressed & finished; Lumber: rough, dressed & finished
Pr: Vicki Klumb O'Neill
**Pr:* Steve Funchess
**Pr:* Vicki O'Neill
**CEO:* C E Klumb Jr
**CFO:* Randall Hudson

KLUMB SOUTHERN DIVISION
See KLUMB LUMBER CO

KLUNE AEROSPACE
See GCM NORTH AMERICAN AEROSPACE LLC

D-U-N-S 96-335-3227
■ **KLUNE HOLDINGS INC**
(*Suby of* PCC) ★
7323 Coldwater Canyon Ave, North Hollywood, CA 91605-4206
Tel (818) 503-8100 *Founded/Ownrshp* 2010
Sales 131.6MM *EMP* 760
SIC 3728 Aircraft parts & equipment; Aircraft parts & equipment
CEO: Allen Ronk
CFO: Clom Plunkett
CFO: Ken Ward
VP: Emanuel Funk
Comm Man: Vicky Dalton
Ex Dir: Lisa Lujan
Prgrm Mgr: Karen Gull
Prgrm Mgr: Cindy Smith
Genl Mgr: Jack Brady
Genl Mgr: Al Eddert
Genl Mgr: Micheal Meehan

D-U-N-S 03-038-7286 IMP
■ **KLUNE INDUSTRIES INC**
(*Suby of* KLUNE HOLDINGS INC) ★
7323 Coldwater Canyon Ave, North Hollywood, CA 91605-4206
Tel (818) 503-8100 *Founded/Ownrshp* 2012
Sales 131.1MM[E] *EMP* 757
SIC 3728 Aircraft parts & equipment; Aircraft parts & equipment
CEO: Joseph I Snowden
CEO: Allen Ronk
CFO: Kenneth Ward
Prgrm Mgr: Blaine Deveraux
Prgrm Mgr: Zac Frampton
Prgrm Mgr: Sara Galovich
Prgrm Mgr: Barbara Greene
Prgrm Mgr: Shirleen Morton
Dir IT: Gerry Mauricio
IT Man: Kurt Olson
QC Dir: Mark Claire
Board of Directors: Jake Blumenthal, Gordon Clune, Richard Crowell, Tom Epley, Richard Roeder, Allen Ronk

KLX AEROSPACE SOLUTIONS
See M&M AEROSPACE HARDWARE INC

KLX AEROSPACE SOLUTIONS
See KLX INC

D-U-N-S 07-947-8159
■ **KLX ENERGY SERVICES LLC**
VISION OIL TOOLS
(*Suby of* KLX AEROSPACE SOLUTIONS) ★
2700 Post Oak Blvd, Houston, TX 77056-5784
Tel (281) 657-3380 *Founded/Ownrshp* 2013
Sales 24.0MM[E] *EMP* 98[E]
SIC 1389 Fishing for tools, oil & gas field
CEO: Amin Khoury
**Pr:* Thomas P McCaffrey
Sales Asso: Dusti Pace

D-U-N-S 07-957-9685
▲ **KLX INC**
KLX AEROSPACE SOLUTIONS
1300 Corporate Center Way # 200, Wellington, FL 33414-8594
Tel (561) 383-5100 *Founded/Ownrshp* 1974
Sales 1.7MMM *EMP* 3,300[E]
Tkr Sym KLXI *Exch* NGS
SIC 3728 2911 1381 Aircraft parts & equipment; Fractionation products of crude petroleum, hydrocarbons; Service well drilling
CEO: Amin J Khoury
Pr: Thomas P McCaffrey
CFO: Michael F Senft
VP: Roger Franks
Board of Directors: John T Collins, Peter V Del Presto, Richard G Hamermesh, Benjamin A Hardesty, Stephen M Ward Jr, Theodore L Weise, John T Whates

D-U-N-S 19-822-6987
KM BUILDERS INC
BARR CONCRETE
8420 Terminal Rd, Lorton, VA 22079-1424
Tel (703) 912-6553 *Founded/Ownrshp* 2000
Sales 20.1MM[E] *EMP* 90
SIC 1542 Commercial & office buildings, renovation & repair; Commercial & office buildings, renovation & repair
Pr: Keith O Martin
CFO: Michael Scroggs
Snr Mgr: Mehrdad Banafshe
Snr Mgr: Mike Bayliss
Snr Mgr: Bill Klein

D-U-N-S 08-668-9403
KM DEVELOPMENT CORP
(*Suby of* TOWNE REALTY, INC.)
710 N Plankinton Ave # 1100, Milwaukee, WI 53203-2418
Tel (414) 274-2800 *Founded/Ownrshp* 1977
Sales 35.0MM[E] *EMP* 189
SIC 1522 8742 6552 Residential construction; Multi-family dwelling construction; Construction project management consultant; Land subdividers & developers, commercial; Land subdividers & developers, residential; Residential construction; Multi-family dwelling construction; Construction project management consultant; Land subdividers & developers, commercial; Land subdividers & developers, residential
Pr: Donald A Mantz
Treas: Stephan Chevalier

Ex VP: Arthur W Wigchers Jr
Sr VP: James F Janz
VP: Robert Braun
VP: Robert Rutkowski
VP: James B Young
Div/Sub He: Kohn Bennett
MIS Mgr: John Janz

D-U-N-S 61-177-2448
KM PLANT SERVICES INC
(*Suby of* K2 INDUSTRIAL SERVICES INC) ★
2552 Industrial Dr, Highland, IN 46322-2625
Tel (219) 933-1100 *Founded/Ownrshp* 2003
Sales 62.3MM^E *EMP* 525^E
SIC 1721 7349 1799 Industrial painting; Cleaning service, industrial or commercial; Fireproofing buildings; Industrial painting; Cleaning service, industrial or commercial; Fireproofing buildings
Pr: Will Colon
COO: Herndon Dennis
**Treas:* Richard S Bartell
**Treas:* David Zipse

D-U-N-S 02-309-7231
KM SUPERMARKETS INC
MACKENTHUN'S COUNTY MARKET
851 Marketplace Dr, Waconia, MN 55387-1548
Tel (952) 442-2512 *Founded/Ownrshp* 1980
Sales 27.8MM^E *EMP* 200
Accts Fdwnk Professional Corporation
SIC 5411 Grocery stores; Grocery stores
Pr: Kevin Mackenthun
**VP:* Jaime Mackenthun
Genl Mgr: Ed Gardeski

D-U-N-S 08-000-2619
KM2 SOLUTIONS LLC
150 E Wilson Bridge Rd, Worthington, OH 43085-2328
Tel (484) 359-7263 *Founded/Ownrshp* 2004
Sales 28.0MM *EMP* 15
SIC 8741 Business management
CEO: David Kreiss
**CFO:* Terry Weikel
**Ex VP:* Gary Myers

D-U-N-S 18-641-3477
KM2 SOLUTIONS LLC
112 Christine Dr, Downingtown, PA 19335-1518
Tel (610) 213-1408 *Founded/Ownrshp* 2004
Sales 44.0MM^E *EMP* 1,000
SIC 8742 Financial consultant; Financial consultant

D-U-N-S 09-012-2037 IMP
KMA ASSOCIATES OF PUERTO RICO INC
LUIS FREIRE
7 Ave Arbolote, Guaynabo, PR 00969-2800
Tel (787) 622-0505 *Founded/Ownrshp* 1988
Sales 23.8MM^E *EMP* 50
SIC 5074 5999 5211 Plumbing & hydronic heating supplies; Sanitary ware, china or enameled iron; Sanitary ware, metal; Plumbing & heating supplies; Bathroom fixtures, equipment & supplies
Pr: Marcelo C Arroyo

D-U-N-S 00-896-5873 IMP
■ KMART CORP
(*Suby of* KMART HOLDING CORP) ★
3333 Beverly Rd, Hoffman Estates, IL 60179-0001
Tel (847) 286-2500 *Founded/Ownrshp* 1916
Sales 7.9MMM^E *EMP* 45,000
SIC 5311 5912 5399 Department stores; Drug stores; Army-Navy goods; Department stores; Drug stores; Army-Navy goods
Pr: Edward Lampert
**Pr:* Ronald D Doirie
Pr: Kevin Mackenthun
**Treas:* Scott E Huckins
Sr VP: Frank Kruszewski
VP: Joel Dubiner
VP: Lisa Schultz
VP: Clay Wahl
Mng Ofcr: John M Foster
Prin: Robert P Woodard
Dist Mgr: Ken Dunn
Dist Mgr: Brad Johnson

D-U-N-S 13-197-8533 IMP
■ KMART HOLDING CORP
(*Suby of* SEARS HOLDINGS CORP) ★
3333 Beverly Rd, Hoffman Estates, IL 60179-0001
Tel (847) 286-2500 *Founded/Ownrshp* 2003
Sales 7.9MMM^E *EMP* 45,000^E
Accts Bdo Seidman Llp Troy Mi
SIC 5311 Department stores, discount; Department stores, discount
Chf Mktg O: Alasdair James
CFO: Robert Schriesheim
Treas: James F Gooch
Chf Mktg O: Paul Guyardo
Chf Mktg O: Mike Valle
Ofcr: Peter Whitsett
Ofcr: Thomas E Zielecki
Ex VP: Ronald Boire
Sr VP: Karen A Austin
Sr VP: James E Defebaugh
Sr VP: Dane Drobny
Sr VP: Donald J Germano
Sr VP: John D Goodman
Sr VP: William Harker
Sr VP: James P Mixon
Sr VP: Irv Neger
Sr VP: William Phelan
Sr VP: Leslie Schultz
VP: Robert Riecker
VP: Judith Rusch
Board of Directors: W Bruce Johnson, Aylwin B Lewis, Allen R Ravas

KMAX TV
See SACRAMENTO TELEVISION STATIONS INC

D-U-N-S 96-301-1358 IMP
KMC ACQUISITION CORP
KIRKHILL
12023 Woodruff Ave, Downey, CA 90241-5603
Tel (562) 803-1117 *Founded/Ownrshp* 1996
Sales 20.9MM^E *EMP* 112
SIC 3069

KMC CONTROLS
See KREUTER MANUFACTURING CO INC

D-U-N-S 02-007-0152 IMP
KMC EXIM CORP
1 Harbor Park Dr, Port Washington, NY 11050-4601
Tel (516) 621-6565 *Founded/Ownrshp* 1997
Sales 48.3MM *EMP* 25
Accts Kpmg New York Ny
SIC 5087 Beauty parlor equipment & supplies; Beauty parlor equipment & supplies
Pr: John Chang

D-U-N-S 00-609-0724
KMC HOLDINGS LLC
KMC STAMPINGS
1221 S Park St, Port Washington, WI 53074-2127
Tel (262) 284-3424 *Founded/Ownrshp* 2008
Sales 44.8MM^E *EMP* 275
SIC 3469

D-U-N-S 79-712-3812 IMP
KMC HOLDINGS LLC
KENNEDY MANUFACTURING CO.
1260 Industrial Dr, Van Wert, OH 45891-2433
Tel (419) 238-2442 *Founded/Ownrshp* 2007
Sales 27.9MM^E *EMP* 130
SIC 3841 3469 5021 Surgical & medical instruments; Boxes: tool, lunch, mail, etc.: stamped metal; Racks; Surgical & medical instruments; Boxes: tool, lunch, mail, etc.: stamped metal; Racks
Genl Mgr: George Garifalis
Dir IT: Nancy Oberhaus
IT Man: Nancy Ferris
Plnt Mgr: Dana Sealscott
VP Sls: Craig Martin
Sls Mgr: Doug Campbell

KMC MUSIC, INC.
See ROKR DISTRIBUTION US INC

KMC STAMPINGS
See KMC HOLDINGS LLC

D-U-N-S 94-507-7527 IMP
KMC SYSTEMS INC
(*Suby of* KOLLSMAN INC) ★
220 Daniel Webster Hwy, Merrimack, NH 03054-4898
Tel (603) 889-2500 *Founded/Ownrshp* 1995
Sales 20.5MM^E *EMP* 100
SIC 3812 3841 3629 Search & navigation equipment; Surgical & medical instruments; Electrochemical generators (fuel cells); Search & navigation equipment; Surgical & medical instruments; Electrochemical generators (fuel cells)
Pr: Patrick McNallen
**Pr:* Patrick Mc Nallen
**VP:* Ron Jellison
Prgrm Mgr: Johnathan Brooks
Prgrm Mgr: Spencer Lovette
Snr Sftwr: Mark Bastille
Snr Sftwr: Eric Martens
IT Man: Jane Ravagni
Opers Mgr: Bill St Onge

D-U-N-S 85-870-4500
KMC THERMO LLC
3 Waterway Square Pl # 475, The Woodlands, TX 77380-3487
Tel (713) 236-3046 *Founded/Ownrshp* 2002
Sales 23.8MM^E *EMP* 59^E
SIC 4911 Generation, electric power
VP: Tony Hopkins
Admn Mgr: Heather McKee

D-U-N-S 07-419-8961 IMP
KMCO LP
KMTEX
16503 Ramsey Rd, Crosby, TX 77532-5916
Tel (832) 607-7050 *Founded/Ownrshp* 2012
Sales 43.8MM^E *EMP* 120
SIC 2899 2992 Chemical preparations; Antifreeze compounds; Brake fluid (hydraulic): made from purchased materials; Chemical preparations; Antifreeze compounds; Brake fluid (hydraulic): made from purchased materials
Pr: Artie Mc Ferrin
Pr: Jeff Mc Ferrin
VP: David Fortune
Exec: Gisele Stein
Prin: Will Baker

KMD
See KAPLAN/MCLAUGHLIN/DIAZ INC

KME FIRE APPARATUS
See KOVATCH MOBILE EQUIPMENT CORP

KMG AMERICA
See KANAWHA INSURANCE CO

D-U-N-S 16-190-5547
■ KMG AMERICA CORP
(*Suby of* HUMANA INC) ★
12600 Whitewater Dr # 150, Minnetonka, MN 55343-4592
Tel (952) 930-4800 *Founded/Ownrshp* 2007
Sales NA *EMP* 505^E
SIC 6311 6321 Life insurance; Accident & health insurance; Life insurance; Accident & health insurance
Pr: Kenneth U Kuk
Pr: R Dale Vaughan
**VP:* Paul F Kraemer
**VP:* Paul Moore
Ex Dir: Scott H Delong III

D-U-N-S 00-974-1745 IMP/EXP
▲ KMG CHEMICALS INC (TX)
9555 W Sam Houston Pkwy S, Houston, TX 77099-2132
Tel (713) 600-3800 *Founded/Ownrshp* 1992
Sales 320.5MM *EMP* 657
Accts Kpmg Llp Houston Texas
Tkr Sym KMG *Exch* NYS
SIC 2899 Chemical preparations; Chemical preparations
Pr: Christopher T Fraser
CFO: Malinda G Passmore
VP: Roger C Jackson
VP: Ernest C Kremling
Plnt Mgr: Ron Wooley
VP Sls: Thomas H Mitchell
Mktg Dir: Ryan Mears
Sls Mgr: Jacob Halpern
Board of Directors: Gerald G Ermentrout, James F Gentilcore, George W Gilman, Robert Harrer, John C Hunter III, Fred C Leonard, Karen A Twitchell

D-U-N-S 80-126-0154 IMP/EXP
■ KMG ELECTRONIC CHEMICALS INC
(*Suby of* KMG CHEMICALS INC) ★
9555 W Sm Hstn Pkwy 600, Houston, TX 77099
Tel (713) 600-3814 *Founded/Ownrshp* 2007
Sales 103.9MM^E *EMP* 272
SIC 1629 Chemical plant & refinery construction; Chemical plant & refinery construction
CEO: Christopher T Fraser
**CFO:* John V Sobchak
**Treas:* Pam Birkholz
**VP:* Ernest C Kremling II

D-U-N-S 09-380-4912
KMG ENTERPRISES INC
IHOP
17619 W 66th Ter, Shawnee Mission, KS 66217-9101
Tel (913) 962-1816 *Founded/Ownrshp* 1984
Sales 12.8MM *EMP* 420
SIC 5812 Restaurant, family: chain; Restaurant, family: chain
Pr: Karen Garrett
**VP:* Alan D Garrett
**VP:* Kevin R Garrett

D-U-N-S 06-472-5083
KMG HAULING INC
14 Bryant Ct Ste B, Sterling, VA 20166-9574
Tel (703) 961-1100 *Founded/Ownrshp* 2001
Sales 21.8MM^E *EMP* 83
Accts James B Veltri Cpa Campbell
SIC 4953 Rubbish collection & disposal
Pr: Hugo M Garcia
Exec: A Costigan

D-U-N-S 03-862-5760
KMG PRESTIGE INC
KEYSTONE MANAGEMENT GROUP
102 S Main St Ste 108, Mount Pleasant, MI 48858-2336
Tel (989) 772-3261 *Founded/Ownrshp* 1992
Sales 29.1MM^E *EMP* 400
SIC 6531 Real estate managers; Real estate managers
Pr: Kenneth C Bovee
Pr: Joe Tandy
**CFO:* Robert Kabbe
VP: Jennifer Allen
**VP:* Joanne Golden
VP: Connie Mathes
Dir Risk M: Amy Howard
MIS Dir: Samuel Brooks
Site Mgr: Thomas Danis
Site Mgr: Amy Ireland
Site Mgr: Rhonda Jackson

D-U-N-S 78-964-1875 IMP
■ KMG-BERNUTH INC
(*Suby of* KMG CHEMICALS INC) ★
9555 W Sam Houston Pkwy S, Houston, TX 77099-2132
Tel (713) 988-9252 *Founded/Ownrshp* 1996
Sales 92.7MM^E *EMP* 118
SIC 5169 2869 Chemicals, industrial & heavy; Industrial organic chemicals; Chemicals, industrial & heavy; Industrial organic chemicals
Ch Bd: David L Hatcher
**Pr:* Neal Butler
**Treas:* John V Sobchak
**VP:* Michael A Hoffman
**VP:* Roger Jackson
**VP:* Ernest C Kremling III

D-U-N-S 07-469-3458 IMP
KMH SYSTEMS INC
6900 Poe Ave, Dayton, OH 45414-2531
Tel (937) 890-0711 *Founded/Ownrshp* 1975
Sales 67.1MM^E *EMP* 120
SIC 5084 7359

D-U-N-S 61-816-2536 IMP/EXP
KMI GROUP INC
320 N Main St, Kenton, TN 38233-1130
Tel (731) 749-8700 *Founded/Ownrshp* 2005
Sales 21.1MM^E *EMP* 35
SIC 2821 Acrylic resins
CEO: Kevin Vakili
**Pr:* Zenat Karandish
**Prin:* Brian Chew
**Prin:* Sina Jashfer
Genl Mgr: Richard Herrera

D-U-N-S 11-748-9369 IMP
KMI SYSTEMS INC
ENGINEERED FINISHING SYSTEMS
4704 3 Oaks Rd, Crystal Lake, IL 60014-8180
Tel (815) 459-5255 *Founded/Ownrshp* 1984
Sales 22.0MM *EMP* 34
SIC 3559 3264 8711 Amusement park equipment; Porcelain electrical supplies; Engineering services; Paint making machinery; Porcelain electrical supplies; Engineering services
Pr: Kevin Coursin
**Treas:* Vikram Desai
**VP:* Terence M Ray
Sales Exec: Lynne Henifin

KMK
See KEATING MUETHING & KLEKAMP PLL

D-U-N-S 78-812-4980
KMM TELECOMMUNICATIONS
9 Law Dr Ste 13, Fairfield, NJ 07004-3233
Tel (973) 244-1380 *Founded/Ownrshp* 1991
Sales 892.8MM *EMP* 125
Accts Dorfman Abrams Music Llc Sad
SIC 5063 Electrical apparatus & equipment; Electrical apparatus & equipment
CEO: Katherine McConvey
**Pr:* Abelardo De La Teja
CFO: Bill Teja
VP: Dennis Smith

KMMG
See KIA MOTORS MANUFACTURING GEORGIA INC

D-U-N-S 04-245-8427
KMOV-TV INC
1 S Memorial Dr, Saint Louis, MO 63102-2425
Tel (314) 444-6333 *Founded/Ownrshp* 1994
Sales 20.4MM^E *EMP* 145
SIC 4833 Television broadcasting stations
Pr: Mark D Pimentel
**COO:* John Knicely
Dir Soc: Mark Reardon
Sls Mgr: Robert Totsch

D-U-N-S 03-060-7774 IMP
KMS INC (KS)
811 E Waterman St Ste 1, Wichita, KS 67202-4716
Tel (316) 264-8833 *Founded/Ownrshp* 1976
Sales 75.6MM *EMP* 25
SIC 5199 5141 General merchandise, non-durable; Groceries, general line; General merchandise, non-durable; Groceries, general line
Pr: Michael S Jabara
CFO: Steven Jess
**VP:* Garrell Dombaugh
**VP:* Larry McKee

D-U-N-S 10-419-2013
KMS INC
3401 Platt Springs Rd, West Columbia, SC 29170-2205
Tel (803) 217-3577 *Founded/Ownrshp* 2002
Sales 24.7MM^E *EMP* 70
SIC 3441 Fabricated structural metal
CEO: Joe Canfield
**Ch Bd:* Jeffrey S Dickson
**COO:* Ed Townsend
Sfty Dirs: Karyn Lynch
QC Dir: Dan Crossman

D-U-N-S 60-293-2274
KMS SOLUTIONS LLC
205 S Whiting St Ste 400, Alexandria, VA 22304-3632
Tel (703) 281-0374 *Founded/Ownrshp* 2005
Sales 60.0MM *EMP* 235
SIC 8748 8711 8742 Business consulting; Business consulting; Engineering services; Training & development consultant
Sr VP: Wayne King
Genl Mgr: Robert Urso

D-U-N-S 19-217-5040 EXP
■ KMT REFRIGERATION INC
KOLPAK
(*Suby of* MANITOWOC FOODSERVICE COMPANIES LLC) ★
2915 Tennessee Ave N, Parsons, TN 38363-5046
Tel (731) 847-6361 *Founded/Ownrshp* 1997
Sales 70.4MM^E *EMP* 1,100
SIC 3585 3448 1711 Refrigeration equipment, complete; Prefabricated metal components; Refrigeration contractor; Refrigeration equipment, complete; Prefabricated metal components; Refrigeration contractor
Genl Mgr: Gerry Senion
**Treas:* Glen Tellock

D-U-N-S 79-253-2660 IMP
KMT US HOLDING CO INC
(*Suby of* KMT WATERJET AB)
635 W 12th St, Baxter Springs, KS 66713-1940
Tel (620) 856-2151 *Founded/Ownrshp* 2005
Sales 37.8MM^E *EMP* 66
SIC 3569 Baling machines, for scrap metal, paper or similar material
CEO: Duane Johnson
**VP:* Brett Lawrie

D-U-N-S 79-508-2374
KMT WIRELESS LLC
CYNERGYHITECH
6080 Northbelt Dr, Norcross, GA 30071-2951
Tel (770) 277-2760 *Founded/Ownrshp* 1999
Sales 56.7MM^E *EMP* 400
SIC 3663 Radio & TV communications equipment; Radio & TV communications equipment
Pr: Darin Mickel
VP: Bill Kemp

KMTEX
See KMCO LP

D-U-N-S 01-708-8972 IMP/EXP
KMW GROUP INC
GREAT LAKES MARINE
5085 Corporate Exch Blvd, Grand Rapids, MI 49512-5515
Tel (616) 656-0755 *Founded/Ownrshp* 1982
Sales 38.8MM^E *EMP* 130
SIC 5047 5091

D-U-N-S 17-947-4002
KMW LTD
535 W Garfield Ave, Sterling, KS 67579-2370
Tel (620) 278-3641 *Founded/Ownrshp* 1997
Sales 21.2MM^E *EMP* 140^E
SIC 3523 3537 Loaders, farm type: manure, general utility; Industrial trucks & tractors; Loaders, farm type: manure, general utility; Industrial trucks & tractors
Pr: Michael Bender
CFO: Lori Crandall
VP: Dave Schneider
Prd Mgr: Larry Hoover
Sls Mgr: Wayne Rosenbaum
Sales Asso: Glenn Dorn
Sales Asso: Russ Wiese

KN RUBBER
See KONETA INC

D-U-N-S 19-935-4218 IMP/EXP
KN RUBBER LLC
KONETA RUBBER
(*Suby of* KINDERHOOK INDUSTRIES LLC) ★
1400 Lunar Dr, Wapakoneta, OH 45895-9796
Tel (419) 739-4200 *Founded/Ownrshp* 2007
Sales 69.2MM^E *EMP* 465
SIC 3069 Rubber automotive products; Rubber automotive products

D-U-N-S 00-523-8324 EXP
KNAACK LLC
KNAACK MANUFACTURING
(*Suby of* WERNER CO) ★
420 E Terra Cotta Ave, Crystal Lake, IL 60014-3611
Tel (815) 459-6020 *Founded/Ownrshp* 1960, 2012
Sales 80.8MM^E *EMP* 100
SIC 3499 Chests, fire or burglary resistive: metal; Chests, fire or burglary resistive: metal
Pr: Chad Severson
VP: Robert Pradelski
CTO: Steve Seibert
Natl Sales: Josh Rizzo

KNAACK MANUFACTURING
See KNAACK LLC

D-U-N-S 00-602-4699 IMP
KNAPE & VOGT MANUFACTURING CO (MI)
(*Suby of* WIND POINT PARTNERS VI, L.P.)
2700 Oak Industrial Dr Ne, Grand Rapids, MI 49505-6081
Tel (616) 459-3311 *Founded/Ownrshp* 1898, 2006
Sales 159.5MM^E *EMP* 640
SIC 2542 2541 3429 Partitions & fixtures, except wood; Shelving, office & store: except wood; Fixtures: display, office or store: except wood; Wood partitions & fixtures; Shelving, office & store, wood; Display fixtures, wood; Furniture builders' & other household hardware; Partitions & fixtures, except wood; Shelving, office & store: except wood; Fixtures: display, office or store: except wood; Wood partitions & fixtures; Shelving, office & store, wood; Display fixtures, wood; Furniture builders' & other household hardware
CEO: Peter Martin
**Ch Bd:* Bill Denton
**VP:* Gordon Kirsch
**VP:* John J Master
**VP:* Daniel D Pickett
VP: Michael Van Rooy
Natl Sales: Cletus Massi
Sls&Mrk Ex: Jim Dahlke

D-U-N-S 00-626-3073 IMP
KNAPHEIDE MANUFACTURING CO (IL)
1848 Westphalia Strasse, Quincy, IL 62305-7604
Tel (217) 222-7131 *Founded/Ownrshp* 1848
Sales 44.6MM^E *EMP* 250
SIC 3713

D-U-N-S 04-012-3275
KNAPHEIDE TRUCK EQUIPMENT CO (MO)
KTEC-JC
6603 Business 50 W, Jefferson City, MO 65109-6310
Tel (573) 893-5200 *Founded/Ownrshp* 1976
Sales 42.3MM^E *EMP* 100
SIC 5531 5013 Truck equipment & parts; Motor vehicle supplies & new parts
Pr: Harold W Knapheide III
**Sec:* Robert Overholser
**VP:* Richard J Green
Rgnl Mgr: Ron Lehman
Genl Mgr: Rich Green

D-U-N-S 00-793-1918
KNAPP CHEVROLET INC (TX)
815 Houston Ave, Houston, TX 77007-7709
Tel (713) 228-4311 *Founded/Ownrshp* 1940
Sales 55.9MM^E *EMP* 117
SIC 5511 Automobiles, new & used; Pickups, new & used; Vans, new & used; Automobiles, new & used; Pickups, new & used; Vans, new & used
Pr: Robert Knapp
Genl Mgr: Bobby Knapp
Sls Mgr: Bob Flanders
Sls Mgr: Mark Klouda
Sls Mgr: Wayne Ledu
Sls Mgr: Lovell Lloyd
Sales Asso: Rey Garcia

D-U-N-S 05-511-5059 IMP
KNAPP MEDICAL CENTER
1401 E 8th St, Weslaco, TX 78596-6640
Tel (956) 968-8567 *Founded/Ownrshp* 2005
Sales 145.3MM^E *EMP* 1,000
Accts Bkd Llp Houston Tx
SIC 8011 Offices & clinics of medical doctors; Offices & clinics of medical doctors
CEO: Bill Adams
Chf Path: Alberto P Gonzalez
Chf Rad: Michael Decandia
**Pr:* James Summersett
CFO: Dinah Gonzalez
CFO: Curtis Haley
VP: Alicia Rodriguez
Dir OR: Tamara Leonard
Dir Risk M: Ruben Garza
Dir Case M: Ellen Williams
Dir Lab: Roberto Velasquez

D-U-N-S 15-618-6475
KNAPP MEDICAL CENTER FOUNDATION INC
(*Suby of* MID VALLEY HEALTH SYSTEM) ★
1401 E 8th St, Weslaco, TX 78596-6640
Tel (956) 969-5112 *Founded/Ownrshp* 1981
Sales 266.1M *EMP* 900
Accts Bkd Llp
SIC 8742 Hospital & health services consultant; Hospital & health services consultant
Pr: James A Summersett
**CFO:* Curtis Haley

D-U-N-S 02-593-3409
KNAPP OIL CO INC
220 Front St, Xenia, IL 62899-1305
Tel (618) 678-2800 *Founded/Ownrshp* 1935
Sales 62.1MM^E *EMP* 175
SIC 5541 5171 Filling stations, gasoline; Petroleum bulk stations; Filling stations, gasoline; Petroleum bulk stations
Pr: Chuck Knapp
**VP:* Rick Forth

D-U-N-S 19-483-0642 IMP
■ **KNAPPCO CORP**
CIVACON
(*Suby of* DOVER CORP) ★
4304 N Mattox Rd, Kansas City, MO 64150-9755
Tel (816) 741-0786 *Founded/Ownrshp* 1995
Sales 44.9MM^E *EMP* 140
SIC 3321 3643 3494 Manhole covers, metal; Caps & plugs, electric: attachment; Valves & pipe fittings; Manhole covers, metal; Caps & plugs, electric: attachment; Valves & pipe fittings
Pr: Rick Potter
**Pr:* Pat Gerard
**CEO:* John F Anderson
**CFO:* Dan Taylor
Ql Cn Mgr: Bob Bobadilla
Natl Sales: Greg Evans
Sls Mgr: Brenda Munci

D-U-N-S 13-487-5983 IMP
KNAUF INSULATION INC
(*Suby of* GEBR. KNAUF VERWALTUNGSGESELLSCHAFT KG)
1 Knauf Dr, Shelbyville, IN 46176-8626
Tel (317) 398-4434 *Founded/Ownrshp* 1979
Sales 364.2MM^E *EMP* 1,126
SIC 3229 Glass fiber products; Glass fiber products
CEO: Tony Robson
**Pr:* Mark Andrews
**CFO:* Robert Claxton
**VP:* Jeffery Brisley
**VP:* Jon Pereira
Assoc Dir: Louis Walton
Dir Bus: Graham Boyd
CIO: Stefan Haverkock
Natl Sales: David Harrison

D-U-N-S 14-434-5147 IMP
KNAUF INSULATION LLC
979 Batesville Rd Ste B, Greer, SC 29651-6819
Tel (517) 629-9464 *Founded/Ownrshp* 2014
Sales 125.3MM^E *EMP* 500
SIC 3296 Fiberglass insulation; Fiberglass insulation
CEO: Mark Andrews
VP: Jeffrey Knight
IT Man: Greg Sanford

D-U-N-S 07-895-1761
KNAUS CHEESE INC (WI)
WEYAUWEGA STAR DAIRY
N5722 County Road C, Rosendale, WI 54974-9717
Tel (920) 922-5200 *Founded/Ownrshp* 1975
Sales 55.9MM^E *EMP* 95
SIC 5143 5147 Cheese; Meats & meat products; Cheese; Meats & meat products
Pr: Daniel Knaus
**VP:* Theresa Knaus
Sfty Mgr: Chris Nesdit

D-U-N-S 07-132-9092
KND DEVELOPMENT 55 LLC
KINDRED HOSPITAL - RANCHO
10841 White Oak Ave, Rancho Cucamonga, CA 91730-3811
Tel (909) 581-6400 *Founded/Ownrshp* 2007
Sales 45.1MM *EMP* 68^E
SIC 8062 General medical & surgical hospitals; General medical & surgical hospitals
CFO: J Hovsepian
Dir Rad: Jenny Hicks
Mktg Dir: Jennifer Benefield

D-U-N-S 11-348-6893
KNEAD BREAD LLC
PANERA BREAD
2053 Niles Rd, Saint Joseph, MI 49085-2505
Tel (269) 983-3888 *Founded/Ownrshp* 1999
Sales 33.8MM^E *EMP* 700
SIC 5461 Bakeries; Bakeries
Prin: Craig S Erikson
**Pr:* Jeff White

D-U-N-S 15-454-8564
KNECHT HOME CENTER OF RAPID CITY LLC
(*Suby of* ACE HARDWARE) ★
320 West Blvd, Rapid City, SD 57701-2671
Tel (605) 342-4840 *Founded/Ownrshp* 1931
Sales 56.5MM^E *EMP* 349^E
SIC 5251 5211 1751 Builders' hardware; Lumber & other building materials; Cabinet & finish carpentry; Builders' hardware; Lumber & other building materials; Cabinet & finish carpentry
Pr: Craig Bradshaw
**Ch:* Robert Mead
Genl Mgr: Wallace Bork

D-U-N-S 02-995-2686
KNEIBERT CLINIC LLC
686 Lester St, Poplar Bluff, MO 63901-5025
Tel (573) 686-2411 *Founded/Ownrshp* 1939
Sales 20.7MM^E *EMP* 120
SIC 8011 5912 Medical centers; Drug stores; Medical centers; Drug stores
Pt: R K Bost MD
Pt: Cynthia Brown MD
Pt: E C Hansbrough MD
Pt: A D Madduri MD
Pt: S D Madduri MD
Pt: Steve Nagy MD
Pt: A N Reddy MD
Pt: Dr Bradley J Stuckenschneider
Pt: John True MD
Pt: Kirby L Turner MD
Pt: Prem Varma MD
Pt: Gary Ward Do

D-U-N-S 08-226-7279
KNEIBERT CLINIC LLC
686 Lester St, Poplar Bluff, MO 63901-5025
Tel (573) 778-7210 *Founded/Ownrshp* 1973
Sales 25.6MM^E *EMP* 150
SIC 8062 General medical & surgical hospitals
Ch: Kirby Turner
Dir Rx: Ellis Odom
Off Mgr: Chad Boyt
Off Mgr: Phyllis Davis
MIS Dir: Mike Collins
Doctor: Roger Bost
Doctor: Wendell Elliott
Doctor: Charles Lawson
Doctor: B Till

D-U-N-S 00-439-3633 IMP
KNEPPER PRESS CORP (PA)
2251 Sweeney Dr, Clinton, PA 15026-1818
Tel (724) 899-4200 *Founded/Ownrshp* 1873
Sales 35.0MM *EMP* 200
SIC 2752 Commercial printing, offset; Commercial printing, offset
CEO: Ted Ford
**Pr:* Bob Hreha
**VP:* William J Knepper
VP: Kent Rafferty
**Prin:* Robert Hreha
Dir IT: Aveek Datta
IT Man: Scott Nock
IT Man: Dennis Ranft
Sales Exec: Paul Jackson
VP Sls: Alain Lemieux
VP Sls: Dena McCall-Crow

K'NEX
See CONNECTOR SET LTD PARTNERSHIP

KNEX BUILDING MTL CO & INSUL
See KNEZ BUILDING MATERIALS CO

D-U-N-S 06-122-6697 IMP/EXP
KNEX INDUSTRIES INC
2990 Bergey Rd, Hatfield, PA 19440-1735
Tel (215) 997-7722 *Founded/Ownrshp* 1992
Sales 27.2MM^E *EMP* 160
SIC 3944 Games, toys & children's vehicles; Games, toys & children's vehicles
CEO: Michael Araten
**Pr:* Joel Glickman
**CFO:* Robert Haines
**Sr VP:* Bob Haines
**Sr VP:* Joseph Smith
VP: Stewart McMeeking
IT Man: John Zimmer
Web Dev: Andrew Emerick
Opers Mgr: Joe Wetzel
Natl Sales: Bill Konkel
VP Sls: Dave Bickel

D-U-N-S 06-148-6940
KNEZ BUILDING MATERIALS CO
KNEX BUILDING MTL CO & INSUL
12300 Se Knez Way, Clackamas, OR 97015-9062
Tel (503) 655-1991 *Founded/Ownrshp* 1974
Sales 66.5MM^E *EMP* 130
SIC 5031 Lumber, plywood & millwork; Wallboard; Lumber, plywood & millwork; Wallboard
Pr: John S Knez J
**Pr:* John Knez Jr
**VP:* Joseph F Knez

D-U-N-S 15-594-2709
KNF&T INC
KNF&T STAFFING RESOURCES
3 Post Office Sq Ste 200, Boston, MA 02109-3941
Tel (617) 574-8200 *Founded/Ownrshp* 1983
Sales 22.5MM *EMP* 35
SIC 7361 Employment agencies; Employment agencies
Pr: Jeanne Fiol
**Sec:* Elizabeth Tucker
VP: Maura Gilbert
Brnch Mgr: Jillian Ciarletta
IT Man: Beth Tucker

KNF&T STAFFING RESOURCES
See KNF&T INC

KNI MARKETING
See KRAEMERS NURSERY INC

D-U-N-S 82-893-4989
KNIA HOLDINGS INC
110 Hopkins St, Buffalo, NY 14220-2131
Tel (914) 241-7430 *Founded/Ownrshp* 2006
Sales NA *EMP* 1,070
SIC 6719 Investment holding companies, except banks; Investment holding companies, except banks
Pr: James Kohlberg

D-U-N-S 13-072-7444
KNICHEL LOGISTICS
5347 William Flynn Hwy, Gibsonia, PA 15044-9644
Tel (724) 449-3300 *Founded/Ownrshp* 2003
Sales 30.4MM^E *EMP* 30
SIC 4731 Transportation agents & brokers
Mng Pt: William Knichel
**Pt:* Kristy Knichel
**Ex VP:* J R Knichel
VP: Jonathon Krystek
Sls Mgr: Vicki Clark

D-U-N-S 00-219-1005
KNICKERBOCKER MACHINE SHOP INC (NJ)
A S P
611 Union Blvd, Totowa, NJ 07512-2402
Tel (973) 256-1616 *Founded/Ownrshp* 1944
Sales 20.0MM^E *EMP* 166
SIC 3494 3432 Valves & pipe fittings; Plumbing fixture fittings & trim; Valves & pipe fittings; Plumbing fixture fittings & trim
Pr: John Simonelli
**VP:* Anthony P Auferio
**VP Mfg:* Annemarie Appleton
Ql Cn Mgr: William Rodriquez

D-U-N-S 02-301-6137
KNICKERBOCKER PROPERTIES INC
8717 W 110th St Ste 240, Shawnee Mission, KS 66210-2103
Tel (913) 451-4466 *Founded/Ownrshp* 1996
Sales 36.0MM *EMP* 40
SIC 6531 Real estate agents & managers; Real estate agents & managers
Pr: Sara Queen
**Treas:* Peter Zapulla
**VP:* Charles Grossman
VP: Robert Leu
Off Mgr: Lisa Dillon

KNIFE RIVER COAL MINING
See KNIFE RIVER CORP

KNIFE RIVER CONSTRUCTION
See BALDWIN CONTRACTING CO INC

D-U-N-S 00-696-2096 IMP
■ **KNIFE RIVER CORP**
KNIFE RIVER COAL MINING
(*Suby of* MDU RESOURCES GROUP INC) ★
1150 W Century Ave, Bismarck, ND 58503-0942
Tel (701) 530-1400 *Founded/Ownrshp* 1922, 1988
Sales 1.3MMM^E *EMP* 2,370
SIC 1442 3273 3241 1221 Construction sand & gravel; Ready-mixed concrete; Cement, hydraulic; Bituminous coal & lignite-surface mining; Construction sand & gravel; Ready-mixed concrete; Cement, hydraulic; Bituminous coal & lignite-surface mining
Ch Bd: Martin White
**Pr:* Dave Barney
**CEO:* Bill Schneider
**Treas:* Larry E Hansen
Ofcr: Steve Baeth
VP: Boyd Clements
**VP:* Larry Duppong
VP: Trevor Hastings
VP: Mary Johnson
VP: Steve Mote
Genl Mgr: Alrick Hale

D-U-N-S 04-725-8306
■ **KNIFE RIVER CORP - NORTH CENTRAL**
(*Suby of* KNIFE RIVER CORP COAL MINING) ★
4787 Shadowwood Dr Ne, Sauk Rapids, MN 56379-9431
Tel (320) 251-9472 *Founded/Ownrshp* 2007
Sales 129.5MM^E *EMP* 750
SIC 1611 1442 3273 2951 Highway & street paving contractor; Gravel mining; Ready-mixed concrete; Asphalt paving mixtures & blocks; Highway & street paving contractor; Gravel mining; Ready-mixed concrete; Asphalt paving mixtures & blocks
CEO: David C Barney
**VP:* Michael Bauerly
Sls Mgr: Alan Johnson

D-U-N-S 00-904-1427 IMP
■ **KNIFE RIVER CORP - NORTHWEST** (OR)
(*Suby of* KNIFE RIVER COAL MINING) ★
32260 Old Highway 34, Tangent, OR 97389-9770
Tel (541) 928-6491 *Founded/Ownrshp* 1962
Sales 151.4MM^E *EMP* 575
SIC 1611 3273 General contractor, highway & street construction; Ready-mixed concrete; General contractor, highway & street construction; Ready-mixed concrete
Pr: Brian R Gray
**Ch Bd:* Martin A White
**Pr:* David Ball
**CEO:* Terry D Hildestad
**VP:* Stephen Frey
Opers Mgr: Dave Bolster

D-U-N-S 78-385-6227
■ **KNIFE RIVER CORP - SOUTH**
(*Suby of* KNIFE RIVER COAL MINING) ★
8320 Central Park Dr A, Waco, TX 76712-6523
Tel (254) 761-2600 *Founded/Ownrshp* 1993
Sales 51.3MM^E *EMP* 700
SIC 1442 3273 1521 Construction sand & gravel; Ready-mixed concrete; Single-family housing construction; Construction sand & gravel; Ready-mixed concrete; Single-family housing construction
Pr: Wayne Dutra
Board of Directors: Terry D Hildestad, William E Schneider

KNIFE RIVER MATERIALS
See LTM INC

KNIFE RIVER MATERIALS
See NORTHSTAR MATERIALS INC

D-U-N-S 00-694-0928
■ **KNIFE RIVER MIDWEST LLC**
(*Suby of* KNIFE RIVER COAL MINING) ★
2220 Hawkeye Dr, Sioux City, IA 51105-2048
Tel (712) 252-2766 *Founded/Ownrshp* 1901, 2004
Sales 72.0MM^E *EMP* 546
SIC 1611 3273 1442

KNIFE RIVER-BILLINGS
See JTL GROUP INC

D-U-N-S 15-198-8771
KNIGHT & WILSON INC
1240 Williams Ave, Memphis, TN 38104-4701
Tel (901) 274-6978 *Founded/Ownrshp* 1979
Sales 39.2MM^E *EMP* 250
SIC 1711 1761

D-U-N-S 83-016-6893
■ **KNIGHT BROKERAGE LLC**
(*Suby of* KNIGHT TRANSPORTATION INC) ★
20002 N 19th Ave, Phoenix, AZ 85027-4250
Tel (602) 272-1500 *Founded/Ownrshp* 2005
Sales 31.2MM^E *EMP* 40
SIC 4731 Freight transportation arrangement
Pr: Greg Ritter
**CFO:* Dave Jackson
**VP:* Scott Pruneau
Sls&Mrk Ex: Bittle Shawn

D-U-N-S 83-587-4892
■ **KNIGHT CAPITAL AMERICAS LP**
KCG
(*Suby of* KNIGHT CAPITAL GROUP INC) ★
545 Washington Blvd Ste 1, Jersey City, NJ 07310-1607
Tel (800) 544-7508 *Founded/Ownrshp* 1998

Sales 101.4MM^E *EMP* 481
SIC 6211 Security brokers & dealers; Security brokers & dealers
Mng Pt: Thomas M Joyce
Pt: James P Smyth Sr
Pt: Gregory C Voetsch
COO: Philip Gough
Mng Dir: Adam Seiden
Software D: Zia Chowdhury
Software D: Vincent Harvey
Software D: Alexander Kondratskiy
Software D: Vlad Lazarenko
Software D: Ujwal Ovaleker
Software D: Andrei Shpakov

D-U-N-S 01-820-3229
■ KNIGHT CAPITAL GROUP INC
(*Suby of* KCG HOLDINGS INC) ★
545 Washington Blvd Ste 1, Jersey City, NJ 07310-1607
Tel (201) 222-9400 *Founded/Ownrshp* 1995, 2013
Sales 590.0MM^E *EMP* 1,524^E
SIC 6211 6282 Security brokers & dealers; Investment advice; Security brokers & dealers; Investment advice
CEO: Daniel B Coleman
Pr: Scott Crammond
Pr: Ignacio Diaz
Pr: Parin Shah
Pr: Viany Taitt
Pr: Jianzhang Xu
**COO:* Steven Bisgay
CFO: Sean Galvin
CFO: Steffen Parratt
Ofcr: Nick Ogurtsov
Assoc VP: Beth Mills
**Ex VP:* Leonard J Amoruso
**Sr VP:* Glenn T Callen
VP: Neeraj Aggarwal
VP: Chuxun Chen
VP: Chris Cochrane
VP: Brooke Jones
**VP:* Caryn Korman
VP: Himanshu Sharma
VP: Peter Sheahan
Board of Directors: William L Bolster, Martin Brand, James W Lewis, James T Milde, Matthew Nimetz, Christopher C Quick, Daniel F Schmitt, Laurie M Shahon, Fred Tomczyk

D-U-N-S 05-605-4380
KNIGHT CONST & SUPPLY INC (WA)
28308 N Cedar Rd, Deer Park, WA 99006-8357
Tel (509) 276-2229 *Founded/Ownrshp* 1968
Sales 21.7MM *EMP* 80
SIC 1629 Dam construction; Industrial plant construction; Dam construction; Industrial plant construction
CEO: James D Knight
**Pr:* Douglas J Knight
**Treas:* David Knight
**VP:* Kenneth L Knight
Dir IT: Dorothy King
IT Man: Erik Wakeling

D-U-N-S 01-209-7523
KNIGHT ELECTRICAL SERVICES CORP
NATIONAL STATES ELC SYSTEMS
599 11th Ave Fl 7, New York, NY 10036-2110
Tel (212) 989-2333 *Founded/Ownrshp* 2003
Sales 27.1MM^E *EMP* 200^E
SIC 1731 General electrical contractor; General electrical contractor
Ch Bd: Bartholomew J Carmody
**Sec:* Bartholomew D Carmody
MIS Dir: Charles Hayek
Mktg Dir: Philip Kielkucki

D-U-N-S 09-694-7742
KNIGHT ENERGY HOLDINGS LLC
2727 Se Evangeline Trwy, Lafayette, LA 70508-2205
Tel (337) 233-0464 *Founded/Ownrshp* 1983
Sales 60.7MM^E *EMP* 300
SIC 7353 Oil field equipment, rental or leasing; Oil field equipment, rental or leasing
CEO: Earl Blackwell
Ch Bd: Mark Knight
Pr: Doug Keller
COO: Pat McLaughlin
CFO: Robert Veazey
VP: Mike Foster
Brnch Mgr: Donald Ramero
VP Opers: Mickey Broussard
Trfc Dir: Drew Duplantis
VP Sls: Rickey Tauzin

KNIGHT ENTERPRISES
See JEFFRY KNIGHT INC

D-U-N-S 06-881-1702
KNIGHT ENTERPRISES INC
40600 Grand River Ave, Novi, MI 48375-2810
Tel (248) 478-3651 *Founded/Ownrshp* 1968
Sales 36.2MM^E *EMP* 85
SIC 5541 5171 Filling stations, gasoline; Petroleum bulk stations
Pr: Carroll L Knight

D-U-N-S 82-481-2887
KNIGHT FACILITIES MANAGEMENT INC
KNIGHT FM
5360 Hampton Pl, Saginaw, MI 48604-9490
Tel (989) 793-8820 *Founded/Ownrshp* 1993
Sales 30.4MM *EMP* 850
SIC 8742 Maintenance management consultant; Maintenance management consultant
Pr: Daniel Waltenburg
**CFO:* Dennis Argyle
**VP:* Chad Hinds
VP Opers: Mark Yohannan
Board of Directors: Deforest Davis, Steve Mitchell

KNIGHT FEDERAL
See AB CLOSING CORP

KNIGHT FM
See KNIGHT FACILITIES MANAGEMENT INC

D-U-N-S 02-258-1537
KNIGHT HAWK COAL LLC
500 Cutler Trico Rd, Percy, IL 62272-2716
Tel (618) 426-3662 *Founded/Ownrshp* 1998
Sales 582.7MM^E *EMP* 380
SIC 1241 1222 Coal mining services; Bituminous coal-underground mining; Coal mining services; Bituminous coal-underground mining
VP: James Smith
Dir Risk M: Jenna Parsons
Genl Mgr: Keith Dailey
Off Mgr: Neil Bradley
IT Man: Jason Thies
Plnt Mgr: Dale Winter

KNIGHT INDUSTRIES
See KNIGHT TEXTILE CORP

D-U-N-S 79-315-1275
KNIGHT OFFICE SOLUTIONS INC
12961 Park Central # 1470, San Antonio, TX 78216-2092
Tel (210) 340-8909 *Founded/Ownrshp* 1995
Sales 20.3MM^E *EMP* 45
SIC 5045 Computer software
Pr: John Chaney
Sls Mgr: Wilson Korona

D-U-N-S 07-838-9986
KNIGHT OIL TOOLS LLC
(*Suby of* KNIGHT ENERGY HOLDINGS LLC) ★
2727 Se Evangeline Trwy, Lafayette, LA 70508-2205
Tel (337) 233-0464 *Founded/Ownrshp* 2011
Sales 25.0MM^E *EMP* 98^E
SIC 1381 Directional drilling oil & gas wells
CEO: Earl Blackwell
**Ch Bd:* Mark Knight
Pr: Doug Keller
**COO:* Mickey Broussard
**CFO:* Robert C Veazey
Genl Mgr: Graham Edgley
Off Mgr: Cindy Pothier
Store Mgr: James Matherne
Dir IT: Barret Lemaire
IT Man: Bobby Crockett
Software D: Michael Blanchard

D-U-N-S 62-259-4492
KNIGHT POINT SYSTEMS LLC
1775 Wiehle Ave Ste 101, Reston, VA 20190-5109
Tel (703) 657-7050 *Founded/Ownrshp* 2005
Sales 68.9MM *EMP* 185
SIC 7374 Data processing & preparation; Data processing & preparation
COO: Doug Duenkel
Prgrm Mgr: Chris Burch
Off Admin: Erin Hood
Off Admin: Tonya Mitchell
Netwrk Eng: Calvin Stanberry
Board of Directors: Daniel Duenkel, Keith McMeans

D-U-N-S 62-759-2843
KNIGHT PROTECTIVE SERVICE INC
6411 Ivy Ln Ste 320, Greenbelt, MD 20770-1405
Tel (301) 808-4669 *Founded/Ownrshp* 1988
Sales 20.4MM^E *EMP* 1,500
Accts Mccalin & Associates Philadel
SIC 7381 Security guard service; Security guard service
Pr: Macon Sims Jr
VP: Denisha Logan

D-U-N-S 10-677-7972
KNIGHT SECURITY SYSTEMS LLC
10105 Tech Blvd W Ste 100, Dallas, TX 75220-4384
Tel (214) 350-1632 *Founded/Ownrshp* 1983
Sales 21.3MM^E *EMP* 60^E
SIC 7382 Security systems services
VP: H West
Dir: Bob Minchew
Dir IT: Brian Bradford
MIS Mgr: Chad Brooks
Sls Mgr: Dan Viotto
Snr PM: Bert Aquila
Snr PM: Clyde Conn

D-U-N-S 05-591-3834
KNIGHT TEXTILE CORP
KNIGHT INDUSTRIES
310 S Main St, Saluda, SC 29138-1779
Tel (803) 445-8115 *Founded/Ownrshp* 1971
Sales 18.3MM^E *EMP* 400
SIC 2339 2331 2369 2325 Slacks: women's, misses' & juniors'; Blouses, women's & juniors': made from purchased material; Girls' & children's outerwear; Men's & boys' trousers & slacks
Pr: Talmadge M Knight

D-U-N-S 78-136-6299
KNIGHT TRANSPORT LLC
1016 W Main St, Auburn, WA 98001-5219
Tel (253) 536-6840 *Founded/Ownrshp* 2008
Sales 28.1MM^E *EMP* 100
SIC 4213 4731 Trucking, except local; Truck transportation brokers

D-U-N-S 01-553-4576
KNIGHT TRANSPORTATION
20431 Franz Rd, Katy, TX 77449-5657
Tel (281) 599-7254 *Founded/Ownrshp* 1996
Sales 32.0MM^E *EMP* 340
SIC 4213 Trucking, except local; Trucking, except local
Div Mgr: Adams Phillips
COO: Dave Jackson
Mktg Dir: Patrick Maher
Sls Dir: Grady Jarl

D-U-N-S 10-720-5536
■ KNIGHT TRANSPORTATION GULF COAST INC
(*Suby of* KNIGHT TRANSPORTATION INC) ★
20002 N 19th Ave, Phoenix, AZ 85027-4250
Tel (602) 269-2000 *Founded/Ownrshp* 2000
Sales 15.3MM^E *EMP* 300
SIC 4213 Trucking, except local; Trucking, except local
CEO: Kevin Knight
**Pr:* Gary Knight
**Treas:* Tim Kohl

D-U-N-S 61-595-6992
▲ KNIGHT TRANSPORTATION INC
20002 N 19th Ave, Phoenix, AZ 85027-4250
Tel (602) 269-2000 *Founded/Ownrshp* 1989
Sales 1.1MMM *EMP* 5,485
Tkr Sym KNX *Exch* NYS
SIC 4213 4212 Trucking, except local; Local trucking, without storage; Trucking, except local; Local trucking, without storage
Pr: David A Jackson
**Ch Bd:* Kevin P Knight
COO: Richard Martin
CFO: Adam Miller
**V Ch Bd:* Gary J Knight
Ex VP: Casey Comen
Ex VP: Matt Hoffman
Ex VP: Kevin Quast
Ex VP: James E Updike Jr
Sr VP: Ramsey Bill
Exec: Jonathan Barnes
Exec: Nathan Barney
Exec: Jeremy Bartell
Exec: Genny Bennett
Exec: Jimie Campbell
Exec: Ryan Campbell
Exec: Edward Christian
Exec: Courtney Dailey
Exec: Kimberly Davis
Exec: Desiree Dufur
Exec: George Duggan
Board of Directors: Donald A Bliss, Michael Garnreiter, Richard C Kraemer, Richard J Lehmann, G D Madden, Kathryn L Munro

D-U-N-S 18-764-3754 IMP/EXP
KNIGHT-CHEMSTAR INC
9204 Emmott Rd, Houston, TX 77040-3328
Tel (713) 466-8751 *Founded/Ownrshp* 2002
Sales 363.3MM *EMP* 10
SIC 5169 5172 Chemicals & allied products; Industrial chemicals; Petroleum products; Naptha
Pr: Steve Knight

KNIGHTED, LLC
See INTELLIGRATED SOFTWARE LLC

KNIGHTEN INDUSTRIES
See KNIGHTEN MACHINE AND SERVICE INC

D-U-N-S 05-369-9906
KNIGHTEN MACHINE AND SERVICE INC
KNIGHTEN INDUSTRIES
3323 N County Rd W, Odessa, TX 79764-6403
Tel (432) 362-0468 *Founded/Ownrshp* 1972
Sales 20.5MM^E *EMP* 45
SIC 3599 7692 Machine shop, jobbing & repair; Welding repair
Pr: William L Knighten
**VP:* Brian Knighten
Area Mgr: Bill Smith
Brnch Mgr: James Bivins
Brnch Mgr: Derrick Katzer
Brnch Mgr: Ron Parault
Opers Mgr: Jamie Williams
Sls Mgr: Alton Holloway
Sales Asso: Herb Mayfield

D-U-N-S 15-369-6930 IMP/EXP
■ KNIGHTS APPAREL INC
ALTA GRACIA
(*Suby of* HANESBRANDS INC) ★
5475 N Blackstock Rd, Spartanburg, SC 29303-4702
Tel (864) 587-9690 *Founded/Ownrshp* 2015
Sales 198.0MM^E *EMP* 325^E
SIC 5091 5699 Sporting & recreation goods; Sporting & recreation goods; Sports apparel
CEO: Joseph Bozich
**Pr:* Donnie Hodge
**CFO:* Jay R Cope

D-U-N-S 05-380-4169
KNIGHTS COMPANIES INC
480 Hodge Rd, Summerville, SC 29483-7607
Tel (843) 821-7600 *Founded/Ownrshp* 1995
Sales 25.0MM *EMP* 140
SIC 3273 Ready-mixed concrete
Pr: Michael B Knight

KNIGHT'S GARAGE NISSAN
See NISSAN

KNIGHTS INN
See WYNDHAM HOTEL GROUP LLC

D-U-N-S 09-026-6078
KNIGHTS MARINE AND INDUSTRIAL SERVICES INC
3421 Industrial Rd, Pascagoula, MS 39581-5213
Tel (228) 769-5550 *Founded/Ownrshp* 1999
Sales 41.6MM^E *EMP* 242
SIC 3441 3732 7361 Fabricated structural metal; Boat building & repairing; Labor contractors (employment agency); Fabricated structural metal; Boat building & repairing; Labor contractors (employment agency)
Pr: Brian Knight
**VP:* David E Knight
**VP:* Jim Patano
Genl Mgr: Melissa Wallis

D-U-N-S 12-177-8583
KNIGHTS MECHANICAL INC
4250 Leitchfield Rd, Cecilia, KY 42724-9642
Tel (270) 765-4141 *Founded/Ownrshp* 1980
Sales 20.7MM^E *EMP* 150
SIC 1711 7692

D-U-N-S 04-120-5329 IMP
KNIGHTS OF COLUMBUS
1 Columbus Plz Ste 1700, New Haven, CT 06510-3326
Tel (203) 752-4000 *Founded/Ownrshp* 1882
Sales NA *EMP* 2,300
SIC 6411 8641 Insurance agents & brokers; Fraternal associations; Insurance agents & brokers; Fraternal associations
VP: Robert Tracz
Pr: Niki Kratzert
CFO: Terry Lescoe
**Treas:* Logan Ludwig

Treas: Michael J O'Connor
VP: Joel Boncek
VP: Lynn Hussey
VP: Patrick Korten
VP: Gilles Marchand
VP: Anthony Minopoli
Snr Ntwrk: John Thompson

D-U-N-S 07-097-8358 IMP
KNIK CONSTRUCTION CO INC
(*Suby of* LYNDEN INC) ★
18000 Intl Blvd Ste 800, Seatac, WA 98188-4263
Tel (206) 439-5525 *Founded/Ownrshp* 1973
Sales 49.7MM^E *EMP* 200
SIC 1611 5032 Airport runway construction; Paving materials; Sand, construction; Gravel; Airport runway construction; Paving materials; Sand, construction; Gravel
Pr: Steve Jansen
**Treas:* Kitty Samuel
**VP:* David W Haugen
VP: Parry Rekers
Exec: Vic Jansen

D-U-N-S 62-191-9141
KNIPP EQUIPMENT INC
KANSAS TRANE SALES COMPANY
120 S Ida St, Wichita, KS 67211-1504
Tel (316) 265-9655 *Founded/Ownrshp* 1990
Sales 21.5MM^E *EMP* 35
SIC 5075 1711 Warm air heating & air conditioning; Warm air heating & air conditioning contractor
Pr: John F Knipp
**VP:* Patricia A Knipp
Off Mgr: Tom Schmidt

D-U-N-S 03-288-8794
KNIPPELMIER CHEVROLET INC
1811 E Us Highway 62, Blanchard, OK 73010-9202
Tel (405) 485-3333 *Founded/Ownrshp* 1969
Sales 22.0MM^E *EMP* 60
SIC 5511 Automobiles, new & used; Pickups, new & used; Automobiles, new & used; Pickups, new & used
Pr: Larry Knippelmier
**VP:* Peggy Knippelmier

D-U-N-S 04-393-9941 IMP
KNIT-RITE INC
120 Osage Ave, Kansas City, KS 66105-1415
Tel (913) 279-6310 *Founded/Ownrshp* 2006
Sales 22.0MM^E *EMP* 170
SIC 3842 Orthopedic appliances; Prosthetic appliances; Elastic hosiery, orthopedic (support); Orthopedic appliances; Prosthetic appliances; Elastic hosiery, orthopedic (support)
Ch Bd: Mark W L Smith
**COO:* Chris H Vering
**Ex VP:* Ron Hercules
Exec: Lisa Trussel
CIO: Janell Haskins
QA Dir: Jennifer Leviner
IT Man: Michael Wright
QI Cn Mgr: Stuart Reynolds
Sls Dir: Evan McGill
Sls Mgr: Jim Gillespie
Snr Mgr: Jeff Dalbey

D-U-N-S 96-194-6238 IMP
KNITWORK PRODUCTIONS II LLC
AMERICAN ATTITUDES/SAY WHAT
1410 Brdy Fl 24, New York, NY 10018
Tel (212) 398-8181 *Founded/Ownrshp* 2007
Sales 38.9MM^E *EMP* 90
SIC 5137 Women's & children's clothing
CEO: Rozita Pnini
**CFO:* David Sapiro
**Ex VP:* Yuval Navon
**Ex VP:* Matthew Pnini
Ex VP: Bernie Slobotkin
**Prin:* Izzy Pnini
**Prin:* Peter Stern

D-U-N-S 04-777-7131
KNOBBE MARTENS OLSON & BEAR LLP
2040 Main St Fl 14, Irvine, CA 92614-8214
Tel (949) 760-0404 *Founded/Ownrshp* 1962
Sales 91.0MM^E *EMP* 600
SIC 8111 General practice law office; General practice law office
Mng Pt: Steven J Nataupsky
**Pt:* William B Bunker
**Pt:* Drew S Hamilton
**Pt:* Ned Israelsen
**Pt:* Steven Nataupsky
**Pt:* William H Nieman
**Pt:* Darrell L Olson
**Pt:* Arthur S Rose
**Pt:* Joseph R RE
**Pt:* Edward A Schlatter
**Pt:* John B Sganga
**Pt:* Gerard Von Hoffman III
**Mng Pt:* James B Bear
VP: Daniel Henry
VP: Edward Treska
Dir Soc: Shannon Keany
Dir Bus: Krista Hosseinzadeh

D-U-N-S 03-953-5752
KNOCHEL BROS INC
K B
1441 E Alameda Dr, Phoenix, AZ 85024-4305
Tel (623) 581-2966 *Founded/Ownrshp* 1983
Sales 27.2MM^E *EMP* 150
SIC 1794 Excavation & grading, building construction; Excavation & grading, building construction
Pr: Nathan Knochel
**VP:* Herb Knochel Jr

D-U-N-S 07-378-8739
KNOEBEL CONSTRUCTION INC
640 Axminister Dr, Fenton, MO 63026-2906
Tel (314) 421-3511 *Founded/Ownrshp* 1999
Sales 30.0MM^E *EMP* 50
SIC 1542 Commercial & office building, new construction
Pr: Randall G Venhaus
**Treas:* Denise S Venhaus

KNOEBEL'S AMUSEMENT RESORT
See H H KNOEBEL SONS INC

KNOEPFLER BODY SHOP
See KNOEPFLER CHEVROLET CO

D-U-N-S 00-798-9411
KNOEPFLER CHEVROLET CO (IA)
KNOEPFLER BODY SHOP
100 Jackson St, Sioux City, IA 51101-1727
Tel (712) 279-7100 Founded/Ownrshp 1922
Sales 39.6MM^E EMP 105
SIC 5511 7515 7538 7532 5521

D-U-N-S 78-131-6096 EXP
▲ KNOLL INC
1235 Water St, East Greenville, PA 18041-2202
Tel (215) 679-7991 Founded/Ownrshp 1938
Sales 1.0MMM EMP 3,343
Tkr Sym KNL Exch NYS
SIC 2521 2522 2299 Wood office furniture; Panel systems & partitions (free-standing), office: wood; Chairs, office: padded, upholstered or plain: wood; Office furniture, except wood; Panel systems & partitions, office: except wood; Chairs, office: padded or plain, office: except wood; Upholstery filling, textile; Wood office furniture; Panel systems & partitions (free-standing), office: wood; Chairs, office: padded, upholstered or plain: wood; Office furniture, except wood; Panel systems & partitions, office: except wood; Chairs, office: padded or plain, except wood; Upholstery filling, textile
CEO: Andrew B Cogan
*Ch Bd: Burton B Staniar
Pr: Roger B Wall
COO: Joseph T Coppola
CFO: Craig B Spray
Ex VP: Benjamin A Pardo
Sr VP: Pamela J Ahrens
Sr VP: Karen E Clary
Sr VP: Michael A Pollner
Dir Bus: Jennyfer Aguilera
Prgrm Mgr: Steven Bright
Board of Directors: Kathleen G Bradley, Stephen F Fisher, Jeffrey A Harris, Christopher G Kennedy, Sidney Lapidus, John F Maypole, Sarah E Nash, Stephanie Stahl

D-U-N-S 06-894-9346
KNOLL MAPLE COMMUNITIES INC
MAPLE KNOLL VILLAGE
11100 Springfield Pike, Cincinnati, OH 45246-4165
Tel (513) 782-2400 Founded/Ownrshp 1848
Sales 43.8MM EMP 600
Accts Plante & Moran Pllc Columbus
SIC 8051 8052 8082 Skilled nursing care facilities; Intermediate care facilities; Home health care services; Skilled nursing care facilities; Intermediate care facilities; Home health care services
VP: Rose Denman
CFO: Kenneth Huff
Bd of Dir: Lucie Ashton
Comm Dir: Megan Gresham
Off Mgr: Nancy Hendricks
Dir IT: Andy Craig

KNOLLS ATOMIC POWER LABORATORY
See KAPL INC

D-U-N-S 07-606-7859
KNOLLS CONVALESCENT HOSPITAL INC
DESERT KNLLS CONVALESCENT HOSP
16890 Green Tree Blvd, Victorville, CA 92395-5618
Tel (760) 245-5361 Founded/Ownrshp 1976
Sales 10.4MM^E EMP 300
SIC 8051 8052 Convalescent home with continuous nursing care; Intermediate care facilities; Convalescent home with continuous nursing care; Intermediate care facilities
Pr: Gary L Bechtold
*VP: Fred Bechtold
Off Mgr: Pam Kowal
HC Dir: Mirella Cervantes

KNOLLWOOD
See ARMY DISTAFF FOUNDATION INC

D-U-N-S 08-055-8406
KNOLLWOOD MANOR GENESIS ELDERCARE
KNOLLWOOD MANOR NURSING HOME
1221 Waugh Chapel Rd, Gambrills, MD 21054-1608
Tel (410) 987-1644 Founded/Ownrshp 1960, 1994
Sales 505.2MM EMP 84
SIC 8051 8052 Skilled nursing care facilities; Intermediate care facilities
Exec: Todd Jones

KNOLLWOOD MANOR NURSING HOME
See KNOLLWOOD MANOR GENESIS ELDERCARE

D-U-N-S 93-264-6748
KNOLOGY BROADBAND INC
1241 Og Skinner Dr, West Point, GA 31833-1789
Tel (706) 645-8553 Founded/Ownrshp 1998
Sales NA EMP 1,157^E
SIC 4841

D-U-N-S 09-801-3613
KNOLOGY INC
(Suby of WIDEOPENWEST FINANCE LLC) ★
1241 Og Skinner Dr, West Point, GA 31833-1789
Tel (334) 644-2611 Founded/Ownrshp 2012
Sales 406.1MM^E EMP 1,861^E
SIC 4813 4841 ; Cable television services
CEO: Rodger L Johnson
COO: Jack Hearst
CFO: Felix L Boccucci Jr
VP: Anthony J Palermo Jr
VP: Wendy Wills
Genl Mgr: Deb Hines
Genl Mgr: Kevin Nolan
Plng Mgr: Lynn Hall
Netwrk Eng: David Reale
Sls Mgr: Parker Redevelopa

D-U-N-S 00-585-4583
KNOLOGY OF VALLEY INC (GA)
(Suby of KNOLOGY INC) ★
910 1st Ave, West Point, GA 31833-1254
Tel (706) 645-0033 Founded/Ownrshp 1895
Sales 20.7MM^E EMP 140
SIC 4813 Local telephone communications; Local telephone communications
CEO: CAM B Lanier III
*Pr: Rodger Johnson
CFO: J D Cox

D-U-N-S 04-513-3899 EXP
KNOPF AUTOMOTIVE INC
3401 Lehigh St, Allentown, PA 18103-7038
Tel (610) 439-1555 Founded/Ownrshp 1969
Sales 37.3MM^E EMP 75
Accts Downey & Company Llp Braintr
SIC 5511 7538 Automobiles, new & used; General automotive repair shops; Automobiles, new & used; General automotive repair shops
Ch: Charles E Knopf Jr
*Pr: David W Helmer
IT Man: Alan Ziegler
VP Mktg: Chris Boland
Sls Mgr: John Buckner
Sls Mgr: Dave Thomas

D-U-N-S 07-484-3871 IMP
KNORR BRAKE CO LLC
(Suby of KNORR BRAKE HOLDING CORP) ★
1 Arthur Peck Dr, Westminster, MD 21157-3074
Tel (410) 875-0900 Founded/Ownrshp 2008
Sales 47.7MM^E EMP 230
SIC 3743 4789 Brakes, air & vacuum: railway; Rapid transit cars & equipment; Railroad maintenance & repair services; Railroad car repair; Brakes, air & vacuum: railway; Rapid transit cars & equipment; Railroad maintenance & repair services; Railroad car repair
Ch: Kenneth Andrews
*Pr: Richard Bowie
Dir Bus: Ignacio Fuster
Prd Mgr: Keith Mutschler
Ql Cn Mgr: John Jeffas
Ql Cn Mgr: Aaron O'Neal
Ql Cn Mgr: Gary Stonge
Sls Mgr: Randy Mitzelfelt

D-U-N-S 80-135-6317 IMP
KNORR BRAKE HOLDING CORP
(Suby of KNORR-BREMSE AG)
748 Starbuck Ave, Watertown, NY 13601-1620
Tel (315) 786-5356 Founded/Ownrshp 1990
Sales 1.3MMM^E EMP 5,304
SIC 3743 5013 Railroad equipment; Motor vehicle supplies & new parts; Railroad equipment; Motor vehicle supplies & new parts
Pr: Heinz Hermann Thiele
Sls Mgr: Heather Komatsoulis

D-U-N-S 55-607-2163 IMP
KNORR BRAKE TRUCK SYSTEMS CO
NEW YORK AIR BRAKE
(Suby of KNORR BRAKE HOLDING CORP) ★
748 Starbuck Ave, Watertown, NY 13601-1620
Tel (315) 786-5200 Founded/Ownrshp 1990
Sales 1.2MMM^E EMP 3,194
Accts Kpmg Llp
SIC 3743 Brakes, air & vacuum: railway; Brakes, air & vacuum: railway
Pr: Heinz Hermann Thiele
*Pr: Mike Hawthorne
*CFO: J Paul Morgan
Treas: Kathleen Gosnell
*V Ch Bd: Peter Riedlinger
VP: Scott Burkhart
VP: Kishor Pendse
Prgrm Mgr: Pat Purtell
Snr Sftwr: Scott Walters
IT Man: Marc Robbins
IT Man: Mark Storms

KNOTT COUNTY BOARD EDUCATION
See KNOTT COUNTY SCHOOL DISTRICT

D-U-N-S 08-620-2041
KNOTT COUNTY SCHOOL DISTRICT
KNOTT COUNTY BOARD EDUCATION
1156 Hindman Byp, Hindman, KY 41822-8673
Tel (606) 785-3153 Founded/Ownrshp 1915
Sales 20.4MM EMP 550
Accts Adams & Holliday Psc Cpa
SIC 8211 Public elementary & secondary schools; Public elementary & secondary schools

KNOTT'S BERRY FARM
See BERRY KNOTTS FARM LLC

D-U-N-S 00-300-2680 IMP/EXP
KNOUSE FOODS COOPERATIVE INC (PA)
800 Pach Glen Idaville Rd, Peach Glen, PA 17375-0001
Tel (717) 677-8181 Founded/Ownrshp 1949
Sales 419.4MM^E EMP 1,200
SIC 2033 Fruits: packaged in cans, jars, etc.; Fruit juices: packaged in cans, jars, etc.; Fruit pie mixes & fillings: packaged in cans, jars, etc.; Apple sauce: packaged in cans, jars, etc.; Fruits: packaged in cans, jars, etc.; Fruit juices: packaged in cans, jars, etc.; Fruit pie mixes & fillings: packaged in cans, jars, etc.; Apple sauce: packaged in cans, jars, etc.
Pr: Kenneth E Guise Jr
*Treas: Craig M Hinkle
*VP: Thomas M Denisco
*VP: Richard W Esser
*VP: Emery C Etter Jr
*VP: Eugene Kelly
VP: Eugene F Kelly
*VP: Linda Kelly
Dir IT: Ron Nichols
MIS Mgr: Harold Heller
Opers Mgr: Arlene Jennings

D-U-N-S 09-279-8354
KNOWLANS SUPER MARKETS INC
FESTIVAL FOODS
111 County Road F E, Vadnais Heights, MN 55127-6933
Tel (651) 483-9242 Founded/Ownrshp 1955
Sales 102.5MM^E EMP 600
SIC 5411 Supermarkets, independent; Supermarkets, independent
CEO: Marie Aarthun
COO: Lauri Youngquist
Genl Mgr: Frank Kirchner
Info Man: Mike Barrett

D-U-N-S 00-723-2429
■ KNOWLEDGE CONSULTING GROUP INC
K C G
(Suby of MANTECH INTERNATIONAL CORP) ★
2000 Edmund Halley Dr # 500, Reston, VA 20191-3466
Tel (703) 467-2000 Founded/Ownrshp 2015
Sales 44.3MM^E EMP 200
SIC 6211 Computer related consulting services; Software programming applications; Computer integrated systems design; Brokers, security
CEO: Dusty Wince
Pr: Maryann Hirsch
Ofcr: Chris Galvan
Ofcr: Nicole Parker
Sr VP: Christopher S Oglesby
VP: Matt Brown
Genl Mgr: Derek Noche
IT Man: Veronica Robinson
Netwrk Mgr: Tony Price
Netwrk Mgr: Bart Stevens
Sales Exec: Paul Rayburn

D-U-N-S 04-841-0489
KNOWLEDGE NETWORKS INC
2100 Geng Rd Ste 210, Palo Alto, CA 94303-3307
Tel (650) 289-2000 Founded/Ownrshp 2011
Sales NA EMP 647
SIC 8732 Market analysis or research; Market analysis, business & economic research

KNOWLEDGE SERVICES
See GUIDESOFT INC

D-U-N-S 16-114-7244
KNOWLEDGE SYSTEMS & RESEARCH INC
K S & R
120 Madison St Ste 15, Syracuse, NY 13202-2813
Tel (315) 233-1071 Founded/Ownrshp 1983
Sales 23.7MM EMP 240
SIC 8732 8742 Market analysis or research; Management consulting services; Market analysis or research; Management consulting services
Pr: Rita Reicher
*Treas: Jerry Scott
Prgrm Mgr: Barbara Ensign
Dir IT: Kathleen McKnight
Dir IT: Paul Scott
Software D: Jaime Chapman
Board of Directors: Lynnette Vandyke, Lucinda Burch, Kris Fischer, Jim Kraus, Robert Mortenson, Michael Nash, Rita Reicher, Craig Reimann, Jerry Scott, Joseph Snyder

D-U-N-S 11-617-4533
KNOWLEDGE UNIVERSE EDUCATION LLC
C D C
650 Ne Holladay St # 1400, Portland, OR 97232-2096
Tel (503) 872-1300 Founded/Ownrshp 2005
Sales 983.5MM^E EMP 32,000
SIC 8299 Music school; Music school
Ch Bd: Mike Milken
*Pr: Elanna S Yalow PHD
CEO: Thomas Pinnau
*CEO: John Thomson Wyatt
*COO: Shelley Bromberek
*CFO: Michael Ensing
CFO: Mark D Morelan
CFO: Mark D Moreland
*Chf Mktg O: Gail Galuppo
*Ex VP: WEI-LI Chong
Ex VP: Gail A Galuppo
Sr VP: Edward Brewington
Sr VP: Diane Colum
*Sr VP: Toni Jaffe
*Sr VP: Eva Kripalani
*Sr VP: Mark Schmitz
Sr VP: Bruce Walters
VP: Linda Hassan Anderson
VP: David Benedict
VP: Jane Delaney
VP: Jill Eiland

KNOWLEDGEPOINT360 GROUP
See KNOWLEDGEPOINT360 PARENT HOLDINGS LLC

D-U-N-S 80-003-6084
KNOWLEDGEPOINT360 GROUP LLC
TGAS ADVISORS
(Suby of ABRY PARTNERS INC) ★
125 Chubb Ave, Lyndhurst, NJ 07071-3504
Tel (201) 553-8880 Founded/Ownrshp 2007
Sales 55.2MM^E EMP 680
SIC 8999 Communication services; Communication services; Art related services
CEO: Jonathan Bigelow
*CFO: Chris Stratton
Sr VP: Angela Cairns
Sr VP: Todd Courcy
Sr VP: Christina Curry
VP: Marcus Furniss
VP: Amy Parke
VP: Sylvia Razzo
VP: Greg Thompson
Exec: Sandra McGechan
Dir Bus: Greg Kloiber

D-U-N-S 96-568-0940
KNOWLEDGEPOINT360 PARENT HOLDINGS LLC
KNOWLEDGEPOINT360 GROUP
(Suby of ABRY PARTNERS INC) ★
125 Chubb Ave, Lyndhurst, NJ 07071-3504
Tel (201) 271-6000 Founded/Ownrshp 2007
Sales 7.7MM^E EMP 650
SIC 7363 Medical help service; Medical help service
CFO: Chris Stratton

D-U-N-S 17-469-2343
KNOWLEDGEWORKS FOUNDATION
1 W 4th St Ste 200, Cincinnati, OH 45202-3624
Tel (513) 241-1422 Founded/Ownrshp 1991
Sales 21.3MM EMP 93
Accts Deloitte Tax Llp Cincinnati
SIC 8299 8742 Educational services; Management consulting services; Educational services; Management consulting services
CEO: Tim Tuff
*Pr: Brian Ross
Chf Mktg O: Meredith Yacso
Ex VP: Patricia Conley
*Sr VP: William E McNeese
*VP: Andrew Benson
*VP: Holly A Brinkman
*VP: Jillian Darwish
VP: Barbara Diamond
VP: Meredith Meyer
VP: Cris Mulder

D-U-N-S 09-556-5545 IMP
■ KNOWLES CAZENOVIA INC
DLI
(Suby of KNOWLES CORP) ★
2777 Us Route 20, Cazenovia, NY 13035-8444
Tel (315) 655-8710 Founded/Ownrshp 1986
Sales 34.0MM EMP 232
SIC 3675 Electronic capacitors; Electronic capacitors
Pr: David Wightman
*Ch Bd: Michael P Busse
COO: Gary Leshkivich
VP: Steve Butcher
*Mng Dir: Howard Ingleson
Dir IT: Allan Drogo
Dir IT: Greg Fox
Sls Mgr: Brian Forte
Sls Mgr: Christine Worfel
Sales Asso: Tatum Cheney

D-U-N-S 07-925-8305
▲ KNOWLES CORP
1151 Maplewood Dr, Itasca, IL 60143-2058
Tel (630) 250-5100 Founded/Ownrshp 2013
Sales 1.1MMM EMP 10,349^E
Accts Pricewaterhousecoopers Llp Ch
Tkr Sym KN Exch NYS
SIC 3651 3675 Household audio & video equipment; Audio electronic systems; Microphones; Speaker systems; Electronic capacitors; Household audio & video equipment; Audio electronic systems; Microphones; Speaker systems; Electronic capacitors
Pr: Jeffrey S Niew
*Ch Bd: Jean-Pierre M Ergas
*COO: Daniel J Giesecke
*CFO: John S Anderson
Ofcr: Alexis Bernard
*Sr VP: Raymond D Cabrera
*Sr VP: Thomas G Jackson
VP: John Donovan
*VP: Bryan E Mittelman
VP: James F Wynn
Mng Dir: Steven Lu
Board of Directors: Keith L Barnes, Robert W Cremin, Hermann Eul, Ronald Jankov, Richard K Lochridge, Donald Macleod

D-U-N-S 00-511-5902
■ KNOWLES ELECTRONICS HOLDINGS INC
(Suby of KNOWLES CORP) ★
1151 Maplewood Dr, Itasca, IL 60143-2058
Tel (630) 250-5100 Founded/Ownrshp 1954, 2014
Sales 228.8MM^E EMP 2,420
SIC 3679 3625 3651 8731 6159 Transducers, electrical; Headphones, radio; Solenoid switches (industrial controls); Sound reproducing equipment; Engineering laboratory, except testing; Commercial research laboratory; Loan institutions, general & industrial; Transducers, electrical; Headphones, radio; Solenoid switches (industrial controls); Sound reproducing equipment; Engineering laboratory, except testing; Commercial research laboratory; Loan institutions, general & industrial
Ch Bd: Jean-Pierre M Ergas
*Pr: Michael A Adell
*Pr: Jeffrey S Niew
*CFO: John S Anderson
*Sr VP: Raymond D Cabrera
*Sr VP: Paul M Dickinson
*VP: Pat Cavanagh
*VP: James H Moyle
*VP: Stephen D Petersen
*Prin: John J Zei

D-U-N-S 02-529-6208 IMP
■ KNOWLES ELECTRONICS LLC
(Suby of KNOWLES CORP) ★
1151 Maplewood Dr, Itasca, IL 60143-2071
Tel (630) 250-5100 Founded/Ownrshp 1999
Sales NA EMP 2,418
SIC 3679 3842 Transducers, electrical; Hearing aids; Transducers, electrical; Hearing aids
Pr: Jeffrey Niew
Pr: Mike Adell
CFO: Mark Godish
Treas: Paul Dickinson
Sr VP: John Anderson
VP: Arno Campostrini
VP: Janson Hung
VP: Pete Loeppert
VP: Jignesh Sampat
VP: Craig Stein
Prgrm Mgr: Kathy Haas

D-U-N-S 17-935-9042
KNOWLES ENTERPRIES LLC
2381 1/2 River Rd, Grand Junction, CO 81505-1323
Tel (970) 434-1912 Founded/Ownrshp 2005
Sales 22.0MM EMP 170
SIC 4212 Petroleum haulage, local; Petroleum haulage, local

D-U-N-S 95-954-9650
KNOWLES HOLDINGS INC
820 N Franklin St Ste 300, Chicago, IL 60610-3191
Tel (312) 640-2500 *Founded/Ownrshp* 1994
Sales 6.0MM *EMP* 350
SIC 7389 Telemarketing services; Telemarketing services
Pr: Cliff Knowles
**VP:* Dave Burr
**VP:* Ann L Knowles

D-U-N-S 82-688-5134 IMP/EXP
■ **KNOWLTON TECHNOLOGIES LLC**
(*Suby of* EASTMAN CHEMICAL CO) ★
213 Factory St, Watertown, NY 13601-2748
Tel (315) 782-0600 *Founded/Ownrshp* 2014
Sales 70.8MM^E *EMP* 130
SIC 2621 Filter paper; Specialty papers; Filter paper; Specialty papers
CEO: Frederick G Rudmann
**Ex VP:* James Ganter
Ex VP: Dick Gray
**VP:* James Lee
Exec: Marybeth La Vallee
QA Dir: Brian Szafranski
IT Man: Richard Gray
Opers Mgr: James Gantner
Plnt Mgr: Nick Cassoni
Plnt Mgr: John Connor
Plnt Mgr: Jamie Ganter

D-U-N-S 82-777-4720
KNOX & ASSOCIATES LLC
CHRISTIAN J KNOX & ASSOCIATES
615 Candlewood Ct, Lodi, CA 95242-4646
Tel (209) 365-1567 *Founded/Ownrshp* 1978
Sales 50.8MM^E *EMP* 3,000
SIC 8741 5812 Restaurant management; Eating places; Restaurant management; Eating places
Pt: Chris Knox
**Pt:* David Knox
**Pt:* Michael Pettit

D-U-N-S 00-544-0250
KNOX AND SCHNEIDER INC (IL)
914 W Superior St, Chicago, IL 60642-5961
Tel (312) 666-9300 *Founded/Ownrshp* 1931, 1999
Sales 26.0MM *EMP* 20
SIC 5084 Packaging machinery & equipment; Packaging machinery & equipment
Pr: David S Goodman
**VP:* Brian Monckton
**VP:* Steven G Packer
**VP:* Daniel Webster
**VP:* Joseph Wolf

D-U-N-S 09-274-4408
KNOX ASSOCIATES INC
KNOX COMPANY, THE
1601 W Deer Valley Rd, Phoenix, AZ 85027-2112
Tel (623) 687-2300 *Founded/Ownrshp* 1975
Sales 27.3MM^E *EMP* 95
SIC 5065 3499 3842 3429 Security control equipment & systems; Safes & vaults, metal; Surgical appliances & supplies; Manufactured hardware (general); Security control equipment & systems; Safes & vaults, metal; Surgical appliances & supplies; Manufactured hardware (general)
Pr: Don Trempala

D-U-N-S 07-356-1128
KNOX ATTORNEY SERVICE INC
KNOX COPY CENTERS
2250 4th Ave Ste 200, San Diego, CA 92101-2124
Tel (619) 233-9700 *Founded/Ownrshp* 1973
Sales 28.9MM^E *EMP* 227
SIC 7334 8111 7389 Photocopying & duplicating services; Legal aid service; Courier or messenger service; Photocopying & duplicating services; Legal aid service; Courier or messenger service
**Pr:* Steve Knox
**CFO:* Steve Todd
**VP:* John Maguire
Exec: Marilyn Menard
Dir IT: Tim Peters
IT Man: Jack Potolski
Sls&Mrk Ex: Eric Watkins

KNOX COMPANY, THE
See KNOX ASSOCIATES INC

D-U-N-S 60-755-2937
KNOX CO
1601 W Deer Valley Rd, Phoenix, AZ 85027-2112
Tel (623) 687-2300 *Founded/Ownrshp* 1975
Sales 22.6MM^E *EMP* 150
SIC 2542 Locker boxes, postal service: except wood; Locker boxes, postal service: except wood
Pr: Don Trempala
Genl Mgr: Rita Barnes
Genl Mgr: Cynthia Jones
IT Man: Erick Lao
IT Man: Glee Thode
Mtls Mgr: Kenneth Keith
Opers Mgr: Julie Benken
VP Sls: Rex Hanson
Sls Mgr: John Thibault

KNOX CO SCHOOL DISTRICT
See KNOX COUNTY SCHOOLS INC

D-U-N-S 07-142-9823
KNOX COLLEGE
2 E South St Rm 212k, Galesburg, IL 61401-4999
Tel (309) 341-7213 *Founded/Ownrshp* 1837
Sales 52.1MM *EMP* 453
SIC 8221

D-U-N-S 05-884-1073
KNOX COMMUNITY HOSPITAL
1330 Coshocton Ave, Mount Vernon, OH 43050-1495
Tel (740) 393-9000 *Founded/Ownrshp* 1977
Sales 116.6MM *EMP* 628
Accts Blue & Co Llc Columbus Oh
SIC 8062 General medical & surgical hospitals; General medical & surgical hospitals
CEO: Bruce White
CEO: Sheila Cochran
**CFO:* Michael Ambrosiani
Chf Nrs Of: Sandra Beidelschies
Chf Nrs Of: James Middleton
Mktg Dir: Jeffrey Scott
Orthpdst: Michael Sullivan
Surgeon: Paul Taiganides
Anesthgy: Zachary Gatton
Doctor: Suzanne Helming
Pharmcst: Andrea McCluskey

D-U-N-S 05-067-8093
KNOX COMMUNITY SCHOOL DISTRICT
2 Redskin Trl, Knox, IN 46534-2238
Tel (574) 772-1600 *Founded/Ownrshp* 1890
Sales 319.4M *EMP* 280
SIC 8211 Public elementary & secondary schools; Public elementary & secondary schools
VP: Wendy McIntire
Schl Brd P: Kirk Bennett

KNOX COPY CENTERS
See KNOX ATTORNEY SERVICE INC

D-U-N-S 08-096-0651
KNOX COUNTY ASSOCIATION FOR RETARDED CITIZENS INC
DOVE MANUFACTURING
2525 N 6th St, Vincennes, IN 47591-2405
Tel (812) 886-4312 *Founded/Ownrshp* 1972
Sales 13.0MM *EMP* 350
Accts Cna Tax Professionals Inc Ind
SIC 2521 7032 Wood office furniture; Sporting & recreational camps; Wood office furniture; Sporting & recreational camps
Pr: Michael R Carney
Ex VP: Jeff Darling

D-U-N-S 79-336-9471
KNOX COUNTY BOARD OF EDUCATION
KNOX COUNTY SCHOOLS
200 Daniel Boone Dr, Barbourville, KY 40906-1104
Tel (606) 546-3157 *Founded/Ownrshp* 1924
Sales 47.8MM *EMP* 800
SIC 8211 Public elementary school; Public junior high school; Public senior high school; Public elementary school; Public junior high school; Public senior high school
Teacher Pr: Sherry Smith

D-U-N-S 09-753-7823
KNOX COUNTY CAREER CENTER
306 Martinsburg Rd, Mount Vernon, OH 43050-4225
Tel (740) 393-2933 *Founded/Ownrshp* 1969
Sales 24.5MM^E *EMP* 125
SIC 8211 Job training & vocational rehabilitation services; Vocational high school
Pr: Richard McLarnan
**VP:* Margie Bennett
Dir IT: Nate Greene
Sls&Mrk Ex: Loretta Lower

KNOX COUNTY HOSPITAL
See KNOX HOSPITAL CORP

D-U-N-S 07-132-0501
KNOX COUNTY HOSPITAL
GOOD SAMARITAN HOSPITAL
305 S 5th St, Vincennes, IN 47591-1117
Tel (812) 882-5220 *Founded/Ownrshp* 1908, 2001
Sales 537.0MM *EMP* 1,900
Accts Bkd Llp Indianapolis Indiana
SIC 8062 General medical & surgical hospitals; General medical & surgical hospitals
Pr: Robert D McLin
COO: Daryl Waldrige
COO: Darryl Waldrup
CFO: Jerry Stump
VP: Fred England
VP: Emily Heineke
VP: Scott Kaminski
VP: Robert McLin
VP: Carol Olson
VP: Adam Thacker
VP: Carol Wahl
Dir OR: Debra Brand
Dir Risk M: Denise Faught
Dir Lab: Steven Jones
Dir Rx: Jim Eskew

KNOX COUNTY SCHOOLS
See KNOX COUNTY BOARD OF EDUCATION

D-U-N-S 96-559-1886
KNOX COUNTY SCHOOLS INC
KNOX CO SCHOOL DISTRICT
912 S Gay St Ste L400, Knoxville, TN 37902-1832
Tel (865) 594-1800 *Founded/Ownrshp* 1988
Sales 22.0MM^E *EMP* 200^E
SIC 8211 Public elementary & secondary schools; Public elementary & secondary schools
Bd of Dir: Michael Martin
Ex Dir: Mitzi Mitchell
Admn Mgr: Julie Thompson
Snr Mgr: Kristin Finck

D-U-N-S 06-346-4622
■ **KNOX CREEK COAL CORP**
(*Suby of* APPALACHIA HOLDING CO) ★
2295 Gvrnor G C Pery Hwy, Raven, VA 24639
Tel (276) 964-4333 *Founded/Ownrshp* 1947
Sales 30.1MM^E *EMP* 450
SIC 1222 Bituminous coal-underground mining; Bituminous coal-underground mining
VP: Richard H Verheij
**Pr:* David Kramer

D-U-N-S 07-786-3553
KNOX HOSPITAL CORP
KNOX COUNTY HOSPITAL
80 Hospital Dr, Barbourville, KY 40906-7363
Tel (606) 545-5500 *Founded/Ownrshp* 1959
Sales 41.2MM^E *EMP* 213
SIC 8062 General medical & surgical hospitals; General medical & surgical hospitals
Ch Bd: James West
Dir OR: Renee Carton
Dir Lab: Carla Dobbs
Dir Rad: Albert Moreland
Dir Rx: Bob Croley

D-U-N-S 04-286-1088
KNOX INDUSTRIES INC (GA)
4865 Martin Ct Se, Smyrna, GA 30082-4935
Tel (770) 434-7401 *Founded/Ownrshp* 1983
Sales 39.7MM^E *EMP* 175^E
SIC 1761 3448 Sheet metalwork; Prefabricated metal buildings; Sheet metalwork; Prefabricated metal buildings
Pr: Jack Knox
IT Man: David Chism

D-U-N-S 04-062-3373
KNOX NELSON OIL CO INC
101 S Pennsylvania St, Pine Bluff, AR 71601-4535
Tel (870) 534-4941 *Founded/Ownrshp* 1996
Sales 21.8MM^E *EMP* 50
SIC 5541 5171 6512 Filling stations, gasoline; Petroleum bulk stations; Commercial & industrial building operation
CEO: Nan Simmons
**Pr:* Dennis Fitzgerald

D-U-N-S 04-020-1519 IMP
KNOX NURSERY INC
940 Avalon Rd, Winter Garden, FL 34787-9701
Tel (407) 654-1972 *Founded/Ownrshp* 1962
Sales 42.3MM^E *EMP* 106^E
Accts Mcgladrey & Pullen Llp Orland
SIC 5193 5191 Flowers & nursery stock; Seeds & bulbs
Pr: Bruce R Knox
**VP:* James M Knox III

D-U-N-S 09-425-0636
■ **KNOX OIL FIELD SUPPLY INC**
(*Suby of* APPLIED INDUSTRIAL TECHNOLOGIES INC) ★
4603 S Jackson St Ste 200, San Angelo, TX 76903-9331
Tel (325) 227-8755 *Founded/Ownrshp* 2014
Sales 21.7MM^E *EMP* 30
SIC 5084 Oil well machinery, equipment & supplies
Pr: Neil A Schrimsher

D-U-N-S 93-990-1054
KNOXVILLE AUTO TRUCK PLAZA INC
BURGER KING
615 N Watt Rd, Knoxville, TN 37934-1112
Tel (865) 531-7676 *Founded/Ownrshp* 1993
Sales 20.1MM^E *EMP* 120
SIC 5812 Truck stops; Fast-food restaurant, chain; Fast-food restaurant, chain
Pr: Walter Smith
Exec: Alicia Mace

D-U-N-S 03-469-9561 IMP
KNOXVILLE BEVERAGE CO INC
1335 E Weisgarber Rd, Knoxville, TN 37909-2616
Tel (865) 637-9411 *Founded/Ownrshp* 1961
Sales 22.0MM^E *EMP* 38
SIC 5182 Liquor; Wine; Liquor; Wine
Pr: Mike Craig
**Ch Bd:* Orvis Milner
**Pr:* Michael Milner
**VP:* Jerrison Claire
VP: Jerry Sinclair

D-U-N-S 96-669-0880
KNOXVILLE COMMUNITY HOSPITAL INC
1002 S Lincoln St, Knoxville, IA 50138-3121
Tel (641) 842-2151 *Founded/Ownrshp* 2011
Sales 30.2MM *EMP* 24
Accts Gronewold Ell Kyhnn & Co Pc A
SIC 8062 General medical & surgical hospitals; General medical & surgical hospitals
CEO: Kevin Kincaid
**CFO:* Maggie Hamilton-Beyer

D-U-N-S 09-651-5283
KNOXVILLE COMMUNITY SCHOOL DISTRICT
309 W Main St, Knoxville, IA 50138-2650
Tel (641) 842-6552 *Founded/Ownrshp* 1879
Sales 17.1MM^E *EMP* 320
SIC 8211 Public elementary & secondary schools; School board; Public elementary & secondary schools; School board
Pr: Randy Flack
**Prin:* Kevin Crawford

D-U-N-S 62-318-2037
KNOXVILLE MILLING CO
(*Suby of* C H GUENTHER & SON INC) ★
1605 Prosser Rd, Knoxville, TN 37914-3459
Tel (865) 546-5511 *Founded/Ownrshp* 1883
Sales 54.2MM^E *EMP* 750
SIC 2041 2099 2045 5149 Flour; Bread & bread-type roll mixes; Corn meal; Grain mills (except rice); Food preparations; Prepared flour mixes & doughs; Flour; Flour; Bread & bread-type roll mixes; Corn meal; Grain mills (except rice); Food preparations; Prepared flour mixes & doughs; Flour
**Ch Bd:* Scott Petty Jr
**VP:* Richard De Gregorio
VP: Kevin Janiga
**VP:* James W Stamper
**VP Opers:* Jerry D Kuhn

D-U-N-S 00-338-0888
■ **KNOXVILLE NEWS-SENTINEL CO** (TN)
(*Suby of* JOURNAL MEDIA GROUP INC) ★
2332 News Sentinel Dr, Knoxville, TN 37921-5766
Tel (865) 523-3131 *Founded/Ownrshp* 1886, 2015
Sales 50.5MM^E *EMP* 580
SIC 2711 Newspapers, publishing & printing; Newspapers, publishing & printing
Pr: Bruce Hartmann
**Sr VP:* Mark G Contreras
**VP:* Rusty Coats
**VP:* Jack McElroy
Advt Dir: Frank B Hughes

D-U-N-S 06-372-7767
KNOXVILLE ROADHOUSE INVESTORS LLC
7100 Kingston Pike Ste B, Knoxville, TN 37919-5709
Tel (865) 584-4245 *Founded/Ownrshp* 1998
Sales 6.1MM^E *EMP* 300
SIC 5812 Steak restaurant; Steak restaurant

D-U-N-S 07-491-6552
KNOXVILLE TVA EMPLOYEES CREDIT UNION
301 Wall Ave, Knoxville, TN 37902-1407
Tel (865) 544-5400 *Founded/Ownrshp* 1934
Sales NA *EMP* 210
SIC 6062 State credit unions, not federally chartered; State credit unions, not federally chartered
CEO: Glenn Siler
**CFO:* Shannon York
Ofcr: Shane Phillips
**VP:* Charlotte Beets
VP: Rebecca Lawson
VP: Betty Norman
Brnch Mgr: Micka Holtzclaw
Brnch Mgr: Darren Lee
CIO: Nathan Brown
Opers Mgr: Mike Snider
Mktg Dir: Jayne Walshaw

D-U-N-S 00-338-7560
KNOXVILLE UTILITIES BOARD
K U B
(*Suby of* CITY OF KNOXVILLE) ★
445 S Gay St, Knoxville, TN 37902-1125
Tel (865) 594-7324 *Founded/Ownrshp* 1939, 1986
Sales 751.7MM *EMP* 500
Accts Rodefer Moss & Co Pllc Knox
SIC 4911 4924 4941 4952 Electric services; Natural gas distribution; Water supply; Sewerage systems; Electric services; Natural gas distribution; Water supply; Sewerage systems
CEO: Mintha Roach
**Ex VP:* Bill Elmore
**Sr VP:* Eddie Black
**Sr VP:* Susan Edwards
Sr VP: Roby Trotter
VP: Debbie Boles
**VP:* Mike Bolin
VP: Derwin Haygood
VP: Dawn Mosteit
**VP:* Mark Walker
IT Man: Dwayne Frye

D-U-N-S 78-999-0561 IMP
KNOXVILLE WHOLESALE FURNITURE CO INC
410 N Peters Rd, Knoxville, TN 37922-2332
Tel (865) 671-5300 *Founded/Ownrshp* 1992
Sales 22.3MM^E *EMP* 90
SIC 5712 5021 Furniture stores; Furniture
Pr: Tim Harris
Treas: Elizabeth Jane Weaer

D-U-N-S 07-491-4243
KNOXVILLES COMMUNITY DEVELOPMENT CORP
K C D C
901 N Broadway St, Knoxville, TN 37917-6663
Tel (865) 403-1100 *Founded/Ownrshp* 1935
Sales 45.5MM *EMP* 140^E
Accts Malcolm Johnson & Company Pa
SIC 6531 Housing authority operator; Housing authority operator
Pr: David Hutchins
**Treas:* Phyllis J Patrick
Exec: John Rochelle
Dir IT: Eric Bellamy
Dir IT: Jeff Ferrell
Dir IT: Patrick Patterson

D-U-N-S 14-050-7190
KNT INC
39760 Eureka Dr, Newark, CA 94560-4808
Tel (510) 651-7163 *Founded/Ownrshp* 2001
Sales 31.5MM^E *EMP* 150
SIC 3599 Machine shop, jobbing & repair; Machine shop, jobbing & repair
CEO: Keith Ngo

D-U-N-S 19-758-9893 IMP
KNU LLC
LA-Z-BOY CONTRACT FURNITURE
1300 N Broad St, Leland, MS 38756-2511
Tel (812) 367-1761 *Founded/Ownrshp* 2005
Sales 27.8MM *EMP* 125^E
Accts Nonte & Company Llc Jasper I
SIC 2599 Hospital furniture, except beds; Hospital furniture, except beds
Pr: Glenn A Lange
Treas: Steven M Wahl
VP: Richard N Franey
Genl Couns: Patrick L Miller

D-U-N-S 00-817-3122 IMP
KNUD NIELSEN CO INC (AL)
EARTH ELEMENTS
217 Park St, Evergreen, AL 36401-2903
Tel (251) 578-1887 *Founded/Ownrshp* 1990
Sales 46.7MM^E *EMP* 325
SIC 3999 Flowers, artificial & preserved; Foliage, artificial & preserved; Flowers, artificial & preserved; Foliage, artificial & preserved
**Pr:* John E Smith
**Ex VP:* Thomas S Nielsen
**VP:* Melissa S Higgenbothan
Sls Mgr: Ken Vickery

D-U-N-S 19-043-7293
KNUDTSEN CHEVROLET CO
1900 E Polston Ave, Post Falls, ID 83854-5365
Tel (208) 664-8107 *Founded/Ownrshp* 1937
Sales 29.0MM^E *EMP* 70
SIC 5511 Automobiles, new & used; Automobiles, new & used
Pr: Eve Knudtsen
Sls Dir: Eric Knudtsen
Sls Mgr: Bob Chapman

D-U-N-S 00-808-7942 IMP
KNUST-SBO LLC
8625 Meadowcroft Dr, Houston, TX 77063-5011
Tel (713) 785-1060 *Founded/Ownrshp* 1946
Sales 39.7MM^E *EMP* 178^E
Accts Ernst & Young

SIC 3599 Machine shop, jobbing & repair; Machine shop, jobbing & repair
Pr: Steve McGowen
Mng Dir: Rick Welch
Prd Mgr: Tim Duke
Ql Cn Mgr: Troy Jeansonne
Ql Cn Mgr: Jim Kidd
Ql Cn Mgr: Juan Mayorga

D-U-N-S 07-869-2845
KNUTE NELSON (MN)
420 12th Ave E, Alexandria, MN 56308-2612
Tel (320) 763-6653 *Founded/Ownrshp* 1969
Sales 19.5MM *EMP* 450
Accts Eide Bailly Llp Minneapolis
SIC 8051 Skilled nursing care facilities; Skilled nursing care facilities
Ex Dir: Mark R Anderson
**CFO:* Marnie Gugisberg
**VP:* Katie Perry
**VP:* Angie Urman
Dir Soc: Kelly Boesen
Nurse Mgr: Cynthia Lerohl

KNUTSON CONSTRUCTION SERVICES
See KNUTSON HOLDINGS INC

D-U-N-S 13-073-2332
KNUTSON CONSTRUCTION SERVICES INC
(*Suby of* KNUTSON CONSTRUCTION SERVICES) ★
7515 Wayzata Blvd, Minneapolis, MN 55426-1621
Tel (763) 546-1400 *Founded/Ownrshp* 1985
Sales 92.5MM^E *EMP* 400
SIC 1542 1541

D-U-N-S 10-232-0975 IMP
KNUTSON CONSTRUCTION SERVICES MIDWEST INC
(*Suby of* KNUTSON CONSTRUCTION SERVICES) ★
2351 Scott Blvd Se, Iowa City, IA 52240-8174
Tel (319) 351-2040 *Founded/Ownrshp* 1985
Sales 24.6MM^E *EMP* 75
SIC 1542 Commercial & office building contractors; Institutional building construction
Pr: Robert A Marsh
Sr VP: Douglas Jandro
VP: Steve Curry
Off Mgr: Kelly Kendle
Snr PM: Scott Wingrove

D-U-N-S 14-466-2632
KNUTSON HOLDINGS INC
KNUTSON CONSTRUCTION SERVICES
7515 Wayzata Blvd, Minneapolis, MN 55426-1621
Tel (763) 546-1400 *Founded/Ownrshp* 1985
Sales 132.1MM^E *EMP* 400^E
SIC 1542 1541 Commercial & office building, new construction; Industrial buildings, new construction; Commercial & office building, new construction; Industrial buildings, new construction
Pr: Steven O Curry
**CFO:* Michael D Wolf
**VP:* Dave Foley

KNVA TELEVISION
See LIN TELEVISION OF TEXAS LP

D-U-N-S 16-491-6871
KNWEBS LLC
C S I
4420 E I 240 Service Rd, Oklahoma City, OK 73135-2609
Tel (405) 526-1030 *Founded/Ownrshp* 2002
Sales 30.8MM *EMP* 285^E
SIC 7376 Computer facilities management; Computer facilities management
Pr: Ken Novotny
**CFO:* Keri Wright
**VP:* Jay Graham

D-U-N-S 80-683-9155
KO OLINA INTANGIBLES LLC
IHILANI RESORT & SPA
92-1001 Olani St, Kapolei, HI 96707-2203
Tel (909) 679-0079 *Founded/Ownrshp* 1993
Sales 167.3M^E *EMP* 400
SIC 7011 Resort hotel; Motels
Pr: Fumio Kanto

D-U-N-S 79-404-6110
KOA DEVELOPMENT INC
13 12th Ave S, Nampa, ID 83651-3922
Tel (208) 461-0022 *Founded/Ownrshp* 1978
Sales 22.5MM *EMP* 51
Accts Quady & Brash & Leal Cpa S
SIC 1522 Residential construction; Residential construction
Pr: Richard D Brazil
**Sec:* Carol Brazil

D-U-N-S 15-415-0523
KOA HOTEL LLC
SHERATON KAUHOU BAY RESORT SPA
78-128 Ehukai St Ste 100, Kailua Kona, HI 96740-2567
Tel (808) 930-4900 *Founded/Ownrshp* 2001
Sales 5.2MM^E *EMP* 300
SIC 7011 Resort hotel; Resort hotel
VP: Rodrick O'Connor
Genl Mgr: Tetsuji Yamazaki
Sls Mgr: Christi Lewis

D-U-N-S 19-795-9638
KOA TRADING CO A DIVISION OF Y HATA
KOA TRADING COMPANY, INC.
(*Suby of* Y HATA & CO LIMITED) ★
2975 Aukele St, Lihue, HI 96766-1463
Tel (808) 245-6961 *Founded/Ownrshp* 2015
Sales 37.7MM^E *EMP* 50
SIC 5141 5144 5146 5142 5182 Groceries, general line; Poultry products; Fish & seafoods; Meat, frozen: packaged; Wine & distilled beverages
Pr: Wesley Park

KOA TRADING COMPANY, INC.
See KOA TRADING CO A DIVISION OF Y HATA

D-U-N-S 62-348-2338
KOB-TV LLC
(*Suby of* HUBBARD BROADCASTING INC) ★
4 Broadcast Plz Sw, Albuquerque, NM 87104-1000
Tel (505) 243-4411 *Founded/Ownrshp* 1957
Sales 33.2MM^E *EMP* 130
SIC 4833 Television broadcasting stations; Television broadcasting stations
Ch: Robert W Hubbard
**VP:* Stanley E Hubbard
Exec: Elena Hernandez
Genl Mgr: Michael Burgess
IT Man: Cook Lee
IT Man: Seanna Ramsey
Prd Mgr: Levi Duran
Trfc Mgr: Jackie Gregory
Sls Mgr: Cris Beck
Sls Mgr: Jeff Finkel
Sls Mgr: Olivia Lawrence

D-U-N-S 04-600-7803
KOBAYASHI TRAVEL SERVICE LTD (HI)
ALOHA WORLD
650 Iwilei Rd Ste 410, Honolulu, HI 96817-5318
Tel (808) 524-5040 *Founded/Ownrshp* 1945
Sales 21.7MM^E *EMP* 113
SIC 4724 4119 Travel agencies; Sightseeing bus
Pr: Michael K Kobayashi
**Sec:* Lawson Teshima
**VP:* Peter Kobayashi
**VP:* Tatsukichi Kobayashi
VP: Carl Tarumi
IT Man: Christopher Wong

D-U-N-S 14-457-6779 IMP
KOBE ALUMINUM AUTOMOTIVE PRODUCTS LLC
KAAP
(*Suby of* KOBE STEEL, LTD.)
1 Kobe Way, Bowling Green, KY 42101-7561
Tel (270) 842-6492 *Founded/Ownrshp* 2003
Sales 47.1MM^E *EMP* 105
SIC 3463 3714 Aluminum forgings; Motor vehicle parts & accessories; Aluminum forgings; Motor vehicle parts & accessories
CEO: Susumu Koike
Treas: Ken McCutchen
IT Man: Eric Davis
Tech Mgr: George Carroll
Ql Cn Mgr: Carol Maedel

D-U-N-S 60-315-5482 IMP/EXP
KOBE STEEL USA HOLDINGS INC
(*Suby of* KOBE STEEL, LTD.)
535 Madison Ave Fl 5, New York, NY 10022-4214
Tel (212) 751-9400 *Founded/Ownrshp* 1988
Sales 226.2MM^E *EMP* 1,512
SIC 3542 3089 Extruding machines (machine tools), metal; Injection molding of plastics; Extruding machines (machine tools), metal; Injection molding of plastics
Pr: Hiroya Kawasaki
Dir IT: Carrie Dugan
IT Man: Onuma Hideki
IT Man: Kazuhiro Ono

D-U-N-S 80-096-1513
KOBELCO ADVANCED COATING (AMERICA) INC
(*Suby of* KOBE STEEL USA HOLDINGS INC) ★
1007 Commerce Ct, Buffalo Grove, IL 60089-2362
Tel (847) 520-6000 *Founded/Ownrshp* 2007
Sales 49.5MM^E *EMP* 788^E
SIC 3479 Coating or wrapping steel pipe
Pr: Kazuki Takahara

D-U-N-S 60-972-8423 IMP/EXP
KOBELCO COMPRESSORS AMERICA INC
(*Suby of* KOBE STEEL, LTD.)
1450 W Rincon St, Corona, CA 92880-9205
Tel (951) 739-3030 *Founded/Ownrshp* 1990
Sales 158.1MM^E *EMP* 280
SIC 1623 3563 Oil & gas line & compressor station construction; Air & gas compressors including vacuum pumps; Oil & gas line & compressor station construction; Air & gas compressors; Air & gas compressors including vacuum pumps
CEO: Takaaki Hayata
**CTO:* Mohamad A Gauhar
Sls Mgr: Kenji Fujimatsu

D-U-N-S 07-880-6272 IMP/EXP
KOBELCO CONSTRUCTION MACHINERY USA INC
(*Suby of* KOBE STEEL, LTD.)
22350 Merchants Way, Katy, TX 77449-7811
Tel (281) 684-8761 *Founded/Ownrshp* 2001
Sales 21.9MM^E *EMP* 25
SIC 5082 3531 Construction & mining machinery; Excavators: cable, clamshell, crane, derrick, dragline, etc.; Tractors, crawler
Pr: Katsuhiko Morita
**VP:* Ronald Hargrave

KOBELCO NORTH WEST
See ROGERS MACHINERY CO INC

D-U-N-S 07-451-9294 IMP
KOBELCO STEWART BOLLING INC
(*Suby of* KOBE STEEL USA HOLDINGS INC) ★
1600 Terex Rd, Hudson, OH 44236-4086
Tel (330) 655-3111 *Founded/Ownrshp* 1923
Sales 41.6MM^E *EMP* 94
SIC 3559 Rubber working machinery, including tires; Rubber working machinery, including tires
Pr: Atsushi Shigeno
**Treas:* Takehiko Fujioka
Genl Mgr: Hiroki Toyoizumi
Opers Mgr: Scott Morgan
Opers Mgr: John Schneider

D-U-N-S 05-240-8739 IMP
KOBERT & CO INC
L H DOTTIE
6131 Garfield Ave, Commerce, CA 90040-3610
Tel (323) 725-1000 *Founded/Ownrshp* 1965
Sales 25.2MM^E *EMP* 90
SIC 5063 5074

KOBI GROUP
See KOBI INTERNATIONAL INC

D-U-N-S 94-835-8700 IMP/EXP
KOBI INTERNATIONAL INC
KOBI GROUP
253 Loy St, Burleson, TX 76028-4922
Tel (817) 297-3200 *Founded/Ownrshp* 1993
Sales 34.0MM *EMP* 18
SIC 5084 Industrial machinery & equipment; Industrial machinery & equipment
Pr: Foued Shade
Creative D: Luke Byford
Dir Bus: Mark Austin
Opers Mgr: T J Hearndon

D-U-N-S 85-840-2993
KOBIE MARKETING INC
100 2nd Ave S Ste 1000, Saint Petersburg, FL 33701-4360
Tel (727) 822-5353 *Founded/Ownrshp* 1989
Sales 20.1MM *EMP* 112
SIC 7311 Advertising agencies; Advertising agencies
Ch: Michael Hemsey
**Ch:* Bonnie Hechtkopf
VP: David Andreadakis
VP: Ashby Green
VP: Matt Stein
CIO: Don Hughes
IT Man: Dennis Sarvis

D-U-N-S 19-502-9723 IMP
KOBO PRODUCTS INC
3474 S Clinton Ave, South Plainfield, NJ 07080-1320
Tel (908) 757-0033 *Founded/Ownrshp* 1987
Sales 31.6MM^E *EMP* 104
SIC 2844 Cosmetic preparations; Cosmetic preparations
Pr: David Schlossman
VP: Yun Shao
Exec: Sandi Tortorella
Plnt Mgr: Sadi Benzemma
Plnt Mgr: Frank Mazzella
Mktg Mgr: Nancy O'Shea

D-U-N-S 00-253-5037
KOBRAND CORP (NY)
1 Manhattanville Rd # 400, Purchase, NY 10577-2126
Tel (212) 490-9300 *Founded/Ownrshp* 1944, 1969
Sales 63.6MM^E *EMP* 180
SIC 5182 5812 Wine; Liquor; Eating places; Wine; Liquor; Eating places
CEO: Robert Deroose
**Ch Bd:* Charles Mueller
Pr: Nick Lopez-Jenkins
**Pr:* Charles Palombini
**CFO:* Richard Reitman
VP: Kathleen Burke
Area Mgr: Gary Gondelman
Dist Mgr: Mike Biagi
Dist Mgr: Mark Cheek
Dist Mgr: Alex Valdes
Dist Mgr: Michael Zinni

D-U-N-S 03-261-5890
KOBRIN BUILDERS SUPPLY LLC
1924 W Princeton St, Orlando, FL 32804-4706
Tel (407) 843-1000 *Founded/Ownrshp* 2010
Sales 58.2MM^E *EMP* 100
SIC 5032 5211 Drywall materials; Lumber & other building materials
Sls Mgr: Clinton Thomas

D-U-N-S 02-327-9474
KOBUSSEN BUSES LTD
W914 County Road Ce, Kaukauna, WI 54130-3712
Tel (920) 722-8572 *Founded/Ownrshp* 1963
Sales 29.1MM^E *EMP* 342
SIC 4151 4141 School buses; Local bus charter service; School buses; Local bus charter service
Ch Bd: James Kobussen
**Pr:* Joe Kobussen
**Sec:* Daniel Kobussen
**VP:* Michael Kobussen
Mng Dir: Pat Campbell
Genl Mgr: Blaise Bodway
Off Admin: Laurie Fischer
Sfty Dirs: Chris Angell
Opers Mgr: Laura O'Rourke
Sls Dir: Larry Brincks

D-U-N-S 19-912-6137
KOCH & CO INC
KOCH CABINETS
1809 North St, Seneca, KS 66538-2415
Tel (785) 336-6022 *Founded/Ownrshp* 1989
Sales 58.3MM *EMP* 450
Accts Illegible
SIC 2434 3442 2431 Wood kitchen cabinets; Metal doors; Doors, wood; Wood kitchen cabinets; Metal doors; Doors, wood
Pr: Jim Koch
**CFO:* Jeffrey R Connor
**Prin:* Dan Koch
IT Man: Eric Schmitz

D-U-N-S 07-972-5044
KOCH AG & ENERGY SOLUTIONS LLC
4111 E 37th St N, Wichita, KS 67220-3203
Tel (316) 828-8310 *Founded/Ownrshp* 2008
Sales 32.1MM^E *EMP* 144^E
SIC 5191 Fertilizers & agricultural chemicals

D-U-N-S 05-447-0351
KOCH AIR LLC
(*Suby of* KOCH HVAC DISTRIBUTION INC) ★
1900 W Lloyd Expy, Evansville, IN 47712-7506
Tel (812) 962-5200 *Founded/Ownrshp* 1999
Sales 150.0MM *EMP* 182
Accts Harding Shymanski & Company
SIC 5075 Air conditioning & ventilation equipment & supplies; Air conditioning & ventilation equipment & supplies
Pr: James H Muehlbauer
**VP:* Glen Muehlbauer
Sls Mgr: Allan Jones

D-U-N-S 06-461-8676
KOCH BUSINESS SOLUTIONS LP
KBS
(*Suby of* KOCH INDUSTRIES INC) ★
4111 E 37th St N, Wichita, KS 67220-3203
Tel (316) 828-5500 *Founded/Ownrshp* 2007
Sales 91.2MM^E *EMP* 240^E
SIC 8748 Business consulting; Business consulting
Pt: David Robertson
Dir IT: Frank Walker
IT Man: Matthew Carnahan
Snr PM: Ann Trotter

KOCH CABINETS
See KOCH & CO INC

D-U-N-S 08-246-8463
KOCH CARBON LLC
(*Suby of* KOCH MINERAL SERVICES LLC) ★
4111 E 37th St N, Wichita, KS 67220-3203
Tel (316) 828-5500 *Founded/Ownrshp* 1976
Sales 31.8MM^E *EMP* 329
SIC 4731 5172 4412 4424 5052 2999 Freight transportation arrangement; Petroleum products; Deep sea foreign transportation of freight; Deep sea domestic transportation of freight; Coal & other minerals & ores; Coke (not from refineries), petroleum; Freight transportation arrangement; Petroleum products; Deep sea foreign transportation of freight; Deep sea domestic transportation of freight; Coal & other minerals & ores; Coke (not from refineries), petroleum
Pr: Ken Hush
CFO: Tom Falkenstein
CFO: Steven Feilmeier
CFO: Dan Solomon

D-U-N-S 10-332-6216 IMP/EXP
KOCH CHEMICAL TECHNOLOGY GROUP LLC
(*Suby of* KOCH RESOURCES LLC) ★
4111 E 37th St N, Wichita, KS 67220-3203
Tel (316) 828-8515 *Founded/Ownrshp* 2001
Sales 341.9MM^E *EMP* 5,101^E
SIC 3443 Metal parts
CEO: Charles Koch
**Pr:* David Robertson
**Ex VP:* David Koch
VP: Bradley E Haddock
Creative D: Joe Robertson
Snr Mgr: Matt Flamini

D-U-N-S 00-637-0357 IMP
KOCH ENTERPRISES INC
14 S 11th Ave, Evansville, IN 47712-5020
Tel (812) 465-9800 *Founded/Ownrshp* 1873
Sales 1.0MMM^E *EMP* 2,482
Accts Harding Shymanski & Company
SIC 3363 5075 3559 5084 2891 3069 Aluminum die-castings; Air conditioning equipment, except room units; Metal finishing equipment for plating, etc.; Industrial machinery & equipment; Sealants; Adhesives; Molded rubber products
Ch: Robert Koch
**Pr:* Kevin R Koch
COO: James H Muelbauer
**CFO:* Susan E Parsons
IT Man: Kevin Peveler
Mktg Dir: Jennifer Slade

D-U-N-S 60-208-4618
KOCH FERTILIZER LLC
KOCH NITROGEN COMPANY, LLC
(*Suby of* KOCH MINERAL SERVICES LLC) ★
4111 E 37th St N, Wichita, KS 67220-3203
Tel (316) 828-5010 *Founded/Ownrshp* 2001
Sales 134.9MM^E *EMP* 314
SIC 2873 5169 2813 Nitrogenous fertilizers; Chemicals & allied products; Industrial gases; Nitrogenous fertilizers; Chemicals & allied products; Industrial gases
Treas: Richard Dinkel

D-U-N-S 02-406-8132 IMP
■ **KOCH FILTER CORP** (KY)
(*Suby of* A S C) ★
625 W Hill St, Louisville, KY 40208-2201
Tel (502) 634-4796 *Founded/Ownrshp* 1966, 2012
Sales 78.4MM^E *EMP* 248
SIC 3585 Refrigeration & heating equipment; Refrigeration & heating equipment
Pr: Gordon Jones
Ex VP: Jourdan Moore
Dist Mgr: Randy Crick
Opers Mgr: Chris Dempsey
Plnt Mgr: Derek Busby
Mktg Mgr: Kevin Sulzer
Manager: Phil Faust
Sls Mgr: Russ Cummins
Sls Mgr: Joey Thurman

D-U-N-S 00-338-5127 EXP
KOCH FOODS INC (TN)
1080 River Oaks Dr A100, Flowood, MS 39232-9779
Tel (601) 732-8911 *Founded/Ownrshp* 1948
Sales 2.0MMM^E *EMP* 3,984
SIC 5144 Poultry: live, dressed or frozen (unpackaged); Poultry products; Eggs; Poultry: live, dressed or frozen (unpackaged); Poultry products; Eggs
Pr: Joe Grundy
CFO: Mark Kaminsky
VP: John Marler
Off Mgr: Regina Little
Ql Cn Mgr: Anita Scott
Sales Exec: Charlene Moncries
Manager: Mike Massey

D-U-N-S 02-443-9153
KOCH FOODS OF CINCINNATI LLC
4100 Port Union Rd, Fairfield, OH 45014-2293
Tel (513) 874-3500 *Founded/Ownrshp* 1999
Sales 26.4MM^E *EMP* 185^E
SIC 2099 Food preparations
Genl Mgr: Brian Reisen
VP: Ted Davis
VP: Bill Kantola
VP: Bruce Mackenzie
Dir Lab: Sammie Smith

Genl Mgr: Brian Reisen
Off Mgr: Cindy Craft
QA Dir: Francis Banahene
QA Dir: Jennifer Meeks
QA Dir: Jennifer Patrick
IT Man: Alejandro Delgado

D-U-N-S 94-319-2658
KOCH FOODS OF GAINESVILLE
(*Suby of* KOCH FOODS INC) ★
221 Meadow Dr, Cumming, GA 30040-2691
Tel (770) 844-8416 *Founded/Ownrshp* 2000
Sales 50.7MM^E *EMP* 300
SIC 2015 Poultry slaughtering & processing; Poultry slaughtering & processing

D-U-N-S 00-819-5638 EXP
KOCH FOODS OF MISSISSIPPI LLC (MS)
(*Suby of* KOCH FOODS INC) ★
4688 Highway 80, Morton, MS 39117-3472
Tel (601) 732-8911 *Founded/Ownrshp* 1981, 1999
Sales 558.1MM^E *EMP* 3,534
SIC 2015 Chicken, processed: fresh; Chicken, processed: frozen; Chicken, slaughtered & dressed; Chicken, processed: fresh; Chicken, processed: frozen; Chicken, slaughtered & dressed

KOCH HOLDINGS
See FORD MILHAM TOYOTA SCION

D-U-N-S 03-106-5394
KOCH HVAC DISTRIBUTION INC
(*Suby of* KOCH ENTERPRISES INC) ★
1900 W Lloyd Expy, Evansville, IN 47712-5138
Tel (812) 962-5200 *Founded/Ownrshp* 1997
Sales 151.3MM *EMP* 191
Accts Harding Shymanski And Company
SIC 5075 Warm air heating & air conditioning; Compressors, air conditioning; Condensing units, air conditioning; Warm air heating & air conditioning; Compressors, air conditioning; Condensing units, air conditioning
Ch Bd: Robert L Koch II
**Pr:* James H Muehlbauer
**CFO:* Cindy Spaetti
Treas: Cindy Mitchell
**Sec:* Susan E Parsons

D-U-N-S 00-694-4334 IMP
KOCH INDUSTRIES INC
4111 E 37th St N, Wichita, KS 67220-3298
Tel (316) 828-5500 *Founded/Ownrshp* 1961
Sales 93.1MMM^E *EMP* 70,000
SIC 5172 2911 5169 Petroleum refining; Chemicals & allied products; Petroleum products; Petroleum products; Petroleum refining; Chemicals & allied products
CEO: Charles G Koch
COO: J F Gostkowski
COO: Bill Hohns
COO: David L Robertson
COO: Allen Wright
CFO: Pat Boushka
CFO: Steven Feilmeier
CFO: Sam Soliman
Ex VP: Richard Fink
Ex VP: James Mahoney
Ex VP: Brad Sanders
Sr VP: Mark Holden
VP: Brian Boulter
VP: James Faith
VP: David H Koch
VP: Lori Little
VP: Rick Moncrief
VP: Steve Pankey
VP: Paul R Wheeler
Dir Risk M: Jeff Parke

D-U-N-S 14-428-1909 IMP/EXP
KOCH KNIGHT LLC
(*Suby of* KOCH-GLITSCH LP) ★
5385 Orchardview Dr Se, East Canton, OH 44730-9568
Tel (330) 488-1651 *Founded/Ownrshp* 2001
Sales 29.6MM^E *EMP* 80
SIC 2911 5172 5169 4922 1311 3559 Petroleum refining; Petroleum products; Chemicals & allied products; Natural gas transmission; Crude petroleum production; Natural gas production; Refinery, chemical processing & similar machinery
Pr: Mike Graeff
**VP:* Mathew Phayer
Opers Mgr: Greg Carle
Sls Dir: Ahmed Zamin
Manager: Matthias Walschburger

D-U-N-S 00-627-0003
KOCH MATERIALS LLC
KOCH PAVEMENT SOLUTIONS
(*Suby of* KOCH INDUSTRIES INC) ★
4111 E 37th St N, Wichita, KS 67220-3203
Tel (316) 828-5500 *Founded/Ownrshp* 1923
Sales 32.4MM^E *EMP* 200
SIC 2951 2899 Asphalt & asphaltic paving mixtures (not from refineries); Waterproofing compounds; Asphalt & asphaltic paving mixtures (not from refineries); Waterproofing compounds
VP: Dale Gibbens
VP: Chris Hamman
VP: Chuck Passannanti
VP: Phillip Wittmer

D-U-N-S 02-518-9853 EXP
KOCH MEAT CO INC (IL)
KOCH POULTRY
(*Suby of* KOCH FOODS INC) ★
1300 Higgins Rd Ste 100, Park Ridge, IL 60068-5766
Tel (847) 384-8018 *Founded/Ownrshp* 1959
Sales 313.7MM^E *EMP* 405
SIC 5142 5144 Poultry, frozen: packaged; Poultry: live, dressed or frozen (unpackaged); Poultry products; Poultry, frozen: packaged; Poultry: live, dressed or frozen (unpackaged); Poultry products
Pr: Joseph Grundy
**Sec:* Mark Kaminsky
Plnt Mgr: David Lebla

D-U-N-S 04-169-7244
KOCH MEMBRANE SYSTEMS INC
(*Suby of* KOCH-GLITSCH LP) ★
850 Main St, Wilmington, MA 01887-3388
Tel (978) 694-7000 *Founded/Ownrshp* 1999
Sales 103.6MM^E *EMP* 480
SIC 3569 3564 Separators for steam, gas, vapor or air (machinery); Air purification equipment; Separators for steam, gas, vapor or air (machinery); Air purification equipment
Ch Bd: David H Koch
**Treas:* Jeanne R Hernandez
VP: Joseph Gullotta
VP: Imran Jaferey
Div/Sub He: William Ekyamp
Rgnl Mgr: Jack Cangiano
Rgnl Mgr: Mark Forbes
Rgnl Mgr: Martin Howard
Rgnl Mgr: Sergio Ribeiro
IT Man: Thomas McCarthy
Mtls Mgr: Stephen Curtis
Board of Directors: John M Van Gelder

D-U-N-S 14-169-0375 IMP/EXP
KOCH MINERAL SERVICES LLC
(*Suby of* KOCH RESOURCES LLC) ★
4111 E 37th St N, Wichita, KS 67220-3203
Tel (316) 828-5500 *Founded/Ownrshp* 2001
Sales 188.6MM^E *EMP* 347^E
SIC 2999 2873 2819 4731 5172 1382 Coke (not from refineries), petroleum; Nitrogenous fertilizers; Industrial inorganic chemicals; Freight transportation arrangement; Petroleum products; Oil & gas exploration services; Coke (not from refineries), petroleum; Nitrogenous fertilizers; Industrial inorganic chemicals; Freight transportation arrangement; Petroleum products; Oil & gas exploration services
CFO: Dan Solomon

D-U-N-S 82-502-3468
KOCH MODULAR PROCESS SYSTEMS LLC
45 Eisenhower Dr Ste 350, Paramus, NJ 07652-1416
Tel (201) 368-2929 *Founded/Ownrshp* 1999
Sales 43.7MM *EMP* 70
SIC 8711 3559 Engineering services; Chemical engineering; Chemical machinery & equipment; Engineering services; Chemical engineering; Chemical machinery & equipment
Pr: George Schlowsky
VP: Alan Erickson
VP: Thomas Schafer
Exec: Sandy Lind

KOCH NATIONALEASE
See STAN KOCH & SONS TRUCKING INC

KOCH NITROGEN COMPANY
See KOCH PIPELINE CO LP

KOCH NITROGEN COMPANY, LLC
See KOCH FERTILIZER LLC

KOCH PAVEMENT SOLUTIONS
See KOCH MATERIALS LLC

D-U-N-S 95-744-1173
KOCH PIPELINE CO LP
KOCH NITROGEN COMPANY
(*Suby of* FLINT HILLS RESOURCES LLC) ★
4111 E 37th St N, Wichita, KS 67220-3203
Tel (316) 828-5511 *Founded/Ownrshp* 2005
Sales 55.2MM^E *EMP* 166
SIC 4612 Crude petroleum pipelines; Crude petroleum pipelines
Pr: Kim Penner
V Ch: Mike Kostelecky
VP: Mike Purkey
Genl Mgr: Jimmy Andrews
IT Man: William Bowen
Counsel: Kristin Westgard
Snr Mgr: Julie Carson
Snr Mgr: Monty Dershem
Snr Mgr: Josh McCabe

KOCH POULTRY
See KOCH MEAT CO INC

D-U-N-S 14-298-1278
KOCH RESOURCES LLC
(*Suby of* KOCH INDUSTRIES INC) ★
4111 E 37th St N, Wichita, KS 67220-3203
Tel (316) 828-5500 *Founded/Ownrshp* 2003
Sales 1.9MMM^E *EMP* 10,000^E
SIC 6221 2911 Commodity traders, contracts; Petroleum refining; Commodity traders, contracts; Petroleum refining
CEO: Charles G Koch
**Pr:* David L Robertson
**Ex VP:* David H Koch
Genl Mgr: Wade Marquardt
Genl Mgr: Anthony Sementelli
VP Opers: Carmen Perri
Board of Directors: Gary Kohn

D-U-N-S 07-512-8595 IMP
KOCH SPECIALTY PLANT SERVICES INC (KS)
KOCH-GLITSCH FIELD SERVICE
(*Suby of* KOCH INDUSTRIES INC) ★
12221 E Sam Huston Pkwy N, Houston, TX 77044-5094
Tel (713) 427-7700 *Founded/Ownrshp* 1971, 1997
Sales 46.6MM^E *EMP* 500
SIC 7699 7389 Industrial machinery & equipment repair; Inspection & testing services; Industrial machinery & equipment repair; Inspection & testing services
Pr: Craig R Alexander
**VP:* Tom Concienne
**VP:* Norman Funderburk
**VP:* Mike Woltemath
Manager: Richard Schmidt

KOCH SUPPLY & TRADING
See KS&T INTERNATIONAL HOLDINGS LP

D-U-N-S 03-115-9093 EXP
KOCH SUPPLY & TRADING LP
KOCH SUPPLY AND TRADING
(*Suby of* KOCH INDUSTRIES INC) ★
4111 E 37th St N, Wichita, KS 67220-3203
Tel (316) 828-5500 *Founded/Ownrshp* 2001
Sales 241.8MM^E *EMP* 350
SIC 2911 Petroleum refining; Petroleum refining
CEO: Charles G Koch
Pt: Bradford T Sanders
Pr: Steve Mawer
CFO: Bradley C Hall
Ex VP: Mark Dobbins
Ex VP: Bill Kovach
IT Man: Donnie Aschenbrenner
IT Man: Tim Shanfelt

KOCH SUPPLY AND TRADING
See KOCH SUPPLY & TRADING LP

KOCH-GLITSCH FIELD SERVICE
See KOCH SPECIALTY PLANT SERVICES INC

D-U-N-S 00-732-4916 IMP/EXP
KOCH-GLITSCH LP
(*Suby of* KOCH INDUSTRIES INC) ★
4111 E 37th St N, Wichita, KS 67220-3203
Tel (316) 828-5110 *Founded/Ownrshp* 1913, 1997
Sales 255.4MM^E *EMP* 900
SIC 3443 Vessels, process or storage (from boiler shops): metal plate; Vessels, process or storage (from boiler shops): metal plate
Pt: Robert Difulgentiz
Pt: Vince Dailey
Pt: Matt Sherwood
Bd of Dir: John Gelder
Dir IT: Justin Sullivan
QC Dir: Patricia Cooke
Mtls Mgr: Charlene Frame
Opers Mgr: Robert Brown
Plnt Mgr: Jim Snodgrass
S&M/VP: Christoph Ender
Manager: Joe Heavrin

D-U-N-S 01-661-4562
KOCOLENE MARKETING CORP
FAST MAX
(*Suby of* KOCOLENE MARKETING LLC) ★
2060 1st Ave, Seymour, IN 47274-3321
Tel (812) 522-2224 *Founded/Ownrshp* 1938, 1973
Sales 32.1MM^E *EMP* 100
SIC 5541 5411 Gasoline service stations; Convenience stores, independent; Gasoline service stations; Convenience stores, independent
Ch Bd: Robert Myers
**Pr:* Gary F Myers
COO: Douglas Prather
CFO: Kevin Johnson

D-U-N-S 07-595-2713
KOCOLENE MARKETING LLC
2060 1st Ave, Seymour, IN 47274-3321
Tel (812) 522-2224 *Founded/Ownrshp* 1973
Sales 193.5MM^E *EMP* 580^E
SIC 5541 5411 Gasoline service stations; Convenience stores, independent; Gasoline service stations; Convenience stores, independent

D-U-N-S 04-791-4759
KOCSIS BROTHERS MACHINE CO
11755 S Austin Ave, Alsip, IL 60803-6002
Tel (708) 597-8110 *Founded/Ownrshp* 1968
Sales 26.7MM^E *EMP* 110
SIC 3599 Machine shop, jobbing & repair; Machine shop, jobbing & repair
Pr: Louis Kocsis
**CFO:* Gerald Sullivan
Dir IT: Chris Ennis
Dir IT: Chris Pawlowski
IT Man: John Quadrizius

KODA DISTRIBUTION GROUP
See RIBELIN SALES INC

D-U-N-S 05-785-3769
KODA DISTRIBUTION GROUP INC
262 Harbor Dr, Stamford, CT 06902-7438
Tel (203) 274-8691 *Founded/Ownrshp* 1998
Sales 115.9MM^E *EMP* 77^E
SIC 5085 5046 5169 Industrial supplies; Commercial equipment; Chemicals & allied products
Pr: Eugene P McDonald
**Treas:* William S Karol

D-U-N-S 11-061-6997
KODA ENTERPRISES GROUP LLC
51 Sawyer Rd Ste 420, Waltham, MA 02453-3488
Tel (781) 891-0467 *Founded/Ownrshp* 1998
Sales 47.4MM^E *EMP* 97
SIC 5075 3585 Automotive air conditioners; Air conditioning, motor vehicle; Automotive air conditioners; Air conditioning, motor vehicle
**Sr VP:* William Leaver
Off Mgr: Kathy Nee

D-U-N-S 07-909-0540 IMP
KODAK ALARIS INC
(*Suby of* KODAK ALARIS HOLDINGS LIMITED)
2400 Mount Read Blvd # 1175, Rochester, NY 14615-2744
Tel (585) 290-2891 *Founded/Ownrshp* 2013
Sales 360.1MM^E *EMP* 700^E
SIC 3861 Photographic equipment & supplies; Photographic equipment & supplies
Ch: Steven Ross
**CFO:* Steven Meyers
**VP:* Phillip Gibbons
**Prin:* Dolores Kruchten
**Prin:* Dennis Olbrich
Snr Sftwr: Bill Moon
Software D: Dan Jarvis

KODAK GALLERY - COHBER
See COHBER PRESS INC

D-U-N-S 01-020-5433
KODIAK AREA NATIVE ASSOCIATION
KANA
3449 Rezanof Dr E, Kodiak, AK 99615-6952
Tel (907) 486-9800 *Founded/Ownrshp* 1966
Sales 25.8MM^E *EMP* 150
SIC 8011 8322 8641 8621 Clinic, operated by physicians; Social service center; Civic social & fraternal associations; Professional membership organizations; Clinic, operated by physicians; Social service center; Civic social & fraternal associations; Professional membership organizations
Pr: Andrew Teuber
**Treas:* Kewan Arnold
**VP:* Marjorie Bezona

KODIAK BUILDING PARTNERS
See KODIAK GYPSUM LLC

D-U-N-S 04-247-8982
KODIAK ELECTRIC ASSOCIATION INC
K E A
1614 Mill Bay Rd, Kodiak, AK 99615-6234
Tel (907) 486-7700 *Founded/Ownrshp* 1941
Sales 25.8MM *EMP* 46^E
SIC 4911 Transmission, electric power; Distribution, electric power; Transmission, electric power; Distribution, electric power
Ch: Cliff Davidson
Pr: Darron Scott
VP: Ron Acarregui
VP: Kate Ballenger
VP: Cliff Davidson

D-U-N-S 14-456-8631
KODIAK FRESH PRODUCE LLC
KODIAK PRODUCE
1033 E Maricopa Fwy, Phoenix, AZ 85034-5505
Tel (602) 253-2236 *Founded/Ownrshp* 2005
Sales 190.4MM^E *EMP* 225
SIC 5148 Fresh fruits & vegetables; Fresh fruits & vegetables
Sfty Mgr: Greg Bennett
Sls Mgr: Louise Carter

D-U-N-S 07-867-2173
KODIAK GYPSUM LLC
KODIAK BUILDING PARTNERS
14800 E Moncrieff Pl, Aurora, CO 80011-1211
Tel (720) 336-0083 *Founded/Ownrshp* 2011
Sales 35.7MM^E *EMP* 180^E
SIC 6799 Investors
CEO: Paul Hylbert
**VP:* Kyle Barker
**VP:* Eric Miller

D-U-N-S 09-983-7122
KODIAK ISLAND BOROUGH
710 Mill Bay Rd Rm 104, Kodiak, AK 99615-6398
Tel (907) 486-9325 *Founded/Ownrshp* 1963
Sales 24.9MM *EMP* 40^E
Accts Altman Rogers & Co Anchorag
SIC 8611 9111 Business associations; Mayors' offices; Business associations; Mayors' offices
Bd of Dir: Janet Buckingham
Exec: Sharon Nault
Dir: Bud Cassidy

D-U-N-S 06-744-2798
KODIAK ISLAND BOROUGH SCHOOL DISTRICT
722 Mill Bay Rd, Kodiak, AK 99615-6340
Tel (907) 481-6200 *Founded/Ownrshp* 1959
Sales 22.2MM^E *EMP* 360
SIC 8211 Elementary school; Public elementary school; Public junior high school; Public senior high school; Elementary school; Public elementary school; Public junior high school; Public senior high school
Prin: Kendra Bartz
Prin: Corrina Eaton
Dir Sec: Steve Doerksen
Schl Brd P: Katie Oliver

D-U-N-S 93-394-6055 IMP
KODIAK MFG INC
(*Suby of* INTERNATIONAL EQUIPMENT SOLUTIONS LLC) ★
8849 Candies Crk, Charleston, TN 37310-5163
Tel (423) 336-2390 *Founded/Ownrshp* 2015
Sales 21.8MM^E *EMP* 80
SIC 3523 Farm machinery & equipment
CEO: Steve Andrews
Plnt Mgr: Marvin Bishop

D-U-N-S 13-010-0048 EXP
KODIAK NETWORKS INC
1501 10th St Ste 130, Plano, TX 75074-8660
Tel (972) 665-0200 *Founded/Ownrshp* 2001
Sales 91.3MM^E *EMP* 190
SIC 4813 Telephone communication, except radio; Telephone communication, except radio
Pr: John Vice
Sr VP: Charles Nelson
**VP:* John Dilley
**VP:* Tim Hall
**VP:* Bruce Lawler
VP: Dipan Mann
**VP:* Kris Patel
VP: Bujji Vempati
Ex Dir: Dave Lafferty
Tech Mgr: Atul Jadhav
Sls Mgr: Steve Moses

KODIAK OIL & GAS CORP
See WHITING CANADIAN HOLDING CO ULC

KODIAK PRODUCE
See KODIAK FRESH PRODUCE LLC

KODIAK ROOFING & WATERPROOFING
See DWAYNE NASH INDUSTRIES INC

D-U-N-S 18-269-4307
KOEDYKER AND KENYON CONSTRUCTION INC
901 W Calle Progreso, Tucson, AZ 85705-6452
Tel (520) 882-7006 *Founded/Ownrshp* 1988
Sales 20.8MM^E *EMP* 250

SIC 1771 1542 1751 1521 1741 Stucco, gunite & grouting contractors; Nonresidential construction; Carpentry work; New construction, single-family houses; Masonry & other stonework; Stucco, gunite & grouting contractors; Nonresidential construction; Carpentry work; New construction, single-family houses; Masonry & other stonework
Pr: John Kenyon III

D-U-N-S 00-532-5030
KOEGEL MEATS INC
3400 W Bristol Rd, Flint, MI 48507-3199
Tel (810) 238-3685 *Founded/Ownrshp* 1916
Sales 32.0MM *EMP* 115
Accts Stork & Co Cpa Pc Grand Bl
SIC 2013 5712 Frankfurters from purchased meat; Bologna from purchased meat; Luncheon meat from purchased meat; Furniture stores; Frankfurters from purchased meat; Bologna from purchased meat; Luncheon meat from purchased meat; Furniture stores
Pr: John C Koegel
**Treas:* Albert J Koegel
**VP:* Kathryn Koegel
Board of Directors: Barbara L Koegel, Edward Neithercut

D-U-N-S 06-091-8729 IMP
KOEHLKE COMPONENTS INC
1201 Commerce Center Dr, Franklin, OH 45005-7206
Tel (937) 435-5435 *Founded/Ownrshp* 1976
Sales 27.2MM^E *EMP* 26
SIC 5065 Electronic parts
Pr: Tom Koehlke
**Sec:* Shirley F Koehlke
CIO: Kris Fenton
Ql Cn Mgr: Kim Moyer

D-U-N-S 88-313-2961 IMP/EXP
■ **KOEHRING CRANES INC**
TEREX CRANES
(*Suby of* TEREX CORP) ★
106 12th St Se, Waverly, IA 50677-4200
Tel (319) 352-3920 *Founded/Ownrshp* 2005
Sales 95.0MM^E *EMP* 245
SIC 3536 Hoists, cranes & monorails; Hoists, cranes & monorails
Pr: Kevin Bradley
Treas: Philip Widman
**VP:* Frank Bardonar
VP: Mike Rodriguez
**Prin:* Steve Silpoth
MIS Mgr: Tim Bruxvoort
MIS Mgr: Dave Stevenson
Ql Cn Mgr: Lee Linderkamp
Snr Mgr: Jim McKenzie

D-U-N-S 06-930-0382 IMP
KOELLMANN GEAR CORP
8 Industrial Park, Waldwick, NJ 07463-1512
Tel (201) 447-0200 *Founded/Ownrshp* 1974
Sales 37.8MM^E *EMP* 250
SIC 3566 Gears, power transmission, except automotive; Reduction gears & gear units for turbines, except automotive; Gears, power transmission, except automotive; Reduction gears & gear units for turbines, except automotive
CEO: Michael Rasovic

D-U-N-S 04-084-6388
KOEN BOOK DISTRIBUTORS INC
1753 Garwood Dr, Cherry Hill, NJ 08003-3205
Tel (856) 235-4444 *Founded/Ownrshp* 1973
Sales 27.9MM^E *EMP* 250
SIC 5192 Books; Books
Pr: Robert Koen
**VP:* Patricia Koen
VP: Sally Lindsay

D-U-N-S 78-322-8369
KOEN-LEVY BOOK WHOLESALERS LLC
(*Suby of* READERLINK LLC) ★
1930 George St Ste 1, Melrose Park, IL 60160-1501
Tel (708) 356-3700 *Founded/Ownrshp* 2011
Sales 8.9MM^E *EMP* 415^E
SIC 5192 Books
VP: Linwood Ferguson
VP: Joe Gallagher

D-U-N-S 01-754-9353
KOENIG EQUIPMENT INC
15213 State Route 274, Botkins, OH 45306-9586
Tel (937) 693-5000 *Founded/Ownrshp* 1974
Sales 200.0MM *EMP* 210
SIC 5999 0782 Farm equipment & supplies; Lawn & garden services; Farm equipment & supplies; Lawn & garden services
CEO: Raymond Koenig
**Pr:* Aaron Koenig
**Treas:* Gene Derringer
Chf Mktg O: Marguerite Kleinedler
**VP:* Jack Koenig
VP: Kenneth Konig

D-U-N-S 93-834-5683
KOEPPEL VOLKSWAGEN INC
5715 Northern Blvd, Woodside, NY 11377-2222
Tel (718) 728-8111 *Founded/Ownrshp* 1994
Sales 20.5MM^E *EMP* 58
SIC 5511 Automobiles, new & used; Automobiles, new & used
Pr: Howard Koeppel
**Sec:* Mark Lacher

D-U-N-S 05-229-9096 IMP
KOERNER DISTRIBUTOR INC (IL)
1305 W Wabash Ave, Effingham, IL 62401-1966
Tel (217) 347-7113 *Founded/Ownrshp* 1952, 1981
Sales 37.0MM^E *EMP* 130
SIC 5181 5182

D-U-N-S 01-326-2803
KOERNER FORD OF SYRACUSE INC
805 W Genesee St, Syracuse, NY 13204-2205
Tel (315) 474-4275 *Founded/Ownrshp* 1982
Sales 27.1MM^E *EMP* 75
SIC 5511 Automobiles, new & used; Automobiles, new & used
Pr: Thomas Licciardello
Sls Mgr: Kevin Dawley

D-U-N-S 18-895-1446 IMP
KOESTER ASSOCIATES INC
3101 Seneca Tpke, Canastota, NY 13032-4525
Tel (315) 697-3800 *Founded/Ownrshp* 1973
Sales 30.0MM^E *EMP* 35
SIC 5084 Industrial machinery & equipment; Materials handling machinery
Pr: Mark Koester
Ofcr: Gregg Palmer
**Sr VP:* Peter J Padosta
**VP:* Thomas J Whetham
Off Admin: Katherine Hurrle
Tech Mgr: John West
Sales Asso: Bill Driscoll
Sales Asso: Jacob Koester
Sales Asso: Bill Rourke

KOESTER FINANCIAL SERVICES
See VIGO COAF INC

D-U-N-S 01-630-0337
KOETTER CONSTRUCTION INC
7393 Pete Andres Rd, Floyds Knobs, IN 47119-8825
Tel (812) 923-9873 *Founded/Ownrshp* 1954
Sales 53.3MM^E *EMP* 125
Accts Monroe Shine & Company Inc Ne
SIC 1542 1541 Commercial & office building, new construction; Commercial & office buildings, renovation & repair; Industrial buildings & warehouses; Renovation, remodeling & repairs: industrial buildings; Commercial & office building, new construction; Commercial & office buildings, renovation & repair; Industrial buildings & warehouses; Renovation, remodeling & repairs: industrial buildings
Ch Bd: Robert Koetter Sr
**Pr:* Robert Koetter Jr
**CEO:* John L Koetter
**Sec:* Gladys Koetter
**VP:* Kenneth Koetter
VP Mktg: Tim Hunt

D-U-N-S 02-623-7206 IMP
KOETTER FIRE PROTECTION LLC
KOETTER FIRE PROTECTION SVC
10351 Olympic Dr, Dallas, TX 75220-4437
Tel (214) 358-8944 *Founded/Ownrshp* 1995
Sales 74.8MM^E *EMP* 165^E
SIC 5063 5087 8734 Fire alarm systems; Signaling equipment, electrical; Firefighting equipment; Hydrostatic testing laboratory; Fire alarm systems; Signaling equipment, electrical; Firefighting equipment; Hydrostatic testing laboratory
Mng Dir: Bethe Hathaway
Opers Mgr: Andy Axtman

D-U-N-S 04-248-1080
KOETTER FIRE PROTECTION OF AUSTIN LLC
16069 Central Commerce Dr, Pflugerville, TX 78660-2005
Tel (512) 252-2534 *Founded/Ownrshp* 1997
Sales 41.5MM^E *EMP* 70
SIC 5063 Alarm systems
Pr: Robert Rabroker

KOETTER FIRE PROTECTION SVC
See KOETTER FIRE PROTECTION LLC

D-U-N-S 00-700-3189 IMP
KOETTER WOODWORKING INC
533 Louis Smith Rd, Borden, IN 47106-8107
Tel (812) 923-8875 *Founded/Ownrshp* 1959
Sales 54.3MM^E *EMP* 330
SIC 2431 Doors & door parts & trim, wood; Moldings, wood: unfinished & prefinished; Staircases & stairs, wood; Doors & door parts & trim, wood; Moldings, wood: unfinished & prefinished; Staircases & stairs, wood
Pr: Randall F Koetter
CFO: Aaron Morgan
**Treas:* Thomas C Koetter Jr
**VP:* Gerald Koetter
VP: David Martin
Genl Mgr: Randell Eldridge
IT Man: Missy Huff
IT Man: Carol Phillips
Web Prj Mg: Mark Farmer
Sfty Mgr: Cory Vern
Prd Mgr: Sam Smith

D-U-N-S 12-175-6308
KOETTING FORD INC
3465 Progress Pkwy, Granite City, IL 62040-6820
Tel (618) 452-5400 *Founded/Ownrshp* 1984
Sales 23.2MM^E *EMP* 40
SIC 5511 Automobiles, new & used
Pr: Gerald R Koetting
**VP:* Loe W Frederking
**VP:* Martin R McCabe
Store Mgr: Keith Langreder

D-U-N-S 14-791-8601 EXP
■ **KOFAX INC**
(FORMERLY KNOWN AS: KOFAX IMAGE PRODUCTS, INC.)
(*Suby of* KOFAX LIMITED) ★
15211 Laguna Canyon Rd, Irvine, CA 92618-3146
Tel (949) 783-1000 *Founded/Ownrshp* 1985
Sales 300.0MM *EMP* 505
SIC 3577 7371 Input/output equipment, computer; Computer software development; Input/output equipment, computer; Computer software development
CEO: Reynolds C Bish
CFO: Stefan Gaiser
CFO: Paul Smith
Ex VP: Howard Dratler
Ex VP: Jim Nicol
Ex VP: Bradford Weller
Sr VP: Karl Doyle
Sr VP: Lynne Scheid
Sr VP: Owen Taraniuk
VP: Colleen Edwards
VP: Daniel Geiger
VP: Rupert Grafendorfer
VP: David Hultquist
VP: Dermot McCauley
VP: Nita Patel
VP: Tom Ullman
VP: Dave Von Klemperer

D-U-N-S 07-925-6419
■ **KOFAX LIMITED**
(*Suby of* LEXMARK INTERNATIONAL INC) ★
15211 Laguna Canyon Rd, Irvine, CA 92618-3146
Tel (949) 783-1000 *Founded/Ownrshp* 2015
Sales 306.5MM^E *EMP* 1,381^E
SIC 7372 Prepackaged software; Business oriented computer software; Prepackaged software; Business oriented computer software
CEO: Reynolds C Bish
CFO: James Arnold Jr
Chf Mktg O: Grant Johnson
Ex VP: Bradford Weller
Sr VP: Lynne Scheid
Mng Dir: Srinivas Reddy
CTO: Anthony Macciola
IT Man: Dean Willo

D-U-N-S 00-207-0753
KOFFEE KUP BAKERY INC
436 Riverside Ave, Burlington, VT 05401-1452
Tel (802) 863-2696 *Founded/Ownrshp* 1967
Sales 33.3MM^E *EMP* 130
SIC 2051 5149 Bread, cake & related products; Bakery products; Bread, cake & related products; Bakery products
Pr: Huburt Aubery
**Pr:* Ronald Roberge
**Treas:* Thomas Beauregard
Ex VP: Brian Carpentier
**VP:* Andrew Matthews
**VP:* Carol Roberge
Dept Mgr: Monte Harrington
Sls Mgr: Dave Bourgea
Sls Mgr: Mark Whitehead

D-U-N-S 04-510-7125 IMP
KOFKOFF EGG FARM HOLDING LIMITED LIABILITY CO
17 Schwartz Rd, Bozrah, CT 06334-1009
Tel (860) 886-2445 *Founded/Ownrshp* 1940
Sales 20.4MM^E *EMP* 175
SIC 0252 Chicken eggs; Chicken eggs
Pr: Craig A Willardson

D-U-N-S 07-767-5049
KOGA ENGINEERING & CONSTRUCTION INC
1162 Mikole St, Honolulu, HI 96819-4320
Tel (808) 845-7829 *Founded/Ownrshp* 1973
Sales 21.1MM *EMP* 100
Accts Sutor Krystad & Rosenfeld Pl
SIC 1611 1623 General contractor, highway & street construction; Water main construction; General contractor, highway & street construction; Water main construction
Pr: Glenn Nohara
**CFO:* Lori Isara
**Ch:* Malcolm Koga
**Sec:* Carol Koga
**VP:* Clay Asato
**VP:* Dennis Okazaki
Sls Mgr: Mark Nakagawa
Snr Mgr: Brian Kunioka

D-U-N-S 00-903-8399
KOGAP ENTERPRISES INC
KOGAP EXCAVATION
115 W Stewart Ave Ste 202, Medford, OR 97501-3607
Tel (541) 776-6500 *Founded/Ownrshp* 1954
Sales 13.2MM *EMP* 5,075^E
SIC 1542 7992 0811 Commercial & office building contractors; Public golf courses; Timber tracts, softwood; Commercial & office building contractors; Public golf courses; Timber tracts, softwood
Pr: Jerry S Lausmann
**Ch:* Donnis Lausmann
VP: Edward Istel
Opers Mgr: Sabrina Reich

KOGAP EXCAVATION
See KOGAP ENTERPRISES INC

D-U-N-S 83-808-8771
KOGER INC
12 N State Rt 17 Ste 111, Paramus, NJ 07652-2644
Tel (201) 291-7747 *Founded/Ownrshp* 1993
Sales 23.4MM^E *EMP* 200
SIC 7379 Computer related consulting services; Computer related consulting services
Pr: George Sipko
QA Dir: Adrian Kelly
VP Opers: Wasseem Ghorayeb

D-U-N-S 92-778-0163 IMP
KOGOK CORP
4011a Penn Belt Pl, District Heights, MD 20747
Tel (301) 736-5300 *Founded/Ownrshp* 1995
Sales 30.1MM^E *EMP* 275
SIC 3444 Sheet metalwork; Sheet metalwork
Pr: Jeffrey W Kogok
Exec: Matthew Jones
Genl Mgr: Joe Poole
Dir IT: Mike Little
Sfty Dirs: Ted Warrington

D-U-N-S 00-506-0959
KOHL & MADDEN PRINTING INK CORP
(*Suby of* SUN CHEMICAL CORP) ★
651 Garden St, Carlstadt, NJ 07072-1609
Tel (201) 935-8666 *Founded/Ownrshp* 1905
Sales 22.7MM^E *EMP* 350
SIC 2893 3565 3555 Printing ink; Packaging machinery; Printing trades machinery; Printing ink; Packaging machinery; Printing trades machinery
Pr: Brad Bergey
**Treas:* Eugene Standora

KOHL WHOLESALE
See N KOHL GROCER CO

KOHLBERG & COMPANY
See KOHLBERG & CO LLC

D-U-N-S 01-255-0153
KOHLBERG & CO LLC
KOHLBERG & COMPANY
111 Radio Circle Dr, Mount Kisco, NY 10549-2609
Tel (914) 241-7430 *Founded/Ownrshp* 1987
Sales 10.4MM^E *EMP* 37,660
SIC 6726 6211 Investment offices; Security brokers & dealers; Investment offices; Security brokers & dealers
**Treas:* Walter W Farley
Chf Inves: Gordon Woodward
Ofcr: Amanda Moore
**VP:* Ted Jeon
**VP:* David A Lorch
VP: Elizabeth Perreten
**VP:* Jean Roberts
VP: Mary-Ann Sievert
Prin: Marion H Antonini
Prin: George T Brophy
IT Man: Warren Winte

D-U-N-S 01-236-5461
KOHLBERG FOUNDATION INC (NY)
111 Radio Circle Dr, Mount Kisco, NY 10549-2609
Tel (914) 242-2312 *Founded/Ownrshp* 1988
Sales 31.2MM *EMP* 4
SIC 8641 Environmental protection organization; Environmental protection organization
Pr: Jerome Kohlberg
Ofcr: Renu Saini
Ex VP: Nancy McCabe

D-U-N-S 06-022-3393 IMP/EXP
■ **KOHLBERG KRAVIS ROBERTS & CO LP**
(*Suby of* KKR & CO LP) ★
9 W 57th St Ste 4200, New York, NY 10019-2707
Tel (212) 750-8300 *Founded/Ownrshp* 1976
Sales 227.0MM^E *EMP* 1,014^E
SIC 6726

D-U-N-S 96-277-1775
KOHLBERG SPORTS GROUP INC
(*Suby of* KOHLBERG & CO) ★
111 Radio Circle Dr, Mount Kisco, NY 10549-2609
Tel (914) 241-7430 *Founded/Ownrshp* 2010
Sales 878.3M^E *EMP* 5,025^E
SIC 3949 Hockey equipment & supplies, general

D-U-N-S 00-607-3225 IMP/EXP
KOHLER CO
444 Highland Dr, Kohler, WI 53044-1500
Tel (920) 457-4441 *Founded/Ownrshp* 1873
Sales 7.9MMM^E *EMP* 30,000^E
Accts Deloitte & Touche Llp Milwauk
SIC 3431 3432 3261 2511 2521 3519 Plumbing fixtures: enameled iron cast iron or pressed metal; Bathroom fixtures, including sinks; Plumbing fixture fittings & trim; Bathroom accessories/fittings, vitreous china or earthenware; Plumbing fixtures, vitreous china; Wood household furniture; Wood office furniture; Gasoline engines; Plumbing fixtures: enameled iron cast iron or pressed metal; Bathroom fixtures, including sinks; Plumbing fixture fittings & trim; Bathroom accessories/fittings, vitreous china or earthenware; Plumbing fixtures, vitreous china; Wood household furniture; Wood office furniture; Gasoline engines
Pr: K David Kohler
Pr: Scott Anderson
Pr: Jeff Mueller
Pr: Jim Westdorp
COO: Jim Hoven
Sr VP: Martin D Agard
**Sr VP:* Laura E Kohler
Sr VP: James M Robinson
Creative D: Tristan Butterfield
Creative D: Michael Huibregtse
Area Mgr: Daniel Goodman
Board of Directors: Natalie A Black, John M Kohler Jr Director, Jeff M Fettig, William C Foote, Glen H Hiner, Jeffrey A Joerres, Rachael D Kohler, Michael H Thaman

KOHLER DISTRIBUTING
See A I G TRUCKING CO INC

D-U-N-S 08-906-6484 IMP/EXP
KOHLER INTERIORS FURNITURE CO
MCGUIRE FURNITURE
(*Suby of* KOHLER CO) ★
1105 22nd St Se, Hickory, NC 28602-9670
Tel (828) 624-7000 *Founded/Ownrshp* 1986
Sales 156.9MM^E *EMP* 716^E
SIC 2511 5021 Wood household furniture; Household furniture; Wood household furniture; Household furniture
Pr: Rachel D Kohler
**CFO:* Martin D Agard
Sr VP: Rick Vaughn
VP: Kevin Ward
Genl Mgr: Tracey Sheedlo
Genl Mgr: Mitch Stotts

KOHLLS PHARMACY
See KOHLLS PHARMACY & HOMECARE INC

D-U-N-S 06-866-1719
KOHLLS PHARMACY & HOMECARE INC
KOHLLS PHARMACY
12739 Q St, Omaha, NE 68137-3211
Tel (402) 895-6812 *Founded/Ownrshp* 1948
Sales 51.9MM^E *EMP* 215
SIC 5912 Drug stores; Proprietary (non-prescription medicine) stores; Drug stores; Proprietary (non-prescription medicine) stores
Pr: David Kohll
**CFO:* Bob Moeller
**VP:* Marvin Kohll
Mktg Mgr: Laurie Dondelinger
Pharmcst: Vince Jorn
Cert Phar: Alexis Dickerson

D-U-N-S 78-740-8996 IMP/EXP
▲ **KOHLS CORP**
N56w17000 Ridgewood Dr, Menomonee Falls, WI 53051-7096
Tel (262) 703-7000 *Founded/Ownrshp* 1962
Sales 19.0MMM *EMP* 137,000

Tkr Sym KSS *Exch* NYS
SIC 5311 5961 Department stores; Department stores, non-discount; Catalog & mail-order houses; Department stores; Department stores, non-discount; Catalog & mail-order houses
Ch Bd: Kevin Mansell
COO: Sona Chawla
CFO: Wesley S McDonald
Ofcr: Richard D Schepp
Board of Directors: Peter Boneparth, Steven A Burd, Dale E Jones, Jonas Prising, John E Schlifske, Frank V Sica, Stephanie A Streeter, Nina G Vaca, Stephen E Watson

D-U-N-S 15-420-2360 IMP
■ KOHLS DEPARTMENT STORES INC
(*Suby of* KOHLS CORP) ★
N56w17000 Ridgewood Dr, Menomonee Falls, WI 53051-7096
Tel (262) 703-7000 *Founded/Ownrshp* 1992
Sales 16.7MMM^E *EMP* 126,000
SIC 5311 Department stores, non-discount; Department stores, non-discount
Ch Bd: Larry Montgomery
Pr: Bernard Powers
**CEO:* Kevin Mansell
COO: Reginald Davis
CFO: Wesley McDonald
**Chf Cred:* Michelle Gass
Ex VP: Kenneth Bonning
Ex VP: Donald A Brennan
Ex VP: David J Campisi
Ex VP: Chris Capuano
Ex VP: Joanne Crevoiserat
Ex VP: Peggy Eskenasi
Ex VP: Telvin Jeffries
Ex VP: John Lesko
Ex VP: Richard Leto
Ex VP: Ron Ota
Sr VP: Anne Horter
Sr VP: Monica Margerum
Sr VP: Randy Meadows
**Sr VP:* Brian F Miller
VP: Jack H Boyle
Board of Directors: James D Ericson, Frank V Sica, Herbert Simon, Peter M Sommerhauser, R Elton White

D-U-N-S 05-044-5342
KOHLS WEELBORG CHEVROLET LLC
1430 Westridge Rd, New Ulm, MN 56073-2335
Tel (507) 233-2000 *Founded/Ownrshp* 2010
Sales 21.8MM^E *EMP* 125
SIC 5511 Automobiles, new & used; Automobiles, new & used

D-U-N-S 02-300-1175
KOHLS WEELBORG FORD INC
1307 E Bridge St, Redwood Falls, MN 56283-1903
Tel (507) 644-2931 *Founded/Ownrshp* 1980
Sales 26.2MM *EMP* 32
Accts Conway Deuth & Schmiesing Pll
SIC 5511 Automobiles, new & used; Automobiles, new & used
Pr: Ronald A Kohls
**Sec:* Gregory Weelborg
**Prin:* Nicole Weelborg
Off Mgr: Jacqueline Reck
Sls Mgr: Bret Weelborg

D-U-N-S 05-306-2824
KOHLWEISS INC (CA)
1205 Veterans Blvd, Redwood City, CA 94063-2608
Tel (650) 367-8424 *Founded/Ownrshp* 1984
Sales 31.4MM^E *EMP* 89
SIC 5013 5531 Automotive supplies & parts; Automotive parts
Pr: Frank Kohlweiss
**CFO:* Theresa Kohlweiss

D-U-N-S 08-258-8880
KOHN PEDERSEN FOX ASSOCIATES PC (NY)
KPF
11 W 42nd St Ste 8a, New York, NY 10036-8002
Tel (212) 977-6500 *Founded/Ownrshp* 1976
Sales 81.6MM^E *EMP* 350
Accts Dgpw New York Ny
SIC 8712 8742 Architectural services; Planning consultant; Architectural services; Planning consultant
Pr: Paul Katz
**Pr:* James Von Klemperer
**CFO:* Peter Catalano
**Treas:* William Louie
**Ex VP:* A Eugene Kohn
**Ex VP:* William Pedersen
VP: Robert Cioppa
Comm Dir: Regina Henry
Dir IT: Felipe Lima
Dir IT: Mark Shattock
Netwrk Mgr: Enrico Cordice

D-U-N-S 10-656-6334
KOHNER PROPERTIES INC
1034 S Brentwood Blvd # 1300, Saint Louis, MO 63117-1213
Tel (314) 862-5955 *Founded/Ownrshp* 1982
Sales 13.7MM^E *EMP* 350
SIC 6531 Real estate managers; Real estate managers
Pr: Debra Pyzyk
**COO:* Laura Ayers
**CFO:* Jeffery Burt
VP: Susan Bozue
**VP:* William Brad Bryan
VP: Steve Gresic
VP: William B Ryan
Mktg Dir: Kristin Pyzyk

D-U-N-S 01-948-4737 IMP
KOI DESIGN LLC
1757 Stanford St, Santa Monica, CA 90404-4115
Tel (310) 828-0055 *Founded/Ownrshp* 2006
Sales 34.1MM^E *EMP* 60
SIC 5137 Uniforms, women's & children's
**Ex VP:* Jeremy Husk

D-U-N-S 00-167-5623 IMP
KOI ENTERPRISES INC
K O I
(*Suby of* FISHER AUTO PARTS INC) ★
2701 Spring Grove Ave, Cincinnati, OH 45225-2221
Tel (513) 357-2427 *Founded/Ownrshp* 1946, 2014
Sales 505.9MM^E *EMP* 1,000
SIC 5013 5531 Automotive supplies & parts; Automotive & home supply stores; Automotive supplies & parts; Automotive & home supply stores
Pr: David Wesselman
**Treas:* Greg Steppe
IT Man: Chuck Smith
Site Mgr: Don Spath

KOIN 6 TV
See MONTECITO PORTLAND LLC

D-U-N-S 14-459-3183
KOINONIA FOSTER HOMES INC
3731 Magnolia St, Loomis, CA 95650-8921
Tel (916) 652-5802 *Founded/Ownrshp* 1982
Sales 21.4MM *EMP* 200
Accts Fechter & Company Cpa S Sacra
SIC 8361 Group foster home; Group foster home
CEO: Cary Nosler
**Ex Dir:* Sam Golden

D-U-N-S 80-965-7476
KOINONIA HOMES INC
6161 Oak Tree Blvd # 400, Cleveland, OH 44131-2516
Tel (216) 588-8777 *Founded/Ownrshp* 1974
Sales 25.2MM *EMP* 500
Accts Howard Wershbale & Co Clevela
SIC 8699 Single-family housing construction; Charitable organization
Prin: William E Tumney
**Prin:* James C Maher
**Prin:* Dineen B Terstage
Snr Mgr: Mary Bondy

D-U-N-S 18-481-3434
KOJAIAN MANAGEMENT CORP
39400 Woodward Ave # 250, Bloomfield Hills, MI 48304-5155
Tel (248) 644-7600 *Founded/Ownrshp* 1985
Sales 20.2MM^E *EMP* 248
SIC 6531 Real estate leasing & rentals; Real estate leasing & rentals
Pr: Mike Kojaian
**Ex VP:* C Michael Kojaian
Sr VP: Richard Stebbins
VP: Anthony G Antone
Mktg Dir: Mark Kakkuri

D-U-N-S 01-017-7031
■ KOKO OHA INVESTMENTS INC (HI)
(*Suby of* PAR PACIFIC HOLDINGS INC) ★
1100 Alakea St Fl 8, Honolulu, HI 96813-2833
Tel (808) 535-5999 *Founded/Ownrshp* 2007, 2015
Sales 101.9MM^E *EMP* 900^E
SIC 5172 6719 Petroleum products; Service station supplies, petroleum; Personal holding companies, except banks
Pr: Jim R Yates
CFO: Kaiyo Sayle Hirashima
VP: David C Hulihee
VP: Bill D Mills
VP: Keith M Yoshida

D-U-N-S 04-281-8401
KOKOMO AUTO WORLD INC
KOKOMO FORD
3813 S Lafountain St, Kokomo, IN 46902-3819
Tel (765) 453-4111 *Founded/Ownrshp* 1976
Sales 25.9MM^E *EMP* 62
SIC 5511 7538 7532 5531 5521 5012 Automobiles, new & used; Pickups, new & used; Vans, new & used; General automotive repair shops; Top & body repair & paint shops; Automotive & home supply stores; Used car dealers; Automobiles & other motor vehicles; Automobiles, new & used; Pickups, new & used; Vans, new & used; General automotive repair shops; Top & body repair & paint shops; Automotive & home supply stores; Used car dealers; Automobiles & other motor vehicles
Pr: Jim Kebrdle
**Sec:* Carla Glos
**VP:* Coleen Kebrdle
Sls Mgr: Michael Kebrdle
Sls Mgr: Chris Welton

KOKOMO FORD
See KOKOMO AUTO WORLD INC

D-U-N-S 01-647-2136
KOKOMO GRAIN CO INC
1002 W Morgan St, Kokomo, IN 46901-2061
Tel (765) 457-7536 *Founded/Ownrshp* 1950
Sales 27.1MM^E *EMP* 50
SIC 5153 Grain elevators; Grain elevators
Pr: Scot Ortman
**Sec:* John Sigler
**VP:* Brad Ortman
Genl Mgr: Meg Burnworth

D-U-N-S 10-064-8146
KOKOMO SCHOOL CORP
LAFAYETTE PARK ELEMENTARY MIDD
1500 S Washington St, Kokomo, IN 46902-2011
Tel (765) 455-8000 *Founded/Ownrshp* 1993
Sales 65.4MM^E *EMP* 1,100
SIC 8211 Public elementary & secondary schools; Public elementary & secondary schools
**Treas:* Joyce Aaron
**Treas:* Geralynn Smalling
Bd of Dir: Ted Schuck
VP: Julie Abney
Dir Bus: Michelle Kronk
Cmptr Lab: Judy Wininger
Tech Mgr: Adam Heady
Pr Dir: Dave Barnes
Schl Brd P: Crystal Sanburn
Board of Directors: James Little

KOKOS CONFECTIONERY & NOVELTY
See A & A GLOBAL INDUSTRIES INC

D-U-N-S 10-769-8706 IMP
KOKOSING CONSTRUCTION CO INC
(*Suby of* KOKOSING INC) ★
6235 Wstrville Rd Ste 200, Westerville, OH 43081
Tel (614) 228-1029 *Founded/Ownrshp* 1981
Sales 705.5MM^E *EMP* 1,061
Accts Crowe Horwath Llp South Bend
SIC 1611 1622 1629 1542 1541 1623 General contractor, highway & street construction; Highway & street paving contractor; Bridge construction; Waste water & sewage treatment plant construction; Commercial & office building, new construction; Industrial buildings, new construction; Renovation, remodeling & repairs: industrial buildings; Sewer line construction; Water main construction; General contractor, highway & street construction; Highway & street paving contractor; Bridge construction; Waste water & sewage treatment plant construction; Commercial & office building, new construction; Industrial buildings, new construction; Renovation, remodeling & repairs: industrial buildings; Sewer line construction; Water main construction
CEO: W Barth Burgett
**CFO:* Kim Freed
**CFO:* James H Geiser
CFO: James Graves
**Ex VP:* Marsha Rinehart
**Sr VP:* Daniel J Compston
**Sr VP:* Daniel Walker
VP: Valerie Matusik
VP: John Neighbors
Area Mgr: Thomas Graf
Area Mgr: Gary Lewis

D-U-N-S 07-778-7984 IMP
KOKOSING CONSTRUCTION INC
1516 Timken Rd, Wooster, OH 44691-9401
Tel (330) 263-4168 *Founded/Ownrshp* 2002
Sales 92.3MM^E *EMP* 2,500
SIC 1611 Highway & street paving contractor; Highway & street paving contractor
Pr: Brian Burgett

D-U-N-S 07-981-3347
KOKOSING INC
6235 Wstrville Rd Ste 200, Westerville, OH 43081
Tel (614) 212-5700 *Founded/Ownrshp* 2015
Sales 818.5MM^E *EMP* 1,900
Accts Crowe Horwath Llp
SIC 1611 General contractor, highway & street construction
CEO: William Brian Burgett
Pr: Dan Compston

D-U-N-S 07-972-9702
KOKOSING INDUSTRIAL INC
(*Suby of* KOKOSING INC) ★
6235 Westerville Rd, Westerville, OH 43081-4041
Tel (614) 212-5700 *Founded/Ownrshp* 2015
Sales 15.0MM^E *EMP* 400
Accts Crowe Horwath Llp
SIC 1623 1629 Water, sewer & utility lines; Dams, waterways, docks & other marine construction
CEO: W Brian Burgett

D-U-N-S 88-425-8369
KOKUSAI SEMICONDUCTOR EQUIPMENT CORP
(*Suby of* HITACHI KOKUSAI ELECTRIC INC.)
2460 N 1st St Ste 290, San Jose, CA 95131-1024
Tel (408) 456-2750 *Founded/Ownrshp* 1992
Sales 169.5MM *EMP* 96
SIC 5065 7629 Semiconductor devices; Communication equipment; Electronic equipment repair; Semiconductor devices; Communication equipment; Electronic equipment repair
CEO: Nobuo Owada
**CFO:* Kenichi Sato
VP: Len Elias

D-U-N-S 09-939-4793
KOLACHE FACTORY INC
23240 Westheimer Pkwy A, Katy, TX 77494-3620
Tel (281) 829-6188 *Founded/Ownrshp* 1982
Sales 24.5MM^E *EMP* 185
SIC 5461 Bakeries
Pr: John Banks
**VP:* Catherine D Nielsen

KOLAR AUTO WORLD
See KOLAR BUICK - GMC TRUCK INC

D-U-N-S 04-539-8245
KOLAR BUICK - GMC TRUCK INC
KOLAR AUTO WORLD
4781 Miller Trunk Hwy, Hermantown, MN 55811-3918
Tel (218) 733-0100 *Founded/Ownrshp* 1968
Sales 22.6MM^E *EMP* 60
SIC 5511 Automobiles, new & used; Trucks, tractors & trailers: new & used
Pr: Bernard J Kolar
Treas: Peter Kolar
VP: Dave Hammer
Sls Mgr: David Ling
Sales Asso: Todd Abrahamson
Sales Asso: Rick Saylor

D-U-N-S 02-997-1124
KOLB GRADING LLC
5731 Westwood Dr, Weldon Spring, MO 63304-7650
Tel (636) 441-0200 *Founded/Ownrshp* 2009
Sales 40.5MM^E *EMP* 190
SIC 1794

D-U-N-S 00-612-7294 IMP/EXP
KOLBE & KOLBE MILLWORK CO INC
KOLBE WINDOWS & DOORS
1323 S 11th Ave, Wausau, WI 54401-5980
Tel (715) 842-5666 *Founded/Ownrshp* 1973
Sales 210.7MM^E *EMP* 1,150
SIC 5031 2431 Millwork; Window frames, wood; Doors, wood; Millwork; Window frames, wood; Doors, wood
CEO: Mike Salsieder
Pr: Judith Gorski
Pr: George Waldvogle
VP: Donald Huehnerfuss
VP: Dave Southworth
VP: George Waldvogel
Rgnl Mgr: Tim Christopherson
Genl Mgr: Scott Orlikowski
Genl Mgr: Ken Wilcox
Dir IT: Dusten Tornow
VP Mfg: Jeffrey De Lonay

KOLBE CYCLE SALES
See KOLBE INC

D-U-N-S 02-966-4653 EXP
KOLBE INC
KOLBE CYCLE SALES
7514 Reseda Blvd, Reseda, CA 91335-2820
Tel (818) 609-7441 *Founded/Ownrshp* 1959
Sales 25.3MM^E *EMP* 100
SIC 5571 5551 5511 Motorcycle dealers; Jet skis; Automobiles, new & used
Pr: Andrew R Kolbe
**CFO:* Barbara Kolbe
VP: David Colby
**VP:* David Kolbe
Sls Mgr: Chris Beigi
Sls Mgr: Michael Jaffari
Sls Mgr: Steve Nussbaum
Sales Asso: Edward Catam
Sales Asso: Hossein Ghaffari
Sales Asso: Robin Worasri

D-U-N-S 79-148-5472
KOLBE LEASING CO LLC
LAKE POINTE HEALTH CENTER
3364 Kolbe Rd, Lorain, OH 44053-1628
Tel (440) 282-2244 *Founded/Ownrshp* 2004
Sales 12.4MM^E *EMP* 290
SIC 8051 Skilled nursing care facilities; Skilled nursing care facilities
Off Mgr: Michelle Dawson
Nrsg Dir: Verona Bair
Dietician: Susan Wright

KOLBE WINDOWS & DOORS
See KOLBE & KOLBE MILLWORK CO INC

D-U-N-S 96-914-5015 IMP
KOLBENSCHMIDT USA INC
(*Suby of* KSPG NORTH AMERICA INC) ★
1731 Industrial Pkwy N, Marinette, WI 54143-3704
Tel (715) 732-0181 *Founded/Ownrshp* 2011
Sales 38.5MM^E *EMP* 987^E
SIC 3592 Pistons & piston rings
Pr: Donald L Cameron
**VP:* Robert Stetfens
**VP:* Robert Turcott

D-U-N-S 96-947-5763 IMP/EXP
■ KOLBERG-PIONEER INC
(*Suby of* ASTEC INDUSTRIES INC) ★
700 W 21st St, Yankton, SD 57078-1506
Tel (605) 665-9311 *Founded/Ownrshp* 1997
Sales 112.0MM^E *EMP* 420
SIC 3532 3531 3535 Mining machinery; Construction machinery; Conveyors & conveying equipment; Mining machinery; Construction machinery; Conveyors & conveying equipment
Pr: Jeff May
VP: Bill Carpenter
Advt Mgr: Curt Peterka

D-U-N-S 13-087-2658 IMP
KOLCRAFT ENTERPRISES INC
1100 W Monroe St Ste 1, Chicago, IL 60607-2528
Tel (312) 361-6315 *Founded/Ownrshp* 1984
Sales 77.5MM^E *EMP* 244
SIC 2515 Mattresses, containing felt, foam rubber, urethane, etc.; Mattresses, containing felt, foam rubber, urethane, etc.
Ch Bd: Sanfred Koltun
**Pr:* Thomas N Koltun
**Sec:* Sharon M Danko
**Sr VP:* Edward Bretschger
**Sr VP:* Andrew Newmark
VP: Elineen Lysaught
MIS Dir: Gary Klosak
QA Dir: MO Anooshah
IT Man: Konrad Werner

D-U-N-S 93-110-5175
KOLD LLC
KOLD TV
(*Suby of* RAYCOM MEDIA INC) ★
7831 N Business Park Dr, Tucson, AZ 85743-9622
Tel (520) 744-1313 *Founded/Ownrshp* 1995
Sales 39.5MM *EMP* 110
SIC 4833 Television broadcasting stations; Television broadcasting stations
Pr: Paul McTear
**VP:* Jim Arnold
Sls Mgr: Bob McCaughey

KOLD TV
See KOLD LLC

D-U-N-S 07-858-6849 IMP/EXP
KOLDER INC
1601 N Closner Blvd, Edinburg, TX 78541-7102
Tel (956) 381-9851 *Founded/Ownrshp* 1982
Sales 69.4MM^E *EMP* 500
SIC 3089

D-U-N-S 80-167-5927
KOLE CONSTRUCTION CO OF LEMONT INC
1235 Naperville Dr, Romeoville, IL 60446-1041
Tel (630) 378-2006 *Founded/Ownrshp* 1989
Sales 21.1MM^E *EMP* 190
SIC 1751 1742 Carpentry work; Drywall; Acoustical & ceiling work; Carpentry work; Drywall; Acoustical & ceiling work
Pr: William Sokolis

D-U-N-S 14-615-7821 IMP
KOLE IMPORTS
BASKET BASICS
24600 Main St, Carson, CA 90745-6332
Tel (310) 834-0004 *Founded/Ownrshp* 1985
Sales 46.2MM^E *EMP* 84
SIC 5199 Gifts & novelties
CEO: Robert Kole

Ex VP: Fernando Garcia
VP: Alma Corral
**VP:* Dan Kole
VP: Amir Shteiwi
VP Bus Dev: Andy Kole
VP Bus Dev: Jason Kole

D-U-N-S 94-840-8372
KOLEASECO INC
4265 Corporate Exch Dr, Hudsonville, MI 49426-1950
Tel (616) 896-5170 *Founded/Ownrshp* 1992
Sales 44.9MM^E *EMP* 210
SIC 4212 Timber trucking, local; Timber trucking, local
Genl Mgr: Al Kruithoff
Sales Exec: John Wondergem

D-U-N-S 18-806-6369
KOLEY JESSEN PC LLO
1125 S 103rd St Ste 800, Omaha, NE 68124-1079
Tel (402) 390-9500 *Founded/Ownrshp* 1988
Sales 23.5MM^E *EMP* 150
SIC 8111 Legal services; Legal services
Pr: Paul C Jessen
**CFO:* Elaine Null
**Ex VP:* Michael M Hupp
**VP:* David M Dvorak
**VP:* Margaret C Hershiser
**VP:* M Shaun McGaughey
**VP:* Gregory C Scaglione
**VP:* Kurt FTjaden

D-U-N-S 03-722-7477
KOLKHORST PETROLEUM CO
RATTLERS COUNTRY STORES
1685 E Washington Ave, Navasota, TX 77868-3244
Tel (936) 825-6868 *Founded/Ownrshp* 1962
Sales 33.9MM^E *EMP* 150
SIC 5984 5411 5171 Liquefied petroleum gas dealers; Convenience stores; Petroleum bulk stations & terminals; Liquefied petroleum gas dealers; Convenience stores; Petroleum bulk stations & terminals
Pr: Jim Kolkhorst
**VP:* Lois Kolkhorst
IT Man: Randy Krumrey
Snr Mgr: Sarah Chisholm

KOLL BREN SCHRBER RLTY ADVSORS
See KBS REALTY ADVISORS LLC

D-U-N-S 02-874-1593
KOLL CO LLC
17755 Sky Park Cir # 100, Irvine, CA 92614-6400
Tel (562) 948-5296 *Founded/Ownrshp* 2001
Sales 64.8MM^E *EMP* 74
SIC 1542 6552 6531 8741 Commercial & office building contractors; Subdividers & developers; Real estate managers; Management services; Commercial & office building contractors; Subdividers & developers; Real estate managers; Management services
**CEO:* Don Koll
CFO: Jim Micell
Ofcr: Kelly Crist
VP: Kevin Deighan
VP: Jeff Dun
VP: Jeff Dunn
VP: Mike Hackett
VP: Lori Klasner
VP: Don Koller
VP: Nancy Rohan
VP: John Woo
Dir Bus: Thomas Tschudin

D-U-N-S 78-217-1946
KOLL MANAGEMENT SERVICES INC
4343 Von Karman Ave # 150, Newport Beach, CA 92660-2099
Tel (949) 833-3030 *Founded/Ownrshp* 1997
Sales 29.1MM^E *EMP* 2,400
SIC 6531 8741 Real estate managers; Management services; Real estate managers; Management services
Ch Bd: Donald M Koll

KOLLER CRAFT PLASTIC PDTS DIV
See KOLLER ENTERPRISES INC

D-U-N-S 00-626-7967 IMP
KOLLER ENTERPRISES INC (MO)
KOLLER CRAFT PLASTIC PDTS DIV
1400 S Old Highway 141, Fenton, MO 63026-5733
Tel (636) 343-9220 *Founded/Ownrshp* 1941
Sales 81.3MM^E *EMP* 331
SIC 3089 5063 Injection molded finished plastic products; Lighting fixtures; Injection molded finished plastic products; Lighting fixtures
Ch Bd: Alois J Koller Jr
**Pr:* Alois J Koller III
CFO: Jim Wyrsch
**Treas:* David Koller
Ql Cn Mgr: Greg Minnich
Sales Asso: Mark Pierce

D-U-N-S 00-111-7290 IMP/EXP
■ **KOLLMORGEN CORP** (NY)
DANAHER MOTION
(*Suby of* DANAHER CORP) ★
203a W Rock Rd, Radford, VA 24141-4026
Tel (540) 639-2495 *Founded/Ownrshp* 1951
Sales 340.9MM^E *EMP* 2,025
SIC 3621 3827 3861 3825 Motors & generators; Servomotors, electric; Generators & sets, electric; Motors, electric; Periscopes; Sighting & fire control equipment, optical; Optical test & inspection equipment; Densitometers; Exposure meters, photographic; Test equipment for electronic & electrical circuits; Motors & generators; Servomotors, electric; Generators & sets, electric; Motors, electric; Periscopes; Sighting & fire control equipment, optical; Optical test & inspection equipment; Densitometers; Exposure meters, photographic; Test equipment for electronic & electrical circuits
Pr: Michael Wall
Ex VP: Larry Kingsley
Ex Dir: John Nixon
Prgrm Mgr: Brian McCahill
Snr Sftwr: Thomas Bannish
IT Man: Alayne Heishman
Sys Mgr: Bill Edinger
Opers Mgr: Richard Acherson
Prd Mgr: Mario Solorio
Ql Cn Mgr: Evan Hagerstrom
Ql Cn Mgr: Frank Sadlowski

D-U-N-S 93-213-5148
KOLLSMAN INC
(*Suby of* ELBIT SYSTEMS OF AMERICA LLC) ★
220 Daniel Webster Hwy, Merrimack, NH 03054-4837
Tel (603) 889-2500 *Founded/Ownrshp* 1995
Sales 76.7MM^E *EMP* 550
SIC 3812 3629 Search & navigation equipment; Electrochemical generators (fuel cells); Search & navigation equipment; Electrochemical generators (fuel cells)
Pr: Ranaan Horowitz
Pr: Jon Lyford
**COO:* Yuval Ramon
Chf Mktg O: Robert Goodwin
VP: Bob Goodnow
VP: Joann Lifehood
Exec: Daniel Guerrette
Ex Dir: Leanne Collazzo
QA Dir: Karen Conti
Dir IT: Ken Jarry
IT Man: Bill Cote

KOLLSMAN INSTRUMENT DIVISION
See SEQUA CORP

KOLLSTAR GOLF COMPANY
See KOLLWOOD GOLF OPERATING LP

D-U-N-S 02-865-0351
KOLLWOOD GOLF OPERATING LP
KOLLSTAR GOLF COMPANY
4343 Von Karman Ave # 150, Newport Beach, CA 92660-2099
Tel (949) 833-3025 *Founded/Ownrshp* 1998
Sales 4.7MM^E *EMP* 400
SIC 7992 Public golf courses; Public golf courses
Pt: Joseph Woodard
Pt: Donald M Koll

D-U-N-S 00-772-7829 IMP/EXP
KOLMAR AMERICAS INC
(*Suby of* KOLMAR GROUP AG)
10 Middle St Ph, Bridgeport, CT 06604-4229
Tel (203) 873-2078 *Founded/Ownrshp* 1998
Sales 194.5MM^E *EMP* 24
SIC 5172 Petroleum products
Pr: Rafael Aviner
CFO: Kevin Luddy
**VP:* Paul Francis Teta

KOLMAR INC. / PORT JERVIS
See KOLMAR LABORATORIES INC

D-U-N-S 00-153-5103 IMP/EXP
KOLMAR LABORATORIES INC (DE)
KOLMAR INC. / PORT JERVIS
(*Suby of* CORPORATION DEVELOPPEMENT KNOWLTON INC)
20 W King St, Port Jervis, NY 12771-3061
Tel (845) 856-5311 *Founded/Ownrshp* 1937, 2015
Sales 110.1MM^E *EMP* 700^E
SIC 2844

D-U-N-S 96-884-1494 IMP
KOLMAR LABS GROUP LLC
20 W King St, Port Jervis, NY 12771-3061
Tel (845) 856-5311 *Founded/Ownrshp* 1996
Sales 188.4MM^E *EMP* 1,000
SIC 2844 7389 2834 Toilet preparations; Packaging & labeling services; Pharmaceutical preparations; Toilet preparations; Packaging & labeling services; Pharmaceutical preparations
Ch Bd: Joseph Healey
**Pr:* Rob Edmonds
COO: James Skelton
Ofcr: Carol Starr
VP: Jack Fallon
VP: Robert Jaegly

D-U-N-S 04-830-0537
■ **KOLMAR PRODUCTS CORP (WIS)**
PEPSICO
(*Suby of* PEPSI-COLA GENERAL BOTTLERS INC) ★
3501 Algonquin Rd, Rolling Meadows, IL 60008-3103
Tel (847) 253-1000 *Founded/Ownrshp* 1964
Sales 109.0MM^E *EMP* 860
SIC 2086 Carbonated soft drinks, bottled & canned; Carbonated soft drinks, bottled & canned
Exec: Larry Young
CIO: Kenneth L Johnsen

D-U-N-S 03-343-2019 IMP
KOLO LLC
1224 Mill St Ste B001, East Berlin, CT 06023-1166
Tel (860) 293-0624 *Founded/Ownrshp* 1998
Sales 21.3MM^E *EMP* 30
SIC 5112 Stationery & office supplies
Pr: Keith Werner
Ex VP: Keith Horner

D-U-N-S 06-884-2319 IMP
KOLONAKI
GEORGIOU
1216 Broadway Plz, Walnut Creek, CA 94596-5129
Tel (415) 554-8000 *Founded/Ownrshp* 1974
Sales 50.5MM^E *EMP* 400
SIC 5137 5621 2339 Sportswear, women's & children's; Ready-to-wear apparel, women's; Women's & misses' outerwear; Sportswear, women's & children's; Ready-to-wear apparel, women's; Women's & misses' outerwear
Pr: George Georgiou
**VP:* Martha Birchett
MIS Dir: Lambert Danglind

D-U-N-S 04-653-5415
KOLOSSO AUTO SALES INC
KOLOSSO TOYOTA
3000 W Wisconsin Ave, Appleton, WI 54914-1707
Tel (920) 738-3666 *Founded/Ownrshp* 1962
Sales 26.4MM^E *EMP* 60
SIC 5511 Automobiles, new & used; Automobiles, new & used
Pr: Joan Kolosso
**Treas:* William Kolosso
**Prin:* Barb Kolosso
Info Man: Bill Koloo
Sales Asso: Tina Ferge
Sales Asso: Bruce Steinike

KOLOSSO TOYOTA
See KOLOSSO AUTO SALES INC

KOLPAK
See KMT REFRIGERATION INC

D-U-N-S 14-722-1910
KOMAN DIVERSIFIED SERVICES LLC
KDS
2700 Gambell St Ste 401, Anchorage, AK 99503-2833
Tel (907) 569-9130 *Founded/Ownrshp* 2003
Sales 20.5MM^E *EMP* 217^E
SIC 1541 2396 8744 8748 Industrial buildings, new construction; Apparel findings & trimmings; Facilities support services; Environmental consultant; Industrial buildings, new construction; Apparel findings & trimmings; Facilities support services; Environmental consultant
Prin: Michael L Kelly
Genl Mgr: Michael Zavosky

D-U-N-S 16-140-8849
KOMAR ALLIANCE LLC
6900 Washington Blvd, Montebello, CA 90640-5424
Tel (323) 890-3000 *Founded/Ownrshp* 2000
Sales 62.6MM^E *EMP* 86^E
SIC 5131 Sewing accessories; Sewing accessories
**CFO:* Jonathan Feldman
Sales Asso: Al Tanner

KOMAR COMPANY, THE
See CHARLES KOMAR & SONS INC

D-U-N-S 61-875-0772 IMP/EXP
KOMATSU AMERICA CORP
(*Suby of* KOMATSU LTD.)
1701 Golf Rd Ste 1-100, Rolling Meadows, IL 60008-4234
Tel (847) 437-5800 *Founded/Ownrshp* 1970
Sales 2.2MMM^E *EMP* 4,000
SIC 5082 3532 3531 Mining machinery & equipment, except petroleum; Mining machinery; Construction machinery; Mining machinery & equipment, except petroleum; Mining machinery; Construction machinery
Ch Bd: Rod Schrader
**Pr:* Max Masayuki Moriyama
**COO:* Hisashi Shinozuka
**Ex VP:* Ken Furuse
**Ex VP:* Gary Kasbeer
Ex VP: Noboru Sato
**Sr VP:* Nob Sato
VP: Ben Norris
VP: Jeff Powell
**VP:* Ed Powers
VP: Erik Wilde

D-U-N-S 15-520-9729 IMP
KOMATSU AMERICA MANUFACTURING CORP
409 Signal Mountain Rd, Chattanooga, TN 37405-1918
Tel (423) 267-1066 *Founded/Ownrshp* 1986
Sales 26.8MM^E *EMP* 150^E
SIC 3531 Construction machinery; Trucks, off-highway; Excavators: cable, clamshell, crane, derrick, dragline, etc.; Loaders, shovel: self-propelled; Construction machinery; Trucks, off-highway; Excavators: cable, clamshell, crane, derrick, dragline, etc.; Loaders, shovel: self-propelled
CEO: Rod Schrader
Pr: Max Moriyama
Treas: J Yamawaki
VP: K Kikuchi
Board of Directors: A Yakota

D-U-N-S 00-701-5365
KOMATSU ENTERPRISES INC
K & K DISTRIBUTORS
94-153 Leonui St Ste H, Waipahu, HI 96797-2251
Tel (808) 677-0046 *Founded/Ownrshp* 1982
Sales 20.1MM^E *EMP* 25
SIC 5145 5149 Candy; Snack foods; Cookies
Pr: Carol Komatsu
**Pr:* Ryan Komatsu
**Treas:* Houston Komatsu
Ex Dir: Michael Bullen

D-U-N-S 00-909-5811 IMP/EXP
KOMATSU EQUIPMENT CO
KOMATSU MACHINERY
(*Suby of* KOMATSU AMERICA CORP) ★
1486 S Dist Dr, Salt Lake City, UT 84104
Tel (801) 972-3660 *Founded/Ownrshp* 1997
Sales 51.7MM^E *EMP* 230
SIC 7359 5082 7353 5085 Equipment rental & leasing; Front end loaders; Heavy construction equipment rental; Industrial supplies; Equipment rental & leasing; Front end loaders; Heavy construction equipment rental; Industrial supplies
Pr: John Pfisterer
**CFO:* Kenneth Youngquist
**Treas:* Gary A Kasbeer
**VP:* Irwin Green
**VP:* Gregg Herdina
**Prin:* Bill Dwyer
Brnch Mgr: Jim Slade
Mktg Mgr: Kris Venkiteswaran
Sls Mgr: Garin Humphrey
Sls Mgr: Doug Tripp

D-U-N-S 10-318-1277
KOMATSU FINANCIAL LIMITED PARTNERSHIP
(*Suby of* KOMATSU AMERICA CORP) ★
1701 Golf Rd Ste 1-300, Rolling Meadows, IL 60008-4208
Tel (847) 437-3330 *Founded/Ownrshp* 2003
Sales NA *EMP* 60
SIC 6159 Machinery & equipment finance leasing
CFO: Gary Kasbeer
**Pt:* William Fruland
**Pr:* Michael Fraser
Treas: Benjamin A Norris
VP: Noboru Satou
Mktg Mgr: Susan Crosby

D-U-N-S 06-207-5619
KOMATSU FORKLIFT RETAIL OPERATIONS INC
(*Suby of* KOMATSU AMERICA CORP) ★
1475 Rock Mountain Blvd, Stone Mountain, GA 30083-1505
Tel (770) 938-5071 *Founded/Ownrshp* 2011
Sales 23.8MM^E *EMP* 61
SIC 5084 7699 7359 Materials handling machinery; Industrial equipment services; Equipment rental & leasing
Pr: Hairra Yamakawa
Genl Mgr: Paul Russell

KOMATSU MACHINERY
See KOMATSU EQUIPMENT CO

D-U-N-S 18-670-8590
KOMET OF AMERICA INC (DEL)
(*Suby of* KOMET GROUP GMBH)
2050 Mitchell Blvd, Schaumburg, IL 60193-4544
Tel (847) 923-8400 *Founded/Ownrshp* 1986
Sales 21.6MM^E *EMP* 186^E
SIC 3541 3365 Machine tools, metal cutting type; Aerospace castings, aluminum; Machine tools, metal cutting type; Aerospace castings, aluminum
Prin: Dr F Hans Grandin
**Pr:* Dietmar Bolkhart
Pr: Komet Ruff
VP: Tom Brand
Snr Mgr: Tim Lewerenz
Snr Mgr: Dave Pattison
Snr Mgr: Brad Wuestenfeld

D-U-N-S 01-712-0713
KOMKAD CORP
KOMKAD INTERNATIONAL
100 Winston Dr Apt 14dn, Cliffside Park, NJ 07010-3298
Tel (201) 833-9400 *Founded/Ownrshp* 2001
Sales 42.0MM *EMP* 72
SIC 5013 Automotive supplies & parts; Automotive supplies & parts
Pr: Michael Bront
**Ex VP:* Alex Vinogradsky
**VP:* Henry Kogan

KOMKAD INTERNATIONAL
See KOMKAD CORP

D-U-N-S 96-573-7856
KOMLI MEDIA INC
(*Suby of* KOMLI MEDIA PRIVATE LIMITED)
444 High St Ste 400, Palo Alto, CA 94301-1671
Tel (646) 736-0650 *Founded/Ownrshp* 2008
Sales 11.8MM^E *EMP* 420
SIC 7311 Advertising agencies; Advertising agencies
Ch: Amar Goel
**CEO:* Prashant Mehta
**CFO:* Rajesh Ghonasgi
CFO: Rakesh Malani
Exec: Naveen Prasad
Admn Mgr: Loretta Silas
Genl Mgr: Kaajal Mathur
Sftwr Eng: Sandhya Bhonsale

D-U-N-S 00-214-2669 IMP/EXP
KOMLINE-SANDERSON ENGINEERING CORP
12 Holland Ave, Peapack, NJ 07977
Tel (908) 234-1000 *Founded/Ownrshp* 1974
Sales 34.1MM^E *EMP* 200
SIC 3569

D-U-N-S 62-758-5896 IMP/EXP
KOMMERLING USA INC
(*Suby of* PROFINE GMBH)
3402 Stanwood Blvd Ne, Huntsville, AL 35811-9021
Tel (256) 851-4099 *Founded/Ownrshp* 2004
Sales 47.6MM^E *EMP* 75
SIC 5169

D-U-N-S 09-000-2577 IMP
KOMODIDAD DISTRIBUTORS INC
GATSBY
Gastby, Caguas, PR 00725-3807
Tel (787) 746-3188 *Founded/Ownrshp* 1965
Sales 221.8MM^E *EMP* 475
Accts De Angel & Compania San Juan
SIC 5137 5136 5094 Women's & children's clothing; Women's & children's lingerie & undergarments; Women's & children's accessories; Men's & boys' clothing; Jewelry; Women's & children's clothing; Women's & children's lingerie & undergarments; Women's & children's accessories; Men's & boys' clothing; Jewelry
Pr: Jorge Galliano
**VP:* Carlos Galliano
Genl Mgr: Gisela Cartagena

D-U-N-S 04-717-7308 IMP
KOMORI AMERICA CORP
(*Suby of* KOMORI CORPORATION)
5520 Meadowbrook Indus Ct, Rolling Meadows, IL 60008-3898
Tel (847) 806-9000 *Founded/Ownrshp* 1982
Sales 42.0MM^E *EMP* 86
SIC 5084 5044 3555 3542 Printing trades machinery, equipment & supplies; Office equipment; Printing trades machinery; Machine tools, metal forming type; Printing trades machinery, equipment & supplies; Office equipment; Printing trades machinery; Machine tools, metal forming type
Pr: Kazuyoshi Miyao
**Ex VP:* Hiro Hoshino
**Ex VP:* Robert J Rath
**Sr VP:* Jacki Hudmon
VP: Mark Hopkins
CIO: Andy Katz
Sls Mgr: Derek Gordon
Snr PM: John Bankson

KONA ENERGY
See IRON ENERGY LLC

D-U-N-S 93-186-1272
▲ KONA GRILL INC
7150 E Camelback Rd # 220, Scottsdale, AZ 85251-1233
Tel (480) 922-8100 *Founded/Ownrshp* 1998
Sales 119.1MM *EMP* 2,743
Tkr Sym KONA *Exch* NGM
SIC 5812 Grills (eating places); Eating places; Grills (eating places)
Pr: Berke Bakay
**Ch Bd:* James R Jundt
CFO: Christi Hing
Ex VP: Jason Merritt
VP: Richard Gaderick
VP: Nicholas Geyer
VP: Rachel Luther
VP: Marci Rude
Exec: Jose Aviles
Genl Mgr: Brian Bevins
Genl Mgr: Michelle Fuller
Board of Directors: Richard J Hauser, Marcus E Jundt, Leonard M Newman, Steven W Schussler, Anthony L Winczewski

KONA INN RESTAURANT
See WIND & SEA RESTAURANTS INC

D-U-N-S 93-393-8052
KONA RESTAURANT GROUP INC
JOHNNY CARINOS ITALIAN KITCHEN
(*Suby of* CARINOS ITALIAN KITCHEN) ★
1514 Rr 620 S, Lakeway, TX 78734-6210
Tel (512) 263-0800 *Founded/Ownrshp* 1995
Sales 11.5MM^E^ *EMP* 400
SIC 5812 Italian restaurant; Italian restaurant
CEO: Creed Ford III
**Pr:* Norman Abdalah
**VP:* Brian Kelly
VP: Rene Lagarrigue

D-U-N-S 07-848-3086
KONA SURF PARTNERS LLC
SHERATON KAUHOU BAY RESORT SPA
78-128 Ehukai St Ste 100, Kailua Kona, HI 96740-2567
Tel (808) 930-4900 *Founded/Ownrshp* 2011
Sales 18.1MM^E^ *EMP* 300
SIC 7011 Resort hotel; Resort hotel
Prin: Steven Lindburg

KONA TOYOTA
See BIG ISLAND TOYOTA INC

D-U-N-S 10-387-4699
KONAMI DIGITAL ENTERTAINMENT INC
(*Suby of* KONAMI HOLDINGS CORPORATION)
2381 Rosecrans Ave # 200, El Segundo, CA 90245-4922
Tel (310) 220-8100 *Founded/Ownrshp* 1996
Sales 26.5MM^E^ *EMP* 110^E^
SIC 7372 Home entertainment computer software
CEO: Shinji Hirano
**Pr:* Tomohiro Uesugi
VP: Yumi Hoashi
**VP:* Azuma Takahiro
VP: Careen Yapp
**Prin:* Kazumi Kitaue
Mktg Mgr: John Choon
Mktg Mgr: Pearl Lu
Manager: Stephen Capa
Sls Mgr: Erik Bladinieres

D-U-N-S 01-562-1964 IMP/EXP
KONAMI GAMING INC
(*Suby of* KONAMI CORPORATION)
585 Konami Cir, Las Vegas, NV 89119-3754
Tel (702) 616-1400 *Founded/Ownrshp* 2011
Sales 82.5MM^E^ *EMP* 150
SIC 3944 Electronic game machines, except coin-operated; Electronic game machines, except coin-operated
Pr: Satoshi Sakamoto
**Pr:* Jay Canaday
**COO:* Steve Sutherland
VP: Ryoichi Kimura
Snr Sftwr: Michael Cassidy
Cmptr Lab: B J Overeem
QA Dir: Loretta Roby
QI Cn Mgr: David Duperault

D-U-N-S 80-668-9936
KONDAUR CAPITAL CORP
333 S Anita Dr Ste 400, Orange, CA 92868-3314
Tel (714) 352-2038 *Founded/Ownrshp* 2007
Sales NA *EMP* 150^E^
SIC 6162 Mortgage bankers & correspondents; Mortgage bankers & correspondents
Pr: John Kontouis
Dir IT: Rodel Bernabe
Board of Directors: Michael J Sekits

D-U-N-S 07-614-2819 IMP/EXP
KONDEX CORP
(*Suby of* DLSM INC) ★
1500 Technology Dr, Lomira, WI 53048-9440
Tel (920) 269-7989 *Founded/Ownrshp* 1982
Sales 42.7MM^E^ *EMP* 150
SIC 3523 3524 3423 Farm machinery & equipment; Lawn & garden equipment; Hand & edge tools; Farm machinery & equipment; Lawn & garden equipment; Hand & edge tools
Pr: Jim Wessing
**CEO:* Scott Moon
**CFO:* James H Bryant
**CFO:* Ken Hahn
**VP:* Brian Bloczynski
VP: Mike Frydryk
VP Mfg: Keith Johnson
S&M/VP: Eric Griesbach

D-U-N-S 11-320-4846 IMP
KONE ELEVATOR
(*Suby of* KONE HOLLAND B.V.)
1 Kone Ct, Moline, IL 61265-1380
Tel (309) 764-6771 *Founded/Ownrshp* 2003
Sales 545.9MM^E^ *EMP* 4,200
SIC 7699 3534 Elevators: inspection, service & repair; Elevators & equipment; Elevators: inspection, service & repair; Elevators & equipment
CEO: Trevor Nink
**Pr:* Heimo Makinen
**Treas:* Bill Bowers
Dist Mgr: Neal Rasmussen
Sales Asso: Matt Delks

D-U-N-S 00-526-2308 IMP
KONE INC
(*Suby of* KONE ELEVATOR) ★
1 Kone Ct, Moline, IL 61265-1380
Tel (309) 764-6771 *Founded/Ownrshp* 1956
Sales 543.2MM^E^ *EMP* 4,253
SIC 7699 3534 1796 Elevators: inspection, service & repair; Escalators, passenger & freight; Walkways, moving; Dumbwaiters; Elevator installation & conversion; Elevators: inspection, service & repair; Escalators, passenger & freight; Walkways, moving; Dumbwaiters; Elevator installation & conversion
CEO: Larry Wash
**CFO:* Eriikka Sderstrm
Treas: Michael Bauschka
Sr VP: Danilo Elez
**Sr VP:* Dennis Gerard
**Sr VP:* David McFadden
**Sr VP:* Charles Moore
**Sr VP:* Kenneth E Schmid Jr
**Sr VP:* Kurt Stepaniak
VP: Stephen Cox
VP: Timo Pakarinen
Dir Risk M: Patricia Pritchard
Dir Bus: Cristobal Gomez

D-U-N-S 03-026-0835
KONECNY BROTHERS LUMBER CO INC
KONECNY SISTER'S TRUCKING
2108 S 1100 W Ste 5, Ogden, UT 84401-0263
Tel (801) 621-3399 *Founded/Ownrshp* 2001
Sales 27.0MM *EMP* 11
SIC 5031 Lumber, plywood & millwork
Pr: John Konecny
**VP:* Tyrone Konecny
IT Man: Michael Carroll

KONECNY SISTER'S TRUCKING
See KONECNY BROTHERS LUMBER CO INC

D-U-N-S 80-474-9505 IMP/EXP
KONECRANES INC
(*Suby of* KONECRANES ABP)
4401 Gateway Blvd, Springfield, OH 45502-9339
Tel (937) 525-5533 *Founded/Ownrshp* 2014
Sales 565.1MM^E^ *EMP* 2,100
SIC 3536 Cranes, industrial plant; Cranes, industrial plant
Pr: Pekka Lundmark
CFO: Teuvo R Ki
**Treas:* Steve Mayes
**VP:* Bernard D'Ambrosi Jr
**VP:* Keith Kings
**VP:* Steve Kosir
**VP:* Sirpa Poitsalo
**VP:* Kim Sullivan
**VP:* Mark Ubl
Exec: Melissa Rider
Brnch Mgr: Lupe Castro
Board of Directors: Teo Ottola, Tom Sothard

D-U-N-S 04-152-5311
KONECRANES NUCLEAR EQUIPMENT & SERVICES LLC
(*Suby of* MORRIS MATERIAL HANDLING INC) ★
5300 S Emmer Dr, New Berlin, WI 53151-7365
Tel (262) 784-1873 *Founded/Ownrshp* 2010
Sales 26.2MM^E^ *EMP* 100
SIC 3536 Hoists, cranes & monorails; Hoists, cranes & monorails
Pr: Steve Waisanen
**Treas:* Steve Mayes
**VP:* Jay Edmundson
**VP:* Mark Stanislawski
**VP:* Debbie Yost

D-U-N-S 96-177-5140 IMP/EXP
KONETA INC
KN RUBBER
1400 Lunar Dr, Wapakoneta, OH 45895-9796
Tel (419) 739-4200 *Founded/Ownrshp* 2007
Sales 29.0MM^E^ *EMP* 150
SIC 3061 Automotive rubber goods (mechanical); Automotive rubber goods (mechanical)
CEO: Christopher Keogh
**CFO:* Christopher McKee
Sls Mgr: Sarah Stechman

KONETA RUBBER
See KN RUBBER LLC

D-U-N-S 82-786-3429 IMP
KONGSBERG ACTUATION SYSTEMS II INC
KONGSBERG AUTOMOTIVE
1 Firestone Dr, Suffield, CT 06078-2611
Tel (860) 668-1285 *Founded/Ownrshp* 1981
Sales 30.4MM^E^ *EMP* 100^E^
SIC 3052 Rubber & plastics hose & beltings; Rubber & plastics hose & beltings
CEO: Hans Peter Havdal
**Pr:* Jonathan Day
**Treas:* James Fuda
IT Man: Leo Moreau

KONGSBERG AUTO POWER PRDCT SYS
See KONGSBERG PWR PROD SYST I INC

KONGSBERG AUTOMOTIVE
See KONGSBERG HOLDING III INC

KONGSBERG AUTOMOTIVE
See KONGSBERG ACTUATION SYSTEMS II INC

D-U-N-S 60-663-3337 IMP
KONGSBERG AUTOMOTIVE INC
(*Suby of* KONGSBERG AUTOMOTIVE ASA)
27275 Haggerty Rd Ste 610, Novi, MI 48377-3635
Tel (248) 449-7455 *Founded/Ownrshp* 2008
Sales 217.5MM^E^ *EMP* 900
SIC 3714 Motor vehicle parts & accessories; Heaters, motor vehicle; Motor vehicle parts & accessories; Heaters, motor vehicle
CEO: Hans Peter Havdal
**Ex VP:* Joachim Magnusson
**Ex VP:* Jarle Nymoen
**Ex VP:* Anders Nystrm
**Ex VP:* Trond Stabekk
Genl Mgr: Scott Trayer
Board of Directors: Hans Peter Havdal

D-U-N-S 80-858-6015 IMP
KONGSBERG DRIVELINE SYSTEMS I INC
(*Suby of* KONGSBERG AUTOMOTIVE ASA)
27275 Haggerty Rd Ste 610, Novi, MI 48377-3635
Tel (248) 468-1221 *Founded/Ownrshp* 2007
Sales 26.2MM^E^ *EMP* 350
SIC 5531 Automotive parts; Automotive parts
Pr: Larry Alberding

D-U-N-S 82-774-1971
KONGSBERG HOLDING III INC
KONGSBERG AUTOMOTIVE
(*Suby of* KONGSBERG AUTOMOTIVE ASA)
27275 Haggerty Rd Ste 610, Novi, MI 48377-3635
Tel (248) 468-1300 *Founded/Ownrshp* 2008
Sales 253.3MM^E^ *EMP* 2,500
SIC 3714 Motor vehicle parts & accessories; Motor vehicle parts & accessories
Pr: Raymond Boyma

D-U-N-S 14-193-9806 IMP
KONGSBERG INTERIOR SYSTEMS I INC
(*Suby of* KONGSBERG AUTOMOTIVE) ★
27275 Haggerty Rd Ste 610, Novi, MI 48377-3635
Tel (956) 465-4541 *Founded/Ownrshp* 2007
Sales 62.0MM *EMP* 32^E^
SIC 3714 Motor vehicle parts & accessories
Pr: Raymond Bonya
**CEO:* Hans Peter Havdal
**Ex VP:* Anders Mystron
**Ex VP:* Trond Stabekk

D-U-N-S 82-916-4172 IMP
KONGSBERG PROTECH SYSTEMS USA CORP
(*Suby of* KONGSBERG DEFENCE & AEROSPACE AS)
210 Industrial Park Rd # 105, Johnstown, PA 15904-1933
Tel (814) 269-5700 *Founded/Ownrshp* 2005
Sales 36.9MM^E^ *EMP* 170^E^
SIC 3489 Ordnance & accessories; Ordnance & accessories
Pr: Gunnar Pedersen
Ofcr: Pamela Turinsky
**VP:* Greg Platee
**VP:* Jeff Wood
Prgrm Mgr: Jaynee Lafferty
IT Man: Scott Burk
IT Man: Chris Glessner
Tech Mgr: Vegard Saeterlid
Software D: Inger Freeman
Software D: Martin Himberg
Opers Mgr: Scott Harrington

D-U-N-S 08-202-1296 IMP
KONGSBERG PWR PROD SYST I INC
KONGSBERG AUTO POWER PRDCT SYS
(*Suby of* KONGSBERG AUTOMOTIVE) ★
300 S Cochran St, Willis, TX 77378-9034
Tel (936) 856-2971 *Founded/Ownrshp* 2008
Sales 185.0MM^E^ *EMP* 2,300
SIC 3714 Motor vehicle parts & accessories; Anti-sway devices, motor vehicle; Motor vehicle parts & accessories; Anti-sway devices, motor vehicle
Ex VP: Scott Paquette
**VP:* Jonathan Reeve
Plnt Mgr: Rick Alf

D-U-N-S 16-862-8035 IMP
KONGSBERG UNDERWATER TECHNOLOGY INC
SIMRAD FISHERIES
(*Suby of* KONGSBERG MARITIME AS)
19210 33rd Ave W, Lynnwood, WA 98036-4749
Tel (425) 712-1107 *Founded/Ownrshp* 2004
Sales 22.0MM *EMP* 40
SIC 3812 Sonar systems & equipment; Sonar systems & equipment
Pr: Tom Healy
Treas: Craig Rominger
Genl Mgr: Andrew Watson
Opers Mgr: Bruce Trimble

D-U-N-S 13-221-1587 IMP
KONGSKILDE INDUSTRIES INC
(*Suby of* KONGSKILDE INDUSTRIES A/S)
19500 N 1425 East Rd, Hudson, IL 61748-7630
Tel (309) 820-1090 *Founded/Ownrshp* 1999
Sales 47.5MM^E^ *EMP* 110
SIC 3535 3523 Pneumatic tube conveyor systems; Soil preparation machinery, except turf & grounds; Fertilizing machinery, farm; Pneumatic tube conveyor systems; Soil preparation machinery, except turf & grounds; Fertilizing machinery, farm
Pr: Hans Rasmussen
Rgnl Mgr: Dave Berger
Prd Mgr: Russ Bryan
Sales Exec: Richard Follmer
Sales Asso: Linda Williams

D-U-N-S 12-521-2154
KONIAG DEVELOPMENT CORP
K D C
(*Suby of* KONIAG INC) ★
4300 B St Ste 408, Anchorage, AK 99503-5933
Tel (907) 261-4040 *Founded/Ownrshp* 2002
Sales 247.0MM *EMP* 820
Accts Kpmg Llp Anchorage Ak
SIC 8741 6719 Management services; Investment holding companies, except banks; Management services; Investment holding companies, except banks
Pr: Thomas Panamaroff
**Ch Bd:* Elizabeth Perry

D-U-N-S 07-820-3361
KONIAG INC
4300 B St Ste 407, Anchorage, AK 99503-5961
Tel (907) 561-2668 *Founded/Ownrshp* 1972
Sales 257.6MM *EMP* 834
Accts Kpmg Llp Anchorage Ak
SIC 6552 6519 6719 Subdividers & developers; Landholding office; Investment holding companies, except banks; Subdividers & developers; Landholding office; Investment holding companies, except banks
**Ch Bd:* Ronald Unger
**Pr:* Thomas Panamaroff
**CEO:* Christopher Morgan
**CEO:* Elizabeth Perry
CFO: Will Anderson
**Ch:* Ron Unger
**Ex VP:* Jessica Graham
VP: Debbie Lukin

D-U-N-S 14-363-6947
KONIAG TECHNOLOGY SOLUTIONS INC
K D C
(*Suby of* K D C) ★
4300 B St Ste 407, Anchorage, AK 99503-5961
Tel (703) 488-3480 *Founded/Ownrshp* 2008
Sales 28.8MM *EMP* 30
Accts Kpmg Llp Anchorage Ak
SIC 8742 7379 Management consulting services; Computer related consulting services
Pr: Ed O'Hare
**CEO:* Thomas Panamaroff
**Prin:* Daniel Nielsen
**Genl Mgr:* Kevin Razzaghi

KONICA MEDICAL
See KONICA MINOLTA MEDICAL IMAGING USA INC

D-U-N-S 00-170-7322 IMP/EXP
KONICA MINOLTA BUSINESS SOLUTIONS USA INC (DE)
MINOLTA BUSINESS SYSTEMS
(*Suby of* KONICA MINOLTA HOLDINGS USA INC) ★
100 Williams Dr, Ramsey, NJ 07446-2907
Tel (201) 825-4000 *Founded/Ownrshp* 1959
Sales 403.3MM^E^ *EMP* 590
SIC 5044 5045 Office equipment; Copying equipment; Computers, peripherals & software; Printers, computer; Office equipment; Copying equipment; Computers, peripherals & software; Printers, computer
CEO: Toshimitsu Taiko
Pr: Daniel Davidson
Pr: Ernest Iovine
CFO: Mark Crossley
CFO: John Thielke
Ex VP: Kazuhiro Goto
Sr VP: Mark Bradord
Sr VP: Sam Errigo
Sr VP: Barbara Stainbrook
VP: Brian Cupka
VP: Todd G Foote
VP: David Hartman
VP: Nelson T Lin
VP: Barry Nickerson
VP: Chris Reale
VP: Don Snowden
VP: Rick Toger
VP: David E Wise
Exec: Jeffrey Fernandez
Exec: Henry Kobayashi
Board of Directors: Jun Haraguchi, William Troxil

D-U-N-S 13-825-6677 IMP
KONICA MINOLTA HOLDINGS USA INC
(*Suby of* KONICA MINOLTA, INC.)
100 Williams Dr, Ramsey, NJ 07446-2907
Tel (201) 825-4000 *Founded/Ownrshp* 2004
Sales 551.3MM^E^ *EMP* 605^E^
SIC 5043 5065 5044 5047 Photographic equipment & supplies; Photographic cameras, projectors, equipment & supplies; Photographic processing equipment; Facsimile equipment; Tapes, audio & video recording; Office equipment; Duplicating machines; Microfilm equipment; Photocopy machines; X-ray film & supplies; X-ray machines & tubes; Photographic equipment & supplies; Photographic cameras, projectors, equipment & supplies; Photographic processing equipment; Facsimile equipment; Tapes, audio & video recording; Office equipment; Duplicating machines; Microfilm equipment; Photocopy machines; X-ray film & supplies; X-ray machines & tubes
Pr: Hideki Okamura
Sr VP: Erik Holdo
Sr VP: John Phillips
VP: Richard Miller
Mktg Mgr: Steven Eisner

D-U-N-S 06-929-3090 IMP/EXP
KONICA MINOLTA MEDICAL IMAGING USA INC
KONICA MEDICAL
(*Suby of* KONICA MINOLTA HOLDINGS USA INC) ★
411 Newark Pompton Tpke, Wayne, NJ 07470-6657
Tel (973) 633-1500 *Founded/Ownrshp* 1973
Sales 42.0MM^E^ *EMP* 85
SIC 5047 3861 3845 Medical & hospital equipment; Photographic equipment & supplies; Electromedical equipment; Medical & hospital equipment; Photographic equipment & supplies; Electromedical equipment
Pr: David Widmann
CFO: Jerry Liebowitz
Treas: Ken Nozaki
Ex VP: Kirk Ichijo
CIO: Nelson T Lin
IT Man: Michael Hunstein
Tech Mgr: Lou Bower
VP Sls: Richard Miller
Sls Mgr: Jeff Andreski
Sls Mgr: Terry Coleman
Sls Mgr: Jon Guidry

D-U-N-S 08-654-7338 IMP/EXP
KONICA MINOLTA PRINTING SOLUTIONS USA INC
101 Williams Dr, Ramsey, NJ 07446-1217
Tel (201) 316-8200 *Founded/Ownrshp* 2004
Sales NA *EMP* 539
SIC 3577 7372

D-U-N-S 60-797-0691 IMP
KONICA MINOLTA SENSING AMERICAS INC
KONICA MNOLTA SENSING AMERICAS
101 Williams Dr, Ramsey, NJ 07446-1217
Tel (201) 236-4300 *Founded/Ownrshp* 2014
Sales 40.9MM^E *EMP* 50
SIC 5084 Measuring & testing equipment, electrical
Pr: Shingo Tsujimoto
**Pr:* Hal Yamazaki
Plng Mgr: Rob Nishiura
Sls Mgr: Julius Powell

D-U-N-S 61-004-5643 IMP
KONICA MINOLTA SUPPLIES MANUFACTURING USA INC
(*Suby of* KONICA MINOLTA HOLDINGS USA INC) ★
51 Hatfield Ln, Goshen, NY 10924-6712
Tel (845) 294-8400 *Founded/Ownrshp* 1987
Sales 100.0MM *EMP* 75
Accts Kpmg Llp Short Hills Nj
SIC 3861 Toners, prepared photographic (not made in chemical plants); Toners, prepared photographic (not made in chemical plants)
Pr: Miyako Asai
MIS Dir: Gary Gould

KONICA MNOLTA SENSING AMERICAS
See KONICA MINOLTA SENSING AMERICAS INC

D-U-N-S 96-177-6069
KONING RESTAURANTS INTERNATIONAL LC
PIZZA HUT
1000 Park Centre Blvd # 134, Miami, FL 33169-5373
Tel (305) 430-1200 *Founded/Ownrshp* 1999
Sales 49.7MM^E *EMP* 2,000
SIC 5812 Pizzeria, chain; Pizzeria, chain
CEO: Alfredo Salas
CFO: Omar Sezer
Genl Couns: Elliot Tunis

D-U-N-S 84-771-8186
KONOCTI UNIFIED SCHOOL DISTRICT
9430 Lake St, Lower Lake, CA 95457-8600
Tel (707) 994-6475 *Founded/Ownrshp* 1987
Sales 20.4MM^E *EMP* 300
SIC 8211 Public elementary & secondary schools; Public elementary & secondary schools
**Pr:* Bill Diener

D-U-N-S 87-983-5775
KONOIKE-PACIFIC (CALIFORNIA) INC
KPAC
(*Suby of* KONOIKE TRANSPORT CO.,LTD.)
1420 Coil Ave, Wilmington, CA 90744-2205
Tel (310) 518-1000 *Founded/Ownrshp* 2000
Sales 25.0MM^E *EMP* 92^E
Accts Deloitte Los Angeles Ca
SIC 4222 Warehousing, cold storage or refrigerated; Warehousing, cold storage or refrigerated
Pr: Bob Smola
**CFO:* Ulises Sam
**VP:* Wayne Lamb
**VP:* Yutaka Kane Urabe
**VP:* Jeffrey Waite

D-U-N-S 36-081-7907 IMP
KONSEI USA INC
401 Commerce Pkwy, Hodgenville, KY 42748-8476
Tel (270) 358-0145 *Founded/Ownrshp* 2003
Sales 21.4MM^E *EMP* 100
SIC 3465 Body parts, automobile: stamped metal
Pr: Yasumasa Kondo

KONTES OF CALIFORNIA
See KIMBLE CHASE LIFE SCIENCE AND RESEARCH PRODUCTS LLC

D-U-N-S 18-141-6173 IMP
KONTOS FOODS INC
100 6th Ave, Paterson, NJ 07524-1406
Tel (973) 278-2800 *Founded/Ownrshp* 1987
Sales 35.3MM^E *EMP* 150
SIC 5149 2051 2099

D-U-N-S 14-739-0793 IMP
KONTRON AMERICA INC
(*Suby of* KONTRON AG)
14118 Stowe Dr, Poway, CA 92064-7147
Tel (858) 677-0877 *Founded/Ownrshp* 2001
Sales 58.6MM^E *EMP* 230
SIC 3571 3577 Electronic computers; Computer peripheral equipment; Electronic computers; Computer peripheral equipment
CEO: Ulrich Gehrmann
Pr: Stefan Milnov
**Pr:* Thomas Sparrvik
**CFO:* Jrgen Kaiser-Gerwens
Ex VP: Eric Sivertson
VP: Buck Fambrough
VP: Michael Kadri
VP: Andy Mason
VP: Fran Moore
Ex Dir: Eric Tarter
Prgrm Mgr: Robert Bezy

D-U-N-S 10-588-9732
KONVISSER CUSTOM SOFTWARE
5109 Deer Run Cir, Orchard Lake, MI 48323-1510
Tel (248) 682-0717 *Founded/Ownrshp* 2002
Sales 214.1MM *EMP* 2
Accts Steakley & Gilbert Pc Okla
SIC 7371 Custom computer programming services; Custom computer programming services
Owner: Mark Konvisser

D-U-N-S 82-866-3349
KONY INC
7380 W Sand Lake Rd # 390, Orlando, FL 32819-5248
Tel (407) 730-5669 *Founded/Ownrshp* 2008
Sales 296.6MM^E *EMP* 1,000
SIC 7372 Application computer software; Application computer software
Pr: Thomas Hogan
Pr: Jim Lambert
**Treas:* Lesli Whisenant
Assoc VP: Sriram Sundaram
**Ex VP:* Hollie Castro
Sr VP: Allison Coats
Sr VP: John Stewart
VP: Jonathan Best
VP: Oscar Clarke
VP: Kevin Corcoran
VP: Theresa Heinz
**VP:* John Joyce
VP: Neeraj Nityanand
VP: Joe Schwartz
**VP:* Robert Turner
Exec: Daniel Jennings
Assoc Dir: Srikanth Alapati
Assoc Dir: SAI Bhamidipati
Assoc Dir: Sreeram Boddupalli
Assoc Dir: Goverdhan Parikimandla
Assoc Dir: Kalpesh Patel

KOO KOO ROO
See BROSNA INC

D-U-N-S 96-239-8046 IMP
KOOIMA CO
2638 310th St, Rock Valley, IA 51247-7534
Tel (712) 476-5600 *Founded/Ownrshp* 1988
Sales 21.9MM^E *EMP* 58
SIC 3599 3523 3541 Machine shop, jobbing & repair; Farm machinery & equipment; Machine tools, metal cutting type
Pr: John Kooima
CFO: Mike Altena
**VP:* Philip Kooima
CTO: Bret Vanoort
IT Man: Peter Zagaeski
Advt Mgr: Nolan Denboer
Sls Mgr: Gene Van Bemmel
Sales Asso: Dan Christensen
Sales Asso: Bob Meyer

D-U-N-S 11-907-7477
KOOL AUTOMOTIVE LLC
1313 High St, Portsmouth, VA 23704-3229
Tel (757) 393-0020 *Founded/Ownrshp* 1984
Sales 20.8MM^E *EMP* 58
SIC 5511 Automobiles, new & used
**VP:* Ross Kool
Sls Mgr: Frank Girouard

D-U-N-S 07-259-2801
KOOL CHEVROLET INC
3770 Plainfield Ave Ne, Grand Rapids, MI 49525-2489
Tel (616) 364-9431 *Founded/Ownrshp* 1977
Sales 36.0MM^E *EMP* 85
SIC 5511

KOOL PAK
See NESS HOLDING CO

D-U-N-S 16-992-2452
KOOL PAK LLC
(*Suby of* KOOL PAK) ★
4550 Kruse Way Ste 350, Lake Oswego, OR 97035-3588
Tel (503) 240-8500 *Founded/Ownrshp* 2011
Sales 30.1MM^E *EMP* 85
SIC 4213 4222 8742 4214 Trucking, except local; Refrigerated warehousing & storage; Management consulting services; Local trucking with storage
Dir IT: Brian Hart
IT Man: Norbert Loske
Opers Mgr: Jan Meng

KOOL SMILES
See BENEVIS LLC

KOONS BALTIMORE FORD
See KOONS FORD OF BALTIMORE INC

KOONS CHEVROLET
See KOONS OFTYSONS CORNER INC

KOONS COLLEGE PARK FORD
See KOONS FORD SILVER SPRING

KOONS FALLS CHURCH FORD
See FORD KOONS INC

D-U-N-S 02-141-8298
■ **KOONS FORD LLC**
(*Suby of* GROUP 1 AUTOMOTIVE INC) ★
8655 Pines Blvd, Pembroke Pines, FL 33024-6533
Tel (954) 443-7000 *Founded/Ownrshp* 2003
Sales 27.2MM^E *EMP* 200
SIC 5511 5012 Automobiles, new & used; Automobiles; Automobiles, new & used; Automobiles

D-U-N-S 04-857-7092
KOONS FORD OF ANNAPOLIS INC
2540 Riva Rd, Annapolis, MD 21401-7468
Tel (410) 224-2100 *Founded/Ownrshp* 1969
Sales 52.9MM^E *EMP* 110
SIC 5511 Automobiles, new & used; Pickups, new & used; Vans, new & used; Automobiles, new & used; Pickups, new & used; Vans, new & used
Pr: Joseph Koons
**Treas:* Michelle Goodson
**Treas:* Nancy Koons
**VP:* Joseph Koons Jr
Sls Mgr: Doug Killian
Sls Mgr: Billy Wynn
Sales Asso: Anthony Biba
Sales Asso: Tedd Bodnar
Sales Asso: Kevin Bracey
Sales Asso: Chris Duke
Sales Asso: Charlita Hearn

D-U-N-S 05-491-2373
KOONS FORD OF BALTIMORE INC
KOONS BALTIMORE FORD
(*Suby of* JIM KOONS MANAGEMENT CO) ★
6970 Security Blvd, Baltimore, MD 21244-2496
Tel (410) 298-3800 *Founded/Ownrshp* 1985
Sales 56.0MM^E *EMP* 150
SIC 5511 Automobiles, new & used; Automobiles, new & used
Pr: Jim Koons
**VP:* Cecelia Koons
**Genl Mgr:* Dennis Koulatsos
DP Exec: Sandra Mc Dermott
IT Man: Todd Pendergrast
IT Man: Paul Sarandos
Sls Mgr: Jarryd Carver

D-U-N-S 07-091-6853
KOONS FORD SILVER SPRING
KOONS COLLEGE PARK FORD
3111 Automobile Blvd, Silver Spring, MD 20904-4902
Tel (301) 890-6100 *Founded/Ownrshp* 1983
Sales 24.3MM^E *EMP* 94
SIC 5511 Automobiles, new & used; Automobiles, new & used
Pr: James E Koons
Sls Mgr: Bary Landa
Sales Asso: Nelly Branson

D-U-N-S 02-379-6311
KOONS OF MANASSAS INC
JOYCE KOONS HONDA
10660 Automotive Dr, Manassas, VA 20109-2643
Tel (703) 368-9100 *Founded/Ownrshp* 1982
Sales 76.0MM^E *EMP* 175^E
SIC 5511 Automobiles, new & used; Pickups, new & used; Automobiles, new & used; Pickups, new & used
CEO: Joyce Koons
CFO: Earl Richardson
VP: Jim Bencivenga
VP: Kody Ronald F
**VP:* David Hish
VP: Eleanor Koons
Genl Mgr: Kevin Runey
IT Man: Derrick Rychlik
Sales Asso: Mike Ausden-Nkwanga

D-U-N-S 78-732-8962 IMP
KOONS OF TYSONS CORNER INC
KOONS CHEVROLET
(*Suby of* JIM KOONS MANAGEMENT CO) ★
2000 Chain Bridge Rd, Vienna, VA 22182-2531
Tel (888) 335-7892 *Founded/Ownrshp* 1992
Sales 41.7MM^E *EMP* 100^E
SIC 5511 New & used car dealers; Automobiles, new & used; New & used car dealers; Automobiles, new & used
Pr: James Koons
Pt: Jason Plyler
CFO: Tim O'Connell
**Treas:* Kerry Elise Hoagland
**VP:* Karl Leckner
VP: Mirza Thomas
Genl Mgr: Walter Johnson
Genl Mgr: Carl Leckner
Genl Mgr: Bryan Murray
Off Mgr: Marie Anderson
Off Mgr: Lisa Clark

KOONS STERLING FORD
See HERNDON MOTOR CO INC

KOONS TYSONS TOYOTA
See KLINETYSONS IMPORTS INC

D-U-N-S 80-951-5377
KOONTZ CONSTRUCTION INC
KOONTZ/MCCOMBS
755 E Mulberry Ave # 100, San Antonio, TX 78212-3129
Tel (210) 826-2600 *Founded/Ownrshp* 2015
Sales 125.0MM *EMP* 100
SIC 1542 1522 Nonresidential construction; Commercial & office building contractors; Hotel/motel & multi-family home construction
Pr: Bart C Koontz
Pr: Gerald Turman
COO: Henry Serry
CFO: Troves B Gilbert
Ex VP: Chris Corso
VP: Robert Grier
Genl Couns: Erwin Caban

D-U-N-S 03-558-5207
KOONTZ ELECTRIC CO INC
1223 E Broadway St, Morrilton, AR 72110-3799
Tel (501) 354-2526 *Founded/Ownrshp* 1957
Sales 65.9MM^E *EMP* 140
SIC 1731

D-U-N-S 17-602-1889
KOONTZ MCCOMBS LLC
755 E Mulberry Ave # 100, San Antonio, TX 78212-3194
Tel (210) 841-9242 *Founded/Ownrshp* 1997
Sales 39.0MM^E *EMP* 42
SIC 6552 Subdividers & developers
CEO: Bart C Koontz
COO: Tim Cliver
**CFO:* Troves B Gilbert
Sr VP: Henry Serry
VP: Robert Grier
**VP:* Loren Gulley
VP: Bill Rhodes
**VP:* Cynthia H Stevens
**VP:* Thomas Wells
Genl Couns: Erwin Caban
Pgrm Dir: Holly Farmer

D-U-N-S 82-882-9643 IMP
■ **KOONTZ-WAGNER CUSTOM CONTROLS HOLDINGS LLC**
KOONTZ-WAGNER ELECTRIC
(*Suby of* GLOBAL POWER EQUIPMENT GROUP INC) ★
3801 Voorde Dr Ste B, South Bend, IN 46628-1643
Tel (713) 419-8886 *Founded/Ownrshp* 2012
Sales 27.8MM^E *EMP* 85
SIC 3448 Prefabricated metal buildings
CEO: Michael Pound
**Pr:* Richard Pfeil
Treas: Keith Snelson
Bd of Dir: Ed Huggil
**VP:* Paul Pritzl
**VP:* Paul Witek

KOONTZ-WAGNER ELECTRIC
See KOONTZ-WAGNER CUSTOM CONTROLS HOLDINGS LLC

KOONTZ/MCCOMBS
See KOONTZ CONSTRUCTION INC

D-U-N-S 01-971-2348
KOOPMAN LUMBER CO INC
TRUE VALUE
665 Church St, Whitinsville, MA 01588-2116
Tel (508) 234-4545 *Founded/Ownrshp* 1987
Sales 33.8MM^E *EMP* 105
SIC 5211 5251 Lumber & other building materials; Cabinets, kitchen; Hardware; Lumber & other building materials; Cabinets, kitchen; Hardware
Pr: Donald H Koopman
**Treas:* Denise Brookhouse
**VP:* Dirk Koopman
IT Man: Eric Sampson
Sales Asso: Matt Nichols

D-U-N-S 01-641-6893
KOORSEN FIRE & SECURITY INC
2719 N Arlington Ave, Indianapolis, IN 46218-3300
Tel (317) 542-1800 *Founded/Ownrshp* 1968
Sales 160.0MM^E *EMP* 625
SIC 5099 7389 5199 5063 1731

D-U-N-S 02-106-2989
KOOS MANUFACTURING INC
2741 Seminole Ave, South Gate, CA 90280-5550
Tel (323) 249-1000 *Founded/Ownrshp* 1985
Sales 92.4MM^E *EMP* 800
SIC 7389 Sewing contractor; Sewing contractor
Pr: U Yul Ku
VP: David Chang
**VP:* Kee H Fong
**VP:* John Hur
Dir Bus: Yul Ku

D-U-N-S 00-378-1994
KOOTENAI ELECTRIC COOPERATIVE INC (ID)
2451 W Dakota Ave, Hayden, ID 83835-7402
Tel (208) 765-1200 *Founded/Ownrshp* 1938
Sales 36.5MM *EMP* 65
Accts Moss Adams Llp Spokane Wa
SIC 4911 Distribution, electric power; Distribution, electric power
Genl Mgr: Robert Crump

D-U-N-S 07-183-6936
KOOTENAI HOSPITAL DISTRICT
KOOTENAI MEDICAL CENTER
2003 Kootenai Health Way, Coeur D Alene, ID 83814-6051
Tel (208) 625-4000 *Founded/Ownrshp* 1983, 1956
Sales 334.7MM^E *EMP* 1,892
SIC 8062 5912 8063 8093 8734 General medical & surgical hospitals; Drug stores & proprietary stores; Psychiatric hospitals; Rehabilitation center, outpatient treatment; Radiation dosimetry laboratory; General medical & surgical hospitals; Drug stores & proprietary stores; Psychiatric hospitals; Rehabilitation center, outpatient treatment; Radiation dosimetry laboratory
CEO: John Ness
Chf Rad: Albert Martinez
**Pr:* Shawn Bassham
CFO: Richard Schutte
**CFO:* Kim Webb
Chf Mktg O: Walter Fairfax
VP: Joe Bujak
VP: Laurie Davis
**VP:* Jeremy S Evans
Dir Risk M: Lorraine Olshesky
Comm Dir: Kim Anderson

KOOTENAI MEDICAL CENTER
See KOOTENAI HOSPITAL DISTRICT

D-U-N-S 19-333-0446 IMP/EXP
■ **KOP-COAT INC**
MARINE DIVISION
(*Suby of* REPUBLIC POWDERED METALS INC) ★
436 7th Ave Ste 1850, Pittsburgh, PA 15219-1847
Tel (412) 227-2700 *Founded/Ownrshp* 1990
Sales 28.1MM^E *EMP* 130
SIC 2851 Marine paints; Varnishes; Wood stains; Marine paints; Varnishes; Wood stains
Pr: Richard Kelly
VP: Dawn Ludgate
VP: Gerald Nessenson
VP: Hans Ward

D-U-N-S 15-460-1496 IMP
■ **KOP-FLEX INC**
(*Suby of* REGAL-BELOIT CORP) ★
999 Corporate Blvd # 300, Linthicum Heights, MD 21090-2271
Tel (410) 768-2000 *Founded/Ownrshp* 2015
Sales 44.0MM^E *EMP* 320
SIC 3568 3462 Power transmission equipment; Mechanical power transmission forgings, ferrous; Power transmission equipment; Mechanical power transmission forgings, ferrous
Pr: Charles F Mansur
Ofcr: James Stevenson Jr
Genl Mgr: Bob Kirby
Tech Mgr: Fran Kuhn

D-U-N-S 01-752-1063
KOPF CONSTRUCTION CORP
420 Avon Belden Rd Ste A, Avon Lake, OH 44012-2294
Tel (440) 933-6908 *Founded/Ownrshp* 1965
Sales 23.1MM^E *EMP* 125^E
SIC 1521 1522 New construction, single-family houses; Multi-family dwelling construction
Pr: Herman R Kopf Jr

D-U-N-S 14-412-3528
▲ **KOPIN CORP**
125 North Dr, Westborough, MA 01581-3341
Tel (508) 870-5959 *Founded/Ownrshp* 1984
Sales 31.8MM *EMP* 180^E
Accts Deloitte & Touche Llp Boston
Tkr Sym KOPN *Exch* NGS
SIC 3674 Semiconductors & related devices; Wafers (semiconductor devices); Semiconductors & related devices; Wafers (semiconductor devices)
Ch Bd: John C C Fan
CFO: Richard A Sneider

Ofcr: Fritz Herrmann
Ex VP: Bor-Yeu Tsaur
Sr VP: Stuart Nixdorff
VP: Frank Alter
VP: Hong Choi
VP: Steven Glaza
VP: Wayne Johnson
VP: Bill Maffucci
VP: Michael J Presz
Exec: Ngwe Cheong
Exec: Edward Yung
Board of Directors: James K Brewington, Andrew H Chapman, Morton Collins, Chi Chia Hsieh, Michael J Landine

D-U-N-S 05-481-0353 IMP
KOPP DRUG INC (PA)
1405 13th Ave, Altoona, PA 16601-3339
Tel (814) 949-9512 *Founded/Ownrshp* 1925, 1968
Sales 22.5MM^E *EMP* 100
SIC 5912 Drug stores
Pr: Morley A Cohn
**VP:* Carol Cohn
VP: Robert A Smith
Sales Asso: Marybeth Hoover

D-U-N-S 61-343-4856
▲ KOPPERS HOLDINGS INC
436 7th Ave, Pittsburgh, PA 15219-1826
Tel (412) 227-2001 *Founded/Ownrshp* 1988
Sales 1.5MMM *EMP* 2,142
Tkr Sym KOP *Exch* NYS
SIC 2865 2491 2895 3312 2899 Cyclic crudes, coal tar; Poles, posts & pilings: treated wood; Carbon black; Coke produced in chemical recovery coke ovens; Coke oven products (chemical recovery); Chemical preparations; Cyclic crudes, coal tar; Poles, posts & pilings: treated wood; Carbon black; Coke produced in chemical recovery coke ovens; Coke oven products (chemical recovery); Chemical preparations
Pr: Leroy M Ball Jr
CFO: Michael J Zugay
Treas: Louann E Tronsberg-Deihle
Sr VP: Steven R Lacy
VP: Markus Spies
Board of Directors: Cynthia A Baldwin, Sharon Feng, David M Hillenbrand, Albert J Neupaver, Louis L Testoni, Stephen R Tritch, Walter W Turner, T Michael Young

D-U-N-S 19-699-1582 IMP/EXP
■ KOPPERS INC
(*Suby of* KOPPERS HOLDINGS INC) ★
436 7th Ave, Pittsburgh, PA 15219-1826
Tel (412) 227-2001 *Founded/Ownrshp* 1988
Sales 523.5MM^E *EMP* 1,589
SIC 2865 2491 3312 2899 Cyclic crudes, coal tar; Poles, posts & pilings: treated wood; Coke produced in chemical recovery coke ovens; Coke oven products (chemical recovery); Oils & essential oils; Cyclic crudes, coal tar; Poles, posts & pilings: treated wood; Coke produced in chemical recovery coke ovens; Coke oven products (chemical recovery); Oils & essential oils
Pr: Leroy M Ball Jr
CFO: Leroy Ball
CFO: Leroy M Ball Jr
Bd of Dir: Sharon Feng
Sr VP: Paul A Goydan
Sr VP: Steven R Lacy
Sr VP: Thomas D Loadman
VP: Ernest S Bryon
VP: James T Dietz
VP: Ian Doherty
VP: Donald E Evans
VP: Mark R McCormack
VP: Kevin Probst
Board of Directors: Cynthia A Baldwin, David M Hillenbrand Phd, James C Stalder, T Michael Young

D-U-N-S 00-211-2944 EXP
■ KOPPERS PERFORMANCE CHEMICALS INC (NY)
(*Suby of* KOPPERS INC) ★
1016 Everee Inn Rd, Griffin, GA 30224-4733
Tel (770) 228-8434 *Founded/Ownrshp* 1934, 2014
Sales 88.8MM^E *EMP* 200
SIC 2491 Preserving (creosoting) of wood; Preserving (creosoting) of wood
Pr: Paul A Goydan
Treas: Tracie McCormick
**Chf Mktg O:* Gary Converse

D-U-N-S 12-851-0455
■ KOPPERS RAILROAD STRUCTURES INC
(*Suby of* KOPPERS INC) ★
4546 Tompkins Dr, Madison, WI 53716-3310
Tel (800) 356-5952 *Founded/Ownrshp* 2014
Sales 26.5MM^E *EMP* 95
SIC 1629 Railroad & railway roadbed construction
Pr: Harry Holekamp
**Ch Bd:* Leroy Ball Jr
VP: Robin Zhu
Plnt Mgr: Dan Baade-Pedersen

D-U-N-S 01-427-9632
KOPPYS PROPANE INC (PA)
8635 State Route 209, Williamstown, PA 17098-9429
Tel (717) 647-7111 *Founded/Ownrshp* 1944, 1957
Sales 33.9MM^E *EMP* 45
Accts Tammy A Specht Cpa Hegins
SIC 5172 5984 Gases; Liquefied petroleum gas dealers
Pr: David H Koppenhaver
**Treas:* Kristen K Koppenhaver
**Sec:* Helen M Koppenhaver
**VP:* Kara K Tucker
IT Man: Glenda Klinger

D-U-N-S 96-261-7143
KOR HOTEL MANAGEMENT LLC
VICEROY HOTEL GROUP
1212 S Flower St Ste 100, Los Angeles, CA 90015-2123
Tel (323) 930-3700 *Founded/Ownrshp* 2008
Sales 28.7MM^E *EMP* 100
SIC 8741 Hotel or motel management
CEO: Bill Walshe
Pr: Anton Bawab
CFO: Mary C Pierson
Sr VP: Kristie Goshow
Sr VP: Michael R Paneri
Sr VP: Brenda Tscharner
Sr VP: Mike Walsh
VP: Joanne Cox
VP: Nicholas A Monteleone
VP: Alex Samek
Genl Mgr: Jennifer Villanueva

KORBEL CHAMPAGNE CELLERS
See F KORBEL & BROS

D-U-N-S 10-872-1361
KORBER MEDIPAK SYSTEMS NA INC
(*Suby of* KORBER AG)
14501 58th St N, Clearwater, FL 33760-2808
Tel (727) 532-6500 *Founded/Ownrshp* 2004
Sales 34.0MM *EMP* 45
SIC 3565 Packaging machinery; Packaging machinery
CEO: Gerhard Breu
**Pr:* Mike Decollibus
**Treas:* Ralf Pehle
**Treas:* Jorg Tafelmaier
Software D: Martin O'Boyle
Sls Mgr: Ernie Bancorfp
Sls Mgr: Kerry Fillmore

KORD KING COMPANY
See KING ASSOCIATES LTD

KORDIAL NTRNTS PROF SPPLEMENTS
See PROGRESSIVE LABORATORIES INC

D-U-N-S 00-809-1071 IMP/EXP
KORDSA INC
(*Suby of* KORDSA GLOBAL ENDUSTRIYEL IPLIK VE KORD BEZI SANAYI VE TICARET ANONIM SIRKETI)
4501 N Access Rd, Chattanooga, TN 37415-3816
Tel (423) 643-8300 *Founded/Ownrshp* 2005
Sales 391.6MM^E *EMP* 1,200
SIC 5169 Chemicals & allied products; Chemicals & allied products
VP: Mesut Ada
**Treas:* Darrell Smutz
**Treas:* Charlise Way
Genl Mgr: Tim Brickley
CIO: Richard Massey
Ql Cn Mgr: Mara Bishop
VP Sls: Bulent Arasli

D-U-N-S 92-847-7251
KORE TELEMATICS INC
3700 Mansell Rd Ste 250, Alpharetta, GA 30022-1520
Tel (678) 389-3146 *Founded/Ownrshp* 2003
Sales 20.1MM^E *EMP* 55^E
SIC 4812 Cellular telephone services; Cellular telephone services
Pr: Alex Brisbourne
V Ch: Richard Burston
Pr: Shane Murphy
**VP:* Chris Francosky
**VP:* Stephen Healy
**VP:* Felix Lluberes
**VP:* Robert Metzler
VP: Pat Verrington
Dir Bus: Bert Gillespie
Dir Bus: Alan McGrady
Natl Sales: Daniel Cebula

D-U-N-S 02-791-4821
KORE WIRELESS GROUP INC
12801 Worldgate Dr # 500, Herndon, VA 20170-4393
Tel (571) 203-7000 *Founded/Ownrshp* 2002
Sales 28.0MM^E *EMP* 100^E
SIC 4812 Cellular telephone services
Pr: Chris Scatliff

KOREA CENTRAL DAILY NEWS
See JOONGANG USA

KOREA DAILY
See JOONG-ANG DAILY NEWS CALIFORNIA INC

D-U-N-S 05-802-8325 IMP
KOREA TIMES LOS ANGELES INC
4525 Wilshire Blvd, Los Angeles, CA 90010-3837
Tel (323) 692-2000 *Founded/Ownrshp* 1969
Sales 63.8MM^E *EMP* 350
SIC 2711

KOREAN CARGO CONSOLIDATED USA
See KCC TRANSPORT SYSTEMS INC

D-U-N-S 87-827-4315 IMP/EXP
KOREAN FARM INC
12500 Slauson Ave, Santa Fe Springs, CA 90670-2658
Tel (562) 789-9988 *Founded/Ownrshp* 1994
Sales 28.4MM^E *EMP* 45
SIC 5141 5149 5142 Groceries, general line; Groceries & related products; Packaged frozen goods
Pr: Steven Yongbin Rhee
COO: Yun Hong
CFO: Michelle Chae
**Treas:* Robin Rhee
IT Man: Kenny Kuwn

D-U-N-S 36-183-5098
KOREAN RED GINSENG CORP INC
12750 Center Court Dr S # 100, Cerritos, CA 90703-8569
Tel (714) 522-2333 *Founded/Ownrshp* 2003
Sales 30.0MM *EMP* 2
SIC 2023 Dietary supplements, dairy & non-dairy based; Dietary supplements, dairy & non-dairy based
CEO: Jin Han Park
**Pr:* Dooki King
Mktg Mgr: Vince Field

D-U-N-S 18-023-8727
KOREAN WOMENS ASSOCIATION
123 E 96th St, Tacoma, WA 98445-2001
Tel (253) 535-4202 *Founded/Ownrshp* 1972
Sales 23.4MM^E *EMP* 127
Accts Dwyer Pemberton & Coulson Pc
SIC 8641 Civic associations; Civic associations
Sr VP: Agnes Park
**Prin:* Jason Park
Ex Dir: Lua Pritchard

D-U-N-S 10-341-3514
KORET FOUNDATION
611 Front St, San Francisco, CA 94111-1963
Tel (415) 882-7740 *Founded/Ownrshp* 1966
Sales 38.5MM *EMP* 20
SIC 6732 Charitable trust management; Charitable trust management
Ch Bd: Susan Koret
Pr: Thaddeus N Taube
CFO: Jeff Fearn
CFO: Claudia Hargin
Sec: Jack R Curley
V Ch Bd: Eugene L Friend
Bd of Dir: Michael Boskin
Bd of Dir: Richard Greene
Bd of Dir: Stanley Herzstein
VP: Tina Frank

KORFUND DYNAMICS
See VIBRATION MOUNTINGS & CONTROLS INC

D-U-N-S 15-135-6615 IMP
KORG USA INC
(*Suby of* KORG INC.)
316 S Service Rd, Melville, NY 11747-3228
Tel (631) 390-6500 *Founded/Ownrshp* 1985
Sales 76.8MM^E *EMP* 112
SIC 5099 Musical instruments; Musical instruments parts & accessories; Musical instruments; Musical instruments parts & accessories
Ch Bd: Joseph Castronovo
**Ex VP:* Mitch Colby
VP: Douglas Nestler
Genl Mgr: Sakae Yoshinaga
Netwrk Eng: Joe Roy
Natl Sales: A J Reitz
VP Sls: Joseph Bredau
Sls Dir: Mia Pizzo
Mktg Mgr: Scott Fiesel
Mktg Mgr: Jennifer Lewis
Sls Mgr: Allan Pearlman

KORMAN COMMUNITIES
See SHK MANAGEMENT INC

D-U-N-S 01-033-3800
KORMEX FOODS INC
TACO BELL
3233 W 11th St Ste 200, Houston, TX 77008-6168
Tel (713) 980-2860 *Founded/Ownrshp* 2000
Sales 12.0MM^E *EMP* 300
SIC 5812 Fast-food restaurant, chain; Fast-food restaurant, chain
Pr: Phillip S Rhee
**VP:* Oscar Saavedra

D-U-N-S 07-649-4129
■ KORN FERRY LEADERSHIP CONSULTING CORP
(*Suby of* KORN/FERRY INTERNATIONAL) ★
33 S 6th St Ste 4900, Minneapolis, MN 55402-3716
Tel (612) 339-0927 *Founded/Ownrshp* 2013
Sales 51.5MM^E *EMP* 575
SIC 8742

D-U-N-S 05-223-9530
▲ KORN/FERRY INTERNATIONAL
1900 Avenue Of The Stars # 2600, Los Angeles, CA 90067-4507
Tel (310) 552-1834 *Founded/Ownrshp* 1969
Sales 1.0MMM *EMP* 3,687
Accts Ernst & Young Llp Los Angeles
Tkr Sym KFY *Exch* NYS
SIC 8742 7361 Management consulting services; Executive placement; Management consulting services; Executive placement
Pr: Gary D Burnison
Pt: John Doyle
Pr: Doug Charles
Pr: Alexandre S Fialho
COO: Bill King
CFO: Robert P Rozek
Ofcr: Patricia Carroll
Ex VP: Linda Hyman
Ex VP: Ian McGinty
Sr VP: Bryan Ackermann
Mng Dir: Carole Gilbert
Board of Directors: William R Floyd, Christina A Gold, Jerry Leamon, Edward D Miller, Debra J Perry, George T Shaheen, Harry L You

D-U-N-S 02-310-8017
■ KORN/FERRY INTERNATIONAL FUTURESTEP INC
FUTURESTEP.COM
(*Suby of* KORN/FERRY INTERNATIONAL) ★
1900 Avenue Of The Stars, Los Angeles, CA 90067-4301
Tel (310) 552-1834 *Founded/Ownrshp* 1997
Sales 21.2MM^E *EMP* 300
SIC 7361 Executive placement; Executive placement
CEO: Byrne Mulrooney
**Ch Bd:* Peter L Dunn
Pr: George Puig
Pr: William Sebra
**COO:* Andrew Watt
**Chf Mktg O:* Michael Distefano
**Ofcr:* Jeanne Macdonald
Ofcr: Victor Wahba
VP: Jaishankar Adhinarayanan
VP: Mir Ali
VP: Lyn Currie
VP: Charlie Eye
VP: Carl Fitch
VP: Dennis Law
Dir Bus: Harold Levy

KORNER GIFT SHOP
See REX HOSPITAL GUILD INC

D-U-N-S 18-292-5339
KORNER MART
DAIRY QUEEN
7101 W 78th St Ste 200, Minneapolis, MN 55439-2531
Tel (507) 377-9225 *Founded/Ownrshp* 1987
Sales 14.0MM^E *EMP* 700
SIC 5812 5411 5541 Ice cream stands or dairy bars; Convenience stores, independent; Gasoline service stations; Ice cream stands or dairy bars; Convenience stores, independent; Gasoline service stations
Pr: Ron Kraus
**VP:* Kathy Kraus

KORNREICH INSURANCE SVCES
See KORNREICH NIA LLC

D-U-N-S 15-219-8602
■ KORNREICH NIA LLC
KORNREICH INSURANCE SVCES
(*Suby of* NIA GROUP LLC) ★
521 5th Ave Fl 12, New York, NY 10175-1275
Tel (212) 867-0070 *Founded/Ownrshp* 1994
Sales NA *EMP* 120
SIC 6411 Insurance brokers
CEO: Paul L Gross
VP: Joyce Corwin
VP: Karen Williams
Off Mgr: Helen Cetta
Sales Exec: Elissa Palmer

D-U-N-S 07-934-1415
KOROSEAL INTERIOR PRODUCTS LLC
3875 Embassy Pkwy Ste 110, Fairlawn, OH 44333-8334
Tel (855) 753-5474 *Founded/Ownrshp* 2014
Sales 100.0MM *EMP* 639^E
SIC 3081 3089 3069 Floor or wall covering, unsupported plastic; Battery cases, plastic or plastic combination; Wallcoverings, rubber
CEO: Rich Runkel
**COO:* John Farrell
Ex VP: Eric Wroldsen
Manager: Stephanie Segall
Sls Mgr: Ann Mather
Sls Mgr: Jim Sherlock

KORRECT OPTICAL
See ALLAN BAKER INC

D-U-N-S 60-590-3293
■ KORRY ELECTRONICS CO
(*Suby of* ESTERLINE TECHNOLOGIES CORP) ★
11910 Beverly Park Rd, Everett, WA 98204-3529
Tel (425) 297-9700 *Founded/Ownrshp* 1989
Sales 114.5MM^E *EMP* 675
SIC 3613 Switchgear & switchboard apparatus; Panel & distribution boards & other related apparatus; Control panels, electric; Switchgear & switchboard apparatus; Panel & distribution boards & other related apparatus; Control panels, electric
Pr: Richard Brad Lawrence
**CFO:* Robert D George
**VP:* Frank E Houston
IT Man: Robert Eikenberry
Plnt Mgr: John Fauska
Ql Cn Mgr: Paul Dorst
Mktg Dir: Peggy Keene

KORTE COMPANY, THE
See KORTE CONSTRUCTION CO

D-U-N-S 08-163-9411
KORTE CONSTRUCTION CO
KORTE COMPANY, THE
5700 Oakland Ave Ste 275, Saint Louis, MO 63110-1375
Tel (314) 231-3700 *Founded/Ownrshp* 1958
Sales 106.3MM *EMP* 170
Accts Rubinbrown Llp Saint Louis
SIC 1541 1542 Industrial buildings & warehouses; Commercial & office building, new construction; Industrial buildings & warehouses; Commercial & office building, new construction
Pr: Todd Korte
Pr: Greg Korte
COO: Jason Mantle
CFO: William D Bououris
Ch: Ralph Korte
Sec: Susan Bowman
Ex VP: Thomas V Korte
Sr VP: Dennis Araujo
Sr VP: Dennis Calvert
Sr VP: Thomas Lyerla

KORTE DOES IT ALL
See KORTE ELECTRIC INC

D-U-N-S 07-429-5114
KORTE ELECTRIC INC
KORTE DOES IT ALL
10920 Stellhorn Rd Ste A, New Haven, IN 46774-9242
Tel (260) 493-2596 *Founded/Ownrshp* 1964
Sales 25.1MM^E *EMP* 80
SIC 1711 1731 Warm air heating & air conditioning contractor; Plumbing contractors; General electrical contractor
Pr: Jerry Korte
**Treas:* Kevin Kratzman
VP: Ryan Martin

D-U-N-S 78-569-5540
KORUM AUTOMOTIVE GROUP INC
100 River Rd, Puyallup, WA 98371-4161
Tel (253) 845-6600 *Founded/Ownrshp* 1999
Sales 66.2MM^E *EMP* 475
SIC 6719 Personal holding companies, except banks; Personal holding companies, except banks
Pr: Jerome M Korum
CFO: John Hall
**VP:* Jermaine Korum
Genl Mgr: Brett Solomon
Sls Mgr: Jeff Beaty
Sls Mgr: Andy Carter
Sales Asso: Freddie Trotter

KORUM MITSUBISHI
See KORUM MOTORS INC

D-U-N-S 15-211-0714
KORUM MOTORS INC
KORUM MITSUBISHI
(*Suby of* KORUM AUTOMOTIVE GROUP INC) ★
100 River Rd, Puyallup, WA 98371-4161
Tel (253) 841-9600 *Founded/Ownrshp* 1986
Sales 37.2MM^E *EMP* 175

SIC 5511 7539 Automobiles, new & used; Automotive repair shops; Automobiles, new & used; Automotive repair shops
Pr: Jerome M Korum
CFO: Carol Skinner
Pr Dir: Diana Soden
Sales Asso: Dean Lawthers

D-U-N-S 11-185-0751
KORVIS LLC
2101 Ne Jack London St, Corvallis, OR 97330-6916
Tel (541) 738-4389 *Founded/Ownrshp* 2002
Sales 22.1MM^E *EMP* 80
SIC 8742 Automation & robotics consultant
CEO: Rich Carone
**Pr:* Ben Wahlstrom
VP: Steve Dunfield
VP: Rod Grant
**VP:* Rod W Holmquist
VP: Rod Holmquist
**VP:* Neal Pierce
Mng Dir: Korvis Asia
Off Mgr: Laura Hay
CTO: Dilip Kuchipudi
Sftwr Eng: Barry Johnson

D-U-N-S 36-192-2446 IMP
■ **KOS PHARMACEUTICALS INC**
(*Suby of* ABBVIE INC) ★
1 Cedarbrook Dr, Cranbury, NJ 08512-3618
Tel (609) 495-0500 *Founded/Ownrshp* 2006
Sales 52.2MM^E *EMP* 1,361^E
SIC 2834 Pharmaceutical preparations; Pharmaceutical preparations
CEO: Adrian Adams

D-U-N-S 08-239-5765
KOSAIR CHARITIES COMMITTEE INC
982 Eastern Pkwy Ste 3, Louisville, KY 40217-1568
Tel (502) 637-7696 *Founded/Ownrshp* 1923
Sales 25.8MM *EMP* 18
Accts Blue & Co Llc Louisville K
SIC 8399 Fund raising organization, non-fee basis; Fund raising organization, non-fee basis
Pr: Randy Coe
CFO: Tom O'Brien
Treas: C Brown Allen
VP: Vicky Weber

D-U-N-S 07-407-9948
KOSAIR CHILDRENS HOSPITAL
(*Suby of* NORTON HOSPITALS INC) ★
231 E Chestnut St Ste 100, Louisville, KY 40202-3800
Tel (502) 629-6000 *Founded/Ownrshp* 1886
Sales 100.4MM^E *EMP* 1,500
SIC 8062 General medical & surgical hospitals; General medical & surgical hospitals
Pr: Thomas D Kmetz
**VP:* Jeff Lilly
Dir Rx: Edward Leist
IT Man: David Ross
Ansthlgy: Edin Jusufbegovic
Opthamlgy: Paul Rychwalski
Pharmcst: Stephanie Fuhrman
Diag Rad: Phillip Silberberg

D-U-N-S 04-028-1073
■ **KOSCIUSKO 21ST CENTURY FOUNDATION INC**
(*Suby of* COMMUNITY HEALTH SYSTEMS INC) ★
2170 N Pointe Dr, Warsaw, IN 46582-9043
Tel (574) 267-6637 *Founded/Ownrshp* 2007
Sales 73.8MM^E *EMP* 839
SIC 8062 General medical & surgical hospitals; General medical & surgical hospitals
Pr: Richard Haddad
Chf Path: Thomas A Kocoshis
Chf OB: Jody Freyre
**CFO:* Doug Bement
Ansthlgy: Christopher Nelson
Doctor: Cathy Campbell

D-U-N-S 00-578-6819
KOSCIUSKO COUNTY RURAL ELECTRIC MEMBERSHIP CORP
KOSCIUSKO R E M C
370 S 250 E, Warsaw, IN 46582-9048
Tel (574) 267-6331 *Founded/Ownrshp* 1938
Sales 44.5MM *EMP* 36
SIC 4911 Distribution, electric power; Distribution, electric power
Pr: Stephen T Rhodes
Off Mgr: Jeff Buell
Opers Supe: Kurt Carver
Board of Directors: V Pres, John Anglin Jr, Don Arnold, Terry Bouse, Steve Miner, Fred Powell, James Romine, Carl Sands, Tom Shively, William Stump Jr

KOSCIUSKO R E M C
See KOSCIUSKO COUNTY RURAL ELECTRIC MEMBERSHIP CORP

D-U-N-S 11-857-4672
KOSHAN INC
PAYLESS FOODS
23501 Avalon Blvd, Carson, CA 90745-5522
Tel (310) 830-8241 *Founded/Ownrshp* 1984
Sales 79.7MM^E *EMP* 550
SIC 5411 Grocery stores, independent; Grocery stores, independent
CEO: Bijan H Rodd
**Treas:* Frank Hendizadeh
**VP:* Sami Khoshbin

KOSMOS ENERGY HOLDINGS
See KOSMOS ENERGY LLC

D-U-N-S 13-873-6678
KOSMOS ENERGY LLC
KOSMOS ENERGY HOLDINGS
8176 Park Ln Ste 500, Dallas, TX 75231-5988
Tel (214) 445-9600 *Founded/Ownrshp* 2003
Sales 24.1MM^E *EMP* 20^E
SIC 1382 Oil & gas exploration services
Pr: Brian F Maxted
**CFO:* W Greg Dunlevy
**Ofcr:* Paul M Nobel
Sr VP: Mike Anderson
Sr VP: Christopher Ball
**Sr VP:* Kenny Goh
**Sr VP:* Eric J Haas
**Sr VP:* William S Hayes
**Sr VP:* Reg Manhas
VP: Gary Brooks
VP: Tom Fauria
VP: Ragnar Fredsted
VP: Mark Katrosh
VP: Ken Keag
VP: Jesse Noah
VP: Douglas Trumbauer
VP: Brad Whitmarsh
Dir Bus: John Curtis
Comm Man: Ruth Adashie

D-U-N-S 00-694-1298
KOSS CONSTRUCTION CO (IA)
5830 Sw Drury Ln, Topeka, KS 66604-2262
Tel (785) 228-2928 *Founded/Ownrshp* 1912
Sales 152.7MM^E *EMP* 350
SIC 1611

D-U-N-S 00-128-6020 IMP
▲ **KOSS CORP**
4129 N Port Washington Rd, Milwaukee, WI 53212-1029
Tel (414) 964-5000 *Founded/Ownrshp* 1958
Sales 24.2MM *EMP* 54^E
Accts Baker Tilly Virchow Krause Ll
Tkr Sym KOSS *Exch* NGM
SIC 3651 3679 Household audio equipment; Headphones, radio; Household audio equipment; Headphones, radio
Ch Bd: Michael J Koss
CFO: David D Smith
VP: Declan Hanley
VP: Lenore E Lillie
Dir IT: Bill Thompson
VP Opers: Lenore Lilli
VP Sls: John Koss Jr
Board of Directors: Thomas L Doerr, Lawrence S Mattson, Theodore H Nixon, John J Stollenwerk

D-U-N-S 07-854-0727
KOSSE PARTNERS I LLC
FORTRESS SOLUTIONS
2100 10th St Ste 300, Plano, TX 75074-8022
Tel (214) 453-5600 *Founded/Ownrshp* 2012
Sales 25.9MM^E *EMP* 227
SIC 7622 Communication equipment repair
CEO: Brendon Mills
COO: Josh Orender
CFO: Brian Alton
Sr VP: David Deas
VP: Grant Davis
VP: Dan Walsh
VP Opers: Joe Uhr
Opers Mgr: James Bridges

D-U-N-S 03-327-2725
KOSSMANS INC
114 N Davis Ave, Cleveland, MS 38732
Tel (662) 843-3686 *Founded/Ownrshp* 1941
Sales 23.0MM *EMP* 34
SIC 5511 7515 Automobiles, new & used; Passenger car leasing; Automobiles, new & used; Passenger car leasing
Pr: S Edward Kossman Jr
**Sec:* Juliet Kossman
**VP:* Kitty S Kossman

D-U-N-S 07-348-0709
KOSSUTH COUNTY HOSPITAL FOUNDATION
KOSSUTH REGIONAL HEALTH CENTER
1515 S Phillips St, Algona, IA 50511-3649
Tel (515) 295-2451 *Founded/Ownrshp* 1973
Sales 33.2MM^E *EMP* 270
SIC 8062 General medical & surgical hospitals; General medical & surgical hospitals
Ch: Jack Munch
**Pr:* Kurt Welp
**CEO:* Scott Curtis
**CFO:* Tom Geelan
**Treas:* Kristie Brown
**VP:* Pat Reding
CIO: Nancy Erickson
Opers Mgr: Lori Reding
Doctor: Prasad Nadkarni

KOSSUTH REGIONAL HEALTH CENTER
See KOSSUTH COUNTY HOSPITAL FOUNDATION

D-U-N-S 01-412-5108 IMP
KOST TIRE DISTRIBUTORS INC
KOST TIRE SALES
2 Griswold St, Binghamton, NY 13904-1688
Tel (607) 723-9471 *Founded/Ownrshp* 1982
Sales 211.6MM^E *EMP* 308
SIC 5014 5531 7538 Tires & tubes; Automotive tires; General automotive repair shops; Tires & tubes; Automotive tires; General automotive repair shops
Ch Bd: Michael G Kost
**VP:* David Kost
VP: Erwin Kost
**VP:* Sam Kost
Opers Mgr: Dan Getter

KOST TIRE SALES
See KOST TIRE DISTRIBUTORS INC

KOSTAL GROUP
See KOSTAL KONTAKT SYSTEME INC

D-U-N-S 96-435-0735 IMP
KOSTAL KONTAKT SYSTEME INC
KOSTAL GROUP
1350 W Hamlin Rd, Rochester Hills, MI 48309-3361
Tel (248) 284-7600 *Founded/Ownrshp* 2010
Sales 37.7MM^E *EMP* 143
SIC 3678 Electronic connectors; Electronic connectors
CEO: Waldemar Schneider
**CFO:* Anna Mueller
Bd of Dir: Jerry Morlewski
Prgrm Mgr: Heath Miller
Snr Sftwr: David Bowden
Snr Sftwr: Daniel McRobb
Prd Mgr: Rayman Hannish
Ql Cn Mgr: Ivan Ramos
Ql Cn Mgr: Wayne Russell
Ql Cn Mgr: Omar Serrano
Ql Cn Mgr: Tengfei Yang

KOSTAL NORTH AMERICA
See KOSTAL OF AMERICA INC

D-U-N-S 00-250-4512 IMP
KOSTAL OF AMERICA INC (MI)
KOSTAL NORTH AMERICA
(*Suby of* KOSTAL BETEILIGUNGSGES. MBH)
350 Stephenson Hwy, Troy, MI 48083-1119
Tel (248) 284-6500 *Founded/Ownrshp* 1987, 2008
Sales 27.8MM^E *EMP* 170
SIC 7389 3714 3643 3613 Design, commercial & industrial; Motor vehicle parts & accessories; Current-carrying wiring devices; Switchgear & switchboard apparatus; Design, commercial & industrial; Motor vehicle parts & accessories; Current-carrying wiring devices; Switchgear & switchboard apparatus
Pr: Walter Maisel
**CFO:* Anna Mueller
Bd of Dir: Octavio Martinez
Ofcr: Colette Kennelly
VP: Karissa Chamberlin
Exec: Fiona Harrison
Dir Bus: Michael Campbell
IT Man: Eric Hanotin

D-U-N-S 04-075-4504 IMP
KOTOCORP (USA) INC
(*Suby of* KOTOBUKI CORPORATION)
5981 E Cork St, Kalamazoo, MI 49048-9609
Tel (269) 349-1521 *Founded/Ownrshp* 1998
Sales 34.7MM^E *EMP* 160
SIC 2531 Personal holding companies, except banks; Stadium seating
Ch: Mike Amemiya
Treas: Brian L Gould

D-U-N-S 11-081-1192
KOUNTRY WOOD PRODUCTS LLC
352 Shawnee St, Nappanee, IN 46550-9061
Tel (574) 773-5673 *Founded/Ownrshp* 1997
Sales 78.1MM^E *EMP* 325^E
SIC 2434 Wood kitchen cabinets; Wood kitchen cabinets
CEO: Ola Yoder
**Pr:* Perry Miller
**CFO:* Greg Shank
**VP:* Virgil Yoder
Opers Mgr: Jeff Walters

D-U-N-S 15-665-5222
KOURT SECURITY PARTNERS LLC
SELECT SECURITY
241 N Plum St, Lancaster, PA 17602-2792
Tel (717) 481-6303 *Founded/Ownrshp* 2003
Sales 25.8MM^E *EMP* 59
SIC 7382 Security systems services

D-U-N-S 02-459-3790
KOURY CORP
2275 Vanstory St Ste 200, Greensboro, NC 27403-3623
Tel (336) 299-9200 *Founded/Ownrshp* 1955
Sales 48.7MM^E *EMP* 1,000
SIC 6512 6513 Commercial & industrial building operation; Shopping center, property operation only; Apartment building operators; Commercial & industrial building operation; Shopping center, property operation only; Apartment building operators
Ch: Koury
**Pr:* Steve Showfety
VP: Ron Mack
CTO: Chad Harper

D-U-N-S 14-315-1095
KOURY VENTURES LP
GRANDOVER RESORT
(*Suby of* KOURY CORP) ★
1000 Club Rd, Greensboro, NC 27407-8286
Tel (336) 323-3838 *Founded/Ownrshp* 1993
Sales 12.4MM^E *EMP* 350
SIC 7011 Hotels & motels; Hotels & motels
Pt: Steve Showfety
Sr VP: Tom Thomas
VP: MO Milani

KOUTS BUD HONDA
See FELDKOUTS LLC

D-U-N-S 00-605-6824
KOVA FERTILIZER INC
1330 N Anderson St, Greensburg, IN 47240-1011
Tel (812) 663-5081 *Founded/Ownrshp* 1947
Sales 68.8MM^E *EMP* 60
SIC 5191 2875 Fertilizers & agricultural chemicals; Fertilizers, mixing only; Fertilizers & agricultural chemicals; Fertilizers, mixing only
Pr: Bradley Reed
VP: Brain Reed
VP: Todd Reed
Dir IT: David Lawson
Sfty Mgr: Roger Dumond
Sales Asso: Greg Bennett

KOVACH BUILDING ENCLOSURES
See KOVACH INC

D-U-N-S 07-447-2275 IMP
KOVACH INC
KOVACH BUILDING ENCLOSURES
3195 W Armstrong Pl, Chandler, AZ 85286-6602
Tel (480) 926-9292 *Founded/Ownrshp* 1969
Sales 105.3MM^E *EMP* 200
SIC 1761 Roofing contractor; Siding contractor; Roofing contractor; Siding contractor
Pr: Stephen E Kovach IV
**Pr:* Scott Bourdo
VP: Eric Kovach
Snr Mgr: Chip Carr

D-U-N-S 00-791-1696
KOVALCHICK SALVAGE CO (PA)
1060 Wayne Ave, Indiana, PA 15701-2951
Tel (724) 349-3300 *Founded/Ownrshp* 1972
Sales 26.5MM^E *EMP* 111
SIC 5088 5082 5085 5093 6519 4011 Railroad equipment & supplies; Mining machinery & equipment, except petroleum; Mill supplies; Junk & scrap; Real property lessors; Railroads, line-haul operating
Pt: Joseph Kovalchick
VP: Nathan Kovalchick

D-U-N-S 00-222-2297
KOVALSKY-CARR ELECTRIC SUPPLY CO INC (NY)
208 Saint Paul St, Rochester, NY 14604-1188
Tel (585) 325-1950 *Founded/Ownrshp* 1921, 1977
Sales 32.8MM^E *EMP* 30
SIC 5063 Electrical apparatus & equipment; Electrical fittings & construction materials; Lighting fixtures
Pr: Arnold M Kovalsky
VP: Don Bausch
**VP:* Laurence Kovalsky
Off Mgr: Jeannie Huss
Opers Mgr: Jerry Turner
Sls Mgr: Rob Gioia
Sales Asso: Dave Aldrich

D-U-N-S 16-496-4954
KOVARUS INC
2000 Crow Canyon Pl # 250, San Ramon, CA 94583-1367
Tel (650) 392-7848 *Founded/Ownrshp* 2004
Sales 24.2MM^E *EMP* 25
SIC 7379 5734 ; Computer software & accessories
CEO: Peter Castaldi
**Pr:* Patrick Cronin
Sr VP: Kevin Potts
VP: Mathew Shuster
**CIO:* Andy Lewis
**CTO:* Steve Rogers
VP Mktg: Sophia Le
Snr PM: Mathias Lee

D-U-N-S 08-177-5447 IMP/EXP
KOVATCH CASTINGS INC
3743 Tabs Dr, Uniontown, OH 44685-9563
Tel (330) 896-9944 *Founded/Ownrshp* 1976
Sales 41.4MM^E *EMP* 150
Accts Meaden & Moore Ltd Akron O
SIC 3324 3369 3366 3365 3325 Commercial investment castings, ferrous; Aerospace investment castings, ferrous; Nonferrous foundries; Copper foundries; Aluminum foundries; Steel foundries; Commercial investment castings, ferrous; Aerospace investment castings, ferrous; Nonferrous foundries; Copper foundries; Aluminum foundries; Steel foundries
Pr: Douglas Kovatch
CFO: Frank Lysik
**VP:* Frank E Lysiak
QC Dir: Martin Prenosil

D-U-N-S 15-214-4010 IMP/EXP
KOVATCH MOBILE EQUIPMENT CORP
KME FIRE APPARATUS
1 Industrial Complex, Nesquehoning, PA 18240-1499
Tel (570) 669-9461 *Founded/Ownrshp* 1985
Sales 173.7MM^E *EMP* 765
Accts Fegley & Associates Pc Plymou
SIC 3711 Chassis, motor vehicle; Fire department vehicles (motor vehicles), assembly of; Automobile assembly, including specialty automobiles; Chassis, motor vehicle; Fire department vehicles (motor vehicles), assembly of; Automobile assembly, including specialty automobiles
Pr: John I Kovatch
**CFO:* Richard T Reaman
CIO: Brian Glitzer
Sls Mgr: Stan Ptaszkowski
Sales Asso: Mark Chai

D-U-N-S 11-945-9589 IMP
KOWA PHARMACEUTICALS AMERICA INC
(*Suby of* KOWA COMPANY,LTD.)
530 Industrial Park Blvd, Montgomery, AL 36117-5543
Tel (334) 288-1288 *Founded/Ownrshp* 2008
Sales 200.0M *EMP* 314
SIC 5122 Pharmaceuticals; Pharmaceuticals
CEO: Ben Stakely
**COO:* Roger Graben
**CFO:* Koji Tamura
**Sr VP:* Lou Mullikan
**VP:* Brad Hardy
**VP:* Kenneth Riester
**VP:* Craig Sponsellor
Dist Mgr: Ivory Gethers
Dist Mgr: David Kodluk
Natl Sales: John Fongaro
Pharmcst: Charles Smith

D-U-N-S 60-494-6707
KOWALIS MOTOR CAR INC
LEXUS OF ORLAND
8300 W 159th St, Orland Park, IL 60462-4941
Tel (708) 614-8700 *Founded/Ownrshp* 1989
Sales 36.0MM^E *EMP* 60
SIC 5511 7538 Automobiles, new & used; General automotive repair shops; Automobiles, new & used; General automotive repair shops
Pr: Eugene A Kowalis
Exec: Caryn Szoldatits
Prin: Jeff Kowalis
Genl Mgr: Mark Mizera
Sls Mgr: Steven Safavi
Sales Asso: Assad Hamzeh
Sales Asso: Gustavo Jaramillo
Sales Asso: Chris Merx
Sales Asso: Sean Pearson

D-U-N-S 06-247-3897
KOWALIS MOTORS INC (IL)
ORLAND TOYOTA
8505 159th St, Tinley Park, IL 60487-1166
Tel (708) 336-7272 *Founded/Ownrshp* 1972
Sales 20.3MM^E *EMP* 50
SIC 5511 Automobiles, new & used
Pr: Eugene Kowalis
**Sec:* Kurt Kowalis
Genl Mgr: Jeff Kowalis
Sls Mgr: Christopher Strozyk
Sales Asso: Adrian Ziarko

D-U-N-S 00-531-8050
KOWALSKI COMPANIES INC
2270 Holbrook St, Detroit, MI 48212-3445
Tel (313) 873-8200 *Founded/Ownrshp* 1989
Sales 51.8MM^E *EMP* 182
SIC 2013 5421 Sausages from purchased meat; Bacon, side & sliced: from purchased meat; Meat extracts from purchased meat; Meat & fish markets; Sausages from purchased meat; Bacon, side & sliced: from purchased meat; Meat extracts from purchased meat; Meat & fish markets
Pr: Michael Kowalski
**Treas:* Ulrich Eggert
Plnt Mgr: Joe Adolph
Plnt Mgr: Shawn Cinco
Sls Mgr: John Oldani

D-U-N-S 10-227-7308 IMP
KOWALSKI COMPANIES INC
8505 Valley Creek Rd, Woodbury, MN 55125-2342
Tel (651) 578-8800 *Founded/Ownrshp* 1984
Sales 185.0MM^E *EMP* 1,200
SIC 5411 Grocery stores, chain; Grocery stores, chain
Pr: James S Kowalski
**COO:* Kristin Kowalski
**CFO:* Tom Beauchamp
**VP:* Mary Anne Kowalski
Genl Mgr: Danielle Wilebski
Store Mgr: Doug Borsch
Store Mgr: Dan Niggeler
CTO: Steve Beaird
MIS Dir: Bob Kowalski
VP Opers: Dale Riley
Mktg Dir: Laurie Bell

D-U-N-S 94-339-2522
KOYITLOTSINA LIMITED
1603 College Rd Ste 2, Fairbanks, AK 99709-4175
Tel (907) 452-8119 *Founded/Ownrshp* 1980
Sales 105.2MM^E *EMP* 650
Accts Rjg Pc Fairbanks Alaska
SIC 6798 8744 7349 Real estate investment trusts; Facilities support services; Building maintenance services; Real estate investment trusts; Facilities support services; Building maintenance services
Pr: Christopher Simon
CFO: Lynn Laycock
CFO: R Lynn Laycock CPA
Treas: Larry Edwards
**Treas:* Julia Simon
**VP:* Fred Bifelt
Adm Dir: Julie Gasparro

KOYO BEARINGS
See JTEKT NORTH AMERICA CORP

D-U-N-S 83-256-3774 IMP
KOYO BEARINGS NORTH AMERICA LLC
(*Suby of* JTEKT NORTH AMERICA CORP) ★
4895 Dressler Rd Nw Ste B, Canton, OH 44718-2571
Tel (330) 994-0890 *Founded/Ownrshp* 2009
Sales 309.6MM^E *EMP* 1,444
SIC 3562 Ball & roller bearings; Ball & roller bearings
Pr: Ken Hopkins
Genl Mgr: Bryan Spinney

D-U-N-S 03-105-7649
KOZENY-WAGNER INC
951 W Outer Rd, Arnold, MO 63010-1300
Tel (636) 296-2012 *Founded/Ownrshp* 1965
Sales 38.6MM *EMP* 80
Accts Wolfe Nilges Nahorski St Lou
SIC 1611 1542 Highway & street paving contractor; Commercial & office building, new construction; Highway & street paving contractor; Commercial & office building, new construction
CEO: Donald J Kozeny
**Pr:* Patrick Kozeny
**CFO:* Roger Loesche
**VP:* Richard V Wagner
**VP:* Gary Walker
Exec: Michael Kozeny
VP Mktg: Rob Lonigro
Board of Directors: Richard Wagner Sr

KOZY HEAT FIREPLACES
See HUSSONG MANUFACTURING CO INC

D-U-N-S 04-319-0917 IMP
KOZY SHACK ENTERPRISES LLC
(*Suby of* LAND O'LAKES INC) ★
83 Ludy St, Hicksville, NY 11801-5114
Tel (516) 870-3000 *Founded/Ownrshp* 1967, 2012
Sales 71.8MM^E *EMP* 450
SIC 2099 5149 Desserts, ready-to-mix; Gelatin dessert preparations; Groceries & related products; Desserts, ready-to-mix; Gelatin dessert preparations; Groceries & related products
CEO: Robert Striano
**CFO:* Sally Olivero

D-U-N-S 12-322-2643
KP HOLDINGS LLC
2000 E 196th St, Westfield, IN 46074-3801
Tel (317) 867-0234 *Founded/Ownrshp* 1999
Sales 53.8MM^E *EMP* 430
SIC 3714 Motor vehicle parts & accessories; Motor vehicle parts & accessories
Pr: John Ball
**VP:* Gregory Griffin

D-U-N-S 14-857-0708
KP KAUFFMAN CO INC
1675 Broadway Ste 2800, Denver, CO 80202-4690
Tel (303) 825-0815 *Founded/Ownrshp* 1984
Sales 72.8MM^E *EMP* 115
SIC 1381 4789 Directional drilling oil & gas wells; Cargo loading & unloading services; Directional drilling oil & gas wells; Cargo loading & unloading services
CEO: Kevin P Kauffman
**COO:* Jeffrey V Kauffman
VP: Ronda Gallup
**VP:* Kent L Gilbert
**VP:* Tony Losacano

D-U-N-S 05-097-3130 IMP
KP LLC (OR)
13951 Washington Ave, San Leandro, CA 94578-3220
Tel (510) 346-0729 *Founded/Ownrshp* 1929, 1967
Sales 110.3MM^E *EMP* 300
SIC 2752 7334 7331 7374 7389 8742 Commercial printing, lithographic; Photocopying & duplicating services; Direct mail advertising services; Computer graphics service; Subscription fulfillment services: magazine, newspaper, etc.; Marketing consulting services; Commercial printing, lithographic; Photocopying & duplicating services; Direct mail advertising services; Computer graphics service; Subscription fulfillment services: magazine, newspaper, etc.; Marketing consulting services
CEO: Joe Atturio
Dir Bus: Steve Bottomley
Prgrm Mgr: Rachel Lee
Opers Mgr: Aaron King
Opers Mgr: Tom Stoneback
Ql Cn Mgr: Wendy Welsh
Pharmcst: Teresa Petrilla

D-U-N-S 05-534-5102
■ **KP MOTORS LLC**
COGGIN PONTIAC GMC ORANGE PARK
(*Suby of* ASBURY AUTOMOTIVE SOUTHERN CALIFORNIA LLC) ★
7245 Blanding Blvd, Jacksonville, FL 32244-4503
Tel (904) 777-9999 *Founded/Ownrshp* 2001
Sales 25.2MM^E *EMP* 80
SIC 5511 Automobiles, new & used; Automobiles, new & used
Off Mgr: Wayne Watkins

D-U-N-S 19-057-7127
KP SANGHVI INC
589 5th Ave Rm 1008, New York, NY 10017-8751
Tel (212) 575-2358 *Founded/Ownrshp* 2003
Sales 27.3MM *EMP* 17
Accts Nissel Cpa Llc New York Ny
SIC 5094 Jewelry & precious stones
Pr: Gautam Begani

D-U-N-S 00-289-4558
KP-SUPPLY CO INC
5 N Pensylvania Ave, Oklahoma City, OK 73107-7051
Tel (405) 235-2621 *Founded/Ownrshp* 1975
Sales 29.5MM^E *EMP* 41^E
SIC 5085 5084 5072 Industrial supplies; Machine tools & metalworking machinery; Hardware; Industrial supplies; Machine tools & metalworking machinery; Hardware
Pr: Tom Hughes
**Sec:* Marsha Pierce
Sls Mgr: Chris Hess
Sls Mgr: Rick Hughes
Sales Asso: Roger Guthery
Sales Asso: John Hamlin
Sales Asso: Glen Mailand
Sales Asso: Jimmy Romero

D-U-N-S 79-669-8863
KPA SERVICES LLC
1380 Frest Pk Cir Ste 140, Lafayette, CO 80026
Tel (303) 228-8750 *Founded/Ownrshp* 2014
Sales 21.1MM^E *EMP* 76^E
SIC 3822 Auto controls regulating residntl & coml environmt & applncs
Pr: Vane Clayton
**CFO:* Gabe Orvis
VP: Kathryn Carlson
VP: Bill Duclos
VP: John Hansen
Dist Mgr: Nick Bujeaud
Dist Mgr: Nick Hardesty
IT Man: Chris Vinall
Software D: Jesse Beckton
Software D: Jim Mitchell
Software D: Scott Peterson

KPAC
See KONOIKE-PACIFIC (CALIFORNIA) INC

D-U-N-S 78-530-8797
KPAUL PROPERTIES LLC
5825 W 74th St, Indianapolis, IN 46278-1757
Tel (317) 243-1750 *Founded/Ownrshp* 2004
Sales 43.4MM^E *EMP* 90^E
SIC 5085 Industrial supplies; Industrial supplies
IT Man: Rochana Chhun

KPC
See KENTWOOD PACKAGING CORP

D-U-N-S 62-638-7570
KPC GROUP LLC
6800 Indiana Ave Ste 130, Riverside, CA 92506-4266
Tel (951) 782-8812 *Founded/Ownrshp* 2006
Sales 20.7MM^E *EMP* 167^E
SIC 8742 Financial consultant

D-U-N-S 13-610-3970
▲ **KPC HEALTHCARE INC**
1301 N Tustin Ave, Santa Ana, CA 92705-8619
Tel (714) 953-3652 *Founded/Ownrshp* 2004
Sales 398.3MM^E *EMP* 3,012
Tkr Sym IHCH *Exch* OTO
SIC 8062 6719 General medical & surgical hospitals; Investment holding companies, except banks; General medical & surgical hospitals; Investment holding companies, except banks
Pr: Suzanne Richards
Ch Bd: Kali Chaudhuri
CFO: John Collins
VP: Randy Overturf
VP: Eric Royal
Dir Lab: Nancy Davis
Prgrm Mgr: Andrea Kosewick
Rgnl Mgr: Randy Rodelo
CIO: SRI Yarramsetti
Mtls Mgr: Rosie Aburto
Sls Mgr: Kathy Kelly
Board of Directors: Robert Jameson, Michael Metzler, Fernando Niebla, William E Thomas

D-U-N-S 05-739-5394
KPC MEDIA GROUP INC
ADVANCE LEADER
102 N Main St, Kendallville, IN 46755-1714
Tel (260) 347-0400 *Founded/Ownrshp* 1911
Sales 29.9MM^E *EMP* 161
SIC 2711 2791 2752 Newspapers, publishing & printing; Typesetting; Commercial printing, lithographic
CEO: Terry R Ward
**Pr:* Terry Housholder
**Pr:* George B Witwer
**CFO:* S Rick Mitchell
Ofcr: John Dixon
VP: Banks Dishmon
**VP:* Grace Householder
**VP:* David Kurtz
**VP:* Richard Stoltz
**VP:* Sally Stoltz
**VP:* Violet Wysong

KPCB
See KLEINER PERKINS CAUFIELD & BYERS LLC

D-U-N-S 09-500-2127
KPD INSURANCE INC
KINGREY PRICE & DUYCK INSUR
1111 Gateway Loop, Springfield, OR 97477-1116
Tel (541) 741-0550 *Founded/Ownrshp* 2001
Sales NA *EMP* 70^E
SIC 6411 6321 6331 Insurance agents; Life insurance agents; Health insurance carriers; Fire, marine & casualty insurance
Pr: Jim Ginger
Treas: John Kennedy Jr
Sr Cor Off: Ike Kingrey
Bd of Dir: Ryan Melvin
VP: Tracie Knowlton
VP: Matt Stopher
Manager: Keith Yam
Board of Directors: Stan Duyck, Gordon Groshong, John Melvin

KPF
See KOHN PEDERSEN FOX ASSOCIATES PC

KPFF CONSULTING ENGINEERS
See KPFF INC

D-U-N-S 04-247-7729
KPFF INC
KPFF CONSULTING ENGINEERS
1601 5th Ave Ste 1600, Seattle, WA 98101-3665
Tel (206) 622-5822 *Founded/Ownrshp* 1960
Sales 169.2MM^E *EMP* 900
SIC 8711 Consulting engineer; Civil engineering; Structural engineering; Consulting engineer; Civil engineering; Structural engineering
Pr: John Gavan
**CFO:* Steve Dill
CFO: Barbara Rothfarb
**VP:* Molly Wilcox
Div Mgr: Jenny Lockheimers
Off Mgr: Kim Anderson
Off Mgr: Kacy Rufener
Off Admin: Leo Castillo
IT Man: Chris Hartley
Sys Mgr: James Lord

D-U-N-S 01-239-4156
KPH ENGINEERED SYSTEMS INC
PL PORTER
(*Suby of* KP HOLDINGS LLC) ★
2000 E 196th St, Westfield, IN 46074-3801
Tel (317) 867-0234 *Founded/Ownrshp* 1999
Sales 53.8MM^E *EMP* 400
SIC 3714 Motor vehicle parts & accessories; Motor vehicle parts & accessories
Pr: John Ball
Pr: Carl Murphy
CFO: Charles Bullard
**VP:* Gregory Griffin
**VP:* Karl A Murphy
VP: Rob Nelson
VP: Rich Phillips
VP: Regina Shoe
**VP:* J Michael Vance
Exec: Dan Byers
Genl Mgr: Rick Schiess

D-U-N-S 00-586-9581 IMP
KPH HEALTHCARE SERVICES INC (NY)
KINNEY DRUGS
29 E Main St, Gouverneur, NY 13642-1401
Tel (315) 287-3600 *Founded/Ownrshp* 1903, 2008
Sales 915.4MM *EMP* 3,400
SIC 5912 Drug stores; Drug stores
Ch Bd: Craig Painter
**Pr:* Bridget-Ann Hart
CFO: Darrell Barber
Bd of Dir: Rebecca Horn
**Ex VP:* Stephen McCoy
**Sr VP:* Michael Burgess
VP: Scott Bouchard
VP: Owen Halloran
**VP:* David C McClure
VP: April Sumner
VP: Jim Wuest
Board of Directors: John Dyer, Warren Wolfson

D-U-N-S 14-781-7175 IMP
KPI CONCEPTS INC
1415 W Mount Pleasant St, West Burlington, IA 52655-1002
Tel (319) 754-5922 *Founded/Ownrshp* 1990
Sales 31.4MM *EMP* 46^E
SIC 2541 5031 Shelving, office & store, wood; Kitchen cabinets; Shelving, office & store, wood; Kitchen cabinets
Pr: Craig Upton
**VP:* Kevin Mueller
Genl Mgr: Brandon Upton

D-U-N-S 08-724-3403 IMP
KPI ULTRASOUND INC (NV)
K P I
23865 Via Del Rio, Yorba Linda, CA 92887-2727
Tel (951) 367-0872 *Founded/Ownrshp* 1999
Sales 29.5MM *EMP* 27

Accts Roorda Piquet & Bessee Inc
SIC 5047 Medical equipment & supplies; Medical laboratory equipment; Medical equipment & supplies; Medical laboratory equipment
Pr: Eunjin Minn
**Sec:* Steven Minn
S&M/VP: Greg Johnson
Sls Mgr: Jose Valdez

D-U-N-S 05-358-9243
KPIT INFOSYSTEMS INC
(*Suby of* KPIT TECHNOLOGIES LIMITED)
379 Thornall St Ste 6, Edison, NJ 08837-2226
Tel (732) 321-0921 *Founded/Ownrshp* 1998
Sales 53.4MM^E *EMP* 292
SIC 7371 Custom computer programming services; Custom computer programming services
CEO: Sachin Tikekar
Sr VP: Anup Sable
Off Mgr: Barbara Stroul
IT Man: Siddharth Ambekar

D-U-N-S 82-779-6579
KPLT HOLDINGS INC
(*Suby of* KOHLBERG & CO) ★
111 Radio Circle Dr, Mount Kisco, NY 10549-2609
Tel (914) 241-7430 *Founded/Ownrshp* 2008
Sales NA *EMP* 29,060
SIC 6719 Investment holding companies, except banks; Investment holding companies, except banks
Prin: Gordon Woodward
**Sec:* Seth Hollander

KPLX FM RADIO
See RADIO METROPLEX INC

D-U-N-S 00-166-7906
KPMG LLP
345 Park Ave Lowr L-4, New York, NY 10154-0016
Tel (212) 758-9700 *Founded/Ownrshp* 1994
Sales 6.1MMM^E *EMP* 24,097
SIC 8721 Certified public accountant; Certified public accountant
CEO: John Veihmeyer
Pt: Brian M Ambrose
Pt: J Richard Andrews Jr
Pt: Patrick L Arsers
Pt: Charles J Bachand
Pt: Jeffrey S Berman
Pt: Kyle A Bibb
Pt: Charles Bruce
Pt: Patricia Carey
Pt: Dominick P Cavuoto
Pt: Charles I Johnson III
Pt: Stephen N Chase
Pt: Joann Chavez
Pt: R Matthew Clark
Pt: Robert D Cleveland
Pt: Charles E Cochran
Pt: Brian Cooper
Pt: Jim Craycroft
Pt: Steven L Cross
Pt: Brian L Cumberland
Pt: Anthony Dalessio
Board of Directors: Stephen G Butler

D-U-N-S 00-690-2134
■ **KPNX BROADCASTING CO**
KPNX TV CHANNEL 12
(*Suby of* TEGNA INC) ★
200 E Van Buren St, Phoenix, AZ 85004-2238
Tel (602) 257-1212 *Founded/Ownrshp* 1929, 1968
Sales 26.3MM^E *EMP* 200
SIC 4833 Television broadcasting stations; Television broadcasting stations
Pr: John Misner
**Treas:* Jimmy L Thomas
VP: Lucia Madrid
**Prin:* Brien Kennedy

KPNX TV CHANNEL 12
See KPNX BROADCASTING CO

KPRC-TV CHANNEL 2
See GRAHAM MEDIA GROUP HOUSTON INC

D-U-N-S 04-687-2078
KPRS CONSTRUCTION SERVICES INC (NV)
2850 Saturn St Ste 110, Brea, CA 92821-1701
Tel (714) 672-0800 *Founded/Ownrshp* 1995
Sales 61.2MM^E *EMP* 95^E
Accts Wahlquist & Company Los Angel
SIC 1542 8711 Nonresidential construction; Building construction consultant; Nonresidential construction; Building construction consultant
Pr: Joel H Stensby
**Treas:* Lev Rabinovich
Genl Mgr: Jeanette Koga-Horen
Off Mgr: Lela Mbernal
Dir IT: Frank Chien

D-U-N-S 07-115-9078 IMP/EXP
KPS CAPITAL PARTNERS LP
485 Lexington Ave Fl 31, New York, NY 10017-2641
Tel (212) 338-5100 *Founded/Ownrshp* 1998
Sales 2.3MMM^E *EMP* 5,497
SIC 3541 6722 3545 5084 Machine tools, metal cutting type; Management investment, open-end; Machine tool accessories; Industrial machinery & equipment; Machine tools, metal cutting type; Management investment, open-end; Machine tool accessories; Industrial machinery & equipment
Mng Pt: Michael G Psaros
**Pt:* Jay Bernstein
**Pt:* Raquel Palmer
**Pt:* David Shapiro
VP: Jeff Bougher
VP: Keith McKinnish
VP: David Peck

D-U-N-S 07-934-6140
■ **KPS LLC** (OH)
(*Suby of* KROGER CO) ★
1014 Vine St, Cincinnati, OH 45202-1141
Tel (513) 762-4000 *Founded/Ownrshp* 2013
Sales 199.7MM^E *EMP* 1^E
SIC 5141 Groceries, general line
CEO: W Rodney McMullen

KPTM-TV CHANNEL 42
See PAPPAS TELECASTING OF MIDLANDS LP

D-U-N-S 00-477-0921
KQED INC (CA)
KQED PUBLIC MEDIA
2601 Mariposa St, San Francisco, CA 94110-1426
Tel (415) 864-2000 *Founded/Ownrshp* 1952
Sales 69.0MM *EMP* 266
Accts Hood & Strong Llp San Francis
SIC 4833 4832 Television broadcasting stations; Radio broadcasting stations;Television broadcasting stations; Radio broadcasting stations
Pr: John Boland
V Ch: James E Canals
**COO:* Donald W Derheim
CFO: Paul Galvin
**CFO:* Mitzie Kelley
CFO: Kim Van
CFO: Gerald Yaffee
Bd of Dir: Michael Ramsay
Sr VP: Kevin Martin
VP: Joanne Corder
VP: Deanne Hamilton
Dir Soc: Heather Lum
Board of Directors: Jayme Burke, Nic Hill, Terrel Hutton, Robin Smith, Tim Wu

KQED PUBLIC MEDIA
See KQED INC

D-U-N-S 55-692-9875
KR ACQUISITION CORP
727 S Wolfe St, Baltimore, MD 21231-3513
Tel (410) 342-2626 *Founded/Ownrshp* 1991
Sales 31.0MM[E] *EMP* 48[E]
SIC 8711 3829 Engineering services; Meteorological instruments
Ch: Bruce R Robinson

D-U-N-S 07-647-5870
KR SWERDFEGER CONSTRUCTION INC
421 E Industrial Blvd, Pueblo, CO 81007-1415
Tel (719) 547-0242 *Founded/Ownrshp* 1968
Sales 51.1MM[E] *EMP* 100
SIC 1623 Water, sewer & utility lines
Pr: Keith R Swerdfeger
Sec: Sharon Swerdfeger
Sfty Mgr: Dan Kraus
Sfty Mgr: John Samec
Snr Mgr: Darryl Stephens

KR3W
See ONE-DISTRIBUTION CO LLC

D-U-N-S 19-728-7501
KRA CORP
11830 W Market Pl Ste M, Fulton, MD 20759-2432
Tel (301) 562-2300 *Founded/Ownrshp* 1981
Sales 23.9MM[E] *EMP* 250[E]
Accts Dembo Jones Healy Penningto
SIC 8742 8299 Management consulting services; Educational services; Educational service, nondegree granting: continuing educ.; Management consulting services; Educational services; Educational service, nondegree granting: continuing educ.
Pr: Knowlton R Atterbeary
**COO:* Patrick Boxall
VP: Mary Geoghegan
VP: Wenda Harbour
VP: Michael Walker
Prgrm Mgr: Anita Davis
Prgrm Mgr: Anthony Featherstone
Prgrm Mgr: Alisha Williams
Opers Mgr: Karen Brown
Corp Couns: Vanessa Atterbeary
Snr Mgr: Brian Carter

KRACAW PRODUCE
See WINNEMUCCA FARMS INC

D-U-N-S 06-209-2895 IMP/EXP
KRACO ENTERPRISES LLC
505 E Euclid Ave, Compton, CA 90222-2890
Tel (310) 639-0666 *Founded/Ownrshp* 2008
Sales 90.5MM[E] *EMP* 164
SIC 5531 3069 5013 Automotive & home supply stores; Motor vehicle supplies & new parts; Automotive trimmings, fabric; Hard rubber & molded rubber products; Automotive & home supply stores; Hard rubber & molded rubber products; Motor vehicle supplies & new parts
**Pr:* Lawrence McIsaac
**CFO:* Blake Barnett
CFO: Dennis Jolicoeur
**Sr VP:* John Fiumefreddo
**Sr VP:* Steve Lazzara
VP: Roger McCallen
Prgrm Mg: Gary Steinberg
Genl Mgr: Brad Vetter
Natl Sales: Oscar Martinez
Natl Sales: Tony Murphy

D-U-N-S 05-556-4686 IMP
KRADJIAN IMPORTING COINC
5018 San Fernando Rd, Glendale, CA 91204-1114
Tel (818) 502-1313 *Founded/Ownrshp* 1987
Sales 35.4MM[E] *EMP* 61
SIC 5149 Groceries & related products
Pr: Raffi Kradjian
**VP:* Viken Kradjian

D-U-N-S 94-869-1498 IMP
KRAEMER CO LLC
820 Wachter Ave, Plain, WI 53577
Tel (608) 546-2255 *Founded/Ownrshp* 1996
Sales 44.9MM[E] *EMP* 175
SIC 1442 Gravel mining; Gravel mining
Ofcr: Dick Marino
Exec: Richard Kraemer

D-U-N-S 07-981-4759
KRAEMER NORTH AMERICA LLC
(*Suby of* OBAYASHI USA LLC) ★
1 Plainview Rd, Plain, WI 53577-9694
Tel (608) 546-2311 *Founded/Ownrshp* 2015
Sales 12.3MM[E] *EMP* 302
SIC 1622 1442 Bridge construction; Gravel mining
Pr: Scott W Peterson
Treas: Tina H Johansen

D-U-N-S 05-707-2969 IMP
KRAEMERS NURSERY INC
KNI MARKETING
14306 Downs Rd Ne, Mount Angel, OR 97362-9738
Tel (503) 845-2283 *Founded/Ownrshp* 1979
Sales 30.8MM[E] *EMP* 200
SIC 0783 Ornamental shrub & tree services; Ornamental shrub & tree services
CEO: Dave Sabalka
**Pr:* Paul J Kraemer
CFO: Michelle Kraemer
CTO: Alan Kraemer
IT Man: Ron Ammon
Trfc Mgr: Pat Schaecher

D-U-N-S 00-797-9974 IMP
KRAFT CHEMICAL CO (IL)
1975 N Hawthorne Ave, Melrose Park, IL 60160-1160
Tel (708) 345-5200 *Founded/Ownrshp* 1935
Sales 34.6MM *EMP* 30
Accts Hansen Plahm & Company Darien
SIC 5169 Chemicals, industrial & heavy; Chemicals, industrial & heavy
Pr: Rick Kraft
Mng Pt: Antoinette Lonero
**CFO:* David Harris
**Prin:* Jerry Planek
Genl Mgr: Kathy Barth
Off Mgr: Cynthia Rodriguez

D-U-N-S 18-884-0425 EXP
■ **KRAFT FOOD INGREDIENTS CORP**
KRAFT FOODS
(*Suby of* HEINZ KRAFT CO) ★
8000 Horizon Center Blvd, Memphis, TN 38133-5197
Tel (901) 381-6500 *Founded/Ownrshp* 1965
Sales 90.8MM[E] *EMP* 300
SIC 5143 5149 2099 Cheese; Dairy products, dried or canned; Flavourings & fragrances; Food preparations; Cheese; Dairy products, dried or canned; Flavourings & fragrances; Food preparations
Pr: Robert Herron
Ex VP: Mark H Berlind
**VP:* Paul Kenny
VP: Michael Strauch
**VP Sls:* Roger Samson
Snr Mgr: Amy Loomis

KRAFT FOODS
See KRAFT PIZZA CO INC

KRAFT FOODS
See MONDELEZ PUERTO RICO LLC

KRAFT FOODS
See KRAFT FOOD INGREDIENTS CORP

D-U-N-S 03-901-0590 IMP/EXP
■ **KRAFT FOODS GROUP INC**
(*Suby of* HEINZ KRAFT CO) ★
3 Lakes Dr, Northfield, IL 60093-2754
Tel (847) 646-2000 *Founded/Ownrshp* 2015
Sales 14.7MMM[E] *EMP* 22,100
SIC 2022 3411 2095 2043 2035 2087 Processed cheese; Natural cheese; Spreads, cheese; Dips, cheese-based; Sausages & other prepared meats; Bacon, side & sliced: from purchased meat; Frankfurters from purchased meat; Luncheon meat from purchased meat; Coffee roasting (except by wholesale grocers); Freeze-dried coffee; Instant coffee; Cereal breakfast foods; Dressings, salad: raw & cooked (except dry mixes); Powders, drink; Processed cheese; Natural cheese; Spreads, cheese; Dips, cheese-based; Food & beverage containers; Coffee roasting (except by wholesale grocers); Freeze-dried coffee; Instant coffee; Cereal breakfast foods; Dressings, salad: raw & cooked (except dry mixes); Powders, drink
Pr: Anthony W Vernon
COO: Georges El-Zoghbi
**CFO:* James Kehoe
Div VP: Doug Skeoch
Ex VP: Tom Duesler
Ex VP: Terry Faulk
**Ex VP:* Diane Johnson May
**Ex VP:* Kim K W Rucker
Sr VP: Matthew Wohl
VP: Bob Becker
VP: Tim Berman
VP: William Eichar
VP: Jennifer Fox
VP: Carol Kellar
VP: William Kelley
VP: Carlos Ricardo
VP: John Ruff
VP: Gary Seagraves
VP: Kevin Wiley
VP: Luca Zaramell
Board of Directors: James Liu

D-U-N-S 80-571-1723
KRAFT GROUP LLC
1 Patriot Pl, Foxborough, MA 02035-1374
Tel (508) 384-4230 *Founded/Ownrshp* 1995
Sales 811.3MM[E] *EMP* 5,000[E]
SIC 2653 Boxes, corrugated: made from purchased materials; Boxes, corrugated: made from purchased materials
Pr: Jonathan A Kraft
CFO: Michael Quattromani
Ch: Robert Kraft
Genl Mgr: Brian Earley
Counsel: Marie Coukos

D-U-N-S 12-236-5625
KRAFT MOTORCAR CO OF TALLAHASSEE INC
KRAFT MOTORCARS NISSAN VOLVO
3277 Mahan Dr, Tallahassee, FL 32308-5536
Tel (850) 576-6171 *Founded/Ownrshp* 2002
Sales 24.8MM[E] *EMP* 62
SIC 5511 Automobiles, new & used; Automobiles, new & used
Owner: Chris Kraft Sr
**Pr:* Christopher L Kraft Sr
**VP:* Eric V Kraft
Sls Mgr: Blaire Bussey

KRAFT MOTORCARS NISSAN VOLVO
See KRAFT MOTORCAR CO OF TALLAHASSEE INC

D-U-N-S 04-200-9001 EXP
KRAFT PIZZA CO INC (WI)
KRAFT FOODS
(*Suby of* NESTLE USA INC) ★
1 Kraft Ct, Glenview, IL 60025
Tel (847) 646-2000 *Founded/Ownrshp* 1962, 2010
Sales 237.2MM[E] *EMP* 1,500
SIC 2038 Pizza, frozen; Snacks, including onion rings, cheese sticks, etc.; Pizza, frozen; Snacks, including onion rings, cheese sticks, etc.
Pr: David S Johnson
Pr: Peter Boyle
Pr: Barbara M Ford
Ex VP: Rajesh Garg
**VP:* Gregory P Banks
**VP:* Brian T Jansen
**VP:* Randal S Tworek
Ql Cn Mgr: Debra Reyes
Mktg Mgr: Thomas Hafen
Manager: Michele Malo

D-U-N-S 01-922-4120 IMP/EXP
KRAFT POWER CORP
199 Wildwood Ave, Woburn, MA 01801-2024
Tel (781) 938-9100 *Founded/Ownrshp* 1965
Sales 122.9MM[E] *EMP* 160
SIC 5084 7699 Industrial machinery & equipment; Industrial machine parts; Industrial machinery & equipment repair; Industrial machinery & equipment; Industrial machine parts; Industrial machinery & equipment repair
Pr: Owen M Duffy
Exec: Angela Champigny
Exec: Ed Johnson
Exec: Patty Rappa
Genl Mgr: Angela Chamtigny
Genl Mgr: Charlie Myers
Sls Mgr: Derwin Fancher
Sls Mgr: Peter Ingrassia

D-U-N-S 00-411-0250 IMP
KRAFT TOOL CO (MO)
8325 Hedge Lane Ter, Shawnee Mission, KS 66227-3544
Tel (913) 422-4848 *Founded/Ownrshp* 1981
Sales 24.2MM[E] *EMP* 180[E]
SIC 3423 Hand & edge tools; Hand & edge tools
Pr: Ron Meyer
VP: Cal Van Sant
IT Man: Vishal Mody
IT Man: Cal Vansant
Mfg Mgr: Mark Kreutzer
Plnt Mgr: Steve Cook
Plnt Mgr: Orval Engling
Snr Mgr: Ron Teague

D-U-N-S 00-537-5852 IMP
KRAFTUBE INC (MI)
925 E Church Ave, Reed City, MI 49677-9196
Tel (231) 832-5562 *Founded/Ownrshp* 1946, 2003
Sales 41.2MM[E] *EMP* 145
SIC 3498 3585 3469 3398 Tube fabricating (contract bending & shaping); Refrigeration & heating equipment; Metal stampings; Metal heat treating; Tube fabricating (contract bending & shaping); Refrigeration & heating equipment; Metal stampings; Metal heat treating
Pr: John Kinnally
Pgrm Dir: Mark Rose

D-U-N-S 09-479-0300
■ **KRAGIE/NEWELL ADVERTISING INC**
K N INTEGER
(*Suby of* INTEGER GROUP L L C) ★
2633 Fleur Dr, Des Moines, IA 50321-1753
Tel (515) 288-7910 *Founded/Ownrshp* 1998
Sales 32.0MM[E] *EMP* 150
SIC 7311 Advertising agencies; Advertising agencies
Pr: Frank Maher
**CFO:* Michelle Diehl
**Chf Mktg O:* Al Tramontina
Sr VP: Xan McNelly
Creative D: Kent Fieldsend

D-U-N-S 87-895-3454 IMP/EXP
KRAJEWSKI CORP
UNIVERSAL VENEER SALES
1776 Tamarack Rd, Newark, OH 43055-1359
Tel (740) 522-1147 *Founded/Ownrshp* 1993
Sales 20.3MM[E] *EMP* 200
SIC 2411 Veneer logs; Veneer logs
Pr: Klaus Krajewski
COO: Patty Showalter

D-U-N-S 06-778-6046
KRAMARS IRON & METAL INC
K LINE METALS
8821 San Fernando Rd, Sun Valley, CA 91352-1408
Tel (818) 767-4303 *Founded/Ownrshp* 1974
Sales 40.4MM[E] *EMP* 45
SIC 5093 Metal scrap & waste materials; Metal scrap & waste materials
Pr: Ronald Kramar
**VP:* Stewart Kramar
**Prin:* Norman Kramar

D-U-N-S 08-677-9774
KRAMER & LEONARD INC
KRAMER & LEONARD OFFICE PDTS
312 Roberts Rd Ste 1000, Chesterton, IN 46304-1570
Tel (219) 926-1171 *Founded/Ownrshp* 1983
Sales 66.9MM[E] *EMP* 56
SIC 5112 5021 5943 Office supplies; Office furniture; Office forms & supplies
CEO: Mary Leonard Fox
**Pr:* Gregory L Fox
**VP:* Julie C Leonard
Genl Mgr: Mary Pomeroy
Dir IT: Bill Vendramin
Sls&Mrk Ex: Kevin Leonard
Mktg Dir: Jennifer Vittands
Sls Mgr: Scott Kimmel

KRAMER & LEONARD OFFICE PDTS
See KRAMER & LEONARD INC

D-U-N-S 01-106-7543
KRAMER BEVERAGE CO LLC
161 S 2nd Rd, Hammonton, NJ 08037-3336
Tel (609) 704-7000 *Founded/Ownrshp* 1975
Sales 60.5MM[E] *EMP* 140
SIC 5181 Beer & ale; Beer & ale
COO: Jack Grenfell
CFO: Lynn Kramer
Dist Mgr: Keith Armstrong
MIS Mgr: Lauri Gardner
S&M/VP: Gregory Swinicki
Mktg Dir: Layne Ell
Sls Mgr: Scott Clark

D-U-N-S 78-515-0991 IMP
KRAMER ELECTRONICS USA INC
96 Route 173 Ste 1, Hampton, NJ 08827-4033
Tel (908) 735-0018 *Founded/Ownrshp* 1997
Sales 21.8MM[E] *EMP* 50
SIC 5065 Electronic parts
Genl Mgr: David Bright
VP: David Haar
Rgnl Mgr: Tom Conforti
Natl Sales: Cheryl Vurckio
Natl Sales: Cheryl Walton
Mktg Mgr: Jamie Kelleher
Manager: David Goldsmith
Sls Mgr: Nick Warshany

D-U-N-S 07-326-6330
KRAMER LEVIN NAFTALIS & FRANKEL LLP
1177 Ave Of The Americas, New York, NY 10036-2714
Tel (212) 715-9236 *Founded/Ownrshp* 1968
Sales 114.9MM[E] *EMP* 700[E]
SIC 8111 General practice law office; General practice law office
Pt: Paul S Pearlman
VP: Elliott Baldeon
Counsel: Eve Preminger

D-U-N-S 02-384-3097 IMP/EXP
KRAMER TIRE CO INC
572 Central Dr Ste 102, Virginia Beach, VA 23454-5253
Tel (800) 876-6676 *Founded/Ownrshp* 1954
Sales 24.3MM[E] *EMP* 200
SIC 5014 5531 7538 Automobile tires & tubes; Automotive tires; General automotive repair shops
Pr: Ronald Kramer
CFO: Mark Palmer

D-U-N-S 03-038-8672 IMP/EXP
KRAMER-WILSON CO INC
CENTURY NATIONAL
16650 Sherman Way, Van Nuys, CA 91406-3782
Tel (818) 760-0880 *Founded/Ownrshp* 1969
Sales NA *EMP* 670
SIC 6331 Fire, marine & casualty insurance & carriers; Fire, marine & casualty insurance & carriers
CEO: Weldon Wilson
**Pr:* Kevin Wilson
**CFO:* Daniel Sherrin
Sls Dir: Lou Balicki

KRAMES PATIENT EDUCATION
See STAYWELL CO LLC

KRAMM HALTHCARE REHABILITATION
See KRAMM HEALTHCARE CENTER INC

D-U-N-S 04-093-8664
KRAMM HEALTHCARE CENTER INC
KRAMM HALTHCARE REHABILITATION
(*Suby of* KRAMM NRSING HM REHABILITATION) ★
743 Mahoning St, Milton, PA 17847-2232
Tel (570) 742-2681 *Founded/Ownrshp* 1982
Sales 925.4MM[E] *EMP* 330
SIC 8051 Skilled nursing care facilities; Skilled nursing care facilities
Pr: Jeffrey Kramm
**Prin:* Steven Kramm DMD
**Prin:* Randall L Kramm

KRAMM NRSING HM REHABILITATION
See KRAMM NURSING HOME INC

D-U-N-S 08-087-7665
KRAMM NURSING HOME INC (PA)
KRAMM NRSING HM REHABILITATION
(*Suby of* MID-ATLANTIC HEALTH CARE LLC) ★
245 E 8th St, Watsontown, PA 17777-1033
Tel (570) 538-2561 *Founded/Ownrshp* 1968
Sales 925.4MM[E] *EMP* 330
SIC 8051 Skilled nursing care facilities; Skilled nursing care facilities
Pr: Randall D Kramm
**Treas:* Jeffrey S Kramm
**VP:* Janet S Kramm
VP: Steven R Kramm

D-U-N-S 61-857-0162 IMP
KRAMS ENTERPRISES INC
ARDEN-BENHAR MILLS
30400 Telg Rd Ste 200, Bingham Farms, MI 48025
Tel (248) 415-8500 *Founded/Ownrshp* 1986
Sales 194.2MM[E] *EMP* 887
SIC 2392 Household furnishings; Cushions & pillows; Dishcloths, nonwoven textile: made from purchased materials; Towels, fabric & nonwoven: made from purchased materials; Household furnishings; Cushions & pillows; Dishcloths, nonwoven textile: made from purchased materials; Towels, fabric & nonwoven: made from purchased materials
Pr: Bob Sachs
**Pr:* Robert S Sachs
**Sec:* Kenneth Sachs
**Ex VP:* John F Connell
**Ex VP:* Ronald P Zemenak
**VP:* Stephen M Ezer
**VP:* Martha M Sachs
**VP:* William N Sachs
Exec: Julie Nowland
Plnt Mgr: Al Smith

D-U-N-S 16-927-7899 EXP
KRANNICH SOLAR INC
KRANNICH SOLAR USA
75 Twinbridge Dr Ste H, Pennsauken, NJ 08110-4205
Tel (856) 802-0991 *Founded/Ownrshp* 2004
Sales 22.8MM[E] *EMP* 60[E]
SIC 5074 Heating equipment & panels, solar
CEO: Juan Romera-Wade
**CEO:* Mark Loeser
**COO:* Kim Mann
**Prin:* Kurt Krannich

KRANNICH SOLAR USA
See KRANNICH SOLAR INC

D-U-N-S 96-731-2583
KRANOS CORP
SCHUTT SPORTS
710 Industrial Dr, Litchfield, IL 62056-3030
Tel (217) 324-3978 *Founded/Ownrshp* 2010
Sales 37.1MM[E] *EMP* 175[E]
SIC 7389 Athletic equipment inspection service
CEO: Robert Erb
**CFO:* Rollen Jones
Exec: Penny Jones
VP Opers: Andrew Fischer
Sls&Mrk Ex: Glenn Beckmann

KRAPF'S COACHES DIVISION
See KRAPFS COACHES INC

D-U-N-S 18-213-9816
KRAPFS COACHES INC
KRAPF'S COACHES DIVISION
1030 Andrew Dr, West Chester, PA 19380-4291
Tel (610) 594-2664 *Founded/Ownrshp* 1983
Sales 63.2MM[E] *EMP* 317
SIC 4142

D-U-N-S 00-698-6483 IMP
KRASDALE FOODS INC (DE)
65 W Red Oak Ln Ste 2, White Plains, NY 10604-3614
Tel (914) 694-6400 *Founded/Ownrshp* 1907
Sales 1.0MMM[E] *EMP* 530
SIC 5141 Groceries, general line; Groceries, general line
Pr: Charles A Krasne
Treas: Steven Silver
Ex VP: Robert Gewelb
Ex VP: Kenneth Krasne
VP: Michael Chayet
VP: Neil Gewelb
VP: Steven Laskowitz
VP: Catherine Taibi
VP: Dennis Wallin
Genl Mgr: David Quintana
CIO: Simon Barker

KRASNY KAPLAN DIVISION
See FORMTEK INC

D-U-N-S 83-264-7247
▲ KRATON PERFORMANCE POLYMERS INC
15710 John F Kennedy Blvd # 300, Houston, TX 77032-2347
Tel (281) 504-4700 *Founded/Ownrshp* 2003
Sales 1.2MMM *EMP* 1,108[E]
Tkr Sym KRA *Exch* NYS
SIC 2821 Plastics materials & resins; Plastics materials & resins
Pr: Kevin M Fogarty
CFO: Stephen E Tremblay
Chf Cred: Holger R Jung
VP: Thomas A Abrey
VP: Richard Brennan
VP: Garret Davies
VP: Stephen Duffy
VP: Lothar P Freund
VP: Richard Ott
VP: James L Simmons
IT Man: Jerome Davidson
Board of Directors: Anna C Catalano, Steven J Demetriou, Dominique Fournier, John J Gallagher III, Barry J Goldstein, Francis S Kalman, Dan F Smith, Karen A Twitchell

D-U-N-S 82-790-0320 IMP
KRATON POLYMERS LLC
(*Suby of* KRATON POLYMERS GMBH)
15710 John F Kennedy Blvd # 300, Houston, TX 77032-2347
Tel (281) 504-4700 *Founded/Ownrshp* 2000
Sales 191.6MM[E] *EMP* 1,019[E]
SIC 2822 Ethylene-propylene rubbers, EPDM polymers; Ethylene-propylene rubbers, EPDM polymers
Pr: Kevin M Fogarty
Pr: Robert Newman
**COO:* David A Bradley
COO: Mark McKarnin
**CFO:* Stephen E Tremblay
VP: Richard Brennan
VP: William H Davis
**VP:* Stephen W Duffy
VP: Michael Oberkirch
VP: James Simmons
VP Bus Dev: Eli Ben
Board of Directors: Nathan H Wright, Richard C Brown, Kelvin L Davis, Steven J Demetriou, Barry J Goldstein, Michael G Macdougall, Kevin G O'brien, Dan F Smith, Karen A Twitchell, Timothy J Walsh

D-U-N-S 01-833-0279 IMP/EXP
KRATON POLYMERS US LLC
(*Suby of* KRATON POLYMERS LLC) ★
15710 John F Kennedy Blvd # 300, Houston, TX 77032-2347
Tel (281) 504-4700 *Founded/Ownrshp* 1999
Sales 182.2MM[E] *EMP* 520
Accts Kpmg Llp Houston Texas
SIC 2822 Synthetic rubber; Synthetic rubber
CEO: Kevin M Fogarty
Treas: Stan Rice
**Ex VP:* Stephen E Tremblay
**Sr VP:* Lothar P Freund
**Sr VP:* Holger R Jung
**VP:* Melinda S Conley
**VP:* G Scott Lee
VP: Eli B Shoshan

D-U-N-S 78-625-0902
■ KRATOS DEFENSE & ROCKET SUPPORT SERVICES INC
(*Suby of* KRATOS DEFENSE & SECURITY SOLUTIONS INC) ★
4820 Estgate Mall Ste 200, San Diego, CA 92121
Tel (858) 812-7300 *Founded/Ownrshp* 2004
Sales 98.9MM[E] *EMP* 1,607
SIC 8711 Engineering services; Engineering services
Pr: Eric M Demarco
CFO: Gary Accord
**Treas:* Laura L Siegal
VP: Michael W Fink
Board of Directors: William A Hoglund

D-U-N-S 88-445-7813
▲ KRATOS DEFENSE & SECURITY SOLUTIONS INC
4820 Estgate Mall Ste 200, San Diego, CA 92121
Tel (858) 812-7300 *Founded/Ownrshp* 1995
Sales 868.0MM *EMP* 3,800
Tkr Sym KTOS *Exch* NGS
SIC 3761 8711 8744 7382 Guided missiles & space vehicles; Engineering services; Facilities support services; Security systems services; Guided missiles & space vehicles; Engineering services; Facilities support services; Security systems services
Pr: Eric M Demarco
Ch Bd: William Hoglund
Pr: Yonah Adelman
Pr: Gerald Beaman
CFO: Deanna H Lund
Chf Cred: Deborah S Butera
Bd of Dir: John Cavuoti
Bd of Dir: Kratos Intranet
Bd of Dir: Amy Zegart
Ex VP: Richard Selvaggio
Sr VP: Mark Bonatucci
VP: James Bae
VP: Cody Baker
VP: Mike Bennett
VP: Lance Bowers
VP: Jim Burger
VP: Jay Dempsey
VP: Jose Diaz
VP: Richard Duckworth
VP: Dan Dunaway
VP: Charles Farmer
Board of Directors: Scott Anderson, Scot Jarvis, Jane Judd, Samuel Liberatore, Amy Zegart

D-U-N-S 13-578-1164
■ KRATOS PUBLIC SAFETY & SECURITY SOLUTIONS INC
(*Suby of* KRATOS DEFENSE & SECURITY SOLUTIONS INC) ★
4820 Estgate Mall Ste 200, San Diego, CA 92121
Tel (858) 812-7300 *Founded/Ownrshp* 2000
Sales 36.9MM[E] *EMP* 99[E]
SIC 7382 Security systems services
Pr: Eric M Demarco
COO: David Knutson
**CFO:* Deanna H Lund
**Treas:* Laura L Siegal
VP: Carol Clay
VP: Michael W Fink
VP: Benjamin Goodwin
VP: Gregory Meacham
CIO: Gina Aven
Mktg Mgr: James Barbour

D-U-N-S 04-850-5366
■ KRATOS TECHNOLOGY & TRAINING SOLUTIONS INC
(*Suby of* KRATOS DEFENSE & SECURITY SOLUTIONS INC) ★
4820 Estgate Mall Ste 200, San Diego, CA 92121
Tel (858) 812-7300 *Founded/Ownrshp* 1966
Sales 117.8MM[E] *EMP* 441[E]
SIC 7372 Business oriented computer software; Business oriented computer software
Pr: Eric M Demarco
Pr: Kenneth Reagan
CFO: Deanna H Lund
**Treas:* Laura L Siegal
Sr VP: Ben Goodwin
VP: Phil Carrai
VP: Michael W Fink
VP: Vic Wilson
Sftwr Eng: Shanna Sood
Sftwr Eng: Myoki Spencer
Sls&Mrk Ex: Robin Reschke

D-U-N-S 96-268-1107
■ KRATOS UNMANNED SYSTEMS SOLUTIONS INC
(*Suby of* KRATOS DEFENSE & SECURITY SOLUTIONS INC) ★
4820 Estgate Mall Ste 200, San Diego, CA 92121
Tel (858) 812-7300 *Founded/Ownrshp* 2010
Sales 56.8MM[E] *EMP* 500
SIC 6719 Investment holding companies, except banks; Investment holding companies, except banks
Pr: Eric M Demarco
Pr: Thomas Mills
COO: Richard Selvaggio
CFO: Deanna H Lund
**Treas:* Laura L Siegal
VP: Michael W Fink

KRATSA PROPERTIES
See PREMIER HOSPITALITY GROUP

D-U-N-S 61-680-2393
KRATZENBERG & ASSOCIATES INC
KEYSTONE MUNICIPAL COLLECTIONS
546 Wendel Rd Ste 100, Irwin, PA 15642-7539
Tel (724) 978-0300 *Founded/Ownrshp* 1986
Sales 24.3MM[E] *EMP* 170
SIC 7389 Tax collection agency; Tax collection agency
Pr: Thomas J Kratzenberg
**VP:* Rose M Harr
**VP:* David K Kratzenberg
**VP:* Joseph W Lazzaro

D-U-N-S 01-461-0547
KRATZER OIL CO INC
150 East Dr, Sunbury, PA 17801-1014
Tel (570) 286-6731 *Founded/Ownrshp* 1957
Sales 39.5MM *EMP* 23
Accts Robert C Caryl Sunbury Pa
SIC 5541 5983 5171 Filling stations, gasoline; Fuel oil dealers; Petroleum bulk stations; Filling stations, gasoline; Fuel oil dealers; Petroleum bulk stations
Pr: Gary Kratzer

KRAUS ANDERSON INSURANCE
See OSBORNE PROPERTIES LIMITED PARTNERSHIP

KRAUS SORCE
See KRAUS USA INC

D-U-N-S 01-457-8660 IMP
KRAUS USA INC
KRAUS SORCE
160 Amsler Ave, Shippenville, PA 16254-4804
Tel (814) 226-9300 *Founded/Ownrshp* 1959
Sales 66.0MM[E] *EMP* 132
SIC 5023 Carpets; Resilient floor coverings: tile or sheet; Wood flooring; Carpets; Resilient floor coverings: tile or sheet; Wood flooring
Pr: Brad Vollrath
**Ch Bd:* Frank Guthier
**Pr:* Vollrath Brad
**Pr:* Richard Martin
VP: David Mumford
Sls Mgr: Anthony Lala

D-U-N-S 00-482-0171
KRAUS-ANDERSON CONSTRUCTION CO (MN)
K A
(*Suby of* KRAUS-ANDERSON INC) ★
525 S 8th St, Minneapolis, MN 55404-1077
Tel (612) 332-7281 *Founded/Ownrshp* 1958
Sales 92.8MM[E] *EMP* 17[E]
SIC 1541 1542

D-U-N-S 00-696-2104
KRAUS-ANDERSON INC (MN)
523 S 8th St, Minneapolis, MN 55404-1030
Tel (612) 332-7281 *Founded/Ownrshp* 1937
Sales 102.5MM[E] *EMP* 17
SIC 6512 Commercial & industrial building operation
Ch Bd: Bruce Engelsma
**Pr:* Daniel W Engelsma
Ex VP: Phillip Boelter
VP: David Rollins
Dir Risk M: Clay Shelton
Off Mgr: Lori Charlesworth
Off Mgr: Jackie Kokaisel
Dir IT: Thuan Nguyen
Sfty Dirs: Jay Vander Leest
Snr PM: Matt Stringfellow

D-U-N-S 61-532-1911
KRAUSE HOLDINGS INC
6400 Westown Pkwy, West Des Moines, IA 50266-7709
Tel (515) 226-0128 *Founded/Ownrshp* 1991
Sales 379.3MM[E] *EMP* 3,500
SIC 5411 Convenience stores, chain; Convenience stores, chain
Pr: Kyle J Krause
**Treas:* Craig A Bergstrom
**Treas:* Brian J Thompson

D-U-N-S 08-259-6115 IMP/EXP
KRAUSS MAFFEI CORP
(*Suby of* KRAUSSMAFFEI TECHNOLOGIES GMBH)
7095 Industrial Rd, Florence, KY 41042-2930
Tel (859) 283-0200 *Founded/Ownrshp* 2013
Sales 136.1MM[E] *EMP* 147
SIC 5084 3559 Chemical process equipment; Plastic products machinery; Plastics working machinery; Chemical machinery & equipment; Chemical process equipment; Plastic products machinery; Plastics working machinery; Chemical machinery & equipment
CEO: Paul Caprio
**CFO:* Sandy Winter
VP: Volker Kiel
**VP:* Sandra K Winter
Mng Dir: A Sangtani
Area Mgr: Steffen Bauer
Genl Mgr: John-Paul Mead
Genl Mgr: Matt Sieverding
Genl Mgr: Martin Stojkovic
CIO: Jeff Spurlock
Mfg Mgr: Andrew Bittner

D-U-N-S 18-901-3498
KRAUTER & CO LLC
1350 Avenue Of The Americ, New York, NY 10019-4806
Tel (212) 596-3400 *Founded/Ownrshp* 2004
Sales NA *EMP* 50[E]
SIC 6411 Insurance agents, brokers & service
CEO: Neil Krauter
**Pr:* Andre Eichenholtz

D-U-N-S 05-900-7807
■ KRAVCO HOLDINGS INC
KRAVCO SIMON COMPANY
(*Suby of* SIMON PROPERTY GROUP INC) ★
234 Mall Blvd Ste G10, King of Prussia, PA 19406-2940
Tel (317) 636-1600 *Founded/Ownrshp* 1948
Sales 17.0MM[E] *EMP* 300
SIC 6531 8742 6512 Real estate agents & managers; Management consulting services; Shopping center, property operation only; Commercial & industrial building operation; Real estate agents & managers; Management consulting services; Shopping center, property operation only; Commercial & industrial building operation
Pt: Jon R Powell
Pt: Robert C Berkbeck
Pt: Clinton Cochrin
Pt: Lisa F Pliskin
Sr VP: Clinton Cochran
VP: Mary Morrow
Dir Sec: Joseph Ward
Snr Mgr: Lisa Pliskin

KRAVCO SIMON COMPANY
See KRAVCO HOLDINGS INC

D-U-N-S 80-002-8297 IMP
KRAVET FABRICS INC
225 Central Ave S, Bethpage, NY 11714-4990
Tel (516) 293-2000 *Founded/Ownrshp* 2002
Sales 83.0MM[E] *EMP* 500[E]
SIC 2392 Mattress pads; Mattress pads
CEO: Cary Kravet
Telecom Mg: Mike Degroso
Netwrk Mgr: John Pfeiffer
Sfty Mgr: Gina Rivera
Opers Mgr: Elliot Halem

D-U-N-S 00-196-5987 IMP
KRAVET INC
LEE JOFA
225 Cent Ave S, Bethpage, NY 11714
Tel (516) 293-2000 *Founded/Ownrshp* 1917
Sales 454.5MM[E] *EMP* 500
SIC 5131 5198 2392 Upholstery fabrics, woven; Drapery material, woven; Trimmings, apparel; Wallcoverings; Household furnishings; Upholstery fabrics, woven; Drapery material, woven; Trimmings, apparel; Wallcoverings; Household furnishings
Ch Bd: Cary Kravet
**CFO:* Mike Wilbur

KRAYDEN
See K R ANDERSON INC

KRAZY GLUE
See TOAGOSEI AMERICA INC

D-U-N-S 02-669-8576
KRC HOLDINGS INC
11250 State Route 30, Irwin, PA 15642-2022
Tel (724) 863-9000 *Founded/Ownrshp* 1988
Sales 73.8MM[E] *EMP* 580
SIC 6719 Investment holding companies, except banks; Investment holding companies, except banks
CEO: James Ross
Store Mgr: Gary Swartz
Sales Asso: Brian Smoody

D-U-N-S 17-558-2972
KRC INC
5635 Clay Ave Sw, Grand Rapids, MI 49548-5760
Tel (616) 531-1850 *Founded/Ownrshp* 1986
Sales 36.1MM[E] *EMP* 250
SIC 4213 7513 4225 Contract haulers; Refrigerated products transport; Truck leasing, without drivers; General warehousing & storage; Contract haulers; Truck leasing, without drivers; General warehousing & storage
Pr: Douglas De Vries
**VP:* David De Vries

D-U-N-S 19-824-9224
■ KRC MEXICO ACQUISITION CORP
(*Suby of* KIMCO REALTY CORP) ★
3333 New Hyde Park Rd, New Hyde Park, NY 11042-1204
Tel (516) 869-9000 *Founded/Ownrshp* 2005
Sales 37.5MM[E] *EMP* 300[E]
SIC 6798 Real estate investment trusts; Real estate investment trusts
CEO: Milton Cooper

D-U-N-S 08-855-2922 IMP
KRC ROCK INC
700 N Twin Oaks Valley Rd, San Marcos, CA 92069-1714
Tel (760) 744-1036 *Founded/Ownrshp* 1984
Sales 36.3MM[E] *EMP* 50
SIC 5191 5999 Phosphate rock, ground; Rock & stone specimens; Phosphate rock, ground; Rock & stone specimens
Pr: Gerald Sebby
**VP:* Cathy Sebby
Opers Mgr: Tom Coyne

D-U-N-S 79-148-5605
KRD INVESTMENTS INC
DAVE MUNGENAST OF NORTH COUNTY
649 Dunn Rd, Hazelwood, MO 63042-1725
Tel (314) 731-4986 *Founded/Ownrshp* 2006
Sales 30.4MM[E] *EMP* 100
SIC 5511 5531 New & used car dealers; Automotive & home supply stores; New & used car dealers; Automotive & home supply stores
Pr: Dave Mungenast
Sls Mgr: Gary Wright

KRD TRUCKING
See K R DRENTH TRUCKING INC

KRDO-TV CH 13
See PIKES PEAK BROADCASTING CO INC

D-U-N-S 01-428-0622
KREAMER FEED INC
215 Kreamer Ave, Kreamer, PA 17833
Tel (570) 374-8148 *Founded/Ownrshp* 1947
Sales 70.6MM *EMP* 50
Accts Frost Pllc Little Rock Arkan
SIC 2048 Prepared feeds; Prepared feeds
Pr: William D Robinson
**Ch Bd:* George W Robinson
**Sec:* Julie Eriksson
**VP:* Edward G Robinson
VP: Jason Robinson
QA Dir: Jennifer Arbogast
Opers Mgr: Andrew Wagner

D-U-N-S 78-330-0692 IMP
KREG ENTERPRISES INC
KREG TOOL
201 Campus Dr, Huxley, IA 50124-9760
Tel (515) 597-6400 *Founded/Ownrshp* 1989
Sales 29.9MM[E] *EMP* 80[E]
SIC 5251 3545 3546 3423 Tools; Tool holders; Power-driven handtools; Hand & edge tools
Pr: Todd Sommerfeld
COO: Tony Hogan

*Sec: Kathie Sommerfeld
*VP: Craig Sommerfeld
Genl Mgr: Tod Summerfield
Prd Mgr: Jarod Shell
Natl Sales: Brett Demello
Mktg Dir: Matt Oakley
Mktg Mgr: Brad Lilienthal

KREG TOOL
See KREG ENTERPRISES INC

D-U-N-S 93-394-1387
KREGER INC
3520 W Howard Ave, Visalia, CA 93277-4058
Tel (559) 884-2585 Founded/Ownrshp 1989
Sales 6.3MM^E EMP 700
SIC 0761 7361 Farm labor contractors; Labor contractors (employment agency); Farm labor contractors; Labor contractors (employment agency)
Pr: Patrick L Kreger

D-U-N-S 09-236-4702 IMP
KREHER STEEL CO LLC
1550 N 25th Ave, Melrose Park, IL 60160-1801
Tel (708) 345-8180 Founded/Ownrshp 1996
Sales 140.0MM EMP 200
SIC 5051 Bars, metal; Bars, metal
VP: Kim Tremmel
Genl Mgr: John Ayello
Manager: Bob Anderson
Sls Mgr: Bruce Parker

D-U-N-S 05-796-8190
KREHLING INDUSTRIES INC
(Suby of RMC USA INC) ★
1425 Wiggins Pass Rd, Naples, FL 34110-6330
Tel (239) 597-3162 Founded/Ownrshp 1966
Sales 17.4MM^E EMP 400
SIC 3273 3271 Ready-mixed concrete; Blocks, concrete or cinder: standard; Ready-mixed concrete; Blocks, concrete or cinder: standard
Pr: Henry W Krehling
*VP: William Ryan
Counsel: L Ingram

KREIDER DAIRY FARMS
See KREIDER FARMS

D-U-N-S 02-435-4755 EXP
KREIDER FARMS
KREIDER DAIRY FARMS
1461 Lancaster Rd, Manheim, PA 17545-9768
Tel (717) 665-4415 Founded/Ownrshp 1935
Sales 88.2MM^E EMP 450
SIC 0291 General farms, primarily animals; General farms, primarily animals
Pr: Ronald Kreider
*Ch: Noah W Kreider Jr
*VP: Dave Andrews
VP Opers: Tom Beachler
Sls Mgr: Pete Lecompte

D-U-N-S 09-177-6377
KREIDER SERVICES INC
HILLTOP GROUP HOME
500 Anchor Rd, Dixon, IL 61021-8854
Tel (815) 288-6691 Founded/Ownrshp 1952
Sales 18.6MM EMP 280
Accts Cliftonlarsonallen Llp Dixon
SIC 8331 8361 2875 4953 Sheltered workshop; Residential care; Fertilizers, mixing only; Recycling, waste materials; Sheltered workshop; Residential care; Fertilizers, mixing only; Recycling, waste materials
CEO: Arlan L McClain
CFO: Edward Roller
Ex Dir: Arlan L Mc Clain
Genl Mgr: Linda Flock
Off Mgr: Sue Ely
Prd Mgr: Bob Owen
Prd Mgr: Paul Roe
Nrsg Dir: Kathy Baker
Board of Directors: Dr Vernon Brickley, Tom Durband, Joseph Fleming, Dan Moats, Richard Piller, Gerry Stevens, Frank Stransky

D-U-N-S 05-529-9960
KREILKAMP TRUCKING INC
6487 State Road 175, Allenton, WI 53002-9785
Tel (262) 629-5000 Founded/Ownrshp 1969
Sales 71.5MM^E EMP 500
SIC 4213

D-U-N-S 02-437-5602
KREISERS INC
2200 W 46th St, Sioux Falls, SD 57105-6560
Tel (605) 336-1155 Founded/Ownrshp 1956
Sales 45.8MM^E EMP 104
SIC 5047 5049

KREISLER INDUSTRIAL
See KREISLER MANUFACTURING CORP

D-U-N-S 00-131-9003
▲ KREISLER MANUFACTURING CORP
KREISLER INDUSTRIAL
180 Van Riper Ave, Elmwood Park, NJ 07407-2610
Tel (201) 791-0700 Founded/Ownrshp 1968
Sales 50.3MM^E EMP 260
Tkr Sym KRSL Exch OTO
SIC 3728 3724 Aircraft body assemblies & parts; Turbines, aircraft type; Aircraft body assemblies & parts; Turbines, aircraft type
Pr: Michael D Stern
*Pr: Edward A Stern

D-U-N-S 00-642-2406 IMP
■ KREMERS URBAN PHARMACEUTICALS INC
(Suby of LANNETT CO INC) ★
902 Carnegie Ctr Ste 360, Princeton, NJ 08540-6530
Tel (609) 936-5940 Founded/Ownrshp 1904, 2015
Sales 138.2MM^E EMP 350^E
SIC 2834 Tablets, pharmaceutical; Syrups, pharmaceutical; Tablets, pharmaceutical; Syrups, pharmaceutical
Pr: George Stevenson
CFO: Mary Ellen Campion

Treas: Jon Thiel
Chf Cred: Frank Stiefel
VP: Xiu Xiu Cheng
VP: Michael Dornhecker
VP: Susan Witham

KREOFSKY BUILDING SUPPLY
See BRUCE KREOFSKY & SONS INC

D-U-N-S 06-363-8837
KREPE KRAFT INC
KREPE-KRAFT
(Suby of MOD-PAC CORP) ★
1801 Elmwood Ave, Buffalo, NY 14207-2463
Tel (716) 826-7086 Founded/Ownrshp 2014
Sales 25.6MM^E EMP 370
SIC 2754 5947 Commercial printing, gravure; Invitations: gravure printing; Cards, except greeting: gravure printing; Gift, novelty & souvenir shop; Commercial printing, gravure; Invitations: gravure printing; Cards, except greeting: gravure printing; Gift, novelty & souvenir shop
Pr: Daniel Keane
Pr: Leo Eckman
*Treas: John M Yessa
VP: Donna Eckman
Prin: Kevin T Keane
Board of Directors: Kevin Keane

KREPE-KRAFT
See KREPE KRAFT INC

KRESA
See KALAMAZOO REGIONAL EDUCATIONAL SERVICE AGENCY

D-U-N-S 08-393-7086
KRESGE FOUNDATION (MI)
3215 W Big Beaver Rd, Troy, MI 48084-2818
Tel (248) 643-9630 Founded/Ownrshp 1924
Sales 203.7MM EMP 27
SIC 6732 Charitable trust management; Charitable trust management
Pr: John Marshal
Pr: Sharon Zimmerman
Ofcr: Jessica Boehland
Ofcr: Andrew Gatewood
Ofcr: Bryan Hogle
Ofcr: George Jacobsen
Ofcr: Helen Johnson
Ofcr: Christopher Kabel
Ofcr: Fred Karnas
Ofcr: John Nordgren
Ofcr: Christine Robinson
Ofcr: Caroline Smith

D-U-N-S 00-597-0967 IMP/EXP
KRESS CORP
227 W Illinois St, Brimfield, IL 61517-8069
Tel (309) 446-3395 Founded/Ownrshp 1965
Sales 34.1MM^E EMP 160
SIC 3531 Trucks, off-highway; Trucks, off-highway
Pr: Rita S Kress
COO: Willie Hedgespeth
Sfty Dirs: Marty Cantwell
Plnt Mgr: Dan Olmsted
Snr Mgr: Bob Prellwitz

D-U-N-S 09-030-4056 IMP/EXP
KRESS STORES OF PUERTO RICO INC
CLICK
598 Calle A, San Juan, PR 00920-2102
Tel (787) 783-5374 Founded/Ownrshp 1972
Sales 74.4MM^E EMP 2,000
Accts Goas Psc San Juan Puerto Ric
SIC 7389 8741 Purchasing service; Personnel management; Purchasing service; Personnel management
Pr: Mark J Berezdivin
*CFO: Moises Berezdivin
*VP: Jeff Berezdivin
*VP: Vivian Lazoff

D-U-N-S 16-757-8017
KRESTMARK INDUSTRIES LP
3950 Bastille Rd Ste 100, Dallas, TX 75212-5903
Tel (214) 237-5055 Founded/Ownrshp 2004
Sales 107.2MM^E EMP 400
SIC 3442 Window & door frames; Window & door frames
Pr: William E Robinson
*Pt: Joe Fojtasek
CFO: Jim Robinson
VP: Steve Rosenthal
Trfc Mgr: Tom Barnett
Sales Exec: Felix Hicks
Sls&Mrk Ex: Lou Simi
Sls Mgr: Mike Smith

D-U-N-S 10-888-1590 IMP/EXP
KRETEK INTERNATIONAL INC
5449 Endeavour Ct, Moorpark, CA 93021-1712
Tel (805) 531-8888 Founded/Ownrshp 1983
Sales 67.2MM^E EMP 120
SIC 5194 Cigarettes; Smoking tobacco; Cigars; Cigarettes; Smoking tobacco; Cigars
CEO: Hugh R Cassar
*COO: Sean Cassar
*CFO: Donald Gormley
*Sec: Lynn K Cassar
Sr VP: Stan Ching
Dir IT: Scott Cormier
Dir IT: Keith Roos
Software D: Ben Buckner
VP Mktg: Elliot Suied
*VP Sls: Eliot Suied
Mktg Dir: John Geoghegan

D-U-N-S 02-448-7436
KRETSINGER GROUP INC (MO)
1700 E Old State Rt 210, Liberty, MO 64068-8306
Tel (816) 781-9600 Founded/Ownrshp 1997
Sales 32.8MM^E EMP 180^E
SIC 4213 7513 Trucking, except local; Truck rental & leasing, no drivers; Truck leasing, without drivers
Pr: Tom Kretsinger Sr
*VP: Carolyn Kretsinger
*VP: Tim Zeyer
VP Opers: Aaron Thompson

D-U-N-S 00-613-2625
KRETZ LUMBER CO INC
W11143 County Hwy G, Antigo, WI 54409
Tel (715) 623-5410 Founded/Ownrshp 2000
Sales 34.8MM^E EMP 171
SIC 2421 2426 4731 Sawmills & planing mills, general; Kiln drying of lumber; Lumber: rough, sawed or planed; Hardwood dimension & flooring mills; Truck transportation brokers; Sawmills & planing mills, general; Kiln drying of lumber; Lumber: rough, sawed or planed; Hardwood dimension & flooring mills; Truck transportation brokers
Ch Bd: Daniel W Kretz
*Pr: Troy Brown
*VP: Diane Bielen
Genl Mgr: Charley Macintosh
Sales Asso: Mike Peterson

D-U-N-S 10-235-6953 IMP
KREUTER MANUFACTURING CO INC
KMC CONTROLS
19476 Industrial Dr, New Paris, IN 46553-9714
Tel (574) 831-4626 Founded/Ownrshp 1977
Sales 35.6MM^E EMP 200
SIC 3625 Control equipment, electric; Control equipment, electric
Pr: Jon Hilberg
VP: Rowland Bradford
VP: Doug Miller
VP: Scott J Taylor
VP Bus Dev: Richard Fellows
Exec: Jan Baker
Telecom Ex: Drew Cullip
Dir IT: Larry Odegaard
IT Man: Andrew Cullip
IT Man: Chris Kenyon
VP Mfg: Joerg Mueller

KREY DISTRIBUTING CO
See BUSCH DISTRIBUTING CO LLC

D-U-N-S 85-971-4151
KRG CAPITAL PARTNERS LLC
1800 Larimer St Ste 2200, Denver, CO 80202-1417
Tel (303) 390-5001 Founded/Ownrshp 1996
Sales 475.0MM^E EMP 2,059
SIC 6726 8742 6411 Investment offices; Management consulting services; Insurance agents, brokers & service; Investment offices; Management consulting services; Insurance agents, brokers & service
Pr: Daniel E Greenleaf
VP: Piotr Biezychudek
Mng Dir: Christopher Bock
Mng Dir: Jay Coughlon
Mng Dir: Mark King
Off Mgr: McKenzie Tyrrell

D-U-N-S 18-537-7520 IMP
KRG ENTERPRISES INC
9901 Blue Grass Rd, Philadelphia, PA 19114-1013
Tel (215) 708-2811 Founded/Ownrshp 1984
Sales 30.5MM^E EMP 125
SIC 2541 Store & office display cases & fixtures; Store & office display cases & fixtures
Pr: Kevin Gottlieb
*Sec: Stevan P Gottlieb
*VP: Maureen Gottlieb
*VP: Gary Waldman
Plnt Mgr: James Szczurowski

D-U-N-S 13-825-6248
KRG TECHNOLOGIES INC
K R G
25000 Ave Stnford Ste 243, Valencia, CA 91355
Tel (661) 257-9967 Founded/Ownrshp 2007
Sales 35.0MM EMP 400
SIC 7371 8748 Software programming applications; Industrial development planning
Pr: Muthuramalingam Umapathi
*Owner: Hemalatha Rajagopala
*Prin: Balamurugan Subbiah

KRIBS FORD CITY
See SUNTRUP FORD WESTPORT

D-U-N-S 09-534-3612
KRICK PLUMBING & HEATING CO INC
5011 46th Ave, Hyattsville, MD 20781-2357
Tel (301) 927-5284 Founded/Ownrshp 1944
Sales 24.9MM^E EMP 125
SIC 1711 Plumbing contractors; Heating & air conditioning contractors; Plumbing contractors; Heating & air conditioning contractors
CEO: Richard J Grier
Ex VP: Barry Gore
Snr Mgr: Bob Osborne

D-U-N-S 08-425-3855
KRIEG DEVAULT ALEXANDER & CAPEHART LLP
1 Indiana Sq Ste 2800, Indianapolis, IN 46204-2017
Tel (317) 636-4341 Founded/Ownrshp 1932
Sales 24.6MM^E EMP 173
SIC 8111 General practice law office; General practice law office
Mng Pt: Michael Williams
Pt: David E Corbitt
Pt: Jeffrey McDermott
Dir IT: George A Smith
Counsel: Steven M Brown

D-U-N-S 02-226-3446
KRIEGER MOTOR CO
501 W By Pass 61, Muscatine, IA 52761
Tel (563) 263-5432 Founded/Ownrshp 1956
Sales 40.5MM^E EMP 115
SIC 5511

D-U-N-S 00-607-6871 IMP
KRIER FOODS INC
520 Wolf Rd, Random Lake, WI 53075-1280
Tel (920) 994-2469 Founded/Ownrshp 1913
Sales 20.4MM^E EMP 80
SIC 2033 2086 Fruit juices: packaged in cans, jars, etc.; Carbonated beverages, nonalcoholic: bottled & canned
Ch Bd: Bruce Krier

*Treas: Thomas Bretza
QI Cn Mgr: Diane Miller

D-U-N-S 61-992-7221
KRIGER CONSTRUCTION INC
859 Enterprise St, Dickson City, PA 18519-1598
Tel (570) 383-2042 Founded/Ownrshp 1971
Sales 31.0MM^E EMP 115
SIC 1623

D-U-N-S 01-933-8797
KRIKORIAN PREMIERE THEATRE LLC
2275 W 190th St, Torrance, CA 90504-6007
Tel (310) 856-1270 Founded/Ownrshp 1979
Sales 62.3MM^E EMP 300
SIC 1542 1522 1541 6531 Nonresidential construction; Multi-family dwelling construction; Industrial buildings & warehouses; Real estate agents & managers; Nonresidential construction; Multi-family dwelling construction; Industrial buildings & warehouses; Real estate agents & managers
Genl Mgr: Ted Goldbeck
VP Opers: Todd Cummings

D-U-N-S 02-665-1908
KRINGLE CANDLE CO LLC (MA)
220 S St Rt 5, Bernardston, MA 01337
Tel (413) 648-3077 Founded/Ownrshp 2010
Sales 23.2MM^E EMP 49^E
SIC 5199 5999 Candles; Candle shops
CFO: Sara Smiarowski
VP Sls: Meseydi Machado
Mktg Dir: Tim Obrien

D-U-N-S 00-253-2091 IMP
KRINOS FOODS LLC (NY)
4700 Northern Blvd, Long Island City, NY 11101-1017
Tel (718) 729-9000 Founded/Ownrshp 1958, 1985
Sales 51.5MM^E EMP 100^E
SIC 5143 2032 5149 Cheese; Canned specialties; Groceries & related products; Canned goods: fruit, vegetables, seafood, meats, etc.; Condiments; Cheese; Canned specialties; Groceries & related products; Canned goods: fruit, vegetables, seafood, meats, etc.; Condiments
VP: Al Castano
Rgnl Mgr: Lisa Pyros
*Genl Mgr: Charles Vergiris
Genl Mgr: Kyriakos Vergiris
QA Dir: Monika Tyagi
Manager: Dennis Miller
Sls Mgr: Birce Ege

D-U-N-S 03-029-1827
KRIPALU CENTER FOR YOGA & HEALTH INC
57 Interlaken Rd, Stockbridge, MA 01262-9100
Tel (413) 448-3400 Founded/Ownrshp 1967
Sales 35.5MM EMP 400
Accts Alexander Aronson Finning & Co
SIC 7999 Yoga instruction; Yoga instruction
CEO: David Lipsius
*Treas: John Gillespie
Treas: John O'Neill
VP: Wendy Adam
Prd Mgr: Patti McCabe
Pgrm Dir: Denise Barack

D-U-N-S 80-227-1551
KRIPKE ENTERPRISES INC
2351 Hill Ave, Toledo, OH 43607-3608
Tel (419) 539-9133 Founded/Ownrshp 1993
Sales 23.7MM^E EMP 40
SIC 5093 Metal scrap & waste materials
Pr: Matthew Kripe
CEO: Larry Kripke
VP: Marvin Finkelstein
VP: Andy Golding
VP: Chad Kripke

KRIS TV CHANNEL SIX
See GULF COAST BROADCASTING CO

D-U-N-S 09-363-4236
KRIS WAY TRUCK LEASING INC
PACLEASE
43 Hemco Rd Ste 1, South Portland, ME 04106-6295
Tel (207) 799-8593 Founded/Ownrshp 1978
Sales 20.7MM^E EMP 224
SIC 7513 7538 7519 5013 Truck leasing, without drivers; General automotive repair shops; Utility trailer rental; Motor vehicle supplies & new parts; Truck leasing, without drivers; General automotive repair shops; Utility trailer rental; Motor vehicle supplies & new parts
Pr: Tom Keefer
COO: Tracy Grass
*Treas: Evelyn Tonks
*VP: Bob Coale
*VP: Jim Ryan
Exec: CIS Tonks
Brnch Mgr: Mark Thomsen

KRISPY KREME
See WESTWARD DOUGH OPERATING CO LLC

KRISPY KREME
See GLAZING SADDLES LTD

KRISPY KREME
See RION LLC

KRISPY KREME
See SWEET TRADITIONS LLC

KRISPY KREME DONUTS
See GLAZED INVESTMENTS LLC

D-U-N-S 01-265-0750 IMP/EXP
■ KRISPY KREME DOUGHNUT CORP
(Suby of KRISPY KREME DOUGHNUTS INC) ★
259 S Stratford Rd, Winston Salem, NC 27103-1817
Tel (336) 733-3780 Founded/Ownrshp 2000
Sales 12.2MM EMP 3,360
SIC 5461 2051 Doughnuts; Pies; Pastries; Doughnuts, except frozen; Pies, bakery: except frozen; Buns, sweet: except frozen; Doughnuts; Pies; Pastries; Doughnuts, except frozen; Pies, bakery: except frozen; Buns, sweet: except frozen

CEO: Jim Morgan
Ch Bd: James H Morgan
Pr: Darryl R Marsch
Pr: Kenneth A May
Pr: John Tate
Treas: Douglas R Muir
Chf Mktg O: Duane Chambers
Ex VP: J Paul Breitbach
Ex VP: John N Mc Aleer
Sr VP: Randy S Casstevens
Sr VP: L Stephen Hendrix
Sr VP: Robert E L Hodges
Sr VP: Fred W Mitchell
VP: R Michael Cecil
VP: Dwayne Chambers
VP: Timothy Honeycutt
VP: Stanley N Lowry
VP: Philip R S Waugh Jr
Board of Directors: Frank E Guthrie, Joseph A McAleer, Robert L McCoy, Steven D Smith

D-U-N-S 11-638-7510 IMP
▲ KRISPY KREME DOUGHNUTS INC
370 Knollwood St Ste 500, Winston Salem, NC 27103-1865
Tel (336) 725-2981 *Founded/Ownrshp* 1937
Sales 490.3MM *EMP* 5,000
Tkr Sym KKD *Exch* NYS
SIC 5461 5149 6794 2051 Doughnuts; Bakery products; Franchises, selling or licensing; Doughnuts, except frozen; Crullers, except frozen; Doughnuts; Bakery products; Franchises, selling or licensing; Doughnuts, except frozen; Crullers, except frozen
Pr: Anthony N Thompson
Pr: Mucha Nathan
CFO: Price Cooper
Chf Mktg O: G Dwayne Chambers
Ex VP: Lorraine Alexander
Sr VP: Cathleen D Allred
Sr VP: Cynthia A Bay
Sr VP: L Stephen Hendrix
Sr VP: Sherry Luper
Sr VP: Darryl R Marsch
Sr VP: Stan L Parker
Sr VP: Mansour Tavangaran
Sr VP: Philip R S Waugh Jr
VP: Chris Brown
VP: Charles W Bruton
VP: G Chambers
VP: Stephen Graves
VP: Sam Hauser
VP: Fred Mitchell
VP: Nathan Mucha
VP: Nathan Mucher
Board of Directors: Tim E Bentsen, Charles A Blixt, Lynn Crump-Caine, Carl E Lee Jr, C Stephen Lynn, Robert S McCoy Jr, James H Morgan, Andrew J Schindler

KRISS SYSTEMS, SA
See KRISS USA INC

D-U-N-S 15-107-7331
KRISS USA INC
KRISS SYSTEMS, SA
(*Suby of* GAMMA APPLIED VISIONS GROUP HOLDING SA)
912 Corporate Ln, Chesapeake, VA 23320-3641
Tel (757) 821-1089 *Founded/Ownrshp* 2002
Sales 24.0MM^E *EMP* 30
SIC 3484 Small arms; Small arms
CEO: Peter Phing

D-U-N-S 01-677-4762
KRIST OIL CO
QUIK FOOD MARTS
303 Selden Rd, Iron River, MI 49935-1899
Tel (906) 265-6144 *Founded/Ownrshp* 1954
Sales 214.2MM^E *EMP* 535
SIC 5541 5411

KRISTEL DISPLAYS
See KRISTEL LIMITED PARTNERSHIP

D-U-N-S 14-791-9302 IMP
KRISTEL LIMITED PARTNERSHIP
KRISTEL DISPLAYS
555 Kirk Rd, Saint Charles, IL 60174-3406
Tel (630) 443-1290 *Founded/Ownrshp* 1985
Sales 39.7MM^E *EMP* 100
SIC 3575 Cathode ray tube (CRT), computer terminal; Cathode ray tube (CRT), computer terminal
Pt: Chris A Petri
Pt: George Kinney
Pt: Keith Petri
Manager: Thomas Eder
Sls Mgr: Dan Baeten
Sls Mgr: Lou Zarakas

D-U-N-S 06-727-3805 IMP
KRISTEN DISTRIBUTING CO
8301 N State Highway 6, Bryan, TX 77807-7431
Tel (979) 775-6322 *Founded/Ownrshp* 1930
Sales 44.1MM^E *EMP* 70
SIC 5181 5149 2086 Beer & other fermented malt liquors; Soft drinks; Water, pasteurized: packaged in cans, bottles, etc.; Beer & other fermented malt liquors; Soft drinks; Water, pasteurized: packaged in cans, bottles, etc.
Pr: Mark A Kristen
**VP:* Bob Gay
Off Mgr: Ashley Grote
Opers Mgr: Randy Brinkman
Mktg Mgr: Nancy Walker
Sls Mgr: Wes Lambard
Sls Mgr: Robert Vilarreal

D-U-N-S 00-891-0150
KRIZ-DAVIS CO
KD
2400 W 3rd St, Grand Island, NE 68803-5324
Tel (308) 382-2230 *Founded/Ownrshp* 1974
Sales 184.1MM^E *EMP* 217
SIC 5063 Electrical apparatus & equipment; Electrical apparatus & equipment
Pr: Timothy P Berry
**VP:* David Brown
**VP:* Ralph J Knobbe
Brnch Mgr: Steve Chambers

Div Mgr: Scott Belden
Div Mgr: Doug Eggers
Div Mgr: Steve Gwiasda
Div Mgr: Ted Myers
Div Mgr: Josh Phillips
Mktg Mgr: Crystal Rasmussen
Sales Asso: Neal Chromy

D-U-N-S 12-707-1434
KRM INC
KRM RESTAURANT GROUP
5921 Nw Barry Rd Ste 100, Kansas City, MO 64154-2579
Tel (816) 455-9008 *Founded/Ownrshp* 1989
Sales 18.4MM^E *EMP* 400
SIC 5812 Eating places; Eating places
Pr: Tom Norsworthy
**VP:* Michael Norsworty

KRM RESTAURANT GROUP
See KRM INC

D-U-N-S 60-888-6685 IMP
KROEHLER FURNITURE MFG CO INC
1800 Conover Blvd E, Conover, NC 28613-9696
Tel (828) 459-9865 *Founded/Ownrshp* 1969
Sales 78.1MM^E *EMP* 400
SIC 2512 Upholstered household furniture; Upholstered household furniture
Ch Bd: Jay Schottenstein
**CFO:* Ed Cornell
**Treas:* Thomas Ketteler
**VP:* David Sadlowski
Exec: Larry Duncan
Genl Mgr: David Fadlowki
Plnt Mgr: Larry Wright
Ql Cn Mgr: Mitch Howze

D-U-N-S 79-156-4297
KROEKER INC
4627 S Chestnut Ave, Fresno, CA 93725-9238
Tel (559) 237-3764 *Founded/Ownrshp* 1991
Sales 25.0MM *EMP* 120
SIC 1795 1629 4953 Wrecking & demolition work; Land reclamation; Earthmoving contractor; Recycling, waste materials; Wrecking & demolition work; Land reclamation; Earthmoving contractor; Recycling, waste materials
Pr: Joyce Kroeker
**Sec:* Jeff Kroeker
**VP:* Ed Kroeker
**Genl Mgr:* Rodney Ainsworth
Genl Mgr: Kevin Foreman
**Off Mgr:* John Ramirez
Snr Mgr: Craig Chasmar

KROENKE SPORTS & ENTERTAINMENT
See KROENKE SPORTS HOLDINGS LLC

D-U-N-S 07-867-3926
KROENKE SPORTS & ENTERTAINMENT LLC
1000 Chopper Cir, Denver, CO 80204-5805
Tel (303) 405-1100 *Founded/Ownrshp* 1999
Sales 45.4MM^E *EMP* 37^E
SIC 7941 6719 Sports field or stadium operator, promoting sports events; Investment holding companies, except banks
Pr: Jim Martin
**COO:* David Ehrlich
**CFO:* Bruce Glazer
VP: Sean Ream
**Prin:* Stan Kroenke
Prd Mgr: Cameron Marcotte
Sales Asso: David Gaston
Sales Asso: Irene Lahana
Sales Asso: Joe Rimar
Sales Asso: Rebecca Schurwonn
Sales Asso: Samantha Sellmeyer

D-U-N-S 04-178-5028
KROENKE SPORTS HOLDINGS LLC
KROENKE SPORTS & ENTERTAINMENT
1000 Chopper Cir, Denver, CO 80204-5805
Tel (303) 405-1100 *Founded/Ownrshp* 1999
Sales 127.9MM^E *EMP* 835^E
SIC 7941 Sports field or stadium operator, promoting sports events; Sports field or stadium operator, promoting sports events
Exec: Stan Kroenke
Pt: Ryan Brach
Ex VP: Paul Andrews
VP: Steve Govett
VP: Christy Grady
VP: Shawn Stokes
VP: Mark Wagner
Exec: Cheryl Miller
Ex Dir: Dick Brockmeier
Ex Dir: Jerry Girkin
Ex Dir: Glenn Hives

D-U-N-S 00-798-0006
KROESCHELL ENGINEERING CO INC (IL)
(*Suby of* KROESCHELL OPERATIONS INC) ★
3222 N Kennicott Ave, Arlington Heights, IL 60004-1428
Tel (312) 649-7980 *Founded/Ownrshp* 1879
Sales 57.1MM^E *EMP* 300
SIC 1711 Heating & air conditioning contractors; Plumbing contractors; Refrigeration contractor; Heating & air conditioning contractors; Plumbing contractors; Refrigeration contractor
CEO: Edward Swietek
Pr: Rory Gilbert
**VP:* Richard Pruchniak
**VP:* Ken Schuette
Dir Bus: Gary Evans
CIO: Lalani Munir
Netwrk Eng: Jason Smith

D-U-N-S 80-343-5338
KROESCHELL OPERATIONS INC
3222 N Kennicott Ave, Arlington Heights, IL 60004-1428
Tel (309) 966-1284 *Founded/Ownrshp* 1932
Sales 89.4MM^E *EMP* 400
Accts Mueller & Company Llp Elgin
SIC 1711 Heating & air conditioning contractors; Plumbing contractors; Refrigeration contractor; Heating & air conditioning contractors; Plumbing contractors; Refrigeration contractor
Pr: William Chambers
**Ch Bd:* Frank Sutfin Sr
**Treas:* Stephen Maloney
**Treas:* Richard A Pruchniak
**Ex VP:* Pablo Mabbun Jr
**Ex VP:* James Q Whalen
VP: Michael McDonough
**VP:* Edward A Swietek
Dir IT: Jason Smith
IT Man: Tony Bianco
Mktg Dir: Adam Swietek

KROFF CHEMICAL COMPANY
See KROFF INC

D-U-N-S 82-990-9493
KROFF INC
KROFF CHEMICAL COMPANY
1 N Shore Ctr Ste 450, Pittsburgh, PA 15212-5837
Tel (412) 321-9800 *Founded/Ownrshp* 2006
Sales 37.2MM^E *EMP* 75^E
SIC 5169 Chemicals & allied products
Pr: Fred Potthoff
Rgnl Mgr: Jeremy Dehaai
Genl Mgr: Timothy Laube
Genl Mgr: David Schwab
Off Mgr: Cindy Jones
Tech Mgr: Gregg Gailey
Sls Dir: Dave Grottenthaler
Manager: Don Tomovich
Sls Mgr: Robert Hansen

KROGER
See FRED MEYER STORES INC

KROGER
See BAKERS SUPERMARKETS INC

KROGER CENTRAL REGIONAL OFFICE
See THLP CO INC

D-U-N-S 00-699-9528 IMP
▲ KROGER CO
1014 Vine St Ste 1000, Cincinnati, OH 45202-1100
Tel (513) 762-4000 *Founded/Ownrshp* 1883
Sales 108.4MMM *EMP* 400,000
Accts Pricewaterhousecoopers Llp Ci
Tkr Sym KR *Exch* NYS
SIC 5411 5912 5541 5944 Supermarkets, chain; Supermarkets, 66,000-99,000 square feet; Convenience stores, chain; Drug stores; Gasoline service stations; Jewelry stores; Supermarkets, chain; Supermarkets, 66,000-99,000 square feet; Convenience stores, chain; Drug stores; Gasoline service stations; Jewelry stores
CEO: W Rodney McMullen
Pr: Dennis Gibson
Pr: Calvin Kaufman
Pr: Steve McKinney
CFO: J Michael Schlotman
CFO: Mike Schlotman
Ex VP: Mike Donnelly
Ex VP: Chris Hjelm
Ex VP: Christopher T Hjelm
Ex VP: Fred Morganthall
Sr VP: Geoff Covert
Sr VP: Michael J Donnelly
Sr VP: Michael L Ellis
Sr VP: M Marnette Perry
Sr VP: James R Thorne
VP: Elizabeth Oflen
VP: M Elizabeth Van Oflen
VP: Christine S Wheatley
Board of Directors: Ronald L Sargent, Nora A Aufreiter, Bobby S Shackouls, Robert D Beyer, Anne Gates, Susan J Kropf, David B Lewis, Jorge P Montoya, Clyde R Moore, Susan M Phillips, James A Runde

D-U-N-S 12-713-0537
■ KROGER CO
(*Suby of* KROGER CO) ★
2000 Nutter Farms Ln, Delaware, OH 43015-9195
Tel (740) 657-2124 *Founded/Ownrshp* 2003
Sales 71.8MM^E *EMP* 1,000
SIC 5411 Supermarkets, chain; Supermarkets, chain
Pr: Bruce Macaulay

D-U-N-S 03-144-4743
KROGER LIMITED PARTNERSHIP I
J C FOOD STORES
10721 Chapman Hwy, Seymour, TN 37865-4765
Tel (865) 609-1909 *Founded/Ownrshp* 1997
Sales 6.0MM^E *EMP* 383^E
SIC 5411 Supermarkets
Pt: Joseph A Pichler

D-U-N-S 36-143-0114 IMP
■ KROGER LIMITED PARTNERSHIP I
JAYC FOOD STORES
(*Suby of* KROGER CO) ★
1014 Vine St Ste 1000, Cincinnati, OH 45202-1119
Tel (513) 762-4000 *Founded/Ownrshp* 1997
Sales 286.3MM^E *EMP* 1,456
SIC 5411 Grocery stores; Grocery stores
Pt: Carver Johnson
Exec: Kelly Ashley
Dist Mgr: Bob Jones
Dist Mgr: Brian Labarge
Dist Mgr: Vic Watson
Dist Mgr: Nate Wolfe
Dist Mgr: Steve Woods
Corp Couns: Michael Majba

D-U-N-S 78-748-9819
KROGER LIMITED PARTNERSHIP II
KENLAKE FOODS
300 N Lp Miller St, Murray, KY 42071-2594
Tel (270) 762-5100 *Founded/Ownrshp* 1982
Sales 45.3MM^E *EMP* 300
SIC 1541 Food products manufacturing or packing plant construction; Food products manufacturing or packing plant construction
Genl Mgr: Peter Placr
CIO: Lisa Stout
CTO: Lisa Stought
Dir IT: Will Baird

D-U-N-S 00-344-8060
■ KROGER TEXAS LP
AMERICA'S BEVERAGE COMPANY
(*Suby of* KROGER CO) ★
19245 David Memorial Dr, Shenandoah, TX 77385-8778
Tel (713) 507-4800 *Founded/Ownrshp* 1999
Sales 1.3MMM^E *EMP* 2,500
SIC 5141 5411 Groceries, general line; Supermarkets, chain; Groceries, general line; Supermarkets, chain
Pt: Bill Breetz

KROLL ACQUISITION CO
See KROLL HOLDINGS INC

D-U-N-S 01-320-4714
KROLL ASSOCIATES INC
(*Suby of* KROLL ACQUISITION CO) ★
600 3rd Ave Fl 4, New York, NY 10016-1919
Tel (212) 593-1000 *Founded/Ownrshp* 1972
Sales 31.3MM^E *EMP* 320
SIC 8741 Management consulting services; Private investigator; Business management
CEO: James Philip Casey
**Pr:* Rod Bazzani
**CEO:* Emanuele A Conti
**CFO:* Ken Roche
**Ch:* Charlie Gottdiener
S&M/Mgr: Guy Raviv

D-U-N-S 96-126-4496
KROLL BACKGROUND AMERICA INC
SEARCH IS ON, THE
(*Suby of* KROLL INC) ★
100 Centerview Dr Ste 300, Nashville, TN 37214-3455
Tel (615) 320-9800 *Founded/Ownrshp* 1999
Sales 12.0MM^E *EMP* 300
SIC 7381 Private investigator; Private investigator
Pr: A Micheal Rosen
**CFO:* Rick King
VP: Robert Brenner
VP: Tom Hartley Jr
Dir Bus: Polly Archer
**Prin:* Jenifer Deloach
Mng Dir: Ken Mate
CTO: Jerry Black
Sftwr Eng: Craig McQuistion

D-U-N-S 17-416-4798
KROLL FACTUAL DATA LLC
N F R
5200 Hahns Peak Dr # 130, Loveland, CO 80538-8853
Tel (970) 663-5700 *Founded/Ownrshp* 2003
Sales NA *EMP* 400
SIC 7375 Information retrieval services

D-U-N-S 96-890-5141
KROLL HOLDINGS INC
KROLL ACQUISITION CO
(*Suby of* KROLL INC) ★
600 3rd Ave Fl 4, New York, NY 10016-1919
Tel (212) 593-1000 *Founded/Ownrshp* 1993
Sales 31.3MM^E *EMP* 323
SIC 8742 Management consulting services; Management consulting services
Prin: Sharon Rowlands
**Pr:* Sabrina Perel
Treas: Nicholas Carpinello
Dir IT: Gary Graham
Corp Couns: Wayne Hoeberlein
Corp Couns: Richard Sibery

D-U-N-S 10-148-7239
KROLL INC
(*Suby of* CORPORATE RISK HOLDINGS LLC) ★
600 3rd Ave Fl 4, New York, NY 10016-1919
Tel (212) 593-1000 *Founded/Ownrshp* 2010
Sales 638.5MM^E *EMP* 3,098
SIC 7381 8742 8748 7389 Detective services; Private investigator; Industry specialist consultants; Business consulting; Tenant screening service; Detective services; Private investigator; Industry specialist consultants; Business consulting; Tenant screening service
Pr: Dean Hager
Recvr: Chris Hughes
**Ch Bd:* William J Bratton
Pr: Lee Kirschbaum
Pr: Mark R Williams
COO: Brian Lapidus
COO: Gregory Olson
CFO: Donald Buzinkai
CFO: Glenn R King Jr
CFO: Ken Roche
Ofcr: Joseph Buczek
Ofcr: Scott Viebranz
Ex VP: Howard Smith
Sr VP: John Loveland
Sr VP: Tom Parker
VP: Patricia Pizzo
Assoc Dir: Bo Li
Adv Bd Mbr: Nicola Reynolds

D-U-N-S 18-956-0592
KROLL INTERNATIONAL LLC
51360 Danview Tech Ct, Shelby Township, MI 48315
Tel (586) 739-9200 *Founded/Ownrshp* 1985
Sales 22.5MM^E *EMP* 37
SIC 5049 5199 Law enforcement equipment & supplies; Advertising specialties
VP: Dan Sobiechowski
Mktg Dir: Diane Sacra

KROLL ONTRACK
See ONTRACK DATA RECOVERY INC

D-U-N-S 14-758-7240
KROLL ONTRACK INC
(*Suby of* KROLL INC) ★
9023 Columbine Rd, Eden Prairie, MN 55347-4182
Tel (952) 937-5161 *Founded/Ownrshp* 2002
Sales 460.4MM^E *EMP* 1,500
SIC 7374 7372 Data processing & preparation; Application computer software; Data processing & preparation; Application computer software
CEO: Mark R Williams
Pr: Ravi Sathyanna

COO: Lee B Lewis
Bd of Dir: Ben Allen
Sr VP: Craig Carpenter
Sr VP: Don O'Brien
Sr VP: Greg Olson
VP: Brett Amdur
VP: Adrian Briscoe
VP: John M Bujan
VP: Lee Lewis
VP: Pamela Roberts
VP: Josh Zylbershlag
Creative D: Lance Paulson
Board of Directors: John E Pence, Roger D Shober, Robert M White

D-U-N-S 01-262-8996
KRON INTERNATIONAL TRUCKS INC
BLUEGRASS INTERNATIONAL
101 Triport Cir, Georgetown, KY 40324-9619
Tel (502) 863-3271 *Founded/Ownrshp* 2001
Sales 42.0MM *EMP* 40E
SIC 7513 5012 7538 5013 Truck leasing, without drivers; Trucks, commercial; General automotive repair shops; Motor vehicle supplies & new parts; Truck leasing, without drivers; Trucks, commercial; General automotive repair shops; Motor vehicle supplies & new parts
Pr: Michael Roberts
**CFO:* Mark Fussinger
**VP:* John Deters
Mktg Dir: Dean Sorensen
Sls Mgr: Frank Nelson

KRON-TV
See CHRONICLE BROADCASTING CO INC

D-U-N-S 07-666-9241 IMP
KRONE NA INC
(*Suby of* FAHRZEUGWERK BERNARD KRONE GMBH)
3363 Miac Cv, Memphis, TN 38118-3600
Tel (901) 260-9901 *Founded/Ownrshp* 1998
Sales 50.9MME *EMP* 105
SIC 5083 Agricultural machinery & equipment; Farm equipment parts & supplies; Agricultural machinery & equipment; Farm equipment parts & supplies
CEO: Thomas F Jones
**Pr:* Rusty Fowler
**CFO:* Dan Witherspoon
**Ch:* Bernard Krone
Sls Mgr: Kory Vering

D-U-N-S 02-611-5521 IMP
KRONES INC
14950 Hathrow Forest Pkwy, Houston, TX 77032-3847
Tel (281) 423-3300 *Founded/Ownrshp* 2008
Sales 221.8MME *EMP* 7,300
SIC 5169 Chemicals & allied products; Chemicals & allied products
Prin: Lawrence Wigdor

D-U-N-S 04-594-8429 IMP/EXP
KRONES INC
(*Suby of* KRONES AG)
9600 S 58th St, Franklin, WI 53132-9107
Tel (414) 409-4000 *Founded/Ownrshp* 1966
Sales 85.2MME *EMP* 520
Accts Kpmg Llp
SIC 3565 Bottling machinery: filling, capping, labeling; Bottling machinery: filling, capping, labeling
CEO: Holger Beckmann
**COO:* Michael M Wiebe
**Ex VP:* Timothy A Raymond
Ex VP: Timothy Raymond
Sr VP: Claudius Wolf
VP: Kristi Menden
VP: Roland Pokorny
VP: Christian Zimmerer
Mng Dir: Feuring Heiko
Mng Dir: Andrew Wilson
Area Mgr: Peter Resch

D-U-N-S 00-695-0125 IMP
KRONHEIM CO
NATIONAL DISTRIBUTING CO
(*Suby of* NATIONAL DISTRIBUTING CO INC) ★
8201 Stayton Dr, Jessup, MD 20794-9633
Tel (301) 604-6991 *Founded/Ownrshp* 1951, 1997
Sales 31.9MME *EMP* 320
SIC 5182 5181 Liquor; Wine; Beer & other fermented malt liquors; Ale; Liquor; Wine; Beer & other fermented malt liquors; Ale
CEO: Michael Carlos
VP: Jeffreuy Mollerick
VP: Andy Quarm
MIS Dir: Jay Davis
MIS Dir: Warren Newman
Trfc Mgr: Beverly Pleasant

D-U-N-S 92-929-0682 IMP
KRONHEIM CO INC
(*Suby of* NATIONAL DISTRIBUTING CO INC) ★
8201 Stayton Dr, Jessup, MD 20794-9633
Tel (410) 724-3300 *Founded/Ownrshp* 1997
Sales 160.0MM *EMP* 300
SIC 5182 5181 Wine & distilled beverages; Beer & other fermented malt liquors; Wine & distilled beverages; Beer & other fermented malt liquors
Ch Bd: Jay Davis
**Pr:* Pat Vogel

D-U-N-S 01-774-9375
KRONHEIMS FURNITURE INC
8888 Brookpark Rd, Cleveland, OH 44129-6818
Tel (216) 398-4663 *Founded/Ownrshp* 1956, 2004
Sales 26.0MME *EMP* 200
SIC 5712 Furniture stores; Furniture stores
Pr: Gregory Koreness
**Ch:* Eugene Phinick
**Treas:* Nancy Koreness
Board of Directors: Bob Stern

D-U-N-S 80-576-8897
KRONOS ACQUISITION CORP
(*Suby of* KRONOS PARENT CORP) ★
297 Billerica Rd, Chelmsford, MA 01824-4119
Tel (978) 250-9800 *Founded/Ownrshp* 2007
Sales 1.0MMME *EMP* 4,128
SIC 7372 7373 6726 Prepackaged software; Computer integrated systems design; Investment offices; Prepackaged software; Computer integrated systems design; Investment offices
Ch: Mark S AIN
**CEO:* Aron J AIN
**CFO:* Mark Julien

D-U-N-S 08-255-0211
KRONOS FOODS CORP
1 Sexton Dr, Glendale Heights, IL 60139-1965
Tel (773) 847-2250 *Founded/Ownrshp* 1994
Sales 98.1MME *EMP* 350E
SIC 2013 2051 Prepared beef products from purchased beef; Breads, rolls & buns; Prepared beef products from purchased beef; Breads, rolls & buns
Ch Bd: Joel Jacks
**Pr:* Howard Eirinberg
**CEO:* Michael Austin
Sr VP: Pat Costello
Sr VP: Bob Michaels
VP: Michael Brosnan
**VP:* T Costello
VP: Mara Deura
**VP:* George Liggett
VP: Bobby Verros
Rgnl Mgr: Peter Bouloukos

D-U-N-S 09-427-3653 IMP/EXP
KRONOS INC (MA)
EZ CALL
(*Suby of* KRONOS ACQUISITION CORP) ★
297 Billerica Rd, Chelmsford, MA 01824-4119
Tel (978) 250-9800 *Founded/Ownrshp* 1977, 2007
Sales 1.0MMME *EMP* 4,128
SIC 7372 7373 Prepackaged software; Computer integrated systems design; Prepackaged software; Computer integrated systems design
Ch Bd: Mark S AIN
Pr: Kristina Lengyel
CEO: Aron J AIN
COO: Donald Grant
CFO: John Butler
CFO: Mark Julien
Sr VP: Peter C George
Sr VP: James J Kizielewicz
Sr VP: James Kizielewicz
Sr VP: Christopher R Todd
VP: David Almeda
VP: Michael Biery
VP: Peter Broderick
VP: Renee Cacchillo
VP: Doug Clute
VP: Charlie Dewitt
VP: Nobu Hara
VP: Laura L Vaughan

D-U-N-S 96-535-0411
■ **KRONOS INTERNATIONAL INC**
(*Suby of* KRONOS WORLDWIDE INC) ★
5430 L B Johnson Fwy 1700, Dallas, TX 75240
Tel (972) 233-1700 *Founded/Ownrshp* 2004
Sales 1.4MMME *EMP* 51E
Accts Pricewaterhousecoopers Llp Da
SIC 2816 Inorganic pigments
Pr: Steven L Watson

D-U-N-S 07-929-6464
KRONOS PARENT CORP
297 Billerica Rd, Chelmsford, MA 01824-4119
Tel (978) 250-9800 *Founded/Ownrshp* 2007
Sales 1.0MMME *EMP* 4,128
SIC 7372 7373 Prepackaged software; Computer integrated systems design; Prepackaged software; Computer integrated systems design
Pr: Aron J AIN
**Treas:* Mark V Julien
**VP:* Alyce Moore

D-U-N-S 19-328-0336
KRONOS TALENT MANAGEMENT LLC
(*Suby of* EZ CALL) ★
11850 Sw 67th Ave Ste 200, Tigard, OR 97223-8972
Tel (503) 596-3102 *Founded/Ownrshp* 2006
Sales 21.5MME *EMP* 235
SIC 7372 Prepackaged software; Prepackaged software
Pr: Christopher Marsh
CFO: Doug Shafer
Bd of Dir: Jeffrey Pfeffer
VP: Michael Biery
Exec: Debbie Burke
QA Dir: Kari Hohnbaum
Dir IT: Joe Kaeding
IT Man: Vinh Truong
Opers Mgr: Derek Vanderzanden
VP Mktg: Chris Reed
Mktg Mgr: Barry Braddick

D-U-N-S 07-929-6498
KRONOS TECHNOLOGY SYSTEMS LIMITED PARTNERSHIP
(*Suby of* EZ CALL) ★
297 Billerica Rd, Chelmsford, MA 01824-4119
Tel (978) 250-9800 *Founded/Ownrshp* 2002
Sales NA *EMP* 399
SIC 6719 Investment holding companies, except banks; Investment holding companies, except banks
Prin: Anthony Newton

D-U-N-S 60-712-1258 IMP
▲ **KRONOS WORLDWIDE INC**
5430 Lbj Fwy Ste 1700, Dallas, TX 75240-2620
Tel (972) 233-1700 *Founded/Ownrshp* 1989
Sales 1.6MMM *EMP* 2,450E
Tkr Sym KRO *Exch* NYS
SIC 2816 Titanium dioxide, anatase or rutile (pigments); Titanium dioxide, anatase or rutile (pigments)
Pr: Bobby D O'Brien
**Ch Bd:* Steven L Watson
CFO: Gregory M Swalwell
Treas: John A St Wrba
Ex VP: Kelly D Luttmer
Sr VP: Douglas Smellage
Sr VP: Tim C Hafer
VP: A Andrew R Louis
Board of Directors: Keith R Coogan, Loretta J Feehan, Cecil H Moore Jr, Thomas P Stafford, R Gerald Turner, C Kern Wildenthal

D-U-N-S 78-397-2727 IMP
KRONOSPAN LLC
1 Kronospan Way, Eastaboga, AL 36260-5316
Tel (256) 741-8755 *Founded/Ownrshp* 2004
Sales 34.6MME *EMP* 120
SIC 2491 Wood products, creosoted
**CFO:* Timothy Pack

D-U-N-S 00-363-8637 IMP
KRONOTEX USA HOLDINGS INC
(*Suby of* KRONO HOLDING AG)
810 Technology Dr, Barnwell, SC 29812-8635
Tel (803) 224-9150 *Founded/Ownrshp* 1897
Sales 60.0MME *EMP* 95
SIC 5031 2431 Building materials, exterior; Building materials, interior; Floor baseboards, wood; Building materials, exterior; Building materials, interior; Floor baseboards, wood
Pr: George R Kelley
**Pr:* Norman Voss
**CFO:* Robert Dichiara
Genl Mgr: Fred Giuggio
Plnt Mgr: Steve Peskar
Natl Sales: Reid Wood
Mktg Mgr: Jennifer Davis

D-U-N-S 08-496-9950
KRONOZ INTERNACIONAL INC
EVOLUCION LOGISTICA
(*Suby of* EVOLUCION LOGISTICA, S.A. DE C.V.)
411 S 12th St Ste 53, McAllen, TX 78501-4923
Tel (305) 677-9232 *Founded/Ownrshp* 2000
Sales 21.1MME *EMP* 145
SIC 4731 Freight forwarding; Freight forwarding
Pr: Alejandro Lasheras
Treas: Luis Lasheras

D-U-N-S 01-624-0970
KROOT CORP
2915 State St, Columbus, IN 47201-7451
Tel (812) 372-8203 *Founded/Ownrshp* 1890, 1965
Sales 25.9MME *EMP* 50
SIC 5093 5051 3341 Metal scrap & waste materials; Steel; Secondary nonferrous metals
Pr: Josh Kroot
**Treas:* Arthur J Kroot
Off Mgr: Julie Moss
Sales Asso: Tony Moss

KROPP FORGE
See PARK-OHIO FORGED & MACHINED PRODUCTS LLC

D-U-N-S 09-467-9859 IMP
KROY INDUSTRIES INC
522 W 26th St, York, NE 68467-9632
Tel (402) 362-6651 *Founded/Ownrshp* 1998
Sales 34.3MME *EMP* 100
SIC 3353 3082 3523 3444 3312 3084 Aluminum sheet, plate & foil; Unsupported plastics profile shapes; Farm machinery & equipment; Sheet metalwork; Blast furnaces & steel mills; Plastics pipe; Aluminum sheet, plate & foil; Unsupported plastics profile shapes; Farm machinery & equipment; Sheet metalwork; Blast furnaces & steel mills; Plastics pipe
Pr: Kenneth Nordlund
Ex VP: Marvin Gilsdorf
VP: Chelsa Andersen
**VP:* Danny Stanton

D-U-N-S 00-621-7855 IMP
KROY LLC (MN)
(*Suby of* PUBCO CORP) ★
3830 Kelley Ave, Cleveland, OH 44114-4534
Tel (216) 391-6300 *Founded/Ownrshp* 1953, 1998
Sales 48.5MME *EMP* 255
SIC 3579 3993 Mailing, letter handling & addressing machines; Signs, not made in custom sign painting shops; Mailing, letter handling & addressing machines; Signs, not made in custom sign painting shops
**CFO:* Maria Szubski
Dir IT: Johnny Hyde
VP Opers: Elenora Grmek
Plnt Mgr: Robert Overcasher
Natl Sales: Adam McFerran
VP Mktg: Benny Bonanno
Mktg Mgr: Kevin Devers
Sls Mgr: Teri Pistininzi
Sls Mgr: Tom Sakony

D-U-N-S 00-699-8389 IMP
KROY LLC
BUCKEYE BUSINESS PRODUCTS
(*Suby of* PUBCO CORP) ★
3830 Kelley Ave Fl 1b, Cleveland, OH 44114-4534
Tel (216) 881-5300 *Founded/Ownrshp* 1986
Sales 73.3MME *EMP* 125
SIC 2671 3955 2761 Packaging paper & plastics film, coated & laminated; Carbon paper & inked ribbons; Manifold business forms; Packaging paper & plastics film, coated & laminated; Carbon paper & inked ribbons; Manifold business forms
Pt: Stephen Kalette

KRS
See KWAJALEIN RANGE SERVICES LLC

D-U-N-S 01-476-3459
KRS GLOBAL BIOTECHNOLOGY INC
KRS GLOBAL BIOTECHNOLOGY MFG
777 Park Of Commerce Dr, Boca Raton, FL 33487-3621
Tel (888) 242-7996 *Founded/Ownrshp* 2001
Sales 27.2MME *EMP* 40
SIC 5122 Pharmaceuticals
Prin: Roger Costa
**Prin:* William L Brown
**Prin:* Kenneth R Johnson
**Prin:* Ricardo Roscetti

KRS GLOBAL BIOTECHNOLOGY MFG
See KRS GLOBAL BIOTECHNOLOGY INC

D-U-N-S 87-622-6721
KRSM INC
41 40th St, Wheeling, WV 26003-4314
Tel (304) 232-8540 *Founded/Ownrshp* 1994
Sales 48.4MM *EMP* 50
SIC 1761 Roofing, siding & sheet metal work; Roofing, siding & sheet metal work
Pr: John L Kalkreuth

D-U-N-S 06-902-4347
KRUEGER ASSOCIATES INC
NATIONAL FULFILLMENT SERVICES
105 Commerce Dr, Aston, PA 19014-3204
Tel (610) 532-4700 *Founded/Ownrshp* 1968
Sales 33.6MME *EMP* 150
SIC 7374 Computer processing services; Computer processing services
Pr: Eugene C Krueger
**Treas:* John Elliott
**VP:* Barbara H Krueger
Sales Asso: Gwen Blayne

D-U-N-S 00-808-4345 IMP
KRUEGER ENGINEERING & MANUFACTURING CO INC
KEMCO
12001 Hirsch Rd, Houston, TX 77050-4503
Tel (281) 442-2537 *Founded/Ownrshp* 1951
Sales 21.1MM *EMP* 83
SIC 3433 3443

KRUEGER FLORAL-N-GIFTS
See KRUEGER WHOLESALE FLORIST INC

D-U-N-S 03-267-2651 IMP
KRUEGER INTERNATIONAL INC
KI
1330 Bellevue St, Green Bay, WI 54302-2197
Tel (920) 468-8100 *Founded/Ownrshp* 1986
Sales 739.3MME *EMP* 2,300
Accts Baker Tilly Virchow Krause Ll
SIC 2531 School furniture; School furniture
CEO: Richard J Resch
**Pr:* Brian Krenke
COO: Mike Hogan
**CFO:* Kelly Andersen
**VP:* Dean Lindsley
VP: Dan Schiltz
Prgrm Mgr: Brian Kontny
Dist Mgr: John Shearer
Off Mgr: Candyce Mros
Dir IT: Tim Lasecki
Sys Mgr: John Bartelt

D-U-N-S 02-687-6524 IMP
KRUEGER SERVICES INC
MAXWELL, DON CHEVROLET
725 S Interstate 35, New Braunfels, TX 78130-4836
Tel (830) 606-3451 *Founded/Ownrshp* 1988
Sales 21.1MME *EMP* 42
SIC 5511 Automobiles, new & used; Trucks, tractors & trailers: new & used
Pr: Valerie Maxwell
Sls Mgr: John David Lewien

D-U-N-S 00-906-7307
KRUEGER SHEET METAL CO (WA)
731 N Superior St, Spokane, WA 99202-2014
Tel (509) 489-0221 *Founded/Ownrshp* 1948, 1986
Sales 20.6MM *EMP* 80E
Accts Schoedel & Schoedel Cpas Pll
SIC 1761 3444 Roofing contractor; Sheet metalwork; Sheet metalwork; Roofing contractor; Sheet metalwork; Sheet metalwork
Pr: Thomas H Brandt
**CFO:* Tony Teeters
**VP:* Alexander E Brandt
**VP:* Robert A Starkey

D-U-N-S 04-314-3270
KRUEGER WHOLESALE FLORIST INC (WI)
KRUEGER FLORAL-N-GIFTS
10706 Tesch Ln, Rothschild, WI 54474-7913
Tel (715) 359-7202 *Founded/Ownrshp* 1963
Sales 59.2MME *EMP* 185
Accts Wipfli Llp
SIC 5193 5992 Florists' supplies; Flowers, fresh; Nursery stock; Flowers, fresh; Florists' supplies; Flowers, fresh; Nursery stock; Flowers, fresh
Pr: James W Krueger
**CFO:* Gary Ruplinger
CFO: Floyd Sliwicki
**VP:* Kevin Krueger

D-U-N-S 00-920-9479 EXP
KRUGER FOODS INC
18362 E Highway 4, Stockton, CA 95215-9433
Tel (209) 941-8518 *Founded/Ownrshp* 1930
Sales 52.4MME *EMP* 155
SIC 2035 Pickles, vinegar; Vegetables, pickled; Pickles, vinegar; Vegetables, pickled
CEO: Kara Kruger
**COO:* Leslie Kruger
Ex VP: Dennis Kruger
Genl Mgr: Bob Chelli
**VP Opers:* Eric Kruger
Opers Mgr: Leah Edge
Plnt Mgr: Gary Brachtenbach

D-U-N-S 07-061-9820
KRUGER LTD
1513 Absco Dr, Longs, SC 29568-8815
Tel (843) 399-2165 *Founded/Ownrshp* 2004
Sales 102.0MM *EMP* 6
SIC 5199 Gifts & novelties; Gifts & novelties
Pr: Joe Kruger
**Owner:* Richard Kruger
**Sec:* Joanne Kruger

D-U-N-S 60-255-7022 IMP/EXP
KRUSE FAMILY ENTERPRISES LLC
WYNCO
324 Main St, Iowa Falls, IA 50126-2207
Tel (641) 648-2529 *Founded/Ownrshp* 2005
Sales 57.0MME *EMP* 370

SIC 5191 5122 5047 Insecticides; Pesticides; Feed; Proprietary (patent) medicines; Biologicals & allied products; Animal medicines; Veterinarians' equipment & supplies; Insecticides; Pesticides; Feed; Proprietary (patent) medicines; Biologicals & allied products; Animal medicines; Veterinarians' equipment & supplies
Pr: Thomas J Kruse
**VP:* Thomas Dougan
**VP:* Duane C Schamerloh

D-U-N-S 00-986-8142
KRUSE INVESTMENT CO INC
31120 W St, Goshen, CA 93227
Tel (559) 302-1000 *Founded/Ownrshp* 1936
Sales 570.0MM^E *EMP* 312
SIC 6799

D-U-N-S 95-755-8443
KRUSH COMMUNICATIONS LLC
1511 N West Shore Blvd # 750, Tampa, FL 33607-4563
Tel (813) 662-5975 *Founded/Ownrshp* 2013
Sales 24.0MM *EMP* 41
SIC 4813 Telephone communication, except radio; Telephone communication, except radio
CFO: Brian Rudolph
Chf Mktg O: Richard Estrada
CTO: Ben Benner

D-U-N-S 05-289-9408 IMP
KRYGER GLASS CO (MO)
1221 Harrison St, Kansas City, MO 64106-3195
Tel (816) 471-6944 *Founded/Ownrshp* 1972
Sales 44.3MM^E *EMP* 150
SIC 5013 7536 Automobile glass; Automotive glass replacement shops; Automobile glass; Automotive glass replacement shops
Prin: Bill Kryger Jr
**Ch:* Wm Kryger Sr
**Co-Pr:* Norma Kryger
**Co-Pr:* W M Kryger Jr
**VP:* Kyle Kryger

KRYPTIQ CORPORATION
See ENLI HEALTH INTELLIGENCE

D-U-N-S 61-415-1814 IMP/EXP
KRYPTON SOLUTIONS LLC
3060 Summit Ave, Plano, TX 75074-7200
Tel (972) 424-3880 *Founded/Ownrshp* 2005
Sales 20.0MM *EMP* 127
SIC 3672 Printed circuit boards; Printed circuit boards
Pr: Surendra Patel

D-U-N-S 17-213-2185
KRYSILIS INC
DEVELOPMENTAL RESOURCES
102 W Park St, Forest City, IA 50436-2132
Tel (641) 585-5450 *Founded/Ownrshp* 1971
Sales 8.2MM^E *EMP* 442
Accts Dk Arndt Pc Forest City I
SIC 8211 School for the retarded; School for physically handicapped; School for the retarded; School for physically handicapped
Ex Dir: Brent Aberg
CFO: Michelle Smith

D-U-N-S 00-792-0804
KRYSTAL CO (TN)
KRYSTAL RESTAURANT
(*Suby of* ARGONNE CAPITAL GROUP LLC) ★
1455 Lincoln Pkwy E # 600, Dunwoody, GA 30346-2200
Tel (423) 757-1550 *Founded/Ownrshp* 1932, 2012
Sales 321.8MM^E *EMP* 7,056
SIC 5812 6794 American restaurant; Franchises, selling or licensing; American restaurant; Franchises, selling or licensing
CEO: James F Exum Jr
**CFO:* James W Bear
**CFO:* Carl Jakaitis
**Chf Mktg O:* Jason Abelkop
**Ofcr:* Tom Murrill
**Sr VP:* Michael C Bass
VP: Gordon L Davenport Jr
VP: Misty Didal
VP: Scott Gallagher
VP: Glen R Griffiths
VP: Chris Kermode
VP: Kathy Pittman

D-U-N-S 16-601-7470
KRYSTAL LOGISTICS USA INC
HAFEN USA
11600 Nw 91st St Unit 11, Medley, FL 33178-2831
Tel (305) 887-5000 *Founded/Ownrshp* 2004
Sales 60.0MM *EMP* 40
SIC 4731 Freight transportation arrangement
Pr: Andres Valdano

KRYSTAL RESTAURANT
See KRYSTAL CO

KS
See KULITE SEMICONDUCTOR PRODUCTS INC

D-U-N-S 17-221-9458
KS ENERGY SERVICES LLC
19705 W Lincoln Ave, New Berlin, WI 53146-1720
Tel (262) 574-5100 *Founded/Ownrshp* 2004
Sales 163.1MM^E *EMP* 300
SIC 1623 Gas main construction; Gas main construction
Pr: Dennis Klumb Jr
**Treas:* Shawn Klumb
**VP:* Michael Klumb Sr
**VP:* Tom Schaitel Sr
Area Mgr: Zak Schwartz

KS FABRICATION & MACHINE
See K S FABRICATION & MACHINE INC

D-U-N-S 15-471-0680
KS INDUSTRIES LP
K S I
6205 District Blvd, Bakersfield, CA 93313-2141
Tel (661) 617-1700 *Founded/Ownrshp* 2002
Sales 250.8MM^E *EMP* 2,500
SIC 1623 Water, sewer & utility lines; Water, sewer & utility lines
CEO: Kevin Small
Sr VP: Mark Payton
VP: Doug Erickson
VP: Mike Lackey
Off Mgr: Donna Diaz
DP Exec: Bret Kingsbury
VP Opers: Allen Vaughn
Sfty Mgr: Robert Mahan
Opers Mgr: Brian Henderson
Sls&Mrk Ex: Jim Dmohowski
Snr PM: David Aguirre

D-U-N-S 61-843-3064 IMP
KS KOLBENSCHMIDT US INC
(*Suby of* KSPG HOLDING USA INC) ★
1731 Industrial Pkwy N, Marinette, WI 54143-3704
Tel (715) 732-0181 *Founded/Ownrshp* 1992
Sales 147.2MM^E *EMP* 870
SIC 3592 Pistons & piston rings; Pistons & piston rings
Pr: Donald L Cameron
VP: Don Cameron
VP: Mark Lennart
**VP:* Robert W Steffens
VP: Robert Steffers
**VP:* Robert G Turcott
VP Opers: Richard Cole
Sfty Mgr: Debbie Vandercook
Opers Mgr: Jim Weidman
Plnt Mgr: Mark Greenlund
Ql Cn Mgr: Kelly Coan

D-U-N-S 06-185-4456
KS MANAGEMENT SERVICES LLC (TX)
(*Suby of* KELSEY-SEYBOLD CLINIC) ★
8900 Lakes At 610 Dr, Houston, TX 77054-2525
Tel (713) 442-0000 *Founded/Ownrshp* 1949
Sales NA *EMP* 2,400
SIC 8741 Management services; Management services
CFO: John Sperry
VP: Mike Fitzgerald
VP Mktg: Phil Price
Doctor: Nancy Byrd
Snr Mgr: Carol Bible

D-U-N-S 00-399-1592 IMP
KS MARKETING INC
632 E Sandhill Ct, Lehi, UT 84043-5931
Tel (801) 768-4125 *Founded/Ownrshp* 2007
Sales 30.0MM^E *EMP* 25
SIC 2782 5942 5192 Scrapbooks; Book stores; Books, periodicals & newspapers; Scrapbooks; Book stores; Books, periodicals & newspapers
Pr: Kory Alan Boyd
**VP:* Randall Hild

D-U-N-S 80-840-8319
KS&T INTERNATIONAL HOLDINGS LP
KOCH SUPPLY & TRADING
(*Suby of* KOCH RESOURCES LLC) ★
4111 E 37th St N, Wichita, KS 67220-3203
Tel (316) 828-5500 *Founded/Ownrshp* 2002
Sales 119.5MM^E *EMP* 366^E
SIC 2911 Petroleum refining

D-U-N-S 09-240-5091
KSA ENGINEERS INC
WISENBAKER FIX
140 E Tyler St Ste 600, Longview, TX 75601-7256
Tel (903) 236-7700 *Founded/Ownrshp* 1978
Sales 22.2MM *EMP* 149
SIC 8711 Civil engineering; Mechanical engineering; Electrical or electronic engineering; Consulting engineer; Civil engineering; Mechanical engineering; Electrical or electronic engineering; Consulting engineer
Pr: Joncie Young
VP: Lanny Buck
**VP:* Mitchell Fortner
**VP:* Walter F Hicks
**VP:* Robert L Thurber
Div Mgr: Bob Fisher
Div Mgr: Scott Hoelzle
Div Mgr: Philip Huseman
Div Mgr: Clayton Scales
Sls&Mrk Ex: Jennifer Cox
Snr PM: Christopher Aylor

D-U-N-S 00-793-0795
KSA INDUSTRIES INC
4400 Post Oak Pkwy # 2800, Houston, TX 77027-3421
Tel (713) 881-3400 *Founded/Ownrshp* 1947
Sales 72.7MM^E *EMP* 587
SIC 7941 1311 0211 5511 6799 Football club; Crude petroleum production; Natural gas production; Beef cattle feedlots; New & used car dealers; Investors; Football club; Crude petroleum production; Natural gas production; Beef cattle feedlots; New & used car dealers; Investors
Pr: Thomas S Smith
**Pr:* Kenneth S Adams Jr
**CFO:* Ric Adchire
**VP:* W R Scofield

D-U-N-S 55-718-6723
KSA INFORMATION TECHNOLOGIES INC
(*Suby of* HEALTH CARE MGT COUNSELORS) ★
1355 Peachtree St Ne # 900, Atlanta, GA 30309-3212
Tel (404) 892-0321 *Founded/Ownrshp* 1990
Sales 11.6MM^E *EMP* 300
SIC 8711 8742 Engineering services; Retail trade consultant; Engineering services; Retail trade consultant
Pr: Bill Page
Snr Mgr: Bill Beckemeyer

D-U-N-S 61-700-4283
KSARIA CORP
300 Griffin Brook Dr, Methuen, MA 01844-1873
Tel (978) 933-0000 *Founded/Ownrshp* 2000
Sales 32.9MM^E *EMP* 95
SIC 3679 3678 Harness assemblies for electronic use: wire or cable; Electronic connectors
CEO: Sebastian J Sicari
**Treas:* Michael A Dipoto
**VP:* Anthony J Christopher
Ql Cn Mgr: Bruce Belanger
Sls Mgr: Blair Worth

D-U-N-S 80-186-9843 IMP/EXP
KSB AMERICA CORP
(*Suby of* PAB PUMPEN- UND ARMATUREN- BETEILIGUNGSGESELLSCHAFT MIT BESCHRANKTER HAFTUNG)
4415 Sarellen Rd, Richmond, VA 23231-4428
Tel (804) 222-1818 *Founded/Ownrshp* 2006
Sales 188.5MM^E *EMP* 508
Accts Ernst & Young Llp
SIC 3561 3559 3494 3625 5084 7699 Industrial pumps & parts; Foundry machinery & equipment; Valves & pipe fittings; Actuators, industrial; Pumps & pumping equipment; Pumps & pumping equipment repair; Industrial pumps & parts; Foundry machinery & equipment; Valves & pipe fittings; Actuators, industrial; Pumps & pumping equipment; Pumps & pumping equipment repair
**Sec:* Karen M Wood
Prin: William A Leech

KSB HOSPITAL
See KATHERINE SHAW BETHEA HOSPITAL

D-U-N-S 07-577-7615 IMP/EXP
KSB INC
(*Suby of* KSB AMERICA CORP) ★
4415 Sarellen Rd, Richmond, VA 23231-4428
Tel (804) 222-1818 *Founded/Ownrshp* 1992
Sales 55.6MM^E *EMP* 82
Accts Keiter Glen Allen Georgia V
SIC 5074 3621 Plumbing & hydronic heating supplies; Motors & generators; Plumbing & hydronic heating supplies; Motors & generators
Mng Dir: Michael Blundell
Ch Bd: Klans Barmann
Pr: Lewis E Harvie
Mng Dir: Andy Ratcliffe
Rgnl Mgr: David Crossley
Rgnl Mgr: Jim Hendery
Manager: John Krepper

D-U-N-S 02-514-1560
KSC & SON CORP
52138 Harrison St, Coachella, CA 92236-2851
Tel (760) 398-6028 *Founded/Ownrshp* 1995
Sales 31.3MM *EMP* 100
SIC 5541 5411 Filling stations, gasoline; Convenience stores; Filling stations, gasoline; Convenience stores
Pr: Nachattar S Chandi
**CFO:* Susana Chandi

KSFCU
See KERN SCHOOLS FEDERAL CREDIT UNION

D-U-N-S 09-880-5252 IMP
KSG DISTRIBUTING INC
1121 Flint Meadow Dr, Kaysville, UT 84037-9564
Tel (801) 771-4053 *Founded/Ownrshp* 1979
Sales 42.8MM^E *EMP* 70
SIC 5099 5192 Video cassettes, accessories & supplies; Phonograph records; Tapes & cassettes, prerecorded; Compact discs; Books
Pr: Don Paddock
**Sec:* Kevin Yates
Dir Bus: Patrick Viets
Manager: Brian Nixon
Manager: Tina Ward

KSI CARTRIDGE SERVICE
See KENT-SUSSEX INDUSTRIES INC

D-U-N-S 04-961-0764
KSI CONVEYOR INC
2345 U Rd, Sabetha, KS 66534-2591
Tel (785) 284-0600 *Founded/Ownrshp* 2001
Sales 34.0MM^E *EMP* 115
SIC 3523 Farm machinery & equipment; Farm machinery & equipment
Pr: Paul Kaeb
**COO:* Harvey Kaeb
**CFO:* Neal Kellenberger
**VP:* Hartzell Kaeb

KSI MANAGEMENT ALEXANDRIA CI
See KETTLER MANAGEMENT INC

D-U-N-S 11-286-1315 IMP
KSI TRADING CORP
CRS AUTOMOTIVE COOLING PDTS
100a Wade Ave, South Plainfield, NJ 07080-1311
Tel (908) 754-7154 *Founded/Ownrshp* 1987
Sales 100.0MM *EMP* 103
SIC 5013 Automotive supplies & parts; Automotive supplies & parts
Pr: Wayne Jan
Opers Mgr: Patrick Lai

D-U-N-S 79-923-8977
KSK PROPERTY MANAGEMENT INC
1 Daniel Burnham Ct 205c, San Francisco, CA 94109-5472
Tel (415) 776-7575 *Founded/Ownrshp* 1991
Sales 13.2MM^E *EMP* 300
SIC 6512 Nonresidential building operators; Nonresidential building operators
Pr: Kun Sam Kim

D-U-N-S 78-932-7947
KSL ARIZONA HOLDINGS III INC
ARIZONA BILTMORE RESORT & SPA
2400 E Missouri Ave, Phoenix, AZ 85016-3106
Tel (602) 955-6600 *Founded/Ownrshp* 2000
Sales 13.0MM^E *EMP* 1,150
SIC 7011 5812 7991 5813 Resort hotel; Eating places; Spas; Drinking places; Resort hotel; Eating places; Spas; Drinking places
Pr: Scott M Dalecio

D-U-N-S 78-883-1233
KSL CAPITAL PARTNERS LLC
100 Fillmore St Ste 600, Denver, CO 80206-4931
Tel (720) 284-6400 *Founded/Ownrshp* 2005
Sales 255.6MM^E *EMP* 1,035
SIC 6799 Investors; Investors
Ofcr: Kevin Rohnstock
VP: John Ege
VP: Bryan O'Shields
Mng Dir: Michael Shannon
VP Sls: Michael E Rickson
Sls Mgr: Nicole German
Sls Mgr: Jana Thompson

D-U-N-S 05-805-1160
KSL MEDIA INC
15910 Ventura Blvd # 900, Encino, CA 91436-2809
Tel (212) 468-3395 *Founded/Ownrshp* 2003
Sales 406.6MM^E *EMP* 130
SIC 7319 Media buying service
Ch Bd: Kalman Liebowitz
**Pr:* Hank Cohen
**CFO:* Russell Meisels
Sr VP: Tyler Liebowitz
VP: Christina Selberis
Mng Dir: Fran McCreary

D-U-N-S 78-700-2521
KSL RANCHO MIRAGE OPERATING CO INC
RANCHO LAS PALMAS RESORT & SPA
41000 Bob Hope Dr, Rancho Mirage, CA 92270-4416
Tel (760) 568-2727 *Founded/Ownrshp* 2006
Sales NA *EMP* 500
SIC 7011 Hotels & motels

D-U-N-S 00-527-9109
KSL RECREATION MANAGEMENT OPERATIONS LLC (DE)
50905 Avenida Bermudas, La Quinta, CA 92253-8910
Tel (760) 564-8000 *Founded/Ownrshp* 2003
Sales NA *EMP* 8,000
SIC 7992 7011

D-U-N-S 94-974-4411
KSL-TV
(*Suby of* BONNEVILLE INTERNATIONAL CORP) ★
55 N 300 W, Salt Lake City, UT 84101-3502
Tel (801) 575-5555 *Founded/Ownrshp* 2000
Sales 15.4MM^E *EMP* 312
SIC 4833 7622 Television broadcasting stations; Television repair shop; Television broadcasting stations; Television repair shop
Pr: Greg James
Sr Cor Off: Candice Madsen
Ex Dir: Shawn Oneil
Dir IT: Huntsman Don
IT Man: Ed Tyler
Sales Exec: Derek Glade
Sls Mgr: Jason Glade
Art Dir: Laura Ellington

D-U-N-S 07-276-5386 IMP
■ **KSLP LIQUIDATION LP**
(*Suby of* HEIL CO) ★
1505 W Main St, Gatesville, TX 76528-1024
Tel (254) 865-7235 *Founded/Ownrshp* 2000
Sales 41.0MM^E *EMP* 100
SIC 3715 Truck trailers; Truck trailers
Mng Pt: Gary Marino
VP: Wesley Chandler
Mng Dir: Ryan Rockafellow
CTO: Lynn Gohlke
Natl Sales: Robert Voss
VP Sls: Lewis Smith
Mktg Mgr: Karl Stabenow
Manager: Jim Lindsey

KSM BUSINESS SERVICES
See KATZ SAPPER & MILLER LLP

D-U-N-S 78-476-2150
KSM CORP
(*Suby of* KSM COMPONENT CO., LTD.)
1959 Concourse Dr, San Jose, CA 95131-1708
Tel (408) 514-2400 *Founded/Ownrshp* 2003
Sales 100.0MM *EMP* 500
SIC 3674 Semiconductors & related devices
CEO: Jooswan Kim
**Pr:* Harvinder P Singh

D-U-N-S 07-987-2560 IMP
KSM ELECTRONICS INC
5607 Hiatus Rd Ste 600, Tamarac, FL 33321-6409
Tel (954) 642-7050 *Founded/Ownrshp* 1975
Sales 68.6MM^E *EMP* 325
SIC 3679 Harness assemblies for electronic use: wire or cable; Harness assemblies for electronic use: wire or cable
Pr: Stephen Benjamin
CFO: Oscar Lopez
VP: Leonard Partyka
Genl Mgr: Red Yang
Off Mgr: Linda Walberer
Mtls Mgr: Vincent Calabria
Ql Cn Mgr: Fritz Adonis
Sales Asso: Ricardo Martinez

K.S.P. COMPANY
See KSP ENTERPRISE INC

D-U-N-S 00-790-6419 IMP/EXP
KSP ENTERPRISE INC
K.S.P. COMPANY
2095 Christie St, Fullerton, CA 92833-5098
Tel (714) 336-8352 *Founded/Ownrshp* 2009
Sales 26.0MM *EMP* 3
SIC 5159 Peanuts (bulk), unroasted; Peanuts (bulk), unroasted
Pr: Brian Chong

D-U-N-S 62-198-1059 IMP
KSPG HOLDING USA INC
(*Suby of* RHEINMETALL AG)
1731 Indl Pkwy, Marinette, WI 54143
Tel (715) 732-0181 *Founded/Ownrshp* 2005
Sales 242.1MM^E *EMP* 1,800
SIC 3592 3714 6719 Pistons & piston rings; Bearings, motor vehicle; Investment holding companies, except banks; Pistons & piston rings; Bearings, motor vehicle; Investment holding companies, except banks
Pr: Dr Peter Merten
**Ex VP:* Richard A Posz
**VP:* Robert G Turcott

Board of Directors: Dr Joerg-Martin Friedrich

D-U-N-S 96-890-7621 IMP
KSPG NORTH AMERICA INC
1731 Industrial Pkwy N, Marinette, WI 54143-3704
Tel (715) 732-0181 Founded/Ownrshp 2011
Sales 43.8MM^E EMP 1,000^E
SIC 3592 Pistons & piston rings; Pistons & piston rings
CEO: Don Cameron
*CFO: Rick Posz

D-U-N-S 12-087-1108
KST DATA INC
3699 Wilshire Blvd # 680, Los Angeles, CA 90010-2740
Tel (213) 384-9555 Founded/Ownrshp 1990
Sales 22.3MM^E EMP 52
SIC 7371 7378 Computer software development & applications; Computer maintenance & repair
Pr: Torres Tansobing
*VP: Mark Edson
Genl Mgr: Eugene Jacobowitz
Tech Mgr: Dean Baroni
Sls Mgr: Lou Szed
Sales Asso: David Oropeza
Snr Mgr: Armando Tan

D-U-N-S 78-051-1668
KST ELECTRIC LTD
(Suby of ROSENDIN ELECTRIC INC) ★
14215 Suncrest Rd, Manor, TX 78653-3899
Tel (512) 278-8435 Founded/Ownrshp 2010
Sales 86.0MM^E EMP 450
SIC 1731 1623 1711 Electrical work; Access control systems specialization; Telephone & communication line construction; Plumbing contractors; Electrical work; Access control systems specialization; Telephone & communication line construction; Plumbing contractors
Pr: Kenneth Tumlinson
Dir Bus: Glenn Garrett
IT Man: Joe Schaefer

D-U-N-S 94-120-6674
KST ENTERPRISES LLC
14215 Suncrest Rd, Manor, TX 78653-3899
Tel (512) 272-8841 Founded/Ownrshp 1994
Sales 15.4MM^E EMP 350
SIC 1731 1623 1711 Electrical work; Access control systems specialization; Telephone & communication line construction; Plumbing contractors; Electrical work; Access control systems specialization; Telephone & communication line construction; Plumbing contractors

D-U-N-S 96-903-7345
KSTATE ATHLETICS INC
1800 College Ave, Manhattan, KS 66502-3308
Tel (785) 532-7199 Founded/Ownrshp 2011
Sales 63.0MM EMP 2
Accts Sink Gordon & Associates Llp
SIC 7941 Sports clubs, managers & promoters; Sports clubs, managers & promoters
Prin: Chad Weiberg

KSU FOUNDATION
See KANSAS STATE UNIVERSITY FOUNDATION INC

D-U-N-S 61-912-3248
KSUS INTERNATIONAL LLC
KARL SCHMIDT UNISIA
(Suby of KSPG HOLDING USA INC) ★
1731 Industrial Pkwy N, Marinette, WI 54143-3704
Tel (715) 732-0181 Founded/Ownrshp 2005
Sales 60.4MM^E EMP 447
SIC 3592 Carburetors, pistons, rings, valves; Pistons & piston rings; Carburetors, pistons, rings, valves; Pistons & piston rings
Pr: Robert W Stellens
VP: Robert G Turcott

KSV
See MILLER GROUP USA LLC

KT
See KEPNER-TREGOE INC

D-U-N-S 96-594-6411
KT MAINTENANCE CO INC
800 Procter St, Port Arthur, TX 77640-6523
Tel (409) 982-9952 Founded/Ownrshp 1993
Sales 21.1MM^E EMP 119
Accts Ralph E Likins Beaumont Tex
SIC 1541 Industrial buildings & warehouses; Industrial buildings & warehouses
Pr: Kenny L Tims Sr
*Treas: William D Maxey

D-U-N-S 00-450-0773
KT-GRANT INC
KT-GRANTS
3073 Route 66, Export, PA 15632-1908
Tel (724) 468-4700 Founded/Ownrshp 1997
Sales 34.4MM^E EMP 175
SIC 7353 3441 3433 Earth moving equipment, rental or leasing; Ship sections, prefabricated metal; Heating equipment, except electric; Earth moving equipment, rental or leasing; Ship sections, prefabricated metal; Heating equipment, except electric
Pr: Marc Glasgow
*Treas: David Holvey
*Ex VP: Louis A Grant Jr
VP: Ruth Grant
Area Mgr: Ron Davis
IT Man: Timothy REA
Sfty Dirs: Dave Smiley
Sales Exec: Rich Thomas
VP Sls: John Wargofchik

KT-GRANTS
See KT-GRANT INC

KTA SUPER STORES
See PUNA PLANTATION HAWAII LIMITED

D-U-N-S 04-720-5232
KTA-TATOR INC
K T A
115 Technology Dr, Pittsburgh, PA 15275-1085
Tel (412) 788-1300 Founded/Ownrshp 1949
Sales 28.4MM^E EMP 204
Accts Cypher & Cypher Canonsburg P
SIC 8711 Consulting engineer; Consulting engineer
Pr: Kenneth A Trimber
*COO: Daniel P Adley
*VP: Eric S Kline
*VP: John Konopka
Off Admin: Pamela Morency
CTO: Charles Barris
QA Dir: Glenda Stilwell

D-U-N-S 86-765-1155
KTB SERVICES LLC
EXPERT AIR
1108 Cedar Bayou Rd, Baytown, TX 77520-2926
Tel (281) 428-7344 Founded/Ownrshp 2009
Sales 204.0MM EMP 12
SIC 1711 Plumbing, heating, air-conditioning contractors; Plumbing, heating, air-conditioning contractors

KTB USA
See MEGATRON INC

KTC
See KIAMICHI TECHNOLOGY CENTERS

KTEC-JC
See KNAPHEIDE TRUCK EQUIPMENT CO

D-U-N-S 10-911-1372
KTG (USA) LP
(Suby of KRUGER PRODUCTS L.P.)
400 Mahannah Ave, Memphis, TN 38107-1021
Tel (901) 577-5555 Founded/Ownrshp 2013
Sales 140.3MM^E EMP 265
SIC 2621 Towels, tissues & napkins: paper & stock; Towels, tissues & napkins: paper & stock
Pt: Phil Shearing
Sfty Dirs: Billy Brooks
Prd Mgr: Jim Szaroletta
Snr Mgr: Randy Adams

D-U-N-S 55-709-8670
KTGY GROUP INC
17911 Von Karman Ave # 250, Irvine, CA 92614-4243
Tel (949) 851-2133 Founded/Ownrshp 1991
Sales 27.8MM^E EMP 100
SIC 8712 Architectural services; Architectural services
CEO: Tricia Esser
Pr: Stan Braden
Assoc Dir: Louie Garcia
Ex Dir: Nick Lehnert
Plng Mgr: Johanna Crooker
Prd Dir: Loreen Arnold
Prd Dir: Kamran Charmsaz
Prd Dir: Ricardo Ramos
Snr PM: Gary Leus
Snr PM: Stan Olsiewski
Snr Mgr: Federico Soifer

D-U-N-S 12-198-2664 IMP
KTH PARTS INDUSTRIES INC
1111 State Route 235 N, Saint Paris, OH 43072-9680
Tel (937) 663-5941 Founded/Ownrshp 1984
Sales 225.7MM^E EMP 826
SIC 3714 Motor vehicle parts & accessories; Motor vehicle parts & accessories
Pr: Toshio Inoue
Pr: Mike Holland
*Ex VP: Sanichi Kanai
*Prin: Fumio Takeuchi
Prgrm Mgr: Joe Martz
Admn Mgr: Andrew Donahoe
Genl Mgr: Timothy Harrigan
Sfty Mgr: Larry Goings
Ql Cn Mgr: Brett Kuhn

D-U-N-S 18-668-1557
KTI INC
RIALTO CONCRETE PRODUCTS
3009 N Laurel Ave, Rialto, CA 92377-3725
Tel (909) 434-1888 Founded/Ownrshp 1987
Sales 35.4MM^E EMP 100
SIC 3272 Concrete products
CEO: Kenneth D Thompson
*Pr: Daniel J Deming
*VP: Jerry Cowden

D-U-N-S 79-339-7613 IMP
KTM NORTH AMERICA INC
1119 Milan Ave, Amherst, OH 44001-1319
Tel (440) 985-3553 Founded/Ownrshp 1992
Sales 44.4MM^E EMP 92
SIC 5012 3751 Motorcycles; Motorcycles, bicycles & parts; Motorcycles; Motorcycles, bicycles & parts
Pr: Rod Bush
*Treas: Jon-Erik Burleson
Ex VP: Tom Beer
VP: Jakob Branner
VP: Paul Brannigan
VP: Doug Frisbie
*VP: John S Harden
*VP: Selvaraj Narayana
Natl Sales: Clay Stuckey
Sls&Mrk Ex: Jack Henderson
VP Sls: Tom Etherington

D-U-N-S 06-127-0682
■ **KTP HOLDING CO INC** (CA)
RAYTHEON
(Suby of RAYTHEON MISSILE SYSTEMS CO) ★
1300 Eubank Blvd Se, Albuquerque, NM 87123-3336
Tel (505) 266-5678 Founded/Ownrshp 1953, 2011
Sales 48.9MM^E EMP 403^E
SIC 8731 8711 7375 7374 3823 3545 Electronic research; Energy research; Engineering services; Information retrieval services; Data processing & preparation; Industrial instrmnts msrmnt display/control process variable; Machine tool accessories; Electronic research; Energy research; Engineering services; Information retrieval services; Data processing & preparation; Industrial instrmnts msrmnt display/control process variable; Machine tool accessories
Pr: Steven E Downie
MIS Dir: Ronald Nolan

D-U-N-S 80-193-6899
■ **KTRK TELEVISION INC**
K T R K T V
(Suby of ABC INC) ★
3310 Bissonnet St, Houston, TX 77005-2195
Tel (713) 666-0713 Founded/Ownrshp 1996
Sales 21.6MM^E EMP 200
SIC 4833 Television broadcasting stations; Television broadcasting stations
Pr: Henry S Florsheim
*Treas: James D Hanford
VP: Steve Hinchman

D-U-N-S 17-713-8252
KTS KITCHENS INC
1065 E Walnut St Ste C, Carson, CA 90746-1384
Tel (310) 764-0850 Founded/Ownrshp 1987
Sales 69.7MM^E EMP 250
SIC 2099 2035 Pizza, refrigerated: except frozen; Dressings, salad: raw & cooked (except dry mixes); Pizza, refrigerated: except frozen; Dressings, salad: raw & cooked (except dry mixes)
CEO: Kathleen D Taggares
CFO: Sheryl Schneider
*Sec: Joan Paris

KTVD CHANNEL 20
See CHANNEL 20 TV CO

D-U-N-S 00-778-5116
KTVK INC
KTVK-TV CHANNEL 3
5555 N 7th Ave, Phoenix, AZ 85013-1701
Tel (602) 207-3333 Founded/Ownrshp 1955
Sales NA EMP 300
SIC 4833

KTVK-TV CHANNEL 3
See KTVK INC

D-U-N-S 06-039-5600
KTVT BROADCASTING CO LP
KTVT TV CHANNEL 11
5233 Bridge St, Dallas, TX 75231
Tel (214) 750-1111 Founded/Ownrshp 2000
Sales 42.9MM^E EMP 300
SIC 4833 Television broadcasting stations; Television broadcasting stations
Pr: Steve Mouldin
*Genl Pt: CBS Corp

KTVT TV CHANNEL 11
See KTVT BROADCASTING CO LP

D-U-N-S 15-083-4752 IMP/EXP
■ **KTVU PARTNERSHIP INC**
KTVU TELEVISION FOX 2
(Suby of FOX TELEVISION STATIONS INC) ★
2 Jack London Sq, Oakland, CA 94607-3727
Tel (510) 834-1212 Founded/Ownrshp 2014
Sales 26.8MM^E EMP 230
SIC 4833 Television broadcasting stations; Television broadcasting stations
CEO: Murdock Lachlan
Exec: Brian Hastings
Dir Bus: Diane Baldwin
Mktg Dir: Steven Poitras

KTVU TELEVISION FOX 2
See KTVU PARTNERSHIP INC

KTXL-FOX 40
See CHANNEL 40 INC

KU ENDOWMENT
See KANSAS UNIVERSITY ENDOWMENT ASSOCIATION

KU MEMORIAL UNIONS
See UNIVERSITY OF KANSAS MEMORIAL CORP

D-U-N-S 11-323-0569 IMP
KUAKINI HEALTH SYSTEM
347 N Kuakini St, Honolulu, HI 96817-2382
Tel (808) 536-2236 Founded/Ownrshp 1900
Sales 1.1MM EMP 1,400
Accts Delo Itte Tax Llp Honolulu H
SIC 8062 General medical & surgical hospitals; General medical & surgical hospitals
Pr: Gary K Kajiwara
*COO: Gregg Oishi
*CFO: Quin Ogawa
CFO: Quinn Ogawa
*VP: June Drumeller
*VP: Nobuyuki Miki
QA Dir: Vicki Philbin

D-U-N-S 07-770-1613
KUAKINI MEDICAL CENTER
(Suby of KUAKINI HEALTH SYSTEM) ★
347 N Kuakini St, Honolulu, HI 96817-2381
Tel (808) 547-9231 Founded/Ownrshp 1995
Sales 133.5MM EMP 1,216
Accts Deloitte Tax Llp Honolulu Hi
SIC 8062 General medical & surgical hospitals; General medical & surgical hospitals
Pr: Gary Kajiwara
*COO: Gregg Oishi
*Treas: Chuck Gee
Ofcr: Tamlyn Miyagawa
*VP: Dawn Ching
*VP: June Drumeller
VP: Nobuyuki Miki
Exec: Devin Brown
Dir Rx: Wendy Zarella
Brnch Mgr: Scott Lopes
Brnch Mgr: Ida Thiede

KUAKINI MEDICAL SYSTEMS
See KUAKINI PLAZA RADIOLOGY INC

D-U-N-S 05-074-5611
KUAKINI PLAZA RADIOLOGY INC
KUAKINI MEDICAL SYSTEMS
321 N Kuakini St Ste 102, Honolulu, HI 96817-2385
Tel (808) 547-9445 Founded/Ownrshp 1979
Sales NA EMP 200
SIC 6324 Hospital & medical service plans; Hospital & medical service plans
CEO: Gary Kajiwara
Doctor: Donn Tokairin
Doctor: Glenn Uto

D-U-N-S 03-199-4155
KUBAT EQUIPMENT & SERVICE CO
KESCO I
1070 S Galapago St, Denver, CO 80223-2804
Tel (303) 777-2044 Founded/Ownrshp 1994
Sales 47.9MM^E EMP 64
SIC 5084 1799 Industrial machinery & equipment; Service station equipment installation, maintenance & repair
Pr: Gene Hoyer
*VP: Craig Hoyer
IT Man: Richard Lorenz
IT Man: Gary Shomaker
Sls Mgr: Jim Kerth

D-U-N-S 00-449-6600 IMP/EXP
KUBETECH CUSTOM MOLDING INC
(Suby of COVERIS FLEXIBLES US LLC) ★
200 Masters Blvd, Anderson, SC 29626-6124
Tel (864) 225-9750 Founded/Ownrshp 2014
Sales 154.0MM^E EMP 500
SIC 2671 3089 Plastic film, coated or laminated for packaging; Injection molding of plastics; Plastic film, coated or laminated for packaging; Injection molding of plastics
Pr: Frank C Brown
*Treas: Lisa R Hysko

D-U-N-S 08-735-1417
KUBICKI DRAPER A PROFESSIONAL ASSOCIATION
25 W Flagler St Ph 1, Miami, FL 33130-1790
Tel (305) 374-1212 Founded/Ownrshp 1962
Sales 27.1MM^E EMP 158
SIC 8111 General practice law office; General practice law office
Pr: Gene Kubicki
COO: Jason Lennon
VP: Charles Kondla
Dir IT: Erick Gonzales

KUBOTA
See BURRIS EQUIPMENT CO

KUBOTA
See HOOBER INC

KUBOTA
See HARTER EQUIPMENT INC

KUBOTA
See COLUMBUS EQUIPMENT CO

KUBOTA
See PINE BUSH EQUIPMENT CO INC

KUBOTA
See LAMB & WEBSTER INC

KUBOTA
See WHITES FARM SUPPLY INC

KUBOTA
See EMPIRE TRACTOR CO INC

KUBOTA
See MARSHALL MACHINERY INC

KUBOTA
See HOPF EQUIPMENT INC

KUBOTA
See JACOBI SALES INC

KUBOTA
See GINOP SALES INC

KUBOTA
See CHAPPELL TRACTOR SALES INC

KUBOTA
See KUNAU IMPLEMENT CO

KUBOTA
See JOHNSON TRACTOR INC

KUBOTA
See WINCHESTER EQUIPMENT CO

KUBOTA
See STOLLER INTERNATIONAL INC

KUBOTA
See BERCHTOLD EQUIPMENT CO INC

KUBOTA
See GARTON TRACTOR INC

KUBOTA
See BURKS TRACTOR CO INC

KUBOTA
See M&L INDUSTRIES LLC

KUBOTA
See BINGHAM EQUIPMENT CO

KUBOTA
See KANEQUIP INC

KUBOTA
See EVOLUTION AG LLC

KUBOTA
See RITCHIE IMPLEMENT INC

KUBOTA
See KANEQUIP INC

KUBOTA
See NORTHERN PLAINS EQUIPMENT CO INC

KUBOTA
See STATE EQUIPMENT INC

KUBOTA
See CROWN POWER & EQUIPMENT CO LLC

KUBOTA
See EAGLE POWER AND EQUIPMENT CORP

D-U-N-S 19-609-6515
KUBOTA CREDIT CORP USA
(Suby of KUBOTA USA INC) ★
3401 Del Amo Blvd, Torrance, CA 90503-1636
Tel (310) 370-3370 Founded/Ownrshp 1982
Sales NA EMP 100
SIC 6141 Consumer finance companies; Consumer finance companies
CEO: David A Sutton
Pr: Yoshiyuki Fujita

D-U-N-S 06-850-0268 IMP/EXP
KUBOTA ENGINE AMERICA CORP
(Suby of KUBOTA USA INC) ★
505 Schelter Rd, Lincolnshire, IL 60069-4220
Tel (847) 955-2500 Founded/Ownrshp 1997
Sales 54.8MM^E EMP 61
SIC 5084 Engines & transportation equipment
Pr: Tomokazu Matsushita
*Pr: Tadahisa Omote
*Sec: Kyota Toyoki

D-U-N-S 17-682-2182 IMP/EXP
KUBOTA INDUSTRIAL EQUIPMENT CORP
(Suby of KUBOTA USA INC) ★
1001 Mcclure Indl Dr, Jefferson, GA 30549-1700
Tel (706) 387-1000 Founded/Ownrshp 2004
Sales NA EMP 720
SIC 3531 3711 Backhoes, tractors, cranes, plows & similar equipment; Truck & tractor truck assembly; Backhoes, tractors, cranes, plows & similar equipment; Truck & tractor truck assembly
CEO: Kazunori Monodane
*CFO: Wataru Ouchi
*Treas: Yasuhiro Kawabata

D-U-N-S 36-066-5376 IMP/EXP
KUBOTA MANUFACTURING OF AMERICA CORPO
(Suby of KUBOTA USA INC) ★
2715 Ramsey Rd, Gainesville, GA 30501-7526
Tel (770) 532-0038 Founded/Ownrshp 1988
Sales 228.8MM^E EMP 850
SIC 3524 3537 Lawn & garden tractors & equipment; Industrial trucks & tractors; Lawn & garden tractors & equipment; Industrial trucks & tractors
CEO: Hironobu Kubota
*CFO: Takehiro Ueda
*Treas: Walter Ouchi
*Ex VP: Kaz Monodane
*VP: Yasu Hiyama
Exec: John Harris

D-U-N-S 06-207-4828 IMP/EXP
KUBOTA TRACTOR CORP
(Suby of KUBOTA USA INC) ★
3401 Del Amo Blvd, Torrance, CA 90503-1636
Tel (310) 370-3370 Founded/Ownrshp 1972
Sales 476.2MM^E EMP 470
SIC 5083 3531 3799 Tractors, agricultural; Farm equipment parts & supplies; Construction machinery; Recreational vehicles; Tractors, agricultural; Farm equipment parts & supplies; Construction machinery; Recreational vehicles
Pr: Yuichi Kitao
Pr: Masto Yoshikawa
CFO: Toby Anderson
Treas: Kosuke Ota
Treas: Takehiro Ueda
VP: Shingo Banada
VP: Kazuhiro Higuchi
Prin: Susan Holmes
Dist Mgr: Bob Gertner
Dist Mgr: Don Lowe
Dist Mgr: Steve Payne

D-U-N-S 18-339-9005 IMP
KUBOTA USA INC
(Suby of KUBOTA CORPORATION)
3401 Del Amo Blvd, Torrance, CA 90503-1636
Tel (310) 370-3370 Founded/Ownrshp 1986
Sales 1.0MMM^E EMP 1,500
SIC 5083 3577 5051 3531 3571 Tractors, agricultural; Disk & diskette equipment, except drives; Castings, rough: iron or steel; Loaders, shovel: self-propelled; Electronic computers; Tractors, agricultural; Disk & diskette equipment, except drives; Castings, rough: iron or steel; Loaders, shovel: self-propelled; Electronic computers
Pr: Yoshiharu Nishiguchi
*Sec: Hiro Okino
Ofcr: Toby Anderson
Top Exec: Sid Winecoop

D-U-N-S 78-377-6201
KUCHTA MINING SERVICES
1933 Sage Dr, Golden, CO 80401-1748
Tel (303) 518-5242 Founded/Ownrshp 2006
Sales 30.0MM EMP 1
SIC 8741 Business management; Business management
Owner: Mark Kuchta

D-U-N-S 07-928-3143
KUDOS TECH LLC
20650 Park Cir E Apt 3, Cupertino, CA 95014-1948
Tel (415) 754-9604 Founded/Ownrshp 2011
Sales 60.0MM EMP 10
SIC 5092 5734 Toys; Computer software & accessories; Toys; Computer software & accessories

D-U-N-S 13-468-4349
KUECKER LOGISTICS GROUP INC
KLG
801 W Markey Rd, Belton, MO 64012-1709
Tel (816) 331-7070 Founded/Ownrshp 1980
Sales 35.1MM^E EMP 36
SIC 5084 Materials handling machinery
CEO: Mike Langdon
*Pr: Stanley J Kuecker
*Sec: Alice Kuecker
VP: Kuecker Jim
VP: Stanley Nicholas Kuecker
Exec: Alice Kueker
Sales Asso: Scott Hooper

D-U-N-S 02-308-0211
KUEHN MOTOR INC
KUEHN MOTOR LEASING
5020 Highway 52 N, Rochester, MN 55901-3143
Tel (507) 346-7339 Founded/Ownrshp 1958
Sales 32.3MM^E EMP 90
SIC 5521 5561 Automobiles, used cars only; Pickups & vans, used; Motor homes; Travel trailers: automobile, new & used; Automobiles, used cars only; Pickups & vans, used; Motor homes; Travel trailers: automobile, new & used
Pr: Charles Kuehn Jr
*Treas: Richard Kuehn
*VP: Jon Kuehn
Genl Mgr: Dar Halverson

KUEHN MOTOR LEASING
See KUEHN MOTOR INC

D-U-N-S 00-985-3664
KUEHNE + NAGEL INC
BLUE ANCHOR LINE
(Suby of KUEHNE + NAGEL INVESTMENT INC) ★
10 Exchange Pl, Jersey City, NJ 07302-3918
Tel (201) 413-5500 Founded/Ownrshp 1992
Sales 782.1MM^E EMP 3,300
SIC 4731 Freight forwarding; Freight forwarding
Pr: John Hextall
Pr: Bill Spiker
CFO: Markus Blanka-Graff
*CFO: Michael Schimpf
*CFO: Gerard Van Kesteren
Sr VP: Dave Mabon
*Sr VP: Greg Martin
*VP: Juerg Bandle
VP: John Franklin
VP: Jon Hettrick
VP: Nadine Jones
*VP: Rainer Wunn
Dir Bus: Tony Goralski

D-U-N-S 80-736-8360
KUEHNE + NAGEL INVESTMENT INC
(Suby of KUEHNE + NAGEL INTERNATIONAL AG)
10 Exchange Pl Fl 19, Jersey City, NJ 07302-4935
Tel (201) 413-5500 Founded/Ownrshp 1992
Sales 1.0MMM^E EMP 5,306^E
SIC 4731 Foreign freight forwarding; Foreign freight forwarding
CEO: Reinhard Lange
*Pr: John Hextall
*CFO: Gerard Van Kesteren
*Ex VP: Peter Messerli
*VP: Klaus-Michael Kuehne
Opers Mgr: Paul Norris

D-U-N-S 01-123-9167 IMP/EXP
KUEHNE CHEMICAL CO INC
86 N Hackensack Ave, Kearny, NJ 07032-4673
Tel (973) 589-0700 Founded/Ownrshp 1966
Sales 113.2MM^E EMP 200
SIC 2819 4226 2812 Sodium & potassium compounds, exc. bleaches, alkalies, alum.; Special warehousing & storage; Alkalies & chlorine; Sodium & potassium compounds, exc. bleaches, alkalies, alum.; Special warehousing & storage; Alkalies & chlorine
Pr: Donald Nicolai
*CFO: Bill Paulin
Dir IT: John Romano
Sfty Mgr: Tony Dias
Sfty Mgr: Tony Diaz
Plnt Mgr: Herbert Uhlig

KUEPERS ARCHITECTS & BUILDERS
See KUEPERS CONSTRUCTION INC

D-U-N-S 10-226-3431
KUEPERS CONSTRUCTION INC
KUEPERS ARCHITECTS & BUILDERS
17018 Commercial Park Rd, Brainerd, MN 56401-6066
Tel (218) 829-0707 Founded/Ownrshp 1976
Sales 43.5MM^E EMP 180
Accts Kummet Larson Bluth & Co Pa
SIC 1542 1521 1522 Commercial & office building, new construction; New construction, single-family houses; Apartment building construction; Commercial & office building, new construction; New construction, single-family houses; Apartment building construction
CEO: Douglas Kuepers
*Ex VP: Steven Kuepers
VP: Kristopher Solseth
Prd Mgr: Jeremy Adams

KUGLER COMPANY
See KUGLER OIL CO

D-U-N-S 03-500-9810
KUGLER OIL CO
KUGLER COMPANY
209 W 3rd St, Mc Cook, NE 69001-3622
Tel (308) 345-2280 Founded/Ownrshp 1956
Sales 79.9MM EMP 140
Accts Bkd Llp Lincoln Nebraska
SIC 5191 Fertilizer & fertilizer materials; Fertilizer & fertilizer materials
CEO: G D Kugler
*Pr: John Kugler
*CFO: James Somers
*Treas: Michael A Kugler
Sfty Dirs: Mike Gapp

KUHLMAN CONSTRUCTION PRODUCTS
See KUHLMAN CORP

D-U-N-S 00-503-5845
KUHLMAN CORP (FL)
KUHLMAN CONSTRUCTION PRODUCTS
1845 Indian Wood Cir, Maumee, OH 43537-4072
Tel (419) 897-6000 Founded/Ownrshp 1901
Sales 48.7MM^E EMP 150
Accts Plante & Moran Pllc Toledo
SIC 4226 5032 3273 Special warehousing & storage; Brick, stone & related material; Brick, except refractory; Building blocks; Sewer pipe, clay; Ready-mixed concrete; Special warehousing & storage; Brick, stone & related material; Brick, except refractory; Building blocks; Sewer pipe, clay; Ready-mixed concrete
Pr: Timothy L Goligoski
*CFO: Terry Schaefer
Treas: Vernon J Nagel
*VP: Kenneth Kuhlman
VP: Steve Wagner
Dir IT: Maria Pacheco
IT Man: Margaret Walldeck
MIS Mgr: Margaret Waldeck
Sls Mgr: Tim Casey

D-U-N-S 86-844-4555 IMP
KUHLMAN ELECTRIC CORP
ABB-KUHLMAN
(Suby of ABB HOLDINGS INC) ★
101 Kuhlman Blvd, Versailles, KY 40383-1527
Tel (800) 435-7365 Founded/Ownrshp 2008
Sales 50.2MM^E EMP 700
SIC 3621 Generating apparatus & parts, electrical; Generating apparatus & parts, electrical
CEO: Thomas Minnich
*CFO: Jonathan N Brooks
*Prin: Etna Kuhlman

D-U-N-S 04-512-4468
KUHLMAN INC
N58 W 16865 Ridgewood Rd N 58 W, Menomonee Falls, WI 53051
Tel (262) 252-9400 Founded/Ownrshp 1957
Sales 24.1MM^E EMP 75^E
SIC 1711 Refrigeration contractor
Owner: Ron Kuhlman
*VP: Dale Kuhlman

D-U-N-S 03-238-2442 IMP
KUHN ACQUISITION LLC
KUHN FLOWERS
3802 Beach Blvd, Jacksonville, FL 32207-4757
Tel (904) 398-8601 Founded/Ownrshp 2001
Sales 26.2MM^E EMP 90
SIC 5193 Flowers, fresh

KUHN FLOWERS
See KUHN ACQUISITION LLC

KUHN HONDA VOLKSWAGEN
See DIRECT AUTOMOTIVE MANGEMENT INC

D-U-N-S 00-723-2333 IMP/EXP
KUHN KRAUSE INC
(Suby of KUHN NORTH AMERICA INC) ★
305 S Monroe St, Hutchinson, KS 67501-1728
Tel (620) 663-6161 Founded/Ownrshp 2011
Sales 5.5MM^E EMP 350
SIC 3523

D-U-N-S 00-608-3240 IMP/EXP
KUHN NORTH AMERICA INC
(Suby of KUHN SA)
1501 W 7th Ave, Brodhead, WI 53520-1637
Tel (608) 897-4508 Founded/Ownrshp 1945
Sales 153.4MM^E EMP 630
SIC 3523 3531 Feed grinders, crushers & mixers; Spreaders, fertilizer; Construction machinery; Feed grinders, crushers & mixers; Spreaders, fertilizer; Construction machinery
CEO: Thierry Krier
CFO: Scott Rupprecht
IT Man: Laurent Maurer
Mktg Mgr: Frank O Brien

KUHNLE BROS TRUCKING
See KUHNLE BROTHERS INC

D-U-N-S 00-294-6523
KUHNLE BROTHERS INC (OH)
KUHNLE BROS TRUCKING
14905 Cross Creek Pkwy, Newbury, OH 44065-9788
Tel (440) 564-7168 Founded/Ownrshp 1963
Sales 270.0MM EMP 150
Accts Demarchi & Associates Clevela
SIC 4213 4212 Trucking, except local; Local trucking, without storage; Trucking, except local; Local trucking, without storage
CEO: Kim Taylor Kuhnle
*Treas: Robert Russell

KUHNS EQUIPMENT COMPANY
See KUHNS EQUIPMENT LLC

D-U-N-S 02-492-6800
KUHNS EQUIPMENT LLC (IL)
KUHNS EQUIPMENT COMPANY
1000 E Columbia St, Arthur, IL 61911-9739
Tel (217) 543-2154 Founded/Ownrshp 1956
Sales 29.0MM EMP 21
SIC 5261 Garden supplies & tools; Garden supplies & tools
Pr: Howard A Kuhns
Prin: Steven Anderson
Off Mgr: Monica Kuhns

KUHN'S MARKET
See QUALITY FOODS CORP

KUIC RADIO
See COAST RADIO CO INC

D-U-N-S 01-125-7615
KUIKEN BROTHERS CO INC
6-02 Fair Lawn Ave, Fair Lawn, NJ 07410-1219
Tel (201) 796-2082 Founded/Ownrshp 1912
Sales 145.9MM EMP 270
Accts Massood & Company Pa Totowa
SIC 5211 5031 3272 Lumber & other building materials; Building materials, exterior; Building materials, interior; Concrete stuctural support & building material; Lumber & other building materials; Building materials, exterior; Building materials, interior; Concrete stuctural support & building material
Pr: Douglas Kuiken
*VP: Nicholas M Fuiken
*VP: Henry Kuiken
IT Man: Frank Chempanos
Sfty Dirs: Louis Cicchella
Sales Asso: Darlene Bryant
Sales Asso: Michael Conte

KUKA AEROSPACE
See KUKA SYSTEMS NORTH AMERICA LLC

D-U-N-S 00-533-4511 IMP
KUKA ASSEMBLY AND TEST CORP
(Suby of KUKA AG)
5675 Dixie Hwy, Saginaw, MI 48601-5828
Tel (989) 777-2111 Founded/Ownrshp 2007
Sales 37.1MM^E EMP 170
SIC 3829 3549 Testing equipment: abrasion, shearing strength, etc.; Assembly machines, including robotic; Testing equipment: abrasion, shearing strength, etc.; Assembly machines, including robotic
Pr: Scott Orendach
CFO: Kurt Kuck
VP: Dan Emrick
Prgrm Mgr: John Lommel
Prgrm Mgr: Mark Pichler
Snr Mgr: Mike Hagedon
Snr Mgr: Scott Wenzel

KUKA ROBOTICS
See KUKA US HOLDING CO LLC

D-U-N-S 05-332-9082 IMP
KUKA SYSTEMS NORTH AMERICA LLC
KUKA AEROSPACE
(Suby of KUKA SYSTEMS GMBH)
6600 Center Dr, Sterling Heights, MI 48312-2666
Tel (586) 795-2000 Founded/Ownrshp 1935, 2007
Sales 572.0MM EMP 940
SIC 3549 Assembly machines, including robotic; Assembly machines, including robotic
Pr: Lawrence A Drake
*CFO: Paul Ambros
Ofcr: Martin Costa
Dir Bus: Ernani Westarb
Prgrm Mgr: Jeff Angel
Prgrm Mgr: Tim Mansfield
Prgrm Mgr: Steve Schiff
Prgrm Mgr: Bob Szymanski
Prgrm Mgr: Steve Verklan
Prgrm Mgr: John Ward
Prgrm Mgr: Dave Wells

D-U-N-S 19-298-7993
KUKA TOLEDO PRODUCTION OPERATIONS LLC
(Suby of KUKA SYSTEMS GMBH)
3770 Stickney Ave, Toledo, OH 43608-1310
Tel (419) 727-5500 Founded/Ownrshp 2004
Sales 39.2MM^E EMP 247
SIC 3713 Truck & bus bodies; Truck & bus bodies
CEO: Lawrence A Drake
*CFO: Paul Ambros
Ql Cn Mgr: Evan Jenkins

D-U-N-S 18-594-7152 IMP
KUKA US HOLDING CO LLC
KUKA ROBOTICS
(Suby of KUKA ROBOTER GMBH)
51870 Shelby Pkwy, Shelby Township, MI 48315-1787
Tel (586) 465-8826 Founded/Ownrshp 2004
Sales 42.4MM^E EMP 100^E
SIC 5084 3549 Industrial machinery & equipment; Assembly machines, including robotic; Industrial machinery & equipment; Assembly machines, including robotic
Pr: Joseph Gemma
Pr: Paul Gazdick
CFO: Peter Mohnen
Sec: Bryan Cermak
VP: Bernard Sagan
VP: Stuart Shepherd
Prgrm Mgr: Todd Bell
IT Man: Lori Rogers
Sls Dir: Chris Lutz

D-U-N-S 01-503-5090
KUKURIN CONTRACTING INC
1169 Route 286, Export, PA 15632-1986
Tel (724) 325-2136 Founded/Ownrshp 1981
Sales 33.8MM^E EMP 90
SIC 1623 1629 1611 Water main construction; Sewer line construction; Land clearing contractor; Earthmoving contractor; Highway & street paving contractor
Pr: William J Kukurin
*VP: Harold R McDade Jr

D-U-N-S 13-190-8571
KULA PRODUCE CO LTD
217 Hoohana St, Kahului, HI 96732-2452
Tel (808) 871-6232 Founded/Ownrshp 2002
Sales 22.0MM EMP 65
SIC 5148 Fresh fruits & vegetables; Fresh fruits & vegetables
Pr: Wayne Teruya

KULICKE & SOFFA INDUSTRIES
See KULICKE AND SOFFA WEDGE BONDING INC

D-U-N-S 00-235-1203
▲ KULICKE AND SOFFA INDUSTRIES INC (PA)
1005 Virginia Dr, Fort Washington, PA 19034-3101
Tel (215) 784-6000 Founded/Ownrshp 1951
Sales 536.4MM EMP 2,373^E
Accts Pricewaterhousecoopers Llp Si
Tkr Sym KLIC Exch NGS
SIC 3674 Semiconductor manufacturing machinery; Packaging machinery; Semiconductors & related devices; Integrated circuits, semiconductor networks, etc.
CEO: Jonathan H Chou
*Ch Bd: Garrett E Pierce
Sr VP: Irene Lee
Sr VP: Yih-Neng Lee
Sr VP: Lester Wong
VP: Alan Schindler
Snr Sftwr: Andrew Stefanowicz
CIO: Oliver Strasser
Board of Directors: Brian R Bachman, Peter T Kong,

Chin Hu Lim, Gregory F Milzcik

D-U-N-S 82-854-4812 IMP
■ KULICKE AND SOFFA WEDGE BONDING INC
KULICKE & SOFFA INDUSTRIES
(*Suby of* KULICKE AND SOFFA INDUSTRIES INC) ★
1821 E Dyer Rd Ste 200, Santa Ana, CA 92705-5700
Tel (949) 660-0440 *Founded/Ownrshp* 2008
Sales 44.1MM^E *EMP* 200
SIC 3699 Electrical equipment & supplies; Electrical equipment & supplies
Pr: Scott Kulicke
Sr VP: Lester Wong
CTO: Jon Codispoti
Sls Mgr: Jerry Muenchow

D-U-N-S 00-180-3089
KULITE SEMICONDUCTOR PRODUCTS INC (NJ)
KS
1 Willow Tree Rd, Leonia, NJ 07605-2239
Tel (201) 461-0900 *Founded/Ownrshp* 1959
Sales 123.0MM *EMP* 828
SIC 3728 3829

D-U-N-S 00-232-0877
KULJIAN CORP
DATA SCAN
(*Suby of* A M D C INC) ★
3700 Market St Fl 2, Philadelphia, PA 19104-3142
Tel (215) 243-1900 *Founded/Ownrshp* 1941, 1961
Sales 20.9MM^E *EMP* 300
SIC 8711 8741 Engineering services; Construction management; Engineering services; Construction management
Ch Bd: Sadhan C Dutt
**Pr:* Arthur H Kuljian
**VP:* Arthur H Ferber
VP: Ronald Szostak
MIS Dir: Shyamal Choundry
Telecom Mg: Sandip Sinha
Snr Mgr: Anindya Sengupta

D-U-N-S 02-661-5195 IMP
KULKONI INC
KULKONI PRECISION METALS
502 Garden Oaks Blvd, Houston, TX 77018-5506
Tel (713) 691-1234 *Founded/Ownrshp* 1963
Sales 24.6MM^E *EMP* 32
SIC 5085 5072 Industrial supplies; Hardware
CEO: Benjamin T Cole
**Pr:* Dun McColum
**Ch:* Hans W Buhrfeind
**VP:* Martin Little
**VP:* Mike Rothermund
**Prin:* Jurgen Prohaska
Off Mgr: Regina Geisendorff
IT Man: Ken Brunot
IT Man: Frank Martinez
Opers Mgr: Robert Borjas
Sls Mgr: Charlie Perkins
Board of Directors: Gerd De Haan, Hermann Jagau, Norbert Preilowski

KULKONI PRECISION METALS
See KULKONI INC

D-U-N-S 61-532-2414 IMP
KUM & GO LC
(*Suby of* KRAUSE HOLDINGS INC) ★
6400 Westown Pkwy, West Des Moines, IA 50266-7709
Tel (515) 226-0128 *Founded/Ownrshp* 1997
Sales 379.3MM^E *EMP* 3,000
SIC 5411 Convenience stores, chain; Convenience stores, chain
Ch: William A Krause
CEO: Kyle J Krause
COO: Mark Hastings
CFO: Craig Bergstrom
CFO: Brian Thompson
Ex VP: Dennis Folden
VP: James Brandt
Ex Dir: Pat Fellers

D-U-N-S 08-218-2999 IMP/EXP
KUMHO TIRE USA INC
(*Suby of* KUMHO TIRE)
133 Peachtree St Ne, Atlanta, GA 30303-1804
Tel (678) 916-3243 *Founded/Ownrshp* 2002
Sales 60.6MM^E *EMP* 90
SIC 5014 Automobile tires & tubes; Truck tires & tubes; Automobile tires & tubes; Truck tires & tubes
CEO: Hai Eok Choi
VP: Armand Allaire
VP: Chris Han
**Prin:* J B Kim
Rgnl Mgr: Dave Walsh
Genl Mgr: Edmund Cho
Dir IT: Ike Chun
VP Sls: Kenneth Lee
Manager: John Barnes
Manager: Martin Davis
Manager: Dan Fessler

D-U-N-S 03-980-3213 IMP
KUMI MANUFACTURING ALABAMA LLC
(*Suby of* KAMCO INDUSTRIES INC) ★
2543 7th St S, Clanton, AL 35046-6304
Tel (205) 280-1265 *Founded/Ownrshp* 2000
Sales 42.0MM *EMP* 94
SIC 3089 Injection molded finished plastic products; Thermoformed finished plastic products
Pr: Chuck Saeki
Exec: Andy Salter
IT Man: Gregg Sandlin

D-U-N-S 78-950-8959 IMP
KUMON NORTH AMERICA INC
(*Suby of* KUMON INSTITUTE OF EDUCATION CO.,LTD.)
300 Frank W Burr Blvd # 6, Teaneck, NJ 07666-6703
Tel (201) 692-3062 *Founded/Ownrshp* 1989
Sales 150.4MM *EMP* 441
Accts Citrin Cooperman & Company Ll
SIC 8299 Educational services; Educational services
Pr: Akira Hamanika

**COO:* Savio Rebelo
VP: James F Coakley Jr
**VP:* Robert Lichtenstein
VP: Joseph Nativo
Brnch Mgr: Caroline Rostkowski
Brnch Mgr: Dawa Samdup
Web Dev: Mariko Fujitsuka
Software D: Joe Larkin
Snr Mgr: Victor Szuper
Snr Mgr: Kyosuke Yamaguchi

D-U-N-S 00-912-1641
■ KUMUKAHI HOLDINGS INC
(*Suby of* KEY PRINCIPAL INVESTING) ★
91-151 Malakole St, Kapolei, HI 96707-1812
Tel (808) 682-2447 *Founded/Ownrshp* 2004
Sales 28.9MM^E *EMP* 192^E
SIC 5031 5039 5033 Lumber, plywood & millwork; Prefabricated buildings; Roofing & siding materials
Pr: Terris Inglett

KUNA FOOD SERVICE
See KUNA MEAT CO INC

D-U-N-S 08-738-8893
KUNA GOOD NEIGHBORS INC (ID)
12689 S Five Mile Rd, Kuna, ID 83634-2661
Tel (208) 362-1907 *Founded/Ownrshp* 1990
Sales 197.0MM *EMP* 15
SIC 8611 Community affairs & services; Community affairs & services
Pr: Patricia Hamm
Sec: Janie Arnold

D-U-N-S 03-105-8423 IMP
KUNA MEAT CO INC
KUNA FOOD SERVICE
704 Kuna Industrial Ct, Dupo, IL 62239-1823
Tel (618) 286-4000 *Founded/Ownrshp* 1994
Sales 114.0MM^E *EMP* 105
SIC 5144 5142 5147 5169 5149 5148 Poultry & poultry products; Packaged frozen goods; Meats & meat products; Specialty cleaning & sanitation preparations; Sanitation preparations; Groceries & related products; Fresh fruits & vegetables; Poultry & poultry products; Packaged frozen goods; Meats & meat products; Specialty cleaning & sanitation preparations; Sanitation preparations; Groceries & related products; Fresh fruits & vegetables
Pr: Daniel F Bippen
**CFO:* Paul Vlaich
Sr VP: John Schuler

D-U-N-S 10-001-5072
KUNA SCHOOL DISTRICT
711 E Porter St, Kuna, ID 83634-1484
Tel (208) 922-1000 *Founded/Ownrshp* 1950
Sales 25.2MM^E *EMP* 500
SIC 8211 Public elementary & secondary schools; Public elementary & secondary schools
**Prin:* Arnette Johnson
Off Mgr: Zonia Brown
Off Mgr: Greta Smith
IT Man: Mike Wiedenfeld

D-U-N-S 02-229-9259 IMP
KUNAU IMPLEMENT CO
KUBOTA
420 W White St, Preston, IA 52069-9570
Tel (563) 689-3311 *Founded/Ownrshp* 1936
Sales 54.5MM *EMP* 42
Accts Winkel Parker & Foster Cpa P
SIC 5083 Agricultural machinery; Agricultural machinery
Pr: Kunau Todd
**VP:* Dan Kunau

D-U-N-S 01-130-9705 IMP
KUNDERT MOTORS INC
KUNDERT VOLVO HASBROUCK HTS
140 State Rt 17, Hasbrouck Heights, NJ 07604-2905
Tel (201) 288-8895 *Founded/Ownrshp* 1942
Sales 36.7MM^E *EMP* 105
SIC 5511 New & used car dealers
Pr: William M Kundert
**Ex VP:* William R Whited
Sales Asso: Jay Tobia

KUNDERT VOLVO HASBROUCK HTS
See KUNDERT MOTORS INC

KUNDINGER CONTROLS
See KUNDINGER FLUID POWER INC

D-U-N-S 01-702-5800
KUNDINGER FLUID POWER INC
KUNDINGER CONTROLS
1771 Harmon Rd, Auburn Hills, MI 48326-1587
Tel (248) 391-6100 *Founded/Ownrshp* 1961
Sales 44.2MM^E *EMP* 60
SIC 5085 Industrial supplies; Industrial supplies
Pr: Thomas J Kundinger
**VP Opers:* John Leece

D-U-N-S 02-320-1890
KUNES COUNTRY CHEVROLET-CADILLAC INC
CREST OLDSMOBILE
1231 E Geneva St, Delavan, WI 53115-2002
Tel (262) 728-9163 *Founded/Ownrshp* 1977
Sales 61.5MM^E *EMP* 200
SIC 5511 7538 Automobiles, new & used; General automotive repair shops; Automobiles, new & used; General automotive repair shops
Pr: Greg Kunes
**VP:* Dennis Kramer
Genl Mgr: Bill Ederer
Genl Mgr: Dan Schlitt
Sls Mgr: Ron Hutter

D-U-N-S 96-667-1026
KUNES COUNTRY FORD-LINCOLN INC
CHEV CADILLAC
1234 E Geneva St, Delavan, WI 53115-2002
Tel (262) 728-5544 *Founded/Ownrshp* 1996
Sales 42.6MM^E *EMP* 70
SIC 5511 Automobiles, new & used; Automobiles, new & used

Pr: Greg Kunes
**VP:* Deborah Kunes
Genl Mgr: Tony Wheatley
Mktg Dir: Jennifer Myers
Sls Mgr: Pat Connor

KUNI AUTOMOTIVE
See KUNI ENTERPRISES INC

D-U-N-S 05-097-0409
KUNI CADILLAC & BMW INC
3725 Sw Cedar Hills Blvd, Beaverton, OR 97005-2024
Tel (503) 643-1543 *Founded/Ownrshp* 1969
Sales 35.7MM *EMP* 98
SIC 5511 Automobiles, new & used; Automobiles, new & used
Pr: Wayne D Kuni
CFO: Carl Cristofferson
**Treas:* Carl Christoferson
**VP:* Sean D Kuni
Dir IT: David Millier
IT Man: Michael Ross
Opers Mgr: Bob Rausch
Sls Mgr: Taji Aslothower
Sls Mgr: Eileen Sorg

D-U-N-S 03-197-5360
KUNI CENTENNIAL MOTORS LLC
KUNI HONDA ON ARAPAHOE
10750 E Arapahoe Rd, Centennial, CO 80112-3823
Tel (303) 708-2000 *Founded/Ownrshp* 2009
Sales 33.6MM^E *EMP* 100^E
SIC 5511 7538 5531 New & used car dealers; General automotive repair shops; Automotive parts; New & used car dealers; General automotive repair shops; Automotive parts
Genl Mgr: Herman Brocksmith
Sls Mgr: James Winslow
Sales Asso: Mark Cook

D-U-N-S 61-970-8563
KUNI DENVER MOTORS INC
KUNI LEXUS
5150 S Quebec St, Greenwood Village, CO 80111-1827
Tel (303) 798-9500 *Founded/Ownrshp* 1991
Sales 33.0MM^E *EMP* 67
SIC 5511 Automobiles, new & used; Automobiles, new & used
Pr: Greg Goodwin
**Ch Bd:* Wayne Kuni
**Sec:* Carl B Christoferson
CTO: Tim Perry
IT Man: Travis Brower
Sls Mgr: Shawn Evans
Sls Mgr: Scott Mendelsohn
Sls Mgr: Mike Parmakian
Sales Asso: Randy Palser

D-U-N-S 78-785-0705
KUNI ENTERPRISES INC
KUNI AUTOMOTIVE
17800 Se Mill Plain Blvd, Vancouver, WA 98683-7586
Tel (503) 372-7457 *Founded/Ownrshp* 1970
Sales 303.4MM^E *EMP* 1,000
SIC 5511 Automotive maintenance services; New & used car dealers
Pr: Greg Goodwin
Pr: Brenda Morgan
COO: Joseph Herman
Ofcr: Matt Newell
VP: Lee Castonguay
VP: Tim Hays
IT Man: Annette Foglio

D-U-N-S 36-278-8841
KUNI GERMAN MOTORS LLC
KUNI GM BMW
10999 Sw Canyon Rd, Beaverton, OR 97005-1818
Tel (503) 748-5400 *Founded/Ownrshp* 2005
Sales 66.2MM^E *EMP* 170
SIC 5511 Automobiles, new & used; Automobiles, new & used
Pr: Todd Bondy
CFO: Laura Carlisle
Genl Mgr: Gregg Stone
Off Mgr: Kristy Payne
IT Man: Matt Hughes
Sls&Mrk Ex: Heather Krieves
Sls Mgr: David Richardson

KUNI GM BMW
See KUNI GERMAN MOTORS LLC

KUNI HONDA ON ARAPAHOE
See KUNI CENTENNIAL MOTORS LLC

KUNI LEXUS
See KUNI DENVER MOTORS INC

D-U-N-S 05-208-3511
KUNI WEST SLOPE MOTORS LLC
LEXUS OF PORTLAND
8840 Sw Canyon Rd, Portland, OR 97225-3416
Tel (503) 297-9017 *Founded/Ownrshp* 1994
Sales 36.8MM^E *EMP* 102
SIC 5511 Automobiles, new & used; Automobiles, new & used
COO: Ron Lane
Ex Dir: Brent Hann
Sales Asso: Evan Whitaker

D-U-N-S 05-302-9086
KUNI WESTSIDE INFINITI
(*Suby of* KUNI AUTOMOTIVE) ★
17305 Highway 99, Lynnwood, WA 98037-3143
Tel (425) 563-6600 *Founded/Ownrshp* 2010
Sales 71.8MM^E *EMP* 935^E
SIC 5511 Automobiles, new & used
Prin: Andrew Clark
Sls Mgr: Mich Allee

D-U-N-S 02-291-1960
KUNKEL CO INC
7464 Washington Ave S, Eden Prairie, MN 55344-3704
Tel (952) 938-3528 *Founded/Ownrshp* 1951
Sales 25.8MM *EMP* 10
SIC 5148

D-U-N-S 10-708-8726 IMP
KUNKEL ENTERPRISES INC
C K ENTERPRISES
1204 Sw Jefferson St, Lees Summit, MO 64081-2844
Tel (816) 524-1304 *Founded/Ownrshp* 1981
Sales 41.6MM^E *EMP* 43
SIC 5169 7349 Industrial chemicals; Building maintenance services
Pr: Charlie Kunkel
**Pr:* Charles Kunkel III
**Sec:* Catherine Kunkel
VP: Rick Carver
VP: Steve Kimble
**VP:* Charles Kunkel IV
Dir Lab: Beth Furnish
Dir Lab: Tarah Henlon
Trfc Mgr: Donna Stines

D-U-N-S 02-254-5586
KUNKEL SERVICE CO
331 Baltimore Pike, Bel Air, MD 21014-4100
Tel (410) 838-3344 *Founded/Ownrshp* 1947
Sales 28.5MM^E *EMP* 350
SIC 5013 5063 5531 Automotive supplies & parts; Motors, electric; Automobile & truck equipment & parts; Automotive supplies & parts; Motors, electric; Automobile & truck equipment & parts
Treas: John N Kunkel
**Pr:* Gerard F Kunkel Sr
**Ex VP:* Gerard F Kunkel Jr

KUNKLE VALVE
See NORTH AMERICAN SAFETY VALVE INDUSTRIES INC

D-U-N-S 78-132-6269
KUNO OIL CO INC
KUNOCO
5830 County Route 27, Canton, NY 13617-6552
Tel (315) 714-2205 *Founded/Ownrshp* 1990
Sales 28.1MM^E *EMP* 55
SIC 5172 Petroleum products; Petroleum products
Pr: Steve Kuno

KUNOCO
See KUNO OIL CO INC

D-U-N-S 00-300-2433
KUNZLER & CO INC (PA)
652 Manor St, Lancaster, PA 17603-5108
Tel (717) 299-6301 *Founded/Ownrshp* 1901, 1961
Sales 107.7MM^E *EMP* 500
SIC 2011 2013 Meat packing plants; Smoked meats from purchased meat; Meat packing plants; Smoked meats from purchased meat
Pr: Christian C Kunzler III
CFO: John Younk
**VP:* John S Kunzler
Rgnl Mgr: Theresa McKinnell
MIS Dir: Steve Henry
Opers Mgr: Craig Dutrow
Prd Mgr: Bill Lambert
Mktg Mgr: Tom Coder
Mktg Mgr: Becca Massey
Manager: Peter Turner
Sls Mgr: Betty Ann Loht

D-U-N-S 15-164-8797
KUONI DESTINATION MANAGEMENT USA INC
ALLIED TPRO
(*Suby of* KUONI HOLDING DELAWARE, INC.)
500 Fashion Ave Fl 9b, New York, NY 10018-0840
Tel (212) 596-1000 *Founded/Ownrshp* 1990
Sales 22.5MM^E *EMP* 106
SIC 4725 Arrangement of travel tour packages, wholesale
Pr: Mark Morello
**Sr VP:* Jane Rossmango
Dir IT: Steven Schinger
IT Man: Greg Eschinger
Opers Mgr: Edward Roizman

D-U-N-S 03-937-8005
KUPPER CHEVROLET INC
1500 2nd St Ne, Mandan, ND 58554-3781
Tel (701) 663-9851 *Founded/Ownrshp* 1988
Sales 54.8MM^E *EMP* 140
SIC 5511 7538 Automobiles, new & used; General automotive repair shops; Automobiles, new & used; General automotive repair shops
Pr: Dave Ressler
**Sec:* Gerri Ressler
Genl Mgr: Bob Cooper
**Genl Mgr:* Robert Kupper
Genl Mgr: Karen Rychlik
IT Man: Dava Ralph
Sales Exec: Bob Kupper
Mktg Mgr: DOT Frank

D-U-N-S 02-081-1123 IMP
KURABE AMERICA CORP
38777 6 Mile Rd Ste 204, Livonia, MI 48152-2660
Tel (734) 464-2120 *Founded/Ownrshp* 2006
Sales 17.4MM^E *EMP* 1,100
SIC 7699 7549 Professional instrument repair services; High performance auto repair & service; Professional instrument repair services; High performance auto repair & service
CEO: Yasuto Kanazawa
**Pr:* Takenobu Kanazawa

D-U-N-S 11-894-9304
KURANI INC
PIZZA HUT
210 Center Ct, Anchorage, AK 99518-1621
Tel (907) 562-2205 *Founded/Ownrshp* 1984
Sales 11.7MM^E *EMP* 400
SIC 5812 Pizzeria, chain; Pizzeria, chain
CEO: Kurban Kurani
Treas: Carolyn Kurani

D-U-N-S 96-493-4756
KURANI PIZZA INC
PIZZA HUT
2825 Breckinridge Blvd # 150, Duluth, GA 30096-7600
Tel (770) 923-2313 *Founded/Ownrshp* 1994
Sales 57.3MM^E *EMP* 2,559

SIC 5812 Pizzeria, chain; Pizzeria, chain
Pr: Sultan Kurani
Off Mgr: Aneela Huwaja

D-U-N-S 94-809-5245 IMP/EXP
KURARAY AMERICA INC
KAI
(*Suby of* KURARAY HOLDINGS USA INC) ★
2625 Bay Area Blvd # 600, Houston, TX 77058-1523
Tel (281) 474-1592 *Founded/Ownrshp* 2000
Sales 263.7MM^E *EMP* 220
SIC 2821 3081 3843 Vinyl resins; Polyvinyl film & sheet; Glue, dental; Vinyl resins; Polyvinyl film & sheet; Glue, dental
Pr: George Avdey
Pr: Bob Chvala
VP: Nobu Hironaka
VP: Lee Nugent
VP: David Schreckengost
VP: Kazu Takeuchi
Exec: Christian Amad
Opers Mgr: Eric Bass
Opers Mgr: Michael Iwanski
Plnt Mgr: Scott Landon
Sales Exec: Ritsu Seike

D-U-N-S 17-470-8540 EXP
KURARAY HOLDINGS USA INC
(*Suby of* KURARAY CO., LTD.)
2625 Bay Area Blvd, Houston, TX 77058-1523
Tel (713) 495-7311 *Founded/Ownrshp* 1996
Sales 263.7MM^E *EMP* 235
SIC 5047 5049 2821 Dental equipment & supplies; Optical goods; Vinyl resins; Dental equipment & supplies; Optical goods; Vinyl resins
Pr: Yuichi Kawarasaki

D-U-N-S 07-915-7735
KURE GROUP LLC
1645 Camden Ave Apt 401, Los Angeles, CA 90025-7546
Tel (310) 498-8460 *Founded/Ownrshp* 2013
Sales 50.0MM *EMP* 5
SIC 2111 5194 Cigarettes; Cigarettes; Cigarettes; Cigarettes
CEO: Monica Ord

D-U-N-S 17-628-0295 IMP
KUREHA AMERICA INC
(*Suby of* KUREHA CORPORATION)
420 Lexington Ave Rm 2510, New York, NY 10170-1402
Tel (212) 867-7040 *Founded/Ownrshp* 1995
Sales 28.7MM^E *EMP* 61
SIC 5169 Chemicals & allied products
Ch Bd: Yoshitsugu Nishibayashi
**Pr:* Naoya Suzuki
VP: Takeshi Matsukata
**VP:* Keisuke Narumi
Mktg Mgr: Gerry Benedicto

D-U-N-S 06-066-5054
KURION INC
2020 Main St Ste 300, Irvine, CA 92614-8232
Tel (949) 398-6350 *Founded/Ownrshp* 2008
Sales 84.7MM^E *EMP* 160
SIC 4953 Radioactive waste materials, disposal
CEO: William Gallo
Pr: Jacques Besnainou
CFO: Jonathan Foster
CFO: Stephen Wright
Treas: Josh Wolfe
Ex VP: David Brockman
Sr VP: David Carlson
Sr VP: Phil Ohl
VP: Gaetan Bonhomme
VP: Yohei Iwasaki
VP: Rich Keenan

D-U-N-S 06-275-3806 IMP
KURITA AMERICA INC
(*Suby of* KURITA WATER INDUSTRIES LTD.)
1313 Valwood Pkwy Ste 370, Carrollton, TX 75006-8382
Tel (972) 484-4438 *Founded/Ownrshp* 1996
Sales 22.0MM *EMP* 31
Accts Cornwell Jackson Pllc Plano
SIC 3589 Sewage treatment equipment; Water treatment equipment, industrial; Sewage treatment equipment; Water treatment equipment, industrial
Pr: Masahiko Mitsuta
CFO: Miko Mat
VP: Bryan Baxley
VP: Bruce Harlan
Off Mgr: Naomi Arai
IT Man: Kathy Laplace
Sls Mgr: Monty Wheeler

D-U-N-S 07-440-3312 IMP/EXP
KURIYAMA OF AMERICA INC (IL)
(*Suby of* KURIYAMA HOLDINGS CORPORATION)
360 E State Pkwy, Schaumburg, IL 60173-5335
Tel (847) 519-0355 *Founded/Ownrshp* 1968
Sales 85.8MM^E *EMP* 150
SIC 5085 3052 Hose, belting & packing; Rubber & plastics hose & beltings; Hose, belting & packing; Rubber & plastics hose & beltings
Pr: Lester A Kraska
**Treas:* Fred Bobzien
Bd of Dir: Masahide Okumura
**VP:* Motohiro Majikima
VP: Motohiro Majikina
Exec: Tsutomu Hitomi
Genl Mgr: Brian Detton
Genl Mgr: Brian Dutton
Genl Mgr: Hassan Salim
IT Man: Dura Hose
Opers Mgr: Chantell Van Leer
Board of Directors: Brian Dutton, Thomas Hanyok, Terry Jackson, Gary Kammes, Gary Kammes

KURK FUEL COMPANY
See GOETZ ENERGY CORP

KURT J LESKER
See KURT J LESKER CO

D-U-N-S 01-497-9595 IMP
KURT J LESKER CO (PA)
KURT J LESKER
1925 Worthington Ave, Clairton, PA 15025
Tel (412) 387-9200 *Founded/Ownrshp* 1968
Sales 76.4MM^E *EMP* 225
SIC 3559 Semiconductor manufacturing machinery; Semiconductor manufacturing machinery
Pr: Kurt J Lesker III
**CFO:* John A Ross
VP: Adam Bartlett
**VP:* Duane Bingaman
**VP:* Allen R Demetrius
**VP:* Chuck Deventura
**VP:* Richard C Johnson
**VP:* Cindy Lesker
**VP:* John Lubic
**VP:* Dennis Sollon
VP: Herbert Tembusch

D-U-N-S 05-968-0165 IMP
KURT MANUFACTURING CO INC
5280 Main St Ne, Minneapolis, MN 55421-1594
Tel (763) 572-1500 *Founded/Ownrshp* 1946
Sales 131.2MM^E *EMP* 410
SIC 3499 3545 3363 3728 3842 3365 Machine bases, metal; Vises, machine (machine tool accessories); Aluminum die-castings; Gears, aircraft power transmission; Wheelchairs; Aluminum foundries; Machine bases, metal; Vises, machine (machine tool accessories); Aluminum die-castings; Gears, aircraft power transmission; Wheelchairs; Aluminum foundries
Ch: William G Kuban
**Pr:* Steven Carlsen
**CEO:* Paul Lillyblad
VP: Dan Moore
**VP:* Kelli Watson
Prgrm Mgr: Tim Laitinen
Prgrm Mgr: Rick Pasche
Dept Mgr: Darren Kitz
Genl Mgr: Gloria Duran
Genl Mgr: Jeff Lenz
Dir IT: Tom Moore

D-U-N-S 00-169-4025 IMP
KURT S ADLER INC
SANTA'S WORLD
7 W 34th St Ste C100, New York, NY 10001-3018
Tel (212) 924-0900 *Founded/Ownrshp* 1946
Sales 49.4MM^E *EMP* 100
SIC 5199 Christmas novelties; Christmas trees, including artificial
CEO: Clifford Adler
**Pr:* Howard Adler
**CFO:* Karen Adler
VP: Louis Benjamin
Genl Mgr: J P Messenkopf
Sls Mgr: Nolan Skolnick

D-U-N-S 00-325-6450
KURT SALMON US INC
HEALTH CARE MGT COUNSELORS
(*Suby of* MANAGEMENT CONSULTING GROUP PLC)
1355 Peachtree St Ne # 900, Atlanta, GA 30309-3257
Tel (404) 892-0321 *Founded/Ownrshp* 1935, 2007
Sales 94.7MM^E *EMP* 1,003
SIC 8742

KURT WEISS FLORIST
See KURT WEISS GREENHOUSES INC

D-U-N-S 01-352-2008 IMP
KURT WEISS GREENHOUSES INC
KURT WEISS FLORIST
95 Main St, Center Moriches, NY 11934-1703
Tel (631) 878-2500 *Founded/Ownrshp* 1960
Sales 393.4MM^E *EMP* 1,000
SIC 0181 5193 Plants, potted: growing of; Plants, potted; Plants, potted: growing of; Plants, potted
Pr: Russell Weiss
**VP:* Kirk Weiss
VP: Wayne Weiss
IT Man: Ravindra Parasram

KURTIS KITCHEN & BATH CENTERS
See KURTIS MANUFACTURING & DISTRIBUTING CORP

D-U-N-S 04-928-3757
KURTIS MANUFACTURING & DISTRIBUTING CORP
KURTIS KITCHEN & BATH CENTERS
12500 Merriman Rd, Livonia, MI 48150-1928
Tel (734) 522-7600 *Founded/Ownrshp* 1969
Sales 36.9MM^E *EMP* 95
SIC 5021 5211 5031 5712 2434 2541 Household furniture; Counter tops; Kitchen cabinets; Cabinet work, custom; Wood kitchen cabinets; Wood partitions & fixtures; Counter tops; Household furniture; Cabinet work, custom; Kitchen cabinets; Wood kitchen cabinets; Wood partitions & fixtures
Pr: Howard Kuretzky
**VP:* Wayne Weintraub
VP: Wayne Winetrap

D-U-N-S 00-433-6079 IMP
KURTZ BROS
400 Reed St, Clearfield, PA 16830-2585
Tel (814) 765-6561 *Founded/Ownrshp* 1999
Sales 25.3MM^E *EMP* 108
SIC 2621 2752 Tablet paper; Promotional printing, lithographic; Tablet paper; Promotional printing, lithographic
CEO: Monty Kunes
**Ch Bd:* Robert M Kurtz
**CFO:* Matthew C Hoover
**VP:* James H Liu
Genl Mgr: Dana Jagger
Plnt Mgr: Dave Strickland
Mktg Mgr: Jeffery Pistner
Sls Mgr: Chris Barrett

D-U-N-S 04-494-4700
KURTZ BROS INC
6415 Granger Rd, Independence, OH 44131-1413
Tel (216) 986-7000 *Founded/Ownrshp* 1974
Sales 41.1MM^E *EMP* 136
SIC 5031 5211

D-U-N-S 19-692-3247 IMP
KURYAKYN HOLDINGS LLC
(*Suby of* MOTORSPORT AFTERMARKET GROUP INC) ★
454 County Road Vv, Somerset, WI 54025-9031
Tel (715) 247-5008 *Founded/Ownrshp* 2010
Sales 53.9MM^E *EMP* 140
SIC 5013 5571 Motorcycle parts; Motorcycle parts & accessories
Pr: Holger Mohr
Pr: Tom Ellsworth
**Prin:* Tom Rudd
Mktg Dir: Marc Wolfram
Sls Dir: John Petta
Mktg Mgr: Bryan Desimone
Sls Mgr: Kelly Bowers
Sls Mgr: Matt Leisch

D-U-N-S 02-232-6677 IMP
KURZ TRANSFER PRODUCTS LP
3200 Woodpark Blvd, Charlotte, NC 28206-4211
Tel (704) 927-3700 *Founded/Ownrshp* 2004
Sales 73.7MM^E *EMP* 190
SIC 3497 Metal foil & leaf; Metal foil & leaf
COO: Drew Beringer
CFO: Thomas Hertlein
Dir IT: Brian Hill
Dir IT: Scott McCarty
Opers Mgr: Kurz Wilcox
Plnt Mgr: Mike Starzubic
Prd Mgr: Larue Cribb
Ql Cn Mgr: Robert Beck
Ql Cn Mgr: Stephen Schwartz
VP Mktg: John Keane

D-U-N-S 01-091-2798
KUSER VILLAGE
160 S Livingston Ave, Livingston, NJ 07039-3033
Tel (973) 992-8200 *Founded/Ownrshp* 1973
Sales 50.0MM^E *EMP* 110
SIC 6513 6531 Apartment building operators; Real estate agents & managers; Apartment building operators; Real estate agents & managers
Mng Pt: Donald Legow

D-U-N-S 80-878-7220 IMP/EXP
KUSHA INC
LT FOODS AMERICA
(*Suby of* LT FOODS LIMITED)
11130 Warland Dr, Cypress, CA 90630-5032
Tel (562) 340-4040 *Founded/Ownrshp* 2007
Sales 21.5MM^E *EMP* 30
SIC 5499 5411 Gourmet food stores; Grocery stores
CEO: Abhinav Arora
**CEO:* Jerry Taylor
**CFO:* Mukesh Agrawal
VP: Mukesh Agarwal
VP: Nadine Curias
VP: Tom De Casteele
VP: SAI Krishnan
VP: Sundeep Lamba
VP: Jatinder Sabhlok
Off Mgr: Punam Ashtana
Ql Cn Mgr: Ankush Kukreja

D-U-N-S 13-048-0437
KUSHNER COMPANIES INC
WESTMINSTER MANAGEMENT
666 5th Ave Fl 15, New York, NY 10103-0001
Tel (212) 527-7000 *Founded/Ownrshp* 1984
Sales 145.1MM^E *EMP* 650
SIC 1521 6513 6531 6512 1522 1531 New construction, single-family houses; Townhouse construction; Apartment building operators; Condominium manager; Cooperative apartment manager; Real estate brokers & agents; Multiple listing service, real estate; Nonresidential building operators; Apartment building construction; Co-op construction; Condominium construction; Condominium developers; Cooperative apartment developers; New construction, single-family houses; Townhouse construction; Apartment building operators; Condominium manager; Cooperative apartment manager; Real estate brokers & agents; Multiple listing service, real estate; Nonresidential building operators; Apartment building construction; Co-op construction; Condominium construction; Condominium developers; Cooperative apartment developers
Pr: Charles Kushner
CFO: Lawrence Lipton
VP: Gladys Vanterpool
**Genl Mgr:* Richard Stadtmauer
Genl Couns: Laurence Rabinowitz
Genl Couns: Sampson Schmitt

KUSI TV CHANNEL 51
See MCKINNON BROADCASTING CO

D-U-N-S 05-566-5624
KUSKOKWIM CORP
4300 B St Ste 207, Anchorage, AK 99503-5951
Tel (907) 243-2944 *Founded/Ownrshp* 1977
Sales 35.7MM^E *EMP* 148
SIC 6799 8742 6512 Security speculators for own account; Management consulting services; Commercial & industrial building operation; Security speculators for own account; Management consulting services; Commercial & industrial building operation
Pr: Mazer Carey
**Pr:* Maver Carey
**Ch:* Leo Morgan

D-U-N-S 96-955-7532 IMP
KUSS FILTRATION INC
2150 Industrial Dr, Findlay, OH 45840-5402
Tel (419) 423-9040 *Founded/Ownrshp* 2011
Sales 198.8MM^E *EMP* 600
SIC 3569 Filters, general line: industrial; Filters, general line: industrial
CEO: Hasnain R Merchant
**Ch Bd:* Nick Galambos
**CFO:* John Byrnes
CFO: Tom Hogan
**VP:* Gary L Rickle
VP: Gary Rickle
Ex Dir: Gulsu Law

Ql Cn Mgr: Pamela Abner
Sls Mgr: Rick Ganfi

D-U-N-S 96-332-2540
KUSSY INC
QUALITY FLOORING JACKSON HOLE
1260 Huff Ln Ste B, Jackson, WY 83001-8504
Tel (307) 739-9465 *Founded/Ownrshp* 1995
Sales 116.2MM *EMP* 2
SIC 1752 5713 Carpet laying; Floor covering stores; Carpet laying; Floor covering stores
Pr: Richard Kussy
**Sec:* Kimmi Kussy
Off Mgr: Kimberly Townsend

D-U-N-S 60-814-3533 IMP
KUSTOM BLENDING LLC
KUSTOM GROUP
3 Carbon Way, Walton, KY 41094-9370
Tel (859) 485-8600 *Founded/Ownrshp* 2003
Sales 22.1MM^E *EMP* 53
SIC 2899 Chemical preparations
Tech Mgr: James Chapman
Opers Mgr: Doug Diem

KUSTOM FOOD
See UWAJIMAYA INC

KUSTOM GROUP
See KUSTOM BLENDING LLC

KUSTOM PAK
See TUR-PAK FOODS INC

D-U-N-S 10-760-7749 IMP
KUSTOM PAK FOODS LTD
SHERMAN FAMILY FOODS
6201 Macarthur St, Sioux City, IA 51111-1313
Tel (712) 255-5108 *Founded/Ownrshp* 1985
Sales 90.6MM^E *EMP* 450
SIC 2015 2011 Chicken, processed; Pork products from pork slaughtered on site; Chicken, processed; Pork products from pork slaughtered on site
CEO: Stan Sherman Jr
Pr: Leroy Zachow
VP: Marc Sherman
VP: Stanley Sherman Jr

D-U-N-S 05-408-5196
KUSTOM SIGNALS INC
(*Suby of* PUBLIC SAFETY EQUIPMENT INC) ★
9652 Loiret Blvd, Lenexa, KS 66219-2406
Tel (913) 492-1400 *Founded/Ownrshp* 1996
Sales 30.1MM^E *EMP* 177
SIC 5731 3812

KUT FROM THE KLOTH
See SWATFAME INC

D-U-N-S 07-800-6301
KUTAK ROCK LLP
1650 Farnam St Fl 2, Omaha, NE 68102-2103
Tel (402) 346-6000 *Founded/Ownrshp* 1965
Sales 106.3MM^E *EMP* 750
SIC 8111 General practice law office; General practice attorney, lawyer; General practice law office; General practice attorney, lawyer
Ch: David A Jacobson
Mng Pt: James D Arundel
Mng Pt: Michael L Curry
Pr: Rosie Forsman
CFO: Vicki L Young
CFO: Vicki Young
Bd of Dir: Michael McDonnell
Chf Mktg O: David Amsden
Exec: Fred Clingman
Genl Mgr: Robert D Binderup
CIO: Kenneth Kroeger

D-U-N-S 00-423-6139 IMP
KUTOL PRODUCTS CO INC (OH)
100 Partnership Way, Sharonville, OH 45241-1571
Tel (513) 527-5500 *Founded/Ownrshp* 1912, 1985
Sales 55.6MM^E *EMP* 140
SIC 2841 Soap & other detergents; Soap & other detergents
Pr: Joseph W Rhodenbaugh
**VP:* Tom Rhodenbaugh
Plnt Mgr: Joe Mast
Plnt Mgr: Greg Nichols
Ql Cn Mgr: Kurt Buffenbarger

D-U-N-S 01-290-1484
KUTSHERS COUNTRY CLUB CORP
Kutsher Rd, Monticello, NY 12701
Tel (845) 794-6000 *Founded/Ownrshp* 1947
Sales 6.2MM^E *EMP* 300
Accts David B Jaffe Cpa
SIC 7011 Resort hotel; Resort hotel
Pr: Mark Kutsher
**Sec:* Helen Kutsher
Genl Mgr: Bella Farquhar

D-U-N-S 10-221-1422
KUTZLER EXPRESS INC
K I X
12737 60th St, Kenosha, WI 53144-7555
Tel (262) 857-7945 *Founded/Ownrshp* 1982
Sales 23.4MM^E *EMP* 110
SIC 4212 4213 Local trucking, without storage; Trucking, except local
Pr: Robert L Kutzler
**COO:* Frank Kutzler
**Sec:* R Scott Kutzler

D-U-N-S 01-167-3647
KUTZTOWN AREA SCHOOL DISTRICT
251 Long Lane Rd, Kutztown, PA 19530-9693
Tel (610) 683-7346 *Founded/Ownrshp* 1962
Sales 18.8MM^E *EMP* 300
SIC 8211 Public elementary & secondary schools; School board; Public elementary & secondary schools; School board
**CFO:* Joseph Pugliese
Exec: Rikki Clark
**Prin:* Brenda A Winkler
Teacher Pr: Barbara Richard

KUTZTOWN BOLOGNA
See GODSHALLS QUALITY MEATS INC

D-U-N-S 06-978-4734
KUTZTOWN UNIVERSITY OF PENNSYLVANIA
(*Suby of* STATE SYSTEM HIGHER EDUCATN PA) ★
15200 Kutztown Rd, Kutztown, PA 19530-9339
Tel (610) 683-4000 *Founded/Ownrshp* 1866
Sales 87.0MM^E *EMP* 844
SIC 8221 9411 University; Administration of educational programs; ; University; Administration of educational programs;
Pr: Javier F Cevallos
Treas: Zach Esposito
Ex VP: Carlos Vargas-Aburto
VP: Jennifer Schlegel
VP: Gerald Silberman
Assoc Dir: Valerie Med
Ex Dir: David Valuska
HC Dir: Nancy Wunderly

KUUPIK ARCTIC SERVICES
See ARCTIC CATERING INC

D-U-N-S 06-497-4263
KUUSAKOSKI US LLC
13543 S Route 30, Plainfield, IL 60544-1100
Tel (815) 782-7125 *Founded/Ownrshp* 2011
Sales 33.4MM^E *EMP* 35^E
SIC 4953 Recycling, waste materials
Pr: Richard Hipp
**CFO:* Timothy Bowers
Rgnl Mgr: Nate Talley

KUVARE HOLDINGS
See KUVARE INSURANCE SERVICES LLC

D-U-N-S 07-990-5812
KUVARE INSURANCE SERVICES LLC
KUVARE HOLDINGS
18 S Michigan Ave Fl 12, Chicago, IL 60603-3200
Tel (312) 276-5200 *Founded/Ownrshp* 2015
Sales NA *EMP* 10
SIC 6311 6371 Life insurance; Pension, health & welfare funds

KUVERA INTERNATIONAL
See VINMAR INTERNATIONAL HOLDINGS LTD

KV VET SUPPLY COMPANY
See KENNEL VACCINE VET SUPPLY CO

D-U-N-S 96-333-4409
KVAERNER AMERICAS INC
(*Suby of* KVARNER ASA)
3600 Briarpark Dr, Houston, TX 77042-5206
Tel (713) 988-2002 *Founded/Ownrshp* 2011
Sales 25.3MM^E *EMP* 150^E
SIC 8711 Engineering services; Construction & civil engineering
Pr: Glyn A Rodgers
VP: Hal Bouknight
VP: MO Islam
VP: Chris Neff
VP: John Siffert
VP: Donald Smuin
Sls Dir: Thomas Hewett

D-U-N-S 79-338-6194
KVAERNER NORTH AMERICAN CONSTRUCTION INC
(*Suby of* KVARNER ASA)
701 Technology Dr Ste 210, Canonsburg, PA 15317-9529
Tel (724) 416-6900 *Founded/Ownrshp* 2011
Sales 432.9MM^E *EMP* 1,500
Accts Grossman Yanak Ford Llp Pitts
SIC 1542 8741 Nonresidential construction; Construction management; Nonresidential construction; Construction management
Pr: Steve Harker
**CFO:* Jerome Myron
**Treas:* Barbara Fettig
Ex VP: Dane Osborn
Ex VP: Keith Vecchini
**VP:* Robert C Hoover
**VP:* Charles W Schropp
Admn Mgr: Peter Holt
Opers Mgr: Bruce Kingsbury

D-U-N-S 00-920-6673 IMP
KVAL INC
KVAL MACHINERY CO
825 Petaluma Blvd S, Petaluma, CA 94952-5134
Tel (707) 762-4363 *Founded/Ownrshp* 1961
Sales 33.2MM^E *EMP* 125
SIC 3553 5084 Woodworking machinery; Industrial machinery & equipment; Woodworking machinery; Industrial machinery & equipment
CEO: Gerald Kvalheim
Treas: Andrew M Kvalhei
**Treas:* Andrew M Kvalheim
Act CFO: Nate Kvalheim
**VP:* Dave Kvalheim
CTO: John Miller
Software D: Dave Schneider
Sftwr Eng: Steve Pinner
Plnt Mgr: Roger King
Surg Cl Rc: Dennis Sellers

KVAL MACHINERY CO
See KVAL INC

KVBC T.V.
See VALLEY BROADCASTING CO INC

D-U-N-S 09-134-8144
KVC BEHAVIORAL HEALTHCARE INC
KAW VALLEY CENTER
(*Suby of* KVC HEALTH SYSTEMS INC) ★
21350 W 153rd St, Olathe, KS 66061-5413
Tel (913) 322-4900 *Founded/Ownrshp* 1968
Sales 38.9MM *EMP* 320
Accts Bkd Llp Kansas City Mo
SIC 8361 Residential care for children; Residential care for children
Pr: Chad Anderson
Bd of Dir: Carrol Maersch
VP: Renny Arensberg
VP: Jodie Austin
**VP:* Danielle Bartelli
VP: Andrew Brookens
VP: Kim Hawekotte
VP: John Hoffman
VP: Jackie Suttington
VP: Frederick Watts
Exec: Tami Seaman
Comm Dir: Jenny Kutz

D-U-N-S 96-489-3676
KVC HEALTH SYSTEMS INC
21350 W 153rd St, Olathe, KS 66061-5413
Tel (913) 322-4904 *Founded/Ownrshp* 1968
Sales 10.5MM *EMP* 701^E
Accts Bkd Llp Kansas City Mo
SIC 8361 Residential care for children; Residential care for children
CEO: B Wayne Sims
**COO:* Anne Roberts
**CFO:* Paul Klayder
**Ex VP:* Renny Arensberg
**Ex VP:* Sandra Gasca-Gonzalez

KVCC
See KALAMAZOO VALLEY COMMUNITY COLLEGE

KVEO TV
See COMMUNICATIONS CORP OF AMERICA

D-U-N-S 09-320-7215 IMP/EXP
▲ KVH INDUSTRIES INC
50 Enterprise Ctr, Middletown, RI 02842-5279
Tel (401) 847-3327 *Founded/Ownrshp* 1978
Sales 172.5MM *EMP* 471
Tkr Sym KVHI *Exch* NGS
SIC 3663 3812 Mobile communication equipment; Navigational systems & instruments; Mobile communication equipment; Navigational systems & instruments
CEO: Martin A Kits Van Heyningen
CFO: Peter A Rendall
Ex VP: Brent C Bruun
Ex VP: Daniel R Conway
Sr VP: Robert J Balog
VP: Daren Benzi
VP: Felise B Feingold
VP: Neal Muhilly
**VP:* Robert W B Kits Van Heyningen
Ex Dir: Werner Trattner
Mng Dir: Mark Woodhead
Board of Directors: Mark S Ain, Stanley K Honey, Bruce J Ryan, Charles R Trimble

KVIA TV
See NPG HOLDINGS INC

D-U-N-S 13-053-6105 IMP/EXP
KVK PRECISION SPECIALTIES INC
425 Quincy Ave, Shenandoah, VA 22849-1739
Tel (540) 652-6102 *Founded/Ownrshp* 1978
Sales 25.3MM^E *EMP* 102
SIC 1761 3599 3444

D-U-N-S 08-401-5536
KVL AUDIO VISUAL SERVICES INC
466 Saw Mill River Rd, Ardsley, NY 10502-2112
Tel (212) 581-8050 *Founded/Ownrshp* 1976
Sales 24.2MM^E *EMP* 150
SIC 7359 5065 Audio-visual equipment & supply rental; Electronic parts & equipment; Audio-visual equipment & supply rental; Electronic parts & equipment
Ch Bd: Leslie L Lieberman
**CFO:* Nick Prignano
**Ex VP:* Bruce Borland
**VP:* Bill Larkin
VP: Robert McKiernan
**VP:* Robert Mickernan
Site Mgr: Matthew Hannan
Opers Mgr: Kyd Ellsworth

D-U-N-S 18-663-7815
KVL HOLDINGS INC
SAINT NICOLAS VINEYARD
37700 Foothill Rd, Soledad, CA 93960-9620
Tel (831) 678-2132 *Founded/Ownrshp* 1980
Sales 21.1MM^E *EMP* 55
SIC 0172 2084 6719 Grapes; Wines; Investment holding companies, except banks
CEO: Nicholaus Hahn

D-U-N-S 95-680-4082
KVOA COMMUNICATIONS INC
KVOA TV
(*Suby of* CORDILLERA COMMUNICATIONS INC) ★
209 W Elm St, Tucson, AZ 85705-6539
Tel (520) 624-2477 *Founded/Ownrshp* 1993
Sales 23.9MM^E *EMP* 100^E
SIC 4833 Television broadcasting stations
Pr: William Shaw
**Treas:* Roger A Berardinis
**VP:* John P Barnwell
Mktg Dir: Yvette Perez
Mktg Mgr: Jean Burleigh

KVOA TV
See KVOA COMMUNICATIONS INC

D-U-N-S 61-610-3107
■ KVS TRANSPORTATION INC
(*Suby of* C J SPECIALTY RENTAL TOOLS) ★
3752 Allen Rd, Bakersfield, CA 93314-9242
Tel (661) 589-5220 *Founded/Ownrshp* 1990
Sales 21.1MM^E *EMP* 170
SIC 4213 4212 Trucking, except local; Local trucking, without storage; Trucking, except local; Local trucking, without storage
CEO: Josh Comstock
**VP:* Ted Moore

D-U-N-S 60-990-3810 EXP
KW 1 ACQUISITION CO LLC
METRO LEXUS
13600 Brookpark Rd, Cleveland, OH 44135-5147
Tel (216) 916-6000 *Founded/Ownrshp* 2004
Sales 61.5MM^E *EMP* 188^E
SIC 5511 New & used car dealers; New & used car dealers
DP Exec: Jack Ross
MIS Dir: Don Holobinko
Sales Asso: Phil Cohen

KW COMPANIES
See KW INTERNATIONAL INC

D-U-N-S 07-985-6701
KW CONTAINER
110 Henderson Hwy, Troy, AL 36079-8240
Tel (334) 566-1563 *Founded/Ownrshp* 1999
Sales 53.9MM^E *EMP* 100
SIC 3081 3089 Polypropylene film & sheet; Plastic containers, except foam

KW FLOORING GROUP
See CARPETLAND INC

D-U-N-S 06-212-5356 IMP
KW INDUSTRIES INC
909 Industrial Blvd, Sugar Land, TX 77478-2887
Tel (281) 240-0909 *Founded/Ownrshp* 1972
Sales 50.3MM^E *EMP* 143
SIC 3648 Public lighting fixtures; Public lighting fixtures
Pr: James A White
**Ch Bd:* E A Kostelnik
**Treas:* Laura Estle

D-U-N-S 96-244-3677
KW INTERNATIONAL INC
KW COMPANIES
18655 Bishop Ave, Carson, CA 90746-4028
Tel (310) 747-1380 *Founded/Ownrshp* 1996
Sales 292.4MM^E *EMP* 600
SIC 4731 4226 8744 Freight transportation arrangement; Freight forwarding; Special warehousing & storage; Facilities support services; Freight transportation arrangement; Freight forwarding; Special warehousing & storage; Facilities support services
CEO: Kil Won Jin
**CFO:* Dj Kim
VP Admn: Dan Schrader
Ex Dir: Julie Gerberding

D-U-N-S 86-837-4406
KW INTERNATIONAL LLC
K W INTERNATIONAL
1223 Brittmoore Rd, Houston, TX 77043-4001
Tel (713) 468-9581 *Founded/Ownrshp* 1988
Sales 133.6MM^E *EMP* 170
SIC 3533 Oil & gas field machinery; Oil & gas field machinery
Pr: Kurt E Wind
Pr: George Foster
Pr: Kelly Froelich
COO: Joe Craft
COO: David Golden
CFO: Tom S Simms
VP: John Thompson
IT Man: Ben Hooten
Mfg Dir: Jeff Duncan
Mfg Dir: Jeff Wagner
Ql Cn Mgr: Lance Semon

KW LUBES
See KELLEY WILLIAMSON CO

D-U-N-S 00-442-6854
KW PLASTICS INC
279 Pike County Lake Rd, Troy, AL 36079
Tel (334) 566-1563 *Founded/Ownrshp* 1998
Sales NA *EMP* 310
SIC 3081 4581 4953 Polypropylene film & sheet; Hangar operation; Refuse systems

D-U-N-S 07-914-8696 IMP
KW PLASTICS RECYCLING DIVISION
279 Pike County Lake Rd, Troy, AL 36079
Tel (334) 566-1563 *Founded/Ownrshp* 1999
Sales 65.5MM^E *EMP* 110
SIC 2821 4581 3081 4953 Plastics materials & resins; Hangar operation; Polypropylene film & sheet; Refuse systems
Genl Mgr: Scott Saunders
Pr: Phillip Harris
Plnt Mgr: Anthony Smith
Prd Mgr: Mike Hukill

D-U-N-S 15-003-2774
KW PROPERTY MANAGEMENT LLC
KW PROPERTY MGT & CONSULTING
8200 Nw 33rd St Ste 300, Doral, FL 33122-1942
Tel (305) 476-9188 *Founded/Ownrshp* 2004
Sales 98.8MM^E *EMP* 630^E
SIC 6531 Real estate managers; Real estate managers
Mng Pt: Trycia Arencibi
Mng Pt: Katalina Cruz
COO: Horwitz Grant
COO: Grant Horwitz
Dist Mgr: Grant Hall
Dist Mgr: Tom Ryan
Dist Mgr: Scott Stewart
Dist Mgr: Sergio Ubilla
Genl Mgr: Mirian Padin
Off Mgr: Alicia Garcia-Perez
Off Mgr: Angela Segrera

KW PROPERTY MGT & CONSULTING
See KW PROPERTY MANAGEMENT LLC

D-U-N-S 00-894-6704
KW RASTALL OIL INC
2600 Us Highway 1, North Brunswick, NJ 08902-4305
Tel (732) 297-5600 *Founded/Ownrshp* 1995
Sales 37.3MM^E *EMP* 80
SIC 5172 Petroleum products; Petroleum products
Pr: Dave Rosenberg

D-U-N-S 00-546-2460
KW SERVICES LLC
3801 Voorde Dr Ste A, South Bend, IN 46628-1643
Tel (574) 232-2051 *Founded/Ownrshp* 1921, 2014
Sales 80.5MM^E *EMP* 140
SIC 6719 Investment holding companies, except banks; Investment holding companies, except banks
Pr: Paul M Witek
VP: William G Harlan Jr
VP: Stephen J Vivian
Plnt Mgr: Phil Meekins
Prd Mgr: Kyle Schriver
Sls Mgr: Trae Claypool
Sls Mgr: Ben Petty
Sales Asso: Nicolette Barone

D-U-N-S 11-435-3365
KWAJALEIN RANGE SERVICES LLC
KRS
(*Suby of* BECHTEL NATIONAL INC) ★
4975 Bradford Dr Nw # 600, Huntsville, AL 35805-1929
Tel (256) 890-8536 *Founded/Ownrshp* 2002
Sales 147.2MM^E *EMP* 1,500
SIC 8744 Facilities support services; Facilities support services
Sls Mgr: Gerard Sims

D-U-N-S 00-706-2011
KWAL-HOWELLS INC
STELLAR PAINT
5575 Dtc Pkwy Ste 100, Greenwood Village, CO 80111-3137
Tel (303) 371-5600 *Founded/Ownrshp* 1982
Sales NA *EMP* 800
SIC 2851 5198

D-U-N-S 78-805-7719 IMP
KWAN WO IRONWORKS INC
31628 Hayman St, Hayward, CA 94544-7122
Tel (415) 822-9628 *Founded/Ownrshp* 1992
Sales 34.4MM^E *EMP* 120^E
SIC 1791 Iron work, structural; Iron work, structural
Pr: Florence Kong
Off Mgr: Ada Tang
Snr Mgr: Stephen Tsoy

D-U-N-S 16-025-5170 IMP/EXP
KWANG JIN AMERICA INC
(*Suby of* KWANG JIN SANG GONG CO., LTD.)
32450 N Avis Dr, Madison Heights, MI 48071-1557
Tel (248) 589-8001 *Founded/Ownrshp* 2009
Sales 60.4MM *EMP* 73^E
Accts Soon B Hong Cpa - Green Accou
SIC 5531 Automotive parts; Automotive parts
Ch Bd: Young Jik Kwon
**Pr:* Yong Joo Lee

D-U-N-S 79-000-9679 IMP
KWANGSUNG AMERICA CORP
(*Suby of* KWANGSUNG CORPORATION LTD.)
217 Thweatt Indus Blvd, Dadeville, AL 36853-2609
Tel (256) 825-8002 *Founded/Ownrshp* 2006
Sales 55.2MM *EMP* 400
Accts Jise Pc Duluth Ga
SIC 5013 Automotive supplies & parts; Automotive supplies & parts
CEO: Moon Wook Kim
**Pr:* Thil Sung

D-U-N-S 62-241-1820
KWD LLD FAMILY ENTERPRISES LLC
PERFORMANCE MOBILITY
9500 W 49th Ave Ste C107, Wheat Ridge, CO 80033-2201
Tel (303) 467-9981 *Founded/Ownrshp* 2006
Sales 20.4MM^E *EMP* 50^E
SIC 5511 Vans, new & used
Sls Mgr: Michelle Lucero

D-U-N-S 10-265-0327 IMP
KWDZ MANUFACTURING LLC
337 S Anderson St, Los Angeles, CA 90033-3742
Tel (323) 526-3526 *Founded/Ownrshp* 1999
Sales 21.6MM^E *EMP* 80
SIC 2361 T-shirts & tops: girls', children's & infants'

D-U-N-S 04-153-4892
■ KWGN INC
C W 2
(*Suby of* TRIBUNE BROADCASTING CO INC) ★
100 E Speer Blvd, Denver, CO 80203-3437
Tel (303) 740-2222 *Founded/Ownrshp* 1966
Sales 28.0MM *EMP* 40
SIC 4833 Television broadcasting stations; Television broadcasting stations
Genl Mgr: Dennis Leonard
VP: Richard Lowden
Sls Mgr: John Strassner

KWI
See KLIGER-WEISS INFOSYSTEMS INC

KWIK CHEK FOOD STORES
See KWIK CHEK REAL ESTATE TRUST INC

D-U-N-S 15-469-3741
KWIK CHEK FOOD STORES INC
K C FOOD
2207 N Center St, Bonham, TX 75418-2112
Tel (903) 583-7484 *Founded/Ownrshp* 1975
Sales 164.3MM^E *EMP* 425
Accts Fox Byrd & Company Pc Dal
SIC 5541 5411 Filling stations, gasoline; Convenience stores, independent; Filling stations, gasoline; Convenience stores, independent
Pr: Doyce Taylor
**CFO:* Becky Moore
**VP:* Bobby Mc Craw
Sales Exec: Sherry Capehart

D-U-N-S 10-528-6640
KWIK CHEK REAL ESTATE TRUST INC
KWIK CHEK FOOD STORES
2207 N Center St, Bonham, TX 75418-2112
Tel (903) 583-7481 *Founded/Ownrshp* 1998
Sales 86.1MM *EMP* 50
SIC 6798 Real estate investment trusts; Real estate investment trusts
Pr: Doyce Taylor
**VP:* Bobby McCraw
Prd Mgr: Lance Davis

D-U-N-S 06-187-9060 IMP/EXP
KWIK GOAL LTD (PA)
140 Pacific Dr, Quakertown, PA 18951-3608
Tel (800) 531-4252 *Founded/Ownrshp* 1981
Sales 30.2MM^E *EMP* 60
SIC 5091 3949 Sporting & recreation goods; Soccer equipment & supplies
CEO: Vincent C Caruso

*Pr: Anthony Caruso
CFO: Doug Propst
VP: Ellen Farewell
Telecom Mg: John Huhn
Plnt Mgr: Arden McCue
Sls&Mrk Ex: James Pepe
Manager: Bill Horvath
Sls Mgr: Tim Tobin

D-U-N-S 00-924-6067 IMP
KWIK LOK CORP (WA)
(Suby of KLC HOLDINGS LTD) ★
2712 S 16th Ave, Yakima, WA 98903-9530
Tel (509) 248-4770 Founded/Ownrshp 1989
Sales 32.5MM[E] EMP 165
SIC 3565 Packaging machinery; Packaging machinery
Pr: Jerre H Paxton
*Sec: Lorne House
IT Man: Mike Paxton

KWIK MART
See HAYS CITY CORP

KWIK SHOP
See RUSSELL PETROLEUM CORP

D-U-N-S 03-127-2206
■ **KWIK SHOP INC**
(Suby of KROGER CO) ★
734 E 4th Ave, Hutchinson, KS 67501-2274
Tel (620) 669-8504 Founded/Ownrshp 2001
Sales 197.0MM[E] EMP 1,507
SIC 5411 Convenience stores, chain; Convenience stores, chain
Pr: Micheal Hoffman
*CFO: Mike Gerwert
Treas: Scott Henderson
Sr VP: William Hjelm
*VP: Pat Edwards
*VP: Kenny Nuss
Dist Mgr: Neal Sewyer
Dir IT: Dennis Farrell
VP Opers: Brian Fisher
VP Opers: Tim Roark
Opers Mgr: Scott Morgaridge

KWIK STOP
See RAINBO OIL CO

D-U-N-S 05-903-9339
KWIK TRIP INC
1626 Oak St, La Crosse, WI 54603-2308
Tel (608) 781-8988 Founded/Ownrshp 1971
Sales 2.1MMM[E] EMP 10,500
Accts Mcgladrey & Pullen Llp Minne
SIC 5411 5541 5993 5921 5983 Convenience stores, chain; Filling stations, gasoline; Tobacco stores & stands; Liquor stores; Fuel oil dealers; Convenience stores, chain; Filling stations, gasoline; Tobacco stores & stands; Liquor stores; Fuel oil dealers
Pr: Don Zietlow
*CFO: Scott Teigen
*VP: Steve Loehr
*VP: Greg Olson
*VP: Thomas Reinhart
*VP: Robert Thorud
VP: David Wills
*VP: Steve Zietlow
Exec: Mila Cabral
Exec: Ed Strahs
Genl Mgr: Gretchen Knudson-Stuhr

KWIKEE
See MULTI-AD SERVICES INC

D-U-N-S 60-286-0520 IMP
■ **KWIKSET CORP**
SPECTRUM BRANDS HDWR HM IMPRV
(Suby of RAYOVAC) ★
19701 Da Vinci, Foothill Ranch, CA 92610-2622
Tel (949) 672-4000 Founded/Ownrshp 2012
Sales 928.2MM[E] EMP 3,200
SIC 3429 Keys, locks & related hardware; Keys, locks & related hardware
CEO: David R Lumley

KWOK'S FOOD SERVICE
See CHARLES AUTIN LIMITED

D-U-N-S 02-510-2492 IMP
KWONG YET LUNG CO INC
UNITED INVESTMENTS
5000 S Decatur Blvd, Las Vegas, NV 89118-1515
Tel (702) 889-2888 Founded/Ownrshp 1980
Sales 53.8MM[E] EMP 100
SIC 5141 5411 Groceries, general line; Grocery stores, independent; Groceries, general line; Grocery stores, independent
Pr: Joyce Kwan

D-U-N-S 15-480-2789
KWONS CORP
2902 Union St, Flushing, NY 11354-2201
Tel (718) 445-5656 Founded/Ownrshp 1984
Sales 26.1MM EMP 40
SIC 5411 Grocery stores, independent; Grocery stores, independent
Pr: Ilyeon Kwon
VP: Sun Huh
Genl Mgr: Daniel Pak

D-U-N-S 05-208-1908
KWS INC
STAAB MANAGEMENT CO
3048 W Stolley Park Rd, Grand Island, NE 68801-7227
Tel (308) 382-1053 Founded/Ownrshp 1981
Sales 43.7MM[E] EMP 1,400
SIC 5812 Pizzeria, chain; Pizzeria, chain
Pr: Kenneth Staab
*Treas: Dean Olson

D-U-N-S 05-867-4342 EXP
KWS MANUFACTURING CO LTD
3041 Conveyor Dr, Burleson, TX 76028-1857
Tel (817) 295-2247 Founded/Ownrshp 2002
Sales 63.1MM[E] EMP 135
SIC 3535 5084 Belt conveyor systems, general industrial use; Industrial machinery & equipment; Belt conveyor systems, general industrial use; Industrial machinery & equipment
Pt: William C Mecke
*VP: Jim Collins
IT Man: Andy Gant
Manager: Jimmy Dufinetz
Manager: Kris Gililland
Manager: Ray Rogers
Manager: Ian Smith
Manager: Kevin Turner
Sls Mgr: Tannen McDonald

D-U-N-S 80-886-0977
KWS-SEEDS INC
(Suby of KWS SAAT SE)
5705 W Old Shakopee Rd # 110, Bloomington, MN 55437-3103
Tel (952) 445-8911 Founded/Ownrshp 2005
Sales 37.7MM[E] EMP 150
SIC 8731 0181 5191 Agricultural research; Seeds, vegetable: growing of; Seeds: field, garden & flower
CFO: Don Weaver
*Sr VP: E Joe Dahmer

KWTV-CHANNEL 9
See GRIFFIN TELEVISION OKC LLC

D-U-N-S 82-516-7427 IMP
■ **KX TECHNOLOGIES LLC**
(Suby of MARMON WATER LLC) ★
55 Railroad Ave, West Haven, CT 06516-4143
Tel (203) 799-9000 Founded/Ownrshp 2004
Sales 29.4MM[E] EMP 150[E]
SIC 3589 Water purification equipment, household type; Water filters & softeners, household type; Water purification equipment, household type; Water filters & softeners, household type
VP Mktg: Kelly Boudreau
Sls Dir: Terry Lemon

D-U-N-S 83-152-1526
KX2 HOLDINGS BUILDING TECHNOLOGIES GROUP LP
(Suby of CLIMATEC) ★
2851 W Kathleen Rd, Phoenix, AZ 85053-4053
Tel (602) 944-3330 Founded/Ownrshp 2008
Sales 43.0MM EMP 150
SIC 4961 Air conditioning supply services; Air conditioning supply services
Pt: Terry Keenen
Pt: Jimeen Hamblen
Pt: Jack Kucera
Pt: Thomas Paterno

KXLY-TV
See SPOKANE TELEVISION INC

D-U-N-S 78-813-0755
■ **KXTV INC**
K X T V CHANNEL 10
(Suby of TEGNA INC) ★
400 Broadway, Sacramento, CA 95818-2041
Tel (916) 441-2345 Founded/Ownrshp 1999
Sales 39.7MM[E] EMP 160
SIC 4833 Television broadcasting stations; Television broadcasting stations
Pr: Maria Barrs
Trfc Mgr: Terri Acevedo
VP Mktg: Elizabeth Bishop

KY RIVER FOOTHILLS HEAD START
See KENTUCKY RIVER FOOTHILLS DEVELOPMENT COUNCIL INC

D-U-N-S 00-685-2263
KY-3 INC (MO)
KYTV
(Suby of SCHURZ COMMUNICATIONS INC) ★
999 W Sunshine St, Springfield, MO 65807-2443
Tel (417) 268-3000 Founded/Ownrshp 1951, 1987
Sales 20.2MM[E] EMP 180
SIC 4833 Television translator station; Television translator station
Pr: Mike Scott
*VP: Angela Moyle

D-U-N-S 10-268-8624
KYADAX CORP
9145 Ellis Rd, Melbourne, FL 32904-1019
Tel (321) 723-5395 Founded/Ownrshp 1985
Sales 29.5MM[E] EMP 162
SIC 6719 Investment holding companies, except banks; Investment holding companies, except banks
Pr: David Christiano

D-U-N-S 00-794-0117 EXP
KYANITE MINING CORP (VA)
BUFFALO WOOD PRODUCTS DIV
30 Willis Mtn Plant Ln, Dillwyn, VA 23936-3433
Tel (434) 983-2085 Founded/Ownrshp 1928, 1945
Sales 148.2MM[E] EMP 300
SIC 1459 Kyanite mining; Kyanite mining
Pr: Dixon Jr Gene Bishop
*Treas: Ron Hudgins
*VP: Dixon Guy Bishop
VP: Guy Dixon
IT Man: Lakshmi Bertram
VP Opers: Barry Jones
S&M/VP: Hank Jamerson

D-U-N-S 18-368-8837 IMP
KYB AMERICAS CORP
(Suby of KYB CORPORATION)
2625 N Morton St, Franklin, IN 46131-8820
Tel (317) 736-7774 Founded/Ownrshp 2001
Sales 105.8MM[E] EMP 500
SIC 3714 Shock absorbers, motor vehicle; Shock absorbers, motor vehicle
Pr: Hiroaki Hirayama
*Pr: A Tanaka
CFO: Richard A Smith
Genl Mgr: Wade Cunningham
Genl Mgr: Dan Pierson
Sfty Mgr: Jerry Reamer
Mfg Mgr: Gil Iames
Ql Cn Mgr: Cole Johnson
Ql Cn Mgr: Kenneth Ralph
Manager: Ryan Dickerman

D-U-N-S 00-915-2752 IMP
KYD INC
KYAMADA DISTRIBUTORS
2949 Koapaka St, Honolulu, HI 96819-1923
Tel (808) 836-3221 Founded/Ownrshp 1948
Sales 41.8MM[E] EMP 92
Accts Chee & Yamasaki Honolulu Haw
SIC 5113 2673 2674 Bags, paper & disposable plastic; Plastic bags: made from purchased materials; Cellophane bags, unprinted: made from purchased materials; Paper bags: made from purchased materials; Bags, paper & disposable plastic; Plastic bags: made from purchased materials; Cellophane bags, unprinted: made from purchased materials; Paper bags: made from purchased materials
Pr: Dexter Yamada
*CEO: Gilbert Yamada
*COO: Glenn Horiuchi
*VP: Carmelita Dayao-Phillips
*VP: Chester Lee
*VP: Gregory Mishima

D-U-N-S 03-952-8021 IMP/EXP
KYKENKEE INC
18719 Hwy 11 N, Vance, AL 35490
Tel (205) 553-8593 Founded/Ownrshp 1938
Sales 27.0MM[E] EMP 53
SIC 2421 Sawmills & planing mills, general
Pr: Kyle Burt
*Treas: L Kendall Burt
*VP: Keefe Burt

D-U-N-S 80-960-8750 IMP
KYKLOS BEARING INTERNATIONAL LLC
K B I
2509 Hayes Ave, Sandusky, OH 44870-5359
Tel (419) 627-7000 Founded/Ownrshp 2008
Sales 143.5MM[E] EMP 900
SIC 3714 Bearings, motor vehicle; Bearings, motor vehicle
Pr: George Thanopoulos
Exec: Chris Kettereer
Dir IT: Anthony Cundari
Sfty Dirs: Bob Voltz
Opers Supe: Christopher Marquart
Manager: Terence Kehres
Plnt Mgr: Debbie Bialorucki
Plnt Mgr: Gene Biroth
Ql Cn Mgr: Pan Balgude
Ql Cn Mgr: Bruce Rockwell

D-U-N-S 96-718-9882
KYLE ENTERPRISES LLC
MILLENNIUM
700 Veterans Pkwy # 204, Lake Geneva, WI 53147-4621
Tel (262) 249-8705 Founded/Ownrshp 2007
Sales 33.7MM EMP 40
SIC 5065 5063 Communication equipment; Electrical apparatus & equipment; Communication equipment; Electrical apparatus & equipment

KYMA TELEVISION
See YUMA BROADCASTING CO

D-U-N-S 07-857-1830 IMP
KYMETA CORP
12277 134th Ct Ne Ste 100, Redmond, WA 98052-2431
Tel (425) 896-3700 Founded/Ownrshp 2012
Sales 30.7MM[E] EMP 100
SIC 3663 Satellites, communications; Television antennas (transmitting) & ground equipment; Satellites, communications; Television antennas (transmitting) & ground equipment
CEO: Nathan Kundtz
*Pr: Vern Fotheringham
*Pr: Bob McCambridge
*CFO: John Schilling
*CFO: Marc Stolzman

D-U-N-S 06-869-2732
KYNETIC LLC
225 Washington St, Conshohocken, PA 19428-4122
Tel (484) 534-8100 Founded/Ownrshp 2011
Sales 364.3MM[E] EMP 920
SIC 8741 5961 Business management; Catalog & mail-order houses; Business management; Catalog & mail-order houses
CEO: Michael G Rubin
CFO: Michael R Conn
VP: Saj Cherian
Genl Couns: Jonathan S Schoenfeld

D-U-N-S 03-319-4572
KYO-YA HOTELS & RESORTS LP
(Suby of KOKUSAI KOGYO KANRI CO.,LTD.)
2255 Kalakaua Ave Fl 2, Honolulu, HI 96815-2515
Tel (808) 931-8600 Founded/Ownrshp 1961
Sales 250.1MM[E] EMP 3,638
SIC 7011 5812 5813 Hotels & motels; Eating places; Bar (drinking places); Hotels & motels; Eating places; Bar (drinking places)
Pr: Takamasa Osano
Pr: Greg Dichkens
COO: Ernest Nishizaki
Sr VP: Nobutada Nagai
Exec: Kevin Gleason
Exec: Nona Tamanaha
Mng Dir: William Hurley
IT Man: Ken Sato
Sys/Mgr: Allan Sato
Board of Directors: Kenichi Uchida

KYOCEARA
See KYOCERA TYCOM CORP

D-U-N-S 17-451-9678 IMP
■ **KYOCERA AMERICA INC**
(Suby of KYOCERA INTERNATIONAL, INC.)
8611 Balboa Ave, San Diego, CA 92123-1580
Tel (858) 576-2600 Founded/Ownrshp 1978
Sales 90.5MM EMP 650
SIC 3674 Integrated circuits, semiconductor networks, etc.; Integrated circuits, semiconductor networks, etc.
CEO: Robert Whisler
*Treas: William Edwards
*VP: Eiji Tanaka
Netwrk Eng: John Powers
Prd Mgr: Kevin Horton
Prd Mgr: Adel Karmouche

D-U-N-S 83-100-2972
■ **KYOCERA COMMUNICATIONS INC**
(Suby of KYOCERA INTERNATIONAL, INC.)
9520 Towne Centre Dr, San Diego, CA 92121-1990
Tel (858) 882-2000 Founded/Ownrshp 2011
Sales 23.0MM[E] EMP 177[E]
SIC 8999 Communication services
Pr: Elichi Toriyawa
*CEO: Yasuhiro Oishi
VP: Kazuhiro Iwabuchi
VP: Ellen Lynch

D-U-N-S 06-446-5503 EXP
■ **KYOCERA DOCUMENT SOLUTIONS AMERICA INC** (CA)
(Suby of KYOCERA DOCUMENT SOLUTIONS INC.)
225 Sand Rd, Fairfield, NJ 07004-1575
Tel (973) 808-8444 Founded/Ownrshp 1973
Sales 176.8MM[E] EMP 700
SIC 5044 5084 5065 Photocopy machines; Printing trades machinery, equipment & supplies; Facsimile equipment; Photocopy machines; Printing trades machinery, equipment & supplies; Facsimile equipment
CEO: Norihiko INA
*CFO: Nicholas Maimone
CFO: Nicholas Maimone
Ex VP: Yoshihiro Suzuki
VP: Ed Bialecki
VP: Mark O'Hara
VP: Mark Ohara
*VP: Calvin Rosen
Assoc Dir: William Cassidy
Area Mgr: Greg Bezdek
Area Mgr: Michel Naud
Board of Directors: Tetsuo Kuba, Takashi Kuki, Nicholas Maimone, John Rigby, Calvin Rosen

D-U-N-S 11-524-7751
■ **KYOCERA DOCUMENT SOLUTIONS NEW ENGLAND INC**
DUPLITRON
(Suby of KYOCERA DOCUMENT SOLUTIONS AMERICA INC) ★
1 Jewel Dr Ste 321, Wilmington, MA 01887-3460
Tel (781) 272-4560 Founded/Ownrshp 2008
Sales 25.0MM EMP 107
SIC 5999

D-U-N-S 07-849-5083 IMP
■ **KYOCERA INDUSTRIAL CERAMICS CORP**
KYOCERA USA
(Suby of KYOCERA INTERNATIONAL, INC.)
100 Industrial Park Rd, Hendersonville, NC 28792-9011
Tel (828) 693-0241 Founded/Ownrshp 1990
Sales 86.5MM[E] EMP 310
SIC 5065 5013 5085 Electronic parts & equipment; Connectors, electronic; Semiconductor devices; Heaters, motor vehicle; Industrial tools; Electronic parts & equipment; Connectors, electronic; Semiconductor devices; Heaters, motor vehicle; Industrial tools
Pr: David M Williams

D-U-N-S 07-934-8788
■ **KYOCERA PRECISION TOOLS INC**
(Suby of KYOCERA INTERNATIONAL, INC.)
102 Industrial Park Rd, Hendersonville, NC 28792-9011
Tel (828) 698-4181 Founded/Ownrshp 2013
Sales 60.2MM[E] EMP 233
SIC 3545 3541 3845 3843 3841 Machine tool accessories; Machine tools, metal cutting type; Endoscopic equipment, electromedical; Cutting instruments, dental; Surgical & medical instruments; Machine tool accessories; Machine tools, metal cutting type; Endoscopic equipment, electromedical; Cutting instruments, dental; Surgical & medical instruments
Pr: Koichi Nosaka
VP: Jim Good

D-U-N-S 03-502-7903 IMP/EXP
■ **KYOCERA SOLAR INC**
(Suby of KYOCERA INTERNATIONAL, INC.)
8800 E Raintree Dr # 280, Scottsdale, AZ 85260-3965
Tel (480) 948-8003 Founded/Ownrshp 1999
Sales 28.1MM[E] EMP 150
SIC 3674 Semiconductors & related devices; Photovoltaic devices, solid state; Solar cells; Semiconductors & related devices; Photovoltaic devices, solid state; Solar cells
Pr: Steve Hill
*Treas: William Edwards
*VP: Michael Rennie
Ql Cn Mgr: Keith Shellkopf
Sls Mgr: Troy Calapp
Sales Asso: Myrian Apatiga

D-U-N-S 82-524-6820 IMP
KYOCERA TYCOM CORP
KYOCEARA
3565 Cadillac Ave, Costa Mesa, CA 92626-1401
Tel (714) 428-3600 Founded/Ownrshp 2008
Sales NA EMP 500
SIC 3541 3845 3843 3841 3545

D-U-N-S 94-095-5057 IMP
■ **KYOCERA UNIMERCO TOOLING INC**
UNIMERCO GROUP A/S
(Suby of KYOCERA UNIMERCO A/S)
6620 State Rd, Saline, MI 48176-9274
Tel (734) 944-4433 Founded/Ownrshp 1995
Sales 23.0MM[E] EMP 48
SIC 5084 7699 3545 Industrial machinery & equipment; Knife, saw & tool sharpening & repair; Cutting tools for machine tools
CFO: Esge Jensen
Exec: Sheila Marrs

Mng Dir: Carsten Mortensen
Sls Mgr: Thomas Linde
Sls Mgr: Anders Varga
Board of Directors: John Erik Foxby, Kenneth Iversen, Jan Ronberg

KYOCERA USA
See KYOCERA INDUSTRIAL CERAMICS CORP

KYOLIC
See WAKUNAGA OF AMERICA CO LTD

D-U-N-S 80-865-6164 IMP
KYOUNG IL USA INC
7710 Balboa Ave Ste 227f, San Diego, CA 92111-2253
Tel (619) 428-9903 *Founded/Ownrshp* 2005
Sales 32.3MM *EMP* 9
Accts Choi Kim & Park Llp San Dieg
SIC 3651 Household audio & video equipment; Household audio & video equipment
CEO: Sang Yoong Lee
**Treas:* Jin Young Lee
**VP:* Jong Hoon Lee

D-U-N-S 15-753-6822 IMP
KYOWA AMERICA CORP
(*Suby of* KYOWA ELECTRIC AND CHEMICAL CO.,LTD.)
1039 Fred White Blvd, Portland, TN 37148-8369
Tel (615) 323-2194 *Founded/Ownrshp* 1973
Sales 155.8MM^E *EMP* 447
SIC 5162 Plastics basic shapes; Plastics basic shapes
Pr: Sumito Furuya
VP: K Nakazawa
**VP:* Fumio Tomita

D-U-N-S 07-983-6257
KYRENE ELEMENTARY DISTRICT
8700 S Kyrene Rd, Tempe, AZ 85284-2108
Tel (480) 541-1000 *Founded/Ownrshp* 2015
Sales 6.3MM^E *EMP* 1,480^E
SIC 8211

D-U-N-S 02-165-7069
KYRENE SCHOOL DISTRICT
8700 S Kyrene Rd, Tempe, AZ 85284-2197
Tel (480) 541-1000 *Founded/Ownrshp* 1888
Sales 131.3MM^E *EMP* 2,000
SIC 8211 Public elementary & secondary schools; Public elementary & secondary schools
**VP:* Bernadette Coggins
VP: Michelle Hirsch
Pr Dir: Kelly Alexander

D-U-N-S 13-235-2415
KYRIBA CORP
(*Suby of* KYRIBA)
9620 Towne Cntre Dr 200, San Diego, CA 92121
Tel (858) 210-3560 *Founded/Ownrshp* 2005
Sales 54.3MM^E *EMP* 260
SIC 8742 Financial consultant; Financial consultant
CEO: Jean-Luc Robert
**COO:* Didier Martineau
**CFO:* Fabrice Lvy
CFO: Gene Lynes
Chf Mktg O: Julie Roy
**Ex VP:* Remy Dubois
Ex VP: Eric Riddle
Sr VP: John Lomoro
**Sr VP:* Catherine Moore
**Sr VP:* Edi Poloniato
VP: Simone Bernardelli
VP: Jean-Francois Brissot
VP: Scott Montigelli
VP: Ben Stollard
Dir Soc: Gretchen Ploen

D-U-N-S 00-602-1141 EXP
■ **KYSOR INDUSTRIAL CORP**
KYSOR WARREN
(*Suby of* MANITOWOC CO INC) ★
2227 Welbilt Blvd, Trinity, FL 34655-5130
Tel (727) 376-8600 *Founded/Ownrshp* 1925, 2009
Sales 207.8MM^E *EMP* 1,342
SIC 3585 3714 Refrigeration & heating equipment; Refrigeration equipment, complete; Counters & counter display cases, refrigerated; Air conditioning condensers & condensing units; Motor vehicle engines & parts; Heaters, motor vehicle; Radiators & radiator shells & cores, motor vehicle; Air conditioner parts, motor vehicle; Refrigeration & heating equipment; Refrigeration equipment, complete; Counters & counter display cases, refrigerated; Air conditioning condensers & condensing units; Motor vehicle engines & parts; Heaters, motor vehicle; Radiators & radiator shells & cores, motor vehicle; Air conditioner parts, motor vehicle
Pr: Richard Osborne
**Treas:* Donald Holmes
Dir IT: Christopher Glomski

KYSOR PANEL SYSTEMS
See WELBILT WALK-INS LP

KYSOR WARREN
See KYSOR INDUSTRIAL CORP

KYTV
See KY-3 INC

D-U-N-S 16-517-0171 IMP
KYUNG IN PRINTING INC
PRINTING MANUFACTURER
7920 Airway Rd Ste A8, San Diego, CA 92154-8311
Tel (619) 662-3920 *Founded/Ownrshp* 1998
Sales 36.3MM *EMP* 198
Accts Choi Kim & Park Llp San Die
SIC 2752 Commercial printing, lithographic; Commercial printing, offset; Commercial printing, lithographic; Commercial printing, offset
Pr: Sung Hwan Lee
**CFO:* Kay Park

D-U-N-S 02-322-4250 IMP
KYUNGSHIN AMERICA CORP
(*Suby of* KYUNGSHIN CORP.)
1201 Og Skinner Dr, West Point, GA 31833-1789
Tel (706) 645-1595 *Founded/Ownrshp* 2008
Sales 355.3MM^E *EMP* 114^E
SIC 3714 Motor vehicle parts & accessories; Automotive wiring harness sets
CEO: Seung Kwan Lee
**CFO:* Chang Jun Lee

D-U-N-S 15-077-1652 EXP
KYUNGSHIN-LEAR SALES AND ENGINEERING LLC
(*Suby of* KYUNGSHIN AMERICA CORP) ★
100 Smothers Rd, Montgomery, AL 36117-5505
Tel (334) 413-0575 *Founded/Ownrshp* 2003
Sales 355.3MM *EMP* 105^E
Accts Mancera Sc Ciudad Juarez
SIC 3714 Automotive wiring harness sets; Automotive wiring harness sets
CEO: Richard Ocallaghan
**Pr:* Seung Kwan Lee
**Genl Mgr:* Charles Kim

D-U-N-S 09-001-4320
KYYBA INC (MI)
28230 Orchard Lake Rd, Farmington Hills, MI 48334-3762
Tel (248) 290-2910 *Founded/Ownrshp* 1998
Sales 32.6MM *EMP* 353^E
SIC 8742 Management information systems consultant; Management information systems consultant
CEO: Tel K Ganesan
**COO:* Thiru Ganesan
VP: Kevin Fitzgerald
VP: Wayne Presley
IT Man: Kavidha Selvaraj
VP Mktg: Maria Jarrous

D-U-N-S 05-895-6921 IMP/EXP
KZRV LP
985 N 900 W, Shipshewana, IN 46565-9139
Tel (260) 768-4016 *Founded/Ownrshp* 2004
Sales 80.2MM^E *EMP* 300
SIC 3792 Trailer coaches, automobile; Trailer coaches, automobile
Genl Pt: Daryl E Zook
Pt: Tonja Zook Nicholas
Pt: Trista Nunemaker
VP: Mark Campbell
Dist Mgr: Art Kalb
Dir IT: Mike Zook
Plnt Mgr: Kurt Walker
S&M/VP: Andy Baer
Sls Dir: Marlene Snyder

L

D-U-N-S 04-122-6028
L & A CONTRACTING CO
100 Simms Rd, Hattiesburg, MS 39401-4642
Tel (601) 264-2100 *Founded/Ownrshp* 1946
Sales 40.1MM^E *EMP* 100
SIC 1622 1611

L & A JUICE
See LANGER JUICE CO INC

D-U-N-S 14-477-8271
L & D GROUP INC
LYON & DITTRICH HOLDING CO
420 N Main St, Montgomery, IL 60538-1367
Tel (630) 892-8941 *Founded/Ownrshp* 1989
Sales NA *EMP* 500
SIC 2542 2522 2599 Shelving, office & store: except wood; Desks, office: except wood; Work benches, factory

D-U-N-S 78-340-8768
L & D MAIL MASTERS INC
110 Security Pkwy, New Albany, IN 47150-9366
Tel (812) 981-7161 *Founded/Ownrshp* 1986
Sales 27.1MM^E *EMP* 123
Accts Harding Shymanski & Co Psc L
SIC 7331 Direct mail advertising services; Direct mail advertising services
Pr: Diane B Fischer
**Treas:* Rocco Celebrezze
**VP:* Krista Fischer
CTO: Sherrie Byrd

D-U-N-S 62-150-1402
L & E MANAGEMENT COMAPNY INC
PERKINS FAMILY RESTAURANT
830 Herbert Rd Ste 101, Cordova, TN 38018-2276
Tel (901) 375-9477 *Founded/Ownrshp* 1990
Sales 13.5MM^E *EMP* 400
SIC 5812 5461 Restaurant, family: chain; Bakeries; Restaurant, family: chain; Bakeries
Pr: Larry Walker

D-U-N-S 08-313-9311 IMP
L & F DISTRIBUTORS LLC
3900 N Mccoll Rd, McAllen, TX 78501-9160
Tel (956) 687-7751 *Founded/Ownrshp* 2007
Sales 155.8MM^E *EMP* 250
SIC 5181 Beer & other fermented malt liquors; Beer & other fermented malt liquors
Genl Mgr: Bobby Casso
IT Man: John Beagle
IT Man: John Duran
IT Man: Gabriel Gomez
Sfty Dirs: Ronald Flores
Mktg Mgr: Brian Desmond
Mktg Mgr: Joshua Sandoval
Sls Mgr: Dion Ruiz

D-U-N-S 02-221-4121
L & G CADDELL INC
2451 Jamacha Rd Ste 105, El Cajon, CA 92019-4324
Tel (619) 401-2150 *Founded/Ownrshp* 1991
Sales 70.0MM *EMP* 3
SIC 6531 Real estate agents & managers; Real estate agents & managers
Pr: Lyle R Caddell

D-U-N-S 80-816-2838
L & G CONCRETE CONSTRUCTION INC
2100 W Expressway 83, Mercedes, TX 78570-9764
Tel (956) 565-6334 *Founded/Ownrshp* 1983
Sales 61.6MM^E *EMP* 275
SIC 1611 Concrete construction: roads, highways, sidewalks, etc.; Concrete construction: roads, highways, sidewalks, etc.
Pr: Erasmo Lopez
**VP:* Pablo J Garza
Sls Mgr: Trevan Williams

D-U-N-S 17-365-9574
L & G MORTGAGEBANC INC
8151 E Evans Rd Ste 10, Scottsdale, AZ 85260-3648
Tel (408) 905-5140 *Founded/Ownrshp* 1985
Sales NA *EMP* 1,000^E
SIC 6162 Mortgage bankers; Mortgage bankers
Ch Bd: Alan D Levin
**CEO:* Mitchell Ginsberg
**VP:* Laura Cohen

D-U-N-S 03-568-8795
L & H CO INC
MEADE ELECTRIC CO
2215 York Rd Ste 304, Oak Brook, IL 60523-4004
Tel (630) 571-7200 *Founded/Ownrshp* 1980
Sales 349.8MM^E *EMP* 2,000
SIC 1731 1611 1623 3621 Electrical work; Lighting contractor; General contractor, highway & street construction; Oil & gas pipeline construction; Motors, electric; Electrical work; Lighting contractor; General contractor, highway & street construction; Oil & gas pipeline construction; Motors, electric
Pr: John S Lizzadro

D-U-N-S 00-623-8406 IMP/EXP
L & H INDUSTRIAL INC
913 L J Ct, Gillette, WY 82718-6542
Tel (307) 682-7238 *Founded/Ownrshp* 1964, 2000
Sales 79.5MM^E *EMP* 275
SIC 3599 7692 Machine shop, jobbing & repair; Welding repair; Machine shop, jobbing & repair; Welding repair
Pr: Mike Wandler
**CFO:* Jim Clikeman
**VP:* Jeff Wandler
Genl Mgr: David R Espanol
Opers Mgr: Christi Surat
Prd Mgr: Joe Drefchinski

D-U-N-S 00-191-3672
L & H SUPPLY INC
(*Suby of* FERGUSON ENTERPRISES INC) ★
190 Oberlin Ave N, Lakewood, NJ 08701-4266
Tel (732) 905-1000 *Founded/Ownrshp* 1998
Sales 42.5MM^E *EMP* 300
SIC 5074 5075 5083 5084 Plumbing & hydronic heating supplies; Air conditioning & ventilation equipment & supplies; Irrigation equipment; Pumps & pumping equipment; Plumbing & hydronic heating supplies; Air conditioning & ventilation equipment & supplies; Irrigation equipment; Pumps & pumping equipment
Pr: Andrew Ciesla
Counsel: James Casey

D-U-N-S 62-664-2250 IMP
L & J GENERAL INTERNATIONAL CORP
EL SEMBRADOR
2424 Nw 46th St, Miami, FL 33142-4652
Tel (305) 638-5161 *Founded/Ownrshp* 1984
Sales 41.3MM^E *EMP* 50
SIC 5142 Packaged frozen goods
Pr: Luis A Hernandez
**Treas:* Gregorio Falla
**Treas:* Gus Hernandez

D-U-N-S 79-350-3079
L & J HOLDING CO LTD
L & J TECHNOLOGIES
5911 Butterfield Rd, Hillside, IL 60162-1457
Tel (708) 236-6000 *Founded/Ownrshp* 1990
Sales 22.7MM^E *EMP* 130
SIC 3829 3491 Measuring & controlling devices; Gauging instruments, thickness ultrasonic; Industrial valves; Measuring & controlling devices; Gauging instruments, thickness ultrasonic; Industrial valves
Pr: Louis Jannotta
CFO: Pam Senn

L & J TECHNOLOGIES
See L & J HOLDING CO LTD

D-U-N-S 11-029-7116 IMP
L & K COFFEE CO LLC
MAGNUM COFFEE ROASTERY
1 Java Blvd, Nunica, MI 49448-9462
Tel (616) 837-0333 *Founded/Ownrshp* 1990
Sales 22.7MM^E *EMP* 60
SIC 5149 Coffee, green or roasted
**CFO:* Jody Kotrch
Genl Mgr: Nick Andres

D-U-N-S 11-868-8902
L & L BUILDERS CO
2205 4th St, Sioux City, IA 51101-2215
Tel (712) 255-0657 *Founded/Ownrshp* 1979
Sales 31.7MM^E *EMP* 50
Accts King Reinsch Prosser & Co
SIC 1542 1541 1522 Commercial & office building, new construction; Industrial buildings, new construction; Residential construction; Commercial & office building, new construction; Industrial buildings, new construction; Residential construction
Pr: John D Lee
VP: Kirk Bohlke
VP: Dana Rand
VP: Charles Salmen

D-U-N-S 04-560-8726
L & L CARPET DISCOUNT CENTERS INC
L & L COMPANY, THE
7459 Mason King Ct, Manassas, VA 20109-5220
Tel (703) 368-5025 *Founded/Ownrshp* 1956
Sales 40.3MM^E *EMP* 174
SIC 5023 1761 Carpets; Roofing, siding & sheet metal work; Carpets; Roofing, siding & sheet metal work
Ch Bd: Eugene J Lane
**Pr:* Mike Geisler
**Pr:* Donald Martin
**CEO:* Daniel J Lane
Treas: Brian Ransom
Mktg Mgr: Eddy Ross

L & L COMPANY, THE
See L & L CARPET DISCOUNT CENTERS INC

D-U-N-S 12-869-1672
L & L FLEETING INC
(*Suby of* SMITH COOPER/T CORP) ★
3027 Hwy 75, Darrow, LA 70725
Tel (225) 473-1025 *Founded/Ownrshp* 1977
Sales 13.6MM^E *EMP* 300
SIC 3731 Barges, building & repairing; Barges, building & repairing
Pr: David J Cooper
**VP:* Richard Murry III

D-U-N-S 11-119-0620
L & L HOLDING CO LLC
L&L NO TRADESTYLE
142 W 57th St Ste 1601, New York, NY 10019-3300
Tel (212) 920-3360 *Founded/Ownrshp* 1995
Sales 20.7MM^E *EMP* 36^E
SIC 6512 Commercial & industrial building operation
CEO: David W Levinson
**Pr:* Robert T Lapidus
**CFO:* Ronald Gentile
**Ex VP:* David C Berkey
Ex VP: David Berkey
Ex VP: Henry Celestino
**Ex VP:* William Potts
**Sr VP:* Howard Slavin
VP: Joshua Carson
VP: Jeffrey Davis
VP: Kevin Fallon
VP: Samantha Fishbone
VP: Scott Lakow
VP: Keith Purcell
VP: Alina Tulman
VP: Laura Yablon

D-U-N-S 00-953-3068 IMP
L & L NURSERY SUPPLY INC (CA)
UNIGRO
2552 Shenandoah Way, San Bernardino, CA 92407-1845
Tel (909) 591-0461 *Founded/Ownrshp* 1953
Sales 186.3MM^E *EMP* 275
SIC 5191 2875 2449 5193 Insecticides; Fertilizer & fertilizer materials; Soil, potting & planting; Potting soil, mixed; Wood containers; Flowers & florists' supplies; Insecticides; Fertilizer & fertilizer materials; Soil, potting & planting; Potting soil, mixed; Wood containers; Flowers & florists' supplies
Ch Bd: Lloyd Swindell
Pr: Harvey Luth
Pr: Tom Medhurst
VP: Mike Fuson
IT Man: Larry Tabert
Sales Exec: Craig Patrick
Sales Asso: Ren Yamada

D-U-N-S 00-552-4111
L & L PACKING CO
527 W 41st St, Chicago, IL 60609-2708
Tel (773) 285-5400 *Founded/Ownrshp* 1975
Sales 20.1MM^E *EMP* 40
SIC 5147 5142 5144 Meats, fresh; Meat, frozen: packaged; Poultry: live, dressed or frozen (unpackaged)
Pr: Joel Lezak
Ch Bd: Alan Lezak
VP: Diane Bond

D-U-N-S 01-238-8856 IMP
L & L PAINTING CO INC
900 S Oyster Bay Rd, Hicksville, NY 11801-3518
Tel (516) 349-1900 *Founded/Ownrshp* 1949
Sales 30.2MM^E *EMP* 200
SIC 1721

D-U-N-S 00-537-1414 IMP/EXP
L & L PRODUCTS INC
(*Suby of* L& L PRODUCTS) ★
160 Mclean, Bruce Twp, MI 48065-4919
Tel (586) 336-1600 *Founded/Ownrshp* 1958
Sales 150.1MM^E *EMP* 775
SIC 3053 Gaskets & sealing devices; Gaskets, all materials; Gaskets & sealing devices; Gaskets, all materials
CEO: John Ligon
**Pr:* Tom Klieno
**Ch:* Larry R Schmidt
**Treas:* Robert M Ligon
Prgrm Mgr: Michelle Bowen
Prgrm Mgr: Steve Brazeau
Prgrm Mgr: Tom Kleino
Prgrm Mgr: Corina Rotkiewicz
Prgrm Mgr: Matt Smith
Prgrm Mgr: Ken Takahashi
Prgrm Mgr: Barb Vitale

D-U-N-S 04-889-6807
L & L SERVICES INC
METRO COMMUNICATION SERVICES
502 N Montgomery Ave Ofc, Sheffield, AL 35660-2864
Tel (256) 383-6940 *Founded/Ownrshp* 1968
Sales 35.6MM *EMP* 150
Accts Leigh King & Associates Pc
SIC 6514 7374 4813 5411 Residential building, four or fewer units: operation; Computer processing services; Local & long distance telephone communications; Grocery stores, independent; Convenience stores, independent; Residential building, four or fewer units: operation; Computer processing services; Local & long distance telephone communications; Grocery stores, independent; Convenience stores, independent
Pr: Bob R Love
**Sec:* Walter Andrews
VP: Vrena Brennan
**VP:* William Kinser

D-U-N-S 04-005-0353
L & L STORES INC
627 E Washington St, Nashville, NC 27856-1737
Tel (252) 459-4475 *Founded/Ownrshp* 1973

Sales 51.2MM *EMP* 150
Accts Pate Horton & Ess Pa Rock
SIC 5411 Convenience stores, chain; Convenience stores, chain
Pr: Wayne J Land
**Treas:* Pamela L Saunders
**Sec:* Cathy Sherrod

D-U-N-S 00-483-4024
L & M BOTRUC RENTAL INC (LA)
18692 W Main St, Galliano, LA 70354-3908
Tel (985) 475-5733 *Founded/Ownrshp* 1961
Sales 21.6MM[E] *EMP* 150
SIC 4499 Boat rental, commercial; Boat rental, commercial
Pr: Minor Cheramie Jr
VP: Jacob Pitre
**VP:* Patrick Pitre
Off Mgr: Susan David
Opers Mgr: Mike Curole

L & M COMPANIES, INC.
See GRACE LOCKE MARINE LLC

D-U-N-S 07-202-8327 IMP/EXP
L & M COMPANIES INC
L & M WEST
2925 Huntleigh Dr Ste 204, Raleigh, NC 27604-3374
Tel (919) 981-8000 *Founded/Ownrshp* 1964
Sales 154.2MM[E] *EMP* 160
SIC 5148 Fresh fruits & vegetables; Fresh fruits & vegetables
Ch: Joseph E McGee
**Pr:* Jonathan C Oxford
**COO:* Gary James
CFO: Maureen Adam
CFO: John Oxford
**Treas:* Thomas F Crowder
VP: Larry Atto
CTO: John McDaniel
Dir IT: Dan Giddens
Dir IT: Jon Gorman
Sls Dir: T J Bauer

D-U-N-S 13-138-6880
L & M DEVELOPMENT PARTNERS INC
1865 Palmer Ave Ste 203, Larchmont, NY 10538-3037
Tel (914) 833-3000 *Founded/Ownrshp* 1984
Sales 24.4MM[E] *EMP* 15[E]
SIC 6552 Land subdividers & developers, residential
Pr: Sandy Lowentheil
**Ch Bd:* Ronald Moelis
V Ch: Sanford Loewentheil
COO: Debra Kenyon
CFO: Lenny Rueben
Ex VP: David Dishy
Ex VP: Lisa Gomez
Ex VP: Gerald Miceli
VP: Jon Cortell
**VP:* Ron Moelis
Ex Dir: Joe Pfeiffer

D-U-N-S 04-339-2083
L & M FABRICATION AND MACHINE INC (PA)
6814 Chrisphalt Dr, Bath, PA 18014-8503
Tel (610) 837-1848 *Founded/Ownrshp* 1967, 1977
Sales 34.0MM[E] *EMP* 80
SIC 3443 3444 3441 Industrial vessels, tanks & containers; Heat exchangers, condensers & components; Boiler & boiler shop work; Liners/lining; Sheet metalwork; Building components, structural steel
Pr: Bruce Lack
**VP:* Keith Ashner
Exec: Jeff Werner

D-U-N-S 12-202-6313
L & M FOOTWEAR INC
ROBERT WAYNE FOOTWEAR
5303 E Washington Blvd, Commerce, CA 90040-2111
Tel (323) 948-4800 *Founded/Ownrshp* 1982
Sales 74.4MM[E] *EMP* 500
SIC 5661 Men's shoes; Women's boots; Men's shoes; Women's boots
CEO: Mark Mintz
Pr: Art Bell
Area Mgr: Jon Robertson
Dist Mgr: Mike Arena
Dist Mgr: Carlos Flores
Dist Mgr: Justin Hotchkiss
Dist Mgr: Mike Padfield
Dist Mgr: Brent Thomas
CTO: Crystal Chadwick

D-U-N-S 09-937-0454
L & M LAMINATES AND MARBLE INC
813 E University Dr, Phoenix, AZ 85034-6505
Tel (602) 254-5629 *Founded/Ownrshp* 1979
Sales 23.9MM[E] *EMP* 250
SIC 3088 3083 5031 Bathroom fixtures, plastic; Laminated plastic sheets; Lumber, plywood & millwork; Kitchen cabinets; Bathroom fixtures, plastic; Laminated plastic sheets; Lumber, plywood & millwork; Kitchen cabinets
Pr: Raymond W St Cyr
**VP:* Joseph P Schott III

D-U-N-S 02-281-8538 IMP/EXP
L & M RADIATOR INC
1414 E 37th St, Hibbing, MN 55746-3629
Tel (218) 263-8993 *Founded/Ownrshp* 1975
Sales 72.7MM *EMP* 500
SIC 3714 3433 3599

D-U-N-S 03-787-9534
L & M SANITATION SOLUTIONS LLC
22564 Frisbee St, Detroit, MI 48219-1864
Tel (248) 266-1103 *Founded/Ownrshp* 2011
Sales 60.0MM *EMP* 8
SIC 7349 7389 Building maintenance services; ; Building maintenance services;

D-U-N-S 02-703-8702
L & M STEEL CO INC
5523 Dietrich Rd, San Antonio, TX 78219-2915
Tel (210) 661-4241 *Founded/Ownrshp* 1965
Sales 25.0MM *EMP* 48
SIC 5051 1791 Concrete reinforcing bars; Concrete reinforcement, placing of
CEO: Lester W Maxey
Pr: Michael A Doucet
VP: Sansa Johnson

D-U-N-S 02-814-0846
L & M TIRE CO INC
EXPRESS TIRE
1148 Indl Ave, Escondido, CA 92029
Tel (760) 741-4044 *Founded/Ownrshp* 1974
Sales 32.6MM[E] *EMP* 360
SIC 7538 5531 General automotive repair shops; Automotive tires; General automotive repair shops; Automotive tires
CEO: Arnulfo Villavicencio
**Pr:* Joseph Jubela

D-U-N-S 13-770-7824
L & M TRANSPORTATION SERVICES INC
2925 Huntleigh Dr Ste 104, Raleigh, NC 27604-3373
Tel (919) 872-9383 *Founded/Ownrshp* 1977
Sales 74.2MM *EMP* 45
Accts Cherry Bekaert & Holland Llp
SIC 4731 Truck transportation brokers; Truck transportation brokers
CEO: John Oxford
**Pr:* Michael Devine
**Treas:* Leeanne Oxford
**Sr VP:* Michael O Moore
**VP:* Thomas Devine
Sls Mgr: George Cowles

L & M WEST
See L & M COMPANIES INC

D-U-N-S 12-252-0377
L & N FEDERAL CREDIT UNION
101 Spring St, London, KY 40741-1447
Tel (606) 878-0662 *Founded/Ownrshp* 1999
Sales NA *EMP* 6
SIC 6061 Federal credit unions; Federal credit unions
Pr: George Mann

D-U-N-S 13-036-1371
L & N FEDERAL CREDIT UNION
9265 Smyrna Pkwy, Louisville, KY 40229-1415
Tel (502) 368-5858 *Founded/Ownrshp* 1954
Sales NA *EMP* 172
SIC 6061 Federal credit unions; Federal credit unions
Pr: George Mann
COO: Sam Jackson
CFO: Chris Brown
Ofcr: Peter Bruers
**Sr VP:* Gwen Paul
**Sr VP:* Linda Snodgrass
**VP:* Richard Gravatte
VP: Gary Lord
VP: Tony Raley
VP: Ryan Wood
Exec: Jan Gittings
Creative D: Greg Epley

D-U-N-S 00-784-6439
L & O POWER COOPERATIVE
1302 S Union St, Rock Rapids, IA 51246-2090
Tel (712) 472-2556 *Founded/Ownrshp* 1952
Sales 28.5MM *EMP* 3
SIC 4911 Distribution, electric power; Distribution, electric power
Pr: Allen Blauwet
Treas: Dale Klinkenborg

D-U-N-S 83-643-5248
L & P BUILDING SUPPLY OF LAS CRUCES INC
101 Archuleta Rd, Las Cruces, NM 88005-4102
Tel (575) 527-8000 *Founded/Ownrshp* 2001
Sales 35.1MM[E] *EMP* 50
SIC 5031 5211 Building materials, exterior; Building materials, interior; Doors & windows; Lumber & other building materials
Pr: Robert Atchley
**Pr:* Paul Bubdain
**Sec:* Wilfred E Binns
**VP:* Ray Florez
**VP:* Phillip Philloippou

D-U-N-S 01-257-8514 IMP
L & R DISTRIBUTORS INC
9301 Avenue D, Brooklyn, NY 11236-1899
Tel (718) 272-2100 *Founded/Ownrshp* 1956
Sales 1.2MMM[E] *EMP* 950
SIC 5131 5122 Notions; Druggists' sundries; Notions; Druggists' sundries
CEO: Marc Bodner
**Pr:* E Reilly Murray
**CEO:* Marc J Bodner
**CFO:* Edward Musantry
**Ex VP:* Annette Lucas
**Sr VP:* Arthur C Walker
VP: Mike Cirilli
**VP:* Ray Delio
VP: Michael Willert
Rgnl Mgr: Robert Gaboriault
Dist Mgr: Denise Trenchard

D-U-N-S 84-740-0751
L & S ASSOCIATES INC
MEDICAID SPECIALISTS
(*Suby of* HUMAN ARC CORP) ★
3245 Technology Blvd, Lansing, MI 48910-8553
Tel (517) 203-7500 *Founded/Ownrshp* 2012
Sales NA *EMP* 180
SIC 6321 Accident & health insurance; Accident & health insurance
Pr: Lynnette J Rhodes
COO: Ann L Andrews

L & S AVIATION LUBRICANTS
See EXXONMOBIL OIL CORP

D-U-N-S 05-308-8829
L & S ELECTRIC INC
5101 Mesker St, Schofield, WI 54476-3056
Tel (715) 359-3155 *Founded/Ownrshp* 1970
Sales 81.3MM *EMP* 350
Accts Gassner & Company Sc Wausa
SIC 5063 7694 3613 8711 Motors, electric; Motor controls, starters & relays: electric; Electric motor repair; Control panels, electric; Electrical or electronic engineering; Motors, electric; Motor controls, starters & relays: electric; Electric motor repair; Control panels, electric; Electrical or electronic engineering
Ch Bd: Alan Lewitzke
**CFO:* David Krause
**Ex VP:* Paul Gullickson
VP: Louis Barto
VP: Hunt Dean
VP: Elaine Lane
Exec: Marsha Wadzinski
Div Mgr: Kevin Campbell
Genl Mgr: Jody Frieders
Genl Mgr: Melvin Lopez
IT Man: Lisa Myles

D-U-N-S 07-579-7928
L & S MOTORS INC
HUNTINGTON HONDA/SAAB
1055 E Jericho Tpke, Huntington, NY 11743-5434
Tel (631) 423-0883 *Founded/Ownrshp* 1974
Sales 39.7MM[E] *EMP* 90
SIC 5511 7389 Automobiles, new & used; Drive-a-way automobile service; Automobiles, new & used; Drive-a-way automobile service
Pr: Don Lia
Off Mgr: Arlene Zoitke
IT Man: Roy Hartmann
Sls Mgr: Fran Lomenzo
Sales Asso: Arthur Massey
Sales Asso: Ryan McHale

D-U-N-S 93-972-2575
L & T MEAT CO
3050 E 11th St, Los Angeles, CA 90023-3606
Tel (323) 262-2815 *Founded/Ownrshp* 1996
Sales 33.2MM[E] *EMP* 80
SIC 5142 Frozen fish, meat & poultry; Frozen fish, meat & poultry
Pr: Chak Por Tea
**VP:* Bobby Lu

D-U-N-S 12-171-0164
L & T PRECISION CORP
12105 Kirkham Rd, Poway, CA 92064-6870
Tel (858) 513-7874 *Founded/Ownrshp* 1984
Sales 37.3MM[E] *EMP* 110
SIC 3444 3599 Sheet metalwork; Machine & other job shop work
Pr: Loc Nguyen
VP: Mimi Moore
VP: Juan Mora
**VP:* Tho Nguyen
**Prin:* Tien D Nguyen
Genl Mgr: Nou Vue
Sfty Mgr: Lan Tran

D-U-N-S 78-713-6654
L & V TRAILER SALES INC
2655 Burlingame Ave Sw # 1, Grand Rapids, MI 49509-2300
Tel (616) 534-1300 *Founded/Ownrshp* 2006
Sales 21.4MM[E] *EMP* 25
SIC 5012 7538 5531 Trailers for trucks, new & used; General truck repair; Truck equipment & parts
Pr: Bob Falahee

D-U-N-S 04-026-1893
L & W ENGINEERING INC
107 Industrial Pkwy E, Middlebury, IN 46540-8511
Tel (574) 825-5351 *Founded/Ownrshp* 1975
Sales 25.6MM[E] *EMP* 80
SIC 3714 3429 3499 3498 3444 3441 Motor vehicle body components & frame; Manufactured hardware (general); Motor vehicle hardware; Bicycle racks, automotive; Metal ladders; Fabricated pipe & fittings; Sheet metalwork; Fabricated structural metal
Pr: Roger Huffman
**Ch Bd:* Wilbur Bontrager
COO: Steve Shaffer
**Sec:* Kennard Weaver
**VP:* Robert M Sutter
Genl Mgr: Joyce Miller
Dir IT: Katie Burkley
Dir IT: Paul Keifer
Plnt Mgr: Maynard Miller

D-U-N-S 17-808-0446 IMP
L & W INC
L&W ENGINEERING
17757 Woodland Dr, New Boston, MI 48164-9265
Tel (734) 397-6300 *Founded/Ownrshp* 1985
Sales 565.7MM[E] *EMP* 1,500
SIC 3469 3465 3441 3429 Stamping metal for the trade; Automotive stampings; Fabricated structural metal; Manufactured hardware (general); Stamping metal for the trade; Automotive stampings; Fabricated structural metal; Manufactured hardware (general)
Ch Bd: Wayne D Jones
Pr: Gene Goins
**Pr:* Scott L Jones
**COO:* Steven Schafer
CFO: John Meng
CFO: Diane Patton
**Treas:* Bob Koss
VP: Mike Alcala
VP: Jeff Allen
**VP:* Mark Lorenger
Mng Dir: Angelo Katakis

D-U-N-S 05-662-5908 EXP
■ **L & W SUPPLY CORP**
DOBY BUILDING SUPPLY
(*Suby of* USG CORP) ★
550 W Adams St, Chicago, IL 60661-3665
Tel (312) 606-4000 *Founded/Ownrshp* 1971
Sales 1.0MMM[E] *EMP* 3,250
SIC 5032 Plastering materials; Plastering materials
Pr: Brendan J Deely
**VP:* John W Cain
VP: Kevin Corrigan
VP: Tim Mahaffey
Brnch Mgr: Brett Christian
Brnch Mgr: Jack Martin
Brnch Mgr: Carl Roy
Brnch Mgr: Chad Thompson
Dir IT: Jorge Angel
Dir IT: Richard Needham
Site Mgr: Thomas Pakulski

D-U-N-S 03-839-8374
■ **L 3 COMMUNICATIONS INTEGRATED SYSTEMS LP**
(*Suby of* L-3 COMMUNICATIONS HOLDINGS INC) ★
1655 Science Pl, Rockwall, TX 75032-6202
Tel (972) 772-2036 *Founded/Ownrshp* 2012
Sales 47.9MM[E] *EMP* 133[E]
SIC 3812 Aircraft/aerospace flight instruments & guidance systems
Pr: John McNellis
**Ex VP:* S Gordon Walsh

D-U-N-S 01-411-1207
L A BROKERS INC
WATSON CHEVROLET OLDSMOBILE
6370 William Penn Hwy, Murrysville, PA 15632-9016
Tel (724) 387-1500 *Founded/Ownrshp* 1992
Sales 60.0MM *EMP* 85
SIC 5511 Automobiles, new & used; Automobiles, new & used
Pr: Patsy Tiani Jr
**Treas:* Maryann Tiani

L A C S D
See LAKE ARROWHEAD COMMUNITY SERVICES DISTRICT

L A CARE HEALTH PLAN
See LOCAL INITIATIVE HEALTH AUTHORITY FOR LOS ANGELES COUNTY

D-U-N-S 62-103-6057
L A FITNESS INTERNATIONAL LLC
LA FITNESS
3021 Michelson Dr, Irvine, CA 92612-0626
Tel (949) 255-7200 *Founded/Ownrshp* 1996
Sales 117.3MM[E] *EMP* 1,510
SIC 7991 6794 Physical fitness facilities; Franchises, selling or licensing; Physical fitness facilities; Franchises, selling or licensing
**Sr VP:* Robert P Bryant
Sr VP: Suzanne Salcedo
VP: Todd Boren
VP: Chris Kelly
CTO: Mindy Stokesberry
IT Man: Angie Wielandt
Software D: Ada Tzeng
Opers Mgr: Gary Alabaugh
Sales Exec: John Bembaron
Mktg Dir: Andrea Ojeda

L A GIRL
See BEAUTY 21 COSMETICS INC

D-U-N-S 00-377-9931 IMP
L A HEARNE CO (CA)
512 Metz Rd, King City, CA 93930-2503
Tel (831) 385-5441 *Founded/Ownrshp* 1938
Sales 77.6MM[E] *EMP* 105
SIC 5191 0723 5699 4214 2048 5261 Fertilizers & agricultural chemicals; Bean cleaning services; Grain drying services; Seed cleaning; Livestock feeds; Local trucking with storage; Western apparel; Lawn & garden supplies; Fertilizers & agricultural chemicals; Bean cleaning services; Grain drying services; Seed cleaning; Western apparel; Local trucking with storage; Livestock feeds; Lawn & garden supplies
Pr: Francis Giudici
**Ch Bd:* Dennis Hearne
**VP:* Frank Hearne

D-U-N-S 08-350-1424
L A LAKEVIEW ASSOCIATERS LP
LAKEVIEW PRO SHOP
1 Lakeview Dr, Morgantown, WV 26508-8061
Tel (304) 594-2011 *Founded/Ownrshp* 1954
Sales 3.6MM[E] *EMP* 300
SIC 7011 7992 Hotels; Public golf courses; Hotels; Public golf courses
Genl Mgr: Steve Sharkey

L A P F C U
See LOS ANGELES POLICE CREDIT UNION

L A PHILHARMONIC
See LOS ANGELES PHILHARMONIC ASSOCIATION

L A RUBBER CO
See MECHANICAL DRIVES CO

D-U-N-S 60-520-8644
L A STRANSPORTATION INC
PRODUCES DAIRY
250 E Belmont Ave, Fresno, CA 93701-1405
Tel (559) 264-6583 *Founded/Ownrshp* 1954
Sales 32.9MM[E] *EMP* 300
SIC 4213 Refrigerated products transport; Refrigerated products transport
Pr: Richard Shehady
**Ch:* Lawrence Shehady

L A UTILITIES
See LAWRENCE ANZALDUA COMPANIES INC

D-U-N-S 02-280-6475 IMP
L AND M SUPPLY INC
TRUE VALUE
1200 E Us Highway 169, Grand Rapids, MN 55744-3235
Tel (218) 326-9451 *Founded/Ownrshp* 1963
Sales 101.5MM[E] *EMP* 450
SIC 5251 5331 5013 Hardware; Variety stores; Motor vehicle supplies & new parts; Hardware; Variety stores; Motor vehicle supplies & new parts
CEO: Erik Andersen
**Sec:* Donald Ley
Sales Exec: Karen Martire

L AND STRUCK CENTER
See LES STUMPF FORD INC

D-U-N-S 79-337-4034
L B & B ASSOCIATES INC
9891 Broken Land Pkwy # 400, Columbia, MD 21046-1165
Tel (301) 621-3944 *Founded/Ownrshp* 1992
Sales 228.4MM[E] *EMP* 1,308[E]
SIC 8744 7338 4225 8742 8748 4581 Facilities support services; Secretarial & court reporting; General warehousing & storage; Transportation consultant; Safety training service; Fixed base operator; Facilities support services; Secretarial & court reporting; General warehousing & storage; Transportation consultant; Safety training service; Fixed base operator
Pr: F Edward Brandon
**COO:* David Van Scoyoc
**CFO:* Rachel Rakes
Ofcr: Shannon Klisiewicz
**Sr VP:* Jeff Mendenhall
**Sr VP:* Reginald Spence
**VP:* Alexander Torrance
**Exec:* Frederick Franz

L B C
See LAWRENCE BUILDING CORP

D-U-N-S 96-376-3669
L B C HOLDINGS U S A CORP
362 E Grand Ave, South San Francisco, CA 94080-6210
Tel (650) 873-0750 *Founded/Ownrshp* 1986
Sales 37.2MM[E] *EMP* 170
SIC 4724 4513 4412 Travel agencies; Air courier services; Deep sea foreign transportation of freight
Ch Bd: Carlos Araneta
Treas: Fely Ruiz

L B CONSTRUCTION
See BURNS LANCASTER CONSTRUCTION INC

D-U-N-S 00-439-2619 IMP/EXP
▲ L B FOSTER CO (PA)
LBFOSTER
415 Holiday Dr Ste 1, Pittsburgh, PA 15220-2793
Tel (412) 928-3400 *Founded/Ownrshp* 1902
Sales 607.1MM *EMP* 830
Accts Ernst & Young Llp Pittsburgh
Tkr Sym FSTR *Exch* NGS
SIC 3312 3272 3317 Railroad crossings, steel or iron; Structural shapes & pilings, steel; Ties, railroad: concrete; Concrete products, precast; Steel pipe & tubes; Railroad crossings, steel or iron; Structural shapes & pilings, steel; Ties, railroad: concrete; Concrete products, precast; Steel pipe & tubes
Pr: Robert P Bauer
**Ch Bd:* Lee B Foster II
CFO: David J Russo
Ofcr: John Gorman
Sr VP: John F Kasel
VP: Steve Burgess
VP: Donald Eadie
VP: Patrick J Guinee
VP: Brian Vidler
VP Bus Dev: Ll Cheng
Dist Mgr: Tim Maier
Board of Directors: Peter McIlroy II, G Thomas McKane, Diane B Owen, Robert S Purgason, William H Rackoff, Suzanne B Rowland

D-U-N-S 02-920-1493 IMP
■ L B FOSTER RAIL TECHNOLOGIES INC
PORTEC RAIL PRODUCTS, INC.
(*Suby of* L B FOSTER CO) ★
415 Holiday Dr Ste 1, Pittsburgh, PA 15220-2793
Tel (412) 928-3448 *Founded/Ownrshp* 2010
Sales 37.7MM[E] *EMP* 200
SIC 5088 Railroad equipment & supplies; Railroad equipment & supplies
Pr: Robert Bauer
Pr: L J Sieja
CFO: David Russo

D-U-N-S 10-709-3416
L B I HOLDINGS I INC
1845 W Empire Ave, Burbank, CA 91504-3402
Tel (818) 563-5722 *Founded/Ownrshp* 1997
Sales 33.8MM[E] *EMP* 522
Accts Ernst & Young Llp
SIC 4832 Radio broadcasting stations; Ethnic programming; Radio broadcasting stations; Ethnic programming
Pr: Jose Liberman
**CFO:* William S Keenan
**Ex VP:* Lenard Liberman
**VP:* Winter Horton
**VP:* Eduardo Leon

D-U-N-S 00-512-1546
L B INDUSTRIES INC
LALLY PIPE & TUBE DIVISION
8770 Railroad Dr, Taylor Mill, KY 41015-9096
Tel (859) 431-8300 *Founded/Ownrshp* 1934
Sales 110.0MM *EMP* 100
SIC 5051

L B P
See LBP MANUFACTURING INC

D-U-N-S 03-855-7005 IMP
L B PLASTICS INC
(*Suby of* LITCHFIELD INVESTMENTS HOLDINGS LIMITED)
482 E Plaza Dr, Mooresville, NC 28115-8021
Tel (704) 663-1543 *Founded/Ownrshp* 1977
Sales 25.8MM[E] *EMP* 125
SIC 3089 2522 3069 Plastic hardware & building products; Windows, plastic; Doors, folding: plastic or plastic coated fabric; Hardware, plastic; Office cabinets & filing drawers: except wood; Mats or matting, rubber
Ch Bd: Leon G Litchfield
**Pr:* Harry H Davis
VP: James Litchfied

D-U-N-S 00-615-3084 IMP/EXP
L B WHITE CO INC
411 Mason St, Onalaska, WI 54650-7035
Tel (608) 783-5691 *Founded/Ownrshp* 1953, 2010
Sales 37.6MM[E] *EMP* 135
SIC 3585 Heating equipment, complete; Heating equipment, complete
CEO: Richard Diermeier
**CFO:* Kevin Gagermeier
CFO: Jack Lauer
VP: Bridgett Crave
IT Man: Dan Jackson
IT Man: Bryan James
IT Man: Melissa Olsen
Mtls Mgr: Bernie Clements
Opers Mgr: Gary Larson
Mktg Dir: Paul Barrington
Mktg Dir: Henry Glover

D-U-N-S 02-247-2468 IMP/EXP
▲ L BRANDS INC
3 Limited Pkwy, Columbus, OH 43230-1467
Tel (614) 415-7000 *Founded/Ownrshp* 1963
Sales 11.4MMM *EMP* 80,100
Accts Ernst & Young Llp Columbus O
Tkr Sym LB *Exch* NYS
SIC 5632 5961 5621 5999 Lingerie (outerwear); Lingerie & corsets (underwear); Toiletries, cosmetics & perfumes; Women's apparel, mail order; Women's clothing stores; Lingerie (outerwear); Lingerie & corsets (underwear); Women's apparel, mail order; Women's clothing stores; Toiletries, cosmetics & perfumes
Ch Bd: Leslie H Wexner
Ch Bd: Jack Listanowsky
Pr: Shashi Batra
Pr: Barry D Kaufman
Pr: Denise Landman
Pr: Jay Margolis
Pr: Joanne Nemeroff
COO: William E May
COO: Charles C McGuigan
COO: Scott Oliver
COO: Bjorn Waring
COO: Dave Webster
CFO: Stuart B Burgdoerfer
Treas: Timothy Faber
Ex VP: Rick Jackson
Ex VP: Michael Keane
Ex VP: Frederick Lamster
Ex VP: Joan Overlock
Ex VP: Martyn Redgrave
Ex VP: Kurt Schnieders
Sr VP: Daniel Finkelman
Board of Directors: Abigail S Wexner, E Gordon Gee, Raymond Zimmerman, Dennis S Hersch, Donna A James, David T Kollat, William R Loomis Jr, Jeffrey H Miro, Michael G Morris, Stephen D Steinour, Allan R Tessler

D-U-N-S 79-691-9447 IMP
■ L BRANDS STORE DESIGN & CONSTRUCTION INC
LIMITED
(*Suby of* L BRANDS INC) ★
3 Ltd Pkwy, Columbus, OH 43230
Tel (614) 415-7000 *Founded/Ownrshp* 1990
Sales 154.5MM[E] *EMP* 230
SIC 1542 Commercial & office building, new construction; Commercial & office building, new construction
Pr: Gene Torcha
**Treas:* Timothy Faber
Bd of Dir: Samuel Fried
Assoc VP: Bryan Yuris
Ex VP: Mark Giresi
Sr VP: Jennie Wilson
**VP:* Rick Felice
VP: Edwin Hofmann
VP: Kent Kleeberger
Prgrm Mgr: Peggy Trueman
Dir IT: Joe Proctor

D-U-N-S 00-242-3994
L BUILDERS SUPPLY INC
BELLEVUE BUILDERS SUPPLY
(*Suby of* US LBM HOLDINGS LLC) ★
500 Duanesburg Rd, Schenectady, NY 12306-1015
Tel (518) 355-7190 *Founded/Ownrshp* 2009
Sales 78.7MM[E] *EMP* 380
SIC 2431 2439 2541 5211 Millwork; Trusses, wooden roof; Trusses, except roof: laminated lumber; Wood partitions & fixtures; Millwork & lumber; Cabinets, kitchen; Home centers; Millwork; Trusses, wooden roof; Trusses, except roof: laminated lumber; Wood partitions & fixtures; Millwork & lumber; Cabinets, kitchen; Home centers
Pr: Greg Gaskell
CFO: Suzanne Firsee
Treas: Monica L Keiss
Dept Mgr: Bill Kanas
Off Mgr: Sally Blum
IT Man: Pat O'Neil
Sfty Mgr: Mark Auspelmyer
Sales Asso: Jim Decaro
Sales Asso: Tim Kenyon
Sales Asso: Jim Telfer
Sales Asso: Peter Zacheus

L C
See LOUISA COUNTY PUBLIC SCHOOLS

D-U-N-S 80-342-7293 IMP
L C ACME BARRICADES
9800 Normandy Blvd, Jacksonville, FL 32221-2038
Tel (904) 781-1950 *Founded/Ownrshp* 1997
Sales 27.2MM[E] *EMP* 82[E]
SIC 3499 7389 Barricades, metal; Flagging service (traffic control)

D-U-N-S 13-263-6619 EXP
L C ALLIED DBD
ALLIED CARIBBEAN DISTRIBUTORS
10992 Nw 92nd Ter, Medley, FL 33178-2515
Tel (305) 463-0038 *Founded/Ownrshp* 1999
Sales 21.2MM[E] *EMP* 47
SIC 5149 Groceries & related products
Pr: Derek Kramer
**VP:* Bill Janco
VP: Jonathan Kramer
Dir Bus: Scott Jahrmarkt

D-U-N-S 00-880-3152 IMP
L C BDP
BASSETT FURNITURE DIRECT
2244 Luna Rd Ste 100, Carrollton, TX 75006-6543
Tel (469) 522-6803 *Founded/Ownrshp* 1996, 2001
Sales 31.3MM *EMP* 150
SIC 5712 Furniture stores; Furniture stores
Pr: Mark Klein
**Treas:* Eric Hall
**VP:* Mike Hall

D-U-N-S 10-715-9972 IMP/EXP
L C BULLFROG INTERNATIONAL
BULLFROG SPAS
668 W 14600 S, Bluffdale, UT 84065-4859
Tel (801) 307-1042 *Founded/Ownrshp* 1996
Sales 22.8MM[E] *EMP* 150
SIC 3999 3949 3088 Hot tubs; Sporting & athletic goods; Plastics plumbing fixtures; Hot tubs; Sporting & athletic goods; Plastics plumbing fixtures
Pr: Jerry Pasley
**VP:* Alan Robins
Sls Dir: Jim Sueppel

D-U-N-S 06-190-6491
L C BUSCH-TRANSOU (MO)
TRI EAGLE SALES
545 River Birch Rd, Midway, FL 32343-2768
Tel (850) 576-1294 *Founded/Ownrshp* 1996
Sales 52.2MM[E] *EMP* 210
SIC 5181 Beer & other fermented malt liquors; Beer & other fermented malt liquors
Mktg Mgr: Amanda Ganley

L C C C
See LORAIN COUNTY COMMUNITY COLLEGE DISTRICT

D-U-N-S 02-409-0503
L C DM GROUP
DIRECTMAIL.COM
5351 Ketch Rd, Prince Frederick, MD 20678-3470
Tel (301) 855-1700 *Founded/Ownrshp* 1972
Sales 44.7MM[E] *EMP* 251
SIC 7331 Direct mail advertising services; Direct mail advertising services
Pr: Kirk Swain
CFO: Lily Swain
VP: Doborah Albro
VP: Lisa Donnelly
VP: Shawn Salta
VP: Mike Savage
VP: Cindy Vance
Dir Bus: Maureen Raymond
Prgrm Mgr: Rebecca Cloud
Prgrm Mgr: Diane Nappi
Web Dev: Natasha Naglowsky

L C E
See LIFE CYCLE ENGINEERING INC

D-U-N-S 08-741-4009
L C ENTERPRISES
LC ENTERPRISES
8100 E 22nd St N Bldg 900, Wichita, KS 67226-2309
Tel (316) 682-3300 *Founded/Ownrshp* 1977
Sales 20.2MM[E] *EMP* 500
SIC 8741 7359 6512 Restaurant management; Equipment rental & leasing; Commercial & industrial building operation; Restaurant management; Equipment rental & leasing; Commercial & industrial building operation
Pr: Larry Cooley
**CEO:* Mathew Shets
**COO:* Gary Greaves

D-U-N-S 11-206-3169 IMP
L C EXCELL MARKETING
5501 Park Ave, Des Moines, IA 50321-1206
Tel (515) 564-4896 *Founded/Ownrshp* 1995
Sales 69.8MM[E] *EMP* 200
SIC 5199 Cards, plastic: unprinted; Cards, plastic: unprinted
Pr: Stan Seidler
**CFO:* Patrick Burton
**CFO:* Steve Jones
Prin: Doug Lindquist
Mktg Dir: Chad Ranck

D-U-N-S 00-319-7803
L C INDUSTRIES INC (NC)
4500 Emperor Blvd, Durham, NC 27703-8420
Tel (919) 596-8277 *Founded/Ownrshp* 1938
Sales 56.3MM *EMP* 800
Accts Dixon Hughes Goodman Llp Ashe
SIC 5943 2675 2515 2253 2392 2676 Office forms & supplies; Folders, filing, die-cut: made from purchased materials; Mattresses & foundations; Shirts (outerwear), knit; Mattress protectors, except rubber; Towels, paper: made from purchased paper; Office forms & supplies; Folders, filing, die-cut: made from purchased materials; Mattresses & foundations; Shirts (outerwear), knit; Mattress protectors, except rubber; Towels, paper: made from purchased paper
Ch: Richard M Hudson
**Pr:* William L Hudson
COO: Jeffrey Schwartz
**CFO:* Richard Stallings
Ex VP: Jeffrey Hawting
VP: Ed Gagne
Store Mgr: Todd Bullard
Store Mgr: Antoine Bush
Store Mgr: Brian Wilson
Dir IT: Del White
IT Man: Nathan Mason

L C N
See EDWARD G SAWYER CO INC

D-U-N-S 03-168-4368
L C RAMNARAIN
HOSPITALITY STAFF OF METRO DC
5010 Nicholson Ln Ste 202, Rockville, MD 20852-3108
Tel (301) 230-6585 *Founded/Ownrshp* 1997
Sales 9.9MM[E] *EMP* 400
SIC 7363 Help supply services; Help supply services

L C S
See LIFE CARE SERVICES LLC

L C S
See LCS CONSTRUCTORS INC

L C S E C O
See LEAVENWORTH CO SPEC ED CO OP

D-U-N-S 03-419-5024
L C SSX
SOUTHERN SCRAP X-PRESS RECYCL
(*Suby of* SOUTHERN RECYCLING LLC) ★
6847 Scenic Hwy, Baton Rouge, LA 70807-6254
Tel (225) 355-4453 *Founded/Ownrshp* 1954
Sales 26.5MM[E] *EMP* 87
SIC 5093 Ferrous metal scrap & waste; Ferrous metal scrap & waste
Pr: Chip Hunter
**CFO:* David Fonge
**Treas:* J D Demarest
Off Mgr: Sam Zurke

L C W
See LANTZ CONSTRUCTION CO OF WINCHESTER INC

D-U-N-S 00-213-0755 EXP
L C WHITFORD CO INC (NY)
164 N Main St, Wellsville, NY 14895-1152
Tel (585) 593-3601 *Founded/Ownrshp* 1916, 1969
Sales 43.9MM *EMP* 200
Accts Proto & Loskey Llc Olean Ne
SIC 1622 1611 1541 3272 7359 3273 Bridge construction; General contractor, highway & street construction; Industrial buildings, new construction; Precast terrazo or concrete products; Prestressed concrete products; Equipment rental & leasing; Ready-mixed concrete; Bridge construction; General contractor, highway & street construction; Industrial buildings, new construction; Precast terrazo or concrete products; Prestressed concrete products; Equipment rental & leasing; Ready-mixed concrete
Pr: L Bradley Whitford
**Pr:* Brad Whitford
**CFO:* Dan Matacale
**VP:* L Chandler Whitford
Admn Mgr: Melissa Niedermaier
Sls Mgr: Dan Whitford
Sales Asso: Karl Graves

L D & S
See L DAGOSTINI & SONS INC

L D C OF LAFAYETTE
See LAFAYETTE DRUG CO INC

D-U-N-S 06-751-9723
L D CONATSER CONTRACTORS INC
5327 Wichita St, Forest Hill, TX 76119-6035
Tel (817) 534-1743 *Founded/Ownrshp* 1986
Sales 11.0MM[E] *EMP* 400
SIC 1794 Excavation work; Excavation work
Pr: Jerry Conatser

D-U-N-S 13-109-9793
L D CUTTING LLC
AMERICAN CLASSIC HOMES
3016 Benson Rd S, Renton, WA 98055-5118
Tel (425) 277-1500 *Founded/Ownrshp* 2003
Sales 30.0MM *EMP* 22
SIC 6531 Real estate agent, residential; Real estate agent, residential

L D I
See LOGISTIC DYNAMICS INC

D-U-N-S 00-446-0317 IMP
L D KICHLER CO (OH)
KICHLER LIGHTING
7711 E Pleasant Valley Rd, Cleveland, OH 44131-5532
Tel (216) 573-1000 *Founded/Ownrshp* 1938
Sales 162.9MM[E] *EMP* 645
SIC 3645 3648 3641 Residential lighting fixtures; Lighting equipment; Electric lamps; Residential lighting fixtures; Lighting equipment; Electric lamps
CEO: Tony Davidson
**Ch Bd:* Harold S Minoff
**Ch:* Barry Minoff
Treas: Nichole Bruening
**VP:* Roy Minoff
**VP:* David Pamer
VP: Bruce Pazula
VP: John Schlinder
Dir Bus: Eric Borden
Genl Mgr: Patrick Shen
Off Mgr: Donna Camarco

D-U-N-S 86-705-3399
L D V INVESTMENTS INC
3850 W 1st Ave, Eugene, OR 97402-5367
Tel (541) 686-2848 *Founded/Ownrshp* 1993
Sales 39.8MM *EMP* 380[E]
Accts Jones & Roth Pc Eugene Or
SIC 3993 7389 7373 Signs & advertising specialties; Design, commercial & industrial; Systems software development services; Signs & advertising specialties; Design, commercial & industrial; Systems software development services
CEO: Kris Londahl
**VP:* William Volm

D-U-N-S 04-927-7882
L DAGOSTINI & SONS INC
L D & S
15801 23 Mile Rd, Macomb, MI 48042-4002
Tel (586) 781-5800 *Founded/Ownrshp* 1961
Sales 26.8MM[E] *EMP* 20
SIC 1623 1794 6552 Sewer line construction; Water main construction; Excavation & grading, building construction; Land subdividers & developers, commercial; Sewer line construction; Excavation & grading, building construction; Land subdividers & developers, commercial
Pr: Antonio D'Agostini
**Sec:* James D'Agostini
**VP:* Robert D'Agostini

D-U-N-S 00-443-2076
L DICKS INC
608 W Frederick Ave, Dundee, FL 33838-4225
Tel (863) 439-1996 *Founded/Ownrshp* 1949

Sales 35.0MM *EMP* 120
SIC 5148 4212 Fruits, fresh; Light haulage & cartage, local; Fruits, fresh; Light haulage & cartage, local
Pr: Richard Dicks
**VP:* Dennis Dicks
**VP:* Ronald Dicks

L E BELCHER
See LEONARD E BELCHER INC

D-U-N-S 06-367-7579 EXP
L E BELL CONSTRUCTION CO INC
1226 County Road 11, Heflin, AL 36264-3533
Tel (256) 253-2676 *Founded/Ownrshp* 1972
Sales 144.2MM[E] *EMP* 300
SIC 1623 Oil & gas pipeline construction; Oil & gas pipeline construction
Pr: Larry Bell
Sec: Jimmie Taylor
VP: Michael Bell
VP: Dan Norton
VP: Jackson Norton
Exec: Elizabeth Bell
Sfty Dirs: Steve Barker
Trfc Dir: James Saxon
Snr Mgr: Britt Sincher
Snr Mgr: Cliff Wakefield

D-U-N-S 05-008-7410
L E COPPERSMITH INC
COPPERSMITH GLOBAL LOGISTICS
525 S Douglas St Ste 100, El Segundo, CA 90245-4828
Tel (310) 607-8000 *Founded/Ownrshp* 2003
Sales 58.6MM[E] *EMP* 156
SIC 4731 Customhouse brokers; Customhouse brokers
CEO: Jeffrey Craig Coppersmith
**CFO:* Douglas S Walkley
VP: Lew Coppersmith Jr
Ex Dir: Diane Eicher
CIO: Dion Cheong
Natl Sales: Bobby Shaida

L E D
See LOUISIANA DEPARTMENT OF ECONOMIC DEVELOPMENT

D-U-N-S 04-304-4919
L E D BRAUN INC
46129 W Kristina Way, Maricopa, AZ 85139-6968
Tel (916) 410-8534 *Founded/Ownrshp* 2010
Sales 28.0MM *EMP* 372
SIC 3229 Glass blanks for electric light bulbs
CEO: Samuel L Thompson
Pr: Scott E Emison
Sr VP: Chandler Harrison

D-U-N-S 17-804-1349
L E F INC
LASER ENNOVATION AND ENGRG
9401 E 54th St, Tulsa, OK 74145-8101
Tel (918) 665-7799 *Founded/Ownrshp* 1987
Sales 21.1MM[E] *EMP* 60
SIC 3444 7692 Sheet metal specialties, not stamped; Welding repair
Pr: George Juanitis
**VP:* Troy Kuske
IT Man: Aimee Lapelle
Sls Mgr: Troy Kusky

D-U-N-S 00-206-3857
L E FARRELL CO INC (VT)
PEPSI COLA BOTTLING CO
405 Pine St, Burlington, VT 05401-4742
Tel (802) 864-6000 *Founded/Ownrshp* 1920
Sales 20.3MM[E] *EMP* 159
SIC 5149 Soft drinks; Soft drinks
Pr: Louis G Farrell
**VP:* Cathy Campbell
Opers Mgr: Larry Moirano

L E I
See LEI COMPANIES INC

D-U-N-S 00-547-0562 IMP/EXP
L E JOHNSON PRODUCTS INC
JOHNSON HARDWARE
2100 Sterling Ave, Elkhart, IN 46516-4909
Tel (574) 293-5664 *Founded/Ownrshp* 1959
Sales 27.8MM[E] *EMP* 210[E]
SIC 3429 Door opening & closing devices, except electrical; Furniture hardware; Door opening & closing devices, except electrical; Furniture hardware
Pr: Larry A Johnson
**Pr:* Larry Johnson
**Treas:* Scott Johnson
**VP:* Stephen Johnson
Mktg Mgr: Michael Myers

D-U-N-S 00-613-4183 IMP
L E JONES CO
1200 34th Ave, Menominee, MI 49858-1695
Tel (906) 863-1043 *Founded/Ownrshp* 1946
Sales 85.7MM[E] *EMP* 390
SIC 3592 3545 Valves, engine; Machine tool accessories; Valves, engine; Machine tool accessories
CEO: David Doll
**Ch Bd:* Peter Vennema
**VP:* Douglas Dooley
Dir IT: Wayne Mills
Info Man: Eric Powers
Ql Cn Mgr: Cathy Molkentine
VP Sls: Lawrence Bowsher
S&M/VP: Daniel Ward

D-U-N-S 00-693-1661
■ L E MYERS CO
(*Suby of* MYR GROUP INC) ★
1701 Golf Rd Ste 3-1012, Rolling Meadows, IL 60008-4276
Tel (847) 290-1891 *Founded/Ownrshp* 1982
Sales 109.7MM[E] *EMP* 280
SIC 1623 Electric power line construction; Electric power line construction
Ch Bd: William A Koertner
**Pr:* Richard S Swartz Jr
**Treas:* Marco A Martinez
**Sr VP:* William Green
**VP:* John A Fluss Sr
Opers Mgr: Warren Beert

L E P A
See LOUISIANA ENERGY & POWER AUTHORITY

D-U-N-S 07-649-0440
L E PHILLIPS CAREER DEVELOPMENT CENTER INC
1515 Ball St, Eau Claire, WI 54703-3261
Tel (715) 834-2771 *Founded/Ownrshp* 1959
Sales 2.7MM *EMP* 320
SIC 8331 Job training & vocational rehabilitation services; Job training & vocational rehabilitation services
IT Man: Gregg Mizerk

L E S
See LOUISIANA ENERGY SERVICES LLC

D-U-N-S 79-008-1814
L E SIMMONS & ASSOCIATES INC
SCF PARTNERS
600 Travis St Ste 6600, Houston, TX 77002-2921
Tel (713) 227-7888 *Founded/Ownrshp* 1989
Sales 470.8MM[E] *EMP* 5,006
SIC 6799 Venture capital companies; Venture capital companies
Pr: L E Simmons
Pt: Ray A Ballantyne
**Pt:* Anthony F Deluca
**VP:* Nicholas B Drake
**VP:* Theresa W Eaton
CIO: Jim Wood
Opers Mgr: Sara Galvan

D-U-N-S 78-625-0357
L EVERITT INDUSTRIAL SUPPLY INC
523 Crockett St, Channelview, TX 77530-4353
Tel (281) 452-6660 *Founded/Ownrshp* 1992
Sales 20.1MM[E] *EMP* 25
SIC 5085

L F D HOME FURNISHINGS
See LFD LLC

D-U-N-S 01-846-4412
L F DONNELL INC
DONNELL AUTO GROUP
(*Suby of* DAVID A FLYNN INC)
7955 Market St, Youngstown, OH 44512-5932
Tel (330) 726-8181 *Founded/Ownrshp* 1982
Sales 33.7MM[E] *EMP* 85
SIC 5511

D-U-N-S 00-678-1769 IMP
L F DRISCOLL CO LLC
401 E City Ave Ste 500, Bala Cynwyd, PA 19004-1124
Tel (610) 668-0950 *Founded/Ownrshp* 1929, 2009
Sales 214.6MM[E] *EMP* 200
Accts Deloitte & Touche Llp Parsipp
SIC 1541 1542 1522 8742 Industrial buildings, new construction; Commercial & office building, new construction; Apartment building construction; Management consulting services; Industrial buildings, new construction; Commercial & office building, new construction; Apartment building construction; Management consulting services
CEO: John J Donnelly
Pr: Frank M Stulb
CFO: Rich Pirollo
Ex VP: Robert J Miller
VP: Michael F Delaney
VP: Kenneth J Innella
Exec: Peggy Cowan
Exec: Jeffrey Hutwelker
Exec: Tom McDonald
Exec: George Schaefer
Exec: David Zoolalian
Dir Bus: Trish Harrington

D-U-N-S 08-836-8113 IMP
L F MANUFACTURING INC
5528 E Highway 290, Giddings, TX 78942-2972
Tel (979) 542-8027 *Founded/Ownrshp* 1996
Sales 24.0MM *EMP* 225
SIC 3089 1629 3088 Plastic & fiberglass tanks; Waste water & sewage treatment plant construction; Plastics plumbing fixtures; Plastic & fiberglass tanks; Waste water & sewage treatment plant construction; Plastics plumbing fixtures
Pr: C A Johnston
Genl Mgr: Jack D Murray
Off Mgr: Bernie Ofczarvak
Sls Mgr: Jamey Finstad
Sales Asso: Nathan Sewvillo

D-U-N-S 08-128-3756 IMP
L F P INC (CA)
FLYNT, LARRY PUBLISHING
8484 Wilshire Blvd # 900, Beverly Hills, CA 90211-3218
Tel (323) 651-3525 *Founded/Ownrshp* 1976
Sales 26.2MM[E] *EMP* 117
SIC 2721 Magazines: publishing & printing; Magazines: publishing & printing
Ch Bd: Larry Flynt
**Pr:* Michael H Klein
COO: Dennis Wang
CFO: James B Chamberlain
Ex VP: Theresa Flynt
VP: Gerry Awang
VP: Darren Davis
VP: Lyn Heller
VP: David Wolinsky
VP: Mike Youtan
VP Bus Dev: Mark Hamilton
Creative D: Wilson Kello
Creative D: Drew Rosenfeld

D-U-N-S 03-033-3165 IMP
L FISHMAN & SON INC
6301 E Lombard St, Baltimore, MD 21224-1779
Tel (410) 633-2500 *Founded/Ownrshp* 1974
Sales 48.7MM[E] *EMP* 150
SIC 5023 5087

D-U-N-S 06-103-4617
■ L G & E POWER INC
L G E-ON COMPANY
(*Suby of* LG&E CAPITAL CORP) ★
220 W Main St Ste 1400, Louisville, KY 40202-1377
Tel (502) 627-2000 *Founded/Ownrshp* 1980
Sales 71.2MM[E] *EMP* 525
SIC 4922 4923 1629 4911 Pipelines, natural gas; Storage, natural gas; Gas transmission & distribution; Power plant construction; Generation, electric power; Pipelines, natural gas; Storage, natural gas; Gas transmission & distribution; Power plant construction; Generation, electric power
Pr: Victor Staffieri
**CFO:* S Bradford Rives
**Treas:* Daniel K Arbough
VP: Cathy Butler
VP: Don Carter
**VP:* John R McCall
Telecom Mg: Steve Kniffley
IT Man: Cheryl Bobzien
IT Man: Danny Katzman
IT Man: Robert Rose
IT Man: Tony Ruckriegel

D-U-N-S 01-065-0414
L G BARCUS AND SONS INC
1430 State Ave, Kansas City, KS 66102-4469
Tel (913) 621-1100 *Founded/Ownrshp* 1941
Sales 91.7MM[E] *EMP* 125
SIC 1629 1622 Pile driving contractor; Bridge construction; Pile driving contractor; Bridge construction
Pr: Richard W Hoener
Ch Bd: Douglas G Barcus
CFO: Stephen Kimsey
V Ch Bd: Lawrence G Barcus
VP: David Grossman
VP: Joshua Shorley
VP: Dale E Stockfleth
Snr Mgr: Daniel Gibson
Snr Mgr: Todd Kalwei

L G E-ON COMPANY
See L G & E POWER INC

D-U-N-S 00-792-0390
L G EVERIST INC (IA)
300 S Phillips Ave # 200, Sioux Falls, SD 57104-6322
Tel (712) 552-1347 *Founded/Ownrshp* 1876
Sales 453.9MM[E] *EMP* 260
SIC 1442 1429 Common sand mining; Gravel mining; Quartzite, crushed & broken-quarrying; Riprap quarrying; Common sand mining; Gravel mining; Quartzite, crushed & broken-quarrying; Riprap quarrying
CEO: Rick Everist
**CFO:* Steve Mousel
CFO: Steven Musel
**VP:* Rob Everist
VP: Denny Fields
VP: Carrie Garry
VP: Todd Schuver
**VP:* Jay Van Den Top
VP: Jay Den Den Top
VP: Jay Den Top
VP: Jay Den Den Top
VP: Jay Den Top

L G H
See LOWELL GENERAL HOSPITAL

D-U-N-S 05-325-1679 IMP/EXP
■ L G SOURCING INC
(*Suby of* LOWES COMPANIES INC) ★
1605 Curtis Bridge Rd, North Wilkesboro, NC 28659
Tel (866) 578-0563 *Founded/Ownrshp* 1997
Sales 141.5MM[E] *EMP* 40
SIC 5023 5031 2499 Home furnishings; Decorative home furnishings & supplies; Building materials, exterior; Building materials, interior; Picture & mirror frames, wood
Pr: Mike Menser
**Treas:* Benjamin S Adams Jr
**VP:* David R Green

D-U-N-S 80-560-3698
L GARY HART ASSOCIATED
13381 440th Ave Sw, East Grand Forks, MN 56721-9004
Tel (520) 297-3237 *Founded/Ownrshp* 2006
Sales 805.6MM *EMP* 1
SIC 8733 Medical research
Owner: Lawrence Gary Hart

L GORDON IRON & METAL COMPANY
See GORDON RECYCLERS INC

L H DOTTIE
See KOBERT & CO INC

D-U-N-S 00-577-9046
L H LACY CO LTD (TX)
LACY CONSTRUCTION
1880 Crown Dr, Dallas, TX 75234-9401
Tel (214) 357-0146 *Founded/Ownrshp* 1919, 1995
Sales 55.7MM *EMP* 275
Accts Cpwr Llp Addison Texas
SIC 1611 1629 1542 1794 Concrete construction: roads, highways, sidewalks, etc.; Trenching contractor; Earthmoving contractor; Nonresidential construction; Excavation work; Concrete construction: roads, highways, sidewalks, etc.; Trenching contractor; Earthmoving contractor; Nonresidential construction; Excavation work
CEO: Mike R Lacy
Pt: George Rivero
CEO: Ron Murawski
Mtls Mgr: Dale McCurley

L H M
See LODGING/HOSPITALITY MANAGEMENT CORP

D-U-N-S 11-739-9261
L H STAMPING CORP
(*Suby of* L.H. INDUSTRIES CORP.)
4420 Clubview Dr, Fort Wayne, IN 46804-4407
Tel (260) 432-5563 *Founded/Ownrshp* 1991
Sales 30.7MM *EMP* 43
Accts Baden Gage & Schroeder Llc F
SIC 3469 Metal stampings; Metal stampings
Ch: Leon Habegger
**Pr:* Bruce Emerick
**CFO:* Dan Brehm
Genl Mgr: Brad Habegger
Plnt Mgr: Jim Turney
Mktg Mgr: Danny McLemore

D-U-N-S 19-431-0991
L H WHITE & SON INC
(*Suby of* R H WHITE COMPANIES INC) ★
41 Central St, Auburn, MA 01501-2304
Tel (508) 832-3295 *Founded/Ownrshp* 1923
Sales 3.0MM *EMP* 300
Accts Ccr Llp
SIC 7353 Heavy construction equipment rental; Heavy construction equipment rental
Pr: David White

L HAMRICK'S
See HAMRICKS INC

D-U-N-S 17-266-0524
L I C H CORP
339 Hicks St, Brooklyn, NY 11201-5509
Tel (718) 780-1000 *Founded/Ownrshp* 1984
Sales 46.1MM[E] *EMP* 3,200
SIC 8062 8092 5912 General medical & surgical hospitals; Kidney dialysis centers; Drug stores; General medical & surgical hospitals; Kidney dialysis centers; Drug stores
Pr: Donald Snell
COO: John Byrne
VP: Catherine Gallogly-Simon
VP: Diana Sullivan
Dir Rad: Deborah Reede
Dir Rx: Michael Delio
IT Man: Ashras Kahn

D-U-N-S 17-375-7360
L I CHILD AND FAMILY DEVELOPMENT SERVICES INC
LONG ISLAND HEAD START
98 Austin St, Patchogue, NY 11772-2615
Tel (631) 758-5200 *Founded/Ownrshp* 1985
Sales 12.9MM[E] *EMP* 325
Accts Deans Archer & Co Valley Stre
SIC 8351 Head start center, except in conjunction with school; Head start center, except in conjunction with school
CEO: Debra Garcia
**Ch Bd:* Terrence Goode
**CFO:* David Ferlauto

L J AVIATION
See LJ ASSOCIATES INC

D-U-N-S 83-643-2070
L J D HOLDINGS INC
B & D FOODS
3494 S Tk Ave, Boise, ID 83705-5278
Tel (208) 344-1183 *Founded/Ownrshp* 1994
Sales 25.4MM[E] *EMP* 160
SIC 2038 2013 Snacks, including onion rings, cheese sticks, etc.; Sausages & other prepared meats; Frozen meats from purchased meat
Pr: Tim Andersen
**VP:* David Durkin
Sls Mgr: Brian Maher

D-U-N-S 00-418-8058 IMP
L J SMITH INC
WOODSMITHS DESIGN & MFG
(*Suby of* MCDONOUGH HOLDINGS INC (FN)) ★
35280 Scio Bowerston Rd, Bowerston, OH 44695-9731
Tel (740) 269-2221 *Founded/Ownrshp* 1913
Sales 48.1MM[E] *EMP* 325
SIC 2431 Millwork; Staircases, stairs & railings; Millwork; Staircases, stairs & railings
Pr: Craig Kurtz
Sls Mgr: David Smith
Sls Mgr: Jim Stingel
Sls Mgr: Jerry Yeager

L J T
See LOCK JOINT TUBE LLC

D-U-N-S 15-570-3713
L J T FLOWERS INC
SKYLINE FLWR GROWERS SHIPPERS
4279 E Hueneme Rd, Oxnard, CA 93033-8204
Tel (805) 488-0879 *Founded/Ownrshp* 1954
Sales 27.4MM[E] *EMP* 105
SIC 5191 0181 Flower & field bulbs; Flowers grown in field nurseries; Flower & field bulbs; Flowers grown in field nurseries
Pr: Joe Goldberg
**VP:* Tom Goldberg

D-U-N-S 07-231-8496 IMP
L J THALMANN CO
CHALET
3132 Lake Ave, Wilmette, IL 60091-1116
Tel (847) 256-0561 *Founded/Ownrshp* 1955
Sales 55.8MM[E] *EMP* 285
SIC 5261 6512 Nursery stock, seeds & bulbs; Commercial & industrial building operation; Nursery stock, seeds & bulbs; Commercial & industrial building operation
Ch Bd: Lawrence J Thalmann Jr
Pr: Lawrence J Thalmann III
CFO: Keith Loeffler

D-U-N-S 10-926-7948
L JOHNSON JERRY & ASSOCIATES INC
6499 Mount Zion Blvd, Morrow, GA 30260-2150
Tel (770) 961-7600 *Founded/Ownrshp* 1991
Sales 26.4MM[E] *EMP* 70
SIC 1542 Commercial & office building contractors; Commercial & office building, new construction; Commercial & office buildings, renovation & repair
Pr: Emory H Palmer
**VP:* Charles W Cobb
**VP:* Wilkes W Palmer

L K M
See LARRY KLINE WHOLESALE MEATS AND PROVISIONS INC

D-U-N-S 08-163-1459
L KEELEY CONSTRUCTION CO (IL)
KEELEY COMPANIES, THE
2901 Falling Springs Rd, Sauget, IL 62206-1133
Tel (314) 421-5933 *Founded/Ownrshp* 1976
Sales 109.0MM *EMP* 50
Accts Sfw Partners Llc St Louis
SIC 1541 1611 1623 Industrial buildings, new construction; Highway & street paving contractor; Sewer line construction; Industrial buildings, new construction; Highway & street paving contractor; Sewer line construction
Prin: Rusty Keeley
**Pr:* LP Rusty Keeley Jr
Exec: Keith Cova

D-U-N-S 07-196-3805
L KELLER OIL PROPERTIES INC
KELLER OIL CO
(*Suby of* KELLER ENTERPRISES INC) ★
1202 N Keller Dr, Effingham, IL 62401-4523
Tel (217) 347-7777 *Founded/Ownrshp* 1938
Sales 33.3MM^E *EMP* 162
SIC 5541 5171 5014 6512 Filling stations, gasoline; Petroleum bulk stations; Automobile tires & tubes; Commercial & industrial building operation; Filling stations, gasoline; Petroleum bulk stations; Automobile tires & tubes; Commercial & industrial building operation
Ch Bd: Charles F Keller
CFO: Kaare J Pedersen

D-U-N-S 01-957-2577 IMP
L KNIFE & SON INC
GREAT BREWERS
35 Elder Ave, Kingston, MA 02364-1503
Tel (781) 585-2364 *Founded/Ownrshp* 1963
Sales 107.4MM^E *EMP* 200
SIC 5181 5182 Beer & other fermented malt liquors; Wine; Beer & other fermented malt liquors; Wine
Pr: Timothy G Sheehan
**Treas:* Douglas S Macdonald
VP: Jeffrey Annis
VP: Tom Schreibel
**Prin:* Gerald Sheehan
Area Mgr: Ethan Rosenbluth
Genl Mgr: Ted Landers
Genl Mgr: J C Panio
IT Man: Debra Lahteine
VP Opers: Brian McGuire
Opers Mgr: Jim Burke

D-U-N-S 00-109-4382 IMP/EXP
L L BEAN INC (ME)
15 Casco St, Freeport, ME 04033-0002
Tel (207) 552-2000 *Founded/Ownrshp* 1912
Sales 1.2MMM^E *EMP* 5,000
SIC 5961 5621 5611 5941 5661 5948

D-U-N-S 00-390-6302
L L P GODFREY SUSMAN (TX)
1000 La St Ste 5100, Houston, TX 77002
Tel (713) 653-7867 *Founded/Ownrshp* 2001
Sales 26.9MM^E *EMP* 180
SIC 8111 General practice law office; General practice law office
CEO: Eva Chen
Genl Pt: Stephen D Susman
Pt: H Lee Godfrey
Pr: Matthew R Berry
Pr: Mary Christie
Pr: Jenni Dunaven
Pr: Mike Leone
CFO: Nikki Thornton
Exec: Jordan Connors
Off Mgr: Jessica Bughman
Off Mgr: Jami Grounds

D-U-N-S 00-284-7101
L L PELLING CO INC
1425 W Penn St, North Liberty, IA 52317-9150
Tel (319) 626-4600 *Founded/Ownrshp* 1985
Sales 59.8MM^E *EMP* 200
SIC 1611 2951 Highway & street paving contractor; Highway & street maintenance; Asphalt paving mixtures & blocks; Highway & street paving contractor; Highway & street maintenance; Asphalt paving mixtures & blocks
Pr: Chuck Finnegan
**Sec:* JC Miller
Div Mgr: Brett Finnegan

D-U-N-S 18-344-9636
L L VANN ELECTRIC INC
833 Purser Dr, Raleigh, NC 27603-4152
Tel (919) 772-2567 *Founded/Ownrshp* 1988
Sales 23.8MM^E *EMP* 130
SIC 1731 General electrical contractor; General electrical contractor
Pr: Leland L Vann
**Sec:* Joan A Vann
Ex VP: Roy Schmick

D-U-N-S 04-503-3453
L LYON WILLIAM & ASSOCIATES INC
LYON REAL ESTATE
3640 American River Dr, Sacramento, CA 95864-5953
Tel (916) 978-4200 *Founded/Ownrshp* 1946
Sales 66.4MM^E *EMP* 1,062
SIC 8741 Management services; Management services
CEO: Larry Knapp
**Pr:* Jean Ll
**CEO:* Patrick M Shea
Off Mgr: David Falcone
Off Mgr: Susan Pierce
Off Admin: Jessica Boatman
Off Admin: Traci McCullough
Off Admin: Andy Siau
Off Admin: Amy Tucker
Off Admin: Holly Ware
Mktg Dir: Cathy Harrington

D-U-N-S 00-790-2380
■ **L M BERRY AND CO**
(*Suby of* BELLSOUTH ENTERPRISES INC)
3170 Kettering Blvd, Moraine, OH 45439-1975
Tel (937) 296-2121 *Founded/Ownrshp* 1910
Sales 49.1MM^E *EMP* 2,600
SIC 7311 2741 Advertising agencies; Miscellaneous publishing; Advertising agencies; Miscellaneous publishing
Pr: Daniel J Graham
Exec: Scott Pomeroy
IT Man: James Oreilly
Sls&Mrk Ex: Carol Betts

L M C
See LIGHT METALS CORP

L M E
See LAKEVILLE MOTOR EXPRESS INC

L M GEAR COMPANY DIVISION
See ANDERSON-COOK INC

L M GROUP
See LUCKMARR PLASTICS INC

L M H
See LM HEAVY CIVIL CONSTRUCTION LLC

L M H
See LAWRENCE MEMORIAL HOSPITAL

D-U-N-S 61-946-6402
L M H CORP
521 East Ave, Lockport, NY 14094-3201
Tel (716) 434-9111 *Founded/Ownrshp* 1985
Sales 72.5MM *EMP* 2
Accts Ernst & Young Llp
SIC 8049 Occupational therapist
CEO: Clare Haar

L M I
See LOGISTICS MANAGEMENT INSTITUTE

L M I
See LIQUID METRONICS INC

L M I
See LARRY METHVIN INSTALLATIONS INC

D-U-N-S 36-128-0951
L M RESTAURANTS INC
6510 Chapel Hill Rd # 200, Raleigh, NC 27607-5010
Tel (919) 858-0404 *Founded/Ownrshp* 1987
Sales 33.1MM^E *EMP* 305
SIC 8742 Restaurant & food services consultants; Restaurant & food services consultants
Pr: Lou Moshakos
VP: Amber Moshakos
**VP:* Joy Moshakos
Genl Mgr: Joel Freeman
Genl Mgr: John Galanos
IT Man: Eric Chiong
VP Opers: Michael Liedberg
Mktg Dir: Katherine Costa
Doctor: J Brown
Art Dir: Christopher Stenger

D-U-N-S 78-625-2635
L MERRILL MICHAEL & ASSOCIATES INC
MERRILL & ASSOCIATES
1305 Pioneer St, Brea, CA 92821-3719
Tel (714) 256-2206 *Founded/Ownrshp* 1988
Sales 22.4MM^E *EMP* 40
SIC 5065 5999 Telephone equipment; Telephone equipment & systems
Pr: Michael L Merrill
VP: Damion Merrill
IT Man: Danielle Ayala
Sls Dir: Charl Luna
Sls Mgr: Barry Welker

L. N. CURTIS & SONS L.N. CURT
See LN CURTIS AND SONS

L O OILFIELD SEVICES
See L O TRANSPORT INC

D-U-N-S 78-303-7984
L O TRANSPORT INC
L O OILFIELD SEVICES
103 Lake Rd, Bridgeport, TX 76426-2223
Tel (940) 683-5286 *Founded/Ownrshp* 2006
Sales 24.0MM *EMP* 109^E
SIC 4731 Transportation agents & brokers; Transportation agents & brokers
CEO: Leslie Paul Oates
**VP:* Mary Denise Oates

L P A
See LPA INC

D-U-N-S 03-475-3558 IMP
L P BROWN CO INC
(*Suby of* FEDERAL COMPRESS & WAREHOUSE CO INC) ★
6060 Primacy Pkwy Ste 454, Memphis, TN 38119-5770
Tel (901) 767-6052 *Founded/Ownrshp* 2007
Sales 32.1MM^E *EMP* 51
SIC 5199 3315 Packaging materials; Bags, textile; Wire products, ferrous/iron: made in wiredrawing plants
Ch: Robert B Cohen
**Pr:* Doyle K Needham
**VP:* Charles S Walker

L P I
See LANCASTER PACKAGING INC

L P K
See LIBBY PERSZYK KATHMAN HOLDINGS INC

L P L FINANCIAL SERVICES
See LPL FINANCIAL CORP

D-U-N-S 03-461-4826
■ **L P SHANKS CO**
(*Suby of* AMCON DISTRIBUTING CO INC) ★
624 Industrial Blvd, Crossville, TN 38555-8764
Tel (931) 484-5155 *Founded/Ownrshp* 2011
Sales 33.5MM^E *EMP* 144
SIC 5194 5141 5145 Cigarettes; Chewing tobacco; Groceries, general line; Candy; Cigarettes; Chewing tobacco; Groceries, general line; Candy
Pr: Scot H Shanks
Opers Mgr: Scott Nelson

D-U-N-S 00-601-3346 IMP/EXP
■ **L PERRIGO CO** (MI)
(*Suby of* PERRIGO CO) ★
515 Eastern Ave, Allegan, MI 49010-9070
Tel (269) 673-8451 *Founded/Ownrshp* 1887, 1981
Sales 1.6MMM^E *EMP* 9,200
SIC 2834 Pharmaceutical preparations; Pharmaceutical preparations
CEO: Joseph Papa
**Ch Bd:* David Gibbons
Ex VP: Celeste Smith
VP: Richard Hansen
**Prin:* Arthur J Shannon
Ql Cn Mgr: Andrea Kirk
Ql Cn Mgr: David Troff
S&M/VP: Don Smith

D-U-N-S 83-184-9935 IMP/EXP
L POWELL ACQUISITION CORP
22 Jericho Tpke Ste 200, Mineola, NY 11501-2949
Tel (516) 699-1000 *Founded/Ownrshp* 2009
Sales 40.5MM^E *EMP* 99
SIC 5021 Furniture; Furniture
Pr: Demetrios Ziozis
**COO:* Larry Woods
**CFO:* Steven Ziosis
**VP:* Jim Papadopoulos
**VP:* Alex Vasilakis
Sls Mgr: Gary Glick

L Q M
See LA QUESERA MEXICANA LLC

D-U-N-S 04-538-9699
L R COSTANZO CO INC (PA)
123 N Main Ave, Scranton, PA 18504-3308
Tel (570) 207-4955 *Founded/Ownrshp* 1967
Sales 67.0MM^E *EMP* 110
SIC 1542 1611 Commercial & office building, new construction; Commercial & office buildings, renovation & repair; Concrete construction: roads, highways, sidewalks, etc.; Commercial & office building, new construction; Commercial & office buildings, renovation & repair; Concrete construction: roads, highways, sidewalks, etc.
Pr: Louis A Costanzo
**Sec:* Anthony L Costanzo
**VP:* Louis E Costanzo
VP: Matthew Michalek
Ql Cn Mgr: Stephen Peterson

L R E C
See LAKE REGION ELECTRIC COOPERATIVE INC

L R G
See LIFTED RESEARCH GROUP INC

L R I
See PIERCE COUNTY RECYCLING & DISPOSAL LLC

L R P
See LRP PUBLICATIONS INC

D-U-N-S 06-323-5287
L R WILLSON & SONS INC
773 Annapolis Rd, Gambrills, MD 21054-1308
Tel (410) 987-5414 *Founded/Ownrshp* 1971
Sales 27.1MM^E *EMP* 150
SIC 1791 7359 Structural steel erection; Equipment rental & leasing; Structural steel erection; Equipment rental & leasing
Pr: Donald Willson
COO: Jim Gregory
**VP:* James Willson
Dir IT: Donald Wilson
Sfty Dirs: Lrwilson Mosebach

D-U-N-S 09-307-9234
L S A ASSOCIATES INC
20 Executive Park Ste 200, Irvine, CA 92614-4739
Tel (949) 553-0666 *Founded/Ownrshp* 1987
Sales 35.9MM^E *EMP* 265
Accts Burr Pilger Mayer
SIC 8748 Environmental consultant; Environmental consultant
CEO: Les Card
**Pr:* Rob McCann
**CFO:* James Baum
Admn Mgr: Jeff Bray
Admn Mgr: Lyndon Calerdine
Admn Mgr: Lynn Calvert-Hayes
Admn Mgr: Rick Harlacher
Admn Mgr: Frank Haselton
Genl Mgr: Christina Belsito
Genl Mgr: Natalie Frey
Off Mgr: Suzanne Giesin

D-U-N-S 80-841-1263
L S F 5 ACCREDITED INVESTMENTS LLC
(*Suby of* LONE STAR FUND V (US) LP) ★
717 N Harwood St Ste 2200, Dallas, TX 75201-6515
Tel (214) 754-8300 *Founded/Ownrshp* 2007
Sales 242.7MM^E *EMP* 2,704^E
SIC 6798 Real estate investment trusts
Prin: Benjamin D Velvin III

L S I
See MKRB LIQUIDATION INC

L S I
See LIGHT SOURCES INC

L S I
See LOGISTIC SERVICES INTERNATIONAL INC

L S I
See LOGICAL SYSTEMS INC

L S I
See LUMINESCENT SYSTEMS INC

L S I
See LAWRENCE STREET INDUSTRY LLC

L S I
See LSI TITLE CO

D-U-N-S 06-709-8343
L S LEE INC
(*Suby of* REH HOLDINGS INC) ★
152 S Sumner St, York, PA 17404-5451
Tel (717) 843-0021 *Founded/Ownrshp* 1986
Sales 30.6MM^E *EMP* 110
SIC 1611 1799 Guardrail construction, highways; Highway & street sign installation; Fence construction; Guardrail construction, highways; Highway & street sign installation; Fence construction
CEO: Basil A Shorb III
**Ch Bd:* Robert E Hirschman
**Pr:* William J Shorb
**VP:* Michael Coffman
**VP:* Patrick Dempsey
**VP:* James R Murin
Dir IT: Basil Shorb
Info Man: Lola Smith

L S R
See LERNER SAMPSON & ROTHFUSS A LEGAL PROFESSIONAL ASSOCIATION

L S R
See LEGEND SMELTING AND RECYCLING INC

D-U-N-S 00-112-5681 IMP
▲ **L S STARRETT CO** (MA)
121 Crescent St, Athol, MA 01331-1915
Tel (978) 249-3551 *Founded/Ownrshp* 1880
Sales 241.5MM *EMP* 1,804
Accts Grant Thornton Llp Boston Ma
Tkr Sym SCX *Exch* NYS
SIC 3545 3423 3999 3425 3823 Precision measuring tools; Micrometers; Verniers (machinists' precision tools); Calipers & dividers; Rules or rulers, metal; Carpenters' hand tools, except saws: levels, chisels, etc.; Tape measures; Saw blades for hand or power saws; Saws, hand: metalworking or woodworking; Industrial instrmnts msrmnt display/control process variable; Precision measuring tools; Micrometers; Verniers (machinists' precision tools); Calipers & dividers; Rules or rulers, metal; Carpenters' hand tools, except saws: levels, chisels, etc.; Tape measures; Saw blades for hand or power saws; Saws, hand: metalworking or woodworking; Industrial instrmnts msrmnt display/control process variable
Pr: Douglas A Starrett
CFO: Francis J O'Brien
VP: Mike Baczewski
VP: James B Taylor
Netwrk Mgr: John Eklund
VP Mktg: Bill Power
VP Sls: Anthony M Aspin
S&M/VP: Dennis Reynolds
Sls Mgr: Michael Edmondson
Board of Directors: Salvador De Camargo Jr, Richard B Kennedy, Ralph G Lawrence, David A Lemoine, Terry A Piper, Stephen F Walsh

L SILVERBERG & COMPANY
See QUALITY METALS INC

D-U-N-S 04-495-8759 IMP
L T C ROLL & ENGINEERING CO
23500 John Gorsuch Dr, Clinton Township, MI 48036-1215
Tel (586) 465-1023 *Founded/Ownrshp* 1967
Sales 34.0MM *EMP* 130
SIC 5013 Automotive supplies & parts; Automotive supplies & parts
Pr: Andrew Ligda
**VP:* Ned M Cavallaro
Sls Dir: Russ Senkowski

D-U-N-S 10-180-3492
L T CORP
2914 Hwy 61 S, Cleveland, MS 38732
Tel (662) 843-4046 *Founded/Ownrshp* 1982
Sales 21.9MM^E *EMP* 95^E
SIC 3443 6141 6311 Tanks for tank trucks, metal plate; Consumer finance companies; Life insurance
Ch Bd: James I Tims

L T D
See LANE TRANSIT DISTRICT

D-U-N-S 02-047-3278
L T HAMPEL CORP
W194n11551 Mccormick Dr, Germantown, WI 53022-3000
Tel (262) 255-4540 *Founded/Ownrshp* 1976
Sales 29.7MM^E *EMP* 105
SIC 3089 Toilets, portable chemical: plastic; Plastic processing; Pallets, plastic
Pr: Lance T Hampel
**Pr:* Paul Lorge
VP: Dave Bamberg
Exec: Heidi Hellesen
IT Man: Mark Sjoberg
Ql Cn Mgr: Dave Lorenz
Mktg Mgr: Joe Weber

L T I
See LOW TEMP INDUSTRIES INC

L T I
See LASER TECHNOLOGY INC

L T I CONTRACTING
See LOW-TEMP INSULATIONS INC

L T L HOME PRODUCTS
See LTL WHOLESALE INC

L T M COLLISION CENTER
See ALLEN IMPORTS LIMITED INC

D-U-N-S 02-237-3120
L T M LTD
CHUCK E. CHEESE'S
1202 24th Ave S, Fargo, ND 58103-5704
Tel (701) 237-0580 *Founded/Ownrshp* 1981
Sales 14.1MM^E *EMP* 387
SIC 8741 8742 Restaurant management; Management consulting services; Restaurant management; Management consulting services
Pr: Thomas M La Velle
**VP:* D K Dockter

L T R
See LIGHTTOWER RENTALS INC

L T S
See LOGISTICS & TECHNOLOGY SERVICES INC

D-U-N-S 06-725-8525 IMP
L THREE INC
12235 Robin Blvd, Houston, TX 77045-4826
Tel (713) 434-7600 Founded/Ownrshp 1973
Sales 20.6MM^E EMP 22^E
SIC 5171 Petroleum bulk stations
Pr: Andrew S Leach

L U A
See LUMBERMENS UNDERWRITING ALLIANCE

L V D
See STRIPPIT INC

L V I
See LION-VALLEN LIMITED PARTNERSHIP

L V STABLER MEMORIAL HOSPITAL
See GREENVILLE HOSPITAL CORP

L V W ELECTRONICS
See LOW VOLTAGE WIRING LTD

L W BLAKE HOSPITAL
See ST LUCIE MEDICAL CENTER AUXILIARY INC

L W C
See LINDSEY WILSON COLLEGE INC

D-U-N-S 02-341-4287
L W MEYER INC
W223n609 Saratoga Dr, Waukesha, WI 53186-0402
Tel (262) 513-2800 Founded/Ownrshp 1987
Sales 25.4MM^E EMP 32
SIC 5085 5072 5084 Industrial supplies; Fasteners, industrial: nuts, bolts, screws, etc.; Power tools & accessories; Industrial machinery & equipment
Pr: Andrew Marker
*Sec: James H Ladew
*VP: John T Kearns
Sales Asso: Robert Dixon

D-U-N-S 82-465-6631
L WOERNER INC
H C R
85 Metro Park, Rochester, NY 14623-2607
Tel (585) 272-1930 Founded/Ownrshp 1986
Sales 29.7MM^E EMP 650
SIC 8322 8742 8082 Geriatric social service; Hospital & health services consultant; Home health care services; Geriatric social service; Hospital & health services consultant; Home health care services
CEO: Louise Woerner
*Pr: Mark Maxim
Pr: Barbara Robinson
*COO: Paul Donnelly
Dir IT: Andrew Bascom

D-U-N-S 00-223-3872 IMP
L& JG STICKLEY INC (NY)
1 Stickley Dr, Manlius, NY 13104-2485
Tel (315) 682-5500 Founded/Ownrshp 1895, 1974
Sales 583.7MM^E EMP 1,325
SIC 5511 5712 2511 5713 Customized furniture & cabinets; Household furniture; Office & public building furniture; Wood household furniture; Rugs; New & used car dealers; Customized furniture & cabinets; Wood household furniture; Rugs
Ch Bd: Aminy I Audi
*Pr: Edward Audi
VP: John Broagen
VP: Roderick McLean
VP: Craig Pelton
VP: Blain Wrench
Creative D: Nancy Dowms
Creative D: Nancy Downs
CIO: Maher Najjar
Dir IT: Janice Schmit
IT Man: Reuben Connor

L& L PRODUCTS
See ZEPHYROS INC

D-U-N-S 01-912-2618
L&B REALTY ADVISORS LLP (DE)
8750 N Central Expy # 800, Dallas, TX 75231-6436
Tel (214) 989-0800 Founded/Ownrshp 2014, 2005
Sales 67.4MM^E EMP 165
SIC 6531 Real estate agents & managers
CEO: G Andrews Smith
Ex VP: Mark Faraldi
Ex VP: John L Gerdes
Ex VP: Victoria W Grissom
VP: Stacie Crown
VP: Eric R Smith
Assoc Dir: David Castillejos
Assoc Dir: Matthew Hood
Assoc Dir: Matt Lewis
Ex Dir: Alexander Fitzenhagen
Ex Dir: Holly Robertson

D-U-N-S 18-764-0891
L&B TRANSPORT LLC
708 Highway 190 W, Port Allen, LA 70767-3818
Tel (225) 387-0894 Founded/Ownrshp 1984
Sales 56.5MM^E EMP 370
Accts Hannis T Bourgeois Llp Denh
SIC 4212 Hazardous waste transport; Hazardous waste transport
Genl Mgr: Blain Houston
IT Man: Joseph Mangano

L&H PACKING
See LEONARD & HARRAL PACKING CO

D-U-N-S 86-770-0668 IMP
L&H THREADED RODS CORP
(Suby of GRAY AMERICA CORP) ★
3050 Dryden Rd, Moraine, OH 45439-1620
Tel (937) 294-6666 Founded/Ownrshp 1986
Sales 24.6MM^E EMP 125
SIC 3312 Rods, iron & steel: made in steel mills; Rods, iron & steel: made in steel mills
Pr: John C Gray
*CFO: Jeff Schroder

Off Mgr: Sharon Thompson
Sls Mgr: Mike McGrew

D-U-N-S 79-094-6730 IMP/EXP
L&K DISTRIBUTORS INC
175 Central Ave S, Bethpage, NY 11714-4940
Tel (718) 643-1141 Founded/Ownrshp 2004
Sales 21.0MM^E EMP 12
SIC 5141 Groceries, general line
Ch Bd: Arthur Kantorovich
*VP: Aleksey Ilishayev

D-U-N-S 78-647-4325
L&L ENERGY INC
130 Andover Park E # 200, Tukwila, WA 98188-2909
Tel (206) 264-8065 Founded/Ownrshp 2006
Sales 198.9MM EMP 1,364
Tkr Sym LLEN Exch OTC
SIC 1241 1221 5052 Coal mining services; Bituminous coal & lignite-surface mining; Coal; Coal mining services; Bituminous coal & lignite-surface mining; Coal
CFO: Ian G Robinson
*VP: Clayton Fong
Exec: Youwei Cramer

D-U-N-S 94-528-3567
L&L FOODS HOLDINGS LLC
(Suby of PEACOCK ENGINEERING CO LLC) ★
333 N Euclid Way, Anaheim, CA 92801-6738
Tel (714) 254-1430 Founded/Ownrshp 2015
Sales 78.5MM^E EMP 200
SIC 4783 Food brokers; Packing goods for shipping
CEO: John Pooley
CFO: Roger Douglas
VP Sls: Matt Sonneman

L&L INSULATIONS
See FLIGG CORP

L&L NO TRADESTYLE
See L & L HOLDING CO LLC

D-U-N-S 08-863-3961
L&L WINGS INC
666 Broadway Rm 200, New York, NY 10012-2317
Tel (212) 481-8299 Founded/Ownrshp 1978
Sales 40.8MM^E EMP 250
SIC 5699 5331 5611 5621 5947 5661 T-shirts, custom printed; Bathing suits; Variety stores; Clothing, sportswear, men's & boys'; Women's sportswear; Gift shop; Souvenirs; Novelties; Shoe stores; T-shirts, custom printed; Bathing suits; Variety stores; Clothing, sportswear, men's & boys'; Women's sportswear; Gift shop; Souvenirs; Novelties; Shoe stores
CEO: Shaul Levy
*Pr: Meir Levy
VP: Ariel Levy
Genl Mgr: Gil Cohen

D-U-N-S 07-646-5491
L&M TECHNOLOGIES INC
4209 Balloon Park Rd Ne A, Albuquerque, NM 87109-5861
Tel (505) 343-0200 Founded/Ownrshp 1986
Sales 25.1MM EMP 170
Accts Ricci & Company Llc Albuquer
SIC 8744 Facilities support services; Facilities support services
Pr: Peter E Harrod
*CFO: Antonette Montoya
Prgrm Mgr: Fil Martinez

D-U-N-S 12-715-1806
L&S LOGISTIC SERVICES INC
9858 Sidney Hayes Rd, Orlando, FL 32824-8127
Tel (407) 582-0900 Founded/Ownrshp 2001
Sales 22.1MM^E EMP 250^E
SIC 4213 Trucking, except local; Trucking, except local
Pr: Leigh Cospito

D-U-N-S 13-415-8141
L&S SERVICES LLC
501 W Broad St, Smithville, TN 37166-1111
Tel (615) 597-6278 Founded/Ownrshp 2003
Sales 16.6MM^E EMP 1,000
SIC 5812 Contract food services; Contract food services
CFO: Bill Stencer

D-U-N-S 17-965-7908
L&T STAFFING INC
STAFFING SOLUTIONS
400 N Tustin Ave Ste 140, Santa Ana, CA 92705-3879
Tel (714) 558-1821 Founded/Ownrshp 2004
Sales 7.0MM EMP 380^E
SIC 7361 Employment agencies; Employment agencies
CEO: Fortino Rivera
*CFO: Lucia Montellano

L&W ENGINEERING
See L & W INC

L- A ELECTRIC
See LAUX/ARNOLD INC

L-1 ENROLLMENT SERVICES DIV
See INTEGRATED BIOMETRIC TECHNOLOGY LLC

D-U-N-S 03-501-6416
■ L-3 APPLIED TECHNOLOGIES INC
PULSE SCIENCES
(Suby of L-3 COMMUNICATIONS CORP) ★
10180 Barnes Canyon Rd, San Diego, CA 92121-2724
Tel (858) 404-7824 Founded/Ownrshp 2011
Sales 28.2MM^E EMP 110^E
SIC 3663 3669 3769 Telemetering equipment, electronic; Receiver-transmitter units (transceiver); Amplifiers, RF power & IF; Signaling apparatus, electric; Intercommunication systems, electric; Guided missile & space vehicle parts & auxiliary equipment; Telemetering equipment, electronic; Receiver-transmitter units (transceiver); Amplifiers, RF power & IF; Signaling apparatus, electric; Intercommunication systems, electric; Guided missile & space vehicle parts & auxiliary equipment
CEO: Michael T Strainese

*Pr: Robert A Huffman
Sr VP: James Stuhmiller

L-3 CMMNCTIONS ELECTRODYNAMICS
See ELECTRODYNAMICS INC

L-3 CMMUNICATIONS CORP GCS DIV
See L-3 COMMUNICATIONS CORP

L-3 COMMUNICATION & THALES
See AVIATION COMMUNICATION & SURVEILLANCE SYSTEMS LLC

D-U-N-S 00-725-0079
■ L-3 COMMUNICATIONS AVIONICS SYSTEMS INC
BF GOODRICH AVIONICS SYS
(Suby of L-3 COMMUNICATIONS CORP) ★
5353 52nd St Se, Grand Rapids, MI 49512-9702
Tel (616) 977-6837 Founded/Ownrshp 2003
Sales 68.7MM^E EMP 479
SIC 3812 Aircraft flight instruments; Gyroscopes; Automatic pilots, aircraft; Radar systems & equipment; Aircraft flight instruments; Gyroscopes; Automatic pilots, aircraft; Radar systems & equipment
CEO: Michael T Strianese
*Pr: Jay Lafoy
VP: Glenn Good
VP: Doug Pell
Dir IT: Henry Vlieg
IT Man: John Miller
IT Man: Eric Smead
Sys Mgr: Karl Domeier
Sftwr Eng: George Bohn
Netwrk Eng: Brandon Roberts
Sls Mgr: Thomas McDonald

D-U-N-S 05-910-6484
■ L-3 COMMUNICATIONS CINCINNATI ELECTRONICS CORP
(Suby of L-3 COMMUNICATIONS CORP) ★
7500 Innovation Way, Mason, OH 45040-9695
Tel (513) 573-6100 Founded/Ownrshp 2004
Sales 181.9MM^E EMP 735
SIC 3812 3769 3823 Detection apparatus: electronic/magnetic field, light/heat; Missile guidance systems & equipment; Guided missile & space vehicle parts & auxiliary equipment; Infrared instruments, industrial process type; Detection apparatus: electronic/magnetic field, light/heat; Missile guidance systems & equipment; Guided missile & space vehicle parts & auxiliary equipment; Infrared instruments, industrial process type
Ch: Patrick J Sweeney
*CEO: Russ Walker
*CFO: David Monaco
*VP: Doug Becker
*VP: Mark Dapore
*VP: Ed English
*VP: Vance King
*VP: Gregg Ridgley
Dir Bus: Steve Carrington
VP Admn: Dale E Lhmann
Prgrm Mgr: Jeff Raines
Board of Directors: Doug Foster, Kevin Haurin, George Macomber, Alison McKinnon

D-U-N-S 00-889-8884 IMP
■ L-3 COMMUNICATIONS CORP (GA)
(Suby of L-3 COMMUNICATIONS HOLDINGS INC) ★
600 3rd Ave, New York, NY 10016-1901
Tel (212) 697-1111 Founded/Ownrshp 1997
Sales 3.5MMM EMP 45,000^E
SIC 3812 3663 3669 3679 3769 Search & navigation equipment; Aircraft control systems, electronic; Telemetering equipment, electronic; Receiver-transmitter units (transceiver); Amplifiers, RF power & IF; Signaling apparatus, electric; Intercommunication systems, electric; Microwave components; Guided missile & space vehicle parts & auxiliary equipment; Search & navigation equipment; Aircraft control systems, electronic; Telemetering equipment, electronic; Receiver-transmitter units (transceiver); Amplifiers, RF power & IF; Signaling apparatus, electric; Intercommunication systems, electric; Microwave components; Guided missile & space vehicle parts & auxiliary equipment
Ch Bd: Michael T Strianese
Pr: Kris Ganase
Pr: Christopher E Kubasik
Pr: John C McNellis
Pr: Dan Sperandio
CFO: Ralph G D'Ambrosio
CFO: Frank Rice
Bd of Dir: Michael Forbes
Ex VP: James Ward
Ex VP: James Winchester
Sr VP: Allen Barber
Sr VP: Curtis Brunson
Sr VP: Holly Clarke
Sr VP: Steven M Post
VP: Dan Azmon
VP: Brian Macdonald
VP: Mark D Simon
Exec: Bob Deegan
Dir Bus: James Appleyard
Dir Bus: Gary Reese
Board of Directors: Alan H Washkowitz, Claude R Canizares, Thomas A Corcoran, Ann E Dunwoody, Lewis Kramer, Robert B Millard, Lloyd W Newton, Vincent Pagano Jr, H Hugh Shelton, Arthur L Simon

D-U-N-S 07-867-8394
L-3 COMMUNICATIONS CORP
COMMUNICATIONS SYSTEM WEST
322 N 2200 W, Salt Lake City, UT 84116-2922
Tel (801) 594-2000 Founded/Ownrshp 1997
Sales 228.8MM^E EMP 3,800
SIC 3812 Defense systems & equipment; Defense systems & equipment
Pr: Susan Oop
VP: John Hill
Dir Lab: Mike Newhouse
*Prin: Michael T Strianese
Mng Dir: Jeff McMullen
Prgrm Mgr: Kristina Williams
Area Mgr: Daniel Wanner
Brnch Mgr: Emily Boykin

CTO: David Hendrickson
IT Man: Jeff Walker
Software D: Garry Garrett

D-U-N-S 19-237-2860
■ L-3 COMMUNICATIONS CORP
(Suby of L-3 COMMUNICATIONS HOLDINGS INC) ★
9 Akira Way, Londonderry, NH 03053-2037
Tel (603) 626-4800 Founded/Ownrshp 2010
Sales 228.8MM^E EMP 1,100
SIC 3827 Optical instruments & lenses; Optical instruments & lenses
Pr: Todd Stirtzinger
Snr Sftwr: Mark Dobrosielski
IT Man: Suzanne Allen
Mktg Dir: Danielle Hoffman
Snr Mgr: Geoff Ziminsky

D-U-N-S 60-623-7220 IMP
■ L-3 COMMUNICATIONS CORP
L-3 HENSCHEL
(Suby of L-3 COMMUNICATIONS HOLDINGS INC) ★
90 Nemco Way, Ayer, MA 01432-1541
Tel (978) 784-1999 Founded/Ownrshp 1989
Sales 25.6MM^E EMP 115
SIC 3669 Intercommunication systems, electric; Intercommunication systems, electric
CEO: Frank Lanza
Pr: Richard Hitchcock
Pr: George Kay
*Pr: Robert Lapenta
*Treas: Stephen Souza
*VP: Lawrence Van Blerkom
IT Man: Paula Ingel
IT Man: Amy Lafleur
VP Opers: Andy Rusnock
Pgrm Dir: Ron Harris

D-U-N-S 82-745-0995
■ L-3 COMMUNICATIONS CORP
(Suby of L-3 COMMUNICATIONS HOLDINGS INC) ★
2200 Arlgtn Downs Rd L, Arlington, TX 76011
Tel (817) 619-2000 Founded/Ownrshp 2008
Sales 23.8MM^E EMP 836^E
SIC 8331 Job training & vocational rehabilitation services
CEO: Michael T Strianese
Pr: Ashok Sisodia
*Treas: Stephen M Souza
VP: Jeff Butler
VP: Mark Gasson
VP: Dan Kelly
VP: Steve Osborne
*VP: Lawrence Van Blerkom
Dir Bus: William Johnson
Prgrm Mgr: Wade Ward
Prgrm Mgr: David Warner

D-U-N-S 92-636-7939
■ L-3 COMMUNICATIONS CORP
L-3 CMMUNICATIONS CORP GCS DIV
(Suby of L-3 COMMUNICATIONS CORP) ★
7640 Omnitech Pl, Victor, NY 14564-9429
Tel (585) 742-9100 Founded/Ownrshp 2007
Sales 29.2MM^E EMP 148
SIC 3663 4899 Radio & TV communications equipment; Satellites, communications; Space satellite communications equipment; Satellite earth stations; Radio & TV communications equipment; Satellites, communications; Space satellite communications equipment; Satellite earth stations
CEO: Michael Strianese
*Treas: Stephen Souza
VP: Lawrence V Blerkom
VP: Kurt Lieberman
*VP: Lawrence Van Blerkom
VP: Ernie Yasso
Exec: Cathy Cronin
Prgrm Mgr: Scott McCombs
Sftwr Eng: Alexander Pita
Mktg Mgr: Meghan Defisher
Manager: David Goldstein

D-U-N-S 62-224-7088
L-3 COMMUNICATIONS CRESTVIEW AEROSPACE CORP
5486 Fairchild Rd, Crestview, FL 32539-8155
Tel (850) 682-2746 Founded/Ownrshp 2006
Sales NA EMP 850
SIC 3728 3721

D-U-N-S 55-661-8267 IMP
■ L-3 COMMUNICATIONS ELECTRON TECHNOLOGIES INC
(Suby of L-3 COMMUNICATIONS HOLDINGS INC) ★
3100 Lomita Blvd, Torrance, CA 90505-5104
Tel (310) 517-6000 Founded/Ownrshp 2000
Sales 174.1MM^E EMP 658
SIC 3671 3764 Traveling wave tubes; Guided missile & space vehicle propulsion unit parts; Traveling wave tubes; Guided missile & space vehicle propulsion unit parts
CEO: Michael Strianese
VP: Frank Lucca
Genl Mgr: Robert Vasquez
IT Man: Mike Luna
VP Opers: Jim Williams
Mfg Mgr: Rick Smith

D-U-N-S 87-768-5933
■ L-3 COMMUNICATIONS EOTECH INC
(Suby of L-3 COMMUNICATIONS CORP) ★
1201 E Ellsworth Rd, Ann Arbor, MI 48108-2420
Tel (734) 741-8868 Founded/Ownrshp 2005
Sales 22.4MM^E EMP 120
SIC 3827 Sighting & fire control equipment, optical; Sighting & fire control equipment, optical
Pr: Paul Mangano
VP: Eric Sieczka
*CTO: Dr Anthony M Tai

D-U-N-S 00-101-8522 IMP
■ L-3 COMMUNICATIONS ESSCO INC
(Suby of L-3 COMMUNICATIONS CORP) ★
90 Nemco Way, Ayer, MA 01432-1541
Tel (978) 568-5100 Founded/Ownrshp 1961, 1998
Sales 28.0MM^E EMP 230^E

SIC 3711 3663 Motor vehicles & car bodies; Radio & TV communications equipment; Motor vehicles & car bodies; Radio & TV communications equipment
Pr: Thomas J Casale
VP: Jim Cataldo
VP Mktg: Jeff Brown
Pdt Mgr: Robert Matson

D-U-N-S 00-889-8843 IMP/EXP
▲ L-3 COMMUNICATIONS HOLDINGS INC
600 3rd Ave, New York, NY 10016-1901
Tel (212) 697-1111 *Founded/Ownrshp* 1997
Sales 12.1MMM *EMP* 45,000
Accts Pricewaterhousecoopers Llp Ne
Tkr Sym LLL *Exch* NYS
SIC 3663 3669 3679 3812 3769 Telemetering equipment, electronic; Receiver-transmitter units (transceiver); Signaling apparatus, electric; Intercommunication systems, electric; Microwave components; Search & navigation equipment; Guided missile & space vehicle parts & auxiliary equipment; Telemetering equipment, electronic; Receiver-transmitter units (transceiver); Signaling apparatus, electric; Intercommunication systems, electric; Microwave components; Search & navigation equipment; Guided missile & space vehicle parts & auxiliary equipment
CEO: Michael T Strianese
Pr: Christopher E Kubasik
CFO: Wendy Barnhart
CFO: Ralph G D'Ambrosio
Ex VP: Curtis Brunson
Sr VP: Richard A Cody
Sr VP: Steven M Post
VP: Dan Azmon
VP: Bruce Burton
VP: Ron Cook
VP: Patricia Craig
VP: Paul Delia
VP: James W Dunn
VP: John Finegan
VP: Vance King
VP: Ronald Mandler
VP: Curt Osterheld
VP: Lou Park
VP: David M Reilly
VP: Glen Roussos
VP: Roman Turchyn
Board of Directors: Alan H Washkowitz, Claude R Canizares, Thomas A Corcoran, Ann E Dunwoody, Lewis Kramer, Robert B Millard, Lloyd W Newton, Vincent Pagano Jr, H Hugh Shelton, Arthur L Simon

D-U-N-S 11-364-1703
■ L-3 COMMUNICATIONS INTEGRATED SYSTEMS LP
(*Suby of* L-3 COMMUNICATIONS HOLDINGS INC) ★
1655 Science Pl, Rockwall, TX 75032-6202
Tel (903) 455-3450 *Founded/Ownrshp* 2002
Sales 1.2MMM^E *EMP* 23,000^E
SIC 4581 Aircraft maintenance & repair services; Aircraft maintenance & repair services
Pr: John McNellis
Pt: Robert Drews
Pr: Sylvain Bdard
Pr: Jim Gibson
Pr: Alison J Hartley
Ex VP: Mark Von Schwarz
Sr VP: Tim Keenan
VP: Nick Farah
VP: Ed Gloviak
VP: Russell Martin
VP: S Gordon Walsh
Exec: Chris White
Dir Risk M: David Debrestian
Dir Bus: Daniel Imbat
Dir Bus: Ziad Safi

D-U-N-S 55-687-2588 IMP
■ L-3 COMMUNICATIONS MOBILE-VISION INC
(*Suby of* L-3 COMMUNICATIONS CORP) ★
90 Fanny Rd Ste 2, Boonton, NJ 07005-1055
Tel (973) 263-1090 *Founded/Ownrshp* 2005
Sales 57.5MM^E *EMP* 99
SIC 5065 3663 Closed circuit television; Television closed circuit equipment; Closed circuit television; Television closed circuit equipment
Pr: Leo Lorenzetti
**VP:* Chief Mike Burridge
VP: Michael Burridge
**VP:* Chris Kadoch
**VP:* Kurt Kessel
Plnt Mgr: Jim Ward
Mktg Mgr: John Powers
Mktg Mgr: Rob Thompkins
Sales Asso: Mark Pavlak

D-U-N-S 17-220-8394
■ L-3 COMMUNICATIONS SECURITY AND DETECTION SYSTEMS INC
(*Suby of* L-3 COMMUNICATIONS CORP) ★
10e Commerce Way, Woburn, MA 01801-1044
Tel (781) 939-3800 *Founded/Ownrshp* 1996
Sales 23.4MM^E *EMP* 230^E
SIC 7382 Security systems services; Security systems services
Pr: Thomas M Ripp
**VP:* Lawrence Van Blerkom
Snr Sftwr: Sarfraz Azmi

D-U-N-S 01-181-4386
■ L-3 COMMUNICATIONS SONOMA EO INC
WESCAM SONOMA OPERATIONS
(*Suby of* L-3 COMMUNICATIONS CORP) ★
428 Aviation Blvd, Santa Rosa, CA 95403-1069
Tel (707) 568-3000 *Founded/Ownrshp* 2005
Sales 52.8MM^E *EMP* 200
SIC 3812 3861 Search & navigation equipment; Heads-up display systems (HUD), aeronautical; Photographic equipment & supplies; Search & navigation equipment; Heads-up display systems (HUD), aeronautical; Photographic equipment & supplies
Genl Mgr: Andy Fordham
Ofcr: Dean Hautanen
IT Man: Betty Burgess
IT Man: Dennis Wood

D-U-N-S 09-144-1089
■ L-3 COMMUNICATIONS VERTEX AEROSPACE LLC
(*Suby of* L-3 COMMUNICATIONS CORP) ★
555 Industrial Dr S, Madison, MS 39110-9072
Tel (601) 856-2274 *Founded/Ownrshp* 1977, 2004
Sales 351.9MM^E *EMP* 4,000^E
Accts Pricewaterhousecoopers Llp
SIC 4581 5088 Aircraft maintenance & repair services; Aircraft & parts; Aircraft maintenance & repair services; Aircraft & parts
CEO: Michael T Strianese
**CFO:* Ralph G D'Ambrosio
**Ex VP:* Curtis Brunson
**Sr VP:* Richard A Cody
**Sr VP:* Steven M Post
**VP:* Dave Merriam
**VP:* R Steve Singfield
Prgrm Mgr: Tom Rachfalski
Prgrm Mgr: William Staber
Dir IT: Lisa Scott
Info Man: Peter Vozzo

D-U-N-S 36-067-4337
■ L-3 COMMUNICATIONS WESTWOOD CORP
L-3 WESTWOOD
(*Suby of* L-3 COMMUNICATIONS HOLDINGS INC) ★
12402 E 60th St, Tulsa, OK 74146-6920
Tel (918) 252-0481 *Founded/Ownrshp* 2002
Sales 38.3MM^E *EMP* 200
SIC 3621 3613 Motors & generators; Switchgear & switchboard apparatus; Motors & generators; Switchgear & switchboard apparatus
Pr: Clayton McClain
**CFO:* Lynn McGowan
**VP:* Ahmad Zahedi

D-U-N-S 61-163-1974
■ L-3 DATA TACTICS CORP
(*Suby of* L-3 COMMUNICATIONS HOLDINGS INC) ★
7901 Jones Branch Dr # 700, Mc Lean, VA 22102-3338
Tel (703) 506-3735 *Founded/Ownrshp* 2014
Sales 29.8MM^E *EMP* 122^E
Accts Dixon Hughes Goodman Llp Tyso
SIC 7374 Data processing & preparation
CEO: Oscar Wood
**CFO:* Lorraine Alexander
Ofcr: Tina Peters
**VP:* Lee Shabe
Dir Sec: Gary Llewellyn
Prgrm Mgr: Gregg Deleaver
Prgrm Mgr: Karen Hayes
Div Mgr: William Conroy
Div Mgr: Francis McCarthy
Div Mgr: John Rogers
Off Admin: Trish Smith

L-3 D.P. ASSOCIATES
See DP ASSOCIATES INC

D-U-N-S 04-160-3077
■ L-3 FUZING AND ORDNANCE SYSTEMS INC
(*Suby of* L-3 COMMUNICATIONS HOLDINGS INC) ★
3975 Mcmann Rd, Cincinnati, OH 45245-2307
Tel (513) 943-2000 *Founded/Ownrshp* 1998
Sales 228.8MM^E *EMP* 575
SIC 3483 Arming & fusing devices for missiles; Arming & fusing devices for missiles
CEO: Michael T Strianese
Pr: Eric Ellis
CFO: Ralph G D'Ambrosio
Ex VP: Curtis Brunson
Sr VP: Richard A Cody
Sr VP: Steven M Post
VP: Richard Hunter
Prgrm Mgr: Leo Brun
Prgrm Mgr: Jim Ferrando
Prgrm Mgr: James Webb
IT Man: Sarah Urban
Board of Directors: Mark Clark, Roy B York

L-3 HENSCHEL
See L-3 COMMUNICATIONS CORP

L-3 INTERSTATE ELECTRONICS
See INTERSTATE ELECTRONICS CORP

L-3 MUSTANG TECHNOLOGY
See MUSTANG TECHNOLOGY GROUP LP

D-U-N-S 07-836-8844
■ L-3 NATIONAL SECURITY SOLUTIONS INC
(*Suby of* L-3 COMMUNICATIONS CORP) ★
11955 Freedom Dr Fl 4, Reston, VA 20190-5673
Tel (703) 434-4000 *Founded/Ownrshp* 2012
Sales 60.2MM^E *EMP* 99^E
SIC 8711 3532 Engineering services; Mining machinery
CEO: Michael T Strianese
**Pr:* Leslie Rose
**CFO:* Ralph G D Ambrosio
Ofcr: Chemise Smith
Sr VP: Lexi Alexander
Sr VP: John Drinkwater
Sr VP: Nick Smith
VP: Jeffrey Sabol
**VP:* Lawrence Van Blerkom
Prgrm Mgr: Joel Lindner
Prgrm Mgr: Jeffrey Ralston

L-3 SPD ELECTRICAL SYSTEMS
See SPD ELECTRICAL SYSTEMS INC

L-3 UNIDYNE
See UNIDYNE

L-3 WESTWOOD
See L-3 COMMUNICATIONS WESTWOOD CORP

L-COM DATA PRODUCTS
See L-COM INC

D-U-N-S 04-019-9572 IMP/EXP
L-COM INC (MA)
L-COM DATA PRODUCTS
45 Beechwood Dr, North Andover, MA 01845-1092
Tel (800) 343-1455 *Founded/Ownrshp* 1982, 2012
Sales 99.1MM^E *EMP* 400^E
SIC 3678 3577 3357 Electronic connectors; Computer peripheral equipment; Nonferrous wiredrawing & insulating; Electronic connectors; Computer peripheral equipment; Nonferrous wiredrawing & insulating
Pr: Jon Jensen
Pr: Nick Nash
**COO:* Bentley Craig
COO: Zig Woronko
**CFO:* George Walter
Ex VP: Bill Miller
Sr VP: Chris Long
VP: William Byrd
VP: Jim Machak
IT Man: Dave Gallagher
IT Man: Scott Johnson

L-CON CONSTRUCTORS
See L-CON INC

D-U-N-S 78-794-2247
L-CON INC
L-CON CONSTRUCTORS
(*Suby of* LEXICON INC) ★
12301 Kurland Dr Ste 200, Houston, TX 77034-4838
Tel (281) 484-5266 *Founded/Ownrshp* 2006
Sales 20.5MM^E *EMP* 100
SIC 8711 Construction & civil engineering
Pr: Kelley McGill
**Sec:* Jeff D Weatherly
Sr VP: Rocco Coletta
**VP:* Mark Davis
**VP:* Brian Rutherford
**VP:* Patrick Schueck
VP: Mark West
Dir Bus: Robert Dias
Board of Directors: Thomas Schueck

D-U-N-S 07-844-8131
L-D SYSTEMS LP
LD SYSTEMS
407 Garden Oaks Blvd, Houston, TX 77018-5503
Tel (713) 695-9400 *Founded/Ownrshp* 2003
Sales 47.7MM^E *EMP* 140
SIC 5719 1731 Lighting fixtures; Sound equipment specialization; Lighting fixtures; Sound equipment specialization
Mng Pt: Rob McKinley

D-U-N-S 05-198-2569
L-O CORONADO HOTEL INC
1500 Orange Ave, Coronado, CA 92118-2918
Tel (619) 435-6611 *Founded/Ownrshp* 1886, 2015
Sales 8.1MM^E *EMP* 1,350
SIC 7011 5812 5813 5941 Hotels; Eating places; Cocktail lounge; Tennis goods & equipment
Pr: Tod Shallon
IT Man: Vic Duvela
Mktg Mgr: Stephanie Jourdan

L-T-D COMMODITIES
See LTD COMMODITIES LLC

D-U-N-S 04-288-1771
L/B CORP (TN)
MCDONALD'S
152 Mcgavock Pike, Nashville, TN 37214-2144
Tel (615) 754-8588 *Founded/Ownrshp* 1982
Sales 16.5MM^E *EMP* 500
SIC 5812 Fast-food restaurant, chain; Fast-food restaurant, chain
Pr: Theodore F Bertuca

D-U-N-S 05-165-8516
L/B WATER SERVICE INC
540 S High St, Selinsgrove, PA 17870-1302
Tel (570) 374-2355 *Founded/Ownrshp* 2002
Sales 89.1MM^E *EMP* 106
SIC 5074 Plumbing fittings & supplies; Pipes & fittings, plastic; Plumbing & heating valves; Plumbing fittings & supplies; Pipes & fittings, plastic; Plumbing & heating valves
CEO: Frederick A Steimling
**Pr:* James F App
**Treas:* Walter C Vannuys
**Treas:* Ann L Wagner
Chf Mktg O: Don Bush
**VP:* Robert Dagle
Mktg Mgr: Ben Reichley
Sales Asso: Ginny Capello
Sales Asso: Joshua Dickert
Sales Asso: Jim Haworth
Sales Asso: Clint Inch

D-U-N-S 05-305-6997
L/P INSURANCE SERVICES INC (NV)
6275 Neil Rd Ste B, Reno, NV 89511-1105
Tel (775) 996-6000 *Founded/Ownrshp* 2010
Sales NA *EMP* 56^E
SIC 6411 Insurance agents, brokers & service
Pr: Nicholas Rossi
**COO:* Joseph Wyatt
**VP:* Lloyd Barnes
**VP:* Richard Bullard

D-U-N-S 88-363-4297 IMP
L2T INC
TRINA TURK
3025 W Mission Rd, Alhambra, CA 91803-1111
Tel (626) 458-7768 *Founded/Ownrshp* 1995
Sales 25.2MM^E *EMP* 100^E
SIC 5621 Boutiques
CEO: Trina Turk
VP: Claudine Covolo
**VP:* Lyne Lee
VP: Cathy Quain
VP: Ray Starck
Opers Mgr: Steve Clima
Board of Directors: Richard Speiss

D-U-N-S 02-073-6880
LA ASOCIACION NACIONAL PRO PERSONAS MAYORES (CA)
NAT'L ASSN FOR HISPANIC ELDERL
234 E Colo Blvd Ste 300, Pasadena, CA 91101
Tel (626) 564-1988 *Founded/Ownrshp* 1975
Sales 12.7MM *EMP* 1,330^E
SIC 8322 Social service center; Social service center
Pr: Carmela G Lacayo
**Ch Bd:* Maria Ramirez
**Treas:* Carole Kracer

D-U-N-S 02-556-4758
LA BEAU BROS INC (IL)
295 N Harrison Ave, Kankakee, IL 60901-4041
Tel (815) 933-5519 *Founded/Ownrshp* 1948, 1983
Sales 70.0MM *EMP* 35
SIC 5012 Trucks, commercial; Trucks, commercial
Pr: Wayne Hove
**VP:* Bruce Hove

LA BELLE DODGE
See LABELLE DODGE CHRYSLER JEEP INC

LA BIOMED
See LOS ANGELES BIOMEDICAL RESEARCH INSTITUTE AT HARBOR-UCLA MEDICAL CENTER

LA BODEGA MEAT AND PRODUCE
See LA BODEGA MEAT INC

D-U-N-S 78-414-9663 IMP
LA BODEGA MEAT INC
LA BODEGA MEAT AND PRODUCE
14330 Gillis Rd, Farmers Branch, TX 75244-3717
Tel (972) 926-6129 *Founded/Ownrshp* 2004
Sales 90.3MM^E *EMP* 99
SIC 5147 Meat brokers; Meat brokers
Pr: Mario Nafal
COO: Jose Torres
**VP:* Khaled Nafal
VP Opers: Terry Wiseman

LA BODEGA WHOLESALE
See HERMANOS LOPEZ INC

LA BOHEME GENTLEMENS CABARET
See STOUT RESTAURANT CONCEPTS INC

LA BONITA
See DIANAS MEXICAN FOOD PRODUCTS INC

LA BOULANGE
See BAY BREAD LLC

D-U-N-S 01-690-0562
LA BOXING FRANCHISE CORP
(*Suby of* U GYM LLC) ★
1241 E Dyer Rd Ste 100, Santa Ana, CA 92705-5611
Tel (714) 668-0911 *Founded/Ownrshp* 1992, 2013
Sales 38.9MM^E *EMP* 222^E
SIC 6794 Franchises, selling or licensing
Pr: Anthony Geisler

D-U-N-S 01-651-1011
LA BREA BAKERY CAFE INC
(*Suby of* LA BREA BAKERY HOLDINGS INC) ★
14490 Catalina St, San Leandro, CA 94577-5516
Tel (818) 742-4242 *Founded/Ownrshp* 1998
Sales 100.0MM^E *EMP* 1,200
SIC 2051 2052 2053 Bread, cake & related products; Cookies & crackers; Frozen bakery products, except bread; Bread, cake & related products; Cookies & crackers; Frozen bakery products, except bread
CEO: John Yamin
**CFO:* Robert Gray
Mktg Mgr: Magen Linden

D-U-N-S 10-624-3681
LA BREA BAKERY HOLDINGS INC
(*Suby of* ARYZTA AG)
14490 Catalina St, San Leandro, CA 94577-5516
Tel (818) 742-4242 *Founded/Ownrshp* 2001
Sales 162.3MM^E *EMP* 1,200
SIC 2051 Bread, all types (white, wheat, rye, etc): fresh or frozen; Bread, all types (white, wheat, rye, etc): fresh or frozen
CEO: John Yamin
CFO: Robert Gray
Ex VP: Rick Anderson
Sr VP: Paul Cannon
Sr VP: Chris D'Alessandro
VP: Conor Costello
VP: Jon Davis
Genl Mgr: Tom Bent
Genl Mgr: Brendan Maguire
Dir IT: Hovik Abrahamyan
Opers Mgr: Mark Loera

D-U-N-S 82-569-4193
LA CADENA INVESTMENTS
3750 University Ave # 610, Riverside, CA 92501-3366
Tel (909) 733-5000 *Founded/Ownrshp* 1983
Sales 71.8MM^E *EMP* 35,000
SIC 5411 Supermarkets, chain; Supermarkets, chain
Pt: Jack H Brown

D-U-N-S 08-269-5289
LA CANADA UNIFIED SCHOOL DISTRICT
K-12 PUBLIC EDUCATION
4490 Cornishon Ave Ste 1, La Canada, CA 91011-3243
Tel (818) 952-8300 *Founded/Ownrshp* 1897
Sales 46.3MM *EMP* 450
Accts Vavrinek Trine Day & Co Ll
SIC 8211 Public senior high school; Public senior high school
Schl Brd P: Ellen Multari
Art Dir: Justin Eick

D-U-N-S 00-900-0514
LA CANASTA MEXICAN FOOD PRODUCTS INC
LA CANASTA TORTILLAS
3101 W Jackson St, Phoenix, AZ 85009-4833
Tel (602) 269-7721 *Founded/Ownrshp* 1961
Sales 23.9MM^E *EMP* 120
SIC 2099 Tortillas, fresh or refrigerated; Tortillas, fresh or refrigerated
Pr: Josie Ippolito
**VP:* Linda Rios
Plnt Mgr: Ben Garduno
Board of Directors: Jesus Gonzalez

LA CANASTA TORTILLAS
See LA CANASTA MEXICAN FOOD PRODUCTS INC

D-U-N-S 15-344-5593 EXP
LA CANTINA DOORS INC
3817 Ocean Ranch Blvd, Oceanside, CA 92056-8607
Tel (760) 597-0281 *Founded/Ownrshp* 2003
Sales 50.4MM^E *EMP* 61^E
SIC 5039 Doors, sliding
CEO: Matthew Power
**VP:* Toby Jones
Opers Mgr: Lee Maughan
Prd Mgr: James Decremer
Natl Sales: Jordon Oberhaus
Sls Mgr: Chase Clark
Sales Asso: Stephen Costantino
Sales Asso: Christian Perry

LA CAPITAL
See LOS ANGELES CAPITAL MANAGEMENT AND EQUITY RESEARCH INC

LA CARPET & RUG
See LONG AFFAIR CARPET AND RUG INC

LA CHIQUITA TORTILLA MFR
See LATINO ENTERPRISES INC

D-U-N-S 07-015-9157
LA CLINICA DE LA RAZA INC
1450 Fruitvale Ave Fl 3, Oakland, CA 94601-2313
Tel (510) 535-4000 *Founded/Ownrshp* 1971
Sales 82.7MM^E *EMP* 2,000
Accts Moss Adams Llp San Francisco
SIC 8099 Medical services organization; Medical services organization
CEO: Jane Garcia
**CFO:* Patricia Aguilera

LA CLIQUE SALONS
See PROFILE GROUP INC

D-U-N-S 79-268-0691
LA COLO LLC
COLO RAILROAD BUILDERS
760 Twin Rail Dr, Minooka, IL 60447-8850
Tel (815) 293-0200 *Founded/Ownrshp* 1978
Sales 52.0MM^E *EMP* 225
SIC 1629 Railroad & subway construction; Railroad & subway construction
COO: Frank Condurelis
Snr Mgr: Kent Strohmaier

LA COLONIAL MEXICAN FOODS
See LA COLONIAL TORTILLA PRODUCTS INC

D-U-N-S 00-825-9186
LA COLONIAL TORTILLA PRODUCTS INC (CA)
LA COLONIAL MEXICAN FOODS
543 Monterey Pass Rd, Monterey Park, CA 91754-2416
Tel (626) 289-3647 *Founded/Ownrshp* 1950, 1957
Sales 43.3MM^E *EMP* 185
SIC 2099 Tortillas, fresh or refrigerated; Tortillas, fresh or refrigerated
Pr: Daniel Robles
VP: Adrian Robles
Plnt Mgr: George Robles

D-U-N-S 82-747-0472
LA CONCHA A RENAISSANCE RESORT
1077 Ave Ashford, San Juan, PR 00907-1128
Tel (787) 721-7500 *Founded/Ownrshp* 2008
Sales 10.4MM^E *EMP* 300
SIC 7011 Hotels & motels; Hotels & motels
Owner: Noraliz Santana

LA COSTA GLEN
See CONTINUING LIFE COMMUNITIES LLC

LA COSTA RESORT & SPA
See LC TRS INC

D-U-N-S 05-220-4949
LA COSTENA USA INC
(*Suby of* LA COSTEIA VIZCAYA SOCIEDAD LIMITADA)
8755 S Rita Rd, Tucson, AZ 85747-9106
Tel (520) 663-4720 *Founded/Ownrshp* 2006
Sales 246.1MM^E *EMP* 835
SIC 2032 Beans & bean sprouts, canned, jarred, etc.
CEO: Albert Basauri
**Pr:* Vincent Rodea

D-U-N-S 93-053-7282
LA COUNTY HIGH DESERT HEALTH SYSTEM
44900 60th St W, Lancaster, CA 93536-7618
Tel (661) 945-8461 *Founded/Ownrshp* 1961
Sales 11.9MM^E *EMP* 400
SIC 8011 8062 8093 Ambulatory surgical center; Hospital, AMA approved residency; Specialty outpatient clinics; Ambulatory surgical center; Hospital, AMA approved residency; Specialty outpatient clinics
Ex Dir: Beryl Brooks
CFO: Camby Smith

LA COUNTY MUSEUM OF ART
See MUSEUM ASSOCIATES

D-U-N-S 12-798-3596 IMP
LA CROSSE FORAGE & TURF SEED CORP
2541 Commerce St, La Crosse, WI 54603-1762
Tel (608) 781-4637 *Founded/Ownrshp* 2000
Sales 34.2MM^E *EMP* 17
SIC 5191 Seeds: field, garden & flower
Pr: Katheen Curran
COO: Dan Foor
**VP:* Jeff Curran
IT Man: Clara Anderson
IT Man: Debbie Knutson

D-U-N-S 15-649-4387
LA CROSSE GRAPHICS INC
3025 East Ave S, La Crosse, WI 54601-7204
Tel (608) 788-2500 *Founded/Ownrshp* 1986
Sales 22.8MM^E *EMP* 87
SIC 2752 Commercial printing, offset
Pr: Tim Morgan
**Treas:* Heath Tschumper

D-U-N-S 00-696-6618
LA CROSSE LUMBER CO (MO)
200 N Main St, Louisiana, MO 63353-1747
Tel (573) 754-4500 *Founded/Ownrshp* 1873
Sales 23.7MM^E *EMP* 110
SIC 5211 Lumber & other building materials; Lumber & other building materials
Pr: Kevin Keely
VP: Doyle Whiskur
**VP:* Doyle Wiskur

D-U-N-S 11-352-5448 EXP
LA CROSSE MILLING CO
105 State Hwy 35, Cochrane, WI 54622
Tel (608) 248-2222 *Founded/Ownrshp* 1984
Sales 48.2MM *EMP* 95
Accts Mcgladrey Llp La Crosse Wis
SIC 2048 2043 2041 Cereal breakfast foods; Flour & other grain mill products; Feed concentrates; Feed concentrates; Cereal breakfast foods; Flour & other grain mill products
Pr: Dan Ward
**VP:* Glenn Hartzell
Dir Lab: Bryan Hoch

D-U-N-S 09-004-7168
LA CRUZ AZUL OF PUERTO RICO INC
(*Suby of* BLUE CROSS) ★
Km 173 Sctor El Mnao Rr 1, San Juan, PR 00926
Tel (877) 730-8108 *Founded/Ownrshp* 1943, 1998
Sales NA *EMP* 400
SIC 6321 Health insurance carriers
Pr: Marcos Vidal
COO: IV N E Col N
**CFO:* Juan A Ortega
VP: Jos F Vazquez

D-U-N-S 01-874-4799
LA CTY FAIRGROUNDS
1101 W Mckinley Ave 12, Pomona, CA 91768-1639
Tel (909) 623-3111 *Founded/Ownrshp* 2010
Sales 68.4MM *EMP* 2^E
SIC 7033 Recreational vehicle parks; Recreational vehicle parks

LA CURACAO
See ADIR INTERNATIONAL LLC

D-U-N-S 15-284-5061 IMP/EXP
■ **LA DARLING CO LLC**
THORCO INDUSTRIES
(*Suby of* MARMON RETAIL SERVICES INC) ★
1401 Highway 49b, Paragould, AR 72450-3139
Tel (870) 239-9564 *Founded/Ownrshp* 1960
Sales 356.8MM^E *EMP* 1,500
SIC 2541 2542 Store fixtures, wood; Fixtures, store: except wood; Racks, merchandise display or storage: except wood; Shelving, office & store: except wood; Store fixtures, wood; Fixtures, store: except wood; Racks, merchandise display or storage: except wood; Shelving, office & store: except wood
Pr: Randy Guthrie
CFO: Bobby Wallis
Sr VP: Mark Garrette
VP: Jerry Keel
**Prin:* Kenneth Recor
S&M/VP: Tom Howe
Snr Mgr: Tim Williams

D-U-N-S 17-510-6462
LA EAST INC
MIDDLEBURY TRAILERS
51790 County Road 39, Middlebury, IN 46540-9661
Tel (574) 825-9518 *Founded/Ownrshp* 2004
Sales 42.0MM^E *EMP* 55^E
SIC 3731 Cargo vessels, building & repairing
Pr: James Bergan
CFO: Joe Kiefer
**Sec:* Georgia Vangilder
Sls Mgr: Jeff Stanley

D-U-N-S 02-148-6329
LA ESPIGA DE ORO - GEORGIA INC (TX)
1202 W 15th St, Houston, TX 77008-3816
Tel (713) 861-4200 *Founded/Ownrshp* 1977
Sales 28.2MM^E *EMP* 200
SIC 2099 Tortillas, fresh or refrigerated; Tortillas, fresh or refrigerated
Pr: Alfredo S Lira
**Sec:* Lyvia Lira

D-U-N-S 08-450-3908
LA FAMILIA HEALTH INC
LA FAMILIA HEALTHCARE
1155 Wstmrland Dr Ste 132, El Paso, TX 79925
Tel (915) 591-7100 *Founded/Ownrshp* 2015
Sales 23.1MM^E *EMP* 520^E
SIC 8082 8059 8361 Home health care services; Home health care services; Rest home, with health care; Rehabilitation center, residential: health care incidental
Pr: Elsa Velazquez
**CFO:* Fernando Acosta
**Treas:* Agustin Velazquez

LA FAMILIA HEALTHCARE
See LA FAMILIA HEALTH INC

LA FE FOODS
See GRACEKENNEDY FOODS (USA) LLC

D-U-N-S 82-508-9303 IMP
LA FE FOODS INC
GONZALEZ AND TAPANES FOODS
230 Moonachie Ave, Moonachie, NJ 07074-1831
Tel (201) 329-6260 *Founded/Ownrshp* 1993
Sales 43.2MM *EMP* 205
SIC 5141

LA FEDE ITALIAN FOODS
See ACE ENDICO CORP

D-U-N-S 09-374-4670
LA FERIA INDEPENDENT SCHOOL DISTRICT
LF
203 E Oleander Ave, La Feria, TX 78559-5102
Tel (956) 797-8300 *Founded/Ownrshp* 1935
Sales 30.6MM^E *EMP* 500
Accts Long Chilton Llp Harlingen
SIC 8211 Public elementary school; Public junior high school; Public senior high school; School board; Public elementary school; Public junior high school; Public senior high school; School board
**Pr:* Juan Briones
**Pr:* Allan Moore
Bd of Dir: Javier Loredo
Bd of Dir: Lisa Montalvo
Bd of Dir: Lalo Sosa
**VP:* Gloria Loya
**Ex Dir:* Cynthia Torres
Instr Medi: Aida Martinez

LA FIESTA SUPERMARKETS
See COXS FIESTA SUPER MARKETS OF SA INC

LA FITNESS
See FITNESS INTERNATIONAL LLC

LA FITNESS
See L A FITNESS INTERNATIONAL LLC

LA FLOR DE MEXICO BAKERY
See LA FLOR DE MEXICO INC

D-U-N-S 02-849-4466
LA FLOR DE MEXICO INC
LA FLOR DE MEXICO BAKERY
495 E Gladstone St, Azusa, CA 91702-4929
Tel (626) 334-0716 *Founded/Ownrshp* 1959
Sales 28.5MM^E *EMP* 52^E
SIC 5149 5461 5411 5812 Bakery products; Bakeries; Pastries; Grocery stores, independent; Mexican restaurant
Pr: Michael Esquivel
**VP:* Irene Esquivel
Genl Mgr: Anthony Esquivel

D-U-N-S 96-587-0624
LA FONDATION DU LYCEE FRANCAIS INTERNATIONAL DE WASHINGTON
9600 Forest Rd, Bethesda, MD 20814-1714
Tel (301) 530-8260 *Founded/Ownrshp* 2010
Sales 20.2MM *EMP* 1^E
Accts Mcgladrey Llp Gaithersburg M
SIC 8299 Educational services; Educational services

D-U-N-S 05-234-4876
LA FONTAINE BLEU LLC
BLEUE BAGUETTE BISTRO
7514 Ritchie Hwy, Glen Burnie, MD 21061-3717
Tel (443) 883-3547 *Founded/Ownrshp* 1986
Sales 12.5MM^E *EMP* 400
SIC 5812 Caterers; Caterers
Prin: Thomas Stuehler
VP: Ann Wood

LA FOODS
See LA FOODS LLC

D-U-N-S 62-486-0334 IMP
LA FOODS LLC
LA FOODS
5115 Clareton Dr Ste 200, Agoura Hills, CA 91301-6313
Tel (818) 587-3757 *Founded/Ownrshp* 1990
Sales 26.7MM^E *EMP* 56
SIC 5142 5149 5199

D-U-N-S 02-324-8727
LA FORCE INC
1060 W Mason St, Green Bay, WI 54303-1863
Tel (920) 497-7100 *Founded/Ownrshp* 1954
Sales 153.6MM^E *EMP* 412
SIC 5072 5031 3442 Builders' hardware; Doors; Window & door frames; Builders' hardware; Doors; Window & door frames
CEO: Kenneth Metzler
Pr: Brian Mannering
CFO: April Johnson
Treas: Jill M Pruski
VP: Michael Latour
VP: Jeff McGlachlin
Mng Dir: Brian Delveaux
CIO: Jeff Mc Glachlin
IT Man: Tery Mallon
IT Man: Rob Russell
Trfc Dir: Andy Roznowski
Board of Directors: Harold Breliant, Tony Cinquini, Tom Gaible, James La Force, Patricia La Force, Bruce Massey

D-U-N-S 00-227-5436 IMP
LA FRANCE CORP
JAT CREATIVE PDTS DIV LAFRANCE
1 Lafrance Way, Concordville, PA 19331
Tel (610) 361-4300 *Founded/Ownrshp* 1946
Sales 131.3MM *EMP* 1,827
Accts Cliftonlarsonallen Llp Plymo
SIC 3089 3364 3993 5013 7389 Injection molded finished plastic products; Zinc & zinc-base alloy die-castings; Name plates: except engraved, etched, etc.: metal; Automotive supplies & parts; Design services; Injection molded finished plastic products; Zinc & zinc-base alloy die-castings; Name plates: except engraved, etched, etc.: metal; Automotive supplies & parts; Design services
Ch: John J Teti
**Pr:* George Barrar
**CFO:* Thomas Sheehan
**Ex VP:* Alan Grodnitzky
VP: Chris Anthony
VP: Rich Bender
VP: Ed Lincoln
**VP:* Brian McHenry
**VP:* Peter Peroni
VP: Lou Venancio
Genl Mgr: Fran Vespa

D-U-N-S 01-210-4626
LA FRIEDA MEATS INC
LA FRIEDA PATK MEATS
3701 Tonnelle Ave, North Bergen, NJ 07047-2421
Tel (201) 537-7915 *Founded/Ownrshp* 1964
Sales 90.0MM^E *EMP* 50
SIC 5147 5144 Meats, fresh; Poultry & poultry products; Meats, fresh; Poultry & poultry products
CEO: Patrick La Frieda Jr
Genl Mgr: Dan Nguyen
Genl Mgr: Mark Pastore
Opers Mgr: Chris Gyuricsek

LA FRIEDA PATK MEATS
See LA FRIEDA MEATS INC

D-U-N-S 02-164-9413
LA FRONTERA CENTER INC
LA FRONTERA CENTER OUT PATIENT
504 W 29th St, Tucson, AZ 85713-3353
Tel (520) 884-9920 *Founded/Ownrshp* 1968
Sales 53.4MM *EMP* 500
Accts Keegan Linscott & Kenon PcT
SIC 8093 Mental health clinic, outpatient; Mental health clinic, outpatient
Pr: Daniel J Ranieri
**CFO:* Michael Prudence
**VP:* Kathy Wells
Ex Dir: Heather Taras
Genl Mgr: Kelly Harshberger
CTO: Pat Penn
IT Man: Estella Rodriguez
Opers Supe: Carmelo Carlone
Psych: Ann Maier
Psych: Roger Owen
Doctor: Amie Hart

LA FRONTERA CENTER OUT PATIENT
See LA FRONTERA CENTER INC

D-U-N-S 60-885-7371
LA GAUGE CO INC
7440 San Fernando Rd, Sun Valley, CA 91352-4398
Tel (818) 767-5374 *Founded/Ownrshp* 2008
Sales 22.8MM^E *EMP* 62
SIC 3599 Machine shop, jobbing & repair
Pr: Harbans Bawa
Genl Mgr: James Corum
Sls Mgr: Brian Walters

L.A. GAY & LESBIAN CENTER
See LOS ANGELES LGBT CENTER

D-U-N-S 11-893-2636 IMP
LA GEM AND JEWELRY DESIGN INC
LA ROCKS
659 S Broadway Fl 7, Los Angeles, CA 90014-2291
Tel (213) 488-1290 *Founded/Ownrshp* 2002
Sales 41.1MM^E *EMP* 100
SIC 3911 5094 Jewelry, precious metal; Jewelry; Jewelry, precious metal; Jewelry
CEO: Joseph W Behney
**CFO:* Ashish Arora

D-U-N-S 12-271-7866
■ **LA GRANGE ACQUISITION LP**
ENERGY TRANSFER COMPANY
(*Suby of* ENERGY TRANSFER PARTNERS LP) ★
800 E Sonterra Blvd, San Antonio, TX 78258-3940
Tel (210) 403-7300 *Founded/Ownrshp* 2002
Sales 415.7MM^E *EMP* 500^E
SIC 4922 Natural gas transmission; Natural gas transmission
Pt: Kelcy L Warren
**Pt:* Ray Davis
**Pt:* Mackie McCrea
**Pr:* Marshall S McCrea
**COO:* Greg Brazaitis
Off Admin: Rachel McPheeters
IT Man: Clint Hoyle
Plnt Mgr: Larry Gray
Genl Couns: Paul Keeler
Snr PM: John Bilhartz
Board of Directors: Josie Castrejana

D-U-N-S 10-007-5365
LA GRANGE INDEPENDENT SCHOOL DISTRICT
560 N Monroe St, La Grange, TX 78945-1944
Tel (979) 968-7000 *Founded/Ownrshp* 1895
Sales 14.4MM^E *EMP* 300^E
Accts Singleton Clark & Company Pc
SIC 8211 Public combined elementary & secondary school; Public combined elementary & secondary school
**Prin:* Mike Michalka
Prin: Sandra Stoever

D-U-N-S 04-423-9606
LA GRANGE MEMORIAL HOSPITAL INC
ADVENTIST MIDWEST HEALTH
5101 Willow Springs Rd, La Grange, IL 60525-2600
Tel (708) 352-1200 *Founded/Ownrshp* 1999
Sales 123.1MM^E *EMP* 1,754
SIC 8062 General medical & surgical hospitals; General medical & surgical hospitals
CEO: Rick Wright
CFO: Keith Richardson
VP: Theodore Suchy
Dir Lab: Ron Longino
Dir Rx: Dave Tsang
CIO: Rich Razwadowski
Dir IT: Rich Rozwadoski
IT Man: Alice Estela
Pharmcst: Lue Baker
Pharmcst: Anne Bran
Pharmcst: Mike Detro
Board of Directors: Keren Gonzalez

D-U-N-S 02-861-3123
LA GRANGE SCHOOL DISTRICT NO 102
333 N Park Rd, La Grange Park, IL 60526-1802
Tel (708) 482-2400 *Founded/Ownrshp* 1900
Sales 25.0MM^E *EMP* 287
SIC 8211 8741 Public elementary & secondary schools; Management services; Public elementary & secondary schools; Management services
HC Dir: Lori Gehrke

D-U-N-S 07-812-6554
LA GRANGE TROUP COUNTY HOSPITAL AUTHORITY
FLORENCE HAND NURSING HOME
1514 Vernon Rd, Lagrange, GA 30240-4131
Tel (706) 882-1411 *Founded/Ownrshp* 1936
Sales 69.7MM^E *EMP* 1,315

SIC 8062 8051 General medical & surgical hospitals; Skilled nursing care facilities; General medical & surgical hospitals; Skilled nursing care facilities
Pr: Gerald Fulke
**CFO:* Paul Perrotti
CFO: Esther Rainey
CFO: Monty Wallace
Ofcr: Marjorie Scott
CIO: Bob Honeycutt
Mktg Dir: Jan Nichols
Obsttrcn: Madhavi Naik
Ansthlgy: Jung Ahn
Doctor: Sylvester Ejeh
Doctor: Bruce James

LA GROU COLD STORAGE PARTNR
See LA GROU MOTOR SERVICE INC

D-U-N-S 00-677-2800
LA GROU MOTOR SERVICE INC (IL)
LA GROU COLD STORAGE PARTNR
3514 S Kostner Ave, Chicago, IL 60632-3818
Tel (773) 523-1800 *Founded/Ownrshp* 1965
Sales 21.7MM^E *EMP* 150
SIC 4214 Household goods moving & storage, local
Pr: Donald Schimmek
VP: Steve Schuldt

D-U-N-S 01-329-0598
LA HABRA CITY SCHOOL DISTRICT
500 N Walnut St, La Habra, CA 90631-3769
Tel (562) 690-2305 *Founded/Ownrshp* 1896
Sales 0.0 *EMP* 550
SIC 8211 Public elementary & secondary schools; Public elementary & secondary schools
Dir IT: Wray Miller
Psych: Lisa Torkzadeh

LA HACIENDA RANCH RESTAURANT
See STEMNONES COMPADRES LTD

D-U-N-S 83-031-1499
LA HOTEL VENTURE LLC
LOS ANGELES MARRIOTT DOWNTOWN
333 S Figueroa St, Los Angeles, CA 90071-1001
Tel (213) 617-1133 *Founded/Ownrshp* 2010
Sales 15.7MM^E *EMP* 400
SIC 7011 Hotels & motels; Hotels & motels
Bd of Dir: Philip Amoils
Genl Mgr: Carl Sprayberry
Sls Dir: Libby Zarrahy

D-U-N-S 02-835-3324
LA JOLLA BEACH & TENNIS CLUB INC
SEA LODGE HOTEL
2000 Spindrift Dr, La Jolla, CA 92037-3237
Tel (858) 454-7126 *Founded/Ownrshp* 1940
Sales 51.3MM^E *EMP* 450
SIC 7011 8742 7997 Hotels; Food & beverage consultant; Membership sports & recreation clubs; Hotels; Food & beverage consultant; Membership sports & recreation clubs
CEO: William J Kellogg
VP: Melony Kurashima
Exec: Bernard Guillas
Genl Mgr: John Campbell
CIO: Bill Kellogg
Dir IT: Matt Forsyth
IT Man: Kathy Lindburg
Sls Dir: Karen Lanning
Sls Dir: Amy Lassalette
Sls Mgr: Suzy Clayton
Sls Mgr: Amy Lasalpce

D-U-N-S 96-476-9009
LA JOLLA COUNTRY DAY SCHOOL
9490 Genesee Ave, La Jolla, CA 92037-1302
Tel (858) 453-3440 *Founded/Ownrshp* 1955
Sales 35.6MM *EMP* 213
Accts Grant Thornton Llp Los Angele
SIC 8211 Elementary & secondary schools; Elementary & secondary schools
Pr: Manish Parikh
**Pr:* Howard Ziment
**Treas:* Chris Richey
**Treas:* Barry Rosenbaum
**VP:* Angela Glynn
**VP:* Peter Hamilton
**VP:* Cameron Rooke
**Prin:* Christopher Schuck

D-U-N-S 06-616-4278
LA JOLLA COUNTRY DAY SCHOOL PARENTS ASSOCIATION
9490 Genesee Ave, La Jolla, CA 92037-1302
Tel (858) 453-3440 *Founded/Ownrshp* 1955
Sales 32.8MM *EMP* 170
SIC 8211 Private combined elementary & secondary school; Private combined elementary & secondary school
VP: Patricia Hughes

D-U-N-S 01-769-6277
LA JOLLA GROUP INC
LJG
14350 Myford Rd, Irvine, CA 92606-1002
Tel (949) 428-2800 *Founded/Ownrshp* 2007
Sales 41.1MM^E *EMP* 173^E
SIC 7389 6794 2326 Apparel designers, commercial; Copyright buying & licensing; Franchises, selling or licensing; Patent buying, licensing, leasing; Men's & boys' work clothing
CEO: Daniel Neukomm
Sr VP: Tobye Lovelace
VP: Ryan Rush
VP Mktg: Steve Ward
VP Sls: Michelle Devine
S&M/VP: Ryan Divel

D-U-N-S 60-388-0287
LA JOLLA INSTITUTE FOR ALLERGY AND IMMUNOLOGY
DIDNRI
9420 Athena Cir, La Jolla, CA 92037-1387
Tel (858) 752-6500 *Founded/Ownrshp* 1988
Sales 49.3MM *EMP* 240
Accts Moss Adams Llp San Diego Cal
SIC 8733 Medical research; Medical research
Pr: Mitchell Kronenberg
Mng Pt: Harold G Buchanan II
CFO: Skip Carpowich
Ex VP: Charles A Carpowich Jr
Ex VP: Stephen Wilson
Dir Lab: Chris Elly
Off Mgr: David Hall
IT Man: Jen Keyes
IT Man: Tai Nguyen
Web Dev: Adam Grofcsik
Snr Mgr: John Stillwagen
Board of Directors: David Dominguez, Robert C Dynes, Leroy Hood, John E Major

D-U-N-S 02-410-2451
LA JOYA INDEPENDENT SCHOOL DISTRICT
201 W Expressway 83, La Joya, TX 78560-4024
Tel (956) 580-5000 *Founded/Ownrshp* 1926
Sales 173.7MM^E *EMP* 2,800
Accts Reyna & Garza Pllc Cpa S Tx
SIC 8211 Public elementary & secondary schools; Public elementary & secondary schools
**Pr:* Juan Jos Jj Pea Jr
MIS Dir: Frank Rivera
Instr Medi: Perriann Huntley

D-U-N-S 19-000-8243
LA LOMITA INC
EL TIGRE FOOD STORE
2105 Remington Ave, Edinburg, TX 78539-3931
Tel (956) 287-8077 *Founded/Ownrshp* 1979
Sales 62.5MM^E *EMP* 189
SIC 5541 5411 5172 5813 Gasoline service stations; Convenience stores; Gasoline; Diesel fuel; Cocktail lounge; Gasoline service stations; Convenience stores; Gasoline; Diesel fuel; Cocktail lounge
Pr: Carlos Garza
**Treas:* Sandra Garza

LA MADELEINE OF LOUISIANA INC
See LA MADELEINE OF LOUISIANA LLC

D-U-N-S 01-882-9296
LA MADELEINE OF LOUISIANA LLC
LA MADELEINE OF LOUISIANA INC
(*Suby of* HEC, INC.)
12201 Merit Dr Ste 900, Dallas, TX 75251-3139
Tel (800) 975-2623 *Founded/Ownrshp* 1994
Sales 17.9MM^E *EMP* 630
SIC 5812 French restaurant; French restaurant
Pr: Mark Menking
**VP:* Harry J Martin Jr

LA MAESTRA COMMUNITY HEALTH CE
See LA MAESTRA FAMILY CLINIC INC

D-U-N-S 77-996-6647
LA MAESTRA FAMILY CLINIC INC
LA MAESTRA COMMUNITY HEALTH CE
4060 Fairmount Ave, San Diego, CA 92105-1608
Tel (619) 584-1612 *Founded/Ownrshp* 1991
Sales 24.2MM *EMP* 300^E
Accts Filipina B Patio San Diego
SIC 8322 Individual & family services; Individual & family services
CEO: Zara Marselian
**Ch Bd:* Carlos Hanessian
**COO:* Alejandrina Areizaga
CFO: Mary David
**CFO:* Alex Pantoja
**V Ch Bd:* Samuel Mirelles
Prgrm Mgr: Brenda Zapata
CIO: Sal Saldivar
IT Man: Garabet Hanessian
Pharmcst: Melissa Jump

D-U-N-S 07-349-9840
LA MAIR-MULOCK-CONDON CO
LMC INSURANCE
(*Suby of* LMC INSURANCE & RISK MANAGEMENT INC) ★
4200 University Ave # 200, West Des Moines, IA 50266-5945
Tel (515) 244-0166 *Founded/Ownrshp* 1965
Sales NA *EMP* 95
SIC 6411 7389 Insurance agents; Financial services
Ch Bd: Roger Hoyt
**Pr:* Greg La Mair
**Treas:* Mark Lyons
Sr VP: Richard Debartolo
**VP:* Gene Clay
**VP:* F M Hrubetz
**VP:* Mark Keairnes
VP: Greg Sieck
IT Man: Jeremy Hepp
IT Man: Greg Lamair
Sales Exec: Karen Cooper

LA MANSION DEL RIO HOTEL
See LA MANSION HOTELS LTD

D-U-N-S 79-453-0329
LA MANSION HOTELS LTD
LA MANSION DEL RIO HOTEL
112 E Pecan St Ste 2810, San Antonio, TX 78205-1586
Tel (210) 518-1000 *Founded/Ownrshp* 1968
Sales 7.9MM^E *EMP* 305
SIC 7011 5812 5813 Hotels; Eating places; Drinking places; Hotels; Eating places; Drinking places
Pt: Patrick J Kennedy

D-U-N-S 01-079-9765
LA MARQUE INDEPENDENT SCHOOL DISTRICT
1727 Bayou Rd, La Marque, TX 77568-5209
Tel (409) 938-4251 *Founded/Ownrshp* 1914
Sales 20.3MM^E *EMP* 380
Accts Null-Lairson Pc Texas City
SIC 8211 Public elementary & secondary schools; High school, junior or senior; Public elementary & secondary schools; High school, junior or senior
Pr Dir: Thomasine Allen
Teacher Pr: Antonio Corrales

D-U-N-S 87-769-8035 IMP
LA MARZOCCO INTERNATIONAL LLC
1553 Nw Ballard Way, Seattle, WA 98107-4712
Tel (206) 706-9104 *Founded/Ownrshp* 1927
Sales 23.0MM *EMP* 39^E
SIC 5084 Brewery products manufacturing machinery, commercial

LA MESA DISPOSAL
See EDCO DISPOSAL CORP

D-U-N-S 05-927-6444
LA MESA R V CENTER INC
7430 Copley Park Pl, San Diego, CA 92111-1122
Tel (858) 874-8001 *Founded/Ownrshp* 1972
Sales 211.9MM^E *EMP* 450
SIC 5561 7538 Motor homes; Travel trailers: automobile, new & used; Recreational vehicle parts & accessories; Recreational vehicle repairs; Motor homes; Travel trailers: automobile, new & used; Recreational vehicle parts & accessories; Recreational vehicle repairs
CEO: James R Kimbrell
**Pr:* James Walters
CFO: Timothy O'Connor
VP: Rick Berardi
**VP:* Laree Howell
Genl Mgr: Vince Meo
Info Man: Jason Boettcher
Sls Dir: Bob Upton
Mktg Mgr: Steve Love
Sls Mgr: Terry Bridgewater
Sls Mgr: Thomas Chelone

D-U-N-S 07-872-8987
LA MESA-SPRING VALLEY SCHOOL DISTRICT
4750 Date Ave, La Mesa, CA 91942-9214
Tel (619) 668-5700 *Founded/Ownrshp* 1915
Sales 88.3MM^E *EMP* 1,500
Accts Christywhite Accountancy Corpo
SIC 8211 Public elementary & secondary schools; Public elementary & secondary schools
Ex VP: Courtney Lanier
VP: Kathy Haase
Schl Brd P: Bob Duff
Psych: Melissa Mackie
HC Dir: Ginger Rabenheimer

LA METHODIST CHILDREN'S HOME
See LOUISIANA UNITED METHODIST CHILDREN AND FAMILY SERVICES INC

D-U-N-S 09-862-5437
LA METROPOLITAN MEDICAL CENTER
(*Suby of* PACIFIC HEALTH CORP) ★
2231 Southwest Dr, Los Angeles, CA 90043
Tel (323) 730-7300 *Founded/Ownrshp* 1984
Sales 39.4MM^E *EMP* 600
SIC 8062 General medical & surgical hospitals; General medical & surgical hospitals
CEO: John Fenton
**Pr:* James W Young
**COO:* Audrey O'Donnell
COO: Ron Stinett
**CFO:* Michael Grubb
Nrsg Dir: Jackie Curtin
Resp Thrpy: Judy Johnson

D-U-N-S 18-968-4405 EXP
LA MINA DE ORO INC
KD DISTRIBUTORS
1874 Tandem, Norco, CA 92860-3605
Tel (951) 372-0877 *Founded/Ownrshp* 2003
Sales 30.0MM^E *EMP* 24
SIC 5999 5122 Perfumes & colognes; Perfumes; Perfumes & colognes; Perfumes
Pr: Desiree C Nutley
**VP:* Ken Nutley

D-U-N-S 09-277-7366
LA MONTANITA FOOD COOPERATIVE
901 Menaul Blvd Ne, Albuquerque, NM 87107-1658
Tel (505) 217-2001 *Founded/Ownrshp* 1976
Sales 39.1MM^E *EMP* 235
Accts Mackie Reid & Company Pa Al
SIC 5411 Supermarkets, independent; Supermarkets, independent
Pr: Marshal Kovitz
**Pr:* Martha Whitman
CFO: John Heckes
**CFO:* John Hectors
**Treas:* Roger Eldridge
**Ex Dir:* Terry Bowling
Opers Mgr: Michelle Franklin

D-U-N-S 14-846-7434
LA NEVADA INC
G & G SYSTEMS
4340 W Hacienda Ave, Las Vegas, NV 89118-2900
Tel (702) 739-0090 *Founded/Ownrshp* 1998
Sales 28.4MM^E *EMP* 180
SIC 1731 General electrical contractor; General electrical contractor
Pr: Robert J Lisowski
**Sec:* Patrick R Armour

D-U-N-S 00-832-7678
LA OPINION LP (CA)
LOZANO ENTERPRISES
(*Suby of* IMPREMEDIA LLC) ★
700 S Flower St Ste 3100, Los Angeles, CA 90017-4218
Tel (213) 896-2196 *Founded/Ownrshp* 1926, 1990
Sales 50.0MM^E *EMP* 420
SIC 2711 Newspapers, publishing & printing; Newspapers, publishing & printing
CEO: Monica C Lozano
Genl Pt: Lozano Communications
CFO: David Torres
VP: La Opini N
Admn Mgr: Jacob Kisner

D-U-N-S 07-251-6164
LA PALMA HOSPITAL MEDICAL CENTER
LA PALMA INTERCOMMUNITY HOSP
(*Suby of* PRIME HEALTHCARE SERVICES INC) ★
7901 Walker St, La Palma, CA 90623-1764
Tel (714) 670-7400 *Founded/Ownrshp* 2006
Sales 54.4MM^E *EMP* 400
SIC 8062 General medical & surgical hospitals; General medical & surgical hospitals
CEO: Virg Narbutas
CFO: Allen Spefanek
Cmptr Lab: Melody Pascual
Mktg Dir: Dana Woods
Advt Mgr: Stephen Dixon

LA PALMA INTERCOMMUNITY HOSP
See LA PALMA HOSPITAL MEDICAL CENTER

D-U-N-S 60-362-2874 IMP
LA PALOMA GENERATING CO LLC
(*Suby of* COMPLETE ENERGY HOLDINGS LLC)
1760 W Skyline Rd, Mc Kittrick, CA 93251
Tel (661) 762-6006 *Founded/Ownrshp* 1998
Sales 31.9MM^E *EMP* 43
SIC 4911 Electric services
Opers Mgr: Mark Wooten

LA PAZ
See MEXICAN SPECIALTY FOODS INC

D-U-N-S 07-447-6441
LA PAZ REGIONAL HOSPITAL INC
1200 W Mohave Rd, Parker, AZ 85344-6349
Tel (928) 669-9201 *Founded/Ownrshp* 1972
Sales 26.0MM *EMP* 200
SIC 8062 8399 8322 General medical & surgical hospitals; Community action agency; Rehabilitation services
CEO: Robert Libberton
Chf Path: Bert Dougherty
**Ch Bd:* Norman Simpson
**CEO:* M Victoria Clark
COO: Bonnie Viloria
**CFO:* James Ehasz
CFO: Dennis Good
**CFO:* Steve Stewart
**Ch:* Cheryl Montijo
**Sec:* Pat Wall
Dir OR: Tori Gilliland
Dir Inf Cn: Diane Brown
Dir Lab: Vivian Le Blanc
Dir Rad: Rick Graybeal
Dir Rx: Larry Sanders
Dir Env Sv: Carlo Lagana

LA PEER HEALTH SYSTEMS
See LA PEER SURGERY CENTER LLC

D-U-N-S 06-544-3371
LA PEER SURGERY CENTER LLC
LA PEER HEALTH SYSTEMS
8920 Wilshire Blvd # 101, Beverly Hills, CA 90211-2007
Tel (310) 360-9119 *Founded/Ownrshp* 2003
Sales 28.3MM *EMP* 78
SIC 8011 Surgeon; Surgeon

LA PERLA TAPATIA
See MANUEL VILLA ENTERPRISES INC

LA PETITE ACADEMY
See LPA INVESTMENT LLC

D-U-N-S 02-722-9863
LA PETITE ACADEMY INC
(*Suby of* LA PETITE HOLDINGS CORP) ★
21333 Haggerty Rd Ste 300, Novi, MI 48375-5537
Tel (877) 861-5078 *Founded/Ownrshp* 1994
Sales 135.8MM^E *EMP* 9,693^E
Accts Deloitte & Touche Llp Chicago
SIC 8351 Child day care services; Preschool center; Montessori child development center
Ch Bd: Stephen P Murray
**CEO:* Barbara J Beck
**COO:* Leigh-Ellen Louie
**CFO:* Mark R Bierley
VP: Joan K Singleton
**VP:* Bill Van Huis
IT Exec: Walt Tracy
CIO: Hugh W Tracy

D-U-N-S 07-833-1475
LA PETITE HOLDINGS CORP
(*Suby of* LEARNING CARE GROUP (US) INC) ★
21333 Haggerty Rd Ste 300, Novi, MI 48375-5537
Tel (248) 697-9000 *Founded/Ownrshp* 1993
Sales 131.2MM^E *EMP* 9,728^E
SIC 8351 Child day care services; Preschool center; Montessori child development center; Child day care services; Preschool center; Montessori child development center

D-U-N-S 19-769-3815
LA PIZZA LOCA INC
9550 Firestone Blvd # 105, Downey, CA 90241-5560
Tel (562) 862-4470 *Founded/Ownrshp* 1985
Sales 23.7MM^E *EMP* 600
SIC 5812 Pizzeria, chain; Pizzeria, chain
Pr: Alex Meruelo

D-U-N-S 07-644-1138
LA PLATA COUNTY
LA PLATA COUNTY TREASURER
1101 E 2nd Ave, Durango, CO 81301-5155
Tel (970) 382-6306 *Founded/Ownrshp* 1883
Sales NA *EMP* 390
Accts Chadwick Steinkirchner Davis
SIC 9121 County commissioner; ; County commissioner;
Ofcr: Marianna Spishock
**Prin:* Wayne Bedor

LA PLATA COUNTY TREASURER
See LA PLATA COUNTY

D-U-N-S 00-387-3627
LA PLATA ELECTRIC ASSOCIATION INC
45 Stewart St, Durango, CO 81303-7915
Tel (970) 247-5786 *Founded/Ownrshp* 1939
Sales 110.7MM *EMP* 113
Accts Schmidt & Compan Llc Lee S Su
SIC 4911 Distribution, electric power; Distribution, electric power
CEO: Steve Gregg
CFO: John Bloom
Bd of Dir: Nancy Andrews
**Prin:* Emery Maez
CTO: Cindy Straight
Dir IT: Harry Peterson

LA PLAYA BEACH AND GOLF RESORT
See LA PLAYA LLC

D-U-N-S 07-960-3827
LA PLAYA BEACH ASSOCIATES LLC
1000 E Hllandale Bch Blvd, Hallandale Beach, FL 33009-4433
Tel (954) 668-2505 Founded/Ownrshp 2014
Sales 100.0MM EMP 20
SIC 6552 Land subdividers & developers, residential; Land subdividers & developers, residential

D-U-N-S 82-722-2142
LA PLAYA LLC
LA PLAYA BEACH AND GOLF RESORT
9891 Gulf Shore Dr, Naples, FL 34108-2019
Tel (239) 597-3123 Founded/Ownrshp 1999
Sales 25.0MM^E EMP 310
SIC 7011 Hotels & motels; Hotels & motels
Genl Mgr: Alan Findlay
Genl Mgr: Deborah Puccio

D-U-N-S 07-432-3957
LA PORTE COMMUNITY SCHOOL CORP
1921 A St, La Porte, IN 46350-6639
Tel (219) 362-7056 Founded/Ownrshp 1864
Sales 49.4MM^E EMP 850
SIC 8211 Public elementary & secondary schools; Public elementary & secondary schools
Schl Brd P: Michael Kellems

LA PORTE HOSPITAL & HLTH SVCS
See INDIANA UNIVERSITY HEALTH LA PORTE HOSPITAL INC

D-U-N-S 08-086-5645
LA PORTE INDEPENDENT SCHOOL DISTRICT
1002 San Jacinto St, La Porte, TX 77571-5461
Tel (281) 604-7001 Founded/Ownrshp 2005
Sales 104.7MM EMP 1,200
Accts Weaver And Tidwell Llp Houst
SIC 8211 Public elementary & secondary schools; Public elementary & secondary schools
Trst: Charles Hilborn
Pr Dir: Terri Cook
Teacher Pr: Isela Montes
HC Dir: Laura Lynch
Snr Mgr: Shelli McIntosh

D-U-N-S 01-975-6055
■ **LA PORTE SAVINGS BANK (INC)**
(Suby of LAPORTE BANCORP INC) ★
710 Indiana Ave, La Porte, IN 46350-3461
Tel (219) 362-7511 Founded/Ownrshp 1891
Sales NA EMP 80
SIC 6035 Federal savings & loan associations; Federal savings banks; Federal savings & loan associations; Federal savings banks
Ch Bd: Joan M Ulrich
*Pr: Lee Brady
CFO: Jared Thompson
Bd of Dir: Mark Krentz
Ofcr: Linda Halter
*Ex VP: Russel Klosinski
Sr VP: Patrick Collins
*Sr VP: Bruce Fisher
Sr VP: Carrie McKibben
VP: Kevin Beres
VP: Carol Gee
VP: Brock Lloyd
VP: Raj Nagarajan
VP: Michael Zappia

D-U-N-S 93-013-1052
LA POSADA AT PARK CENTRE INC
LA POSADA HEALTHCARE
350 E Morningside Rd, Green Valley, AZ 85614-5152
Tel (520) 648-8131 Founded/Ownrshp 1997
Sales 37.5MM EMP 500^E
Accts Cbiz Mhm Llc Phoenix Az
SIC 6513 8051 8052 8069 Retirement hotel operation; Skilled nursing care facilities; Intermediate care facilities; Specialty hospitals, except psychiatric; Retirement hotel operation; Skilled nursing care facilities; Intermediate care facilities; Specialty hospitals, except psychiatric
Pr: Lisa Israel
*COO: Joni Condit
CFO: Paul Ide Sr
VP: Tim Carmichael
Dir IT: Jerry Weyjing
IT Man: Suzanne Caldarello
IT Man: Vicky Oupkes

LA POSADA HEALTHCARE
See LA POSADA AT PARK CENTRE INC

LA POSTE OFFICE OF EXCHANGE
See ASENDIA USA INC

LA PRAIRIE GROUP
See LA PRAIRIE INC

D-U-N-S 09-284-8621 IMP/EXP
LA PRAIRIE INC
LA PRAIRIE GROUP
(Suby of BEIERSDORF INC) ★
680 5th Ave Fl 14, New York, NY 10019-5429
Tel (212) 459-1600 Founded/Ownrshp 1991
Sales 22.2MM^E EMP 24
SIC 5122 Cosmetics; Cosmetics, perfumes & hair products
CEO: Patrick Rasquinet
*Ch Bd: Lynne M Florio
*CFO: Dr Karsten Boyens
Sr VP: Charlene Holt
*VP: Brigitte Bruggmann
*VP: Edouard Feller
VP: Peter Gladel
VP: Sven Gohla
VP: Elizabeth Lamont
*VP: Francois Le Gloan
VP: Jaime Maser
*VP: Nunzi Richardson

D-U-N-S 02-519-8227 IMP
LA PREFERIDA INC (IL)
WORLDWIDE FOODS
3400 W 35th St, Chicago, IL 60632-3399
Tel (773) 254-7200 Founded/Ownrshp 2001
Sales 54.5MM^E EMP 70
SIC 5149 5148 Groceries & related products; Fresh fruits & vegetables
Owner: David A Steinbarth
*Ch Bd: Ralph H Steinbarth
*Pr: Richard J Steinbarth
*CFO: Gregory M Gondek
Ex VP: Bob Gouwens
*VP: Robert R Gouwens
*VP: Breck W Grigas
IT Man: Art Sandival
IT Man: Nestor Soto
Natl Sales: Trent Otto
Mktg Mgr: Jaime Munoz

D-U-N-S 14-621-3983
LA QUESERA MEXICANA LLC
L Q M
121 Hankins St, Greeneville, TN 37745-3539
Tel (423) 638-8189 Founded/Ownrshp 2003
Sales 27.6MM^E EMP 80
SIC 2024 Dairy based frozen desserts

LA QUINTA INN
See LQ MANAGEMENT LLC

D-U-N-S 03-718-5329
■ **LA QUINTA LLC**
(Suby of LA QUINTA HOLDINGS INC.)
909 Hidden Rdg Ste 600, Irving, TX 75038-3822
Tel (214) 492-6600 Founded/Ownrshp 2006
Sales 1.1MMM^E EMP 9,400
SIC 7011 6794 8741 Hotels & motels; Franchises, selling or licensing; Hotel or motel management; Hotels & motels; Franchises, selling or licensing; Hotel or motel management
Pr: Wayne B Goldberg
Pr: Feliz Jarvis
*CFO: Robert Harshbarber
CFO: Robert M Harshberger
CFO: David L REA
Sr Cor Off: Clive Bode
*Ex VP: Julie Cary
Ex VP: Murry Cathlina
*Ex VP: Mark M Chloupek
*Ex VP: Keith A Cline
Ex VP: Kevin Dailey
Ex VP: Angelo Lombarbi
*Ex VP: Angelo J Lombardi
Ex VP: James Mitchell
Ex VP: Alicia Novak
Ex VP: Susan Salazar
Ex VP: Vivek Shaiva
*Ex VP: Rajiv K Trivedi
Ex VP: Mark Workman
Sr VP: Alise Deeb
Sr VP: Noel Ferguson

D-U-N-S 01-238-2955
LA RABIDA CHILDRENS HOSPITAL
6501 S Promontory Dr, Chicago, IL 60649-1002
Tel (773) 363-6700 Founded/Ownrshp 2010
Sales 56.1MM EMP 40
Accts Mcgladrey Llp Chicago Il
SIC 8069 Children's hospital; Children's hospital
Owner: Brenda Wolf
Dir Lab: Cathy Coleman

D-U-N-S 06-999-2477
LA RABIDA CHILDRENS HOSPITAL
6501 S Promontory Dr, Chicago, IL 60649-1002
Tel (773) 363-6700 Founded/Ownrshp 1895
Sales 58.0MM EMP 450
SIC 8069 Children's hospital; Children's hospital
Ch Bd: Allen Kanter
*Pr: Paula Jaudes MD
CFO: Mark Renfree
Chf Mktg O: Dilek A Bishku
VP: Janet Haines
VP: Aden Henry
Dir Rad: Diane Knetl
Prgrm Mgr: Carol Muhammad
Telecom Ex: Joyce Williams
QA Dir: Patricia Difiglio
IT Man: Sue Porzel

LA RAZA
See IMPREMEDIA LLC

LA REINA
See OLD PUEBLO RANCH INC

D-U-N-S 06-874-5603
LA ROCHE COLLEGE
9000 Babcock Blvd, Pittsburgh, PA 15237-5898
Tel (412) 367-9300 Founded/Ownrshp 1963
Sales 40.3MM EMP 200
Accts Baker Tilly Virchow Krause Llp
SIC 8221 College, except junior; College, except junior
Pr: Candace Introcaso
Pr: Janet Shearer
*CFO: Bob Bogo
*Treas: Fred Vey Jr
*Ex VP: Dan Soller
*Sr VP: Carolyn Winschel
*VP: Roger Carothers
VP: June Fischerkeller
VP: Arthur Shaker
Telecom Ex: Reem Almasri
CTO: Greg Kemper

LA ROCKS
See LA GEM AND JEWELRY DESIGN INC

D-U-N-S 05-522-5064
LA ROSA DEL MONTE EXPRESS INC
1133 Tiffany St 35, Bronx, NY 10459-2398
Tel (718) 991-5560 Founded/Ownrshp 1969
Sales 34.6MM^E EMP 300
SIC 4212 7389 Moving services; Local trucking with storage; Trucking, except local; Moving services; Relocation service
Pr: Hiran Rodriguez

*VP: Isabel Rodriguez
Sales Exec: Carlos Figueroa

D-U-N-S 07-142-1994
LA SALLE COUNTY OF ILLINOIS
707 E Etna Rd, Ottawa, IL 61350-1047
Tel (815) 434-8200 Founded/Ownrshp 1831
Sales NA EMP 530
Accts Wipfli Llp Mendota Il
SIC 9111 County supervisors' & executives' offices; ; County supervisors' & executives' offices;
Ch Bd: Jerry Hicks

D-U-N-S 03-933-4826
LA SALLE STREET SECURITIES LLC (DE)
940 N Industrial Dr, Elmhurst, IL 60126-1139
Tel (630) 600-0500 Founded/Ownrshp 1975
Sales 28.3MM^E EMP 128
SIC 6211 6282 Brokers, security; Investment advisory service; Brokers, security; Investment advisory service
Pr: John W Mc Dermott
*CFO: Daniel Schlesser
CFO: Robert Widman
Sr VP: Dave Dingle
VP: Jay Carstensen
VP: Bill Powell
IT Man: Chris Venasco

LA SALLE UNIVERSITY
See LASALLE UNIVERSITY

LA SCALA
See PREMIERE RESIDENTIAL LLC

D-U-N-S 17-437-5167 IMP/EXP
LA SCRAP EXPORT INC
2225 W Commonwealth Ave # 116, Alhambra, CA 91803-1333
Tel (626) 588-2211 Founded/Ownrshp 2004
Sales 44.9MM EMP 4
Accts Newcentury Cpa
SIC 5093 4953 Metal scrap & waste materials; Recycling, waste materials; Metal scrap & waste materials; Recycling, waste materials
CEO: Steve Yu

D-U-N-S 62-759-9988
LA SIERRA UNIVERSITY
4500 Riverwalk Pkwy, Riverside, CA 92505-3332
Tel (951) 785-2000 Founded/Ownrshp 1968
Sales 85.3MM EMP 282
Accts Ahern Adcock Devlin Llp River
SIC 8221 University; University
CEO: Randal R Wisbey
COO: Deanne Knipschild
Treas: Mylon McDonald
Ofcr: Debra Marovitch
Ofcr: Paul Wells
VP: Yamilet Bazan
VP: Carol Bradfield
*VP: David Geriguis
VP: David Lofthouse
VP: Jeff Swanson
VP: Marilyn Thompson

D-U-N-S 13-969-3261
LA SPECIALTY PRODUCE CO
SAN FRANSISCO SPECIALITY PROD
13527 Orden Dr, Santa Fe Springs, CA 90670-6338
Tel (562) 741-2200 Founded/Ownrshp 1985
Sales 347.4MM^E EMP 475
SIC 5148 Fresh fruits & vegetables; Fresh fruits & vegetables
Pr: Michael Glick
*VP: Kathleen Glick
VP: Scott Matthews
Exec: Joycee Del Toro
Brnch Mgr: John Bird
Opers Mgr: Scott Mathews
Opers Mgr: Bounthan Panyanouvong
Opers Mgr: Boris Rosa
Sls Dir: Paul Bernardini
Sls Dir: Rick Fischer
Sls Dir: Richard Fisher

LA SPORTS ARENA
See LOS ANGELES MEMORIAL COLISEUM COMMISSION

D-U-N-S 00-917-7106
LA TAPATIA TORTILLERIA INC
104 E Belmont Ave, Fresno, CA 93701-1403
Tel (559) 441-1030 Founded/Ownrshp 1993
Sales 31.9MM^E EMP 170
SIC 2099 Tortillas, fresh or refrigerated; Tortillas, fresh or refrigerated
CEO: Helen Chavez-Hansen
*Sr VP: John Hansen

D-U-N-S 87-267-3637
LA TERRA FINA USA INC
1300 Atlantic St, Union City, CA 94587-2004
Tel (510) 404-5888 Founded/Ownrshp 2015
Sales 30.7MM^E EMP 70
SIC 2099 Seasonings & spices
Pr: Peter Molloy
VP: Stephen Cottrell
Off Mgr: Elizabeth Evans

LA TESTING
See EMSL ANALYTICAL INC

D-U-N-S 94-496-5651
LA TORRETTA LAKE RESORT & SPA
600 La Torretta Blvd, Montgomery, TX 77356-5309
Tel (936) 448-4400 Founded/Ownrshp 2009
Sales 20.4MM^E EMP 300
SIC 7011 Resort hotel; Resort hotel
Genl Mgr: John Hamati
Dir IT: Jay Pyles
IT Man: Clint Garrison
Mktg Mgr: Martin Valdez
Sls Mgr: Krista Gibson
Sls Mgr: Heidi Gwinn
Sls Mgr: Laurie Lea
Sls Mgr: Michelle Rayburn
Sls Mgr: Jessica Thornbrough
Sls Mgr: Chelsa Waller

D-U-N-S 08-721-2270
LA TORTILLA FACTORY INC (CA)
3300 Westwind Blvd, Santa Rosa, CA 95403-8273
Tel (707) 586-4000 Founded/Ownrshp 1977
Sales 147.3MM^E EMP 310
SIC 5149 2051 Specialty food items; Bakery products; Bread, cake & related products; Specialty food items; Bakery products; Bread, cake & related products
CEO: Samuel Carlos Tamayo
*Pr: Carlos Tamayo
COO: Dave Davis
CFO: David Trogdon
*VP: Willie E Tamayo
Exec: Earl Oakley
Dist Mgr: Jake Hammack
QA Dir: Julia Cooper
QA Dir: Cheriene Griffith
IT Man: Clarke Katz
VP Opers: Katie Evans

D-U-N-S 04-723-0508 IMP
LA TORTILLERIA INC
2900 Lowery St, Winston Salem, NC 27101-6126
Tel (336) 773-0010 Founded/Ownrshp 1995
Sales 23.9MM^E EMP 82
SIC 2099 5141 Tortillas, fresh or refrigerated; Food brokers
Pr: Daniel Calhoun

LA TOUCH
See EVY OF CALIFORNIA INC

D-U-N-S 15-553-2034 IMP
LA TOURANGELLE INC
125 University Ave # 201, Berkeley, CA 94710-1601
Tel (510) 970-9960 Founded/Ownrshp 2002
Sales 24.0MM EMP 48
SIC 5159 Oil nuts, kernels, seeds
CEO: Matthieu Kohlmeyer
*CFO: Gwenn Goffin

D-U-N-S 94-979-4101
LA TROPICANA FOOD INC
2600 W 35th St, Chicago, IL 60632-1602
Tel (773) 376-1717 Founded/Ownrshp 1996
Sales 25.0MM^E EMP 37
Accts Robert J Helmsdorfer Ea-H
SIC 5141 Groceries, general line; Groceries, general line
*Prin: David Ortiz
*Genl Mgr: Edgar Navarro

D-U-N-S 12-125-2998 EXP
LA TURBINE
28557 Industry Dr, Valencia, CA 91355-5424
Tel (661) 294-8290 Founded/Ownrshp 2003
Sales 30.3MM^E EMP 72^E
SIC 3511 Turbines & turbine generator sets & parts; Turbines & turbine generator sets & parts
CEO: John Maskaluk
*Pr: Danny Mascari
*CFO: Dominique Maskaluk
Off Mgr: Michelle French
Ql Cn Mgr: Frank Loth
Mktg Dir: Shawne Thiry
Manager: John Harkrider
Sls Mgr: Troy O'Steen
Sls Mgr: Tigran Zakharyan

D-U-N-S 80-875-2278
LA USD
333 S Beaudry Ave, Los Angeles, CA 90017-1466
Tel (310) 306-3249 Founded/Ownrshp 2007
Sales 28.2MM^E EMP 191^E
SIC 8211 Elementary & secondary schools
Prin: Monica Garcia
Ofcr: Sara Perochena
VP: Adrian Barcenas
Dir Teleco: Cathy Judge
Dir Risk M: Gregg Breed
Info Man: Beverly Wakefield
Plnt Mgr: Omar Bracy
Plnt Mgr: Gary Pun
Psych: Zamecia McCorvey
Snr PM: Mike Bagheri
Snr Mgr: Aixle Aman

D-U-N-S 04-211-4341
LA VALENCIANA AVOCADOS CORP (TX)
2101 W Military Hwy K8, McAllen, TX 78503-5702
Tel (956) 994-0561 Founded/Ownrshp 2011
Sales 35.0MM EMP 6
SIC 5148 0179 Fruits; Avocado orchard; Fruits; Avocado orchard
Pr: Sergio F Zurita-Valencia

D-U-N-S 01-049-2890
LA VEGA INDEPENDENT SCHOOL DISTRICT
400 E Loop 340, Waco, TX 76705-3420
Tel (254) 299-6700 Founded/Ownrshp 1960
Sales 24.0MM EMP 400
SIC 8211 Public elementary & secondary schools; Public elementary & secondary schools
Bd of Dir: Kevin P Harris
Prin: Bonnie McRae
Pr Dir: Lori Mynarcik
HC Dir: Patricia Lednicky

D-U-N-S 03-831-2328
LA VIDA LLENA
LA VIDA LLENA HEALTH CARE CTR
10501 Lagrima De Oro Rd N, Albuquerque, NM 87111-6926
Tel (505) 296-6700 Founded/Ownrshp 1979
Sales 24.3MM EMP 215
Accts Cliftonlarsonallen Llp St Lou
SIC 8361 8051 8052 Rest home, with health care incidental; Convalescent home with continuous nursing care; Personal care facility; Rest home, with health care incidental; Convalescent home with continuous nursing care; Personal care facility
Ch Bd: Chris Kerchner
CFO: Deanne Eaton
Nrsg Dir: Carolyn Rupert
HC Dir: Pauline Perry

LA VIDA LLENA HEALTH CARE CTR
See LA VIDA LLENA

D-U-N-S 03-666-7488
LA VIDA MULTISPECIALTY MEDICAL CENTERS INC
1400 S Grand Ave, Los Angeles, CA 90015-3048
Tel (213) 765-7500 Founded/Ownrshp 2000
Sales 23.0MM EMP 60
SIC 8011 Offices & clinics of medical doctors; Offices & clinics of medical doctors
Pr: Chuca Chidi
Off Mgr: Marcy Flowers

LA VOX THE HOUSTON NEWSPAPER
See LA VOZ PUBLISHING CORP

D-U-N-S 10-701-5406
LA VOZ PUBLISHING CORP
LA VOX THE HOUSTON NEWSPAPER
4747 Southwest Fwy, Houston, TX 77027-6901
Tel (713) 664-4404 Founded/Ownrshp 1980
Sales 26.1MM^E EMP 1,000
SIC 2711 Newspapers: publishing only, not printed on site; Newspapers: publishing only, not printed on site
VP: Erquiaga Angel

D-U-N-S 00-508-5386 IMP/EXP
LA-CO INDUSTRIES INC (IL)
MARKAL COMPANY
1201 Pratt Blvd, Elk Grove Village, IL 60007-5746
Tel (847) 427-3220 Founded/Ownrshp 1935, 1975
Sales 34.6MM^E EMP 145^E
SIC 2891 2899 Sealants; Fluxes: brazing, soldering, galvanizing & welding; Sealants; Fluxes: brazing, soldering, galvanizing & welding
CEO: Daniel Kleiman
*Pr: George Bowman
Exec: Scott Prochaska
Rgnl Mgr: Jay Campbell
Genl Mgr: Valerie Smith
IT Man: Jordan Constabileo
IT Man: Skip Laubach
Sfty Mgr: Julie Gann
Mfg Mgr: Eric Person
Plnt Mgr: Ed Labedz
Natl Sales: Chris Dietel

LA-Z-BOY
See FURNITURE ENTERPRISES OF ALASKA INC

LA-Z-BOY
See LZB MANUFACTURING INC

D-U-N-S 07-988-1556
■ **LA-Z-BOY CASEGOODS INC**
KINCAID FURNITURE
(Suby of LA-Z-BOY INC) ★
240 Pleasant Hill Rd, Hudson, NC 28638-2244
Tel (828) 728-3261 Founded/Ownrshp 2014
Sales 56.8MM^E EMP 250
SIC 5021 2512 Furniture; Upholstered household furniture
Pr: Steven Kincaid

LA-Z-BOY CONTRACT FURNITURE
See KNU LLC

LA-Z-BOY FURNITURE GALLERIES
See EBCO INC

LA-Z-BOY FURNITURE GALLERIES
See FURNITURE GALLERIES OF ATLANTA LLC

LA-Z-BOY FURNITURE GALLORIES
See LEBCO INDUSTRIES LP

D-U-N-S 00-504-2841 IMP/EXP
▲ **LA-Z-BOY INC** (MI)
1 La Z Boy Dr, Monroe, MI 48162
Tel (734) 242-1444 Founded/Ownrshp 1927
Sales 1.4MMM EMP 8,270
Accts Pricewaterhousecoopers Llp De
Tkr Sym LZB Exch NYS
SIC 2512 2511 5712 Chairs: upholstered on wood frames; Couches, sofas & davenports: upholstered on wood frames; Recliners: upholstered on wood frames; Rockers: upholstered on wood frames; Wood household furniture; Furniture stores; Chairs: upholstered on wood frames; Couches, sofas & davenports: upholstered on wood frames; Recliners: upholstered on wood frames; Rockers: upholstered on wood frames; Wood household furniture; Furniture stores
Ch Bd: Kurt L Darrow
CFO: Louis M Riccio Jr
Ofcr: J Douglas Collier
Sr VP: Mark S Bacon Sr
Sr VP: Darrell D Edwards
Sr VP: Darrell Edwards
Sr VP: Greg White
VP: Chris Jackson
VP: Michael Martinelli
VP: Margaret Mueller
Exec: Daniel Deland
Creative D: Matt Hartman
Board of Directors: Richard M Gabrys, David K Hehl, Edwin J Holman, Janet E Kerr, Michael T Lawton, H George Levy, W Alan McCollough

D-U-N-S 00-609-7414 IMP/EXP
LAACKE & JOYS CO LLC (WI)
HALL SADDLERY
19233 W Bluemound Rd, Brookfield, WI 53045-5939
Tel (414) 271-7885 Founded/Ownrshp 1884, 1996
Sales 20.5MM^E EMP 110
SIC 5941 5699 2394 5712 Sporting goods & bicycle shops; Sports apparel; Canvas & related products; Outdoor & garden furniture
*Sr VP: Dean Pecard
Dept Mgr: Sedate Kohler
Genl Mgr: Rachelle Bears
VP Mfg: Rachel Bares
Mktg Mgr: Ryan Hillgartner

D-U-N-S 00-690-7927
LAACO LTD
STORAGE WEST
431 W 7th St, Los Angeles, CA 90014-1601
Tel (213) 622-1254 Founded/Ownrshp 1986
Sales 20.9MM^E EMP 350
SIC 6519 7997 7011 5812 Real property lessors; Yacht club, membership; Hotels; Resort hotel; Eating places; Real property lessors; Yacht club, membership; Hotels; Resort hotel; Eating places
Pr: Karen L Hathaway
Mng Pt: Karen Lewis
*CFO: Bryan J Cusworth
*VP: John K Hathaway
VP: Charles Michaels
VP: John Wolff
VP: Fred Zepeda
Info Man: Diane Williams
Counsel: Christopher Piano

LAAD AMERICAS NV
See LATIN AMERICAN AGRIBUSINESS DEVELOPMENT CORP SA

LAAPOA
See LOS ANGELES AIRPORT PEACE OFFICERS ASSOCIATION

D-U-N-S 60-270-4616 IMP
LAARS HEATING SYSTEMS CO INC
(Suby of BRADFORD-WHITE CORP) ★
20 Industrial Way, Rochester, NH 03867-4296
Tel (603) 335-6300 Founded/Ownrshp 2005
Sales 52.8MM^E EMP 165
SIC 3567 Heating units & devices, industrial: electric; Heating units & devices, industrial: electric
CEO: Bob Carnevale
Pr: Bill Root
*VP: William R Root
*VP: Angelo Sinisi
*Prin: Steven Bailey
Rgnl Mgr: Van Culberson
IT Man: Paul Upson
Plnt Mgr: Mark Farrell
Ql Cn Mgr: David Macdowell

D-U-N-S 80-613-5435
LAB DEVELOPMENT LLC
CONNEXION
1700 Leider Ln, Buffalo Grove, IL 60089-6622
Tel (847) 499-8300 Founded/Ownrshp 2006
Sales 70.4MM^E EMP 39^E
SIC 5063 Electrical apparatus & equipment
CFO: Michael Nuccil

D-U-N-S 62-788-7990
LAB HOLDINGS INC
7901 Xerxes Ave S Ste 201, Minneapolis, MN 55431-1219
Tel (612) 607-1700 Founded/Ownrshp 1999
Sales 269.1MM^E EMP 1,400^E
SIC 8734 8731 Hazardous waste testing; Soil analysis; Water testing laboratory; Commercial physical research; Hazardous waste testing; Soil analysis; Water testing laboratory; Commercial physical research
CEO: Rodney Burwell

LAB ITALEE
See ITALEE OPTICS INC

LAB NET
See DENTRIX DENTAL SYSTEMS INC

LAB SAFETY SUPPLY
See GHC SPECIALTY BRANDS LLC

D-U-N-S 10-093-7150
LAB SCHOOL OF WASHINGTON
4759 Reservoir Rd Nw, Washington, DC 20007-1921
Tel (202) 965-6600 Founded/Ownrshp 1967
Sales 21.9MM EMP 340
Accts Anderson Davis & Associates Cp
SIC 8211 Private special education school; Public adult education school; Private special education school; Public adult education school
Ch: Mimi W Dawson
*Ch Bd: Susan Hager
*Treas: Bill Tennis
*VP: John Clifford
Assoc Dir: Tanya Rorie-Bryan
Assoc Dir: Nancy Rowland
Comm Dir: Victoria McDonough
HC Dir: Susan Feeley
HC Dir: Bob Lane

D-U-N-S 05-991-0075
LABADIE AUTO CO
711 S Euclid Ave, Bay City, MI 48706-3303
Tel (989) 460-0316 Founded/Ownrshp 1997
Sales 44.8MM^E EMP 150
SIC 5511 Automobiles, new & used; Automobiles, new & used
Pr: Gary Labadie
*VP: Mark Labadie
Dir IT: Thomas Suchyta
Snr Mgr: Todd Herremans

LABADIE CADILLAC
See LABADIE OLDSMOBILE CADILLAC GMC TRUCK INC

D-U-N-S 05-566-2936
LABADIE OLDSMOBILE CADILLAC GMC TRUCK INC
LABADIE CADILLAC
711 S Euclid Ave, Bay City, MI 48706-3303
Tel (989) 667-2000 Founded/Ownrshp 1959
Sales 41.9MM^E EMP 140
SIC 5511 7532 5521 Automobiles, new & used; Pickups, new & used; Top & body repair & paint shops; Used car dealers; Automobiles, new & used; Pickups, new & used; Top & body repair & paint shops; Used car dealers
Pr: Gary Labadie
*VP: Marl Labadie

LABANSWER
See DIGITAL CONSULTING & SOFTWARE SERVICES INC

D-U-N-S 12-260-9878 IMP/EXP
■ **LABARGE PIPE AND STEEL CO**
M R C
(Suby of MCJUNKIN RED MAN CORP) ★
3672 State Route 111, Granite City, IL 62040-6612
Tel (314) 231-3400 Founded/Ownrshp 2008
Sales 73.3MM^E EMP 150
SIC 5051 3498 3317 Structural shapes, iron or steel; Tube fabricating (contract bending & shaping); Steel pipe & tubes; Structural shapes, iron or steel; Tube fabricating (contract bending & shaping); Steel pipe & tubes
Pr: Pierre L Labarge III
*CFO: Michael J Brand
VP: Jack McCarthy
IT Man: Tony Kampwerth
Sls Mgr: David Kersting

D-U-N-S 07-773-7153
LABATON SUCHAROW LLP
140 Broadway Ste 2300, New York, NY 10005-1134
Tel (212) 907-0700 Founded/Ownrshp 1994
Sales 30.1MM^E EMP 135^E
SIC 8111 General practice law office; General practice law office
*Sr Pt: Edward Labaton
*Pt: Martis A Alix
*Pt: Mark Arisohn
*Pt: Stacy Auer
*Pt: Eric J Belfi
*Pt: Joel Bernstein
*Pt: Ryan Caplan
*Pt: Edmond Coller
*Pt: Peter Corrigan
*Pt: Jeffrey Galant
*Pt: Louis Gottlieb
*Pt: Lynda Grant
*Pt: Barbara Hart
*Pt: Ira Hecht
*Pt: James Johnson
*Pt: Diane Kilka
*Pt: Emily Komlossy
*Pt: Richard M Mc Gonical
*Pt: Kenneth McCallion
*Pt: Joel Negrin
*Pt: Bernard Persky

LABATT FOOD SERVICE
See LABATT INSTITUTIONAL SUPPLY CO INC

D-U-N-S 83-094-3812
LABATT FOOD SERVICE LLC
(Suby of LABATT FOOD SERVICE) ★
4500 Industry Park Dr, San Antonio, TX 78218-5427
Tel (210) 661-4216 Founded/Ownrshp 2007
Sales 99.9MM^E EMP 235^E
SIC 8742 Restaurant & food services consultants; Restaurant & food services consultants
Pr: Blair Labatt
COO: Al Silva
VP: Jason Beinart
VP: Tony Canti
VP: Rodney Carrillo
VP: Chas Demott
*VP: Alfredo Silvia
Brnch Mgr: Pat Wilson
Dist Mgr: Tony McCormick
Genl Mgr: Frank Anglin
Genl Mgr: Dean Atkinson

D-U-N-S 04-627-5301
LABATT INSTITUTIONAL SUPPLY CO INC (TX)
LABATT FOOD SERVICE
4500 Industry Park Dr, San Antonio, TX 78218-5427
Tel (210) 661-4216 Founded/Ownrshp 1968
Sales 407.6MM^E EMP 1,200
SIC 5141

D-U-N-S 05-730-7696 IMP
LABBEEMINT INC
11793 Fort Rd, White Swan, WA 98952-9632
Tel (509) 848-2022 Founded/Ownrshp 1971
Sales 60.0MM^E EMP 35
SIC 2899

D-U-N-S 02-935-8231 IMP
LABCON NORTH AMERICA
(Suby of HELENA LABORATORIES CORP) ★
3700 Lakeville Hwy # 200, Petaluma, CA 94954-7611
Tel (707) 766-2100 Founded/Ownrshp 1981
Sales 74.7MM^E EMP 200
SIC 3089 Injection molding of plastics; Injection molding of plastics
Pr: James A Happ
*CFO: Connie Hansen
Prd Mgr: Steve Bumstead
Sales Exec: Tom Kennedy
Natl Sales: Russ McNamee
Mktg Dir: Tom Moulton

D-U-N-S 00-711-8235 IMP/EXP
LABCONCO CORP (MO)
8811 Prospect Ave, Kansas City, MO 64132-2696
Tel (816) 333-8811 Founded/Ownrshp 1929
Sales 30.9MM^E EMP 250
SIC 3821

LABCORP OF AMERICA
See LABORATORY CORP OF AMERICA

LABCORPDYNACARE NORTHWEST
See DYNACARE NORTHWEST INC

D-U-N-S 02-123-9814
LABCYTE INC
1190 Borregas Ave, Sunnyvale, CA 94089-1302
Tel (408) 747-2000 Founded/Ownrshp 2000
Sales 20.3MM^E EMP 74^E
SIC 3821 Laboratory equipment: fume hoods, distillation racks, etc.
CEO: Mark F Colbrie
*Ex VP: Stephen Bates
VP: A Bramwell
VP: Mark A Bramwell
VP: Mathew Bramwell
VP: Brent Browning
Exec: Jovica Pavlovic
Mng Dir: Nick Samaras
*CTO: Richard Ellson
IT Man: Lisa Hazen
IT Man: Barry Lou

LABEL ART
See W S PACKAGING

LABEL GROUP
See MEYERS PRINTING COMPANIES INC

LABEL SHOPPER
See HUCK FINN CLOTHES INC

D-U-N-S 08-962-2211
LABEL SYSTEMS INC
56 Cherry St, Bridgeport, CT 06605-2370
Tel (203) 333-5503 Founded/Ownrshp 1996
Sales 26.7MM^E EMP 155
SIC 2672 2671 Coated paper, except photographic, carbon or abrasive; Labels (unprinted), gummed: made from purchased materials; Packaging paper & plastics film, coated & laminated; Coated paper, except photographic, carbon or abrasive; Labels (unprinted), gummed: made from purchased materials; Packaging paper & plastics film, coated & laminated
Pr: Michael Zubretsky
*Treas: Kenneth Felis

D-U-N-S 10-340-5999 IMP
LABEL TECHNOLOGY INC
2050 Wardrobe Ave, Merced, CA 95341-6409
Tel (209) 384-1000 Founded/Ownrshp 1986
Sales 26.7MM^E EMP 105
SIC 2759 Commercial printing
Ch Bd: John Bankson
Pr: David Bankson
CFO: Vinton Thengvall
VP: Brent Davies
VP: Dennis Deisenroth
Dir IT: John Lawrence
Dir IT: Jason Roberts
Sfty Mgr: Stan Roberts
VP Sls: Phill Henderson
Manager: Marygrace Quigley

D-U-N-S 03-425-7307
LABELLA ASSOCIATES DPC
(Suby of LABELLA ENGINEERING SL.)
300 State St Ste 201, Rochester, NY 14614-1098
Tel (585) 454-6110 Founded/Ownrshp 1978
Sales 31.0MM^E EMP 270
SIC 8711 8712 Engineering services; Architectural services; Engineering services; Architectural services
Ch Bd: Serio Esteban
*CFO: Robert Pepe
*VP: Robert Healy
*Prin: Jim Mc Intosh

D-U-N-S 09-167-0117
LABELLA ASSOCIATES PC
300 State St Ste 201, Rochester, NY 14614-1098
Tel (585) 454-6110 Founded/Ownrshp 1978
Sales 31.1MM EMP 170
Accts Mengel Metzger Barr & Co Cpa
SIC 8711 8712 Civil engineering; Structural engineering; Mechanical engineering; Architectural engineering; Civil engineering; Structural engineering; Mechanical engineering; Architectural engineering
Pr: Sergio Esteban
*Ch Bd: Salvatore Labella
*Pr: Robert Healy
*VP: James R McIntosh

D-U-N-S 09-806-1500
LABELLE DODGE CHRYSLER JEEP INC
LA BELLE DODGE
501 S Main St Hwy 29, Sarasota, FL 34240
Tel (863) 675-2701 Founded/Ownrshp 1996
Sales 27.5MM^E EMP 80
SIC 5511 Automobiles, new & used; Pickups, new & used; Vans, new & used; Automobiles, new & used; Pickups, new & used; Vans, new & used
Pr: Doug Plattner
*VP: Vernon Plattner
Genl Mgr: Jim Shelly

D-U-N-S 06-560-5636
LABELLE ELECTRIC SERVICES INC
24546 21 Mile Rd, Macomb, MI 48042-5111
Tel (586) 598-7360 Founded/Ownrshp 1969
Sales 24.5MM EMP 110
Accts Doeren Mayhew Troy Michigan
SIC 1731 General electrical contractor; General electrical contractor
Pr: Christopher Belle
VP: Dennis Jarzombek

LABELMASTER DIVISION
See AMERICAN LABELMARK CO INC

LABELS UNLIMITED
See DISCOUNT LABELS LLC

D-U-N-S 86-754-6269 IMP
LABELTEX MILLS INC
6100 Wilmington Ave, Los Angeles, CA 90001-1826
Tel (323) 582-0228 Founded/Ownrshp 1994
Sales 31.4MM^E EMP 215
SIC 2241 3965 2253 Narrow fabric mills; Labels, woven; Fasteners, buttons, needles & pins; Collar & cuff sets, knit; Narrow fabric mills; Labels, woven; Fasteners, buttons, needles & pins; Collar & cuff sets, knit
CEO: Torag Pourshamtobi
*Pr: Shahrokh Shamtobi
Ofcr: Kami Valafar
*VP: Ben Younessi

D-U-N-S 08-311-9693
LABETTE COMMUNITY COLLEGE
200 S 14th St, Parsons, KS 67357-4299
Tel (620) 421-6700 Founded/Ownrshp 1923
Sales 956.0M EMP 302^E
SIC 8222 Community college; Community college
Pr: Ronald Fundis
VP: Tammy Fuentez
Dir IT: Tony Robiy
IT Man: Jodie Burzinski

Pr Dir: Lindi Forbes
HC Dir: Angela Holmes

D-U-N-S 96-409-8136
LABETTE COUNTY MEDICAL CENTER
1902 S Us Highway 59 D, Parsons, KS 67357-4948
Tel (620) 421-4880 *Founded/Ownrshp* 2010
Sales 54.5MM *EMP* 39E
Accts Wendling Noe Nelson & Johnson
SIC 8011 Offices & clinics of medical doctors
CEO: William Mahoney
**CFO:* Thomas Macaronas
Dir Rx: Ashley Harlow
IT Man: Tom Macaronas

D-U-N-S 07-629-0675
LABETTE HEALTH FOUNDATION INC (KS)
1902 S Us Highway 59, Parsons, KS 67357-4948
Tel (620) 421-4881 *Founded/Ownrshp* 1961
Sales 163.5M *EMP* 500
Accts Jennifer L Okinger Cpa Llcm
SIC 8062 General medical & surgical hospitals; General medical & surgical hospitals
Pr: Vincent Schibi
Chf OB: Javine McLaughlan
**CEO:* William Mahoney
**CFO:* Tom Macaronas
**Treas:* Melissa Morris
Ofcr: Audra Cochran
Ofcr: Jodi Schmidt
**VP:* Wl Dillon
**VP:* Perry Sorrell
Dir Rad: Robert Gibbs
Prgrm Mgr: Linda Johnson

D-U-N-S 05-531-9482
LABINAL LLC
LABINAL POWER SYSYEMS
(*Suby of* SAFRAN USA INC) ★
3790 Russell Newman Blvd # 100, Denton, TX 76208-2936
Tel (940) 272-5700 *Founded/Ownrshp* 1993
Sales 352.1MME *EMP* 900
SIC 3728 Aircraft parts & equipment; Aircraft parts & equipment
Pr: Jorge Ortega
**Treas:* David Anderson
IT Man: Carl Johnson
Mfg Mgr: Marivel Romo
Snr Mgr: Priscillia Roberson

LABINAL POWER SYSYEMS
See LABINAL LLC

D-U-N-S 86-930-5961 IMP
LABINAL SALISBURY LLC
(*Suby of* SAFRAN USA INC) ★
600 Glen Ave, Salisbury, MD 21804-5250
Tel (410) 548-7800 *Founded/Ownrshp* 2010
Sales 140.1MME *EMP* 800E
SIC 3728 Aircraft parts & equipment; Aircraft parts & equipment
VP: Marc Renick
**Pr:* Greg Moffitt
Prgrm Mgr: Bob Lenaghan
IT Man: James Smith
S&M/VP: Steve Burke

D-U-N-S 17-779-4450
LABINAL-CORINTH INC
(*Suby of* SAFRAN USA INC) ★
7701 S Stemmons Ste 220, Corinth, TX 76210
Tel (940) 270-5700 *Founded/Ownrshp* 2006
Sales 75.2MME *EMP* 894E
SIC 3679 Electronic circuits; Electronic circuits
Pr: Jorge Ortega
**Treas:* David Anderson

D-U-N-S 02-433-6778
LABOLT FARMERS GRAIN CO (SD)
102 Georgia Ave, Labolt, SD 57246
Tel (605) 623-4581 *Founded/Ownrshp* 1906
Sales 20.4MME *EMP* 20
SIC 5153 5191 Grain elevators; Farm supplies; Feed; Seeds: field, garden & flower; Fertilizer & fertilizer materials; Grain elevators; Farm supplies; Feed; Seeds: field, garden & flower; Fertilizer & fertilizer materials
Pr: Bruce Granquist

D-U-N-S 18-922-2334 IMP
■ **LABONE INC**
QUEST DIAGNOSTICS
(*Suby of* QUEST DIAGNOSTICS INC) ★
10101 Renner Blvd, Lenexa, KS 66219-9752
Tel (913) 888-1770 *Founded/Ownrshp* 2005
Sales 69.6MME *EMP* 1,500
SIC 8071 6411 Testing laboratories; Blood analysis laboratory; Urinalysis laboratory; Insurance information & consulting services; Testing laboratories; Blood analysis laboratory; Urinalysis laboratory; Insurance information & consulting services
VP: Joseph Benage
Pr: Barry Bauer
Pr: Staci Birk
Pr: Bob Morris
Pr: Kaye Smith
Ofcr: Aaron Atkinson
**Ex VP:* Troy Hartman
Ex VP: Patrick James
Sr VP: Darren Dombrosky
Sr VP: Kathleen Willms
VP: Roger Betts
VP: Monica Learned
Dir Bus: Phil Williamson

LABONNE'S EPICURE MARKET
See HY LABONNE AND SONS INC

LABOR COMMISSIONER
See OREGON BUREAU OF LABOR AND INDUSTRIES

LABOR, COMMISSIONER OF
See GEORGIA DEPARTMENT OF LABOR

LABOR FINDERS
See DMD INC

D-U-N-S 96-489-7917
LABOR HEALTH & WELTR FNDNE CA
220 Campus Ln, Fairfield, CA 94534-1497
Tel (707) 864-2800 *Founded/Ownrshp* 2010
Sales 157.2MM *EMP* 2
Accts Hemming Morse Cpa S And Consul
SIC 8099 Health & allied services

D-U-N-S 78-129-1182
LABOR MANAGEMENT CONCEPTS INC
200 Belleville Tpke, North Arlington, NJ 07031-6235
Tel (212) 941-6862 *Founded/Ownrshp* 1989
Sales 10.0MME *EMP* 500
SIC 7381 Security guard service; Detective agency; Security guard service; Detective agency
Pr: John Munro
VP: Gary Munro

D-U-N-S 80-367-7769
LABOR MANAGEMENT HEALTHCARE FU
3786 Broadway St, Buffalo, NY 14227-1123
Tel (716) 601-7980 *Founded/Ownrshp* 2007
Sales 199.1MM *EMP* 7E
Accts Toski & Co Cpas Pc Buffalo N
SIC 8011 Clinic, operated by physicians; Clinic, operated by physicians
Prin: Vicki Martino

D-U-N-S 14-635-4480
LABOR ON DEMAND INC
851 Culebra Rd, San Antonio, TX 78201-6211
Tel (210) 736-1400 *Founded/Ownrshp* 2003
Sales 22.9MME *EMP* 300
SIC 7361 Employment agencies; Employment agencies
Pr: Lucinda Martinez
**VP:* Richard M Leal
Mktg Dir: Richard Tovar

D-U-N-S 12-357-2377
■ **LABOR READY INC**
(*Suby of* TRUEBLUE INC) ★
1015 A St Unit A, Tacoma, WA 98402-5122
Tel (253) 680-8487 *Founded/Ownrshp* 2011
Sales 50.4MME *EMP* 939E
SIC 7363 Manpower pools
Pr: Wayne Larkin
**CEO:* Steve Cooper
**Treas:* Derrek Gafford
**Treas:* Bruce Marley
**VP:* James Defebaugh
VP: Billie R Otto
Brnch Mgr: Kevin Welsh
Dist Mgr: Glenn Capps
VP Opers: Chris D Burger
Genl Couns: James E Defebaugh

D-U-N-S 12-354-8716
■ **LABOR READY MID-ATLANTIC INC**
(*Suby of* TRUEBLUE INC) ★
1015 A St Unit A, Tacoma, WA 98402-5122
Tel (253) 383-9101 *Founded/Ownrshp* 1989
Sales 11.9MME *EMP* 300
SIC 7363 Temporary help service; Temporary help service
Pr: Joe Sameataro
CFO: Joseph P Sambataro
VP: Ralph E Peterson

D-U-N-S 12-355-1108
■ **LABOR READY MIDWEST INC**
(*Suby of* TRUEBLUE INC) ★
1015 A St Unit A, Tacoma, WA 98402-5122
Tel (253) 383-9101 *Founded/Ownrshp* 1998
Sales 38.5MME *EMP* 2,600
SIC 7363 Temporary help service; Temporary help service
Pr: Joe Sambataro

D-U-N-S 12-357-3011
■ **LABOR READY NORTHWEST INC**
(*Suby of* TRUEBLUE INC) ★
P.O. Box 2910 (98401-2910)
Tel (253) 383-9101 *Founded/Ownrshp* 1998
Sales 78.9MME *EMP* 5,310
SIC 7363 Temporary help service; Temporary help service
Pr: Richard King

D-U-N-S 12-353-6794
■ **LABOR READY SOUTHEAST III LP**
(*Suby of* TRUEBLUE INC) ★
1015 A St Unit A, Tacoma, WA 98402-5122
Tel (253) 383-9101 *Founded/Ownrshp* 1998
Sales 75.2MME *EMP* 2,000
SIC 7363 Temporary help service; Temporary help service
Prin: Robert Breen
Brnch Mgr: Robin Camirand
Brnch Mgr: Contessa Davis
Brnch Mgr: Carol Fulbright
Brnch Mgr: Kris Gallant
Brnch Mgr: Latonya Glover
Brnch Mgr: Christina Martinez
Brnch Mgr: Alex Munoz
Brnch Mgr: Ivonne Suarez
Brnch Mgr: Stephen Torrez
Dist Mgr: Dave Gallipeau

D-U-N-S 12-355-8145
■ **LABOR READY SOUTHEAST INC**
(*Suby of* TRUEBLUE INC) ★
1016 S 28th St, Tacoma, WA 98409-8020
Tel (253) 383-9101 *Founded/Ownrshp* 2000
Sales 107.3MME *EMP* 1,830
SIC 7363 Temporary help service; Temporary help service
CEO: Joe Sambataro

D-U-N-S 09-529-6158
LABOR SERVICES CO
(*Suby of* ALLSTATE DLVRY SVC LABOR SVCS) ★
55 W 78th St, Minneapolis, MN 55420-1110
Tel (952) 884-0765 *Founded/Ownrshp* 1970
Sales 11.0MM *EMP* 350
SIC 7361 Employment agencies; Employment agencies
Pr: Dale B Robison
**Treas:* Kristina Robison

D-U-N-S 01-118-4890
▲ **LABOR SMART INC**
3270 Florence Rd Ste 200, Powder Springs, GA 30127-3831
Tel (770) 222-5888 *Founded/Ownrshp* 2011
Sales 23.9MM *EMP* 300
Accts Singerlewak Llp Los Angeles
Tkr Sym LTNC *Exch* OTC
SIC 7363 Help supply services; Temporary help service; Help supply services; Temporary help service
Ch Bd: Ryan Schadel
COO: Kimberly Thompson
Board of Directors: James Robert Edmonds

D-U-N-S 07-800-1810
LABOR STAFFING INC
126 New St Ste A, Decatur, GA 30030-5364
Tel (404) 209-1112 *Founded/Ownrshp* 1999
Sales 21.9MM *EMP* 800
SIC 7363 Help supply services; Help supply services
Pr: Jonathan Walchle
**VP:* James Walchle
Brnch Mgr: Manuel Centeno
Brnch Mgr: Ed Romano

D-U-N-S 00-819-5690
LABORATORY ALLIANCE OF CENTRAL NEW YORK LLC
1304 Buckley Rd Ste 300, Syracuse, NY 13212-4318
Tel (315) 461-3008 *Founded/Ownrshp* 1997
Sales 17.2MME *EMP* 300
SIC 8071 Medical laboratories; Medical laboratories
VP: Karen Carter
VP Opers: Marilyn Leclair

D-U-N-S 01-282-2243 IMP
■ **LABORATORY CORP OF AMERICA**
LABCORP OF AMERICA
(*Suby of* LABORATORY CORP OF AMERICA HOLDINGS) ★
358 S Main St Ste 458, Burlington, NC 27215-5837
Tel (336) 229-1127 *Founded/Ownrshp* 1997
Sales 685.8MME *EMP* 10,953
SIC 8071

D-U-N-S 86-142-2434
▲ **LABORATORY CORP OF AMERICA HOLDINGS**
358 S Main St, Burlington, NC 27215-5837
Tel (336) 229-1127 *Founded/Ownrshp* 1971
Sales 6.0MMM *EMP* 36,000
Tkr Sym LH *Exch* NYS
SIC 8071 Testing laboratories; Pathological laboratory; Medical laboratories; Testing laboratories; Pathological laboratory
Ch Bd: David P King
Pr: William E Klitgaard
CEO: James T Boyle Jr
CEO: Deborah Keller
CFO: Glenn A Eisenberg
Chf Mktg O: Mark E Brecher
Ofcr: Lisa J Uthgenannt
Sr VP: Lance V Berberian
Sr VP: Edward T Dodson
Board of Directors: D Gary Gilliland, Robert E Mittelstaedt Jr, Peter M Neupert, Adam H Schechter, R Sanders Williams

D-U-N-S 08-648-5455
LABORATORY SCIENCES OF ARIZONA LLC
(*Suby of* BANNER HEALTH) ★
1255 W Washington St, Tempe, AZ 85281-1210
Tel (602) 685-5000 *Founded/Ownrshp* 1996
Sales 81.8MME *EMP* 1,760E
SIC 8071 8011 8331 Medical laboratories; Clinic, operated by physicians; Job training & vocational rehabilitation services; Job counseling; Medical laboratories; Clinic, operated by physicians; Job training & vocational rehabilitation services; Job counseling
CEO: David A Dexter
CFO: Jennifer Andrew
Ex Dir: Anne T Daley
CIO: Robert Dowd

D-U-N-S 06-156-2641 IMP/EXP
LABORATORY SUPPLY CO
LABSCO
(*Suby of* FRAZIER HEALTHCARE II LP) ★
1951 Bishop Ln Ste 300, Louisville, KY 40218-1950
Tel (502) 363-1891 *Founded/Ownrshp* 2011
Sales 179.1MME *EMP* 200
SIC 5047 Medical & hospital equipment; Medical laboratory equipment; Medical & hospital equipment; Medical laboratory equipment
CEO: Hendrik Struik
Pr: Dan Eckert
CFO: George Willett
Sec: Charles E Davis Jr
Ex VP: Joel Weihe
VP: Charles E Davis Sr
VP: Patrick Dunigan
VP: John Hardesky
VP Opers: Tim Wolf
Opers Mgr: James Ardoin
Opers Mgr: Jason Condon
Board of Directors: Rod Wolford

D-U-N-S 06-502-6734
LABORATORY TESTING INC
LT
2331 Topaz Dr, Hatfield, PA 19440-1936
Tel (215) 997-9080 *Founded/Ownrshp* 1995
Sales 23.4MME *EMP* 105
SIC 8734 3599 Metallurgical testing laboratory; Calibration & certification; Product testing laboratories; Machine shop, jobbing & repair
Pr: Mike McVaugh
COO: Phil Trach
**CFO:* Loretta Tubiello Harr
**Sec:* Joan Bentley
**VP:* Thomas Mc Vaugh
DP Exec: Mike Sagel
QA Dir: Heather Heathwood
Mktg Dir: Rick Heist
Mktg Mgr: Sharon Bentzley
Sales Asso: Eric Baum
Sales Asso: Joe Farrell

D-U-N-S 05-116-0042 IMP
LABORATORY TOPS INC
DURCON
(*Suby of* WILSONART LLC) ★
206 Allison, Taylor, TX 76574-3805
Tel (512) 595-8000 *Founded/Ownrshp* 2013
Sales 58.2MME *EMP* 340
SIC 3821

D-U-N-S 83-937-6894
LABORDE MARINE LLC
601 Poydras St Ste 1725, New Orleans, LA 70130-6033
Tel (504) 410-8000 *Founded/Ownrshp* 1995
Sales 24.4MME *EMP* 175
SIC 4499 Marine salvaging & surveying services; Marine salvaging & surveying services

D-U-N-S 11-742-1412 EXP
LABORDE PRODUCTS INC
DIESEL AMERICA
74257 Highway 25, Covington, LA 70435-5679
Tel (985) 892-0107 *Founded/Ownrshp* 1998
Sales 30.8MM *EMP* 28E
SIC 5084 5088 Compressors, except air conditioning; Marine propulsion machinery & equipment
Pr: John Laborde
**Pr:* Brian Laborde
**Ch:* John P Laborde
**VP:* Doug Oehrlein
Genl Mgr: Roger Markwardt
Opers Mgr: Casey Symonds
Manager: David Disalvo
Sls Mgr: Joe Manning
Sales Asso: Chris Wright

LABORERS CMBNED FNDS WSTN PNNS
See LABORERS COMBINED FUNDS OF WESTERN PENNSYLVANIA

D-U-N-S 08-756-1346
LABORERS COMBINED FUNDS OF WESTERN PENNSYLVANIA
LABORERS CMBNED FNDS WSTN PNNS
1425 Forbes Ave Ste 600, Pittsburgh, PA 15219-5140
Tel (412) 263-0900 *Founded/Ownrshp* 1978
Sales NA *EMP* 49
Accts Deloitte & Touche Llp Pittsbu
SIC 6371 Pension funds; Pension funds
Pr: Paul A Quarantillo
CFO: Paul A Qurntillo
**Sec:* John Busse
Dept Mgr: Reges Urban
Dir IT: Jason Hawes
IT Man: Robert Buzzanco

D-U-N-S 12-381-7694
LABORERS DISTRICT COUNCIL HEAVY AND HIGHWAY CONSTRUCTION HEALTH AND WELFARE FUND
665 N Broad St Fl 1, Philadelphia, PA 19123-2418
Tel (215) 765-4633 *Founded/Ownrshp* 1954
Sales 24.7MM *EMP* 7
SIC 8322 General counseling services; General counseling services

D-U-N-S 08-451-9503
LABORERS FUNDS ADMINISTRATIVE OFFICE OF NORTHERN CALIFORNIA INC
LABORERS TRUST FUNDS NTHRN CAL
220 Campus Ln, Fairfield, CA 94534-1498
Tel (707) 864-2800 *Founded/Ownrshp* 1963
Sales NA *EMP* 110
Accts Guidestar
SIC 6371 Union welfare, benefit & health funds
Dir IT: Bill Eisley

D-U-N-S 80-202-5192
LABORERS HEALTH & WELFARE TRUST FUND FOR SOUTHERN
4399 Santa Anita Ave # 200, El Monte, CA 91731-1648
Tel (626) 279-3000 *Founded/Ownrshp* 2007
Sales 155.7MM *EMP* 3
Accts Miller Kaplan Arase Llp North
SIC 8631 Labor unions & similar labor organizations; Labor unions & similar labor organizations

D-U-N-S 07-780-8913
LABORERS INTERNATIONAL UNION OF NORTH AMERICA (DC)
LIUNA
905 16th St Nw, Washington, DC 20006-1703
Tel (202) 737-8320 *Founded/Ownrshp* 1903
Sales 98.7MME *EMP* 659
SIC 8631 Labor union; Labor union
Pr: Terence M O'Sullivan
**Sec:* Armand E Sabitoni
Ofcr: Andrew Dale
Ofcr: Diane Respall
VP: Faye Bice
VP: Rocco Davis
Exec: Darryl Carver
Comm Man: Lisa Martin
CIO: Matthew Richard
Dir IT: Darrell Wilson
Genl Couns: Michael Barrett

D-U-N-S 96-941-9899
LABORERS NATIONAL HEALTH AND WELFARE FUND
10440 Little Patuxent Pkwy, Columbia, MD 21044-3561
Tel (410) 884-1417 *Founded/Ownrshp* 2011
Sales NA *EMP* 2
Accts Calibre Cpa Group Pllc Bethes
SIC 6371 Pension, health & welfare funds; Pension, health & welfare funds

D-U-N-S 07-442-1058
LABORERS PENSION & WELFARE FUNDS
HEALTH AND WELFARE DEPT OF THE
11465 W Cermak Rd, Westchester, IL 60154-5768
Tel (708) 562-0200 *Founded/Ownrshp* 1950
Sales NA *EMP* 82E

Accts Bansley And Kiener Llp Chicag
SIC 6371 Pension funds; Union welfare, benefit & health funds; Welfare pensions; Pension funds; Union welfare, benefit & health funds; Welfare pensions
MIS Dir: Sally Etz

LABORERS TRUST FUNDS NTHRN CAL
See LABORERS FUNDS ADMINISTRATIVE OFFICE OF NORTHERN CALIFORNIA INC

D-U-N-S 96-967-6712
LABORERS VACATION HOLIDAY TRUST FUND FOR NORTHERN CALIFORNIA
220 Campus Ln, Fairfield, CA 94534-1497
Tel (707) 864-2800 *Founded/Ownrshp* 2011
Sales 69.8MM *EMP* 3^E
Accts Hemming Morse Cpa S And Consul
SIC 8631 Labor unions & similar labor organizations; Labor unions & similar labor organizations
Prin: Leo Ferrer

D-U-N-S 96-454-4576
LABORERS-EMPLOYERS BENEFIT PLAN COLLECTION TRUST
905 16th St Nw, Washington, DC 20006-1703
Tel (202) 393-7344 *Founded/Ownrshp* 2010
Sales NA *EMP* 2^E
Accts Calibre Cpa Group Pllc Washin
SIC 6411 Pension & retirement plan consultants; Pension & retirement plan consultants
Prin: Tracey Barrick

LABORS LOCAL NO 472
See HEAVY & GENERAL CONSTRUCTION LABORERS UNION LOCAL NO 472

D-U-N-S 01-731-0553
LABORWORKS INDUSTRIAL STAFFING SPECIALISTS INC
7201 Pioneer Way Ste B101, Gig Harbor, WA 98335-1161
Tel (253) 853-3444 *Founded/Ownrshp* 1998
Sales 30.0MM^E *EMP* 600
SIC 7361 7363 Employment agencies; Help supply services; Employment agencies; Help supply services
Pr: J Scott Sabo
**CFO:* Al Bacon
Brnch Mgr: Scott Isaacson
Brnch Mgr: Anthony Warner
Dir IT: Jeff Shearer

LABOUR DEPARTMENT
See HARBOR HOSPITAL CENTER INC

D-U-N-S 09-105-7885 IMP/EXP
LABRADA DISTRIBUTORS INC
Calle 272 Bloq 1c 6 Count St Cal, Carolina, PR 00982
Tel (787) 757-2721 *Founded/Ownrshp* 1972
Sales 33.9MM^E *EMP* 73
Accts Diaz Bergnes Cid San Juan Pu
SIC 5149 Pizza supplies
Pr: Jorge Labrada
**Treas:* Guillermo Labrada Blanzaco

LABREE'S BAKERY
See LABREES INC

D-U-N-S 00-110-4058 IMP
LABREES INC (ME)
LABREE'S BAKERY
169 Gilman Falls Ave, Old Town, ME 04468-1325
Tel (207) 827-6121 *Founded/Ownrshp* 1948
Sales 65.5MM^E *EMP* 300
SIC 2053 Frozen bakery products, except bread; Doughnuts, frozen; Cakes, bakery: frozen; Pastries (danish): frozen; Frozen bakery products, except bread; Doughnuts, frozen; Cakes, bakery: frozen; Pastries (danish): frozen
Pr: Bernie Labree
**CFO:* David L Dorr
**Treas:* Damian Labree
Plnt Mgr: Ken Mitchell
Prd Mgr: Jay Macdonald
Ql Cn Mgr: Peggy Severance
Manager: Anya Kucheryavenko

D-U-N-S 11-806-9699
LABREPCO LLC
101 Witmer Rd Ste 700, Horsham, PA 19044-2262
Tel (215) 442-9200 *Founded/Ownrshp* 1983
Sales 25.2MM *EMP* 42
Accts Stephano Slack & Katz Llc Ply
SIC 3821 Laboratory apparatus & furniture; Laboratory apparatus & furniture
COO: Vanessa Good
Treas: Pearl Wayne
Sr VP: James Weldon
**VP:* George Koutris
**VP:* Dan Morris
Exec: Richard Doughtery
Prgrm Mgr: Jim Owens
Genl Mgr: Regis Rauch
Off Mgr: Matthew Aldrich
Off Mgr: David Cabral
IT Man: Elizabeth Smecker

LABRIOLA
See RJL INC

D-U-N-S 80-817-8466
LABS INC
(*Suby of* ALLOSOURCE) ★
6933 S Revere Pkwy Unit B, Centennial, CO 80112-3762
Tel (303) 365-9000 *Founded/Ownrshp* 2007
Sales 27.0MM^E *EMP* 143
SIC 8734 Testing laboratories
Pr: Todd G Johnson
Pr: Elizabeth Hearty
COO: Robert Brook
VP: Sarah Dennison
VP: Chad Ronholdt
Dir Lab: Sara Dionne
IT Man: Patrick Meyer
Mktg Mgr: Jessica O'Neale
Sls Mgr: Amy Ferguson
Board of Directors: Kevin M Smith

LABSCO
See LABORATORY SUPPLY CO

D-U-N-S 09-551-9989 IMP
LABSPHERE INC
(*Suby of* HALMA PUBLIC LIMITED COMPANY)
231 Shaker St, North Sutton, NH 03260
Tel (603) 927-4266 *Founded/Ownrshp* 2007
Sales 28.9MM^E *EMP* 105
SIC 3826 Analytical instruments; Analytical instruments
Pr: John Kelly
**CFO:* Gail Devoid
**Treas:* Steve Sowell
VP: Blaine Flores
**VP:* Greg McKee
**VP:* David McManus
**VP:* Peter Weitzman
Sftwr Eng: David Herr
Mktg Dir: Kimberly Fasano

D-U-N-S 94-946-3483
LABTEST EQUIPMENT CO
72 Timber Dr, Valparaiso, IN 46385-9685
Tel (219) 462-3300 *Founded/Ownrshp* 1979
Sales 30.0MM *EMP* 83
SIC 3826 Analytical instruments; Analytical instruments
Owner: James Mattel

D-U-N-S 02-340-6069 IMP
LABUDDE GROUP INC
W63n583 Hanover Ave, Cedarburg, WI 53012-1969
Tel (262) 375-9111 *Founded/Ownrshp* 1985
Sales 48.0MM *EMP* 75
Accts Anderson Tackman & Company P
SIC 5191 Animal feeds; Animal feeds
CEO: Richard Erickson
**Sec:* Mary Sciascia
VP: Chris Wills
Off Mgr: Penny Taylor
Mktg Dir: Joel Deutmeyer

D-U-N-S 79-327-5504
LABVANTAGE SOLUTIONS INC
265 Davidson Ave Ste 220, Somerset, NJ 08873-4120
Tel (908) 707-4100 *Founded/Ownrshp* 1993
Sales 39.2MM^E *EMP* 160
SIC 7372 Prepackaged software; Prepackaged software
CEO: Peter Bailey
**Sr VP:* Jerry Hacker
VP: Fernando Casanova
VP: Stephen Saukaitis
VP Bus Dev: Kim Ahmed
Exec: John Fitzgerald
Off Mgr: Jennifer Gerald
IT Man: Barry Polhemus
Tech Mgr: William Musil

D-U-N-S 79-691-3192
LABWARE HOLDINGS INC
3 Mill Rd Ste 102, Wilmington, DE 19806-2154
Tel (302) 658-8444 *Founded/Ownrshp* 1988
Sales 97.0MM *EMP* 300
SIC 7371 7372 6719 Computer software development & applications; Business oriented computer software; Personal holding companies, except banks; Computer software development & applications; Business oriented computer software; Personal holding companies, except banks
Pr: Vance Kershner
**VP:* David Nixon

D-U-N-S 83-043-4580
LABWARE INC
(*Suby of* LABWARE HOLDINGS INC) ★
3 Mill Rd Ste 102, Wilmington, DE 19806-2154
Tel (302) 658-8444 *Founded/Ownrshp* 2007
Sales 27.7MM^E *EMP* 200
SIC 7371 Computer software development & applications; Computer software development & applications
Pr: Vance Kershner
CFO: Clem Padin
Treas: David Nixon
Mng Dir: Bob Hilhouse
Off Mgr: Alice Campbell
IT Man: John Newtown
IT Man: John Raiford
Web Dev: Simon Watts
Ql Cn Mgr: Doug Judge
Mktg Dir: Michael Kelly
Mktg Mgr: Jo Webber

D-U-N-S 06-361-6700
LAC COURTE OREILLES BAND OF LAKE SUPERIOR CHIPPEWA INDIANS OF WI
LAC CRTE ORLLES TRBAL GVRNMENT
13394 W Trepania Rd, Hayward, WI 54843-2186
Tel (715) 634-8934 *Founded/Ownrshp* 1843
Sales NA *EMP* 922
SIC 9131 Indian reservation; ; Indian reservation;
Ch Bd: Michael Isham Jr
**Ch Bd:* Louis Taylor
**Ch:* Russell Barber
**Sec:* Donald Carley
Ofcr: Rose Oshogay
Board of Directors: Connie Corbine

LAC CRTE ORLLES TRBAL GVRNMENT
See LAC COURTE OREILLES BAND OF LAKE SUPERIOR CHIPPEWA INDIANS OF WI

D-U-N-S 07-478-1584
LAC DU FLAMBEAU BAND OF LAKE SUPERIOR CHIPPEWA INDIANS (INC)
LAC DU FLAMBEAU TRIBAL COUNCIL
418 Little Pines Rd, Lac Du Flambeau, WI 54538-9124
Tel (715) 588-3303 *Founded/Ownrshp* 1936
Sales 538.4MM^E *EMP* 2,122
SIC 3825 8011 7999 5411 5541 8031 Instruments to measure electricity; Test equipment for electronic & electric measurement; Medical centers; Bingo hall; Grocery stores, independent; Filling stations, gasoline; Offices & clinics of osteopathic physicians; Instruments to measure electricity; Test equipment for electronic & electric measurement; Medical centers; Bingo hall; Grocery stores, independent; Filling stations, gasoline; Offices & clinics of osteopathic physicians
Pr: Thomas Maulson
**Treas:* Rose Mitchell
**Treas:* Mary Peterson
**VP:* Michael Ellen
IT Man: Patricia O'Neil
IT Man: Wanda Wayman

LAC DU FLAMBEAU TRIBAL COUNCIL
See LAC DU FLAMBEAU BAND OF LAKE SUPERIOR CHIPPEWA INDIANS (INC)

LAC GROUP
See LIBRARY ASSOCIATES INC

D-U-N-S 78-528-0744
LAC USC MEDICAL CENTER
LOS ANGELES COUNTY HOSPITAL
1200 N State St Rm 5250, Los Angeles, CA 90033-1083
Tel (323) 226-7858 *Founded/Ownrshp* 1992
Sales 73.2MM^E *EMP* 178^E
SIC 8062 6324 General medical & surgical hospitals; Hospital & medical service plans
COO: Henry Ornelas
CFO: Hung Jeff
Dir Inf Cn: Carol Salminen
**Prin:* Michael Siegel
Netwrk Mgr: Kinly KAO
Pr Dir: Adelaida Dela Cerda
Pathlgst: Gregory S Pinsky
Pathlgst: Sunita Saxena
Pathlgst: Gian A Ykoub
Surgeon: Jennifer A Smith
Doctor: Joseph Kim

D-U-N-S 17-186-8698
LAC VIEUX DESERT BAND OF LAKE SUPERIOR CHIPPEWA INDIANS
E23968 Pow Wow Trl, Watersmeet, MI 49969
Tel (906) 358-4577 *Founded/Ownrshp* 1999
Sales NA *EMP* 490^E
Accts Roe Meyer Sc Brule Wiscon
SIC 9131 Indian reservation; ; Indian reservation;
Ch: Alan Shively
COO: Henry Smith
**Treas:* Suzie McGeshick

D-U-N-S 01-473-6748 IMP
LACAS COFFEE CO LLC (PA)
7950 National Hwy F, Pennsauken, NJ 08110-1412
Tel (800) 220-1133 *Founded/Ownrshp* 1921, 1993
Sales 34.2MM^E *EMP* 58
SIC 5149 Coffee, green or roasted; Tea; Chocolate
Pr: Jonathan Del RE
CFO: Michael Vlahos
VP: Daniel M Berger
VP: John Vastardis
Manager: Gordon Scherer

D-U-N-S 03-440-9854
LACASSAGNES LLC
495 N 49th St, Baton Rouge, LA 70806-3453
Tel (225) 218-0237 *Founded/Ownrshp* 1935
Sales 23.5MM^E *EMP* 25
SIC 5142 5149 5143 Packaged frozen goods; Dried or canned foods; Dairy products, except dried or canned
VP: Herbert L Lacassagne Jr
**Pr:* Louis H Lacassagne
**Treas:* Cathy S Lacassagne

D-U-N-S 13-085-0076
LACAVA & SOWERSBY INC
1375-1377 Plymouth Ave, Fall River, MA 02721
Tel (508) 675-0512 *Founded/Ownrshp* 1985
Sales 26.0MM^E *EMP* 80
SIC 5013 5531 Automotive supplies & parts; Automotive parts
Pr: William E Sowersby
**Treas:* Paul A Lacava
**VP:* John Lacava

D-U-N-S 80-850-9335
LACEK GROUP INC
(*Suby of* OGILVY & MATHER WORLDWIDE INC) ★
900 2nd Ave S Ste 1800, Minneapolis, MN 55402-3342
Tel (612) 359-3700 *Founded/Ownrshp* 2000
Sales 63.2MM^E *EMP* 250
SIC 7311 Advertising consultant; Advertising consultant
Pr: Bill Baker
Sr Pt: Francesco Favazza
VP: Julie Bustos
VP: Brad Fiery
VP: Tim Manoles
VP: Jeffrey McLaughlin
VP: Laura Wadzinski
QA Dir: David Griebel
QA Dir: Brent Miltner
QA Dir: Jeremiah Steele
Dir IT: Evan Davies

LACERA
See LOS ANGELES COUNTY EMPLOYEES RETIREMENT ASSOCIATION

D-U-N-S 95-821-2029 IMP
LACEY MANUFACTURING CO LLC
(*Suby of* PEP) ★
1146 Barnum Ave, Bridgeport, CT 06610-2794
Tel (203) 336-7427 *Founded/Ownrshp* 2008
Sales 97.7MM^E *EMP* 310
SIC 3841 3089 Surgical instruments & apparatus; Injection molding of plastics; Surgical instruments & apparatus; Injection molding of plastics
Pr: Ken Lisk
Exec: Keysha Johnson
Prgrm Mgr: Larry Lucas
IT Man: Lisa Rotella
Sfty Dirs: Jim Rogers
Ql Cn Mgr: Gary Chaffee
Ql Cn Mgr: Bob Clancey
Sales Exec: Gerry Lapke
Mktg Mgr: Craig Mikita
Snr Mgr: Craig Stevens

D-U-N-S 08-563-9912
LACEY TOWNSHIP BOARD OF EDUCATION
200 Western Blvd, Lanoka Harbor, NJ 08734-1538
Tel (609) 971-2000 *Founded/Ownrshp* 1924
Sales 26.8MM^E *EMP* 608
SIC 8211 Public elementary & secondary schools; High school, junior or senior; School board; Public elementary & secondary schools; High school, junior or senior; School board

D-U-N-S 07-939-2490
LACEY TOWNSHIP SCHOOL DISTRICT
200 Western Blvd, Lanoka Harbor, NJ 08734-1538
Tel (609) 971-2000 *Founded/Ownrshp* 2014
Sales 15.8MM^E *EMP* 664^E
SIC 8211 Elementary & secondary schools
Prin: Vanessa Clark
Schl Brd P: Linda Downing
HC Dir: Michael Maschi

D-U-N-S 07-599-0416
LACKAWANNA CASUALTY CO INC
(*Suby of* PAGNOTTI ENTERPRISES INC) ★
46 Public Sq Ste 501, Wilkes Barre, PA 18701-2609
Tel (570) 824-1400 *Founded/Ownrshp* 1996
Sales NA *EMP* 45
SIC 6411 Insurance agents, brokers & service; Insurance agents, brokers & service
Pr: Michelene M Kennedy
**Treas:* Mark H Destefano
**VP:* David J Austin
**VP:* Mary Ann Eggleston
VP: C Parenti
Mktg Mgr: Dave Kalinowski

D-U-N-S 07-400-0522
LACKAWANNA CITY SCHOOL DISTRICT
245 S Shore Blvd, Buffalo, NY 14218-1711
Tel (716) 827-6708 *Founded/Ownrshp* 1909
Sales 15.6MM^E *EMP* 300
SIC 8211 Public elementary & secondary schools; Public elementary & secondary schools
Prin: Aldo Filipetti
CIO: Matteo Anello
Schl Brd P: Leonard Kowalski

D-U-N-S 07-599-1505
LACKAWANNA COLLEGE
LACKAWANNA COLLEGE BOOK STORE
501 Vine St, Scranton, PA 18509-3251
Tel (570) 961-7810 *Founded/Ownrshp* 1894
Sales 24.2MM *EMP* 115
Accts Mcgrail Merkel Quinn & Assoc
SIC 8221 Colleges & universities; Colleges & universities
Pr: Raymond S Angeli
CTO: Sharyn Brown
IT Man: Jack Truschel

LACKAWANNA COLLEGE BOOK STORE
See LACKAWANNA COLLEGE

D-U-N-S 07-915-9141
LACKAWANNA COUNTY GOVERNMENT (PA)
1302 Madison Ave, Scranton, PA 18509-2424
Tel (570) 963-6800 *Founded/Ownrshp* 1878
Sales NA *EMP* 1,400
SIC 9111 Executive offices; ; Executive offices;

D-U-N-S 09-933-1811 IMP
LACKAWANNA PRODUCTS CORP
8545 Main St Ste 1, Williamsville, NY 14221-7457
Tel (716) 633-1940 *Founded/Ownrshp* 1982
Sales 112.2MM^E *EMP* 70
SIC 5191 5153 Animal feeds; Grains; Animal feeds; Grains
Pr: David A Olshan
**Ch Bd:* Tunnen Murchie

D-U-N-S 06-594-0512
LACKMANN FOOD SERVICE INC
LACKMANN FOOD SVCE
303 Crossways Park Dr, Woodbury, NY 11797-2099
Tel (516) 364-2300 *Founded/Ownrshp* 1963
Sales 33.4MM^E *EMP* 1,200
SIC 5812 Contract food services; Contract food services
CEO: Matthew Lackmann
**Pr:* Peter Alessio
**CEO:* Andrew Lackmann
Genl Mgr: Marianee Walker

LACKMANN FOOD SVCE
See LACKMANN FOOD SERVICE INC

D-U-N-S 61-681-1659
LACKS ENTERPRISES INC
5460 Cascade Rd Se, Grand Rapids, MI 49546-6406
Tel (616) 949-6570 *Founded/Ownrshp* 1985
Sales 888.4MM^E *EMP* 2,800
SIC 3089 Molding primary plastic; Molding primary plastic
Pr: Richard Lacks Jr
**Treas:* Chester Anisko
**Ex VP:* Kurt Lacks
VP: Chet Anisko
VP: Dave McNulty
**Prin:* John Lacks
**Prin:* Chris Walker
Dir Sec: A J Ponstein
Genl Mgr: Bob Bieri
Genl Mgr: Jeff Lacross
CIO: Nancy Bussler

D-U-N-S 02-648-6253 IMP
LACKS EXTERIOR SYSTEMS LLC
LACKS TRIM SYSTEMS
(*Suby of* LACKS ENTERPRISES INC) ★
5460 Cascade Rd Se, Grand Rapids, MI 49546-6406
Tel (616) 949-6570 *Founded/Ownrshp* 1966

Sales 327.3MM^E *EMP* 1,700
SIC 3089 Plastic hardware & building products; Plastic hardware & building products
CFO: Chet Anisko
CFO: Mike Clover
**VP:* Kurt Lacks
Ql Cn Mgr: Kim Zoerman

D-U-N-S 00-601-4666 IMP
LACKS INDUSTRIES INC
(*Suby of* LACKS ENTERPRISES INC) ★
5460 Cascade Rd Se, Grand Rapids, MI 49546-6499
Tel (616) 949-6570 *Founded/Ownrshp* 1964
Sales 137.8MM^E *EMP* 1,900
SIC 3089

LACKS TRIM SYSTEMS
See LACKS EXTERIOR SYSTEMS LLC

D-U-N-S 02-682-0175 IMP/EXP
LACKS VALLEY STORES LTD
1300 San Patricia Dr, Pharr, TX 78577-2158
Tel (956) 702-3361 *Founded/Ownrshp* 1953
Sales 201.2MM^E *EMP* 800
SIC 5712 5722

D-U-N-S 11-098-4320 IMP
LACLEDE CHAIN MANUFACTURING CO LLC
1549 Fenpark Dr, Fenton, MO 63026-2915
Tel (636) 680-2320 *Founded/Ownrshp* 2001
Sales 39.9MM^E *EMP* 180
SIC 3315 Chain link fencing; Chain link fencing
**Bd of Dir:* Steve Heuett
Plnt Mgr: Alan Sheets
Manager: Jay Wilson

D-U-N-S 00-696-6576
LACLEDE ELECTRIC COOPERATIVE
1400 E Route 66, Lebanon, MO 65536-5332
Tel (417) 532-3164 *Founded/Ownrshp* 1938
Sales 66.5MM *EMP* 123
SIC 4911 Distribution, electric power; Distribution, electric power
CEO: Kenneth Miller
Bd of Dir: Darrel Bishop
VP: Joel Cravens
Off Admin: Julie Lucas
Dir IT: Darlene Ritchie
Opers Mgr: Michael Kirkland

D-U-N-S 00-696-7798
■ **LACLEDE GAS CO**
(*Suby of* LACLEDE GROUP INC) ★
700 Market St, Saint Louis, MO 63101-1829
Tel (314) 342-0500 *Founded/Ownrshp* 1857
Sales 1.4MMM *EMP* 2,311
Accts Deloitte & Touche Llp St Lou
SIC 4924 Natural gas distribution; Natural gas distribution
Ch Bd: Suzanne Sitherwood
**Pr:* Steven L Lindsey
**CFO:* Steven P Rasche
**Sr VP:* Mary C Kullman
Sr VP: R E Shively
VP: D P Abernathy
VP: Muawiya A Huneidi
VP: Peter J Palumbo Jr
VP: M C Pendergast
Exec: Benjamin McReynolds
Sls Mgr: Cliff Garrett

D-U-N-S 05-947-0943
▲ **LACLEDE GROUP INC**
700 Market St, Saint Louis, MO 63101-1829
Tel (314) 342-0878 *Founded/Ownrshp* 2001
Sales 1.9MMM *EMP* 6,024
Tkr Sym LG *Exch* NYS
SIC 4924 Natural gas distribution; Natural gas distribution
Pr: Suzanne Sitherwood
**Ch Bd:* Edward L Glotzbach
COO: Steven L Lindsey
CFO: Steven P Rasche
Chf Cred: Mark C Darrell
Sr VP: L Craig Dowdy
VP: Craig R Hoeferlin

LACOE
See LOS ANGELES COUNTY OFFICE OF EDUCATION

D-U-N-S 18-463-4095
LACONIA SCHOOL DISTRICT
39 Harvard St, Laconia, NH 03246-3056
Tel (603) 524-5710 *Founded/Ownrshp* 1972
Sales NA *EMP* 339
Accts Plodzik & Sanderson Pa
SIC 9411 Administration of educational programs; Administration of educational programs
**Prin:* Terry Foreten
IT Man: Louann Breen

D-U-N-S 84-164-4102
LACORR PACKAGING LLC
13890 Nelson Ave, City of Industry, CA 91746-2050
Tel (626) 369-6446 *Founded/Ownrshp* 1999
Sales 55.6MM^E *EMP* 150
SIC 2653 Corrugated boxes, partitions, display items, sheets & pad
**Pr:* John Perullo

D-U-N-S 18-612-1208
LACOSTA INC
PREMIER FACILITY SERVICES ILL
440 W Bonner Rd, Wauconda, IL 60084-1102
Tel (847) 526-9556 *Founded/Ownrshp* 1988
Sales 114.0MM^E *EMP* 2,800^E
SIC 7349 Building & office cleaning services; Building & office cleaning services
Pr: Karla Mota
VP: Mark Cones
VP: Bill McKenna
Rgnl Mgr: Ann Donnelley
Manager: Bonnie Barkan
Snr Mgr: Tom Herzberg

D-U-N-S 80-590-6641 IMP
LACOSTE USA INC
(*Suby of* LACOSTE OPERATIONS)
551 Madison Ave Ste 1300, New York, NY 10022-3264
Tel (212) 750-1900 *Founded/Ownrshp* 1992
Sales 39.4MM^E *EMP* 40
SIC 5137 5136 5611 5621 Women's & children's clothing; Men's & boys' clothing; Men's & boys' clothing stores; Women's clothing stores
CEO: Steve Birkhold
Pr: Mari Goldberg
**Pr:* Robert Ross
**CFO:* Gerard Pena
**Ch:* Robert Siegal
Ex VP: Berta Barbier
Sr VP: Livia Lee
VP: Emily Coppock
VP: Ben Rosenfeld
Mng Dir: Veronica Castellano
Mng Dir: Jena Jensen

D-U-N-S 08-541-0694
LACOUNTY MUSEUM NATLHSTRYFDTN
900 Exposition Blvd, Los Angeles, CA 90007-4057
Tel (213) 763-3466 *Founded/Ownrshp* 1965
Sales NA *EMP* 350
Accts Singerlewak Llp Los Angeles
SIC 9111 8399 8412 County supervisors' & executives' offices; Fund raising organization, non-fee basis; Museums & art galleries; County supervisors' & executives' offices; Fund raising organization, non-fee basis; Museums & art galleries
Pr: Jane Pisano
Exec: Gordon Hendler
Exec: Kim Townsend
IT Man: Jeri Gutierrez

D-U-N-S 00-507-2079
LACROIX OPTICAL CO INC (AR)
50 Lacroix Dr, Batesville, AR 72501
Tel (870) 698-1881 *Founded/Ownrshp* 1947
Sales 21.7MM^E *EMP* 105
SIC 3827 3231 3229 3211 Optical instruments & lenses; Products of purchased glass; Pressed & blown glass; Flat glass
Pr: Raymond Lacroix
**VP:* Diane Lacroix
Sls Mgr: Kirk Warden

D-U-N-S 11-622-7315 IMP
LACROSSE FOOTWEAR INC
(*Suby of* ABC-MART,INC.)
17634 Ne Airport Way, Portland, OR 97230-4999
Tel (503) 262-0110 *Founded/Ownrshp* 2012
Sales 102.8MM^E *EMP* 713^E
SIC 3021 Rubber & plastics footwear; Rubber & plastics footwear
CEO: Joseph P Schneider
Pr: Yasushi Akaogi
Pr: Robert Sasaki
CFO: David P Carlson
VP: Gary Carlson
VP: Joseph Fahey
VP: Wayne Lorek
VP: Nina Palludan
VP: Robert G Rinehart
VP: Dave Strouse
VP Admn: Greg S Inman
Board of Directors: Stephen F Loughlin, Charles W Smith, John D Whitcombe, William H Williams

D-U-N-S 13-168-7790 IMP/EXP
LACTALIS AMERICAN GROUP INC
SORRENTO LACTALIS
(*Suby of* PARMALAT SPA)
2376 S Park Ave, Buffalo, NY 14220-2670
Tel (716) 823-6262 *Founded/Ownrshp* 1980
Sales 376.9MM^E *EMP* 1,500
SIC 2022 Cheese, natural & processed; Cheese, natural & processed
CEO: Frederick Bouisset
CFO: John Zielinski
VP: Alban Damour
VP: Paul Peterson
Dir Lab: Vesna Korjenic
Dir IT: William Packard
Opers Mgr: Gary Marcinkowski
Plnt Mgr: Bill Senay
Natl Sales: Jeffrey Pugliese
Natl Sales: Ed Sullivan
VP Sls: Peter Deeb

D-U-N-S 02-906-8202 IMP/EXP
LACTALIS DELI INC
(*Suby of* GROUPE LACTALIS)
77 Water St Fl Mezz, New York, NY 10005-4421
Tel (212) 758-6666 *Founded/Ownrshp* 1980
Sales 180.2MM^E *EMP* 765
SIC 5143 2022 Cheese; Cheese, natural & processed; Cheese; Cheese, natural & processed
CEO: Frederick Bouisset
**Pr:* Philippe Surget
CFO: Michael Picirillo
VP: Alain Gerard
**Prin:* Erick Boutry
QA Dir: Loren Green
IT Man: Michael Vendura
VP Sls: Yann Connan
Sls Dir: Julien Lapraz
Mktg Mgr: Marjolaine Besnard
Sls Mgr: Kurt Wolfram

D-U-N-S 13-979-1631 IMP
LACTALIS USA INC
(*Suby of* LACTALIS AMERICAN GROUP INC) ★
218 S Park St, Belmont, WI 53510-9639
Tel (608) 762-5173 *Founded/Ownrshp* 1999
Sales 21.7MM^E *EMP* 150^E
SIC 2022 Cheese, natural & processed; Cheese, natural & processed
Pr: Philippe Surget
**VP:* Jean-Marc Desroches
VP: Robert J Woeppel
Exec: Yann Rohou
Plnt Mgr: Lenny Bass

LACY CONSTRUCTION
See L H LACY CO LTD

D-U-N-S 60-584-4505
LACY DISTRIBUTION INC
(*Suby of* LDI LTD., LLC)
54 Monument Cir Ste 800, Indianapolis, IN 46204-2949
Tel (317) 237-5400 *Founded/Ownrshp* 1989
Sales 386.8MM^E *EMP* 1,550
SIC 5015 Automotive parts & supplies, used; Automotive parts & supplies, used
Ch: Andre Lacy
MIS Dir: Kathy Randell
IT Man: Brian Reed
IT Man: Vangie Sison

D-U-N-S 09-928-8888
LADACIN NETWORK INC
1701 Kneeley Blvd, Ocean, NJ 07712-7622
Tel (732) 493-5900 *Founded/Ownrshp* 1960
Sales 23.1MM *EMP* 500
Accts Cohn Reznick Llp Eatontown
SIC 8331 Job training & vocational rehabilitation services; Job training & vocational rehabilitation services
Pr: James R Klagholz
**Treas:* Stephen F Bell
**VP:* Kelly Siegfried

D-U-N-S 07-326-7304
LADAS & PARRY LLP
1040 Ave Of The Amrcs 5, New York, NY 10018-3738
Tel (212) 246-8959 *Founded/Ownrshp* 1912
Sales 25.4MM^E *EMP* 220
SIC 8111 Legal services; Legal services
Pt: Lanning Bryer
Pt: Geraldine Marti
CFO: Chuck Bernstein
Genl Mgr: Lou Pezzullo
Off Mgr: Cindy Revere
CIO: Garhard Paulman

D-U-N-S 80-887-0281
LADBROKE RACING MANAGEMENT PENNSYLVANIA
475 Johnson Rd, Washington, PA 15301-8913
Tel (724) 225-9300 *Founded/Ownrshp* 1991
Sales 7.5MM^E *EMP* 600
SIC 7999 Off-track betting; Off-track betting
Prin: Mike Juno
CIO: Tony Mediate

D-U-N-S 05-363-1214 EXP
LADCO INC
7900 Washington Ave, Houston, TX 77007-1000
Tel (713) 868-2828 *Founded/Ownrshp* 1988
Sales 27.1MM^E *EMP* 40
SIC 5021 Household furniture
Pr: Phillip V Ladin
**VP:* Ronald M Ladin

D-U-N-S 15-068-0007 IMP
LADD DISTRIBUTION LLC
(*Suby of* TE CONNECTIVITY) ★
4849 Hempstead Station Dr, Kettering, OH 45429-5156
Tel (937) 438-2646 *Founded/Ownrshp* 2012
Sales 32.0MM^E *EMP* 125
SIC 5065 Connectors, electronic; Connectors, electronic

LADD HANFORD MAZDA JEEP EAGLE
See LADD MOTORS INC

D-U-N-S 07-763-6785
LADD MEMORIAL HOSPITAL INC
OSCEOLA MEDICAL CENTER
2600 65th Ave, Osceola, WI 54020-4370
Tel (715) 294-2116 *Founded/Ownrshp* 1932
Sales 25.0MM *EMP* 250^E
Accts Heather A Peterkin Cfo
SIC 8062 General medical & surgical hospitals; General medical & surgical hospitals
CEO: Tom Geskermann
CFO: Heather Peterkin
Dir Lab: Greg Schuer
Dir Rad: Brad Feltz
Dir Rx: Nancy Blain
Surgeon: Warren Abell
Doctor: Shelly Anderson
Doctor: Tom Johnson
HC Dir: Julie Peper
Snr Mgr: Rob Dybvig

D-U-N-S 01-431-8455
LADD MOTORS INC
LADD HANFORD MAZDA JEEP EAGLE
2247 Cumberland St, Lebanon, PA 17042-2521
Tel (717) 273-4585 *Founded/Ownrshp* 1925
Sales 26.4MM^E *EMP* 65
SIC 5511 5521 7538 Automobiles, new & used; Used car dealers; General automotive repair shops; Automobiles, new & used; Used car dealers; General automotive repair shops
Pr: A L Hanford III
Sales Asso: Michael Ebling
Sales Asso: James Green
Sales Asso: Zachary Lesher
Sales Asso: Chad Wartluft

D-U-N-S 08-004-7467 IMP
LADDAWN INC (MA)
NORTHEAST POLY BAG
155 Jackson Rd, Devens, MA 01434-5614
Tel (800) 446-3639 *Founded/Ownrshp* 1976
Sales 72.0MM^E *EMP* 173
SIC 2673 3081 Plastic bags: made from purchased materials; Polyethylene film; Plastic bags: made from purchased materials; Polyethylene film
Ch: Paul F Lavallee
**Pr:* Steven R Graham
CFO: Donald Hafer
**VP:* Ladd Lavallee
**VP:* Dawn Seiple
Dir IT: James Maloy
VP Opers: Karen Minasian
Mfg Dir: Gregory Scheidemantel
Prd Mgr: Jim Dennison
Prd Mgr: Eric Rosinski
Sales Asso: David Wornham

D-U-N-S 07-908-9494
▲ **LADDER CAPITAL CORP**
345 Park Ave Fl 8, New York, NY 10154-0017
Tel (212) 715-3170 *Founded/Ownrshp* 2008
Sales 376.4MM *EMP* 66^E
Tkr Sym LADR *Exch* NYS
SIC 6798 6162 Real estate investment trusts; Mortgage bankers & correspondents
CEO: Brian Harris
Pr: Michael Mazzei
CFO: Marc Fox
Dir Sec: Pamela McCormack
CIO: Greta Guggenheim

D-U-N-S 82-594-2253
LADDER TOWER CO
AMERICAN LAFRANCE AERIALS
64 Cocalico Creek Rd, Ephrata, PA 17522-9455
Tel (717) 859-1176 *Founded/Ownrshp* 2014
Sales NA *EMP* 300
SIC 3446 3711

D-U-N-S 06-516-0819
LADEKI RESTAURANT GROUP
ROPPONGI
7596 Eads Ave Ste 200, La Jolla, CA 92037-4899
Tel (858) 454-2222 *Founded/Ownrshp* 1998
Sales 52.5MM^E *EMP* 2,000
SIC 8741 Restaurant management; Restaurant management
Pr: Sami Ladeki
**CFO:* Anthony Kulick
Genl Mgr: Alan Hagoriles
Genl Mgr: Heather Lugo
Genl Mgr: Aaron McDaniel
Genl Mgr: Richard Stephan
IT Man: Mark Miller
VP Opers: Dan Smith
Mktg Dir: Nicole Abraham
Mktg Mgr: Joanna Train

D-U-N-S 00-178-9242
LADELLE INVESTMENT CO INC
473 N Kirkwood Rd, Saint Louis, MO 63122-3911
Tel (314) 821-7007 *Founded/Ownrshp* 1960
Sales 6.8MM^E *EMP* 300
SIC 8051 Skilled nursing care facilities; Skilled nursing care facilities
Pr: George Menos
**Treas:* William Koch

D-U-N-S 00-698-6574
■ **LADENBURG THALMANN & CO INC**
(*Suby of* LADENBURG THALMANN FINANCIAL SERVICES INC) ★
153 E 53rd St, New York, NY 10022-4611
Tel (212) 954-0560 *Founded/Ownrshp* 1972, 2001
Sales 33.5MM^E *EMP* 160^E
Accts Pricewaterhousecoopers Llp
SIC 6211 6282 Investment bankers; Dealers, security; Investment advisory service; Investment bankers; Dealers, security; Investment advisory service
Ch: Mark Klein
**Pr:* Peter H Blum
**Pr:* David Rosenberg
**COO:* Robert Gorczakowski
Sr VP: Lawrence P Caplan
**Sr VP:* Joseph Giovanniello Jr
Sr VP: David Rosensweet
VP: Alfred Castaneda
**VP:* Joan D Levine
**VP:* John H Ruggiero

D-U-N-S 00-222-7036
▲ **LADENBURG THALMANN FINANCIAL SERVICES INC** (FL)
4400 Biscayne Blvd Fl 12, Miami, FL 33137-3212
Tel (305) 572-4100 *Founded/Ownrshp* 1876
Sales 921.2MM *EMP* 715^E
Accts Eisneramper Llp New York New
Tkr Sym LTS *Exch* ASE
SIC 6211 6282 Investment bankers; Investment firm, general brokerage; Investment advisory service; Investment bankers; Investment firm, general brokerage; Investment advisory service
Pr: Richard J Lampen
**Ch Bd:* Phillip Frost
**V Ch:* Howard M Lorber
COO: Adam Malamed
CFO: Brett Kaufman
**Ex VP:* Mark Zeitchick
Sr VP: Diane Chillemi
Sr VP: Joseph Giovanniello Jr
Sr VP: Carly P Maher
Sr VP: Oksana Poznak
VP: Dennis Brennan
VP: Michael Mundo
VP: Noel Parks
VP: David Rosenberg
Board of Directors: Henry C Beinstein, Brian S Genson, Saul Gilinski, Richard M Krasno, Jeffrey S Podell, Jacqueline M Simkin

D-U-N-S 94-580-9077
■ **LADENBURG THALMANN GROUP INC**
(*Suby of* NEW VALLEY LLC) ★
520 Lexington Ave Fl 11, New York, NY 10017-1219
Tel (212) 409-2000 *Founded/Ownrshp* 1980
Sales 21.9MM^E *EMP* 150^E
SIC 6211 Investment bankers; Investment bankers
CEO: Ronald J Kramer
CFO: Hal Strong
Bd of Dir: Vincent A Mangone
Sr VP: Robert Gorczakowski
Mng Dir: Michael Kramer
IT Man: Eugene Kvasov

LADERA RANCH
See RANCHO MISSION VIEJO LLC

D-U-N-S 09-213-1481 IMP
LADESSERTS INC
IVY, THE
113 N Robertson Blvd, Los Angeles, CA 90048-3101
Tel (310) 274-8303 *Founded/Ownrshp* 1977
Sales 23.0MM^E *EMP* 225

SIC 5461 5812 Bakeries; Eating places; Bakeries; Eating places
Pr: Richard Irving
**VP:* Lyn Von Kersting
Genl Mgr: Ann Parkar

LADI
See LATIN AMERICAN DISTRIBUTORS INC

D-U-N-S 06-647-7480
LADIES PROFESSIONAL GOLF ASSOCIATION
LPGA
100 International Golf Dr, Daytona Beach, FL 32124-1082
Tel (386) 274-2073 *Founded/Ownrshp* 1950
Sales 102.8MM *EMP* 85
Accts Grant Thornton Llp Orlando F
SIC 8699 Professional golf association; Professional golf association
Pt: Greg Downey
CFO: Kathy Milthorpe
Sr VP: Mindy Moore
VP: Heather Donofrio
VP: Jane Geddes
VP: Rob Neal
VP Bus Dev: Edward Willett
Ex Dir: Tim Erensen
CIO: Jack Sumner
Netwrk Mgr: Fred Weston
Software D: Shawn Cooper

D-U-N-S 08-360-3175 IMP
LADOVE INC
5701 Miami Lakes Dr E, Miami Lakes, FL 33014-2417
Tel (305) 823-8051 *Founded/Ownrshp* 1977
Sales 26.3MM^E *EMP* 55
SIC 2844 Shampoos, rinses, conditioners: hair
Pr: Sheree Kent
**CFO:* Julian Cecio
**Genl Mgr:* Michael Bass

LADS PET SUPPLIES
See WILBUR H SMITH INC

LADUE SCHOOL DISTRICT
See LADUE SCHOOLS

D-U-N-S 05-587-3657
LADUE SCHOOLS
LADUE SCHOOL DISTRICT
9703 Conway Rd, Saint Louis, MO 63124-1646
Tel (314) 983-5321 *Founded/Ownrshp* 1952
Sales 42.7MM^E *EMP* 650
SIC 8211 Public elementary & secondary schools; Public elementary & secondary schools
Dir IT: Rob Highfill

LADWP
See LOS ANGELES DEPARTMENT OF WATER AND POWER

LADY BLUE
See CITY BLUE INC

D-U-N-S 06-190-1500 IMP
LADY BURD EXCLUSIVE COSMETICS INC
LADY BURD PRIVATE LABEL COSMT
44 Executive Blvd Ste 1, Farmingdale, NY 11735-4706
Tel (631) 454-0444 *Founded/Ownrshp* 1967
Sales 20.3MM^E *EMP* 120
SIC 2844 Cosmetic preparations; Cosmetic preparations
Pr: Roberta Burd
VP: Alan Burd
**VP:* Allan Burd
**VP:* Christina Burd
**VP:* Lawrence Burd
**VP:* Tina Burd

LADY BURD PRIVATE LABEL COSMT
See LADY BURD EXCLUSIVE COSMETICS INC

D-U-N-S 03-770-2601
LADY JANES HAIR CUTS FOR MEN HOLDING CO LLC
3921 Rochester Rd, Troy, MI 48083-5246
Tel (248) 689-0997 *Founded/Ownrshp* 2007
Sales 13.2MM^E *EMP* 406^E
SIC 7241 5999 Hair stylist, men; Hair care products
Ch Bd: Chad Johnson
**Pr:* Tim McCollum
VP: David Hartford
Dir Bus: Jeff Anderman

D-U-N-S 02-520-7622
LADY LITTLE FOODS INC (IL)
PRIMERRO FROZEN FOODS
2323 Pratt Blvd, Elk Grove Village, IL 60007-5918
Tel (847) 806-1440 *Founded/Ownrshp* 1960, 1984
Sales 135.0MM^E *EMP* 420
SIC 2038 2099 Pizza, frozen; Food preparations; Pizza, frozen; Food preparations
CEO: John Geocaris
**CEO:* Rick Anderson
**COO:* Dan Geocaris
**CFO:* James Sharwarko
Dir Bus: David Foran
Dir IT: Eric Parker
Dir IT: Dan Rich
Dir IT: Ellie Stevanovic
VP Opers: Steven Kunkle
Sfty Mgr: Steven Jacobson
Opers Mgr: Jim Dinklenburg

LADY OF SEA GENERAL HOSPITAL
See LAFOURCHE PARISH HOSPITAL SERVICE DISTRICT 1

LAEMMLE THEATRES ETC
See LAEMMLE THEATRES LLC

D-U-N-S 07-412-2870
LAEMMLE THEATRES LLC
LAEMMLE THEATRES ETC
11523 Santa Monica Blvd, Los Angeles, CA 90025-3094
Tel (310) 478-1041 *Founded/Ownrshp* 1963
Sales 70.0MM *EMP* 200
SIC 7832 Motion picture theaters, except drive-in; Motion picture theaters, except drive-in
VP: Kevin Gallagher
Genl Mgr: Cassie Gratton

D-U-N-S 04-279-1152 IMP
LAERDAL MEDICAL CORP
167 Myers Corners Rd, Wappingers Falls, NY 12590-3869
Tel (845) 297-7770 *Founded/Ownrshp* 1967
Sales 76.0MM^E *EMP* 310
SIC 5047 3845 3841 Medical & hospital equipment; Oxygen therapy equipment; Defibrillator; Surgical & medical instruments; Medical & hospital equipment; Oxygen therapy equipment; Defibrillator; Surgical & medical instruments
Pr: Clyde Patrickson
Ch Bd: David Johnson
Pr: John Beck
Bd of Dir: Cindy Baxter
Creative D: Ramon Sosa
Rgnl Mgr: George Besant
MIS Dir: Paul Singleton
QA Dir: Ronald Weyhrauch
Dir IT: David Diprete
VP Opers: John Kuphal
Opers Mgr: Brenda Buckner
Board of Directors: Hans H Dahll, Tore Laerdal

D-U-N-S 16-018-8389 IMP
LAERDAL MEDICAL CORP
(*Suby of* MEDICAL PLASTICS LABORATORY INC) ★
167 Myers Corners Rd, Wappingers Falls, NY 12590-3869
Tel (254) 865-7221 *Founded/Ownrshp* 1993
Sales 220.0M^E *EMP* 310
SIC 5046 Mannequins; Mannequins
Pr: David Johnson
**Pr:* David Broussard
**CEO:* Clive Patrickson
**CFO:* Egil Mathisen
**VP:* Lars Kirkeskov Srup

D-U-N-S 04-726-4742
LAETHEM RAY PONTIAC-BUICK-GMC TRUCKS INC
RAY LAETHEM BUICK
17677 Mack Ave, Detroit, MI 48224-1470
Tel (313) 417-8432 *Founded/Ownrshp* 1980
Sales 29.5MM^E *EMP* 70
SIC 5511 5521 Automobiles, new & used; Pickups, new & used; Vans, new & used; Used car dealers; Automobiles, new & used; Pickups, new & used; Vans, new & used; Used car dealers
Pr: Ray Laethem
**Pr:* Jeff Laethem
**Sec:* Philip Castiglione
**Genl Mgr:* Jim Castiglione
Genl Mgr: David Okonoski
Store Mgr: Eugene Kornetti

LAFALLE GENERAL HOSPITAL
See HOSPITAL SERVICE DISTRICT NO 2 OF LASALLE

D-U-N-S 11-531-8230 IMP
LAFARGE BUILDING MATERIALS INC
(*Suby of* LAFARGE NORTH AMERICA INC) ★
8700 W Bryn Mawr Ave 300n, Chicago, IL 60631-3512
Tel (678) 746-2000 *Founded/Ownrshp* 2009
Sales 462.6MM^E *EMP* 2,600
SIC 3241 3274 3273 3271 Masonry cement; Natural cement; Portland cement; Lime; Ready-mixed concrete; Blocks, concrete or cinder: standard; Masonry cement; Natural cement; Portland cement; Lime; Ready-mixed concrete; Blocks, concrete or cinder: standard
CEO: Jean M Lechene
**CEO:* Peter L Keeley
**CFO:* Robert Fiolek

D-U-N-S 00-384-4875
LAFARGE DAKOTA INC
(*Suby of* LAFARGE NORTH AMERICA INC) ★
684 15th Ave Sw, Valley City, ND 58072-3629
Tel (701) 845-2421 *Founded/Ownrshp* 1962
Sales 34.0MM *EMP* 20
SIC 5032 Cement; Cement
Pr: Martin Warborg
Genl Mgr: Roy Sander
Trfc Dir: Tony Hymel

D-U-N-S 13-148-6177
LAFARGE MID-ATLANTIC LLC
300 E Joppa Rd Ste 200, Baltimore, MD 21286-3015
Tel (410) 847-3300 *Founded/Ownrshp* 2006
Sales 103.8MM^E *EMP* 500
SIC 3273 1422 Ready-mixed concrete; Crushed & broken limestone; Ready-mixed concrete; Crushed & broken limestone
Opers Supe: James Wallace

D-U-N-S 06-756-8246 IMP
LAFARGE NORTH AMERICA INC
(*Suby of* SOCIETE LAFARGE)
8700 W Bryn Mawr Ave Ll, Chicago, IL 60631-3535
Tel (703) 480-3600 *Founded/Ownrshp* 2006
Sales 2.6MMM^E *EMP* 16,600
SIC 3241 3273 3272 3271 1442 2951 Cement, hydraulic; Portland cement; Ready-mixed concrete; Concrete products; Precast terrazo or concrete products; Prestressed concrete products; Cylinder pipe, prestressed or pretensioned concrete; Blocks, concrete or cinder: standard; Construction sand & gravel; Construction sand mining; Gravel mining; Asphalt paving mixtures & blocks; Paving mixtures; Asphalt & asphaltic paving mixtures (not from refineries); Cement, hydraulic; Portland cement; Ready-mixed concrete; Concrete products; Precast terrazo or concrete products; Prestressed concrete products; Cylinder pipe, prestressed or pretensioned concrete; Blocks, concrete or cinder: standard; Construction sand & gravel; Construction sand mining; Gravel mining; Asphalt paving mixtures & blocks; Paving mixtures; Asphalt & asphaltic paving mixtures (not from refineries)
Pr: John Stull
**CEO:* Bernard L Kasriel
**CEO:* Isaac Preston
CFO: John Cheong
**CFO:* Robert Fiolek
Ex VP: Jean Gauthier
Ex VP: Ulrich Glaunach
Ex VP: Eric Meuriot
Ex VP: Jean-Marc Lech Ne
VP: Ed Claggett
VP: Sandip Ghose
**VP:* Peter Keeley
VP: Nicolas Mathon
VP: Stephen Smith
Dir Soc: Dawn Stefano
Board of Directors: Michel Rose, Marshall A Cohen, Lawrence M Tanenbaum, Philippe P Dauman, Gerald H Taylor, Bruno Lafont, Claudine B Malone, Blythe J McGarvie, James M Micali, Robert W Murdoch, Bertin F Nadeau, John D Redfern

D-U-N-S 02-384-2953
LAFARGE ROAD MARKING INC
400 Lanidex Plz, Parsippany, NJ 07054-2722
Tel (973) 884-0300 *Founded/Ownrshp* 2003
Sales 28.8MM^E *EMP* 250^E
SIC 2851 3953
Pr: Robert A Dirienzo
**VP:* Anthony Cipolla
**VP:* Steve Shinners

D-U-N-S 61-253-6680
LAFARGE SOUTHWEST INC
(*Suby of* LAFARGE NORTH AMERICA INC) ★
1500 N Rnaissance Blvd Ne, Albuquerque, NM 87107-7002
Tel (505) 343-7800 *Founded/Ownrshp* 1989
Sales 24.7MM^E *EMP* 350
SIC 3273 1611 2951 Ready-mixed concrete; Highway & street construction; Asphalt paving mixtures & blocks; Ready-mixed concrete; Highway & street construction; Asphalt paving mixtures & blocks
CEO: Bob Cartmel
Mktg Dir: Ted Matson

D-U-N-S 16-087-5381
LAFARGE WEST INC
WESTERN PAVING CONSTRUCTION
(*Suby of* LAFARGE NORTH AMERICA INC) ★
10170 Church Ranch Way # 200, Westminster, CO 80021-6060
Tel (303) 657-4355 *Founded/Ownrshp* 2003
Sales 191.2MM^E *EMP* 1,400
SIC 5032 1611 3273

D-U-N-S 93-308-8643 IMP
LAFAYETTE 148 INC
148 Lafayette St Fl 2, New York, NY 10013-3115
Tel (646) 708-7010 *Founded/Ownrshp* 1996
Sales 152.5MM *EMP* 250^E
Accts Friedman Llp New York Ny
SIC 5137 Women's & children's accessories; Women's & children's accessories
Pr: Deirdre Quinn
Sr VP: Debra Clark
VP: Sandra Francisco
VP: Barbara Gast
DP Exec: Albert Chu
Dir IT: Kinsen Siu
VP Prd: Irene Tam
Sls Dir: Candace Amesbury
Sls Dir: Michelle TSE

D-U-N-S 00-791-0631
■ **LAFAYETTE AMBASSADOR BANK** (PA)
FULTON FINANCIAL ADVISORS
(*Suby of* FULTON FINANCIAL CORP) ★
360 Northampton St, Easton, PA 18042-3599
Tel (610) 758-7330 *Founded/Ownrshp* 1922
Sales NA *EMP* 337
SIC 6022 State trust companies accepting deposits, commercial; State trust companies accepting deposits, commercial
Pr: Robert Rupel
CFO: Lou Maynard
Ofcr: Gary Maurer
VP: Jim Hartman
VP: Diane Hepburn
VP: Mark Jobes
VP: Celeste Rau
**Exec:* Ronald J De Bona
**Exec:* Talbot R Houck Jr
Site Mgr: Sharon Fontana

D-U-N-S 01-038-4899
LAFAYETTE ASSOCIATION FOR RETARDED CITIZENS INC (LA)
LARC
303 New Hope Rd, Lafayette, LA 70506-7407
Tel (337) 981-7900 *Founded/Ownrshp* 1954
Sales 7.0MM *EMP* 325
Accts John S Dowling & Company Opel
SIC 8322 Social services for the handicapped; Social services for the handicapped

LAFAYETTE AUTO SUPPLY
See LAFAYETTE WAREHOUSE INC

D-U-N-S 07-505-4536
LAFAYETTE CITY PARISH CONSOLIDATED GOVERNMENT
705 W University Ave, Lafayette, LA 70506-3543
Tel (337) 291-8353 *Founded/Ownrshp* 1840
Sales NA *EMP* 2,022
Accts Kolder Champagne Slaven & Co
SIC 9111 Executive offices; Executive offices;
Pr: Walter S Comeaux Jr
Exec: Paul Mouton
Comm Man: Tracy Mouton
Ex Dir: Max Ulmer
**Adm/Dir:* Rebecca Lalumia
Snr Mgr: Robert Benoit

D-U-N-S 04-136-4522
LAFAYETTE COLLEGE
730 High St, Easton, PA 18042-1761
Tel (610) 330-5000 *Founded/Ownrshp* 1826
Sales 145.6MM *EMP* 675^E
Accts Grant Thornton Llp Philadelph
SIC 8221 Colleges universities & professional schools; Colleges universities & professional schools
Pr: Arthur J Rothkopf
**Treas:* Frederick J Quivey
Chf Inves: Joseph Bohrer
Ofcr: John O'Keefe
VP: James Dicker
**VP:* Gary Evans
VP: Brian McAtee
VP: Leslie F Muhlfelder
VP: Steph Roebelen
VP: Casey Schmalacker
VP: Kimberly A Spang
Assoc Dir: Matt Blackton

D-U-N-S 80-968-1476
LAFAYETTE CONSOLIDATED GOVERNMENT
705 W University Ave, Lafayette, LA 70506-3543
Tel (337) 291-5600 *Founded/Ownrshp* 2008
Sales NA *EMP* 2,500
Accts Kolder Champagne Slaven & Co
SIC 9111 Executive offices
Pr: Joey Durel
CFO: Lorrie Toups
Ofcr: Dee Stanley
Comm Man: Mark Pope
Comm Man: Darin Smalley
Brnch Mgr: Larry Richard
CIO: Kevin Samples
IT Man: Sheila Courville

D-U-N-S 05-452-2107
LAFAYETTE COUNTY SCHOOL DISTRICT (MS)
100 Commodore Dr, Oxford, MS 38655-8182
Tel (662) 234-3271 *Founded/Ownrshp* 1800, 1965
Sales 15.7MM^E *EMP* 300^E
Accts Ramona Hill Cpa
SIC 8211 Public elementary school; Public senior high school; Public elementary school; Public senior high school
Schl Brd P: Johnny Parker
Board of Directors: Garydruckemiller Superintende

LAFAYETTE CY PARISH GOVERNMENT
See LAFAYETTE UTILITY SYSTEM

D-U-N-S 06-264-8118
LAFAYETTE DRUG CO INC
L D C OF LAFAYETTE
(*Suby of* ACADIA WHOLESALE & TOBACCO CO INC) ★
220 N University Ave, Church Point, LA 70525
Tel (337) 684-5411 *Founded/Ownrshp* 1941
Sales 29.6MM^E *EMP* 50
SIC 5122 Drugs, proprietaries & sundries
Pr: John M Chachere
**Sec:* Celia Chachere
**VP:* Richard Chachere
VP Sls: Ricky Castille

LAFAYETTE EXTENDED CARE
See PRIME HEALTHCARE LLC

D-U-N-S 96-633-3457
LAFAYETTE GENERAL HEALTH SYSTEM INC
LGH
1214 Coolidge Blvd, Lafayette, LA 70503-2621
Tel (337) 289-8125 *Founded/Ownrshp* 2002
Sales 495.5MM *EMP* 2,600^E
Accts Laporte Apac Metairie La
SIC 8062 General medical & surgical hospitals; General medical & surgical hospitals
Ch Bd: Clay M Allen
**Pr:* David Callecod
Snr Mgr: Diana Motty

LAFAYETTE GENERAL HOSPITAL GIF
See LAFAYETTE GENERAL MEDICAL CENTER INC

D-U-N-S 04-342-7426
LAFAYETTE GENERAL MEDICAL CENTER INC
LAFAYETTE GENERAL HOSPITAL GIF
1214 Coolidge Blvd, Lafayette, LA 70503-2621
Tel (337) 289-7991 *Founded/Ownrshp* 1905
Sales 357.8MM *EMP* 1,626
SIC 8062 General medical & surgical hospitals; General medical & surgical hospitals
Ex Dir: Caroline Huval
Pr: Wendy Alexander
Sr VP: Susan Johnson
Dir Lab: Chelle Lefleur
Ex Dir: John Burdin
Mtls Dir: Chance Harst
Nutrtnst: Hilary Touchet
Doctor: Reynaldo Rosa
Pharmcst: Michael Moresi
Diag Rad: Joseph Horton
Snr Mgr: Stacy Mistric

D-U-N-S 19-598-7248
LAFAYETTE GENERAL SURGICAL HOSPITAL LLC
1000 W Pinhook Rd Ste 206, Lafayette, LA 70503-2460
Tel (337) 289-8060 *Founded/Ownrshp* 2003
Sales 16.0MM^E *EMP* 1,200
SIC 8062 General medical & surgical hospitals

D-U-N-S 14-449-6817
LAFAYETTE HEALTH VENTURES INC
MEDICAL DIMENSIONS
(*Suby of* LAFAYETTE GENERAL HOSPITAL GIF) ★
459 Heymann Blvd, Lafayette, LA 70503-2616
Tel (337) 289-8969 *Founded/Ownrshp* 1984
Sales 26.4MM *EMP* 70
SIC 8742 7322 6411 Business consultant; Collection agency, except real estate; Advisory services, insurance; Business consultant; Collection agency, except real estate; Advisory services, insurance
Ex VP: Jelena Bertrand
VP: Larry E Baker
VP: Larry E Bakr

LAFAYETTE INTERIOR FASHIONS
See LAFAYETTE VENETIAN BLIND INC

D-U-N-S 00-693-8989
LAFAYETTE LIFE INSURANCE CO INC
(*Suby of* WESTERN & SOUTHERN FINANCIAL GROUP INC) ★
400 Broadway St, Cincinnati, OH 45202-3312
Tel (800) 443-8793 *Founded/Ownrshp* 1905
Sales NA *EMP* 204
SIC 6311 Life insurance; Life insurance
Pr: Larry Grypp
**COO:* William Olds
**Treas:* Ronald Heibert
**Sr VP:* Jeffrey A Poxon
VP: Keith Baumgarn
VP: Becky Cummings
VP: Michael Donahue
VP: Pat Raftery
VP: Cheryl Rogers
Software D: Jack Hurless

LAFAYETTE LUMBER
See STERLING LUMBER AND INVESTMENT CO

D-U-N-S 02-087-8674
LAFAYETTE PARISH SCHOOL BOARD
113 Chaplin Dr, Lafayette, LA 70508-2101
Tel (337) 521-7000 *Founded/Ownrshp* 1870
Sales 346.3MM *EMP* 3,400
Accts Kolder Champagne Slaven & Co
SIC 8211 Public elementary & secondary schools; Public elementary & secondary schools
**Pr:* Hunter Beasley
**VP:* Tommy Angelle
Off Admin: Phyllis Collette
Off Admin: Paula Jameyson
Teacher Pr: Bruce C Leininger
Instr Medi: Patrick Hanisee

LAFAYETTE PARK ELEMENTARY MIDD
See KOKOMO SCHOOL CORP

D-U-N-S 15-108-4811
LAFAYETTE PARK HOTEL CORP
1100 Alma St Ste 106, Menlo Park, CA 94025-3344
Tel (650) 330-8888 *Founded/Ownrshp* 1984
Sales 19.9MM^E *EMP* 500
SIC 7011 Hotels; Hotels
Pr: Ellis J Alden
**Pr:* Katherine H Alden

D-U-N-S 07-305-8257
LAFAYETTE REGIONAL HEALTH CENTER AUXILIARY INC
HCA MIDWEST CENTER
1500 State St, Lexington, MO 64067-1107
Tel (660) 259-6882 *Founded/Ownrshp* 2003
Sales 20.7MM^E *EMP* 195^E
SIC 8062 General medical & surgical hospitals; General medical & surgical hospitals
**CEO:* Darrel Box
CFO: Teri James
Dir Lab: Rachel Pahayo
CTO: Marla Harvey
DP Dir: Florence Barron
Ansthlgy: Jim Lloyd
Doctor: Cheryl Cooley
Nrsg Dir: Gloria Driver
HC Dir: Cheryl Kooley

D-U-N-S 07-206-0163
LAFAYETTE SCHOOL CORP
2300 Cason St, Lafayette, IN 47904-2692
Tel (765) 771-6000 *Founded/Ownrshp* 1963
Sales 71.7MM^E *EMP* 1,200
Accts State Board Of Accounts India
SIC 8211 Public elementary & secondary schools; Public elementary school; Public junior high school; Public senior high school; Public elementary & secondary schools; Public elementary school; Public junior high school; Public senior high school
COO: Debbie Vanness
**CFO:* Eric Rody
**Treas:* Robert Forman
Bd of Dir: Kim Parthun
**VP:* Rebecca Sprague
Off Mgr: Diane Troxel
IT Man: Sherry Burchett

D-U-N-S 08-071-1450
LAFAYETTE SCHOOL DISTRICT
3477 School St, Lafayette, CA 94549-4503
Tel (925) 927-3500 *Founded/Ownrshp* 1881
Sales 18.7MM^E *EMP* 350
SIC 8211 Public elementary & secondary schools; Public elementary & secondary schools
Off Mgr: Sheryl Kelley
Psych: Marjolein Byl

LAFAYETTE STEEL AND ALUM SLS
See OSCAR WINSKI CO INC

D-U-N-S 00-386-1689
LAFAYETTE STEEL ERECTOR INC (LA)
LSE
313 Westgate Rd, Lafayette, LA 70506-2714
Tel (337) 234-9435 *Founded/Ownrshp* 1957
Sales 27.5MM^E *EMP* 90
Accts Major Morrison And David New
SIC 1791 Structural steel erection
Pr: John B Prudhomme II
CFO: Erin Ramos
**Sec:* Marlynn Cynthia Prudhomme
**VP:* Ronnie M Prudhomme

LAFAYETTE STEEL PROCESSING
See OLYMPIC STEEL LAFAYETTE INC

D-U-N-S 17-937-0999
LAFAYETTE SURGICAL HOSPITAL LLC
LAFAYETTE SURGICAL SPECIALTY H
1101 Kaliste Saloom Rd, Lafayette, LA 70508-5705
Tel (337) 769-4100 *Founded/Ownrshp* 2002
Sales 40.2MM *EMP* 150
SIC 8062 General medical & surgical hospitals
CEO: Buffy Domingue
CEO: Gary Keller
CFO: Stephanie Geary
Dir Rad: Thomas Martin
Dir Rx: Neil Fontenot
Chf Nrs Of: Selina Guidry
Orthpdst: Barry Henry
Doctor: Thomas V Bertuccini
Cert Phar: Danielle Jackson
HC Dir: Kathy Lafleur

LAFAYETTE SURGICAL SPECIALTY H
See LAFAYETTE SURGICAL HOSPITAL LLC

D-U-N-S 08-943-2954
LAFAYETTE TEXTILE INDUSTRIES LLC
2734 E 46th St, Vernon, CA 90058-2303
Tel (323) 264-2212 *Founded/Ownrshp* 1998
Sales 20.9MM^E *EMP* 85
SIC 5131 Piece goods & notions

D-U-N-S 02-680-3796
LAFAYETTE UTILITY SYSTEM
LAFAYETTE CY PARISH GOVERNMENT
705 W University Ave, Lafayette, LA 70506-3543
Tel (337) 291-8280 *Founded/Ownrshp* 2007
Sales 30.9MM^E *EMP* 200
SIC 1623 Water, sewer & utility lines; Water, sewer & utility lines
**Pr:* Lj Durel
VP: Mike Talley
IT Man: Tonia Khosropour

D-U-N-S 00-508-0908 IMP
LAFAYETTE VENETIAN BLIND INC
LAFAYETTE INTERIOR FASHIONS
3000 Klondike Rd, West Lafayette, IN 47906-5210
Tel (765) 464-2500 *Founded/Ownrshp* 1950
Sales 192.3MM^E *EMP* 1,000
SIC 2591 2391 Drapery hardware & blinds & shades; Venetian blinds; Mini blinds; Blinds vertical; Draperies, plastic & textile: from purchased materials; Drapery hardware & blinds & shades; Venetian blinds; Mini blinds; Blinds vertical; Draperies, plastic & textile: from purchased materials
Pr: Joseph N Morgan
CFO: Tom Moore
**Sec:* Dennis Morgan
Telecom Ex: Estella Morgan
Dir IT: Joseph Lamay
IT Man: Rick Haan
Info Man: Ted Nottingham
Plnt Mgr: Jay Cleaver
Sls Mgr: Marc Accristo
Sls Mgr: Tim Bertrand
Sls Mgr: Ralph Gonzales

D-U-N-S 04-610-3073
LAFAYETTE WAREHOUSE INC
LAFAYETTE AUTO SUPPLY
115 S 3rd St, Lafayette, IN 47901-1691
Tel (765) 742-5065 *Founded/Ownrshp* 1984
Sales 26.3MM^E *EMP* 100
SIC 5084 5083 5013 4226

D-U-N-S 07-180-0856
LAFCU YOUR CREDIT UNION
106 N Marketplace Blvd, Lansing, MI 48917-7753
Tel (517) 622-6560 *Founded/Ownrshp* 2011
Sales NA *EMP* 15^E
SIC 6061 Federal credit unions
Prin: Robin Frucci
CFO: Pamela McPherson
Ofcr: Jim Thelen
CIO: Harry Bauer
MIS Dir: Tom Kopenhafer

D-U-N-S 93-239-2582
LAFERIA SCHOOL DISTRICT INC
203 E Oleander Ave, La Feria, TX 78559-5102
Tel (956) 797-2741 *Founded/Ownrshp* 2003
Sales 7.9MM^E *EMP* 505
SIC 8211 Public elementary & secondary schools; Public elementary & secondary schools

D-U-N-S 01-507-0055
LAFFERTY CHEVROLET CO
829 W Street Rd, Warminster, PA 18974-3132
Tel (215) 672-2000 *Founded/Ownrshp* 1960
Sales 27.7MM^E *EMP* 70
SIC 5511 Automobiles, new & used; Automobiles, new & used
Pr: John J Lafferty III
COO: Joe Taber
Sls Mgr: Bill Siegle
Sales Asso: Joseph Costa
Sales Asso: John Lloyd
Sales Asso: Timothy Taber

D-U-N-S 07-490-1141
■ **LAFOLLETTE MEDICAL CENTER INC**
HMA
(*Suby of* HEALTH MANAGEMENT ASSOCIATES INC) ★
923 E Central Ave, La Follette, TN 37766-2768
Tel (423) 907-1200 *Founded/Ownrshp* 1956
Sales 59.8MM *EMP* 485
SIC 8051 8062 8052 Convalescent home with continuous nursing care; Hospital, AMA approved residency; Intermediate care facilities; Convalescent home with continuous nursing care; Hospital, AMA approved residency; Intermediate care facilities
CEO: Michael Garfield
**CFO:* West Griffith
**CFO:* Glenn McGuire
**Prin:* James Heitzenrater
Off Mgr: Don Manis
Diag Rad: Thomas L Cohen

D-U-N-S 14-776-0540
LAFONTAINE CADILLAC BUICK GMC INC
LAFONTINE PRE OWNED AUTO WORLD
4000 W Highland Rd, Highland, MI 48357-4007
Tel (248) 887-4747 *Founded/Ownrshp* 1984
Sales 71.8MM^E *EMP* 200
SIC 5511 Automobiles, new & used; Automobiles, new & used
Pr: Michael Lafontaine
**Treas:* Michael Lafontaine Jr
**VP:* Maureen Lafontaine
Dir Bus: Carlificw Irtiojica
Store Mgr: Mike Figurelle
Sls Mgr: Paul Jordan
Sls Mgr: Scott Tarwacki
Sales Asso: Kenn Elliott
Sales Asso: Joseph Vulai

D-U-N-S 05-990-8426
LAFONTAINE MOTORS INC
LAFONTAINE TOYOTA
2027 S Telegraph Rd, Dearborn, MI 48124-2516
Tel (313) 561-6600 *Founded/Ownrshp* 1980
Sales 33.8MM^E *EMP* 71
SIC 5511 Automobiles, new & used; Automobiles, new & used
Pr: Michael T Lafontaine
Off Mgr: Diane Hare
Mktg Mgr: Jason Stum
Sls Mgr: John Berghoefer

LAFONTAINE TOYOTA
See LAFONTAINE MOTORS INC

LAFONTINE PRE OWNED AUTO WORLD
See LAFONTAINE CADILLAC BUICK GMC INC

LAFORGE & BUDD
See LAFORGE AND BUDD CONSTRUCTION CO INC

D-U-N-S 00-714-6947
LAFORGE AND BUDD CONSTRUCTION CO INC (KS)
LAFORGE & BUDD
2020 N 21st St, Parsons, KS 67357-8090
Tel (620) 421-4470 *Founded/Ownrshp* 1960
Sales 27.8MM^E *EMP* 100
SIC 1542 1611 1541 Commercial & office building, new construction; Highway & street construction; Industrial buildings & warehouses; Commercial & office building, new construction; Highway & street construction; Industrial buildings & warehouses
Ch: Paul F Laforge
**Pr:* Patrick Laforge
**VP:* Bernard Dougherty

D-U-N-S 16-629-3571
LAFOURCHE ARC
100 W Main St, Thibodaux, LA 70301-5216
Tel (985) 447-6214 *Founded/Ownrshp* 1963
Sales 12.2MM *EMP* 700
Accts Bourgeois Bennett Llc Cpa S
SIC 8322 Association for the handicapped; Association for the handicapped
**Pr:* Richard Booterie Jr
**Treas:* James Peltier
Ex Dir: Lester Adams

LAFOURCHE PARISH COUNCIL
See PARISH OF LAFOURCHE

D-U-N-S 07-508-5076
LAFOURCHE PARISH HOSPITAL SERVICE DISTRICT 1
LADY OF SEA GENERAL HOSPITAL
200 W 134th Pl, Cut Off, LA 70345-4143
Tel (985) 325-2676 *Founded/Ownrshp* 1953
Sales 26.4MM^E *EMP* 185
SIC 8062 General medical & surgical hospitals; General medical & surgical hospitals
CEO: Karen Collins
**CEO:* John Werner Jr
**COO:* Lloyd Guidry Jr
**CFO:* Randy Tabor
Exec: Gayle Duet
S&M/Dir: Charlotte Randolph
Doctor: Bud Sayes

D-U-N-S 07-945-2736
LAFOURCHE PARISH HOSPITAL SERVICE DISTRICT NO 2
ST ANNE'S GENERAL HOSPITAL
4608 Highway 1, Raceland, LA 70394-2623
Tel (985) 537-6841 *Founded/Ownrshp* 1967
Sales 24.7MM^E *EMP* 313
SIC 8062 General medical & surgical hospitals; General medical & surgical hospitals
Chf Path: Andrew Hoffmann III
Chf OB: Charles H Faucheux
Chf Rad: Gorst Duplessis
CFO: Erika Anderson
VP: Marsha Arabie
Dir OR: Sharon Mc Clain
Dir Inf Cn: Kirk Carlos
Dir Soc: Wanda Bordelon
Dir Rad: John Flannery
IT Man: Susan Boudreaux
Psych: Stacie Gold

D-U-N-S 09-354-6901
LAFOURCHE PARISH SCHOOL BOARD INC
LAFOURCHE PUBLIC SCHOOLS
805 E 7th St, Thibodaux, LA 70301-3606
Tel (985) 446-5631 *Founded/Ownrshp* 1906
Sales 98.3MM^E *EMP* 2,218
Accts Stagni & Company Llc Thiboda
SIC 8211 Public elementary & secondary schools; Public elementary & secondary schools
Bd of Dir: Richmond Boyd Jr
IT Man: Ben Gautreaux
Psych: Elizabeth Hodnett
Psych: Claire Pellegrin

D-U-N-S 07-980-2903
LAFOURCHE PARISH SCHOOL DISTRICT
805 E 7th St, Thibodaux, LA 70301-3606
Tel (985) 446-5631 *Founded/Ownrshp* 2015
Sales 43.6MM^E *EMP* 2,004^E
SIC 8211 Public elementary & secondary schools
Pr Dir: Floyd Benoit
Teacher Pr: Louis Voiron
HC Dir: Charles Michel

LAFOURCHE PUBLIC SCHOOLS
See LAFOURCHE PARISH SCHOOL BOARD INC

D-U-N-S 02-102-6257 IMP
LAFOURCHE SUGARS LLC
141 Leighton Quarters Rd, Thibodaux, LA 70301-6489
Tel (985) 447-3210 *Founded/Ownrshp* 1937, 1999
Sales 20.7MM^E *EMP* 90
SIC 2061 2493 Blackstrap molasses made from sugar cane; Raw cane sugar; Bagasse board; Blackstrap molasses made from sugar cane; Raw cane sugar; Bagasse board
Genl Mgr: Greg Noland

LAFRANCAISE BAKERY
See CHEF SOLUTIONS INC

D-U-N-S 78-246-9498
LAGARDERE NORTH AMERICA INC
(*Suby of* LAGARDERE MEDIA)
60 E 42nd St Ste 1940, New York, NY 10165-6201
Tel (212) 477-7373 *Founded/Ownrshp* 2004
Sales 501.5MM^E *EMP* 7,024^E
SIC 2721 Magazines: publishing only, not printed on site; Magazines: publishing only, not printed on site
Sr VP: David Leckey
VP: Anne Billaz
**VP:* Richard Rabinowitz
Genl Mgr: Charn Lee
Genl Mgr: Nickolay Stoyanov

D-U-N-S 00-816-1523 IMP/EXP
■ **LAGASSE INC**
LAGASSE SWEET
(*Suby of* ESSENDANT CO) ★
1 Parkway North Blvd # 100, Deerfield, IL 60015
Tel (847) 627-7000 *Founded/Ownrshp* 1996
Sales 961.1MM^E *EMP* 500
SIC 5087 5141 Janitors' supplies; Food brokers; Janitors' supplies; Food brokers
Pr: Paul Barrett
VP: Christopher Adams
**VP:* Eric A Blanchard
**VP:* Robert J Kelderhouse
IT Man: Heidi Chapman
Opers Mgr: Dan Elko
Opers Mgr: Vic Moretti
VP Sls: Dane James
Sls Dir: Terry Girifalco
Mktg Mgr: Sara McCarthy
Manager: Tim Aland

LAGASSE SWEET
See LAGASSE INC

D-U-N-S 62-061-7407
LAGNIAPPE PHARMACY SERVICES LLC
LPS
2601 Scott Ave Ste 600, Fort Worth, TX 76103-2307
Tel (817) 531-8992 *Founded/Ownrshp* 1990
Sales 41.2MM^E *EMP* 125^E
Accts Hatter & Associates Llp
SIC 7371 Computer software development; Computer software development
Pr: Rex Akers
Treas: Tracy Ward
Sr VP: Christina McCormack
VP: Mike McManus
VP: Brooke Miller
Sls&Mrk Ex: Clarence Lea

LAGOON AMUSEMENT PARK
See LAGOON CORP INC

D-U-N-S 03-739-7085 IMP
LAGOON CORP INC
LAGOON AMUSEMENT PARK
375 Lagoon Dr, Farmington, UT 84025-2554
Tel (801) 451-8000 *Founded/Ownrshp* 1973
Sales 21.2MM^E *EMP* 200
SIC 7999 7033 Recreation center; Campgrounds; Recreation center; Campgrounds
Pr: David W Freed
**Treas:* Kristen Freed O'Bagy
Ex VP: Dick Andrew
VP: Kristen Freed
Software D: Chad Smith
Sftwr Eng: David Larsen

D-U-N-S 07-247-7813
LAGRANGE COLLEGE
601 Broad St, Lagrange, GA 30240-2999
Tel (706) 880-8000 *Founded/Ownrshp* 1831
Sales 41.1MM *EMP* 225
Accts Mauldin & Jenkins Llc Atlant
SIC 8221 College, except junior; College, except junior
CEO: Dan McAlexander
**CFO:* Martin Pirrman
Treas: Robert Harste
VP: Linda Buchanan
VP: William Jones
Exec: Jackie Belcher
Exec: Jeff Geeter
CIO: Tiffany Mixon
Dir IT: Andrew Rokitka
Mtls Mgr: Kendall Todd
Pr Dir: Jonathan Compton

LAGRAPHICO
See MIDNIGHT OIL AGENCY INC

D-U-N-S 04-607-2344
LAGRASSO BROS INC
5001 Bellevue St, Detroit, MI 48211-3278
Tel (313) 579-1455 *Founded/Ownrshp* 1944
Sales 87.7MM^E *EMP* 108
SIC 5148 Fruits, fresh; Vegetables, fresh; Fruits, fresh; Vegetables, fresh
Pr: Thomas La Grasso Jr
Pr: Steve Schultz
VP: Frank L Grasso
**VP:* Joseph H La Grasso
**VP:* Michael La Grasso
Exec: Barbara Lehto

D-U-N-S 05-594-1231
LAGROU DISTRIBUTION SYSTEM INC
3514 S Kostner Ave, Chicago, IL 60632-3818
Tel (773) 523-1800 *Founded/Ownrshp* 1982
Sales 30.0MM^E *EMP* 150
SIC 4789 Freight car loading & unloading; Freight car loading & unloading
Pr: Donald E Schimek
Pr: Tim Kelly
**Sec:* James Stancel
**VP:* Timothy Kelly
**VP:* Steve Schuldt

VP: Mark Stevens
VP: Jack Stewart

D-U-N-S 01-328-4047
LAGUNA BEACH UNIFIED SCHOOL DISTRICT
550 Blumont St, Laguna Beach, CA 92651-2356
Tel (949) 497-7711 *Founded/Ownrshp* 1996
Sales 21.5MM^E *EMP* 250
SIC 8211 Public elementary & secondary schools; Public elementary & secondary schools
Prin: Joanne Culverhouse
Prin: Chris Duddy
Prin: Ron Lamotte
CTO: Sean Colt
Pr Dir: Lisa Winston
HC Dir: Irene White

D-U-N-S 15-937-3216
LAGUNA DEPARTMENT OF EDUCATION
LAGUNA MIDDLE SCHOOL
I-40 W Exit 114 Bldg 1125, Laguna, NM 87026
Tel (505) 552-6544 *Founded/Ownrshp* 1992
Sales 21.8MM^E *EMP* 200
SIC 8211 Public junior high school; Public junior high school

D-U-N-S 14-448-2429
LAGUNA DEVELOPMENT CORP
14500 Central Ave Sw I40, Albuquerque, NM 87121-1450
Tel (505) 352-7877 *Founded/Ownrshp* 1998
Sales 114.8MM^E *EMP* 1,400
SIC 7011 5411 Casino hotel; Grocery stores, independent; Casino hotel; Grocery stores, independent
Ch: Debra Haaland
**CEO:* Jerry Smith
**COO:* Kevin Greer
**CFO:* Howard Funchess
Board of Directors: Debra Haaland

LAGUNA MIDDLE SCHOOL
See LAGUNA DEPARTMENT OF EDUCATION

D-U-N-S 01-920-0164 IMP/EXP
LAGUNA TUBULAR PRODUCTS CORP
(*Suby of* TUBERIA LAGUNA, S.A. DE C.V.)
16952 Leonard Rd, Houston, TX 77049-1800
Tel (832) 734-0044 *Founded/Ownrshp* 2007
Sales 34.7MM^E *EMP* 75
SIC 3399 Laminating steel
CEO: Eduardo Anaya Kessler
COO: Chris Rowland
**CFO:* Ignacio Aguirre
VP: Brian C Doner
Sls Mgr: Katherine Carter
Sales Asso: Ricardo Salas

D-U-N-S 86-788-6848
LAGUNA WOODS VILLAGE
24351 El Toro Rd, Laguna Beach, CA 92653
Tel (949) 597-4267 *Founded/Ownrshp* 1964
Sales 32.6MM^E *EMP* 1,000
SIC 6531 Real estate agents & managers; Real estate agents & managers

D-U-N-S 92-857-5885 IMP
LAGUNITAS BREWING CO
1280 N Mcdowell Blvd, Petaluma, CA 94954-1113
Tel (707) 778-8776 *Founded/Ownrshp* 1996
Sales 71.9MM^E *EMP* 200^E
SIC 2082 Malt beverages; Malt beverages
Pr: Tony Magee
COO: Todd Stevenson
**Treas:* Carissa Brader
Ex VP: Ash Notaney
VP: Jon Richey
Exec: Ian Jacobs
Exec: Sean McHugh
Exec: Tommy Nuckols
Exec: Lauren Young
Rgnl Mgr: Jeremy Grenert
Dir IT: Jason Gregori

D-U-N-S 14-518-5943
LAHAINA PETROLEUM LLC
1200 I St, Sacramento, CA 95814-2905
Tel (916) 488-3666 *Founded/Ownrshp* 2002
Sales 25.0MM *EMP* 60
SIC 5541 Gasoline service stations; Gasoline service stations

D-U-N-S 04-170-6300
LAHEY CLINIC FOUNDATION INC
(*Suby of* LAHEY HEALTH SYSTEM INC) ★
41 Mall Rd, Burlington, MA 01805-0002
Tel (781) 273-5100 *Founded/Ownrshp* 2012
Sales 9.3MM *EMP* 5,000^E
Accts Pricewaterhousecoopers Llp Bo
SIC 8059 Rest home, with health care; Rest home, with health care
Pr: David M Barrett MD
**Treas:* Timothy P O'Connor
IT Man: Jim Drewett
Ansthlgy: Carl J Borromeo
Ansthlgy: Michael D Kaufman
Opthamlgy: Geetha K Athappilly
Opthamlgy: Patrick L Bessette
Diag Rad: Nancy D Baker

D-U-N-S 18-345-2549
LAHEY CLINIC HOSPITAL INC
(*Suby of* LAHEY CLINIC FOUNDATION INC) ★
41 Mall Rd, Burlington, MA 01805-0002
Tel (781) 273-5100 *Founded/Ownrshp* 2012
Sales 800.6MM *EMP* 5,000
SIC 8062 General medical & surgical hospitals; General medical & surgical hospitals
CEO: Howard R Grant JD
**CEO:* David Barrett MD
COO: Richard Bias
**Ch:* Bernard Gordon
Treas: Timothy P Connor
Ofcr: Kathleen Jose
Sr VP: Derek C Bellin
**VP:* Donna Cameron
Nurse Mgr: Marty Allard
Nurse Mgr: Terri Burnell
Doctor: Bonney Myles

D-U-N-S 88-385-0364
LAHEY CLINIC INC
LAHEY CLINIC MEDICAL CENTER
(*Suby of* LAHEY CLINIC FOUNDATION INC) ★
41 Mall Rd, Burlington, MA 01805-0002
Tel (781) 744-5100 *Founded/Ownrshp* 1923
Sales 424.7MM^E *EMP* 5,000
SIC 8062 General medical & surgical hospitals; General medical & surgical hospitals
Ch: Ann Marie Connolly
V Ch: James W Henderson
**Pr:* Howard R Grant JD
**CEO:* David Barret MD
COO: Jeffrey P Doran
COO: Robert J Schneider
**CFO:* Timothy P Oconnor
Trst: Eric M Bailey
Trst: Craig R Benson
Trst: Bernard Cammarata
Trst: Jerald G Fishman
Trst: Charles M Leighton
Trst: John W Poduska Sr
Trst: James A Radley
Trst: Robert L Reynolds
Ofcr: Kathleen S Jose
Ofcr: David J Schoetz Jr
Ex VP: Richard W Nesto
Sr VP: Joan M Robbio
VP: Allen S Danis
VP: Elizabeth Garvin

LAHEY CLINIC MEDICAL CENTER
See LAHEY CLINIC INC

D-U-N-S 07-860-1824
LAHEY HEALTH SYSTEM INC
41 Mall Rd, Burlington, MA 01805-0001
Tel (781) 273-5100 *Founded/Ownrshp* 2012
Sales 3.0MM *EMP* 5,056^E
Accts Feeley & Driscoll Pc Boston
SIC 8059 Rest home, with health care
Pr: Howard R Grant
**Treas:* Timothy P O'Connor
VP: Eric Berger
VP: Tonya Hongsermeier
Pr Dir: Andrew Mastrangelo
Doctor: Ghazwan Acash
Doctor: Yevgeniy Arshanskiy

D-U-N-S 00-923-7686 IMP
LAHLOUH INC
1649 Adrian Rd, Burlingame, CA 94010-2103
Tel (650) 692-6600 *Founded/Ownrshp* 1981
Sales 56.8MM^E *EMP* 185
SIC 2752 Commercial printing, lithographic; Commercial printing, lithographic
Pr: John Lahlouh
**VP:* Fadi Lahlouh
Mktg Mgr: Scott James
Snr Mgr: Jim Hildinger

LAHR CONSTRUCTION
See LECESSE CONSTRUCTION SERVICES LLC

D-U-N-S 62-794-2048
LAHR CONSTRUCTION CORP
LECESSE CONSTRUCTION COMPANY
75 Thruway Park Dr Ste 1, West Henrietta, NY 14586-9793
Tel (585) 334-4490 *Founded/Ownrshp* 1990
Sales 120.0MM *EMP* 95
SIC 1521 1541 Single-family housing construction; Industrial buildings & warehouses; Single-family housing construction; Industrial buildings & warehouses
Pr: Andrew Hislop
**COO:* Tayloe M Call
COO: Mary Merritt
CFO: Evelyn Hartwell
**Ch:* Gary Henehan
**Treas:* David Luxenberg
Treas: Bill Tehan
**VP:* William O Hanlon
VP: Ken Ogden
**VP:* Christopher Phillips
Exec: Daniel Gasbarre
Exec: Kevin Morgan

D-U-N-S 61-859-1515
LAI ACQUISITION CORP
12600 N Featherwood Dr # 400, Houston, TX 77034-4443
Tel (832) 300-1300 *Founded/Ownrshp* 2014
Sales NA *EMP* 85
SIC 6159 Automobile finance leasing; Truck finance leasing
Pr: Mark A Sprague
COO: Eric King

D-U-N-S 84-799-9158
LAI INTERNATIONAL INC
LAI MIDWEST
7645 Baker St Ne, Minneapolis, MN 55432-3421
Tel (763) 780-0060 *Founded/Ownrshp* 2012
Sales 60.0MM *EMP* 285
SIC 3728

LAI MIDWEST
See LAI INTERNATIONAL INC

LAICO INDUSTRIES
See LIFETIME ASSISTANCE INC

D-U-N-S 06-470-8357
LAIDIG INC
14535 Dragoon Trl, Mishawaka, IN 46544-6814
Tel (574) 256-0204 *Founded/Ownrshp* 1983
Sales 22.9MM^E *EMP* 50
SIC 3523 3537 3448 3423 Silo fillers & unloaders; Industrial trucks & tractors; Prefabricated metal buildings; Hand & edge tools
Pr: Jonathon Laidig
**Pr:* Wyn Laidig
Pr: Tom Lindenman
VP: Thomas Linderman
MIS Mgr: Kevin Harris

D-U-N-S 60-389-1503
LAIDLAW & CO (UK) LTD
546 5th Ave Fl 5, New York, NY 10036-5000
Tel (212) 953-4900 *Founded/Ownrshp* 1999
Sales 36.5MM^E *EMP* 135^E
SIC 6211 Security brokers & dealers; Security brokers & dealers
Pr: Alex Shtaynberger
Mng Pt: James Ahern
**Co-Pr:* Marc Ellis
VP: Timothy Behr
VP: Luke Kotke
VP: Christopher Oppito
Mng Dir: Jeffrey Glazer
Mng Dir: Richard Kirschner
Mng Dir: Peter Malone
IT Man: Michael Lee
Board of Directors: Kevin Connors, Jay Russo, Moshe Silver

D-U-N-S 13-387-1439 IMP
LAIDLAW INTERNATIONAL INC
FIRSTGROUP AMERICA
(*Suby of* FIRSTGROUP PLC)
55 Shuman Blvd Ste 400, Naperville, IL 60563-8248
Tel (214) 849-8100 *Founded/Ownrshp* 2007
Sales 1.4MMM^E *EMP* 17,200
SIC 4151 4111 4131 School buses; Bus transportation; Intercity bus line; School buses; Bus transportation; Intercity bus line
Pr: Kevin E Benson
CFO: Jeffrey W Sanders
Treas: Jeffrey A McDougle
Ex VP: Beth B Corvino
VP: Bill Shuman
VP: Beverly A Wyckoff
Exec: Diane Orndorff
Exec: Dean Suhre

D-U-N-S 10-647-8105
LAIDLAW TRANSIT SERVICES INC
(*Suby of* FIRST GROUP OF AMERICA) ★
600 Vine St Ste 1400, Cincinnati, OH 45202-2426
Tel (513) 241-2200 *Founded/Ownrshp* 2007
Sales 138.2MM^E *EMP* 6,000
SIC 4131 Intercity & rural bus transportation; Intercity & rural bus transportation
Pr: Mike Rushin
CFO: Larry Sisel
**VP:* Jeff C Baker

D-U-N-S 02-948-3385
LAIDLAWS HARLEY-DAVIDSON SALES INC
1919 Puente Ave, Baldwin Park, CA 91706-6043
Tel (626) 851-0412 *Founded/Ownrshp* 1946
Sales 20.4MM^E *EMP* 70
SIC 5571 Motorcycle dealers; Mopeds; Motor scooters; Motorcycle dealers; Mopeds; Motor scooters
Pr: Walter R Laidlaw
**Sec:* Jarold R Laidlaw
**VP:* Brent Laidlaw
Genl Mgr: Richard Litchfield
Sls Mgr: Matt Laidlaw

LAIKA ENTERTAINMENT
See LAIKA LLC

D-U-N-S 09-700-2026
LAIKA LLC
LAIKA ENTERTAINMENT
22990 Nw Bennett St, Hillsboro, OR 97124-5855
Tel (503) 615-3344 *Founded/Ownrshp* 1984
Sales 40.9MM^E *EMP* 220
SIC 7812 Commercials, television: tape or film; Television film production; Commercials, television: tape or film; Television film production
CEO: Travis Knight
**Pr:* Lourri Hammach
**CFO:* Gary Raksis
**VP:* Al Cupillas
**VP:* Dan Philips
VP: Cindy Rabe
DP Dir: Michael Hix
Dir IT: Jonathan Rozes
Dir IT: Mahlon Smith
Sftwr Eng: Owen Nelson
Prd Mgr: Peter McCown

D-U-N-S 18-934-7859
LAINGSBURG COMMUNITY SCHOOL DISTRICT
205 S Woodhull Rd, Laingsburg, MI 48848-9331
Tel (517) 651-6381 *Founded/Ownrshp* 1800
Sales 25.8MM *EMP* 130
Accts Cantor & Cantor Cpa S Farming
SIC 8211 Public elementary & secondary schools; Secondary school; High school, junior or senior; Public elementary & secondary schools; Secondary school; High school, junior or senior
**Pr:* Patrich Dolan
Sls Mgr: Jackie Bobb

D-U-N-S 06-314-0990 IMP
LAIRD & CO
1 Laird Rd, Eatontown, NJ 07724-9724
Tel (732) 542-0312 *Founded/Ownrshp* 1780
Sales 44.0MM *EMP* 56
Accts Wiss & Company Llp Flemingto
SIC 2084 5182 Brandy; Brandy & brandy spirits; Brandy; Brandy & brandy spirits
Pr: Larrie W Laird
**Ex VP:* John E Laird III
Plnt Mgr: Ray Murdock

D-U-N-S 01-457-0980
LAIRD CONTROLS HOLDINGS INC
(*Suby of* LAIRD PLC)
655 N River Rd Nw Ste A, Warren, OH 44483-2254
Tel (234) 806-0018 *Founded/Ownrshp* 2010
Sales 31.3MM^E *EMP* 150
SIC 3625 7622 5065 5063 7359 3536 Relays & industrial controls; Communication equipment repair; Communication equipment; Closed circuit television; Electric alarms & signaling equipment; Equipment rental & leasing; Hoists, cranes & monorails; Relays & industrial controls; Communication equipment repair; Communication equipment; Closed circuit television; Electric alarms & signaling equipment; Equipment rental & leasing; Hoists, cranes & monorails
Pr: Rick Morse
**Sec:* Lori Grace
VP: Thomas McFall

D-U-N-S 15-474-8813
LAIRD HOSPITAL INC
25117 Highway 15, Union, MS 39365-9099
Tel (601) 774-8214 *Founded/Ownrshp* 2001
Sales 23.0MM^E *EMP* 167
Accts Horne Llp Ridgeland Ms
SIC 8062 General medical & surgical hospitals; General medical & surgical hospitals
VP: Gunn Thena
Opers Mgr: Kim Martos

D-U-N-S 03-130-9172
LAIRD NOLLER AUTOMOTIVE INC
935 W 23rd St, Lawrence, KS 66046-4464
Tel (785) 843-3500 *Founded/Ownrshp* 1977
Sales 40.6MM^E *EMP* 100
SIC 5511 5531 New & used car dealers; Automotive parts; New & used car dealers; Automotive parts
Pr: Gary Bennett
**Sec:* Laird Noller
**VP:* Barry Noller
VP: David Sherman
Genl Mgr: Bill Egan
Sales Exec: Marc Hauser
Sls Mgr: Ron Bozarth
Sls Mgr: Jimmy Brough
Sls Mgr: Heath Cheatham
Sls Mgr: Jeff Morel
Sls Mgr: Cody Reich

D-U-N-S 03-141-1887
LAIRD NOLLER FORD INC
2245 Sw Topeka Blvd, Topeka, KS 66611-1284
Tel (785) 235-9211 *Founded/Ownrshp* 2005
Sales 48.4MM^E *EMP* 135
SIC 5511 5531 7538 Automobiles, new & used; Pickups, new & used; Automotive parts; General automotive repair shops; Automobiles, new & used; Pickups, new & used; Automotive parts; General automotive repair shops
Pr: Laird Noller
Genl Mgr: Mark Harris
Store Mgr: Becky Taylor
Sls Mgr: Jeremy Lamb

D-U-N-S 00-696-3805
LAIRD NORTON CO LLC (MN)
801 2nd Ave Ste 1300, Seattle, WA 98104-1517
Tel (206) 464-5245 *Founded/Ownrshp* 1855
Sales 581.3MM^E *EMP* 7,500
SIC 5211 Home centers; Home centers
Pr: Jeffery Vincent
**Ch Bd:* Elizabeth Williams
**CFO:* Kim Hillyard
**CFO:* Nick Pavelich

D-U-N-S 96-946-0018
LAIRD NORTON INVESTMENT MANAGEMENT INC
801 2nd Ave Ste 1300, Seattle, WA 98104-1517
Tel (206) 464-5245 *Founded/Ownrshp* 2011
Sales 23.0MM^E *EMP* 82^E
SIC 6282 Investment advice

D-U-N-S 00-253-1317 IMP
LAIRD PLASTICS INC
6800 Broken Sound Pkwy Nw # 150, Boca Raton, FL 33487-5711
Tel (561) 443-9100 *Founded/Ownrshp* 1944, 2004
Sales 376.4MM^E *EMP* 500^E
SIC 5162 3089 Plastics materials; Plastics sheets & rods; Plastics film; Windows, plastic; Plastics materials; Plastics sheets & rods; Plastics film; Windows, plastic
Pr: Mark W Kramer
CFO: Willy Figueran
**CFO:* Wilfredo W Figueras
CFO: Dolores Willis
**Ch:* Douglas T McNair
**Ex VP:* Peter Edelstein
VP: Gerald Burnett
VP: Larry A Stafford
Exec: Chris Muth
Brnch Mgr: Gary King
Sales Asso: Dale Bartley

LAIRD TECHNOLOGIES
See CENTURION WIRELESS TECHNOLOGIES INC

LAIRD TECHNOLOGIES
See THERMAGON INC

D-U-N-S 00-216-1685 IMP
LAIRD TECHNOLOGIES INC
(*Suby of* LAIRD PLC)
3481 Rider Trl S, Earth City, MO 63045-1110
Tel (636) 898-6000 *Founded/Ownrshp* 1938, 1991
Sales 345.3MM^E *EMP* 1,440
SIC 3469 3663 Stamping metal for the trade; Cellular radio telephone; Stamping metal for the trade; Cellular radio telephone
CEO: David Lockwood
**Pr:* Tom Cochran
CFO: Jonathan Silver
Ofcr: Mark David
Sr VP: Jennifer Burton
VP: Craig Fix
VP: Joseph Sun
Dir Rx: Steven Ye
Prgrm Mgr: Troy Anderson
Prgrm Mgr: Yang Cao
Prgrm Mgr: Shane Demarais
Board of Directors: W Brewster Kopp, Paul Kozloff, John Thomas O'donnell, Thomas Witmer

D-U-N-S 00-819-3799 IMP/EXP
LAITRAM LLC
220 Laitram Ln, Harahan, LA 70123-5308
Tel (504) 733-6000 *Founded/Ownrshp* 1949
Sales 352.6MM^E *EMP* 1,400
SIC 3535 3556 7359 3446 6719 Conveyors & conveying equipment; Food products machinery; Equipment rental & leasing; Stairs, staircases, stair treads: prefabricated metal; Investment holding companies, except banks; Conveyors & conveying equipment; Food products machinery; Equipment rental & leasing; Stairs, staircases, stair treads: prefabricated metal; Investment holding companies, except banks
**Brnch Mgr:* Clay Beery
CIO: Donald Lalonde
IT Man: Lori Neupert
Netwrk Eng: Aimee Moll
Sfty Mgr: Gloria Bowman
Advt Mgr: Doug Champagne
Mktg Mgr: Karen Quaas
Corp Couns: Adrian Haynes
Board of Directors: Andrew B Lapeyre, Charles Lapeyre, James M Lapeyre Jr, Philip F Lapeyre, Robert S Lapeyre, Monique Lapeyre McCleskey

D-U-N-S 09-604-8855 IMP
LAITRAM MACHINERY INC
220 Laitram Ln, Harahan, LA 70123-5308
Tel (504) 733-6000 *Founded/Ownrshp* 1980
Sales 40.4MM^E *EMP* 125
SIC 5084 7359 3556 Food products machinery; Food product manufacturing machinery; Equipment rental & leasing; Food product manufacturing machinery; Equipment rental & leasing; Food products machinery
CEO: James M Lapeyre
**Sec:* Lawrence Oertling
Dir IT: Chris Creel
Dir IT: Patricia Smith
Dir IT: Mark Sutton
Software D: Jared Mumphrey
Prd Mgr: Wayne Waguespack
Sales Asso: Annie Edwards

D-U-N-S 08-250-0943
LAKE & PENINSULA SCHOOL DISTRICT
101 Jensen Dr, King Salmon, AK 99613
Tel (907) 533-3220 *Founded/Ownrshp* 1976
Sales 18.1MM^E *EMP* 350
SIC 8211 Public combined elementary & secondary school; Public elementary school; School board; Public combined elementary & secondary school; Public elementary school; School board
Dir IT: David Smith

D-U-N-S 00-625-2035 IMP
LAKE AIR METAL STAMPING LLC (MN)
TABER BUSHNELL
7709 Winpark Dr, Minneapolis, MN 55427-2060
Tel (763) 546-0994 *Founded/Ownrshp* 1958, 2001
Sales 38.0MM^E *EMP* 150
SIC 3469 3544 Metal stampings; Industrial molds; Metal stampings; Industrial molds
CEO: Brad Severson
**CFO:* Carol Scott
Mktg Dir: Bruce Grant

D-U-N-S 00-618-9975
LAKE AND PARK SCHOOL
3201 Hunter Blvd S, Seattle, WA 98144-7029
Tel (206) 721-3480 *Founded/Ownrshp* 2010
Sales 636.4M *EMP* 343
Accts Jones & Associates Llc Cpas S
SIC 8211 Elementary & secondary schools; Elementary & secondary schools
Prin: Camille Hayward

D-U-N-S 07-255-9644
LAKE APOPKA NATURAL GAS DISTRICT (INC)
1320 Wntr Gdn Vnlnd Rd, Winter Garden, FL 34787-4341
Tel (407) 656-2734 *Founded/Ownrshp* 1959
Sales 24.0MM^E *EMP* 52
SIC 4924 Natural gas distribution; Natural gas distribution
Genl Mgr: George Crabtree

D-U-N-S 80-029-9047
LAKE AREA CORN PROCESSORS CO-OPERATIVE
46269 Sd Highway 34, Wentworth, SD 57075-6934
Tel (605) 483-2676 *Founded/Ownrshp* 1999
Sales 96.4MM *EMP* 40^E
Accts Mcgladrey & Pullen Llp Des M
SIC 2869 Ethanolamines; Ethanolamines
Pr: Greg Vanzaten
**Treas:* Roger Orton
**VP:* Doyle Paul

LAKE AREA MEDICAL CENTER
See WOMEN & CHILDRENS HOSPITAL LLC

D-U-N-S 05-005-5458
LAKE ARROWHEAD COMMUNITY SERVICES DISTRICT (CA)
L A C S D
28200 Highway 189, Lake Arrowhead, CA 92352-9700
Tel (909) 336-1359 *Founded/Ownrshp* 1961, 1978
Sales 31.8MM^E *EMP* 65
Accts Leaf & Cole Llp San Diego C
SIC 4941 Water supply
Genl Mgr: Marvin Shaw
Bd of Dir: Ralph Wagner
VP: David Hur
Genl Mgr: Leo Havener
Opers Mgr: Matt Brooks

D-U-N-S 80-554-3845
LAKE ATK CITY AMMUNITION
101 N M 7 Hwy, Independence, MO 64056
Tel (816) 796-7101 *Founded/Ownrshp* 2000
Sales 228.8MM^E *EMP* 2,800
SIC 3761 Rockets, space & military, complete; Rockets, space & military, complete
CEO: Mark W Deyoung
**Pr:* Karen Davis
**VP:* Mark Hissong
Opers Mgr: Kerry Bricker

D-U-N-S 00-199-8566
LAKE BEVERAGE CORP (NY)
900 John St, West Henrietta, NY 14586-9748
Tel (585) 427-0090 *Founded/Ownrshp* 1933, 1973
Sales 42.2MM^E *EMP* 85
SIC 5181 Beer & other fermented malt liquors; Beer & other fermented malt liquors
Ch: Horst H Schroeder
**Pr:* Bernard H Schroeder
**VP:* Jeff Dodsworth
CTO: Wendy Felker
Opers Mgr: Robbie Ratliff
Sls&Mrk Ex: John Mula

D-U-N-S 06-442-0755 IMP/EXP
LAKE BOOK MANUFACTURING INC
2085 Cornell Ave, Melrose Park, IL 60160-1002
Tel (708) 345-7000 *Founded/Ownrshp* 1970
Sales 82.3MM^E *EMP* 300
SIC 2732 Book printing; Bookbinding & related work; Books: printing & binding
CEO: Ralph P Genovese
**Pr:* Dan Genovese
**Pr:* Bill Richards
**VP:* Robert Flatow
VP: Bill Flavin
**VP:* Paul Genovese
**VP:* Nick Vergoth
IT Man: Joseph Bongiovanni
Sfty Dirs: John Sarrantino
Mfg Mgr: Steve Quagliato
Opers Mgr: Ed Coco

D-U-N-S 14-866-0194
LAKE BRANTLEY PLANT CORP
1931 W Lake Brantley Rd, Longwood, FL 32779-4794
Tel (407) 869-6545 *Founded/Ownrshp* 1984
Sales 46.0MM^E *EMP* 75
SIC 5193 Nursery stock
Pr: Daniel J Klinger
**Treas:* William L Klinger
**VP:* Paul E Klinger Jr
Off Mgr: Ashley Klinger

D-U-N-S 05-906-4139
LAKE BUSINESS PRODUCTS INC
37200 Research Dr, Eastlake, OH 44095-1869
Tel (440) 953-1199 *Founded/Ownrshp* 1962
Sales 38.2MM^E *EMP* 175
SIC 5044 5065 5112

D-U-N-S 92-741-0308 IMP
LAKE CABLE LLC
529 Thomas Dr, Bensenville, IL 60106-1620
Tel (847) 238-3000 *Founded/Ownrshp* 1995
Sales 71.0MM *EMP* 194
SIC 3496 Miscellaneous fabricated wire products; Miscellaneous fabricated wire products
Pr: William Runzel
**COO:* Emile Tohme
**CFO:* Mary Oziemkowski
**Ex VP:* John Murakami
Opers Mgr: Joel Gonzalez
Plnt Mgr: Bill Ballinger
Plnt Mgr: Alberto Borja
Prd Mgr: Gabriel Lutin
VP Sls: Everett McCarty
Sls Mgr: Julie Ketter
Sls Mgr: Somie Mossell

D-U-N-S 16-724-8983
LAKE CABLE OF INDIANA LLC
2700 Evans Ave, Valparaiso, IN 46383-4440
Tel (847) 238-3000 *Founded/Ownrshp* 2003
Sales 29.7MM^E *EMP* 103
SIC 3496 Miscellaneous fabricated wire products
Pr: William L Runzel
**CFO:* Mary Oziemkowski

D-U-N-S 85-842-1030
LAKE CAPITAL MANAGEMENT LLC
676 N Michigan Ave # 3900, Chicago, IL 60611-2896
Tel (312) 640-7050 *Founded/Ownrshp* 1995
Sales 475.7MM^E *EMP* 11,735
SIC 6799

LAKE CAPOTE PARK
See SOUTHERN UTE INDIAN TRIBE

LAKE CATHERINE FOOTWEAR CO
See MUNRO & CO INC

D-U-N-S 78-407-7646
LAKE CENTER INDUSTRIES TRANSPORTATION INC
T R W
(*Suby of* KELSEY-HAYES CO) ★
5676 Industrial Park Rd, Winona, MN 55987-1420
Tel (507) 457-3750 *Founded/Ownrshp* 2006
Sales 41.2MM^E *EMP* 250
SIC 4213 Trucking, except local; Trucking, except local
CEO: John Plant
**Genl Mgr:* Ken Kaiser

D-U-N-S 07-701-4660
LAKE CENTRAL SCHOOL CORP
8260 Wicker Ave, Saint John, IN 46373-9711
Tel (219) 365-8507 *Founded/Ownrshp* 1967
Sales 76.4MM^E *EMP* 1,300
SIC 8211 Public combined elementary & secondary school; Public special education school; Public combined elementary & secondary school; Public special education school
Treas: Lorri Miskus
**Prin:* Al Gandolfi
Dir Sec: Brett Sidenbender

D-U-N-S 00-685-0184
LAKE CHAMPLAIN TRANSPORTATION CO (VT)
BURLINGTON FERRY
1 King St, Burlington, VT 05401-5275
Tel (802) 864-9804 *Founded/Ownrshp* 1826, 2000
Sales 22.3MM^E *EMP* 150
SIC 4482 Ferries; Car lighters (ferries); Ferries; Car lighters (ferries)
Pr: Ray Pecor III
Treas: Henry Sorrell
Board of Directors: Patrick Robins, Alan Sylvester

D-U-N-S 09-518-0519 IMP
■ **LAKE CHARLES LNG CO LLC**
(*Suby of* ENERGY TRANSFER EQUITY LP) ★
1300 Main St, Houston, TX 77002-6803
Tel (713) 989-2000 *Founded/Ownrshp* 2014
Sales 62.5MM^E *EMP* 79
SIC 4923 Gas transmission & distribution; Gas transmission & distribution
CEO: Kelcy L Warren
**Pr:* Richard A Cargile
**Pr:* Marshall S McCrea III
**CFO:* Martin Salinas
**Ex VP:* Ryan Coffey
Off Mgr: Fay Riggs

LAKE CHARLES MEMORIAL HOSPITAL
See SOUTHWEST LOUISIANA HOSPITAL ASSOCIATION

D-U-N-S 12-511-8294
LAKE CHARLES MEMORIAL HOSPITAL
1701 Oak Park Blvd, Lake Charles, LA 70601-8911
Tel (337) 494-2121 *Founded/Ownrshp* 2002
Sales 132.5MM *EMP* 4^E
SIC 8011 General & family practice, physician/surgeon; General & family practice, physician/surgeon
Prin: James Maze

D-U-N-S 03-430-9690 IMP
LAKE CHARLES RUBBER & GASKET CO LLC
930 3rd Ave, Lake Charles, LA 70601-4639
Tel (337) 433-1002 *Founded/Ownrshp* 1957
Sales 23.7MM^E *EMP* 30
SIC 5085 Industrial supplies; Hose, belting & packing; Gaskets; Industrial fittings
Sls Mgr: Allen Billups

LAKE CHELAN COMMUNITY HOSPITAL
See CHELAN COUNTY PUBLIC HOSPITAL DIST 2

D-U-N-S 00-880-1693
LAKE CHEVROLET (CA)
31201 Auto Center Dr, Lake Elsinore, CA 92530
Tel (951) 674-3116 *Founded/Ownrshp* 1998
Sales 48.1MM^E *EMP* 133
SIC 5511 7515 5521 Automobiles, new & used; Passenger car leasing; Used car dealers; Automobiles, new & used; Passenger car leasing; Used car dealers
Pr: Robert Gregory
**Pr:* Renard Bergstrom
S&M/VP: Ray Knight

D-U-N-S 08-792-0831
■ **LAKE CITY BANK**
(*Suby of* LAKELAND FINANCIAL CORP) ★
202 E Center St, Warsaw, IN 46580-2853
Tel (574) 267-6144 *Founded/Ownrshp* 1999
Sales NA *EMP* 400
SIC 6022 6163 State commercial banks; Loan brokers; State commercial banks; Loan brokers
Pr: David M Findlay
**Ch Bd:* Michael L Kubacki
Pr: Mary Horan
CFO: Lisa M O'Neill
Treas: Ken Mishler
Chf Cred: Michael E Gavin
Chf Inves: Andrew R Haddock
Ofcr: Jared Burns
Ofcr: Laura Hartley
Ofcr: Eric Neuenschwander
Ofcr: Ben Rice
Ofcr: Eric Wagoner
Ofcr: Michelle Wedeven
Trst Ofcr: James Westerfield
Ex VP: Kevin L Deardorff
Sr VP: Andrew Haddock
Sr VP: Meyer Kretchman
Sr VP: Bill Redman
Sr VP: Jonathan P Steiner
VP: Drew Dunlavy
VP: Lisa Fulton
Board of Directors: Blake W Augsburger, Daniel F Evans Jr, Brian J Smith, Brad Toothaker, Ron Truex

D-U-N-S 60-659-8642
LAKE CITY COMMUNITY HOSPITAL
LOWER FLORENCE COUNTY HOSPITAL
258 N Ron Mcnair Blvd, Lake City, SC 29560-2462
Tel (843) 374-2036 *Founded/Ownrshp* 2005
Sales 53.3MM^E *EMP* 278
SIC 8062 General medical & surgical hospitals; General medical & surgical hospitals
Prin: Mary Chandler Duke
CFO: Butch McCutcheon
Ofcr: Henry McCutcheon
Ofcr: Ann Poston
Dir Case M: Lois Miles
Dir Lab: Loretta Isaac
Dir Rx: Sherry Galloway
QA Dir: Deniel Dickson
Dir IT: Frida Evans
Sfty Dirs: Mike Faucett
Plnt Mgr: Mike Faucette

LAKE CITY FORGE
See LC MANUFACTURING LLC

LAKE CITY MEDICAL CENTER
See NOTAMI HOSPITALS OF FLORIDA INC

D-U-N-S 07-844-1920
LAKE CLEAR CITY WATER AUTHORITY
900 Bay Area Blvd, Houston, TX 77058-2691
Tel (281) 488-1164 *Founded/Ownrshp* 1963
Sales 23.5MM *EMP* 60
Accts Mccall Gibson Swedlund Barfoot
SIC 4941 Water supply; Water supply
COO: David Plaisance
VP: Bill Farries
IT Man: Shirley Kelly
IT Man: Taleen Moore

D-U-N-S 60-984-3388 IMP
LAKE CLEAR PARTNERS LTD
HONDA OF CLEAR LAKE
20233 Gulf Fwy, Webster, TX 77598-4809
Tel (281) 338-6666 *Founded/Ownrshp* 1989
Sales 22.8MM^E *EMP* 55
SIC 5511 Automobiles, new & used
Pt: Tom Tyrrell
Pt: Nick Hill
Genl Mgr: Harvey Bishop
Sls Dir: Bennett Johnson
Sls Mgr: Samir Al-Busaidy
Sls Mgr: Samir Busaidy

D-U-N-S 03-803-3200
LAKE CLEAR VOLKSWAGEN
15100 Gulf Fwy, Houston, TX 77034-5357
Tel (281) 848-5500 *Founded/Ownrshp* 2002
Sales 28.0MM^E *EMP* 100
SIC 5511 Automobiles, new & used; Automobiles, new & used
Pr: Anthony Mitchell

D-U-N-S 18-629-8642
LAKE COUNTRY CHEVROLET CADILLAC LLC
144 W Shawnee St, Muskogee, OK 74401-4147
Tel (918) 683-0311 *Founded/Ownrshp* 2001
Sales 24.2MM^E *EMP* 70
SIC 5511 Automobiles, new & used; Pickups, new & used; Automobiles, new & used; Pickups, new & used
Off Mgr: Shirley Miranda
Store Mgr: Gary Andrews
Sls Mgr: Zac Jones
Sls Mgr: Greg Stout

D-U-N-S 06-729-1187
LAKE COUNTRY CORP
CROWNE PLAZA LANSING WEST
(*Suby of* AUTO-OWNERS INSURANCE CO) ★
925 S Creyts Rd, Lansing, MI 48917-9222
Tel (517) 323-7100 *Founded/Ownrshp* 1982
Sales 42.0MM^E *EMP* 1^E
SIC 7011 Hotels & motels
CEO: Jeffrey Harrold
**Pr:* Jeffrey Tagsold
**Ex VP:* Rodney Rupp

D-U-N-S 13-019-1711
LAKE COUNTRY CORP
225 Commerce St, Mayville, WI 53050-1421
Tel (800) 472-5720 *Founded/Ownrshp* 1985
Sales 28.2MM^E *EMP* 45
SIC 5162 3089 5085 Plastics materials; Plastic processing; Industrial supplies
CEO: Richard Gillette
**Pr:* Alan Gillette
VP: Ronald Hron
VP: Lauren Rankin
**VP:* James Underberg

D-U-N-S 79-728-6754 IMP/EXP
LAKE COUNTRY FOODS INC
LCFMGF
132 S Concord Rd, Oconomowoc, WI 53066-3555
Tel (262) 567-5521 *Founded/Ownrshp* 1998
Sales 27.0MM^E *EMP* 95
SIC 2066 2099 Cocoa & cocoa products; Sauces: dry mixes; Gravy mixes, dry; Cocoa & cocoa products; Sauces: dry mixes; Gravy mixes, dry
Pr: Phillip Kemppianen
**CFO:* Josh Waltenberry
**Ex VP:* Myron Jones
**VP:* Phillip K Vanderhyden
Site Mgr: Mike Hans
Opers Mgr: Ryan Klemme
Plnt Mgr: Tom Gnewuch

LAKE COUNTY ADMINISTRATION CTR
See COUNTY OF LAKE

LAKE COUNTY BOCC
See COUNTY OF LAKE

D-U-N-S 07-674-8870
LAKE COUNTY COMMUNITY COLLEGE DISTRICT
LAKELAND COMMUNITY COLLEGE
7700 Clocktower Dr, Willoughby, OH 44094-5198
Tel (440) 525-7000 *Founded/Ownrshp* 1967
Sales 16.5MM *EMP* 1,100^E
Accts Plante & Moran Pllc Clevelan
SIC 8222 Community college; Community college
Pr: Morris W Beverage Jr
**CFO:* Michael E Mayher
**VP:* Mary Ann Plakeley
**VP:* Dawn Plante
Exec: Cathy Bush
**Prin:* Margaret Sbartow
Off Admin: Bernice Connolly
Off Admin: Karen Tarasco
CTO: Tiffany Heindel
Psych: Sarah Amoroso
Psych: Ricky Amster

D-U-N-S 09-253-3637
LAKE COUNTY FAMILY YMCA
980 N Michigan Ave # 1400, Chicago, IL 60611-4501
Tel (847) 360-5676 *Founded/Ownrshp* 1895
Sales 12.5MM^E *EMP* 300
Accts Craig & Associates Llc Northb
SIC 8641 8322 Youth organizations; Recreation association; Individual & family services

D-U-N-S 08-963-4273
LAKE COUNTY FOREST PRESERVE DISTRICT
1899 W Winchester Rd, Libertyville, IL 60048-5367
Tel (847) 367-6640 *Founded/Ownrshp* 1958
Sales 56.6MM *EMP* 300
Accts Mcgladrey Llp Schaumburg Ill
SIC 0851 Forest management services; Forest management services
Pr: Ann B Maine
VP: Carol Calabresa
**VP:* Linda Pedersen
Ex Dir: Thomas Hahn

Ex Dir: Alex Kovach
IT Man: Michael Stevensen

D-U-N-S 02-434-1182
LAKE COUNTY INTERNATIONAL INC
45313 Sd Highway 34, Madison, SD 57042-6810
Tel (605) 256-3521 *Founded/Ownrshp* 1962
Sales 25.8MM *EMP* 19
Accts Thurman Comes Foley & Co Llp
SIC 5083 7699 Agricultural machinery & equipment; Farm machinery repair; Agricultural machinery & equipment; Farm machinery repair
Pr: Jeffrey Bloom
**VP:* Tom Bloom

D-U-N-S 07-686-5260
LAKE COUNTY OF INDIANA
LAKE COUNTY PARKS
2293 N Main St, Crown Point, IN 46307-1854
Tel (219) 755-3465 *Founded/Ownrshp* 1937
Sales NA *EMP* 2,552
SIC 9111 ;
**Treas:* Peggy Holinga
Ofcr: Oscar Martinez
Ofcr: Steven Trajkovich
Ofcr: John Zenone
Ex Dir: Milan Grozdanich
Brnch Mgr: John Dull
Genl Mgr: Anna Nunez
IT Man: Lori Burke
Sls Mgr: Brenda Koselke
Snr Mgr: Edward Davies
Snr Mgr: Dan Murchek

LAKE COUNTY PARKS
See LAKE COUNTY OF INDIANA

D-U-N-S 05-191-9041
LAKE COUNTY PRESS INC
98 Noll St, Waukegan, IL 60085-3031
Tel (847) 336-4333 *Founded/Ownrshp* 1970
Sales 87.2MM^E *EMP* 223^E
SIC 2791 7334 Typesetting; Blueprinting service; Typesetting; Blueprinting service
Pr: Ralph L Johnson
Pr: Ned Steck
**Sr VP:* Peter Douglas
**Sr VP:* Robert Hilliard
Sr VP: Russ Schoenherr
**VP:* Russell Schoenherr
Opers Mgr: Mark Hammel
Plnt Mgr: Dan Murphy
Plnt Mgr: Thomas Oberembt
Sales Asso: Mark Boothe

D-U-N-S 07-921-4185
LAKE COUNTY SCHOOLS
201 W Burleigh Blvd, Tavares, FL 32778-2407
Tel (352) 253-6500 *Founded/Ownrshp* 1950
Sales 134.1MM^E *EMP* 3,777
Accts Auditor General State Of Flori
SIC 8211 Public elementary & secondary schools; Public elementary school; Public junior high school; Public senior high school; Public elementary & secondary schools; Public elementary school; Public junior high school; Public senior high school
**Ch Bd:* Debbie Stivender
**Ch:* Larry Metz

D-U-N-S 08-232-6992
LAKE COUNTY YMCA
933 Mentor Ave Fl 2, Painesville, OH 44077-2519
Tel (440) 352-3303 *Founded/Ownrshp* 1867
Sales 18.3MM^E *EMP* 575
Accts Neece Malec Seifert & Vitaz C
SIC 8641 7991 8351 7032 8322 Youth organizations; Physical fitness facilities; Child day care services; Youth camps; Individual & family services; Youth organizations; Physical fitness facilities; Child day care services; Youth camps; Individual & family services
CEO: Richard Bennett
COO: Bob Diak
Ex Dir: Jessica Martin
Off Mgr: C Frisby
Pgrm Dir: Elaine Barnard
Pgrm Dir: Abby Begeman
Pgrm Dir: Greg Church
Pgrm Dir: Kevin Sraj
Snr Mgr: Scott Taylor

D-U-N-S 78-748-1746 IMP
LAKE COURT MEDICAL SUPPLIES INC
27733 Groesbeck Hwy, Roseville, MI 48066-2758
Tel (800) 860-3130 *Founded/Ownrshp* 1991
Sales 88.9MM^E *EMP* 65^E
SIC 5047 Medical equipment & supplies
Pr: Charles Elliott
**CFO:* Sandy Wagner
VP Sls: Phil Benvenuti
Mktg Dir: William Troesken
Sls Mgr: Dan Neill

D-U-N-S 01-534-0796
LAKE CUMBERLAND DISTRICT HEALTH DEPARTMENT
LCDHD
500 Bourne Ave, Somerset, KY 42501-1916
Tel (606) 678-4761 *Founded/Ownrshp* 2010
Sales 22.4MM^E *EMP* 270
SIC 8621 Health association; Health association
Ex Dir: Shawn D Crabtree

D-U-N-S 06-830-2314
LAKE CUMBERLAND REGIONAL MENTAL HEALTH-MENTAL RETARDATION BOARD INC
ADANTA GROUP, THE
130 Southern School Rd, Somerset, KY 42501-3223
Tel (606) 679-4782 *Founded/Ownrshp* 1966
Sales 25.3MM *EMP* 500
Accts Phillips & Phillips Barbourvi
SIC 8322 General counseling services; General counseling services
CEO: Jamie S Burton
Treas: Nola Mills
Ofcr: Dan Luchtefeld
VP: Byron Owens

Ex Dir: Judy Wilson
MIS Dir: Linda Adams
IT Man: Tracie Horton

D-U-N-S 00-777-8665
LAKE DALLAS INDEPENDENT SCHOOL DISTRICT
315 E Hundley Dr, Lake Dallas, TX 75065-2629
Tel (940) 497-5244 *Founded/Ownrshp* 1929
Sales 21.6MM^E *EMP* 450
SIC 8299 8211 Educational services; Public elementary school; Educational services; Public elementary school
Trst: Tim Hicks
Trst: Courtney Tankersley
Pr Dir: Melaynee Broadstreet

D-U-N-S 80-094-0959
LAKE DEVILS PUBLIC SCHOOL DISTRICT
DEVILS LAKE PUBLIC SCHOOL
1601 College Dr N, Devils Lake, ND 58301-1550
Tel (701) 662-1200 *Founded/Ownrshp* 1992
Sales 11.7MM^E *EMP* 278
SIC 8211 Public elementary & secondary schools; Public elementary & secondary schools

D-U-N-S 17-354-7183
LAKE ELECTRIC CO INC
4362 Providence Mill Rd, Maiden, NC 28650-8594
Tel (704) 483-4000 *Founded/Ownrshp* 1988
Sales 26.6MM^E *EMP* 100
SIC 1731 General electrical contractor
Pr: Bynum D Caldwell

D-U-N-S 07-880-3615
LAKE ELK CAPITAL LLC (PA)
149 Penn Ave, Scranton, PA 18503-2055
Tel (570) 348-9101 *Founded/Ownrshp* 2011
Sales 23.0MM^E *EMP* 115^E
SIC 6799 Investors
Mng Pt: Matthew E Haggerty
**Mng Pt:* Robert J Lynett

D-U-N-S 05-314-4189
LAKE ELSINORE FORD INC
450 W Vista Way, Vista, CA 92083-5829
Tel (760) 945-9900 *Founded/Ownrshp* 1998
Sales 37.5MM^E *EMP* 202
SIC 5521 5511 Used car dealers; Automobiles, new & used; Used car dealers; Automobiles, new & used
Pr: Jeffrey Freistedt

D-U-N-S 01-350-3255
LAKE ELSINORE UNIFIED SCHOOL DISTRICT
ACOUNTS PAYABLE DEPT
545 Chaney St, Lake Elsinore, CA 92530-2712
Tel (951) 253-7000 *Founded/Ownrshp* 1884
Sales 78.1MM^E *EMP* 1,919
SIC 8211 Public elementary school; Public elementary school
IT Man: Carol Cole

D-U-N-S 79-731-5348
LAKE ERIE COLLEGE OF OSTEOPATHIC MEDICINE INC
LECOM
1858 W Grandview Blvd, Erie, PA 16509-1025
Tel (814) 866-3986 *Founded/Ownrshp* 1993
Sales 124.6MM *EMP* 180
Accts Carbis Walker Llp Pittsburgh
SIC 8221 Colleges universities & professional schools; Colleges universities & professional schools
Pr: John M Ferretti
**Treas:* Richard Olinger
Ofcr: Denay Hunter
**VP:* Hershey Bell
**VP:* Silvia M Ferretti
**VP:* Irving Freeman
Mng Dir: Richard Raymond
Genl Mgr: Gregory Balo
IT Man: Keith Hein
VP Mktg: Robert George
Pathlgst: Lisa Stevens

D-U-N-S 09-217-2824
LAKE ERIE MEDICAL & SURGICAL SUPPLY INC
7560 Lewis Ave, Temperance, MI 48182-9539
Tel (734) 847-3847 *Founded/Ownrshp* 1978
Sales 24.9MM^E *EMP* 66
Accts Plante & Moran Pllc Toledo O
SIC 5047 3826 3841 Medical & hospital equipment; Analytical instruments; Surgical & medical instruments
Pr: Michael W Holmes
**Treas:* Jeannie Sieren
**VP:* Robert Holmes
**Prin:* Joeseph Braker

D-U-N-S 07-458-6678
LAKE FOREST ACADEMY
1500 W Kennedy Rd, Lake Forest, IL 60045-1099
Tel (847) 234-3210 *Founded/Ownrshp* 1857
Sales 27.7MM *EMP* 102
Accts Pasquest Sheppard Llc Lake Fo
SIC 8211 Preparatory school; Preparatory school
Pr: John Strudwick
**CFO:* Andrew Kerr
Comm Dir: Ruth Keyso

D-U-N-S 55-627-8224
■ **LAKE FOREST BANK AND TRUST CO**
(*Suby of* WINTRUST FINANCIAL CORP) ★
727 N Bank Ln Fl 1, Lake Forest, IL 60045-1898
Tel (847) 234-2882 *Founded/Ownrshp* 1997
Sales NA *EMP* 211
SIC 6022 State commercial banks; State commercial banks
Pr: David E Lee
Ch Bd: Edward Wehmer
CFO: David A Dykstra
Ch: John J Meierhoff
Ofcr: Zack Adamovic
Ofcr: Sitha Bouy
Ofcr: Lisa Meggs
Ofcr: Katie Wiswald

Ex VP: Lynn Cleave
Ex VP: Kurt Prinz
Sr VP: David Bruskin
Sr VP: James Draths
Sr VP: Lori Higgins
Sr VP: Mark Jacobson
Sr VP: Thomas Littau
Sr VP: Louman Mancusi
Sr VP: Casandra Slade
VP: Christopher Baker
VP: Paul Blake
VP: Kelly Breasbois
VP: Brad Bremen

D-U-N-S 07-458-3899
LAKE FOREST COLLEGE
555 N Sheridan Rd, Lake Forest, IL 60045-2399
Tel (847) 234-3100 *Founded/Ownrshp* 1857
Sales 107.9MM *EMP* 385
SIC 8221 College, except junior; College, except junior
V Ch: Peter G Schiff
**Pr:* Stephen D Schutt
**Treas:* Leslie T Chapman
Trst: Daniel Gescheidle
Trst: Robert Lansing
VP: Lisa Hinkley
**VP:* Philip R Hood
**VP:* Bill Motzer
**VP:* Fred Vansickle
Trfc Dir: James Rissell
Schl Brd P: David Harris

D-U-N-S 09-530-7443
LAKE FOREST COMMUNITY HIGH SCHOOL DISTRICT 115
300 S Waukegan Rd, Lake Forest, IL 60045-2643
Tel (847) 234-3600 *Founded/Ownrshp* 1949
Sales 55.1MM *EMP* 308^E
Accts Miller Cooper & Co Ltd De
SIC 8211 Public senior high school; Public senior high school
Bd of Dir: Dick Block
Bd of Dir: Ingrid Booker
Bd of Dir: B Edson
Bd of Dir: Ted Moorman
Bd of Dir: John Powers
Bd of Dir: Dave Schreiber
Top Exec: Jaclyn Cardenas
Top Exec: Chris Chouinard
Top Exec: Steve Clegg
Top Exec: Candice Davenport
Top Exec: Alison Gildemeister
Top Exec: Jay Kleeman
Top Exec: Shelly Lindsey
Top Exec: Megan Miles
Top Exec: Denise Murphy
Top Exec: Kurt Schuessler
Top Exec: Kyle Wilhelm

D-U-N-S 61-672-1148
LAKE FOREST HOSPITAL FOUNDATION
660 N Westmoreland Rd, Lake Forest, IL 60045-1659
Tel (847) 234-5600 *Founded/Ownrshp* 1982
Sales 63.9MM^E *EMP* 1,500
SIC 8062 General medical & surgical hospitals; General medical & surgical hospitals
CEO: Thomas McAsee
Chf Rad: Ahmed Faraq
CFO: Regina Rizzo
Bd of Dir: Robert Shaw
VP: Mathew Koschmann
Dir Risk M: Richard Paulus
Dir Rx: Satya RAO
Ex Dir: Jane Paley
Brnch Mgr: Vida Ludington
Genl Mgr: Rich Menely
Dir IT: Sue Atkinson

D-U-N-S 10-218-3373
LAKE FOREST PUBLIC SCHOOL DISTRICT 67
300 S Waukegan Rd, Lake Forest, IL 60045-2643
Tel (847) 234-6010 *Founded/Ownrshp* 1869
Sales 12.4MM^E *EMP* 285
Accts Milburn Cain & Co Gurnee Il
SIC 8211 8741 Public elementary & secondary schools; Public junior high school; Management services; Public elementary & secondary schools; Public junior high school; Management services
Bd of Dir: Laurie Rose
MIS Dir: Cornelius D Bose
Dir IT: Grace Frantz

D-U-N-S 12-487-6046
LAKE FOREST SCHOOL DISTRICT
5423 Killens Pond Rd, Felton, DE 19943-1901
Tel (302) 284-3020 *Founded/Ownrshp* 1970
Sales 29.8MM^E *EMP* 400
SIC 8211 Public elementary & secondary schools; Public elementary & secondary schools
Prin: Daniel Curry
MIS Dir: Ron Usilton

LAKE FRONT SUPPLY
See JESUS PEOPLE USA FULL GOSPEL MINISTRIES

D-U-N-S 10-008-3195
LAKE GENEVA-GENOA CITY UNION HIGH SCHOOL DISTRICT
208 E South St, Lake Geneva, WI 53147-2436
Tel (262) 348-1000 *Founded/Ownrshp* 1872
Sales 25.7MM^E *EMP* 400
SIC 8211 Public elementary & secondary schools; Public elementary & secondary schools

D-U-N-S 03-043-2033
LAKE GRENADA MEDICAL CENTER INC
UMMC GRENADA
960 Avent Dr, Grenada, MS 38901-5230
Tel (662) 227-7000 *Founded/Ownrshp* 1967
Sales 51.5MM *EMP* 360^E
SIC 8062 8082 General medical & surgical hospitals; Home health care services; General medical & surgical hospitals; Home health care services
CEO: David Putt
**CFO:* John Harrington
CFO: Keith Heartsill

Ofcr: Tracie Turbeville
Ex VP: Kevin Whalley
Dir Rx: Valorie Woods
QA Dir: Diana Jones
QA Dir: Joyce Williams
Doctor: Eddy Cresswell
Doctor: Cynthia Dotson

D-U-N-S 03-862-7196
LAKE GULL COMMUNITY SCHOOLS INC
11775 E D Ave, Richland, MI 49083-9669
Tel (269) 488-5000 *Founded/Ownrshp* 1962
Sales 29.2MM *EMP* 310
Accts Plante & Moran Pllc Portage
SIC 8211 Public elementary school; Public junior high school; Public senior high school; School board; Public elementary school; Public junior high school; Public senior high school; School board
Off Mgr: Bonnie Kuepser
MIS Dir: Tony Nuisner
IT Man: Lynn Hittle
Site Mgr: Whitney Brockway
Psych: Sandy Schreiber

D-U-N-S 83-544-3805
LAKE HAMILTON SCHOOL DISTRICT
205 Wolf St, Pearcy, AR 71964-9449
Tel (501) 760-6800 *Founded/Ownrshp* 1945
Sales 32.6MM^E *EMP* 500
SIC 8211 Public elementary & secondary schools; Public elementary & secondary schools
**VP:* Mark Curry
Ex Dir: Kay Ekey
Schl Brd P: Vance Dobyns

D-U-N-S 00-654-5164
LAKE HARLEYSVILLE STATES INSURANCE CO
(*Suby of* HARLEYSVILLE GROUP INC) ★
600 E Front St Ste 200, Traverse City, MI 49686-2892
Tel (231) 946-6390 *Founded/Ownrshp* 1915
Sales NA *EMP* 50
Accts Kpmg Llp
SIC 6331 Fire, marine & casualty insurance; Property damage insurance; Fire, marine & casualty insurance; Property damage insurance
Pr: Daniel E Barr
Treas: Mark Cummins
VP: Richard A Fasa

LAKE HARRIS HEALTH CENTER
See LAKE PORT PROPERTIES LLC

D-U-N-S 00-290-2351
LAKE HAVASU UNIFIED SCHOOL DISTRICT 1
2200 Havasupai Blvd, Lake Havasu City, AZ 86403-3122
Tel (928) 505-6900 *Founded/Ownrshp* 1964
Sales 39.9MM^E *EMP* 700
Accts Heinfeld Meech & Co Pc C
SIC 8211 Public elementary & secondary schools; Public elementary & secondary schools
Bd of Dir: Juliane Grandell
Off Admin: Billie Vandenheuvel
Netwrk Mgr: Ellen Went
Netwrk Mgr: Becky Yost
Schl Brd P: Jo Navaretta
Teacher Pr: Denise Minor

LAKE HEALTH
See LAKE HOSPITAL SYSTEM INC

D-U-N-S 04-132-7099
LAKE HEMET MUNICIPAL WATER DISTRICT (INC)
26385 Fairview Ave, Hemet, CA 92544-6607
Tel (951) 927-1816 *Founded/Ownrshp* 1955
Sales 24.6MM^E *EMP* 58
Accts Cox Valdez & Silbermann Heme
SIC 4941 4971 Water supply; Water distribution or supply systems for irrigation
Genl Mgr: Tom Wagoner

D-U-N-S 08-472-4400
LAKE HIGHLAND PREPARATORY SCHOOL INC
901 Highland Ave, Orlando, FL 32803-3233
Tel (407) 206-1900 *Founded/Ownrshp* 1970
Sales 37.5MM^E *EMP* 500
Accts Batts Morrison Wales & Lee Pa
SIC 8211 Private combined elementary & secondary school; Kindergarten; Private elementary & secondary schools; Private combined elementary & secondary school; Kindergarten; Private elementary & secondary schools
Ch Bd: Randall Rex
**Pr:* Warren Hudson
**CFO:* Jim Bartlett
**Treas:* Robert W Meherg
Ex Dir: Robert Meherg
Store Mgr: Debbie Saul
Dir IT: Sally Obrien

D-U-N-S 61-968-0739
LAKE HOSPITAL HOME HEALTH SERVICES
7590 Auburn Rd, Painesville, OH 44077-9176
Tel (440) 639-0900 *Founded/Ownrshp* 1987
Sales 364.1MM *EMP* 50
SIC 8082 Home health care services; Home health care services
Dir OR: Mary Gallik
Dir IT: Jerry Peter
Obsttrcn: Phillip Brzozowski

D-U-N-S 07-775-7292
LAKE HOSPITAL SYSTEM INC
LAKE HEALTH
7590 Auburn Rd, Painesville, OH 44077-9176
Tel (440) 354-2400 *Founded/Ownrshp* 1902
Sales 350.6MM *EMP* 2,200
SIC 8062 General medical & surgical hospitals; General medical & surgical hospitals
Pr: Cynthia Moore-Hardy
Bd of Dir: Connie Zwegat
**Sr VP:* Richard Cicero
**Sr VP:* Michael E Kittoe
VP: Mary Ogrinc

VP: Joyce Taylor
VP: Andrea Wasdovich
Exec: Donna Colucci
Dir Inf Cn: Pat Cassella
Dir Lab: Becky Pesta
Dir Lab: Ross Waite

D-U-N-S 55-689-5949
LAKE HOSPITAL SYSTEMS
7956 Tyler Blvd, Mentor, OH 44060-4806
Tel (440) 255-6400 *Founded/Ownrshp* 2005
Sales 309.6MM *EMP* 1
Accts Plante & Moran Pllc Columbus
SIC 8062 General medical & surgical hospitals; General medical & surgical hospitals
Prin: Paul V Miotto MD

D-U-N-S 02-103-5076
LAKE HOUGHTON COMMUNITY SCHOOLS
6001 W Houghton Lake Dr, Houghton Lake, MI 48629-9704
Tel (989) 366-2032 *Founded/Ownrshp* 1928
Sales 11.4MM[E] *EMP* 300
SIC 8211 9411 Public combined elementary & secondary school; Administration of educational programs; Public combined elementary & secondary school; Administration of educational programs
Opers Mgr: John Early

D-U-N-S 07-559-8359
LAKE LAND COLLEGE
5001 Lake Land Blvd, Mattoon, IL 61938-9366
Tel (217) 234-5253 *Founded/Ownrshp* 1967
Sales 18.4MM *EMP* 1,012
Accts Doehring Winders & Co Llp
SIC 8222 8221 Junior college; Community college; Colleges universities & professional schools; Junior college; Community college; Colleges universities & professional schools
Pr: Scott Lensink
Bd of Dir: Donna Sherman
VP: Connie Compton
* *VP:* Ray Rieck
VP: Tina Stovall
CTO: Nan Caldwell
Dir IT: Lee Spaniol
IT Man: Madge Shoot

LAKE LAWN RESORT
See DELAVAN RESORT HOLDINGS LLC

D-U-N-S 09-327-9560
LAKE LOCAL BOARD OF EDUCATION
436 King Church Ave Sw, Uniontown, OH 44685-5100
Tel (330) 877-9383 *Founded/Ownrshp* 1860
Sales 16.5MM[E] *EMP* 450
SIC 8211 Public elementary school; Public junior high school; Public senior high school; School board; Public elementary school; Public junior high school; Public senior high school; School board
Pr: David Vanderkaay
* *Treas:* Robert Moffat

D-U-N-S 79-119-8463
LAKE LOCAL SCHOOL DISTRICT
436 King Church Ave Sw, Uniontown, OH 44685-5100
Tel (330) 877-9383 *Founded/Ownrshp* 2007
Sales 19.6MM[E] *EMP* 333[E]
Accts Dave Yost Auditor Of State C
SIC 8211 School board
Treas: Nicole Nichols
Bd of Dir: Scott Swartz
VP: David Vanderkaay
Exec: Phil Burns
MIS Dir: Pat Carroll
Schl Brd P: David Poling
Psych: Mike Coldsnow
Psych: Angela Rapp
Psych: Jake Thomas

D-U-N-S 01-872-2319
LAKE LONG LTD
POSTWOOD BUILDERS
15915 Katy Fwy Ste 405, Houston, TX 77094-1710
Tel (281) 646-1727 *Founded/Ownrshp* 1997
Sales 27.1MM[E] *EMP* 50
SIC 1521 Single-family housing construction
Pt: Roger B Medors

D-U-N-S 04-124-2272
LAKE MANAWA NISSAN INC
AUTOMART 150
920 32nd Ave, Council Bluffs, IA 51501-8096
Tel (712) 366-9481 *Founded/Ownrshp* 1967
Sales 39.1MM[E] *EMP* 100
SIC 5511 Automobiles, new & used; Automobiles, new & used
Pr: Dennis Gascoigne
Treas: Robert Mc Intyre
* *Treas:* Timothy L O'Neill
* *VP:* David Edwards
Sls Mgr: Art Batten
Sls Mgr: Heath Gunderson
Sls Mgr: Larry McGee

D-U-N-S 03-809-3035
LAKE METROPARKS
11211 Spear Rd, Painesville, OH 44077-8902
Tel (440) 639-7275 *Founded/Ownrshp* 1958
Sales 25.3MM *EMP* 350[E]
Accts Dave Yost Cleveland Ohio
SIC 7999 7992 Recreation services; Public golf courses; Recreation services; Public golf courses
Ex Dir: Paul Palagyi
Mktg Dir: Stella Kohler
Sls Mgr: Amy Kapostasy
Snr Mgr: Brian Fowler
Snr Mgr: John Grantham
Snr Mgr: Daniel Llewellyn
Snr Mgr: Sharon Metzung
Board of Directors: Joe Iddo

LAKE MICH COLLEGE MENDEL CTR
See LAKE MICHIGAN COLLEGE (INC)

D-U-N-S 07-891-6889
LAKE MICHIGAN COLLEGE (INC)
LAKE MICH COLLEGE MENDEL CTR
2755 E Napier Ave, Benton Harbor, MI 49022-1881
Tel (269) 927-1000 *Founded/Ownrshp* 1946
Sales 22.6MM[E] *EMP* 580
Accts Rehmann Robson Grand Rapids
SIC 8222 Community college; Community college
Ch: David Maysick
* *Pr:* Robert Harrison
* *Treas:* Michael Lindley
Ex Dir: Amy Walker
Mktg Dir: Candice Elders

D-U-N-S 07-257-7042
LAKE MICHIGAN CREDIT UNION
C U FINANCIAL GROUP
4027 Lake Dr Se Ste 100, Grand Rapids, MI 49546-8812
Tel (616) 242-9790 *Founded/Ownrshp* 1933
Sales NA *EMP* 130
SIC 6062 State credit unions, not federally chartered; State credit unions, not federally chartered
Ch Bd: Dr Marinus Swets
Pr: Sandy Jelinski
V Ch Bd: Rodger Northuis
Bd of Dir: Ken Larsen
Bd of Dir: Mike Rice
Ofcr: Chuck Bauss
Ofcr: Mark Breon
Ofcr: Laurie Cordes
Ofcr: Dave Lukomski
Ofcr: Jon Mulder
Ofcr: Jason Pewinski
Ofcr: Jordan Rupkey
Ofcr: Bill Wilson
Sr VP: Eric Burgoon
Sr VP: Mark Hoffhines
Sr VP: Jim Koessel
VP: Audrey Andrews
VP: Corbin Buttleman
VP: Carla Grice
VP: Sara Hendrickson
VP: Jim Maskell

LAKE MOULTRIE NURSING HOME
See SAINT STEPHEN NURSING FACILITY INC

LAKE NORMAN CHRYSLER JEEP DODG
See TT OF LAKE NORMAN LLC

D-U-N-S 15-846-0092
LAKE NORMAN MOTOR SALES LLC
TOYOTA NORTH CHARLOTTE
13429 Statesville Rd, Huntersville, NC 28078-9035
Tel (704) 875-9199 *Founded/Ownrshp* 2000
Sales 44.7MM[E] *EMP* 137
SIC 5511 Automobiles, new & used; Automobiles, new & used
Dir Bus: Brian Doyle
Sls Mgr: Jackie Crane
Sales Asso: Michael Brown
Sales Asso: Joseph Daniels
Sales Asso: Steve Gregory

D-U-N-S 61-195-5613
LAKE NORMAN REGIONAL MEDICAL CENTRE
171 Fairview Rd, Mooresville, NC 28117-9500
Tel (704) 660-4000 *Founded/Ownrshp* 2003
Sales 127.8MM *EMP* 21[E]
SIC 8062 General medical & surgical hospitals; General medical & surgical hospitals
CEO: Greg Lowe

D-U-N-S 02-084-2068
LAKE ORION COMMUNITY SCHOOLS
315 N Lapeer St, Lake Orion, MI 48362-3165
Tel (248) 693-5400 *Founded/Ownrshp* 1890
Sales 91.5MM *EMP* 1,000
Accts Plante & Moran Pllc Auburn Hi
SIC 8211 Public elementary & secondary schools; School board; Public elementary & secondary schools; School board
HC Dir: Heidi Mercer

D-U-N-S 03-336-3433
LAKE OSWEGO SCHOOL DISTRICT
2455 Country Club Rd, Lake Oswego, OR 97034-2024
Tel (503) 534-2000 *Founded/Ownrshp* 1800
Sales 78.9MM *EMP* 800
Accts Grove Mueller & Swank Pc
SIC 8211 Public elementary & secondary schools; School board; Public elementary & secondary schools; School board
Ofcr: Brenda Hanson
Dir IT: Robert Dreier
Dir IT: Donna Watson
Schl Brd P: Linda Brown
Schl Brd P: Liz Hartman

D-U-N-S 00-231-4529
LAKE PACIFIC PARTNERS LLC
120 S La Salle St # 1510, Chicago, IL 60603-3574
Tel (312) 578-1110 *Founded/Ownrshp* 2000
Sales 42.8MM[E] *EMP* 500
SIC 6211 3089 2013 2011 Investment firm, general brokerage; Food casings, plastic; Sausages & other prepared meats; Meat packing plants; Investment firm, general brokerage; Food casings, plastic; Sausages & other prepared meats; Meat packing plants
Adv Bd Mbr: Paul Murphy
Mng Dir: William Voss

D-U-N-S 09-176-4829
LAKE PARK COMMUNITY HIGH SCHOOL DISTRICT NO 108
LAKE PARK HIGH SCHOOL
590 Medinah Rd, Roselle, IL 60172-1978
Tel (630) 529-4500 *Founded/Ownrshp* 1955
Sales 23.4MM[E] *EMP* 325
Accts Clifton Gunderson Llc Cpa S
SIC 8211 Public elementary & secondary schools; Public elementary & secondary schools
Bd of Dir: P Olzen
Trst: Dean Bladel
Trst: Jennifer Jungel
VP: Bob Marino
IT Man: Kathleen Lovelace-Birk
IT Man: Kathleen Schenone
Netwrk Mgr: Tim Richmond
Pr Dir: Sherri Anderson
Schl Brd P: Barbara Layer
Instr Medi: Carolyn Roys

LAKE PARK HIGH SCHOOL
See LAKE PARK COMMUNITY HIGH SCHOOL DISTRICT NO 108

D-U-N-S 83-215-6884
LAKE PEND ORIELLE SCHOOL DISTRICT 84
901 N Triangle Dr, Ponderay, ID 83852-9747
Tel (208) 263-2184 *Founded/Ownrshp* 2012
Sales 20.5MM[E] *EMP* 457[E]
SIC 8211 Public elementary & secondary schools
Adm Dir: Gail Curless
MIS Dir: Randy Wittwer
Teacher Pr: Thoretta Short

LAKE POINTE HEALTH CENTER
See KOLBE LEASING CO LLC

LAKE POINTE MEDICAL CENTER
See LAKEPOINTE EMERGENCY CONSULTANTS PLLC

D-U-N-S 07-077-2268
LAKE POINTE MEDICAL CENTER
6800 Scenic Dr, Rowlett, TX 75088-4552
Tel (972) 412-2273 *Founded/Ownrshp* 2011
Sales 64.6MM[E] *EMP* 700[E]
SIC 8011 Medical centers; Medical centers
CEO: Brett Lee
COO: Eric Evans
Dir Inf Cn: Maria Sparks
Chf Nrs Of: Debbie Moeller
Dir IT: Charles Sitzes
IT Man: Susan Miklis
Phys Thrpy: Robert Montgomery
Snr Mgr: Chris Cottrell
Snr Mgr: John Lee

D-U-N-S 18-184-4531
LAKE PORT PROPERTIES LLC
LAKE HARRIS HEALTH CENTER
800 Lake Port Blvd Ofc, Leesburg, FL 34748-7654
Tel (352) 323-0889 *Founded/Ownrshp* 1986
Sales 15.7MM[E] *EMP* 400
SIC 6513 Retirement hotel operation; Retirement hotel operation

LAKE POWELL RESORTS & MARINOS
See ARAMARK SPORTS AND ENTERTAINMENT SERVICES LLC

D-U-N-S 02-433-7461
LAKE PRESTON COOPERATIVE ASSOCIATION
LAKE PRESTON FARM SUPPLY
106 2nd St Nw, Lake Preston, SD 57249
Tel (605) 847-4414 *Founded/Ownrshp* 1939
Sales 125.9MM *EMP* 30
Accts Gardiner Thomsen Pc Sioux
SIC 5153 5191 5172 Grains; Fertilizer & fertilizer materials; Feed; Chemicals, agricultural; Petroleum products; Grains; Fertilizer & fertilizer materials; Feed; Chemicals, agricultural; Petroleum products

LAKE PRESTON FARM SUPPLY
See LAKE PRESTON COOPERATIVE ASSOCIATION

D-U-N-S 08-984-7487
LAKE RANDOM SCHOOL DISTRICT
605 Random Lake Rd, Random Lake, WI 53075-1646
Tel (920) 994-2498 *Founded/Ownrshp* 1961
Sales 11.0MM[E] *EMP* 495[E]
SIC 8211 Public elementary school; Public senior high school; Public elementary school; Public senior high school

D-U-N-S 00-696-2906
LAKE REGION ELECTRIC COOPERATIVE
1401 S Brdwy, Pelican Rapids, MN 56572
Tel (218) 863-1171 *Founded/Ownrshp* 1937
Sales 50.6MM *EMP* 72[E]
Accts Cliftonlarsonallen Llp Austin
SIC 4911 Distribution, electric power; Distribution, electric power
CEO: Tim Thompson
* *Ch Bd:* Charles Kvare
* *Ch Bd:* Dennis Tollefson
VP: Joe Belz
VP Mktg: Dan Husted

D-U-N-S 00-585-6216
LAKE REGION ELECTRIC COOPERATIVE INC (OK)
L R E C
516 S Lake Region Rd, Hulbert, OK 74441-2685
Tel (918) 772-2526 *Founded/Ownrshp* 1949
Sales 37.8MM *EMP* 83
Accts Briscoe Burke & Grigsby Llp
SIC 4911 Distribution, electric power; Distribution, electric power
CEO: Hamid Vahdatipour
Sfty Dirs: David Rittenhouse

D-U-N-S 07-176-4062
LAKE REGION HEALTHCARE CORP
LAKE REGION REHAB SERVICE
712 S Cascade St, Fergus Falls, MN 56537-2913
Tel (218) 736-8000 *Founded/Ownrshp* 2005
Sales 103.1MM *EMP* 868[E]
SIC 8062 General medical & surgical hospitals; General medical & surgical hospitals
CEO: Larry Schulz
* *Ch Bd:* Stephen Rufer
* *Pr:* Paul Wilson
* *CFO:* Brett Longtin
* *CFO:* Edward Strand
* *Treas:* Dennis Emmen
Sr VP: Jeff Shackor
Dir OR: Holly Leonard
Dir Rx: Mark Dewey
Dir Rx: Brett A Leitch
Cmptr Lab: Leanne Stoll

D-U-N-S 04-229-6665
■ **LAKE REGION MANUFACTURING INC**
LAKE REGION MEDICAL
(*Suby of* LAKE REGION MEDICAL INC) ★
100 Fordham Rd, Wilmington, MA 01887-2168
Tel (952) 361-2515 *Founded/Ownrshp* 2014
Sales 386.7MM[E] *EMP* 1,630
SIC 3841 3845 Surgical instruments & apparatus; Electromedical equipment; Surgical instruments & apparatus; Electromedical equipment
Ch Bd: Donald J Spence
* *CEO:* Joe Fleischhacker
VP: Sharon Barber
Ql Cn Mgr: David Devett
Sales Asso: Steve Rudin

LAKE REGION MEDICAL
See LAKE REGION MANUFACTURING INC

LAKE REGION MEDICAL
See ACCELLENT LLC

D-U-N-S 79-955-4931 IMP
■ **LAKE REGION MEDICAL INC**
(*Suby of* GREATBATCH INC) ★
100 Fordham Rd, Wilmington, MA 01887-2168
Tel (978) 570-6900 *Founded/Ownrshp* 2015
Sales 712.7MM[E] *EMP* 3,190
SIC 3841 Surgical & medical instruments; Surgical & medical instruments
Pr: Donald J Spence
CFO: Richard E Johnson
VP: Jeremy M Farina
VP: Jeremy Friedman
VP: Ron Honig
Prgrm Mgr: Sean Silva
Site Mgr: Carol Simon
Prd Mgr: Christopher Metcalf
Ql Cn Mgr: Kathy Cody
Ql Cn Mgr: James Madden
Sales Asso: Adam Carr

LAKE REGION REHAB SERVICE
See LAKE REGION HEALTHCARE CORP

D-U-N-S 08-500-8217
LAKE REGIONAL HEALTH SYSTEM
LAKE REGIONAL HOSPITAL
54 Hospital Dr, Osage Beach, MO 65065-3050
Tel (573) 348-8000 *Founded/Ownrshp* 1978
Sales 175.5MM *EMP* 1,300
Accts Bkd Llp Springfield Missour
SIC 8062 General medical & surgical hospitals; General medical & surgical hospitals
CEO: Michael E Henze
Chf Rad: Michael Vierra
Pr: Denise Coombs
* *Pr:* Dennis Michaelree
Pr: Ron Warren
Sr VP: David Halsell
Sr VP: Robert Hyatt
* *VP:* Cory Ten Bensel
Dir Rx: Tom Myler
Nurse Mgr: Alison Williams
CTO: Sally Burke

LAKE REGIONAL HOSPITAL
See LAKE REGIONAL HEALTH SYSTEM

D-U-N-S 07-714-3295
LAKE REND COLLEGE
REND LAKE DISTRICT #521
468 N Ken Gray Pkwy, INA, IL 62846-2408
Tel (618) 437-5321 *Founded/Ownrshp* 1967
Sales 3.4MM *EMP* 550
Accts Cliftonlarsonallen Llp Peoria
SIC 8221 8222 Colleges universities & professional schools; Community college; Colleges universities & professional schools; Community college
Pr: Terry Wilkerson
* *CFO:* Angie Kissner
CFO: Larry West
VP: James Hull
Exec: Mark Kern
Exec: Gloria Oliver
Dir IT: Kevin Majca
Dir IT: Kim Robert
IT Man: Wendy Smith
HC Dir: Vickie Schulte

D-U-N-S 07-001-0442
LAKE RIDGE SCHOOLS
6111 W Ridge Rd, Gary, IN 46408-1797
Tel (219) 989-7823 *Founded/Ownrshp* 1956
Sales 20.5MM[E] *EMP* 325
SIC 8211 Public elementary school; Public junior high school; Public senior high school; Public elementary school; Public junior high school; Public senior high school
* *Treas:* Kim Tusateri
Bd of Dir: Jonathan Evans
Opers Mgr: Jim Wadkins

D-U-N-S 11-075-4145 IMP
LAKE ROAD GENERATING CO LIMITED PARTNERSHIP
56 Alexander Pkwy, Dayville, CT 06241-1134
Tel (860) 779-8300 *Founded/Ownrshp* 1997
Sales 27.5MM[E] *EMP* 32
SIC 4911 Electric services
Pt: Robert Heley
Off Mgr: Heidi Lavine

D-U-N-S 11-374-3454
LAKE ROUND AREA SCHOOLS
COMMUNITY UNIT DISTRICT 116
316 S Rosedale Ct, Round Lake, IL 60073-2944
Tel (847) 270-9000 *Founded/Ownrshp* 1941
Sales 38.0MM[E] *EMP* 620
SIC 8211 Public elementary & secondary schools; Public elementary & secondary schools
Admn Mgr: Paul Flately

D-U-N-S 05-498-1766
LAKE SARANAC CENTRAL SCHOOL DISTRICT
SARANAC LAKE CENTRAL SCHL DST
79 Canaras Ave, Saranac Lake, NY 12983-1590
Tel (518) 891-5460 *Founded/Ownrshp* 1926
Sales 11.9MM^E *EMP* 300
SIC 8211 Public elementary & secondary schools; Public junior high school; Public senior high school; Public elementary & secondary schools; Public junior high school; Public senior high school
Prin: Lynda Neveu
IT Man: Joe Marocco
Schl Brd P: Clyde Baker

D-U-N-S 96-935-0599
LAKE SHEFFIELD-SHEFFIELD CITY SCHOOL DISTRICT
1824 Harris Rd, Sheffield Village, OH 44054-2628
Tel (440) 949-6181 *Founded/Ownrshp* 2011
Sales 9.9MM^E *EMP* 277^E
SIC 8211 Elementary & secondary schools
Prin: Will Folger
Treas: Penny Plouffe
HC Dir: Sharon Young

D-U-N-S 62-056-0370
■ LAKE SHORE BANCORP INC
(*Suby of* LAKE SHORE MHC) ★
31 E 4th St, Dunkirk, NY 14048-2112
Tel (716) 366-4070 *Founded/Ownrshp* 2006
Sales NA *EMP* 122^E
Tkr Sym LSBK *Exch* NGM
SIC 6035 Savings institutions, federally chartered; Savings institutions, federally chartered
Pr: Daniel P Reininga
**Ch Bd:* Gary W Winger
CFO: Rachel A Foley
**V Ch Bd:* Nancy L Yocum
Bd of Dir: Tracy Bennett
Ex VP: Jeffrey Werdein
CIO: Dan Reininga
Web Dev: Lori Danforth

LAKE SHORE CENTRAL SCHOOL
See EVANS BRANT CENTRAL SCH DIST

D-U-N-S 15-514-4801
LAKE SHORE FORD TOYOTA SCION
LAKE SHORE TOYOTA
244 Melton Rd, Chesterton, IN 46304-9434
Tel (219) 787-8600 *Founded/Ownrshp* 1985
Sales 25.5MM^E *EMP* 75
SIC 5511 7538 Automobiles, new & used; General automotive repair shops; Automobiles, new & used; General automotive repair shops
Pr: John M Kerr
**VP:* Robert Kerr
Sales Asso: Bill Ozug

LAKE SHORE HEALTH CARE CENTER
See LAKE SHORE HOSPITAL

D-U-N-S 07-402-5073
LAKE SHORE HOSPITAL
LAKE SHORE HEALTH CARE CENTER
845 Route 5 And 20, Irving, NY 14081-9716
Tel (716) 934-2654 *Founded/Ownrshp* 1965
Sales 36.2MM^E *EMP* 599
SIC 8062 8063 8082 General medical & surgical hospitals; Psychiatric hospitals; Home health care services; General medical & surgical hospitals; Psychiatric hospitals; Home health care services
Dir Recs: Rebecca Woods
Dir Vol: Cindy Wlodarek
**Pr:* Timothy J Cooper
Ch: John Keyes
Ch: Carl Roth
**Sec:* Jeanne Lavin
Ofcr: Louis Dirinzo
**VP:* James M Merrins
Dir Lab: Ray Conner
Off Mgr: Barbara McCoroskey
CIO: Roger Benn

D-U-N-S 96-958-4585
▲ LAKE SHORE MHC
125 E 4th St, Dunkirk, NY 14048-2222
Tel (716) 366-4070 *Founded/Ownrshp* 2006
Sales NA *EMP* 119^E
SIC 6035 Savings institutions, federally chartered; Savings institutions, federally chartered
CEO: Daniel P Reininga

LAKE SHORE ORTHOPEDICS
See ILLINOIS BONE & JOINT INSTITUTE

D-U-N-S 60-335-5319
LAKE SHORE SAVINGS
128 E 4th St, Dunkirk, NY 14048-2226
Tel (716) 673-9556 *Founded/Ownrshp* 2005
Sales NA *EMP* 121
SIC 6035 Savings institutions, federally chartered; Savings institutions, federally chartered
Pr: David C Mancuso
**Ch Bd:* Michael E Brunecz
CFO: Robert L Smith
Sec: Beverley Mulkin
Ofcr: Nicole May
Brnch Mgr: Magdalena Dye

LAKE SHORE TOYOTA
See LAKE SHORE FORD TOYOTA SCION

D-U-N-S 06-048-7915
LAKE SPIRIT TRIBE
816 3rd Ave N, Fort Totten, ND 58335-9998
Tel (701) 766-1270 *Founded/Ownrshp* 1870
Sales 118.2MM^E *EMP* 1,000
SIC 3795 0191 2394 2298 7999 Specialized tank components, military; General farms, primarily crop; Canvas & related products; Sails: made from purchased materials; Camouflage nets, not made in weaving mills; Gambling establishment; Specialized tank components, military; General farms, primarily crop; Canvas & related products; Sails: made from purchased materials; Camouflage nets, not made in weaving mills; Gambling establishment
Ch Bd: Myra Pierson
**Sec:* Bryan Pierson
Dir: Ila McKay
Ex Dir: Linda Thompson
Brnch Mgr: Valentino White

D-U-N-S 78-674-6008
LAKE STATE RAILWAY CO
750 N Washington Ave, Saginaw, MI 48607-1374
Tel (989) 393-9800 *Founded/Ownrshp* 1992
Sales 21.6MM *EMP* 70
Accts Larkin & Associates Pllc Liv
SIC 4011 Railroads, line-haul operating; Railroads, line-haul operating
Pr: John Rickoff
**CFO:* Kevin Mitrzyk
VP: Mark Nagy
**VP:* Mike Stickel

D-U-N-S 09-827-9276 IMP
LAKE STATES LUMBER INC
312 S Chester St, Sparta, WI 54656-1813
Tel (608) 269-6714 *Founded/Ownrshp* 1979
Sales 76.1MM^E *EMP* 200
SIC 5031

D-U-N-S 10-008-0670
LAKE STEVENS SCHOOL DISTRICT
EDUCATIONAL SERVICE CENTER
12309 22nd St Ne, Lake Stevens, WA 98258-9500
Tel (425) 335-1500 *Founded/Ownrshp* 1928
Sales 80.3MM *EMP* 1,000
Accts Briann Sontag Cgfm
SIC 8211 Public elementary school; Public junior high school; Public senior high school; Public elementary school; Public junior high school; Public senior high school
Pr Dir: Jayme Taylor
Schl Brd P: John Boerger
Teacher Pr: Ken Collins

D-U-N-S 00-506-1056
LAKE STORM COMMUNITY SCHOOL DISTRICT
ADMINISTRATION OFFICE
419 Lake Ave, Storm Lake, IA 50588-2436
Tel (712) 732-8060 *Founded/Ownrshp* 1865
Sales 16.9MM^E *EMP* 310
SIC 8211 Public elementary & secondary schools; Public elementary & secondary schools
Bd of Dir: Dave Skibsted
Instr Medi: Julie Weeda

D-U-N-S 01-976-6021
■ LAKE SUNAPEE BANK FSB
(*Suby of* LAKE SUNAPEE BANK GROUP) ★
9 Main St Ste 1, Newport, NH 03773-1598
Tel (603) 863-5772 *Founded/Ownrshp* 1989
Sales NA *EMP* 165
SIC 6035 6163 Federal savings banks; Loan brokers; Federal savings banks; Loan brokers
Ch Bd: John Kiernan
Pr: Stephen W Ensign
Pr: Stephen R Theroux
CFO: Laura Jacobi
Ex VP: Bill McIver
Sr VP: Joe Boyd
VP: Dean Cashman
VP: John Duddie
VP: Stevan Geiger
VP: Jodi Hoyt
VP: Cathy Murray
VP: Marie Pelletier
VP: Meghan Wilkie
VP: Janet Zutell
Board of Directors: Catherine A Feeney

D-U-N-S 60-319-8185
▲ LAKE SUNAPEE BANK GROUP
9 Main St Ste 1, Newport, NH 03773-1598
Tel (603) 863-0886 *Founded/Ownrshp* 1989
Sales NA *EMP* 361
Tkr Sym LSBG *Exch* NGM
SIC 6035 Savings institutions, federally chartered; Federal savings & loan associations; Savings institutions, federally chartered; Federal savings & loan associations
Pr: Stephen R Theroux
**Ch Bd:* Stephen W Ensign
COO: William J McIver
CFO: Laura Jacobi
Chf Cred: Sharon Whitaker
Sr VP: Frances E Clow
Sr VP: Scott W Laughinghouse
Sr VP: Karen Lynch
Sr VP: Sharon L Whitaker
VP: Steve Declue
VP: Ed Killam
VP: Sue Shaw
VP: Sharon Whitaker

D-U-N-S 79-373-7656
LAKE SUPERIOR COLLEGE FOUNDATION INC
(*Suby of* BEMIDJI STATE UNIVERSITY) ★
2101 Trinity Rd, Duluth, MN 55811-3349
Tel (218) 733-7600 *Founded/Ownrshp* 1983
Sales 614.2M *EMP* 437
Accts Licari Larsen And Company Dul
SIC 8221 9411 Colleges universities & professional schools; Administration of educational programs; ; Colleges universities & professional schools; Administration of educational programs;
Pr: Gary Tridgell
**Pr:* Kathleen Nelson
**Treas:* Tim Peterson
VP: Mike Seymour
**VP:* Dick Wolleat
VP Admn: Al Finlayson
IT Man: Terri Schumacher
Mktg Dir: Janet Blixt

D-U-N-S 14-401-6305
LAKE SUPERIOR CONSULTING LLC
130 W Superior St Ste 610, Duluth, MN 55802-4020
Tel (218) 491-7302 *Founded/Ownrshp* 2002
Sales 29.3MM^E *EMP* 89
SIC 8711 Consulting engineer

LAKE SUPERIOR CONTRACTING
See LASALLE GROUP INC

LAKE SUPERIOR MACK SALES
See EAU CLAIRE MACK SALES INC

D-U-N-S 17-440-5555
LAKE SUPERIOR SCHOOL DISTRICT 381
TWO HARBORS HIGH SCHOOL
1640 Highway 2, Two Harbors, MN 55616-4017
Tel (218) 834-8216 *Founded/Ownrshp* 1913
Sales 33.6MM^E *EMP* 690
Accts Eikill & Schilling Ltd Dulu
SIC 8211 Public senior high school; Public senior high school

D-U-N-S 07-478-7789
LAKE SUPERIOR STATE UNIVERSITY FOUNDATION
BOARD OF TRUSTEES
650 W Easterday Ave, Sault Sainte Marie, MI 49783-1626
Tel (906) 635-2674 *Founded/Ownrshp* 1970
Sales 3.2MM *EMP* 376
Accts Rehmann Traverse City Mi
SIC 8221 University; University
Pr: Dr Tony McLain
Ofcr: Jennifer Constantino
Ofcr: Don Haist
Ofcr: R J Macker
Ofcr: Pat Victor
Ofcr: Sara Webb
VP: William Crawford
VP: Brittnee Dault
Off Mgr: Carol Schmitigal
CTO: Aaron Westrick
Opers Mgr: Jackie Kellerman

LAKE TAHOE HORZN CASINO RESORT
See TROPICANA CASINOS AND RESORTS INC

LAKE TAHOE HORZN CASINO RESORT
See COLUMBUS EAST LANSING HOTEL INC

D-U-N-S 07-609-5058
LAKE TAHOE UNIFIED SCHOOL DISTRICT
1021 Al Tahoe Blvd, South Lake Tahoe, CA 96150-4502
Tel (530) 541-2850 *Founded/Ownrshp* 1948
Sales 25.9MM^E *EMP* 407
Accts Goodell Porter & Frederick L
SIC 8211 Public elementary & secondary schools; Public elementary & secondary schools
Adm Dir: Don Borges
Pr Dir: Shannon Chandler
HC Dir: Annamarie Cohen

D-U-N-S 19-974-7049
LAKE TAYLOR TRANSITIONAL CARE HOSPITAL FOUNDATION
1309 Kempsville Rd, Norfolk, VA 23502-2205
Tel (757) 461-5001 *Founded/Ownrshp* 1890
Sales 67.0MM^E *EMP* 400
SIC 8062

D-U-N-S 07-862-3659
LAKE TRAVIS INDEPENDENT SCHOOL DISTRICT
3322 Ranch Road 620 S, Austin, TX 78738-6804
Tel (512) 533-6000 *Founded/Ownrshp* 1981
Sales 122.2M *EMP* 900
SIC 8211 Public elementary & secondary schools; Public elementary & secondary schools
Pr Dir: Marco Alvarado
Psych: Lisa Colley

D-U-N-S 10-675-6067
LAKE TRUST CREDIT UNION
4605 S Old Us Highway 23, Brighton, MI 48114-7521
Tel (517) 267-7200 *Founded/Ownrshp* 1937
Sales NA *EMP* 61
SIC 6062 State credit unions, not federally chartered; State credit unions, not federally chartered
CEO: Stephan L Winninger
**Pr:* William J Thiess
CFO: Diana Scott
Ofcr: Bill Thomas
Sr VP: Jane Kile
VP: Stuart Dodge
VP: Raynor Zillgitt
Brnch Mgr: Emily Malone
Brnch Mgr: Jennie Olsen
Brnch Mgr: Daniel Valley

LAKE UNION CONF OF S.D.A.
See LAKE UNION CONFERENCE OF SEVENTH DAY ADVENTISTS (INC)

D-U-N-S 07-430-5343
LAKE UNION CONFERENCE OF SEVENTH DAY ADVENTISTS (INC) (MI)
LAKE UNION CONF OF S.D.A.
8903 Us Highway 31, Berrien Springs, MI 49104-1001
Tel (269) 473-8200 *Founded/Ownrshp* 1901
Sales 16.3MM^E *EMP* 374
SIC 8661 Seventh Day Adventist Church; Seventh Day Adventist Church
Pr: Don Livesay
**Treas:* Glynn Scott
Assoc Dir: Joanna Sudds
MIS Dir: Sean Parker

LAKE UNION SEA RAY
See SEA RAY SPORT YACHTS INC

D-U-N-S 16-539-0290
LAKE WALES CHARTER SCHOOLS INC
130 E Central Ave, Lake Wales, FL 33853-4166
Tel (863) 678-4244 *Founded/Ownrshp* 2004
Sales 32.8MM *EMP* 400
Accts Bkhm Pa Winter Park Flori
SIC 8211 Elementary & secondary schools; Elementary & secondary schools
**CFO:* Brian Fisher
Corp Couns: Robin Gibson

LAKE WALES HOSPITAL
See LAKE WALES MEDICAL CENTERS INC

D-U-N-S 14-254-6204
■ LAKE WALES HOSPITAL CORP
(*Suby of* COMMUNITY HEALTH SYSTEMS INC) ★
410 S 11th St, Lake Wales, FL 33853-4256
Tel (863) 676-1433 *Founded/Ownrshp* 2002
Sales 313.5M *EMP* 340
SIC 8062 General medical & surgical hospitals; General medical & surgical hospitals
Pr: Julie Travis
**CFO:* Richard White
VP: Joe Connell
Nrsg Dir: Nancy Kovencz
Nrsg Dir: Brian Stone

D-U-N-S 06-966-7293
LAKE WALES MEDICAL CENTERS INC (FL)
LAKE WALES HOSPITAL
410 S 11th St, Lake Wales, FL 33853-4203
Tel (863) 676-1433 *Founded/Ownrshp* 1929
Sales 93.1MM^E *EMP* 656
Accts Price Waterhouse Llp
SIC 8062 8059 Hospital, affiliated with AMA residency; Convalescent home; Hospital, affiliated with AMA residency; Convalescent home
CEO: Joe M Connell
**CFO:* Karen Cheshire
CFO: Joelaine Zink
Mktg Dir: Maryemma Bachelder
HC Dir: Annette Cox

D-U-N-S 02-083-5294
LAKE WALLED CONSOLIDATED SCHOOL DISTRICT
850 Ladd Rd Bldg D, Walled Lake, MI 48390-3019
Tel (248) 956-2000 *Founded/Ownrshp* 1922
Sales 180.7MM *EMP* 1,482
Accts Plante & Moran Pllc Auburn H
SIC 8211 Public elementary school; Public junior high school; Public senior high school; Public vocational/technical school; Public elementary school; Public junior high school; Public senior high school; Public vocational/technical school
Trst: Denise Bither

D-U-N-S 11-684-8412
LAKE WASHINGTON INSTITUTE OF TECHNOLOGY
11605 132nd Ave Ne, Kirkland, WA 98034-8505
Tel (425) 739-8100 *Founded/Ownrshp* 1991
Sales 531.9M *EMP* 573^E
Accts Peterson Sullnan Llp Cpa S Se
SIC 8222 Technical institute; Technical institute
VP: Bill Thomas
Comm Dir: Leslie Cohan
Opers Supe: Rhonda McElroy

D-U-N-S 08-683-5287
LAKE WASHINGTON SCHOOL DISTRICT
16250 Ne 74th St, Redmond, WA 98052-7817
Tel (425) 936-1200 *Founded/Ownrshp* 1944
Sales 256.6MM^E *EMP* 3,100
SIC 8211 Public elementary school; Public junior high school; Public senior high school; Public special education school; Public elementary school; Public junior high school; Public senior high school; Public special education school
Bd of Dir: Ravi Shahani
Off Mgr: Melody Kieffer
Off Mgr: Brigitte Tennis
Pr Dir: Kathryn Reith
Teacher Pr: Pat Fowler-Fung
Psych: Sue Gallo
HC Dir: Nancy Johnson

D-U-N-S 01-726-9580
■ LAKE WELDING SUPPLY CO INC
(*Suby of* PRAXAIR DISTRIBUTION INC) ★
363 Ottawa St, Muskegon, MI 49442-1032
Tel (231) 722-3773 *Founded/Ownrshp* 2014
Sales 22.8MM^E *EMP* 38
SIC 5084 5085 Welding machinery & equipment; Industrial supplies
Pr: Thomas Lesneski
Treas: Gregory Teerman

D-U-N-S 00-401-4515
LAKE WEST FUNDING INC
9210 Arboretum Pkwy, North Chesterfield, VA 23236-3472
Tel (804) 393-7400 *Founded/Ownrshp* 2000
Sales NA *EMP* 31
SIC 6163 Mortgage brokers arranging for loans, using money of others; Mortgage brokers arranging for loans, using money of others
CEO: Robert D Edwards Sr
**Sec:* Loretta C Edwards
**Ex VP:* Ricardo Edwards
**VP:* Robert D Edwards II
Ex Dir: Sharon Edwards

D-U-N-S 02-054-9846
LAKE WORTH DRAINAGE DISTRICT
13081 S Military Trl, Delray Beach, FL 33484-1199
Tel (561) 737-3835 *Founded/Ownrshp* 1915
Sales 21.8MM^E *EMP* 92
Accts Rachlin Cohen & Holtz
SIC 4952 Sewerage systems; Sewerage systems
Pr: James Alderman
Treas: Carol Connelly
**Treas:* Carol Connolly
Ex Dir: Robert Brown
IT Man: Juan Tobar

D-U-N-S 79-435-9059
LAKE WORTH INDEPENDENT SCHOOL DISTRICT
6805 Telephone Rd, Fort Worth, TX 76135-2855
Tel (817) 306-4200 *Founded/Ownrshp* 1938
Sales 36.6MM *EMP* 352
Accts Kirk Richardson & Poole Pc
SIC 8211 Public elementary & secondary schools; Public elementary & secondary schools
Dir IT: Dru Mgodwin
IT Man: Cynthia Walter
Psych: Carla Smith

LAKE ZURICH SCHOOL DISTRICT 95
See COMMUNITY UNIT SCHOOL DISTRICT 95

D-U-N-S 02-711-0386
LAKE-LEHMAN SCHOOL DISTRICT
18612 Market St, Lehman, PA 18627
Tel (570) 675-2165 Founded/Ownrshp 1966
Sales 26.2MM EMP 213
Accts Bonita & Rainey Plains Pa
SIC 8211 Public elementary & secondary schools; Elementary school; Public elementary & secondary schools; Elementary school
*Pr: Moderno Rossi Jr
*Treas: Rosemary Howard
*VP: Robert Allardyce
*VP: Lois Kopcha
Teacher Pr: Tabitha Miscavhe

D-U-N-S 79-910-0367 IMP
LAKEFRONT BREWERY INC
1872 N Commerce St, Milwaukee, WI 53212-3701
Tel (414) 372-4144 Founded/Ownrshp 1987
Sales 21.1MM^E EMP 105
SIC 2082 Beer (alcoholic beverage)
Pr: Russell Klisch
Mktg Dir: Chris Johnson
Sls Mgr: Kevin Pearson

D-U-N-S 14-125-5401
LAKEFRONT CAPITAL LLC
28175 Haggerty Rd 143, Novi, MI 48377-2903
Tel (248) 994-9001 Founded/Ownrshp 2002
Sales 33.0MM EMP 6
SIC 7377 Computer hardware rental or leasing, except finance leasing; Computer hardware rental or leasing, except finance leasing
IT Man: Christine Prendergast

D-U-N-S 07-858-4902
LAKEFRONT LINES INC
(Suby of COACH USA INC) ★
13315 Brookpark Rd, Brookpark, OH 44142-1822
Tel (216) 267-8810 Founded/Ownrshp 2012
Sales 25.9MM^E EMP 200
SIC 4119 4142 4141 Local passenger transportation; Bus charter service, except local; Local bus charter service; Local passenger transportation; Bus charter service, except local; Local bus charter service
Genl Mgr: Tom Goebel
Genl Mgr: Christopher Goebel
Genl Mgr: Mike Schmuhl
Dir IT: Scott Nazio

D-U-N-S 06-335-4146
LAKEHAVEN UTILITY DISTRICT
31627 1st Ave S, Federal Way, WA 98003-5201
Tel (253) 941-1516 Founded/Ownrshp 1950
Sales 28.9MM EMP 102
Accts Troy Kelley Federal Way Wash
SIC 4952 4941 Sewerage systems; Water supply; Sewerage systems; Water supply
Genl Mgr: Donald Perry
CFO: Judy Taylor
Exec: Dennis Morgan
Dir Risk M: Lindal Kochmar
Dir IT: Don Feierabend
IT Man: Max Rawson
Software D: Dennis Alfredson

D-U-N-S 00-880-7679
LAKEHEAD CONSTRUCTORS INC
(Suby of LAKEHEAD HOLDING CORP) ★
2916 Hill Ave, Superior, WI 54880-5560
Tel (715) 392-5181 Founded/Ownrshp 1986
Sales 95.3MM^E EMP 250^E
SIC 1541 1542 Industrial buildings, new construction; Renovation, remodeling & repairs: industrial buildings; Commercial & office building contractors; Industrial buildings, new construction; Renovation, remodeling & repairs: industrial buildings; Commercial & office building contractors
CEO: Brian C Maki
*Pr: Dennis M Hallberg
*Sec: Mark Hubbard
*VP: Don Odermann
Genl Mgr: Bruce Beste
Sfty Dirs: Ryan Nelson

D-U-N-S 16-196-2261
LAKEHEAD HOLDING CORP
2916 Hill Ave, Superior, WI 54880-5504
Tel (715) 392-5181 Founded/Ownrshp 1987
Sales 95.3MM^E EMP 250
Accts Mcgladrey & Pullen
SIC 1541 1542 Industrial buildings, new construction; Renovation, remodeling & repairs: industrial buildings; Commercial & office building contractors; Industrial buildings, new construction; Renovation, remodeling & repairs: industrial buildings; Commercial & office building contractors
Pr: Dennis M Hallberg

D-U-N-S 19-615-8646
■ LAKELAND AUTO AUCTION INC
(Suby of MANHEIM INVESTMENTS INC) ★
Interstate 4 At Hwy 33, Lakeland, FL 33805
Tel (863) 984-1551 Founded/Ownrshp 1985
Sales 24.8MM^E EMP 293
SIC 5012 Automobile auction; Automobile auction
Pr: Darryll M Ceccoli
*CFO: Robert Gartin
Treas: James A Htcher
*Sec: James A Hatcher

LAKELAND AUTO MALL
See MUTZ MOTORS LTD PARTNERSHIP

D-U-N-S 01-167-8893
LAKELAND AUTOMOTIVE INC
CRESTMONT TOYOTA
730 State Rt 23, Pompton Plains, NJ 07444-1424
Tel (973) 839-4000 Founded/Ownrshp 1989
Sales 35.0MM^E EMP 100
SIC 5511 7515 7514 7513 5521 5012 Automobiles, new & used; Passenger car leasing; Passenger car rental; Truck rental & leasing, no drivers; Used car dealers; Automobiles & other motor vehicles; Automobiles, new & used; Passenger car leasing; Passenger car rental; Truck rental & leasing, no drivers; Used car dealers; Automobiles & other motor vehicles
Pr: William L Strauss III
*Ch: Daniel Peyton
Sls Mgr: Rob Bojarun
Sales Asso: John Fletcher

D-U-N-S 80-876-7933
▲ LAKELAND BANCORP INC
250 Oak Ridge Rd, Oak Ridge, NJ 07438-8906
Tel (973) 697-2000 Founded/Ownrshp 1989
Sales NA EMP 566^E
Tkr Sym LBAI Exch NGS
SIC 6022 State commercial banks; State commercial banks
Pr: Thomas J Shara
*Ch Bd: Mary Ann Deacon
Pr: Patrick Lasslett
Pr: Karen McDougal
COO: Robert A Vandenbergh
CFO: Joseph F Hurley
Chf Cred: James R Noonan
Ofcr: Ronald E Schwarz
Ofcr: David S Yanagisawa
Ex VP: Jeffrey J Buonforte
Ex VP: Timothy J Matteson
VP: Bruce Bready
VP: Steven Breeman
VP: Frank Doyle
VP: Scott Heiman
Exec: Patricia Carson
Board of Directors: Bruce D Bohuny, Edward B Deutsch, Brian Flynn, Mark J Fredericks, Thomas J Marino, Robert E McCracken, Robert B Nicholson III, Joseph P O'dowd, Stephen R Tilton Sr

D-U-N-S 18-726-9873
■ LAKELAND BANK
(Suby of LAKELAND BANCORP INC) ★
250 Oak Ridge Rd, Oak Ridge, NJ 07438-8906
Tel (973) 697-2000 Founded/Ownrshp 1988
Sales NA EMP 500
SIC 6022 State commercial banks; State commercial banks
CEO: Thomas J Shara
Ch Bd: Mary Ann Deacon
Pr: Bill Schachtel
Pr: Robert A Vandenbergh
CFO: Giuseppe Cascio
CFO: Joseph Hurley
Treas: Thomas Post
Chf Cred: James R Noonan
Ofcr: R David Korngruen
Ofcr: Lisa Nienaber
Ofcr: Frank Walka
Ex VP: Jeff Buonforte
Ex VP: Michele Gilchrist
Ex VP: Timothy J Matteson
Ex VP: Stewart McClure
Ex VP: Mary Nandone
Ex VP: Ronald Schwarz
Sr VP: Karen Garrera
Sr VP: Christopher Gorey
Sr VP: Thomas Keady
Sr VP: Ellen Lalwani

D-U-N-S 96-468-1469
LAKELAND CARE DISTRICT
N6654 Rolling Meadows Dr, Fond Du Lac, WI 54937-9471
Tel (920) 906-5100 Founded/Ownrshp 2010
Sales NA EMP 175^E
SIC 6321 Accident & health insurance; Accident & health insurance
Ex Dir: Katie Mnuk
Ql Cn Mgr: Katie Calmes

D-U-N-S 07-056-4992
LAKELAND CENTRAL SCHOOL DISTRICT OF SHRUB OAK INC
LAKELAND CENTRAL SCHOOL DST
1086 E Main St, Shrub Oak, NY 10588-1507
Tel (914) 245-1700 Founded/Ownrshp 1951
Sales 60.3MM^E EMP 1,200
SIC 8211 Public combined elementary & secondary school; Public combined elementary & secondary school
Prin: Dr George Stone
Ofcr: Jason Hilliard
Ofcr: Larry Paniccia
Comm Dir: James Develde
Off Admin: Stephanie Elio
Off Admin: Nancy Gentile
Psych: Melissa Gilmore
Psych: Kathleen Giordano
Psych: Catherine Leblanc
Psych: Laurainne Mosca
Psych: Mary Mulligan

LAKELAND CENTRAL SCHOOL DST
See LAKELAND CENTRAL SCHOOL DISTRICT OF SHRUB OAK INC

LAKELAND CMNTY HOSP WATERVLIET
See COMMUNITY HOSPITAL INC

D-U-N-S 07-614-7321
LAKELAND COLLEGE
W3718 South Dr, Plymouth, WI 53073-4878
Tel (920) 565-2111 Founded/Ownrshp 1862
Sales 33.5MM EMP 1,123
Accts Schenck Cpas Green Bay Wisco
SIC 8221 College, except junior; College, except junior
Ch: Robert T Melzer
*Pr: Daniel Eck
Pr: Ann Flad-Jesion
*Pr: Stephen Gould
COO: Annette Gamache
*CFO: Joseph Botana II
CFO: Carole Robertson
Trst: Deb Ansay
Sr VP: Dan Eck
VP: Brye Aanonsen
VP: Meg Albrinck
VP: Rebecca Boyko
VP: Nete Dehme
VP: Nate Dehne
VP: Anthony Fessler
VP: Andre Glass
VP: Taras Saruk
VP: Ken Strmiska
VP: Tim Stromiska
VP: Zach Voelz
VP: Ben Zuengler

LAKELAND COMMUNITY COLLEGE
See LAKE COUNTY COMMUNITY COLLEGE DISTRICT

D-U-N-S 80-984-3597
LAKELAND COOPERATIVE
229 Railroad St, Ridgeland, WI 54763
Tel (715) 949-1165 Founded/Ownrshp 2008
Sales 23.4MM^E EMP 110
SIC 5999 Feed & farm supply
Pr: David Store
VP: Carl Varnes
*Genl Mgr: Karl Varnes

D-U-N-S 03-595-6879
LAKELAND EQUIPMENT CORP
JOHN DEERE
13330 State Route 31, Savannah, NY 13146-8703
Tel (315) 365-2888 Founded/Ownrshp 1983
Sales 27.8MM^E EMP 120
SIC 5999 7699 Farm equipment & supplies; Farm machinery repair
Pr: Martin Phillippe
*VP: Robert A Mc Namara Jr
*VP: Mike Wilson
Genl Mgr: Tom Beaty
Sales Asso: Patrick Fortune

D-U-N-S 10-235-6003
▲ LAKELAND FINANCIAL CORP
202 E Center St, Warsaw, IN 46580-2842
Tel (574) 267-6144 Founded/Ownrshp 1983
Sales NA EMP 497^E
Tkr Sym LKFN Exch NGS
SIC 6022 State commercial banks; State commercial banks
Pr: David M Findlay
*Ch Bd: Michael L Kubacki
CFO: Lisa M O'Neill
Ex VP: Kevin L Deardorff
Ex VP: Eric H Ottinger
Ex VP: Kristin L Pruitt
Sr VP: Jill Debatty
VP: Teresa Bartman
VP: Andrew Haddock
VP: Lawrence Moeller

LAKELAND HEALTH
See LAKELAND HOSPITALS AT NILES & ST JOSEPH INC

LAKELAND HEALTH
See LAKELAND REGIONAL HEALTH SYSTEM

D-U-N-S 08-062-4257
LAKELAND HILLS FAMILY YMCA ASSOCIATION INC
100 Fanny Rd, Mountain Lakes, NJ 07046-1021
Tel (973) 334-2820 Founded/Ownrshp 1876
Sales 8.1MM EMP 350
Accts Best & Sweeney Cpa Associates
SIC 8641 7991 8351 7032 8322 Youth organizations; Physical fitness facilities; Child day care services; Youth camps; Individual & family services; Youth organizations; Physical fitness facilities; Child day care services; Youth camps; Individual & family services
Pr: James McCrudden
*Ch: Mike Naughton
*Treas: Vincent Aniello

D-U-N-S 10-979-5299
■ LAKELAND HOLDINGS LLC
WORLDSTRIDES
(Suby of CARLYLE GROUP L P) ★
218 W Water St Ste 401, Charlottesville, VA 22902-5531
Tel (434) 982-8600 Founded/Ownrshp 2011
Sales 29.5MM^E EMP 397^E
SIC 4724 Tourist agency arranging transport, lodging & car rental; Tourist agency arranging transport, lodging & car rental
CEO: Jim Hall
Pr: Jim Creighton
*COO: Terri Morgolione
CFO: James Gerber
Sr VP: Steven Borenstein
Sr VP: Beau Burris
Sr VP: Earl Grossman
Sr VP: Jim Langas
Sr VP: Jim Yu
VP: Mike Bardaro
VP: Carol Hoselton
VP: Rick Rosenfeld
VP: Neal Waldman
VP: Doug White

LAKELAND HOSP ACQUISITION CORP
See LAKELAND HOSPITAL ACQUISITION LLC

D-U-N-S 12-131-9768
■ LAKELAND HOSPITAL ACQUISITION LLC
LAKELAND HOSP ACQUISITION CORP
(Suby of ACADIA HEALTHCARE CO INC) ★
440 S Market Ave, Springfield, MO 65806-2026
Tel (417) 865-5581 Founded/Ownrshp 2011
Sales 25.0MM^E EMP 350
SIC 8063 Psychiatric hospitals; Psychiatric hospitals
CEO: Nate Duncan
*CFO: Rick Crump
Nrsg Dir: Julee Corey
HC Dir: Sara Wolfe

D-U-N-S 08-678-0400
LAKELAND HOSPITALS AT NILES & ST JOSEPH INC
LAKELAND HEALTH
1234 Napier Ave, Saint Joseph, MI 49085-2112
Tel (269) 983-8300 Founded/Ownrshp 1977
Sales 327.1MM EMP 4,000
Accts Plante & Moran Pllc
SIC 8062 General medical & surgical hospitals; General medical & surgical hospitals
Pr: Loren Hamel
*Pr: Joseph Wasserman
COO: Daniel Bacchiocchi
*CFO: Tim Calhoun
VP: Laurie Fleming
VP: David O'Conner
VP: Mary Ann Peter
VP: Norma Tirado
Dir OR: Angela Kacynski
Dir Rx: Mark Paulson
Off Mgr: Debbie Burkett

D-U-N-S 05-588-3458 EXP
▲ LAKELAND INDUSTRIES INC
3555 Vtrans Mem Hwy Ste C, Ronkonkoma, NY 11779-7636
Tel (631) 981-9700 Founded/Ownrshp 1982
Sales 99.7MM EMP 1,427^E
Tkr Sym LAKE Exch NGM
SIC 3842 2389 Personal safety equipment; Clothing, fire resistant & protective; Gloves, safety; Disposable garments & accessories; Personal safety equipment; Clothing, fire resistant & protective; Gloves, safety; Disposable garments & accessories
Pr: Christopher J Ryan
Ch Bd: Duane W Albro
COO: Stephen M Bachelder
CFO: Gary Pokrassa
VP: Todd Moncrief
VP: Charles D Roberson
Mng Dir: Martin Lill
Genl Mgr: Martin Watkin
Board of Directors: Douglas B Benedict, James M Jenkins, A John Kreft, Thomas McAteer

D-U-N-S 10-001-5080
LAKELAND JOINT SCHOOL DISTRICT 272
15506 N Washington St, Rathdrum, ID 83858-8317
Tel (208) 687-0431 Founded/Ownrshp 1949
Sales 27.7MM^E EMP 575
SIC 8211 Public elementary & secondary schools; School board; Public elementary & secondary schools; School board
*Treas: Cindy Happeny
HC Dir: Judy Gerstenberger

D-U-N-S 01-321-3723
LAKELAND LUMBER CORP
1248 E Main St, Shrub Oak, NY 10588-1425
Tel (914) 245-5050 Founded/Ownrshp 1954
Sales 25.8MM EMP 36
Accts Fishkin Associates Marlboro
SIC 5211 5251 Lumber & other building materials; Hardware; Lumber & other building materials; Hardware
Pr: Herbert Kahan
*Treas: Miriam Golden
*VP: Jack J Kahan
Sales Asso: Jim Sundae

D-U-N-S 00-901-9619
LAKELAND MEDICAL HEALTH CENTER
1234 Napier Ave, Saint Joseph, MI 49085-2112
Tel (269) 982-4935 Founded/Ownrshp 2010
Sales 344.1MM EMP 3
SIC 8099 Health & allied services; Health & allied services

LAKELAND PHARMACY
See MIKE STUART ENTERPRISES INC

D-U-N-S 79-849-7756
LAKELAND REGIONAL HEALTH SYSTEM
LAKELAND HEALTH
1234 Napier Ave, Saint Joseph, MI 49085-2112
Tel (269) 983-8300 Founded/Ownrshp 1985
Sales 650.0MM EMP 2,430
Accts Plante & Moran Pllc St Jose
SIC 8741 8062 Hospital management; Nursing & personal care facility management; Business management; Hospital management; Nursing & personal care facility management; Business management; General medical & surgical hospitals
Pr: Loren B Hamel MD
COO: Gerard Guinane
*CFO: Timothy Calhoun
Ofcr: Cameron Coburn
*VP: Linda Beushausen Rn
*VP: Ray Cruse
*VP: Lowell Hamel
VP: Lindsay Neubarth
*VP: David O'Connor
Dir Inf Cn: Jim Rockhill
Dir Rad: Crystal F Darling

D-U-N-S 96-344-5049
LAKELAND REGIONAL HEALTH SYSTEMS INC
1324 Lakeland Hills Blvd, Lakeland, FL 33805-4543
Tel (863) 687-1100 Founded/Ownrshp 1986
Sales 685.8MM EMP 3,124
Accts Pershing Yoakley & Associates
SIC 8062 General medical & surgical hospitals; General medical & surgical hospitals
Pr: Jack T Stephens
*VP: Paul A Powers
Exec: Karen Stebbins

D-U-N-S 06-025-3150
LAKELAND REGIONAL MEDICAL CENTER INC
LRMC
1324 Lakeland Hills Blvd, Lakeland, FL 33805-4500
Tel (863) 687-1100 Founded/Ownrshp 1988
Sales 618.3MM EMP 3,100
Accts Kpmg Llp Tampa Fl

SIC 8062 General medical & surgical hospitals; General medical & surgical hospitals
CEO: Elaine C Thompson
Chf Rad: Joseph McDowell
Treas: Dick Schaw
Sr VP: Janine Wiggins
VP: Wendell Blake
VP: Carl Gil
VP: Vesta Hudson
VP: Debra Lineberger
VP: Debra Marion
VP: Mary A Pater
VP: Jeff Payne
Exec: Michelle Benjamin
Exec: Cheryle Smith
Dir Risk M: Carl Heaberlin
Dir Risk M: Debi Hodges
Dir Risk M: Jennifer Szanyi
Dir Rad: Thelma L Chishom
Dir Rad: Larry M Dietrich
Dir Rad: Carol J Ebersole
Dir Rad: Gregg Jacob

D-U-N-S 18-157-8790
LAKELAND SCHOOL CORP
825 E 075 N, Lagrange, IN 46761-2099
Tel (260) 499-2400 *Founded/Ownrshp* 1964
Sales 13.0MM *EMP* 285
SIC 8211 Public elementary & secondary schools; Public elementary & secondary schools
**Treas:* Barbara Drake

D-U-N-S 12-159-4675
LAKELAND SUPPLY INC
N8w22380 Johnson Dr, Waukesha, WI 53186-1666
Tel (262) 549-6800 *Founded/Ownrshp* 1984
Sales 20.3MM^E *EMP* 40
SIC 5199 5087 5113 Packaging materials; Cleaning & maintenance equipment & supplies; Industrial & personal service paper
Pr: Lawrence Schmidt II
VP: Dave Ebenhoh
**VP:* Vince Schmidt
Dept Mgr: Craig Knueppel
Mfg Dir: Jim Strecher

D-U-N-S 06-478-3319
LAKELAND TOOL AND ENGINEERING INC
2939 6th Ave, Anoka, MN 55303-1144
Tel (763) 422-8866 *Founded/Ownrshp* 1973
Sales 30.3MM^E *EMP* 170^E
SIC 3089 3544 Injection molding of plastics; Industrial molds; Injection molding of plastics; Industrial molds
CEO: Donald Gross
**Sec:* Martin Sweerin
Exec: Debbie Bolin
Dir IT: Jerry Garvey
Sls Mgr: Susan Reichert

D-U-N-S 04-782-2270
■ LAKELAND TOURS LLC
WORLDSTRIDES
(*Suby of* LAKELAND HOLDINGS LLC) ★
218 W Water St Ste 401, Charlottesville, VA 22902-5531
Tel (434) 982-8600 *Founded/Ownrshp* 1998
Sales 27.7MM^E *EMP* 359
SIC 7999 Travel agent school; Tour & guide services
Sr VP: Beau Burris
Assoc Dir: Jackie Busa
Dir IT: Roger Evan
VP Mktg: Wayne Williams

LAKELAND TOYOTA
See MEMORIAL MOTORS INC

D-U-N-S 07-303-0207
LAKEMARY CENTER INC
LMC INDUSTRIES
100 Lakemary Dr, Paola, KS 66071-1855
Tel (913) 557-4000 *Founded/Ownrshp* 1969
Sales 21.9MM *EMP* 369
Accts Agler & Gaeddert Chartered Ot
SIC 8361 8211 Home for the mentally retarded; School for the retarded; Home for the mentally retarded; School for the retarded
Pr: William Craig
**Ch Bd:* Paul Sokoloff
**Pr:* Mike Everett
**CFO:* Shawn Kelsey
**Treas:* Carolyn Jacobs
**V Ch Bd:* Gail Richardson
**VP:* Tom Walsh
Prgrm Mgr: Teresa Galutia
Sls&Mrk Ex: Tracy Price
Mktg Dir: Mary Wheeler
Board of Directors: Mike Everett, Barry Fink, Ron Herman, Edward Kerrigan, Lydia Marien, Gayle Richardson, Harold Sevy, Gary Weinberg

LAKENORMAN REGIONAL MED CTR
See MOORESVILLE HOSPITAL MANAGEMENT ASSOCIATES LLC

D-U-N-S 14-422-0613
LAKEPARK INDUSTRIES INC
MIDWAY PRODUCTS GROUP
(*Suby of* MIDWAY PRODUCTS GROUP INC) ★
40 Seminary St, Greenwich, OH 44837-1040
Tel (419) 752-4471 *Founded/Ownrshp* 1985
Sales 30.8MM^E *EMP* 150
SIC 3469 3465 Metal stampings; Automotive stampings; Metal stampings; Automotive stampings
Pr: James Hoyt
**VP:* Lloyd A Miller
Plnt Mgr: Jeff Price
Prd Mgr: John Crider
Ql Cn Mgr: Jeanne Carpenter
Ql Cn Mgr: Grady Dias
Ql Cn Mgr: Nilesh Soni

D-U-N-S 16-143-3800
■ LAKEPOINTE EMERGENCY CONSULTANTS PLLC
LAKE POINTE MEDICAL CENTER
(*Suby of* TENET HEALTHCARE CORPORATION)
6800 Scenic Dr, Rowlett, TX 75088-4552
Tel (972) 412-2273 *Founded/Ownrshp* 1997
Sales 48.9MM^E *EMP* 575
SIC 8062 8051 8082 8011 General medical & surgical hospitals; Skilled nursing care facilities; Home health care services; Medical centers; General medical & surgical hospitals; Skilled nursing care facilities; Home health care services; Medical centers
CEO: Brett D Lee
Ofcr: Patti Gilliano
Ansthlgy: Jay Moore
Snr Mgr: John Klitsch
Board of Directors: David M French, Clyde Goins

D-U-N-S 19-751-4946
LAKEPORT CREDIT UNION
COMMUNITY FIRST CREDIT UNION
1100 S 30th St, Manitowoc, WI 54220-5594
Tel (920) 684-7148 *Founded/Ownrshp* 1953
Sales 8.9MM^E *EMP* 300
SIC 7323 Credit reporting services; Credit reporting services
Pr: Cathie Tierney

D-U-N-S 12-316-9898
LAKER SCHOOLS
6136 Pigeon Rd, Pigeon, MI 48755-9585
Tel (989) 453-4600 *Founded/Ownrshp* 1975
Sales 21.2MM^E *EMP* 121
Accts John Walsh Cpa Pigeon Mi
SIC 8211 Public elementary & secondary schools; Public elementary & secondary schools
CFO: Mike Klosowski

D-U-N-S 05-731-6457
LAKERIDGE PAVING CO LLC
19606 Se 252nd St, Covington, WA 98042-6707
Tel (801) 975-9900 *Founded/Ownrshp* 1980
Sales 22.9MM *EMP* 37
Accts Petersen Cpas And Advisors Pl
SIC 1771 1623 1611 Blacktop (asphalt) work; Underground utilities contractor; Highway & street construction; Blacktop (asphalt) work; Underground utilities contractor; Highway & street construction

D-U-N-S 14-179-0592
LAKES ENTERPRISES INC
MAURER MANUFACTURING
(*Suby of* DEMCO) ★
1300 38th Ave W, Spencer, IA 51301-2547
Tel (712) 262-2992 *Founded/Ownrshp* 2000
Sales 20.0MM^E *EMP* 75
SIC 3715 3523 Truck trailers; Farm machinery & equipment; Trailers & wagons, farm
Genl Mgr: Cris Tostnrud
**Genl Mgr:* John Tatman
Genl Mgr: Chris Tostenrud
S&M/VP: Gene Montgomery
Sls Mgr: Chris Taylor

D-U-N-S 02-279-6114
LAKES GAS CO
655 Lake St S, Forest Lake, MN 55025-2651
Tel (651) 464-3345 *Founded/Ownrshp* 1959
Sales 37.0MM^E *EMP* 170
SIC 5984 Propane gas, bottled; Propane gas, bottled
Pr: Howard Sargeant
**VP:* Steve Sargeant
Exec: Jane Boyer
Dist Mgr: Tony Buck

D-U-N-S 12-277-8277
LAKES REGION COMMUNITY SERVICES COUNCIL INC
LRCSC
719 N Main St Rm 105, Laconia, NH 03246-2741
Tel (603) 524-8811 *Founded/Ownrshp* 1975
Sales 22.8MM *EMP* 300
Accts Leone Mcdonnell & Roberts Prof
SIC 8331 8322 8399 8742 8361 Job training & vocational rehabilitation services; Travelers' aid; Community development groups; Human resource consulting services; Residential care; Job training & vocational rehabilitation services; Travelers' aid; Community development groups; Human resource consulting services; Residential care
Pr: Christine Satanillo
Ex Dir: Richard Crocker
IT Man: Shelley Kelleher

D-U-N-S 07-289-1542
LAKES REGIONAL HEALTHCARE
2301 Highway 71, Spirit Lake, IA 51360-1185
Tel (712) 336-1230 *Founded/Ownrshp* 2009
Sales 23.7MM^E *EMP* 250^E
SIC 8062 General medical & surgical hospitals; General medical & surgical hospitals
Pr: Richard C Kielman
COO: Jason Harrington
**CFO:* Gordon Larson
Ofcr: Carolyn Hansman
Dir Rad: Tracy Evens
Pharmcst: Cheryl Ramsey

D-U-N-S 12-271-2151 EXP
LAKESHIRTS INC
BLUE 84
750 Randolph Rd, Detroit Lakes, MN 56501-3701
Tel (218) 847-2171 *Founded/Ownrshp* 1984
Sales 58.0MM *EMP* 320
SIC 2395 7336 5699 Emblems, embroidered; Silk screen design; T-shirts, custom printed; Customized clothing & apparel; Emblems, embroidered; Silk screen design; T-shirts, custom printed; Customized clothing & apparel
Pr: Mark Fritz
**CEO:* Mike Hutchinson
Opers Mgr: Kara Bren

D-U-N-S 61-870-5420 IMP
LAKESHORE CHRYSLER DODGE JEEP INC
330 E Howze Beach Rd, Slidell, LA 70461-4644
Tel (985) 641-9595 *Founded/Ownrshp* 1990
Sales 28.1MM^E *EMP* 78^E
SIC 5511 7538 7532 5521 Automobiles, new & used; General automotive repair shops; Top & body repair & paint shops; Used car dealers; Automobiles, new & used; General automotive repair shops; Top & body repair & paint shops; Used car dealers
Pr: Otis Favre
**VP:* Lonnie S Favre

D-U-N-S 07-927-4718
LAKESHORE COMMUNITY HOSPITAL INC
MERCY HEALTH
72 S State St, Shelby, MI 49455-1228
Tel (231) 861-2156 *Founded/Ownrshp* 1925
Sales 24.1MM^E *EMP* 110
SIC 8062 General medical & surgical hospitals; General medical & surgical hospitals
Ex Dir: Jay Bryan
COO: Jeff Alexander
**CFO:* Mark Gross
Mng Ofcr: Elizabeth Le Vasseu

D-U-N-S 62-505-0752
LAKESHORE COMMUNITY SERVICES INC
1352 W 26th St, Erie, PA 16508
Tel (814) 456-9962 *Founded/Ownrshp* 1987
Sales 19.1MM *EMP* 550^E
Accts Malin Bergquist & Company Llp
SIC 8059 Home for the mentally retarded, exc. skilled or intermediate; Home for the mentally retarded, exc. skilled or intermediate
Ex Dir: Richard Ruedy
CFO: Dave Meehl

D-U-N-S 78-225-4028
LAKESHORE CUTTING SOLUTIONS INC
LCS
411 E Roosevelt Ave, Zeeland, MI 49464-1341
Tel (616) 772-2888 *Founded/Ownrshp* 2006
Sales 23.6MM^E *EMP* 43^E
SIC 5074 Water softeners
Pr: Tracy Ayers

D-U-N-S 12-284-3381
LAKESHORE ENERGY SERVICES LLC
(*Suby of* CONTINUUM ENERGY SERVICES LLC) ★
1415 La St Ste 4200, Houston, TX 77002
Tel (888) 200-3788 *Founded/Ownrshp* 2008
Sales 173.8MM *EMP* 35
SIC 4924 Natural gas distribution; Natural gas distribution
VP: Robert Giles

D-U-N-S 02-879-7546 IMP/EXP
LAKESHORE EQUIPMENT CO INC
LAKESHORE LEARNING MATERIALS
2695 E Dominguez St, Carson, CA 90895-1000
Tel (310) 537-8600 *Founded/Ownrshp* 1992
Sales 459.3MM^E *EMP* 1,800
SIC 5999 5961 Education aids, devices & supplies; Educational supplies & equipment, mail order; Toys & games (including dolls & models), mail order; Education aids, devices & supplies; Educational supplies & equipment, mail order; Toys & games (including dolls & models), mail order
Pr: Michael A Kaplan
CFO: Mike Baltzer
**CFO:* Renee Billele
CFO: Karen Townsend
CFO: Renee Villea
Treas: Irl Cramer
**Treas:* Joshua Kaplan
Chf Mktg O: Diane Seidel
Ofcr: Monika Lee
VP: Jeniffer Centazzo
VP: Jennifer Centazzo
VP: Blaine Dyne
**VP:* Charles P Kaplan
VP: Jarrett Klein
VP: Pamela Moreno
VP: Bob Musso
VP: Mario Savastano
VP: Jon Spiegelhoff

D-U-N-S 06-470-7896
LAKESHORE FOODS CORP
AL'S SUPERMARKET
100 Commerce Sq, Michigan City, IN 46360-3281
Tel (219) 326-7500 *Founded/Ownrshp* 1947
Sales 44.1MM^E *EMP* 400
SIC 5411 Supermarkets, independent; Supermarkets, independent
Pr: Gil R Pontius
**CFO:* Jim Ziska
VP: Robert Bline
Sls&Mrk Ex: Kyle Johnson

D-U-N-S 02-949-4105
LAKESHORE HEALTH PARTNERS
3235 N Wellness Dr 120b, Holland, MI 49424-8035
Tel (616) 399-9522 *Founded/Ownrshp* 2010
Sales 69.0MM^E *EMP* 1,199^E
SIC 8062 General medical & surgical hospitals
Prin: Dale Sowders
Podiatrist: Ritu Mathur

LAKESHORE LEARNING MATERIALS
See LAKESHORE EQUIPMENT CO INC

D-U-N-S 00-360-9633
LAKESHORE MANAGEMENT GROUP INC (IL)
70 E Lake St Ste 1600, Chicago, IL 60601-7446
Tel (773) 981-1452 *Founded/Ownrshp* 1997
Sales 20.9MM^E *EMP* 1,500
SIC 7991 Health club; Health club
CEO: Robert Johnson
**Pr:* Jordon Kaiser
**Treas:* Walter Kaiser
**Ex VP:* Michael Sons
**VP:* Michael Dow

D-U-N-S 02-160-2226
LAKESHORE MANAGEMENT INC
8833 Gross Point Rd # 310, Skokie, IL 60077-1859
Tel (847) 626-0400 *Founded/Ownrshp* 2001
Sales 28.3MM^E *EMP* 170
SIC 8741 Management services
Pr: Joseph Wolf

D-U-N-S 12-347-4314
LAKESHORE PUBLIC SCHOOL
28850 Harper Ave, Saint Clair Shores, MI 48081-1249
Tel (586) 285-8480 *Founded/Ownrshp* 1898
Sales 21.7MM^E *EMP* 400
SIC 8211 Public elementary & secondary schools; Public elementary & secondary schools

D-U-N-S 08-677-2662
LAKESHORE PUBLIC SCHOOLS
5771 Cleveland Ave, Stevensville, MI 49127-9481
Tel (269) 428-1400 *Founded/Ownrshp* 1957
Sales 19.9MM^E *EMP* 409
SIC 8211 8741 Public elementary & secondary schools; High school, junior or senior; Management services; Public elementary & secondary schools; High school, junior or senior; Management services
**CFO:* Robert L Burgess
**Prin:* Michael Mulligan
Adm Dir: Kim Fowler

D-U-N-S 07-877-8361
LAKESHORE RECYCLING SYSTEMS LLC
LAKESHORE WASTE SERVICES
6132 Oakton St, Morton Grove, IL 60053-2718
Tel (773) 685-8811 *Founded/Ownrshp* 2012
Sales 93.3MM^E *EMP* 419
SIC 4953 Refuse systems; Refuse systems
CEO: Alan T Handley
Mng Pt: Joshua Connell
COO: Sylvia Corona
VP Opers: John J Larsen
Sales Asso: Charlie Zimmerman

D-U-N-S 15-359-1490
■ LAKESHORE SYSTEM SERVICES INC
HEALTHSOUTH
(*Suby of* HEALTHSOUTH CORP) ★
1 Healthsouth Pkwy S, Birmingham, AL 35243-2358
Tel (205) 967-7116 *Founded/Ownrshp* 1987
Sales 60.6MM^E *EMP* 800
SIC 8741 8361 8093 Hospital management; Rehabilitation center, residential: health care incidental; Specialty outpatient clinics; Hospital management; Rehabilitation center, residential: health care incidental; Specialty outpatient clinics
Pr: Jim Bennett
Pr: Adriene Dudley
Pr: Mia Haynes
**CFO:* Dave Clemente
VP: James Foxworthy
VP: Debra Larson
**VP:* Michael E Stephens
VP: Fred Wright
Dir Risk M: Susan Nance
Dir Rx: Lance Kephart
Chf Nrs Of: Maryjean Ricci

D-U-N-S 07-477-4324
LAKESHORE TECHNICAL COLLEGE
1290 North Ave, Cleveland, WI 53015-1412
Tel (920) 693-1000 *Founded/Ownrshp* 1912
Sales 15.9MM *EMP* 741
Accts Schenck Sc Sheboygan Wiscons
SIC 8222 Technical institute; Technical institute
Pr: Mike Lanser
Psych: Sue Hein
Cert Phar: Dave Brown

D-U-N-S 09-868-1364
LAKESHORE UTILITY TRAILER INC
18239 Telegraph Rd, Romulus, MI 48174-9546
Tel (734) 285-4560 *Founded/Ownrshp* 1979
Sales 20.4MM^E *EMP* 50
SIC 5511 7539 7336 Trucks, tractors & trailers: new & used; Trailer repair; Art design services
Pr: Charles M Pfeffer
Opers Mgr: Dave Bielak
Sls Mgr: Richard Tiseo

LAKESHORE WASTE SERVICES
See LAKESHORE RECYCLING SYSTEMS LLC

D-U-N-S 00-552-2578
LAKESIDE BANK (INC) (IL)
55 W Wacker Dr Lbby, Chicago, IL 60601-1699
Tel (312) 435-5100 *Founded/Ownrshp* 1965, 1993
Sales NA *EMP* 115
SIC 6022 State commercial banks; State commercial banks
Ch Bd: Victor Cacciatore
Pr: Raymond J Spaeth
CFO: Shively Verrette
CFO: Connie S Watkins
Bd of Dir: Raymond Chin
Bd of Dir: Terry Gabinski
Sr VP: Jeff Mancuso
Sr VP: Lyles McDaniel
VP: Bonnie Kotara
VP: David Pinkerton
VP: Desi White
Exec: Susan Schliep
Board of Directors: William F Cellini, Raymond M Chin, John P Davey, Charles C Haffner III, Elonzo Hill, Robert Mariano, Kenneth McHugh, Dan Webb, William Weibel

D-U-N-S 15-284-0278
LAKESIDE BEHAVIORAL HEALTH SYSTEM LLC
2911 Brunswick Rd, Memphis, TN 38133-4105
Tel (901) 377-4733 *Founded/Ownrshp* 1973
Sales 14.3MM^E *EMP* 325
SIC 8063 8069 Psychiatric hospitals; Substance abuse hospitals; Psychiatric hospitals; Substance abuse hospitals
CFO: Ron Hart

LAKESIDE BEHAVIORAL HEALTHCARE
See ASPIRE HEALTH PARTNERS INC

D-U-N-S 00-518-2985 IMP
LAKESIDE EQUIPMENT CORP
1022 E Devon Ave, Bartlett, IL 60103-4796
Tel (630) 837-5640 *Founded/Ownrshp* 1928, 1990
Sales 30.0MM *EMP* 40
SIC 3589 3561

D-U-N-S 01-096-6117
LAKESIDE FAMILY & CHILDRENS SERVICES INC (NY)
235 N Main St Ste 14, Spring Valley, NY 10977-4014
Tel (845) 222-2469 *Founded/Ownrshp* 1923
Sales 304.4M *EMP* 300
SIC 8322 Individual & family services
Pr: Robert M Lederman

LAKESIDE FAMILY PHYSICIANS
See NOVANT HEALTH INC

D-U-N-S 60-575-4399
LAKESIDE FOOD INC
7 E 13th St Ste 322, Anniston, AL 36201-4603
Tel (256) 238-9281 *Founded/Ownrshp* 1989
Sales 20.4MM *EMP* 7
SIC 5144 Poultry & poultry products; Poultry & poultry products
Pr: Allen Bodner
**VP:* Lavern Holifield

D-U-N-S 00-607-2037 IMP/EXP
LAKESIDE FOODS INC (WI)
808 Hamilton St, Manitowoc, WI 54220-5326
Tel (920) 684-3356 *Founded/Ownrshp* 1921
Sales 413.2MM^E *EMP* 970
SIC 2033 2037 2032 2038 Canned fruits & specialties; Vegetables & vegetable products in cans, jars, etc.; Fruits & fruit products in cans, jars, etc.; Jams, jellies & preserves: packaged in cans, jars, etc.; Frozen fruits & vegetables; Canned specialties; Frozen specialties; Canned fruits & specialties; Vegetables & vegetable products in cans, jars, etc.; Fruits & fruit products in cans, jars, etc.; Jams, jellies & preserves: packaged in cans, jars, etc.; Frozen fruits & vegetables; Canned specialties; Frozen specialties
Pr: David J Yanda
Pr: Denise Kitzerow
Sr VP: Gordon J Lund
VP: David Aggen
VP: Michael Gilbertson
VP: Nathan Hartman
**VP:* James I Ferguson
**VP:* Robert Popple
VP: John Rusiniak
VP Opers: Bruce Jacobson
QI Cn Mgr: Brian Herbrand
Board of Directors: Elizabeth Kocourek, Henry F White Jr

LAKESIDE FORD
See FERRIDAY AUTO VENTURES LLC

LAKESIDE HOSPITAL
See MEDICAL CENTER OF BATON ROUGE INC

D-U-N-S 78-680-6685
LAKESIDE IMPORTS INC
LAKESIDE TOYOTA
3701 N Causeway Blvd, Metairie, LA 70002-1722
Tel (504) 837-5623 *Founded/Ownrshp* 1990
Sales 69.9MM^E *EMP* 196
SIC 5511 7538 7515 7514 5531 5521 Automobiles, new & used; General automotive repair shops; Passenger car leasing; Passenger car rental; Automotive & home supply stores; Used car dealers; Automobiles, new & used; General automotive repair shops; Passenger car leasing; Passenger car rental; Automotive & home supply stores; Used car dealers
Pr: Anthony Gullo Sr
**VP:* Keith Hanks
Sls Mgr: Troy Campise
Sls Mgr: Mike Chosa
Sls Mgr: John Prindle

D-U-N-S 05-835-2022 IMP
LAKESIDE INDUSTRIES INC
6505 226th Pl Se Ste 200, Issaquah, WA 98027-8905
Tel (425) 313-2600 *Founded/Ownrshp* 1952
Sales 366.3MM^E *EMP* 750
SIC 1611 2951 5032 Highway & street paving contractor; Asphalt & asphaltic paving mixtures (not from refineries); Gravel; Highway & street paving contractor; Asphalt & asphaltic paving mixtures (not from refineries); Gravel
Ch: Rhoady R Lee Jr
**Pr:* Michael J Lee
**CEO:* Timothy Lee Jr
**CFO:* Hank Waggoner
CFO: Dax Woolston
VP: Ron Green
Div Mgr: Tony Hammett
CTO: Bruce Fyfe
Dir IT: Mike Smith
IT Man: Eric Carlson
IT Man: Doug Stillgebauer

D-U-N-S 36-450-4803
LAKESIDE INTERIOR CONTRACTORS INC
26970 Eckel Rd, Perrysburg, OH 43551-1214
Tel (419) 867-1300 *Founded/Ownrshp* 1989
Sales 24.3MM^E *EMP* 175
SIC 1742 1791 1751 1752 1721

D-U-N-S 11-753-2507
LAKESIDE INTERNATIONAL LLC
LAKESIDE INTERNATIONAL TRUCKS
11000 W Silver Spring Dr, Milwaukee, WI 53225-3134
Tel (414) 353-4800 *Founded/Ownrshp* 1995
Sales 128.9MM^E *EMP* 285
SIC 5511 5531 7538 7532 6159 7513 Trucks, tractors & trailers: new & used; Truck equipment & parts; General truck repair; Body shop, trucks; Truck finance leasing; Truck rental, without drivers; Trucks, tractors & trailers: new & used; Truck equipment & parts; General truck repair; Body shop, trucks; Truck finance leasing; Truck rental, without drivers
Pr: Bill Reilley Jr
**CFO:* Jim Daugherty
Genl Mgr: Dan Lindberg
Sales Asso: David Considine

LAKESIDE INTERNATIONAL TRUCKS
See LAKESIDE INTERNATIONAL LLC

D-U-N-S 00-609-1599 IMP
LAKESIDE MANUFACTURING INC (WI)
ARIS MANUFACTURING COMPANY
4900 W Electric Ave, Milwaukee, WI 53219-1629
Tel (414) 645-0630 *Founded/Ownrshp* 1946, 2003
Sales 29.6MM^E *EMP* 120
SIC 2599 Carts, restaurant equipment; Carts, restaurant equipment
Ch Bd: Lawrence Moon
**Pr:* Joseph Carlson
COO: Don Combs
**Sr VP:* James Anderson
VP Opers: Jim Fleuchaus
**Plnt Mgr:* Jeff Goodman
VP Sls: Brian Emmer
Mktg Mgr: Ken Bindas
Manager: Jason Fox
Manager: Jeff Gudex
Manager: Marianne Schussler-Yenor

D-U-N-S 07-602-2664
LAKESIDE MEDICAL CENTER
GLADES GENERAL HOSPITAL
(*Suby of* HEALTH CARE DISTRICT OF PALM BEACH COUNTY) ★
39200 Hooker Hwy, Belle Glade, FL 33430-5368
Tel (561) 996-6571 *Founded/Ownrshp* 2004
Sales 22.3MM *EMP* 260
SIC 8062 General medical & surgical hospitals; General medical & surgical hospitals
**QC Dir:* Nancy O'Neal
Pathlgst: Thomas Bolton
HC Dir: Monica Bevill

LAKESIDE MEDICAL SYSTEMS
See LAKESIDE SYSTEMS INC

D-U-N-S 06-791-3269
LAKESIDE MEMORIAL HOSPITAL INC
DAISY MARQUIS JONES FAMILY WEL
170 West Ave, Brockport, NY 14420-1227
Tel (585) 395-6043 *Founded/Ownrshp* 1939
Sales 10.7MM *EMP* 600
SIC 8062 General medical & surgical hospitals; General medical & surgical hospitals
CEO: Mike Stapleton
CFO: Michelle Richman
VP: Terry Klinetob
VP: Carolyn Vacanti
Dir Rad: Michael Heary
VP Admn: Krys Staub
Prgrm Mgr: Bonnie Hewett
CIO: Bridget Reed
IT Man: Chris Maltese
IT Man: Gary Torok
Doctor: Mitchell Chess

D-U-N-S 60-929-1737 IMP
LAKESIDE METALS INC
7000 S Adams St Ste 210, Willowbrook, IL 60527-8443
Tel (630) 850-3800 *Founded/Ownrshp* 1989
Sales 27.6MM^E *EMP* 65
SIC 5051 Tin plate; Tin plate
Pr: Ira Nadler
**Pr:* Lee Nadler
**VP:* Harold Tannenbaum

D-U-N-S 18-610-5552
LAKESIDE PIC-N-PAC LLC
7131 W Olive Rd, Holland, MI 49424-8470
Tel (616) 399-3922 *Founded/Ownrshp* 2003
Sales 11.6MM^E *EMP* 400
SIC 0191 General farms, primarily crop; General farms, primarily crop

LAKESIDE PUBLIC SCHOOLS
See LAKESIDE SCHOOL DISTRICT /MAIN OFFICE

D-U-N-S 08-933-7984
LAKESIDE SCHOOL
14050 1st Ave Ne, Seattle, WA 98125-3025
Tel (206) 368-3600 *Founded/Ownrshp* 1923
Sales 35.8MM *EMP* 303
SIC 8211

D-U-N-S 09-856-6649
LAKESIDE SCHOOL DISTRICT /MAIN OFFICE
LAKESIDE PUBLIC SCHOOLS
2837 Malvern Ave, Hot Springs, AR 71901-8321
Tel (501) 262-1880 *Founded/Ownrshp* 1930
Sales 21.4MM^E *EMP* 325
SIC 8211 Public combined elementary & secondary school; Public combined elementary & secondary school
MIS Dir: Melinda Dodd

D-U-N-S 08-307-8147
LAKESIDE SCREW PRODUCTS INC (IL)
1395 W Jeffrey Dr, Addison, IL 60101-4331
Tel (630) 705-9274 *Founded/Ownrshp* 1977
Sales 20.6MM^E *EMP* 105
SIC 3451 Screw machine products
Pr: Zygmunt Soszko

D-U-N-S 01-778-5445
LAKESIDE SUPPLY CO (OH)
3000 W 117th St, Cleveland, OH 44111-1667
Tel (216) 941-6800 *Founded/Ownrshp* 1932
Sales 36.0MM^E *EMP* 39
SIC 5085 5074 5075 Industrial supplies; Valves & fittings; Plumbing fittings & supplies; Warm air heating equipment & supplies
Co-Pr: Kenneth Mathews
**Treas:* Mary Lou Mathews
**Co-Pr:* Lawrence G Mathews
**VP:* Brian Driscoll
**VP:* John Joseph Mathews
Off Mgr: Pamela Bonham
Sales Asso: Sarah Candow
Sales Asso: Pat Charvat

D-U-N-S 93-359-2768
LAKESIDE SYSTEMS INC
LAKESIDE MEDICAL SYSTEMS
(*Suby of* HERITAGE PROVIDER NETWORK INC) ★
8510 Balboa Blvd Ste 150, Northridge, CA 91325-5810
Tel (866) 654-3471 *Founded/Ownrshp* 2009
Sales 31.2MM^E *EMP* 700
SIC 8741 8742 6411 Management services; Management consulting services; Insurance agents, brokers & service; Management services; Management consulting services; Insurance agents, brokers & service
CEO: Richard Merkin
Exec: Karol Cabrera

LAKESIDE TOYOTA
See LAKESIDE IMPORTS INC

D-U-N-S 07-875-3001
LAKESIDE UNION SCHOOL DISTRICT
12335 Woodside Ave, Lakeside, CA 92040-3015
Tel (619) 390-2600 *Founded/Ownrshp* 1923
Sales 32.3MM^E *EMP* 600
SIC 8211 Public elementary school; Public junior high school; Public elementary school; Public junior high school
Exec: Andy Parr

D-U-N-S 02-541-6025 IMP
LAKESTAR SEMI INC
888 7th Ave Ste 3300, New York, NY 10106-3402
Tel (212) 974-6254 *Founded/Ownrshp* 2013
Sales 62.3MM^E *EMP* 315^E
SIC 3674 5065 Semiconductors & related devices; Semiconductor devices; Semiconductors & related devices; Semiconductor devices
Pr: Sailesh Chittipeddi
Pr: Shiva Gowni
COO: Naresh Malipeddi
COO: Daniel A Marotta
Ch: Shu Li
Sec: Julie Hall
Sr Cor Off: Balakrishnan Siyer
Ofcr: Mark D Peterson
Sr VP: Moiz M Beguwala
Sr VP: Raouf Y Halim
Sr VP: Phillip E Pompa
Sr VP: James P Spoto
Sr VP: Thomas A Stites
Sr VP: Kevin V Strong
Sr VP: Paul D Walker
Sr VP: Bradley W Yates
VP: Steven Bakos
VP: Steve Bergeron
VP: Jeff Crosby
VP: Greg Fischer
VP: Dennis E O Reilly

LAKEVIEW APPLIANCE DISTRG
See DKMR PARTNERS LLC

D-U-N-S 01-315-0651
LAKEVIEW AUTO SALES AND SERVICE INC (NY)
MERCEDES-BENZ ROCKVILLE CENTRE
110 W Graham Ave, Hempstead, NY 11550-6102
Tel (516) 766-6900 *Founded/Ownrshp* 1965, 2001
Sales 32.5MM^E *EMP* 100^E
SIC 5511 Automobiles, new & used; Automobiles, new & used
Pr: David Meyer
Exec: Russell Bliss
Sls Mgr: Bob Lantz

D-U-N-S 09-892-9524
LAKEVIEW CENTER INC
1221 W Lakeview Ave, Pensacola, FL 32501-1836
Tel (850) 432-1222 *Founded/Ownrshp* 1961
Sales 217.4MM *EMP* 1,900^E
Accts Ernst & Young Llp
SIC 8069 8093 7389 7371 7373 Specialty hospitals, except psychiatric; Mental health clinic, outpatient; Substance abuse clinics (outpatient); Psychiatric hospitals; Home health care services; Specialty hospitals, except psychiatric; Substance abuse hospitals; Alcoholism rehabilitation hospital; Drug addiction rehabilitation hospital; Substance abuse clinics (outpatient); Detoxification center, outpatient; Personal service agents, brokers & bureaus; Custom computer programming services; Computer integrated systems design
Pr: Gary L Bembry
COO: Tra Williams
CFO: Xan Smith
VP: Rich Gilmartin
VP: Dennis Goodspeed
VP: Allison Hill
VP: Shawn Salamida
VP: Sandy Whitaker
Ex Dir: Alicia Hall

D-U-N-S 83-142-1149 IMP
LAKEVIEW CHEESE CO LLC
3030 N Lamb Blvd Ste 114, Las Vegas, NV 89115-3496
Tel (702) 233-2439 *Founded/Ownrshp* 2009
Sales 47.1MM^E *EMP* 70^E
SIC 5143 Dairy products, except dried or canned; Dairy products, except dried or canned

D-U-N-S 05-293-1672
LAKEVIEW COMMUNITY HOSPITAL AUTHORITY AUXILIARY (MI)
408 Hazen St, Paw Paw, MI 49079-1019
Tel (269) 657-3141 *Founded/Ownrshp* 1954
Sales 40.2MM^E *EMP* 558
SIC 8062 8051 Hospital, affiliated with AMA residency; Convalescent home with continuous nursing care; Hospital, affiliated with AMA residency; Convalescent home with continuous nursing care
CEO: Frank J Sardone
**Pr:* Sue E Johnson-Phillippe
Dir Lab: Diane Branch
Dir Rx: Larry Pokryfke
VP Opers: Sally Berglin
Mktg Mgr: Mike Matthews
Pharmcst: Sara Bartells

D-U-N-S 78-669-4570
LAKEVIEW COMMUNITY SCHOOL
123 5th St, Lakeview, MI 48850-9153
Tel (989) 352-6226 *Founded/Ownrshp* 1880
Sales 13.7MM *EMP* 405
Accts Rehmann Robson Llc Grand Rap
SIC 8211 Public elementary & secondary schools

D-U-N-S 80-008-3289
LAKEVIEW CONSTRUCTION INC
10505 Corp Dr Ste 200, Pleasant Prairie, WI 53158
Tel (262) 857-3336 *Founded/Ownrshp* 1993
Sales 66.7MM^E *EMP* 112
Accts Raimondo Callahan & Associate
SIC 1542 Shopping center construction; Shopping center construction
Pr: Kent Moon
**VP:* Marc Delsman
**VP:* Bryan Dunn
**VP:* Rob Schoenberg
Opers Mgr: Gary Sills

D-U-N-S 07-891-4454
LAKEVIEW CONTINUING CARE CENTER
(*Suby of* LAKEVIEW COMMUNITY HOSPITAL AUTHORITY AUXILIARY) ★
99 Walker St, Lawton, MI 49065-9703
Tel (269) 624-4311 *Founded/Ownrshp* 1987
Sales 6.1MM^E *EMP* 558
SIC 8051 8069 Skilled nursing care facilities; Specialty hospitals, except psychiatric; Skilled nursing care facilities; Specialty hospitals, except psychiatric
Pr: Laura Hamann
**Ch Bd:* Charles Randall
Pr: Deb Goble

D-U-N-S 19-146-6739
LAKEVIEW FARMS LLC
229 E 2nd St, Delphos, OH 45833-1702
Tel (419) 695-9925 *Founded/Ownrshp* 2015
Sales 117.7MM^E *EMP* 230
SIC 2026 2099 2022 Cream, sour; Dips, sour cream based; Dips, except cheese & sour cream based; Gelatin dessert preparations; Cheese, natural & processed; Cream, sour; Dips, sour cream based; Dips, except cheese & sour cream based; Gelatin dessert preparations; Cheese, natural & processed
Pr: Ernest E Graves
CFO: Gerald Fischer
Treas: Martin Garlock
Dir IT: Doug Metzger
Plnt Mgr: Phil Baldauf
Plnt Mgr: Delbert Collins
Plnt Mgr: Del Hanf
Plnt Mgr: Brian Smith
QI Cn Mgr: Lynda Stewart
Mktg Dir: John Kopilchack

D-U-N-S 03-923-9138
LAKEVIEW FORD-LINCOLN INC
295 W Dickman Rd, Battle Creek, MI 49037-8453
Tel (269) 441-2500 *Founded/Ownrshp* 2010
Sales 23.5MM^E *EMP* 54
SIC 5511 Automobiles, new & used
Pr: Vincent Pavone

D-U-N-S 87-924-5855
LAKEVIEW HEALTH SYSTEMS LLC
1100 Park Central Blvd S # 3400, Pompano Beach, FL 33064-2265
Tel (954) 491-1707 *Founded/Ownrshp* 2013
Sales 26.0MM *EMP* 250
SIC 8069 Alcoholism rehabilitation hospital
CEO: Roy Scrta
Ex VP: James Long
Mktg Dir: John Howe

LAKEVIEW HOSPITAL
See LAKEVIEW MEMORIAL HOSPITAL ASSOCIATION INC

LAKEVIEW HOSPITAL
See HOSPITAL CORP OF UTAH

D-U-N-S 07-839-0061
LAKEVIEW HOSPITAL
630 Medical Dr, Bountiful, UT 84010-4908
Tel (801) 292-6231 *Founded/Ownrshp* 2012
Sales 82.3MM *EMP* 160^E
SIC 8062 General medical & surgical hospitals; General medical & surgical hospitals
Pathlgst: Hu Ding
Doctor: Scott H West MD
Pharmcst: Greg Mendiola

D-U-N-S 12-644-8823 IMP/EXP
LAKEVIEW INTERNATIONAL CORP
100 Lakeview Pkwy, Vernon Hills, IL 60061-1547
Tel (847) 484-0040 *Founded/Ownrshp* 1995
Sales 50.4MM^E *EMP* 100
SIC 5084 Engines & transportation equipment
Pr: Ivano Passini

D-U-N-S 06-156-9872
LAKEVIEW MANAGEMENT INC
NEURO REHABILATATION
2011 Rutland Dr, Austin, TX 78758-5421
Tel (512) 973-9700 *Founded/Ownrshp* 1995
Sales 27.5MM^E *EMP* 302
SIC 8322 Rehabilitation services; Rehabilitation services
CEO: Anton C Merka
**Pr:* Carolyne McDermott
**CFO:* Ken Kosowizz

LAKEVIEW MANOR
See COUNTY OF WAUPACA

LAKEVIEW MEDICAL CENTER
See NOTAMI HOSPITALS OF LOUISIANA INC

D-U-N-S 01-006-5779
LAKEVIEW MEDICAL CENTER INC
2000 Meade Pkwy, Suffolk, VA 23434-4260
Tel (757) 539-0251 *Founded/Ownrshp* 1969
Sales 23.7MM^E *EMP* 300
SIC 8011 8093 8071 Medical centers; Specialty outpatient clinics; Medical laboratories; Medical centers; Specialty outpatient clinics; Medical laboratories
CFO: Kimberly W Garrett
**Pr:* William Delacey
Top Exec: Frederick L Assen
VP: Serena Barakat
Dir Lab: Kitty Quillin

D-U-N-S 07-763-7569
LAKEVIEW MEDICAL CENTER INC OF RICE LAKE
1700 W Stout St, Rice Lake, WI 54868-5000
Tel (715) 234-1515 *Founded/Ownrshp* 1920
Sales 69.0MM *EMP* 360ᴱ
SIC 8062 General medical & surgical hospitals; General medical & surgical hospitals
Pr: Edward H Wolf
CFO: Jackie Klein
Treas: Delores Bantz
Chf Mktg O: John Olson
**VP:* Scott Moebius
VP: Bev Prock
Dir OR: Kelly Flach
Dir Lab: Jim Berndt
Dir Rad: Kristine Curtis
Dir Rad: Terry Larson
Dir Rx: Ken Engel
Dir Rx: Kate Hillyer

D-U-N-S 07-763-4079
LAKEVIEW MEMORIAL HOSPITAL ASSOCIATION INC
LAKEVIEW HOSPITAL
927 Churchill St W, Stillwater, MN 55082-6605
Tel (651) 439-5330 *Founded/Ownrshp* 1958
Sales 70.3MMᴱ *EMP* 500ᴱ
Accts Larsonallen Llp Minneapolis
SIC 8062 General medical & surgical hospitals; General medical & surgical hospitals
Pr: Jeffrey Robertson
Chf Rad: John Knoedler
V Ch: Mary Weber
CEO: Debb Marshall
CFO: Doug Johnson
Bd of Dir: Joshua Peltier
Bd of Dir: Pat Riley
CIO: Chris Peterson
MIS Dir: Bill Overby
Software D: Karen Heilsberg
Sfty Dirs: Corey Seidie

D-U-N-S 94-211-6674
LAKEVIEW NEUROREHAB CENTER MIDWEST INC
LAKEVIEW SPECIALTY HOSPITAL
(*Suby of* LAKEVIEW MANAGEMENT INC) ★
1701 Sharp Rd, Waterford, WI 53185-5214
Tel (262) 534-7297 *Founded/Ownrshp* 1994
Sales 27.5MMᴱ *EMP* 300
SIC 8093 Rehabilitation center, outpatient treatment; Rehabilitation center, outpatient treatment
Ch: Anton Merka
**Pr:* Carolyne McDermott
**CEO:* Christopher Slover
**COO:* Tina Trudell
Dir Rx: Joanne Narut
Chf Nrs Of: Chris Mc Mahon
QA Dir: Mona Payne
Dir IT: David Gilligan
Site Mgr: Mary Lasanta
Psych: Bob Davis
Psych: Cynthia Sorenson

D-U-N-S 62-772-2960
LAKEVIEW NEUROREHABILITATION CENTER INC
244 High Watch Rd, Effingham, NH 03882-8336
Tel (603) 539-7451 *Founded/Ownrshp* 1993
Sales 21.1MMᴱ *EMP* 350
SIC 8069 8361 Specialty hospitals, except psychiatric; Residential care; Rehabilitation center, residential: health care incidental; Specialty hospitals, except psychiatric; Residential care; Rehabilitation center, residential: health care incidental
Pr: Carolyn G McDermott
**Treas:* Anton C Merka
Board of Directors: Patricia Reed

LAKEVIEW PRO SHOP
See L A LAKEVIEW ASSOCIATERS LP

LAKEVIEW REC PLEX
See VILLAGE OF PLEASANT PRAIRIE

D-U-N-S 15-918-4543
■ **LAKEVIEW REGIONAL MEDICAL CENTER AUXILIARY INC**
(*Suby of* HCA INC) ★
95 Judge Tanner Blvd, Covington, LA 70433-7500
Tel (985) 867-3800 *Founded/Ownrshp* 2001
Sales 33.6M *EMP* 800
SIC 8062 8011 General medical & surgical hospitals; Offices & clinics of medical doctors; General medical & surgical hospitals; Offices & clinics of medical doctors
Pr: June Selzer
Sr VP: Karen Cole
CTO: Marilyn Summerville
Doctor: Anthony Morales
HC Dir: Deborah Hesling
Snr Mgr: Sheila Anderson

D-U-N-S 02-103-5357
LAKEVIEW SCHOOL DISTRICT (MI)
15 Arbor St, Battle Creek, MI 49015-2903
Tel (269) 565-2411 *Founded/Ownrshp* 1921
Sales 35.7MM *EMP* 500
Accts Plante & Moran Pllc Portage
SIC 8211 8661 Public elementary & secondary schools; High school, junior or senior; Religious organizations; Public elementary & secondary schools; High school, junior or senior; Religious organizations
Prin: Robert Ward
Dir Sec: Marty Pessetti
Genl Mgr: David Peterson
IT Man: Fred Harris
HC Dir: Sharon Davids

LAKEVIEW SPECIALTY HOSPITAL
See LAKEVIEW NEUROREHAB CENTER MIDWEST INC

D-U-N-S 07-305-1518
LAKEVIEW VILLAGE INC
LAKEVIEW VILLAGE RETIREMENT CO
9100 Park St, Lenexa, KS 66215-3353
Tel (913) 888-1900 *Founded/Ownrshp* 1961
Sales 37.0MM *EMP* 550
Accts Cliftonlarsonallen Llp St L
SIC 6513 8052 Retirement hotel operation; Intermediate care facilities; Personal care facility; Retirement hotel operation; Intermediate care facilities; Personal care facility
CEO: James K Frazier
**Ch Bd:* Tedrick Housh
**COO:* Mary Schworer
**CFO:* Robert Clausen
Nrsg Dir: Delores Gilliland
Board of Directors: Donald Horine

LAKEVIEW VILLAGE RETIREMENT CO
See LAKEVIEW VILLAGE INC

D-U-N-S 01-039-2751
LAKEVILLE AREA PUBLIC SCHOOLS
LAKEVILLE PUBLIC SCHOOL
8670 210th St W, Lakeville, MN 55044-7000
Tel (952) 232-2000 *Founded/Ownrshp* 2000
Sales 131.5MM *EMP* 1,270
Accts Malloy Montague Karnowski R
SIC 8211 Public elementary & secondary schools; Public elementary & secondary schools
**Schl Brd P:* Roz Peterson
Psych: Jessica Davich
Board of Directors: Stan Frederickson, Gayle Smaley-Rader, Lonnie Smith, Linda Swanson, Greg Utchetc

D-U-N-S 05-957-2644
LAKEVILLE GROWERS
PETALUMA POULTRY
2700 Lakeville Hwy, Petaluma, CA 94954-5606
Tel (707) 763-1904 *Founded/Ownrshp* 1972
Sales 34.5MMᴱ *EMP* 200
SIC 0251 Broiler, fryer & roaster chickens; Broiler, fryer & roaster chickens
Genl Pt: Matt Junkeo
Pt: Dave Martinelli
Sls Mgr: Brian Starr

D-U-N-S 00-986-9918
LAKEVILLE MOTOR EXPRESS INC
L M E
500 County Road D W, Saint Paul, MN 55112-3520
Tel (651) 636-8900 *Founded/Ownrshp* 2009
Sales 56.4MMᴱ *EMP* 300ᴱ
SIC 4212 Local trucking, without storage; Local trucking, without storage
CEO: Roger Wilsey
Bd of Dir: John Wren
VP: Roger McGillis
VP: Mike Sanford
VP: Dan Stadick
VP: Karen Vanney
Dir Bus: Luke Olson
Sfty Dirs: Tom Hughes
Sls Dir: Gill Huskins

LAKEVILLE PUBLIC SCHOOL
See LAKEVILLE AREA PUBLIC SCHOOLS

LAKEVILLE SANITARY
See DICKS SANITATION SERVICE INC

D-U-N-S 07-903-1746
LAKEWAY CONTAINER INC (TN)
5715 Superior Dr, Morristown, TN 37814-1075
Tel (423) 581-2164 *Founded/Ownrshp* 1975
Sales 22.0MM *EMP* 96
Accts Crane Thompson & Jones Pc
SIC 2653 Boxes, corrugated: made from purchased materials; Boxes, corrugated: made from purchased materials
Pr: Gene Jolley
**VP:* Randall E Jolley

D-U-N-S 82-513-2202
■ **LAKEWAY HOSPITAL CORP**
LAKEWAY REGIONAL HOSPITAL
(*Suby of* COMMUNITY HEALTH SYSTEMS INC) ★
726 Mcfarland St, Morristown, TN 37814-3989
Tel (423) 522-6000 *Founded/Ownrshp* 1993
Sales 55.8MMᴱ *EMP* 350
SIC 8062 General medical & surgical hospitals; General medical & surgical hospitals
CEO: Pricilla Mills
**CFO:* Alan Archbold
Dir Lab: Ellen Maddron
Dir Rad: Amy Gillard
Dir Rx: Todd Webb
Mktg Dir: Pam Snyder
Pharmcst: Tex Springfield

D-U-N-S 00-339-1778
LAKEWAY PUBLISHERS INC (TN)
CITIZENS TRIBUNE
1609 W 1st North St, Morristown, TN 37814-3724
Tel (423) 318-8848 *Founded/Ownrshp* 1966
Sales 36.2MMᴱ *EMP* 250
SIC 2711 2752 Newspapers, publishing & printing; Commercial printing & newspaper publishing combined; Commercial printing, lithographic; Newspapers, publishing & printing; Commercial printing & newspaper publishing combined; Commercial printing, lithographic
Pr: R Jack Fishman
**Sec:* Jack Strate
Dist Mgr: Donna Haase

LAKEWAY REGIONAL HOSPITAL
See LAKEWAY HOSPITAL CORP

D-U-N-S 00-394-7229
LAKEWAY REGIONAL MEDICAL CENTER LLC
LRMC
100 Medical Pkwy, Lakeway, TX 78738-5621
Tel (512) 571-5000 *Founded/Ownrshp* 2007
Sales 87.4MMᴱ *EMP* 450
SIC 8062 General medical & surgical hospitals; General medical & surgical hospitals
CEO: Joyce Hein
CFO: Francis Curry
CFO: Thomas Marshall
Dir Lab: Lugard Igharo
Dir Rx: Pam Leal
IT Man: Matt Pace
QI Cn Mgr: Laura Cornelson
Mktg Dir: Odalis Mehta

D-U-N-S 08-094-8540
LAKEWOOD BOARD OF EDUCATION (INC) (NJ)
LAKEWOOD PUBLIC SCHOOLS
200 Ramsey Ave, Lakewood, NJ 08701-2085
Tel (732) 730-1606 *Founded/Ownrshp* 1910, 1970
Sales 49.1MMᴱ *EMP* 1,000
SIC 8211 Public elementary & secondary schools; Public elementary & secondary schools
Pr: Isaac Zlatkin
**VP:* Tracey Tift
Dir Sec: John Stillwell

D-U-N-S 08-404-3918
LAKEWOOD CHEDER SCHOOL
1785 Swarthmore Ave, Lakewood, NJ 08701-4532
Tel (732) 370-6400 *Founded/Ownrshp* 1962
Sales 21.9MM *EMP* 330
Accts Gershon Biegeleisen & Co Cpa
SIC 8211 Private elementary school; Private elementary school

D-U-N-S 02-081-9389
LAKEWOOD CHURCH (TX)
JOEL OSTEEN MINISTRIES
3700 Southwest Fwy, Houston, TX 77027-7514
Tel (713) 635-4154 *Founded/Ownrshp* 1959
Sales 24.3MMᴱ *EMP* 348
SIC 8661 Inter-denominational church; Inter-denominational church

D-U-N-S 07-980-0868
LAKEWOOD CITY SCHOOL DISTRICT
1470 Warren Rd, Cleveland, OH 44107-3918
Tel (216) 529-4092 *Founded/Ownrshp* 1916
Sales 65.5MM *EMP* 707
SIC 8211 Public elementary & secondary schools; Public elementary & secondary schools

D-U-N-S 79-498-6542
LAKEWOOD CITY SCHOOL DISTRICT
LAKEWOOD CITY SCHOOLS
1470 Warren Rd, Lakewood, OH 44107-3918
Tel (216) 529-4000 *Founded/Ownrshp* 2010
Sales 37.3MMᴱ *EMP* 707
Accts Dave Yost Cleveland Oh
SIC 8211 Public elementary & secondary schools; Public elementary school; Public junior high school; Public senior high school; Public elementary & secondary schools; Public elementary school; Public junior high school; Public senior high school
Bd of Dir: Linda Beebe
Bd of Dir: Betsy Shaughnessy
Ex Dir: Missy Toms
Sfty Dirs: John Crane
HC Dir: Christine Palumbo

LAKEWOOD CITY SCHOOLS
See LAKEWOOD CITY SCHOOL DISTRICT

LAKEWOOD FORD
See TITUS-WILL INVESTMENTS LLC

D-U-N-S 08-448-8139
LAKEWOOD HEALTH SYSTEM
49725 County 83, Staples, MN 56479-5280
Tel (218) 894-1515 *Founded/Ownrshp* 1973
Sales 95.6MM *EMP* 800ᴱ
Accts Wipfli Llp Minneapolis Mn
SIC 8062 8051 General medical & surgical hospitals; Extended care facility; General medical & surgical hospitals; Extended care facility
Pr: Tim Rice
Dir Vol: Marnie Pogreba
**CFO:* Jim Dregney
Bd of Dir: Julie Benson
Dir Lab: Cheryl Houselog
Dir IT: Corrine Neisess
Dir IT: Jim Thurner
Sfty Dirs: Robin Johnson
Nrsg Dir: Patrick Collins
Nrsg Dir: Cindy Denning
Pharmcst: Michael Brauch

LAKEWOOD HEALTHCARE CENTER
See HEALTHCARE CENTER OF DOWNEY LLC

D-U-N-S 07-778-2241
LAKEWOOD HOSPITAL ASSOCIATION
(*Suby of* CLEVELAND CLINIC FOUNDATION) ★
14519 Detroit Ave, Lakewood, OH 44107-4383
Tel (216) 529-7160 *Founded/Ownrshp* 1907
Sales 116.8MM *EMP* 750
SIC 8062 General medical & surgical hospitals; General medical & surgical hospitals
CEO: Fred Degrandis
VP: W C Geiger III
Chf Nrs Of: Mary Sauer
Cmptr Lab: Barb Garrard
Doctor: Krisin Broadben

D-U-N-S 10-006-3015
LAKEWOOD LOCAL SCHOOL DISTRICT
525 E Main St, Hebron, OH 43025-9702
Tel (740) 928-5878 *Founded/Ownrshp* 1950
Sales 17.9MMᴱ *EMP* 283
Accts Wilson Shannon And Snow Inc
SIC 8211 Public elementary & secondary schools; Public elementary & secondary schools
Prin: Jay Gaulpt
**Treas:* Doran Hammett
**Treas:* Glenna Plaisted
HC Dir: Christina Stager

D-U-N-S 07-363-0071
LAKEWOOD MANOR BAPTIST RETIREMENT COMMUNITY INC
(*Suby of* VIRGINIA BAPTIST HOMES, INCORPORATED)
1900 Lauderdale Dr, Richmond, VA 23238-3933
Tel (804) 740-2900 *Founded/Ownrshp* 1984
Sales 25.3MM *EMP* 100
Accts Larsonallen Llp Charlotte Nc
SIC 8059 Nursing home, except skilled & intermediate care facility; Nursing home, except skilled & intermediate care facility
Ch Bd: Oliver Way
Dir Recs: Donna Massey
**Pr:* Randall Robinson
Treas: Kevin Quinn
Dir Env Sv: John Topolosky
**Ex Dir:* Jeffery McInnis
Nrsg Dir: Valerie Bing

D-U-N-S 94-094-6226
LAKEWOOD MIDSTREAM LLC
(*Suby of* ENERGY SPECTRUM PARTNERS VI LP) ★
6655 S Lewis Ave Ste 200, Tulsa, OK 74136-1031
Tel (918) 392-9356 *Founded/Ownrshp* 2013
Sales 98.1MM *EMP* 122
SIC 4932 Gas & other services combined
Plnt Mgr: Blake Dacus
VP Sls: Doug Billings

LAKEWOOD OHIO
See CITY OF LAKEWOOD

LAKEWOOD PARK HEALTH CENTER
See MENTAL HEALTH CONVELESCENT SERVICES INC

LAKEWOOD PUBLIC SCHOOLS
See LAKEWOOD BOARD OF EDUCATION (INC)

D-U-N-S 79-831-7418
LAKEWOOD SCHOOL DISTRICT
200 Ramsey Ave, Lakewood, NJ 08701-2085
Tel (732) 905-3630 *Founded/Ownrshp* 1960
Sales 54.0MM *EMP* 650
SIC 8211 Public elementary & secondary schools; Public elementary & secondary schools
Prin: Dr Ernest Cannava
Psych: Rita Hocking
Psych: Marta Holsinger
Psych: Jim Roan

D-U-N-S 02-245-2825
LAKEWOOD SCHOOL DISTRICT 306
17110 16th Dr Ne, Marysville, WA 98271-5415
Tel (360) 652-4500 *Founded/Ownrshp* 1914
Sales 19.9MM *EMP* 300
SIC 8211 Public elementary & secondary schools; Public elementary & secondary schools
Dir IT: Denny Alford
Dir IT: Danny Alfred
Pr Dir: Robin Barker
Schl Brd P: Kelly Allen
Teacher Pr: Valori Smith
HC Dir: Marie Eisman

D-U-N-S 05-447-8565
LAKEWOOD TOWNSHIP (NJ)
231 3rd St, Lakewood, NJ 08701-3220
Tel (732) 363-0200 *Founded/Ownrshp* 1893
Sales NA *EMP* 400
Accts Holman Frenia Allison Pc Med
SIC 9121 Legislative bodies, state & local; Legislative bodies, state & local
Sls&Mrk Ex: Robert Lawson

D-U-N-S 19-150-3361
LAKHANI COMMERCIAL CORP
6828 Kaw Dr, Kansas City, KS 66111-2410
Tel (913) 677-1100 *Founded/Ownrshp* 2002
Sales 28.5MMᴱ *EMP* 100ᴱ
SIC 5541 7542 Gasoline service stations; Carwashes; Gasoline service stations; Carwashes
Pr: Hanif Lakhani
COO: Terry Wheeler

LAKIN GENERAL
See A LAKIN & SONS INC

D-U-N-S 09-721-2252 EXP
LAKIN TIRE EAST INC
220 Frontage Rd, West Haven, CT 06516-4129
Tel (203) 932-5801 *Founded/Ownrshp* 1979
Sales 55.3MMᴱ *EMP* 200
SIC 5014 Tires, used; Tires, used
Pr: Robert Lakin
**VP:* Bruce P Hayn
VP: Chris Rodriguez
**VP:* Randall Roth
Sls Mgr: Jose Martinez

LAKIN TIRE OF CALIF
See LAKIN TIRE WEST INC

D-U-N-S 06-861-7570 EXP
LAKIN TIRE WEST INC
LAKIN TIRE OF CALIF
15305 Spring Ave, Santa Fe Springs, CA 90670-5645
Tel (562) 802-2752 *Founded/Ownrshp* 1978
Sales 92.7MMᴱ *EMP* 180ᴱ
SIC 5014 5531 Tires, used; Automotive & home supply stores; Tires, used; Automotive & home supply stores
CEO: Robert Lakin
CFO: Francisco Ochoa
**VP:* David Lakin
VP: Randolph Roth
Genl Mgr: Debbie Vincent
MIS Mgr: David Hui

LAKIS FORD
See LOUIS FORD LAKIS INC

D-U-N-S 00-507-3341 IMP
LAKONE CO (IL)
1003 Aucutt Rd, Montgomery, IL 60538-1176
Tel (630) 892-4251 *Founded/Ownrshp* 1944
Sales 21.1MMᴱ *EMP* 100

SIC 3089 3083 Molding primary plastic; Laminated plastics plate & sheet
Pr: Bruce Rhoades

LAKOS SEPARATORS INTERNATIONAL
See CLAUDE LAVAL CORP

D-U-N-S 03-095-4713
LAKOTA LOCAL SCHOOL DISTRICT
5572 Princeton Rd, Liberty Twp, OH 45011-9726
Tel (513) 874-5505 *Founded/Ownrshp* 1970
Sales 90.4MM^E *EMP* 1,800^E
SIC 8211 Public elementary school; Public junior high school; Public senior high school; Public elementary school; Public junior high school; Public senior high school
Treas: Beth Dodson
**Treas:* Jenni Logan
Prin: Clayton Ash
Prin: Matthew Glover
Prin: Linda Lee
Prin: Cathleen Newkirk
Prin: David Pike
Prin: Ed Rudder
Prin: Ron Spurlock
Prin: David Tobergte
Prin: Robert Winterberger
Board of Directors: Ben Dibble, Ray Murray, Lynda Oconnor, Todd Parnell, Julie Shaffer

D-U-N-S 11-879-8073
LAKS MOTORS INC
RAY LAKS HONDA
100 Orchard Park Rd, West Seneca, NY 14224-2614
Tel (716) 826-4200 *Founded/Ownrshp* 1984
Sales 41.5MM^E *EMP* 150
Accts Lonestrom & Mccormick Cpa
SIC 5511 Automobiles, new & used; Automobiles, new & used
Pr: Raymond Laks
Pr: Vicki Poponi
**Treas:* Patrick Kelly
Off Mgr: Ray L Honda
Dir IT: Aaron Williams
Sales Asso: Chuck Riso

D-U-N-S 07-970-4009
LAKSHMI NARAYAN HOSPITALITY GROUP LOUISVILLE LLC
1325 S Hurstbourne Pkwy, Louisville, KY 40222-5707
Tel (650) 826-1954 *Founded/Ownrshp* 2014
Sales 9.5MM *EMP* 500
SIC 7011 Hotels
Owner: Robert Patel

D-U-N-S 80-921-3817
LALA BRANDED PRODUCTS INC
GILSA DAIRY PRODUCTS
(*Suby of* BORDEN DAIRY CO) ★
8750 N Central Expy # 400, Dallas, TX 75231-6436
Tel (214) 459-1100 *Founded/Ownrshp* 2015
Sales 212.0MM^E *EMP* 300^E
SIC 5143 Milk; Dairy products, except dried or canned
VP: Diego Rosenfiedt
Mktg Dir: Mauricio Galvan

D-U-N-S 16-188-4418
LALLY PIPE & TUBE CO
(*Suby of* L B INDUSTRIES INC) ★
8770 Railroad Dr, Taylor Mill, KY 41015-9096
Tel (606) 371-5600 *Founded/Ownrshp* 1984
Sales 120.0MM *EMP* 100
SIC 5014 Tires & tubes
Pr: Timothy Lally
**Ch Bd:* John B Lally
**VP:* Brendan Lally

LALLY PIPE & TUBE DIVISION
See L B INDUSTRIES INC

D-U-N-S 07-818-1047 IMP
LALLY-PAK INC
1209 Central Ave, Hillside, NJ 07205-2613
Tel (908) 351-4141 *Founded/Ownrshp* 1973
Sales 24.0MM *EMP* 75
SIC 3081 2759 2671 Packing materials, plastic sheet; Bags, plastic: printing; Plastic film, coated or laminated for packaging
Pr: Henry Herbst
VP Opers: Benjamin Herbst

D-U-N-S 83-872-1199
LALVAREZ LINCOLN MERCURY INC
8051 Auto Dr, Riverside, CA 92504-4100
Tel (951) 687-1212 *Founded/Ownrshp* 1995
Sales 20.5MM^E *EMP* 52
SIC 5511 5521 Automobiles, new & used; Used car dealers; Automobiles, new & used; Used car dealers
Pr: Ramon Alvarez
Exec: Vanessa Martinez

D-U-N-S 05-181-4515
LAM HOLDINGS 1 INC
1 Scrivner Dr Ste 1, Buffalo, NY 14227-2742
Tel (716) 693-9999 *Founded/Ownrshp* 1976
Sales 26.7MM^E *EMP* 70
SIC 5141 5411 Food brokers; Grocery stores, independent; Food brokers; Grocery stores, independent
Ch Bd: Charles O Marazzo
**CEO:* John Brodfuehrer
**CFO:* Ann Sidoni
Genl Mgr: Charles Marazzo Jr

D-U-N-S 03-813-7956 IMP
▲ LAM RESEARCH CORP
4650 Cushing Pkwy, Fremont, CA 94538-6401
Tel (510) 572-0200 *Founded/Ownrshp* 1980
Sales 5.2MMM *EMP* 7,300
Accts Ernst & Young Llp San Jose C
Tkr Sym LRCX *Exch* NGS
SIC 3674 Semiconductor manufacturing machinery; Semiconductors & related devices; Wafers (semiconductor devices)
Pr: Martin B Anstice
**Ch Bd:* Stephen G Newberry
COO: Timothy M Archer
CFO: Douglas R Bettinger
Ex VP: Richard A Gottscho
Sr VP: Gary Bultman
VP: Kaihan Ashtiani
VP: Joy Cartun
VP: Tina Correia
VP: David J Hemker
VP: Chung-Ho Huang
VP: Thorsten Lill
VP: Mike Morita
VP: Rangesh Raghavan
VP: Jackie Seto
Board of Directors: Eric K Brandt, Michael R Cannon, Christine A Heckart, Grant M Inman, Catherine P Lego, Youssef A El-Mansy, William R Spivey

LAMTECH
See LAMINATE TECHNOLOGIES INC

D-U-N-S 01-487-1797 IMP
LAMACAR INC
KELLI'S GIFT SHOP SUPPLIERS
3311 Boyington Dr Ste 400, Carrollton, TX 75006-5090
Tel (972) 759-7000 *Founded/Ownrshp* 2000
Sales 48.6MM^E *EMP* 90
SIC 5199 Gifts & novelties
Pr: Julius Cohen
**CEO:* Michael Cohen
**VP:* Lori Cohen
Sales Asso: Donny Young

D-U-N-S 83-275-2294
LAMAJ FUEL LLC
1200 Dale Rd, Linden, NJ 07036
Tel (212) 837-7985 *Founded/Ownrshp* 2009
Sales 39.0MM *EMP* 13
SIC 4213 4214 Trucking, except local; Local trucking with storage

D-U-N-S 02-819-4520 IMP
LAMANUZZI & PANTALEO LLC
11767 Road 27 1/2, Madera, CA 93637-9108
Tel (559) 432-3170 *Founded/Ownrshp* 1937
Sales 30.8MM *EMP* 90^E
Accts Price Page & Company Clovis
SIC 0172 4222 Grapes; Warehousing, cold storage or refrigerated; Grapes; Warehousing, cold storage or refrigerated

D-U-N-S 78-812-1481
▲ LAMAR ADVERTISING CO
5321 Corporate Blvd, Baton Rouge, LA 70808-2506
Tel (225) 926-1000 *Founded/Ownrshp* 1902
Sales 1.2MMM *EMP* 3,200
Tkr Sym LAMR *Exch* NGS
SIC 7312 6798 Outdoor advertising services; Billboard advertising; Poster advertising, outdoor; Outdoor advertising services; Billboard advertising; Poster advertising, outdoor; Real estate investment trusts
Ch Bd: Kevin P Reilly Jr
Pr: Luis Betancourt
Pr: Christina Butler
Pr: Claire Sherman
CEO: Sean E Reilly
CFO: Keith A Istre
Ex VP: Rhett Enzor
Ex VP: Stan Geier
VP: Brian Conley
VP: Sam Iuvino
VP: Korbe Palmer
VP: Robert B Switzer
Exec: Leisje Coyle
Creative D: Justin Hart
Board of Directors: John Maxwell Hamilton, John E Koerner III, Stephen P Mumblow, Thomas V Reifenheiser, Anna Reilly, Wendell Reilly

D-U-N-S 80-665-2934
LAMAR BRUNI VERGARA TRUST
108 Del Ct, Laredo, TX 78041-2276
Tel (956) 712-9190 *Founded/Ownrshp* 2007
Sales 20.9MM *EMP* 2
SIC 6733 Trusts
Prin: Casseb Solomon

D-U-N-S 09-964-4353
LAMAR CO SCHOOL SYSTEM
LAMAR COUNTY SCHOOL DISTRICT
424 Martin Luther King Dr, Purvis, MS 39475-5028
Tel (601) 794-1030 *Founded/Ownrshp* 1900
Sales 55.2MM^E *EMP* 1,200
SIC 8211 Public elementary & secondary schools; Public elementary & secondary schools
Prin: Tess R Smith
Dir IT: Ross Randall
HC Dir: Tricia Cox

D-U-N-S 82-763-3632
LAMAR COMMUNITY CARE CENTER LLC
WINDHAM HOUSE OF HATTIESBURG
(*Suby of* COMMCARE CORP) ★
37 Hillcrest Dr Ofc, Hattiesburg, MS 39402-8622
Tel (601) 264-0058 *Founded/Ownrshp* 2008
Sales 5.5MM *EMP* 1,035^E
SIC 8051 Skilled nursing care facilities

LAMAR COMPANIES
See LAMAR TEXAS LIMITED PARTNERSHIP

D-U-N-S 08-356-9764
LAMAR CONSOLIDATED INDEPENDENT SCHOOL DISTRICT (INC)
CSID
3911 Avenue I, Rosenberg, TX 77471-3901
Tel (832) 223-0000 *Founded/Ownrshp* 1947
Sales 258.1MM^E *EMP* 4,200
Accts Null-Lairson Pc Houston Tx
SIC 8211 Public combined elementary & secondary school; Public senior high school; Public combined elementary & secondary school; Public senior high school
**Pr:* Julie Thompson
**VP:* Rhonda Zacharias
**Prin:* Sam Hopkins
Dir Sec: Trudy Harris
MIS Dir: David Jacobson
MIS Dir: Linda Tayler
Pr Dir: Mike Rockwood
Teacher Pr: Kathleen Bowen
HC Dir: Judy Smith

D-U-N-S 00-485-3651
LAMAR CONSTRUCTION CO (MI)
4404 Central Pkwy, Hudsonville, MI 49426-7831
Tel (616) 662-2933 *Founded/Ownrshp* 1999
Sales 211.7MM *EMP* 125^E
SIC 1542 1541

D-U-N-S 10-001-4000
LAMAR COUNTY BOARD OF EDUCATION
100 Victory Ln, Barnesville, GA 30204-1581
Tel (770) 358-5891 *Founded/Ownrshp* 1921
Sales 17.9MM^E *EMP* 374
Accts Russell W Hinton Cpa Cgfm
SIC 8211 School board; School board
Ofcr: Joe Sims
Ex Dir: Sam Walker
Info Man: Jarrod Fletcher
Psych: Daniel Sergent
Psych: Jessica Traylor

D-U-N-S 00-480-6097
LAMAR COUNTY ELECTRIC CO-OPERATIVE ASSOCIATION
1485 N Main St, Paris, TX 75460-2651
Tel (903) 784-4303 *Founded/Ownrshp* 1938
Sales 26.7MM *EMP* 30
Accts Bolinger Segars Gilbert & Mo
SIC 4911 Distribution, electric power; Distribution, electric power
CEO: Jerry D Williams
**Pr:* Allen C Branch
**VP:* Charles Dooley
Dir IT: Terry McFadden
Sfty Dirs: Scott Sansom

D-U-N-S 94-133-9012
LAMAR COUNTY HEADSTART
1350 6th St Ne, Paris, TX 75460-2626
Tel (903) 737-7469 *Founded/Ownrshp* 1993
Sales 36.9MM *EMP* 42
Accts Malnory Mcneal & Company Pc
SIC 8351 Head start center, except in conjunction with school; Head start center, except in conjunction with school
Ex Dir: Judie Fortehuff

LAMAR COUNTY SCHOOL DISTRICT
See LAMAR CO SCHOOL SYSTEM

D-U-N-S 02-125-1285
LAMAR COUNTY SCHOOL DISTRICT
BOARD OF EDUCATION
150 Butler Cir Sw, Vernon, AL 35592-5244
Tel (205) 695-7615 *Founded/Ownrshp* 1928
Sales 14.9MM^E *EMP* 350
SIC 8211 Public elementary & secondary schools; Public elementary & secondary schools
Schl Brd P: Jonathan Betsley

D-U-N-S 07-979-6832
LAMAR COUNTY SCHOOLS
100 Victory Ln, Barnesville, GA 30204-1581
Tel (770) 358-5891 *Founded/Ownrshp* 2015
Sales 5.6MM^E *EMP* 386^E
SIC 8211 Public elementary & secondary schools

D-U-N-S 06-953-6116
■ LAMAR MEDIA CORP
(*Suby of* LAMAR ADVERTISING CO) ★
5321 Corporate Blvd, Baton Rouge, LA 70808-2506
Tel (225) 926-1000 *Founded/Ownrshp* 1902
Sales 1.2MMM *EMP* 3,200
SIC 7312 Outdoor advertising services; Billboard advertising; Poster advertising, outdoor; Outdoor advertising services; Billboard advertising; Poster advertising, outdoor
CEO: Sean E Reilly
**Ch Bd:* Kevin P Reilly Jr
CFO: Keith A Istre
Board of Directors: John Maxwell Hamilton, John E Koerner III, Stephen P Mumblow, Thomas Reifenheiser, Anna Reilly, Wendell S Reilly

D-U-N-S 11-861-5058
LAMAR POWER PARTNERS LP
3205 Farm Road 137, Paris, TX 75460-1942
Tel (903) 785-9562 *Founded/Ownrshp* 1999
Sales 23.6MM^E *EMP* 34
SIC 4911 Generation, electric power
Pt: Brian Tobin

D-U-N-S 10-004-1474
LAMAR R-I SCHOOL DISTRICT
202 W 7th St, Lamar, MO 64759-1285
Tel (417) 682-3527 *Founded/Ownrshp* 1984
Sales 14.7MM^E *EMP* 279
SIC 8211 9411 Public elementary & secondary schools; School board; Administration of educational programs; Public elementary & secondary schools; School board; Administration of educational programs
Prin: Marsha Berry

D-U-N-S 96-693-3764
LAMAR STATE COLLEGE-PORT ARTHUR
(*Suby of* TEXAS STATE UNIVERSITY SYSTEM) ★
1500 Procter St, Port Arthur, TX 77640-6604
Tel (409) 983-4921 *Founded/Ownrshp* 2001
Sales 33.8MM^E *EMP* 300
SIC 8221 Colleges universities & professional schools; Colleges universities & professional schools
Pr: W Sam Monroe

D-U-N-S 14-720-6515
LAMAR TEXAS LIMITED PARTNERSHIP
LAMAR COMPANIES
5321 Corporate Blvd, Baton Rouge, LA 70808-2506
Tel (800) 235-2627 *Founded/Ownrshp* 1995
Sales 65.1MM^E *EMP* 3,000
SIC 7312 Outdoor advertising services

D-U-N-S 96-731-5706
LAMAR UNIVERSITY
LAMAR UNIVERSITY-BEAUMONT
(*Suby of* TEXAS STATE UNIVERSITY SYSTEM) ★
4400 S M L King Jr Pkwy, Beaumont, TX 77705-5748
Tel (409) 880-8932 *Founded/Ownrshp* 1923
Sales 89.4MM^E *EMP* 836
SIC 8221 University; University
Prin: Carroll David
VP: Norman Bellard
VP: Stephen Doblin
VP: Kevin Smith
Dir Lab: Robert Corbett
Dir IT: Fatai Oyejobi
IT Man: Shellie Fischer
Netwrk Mgr: Jamie Turner
Doctor: Lawrence Osborne
Snr Mgr: William Holmes

LAMAR UNIVERSITY-BEAUMONT
See LAMAR UNIVERSITY

LAMARQUE FORD SERVICE
See LAMARQUE MOTOR CO

D-U-N-S 07-947-2361
LAMARQUE MOTOR CO
LAMARQUE FORD SERVICE
3101 Williams Blvd, Kenner, LA 70065-4504
Tel (504) 443-2500 *Founded/Ownrshp* 1981
Sales 42.3MM^E *EMP* 91
SIC 5511 Automobiles, new & used; Automobiles, new & used
Pr: Ronald Lamarque
**Sec:* Kristi Lamarque
IT Man: Don Heaton
Sls Mgr: Christopher Cazaubon
Sales Asso: Frank Romano

LAMARS DONUTS
See DONUT HOLDINGS INC

D-U-N-S 00-215-8418 IMP
LAMART CORP
16 Richmond St, Clifton, NJ 07011-2899
Tel (973) 772-6262 *Founded/Ownrshp* 1956
Sales 31.9MM^E *EMP* 90
SIC 2672 Tape, pressure sensitive: made from purchased materials; Adhesive backed films, foams & foils; Adhesive papers, labels or tapes: from purchased material; Metallic covered paper: made from purchased materials; Tape, pressure sensitive: made from purchased materials; Adhesive backed films, foams & foils; Adhesive papers, labels or tapes: from purchased material; Metallic covered paper: made from purchased materials
Pr: Steven B Hirsh
CFO: Graeme Silbert
Bd of Dir: Gene Jung
**VP:* Alan Hirsh
VP: Jonathan Hirsh
Sftwr Eng: Gary Shank
Mtls Mgr: Michael Kehr
Opers Mgr: Judy Sondej
Plnt Mgr: R Van
Plnt Mgr: Ray Vanhouten
Sls Mgr: Jim Pepperdine

D-U-N-S 01-711-3614
LAMB & ASSOCIATES PACKAGING INC (AR)
1700 Murphy Dr, North Little Rock, AR 72113-6192
Tel (501) 851-0800 *Founded/Ownrshp* 1981
Sales 38.6MM^E *EMP* 62
SIC 5113 Boxes, paperboard & disposable plastic; Shipping supplies
Pr: Kyle Lamb
CEO: Jerry Lamb
Sec: Laurie Adcock
VP: Laurie Lamb
Plnt Mgr: Todd Welborn
Sales Exec: Mike Arnold

D-U-N-S 01-323-3689
LAMB & WEBSTER INC
KUBOTA
601 W Main St, Springville, NY 14141-1088
Tel (716) 592-4923 *Founded/Ownrshp* 1990
Sales 22.0MM^E *EMP* 75
SIC 5999 5261

D-U-N-S 03-593-7127
LAMB CHEVROLET INC
LAMB-CHEVROLET-OLDSMOBILE
400 Prescott Lakes Pkwy, Prescott, AZ 86301-6532
Tel (928) 778-5262 *Founded/Ownrshp* 1964
Sales 22.1MM^E *EMP* 55
SIC 5511 Automobiles, new & used; Automobiles, new & used
Pr: Ted F Lamb
**Sec:* Blasita Rodriguez
**VP:* Sherene Lamb
Exec: Jim Daddio

D-U-N-S 00-387-9277
LAMB COUNTY ELECTRIC COOPERATIVE INC (TX)
2415 Phelps Ave, Littlefield, TX 79339-5699
Tel (806) 894-8000 *Founded/Ownrshp* 1938
Sales 40.9MM *EMP* 41
Accts Bolinger Segars Gilbert And Mo
SIC 4911 Distribution, electric power; Transmission, electric power; Distribution, electric power; Transmission, electric power
Genl Mgr: Boyd McCamish
Genl Mgr: Boyd McCanish

LAMB NISSAN
See NISSAN LAMB INC

LAMB-CHEVROLET-OLDSMOBILE
See LAMB CHEVROLET INC

D-U-N-S 18-641-3381
LAMBDA LEGAL DEFENSE & EDUCATION FUND INC
120 Wall St Fl 19, New York, NY 10005-3919
Tel (212) 809-8585 *Founded/Ownrshp* 1973
Sales 25.8MM *EMP* 91

Accts Marks Paneth Llp New York Ny
SIC 8111 Specialized legal services; Specialized legal services
Ex Dir: Kevin M Cathcart
CFO: Mark A Gasparini
Bd of Dir: Andrew Bernstein
Bd of Dir: Kenneth Weissenberg
Ofcr: Erin Baer
Ofcr: Jason Howe
Ofcr: Maura Leahy
Ofcr: Tika Milan
Dir: John Westfall
**Ex Dir:* Kevin M Cathcart J D
Off Admin: Carla Avila

LAMBERT MATERIAL HANDLING
See GLOBAL MATERIAL HANDLING INC

D-U-N-S 08-959-4506 EXP
LAMBERT VET SUPPLY LLC
714 5th St, Fairbury, NE 68352-2626
Tel (402) 729-3044 *Founded/Ownrshp* 1993
Sales 125.0MM^E *EMP* 92
SIC 5047 Veterinarians' equipment & supplies
Ex VP: Tammy Shin
IT Man: Greg Meyer
Mktg Dir: Nels Sorensen

D-U-N-S 55-636-8186
LAMBERT-ST LOUIS INTERNATIONAL AIRPORT CORP
(*Suby of* CITY OF ST LOUIS) ★
4780 Saint Andrew Ln, Bridgeton, MO 63044-2331
Tel (314) 551-5302 *Founded/Ownrshp* 2005
Sales 23.8MM^E *EMP* 1^E
SIC 4581 Airport
Sys Mgr: Wali Tabiat

D-U-N-S 79-667-6117
LAMBERTI SYNTHESIS USA INC
(*Suby of* LAMBERTI SPA)
4001 N Hawthorne St, Chattanooga, TN 37406-1314
Tel (423) 697-0526 *Founded/Ownrshp* 2006
Sales 9.2MM^E *EMP* 3,000
SIC 8741 Management services
Pr: Anthony Philip

D-U-N-S 04-002-7955
■ **LAMBERTS CABLE SPLICING CO LLC**
(*Suby of* DYCOM INDUSTRIES INC) ★
2521 S Wesleyan Blvd, Rocky Mount, NC 27803-8847
Tel (252) 442-9777 *Founded/Ownrshp* 1967
Sales 47.4MM^E *EMP* 292
SIC 1799 1731 Cable splicing service; Electrical work; Cable splicing service; Electrical work
Pr: Thomas L Lambert
VP: John Gilbert
IT Man: Brandon Stussie
Sfty Mgr: Jimmy Carter
VP Mktg: Karen Allen
VP Mktg: James Vaughan

D-U-N-S 01-655-1277
LAMBERTS DISTRIBUTORS INC
142 W Main St, New Albany, IN 47150-5999
Tel (812) 948-1614 *Founded/Ownrshp* 1961
Sales 26.6MM *EMP* 11
Accts Monroe Shine New Albany Indi
SIC 5194 5145 5113 Tobacco & tobacco products; Cigarettes; Chewing tobacco; Cigars; Candy; Industrial & personal service paper; Bags, paper & disposable plastic; Towels, paper; Napkins, paper; Tobacco & tobacco products; Candy; Industrial & personal service paper
Pr: Mary C Schroeder
**Sec:* Thomas Schroeder

LAMBOS AMOCO
See LANMAN OIL CO INC

D-U-N-S 03-965-2391 IMP/EXP
LAMBRETTA SOUTH INC
RIVA MOTORSPORTS
3671 N Dixie Hwy, Pompano Beach, FL 33064-4413
Tel (954) 785-4820 *Founded/Ownrshp* 1979
Sales 47.0MM^E *EMP* 96
SIC 5571 5012 Motorcycle dealers; Motorized cycles; Motorcycle dealers; Motorized cycles
Pr: David Bamdas
**Treas:* Stephen Bamdas
**VP:* Joseph Bamdas

D-U-N-S 04-383-3144 IMP
LAMBRO INDUSTRIES INC
115 Albany Ave, Amityville, NY 11701-2632
Tel (631) 842-8088 *Founded/Ownrshp* 1967
Sales 22.7MM^E *EMP* 140
SIC 3444 Ventilators, sheet metal; Ventilators, sheet metal
Ch Bd: Shiv Anand CPA
Mktg Dir: Robert Lange

LAMB'S MARKET
See LAMKO LLC

LAMCOTEC
See LAMINATING COATING TECHNOLOGIES INC

D-U-N-S 06-545-1080
LAMERS BUS LINES INC (WI)
2407 S Point Rd, Green Bay, WI 54313-5498
Tel (920) 496-3600 *Founded/Ownrshp* 1944
Sales 154.3MM^E *EMP* 1,300
SIC 4151 4142 4119 4725 4141 School buses; Bus charter service, except local; Local passenger transportation; Limousine rental, with driver; Tour operators; Local bus charter service; School buses; Bus charter service, except local; Local passenger transportation; Limousine rental, with driver; Tour operators; Local bus charter service
Prin: Allen Lamers

D-U-N-S 00-705-4315
LAMESA INDEPENDENT SCHOOL DISTRICT
LAMESA ISD
212 N Houston Ave, Lamesa, TX 79331-5442
Tel (806) 872-8385 *Founded/Ownrshp* 1903, 2006
Sales 20.0MM *EMP* 341
SIC 8211 Public elementary school; Public junior high school; Public senior high school; Public elementary school; Public junior high school; Public senior high school
**CFO:* Leslie Vann
Schl Brd P: Sonya Raney
Teacher Pr: Brian Yearwood

LAMESA ISD
See LAMESA INDEPENDENT SCHOOL DISTRICT

D-U-N-S 14-759-0731 IMP/EXP
LAMEX FOODS INC
(*Suby of* LAMEX FOODS UK LIMITED)
8500 Normandale Ste 1150, Bloomington, MN 55437
Tel (952) 844-0585 *Founded/Ownrshp* 1986
Sales 107.0MM^E *EMP* 47
SIC 5144 5147 Poultry: live, dressed or frozen (unpackaged); Meats & meat products
CEO: Phillip O Wallace
**Pr:* Steve Anderson
**VP:* Mark Barrett
VP: Dave Huber
**VP:* Robert Lucas
Off Admin: Luz Hernandez
Opers Mgr: Megan Abbott

D-U-N-S 11-434-1506 IMP
LAMI PRODUCTS INC
860 Welsh Rd, Huntingdon Valley, PA 19006-6000
Tel (215) 947-5333 *Founded/Ownrshp* 1976
Sales 207.8MM^E *EMP* 450
SIC 5199 General merchandise, non-durable; General merchandise, non-durable
Pr: Michael Dion
CFO: Jeff Mazer
VP: Larry Dion
Rgnl Mgr: Bill Smith
Genl Mgr: Dan Demara
Genl Mgr: Debbie Dion

D-U-N-S 00-535-3792
LAMINA INC
ANCHOR DANLY
(*Suby of* ANCHOR DIE SUPPLY) ★
38505 Country Club Dr # 100, Farmington Hills, MI 48331-3403
Tel (248) 489-9122 *Founded/Ownrshp* 1992, 2005
Sales 34.8MM^E *EMP* 212
SIC 3545 3546 Machine tool attachments & accessories; Drills, portable, except rock: electric or pneumatic; Machine tool attachments & accessories; Drills, portable, except rock: electric or pneumatic
Pr: Roy Verstraete
**CFO:* Steve Zerio
**Treas:* Craig Swoish
**VP:* Todd Castile
CTO: Amber Reatan
Plnt Mgr: Dietrich Heyde

D-U-N-S 02-187-7436
LAMINATE CO (VA)
AMERICAN STAIR AND CABINETRY
6612 James Madison Hwy, Haymarket, VA 20169-2713
Tel (703) 753-0699 *Founded/Ownrshp* 1980, 1991
Sales 88.5MM^E *EMP* 253
SIC 5031 2431 Kitchen cabinets; Staircases, stairs & railings; Kitchen cabinets; Staircases, stairs & railings
CEO: John Lombardozzi
**VP:* John Hall
**VP:* Mary Jeanne Helton

D-U-N-S 18-356-9672 IMP
LAMINATE TECHNOLOGIES INC
LAM TECH
161 Maule Rd, Tiffin, OH 44883-9400
Tel (419) 448-0812 *Founded/Ownrshp* 1985
Sales 24.6MM^E *EMP* 130
Accts Spilman Hills & Heidebrink To
SIC 2439 2891 2672 Structural wood members; Adhesives & sealants; Coated & laminated paper
Pr: Frederick E Zoeller
**CFO:* Allan Funkhouser
**VP:* A Louise Zoeller
Genl Mgr: Randy Wiser
VP Mfg: Beth Welly
Plnt Mgr: Mark Thomas

D-U-N-S 10-472-7917
LAMINATE WORKS INC
15900 College Blvd # 200, Lenexa, KS 66219-1334
Tel (913) 800-8263 *Founded/Ownrshp* 1999
Sales 22.0MM *EMP* 70
SIC 2493 Particleboard, plastic laminated
Pr: Bert Clothier
CFO: Gary Fenton
**Sec:* Gretchen Clothier

D-U-N-S 15-724-7701 IMP
LAMINATING COATING TECHNOLOGIES INC
LAMCOTEC
152 Bethany Rd, Monson, MA 01057-9538
Tel (413) 267-4808 *Founded/Ownrshp* 1986
Sales 21.0MM^E *EMP* 69
SIC 2295 Laminating of fabrics; Laminating of fabrics
Pr: Richard Anderson Sr
COO: Bob Champigny
**VP:* Richard Anderson Jr
VP: Rick Malo

D-U-N-S 00-303-8775 IMP
LAMINATIONS INC (PA)
101 Power Blvd, Archbald, PA 18403-2012
Tel (570) 876-8199 *Founded/Ownrshp* 1953
Sales 43.7MM^E *EMP* 150^E
SIC 3083 3089 3081 2821 Laminated plastics plate & sheet; Molding primary plastic; Unsupported plastics film & sheet; Plastics materials & resins; Laminated plastics plate & sheet; Molding primary plastic; Unsupported plastics film & sheet; Plastics materials & resins
Pr: Michael Lynch
Pr: Michael Ahern
**CFO:* Jim Gavigan
Sr VP: Oscar Palmquist
Genl Mgr: John Breslin
CTO: Scott Harrison
IT Man: Gary Bosardman
IT Man: John Byrdsell
S&M/VP: John Ploskonka
Sales Asso: Michele Smith

D-U-N-S 02-775-7715
LAMKO LLC
LAMB'S MARKET
8255 Sw Wilsonville Rd, Wilsonville, OR 97070-7718
Tel (503) 682-9053 *Founded/Ownrshp* 1997
Sales 82.8MM^E *EMP* 490
SIC 5411 Grocery stores, independent

D-U-N-S 36-159-3296
LAMKONE RESTAURANTS INC
WAHOO'S FISH TACO
2855 Pullman St, Santa Ana, CA 92705-5713
Tel (949) 222-0670 *Founded/Ownrshp* 1990
Sales 22.1MM^E *EMP* 550
SIC 5812 6794 Fast-food restaurant, chain; Franchises, selling or licensing; Fast-food restaurant, chain; Franchises, selling or licensing
CEO: Renato Mingo Lee
**Treas:* Ed Lam
**VP:* Wing Lam
VP: Tom Orbe
Dist Mgr: Juan Reyes
Mktg Dir: Kasey Willis

D-U-N-S 11-278-0689
LAMMICO
1 Galleria Blvd Ste 700, Metairie, LA 70001-7510
Tel (504) 841-5243 *Founded/Ownrshp* 1981
Sales NA *EMP* 150
SIC 6351 Liability insurance; Liability insurance
CEO: Thomas McCormick
Pr: Joe Hahnenfeld
**Pr:* John E Lemoine MD
Top Exec: Linda Berggreen
**VP:* Frank J George
VP: James Kennedy
**VP:* Philip Robichaux
**VP:* Richard Zepernick
**Prin:* Henry J Jumonville III

D-U-N-S 00-233-3466 IMP
LAMONICA FINE FOODS LLC
CAPE MAY FOODS
48 Gorton Rd, Millville, NJ 08332-6202
Tel (856) 776-2126 *Founded/Ownrshp* 1949
Sales 34.5MM^E *EMP* 200
SIC 2091 2092 Clams: packaged in cans, jars, etc.; Juice, clam: packaged in cans, jars, etc.; Seafoods, fresh: prepared
Pr: Danny Lavecchia
CFO: Dennis Guckin
**VP:* Chris Douthett
**VP:* Michael Lavecchia
Plnt Mgr: Mary Annsafchinsky
Plnt Mgr: Mary Safchinski
Plnt Mgr: Chris Schreiber
Mktg Dir: Steve Zevitas

D-U-N-S 87-487-9562 IMP
LAMONICAS PIZZA DOUGH CO INC
3706 E 26th St, Vernon, CA 90058-4106
Tel (323) 263-0644 *Founded/Ownrshp* 1991
Sales 25.5MM^E *EMP* 60
SIC 5142

D-U-N-S 00-808-2976 IMP
■ **LAMONS GASKET CO**
(*Suby of* TRIMAS CORP) ★
7300 Airport Blvd, Houston, TX 77061-3932
Tel (713) 547-9527 *Founded/Ownrshp* 1945, 2002
Sales 150.9MM^E *EMP* 495
SIC 3053 5085 Gaskets, all materials; Hose, belting & packing; Gaskets, all materials; Hose, belting & packing
Pr: Kurt Allen
Tech Mgr: Kris Kolb
Mtls Mgr: Jeff Warren
Mktg Dir: Dave Metzer
Sls Mgr: Ron Kovilaritch

LAMONTS GIFTS & SUNDRY
See FOOD PANTRY LTD

D-U-N-S 08-575-2327
LAMOTHERMIC CORP
391 Route 312, Brewster, NY 10509-2328
Tel (845) 278-6118 *Founded/Ownrshp* 1975
Sales 20.5MM^E *EMP* 75
SIC 3369 Castings, except die-castings, precision
Ch Bd: Amos Noach
**VP:* Gideon Noach
Ql Cn Mgr: Ed Calabrese

D-U-N-S 00-306-2866 IMP/EXP
LAMOTTE CHEMICAL PRODUCTS CO
(*Suby of* ARTHUR H THOMAS CO) ★
802 Washington Ave, Chestertown, MD 21620-1015
Tel (410) 778-3100 *Founded/Ownrshp* 1920
Sales 29.7MM^E *EMP* 108
SIC 3826 2899 3564 Water testing apparatus; Soil testing kits; Purification & dust collection equipment; Water testing apparatus; Soil testing kits; Purification & dust collection equipment
Ch Bd: Edward B Patterson Jr
**Pr:* David Lamotte Jr
**Treas:* Edward L Sudnick
**VP:* James Trumbauer
VP: Jim Trumbauer
Exec: Timothy Parent
Exec: Ernie Rector
Comm Dir: Libby Woolever
Dir Bus: Robert Gingell
Dir Bus: Marta Girone
Sfty Dirs: Dawn Hofstetter
Board of Directors: Leif Culbrandsen, Michael Curtin, Leif Gulbrandsen, Maria Landskroener, Nancy Smaroff, Herman Wefelmeyer

D-U-N-S 13-903-3075
LAMOUNTAIN BROS INC
37 Federal Hill Rd, Oxford, MA 01540-1301
Tel (508) 987-5322 *Founded/Ownrshp* 1985
Sales 25.5MM^E *EMP* 83
SIC 1542 Nonresidential construction; Nonresidential construction
Pr: Peter Lamountain
Treas: Hank Lamountain
**VP:* Michael Voas

D-U-N-S 00-780-2358
LAMP INC
460 N Grove Ave, Elgin, IL 60120-3612
Tel (847) 741-7220 *Founded/Ownrshp* 1932
Sales 29.0MM *EMP* 44
Accts Borhart Spellmeyer Elgin Il
SIC 1542 Commercial & office building, new construction
Pr: Craig Lamp
**Ch Bd:* Earl W Lamp
**Sec:* Steven Lamp
**VP:* Greg Bohlin
Ex Dir: Debbie Hudnall
**VP Sls:* Ian Lamp

D-U-N-S 04-703-9938
LAMP RYNEARSON & ASSOCIATES INC
14710 W Dodge Rd Ste 100, Omaha, NE 68154-2027
Tel (402) 496-2498 *Founded/Ownrshp* 2000
Sales 23.3MM^E *EMP* 135
SIC 8711 8713 Consulting engineer; Surveying services; Consulting engineer; Surveying services
Pr: Michael McMeekin
CFO: George Goos
Treas: Brett J Wawers
**Sr VP:* Daniel Owens
**Sr VP:* Loren Steenson
**Sr VP:* Brett Wawers
**VP:* Terence Atkins
**VP:* Nancy Pridal
Mktg Dir: Leslie Peterson
Board of Directors: Terence Atkins, Michael McMeekin, Dennis O'neal, Daniel Owens, Nancy Pridal, Loren Steenson, Brett Wawers, Lynn Ziegenbein

D-U-N-S 10-007-5415
LAMPASAS INDEPENDENT SCHOOL DISTRICT
207 W 8th St, Lampasas, TX 76550-3125
Tel (512) 556-8291 *Founded/Ownrshp* 1947
Sales 22.1MM^E *EMP* 500
SIC 8211 Public elementary & secondary schools; Public elementary & secondary schools
Prin: Randall Hoyer

D-U-N-S 00-696-3342
LAMPERT YARDS INC (MN)
LAMPERTS
1850 Como Ave, Saint Paul, MN 55108-2715
Tel (651) 695-3600 *Founded/Ownrshp* 1887
Sales 130.6MM^E *EMP* 500
SIC 5211 1521 2439 2426

LAMPERTS
See LAMPERT YARDS INC

D-U-N-S 10-006-9699
LAMPETER-STRASBURG SCHOOL DISTRICT
1600 Book Rd, Lampeter, PA 17537
Tel (717) 464-3311 *Founded/Ownrshp* 1954
Sales 31.2MM^E *EMP* 480
SIC 8211 9411 Public elementary & secondary schools; School board; Administration of educational programs; Public elementary & secondary schools; School board; Administration of educational programs

D-U-N-S 09-196-3538
LAMPHERE SCHOOLS
31201 Dorchester Ave, Madison Heights, MI 48071-1075
Tel (248) 589-0708 *Founded/Ownrshp* 1864
Sales 20.3MM^E *EMP* 325
Accts Hungerford & Co Southgate M
SIC 8211 Public elementary school; Public junior high school; Public senior high school; Public elementary school; Public junior high school; Public senior high school
Pr Dir: Jeanne Berlin
Teacher Pr: Rita Lewis

D-U-N-S 00-643-8162 IMP/EXP
LAMPLIGHT FARMS INC (WI)
(*Suby of* W C BRADLEY CO) ★
W140n4900 Lilly Rd, Menomonee Falls, WI 53051-7035
Tel (262) 781-9590 *Founded/Ownrshp* 1964
Sales 123.4MM^E *EMP* 301
SIC 3648 3999 3229 2911 Lighting equipment; Candles; Pressed & blown glass; Oils, illuminating; Lighting equipment; Candles; Pressed & blown glass; Oils, illuminating
Pr: Joel R Borgardt
**VP:* Thomas Risch

D-U-N-S 92-756-5648
LAMPO GROUP INC
RAMSEY SOLUTIONS
1749 Mallory Ln Ste 100, Brentwood, TN 37027-2931
Tel (615) 371-8881 *Founded/Ownrshp* 1991
Sales 27.3MM^E *EMP* 240
SIC 8299 Investment advice; Educational services
Pr: David Ramsey III
VP: Chris Locurto
VP: Matt Woodburn
Assoc Dir: Chandler Gaines
CIO: Tony Bradshaw
IT Man: Eli Tapolcsanyi
Web Dev: Leon Oosterwijk
Software D: Doug Smith
Snr Mgr: Jim Ebert

D-U-N-S 08-111-0124 IMP/EXP
LAMPS PLUS INC
20250 Plummer St, Chatsworth, CA 91311-5300
Tel (818) 886-5267 *Founded/Ownrshp* 1976
Sales 291.4MM^E *EMP* 1,200
SIC 5719 Lighting, lamps & accessories; Lighting, lamps & accessories
CEO: Dennis K Swanson

*COO: Jerry Bass
*CFO: Clark Linstone
Ofcr: Erik Swanson
VP: Elie Boutros
VP: Bill Gratke
VP: Katja Hockenberg
*VP: Manja Swanson
Exec: Mel Almeda
Dist Mgr: Pauline Beauchamp
Dist Mgr: Iskender Berberoglu

D-U-N-S 00-960-1944
LAMPSON INTERNATIONAL LLC
(Suby of NEIL F LAMPSON INC) ★
607 E Columbia Dr, Kennewick, WA 99336-3778
Tel (509) 586-0411 Founded/Ownrshp 2000
Sales 31.9MM^E EMP 200
SIC 7353 Cranes & aerial lift equipment, rental or leasing; Cranes & aerial lift equipment, rental or leasing
Pr: William N Lampson
CFO: Ryan Cooper
VP: Jenny L Lampson
Genl Mgr: Steve Helton
Off Mgr: Annette Flores
Mtls Mgr: Rusty Rutherford
Opers Mgr: Jim Maiocco
Opers Mgr: Patrick Mansfield
Sls&Mrk Ex: Jeff Abersfeller

D-U-N-S 03-144-4433
LAMPTON WELDING SUPPLY CO INC
601 N Washington St, Wichita, KS 67214-3839
Tel (316) 263-3293 Founded/Ownrshp 1946
Sales 48.2MM^E EMP 100
SIC 5084 Welding machinery & equipment; Welding machinery & equipment
CEO: Marvin E Lampton
*Pr: Guy Marlin
*Treas: Sheila Lampton
*VP: Doug Lampton

D-U-N-S 05-602-7980
LAMPTON-LOVE INC
(Suby of ERGON INC) ★
2829 Lakeland Dr Ste 1505, Jackson, MS 39232-8880
Tel (601) 933-3400 Founded/Ownrshp 1967
Sales 117.9MM^E EMP 328
SIC 5171 Petroleum bulk stations & terminals; Petroleum bulk stations & terminals
Ch Bd: Leslie B Lampton Sr
*Pr: Robert Love
*VP: Ken Hodges
VP: Robert H Lampton
*VP: Kathryn Stone
IT Man: Mike Donaldson

LAMRITE COMPLETE
See HULL SUPPLY CO INC

D-U-N-S 01-778-6245 IMP
LAMRITE WEST INC
DARICE
13000 Darice Pkwy, Strongsville, OH 44149-3800
Tel (440) 238-9150 Founded/Ownrshp 1964
Sales 161.0MM^E EMP 600
SIC 5999 5199 5092 Artists' supplies & materials; Artificial flowers; Art goods & supplies; Toys & hobby goods & supplies; Artists' supplies & materials; Artificial flowers; Art goods & supplies; Toys & hobby goods & supplies
Pr: Michael Catanzarite
*CFO: Joe Rudolph
*VP: David Catanzarite
Trfc Mgr: Al Bagoly

D-U-N-S 79-893-0582
LAMSCO WEST INC
SHIMTECH US
(Suby of SHIMTECH INDUSTRIES GROUP LIMITED)
29101 The Old Rd, Valencia, CA 91355-1014
Tel (661) 295-8620 Founded/Ownrshp 2013
Sales 25.0MM^E EMP 150
SIC 3728 Laminated plastics plate & sheet; Metal stampings; Aircraft parts & equipment
Pr: Gladden John Baldwin
*COO: Rick Casillas
*CFO: Scott Wilkenson
Exec: Kathy Fischer
IT Man: Stan Walker
*VP Sls: Steve Griffith

D-U-N-S 08-297-9717 IMP/EXP
LAMTEC CORP (PA)
5010 River Rd, Mount Bethel, PA 18343-5610
Tel (570) 897-8200 Founded/Ownrshp 2010
Sales 90.0MM^E EMP 135
SIC 2679 Insulating paper: batts, fills & blankets; Foil board: made from purchased material; Insulating paper: batts, fills & blankets; Foil board: made from purchased material
Pr: John Post
*CFO: Paul Bocchino
*VP: Paul Leonardelli
CTO: Steve Williams
Dir IT: Lynda Mohring
Tech Mgr: Charlie Petty
Sfty Mgr: Bob Hodges
Trfc Mgr: John Fitzsimmons
S&M/VP: Norman Parker

L'AMY AMERICA
See LAMY INC

D-U-N-S 10-133-2278 IMP
LAMY INC
L'AMY AMERICA
(Suby of L AMY SA)
37 Danbury Rd, Wilton, CT 06897-4405
Tel (203) 761-0611 Founded/Ownrshp 1978
Sales 37.7MM^E EMP 92
SIC 5048 Ophthalmic goods; Ophthalmic goods
Pr: Aymeric Chaumet
*Pr: Marc Lamy
*VP: Stephen Rappoport
Dir IT: Seth Sanford
Sls Dir: Eddie Oates
Manager: Doug Davis
Sls Mgr: Sharon Brock
Sls Mgr: Alan Hites
Sls Mgr: Elyse Klein
Sls Mgr: Sherri Parrett
Sls Mgr: Russ Rogers

D-U-N-S 62-661-9949
LAN CARGO SA
(Suby of LATAM AIRLINES GROUP S.A.)
6500 Nw 22nd St, Miami, FL 33122-2234
Tel (786) 265-6000 Founded/Ownrshp 1990
Sales 87.3MM^E EMP 800^E
SIC 4789 Cargo loading & unloading services; Cargo loading & unloading services
CEO: Christian Ureta
*COO: Federico Germani
*CFO: Andres Bianchi
CIO: Francisco Garcia

LAN SYSTEMS
See COLLEGE PARK UNIVERSITY

D-U-N-S 80-823-6327
LAN-TEL COMMUNICATIONS INC
1400 Bston Prvidence Tpke, Norwood, MA 02062-5044
Tel (781) 551-8599 Founded/Ownrshp 1992
Sales 27.8MM EMP 75
Accts Luca Deblasio & Co Inc Wo
SIC 1731 Communications specialization; Voice, data & video wiring contractor; Communications specialization; Voice, data & video wiring contractor
CEO: Joseph H Bodio
Dir Bus: Kate Waldron
*Prin: William R Woodbury
Sales Exec: Paul Bateman

D-U-N-S 01-378-9149 IMP
LANA FASHIONWEAR INC
LANA WINER INTERNATIONAL
(Suby of LANA FASHIONWEAR COMPANY LIMITED)
240 W 37th St Fl 4, New York, NY 10018-5733
Tel (212) 868-8383 Founded/Ownrshp 1981
Sales 40.0MM EMP 50
SIC 5137 Women's & children's clothing; Women's & children's clothing
CEO: Joseph Wong
*Pr: Martin Richter
*Treas: Vincent Au
*VP: Herb Frichner
*VP: Bonnie Mercedes
*VP: Maria Murphy
*VP: Lawrence Winer

LANA WINER INTERNATIONAL
See LANA FASHIONWEAR INC

D-U-N-S 06-629-0602 IMP
LANAI RESORTS LLC
LODGE AT KOELE
(Suby of CASTLE & COOKE, INC.)
1311 Fraser Ave, Lanai City, HI 96763
Tel (808) 565-3000 Founded/Ownrshp 2012
Sales 440.7MM^E EMP 800
SIC 6552 6512 Land subdividers & developers, commercial; Commercial & industrial building operation; Land subdividers & developers, commercial; Commercial & industrial building operation
*COO: Kurt Matsumoto
*Sr VP: Arlan Chun
Sr VP: Miyazawa Frank
*Sr VP: Lesley Kaneshiro
*VP: Kimberly Miyazawa Frank
VP: John Uchiyama

LANB
See LOS ALAMOS NATIONAL BANK

D-U-N-S 83-757-7469
LANCASHIRE GROUP INC
TLG
37053 Cherry St Ste 210, Newark, CA 94560-3782
Tel (510) 792-9384 Founded/Ownrshp 1999
Sales 26.9MM^E EMP 279
SIC 8742 Industry specialist consultants; Industry specialist consultants
Pr: Ian McDonnell
CFO: John Cerelli
*Sr VP: John Lambert
Off Mgr: Rosie Abigana

LANCASTER
See MERIT DISTRIBUTION GROUP LLC

D-U-N-S 10-166-1932 IMP/EXP
LANCASTER ARCHERY SUPPLY INC
TRADTECH ARCHERY
21 Graybill Rd, Leola, PA 17540-1910
Tel (717) 656-7229 Founded/Ownrshp 1983
Sales 27.5MM^E EMP 62^E
SIC 5091 5941 Archery equipment; Archery supplies
Pr: Robert Kaufhold
*Pr: A Robert Kaufhold
VP: Ted Houser
IT Man: Eric Eschbach
Mktg Mgr: Rebecca Wolf
Sls Mgr: Jim Kish

D-U-N-S 07-119-9277
LANCASTER BIBLE COLLEGE (PA)
901 Eden Rd, Lancaster, PA 17601-5036
Tel (717) 569-7071 Founded/Ownrshp 1933
Sales 24.3MM EMP 150^E
Accts Tait Weller & Baker Llp Phil
SIC 8221 College, except junior; College, except junior
Ch: Phillip Klemens
*Pr: Dr Peter W Teague
Bd of Dir: Charlie Kreider
VP: Gary Bredfeldt
*VP: Philip Dearborn
Mktg Dir: Jill Armstrong

LANCASTER BOARD OF EDUCATION
See LANCASTER CITY SCHOOL DISTRICT

D-U-N-S 05-429-5456
LANCASTER CENTRAL SCHOOLS DISTRICT
177 Central Ave, Lancaster, NY 14086-1897
Tel (716) 686-3200 Founded/Ownrshp 1950
Sales 87.3MM EMP 900
Accts Drescher & Malecki Llp Cheekt
SIC 8211 9411 Public elementary school; Public junior high school; Public senior high school; Kindergarten; Administration of educational programs; Public elementary school; Public junior high school; Public senior high school; Kindergarten; Administration of educational programs
*CIO: Edward Myszka
Pr Dir: Patricia Burgio
Teacher Pr: Cheryl Reukauf
Psych: Trish Gang

D-U-N-S 03-227-5588
LANCASTER CITY SCHOOL DISTRICT
LANCASTER BOARD OF EDUCATION
345 E Mulberry St, Lancaster, OH 43130-3166
Tel (740) 687-7315 Founded/Ownrshp 1900
Sales 47.1MM^E EMP 766
Accts Dave Yost Columbus Ohio
SIC 8211 Public senior high school; Public junior high school; Public elementary school; Public senior high school; Public junior high school; Public elementary school
Pr: Amy Eyman
Bd of Dir: Bart Pickenpaugh
VP: Kathy Kittredge
*VP: Lise Ricketts
Off Mgr: Sandra McDaniel
MIS Dir: Jackie McCurdy
Dir IT: Ray Miller
Dir IT: Scott Thomas
Teacher Pr: Nathan Hale
Psych: Sheila Coleman-Gross

LANCASTER CNTY SCHL DISTRCT 1
See LINCOLN PUBLIC SCHOOLS INC

D-U-N-S 00-192-8035 IMP/EXP
▲ **LANCASTER COLONY CORP** (OH)
37 W Broad St Ste 500, Columbus, OH 43215-4177
Tel (614) 224-7141 Founded/Ownrshp 1961
Sales 1.1MMM EMP 2,600
Accts Deloitte & Touche Llp Columb
Tkr Sym LANC Exch NGS
SIC 2035 2038 Dressings, salad: raw & cooked (except dry mixes); Seasonings & sauces, except tomato & dry; Frozen specialties; Dressings, salad: raw & cooked (except dry mixes); Seasonings & sauces, except tomato & dry; Frozen specialties
Ch Bd: John B Gerlach Jr
CFO: Douglas A Fell
VP: Bruce L Rosa

D-U-N-S 06-594-6603
LANCASTER COMMUNITY HOSPITAL
38600 Medical Center Dr, Palmdale, CA 93551-4483
Tel (661) 940-1321 Founded/Ownrshp 2011
Sales 9.6MM^E EMP 284^E
SIC 8062 General medical & surgical hospitals
Prin: Penny Hammer
CFO: Kurt Broten
Pharmcst: Margaret Rice

D-U-N-S 15-132-4167
LANCASTER COMMUNITY SERVICES FOUNDATION INC
LANCASTER REDEVELOPMENT AGENCY
44933 Fern Ave, Lancaster, CA 93534-2461
Tel (661) 723-6000 Founded/Ownrshp 1977
Sales NA EMP 300
Accts White Nelson Diehl Evans Llp
SIC 9111 City & town managers' offices; City & town managers' offices
CEO: R Rex Tarris
Ofcr: Jeff Thompson
Ofcr: Yolanda Williams
Exec: Mayra Montero
Comm Man: Nicole Allen
Comm Man: Joseph Cabral
IT Man: Franklin Debra
IT Man: Patti Galloway
IT Man: Mike Sanderson

D-U-N-S 01-429-2809
LANCASTER COUNTY MOTORS INC
5260 Main St, East Petersburg, PA 17520-1608
Tel (717) 569-4514 Founded/Ownrshp 1974
Sales 52.8MM^E EMP 107
SIC 5511 Automobiles, new & used; Automobiles, new & used
Pr: Michael Mann
*Sec: George B Mann
*VP: Frank L Nolt
Sls Mgr: Alex Knight
Sls Mgr: Steve Lehman
Sales Asso: Matt Harnish

D-U-N-S 08-471-3015
LANCASTER COUNTY SCHOOL DISTRICT
300 S Catawba St, Lancaster, SC 29720-2458
Tel (803) 286-6972 Founded/Ownrshp 1935
Sales 116.3MM EMP 1,600
Accts Mcgregor & Company Llp Columb
SIC 8211 Public elementary & secondary schools; Public elementary & secondary schools
*CFO: Tony Walker
Ex Dir: Lydia Quinn
Schl Brd P: Robert Parker
Psych: Tracey Snipes-Purser
HC Dir: Kathy Durbin

D-U-N-S 06-709-5828
LANCASTER COUNTY SOLID WASTE MANAGEMENT AUTHORITY
1299 Harrisburg Ave, Lancaster, PA 17603-2515
Tel (717) 397-9968 Founded/Ownrshp 1954
Sales 52.2MM EMP 84
Accts Trout Ebersole & Groff Llp
SIC 4953 Sanitary landfill operation; Sanitary landfill operation
CEO: James D Warner
*COO: Robert B Zorbaugh
Admn Mgr: Dave Anderson
Admn Mgr: Robert Eshbach
Genl Mgr: Tim Odonnell
Board of Directors: William Ebel Jr, John Kassees, lester Houck,, Barbara Hammel, musser John, J Scott Ulrich, Karen Weibel, r Edward Gor

D-U-N-S 62-711-9928
LANCASTER COUNTY WATER & SEWER DISTRICT
1400 Pageland Hwy, Lancaster, SC 29720-8540
Tel (803) 285-6919 Founded/Ownrshp 1958
Sales 21.5MM EMP 55
Accts Mcabee Talbert Halliday & Co
SIC 4941 4952 Water supply; Sewerage systems; Water supply; Sewerage systems

D-U-N-S 78-780-0408
LANCASTER COUNTY WEEKLIES
EPHRATA RVIEW SUSQUEHANNA PRTG
(Suby of BUSINESS INTELLHGENCER JOURNAL) ★
1 E Main St, Ephrata, PA 17522-2713
Tel (717) 626-2191 Founded/Ownrshp 1987
Sales 30.5MM^E EMP 550
SIC 2711 Newspapers; Newspapers
Pr: Bill Burgess

D-U-N-S 01-350-3032
LANCASTER DEVELOPMENT INC (NY)
145 Podpadic Rd, Richmondville, NY 12149-2295
Tel (518) 294-9964 Founded/Ownrshp 1946
Sales 30.7MM^E EMP 75
SIC 1611 General contractor, highway & street construction; Resurfacing contractor
Ch Bd: Mark A Galasso
*CFO: Tim Gaffney
*Ex VP: Martin A Galasso Jr
*VP: James F Crum
*VP: Francis P George
MIS Dir: Craig Watson
Snr Mgr: Darren Collins

D-U-N-S 08-162-3241 IMP
LANCASTER FOODS LLC (DE)
(Suby of GUEST SERVICES INC) ★
7700 Conowingo Ave, Jessup, MD 20794-9473
Tel (410) 799-0010 Founded/Ownrshp 1983, 1992
Sales 221.8MM^E EMP 280
SIC 5148 Fresh fruits & vegetables; Fresh fruits & vegetables
Pr: John Gates
COO: Gerry Gabrys
*VP: Jerold Chadwick
*VP: Kevin Jones
Off Mgr: Monika Griffith
Prd Mgr: Paul Manu
Sls Mgr: Christina Sikorski

LANCASTER GEN HOSP SSQHNNA DIV
See COLUMBIA HOSPITAL

D-U-N-S 60-644-6227
LANCASTER GENERAL HEALTH
555 N Duke St, Lancaster, PA 17602-2250
Tel (717) 290-5511 Founded/Ownrshp 1983
Sales 299.1M EMP 5,000
SIC 8062 General medical & surgical hospitals; General medical & surgical hospitals
Pr: Thomas Beeman
*Ch Bd: Robert Bolinger
CFO: F Joseph Byroick
Ofcr: James Stuccio
Ex VP: Jan L Bergen
Sr VP: F J Byorick
Sr VP: Joseph Byorick
Sr VP: Robert Macina
Sr VP: Regina Mingle
VP: Geoffrey Eddowes
Dir Rx: Rich Paoletti
Board of Directors: Mark A Brazitis, Robert P Macina

D-U-N-S 06-978-4924
LANCASTER GENERAL HOSPITAL
LGH
555 N Duke St, Lancaster, PA 17602-2207
Tel (717) 544-5511 Founded/Ownrshp 1893
Sales 867.9MM EMP 5,000
SIC 8062 Hospital, professional nursing school with AMA residency; Hospital, professional nursing school with AMA residency
CEO: Jan L Bergen
Chf Rad: Leigh Shuman
CFO: Joseph Byorick
CFO: Dennis R Roemer
Bd of Dir: Christine Vlassis
Ex VP: Robert P Macina
Ex VP: Joel Perlish
Sr VP: Geoffrey W Eddowes
VP: Gary Davidson
Assoc Dir: Gladys Frye
Dir Rx: Tammy Keith

D-U-N-S 07-285-3559
■ **LANCASTER HMA INC**
HEART LNCSTER REGIONAL MED CTR
(Suby of HEALTH MANAGEMENT ASSOCIATES INC) ★
1500 Highlands Dr, Lititz, PA 17543-7694
Tel (717) 625-5000 Founded/Ownrshp 1999
Sales 65.1MM^E EMP 420
SIC 8062 General medical & surgical hospitals; General medical & surgical hospitals
CEO: Karen Metz
Chf Rad: Kartik Shah
Dir Lab: Jim Kantoski
Dir Rx: Chris Dimaulo
Off Mgr: Betty Gross
QA Dir: Dawn Shafferman
Obsttrcn: Thomas Fromuth
Ansthlgy: Seth Gunderson
Nrsg Dir: Peter Mecouch
Pharmcst: John Mariano
HC Dir: Teri Sipe

LANCASTER HONDA & AV KIA
See CLUTTER MOTORS INC

D-U-N-S 88-377-9902
■ **LANCASTER HOSPITAL CORP**
SPRINGS MEMORIAL HOSPITAL
(Suby of COMMUNITY HEALTH SYSTEMS INC) ★
800 W Meeting St, Lancaster, SC 29720-2202
Tel (803) 286-1214 Founded/Ownrshp 1995
Sales 27.8MM^E EMP 660

SIC 8062 General medical & surgical hospitals; General medical & surgical hospitals
CFO: Nathan Crabtree
MIS Dir: Chrys Steele

LANCASTER HOST RESORT
See HOSPITALITY ASSOCIATES OF LANCASTER LP

D-U-N-S 07-487-5931
LANCASTER INDEPENDENT SCHOOL DISTRICT
422 S Centre Ave, Lancaster, TX 75146-3829
Tel (972) 218-1400 *Founded/Ownrshp* 1865
Sales 61.2MM^E *EMP* 800
Accts Pattillo Brown & Hill Llp W
SIC 8211 Public elementary school; Public junior high school; Public senior high school; Kindergarten; Public elementary school; Public junior high school; Public senior high school; Kindergarten
Ex VP: Cynthia Jarvis
VP: Ellen Clark
Dir IT: Joe Williams
IT Man: Brenda Gray
Schl Brd P: Ty Jones
HC Dir: Maelene Grant

D-U-N-S 00-791-2116 IMP/EXP
■ **LANCASTER LEAF TOBACCO CO OF PENNSYLVANIA INC** (VA)
(*Suby of* UNIVERSAL LEAF TOBACCO CO INC) ★
198 W Liberty St, Lancaster, PA 17603-2712
Tel (717) 394-2676 *Founded/Ownrshp* 1941, 2011
Sales 51.1MM^E *EMP* 120
SIC 5159 2141 Tobacco distributors & products; Tobacco stemming & redrying; Tobacco distributors & products; Tobacco stemming & redrying
Ch: Claude Martin
**Pr:* G E Bossert
**Pr:* T K Walsh Jr
**CFO:* Michael Dooley
**Treas:* Thomas Stephenson
**Sec:* D C Moore
VP: Frank Miller
VP: August Payne
**VP:* T E Stephenson
VP: Thomas Walsh

D-U-N-S 83-308-8011
LANCASTER MANOR REHABILITATION CENTER LLC
1001 South St, Lincoln, NE 68502-2296
Tel (402) 441-7101 *Founded/Ownrshp* 2009
Sales 950.0M *EMP* 290
SIC 8059 Personal care home, with health care; Personal care home, with health care

D-U-N-S 36-395-6392 IMP
LANCASTER OIL CO
ENVIRONMENTAL RECOVERY CORP PA
1076 Old Manheim Pike, Lancaster, PA 17601-3177
Tel (717) 393-2627 *Founded/Ownrshp* 1988
Sales 46.6MM^E *EMP* 68^E
SIC 4953 5093 Recycling, waste materials; Oil, waste
Pr: Richard L Middleton
**Pr:* Kenneth D Lefever
**VP:* Peter C Haiges
**VP:* Kevin L Rohrbach
**Genl Mgr:* Terry Leatherman

D-U-N-S 62-065-8674
LANCASTER PACKAGING INC
L P I
560 Main St Ste 1, Hudson, MA 01749-2919
Tel (978) 562-0100 *Founded/Ownrshp* 1989
Sales 21.5MM^E *EMP* 19^E
SIC 5087 5199 Cleaning & maintenance equipment & supplies; Packaging materials
Pr: Marianne Lancaster

D-U-N-S 82-984-9269
LANCASTER POLLARD MORTGAGE CO LLC
65 E State St Ste 1600, Columbus, OH 43215-4237
Tel (614) 224-8800 *Founded/Ownrshp* 1988
Sales NA *EMP* 110
SIC 6159 6162 6282 Intermediate investment banks; Mortgage bankers; Investment advisory service; Intermediate investment banks; Mortgage bankers; Investment advisory service
CEO: Thomas R Green
CFO: Kevin J Beerman
Ex VP: Timothy J Dobyns

LANCASTER REDEVELOPMENT AGENCY
See LANCASTER COMMUNITY SERVICES FOUNDATION INC

D-U-N-S 07-284-6017
■ **LANCASTER REGIONAL MEDICAL CENTER**
(*Suby of* HEALTH MANAGEMENT ASSOCIATES INC) ★
250 College Ave, Lancaster, PA 17603-3378
Tel (717) 358-7349 *Founded/Ownrshp* 1877
Sales 156.1MM^E *EMP* 1,100
SIC 8062 General medical & surgical hospitals; General medical & surgical hospitals
CEO: Bradley Nurkin
**CEO:* Bob Moore
COO: Debra Wilwerth
**CFO:* Fred Ashworth
Dir Rx: John Sokso
Chf Nrs Of: Joanne Lucas
Board of Directors: Joe Legenstein

D-U-N-S 09-999-9492
LANCASTER SCHOOL DISTRICT
44711 Cedar Ave, Lancaster, CA 93534-3216
Tel (661) 948-4661 *Founded/Ownrshp* 1890
Sales 102.9MM^E *EMP* 2,500
Accts Christy White Accountancy Corp
SIC 8211 Public elementary school; Public elementary school
CFO: Leona Smith
Exec: Candy Strand
CTO: Judy Brenneman
Schl Brd P: Chris Grado
Schl Brd P: John Miller
HC Dir: Jullie Eutsler

D-U-N-S 17-374-5746
LANCASTER SYSTEMS
411 Theodore Fremd Ave, Rye, NY 10580-1410
Tel (914) 967-5700 *Founded/Ownrshp* 1999
Sales 29.0MM *EMP* 64
SIC 7379 Data processing consultant; Data processing consultant
Ch Bd: Nadine Diciccio
**Sec:* Joan Ferrari

D-U-N-S 09-187-3984
LANCASTER-LEBANON INTERMEDIATE UNIT 13 (INC)
1020 New Holland Ave, Lancaster, PA 17601-5606
Tel (717) 606-1600 *Founded/Ownrshp* 1971
Sales 76.1M^E *EMP* 1,800
Accts Trout Ebersole & Groff Llp La
SIC 8299 Educational services; Educational services
Ex Dir: Cynthia Burkhart
**CFO:* Gina Brillhart
Instr Medi: Pam Mc Artney
Phys Thrpy: Barbara Miller

D-U-N-S 00-967-5158 IMP
LANCE CAMPER MFG CORP
LANCE MANUFACTURING
43120 Venture St, Lancaster, CA 93535-4510
Tel (661) 949-3322 *Founded/Ownrshp* 1981
Sales 76.5MM^E *EMP* 300
SIC 3792 Campers, for mounting on trucks; Campers, for mounting on trucks
CEO: Earl Jackson Cole
**Pr:* Jack Cole
VP: Jan Kurahara
**VP:* Jeff Souleles
IT Man: Dan Goldberg
Plnt Mgr: Victor Garcia
Sls Dir: Gary Connely
Pathlgst: Eric Cleveland

LANCE CUNNINGHAM FORD
See TT OF KNOXVILLE INC

D-U-N-S 05-455-0140
LANCE INVESTIGATION SERVICE INC
1438 Boston Rd, Bronx, NY 10460-4963
Tel (718) 893-1400 *Founded/Ownrshp* 1965
Sales 21.0MM^E *EMP* 1,800
Accts Zeligson Granito & Epstein L
SIC 7381 1731 Protective services, guard; Detective services; Fire detection & burglar alarm systems specialization; Protective services, guard; Detective services; Fire detection & burglar alarm systems specialization
Pr: Ralph V Johnson
**VP:* Lance W Johnson
Genl Mgr: Mark Creighton

LANCE MANUFACTURING
See LANCE CAMPER MFG CORP

LANCE PRIVATE BRANDS
See VISTA BAKERY INC

D-U-N-S 95-838-7367
LANCE S SUPER DOLLAR INC
LANCES NEWMARKETS
18 W Washington St, Huntington, IN 46750-2658
Tel (260) 356-1292 *Founded/Ownrshp* 1973
Sales 55.0MM *EMP* 600
SIC 5411 Grocery stores; Grocery stores
Pr: Dan Lance
**VP:* Doug Lance

D-U-N-S 04-701-3412 IMP/EXP
LANCER CORP
INDUSTRIAS LANCERMEX SA DE CV
(*Suby of* HOSHIZAKI AMERICA INC) ★
6655 Lancer Blvd, San Antonio, TX 78219-4735
Tel (210) 661-6964 *Founded/Ownrshp* 1969
Sales 153.1MM^E *EMP* 515
SIC 3585 Ice making machinery; Soda fountain & beverage dispensing equipment & parts; Beer dispensing equipment; Carbonators, soda water; Ice making machinery; Soda fountain & beverage dispensing equipment & parts; Beer dispensing equipment; Carbonators, soda water
Pr: Luis Alvarez
VP: Jose A Canales
VP: David Ewing
**VP:* Richard Laughlin
VP: Chuck Thomas

D-U-N-S 80-735-4410
LANCER INSURANCE CO
1 Fairchild Ct Ste 200, Plainview, NY 11803-1720
Tel (541) 472-0950 *Founded/Ownrshp* 1985
Sales NA *EMP* 430
SIC 6331 Fire, marine & casualty insurance; Fire, marine & casualty insurance
Pr: David P Delaney Jr
**CFO:* Alistair T Lind
Ex VP: Robert Boyle
Ex VP: Thomas L Theiler
Sr VP: Randy O'Neill
VP: Elsa Aleman
VP: Kim Aquilino
VP: Paul Berne
VP: Robert Burns
VP: Michael Byrne
**VP:* Bob Crescenzo
VP: Mark Libertine
VP: Bill Madtes
VP: Pamela Marin
VP: Kieran McGowan
VP: Matthew Mushorn
VP: Shirley Ortego
**VP:* Gail Riley
VP: Steve Shapiro
VP: Fran Walsh
VP: Jeffrey Willmann

LANCER LABEL
See RILEY CO

D-U-N-S 00-816-4592
LANCER PARTNERSHIP LTD
6655 Lancer Blvd, San Antonio, TX 78219-4735
Tel (210) 310-7000 *Founded/Ownrshp* 1996
Sales 12.9MM^E *EMP* 300
SIC 8732 Market analysis or research; Market analysis or research
Pt: Chris Hughes
Pt: Scott Adams
Pt: Anthony Canalis
Pt: Mark Freitas

LANCE'S NEW MARKET
See LANCES SUPER VALU INC

LANCES NEWMARKETS
See LANCE S SUPER DOLLAR INC

D-U-N-S 60-391-2155
LANCES SUPER VALU INC
LANCE'S NEW MARKET
18 W Washington St, Huntington, IN 46750-2658
Tel (260) 356-1292 *Founded/Ownrshp* 1981
Sales 24.5MM^E *EMP* 400
SIC 5411 Grocery stores, independent; Grocery stores, independent
Pr: Todd Taylor
**Pr:* Dan Lance
**VP:* Doug Lance

D-U-N-S 15-461-0971
LANCESOFT INC
13454 Sunrise Valley Dr # 120, Herndon, VA 20171-3278
Tel (703) 674-4500 *Founded/Ownrshp* 2000
Sales 46.4MM *EMP* 650
SIC 7361 Computer related consulting services; Computer software development & applications; Labor contractors (employment agency)
CEO: Ramkumar Karuppusamy
**CFO:* Richard Todd
**VP:* Prashant Arni
VP: Aditya Shrimali
**VP:* Parag Tandon
VP: Krishna Valiyatodi
CTO: Asha Tambare
IT Man: Karthik Eyan
Sls Mgr: Ruchi Jain

D-U-N-S 13-054-8659 IMP/EXP
LANCO & HARRIS CORP
600 Mid Florida Dr, Orlando, FL 32824-7008
Tel (407) 240-4000 *Founded/Ownrshp* 2003
Sales 25.4MM^E *EMP* 60
SIC 2851 Paints & paint additives
Pr: Sergio Blanco
**Treas:* Guillermo Blanco
**VP:* Inrique Blanco
Genl Mgr: Manny Sayago
Prd Mgr: Ruben Melendez
VP Sls: Javier Betancourt

D-U-N-S 10-817-8369
LANCO ASSEMBLY SYSTEMS INC
LANCO SYSTEMS
12 Thomas Dr, Westbrook, ME 04092-3824
Tel (207) 773-2060 *Founded/Ownrshp* 2001
Sales 21.6MM^E *EMP* 90
SIC 3559 Robots, molding & forming plastics; Robots, molding & forming plastics
Pr: Thomas A Zack
Off Mgr: Lisa Letellier
IT Man: Ed Karabec
Opers Mgr: David Walden
VP Sls: Matt Bresnahan
VP Sls: Tim Neale
Manager: Kevin Forshee
Snr Mgr: Alexander Baker
Snr Mgr: Peter Brazier
Snr Mgr: Matthew Mingo

D-U-N-S 17-511-5765 IMP/EXP
LANCO CORP
BRIJON
2905 Vtrans Mem Hwy Ste 3, Ronkonkoma, NY 11779-7655
Tel (631) 231-2300 *Founded/Ownrshp* 1983
Sales 50.8MM^E *EMP* 250
SIC 3993 2066 5149 2064 Signs & advertising specialties; Chocolate & cocoa products; Chocolate; Candy & other confectionery products; Signs & advertising specialties; Chocolate & cocoa products; Chocolate; Candy & other confectionery products
Pr: Brian Landow
COO: Mike Zimmerman
**VP:* Irwin Landow
Rgnl Mgr: Marion Cross
Rgnl Mgr: Tom Kronberger
Sfty Mgr: Donald Landeu
Opers Mgr: Joe Barone
Prd Mgr: Bernardo Romero
Manager: Robin Daniel
Manager: Robert McGilton
Manager: Mark Whitner

D-U-N-S 04-252-4272 EXP
LANCO INTERNATIONAL INC
LANTECH LOGISTICS
3111 167th St, Hazel Crest, IL 60429-1025
Tel (708) 596-5200 *Founded/Ownrshp* 1955
Sales 194.5MM^E *EMP* 650
SIC 3531 8711 5084 3536 7353 3537 Construction machinery; Designing: ship, boat, machine & product; Cranes, industrial; Cranes, overhead traveling; Heavy construction equipment rental; Industrial trucks & tractors; Construction machinery; Designing: ship, boat, machine & product; Cranes, industrial; Cranes, overhead traveling; Heavy construction equipment rental; Industrial trucks & tractors
Pr: John J Lanigan Jr
COO: Rakesh Gupta
**CFO:* Stephen J Bayers
**Ex VP:* Mike T Lanigan
**Ex VP:* William P Lanigan
**VP:* Jack Wepfer
Genl Mgr: C Rog
IT Man: Jason Morris
VP Sls: Ray Tippit
Sls Mgr: Dan Gray
Board of Directors: Daniel P Lanigan

D-U-N-S 09-046-9834 IMP
LANCO MANUFACTURING CORP
5 Urb Aponte, San Lorenzo, PR 00754-3003
Tel (787) 736-4221 *Founded/Ownrshp* 1974, 1978
Sales 72.7MM^E *EMP* 200
Accts Nigaglioni & Rivera Carreras
SIC 2891 2851 Adhesives; Paints & paint additives; Adhesives; Paints & paint additives
Pr: Sergio Blanco

LANCO SYSTEMS
See LANCO ASSEMBLY SYSTEMS INC

D-U-N-S 11-030-5591
LANCOPE INC
3650 Brookside Pkwy # 500, Alpharetta, GA 30022-1424
Tel (770) 225-6500 *Founded/Ownrshp* 2000
Sales 27.6MM^E *EMP* 53^E
Accts Frazier & Deeter Llc Atlanta
SIC 7372 7374 Business oriented computer software; Service bureau, computer
Pr: Mike Potts
**Ch Bd:* Brian Cohen
**COO:* David Cocchiara
**VP:* Jason Anderson
**VP:* John Balsam
**VP:* Mark Gothard
VP: Steven Newman
**VP:* Ken O'Reilly
VP: Kenneth O'Reilly
VP: Gavin Reid
**VP:* David Scruggs
VP: John Sellers
VP: Jim Ulam
Dir Bus: Sam Davis
Dir Bus: Jeff Wells

LAND & PERSONNEL MANAGEMENT
See HALL MANAGEMENT CORP

D-U-N-S 16-035-9384
LAND AIR EXPRESS INC
6377 Cemetery Rd, Bowling Green, KY 42103-9814
Tel (270) 781-0655 *Founded/Ownrshp* 1983
Sales 48.4MM^E *EMP* 180
SIC 4513 4212 Air courier services; Delivery service, vehicular; Air courier services; Delivery service, vehicular
Pr: Joseph P Schneller Sr
**Pr:* Jerry Schneller
**Treas:* Diane Bush
**VP:* Joseph P Schneller Jr
Rgnl Mgr: Jim Stallbaumer

D-U-N-S 05-089-8463
LAND COAST INSULATION INC
4017 2nd St, New Iberia, LA 70560-0515
Tel (337) 367-7741 *Founded/Ownrshp* 1973
Sales 63.2MM^E *EMP* 380
Accts Hannis T Bourgeois Llp Denh
SIC 1799 1721 Insulation of pipes & boilers; Industrial painting; Insulation of pipes & boilers; Industrial painting
CEO: Michael Morton
**Pr:* R Michael Morton
CFO: Robin Seibert
**VP:* Timothy S Morton

D-U-N-S 00-360-5271
LAND HOUSE CO LLC
HOUSE LAND DEVELOPEMENT CO
35631 Trevino Trl, Beaumont, CA 92223-6221
Tel (909) 227-2011 *Founded/Ownrshp* 1994
Sales 30.0MM *EMP* 5
SIC 6552 Land subdividers & developers, residential; Land subdividers & developers, residential
COO: Brent Brodie

D-U-N-S 60-502-7457
LAND MARK PRODUCTS INC
PICCADILLY CIRCUS PIZZA
1007 Okoboji Ave, Milford, IA 51351-1376
Tel (712) 338-2771 *Founded/Ownrshp* 1980
Sales 42.8MM *EMP* 75
Accts Brinkman & Reed Cpa S Estherv
SIC 2099 6794 Pizza, refrigerated: except frozen; Franchises, selling or licensing; Pizza, refrigerated: except frozen; Franchises, selling or licensing
Prin: Rodney D Simonson
**Ex VP:* Jason Farrell
**Sr VP:* Jerry Ryker
**VP:* Lamont Glendinning
Exec: Dana Evaro

D-U-N-S 07-845-6993 EXP
■ **LAND N SEA DISTRIBUTING INC** (FL)
LAND N SEA FORT MYERS
(*Suby of* BRUNSWICK CORP) ★
3131 N Andrews Avenue Ext, Pompano Beach, FL 33064-2118
Tel (954) 792-9971 *Founded/Ownrshp* 1975, 2003
Sales 236.2MM^E *EMP* 350
SIC 5088 5091 5046 5531 Marine supplies; Sporting & recreation goods; Commercial equipment; Automotive parts; Marine supplies; Sporting & recreation goods; Commercial equipment; Automotive parts
Pr: Thomas Schuessler
Pr: Carl Parisi
Sr VP: Karen Hodum
**VP:* David R Swick
**VP:* Judith P Zelisko
Genl Mgr: Ryan O'Connor
Genl Mgr: Jim Paulick
MIS Dir: Betty Alvarez
IT Man: Donald Stoll
Mktg Mgr: Barret Dickinson

LAND N SEA FORT MYERS
See LAND N SEA DISTRIBUTING INC

D-U-N-S 00-121-5086 IMP/EXP
LAND N SEA INC (NY)
1375 Broadway Fl 2, New York, NY 10018-7073
Tel (212) 703-2980 *Founded/Ownrshp* 1958
Sales 38.1MM^E *EMP* 100

SIC 2369 2361 2331 2339 5651 Girls' & children's outerwear; Blouses: girls', children's & infants'; Blouses, women's & juniors': made from purchased material; Women's & misses' outerwear; Family clothing stores; Girls' & children's outerwear; Blouses: girls', children's & infants'; Blouses, women's & juniors': made from purchased material; Women's & misses' outerwear; Family clothing stores
Ch Bd: Robert Sobel
*Ch Bd: Kirk Gellin
*COO: Fred Mandato
VP: Scott Aimetti
Area Mgr: Ed Vanduzer
Info Man: Owen Perry
Opers Mgr: Tom Schueffler
Opers Mgr: Heather Smith
VP Sls: Michael Conners
Merch Mgr: Katie Tiernan

D-U-N-S 78-634-6689
LAND OF LINCOLN GOODWILL IND
2305 W Monroe St, Springfield, IL 62704-1438
Tel (217) 726-6846 Founded/Ownrshp 2006
Sales 21.0MM EMP 2E
Accts Kerber Eck & Braeckel Llp Spr
SIC 8331 Sheltered workshop; Sheltered workshop
Pr: Sharon Durbin

D-U-N-S 10-928-4257
LAND OF LINCOLN GOODWILL INDUSTRIES INC SPRINGFIELD ILLINOIS
1220 Outer Park Dr, Springfield, IL 62704-4409
Tel (217) 789-0400 Founded/Ownrshp 1938
Sales 24.2MM EMP 480
Accts Kerber Eck & Braeckel Llp Sp
SIC 8331 Vocational rehabilitation agency; Vocational rehabilitation agency
CEO: Sharon Durbin

D-U-N-S 04-703-1190 IMP
LAND OFROST INC
16850 Chicago Ave, Lansing, IL 60438-1115
Tel (708) 474-7100 Founded/Ownrshp 1958
Sales 7.5MM EMP 900
Accts Swartz Retson & Co Pc Merrill
SIC 2013 2099 Sausages & other prepared meats; Smoked meats from purchased meat; Prepared beef products from purchased beef; Ready-to-eat meals, salads & sandwiches; Sausages & other prepared meats; Smoked meats from purchased meat; Prepared beef products from purchased beef; Ready-to-eat meals, salads & sandwiches
Pr: David Van Eekeren
*Ch Bd: Donna Van Eekeren
*CFO: George Smolar
Treas: Donna Vaneekeren
Sr VP: Dave Funk
VP: John Horton
Plnt Mgr: Paul Schlundt
Ql Cn Mgr: Greg Kammerer
VP Sls: Anthony Palesotti

LAND OLAKES ANIMAL MILK PDTS
See PURINA ANIMAL NUTRITION LLC

D-U-N-S 00-625-3835 IMP/EXP
LAND OLAKES INC (TN)
4001 Lexington Ave N, Arden Hills, MN 55126-2998
Tel (651) 375-2222 Founded/Ownrshp 1921
Sales 14.9MMM EMP 9,100
SIC 2879

D-U-N-S 96-826-2048
LAND OSUN MANAGEMENT CORP
FASTTRACK FOODS
3715 Nw 97th Blvd Ste A, Gainesville, FL 32606-7373
Tel (352) 333-3011 Founded/Ownrshp 1988
Sales 133.4MME EMP 300
SIC 5541 5411 Filling stations, gasoline; Convenience stores; Filling stations, gasoline; Convenience stores
Pr: Alan Fogg
*VP: Stephen Fogg
*VP: Richard Rentz

LAND PRIDE
See GREAT PLAINS MANUFACTURING INC

D-U-N-S 82-975-3735
LAND REMEDIATION INC
1644 State Route 43, Averill Park, NY 12018-3426
Tel (518) 766-4105 Founded/Ownrshp 2006
Sales 24.0MM EMP 35
SIC 8744 7389 ;
Ch Bd: William Lindheimer
*Sls&Mrk Ex: Keith Decker

LAND ROVER
See BAKER MOTOR CO OF CHARLESTON INC

LAND ROVER
See FRED LAVERY CO

D-U-N-S 96-041-1445
LAND ROVER AUSTIN LP
(Suby of DON SNELL BUICK LP) ★
1515 W 5th St, Austin, TX 78703-5131
Tel (512) 236-0000 Founded/Ownrshp 1995
Sales 51.6MME EMP 191
SIC 5511 New & used car dealers; New & used car dealers
Pt: Donald Snell
*Sec: Jim Bush
Genl Mgr: Alan Cirota

LAND ROVER CHICAGO
See HOWARD ORLOFF IMPORTS INC

D-U-N-S 93-256-7787 EXP
LAND ROVER DALLAS LP
(Suby of DON SNELL BUICK LP) ★
11400 N Central Expy, Dallas, TX 75243-6602
Tel (214) 691-4294 Founded/Ownrshp 1995
Sales 32.5MME EMP 75
SIC 5511 New & used car dealers; New & used car dealers
Pr: Jim Snell
*VP: Donald Snell
Sls Mgr: Tony Ventura

D-U-N-S 00-672-9938 EXP
LAND ROVER LAS VEGAS
5325 W Sahara Ave, Las Vegas, NV 89146-3345
Tel (702) 579-0400 Founded/Ownrshp 2001
Sales 35.6MME EMP 100
SIC 5511 New & used car dealers; New & used car dealers
Pr: Clifford Finley

LAND ROVER METRO WEST
See FOREIGN MOTORS WEST INC

LAND ROVER OF SMITHTOWN
See LONG ISLAND UK AUTO INC

D-U-N-S 36-076-3903
LAND SERVICES USA INC
1835 Market St Ste 420, Philadelphia, PA 19103-2933
Tel (215) 563-5468 Founded/Ownrshp 2005
Sales NA EMP 45E
SIC 6411
Pr: Gordon Daniels
Pr: Kurt Scheivert
Ofcr: Melissa Ennis
Ofcr: Katrina Orlando
Ofcr: Melissa Pertz
Ofcr: Marianne Young
VP: Jesse Silverman
IT Man: Bob Finnimore

D-U-N-S 83-837-0682
LAND SOUTHERN CO LLC
WESTHAVEN REALTY
1550 W Mcewen Dr Ste 200, Franklin, TN 37067-1771
Tel (615) 778-3150 Founded/Ownrshp 1995
Sales 120.9MME EMP 250E
SIC 6552 Subdividers & developers; Subdividers & developers
CEO: Tim Downey
Pr: Brian Sewell
CFO: Ken Howell
Sr VP: Sharon Hatfield
Sr VP: Mike Hathaway
VP: Michael McNally
VP: Kathy Shelling
VP: Cliff Smith
VP: Tim Snook
VP: Creighton Wright
Dir Soc: Marlena Karlsson

LAND SPAN LOGISTICS
See OLD LS INC

D-U-N-S 80-711-0528
LAND TITLE GUARANTEE CO
1561 Oxbow Dr Unit 200, Montrose, CO 81401-4701
Tel (970) 249-9131 Founded/Ownrshp 2007
Sales NA EMP 99
SIC 6361 Title insurance
Pr: John E Freyer

D-U-N-S 07-576-3540
LAND TITLE GUARANTEE CO INC
3033 E 1st Ave Ste 600, Denver, CO 80206-5625
Tel (303) 321-1880 Founded/Ownrshp 1994
Sales NA EMP 600
SIC 6411 Insurance agents, brokers & service; ; Insurance agents, brokers & service;
Ch Bd: W B Vollbracht
*Pr: John E Fryer Sr
*CFO: Dan Every
Bd of Dir: Tina Rutherford
Ofcr: Debi Bright
Ofcr: Ryan Brito
Ofcr: Christy Brown
Ofcr: Nancy Crowder
Ofcr: Heidi Crue
Ofcr: Sarah Dorman
Ofcr: Dave Fischer
Ofcr: Sandra Johnson
Ofcr: Ben Lowe
Ofcr: Melissa Martino
Ofcr: Dixie Powers
Ofcr: Lisa Romo
Ofcr: Scott Seymour
Ofcr: Kim Shultz
Ofcr: Robin Trent
Ofcr: Kim Zimmerman
Ex VP: John Freyer

D-U-N-S 19-311-3651
LAND TITLE INC
2200 County Road C W # 2205, Saint Paul, MN 55113-2551
Tel (651) 638-1900 Founded/Ownrshp 1985
Sales NA EMP 85
SIC 6361 6531 Title insurance; Real estate agents & managers
Pr: Jeff Christian
Pr: Greg Booth
COO: Sandy Casillas
Treas: Becky Wagner
Sls&Mrk Ex: Annette Theis

D-U-N-S 11-751-6757
LAND VIEW INC
20504 4th St, Rupert, ID 83350-9428
Tel (208) 531-4100 Founded/Ownrshp 1984
Sales 87.0MME EMP 150
SIC 2879 2873 2874 5999 5261 5169 Agricultural chemicals; Nitrogenous fertilizers; Phosphatic fertilizers; Feed & farm supply; Fertilizer; Chemicals & allied products; Alkalines & chlorine; Agricultural chemicals; Nitrogenous fertilizers; Phosphatic fertilizers; Feed & farm supply; Fertilizer; Chemicals & allied products; Alkalines & chlorine
Pr: Roy Young
CFO: Lance Whitney
*VP: Gregg M Harman
*VP: V Paul Hobson
Exec: Lance Wihitney

D-U-N-S 61-925-8734
LAND-AIR EXPRESS OF NEW ENGLAND LTD
59 Avenue C, Williston, VT 05495-8109
Tel (802) 863-5062 Founded/Ownrshp 1990
Sales 73.8MME EMP 650
SIC 4214

D-U-N-S 87-805-3321 EXP
■ **LAND-O-SUN DAIRIES LLC**
PET DAIRY
(Suby of DEAN FOODS CO) ★
2900 Bristol Hwy, Johnson City, TN 37601-1502
Tel (423) 283-5700 Founded/Ownrshp 1998
Sales 220.8MME EMP 1,900
SIC 2026 2024 5143 Fluid milk; Ice cream & frozen desserts; Dairy products, except dried or canned; Fluid milk; Ice cream & frozen desserts; Dairy products, except dried or canned
Pr: Rick Fehr
*CFO: Loren White
Treas: A M Allem
Treas: A Allem
MIS Dir: Rod Barnett
Sales Exec: Jeff Monroe

D-U-N-S 03-207-6395 EXP
LAND-RON INC
6753 Kingspointe Pkwy # 109, Orlando, FL 32819-8598
Tel (407) 816-7035 Founded/Ownrshp 1999
Sales 24.9MM EMP 20
Accts Alecia D Spence Cpa Orlando
SIC 1542 Commercial & office buildings, renovation & repair; Commercial & office buildings, renovation & repair
Pr: Ronald Karpiuk
*CFO: Roy Karpiuk

LANDAAL PACKAGING SYSTEMS
See FLINT PACKAGING INC

D-U-N-S 12-283-9462
LANDAIR TRANSPORT INC
1110 Myers St, Greeneville, TN 37743-5216
Tel (423) 783-1300 Founded/Ownrshp 2002
Sales 116.9MME EMP 951E
SIC 4213 4225 Trucking, except local; General warehousing & storage; Trucking, except local; General warehousing & storage
CEO: John A Tweed
*CFO: Chris E Horner
*Ch: Scott M Niswonger
*Sr VP: Matt T Anderson
*Sr VP: Gary Funk
*Sr VP: Kris Kohls
VP: Eric Johnson
*VP: Jim Massengill
*VP: Richard Roberts
Genl Mgr: Mike Chesser
Opers Mgr: Sasha Catron

LANDAU
See HYMAN COMPANIES INC

D-U-N-S 83-224-2692
LANDAU APARTMENTS LIMITED PARTNERSHIP
1321 S Broad St, Clinton, SC 29325-9430
Tel (864) 833-3215 Founded/Ownrshp 2009
Sales 39.2MME EMP 3,900
SIC 6513 Apartment building operators; Apartment building operators
Prin: Margaret Stannard
Sr VP: Leeann Morein

D-U-N-S 04-217-0829 IMP/EXP
LANDAU UNIFORMS INC
8410 W Sandidge Rd, Olive Branch, MS 38654-3412
Tel (662) 895-7200 Founded/Ownrshp 1959
Sales 89.1MME EMP 500E
SIC 2326 2337 2339 Work uniforms; Medical & hospital uniforms, men's; Uniforms, except athletic: women's, misses' & juniors'; Women's & misses' outerwear; Work uniforms; Medical & hospital uniforms, men's; Uniforms, except athletic: women's, misses' & juniors'; Women's & misses' outerwear
CEO: Bruce Landau
*Pr: Nathaniel Landau
*Sec: Nancy E Russell
VP: Donna Cates
VP: Russ Goddard
VP: David Jones
*VP: Gregg A Landau
Dept Mgr: Janice Credille
Genl Mgr: Mauricio Mayer
MIS Dir: Ron Richins
Dir IT: Tim Shelton
Board of Directors: Dale Scott

D-U-N-S 18-980-7159 IMP
▲ **LANDAUER INC**
2 Science Rd, Glenwood, IL 60425-1586
Tel (708) 755-7000 Founded/Ownrshp 1987
Sales 151.3MM EMP 600E
Accts Pricewaterhousecoopers Llp Ch
Tkr Sym LDR Exch NYS
SIC 8734 5047 3829 Radiation laboratories; Radiation dosimetry laboratory; Instruments, surgical & medical; X-ray film & supplies; Radiation laboratories; Radiation dosimetry laboratory; Instruments, surgical & medical; X-ray film & supplies; Measuring & controlling devices
Pr: Michael T Leatherman
Pr: Peter Cempellin
CFO: Dan Fujii
CFO: Mark Zorko
Sr VP: R Craig Yoder
VP: Diana Gehring
VP: Michael Kennedy
VP: Timothy Keys
VP: Doug King
Exec: Douglas R Gipson
CTO: Sue Morrow
Board of Directors: Jeffrey Bailey, Robert J Cronin, William G Dempsey, David E Meador, Stephen C Mitchel, Thomas M White

LANDAUER MEDSTAR
See MED STAR SURGICAL & BREATHING EQUIPMENT INC

LANDAUER-METROPOLITAN, INC.
See LMI LEGACY HOLDINGS II INC

D-U-N-S 02-817-2336
LANDAVAZO BROS INC
29280 Pacific St, Hayward, CA 94544-6016
Tel (510) 888-1043 Founded/Ownrshp 1988
Sales 20.7MME EMP 175E
SIC 1771 Foundation & footing contractor; Foundation & footing contractor
CEO: George C Landavazo
*Pr: Theodore V Landavazo
*Treas: Derrick P Landavazo
Off Mgr: Pat McCarron

D-U-N-S 01-299-5176
LANDCARE USA INC
(Suby of SERVICEMASTER CO LLC) ★
2603 Augusta Dr Ste 1300, Houston, TX 77057-5428
Tel (713) 692-6371 Founded/Ownrshp 1998, 1999
Sales 30.2MME EMP 2,000
SIC 0783 0782 Planting, pruning & trimming services; Tree trimming services for public utility lines; Removal services, bush & tree; Highway lawn & garden maintenance services; Landscape contractors; Planting, pruning & trimming services; Tree trimming services for public utility lines; Removal services, bush & tree; Highway lawn & garden maintenance services; Landscape contractors
Ch Bd: William F Murdy
*Sr VP: William L Fiedler
*Sr VP: Kenneth V Garcia
*VP: Harold D Cranston
*VP: Peter C Forbes

D-U-N-S 12-154-8270
LANDCARE USA LLC
9416 Doctor Perry Rd, Ijamsville, MD 21754-8700
Tel (301) 874-3300 Founded/Ownrshp 2011
Sales 795.8MME EMP 4,200
SIC 0782 Landscape contractors; Lawn services; Landscape contractors; Lawn services
CEO: Michael Bogan
CFO: Dan Krems
VP: John A Mann
VP: Kevin Sherwood
Area Mgr: Josh Hedrick
Area Mgr: Rick Herndon
Area Mgr: Ramon Valdes
Brnch Mgr: Tim Liebmann
Brnch Mgr: Larry Roscini
Brnch Mgr: Joe Russo
Brnch Mgr: Cynthia Smith

D-U-N-S 15-338-4503
LANDCASTLE TITLE LLC
7000 Cntl Pkwy Ne Ste 300, Atlanta, GA 30328
Tel (678) 298-2100 Founded/Ownrshp 2003
Sales 15.4MME EMP 495
SIC 6541 Title abstract offices; Title abstract offices

D-U-N-S 12-259-8563
LANDCO CONSTRUCTION LLC
2 Cityplace Dr Ste 10, Saint Louis, MO 63141-7096
Tel (314) 275-7400 Founded/Ownrshp 2001
Sales 28.2MM EMP 40
SIC 1542 Commercial & office building, new construction; Commercial & office building, new construction
Pr: Ronald L Landolt
Opers Mgr: Steve Brown

D-U-N-S 10-185-0774
LANDCOM HOSPITALITY MANAGEMENT INC
4314 Pablo Oaks Ct, Jacksonville, FL 32224-9631
Tel (904) 992-3700 Founded/Ownrshp 1991
Sales 29.0MME EMP 600
SIC 8741 6552 7011 Hotel or motel management; Land subdividers & developers, commercial; Hotels & motels; Hotel or motel management; Land subdividers & developers, commercial; Hotels & motels
Ch Bd: H Kenneth O'Steen Jr
*Pr: Charles R Johnson
CFO: Nanette Orlins
*CFO: Mary A Toomey
*Sr VP: Henry B Fonde Jr

D-U-N-S 06-755-8087
LANDCON LLC
1804 Sw Palmer Crk, Bentonville, AR 72712-7903
Tel (479) 250-1461 Founded/Ownrshp 2013
Sales 25.0MM EMP 12
SIC 7389

D-U-N-S 09-546-2867
LANDDESIGN INC
223 N Graham St, Charlotte, NC 28202-1431
Tel (704) 333-0325 Founded/Ownrshp 1978
Sales 227.8MME EMP 85
SIC 0781

D-U-N-S 17-707-0794
▲ **LANDEC CORP**
3603 Haven Ave, Menlo Park, CA 94025-1010
Tel (650) 306-1650 Founded/Ownrshp 1986
Sales 539.2MM EMP 550E
Accts Ernst & Young Llp San Francis
Tkr Sym LNDC Exch NGS
SIC 2033 5148 5999 Fruits: packaged in cans, jars, etc.; Vegetables: packaged in cans, jars, etc.; Fresh fruits & vegetables; Medical apparatus & supplies; Fruits: packaged in cans, jars, etc.; Vegetables: packaged in cans, jars, etc.; Fresh fruits & vegetables; Medical apparatus & supplies
Ch Bd: Gary T Steele
*COO: Molly A Hemmeter
CFO: Gregory S Skinner
VP: Steven P Bitler
VP: Larry Greene
VP: Larry D Hiebert
VP: Ronald L Midyett
Mng Dir: Rose Albar
IT Man: Nicholas Tompkins
Opers Mgr: Richard Schneider
Board of Directors: Albert D Bolles, Frederick Frank, Steven Goldby, Tonia Pankopf, Catherine A Sohn, Robert Tobin, Nicholas Tompkins

D-U-N-S 03-517-6916
LANDELL-THELEN INC
323 E Highway 30, Shelton, NE 68876-1627
Tel (308) 647-9100 *Founded/Ownrshp* 1961
Sales 32.8MM *EMP* 20
SIC 5999 7699 Farm equipment & supplies; Farm machinery repair; Farm equipment & supplies; Farm machinery repair
Pr: Lee Landell
**Sec:* Patrick Thelen

D-U-N-S 07-370-8208
LANDER UNIVERSITY
320 Stanley Ave, Greenwood, SC 29649-2099
Tel (864) 388-8300 *Founded/Ownrshp* 1872
Sales 34.7MM *EMP* 386
Accts Elliott Davis Llc Greenville
SIC 8221 University; University
Pr: Daniel W Ball
Pr: Sadie Erwin
Ofcr: Jeff Boyd
Ofcr: Eddie Briggs
Ofcr: James Burke
Ofcr: Casey Goff
Ofcr: Rachel Griggs
Ofcr: Laura Riddle
VP: Shelby Dominick
Assoc Dir: Chandler Darling
Ex Dir: Cecily Ferguson

LANDER VLY MED CTR HOSPITALIST
See SAGEWEST HEALTH CARE

D-U-N-S 94-586-1466
LANDERS AUTO GROUP INC
LANDERS CHEVROLET
21099 Interstate 30 S, Benton, AR 72022-6239
Tel (501) 315-2500 *Founded/Ownrshp* 2001
Sales 24.0MM^E *EMP* 70
SIC 5511 5521 5531 Automobiles, new & used; Used car dealers; Automotive parts; Automobiles, new & used; Used car dealers; Automotive parts
Pr: Steve Landers
**Pr:* Dwight Everett
Sls Mgr: Pat Campbell
Sls Mgr: Matt Trumbo
Sales Asso: Vince Hunter
Sales Asso: Jordan Jackson

D-U-N-S 01-030-8195 IMP
■ **LANDERS AUTO SALES LLC**
LANDERS CHRYSLER JEEP DODGE
(*Suby of* PENSKE AUTOMOTIVE GROUP INC) ★
7800 Alcoa Rd, Bryant, AR 72019-8535
Tel (501) 316-4400 *Founded/Ownrshp* 2004
Sales 46.3MM^E *EMP* 100
SIC 5511 Automobiles, new & used; Pickups, new & used; Automobiles, new & used; Pickups, new & used
Pr: Dwight Everett
CFO: Ben Brook
Genl Mgr: Kevin Wilson
Off Mgr: Donna Ramsey

LANDERS CHEVROLET
See LANDERS AUTO GROUP INC

LANDERS CHRYSLER JEEP DODGE
See LANDERS AUTO SALES LLC

LANDERS DODGE
See SHREVEPORT DODGE LLC

D-U-N-S 36-268-7816
■ **LANDERS FORD INC**
(*Suby of* PENSKE AUTOMOTIVE GROUP INC) ★
2082 W Poplar Ave, Collierville, TN 38017-0606
Tel (662) 349-5557 *Founded/Ownrshp* 1999
Sales 71.8MM^E *EMP* 195
SIC 5511 Automobiles, new & used; Automobiles, new & used
**Genl Mgr:* Don Kitchens
Sales Asso: Charlie James

LANDERS MCLARTY CHEVROLET
See R M L HUNTSVILLE CHEVROLET LLC

D-U-N-S 12-090-8199
LANDERS MCLARTY NISSAN
REGAL AUTO PLAZA
6520 University Dr Nw, Huntsville, AL 35806-1718
Tel (256) 837-5752 *Founded/Ownrshp* 1984
Sales 32.7MM^E *EMP* 72
SIC 5511 7532 Automobiles, new & used; Body shop, automotive; Automobiles, new & used; Body shop, automotive
Pt: David Richardson
**Pt:* John H Shields II
Dir IT: Brad Tipton
Opers Mgr: Tim Dyer
Sls Mgr: Robert Callis
Sls Mgr: Abraham Demsas

D-U-N-S 62-036-8675
LANDERS MCLARTY OLATHE KS LLC
OLATHE DODGE CHRYSLER JEEP
15500 W 117th St, Olathe, KS 66062-1048
Tel (913) 780-3700 *Founded/Ownrshp* 2005
Sales 44.8MM^E *EMP* 110
SIC 5511 Automobiles, new & used; Automobiles, new & used
Genl Mgr: Jeff Brooks
Sales Asso: Karl Petersen

D-U-N-S 96-285-5339
LANDES FOODS LLC
7777 Hines Pl, Dallas, TX 75235-3312
Tel (972) 388-8000 *Founded/Ownrshp* 2010
Sales 58.3MM^E *EMP* 200
SIC 2099 Tortillas, fresh or refrigerated; Tortillas, fresh or refrigerated
Pr: Matt Landes
CEO: Irwin Gordon
VP: Thomas Rowell
VP: Tommy Rowland
QA Dir: Nohely Becerra
IT Man: Mayra Delgado
Ql Cn Mgr: Pauline Garcia
Manager: Rod Joffre

D-U-N-S 11-973-2696
LANDESK SOFTWARE INC
SHAVLIK
698 W 10000 S Ste 500, South Jordan, UT 84095-4054
Tel (801) 208-1500 *Founded/Ownrshp* 2002
Sales 286.4MM^E *EMP* 810^E
SIC 7371 Computer software development & applications; Computer software development & applications
Pr: Stephen M Daly
Pt: John White
**CFO:* Mark McBride
CFO: Robert Schriesheim
**Chf Mktg O:* Steve Morton
Ex VP: Josh Baxter
Ex VP: Tom Davis
VP: Michael W Hall
**VP:* Matthew Smith
Exec: Jared Barneck
Dir Sec: Linda Gilliam

D-U-N-S 11-962-1808
LANDFORCE EXPRESS CORP
17201 N D St, Victorville, CA 92394-1401
Tel (760) 843-7839 *Founded/Ownrshp* 2000
Sales 30.6MM^E *EMP* 120
SIC 4213 Trucking, except local
CEO: Rajinder Bhangu
Trfc Dir: Rick Thieme

LANDHOPE FARMS
See LANDHOPE REALTY CO

D-U-N-S 04-858-8461 IMP
LANDHOPE REALTY CO
LANDHOPE FARMS
101 E Street Rd, Kennett Square, PA 19348-1701
Tel (610) 444-3141 *Founded/Ownrshp* 1959
Sales 23.0MM^E *EMP* 180
SIC 5411 Convenience stores, chain; Convenience stores, chain
Pr: W B Dixon Stroud Jr
**VP:* W B Dixon Stroud Sr

D-U-N-S 60-343-1842
LANDINGS CLUB INC
71 Green Island Rd, Savannah, GA 31411-1202
Tel (912) 598-8050 *Founded/Ownrshp* 1991
Sales 27.6MM *EMP* 350^E
Accts Condon O Meara Mcginty & Donne
SIC 8741 Membership sports & recreation clubs; Golf club, membership; Tennis club, membership; Country club, membership; Health club; Management services
CEO: Steven Freund
**Pr:* Bruce Fischer
**CFO:* Jesse Ruben
**Treas:* Mdonald Roehm
Genl Mgr: Alan Gamble
Snr Mgr: Nicole Weller

LANDIS COMPANY
See LANDIS CONSTRUCTION CO LLC

D-U-N-S 86-858-9763 IMP
LANDIS CONSTRUCTION CO LLC
LANDIS COMPANY
8300 Earhart Blvd Ste 300, New Orleans, LA 70118-4430
Tel (504) 833-6070 *Founded/Ownrshp* 1999
Sales 59.1MM *EMP* 73
SIC 1542 Specialized public building contractors; Specialized public building contractors
CEO: James C Landis
V Ch: James Lewis
**Ex VP:* James M Lewis
**Sr VP:* George W Voss
**VP:* Christian Generes
**VP:* Anne Teague Landis
Genl Mgr: James Christovich
Snr Mgr: Maro Hihar

D-U-N-S 86-699-2910
LANDIS CONSULTING LLC
8300 Earhart Blvd, New Orleans, LA 70118-4428
Tel (504) 833-6070 *Founded/Ownrshp* 1999
Sales 60.2MM *EMP* 80
SIC 1542 Commercial & office building, new construction; Commercial & office building, new construction

LANDIS GYR
See LANDIS+GYR TECHNOLOGIES INC

D-U-N-S 07-533-2726
LANDIS HOMES RETIREMENT COMMUNITY (PA)
1001 E Oregon Rd, Lititz, PA 17543-9205
Tel (717) 569-3271 *Founded/Ownrshp* 1964
Sales 32.5MM *EMP* 413
Accts Parentebeard Llc Philadelphia
SIC 8361 8052 8051 8322 Rest home, with health care incidental; Intermediate care facilities; Skilled nursing care facilities; Adult day care center; Rest home, with health care incidental; Intermediate care facilities; Skilled nursing care facilities; Adult day care center
Pr: Larry Zook
**Ch Bd:* John EBY
**Treas:* Jonathan Hollinger
**V Ch Bd:* Glen Moffett
VP: Allen Heinly
Comm Dir: Larry Guengerich
Nurse Mgr: Stephanie Hoffman
CIO: Stu Landis
IT Man: Ryan Martin
Mktg Dir: Deborah Laws-Landis
Nrsg Dir: Danine Bitting

D-U-N-S 01-462-0017
LANDIS SUPERMARKET INC
2685 County Line Rd, Telford, PA 18969-1075
Tel (215) 723-1157 *Founded/Ownrshp* 1939
Sales 90.1MM^E *EMP* 600
SIC 5411 5812

D-U-N-S 00-510-5408
LANDIS+GYR INC (GA)
LANDISGYR
2800 Duncan Rd, Lafayette, IN 47904-5012
Tel (765) 742-1001 *Founded/Ownrshp* 2002, 2006
Sales 539.9MM^E *EMP* 5,139
SIC 3825 Meters: electric, pocket, portable, panelboard, etc.; Measuring instruments & meters, electric; Demand meters, electric; Meters: electric, pocket, portable, panelboard, etc.; Measuring instruments & meters, electric; Demand meters, electric
CEO: Richard Mora
**CEO:* Andreas Umbach
**CFO:* Jonathan Elmer
**VP:* Donald Shipley
Opers Mgr: Paul Snowden
Ql Cn Mgr: Thierry Kieffer
Sls&Mrk Ex: Hassan Ali
Sls&Mrk Ex: Dave Schnelle

D-U-N-S 16-456-7484
LANDIS+GYR TECHNOLOGIES INC
LANDIS GYR
(*Suby of* LANDIS & GYR HOLDINGS PTY LTD)
30000 Mill Creek Ave # 100, Alpharetta, GA 30022-1555
Tel (678) 258-1500 *Founded/Ownrshp* 2007
Sales 146.4MM^E *EMP* 375
Accts Deloitte & Touche Llp
SIC 7389 Meter readers, remote; Meter readers, remote
CEO: Richard Mora
**CEO:* Andreas Umbach
**COO:* Jerry Figurilli
**CFO:* John Lutz
**Ex VP:* Jonathan Elmer
Ex VP: Chris Hickman
**VP:* Randolph Houchins

D-U-N-S 13-924-6375
LANDIS+GYR TECHNOLOGIES LLC
HUNT TECHNOLOGIES
(*Suby of* TOSHIBA CORPORATION)
6436 County Road 11, Pequot Lakes, MN 56472-3107
Tel (218) 562-4877 *Founded/Ownrshp* 2006
Sales 44.5MM^E *EMP* 200
Accts Brady Martz
SIC 3825 8711 Meters: electric, pocket, portable, panelboard, etc.; Test equipment for electronic & electrical circuits; Designing: ship, boat, machine & product; Meters: electric, pocket, portable, panelboard, etc.; Test equipment for electronic & electrical circuits; Designing: ship, boat, machine & product
Pr: Andreas Umbach
CFO: Matt Goddman
**VP:* Jonathan Elmer
VP Admn: Matthew Goodman
MIS Dir: James Barutt
Ql Cn Mgr: Robert Nies

D-U-N-S 16-456-7815
LANDIS+GYR TECHNOLOGY INC
LANDISGYR
(*Suby of* LANDIS GYR) ★
30000 Mill Creek Ave # 100, Alpharetta, GA 30022-1555
Tel (678) 258-1295 *Founded/Ownrshp* 2004
Sales 28.3MM^E *EMP* 70^E
SIC 3613 3824 Metering panels, electric; Mechanical measuring meters; Water meters
CEO: Andreas Umbach
Pt: Dave Elve
**Ex VP:* Roger Amhof
**Ex VP:* Jonathan Elmer
**Ex VP:* Richard Mora
Sr VP: Tracy Moore
VP: H Ward Camp
VP: Gary High
VP: Clark Pierce
Mktg Dir: J Phua

LANDISGYR
See LANDIS+GYR INC

LANDISGYR
See LANDIS+GYR TECHNOLOGY INC

D-U-N-S 02-019-6890
LANDLOVERS LLC
LOANS 4 HOMES
1833 Executive Dr Ste 105, Oconomowoc, WI 53066-4841
Tel (262) 560-9786 *Founded/Ownrshp* 2001
Sales NA *EMP* 20
SIC 6163 Mortgage brokers arranging for loans, using money of others; Mortgage brokers arranging for loans, using money of others

D-U-N-S 01-411-5248
LANDMARK APARTMENT TRUST INC
4901 Dickens Rd Ste 101, Richmond, VA 23230-1952
Tel (804) 237-1335 *Founded/Ownrshp* 2005
Sales 262.2MM *EMP* 768^E
SIC 6798 6513 Real estate investment trusts; Apartment building operators; Real estate investment trusts; Apartment building operators
Pr: Stanley J Olander Jr
CFO: Greg E Brooks
Ofcr: Gustav G Remppies
Ex VP: Debra Claytor
Sr VP: Laura Wood
Snr Mgr: Mechelle Lafon

D-U-N-S 79-915-0888
LANDMARK APARTMENT TRUST OF AMERICA HOLDINGS LP
(*Suby of* LANDMARK APARTMENT TRUST INC) ★
3505 E Frontage Rd # 150, Tampa, FL 33607-1749
Tel (813) 281-2907 *Founded/Ownrshp* 2005
Sales 21.7MM^E *EMP* 748^E
SIC 6798 Real estate investment trusts

LANDMARK AUDIO BOOKS
See RECORDED BOOKS LLC

LANDMARK AVIATION
See PIEDMONT HAWTHORNE AVIATION LLC

LANDMARK AVIATION
See LANDMARK FBO LLC

D-U-N-S 06-607-4217
▲ **LANDMARK BANCORP INC**
701 Poyntz Ave, Manhattan, KS 66502-6052
Tel (785) 565-2000 *Founded/Ownrshp* 2001
Sales NA *EMP* 292^E
Tkr Sym LARK *Exch* NGM
SIC 6021 National commercial banks; National commercial banks
Pr: Michael E Scheopner
**Ch Bd:* Patrick L Alexander
CFO: Mark A Herpich
CFO: Mark Herpich
Ofcr: Cheryl Chaffin
VP: Linda Burris
Exec: Bradly Chindamo
IT Man: Jeremy Hinkle
Netwrk Eng: Scott Woborny

LANDMARK BANK COMPANY NA
See LANDMARK BANK NA

D-U-N-S 02-073-4299
LANDMARK BANK NA
LANDMARK BANK COMPANY NA
(*Suby of* LANDRUM CO INC) ★
128 Plaza, Madill, OK 73446-2249
Tel (580) 795-5503 *Founded/Ownrshp* 1942, 1978
Sales NA *EMP* 200
SIC 6021 6163 National commercial banks; Loan brokers; National commercial banks; Loan brokers
Pr: Basil Bigbe
Pr: Jay Alexander
VP: Roberta Morgan
VP: Verna Shivers
VP Mktg: Sam Huffman

D-U-N-S 87-933-0330
LANDMARK BANK NATIONAL ASSOCIATION
(*Suby of* LANDRUM CO INC) ★
801 E Broadway, Columbia, MO 65201-4855
Tel (573) 449-3911 *Founded/Ownrshp* 2009
Sales NA *EMP* 355
SIC 6021 National commercial banks; National commercial banks
Pr: Jeffrey Maclellan
Pr: Brenda Nicolay
Treas: Kris Bloom
Chf Inves: Nicholas Thurwanger
Sr VP: Ron Bennett
Sr VP: Brenda Emerson
Sr VP: Susan Gowin
Sr VP: Sam Henry
Sr VP: Cheryl Jarvis
Sr VP: Larry R Niedergerke
Sr VP: Scott Wilson
VP: Cathy Eubank
VP: Laura Glass
VP: Amy Hammon
VP: Jo Mooney
VP: David Mordy
VP: Aaron Quarles
VP: Chris Steuber

D-U-N-S 07-784-8117
LANDMARK BUILDERS OF TRIAD INC
3520 Triad Ct, Winston Salem, NC 27107-4571
Tel (336) 373-1900 *Founded/Ownrshp* 2012
Sales 52.3MM^E *EMP* 85
SIC 1542 1541 Commercial & office building, new construction; Industrial buildings, new construction; Commercial & office building, new construction; Industrial buildings, new construction
CEO: H A Garrett
**Pr:* Rusty Garrett
**CFO:* Barton L Tiffany
**Ex VP:* Samuel Stephens
VP: Randy Elliott
Dir Bus: John Martin
Genl Mgr: Rodney Cheek
Snr PM: Tom Gibbs
Snr Mgr: Russell Powell

D-U-N-S 80-780-1100
LANDMARK CHRYSLER DODGE JEEP OF MONROE LLC
4145 Atlanta Hwy, Athens, GA 30606-0809
Tel (706) 549-7555 *Founded/Ownrshp* 2002
Sales 21.1MM^E *EMP* 70
SIC 5511 7539 Automobiles, new & used; Automotive repair shops; Automobiles, new & used; Automotive repair shops
Genl Mgr: Wes Smithey

D-U-N-S 10-219-9817
LANDMARK CHRYSLER-JEEP INC
2331 Prairie Crossing Dr, Springfield, IL 62711-9495
Tel (217) 862-5300 *Founded/Ownrshp* 1980
Sales 28.4MM^E *EMP* 70
SIC 5511 Automobiles, new & used; Automobiles, new & used
Pr: William T Grant Jr
COO: Sean Grant
**VP:* William Hopper
**Prin:* Lyle Snow
Genl Mgr: Kurt Lowrey
Genl Mgr: Bill Lynch
Genl Mgr: Nick Short
Genl Mgr: Jeff Tesio
Sales Exec: Tom Leepper
Mktg Dir: Jeff Hutchison
Sls Mgr: Mark Bott

D-U-N-S 12-278-4374
LANDMARK COLLEGE INC
19 River Rd S, Putney, VT 05346-8517
Tel (802) 387-4767 *Founded/Ownrshp* 1986
Sales 37.4MM *EMP* 220
Accts O Brien Shortle Reynolds & Sab
SIC 8221 College, except junior; College, except junior
Pr: Dr Peter Eden
Treas: Roy Vogt
VP: Manju Banerjee
VP: Maclean Gander

Off Mgr: Sarah Downing
Psych: Clark Ljohnson

LANDMARK COLLISION CENTER
See TUSCALOOSA HYUNDAI INC

D-U-N-S 05-812-9615
LANDMARK COMMUNITY BANK
5880 Ridge Bnd, Collierville, TN 38017
Tel (901) 850-0555 *Founded/Ownrshp* 1999
Sales NA *EMP* 14ᴱ
SIC 6029 Commercial banks; Commercial banks
Pr: Mike Russell
**Pr:* James Jake Farrell
**CFO:* Charles Buddy Dickey
Sr VP: David May

D-U-N-S 06-833-8367 IMP
LANDMARK COMMUNITY NEWSPAPERS LLC
(*Suby of* LANDMARK MEDIA ENTERPRISES LLC) ★
601 Taylorsville Rd, Shelbyville, KY 40065-9125
Tel (502) 633-4334 *Founded/Ownrshp* 1973
Sales 81.2MMᴱ *EMP* 1,280
SIC 2711 2759 Commercial printing & newspaper publishing combined; Commercial printing; Commercial printing & newspaper publishing combined; Commercial printing
Pr: Michael Abernathy
VP: Dan Sykes
Dir IT: James Bryant
Dir IT: Danny Correll
Opers Mgr: Jay Bondurant
Advt Dir: Tony Martinette

D-U-N-S 06-833-8359
LANDMARK COMMUNITY NEWSPAPERS OF KENTUCKY LLC (NM)
(*Suby of* LANDMARK COMMUNITY NEWSPAPERS LLC) ★
601 Taylorsville Rd, Shelbyville, KY 40065-9125
Tel (502) 633-4334 *Founded/Ownrshp* 1968, 2015
Sales 47.8MMᴱ *EMP* 1,100
SIC 2711 2752 Commercial printing & newspaper publishing combined; Commercial printing, lithographic; Commercial printing & newspaper publishing combined; Commercial printing, lithographic
Pr: Michael Abernathy
Board of Directors: John O Wynne

D-U-N-S 11-916-8722
LANDMARK CONSTRUCTION CO INC
3255 Industry Dr, North Charleston, SC 29418-8453
Tel (843) 552-6186 *Founded/Ownrshp* 1967
Sales 101.1MMᴱ *EMP* 150
SIC 1542 1541 1623 1771 1794 Commercial & office building, new construction; Industrial buildings, new construction; Water, sewer & utility lines; Concrete work; Excavation work; Excavation & grading, building construction; Commercial & office building, new construction; Industrial buildings, new construction; Water, sewer & utility lines; Concrete work; Excavation work; Excavation & grading, building construction
Ch Bd: Ann B Mixson
**Pr:* Cynthia Mixson
Treas: Cynthia M Eagerton
**VP:* Fredrick B Mixson
Dir Bus: Sam Hayes
Telecom Ex: Sandra Davies
CTO: Jeff Bailey
Sfty Mgr: Preston Cain

D-U-N-S 04-078-9380
LANDMARK CREDIT UNION
5445 S Westridge Dr, New Berlin, WI 53151-7948
Tel (262) 796-4500 *Founded/Ownrshp* 1933
Sales NA *EMP* 435
SIC 6062 State credit unions, not federally chartered; State credit unions, not federally chartered
CEO: Jay Magulski
**Ch Bd:* Michael Maxwell
**Pr:* Ron Kase
Ofcr: Patrick Hansen
Sr VP: Eric Kase
Sr VP: Sharon Mather
Sr VP: David Powers
VP: Bob Bruemmer
VP: Donald Cohen
VP: Betty Feierstein
VP: Kyle Mather
VP: Charles Schuyler

D-U-N-S 60-613-2343
LANDMARK DISTRIBUTION LLC
LANDMARK GLOBAL
34 E Sola St, Santa Barbara, CA 93101-2506
Tel (805) 965-3058 *Founded/Ownrshp* 2013
Sales 25.0MMᴱ *EMP* 75
SIC 4789 4731 Cargo loading & unloading services; Foreign freight forwarding
Pr: Dave Mays
Sr VP: John Jensen
VP: Peter Browne
VP: Todd Denholm
VP: Julie-Anne Fiore
VP: Jeff Oswalt
Dir Bus: Mike Benson
Mktg Mgr: Stijn Sommerijns

D-U-N-S 03-503-5726
LANDMARK DIVIDEND LLC
2141 Rosecrans Ave # 2050, El Segundo, CA 90245-4747
Tel (800) 843-2024 *Founded/Ownrshp* 2010
Sales 42.4MMᴱ *EMP* 75ᴱ
SIC 6531 Real estate agent, commercial
CEO: Jeff Knyal
CFO: George Doyle
VP: Sean Burke
VP: Angela Debibi
VP: John Goodhew
VP: George Matthews
VP: Rob Phillips
VP: Oliver Piclo
VP: Don Reitz
VP: Matthew Scott
VP: Brent Stallo
VP: Maranda Walker-Dowell

D-U-N-S 62-681-5518
LANDMARK EDUCATION CORP
353 Sacramento St Ste 200, San Francisco, CA 94111-3639
Tel (415) 981-8850 *Founded/Ownrshp* 1991
Sales NA *EMP* 450
SIC 8299 Educational service, nondegree granting: continuing educ.

D-U-N-S 60-223-8891 EXP
LANDMARK EQUIPMENT INC
1351 S Loop 12, Irving, TX 75060-6319
Tel (972) 579-9999 *Founded/Ownrshp* 1989
Sales 25.2MMᴱ *EMP* 52
SIC 5083 5261 5082 7359 Farm & garden machinery; Lawn & garden equipment; Contractors' materials; Lawn & garden equipment rental
CEO: Gary Lyle
**Pr:* Mike Lyle
CFO: Kathy Ford
**VP:* Todd Vollmering
Manager: Jeff Burns

D-U-N-S 82-935-7727
LANDMARK FBO LLC
LANDMARK AVIATION
1500 Citywest Blvd # 600, Houston, TX 77042-2280
Tel (713) 895-9243 *Founded/Ownrshp* 2007
Sales 620.9MMᴱ *EMP* 1,492ᴱ
SIC 4581 Airports, flying fields & services; Airports, flying fields & services
Pr: Daniel T Bucaro
Pr: Charlie Ferraro
Pr: Bryan Greer
**CFO:* David E Barnes Jr
**Treas:* Louie Hamilton
Treas: Marlene Henry
VP: Tyson Goetz
VP: Skip Madsen
Exec: Kenneth Barton
Exec: Erwin Bernardino
Genl Mgr: Eddie Allison

D-U-N-S 16-140-0031
LANDMARK FINANCIAL GROUP INC
600 S State St Ste 100, Belvidere, IL 61008-4329
Tel (815) 544-2400 *Founded/Ownrshp* 1985
Sales NA *EMP* 289
SIC 6141 Personal credit institutions; Personal credit institutions
CFO: R Robert Funderberg
**CFO:* John Crone
**Treas:* Park Johnston
Sr VP: Palmer Klaas

D-U-N-S 06-801-0586
LANDMARK FOOD CORP
LANDMARK FOODS
865 Waverly Ave, Holtsville, NY 11742-1109
Tel (631) 654-4500 *Founded/Ownrshp* 1973
Sales 87.3MMᴱ *EMP* 90
Accts Laurence Rothblatt & Company
SIC 5142 5141 5148 5147 Packaged frozen goods; Groceries, general line; Fruits, fresh; Meats & meat products; Packaged frozen goods; Groceries, general line; Fruits, fresh; Meats & meat products
Ch Bd: Gordon Kerner
**Sec:* Victor Cardinali Jr
Dir IT: Kris Sagginario

LANDMARK FOODS
See LANDMARK FOOD CORP

D-U-N-S 02-585-8069
LANDMARK FORD INC
FORD-RENT-A-CAR SYSTEM
2401 Prairie Crossing Dr, Springfield, IL 62711-9485
Tel (217) 862-5200 *Founded/Ownrshp* 1974
Sales 71.7MMᴱ *EMP* 125
SIC 5511 7538 7515 5531 5521 Automobiles, new & used; General automotive repair shops; Passenger car leasing; Automotive & home supply stores; Used car dealers; Automobiles, new & used; General automotive repair shops; Passenger car leasing; Automotive & home supply stores; Used car dealers
Pr: William T Grant Jr
**CFO:* David W Seadler
CFO: David Seadler
**Sr VP:* Sean B Grant
**VP:* William B Hopper
CIO: Nadim Khan
IT Man: Don Hitchings
Sls Mgr: Shawn Crenshaw
Sls Mgr: William Grant III
Sls Mgr: Ryan Maisenbacher

D-U-N-S 09-699-4744
LANDMARK FORD INC
LANDMARK FORD PARTS SALES
12000 Sw 66th Ave, Tigard, OR 97223-8599
Tel (503) 639-1131 *Founded/Ownrshp* 1979
Sales 71.8MMᴱ *EMP* 200
SIC 5511 Automobiles, new & used; Automobiles, new & used
Pr: James L Corliss
Genl Mgr: Nadim Khan
Manager: Douglas Osborn
Sls Mgr: Greg Mills
Sales Asso: Jeff Kerr
Snr Mgr: Larry Baker

LANDMARK FORD PARTS SALES
See LANDMARK FORD INC

LANDMARK GLOBAL
See LANDMARK DISTRIBUTION LLC

D-U-N-S 06-722-1796
■ **LANDMARK GRAPHICS CORP**
(*Suby of* HALLIBURTON DELAWARE INC) ★
2107 Citywest Blvd Bldg 2, Houston, TX 77042-2827
Tel (713) 839-2000 *Founded/Ownrshp* 1996
Sales 113.7MMᴱ *EMP* 1,946
SIC 7371 7373 Software programming applications; Computer-aided design (CAD) systems service; Software programming applications; Computer-aided design (CAD) systems service
VP: Jonathan Lewis
Mng Pt: Martha Sandia
**Pr:* Peter Bernard
**Ex VP:* Al Escher
Ex VP: Beverly Stafford
**VP:* Jeff Donnellan
**VP:* Christian Garcia
**VP:* Glenn Goodwin
VP: Paul Koeller
VP: Maggie Montaigne
**VP:* William Trebinski
Exec: Brian Moloney
Board of Directors: David Lesar

D-U-N-S 93-788-1324
LANDMARK HEALTHCARE FACILITIES LLC
839 N Jefferson St # 600, Milwaukee, WI 53202-3740
Tel (414) 277-0500 *Founded/Ownrshp* 1995
Sales 74.8MM *EMP* 42
Accts Baker Tilly Virchow Krause Ll
SIC 1542 Hospital construction; Hospital construction
CEO: Joseph W Checota
VP: Stuart Armstrong
Snr Mgr: William Komlo

D-U-N-S 15-514-6173
LANDMARK HEALTHCARE INC
3455 Ne Loop 820, Fort Worth, TX 76137-2414
Tel (817) 338-0007 *Founded/Ownrshp* 1999
Sales 20.4MMᴱ *EMP* 65ᴱ
SIC 5047 Medical & hospital equipment
Pr: Ronald N Majerus
**CFO:* Michael Everage
**Sr VP:* Marvin Cobern
**VP:* David M Everage
Dir Rx: John Shafer
Brnch Mgr: Desiree Jarvis
Software D: Seth Oneal
Sls Mgr: Mark Vandyke

D-U-N-S 78-564-1395
LANDMARK HEALTHCARE PROPERTIES FUND LLC
839 N Jefferson St # 600, Milwaukee, WI 53202-3761
Tel (414) 277-0500 *Founded/Ownrshp* 2003
Sales 50.8MM *EMP* 7
Accts Virchow Krause And Company
SIC 6512 Commercial & industrial building operation; Commercial & industrial building operation
CFO: Beth L Schumacher
VP: Thomas P Beckes

D-U-N-S 07-853-4466
LANDMARK HOLDINGS OF MISSOURI LLC
240 S Mount Auburn Rd, Cape Girardeau, MO 63703-4918
Tel (573) 331-8026 *Founded/Ownrshp* 2004
Sales 77.7MMᴱ *EMP* 663ᴱ
SIC 8062 General medical & surgical hospitals; General medical & surgical hospitals
CEO: Craig Boudreaux
Pr: William K Kapp III
CFO: Brent Upchurch

D-U-N-S 36-398-8630
LANDMARK HOSPITAL
(*Suby of* LANDMARK HOLDINGS OF MISSOURI LLC) ★
3255 Independence St, Cape Girardeau, MO 63701-4914
Tel (417) 627-1300 *Founded/Ownrshp* 2004
Sales 46.4MM *EMP* 638
SIC 8062 General medical & surgical hospitals; General medical & surgical hospitals
COO: Lori Johnson
CFO: Brent Upchurch
Ofcr: Deborah Sabella
Dir Rx: Bill Paylor
CIO: Renee Hesselrode
Snr Mgr: Adam Clapper
Snr Mgr: Vivian Goff

LANDMARK IDEALEASE
See LANDMARK INTERNATIONAL TRUCKS INC

D-U-N-S 10-582-7166
LANDMARK INDUSTRIES HOLDINGS LTD
TIMEWISE FOOD STORES
11111 S Wilcrest Dr, Houston, TX 77099-4310
Tel (713) 789-0310 *Founded/Ownrshp* 1983
Sales 132.7MMᴱ *EMP* 900
SIC 5411 5541 Convenience stores, independent; Filling stations, gasoline; Convenience stores, independent; Filling stations, gasoline
Pt: Marshall Dujka
**Pt:* J Kent Brotherton
**Pt:* Robert E Duff
**Pt:* Stephen C Dujka
Dist Mgr: Walter Graham
Snr Sftwr: Christopher Fahey
Dir IT: Manzoor Ahmed
IT Man: Nathan Wells
Mktg Mgr: Randy Krause
Sls Mgr: Stephen McQuarrie
Sls Mgr: Swanta Pratt

D-U-N-S 09-638-1892
LANDMARK INTERNATIONAL TRUCKS INC
LANDMARK IDEALEASE
4550 Rutledge Pike, Knoxville, TN 37914-3221
Tel (865) 637-4881 *Founded/Ownrshp* 2003
Sales 44.6MMᴱ *EMP* 102
SIC 5012 Trucks, commercial; Trucks, commercial
Pr: Jim Jablonski
**Sec:* Gregory D Sharpe
**Ex VP:* Diane Jablonski
**VP:* Andrew Jablonski
Sls Mgr: Gary Dennis

D-U-N-S 13-198-2980
LANDMARK LENDING GROUP INC
1327 Se 2nd Ave, Fort Lauderdale, FL 33316-1809
Tel (954) 763-4931 *Founded/Ownrshp* 2000
Sales NA *EMP* 3
SIC 6163 Mortgage brokers arranging for loans, using money of others; Mortgage brokers arranging for loans, using money of others
Pr: Charles Restrepo
**VP:* Claudia Restrepo
Sales Exec: Dedrick Brown
Sales Exec: Maria Cipagauta

D-U-N-S 00-717-7660 IMP
LANDMARK MANUFACTURING CORP (MO)
28100 Quick Ave, Gallatin, MO 64640-8170
Tel (660) 663-2185 *Founded/Ownrshp* 1953
Sales 28.0MM *EMP* 200
SIC 3444 3469 3544 Sheet metalwork; Metal stampings; Special dies, tools, jigs & fixtures
CEO: David Critten
**CFO:* Kevin McCullough
**Treas:* Lola Critten
Ofcr: Kent Brinkley
**VP:* Kenneth Critten
CIO: Jeremy Dowell
IT Man: Greg Bunner
Plnt Mgr: Greg Houghton
Prd Mgr: Steve Perry
Sls Mgr: James Critten

D-U-N-S 82-853-8988
LANDMARK MEDIA ENTERPRISES LLC
150 Granby St, Norfolk, VA 23510-1604
Tel (757) 351-7000 *Founded/Ownrshp* 2008
Sales 800.0MM *EMP* 4,600
SIC 2711 5045 2721 6531 Newspapers, publishing & printing; Television broadcasting stations; Computer software; Newspapers, publishing & printing; Computer software; Periodicals; Real estate listing services
Ch Bd: Frank Batten Jr
**Pr:* Jack J Ross
**CFO:* Teresa F Blevins
**Treas:* Colleen R Pittman
**Ex VP:* Guy R Friddell III

D-U-N-S 07-572-6141
LANDMARK MEDICAL CENTER
115 Cass Ave, Woonsocket, RI 02895-4731
Tel (401) 769-4100 *Founded/Ownrshp* 1988
Sales 117.5MM *EMP* 1,200
SIC 8062 General medical & surgical hospitals

D-U-N-S 08-245-9165
■ **LANDMARK NATIONAL BANK**
(*Suby of* LANDMARK BANCORP INC) ★
Central & Spruce Sts, Dodge City, KS 67801
Tel (620) 225-1745 *Founded/Ownrshp* 2001
Sales NA *EMP* 81ᴱ
SIC 6035 Federal savings & loan associations; Federal savings & loan associations
Pr: Patrick Alexander
**CFO:* Mark Herpich
Exec: M Oliphant
Mktg Mgr: Gary L Watkins

D-U-N-S 11-491-2793 IMP
LANDMARK PLASTIC CORP
1331 Kelly Ave, Akron, OH 44306-3773
Tel (330) 785-2200 *Founded/Ownrshp* 1984
Sales 51.6MMᴱ *EMP* 200
SIC 3089 Plastic containers, except foam; Plastic containers, except foam
CEO: Robert G Merzweiler
COO: Gerald D Stetham
CFO: Jeff Fostyk
Exec: Samantha Ponting
Exec: Jerry Stethem
Rgnl Mgr: Joe Donley
Sftwr Eng: Maija McClure
Prd Mgr: Paul Wallbrown
VP Sls: Steve Beall

D-U-N-S 15-868-2307
LANDMARK PROPERTIES INC
455 Epps Bridge Pkwy # 201, Athens, GA 30606-3347
Tel (706) 543-1910 *Founded/Ownrshp* 2003
Sales 20.8MMᴱ *EMP* 53ᴱ
SIC 6512 8742 6531 Nonresidential building operators; Real estate consultant; Real estate brokers & agents
CEO: J Wesley Rogers
**COO:* James B Whitley
COO: James Whitley
VP: Jason Doornbos
VP: Blair Sweeney

D-U-N-S 17-857-0917
LANDMARK PROTECTION INC
675 N 1st St Ste 620, San Jose, CA 95112-5145
Tel (408) 293-6300 *Founded/Ownrshp* 1997
Sales 10.0MM *EMP* 300
SIC 5136 5099 7381 Uniforms, men's & boys'; Safety equipment & supplies; Guard services; Security guard service; Uniforms, men's & boys'; Safety equipment & supplies; Guard services; Security guard service
Pr: Daniel Miranda

D-U-N-S 05-600-4385
LANDMARK SCHOOL INC
429 Hale St, Prides Crossing, MA 01965
Tel (978) 236-3202 *Founded/Ownrshp* 1964
Sales 29.4MM *EMP* 310
Accts K E Mcgillivray & Company Llc
SIC 8211 Specialty education; Specialty education
Ch Bd: Nicholas A Lopardo
**Pr:* Robert J Broudo
**Treas:* Martin Slark
Dir IT: Michael Brown

D-U-N-S 00-886-6840
LANDMARK SERVICES COOPERATIVE
CENEX HOME & FARM CENTER
207 W Cottage Grove Rd, Cottage Grove, WI 53527-9391
Tel (608) 819-3115 *Founded/Ownrshp* 1933
Sales 569.7MMᴱ *EMP* 400
SIC 5171 4221 5191 1711 Petroleum bulk stations; Grain elevator, storage only; Feed; Seeds: field, garden & flower; Fertilizer & fertilizer materials; Plumbing, heating, air-conditioning contractors; Petroleum bulk stations; Grain elevator, storage only; Feed; Seeds: field, garden & flower; Fertilizer & fertilizer materials; Plumbing, heating, air-conditioning contractors
CEO: Bob Carlson

*Pr: John Blaska
*COO: Mike Elder
*COO: Brad Gjermo
*CFO: Jason Brancel
*Sec: Joanne Reichling
*Ex VP: Doug Cropp
*Ex VP: Dave Haberman
*Sr VP: Mike Bandt
*VP: Dan Difonzo
*VP: Junior Manthe

LANDMARK THEATRES
See SILVER CINEMAS ACQUISITION CO

D-U-N-S 83-254-1267
LANDMARK WORLDWIDE LLC
353 Sacramento St Ste 200, San Francisco, CA 94111-3639
Tel (415) 981-8850 Founded/Ownrshp 2002
Sales 14.3MM^E EMP 410^E
SIC 8299 Educational service, nondegree granting: continuing educ.
VP: Gale Legassick
Mktg Mgr: Michelle Fadeley
Snr Mgr: Jerry Fishman

D-U-N-S 03-133-1051 IMP/EXP
LANDOLL CORP
1900 North St, Marysville, KS 66508-1271
Tel (785) 562-5381 Founded/Ownrshp 1963
Sales 98.7MM^E EMP 460
SIC 3728 3715 3523 3537 Aircraft parts & equipment; Deicing equipment, aircraft; Truck trailers; Plows, agricultural: disc, moldboard, chisel, listers, etc.; Trailers & wagons, farm; Forklift trucks; Aircraft parts & equipment; Deicing equipment, aircraft; Truck trailers; Plows, agricultural: disc, moldboard, chisel, listers, etc.; Trailers & wagons, farm; Forklift trucks
Pr: Don Landoll
COO: Jeff Keating
*Treas: Dan Caffrey
VP: Dan Caffery
Exec: Kerry Smith
QA Dir: Hank Brucker
IT Man: Lynn Ranaball
IT Man: Lynn Ronnebaum
IT Man: Shawn Schiender
Mfg Dir: Shawn Rose
Plnt Mgr: Richard Robinson

D-U-N-S 78-885-8066
LANDON IP INC
(Suby of CPA GLOBAL (ASIA) LIMITED)
1725 Jamieson Ave, Alexandria, VA 22314-5741
Tel (703) 486-1150 Founded/Ownrshp 2014
Sales 20.2MM^E EMP 110
SIC 7389 Patent brokers
CEO: David Hunt
*Pr: Brad Buehler
*CFO: Mary Malone
Sr VP: Ted Klekman
*VP: Julie Cook
VP: Matthew Rodgers
Sls Dir: Gary Yarco

D-U-N-S 07-265-4825
LANDON SCHOOL CORP
6101 Wilson Ln, Bethesda, MD 20817-3107
Tel (301) 320-3200 Founded/Ownrshp 1929
Sales 29.2MM EMP 175
Accts Mcgladrey Llp Gaithersburg M
SIC 8211 Private combined elementary & secondary school; Private combined elementary & secondary school
Prin: David Marmstrong
V Ch: Mary Shue
*CFO: Timothy Harrison
*Ch: H Sherman Joyce
*Treas: Carter Herbert
VP: Stephen Bou
VP: Frenchi Mack
Dir Soc: Addison Hunt
Mtls Mgr: Paul Miller

D-U-N-S 07-463-5079
LANDOR ASSOCIATES INTERNATIONAL LTD
(Suby of YOUNG & RUBICAM GROUP) ★
1001 Front St, San Francisco, CA 94111-1467
Tel (415) 365-1700 Founded/Ownrshp 2006
Sales 66.8MM^E EMP 700
SIC 7336 Commercial art & graphic design; Commercial art & graphic design
CEO: Lois Jacobs
V Ch: Pete Harleman
*Pr: Cheryl Giovannoni
CFO: James Bruce
*CFO: Ran Wadleigh
*Ch: Craig Branigan
Ofcr: Thomas Ordahl
VP: Susan Nelson
*Prin: Peter Law-Gisiko
IT Man: Eliisa M Hilla
Prd Mgr: Ed Sarge

D-U-N-S 15-449-7846
LANDOR INTERNATIONAL INC
2120 Staples Mill Rd # 300, Richmond, VA 23230-2917
Tel (804) 346-8200 Founded/Ownrshp 1985
Sales 96.4MM^E EMP 345
SIC 6552 8741 4724 Subdividers & developers; Management services; Travel agencies; Subdividers & developers; Management services; Travel agencies
CEO: John L Holt III
*Pr: Ronald T Holt
Pr: Diana Wright
COO: Virginia Eyler
VP: John Ruch
Dir IT: Jim Moncrieff

LANDROVER ALEXANDRIA
See GREAT EXPERIMENT L L C

LANDROVER NORTHPOINT
See HENNESSY CADILLAC INC

D-U-N-S 10-240-1015
LANDRUM CO INC
801 E Broadway, Columbia, MO 65201-4855
Tel (573) 449-3911 Founded/Ownrshp 1978
Sales NA EMP 919
SIC 6021 National trust companies with deposits, commercial; National trust companies with deposits, commercial
Ch: Marcus Landrum
*Pr: Jeffrey Maclellan
Pr: Jim Stock
*Sr VP: Basil Bigbie
*Sr VP: Larry Niedergerke
*Sr VP: Hal Pennington
*Sr VP: James Stock
Sr VP: Steve Tanzey
*Sr VP: Daniel Thompson
VP: Stuart Freeny
VP: Carol Karle
VP: Eva Moore
VP Bus Dev: Jay Thompson

D-U-N-S 03-561-9741
LANDRUM STAFFING SERVICES INC (FL)
6723 Plantation Rd, Pensacola, FL 32504-6357
Tel (850) 244-0026 Founded/Ownrshp 1973
Sales 29.5MM EMP 25
Accts Saltmarsh Cleaveland & Gund
SIC 7361 Ship crew agency; Ship crew agency
Pr: Britt H Landrum Jr
COO: Denise McLeod
Treas: Andy Remke
VP: Bill Cleary
VP: William A Cleary
VP: Denise T McLeod
VP: Michael A Perkins
Exec: Yvonne Nellums
Dir Bus: Sandra Smith
MIS Dir: Andy Cianciotto
Dir IT: Jason Heuer

LANDRY FAMILY CHARITABLE TRUST
See C KEVIN LANDRY CHARITABLE FOUNDATION

D-U-N-S 82-534-7987
LANDRYS CRAB SHACK INC
(Suby of LANDRYS INC) ★
9900 Westpark Dr Ste 300, Houston, TX 77063-5287
Tel (713) 953-1938 Founded/Ownrshp 2013
Sales 4.7MM^E EMP 349^E
SIC 5812 Eating places
Prin: Tilman J Fertitta

D-U-N-S 82-546-7629
LANDRYS GAMING INC
(Suby of LANDRYS INC) ★
1510 West Loop S, Houston, TX 77027-9505
Tel (713) 850-1010 Founded/Ownrshp 2005
Sales 215.5MM^E EMP 3,500^E
SIC 7011 Casino hotel; Casino hotel
Pr: Tilman J Fertitta
*Treas: Rick Liem
*Sec: Steven L Scheinthal

D-U-N-S 10-266-4935
LANDRYS INC
LANDRY'S SEAFOOD HOUSE
(Suby of FERTITTA GROUP INC) ★
1510 West Loop S, Houston, TX 77027-9505
Tel (713) 850-1010 Founded/Ownrshp 2010
Sales 2.0MM^E EMP 30,000
SIC 5812 Eating places; Seafood restaurants; Eating places; Seafood restaurants
CEO: Tilman J Fertitta
Pr: Jeffrey L Cantwe
Pr: Wayne Stancil
*CFO: Richard H Liem
*CFO: Rick Lim
CFO: Susan Moher
*Ofcr: K Kelly Roberts
*Ex VP: Steven L Scheinthal
*Sr VP: Jeffrey L Cantwell
VP: Joseph Leighy
VP: Peter Wagle
Exec: Michael Frietsch
Exec: Jeff Lhotsky
Exec: Oscar Mejia
Exec: Miguel Moreno
Exec: John Robinson
Exec: Ric Rosser

D-U-N-S 82-546-8668
LANDRYS LIMITED INC
(Suby of LANDRYS INC) ★
1510 West Loop S, Houston, TX 77027-9505
Tel (713) 850-1010 Founded/Ownrshp 1993
Sales 66.7MM^E EMP 300^E
SIC 6512 8741 Auditorium & hall operation; Hotel or motel management; Auditorium & hall operation; Hotel or motel management
Pr: Tilman J Fertitta
Treas: Rick Liem

D-U-N-S 60-085-6459
LANDRYS MANAGEMENT L P
(Suby of LANDRYS LIMITED INC) ★
1510 West Loop S, Houston, TX 77027-9505
Tel (713) 850-1010 Founded/Ownrshp 1993
Sales 66.7MM^E EMP 300^E
SIC 2599 Food wagons, restaurant; Food wagons, restaurant
Pt: Tilman Fertitta
CFO: Rick Lien
Sec: Val Williams
Sec: Susan Young

LANDRY'S SEAFOOD HOUSE
See LANDRYS INC

D-U-N-S 82-538-0863
LANDRYS SEAFOOD HOUSE - COLORADO INC
(Suby of LSRI HOLDINGS INC) ★
1510 West Loop S, Houston, TX 77027-9505
Tel (713) 850-1010 Founded/Ownrshp 1994
Sales 2.1MM^E EMP 345^E
SIC 5812 Seafood restaurants
Prin: Tilman J Fertitta

D-U-N-S 82-542-0735
LANDRYS SEAFOOD HOUSE - FLORIDA INC
(Suby of LSRI HOLDINGS INC) ★
1510 West Loop S, Houston, TX 77027-9505
Tel (713) 850-1010 Founded/Ownrshp 1994
Sales 3.2MM^E EMP 333^E
SIC 5812 Seafood restaurants
Prin: Tilman J Fertitta

D-U-N-S 82-542-1980
LANDRYS SEAFOOD HOUSE - NEVADA INC
(Suby of LSRI HOLDINGS INC) ★
1510 West Loop S, Houston, TX 77027-9505
Tel (713) 850-1010 Founded/Ownrshp 1995
Sales 2.2MM^E EMP 542^E
SIC 5812 Seafood restaurants
Genl Mgr: Laurie Danieley

D-U-N-S 79-552-8793
LANDRYS SEAFOOD INN & OYSTER BAR II INC
GROTTO
(Suby of LSRI HOLDINGS INC) ★
1510 West Loop S, Houston, TX 77027-9505
Tel (713) 850-1010 Founded/Ownrshp 1993
Sales 5.0MM^E EMP 898^E
SIC 5812 Italian restaurant
Pr: Tillman J Fertitta
*VP: Al Jaska
Genl Mgr: Callum Gray
Genl Mgr: Richard Villarreal

D-U-N-S 02-519-7609
▲ LANDS END INC
1 Lands End Ln, Dodgeville, WI 53595-0001
Tel (608) 935-9341 Founded/Ownrshp 1963
Sales 1.5MMM EMP 6,000
Tkr Sym LE Exch NAS
SIC 5961 5611 5621

LANDSBERG ORORA
See ORORA NORTH AMERICA

D-U-N-S 05-662-1899
LANDSCAPE CONCEPTS INC (IL)
31711 N Alleghany Rd, Grayslake, IL 60030-9509
Tel (847) 223-3800 Founded/Ownrshp 1971, 1986
Sales 52.6MM^E EMP 350^E
SIC 0781 0782 Landscape services; Lawn services; Landscape services; Lawn services
Pr: Michael Kerton
Sales Exec: Dorin Petre

D-U-N-S 07-993-5962
LANDSCAPE CONTRACTORS AND DESIGNERS LLC
Km 17 2 Rr 167, TOA Baja, PR 00951
Tel (787) 794-2620 Founded/Ownrshp 1999
Sales 11.0MM EMP 300
SIC 0781 Landscape services
Pr: Hoaquin Martinez Sr
Pr: Joaquin Martinez Sr
Prin: Caridad Perez

D-U-N-S 11-273-5840 IMP
LANDSCAPE DEVELOPMENT INC
28447 Witherspoon Pkwy, Valencia, CA 91355-4174
Tel (661) 295-1970 Founded/Ownrshp 1983
Sales 77.3MM^E EMP 500
SIC 0782 5039 Lawn & garden services; Landscape contractors; Soil erosion control fabrics; Lawn & garden services; Landscape contractors; Soil erosion control fabrics
CEO: Gary Horton
*CFO: Jenny Lunde
*CFO: Tim Myers
*VP: Casper Correll
VP: Fred Haskett
Off Mgr: Patrick Reinoso
IT Man: Bruce Pedersen
Sales Exec: Caroline De Biase
Snr PM: Glenn Austin
Snr Mgr: Keri Jeffris

D-U-N-S 04-923-8363 IMP/EXP
LANDSCAPE FORMS INC
431 Lawndale Ave, Kalamazoo, MI 49048-9543
Tel (269) 381-0396 Founded/Ownrshp 1969
Sales 74.4MM^E EMP 299
SIC 2531 2522 2511 2449 3648

D-U-N-S 13-989-7941
LANDSCAPE INNOVATIONS LLC
11101 Fairview 189, Eagle, ID 83616
Tel (208) 841-7666 Founded/Ownrshp 2002
Sales 90.0MM EMP 14
SIC 0781 Landscape counseling & planning; Landscape counseling & planning

D-U-N-S 10-313-7857
LANDSCAPE SPECIALISTS INC
ARTISTIC MAINTENANCE
23676 Birtcher Dr, Lake Forest, CA 92630-1769
Tel (949) 581-9737 Founded/Ownrshp 1983
Sales 29.5MM^E EMP 262
SIC 0782 7359 5193 Lawn & garden services; Lawn & garden equipment rental; Nursery stock; Lawn & garden services; Lawn & garden equipment rental; Nursery stock
Pr: Dirk G Herrmann
*Sec: Tom Hernandez

D-U-N-S 06-478-9787 IMP
LANDSCAPE STRUCTURES INC
601 7th St S, Delano, MN 55328-8605
Tel (763) 972-3391 Founded/Ownrshp 1971
Sales 90.3MM^E EMP 420
SIC 3949 2531 Playground equipment; Picnic tables or benches, park; Playground equipment; Picnic tables or benches, park
CEO: Steven King
*Pr: Pat Faust
CFO: Fred Caslavka
Bd of Dir: Charlie Thomas
IT Man: Matt Frank
IT Man: Elaine Harkess
Tech Mgr: Brian Mellgren

D-U-N-S 17-811-5309
LANDSCAPE WORKSHOP INC
3601 Parkwood Rd, Bessemer, AL 35022-5171
Tel (205) 424-0244 Founded/Ownrshp 1986
Sales 24.7MM^E EMP 210
SIC 0782 Landscape contractors; Landscape contractors
CEO: Joseph G Dobbs
*Pr: Stephen Presley
CFO: Katherin Fickling
*Sec: Amy T Dobbs
Brnch Mgr: Paige Paracca
Brnch Mgr: Scott Watson
Dist Mgr: Brandon Smith

LANDSCAPERS PRIDE
See NEW WAVERLY VENTURES LTD CO

D-U-N-S 08-021-9421
LANDSCAPES UNLIMITED LLC
1201 Aries Dr, Lincoln, NE 68512-9338
Tel (402) 423-6653 Founded/Ownrshp 1976
Sales 236.2MM^E EMP 500
SIC 1629 Golf course construction; Golf course construction
CFO: Mike Surls
Treas: Myrna J Kubly
Ex VP: Kurt Huseman
VP: Eric Heskje
VP: Matt Stotler
Exec: Myrna Kubly
Prgrm Mgr: Steve Hill
Rgnl Mgr: Ty Arndt
Genl Mgr: Renae Feilmeier
Genl Mgr: Mark Ruhga
Dir IT: Brad Jurgensen

LANDSDALE HOSPITAL
See LANSDALE HOSPITAL

D-U-N-S 05-397-7120 IMP
LANDSHIRE INC
LANDSHIRE SANDWICHES
727 N 1st St, Saint Louis, MO 63102-2548
Tel (800) 468-3354 Founded/Ownrshp 1961
Sales 151.8MM^E EMP 435
SIC 2099 5149 Sandwiches, assembled & packaged: for wholesale market; Coffee, green or roasted; Sandwiches, assembled & packaged: for wholesale market; Coffee, green or roasted
CEO: Joseph E Trover Jr
*Pr: Dale J Musick
Dir Bus: Craig Mehner
Rgnl Mgr: Jim Anderson
Rgnl Mgr: George Kelley
Rgnl Mgr: Kevin McAlester
Dist Mgr: John Bonsuk
Dist Mgr: Frank Johnson
Dist Mgr: Eric McLear
Dist Mgr: Jim Parsons
Dist Mgr: Bill Riner

LANDSHIRE SANDWICHES
See LANDSHIRE INC

D-U-N-S 06-790-6107
LANDSMAN DEVELOPMENT CORP (NY)
3 Townline Cir, Rochester, NY 14623-2537
Tel (585) 427-7570 Founded/Ownrshp 1971
Sales 41.5MM^E EMP 100
SIC 6552 6531 Subdividers & developers; Real estate managers
Pr: Elliott Landsman
*VP: Deborah Goldman

D-U-N-S 06-382-0773 IMP
LANDSTAR DEVELOPMENT CORP
LANDSTAR HOMES
550 Biltmore Way Ste 1110, Coral Gables, FL 33134-5721
Tel (305) 461-2440 Founded/Ownrshp 1982
Sales 29.4MM^E EMP 162
SIC 1521 1542 New construction, single-family houses; Commercial & office building, new construction; New construction, single-family houses; Commercial & office building, new construction
Pr: Rodolfo Stern
*CFO: Virginia Cepero
*Treas: David Serviansky
*VP: Roberto Horwitz
*VP: Eduardo Stern
*Genl Mgr: William Morrissey

D-U-N-S 60-929-6777
■ LANDSTAR EXPRESS AMERICA INC
(Suby of LANDSTAR GLOBAL LOGISTICS INC) ★
13410 Sutton Park Dr S, Jacksonville, FL 32224-5270
Tel (904) 398-9400 Founded/Ownrshp 1995
Sales 21.0MM^E EMP 65^E
SIC 4731 Freight transportation arrangement
Ch: Henry H Gerkens
*CEO: Jim B Gattoni
*VP: Joe Beacom
*VP: Michael Kneller
*VP: Patrick Omalley
Exec: Andrew Staier

D-U-N-S 78-778-4487
■ LANDSTAR GLOBAL LOGISTICS INC
(Suby of LANDSTAR SYSTEM HOLDINGS INC) ★
13410 Sutton Park Dr S, Jacksonville, FL 32224-5270
Tel (904) 398-9400 Founded/Ownrshp 1989
Sales 65.5MM^E EMP 82
SIC 4731 Brokers, shipping; Brokers, shipping
Pr: Patrick J O'Malley III
Treas: James B Gattoni
VP: Patrick J Murphy

LANDSTAR HOMES
See LANDSTAR DEVELOPMENT CORP

D-U-N-S 05-558-5517
■ LANDSTAR INWAY INC
(Suby of LANDSTAR SYSTEM HOLDINGS INC) ★
1000 Simpson Rd, Rockford, IL 61102-4625
Tel (815) 972-5000 Founded/Ownrshp 1981
Sales 60.8MM^E EMP 298^E

Accts Kpmg Llp Stamford Ct
SIC 4213 8742 Contract haulers; Transportation consultant; Contract haulers; Transportation consultant
Pr: Patrick J O'Malley
**Pr:* Michael K Kneller
**CFO:* Lawrence E Zimmer
**Ex VP:* Jim B Gattoni
**VP:* Joe Beacom
**VP:* John J Collins
VP: Teri Schoepski
**VP:* Larry S Thomas

D-U-N-S 00-877-8847
■ LANDSTAR LIGON INC
(*Suby of* LANDSTAR SYSTEM HOLDINGS INC) ★
13410 Sutton Park Dr S, Jacksonville, FL 32224-5270
Tel (904) 398-9400 *Founded/Ownrshp* 1982
Sales 104.8MM[E] *EMP* 900
SIC 4213 Trucking, except local; Building materials transport; Contract haulers; Trucking, except local; Building materials transport; Contract haulers
CEO: Jim Gattoni
**Pr:* Henry H Gerkens
Ex VP: Rachel Gupton
VP: Al Jordan
**VP:* Larry Thomas
Exec: Patrick J Malley

D-U-N-S 19-466-0387 IMP/EXP
■ LANDSTAR SYSTEM HOLDINGS INC
(*Suby of* LANDSTAR SYSTEM INC) ★
13410 Sutton Park Dr S, Jacksonville, FL 32224-5270
Tel (904) 398-9400 *Founded/Ownrshp* 1988
Sales 467.4MM[E] *EMP* 1,200
SIC 4213 Trucking, except local; Contract haulers; Building materials transport; Trucking, except local; Contract haulers; Building materials transport
Pr: Henry H Gerkens
**Pr:* James B Gattoni
VP: Frank Albanese
**VP:* Joe Beacom
Area Mgr: Rick Pogliano
Area Mgr: Josh Waggle
QA Dir: Renee Nelson
QA Dir: Patricia Wong
Dir IT: John Bradley
Dir IT: Paula Deppe
IT Man: Michael Cashner

D-U-N-S 62-386-4857
▲ LANDSTAR SYSTEM INC
13410 Sutton Park Dr S, Jacksonville, FL 32224-5270
Tel (904) 398-9400 *Founded/Ownrshp* 1968
Sales 3.1MMM *EMP* 1,211[E]
Tkr Sym LSTR *Exch* NGS
SIC 4789 Cargo loading & unloading services; Cargo loading & unloading services
Pr: James B Gattoni
CFO: L Kevin Stout
VP: Joseph J Beacom
VP: Michael K Kneller
VP: Patrick J O'Malley
VP: Larry S Thomas
Board of Directors: David G Bannister, Michael A Henning, Diana M Murphy, Larry J Thoele

D-U-N-S 92-946-6183
LANDTECH CONTRACTORS INC
525 Laredo St, Aurora, CO 80011-9214
Tel (303) 366-0501 *Founded/Ownrshp* 1987
Sales 24.8MM[E] *EMP* 150
Accts Malouff & Company Pc Engle
SIC 0782 0781 Lawn & garden services; Landscape counseling & planning
Pr: Larry Overley
CFO: Hermine Schechs
VP: James Smallwood
Opers Mgr: Kevin Fisher

D-U-N-S 80-509-0248 IMP
LANDTEK GROUP INC
235 County Line Rd, Amityville, NY 11701-2908
Tel (631) 691-2381 *Founded/Ownrshp* 1980
Sales 78.6MM *EMP* 150
Accts Grassi & Co Cpas Pc Jeri
SIC 1629 0783 0782 Golf course construction; Athletic field construction; Ornamental shrub & tree services; Landscape contractors; Golf course construction; Athletic field construction; Ornamental shrub & tree services; Landscape contractors
Ch Bd: Mike Ryan
CFO: Vito Demonte
VP: John Holden
VP: Ed Ryan
**VP:* Gregory Sharp
VP: John Sulinski
Off Mgr: Linda Olsen
IT Man: Michael Pizzo
Opers Mgr: Joe Gusmano
Sales Asso: Chris Hines

D-U-N-S 04-193-5875 IMP
LANE AUTOMOTIVE INC
MOTOR STATE DISTRIBUTING
8300 Lane Dr, Watervliet, MI 49098-9583
Tel (269) 463-4113 *Founded/Ownrshp* 1965
Sales 159.5MM[E] *EMP* 200
SIC 5013 5531 Automotive supplies & parts; Speed shops, including race car supplies; Automotive supplies & parts; Speed shops, including race car supplies
Pr: George Lane
Pr: Dean Akins
Pr: Bill Hartman
Pr: John Motycka
Pr: Bryan Postelli
Pr: Joe Stewart
**Treas:* David Lane
**VP:* Doug Lane
Dir IT: Jerry Drake
Dir IT: Brad Picardat
Dir IT: Brian Robbins

D-U-N-S 00-477-3750
LANE AVIATION CORP (OH)
4389 International Gtwy # 228, Columbus, OH 43219-3819
Tel (614) 237-3747 *Founded/Ownrshp* 1935
Sales 59.4MM[E] *EMP* 130
SIC 5599 4581 4522 4512 Aircraft, self-propelled; Aircraft instruments, equipment or parts; Aircraft servicing & repairing; Air passenger carriers, nonscheduled; Air transportation, scheduled
CEO: Donna L Earl
**Pr:* Brad Primm
Dir IT: Dave Rousselle
Mktg Dir: Mark Myers

D-U-N-S 00-891-7668 IMP
■ LANE BRYANT INC
(*Suby of* CHARMING SHOPPES INC) ★
3344 Morse Xing, Columbus, OH 43219-3092
Tel (614) 476-9281 *Founded/Ownrshp* 2001
Sales 1.0MMM[E] *EMP* 9,000
SIC 5621 Ready-to-wear apparel, women's; Ready-to-wear apparel, women's
CEO: Linda Heasley
Pr: Lorna E Nagler
Assoc VP: Evan Jacobs
Sr VP: Luann Bett
Sr VP: Elizabeth Crystal
VP: Alan Bobman
VP: Deb Camarota
VP: Rob Carter
VP: Nick Haffer
VP: Alice Hilliard
Creative D: Mike Teal
Dir Bus: Margie Hegg

D-U-N-S 13-120-3309
LANE CLEARWATER LIMITED PARTNERSHIP
LANE INDUSTRIES
1200 Shermer Rd, Northbrook, IL 60062-4500
Tel (847) 498-6650 *Founded/Ownrshp* 1985
Sales 100.0MM *EMP* 50
SIC 7011 Hotels; Hotels

LANE COMPANY
See LANE SERVICES LLC

D-U-N-S 07-352-6691
LANE COLLEGE
545 Lane Ave, Jackson, TN 38301-4598
Tel (731) 426-7500 *Founded/Ownrshp* 1882
Sales 25.6MM *EMP* 165
Accts Hoskins & Company Pc Nashvill
SIC 8221 College, except junior; College, except junior
Pr: Wesley Cornelious McClure
Ofcr: Virginia Crump
Ex VP: Michelle Curtain
**VP:* Sharron Burnett
VP: Richard Donnell
**VP:* Melvin Hamlett
**VP:* Dr Vicki Lott
**VP:* D'Nese Moore
CIO: Tori Haliburton
Dir IT: Ernest Mitchell
IT Man: Adrian Ingram

D-U-N-S 04-898-0288
LANE COMMUNITY COLLEGE
4000 E 30th Ave, Eugene, OR 97405-0640
Tel (541) 463-3000 *Founded/Ownrshp* 1964
Sales 58.5MM[E] *EMP* 1,888
Accts Kenneth Kuhns & Co Salem Or
SIC 8222 Community college; Community college
Pr: Mary Spilde
CFO: Greg Holmes
VP: Sonya Christian
VP: Wendy Shaeffer
VP: Roxanne Watson
Exec: Irene Willoughby
CIO: Bill Hughes
CIO: Bill Shoots
CTO: Esther Johnsen
Sys Mgr: Dave Keebler
Snr Mgr: King Provenmire

D-U-N-S 00-691-7504
LANE CONSTRUCTION CORP
(*Suby of* LANE INDUSTRIES INC) ★
90 Fieldstone Ct, Cheshire, CT 06410-1212
Tel (203) 235-3351 *Founded/Ownrshp* 1902
Sales 1.0MMM *EMP* 3,500
Accts Pricewaterhousecoopers Llp Ha
SIC 1622 1611 1629 3272 5032 Highway construction, elevated; Bridge construction; Airport runway construction; Subway construction; Dam construction; Power plant construction; Building materials, except block or brick: concrete; Paving materials; Highway construction, elevated; Bridge construction; Airport runway construction; Subway construction; Dam construction; Power plant construction; Building materials, except block or brick: concrete; Paving materials
Pr: Robert E Alger
Pr: Thomas R Larson
**CFO:* James M Ferrell
**Treas:* Vincent J Caiola
**Ex VP:* David F Benton
**Ex VP:* Micheal M Cote
**Ex VP:* Jay S Cruickshank
**Ex VP:* Donald P Dobbs
**Ex VP:* Kirk D Junco
VP: Farid Hamad
VP: James O Hughes
VP: Lawrence G Hurley
VP: Michael L Johnson
VP: Mark A Schiller
VP: Mark Tomkalski
Dir Bus: George Hassfurter

D-U-N-S 05-143-0239
LANE CONVEYORS & DRIVES INC
LANE SUPPLY COMPANY
15 Industrial Plaza Dr, Brewer, ME 04412-2241
Tel (207) 989-4560 *Founded/Ownrshp* 2007
Sales 27.7MM[E] *EMP* 52[E]
SIC 5085 3441 3599 Industrial supplies; Fabricated structural metal; Machine shop, jobbing & repair
Pr: Robert Taylor
VP: Tim Cowan

D-U-N-S 10-795-7268
LANE COUNCIL OF GOVERNMENTS
859 Willamette St Ste 500, Eugene, OR 97401-2910
Tel (541) 682-4283 *Founded/Ownrshp* 1945
Sales 22.9MM *EMP* 238
Accts Pauly Rogers And Co Pc T
SIC 8999 Personal services; Personal services
Ex Dir: Brenda Wilson
Prgrm Mgr: Steve Dignam
Telecom Mg: Russell Rubrecht

D-U-N-S 03-078-3922
LANE COUNTY SCHOOL DISTRICT 28J
FERNRIDGE SCHOOL DISTRICT
88834 Territorial Rd, Elmira, OR 97437-9758
Tel (541) 935-2253 *Founded/Ownrshp* 1960
Sales 8.5MM[E] *EMP* 283
Accts Pauly Rogers And Co Pc T
SIC 8211 Public elementary & secondary schools; High school, junior or senior; Public elementary & secondary schools; High school, junior or senior

D-U-N-S 00-279-7348
LANE ELECTRIC COOPERATIVE INC
787 Bailey Hill Rd, Eugene, OR 97402-5451
Tel (541) 484-1151 *Founded/Ownrshp* 1939
Sales 22.6MM *EMP* 53
SIC 4911 Transmission, electric power; Distribution, electric power; Transmission, electric power; Distribution, electric power
Pr: Jeri I Nelson
Treas: Jack Billings
**Treas:* Charles J Leighter
Bd of Dir: Ed Bangle
VP: Susan Knudsen
**VP:* Loy Sparks
Genl Mgr: Frederick Crinklaw
Genl Mgr: Rick Crinklaw
Genl Mgr: Matt Michel
IT Man: Andy Cave
IT Man: Richard Crinklaw

D-U-N-S 06-562-2169 EXP
LANE ENTERPRISES INC (PA)
3905 Hartzdale Dr Ste 514, Camp Hill, PA 17011-7837
Tel (717) 761-8175 *Founded/Ownrshp* 1934, 1986
Sales 71.7MM[E] *EMP* 250
SIC 3479 3444 Pipe, sheet metal; Coating of metals & formed products; Coating of metals & formed products; Pipe, sheet metal
Pr: Thomas J Wonsiewicz
**Pr:* Patrick X Collings
**Sec:* Daniel N Gallagher
Ofcr: Gene Anderson
**VP:* Marlin J Cathers
**VP:* Jerry A Saylor
**VP:* Richard A Walter
**VP:* Gregg L Weaver
**VP:* Lynnwood G Will
Plnt Mgr: Paul Vaughn

LANE FURNITURE
See LFI WIND DOWN INC

D-U-N-S 17-445-1047
LANE HOSPITALITY INC
60 Pointe Cir, Greenville, SC 29615-3568
Tel (847) 498-6650 *Founded/Ownrshp* 1980
Sales NA *EMP* 910
SIC 7011 8741 6719

LANE HOSPITALITY SOUTHWEST REG
See SUNBELT HOTELS LIMITED PARTNERSHIP

LANE INDUSTRIES
See LANE CLEARWATER LIMITED PARTNERSHIP

D-U-N-S 06-849-9094
LANE INDUSTRIES INC
1200 Shermer Rd Ste 400, Northbrook, IL 60062-4561
Tel (847) 498-6650 *Founded/Ownrshp* 1968
Sales 58.9MM[E] *EMP* 910[E]
Accts Grant Thornton Llp Chicago I
SIC 3579 3589 7011 1731 Binding machines, plastic & adhesive; Shredders, industrial & commercial; Hotels & motels; Safety & security specialization; Binding machines, plastic & adhesive; Shredders, industrial & commercial; Hotels & motels; Safety & security specialization
Pr: Forrest Schneider
**VP:* William Keating

D-U-N-S 10-125-8739
LANE INDUSTRIES INC
90 Fieldstone Ct, Cheshire, CT 06410-1212
Tel (203) 235-3351 *Founded/Ownrshp* 1982
Sales 1.2MMM *EMP* 4,500
Accts Pricewaterhousecoopers Llp Ha
SIC 1629 5032 1622 3272 1611 Subway construction; Dam construction; Power plant construction; Highway construction, elevated; Bridge construction; Airport runway construction; Building materials, except block or brick: concrete; Paving materials; Subway construction; Paving materials; Highway construction, elevated; Building materials, except block or brick: concrete; Airport runway construction
Pr: Robert E Alger
**Treas:* Vincent J Caiola
**Ex VP:* Mike Cote
**Ex VP:* Donald P Dobbs
**Ex VP:* James M Ferrell
**Ex VP:* Kirk Junco
**VP:* David F Benton
**VP:* Jay S Cruickshank

D-U-N-S 08-667-8018
LANE MARSETTA TEMP SERVICES INC
P.O. Box 746, Ingomar (15127-0746)
Tel (412) 364-1561 *Founded/Ownrshp* 1977
Sales 7.7MM[E] *EMP* 410
SIC 7363 Temporary help service; Temporary help service
Pr: Marsetta Schweiger
**VP:* Diane Bogut

D-U-N-S 01-210-6183
LANE OFFICE FURNITURE INC
205 Lexington Ave Fl 11, New York, NY 10016-6022
Tel (212) 233-4100 *Founded/Ownrshp* 1992
Sales 21.2MM[E] *EMP* 48
SIC 5712 5021

LANE PACKING CO
See SOUTHERN ORCHARD SUPPLY CO INC

D-U-N-S 96-906-6211
LANE PENNY FAMILY CENTER
15305 Rayen St, North Hills, CA 91343-5117
Tel (818) 894-3384 *Founded/Ownrshp* 2011
Sales 53.2MM *EMP* 3[E]
Accts Harrington Group Cpas Llp Pas
SIC 8322 Adoption services
VP: Sylvia Duarte

D-U-N-S 03-225-6117
LANE PONTIAC-BUICK-GMC INC
510 E Nasa Blvd, Melbourne, FL 32901-1987
Tel (321) 724-5263 *Founded/Ownrshp* 1974
Sales 31.3MM[E] *EMP* 70
SIC 5511 7538 5531 Automobiles, new & used; General automotive repair shops; Automotive parts; Automobiles, new & used; General automotive repair shops; Automotive parts
Pr: Leonard Lane
**VP:* Amy E Obrzut
Genl Mgr: Amy Lane

D-U-N-S 06-958-6006
LANE POWELL PC (OR)
1420 5th Ave Ste 4200, Seattle, WA 98101-2375
Tel (206) 223-7000 *Founded/Ownrshp* 1880
Sales 91.4MM *EMP* 420
Accts Moss Adams Llp Seattle Washi
SIC 8111 Legal services; Legal services
Pr: Charles W Riley Jr
COO: Randy L Leitzke
**VP:* Thomas W Sondag
Dir Bus: Sanjiv N Kripalani
Counsel: Michaela A Lbon
Counsel: Leigh D Stephenson-Kuhn

D-U-N-S 00-207-0811 IMP
LANE PRESS INC (VT)
87 Meadowland Dr, South Burlington, VT 05403-7605
Tel (802) 863-5555 *Founded/Ownrshp* 1904
Sales 66.9MM[E] *EMP* 200
SIC 2759 Periodicals: printing; Magazines: printing; Periodicals: printing; Magazines: printing
Pr: Philip M Drumheller
Treas: William Gentes
VP: David Briggs
VP: Bob Morris
VP: Robert Morris
IT Man: Darrin Green
IT Man: Scott Luck
Sales Asso: Rob Leonard

LANE REGIONAL MEDICAL CENTER
See HOSPITAL SERVICE DISTRICT 1 OF EAST BATON ROUGE PARISH

D-U-N-S 61-526-9045
LANE SERVICES LLC
LANE COMPANY
303 Perimeter Ctr N # 200, Atlanta, GA 30346-3402
Tel (678) 681-7200 *Founded/Ownrshp* 2005
Sales 43.5MM[E] *EMP* 1,000
SIC 6512 Property operation, retail establishment; Property operation, retail establishment
COO: Melanie Gersper
Dir Bus: Daniel Leone

D-U-N-S 07-453-0320
LANE STEEL CO INC (PA)
4 River Rd Ste 2, Mc Kees Rocks, PA 15136-2810
Tel (412) 331-1400 *Founded/Ownrshp* 1982
Sales 89.3MM *EMP* 55
Accts Listwak Finke & Associates P
SIC 5051 Plates, metal; Plates, metal
Ch: Al Gedeon
**Pr:* Paul D Gedeon
**VP:* Kathleen Gedeon
**VP:* Michael J Gedeon
**VP:* Richard H Zabrowski
QA Dir: Tom Joyce

LANE SUPPLY COMPANY
See LANE CONVEYORS & DRIVES INC

D-U-N-S 06-218-5186
LANE SUPPLY INC
120 Fairview St, Arlington, TX 76010-7221
Tel (817) 261-9116 *Founded/Ownrshp* 2002
Sales 21.5MM[E] *EMP* 130
SIC 3446 3448 3449 3444 Architectural metalwork; Prefabricated metal buildings; Miscellaneous metalwork; Sheet metalwork; Architectural metalwork; Prefabricated metal buildings; Miscellaneous metalwork; Sheet metalwork
CEO: Ronnie Jones
**CFO:* Steve Golovich
**Ch:* Billy Carnahan
Plnt Mgr: Cliff Ralph

D-U-N-S 06-058-8639
LANE TRANSIT DISTRICT
L T D
3500 E 17th Ave, Eugene, OR 97403-2375
Tel (541) 687-5555 *Founded/Ownrshp* 1970
Sales 17.5MM *EMP* 300
Accts Grove Mueller & Swank Pc
SIC 4131 Intercity bus line; Intercity bus line
Genl Mgr: Mark Pangborn
**Genl Mgr:* Ronald J Kilcoyne

D-U-N-S 06-864-5147
LANE-VALENTE INDUSTRIES INC (NY)
20 Keyland Ct, Bohemia, NY 11716-2620
Tel (631) 454-9100 *Founded/Ownrshp* 1998
Sales 56.8MM[E] *EMP* 250[E]
Accts Richard S Martin Commack Ny
SIC 1542 Institutional building construction; Institutional building construction
Ch Bd: George Lane

*CFO: Jim Hickey
Sr VP: Ken Wrenn
*VP: Chris Mc Cauley
VP: Elias Stambolis
VP: Chris Trujillo
*VP: Paul Valente
Prgrm Mgr: Alexzander Greenfield
Prgrm Mgr: Josi Nappi
Prgrm Mgr: Ken Zundel
Opers Mgr: Mike Akard

D-U-N-S 13-921-6428
LANEHART ELECTRICAL CONTRACTORS INC
2411 River Hill Rd, Irving, TX 75061-8909
Tel (972) 721-1304 Founded/Ownrshp 1984
Sales 23.9MM^E EMP 150
SIC 1731 General electrical contractor; General electrical contractor
CEO: John T Lanehart Jr
*VP: Randy Garrett

D-U-N-S 05-419-0496
LANEMART LLC
DUDLEY MARTIN CHEVROLET
8000 Sudley Rd, Manassas, VA 20109-2807
Tel (703) 368-2111 Founded/Ownrshp 1997
Sales 20.3MM^E EMP 80
SIC 5511 5521 Automobiles, new & used; Used car dealers; Automobiles, new & used; Used car dealers
Sls Mgr: Michael Martin
Sls Mgr: Bob Rice

D-U-N-S 07-920-6104
LANETERRALEVER LLC
725 W Mcdowell Rd, Phoenix, AZ 85007-1727
Tel (602) 258-5263 Founded/Ownrshp 2013
Sales 27.9MM^E EMP 120
SIC 7311 Advertising agencies
CEO: Beau Lane
*Pr: Chris Johnson
*CFO: Richard Skufza
*Sr VP: Dave Foster
*Sr VP: Isabelle Jazo
VP: Rikki Kopack

D-U-N-S 60-361-6319 IMP/EXP
LANEY DIRECTIONAL DRILLING CO
831 Crossbridge Dr, Spring, TX 77373-3501
Tel (281) 540-6615 Founded/Ownrshp 2014
Sales 28.8MM^E EMP 55
SIC 1629 Dam construction
Pr: J Marcus Laney
*VP: Robert Hamil
VP: Mauricio Perini
Mtls Mgr: Sam Norwood

D-U-N-S 00-685-0069
LANFORD BROTHERS CO INC (VA)
122 N Commerce St, Roanoke, VA 24019-8684
Tel (540) 992-2140 Founded/Ownrshp 1960
Sales 26.6MM EMP 150
Accts Brown Edwards & Company Ll
SIC 1622 1611 Bridge, tunnel & elevated highway; General contractor, highway & street construction; Bridge, tunnel & elevated highway; General contractor, highway & street construction
Ch: Stanard F Lanford Jr
*Pr: Kenneth L Lanford
*Treas: Lynn Kirby
*Sec: Marjorie L Cundiff
*Ex VP: Patrick N McDaniel
*VP: Rodney Keffer
*VP: Steve Lattimore
*VP: John R Milliron
*VP: Alan G Soltis

D-U-N-S 00-893-1446
LANG CHEVROLET CO
LANG CHEVROLET GEO
635 Orchard Ln, Beavercreek Township, OH 45434-6163
Tel (937) 426-2313 Founded/Ownrshp 1982
Sales 32.8MM^E EMP 100
SIC 5511 7538 7532 7515 5521 Automobiles, new & used; Trucks, tractors & trailers: new & used; General automotive repair shops; Top & body repair & paint shops; Passenger car leasing; Used car dealers; Automobiles, new & used; Trucks, tractors & trailers: new & used; General automotive repair shops; Top & body repair & paint shops; Passenger car leasing; Used car dealers
Owner: Richard F Lang
*Co-Ownr: Keith Bockbrader
*Co-Ownr: Judy Lang
Div Mgr: Joe Carrico
Off Mgr: Donna Holmes
IT Man: Kyle Bishop
Opers Mgr: Steve Sexton
Sls Mgr: Casey McCormick
Sls Mgr: Doug Phillippi
Sales Asso: Patty Groarth

LANG CHEVROLET GEO
See LANG CHEVROLET CO

D-U-N-S 02-406-9031
LANG CO
540 S 13th St, Louisville, KY 40203-1796
Tel (502) 584-2383 Founded/Ownrshp 2010
Sales 22.7MM^E EMP 70
SIC 5044 Office equipment; Duplicating machines
Pr: Thomas Welter
*Sec: Nancy Welter
VP Admn: Bill Tanner
Sls Mgr: Darin McCarthy
Sales Asso: Matthew Goetz
Snr Mgr: Ryan Penrose
Snr Mgr: Brandon Teri

D-U-N-S 96-168-2155 IMP
LANG COMPANIES INC
N19 W23993 Ridgeview, Waukesha, WI 53188-1000
Tel (262) 523-9235 Founded/Ownrshp 2009
Sales 22.1MM^E EMP 60^E
SIC 2678 Stationery products
CEO: Alan Patrick
*CFO: John Corrigan
*Chf Mktg O: Julie Smith
*Sr VP: Keith Strom
*VP: John Payne
Genl Mgr: Jennie Ortega
Natl Sales: Rich Coleman
Natl Sales: Ann Phillips
Natl Sales: Mike Salerno
Mktg Mgr: Carrie Lauer
Snr Mgr: Jeanne Simons

LANG EXPLORATORY DRLG DL MAHER
See BOART LONGYEAR CO

D-U-N-S 02-046-9631
LANG OIL INC
15 Sterling Ave, Oshkosh, WI 54901-4569
Tel (920) 232-7600 Founded/Ownrshp 1975
Sales 26.1MM EMP 60
Accts Nigl & Sullivan Llp Oshkosh
SIC 5541 5411 Filling stations, gasoline; Convenience stores, independent; Filling stations, gasoline; Convenience stores, independent
Pr: James H Lang
*Sec: Julie Corcoran
Dir Opers: Nicholas Lang

D-U-N-S 00-448-6973 IMP
LANG STONE CO INC (OH)
4099 E 5th Ave, Columbus, OH 43219-1812
Tel (614) 235-4099 Founded/Ownrshp 1856
Sales 22.0MM^E EMP 55^E
SIC 5032 5211 3281 3272 1422 Building stone; Marble building stone; Granite building stone; Lumber & other building materials; Masonry materials & supplies; Cut stone & stone products; Concrete products; Crushed & broken limestone
Pr: E Dean Coffman
COO: Bryan Bragg
CFO: Lori Palmer
*VP: Joann Coffman
VP: Tom Coffman
VP Admn: Joan First

D-U-N-S 07-888-8726
LANG-MEKRA NORTH AMERICA HOLDINGS INC
101 Tillessen Blvd, Ridgeway, SC 29130-9424
Tel (803) 337-5264 Founded/Ownrshp 2013
Sales NA EMP 350
SIC 6719 ; Investment holding companies, except banks
COO: Daniel Rodriguez
CFO: Jimmie Player
Mng Dir: Dave Sparks
Ql Cn Mgr: Reginald Howell

D-U-N-S 02-048-9001
LANG-NELSON ASSOCIATES INC
4601 Excelsior Blvd # 650, Minneapolis, MN 55416-4996
Tel (952) 920-0400 Founded/Ownrshp 1974
Sales 13.1MM^E EMP 400
SIC 6531 Real estate managers; Real estate managers
CEO: Francis W Lang
*Ex VP: Eugene Nelson
Genl Mgr: Shari Frisk

D-U-N-S 19-141-1016
LANGAN ENGINEERING AND ENVIRONMENTAL SERVICES INC
LANGAN ENGR ENVIRONMNTL SURVEY
(Suby of LANGAN ENGINEERING ENVIRONMENTAL SURVEYING AND LANDSCAPE ARCHITECTURE DPC) ★
619 River Dr, Elmwood Park, NJ 07407-1317
Tel (201) 794-6900 Founded/Ownrshp 2013
Sales 156.3MM^E EMP 550
SIC 8711 Consulting engineer; Consulting engineer
Pr: David T Gockel
*Treas: Michael Semeraro
VP: Caryn Barnes
VP: Archabal Roger
Exec: Dan Bendig
*Prin: Richard Burrow
*Prin: Gerard Cosci
*Prin: Marc Gallagher
*Prin: Chris Hager
Brnch Mgr: Jerald Bonta
Off Admin: Andrew Diaz

D-U-N-S 07-870-3163
LANGAN ENGINEERING ENVIRONMENTAL SURVEYING AND LANDSCAPE ARCHITECTURE DPC (NY)
619 River Dr, Elmwood Park, NJ 07407-1317
Tel (212) 479-5400 Founded/Ownrshp 2012
Sales 161.6MM^E EMP 730^E
SIC 8711 8748 1389 0781 Engineering services; Environmental consultant; Testing, measuring, surveying & analysis services; Landscape architects; Engineering services; Environmental consultant; Testing, measuring, surveying & analysis services; Landscape architects
Pr: David Gockel

LANGAN ENGR ENVIRONMNTL SURVEY
See LANGAN ENGINEERING AND ENVIRONMENTAL SERVICES INC

LANGAN MOTORCAR
See COLONIE MOTORS INC

LANGBEIN ENGELBRACHT AMERICAN
See TANN CORP

D-U-N-S 17-352-3416 IMP/EXP
LANGBOARD INC
LANGBOARD OSB
(Suby of LANGDALE INDUSTRIES INC) ★
320 Langboard Ln, Quitman, GA 31643-6335
Tel (229) 244-4154 Founded/Ownrshp 1985
Sales 419.5M^E EMP 301
SIC 2493 Strandboard, oriented; Strandboard, oriented
CEO: John W Langdale
*Ch Bd: Harley Langdale Jr
*CFO: Gregory J Miller
*Sec: Donna C Cain
*VP: Robert H Langdale
Exec: Willie Jean
Plnt Mgr: Tommy Gibbs

LANGBOARD OSB
See LANGBOARD INC

D-U-N-S 00-330-0506 EXP
LANGDALE CO (GA)
1202 Madison Hwy, Valdosta, GA 31601-6033
Tel (229) 242-7450 Founded/Ownrshp 1894
Sales 98.7MM^E EMP 425^E
SIC 2421 2491 7011 7699 5031 5171 Sawmills & planing mills, general; Planing mills; Preserving (creosoting) of wood; Motels; Knife, saw & tool sharpening & repair; Lumber: rough, dressed & finished; Petroleum bulk stations & terminals; Sawmills & planing mills, general; Planing mills; Preserving (creosoting) of wood; Motels; Knife, saw & tool sharpening & repair; Lumber: rough, dressed & finished; Petroleum bulk stations & terminals
Pr: John W Langdale III
Ch Bd: Harley Langdale Jr
CFO: Gregory J Miller
Treas: Delores M Parrish
VP: Larry Fudge
VP: James Harley Langdale
VP: Chris Reid
VP: Donald K Warren
Genl Mgr: Ronnie Lightsey
Sls Mgr: Rick Sanders

D-U-N-S 18-065-8205 IMP/EXP
LANGDALE INDUSTRIES INC
(Suby of LANGDALE CO) ★
1202 Madison Hwy, Valdosta, GA 31601-6033
Tel (229) 242-7450 Founded/Ownrshp 1986
Sales 543.5M EMP 390^E
SIC 2493 2421 2491 5031 Strandboard, oriented; Sawmills & planing mills, general; Wood preserving; Lumber: rough, dressed & finished; Strandboard, oriented; Sawmills & planing mills, general; Wood preserving; Lumber: rough, dressed & finished
CEO: John W Langdale
*CFO: Gregory J Miller
Genl Mgr: Tim Adams

D-U-N-S 80-908-7336
■ **LANGDON WIND LLC**
(Suby of NEXTERA ENERGY INC) ★
10812 Highway 66, Osnabrock, ND 58269-9660
Tel (701) 256-5316 Founded/Ownrshp 2007
Sales 41.3MM^E EMP 99^E
SIC 4911 Electric services
Pr: T J Tuscai

D-U-N-S 11-905-1709
LANGE LOGISTICS INC
(Suby of TOM LANGE CO INC) ★
755 Apple Orchard Rd, Springfield, IL 62703-5914
Tel (217) 786-3300 Founded/Ownrshp 2002
Sales 80.0MM EMP 30
SIC 4731 Transportation agents & brokers
Pr: F W Gumpert
Pr: Greg Reinauer
Treas: Hugh Seelbach
Off Mgr: Tom Linky

D-U-N-S 04-923-6425
LANGE MECHANICAL SERVICES LP
933 Wakefield Dr, Houston, TX 77018-6203
Tel (713) 688-3861 Founded/Ownrshp 2008
Sales 28.1MM^E EMP 110
SIC 1711 1731 Warm air heating & air conditioning contractor; Energy management controls; Warm air heating & air conditioning contractor; Energy management controls
Pt: Jamie Piske
Pt: Bill Piske
VP: Felipe Sandoval
Off Mgr: Brenda Duerer
Secur Mgr: Jay Broughton
Snr Mgr: Bobby Durrett

D-U-N-S 09-485-8677
LANGE TRUCKING INC
2226 Campbell St, Oakland, CA 94607-1719
Tel (510) 836-1105 Founded/Ownrshp 1979
Sales 25.9MM^E EMP 350
Accts Gerald L Cockrill Cpa Haywar
SIC 4213 Contract haulers; Contract haulers
Pr: Bill Lange
*Pr: Twan Lange
*VP: Bob Lange
*Prin: Willy Lange

D-U-N-S 07-827-7650
LANGEHAUMER CONSTRUCTION INC (IL)
321 N Clark St Fl 5, Chicago, IL 60654-4714
Tel (312) 445-6315 Founded/Ownrshp 2010
Sales 30.0MM EMP 15
SIC 1542 Commercial & office building contractors; Commercial & office building contractors
Pr: Jeff Lange

D-U-N-S 80-939-9272 IMP
■ **LANGELOTH METALLURGICAL CO LLC**
(Suby of THOMPSON CREEK MINING CO) ★
10 Langeloth Plant Dr, Langeloth, PA 15054
Tel (724) 947-2201 Founded/Ownrshp 1993
Sales 54.9MM^E EMP 156
SIC 1061 Ferroalloy ores, except vanadium; Ferroalloy ores, except vanadium
Genl Mgr: Robert Dorfler
IT Man: Dave Chapman
IT Man: Dave Smydo
Tech Mgr: Alyssa Matalik
VP Opers: Bob Dorfler
Sfty Mgr: Matthew Lucas

D-U-N-S 04-435-8042
LANGER INDUSTRIES INC
420 State Rt 440, Jersey City, NJ 07305-4813
Tel (201) 434-1600 Founded/Ownrshp 1960
Sales 41.6MM^E EMP 500
SIC 4213 Contract haulers; Contract haulers
VP: Rudolph Langer

D-U-N-S 08-718-3737 IMP/EXP
LANGER JUICE CO INC
L & A JUICE
16195 Stephens St, City of Industry, CA 91745-1718
Tel (626) 336-3100 Founded/Ownrshp 1957
Sales 155.9MM^E EMP 250
SIC 2037 Fruit juices
Pr: Nathan Langer
*Treas: Bruce Langer
*VP: David Langer
Prd Mgr: Chino Resendez
S&M/VP: Jenny San

D-U-N-S 00-178-0337
LANGER ROOFING & SHEET METAL INC (WI)
A A A DISTRIBUTORS
345 S Curtis Rd, Milwaukee, WI 53214-1069
Tel (414) 476-5800 Founded/Ownrshp 1923
Sales 29.3MM^E EMP 130
Accts Benes & Krueger Sc Waukesha
SIC 1761 Roofing contractor; Sheet metalwork
Pr: Mark E Langer
*Ch Bd: Gllenn E Langer
*CFO: Edward C Josephson
*VP: Scott L Harms

D-U-N-S 00-591-6432
LANGER TRANSPORT CORP
(Suby of LANGER INDUSTRIES INC) ★
420 State Rt 440, Jersey City, NJ 07305-4813
Tel (201) 434-1600 Founded/Ownrshp 1918, 1960
Sales 41.6MM^E EMP 250
SIC 4213 Liquid petroleum transport, non-local; Liquid petroleum transport, non-local
Pr: Fannie Langer
*Pr: Rudy Langer
*VP: Abraham Langer
*VP: Rudolph J Langer
Dir IT: Jonathan Dalia
Opers Mgr: Evan Katz

D-U-N-S 87-695-7056
LANGETWINS WINE CO INC
LANGETWINS WINERY & VINEYARDS
1525 E Jahant Rd, Acampo, CA 95220-9187
Tel (209) 334-9780 Founded/Ownrshp 2005
Sales 20.0MM EMP 22
Accts Croce & Company Stockton Cal
SIC 2084 Wines, brandy & brandy spirits; Wines, brandy & brandy spirits
Pr: Marissa Lange
*CFO: Aaron Lange
*VP: Kendra Altnow
Rgnl Mgr: Debi Dabasinskas
Dist Mgr: Andrea Roselli
VP Sls: Steven Folb

LANGETWINS WINERY & VINEYARDS
See LANGETWINS WINE CO INC

D-U-N-S 05-345-0169
LANGFIELD GROUP INC
HERITAGE WHOLESALERS
185 Commercial St, Malden, MA 02148-6708
Tel (781) 324-8100 Founded/Ownrshp 1970
Sales 22.5MM^E EMP 36
SIC 5033 Siding, except wood; Roofing, asphalt & sheet metal
Pr: Steven Field
*VP: Mark Ferullo
*VP: Thomas Wright
Dist Mgr: Jon Marron
Mktg Mgr: Peter Marecka
Sls Mgr: Doug McNamara
Sales Asso: Chris Bennett
Sales Asso: Al Butler
Sales Asso: Dick Fennelly
Sales Asso: Matt Long
Sales Asso: Chris Perfetto

D-U-N-S 01-011-8842
LANGFORD CONSTRUCTION CO
314 Greenville St, Lagrange, GA 30241-3232
Tel (706) 884-1776 Founded/Ownrshp 1975
Sales 20.2MM EMP 25^E
SIC 1542

D-U-N-S 02-812-6965
LANGFORD WIND POWER NRG
112 Telly St, New Roads, LA 70760-2521
Tel (225) 618-4034 Founded/Ownrshp 2010
Sales 42.3MM^E EMP 53^E
SIC 4911

D-U-N-S 15-107-0781 IMP
LANGHAM HOTELS INTERNATIONAL
400 5th Ave 4, New York, NY 10018-2753
Tel (201) 222-8401 Founded/Ownrshp 2004
Sales 5.0MM^E EMP 300
SIC 7011 Hotels; Hotels

D-U-N-S 60-579-5616
LANGHAM LOGISTICS INC
5335 W 74th St, Indianapolis, IN 46268-4180
Tel (317) 290-0227 Founded/Ownrshp 1988
Sales 32.1MM EMP 80
Accts Katz Sapper & Miller Llp Indi
SIC 4522 8742 4225 4731 Air cargo carriers, nonscheduled; Transportation consultant; General warehousing & storage; Truck transportation brokers; Air cargo carriers, nonscheduled; Transportation consultant; General warehousing & storage; Truck transportation brokers
CEO: Cathy Langham
*VP: John Langham
Dir IT: John Huybers
Dir IT: Scott Scull
Software D: Jonathan Terry
Sls Dir: Alice Cota

D-U-N-S 03-017-6028
LANGLADE HOSPITAL - HOTEL DIEU OF ST JOSEPH OF ANTIGO WISCONSIN (WI)
112 E 5th Ave, Antigo, WI 54409-2710
Tel (715) 623-2331 Founded/Ownrshp 1933
Sales 72.5MM^E EMP 800
Accts Wipfli Llp Wausau Wisconsin

SIC 8062 General medical & surgical hospitals; General medical & surgical hospitals
CEO: David R Schneider
Chf Rad: Ken Bowman
VP: Sarah Olafson
Dir Rad: Howard Graves
Dir Rx: Stacy Brownell
Dir IT: Margaret Bowman
IT Man: Patrick Tincher
Mktg Dir: Betsy Kommerf
Nrsg Dir: Sherry Bunten
Pharmcst: Clark Palmer
Phys Thrpy: Diane Peterson

D-U-N-S 18-247-3413
LANGLAS & ASSOCIATES INC
2270 Grant Rd Ste C, Billings, MT 59102-7457
Tel (406) 656-0629 *Founded/Ownrshp* 1972
Sales 33.1MM^E *EMP* 100
Accts Anderson Zurmuehlen & Co Pc
SIC 1542 Commercial & office building, new construction; Commercial & office buildings, renovation & repair; Commercial & office building, new construction
Pr: Stephen R Langlas
**Sec:* William Langlas
**VP:* David Langlas

D-U-N-S 07-793-7688
LANGLEY FEDERAL CREDIT UNION (INC)
721 Lkefront Cmns Ste 400, Newport News, VA 23606
Tel (757) 827-5328 *Founded/Ownrshp* 1936
Sales NA *EMP* 400
SIC 6061 Federal credit unions; Federal credit unions
Ch: William E Griffith Jr
**CEO:* Tom Ryan
Ofcr: Jay Mathieu
Ofcr: Diane Nortness
Ofcr: Erin Sullivan
VP: Ann Johnson
VP: Natasha Merz
VP: Krista Moses
Exec: Joy Davis
Brnch Mgr: Artie Shell
Brnch Mgr: Ron Wells

LANGLEY PROVIDER GROUP
See ROI ACCESS MANAGEMENT SERVICES LLC

D-U-N-S 05-230-8244
LANGLEY RECYCLING INC
3557 Stadium Dr, Kansas City, MO 64129-1734
Tel (816) 924-8452 *Founded/Ownrshp* 1931
Sales 25.8MM^E *EMP* 70
SIC 5093 Ferrous metal scrap & waste
Ch: Henry D Langley
**Pr:* Greg Bice
**VP:* Blaine Liebig

D-U-N-S 96-836-9751 IMP
LANGLEY/EMPIRE CANDLE LLC
2925 Fairfax Trfy, Kansas City, KS 66115-1317
Tel (913) 621-4555 *Founded/Ownrshp* 1999
Sales 34.2MM^E *EMP* 130^E
SIC 3999 Candles; Candles
Pr: Richard W Langley Jr
CFO: Tim Batchman
Ch: Mike Rainen
Prin: Larry Van Tuyl
VP Opers: Mike Stokes
Sales Exec: Fred Rutherford
Mktg Dir: Mercie Ritter
Sls Dir: Deb Swisher

LANGSTON BAG COMPANY
See LANGSTON COMPANIES INC

D-U-N-S 00-702-5166 IMP
LANGSTON COMPANIES INC (TN)
LANGSTON BAG COMPANY
1760 S 3rd St, Memphis, TN 38109-7712
Tel (901) 774-4440 *Founded/Ownrshp* 1946
Sales 80.7MM *EMP* 600
Accts Reynolds Bone Griesbeck Memph
SIC 2674 2393 2673 3315 3496 5199 Shipping bags or sacks, including multiwall & heavy duty; Shipping bags or sacks, including multiwall & heavy duty; Textile bags; Plastic & pliofilm bags; Steel wire & related products; Miscellaneous fabricated wire products; Fabrics, yarns & knit goods
Pr: Robert E Langston
**COO:* George Parkey
**CFO:* James Harris
Treas: George Parky
Opers Mgr: Jay Reese
Plnt Mgr: Wayne Croom
Plnt Mgr: Glenn Johnson

D-U-N-S 19-066-2122
LANGSTON SNYDER L P
SNYDER LANGSTON
17962 Cowan, Irvine, CA 92614-6026
Tel (949) 863-9200 *Founded/Ownrshp* 1986
Sales 53.5MM^E *EMP* 91
Accts Squar Milner Peterson Miran
SIC 1542 8742 1522 Commercial & office building, new construction; Real estate consultant; Residential construction; Commercial & office building, new construction; Real estate consultant; Residential construction
Ch Bd: Stephen Jones
Pr: John Rochford
CFO: Paul Pfeiffer
VP: Robert Barnett
VP: Timothy Bray
VP: Michael Gorelick
VP: Jo-E Immel
VP: Steven Nelson
VP: Lee Watkins
Exec: John Gunther
Exec: Bill V Leuven
Exec: Randy Stephenson

D-U-N-S 07-122-2780
LANGSTON UNIVERSITY
1233 Langston University, Langston, OK 73050
Tel (405) 466-2231 *Founded/Ownrshp* 1897
Sales 26.5MM *EMP* 350
Accts Cole & Reed Pc Oklahoma Cit
SIC 8221 University; University
Pr: Kent J Smith Jr
**Pr:* Joann W Haysbert
CIO: Clark Williams

D-U-N-S 79-153-5151
LANGUAGE ASSOCIATES LLC
DIPLOMATIC LANGUAGE SERVICES
1901 Fort Myer Dr Ste 600, Arlington, VA 22209-1604
Tel (703) 243-4855 *Founded/Ownrshp* 2006
Sales 37.3MM^E *EMP* 350
SIC 7389 8299 7338 Translation services; Reading & speaking schools; Language school; Meditation therapy; Editing service; Word processing service; Translation services; Reading & speaking schools; Language school; Meditation therapy; Editing service; Word processing service
CEO: Jim Bellas
Pr: Chris Bellas
Ex VP: Raluca Angelescu

D-U-N-S 17-000-9687
LANGUAGE LINE HOLDINGS INC
1 Lower Ragsdale Dr # 2, Monterey, CA 93940-5747
Tel (831) 648-5800 *Founded/Ownrshp* 2004
Sales 72.9MM^E *EMP* 1,000^E
SIC 7389 Translation services; Translation services
CEO: Dennis Dracup
**CFO:* Matthew Gibbs

D-U-N-S 05-968-2471
LANGUAGE LINE LLC
LANGUAGE LINE SERVICES
(*Suby of* LANGUAGE LINE HOLDINGS INC) ★
1 Lower Ragsdale Dr # 2, Monterey, CA 93940-5747
Tel (831) 648-5800 *Founded/Ownrshp* 1999
Sales 59.2MM^E *EMP* 549
SIC 7389 Translation services; Translation services
Ch: Dennis G Dracup
**CEO:* Scott W Klein
**Sr VP:* Winnie Heh
**VP:* Dave Bethea
**VP:* Vanessa Eke

LANGUAGE LINE SERVICES
See LANGUAGE LINE LLC

D-U-N-S 80-821-8689
LANGUAGE SERVICES ASSOCIATES INC
455 Business Center Dr # 100, Horsham, PA 19044-3439
Tel (215) 259-7000 *Founded/Ownrshp* 1991
Sales 25.2MM^E *EMP* 200
SIC 7389 Translation services; Translation services
CEO: Laura Kt Schriver
CFO: Arthur Seefahart
Treas: Starla Keith
Ex VP: Gene Schriver
Exec: Frank Johnson
Creative D: Tony Lannutti
QA Dir: Molly Capriotti
QA Dir: Melissa Thompson
IT Man: Jim Dean
Software D: Amanda Dowell

D-U-N-S 11-886-2528
LANI KEA LIMITED PARTNERSHIP
FAIRMONT KEA LANI MAUI
4100 Wailea Alanui Dr, Kihei, HI 96753-8449
Tel (808) 875-4100 *Founded/Ownrshp* 2002
Sales 11.6MM^E *EMP* 500
SIC 6531 Real estate agents & managers; Real estate agents & managers
Genl Mgr: Christof Luedi
Pr Mgr: Lynelle Miyashiro

LANIER BUSINESS PRODUCTS
See MCENROE VOICE & DATA CORP

LANIER HEALTH SERVICES
See CHATTAHOOCHEE VALLEY HOSPITAL SOCIETY (INC)

LANIER J SMITH FINANCIAL SVCS
See LEAVITT FINANCIAL GROUP INC

D-U-N-S 84-268-2999
LANIER PARKING HOLDINGS INC
LANIER PARKING SOLUTIONS
233 Peachtree St Ne # 2600, Atlanta, GA 30303-1510
Tel (404) 881-6076 *Founded/Ownrshp* 1989
Sales 84.3MM *EMP* 2,000
Accts Habif Arogeti And Wynne Llp A
SIC 7521 Automobile parking; Automobile parking
CEO: Jerry Skillett
**Pr:* Bijan Eghtedari
**COO:* Richard C Graham
**CFO:* David A Klarman
CFO: Leo Politz
**CFO:* Karen Quinn
**Ex VP:* Micheal Brown
Ex VP: Mickey A Brown
Ex VP: Sam Coppage
**Ex VP:* Scott Diggs
VP: Bret Almassy
VP: Andrea Gappell
VP: Kirk Hoffman
VP Bus Dev: Lance McCormack
Dir Bus: Tim Dougherty

LANIER PARKING SOLUTIONS
See LANIER PARKING HOLDINGS INC

D-U-N-S 07-220-8825
LANIER VILLAGE ESTATES INC
375 Morris Rd, West Point, PA 19486
Tel (215) 661-8330 *Founded/Ownrshp* 2001
Sales 21.1MM *EMP* 2
SIC 6513 Retirement hotel operation; Retirement hotel operation
Pr: Marvin Mashner
VP: Jerry Grant

D-U-N-S 15-063-4004 IMP
LANIER WORLDWIDE INC
(*Suby of* RICOH USA INC) ★
4667 N Royal Atlanta Dr, Tucker, GA 30084-3802
Tel (770) 493-2100 *Founded/Ownrshp* 2011
Sales 1.0MMM^E *EMP* 7,350
Accts Kpmg Llp
SIC 5044 5999 7359 7629 Office equipment; Telephone & communication equipment; Business machine & electronic equipment rental services; Business machine repair, electric; Office equipment; Telephone & communication equipment; Business machine & electronic equipment rental services; Business machine repair, electric
Pr: Nori Goto
VP: Tony Eugene Amason
VP: Allen Hans
**VP:* Randy Humphrey
VP: Masayoshi Ikeda
VP: Steven McBrayer
**VP:* Mark Miller
VP: Bradford L Nelson
**VP:* Paul Nix
VP: Larry Pelletier
**VP:* Barry Ward
Exec: Debbie Carsillo
Exec: Gail Guillotte
Exec: Chris Lindsay
Exec: Lisa Monica
Exec: Mark Snyder
Board of Directors: Y Mizutani, K Yoshida

D-U-N-S 02-166-7735
LANIGAN HOLDINGS LLC
3111 167th St, Hazel Crest, IL 60429-1025
Tel (708) 596-5200 *Founded/Ownrshp* 2001
Sales 28.0MM^E *EMP* 100^E
SIC 5082 3531 7948 8743 General construction machinery & equipment; Crane carriers; Race track operation; Promotion service; General construction machinery & equipment; Crane carriers; Race track operation; Promotion service
Pr: John J Lanigan Jr
**Ch Bd:* John J Lanigan Sr
**CFO:* Stephen J Bayers
**Ex VP:* Mike T Lanigan
**Ex VP:* William Lanigan

D-U-N-S 05-133-5321
LANK OIL CO
2203 W Mcnab Rd, Pompano Beach, FL 33069-4304
Tel (954) 978-6600 *Founded/Ownrshp* 1965
Sales 30.0MM^E *EMP* 38^E
SIC 5172 Petroleum products; Petroleum products
Pr: William C Lank Jr
**Ch Bd:* Mary G Lank
**VP:* Monty A Michel

D-U-N-S 07-843-4416
LANKENAU MEDICAL CENTER FOUNDATION (PA)
NEMOURS
100 E Lancaster Ave # 12, Wynnewood, PA 19096-3400
Tel (484) 476-2000 *Founded/Ownrshp* 1981
Sales 29.6MM *EMP* 3
SIC 8011 Offices & clinics of medical doctors
CEO: David J Bailey
**Sr VP:* Steven R Sparks
Pathlgst: Shotaro Imaizumi
Ansthlgy: Shyla Banvi
Ansthlgy: Cynthia Rogalski

LANKFORD - SYSCO FOOD SERVICES
See SYSCO EASTERN MARYLAND LLC

D-U-N-S 04-424-4077
LANKFORD CONSTRUCTION CO
1455 Karlens Way, Johnsburg, IL 60051-8413
Tel (847) 223-4200 *Founded/Ownrshp* 1986
Sales 20.6MM^E *EMP* 50
SIC 1542

D-U-N-S 07-227-7002
LANKFORD PROTECTIVE SERVICE INC
2711 Pinedale Rd Ste B, Greensboro, NC 27408-4706
Tel (336) 288-7922 *Founded/Ownrshp* 1995
Sales 7.4MM^E *EMP* 300
SIC 7381 Security guard service; Security guard service
Pr: Sam Lankford
**CEO:* Deborah Lankford
**VP:* Howard Holt
VP Opers: Jeff Mitchell

LANL FOUNDATION
See LOS ALAMOS NATIONAL LABORATORY FOUNDATION

D-U-N-S 08-964-8075
LANMAN OIL CO INC (IL)
LAMBOS AMOCO
10943 E County Road 900n A, Mattoon, IL 61938-3601
Tel (217) 348-8020 *Founded/Ownrshp* 1947
Sales 27.9MM^E *EMP* 35
SIC 5171 5411 Petroleum bulk stations; Convenience stores, independent
Pr: Michael J Lanman

D-U-N-S 61-353-6932
LANMARK GROUP INC
2125 Mill Ave, Brooklyn, NY 11234-6307
Tel (347) 462-4000 *Founded/Ownrshp* 2005
Sales 20.4MM *EMP* 48
Accts Grassi & Co Jericho New Yor
SIC 1542 Nonresidential construction; Nonresidential construction
Pr: Eleftherios Kougentakis

D-U-N-S 01-972-3717
LANNAN CHEVROLET OLDS INC (MA)
LANNAN OLDSMOBILE
40 Winn St, Woburn, MA 01801-2835
Tel (781) 935-2000 *Founded/Ownrshp* 1954
Sales 27.0MM^E *EMP* 70^E
SIC 5511 Automobiles, new & used; Automobiles, new & used
Pr: Peter Lannan
**Treas:* Stephen Lannan
Off Mgr: Phil Chiraluce

LANNAN OLDSMOBILE
See LANNAN CHEVROLET OLDS INC

D-U-N-S 00-227-7481
▲ **LANNETT CO INC**
9000 State Rd, Philadelphia, PA 19136-1615
Tel (215) 333-9000 *Founded/Ownrshp* 1942
Sales 406.8MM *EMP* 502^E
Accts Grant Thornton Llp Philadelph
Tkr Sym LCI *Exch* NYS
SIC 2834 Pharmaceutical preparations; Pharmaceutical preparations
CEO: Arthur P Bedrosian
**Ch Bd:* Jeffrey Farber
V Ch: Ronald A West
**Pr:* Michael J Bogda
**COO:* William F Schreck
**CFO:* Martin P Galvan
VP: John ABT
VP: Rohit Desai
**VP:* Robert Ehlinger
Exec: Ron Wenger
VP Mktg: Rich Matchett
Board of Directors: David Drabik, James M Maher, Albert Paonessa III, Paul Taveira

D-U-N-S 06-965-2865
LANNING TIRE SALES INC (FL)
1235 N Lime Ave, Sarasota, FL 34237-2807
Tel (941) 365-0400 *Founded/Ownrshp* 1974
Sales 24.3MM^E *EMP* 62
SIC 5014 5531 Truck tires & tubes; Automotive tires
Pr: Stephen Lanning

LANNINGS FOODS
See S AND S GILARDI INC

LANNIS FENCE SYSTEMS
See MIDWAY STRUCTURAL PIPE AND SUPPLY INC

D-U-N-S 09-369-2408 IMP/EXP
■ **LANOGA CORP**
UNITED BUILDING CENTERS
(*Suby of* PROBUILD HOLDINGS LLC) ★
17946 Ne 65th St, Redmond, WA 98052-4963
Tel (425) 883-4125 *Founded/Ownrshp* 2006
Sales 480.9MM^E *EMP* 5,600
SIC 5211 5031

D-U-N-S 09-641-0436
LANOHA NURSERIES INC (NE)
19111 W Center Rd, Omaha, NE 68130-2804
Tel (402) 289-4103 *Founded/Ownrshp* 1976
Sales 27.3MM^E *EMP* 80
SIC 5261 0782 1711 Nursery stock, seeds & bulbs; Lawn services; Irrigation sprinkler system installation
Pr: Dave Lanoha
Ex VP: Jason Lanoha
VP: Christopher Lanoha
**VP:* Patty Lanoha
IT Man: Michael Arp

LANOUE CONSULTING
See HEADWORKS INC

D-U-N-S 04-127-4325
LANPHERE ENTERPRISES INC
BEAVERTON HONDA
12505 Sw Brdwy St, Beaverton, OR 97005
Tel (503) 643-5577 *Founded/Ownrshp* 1964
Sales 307.8MM^E *EMP* 675
SIC 5571 5511 5261 Motorcycle dealers; Automobiles, new & used; Lawn & garden equipment; Motorcycle dealers; Automobiles, new & used; Lawn & garden equipment
Ch Bd: Robert D Lanphere Sr
**Pr:* Robert D Lanphere Jr
**CFO:* Robb Walther
**Sec:* Sharon Lenz
Exec: Cheryl Daquilante
**Prin:* Pat Blanchat
**Prin:* Ryan Malone
IT Man: Greg Miller
Sls Mgr: Dan Priest
Sales Asso: Jeff Holley

D-U-N-S 60-221-5667
LANPHERE ENTERPRISES OF WASHINGTON INC
RENTON HONDA AUTOMOBILES
(*Suby of* BEAVERTON HONDA) ★
3701 E Valley Rd, Renton, WA 98057-4948
Tel (425) 271-3131 *Founded/Ownrshp* 1990
Sales 54.3MM^E *EMP* 165
SIC 5511 Automobiles, new & used; Automobiles, new & used
Ch: Robert D Lanphere Sr
**Pr:* Robert D Lanphere Jr
Exec: Patrick Brown
Ex Dir: Tim Collins
Store Mgr: Eric Robinson
Mktg Dir: Kevin Nghiem
Sls Mgr: Travis Holt
Sls Mgr: Carlos Silva

D-U-N-S 13-525-0004
LANSA HOLDINGS INC
2001 Butterfield Rd # 102, Downers Grove, IL 60515-5491
Tel (630) 874-7000 *Founded/Ownrshp* 2000
Sales 32.2MM^E *EMP* 232^E
SIC 7371 Computer software development
CEO: Martin Fincham
**CFO:* Mark Fredericks

D-U-N-S 19-461-6678
LANSA INC
(*Suby of* LANSA HOLDINGS INC) ★
2001 Butterfield Rd # 102, Downers Grove, IL 60515-5491
Tel (630) 874-7042 *Founded/Ownrshp* 1996
Sales 32.2MM^E *EMP* 225
SIC 7371 7372 Computer software development; Educational computer software; Computer software development; Educational computer software
CEO: Pete Draney
**Pr:* Steven Gapp
**VP:* Mark Fredericks
Software D: Riaz Mohamed
Board of Directors: Pete Draney

D-U-N-S 04-225-9903
LANSDALE AUTO GROUP INC
LANSDALE PLYMOUTH
710 Bethlehem Pike, Montgomeryville, PA 18936-9601
Tel (267) 218-7606 *Founded/Ownrshp* 1967
Sales 23.8MM^E *EMP* 50
SIC 5511 Automobiles, new & used; Automobiles, new & used
Pr: Joseph Haenn
**Pr:* Jay Michael Haenn Jr
**Treas:* Mark Haenn
IT Man: Karen Link

D-U-N-S 83-154-4403
LANSDALE HOSPITAL
LANSDALE HOSPITAL
100 Medical Campus Dr, Lansdale, PA 19446-1259
Tel (215) 853-8300 *Founded/Ownrshp* 2008
Sales 80.7MM *EMP* 650
Accts Withumsmithbrown Pc Morristow
SIC 8062 General medical & surgical hospitals; General medical & surgical hospitals
CEO: Gary R Candia

LANSDALE PLYMOUTH
See LANSDALE AUTO GROUP INC

LANSDOWNE RESORT
See LHO LEESBURG ONE LESSEE INC

D-U-N-S 02-083-5245
LANSE CREUSE PUBLIC SCHOOLS
24076 Frdrick Pankow Blvd, Clinton Township, MI 48036
Tel (586) 783-6300 *Founded/Ownrshp* 1954
Sales 53.0MM^E *EMP* 1,200
Accts Plante & Moran Pllc Clinton
SIC 8211 Public elementary & secondary schools; High school, junior or senior; Vocational high school; Public elementary & secondary schools; High school, junior or senior; Vocational high school
Dir IT: Lawrence Chockley
Sales Exec: Anita Monte
Schl Brd P: Linda McLatcher

D-U-N-S 06-983-0503
LANSING AUTOMAKERS FEDERAL CREDIT UNION
106 N Marketplace Blvd, Lansing, MI 48917-7753
Tel (517) 321-6600 *Founded/Ownrshp* 1936
Sales NA *EMP* 110
SIC 6061 Federal credit unions; Federal credit unions
Pr: Robin Frucci
COO: Carolyn Coffman
CFO: Tamela McPherson
CFO: Tammy McPherson
Ex VP: Sharon Gillison
Ex VP: Jon Looman

D-U-N-S 80-999-2055
LANSING BOARD OF WATER AND LIGHT
LANSING BOARD WATER AND LIGHT
830 E Hazel St, Lansing, MI 48912-1020
Tel (517) 702-6000 *Founded/Ownrshp* 1985
Sales 21.5MM *EMP* 740^E
SIC 4941 4911 Water supply; Electric services; Water supply; Electric services
CEO: J Peter Lark
**CFO:* Susan Devon
VP: Dennis McFarland
CIO: Adam Norbut
Dir IT: Marvin Harris

LANSING BOARD WATER AND LIGHT
See LANSING BOARD OF WATER AND LIGHT

D-U-N-S 00-313-6587 IMP
LANSING BUILDING PRODUCTS INC (VA)
8501 Sanford Dr, Richmond, VA 23228-2812
Tel (804) 266-8893 *Founded/Ownrshp* 1957
Sales 298.0MM^E *EMP* 550
SIC 5033 5031 5032 Roofing & siding materials; Windows; Brick, stone & related material; Roofing & siding materials; Windows; Brick, stone & related material
Pr: J C Lansing
Ex VP: Larry Wilson
Ex VP: John Witt
VP: Kevin Kruchem
**VP:* Lynn K Whyte
VP Admn: Lynn White
Rgnl Mgr: John Martin
Brnch Mgr: Brian Daley
Brnch Mgr: Matt Equinoa
Brnch Mgr: John Long
Brnch Mgr: Steven Salcedo
Board of Directors: W B Douglass III

D-U-N-S 07-633-6882
LANSING COMMUNITY COLLEGE
610 N Capitol Ave, Lansing, MI 48933-1212
Tel (517) 483-1957 *Founded/Ownrshp* 1957
Sales 40.2MM *EMP* 2,500
Accts Rehmann Robson Llc Jackson
SIC 8222 Community college; Community college
CEO: Brent Knight
**CFO:* Catherine Fisher
Assoc VP: Vicki Deketelaere
Sr VP: Lisa Webbsharpe
CIO: Peter Lincolnhol
CTO: Debra Szwejda
Dir IT: Karl Dietrich
Dir IT: Gary Heisler
Dir IT: Randy Jobksi
Dir IT: Jonathan Kavanagh
Dir IT: Stephen Potoczek

LANSING FARMING CO
See WOOLF FARMING CO OF CALIFORNIA INC

D-U-N-S 61-094-3115 IMP
LANSING L MPT L C
MAGNA POWERTRAIN LANSING
(*Suby of* MAGNA POWERTRAIN TROY) ★
3140 Spanish Oak Dr Ste A, Lansing, MI 48911-4291
Tel (517) 316-1013 *Founded/Ownrshp* 2005
Sales 205.9MM^E *EMP* 140
SIC 3714 Motor vehicle engines & parts
Mtls Mgr: Heather Bickford
QI Cn Mgr: Larry Burk

D-U-N-S 06-132-0255
■ **LANSING MALL LIMITED PARTNERSHIP**
(*Suby of* GGP INC) ★
110 N Wacker Dr, Chicago, IL 60606-1511
Tel (312) 960-5000 *Founded/Ownrshp* 1986
Sales 33.4MM^E *EMP* 1,450
SIC 6512 7311 Shopping center, property operation only; Advertising agencies; Shopping center, property operation only; Advertising agencies
CEO: Ric Clark
Ch Bd: Matthew Bucksbaum
Pr: Robert A Michaels
CFO: Bernard Freibaum
VP: Linda White
Prin: John Bucksbaum
Genl Mgr: Glen Harrell
Genl Mgr: Ed Kubes
Genl Mgr: Pamela Weller

LANSING MANOR APARTMENTS
See SENIOR RELATED WORLD LLC

D-U-N-S 00-896-4884 IMP
LANSING MPS INC (MI)
HORTA CRAFT DIVISION
(*Suby of* JOHN HENRY HOLDINGS INC) ★
5800 W Grand River Ave, Lansing, MI 48906-9111
Tel (517) 323-9000 *Founded/Ownrshp* 1946, 2004
Sales 196.0MM^E *EMP* 1,800
SIC 2759 2731 2761 3089 5092 2671 Commercial printing; Screen printing; Letterpress printing; Tags: printing; Books: publishing & printing; Continuous forms, office & business; Identification cards, plastic; Arts & crafts equipment & supplies; Packaging paper & plastics film, coated & laminated; Commercial printing; Screen printing; Letterpress printing; Tags: printing; Books: publishing & printing; Continuous forms, office & business; Identification cards, plastic; Arts & crafts equipment & supplies; Packaging paper & plastics film, coated & laminated
Pr: Shahriar Ghoddousi
MIS Dir: Jane Schaffer
Dir IT: Frank Golupski
VP Mktg: Erin Willigan
Mktg Dir: Brenda Vaughn
Advt Mgr: Jeff Fillion

D-U-N-S 07-637-3687
LANSING SCHOOL DISTRICT
519 W Kalamazoo St, Lansing, MI 48933-2080
Tel (517) 755-1000 *Founded/Ownrshp* 1847
Sales 90.4MM^E *EMP* 2,000
Accts Maner Costerisan & Ellis Pc
SIC 8211 Public elementary & secondary schools; Public elementary & secondary schools
VP: Steve Maiville

D-U-N-S 01-719-5611 IMP/EXP
LANSING TRADE GROUP LLC
10975 Benson Dr Ste 400, Overland Park, KS 66210-2137
Tel (913) 748-3000 *Founded/Ownrshp* 1965
Sales 6.6MMM *EMP* 400
SIC 5153 6221 Grains; Commodity contracts brokers, dealers; Grains; Commodity contracts brokers, dealers
CEO: Bill Krueger
CFO: Mark O'Donnell
**CFO:* Mark Odonnell
Ex VP: Tom Irmen
**Ex VP:* Scott Mills
Sr VP: Steve Speck
VP: Weston Heide
VP: Mike Lemke
VP: Dwight Pflipsen
VP: Eric Watts
Dir Bus: Scott Wernimont

D-U-N-S 09-378-2381 IMP
LANTAL TEXTILES INC
1300 Langenthal Dr, Rural Hall, NC 27045-9800
Tel (336) 969-9551 *Founded/Ownrshp* 1979
Sales 26.6MM^E *EMP* 150
SIC 2231 2211 5131 Upholstery fabrics, wool; Upholstery fabrics, cotton; Upholstery fabrics, woven; Upholstery fabrics, wool; Upholstery fabrics, cotton; Upholstery fabrics, woven
Ch Bd: URS Baumann
Pr: Scott C Walker
Treas: Jamey Hughes
Prin: Kim Lawson
IT Man: Wayne Stonestreet
Opers Mgr: William Smith
Sls Mgr: Jennifer Rico-Stewart

LANTECH LOGISTICS
See LANCO INTERNATIONAL INC

D-U-N-S 05-759-4749 IMP/EXP
LANTECH.COM LLC
11000 Bluegrass Pkwy, Louisville, KY 40299-2399
Tel (502) 267-4200 *Founded/Ownrshp* 1971
Sales 107.9MM *EMP* 390
Accts Crowe Horwath Llp Louisville
SIC 3565 Packaging machinery; Packaging machinery
Sr VP: Allison Myers
VP: Chris Kist
Exec: Cathy Taylor
QA Dir: Kevin Hill
QA Dir: Larry Talkington
Opers Mgr: Annette Noel
Sales Exec: Jim Lancaster
Natl Sales: Neil Bennett
Natl Sales: David Carroll
Natl Sales: Mike Castelli
Natl Sales: Ken Robinson

D-U-N-S 19-433-3654
LANTER DELIVERY SYSTEMS INC
1600 Wayne Lanter Ave, Madison, IL 62060-1466
Tel (618) 452-5300 *Founded/Ownrshp* 1995
Sales 41.4MM^E *EMP* 175
SIC 4731 4212 Freight forwarding; Delivery service, vehicular
Pr: Steve Lanter
**Pr:* Kevin Bontemps
**VP:* Chris Lanter
**VP:* Michelle Morio
**VP:* Kevin Westervelt
Rgnl Mgr: Scott Wicks

D-U-N-S 14-492-3690
LANTERN MOON INC
3324 Ne 32nd Ave, Portland, OR 97212-2627
Tel (503) 460-0003 *Founded/Ownrshp* 2001
Sales NA *EMP* 10
SIC 6111 5199 Export/Import Bank; Knit goods; Export/Import Bank; Knit goods
Pr: Joel Woodcock
**CFO:* Sharon Woodcock
**VP:* Bruce Feller

D-U-N-S 07-854-0805
▲ **LANTHEUS HOLDINGS INC**
331 Treble Cove Rd, North Billerica, MA 01862-2849
Tel (978) 671-8001 *Founded/Ownrshp* 1956
Sales 301.6MM *EMP* 443^E
Tkr Sym LNTH *Exch* NGM
SIC 2835 2834 Pharmaceutical preparations; In vitro & in vivo diagnostic substances; Pharmaceutical preparations
Pr: Mary Anne Heino
CFO: John Bakewell
CFO: Jack Crowley
Chf Mktg O: Cesare Orlandi
VP: Michael Duffy
Board of Directors: David Burgstahler, James C Clemmer, Samuel Leno, Brian Markison, Patrick O'neill

D-U-N-S 17-678-6812 IMP
LANTHEUS MEDICAL IMAGING INC
(*Suby of* LANTHEUS MI INTERMEDIATE INC) ★
331 Treble Cove Rd, North Billerica, MA 01862-2849
Tel (978) 671-8001 *Founded/Ownrshp* 2008
Sales 112.3MM^E *EMP* 519^E
SIC 3841 2834 Diagnostic apparatus, medical; Pharmaceutical preparations; Diagnostic apparatus, medical; Pharmaceutical preparations
Pr: Jeffrey Bailey
COO: Mary Anne Heino
CFO: John K Bakewell
CFO: John Golubieski
Chf Mktg O: Cesare Orlandi
VP: Jack Crowley
VP: Michael Duffy
VP: Simon Robinson
VP: Mary Taylor
VP: Cyrille Villeneuve
VP: Dana Washburn
VP: Nigel Williams
Assoc Dir: Sunil Anklekar
Assoc Dir: Anne Butterworth
Assoc Dir: Candace Grasse
Assoc Dir: Amanda Hayden
Assoc Dir: Mitchell Hollander
Assoc Dir: Laura Lee
Assoc Dir: John Singelais
Assoc Dir: Robyn Strassel
Assoc Dir: Charles Vankirk
Board of Directors: David Burgstahler, Samuel Leno, Brian Markison, Patrick O'niell

D-U-N-S 07-959-5362
LANTHEUS MI INTERMEDIATE INC
331 Treble Cove Rd, North Billerica, MA 01862-2849
Tel (978) 671-8001 *Founded/Ownrshp* 2007
Sales 301.6MM *EMP* 519^E
SIC 3841 2834 Diagnostic apparatus, medical; Pharmaceutical preparations; Diagnostic apparatus, medical; Pharmaceutical preparations
Pr: Jeffrey Bailey
CFO: John K Bakewell

D-U-N-S 09-609-7639
LANTING HAY DEALER INC
9032 Merrill Ave, Ontario, CA 91762-7234
Tel (909) 563-5601 *Founded/Ownrshp* 1974
Sales 21.1MM^E *EMP* 75
SIC 5191 Hay; Hay
Pr: Ronald J Lanting
**Sec:* Lorraine Lanting
**VP:* Bradley M Lanting

D-U-N-S 10-910-2376
LANTIS ENTERPRISES INC
4755 E Colorado Blvd, Spearfish, SD 57783-9405
Tel (605) 642-7736 *Founded/Ownrshp* 1990
Sales 89.6MM^E *EMP* 2,500
SIC 8051 8052 Skilled nursing care facilities; Intermediate care facilities; Skilled nursing care facilities; Intermediate care facilities
CEO: Travis Lantis
**Pr:* Will Lantis
**Sec:* Mary Ellen Lantis
**Ex Dir:* Lynne Follmer
CTO: Greg Rinard
VP Opers: Jerry Smyle

D-U-N-S 03-654-1787 IMP
LANTMANNEN UNIBAKE USA INC
(*Suby of* LANTMANNEN UNIBAKE HOLDING A/S)
5007 Lincoln Ave Ste 300, Lisle, IL 60532-4187
Tel (630) 963-4781 *Founded/Ownrshp* 1995
Sales 190.2MM^E *EMP* 360
SIC 5142 Bakery products, frozen; Bakery products, frozen
Pr: Scott Kolinski
CFO: Per Nyman
Comm Man: Mira Perander
Genl Mgr: Giulio Anceschi
Genl Mgr: Greg Harnwell
Genl Mgr: Thomas Jarnum
IT Man: Mike Fowler
Natl Sales: George Haddad
Natl Sales: Mike Minden
Natl Sales: Monia Parker
Mktg Dir: Anette Kalle

D-U-N-S 60-544-4645 IMP
▲ **LANTRONIX INC**
7535 Irvine Center Dr # 100, Irvine, CA 92618-2966
Tel (949) 453-3990 *Founded/Ownrshp* 1989
Sales 42.9MM *EMP* 110^E
Accts Squar Milner Llp (Formerly Sq
Tkr Sym LTRX *Exch* NAS
SIC 3577 Computer peripheral equipment; Data conversion equipment, media-to-media: computer; Computer peripheral equipment; Data conversion equipment, media-to-media: computer
Pr: Jeffrey W Benck
**Ch Bd:* Bernhard Bruscha
CFO: Jeremy R Whitaker
Sr VP: Jeff Kost
VP: Michael A Fink
VP: Mak Mahesh
VP: Robert O Robinson
VP: Kurt E Scheuerman
Snr Sftwr: Matt Davison
Dir IT: Murthy Subramanymurthy
IT Man: Sarah Houston
Board of Directors: Bruce C Edwards, Paul F Folino

D-U-N-S 00-978-1758
LANTZ CONSTRUCTION CO
539 S Main St, Broadway, VA 22815-9548
Tel (540) 896-8911 *Founded/Ownrshp* 1960
Sales 42.4MM *EMP* 115
Accts Yount Hyde & Barbour Pc Wi
SIC 1541 1542 5211 1751 Commercial & office building, new construction; School building construction; Hospital construction; Shopping center construction; Industrial buildings, new construction; Warehouse construction; Garage doors, sale & installation; Industrial buildings, new construction; Warehouse construction; Commercial & office building, new construction; School building construction; Hospital construction; Shopping center construction; Garage doors, sale & installation; Garage door, installation or erection
CEO: Douglas G Driver
**CFO:* Richard R Minnick
Sfty Dirs: Darren Hedrick
Sls Dir: Steven Hottle
Snr Mgr: Drew Meyerhoeffer

D-U-N-S 79-881-6369
LANTZ CONSTRUCTION CO OF WINCHESTER INC
L C W
221 Aviation Dr, Winchester, VA 22602-4571
Tel (540) 665-0130 *Founded/Ownrshp* 1984
Sales 23.5MM^E *EMP* 52
SIC 1542 1541 Commercial & office building, new construction; Commercial & office buildings, renovation & repair; Institutional building construction; Industrial buildings, new construction; Renovation, remodeling & repairs: industrial buildings
Ch Bd: Max A Clatterbuck
**Pr:* Max Clatterbuck
**VP:* Steven L Diehl
**Prin:* Allen Delano Ervin

D-U-N-S 83-591-6412
LANTZ SECURITY SYSTEMS INC
43440 Sahuayo St, Lancaster, CA 93535-4659
Tel (661) 949-3565 *Founded/Ownrshp* 1994
Sales 9.7MM^E *EMP* 500
SIC 7381 Security guard service; Security guard service
Pr: Jack E Lantz
**VP:* Jose Reyes

D-U-N-S 14-585-8770 EXP
LANXESS CORP
(*Suby of* LANXESS DEUTSCHLAND GMBH)
111 Parkwest Dr, Pittsburgh, PA 15275-1112
Tel (800) 526-9377 *Founded/Ownrshp* 2004
Sales 624.2MM^E *EMP* 1,620
SIC 2869 2821 2822 2816 2819 Industrial organic chemicals; Amines, acids, salts, esters; Aldehydes & ketones; Plastics materials & resins; Plasticizer/additive based plastic materials; Synthetic rubber; Butadiene rubbers; Inorganic pigments; Industrial inorganic chemicals; Industrial organic chemicals; Amines, acids, salts, esters; Aldehydes & ketones; Plastics materials & resins; Plasticizer/additive based plastic materials; Synthetic rubber; Butadiene rubbers; Inorganic pigments; Industrial inorganic chemicals
Pr: Flemming B Bjoernslev
CFO: Ray Newhouse
CFO: Thierry Petinaux
Top Exec: James Kok
Exec: Asmita Bhalla
Exec: Erin Bunda
Exec: Martin Bury
Dir Lab: Fernanda Albino
Comm Man: Philippe Van Wassenhove
**Prin:* Randall Dearth
Mng Dir: Kim Oconnor

D-U-N-S 60-855-6809 IMP/EXP
LANXESS SYBRON CHEMICALS INC
(*Suby of* LANXESS CORP) ★
200 Birmingham Rd, Birmingham, NJ 08011
Tel (609) 893-1100 *Founded/Ownrshp* 2000
Sales 131.0MM^E *EMP* 913
SIC 2843 2899 3589 Surface active agents; Textile processing assistants; Water treating compounds; Water filters & softeners, household type; Surface active agents; Textile processing assistants; Water treating compounds; Water filters & softeners, household type
Pr: Markus Linke
Mktg Mgr: Dwight Tamaki

D-U-N-S 62-130-0185
LANYON INC
(*Suby of* VISTA EQUITY PARTNERS LLC) ★
717 N Harwood St Ste 2200, Dallas, TX 75201-6515
Tel (866) 840-9987 *Founded/Ownrshp* 2013
Sales 37.3MM^E *EMP* 70^E
SIC 7371 5045 7389 5122 8741 Custom computer programming services; Computer software; Financial services; Pharmaceuticals; Management services
Ch: Nick Lanyon
Pr: Brent Traidman
**Pr:* Todd E Tyler
**CEO:* David Bonnette
**COO:* Kenny Cobern
**CFO:* John Mills

Sr VP: Teresa Grau
**Sr VP:* Anthony Miller
VP: Dee Thomas
Dir Soc: Amanda Bigley
**Prin:* John Pulling

D-U-N-S 08-895-1939
LANYON SOLUTIONS INC
RESERVEAMERICA
717 N Harwood St Ste 2200, Dallas, TX 75201-6515
Tel (817) 226-5656 *Founded/Ownrshp* 2013
Sales 100.0MM *EMP* 850
SIC 5734 Information services, consumer; Telephone communication, except radio; Software, business & non-game
CEO: David Bonnette
Pr: Josh Schlesser
CFO: Mark Miller
**CFO:* John Mills
Ofcr: Matt Ehrlichman
Ex VP: Kevin Biggs
Sr VP: Kourosh Vossoughi
VP: Kristin Carroll
VP: Andy George
VP: Frank Helwig
VP: Mike Reilly
Exec: Elisa Cheng
Board of Directors: David Alberga, Thomas N Clancy, Bruns H Grayson, Stephen L Green, Matthew Landa, Joseph Levin, Edward Neppl

D-U-N-S 02-763-6521 IMP
LANZ CABINET SHOP INC
LANZ CABINETS
3025 W 7th Pl, Eugene, OR 97402-6911
Tel (541) 485-4050 *Founded/Ownrshp* 1960
Sales 66.0MM^E *EMP* 250
SIC 2434 Wood kitchen cabinets; Wood kitchen cabinets
Pr: Brent Lanz
**VP:* Lori Lanz
Brnch Mgr: Matt Vultaggio
Sfty Mgr: James Cowells
VP Sls: Tami Anderson

LANZ CABINETS
See LANZ CABINET SHOP INC

D-U-N-S 82-818-8198
LANZATECH INC
FREEDOM PINES
(*Suby of* LANZATECH NEW ZEALAND LIMITED)
8045 Lamon Ave Ste 400, Skokie, IL 60077-5318
Tel (630) 439-3050 *Founded/Ownrshp* 2007
Sales 27.8MM^E *EMP* 80^E
SIC 2869 Industrial organic chemicals; Industrial organic chemicals
CEO: Jennifer Holmgren
Ex VP: Jean Paul Michel
VP: Mark Burton
VP: Ken C Lai
Board of Directors: Jennifer Holmgren

D-U-N-S 00-532-3456 IMP
LANZEN INC
30980 Groesbeck Hwy, Roseville, MI 48066-1511
Tel (586) 771-7070 *Founded/Ownrshp* 1960
Sales 21.9MM^E *EMP* 45
SIC 3444 3489 2531 Sheet metal specialties, not stamped; Metal housings, enclosures, casings & other containers; Ordnance & accessories; Vehicle furniture
Pr: Terry K Lanzen
VP: Archie Coffman
Plnt Mgr: Charles Fick
Snr Mgr: Scott Coon
Snr Mgr: Chuck Gravelle

D-U-N-S 14-481-4662
LANZO CONSTRUCTION CO FLORIDA
(*Suby of* LANZO CONSTRUCTION CO INC) ★
125 Se 5th Ct, Deerfield Beach, FL 33441-4749
Tel (954) 979-0802 *Founded/Ownrshp* 1980
Sales 87.1MM^E *EMP* 150^E
SIC 1623 Sewer line construction; Water main construction; Pumping station construction; Sewer line construction; Water main construction; Pumping station construction
Ch Bd: Quirino D'Alessandro
**Sec:* Rose Torres
**VP:* Angelo D'Alessandro
**VP:* Quirino D'Alessandro Jr

D-U-N-S 00-491-3802
LANZO CONSTRUCTION CO INC (MI)
LANZO TRENCHLESS TECH N
28135 Groesbeck Hwy, Roseville, MI 48066-2395
Tel (586) 775-7566 *Founded/Ownrshp* 1965
Sales 87.1MM^E *EMP* 250
SIC 1623 Sewer line construction; Water main construction; Pumping station construction; Sewer line construction
Pr: Quirino D'Alessandro Sr
**VP:* Angelo D'Alessandro
**VP:* Quirino D'Alessandro Jr
**VP:* Rose D'Alessandro-Torres
VP: Guiseppe Dalessandro
Off Mgr: Helen Habuda

LANZO TRENCHLESS TECH N
See LANZO CONSTRUCTION CO INC

D-U-N-S 80-296-2969
LAP ENTERPRISES INC
FOUR CORNERS SERVICE COMPANY
28 Equennes Dr, Little Rock, AR 72223-9166
Tel (501) 372-6577 *Founded/Ownrshp* 1987
Sales 5.3MM^E *EMP* 300
SIC 7349 Janitorial service, contract basis; Janitorial service, contract basis
Pr: Doug Beaver

D-U-N-S 10-897-3173
LAPARKAN TRADING LIMITED CO
(*Suby of* LAPARKAN INVESTMENTS LTD)
3775 Nw 77th St, Miami, FL 33147-4434
Tel (305) 836-4393 *Founded/Ownrshp* 1983
Sales 44.9MM^E *EMP* 154
SIC 4731 Freight transportation arrangement; Freight consolidation; Freight transportation arrangement; Freight consolidation
CEO: Glen Khan
V Ch: Hussein Haniff
**CFO:* Tallim Samad
**VP:* Gordon Berment
IT Man: Imtiaz Samad
MIS Mgr: Phillipe Santana

D-U-N-S 14-733-2571
LAPC OASIS INC
ALEXIS PARK RESORT HOTEL
375 E Harmon Ave, Las Vegas, NV 89169-7081
Tel (702) 796-3300 *Founded/Ownrshp* 1985
Sales 17.2MM^E *EMP* 325
SIC 7011 7299 Resort hotel; Banquet hall facilities; Resort hotel; Banquet hall facilities
Ex Dir: Constance Garceau
Sls Mgr: Jeff Carden
Sls Mgr: Terry Clark
Sls Mgr: Sarah Suppe

LAPEER BOARD OF EDUCATION
See LAPEER COMMUNITY SCHOOLS

D-U-N-S 08-832-8737
LAPEER COMMUNITY SCHOOLS
LAPEER BOARD OF EDUCATION
250 2nd St, Lapeer, MI 48446-1445
Tel (810) 538-1638 *Founded/Ownrshp* 1900
Sales 56.6MM *EMP* 730
Accts Plante & Moran Pllc Auburn H
SIC 8211 Public elementary & secondary schools; School board; Public elementary & secondary schools; School board
CTO: Thomas Kaiser
MIS Dir: Brenda Weir
Pr Dir: Jared Field
Teacher Pr: Kim Seifferly
Teacher Pr: Kim Seifferty

D-U-N-S 07-279-0165
LAPEER COUNTY MEDICAL CARE FACILITY
SUNCREST
1455 Suncrest Dr, Lapeer, MI 48446-1151
Tel (810) 664-8571 *Founded/Ownrshp* 1966
Sales 24.3MM *EMP* 400
SIC 8051 Extended care facility; Extended care facility
Bd of Dir: Kenneth Ewing
**Prin:* Doug Campbell
**Prin:* Linda Stone
Ex Dir: Diann Miller

D-U-N-S 07-633-8466 IMP
LAPEER INDUSTRIES INC
400 Mccormick Dr, Lapeer, MI 48446-2572
Tel (810) 664-1816 *Founded/Ownrshp* 1974
Sales 36.5MM^E *EMP* 110^E
Accts Janz & Knight Plc
SIC 3728 3544 Military aircraft equipment & armament; Turrets & turret drives, aircraft; Turret test fixtures, aircraft; Special dies & tools; Military aircraft equipment & armament; Turrets & turret drives, aircraft; Turret test fixtures, aircraft; Special dies & tools
CEO: Ray Bellan
**Pr:* Daniel C Schreiber
**CFO:* Alan Przekora
**Ex VP:* Eddie Hollomon
**VP:* Michael C Schreiber
Dir Bus: Jeff Brannon
Dir Bus: John Spearing
**Prin:* Chris Olson
Prgrm Mgr: Brandon Bland
Prgrm Mgr: Matt Phelps
Prgrm Mgr: Henry Rise

D-U-N-S 96-336-9785
LAPEER PLATING & PLASTICS INC
395 Demille Rd, Lapeer, MI 48446-3055
Tel (810) 667-4240 *Founded/Ownrshp* 2011
Sales 71.5MM^E *EMP* 225
SIC 2431 3089 Moldings & baseboards, ornamental & trim; Injection molded finished plastic products; Moldings & baseboards, ornamental & trim; Injection molded finished plastic products
CEO: Larry Gatt
Prgrm Mgr: Tim Van
S&M/VP: Tom Prusha

LAPEER REGION MEDICAL CENTER
See MCLAREN LAPEER REGION

D-U-N-S 82-868-9617
LAPEER REGIONAL MEDICAL CENTER
(*Suby of* MCLAREN HEALTH CARE CORP) ★
1375 N Main St, Lapeer, MI 48446-1350
Tel (810) 667-5500 *Founded/Ownrshp* 2013
Sales 121.7MM *EMP* 800
SIC 8062 General medical & surgical hospitals; General medical & surgical hospitals
Pr: Philip Incarnati
**COO:* Michael Taylor
CFO: Mary Beth
CFO: Mary Callahan
**CFO:* Dave Mazurkiewicz
**Ex VP:* Michael McKenna
**Sr VP:* Gregory Lane
**Prin:* Barton Buxton
HC Dir: Susan Engelbrink

D-U-N-S 07-422-5806
LAPEER REGIONAL MEDICAL CENTER FOUNDATION
(*Suby of* MCLAREN HEALTH CARE CORP) ★
1375 N Main St, Lapeer, MI 48446-1350
Tel (810) 245-3668 *Founded/Ownrshp* 1994
Sales 200.8M *EMP* 700
Accts Plante & Moran Pllc Portage
SIC 8322 Rehabilitation services; Rehabilitation services
Pr: Barton Buxton
**CFO:* Mary Beth Callahan
**VP:* Clarence Sevillian

D-U-N-S 00-693-0986 IMP
LAPHAM-HICKEY STEEL CORP
5500 W 73rd St, Chicago, IL 60638-6587
Tel (708) 496-6111 *Founded/Ownrshp* 1956
Sales 229.3MM^E *EMP* 450
SIC 5051 3398 3355 3317 3316 Bars, metal; Strip, metal; Tubing, metal; Metal heat treating; Aluminum rolling & drawing; Steel pipe & tubes; Cold finishing of steel shapes; Bars, metal; Strip, metal; Tubing, metal; Metal heat treating; Aluminum rolling & drawing; Steel pipe & tubes; Cold finishing of steel shapes
Pr: William M Hickey Jr
**CFO:* Bob Piland
VP: Rick Oconnell
**Prin:* Bill Hickey
Brnch Mgr: Mike Dedic
Genl Mgr: Stephen Ford
Dir IT: Christine Colon
IT Man: Robert Carlisle
IT Man: Mandy O'Brien
Sfty Mgr: Ryan Cluckey
Opers Mgr: Dennis Berger

D-U-N-S 05-454-8284 IMP
LAPINE ASSOCIATES INC (CT)
(*Suby of* DAVID S LAPINE INC) ★
15 Commerce Rd Lowr 1, Stamford, CT 06902-4553
Tel (203) 327-9099 *Founded/Ownrshp* 1983
Sales 29.6MM^E *EMP* 60^E
SIC 5064

LAPLAYA BEACH AND GOLF RESORT
See WEST GROUP LAPLAYA LLC

D-U-N-S 13-884-9877
LAPMASTER INTERNATIONAL LLC
BARNES BORE HONING
(*Suby of* LAPMASTER GROUP HOLDINGS LLC)
501 W Algonquin Rd, Mount Prospect, IL 60056-5788
Tel (224) 659-7101 *Founded/Ownrshp* 2003
Sales 53.4MM^E *EMP* 95
SIC 8711 Machine tool design
CFO: Tom Martin
Genl Mgr: Kelly Cavitt
Ql Cn Mgr: Rolf Bastian
Ql Cn Mgr: Sal Khan

D-U-N-S 02-471-8178 IMP/EXP
▲ LAPOLLA INDUSTRIES INC
15402 Vantage Pkwy E # 322, Houston, TX 77032-1966
Tel (281) 219-4700 *Founded/Ownrshp* 1989
Sales 72.0MM *EMP* 73
Accts Hein & Associates Llp Houston
Tkr Sym LPAD *Exch* OTC
SIC 2952 2851 3069 2891 Roofing felts, cements or coatings; Paints & paint additives; Foam rubber; Adhesives & sealants; Roofing felts, cements or coatings; Paints & paint additives; Foam rubber; Adhesives & sealants
Pr: Douglas J Kramer
Ch Bd: Richard J Kurtz
COO: Kevin Conners
COO: Harvey L Schnitzer
CFO: Jomarc C Marukot
CFO: David C Stearnes
CFO: Charles Zajaczkowsk
V Ch Bd: Jay C Nadel
Ex VP: Michael T Adams
VP: Pete Pierangeli
Tech Mgr: Mike Chambers

D-U-N-S 80-915-1975
▲ LAPORTE BANCORP INC
710 Indiana Ave, La Porte, IN 46350-3404
Tel (219) 362-7511 *Founded/Ownrshp* 2012
Sales NA *EMP* 112^E
Tkr Sym LPSB *Exch* NAS
SIC 6035 Savings institutions, federally chartered; Savings institutions, federally chartered
CEO: Lee A Brady
**Ch Bd:* Paul G Fenker
**Pr:* Michele M Thompson
**V Ch Bd:* Jerry L Mayes
Chf Cred: Daniel P Carroll
Bd of Dir: L Lukmann
Sr VP: Kevin N Beres
Sr VP: Patrick W Collins

D-U-N-S 96-412-7398
LAPORTE HOSPITAL INC
Tunnel 7 Lincoln Way, La Porte, IN 46350
Tel (219) 326-2305 *Founded/Ownrshp* 2010
Sales 155.8MM *EMP* 39^E
SIC 8062 General medical & surgical hospitals
Prin: Sarah Evans Barker
VP: Jeffrey Anderson
VP: Connie Ford
Dir Rad: Matt Shebel
Opers Mgr: Dennis Marshall
Pathlgst: Lisa Ostrowski
Diag Rad: Krishna Pillai

D-U-N-S 94-801-2596 IMP
LAPP HOLDING NA INC
(*Suby of* LAPP BETEILIGUNGS-KG)
29 Hanover Rd, Florham Park, NJ 07932-1408
Tel (973) 660-9700 *Founded/Ownrshp* 1988
Sales 136.5MM^E *EMP* 199^E
SIC 3355 Aluminum wire & cable; Aluminum wire & cable
Pr: Marc Mackin
Ex VP: Tom McPherson

D-U-N-S 11-832-3252 IMP
LAPP INSULATORS LLC
130 Gilbert St, Le Roy, NY 14482-1392
Tel (585) 768-6221 *Founded/Ownrshp* 1916
Sales 23.1MM^E *EMP* 125
SIC 3264 3644 Insulators, electrical: porcelain; Noncurrent-carrying wiring services; Insulators & insulation materials, electrical; Insulators, electrical: porcelain; Noncurrent-carrying wiring services; Insulators & insulation materials, electrical
CEO: Bernhard Kahl
**Pr:* Rob Johnson
**CFO:* Veronika Capek
Dir Soc: Julie Roth
Genl Mgr: Geoffrey Buell
CIO: Robert Vanderstouw
QA Dir: Eric Kress
Dir IT: Bob Vanderstouw
Plnt Mgr: Wayne Subject
Natl Sales: Jim Pries
Manager: Paul Chang

D-U-N-S 08-298-3172 IMP
LAPP USA LLC
(*Suby of* LAPP HOLDING NA INC) ★
29 Hanover Rd, Florham Park, NJ 07932-1408
Tel (973) 660-9700 *Founded/Ownrshp* 1976
Sales 112.5MM^E *EMP* 132
SIC 5063 Control & signal wire & cable, including coaxial; Control & signal wire & cable, including coaxial
Pr: Andreas Lapp
**COO:* Marc K Mackin
Ex VP: Thomas Barmann
**Ex VP:* Rob Conway
Ex VP: Geoff Grace
Ex VP: David Solano
**VP:* George Dann
VP: Randy Sadler
Ex Dir: Jim Takacs
CTO: Jay Cordero
Dir IT: Tom Mackin

D-U-N-S 11-816-3898
LAPTALO ENTERPRISES INC
J L PRECISION SHEET METAL
2360 Zanker Rd, San Jose, CA 95131-1115
Tel (408) 727-6633 *Founded/Ownrshp* 1984
Sales 33.2MM^E *EMP* 100
SIC 3444 Sheet metalwork
CEO: Jakov Laptalo
**Pr:* Michael Laptalo
VP: Todd Morey
Ql Cn Mgr: Ray Sanchez

D-U-N-S 08-001-6967
LAQUEY SCHOOL DISTRICT OF PULASKI COUNTY
27600 Highway Aa, Laquey, MO 65534-7694
Tel (573) 765-3716 *Founded/Ownrshp* 1948
Sales 15.0MM^E *EMP* 785
SIC 8211 Public combined elementary & secondary school; Public combined elementary & secondary school
**Prin:* Eric Shaw
**Prin:* Jerry Stenson

LAQUILA/PINNACLE
See PINNACLE CONCRETE CORP

LAR LU
See WINCRAFT INC

D-U-N-S 61-277-9041
LARAMAR GROUP LLC
222 S Riverside Plz, Chicago, IL 60606-5808
Tel (312) 669-1200 *Founded/Ownrshp* 2001
Sales 16.4MM^E *EMP* 500^E
SIC 6531 Cooperative apartment manager; Cooperative apartment manager
Pr: Jeff Elowe

LARAMIE AUTO CENTER
See LARAMIE GM AUTO CENTER INC

D-U-N-S 80-488-5754
LARAMIE COUNTY COMMUNITY COLLEGE
1400 E College Dr, Cheyenne, WY 82007-3295
Tel (307) 778-5222 *Founded/Ownrshp* 1968
Sales 19.7MM *EMP* 502
Accts Mcgee Hearne & Paiz Llp Che
SIC 8222 Community college; Community college
Pr: Darrel L Hammon
**Pr:* Dr Joe Schaffer
COO: Chad Marley
Ex VP: Peggie Kresl-Hotz
Ex VP: Marlene Tignor
VP: Carol Hoglund
Exec: Terry Cook
Exec: Kelli Griffith
Exec: Ann Murray
Prgrm Mgr: Nicole Sackrider
Prgrm Mgr: Jacob Sones

D-U-N-S 07-576-2971
LARAMIE COUNTY SCHOOL DISTRICT 1
2810 House Ave, Cheyenne, WY 82001-2860
Tel (307) 771-2100 *Founded/Ownrshp* 1890
Sales 227.5MM *EMP* 1,600
Accts Mcgee Hearne & Paiz Llp Che
SIC 8211 Private elementary & secondary schools; Private elementary & secondary schools
CEO: Mark Stock
Bd of Dir: Alfred Atkins
Bd of Dir: Anne Beckle
Trfc Dir: Mike Larson

D-U-N-S 03-378-9132
LARAMIE COUNTY WYOMING
COUNTY CLERK
309 W 20th St, Cheyenne, WY 82001-3601
Tel (307) 633-4264 *Founded/Ownrshp* 1872
Sales NA *EMP* 325
Accts Porter Muirhead Cornia & How
SIC 9111 County supervisors' & executives' offices; ; County supervisors' & executives' offices;
Ch: Diane Humprey
**Ch Bd:* Jack Knudsen
V Ch: Buck Holmes
Plng Mgr: Barbara Kloth
Plng Mgr: Brett Walker
Dir IT: Rick Fortney
IT Man: David Flood
Snr Mgr: Dan Cooley
Board of Directors: Diane Humphries, Jeff Ketcham As Commission

D-U-N-S 06-742-9352
LARAMIE GM AUTO CENTER INC
LARAMIE AUTO CENTER
3600 E Grand Ave, Laramie, WY 82070-5110
Tel (307) 745-8961 *Founded/Ownrshp* 2001
Sales 34.4MM^E *EMP* 91

SIC 5511 Automobiles, new & used; Pickups, new & used; Automobiles, new & used; Pickups, new & used
Genl Mgr: Mike Haigler
Sls Mgr: Joe Hedley
Sls Mgr: Barrett Shipman
Sales Asso: Joe Gossman
Sales Asso: Aaron Hardesty
Sales Asso: Sue Morgan
Sales Asso: Adrian Trujillo
Sales Asso: Kevin Watkins

LARAMIE TIRES
See TREADWAYS CORP

LARC
See LAFAYETTE ASSOCIATION FOR RETARDED CITIZENS INC

D-U-N-S 78-133-5773
LARCHMONT IMAGING ASSOCIATES LLC
1295 Route 38, Hainesport, NJ 08036-2702
Tel (609) 261-4500 *Founded/Ownrshp* 1991
Sales 32.5MM^E *EMP* 275
SIC 8011 Radiologist; Radiologist
Pr: Edwin Wilson MD
Off Mgr: Ginnie Guchini
IT Man: Robert Walsh
Diag Rad: William Morgan
Diag Rad: Vincent J Taormina

LARCO CONSTRUCTION CO
See SLOAN CONSTRUCTION CO INC

D-U-N-S 60-815-0876
LARCO ENTERPRISES INC
SONIC DRIVE-IN
29 S Main St, Miami, OK 74354-7022
Tel (918) 542-1679 *Founded/Ownrshp* 1976
Sales 20.7MM^E *EMP* 665
SIC 5812 Drive-in restaurant; Drive-in restaurant
Pr: Larry Smith
CFO: Tom Franz
**Sys/Asst:* Kristi Radebaugh
VP Opers: Greg Smith

D-U-N-S 15-574-9864
LARD OIL CO INC
914 Florida Ave Sw, Denham Springs, LA 70726-4340
Tel (800) 738-7738 *Founded/Ownrshp* 1959
Sales 34.0MM^E *EMP* 48
SIC 5172 Diesel fuel; Gasoline; Lubricating oils & greases; Diesel fuel; Gasoline; Lubricating oils & greases
Pr: Johnny Milazzo
CFO: Mills Murrey
**Treas:* J Mills Murrey
Opers Mgr: Fred Guedry
Plnt Mgr: Craig Petry
S&M/VP: Steve Faulk
Sls Mgr: Brian Babin
Sls Mgr: Mike Ezell
Sls Mgr: Glenn Ferachi
Sls Mgr: Doug Schexnayder
Sls Mgr: Keith Stanley

D-U-N-S 17-864-4993
LAREDO ALARM SYSTEMS INC
1601 Jacaman Rd, Laredo, TX 78041-6140
Tel (956) 723-2738 *Founded/Ownrshp* 1992
Sales 22.2MM^E *EMP* 65
SIC 5063 1731 Alarm systems; Fire detection & burglar alarm systems specialization
Pr: Fidel Gonzalez
**VP:* Rose M Gonzalez

D-U-N-S 00-812-0412
■ **LAREDO COCA-COLA BOTTLING CO**
(*Suby of* AUSTIN COCA-COLA BOTTLING CO) ★
1402 Industrial Blvd, Laredo, TX 78041-2508
Tel (956) 726-2671 *Founded/Ownrshp* 1930
Sales 74.5MM^E *EMP* 399
SIC 5149 Soft drinks; Soft drinks
Sfty Mgr: Tino Villarreal

D-U-N-S 07-461-5550
LAREDO COMMUNITY COLLEGE
1 W End Washington St, Laredo, TX 78040-4301
Tel (956) 722-0521 *Founded/Ownrshp* 1947
Sales 30.9MM^E *EMP* 610
Accts Canales Garza & Baum Pllc La
SIC 8222 Junior college; Junior college
Pr: Juan L Maldonado
CFO: Daniel Flores
VP: Dianna Miller
VP: Janette Perez
Dir Risk M: Martin Villarreal
Mng Ofcr: Orlando Zepeda
CTO: Jose Pena
Psych: Sylvia Trevino
Pgrm Dir: Albert Hernandez

D-U-N-S 12-471-8292
LAREDO ENERGY ARENA
6700 Arena, Laredo, TX 78041-1949
Tel (956) 791-9192 *Founded/Ownrshp* 2002
Sales 27.0MM^E *EMP* 325
SIC 1542 Commercial & office building contractors; Commercial & office building contractors
CFO: Ray Reyes
Genl Mgr: Roy Medina
Opers Mgr: Andy Ysaguirre
Secur Mgr: Rolando Flores
Sales Exec: Amanda Mendiola

D-U-N-S 79-106-2909
LAREDO ENERGY IV GP LLC
840 Houston Ave, Houston, TX 77007
Tel (713) 600-6000 *Founded/Ownrshp* 2006
Sales 28.7MM^E *EMP* 30
SIC 1311 Natural gas production
CEO: Glenn D Hart
Pr: Douglas Fogle
CFO: P Gessinger
VP: Mark Lange
VP: Douglas Swanson
VP Opers: Jeff Shyer
Prd Mgr: Douglas Kaiser
Snr Mgr: Paul Thompson

D-U-N-S 00-176-3130
LAREDO FIREFIGHTERS RETIREMENT SYSTEM
5219 Tesoro Plz, Laredo, TX 78041-5752
Tel (956) 725-9362 *Founded/Ownrshp* 1942
Sales NA *EMP* 8
SIC 6411 Pension & retirement plan consultants; Pension & retirement plan consultants
Ch: Joe Cavares

LAREDO FREIGHT DISPATCH
See FREIGHT DISPATCH SERVICE AGENCY LTD

D-U-N-S 02-673-4293
LAREDO GONZALEZ AUTO PARTS LTD
4220 San Bernardo Ave, Laredo, TX 78041-4447
Tel (956) 726-9766 *Founded/Ownrshp* 1934
Sales 31.8MM^E *EMP* 112
SIC 5531 5013 Automotive parts; Automotive accessories; Automotive supplies & parts
Genl Pt: Roberto Gonzalez
Pt: Javier Gonzalez
Prin: Joseph Gage Jr

D-U-N-S 05-757-0640
LAREDO INDEPENDENT SCHOOL DISTRICT EDUCATIONAL FOUNDATION
LAREDO ISD
1702 Houston St, Laredo, TX 78040-4906
Tel (956) 795-3200 *Founded/Ownrshp* 1946
Sales 172.1MM^E *EMP* 3,800
Accts Weaver And Tidwell Llp Housto
SIC 8211 Public elementary & secondary schools; Public elementary & secondary schools
CFO: Florinda Ayala-Delgado
**CFO:* Alvaro Perez
Dir IT: Elizabeth Garcia

LAREDO ISD
See LAREDO INDEPENDENT SCHOOL DISTRICT EDUCATIONAL FOUNDATION

D-U-N-S 05-511-6214 IMP
■ **LAREDO MEDICAL CENTER**
(*Suby of* COMMUNITY HEALTH SYSTEMS INC) ★
1700 E Saunders St, Laredo, TX 78041-5474
Tel (956) 796-5000 *Founded/Ownrshp* 2003
Sales 412.8MM *EMP* 1,600
SIC 8062 General medical & surgical hospitals; General medical & surgical hospitals
CEO: Aaron Hazard
**Pr:* Abraham Martinez
**COO:* John Ulbricht
**CFO:* Ed Romero
Dir Risk M: Veronica Gonzalez
Dir Lab: Edna Solis
Dir Lab: Edna Soliz
Dir Rad: David Claudio
Dir Rx: Elizabeth Kaczmarek
Dir Sec: David Moreno
Dir IT: Elvia Gonzalez

D-U-N-S 07-908-7530
■ **LAREDO MIDSTREAM SERVICES LLC**
(*Suby of* LAREDO PETROLEUM INC) ★
15 W 6th St Ste 1800, Tulsa, OK 74119-5412
Tel (918) 513-4570 *Founded/Ownrshp* 2013
Sales 11.7MM^E *EMP* 340
SIC 1311 Crude petroleum & natural gas production; Crude petroleum & natural gas production
CEO: Randy A Foutch

D-U-N-S 02-083-7686
LAREDO PETROLEUM INC
508 W Wall St Ste 600, Midland, TX 79701-5073
Tel (432) 684-9955 *Founded/Ownrshp* 2008
Sales 44.5MM^E *EMP* 50
SIC 5172 Petroleum products
CEO: Randy A Foutch
**VP:* Patrick J Curth

D-U-N-S 07-833-0012
▲ **LAREDO PETROLEUM INC**
15 W 6th St Ste 1800, Tulsa, OK 74119-5412
Tel (918) 513-4570 *Founded/Ownrshp* 2011
Sales 793.8MM *EMP* 420^E
Tkr Sym LPI *Exch* NYS
SIC 1311 Crude petroleum & natural gas production; Crude petroleum & natural gas production
Ch Bd: Randy A Foutch
**Pr:* Jay P Still
CFO: Richard C Buterbaugh
Ex VP: Jerry Schuyler
Sr VP: Kenneth E Dornblaser
Sr VP: John Minton
VP: Michael T Beyer
VP: Mark Elliot
VP: Mark King
VP: Gary Smallwood
Exec: James R Courtier
Board of Directors: Peter R Kagan, James R Levy, Bill Z Parker, Pamela S Pierce, Francis Rooney, Myles W Scoggins, Edmund P Segner III, Donald D Wolf

D-U-N-S 79-885-8887
LAREDO PETROLEUM LLC
15 W 6th St Ste 1800, Tulsa, OK 74119-5412
Tel (918) 513-4570 *Founded/Ownrshp* 2007
Sales 51.8MM^E *EMP* 35^E
SIC 1311 Crude petroleum & natural gas
Pr: Jay P Still
Pr: Jerry R Schuyler
CEO: Randy A Foutch

D-U-N-S 10-855-9873
LAREDO REAL FOODS INC
DANNYS RESTAURANT
1319 Hidalgo St, Laredo, TX 78040-5746
Tel (956) 712-2140 *Founded/Ownrshp* 1998
Sales 14.8MM^E *EMP* 350
SIC 5812 Mexican restaurant; Grills (eating places); Mexican restaurant; Grills (eating places)
Pr: Daniel Lopez
**VP:* Miguel Lopez

D-U-N-S 80-583-1901
■ **LAREDO REGIONAL MEDICAL CENTER L P**
DOCTORS HOSPITAL OF LAREDO
(*Suby of* UNIVERSAL HEALTH SERVICES INC) ★
10700 Mcpherson Rd, Laredo, TX 78045-6268
Tel (956) 523-2000 *Founded/Ownrshp* 1999
Sales 134.8MM *EMP* 300
SIC 8062 8071 General medical & surgical hospitals; Medical laboratories; General medical & surgical hospitals; Medical laboratories
Pt: Rene Lopez
Genl Pt: Alan B Miller
Pt: Marc Miller
Dir Teleco: Maribel Mata
Dir Rad: Carlos Farias
Dir Rx: Daniel Crossley

LAREDO WATERWORKS SYSTEM
See CITY OF LAREDO

D-U-N-S 14-613-0559
LAREDO WLE LP
TOPAZ POWER GROUP
7300 Cpl Rd, Laredo, TX 78041-2531
Tel (956) 721-5607 *Founded/Ownrshp* 2004
Sales 26.5MM^E *EMP* 36
SIC 4911 Generation, electric power
Pt: J Darren Stephens
Tech Mgr: Cecilia Garcia
Plnt Mgr: Joe C Guerra
Plnt Mgr: Warren O'Shields
Plnt Mgr: Tom Walker

D-U-N-S 61-361-9782
LARGO CONCRETE INC
2741 Walnut Ave Ste 110, Tustin, CA 92780-7040
Tel (714) 731-3600 *Founded/Ownrshp* 1989
Sales 85.1MM^E *EMP* 500
SIC 1771

LARGO MED CTR
See LARGO MEDICAL CENTER INC

D-U-N-S 60-991-6762 IMP
■ **LARGO MEDICAL CENTER INC**
LARGO MED CTR
(*Suby of* HCA INC) ★
201 14th St Sw, Largo, FL 33770-3199
Tel (727) 588-5200 *Founded/Ownrshp* 1984
Sales 249.3MM^E *EMP* 755^E
SIC 8062 General medical & surgical hospitals; General medical & surgical hospitals
CEO: Anthony Degina
**Pr:* Richard H Satcher
**CFO:* Robert Billings
**Treas:* Vicky A Chiszar
Dir IT: David Saly
Mktg Mgr: Holly Borota
Surgeon: Wesley Gladin
Doctor: Paul Steele MD
Pharmcst: Earl Statzer
Dir Health: Trish McWhorter

D-U-N-S 05-515-1166 IMP
■ **LARIAT SERVICES INC**
(*Suby of* SANDRIDGE ENERGY INC) ★
123 Robert S Kerr Ave, Oklahoma City, OK 73102-6406
Tel (405) 753-5500 *Founded/Ownrshp* 2010
Sales 392.3MM^E *EMP* 888^E
SIC 1382 Oil & gas exploration services; Oil & gas exploration services
Pr: N Malone Mitchell III

LARICHE CHEVROLET-CADILLAC
See LARICHE SUBARU INC

D-U-N-S 13-506-9995
LARICHE SUBARU INC
LARICHE CHEVROLET-CADILLAC
215 E Main Cross St, Findlay, OH 45840-4818
Tel (419) 422-1855 *Founded/Ownrshp* 1985
Sales 32.3MM^E *EMP* 72
SIC 5511 5521 7515 7538 Automobiles, new & used; Pickups, new & used; Used car dealers; Passenger car leasing; General automotive repair shops; Automobiles, new & used; Pickups, new & used; Used car dealers; Passenger car leasing; General automotive repair shops
Pr: Lou Lariche
**Sec:* Scott Lariche
**VP:* John Lariche
IT Man: Sam Maidlow
Sls Mgr: Chuck Baker
Sls Mgr: Jennie Collazo

D-U-N-S 00-694-4201
LARIO OIL & GAS CO
301 S Market St, Wichita, KS 67202-3805
Tel (316) 265-5611 *Founded/Ownrshp* 2011
Sales 53.7MM^E *EMP* 67
SIC 1311 1382 Crude petroleum production; Natural gas production; Oil & gas exploration services; Crude petroleum production; Natural gas production; Oil & gas exploration services
Ch Bd: Patrick E O Shaughnessy
**Pr:* Michael W O Shaughnessy
**CFO:* David Loger
**VP:* Rick Stinson

D-U-N-S 04-485-3018
LARIOT CORP
KFC
4404 S 6th St, Klamath Falls, OR 97603-4866
Tel (541) 882-7288 *Founded/Ownrshp* 1980
Sales 7.9MM^E *EMP* 300
SIC 5812 Fast-food restaurant, chain; Fast-food restaurant, chain
Pr: Larry Stewart
**VP:* Barry Thiriot

D-U-N-S 17-712-6885 IMP/EXP
■ **LARK ENGINEERING CO**
(*Suby of* RUGGED PORTABLE SYSTEMS) ★
2000 W Corporate Way, Anaheim, CA 92801-5373
Tel (949) 240-1233 *Founded/Ownrshp* 2013
Sales 31.9MM^E *EMP* 175
SIC 3679 Microwave components
CEO: Allen Ronk
CFO: Nancy Baier
CFO: Andrew Lewis
VP: Alfonso Martinez
VP Sls: Javier Merino
Sales Asso: Daisy Tan

D-U-N-S 18-504-8824
LARK INDUSTRIES INC
RESIDENTIAL DESIGN SERVICE
4900 E Hunter Ave, Anaheim, CA 92807-2057
Tel (714) 701-4200 *Founded/Ownrshp* 1988
Sales 61.1MM^E *EMP* 200^E
SIC 7389 Interior design services; Interior design services
CEO: Richard D Scholten
Ex VP: Bob Adams
**Ex VP:* Kip Cruze
VP: Scott Cheeseman
VP: Kelli Finale
VP: Paul Forgay
Genl Mgr: Jennifer Huse
Dir IT: Jennifer Kamenca
S&M/VP: Beverly Messemer

D-U-N-S 01-910-1740
LARK INNS LP UNIVERSITY INN
HOWARD JOHNSON
5 Dorset St, South Burlington, VT 05403-6232
Tel (802) 863-5541 *Founded/Ownrshp* 1980
Sales 16.9MM^E *EMP* 408
SIC 7011 7991 5812 Hotels & motels; Physical fitness facilities; Eating places; Hotels & motels; Hotels; Physical fitness facilities; Eating places
Genl Mgr: Mike Sherran
Pt: John Larkin
Pt: Richard Tarrant

D-U-N-S 04-198-5441
LARKEN INC (IA)
824 N St Sw, Cedar Rapids, IA 52404-2708
Tel (319) 366-8201 *Founded/Ownrshp* 1967
Sales 19.2MM^E *EMP* 750^E
SIC 7011 8741 Hotels & motels; Hotel or motel management
Pr: Lawrence Cahill
**VP:* Kenneth Cahill

D-U-N-S 07-608-9622
LARKIN COMMUNITY HOSPITAL INC
7031 Sw 62nd Ave, South Miami, FL 33143-4701
Tel (305) 284-7500 *Founded/Ownrshp* 1997
Sales 101.5MM *EMP* 525
SIC 8062 General medical & surgical hospitals; General medical & surgical hospitals
Pr: Jack Michel
Chf Rad: Patricio Rossi
CFO: Estephany Giraldo
VP: Edgar Castillo
VP: Gary Levin
Exec: Vanessa Aguirre
Dir Lab: Millie Fennema
Off Mgr: Cindy Cortez
Off Admin: Madeleine Gonzalez
CTO: Juan Oms
Surgeon: Quoc Dang

D-U-N-S 09-172-7644
LARKIN HOFFMAN DALY & LINDGREN LTD
8300 Norman Center Dr # 10, Minneapolis, MN 55437-1027
Tel (952) 835-3800 *Founded/Ownrshp* 1969
Sales 24.7MM^E *EMP* 150
SIC 8111 Legal services; Legal services
Pr: William Griffith
Pr: Rachel Crary
**COO:* Richard A Knutson
CFO: Charles Modell
CTO: Mark Brauch
MIS Dir: Mark Brak
Dir IT: Peter Coyle

D-U-N-S 95-850-3070
LARKSPUR HOSPITALITY DEVELOPMENT AND MANAGEMENT CO LLC
125 E Sir F Drake Blvd, Larkspur, CA 94939
Tel (415) 945-5000 *Founded/Ownrshp* 1996
Sales 19.9MM^E *EMP* 650
SIC 7011 Hotels & motels; Hotels & motels
VP: Michael J Sherwood
VP: Mike Speckman
Genl Mgr: Greg Mauldin
CTO: Patrick Falls
Sales Asso: Donna Lombardo

D-U-N-S 07-872-2924
LARNED STATE HOSPITAL
1301 K264 Hwy, Larned, KS 67550-5353
Tel (620) 285-4392 *Founded/Ownrshp* 1911
Sales 23.5MM^E *EMP* 99
SIC 8063 Psychiatric hospitals
Psych: Angela Burcham
Psych: Robert Connell
Psych: John Reid

D-U-N-S 02-609-3989
LAROCHE CHEVROLET-CADILLAC INC
900 Highway 290 W, Brenham, TX 77833-5422
Tel (979) 836-6666 *Founded/Ownrshp* 1962
Sales 26.0MM^E *EMP* 68
SIC 5511 Automobiles, new & used; Pickups, new & used; Vans, new & used; Automobiles, new & used; Pickups, new & used; Vans, new & used
Pr: Darrell Blum
**Pr:* Paul F Laroche Jr
**Treas:* Michelle Wellmann
**VP:* Paul P Laroche III
Dir Rx: Robert Klingsporn

D-U-N-S 79-181-5848
LAROHN INC
DEVEROES
7606 Lesourdsville W, West Chester, OH 45069-1233
Tel (513) 352-0657 *Founded/Ownrshp* 1992
Sales 22.1MM *EMP* 170
SIC 5611 5661

D-U-N-S 02-069-2612 IMP
LARON INC
4255 N Santa Fe Dr, Kingman, AZ 86401-6727
Tel (928) 757-8424 *Founded/Ownrshp* 1989
Sales 48.0MM^E *EMP* 250
SIC 3443 3599 5063 7692 Fabricated plate work (boiler shop); Machine shop, jobbing & repair; Electrical apparatus & equipment; Welding repair; Fabricated plate work (boiler shop); Machine shop, jobbing & repair; Electrical apparatus & equipment; Welding repair
CEO: Glenn Thoroughman
**COO:* John Hansen
**CFO:* Gary Maclay
**Sec:* Toni Alexander
Genl Mgr: Tim Juvera
Opers Mgr: Susie Nicks
Sls Mgr: Dave Taylor

D-U-N-S 80-810-7242
LARON PHARMA INC
500 Office Center Dr # 400, Fort Washington, PA 19034-3219
Tel (267) 575-1470 *Founded/Ownrshp* 2006
Sales 300.0MM *EMP* 15
SIC 2834 5122 Pharmaceutical preparations; Pharmaceuticals; Pharmaceutical preparations; Pharmaceuticals
CEO: Afoluso Adesanya
**Pr:* Adenekan H Adesanya

D-U-N-S 01-765-2074
LAROSAS INC
2334 Boudinot Ave, Cincinnati, OH 45238-3492
Tel (513) 347-5660 *Founded/Ownrshp* 1954
Sales 69.8MM^E *EMP* 1,500
SIC 5812 6794 5141 5921 Pizzeria, chain; Franchises, selling or licensing; Groceries, general line; Wine; Pizzeria, chain; Franchises, selling or licensing; Groceries, general line; Wine
CEO: Mike La Rosa
**Ch Bd:* Tillman D Hughes
COO: Kevin Burrill
**CFO:* Michael J Selker
**Ch:* Donald S Larosa
**Treas:* Joanne Larosa
Treas: Joanne L Rosa
**Sec:* Mark Larosa
Dist Mgr: Rob Kaiser
Genl Mgr: Cory Brumleve
Genl Mgr: Chris Desalvo

D-U-N-S 82-819-3008 IMP
LAROSE INDUSTRIES LLC
PEN MASTER
1578 Sussex Tpke, Randolph, NJ 07869-1833
Tel (973) 543-2037 *Founded/Ownrshp* 2008
Sales 58.1MM^E *EMP* 111
SIC 5092 3269 3944 Arts & crafts equipment & supplies; Stationery articles, pottery; Craft & hobby kits & sets
CEO: Lawrence Rosen
VP: Vito Amato
VP: Uday Patel
IT Man: Chris Frazier
Ql Cn Mgr: Randy Leake
VP Sls: Paul Mashington

D-U-N-S 05-662-4868
LARRETT ENERGY SERVICES INC
6712 Fm 1836, Kaufman, TX 75142-7935
Tel (972) 962-3400 *Founded/Ownrshp* 2010
Sales 50.0MM *EMP* 662
Accts Theresa P Cryer Cpa Gun Bar
SIC 1623 1541 Pipeline construction; Industrial buildings & warehouses; Pipeline construction; Industrial buildings & warehouses
Pr: James Scott Driver
Sfty Dirs: Burt Gilliland
Opers Mgr: Billy Bourland

D-U-N-S 18-160-0016 IMP
LARROC INC
6420 Boeing Dr, El Paso, TX 79925-1007
Tel (915) 772-3733 *Founded/Ownrshp* 1987
Sales 164.7MM *EMP* 25
Accts Strickler & Prieto Llp El Pa
SIC 5141 5149 Groceries, general line; Groceries & related products; Groceries, general line; Groceries & related products
Owner: Enrique Munoz
**Prin:* Olga Munoz

D-U-N-S 02-691-3624
LARRY & MATT INC
B & G ELECTRIC
241 Western St, Pampa, TX 79065
Tel (806) 665-4418 *Founded/Ownrshp* 1999
Sales 48.2MM^E *EMP* 97^E
SIC 1389 5085 1731 4971 5083 Oil field services; Industrial supplies; Electric power systems contractors; Irrigation systems; Irrigation equipment
Pr: Matt Hinton
**Sec:* Larry Beck

D-U-N-S 02-074-7721 IMP
LARRY BLOCK ENTERPRISES INC
BLOCKSURF
440 E Easy St Ste 2, Simi Valley, CA 93065-7545
Tel (805) 583-0057 *Founded/Ownrshp* 1971
Sales 23.0MM *EMP* 14
SIC 5091 Surfing equipment & supplies; Surfing equipment & supplies
Pr: Larry Block

D-U-N-S 06-712-3133
LARRY BLUMBERG & ASSOCIATES INC (AL)
2733 Ross Clark Cir, Dothan, AL 36301-3214
Tel (334) 793-6855 *Founded/Ownrshp* 1972
Sales 26.5MM^E *EMP* 384
SIC 7011 6552 Hotels & motels; Subdividers & developers; Hotels & motels; Subdividers & developers
Ch Bd: Larry Blumberg
**Pr:* Barry Kraselsky
VP: Melissa Bilka
VP: Clint Smith
Admn Mgr: Heather Robinson
Genl Mgr: Glenn Aycock
Genl Mgr: Tammy Buckley
Genl Mgr: Shane Bussino
Genl Mgr: Amy Cantrell
Genl Mgr: Mike Donnelly
Genl Mgr: Deanna Gamble

D-U-N-S 61-988-1360
LARRY C MCCRAE INC
3333 W Hunting Park Ave, Philadelphia, PA 19132-1889
Tel (215) 227-5060 *Founded/Ownrshp* 1989
Sales 24.6MM^E *EMP* 120
Accts Ratner Goodman Limor Lynn
SIC 1731 1542 1521 General electrical contractor; Commercial & office building, new construction; Commercial & office buildings, renovation & repair; New construction, single-family houses; General remodeling, single-family houses; General electrical contractor; Commercial & office building, new construction; Commercial & office buildings, renovation & repair; New construction, single-family houses; General remodeling, single-family houses
Pr: Larry C McCrae
CFO: Susan Parker
**VP:* Joe Williams

D-U-N-S 07-215-2648
LARRY D MAYS
MAYS SPORTING GDS & AWARD CTR
4726 Pittsburgh Ave, Erie, PA 16509-6204
Tel (814) 833-7988 *Founded/Ownrshp* 1974
Sales 21.8MM^E *EMP* 20
Accts Maloney Reed Scarpitti & Com
SIC 2261 5199 5999 2395 Screen printing of cotton broadwoven fabrics; Advertising specialties; Trophies & plaques; Embroidery & art needlework
Owner: Larry D Mays
VP: Gregory Mays

D-U-N-S 03-221-3175
LARRY DIMMITT CADILLAC INC
DIMMITT LAND ROVER
25191 Us Highway 19 N, Clearwater, FL 33763-2102
Tel (727) 797-7070 *Founded/Ownrshp* 1999
Sales 71.8MM^E *EMP* 146
SIC 5511 7538 Automobiles, new & used; General automotive repair shops; New & used car dealers; General automotive repair shops
CEO: Richard Dimmitt
**COO:* Scott Larguier
**CFO:* Kris Jordan
Exec: Marcia Kuzeria
Genl Mgr: Peter Dimmitt
Store Mgr: Kevin Bower
CIO: Iain Sherk

D-U-N-S 19-328-2196
LARRY FORD HILL INC
2496 S Lee Hwy, Cleveland, TN 37311-7340
Tel (423) 472-5454 *Founded/Ownrshp* 2005
Sales 20.5MM^E *EMP* 47
SIC 5511 Automobiles, new & used
Pr: Larry Hill

LARRY GEWEKE FORD
See GEWEKE CO

D-U-N-S 62-049-3221
LARRY H MILLER
CHRYSLER-PLYMOUTH-JEEP
10990 S Auto Mall Dr, Sandy, UT 84070-4180
Tel (801) 553-5300 *Founded/Ownrshp* 1984
Sales 47.7MM^E *EMP* 200
SIC 5511 Automobiles, new & used; Automobiles, new & used
Pr: Gail Miller
**Sec:* Larry H Miller
Genl Mgr: Travis Johnson

D-U-N-S 78-366-2554
LARRY H MILLER ARENA CORP
DELTA CENTER, THE
301 W South Temple, Salt Lake City, UT 84101-1216
Tel (801) 325-2000 *Founded/Ownrshp* 1989
Sales 45.3MM^E *EMP* 520
SIC 7389 7941 5812 Convention & show services; Sports field or stadium operator, promoting sports events; Eating places; Convention & show services; Sports field or stadium operator, promoting sports events; Eating places
Pr: Gayle Miller
**VP:* Jay Francis
**VP:* Robert Hyde
**VP:* Scott Williams
Exec: Paul Welsh
CTO: James Bell
MIS Dir: Shawn Waters
Netwrk Eng: Josh Barney

LARRY H MILLER CHEVROLET
See LARRY H MILLER CHEVROLET MURRAY

D-U-N-S 16-194-9248
LARRY H MILLER CHEVROLET MURRAY
LARRY H MILLER CHEVROLET
5500 S State St, Salt Lake City, UT 84107-6031
Tel (866) 789-1427 *Founded/Ownrshp* 1979
Sales 47.5MM^E *EMP* 144
SIC 5511 Automobiles, new & used; Automobiles, new & used
Pr: Karen G Miller
**Sec:* Larry H Miller
**VP:* Gregory Miller

LARRY H. MILLER CHRYSLER DODGE
See LHM CORPTCD

D-U-N-S 04-130-7661
LARRY H MILLER CORP
CHAMPION FORD
(*Suby of* LARRY H MILLER TOYOTA) ★
200 W 9000 S, Sandy, UT 84070-2050
Tel (801) 566-2441 *Founded/Ownrshp* 2004
Sales 35.4MM^E *EMP* 120
SIC 5511 Automobiles, new & used; Automobiles, new & used
Pr: Karen G Miller
**Sec:* Stephen F Miller
**VP:* Roger L Miller
Off Mgr: Kathy Davis
Telecom Ex: Steven Petorius
Genl Couns: Robert Tingey

D-U-N-S 08-038-4951
LARRY H MILLER CORP - NEW MEXICO
AMERICAN TOYOTA
5995 Alameda Blvd Ne, Albuquerque, NM 87113-2003
Tel (505) 823-4440 *Founded/Ownrshp* 1976, 1988
Sales 37.5MM^E *EMP* 95
SIC 5511 7538 5531 5521 Automobiles, new & used; General automotive repair shops; Automotive & home supply stores; Used car dealers; Automobiles, new & used; General automotive repair shops; Automotive & home supply stores; Used car dealers
Pr: David Chavez
Genl Mgr: Michelle Aragon
Sls Mgr: Allan Le
Sales Asso: Renee Brown
Sales Asso: Sandra Dickson
Sales Asso: Nur Rodriguez

LARRY H MILLER HONDA
See HERITAGE IMPORTS

D-U-N-S 95-957-1480
LARRY H MILLER OF COLORADO SPRINGS
LIBERTY TOYOTA
15 E Motor Way, Colorado Springs, CO 80905-7002
Tel (719) 471-3100 *Founded/Ownrshp* 1989
Sales 36.2MM^E *EMP* 118
SIC 5511 7538 7532 7515 5521 5531 Automobiles, new & used; General automotive repair shops; Top & body repair & paint shops; Passenger car leasing; Used car dealers; Automotive parts; Automobiles, new & used; General automotive repair shops; Top & body repair & paint shops; Passenger car leasing; Used car dealers; Automotive parts
Pr: Edward S Mansfield
**Sec:* Lawrence Miller
**VP:* Thomas Fitchett
**Genl Mgr:* Ray Reilly
Genl Mgr: Bill Stahelin

D-U-N-S 82-946-0117
LARRY H MILLER THEATRES INC
35 E 9270 S, Sandy, UT 84070-2660
Tel (801) 304-4500 *Founded/Ownrshp* 1998
Sales 28.0MM^E *EMP* 1,100
SIC 7832 Motion picture theaters, except drive-in; Motion picture theaters, except drive-in
CFO: Steve Tarbet

LARRY H MILLER TOYOTA
See MARK MILLER SUBARU LLC

D-U-N-S 09-777-2115
LARRY H MILLER TOYOTA INC
(*Suby of* LARRY H MILLER TOYOTA) ★
5650 S State St, Salt Lake City, UT 84107-6194
Tel (801) 264-3200 *Founded/Ownrshp* 1986
Sales 23.6MM^E *EMP* 80
SIC 5511 Automobiles, new & used; Automobiles, new & used
Pr: Gaile Miller
**Sec:* Larry H Miller
Ex VP: Howard Weiner
**VP:* Tony Divino
Tech Mgr: Brent Bigelow
Mktg Dir: Paul Nygaard
Sls Dir: Jason Doherty

LARRY H MLLER DODGE RAM TUCSON
See LHM CORP TDR

D-U-N-S 03-596-4733
LARRY HMILLER CHRYSLER JEEP TUCSON
TUCSON CHRYSLER JEEP, INC.
7800 E 22nd St, Tucson, AZ 85710-8528
Tel (520) 327-5561 *Founded/Ownrshp* 2007
Sales 22.2MM^E *EMP* 62
SIC 5511

LARRY HOPKINS HONDA
See LARRY HOPKINS INC

D-U-N-S 02-951-4775
LARRY HOPKINS INC
LARRY HOPKINS HONDA
1048 W El Camino Real, Sunnyvale, CA 94087-1024
Tel (408) 720-1888 *Founded/Ownrshp* 1947
Sales 34.0MM^E *EMP* 100
SIC 5511 7538 5531 5521 Automobiles, new & used; General automotive repair shops; Automotive & home supply stores; Used car dealers; Automobiles, new & used; General automotive repair shops; Automotive & home supply stores; Used car dealers
Pr: Steven E Hopkins
Off Mgr: Darcie Lopez
Sls Mgr: Michael Quigley
Sales Asso: Jonathan Wilson

D-U-N-S 04-099-8387
LARRY KLINE WHOLESALE MEATS AND PROVISIONS INC
L K M
350 Goolsby Blvd, Deerfield Beach, FL 33442-3005
Tel (954) 420-0071 *Founded/Ownrshp* 1976
Sales 39.6MM^E *EMP* 60^E
SIC 5147 5144 5149 Meats, fresh; Meats, cured or smoked; Poultry & poultry products; Groceries & related products; Meats, fresh; Meats, cured or smoked; Poultry & poultry products; Groceries & related products
Pr: David Kline
**CEO:* Steven Caine
**Treas:* Debbie Freeman
**VP:* Douglas Freeman

D-U-N-S 08-851-2603 IMP
LARRY METHVIN INSTALLATIONS INC
L M I
501 Kettering Dr, Ontario, CA 91761-8150
Tel (909) 563-1700 *Founded/Ownrshp* 1975
Sales 60.8MM^E *EMP* 350
SIC 3231 3431 1751 Doors, glass: made from purchased glass; Shower stalls, metal; Carpentry work; Window & door (prefabricated) installation; Doors, glass: made from purchased glass; Shower stalls, metal; Carpentry work; Window & door (prefabricated) installation
CEO: Larry Methvin
**VP:* Eileen Methvin
Dir Risk M: Laura Stewart
Dir IT: Jason Eberwein
IT Man: Richard Harvey
Opers Mgr: Sande Chapman

LARRY MILLER DODGE
See MILLER LARRY DODGE INC

LARRY MILLER SUNDANCE DODGE
See SUNDANCE DODGE INC

LARRY MILLER'S NISSAN
See DOUGLAS MOTORS INC

D-U-N-S 82-511-3665
LARRY ROESCH AUTOMOTIVE GROUP INC
ROESCH, LARRY MITSUBISHI
313 W Grand Ave, Bensenville, IL 60106-3329
Tel (630) 279-6000 *Founded/Ownrshp* 1997
Sales 27.5MM^E *EMP* 64
SIC 5511 Automobiles, new & used; Automobiles, new & used
Pr: Dan Roesch
Brnch Mgr: Nick Pontarelli
Sls Mgr: Ed Burke
Sales Asso: Michael Sinacola

D-U-N-S 04-430-6892
LARRY ROESCH CHEVROLET INC
333 W Grand Ave, Bensenville, IL 60106-3329
Tel (630) 860-4000 *Founded/Ownrshp* 1954
Sales 27.5MM^E *EMP* 120
SIC 5511 7538 Automobiles, new & used; Pickups, new & used; General automotive repair shops; Automobiles, new & used; Pickups, new & used; General automotive repair shops
Pr: Lawrence F Roesch
CFO: Marijana Malencic
**VP:* David Roesch
Mktg Mgr: Jeff Doladee

D-U-N-S 02-545-2947
LARRY ROESCH CHRYSLER-JEEP INC (IL)
200 W Grand Ave, Elmhurst, IL 60126-1136
Tel (630) 834-8000 *Founded/Ownrshp* 1944
Sales 31.9MM^E *EMP* 80
SIC 5511 7538 5521 Automobiles, new & used; General automotive repair shops; Used car dealers; Automobiles, new & used; General automotive repair shops; Used car dealers
Pr: Lawrence F Roesch
**CFO:* Mike Parilla
Sls Mgr: Bob Gatelis
Sls Mgr: John Sagat

D-U-N-S 02-327-9599
LARRYS MARKETS INC
PIGGLY WIGGLY
300 E Ann St, Kaukauna, WI 54130-3969
Tel (920) 766-6080 *Founded/Ownrshp* 1936
Sales 48.9MM^E *EMP* 425
SIC 5411 Supermarkets, chain; Supermarkets, chain
Ch: Thomas Verhagen

D-U-N-S 82-892-1002 EXP
LARS LLC
HARDWARE IMAGINATION TECH
4300 Nw 37th Ave, Miami, FL 33142-4226
Tel (305) 635-3300 *Founded/Ownrshp* 2004
Sales 26.1MM^E *EMP* 62
SIC 5072 Hardware

LARSEN
See COWTAN AND TOUT INC

D-U-N-S 16-069-1288
LARSEN & TOUBRO INFOTECH LIMITED
(*Suby of* LARSEN AND TOUBRO LIMITED)
2035 State Route 27 # 3000, Edison, NJ 08817-3351
Tel (732) 248-6111 *Founded/Ownrshp* 1997
Sales 478.6MM *EMP* 20,000
Accts Ramesh Sarva Cpa Pc For
SIC 7379 Computer related consulting services; Computer related consulting services
CEO: Sanjay Jalona
**CFO:* Ashok Sonthalia
Top Exec: Parsh Ramanathan
**Ex VP:* Sunil Pande
VP: Satish Khurana
VP: Harsh Naidu
VP: Anil Vazirani
Dir Bus: Raveen Singh
IT Man: Ninad Jambhekar
Sls Dir: Dave Aiken
Snr Mgr: Mukesh Aghi

D-U-N-S 02-330-8141
LARSEN COOPERATIVE CO
8290 County Hwy T, Larsen, WI 54947-9701
Tel (920) 982-1111 *Founded/Ownrshp* 1919
Sales 179.5MM *EMP* 150
SIC 5191 5172 5541

D-U-N-S 07-082-6032 IMP
LARSEN MANUFACTURING LLC
1201 Allanson Rd, Mundelein, IL 60060-3807
Tel (224) 475-0683 *Founded/Ownrshp* 1999
Sales 44.0MM^E *EMP* 200
SIC 3469 Electronic enclosures, stamped or pressed metal; Electronic enclosures, stamped or pressed metal
CFO: Bob Kaliicki
Genl Mgr: Jim Lacroix
Opers Mgr: Al Manges

D-U-N-S 02-946-9061 IMP
LARSEN SUPPLY CO
LASCO
12055 Slauson Ave, Santa Fe Springs, CA 90670-2601
Tel (562) 698-0731 *Founded/Ownrshp* 1930
Sales 38.0MM^E *EMP* 120

Accts Vilmure Peeler & Boucher Llp
SIC 5074 5075 Plumbing & hydronic heating supplies; Warm air heating & air conditioning; Plumbing & hydronic heating supplies; Warm air heating & air conditioning
Ch Bd: Richard Larsen
**VP:* Rella Bodinus
Exec: Sandy Soto
IT Man: Daniel Pro
VP Sls: Matthew Parker

D-U-N-S 07-587-8376
LARSEN TRUCKING INC
5688 Vining Rd, Greenville, MI 48838-9785
Tel (616) 754-4925 *Founded/Ownrshp* 2003
Sales 20.2MM^E *EMP* 62
SIC 4213 Trucking, except local
Pr: Peter Larsen
**Sec:* Maureen Larsen

D-U-N-S 96-170-1393 IMP/EXP
LARSON BOATS LLC
(*Suby of* J&D ACQUISITIONS LLC) ★
700 Paul Larson Mem Dr, Little Falls, MN 56345-1124
Tel (320) 632-5481 *Founded/Ownrshp* 2011
Sales 41.4MM^E *EMP* 99
SIC 3732 Boat building & repairing
CFO: Linda Thesing
Trfc Mgr: Ben Waltman

D-U-N-S 02-356-9262
LARSON CHEVROLET-OLDSMOBILE INC
1420 Ogden Ave, Superior, WI 54880-1500
Tel (715) 392-5111 *Founded/Ownrshp* 1954
Sales 30.0MM *EMP* 42
SIC 5511 Automobiles, new & used; Automobiles, new & used
Pr: Ralph R Kriesel
**VP:* Ralph Grimsrud

D-U-N-S 87-970-1860
LARSON DESIGN GROUP INC
1000 Commerce Park Dr # 201, Williamsport, PA 17701-5475
Tel (570) 323-6603 *Founded/Ownrshp* 1987
Sales 35.9MM *EMP* 250
Accts Stambaugh Ness Pc York Penn
SIC 8711 8713 Consulting engineer; Surveying services; Consulting engineer; Surveying services
CEO: Keith S Kuzio
Ofcr: Marty Muggleton
Ex VP: Shaun Smith
**Sr VP:* Brenda Nichols
**VP:* David Deblander
**VP:* Robert J Gehr
VP: Robert Gehr
**VP:* Andrew D Keister
VP: Doug Smith
CIO: Stephen Murgas
Snr PM: Keith Miller

D-U-N-S 07-407-4030
LARSON ENGINEERING INC
LARSON ENGINEERING MINNESOTA
3524 Labore Rd, White Bear Lake, MN 55110-5126
Tel (651) 481-9120 *Founded/Ownrshp* 1979
Sales 42.6MM^E *EMP* 180
SIC 8711 Structural engineering; Consulting engineer; Structural engineering; Consulting engineer
Pr: Lee Granquist
CFO: Phillip Deimel
**CFO:* Pllilip Dymell
**Sec:* Kesh Ramdular
**VP:* John Pastore
Exec: Kirk Haverland
Mktg Mgr: Tess Maclin

LARSON ENGINEERING MINNESOTA
See LARSON ENGINEERING INC

D-U-N-S 02-605-6267
LARSON ENTERPRISES INC
MCDONALD'S
2617 Highway 41a Byp, Clarksville, TN 37043-3904
Tel (931) 552-3000 *Founded/Ownrshp* 1964
Sales 7.1MM^E *EMP* 300
SIC 5812 Fast-food restaurant, chain; Fast-food restaurant, chain
Pr: Howard Eric Larson II
**Pr:* Eric Larson
Treas: Sherri Larson
**Sec:* Sherri Lynn Clay

D-U-N-S 08-776-8909
LARSON FARM & LAWN INC
4655 E Us Highway 60, Rogersville, MO 65742-8811
Tel (417) 881-2677 *Founded/Ownrshp* 2000
Sales 80.0MM *EMP* 175
Accts Roberts Mckenzie Mangan & Cu
SIC 5999 5261 Farm equipment & supplies; Lawn & garden equipment; Farm equipment & supplies; Lawn & garden equipment
Pr: Glenn Larson
**Sec:* Mike Headley
Store Mgr: Jeremy Knuth
Sales Exec: Brian Craven
Mktg Dir: Melisa Thomas

D-U-N-S 05-816-5929
LARSON FORD INC
LARSON FORD SUZUKI
1150 Ocean Ave, Lakewood, NJ 08701-4594
Tel (732) 363-8100 *Founded/Ownrshp* 1956
Sales 26.2MM^E *EMP* 70
SIC 5511 Automobiles, new & used; Pickups, new & used; Automobiles, new & used; Pickups, new & used
Pr: Paul A Larson Jr
**Treas:* Cathy Larson
**VP:* Robert Larson
Sls Mgr: Chris Mercer

LARSON FORD SUZUKI
See LARSON FORD INC

D-U-N-S 05-175-3546
LARSON GROUP
TLG
3026 N Mulroy Rd, Strafford, MO 65757-7213
Tel (417) 865-5355 *Founded/Ownrshp* 2000
Sales 359.7MM *EMP* 58^E
Accts Roberts Mckenzie Mangan & Cu
SIC 3713 Truck & bus bodies; Truck & bus bodies
Prin: Glenn Larson
CFO: Mike Headley
VP: Don Porthan
VP: Mike Thurston
Mktg Mgr: Barbie Langston
Sales Asso: Bonnie Shockley

D-U-N-S 80-795-0613 IMP
LARSON MANUFACTURING CO INC
(*Suby of* LARSON MANUFACTURING CO OF SOUTH DAKOTA INC) ★
2333 Eastbrook Dr, Brookings, SD 57006-2899
Tel (605) 692-6115 *Founded/Ownrshp* 1954
Sales 111.2MM^E *EMP* 240
SIC 5031 Doors & windows; Windows; Doors & windows; Windows
Pr: Dale Larson
Pr: Bill Retterath
**Sec:* Craig H Johnson
VP: Dan Beinhorn
Genl Mgr: Daren Meints
MIS Dir: Ted Weinrich
Sfty Dirs: Scott Hegdahl
Sfty Dirs: Scott Holm
Sfty Mgr: Joel Osbeck
Plnt Mgr: Glenn Kuschel
Plnt Mgr: Steven Wagner

D-U-N-S 00-528-7420 IMP
LARSON MANUFACTURING CO OF IOWA INC (SD)
2333 Eastbrook Dr, Brookings, SD 57006-2899
Tel (605) 692-6115 *Founded/Ownrshp* 1952
Sales 29.7MM^E *EMP* 282
SIC 3442 Metal doors, sash & trim; Metal doors; Screen & storm doors & windows; Metal doors, sash & trim; Metal doors; Screen & storm doors & windows
Pr: Dale L Larson
**Treas:* Craig H Johnson
**VP:* Bill R Hay

D-U-N-S 00-622-6237
LARSON MANUFACTURING CO OF SOUTH DAKOTA INC
2333 Eastbrook Dr, Brookings, SD 57006-2899
Tel (605) 692-6115 *Founded/Ownrshp* 1964
Sales 205.4MM^E *EMP* 1,000
SIC 3442 Metal doors, sash & trim; Metal doors; Screen & storm doors & windows; Metal doors, sash & trim; Metal doors; Screen & storm doors & windows
Pr: Jeff Rief
**Treas:* Maree Larson
Sls Mgr: Mark Popowski

D-U-N-S 00-145-9536 IMP
LARSON TOOL & STAMPING CO (MA)
90 Olive St, Attleboro, MA 02703-3802
Tel (508) 222-0897 *Founded/Ownrshp* 1920
Sales 24.7MM^E *EMP* 70
Accts Carlucci & Dugan Lincoln Rho
SIC 3469 3443 Metal stampings; Cylinders, pressure: metal plate; Metal stampings; Cylinders, pressure: metal plate
Pr: Charles Cederberg
**CFO:* William E Larson
Board of Directors: Richard Cederberg

D-U-N-S 00-580-0743
LARSON-DANIELSON CONSTRUCTION CO INC
302 Tyler St, La Porte, IN 46350-3299
Tel (219) 362-2127 *Founded/Ownrshp* 1968
Sales 64.7MM *EMP* 300
Accts Angelo And Rardin Laporte In
SIC 1542 1541 Commercial & office building, new construction; Industrial buildings, new construction; Commercial & office building, new construction; Industrial buildings, new construction
Pr: Timothy F Larson
CFO: Patti Obrien
**Sec:* Terry A Larson
**VP:* Mark A Danielson
**VP:* Thomas A Walter
Assoc Dir: Mike Smith
IT Man: George Chavez
Snr Mgr: John Stalbaum

D-U-N-S 00-617-2589 IMP/EXP
■ **LARSON-JUHL US LLC** (GA)
(*Suby of* ALBECCA INC) ★
3900 Steve Reynolds Blvd, Norcross, GA 30093-3090
Tel (770) 279-5200 *Founded/Ownrshp* 1893, 2002
Sales 343.1MM^E *EMP* 1,172
SIC 2499 3499 2431 Picture frame molding, finished; Picture frames, metal; Millwork; Picture frame molding, finished; Picture frames, metal; Millwork
CEO: Drew P Van Pelt
Pr: Rich Jamison
VP: Lynn Duncan
VP: Mark Marschke
Genl Mgr: Damien Howard
QA Dir: Bertha Ray
Dir IT: James Baker
Dir IT: Mike Trammel
Opers Mgr: Ron Lanham
Opers Mgr: Brian Layfield
Opers Mgr: Brian Maher

D-U-N-S 19-197-4450
LARTOM INC
CITY AUTO SUPPLY
445 Littlefield Ave, South San Francisco, CA 94080-6106
Tel (650) 616-4968 *Founded/Ownrshp* 1986
Sales 30.5MM^E *EMP* 80
SIC 5531 5013 Automobile & truck equipment & parts; Automotive supplies & parts

Pr: Larry Chew
**Treas:* Tomo Endo
**VP:* Evans Chew
Genl Mgr: Blaise Brown
Opers Mgr: Wilber Castro

D-U-N-S 15-935-0875
LARUE COUNTY SCHOOL DISTRICT
ABRAHAM LNCOLN ELEMENTARY SCHL
208 College St, Hodgenville, KY 42748-1404
Tel (270) 358-4112 *Founded/Ownrshp* 1800
Sales 13.1MM *EMP* 350
SIC 8211 Public elementary & secondary schools; Public elementary & secondary schools
Board of Directors: Phil Fulkerson Asst Chb, Ronnie Chelf, Shirley Childress, Anita Cruse, Dale Morris Chb

D-U-N-S 03-416-8950
LAS AMIGAS
CODAC BEHAVIORAL HEALTH
502 N Silverbell Rd, Tucson, AZ 85745-2626
Tel (520) 882-5898 *Founded/Ownrshp* 2001
Sales 32.8MM *EMP* 12
SIC 8093 Rehabilitation center, outpatient treatment; Rehabilitation center, outpatient treatment
Ex Dir: Deb Leyda

D-U-N-S 62-803-4233
LAS COLINAS BAPTIST CHURCH
2450 N Highway 121, Grapevine, TX 76051-2002
Tel (972) 304-8300 *Founded/Ownrshp* 1990
Sales 3.5MM^E *EMP* 350
SIC 8661 Baptist Church; Baptist Church

D-U-N-S 02-640-2230 IMP
LAS COLINAS INTERNATIONAL INC
FORMOSA FOODS
1414 Round Table Dr # 1415, Dallas, TX 75247-3508
Tel (214) 631-5903 *Founded/Ownrshp* 1979
Sales 45.0MM^E *EMP* 50
SIC 5146 5149 5147 5113 5144 Seafoods; Dried or canned foods; Rice, polished; Sugar, refined; Canned goods: fruit, vegetables, seafood, meats, etc.; Meats & meat products; Disposable plates, cups, napkins & eating utensils; Cups, disposable plastic & paper; Towels, paper; Poultry & poultry products; Seafoods; Dried or canned foods; Rice, polished; Sugar, refined; Canned goods: fruit, vegetables, seafood, meats, etc.; Meats & meat products; Disposable plates, cups, napkins & eating utensils; Cups, disposable plastic & paper; Towels, paper; Poultry & poultry products
Ch Bd: Mao Shung Chang
**Pr:* Jesse Chang
Sales Exec: Emily Chang

LAS COLINAS MEDICAL CENTER
See COLUMBIA MEDICAL CENTER OF LAS COLINAS INC

D-U-N-S 15-834-9626
LAS CRUCES AUTOMOTIVE GROUP INC
BRAVO CHEVROLET-CADILLAC
1601 S Main St, Las Cruces, NM 88005-3117
Tel (575) 527-3800 *Founded/Ownrshp* 2004
Sales 28.6MM^E *EMP* 100
SIC 5511 Automobiles, new & used; Automobiles, new & used
Pr: Raymond Palacios
**Sec:* Marion Stevens
Genl Mgr: Mike Armstrong

D-U-N-S 11-416-5694
■ **LAS CRUCES MEDICAL CENTER LLC**
MOUNTAINVIEW REGIONAL MED CTR
(*Suby of* COMMUNITY HEALTH SYSTEMS INC) ★
4311 E Lohman Ave, Las Cruces, NM 88011-8255
Tel (575) 556-7600 *Founded/Ownrshp* 2007
Sales 109.5MM^E *EMP* 700
SIC 8062 General medical & surgical hospitals; General medical & surgical hospitals
CFO: Gene Alexander
Ofcr: Randall Hempling
Prin: Denten Park
Cmptr Lab: Jennifer Jimenez
Surgeon: Edward Sweetser
Dir Health: Mary Noebels

LAS CRUCES PUBLIC RELATIONS OF
See LAS CRUCES PUBLIC SCHOOLS

D-U-N-S 09-413-8740
LAS CRUCES PUBLIC SCHOOLS
LAS CRUCES PUBLIC RELATIONS OF
505 S Main St Ste 249, Las Cruces, NM 88001-1243
Tel (575) 527-5893 *Founded/Ownrshp* 1938
Sales 168.5MM^E *EMP* 3,100
Accts Moss Adams Llp Albuquerque N
SIC 8211 Public elementary & secondary schools; Public elementary school; Public junior high school; Public senior high school; Public elementary & secondary schools; Public elementary school; Public junior high school; Public senior high school
Prin: Irene Gomez
MIS Dir: Jeff Harris
Pr Dir: Jo Galvan-Nash
Schl Brd P: Bonnie Votaw
Teacher Pr: Elizabeth Marrufo
Teacher Pr: Tracy O'Hara

D-U-N-S 09-046-5055 IMP
LAS FLORES METALARTE INC
Carr 153 Km 12 1 Sec St Ca, Coamo, PR 00769
Tel (787) 825-1508 *Founded/Ownrshp* 1974
Sales 20.5MM^E *EMP* 160
Accts Reyes-Ramis Cpa Group Psc Po
SIC 2512 2434 Upholstered household furniture; Wood kitchen cabinets
Pr: Hernan Torres
**Treas:* Rosa Zayas
**VP:* Miguel Marreo
**VP:* Jaime Peifer
**VP:* Gilberto Rodriguez

D-U-N-S 00-582-4034
■ **LAS PALMAS MEDICAL CENTER AUXILIARY** (TX)
COLUMBIA HCA
(*Suby of* HCA INC) ★
1801 N Oregon St, El Paso, TX 79902-3524
Tel (915) 521-1200 *Founded/Ownrshp* 2009
Sales 6.7M *EMP* 800^E
Accts Vargas Cpa Pc Anthony Tx
SIC 8011 Medical centers; Medical centers
CEO: Carol Phillips
Chf Rad: Ira Kuptz
**Pr:* Charles Rosenbaum
Dir Lab: Elizabeth Escobar
Adm Dir: Tim Meeks
Dir Sec: Jim Booher
QA Dir: Wendy Adams
Dir IT: James Raab
Sfty Dirs: Veronica Becerra
Obsttrcn: Jorge Kareh
Nrsg Dir: Mary Webster

D-U-N-S 60-688-6596
LAS VEGAS / LA EXPRESS INC
1000 S Cucamonga Ave, Ontario, CA 91761-3461
Tel (909) 972-3100 *Founded/Ownrshp* 1995
Sales 46.5MM^E *EMP* 256
SIC 4213 Trucking, except local; Trucking, except local
CEO: Ronald Cain Jr
**VP:* Beverly A Adley
VP: Richard Hunt

D-U-N-S 11-828-6293
LAS VEGAS ATHLETIC CLUBS
(*Suby of* LVC ACQUISITION CORP) ★
2655 S Maryland Pkwy, Las Vegas, NV 89109-1645
Tel (702) 734-5822 *Founded/Ownrshp* 1991
Sales 22.7MM^E *EMP* 460
SIC 7991 Athletic club & gymnasiums, membership; Athletic club & gymnasiums, membership
Ch: Rudy Smith
**Pr:* Andrew Palluck
**CFO:* Thomas White

D-U-N-S 10-005-3990
LAS VEGAS CITY SCHOOLS
901 Douglas Ave, Las Vegas, NM 87701-3928
Tel (505) 454-5700 *Founded/Ownrshp* 1920
Sales 14.4MM^E *EMP* 340
SIC 8211 8611 Public elementary & secondary schools; Business associations; Public elementary & secondary schools; Business associations
Dir IT: Erwin Baca
Instr Medi: Francis Martinez
HC Dir: Michelle Aragon

D-U-N-S 84-001-5929
LAS VEGAS COLOR GRAPHICS INC
4265 W Sunset Rd, Las Vegas, NV 89118-3873
Tel (702) 617-9000 *Founded/Ownrshp* 2000
Sales 22.2MM^E *EMP* 105
SIC 7336 Commercial art & graphic design
CEO: John G Scheffler
**Pr:* Heidi Scheffler Bridges
Pr: George Posanke
**CFO:* William Vargas
**Ch:* Larry Scheffler
Exec: Judy Cates
VP Opers: Efren Nuno
Mfg Dir: Tracy Grinnell
Sales Exec: Teri Hofstetter
Sales Exec: Lisa Montano

D-U-N-S 07-901-0708
LAS VEGAS CONVENTION & VISITORS AUTHORITY
LAS VEGAS CONVENTION CENTER
3150 Paradise Rd, Las Vegas, NV 89109-9096
Tel (702) 892-0711 *Founded/Ownrshp* 1955
Sales 298.9MM *EMP* 1,100
Accts Piercy Bowler Taylor & Kern L
SIC 7389 Advertising, promotional & trade show services; Advertising, promotional & trade show services
Pr: Rossi Ralenkotter
COO: Timothy Cox
Treas: Jennifer Diblasi
Bd of Dir: Steve Stallworth
**Sr VP:* Terry Jicinsky
VP: John Bischoff
VP: Caroline Coyle
VP: Lisa Culpepper
VP: Jeremy Handel
VP: Miles Rodela
VP: Thomas Smith
Exec: Andrew Atwell
Exec: Valarie Segarra
Comm Dir: Laura Guarneri

LAS VEGAS CONVENTION CENTER
See LAS VEGAS CONVENTION & VISITORS AUTHORITY

D-U-N-S 13-495-5616
LAS VEGAS EVENTS INC
770 E Warm Springs Rd # 140, Las Vegas, NV 89119-4381
Tel (702) 260-8605 *Founded/Ownrshp* 1983
Sales 23.0MM *EMP* 15
Accts Mcgladrey Llp Las Vegas Nv
SIC 7929 Entertainment service; Entertainment service
VP: Bo Gardner

LAS VEGAS HARLEY DAVIDSON
See SOUTHERN NEVADA HARLEY-DAVIDSON SALES INC

LAS VEGAS LIMOUSINE SERVICES
See PHYLLIS FRIAS

D-U-N-S 96-403-0824
LAS VEGAS MONORAIL CO
3770 Howard Hughes Pkwy # 295, Las Vegas, NV 89169-0998
Tel (702) 699-8200 *Founded/Ownrshp* 2000
Sales 20.7MM *EMP* 32
Accts Bdo Usa Llp La Jolla Ca
SIC 1629 Railroad & subway construction

Ch: Donald L Shalmy
**Pr:* Curtis L Myules III
**Treas:* Terry Cordell
Bd of Dir: William Bible
IT Man: Anthony Charles
Mktg Mgr: Jennifer Balsat
Mktg Mgr: Jennifer Breed

LAS VEGAS MOTOR SPEEDWAY
See NEVADA SPEEDWAY LLC

D-U-N-S 08-839-1644
LAS VEGAS PAIUTE TRIBE
1 Paiute Dr, Las Vegas, NV 89106-3261
Tel (702) 386-3926 *Founded/Ownrshp* 1965
Sales 61.1MM^E *EMP* 300
SIC 5993 7992 Cigarette store; Public golf courses; Cigarette store; Public golf courses
Ch Bd: Benny TSO
Sr VP: Marcia R Mahone
Exec: Frank Toth
Genl Mgr: Chad Gunier

D-U-N-S 00-959-6032
LAS VEGAS PAVING CORP
4420 S Decatur Blvd, Las Vegas, NV 89103-5803
Tel (702) 251-5800 *Founded/Ownrshp* 1958
Sales 225.4MM^E *EMP* 700
SIC 1611 1629

LAS VEGAS REVIEW-JOURNAL
See STEPHENS MEDIA LLC

D-U-N-S 16-720-2667
▲ LAS VEGAS SANDS CORP
3355 Las Vegas Blvd S, Las Vegas, NV 89109-8941
Tel (702) 414-1000 *Founded/Ownrshp* 2004
Sales 14.5MMM *EMP* 48,500
Tkr Sym LVS *Exch* NYS
SIC 7011 Casino hotel; Resort hotel; Casino hotel; Resort hotel
Ch Bd: Sheldon G Adelson
Pr: Mark Brown
**Pr:* Robert G Goldstein
Pr: Andy Grisnik
Pr: Nigel Roberts
COO: William P Weidner
Chf Mktg O: Eric Bello
Chf Mktg O: Cynthia Crespo
Ex VP: Ira H Raphaelson
Sr VP: Rocio Beck
Sr VP: Andrew Lazzaro
Sr VP: John Morland
Sr VP: Paul Pusateri
Sr VP: Michael Quartieri
Sr VP: Pim Robberechts
VP: David Little
VP: Michael C Shindler
VP: Mark Signorio
Exec: Olivier Dubreuil

D-U-N-S 17-891-8330
■ LAS VEGAS SANDS LLC
VENETIAN, THE
(*Suby of* LAS VEGAS SANDS CORP) ★
3355 Las Vegas Blvd S, Las Vegas, NV 89109-8941
Tel (702) 414-1000 *Founded/Ownrshp* 1988
Sales 375.1MM^E *EMP* 10,000
SIC 7011 Casino hotel; Casino hotel
Ch Bd: Sheldon Adelson
Pr: Kim Grange
Pr: Frederick Kraus
**Pr:* William Weidner
**COO:* Michael Alan Leven
COO: Bill Weidner
**Ex VP:* Bradley H Stone
**Sr VP:* Robert Goldstein
Sr VP: Scott Henry
VP: Chad Forster
VP: David Pitney
VP: Gary Visu
VP: Jeff Zabriskie
Dir Soc: Bruce Lu
Dir Soc: Scot Mularkey

D-U-N-S 84-862-2783
LAS VEGAS UROLOGY LLP
SUSSMAN KURTZ & GRIGORIEV
7500 Smoke Ranch Rd # 200, Las Vegas, NV 89128-0324
Tel (702) 233-0727 *Founded/Ownrshp* 1993
Sales 22.9MM *EMP* 22^E
SIC 8011 Urologist; Urologist
Pt: Ernest M Sussman
CFO: Connie Neeley
Off Mgr: Patricia Iorizzo
Doctor: Joseph Candela
Doctor: Vijay Goli
Doctor: Victor Grigoriev
Doctor: Steven Kurtz
Doctor: Ernest Sussman

D-U-N-S 04-167-0829 IMP
LAS VEGAS VALLEY WATER DISTRICT
1001 S Valley View Blvd, Las Vegas, NV 89107-4447
Tel (702) 870-2011 *Founded/Ownrshp* 1947
Sales 336.4MM *EMP* 1,200
Accts Piercy Bowler Taylor & Kern L
SIC 4941 Water supply; Water supply
Genl Mgr: Patricia Mulroy
COO: Shirley Schieck
CFO: David Wright
**Treas:* Cary M Casey
Bd of Dir: Mary Scow
Ofcr: Terri Robertson
Ex VP: Cynthia Bodnar
Exec: Jacinta Allen
**Exec:* Karen Hayes
Exec: Richard Hyte
**Prin:* John Entsminger
Board of Directors: Yvonne Atkinson Gates, Myrna Williams

D-U-N-S 04-800-9641
LAS VEGS-CLRK CNTY LBRY DIST F
7060 W Windmill Ln, Las Vegas, NV 89113-4678
Tel (702) 507-3500 *Founded/Ownrshp* 1965
Sales 26.6MM^E *EMP* 737
SIC 8231 Public library; Public library
Pr: Tom Lawyer

**CFO:* Fred James
Treas: Verlia Davis-Hoggard
**Ex Dir:* Jeannie Goodrich

D-U-N-S 07-228-0019
LAS VIRGENES MUNICIPAL WATER DISTRICT
4232 Las Virgenes Rd Lbby, Calabasas, CA 91302-3594
Tel (818) 251-2100 *Founded/Ownrshp* 1958
Sales 48.3MM *EMP* 125
Accts White Nelson Diehl Evans Llp
SIC 4941 Water supply; Water supply
Pr: Charles Caspary
**Treas:* Jeff Smith
**VP:* Lee Renger
**Genl Mgr:* John R Mundy
CIO: Janice Jarmillo

D-U-N-S 04-035-2452
LAS VIRGENES UNIFIED SCHOOL DIST
4111 Las Virgenes Rd, Calabasas, CA 91302-1886
Tel (818) 880-4000 *Founded/Ownrshp* 1962
Sales 48.3MM^E *EMP* 607
Accts Vavrinek Trine Day & Co Ll
SIC 8211 Public elementary school; Public junior high school; Public senior high school; Public elementary school; Public junior high school; Public senior high school
Bd of Dir: Felicia Esqueda
Bd of Dir: Angie Falk
VP: Lesli Stein
Netwrk Eng: Douglas Macduff
Schl Brd P: Jill Gaines
Psych: Holly Baxter
Psych: Erin Howard

D-U-N-S 03-493-8928
LAS-CAL CORP
TACO BELL
3225 S Rainbow Blvd # 102, Las Vegas, NV 89146-6216
Tel (702) 880-5818 *Founded/Ownrshp* 1967
Sales 54.5MM^E *EMP* 1,500
SIC 5812 Fast-food restaurant, chain; Fast-food restaurant, chain
Pr: Bill Allmon
**VP:* David Bonanni
**VP:* Dewey Doolen
Admn Mgr: Wendye Lee
Dist Mgr: Eddie Coloma
Dist Mgr: Sofia Hernandez
Dist Mgr: Ken Parolini
Dist Mgr: Ron Rowe
Dist Mgr: Tanya Szabo
Dist Mgr: Rich Wierzbowski
Off Mgr: Evamoreno Moreno

LASAINT LOGISTICS
See MULTI FITTINGS CORP

LASALLE BRISTOL
See BRISTOL LASALLE CORP

D-U-N-S 10-904-7287
LASALLE CAPITAL GROUP LP
70 W Madison St Ste 5710, Chicago, IL 60602-4370
Tel (312) 236-7041 *Founded/Ownrshp* 1987
Sales 45.9MM^E *EMP* 156
SIC 6799 Venture capital companies
Genl Pt: Jeff M Walters
**Pt:* Rocco J Martino
CFO: Andrew D Shackelford
VP: Gregory Brewer
VP: Brain M Carey
VP: Nicholas S Christopher
Mng Dir: Kelly A Cornelis

D-U-N-S 12-482-3964
LASALLE COLLEGE HIGH SCHOOL
8605 Cheltenham Ave, Glenside, PA 19038-7121
Tel (215) 233-2911 *Founded/Ownrshp* 1858
Sales 22.0MM *EMP* 145
Accts Bbd Llp Philadelphia Pennsy
SIC 8211 Private elementary & secondary schools; Private elementary & secondary schools
Pr: James L Butler
**Pr:* Richard Castor
**Prin:* Joseph Marchese

D-U-N-S 62-666-3868
LASALLE GROUP INC
5002 Dewitt Rd, Canton, MI 48188-2405
Tel (734) 394-0650 *Founded/Ownrshp* 1990
Sales 67.8MM^E *EMP* 150
SIC 1541 1542

D-U-N-S 88-492-3756
LASALLE GROUP INC
LAKE SUPERIOR CONTRACTING
545 E John Carpenter Fwy # 545, Irving, TX 75062-8143
Tel (214) 845-4500 *Founded/Ownrshp* 1990
Sales 28.9MM^E *EMP* 50
SIC 1542

D-U-N-S 11-921-6992
LASALLE HOTEL LESSEE INC
DOLCE SEAVIEW
401 S New York Rd, Galloway, NJ 08205-9753
Tel (609) 652-1800 *Founded/Ownrshp* 2008
Sales 9.8MM^E *EMP* 450
SIC 7011 Hotels & motels; Hotels & motels
Genl Mgr: Hans Muller

D-U-N-S 80-700-2204
LASALLE HOTEL OPERATING PARTNERSHIP LP
(*Suby of* LASALLE HOTEL PROPERTIES) ★
7550 Wisconsin Ave Fl 10, Bethesda, MD 20814-3559
Tel (301) 941-1500 *Founded/Ownrshp* 2007
Sales 977.0MM *EMP* 36
SIC 8741 Hotel or motel management; Hotel or motel management
CEO: Michael Barnello

D-U-N-S 07-322-7121
LASALLE HOTEL PROPERTIES
7550 Wisconsin Ave # 100, Bethesda, MD 20814-6599
Tel (301) 941-1500 *Founded/Ownrshp* 1998
Sales 1.1MMM *EMP* 35
Accts Kpmg Llp Chicago Illinois
SIC 6798 Real estate investment trusts; Real estate investment trusts
Pr: Michael D Barnello
COO: Alfred L Young
CFO: Bruce A Riggins
VP: Ken Fuller
VP: Larry Kaminsky
Board of Directors: Denise M Coll, Jeffrey T Foland, Darryl Hartley-Leonard, William S McCalmont, Stuart L Scott, Donald A Washburn

D-U-N-S 83-153-3521
LASALLE INCOME & GROWTH FUND IV
I & G BELLEVUE
200 E Randolph St Fl 44, Chicago, IL 60601-6520
Tel (312) 228-2087 *Founded/Ownrshp* 2005
Sales 101.6MM *EMP* 12
Accts Deloitte & Touche Llp Chicago
SIC 6531 Real estate agents & managers; Real estate agents & managers

D-U-N-S 10-664-5414
■ LASALLE INVESTMENT MANAGEMENT INC
(*Suby of* JONES LANG LASALLE INC) ★
333 W Wacker Dr Ste 2000, Chicago, IL 60606-1288
Tel (312) 782-5800 *Founded/Ownrshp* 2002
Sales 109.6MM^E *EMP* 150^E
SIC 6531 Real estate agents & managers; Real estate agents & managers
CEO: Jeff Jacobson
**CEO:* Jason Kern
COO: Gerardo Ruiz
CFO: Michael Ricketts
Sr VP: Allan Marques
Sr VP: Erick Paulson
VP: Janet Healy
VP: Holly Marquez
VP: Jessica Posey
Assoc Dir: Daniel Demarco
Assoc Dir: Will Hardyment
Assoc Dir: Gavin Ingram
Assoc Dir: Andrew Miller
Assoc Dir: Shaun Reed
Assoc Dir: David Robinson
Assoc Dir: Norbert Stangelmayer
Comm Dir: John Wallace

LASALLE NETWORK
See LASALLE STAFFING INC

D-U-N-S 02-336-3518
LASALLE PARISH SCHOOL DISTRICT
3012 N 1st St, Jena, LA 71342
Tel (318) 992-2161 *Founded/Ownrshp* 2005
Sales 28.8MM *EMP* 410
SIC 8211 Public combined elementary & secondary school; Public combined elementary & secondary school
Pr: Billy Fowler

D-U-N-S 94-148-0550
LASALLE PARTNERS MANAGEMENT LTD
200 E Randolph St # 4300, Chicago, IL 60601-6500
Tel (312) 782-5800 *Founded/Ownrshp* 1977
Sales 51.0MM *EMP* 100
SIC 6531 Real estate managers; Real estate managers
Genl Pt: Robert C Spoerri
VP: Vivian I Mumaw

LASALLE SOLUTIONS
See LASALLE SYSTEMS LEASING INC

D-U-N-S 07-999-1225
LASALLE STAFFING INC
LASALLE NETWORK
200 N La Salle St # 2500, Chicago, IL 60601-1014
Tel (312) 419-1700 *Founded/Ownrshp* 1998
Sales 40.7MM *EMP* 85
Accts Fgmk Llc Bannockburn Illino
SIC 7363 Help supply services; Help supply services
Pr: Tom Gimbel
**CFO:* Lawrence Casas
VP: Sirmara J Campbell
Mng Dir: Maureen Brown
Off Mgr: Kasey Shafer
Off Admin: Jackie Hyde
QI Cn Mgr: Jenn Delp
Sales Exec: Maureen Hoersten
Snr Mgr: Alan Jagnandan

D-U-N-S 03-704-0219
■ LASALLE SYSTEMS LEASING INC
LASALLE SOLUTIONS
(*Suby of* MB FINANCIAL BANK NA) ★
9550 W Higgins Rd, Rosemont, IL 60018-4906
Tel (847) 823-9600 *Founded/Ownrshp* 2002
Sales 85.0MM^E *EMP* 85
SIC 7377 7374 Computer hardware rental or leasing, except finance leasing; Computer peripheral equipment rental & leasing; Computer processing services
Pr: Robert J Metzen
**Ch Bd:* Charles M Gately
Pr: John Christopher
**CFO:* James Brustad
**VP:* David Hackman
VP: Neil Kuhn
**VP:* Steven Robb
**VP:* Robert Zanchelli
Exec: Blair Walsh
Dir Bus: Jonathan Cohen
Dir Bus: Lex Darr

D-U-N-S 07-161-7880
LASALLE UNIVERSITY
LA SALLE UNIVERSITY
1900 W Olney Ave, Philadelphia, PA 19141-1199
Tel (215) 951-1000 *Founded/Ownrshp* 1863
Sales 131.5MM *EMP* 900
Accts Kpmg Llp Philadelphia Pa
SIC 8221 University; University

Pr: Colleen M Hanycz
Pr: Jon C Aroulis
**Treas:* David C Fleming
VP: Swee-Lim Chia
VP: Larry Nguyen
VP Bus Dev: Kathleen Finnegan
Exec: Chris Kane
Exec: Royer Smith
Exec: Anthony Walker
Assoc Dir: Mark A Badstubner
Assoc Dir: Dina Oleksiak

D-U-N-S 61-941-5623
LASBERG CONSTRUCTION ASSOCIATES INC
200 Bsineny Pk Dr Ste 305, Armonk, NY 10504
Tel (914) 273-4266 *Founded/Ownrshp* 1988
Sales 27.0MM *EMP* 20
SIC 1611 1521 1542 General contractor, highway & street construction; Single-family home remodeling, additions & repairs; Commercial & office building contractors; General contractor, highway & street construction; Single-family home remodeling, additions & repairs; Commercial & office building contractors
Pr: Ellis M Lasberg
**Pr:* Lee Lasberg

LASCO
See LARSEN SUPPLY CO

D-U-N-S 18-408-6023
LASCO ACOUSTICS & DRYWALL INC
11050 Ables Ln, Dallas, TX 75229-4524
Tel (972) 488-5556 *Founded/Ownrshp* 1988
Sales 54.2MM *EMP* 620
Accts Blackburn May & Co Llp D
SIC 1742 Plaster & drywall work; Acoustical & insulation work; Plaster & drywall work; Acoustical & insulation work
Pr: Jeff Thomas
**VP:* Jason Thomas
Genl Mgr: Stan Greene
Board of Directors: Betsy Jubera

D-U-N-S 13-323-0636 IMP
■ LASCO COMPOSITES LP
(*Suby of* CRANE COMPOSITES INC) ★
8015 Dixon Dr, Florence, KY 41042-2992
Tel (859) 371-7720 *Founded/Ownrshp* 2002
Sales 27.5MM^E *EMP* 230
SIC 3088 Shower stalls, fiberglass & plastic; Shower stalls, fiberglass & plastic
Pr: Rich Schueller
Sales Exec: Jack Stambaugh

D-U-N-S 00-222-5002
LASCO ENTERPRISES LLC
MAX'S WINE DIVE TASTING ROOM
7026 Old Katy Rd Ste 250, Houston, TX 77024-2135
Tel (713) 622-4003 *Founded/Ownrshp* 2007
Sales 19.9MM^E *EMP* 300
SIC 5813 Wine bar; Wine bar
Exec: Brian Evans
Exec: Erick Madden
Genl Mgr: Kendra Mejia
Genl Mgr: Jeff Solomon
S&M/VP: Jonathan Horowitz
Snr Mgr: Laura Lasco

D-U-N-S 11-136-7202 IMP/EXP
LASCO FITTINGS INC
(*Suby of* AALBERTS INDUSTRIES N.V.)
414 Morgan St, Brownsville, TN 38012-9324
Tel (731) 772-3180 *Founded/Ownrshp* 2007
Sales 205.7MM^E *EMP* 490
SIC 3494 Valves & pipe fittings; Valves & pipe fittings
Pr: John C McDonald
Treas: Daniel J Disser
**VP:* Randy Stewart
Plnt Mgr: Jack Shamburger
QI Cn Mgr: Tom Allen
Manager: David Beyer
Manager: Don Caver
Manager: Bryan Jackman
Sales Asso: Karen Draver
Sales Asso: Lyn Mojonnier

D-U-N-S 07-657-6313
LASELL COLLEGE
1844 Commonwealth Ave, Auburndale, MA 02466-2716
Tel (617) 243-2000 *Founded/Ownrshp* 1851
Sales 53.6MM *EMP* 336
Accts Mayer Hoffman Mccann Pc Bos
SIC 8221 College, except junior; College, except junior
Pr: Michael B Alexander
**Pr:* Thomas E J Dewitt
**Ch:* Eric Turner
**Treas:* Susan Hass
VP: Steven Bloom
**VP:* Elizabeth Winter
**Prin:* Richard Blankstein
**Prin:* Michael Hoyle
Ex Dir: Emily Meyer
Sls Mgr: Adrienne Griffith

D-U-N-S 02-918-7502
LASER ACCESS INC
(*Suby of* JEDCO INC) ★
1645 Broadway Ave Nw, Grand Rapids, MI 49504-2026
Tel (616) 459-5496 *Founded/Ownrshp* 1998
Sales 20.8MM^E *EMP* 120
SIC 3699 7692 Laser welding, drilling & cutting equipment; Welding repair; Laser welding, drilling & cutting equipment; Welding repair
Pr: Daniel Szymanski
Sys Mgr: Ted Terhune

LASER DIVISION
See SPECTRA-PHYSICS INC

LASER ENNOVATION AND ENGRG
See L E F INC

D-U-N-S 13-418-5987 IMP
LASER EXPRESS OF WISCONSIN INC
1002 Stewart St, Madison, WI 53713-3259
Tel (608) 274-8450 *Founded/Ownrshp* 1998
Sales 22.2MM^E^ *EMP* 47
SIC 5065 Electronic parts & equipment
Pr: Brian Faust

D-U-N-S 18-508-3748
LASER INDUSTRIES INC
1351 Manhattan Ave, Fullerton, CA 92831-5216
Tel (657) 999-6548 *Founded/Ownrshp* 1986
Sales 24.7MM^E^ *EMP* 65
SIC 3599 Machine shop, jobbing & repair
Pr: Robert Karim
**Sec:* Joseph Butterly
**VP:* John Krickl
**VP:* Gary Nadau
VP: Gary Nadeau
Sls Mgr: Debby Nolan

D-U-N-S 62-074-4565 IMP
LASER PROS INTERNATIONAL CORP
1 Intrntnal Ln Rhnelander Rhinelander, Rhinelander, WI 54501
Tel (715) 369-5995 *Founded/Ownrshp* 1990
Sales 70.2MM^E^ *EMP* 114
SIC 5045 7629 3577 Printers, computer; Business machine repair, electric; Computer peripheral equipment; Printers, computer; Business machine repair, electric; Computer peripheral equipment
Pr: Steven T Spencer
**Treas:* Shane Spencer
**VP:* Scott Spencer
IT Man: Wendy Kuckkahn
IT Man: Anna Pasanen
IT Man: Sam Soper
Sales Asso: Robert Borem
Sales Asso: Susan Holtorp
Sales Asso: Nick Olcikas

D-U-N-S 06-848-7615 IMP/EXP
LASER SHOT INC
4214 Bluebonnet Dr, Stafford, TX 77477-2911
Tel (281) 240-1122 *Founded/Ownrshp* 1998
Sales 22.3MM^E^ *EMP* 110
SIC 3699 Laser systems & equipment; Laser systems & equipment
Pr: Paige Manard
**Pr:* Chris Chambers
VP: Don Andrus
**VP:* Alan Winslette
Prgrm Mgr: Kevin Althaus
Sftwr Eng: Timothy Powell
Site Mgr: Dan Maclean
Pr Mgr: Robert Findlay
Sls Mgr: Meena Stewart
Genl Couns: A J Alexander
Snr Mgr: Gregory Mihaly

D-U-N-S 18-001-2770
LASER SPINE INSTITUTE LLC
LSI
3031 N Rocky Point Dr W # 300, Tampa, FL 33607-5805
Tel (813) 289-9613 *Founded/Ownrshp* 2005
Sales 77.5MM^E^ *EMP* 260
SIC 8011 Neurosurgeon; Neurosurgeon
CEO: William Horne
**COO:* Dotty Bollinger
**CFO:* Mark Andrzejewski
Sr VP: Erika Mangrum
VP: Nicole Gritton
VP: Clay Grossman
VP: Justin Horne
Ex Dir: Mark Lindberg
Brnch Mgr: K Howse
CTO: Jenny Pietrick
Web Dev: Aaron Clayton

D-U-N-S 14-752-8319 IMP
LASER TECHNOLOGIES INC
1120 Frontenac Rd, Naperville, IL 60563-1749
Tel (630) 761-1200 *Founded/Ownrshp* 1985
Sales 40.6MM^E^ *EMP* 147
SIC 3541 Machine tool replacement & repair parts, metal cutting types; Numerically controlled metal cutting machine tools; Machine tool replacement & repair parts, metal cutting types; Numerically controlled metal cutting machine tools
Pr: Keri L Foster
**VP:* Jeffrey Foster
Opers Mgr: Steve Jenson
Mktg Mgr: Keri Alwin

D-U-N-S 14-856-7183 IMP
LASER TECHNOLOGY INC
L T I
6912 S Quentin St, Centennial, CO 80112-3945
Tel (303) 649-1000 *Founded/Ownrshp* 1984
Sales 59.1MM^E^ *EMP* 90
SIC 3699 Laser systems & equipment; Laser systems & equipment
CEO: David Williams
Pr: Eric Miller
CFO: Pamela Sevy
VP: Chris Budden
**VP:* Jeremy G Dunne
VP: Mary Huska
VP: Pamela Sezy
Dir IT: Jeremy Dunne
IT Man: Steve Rounds
IT Man: Richard Schwartz
Sftwr Eng: Anthony Zambai

LASER-DYNAMICS
See GREAT LAKES LASER DYNAMICS INC

D-U-N-S 03-961-4557
LASERAGE TECHNOLOGY CORP
3021 N Delany Rd, Waukegan, IL 60087-1826
Tel (847) 249-5900 *Founded/Ownrshp* 1979
Sales 25.0MM^E^ *EMP* 165
SIC 3841 3449 Surgical & medical instruments; Inhalation therapy equipment; Curtain wall, metal
Ch Bd: Stephen L Capp
**CFO:* Michael W Wimmer
**VP:* Joseph S Coel
Dir IT: Stephen Tupper
VP Mktg: Patrick Capp

LASERFICHE DOCUMENT IMAGING
See COMPULINK MANAGEMENT CENTER INC

D-U-N-S 79-831-7483
LASERFLEX CORP
3649 Parkway Ln, Hilliard, OH 43026-1214
Tel (614) 850-9600 *Founded/Ownrshp* 1992
Sales 26.7MM^E^ *EMP* 88
SIC 7389 7699 7692 3599 3441 2295 Metal cutting services; Finishing services; Industrial machinery & equipment repair; Welding repair; Machine shop, jobbing & repair; Fabricated structural metal; Metallizing of fabrics
Pr: Ken Kinkopf
**VP:* Gene White
Sls Mgr: Mike Shirley
Sales Asso: James Dailey

LASERGIFTS
See ORION PHOTO INDUSTRIES INC

D-U-N-S 82-713-5021 IMP
LASERMASTERS LLC
LMI SOLUTIONS
4857 W Van Buren St, Phoenix, AZ 85043-3814
Tel (602) 278-5234 *Founded/Ownrshp* 1997
Sales 65.0MM^E^ *EMP* 290^E^
SIC 3861 Toners, prepared photographic (not made in chemical plants); Toners, prepared photographic (not made in chemical plants)
CFO: Robert Zack
Dir Bus: Raquel Cavazos
Area Mgr: Nick Leko
Manager: Mike Mandeville
Plnt Mgr: Juan Camargo
Sales Asso: Joe Kohn
Sales Asso: Nancy Molski

D-U-N-S 18-772-5569
LASERSHIP INC
1912 Woodford Rd Ste Ll, Vienna, VA 22182-3740
Tel (703) 761-9030 *Founded/Ownrshp* 1986
Sales 120.1MM^E^ *EMP* 475
SIC 7389 Courier or messenger service; Courier or messenger service
CEO: Ali Dilmaghani
**Pr:* Fred Aryan
**COO:* Helen Campbell
COO: Brad Mandart
**CFO:* Kathleen Hughes
**CFO:* Guy Jackson
**Ex VP:* Mehran Aliakbar
**Ex VP:* Blake W Averill
VP: Averill Blake
VP: Joseph Jarvis
Exec: Rene Tingleff
Dir Risk M: Mimi Connelly

D-U-N-S 60-296-8976 IMP
LASERTONE CORP
10203 Avenue D, Brooklyn, NY 11236-1917
Tel (718) 545-7100 *Founded/Ownrshp* 1989
Sales 21.4MM^E^ *EMP* 25
SIC 5045 5734 Computer peripheral equipment; Computer peripheral equipment
Ch Bd: Isaac Deutsch

LASH GROUP HEALTHCARE CONS
See LASH GROUP INC

D-U-N-S 00-253-4795
■ **LASH GROUP INC**
LASH GROUP HEALTHCARE CONS
(*Suby of* AMERISOURCEBERGEN CORP) ★
3735 Glenlake Dr Ste 100, Charlotte, NC 28208-6865
Tel (704) 329-0002 *Founded/Ownrshp* 1996, 1998
Sales 7.4MM^E^ *EMP* 900
SIC 8399 Health systems agency; Health systems agency
Pr: Tracy Foster
Pr: Tom Jordak
Pr: Debbie Maggio
Sr VP: Loreen Brown
VP: Kelly Gasper
VP: Jeff Harding
VP: Jennifer McDonough
Prgrm Mgr: Mark Anzalone
Prgrm Mgr: Amy Busby
Prgrm Mgr: Denise Butler
Prgrm Mgr: Krista Vihma

LASHER WES ADI/ DDG/VOLKSWAGEN
See WESLEY B LASHER INVESTMENT CORP

LASHIP
See NORTH AMERICAN FABRICATORS LLC

D-U-N-S 96-928-5381
LASHIP LLC
352 Dickson Rd, Houma, LA 70363-7309
Tel (985) 601-4444 *Founded/Ownrshp* 2006
Sales 45.4MM^E^ *EMP* 128^E^
SIC 4499 Boat rental, commercial
CFO: Charlie Comeaux
Ofcr: Sarah Anyemi
Off Mgr: Danny Vedros
CTO: Rogerio Lacourt

D-U-N-S 00-379-0227
LASHLEE-RICH INC (TN)
1100 W Main St, Humboldt, TN 38343
Tel (731) 784-2461 *Founded/Ownrshp* 1940, 1959
Sales 21.2MM *EMP* 75^E^
Accts Horne Llp Jackson Tennessee
SIC 1542 1541 5211 Commercial & office building, new construction; Industrial buildings, new construction; Lumber & other building materials; Commercial & office building, new construction; Industrial buildings, new construction; Lumber & other building materials
Pr: Thomas G Lashlee
**VP:* Charles Randolph

D-U-N-S 06-791-3194
LASHORE WINDS
425 Beach Ave, Rochester, NY 14612-2011
Tel (585) 663-0930 *Founded/Ownrshp* 1956
Sales 5.7MM^E^ *EMP* 350
SIC 8051 Skilled nursing care facilities; Skilled nursing care facilities
Prin: Frank P Di Marciso MD
Prin: Robert Hurlbut

LASIK
See TLC VISION (USA) CORP

LASITER ASPHALT MAINTENANCE CO
See REDSTONE CONSTRUCTION GROUP INC

D-U-N-S 02-337-6853 IMP/EXP
LASKO GROUP INC
820 Lincoln Ave, West Chester, PA 19380-4469
Tel (610) 692-7400 *Founded/Ownrshp* 1997
Sales 223.4MM^E^ *EMP* 1,400
SIC 4789 3634 Railroad car repair; Ceiling fans; Railroad car repair; Ceiling fans
Pr: Oscar Lasko
Pr: Vasanthi Iyer
**Ex VP:* Edward Mc Assey
QA Dir: Scott White
Web Dev: Eric Miller
Software D: Kelly Nie
Mfg Mgr: Mark Stevenson
Ql Cn Mgr: Louis Delarosa
Genl Couns: Bradford Brush

D-U-N-S 00-232-9779
LASKO PRODUCTS INC (PA)
GALAXY FANS & HEATERS
(*Suby of* LASKO GROUP INC) ★
820 Lincoln Ave, West Chester, PA 19380-4469
Tel (610) 692-7400 *Founded/Ownrshp* 1906
Sales 201.0MM^E^ *EMP* 1,000
SIC 4789 3585 3564 Railroad car repair; Refrigeration & heating equipment; Blowers & fans; Railroad car repair; Refrigeration & heating equipment; Blowers & fans
Pr: William Lasko
**CFO:* Yen Tsai
Treas: Pat Farrell
**Treas:* Patricia Farrell
**VP:* Edward McAssey
**VP:* James Perella
QA Dir: Cheng MA
Software D: Jonathan Hartline
Mfg Dir: Ralph Topper
Manager: Julian Quiroz
Ql Cn Mgr: George Gilley

D-U-N-S 06-688-9809
LASKYS SERVICE INC
2101 Delafield St, Waukesha, WI 53188-2261
Tel (414) 327-2892 *Founded/Ownrshp* 1975
Sales 20.2MM^E^ *EMP* 120
SIC 5143 5962 Milk; Food vending machines; Milk; Food vending machines
Pr: Mike Lasky
Genl Mgr: Kenny Lyieman

D-U-N-S 04-549-6196
LASS CORP
LASS OIL & GAS MGT CONSULTING
12019 Bammel N Houston Rd, Houston, TX 77066-4703
Tel (713) 826-8377 *Founded/Ownrshp* 2010
Sales 11.8MM^E^ *EMP* 350
SIC 8748 Business consulting; Business consulting
Ch Bd: Samuel Chellam Jr

LASS OIL & GAS MGT CONSULTING
See LASS CORP

D-U-N-S 02-790-0489 EXP
LASSEN CANYON NURSERY INC
1300 Salmon Creek Rd, Redding, CA 96003-9641
Tel (530) 223-1075 *Founded/Ownrshp* 1964
Sales 47.3MM^E^ *EMP* 250
SIC 0171 5141 5191 Berry crops; Raspberry farm; Strawberry farm; Groceries, general line; Hay; Berry crops; Raspberry farm; Strawberry farm; Groceries, general line; Hay
CEO: Elizabeth Elwood Ponce
**Pr:* Kenneth Elwood Jr
Plnt Mgr: William Welty
Snr Mgr: Liz Ponce

LASSIE NATURALS
See CLASSIC MEDIA LLC

D-U-N-S 00-798-4933
LASSUS BROS OIL INC
LASSUS HANDY DANDY
1800 Magnavox Way, Fort Wayne, IN 46804-1540
Tel (260) 436-1415 *Founded/Ownrshp* 1925, 1972
Sales 221.0MM *EMP* 375
Accts Krouse Kern & Co Inc Fort
SIC 5541 5411 Filling stations, gasoline; Convenience stores, independent; Filling stations, gasoline; Convenience stores, independent
Pr: Todd Lassus
Pr: Greg Lassus
COO: Mike Bates
**CFO:* David Fledderjohann
CFO: Fledder Johann
Sr VP: Karissa Pape
VP: Timicka Addison
MIS Dir: Greg Smith
Dir IT: Gregory Smith
Snr Mgr: Mike Taylor

LASSUS HANDY DANDY
See LASSUS BROS OIL INC

D-U-N-S 07-841-9356
LAST CALL OPERATING CO I INC
1551 N Waterfront Pkwy, Wichita, KS 67206-6604
Tel (866) 682-6773 *Founded/Ownrshp* 2014
Sales 23.9MM^E^ *EMP* 500^E^
SIC 5812 Grills (eating places)
CEO: John Siberus

D-U-N-S 82-969-0080
LAST FRONTIER HEALTHCARE DISTRICT
MODOC MEDICAL CENTER
228 W Mcdowell Ave, Alturas, CA 96101-3934
Tel (530) 233-7036 *Founded/Ownrshp* 2012
Sales 33.4MM^E^ *EMP* 161
Accts Wipfli Llp Spokane Washingto
SIC 8062 General medical & surgical hospitals
CEO: Kevin Kramer
Chf Rad: Duwine Matthew
**CFO:* Jo Knoch
Dir Soc: Camila Lopez'pasos
Chf Nrs Of: Michele McQuillan
CIO: Andrew Camacho
Board of Directors: Leta Bethel, Carol Callaghan, Jim Cavasso, Dick Steyer, Guy Young

LAST MINUTE GOURMET
See TAYLOR FARMS ILLINOIS INC

D-U-N-S 10-149-5778 IMP
LASTAR INC
C2G
(*Suby of* LEGRAND FRANCE)
3555 Kettering Blvd, Moraine, OH 45439-2014
Tel (937) 224-0639 *Founded/Ownrshp* 2014
Sales 5.8MM^E^ *EMP* 420
SIC 1731 5063 5045 3643 3357 Communications specialization; Cable conduit; Computer peripheral equipment; Current-carrying wiring devices; Nonferrous wiredrawing & insulating; Communications specialization; Cable conduit; Computer peripheral equipment; Current-carrying wiring devices; Nonferrous wiredrawing & insulating
Pr: Bill Diederich
CFO: John Kuhnash
**Ch:* Michael Shane
**Ex VP:* Gregory Billhardt
**Sr VP:* Michael Caruso
**VP:* Jim Bush
Exec: Joel Liffick
**Prin:* Jeffrey Schatz
Opers Supe: Sandy Hall
Prd Mgr: Tim Kerby
Natl Sales: Dorothy Callen

LASTEC
See WOOD-MIZER HOLDINGS INC

D-U-N-S 05-430-3669 IMP
LASZERAY TECHNOLOGY LLC (OH)
12315 York Delta Dr, North Royalton, OH 44133-3544
Tel (440) 582-8430 *Founded/Ownrshp* 1997
Sales 25.4MM^E^ *EMP* 81
SIC 3089 3544 Injection molding of plastics; Special dies, tools, jigs & fixtures
CEO: Greg Clark
VP: Steve Patton

LAT SPORTS WEAR
See LAT SPORTSWEAR LLC

D-U-N-S 18-053-1923 IMP
LAT SPORTSWEAR LLC
LAT SPORTS WEAR
1200 Airport Dr, Ball Ground, GA 30107-4545
Tel (770) 479-1877 *Founded/Ownrshp* 2001
Sales 92.5MM^E^ *EMP* 180
SIC 5136 5137 2361 2329 2339 2331 Men's & boys' clothing; Sportswear, men's & boys'; Shirts, men's & boys'; Coats, men's & boys'; Women's & children's clothing; Sportswear, women's & children's; Coats: women's, children's & infants'; Infants' wear; Girls' & children's dresses, blouses & shirts; T-shirts & tops: girls', children's & infants'; Dresses: girls', children's & infants'; Men's & boys' sportswear & athletic clothing; Shirt & slack suits: men's, youths' & boys'; Sportswear, women's; T-shirts & tops, women's: made from purchased materials; Men's & boys' clothing; Sportswear, men's & boys'; Shirts, men's & boys'; Coats, men's & boys'; Women's & children's clothing; Sportswear, women's & children's; Coats: women's, children's & infants'; Infants' wear; Girls' & children's dresses, blouses & shirts; T-shirts & tops: girls', children's & infants'; Dresses: girls', children's & infants'; Men's & boys' sportswear & athletic clothing; Shirt & slack suits: men's, youths' & boys'; Sportswear, women's; T-shirts & tops, women's: made from purchased materials
Pr: Gina Watson
**CFO:* Mickie Schneider
**Chf Mktg O:* Rebecca Clements
**Ex VP:* Chuck Phares
**VP:* Mindy Anastos
Off Mgr: Dawn Trahan
Dir IT: Paul Watson
IT Man: Rob Smith
Natl Sales: Reg Dunston
Natl Sales: Dawn Williams
Manager: Mike Manning

LATA
See LOS ALAMOS TECHNICAL ASSOCIATES INC

D-U-N-S 82-976-0797
LATA ENVIRONMENTAL SERVICES OF KENTUCKY LLC
(*Suby of* LATA) ★
761 Veterans Ave, Kevil, KY 42053-9000
Tel (270) 441-5000 *Founded/Ownrshp* 2009
Sales 38.4MM^E^ *EMP* 90
SIC 3822 8744 Air conditioning & refrigeration controls;
Prin: Ann Gough
Prin: Eddie Magness
Prin: Myrna Redfield
Opers Mgr: Bill Franz
Ql Cn Mgr: Michelle Dudley

D-U-N-S 03-397-9873
LATAH SANITATION INC
3299 Highway 8, Moscow, ID 83843
Tel (208) 882-5724 *Founded/Ownrshp* 1979
Sales 21.1MM^E^ *EMP* 39
SIC 4953 Refuse collection & disposal services
Pr: Diane K Johnson

D-U-N-S 79-094-4545
LATAM AIRLINES GROUP SA INC
(*Suby of* LATAM AIRLINES GROUP S.A.)
6500 Nw 22nd St, Miami, FL 33122-2234
Tel (786) 265-6050 *Founded/Ownrshp* 2007
Sales 91.1MM^E^ *EMP* 800
SIC 4512 Air transportation, scheduled; Air transportation, scheduled

VP: Pablo Chiozza
Pr: Ernesto Ramirez
**Treas:* Eduardo Opazo
Bd of Dir: Juan Sierra
Sr VP: Enrique Hirmas
VP: Luis Riquelme
Exec: Andres Fernandez
Genl Mgr: Maximiliano Naranjo
CTO: Salvador Jofre
Sls Dir: Juan Perez
Mktg Mgr: Ursula Velarde

D-U-N-S 03-012-8614
LATAMSCIENCE LLC
2151 S Le Jeune Rd # 307, Miami, FL 33134-4200
Tel (305) 871-0701 *Founded/Ownrshp* 2007
Sales 92.7MM *EMP* 41
SIC 8731 8999 Medical research, commercial; Scientific consulting
CEO: Edmundo G Stahl
**COO:* Annette O Austin
**CFO:* Gustavo Zingg

D-U-N-S 07-125-3470
LATCO INC
2265 E Pridemore Dr, Lincoln, AR 72744-8661
Tel (479) 824-3282 *Founded/Ownrshp* 1973
Sales NA *EMP* 325
SIC 1542

D-U-N-S 02-110-7615 IMP
LATE MODEL RESTORATION INC
400 Jan Dr, Hewitt, TX 76643-2978
Tel (254) 662-1714 *Founded/Ownrshp* 1999
Sales 27.0MM^E *EMP* 72
SIC 5961 Mail order house
Pr: Shannon Guderian
S&M/VP: Scott Springer

D-U-N-S 00-692-5721
LATEX CONSTRUCTION CO INC (GA)
1353 Farmer Rd Nw, Conyers, GA 30012-3488
Tel (770) 760-0820 *Founded/Ownrshp* 1946
Sales 143.0MM^E *EMP* 400^E
Accts Birdsong & Associates Llc Su
SIC 1623 Oil & gas pipeline construction; Water main construction; Oil & gas pipeline construction; Water main construction
Pr: John D Stotz
**Sec:* Tim B Elder
**VP:* David Williams
Genl Mgr: Holly Andrews
Snr Mgr: Max Gayler

D-U-N-S 08-084-3774 IMP/EXP
LATEX FOAM INTERNATIONAL HOLDINGS INC (CT)
LATEX INTERNATIONAL
510 River Rd, Shelton, CT 06484-4517
Tel (203) 924-0700 *Founded/Ownrshp* 1975
Sales 53.8MM^E *EMP* 220
SIC 3069 Latex, foamed; Latex, foamed
Pr: David T Fisher
**CFO:* Steven Watson
Dir IT: Dave Welch
Sls Dir: Jeff Gober

D-U-N-S 84-078-0287 EXP
LATEX FOAM INTERNATIONAL LLC
LATEX FOAM PRODUCTS
(*Suby of* LATEX FOAM INTERNATIONAL HOLDINGS INC) ★
510 River Rd, Shelton, CT 06484-4517
Tel (203) 924-0700 *Founded/Ownrshp* 1999
Sales 53.8MM^E *EMP* 160^E
SIC 3069 2392 Household furnishings; Foam rubber; Foam rubber; Household furnishings
CEO: David Fisher
Chf Mktg O: Mark Garcia
VP: Frank Beafore
Dir IT: Terri Vaccaro
Manager: Mike Tilki

LATEX FOAM PRODUCTS
See LATEX FOAM INTERNATIONAL LLC

LATEX INTERNATIONAL
See LATEX FOAM INTERNATIONAL HOLDINGS INC

D-U-N-S 07-622-1159
LATHAM & WATKINS LLP
355 S Grand Ave Ste 1000, Los Angeles, CA 90071-3419
Tel (213) 485-1234 *Founded/Ownrshp* 1934, 1972
Sales 782.9MM^E *EMP* 4,100
SIC 8111 Legal services; Legal services
Mng Pt: Robert Dell
Pt: Christopher J Allen
Pt: James P Beaubien
Pt: Joseph A Bevash
Pt: Jose Luis Blanco
Pt: James E Brandt
Pt: Rowland Cheng
Pt: John Clair
Pt: Nicholas A Cline
Pt: Fabio Coppola
Pt: Michael E Dillard
Pt: Olivier Du Mottay
Pt: Alice S Fisher
Pt: Mark A Flagel
Pt: Thomas Fox
Pt: Peter M Gilhuly
Pt: David A Gordon
Pt: Ursula Hyman
Pt: Holger Iversen
Pt: Jorg Kirchner
Pt: Brad Kotler

LATHAM FORD
See LATHAM MOTORS INC

D-U-N-S 00-395-7099 IMP
■ **LATHAM INTERNATIONAL INC** (DE)
(*Suby of* LITTLEJOHN & CO LLC) ★
787 Watervliet Shaker Rd, Latham, NY 12110-2211
Tel (518) 951-1000 *Founded/Ownrshp* 2004
Sales 203.1MM^E *EMP* 1,400
SIC 3086 3081 Plastics foam products; Vinyl film & sheet; Plastics foam products; Vinyl film & sheet
Pr: Mark Laven
CFO: Chuck Ryan
Treas: Ray Ludwig
CTO: Craig Harris
QA Dir: Ryan Legere
Dir IT: Gary Jones
VP Opers: Gary Whitcher
Sfty Mgr: Lynn Hyatt
Plnt Mgr: Tom Correll
Prd Mgr: Corey Akstull
Mktg Dir: Bill Wiley

D-U-N-S 79-887-0457 IMP
■ **LATHAM MANUFACTURING CORP**
FORT WAYNE POOLS
(*Suby of* LATHAM INTERNATIONAL INC) ★
787 Watervliet Shaker Rd, Latham, NY 12110-2211
Tel (518) 783-7776 *Founded/Ownrshp* 2004
Sales 161.4MM^E *EMP* 300
SIC 3086 3081 3083 3949 Plastics foam products; Vinyl film & sheet; Laminated plastics plate & sheet; Swimming pools, plastic; Plastics foam products; Vinyl film & sheet; Laminated plastics plate & sheet; Swimming pools, plastic
Pr: Mark P Laven
Dir IT: Gary Jones
VP Opers: Gary Whitcher

D-U-N-S 01-281-8282
LATHAM MOTORS INC
LATHAM FORD
637 Columbia St Ext, Latham, NY 12110-3001
Tel (518) 785-4161 *Founded/Ownrshp* 1956
Sales 21.6MM *EMP* 70
SIC 5511 Automobiles, new & used; Pickups, new & used; Vans, new & used; Automobiles, new & used; Pickups, new & used; Vans, new & used
Pr: Robert Selkis
**VP:* John Selkis III
**VP:* Thomas Selkis
Exec: Bill Carberry
Sales Exec: Joe Aliberti

D-U-N-S 96-338-0139
■ **LATHAM POOL PRODUCTS INC**
(*Suby of* FORT WAYNE POOLS) ★
787 Watervliet Shaker Rd, Latham, NY 12110-2211
Tel (518) 951-1000 *Founded/Ownrshp* 2010
Sales 121.6MM^E *EMP* 300^E
SIC 3949 Swimming pools, except plastic; Swimming pools, except plastic
Pr: Mark Laven
Mktg Dir: Michelle Zollinger
Manager: Tim Denning
Manager: Andrew Gawinski
Manager: Aaron Young

D-U-N-S 03-892-8586 IMP
LATHEM TIME CORP
200 Selig Dr Sw, Atlanta, GA 30336-2033
Tel (404) 691-0400 *Founded/Ownrshp* 1946
Sales 68.4MM^E *EMP* 140
SIC 5084 Recording instruments & accessories; Recording instruments & accessories
Pr: William C Lathem
CFO: David Tetzlaff
Tech Mgr: David Johnson
Trfc Mgr: Terry Rackley
Natl Sales: Donna Lathem

D-U-N-S 07-303-3888
LATHROP & GAGE LLP (MO)
2345 Grand Blvd Ste 2200, Kansas City, MO 64108-2618
Tel (816) 292-2000 *Founded/Ownrshp* 1872, 1970
Sales 107.0MM^E *EMP* 645
SIC 8111 General practice law office; General practice law office
Mng Pt: Mark Bluhm
Pt: Joel B Voran
Off Admin: Maria Harper
Off Admin: Linda Stepney
Counsel: Amanda Cochran
Counsel: William Cramer
Counsel: Stacy Harper
Counsel: Stephen Mitchell
Counsel: Jenny Mosh
Counsel: Maurice Osullivan
Counsel: Julie Roth

D-U-N-S 00-790-4519
LATHROP CO INC
(*Suby of* TURNER CONSTRUCTION CO INC) ★
460 W Dussel Dr, Maumee, OH 43537-1643
Tel (419) 893-7000 *Founded/Ownrshp* 1986
Sales 28.7MM^E *EMP* 75
SIC 1542 8741 1541 Commercial & office building, new construction; Construction management; Industrial buildings & warehouses; Commercial & office building, new construction; Construction management; Industrial buildings & warehouses
Pr: Thomas J Manahan Jr
**Treas:* Mark T Kusner
**VP:* Joseph R Kovaleski
VP: Joe Kovgleski
**VP:* Douglas F Martin
Snr PM: Carl Benz

LATHROP PAINT
See HIRSHFIELDS INC

D-U-N-S 00-116-8343 IMP/EXP
LATICRETE INTERNATIONAL INC (CT)
1 Laticrete Park N 91, Bethany, CT 06524-3444
Tel (203) 393-0010 *Founded/Ownrshp* 1962
Sales 106.2MM^E *EMP* 350
SIC 2899 2891

D-U-N-S 07-699-3906
LATIN AMERICAN AGRIBUSINESS DEVELOPMENT CORP SA
LAAD AMERICAS NV
2800 Ponce De Leon Blvd, Coral Gables, FL 33134-6913
Tel (305) 445-1341 *Founded/Ownrshp* 1970
Sales NA *EMP* 44
SIC 6159 8732 Agricultural loan companies; Market analysis or research; Agricultural loan companies; Market analysis or research
Pr: Benjamin Fernandez

D-U-N-S 05-593-3675 IMP
LATIN AMERICAN DISTRIBUTORS INC
LADI
100 Crows Mill Rd, Keasbey, NJ 08832-1005
Tel (732) 738-7390 *Founded/Ownrshp* 1984
Sales 23.9MM *EMP* 95
Accts Leaf Miele Manganelli Fortu
SIC 5122 5072 Proprietary (patent) medicines; Cosmetics; Toiletries; Hardware; Proprietary (patent) medicines; Cosmetics; Toiletries; Hardware
Pr: Antonio Bomnin
**Owner:* Odalys Bomnin

D-U-N-S 83-225-5793 EXP
LATIN AMERICAN POLYMERS LLC
(*Suby of* OSTERMAN & CO INC) ★
726 S Main St, Cheshire, CT 06410-3472
Tel (203) 272-2233 *Founded/Ownrshp* 2009
Sales 46.5MM^E *EMP* 14^E
SIC 5162 Plastics materials & basic shapes; Plastics resins
**CFO:* Jennifer A Vestergaard

D-U-N-S 07-685-5840
LATIN SCHOOL OF CHICAGO
59 W North Blvd, Chicago, IL 60610-1403
Tel (312) 582-6000 *Founded/Ownrshp* 1888
Sales 48.2MM *EMP* 243
Accts Plante & Moran Pllc Chicago
SIC 8211 Private combined elementary & secondary school; Private combined elementary & secondary school
VP: Tomy Alexander
VP: Shelley Greenwood
Comm Dir: Katie Odea
Ex Dir: Catherine Curry
Cmptr Lab: Brian Woodhouse
Pgrm Dir: Valerie Warnsby

D-U-N-S 03-838-8203
LATINO ENTERPRISES INC
LA CHIQUITA TORTILLA MFR
3451 Atlnta Indus Pkwy Nw, Atlanta, GA 30331-1039
Tel (404) 351-9822 *Founded/Ownrshp* 1977
Sales 46.5MM^E *EMP* 150
SIC 2099 Tortillas, fresh or refrigerated; Tortillas, fresh or refrigerated
Pr: Marcelino Solis
**COO:* Adam Oliaro
VP: Shane Stogner
Exec: Israel Sanchez
Exec: Jose Solis
Exec: Carroll Todd
QA Dir: Regina Cook
QA Dir: Cathy Norman

D-U-N-S 09-609-1371
LATINWORKS MARKETING LLC
206 E 9th St, Austin, TX 78701-2518
Tel (512) 479-6200 *Founded/Ownrshp* 1998
Sales 24.8MM^E *EMP* 100
SIC 8742 Marketing consulting services
Pr: Manny Flores
**Pt:* Alejandro Ruelas
Mng Pt: Alejrando Rueales
VP: Sergio Alcocer
VP: Christian Filli
VP: Greg Knipp
VP: Victor Paredes
VP: Jim Wegerbaue
VP: Jim Wegerbauer
Creative D: Alejandro Egozcue
Creative D: Gabriel Garcia
Creative D: Erik Hernandez
Creative D: Pablo Maldonado
Creative D: Alejandro Pere
Creative D: Rafael Serrano
Dir Bus: Kristie Allen

D-U-N-S 82-538-9989
LATISYS CORP
(*Suby of* LATISYS HOLDINGS LLC) ★
393 Inverness Pkwy, Englewood, CO 80112-5816
Tel (303) 268-1470 *Founded/Ownrshp* 2007
Sales 22.8MM^E *EMP* 60^E
SIC 7376 Computer facilities management
CEO: Peter Stevenson
**COO:* Evan Mullan
**CFO:* Doug Butler
Ofcr: Randal Thompson
VP: Jonathan Sharp
Genl Mgr: John McCreary
CIO: Steve Merkel
IT Man: Joe Morgan
Sftwr Eng: Brad Bailey
Netwrk Eng: Phillip Stansell
Sls Dir: Tim Cooper

D-U-N-S 80-738-4354
LATISYS HOLDINGS LLC
393 Inverness Pkwy, Englewood, CO 80112-5816
Tel (303) 268-1470 *Founded/Ownrshp* 2007
Sales 22.8MM^E *EMP* 70
SIC 7374 Data processing & preparation
CEO: Peter Stevenson
**COO:* Evans Mullan
**CFO:* Doug Butler
**Dir Sec:* Randal Thompson
VP Mktg: Jonathan Sharp

D-U-N-S 03-227-8848
LATITE ROOFING AND SHEET METAL LLC
2280 W Copans Rd, Pompano Beach, FL 33069-1230
Tel (954) 772-3446 *Founded/Ownrshp* 1986
Sales 66.2MM^E *EMP* 350
SIC 1761

D-U-N-S 84-421-5975
LATITUDE 36 INC
810 Crescent Centre Dr # 120, Franklin, TN 37067-6233
Tel (615) 468-0188 *Founded/Ownrshp* 2000
Sales 37.0MM *EMP* 200
Accts Joe Osterfield Cpa Columbia
SIC 7361 Employment agencies; Employment agencies
Pr: Dean Farling
**COO:* Jason Pyle
Sr Cor Off: John Magagnini
VP: Jyotindra Patel
Opers Mgr: Scott Dickson
Manager: Keegan Ballenger
Board of Directors: John P Kendrick

D-U-N-S 07-829-2673 IMP
LATITUDE 360 INC
LATITUDE30
8367 Baymeadows Way, Jacksonville, FL 32256-8222
Tel (904) 365-5555 *Founded/Ownrshp* 2014
Sales 40.3MM^E *EMP* 475
SIC 7929 5812 Entertainment service; Grills (eating places); Entertainment service; Grills (eating places)
CEO: Brent W Brown
**Pr:* Gregory Garson
**CFO:* Alan J Greenstein
**Sec:* Thomas Bass

D-U-N-S 36-167-4174
LATITUDE 360 INC
8367 Baymeadows Way, Jacksonville, FL 32256-8222
Tel (972) 771-4205 *Founded/Ownrshp* 2011
Sales 17.9MM *EMP* 477
Tkr Sym KGKO *Exch* OTO
SIC 7929 5812 Entertainment service; Grills (eating places)
Ch Bd: Brent W Brown
**Pr:* Gregory Garson
CFO: Alan Greenstein
Chf Mktg O: Philip Alia
Sls Dir: Sarah Baird
Sales Asso: Sam Karlo
Board of Directors: John Alexon, Tim Gannon, Casey Gunnell, Michael P Norris, Michael G Simon

D-U-N-S 80-810-8331 IMP
LATITUDE BEVERAGE CO
NINETY PLUS CELLARS
1354 Commonwealth Ave # 2, Boston, MA 02134-3809
Tel (617) 396-8220 *Founded/Ownrshp* 2006
Sales 21.4MM *EMP* 48
SIC 5182 Brandy & brandy spirits; Brandy & brandy spirits
CEO: Kevin Mehra
**VP:* Brett Vankoski

LATITUDE30
See LATITUDE 360 INC

D-U-N-S 07-917-1535
LATIUM USA TRADING INC
FOUR SEASONS SUNROOMS
5005 Veterans Mem Hwy, Holbrook, NY 11741-4506
Tel (631) 563-4000 *Founded/Ownrshp* 2013
Sales 42.5MM^E *EMP* 150
SIC 3448 Sunrooms, prefabricated metal
Pr: Shaun Kennedy

LATONA TRUCKING AND EXCAVATING
See LATONA TRUCKING INC

D-U-N-S 07-599-1901
LATONA TRUCKING INC
LATONA TRUCKING AND EXCAVATING
620 S Main St, Pittston, PA 18640-3219
Tel (570) 654-3525 *Founded/Ownrshp* 1968
Sales 22.0MM *EMP* 100
Accts Parentebeard Llc Wilkes-Barre
SIC 1794 4212 Excavation & grading, building construction; Local trucking, without storage; Excavation & grading, building construction; Local trucking, without storage
Pr: Leo Latona
**CFO:* Mark Destefano
**Sec:* Charles Latona
**VP:* Joseph Latona

D-U-N-S 60-245-3128
LATOUR MANAGEMENT INC
2949 N Rock Rd Ste 100, Wichita, KS 67226-2279
Tel (316) 524-2290 *Founded/Ownrshp* 1987
Sales 7.0MM *EMP* 400
SIC 8741 5812 8742 Restaurant management; Eating places; Management consulting services; Restaurant management; Eating places; Management consulting services
Pr: Naji Toubia
**VP:* Joumana Toubia
Mktg Mgr: Pat McCombs

D-U-N-S 07-495-6582
LATROBE AREA HOSPITAL INC (PA)
(*Suby of* EXCELA HEALTH HOLDING CO INC) ★
1 Mellon Way, Latrobe, PA 15650-1197
Tel (724) 537-1000 *Founded/Ownrshp* 1908
Sales 68.0MM^E *EMP* 1,060^E
SIC 8062 General medical & surgical hospitals; General medical & surgical hospitals
Pr: Peggy Hayden
Dir Rx: Walter McGuire
Pharmcst: Annette Scaccia

D-U-N-S 00-439-3468 IMP
■ **LATROBE SPECIALTY METALS CO**
(*Suby of* CARPENTER TECHNOLOGY CORP) ★
2626 Ligonier St, Latrobe, PA 15650-3246
Tel (724) 537-7711 *Founded/Ownrshp* 2012
Sales 208.3MM^E *EMP* 860
SIC 3312 3369 Tool & die steel; Castings, except die-castings, precision; Tool & die steel; Castings, except die-castings, precision
Pr: B Christopher Disantis
Ofcr: Jim Ruelh
**VP:* Dale Mikus
IT Man: Randall Strayer
IT Man: Eric Thomson
VP Mfg: Dan Hennessy
VP Mktg: Mark Weberding
Sales Asso: Shelby Tapper

D-U-N-S 01-921-7355 IMP
■ LATROBE SPECIALTY METALS DISTRIBUTION INC
(Suby of CARPENTER TECHNOLOGY CORP) ★
1551 Vienna Pkwy, Vienna, OH 44473-8703
Tel (330) 609-5137 Founded/Ownrshp 2012
Sales 95.0MM EMP 80
SIC 5051 3312 Steel; Steel; Stainless steel
Ch Bd: Gregory A Pratt
*VP: Timothy R Armstrong
*VP: Thomas F Cramsey
*VP: James D Dee
*VP: Matthew S Enoch
*VP: David Murray
*VP: Joe Wakeling
Mktg Mgr: Tim Wise

LATSHAW DRILLING
See MUSTANG HEAVY HAUL LLC

D-U-N-S 11-530-3096
LATSHAW DRILLING & EXPLORATION CO
LATSHAW DRLG CO
4500 S 129th East Ave # 150, Tulsa, OK 74134-5801
Tel (918) 355-4380 Founded/Ownrshp 1981
Sales 367.2MM^E EMP 1,100^E
SIC 1381 Drilling water intake wells; Drilling water intake wells
Pr: Trent B Latshaw
Dir Risk M: Cindy Lozano
Dir IT: Brusse James
Sfty Mgr: Jason Fox
Opers Mgr: Matt Hooker
Opers Mgr: Jimmy Johnson
Opers Mgr: Joey Stockton

LATSHAW DRLG CO
See LATSHAW DRILLING & EXPLORATION CO

D-U-N-S 00-714-5964
LATSHAW ENTERPRISES INC
2533 S West St, Wichita, KS 67217-1025
Tel (316) 942-7266 Founded/Ownrshp 1946
Sales NA EMP 750
SIC 3823 3643 3714 3089

D-U-N-S 01-168-3347
LATSKO AUTOMOTIVE LP
BEAVER CNTY DDGE CHRYSLER JEEP
2761 Constitution Blvd, Beaver Falls, PA 15010-1291
Tel (724) 847-7770 Founded/Ownrshp 2006
Sales 33.6MM^E EMP 80
SIC 5511 Automobiles, new & used; Automobiles, new & used
Genl Pt: Paul Latsko
Genl Mgr: Pj Latsko

D-U-N-S 08-892-2091
LATTER & BLUM INC
430 Notre Dame St, New Orleans, LA 70130-3610
Tel (504) 525-1311 Founded/Ownrshp 1986
Sales 40.4MM^E EMP 1,000
SIC 6531 Real estate brokers & agents; Appraiser, real estate; Real estate brokers & agents; Appraiser, real estate
Ch Bd: Robert W Merrick
*Pr: Arthur Sterbcow
*CFO: Robert C Penick
*Ex VP: Patrick Egan
Off Mgr: Heather Sweatman
Dir IT: Gillian Sims
Sales Asso: Chris Gremillion

D-U-N-S 02-867-5958
LATTICE ENGINES INC
1825 S Grant St Ste 510, San Mateo, CA 94402-2661
Tel (877) 460-0010 Founded/Ownrshp 2010
Sales 48.0MM^E EMP 120^E
SIC 7379 Computer related consulting services
CEO: Shashi Upadhyay
Pr: Timothy Carruthers
Pr: Andrew Dong
Pr: Kent McCormick
CFO: Howie Shohet
Chf Mktg O: Brian Kardon
Sr VP: Patrick Donnelly
Sr VP: Andrew Somosi
VP: A J Gandhi
VP: Brandt Hurd
VP: Gregory Leibman
VP: Ray Patterson
VP: Ian J Scott
VP: Indraneel Sheorey
VP: Scott Slater
Dir Soc: Michelle Pappas
Comm Dir: Caitlin Ridge
Board of Directors: Robert Heimann, Doug Leone, Pete Sonsini

D-U-N-S 10-301-7299 IMP
▲ LATTICE SEMICONDUCTOR CORP
111 Sw 5th Ave Ste 700, Portland, OR 97204-3641
Tel (503) 268-8000 Founded/Ownrshp 1983
Sales 366.1MM EMP 783^E
Tkr Sym LSCC Exch NGS
SIC 3674 Integrated circuits, semiconductor networks, etc.; Integrated circuits, semiconductor networks, etc.
Pr: Darin G Billerbeck
COO: Glen Hawk
CFO: Joseph Bedewi
VP: Tim Dixon
VP: Demetri Elias
VP: Steven A Laub
VP: Stewart Logie
VP: Byron W Milstead
VP: Sean P Riley
VP: Brian Schwarz
VP: Stephen A Skaggs
VP: Mustafa Veziroglu
VP: Rick White
Board of Directors: Robin Abrams, John Bourgoin, Robert R Herb, Mark Jensen, D Jeffrey Richardson

D-U-N-S 11-323-5766
LATTIMORE BLACK MORGAN & CAIN PC
LBMC
5250 Virginia Way Ste 300, Brentwood, TN 37027-7576
Tel (615) 377-4600 Founded/Ownrshp 1984
Sales 54.7MM^E EMP 400
SIC 8721 Certified public accountant; Certified public accountant
Pr: David Morgan
*Mng Pt: Dennis Blanton
*Mng Pt: Greg Gilbert
CFO: Joyce Legieza
*Sec: Michael Cain
Bd of Dir: Connie Leggett
VP: Ben Alexander
Software D: Marcus Hogins
Snr Mgr: Andy Jordan
Snr Mgr: Susan Schuett

D-U-N-S 02-632-9623 IMP
LATTIMORE MATERIALS CO LP
LATTIMORE READY MIX
(Suby of AGGREGATE INDUSTRIES) ★
15900 Dooley Rd, Addison, TX 75001-4243
Tel (972) 221-4646 Founded/Ownrshp 1990
Sales 205.1MM^E EMP 1,100
SIC 3273 1422 1442 Ready-mixed concrete; Limestones, ground; Sand mining; Ready-mixed concrete; Limestones, ground; Sand mining
Pt: Scott Chrimes

LATTIMORE READY MIX
See LATTIMORE MATERIALS CO LP

D-U-N-S 06-676-3335
LATVA MACHINE INC
LM
744 John Stark Hwy, Newport, NH 03773-2607
Tel (603) 863-5155 Founded/Ownrshp 1973
Sales 27.1MM^E EMP 105
SIC 3599 Machine & other job shop work
Pr: Mitchell William Latva
*VP: William E Latva Jr

D-U-N-S 15-799-1774 EXP
■ LAU INDUSTRIES INC
SUPREME FAN/INDUSTRIAL AIR
(Suby of JOHNSON CONTROLS INC) ★
4509 Springfield St, Dayton, OH 45431-1042
Tel (937) 476-6500 Founded/Ownrshp 1990
Sales 194.0MM^E EMP 1,865^E
SIC 3564 Ventilating fans: industrial or commercial; Ventilating fans: industrial or commercial
Pr: Damian Macaluso
*VP: Dan Disser
*VP: Christopher Wampler
Sls Mgr: Greg Mattox

D-U-N-S 09-926-5217
LAUBER IMPORTS LTD
SUMMIT ESTATES DIVISION
(Suby of SOUTHERN WINE & SPIRITS FLA) ★
24 Columbia Rd Ste 100, Branchburg, NJ 08876-3577
Tel (908) 725-2100 Founded/Ownrshp 1979
Sales 20.7MM^E EMP 91
SIC 5182 Wine
Ch Bd: Edward C Lauber
*Pr: Mark Lauber
Rgnl Mgr: Keith Bader
Mktg Mgr: William Sciambi
Sls Mgr: Diane Newman

L'AUBERGE DU LAC CASINO RESORT
See PNK (LAKE CHARLES) LLC

D-U-N-S 13-239-8236
LAUD COLLIER & CO LLC
LC&CO
466 Southern Blvd Ste 2, Chatham, NJ 07928-1462
Tel (973) 822-1234 Founded/Ownrshp 2002
Sales NA EMP 96
SIC 6153 Working capital financing; Working capital financing

D-U-N-S 03-688-7701 IMP/EXP
LAUDADIO POLYMERS INC (TX)
449 Louisiana Ave, Corpus Christi, TX 78404-1707
Tel (361) 881-8729 Founded/Ownrshp 1996
Sales 31.0MM EMP 16
SIC 5162 Plastics materials & basic shapes; Plastics materials & basic shapes
Pr: Paul Laudadio
*VP: Paul Laudadio II

LAUDERDALE CNTY BD SUPERVISORS
See COUNTY OF LAUDERDALE

LAUDERDALE CNTY SCHL BD EDCATN
See LAUDERDALE COUNTY SCHOOL DISTRICT

D-U-N-S 02-125-1236
LAUDERDALE COUNTY BOARD OF EDUCATION
LAUDERDALE COUNTY SCHOOL SYSTE
355 County Road 61, Florence, AL 35634-2559
Tel (256) 760-1300 Founded/Ownrshp 1889
Sales 77.3MM EMP 1,000
SIC 8211 Public elementary & secondary schools; Public elementary & secondary schools
Schl Brd P: Chad Holden

D-U-N-S 07-895-5176
LAUDERDALE COUNTY SCHOOL DISTRICT
410 Constitution Ave Fl 3, Meridian, MS 39301-5161
Tel (601) 482-9746 Founded/Ownrshp 1833
Sales 38.0MM EMP 1,120
SIC 8211 Public elementary & secondary schools; Public elementary & secondary schools
Schl Brd P: Pam Frazier
HC Dir: Diane Freeman

D-U-N-S 36-126-8204
LAUDERDALE COUNTY SCHOOL DISTRICT
LAUDERDALE CNTY SCHL BD EDCATN
321 Armory St, Ripley, TN 38063-3434
Tel (731) 635-2941 Founded/Ownrshp 1990
Sales 37.0MM^E EMP 750^E
SIC 8211 Public elementary & secondary schools; Public elementary & secondary schools
Prin: David P Carmack
Prin: James G Douglas
Prin: Jack Phillips
Prin: Pam Sirmans.
Prin: Sue Toles
Prin: Alan Wallace
Adm Dir: Mark Newman

LAUDERDALE COUNTY SCHOOL SYSTE
See LAUDERDALE COUNTY BOARD OF EDUCATION

D-U-N-S 07-979-9000
LAUDERDALE COUNTY SCHOOL SYSTEM
355 County Road 61, Florence, AL 35634-2559
Tel (256) 760-1300 Founded/Ownrshp 2015
Sales 32.5MM^E EMP 915^E
SIC 8211 Public elementary & secondary schools
Dir Sec: John Mansell
MIS Dir: Jason Truiet
HC Dir: Brenda Foster
HC Dir: Kelly Stanhope

D-U-N-S 05-263-5641 EXP
LAUDERHILL AUTO INVESTORS I LLC
PHIL SMITH CHEVROLET
1640 N State Road 7, Lauderhill, FL 33313-5814
Tel (954) 777-7770 Founded/Ownrshp 2000
Sales 40.8MM^E EMP 100
SIC 5511 Automobiles, new & used; Automobiles, new & used
Pr: Philip P Smith
Sales Asso: Tom Timpanaro

LAUFEN INTERNATIONAL DIST
See ROCA USA INC

D-U-N-S 01-210-8403
LAUFER GROUP INTERNATIONAL LTD
20 Vesey St Rm 601, New York, NY 10007-4233
Tel (212) 945-6000 Founded/Ownrshp 1989
Sales 58.5MM^E EMP 150
SIC 4731 Freight transportation arrangement; Customhouse brokers; Freight transportation arrangement; Customhouse brokers
Ch Bd: Mark Laufer
Sr VP: Adriane Fulcher
VP: Michael Van Hagen
Dir Bus: Michael Goldsmith
Brnch Mgr: Martin Karczewski
Off Mgr: Louise Bayles
Dir IT: Zlatko Talevski
Opers Mgr: Alex Baes
Manager: Janis Efronson
Sls Mgr: Russell Grant

D-U-N-S 15-082-6873
LAUGHLIN FALBO LEVY MORESI LLP
555 12th St Ste 1900, Oakland, CA 94607-4098
Tel (510) 628-0496 Founded/Ownrshp 1985
Sales 33.8MM^E EMP 278
SIC 8111 Specialized law offices, attorneys; Labor & employment law; Specialized law offices, attorneys; Labor & employment law
Mng Pt: James Pettibone
Pt: John Bennett Jr
Pt: Phillip J Klein
Pt: James Wesolowski
Mng Pt: Kevin Calegari
Mng Pt: Marijo Kuperman
Pr: Carolyn Archibald
Pr: Cathey Bayless
Ex Dir: Bruce R Wright
Ex Dir: Bruce Wright
Off Mgr: Rockford Hearn

D-U-N-S 93-189-8969
LAUGHLIN MARINACCIO & OWENS INC
LM&O ADVERTISING
1776 Wilson Blvd Fl 5, Arlington, VA 22209-2517
Tel (703) 875-2193 Founded/Ownrshp 1995
Sales 25.2MM^E EMP 73^E
SIC 7311 8743 7313 Advertising agencies; Public relations services; Radio, television, publisher representatives
Pr: Christopher Laughlin
*Ch: Doug Laughlin
*Sr VP: Dave Marinaccio
VP: Lois Golden
*VP: Scott Laughlin
Off Mgr: Carol Williams
Off Admin: Ray Tehrani
MIS Dir: Elizabeth Fishkin
IT Man: Dirk Cassard
Prd Mgr: Kristen Butts
Mktg Mgr: Tiffany Matthews

D-U-N-S 06-650-5975
LAUGHLIN MEMORIAL HOSPITAL INC
1420 Tusculum Blvd, Greeneville, TN 37745-5825
Tel (423) 787-5000 Founded/Ownrshp 1963
Sales 67.0MM EMP 680
Accts Bkd Llp Louisville Kentucky
SIC 8062 8051 General medical & surgical hospitals; Skilled nursing care facilities; General medical & surgical hospitals; Skilled nursing care facilities
CEO: Chuck Whitfield
CFO: Mark Crompton
*Treas: Jack G Wilson
Dir Rad: Jesse Taylor
Dir Rx: Rick Ealy
Off Mgr: Erin Ricker
Snr Ntwrk: Dave Johnson
CIO: Mark Compton
IT Man: David Waldrupe
Software D: Brian Cook
QC Dir: Angel Carter

D-U-N-S 06-774-9382
LAUGHLIN RECREATIONAL ENTERPRISES INC
1650 S Casino Dr, Laughlin, NV 89029-1512
Tel (702) 298-2535 Founded/Ownrshp 1973
Sales 43.4MM^E EMP 2,000
SIC 6512 Nonresidential building operators; Nonresidential building operators
Pr: Donald J Laughlin
*Treas: Dan P Laughlin
Exec: Herve Allain
Dir Sec: Larry Covey
Dir Sec: Terry Donaho
MIS Dir: Robert Deering
Netwrk Mgr: Thomas Simonds
Sfty Mgr: Valerie Lopez
Opers Mgr: Dell Newman
VP Mktg: Jesse James
VP Mktg: Pam Morrill

D-U-N-S 05-014-8220 IMP
LAUGHLIN-CARTRELL INC
12850 Ne Hendricks Rd, Carlton, OR 97111
Tel (503) 852-7151 Founded/Ownrshp 1982
Sales 108.2MM EMP 13
Accts Boldt Carlisle + Smith Salem
SIC 5191 Feed; Fertilizer & fertilizer materials; Feed; Fertilizer & fertilizer materials
Pr: Tillman J Stone
*Ch Bd: Robert S Laughlin
*VP: Lawrence Kubes

D-U-N-S 08-048-6616
LAUGHLIN/CONSTABLE INC (WI)
LC
207 E Michigan St Stop 1, Milwaukee, WI 53202-4996
Tel (414) 272-2400 Founded/Ownrshp 1976
Sales 26.0MM^E EMP 135
SIC 7311 Advertising agencies; Advertising agencies
Pr: Steven Laughlin
*Sec: Mitch Winter
Ex VP: Kris Naidl
Sr VP: Paul Brienza
Sr VP: Brian Knox
Sr VP: Patrick McAuley
VP: Brian Doherty
VP: Jim McDonald
VP: Brady Pierzchlaski
VP: Phil Smith
VP: Lisa Todd
VP: Ben Wohlers
VP: Anna Zeck
Creative D: Mark Drewek
Creative D: Steve Drifka
Creative D: Kirk Ruhnke
Creative D: Jay Sharfstein

LAUNCH EQUIPMENT SUPPORT SHOP
See UNITED SPACE ALLIANCE LLC

LAUNCHPAD COMMUNICATIONS
See CONSUMER RESOURCE NETWORK LLC

LAUNDRY LUX
See BERMIL INDUSTRIES CORP

D-U-N-S 96-709-7515
LAURA AND JOHN ARNOLD FOUNDATION
2800 Post Oak Blvd # 225, Houston, TX 77056-6169
Tel (713) 554-1349 Founded/Ownrshp 2008
Sales 418.7MM EMP 2
SIC 8699 Charitable organization; Charitable organization
Ch: Laura E Arnold
*Pr: Denis Calacrese
*Ch: John Arnold
*Treas: Elizabeth Banks
VP: Ed Young
Genl Couns: Lesley Briones

D-U-N-S 02-537-2103
LAURA BUICK - GMC INC (IL)
903 N Bluff Rd, Collinsville, IL 62234-5820
Tel (618) 344-0121 Founded/Ownrshp 1981
Sales 22.6MM^E EMP 47
SIC 5511

LAURA LIGHTING
See EXPRESSIVE LIGHTING INC

D-U-N-S 12-183-6816
LAURAND ASSOCIATES INC
11 Grace Ave Ste 405, Great Neck, NY 11021-2417
Tel (516) 829-8821 Founded/Ownrshp 2000
Sales 110.0MM EMP 8
SIC 5051 Aluminum bars, rods, ingots, sheets, pipes, plates, etc.
Pr: Laurence A Goldfarb
Opers Mgr: Patricia Romero

D-U-N-S 16-190-7613
LAUREATE EDUCATION INC
650 S Exeter St Fl 7, Baltimore, MD 21202-4574
Tel (410) 843-6100 Founded/Ownrshp 2007
Sales 773.7MM^E EMP 23,210
SIC 8299 Educational services; Educational services
Ch Bd: Douglas L Becker
Pr: Raph Appadoo
Pr: Neal Cohen
Pr: Paula R Singer
CFO: Eilif Serck-Hanssen
Bd of Dir: Wolf H Engst
Bd of Dir: Jonathan Smidt
Ex VP: Daniel M Nickel
Sr VP: Robert W Zentz
VP: Cristina Onaghten
VP: Hernando Ramirez
VP: Chris Symanoskie
Board of Directors: George Munoz, Judith Rodin, Robert B Zoellick

D-U-N-S 60-662-7396
LAUREATE PSYCHIATRIC CLINIC & HOSPITAL
SAINT FRANCIS HOSPITAL
(Suby of SAINT FRANCIS HOSPITAL INC) ★
6655 S Yale Ave, Tulsa, OK 74136-3326
Tel (918) 491-3700 Founded/Ownrshp 1989
Sales 36.5MM EMP 300
Accts Ernst & Young Us Llp Columbus
SIC 8063 Psychiatric hospitals; Psychiatric hospitals
VP: Craig Koele
*CFO: Barry Steichen
Ofcr: Bill Schloss
Sr VP: Judy Kishner
VP: Mark Snyderman
Dir Risk M: Sandy Shirley
CIO: Meredith Coburn
CIO: Mark Stastny
CTO: Angela Smith
QA Dir: Jeannie Carl
Dir IT: John Cash

LAUREL BAYE HEALTHCARE
See LAUREL BAYE MEDICAL LLC

D-U-N-S 05-962-9787
LAUREL BAYE HEALTHCARE OF BLACKVILLE L L C
(Suby of LAUREL BAYE HEALTHCARE) ★
1612 Jones Bridge Rd, Blackville, SC 29817-3066
Tel (803) 284-4313 Founded/Ownrshp 1997
Sales 4.4MM EMP 347
SIC 8051 Skilled nursing care facilities; Skilled nursing care facilities
Pr: Dennis Wheeler

D-U-N-S 03-011-4813
LAUREL BAYE HEALTHCARE OF ORANGEBURG LLC (SC)
(Suby of LAUREL BAYE HEALTHCARE) ★
575 Stnewall Jackson Blvd, Orangeburg, SC 29115-7250
Tel (803) 535-3549 Founded/Ownrshp 1965, 2003
Sales 19.3MM^E EMP 450
SIC 8051 8361 Skilled nursing care facilities; Geriatric residential care; Skilled nursing care facilities; Geriatric residential care
Ex Dir: Tae Jone
Off Mgr: Lindsey Rudd
Off Mgr: Rowe Tuttle
Nrsg Dir: Debbie Metts
HC Dir: Tracie Crafts

D-U-N-S 07-880-1399
LAUREL BAYE HEALTHCARE OF SOUTH CAROLINA LLC (SC)
3409 Salterbeck Ct, Mount Pleasant, SC 29466-7117
Tel (843) 216-6800 Founded/Ownrshp 1997
Sales 21.8MM^E EMP 500
SIC 8099 Medical services organization; Medical services organization
CFO: Thomas Tiller

D-U-N-S 03-187-6688
LAUREL BAYE MEDICAL LLC
LAUREL BAYE HEALTHCARE
3409 Salterbeck Ct, Mount Pleasant, SC 29466-7117
Tel (843) 216-6800 Founded/Ownrshp 1997
Sales 40.5MM^E EMP 489
SIC 8051 Skilled nursing care facilities; Skilled nursing care facilities
VP: Lorri Isenhath
Ex Dir: Nick Guzman
Ex Dir: Margaret Lewis

LAUREL CANYON COFFEE COMPANY
See LAUREL FOODSYSTEMS INC

D-U-N-S 07-131-9966
LAUREL COUNTY BOARD OF EDUCATION
LAUREL COUNTY PUBLIC SCHOOLS
718 N Main St, London, KY 40741-1222
Tel (606) 862-4608 Founded/Ownrshp 1925
Sales 90.0MM EMP 1,300
SIC 8211 Public senior high school; Public junior high school; Public elementary school; Public senior high school; Public junior high school; Public elementary school

LAUREL COUNTY PUBLIC SCHOOLS
See LAUREL COUNTY BOARD OF EDUCATION

D-U-N-S 07-982-7311
LAUREL COUNTY PUBLIC SCHOOLS
718 N Main St, London, KY 40741-1222
Tel (606) 862-4600 Founded/Ownrshp 2015
Sales 20.8MM^E EMP 780^E
SIC 8211 Public elementary & secondary schools
Pr Dir: Charlie House
HC Dir: Amy Sams

D-U-N-S 07-214-9149
LAUREL FOODSYSTEMS INC
LAUREL CANYON COFFEE COMPANY
4590 Campbells Run Rd, Pittsburgh, PA 15205-1314
Tel (412) 494-4400 Founded/Ownrshp 1974
Sales 39.1MM^E EMP 228^E
SIC 5962 5812 7389 Cigarettes vending machines; Sandwich & hot food vending machines; Cafeteria; Coffee service; Cigarettes vending machines; Sandwich & hot food vending machines; Cafeteria; Coffee service
Ch Bd: Thomas S Diffendal Sr
*Pr: Thomas S Diffendal Jr
*Treas: Donald Diffendal
*VP: David Diffendal
Exec: Trish Martin
S&M/VP: Rick Lawry

D-U-N-S 03-336-8192
LAUREL FORD LINCOLN-KIA INC
LAUREL KIA
2018 Highway 15 N, Laurel, MS 39440-1837
Tel (601) 649-4511 Founded/Ownrshp 1992
Sales 32.5MM EMP 60
SIC 5511 5521 Automobiles, new & used; Used car dealers; Automobiles, new & used; Used car dealers
Pr: Jimmy Walker
*Off Mgr: Jim Swartzfager

D-U-N-S 00-799-1979
LAUREL GROCERY CO LLC (KY)
129 Barbourville Rd, London, KY 40744-9301
Tel (606) 878-6601 Founded/Ownrshp 1920, 1944
Sales 510.1MM^E EMP 411
SIC 5141 5147 5122 5143 Groceries, general line; Meats, fresh; Drugs, proprietaries & sundries; Dairy products, except dried or canned; Groceries, general line; Meats, fresh; Drugs, proprietaries & sundries; Dairy products, except dried or canned
*V Ch: Winston Griffin
Advt Dir: Barry Williams
Mktg Dir: John McCurry

D-U-N-S 78-599-2520
LAUREL HEALTH CARE CO
(Suby of LAUREL HEALTH CARE CO OF NORTH WORTHINGTON) ★
8181 Worthington Rd Uppr, Westerville, OH 43082-8071
Tel (614) 794-8800 Founded/Ownrshp 1992
Sales 52.4MM^E EMP 1,041^E
SIC 8741 Nursing & personal care facility management
Pr: Bradford Payne
CFO: Lynette Mocksherman
*VP: Jack Alcott
*VP: Carol Bailey
*VP: Timothy Patton
Comm Man: Natalie Kennedy
Rgnl Mgr: Mark Morley
Dir IT: Kelly Foster
IT Man: Matt Moore
Opers Mgr: Jeff Shepard
Doctor: Lynette Mochsherman

D-U-N-S 83-607-5028
LAUREL HEALTH CARE CO OF NORTH WORTHTINGTON
8181 Worthington Rd, Westerville, OH 43082-8067
Tel (614) 794-8800 Founded/Ownrshp 1995
Sales 149.1MM^E EMP 2,018
SIC 8059 8741 Nursing home, except skilled & intermediate care facility; Nursing & personal care facility management; Nursing home, except skilled & intermediate care facility; Nursing & personal care facility management
Pr: Brad Payne

D-U-N-S 10-805-0394
LAUREL HEALTH SYSTEM INC
22 Walnut St, Wellsboro, PA 16901-1526
Tel (570) 724-1010 Founded/Ownrshp 1989
Sales 670.3M EMP 1,100
SIC 8082 8741 8011 Home health care services; Management services; Offices & clinics of medical doctors; Home health care services; Management services; Offices & clinics of medical doctors
CEO: Steven P Johnson
CFO: Ron Gilbert
*Treas: Craig Litchfield
*Ex VP: Jan E Fisher
*VP: Ronald M Gilbert Jr
CIO: Joseph F Bubacz Jr
Opers Mgr: Ben Weiskopff
HC Dir: Sandy Moffett
Pgrm Dir: Susan Sticklin

D-U-N-S 15-778-2991
LAUREL HEALTHCARE LLC
LAUREL HEIGHTS
5900 Forest Hills Dr Ne, Albuquerque, NM 87109-4129
Tel (505) 822-6000 Founded/Ownrshp 2000
Sales 5.6MM^E EMP 300
SIC 8059 8051 Nursing home, except skilled & intermediate care facility; Skilled nursing care facilities; Nursing home, except skilled & intermediate care facility; Skilled nursing care facilities
Exec: Clare Strickman

D-U-N-S 13-680-3595
LAUREL HEALTHCARE PROVIDERS LLC
103 Hospital Loop Ne, Albuquerque, NM 87109-2115
Tel (505) 348-8300 Founded/Ownrshp 1999
Sales 9.6MM^E EMP 780
SIC 8051 8322 Skilled nursing care facilities; Rehabilitation services; Skilled nursing care facilities; Rehabilitation services

LAUREL HEIGHTS
See LAUREL HEALTHCARE LLC

D-U-N-S 08-072-9064
LAUREL HIGHLANDS SCHOOL DISTRICT (PA)
304 Bailey Ave, Uniontown, PA 15401-2497
Tel (724) 437-2821 Founded/Ownrshp 1965
Sales 36.1MM EMP 375
SIC 8211 Public elementary school; Public junior high school; Public senior high school; Public elementary school; Public junior high school; Public senior high school
Prin: Jeanne Moore

D-U-N-S 03-510-3746 IMP
LAUREL HILL ENTERPRISES INC
REGENCY CARE CTR WALLA WALLA
3326 160th Ave Se Ste 120, Bellevue, WA 98008-6418
Tel (425) 392-4066 Founded/Ownrshp 1966
Sales 9.8MM^E EMP 340
SIC 8051 Convalescent home with continuous nursing care; Convalescent home with continuous nursing care
Pr: James L Clay
CFO: Doug Devore

D-U-N-S 07-806-3831
LAUREL HILL INC
(Suby of HMR ADVANTAGE HEALTH SYSTEMS INC) ★
716 E Cedar Rock St, Pickens, SC 29671-2324
Tel (864) 878-4739 Founded/Ownrshp 1969
Sales 569.4MM EMP 225
SIC 8052 8051 Intermediate care facilities; Skilled nursing care facilities; Intermediate care facilities; Skilled nursing care facilities
Prin: Mary Reed
*Sec: John P O'Brien Jr
*VP: Larry Lollis
Exec: Heather Harbinson

D-U-N-S 08-620-9269
LAUREL HOLDINGS INC
111 Roosevelt Blvd, Johnstown, PA 15906-2736
Tel (814) 533-5777 Founded/Ownrshp 1974
Sales 92.4MM^E EMP 311
SIC 4941 5063 3599 4724 7349 Water supply; Batteries, dry cell; Machine shop, jobbing & repair; Travel agencies; Janitorial service, contract basis; Water supply; Batteries, dry cell; Machine shop, jobbing & repair; Travel agencies; Janitorial service, contract basis
Pr: Kim Kunkle
Treas: Mike Brosig

LAUREL IMPORTS
See LAUREL MOTORS HOLDING CO INC

LAUREL KIA
See LAUREL FORD LINCOLN-KIA INC

D-U-N-S 19-347-0358
LAUREL LAKE RETIREMENT COMMUNITY INC
CROWN CENTER
200 Laurel Lake Dr Rear, Hudson, OH 44236-2160
Tel (330) 650-0681 Founded/Ownrshp 1985
Sales 31.2MM^E EMP 350
SIC 8361 8051 Rest home, with health care incidental; Skilled nursing care facilities; Rest home, with health care incidental; Skilled nursing care facilities
Ex Dir: David A Oster
Exec: Lisa Powell
Advt Mgr: Donna Anderson

D-U-N-S 00-817-6935
LAUREL MACHINE AND FOUNDRY CO
LMF
810 Front St, Laurel, MS 39440-3548
Tel (601) 428-0541 Founded/Ownrshp 1904
Sales 43.1MM^E EMP 140
SIC 3599 3441 5051 3443 5085 3321 Machine shop, jobbing & repair; Fabricated structural metal; Metals service centers & offices; Fabricated plate work (boiler shop); Mill supplies; Gray & ductile iron foundries; Machine shop, jobbing & repair; Fabricated structural metal; Metals service centers & offices; Fabricated plate work (boiler shop); Mill supplies; Gray & ductile iron foundries
CEO: Patrick Mulloy
*Pr: Trent A Mulloy
*CFO: Chuck Bridges
VP: James Mulloy
Opers Mgr: Jerry Hinton
Sls Mgr: Mike Cochran
Sls Mgr: Jeff Walters
Board of Directors: Chuck Bridges

D-U-N-S 00-882-3171
LAUREL MANAGEMENT GROUP
166 60th St, Parkersburg, WV 26105-8002
Tel (304) 295-3311 Founded/Ownrshp 1948
Sales 22.1MM^E EMP 50
Accts Rea & Associates
SIC 1761 Roofing contractor; Sheet metalwork
CEO: Harry H Esbenshade III
*VP: Michael D Cain
*VP: Thomas Davies
*VP: M Michael Richardson

D-U-N-S 78-762-0442
LAUREL MOTORS HOLDING CO INC
LAUREL IMPORTS
933 Eisenhower Blvd, Johnstown, PA 15904-3320
Tel (814) 269-3400 Founded/Ownrshp 1991
Sales 56.7MM^E EMP 170
SIC 5511 Automobiles, new & used; Automobiles, new & used
Pr: Michael B Smith
Treas: Jeff Bloom
*VP: Matthew Smith
Sls Mgr: Bill Gianotti
*Sls Mgr: Scott Long
Sls Mgr: Larry Mummert
Sales Asso: Alf Dipaola
Sales Asso: Carrie Hoover
Sales Asso: Alyssa Kvarta
Sales Asso: Doug Thomas

D-U-N-S 83-736-2060
LAUREL MOUNTAIN PARTNERS LLC
LIBERTY CARE RECYCLING
1251 Waterfront Pl # 400, Pittsburgh, PA 15222-4227
Tel (412) 562-0247 Founded/Ownrshp 1995
Sales 53.8MM^E EMP 200^E
SIC 7922 Theatrical producers; Theatrical producers

LAUREL PARK
See LAUREL RACING ASSOCIATION LIMITED PARTNERSHIP

D-U-N-S 80-280-2686
■ **LAUREL PIPE LINE CO LP**
(Suby of BUCKEYE PARTNERS LP) ★
3900 Hamilton Blvd # 208, Allentown, PA 18103-6122
Tel (610) 485-0231 Founded/Ownrshp 1986
Sales 12.6MM^E EMP 543
SIC 4613 Refined petroleum pipelines; Refined petroleum pipelines
Genl Pt: Clark Smith

D-U-N-S 12-230-9222
LAUREL RACING ASSOCIATION LIMITED PARTNERSHIP
LAUREL PARK
Racetrack Rd Rr 198, Laurel, MD 20724
Tel (301) 725-0400 Founded/Ownrshp 2002
Sales 50.6MM EMP 600
Accts Ernst & Young Llp Baltimore
SIC 7948 Thoroughbred horse racing; Thoroughbred horse racing
Pt: Thomas Chuckas Jr
Genl Pt: Laurel Racing Assoc
CFO: Douglas J Illig
Ex VP: Robert Di Pietro
VP: Dennis Smoter

LAUREL REGIONAL HOSPITAL
See PUBLIC RELATIONS & DEVELOPMENT

LAUREL RIDGE APARTMENTS
See MOSAIC RESIDENTIAL INC

LAUREL RIDGE TREATMENT CENTER
See TEXAS LAUREL RIDGE HOSPITAL LP

D-U-N-S 07-116-9841
LAUREL SAND & GRAVEL INC
SW BARRICK & SONS
14504 Greenview Dr # 210, Laurel, MD 20708-3225
Tel (410) 792-7234 Founded/Ownrshp 1982
Sales 135.2MM^E EMP 215
SIC 1422 1442 Crushed & broken limestone; Construction sand & gravel; Crushed & broken limestone; Construction sand & gravel
Pr: Ronald Matovick
VP: Ed Barhauser
*VP: Edward Barnhouser

D-U-N-S 09-761-0323
LAUREL SCHOOL
1 Lyman Cir, Cleveland, OH 44122-2199
Tel (216) 464-1441 Founded/Ownrshp 1896
Sales 22.5MM EMP 165^E
Accts Maloney Novotny Llc Cleveland
SIC 8351 8211 Preschool center; Private combined elementary & secondary school; Preschool center; Private combined elementary & secondary school
Prin: Ann Klotz
*Pr: Heather Ettinger
CFO: Linda Hurley
Ofcr: Rolanda Sims
Assoc Dir: Missy Rose
IT Man: Pam Wingenfeld
Pr Dir: Kate Floyd
Psych: Ilissa Pearlman

D-U-N-S 08-355-2976
LAUREL SCHOOL DISTRICT
303 W 8th St, Laurel, MS 39440-3483
Tel (601) 649-6391 Founded/Ownrshp 1940
Sales 32.3MM EMP 500
Accts Watkins Ward & Stafford Pllc
SIC 8211 Public elementary & secondary schools; Public elementary & secondary schools

LAURELWOOD CLC
See CLC OF LAUREL LLC

LAURELWOOD CTR FOR BHVRAL HLTH
See LAURELWOOD HOSPITAL

D-U-N-S 07-675-6725
LAURELWOOD HOSPITAL
LAURELWOOD CTR FOR BHVRAL HLTH
35900 Euclid Ave, Willoughby, OH 44094-4648
Tel (440) 953-3000 Founded/Ownrshp 2007
Sales 12.8MM^E EMP 319
SIC 8063 8069 Psychiatric hospitals; Substance abuse hospitals; Psychiatric hospitals; Substance abuse hospitals
Pr: Richard Warden
Doctor: Ruth S Martin

LAUREN BY RALPH LAUREN
See CAROLEE LLC

D-U-N-S 19-853-7367
LAUREN CORP
901 S 1st St, Abilene, TX 79602-1502
Tel (325) 670-9660 Founded/Ownrshp 1988
Sales 287.0MM EMP 1,700
SIC 1629 Chemical plant & refinery construction; Chemical plant & refinery construction; Power plant construction; Oil refinery construction
Pr: C Cleve Whitener
CFO: Thomas Modisett
Off Admin: Grace Ingram
Site Mgr: Ted Hapworth
Snr PM: Jason Fuchs

D-U-N-S 12-092-8700
LAUREN ENGINEERS & CONSTRUCTORS INC
(Suby of LAUREN CORP) ★
901 S 1st St, Abilene, TX 79602-1502
Tel (325) 670-9660 Founded/Ownrshp 1994
Sales 237.4MM EMP 1,100
SIC 1541 Industrial buildings & warehouses; Industrial buildings & warehouses
Pr: C Cleve Whitener
Pr: Margarett Barbee
Pr: Charlie Thompson
*COO: Ron Johnson
*COO: Clint Rosenbaum
*CFO: Leslie Hammond
Treas: Christopher R Keays
Ex VP: Bob Fasciana
Ex VP: Jack Shoemate
VP: Rod Phipps
VP: Robert W Roy

D-U-N-S 19-449-7405
LAUREN HOLDING INC
781 North St, Greenwich, CT 06831-3105
Tel (239) 514-7329 Founded/Ownrshp 2005
Sales 200.0MM^E EMP 100
SIC 6211 Investment bankers
Pr: Lauren Corrigan

D-U-N-S 00-398-3269 IMP
LAUREN INTERNATIONAL LTD (OH)
LAUREN MANUFACTURING
2228 Reiser Ave Se, New Philadelphia, OH 44663-3334
Tel (330) 339-3373 Founded/Ownrshp 1965, 2011
Sales 160.6MM^E EMP 450
Accts Four Fifteen Group Canton Oh
SIC 3069 Molded rubber products; Molded rubber products
Pr: Kevin E Gray
*CFO: David Gingrich
VP: Craig Janusz
Genl Mgr: Eric Alander
Tech Mgr: Chris Porter
Info Man: Cindy Felgenhauer
Sftwr Eng: Jonathan Gentsch
Prd Mgr: John Luers
Mktg Dir: Cynthia Miller
Mktg Mgr: Sheryl Montan
Sls Mgr: Allen Johnson
Board of Directors: Philip Eykamp, Dale Foland, Kevin Gray, William High, Thad Rosenberry

LAUREN MANUFACTURING
See LAUREN INTERNATIONAL LTD

D-U-N-S 94-344-1998 IMP
LAUREN MANUFACTURING LLC
(Suby of LAUREN INTERNATIONAL LTD) ★
2228 Reiser Ave Se, New Philadelphia, OH 44663-3334
Tel (330) 339-3373 Founded/Ownrshp 1994
Sales 51.3MM^E EMP 288

SIC 3069 3061 Molded rubber products; Mechanical rubber goods; Molded rubber products; Mechanical rubber goods
CEO: Kevin E Gray
Ch Bd: Dale Foland
Pr: Lisa Huntsman
Pr: Chuck Laney
VP: Jim Hummel
Software D: Matt Mastroine
Natl Sales: Bob Mecomonaco

D-U-N-S 18-003-8465 IMP
LAURENS CB&I INC
(*Suby of* SHAW GROUP INC) ★
366 Old Airport Rd, Laurens, SC 29360-7636
Tel (864) 682-4000 *Founded/Ownrshp* 1987
Sales 45.6MM^E *EMP* 200
SIC 3498 Pipe fittings, fabricated from purchased pipe; Pipe fittings, fabricated from purchased pipe
CEO: Jim Bernhard Jr
Genl Mgr: Joe Harrison

LAURENS COUNTY BOARD EDUCATION
See LAURENS COUNTY SCHOOL DISTRICT

D-U-N-S 07-805-0903
LAURENS COUNTY HEALTH CARE SYSTEM
22725 Highway 76 E, Clinton, SC 29325-7527
Tel (864) 833-9100 *Founded/Ownrshp* 1982
Sales 63.1MM^E *EMP* 450
Accts Larsonallen Llp Charlotte No
SIC 8062 General medical & surgical hospitals; General medical & surgical hospitals
CEO: Michael C Riordan
**Treas:* J Alton Davis Jr
Ex VP: Robert Staton
VP: Willis Jackson Brand
VP: Genevra Kelly
VP: Marion Reeder

D-U-N-S 83-897-3659
LAURENS COUNTY HOSPITAL (INC)
76 W Clinton, Clinton, SC 29325
Tel (864) 833-9100 *Founded/Ownrshp* 1989
Sales 78.8MM *EMP* 500
SIC 8062 General medical & surgical hospitals; General medical & surgical hospitals
Pr: Rich D Alberto
Off Mgr: Regina Stopman
Nrsg Dir: Robert Councilman

D-U-N-S 10-001-3630
LAURENS COUNTY SCHOOL DISTRICT
LAURENS COUNTY BOARD EDUCATION
467 Firetower Rd, Dublin, GA 31021-2682
Tel (478) 272-4767 *Founded/Ownrshp* 1873
Sales 45.0MM^E *EMP* 831
Accts Russell W Hinton Atlanta Geo
SIC 8211 Public elementary & secondary schools; Public elementary & secondary schools
Trst: Jo Wilson
Ofcr: Liliana Ruiz
MIS Dir: Debbie Floyd
Dir IT: Paul Hodges
IT Man: Leon Horne
IT Man: Diane Ikner
Instr Medi: Lance Smith
Psych: Tammy Edge

D-U-N-S 10-007-1455
LAURENS COUNTY SCHOOL DISTRICT 55
1029 W Main St, Laurens, SC 29360-2654
Tel (864) 984-3568 *Founded/Ownrshp* 1955
Sales 61.0MM *EMP* 650
Accts Mckinley Cooper & Co Llc G
SIC 8211 Public combined elementary & secondary school; Public combined elementary & secondary school

D-U-N-S 03-740-0165
LAURENS COUNTY SCHOOL DISTRICT 56
211 N Broad St Ste B, Clinton, SC 29325-2303
Tel (864) 833-0800 *Founded/Ownrshp* 1951
Sales 26.7MM^E *EMP* 452
Accts Mckinley Cooper & Co Llp
SIC 8211 Public combined elementary & secondary school; Public combined elementary & secondary school
IT Man: David O'Shields
IT Man: Carol Barnes

LAURENS COUNTY SHERIFF DEPT
See COUNTY OF LAURENS

D-U-N-S 00-379-3205
LAURENS ELECTRIC COOPERATIVE INC (SC)
2254 Highway 14, Laurens, SC 29360-5164
Tel (864) 682-3141 *Founded/Ownrshp* 1939
Sales 113.9MM *EMP* 160
SIC 4911 Distribution, electric power; Distribution, electric power
Pr: J David Wasson Jr
Dir IT: Bobby Smith
IT Man: Daniel Ott
Board of Directors: Helen Abrams, Louis Harrison, Ralph Hendrix, V Pres

D-U-N-S 80-220-8736
LAURENS RESTORATION INC
1870 Elmdale Ave, Glenview, IL 60026-1356
Tel (847) 486-9111 *Founded/Ownrshp* 1996
Sales 20.6MM^E *EMP* 92
SIC 1521 Single-family home remodeling, additions & repairs
Pr: Jonathan Laurens
COO: Keith White
CFO: Brad Rosen
Off Mgr: Julie Gathman
Opers Mgr: Zachary Laurens
Mktg Dir: Robert Caras

D-U-N-S 02-531-2724 IMP/EXP
LAURIDSEN GROUP INC
2425 Se Oak Tree Ct, Ankeny, IA 50021-7102
Tel (515) 289-7600 *Founded/Ownrshp* 1994
Sales 146.8MM^E *EMP* 750
SIC 2099 Food preparations; Food preparations
Pr: John F Wheeler
COO: Bill Bernardo
**VP:* Mel Berg
**VP:* Jerry Frankl
VP: Christine Lauridsen
**VP:* Louis Russell
**VP:* John Wheeler
Exec: Linda Wilson
Genl Mgr: Tomasz Radomyski
Mktg Mgr: Carol Pahl
Mktg Mgr: Beth Saxton

D-U-N-S 96-568-2102
LAURIE M TISCH FOUNDATION INC
655 Madison Ave Fl 19, New York, NY 10065-8043
Tel (212) 521-2930 *Founded/Ownrshp* 2010
Sales 22.4MM *EMP* 2
SIC 8699 Charitable organization; Charitable organization
Prin: M J Krinsky CPA

D-U-N-S 01-217-7171
LAURIER ENTERPRISES INC (ID)
MCDONALD'S
1235 Market St Ste A, Kirkland, WA 98033-5440
Tel (425) 822-1055 *Founded/Ownrshp* 1986
Sales 20.0MM *EMP* 650
SIC 5812 Fast-food restaurant, chain; Fast-food restaurant, chain
Pr: Brian Beaulaurier
**VP:* Cathy Beaulaurier

D-U-N-S 08-462-1325
LAURITZEN CORP
1620 Dodge St, Omaha, NE 68197-0003
Tel (402) 341-2535 *Founded/Ownrshp* 1985
Sales NA *EMP* 102
SIC 6021 6022 National commercial banks; State commercial banks; National commercial banks; State commercial banks
Pr: Bruce Lauritzen
**Treas:* Joe Ramaeker
**Ex VP:* Daniel O'Neil
**VP:* Neil Stanley

D-U-N-S 02-879-3664
LAURUS CAPITAL MANAGEMENT LLC
LAURUS FUNDS
230 Park Ave Rm 1152, New York, NY 10169-1161
Tel (212) 541-5800 *Founded/Ownrshp* 2001
Sales 62.7MM^E *EMP* 185
SIC 6211 Stock brokers & dealers; Stock brokers & dealers
IT Man: Davin Singh
Counsel: Jessica Atkins

LAURUS FUNDS
See LAURUS CAPITAL MANAGEMENT LLC

D-U-N-S 82-775-9809
LAURUS INTERNATIONAL ENTERPRISES LLC
7362 Futures Dr Ste 26, Orlando, FL 32819-9088
Tel (407) 352-8912 *Founded/Ownrshp* 2010
Sales 18.2MM^E *EMP* 650^E
SIC 7361 Employment agencies; Employment agencies
CEO: Rodolfo Ganna
CFO: Tim Murphy
**VP:* Matt Charles
**VP:* Cleatous Simmons
**VP:* Gregory Waddell

LAUSD
See LOS ANGELES UNIFIED SCHOOL DISTRICT

D-U-N-S 09-001-3624 IMP/EXP
LAUSELL INC
ALUMINIO DEL CARIBE
Carr 2 Km 14 St Ca, Bayamon, PR 00960
Tel (787) 798-7610 *Founded/Ownrshp* 1951, 1997
Sales 74.8MM^E *EMP* 567
SIC 3442 Metal doors, sash & trim; Louver doors, metal; Louver windows, metal; Metal doors, sash & trim; Louver doors, metal; Louver windows, metal
Pr: Alberto M Recio
**CFO:* Manuel Villapol
**VP:* Eduardo Recio

LAUTENBERG FMLY JCC GR MORRIS
See UNITED JEWISH FEDERATION OF METRO WEST

D-U-N-S 17-189-2599
LAUTERBACH INC
TRACE32
(*Suby of* LAUTERBACH GMBH)
4 Mount Royal Ave Ste 320, Marlborough, MA 01752-1961
Tel (508) 303-6812 *Founded/Ownrshp* 1979
Sales 26.5MM *EMP* 5
SIC 5065 Electronic parts & equipment; Electronic parts & equipment
Pr: Lothar Lauterbach
Mng Dir: Barry Lock
Opers Mgr: Ginger Gibeault
Sls&Mrk Ex: Evi Ederer
Sls&Mrk Ex: Jerry Flake

D-U-N-S 08-704-1463
LAUTH PROPERTIES LLC
EATON & LAUTH
111 Cngrnnal Blvd Ste 300, Carmel, IN 46032
Tel (317) 848-6500 *Founded/Ownrshp* 1977
Sales 48.8MM^E *EMP* 425
SIC 6531 1542 6552 Real estate managers; Real estate leasing & rentals; Real estate brokers & agents; Commercial & office building contractors; Commercial & office building, new construction; Subdividers & developers; Real estate managers; Real estate leasing & rentals; Real estate brokers & agents; Commercial & office building contractors; Commercial & office building, new construction; Subdividers & developers
Ch Bd: Robert L Lauth
**Pr:* Gregory C Gurnik
CFO: Jonathon L Goodburn
**CFO:* Lawrence B Palmer
Sr VP: Eric Mallory
Sr VP: Francis Teague
VP: Michael Corless
VP: Ora Downs
VP: Brian Metallic
VP: David Sior
VP Opers: Jeff Todd

D-U-N-S 03-877-4709
LAUTREC LTD
OAKLAND LEASING COMPANY
31550 Northwestern Hwy, Farmington Hills, MI 48334-2571
Tel (248) 851-2700 *Founded/Ownrshp* 1976
Sales 15.3MM^E *EMP* 450
SIC 6531 Real estate managers; Real estate managers
Pr: James Galbraith
**Sec:* Anna Mae Burke
**VP:* Ralph Thompson
Rgnl Mgr: Kevin Trealout

D-U-N-S 60-335-4457
LAUX/ARNOLD INC
L A ELECTRIC
902 Incentive Dr, Fort Wayne, IN 46825-3276
Tel (260) 497-0520 *Founded/Ownrshp* 1988
Sales 23.1MM^E *EMP* 85
SIC 1731 General electrical contractor
CEO: William G Arnold
**Pr:* Bill Arnold
**CEO:* William Arnold
CFO: Sherry Oliver
**Ex VP:* Scott Arnold
**VP:* Steve Arnold
VP: Mark Hossler
**VP:* Chris Stronczek

D-U-N-S 11-255-1262 IMP
LAVA LITE LLC
1200 Thorndale Ave, Elk Grove Village, IL 60007-6749
Tel (630) 315-3300 *Founded/Ownrshp* 2008
Sales 20.3MM *EMP* 18
Accts Detterbeck Johnson & Monsen Cp
SIC 3645 3596 Residential lighting fixtures; Bathroom scales; Residential lighting fixtures; Bathroom scales
Pr: Clay Farnsworth
**CFO:* Joe Kostelc
**Sr VP:* Michael Kehrmann

D-U-N-S 78-815-5500
■ **LAVA TRADING INC**
(*Suby of* CITIGROUP INC) ★
95 Morton St Fl 6, New York, NY 10014-3336
Tel (212) 609-0100 *Founded/Ownrshp* 1999
Sales 21.5MM^E *EMP* 185
SIC 7371 Computer software development; Computer software development
CEO: Richard Korhammer
Pt: Joseph Lalicata
**CFO:* James Paddon
Sr VP: Sreeram Ramanathan
VP: Carl Gertz
VP: Joseph Isaacs
CIO: Jennifer Debski
Software D: Han-Jun Li
Software D: Conred Wang
Netwrk Eng: Saleem Nathoo

D-U-N-S 07-014-3037
LAVACA HOSPITAL DISTRICT
LAVACA MEDICAL CENTER
1400 N Texana St, Hallettsville, TX 77964-2021
Tel (361) 798-3671 *Founded/Ownrshp* 1976
Sales 26.1MM^E *EMP* 107
SIC 8062 General medical & surgical hospitals
CFO: Tracy Green
Dir Lab: Noreen Fojt
Dir Rad: Keith Kutac
Dir Rx: Michael Holescher
Dir Pat Ac: Tammy Horton
CIO: Dale Zoch
DP Dir: Dale Zoch-Hardilek
Surgeon: Marie Migl
Phys Thrpy: Kim Brandt
HC Dir: Nicole Bell

LAVACA MEDICAL CENTER
See LAVACA HOSPITAL DISTRICT

D-U-N-S 04-356-4319
LAVACA TELEPHONE CO INC (AR)
PINNACLE COMMUNICATIONS
301 N Highway 96, Lavaca, AR 72941
Tel (479) 674-2211 *Founded/Ownrshp* 1950, 1957
Sales 29.0MM^E *EMP* 14
SIC 4813 Local telephone communications; Local telephone communications
CEO: Keith Gibson
**Ch Bd:* Clyde Gibson
**Sec:* Ruby Jo Gibson
Plnt Mgr: Greg Gibson

LAVALETTE FOODFAIR
See FORTHS FOODS INC

D-U-N-S 01-399-0044
LAVALLE TRANSPORTATION INC (NY)
LTI
20 Madrid Ave, Potsdam, NY 13676-1015
Tel (315) 265-5800 *Founded/Ownrshp* 1994
Sales 29.0MM^E *EMP* 100
SIC 4213 Trucking, except local
Ch Bd: Randy Lavalley

D-U-N-S 01-895-3430
LAVALLEY BUILDING SUPPLY INC
FLOORING AMERICA
351 Sunapee St, Newport, NH 03773-1489
Tel (603) 863-1050 *Founded/Ownrshp* 1962
Sales 52.5MM^E *EMP* 225
SIC 5211 Lumber & other building materials; Lumber & other building materials
Ch Bd: Harold A Lavalley
**Pr:* Lawrence Huot
**Treas:* Geraldine K Lavalley
Chf Mktg O: Jeremy Stout
Genl Mgr: Andy Carberry
Store Mgr: Bob Jackman
DP Exec: Jo Cross
Mktg Dir: Clint Hamilton
Sls Mgr: Ron Godfrey
Sales Asso: Gary Ball
Sales Asso: Scott Brown

LAVAN & NEIDENBERG
See DISABILITY LAW CLAIMS PA

D-U-N-S 05-895-9446 IMP
LAVANTURE PRODUCTS CO INC
3806 Gallatin Way, Elkhart, IN 46514-7650
Tel (574) 264-0658 *Founded/Ownrshp* 1969
Sales 23.2MM^E *EMP* 42
SIC 5063 5072 5085 5031 5013 Electrical apparatus & equipment; Hardware; Industrial supplies; Lumber, plywood & millwork; Automotive supplies & parts
Pr: Richard E Lavanture
**VP:* Rich Ward
**Prin:* Dick Lavanture
Off Mgr: Tracy Dewitte
IT Man: Brandon Weise

D-U-N-S 19-487-6132 IMP
LAVAZZA PREMIUM COFFEES CORP
(*Suby of* LUIGI LAVAZZA SPA)
120 Wall St Fl 27, New York, NY 10005-4011
Tel (212) 725-8800 *Founded/Ownrshp* 2001
Sales 66.2MM *EMP* 73
Accts Funaro & Co Pc New York Ny
SIC 5149 Coffee, green or roasted; Coffee, green or roasted
Pr: Alberto Lavazza
**CEO:* Ennio Ranaboldo
VP: Giuseppe Lavazza
Dir Bus: Alfredo D'Innocenzo
Rgnl Mgr: Patrizia Tucker
Natl Sales: Lana Overton
Sls&Mrk Ex: Debbie Grabarz
Manager: Joe Sherratt

D-U-N-S 00-290-1627
LAVEEN ELEMENTARY SCHOOL DISTRICT NO 59
5001 W Dobbins Rd, Laveen, AZ 85339-9733
Tel (602) 237-9100 *Founded/Ownrshp* 1900
Sales 30.6MM^E *EMP* 338
SIC 8211 Public elementary school; Public junior high school; Public elementary school; Public junior high school
Adm Dir: Diana Wyon
Pr Dir: Kristen Landry
Schl Brd P: Susan Sanbourn
Teacher Pr: Jeff Sprout
HC Dir: Nichole Enler

D-U-N-S 06-248-5065 IMP/EXP
LAVELLE INDUSTRIES INC
665 Mchenry St, Burlington, WI 53105-2129
Tel (262) 763-2434 *Founded/Ownrshp* 1912
Sales 53.4MM^E *EMP* 280
SIC 3069 3061 Hard rubber & molded rubber products; Plumbers' rubber goods; Mechanical rubber goods; Hard rubber & molded rubber products; Plumbers' rubber goods; Mechanical rubber goods
Pr: Rhonda L Sullivan
**CFO:* Deborah Scheffler
**VP:* Paul J Sullivan
**VP:* Kathryn Turke
Admn Mgr: Chris Kurth
Off Mgr: Laurie Durham
Telecom Ex: Jeremy Zabel
IT Man: Paul Fisher
IT Man: Natalie Koller
Opers Supe: Steve Hayes
Plnt Mgr: Burt Anderson

D-U-N-S 11-430-3712
LAVENDER INC
1204 Lavender Dr Sw, Aliceville, AL 35442-2600
Tel (205) 373-8387 *Founded/Ownrshp* 1992
Sales 99.7MM^E *EMP* 290
SIC 1541 1796 Paper/pulp mill construction; Machinery installation; Paper/pulp mill construction; Machinery installation
Pr: Lamont Lavender

D-U-N-S 08-303-8356
LAVERDIERE CONSTRUCTION INC (IL)
COMMERCIAL RENTAL
9965 Us Highway 136, Macomb, IL 61455-7741
Tel (309) 837-1258 *Founded/Ownrshp* 1974
Sales 44.9MM^E *EMP* 120
SIC 1542

D-U-N-S 02-860-3900
LAVERNE PUBLIC SCHOOLS
615 W Jane Jayroe Blvd, Laverne, OK 73848
Tel (580) 921-3361 *Founded/Ownrshp* 1922
Sales 11.5MM^E *EMP* 500
SIC 8211 Public elementary & secondary schools; Public elementary & secondary schools
IT Man: Pam Crocker

D-U-N-S 04-791-2209
LAVEZZI PRECISION INC
999 Regency Dr, Glendale Heights, IL 60139-2281
Tel (630) 582-1230 *Founded/Ownrshp* 1908
Sales 21.1MM^E *EMP* 108
SIC 3861 3841 7359 3568 Motion picture apparatus & equipment; Surgical & medical instruments; Aircraft assemblies, subassemblies & parts; Equipment rental & leasing; Power transmission equipment; Motion picture apparatus & equipment; Surgical & medical instruments; Equipment rental & leasing; Power transmission equipment
Pr: Albert J La Vezzi
**VP:* Douglas Kremer
Off Mgr: Pat Davis
Plnt Mgr: Victor Guida
Prd Mgr: Bill Konecny
Ql Cn Mgr: Phil Heffner

D-U-N-S 03-998-5437 IMP/EXP
LAVI INDUSTRIES
27810 Avenue Hopkins, Valencia, CA 91355-3409
Tel (877) 275-5284 *Founded/Ownrshp* 1979
Sales 20.0MM^E *EMP* 100

SIC 3446 Architectural metalwork
Pr: Gavriel Lavi
COO: Yariv Blumkine
**CFO:* Christa Harris
Prgrm Mgr: Shawna Kessler
Prgrm Mgr: Mary Moriarty
Prgrm Mgr: Heather Pilkinton
Prgrm Mgr: Maria Rodriguez
Dir IT: Michael Ikona
IT Man: Peter Roxas
Prd Mgr: David Bednar
Prd Mgr: Juan Pena

D-U-N-S 82-987-6528
LAVIDA COMMUNITIES INC
500 Stevens Ave Ste 100, Solana Beach, CA 92075-2055
Tel (858) 792-9300 *Founded/Ownrshp* 2009
Sales 12.8MM^E *EMP* 1,228
SIC 6513 6512 6531 6553 Apartment building operators; Nonresidential building operators; Real estate agents & managers; Cemetery subdividers & developers; Apartment building operators; Nonresidential building operators; Real estate agents & managers; Cemetery subdividers & developers
Prin: J Wickliffe Peterson

LAVIE CARE CENTER
See SEA CREST HEALTH CARE MANAGEMENT LLC

D-U-N-S 61-194-9777
LAVIGNE MANUFACTURING INC
15 Western Industrial Dr, Cranston, RI 02921-3402
Tel (401) 490-4627 *Founded/Ownrshp* 1989
Sales 22.1MM^E *EMP* 110
SIC 3599 Machine shop, jobbing & repair; Machine shop, jobbing & repair
Pr: David T Lavigne
**Treas:* Gerard E Lavigne
**VP:* Daniel W Lavigne
QA Dir: Michelle Mendonca
IT Man: Greg Armstrong

D-U-N-S 01-529-4849
LAVIGNE OIL CO OF BATON ROUGE LLC
11203 Proverbs Ave, Baton Rouge, LA 70816-4182
Tel (225) 952-7900 *Founded/Ownrshp* 2008
Sales 42.7MM^E *EMP* 25
SIC 5172 Fuel oil
Prin: Milton E Lavigne III
VP: Mohamed Makky
Genl Mgr: Ronnie St Zxqromain
IT Man: Karen Barranco

D-U-N-S 14-428-1292
LAVIN ONEIL CEDRONE & DISIPIO
190 N Independence Mall W, Philadelphia, PA 19106-1554
Tel (215) 627-0303 *Founded/Ownrshp* 1985
Sales 26.7MM^E *EMP* 185
SIC 8111 General practice law office; General practice law office
Pr: Basil Disipio
**VP:* Joseph O'Neil
**VP:* William Ricci
IT Man: John Gorman

D-U-N-S 17-352-2707 EXP
LAVOI CORP
EPI BREADS
1749 Tullie Cir Ne, Atlanta, GA 30329-2305
Tel (404) 325-1016 *Founded/Ownrshp* 1985
Sales 96.2MM^E *EMP* 280
SIC 2045 2053 2051 5149 Prepared flour mixes & doughs; Frozen bakery products, except bread; Bread, cake & related products; Breads, rolls & buns; Bakery products; Prepared flour mixes & doughs; Frozen bakery products, except bread; Bread, cake & related products; Breads, rolls & buns; Bakery products
CEO: Bob Gansel
**CFO:* Jim Kelley
**Ch:* Nicholas Mulliez
VP: Alan Radda
Sfty Dirs: Maria Favila

D-U-N-S 00-511-8666
LAW BULLETIN PUBLISHING CO INC (DE)
REAL ESTATE COMMUNICATIONS
415 N State St Ste 1, Chicago, IL 60654-4674
Tel (312) 416-1860 *Founded/Ownrshp* 1854
Sales 70.8MM^E *EMP* 288
SIC 2741 Guides: publishing & printing; Directories: publishing & printing; Business service newsletters: publishing & printing; Guides: publishing & printing; Directories: publishing & printing; Business service newsletters: publishing & printing
Pr: B Macfarland
**Ch Bd:* L Macfarland Jr
**Pr:* Brewster McFarland
**Treas:* James Banich
Ex VP: Peter Fazio
**VP:* Jeff Bope Sr
Ex Dir: Ed Graziano
Off Mgr: Debbie Dewolf
MIS Dir: Fred Faulkner

D-U-N-S 00-781-3587
LAW CO INC
345 N Rverview St Ste 300, Wichita, KS 67203
Tel (316) 268-0200 *Founded/Ownrshp* 1959
Sales 120.1MM^E *EMP* 250
Accts Gutschenritter & Johnson Ll
SIC 1542 1522 Nonresidential construction; Multi-family dwelling construction; Nonresidential construction; Multi-family dwelling construction
Ch: Richard Kerschen
**Pr:* Dennis Kerschen
**Treas:* Josh Gordon
**Ex VP:* Marc Porter
VP: Hassan Jabara
**VP:* Doug Kimple
**VP:* Bill Reynolds
CTO: Glen Bailey
CTO: Andrew Bustraan
IT Man: Ezhini Natarajan
Sfty Mgr: Bill Brand

D-U-N-S 17-729-2034
LAW ENFORCEMENT HEALTH BENEFITS INC
LEHB
2233 Spring Garden St, Philadelphia, PA 19130-3511
Tel (215) 763-8290 *Founded/Ownrshp* 1987
Sales 125.1MM *EMP* 19
Accts Fischer Dorwart Pc Audubon N
SIC 8621 Health association; Health association

LAW MED PERSONNEL
See AUTOMATION PERSONNEL SERVICES INC

LAW OFFCES DAN NEWLIN PARTNERS
See DANIEL J NEWLIN PA

D-U-N-S 82-797-0265
LAW OFFICES OF ETHERIDGE & OUGRAH LLP
340 N Sam Houston Pkwy E, Houston, TX 77060-3305
Tel (832) 563-3620 *Founded/Ownrshp* 2008
Sales 100.0MM *EMP* 4
SIC 8111 Legal services; Legal services
Genl Pt: Krishna Ougrah
Pt: Chad Etheridge

LAW OFFICES OF PETER G ANGELOS
See PETER G ANGELOS

LAW OFFICES OF SHEPARD HOFFMAN
See SHEPARD A HOFFMAN ESQUIRE

D-U-N-S 09-998-6259
LAW SCHOOL ADMISSION COUNCIL INC
662 Penn St, Newtown, PA 18940-2176
Tel (215) 968-1101 *Founded/Ownrshp* 1980
Sales 57.5MM *EMP* 300
Accts Eisneramper Llp Iselin Nj
SIC 8748 Testing service, educational or personnel; Testing service, educational or personnel
CEO: Daniel O Bernstine
**CFO:* Marjorie R Larue
VP: Bruce Bachman
**VP:* Stephen Schreiber
Comm Dir: Wendy Margolis
Snr Sftwr: Larry Lewis
QA Dir: Mark Burstein
QA Dir: Lori Templeton
QA Dir: Faina Vainberg
Dir IT: Jerry Goldman
IT Man: Teresa Beverly

D-U-N-S 60-701-9023
LAWEB OFFSET PRINTING INC
CHINESE-LA DAILY NEWS
9639 Telstar Ave, El Monte, CA 91731-3003
Tel (626) 454-2469 *Founded/Ownrshp* 1990
Sales 23.5MM^E *EMP* 165
SIC 2759 2752 Newspapers: printing; Commercial printing, offset; Newspapers: printing; Commercial printing, offset
Pr: Walter Chang
**Treas:* CHI-Kwang Chiang
MIS Mgr: Sean Chen
Plnt Mgr: George Parra
S&M/VP: Steve Chiang
Sls Mgr: Daniel Chiu

D-U-N-S 08-647-9417 IMP
LAWLER FOODS INC
LAWLER'S
1219 Carpenter Rd, Humble, TX 77396-1535
Tel (281) 446-0059 *Founded/Ownrshp* 1988
Sales 48.1MM^E *EMP* 250
SIC 2051 2053 Cakes, pies & pastries; Cakes, bakery: except frozen; Frozen bakery products, except bread; Cakes, pies & pastries; Cakes, bakery: except frozen; Frozen bakery products, except bread
Pr: Carol M Lawler
**CFO:* Kristi Smith
**VP:* William L Lawler
DP Exec: Mike Callier
VP Prd: Aurelio Jaramillo
Prd Mgr: Fausto Hernandez
Mktg Mgr: Wes Stasny

LAWLER'S
See LAWLER FOODS INC

LAWLEY AUTOMOTIVE CENTER
See LAWLEY MOTORS LLC

D-U-N-S 83-745-8504 IMP
LAWLEY MOTORS LLC
LAWLEY AUTOMOTIVE CENTER
2900 E Fry Blvd, Sierra Vista, AZ 85635-2804
Tel (520) 459-2000 *Founded/Ownrshp* 1995
Sales 34.0MM^E *EMP* 90
SIC 5511 Automobiles, new & used; Automobiles, new & used
Genl Mgr: Bill Klaer

D-U-N-S 07-401-7252
LAWLEY SERVICE INC
GMAC INSURANCE
361 Delaware Ave, Buffalo, NY 14202-1622
Tel (716) 849-8618 *Founded/Ownrshp* 1939
Sales NA *EMP* 200
SIC 6411 Insurance agents, brokers & service; Insurance agents, brokers & service
Ch Bd: William J Lawley Sr
Mng Pt: T J-Revelas
**Pr:* Christopher Ross
CFO: Mark Higgins
**VP:* Todd F Best
**VP:* Mike Lawley
VP: Kathy Quider
Telecom Ex: Fred Holinder
Dir IT: Thomas Lippard
IT Man: Deborah Jindra
Sales Exec: John Cureo

D-U-N-S 15-928-8518
LAWLORS CUSTOM SPORTSWEAR INC
4414 S 84th St, Omaha, NE 68127-1733
Tel (402) 333-8610 *Founded/Ownrshp* 2000
Sales 25.3MM^E *EMP* 16^E
SIC 2261 Screen printing of cotton broadwoven fabrics

Pr: Patrick Lawlor
Sls Mgr: Matt Berezay

D-U-N-S 09-166-6263
LAWMAN HEATING & COOLING INC
206 Ambrose St, Sackets Harbor, NY 13685-3179
Tel (315) 646-2919 *Founded/Ownrshp* 1978
Sales 52.1MM^E *EMP* 275
SIC 1711 Heating systems repair & maintenance; Heating systems repair & maintenance
Ch Bd: Michael Lawler
Sec: Elaine Huttemann
VP: Patrick Lawler
Genl Mgr: Neil Lawler
IT Man: Elaine Huttemann

D-U-N-S 05-414-4779
LAWN EQUIPMENT PARTS CO
LEPCO
1475 River Rd, Marietta, PA 17547-9401
Tel (717) 426-5200 *Founded/Ownrshp* 1999
Sales 38.0MM^E *EMP* 60
SIC 5083 5084 Lawn machinery & equipment; Garden machinery & equipment; Chainsaws
**Pr:* Jeff Clark
**Ch:* Merrell F Clark
**VP:* Mark Hessinger
**Genl Mgr:* Phil Stone
Snr Sftwr: Gary Barnes
Mktg Mgr: Walter Stoltz
Sales Asso: Mary Bouder

LAWN MOWERS DIRECT
See POWER EQUIPMENT DIRECT INC

LAWNABILITY
See CHALLENGE ENTERPRISES OF NORTH FLORIDA INC

D-U-N-S 14-657-5873
LAWNDALE SCHOOL DISTRICT
4161 W 147th St, Lawndale, CA 90260-1709
Tel (310) 973-1300 *Founded/Ownrshp* 1906
Sales 55.7MM *EMP* 725
Accts J An Paic Preparer Lawndale
SIC 8211 Public elementary & secondary schools; Public elementary & secondary schools
CEO: Elizabeth Ramirez
Trst: Cathy Burris
Trst: Ann Phillips
Trst: Shirley Rudolph
Off Mgr: Norma Garcia
Dir IT: Todd Barker
Dir IT: Mike Tu
Opers Mgr: Arlene Hart
Psych: Stephanie Swick

LAWNSCAPES BY DYNASERV INDS
See DYNASERV INDUSTRIES INC

D-U-N-S 19-408-4547
■ **LAWNWOOD MEDICAL CENTER INC**
COLUMBIA HCA
(*Suby of* HCA INC) ★
1700 S 23rd St, Fort Pierce, FL 34950-4899
Tel (772) 461-4000 *Founded/Ownrshp* 1994
Sales 283.8MM *EMP* 1,200
SIC 8062 8063 8069 General medical & surgical hospitals; Psychiatric hospitals; Specialty hospitals, except psychiatric; General medical & surgical hospitals; Psychiatric hospitals; Specialty hospitals, except psychiatric
CEO: Rodney Smith
**CFO:* Robert Dunwoody Jr
VP: Marge Humphrey
Nurse Mgr: Debbie Boyer
Surgeon: Chris Cromwell
Surgeon: Victor R Dasilva
Surgeon: Brad McCollom
Surgeon: Christian Schuetz
Surgeon: William Stanton
Ansthlgy: Ali M Ahed-Elain
Ansthlgy: Ali Ahed-Elain

D-U-N-S 06-925-3946 IMP
LAWRENCE & MEMORIAL HOSPITAL INC
LAWRENCE + MEMORIAL
(*Suby of* LAWRENCE + MEMORIAL CORP) ★
365 Montauk Ave, New London, CT 06320-4769
Tel (860) 442-0711 *Founded/Ownrshp* 1912, 2005
Sales 337.1MM *EMP* 2,200
SIC 8011 8062 Offices & clinics of medical doctors; General medical & surgical hospitals; Offices & clinics of medical doctors; General medical & surgical hospitals
Pr: Bruce D Cummings
**Ch Bd:* Ulysses Hammond
COO: Cynthia Kane
**Treas:* Fred Conti
VP: Lugene Inzana
Exec: Sal Argento
Dir OR: Karen Buck
Dir Rx: Warren Rogers
**Prin:* Timothy Bates
CIO: Robert Aubin
MIS Dir: Bob Aubin
Board of Directors: Timothy Bates

D-U-N-S 07-012-1090
LAWRENCE & SCHILLER INC
3932 S Willow Ave, Sioux Falls, SD 57105-6293
Tel (605) 338-8000 *Founded/Ownrshp* 1976
Sales 25.8MM^E *EMP* 75
Accts Paul East Sioux Falls Sd
SIC 7311 Advertising agencies
CEO: Paul Schiller
Pr: Troy Holt
Sr VP: Tom Helland
VP: Mark Glissendorf
VP: John Pohlman
Exec: Dan Edmonds
Creative D: Kristy Laue
Creative D: Scott Wiechmann
Prd Mgr: Kevin Van Westen
Art Dir: Sarah Pitts
Art Dir: Wade Thurman

LAWRENCE + MEMORIAL
See LAWRENCE & MEMORIAL HOSPITAL INC

D-U-N-S 62-341-6211
LAWRENCE + MEMORIAL CORP
365 Montauk Ave, New London, CT 06320-4700
Tel (860) 442-0711 *Founded/Ownrshp* 1984
Sales 3.4MM *EMP* 2,253
Accts Pricewaterhousecoopers Llp Bo
SIC 8741 Hospital management; Hospital management
Pr: Bruce D Cummings
**Ch:* Ulysses B Hammond
**VP:* Crista Durand
**VP:* Dan Rissi
**VP:* William Stanley
**VP:* Lauren Williams
Dir Lab: Judy Portelance
Mtls Mgr: Brenda Hodge
Opers Mgr: Carol Gessner
Pharmcst: Larry Cole
Pharmcst: Cheryl Guillet

D-U-N-S 17-856-6287
LAWRENCE ANZALDUA COMPANIES INC
L A UTILITIES
206 Brand Ln, Stafford, TX 77477-4804
Tel (281) 969-8321 *Founded/Ownrshp* 1987
Sales 21.5MM^E *EMP* 230
Accts Morris Ligon & Rodriguez Cpa
SIC 1623 Underground utilities contractor; Underground utilities contractor
Pr: Jim Toungate
**CFO:* Steve Hobbs
**VP:* Jim Holt

D-U-N-S 60-710-4049
LAWRENCE AUTOMOTIVE INC
LAWRENCE LEXUS
2630 Us Highway 1, Lawrenceville, NJ 08648-4105
Tel (609) 375-1000 *Founded/Ownrshp* 1989
Sales 20.0MM^E *EMP* 67
SIC 5511 Automobiles, new & used; Automobiles, new & used
Pr: Allan C Haldeman
**Sec:* Scott Haldeman
**VP:* Brian Bennett
Sales Exec: Joseph Albanese
Sales Exec: Bruce Bressler
Sales Exec: Jabian Caceres
Sales Exec: Robert Dieffenbach
Sales Exec: Gayle Dimitri
Sales Exec: Kevin Dunn
Sales Exec: Scott Hallman
Sales Exec: Thomas Harding

D-U-N-S 07-060-6854 IMP
LAWRENCE BERKELEY NATIONAL LAB
1 Cyclotron Rd, Berkeley, CA 94720-8099
Tel (510) 486-6792 *Founded/Ownrshp* 1989
Sales 206.1MM^E *EMP* 6,000
SIC 8071 Medical laboratories; Biological laboratory; Testing laboratories; Medical laboratories; Biological laboratory; Testing laboratories
COO: Glenn D Kubiak
CFO: Kim Williams
Exec: Vera Potapenko
Dir Lab: Scott Taylor
Dir Bus: Michael Chartock
Admn Mgr: Carmen Ross
CIO: Rosio Alvarez
CIO: Craig Leres
Dir IT: Mark Dedlow
Dir IT: Trever Nightengale
Netwrk Eng: David Batzloff

LAWRENCE BROTHERS
See MAL ENTERPRISES INC

D-U-N-S 80-092-2713
LAWRENCE BUILDING CORP
L B C
8401 Fritz Rd, Fort Wayne, IN 46818-9307
Tel (260) 469-8400 *Founded/Ownrshp* 2007
Sales 20.5MM^E *EMP* 55
SIC 1542 1799 Commercial & office building, new construction; Petroleum storage tank installation, underground
Pr: Haley Lawrence
**VP:* Ross Lawrence

D-U-N-S 01-438-7930
LAWRENCE CHEVROLET INC (PA)
6445 Carlisle Pike, Mechanicsburg, PA 17050-5233
Tel (717) 766-0284 *Founded/Ownrshp* 1961, 1980
Sales 25.3MM^E *EMP* 56
SIC 5511 Automobiles, new & used; Automobiles, new & used
Pr: Gary L Lawrence
**Sec:* Joan Lawrence
**VP:* Randy Lawrence
Genl Mgr: Bob Blochker
Sales Asso: Maley Lysle

LAWRENCE COUNTY AMBULANCE SERV
See COUNTY OF LAWRENCE

LAWRENCE COUNTY BOARD EDUCATN
See LAWRENCE COUNTY SCHOOL DISTRICT

D-U-N-S 09-492-0337
LAWRENCE COUNTY BOARD OF EDUCATION
LAWRENCE COUNTY SCHOOL DST
346 Thomas E Jolly Dr W, Monticello, MS 39654-4600
Tel (601) 587-2506 *Founded/Ownrshp* 1954
Sales 20.4MM *EMP* 350
Accts Charles L Shivers Cpa Ridge
SIC 8211 8641 Public elementary & secondary schools; Civic social & fraternal associations; Public elementary & secondary schools; Civic social & fraternal associations

D-U-N-S 11-500-8146
LAWRENCE COUNTY MEMORIAL HOSPITAL AUXILIARY
2200 State St, Lawrenceville, IL 62439-1852
Tel (618) 943-1000 *Founded/Ownrshp* 1950
Sales 31.1MM^E *EMP* 164
SIC 8062 General medical & surgical hospitals
CEO: Doug Florkowski
CFO: Rita Garvey

*CFO: Larry Spour
Dir Risk M: Roxana Schultz
Dir Lab: Donnetta Doyle
Dir Rad: Debra Miller
Dir Rx: Kim Weber
Off Mgr: Julia Hoalt
Dir IT: Gary Theriac
HC Dir: Lynn Tredway

D-U-N-S 07-979-8769
LAWRENCE COUNTY SCHOOL DISTRICT
346 Thomas E Jolly Dr W, Monticello, MS 39654-4600
Tel (601) 587-2506 Founded/Ownrshp 2015
Sales 5.1MM^E EMP 290^E
SIC 8211 Public elementary & secondary schools

D-U-N-S 10-007-3063
LAWRENCE COUNTY SCHOOL DISTRICT
700 Mahr Ave, Lawrenceburg, TN 38464-2621
Tel (931) 762-3581 Founded/Ownrshp 2009
Sales 15.2MM^E EMP 276
SIC 8211 Elementary & secondary schools; Elementary & secondary schools

D-U-N-S 15-943-6153
LAWRENCE COUNTY SCHOOL DISTRICT
50 Bulldog Ln, Louisa, KY 41230-9601
Tel (606) 638-9671 Founded/Ownrshp 1980
Sales 16.9MM^E EMP 400
SIC 8211 9411 Public elementary & secondary schools; School board; Administration of educational programs; Public elementary & secondary schools; School board; Administration of educational programs
Cmptr Lab: Jan Brewer

D-U-N-S 94-334-6791
LAWRENCE COUNTY SCHOOL DISTRICT
LAWRENCE COUNTY BOARD EDUCATN
14131 Market St, Moulton, AL 35650-1407
Tel (256) 905-2400 Founded/Ownrshp 1920
Sales 48.3M EMP 705
Accts Teri G Littrell Cpa Moulton
SIC 8211 Public elementary & secondary schools; Public elementary & secondary schools
CFO: Susan Terry
Cmptr Lab: Belinda Burch
Cmptr Lab: Lorie Walker
Teacher Pr: Donna Flanagan

LAWRENCE COUNTY SCHOOL DST
See LAWRENCE COUNTY BOARD OF EDUCATION

LAWRENCE DAILY JOURNAL WORLD
See WORLD CO

LAWRENCE ENVIRONMENTAL GROUP
See LAWRENCE SANITARY CO INC

D-U-N-S 03-762-1679 IMP
LAWRENCE EQUIPMENT INC
2034 Peck Rd, El Monte, CA 91733-3727
Tel (626) 442-2894 Founded/Ownrshp 1981
Sales 43.6MM^E EMP 200^E
SIC 3556 Food products machinery; Flour mill machinery; Bakery machinery; Food products machinery; Flour mill machinery; Bakery machinery
CEO: John Lawrence
COO: Jim Hopton
*VP: Linda Lawrence
*VP: Glenn Shelton
Dir IT: Karen Foster
VP Mfg: Doug Kirkpatrick

D-U-N-S 08-158-5804
LAWRENCE F QUIGLEY MEMORIAL HOSPITAL INC
SOLDIERS HOME IN MAS
91 Crest Ave, Chelsea, MA 02150-2154
Tel (617) 884-5660 Founded/Ownrshp 1947
Sales 32.1MM^E EMP 410
SIC 8062 8361 8093 8051 General medical & surgical hospitals; Residential care; Specialty outpatient clinics; Skilled nursing care facilities; General medical & surgical hospitals; Residential care; Specialty outpatient clinics; Skilled nursing care facilities
CEO: Michael Resca
CFO: Richard C White
Ofcr: Pat Cunnigham
Prin: John Cronin
CTO: Daniel Roderigues
Nrsg Dir: Tina Wroblewski

D-U-N-S 00-510-6174
LAWRENCE FOODS INC
2200 Lunt Ave, Elk Grove Village, IL 60007-5685
Tel (847) 437-2400 Founded/Ownrshp 1930
Sales 86.9MM^E EMP 250
SIC 2033 2099 Canned fruits & specialties; Food preparations; Canned fruits & specialties; Food preparations
CEO: Lester Lawrence
Ex VP: Keith Appling
Ex VP: Lisa Will
VP: Jeffrey Jenniges
Genl Mgr: Andy Balafas
IT Man: Kim Pantano
Natl Sales: John Foster
S&M/VP: Bill Evans
Sls Dir: Shelly Campbell
Manager: Rex Durdel
Sls Mgr: Cameron Austin

D-U-N-S 36-421-4692
LAWRENCE FROMMER & LLP HAUG
745 5th Ave Fl 10, New York, NY 10151-1206
Tel (202) 292-1530 Founded/Ownrshp 1997
Sales 20.5MM^E EMP 73^E
SIC 8111 Legal aid service
Pt: Edgar H Haug
Pt: Steven M Amundson
Pt: Michael F Brockmeyer
Pt: Angus Chen
Pt: Robert E Colletti
Pt: John F Collins
Pt: Porter F Fleming
Pt: William S Frommer
Pt: Arthur L Hoag
Pt: William F Lawrence
Pt: Richard E Parke
Pt: Charles J Raubicheck
Pt: Matthew K Ryan
Pt: Ronald R Santucci
Pt: Barry White

D-U-N-S 07-951-7611
LAWRENCE GENERAL HOSPITAL
(Suby of LAWRENCE GENERAL REGIONAL HEALTH SYSTEM INC) ★
1 General St, Lawrence, MA 01841-2997
Tel (978) 683-4000 Founded/Ownrshp 1875
Sales 185.5MM EMP 1,405
SIC 8062 General medical & surgical hospitals; General medical & surgical hospitals
CEO: Dianne J Anderson
*Pr: Joseph S Mc Manus
*Ex VP: Gerard Foley
*VP: Robert Tremblay
Dir Lab: Richard Battles
Nurse Mgr: Linda Cardoza
Nurse Mgr: Mariann Gibson
Info Man: Michael Leblond
Doctor: Daniel Concaugh
Doctor: Richard Okeeffe
Pharmcst: Margaret Lee

D-U-N-S 14-412-5945
LAWRENCE GENERAL REGIONAL HEALTH SYSTEM INC
1 General St, Lawrence, MA 01841-2961
Tel (978) 683-4000 Founded/Ownrshp 1985
Sales 185.5MM^E EMP 1,405
SIC 8082 Home health care services; Home health care services
Pr: Dianne J Anderson
*Pr: Joseph S McManus
*COO: Gerard Foley
*CFO: Robert B Tremblay
CFO: Robert B Tremblay
*VP: Denise Palumbo
Doctor: Peter Cole

LAWRENCE GROUP ARCHITECTS
See LAWRENCE GROUP INC

D-U-N-S 79-650-5881
LAWRENCE GROUP INC
LAWRENCE GROUP ARCHITECTS
319 N 4th St Ste 1000, Saint Louis, MO 63102-1937
Tel (314) 231-5700 Founded/Ownrshp 1987
Sales 41.7MM^E EMP 180^E
SIC 8712 Architectural engineering; Architectural engineering
Pr: Stephen Smtih
*Sec: Laura Sciarratta
*VP: Paul C Doerner
*VP: Linda Loewenstein
Assoc Dir: Mary Sutton
Assoc Dir: Beth Trueblood
Genl Mgr: Debra Taylor
Corp Couns: Amanda Auer
Art Dir: Alex Duenwald

D-U-N-S 12-748-6728
LAWRENCE HALL CHEVROLET INC
1385 S Danville Dr, Abilene, TX 79605-4697
Tel (325) 695-8800 Founded/Ownrshp 1989
Sales 59.3MM^E EMP 165
SIC 5511 Automobiles, new & used; Automobiles, new & used
Pr: Larry Hall
Sec: Darrell Lindberg
VP: Mitch Hall

LAWRENCE HALL LNCLN-MERC-MAZDA
See HALL MOTORS

D-U-N-S 07-915-8881
LAWRENCE HOLDING INC
(Suby of HUAXIANG CO., LTD.)
803 S Black River St, Sparta, WI 54656-2221
Tel (608) 269-6911 Founded/Ownrshp 2011
Sales 258.8MM^E EMP 1,200^E
SIC 3469 3089 3544 Stamping metal for the trade; Automotive parts, plastic; Special dies, tools, jigs & fixtures; Stamping metal for the trade; Automotive parts, plastic; Special dies, tools, jigs & fixtures
VP: Bruce Dinger

D-U-N-S 79-333-6707
LAWRENCE HOLDINGS INC
34b Barnes Indus Rd S, Wallingford, CT 06492-2438
Tel (203) 949-1600 Founded/Ownrshp 2006
Sales 44.8MM^E EMP 61^E
SIC 3469 3089 3544 Stamping metal for the trade; Automotive parts, plastic; Special dies, tools, jigs & fixtures
CEO: Lawrence Buhl III
*CFO: K C Jones

D-U-N-S 07-270-1832
LAWRENCE HOSPITAL CENTER
LAWRENCE MEDICAL ASSOCIATE
55 Palmer Ave, Bronxville, NY 10708-3491
Tel (914) 787-1000 Founded/Ownrshp 1988
Sales 194.1MM EMP 15,000
Accts Deloitte Tax Llp Jericho Ny
SIC 8062 General medical & surgical hospitals; General medical & surgical hospitals
Pr: Edward M Dinan
Pr: Rita Dipippo
*CFO: Murray Askinazi
Chf Mktg O: Mark Fox
*Ex VP: James Y Lee
VP: Tracy Conte
VP: John Evanko
*VP: Timothy J Hughes
*VP: James Keogh
VP: Rachel Negron
VP: Roseanne O'Hare
Dir Inf Cn: Mary Hauff
Dir Case M: Eileen Mullaney
Dir Lab: Jackie Reiner
Dir Rx: Lisa Oronzio
Board of Directors: George Austin, Paul Brenner, Arthur Nagle

D-U-N-S 78-972-8052 IMP
■ **LAWRENCE INSTRON CORP**
(Suby of ILLINOIS TOOL WORKS INC) ★
825 University Ave, Norwood, MA 02062-2643
Tel (781) 828-2500 Founded/Ownrshp 2007
Sales 40.0MM^E EMP 200
SIC 3829 Testing equipment: abrasion, shearing strength, etc.; Testing equipment: abrasion, shearing strength, etc.
CEO: Steven Martindale
VP: David Hargreaves
VP: Mark Ritter
Dir Lab: Dan Raynor
Genl Mgr: Jack Bowen
Snr Sftwr: Michael Ashman
Dir IT: Andy Day
Dir IT: Ronna Ungar
IT Man: Detorres Pablo
IT Man: Johan Van Jaarsveld
Info Man: Brian Muratori

D-U-N-S 84-900-1904
LAWRENCE LEASING INC
LAWRENCE NATIONAL LEASE
(Suby of LAWRENCE TRANSPORTATION) ★
860 Bench St, Red Wing, MN 55066-9502
Tel (651) 388-7067 Founded/Ownrshp 1991
Sales 25.1MM^E EMP 167
SIC 7513 Truck rental & leasing, no drivers
CEO: Steve Lawrence
*Pr: William Schultz
*CFO: Jason Krell
Treas: Robert Kastner
Sales Exec: Bill Schultz

LAWRENCE LEXUS
See LAWRENCE AUTOMOTIVE INC

D-U-N-S 00-454-8530
LAWRENCE LIVERMORE NATIONAL LABORATORY
7000 East Ave, Livermore, CA 94550-9698
Tel (925) 422-1100 Founded/Ownrshp 1952
Sales NA EMP 6,000^E
SIC 9711 National security
CFO: Kathy Baker
Bd of Dir: Adam Bertsch
Bd of Dir: Rob Swanson
Bd of Dir: John Westlund
Bd of Dir: Lawrence Wright
Comm Dir: Lynda Seaver
Dir Bus: Catherine Elizondo
Dir Bus: Charity Follett
Dir Bus: Annemarie Meike
Dir Bus: Genaro Mempin
Comm Man: Tim Carnes

LAWRENCE MEDICAL ASSOCIATE
See LAWRENCE HOSPITAL CENTER

LAWRENCE MEMORIAL HOSPITAL
See HALLMARK HEALTH CORP

D-U-N-S 96-112-3254
LAWRENCE MEMORIAL HOSPITAL
L M H
325 Maine St, Lawrence, KS 66044-1360
Tel (785) 749-5800 Founded/Ownrshp 1996
Sales 198.7MM EMP 1,200
SIC 8062 General medical & surgical hospitals; General medical & surgical hospitals
Pr: Gene Meyer
Chf Rad: James Mandigo
*CFO: Simon Scholtz
*VP: Sheryle D Amico
*VP: Carolyn Bowmer
*VP: Janice Early
*VP: Dana Hale
*VP: Karen Shumate
*VP: Deborah Thompson
*VP: Kathy Clausing Willis
Dir Rx: Michael Bennett

D-U-N-S 07-305-3282
LAWRENCE MEMORIAL HOSPITAL ENDOWMENT ASSOCIATION
LMH
330 Arkansas St Ste 201, Lawrence, KS 66044-1335
Tel (785) 505-3318 Founded/Ownrshp 1921
Sales 2.8MM EMP 1,200
Accts Ss&C Solutions Inc Lawrence
SIC 8051 8062 Skilled nursing care facilities; General medical & surgical hospitals; Skilled nursing care facilities; General medical & surgical hospitals
CEO: Gene Meyer
*Pr: Eugene W Meyer
*Pr: Deborah Thomson
*CFO: Simon Scholtz
*VP: Sheryle D Amico
*VP: Carolyn Bowmer
*VP: Janice Early
*VP: Kathy Clausing Willis
CIO: Jane A Maskus
Board of Directors: Kelli Hilmes, Patrick Parker, Terri Barnes, Kevin Howser, Teresa Sikes, Connie Bores, Nancy Knagg, Patty Winslow, Connie Broers, Corey Koester, Stacy Cope, Allyson Leland, Cheryl D'amico, Angela Lowe, Tom Damewood, Denise Martinek, Linda Gall, Patrick Mc Cool, Dana Hale, Debbie Miers, Joan Harvey, Lida Osbern

LAWRENCE NATIONAL LEASE
See LAWRENCE LEASING INC

D-U-N-S 07-206-3746
LAWRENCE NORTH COMMUNITY SCHOOLS
ORANG-LWRNC-JCKSN-MRTIN-GREENE
460 W St, Bedford, IN 47421-1954
Tel (812) 279-3521 Founded/Ownrshp 1965
Sales NA EMP 800^E
SIC 9411 8211 Administration of educational programs; Public elementary school; Administration of educational programs; Public elementary school
Schl Brd P: Larry Arnold

LAWRENCE PACKAGING
See LPS INDUSTRIES INC

D-U-N-S 00-712-7558
LAWRENCE PAPER CO (KS)
2801 Lakeview Rd, Lawrence, KS 66049-8950
Tel (785) 843-8111 Founded/Ownrshp 1882
Sales 53.6MM^E EMP 225
Accts Mize & Houser & Company Pa
SIC 2653 Corrugated & solid fiber boxes; Corrugated & solid fiber boxes
Pr: Justin D Hill
Tech Mgr: Jon Henry
Plnt Mgr: Dave Weise
Plnt Mgr: Dave Wiese
Prd Mgr: Kevin Bryant
Ql Cn Mgr: Greg Kahnk

LAWRENCE PHOTO-GRAPHIC
See HEARTLAND IMAGING COMPANIES INC

LAWRENCE PUBLIC SCHOOLS
See LAWRENCE UNION FREE SCHOOL DISTRICT

LAWRENCE PUBLIC SCHOOLS
See LAWRENCE SCHOOL DISTRICT

D-U-N-S 03-069-3642
LAWRENCE PUBLIC SCHOOLS
110 Mcdonald Dr, Lawrence, KS 66044-1055
Tel (785) 832-5000 Founded/Ownrshp 1966
Sales 105.9MM^E EMP 1,700
SIC 8211 Public combined elementary & secondary school; Public combined elementary & secondary school
Pr: Leonard Ortiz
*Treas: Katharine S Johnson
Bd of Dir: Mary Loveland
Bd of Dir: Randy Masten
Bd of Dir: Marlene Merrill
Bd of Dir: Adina Morse
*VP: Sue Morgan
Brnch Mgr: Susan Cranston
Dir IT: Melinda Stanley
IT Man: Terry McEwen
IT Man: Brandon Mellen

LAWRENCE REHABILITATION
See AMERICAN TRAINING INC

D-U-N-S 02-391-1662
LAWRENCE SANITARY CO INC
LAWRENCE ENVIRONMENTAL GROUP
5220 Klockner Dr, Richmond, VA 23231-4335
Tel (804) 236-0090 Founded/Ownrshp 1944
Sales 21.1MM^E EMP 32
SIC 5169 Aromatic chemicals
Pr: Roy O Jorstad
VP: Nat Cross
*VP: David A Fritter

D-U-N-S 00-121-7926 IMP
LAWRENCE SCHIFF SILK MILLS INC (CA)
SCHIFF RIBBONS
590 California Rd, Quakertown, PA 18951-2409
Tel (215) 538-2880 Founded/Ownrshp 1933, 2012
Sales 37.6MM^E EMP 175
SIC 2241 Fabric tapes; Ribbons; Fabric tapes; Ribbons
CEO: Robert Loring
*VP: Robert Schiff
Genl Mgr: Mark McAlpine
Sales Asso: Jane Reiser

D-U-N-S 80-433-7111
LAWRENCE SCHOOL DISTRICT
LAWRENCE PUBLIC SCHOOLS
233 Haverhill St, Lawrence, MA 01840-1405
Tel (978) 975-5905 Founded/Ownrshp 1848
Sales 156.0MM EMP 2,300^E
SIC 8211 Public elementary & secondary schools
Ch Bd: William Lantigua
Ch Bd: Samuel Reyes
Treas: Deborah Nowicki
Opers Mgr: Pamela Gilbert
Pr Dir: Lynne Garcia
Instr Medi: Greg Limperis
HC Dir: Mary Lou Bergeron

D-U-N-S 08-585-9221 IMP
LAWRENCE SCREW PRODUCTS INC (IL)
7230 W Wilson Ave, Harwood Heights, IL 60706-4797
Tel (708) 867-5150 Founded/Ownrshp 1977
Sales 57.2MM EMP 66
SIC 3965 Fasteners; Fasteners
Pr: Howard Levinson
*VP: Phil Levine
Exec: Gene Amistani
Opers Mgr: Bob Hayslip

D-U-N-S 18-488-9256
LAWRENCE STREET INDUSTRY LLC
L S I
6305 Ivy Ln Ste 720, Greenbelt, MD 20770-6301
Tel (240) 455-2932 Founded/Ownrshp 2005
Sales 21.0MM^E EMP 45
SIC 5064 Garbage disposals
Genl Mgr: Bill Fields
Opers Mgr: Mario Dimaio

D-U-N-S 07-422-6572
LAWRENCE TECHNOLOGICAL UNIVERSITY
21000 W 10 Mile Rd, Southfield, MI 48075-1051
Tel (248) 204-4000 Founded/Ownrshp 1932
Sales 87.7MM EMP 560
SIC 8221 University; University
Pr: Virinder K Moudgil
Pr: Karem Amerson
Treas: Rosemary Hartzer
Bd of Dir: John Davis
Ofcr: Angeline Zelenak
VP: Vince Daniele
VP: Adam Dumas
VP: Dennis Howie
Creative D: Mike Ward
Admn Mgr: Michael Cooper
Off Mgr: Donna Kress

D-U-N-S 13-661-0920
LAWRENCE TOWNSHIP SCHOOL DISTRICT INC
2565 Princeton Pike, Lawrenceville, NJ 08648-3631
Tel (609) 671-5500 Founded/Ownrshp 1910

Sales 26.1MM^E *EMP* 475
SIC 8211 Public elementary & secondary schools; Public elementary & secondary schools
**Prin:* William Buss
**Prin:* Sheila Macdonald
**Prin:* Judith A McLaughlin
**Prin:* Patricia Wendell

D-U-N-S 05-327-7125
LAWRENCE TOYOTA INC
2871 Us Highway 1, Lawrenceville, NJ 08648-2418
Tel (609) 883-4200 *Founded/Ownrshp* 1968
Sales 33.7MM^E *EMP* 90
SIC 5511 7538 7532 5521 Automobiles, new & used; General automotive repair shops; Top & body repair & paint shops; Used car dealers; Automobiles, new & used; General automotive repair shops; Top & body repair & paint shops; Used car dealers
Pr: Paul Muller III
Genl Mgr: Jeff Robinson
DP Exec: Karen Whybark

D-U-N-S 05-036-6988 IMP
LAWRENCE TRACTOR CO INC
JOHN DEERE
2530 E Main St, Visalia, CA 93292-6731
Tel (559) 734-7406 *Founded/Ownrshp* 1970
Sales 30.5MM^E *EMP* 98
SIC 5083 7699 Agricultural machinery; Farm implements; Farm equipment parts & supplies; Farm machinery repair; Agricultural machinery; Farm implements; Farm equipment parts & supplies; Farm machinery repair
Pr: Mark Lawrence
**Sec:* Richard Nunes
**VP:* Steven Lawrence
Sls Mgr: Doug Breschini
Sales Asso: Brent Branco

LAWRENCE TRANSPORTATION
See LTX INC

D-U-N-S 00-278-0666
LAWRENCE TRANSPORTATION SYSTEMS INC (VA)
UNITED VAN LINES
872 Lee Hwy, Roanoke, VA 24019-8516
Tel (540) 966-4000 *Founded/Ownrshp* 1932
Sales 111.2MM^E *EMP* 500
Accts J Moore & Company Pc Roan
SIC 4225 4213 4212 General warehousing; Household goods transport; Local trucking, without storage; General warehousing; Household goods transport; Local trucking, without storage
CEO: Weldon S Lawrence
**Pr:* Ronald E Spangler
**Treas:* Lawrence Harris
VP: J D Robinson
Brnch Mgr: Billy Wills
Natl Sales: Regina Durnal
S&M/VP: Barry Barnes

D-U-N-S 04-046-6716
LAWRENCE UNION FREE SCHOOL DISTRICT
LAWRENCE PUBLIC SCHOOLS
195 Broadway, Lawrence, NY 11559-1737
Tel (516) 295-7000 *Founded/Ownrshp* 1890
Sales 93.4MM *EMP* 755
Accts Coughlin Foundotos Cullen & Da
SIC 8211 Public senior high school; Public junior high school; Public elementary school; Public senior high school; Public junior high school; Public elementary school
Genl Mgr: Kathleen Halbach
IT Man: Lee Comeau

D-U-N-S 04-141-0226
LAWRENCE UNIVERSITY OF WISCONSIN
115 S Drew St, Appleton, WI 54911-5798
Tel (920) 832-7000 *Founded/Ownrshp* 1847
Sales 56.1MM *EMP* 392
Accts Baker Tilly Virchow Krause L
SIC 8221 Colleges universities & professional schools; Colleges universities & professional schools
Pr: Mark Burstein
**Pr:* Jill Beck
**Ex VP:* Brian Riste
Creative D: Tom Neff
Ex Dir: David Gerard
HC Dir: Susan Muenster

D-U-N-S 10-872-8254 IMP
LAWRENCE WHOLESALE LLC
ARGOSY FOODS
4353 Exchange Ave, Vernon, CA 90058-2619
Tel (323) 235-7525 *Founded/Ownrshp* 2000
Sales 805.0MM^E *EMP* 20^E
SIC 5147 Meat brokers; Meat brokers
CEO: Mark Liszt
COO: Max Liszt
CFO: Robert Francis

D-U-N-S 05-888-7738
LAWRENCE-LYNCH MATERIALS CORP
396 Gifford St, Falmouth, MA 02540-2912
Tel (508) 548-1800 *Founded/Ownrshp* 1972
Sales 38.5MM^E *EMP* 100^E
SIC 1629 Dams, waterways, docks & other marine construction
Pr: Christopher M Lynch
VP: Robert Gent

D-U-N-S 04-949-6995
LAWRENCEBURG UTILITY SYSTEMS
1607 N Locust Ave, Lawrenceburg, TN 38464-2213
Tel (931) 762-7161 *Founded/Ownrshp* 1939
Sales 61.7MM^E *EMP* 120^E
SIC 4911 Transmission, electric power; Transmission, electric power
Ofcr: Renee Chandler
VP: Reggie Holt
Tech Mgr: Lonnie Bailey
Sfty Dirs: Brandon Brown
Sfty Dirs: Bill Pettus
Pgrm Dir: Charles Love

D-U-N-S 82-999-3976
LAWRENCEVILLE SCHOOL
TRUSTEES LAWRENCEVILLE SCHOOLS
2500 Main St, Lawrenceville, NJ 08648-1699
Tel (609) 896-0400 *Founded/Ownrshp* 1700
Sales 79.3MM *EMP* 490^E
Accts Withum Smith Brown Pc Princet
SIC 8211 Private elementary & secondary schools; Private elementary & secondary schools
CEO: Elizabeth A Duffy
Trst: Fahad Al-Rashid
Trst: Frederick McCord
Trst: Paul Mott
Trst: Raymond Viault
Trst: Loyal Wilson
Genl Mgr: Robert Freeman
Off Mgr: Janet Moskus
Dir IT: Niki Emanuel
Dir IT: Harriet Huston
Dir IT: Alyssa Totoro

D-U-N-S 02-854-1621
LAWRYS RESTAURANTS INC
TAM O' SHANTER
234 E Colo Blvd Ste 500, Pasadena, CA 91101
Tel (626) 440-5234 *Founded/Ownrshp* 1937
Sales 25.2MM^E *EMP* 550
SIC 5812 5813 Eating places; Cocktail lounge; Eating places; Cocktail lounge
Pr: Richard R Frank
**Ch Bd:* John Van De Kamp
**Treas:* Anna Martirelli
**Sr VP:* David E Stockman
Exec: Steve Kling
Genl Mgr: Ed Lepere

D-U-N-S 00-583-8644
LAWSON ELECTRIC CO INC (TN)
409 Spring St, Chattanooga, TN 37405-3848
Tel (423) 267-5471 *Founded/Ownrshp* 1925, 1957
Sales 49.1MM^E *EMP* 350
SIC 1731

D-U-N-S 00-296-5580 EXP
LAWSON INDUSTRIES INC (FL)
8501 Nw 90th St, Miami, FL 33166-2187
Tel (305) 696-8660 *Founded/Ownrshp* 1965
Sales 79.1MM^E *EMP* 400
SIC 3231 3442 Doors, glass: made from purchased glass; Metal doors, sash & trim; Doors, glass: made from purchased glass; Metal doors, sash & trim
Pr: Harold Bailey
**Treas:* Ron Bailey
Brnch Mgr: Frank Carson

LAWSON KEITH MECHANICAL CONTRS
See KEITH LAWSON CO INC

D-U-N-S 00-945-8407
LAWSON MECHANICAL CONTRACTORS (CA)
6090 S Watt Ave, Sacramento, CA 95829-1302
Tel (916) 381-6704 *Founded/Ownrshp* 1947
Sales 29.1MM^E *EMP* 100^E
SIC 1711 Plumbing contractors; Heating & air conditioning contractors; Mechanical contractor; Plumbing contractors; Heating & air conditioning contractors; Mechanical contractor
Pr: Rodney Lawson
**Sec:* David Lawson
**VP:* Rod Barbour
VP: Stephen Humason
Telecom Ex: Larry Craig
Dir IT: Paul Nelson
Trfc Dir: Roger Reynolds
Sfty Mgr: David Kincaid
Snr PM: Sean Bakey
Snr Mgr: Jason Harris
Board of Directors: Carroll Keys, Donald Wkstrom

D-U-N-S 06-976-7895
LAWSON OIL CO OF LAWTON (MI)
110 E 3rd St, Lawton, MI 49065-8715
Tel (269) 624-4851 *Founded/Ownrshp* 1964
Sales 23.5MM *EMP* 48
Accts Brad Smith Cpa Pc Paw Paw
SIC 5541 5172 Gasoline service stations; Gasoline; Lubricating oils & greases; Fuel oil; Gasoline service stations; Gasoline; Lubricating oils & greases; Fuel oil
Pr: Kenneth E Lawson

D-U-N-S 00-543-8890 IMP
▲ LAWSON PRODUCTS INC
8770 W Bryn Mawr Ave # 639, Chicago, IL 60631-3526
Tel (773) 304-5050 *Founded/Ownrshp* 1952
Sales 285.6MM *EMP* 1,510
Accts Bdo Usa Llp Chicago Il
Tkr Sym LAWS *Exch* NGS
SIC 5072 5085 5084 5013 Screws; Nuts (hardware); Rivets; Fasteners & fastening equipment; Industrial fittings; Hose, belting & packing; Welding machinery & equipment; Automotive supplies & parts; Automotive servicing equipment; Hardware; Nuts (hardware); Rivets; Screws; Fasteners & fastening equipment; Industrial fittings; Hose, belting & packing; Welding machinery & equipment; Automotive supplies & parts; Automotive servicing equipment
Pr: Michael G Decata
Pr: John J Murray
CFO: Ronald J Knutson
Ex VP: Steve R Broome
Ex VP: Neil E Jenkins
Sr VP: Allen D Jacobson
Sr VP: Lawrence Krema
Sr VP: Shane T McCarthy
VP: John Del Sasso
Area Mgr: Bill Patterson
Dist Mgr: Dave Lifford
Board of Directors: Andrew B Albert, I Steven Edelson, James S Errant, Lee S Hillman, Thomas S Postek, Wilma J Smelcer

D-U-N-S 06-710-9926
LAWSON STATE COMMUNITY COLLEGE (AL)
3060 Wilson Rd Sw, Birmingham, AL 35221-1717
Tel (205) 925-2515 *Founded/Ownrshp* 1949
Sales 50.7M^E *EMP* 509^E
SIC 8222 Community college; Community college
Pr: Perry W Ward
Ofcr: Rose Hall
Ofcr: Tammie Turner
VP: Leeann Best
Exec: Vergie Spears
Opers Supe: Rebecca Ephraim
Snr Mgr: Nick Shields

D-U-N-S 96-805-9019 IMP
LAWTER INC
(*Suby of* LAWTER CAPITAL B.V.)
200 N La Salle St # 2600, Chicago, IL 60601-1060
Tel (312) 662-5700 *Founded/Ownrshp* 2011
Sales 148.3MM^E *EMP* 582
SIC 2899 2851 Chemical preparations; Paints & allied products; Chemical preparations; Paints & allied products
Pr: Ichiro Taninaka
**COO:* Jeroen Triesscheijn
**Ch:* Yoshihiro Hasegawa
Treas: Hideo Takahira
**Chf Cred:* Rich Tuttle
**VP:* Peter Biesheuvel

D-U-N-S 08-248-2647
LAWTON INTER-TRIBAL INDIAN HEALTH ADVISORY BOARD
OPERATNAL MNTANCE ORGANIZATION
1515 Ne Lawrie Tatum Rd, Lawton, OK 73507-3002
Tel (580) 354-5000 *Founded/Ownrshp* 1976
Sales 2.7MM^E *EMP* 300
SIC 8062 General medical & surgical hospitals; General medical & surgical hospitals
CEO: Gregg Ketcher
QC Dir: Michael Holmes

D-U-N-S 08-247-1038
LAWTON PUBLIC SCHOOL DISTRICT I-008
753 Nw Fort Sill Blvd, Lawton, OK 73507-5421
Tel (580) 357-6900 *Founded/Ownrshp* 1901, 1902
Sales 200.0MM^E *EMP* 2,200
SIC 8211 Public elementary & secondary schools; Public elementary school; Public junior high school; Public senior high school; Public elementary & secondary schools; Public elementary school; Public junior high school; Public senior high school
CFO: Dianne Branstette
Dir Sec: Mike Moore
HC Dir: Chris Sharkey

D-U-N-S 04-646-3543
LAWYER MECHANICAL SERVICES INC
LMS BUILDING SERVICES
3036 S Valley View Blvd, Las Vegas, NV 89102-7805
Tel (702) 876-7530 *Founded/Ownrshp* 1969
Sales 34.3MM^E *EMP* 50
SIC 5075 7623 Warm air heating & air conditioning; Refrigeration service & repair; Air conditioning repair
CEO: Thomas C Lawyer
**Pr:* John Kotek

D-U-N-S 12-084-0269
LAWYERS COMMITTEE FOR CIVIL RIGHTS UNDER LAW
1401 New York Ave Nw # 400, Washington, DC 20005-2124
Tel (202) 662-8600 *Founded/Ownrshp* 1963
Sales 33.3MM *EMP* 48
Accts Tate And Tryon Washington Dc
SIC 8111 Legal services
Prin: Jon M Greenbaum
**CFO:* Michael A Brown
Treas: William Robinson
Trst: Philip Anderson
Trst: William Bradley
Trst: Michael J Brown
Trst: Eddie Correia
Trst: Armand Derfner
Trst: Colin Diver
Trst: Johnita Due
Trst: James Ferguson
Trst: Charles Hamilton
Trst: Mark Harrison
Trst: Joseph Hatchett
Trst: Tim Hoy
Trst: James Hubbell
Trst: Percy Julian
Trst: Robert McDuff
Trst: Aasia Mustakeem
Trst: Karen Narasaki
Trst: Richard Rawson

D-U-N-S 03-998-0867
LAWYERS MUTUAL INSURANCE CO
3110 W Empire Ave, Burbank, CA 91504-3107
Tel (818) 565-5512 *Founded/Ownrshp* 1978
Sales NA *EMP* 32
SIC 6351 Liability insurance
Ch Bd: Richard D Barger
Pr: Thomas Ault
Treas: Anna Chiong
Ex VP: Andrew Chick
VP: Willis Baughman
VP: John Burke
VP: Robert Riddick
VP: Gerald Sherman
CTO: Gabriel Macu
Genl Couns: Gary Davis

D-U-N-S 07-622-0433
■ LAWYERS TITLE CO
(*Suby of* FIDELITY NATIONAL FINANCIAL INC) ★
7530 N Glenoaks Blvd, Burbank, CA 91504-1052
Tel (818) 767-0425 *Founded/Ownrshp* 1984
Sales NA *EMP* 786
SIC 6361 6531 Real estate title insurance; Escrow agent, real estate; Real estate title insurance; Escrow agent, real estate
CEO: Edward Zerwekh
Ofcr: Monica Thomas
**Sr VP:* Edward Beierle
**VP:* Steve Bauer
VP: Peg Jordan
**VP:* William Star
Brnch Mgr: Jennifer Hall
Opers Mgr: Lisa Lagunas
Sales Exec: Susan Georgeson
Sales Exec: Candy Jackson
Sales Exec: Ling Ting

D-U-N-S 00-794-1180
■ LAWYERS TITLE INSURANCE CORP
(*Suby of* FIDELITY NATIONAL FINANCIAL INC) ★
601 Riverside Ave, Jacksonville, FL 32204-2946
Tel (888) 866-3684 *Founded/Ownrshp* 1988, 2008
Sales NA *EMP* 11,000
SIC 6361 7372 5734 Guarantee of titles; Real estate title insurance; Prepackaged software; Computer peripheral equipment; Computer software & accessories; Guarantee of titles; Real estate title insurance; Prepackaged software; Computer peripheral equipment; Computer software & accessories
CEO: Theodore L Chandler Jr
Pr: Kenneth Astheimer
Pr: Melissa A Hill
Pr: Jeffrey C Selby
Pr: Albert V Will
Ex VP: Ross W Dorneman
Ex VP: G William Evans
Ex VP: Margaret M Foster
Ex VP: Michelle H Gluck
Ex VP: Richard P Gonzalez
Ex VP: John A Magness
Ex VP: Glyn Nelson
Ex VP: John M Obzud
Ex VP: Lynn M Riedel
Ex VP: James E Sindoni
Ex VP: William C Thornton
Ex VP: Jeffrey D Vaughan
Ex VP: Marcy A Welburn
VP: Marty Austin
VP: Jordan Kanter
VP: Toni Reichow

D-U-N-S 07-245-5868
■ LAWYERS TITLE OF ARIZONA INC
(*Suby of* FIDELITY NATIONAL FINANCIAL INC) ★
3131 E Camelback Rd # 220, Phoenix, AZ 85016-4500
Tel (602) 257-2600 *Founded/Ownrshp* 2007
Sales NA *EMP* 185
SIC 6361 6531 6541 Title insurance; Escrow agent, real estate; Title abstract offices; Title insurance; Escrow agent, real estate; Title abstract offices
Pr: Dan Robledo
**Ex VP:* Douglas Thompson
**VP:* Edna M Fraser
Board of Directors: Steven Veltri, Edward Zerwekh

LAWYER'S TRAVEL
See OVATION TRAVEL GROUP INC

D-U-N-S 10-417-2283 IMP
LAX-C INC
1100 N Main St, Los Angeles, CA 90012-1832
Tel (323) 343-9000 *Founded/Ownrshp* 1996
Sales 22.6MM^E *EMP* 50
SIC 5141 Groceries, general line
Pr: Suprata Bovornsivamon

LAXMI DIAMOND NY
See ANERI JEWELS LLC

D-U-N-S 12-647-1676
LAY MANAGEMENT CORP OF GEORIGA
790 Dixon Rd Apt J7, Jonesboro, GA 30238-3165
Tel (678) 558-5631 *Founded/Ownrshp* 2002
Sales 35.1MM^E *EMP* 2,000
SIC 8741 Management services; Management services
Pr: David Lay
**VP:* Laquallis McGee

LAYCO
See YARGUS MANUFACTURING INC

D-U-N-S 12-821-6574 IMP
LAYCO INC
E MOTORSONLINE.COM
6707 E 12th St, Tulsa, OK 74112-5606
Tel (918) 796-8000 *Founded/Ownrshp* 1984
Sales 28.2MM^E *EMP* 40
SIC 5063 Motor controls, starters & relays: electric; Motors, electric
Pr: B Mike Lay
IT Man: Debra Lay
VP Sls: Shawn Lay

LAYERS
See GREAT OUTDOOR PROVISION CO

D-U-N-S 06-364-8069
LAYERS LLC
PATXIS CHICAGO PIZZA
(*Suby of* KARPREILLY LLC) ★
30 Liberty Ship Way # 3225, Sausalito, CA 94965-3324
Tel (415) 887-9315 *Founded/Ownrshp* 2014
Sales 12.9MM^E *EMP* 320
SIC 5812 Pizza restaurants; Pizza restaurants
CEO: William Freeman

D-U-N-S 17-640-3280 IMP
LAYFIELD USA CORP
(*Suby of* LAYFIELD GROUP LIMITED)
2500 Swetwater Sprng Blvd, Spring Valley, CA 91978-2007
Tel (619) 562-1200 *Founded/Ownrshp* 2004
Sales 24.5MM^E *EMP* 120^E
SIC 1799 Building board-up contractor
CEO: Thomas Rose
**Pr:* Gary Pinkerton
Genl Mgr: Robert Remtel

D-U-N-S 80-702-4521
LAYLINE PETROLEUM LLC
820 Gessner Rd Ste 1145, Houston, TX 77024-4265
Tel (713) 465-4100 *Founded/Ownrshp* 2006
Sales 26.0MM^E *EMP* 43^E
SIC 1382 Oil & gas exploration services
Off Mgr: Sara Duchhorn

D-U-N-S 02-395-2492
LAYMAN CANDY CO INC
LAYMAN DISTRIBUTING
1630 W Main St, Salem, VA 24153-3116
Tel (540) 389-2000 *Founded/Ownrshp* 1948
Sales 42.4MM^E *EMP* 60

SIC 5194 5145 5141 Tobacco & tobacco products; Confectionery; Groceries, general line; Tobacco & tobacco products; Confectionery; Groceries, general line
Pr: Juanita L Neely
Pr: Justin Keen
**Sec:* Judy Ross
**VP:* Glenn Bowe
**VP:* Kenneth Keen
IT Man: Matt Byrd
VP Sls: Scott Thomasson
Sales Asso: Mandy Thomasson

LAYMAN DISTRIBUTING
See LAYMAN CANDY CO INC

D-U-N-S 61-300-4290 IMP
LAYMAN WHOLESALE NURSERIES INC
(*Suby of* COSTA NURSERY FARMS INC) ★
73 Green House Rd, Trenton, SC 29847-2101
Tel (803) 275-0656 *Founded/Ownrshp* 2012
Sales 75.3MM^E *EMP* 375^E
SIC 5193 Nursery stock; Nursery stock
Pr: Barry Layman

D-U-N-S 00-696-5917 IMP
▲ LAYNE CHRISTENSEN CO
1800 Hughes Landing Blvd, The Woodlands, TX 77380-1682
Tel (281) 475-2600 *Founded/Ownrshp* 1981
Sales 797.6MM *EMP* 3,380
Accts Deloitte & Touche Llp Housto
Tkr Sym LAYN *Exch* NGS
SIC 1781 1623 5084 7699 1481 8748 Water well drilling; Water well servicing; Water, sewer & utility lines; Materials handling machinery; Pumps & pumping equipment; Water pumps (industrial); Aircraft & heavy equipment repair services; Pumps & pumping equipment repair; Nonmetallic minerals development & test boring; Mine exploration, nonmetallic minerals; Test boring for nonmetallic minerals; Environmental consultant; Water well drilling; Water well servicing; Water, sewer & utility lines; Materials handling machinery; Pumps & pumping equipment; Water pumps (industrial); Aircraft & heavy equipment repair services; Pumps & pumping equipment repair; Nonmetallic minerals development & test boring; Mine exploration, nonmetallic minerals; Test boring for nonmetallic minerals; Environmental consultant
Pr: Michael J Caliel
**Ch Bd:* David A B Brown
CFO: Andrew Atchison
CFO: Andy T Atchison
Sr VP: Steven F Crooke
Sr VP: Gernot E Penzhorn
Sr VP: David Singleton
Sls Mgr: John Slider
Board of Directors: J Samuel Butler, Robert R Gilmore, John T Nesser III, Nelson Obus

D-U-N-S 04-905-9702 IMP
■ LAYNE HEAVY CIVIL INC
(*Suby of* LAYNE CHRISTENSEN CO) ★
4520 N State Road 37, Orleans, IN 47452-9035
Tel (812) 865-3232 *Founded/Ownrshp* 2005
Sales 365.3MM^E *EMP* 650
SIC 1623 1781 1629 Water main construction; Sewer line construction; Pumping station construction; Water well drilling; Waste disposal plant construction; Water main construction; Sewer line construction; Pumping station construction; Water well drilling; Waste disposal plant construction
Pr: Mark Accetturo
Treas: Steven Crooke
**Treas:* James R Easter
Ex VP: Jerry Fanska
Ex VP: Patrick Schmidt
VP: Kevin Collenbaugh
VP: Mark Harris
**VP:* Larry Purlee
VP: William K Reynolds
**VP:* Jim Stutler
**VP:* Andrew M Zalla
Board of Directors: Patrick Schmidt- Dir

D-U-N-S 13-073-4267 IMP
■ LAYNE INLINER LLC
(*Suby of* LAYNE HEAVY CIVIL INC) ★
4520 N State Rd State 37, Orleans, IN 47452
Tel (812) 865-3232 *Founded/Ownrshp* 2002
Sales 98.1MM^E *EMP* 295
SIC 1623 Water, sewer & utility lines; Water, sewer & utility lines
CEO: Jeff Reynolds
**Ch Bd:* David AB Brown

D-U-N-S 05-161-3032
LAYTON CITY CORP (UT)
437 Wasatch Dr, Layton, UT 84041-3275
Tel (801) 336-3800 *Founded/Ownrshp* 1885
Sales NA *EMP* 600
Accts Hansen Bradshaw Malmrose & E
SIC 9111 City & town managers' offices; ; City & town managers' offices;
Treas: Seth Pilkington
Genl Mgr: Jim Mason
Dir IT: Ed Frazier
IT Man: Ed Frasier

D-U-N-S 00-780-9676
LAYTON COMPANIES INC
ROCKY MOUNTAIN PIES
9090 S Sandy Pkwy, Sandy, UT 84070-6409
Tel (801) 568-9090 *Founded/Ownrshp* 1948
Sales 8.3M *EMP* 650^E
SIC 1542 1541 Commercial & office building, new construction; Industrial buildings, new construction; Commercial & office building, new construction; Industrial buildings, new construction
Pr: David S Layton
**CFO:* Dallis Christensen
CFO: Tyler Layton
**Sec:* Gerald Monson
**Ex VP:* Jason Hill
**Ex VP:* Bryan Webb
VP: Bil Munck
VP: Randy Patterson
Exec: Gerald Beisinger
Off Mgr: Meg Howell
Dir IT: John Zinger

D-U-N-S 11-271-9989
LAYTON CONSTRUCTION CO INC
CORPORATE CONSTRUCTION
(*Suby of* LAYTON COMPANIES INC) ★
9090 S Sandy Pkwy, Sandy, UT 84070-6409
Tel (801) 568-9090 *Founded/Ownrshp* 2000
Sales 80.0MM^E *EMP* 450
SIC 1541 1542 Industrial buildings, new construction; Commercial & office building contractors; Industrial buildings, new construction; Commercial & office building contractors
Pr: David S Layton
**CFO:* Dallis J Christensen
**Sec:* Gerry Monson

D-U-N-S 17-730-8533
LAYTON CONSTRUCTION CO OF ARIZONA INC
(*Suby of* LAYTON COMPANIES INC) ★
4686 E Van Buren St # 100, Phoenix, AZ 85008-6960
Tel (602) 840-8655 *Founded/Ownrshp* 1987
Sales 25.8MM^E *EMP* 75
SIC 1542 1541 Commercial & office building, new construction; Industrial buildings, new construction
Pr: David Layton
**CFO:* Dallis Christensen
**Sec:* Gerald Monson
Bd of Dir: Brent Gourley
Ex VP: Steve Brecker
**VP:* Jeff Beecher
**VP:* Craig Bergstrom
Exec: Meg Howell
Dir IT: Shane Zilcox
Snr PM: Darcy Gray

D-U-N-S 09-467-4785
LAYTON HILLS DODGE INC
1234 N Main St, Layton, UT 84041-5280
Tel (801) 544-5800 *Founded/Ownrshp* 1979
Sales 33.5MM^E *EMP* 110
SIC 5511 Automobiles, new & used; Automobiles, new & used
Pr: Homer K Cutrubus
**VP:* Phidia Cutrubus
Exec: Camie Hansen

D-U-N-S 00-594-2180
■ LAYTON HOMES CORP
(*Suby of* SKYLINE CORP) ★
2520 Bypass Rd, Elkhart, IN 46514-1518
Tel (574) 294-6521 *Founded/Ownrshp* 1962
Sales 21.6MM^E *EMP* 139
SIC 3792 Travel trailers & campers; Travel trailers & campers
Pr: Ronald Kloska
**VP:* Joseph Fanchi

LAYTON TRUCK EQUIPMENT
See LTE OLDCO LLC

D-U-N-S 82-698-7083
LAZ KARP ASSOCIATES INC
15 Lewis St Fl 5, Hartford, CT 06103-2503
Tel (860) 522-7641 *Founded/Ownrshp* 2003
Sales 20.9MM^E *EMP* 7,000
SIC 7521 1799 Automobile parking; Parking lot maintenance
Pr: Jeffery Karp
**CEO:* Alan Lazowski
**VP:* Michael Kuziak

D-U-N-S 96-746-7569
LAZ KARP ASSOCIATES LLC
15 Lewis St Fl 5, Hartford, CT 06103-2503
Tel (860) 522-7641 *Founded/Ownrshp* 2007
Sales 850.0MM^E *EMP* 7,000
SIC 1799 Parking lot maintenance
CEO: Alan B Lazowski
Pr: Jeffrey N Karp
COO: Michael J Kuziak
CFO: Nathan Owen
Treas: Raymond H Skoglund
Ofcr: Heather Mortimer

D-U-N-S 00-736-9516
LAZ PARKING LTD
(*Suby of* LAZ KARP ASSOCIATES LLC) ★
9333 Genesee Ave Ste 220, San Diego, CA 92121-2113
Tel (858) 587-8888 *Founded/Ownrshp* 1981
Sales 32.5MM^E *EMP* 6,000
SIC 7521 Parking lots; Parking lots
CEO: Alan Lazowski
**Treas:* Raymond Skoglund
**VP:* Bert Kaplowitz

D-U-N-S 10-851-2856 IMP
LAZ PARKING LTD LLC
(*Suby of* LAZ KARP ASSOCIATES LLC) ★
15 Lewis St Fl 5, Hartford, CT 06103-2500
Tel (860) 713-2030 *Founded/Ownrshp* 1981
Sales 233.2MM^E *EMP* 2,003
SIC 7521 Automobile parking; Parking garage
CEO: Alan Lazowski
**Pr:* Jeffrey N Karp
Pr: Barbara Lao
Rgnl VP: Steven Greshis
VP: Bert Kaplowitz
**VP:* Mike Kusiak
VP: Stacy Rosenberg
Dir Bus: Jason Marovick
Dir Bus: David Zell
Rgnl Mgr: Pat O'Day
Area Mgr: Girma Mammo

D-U-N-S 62-086-2677
LAZ-MD HOLDINGS LLC
(*Suby of* LAZARD LTD)
30 Rockefeller Plz, New York, NY 10112-0015
Tel (212) 632-6000 *Founded/Ownrshp* 2004
Sales 379.1MM^E *EMP* 2,511
SIC 6211 6221 Flotation companies; Investment certificate sales; Commodity contracts brokers, dealers; Flotation companies; Investment certificate sales; Commodity contracts brokers, dealers
CEO: Charles Ward III
Mng Dir: William B Buchanan

D-U-N-S 10-803-7375 IMP/EXP
LAZAR INDUSTRIES LLC
3025 Hamp Stone Rd, Siler City, NC 27344-1426
Tel (919) 742-9303 *Founded/Ownrshp* 1983
Sales 55.2MM^E *EMP* 250
SIC 2512 Upholstered household furniture; Upholstered household furniture
Pr: Robert Luce
CFO: Jeff Sims
Exec: Angelina Mendez
Mfg Dir: Ronnie Murphy
Snr Mgr: James Thompson

D-U-N-S 78-412-9830
LAZARD ASSET MANAGEMENT LLC
(*Suby of* LAZARD FRERES & CO LLC) ★
30 Rockefeller Plz Fl 57, New York, NY 10112-0015
Tel (212) 632-1890 *Founded/Ownrshp* 2002
Sales NA *EMP* 105^E
SIC 6351 Assessment associations, surety & fidelity insurance
Sr VP: Frank Aiello
Sr VP: Bruce Bickerton
Sr VP: Jason Campisi
**Sr VP:* James F Harmon
**Sr VP:* Richard Kowal
Sr VP: Ryan Mims
Sr VP: SRI Nadesan
Sr VP: Richard K Owal
VP: Kerryn Andrews
VP: Ramana Bondugula
**VP:* Stephen S Clair
VP: Joann Disantis
VP: Neal Doying
VP: Dylan Heck
VP: John Labadia
VP: Kevin Ledger
VP: Ross Seiden
VP: Mon Stacey

D-U-N-S 00-698-6723
LAZARD FRERES & CO LLC
(*Suby of* LAZARD GROUP LLC) ★
30 Rockefeller Plz, New York, NY 10112-0015
Tel (212) 632-6000 *Founded/Ownrshp* 1848, 1992
Sales 328.0MM^E *EMP* 1,300
SIC 6211 Dealers, security; Investment bankers; Dealers, security; Investment bankers
Ch Bd: Kenneth M Jacobs
**COO:* Alexander F Stern
Sr VP: John Ceglia
VP: Chris Leelum
VP: David Tan
Dir Risk M: Zoe Chen
Mng Dir: Charles Burgdorf
Mng Dir: James Donald
Mng Dir: Holcombe T Green
Mng Dir: Peter Lewis
Mng Dir: Daniel T Motulsky

D-U-N-S 02-611-5597
LAZARD GROUP LLC
(*Suby of* LAZARD LTD)
30 Rockefeller Plz, New York, NY 10112-0015
Tel (212) 632-6000 *Founded/Ownrshp* 1848
Sales 2.3MMM *EMP* 2,523^E
Accts Deloitte & Touche Llp New Yo
SIC 6282 6211 Investment advisory service; Investment bankers; Securities flotation companies; Investment advisory service; Investment bankers; Securities flotation companies
Ch Bd: Kenneth M Jacobs
COO: Alexander F Stern
CFO: Matthieu Bucaille
**Chf Inves:* Ashish Bhutani
Sr VP: Greg Bernhardt
Sr VP: Guy Fiumarelli
Sr VP: Claire Nordin
Sr VP: Andrew Rogers
Mng Dir: Joseph Cassanelli
Mng Dir: Alexander Hecker
Mng Dir: Christopher Winger
Board of Directors: Andrew M Alper, Steven J Heyer, Sylvia Jay, Philip A Laskawy, Laurent Mignon, Richard D Parsons, Hal S Scott, Michael J Turner

D-U-N-S 78-672-0776
▲ LAZARUS ENERGY HOLDINGS LLC
LAZARUS ENERGY SERVICES
801 Travis St Ste 2100, Houston, TX 77002-5705
Tel (713) 850-0500 *Founded/Ownrshp* 2006
Sales 388.0MM^E *EMP* 70
SIC 2911 Petroleum refining
IT Man: Jonathan Carroll
Brnch Mgr: Tommy Byrd
Brnch Mgr: Fred Marshall
Genl Mgr: Jason Heuring

LAZARUS ENERGY SERVICES
See LAZARUS ENERGY HOLDINGS LLC

D-U-N-S 14-733-6197
LAZEAR CAPITAL PARTNERS LTD
401 N Front St Ste 350, Columbus, OH 43215-2249
Tel (614) 221-1616 *Founded/Ownrshp* 1998
Sales 54.2MM^E *EMP* 118^E
SIC 8741 Management services
Prin: Bruce C Lazear
**Pr:* Bruce Lazear

D-U-N-S 01-514-9599
LAZER SPOT INC
6525 Shiloh Rd Ste 900, Alpharetta, GA 30005-1615
Tel (770) 886-6851 *Founded/Ownrshp* 2015
Sales 280.4MM^E *EMP* 1,300
SIC 0762 4212 Farm management services; Farm management services; Farm to market haulage, local
CEO: Wesley Newsome
COO: Adam Newsome
CFO: Clay Herron
Ex VP: Jerry Edwards
Ex VP: Phil Newsome
VP: Jerry Hudgins
VP: Brent Parker
Rgnl Mgr: John Chambers
Rgnl Mgr: Bill Norris
Rgnl Mgr: George Sanders
Area Mgr: Chris Chapman

D-U-N-S 61-866-2647
LAZY ACRES MARKET INC
302 Meigs Rd, Santa Barbara, CA 93109-1984
Tel (805) 564-4410 *Founded/Ownrshp* 1990
Sales 21.0MM^E *EMP* 220
SIC 5411 Grocery stores, independent; Grocery stores, independent
CEO: Kevin Davis
**VP:* Sam Masterson

D-U-N-S 96-916-9163
LAZY DAYS RV CENTER INC
LAZYDAYS
6130 Lazy Days Blvd, Seffner, FL 33584-2968
Tel (813) 246-4999 *Founded/Ownrshp* 1977
Sales 20.2MM^E *EMP* 118^E
SIC 4724 4725 Travel agencies; Tour operators
Pr: John Horton
CFO: Randall R Lay
**VP:* Randall Lay

LAZYDAYS
See LAZY DAYS RV CENTER INC

LAZYDAYS RV CAMPGROUND
See LDRV HOLDINGS CORP

D-U-N-S 04-178-3585
LAZZARA INTERNATIONAL YACHT SALES
801 Seabreeze Blvd, Fort Lauderdale, FL 33316-1629
Tel (954) 522-2118 *Founded/Ownrshp* 2001
Sales 28.0MM^E *EMP* 500
SIC 5551 Motor boat dealers; Motor boat dealers
Pt: Steven Lazzara

D-U-N-S 00-168-6294
LB ELECTRIC SUPPLY CO INC (NY)
5202 New Utrecht Ave, Brooklyn, NY 11219-3899
Tel (718) 438-4700 *Founded/Ownrshp* 1930
Sales 51.9MM^E *EMP* 50
SIC 5063 5719 Electrical supplies; Lighting fixtures; Lighting fixtures
Pr: Carol Lifton
**Pr:* Jonathan Lifton
**Treas:* Cheryl Lifton
**VP:* Steve Andreala
**VP:* Bruce Hordon
**VP:* Lisa Lifton
**VP:* Richard Lifton
MIS Mgr: Barry Hanold
Sales Asso: Joseph O'Leary
Sales Asso: Joe Oleary

D-U-N-S 62-129-6912
LB INTERNATIONAL INC
LB INTERNATIONAL TRADING CO
417 B N Foothill Blvd, Glendora, CA 91740
Tel (626) 914-0367 *Founded/Ownrshp* 1982
Sales 30.0MM *EMP* 15
SIC 5172 6099 5094 Crude oil; Foreign currency exchange; Bullion, precious metals; Crude oil; Foreign currency exchange; Bullion, precious metals
Pr: Leo Batista
**VP:* Karen Batista

LB INTERNATIONAL TRADING CO
See LB INTERNATIONAL INC

D-U-N-S 10-118-9434 IMP
LB STEEL LLC
TOPEKA METAL SPECIALTIES
15700 Lathrop Ave, Harvey, IL 60426-5118
Tel (708) 331-2600 *Founded/Ownrshp* 2001
Sales 151.2MM^E *EMP* 350
SIC 3599 Machine shop, jobbing & repair; Machine shop, jobbing & repair
Sr VP: Richard Kovak
VP: Richard Kovac
IT Man: Debbie Carnahan
IT Man: Joyce Howard
VP Opers: Terry Byers
Prd Mgr: Marco Zagorac
Trfc Mgr: Janet Arana
Sales Exec: Matt Imer
VP Sls: Janet Cahill
VP Sls: Robert Richards
Manager: Steve Deringer

LBA MORTAGE SERVICES
See EMPIRE STATE MORTGAGE

D-U-N-S 17-133-7483
LBA REALTY LLC
3347 Michelson Dr Ste 200, Irvine, CA 92612-0687
Tel (949) 833-0400 *Founded/Ownrshp* 2004
Sales 30.3MM^E *EMP* 100
SIC 6531 Real estate brokers & agents
Sr VP: Tom Rutherford
VP: Henry Baldenegro
VP: Scott Perry
VP: Loretta Pollack
Exec: Perry Schonfeld
Ex Dir: Alice Wilson
Genl Mgr: Frank Arellano
Genl Mgr: June Butler
IT Man: Tracy Harper
IT Man: Anjly Khurana
Opers Mgr: Melanie Colbert

LBC
See BINGO LANCASTER CO INC

D-U-N-S 18-854-1924
LBC MUNDIAL CORP
(*Suby of* L B C HOLDINGS U S A CORP) ★
3563 Inv Blvd Ste 3, Hayward, CA 94545
Tel (650) 873-0750 *Founded/Ownrshp* 1985
Sales 39.5MM^E *EMP* 170
SIC 4513 4215 6099 6221 Air courier services; Courier services, except by air; Foreign currency exchange; Commodity contracts brokers, dealers; Air courier services; Courier services, except by air; Foreign currency exchange; Commodity contracts brokers, dealers
Pr: Hugo Bonilla
**Ch Bd:* Carlos Araneta

*Sec: Fely Ruiz
Advt Mgr: Patricia Garcia

D-U-N-S 07-877-2179
LBDB HOLDINGS INC
6100 Tower Cir Ste 500, Franklin, TN 37067-1466
Tel (615) 778-2898 Founded/Ownrshp 2007
Sales 46.5MM^E EMP 50^E
SIC 2869 6221 5989 Fuels; Commodity traders, contracts; Wood (fuel)
CEO: Chad Martin
*COO: Gwaine Ton
*VP: Josh Bailey
*VP: Chad Conn
*VP: Mike Ocheltree

L'BEL
See VENTURA CORP LIMITED

D-U-N-S 07-655-1217
LBF ENTERPRISES
LBF POWERMATIC ASSOCIATES
1057 Serpentine Ln, Pleasanton, CA 94566-8465
Tel (925) 461-7171 Founded/Ownrshp 1980
Sales 31.0MM^E EMP 31
SIC 5063 Electrical apparatus & equipment
CEO: Mark Raymond Woltering
*Pr: Lawrence B Fitzgerald
Mktg Dir: Frank Nudo
Sales Asso: Ben Bernardo
Sales Asso: Sean Ghoddoucy
Sales Asso: Courtney Green
Sales Asso: Sandy Johnson
Sales Asso: Ryan Marks
Sales Asso: Pekka Moilanen

LBF POWERMATIC ASSOCIATES
See LBF ENTERPRISES

D-U-N-S 05-769-4430
LBF TRAVEL INC
4545 Murphy Canyon Rd # 210, San Diego, CA 92123-4363
Tel (858) 429-7599 Founded/Ownrshp 2010
Sales 53.4MM^E EMP 300
SIC 4724 Travel agencies; Travel agencies
CEO: Michael H Thomas
*CFO: Philip Ferri
*Ex VP: Steve Pello

LBFOSTER
See L B FOSTER CO

LBG-GUYTON ASSOCIATES
See LEGGETTE BRASHEARS & GRAHAM INC

D-U-N-S 79-119-8976
LBI MEDIA HOLDINGS INC
(Suby of LIBERMAN BROADCASTING INC) ★
1845 W Empire Ave, Burbank, CA 91504-3402
Tel (818) 563-5722 Founded/Ownrshp 2007
Sales 117.5MM EMP 697^E
SIC 4832 4833 Radio broadcasting stations; Television broadcasting stations; Radio broadcasting stations; Television broadcasting stations
Pr: Lenard Liberman
*COO: Winter Horton
CFO: Blima Tuller
Sr VP: Andy Weir
Sls Mgr: Ozzie Mendoza

D-U-N-S 07-935-3125
LBI MEDIA INC
(Suby of LBI MEDIA HOLDINGS INC) ★
1845 W Empire Ave, Burbank, CA 91504-3402
Tel (818) 729-5316 Founded/Ownrshp 2014
Sales 217.3M^E EMP 408^E
SIC 4832 Radio broadcasting stations
VP: Dana Sparber
Dir IT: Keith Geistweit
Sales Exec: Andy Mars
Sls&Mrk Ex: Wynette Ortiz
Mktg Dir: Carlos King
Manager: Laura McEwen
Sls Mgr: Noemi Ramirez
Pgrm Dir: Jorge Cruz
Snr Mgr: Mike Todd

LBI US
See MRY US LLC

D-U-N-S 05-406-0405 EXP
LBM ADVANTAGE INC
ENAP
555 Hudson Valley Ave # 200, New Windsor, NY 12553-4749
Tel (845) 564-4900 Founded/Ownrshp 1967
Sales 287.7MM^E EMP 80
SIC 5031 Lumber: rough, dressed & finished; Building materials, exterior; Building materials, interior; Lumber: rough, dressed & finished; Building materials, exterior; Building materials, interior
Ch: Patrick Rooney
*Pr: Steve Sallah
VP: Brad Waller
Natl Sales: David Merryman
Sls Dir: Angie Maxwell
Mktg Mgr: Donna Cramsie
Manager: Neal Bavousett
Sales Asso: Kevin Epstein

LBMC
See LATTIMORE BLACK MORGAN & CAIN PC

D-U-N-S 96-206-9832
LBMC FINANCIAL SERVICES LLC
5250 Virginia Way Ste 250, Brentwood, TN 37027-7576
Tel (615) 377-4600 Founded/Ownrshp 1998
Sales 24.8MM^E EMP 452^E
SIC 7379 7361 8742 7373 7372 Computer related consulting services; Employment agencies; Management consulting services; Computer integrated systems design; Prepackaged software; Computer related consulting services; Employment agencies; Management consulting services; Computer integrated systems design; Prepackaged software
Pr: Mike Cain

D-U-N-S 03-369-4238 IMP
LBP MANUFACTURING INC
L B P
1325 S Cicero Ave, Cicero, IL 60804-1404
Tel (708) 652-5600 Founded/Ownrshp 2001
Sales NA EMP 550
SIC 2657 Folding paperboard boxes

D-U-N-S 05-238-9863
LBS FINANCIAL CREDIT UNION
5505 Garden Grove Blvd # 500, Westminster, CA 92683-1894
Tel (714) 893-5111 Founded/Ownrshp 1935
Sales NA EMP 240
SIC 6111 6163 6061 Federal & federally sponsored credit agencies; Loan brokers; Federal credit unions; Federal & federally sponsored credit agencies; Loan brokers; Federal credit unions
Pr: Jeffrey A Napper
*Ch Bd: Gene Allen
*Treas: Dug Woog
Ofcr: Charles Thomas
VP: Melissa Martinez
VP: Colleen Savage
VP: Heather Summers
VP: Jennifer Trejo
IT Man: John Salgado
Mktg Mgr: Rosalina Vergara

D-U-N-S 11-570-9482
LBTC HOLDINGS LLC
LEX BRODIE'S TIRES CO
701 Queen St, Honolulu, HI 96813-5109
Tel (808) 536-9381 Founded/Ownrshp 2006
Sales 41.5MM^E EMP 100
SIC 5531 5541 Automotive tires; Filling stations, gasoline
Pr: Scott D Williams
Pr: David Sands
VP: John Kelly
VP: Keith Kobayashi
Genl Mgr: Scott Williams
Sales Asso: Mike Ng

D-U-N-S 03-892-9001
LBU INTERNATIONAL INC
LIGHT BULBS UNLIMITED
1287 E Newport Center Dr # 207, Deerfield Beach, FL 33442-7706
Tel (954) 354-0202 Founded/Ownrshp 2000
Sales 21.9MM EMP 93
Accts Keefe Mccullough Fort Lauderd
SIC 5719 5063 Lighting, lamps & accessories; Light bulbs & related supplies; Lighting, lamps & accessories; Light bulbs & related supplies
Pr: Stanley Civin
*CFO: Jake Gersowsky

LBUSD
See LONG BEACH UNIFIED SCHOOL DISTRICT

D-U-N-S 05-391-2700 IMP/EXP
LBX CO LLC
(Suby of SUMITOMO(S.H.I)CONSTRUCTION MACHINERY CO.,LTD.)
2004 Buck Ln, Lexington, KY 40511-1073
Tel (859) 245-3900 Founded/Ownrshp 2010
Sales 32.5MM^E EMP 62
SIC 1794 Excavation work
Pr: Eric Sauvage
*Pr: Robert Harvell
*CFO: Tom Roberts
*VP: Rod Boyer
*VP: Don Harvell
*VP: Joe Onan
Genl Mgr: Dave Baldridge
IT Man: Kevin Becknell
Tech Mgr: Scott Riemer
Sls Mgr: Steve Barber

LC
See LAUGHLIN/CONSTABLE INC

LC ENTERPRISES
See L C ENTERPRISES

D-U-N-S 09-295-0518
LC MANUFACTURING LLC
LAKE CITY FORGE
(Suby of MW UNIVERSAL INC) ★
4150 N Wolcott Rd, Lake City, MI 49651-9126
Tel (231) 839-7102 Founded/Ownrshp 2004, 2015
Sales 41.6MM^E EMP 192
SIC 3462 3544 Automotive forgings, ferrous: crankshaft, engine, axle, etc.; Special dies & tools; Automotive forgings, ferrous: crankshaft, engine, axle, etc.; Special dies & tools
CEO: Peter Baenen
VP: Sue Novakovich

D-U-N-S 06-445-6221
LCTRS INC
LA COSTA RESORT & SPA
2100 Costa Del Mar Rd, Carlsbad, CA 92009-6823
Tel (760) 438-9111 Founded/Ownrshp 2010
Sales 63.6MM^E EMP 872
SIC 7011 5812 Resort hotel; Eating places; Resort hotel; Eating places
Pr: Mike Shannon
VP: Scott Dalecio
VP: Chevis Hosea
Exec: Hans Wiegand
Genl Mgr: Dave Nelson
Telecom Ex: Eddie Schwartz
Opers Mgr: Jeremy McCarthy
Sales Exec: Ned Nawsome
Natl Sales: Lori Ball
Natl Sales: Kathy Espinola
Sls Dir: George Allen

LC&CO
See LAUD COLLIER & CO LLC

D-U-N-S 16-107-7169
LCA-VISION INC
(Suby of VISION ACQUISITION LLC) ★
7840 Montgomery Rd, Cincinnati, OH 45236-4348
Tel (513) 792-9292 Founded/Ownrshp 2015
Sales 34.3MM^E EMP 138^E
SIC 8011 Eyes, ears, nose & throat specialist: physician/surgeon
CEO: Craig Joffe
Sr VP: Marcello J Celentano
Exec: Carmen Lorenzo
Adm Dir: Barb Kise
CTO: Joe Hauck
Software D: Charlene Cavanaugh
Doctor: Ronald Allen MD
Doctor: Sally Thompson MD

LCAS
See LORAIN COUNTY AUTOMOTIVE SYSTEMS INC

LCC
See COLUMBIA LOWER COLLEGE

D-U-N-S 80-779-8231
LCC DEPLOYMENT SERVICES INC
WFI DEPLOYMENTS SERVICES
(Suby of LIGHTBRIDGE COMMUNICATIONS CORP) ★
7900 Westpark Dr Ste T700, Mc Lean, VA 22102-4276
Tel (703) 873-2700 Founded/Ownrshp 2008
Sales 41.9MM^E EMP 150
SIC 8748 Telecommunications consultant; Telecommunications consultant
CEO: Kenny Young
CFO: Robert J Joubran
Sr VP: Randy Gayer
VP: Nancy Feeney
VP: John Logan
Brnch Mgr: David Knutson

D-U-N-S 96-612-8212
LCC DESIGN SERVICES INC
(Suby of LCC INTERNATIONAL INC) ★
7900 Westpark Dr Ste T700, Mc Lean, VA 22102-4276
Tel (703) 873-2352 Founded/Ownrshp 1994
Sales 30.7MM^E EMP 400
SIC 8748 Communications consulting; Communications consulting
CEO: Kenneth Young
*Pr: Ananthan Veluppillai
*CFO: Rebecca Stahl
*VP: Nancy Feeney
*Genl Couns: Brian Dunn

D-U-N-S 15-324-8695
LCC INTERNATIONAL INC
(Suby of TECH MAHINDRA LIMITED)
7900 Westpark Dr Ste T700, Mc Lean, VA 22102-4276
Tel (703) 873-2065 Founded/Ownrshp 1996
Sales 153.7MM^E EMP 5,500^E
SIC 4813 4812 Telephone communication, except radio; Data telephone communications; Radio telephone communication; Telephone communication, except radio; Data telephone communications; Radio telephone communication
Pr: Kenneth Young
*Sr Pt: Keith Paglusch
CFO: Simone D Carri
*CFO: Rebecca Stahl
Treas: Louis Salamone Jr
*Sr VP: Brian J Dunn
Sr VP: Doreen Trant
*VP: Nancy O Feeney
VP: Daniel Mieszala
VP: Brian Thompson
Mng Dir: Raffaele Annunziata

LCDHD
See LAKE CUMBERLAND DISTRICT HEALTH DEPARTMENT

LCEC
See LEE COUNTY ELECTRIC COOPERATIVE INC

LCFMGF
See LAKE COUNTRY FOODS INC

LCFS
See LUTHERAN CHILD AND FAMILY SERVICES OF ILLINOIS

LCG FACADES
See LINFORD CONTRACT GLAZING LLC

D-U-N-S 13-430-1238
LCG PENCE CONSTRUCTION LLC
2720 Sw Corbett Ave, Portland, OR 97201-4804
Tel (503) 252-3802 Founded/Ownrshp 2002
Sales 67.8MM^E EMP 120
SIC 1542 Nonresidential construction; Nonresidential construction
Mktg Dir: Leed Olson
Snr PM: Jeffrey Perrin
Snr PM: Eric Ross

LCHC
See CHRISTIAN LAWNDALE HEALTH CENTER

LCI
See C & L INDUSTRIES INC

D-U-N-S 05-492-7000
LCI HOLDCO LLC
(Suby of LCI INTERMEDIATE HOLDCO INC) ★
5340 Legacy Dr Bldg 4150, Plano, TX 75024-3178
Tel (469) 241-2100 Founded/Ownrshp 2005
Sales 448.8MM^E EMP 7,800^E
SIC 8069 8051 Specialty hospitals, except psychiatric; Skilled nursing care facilities; Specialty hospitals, except psychiatric; Skilled nursing care facilities
CEO: Phillip B Douglas
*COO: Stuart Archer
*Ex VP: Grant B Asay
*Sr VP: Greg Floyd

D-U-N-S 07-835-7916 IMP
LCI HOLDING CO INC
(Suby of CARLYLE PARTNERS IV LP) ★
5340 Legacy Dr Bldg 4150, Plano, TX 75024-3178
Tel (469) 241-2100 Founded/Ownrshp 2005
Sales 448.8MM^E EMP 14,400^E
SIC 8069 8051 Specialty hospitals, except psychiatric; Skilled nursing care facilities; Specialty hospitals, except psychiatric; Skilled nursing care facilities
CEO: Neil Douglas

D-U-N-S 60-656-0233 IMP/EXP
■ LCI HOLDINGS INC
(Suby of KATE SPADE & CO) ★
5901 W Side Ave, North Bergen, NJ 07047-6451
Tel (201) 295-6300 Founded/Ownrshp 1988
Sales 498.3MM^E EMP 6,800
SIC 5651 5136 5137 5094 5122 5944 Family clothing stores; Men's & boys' clothing; Women's & children's clothing; Jewelry; Perfumes; Jewelry stores; Family clothing stores; Men's & boys' clothing; Women's & children's clothing; Jewelry; Perfumes; Jewelry stores
CEO: Paul R Charron
*CFO: Mike Scarpa
*Treas: Robert Vill
VP: Steven Duva
VP: Kerry Fogarty
*VP: Elaine H Goodell
VP: Geri Lynn
VP: Priya Trivedi
Exec: Patty Polise
*CIO: John Sullivan
MIS Dir: John Ference

D-U-N-S 07-835-8372
LCI INTERMEDIATE HOLDCO INC
(Suby of LCI HOLDING CO INC) ★
5340 Legacy Dr Bldg 4150, Plano, TX 75024-3178
Tel (469) 241-2100 Founded/Ownrshp 2005
Sales 448.8MM^E EMP 11,100^E
SIC 8069 8051 Specialty hospitals, except psychiatric; Skilled nursing care facilities
CEO: Phillip B Douglas

D-U-N-S 06-467-1373
■ LCI SHIPHOLDINGS INC
(Suby of INTERNATIONAL SHIPHOLDING CORP) ★
11 N Water St Ste 18290, Mobile, AL 36602-5018
Tel (251) 243-9100 Founded/Ownrshp 1968
Sales 23.7MM^E EMP 600
SIC 4412 Deep sea foreign transportation of freight; Deep sea foreign transportation of freight
Pr: Niels M Johnsen
CFO: Manuel G Estrada
Treas: David Drake
Ex VP: Peter M Johnston
Dir Risk M: Ken Strong
Board of Directors: Erik F Johnsen, Niels W Johnsen

D-U-N-S 16-805-2913
▲ LCNB CORP
2 N Broadway St Lowr, Lebanon, OH 45036-1795
Tel (513) 932-1414 Founded/Ownrshp 1998
Sales NA EMP 248^E
Tkr Sym LCNB Exch NAS
SIC 6021 National commercial banks; National commercial banks
Ch Bd: Stephen P Wilson
Pr: Tom Beard
*Pr: Steve P Foster
CFO: Robert C Haines II
Ex VP: Christina Harris
Ex VP: Matthew P Layer
VP: Chip Bonny
VP: Amy Butler
VP: John Calhoun
VP: Harry E Campbell
VP: Kelly Haworth
VP: Dan Nielsen
VP: Scott Roman
VP: Lonnie D Schear
VP: Beverly Taylor
VP: Dave Theiss
VP: Bernard H Wright
Board of Directors: Rick L Blossom, Spencer S Cropper, William H Kaufman, John H Kochensparger III

D-U-N-S 00-790-3255
■ LCNB NATIONAL BANK
(Suby of LCNB CORP) ★
2 N Broadway St Lowr, Lebanon, OH 45036-1795
Tel (513) 932-1414 Founded/Ownrshp 1998
Sales NA EMP 230
SIC 6021 National commercial banks; National commercial banks
Ch Bd: Stephen P Wilson
Pr: Steve Foster
CFO: Bernard Wright Jr
Chf Cred: Timothy J Sheridan
Ofcr: Matthew P Layer
Ex VP: Rob Haines
Ex VP: Ben Jackson
Ex VP: Leroy F McKay
Ex VP: Roy McKay
Ex VP: Eric J Meilstrup
Sr VP: Kenneth R Layer
Sr VP: Ann M Smith
VP: Stephen P Anglin
VP: Brian N Bausmith
VP: David Bock
VP: Harry E Campbell
VP: Bill Childers
VP: Bud Mattingly
VP: Pat Mitchell
VP: Lonnie D Schear
VP: Connie Sears
Board of Directors: Marvin E Young, M Russell Horn, Sam Kaufman, William M Kaufman, George L Leasure, James B Miller, Corwin M Nixon, Kathleen Porter Stolle, Howard E Wilson, Stephen P Wilson

LCNW
See LIFECENTER NORTHWEST

D-U-N-S 12-579-8392 IMP
LCO DESTINY LLC
TIMELESS FRAMES
22476 Fisher Rd, Watertown, NY 13601-1090
Tel (315) 782-3302 Founded/Ownrshp 1999
Sales 45.9MM^E EMP 300
SIC 2499 Picture & mirror frames, wood; Picture & mirror frames, wood
*CFO: Greg Gaston
Dir IT: Jordan Aanei
Dir IT: Tom Young
Web Dev: Allison Christiansen
Natl Sales: Kay Kwenski

D-U-N-S 07-994-5880
■ **LCO HOTEL LLC**
(*Suby of* LOEWS CORP) ★
5300 N River Rd, Rosemont, IL 60018-5400
Tel (847) 447-4101 *Founded/Ownrshp* 2014
Sales 40.0MM *EMP* 400
SIC 4212 4789 Local trucking, without storage; Pipeline terminal facilities, independently operated
Genl Mgr: Paul OHM

LCPS
See LOUDOUN COUNTY PUBLIC SCHOOL DISTRICT

D-U-N-S 00-810-6866 IMP/EXP
LCR-M LIMITED PARTNERSHIP
PLUMBING WAREHOUSE, THE
(*Suby of* HAJOCA CORP) ★
6232 Siegen Ln, Baton Rouge, LA 70809-4157
Tel (225) 292-9910 *Founded/Ownrshp* 1995
Sales 225.7MM^E *EMP* 650
SIC 5074 Pipes & fittings, plastic; Plumbing & heating valves; Plumbers' brass goods & fittings; Pipes & fittings, plastic; Plumbing & heating valves; Plumbers' brass goods & fittings
Genl Pt: Richard Klau
**Pt:* C Tom Bromley
**Pt:* Mark D Hanley
**Pt:* Karen V Landry
**Pt:* John D Lyle
**Pt:* A Lavoy Moore
**Pt:* Karl W Triche
Treas: C Pappo
Exec: Cherie Bourgeois
Genl Mgr: Roderick Johnson

LCRA
See LOWER COLORADO RIVER AUTHORITY

LCS
See LIFE CARE SERVICES CORP

LCS
See LAKESHORE CUTTING SOLUTIONS INC

D-U-N-S 79-007-1278 IMP
LCS CONSTRUCTORS INC
L C S
15205 Alton Pkwy, Irvine, CA 92618-2360
Tel (949) 425-5440 *Founded/Ownrshp* 1980
Sales 45.0MM^E *EMP* 90
SIC 1542 Specialized public building contractors; Specialized public building contractors
CEO: Dominick Ranalli
**CFO:* David Skinner
**VP:* Dennis Brewer
**VP:* Stephen A Metzger
**VP:* Marc Scott
Brnch Mgr: Randy Bradford
Div Mgr: Godkin David
IT Man: Melanie Tunget
Sls Mgr: Jody Christman
Sls Mgr: Vern Doering
Sls Mgr: Tom Krause

D-U-N-S 83-223-6678
LCS CORRECTIONS SERVICES INC
2475 Entp Rd Ste 300, Clearwater, FL 33763
Tel (337) 234-1533 *Founded/Ownrshp* 1990
Sales NA *EMP* 650
SIC 9223 Prison, government; Prison, government
CEO: Michael Leblanc
**Ch Bd:* Jerry Gottlieb
**Pr:* David Myers
**Treas:* Albert H Rohrbaugh
**Ex VP:* Richard Harbison
**Ex VP:* Michael Striedel
**Prin:* Michael Magee
Off Mgr: Dianne Roger

D-U-N-S 10-733-5184
LCS HOLDINGS INC
400 Locust St Ste 820, Des Moines, IA 50309-2334
Tel (515) 875-4500 *Founded/Ownrshp* 1983
Sales 50.6MM^E *EMP* 400^E
SIC 8399 Community development groups; Community development groups
Pr: Edward R Kenny
**Pr:* Joel Nelson
**Treas:* Diane Bridgewater
Ex VP: Joel Nelson
VP: Mary Harrison
**VP:* Kent Larson
**Ex Dir:* Rick Exline

LCSC
See LEWIS-CLARK STATE COLLEGE FOUNDATION INC

LCTCS
See LOUISIANA COMMUNITY & TECHNICAL COLLEGE SYSTEM

LCUB
See LENOIR CITY UTILITIES BOARD

LCW WIRELESS
See LEAP WIRELESS INTERNATIONAL INC

D-U-N-S 00-674-7827
LCWW PARTNERS
WESTIN LA CANTERA RESORT, THE
16641 La Cantera Pkwy, San Antonio, TX 78256-2401
Tel (210) 558-6500 *Founded/Ownrshp* 1999
Sales 35.0MM^E *EMP* 500
SIC 7011 8699 Hotels & motels; Professional golf association; Hotels & motels; Professional golf association
Genl Pt: Tony Cherone
Pr: Stephen Treibs
Ex Dir: Michael Vardeman
IT Man: Michael Guin
Sls Mgr: Melissa Demasters

D-U-N-S 14-235-5051 IMP/EXP
LCY ELASTOMERS LP
(*Suby of* LCY CHEMICAL CORP.)
4803 Decker Dr, Baytown, TX 77520-1447
Tel (281) 424-6100 *Founded/Ownrshp* 2003
Sales 72.6MM^E *EMP* 84
Accts Hrss Llp Houston Texas
SIC 2822 Styrene-butadiene rubbers, (over 50% butadiene), SBR, GRS; Styrene-butadiene rubbers, (over 50% butadiene), SBR, GRS
Genl Pt: Bowei Lee
Genl Mgr: Cliferd Menezes
Genl Mgr: Nolan Smith
IT Man: Edward Nolan
Plnt Mgr: Garry Osan
Sls Mgr: Gaylord Garner
Sls Mgr: Mike Nuzzolo

D-U-N-S 00-314-0647
LD AMORY & CO INC (VA)
AMORY'S SEAFOOD
101 S King St, Hampton, VA 23669-4025
Tel (757) 722-1915 *Founded/Ownrshp* 1917
Sales 31.8MM^E *EMP* 100
SIC 5146 4213 2097 2092 Seafoods; Refrigerated products transport; Manufactured ice; Fresh or frozen packaged fish; Seafoods; Refrigerated products transport; Manufactured ice; Fresh or frozen packaged fish
CEO: Charles Amory Jr
**VP:* Meade Amory
Genl Mgr: Richard Coughenour

D-U-N-S 96-545-6275
LD COMMODITIES CITRUS HOLDINGS LLC
(*Suby of* LOUIS DREYFUS COMMODITIES LLC) ★
40 Danbury Rd, Wilton, CT 06897-4441
Tel (203) 761-2000 *Founded/Ownrshp* 2010
Sales 85.2MM^E *EMP* 134^E
SIC 6221 Commodity contracts brokers, dealers
Pr: Peter Hahn
Pr: Robert Eckert
COO: H Thomas Hayden
Treas: Serge Stepanov
Sec: Elizabeth Listner
VP: Erik Anderson
VP: Mark Gerardi
VP: Jeffery Zanchelli

D-U-N-S 80-040-0983 EXP
LD COMMODITIES COTTON LLC
ALLENBERG COTTON CO.
(*Suby of* LOUIS DREYFUS COMMODITIES LLC) ★
7255 Goodlett Farms Pkwy, Cordova, TN 38016-4909
Tel (901) 383-5000 *Founded/Ownrshp* 2010
Sales 86.3MM^E *EMP* 85^E
SIC 5159 5131 Cotton merchants & products; Textiles, woven
CEO: Tommy Hayden
**Pr:* Anthony Tancredi
**CEO:* Joe Nicosia
**COO:* Thomas F Malone Jr
**Ch:* Jerry D Harris
Ofcr: Luciano Cocito
**Ex VP:* Frank M Weathersby

D-U-N-S 96-545-5525
LD COMMODITIES GRAINS AND OILSEEDS HOLDINGS LLC
(*Suby of* LOUIS DREYFUS COMMODITIES LLC) ★
40 Danbury Rd, Wilton, CT 06897-4441
Tel (203) 761-2000 *Founded/Ownrshp* 2010
Sales 58.1MM^E *EMP* 237^E
SIC 6221 Commodity contracts brokers, dealers
Pr: Erik Anderson
COO: H Thomas Hayden
CFO: Robert Eckert
Treas: Serge Stepanov
Sec: Elizabeth Listner
VP: Steven Campbell
VP: Bruce Chapin
VP: Sean Doyle
VP: Mark Gerardi
VP: Sean Martin
VP: Harvey Yaguchi
VP: Jeffery Zanchelli

D-U-N-S 00-906-2597 EXP
LD MCFARLAND CO LIMITED
MCFARLAND CASCADE
1640 E Marc St, Tacoma, WA 98421
Tel (253) 572-5670 *Founded/Ownrshp* 1916
Sales 116.8MM^E *EMP* 500
SIC 2499 2491 2411 Poles, wood; Poles & pole crossarms, treated wood; Logging; Poles, wood; Poles & pole crossarms, treated wood; Logging
CEO: B Corry Mc Farland
Pr: Wayne Wilkinson
VP: L W Docter
VP: Bob Hammond
VP: Greg D Mc Farland
VP: Gregory McFarland
Manager: Mark Fleagle
Sls Mgr: John Small

D-U-N-S 03-284-1298 EXP
LD MULLINS LUMBER CO (FL)
1191 W 15th St, Riviera Beach, FL 33404-5422
Tel (561) 844-4321 *Founded/Ownrshp* 1946
Sales 26.6MM *EMP* 18
SIC 5211

D-U-N-S 18-850-5213 IMP
LD PRODUCTS INC
4INKJETS.COM
3700 Cover St, Long Beach, CA 90808-1782
Tel (562) 986-6940 *Founded/Ownrshp* 2005
Sales 151.3MM^E *EMP* 150
Accts Woo San Ramon Ca
SIC 5045 Printers, computer; Printers, computer
CEO: Aaron D Leon
**Sr VP:* Patrick Devane
QA Dir: Eric Chun
IT Man: Michael Fernandez
Web Dev: Michael Dailey
Software D: Lewis Lee
Software D: Huy Nguyen
Netwrk Eng: James Easter
Mktg Dir: Daniel Alfi
Snr Mgr: Chad Abercrombie
Snr Mgr: Brenna Welch

LD SYSTEMS
See L-D SYSTEMS LP

LDAF
See LOUISIANA DEPARTMENT OF AGRICULTURE AND FORESTRY

D-U-N-S 00-414-6700
LDB CORP
444 Sidney Baker St S, Kerrville, TX 78028-5919
Tel (830) 257-2000 *Founded/Ownrshp* 1960
Sales 7.4MM^E *EMP* 298
SIC 5812 Pizzeria, chain; Pizzeria, chain
Ch Bd: Lloyd D Brinkman
Ex VP: Bryon Smith

D-U-N-S 80-009-2590
LDC HOLDING INC
(*Suby of* LOUIS DREYFUS COMMODITIES B.V.)
40 Danbury Rd, Wilton, CT 06897-4441
Tel (203) 761-2000 *Founded/Ownrshp* 2006
Sales 13.8MM^E *EMP* 2,000
SIC 6221 Commodity contracts brokers, dealers; Commodity contracts brokers, dealers
Pr: Erik Anderson
**COO:* H Thomas Hayden
**CFO:* Robert Eckert
**Treas:* Serge A Stepanov
**Ex VP:* Ciro Echestortu
**Ex VP:* Claude Ehlinger
**VP:* Mark Gerardi
**VP:* Kevin Grimes
**VP:* Joseph Nicosia
**VP:* Jeff Zanchelli

LDF FOOD GROUP
See LDF SALES & DISTRIBUTING INC

D-U-N-S 09-144-3333
LDF FOOD GROUP INC
WENDY'S
10610 E 26th Cir N, Wichita, KS 67226-4536
Tel (316) 630-0677 *Founded/Ownrshp* 1977
Sales 5.0MM *EMP* 1,400
SIC 5812 Fast-food restaurant, chain; Fast-food restaurant, chain
Ch Bd: Larry D Fleming
**Pr:* Don Haynes
**Treas:* Dennis Kirkhart
Sr VP: Jim Cook
**VP:* Rick Albrecht
VP: Gary Fleming

D-U-N-S 10-407-5874
LDF SALES & DISTRIBUTING INC
LDF FOOD GROUP
10610 E 26th Cir N, Wichita, KS 67226-4536
Tel (316) 636-5575 *Founded/Ownrshp* 1950
Sales 381.3MM^E *EMP* 1,500^E
SIC 5181 Beer & other fermented malt liquors; Beer & other fermented malt liquors
Ch Bd: Larry D Fleming
**Sr VP:* Dennis Kirkhart
**VP:* Rick Albreck
**VP:* David Alferd
Area Mgr: Roger Kelough
IT Man: Chris Herman
VP Opers: Brad Knott

LDH U S ASSET HOLDINGS LLC
See CCI US ASSET HOLDINGS LLC

LDI
See LESLIE DIGITAL IMAGING LLC

LDI
See STEINER EOPTICS INC

D-U-N-S 00-642-5367 IMP
LDI INDUSTRIES INC (WI)
FLODAR FLUID PWR FITTINGS DIV
1864 Nagle Ave, Manitowoc, WI 54220-1702
Tel (920) 682-6877 *Founded/Ownrshp* 1962
Sales 30.4MM^E *EMP* 150
SIC 3569 3494 3823 3643 3594 3545 Lubrication equipment, industrial; Pipe fittings; Industrial instrmnts msrmnt display/control process variable; Current-carrying wiring devices; Fluid power pumps & motors; Machine tool accessories; Lubrication equipment, industrial; Pipe fittings; Industrial instrmnts msrmnt display/control process variable; Current-carrying wiring devices; Fluid power pumps & motors; Machine tool accessories
Pr: Rick Breden
**CFO:* Tom Lukas
**VP:* John Lukas
IT Man: Jen Taylor
Mfg Mgr: Erwin Haban

D-U-N-S 05-116-6782
LDI LTD LLC
(*Suby of* LACY DISTRIBUTION INC) ★
54 Monument Cir, Indianapolis, IN 46204-2942
Tel (317) 237-5400 *Founded/Ownrshp* 2010
Sales 386.8MM^E *EMP* 1,000
SIC 4731 Agents, shipping; Brokers, shipping; Agents, shipping; Brokers, shipping
CEO: Ja Lacy
**Treas:* Jon Black
**VP:* Bill Himebrook
**VP:* Ryan Polk

D-U-N-S 05-876-3913
LDI MECHANICAL INC
1587 E Bentley Dr, Corona, CA 92879-1738
Tel (951) 340-9685 *Founded/Ownrshp* 1985
Sales 94.3MM^E *EMP* 400^E
SIC 1711 Heating & air conditioning contractors; Heating & air conditioning contractors
Pr: Lloyd Smith
CFO: Robert Sylvester
Treas: Sandy Smith
Chf Mktg O: Bridgett Robinson
**Sr VP:* Mike Smith
**VP:* Steve Buren
**VP:* Jeff Minarik
Exec: Jennifer Minarik
IT Man: Luis Garcia

D-U-N-S 80-867-8317 IMP/EXP
LDISCOVERY LLC
8201 Greensboro Dr # 717, Mc Lean, VA 22102-3818
Tel (703) 288-3380 *Founded/Ownrshp* 2005
Sales 78.0MM^E *EMP* 299^E
SIC 7374 Data processing & preparation; Data processing & preparation
CFO: Douglas S Strahan
VP: Andrew Jewel
VP: Taffi Schurz
Software D: Shane Levengood
VP Sls: Bob Adamson
Snr PM: Karisa Davison

D-U-N-S 83-317-4837
LDLA CLOTHING LLC
LIVING DOLL
5741 Rickenbacker Rd # 5745, Commerce, CA 90040-3052
Tel (323) 312-2805 *Founded/Ownrshp* 2009
Sales 50.0MM *EMP* 60
SIC 5137 Women's & children's clothing; Women's & children's clothing
Owner: Amy Powers
**CFO:* Richard Swartz

D-U-N-S 78-581-5312
LDR HOLDING CORP
13785 Res Blvd Ste 200, Austin, TX 78750
Tel (512) 344-3333 *Founded/Ownrshp* 2006
Sales 141.2MM *EMP* 290^E
Accts Kpmg Llp Austin Texas
Tkr Sym LDRH *Exch* NGS
SIC 3841 Surgical & medical instruments; Surgical & medical instruments
Ch Bd: Christophe Lavigne
COO: James Burrows
CFO: Robert McNamara
CFO: Robert E McNamara
Ex VP: Herv Dinville
Ex VP: Andr Potgieter
Ex VP: Patrick Richard
Ex VP: Scott Way
Prin: Joseph Aragona
Prin: William W Burke
Prin: Matthew Crawford
Board of Directors: Joseph Aragona, William W Burke, Matthew Crawford, Kevin M Lalande, Alan Milinazzo, Thomas A Raffin, Pierre Remy, Stefan Widensohler

D-U-N-S 08-136-7104
LDRV HOLDINGS CORP
LAZYDAYS RV CAMPGROUND
6130 Lazy Days Blvd, Seffner, FL 33584-2968
Tel (813) 246-4333 *Founded/Ownrshp* 2004
Sales 293.8MM^E *EMP* 500^E
SIC 5561 Travel trailers: automobile, new & used; Motor homes; Recreational vehicle parts & accessories; Travel trailers: automobile, new & used; Motor homes; Recreational vehicle parts & accessories
Pr: John Horton
CFO: Randall Lay
Sls Mgr: James Paredes
Sales Asso: Todd Earwood
Sales Asso: Todd Wallace

D-U-N-S 10-383-6698
LDS FAMILY SERVICES
(*Suby of* CHURCH OF JSUS CHRST OF LD STS) ★
50 E North Temple Fl 8, Salt Lake City, UT 84150-0008
Tel (801) 240-3339 *Founded/Ownrshp* 1970
Sales 16.7MM^E *EMP* 375
SIC 8322 Social service center; Social service center

D-U-N-S 80-041-5940
LDS HOSPITAL
8th Ave C St, Salt Lake City, UT 84143-0001
Tel (801) 408-1100 *Founded/Ownrshp* 1983
Sales 256.4MM *EMP* 70^E
SIC 6211 Security brokers & dealers
Pr: Bill Nelson
COO: Becky Kapp
CFO: David Larsen
VP: Sandra Smith
Exec: Heather Ashby
Exec: Mary Virden
Dir Rad: Edgar J Booth
Dir Rad: Margaret F Ensign
Dir Rad: Frank V Gabor
Dir Rad: Colleen P Harker
Dir Rad: John M Jacobs
Dir Rad: Denise Rodgers

D-U-N-S 08-984-5598 EXP
LDV INC
180 Industrial Dr, Burlington, WI 53105-2307
Tel (262) 763-0147 *Founded/Ownrshp* 1977
Sales 44.0MM^E *EMP* 243
SIC 7532 5013 Van conversion; Customizing services, non-factory basis; Truck parts & accessories; Van conversion; Customizing services, non-factory basis; Truck parts & accessories
Pr: David Lynch
**Pr:* Kurt Petrie
COO: Jason Gaulke
VP: Nancy E Strelow
Sales Exec: Jerry Phillips

LE & CMPA
See LOCOMOTIVE ENGINEERS AND CONDUCTORS MUTUAL PROTECTIVE ASSOCIATION

D-U-N-S 00-288-2744
LE BEL INC
WALSH MECHANICAL CONRACTORS
380 North Ave, Abington, MA 02351-1817
Tel (781) 878-7279 *Founded/Ownrshp* 1988
Sales 30.2MM^E *EMP* 97
SIC 1711 3444 Warm air heating & air conditioning contractor; Ventilation & duct work contractor; Mechanical contractor; Sheet metalwork
Pr: Paul M Lebel
Exec: Richard Lebel

D-U-N-S 78-041-3167 IMP/EXP
LE BLEU CORP
3134 Cornatzer Rd, Advance, NC 27006-7212
Tel (336) 998-1199 *Founded/Ownrshp* 1990
Sales 21.9MM^E *EMP* 115^E

SIC 2086 Water, pasteurized: packaged in cans, bottles, etc.; Water, pasteurized: packaged in cans, bottles, etc.
Pr: Jerry W Smith
CFO: George Andrews
VP: Brock Agee
VP: Achan Smith
Rgnl Mgr: Jack Tally
Genl Mgr: Ed Coney
Genl Mgr: Alex Doyle
Off Mgr: Sandra Riley
Off Mgr: Tracy Shaver
Off Admin: Tanya Hill
QC Dir: Edward Hauser

D-U-N-S 02-404-7953
LE BOULANGER INC (CA)
305 N Mathilda Ave, Sunnyvale, CA 94085-4207
Tel (408) 774-9000 *Founded/Ownrshp* 1981
Sales 17.5MM^E *EMP* 325
SIC 5812 5149 5461

D-U-N-S 86-750-8595
LE BUS BAKERY INC
480 Shoemaker Rd, King of Prussia, PA 19406-4237
Tel (215) 692-0298 *Founded/Ownrshp* 1993
Sales 64.5MM^E *EMP* 100^E
SIC 5149 5461 2051 Bakery products; Bakeries; Bread, cake & related products
CEO: David Braverman
**Treas:* Ruth Drye
**Ex Dir:* Winnie Clowry

LE CHEF BAKERY
See LE PAFE INC

D-U-N-S 13-036-0985
LE CLAIR INDUSTRIES INC
2604 Sunset Dr, Grenada, MS 38901-2845
Tel (662) 226-8075 *Founded/Ownrshp* 1979
Sales 24.1MM^E *EMP* 145
SIC 3086 Insulation or cushioning material, foamed plastic; Insulation or cushioning material, foamed plastic
Pr: Tim Le Clair

D-U-N-S 00-596-8425
LE CLAIRE MFG CO (IA)
3225 Zimmerman Dr, Bettendorf, IA 52722-5582
Tel (563) 332-6550 *Founded/Ownrshp* 1966
Sales 34.0MM^E *EMP* 130
SIC 3365 Machinery castings, aluminum; Machinery castings, aluminum
Pr: Robert Zimmerman
**Co-Pr:* Ralph Zimmerman
**VP:* Jim Mappin
**Prin:* Robert L Zimmerman Jr
Sfty Dirs: Steve Kane
QC Dir: Robert Moore
VP Sls: Tom Mappin

LE CREUSET
See SCHILLER STORES INC

D-U-N-S 08-470-7694 IMP/EXP
LE CREUSET OF AMERICA INC
(*Suby of* LE CREUSET)
114 Bob Gifford Blvd, Early Branch, SC 29916-4138
Tel (803) 943-4308 *Founded/Ownrshp* 1977
Sales 104.8MM^E *EMP* 400
SIC 5023 Kitchen tools & utensils; Kitchen tools & utensils
CEO: Faye Gooding
**Sec:* Andrew J Belger Jr
VP: Donald Hilberand
VP: Stephen Jones
Mng Dir: Monica Pinto
Mktg Dir: Judy Baker
Sls Mgr: Deb Apuli

D-U-N-S 80-101-5306
LE DIPLOMATE INC
14299 Firestone Blvd, La Mirada, CA 90638-5523
Tel (714) 739-8500 *Founded/Ownrshp* 1987
Sales 5.7MM^E *EMP* 300
SIC 5812 Cafe; Cafe
Pr: Antonie C Daoud
**VP:* Walid Daoud

D-U-N-S 07-879-2909
LE DUFF AMERICA INC
(*Suby of* HOLDING LE DUFF "HLD")
12201 Merit Dr Ste 900, Dallas, TX 75251-3139
Tel (214) 540-1867 *Founded/Ownrshp* 2011
Sales 231.7MM^E *EMP* 7,690^E
SIC 5812 American restaurant
CEO: Claude Bergeron
**COO:* Miguel Fernandez
**CFO:* Mike Clock

D-U-N-S 19-757-8073 IMP/EXP
LE ELEGANT BATH INC
AMERICAN BATH FACTORY
13405 Estelle St, Corona, CA 92879-1877
Tel (951) 734-0238 *Founded/Ownrshp* 1984
Sales 23.1MM^E *EMP* 120
SIC 3088 Tubs (bath, shower & laundry), plastic; Tubs (bath, shower & laundry), plastic
Pr: Richard Wheeler

LE GOURMET CHEF
See KITCHEN COLLECTION LLC

D-U-N-S 05-503-8962
LE GRAND JOHNSON CONSTRUCTION CO
1000 S Main St, Logan, UT 84321-6877
Tel (435) 752-2000 *Founded/Ownrshp* 1935
Sales 40.7MM^E *EMP* 110
SIC 1611 3273 General contractor, highway & street construction; Ready-mixed concrete

D-U-N-S 60-339-8488
LE JEUNE STEEL CO
(*Suby of* API GROUP INC) ★
118 W 60th St, Minneapolis, MN 55419-2319
Tel (612) 861-3321 *Founded/Ownrshp* 1989
Sales 180.3MM *EMP* 105
Accts Kpmg Llp Minneapolis Mn
SIC 3441 Fabricated structural metal; Building components, structural steel; Fabricated structural metal for bridges; Fabricated structural metal; Building components, structural steel; Fabricated structural metal for bridges
Pr: Jim Torborg
CFO: Bryan L Kuha
**Treas:* Gregory Keup
**Sr VP:* Mike Histon
VP: Brian Blair
MIS Dir: Clay Kimber
Dir IT: Chris Sharp
Plnt Mgr: Tim Crews
Snr Mgr: Matt Vanderpol

D-U-N-S 07-883-3274
LE LYCEE FRANCAIS DE LOS ANGELES
LE LYCEE FRANCAIS SCHOOL
3261 Overland Ave, Los Angeles, CA 90034-3589
Tel (310) 836-3464 *Founded/Ownrshp* 1964
Sales 20.1MM *EMP* 145^E
Accts Eric Alden Accountancy Corpora
SIC 8211 Public elementary & secondary schools; Public elementary & secondary schools
Pr: Claralisa Kabbaz

LE LYCEE FRANCAIS SCHOOL
See LE LYCEE FRANCAIS DE LOS ANGELES

D-U-N-S 04-091-9144
■ **LE MARS INSURANCE CO**
LE MARS MUTUAL INSURANCE
(*Suby of* DONEGAL GROUP INC) ★
1 Park Ln, Le Mars, IA 51031-3338
Tel (712) 546-7847 *Founded/Ownrshp* 1901
Sales NA *EMP* 40^E
SIC 6411 Insurance agents, brokers & service
Ch Bd: Dennis Bixeman
**Pr:* Donald Nikolaus
Pr: Renae Strand
Sr VP: Arlene Sitzman
VP: Randall Farless
VP: Cyril Greenya
VP: Robert Shenk
Manager: Rob Faber
Manager: Kelly Sunde
Sales Asso: Eileen Dreckman

LE MARS MUTUAL INSURANCE
See LE MARS INSURANCE CO

D-U-N-S 00-613-6162
LE MASTER GROUP LLC
WISCONSIN BOX
929 Townline Rd, Wausau, WI 54403-6681
Tel (715) 842-2248 *Founded/Ownrshp* 1900
Sales 33.4MM^E *EMP* 165
SIC 2449 Rectangular boxes & crates, wood; Boxes, wood: wirebound; Rectangular boxes & crates, wood; Boxes, wood: wirebound
Pr: W Jeff Davis
Plnt Mgr: Bob Schultz

LE MERDIEN DLFINA SANTA MONICA
See BLUE DEVILS LESSEE LLC

D-U-N-S 02-324-9113
LE MIEUX & SON INC
LE MIEUX TOYOTA
2550 S Oneida St, Green Bay, WI 54304-5245
Tel (920) 496-2200 *Founded/Ownrshp* 1956
Sales 21.4MM^E *EMP* 53
SIC 5511 Automobiles, new & used
Pr: Robert R Le Mieux Sr
**Sec:* DEA Le Mieux
Sls Mgr: Josh Couzzo

LE MIEUX TOYOTA
See LE MIEUX & SON INC

D-U-N-S 05-372-3094
LE MOYNE COLLEGE
1419 Salt Springs Rd, Syracuse, NY 13214-1301
Tel (315) 445-4100 *Founded/Ownrshp* 1946
Sales 116.3MM *EMP* 500
Accts Kpmg Llp Hartford Ct
SIC 8221 College, except junior; College, except junior
Pr: Linda Lamura
Pr: Judy Owen
Pr: Jed Schneider
**Treas:* Roger W Stackpoole
VP: Bill Brower
Assoc Dir: Adrienne Graves
Assoc Dir: Christine Liggio
Adm Dir: Philip George
Nurse Mgr: Cynthia Daniels
MIS Dir: Michael Donlin
Doctor: Edward Wolfe

D-U-N-S 96-612-2835
LE NORMAN OPERATING LLC
(*Suby of* TEMPLAR ENERGY LLC) ★
4700 Gaillardia Pkwy # 200, Oklahoma City, OK 73142-1839
Tel (405) 548-1200 *Founded/Ownrshp* 2010
Sales 26.0MM^E *EMP* 14
SIC 1382 1321 1311 Oil & gas exploration services; Natural gas liquids; Crude petroleum & natural gas
Pr: David D Le Norman
Pr: Chris McCormick
VP: Robert Potts

D-U-N-S 10-303-6059 IMP
LE PAFE INC
LE CHEF BAKERY
7547 Telegraph Rd, Montebello, CA 90640-6516
Tel (323) 888-2929 *Founded/Ownrshp* 1919
Sales 45.2MM^E *EMP* 170
SIC 2051 Bread, cake & related products; Bread, cake & related products
Pr: Jonathan Lau
**VP:* Valerie Lau
Plnt Mgr: Hua Liang
Mktg Dir: Rita Kwok

LE PAIN QUOTIDIEN
See PQ NEW YORK INC

LE PEEP RESTAURANT
See RHOADS HOLDINGS LTD

D-U-N-S 07-649-0754
LE PIERS INC
320 1st St E, Fosston, MN 56542-1326
Tel (218) 435-1040 *Founded/Ownrshp* 1983
Sales 25.0MM^E *EMP* 25
SIC 4953 5172 Hazardous waste collection & disposal; Petroleum products
CEO: Larry Le Pier
**Pr:* Larryr Lepier
**VP:* Tami Le Pier
Area Mgr: Arthur Kazarau
Genl Mgr: Tami Hammish
Sls Mgr: Vladimir Gladkikh

LE SALON
See SALON DEVELOPMENT CORP

D-U-N-S 00-541-8041 IMP
LE SMITH CO (OH)
1030 E Wilson St, Bryan, OH 43506-9358
Tel (419) 636-4555 *Founded/Ownrshp* 1950
Sales 23.0MM^E *EMP* 140
SIC 2431 5072 2541 Interior & ornamental woodwork & trim; Builders' hardware; Wood partitions & fixtures
Pr: Laura Juarez
**COO:* Craig Francisco
**CFO:* Mindy Hess
Dir Bus: Amy Miller
**Prin:* Steve Smith
Opers Mgr: Rod Luzar
Opers Mgr: Aaron Walz
Mktg Mgr: Craig Rex
Mktg Mgr: Brian Smith

D-U-N-S 83-649-3700
LE SUEUR CHEESE CO
DAVISCO FOODS INTERNATIONAL
704 N Main St, Le Sueur, MN 56058-1403
Tel (507) 665-8811 *Founded/Ownrshp* 1952
Sales 24.1MM^E *EMP* 120
SIC 2022 Natural cheese; Natural cheese
CEO: Mark E Davis
**VP:* Jim Ward
Sls Mgr: Matus Knoblich

LE SUEUR CHEESE DIVISION
See DAVISCO FOODS INTERNATIONAL INC

D-U-N-S 00-624-9627 IMP
LE SUEUR INC (MN)
ALUMINUM DIV
1409 Vine St, Le Sueur, MN 56058-1125
Tel (507) 665-6204 *Founded/Ownrshp* 1946
Sales 113.3MM^E *EMP* 630
SIC 3363 3089 3544 3369 Aluminum die-castings; Injection molding of plastics; Special dies, tools, jigs & fixtures; Nonferrous foundries; Aluminum die-castings; Injection molding of plastics; Special dies, tools, jigs & fixtures; Nonferrous foundries
CEO: Mark C Mueller
Pr: Henry J Prevot
Treas: Janet Mueller
VP: Robert Hoyt
Telecom Ex: Karl Lamm
CTO: Dave Gagnon
Mtls Mgr: Carol Franzen
Sfty Mgr: Eric Retzlaff
Sfty Mgr: Frank Weber
Opers Mgr: Tony Zwart
Ql Cn Mgr: Clete Dahm

D-U-N-S 02-861-4931 IMP/EXP
LE VECKE CORP
LE VECKE GROUP
10810 Inland Ave, Mira Loma, CA 91752-3235
Tel (951) 681-8600 *Founded/Ownrshp* 1949
Sales 53.4MM^E *EMP* 64
SIC 5181 Beer & other fermented malt liquors; Beer & other fermented malt liquors
CEO: Joseph Neil Levecke
**Pr:* Neil Levecke
CFO: Sheila Checkley
VP: Mike Olsker
VP: Steve Vento
Genl Mgr: Phil Deconinck
Genl Mgr: Tim Levecke
Off Mgr: Joy Albridge
Manager: Martin Rezac
Prd Mgr: Dexter Pierce
Mktg Mgr: Melissa Venglass

LE VECKE GROUP
See LE VECKE CORP

D-U-N-S 03-623-7472 IMP
LE VIAN CORP
ARUSHA TANZANITE
235 Great Neck Rd, Great Neck, NY 11021-3301
Tel (877) 253-8426 *Founded/Ownrshp* 1998
Sales 21.7MM^E *EMP* 85^E
SIC 3911 Jewelry, precious metal
Ch Bd: Lawrence Levian
Pr: Moosa Levian
CEO: Eddie Levian
Ch: Larry Levian
IT Man: David Levian
Sales Exec: Cheryl Layton
Sales Exec: Bryan McAllister
Sls Dir: Leonardo Kashi
Sls Mgr: Jonathan Levian

D-U-N-S 87-463-4814
LE-MAR HOLDINGS INC
EDWARDS MAIL SERVICE
420 Erskine St, Lubbock, TX 79403-3318
Tel (806) 744-8577 *Founded/Ownrshp* 2006
Sales 54.0MM^E *EMP* 240^E
SIC 4213 Contract haulers; Contract haulers
Pr: Lawrence Edwards

D-U-N-S 07-036-3288
LEA CHARLES CENTER INC
WORKABILITY
195 Burdette St, Spartanburg, SC 29307-1003
Tel (864) 585-0322 *Founded/Ownrshp* 1965
Sales 23.6MM *EMP* 600
Accts Mcabee Schwartz Halliday & Co
SIC 8322 8331 8361 Individual & family services; Job training & vocational rehabilitation services; Residential care; Individual & family services; Job training & vocational rehabilitation services; Residential care
Ex Dir: Jerry Bernard
CFO: Elaine Bond
**CFO:* Robert Decker
Comm Dir: Pam Prevatte
IT Man: Vanessa Pressley
IT Man: Judson Stubbs
Pr Dir: Katie Brannan
Pr Dir: Katie Freseman

D-U-N-S 00-985-8655
LEA COUNTY ELECTRIC COOPERATIVE INC
1300 W Avenue D, Lovington, NM 88260-3806
Tel (575) 396-3631 *Founded/Ownrshp* 1946
Sales 70.7MM^E *EMP* 79^E
Accts Bolinger Segars Gilbert And Mo
SIC 4911 Distribution, electric power; Transmission, electric power; Distribution, electric power; Transmission, electric power
Pr: John Ingle
**Prin:* Billy Royce Medlin
Admn Mgr: Jeanette Faris
DP Dir: Kyle Coleman
Mktg Dir: Suzie Brown
Board of Directors: John Ingle

D-U-N-S 06-411-9860
LEA REGIONAL HOSPITAL LLC
LEA REGIONAL MEDICAL CENTER
5419 N Lovington Hwy, Hobbs, NM 88240-9125
Tel (575) 492-5000 *Founded/Ownrshp* 1994
Sales 16.7M *EMP* 436^E
SIC 8062 General medical & surgical hospitals; General medical & surgical hospitals
CEO: Timothy N Thornell
Chf Rad: Aemon Techeira
**CFO:* Steve Smith
Dir Lab: Doug Moore
Dir Lab: Nancy Nix
Dir Rad: Christina Seed
Chf Nrs Of: Wade Tyrrell
MIS Dir: Tom Monejzik
Doctor: Barbara Seay
Nrsg Dir: Patrick Dunn

LEA REGIONAL MEDICAL CENTER
See LEA REGIONAL HOSPITAL LLC

D-U-N-S 96-160-1473
LEA WILLIAMS INC
(*Suby of* DEUTSCHE POST AG)
1 Dag Hammarskjold Plz # 8, New York, NY 10017-2201
Tel (212) 351-9000 *Founded/Ownrshp* 2011
Sales 288.0MM^E *EMP* 3,000
SIC 8741 Management services; Management services
CEO: Justin Barton
Pr: John Snowdon
CEO: Deb Dulsky
CEO: Todd Handcock
CEO: Tim Rodber
COO: Aurora Coya
CFO: Liz Catchpole
Ofcr: Conor Davey
Sr VP: Frank Olivieri
VP: Ajit Kara
VP: Edwin Kiernan
VP: Ray Krienke
VP: Christopher Lamb
VP: Adam Lindstrom
VP: Darren O'Meara
VP: James Oliver
VP: David Pennino
VP: Joanne Prifti
VP: Marc Quinlivan
VP Bus Dev: Andrew Parrish
Exec: Minnie Calo

D-U-N-S 60-322-4452
LEABO FOODS DISTRIBUTION INC
1975 E Locust St Ste B, Ontario, CA 91761-7640
Tel (909) 923-9060 *Founded/Ownrshp* 1987
Sales 30.4MM^E *EMP* 30
SIC 5142 Frozen vegetables & fruit products; Fruit juices, frozen; Frozen fish, meat & poultry; Bakery products, frozen
CEO: Davis Preuss
Opers Mgr: Tom Kellersberger

D-U-N-S 94-549-4888
LEACH BROTHERS BROKERAGE INC
862 E Third St, Forest, MS 39074-4319
Tel (601) 469-4112 *Founded/Ownrshp* 1979
Sales 22.4MM *EMP* 5
SIC 7389 Brokers' services; Brokers' services
Pr: Charles E Leach
**Treas:* Cindy Leach
**VP:* Glenn Leach

LEACH GARNER - A BERKSHIRE
See HALLMARK HEALY GROUP INC

D-U-N-S 60-201-7709 IMP
■ **LEACH GARNER - A BERKSHIRE HATHAWAY CO**
(*Suby of* STERN METALS, INC.)
49 Pearl St, Attleboro, MA 02703-3940
Tel (508) 222-7400 *Founded/Ownrshp* 2012
Sales 178.6MM^E *EMP* 500
SIC 5094 Jewelry & precious stones; Jewelry & precious stones
Pr: Joe White
VP: Dennis Breneiser
**VP:* Fred Poluhovich
VP: Edward Rigano
VP Mktg: Peter Clark
VP Mktg: Dick Smith
Mktg Dir: Ed Rigano

D-U-N-S 08-258-8559
■ LEACH INTERNATIONAL CORP
LEACH INTERNATIONAL NORTH AMER
(*Suby of* ESTERLINE TECHNOLOGIES CORP) ★
6900 Orangethorpe Ave, Buena Park, CA 90620-1390
Tel (714) 739-0770 *Founded/Ownrshp* 1919, 2004
Sales 194.7MM^E *EMP* 1,000
SIC 3679 Electronic circuits; Electronic circuits
CEO: Richard Brad Lawrence
**Pr:* Mark Thek
Ofcr: Shyla Lange
**VP:* Alain Durand
Dir Bus: Franck Kolczak
Ex Dir: Grace Quintero
Genl Mgr: Marlyne Zalma
MIS Dir: Phil Sealana
QA Dir: Russell Price
Sftwr Eng: David Lawton
VP Sls: Tim Ostrosky

LEACH INTERNATIONAL NORTH AMER
See LEACH INTERNATIONAL CORP

D-U-N-S 00-985-8663
LEACO RURAL TELEPHONE COOPERATIVE INC
220 W Broadway St, Hobbs, NM 88240-6038
Tel (575) 370-5010 *Founded/Ownrshp* 1954
Sales 21.9MM^E *EMP* 56
SIC 4813 Local & long distance telephone communications
CEO: Laura Angel
**Pr:* Wanda Munson
**Pr:* Danny Watson
**Sec:* Leon Hemann

D-U-N-S 87-804-9860
LEAD DOG MARKETING GROUP INC
440 9th Ave Fl 17, New York, NY 10001-1612
Tel (212) 488-6547 *Founded/Ownrshp* 1998
Sales 24.1MM^E *EMP* 70^E
SIC 8742 Marketing consulting services
Ch Bd: Daniel Mannix
COO: Donna Providenti
Sr VP: Karen Ashnault
Sr VP: Lisa Hyman
Sr VP: JG Robilotti
VP: Daniel Jahn
Mng Dir: Brian Lefkowitz

D-U-N-S 96-753-1711
LEAD IT CORP
1999 Wabash Ave Ste 210, Springfield, IL 62704-5368
Tel (217) 726-7250 *Founded/Ownrshp* 2009
Sales 9.8MM *EMP* 312
SIC 7371 Computer software development & applications
COO: Suman Akula
Snr Sftwr: Naveen Mangu
Software D: Rajesh Subramaniam
Sls Mgr: Leroy Singleton
Board of Directors: Ram P Talluri

D-U-N-S 96-187-7466
LEADER BANCORP INC
180 Massachusetts Ave, Arlington, MA 02474-8448
Tel (781) 646-3900 *Founded/Ownrshp* 2010
Sales NA *EMP* 130^E
SIC 6021 National commercial banks
CEO: Sushil Tuli

D-U-N-S 12-416-0875
LEADER BANK
LEADER BANK NATIONAL ASSOCIATION
(*Suby of* LEADER BANCORP INC) ★
180 Mmchsetts Ave Ste 204, Arlington, MA 02474
Tel (781) 646-3900 *Founded/Ownrshp* 2002
Sales NA *EMP* 47
SIC 6029 Commercial banks; Commercial banks
Pr: Sushil Tuli
Pr: Paul Mitchell
**CFO:* Brian Taylor
Chf Mktg O: Carrie Cussin
Ofcr: Michael Kidwell
Ex VP: Michael Bonsey
Sr VP: Alfred Odoardi
Sr VP: Matthew Pierce
Sr VP: Steve Ritter
VP: Kevin Cuff
VP: Jeffrey Esterkes
VP: Greg Farber
VP: Cheryl Glantz
VP: Mark Haroutunian
VP: Vincent Hayes
VP: Donna Haynes
VP: Ken Masterson
VP: John McNally
VP: Matt Miller
VP: Liza Pero
VP: Gary Roche-Bernard

LEADER BANK NATIONAL ASSOCIATION
See LEADER BANK

D-U-N-S 04-665-7412
LEADER COMMUNICATIONS INC
6421 S A Depo Blvd Ste A, Oklahoma City, OK 73135
Tel (405) 622-2200 *Founded/Ownrshp* 1999
Sales 22.2MM *EMP* 179
Accts Finley & Cook Pllc Shawnee
SIC 8742 Management information systems consultant; Management information systems consultant
CEO: Michael Lyles

LEADER DRUG STORE
See MILLER DRUG

LEADER DRUG STORE
See PROVIDENCE LITTLE CO OF MARY FOUNDATION

LEADER DRUG STORE
See PRESBYTERIAN VILLAGE NORTH INC

D-U-N-S 04-845-1087 IMP/EXP
LEADER GASKET TECHNOLOGIES INC
INTERNATIONAL GASKET & SUPPLY
(*Suby of* ERIKS CORP) ★
905 W 13th St, Deer Park, TX 77536-3163
Tel (281) 542-0600 *Founded/Ownrshp* 1999
Sales 27.7MM^E *EMP* 248^E
SIC 3053 5072 5085 Gaskets, packing & sealing devices; Bolts, nuts & screws; Gaskets & seals; Gaskets, packing & sealing devices; Bolts, nuts & screws; Gaskets & seals
CEO: Kevin Kolb
Pr: Reid Meyer
**CFO:* Tim Howell

D-U-N-S 78-134-4346
■ LEADER NURSING & REHABILITATION CENTER OF SCOTT TOWNSHIP INC
HCR MANOR CARE
(*Suby of* HCR MANORCARE MEDICAL SERVICES OF FLORIDA LLC) ★
333 N Summit St, Toledo, OH 43604-1531
Tel (419) 252-5718 *Founded/Ownrshp* 1985
Sales 19.5MM^E *EMP* 300
SIC 8051 Skilled nursing care facilities; Skilled nursing care facilities
Pr: Paul A Ormond
**COO:* Steven Guillard
COO: Bruce Schroeder
**CFO:* Steve Cavanaugh
Telecom Ex: Charles Brown
Software D: Jeremy Barr
Software D: David Claydon
Doctor: Alice Brandon
HC Dir: Ernani Porter
Counsel: Cindy Zewleski

D-U-N-S 83-954-9904 IMP
LEADER PROMOTIONS INC
LEADERPROMOS.COM
790 E Johnstown Rd, Columbus, OH 43230-2116
Tel (614) 416-6565 *Founded/Ownrshp* 1995
Sales 52.7MM^E *EMP* 80
SIC 5199 Advertising specialties
CEO: Stephanie Leader
**CFO:* Kathy Weible
Chf Mktg O: Susie Barger

D-U-N-S 12-196-4688
■ LEADER TECH INC
HEICO COMPANY
(*Suby of* HEICO ELECTRONIC TECHNOLOGIES CORP) ★
12420 Race Track Rd, Tampa, FL 33626-3117
Tel (813) 855-6921 *Founded/Ownrshp* 1999
Sales 23.4MM^E *EMP* 100
SIC 3469 Metal stampings
Pr: Robert McKenna
**Treas:* Carlos L Macau
Dir IT: Debbie Clements
Sls Mgr: Tim Black

LEADER TELEGRAM
See EAU CLAIRE PRESS CO

LEADERPROMOS.COM
See LEADER PROMOTIONS INC

LEADERS CASUAL FURNITURE
See LEADERS HOLDING CO

D-U-N-S 93-883-3035
LEADERS GROUP INC
T L G
26 W Dry Creek Cir # 575, Littleton, CO 80120-8063
Tel (303) 797-9080 *Founded/Ownrshp* 1995
Sales 46.8MM *EMP* 11
Accts Spicer Jeffries Llp Greenwood
SIC 6211 Security brokers & dealers; Security brokers & dealers
Pr: David Wickersham
**Sec:* Bernadette Wickersham
VP: Z Riley

D-U-N-S 15-037-0849 EXP
LEADERS HOLDING CO
LEADERS CASUAL FURNITURE
6303 126th Ave, Largo, FL 33773-1864
Tel (727) 538-5577 *Founded/Ownrshp* 1986
Sales 35.1MM^E *EMP* 163
SIC 5712 5021 Furniture stores; Furniture; Furniture stores; Furniture
Pr: Jerry O Newton
**Sec:* Linda Newton
Sales Asso: Victoria Vokes
Snr Mgr: Chris Demato
Board of Directors: Jerry O Newton, Linda Newton

D-U-N-S 79-923-4125 IMP
LEADERTECH SYSTEMS OF CHICAGO INC
210 Mittel Dr, Wood Dale, IL 60191-1120
Tel (630) 238-9988 *Founded/Ownrshp* 1992
Sales 35.4MM^E *EMP* 54
SIC 5045 Computers, peripherals & software
Pr: Leechin Su
**Treas:* Yung Ting Su
Sls Mgr: Chen Henry

LEADING COMMUNICATION CONTRS
See PRINCE TELECOM LLC

LEADING EDGE ARCFT DETAILING
See LEADING EDGE AVIATION SERVS INC

D-U-N-S 00-765-4051
LEADING EDGE AVIATION SERVICES OF AMARILLO INC
10801 Baker St, Amarillo, TX 79111-1235
Tel (806) 335-2616 *Founded/Ownrshp* 1997
Sales 22.7MM^E *EMP* 200
SIC 4581 Aircraft maintenance & repair services; Aircraft maintenance & repair services
Pr: Michael Manclark
Site Mgr: Brenda Whitten

D-U-N-S 61-712-1637
LEADING EDGE AVIATION SERVS INC
LEADING EDGE ARCFT DETAILING
5251 California Ave # 170, Irvine, CA 92617-3074
Tel (714) 556-0576 *Founded/Ownrshp* 1989
Sales 133.8MM^E *EMP* 700
SIC 1721 4581 3721 Aircraft painting; Aircraft maintenance & repair services; Motorized aircraft; Aircraft painting; Aircraft maintenance & repair services; Motorized aircraft
CEO: Niall Cunningham
**Ch Bd:* Mike Manclark
**Pr:* William M Manclark
**COO:* Rod Friese
**COO:* Chris Harano
**CFO:* Daniel Zeddy
VP: Sean Deshler
**VP:* Dave Patterson
Genl Mgr: Dale Mullinax
Off Mgr: Nikki Thomas
Mktg Mgr: Alicia Castle

D-U-N-S 00-593-9665 IMP
LEADING EDGE GROUP INC (IL)
LEADING EDGE HYDRAULICS
1800 16th Ave, Rockford, IL 61104-5453
Tel (815) 316-3500 *Founded/Ownrshp* 1966, 1989
Sales 28.8MM^E *EMP* 125
SIC 3599 3498 3594 3547 3317 Machine shop, jobbing & repair; Tube fabricating (contract bending & shaping); Fluid power pumps & motors; Rolling mill machinery; Steel pipe & tubes; Machine shop, jobbing & repair; Tube fabricating (contract bending & shaping); Fluid power pumps & motors; Rolling mill machinery; Steel pipe & tubes
CEO: Russell Dennis Sr
**Pr:* Russell Dennis Jr
Genl Mgr: John Dennis
Opers Mgr: Mike Dzielak
Ql Cn Mgr: Chuck Westholder
Sales Asso: Kim Rizvi

LEADING EDGE HYDRAULICS
See LEADING EDGE GROUP INC

D-U-N-S 60-409-9387
LEADING EDGE RECOVERY SOLUTIONS LLC
(*Suby of* GLOBAL CREDIT & COLLECTION INC)
5440 N Cumberland Ave # 300, Chicago, IL 60656-1490
Tel (773) 380-8800 *Founded/Ownrshp* 2014
Sales 59.9MM^E *EMP* 407
SIC 7322 Adjustment & collection services; Adjustment & collection services
Pr: Bryan Lubeck
Ex VP: Stanley Moore
Div Mgr: Adam Gow
Div Mgr: Leonard Outlaw
CIO: Derrick Crews
Web Dev: Alex Angeles

D-U-N-S 87-823-4616
LEADING EDGE TECHNOLOGY SOLUTIONS INC
MICRO GLOBAL
2913 N Ontario St, Burbank, CA 91504-2017
Tel (818) 569-7022 *Founded/Ownrshp* 1991
Sales 31.1MM *EMP* 20
SIC 5045 5734 Computers, peripherals & software; Computer & software stores; Computers, peripherals & software; Computer & software stores
Pr: Jeff Mironer
**CFO:* Anna Mazisyuk
Off Mgr: Letty Dennis

D-U-N-S 05-455-3565
LEADING HOTELS OF WORLD LTD
(*Suby of* HOTEL REPRESENTATIVE INC) ★
485 Lexington Ave Rm 401, New York, NY 10017-2650
Tel (212) 515-5600 *Founded/Ownrshp* 1989
Sales 53.9MM^E *EMP* 300
SIC 7389 8742 Hotel & motel reservation service; Marketing consulting services; Hotel & motel reservation service; Marketing consulting services
Pr: Joseph A Giacoponello
**Pr:* Theodore Teng
**Ex VP:* Paul McManus
Sr VP: Patrick Fahnestock
Sr VP: Philip Ho
**Sr VP:* Joe Ioppolo
Sr VP: Daniel Neumann
**Sr VP:* Tova Simonsen
Sr VP: Chris Walker
Sr VP: See-Tho Wilke
VP: Claudia Kaplan
VP: Phil Koserowski
**VP:* Norbert Kublius
VP: Jon Londeen
VP: Claudia Seely-Kirk
VP: Susan Ziluca
Assoc Dir: Yina Mao

D-U-N-S 02-237-9994 IMP/EXP
LEADING INDUSTRY INC
PINNACLE PLASTIC CONTAINERS
1151 Pacific Ave, Oxnard, CA 93033-2472
Tel (805) 385-4100 *Founded/Ownrshp* 1981
Sales 27.1MM^E *EMP* 100
SIC 3089 Plastic processing
Pr: Samuel Hong
**VP:* Dale Hong
Genl Mgr: Brian Yamaguchi

D-U-N-S 61-163-8920
LEADING INSURANCE SERVICES INC
KBIC
(*Suby of* KB INSURANCE CO.,LTD.)
400 Kelby St Ste 14, Fort Lee, NJ 07024-2938
Tel (201) 720-2100 *Founded/Ownrshp* 1990
Sales NA *EMP* 45^E
SIC 6411 Insurance agents, brokers & service
CEO: Jonguk Lee
**COO:* John Tszdpelki

D-U-N-S 86-766-5747
LEADING TECHNOLOGY COMPOSITES INC
LTC
2626 W May St, Wichita, KS 67213-1854
Tel (316) 944-0011 *Founded/Ownrshp* 1993
Sales 38.1MM^E *EMP* 200^E
SIC 5731 3711 3365 3312 3399

D-U-N-S 07-265-3827
LEADINGAGE INC (NY)
2519 Connecticut Ave Nw, Washington, DC 20008-1520
Tel (202) 783-2242 *Founded/Ownrshp* 1965
Sales 20.1MM *EMP* 90^E
Accts Tate And Tryon Washington Dc
SIC 8611 8621 Business associations; Professional membership organizations; Business associations; Professional membership organizations
Pr: William Minnix Jr
**VP:* Majd Alwan
VP: Linda Bloxham
VP: Cheryl Jackson
VP: Leslie Knight
**VP:* Cheryl Phillips
VP: Mary Reilly
**VP:* Robyn I Stone
VP: Bruce Rosenthal
**VP:* Katrinka Smith Sloan
**VP:* Sharon Sullivan
Assoc Dir: Cynthia Wokas
Comm Man: Sarah Mashburn

D-U-N-S 07-860-3929
LEADINGRESPONSE LLC
(*Suby of* HURON CAPITAL PARTNERS LLC) ★
263 Tresser Blvd, Stamford, CT 06901-3236
Tel (210) 387-7272 *Founded/Ownrshp* 2012
Sales 654.0M^E *EMP* 342^E
SIC 7375 Data base information retrieval
CEO: Charles R Dallacqua

D-U-N-S 18-865-3042
LEAF COMMERCIAL CAPITAL INC
2005 Market St Fl 14, Philadelphia, PA 19103-7042
Tel (800) 819-5556 *Founded/Ownrshp* 1995
Sales NA *EMP* 230
SIC 6159 7359 Equipment & vehicle finance leasing companies; Equipment rental & leasing; Equipment & vehicle finance leasing companies; Equipment rental & leasing
Ch Bd: Crit S Dement
**Pr:* Miles Herman
Pr: Bryan Spence
**CFO:* Robert Moskovitz
**Ex VP:* David English
Sr VP: Vincent Faino
Sr VP: Lori Wilson
VP: Paul Tyczkowski
Genl Mgr: John Beard
Genl Mgr: Nick Capparelli
Genl Mgr: Nick Siserone

D-U-N-S 78-449-6283 EXP
LEAF RIVER CELLULOSE LLC
(*Suby of* GP CELLULOSE LLC) ★
157 Buck Creek Rd, New Augusta, MS 39462-6070
Tel (601) 964-8411 *Founded/Ownrshp* 2004
Sales 137.5MM^E *EMP* 300
SIC 2676 Diapers, paper (disposable): made from purchased paper; Diapers, paper (disposable): made from purchased paper
Dir Lab: Arlis Hicks
Sfty Mgr: Scott Roberts

D-U-N-S 79-196-9640
LEAFFILTER NORTH LLC
1595 Georgetown Rd Ste G, Hudson, OH 44236-4045
Tel (330) 655-7950 *Founded/Ownrshp* 2007
Sales 31.1MM^E *EMP* 197^E
SIC 1761 Gutter & downspout contractor
Prin: Matt Kaulig

D-U-N-S 02-522-1025
LEAFGUARD BY BELDON INC (TX)
5039 West Ave, San Antonio, TX 78213-2711
Tel (210) 775-6722 *Founded/Ownrshp* 2008
Sales 28.3MM^E *EMP* 250^E
SIC 1761 Roofing, siding & sheet metal work
Prin: Chris Edelen

D-U-N-S 12-332-3008
LEAGUE OF CONSERVATION VOTERS INC
1920 L St Nw Ste 800, Washington, DC 20036-5045
Tel (202) 785-8683 *Founded/Ownrshp* 1970
Sales 37.0MM *EMP* 25^E
Accts Lane & Company Cpa S Washing
SIC 8641 Environmental protection organization; Environmental protection organization
Pr: Gene Karpinski
Ofcr: Seth Beer
Sr VP: Mark Longabaugh
VP: Amanda Hoffman
Comm Dir: Mike Palamuso

D-U-N-S 04-080-1995
LEAGUE TREATMENT CENTER INC
JOAN FENICHEL THERAPEUTIC NURS
483 Clermont Ave, Brooklyn, NY 11238-2253
Tel (718) 643-5300 *Founded/Ownrshp* 1953
Sales 664.1M *EMP* 350
Accts Loeb & Troper Llp New York N
SIC 8211 8093 School for the retarded; Family planning clinic; School for the retarded; Family planning clinic
CEO: Edward Spauster
**Pr:* Steve Katz
CFO: Steven Fainer
**CFO:* Ron Signore
**Treas:* Rochelle Yates
Ex Dir: Hannah Achtenberg
Dir IT: Brian Riley
Psych: Cara Millington

D-U-N-S 08-550-0742
LEAKE & WATTS SERVICES INC
463 Hawthorne Ave, Yonkers, NY 10705-3441
Tel (914) 375-8700 *Founded/Ownrshp* 1831
Sales 68.3MM *EMP* 900
Accts Loeb & Troper Llp New York N
SIC 8322 Child related social services; Family counseling services; Child related social services; Family counseling services
Pr: G Crossan Seybolt Jr
**Pr:* William A Kirk Jr
CFO: Dorene Clacken
CFO: Michael Mazzocco
Treas: Joseph C Hoopes Jr
**Treas:* G Crossan Seyboltjr
Bd of Dir: Bernard Smith
**VP:* Marjorie E Ames
**VP:* Dr Patricia Garland Morisey Ds

VP: Lois Simmonds
Assoc Dir: Belinda Conway

D-U-N-S 09-354-5291
LEAKE COUNTY BOARD OF EDUCATION (MS)
LEAKE COUNTY SCHOOL DISTRICT
123 W Main St, Carthage, MS 39051-4139
Tel (601) 267-4579 *Founded/Ownrshp* 1954
Sales 24.6MM^E *EMP* 500^E
SIC 8211 Public elementary & secondary schools; Public elementary & secondary schools

LEAKE COUNTY SCHOOL DISTRICT
See LEAKE COUNTY BOARD OF EDUCATION

D-U-N-S 11-737-7325
LEAKTITE CORP
40 Francis St, Leominster, MA 01453-4911
Tel (978) 537-8000 *Founded/Ownrshp* 1984
Sales 20.4MM^E *EMP* 86^E
SIC 3089 3411 Plastic containers, except foam; Metal cans
Pr: Rodney G Sparrow
CFO: Ken Valera
Natl Sales: Jay Brooks
Sls&Mrk Ex: Forsberg Thomas

D-U-N-S 01-704-8351
LEAMAN LOGISTICS LLC
1777 Sentry Pkwy W, Blue Bell, PA 19422-2207
Tel (215) 461-3801 *Founded/Ownrshp* 1998
Sales 26.4MM^E *EMP* 90
SIC 8741 Management services
Prin: J Stephen Hamilton
CFO: Francis Ezeuzoh

D-U-N-S 18-702-1329
LEANCOR LLC
7660 Turfway Rd Ste 200, Florence, KY 41042-1367
Tel (859) 283-9933 *Founded/Ownrshp* 2005
Sales 39.9MM^E *EMP* 228
SIC 8742 Management consulting services; Management consulting services
Pr: Brad Bossence
Pr: David Evans
Sr VP: Vimal Patel
IT Man: Christy Burnett
Opers Mgr: Kyle Gage
Opers Mgr: Scott Stecher
Sls Mgr: Chris Kushmaul
Snr Mgr: Matt Irwin
Snr Mgr: Gwen Lewis
Snr Mgr: Colin Willis

D-U-N-S 01-053-6910
LEANDER INDEPENDENT SCHOOL DISTRICT
204 W South St, Leander, TX 78641-1719
Tel (512) 570-0000 *Founded/Ownrshp* 1948
Sales 120.6MM^E *EMP* 2,700
SIC 8211 Public elementary school; Public junior high school; Public senior high school; Public elementary school; Public junior high school; Public senior high school
Comm Dir: Dick Ellis
Pr Dir: Lisa Napper
Schl Brd P: Pamela Waggoner
Psych: Sullivan James

D-U-N-S 60-962-5256
LEANIN TREE INC
CELEBRATION GREETINGS
6055 Longbow Dr, Boulder, CO 80301-3296
Tel (303) 581-2100 *Founded/Ownrshp* 1949
Sales 52.1MM^E *EMP* 210
SIC 2771 3999 2741 Greeting cards; Novelties, bric-a-brac & hobby kits; Art copy: publishing & printing; Greeting cards; Novelties, bric-a-brac & hobby kits; Art copy: publishing & printing
Ch Bd: Edward P Trumble
**Pr:* Thomas E Trumble
**COO:* Pete Mahlstedt
Chf Mktg O: Dana Pauley
**Sr VP:* Jane Trumble
**VP:* Nancy Trumble Fox
**VP:* Timothy Trumble
Genl Mgr: Guynna Manley
Dir IT: Alan Hermance
Info Man: Susan Powers
Netwrk Eng: Sam Morgante

D-U-N-S 12-421-5133
LEANLOGISTICS INC
1351 S Waverly Rd, Holland, MI 49423-8570
Tel (616) 738-6400 *Founded/Ownrshp* 2008
Sales 33.2MM^E *EMP* 160^E
SIC 8741 Management services; Management services
Pr: Dan Dershem
**COO:* Eric Meister
**CFO:* Stephen Pietenpol
Ofcr: Matt Ahearn
VP: Jason Nurmi
**VP:* Jeff Potts
Genl Mgr: Tim Dalton
Software D: Ray Germain
Software D: Nate Martin
Software D: Vic Polites
Software D: Erin Vickers

D-U-N-S 03-807-4188
■ **LEAP WIRELESS INTERNATIONAL INC**
LCW WIRELESS
(*Suby of* AT&T INC) ★
5887 Copley Dr, San Diego, CA 92111-7906
Tel (858) 882-6000 *Founded/Ownrshp* 2014
Sales 895.2MM^E *EMP* 2,984^E
SIC 4813 Telephone communication, except radio; Telephone communication, except radio
CEO: S Douglas Hutcheson
Pr: Jerry V Elliott
COO: Cherrie Nanninga
CFO: R Perley McBride
Ofcr: William D Ingram
Ofcr: Perley McBride
Sr VP: Erik Gerson
Sr VP: Colin E Holland
Sr VP: Anne Liu
Sr VP: Aaron P Maddox
Sr VP: Catherine Shackleford
Sr VP: Leonard C Stephens
VP: John H Casey III
VP: Janna Ducich
VP: Jennifer Tillson
VP: Amy Wakeham
Board of Directors: Nick W Jones

D-U-N-S 15-227-7687 IMP
LEAPERS INC
32700 Capitol St, Livonia, MI 48150-1742
Tel (734) 542-1500 *Founded/Ownrshp* 1992
Sales 30.0MM *EMP* 70
Accts Post Smythe Lutz And Ziel Ply
SIC 5091 3827 Sporting & recreation goods; Gun sights, optical; Sporting & recreation goods; Gun sights, optical
Pr: Tina Ding
**VP:* David Ding
IT Man: John Pan
Sls Mgr: Steven Yu

D-U-N-S 87-928-8470 IMP
▲ **LEAPFROG ENTERPRISES INC**
6401 Hollis St Ste 100, Emeryville, CA 94608-1463
Tel (510) 420-5000 *Founded/Ownrshp* 1995
Sales 339.1MM *EMP* 579
Accts Pricewaterhousecoopers Llp Sa
Tkr Sym LF *Exch* NYS
SIC 3944 Games, toys & children's vehicles; Games, toys & children's vehicles
CEO: John Barbour
**Ch Bd:* William B Chiasson
**V Ch:* Thomas J Kalinske
CFO: Raymond L Arthur
Chf Mktg O: Gregory B Ahearn
Ex VP: Nancy G Macintyre
Ex VP: Nancy Macintyre
Ex VP: Nancy G Macintyre
Sr VP: Kenneth A Adams
Sr VP: William K Campbell
Sr VP: Craig R Hendrickson
Sr VP: Craig Relyea
Sr VP: Brad Rodrigues
Sr VP: Christopher Spalding
Sr VP: Hilda S West
VP: Eugene Faulkner
VP: Mike Houlahan
VP: Saydeah Howard
VP: Robert L Lattuga
VP: Karen L Luey
VP: Tracy Rogers
Board of Directors: Stanley E Maron, E Stanton McKee Jr, Joanna Rees, Randy O Rissman

D-U-N-S 12-848-4602
LEAPFROG ONLINE CUSTOMER ACQUISITION LLC
807 Greenwood St, Evanston, IL 60201-4311
Tel (847) 492-1968 *Founded/Ownrshp* 1995
Sales 25.6MM^E *EMP* 130
SIC 8742 Marketing consulting services
CEO: Dave Husain
**Pr:* Scott Epskamp
Pr: Dennis Reid
**CEO:* David Husain
**Ex VP:* Jason Wadler
VP: Mark Bradford
VP: Tony Denunzio
VP: George Seletos
Dir Rx: Brian Ames
Prgrm Mgr: Robyn Armes
Prgrm Mgr: Jim Fu

LEAR ASTRONICS
See BAE SYSTEMS AIRCRAFT CONTROLS INC

D-U-N-S 15-780-3792
LEAR CAPITAL INC
1990 S Bundy Dr Ste 600, Los Angeles, CA 90025-5256
Tel (310) 571-0190 *Founded/Ownrshp* 2013
Sales 400.0MM^E *EMP* 72
SIC 6211 Mineral, oil & gas leasing & royalty dealers; Mineral, oil & gas leasing & royalty dealers
Pr: Kevin Demerit
CFO: Scott Robinson
Exec: Warren Wilson
Mktg Dir: Janine Carlson
Mktg Dir: Cher Cusumano
Mktg Dir: Larrin Devereaux

D-U-N-S 17-559-2476 IMP
▲ **LEAR CORP**
21557 Telegraph Rd, Southfield, MI 48033-4248
Tel (248) 447-1500 *Founded/Ownrshp* 1917
Sales 17.7MMM *EMP* 125,200
Tkr Sym LEA *Exch* NYS
SIC 3714 2531 2396 3643 Motor vehicle electrical equipment; Instrument board assemblies, motor vehicle; Automotive wiring harness sets; Motor vehicle body components & frame; Seats, automobile; Automotive & apparel trimmings; Current-carrying wiring devices; Motor vehicle electrical equipment; Instrument board assemblies, motor vehicle; Automotive wiring harness sets; Motor vehicle body components & frame; Seats, automobile; Automotive & apparel trimmings; Current-carrying wiring devices
Pr: Matthew J Simoncini
Pr: Jim Brackenbury
Pr: Miguel Herrera-Lasso
Pr: Lou Salvatore
Pr: Ray Scott
Pr: Joe Zimmer
CFO: Jeffrey H Vanneste
Treas: Shari L Burgess
Ex VP: Terrence B Larkin
Sr VP: Roger A Jackson
VP: Oscar Dominguez
VP: Wendy L Foss
Exec: Sachin S Deshpande
Exec: Jitendra A Garge
Dir Bus: Eric Kerr
Comm Man: Bobby Hamilton
Board of Directors: Richard H Bott, Thomas P Capo, Jonathan F Foster, Kathleen A Ligocki, Conrad L Mallett Jr, Donald L Runkle, Gregory C Smith, Henry D G Wallace

D-U-N-S 96-055-9383 IMP/EXP
■ **LEAR OPERATIONS CORP**
(*Suby of* LEAR CORP) ★
21557 Telegraph Rd, Southfield, MI 48033-4248
Tel (248) 447-1500 *Founded/Ownrshp* 1995
Sales 372.2MM^E *EMP* 4,011
SIC 3089 Plastic processing; Plastic processing
Pr: Robert Rossiter
**Treas:* Sherri Burgess

D-U-N-S 78-424-7715
LEAR SIEGLER LOGISTICS INTERNATIONAL INC
20501 Seneca Meadows Pkwy # 300, Germantown, MD 20876-7016
Tel (301) 944-3100 *Founded/Ownrshp* 2005
Sales 26.6MM *EMP* 95
SIC 4581 Airports, flying fields & services; Airports, flying fields & services
Pr: Randy Woltring
**Treas:* Greg Robinson

D-U-N-S 06-243-7058
LEARFIELD COMMUNICATIONS INC
505 Hobbs Rd, Jefferson City, MO 65109-5788
Tel (573) 893-7200 *Founded/Ownrshp* 2013
Sales 203.4MM^E *EMP* 465
SIC 4832 4841 Radio broadcasting stations; Cable & other pay television services; Radio broadcasting stations; Cable & other pay television services
Pr: Clyde G Lear
Ex VP: Phil Atkinson
Ex VP: Robert Feldwisch
Ex VP: Stan Koenigsfeld
Sr VP: Mike Behymer
VP: David A Rawlings
**VP:* Andy Rollings
VP: Aaron Worsham
VP: James A Worsham
Sales Asso: Aaron Smith
Snr Mgr: Michelle Smith

D-U-N-S 83-509-1125
LEARFIELD SPORTS LLC
(*Suby of* LEARFIELD COMMUNICATIONS INC) ★
2400 Dallas Pkwy Ste 500, Plano, TX 75093-4383
Tel (469) 241-9191 *Founded/Ownrshp* 1979
Sales 27.0MM^E *EMP* 465^E
SIC 7941 Stadium event operator services; Stadium event operator services
VP: Greg Brown

D-U-N-S 00-723-4313 IMP
LEARJET INC
BOMBARDIER AVIATION SERVICES
(*Suby of* BOMBARDIER INC)
1 Learjet Way, Wichita, KS 67209-2924
Tel (316) 946-2000 *Founded/Ownrshp* 1990
Sales 884.4MM^E *EMP* 4,482
SIC 3721 3812 Aircraft; Search & navigation equipment; Aircraft; Search & navigation equipment
VP: Jim Ziegler
CFO: Sylvie Desjardins
VP: Paul Comeau
VP: Chris Crawshaw
VP: Ed Thomas
Prgrm Mgr: Brian Botts
Prgrm Mgr: Gabriel Ivascu
Rgnl Mgr: Dick Wolf
Genl Mgr: Sergio Marrone
Dir IT: Jocelyn Gauthier
Dir IT: Dennis Nelson

D-U-N-S 10-125-9596
LEARN
44 Hatchetts Hill Rd, Old Lyme, CT 06371-1512
Tel (860) 434-4800 *Founded/Ownrshp* 1966
Sales 37.6MM *EMP* 1,000^E
Accts Cohn Reznick Llp New London
SIC 8299 Educational services; Educational services
Ex Dir: Dr Eileen Howley
**CEO:* Mary Royce
**CFO:* Jean Paul Leblanc
**Ex Dir:* Virginia Seccombe
Off Mgr: Gail Foley

LEARN 4 LIFE
See DESERT SANDS PUBLIC CHARTER INC

D-U-N-S 04-006-2473
LEARNING ALLY INC
20 Roszel Rd, Princeton, NJ 08540-6206
Tel (609) 452-0606 *Founded/Ownrshp* 1951
Sales 31.4MM^E *EMP* 425
Accts Grant Thornton Llp Edison Ne
SIC 8742 8741 8299 Personnel management consultant; Management services; Personal development school; Personnel management consultant; Management services; Personal development school
Pr: Andrew Friedman
Dir Vol: Gigi Franklin
**COO:* Cynthia Hamburger
**CFO:* Tim Wilson
**Ex VP:* Jim Halliday
Sr VP: Barbara Vanderkolk
**VP:* Paul Edelblut
**VP:* Stephen Ferranti
VP: James Pritchett
Ex Dir: Jodi Button
Ex Dir: Mary McDermott

D-U-N-S 96-824-6061
LEARNING CARE GROUP (US) INC
21333 Haggerty Rd Ste 300, Novi, MI 48375-5537
Tel (248) 697-9000 *Founded/Ownrshp* 2014
Sales 744.8MM^E *EMP* 17,000^E
SIC 8351 Child day care services; Child day care services
CEO: Barbara J Beck
COO: Leigh-Ellen Louie
CFO: Robert T Vanhees

D-U-N-S 80-727-4923
LEARNING CARE GROUP INC
(*Suby of* LA PETITE ACADEMY) ★
130 S Jefferson St # 300, Chicago, IL 60661-3687
Tel (312) 469-5656 *Founded/Ownrshp* 1993
Sales 420.8MM *EMP* 6
Accts Deloitte & Touche Llp Chicago
SIC 8351 Child day care services; Child day care services
Pr: Gary A Graves
**Ch Bd:* Stephen P Murray
CFO: Neil P Dyment
Treas: Daniel J Knight
Ofcr: William H Van Huis
VP: Lawrence Appell
VP: Bill Buckland
VP: William C Buckland
VP: Gregory S Davis
VP: Stephan Laudicino
VP: Lisa J Miskimins
VP: Leah L Oliva
VP: Stephanie L Pasche
VP: Hugh W Tracy

D-U-N-S 93-395-1618
LEARNING CARE GROUP INC
(*Suby of* LEARNING CARE GROUP (US) INC) ★
21333 Haggerty Rd Ste 300, Novi, MI 48375-5537
Tel (248) 697-9000 *Founded/Ownrshp* 2008
Sales 608.2MM^E *EMP* 17,000
SIC 8351 8299 Child day care services; Educational services; Child day care services; Educational services
Ch Bd: Benjamin Jacobson
CEO: Barbara J Beck
COO: Kathryn L Myers
COO: Erin J Wallace
CFO: Mark R Bierley
CFO: Frank M Jerneycic
Chf Mktg O: John Lichtenberg
VP: Bill Burgess
VP: Linda Cassidy
VP: Kathryn Peel
Dir Risk M: Teri Davidson
Assoc Dir: Courtney Hemberger

D-U-N-S 08-560-6556
LEARNING CENTER FOR DEAF INC
848 Central St, Framingham, MA 01701-4815
Tel (508) 879-5110 *Founded/Ownrshp* 1970
Sales 20.1MM *EMP* 310
Accts Kirkland Albrecht & Fredrickso
SIC 8211 8299 School for physically handicapped; Survival school; School for physically handicapped; Survival school
Ex Dir: Judy Vreeland
**CFO:* Robert Kulchuk
VP: Peter Bailey
VP: Patrick Costello

LEARNING DISABILITIES ASSOCIAT
See WILDWOOD PROGRAMS INC

LEARNING EXPERIENCE, THE
See LEARNING EXPERIENCE HOLDING CORP

D-U-N-S 13-095-0939
LEARNING EXPERIENCE HOLDING CORP
LEARNING EXPERIENCE, THE
4855 Tech Way Ste 700, Boca Raton, FL 33431
Tel (561) 886-6400 *Founded/Ownrshp* 2003
Sales 21.9MM^E *EMP* 200
SIC 8351 Child day care services; Child day care services
Ch Bd: Michael Weissman
Pr: Joshua Kulberg
Pr: Michael Shafir
**COO:* Andrew Alfano
CFO: Kevin Holbrook
**VP:* Weissman Richard S

LEARNING EXPRESS TOYS
See CASTON HOLDINGS LLC

D-U-N-S 96-348-6717
■ **LEARNING HOUSE INC**
(*Suby of* WELD NORTH LLC) ★
427 S 4th St Ste 300, Louisville, KY 40202-3493
Tel (502) 589-9878 *Founded/Ownrshp* 2011
Sales 31.1MM^E *EMP* 248^E
SIC 8748 Educational consultant
Pr: David T Richardson
Chf Mktg O: Todd Zipper
VP: Victoria Alexander
VP: John Anderson
VP: Mac Bornhauser
VP: Matt Cobb
VP Mktg: Wendy Parrish

D-U-N-S 14-478-3354 IMP/EXP
LEARNING RESOURCES INC
380 N Fairway Dr, Vernon Hills, IL 60061-1836
Tel (847) 573-9471 *Founded/Ownrshp* 1984
Sales 31.7MM^E *EMP* 122
SIC 3999 5092 Education aids, devices & supplies; Educational toys; Education aids, devices & supplies; Educational toys
Pr: Richard M Woldenberg
CFO: Ed Stassen
**VP:* Scott McCabe
VP: Kim McLynn
VP: Barb Plain
IT Man: Wendy Zachrisen
Netwrk Mgr: Christian Castro
Sls&Mrk Ex: Eric Toriumi
VP Sls: Ann Mazurski
Mktg Dir: Bill Hinkle
Mktg Mgr: Deanna Holmes

D-U-N-S 14-814-8869
LEARNING SERVICES CORP
131 Langley Dr Ste B, Lawrenceville, GA 30046-6909
Tel (470) 235-4700 *Founded/Ownrshp* 1985
Sales 19.9MM^E *EMP* 400
SIC 8093 8051 Rehabilitation center, outpatient treatment; Skilled nursing care facilities; Rehabilitation center, outpatient treatment; Skilled nursing care facilities
Ch Bd: Thomas Rosse
**VP:* Jeannie Mack
**Prin:* Debra Braunling-Mcmorrow
IT Man: Cathi Aucoin

LEARNING SKILLS CENTER
See CALIFORNIA STATE UNIVERSITY SACRAMENTO

D-U-N-S 09-946-4729
▲ LEARNING TREE INTERNATIONAL INC
1831 Michael Faraday Dr, Reston, VA 20190-5304
Tel (703) 709-9119 *Founded/Ownrshp* 1974
Sales 94.8MM *EMP* 381ᴱ
Accts Bdo Usa Llp Bethesda Maryla
Tkr Sym LTRE *Exch* NGM
SIC 8243 Data processing schools; Data processing schools
CEO: Richard A Spires
Pr: Max Shevitz
COO: Gregory L Adams
CFO: David W Asai
VP: John Moriarty
VP: Kathy Pelech
VP: Dan Rush
VP: Knut Skare
Creative D: Dominique Nguyen
Prgrm Mgr: Beth Haden
CIO: Magnus Nylund
Board of Directors: Howard A Bain III, Mary C Collins, Henri Hodara, W Mathew Juechter, John R Phillips, Richard A Spires

D-U-N-S 78-489-6508
■ LEARNING TREE INTERNATIONAL USA INC
(*Suby of* LEARNING TREE INTERNATIONAL INC) ★
1831 Michael Faraday Dr, Reston, VA 20190-5304
Tel (703) 709-9119 *Founded/Ownrshp* 1974
Sales 12.0MMᴱ *EMP* 375
SIC 8243 Data processing schools; Data processing schools
Pr: Donald Berbary
Prgrm Mgr: Kendall Benner
Genl Mgr: Kathy Hannon
Sls&Mrk Ex: Jackie Davey

D-U-N-S 80-749-5254
LEASE CRUTCHER LEWIS LLC
(*Suby of* W LEASE LEWIS CO) ★
550 Sw 12th Ave, Portland, OR 97205-2300
Tel (503) 223-2245 *Founded/Ownrshp* 2000
Sales 62.5MMᴱ *EMP* 125
SIC 1542 Nonresidential construction; Nonresidential construction
Pr: Bill Lewis
CFO: J Philo Hall
VP: Matt Pearson
Genl Mgr: Bart Ricketts
Sfty Mgr: Pat Rank

D-U-N-S 04-182-8294 EXP
LEASE PLAN USA INC
LEASEPLAN
(*Suby of* LEASEPLAN CORPORATION N.V.)
1165 Sanctuary Pkwy Frnt, Alpharetta, GA 30009-4797
Tel (770) 933-9090 *Founded/Ownrshp* 1983
Sales 122.7MMᴱ *EMP* 480
SIC 7515 8741 Passenger car leasing; Management services; Passenger car leasing; Management services
Pr: Michael A Pitcher
Pr: Tom Jacob
CFO: George Astrauckas
**CFO:* David G Dahm
Sr VP: Brian Barber
**Sr VP:* Mary Christy
**Sr VP:* John Jaje
**Sr VP:* Paul Kennedy
**Sr VP:* Tim Martin
Sr VP: Bryan Steele
**Sr VP:* Jon Toups
VP: Steve Arkon
VP: John Boyd
VP: David Brooksher
VP: Paul Casler
VP: John Claybrooks
VP: Joseph Danca
VP: Kimberly English
VP: John Hayes
VP: Robert Hughes
VP: John Karoly
Board of Directors: Hans Peter Lutzenkirchen, Abe Tomas

LEASEPLAN
See LEASE PLAN USA INC

D-U-N-S 06-128-1309
LEASING ASSOCIATES INC
(*Suby of* LAI ACQUISITION CORP) ★
12600 N Featherwood Dr # 400, Houston, TX 77034-4444
Tel (832) 300-1300 *Founded/Ownrshp* 2014
Sales NA *EMP* 85
SIC 6159 Automobile finance leasing; Truck finance leasing; Automobile finance leasing; Truck finance leasing
Pr: Mark Sprague
**VP:* Ron Janak
Brnch Mgr: Brian Murtha
Genl Mgr: Dan Burrows
DP Exec: Mike Nachman

LEASING EQUIPMENT
See ATEL CAPITAL GROUP

D-U-N-S 09-723-3274 IMP
LEATHERLAND CORP
154 F St, Perrysburg, OH 43551-4428
Tel (419) 822-4590 *Founded/Ownrshp* 1976
Sales 15.8MMᴱ *EMP* 300
Accts John A Nomina Delphos Oh
SIC 5699 Leather garments; Leather garments
Pr: Jeffrey R Bell
**Sec:* Janis Chamberlin

D-U-N-S 06-872-5860
LEATHERMAN NURSING CENTERS CORP
200 Smokerise Dr Ste 300, Wadsworth, OH 44281-9499
Tel (330) 336-6684 *Founded/Ownrshp* 1976
Sales 35.8MMᴱ *EMP* 550
SIC 8741 Management services; Management services
Pr: Robert Leatherman
**Sec:* Phyllis Leatherman

D-U-N-S 14-497-8772 IMP/EXP
LEATHERMAN TOOL GROUP INC
12106 Ne Ainsworth Cir, Portland, OR 97220-9001
Tel (503) 253-7826 *Founded/Ownrshp* 1983
Sales 73.5MMᴱ *EMP* 450ᴱ
SIC 3421

D-U-N-S 02-765-1090
LEATHERS ENTERPRISES INC
LEATHERS OIL COMPANY
255 Depot St, Fairview, OR 97024
Tel (503) 661-1244 *Founded/Ownrshp* 1959
Sales 94.8MM *EMP* 75
SIC 5541 6519 Filling stations, gasoline; Real property lessors; Filling stations, gasoline; Real property lessors
Pr: Lila Leathers-Fitz
**VP:* Kathryn Leathers
**Prin:* Brent Leathers
Site Mgr: Sue Hanson
Sls Mgr: Braxton Peterson

LEATHERS OIL COMPANY
See LEATHERS ENTERPRISES INC

D-U-N-S 83-581-4740
LEAVENWORTH CO SPEC ED CO OP
L C S E C O
210 E Mary St, Lansing, KS 66043-1633
Tel (913) 727-1755 *Founded/Ownrshp* 1960
Sales 4.7MMᴱ *EMP* 300
SIC 8299 Airline training; Airline training

D-U-N-S 08-313-0773
LEAVENWORTH UNIFIED SCHOOL DISTRICT 453
200 N 4th St, Leavenworth, KS 66048-1963
Tel (913) 682-5932 *Founded/Ownrshp* 1920
Sales 27.4MMᴱ *EMP* 750
SIC 8211 Public elementary & secondary schools; Public elementary & secondary schools
Treas: Beth Mattox

D-U-N-S 00-145-9049 IMP
LEAVERS LACE CORP (RI)
144 Mishnock Rd, West Greenwich, RI 02817-1669
Tel (401) 397-5555 *Founded/Ownrshp* 1975, 1984
Sales 22.0MM *EMP* 25
SIC 2258 Lace, knit; Lace, knit
Pr: Mark Klauber
**Treas:* York Roberts
**VP:* Gordon Klauber

D-U-N-S 88-414-3280
LEAVITT FINANCIAL GROUP INC
LANIER J SMITH FINANCIAL SVCS
800 3rd Ave, West Point, GA 31833-1529
Tel (706) 645-8201 *Founded/Ownrshp* 1994
Sales 25.0MM *EMP* 2
SIC 6211 Security brokers & dealers; Security brokers & dealers
Pr: Leavitt Sanders
**VP:* Debra Sanders
Off Mgr: Bennie Dorough

D-U-N-S 00-759-7313
LEAVITT GROUP ENTERPRISES INC
216 S 200 W, Cedar City, UT 84720-3207
Tel (435) 586-1555 *Founded/Ownrshp* 1962
Sales 211.0MM *EMP* 1,272
Accts Bdo Usa Llp Las Vegas Nv
SIC 8741 6153 6411 Management services; Working capital financing; Insurance agents, brokers & service; Management services; Working capital financing; Insurance agents, brokers & service
CEO: Eric Leavitt
**Pr:* Vance Smith
**CFO:* Mark Kenney
**Sr VP:* Bruce Crankshaw
**Sr VP:* Nathan Esplin
**Sr VP:* Rod Leavitt
**Sr VP:* Kelly Russell
VP: Julie Beezley
**VP:* Michael Chidester
VP: Gregory Gates
VP: Greg Massey
VP: Terri Peckinpaugh
VP: Derek Snow
VP: Stacy Torneten
VP: Chris Utterback

D-U-N-S 00-967-2163
LEAVITTS FREIGHT SERVICE INC (OR)
3855 Marcola Rd, Springfield, OR 97477-7953
Tel (541) 747-4236 *Founded/Ownrshp* 1946, 1994
Sales 44.6MMᴱ *EMP* 150
Accts Kernutt Strokes Brandt & Co L
SIC 4213 4212 Trucking, except local; Heavy hauling; Local trucking, without storage; Trucking, except local; Heavy hauling; Local trucking, without storage
Pr: Terry Leavitt
CFO: Tiffany Collier
**Sr VP:* Duane Leavitt
**VP:* Ron Riddle
Dir Risk M: Billy Dover
**Prin:* Elizabeth Price
Sfty Dirs: Wendy Schleis
Sls Mgr: Rod Brady

D-U-N-S 01-722-2407
LEAWOOD CITY OF (INC)
4800 Town Center Dr, Leawood, KS 66211-2038
Tel (913) 339-6700 *Founded/Ownrshp* 1948
Sales NA *EMP* 285
Accts Rubinbrown Llp Overland Park
SIC 9111 Executive offices; Executive offices
**Treas:* Dawn Long
Ofcr: Emily Craighead
Ofcr: Paul Day
Ofcr: Eric Gould
Ofcr: Andrew Maxwell
Ofcr: Ted McLntosh
VP: Mark Endrastic
Snr Mgr: Trevor Davis

LEB USA
See QUALIDEN INC

D-U-N-S 10-329-2082
LEBANESE AMERICAN UNIVERSITY
211 E 46th St Fl 3, New York, NY 10017-2912
Tel (212) 203-4333 *Founded/Ownrshp* 1950
Sales 203.6MM *EMP* 5ᴱ
Accts Plante & Moran Pllc Auburn Hi
SIC 8221 University; University
Pr: Dr Joseph G Jabbra

D-U-N-S 06-894-9890
LEBANON CITY SCHOOLS
700 Holbrook Ave, Lebanon, OH 45036-1648
Tel (513) 934-5770 *Founded/Ownrshp* 1925
Sales 28.8MM *EMP* 560
SIC 8211 Public senior high school; Public junior high school; Public elementary & secondary schools; Public elementary school; Public senior high school; Public junior high school; Public elementary & secondary schools; Public elementary school
Schl Brd P: Donna Davis-Norris
Psych: Sarah Kinnison
Psych: Karen Mills

LEBANON COMMUNITY HOSPITAL
See MID-VALLEY HEALTHCARE INC

D-U-N-S 07-206-1054
LEBANON COMMUNITY SCHOOL CORP
1810 N Grant St, Lebanon, IN 46052-1242
Tel (765) 482-0380 *Founded/Ownrshp* 1963
Sales 36.0MM *EMP* 452
SIC 8211 Public elementary school; Public junior high school; Public senior high school; School board; Public elementary school; Public junior high school; Public senior high school; School board
Snr Mgr: Mary Shirley

D-U-N-S 06-876-8977
LEBANON COMMUNITY SCHOOLS
485 S 5th St, Lebanon, OR 97355-2602
Tel (541) 451-1800 *Founded/Ownrshp* 1898
Sales 28.9MMᴱ *EMP* 620
SIC 8211 Public elementary & secondary schools; Public elementary & secondary schools
Sls&Mrk Ex: Ann Rapoza
HC Dir: Lesser Shortridge

D-U-N-S 01-057-7724
LEBANON COUNTY
400 S 8th St Ste 1, Lebanon, PA 17042-6794
Tel (717) 274-2801 *Founded/Ownrshp* 1813
Sales NA *EMP* 1,190
SIC 9111 Executive offices; ; Executive offices;
Treas: Sally Neuin
IT Man: Stephanie Axarlis
IT Man: Derek Black
IT Man: Brian Deiderick
IT Man: James Holtry

LEBANON DEMOCRAT
See LEBANON PUBLISHING CO INC

LEBANON FORD
See FORD LEBANON INC

D-U-N-S 09-566-8091
■ LEBANON HMA LLC
UNIVERSITY MEDICAL CENTER HOSP
(*Suby of* HEALTH MANAGEMENT ASSOCIATES INC) ★
1411 W Baddour Pkwy, Lebanon, TN 37087-2513
Tel (615) 444-8262 *Founded/Ownrshp* 2003
Sales 99.5MM *EMP* 700
SIC 8062 General medical & surgical hospitals; General medical & surgical hospitals
CEO: Vins Cherry
**CEO:* Matt Caldwell
**COO:* Greg Carda
Dir Rx: Charles Waters
Off Mgr: Harold Galbraith
Doctor: Haroon Kahn
Doctor: Robert Patti
Pharmcst: Tom Keifer

D-U-N-S 10-062-6949
LEBANON NURSING & REHABILITATION CENTER LLC
115 Oregonia Rd, Lebanon, OH 45036-1983
Tel (513) 932-1121 *Founded/Ownrshp* 2007
Sales 40.0MM *EMP* 65
SIC 8051 Skilled nursing care facilities; Skilled nursing care facilities
Pt: Steve Feigenbaum

D-U-N-S 00-405-0761
LEBANON PUBLISHING CO INC (TN)
LEBANON DEMOCRAT
(*Suby of* JOHNSON CITY PRESS) ★
402 N Cumberland St, Lebanon, TN 37087-2306
Tel (615) 444-3952 *Founded/Ownrshp* 1889, 2002
Sales 22.2MMᴱ *EMP* 300
SIC 2711 Newspapers, publishing & printing; Newspapers, publishing & printing
VP: Joseph H Adams
VP: Jesse Lindsey
Prd Mgr: J M Rodgers
Prd Mgr: Mark Rodgers
Advt Dir: Melanie Ray
Mktg Dir: Charity Toombs
Board of Directors: Katherine Jones

D-U-N-S 07-992-5038
LEBANON R-III SCHOOL DISTRICT
1310 E Route 66, Lebanon, MO 65536-5331
Tel (417) 532-9141 *Founded/Ownrshp* 1860, 2006
Sales 33.7MMᴱ *EMP* 675
Accts Clark Schaefer Hackett & Co
SIC 8211 Public elementary & secondary schools; Public elementary & secondary schools
VP: Jim Carr

D-U-N-S 03-842-1954
LEBANON SCHOOL DISTRICT
1000 S 8th St, Lebanon, PA 17042-6727
Tel (717) 273-9391 *Founded/Ownrshp* 1816
Sales 30.7MMᴱ *EMP* 525
SIC 8211 Public elementary & secondary schools; Public elementary & secondary schools
**Treas:* Brian G Zimmerman
Adm Dir: Donyell Traston
CTO: William Waste
Cmptr Lab: Frances Muhr
Dir IT: Shawn Canady
Schl Brd P: Anne Dall
Board of Directors: Anna H Dinulos, Rose Marie R Kotay, Kim Moyer, Jacqueline Parker, John P Shott, George Zimmerman

D-U-N-S 00-300-5477 IMP/EXP
LEBANON SEABOARD CORP (PA)
1600 E Cumberland St, Lebanon, PA 17042-8323
Tel (717) 273-1685 *Founded/Ownrshp* 1947
Sales 139.5MMᴱ *EMP* 300
SIC 5191 2875 2048

D-U-N-S 19-306-7642
LEBANON SPECIAL SCHOOL DISTRICT
701 Coles Ferry Pike, Lebanon, TN 37087-5631
Tel (615) 449-6060 *Founded/Ownrshp* 1901
Sales 18.6MMᴱ *EMP* 350
SIC 8211 9411 Public elementary & secondary schools; Administration of educational programs; Public elementary & secondary schools; Administration of educational programs

LEBANON SUPPLY COMPANY
See INDEPENDENT STAVE CO LLC

D-U-N-S 00-300-5121
LEBANON TOOL CO INC
LTC
(*Suby of* P R L INC) ★
330 N 7th Ave, Lebanon, PA 17046-4000
Tel (717) 273-3711 *Founded/Ownrshp* 1985
Sales 20.9MMᴱ *EMP* 125
SIC 3599 Machine shop, jobbing & repair; Machine shop, jobbing & repair
Pr: Janis Herschkowitz
**Sec:* L Saylor Zimmerman III
**VP:* Ronald C Bailor

D-U-N-S 08-244-1676
LEBANON VALLEY BRETHREN HOME (PA)
1200 Grubb Rd, Palmyra, PA 17078-3514
Tel (717) 838-5406 *Founded/Ownrshp* 1973
Sales 18.9MM *EMP* 280
SIC 8051 7299

D-U-N-S 06-979-1457
LEBANON VALLEY COLLEGE
101 N College Ave, Annville, PA 17003-1400
Tel (717) 867-6100 *Founded/Ownrshp* 1866
Sales 57.5MM *EMP* 300ᴱ
Accts Baker Tilly Virchow Krause Ll
SIC 8221 College, except junior; College, except junior
Pr: Stephen Macdonald
Ex VP: Kevin Yeiser
**VP:* Deborah Fullam
**VP:* Robert Hamilton
VP: Gregory Krikorian
VP: Steven Schuetz
Ex Dir: Ken Andrews
Ex Dir: Jenny Murphy-Shifflet
Info Man: Matthew P Velazquez
Pr Mgr: Ann Myers

LEBAUER HEALTH CARE
See LEBAUER WEINTRAUB BRODIE & PATTERSON ASSOCIATES DRS PA

D-U-N-S 06-030-0050
LEBAUER WEINTRAUB BRODIE & PATTERSON ASSOCIATES DRS PA
LEBAUER HEALTH CARE
(*Suby of* ANNIE PENN HOSPITAL) ★
520 N Elam Ave, Greensboro, NC 27403-1127
Tel (336) 547-1700 *Founded/Ownrshp* 1931
Sales 25.1MMᴱ *EMP* 350
SIC 8011 Offices & clinics of medical doctors; Offices & clinics of medical doctors
Pr: Jeffrey Katz
**Treas:* Dr Eugene Lebauer
VP: Angel White
Off Mgr: Ashley Smith
Site Mgr: Annie Bason
Psych: Curtis Graves
Doctor: Daniel Bensimhon
Doctor: Dora Brodie
Doctor: M T Stark

D-U-N-S 07-673-6404 IMP
LEBCO INDUSTRIES LP
LA-Z-BOY FURNITURE GALLORIES
10676 King William Dr, Dallas, TX 75220-2413
Tel (214) 631-1813 *Founded/Ownrshp* 1975
Sales 29.5MMᴱ *EMP* 130
SIC 5712 Furniture stores
Pt: Lewis E Brown Jr

D-U-N-S 78-841-9690
LEBENTHAL HOLDINGS
ALEXANDRA & JAMES
230 Park Ave Fl 32, New York, NY 10169-3204
Tel (212) 425-6006 *Founded/Ownrshp* 2006
Sales 33.6MMᴱ *EMP* 125ᴱ
SIC 6211 Stock brokers & dealers; Stock brokers & dealers
Ofcr: Keith Flood
Mng Dir: Vijay Chopra
Mng Dir: Leila Heckman
Snr Mgr: Judith Feder
Snr Mgr: John Mullin

D-U-N-S 04-775-7059
LEBEOUF BROS TOWING L L C
124 Dry Dock Rd, Bourg, LA 70343-3815
Tel (985) 594-6691 *Founded/Ownrshp* 1957
Sales 28.0MMᴱ *EMP* 100
SIC 4449 3731 4492 Canal barge operations; Shipbuilding & repairing; Towing & tugboat service; Canal barge operations; Shipbuilding & repairing; Towing & tugboat service
Pr: Richard A Gonsoulin
Pr: Mark Bourgeois
MIS Dir: Jean Pontiff

D-U-N-S 00-130-4534 IMP
LEBHAR-FRIEDMAN INC (NY)
CHAIN STORES AGE
150 W 30th St Fl 19, New York, NY 10001-4119
Tel (212) 756-5000 *Founded/Ownrshp* 1925
Sales 110.3MM^E *EMP* 460
SIC 2721 2711 Magazines: publishing only, not printed on site; Newspapers: publishing only, not printed on site; Magazines: publishing only, not printed on site; Newspapers: publishing only, not printed on site
Pr: J Roger Friedman
**Pr:* Daniel J Mills
COO: Bruce Smith
Ofcr: Paul Frumkin
Creative D: Darren Ursino
Area Mgr: Catherine Stephany
Sls Dir: Chris Keating
Sls Dir: Michael Morrissey
Assoc Ed: Drew Buono

LEBLANC AUTOMOBILES
See LEXUS OF NEW ORLEANS

D-U-N-S 60-682-1650
■ **LEBO AUTOMOTIVE INC**
SOUTH BAY LINCOLN MERCURY
(*Suby of* AUTONATION INC) ★
1500 N Sepulveda Blvd, Manhattan Beach, CA 90266-5110
Tel (310) 546-4848 *Founded/Ownrshp* 2000
Sales 38.2MM^E *EMP* 90
SIC 5511 Automobiles, new & used; Automobiles, new & used
CEO: Darrell L Sperber
**Prin:* Leo R Boese
Mktg Dir: Albert Wise

D-U-N-S 00-733-0137 IMP
LEBUS INTERNATIONAL INC
215 Industrial Dr, Longview, TX 75602-4719
Tel (903) 758-5521 *Founded/Ownrshp* 1901
Sales 30.0MM *EMP* 130^E
SIC 3496 3443 3429 7699 Wire winding; Drums, knockout (reflux, etc.): metal plate; Pulleys metal; Aircraft & heavy equipment repair services; Wire winding; Drums, knockout (reflux, etc.): metal plate; Pulleys metal; Aircraft & heavy equipment repair services
CEO: Charles F Lebus
**Pr:* Frank L Lebus III
**Treas:* Daniel Tucker
**Chf Mktg O:* David Green
IT Man: Richard Nelson
**VP Sls:* Jimmy Deweese
Board of Directors: David Green

D-U-N-S 79-430-5102
LECASA INC
WILDE LEXUS OF SARASOTA
4883 Clark Rd, Sarasota, FL 34233-3219
Tel (941) 924-3040 *Founded/Ownrshp* 1992
Sales 28.9MM^E *EMP* 70
SIC 5511 Automobiles, new & used; Automobiles, new & used
VP: Mark Wilde
Sls Mgr: Kenny Clark

LECESSE CONSTRUCTION COMPANY
See LAHR CONSTRUCTION CORP

D-U-N-S 00-940-4238
LECESSE CONSTRUCTION SERVICES LLC
LAHR CONSTRUCTION
(*Suby of* PIKE CO INC) ★
75 Thruway Park Dr Ste 1, West Henrietta, NY 14586-9793
Tel (585) 334-4490 *Founded/Ownrshp* 2012
Sales 22.0MM^E *EMP* 75
SIC 1522 1542 Residential construction; Multi-family dwelling construction; Multi-family dwellings, new construction; Nonresidential construction; Commercial & office building, new construction; Specialized public building contractors
Pr: Andrew Hislop
**VP:* Barry Ingalsbe

D-U-N-S 03-651-9767
LECHASE CONSTRUCTION SERVICES LLC
205 Indigo Creek Dr, Rochester, NY 14626-5100
Tel (585) 254-3510 *Founded/Ownrshp* 1997
Sales 685.4MM^E *EMP* 780
SIC 1541 1542 Industrial buildings, new construction; Renovation, remodeling & repairs: industrial buildings; Nonresidential construction; Institutional building construction; Commercial & office building, new construction; Commercial & office buildings, renovation & repair; Industrial buildings, new construction; Renovation, remodeling & repairs: industrial buildings; Nonresidential construction; Institutional building construction; Commercial & office building, new construction; Commercial & office buildings, renovation & repair
CEO: William H Goodrich
**Pr:* William H Goodrich
**Pr:* William L Mack
Pr: Thomas W Porter
COO: Bill Goodrich
**Ch:* Wayne Le Chase
Ex VP: Will Mack
VP: William Herbert
VP: Joe Morgigno
VP: James Mulcahy
Exec: Sean Cahill
Exec: Ryan Faulkner
Exec: Paul Klinko
**Exec:* Raymond F Lechase II
Dir Risk M: Michelle Keller

D-U-N-S 18-344-1732
LECLAIRRYAN A PROFESSNL CORP
951 E Byrd St Fl 8, Richmond, VA 23219-4055
Tel (804) 783-2003 *Founded/Ownrshp* 1989
Sales 124.4MM^E *EMP* 715
SIC 8111 General practice law office; General practice law office
CEO: David C Freinberg
**Ch Bd:* Gary D Leclair
**Pr:* Micheal L Hern
**COO:* Dennis M Ryan
**CFO:* Joseph D Cheely
CFO: Joseph Cheely
VP: Charles Meyer
**VP:* Douglas L Sbertoli
VP: Robert Yates
CIO: Peter Mederos
CIO: Lara Pasternack

D-U-N-S 00-474-6683 IMP
LECLERC FOODS TENNESSEE LLC (TN)
(*Suby of* BISCUITS LECLERC LTEE)
10444 Wallace Alley St, Kingsport, TN 37663-3934
Tel (423) 212-2240 *Founded/Ownrshp* 2008
Sales 34.5MM^E *EMP* 52^E
SIC 5149 Groceries & related products; Cookies; Crackers; Chocolate
Ex VP: Jean-Marc Lemoine

D-U-N-S 13-760-3903
LECLERC FOODS USA INC
(*Suby of* BISCUITS LECLERC LTEE)
44 Park Dr, Montgomery, PA 17752-8534
Tel (570) 547-6295 *Founded/Ownrshp* 2002
Sales 24.9MM^E *EMP* 100
SIC 2052 5411 Pretzels; Supermarkets
Pr: Denis Leclerc
**VP:* Jean Leclerc
**VP:* Sebastien Leclerc
VP: Lyne Normand
Plnt Mgr: Kevin Rosenow
Sls Dir: Shelby Counsil

D-U-N-S 00-506-8861 IMP
LECO CORP
TEM-PRESS DIVISION
3000 Lakeview Ave, Saint Joseph, MI 49085-2319
Tel (269) 983-5531 *Founded/Ownrshp* 1936
Sales 186.9MM^E *EMP* 725
Accts Bdo Usa Llp Kalamazoo Mi
SIC 3821 4493 3826 3825 3823 3264 Laboratory apparatus, except heating & measuring; Chemical laboratory apparatus; Boat yards, storage & incidental repair; Marine basins; Analytical instruments; Instruments to measure electricity; Industrial instrmnts msrmnt display/control process variable; Porcelain electrical supplies; Laboratory apparatus, except heating & measuring; Chemical laboratory apparatus; Boat yards, storage & incidental repair; Marine basins; Analytical instruments; Instruments to measure electricity; Industrial instrmnts msrmnt display/control process variable; Porcelain electrical supplies
Pr: Robert J Warren
**Pr:* B John Hawkins
**Pr:* Larry S O'Brien
**Pr:* Elizabeth S Warren
Genl Mgr: Melissa Rogers
Web Dev: Tyler Newton
Ql Cn Mgr: Bradley Wilson
Sls Dir: Nick Hall
Snr Mgr: Arthur Klein

LECOM
See LAKE ERIE COLLEGE OF OSTEOPATHIC MEDICINE INC

D-U-N-S 60-120-8770
LECON INC
4302 Creekmont Dr, Houston, TX 77091-5330
Tel (713) 681-4366 *Founded/Ownrshp* 1988
Sales 20.8MM^E *EMP* 106
SIC 1794 1629 Excavation & grading, building construction; Dredging contractor; Excavation & grading, building construction; Dredging contractor
Pr: Daniel D Lloyd
**VP:* Candy C Lloyd
IT Man: Susan Cribbs
Sfty Mgr: Caleb King

D-U-N-S 07-490-0317
LECONTE MEDICAL CENTER
FORT SANDERS-SEVIER MEDICAL CENTER
(*Suby of* COVENANT HEALTH) ★
742 Middle Creek Rd, Sevierville, TN 37862-5019
Tel (865) 429-6100 *Founded/Ownrshp* 1981
Sales 70.3MM *EMP* 450
SIC 8062 8051 Hospital, affiliated with AMA residency; Convalescent home with continuous nursing care; Hospital, affiliated with AMA residency; Convalescent home with continuous nursing care
Pr: Ellen Wilhoit
**VP:* Rick Carringer
Pharmcst: Amanda Miller
Pharmcst: Dennis Woods
Board of Directors: Mandy Conner

D-U-N-S 80-540-7939
LECOQ CUISINE CORP
35 Union Ave Ste 1, Bridgeport, CT 06607-2335
Tel (203) 334-1010 *Founded/Ownrshp* 1991
Sales 32.5MM^E *EMP* 72
SIC 5149 5461 Bakery products; Pastries
CEO: Eric Lecoq
COO: Michael Maduri
IT Man: Sam Ezell

D-U-N-S 78-475-9110
LECS LTD
11226 Jones Rd W, Houston, TX 77065-3617
Tel (281) 897-9775 *Founded/Ownrshp* 1989
Sales 31.3MM^E *EMP* 175
SIC 1731

LECTORA
See TRIVANTIS CORP

D-U-N-S 05-668-5530 IMP
LECTORUM PUBLICATIONS INC (NY)
205 Chubb Ave Bldg A-1, Lyndhurst, NJ 07071-3520
Tel (201) 559-2200 *Founded/Ownrshp* 1960, 1996
Sales 30.6MM^E *EMP* 48
Accts David T Ontell & Co Pa Liv
SIC 5192 5942 Books; Book stores
Pr: Alex Correa
**Treas:* Fernando Febus
Prd Mgr: Margie Samper

D-U-N-S 15-191-9834
LECTRA USA INC
(*Suby of* LECTRA)
5000 Highlands Pkwy Se # 250, Smyrna, GA 30082-5148
Tel (770) 422-8050 *Founded/Ownrshp* 1980
Sales 29.6MM^E *EMP* 117^E
SIC 7373 3541 1796 5045 Computer-aided manufacturing (CAM) systems service; Machine tools, metal cutting type; Machinery installation; Computers, peripherals & software; Computer-aided manufacturing (CAM) systems service; Machine tools, metal cutting type; Machinery installation; Computers, peripherals & software
Ch: Andr Harari
**Pr:* David Siegelman
**CEO:* Daniel Harari
Off Admin: Michel Cavalier
CIO: Veronique Zoccoletto
IT Man: Chris Bonney
Sls Mgr: Chris Young
Sales Asso: James Chambers

D-U-N-S 03-408-8083 EXP
LECTRODRYER LLC (KY)
135 Quality Dr, Richmond, KY 40475-9621
Tel (859) 624-2091 *Founded/Ownrshp* 1932, 2001
Sales 27.5MM^E *EMP* 40
SIC 3569 Liquid automation machinery & equipment; Filter elements, fluid, hydraulic line
CEO: Ted Warren

D-U-N-S 05-268-9361
LECTROSONICS INC (NM)
581 Laser Rd Ne, Rio Rancho, NM 87124-4508
Tel (505) 892-4501 *Founded/Ownrshp* 1971, 1981
Sales 25.0MM *EMP* 161
SIC 3651 3663 Microphones; Sound reproducing equipment; Radio & TV communications equipment; Microphones; Sound reproducing equipment; Radio & TV communications equipment
Ch Bd: John Arasim Jr
**Pr:* Lawrence E Fisher
**Treas:* Phillip Herkenhoff
**Sec:* Lawrence L Leyba
**Sec:* John A Westman
**VP:* Robert G Cunnings
**VP:* Wesley B Herron
**VP:* Bruce Jones
**VP:* John G Moore
Dir IT: Rich Weber
Netwrk Mgr: Richard Webber

D-U-N-S 61-346-7661 IMP
LECTRUS CORP
1919 W Polymer Dr, Chattanooga, TN 37421-2204
Tel (423) 894-9268 *Founded/Ownrshp* 1976
Sales 124.6MM^E *EMP* 393
SIC 3444 Metal housings, enclosures, casings & other containers; Metal housings, enclosures, casings & other containers
Pr: Brian Fine
COO: Karen Cameron
**CFO:* Gordon Stewart
VP: Thomas Bigger
VP: Andrew Whelan
Mtls Mgr: Brent Houts

LEDBETTER PACKING
See EMPIRE PACKING CO LP

D-U-N-S 78-670-6296
LEDCOR CMI INC
6405 Mira Mesa Blvd # 100, San Diego, CA 92121-4120
Tel (602) 595-3017 *Founded/Ownrshp* 2003
Sales 158.5MM^E *EMP* 5,000
SIC 1541 1611 1629 1623 1522 8999 Industrial buildings & warehouses; Highway & street construction; Mine loading & discharging station construction; Industrial plant construction; Pipeline construction; Condominium construction; Communication services; Industrial buildings & warehouses; Highway & street construction; Mine loading & discharging station construction; Industrial plant construction; Pipeline construction; Condominium construction; Communication services
CEO: David W Lede

D-U-N-S 79-253-6588 IMP
LEDCOR CONSTRUCTION HAWAII LLC
1003 Bishop St Ste 2150, Honolulu, HI 96813-6438
Tel (808) 540-0777 *Founded/Ownrshp* 2005
Sales 20.4MM^E *EMP* 250
SIC 1522 1541 Hotel/motel & multi-family home construction; Industrial buildings & warehouses; Hotel/motel & multi-family home construction; Industrial buildings & warehouses
Ex VP: Hugh Brown

D-U-N-S 07-633-0500
LEDCOR CONSTRUCTION INC
LEDCOR GROUP
(*Suby of* LEDCOR HOLDINGS INC)
6405 Mira Mesa Blvd # 100, San Diego, CA 92121-4120
Tel (858) 527-6400 *Founded/Ownrshp* 2001
Sales 83.7MM^E *EMP* 150
SIC 1542 Commercial & office building, new construction; Commercial & office building, new construction
CEO: Christopher Bourassa
**CFO:* James Logan
VP: Lee Coonfer
VP: Ron Hughes
Exec: Dave Jeffrey
Rgnl Mgr: Darko Brkin
Sfty Dirs: Nicolette Drake
Sfty Dirs: Vanessa Harper
Sfty Mgr: Neil Paterson
Opers Mgr: Brian Knysh
Ql Cn Mgr: Martin Valkenburg

LEDCOR GROUP
See LEDCOR CONSTRUCTION INC

LEDEX & DORMEYER PRODUCTS
See SAIA-BURGESS LCC

D-U-N-S 60-513-6415
LEDGER
LEDGER PUBLISHING COMPANY
(*Suby of* HALIFAX MEDIA HOLDINGS LLC) ★
300 W Lime St, Lakeland, FL 33815-4649
Tel (863) 802-7000 *Founded/Ownrshp* 2012
Sales 57.4MM^E *EMP* 385
SIC 2759 2711 Commercial printing; Newspapers, publishing & printing; Commercial printing; Newspapers, publishing & printing
Ch: Arthur Ochs Sulzberger
CFO: Alan Greene
Treas: Laurena L Emhoff
VP: R A Benten
Exec: Susan Gossett
Dir Bus: Anthony Tucker

LEDGER PUBLISHING COMPANY
See LEDGER

D-U-N-S 17-434-5934
LEDGEWOOD HEALTH CARE CORP
LEDGEWOOD NURSING CARE CENTER
87 Herrick St, Beverly, MA 01915-2773
Tel (978) 524-6100 *Founded/Ownrshp* 1984
Sales 1.4MM^E *EMP* 140
SIC 8051 Skilled nursing care facilities; Skilled nursing care facilities
**Pr:* James Dunn
**Treas:* Greg Sorrell
**VP:* Richard Blinn
Exec: Betty Liacos

LEDGEWOOD NURSING CARE CENTER
See LEDGEWOOD HEALTH CARE CORP

D-U-N-S 05-451-8139
LEDIC MANAGEMENT GROUP LLC
2650 Thousand Oaks Blvd # 3100, Memphis, TN 38118-2459
Tel (901) 761-9300 *Founded/Ownrshp* 1979
Sales 28.9MM^E *EMP* 50
SIC 6531 Real estate managers
Dir Bus: Michael Phelan
Dist Mgr: Merrie Long

D-U-N-S 00-562-9605 IMP
LEDRA BRANDS INC
BRUCK LIGHTING
15774 Gateway Cir, Tustin, CA 92780-6469
Tel (714) 259-9959 *Founded/Ownrshp* 1993
Sales 25.9MM^E *EMP* 55
SIC 5023 Lamps: floor, boudoir, desk
Pr: Alex Ladjevardi

D-U-N-S 11-541-1845 IMP
LEDTRONICS INC
23105 Kashiwa Ct, Torrance, CA 90505-4026
Tel (310) 534-1505 *Founded/Ownrshp* 1983
Sales 30.9MM^E *EMP* 130
SIC 3674 3825 3641 Light emitting diodes; Instruments to measure electricity; Electric lamps; Light emitting diodes; Instruments to measure electricity; Electric lamps
Pr: Pervaiz Lodhie
CFO: Mazvar Rizvi
**VP:* Almas Lodhie
Sfty Mgr: Kevin Sweeney
Ql Cn Mgr: Ron Draucker
Mktg Mgr: Raffi Shubukian
Sales Asso: Kurt Gamlin

D-U-N-S 00-805-3027 IMP/EXP
LEDWELL & SON ENTERPRISES INC
OFFICE SOURCE
3300 Waco St, Texarkana, TX 75501-6645
Tel (903) 838-6531 *Founded/Ownrshp* 1946
Sales 46.1MM^E *EMP* 214^E
SIC 3715 5013 Truck trailers; Trailer parts & accessories; Truck trailers; Trailer parts & accessories
Pr: Stephen H Ledwell
**Sec:* Steven Ledwell
**Ex VP:* Mary Elizabeth Ledwell
QA Dir: Dennis Hughes
QA Dir: Chuck Kift
IT Man: James Greger

LEDYARD DEPARTMENT EDUCATION
See LEDYARD PUBLIC SCHOOLS

D-U-N-S 79-457-1240
LEDYARD NATIONAL BANK
(*Suby of* LEDYARD FINANCIAL GROUP, INC.)
320 Main St, Norwich, VT 05055-4418
Tel (802) 649-2050 *Founded/Ownrshp* 1991
Sales NA *EMP* 85
SIC 6021 National commercial banks; National commercial banks
Pr: Catherin G Underwood
CFO: Greg Steverson
Trst Ofcr: Robert T Boon

D-U-N-S 96-810-7268
LEDYARD PUBLIC SCHOOLS
LEDYARD DEPARTMENT EDUCATION
4 Blonder Park Rd, Ledyard, CT 06339-1504
Tel (860) 464-9255 *Founded/Ownrshp* 1850
Sales 18.7MM^E *EMP* 300
SIC 8211 Public elementary & secondary schools; Public elementary & secondary schools
Treas: Carolyn Hollis
IT Man: Theodore Doyle
IT Man: Terry Samokar
Teacher Pr: Therese Roush

D-U-N-S 04-304-3967
LEE & CATES GLASS INC
5355 Shawland Rd, Jacksonville, FL 32254-1649
Tel (904) 354-4643 *Founded/Ownrshp* 1926
Sales 24.3MM^E *EMP* 145
SIC 7536 1793 Automotive glass replacement shops; Glass & glazing work; Automotive glass replacement shops; Glass & glazing work
Ch Bd: Thomas D Lee Jr
**Pr:* Thomas D Lee III
**VP:* Rick Padgett
Dist Mgr: Randy Mann
VP Opers: Scott Cates

Sls&Mrk Ex: Bob Gardner
Snr PM: Vince Simeone

D-U-N-S 05-347-3790
LEE & LEE SUPPLIES INC
GRANT SUPPLIES
411 Alfred Ave, Teaneck, NJ 07666-5755
Tel (718) 729-2373 *Founded/Ownrshp* 2009
Sales 21.2MM^E *EMP* 20
SIC 5074 Plumbing fittings & supplies
Pr: Anna Lee

D-U-N-S 60-915-9868
LEE AEROSPACE INC
TRIUMPH ARSPC SYSTEMS- WICHITA
9323 E 34th St N, Wichita, KS 67226-2621
Tel (316) 636-9200 *Founded/Ownrshp* 2014
Sales 49.3MM^E *EMP* 142
SIC 3728 Aircraft body assemblies & parts; Aircraft body assemblies & parts
Pr: James Lee
COO: Cub Marion
Treas: David Kornblatt
VP: Tim Dugan
Genl Mgr: Greg Piland
IT Man: James Edwards

D-U-N-S 02-452-5826
LEE AIR CONDITIONERS INC
5109 Neal Rd, Durham, NC 27705-2364
Tel (919) 383-1588 *Founded/Ownrshp* 1951
Sales 23.3MM^E *EMP* 100^E
SIC 1711 Heating & air conditioning contractors
Pr: Joseph M Lee III
CFO: Tom Armstrong
**VP:* Scott Lee
Genl Mgr: Miles Standish

D-U-N-S 19-788-3366 IMP
LEE AND JAMES LTD
75 Albrecht Dr, Lake Bluff, IL 60044-2226
Tel (847) 615-2110 *Founded/Ownrshp* 1988
Sales 24.3MM^E *EMP* 150
SIC 5961 Catalog sales; Catalog sales
Pr: Karen B Scott
**Treas:* Ian Scott
VP: Linda Lomax
Mktg Mgr: Mary Knabe

D-U-N-S 11-284-6977 IMP/EXP
LEE ANDERSON CO INC
EXXON
100 Westwood Ln, Brenham, TX 77833-5696
Tel (979) 830-0830 *Founded/Ownrshp* 1983
Sales 22.1MM^E *EMP* 70^E
SIC 5541 5411 5812 5947 Filling stations, gasoline; Convenience stores, independent; Restaurant, family: chain; Gift shop
Pr: Brett L Smith

D-U-N-S 00-713-1501
■ LEE APPAREL CO INC (PA)
(*Suby of* VF CORP) ★
1 Lee Dr, Shawnee Mission, KS 66202-3620
Tel (913) 789-0330 *Founded/Ownrshp* 1889
Sales 463.6MM^E *EMP* 10,300
SIC 2325 2339 Jeans: men's, youths' & boys'; Jeans: women's, misses' & juniors'; Jeans: men's, youths' & boys'; Jeans: women's, misses' & juniors'
Pr: Terry Lay
Pr: Claudia Broddus
CFO: Mike Mitchell
Board of Directors: William C Hardy, G G Johnson, Mackey J McDonald, Frank C Pickard III, L R Pugh

LEE AUTO MALL
See LEE CHRYSLER PLYMOUTH

D-U-N-S 10-183-2681
LEE AUTOMOTIVE GROUP
LEE CHRYSLER DODGE
541 M Esther Cut Off Nw, Fort Walton Beach, FL 32548
Tel (850) 244-7611 *Founded/Ownrshp* 1981
Sales 23.5MM^E *EMP* 79
SIC 5511 Automobiles, new & used; Automobiles, new & used
Pr: Robert E Lee

D-U-N-S 02-348-5667 IMP
LEE BEVERAGE CO INC
2850 S Oakwood Rd, Oshkosh, WI 54904-6378
Tel (920) 235-1140 *Founded/Ownrshp* 1962
Sales 30.4MM^E *EMP* 84
SIC 5181 Beer & ale; Beer & ale
Pr: Jeff Lindemann
Sls Mgr: Craig Plaszcz

D-U-N-S 10-690-7751 IMP
LEE BRASS CO
1800 Golden Springs Rd, Anniston, AL 36207-8324
Tel (256) 831-4615 *Founded/Ownrshp* 2008
Sales 57.2MM^E *EMP* 250
SIC 3366 Brass foundry; Brass foundry
Pr: Bruce Jameson
CFO: Reiber Heath
IT Man: Duska Lewis
Mtls Mgr: Debbie Ferguson
S&M/VP: Phillip Stephens
Sls Mgr: Robyn Stephens

D-U-N-S 60-253-1118
LEE BRASS FOUNDRY LLC
(*Suby of* MORRIS CAPITAL MANAGEMENT LLC) ★
1800 Golden Springs Rd, Anniston, AL 36207-8324
Tel (256) 831-2501 *Founded/Ownrshp* 2012
Sales 37.6MM^E *EMP* 216
SIC 3366 Machinery castings: brass; Machinery castings: brass
Pr: Ken Dickson
**COO:* David Smith
**CFO:* Reiber Heath

LEE BRICK & BLOCK
See LEE MASONRY PRODUCTS INC

D-U-N-S 13-161-2335 IMP
LEE BROS FOODSERVICES INC
LEE INDUSTRIAL CATERING
660 E Gish Rd, San Jose, CA 95112-2707
Tel (408) 275-0700 *Founded/Ownrshp* 1985
Sales 86.1MM^E *EMP* 150
SIC 5141 5142 Groceries, general line; Packaged frozen goods; Groceries, general line; Packaged frozen goods
CEO: Chieu Van Le
COO: Tu Lee
**VP:* Huong Le
**VP:* Jimmy Lee
MIS Dir: David Hui

LEE CHRYSLER DODGE
See LEE AUTOMOTIVE GROUP

LEE CHRYSLER JEEP DODGE
See ADVANCE AUTO SALES INC

D-U-N-S 84-702-6978
LEE CHRYSLER PLYMOUTH
LEE AUTO MALL
200 Main St, Westbrook, ME 04092-4733
Tel (207) 856-6685 *Founded/Ownrshp* 1993
Sales 71.3MM^E *EMP* 259
SIC 5511 Automobiles, new & used; Automobiles, new & used
Pr: Don Lee
Sales Asso: Dan Mahoney

D-U-N-S 00-116-2395 IMP
LEE CO (CT)
2 Pettipaug Rd, Westbrook, CT 06498-1500
Tel (860) 399-6281 *Founded/Ownrshp* 1949
Sales 227.0MM^E *EMP* 915
SIC 3823 3841 3812 3728 3714 Fluidic devices, circuits & systems for process control; Surgical & medical instruments; Search & navigation equipment; Aircraft parts & equipment; Motor vehicle parts & accessories; Fluidic devices, circuits & systems for process control; Surgical & medical instruments; Search & navigation equipment; Aircraft parts & equipment; Motor vehicle parts & accessories
Pr: William W Lee
**CFO:* Alex M Corl
**Ch:* Leighton Lee III
Chf Mktg O: John Kingsbury
**Ex VP:* Robert M Lee
VP: William Buckridge
VP: Jeffrey Dickey
VP: Bob Hawtin
Exec: Michael Curtis
Dist Mgr: Ryan Dieterle
Dist Mgr: Jeff Svadlenak

D-U-N-S 06-908-8680
LEE CO (TN)
TENNESSEE LEE COMPANY
331 Mallory Station Rd, Franklin, TN 37067-8257
Tel (615) 567-1000 *Founded/Ownrshp* 1965
Sales 136.5MM *EMP* 820
Accts Crowe Horwath
SIC 1711 Plumbing contractors; Warm air heating & air conditioning contractor; Refrigeration contractor; Plumbing contractors; Warm air heating & air conditioning contractor; Refrigeration contractor
CEO: William B Lee
**Pr:* Richard C Perko
Pr: Gerry Vance
**CFO:* Roy B Osborne
**Ex VP:* Gerald R Vance
**Sr VP:* Stuart L Price
VP: Richard Perko
**VP:* Steve Scott
Dir IT: Tom Goddard
Dir IT: Chris Young
IT Man: Jamie Holmes

D-U-N-S 60-956-3440 EXP
LEE CONTAINER CORP INC
275 Chambers Blvd, Homerville, GA 31634
Tel (912) 487-3632 *Founded/Ownrshp* 1989
Sales 20.8MM^E *EMP* 175
SIC 3085

D-U-N-S 79-151-5455
LEE CONTRACTING INC
LEE INDUSTRIAL CONTRACTING
631 Cesar E Chavez Ave, Pontiac, MI 48342-1074
Tel (248) 332-4646 *Founded/Ownrshp* 1995
Sales 128.5MM^E *EMP* 150
SIC 1731 1542 1541 Electrical work; Commercial & office building, new construction; Industrial buildings, new construction; Electrical work; Commercial & office building, new construction; Industrial buildings, new construction
Pr: Edward E Lee
Dir Bus: Conston Taylor
Snr Mgr: Clint Knoblock

D-U-N-S 10-064-6165
LEE COUNTY BOARD OF EDUCATION
LEE COUNTY SCHOOL SYSTEM
126 Starksville Ave N, Leesburg, GA 31763-4548
Tel (229) 903-2100 *Founded/Ownrshp* 2002
Sales 55.3MM *EMP* 800
SIC 8211 Public elementary & secondary schools; Public elementary & secondary schools

D-U-N-S 09-884-8468
LEE COUNTY BOARD OF EDUCATION
LEE COUNTY SCHOOL DISTRICT
2410 Society Hill Rd, Opelika, AL 36804-4856
Tel (334) 745-9770 *Founded/Ownrshp* 1950
Sales 50.5MM^E *EMP* 1,200
SIC 8211 Public elementary & secondary schools; Public elementary & secondary schools
**Pr:* Mr Napoleon Stringer
**VP:* Mr Larry Boswell
MIS Dir: Richard Morgan
Pr Dir: Billie Williamson

LEE COUNTY BOARD SUPERVISORS
See COUNTY OF LEE

D-U-N-S 00-384-0337
LEE COUNTY ELECTRIC COOPERATIVE INC
LCEC
4980 Bayline Dr, Fort Myers, FL 33917-3998
Tel (800) 599-2356 *Founded/Ownrshp* 1940
Sales 405.9MM *EMP* 400
SIC 4911 Electric services; Electric services
CEO: Dennie Hamilton
**CFO:* Donald Schleicher
Trst: William Mathis
Snr Ntwrk: Mark Monteleone
IT Man: Susan Crisafulli
IT Man: Stanley Hyde
Software D: Cindy Neumann
Netwrk Eng: Brian Klepper
Mktg Dir: Barbara Panellino
Mktg Mgr: Melissa Miller

D-U-N-S 06-743-9703
LEE COUNTY OF (INC)
106 Hillcrest Dr, Sanford, NC 27330-4021
Tel (919) 718-4600 *Founded/Ownrshp* 1907
Sales NA *EMP* 515
Accts Martin Starnes & Associates C
SIC 9111 County supervisors' & executives' offices; County supervisors' & executives' offices
Ofcr: Carol Kivett
Ofcr: Frank McDaniel
Ofcr: Bettina Seymoure
Ofcr: Charles Thomas
Ofcr: Omayra Zagada
IT Man: Core Eckel
IT Man: Dawn Owen

D-U-N-S 01-362-9574
LEE COUNTY PORT AUTHORITY
11000 Terminal Access Rd # 8671, Fort Myers, FL 33913-8213
Tel (239) 590-4515 *Founded/Ownrshp* 2009
Sales NA *EMP* 360
SIC 9621 Port authority or district: government, non-operating
Ex Dir: Robert Ball

D-U-N-S 06-591-2354
LEE COUNTY PUBLIC SCHOOLS
(*Suby of* COUNTY OF LEE) ★
2855 Colonial Blvd, Fort Myers, FL 33966-1012
Tel (239) 337-8523 *Founded/Ownrshp* 1934
Sales 845.4MM *EMP* 1,000
SIC 8211 Public elementary & secondary schools; Elementary school; High school, junior or senior; Public elementary & secondary schools; Elementary school; High school, junior or senior
Bd of Dir: Cathleen Morgan
Ex Dir: William Tubb

LEE COUNTY ROAD DEPT
See COUNTY OF LEE

D-U-N-S 07-985-4451
LEE COUNTY RV SALES CO
NORTHTRAIL R V CENTER
5270 Orange River Blvd, Fort Myers, FL 33905-2750
Tel (239) 693-8200 *Founded/Ownrshp* 1986
Sales 43.2MM^E *EMP* 110
SIC 5561 Recreational vehicle dealers
Pr: Albert J Erp
**Prin:* Alan C Erp
Genl Mgr: Ryan Lewis
Sales Asso: John Dyer
Sales Asso: Ismary Fernandez
Sales Asso: Ray Gering
Sales Asso: Doyle Howard
Sales Asso: Ben Rutkin

LEE COUNTY SCHOOL DISTRICT
See LEE COUNTY BOARD OF EDUCATION

D-U-N-S 07-989-3932
LEE COUNTY SCHOOL DISTRICT
2410 Society Hill Rd, Opelika, AL 36804-4830
Tel (334) 745-9770 *Founded/Ownrshp* 2015
Sales 25.5MM^E *EMP* 752^E
SIC 8211 Public elementary & secondary schools
Psych: Delucca Christi

D-U-N-S 10-007-1463
LEE COUNTY SCHOOL DISTRICT
LEE COUNTY SCHOOLS
310 Roland St, Bishopville, SC 29010-1140
Tel (803) 484-5327 *Founded/Ownrshp* 1940
Sales 24.1MM^E *EMP* 450
SIC 8211 Public elementary & secondary schools; Public elementary & secondary schools

D-U-N-S 10-067-4191
LEE COUNTY SCHOOL DISTRICT
153 School Board Pl, Jonesville, VA 24263-7500
Tel (276) 346-2107 *Founded/Ownrshp* 1869
Sales 35.0MM *EMP* 660^E
SIC 8211 Public elementary & secondary schools; School board; Public elementary & secondary schools; School board
MIS Dir: Chris Fee
Pr Dir: Kathy Burgan
HC Dir: Jan Mosley

D-U-N-S 17-424-6421
LEE COUNTY SCHOOL DISTRICT
1280 College View St, Tupelo, MS 38804-5954
Tel (662) 841-9144 *Founded/Ownrshp* 1860
Sales 39.7MM^E *EMP* 756
Accts M M Winkler & Associates Tu
SIC 8211 Public elementary & secondary schools; Kindergarten; High school, junior or senior; Public elementary & secondary schools; Kindergarten; High school, junior or senior
Teacher Pr: Katherine Bass
Psych: Courtney Spencer

LEE COUNTY SCHOOL SYSTEM
See LEE COUNTY BOARD OF EDUCATION

D-U-N-S 07-979-8925
LEE COUNTY SCHOOL SYSTEM
126 Starksville Ave N, Leesburg, GA 31763-4548
Tel (229) 903-2100 *Founded/Ownrshp* 2015
Sales 22.7MM^E *EMP* 539^E
SIC 8211 Public elementary & secondary schools

LEE COUNTY SCHOOLS
See LEE COUNTY SCHOOL DISTRICT

D-U-N-S 10-005-8734
LEE COUNTY SCHOOLS
106 Gordon St, Sanford, NC 27330-3960
Tel (919) 774-6226 *Founded/Ownrshp* 1977
Sales 53.9MM^E *EMP* 1,000
SIC 8211 Public elementary & secondary schools; School board; Public elementary & secondary schools; School board
Bd of Dir: Sylvia Womble

D-U-N-S 01-441-9532
LEE COUNTY SHERIFF DEPARTMENT
14750 6 Mile Cypress Pkwy, Fort Myers, FL 33912-4406
Tel (239) 477-1000 *Founded/Ownrshp* 1887
Sales NA *EMP* 1,800
SIC 9221 Police protection

D-U-N-S 01-874-7915
LEE DAVID MARKETING INC
14921 N Lincoln Blvd, Edmond, OK 73013-3423
Tel (405) 341-7753 *Founded/Ownrshp* 1973
Sales 36.0MM *EMP* 15
SIC 5064 Radios, motor vehicle; High fidelity equipment; Radios, motor vehicle; High fidelity equipment
Pr: David Lee
**VP:* Kelly Lee
**VP:* Lynne Lee
Sls Mgr: David Toliver

D-U-N-S 02-340-1966
LEE DESIGN & MANAGEMENT GROUP INC
795 Lanier Ave E Ste D, Fayetteville, GA 30214-2205
Tel (770) 716-0081 *Founded/Ownrshp* 1998
Sales 21.3MM *EMP* 175^E
Accts Kpmg Llp Miami Fl
SIC 7349 Building maintenance services
CEO: Joe E Lee
**VP:* Donna Lee

LEE DESIGN STUDIO
See LEE SUPPLY CORP

D-U-N-S 04-370-1577
LEE DODGE INC
BROOKLYN AUTO GROUP
2686 Middle Country Rd, Lake Grove, NY 11755-3307
Tel (718) 713-3000 *Founded/Ownrshp* 1998
Sales 30.0MM *EMP* 21
SIC 5511 Automobiles, new & used; Automobiles, new & used
Pr: Robert A Lee Jr
Sls Mgr: Joe Rueda

D-U-N-S 17-705-7627
LEE ELECTRICAL CONSTRUCTION INC
12828 Us Highway 15 501, Aberdeen, NC 28315-4902
Tel (910) 944-9728 *Founded/Ownrshp* 1985
Sales 152.6MM^E *EMP* 500
SIC 1731 Lighting contractor; Electric power systems contractors; Lighting contractor; Electric power systems contractors
Pr: Jerry Lee
**VP:* Donald Lee
Sfty Dirs: Todd Williams

D-U-N-S 00-526-4064
▲ LEE ENTERPRISES INC
201 N Harrison St Ste 600, Davenport, IA 52801-1924
Tel (563) 383-2100 *Founded/Ownrshp* 1890
Sales 648.5MM *EMP* 4,700
Accts Kpmg Llp Chicago Illinois
Tkr Sym LEE *Exch* NYS
SIC 2711 Newspapers; Newspapers, publishing & printing; Newspapers; Newspapers, publishing & printing
Ch Bd: Mary E Junck
Pr: John M Humenik
COO: Kevin D Mowbray
CFO: Carl G Schmidt
VP: Nathan E Bekke
VP: Paul M Farrell
VP: Ray Farris
VP: James A Green
VP: James Green
VP: Michael R Gulledge
VP: Bill Masterson
VP: Michael E Phelps
**VP:* Gregory P Schermer
Board of Directors: Richard R Cole, Nancy S Donovan, Leonard J Elmore, Brent Magid, William E Mayer, Herbert W Moloney III, Andrew E Newman, Mark B Vittert

LEE FINANCIAL SERVICES
See FRESNO TRUCK CENTER

D-U-N-S 02-449-3777
LEE FORREST BUICK PONTIAC GMC
BUICK KEFFER PONTIAC
1001 Tyvola Rd, Charlotte, NC 28217-3513
Tel (704) 525-7650 *Founded/Ownrshp* 1974
Sales 25.2MM^E *EMP* 86
SIC 5511 Automobiles, new & used; Pickups, new & used; Automobiles, new & used; Pickups, new & used
Pr: Richard W Keffer Jr

D-U-N-S 96-464-6574
LEE GALLES CADILLAC INC
6401 San Mateo Blvd Ne, Albuquerque, NM 87109-3500
Tel (505) 837-5200 *Founded/Ownrshp* 1996
Sales 22.0MM^E *EMP* 120
SIC 5511 Automobiles, new & used; Automobiles, new & used
Pr: Lawton Davis

D-U-N-S 00-313-5779
LEE HARTMAN & SONS INC (VA)
3236 Cove Rd Nw, Roanoke, VA 24017-2804
Tel (540) 366-3493 *Founded/Ownrshp* 1936
Sales 30.5MM *EMP* 60

Accts Johnson Equi & Co Plc Cpas
SIC 7359 Equipment rental & leasing; Audio-visual equipment & supply rental; Equipment rental & leasing; Audio-visual equipment & supply rental
CEO: Stephen M Hartman
**Pr:* Lee C Hartman Jr
**Treas:* Robert Hartman Jr
**VP:* Steve Hartman
Area Mgr: Larry Cox
Brnch Mgr: Nick Hatgimisios
Sls Mgr: Jim Powell

D-U-N-S 08-040-7810
LEE HECHT HARRISON LLC
(*Suby of* ADECCO S.A.)
50 Tice Blvd Ste 115, Woodcliff Lake, NJ 07677-8429
Tel (201) 930-9333 *Founded/Ownrshp* 1974
Sales 119.7MME *EMP* 1,180
SIC 8742 8741 Management consulting services; Management services; Management consulting services; Management services
Pr: Peter Alcide
**CFO:* Karine Storm
**Ofcr:* Massimiliano Savarese
**Ex VP:* Barbara Barra
**Ex VP:* Kevin Gagan
**Ex VP:* James Greenway
**Ex VP:* Waseem Razzaq
Sr VP: Ed Epstein
VP: Deleise Lindsay
VP: Lynn Schumacher
VP: Carmel Urgo
Dir Bus: Avelynn Chen
Dir Bus: Stella Lu
Dir Bus: James McCloy

D-U-N-S 06-662-3398
LEE IMPORTED CARS INC
VOLVO
6 Courthouse Ln Unit 15, Chelmsford, MA 01824-1727
Tel (781) 416-1256 *Founded/Ownrshp* 1968
Sales 31.4MME *EMP* 91
SIC 5511 7538 5531 Automobiles, new & used; General automotive repair shops; Automobile & truck equipment & parts; Automobiles, new & used; General automotive repair shops; Automobile & truck equipment & parts
Pr: Christopher J Lee
**VP:* Dana B Lee
Opers Mgr: Andrew Rafter
Sales Asso: Robert Fish

LEE INDUSTRIAL CATERING
See LEE BROS FOODSERVICES INC

LEE INDUSTRIAL CONTRACTING
See LEE CONTRACTING INC

D-U-N-S 00-300-7093 IMP/EXP
LEE INDUSTRIES INC (PA)
FLUID TRANSFER
50 W Pine St, Philipsburg, PA 16866-2430
Tel (814) 342-0460 *Founded/Ownrshp* 1927, 1986
Sales 63.6MME *EMP* 225
SIC 3556 3559 3531 3494 3443 3324 Food products machinery; Pharmaceutical machinery; Chemical machinery & equipment; Construction machinery; Valves & pipe fittings; Fabricated plate work (boiler shop); Steel investment foundries; Food products machinery; Pharmaceutical machinery; Chemical machinery & equipment; Construction machinery; Valves & pipe fittings; Fabricated plate work (boiler shop); Steel investment foundries
Pr: Robert W Montler
**Treas:* John F Horon
VP: Josh Montler
**VP:* Joshua Montler
**VP:* Greg Wharton
Sfty Mgr: Bruce Kephart
Plnt Mgr: Joe Bordack
Sales Asso: Lisa Byron
Art Dir: Quynh Vo

D-U-N-S 04-846-1024 IMP/EXP
LEE INDUSTRIES INC
210 4th St Sw, Conover, NC 28613-2628
Tel (828) 464-8318 *Founded/Ownrshp* 1969
Sales 89.4MME *EMP* 400
SIC 2512 Couches, sofas & davenports: upholstered on wood frames; Chairs: upholstered on wood frames; Couches, sofas & davenports: upholstered on wood frames; Chairs: upholstered on wood frames
Pr: Bill G Coley
Ofcr: Tonia Starnes
Dept Mgr: Lidia Epperson
Dir IT: Marvin Cutshall
Plnt Mgr: Darryl Leonhardt

D-U-N-S 95-834-2917
■ **LEE JEANS CO INC**
(*Suby of* VF CORP) ★
9001 W 67th St, Merriam, KS 66202-3699
Tel (913) 384-4000 *Founded/Ownrshp* 2000
Sales 7.7MME *EMP* 2,350E
SIC 2325 2339 2369 Jeans: men's, youths' & boys'; Jeans: women's, misses' & juniors'; Jeans: girls', children's & infants'
Pr: Mike Lettera
VP: Kent Pech

LEE JEEP EAGLE
See LEE PONTIAC-OLDSMOBILE-GMC TRUCK INC

LEE JOFA
See KRAVET INC

LEE JOFA PORTFOLIO TEXTILES
See KLJM

D-U-N-S 02-733-9217
LEE JOHNSON CHEVROLET INC
LEE JOHNSON MAZDA
11845 Ne 85th St, Kirkland, WA 98033-8042
Tel (425) 827-0521 *Founded/Ownrshp* 1933
Sales 57.1MME *EMP* 140
SIC 5511 5521 Automobiles, new & used; Pickups, new & used; Used car dealers; Automobiles, new & used; Pickups, new & used; Used car dealers
Pr: Tod Johnson
CFO: Robert Jay
**VP:* Richard Meyer
CIO: Marty Duke
Mktg Mgr: Chris Pillings
Sales Asso: Jared Stockdale

LEE JOHNSON MAZDA
See LEE JOHNSON CHEVROLET INC

D-U-N-S 08-898-6179
LEE KENNEDY CO INC
122 Quincy Shore Dr Ste 1, Quincy, MA 02171-2906
Tel (617) 825-6930 *Founded/Ownrshp* 1978
Sales 276.2MM *EMP* 75
Accts Feeley & Driscoll Pc Bosto
SIC 1542 Commercial & office buildings, renovation & repair; Commercial & office building, new construction; Commercial & office buildings, renovation & repair; Commercial & office building, new construction
Ch Bd: Lee M Kennedy
**CFO:* Michael Heath
CFO: Mike Kennedy
**Sr VP:* Chris Pennie
VP: Michael Boyle
VP: Shaila Garland
**VP:* Eugene Kennedy
Exec: Brian Burnes
Exec: Marie Cunningham
Genl Mgr: Nancy Notarangelo
CTO: Mahmoud Yassine

D-U-N-S 11-425-9435 IMP
LEE KUM KEE (USA) INC
LEE'S KITCHEN
14841 Don Julian Rd, City of Industry, CA 91746-3110
Tel (626) 709-1888 *Founded/Ownrshp* 1983
Sales 53.3MME *EMP* 49
SIC 5149 2099 2035 Sauces; Food preparations; Pickles, sauces & salad dressings
CEO: Simon Wu
**Pr:* David H W Lee
CFO: Alan Lui
Ex VP: Kelly Lam
Exec: Canny Luk
Exec: Raymond Wong
Dir Bus: William Tzou
Genl Mgr: Kasik Chan
Genl Mgr: Norman Ho
Genl Mgr: Mahnaz Lee
Dir IT: Elizabeth Mok

D-U-N-S 04-092-3021
LEE LEWIS CONSTRUCTION INC
7810 Orlando Ave, Lubbock, TX 79423-1942
Tel (806) 797-8400 *Founded/Ownrshp* 1975
Sales 118.6MME *EMP* 200
SIC 1542 1541 Commercial & office building, new construction; Industrial buildings & warehouses; Commercial & office building, new construction; Industrial buildings & warehouses
CEO: Lee Lewis
**Pr:* Tom Ferguson
COO: Liz Longer
**Treas:* Kelly Messersmith
VP: James Candle
VP: Bob Fullington
Off Mgr: Sharon Story
Sfty Dirs: Frank Call
Sfty Dirs: Jeff Goolsby
Ql Cn Mgr: Dan Morgan
Snr Mgr: Randy Bias

D-U-N-S 02-520-1427
LEE LUMBER & BUILDING MATERIAL CORP
SPACES AND VIEWS
633 W Pershing Rd, Chicago, IL 60609-2687
Tel (773) 927-8282 *Founded/Ownrshp* 1952
Sales 42.7MME *EMP* 145
SIC 5211 Lumber & other building materials; Windows, storm: wood or metal; Bathroom fixtures, equipment & supplies; Cabinets, kitchen; Lumber & other building materials; Windows, storm: wood or metal; Bathroom fixtures, equipment & supplies; Cabinets, kitchen
Pr: Rick Baumgarten
**Ch Bd:* Lee Baumgarten
**Pr:* Richard Baumgarten
COO: Arthur Baumgarten
**Sec:* Randy Baumgarten
IT Man: Chad Ackerpatt
Snr Mgr: Debra Gold

LEE MAR AQUARIUM & PET SUPS
See LEE-MAR AQUARIUM & PET SUPPLIES

D-U-N-S 05-004-7448
LEE MASONRY PRODUCTS INC
LEE BRICK & BLOCK
309 Dishman Ln, Bowling Green, KY 42101-4001
Tel (270) 781-9813 *Founded/Ownrshp* 1976
Sales 78.7MME *EMP* 305
SIC 3271 5032 5031 3272 Blocks, concrete or cinder: standard; Brick, except refractory; Building materials, exterior; Metal doors, sash & trim; Door frames, all materials; Concrete products; Blocks, concrete or cinder: standard; Brick, except refractory; Building materials, exterior; Metal doors, sash & trim; Door frames, all materials; Concrete products
Pr: Carol Todd Lee
**Treas:* Barry Lee
**VP:* Allen R Lee
CIO: Kirk Patton

D-U-N-S 15-020-2786
LEE MECHANICAL CONTRACTORS INC
508 Parkway Dr, Park Hills, MO 63601-4502
Tel (573) 431-2511 *Founded/Ownrshp* 1985
Sales 53.6MME *EMP* 245
Accts Frank Payne Park Hills Mo
SIC 1711 Mechanical contractor; Mechanical contractor
Pr: Nick Gibson
Treas: Nicholas Gibson
**VP:* William Dickerson
VP Admn: Lora Dickens

D-U-N-S 01-052-0674
LEE MEMORIAL HEALTH SYSTEM FOUNDATION INC (FL)
BRIGHT IDEAS GIFT SHOP
2776 Cleveland Ave, Fort Myers, FL 33901-5864
Tel (239) 343-2000 *Founded/Ownrshp* 1916
Sales 722.8MME *EMP* 7,870
SIC 8741 8062 8082 8051 Hospital management; General medical & surgical hospitals; Home health care services; Skilled nursing care facilities; Hospital management; General medical & surgical hospitals; Home health care services; Skilled nursing care facilities
Pr: James R Nathan
Dir Vol: Jill Palmer
CFO: Michael German
CFO: Ben Spence
Treas: Marilyn Stout
Bd of Dir: Jessica Carter
Bd of Dir: George Kenneke
Bd of Dir: Guy Rhoades
Bd of Dir: Hatton Rogers
Bd of Dir: Alexander Roulston
Bd of Dir: Julie K Smith
**Ofcr:* C B Rebsamen
Ofcr: Charles Swain
VP: Jennifer Higgins
VP: Dianne Rushton
Dir Lab: Susan Lawless
Comm Dir: Brandy Church
Dir Rx: Koth Cassavaugh

D-U-N-S 02-849-3944
LEE MEMORIAL HEALTH SYSTEMS
1569 Matthew Dr, Fort Myers, FL 33907-1734
Tel (239) 481-4111 *Founded/Ownrshp* 2010
Sales 29.8MME *EMP* 643E
SIC 8082 Home health care services
Pr: Jim Nathan
Exec: Tina Reed
Dir Rx: Lozano Yanela
Doctor: Sebastian Draulans
Doctor: Javaad Khan
Doctor: Bala Prabakaran
Doctor: Piedade Silva
Cert Phar: Michele Dotson
Cert Phar: Kellie Griffiths
Cert Phar: Edie King

D-U-N-S 07-430-7794
LEE MEMORIAL HOSPITAL (MI)
BORGESS-LEE MEMORIAL HOSPITAL
420 W High St, Dowagiac, MI 49047-1943
Tel (269) 782-8681 *Founded/Ownrshp* 1918
Sales 25.3MM *EMP* 275
Accts Deloitte Tax Llp Cincinnati
SIC 8062 General medical & surgical hospitals; General medical & surgical hospitals
Pr: Paul Spaude
**COO:* Joy Strands
**CFO:* Ken Holst
Dir Rad: Larry Frank
Dir Rx: Andrew Capes
Dir Rx: Mike Miller
Ex Dir: Greg Otto
CTO: Bill Schurr
Dir IT: Joyce Campbell
VP Opers: Linda Lawton
Opers Mgr: Jan Hansen

D-U-N-S 08-536-9044
LEE MEMORIAL HOSPITAL
2776 Cleveland Ave, Fort Myers, FL 33901-5855
Tel (239) 343-2000 *Founded/Ownrshp* 1992
Sales 58.3MME *EMP* 1,159
SIC 8062 General medical & surgical hospitals; General medical & surgical hospitals
Pr: Jim Nathan
V Ch: Stanley Freeman
CFO: Dennis Pettigrew
Bd of Dir: Donald Brown
Exec: Frank Rosa
Exec: Jason Yost
Dir OR: Kandy Dewitt
Dir Risk M: Mary Lorah
Dir Lab: Demeritt Darrell
Dir Lab: Karla Simpson
Dir Rad: Jessica Lindsey

LEE MICHAELS FINE JEWELRY
See LEE MICHAELS JEWELERS INC

D-U-N-S 09-268-3770 IMP
LEE MICHAELS JEWELERS INC
LEE MICHAELS FINE JEWELRY
11314 Cloverland Ave, Baton Rouge, LA 70809-4279
Tel (225) 291-9094 *Founded/Ownrshp* 1978
Sales 21.8MME *EMP* 150
Accts Hannis T Bourgeois Llp Bato
SIC 5944 Jewelry, precious stones & precious metals
Pr: Lee Michael Berg
**Pr:* Scott Berg
**CFO:* Jane Harrington
**Sec:* Brenda Berg
Sr VP: Johnny Tate
**VP:* Ryan Berg
Store Mgr: Michael Crane
Advt Mgr: Amy Graham
Sales Asso: Victoria Beavers

D-U-N-S 00-249-0688
LEE NATIONAL CORP
645 5th Ave Fl 8, New York, NY 10022-5910
Tel (212) 848-0271 *Founded/Ownrshp* 1915, 1978
Sales 21.7MME *EMP* 175
SIC 6552 6531 6211 6162 Subdividers & developers; Real estate managers; Investment bankers; Mortgage brokers, using own money
Pr: Alvin Dworman
MIS Dir: Anne Goeletz

D-U-N-S 61-453-0905
■ **LEE OIL CO INC**
LEE'S FOOD MART 3
(*Suby of* HEARTLAND INC) ★
1005 N 19th St, Middlesboro, KY 40965-1805
Tel (606) 248-2035 *Founded/Ownrshp* 2008
Sales 22.1MME *EMP* 18
SIC 5171 5411 Petroleum bulk stations & terminals; Convenience stores, independent
Pr: Terry L Lee
**Treas:* Gary D Lee

D-U-N-S 03-231-4643
LEE PONTIAC-OLDSMOBILE-GMC TRUCK INC
LEE JEEP EAGLE
235 Miracle Strip Pkwy Sw, Fort Walton Beach, FL 32548-6616
Tel (850) 243-3123 *Founded/Ownrshp* 1950
Sales 26.1MME *EMP* 85
SIC 5511 Automobiles, new & used; Pickups, new & used; Vans, new & used; Automobiles, new & used; Pickups, new & used; Vans, new & used
Pr: David Lee
Sec: Gary E Lee Jr
Sls Dir: Jay McQuaig
Board of Directors: James Lee

D-U-N-S 00-516-0635
■ **LEE PUBLICATIONS INC** (DE)
TIMES-NEWS, THE
(*Suby of* LEE ENTERPRISES INC) ★
201 N Harrison St Ste 600, Davenport, IA 52801-1918
Tel (563) 383-2100 *Founded/Ownrshp* 1972, 2002
Sales 234.9MME *EMP* 2,500
SIC 2711 Newspapers: publishing only, not printed on site; Newspapers: publishing only, not printed on site
Pr: Mary E Junck
VP: Brian E Kardell
VP: Gregory Schermer
VP: Carl Schmidt

LEE RANCH COAL
See PEABODY NATURAL RESOURCES

LEE RAY SANDBLASTING
See CJI PROCESS SYSTEMS INC

D-U-N-S 01-145-3792
LEE REGIONAL HEALTH SYSTEM INC
132 Walnut St Ste 3, Johnstown, PA 15901-1621
Tel (814) 533-0751 *Founded/Ownrshp* 1981
Sales 25.6MME *EMP* 1,487
SIC 8399 Fund raising organization, non-fee basis; Fund raising organization, non-fee basis
Ch Bd: John W Augustine
VP: Robert E Barrett

D-U-N-S 05-254-5431
LEE RJ GROUP INC
350 Hochberg Rd, Monroeville, PA 15146-1516
Tel (724) 325-1776 *Founded/Ownrshp* 1980
Sales 66.9MME *EMP* 259
SIC 8731 7372 3826 3825 3823 3577 Industrial laboratory, except testing; Prepackaged software; Analytical instruments; Instruments to measure electricity; Industrial instrmnts msrmnt display/control process variable; Computer peripheral equipment; Industrial laboratory, except testing; Prepackaged software; Analytical instruments; Instruments to measure electricity; Industrial instrmnts msrmnt display/control process variable; Computer peripheral equipment
Pr: Richard J Lee
**Pr:* Alex Scuilli
**CFO:* David James
**VP:* Gary Casuccio
VP: Duane Conley
VP: David Crawford
VP: Glenn Harmon
VP: Apostolos Ioannidis
VP: Ludvigsen Phillip
Off Mgr: Annie Estes
Off Admin: Kristine Thomas

LEE RODGERS TIRE CO
See LEE-RODGERS TIRE & BATTERY CO

D-U-N-S 02-628-9090
LEE ROY JORDAN REDWOOD LUMBER CO
2425 Burbank St, Dallas, TX 75235-3128
Tel (214) 357-7317 *Founded/Ownrshp* 1977
Sales 41.3MME *EMP* 70E
Accts Gandy Calverley & Company Pc
SIC 5031 5211 Lumber: rough, dressed & finished; Millwork & lumber; Lumber: rough, dressed & finished; Millwork & lumber
Pr: Lee Roy Jordan
**VP:* David Jordan
Sales Asso: David Gibbs
Sales Asso: Blake Prestridge

D-U-N-S 14-902-0534 IMP
LEE SANDUSKY CORP
75 Park Ave, Littlestown, PA 17340-1328
Tel (717) 359-4111 *Founded/Ownrshp* 2004
Sales 23.3MME *EMP* 70E
SIC 5021 2514 Furniture; Metal household furniture
Pr: Mitchell Liss

LEE SPRING COMPANY DIV
See UNIMEX CORP

D-U-N-S 17-373-6984 IMP
LEE SPRING CO LLC
(*Suby of* LEE SPRING CO DIV) ★
140 58th St Ste 3c, Brooklyn, NY 11220-2560
Tel (718) 362-5183 *Founded/Ownrshp* 1955
Sales 33.2MME *EMP* 277
SIC 3495 3493 3315 5085 Mechanical springs, precision; Steel springs, except wire; Wire & fabricated wire products; Springs; Mechanical springs, precision; Steel springs, except wire; Wire & fabricated wire products; Springs
Pr: Al Mangels Jr
VP: Ralph Mascolo
VP: Paul Ng
Exec: Michael Gisonda
Dir IT: Mike Josanda
IT Man: Mike Jisonda
Opers Mgr: John Staskauskas
Plnt Mgr: Jamie Collazo
Plnt Mgr: Jorge Cortes
Prd Mgr: Laura Hoffman
VP Sls: Sanjeev Rivera

D-U-N-S 00-293-6920 IMP
LEE STEEL CORP (MI)
45525 Grand River Ave, Novi, MI 48374-1308
Tel (855) 533-7833 *Founded/Ownrshp* 1947
Sales 100.0MM *EMP* 65
SIC 5051 Steel

D-U-N-S 07-867-5566
LEE SUMMER HOLDINGS LLC
600 Travis St Ste 5800, Houston, TX 77002-3008
Tel (713) 993-4610 *Founded/Ownrshp* 2006, 2012
Sales 152.7MM^E *EMP* 999^E
SIC 6799 Venture capital companies; Venture capital companies

D-U-N-S 01-395-1447 IMP
LEE SUPPLY CO INC
305 1st St, Charleroi, PA 15022-1427
Tel (724) 483-3543 *Founded/Ownrshp* 1954
Sales 113.2MM *EMP* 127
SIC 5082 5084 Mining machinery & equipment, except petroleum; Industrial machinery & equipment; Mining machinery & equipment, except petroleum; Industrial machinery & equipment
CEO: Michael H Lee
**Pr:* Kevin M Lee
**CFO:* David Lee
Treas: Eileen Nucci
**VP:* Shawn Lee
Sales Exec: Joe Murphy
Sales Asso: Jeff Dumm
Sales Asso: John Kite

D-U-N-S 00-604-5678
LEE SUPPLY CORP
LEE DESIGN STUDIO
6610 Guion Rd, Indianapolis, IN 46268-2534
Tel (317) 290-2500 *Founded/Ownrshp* 1973, 1980
Sales 110.6MM^E *EMP* 190
SIC 5074 5075 5064 5085 5031 Plumbing & hydronic heating supplies; Air conditioning & ventilation equipment & supplies; Electric household appliances; Industrial supplies; Lumber, plywood & millwork; Plumbing & hydronic heating supplies; Air conditioning & ventilation equipment & supplies; Electric household appliances; Industrial supplies; Lumber, plywood & millwork
Pr: Robert T Lee
**Treas:* Charles Lee
Brnch Mgr: Jim Hanchar
Brnch Mgr: Kevin Kreutzberger
IT Man: David Barnes
Info Man: Kevin Stewart

D-U-N-S 16-703-0290
LEE THOMAS H EQUITY FUND V LIMITED PARTNERSHIP
100 Federal St Ste 3500, Boston, MA 02110-1802
Tel (617) 737-3261 *Founded/Ownrshp* 2007
Sales 227.1MM^E *EMP* 8,040
SIC 3585 3444 3634 2431 3699 Refrigeration & heating equipment; Sheet metalwork; Electric housewares & fans; Millwork; Electrical equipment & supplies; Refrigeration & heating equipment; Sheet metalwork; Electric housewares & fans; Millwork; Electrical equipment & supplies
Genl Pt: Thomas H Lee

D-U-N-S 11-289-6956
LEE TRUCK BROKER INC
2302 S Main St, Stuttgart, AR 72160-7003
Tel (870) 673-6921 *Founded/Ownrshp* 2008
Sales 21.4MM *EMP* 18
SIC 4731 Truck transportation brokers; Truck transportation brokers
Pr: Randy Lee
VP Opers: Derrick McCarley

D-U-N-S 07-153-5728
LEE UNIVERSITY
1120 N Ocoee St Ste 102, Cleveland, TN 37311-4475
Tel (423) 614-8000 *Founded/Ownrshp* 1946
Sales 98.3MM^E *EMP* 635
Accts Elliott Davis Decosimo Llc Pll
SIC 8221 8661 College, except junior; Religious organizations; College, except junior; Religious organizations
Pr: Paul Conn
VP: Jerome Hammond
VP: Walt C Mauldin
VP: Deborah Murray
Exec: Alan McClung
Dir Lab: Allison Laframboise
Ex Dir: Kevin Hudson
Store Mgr: Skip Gienapp
CTO: Marybeth Wickes
Dir IT: William Lamb
Psych: David Quagliana

D-U-N-S 06-445-1073 IMP
LEE-MAR AQUARIUM & PET SUPPLIES
LEE MAR AQUARIUM & PET SUPS
2459 Dogwood Way, Vista, CA 92081-8421
Tel (760) 727-1300 *Founded/Ownrshp* 2007
Sales 23.4MM^E *EMP* 100
SIC 5199 3999 Pet supplies; Pet supplies
Pr: Terran R Boyd
VP Sls: Jeff Boyd

D-U-N-S 00-403-4633 IMP
LEE-RODGERS TIRE & BATTERY CO (AL)
LEE RODGERS TIRE CO
3500 3rd Ave S, Birmingham, AL 35222-1817
Tel (205) 322-8552 *Founded/Ownrshp* 1922, 1972
Sales 41.7MM^E *EMP* 78
SIC 5531 7534 Automotive tires; Tire recapping
Pr: William Rodgers

D-U-N-S 00-350-0188
LEE-SMITH INC (TN)
UNIVERSAL TRUCK PARTS
2600 8th Ave, Chattanooga, TN 37407-1195
Tel (423) 622-4161 *Founded/Ownrshp* 1939
Sales 71.8MM^E *EMP* 105
SIC 5511 7532 7538 5012 Trucks, tractors & trailers: new & used; Top & body repair & paint shops; General automotive repair shops; Automobiles & other motor vehicles; Trucks, tractors & trailers: new & used; Top & body repair & paint shops; General automotive repair shops; Automobiles & other motor vehicles
Ch Bd: Lesslie W Lee Sr
Pr: Lesslie W Lee Jr
CFO: Ronald V Duggard II
CFO: Victor Duggard
VP: David Martin
Exec: Kristin Young
Info Man: Corey Cavett
VP Sls: Cliff Hellard
Sls Mgr: Mark Bailey

D-U-N-S 08-171-5260 IMP
LEE-WRIGHT INC
PROFESSIONAL FLOORING SUP CO
6320 Airport Fwy Ste A, Haltom City, TX 76117-6603
Tel (817) 834-4737 *Founded/Ownrshp* 1977
Sales 43.6MM^E *EMP* 65
SIC 5023 Floor coverings; Floor cushion & padding
Pr: Dan Lee
Pr: Vance Haas
**CFO:* Debra Lee
**Treas:* Debbie Lee
Brnch Mgr: Chad Brannan
Brnch Mgr: Jessie Garcia
Brnch Mgr: Doug Gordon
Brnch Mgr: Raul Nombrano
Brnch Mgr: Brian Trojans
Brnch Mgr: Isaac Wiebe
Opers Mgr: Nathan Fleming

LEEANN CHIN RESTAURANT
See CHIN LEEANN INC

D-U-N-S 17-488-7430
LEEBOS STORES INC
2049 N Mall Dr, Alexandria, LA 71301-3665
Tel (318) 445-2814 *Founded/Ownrshp* 1987
Sales 31.4MM *EMP* 100
SIC 5411 Convenience stores, independent; Convenience stores, independent
Pr: Lance Harris
CFO: Randy Rabalais

D-U-N-S 19-267-6229
LEECH LAKE PALACE & CASINO CORP
PALACE BINGO & CASINO, THE
6280 Uppr Cass Frontage, Cass Lake, MN 56633-3058
Tel (218) 335-7000 *Founded/Ownrshp* 1983
Sales 26.7MM^E *EMP* 900
SIC 7011 Casino hotel; Casino hotel
Genl Mgr: Dawn Fairbanks
Dir Sec: Rod Northbird
Dir IT: Kindra Walker

D-U-N-S 06-651-1122
LEECH LAKE RESERVATION BUSINESS COMMITTEE INC
LEECH LK RSRVTION TRBAL CUNCIL
425 7th St Nw, Cass Lake, MN 56633-3360
Tel (218) 335-8206 *Founded/Ownrshp* 1934
Sales NA *EMP* 658
SIC 9131 Indian reservation; ; Indian reservation
Ch: Eli Hunt
Ex Dir: Steve Mortensen

LEECH LK RSRVTION TRBAL CUNCIL
See LEECH LAKE RESERVATION BUSINESS COMMITTEE INC

D-U-N-S 05-057-6552 IMP/EXP
LEECO STEEL LLC (AL)
(*Suby of* ONEAL INDUSTRIES INC) ★
1011 Warrenville Rd # 500, Lisle, IL 60532-0933
Tel (630) 427-2100 *Founded/Ownrshp* 1882, 2005
Sales 48.7MM^E *EMP* 80
SIC 5051

LEED ENERGY SERVICES
See LEED TOOL CORP

D-U-N-S 07-919-1952
LEED HR LLC
2650 Eastpoint Pkwy # 280, Louisville, KY 40223-5135
Tel (502) 253-4000 *Founded/Ownrshp* 2012
Sales 39.8MM^E *EMP* 160
SIC 7361 Employment agencies

D-U-N-S 00-700-7248
LEED SELLING TOOLS CORP
9700 Highway 57, Evansville, IN 47725-9704
Tel (812) 867-4340 *Founded/Ownrshp* 1962
Sales 31.5MM^E *EMP* 275
SIC 2789 2782 Swatches & samples; Sample books; Swatches & samples; Sample books
Pr: Douglas Edwards
**Ex VP:* George K Grace
**VP:* Richard A Edwards

D-U-N-S 00-933-9560
LEED TOOL CORP
LEED ENERGY SERVICES
1352 Factory Cir, Fort Lupton, CO 80621
Tel (303) 457-4321 *Founded/Ownrshp* 1977
Sales 24.4MM^E *EMP* 160
SIC 1389 Gas field services; Gas field services
Pr: Jeff Kaufman

LEEDO CABINETRY
See LEEDO MANUFACTURING CO LP

D-U-N-S 05-030-6729 IMP
LEEDO MANUFACTURING CO LP (TX)
LEEDO CABINETRY
16856 Cabinet Rd, East Bernard, TX 77435-5064
Tel (866) 465-3336 *Founded/Ownrshp* 2001
Sales 93.8MM^E *EMP* 330^E
SIC 2434 Wood kitchen cabinets; Vanities, bathroom: wood; Wood kitchen cabinets; Vanities, bathroom: wood
Pr: Ken Hirshman
CFO: Howard Maymon
CFO: Jonathan Risch
Ch: George Hagle
Ofcr: Cindy Ward
VP: David Burke
IT Man: Charles Russell
Sfty Mgr: Don Kaingely
Opers Mgr: Darren Schmidt

D-U-N-S 01-427-2681
LEEDS EQUITY PARTNERS LLC
350 Park Ave Fl 23, New York, NY 10022-6050
Tel (212) 835-2000 *Founded/Ownrshp* 2001
Sales NA *EMP* 78
SIC 6159 Small business investment companies
VP: Angela Chubb
VP: Dan Higgins
VP: Scott Vanhoy
Mng Dir: Jacques Galante

D-U-N-S 86-700-0580
LEEDSTONE INC
222 County Road 173 Se, Melrose, MN 56352-1602
Tel (320) 256-4252 *Founded/Ownrshp* 1994
Sales 29.6MM^E *EMP* 40
SIC 5083 5047 Dairy machinery & equipment; Veterinarians' equipment & supplies
CEO: David Tomsche
**CFO:* Brendon Van Der Hagen
**VP:* Daniel Tomsche
Board of Directors: Daniel Tomsche, David Tomsche, Grant Tomsche, Margaret Tomsche, Brendon Van Der Hagen

D-U-N-S 15-374-6201 IMP
LEEDSWORLD INC
(*Suby of* POLYCONCEPT NORTH AMERICA INC) ★
400 Hunt Valley Rd, New Kensington, PA 15068-7059
Tel (724) 334-9000 *Founded/Ownrshp* 1983
Sales 400.1MM^E *EMP* 800^E
SIC 5199 5111 5112 3172 3161 2394 Advertising specialties; Writing paper; Writing instruments & supplies; Personal leather goods; Luggage; Canvas & related products; Advertising specialties; Writing paper; Writing instruments & supplies; Personal leather goods; Luggage; Canvas & related products
CEO: Michael Bernstein
**Pr:* David Nicholson
VP: Colleen Blackham
VP: Peter Healy
Rgnl Mgr: Brian Frazer
QA Dir: Richard Gorman
Software D: Paul Fleischman
VP Sls: Samuel Dibiase
Mktg Mgr: Martin Dornisch
Mktg Mgr: Patty Solar
Manager: Bill Levasseur

D-U-N-S 00-602-3394 IMP
LEEDY MANUFACTURING CO LLC
210 Hall St Sw, Grand Rapids, MI 49507-1034
Tel (616) 245-0517 *Founded/Ownrshp* 1978
Sales 23.2MM^E *EMP* 70
SIC 3714 3531 3568 3536 Gears, motor vehicle; Transmissions, motor vehicle; Winches; Sprockets (power transmission equipment); Pulleys, power transmission; Hoists, cranes & monorails
QC Dir: Roy Hagle

LEEE FOUNDATION
See IEEE FOUNDATION INC

D-U-N-S 01-676-9921 IMP
LEEHAN AMERICA INC (AL)
(*Suby of* LEEHAN CORPORATION)
1230 County Road 177, Cusseta, AL 36852-2762
Tel (334) 756-0200 *Founded/Ownrshp* 2007
Sales 39.3MM *EMP* 80
SIC 5571 All terrain vehicle parts and accessories; All terrain vehicle parts and accessories
Pr: Haksum Lee
**Prin:* Steve B Park

D-U-N-S 04-456-2288
LEELANAU FRUIT CO
2900 S West Bay Shore Dr, Suttons Bay, MI 49682-9614
Tel (231) 271-3514 *Founded/Ownrshp* 1975
Sales 26.5MM^E *EMP* 50
SIC 5142 Packaged frozen goods
Genl Mgr: Allen Steimel
Opers Mgr: Renee Spalding

D-U-N-S 05-458-1848 IMP
LEEMAH CORP
155 S Hill Dr, Brisbane, CA 94005-1203
Tel (415) 394-1288 *Founded/Ownrshp* 1971
Sales 103.5MM^E *EMP* 300
SIC 3671 3672 3669 3663 3577 Electron tubes; Printed circuit boards; Intercommunication systems, electric; Radio & TV communications equipment; Computer peripheral equipment; Electron tubes; Printed circuit boards; Intercommunication systems, electric; Radio & TV communications equipment; Computer peripheral equipment
CEO: Efrem Mah
**Pr:* Bing Hong Mah
**CFO:* Warren Gee

D-U-N-S 62-187-3934 IMP
LEEMAH ELECTRONICS INC
(*Suby of* LEEMAH CORP) ★
155 S Hill Dr, Brisbane, CA 94005-1203
Tel (415) 394-1288 *Founded/Ownrshp* 1984
Sales 50.0MM *EMP* 250
SIC 3699

D-U-N-S 07-916-1395
LEEMAK LP (TX)
17171 Park Row Ste 295, Houston, TX 77084-5640
Tel (281) 492-9555 *Founded/Ownrshp* 2006
Sales 53.0MM *EMP* 350
SIC 1389 Oil field services; Oil field services
CFO: Omer Malik

D-U-N-S 07-912-7461
LEEMAN AND ASSOCIATES LLC
42-103 Aleka Pl, Kailua, HI 96734-5708
Tel (808) 542-7676 *Founded/Ownrshp* 1999
Sales 11.4MM^E *EMP* 808
SIC 8742 ; Management consulting services

D-U-N-S 05-434-2175
LEEPS SUPPLY CO INC
DO IT BEST
8001 Tyler St, Merrillville, IN 46410-5345
Tel (219) 756-5337 *Founded/Ownrshp* 1997
Sales 59.1MM^E *EMP* 72
SIC 5074 3261 Plumbing & hydronic heating supplies; Vitreous plumbing fixtures; Plumbing & hydronic heating supplies; Vitreous plumbing fixtures
Pr: John Hamstra
Brnch Mgr: Chet Kwiatkowski
Sls Mgr: Eric McCleary
Sales Asso: Sean Corbett
Sales Asso: Tim Oliver

LEER
See TRUCK ACCESSORIES GROUP LLC

D-U-N-S 79-178-0612 IMP/EXP
LEER INC
(*Suby of* DEXTER APACHE HOLDINGS INC) ★
206 Leer St, New Lisbon, WI 53950-1163
Tel (608) 562-3161 *Founded/Ownrshp* 2008
Sales 44.0MM^E *EMP* 165
SIC 3585 Ice boxes, industrial; Ice boxes, industrial
CEO: Patrick D Albregts
Genl Mgr: Mark Edmonds
IT Man: David Gregoire
Plnt Mgr: Dan Smithburg
Ql Cn Mgr: Allen Schneeberger
Natl Sales: Sheila Palinkas
Mktg Mgr: Brett McCabe
Sls Mgr: Shiela Plainkas

LEE'S FOOD MART 3
See LEE OIL CO INC

D-U-N-S 02-807-8723
LEES IMPERIAL WELDING INC
3300 Edison Way, Fremont, CA 94538-6150
Tel (510) 657-4900 *Founded/Ownrshp* 1958
Sales 43.6MM^E *EMP* 150
SIC 3441 Fabricated structural metal; Fabricated structural metal
CEO: Gary Lee
CFO: Dave Geserick
VP: John Gall
VP: Keith Lee
Exec: Tim Arnold
Opers Mgr: John Montes
VP Sls: Cary Mathewes
VP Sls: Carey Matthews

D-U-N-S 07-958-7168
LEES INNS OF AMERICA INC
130 N State St, North Vernon, IN 47265-1724
Tel (812) 346-5072 *Founded/Ownrshp* 2011
Sales 15.5MM^E *EMP* 400
SIC 7011 6163 7389 Motel, franchised; Mortgage brokers arranging for loans, using money of others; Interior designer; Motel, franchised; Mortgage brokers arranging for loans, using money of others; Interior designer
Pr: Lester L Lee
Pr: Debra Brown
**Treas:* Lisa Klosterman
Rgnl Mgr: Phyllis M Artin

LEE'S KITCHEN
See LEE KUM KEE (USA) INC

D-U-N-S 80-079-0888
LEES MARKETPLACE INC
555 E 1400 N, Logan, UT 84341-2453
Tel (435) 750-0258 *Founded/Ownrshp* 1981
Sales 77.3MM^E *EMP* 270
SIC 5141 Groceries, general line; Groceries, general line
CEO: John Bedger
**VP:* Shari Bedger
Mktg Dir: Tim Rigby

D-U-N-S 18-844-5480
LEES PET CLUB INC
3535 Hollis St, Corte Madera, CA 94925
Tel (510) 595-8120 *Founded/Ownrshp* 1990
Sales 25.6MM^E *EMP* 150
SIC 5999 Pet food
Pr: Wilson Lee
**VP:* Winfield Lee

D-U-N-S 07-622-6554 IMP
LEES POTTERY INC
TRENDSPOT
1595 E San Bernardino Ave, San Bernardino, CA 92408-2946
Tel (909) 937-1141 *Founded/Ownrshp* 1972
Sales 25.0MM^E *EMP* 49^E
SIC 5023 Pottery; Pottery
CEO: William Lee
**CFO:* Edward Lee
Off Mgr: Wendy Salgado
Art Dir: Susan Ishida

D-U-N-S 03-444-8991
LEES SEAFOOD HOLDINGS LLC
19 Neds Point Rd, Mattapoisett, MA 02739-2113
Tel (774) 206-8611 *Founded/Ownrshp* 2010
Sales 23.8MM^E *EMP* 200
SIC 2091 Seafood products: packaged in cans, jars, etc.
COO: George Tarabaih
CFO: Kimberly Lannigan
VP: Rick Marino
Plnt Mgr: Chris Cook
Ql Cn Mgr: Willie Johnson
Sls&Mrk Ex: John Bokel

LEE'S SUMMIT CITY ADMIN
See CITY OF LEES SUMMIT

LEES SUMMIT HONDA
See STADIUM INC

D-U-N-S 08-069-3591
LEES SUMMIT R-7 SCHOOL DISTRICT
301 Ne Tudor Rd, Lees Summit, MO 64086-5702
Tel (816) 986-1000 *Founded/Ownrshp* 1889
Sales 142.3MM^E *EMP* 2,503

SIC 8211 Public elementary school; Public junior high school; Public senior high school; Public elementary school; Public junior high school; Public senior high school
Instr Medi: Laura Maxwell

D-U-N-S 07-905-6081
LEES-MCRAE COLLEGE INC (NC)
191 Main St, Banner Elk, NC 28604-9626
Tel (800) 280-4562 *Founded/Ownrshp* 1900
Sales 30.7MM *EMP* 180
SIC 8221 College, except junior; College, except junior
Pr: Barry M Buxton
**CFO:* Scott McKinney

D-U-N-S 02-510-4311
LEESAR INC
LEESAR REGIONAL SERVICE CENTER
2727 Winkler Ave, Fort Myers, FL 33901-9358
Tel (239) 939-8800 *Founded/Ownrshp* 1998
Sales 195.4MM *EMP* 280
Accts Bobbitt Pittenger & Company Pa
SIC 5047 Medical equipment & supplies; Medical equipment & supplies
Pr: Robert Simpson
**CEO:* Bob Simpson
**CFO:* Gayle Reynolds
**VP:* Paul McWhinnie
IT Man: Vickie Dragich

LEESAR REGIONAL SERVICE CENTER
See LEESAR INC

D-U-N-S 79-661-9922
■ **LEESBURG KNITTING MILLS INC**
(*Suby of* FRUIT OF LOOM) ★
400 Industrial Blvd, Leesburg, AL 35983-3745
Tel (256) 526-6522 *Founded/Ownrshp* 1998
Sales 58.1MM^E *EMP* 1,470
SIC 2281 0724 Yarn spinning mills; Cotton ginning; Yarn spinning mills; Cotton ginning
Pr: Jim Browning

LEESBURG REGIONAL MEDICAL CENT
See CENTRAL FLORIDA HEALTH ALLIANCE INC

D-U-N-S 05-594-7949
LEESBURG REGIONAL MEDICAL CENTER
600 E Dixie Ave, Leesburg, FL 34748-5925
Tel (352) 323-5070 *Founded/Ownrshp* 1963
Sales 5.7MM^E *EMP* 380
SIC 5947 5932 5812 8062 Gift shop; Used merchandise stores; Snack bar; General medical & surgical hospitals; Gift shop; Used merchandise stores; Snack bar; General medical & surgical hospitals
Pr: Richard Wooton
**Pr:* Jeorgia Carpenter
**Treas:* Alice Spears
VP: Phyllis Baum
VP: Darlene Stone

D-U-N-S 01-082-1858
LEESBURG REGIONAL MEDICAL CENTER INC
600 E Dixie Ave, Leesburg, FL 34748-5999
Tel (352) 323-5762 *Founded/Ownrshp* 1986
Sales 222.2MM *EMP* 1,900
Accts Kpmg Llp Greensboro Nc
SIC 8062 General medical & surgical hospitals; General medical & surgical hospitals
CEO: Don Henderson
V Ch: Gregory Lewis
Treas: Roger Beyers
Ofcr: Rob Brown
**Sr VP:* Diane Harden
**VP:* Phyllis Baum
VP: Alex Chang
Dir Rx: Laverne Ford
Prac Mgr: Deborah Cook
CIO: Dave Steele
IT Man: Ron Roweton

D-U-N-S 04-218-6965
LEESBURG SOUTHERN ELECTRIC INC
SOUTHERN ELECTRICAL SERVICE CO
103 Sycolin Rd Se Ste A, Leesburg, VA 20175-4111
Tel (703) 478-8368 *Founded/Ownrshp* 1962
Sales 29.0MM^E *EMP* 180
SIC 1731 1711 7538 General electrical contractor; Warm air heating & air conditioning contractor; General automotive repair shops; General electrical contractor; Warm air heating & air conditioning contractor; General automotive repair shops
Pr: Joseph D Lee Sr
**VP:* Daniel Lee
VP: James Santos
**VP:* O Ronald Smith

D-U-N-S 60-822-4705 IMP
■ **LEESBURG YARN MILLS INC**
(*Suby of* FRUIT OF LOOM) ★
Highway 68, Leesburg, AL 35983
Tel (256) 526-6522 *Founded/Ownrshp* 1987
Sales 24.4MM^E *EMP* 250
SIC 2281 Cotton yarn, spun; Cotton yarn, spun
CEO: John Holland
**Ex VP:* Ralph Wakeland
VP Mfg: Jim Browning
Plnt Mgr: Michael Priest

D-U-N-S 06-687-2706 IMP/EXP
■ **LEESON ELECTRIC CORP**
(*Suby of* REGAL-BELOIT CORP) ★
1051 Cheyenne Ave, Grafton, WI 53024-9541
Tel (262) 377-8810 *Founded/Ownrshp* 2000
Sales 62.5MM^E *EMP* 1,000
SIC 3621 Motors, electric; Motors, electric
VP: Mike Catania
VP: Keith Tipper
Exec: Barb Sexton
DP Exec: Ben He
IT Man: Pat Gasser
Sales Asso: David Pierson

D-U-N-S 16-080-8502 IMP
LEEVAC SHIPYARDS JENNINGS LLC
(*Suby of* CARI CO) ★
111 Bunge St, Jennings, LA 70546
Tel (337) 824-2210 *Founded/Ownrshp* 1998
Sales 119.4MM^E *EMP* 260
SIC 3731 Shipbuilding & repairing; Shipbuilding & repairing
CEO: Christian G Vaccari
**VP:* Richard Ortego
**VP:* Troy W Skelton
Sls Mgr: Tom Church
Sls Mgr: Pat Dalton

D-U-N-S 87-908-1149 IMP
LEEVAC SHIPYARDS LLC
(*Suby of* CARI CO) ★
217 N Columbia St, Covington, LA 70433-3245
Tel (337) 824-2210 *Founded/Ownrshp* 1986
Sales 86.6MM^E *EMP* 300
SIC 3731 Shipbuilding & repairing; Shipbuilding & repairing
CEO: Christian G Vaccari
VP: Dan Gaiennie
VP Opers: Troy Skelton

D-U-N-S 03-219-5245
LEEVERS FOODS PARTNERSHIP LLP
501 4th St Se, Devils Lake, ND 58301-3703
Tel (701) 662-8646 *Founded/Ownrshp* 1997
Sales 92.5MM^E *EMP* 950
SIC 5411 Grocery stores; Grocery stores
Pr: Robert Leevers
**VP:* Al Hanson

LEEVERS FRESH FOODS
See LEEVERS SUPERMARKETS INC

D-U-N-S 03-180-9015
LEEVERS SUPERMARKETS INC
LEEVERS FRESH FOODS
2195 N State, Franktown, CO 80116
Tel (303) 814-8646 *Founded/Ownrshp* 1938
Sales 20.6MM^E *EMP* 90
SIC 5411 Supermarkets, independent
Ch Bd: John N Leevers
CFO: Sharon Leevers
**CFO:* Kirk J Rustvold
**VP:* Christopher Leevers
VP Opers: Dale Brown

LEEWARD CONSTRUCTION
See E R LINDE CONSTRUCTION CORP

D-U-N-S 80-004-9553 IMP/EXP
LEEWARD CONSTRUCTION INC
9 Collan Park, Honesdale, PA 18431-7654
Tel (570) 253-4090 *Founded/Ownrshp* 1993
Sales 23.3MM^E *EMP* 70
SIC 1794 1623 Excavation work; Water, sewer & utility lines
Pr: Gary F Linde
Pr: Tom Ludwig
**Treas:* Karl Harkenreader
**VP:* Thomas Quinnan
IT Man: Kristin Connolly
Sfty Mgr: Shane Ellis

D-U-N-S 14-838-0348
LEEWARD DISTRICT OFFICE
(*Suby of* EDUCATION BOARD) ★
601 Kamokila Blvd Ste 588, Kapolei, HI 96707-2037
Tel (808) 692-8000 *Founded/Ownrshp* 1950
Sales NA *EMP* 2,000
SIC 9411 Administration of educational programs; ; Administration of educational programs;

D-U-N-S 83-309-0264
LEEWARD MEMBER LLC
6688 N Central Expy # 500, Dallas, TX 75206-3914
Tel (214) 515-1100 *Founded/Ownrshp* 2009
Sales 85.4MM^E *EMP* 110
SIC 4911 Energy conservation engineering; Generation, electric power
CEO: Craig Carson
**CEO:* David Smith
**VP:* Andrew Flanagan
**VP:* Greg Flowers
**VP:* Christopher Loehr
Board of Directors: Randy Barnes, Matthew McGowan

D-U-N-S 83-104-0915
■ **LEEWARD STRATEGIC PROPERTIES INC**
(*Suby of* GENERAL ELECTRIC CAPITAL CORP) ★
901 Main Ave, Norwalk, CT 06851-1168
Tel (203) 840-6300 *Founded/Ownrshp* 2010
Sales 53.3MM^E *EMP* 162^E
SIC 6726 Investment offices
Pr: Alec Burger
VP: Carl Jacobson
VP: Michael G Rowan

LEFELD SUPPLIES RENTAL
See LEFELD WELDING AND STEEL SUPPLIES INC

D-U-N-S 00-505-5835 IMP
LEFELD WELDING AND STEEL SUPPLIES INC (OH)
LEFELD SUPPLIES RENTAL
600 N 2nd St, Coldwater, OH 45828-9777
Tel (419) 678-2397 *Founded/Ownrshp* 1953, 1968
Sales 30.6MM^E *EMP* 46
SIC 5084 7353 1799 3441 Welding machinery & equipment; Heavy construction equipment rental; Welding on site; Fabricated structural metal
CEO: Stanley E Lefeld
**Pr:* Gary Lefeld
Sales Asso: Steve Vogel

D-U-N-S 08-244-5180
LEFFINGWELL AG SALES CO INC
942 E Honolulu St, Lindsay, CA 93247-2616
Tel (559) 562-4946 *Founded/Ownrshp* 1985
Sales 40.3MM^E *EMP* 28
Accts Pine Pedroncelli & Aguilar In
SIC 5191 Chemicals, agricultural; Fertilizer & fertilizer materials; Insecticides; Pesticides
CEO: Dana D Gilleastie
**Treas:* Geary Austin
**VP:* Dwight Kissick

LEFFLER ENERGY
See RICHLAND PARTNERS LLC

D-U-N-S 88-490-2065
LEFLORE COUNTY HOSPITAL AUTHORITY
EASTERN OKLAHOMA MEDICAL CTR
105 Wall St, Poteau, OK 74953-4433
Tel (918) 647-8161 *Founded/Ownrshp* 1977
Sales 25.0MM^E *EMP* 250
SIC 8062 8011 General medical & surgical hospitals; Offices & clinics of medical doctors; General medical & surgical hospitals; Offices & clinics of medical doctors
CEO: Michael Carter
CFO: Nancy Frier
Dir Sec: Mark Kannady
QA Dir: Tiffany Griffis
IT Man: Michael Huggins
Mtls Mgr: Sheryl Brown
Trfc Mgr: Lonnie Mitchell
Doctor: William Willis
Phys Thrpy: David Hoegh

D-U-N-S 10-003-9932
LEFLORE COUNTY SCHOOL DISTRICT (INC)
1901 Highway 82 W, Greenwood, MS 38930-2795
Tel (662) 453-8566 *Founded/Ownrshp* 1840
Sales 18.0MM^E *EMP* 500
Accts Charles L Shivers Cpa Ridge
SIC 8211 Public elementary school; Public senior high school; Public elementary school; Public senior high school
Pr Dir: Maxine Greenleaf

D-U-N-S 04-915-5591
LEFRAK ORGANIZATION INC
40 W 57th St Fl 23, New York, NY 10019-4011
Tel (212) 707-6600 *Founded/Ownrshp* 1905
Sales 89.7MM^E *EMP* 245
SIC 6513 6512

LEFT AT ALBUQUERQUE
See CHALK BLUE CAFE INC

D-U-N-S 04-821-8570
LEFTFIELD ENTERTAINMENT LLC
(*Suby of* ITV STUDIOS INC) ★
460 W 34th St Fl 16, New York, NY 10001-2320
Tel (212) 564-2607 *Founded/Ownrshp* 2012
Sales 25.9MM^E *EMP* 398^E
SIC 7812 7922 Motion picture production & distribution, television; Commercials, television: tape or film; Television program, including commercial producers; Motion picture production & distribution, television; Commercials, television: tape or film; Television program, including commercial producers
CEO: Brent Montgomery
**COO:* Chris Valentini
**CFO:* John Brohel
**Ex VP:* Heath Banks
**Ex VP:* David George
VP: Kris Cerny
VP: Jordana Hochman
VP: Tonko Soljan
Off Mgr: Michael Turner
Prd Mgr: Anthony Barsness
Prd Mgr: Jen Berrio

D-U-N-S 02-056-4501
LEFTHAND NETWORKS INC (DE)
2580 55th St, Boulder, CO 80301-5714
Tel (303) 449-4100 *Founded/Ownrshp* 2000
Sales 21.3MM^E *EMP* 140
SIC 3572 Computer storage devices; Computer storage devices
Pr: William Chambers
CFO: John Hillyard
CTO: Raju Bopardikar
Manager: Shaun Soria
Sls Mgr: David Doyle

D-U-N-S 82-903-2965 IMP
LEG APPAREL LLC
(*Suby of* 29 PALMS) ★
65 Railroad Ave Ste 4, Ridgefield, NJ 07657-2130
Tel (201) 840-6766 *Founded/Ownrshp* 2008
Sales 26.1MM^E *EMP* 30^E
SIC 5136 Men's & boys' sportswear & work clothing

D-U-N-S 82-891-6577 IMP
LEG RESOURCE INC
350 5th Ave Ste 6408, New York, NY 10118-6408
Tel (212) 736-4574 *Founded/Ownrshp* 1993
Sales 25.0MM *EMP* 50
SIC 2251 2252 Tights, women's; Hosiery; Men's, boys' & girls' hosiery; Socks
Pr: Wayne Lederman
Sls Mgr: Nancy Felgueiras

LEGACY BANK
See MIDSTATE BANCORP INC

D-U-N-S 03-635-2466
LEGACY BANK (OK)
FIRST STATE BANK
(*Suby of* LEGACY BANK) ★
2801 W Memorial Rd, Oklahoma City, OK 73134-8029
Tel (405) 751-2900 *Founded/Ownrshp* 1902, 1954
Sales NA *EMP* 250
SIC 6029 Commercial banks; Commercial banks
CEO: R Stephen Carmack
**Pr:* Michael Chaloner
**CFO:* Thomas Collins
Sr VP: Kirk Bredy
Sr VP: Barry Burget
VP: John Thompson
VP: Callie Troglin
Genl Couns: Michael Brown
Snr Mgr: Deborah Cardoza

D-U-N-S 61-333-0703
LEGACY BANK INC
101 W Main St, Hinton, OK 73047-9160
Tel (405) 542-3101 *Founded/Ownrshp* 1986
Sales NA *EMP* 69
SIC 6712 Bank holding companies; Bank holding companies
Pr: R Stephen Carmack
**VP:* Samuel Carmack
VP: Dave Fuller

D-U-N-S 78-705-2195
LEGACY BUILDERS/DEVELOPERS CORP
519 8th Ave Fl 7, New York, NY 10018-6506
Tel (212) 644-1603 *Founded/Ownrshp* 2006
Sales 35.2MM^E *EMP* 82
SIC 1542 1522 Commercial & office building contractors; Multi-family dwellings, new construction
Pr: John Bennardo
**CFO:* Harry Zapiti

D-U-N-S 05-279-5525
LEGACY BUSINESS SOLUTIONS LLC
1144 Shine Ave, Myrtle Beach, SC 29577-1503
Tel (843) 945-4358 *Founded/Ownrshp* 2015
Sales 7.4MM^E *EMP* 1,300
SIC 7011 Hotels & motels; Resort hotel
Ex Dir: Nabil Ghanan

LEGACY COMMERCIAL FINISHES
See LEGACY COMMERCIAL FLOORING LTD

D-U-N-S 19-298-4446
LEGACY COMMERCIAL FLOORING LTD
LEGACY COMMERCIAL FINISHES
800 Morrison Rd, Columbus, OH 43230-6643
Tel (614) 476-1043 *Founded/Ownrshp* 2005
Sales 32.6MM^E *EMP* 251^E
Accts Gbq Partners Llc Columbus Oh
SIC 1752 Floor laying & floor work; Floor laying & floor work
Pr: Tony Nixon
**VP:* George Holinga

D-U-N-S 83-017-0044
LEGACY COMMODITIES INC
6565 Shoreline Dr, Little Elm, TX 75068-3115
Tel (972) 292-1007 *Founded/Ownrshp* 2008
Sales 26.0MM *EMP* 3
SIC 5191 7389 Animal feeds; ; Animal feeds;
Pr: Stuart Rickert

D-U-N-S 18-794-4491
LEGACY COMMUNITY HEALTH SERVICES INC
1415 California St, Houston, TX 77006-2602
Tel (713) 830-3000 *Founded/Ownrshp* 1982
Sales 74.9MM *EMP* 132
Accts Bkd Llp Springfield Mo
SIC 8093 8011 Specialty outpatient clinics; Offices & clinics of medical doctors; Specialty outpatient clinics; Offices & clinics of medical doctors
Ch Bd: Ray Purser
**COO:* Jeff Perry
**CFO:* Ben Glisan
**CFO:* Judi McNall
Ofcr: Sammy Nesbit
VP: Tina Megdal
**Ex Dir:* Katy Caldwell
IT Man: Theron Bretz
VP Opers: Michelle Barrera
Pr Mgr: Terri Boyko
Doctor: Mark Levine

D-U-N-S 05-097-3098
LEGACY EMANUEL HOSPITAL & HEALTH CENTER
2801 N Gantenbein Ave, Portland, OR 97227-1623
Tel (503) 413-2200 *Founded/Ownrshp* 1912
Sales 705.0MM *EMP* 3,619
SIC 8062 General medical & surgical hospitals; Hospital, AMA approved residency; General medical & surgical hospitals; Hospital, AMA approved residency
Pr: George J Brown MD
Ofcr: Bryce Helgerson
Ofcr: Lori Morgan
Ofcr: M D Morgan
Dir Soc: Mike Morrison
CIO: Matthew Calais
Podiatrist: Gary Chiotti
Doctor: Duncan Neilson

D-U-N-S 02-247-0635
LEGACY EQUIPMENT INC
(*Suby of* GA WEST & CO INC) ★
12526 Celeste Rd, Chunchula, AL 36521-3578
Tel (251) 679-1965 *Founded/Ownrshp* 2008
Sales 105.8MM *EMP* 10
SIC 5046 Commercial equipment; Commercial equipment
Pr: Gary A West

D-U-N-S 01-802-3770
LEGACY FARMERS COOPERATIVE
6566 County Road 236, Findlay, OH 45840-9769
Tel (419) 423-2611 *Founded/Ownrshp* 1989
Sales 278.4MM *EMP* 122
Accts Balestra Harr & Scherer Cpas
SIC 5153 5191 5984 2875 2048 2041 Grains; Farm supplies; Seeds: field, garden & flower; Fertilizer & fertilizer materials; Liquefied petroleum gas dealers; Fertilizers, mixing only; Prepared feeds; Flour & other grain mill products; Grains; Farm supplies; Seeds: field, garden & flower; Fertilizer & fertilizer materials; Liquefied petroleum gas dealers; Fertilizers, mixing only; Prepared feeds; Flour & other grain mill products
Pr: Mark Sunderman
**Ch Bd:* Andrew Jones
**Treas:* Gary Herringshaw
**V Ch Bd:* Marvin Maas
VP: William Tong
Brnch Mgr: Tim Meyer
IT Man: Sam Clark

D-U-N-S 07-782-4337 IMP
LEGACY FARMS LLC
6625 Caballero Blvd, Buena Park, CA 90620-1131
Tel (714) 736-1800 *Founded/Ownrshp* 1991
Sales 107.1MM^E *EMP* 120
SIC 5148 Fresh fruits & vegetables; Fresh fruits & vegetables

*Prin: Rick Baxter
*Prin: Vince Mendoza
*Prin: Ron Shimizu
*Prin: Wally Sinner
Genl Mgr: Phil Trotter
Opers Mgr: Kevin Shimizu
Sales Asso: Steve Bradley

D-U-N-S 12-496-2320 EXP
LEGACY FISHERMAN INC
10 S Bryan Rd, Dania, FL 33004-3114
Tel (954) 927-6828 Founded/Ownrshp 2000
Sales 25.0MM EMP 35
SIC 5551

D-U-N-S 78-777-1484
LEGACY FORD OF MCDONOUGH INC
413 Industrial Blvd, McDonough, GA 30253-6608
Tel (770) 914-2800 Founded/Ownrshp 1992
Sales 62.3MM^E EMP 190
Accts Overcash Walker & Co Pc
SIC 5511 5521 7538 Automobiles, new & used; Pickups, new & used; Vans, new & used; Used car dealers; General automotive repair shops; Automobiles, new & used; Pickups, new & used; Vans, new & used; Used car dealers; General automotive repair shops
CEO: Emanuel D Jones
*CFO: Brenda Lankford
Genl Mgr: Ray Obrian
Sls Mgr: Robert Prine

D-U-N-S 07-961-2506
LEGACY FRUIT PACKERS LLC (WA)
12 Hoffer Rd, Wapato, WA 98951-8525
Tel (509) 877-4188 Founded/Ownrshp 2014
Sales 63.0MM EMP 300
SIC 0723 Fruit (fresh) packing services; Fruit (fresh) packing services

D-U-N-S 79-885-4824
■ **LEGACY FUNERAL SERVICES OF TEXAS LLC**
(Suby of SCI SPECIAL INC) ★
3103 Sackett St, Houston, TX 77098-2016
Tel (713) 522-5141 Founded/Ownrshp 1962
Sales 8.8MM^E EMP 500
SIC 7261 Funeral service & crematories; Funeral service & crematories
CEO: Robert Waltrip

LEGACY GLOBAL LOGISTICS SVCS
See LEGACY TRANSPORTATION SERVICES INC

D-U-N-S 04-980-6789
LEGACY GOOD SAMARITAN HOSPITAL AND MEDICAL CENTER
LEGACY GOOD SAMARITAN MEDICAL
1015 Nw 22nd Ave, Portland, OR 97210-3025
Tel (503) 413-7711 Founded/Ownrshp 1989
Sales 318.7MM EMP 1,900
SIC 8069

LEGACY GOOD SAMARITAN MEDICAL
See LEGACY GOOD SAMARITAN HOSPITAL AND MEDICAL CENTER

D-U-N-S 02-066-3530
■ **LEGACY GROUP INC**
(Suby of BERKSHIRE BANK) ★
99 North St, Pittsfield, MA 01201-5114
Tel (413) 443-4421 Founded/Ownrshp 1997
Sales NA EMP 182
SIC 6036 State savings banks, not federally chartered

D-U-N-S 12-825-4682
LEGACY GROUP L L C
400 112th Ave Ne Ste 300, Bellevue, WA 98004-5540
Tel (425) 562-8272 Founded/Ownrshp 2002
Sales NA EMP 69^E
SIC 6399 Bank deposit insurance
COO: Dan Flitsch
Ex VP: Brent Eley
Prd Mgr: Shannon Kershaw

D-U-N-S 03-079-8441
LEGACY HEALTH
1919 Nw Lovejoy St, Portland, OR 97209-1503
Tel (503) 415-5600 Founded/Ownrshp 1970
Sales 1.6MM EMP 8,000
SIC 8011 Medical centers; Medical centers
CEO: George J Brown MD
V Ch: Wilma G Kaplan
CFO: Dave Eager
CFO: Beverly Peacock
Treas: Kelly A Higgins
Ofcr: Allyson Anderson
Ofcr: Jonathan Avery
Ofcr: Carla D Harris
Ofcr: Bryce Helgerson
Ofcr: Bronwyn Houston
Ofcr: Lori Morgan
Ofcr: Richard Rico
Sr VP: Carol Bradley Rn
Sr VP: Maureen Bradley
Sr VP: Jack Cioffi
Sr VP: Rob Dewitt
Sr VP: Trent Green
VP: Molly Burchell
VP: Dan Harris
VP: Lowell Johnson
VP: Stephen Jones

LEGACY HEALTH SERVICES
See DMD MANAGEMENT INC

D-U-N-S 12-052-0817
LEGACY HEALTHCARE SERVICES INC
3001 Spring Forest Rd, Raleigh, NC 27616-2815
Tel (919) 424-5080 Founded/Ownrshp 1999
Sales 21.7MM^E EMP 300
SIC 8093 Specialty outpatient clinics; Specialty outpatient clinics
Pr: Sandra Hoskins
*CFO: John Daratony
Sr VP: Phil Jones
VP: Melissa Hanson
VP: Ann Irwin
VP Opers: Anne Shimek

LEGACY HOLDING COMPANY
See LEGACY SUPPLY CHAIN HOLDINGS INC

LEGACY HOME
See FRIENDLY HEARTS LTD

LEGACY HOME INFUSION
See VNA HEALTH SERVICES

LEGACY HOMES
See LEGACY/MONTEREY HOMES LP

D-U-N-S 55-741-4815 IMP
LEGACY HOUSING LTD
4801 Mark Iv Pkwy, Fort Worth, TX 76106-2217
Tel (817) 624-7565 Founded/Ownrshp 2005
Sales 141.2MM^E EMP 500
SIC 2451 Mobile homes, personal or private use; Mobile homes, personal or private use
Genl Pt: Kenny Shipley
Pt: Conley Bigham
Pt: Curtis Hodgson
COO: Mick Barker
CFO: Jeff Burt
Genl Mgr: Ray McKay
Opers Mgr: Andy Nauert
Sales Exec: Christi Lancaster
Sls Mgr: Ed Spaeth
Genl Couns: Drew Chapman

D-U-N-S 82-514-4921
LEGACY INFINITI LTD
ATLANTIC INFINITI
200 Charlotte Ave, Hicksville, NY 11801-2645
Tel (516) 536-9000 Founded/Ownrshp 2003
Sales 29.0MM^E EMP 70
SIC 5511 Automobiles, new & used; Automobiles, new & used
CEO: John Chmela
Sales Asso: Shawn Hassan
Sales Asso: Steve Weintraub

D-U-N-S 83-211-2671
LEGACY LABORATORY SERVICES LLC
(Suby of LEGACY EMANUEL HOSPITAL & HEALTH CENTER) ★
1225 Ne 2nd Ave, Portland, OR 97232-2003
Tel (503) 413-5050 Founded/Ownrshp 2009
Sales 10.4MM^E EMP 500
SIC 8071 Medical laboratories; Medical laboratories
Prin: George J Brown
*VP: Donald Toussaint
Ex Dir: Angelo Turner

D-U-N-S 15-287-6566
LEGACY LEARNING LLC
PROFESSIONAL EDUCATION INST
9020 S Sandy Pkwy, Sandy, UT 84070-6409
Tel (800) 417-5037 Founded/Ownrshp 2000
Sales 12.2MM^E EMP 400^E
SIC 8299 6282 Educational services; Investment advice; Educational services; Investment advice
COO: Dave Ellis
CFO: Troie Price
Genl Mgr: Cathie Woods
Dir IT: Kim Macdonald
IT Man: Britton Child
Plnt Mgr: Fred Kocher
Mktg Mgr: Tom White

LEGACY LODGE
See ISLANDS MANAGEMENT CO LLC

LEGACY MANUFACTURING COMPANY
See WEEMS INDUSTRIES INC

D-U-N-S 14-557-2686
LEGACY MARKETING PARTNERS LLC
640 N Lasalle Dr Fl 5, Chicago, IL 60654
Tel (312) 799-5400 Founded/Ownrshp 2003
Sales 43.1MM^E EMP 200
SIC 8742 Marketing consulting services; Marketing consulting services
CTO: Cheryl Fein
Ex VP: Mark Driggs
Sr VP: Ed Swiderski
VP: Dan Eisenberg
VP: Yolanda Luszcz
VP: Jennifer Shankman
VP: Amanda Turnbull
Exec: Dave Donadeo
Exec: Allicia Rajhel
Exec: Joe Rovner
Exec: Andrea Tomasi
Creative D: April Quealy

D-U-N-S 12-793-6610
LEGACY MECHANICAL & ENERGY SERVICES INC
3130 Crow Canyon Pl # 410, San Ramon, CA 94583-1346
Tel (925) 820-6938 Founded/Ownrshp 2002
Sales 25.5MM^E EMP 100
SIC 1711 Heating & air conditioning contractors
Pr: Richard Almini
CFO: Rich Cardillo
*VP: Chip Eskildsen
*VP: Jack Larkin
*VP: Bill Longbotham
IT Man: Linda Jardin
Snr PM: Chad Barnes

D-U-N-S 16-721-3938
LEGACY MECHANICAL INC
1455 S Platte River Dr, Denver, CO 80223-3463
Tel (720) 898-3446 Founded/Ownrshp 2004
Sales 30.9MM^E EMP 80
SIC 1711 Mechanical contractor
Pr: Scott Krum
*VP: Eric Alstrup
VP: Michael Spiller

D-U-N-S 15-401-9673
LEGACY MERIDIAN PARK HOSPITAL
19300 Sw 65th Ave, Tualatin, OR 97062-7706
Tel (503) 692-1212 Founded/Ownrshp 1970
Sales 188.0MM EMP 458
SIC 8062 8011 General medical & surgical hospitals; Primary care medical clinic; General medical & surgical hospitals; Primary care medical clinic
CEO: George J Brown
*COO: Mike Newcomb
*CFO: Linda Hoff
*Sr VP: Carol Bradley
*Sr VP: David Eager
Diag Rad: Carl Lopez

D-U-N-S 14-769-4160
LEGACY MOUNT HOOD MEDICAL CENTER
24800 Se Stark St, Gresham, OR 97030-3378
Tel (503) 674-1122 Founded/Ownrshp 1984
Sales 136.4MM EMP 306
Accts Kpmg Llp Portland Or
SIC 8062 5912 Hospital, affiliated with AMA residency; Drug stores; Hospital, affiliated with AMA residency; Drug stores
Pr: George J Brown
Off Mgr: Kelly Buker
Pharmcst: Thien Nguyen

LEGACY MUTUAL MORTGAGE
See GARDNER FINANCIAL SERVICES LTD

D-U-N-S 62-237-7195
LEGACY OF VINE MINISTRIES
SAMARITIAN FEET INTERNATIONAL
1900 Associates Ln, Charlotte, NC 28217-2816
Tel (704) 341-1630 Founded/Ownrshp 2003
Sales 32.2MM EMP 15
SIC 8322 Individual & family services; Individual & family services
Pr: Emmanuel T Ohonme
VP: Raj Pragasam
Off Mgr: Ron Pegram

D-U-N-S 12-530-6493 IMP/EXP
LEGACY PADDLESPORTS LLC
210 Old Airport Rd, Fletcher, NC 28732-9273
Tel (828) 684-1933 Founded/Ownrshp 2006
Sales 23.6MM^E EMP 110
SIC 3732

D-U-N-S 12-280-2262
LEGACY PARTNERS RESIDENTIAL INC
(Suby of STEELWAVE INC) ★
4000 E 3rd Ave Ste 600, Foster City, CA 94404-4828
Tel (650) 571-2250 Founded/Ownrshp 1995
Sales 57.1MM^E EMP 1,000
SIC 8741 Management services; Management services
Ch Bd: C Preston Butcher
CFO: Tim McCarthy
*CFO: Gary J Rossi
Mng Dir: Spencer R Stuart Jr

D-U-N-S 78-280-1414
▲ **LEGACY RESERVES LP**
303 W Wall St Ste 1800, Midland, TX 79701-5106
Tel (432) 689-5200 Founded/Ownrshp 2005
Sales 532.3MM EMP 254^E
Accts Bdo Usa Llp Houston Texas
Tkr Sym LGCY Exch NGS
SIC 1311 Crude petroleum & natural gas; Crude petroleum & natural gas production; Crude petroleum & natural gas; Crude petroleum & natural gas production
Pr: Paul T Horne
Genl Pt: Legacy Reserves GP
*Ch Bd: Cary D Brown
COO: Kyle M Hammond
Ex VP: Tom Fitzsimmons
Ex VP: Kyle A McGraw
Off Mgr: Betty Chapman
Prd Mgr: Ernie Hanson
Genl Couns: Bert Ferrara
Board of Directors: Dale A Brown, William R Granberry, G Larry Lawrence, Kyle A McGraw, William D Sullivan, Kyle D Vann

LEGACY RETIREMENT COMMUNITIES
See CHERRY HILL CO LLC

D-U-N-S 01-851-0102 IMP
LEGACY SPORTS INTERNATIONAL INC
4750 Longley Ln Ste 209, Reno, NV 89502-5982
Tel (775) 828-0555 Founded/Ownrshp 2005
Sales 50.0MM EMP 25
SIC 5091 Sporting & recreation goods; Sporting & recreation goods
CEO: Gene Lumsden
*CFO: Douglas Miller

D-U-N-S 07-918-3250
LEGACY SUPPLY CHAIN HOLDINGS INC
LEGACY HOLDING COMPANY
99 Bow St Ste 300w, Portsmouth, NH 03801-3995
Tel (603) 422-0777 Founded/Ownrshp 2013
Sales 33.9MM^E EMP 112^E
SIC 4225 General warehousing & storage
VP: Rick Dempsey

LEGACY SUPPLY CHAIN SERVICES
See TRI-STARR MANAGEMENT SERVICES INC

D-U-N-S 07-956-3083
LEGACY TRADERS INC (CA)
SOUTH BAY WHOLESALE
17240 S Main St, Gardena, CA 90248-3101
Tel (310) 225-3700 Founded/Ownrshp 2011
Sales 24.0MM EMP 7
SIC 5399 Army-Navy goods; Army-Navy goods
Pr: Emad Hanna

D-U-N-S 10-798-5632
LEGACY TRANSPORTATION SERVICES INC
VITRAN LOGISTICS
1000 S Cucamonga Ave, Ontario, CA 91761-3461
Tel (909) 972-3100 Founded/Ownrshp 2015
Sales 21.9MM^E EMP 46
SIC 4731 Freight forwarding; Freight consolidation
CEO: Richard E Gaetz

D-U-N-S 78-583-6842
LEGACY TRANSPORTATION SERVICES INC
LEGACY GLOBAL LOGISTICS SVCS
935 Mclaughlin Ave, San Jose, CA 95122-2612
Tel (408) 294-9800 Founded/Ownrshp 1991
Sales 48.7MM^E EMP 180
SIC 4214 4213 Local trucking with storage; Trucking, except local; Local trucking with storage; Trucking, except local
Pr: John Migliozzi
*Ex VP: Shelly Gipson
*Ex VP: Michael Quinn
*VP: Shelly J McAllister
VP: John Otten
IT Man: Jerry Welch
Opers Mgr: Tony Jensen
Prd Mgr: Ken Schramm
Sales Exec: Beverly Dygert
Sls Dir: John Ordaz

D-U-N-S 06-988-8246
LEGACY TREATMENT SERVICES INC
1289 Route 38 Ste 203, Hainesport, NJ 08036-2730
Tel (609) 267-5656 Founded/Ownrshp 1864
Sales 20.5MM EMP 740
SIC 8093 8361 8322 Mental health clinic, outpatient; Home for the mentally retarded; Individual & family services; Mental health clinic, outpatient; Home for the mentally retarded; Individual & family services
Ex Dir: Roy Leitstein
CFO: Betty Garrison

D-U-N-S 07-962-7448
LEGACY TRUCK CENTERS INC
SHAW MACK SALES & SERVICE-DIV
(Suby of SHAW MACK SALES & SERVICE-DIV) ★
178 Lewis Dr, Somerset, PA 15501-1074
Tel (814) 445-9617 Founded/Ownrshp 2014
Sales 57.4MM EMP 175
SIC 5511 Trucks, tractors & trailers: new & used
Pr: Matthew Niebauer
*VP: John Niebauer III

D-U-N-S 14-045-5788
LEGACY VACATION CLUB LLC
RESORT WORLD MANAGEMENT
2800 N Poinciana Blvd, Kissimmee, FL 34746-5258
Tel (407) 997-5000 Founded/Ownrshp 1998
Sales 30.2MM^E EMP 400
SIC 7011 Time-sharing real estate sales, leasing & rentals; Resort hotel
Pr: Anthony J Picciano
Exec: Gina Somers
Genl Mgr: Steve Blake
Mktg Mgr: Kali Mosalli
Sls Mgr: Ashlee Conley

D-U-N-S 06-060-1929
LEGACY VISITING NURSE ASSOCIATION
LEGENCY VISITING NURSE ASSOC
(Suby of LEGACY HEALTH) ★
815 Ne Davis St, Portland, OR 97232-2964
Tel (503) 220-1000 Founded/Ownrshp 1902
Sales 12.8MM EMP 5,094
Accts Kpmg Llp Portland Or
SIC 8399 5999 8082 Health systems agency; Hospital equipment & supplies; Home health care services; Health systems agency; Hospital equipment & supplies; Home health care services
Pr: Steve Johnson
VP: Dave Loboy
VP: Russ McGillivray
VP: Darwin Murray
VP: Brian Smith
VP: Jeff Vinson
Div Mgr: Stephen Fischer
Div Mgr: Doug Fisher
Div Mgr: Tom Mulligan
Genl Mgr: Chuck Whitaker
IT Man: Brandi Payton

LEGACY VULCAN CORP.
See LEGACY VULCAN LLC

D-U-N-S 00-339-6025 IMP/EXP
■ **LEGACY VULCAN LLC**
LEGACY VULCAN CORP.
(Suby of VULCAN MATERIALS CO) ★
1200 Urban Center Dr, Vestavia, AL 35242-2545
Tel (205) 298-3000 Founded/Ownrshp 1956, 2007
Sales NA EMP 6,598
SIC 1422 1423 1442 2951 3273 Crushed & broken limestone; Crushed & broken granite; Construction sand mining; Gravel mining; Paving mixtures; Ready-mixed concrete; Crushed & broken limestone; Crushed & broken granite; Construction sand mining; Gravel mining; Paving mixtures; Ready-mixed concrete
CFO: Daniel F Sansone
Pr: John L Holland
*Pr: John R McPherson
Sr VP: Guy M Badgett
*Sr VP: William F Denson III
Sr VP: James W Smack
*Sr VP: Robert A Wason IV
*VP: Ejaz A Khan
VP: Michael R Mills
VP: James W O'Brien
Brnch Mgr: Rob McMahan

D-U-N-S 08-001-1459
■ **LEGACY VULCAN LLC**
(Suby of VULCAN MATERIALS CO) ★
1200 Urban Center Dr, Shoal Creek, AL 35242-2545
Tel (205) 298-3000 Founded/Ownrshp 2015
Sales 21.7MM EMP 4,623^E
SIC 1422 1423 1442 2951 3273

D-U-N-S 18-542-4363
LEGACY/MONTEREY HOMES LP
LEGACY HOMES
909 Hidden Rdg Ste 400, Irving, TX 75038-3823
Tel (972) 678-5022 Founded/Ownrshp 1997
Sales 20.8MM^E EMP 110
SIC 1531 6531 1521 Speculative builder, single-family houses; Real estate agents & managers; Single-family housing construction
Pt: Jim Bauer
Off Mgr: Lisa Ware
VP Opers: Eddie Servigon

D-U-N-S 03-942-7831
■ LEGACYSTAR SERVICES LLC
(*Suby of* NUSTAR ENERGY LP) ★
2435 N Central Expy # 700, Richardson, TX 75080-2753
Tel (972) 699-4062 *Founded/Ownrshp* 2005
Sales 17.8MM^E *EMP* 1,078
SIC 4613 5172 Refined petroleum pipelines; Gasoline; Diesel fuel; Refined petroleum pipelines; Gasoline; Diesel fuel
VP: Howard C Wadsworth

D-U-N-S 05-083-7962
■ LEGACYTEXAS BANK
(*Suby of* LEGACYTEXAS FINANCIAL GROUP INC) ★
2101 Custer Rd, Plano, TX 75075-2962
Tel (972) 578-5000 *Founded/Ownrshp* 2015
Sales NA *EMP* 285
SIC 6022 State commercial banks; State commercial banks
CEO: Donald R St Clair
Pr: Phil Dyer
Pr: Gayland Lawshe
CFO: Rewaz Chowdhury
Ofcr: Jeff G Chase
Ofcr: Susan Keene
Ofcr: Penny Wadsworth
Ex VP: Yaeger Brad
Ex VP: Mays Davenport
Ex VP: Audrey Duncan
Ex VP: Tom Risley
Ex VP: Dan Strother
Ex VP: Gerry Taylor
Ex VP: Alan Williams
Ex VP: Steve Young
Sr VP: Pamela Austin
Sr VP: Mary Bank
Sr VP: Pam Best
Sr VP: Carroll Dyer
Sr VP: Eric Sonneborn
Sr VP: Dawn Velekei

D-U-N-S 15-406-8956
▲ LEGACYTEXAS FINANCIAL GROUP INC
5851 Legacy Cir, Plano, TX 75024-5966
Tel (972) 578-5000 *Founded/Ownrshp* 2010
Sales NA *EMP* 576^E
Accts Ernst & Young Llp Dallas Tex
Tkr Sym LTXB *Exch* NGS
SIC 6022 Real estate brokers & agents; State commercial banks
Pr: Kevin J Hanigan
**Ch Bd:* Anthony J Levecchio
CFO: J Mays Davenport
Chf Cred: Mark L Williamson
Ex VP: Scott A Almy
Ex VP: Charles D Eikenberg
Ex VP: Pathie McKee
Ex VP: Rick M Robertson
Sr VP: Kari Anderson
Sr VP: Stephanie Moushon
VP: Dan Bailey
VP: Jamie Richardson

D-U-N-S 02-379-8291
LEGAL & GENERAL AMERICA INC
(*Suby of* LEGAL AND GENERAL ASSURANCE SOCIETY LIMITED)
3275 Bennett Creek Ave, Frederick, MD 21704-7608
Tel (301) 279-4198 *Founded/Ownrshp* 1981
Sales NA *EMP* 309^E
SIC 6411 6311 Insurance agents, brokers & service; Life insurance; Insurance agents, brokers & service; Life insurance
Ex VP: Gene R Gilbertson
Pr: Mary Simonelli
**Sr VP:* Thomas Sima
VP: Grant Andrew
VP: Gwin Banks
**VP:* Ramanathan Esau
VP: Richard Knee
Dir Risk M: Amy Butler
Dir Soc: Anita Macmaster
Software D: Manny Benton
Sftwr Eng: Glen Griffith

D-U-N-S 17-267-7929
LEGAL ACQUISITIONS SUPPORT SERVICES LLC
1170 Peachtree St Ne # 1200, Atlanta, GA 30309-7649
Tel (404) 546-7290 *Founded/Ownrshp* 2004
Sales 134.6MM *EMP* 76
SIC 6531 Real estate agent, commercial; Real estate agent, commercial

D-U-N-S 08-995-1966
LEGAL AID BUREAU INC (MD)
500 E Lexington St, Baltimore, MD 21202-3560
Tel (410) 951-7777 *Founded/Ownrshp* 1911
Sales 23.8MM *EMP* 285
SIC 8111

D-U-N-S 08-416-8566
LEGAL AID OF NORTH CAROLINA INC (NC)
224 S Dawson St, Raleigh, NC 27601-1306
Tel (919) 856-2564 *Founded/Ownrshp* 1976
Sales 22.8MM *EMP* 225
Accts Romeo Wiggins & Company Llp R
SIC 8111 Legal aid service; Legal aid service
CEO: George R Hausen Jr
Pr: Delina Locklear
Off Mgr: Tonya Pruitt-Lyons

D-U-N-S 07-329-7541
LEGAL AID SOCIETY
199 Water St Frnt 3, New York, NY 10038-3526
Tel (212) 577-3346 *Founded/Ownrshp* 1876
Sales 224.7MM *EMP* 1,600
Accts Mcgladrey Llp New York Ny
SIC 8111 Legal aid service; Legal aid service
Ch Bd: Richard J Davis
**Pr:* Blaine Sogg
Treas: George Albro
Ofcr: Patricia Bath
VP: Adriene Holder
Dir IT: John Woroblewski
Genl Couns: Janet Sabel
Board of Directors: Gregory A Markel

D-U-N-S 96-541-7645
LEGAL PLACEMENTS INC
1413 Eye St Nw 750 Fl 2, Washington, DC 20005
Tel (202) 682-1661 *Founded/Ownrshp* 1996
Sales 17.1MM^E *EMP* 350
SIC 7363 7361 Temporary help service; Employment agencies; Temporary help service; Employment agencies
Pr: L Dicesare Richichi
**Pr:* Lori Dicesare Richichi
**VP:* Thomas Richichi
**Prin:* Kerry Purcell
Mng Dir: Joanna Davis
Opers Mgr: John Kuzer

D-U-N-S 10-790-5085
LEGAL SEA FOODS LLC
1 Seafood Way, Boston, MA 02210-2702
Tel (617) 530-9000 *Founded/Ownrshp* 1950
Sales 116.0MM^E *EMP* 3,000
SIC 5812 5146 5961 Seafood restaurants; Fish & seafoods; Catalog & mail-order houses; Seafood restaurants; Fish & seafoods; Catalog & mail-order houses
Ch Bd: George Berkowitz
**Pr:* Roger Berkowitz
Pr: Jeffrey Lipson
COO: J Frump
**CFO:* Mark Synnott
**Treas:* Mary Cronin
VP: Ken Chaisson
VP: Scott Flanagan
VP: Richard Heller
VP: Bill Holler
VP: William P Holler
VP: Regina Jerome
VP: Brian Schwanke

D-U-N-S 02-029-4500
■ LEGAL SERVICES CORP (DC)
(*Suby of* EXECUTIVE OFFICE OF UNITED STATES GOVERNMENT) ★
3333 K St Nw Ste 1, Washington, DC 20007-3522
Tel (202) 295-1500 *Founded/Ownrshp* 1974
Sales 370.5MM *EMP* 130
Accts Withumsmith & Brownm Silver Sp
SIC 6732 9199 Trusts: educational, religious, etc.; General government administration; ; Trusts: educational, religious, etc.; General government administration;
Pr: James Sandman
**Ch Bd:* John G Levi
**Treas:* David Richardson
**V Ch Bd:* Martha Minow
Ofcr: Charlie Jeffress
VP: Ron Flagg
Plnt Mgr: Leonard Koczur
Counsel: Mary-Christy Fisher
Snr Mgr: John Meyer

LEGAL SERVICES FOR NEW YORK CY
See LEGAL SERVICES NYC

D-U-N-S 14-464-0430
LEGAL SERVICES NYC
LEGAL SERVICES FOR NEW YORK CY
40 Worth St Fl 606, New York, NY 10013-2904
Tel (646) 442-3600 *Founded/Ownrshp* 1967
Sales 7.7MM *EMP* 282
Accts Mcgladrey Llp
SIC 8111 Legal services; Legal services
Ch Bd: Mark G Cunha
**COO:* Jeanne Perry
**CFO:* John A Butler
Treas: Carol Rosenbaum
Ex Dir: Dennis Kaufman
**Ex Dir:* Michael Young
Mng Dir: Michael Weisberg
Off Mgr: Sandra Ross
CTO: John Greiner
IT Man: Michael Hernandez
Snr Mgr: Betty Caines

D-U-N-S 96-525-1135
LEGAL SERVICES OF NEW JERSEY
100 Metroplex Dr Ste 402, Edison, NJ 08817-2684
Tel (732) 572-9100 *Founded/Ownrshp* 1973
Sales 28.6MM *EMP* 100
SIC 8111 Legal aid service; Legal aid service
Pr: Melville D Miller Jr
Ex VP: Dawn Miller
Sr VP: Claudine Langrin
VP: Margaret Jurow
VP: Rita Robles
VP: Harold Rubenstein
Ex Dir: Felipe Chavana
Ex Dir: Timothy Madden
Web Dev: Rosita Crooke
Pgrm Dir: Martha Gonzalez
Snr Mgr: Rebecca Schore

LEGAL SHIELD
See PRE-PAID LEGAL SERVICES INC

D-U-N-S 08-009-5658
LEGAL SOLUTIONS HOLDINGS INC
GETMEDLEGAL
955 Overland Ct Ste 200, San Dimas, CA 91773-1747
Tel (800) 244-3495 *Founded/Ownrshp* 1986
Sales 29.3MM *EMP* 237
SIC 8111 Legal services
CEO: Greg Webber

D-U-N-S 96-675-2743
LEGALINK INC
(*Suby of* MERRILL CORP) ★
1 Merrill Cir, Saint Paul, MN 55108-5264
Tel (800) 688-4400 *Founded/Ownrshp* 2006
Sales 13.7MM^E *EMP* 358
SIC 7338 Court reporting service; Court reporting service
Pr: Perry Solomon
IT Man: Ray Heppner

D-U-N-S 08-248-5350
LEGALSHIELD (TN)
(*Suby of* MIDOCEAN PARTNERS) ★
1 Prepaid Way, Ada, OK 74820-5813
Tel (323) 325-3198 *Founded/Ownrshp* 1976, 2011
Sales 132.5MM^E *EMP* 719^E
SIC 8111 General practice attorney, lawyer; General practice attorney, lawyer
Ch Bd: Ralph Mason III
**Pr:* Alan Fearnley
Pr: James Rosseau
**Pr:* Harland C Stonecipher
**CEO:* Jeff Bell
**COO:* Randy Harp
**CFO:* Steve Williamson
Bd of Dir: Mark Sullivan
**Chf Mktg O:* Mark Brown
Ex VP: Darnell Self
Sr VP: Christa Aufdemberg
Sr VP: Bob Levy
VP: Steve Baker
VP: John Long
VP: Viki Mapp
**VP:* Keri Norris
**VP:* Kathleen S Pinson
VP: George Rivera
VP: Charles Rosenberry
VP: Keith Sherman

D-U-N-S 12-279-2831
LEGAN INC
1225 17th St Ste 2440, Denver, CO 80202-5524
Tel (303) 376-1400 *Founded/Ownrshp* 1984
Sales 11.4MM^E *EMP* 437
SIC 6514 Dwelling operators, except apartments; Dwelling operators, except apartments
Pr: Ralph Nagel
**VP:* Edward L Hock Sr

LEGENCY VISITING NURSE ASSOC
See LEGACY VISITING NURSE ASSOCIATION

D-U-N-S 09-331-2866
LEGEND AUTORAMA LTD
PORSCHE-LEGEND AUTORAMA
158 Merrick Rd, Amityville, NY 11701-3439
Tel (631) 691-7700 *Founded/Ownrshp* 1980
Sales 20.9MM^E *EMP* 60
SIC 5511 7515 5013 5531 7538 Automobiles, new & used; Passenger car leasing; Automotive supplies & parts; Automotive parts; General automotive repair shops; Automobiles, new & used; Passenger car leasing; Automotive supplies & parts; Automotive parts; General automotive repair shops
Pr: Roy Siegel
**Sec:* Michael Siegel
**Prin:* Wayne Siegel
Sales Asso: Daniel Rosa

D-U-N-S 60-611-3264
LEGEND BANK NA
101 W Tarrant St, Bowie, TX 76230-5029
Tel (940) 872-2221 *Founded/Ownrshp* 1988
Sales NA *EMP* 116
Accts Jones Baggett Llp Dallas Tex
SIC 6021 National commercial banks; National commercial banks
Pr: Jim Woodall
COO: Toni Simmons
CFO: Todd McMurray
Treas: James A Glser
Ofcr: Karen Johnson
Ofcr: Karen Songer
Ex VP: Jeff Brooks
Ex VP: Mickey Faulconer
Ex VP: Bret Meekins
Sr VP: Brian Mantzey
Sr VP: Jodie Payne
VP: Bobby Evartt
VP: Tim Lambert
VP: Chris Simpson

LEGEND BRANDS
See SKAGIT NORTHWEST HOLDINGS INC

D-U-N-S 79-669-0076 IMP
LEGEND DISTRIBUTING LLC
5032 W Colter St, Glendale, AZ 85301-7013
Tel (602) 751-2405 *Founded/Ownrshp* 2004
Sales 29.3MM^E *EMP* 45
SIC 5148 Fresh fruits & vegetables

D-U-N-S 04-945-5606
LEGEND ENERGY SERVICES LLC
5801 Broadway Ext Ste 210, Oklahoma City, OK 73118-7491
Tel (405) 600-1264 *Founded/Ownrshp* 2010
Sales 90.0MM *EMP* 210
SIC 1389 Cementing oil & gas well casings; Cementing oil & gas well casings
CEO: Trey Ingram
**COO:* Matt Goodson
**CFO:* Josh Pruett
Dist Mgr: Michael Moore
Opers Mgr: Reid Thompson

D-U-N-S 00-126-7967
LEGEND HEALTH SYSTEMS INC
LEGEND PHARMACY
1111 Broadhollow Rd # 319, Farmingdale, NY 11735-4820
Tel (631) 630-4713 *Founded/Ownrshp* 1999
Sales 200.0MM *EMP* 60
SIC 5912 Drug stores; Drug stores
Pr: John Marmero

LEGEND HEALTHCARE
See WIND RIVER GROUP PT LLC

LEGEND PHARMACY
See LEGEND HEALTH SYSTEMS INC

D-U-N-S 61-930-8240
LEGEND SEEDS INC
103 Us Highway 14 E, De Smet, SD 57231-2431
Tel (605) 854-3346 *Founded/Ownrshp* 1990
Sales 60.4MM *EMP* 85^E
Accts Mcgladrey Llp Sioux Falls So
SIC 5191 Seeds: field, garden & flower; Seeds: field, garden & flower
Pr: Glen Davis
**CFO:* Dennis Cook
**Sec:* Janet Davis
Off Mgr: Jodi Cook
IT Man: Elijah Rodriguez
Manager: Bob Lee
Sls Mgr: Steve Fresk

D-U-N-S 15-860-3373
LEGEND SMELTING AND RECYCLING INC
L S R
717 O Neill Dr, Hebron, OH 43025-9680
Tel (740) 928-0139 *Founded/Ownrshp* 1989
Sales 25.5MM^E *EMP* 75
SIC 5093 Nonferrous metals scrap
Pr: Randy Hess
**VP:* Mark Sasko
Dir Teleco: John Ellis

LEGEND TRANSPOTATION
See NEW LEGEND INC

D-U-N-S 01-966-6259
LEGENDARY HOLDING INC
4471 Legendary Dr, Destin, FL 32541-5324
Tel (850) 654-6500 *Founded/Ownrshp* 1991
Sales 20.5MM^E *EMP* 461
SIC 5947 Gifts & novelties

D-U-N-S 18-315-0671 EXP
LEGENDARY INC
4471 Legendary Dr, Destin, FL 32541-5324
Tel (850) 337-8000 *Founded/Ownrshp* 1991
Sales 28.6MM^E *EMP* 450
SIC 5812 5947 Eating places; Gift shop; Eating places; Gift shop
CEO: Peter H Bos Jr
**CFO:* Tracey Blocker
**Ex VP:* Pete Knowles
**VP:* Bruce Craul
VP: Michael Havener
**VP:* John W Lewis
**VP:* Hugh Sawyer
VP: Jim Stout
Genl Mgr: Jackie Gibson
IT Man: Bob Perdue
Sales Asso: Joan Russo

D-U-N-S 05-236-6320 EXP
LEGENDARY MARINE LLC
(*Suby of* ONEWATER MARINE HOLDINGS, LLC)
4601 Legendary Marina Dr, Destin, FL 32541-6300
Tel (850) 337-8300 *Founded/Ownrshp* 2014
Sales 36.4MM^E *EMP* 65
SIC 5551 Boat dealers
Prin: Todd Royall

D-U-N-S 61-215-0540 IMP/EXP
LEGENDS FURNITURE INC
10300 W Buckeye Rd, Tolleson, AZ 85353-9210
Tel (623) 931-6500 *Founded/Ownrshp* 1990
Sales 29.5MM^E *EMP* 182
SIC 2511 5021 Wood household furniture; Furniture; Wood household furniture; Furniture
Pr: Richard G Schmidgall
CFO: Kenneth Kuch
**VP:* Robin Schmidgall
IT Man: Tom Schlolosky
Sales Exec: Jim Cherry
Mktg Dir: Timothy Donk

D-U-N-S 94-553-5078
LEGENDS GROUP LTD
LEGENDS REAL ESTATE
1500 Legends Rd, Myrtle Beach, SC 29579-6808
Tel (843) 236-5165 *Founded/Ownrshp* 1989
Sales 8.0MM^E *EMP* 500
SIC 7011 7992 5812 5813 6531 Hotels & motels; Public golf courses; Eating places; Drinking places; Real estate managers; Hotels & motels; Public golf courses; Eating places; Drinking places; Real estate managers
Pr: Larry Young
CFO: Robert Garcia
**Sec:* Judy Young
Tech Mgr: Tasha Gaddy

D-U-N-S 01-048-8774
LEGENDS HOSPITALITY LLC
805 3rd Ave Fl 31, New York, NY 10022-7588
Tel (212) 317-3200 *Founded/Ownrshp* 2007
Sales 250.0MM *EMP* 10,000
SIC 8742 Restaurant & food services consultants
CEO: David Checketts
Pr: Shervin Mirhashemi
CFO: David Hammer
VP: Mark Pizzariello
Genl Mgr: Brendan Long
Genl Couns: John Ruzich

D-U-N-S 82-907-4587 IMP
LEGENDS HOSPITALITY LLC
(*Suby of* LEGENDS HOSPITALITY MANAGEMENT LIMITED LIABILITY CO) ★
400 Broadacres Dr Ste 200, Bloomfield, NJ 07003-3156
Tel (973) 707-2800 *Founded/Ownrshp* 2008
Sales 69.1MM^E *EMP* 634^E
SIC 7929 Entertainers
CEO: Michael Rawlings
**Pr:* Martin Greenspun
**Pr:* Daniel Smith
**COO:* Michael Ondrejko
**CFO:* David Hammer

D-U-N-S 01-895-2728
LEGENDS HOSPITALITY MANAGEMENT LIMITED LIABILITY CO
400 Broadacres Dr Ste 260, Bloomfield, NJ 07003-3156
Tel (646) 977-8521 *Founded/Ownrshp* 2007
Sales 69.1MM^E *EMP* 652^E
SIC 8741 8744 8742 Business management; Facilities support services; Hospital & health services consultant; Food & beverage consultant; Merchandising consultant
CEO: Mike Rawlings
**Pr:* Marty Greenspun
**COO:* Dan Smith
**CFO:* Jim Sheppard
**Sr VP:* Amy Phillips
**Sr VP:* Mike Phillips
VP: Todd Fleming

VP: Jon Muscalo
VP Sls: Al Guido

LEGENDS OLDSMOBILE
See EARNHARTT CADILLAC

LEGENDS REAL ESTATE
See LEGENDS GROUP LTD

D-U-N-S 80-586-3396 IMP
LEGENT INTERNATIONAL LTD
302 N Water St, Newburgh, NY 12550-6849
Tel (845) 562-4922 *Founded/Ownrshp* 1992
Sales 23.8MM^E *EMP* 165
SIC 5137 5199 Handbags; Bags, baskets & cases; Handbags; Bags, baskets & cases
Pr: Charles Atanasio

D-U-N-S 01-016-3418
LEGERE GROUP LTD
LEGERE WOODWORKING
80 Darling Dr, Avon, CT 06001-4217
Tel (860) 674-0392 *Founded/Ownrshp* 1975
Sales 29.7MM^E *EMP* 125
SIC 2434 2431 3442 2499 Wood kitchen cabinets; Millwork; Metal doors, sash & trim; Decorative wood & woodwork
CEO: Craig Froh
**Pr:* Ronald Legere
**VP:* Bill Bruneau
**VP:* Francis Legere
**VP:* Steve Nagle

LEGERE WOODWORKING
See LEGERE GROUP LTD

LEGG MASON
See GROSVENOR INVESTMENT MANAGEMENT US INC

D-U-N-S 10-145-8883
▲ LEGG MASON INC
100 International Dr, Baltimore, MD 21202-4673
Tel (410) 539-0000 *Founded/Ownrshp* 1899
Sales 2.8MMM *EMP* 2,982^E
Accts Pricewaterhousecoopers Llp Ba
Tkr Sym LM *Exch* NYS
SIC 6282 6211 6162 Manager of mutual funds, contract or fee basis; Investment advisory service; Security brokers & dealers; Brokers, security; Dealers, security; Traders, security; Mortgage bankers; Manager of mutual funds, contract or fee basis; Investment advisory service; Security brokers & dealers; Brokers, security; Dealers, security; Traders, security; Mortgage bankers
Ch Bd: Joseph A Sullivan
Pr: Otto Callen
Pr: Martha Casner
Pr: Shelly Gottesfeld
Pr: Mark Nigro
Pr: Samuel Yen
CEO: Kyle Prechtl Legg
COO: Nancy E McColgan
CFO: Peter H Nachtwey
Ch: Bill Miller
Chf Inves: Robert Hagstrom
Chf Inves: Roger Paradiso
Ofcr: Damon Reed
Ofcr: Ursula Schliessler
Assoc VP: Brian Dannemiller
Ex VP: Richard Himelfarb
Ex VP: Thomas K Hoops
Ex VP: Terence Johnson
Ex VP: Thomas C Merchant
Ex VP: Jeffrey Nattans
Sr VP: Thomas P Mulroy
Board of Directors: Kurt L Schmoke, Robert E Angelica, Carol A Davidson, Barry W Huff, Dennis M Kass, Cheryl Gordon Krongard, John V Murphy, John H Myers, W Allen Reed, Margaret Milner Richardson

D-U-N-S 62-417-1927
■ LEGG MASON INVESTMENT COUNSEL LLC
(*Suby of* LEGG MASON INC) ★
1 South St Ste 2500, Baltimore, MD 21202-3310
Tel (410) 539-0000 *Founded/Ownrshp* 2004
Sales 53.8MM *EMP* 30
SIC 6726 Investment offices; Investment offices
VP: Aimee Eudy
VP: Eileen Stoner
VP: Jacquelyn Weber
Prin: Margaret Hugh
Mng Dir: Charles King
Mng Dir: Steve Sands
Mng Dir: Victoria M Schwatka

D-U-N-S 00-714-0064 IMP/EXP
▲ LEGGETT & PLATT INC
1 Leggett Rd, Carthage, MO 64836-9649
Tel (417) 358-8131 *Founded/Ownrshp* 1883
Sales 3.7MMM *EMP* 19,000
Accts Pricewaterhousecoopers Llp St
Tkr Sym LEG *Exch* NYS
SIC 2515 2514 3495 2392 2542 3363 Box springs, assembled; Mattresses, innerspring or box spring; Chair & couch springs, assembled; Bedsprings, assembled; Frames for box springs or bedsprings: metal; Beds, including folding & cabinet, household: metal; Wire springs; Mattress pads; Fixtures: display, office or store: except wood; Aluminum die-castings; Box springs, assembled; Mattresses, innerspring or box spring; Chair & couch springs, assembled; Bedsprings, assembled; Frames for box springs or bedsprings: metal; Beds, including folding & cabinet, household: metal; Wire springs; Mattress pads; Fixtures: display, office or store: except wood; Aluminum die-castings
Ch Bd: David S Haffner
**Pr:* Karl G Glassman
Pr: Elliott J Lyons
CFO: Matthew C Flanigan
Ex VP: Karl G Lassman
Sr VP: Scott S Douglas
Sr VP: William S Weil
VP: Lee Loop
VP: Vincent S Lyons
Exec: Nora Tebbets
Dir Bus: Bren Flanigan
Board of Directors: Robert E Brunner, Ralph W Clark, Robert G Culp III, R Ted Enloe III, Manuel A Fernandez, Richard T Fisher, Joseph W McClanathan, Judy C Odom, Phoebe A Wood

LEGGETT PLATT
See MASTERACK INC

D-U-N-S 07-329-9257
LEGGETTE BRASHEARS & GRAHAM INC
LBG-GUYTON ASSOCIATES
4 Research Dr Ste 204, Shelton, CT 06484-6242
Tel (203) 929-8555 *Founded/Ownrshp* 1976
Sales 26.7MM^E *EMP* 185
SIC 8999 8711 Geological consultant; Engineering services; Geological consultant; Engineering services
Pr: John Naso
**CFO:* William Bittner
Treas: Donald R Machir
**Sr VP:* William Beckman
**Sr VP:* Dan Buzea
**Sr VP:* Frank Getchell
**VP:* Tom Cusack
**VP:* Robert Good
**VP:* Tim Kenyon
**VP:* Charles Kreitler
**VP:* Jeffrey Lennox
VP: Michael Manolakas
**VP:* Mathew Peramiki
**VP:* J Kevin Powers
**VP:* John Seifert
**VP:* Dave Terry
**VP:* David Wiley

D-U-N-S 07-976-4764
LEGION CREATIVE GROUP
1680 Vine St Ste 700, Los Angeles, CA 90028-8804
Tel (323) 498-1100 *Founded/Ownrshp* 2015
Sales 40.0MM *EMP* 25
SIC 2759 Advertising literature: printing
Owner: Kathleen Fliller

D-U-N-S 83-966-6997
LEGION INDEMNITY CO INC
1 Logan Sq Fl 14, Philadelphia, PA 19103-6908
Tel (215) 963-1200 *Founded/Ownrshp* 2002
Sales NA *EMP* 109
SIC 6351 Surety insurance
Pr: Joseph M Boyle
**Ch Bd:* Robert Mulderig
**Treas:* Gregg C Frederick
**Ex VP:* Glenn Partridge
**Sr VP:* Andrew Walsh
**VP:* Roger Bone
VP: Auvel McLaughlin
VP: David Rampson
VP: Richard Turner
Board of Directors: Glenn R Partridge, Sharon W Abel, Fred H Pearson, Allen G Barry III, Michael I Quist, Robert M Cass, Richard G Turner, John V Clark, Andrew S Walsh, Greg C Frederick, John M Haker, Ronald A Jacks, John Kessock Jr, Robert A Mulderig

D-U-N-S 83-194-1302
LEGION LOGISTICS LLC
600 Meijer Dr Ste 304, Florence, KY 41042-4878
Tel (859) 384-1726 *Founded/Ownrshp* 2009
Sales 38.4MM^E *EMP* 45
SIC 4731 Freight transportation arrangement
Pr: Lacy Starling
**VP Opers:* Levi Papai

LEGISLATIVE ASSEMBLY
See LEGISLATIVE OFFICE OF STATE OF ARIZONA

D-U-N-S 94-172-3421
LEGISLATIVE AUDITOR LOUISIANA
(*Suby of* EXECUTIVE OFFICE OF STATE OF LOUISIANA) ★
State Capitol Building, Baton Rouge, LA 70804
Tel (225) 342-3099 *Founded/Ownrshp* 1999
Sales NA *EMP* 846^E
SIC 9311 Finance, taxation & monetary policy;
CEO: Daniel G Kyle

LEGISLATIVE COUNCIL
See COLORADO STATE GENERAL ASSEMBLY

LEGISLATIVE OFFICE OF THE
See COMPTROLLER OFFICE OF COMMONWEALTH OF PUERTO RICO

D-U-N-S 82-520-1932
LEGISLATIVE OFFICE OF COMMONWEALTH OF MASSACHUSETTS
(*Suby of* COMMONWEALTH OF MASSACHUSETTS) ★
24 Beacon St Rm 360, Boston, MA 02133-1099
Tel (617) 725-4000 *Founded/Ownrshp* 1788
Sales NA *EMP* 900
SIC 9111 Executive offices; ; Executive offices;
Prin: Tim Murry

D-U-N-S 79-620-6993
LEGISLATIVE OFFICE OF COMMONWEALTH OF PENNSYLVANIA
(*Suby of* COMMONWEALTH OF PENNSYLVANIA) ★
Main Capitol Bldg Rm 225, Harrisburg, PA 17120-0001
Tel (717) 787-5962 *Founded/Ownrshp* 1901
Sales NA *EMP* 2,583
SIC 9121 Legislative bodies, state & local; ; Legislative bodies, state & local;

D-U-N-S 80-955-8802
LEGISLATIVE OFFICE OF FLORIDA
(*Suby of* STATE OF FLORIDA) ★
400 S Monroe St, Tallahassee, FL 32399-6536
Tel (850) 488-4505 *Founded/Ownrshp* 1845
Sales NA *EMP* 2,515
SIC 9121 Legislative bodies, state & local; ; Legislative bodies, state & local;

D-U-N-S 80-388-9302
LEGISLATIVE OFFICE OF MICHIGAN
(*Suby of* STATE OF MICHIGAN) ★
George Romney Building, Lansing, MI 48933
Tel (517) 373-3400 *Founded/Ownrshp* 1837
Sales NA *EMP* 1,308
SIC 9121 Legislative bodies, state & local; ; Legislative bodies, state & local;

D-U-N-S 80-939-4612
LEGISLATIVE OFFICE OF NORTH CAROLINA
(*Suby of* STATE OF NORTH CAROLINA) ★
16 W Jones St, Raleigh, NC 27601-1030
Tel (919) 833-7352 *Founded/Ownrshp* 1789
Sales NA *EMP* 882
SIC 9121 Legislative bodies, state & local; ; Legislative bodies, state & local;
Web Dev: Kelly Stallings
Snr Mgr: Hugh Holliman

D-U-N-S 80-565-2526
LEGISLATIVE OFFICE OF STATE OF ARIZONA
LEGISLATIVE ASSEMBLY
(*Suby of* GOVERNORS OFFICE) ★
1700 W Washington St, Phoenix, AZ 85007-2812
Tel (602) 542-4900 *Founded/Ownrshp* 1912
Sales NA *EMP* 637
SIC 9121 Legislative bodies, state & local; ; Legislative bodies, state & local;
Ofcr: Raymond Rees
Off Mgr: Fernando Reyes
Telecom Mg: Lawrence Heinz
IT Man: Howard Dickerson
IT Man: Stacey Echternach
IT Man: Howard Richardson
Netwrk Mgr: Richard Blair
Netwrk Mgr: Rod Franklin
Snr Mgr: Angela Calabrasi
Snr Mgr: Ron Huettner
Snr Mgr: Susan Russell

D-U-N-S 80-748-1031
LEGISLATIVE OFFICE OF STATE OF CONNECTICUT
GENERAL ASSEMBLY
(*Suby of* STATE OF CONNECTICUT) ★
300 Capitol Ave, Hartford, CT 06106-1553
Tel (860) 240-0100 *Founded/Ownrshp* 1788
Sales NA *EMP* 40,970
SIC 9121 Legislative bodies; ; Legislative bodies;
Ofcr: Dan Carter
Off Admin: Susan Keane
Mktg Dir: Carmen Calderon
Mktg Dir: Heidi Lawrence
Mktg Dir: Diane Mazar-Roberts

D-U-N-S 80-674-4660
LEGISLATIVE OFFICE OF STATE OF GEORGIA
GENERAL ASSEMBLY
(*Suby of* STATE OF GEORGIA) ★
332 State Capitol Sw # 332, Atlanta, GA 30334-1600
Tel (404) 656-5020 *Founded/Ownrshp* 1789
Sales NA *EMP* 823
SIC 9121 Legislative bodies, state & local; ; Legislative bodies, state & local;
Dir IT: Chris Hackett

D-U-N-S 82-469-7858
LEGISLATIVE OFFICE OF STATE OF IDAHO
(*Suby of* STATE OF IDAHO) ★
State Capitol Bldg E Wing, Boise, ID 83720-0001
Tel (208) 334-2475 *Founded/Ownrshp* 1890
Sales NA *EMP* 388
SIC 9121 Legislative bodies, state & local; ; Legislative bodies, state & local;

D-U-N-S 80-632-8365
LEGISLATIVE OFFICE OF STATE OF ILLINOIS
(*Suby of* STATE OF ILLINOIS) ★
2 1/2 State House, Springfield, IL 62706-0001
Tel (217) 782-6871 *Founded/Ownrshp* 1991
Sales NA *EMP* 298
SIC 9121 9111 Legislative bodies, state & local; ; Governors' offices; ; Legislative bodies, state & local; ; Governors' offices;
Ex Dir: Michael Madigan

D-U-N-S 82-469-7213
LEGISLATIVE OFFICE OF STATE OF INDIANA
GENERAL ASSEMBLY
(*Suby of* STATE OF INDIANA) ★
200 W Wash St Swt 302, Indianapolis, IN 46204
Tel (317) 924-8401 *Founded/Ownrshp* 1816
Sales NA *EMP* 320
SIC 9121 Legislative bodies, state & local; ; Legislative bodies, state & local;
Off Mgr: Monica Durrett
Snr Mgr: David Rosenberg

D-U-N-S 80-974-7843
LEGISLATIVE OFFICE OF STATE OF LOUISIANA INC
(*Suby of* STATE OF LOUISIANA) ★
900 N 3rd St, Baton Rouge, LA 70802-5236
Tel (225) 342-7015 *Founded/Ownrshp* 1812
Sales NA *EMP* 895
Accts Duplantier Hrapmann Hogan &
SIC 9121 Legislative bodies, state & local; ; Legislative bodies, state & local;

D-U-N-S 80-917-4709
LEGISLATIVE OFFICE OF STATE OF MAINE
(*Suby of* STATE OF MAINE) ★
115 State House Sta Fl 1, Augusta, ME 04333-0115
Tel (207) 287-1615 *Founded/Ownrshp* 1820
Sales NA *EMP* 300
SIC 9121 Legislative bodies, state & local; ; Legislative bodies, state & local;
Ex Dir: David Boulter
Prin: Jackie Calcagni

D-U-N-S 80-534-7168
LEGISLATIVE OFFICE OF STATE OF MINNESOTA
(*Suby of* STATE OF MINNESOTA) ★
100 Rev Dr M L King Jr Bl, Saint Paul, MN 55155-0001
Tel (651) 296-2146 *Founded/Ownrshp* 1858
Sales NA *EMP* 1,038
SIC 9121 Legislative bodies, state & local; ; Legislative bodies, state & local;
MIS Dir: Laurie Lashbrook

D-U-N-S 87-807-2719
LEGISLATIVE OFFICE OF STATE OF MISSOURI
(*Suby of* STATE OF MISSOURI) ★
201 W Capitol Ave, Jefferson City, MO 65101-1556
Tel (573) 751-3829 *Founded/Ownrshp* 1820
Sales NA *EMP* 1,262
SIC 9121 Legislative bodies, state & local; ; Legislative bodies, state & local;
Prin: Matt Bount
**Prin:* Jay Nixon

D-U-N-S 82-480-0213
LEGISLATIVE OFFICE OF STATE OF NEBRASKA
(*Suby of* STATE OF NEBRASKA) ★
State Capitol Rm 1007, Lincoln, NE 68509
Tel (402) 471-2263 *Founded/Ownrshp* 1867
Sales NA *EMP* 454
SIC 9121 Legislative bodies, state & local; ; Legislative bodies, state & local;
Ex Dir: Tom Berquist

D-U-N-S 82-490-1359
LEGISLATIVE OFFICE OF STATE OF NEVADA
NEVADA LEGISLATURE
(*Suby of* STATE OF NEVADA) ★
401 S Carson St, Carson City, NV 89701-4747
Tel (775) 684-6800 *Founded/Ownrshp* 1864
Sales NA *EMP* 389
SIC 9121 Legislative bodies, state & local; ; Legislative bodies, state & local;
V Ch: Lucy Flores
IT Man: Gary Buonacorsi
IT Man: Madelyn Vike
Netwrk Mgr: Eric Dugger
Counsel: Eileen Ogrady
Snr Mgr: Bradley Wilkinson
Board of Directors: Gary White

D-U-N-S 80-833-9998
LEGISLATIVE OFFICE OF STATE OF NEW HAMPSHIRE
GOVERNOR'S OFICE
(*Suby of* STATE OF NEW HAMPSHIRE) ★
107 N Main St Rm 208, Concord, NH 03301-4951
Tel (603) 271-2121 *Founded/Ownrshp* 1788
Sales NA *EMP* 569
SIC 9121 Legislative bodies, state & local; ; Legislative bodies, state & local;
Prin: John H Lynch
CIO: Richard Bailey

D-U-N-S 80-670-4565
LEGISLATIVE OFFICE OF STATE OF NEW JERSEY
GOVERNOR'S OFFICE
(*Suby of* STATE OF NEW JERSEY) ★
125 W State St, Trenton, NJ 08608-1101
Tel (609) 292-6000 *Founded/Ownrshp* 1787
Sales NA *EMP* 885
SIC 9111 Governors' offices; ; Governors' offices;
Prin: Chris Christie
Treas: Charles Chianese
Ex Dir: Rowena Madden
IT Man: Margie Villane
Snr Mgr: Maria Comella
Snr Mgr: Matt McDermott

D-U-N-S 07-839-0411
LEGISLATIVE OFFICE OF STATE OF RHODE ISLAND
(*Suby of* STATE OF RHODE ISLAND AND PROVIDENCE PLANTATIONS) ★
82 Smith St, Providence, RI 02903-1105
Tel (401) 222-2080 *Founded/Ownrshp* 1790
Sales NA *EMP* 600
SIC 9121 Legislative bodies, state & local; ; Legislative bodies, state & local;
Prin: Gov Donald L Carcieri
IT Man: Donald Clayborne
Board of Directors: James R Langevin, Sheldon Whitehouse

D-U-N-S 80-834-4931
LEGISLATIVE OFFICE OF STATE OF SOUTH CAROLINA INC
CLERKS OFFICE OF THE HOUSE REP
(*Suby of* STATE OF SOUTH CAROLINA) ★
1200 Gervais St, Columbia, SC 29201-3207
Tel (803) 734-2010 *Founded/Ownrshp* 1800
Sales NA *EMP* 360
SIC 9121 Legislative bodies; ; Legislative bodies;

D-U-N-S 80-897-3051
LEGISLATIVE OFFICE OF STATE OF WASHINGTON
OFFICE OF THE GOVERNOR
(*Suby of* GOVERNORS OFFICE) ★
Legislative Building, Olympia, WA 98504-0001
Tel (360) 753-6780 *Founded/Ownrshp* 1889
Sales NA *EMP* 343
SIC 9121 Legislative bodies, state & local; ; Legislative bodies, state & local;
Snr Mgr: Bernard Dean

D-U-N-S 80-955-8612
LEGISLATIVE OFFICE OF STATE OF WISCONSIN
(*Suby of* STATE OF WISCONSIN) ★
1 E Main St Ste 401, Madison, WI 53703-3382
Tel (608) 266-1304 *Founded/Ownrshp* 1848
Sales NA *EMP* 301
SIC 9121 Legislative bodies, state & local; ; Legislative bodies, state & local;
Ex Dir: Robert Lang

D-U-N-S 87-843-4414
LEGISLATIVE OFFICE OF TENNESSEE
(*Suby of* STATE OF TENNESSEE) ★
1 Legislative Plz, Nashville, TN 37243-0001
Tel (615) 741-2368 *Founded/Ownrshp* 1796
Sales NA *EMP* 801
SIC 9121 Legislative bodies, state & local; ; Legislative bodies, state & local;
Prin: Phil Dredesen

D-U-N-S 80-987-8465
LEGISLATIVE OFFICE OF VIRGINIA
(*Suby of* COMMONWEALTH OF VIRGINIA) ★
General Assmbly Bldg Fl 2, Richmond, VA 23219
Tel (804) 786-2211 *Founded/Ownrshp* 1788
Sales NA *EMP* 566
SIC 9121 Legislative bodies, state & local;
IT Man: David Hines

D-U-N-S 80-719-6688
LEGISLATIVE OFFICE STATE OF NY
NEW YORK STATE ASSEMBLY
(*Suby of* STATE OF NEW YORK) ★
State Capital Bldg, Albany, NY 12248-0001
Tel (518) 455-4100 *Founded/Ownrshp* 1788
Sales NA *EMP* 3,519
SIC 9121 Legislative bodies, state & local; ; Legislative bodies, state & local;
Prin: Sheldon Silver

D-U-N-S 80-673-2327
LEGISLATIVE OFFICE TEXAS
(*Suby of* STATE OF TEXAS) ★
1200 N Congress Ave Ste 2, Austin, TX 78701
Tel (512) 463-0001 *Founded/Ownrshp* 1845
Sales NA *EMP* 4,258
SIC 9121 Legislative bodies, state & local; ; Legislative bodies, state & local;

D-U-N-S 10-325-6124
LEGISLATIVE RESEARCH COMMISSION KENTUCKY
(*Suby of* EXECUTIVE OFFICE OF COMMONWEALTH OF KENTUCKY) ★
700 Capital Ave Rm 64, Frankfort, KY 40601-3415
Tel (502) 564-8100 *Founded/Ownrshp* 1786
Sales NA *EMP* 400
SIC 9222 Attorney General's office; ; Attorney General's office;
Ofcr: Liz A Burton
Dir IT: Marsha Napier

D-U-N-S 80-930-1823
LEGISLATIVE STATE OF IOWA OFFICE OF
GOVERNORS OFFICE
(*Suby of* STATE OF IOWA) ★
1007 E Grand Ave, Des Moines, IA 50319-1001
Tel (515) 281-5211 *Founded/Ownrshp* 1846
Sales NA *EMP* 594
SIC 9121 Legislative bodies, state & local; ; Legislative bodies, state & local;
Prin: Elizabeth Buck
Treas: Debra Liljedahl
Ofcr: Matthew Kruse
Ofcr: Mark Lyon
**Prin:* Tom Bilsack

LEGO BRAND RETAIL
See LEGO SYSTEMS INC

D-U-N-S 07-958-4394
LEGO BRAND RETAIL INC
LEGO EDUCATION
555 Taylor Rd, Enfield, CT 06082-2372
Tel (860) 749-2291 *Founded/Ownrshp* 2000
Sales 14.6MM^E *EMP* 873
SIC 5945 Toys & games; Toys & games
Pr: Eric Wolfe

LEGO EDUCATION
See LEGO BRAND RETAIL INC

D-U-N-S 06-483-5549 IMP
LEGO SYSTEMS INC
LEGO BRAND RETAIL
(*Suby of* LEGO A/S)
555 Taylor Rd, Enfield, CT 06082-2372
Tel (860) 749-2291 *Founded/Ownrshp* 1973
Sales 454.6MM^E *EMP* 1,450
SIC 3944 5092 Erector sets, toy; Structural toy sets; Blocks, toy; Toys & hobby goods & supplies; Erector sets, toy; Structural toy sets; Blocks, toy; Toys & hobby goods & supplies
Pr: Soren Torp Laursen
Chf Mktg O: Findlay Robb
Creative D: Camilla Calamandrei
Opers Mgr: Peter Bernhard
Mktg Mgr: Christina Holmes
Art Dir: Sanne Koldbk
Board of Directors: V H Andersen, Niels Christian Jensen

D-U-N-S 86-934-8102 IMP
LEGOLAND CALIFORNIA LLC
1 Legoland Dr, Carlsbad, CA 92008-4610
Tel (760) 918-5346 *Founded/Ownrshp* 2001
Sales 41.4MM^E *EMP* 400
SIC 7996 Theme park, amusement; Theme park, amusement
COO: Clark Kim
Top Exec: Tyler Tummolo
Exec: Paul Geasland
Area Supr: Andy Mackey
CIO: Christelle Stubbs
Opers Mgr: Bob Lorenzini
Mktg Dir: Robert Baracz
Sls Mgr: Debbie Brassey

D-U-N-S 13-210-0673
LEGRAND HOLDING INC
(*Suby of* LEGRAND FRANCE)
60 Woodlawn St, West Hartford, CT 06110-2326
Tel (860) 233-6251 *Founded/Ownrshp* 1984
Sales 1.1MMM^E *EMP* 2,736
SIC 3643 Current-carrying wiring devices; Current-carrying wiring devices
CEO: John P Selldorff
Pr: Giles Schnep
Treas: Robert Julian
VP: Antoine Burel
VP: Mario Gonzalez
VP: Susan Rochford
VP: Kenneth Ruh
VP: Daniel Wilhoit
Exec: Greg Chouinard
Exec: Cameron Cole
Exec: Joey Hill
Exec: Marianne Michalek

D-U-N-S 07-776-7577 IMP
LEGRAND HOME SYSTEMS INC
ON Q HOME
(*Suby of* LEGRAND HOLDING INC) ★
301 Fulling Mill Rd Ste G, Middletown, PA 17057-5966
Tel (877) 295-3472 *Founded/Ownrshp* 2012
Sales 28.5MM^E *EMP* 161
SIC 3315 3661 3651 3577 Wire & fabricated wire products; Telephone & telegraph apparatus; Household audio & video equipment; Computer peripheral equipment; Wire & fabricated wire products; Telephone & telegraph apparatus; Household audio & video equipment; Computer peripheral equipment
Pr: Douglas Fikse
Pr: Stu Rutherford
**Treas:* James Laperriere
VP: Jim Devin
**VP:* Bob Fallert
VP: David Hanchette
**VP:* Robert Julian
VP: Steve Schoffstall
**VP:* Fritz Werder
Exec: Steve Baker

D-U-N-S 01-981-2339
LEGRAND NORTH AMERICA LLC
(*Suby of* LEGRAND HOLDING INC) ★
60 Woodlawn St, West Hartford, CT 06110-2326
Tel (860) 233-6251 *Founded/Ownrshp* 2005
Sales 156.3MM^E *EMP* 983^E
SIC 8711 Electrical or electronic engineering; Electrical or electronic engineering
Pr: John Selldorff
CFO: Steve Schneider
**Treas:* James Laperriere
**VP:* Robert Julian
VP: Steven Liu
VP: Ken Mills
VP: Dan Settles
Sales Asso: Sal Bautista
Genl Couns: Hoyt Webb

LEGRAND ORTRONICS
See ORTRONICS INC

LEHB
See LAW ENFORCEMENT HEALTH BENEFITS INC

D-U-N-S 19-516-5774
LEHI VALLEY TRADING CO INC
LEHI VALLEY WHOLESALE
4955 E Mckellips Rd, Mesa, AZ 85215-2531
Tel (877) 962-5017 *Founded/Ownrshp* 1985
Sales 28.0MM^E *EMP* 50
SIC 5149 5145 Fruits, dried; Nuts, salted or roasted; Candy
Pr: Lewis Freeman
**VP:* Trecia Freeman
VP: Aubrey Wadsworth
IT Man: Justin Patterson
VP Mktg: Ryan Mecham
Mktg Mgr: Brady Freeman
Mktg Mgr: Kristopher Olson

LEHI VALLEY WHOLESALE
See LEHI VALLEY TRADING CO INC

D-U-N-S 03-975-3785
LEHIGH CARBON COMMUNITY COLLEGE
4525 Education Park Dr, Schnecksville, PA 18078-2502
Tel (610) 799-2121 *Founded/Ownrshp* 1975
Sales 19.4MM *EMP* 720
Accts Baker Tilly Virchow Krause Ll
SIC 8222 8221 Community college; Colleges universities & professional schools; Community college; Colleges universities & professional schools
Pr: Ann D Bieber
V Ch: Kenneth H Mohr Jr
**Pr:* Dr Ann D Bieber
CFO: Larry Ross
VP: Ann Bieber
**VP:* Cindy M Haney
**VP:* Brian L Kahler
**VP:* Dr Thomas Meyer
VP: Jim Moretti
Adv Bd Mbr: Miriam Harris-Botzum
Ex Dir: Tim Herrlinger

D-U-N-S 06-051-0062
LEHIGH CAREER & TECHNICAL INSTITUTE
4500 Education Park Dr, Schnecksville, PA 18078-2501
Tel (610) 799-1335 *Founded/Ownrshp* 1969
Sales 28.0MM *EMP* 200
Accts Herbein & Company Inc Readin
SIC 8211 Public elementary & secondary schools; Public elementary & secondary schools
Ex Dir: Sandra Himes
CTO: David Lapinsky
Snr Mgr: John Oconnell

D-U-N-S 01-391-5939 IMP
LEHIGH CEMENT CO
LEHIGH NORTHEAST CEMENT
(*Suby of* DYCKERHOFF GMBH)
313 Warren St, Glens Falls, NY 12801-3820
Tel (518) 792-1137 *Founded/Ownrshp* 2007
Sales 28.0MM^E *EMP* 170
SIC 3241 Portland cement; Masonry cement; Portland cement; Masonry cement
Pr: Dan Harrington
Dir Lab: Hermanus Potgieter
Trfc Dir: Justin Denison
Ql Cn Mgr: Mark Trybendis

D-U-N-S 00-131-6355 IMP
LEHIGH CEMENT CO LLC
(*Suby of* HANSON LEHIGH INC) ★
7660 Imperial Way Fl 4th, Allentown, PA 18195-1016
Tel (610) 366-4600 *Founded/Ownrshp* 2008, 2011
Sales 694.8MM^E *EMP* 2,249
SIC 3241 3273 5032 Portland cement; Ready-mixed concrete; Aggregate; Portland cement; Ready-mixed concrete; Aggregate
Ch Bd: Helmut S Erhard
**Pr:* Robert Breyer
COO: Paul Jurgens
CFO: Michael H Hyer
CFO: Mike Lewis
CFO: Larry A Prudhomme
CFO: Kenneth R Rohrbach
Ch: Donald Fallon
**VP:* Jeffry H Brozyna
VP: Jeffry Brozyna
VP: Helmut Leube
VP: Thor Lindberg
VP: Wolfgang Linke
VP: Gerhard Muehlbeyer
VP: Dana Osborne
VP: Pierre Rogmar
VP: Gerhard Seitz
VP: Brian Serra
VP: F R Snyder
VP: Erich Sulzer
VP: Peter B Tait

D-U-N-S 07-847-3430
LEHIGH CEMENT CO LLC
(*Suby of* HANSON LEHIGH INC) ★
300 E John Carpenter Fwy, Irving, TX 75062-2727
Tel (877) 534-4442 *Founded/Ownrshp* 1970
Sales 72.7MM^E *EMP* 29^E
SIC 1442 Sand mining; Gravel & pebble mining
Pr: Daniel M Harrington
**Pr:* Jim Derkatch
Sr VP: Helmut Fischer
**Sr VP:* Seyda Pirnccioglu
VP: Larry Baloun
**VP:* Kelly Bennett
VP: Kyle Gilmour
VP: A King
VP: George Lefler
Exec: Jim Rennie
Rgnl Mgr: Mike Smith

D-U-N-S 10-861-2722
LEHIGH CONSTRUCTION GROUP INC
4327 S Taylor Rd, Orchard Park, NY 14127-2270
Tel (716) 662-2151 *Founded/Ownrshp* 1984
Sales 23.2MM^E *EMP* 64
Accts Schaefer Schiarrino & Schulen
SIC 1542 1541 Commercial & office building contractors; Industrial buildings, new construction
Ch Bd: David Knauss
CFO: Doug Stormer
**CFO:* Douglas Stormer
Snr Mgr: Jody Potter

D-U-N-S 09-641-3575 IMP/EXP
■ **LEHIGH CONSUMER PRODUCTS LLC**
LEHIGH GROUP, THE
(*Suby of* JARDEN CORP) ★
3901 Liberty St, Aurora, IL 60504-8122
Tel (630) 851-7330 *Founded/Ownrshp* 2003
Sales 75.3MM^E *EMP* 300
SIC 3965 2298 3462 3452 8742 Fasteners, buttons, needles & pins; Ropes & fiber cables; Iron & steel forgings; Bolts, nuts, rivets & washers; Fasteners, buttons, needles & pins; Ropes & fiber cables; Iron & steel forgings; Bolts, nuts, rivets & washers; Financial consultant
Pr: Thomas Russo

D-U-N-S 09-536-1978
LEHIGH COUNTY AUTHORITY
1053 Spruce Rd, Allentown, PA 18106-9408
Tel (610) 398-2503 *Founded/Ownrshp* 1966
Sales 56.3MM *EMP* 40^E
Accts Zelenkofske Axelford Llc Harr
SIC 4941 Water supply; Water supply
Genl Mgr: Aurel Arndt
Opers Mgr: Frank Leist

LEHIGH DIRECT
See LEHIGH PRESS LLC

LEHIGH GROUP, THE
See LEHIGH CONSUMER PRODUCTS LLC

D-U-N-S 80-980-3018 EXP
LEHIGH HEAVY FORGE CORP
(*Suby of* WHEMCO INC) ★
275 Emery St, Bethlehem, PA 18015-1984
Tel (610) 317-3113 *Founded/Ownrshp* 2004
Sales 55.6MM^E *EMP* 165
SIC 3312 Blast furnaces & steel mills; Blast furnaces & steel mills
Pr: Charles R Novelli
Pr: Jim Romeo
**CFO:* Carl Maskiewicz
VP: Allan Robertson
MIS Mgr: Robert Werley
Ql Cn Mgr: David Laudenslager
**VP Sls:* James Romeo
Snr Mgr: Lee Decker
Snr Mgr: Mark Royer
Snr Mgr: Bruce Somers
Snr Mgr: Paul Vattimo
Board of Directors: Charles R Novelli, Daniel K Park, Kelly C Park

LEHIGH MASONRY CEMENT
See HANSON AGGREGATES PENNSYLVANIA LLC

LEHIGH NORTHEAST CEMENT
See LEHIGH CEMENT CO

D-U-N-S 08-866-5393 IMP/EXP
■ **LEHIGH OUTFITTERS LLC**
(*Suby of* ROCKY BRANDS INC) ★
39 E Canal St, Nelsonville, OH 45764-1247
Tel (740) 753-1951 *Founded/Ownrshp* 2005
Sales 129.2MM^E *EMP* 1,600
SIC 5661 5139 Men's shoes; Women's shoes; Shoes; Men's shoes; Women's shoes; Shoes
Pr: Joseph J Sebes
Sales Asso: Tracy McMahon

LEHIGH PHOENIX
See PHOENIX COLOR CORP

D-U-N-S 00-233-7749 IMP
LEHIGH PRESS LLC
LEHIGH DIRECT
1900 S 25th Ave, Broadview, IL 60155-2800
Tel (708) 681-3612 *Founded/Ownrshp* 2008
Sales NA *EMP* 290
SIC 8742 Marketing consulting services

D-U-N-S 15-247-7717 IMP
LEHIGH SOUTHWEST CEMENT CO
(*Suby of* HANSON LEHIGH INC) ★
2300 Clayton Rd Ste 300, Concord, CA 94520-2175
Tel (925) 609-6920 *Founded/Ownrshp* 2011
Sales 92.6MM^E *EMP* 334
SIC 3241 2891 5032 5211 Portland cement; Masonry cement; Pozzolana cement; Cement, except linoleum & tile; Cement; Cement; Portland cement; Masonry cement; Pozzolana cement; Cement, except linoleum & tile; Cement; Cement
CEO: Dan Harrington
VP: Zale Asbell
VP: Bill Boughton
VP: Mike Lewis
VP: Mike Roth
Mng Dir: Alex Schwartz

D-U-N-S 19-948-8524
LEHIGH SPECIALTY MELTING INC
(*Suby of* WHEMCO INC) ★
275 Emery St, Bethlehem, PA 18015-1984
Tel (724) 537-7731 *Founded/Ownrshp* 2004
Sales 20.4MM^E *EMP* 65
SIC 3312 Blast furnaces & steel mills
Pr: Charles F Ireland
**VP:* Chad Ireland
**Prin:* Jerald Krueger
VP Opers: Dennis Faiz
Opers Mgr: Daniel Cornelis

D-U-N-S 06-857-0936
LEHIGH UNIVERSITY
27 Memorial Dr W Unit 8, Bethlehem, PA 18015-3005
Tel (610) 758-3000 *Founded/Ownrshp* 1865
Sales 333.0MM^E *EMP* 4,000
Accts Kpmg Llp Philadelphia Pa
SIC 8221 University; University
Pr: Alice P Gast
Trst: Nancy M Beran
Trst: Robert L Brown
Trst: James J Duane
Trst: Oldrich Foucek
Trst: John E McGlad
Ofcr: Mark Ferencin
Ofcr: Ricky Rupp
Assoc VP: K Sivakumar
Ex VP: John D Simon
VP: Patricia A Johnson
VP: Joseph P Kender
VP: Max Muheim
Assoc Dir: David Sudol
Comm Dir: Emily Groff

LEHIGH VALLEY ACURA
See VINART ENTERPRISES INC

LEHIGH VALLEY DAIRY FARMS
See TUSCAN/LEHIGH DAIRIES INC

LEHIGH VALLEY HEALTH NETWORK
See LEHIGH VALLEY HOSPITAL INC

D-U-N-S 10-620-7889
LEHIGH VALLEY HEALTH NETWORK INC
1247 S Cedar Crest Blvd, Allentown, PA 18103-6298
Tel (610) 402-8000 *Founded/Ownrshp* 1982
Sales 1.6MMM *EMP* 12,000
Accts Kpmg Llp Philadelphia Pennsy
SIC 8062 General medical & surgical hospitals; General medical & surgical hospitals
Pr: Elliot J Sussman
**Ch Bd:* J B Relly
**CEO:* Ronald Swinfard
COO: Terry Capuano
CFO: Edward O'Dea
Trst: John T Dickson
Trst: Edward M Mullin
Sr VP: James Geiger
Sr VP: Anne Panik
VP: Mary K Grim
VP: Dorothy Jacquez
VP: Brian Leader
VP: Harry Lukens
VP: Stephanie Marshall
**VP:* Stuart Paxton
VP: Lise Twiford
Dir Rx: Robert Begliomini
Dir Rx: Mary B Karoly

D-U-N-S 15-074-5404
LEHIGH VALLEY HEALTH SERVICES INC
(*Suby of* LEHIGH VALLEY HEALTH NETWORK INC) ★
2166 S 12th St, Allentown, PA 18103-8701
Tel (610) 791-3682 *Founded/Ownrshp* 1983
Sales 82.6MM^E *EMP* 625
SIC 4813 8741 8721 Telephone communication, except radio; Management services; Accounting, auditing & bookkeeping; Telephone communication, except radio; Management services; Accounting, auditing & bookkeeping

LEHIGH VALLEY HONDA
See PWP ENTERPRISES INC

D-U-N-S 06-857-2015
LEHIGH VALLEY HOSPITAL INC
LEHIGH VALLEY HEALTH NETWORK
(*Suby of* LEHIGH VALLEY HEALTH NETWORK INC) ★
1200 S Cedar Crest Blvd, Allentown, PA 18103-6202
Tel (610) 402-8000 *Founded/Ownrshp* 1974
Sales 1.5MMM^E *EMP* 12,000
SIC 8062 General medical & surgical hospitals; General medical & surgical hospitals

CEO: Ronald Swinfard
**Ch Bd:* William Hecht
**Ch Bd:* J B Reilly
**COO:* Stuart Paxton
**CFO:* Vaughn C Gower
CFO: Vaughn Gower
**CFO:* Edward O'Dea
Sr VP: Anne Panik
VP: John Ward
Assoc Dir: Doug Lotz
Assoc Dir: Carlton McCullough
Dir Rad: Gary Marshall

LEHIGH VALLEY INTL ARPRT
See LEHIGH-NORTHAMPTON AIRPORT AUTHORITY

D-U-N-S 83-769-3522
LEHIGH VALLEY PHYSICIANS GROUP
LVPG
(*Suby of* LEHIGH VALLEY HEALTH NETWORK INC) ★
1605 N Cedar Crest Blvd # 110, Allentown, PA 18104-2351
Tel (610) 439-7500 *Founded/Ownrshp* 1993
Sales 198.2MM^E *EMP* 1,500^E
SIC 8011 General & family practice, physician/surgeon; General & family practice, physician/surgeon
Ex Dir: Joseph Lyons
Dir IT: Louis Bottitta

D-U-N-S 05-660-2535
LEHIGH VALLEY PLASTICS INC (PA)
187 N Commerce Way, Bethlehem, PA 18017-8933
Tel (484) 893-5500 *Founded/Ownrshp* 1971
Sales 24.3MM^E *EMP* 90
SIC 3083 3082 2821 Laminated plastics plate & sheet; Rods, unsupported plastic; Tubes, unsupported plastic; Plastics materials & resins
Pr: Dave Keim
CFO: John Nothelfer
**VP:* Edythe Ressler
Opers Mgr: Dru Hayward
Manager: Eli Brandt
Sls Mgr: Curt Hill

D-U-N-S 80-483-2152
LEHIGH VALLEY RESTAURANT GROUP INC
RED ROBIN
6802a Hamilton Blvd, Allentown, PA 18106-9644
Tel (610) 481-0436 *Founded/Ownrshp* 1993
Sales 68.7MM^E *EMP* 2,000
SIC 5812 Restaurant, family: chain; Restaurant, family: chain
CEO: James W Ryan
**CFO:* Chris Defrain
**Sec:* Lucinda Lobach
Ofcr: David Novick
**VP:* Joseph Fusco Jr
Genl Mgr: Joe McCarthy
Genl Mgr: Tischelle Wolfe
IT Man: Ed Kruczek
IT Man: Jason Rezac
VP Opers: Mike Axiotis

LEHIGH VLY HOSPITAL-HAZLETON
See NORTHEASTERN PENNSYLVANIA HEALTH CORP

D-U-N-S 04-514-0415
LEHIGH-NORTHAMPTON AIRPORT AUTHORITY
LEHIGH VALLEY INTL ARPRT
3311 Airport Rd, Allentown, PA 18109-3074
Tel (610) 266-6000 *Founded/Ownrshp* 1929
Sales 55.3MM^E *EMP* 206
Accts Campbell Rappold & Yurasits L
SIC 4581 Airport; Airport
Ch Bd: Jim Seitzinger
**Sec:* Larry Bernhard
Ofcr: John Blair
Ofcr: Joe Nunes
Sr VP: Tom Doster
**Ex Dir:* George Doughty
Opers Mgr: Steven Hanson

D-U-N-S 10-006-9715
LEHIGHTON AREA SCHOOL DISTRICT
1000 Union St, Lehighton, PA 18235-1798
Tel (610) 377-4490 *Founded/Ownrshp* 1885
Sales 27.0MM *EMP* 367
Accts Berg Schultz & Green Cpas
SIC 8211 Public elementary & secondary schools; School board; Public elementary & secondary schools; School board
Dir IT: Marcus Statham

D-U-N-S 07-940-5229
LEHMAN BROTHERS CORE BOND FUND
(*Suby of* NEUBERGER BERMAN MANAGEMENT LLC) ★
605 3rd Ave Fl 41, New York, NY 10158-0180
Tel (212) 476-8800 *Founded/Ownrshp* 2014
Sales 41.3MM^E *EMP* 962^E
SIC 6722 Money market mutual funds

D-U-N-S 11-291-5566
LEHMAN BROTHERS HOLDINGS INC
1271 Ave Of The Americas, New York, NY 10020-1304
Tel (646) 285-9000 *Founded/Ownrshp* 1983
Sales 133.3MM^E *EMP* 125
Accts Ernst & Young Llp New York N
SIC 6211 Security brokers & dealers; Underwriters, security; Investment bankers; Traders, security; Security brokers & dealers; Underwriters, security; Investment bankers; Traders, security
Ch: Bryan Marsal
V Ch: Howard L Clark
Pr: John K Suckow
CFO: William J Fox
Ofcr: Thomas A Russo
Assoc VP: Doug Boreham
Assoc VP: Stephen Capozzoli
Assoc VP: Glenn Dowling
Ex VP: George Andrus
Ex VP: Jeff ABT
Ex VP: Liz Beckford
Ex VP: John Bottega
Ex VP: Matthew Cantor
Ex VP: Karen Coviello
Ex VP: Scott Freidheim
Ex VP: James Kane
Ex VP: Mary Langevin
Ex VP: Natalie Louie
Ex VP: Jillian Munroe
Ex VP: John Ng
Ex VP: Saul Smith

D-U-N-S 78-936-4585
LEHMAN BROTHERS HOLDINGS INTERNATIONAL INC
(*Suby of* LEHMAN BROTHERS/GP INC) ★
745 7th Ave, New York, NY 10019-6801
Tel (212) 526-7000 *Founded/Ownrshp* 1990
Sales 25.5MM^E *EMP* 80^E
SIC 6282 Investment advisory service
CEO: Jermery Isaacs
CFO: Ian T Lowi
CFO: Andrew Wright
Sr VP: Sailesh Buddhavarapu
Sr VP: Chaka Wade
VP: Timothy Cassidy
VP: Ashok Kalyanswamy
VP: Megan T McGrath
Mng Dir: Lawrence Brandman
Genl Mgr: Felipe Maclean
CIO: Sal Cucco

D-U-N-S 00-891-7783
LEHMAN BROTHERS/GP INC
(*Suby of* LEHMAN BROTHERS HOLDINGS INC) ★
1301 Ave Of Amrcas Bsmt 1, New York, NY 10019
Tel (212) 526-0836 *Founded/Ownrshp* 1984
Sales 39.4MM^E *EMP* 44
SIC 6211 6282 6099 6221 Security brokers & dealers; Underwriters, security; Investment bankers; Traders, security; Investment advisory service; Investment research; Foreign currency exchange; Commodity traders, contracts
Ch Bd: Richard S Fuld Jr
**CFO:* Christopher M O'Meara
VP: Anthony Derose
VP: Chip Dickson
VP: Scott Dorey
VP: Hector Ivelez
VP: James Killerlane
VP: Thomas Kvogel
VP: Andrew Lee
VP: David Martin
VP: Elizabeth Moran
VP: Runa Saeki
VP: Anthony Viscardi
VP: Vivian Yiu
VP: Hong Zhang

D-U-N-S 92-903-8545 EXP
LEHMAN DEALERSHIP ENTERPRISES INC
21400 Nw 2nd Ave, Miami, FL 33169-2126
Tel (305) 653-7111 *Founded/Ownrshp* 1984
Sales 85.7MM^E *EMP* 243^E
SIC 5511 Automobiles, new & used; Automobiles, new & used
Pr: William Lehman Jr

D-U-N-S 01-809-8384 IMP/EXP
LEHMAN HARDWARE AND APPLIANCES INC (OH)
LEHMAN'S
289 Kurzen Rd N, Dalton, OH 44618-9009
Tel (330) 828-8828 *Founded/Ownrshp* 1954
Sales 25.4MM^E *EMP* 120
SIC 3639

D-U-N-S 03-252-4340 IMP/EXP
LEHMAN PIPE AND PLUMBING SUPPLY INC
230 Nw 29th St, Miami, FL 33127-3969
Tel (305) 576-3054 *Founded/Ownrshp* 1946
Sales 26.5MM *EMP* 48
SIC 3494 Valves & pipe fittings; Plumbing & heating valves; Valves & pipe fittings; Plumbing & heating valves
Ch Bd: Julian D Lehman
**Pr:* Dennis Jay Lehman
**Sec:* Betty D Lehman
Genl Mgr: Josh Aberman
Genl Mgr: Charles Berkowtc
Sls Mgr: Carlos Chacon
Sales Asso: Jeff Thomas
Sales Asso: Lorraine Williams

D-U-N-S 05-044-0981 EXP
LEHMAN TOYOTA INC
444 Nw 165th St, Miami, FL 33169-6429
Tel (305) 652-6500 *Founded/Ownrshp* 1986
Sales 30.7MM^E *EMP* 114
SIC 5511 7537 5531 5012

D-U-N-S 00-703-6676
LEHMAN-ROBERTS CO
1111 Wilson St, Memphis, TN 38106-2329
Tel (901) 774-4000 *Founded/Ownrshp* 1939
Sales 162.6MM^E *EMP* 400
SIC 1611 2951 Highway & street paving contractor; Asphalt & asphaltic paving mixtures (not from refineries); Highway & street paving contractor; Asphalt & asphaltic paving mixtures (not from refineries)
Pr: Patrick Nelson
Treas: Gilbert Wilson
**VP:* Johnny Driver
**VP:* John Paul Finerson
**VP:* David Greene
**VP:* Jobe Madison

LEHMAN'S
See LEHMAN HARDWARE AND APPLIANCES INC

D-U-N-S 01-415-4900
LEHMANS EGG SERVICE INC
1226 Kauffman Rd W, Greencastle, PA 17225-9030
Tel (717) 375-2261 *Founded/Ownrshp* 1979
Sales 27.5MM^E *EMP* 75
SIC 5144 5143 Eggs; Butter; Cheese; Eggs; Butter; Cheese
Pr: Gregg A Buckwalter
**Pr:* Ron Kissel
**VP:* Anthony A Dryak

D-U-N-S 02-804-3370
LEHMERS
CONCORD, BUICK, PONTIAC GMC
1905 Market St, Concord, CA 94520-2626
Tel (925) 685-4481 *Founded/Ownrshp* 1937
Sales 25.7MM^E *EMP* 52
SIC 5511 Automobiles, new & used; Automobiles, new & used
Pr: Carolyn Anderson
**Sec:* Russ Anderson Sr
**VP:* Darren Anderson
Off Mgr: Barbara Black
Sls Mgr: Ivan Mumm
Sls Mgr: Carl Rogers
Sales Asso: Dwayne Ferriera
Sales Asso: Jason McNeil

D-U-N-S 17-363-2985
LEHMS INC
CARPETLAND
4301 Industrial Ave, Lincoln, NE 68504-1108
Tel (402) 467-6363 *Founded/Ownrshp* 1981
Sales 23.0MM^E *EMP* 19
SIC 5713 Carpets; Carpets
Pr: Jeffrey W Lehms
**Sec:* Mary Lehms

D-U-N-S 06-384-3502
LEHR BROTHERS INC
BIG L PACKERS
12901 Packing House Rd, Edison, CA 93220
Tel (661) 366-3244 *Founded/Ownrshp* 1979
Sales 23.0MM *EMP* 50^E
SIC 0134 0174 0161 Irish potatoes; Orange grove; Carrot farm; Irish potatoes; Orange grove; Carrot farm
CEO: Ronald R Ejr
**Pr:* Ronald Lehr
**VP:* Ronald Lehr Jr
Off Mgr: Scott Pursel

D-U-N-S 00-623-5857
LEHRKINDS INC (MT)
MOUNTAIN COUNTRY DISTRIBUTING
1715 N Rouse Ave, Bozeman, MT 59715-2426
Tel (406) 587-9216 *Founded/Ownrshp* 1906
Sales 45.0MM *EMP* 115
Accts Hubley Phillips & Williams P
SIC 2086 5181 5149 Soft drinks: packaged in cans, bottles, etc.; Beer & other fermented malt liquors; Water, distilled; Soft drinks: packaged in cans, bottles, etc.; Beer & other fermented malt liquors; Water, distilled
Pr: Carl Lehrkind III
**Pr:* Carl IV Lehrkind
**Treas:* Robert M Lehrkind
**VP:* Harry T Lehrkind
**VP:* Robert H Lehrkind
**Genl Mgr:* Carl Lehrkind IV

LEI AG SEATTLE
See LOWE ENTERPRISES INC

D-U-N-S 12-280-6834
LEI COMPANIES INC
L E I
2017 Curtis St, Denver, CO 80205-2516
Tel (303) 865-5209 *Founded/Ownrshp* 2002
Sales 23.4MM^E *EMP* 56
SIC 1731 Electrical work
Pr: Brandon J Berumen
**VP:* Lenee M Koch
Mktg Mgr: Emilee Cook

D-U-N-S 06-344-0460
LEICA BIOSYSTEMS IMAGING INC
APERIO
1360 Park Center Dr, Vista, CA 92081-8300
Tel (760) 539-1100 *Founded/Ownrshp* 1999
Sales 51.5MM^E *EMP* 182
SIC 3841 Surgical & medical instruments; Surgical & medical instruments
VP: James F O'Reilly
**COO:* Keith B Hagen
**Ofcr:* Jared N Schwartz
**VP:* Greg Crandall
VP: Steven V Russell
Dir Bus: Maya Tanaka
Ql Cn Mgr: Gina Martin
Manager: Kimberly Bosworth
Sls Mgr: Sandra Boyte
Pathlgst: Dave Marr
Board of Directors: Thomas Bologna, David Schlotterbeck

D-U-N-S 08-293-0884 IMP/EXP
LEICA BIOSYSTEMS RICHMOND INC (IL)
5205 Rte 12, Richmond, IL 60071
Tel (815) 678-2000 *Founded/Ownrshp* 1977
Sales 188.8MM^E *EMP* 775
SIC 3842

D-U-N-S 19-442-7571 IMP
LEICA CAMERA INC
(*Suby of* LEICA CAMERA AG)
1 Pearl Ct Ste A, Allendale, NJ 07401-1658
Tel (201) 995-0051 *Founded/Ownrshp* 1990
Sales 77.4MM *EMP* 63
Accts Wilkin & Guttenplan Pc East
SIC 5043 Cameras & photographic equipment; Photographic cameras, projectors, equipment & supplies; Binoculars & telescopes; Cameras & photographic equipment; Photographic cameras, projectors, equipment & supplies
Pr: Roger W Horn
**VP:* Raymond L Tomaselli
Sls Mgr: Ebi Kuehne

D-U-N-S 05-479-0980
LEICA GEOSYSTEMS HOLDINGS INC (DE)
(*Suby of* LEICA GEOSYSTEMS AG)
5051 Peachtree Corners Ci, Norcross, GA 30092-2592
Tel (770) 776-3402 *Founded/Ownrshp* 1998, 2000
Sales 71.6MM^E *EMP* 312
SIC 5049 Drafting supplies; Drafting supplies
Pr: Bob Williams
COO: Simon Mears
CFO: Christian Leu
CFO: Schwyter Walter
**Sec:* Steven Shelling
Ofcr: Eric Poll
Ex VP: Sergio Giacoletto
Sr VP: Geoffrey Jacobs
VP: Doug Flint
VP: Sue McGrath
VP: Guy Perkins
VP: Mladen Stojic
VP: Martin Tremp
Dir Bus: Joel Hurt

D-U-N-S 01-959-0731 IMP/EXP
LEICA GEOSYSTEMS INC
(*Suby of* LEICA GEOSYSTEMS HOLDINGS INC) ★
5051 Peachtree Corners Ci, Norcross, GA 30092-2592
Tel (770) 776-3400 *Founded/Ownrshp* 1997
Sales 70.4MM^E *EMP* 210^E
SIC 5084 Measuring & testing equipment, electrical; Measuring & testing equipment, electrical
Pr: Ken Mooyan
**CFO:* Andrew Gotman
**Treas:* Patricia Arroyo
Manager: Yolonda Williams
VP Mktg: Wendy Watson

D-U-N-S 15-351-0730 IMP
■ **LEICA MICROSYSTEMS INC**
(*Suby of* DANAHER CORP) ★
1700 Leider Ln, Buffalo Grove, IL 60089-6622
Tel (847) 405-0123 *Founded/Ownrshp* 2006
Sales 93.4MM^E *EMP* 400
SIC 3827 3841 3821 Optical instruments & lenses; Optical instruments & apparatus; Diagnostic apparatus, medical; Laboratory apparatus & furniture; Optical instruments & lenses; Optical instruments & apparatus; Diagnostic apparatus, medical; Laboratory apparatus & furniture
Pr: Matthias Weber
Treas: Charles Schwertner
**Sec:* Albin Szklany
**VP:* Karen Bergendorf
VP: Christopher McMahon
VP: Dan Simkowski
VP: Clyde Spencer
VP: Bill Standwill
Area Mgr: Kyle Kisiel
Sales Exec: Evanne Maher
Manager: Patrick Truluck
Board of Directors: Daniel L Comas, Robert L Comas, Terrence Grant, Robert S Lutz, Vincent Vaccerelli

LEICHTAG ASSISTED LIVING
See SAN DIEGO HEBREW HOMES

D-U-N-S 00-418-0113
LEIDEN CABINET CO
2385 Edison Blvd, Twinsburg, OH 44087-2376
Tel (330) 425-8555 *Founded/Ownrshp* 1940
Sales 24.8MM^E *EMP* 130
SIC 2541 Store fixtures, wood; Cabinets, except refrigerated: show, display, etc.: wood; Store fixtures, wood; Cabinets, except refrigerated: show, display, etc.: wood
CEO: Thomas Leiden
COO: Dave Marusa
CFO: Melissa Durst
**VP:* Melissa Hale
**VP:* Michael Hopp
Plnt Mgr: Chris Rhoa
Sls Dir: Ken Lucas
Snr PM: Jason Fordyce

D-U-N-S 15-999-0456
■ **LEIDOS BIOMEDICAL RESEARCH INC**
(*Suby of* LEIDOS INC) ★
1050 Boyles St, Frederick, MD 21702-9242
Tel (301) 846-5031 *Founded/Ownrshp* 2000
Sales 98.4MM^E *EMP* 22,000
SIC 8733 Noncommercial research organizations; Noncommercial research organizations
Pr: David Heimbrook
**Treas:* David Bufter
**Ex VP:* Douglas Scott
Prgrm Mgr: Craig Gladden
Dir IT: Jing Fong
IT Man: Laura Knott
IT Man: Dwight Nissley
Netwrk Mgr: William Boyer
Web Dev: Jason Holbert

D-U-N-S 05-165-0752
■ **LEIDOS ENGINEERING LLC**
(*Suby of* LEIDOS HOLDINGS INC) ★
9400 Broadway Ext Ste 300, Oklahoma City, OK 73114-7407
Tel (405) 478-5353 *Founded/Ownrshp* 2007
Sales 19.9MM^E *EMP* 849
SIC 8711 1541 Engineering services; Industrial buildings & warehouses; Engineering services; Industrial buildings & warehouses
Mng Pt: Tom Roach
V Ch: Connie Mullins
Pr: Ken Morris
Treas: Stephen Bingham
VP: Wally Hunt
VP: Napoliello Jeff
VP: Charles Weaver
Dir: Clare Woodside
Creative D: David Benham
Dir Bus: Robert Bogues
Dir Bus: Randal Paquette

LEIDOS HEALTH
See MAXIT HEALTHCARE LLC

D-U-N-S 61-164-1312
▲ **LEIDOS HOLDINGS INC**
11951 Freedom Dr Ste 500, Reston, VA 20190-5650
Tel (571) 526-6000 *Founded/Ownrshp* 1969
Sales 5.0MMM *EMP* 19,000
Accts Deloitte & Touche Llp Mclean
Tkr Sym LDOS *Exch* NYS

SIC 8731 7371 7373 8742 3674 Commercial physical research; Energy research; Environmental research; Medical research, commercial; Computer software development; Systems engineering, computer related; Training & development consultant; Integrated circuits, semiconductor networks, etc.; Commercial physical research; Energy research; Environmental research; Medical research, commercial; Computer software development; Systems engineering, computer related; Training & development consultant; Integrated circuits, semiconductor networks, etc.
Ch Bd: Roger A Krone
Pr: Deborah H Alderson
Pr: Shawn Goltzene
Pr: Karl Kropp
Pr: Larry J Peck
Pr: George T Singley III
Pr: John Szymanski
Pr: Kevin Vest
CFO: Mark W Sopp
Ofcr: Sarah Allen
Assoc VP: Roberto Estrada
Ex VP: Vincent A Maffeo
Ex VP: William A Roper Jr
Ex VP: John H Warner Jr
Sr VP: Lucy Reilly Fitch
Sr VP: John R Hartley
Sr VP: David Lacquement
Sr VP: Paul E Levi
Sr VP: Martin Miner
Sr VP: Steven Russell
Sr VP: Ken Sharp

D-U-N-S 05-478-1240 EXP
■ LEIDOS INC
(*Suby of* LEIDOS HOLDINGS INC) ★
11951 Freedom Dr Ste 500, Reston, VA 20190-5650
Tel (571) 526-6000 *Founded/Ownrshp* 1969
Sales 5.0MMM *EMP* 19,000
Accts Deloitte & Touche Llp Mclean
SIC 8731 7373 Commercial physical research; Energy research; Environmental research; Medical research, commercial; Systems engineering, computer related; Commercial physical research; Energy research; Environmental research; Medical research, commercial; Systems engineering, computer related
Ch Bd: Roger A Krone
Ofcr: Sarah Allen
Ex VP: James E Cuff
Ex VP: Deborah Lee James
Ex VP: Michael E Leiter
Ex VP: Vincent A Maffeo
Sr VP: Julius Caesar
Sr VP: Paul E Levi
Sr VP: Terry M Ryan
Sr VP: Kenneth P Sharp
Sr VP: Travis Slocumb
Sr VP: Jennifer E Smith
Sr VP: Paul W Sullivan
Sr VP: John Sweeney
VP: Kenneth Kicia
Exec: Charles Beard
Exec: Roger Hoopengardner
Dir Risk M: Tom Kennelly
Dir Bus: James Housman
Dir Bus: Michael Stephens
Dir Bus: Adam West
Board of Directors: David G Fubini, John J Hamre, Miriam E John, John J Jumper, Harry M J Kraemer Jr, Gary S May, Lawrence C Nussdorf, Robert S Shapard, Noel B Williams

LEIDY CHEVROLET OLDSMOBILE
See BRENNER CADILLAC INC

D-U-N-S 01-458-7984
LEIDYS INC
(*Suby of* ALL HOLDING CO INC) ★
266 W Cherry Ln, Souderton, PA 18964-2819
Tel (215) 723-4606 *Founded/Ownrshp* 2008
Sales 36.5MM^E *EMP* 270^E
SIC 2011 5147 Meat packing plants; Meats, fresh; Meat packing plants; Meats, fresh
Pr: James Vanstone
CFO: Bill Morral
**Treas:* Scott A Schanzenbach
**VP:* Thomas K Leidy
**VP:* Fred Winter
Dir IT: Bob Hardner
IT Man: Todd Wood
Info Man: Larry Hertzog
Sales Exec: Jerry Mc Millan
Pr Mgr: Jeff Bohmueller
Sls Mgr: Jerry McMillan

D-U-N-S 19-674-0419
LEIF JOHNSON FORD II LTD
501 E Koenig Ln, Austin, TX 78751-1426
Tel (512) 454-3711 *Founded/Ownrshp* 1984
Sales 58.4MM^E *EMP* 230^E
SIC 5531 Automotive parts; Automotive parts
CEO: Robert Johnson

D-U-N-S 05-264-3350 EXP
LEIF JOHNSON FORD INC (TX)
TRUCK CITY FORD
501 E Koenig Ln, Austin, TX 78751-1426
Tel (512) 454-3711 *Founded/Ownrshp* 1947
Sales 158.4MM^E *EMP* 410
SIC 5521 5511 Used car dealers; Automobiles, new & used; Used car dealers; Automobiles, new & used
CEO: Robert Johnson
Pt: Curt Johnson
VP: Brook A Broesche
Genl Mgr: Fred Trudeau
IT Man: Lee Raines
Sales Exec: Chris Tohill
Mktg Mgr: Chris Stclair
Sls Mgr: Jeff Buhl
Sls Mgr: Chip Clester
Sls Mgr: James Figurell
Sls Mgr: Mike Frits

D-U-N-S 80-321-9716
LEIGH ENGINEERING INC
RONE ENGINEERING
8908 Ambassador Row, Dallas, TX 75247-4510
Tel (214) 630-9745 *Founded/Ownrshp* 1972
Sales 22.9MM^E *EMP* 150
SIC 8711 8748 7389 Consulting engineer; Environmental consultant; Inspection & testing services; Consulting engineer; Environmental consultant; Inspection & testing services
CEO: Harold W Leigh
**Pr:* Richard Leigh
**VP:* Larry Bracken
**VP:* Scot Gordon
**VP:* Mark D Gray
VP: Scot Pe
Sfty Mgr: John Moody

D-U-N-S 00-695-2501 IMP
LEIGH FIBERS LLC
1101 Syphrit Rd, Wellford, SC 29385-9460
Tel (864) 439-4111 *Founded/Ownrshp* 1921
Sales 77.0MM^E *EMP* 250
SIC 2299 2221 2824 Fibers, textile: recovery from textile mill waste & rags; Broadwoven fabric mills, manmade; Organic fibers, noncellulosic; Fibers, textile: recovery from textile mill waste & rags; Broadwoven fabric mills, manmade; Organic fibers, noncellulosic
Pr: Donald Bockoven
**Ch:* Heidi M Lehner
**Treas:* Carl P Lehner
Sr Cor Off: David Blalock
**VP:* Bruce Howell
VP: Paul Lehner
Sfty Mgr: Barry Ward
Opers Mgr: Lindy Summey
Advt Mgr: Parris Chernez

D-U-N-S 00-958-6108 IMP
LEIGHT SALES CO INC
1611 S Catalina Ave L45, Redondo Beach, CA 90277-5299
Tel (310) 223-1000 *Founded/Ownrshp* 1974
Sales 56.5MM^E *EMP* 75
SIC 5072 Hardware; Hand tools; Hardware; Hand tools
CEO: Bryan Moskowitz
**Sec:* Helene Moskowitz
**Prin:* Alan Moskowitz
Dir IT: Liz Jiang
VP Sls: Paul Kruger
VP Sls: Steve Phillips

LEIGHTON BROADCASTING
See LEIGHTON ENTERPRISES INC

D-U-N-S 05-759-7114
LEIGHTON ENTERPRISES INC
LEIGHTON BROADCASTING
619 W Saint Germain St # 1, Saint Cloud, MN 56301-3663
Tel (320) 251-1450 *Founded/Ownrshp* 1971
Sales 24.9MM^E *EMP* 117
SIC 4832 Radio broadcasting stations; Radio broadcasting stations
CEO: Bob Leighton
**Pr:* John Sowada
VP: Denny Niess
Mng Dir: Dan Soldner
Pgrm Dir: Derek Lee
Pgrm Dir: Dan Ochsner
Pgrm Dir: Mike Ryan

D-U-N-S 01-938-3244
LEIGHTON GROUP INC
17781 Cowan, Irvine, CA 92614-6009
Tel (949) 477-4040 *Founded/Ownrshp* 1961
Sales 25.9MM^E *EMP* 270
SIC 8744 ;
Ch Bd: Terry Brennan
CFO: Scott Cosper
VP: Chris Lutton
VP: Tom Mills
Off Mgr: Kris Lutton
Sys Mgr: Donald Brockway
Sys Mgr: Buu Tran
Sfty Mgr: Debbie Morin

D-U-N-S 01-844-3465
LEIKIN MOTOR COMPANIES INC
38750 Mentor Ave, Willoughby, OH 44094-7929
Tel (440) 946-6900 *Founded/Ownrshp* 1968
Sales 28.0MM^E *EMP* 62
SIC 5511 7532 7514 5531 5521 Automobiles, new & used; Top & body repair & paint shops; Passenger car rental; Automotive & home supply stores; Used car dealers; Automobiles, new & used; Top & body repair & paint shops; Passenger car rental; Automotive & home supply stores; Used car dealers
Pr: Ronald Leikin
Sales Exec: Kevin Conant

D-U-N-S 03-551-8237
LEILA A MANKARIOUS
MASSACHUSETS EYE EAR INFERMERY
243 Charles St, Boston, MA 02114-3002
Tel (617) 573-3413 *Founded/Ownrshp* 2001
Sales 221.6MM *EMP* 4
SIC 8011 Offices & clinics of medical doctors; Offices & clinics of medical doctors
Owner: Leila A Mankarious PHD
Treas: Joseph B Nadol Jr

D-U-N-S 02-488-8935
LEINBACH MOSELEY INC
5000 Reynolda Rd, Winston Salem, NC 27106-8601
Tel (336) 924-4115 *Founded/Ownrshp* 1945
Sales 20.1MM^E *EMP* 90
SIC 5083 3523 5999 Agricultural machinery & equipment; Farm machinery & equipment; Farm equipment & supplies; Agricultural machinery & equipment; Farm machinery & equipment; Farm equipment & supplies
Pr: Janet Bates

D-U-N-S 03-947-9332
■ LEINER HEALTH PRODUCTS INC
(*Suby of* ARCO PHARMACEUTICAL) ★
901 E 233rd St, Carson, CA 90745-6204
Tel (310) 513-2116 *Founded/Ownrshp* 1952
Sales 142.9MM^E *EMP* 2,538
SIC 2834 5122 Vitamin, nutrient & hematinic preparations for human use; Vitamins & minerals; Vitamin, nutrient & hematinic preparations for human use; Vitamins & minerals
CEO: Jeffrey A Nagel
Pr: Robert J La Ferriere
Pr: Crystal Wright
**CFO:* Michael Collins
**V Ch Bd:* Harvey Kamil
Sr VP: Patrick Dunn
VP Mktg: Brenda Cheng

D-U-N-S 60-707-5595
■ LEISERV INC
(*Suby of* BRUNSWICK CORP) ★
1 N Field Ct, Lake Forest, IL 60045-4810
Tel (847) 735-4700 *Founded/Ownrshp* 1985
Sales 20.0MM^E *EMP* 400
SIC 7933 Bowling centers; Bowling centers
Pr: Warren N Hardie
**VP:* William V Briody Jr

D-U-N-S 15-058-5081 IMP
LEISTRITZ ADVANCED TECHNOLOGIES CORP
LEISTRITZ PUMP
(*Suby of* LEISTRITZ AG)
165 Chestnut St Ste 1, Allendale, NJ 07401-2230
Tel (201) 934-8262 *Founded/Ownrshp* 1985
Sales 32.1MM^E *EMP* 27
SIC 5084 Pumps & pumping equipment; Hydraulic systems equipment & supplies; Machine tools & accessories
Pr: Jeffrey De Daul
COO: Dolares Sydoruk
**CFO:* Robert Richter
Bd of Dir: Elmar Schwarz
Ofcr: Jack Martone
IT Man: Ulla Olsen
Mktg Dir: Michael Thummert
Sls Mgr: Tim Danckwerth
Sls Mgr: K Goga
Sales Asso: Chris Rogers

LEISTRITZ PUMP
See LEISTRITZ ADVANCED TECHNOLOGIES CORP

D-U-N-S 04-071-4441 IMP
LEISTRIZ ADVANCED TURBINE COMPONENTS INC
(*Suby of* ELLWOOD CITY FORGE CO) ★
3050 Wstnghuse Rd Ste 190, Rural Hall, NC 27045
Tel (336) 969-5291 *Founded/Ownrshp* 2012
Sales 22.0MM^E *EMP* 165
SIC 3511 Turbines & turbine generator set units, complete; Turbines & turbine generator set units, complete
Pr: Ernst Rothstein
**VP:* Ernie Konkoli

D-U-N-S 19-368-8595 IMP/EXP
LEISURE BAY INDUSTRIES INC
RECREATION FACTORY WAREHOUSE
450 S Ronald Reagan Blvd, Longwood, FL 32750-5405
Tel (407) 297-0141 *Founded/Ownrshp* 1995
Sales NA *EMP* 600^E
SIC 3949

D-U-N-S 02-131-7003
LEISURE CARE LLC
1601 5th Ave Ste 1900, Seattle, WA 98101-3615
Tel (206) 436-7827 *Founded/Ownrshp* 2003
Sales 66.2MM^E *EMP* 1,900
SIC 6513 Apartment building operators; Apartment building operators
CEO: Dan Madsen
**CFO:* Judy Marczewski

D-U-N-S 62-161-1466 EXP
LEISURE PROPERTIES LLC
CROWNLINE BOATS
11884 Country Club Rd, West Frankfort, IL 62896-5064
Tel (618) 937-6426 *Founded/Ownrshp* 1990
Sales 172.1MM^E *EMP* 550
SIC 3732 Boats, fiberglass: building & repairing; Boats, fiberglass: building & repairing
**Pr:* Scott Lahrman
CFO: Guy Coons
Prd Mgr: Lorraine Leadabrand

D-U-N-S 04-429-8685
LEISURE SPORTS INC
CLUBSPORT OF PLEASANTON
4670 Willow Rd Ste 100, Pleasanton, CA 94588-8587
Tel (925) 600-1966 *Founded/Ownrshp* 1991
Sales 213.0MM^E *EMP* 1,300
SIC 6719 Investment holding companies, except banks; Personal holding companies, except banks; Investment holding companies, except banks; Personal holding companies, except banks
Pr: Steve Gilmour
**CFO:* Patrick O'Brien
VP: Janine Williams

LEISURE SUPPLY
See KELLER SUPPLY CO

LEISURE VALE RETIREMENT HOTEL
See BV GENERAL INC

D-U-N-S 62-342-7671
LEISURE WORLD OF MARYLAND CORP
LWCC
3701 Rossmoor Blvd Ste 1, Silver Spring, MD 20906-1565
Tel (301) 598-4222 *Founded/Ownrshp* 1977
Sales 38.1MM^E *EMP* 224
Accts Deleon & Stang Gaithersburg
SIC 6531 Real estate managers; Real estate managers
Ch Bd: Barbara Cronin
**Pr:* Kevin B Flannery
Treas: Jennifer Peacock
VP: Mark Ellis
**Prin:* Paul Bessel
Off Mgr: Leslie Vizzi
Dir IT: Jamie McDonald
IT Man: Mike Johnson

D-U-N-S 03-120-8390
LEISZLER OIL CO INC
SHORT STOP
635 W Crawford St, Clay Center, KS 67432-2337
Tel (785) 632-5648 *Founded/Ownrshp* 1931
Sales 173.9MM^E *EMP* 175
Accts Sink Gordon & Associates Llp
SIC 5171 5411 5541 Petroleum bulk stations; Grocery stores; Gasoline service stations; Petroleum bulk stations; Grocery stores; Gasoline service stations
Pr: Charles Arthur III
**VP:* Alison R Leiszler
VP: Samantha Liby
Rgnl Mgr: Luke Bauer

LEITH AUTO CENTER SERVICE
See LEITH INC

LEITH DODGE
See AUTO PARTS EAST INC

D-U-N-S 04-736-8238
LEITH INC
LEITH AUTO CENTER SERVICE
5607 Capital Blvd, Raleigh, NC 27616-2933
Tel (919) 876-5432 *Founded/Ownrshp* 1968
Sales 320.3MM^E *EMP* 800
SIC 5511 7515 7513 5012 Automobiles, new & used; Pickups, new & used; Passenger car leasing; Truck rental & leasing, no drivers; Automobiles & other motor vehicles; Automobiles, new & used; Pickups, new & used; Passenger car leasing; Truck rental & leasing, no drivers; Automobiles & other motor vehicles
Pr: Michael J Leith
**CFO:* Linda Leith
Genl Mgr: Don Sigmon
Off Mgr: Kathy Braswell
Sls Mgr: Russ Clark
Sls Mgr: Warren Taylor
Sales Asso: Steven Bonanza
Sales Asso: David Wells
Sales Asso: Richard Williams

LEITZINGER IMPORTS
See DRISCOLL AUTOMOTIVE GROUP LLC

D-U-N-S 96-412-2881
LEJEUNE AUTO WHOLESALE INC
CAR FACTORY OUTLET
709 Nw 42nd Ave, Miami, FL 33126-5523
Tel (305) 642-6757 *Founded/Ownrshp* 1996
Sales 34.0MM *EMP* 29
SIC 5012 5521 Automobiles & other motor vehicles; Automobiles, used cars only; Automobiles & other motor vehicles; Automobiles, used cars only
Pr: Eloy Garcia Jr
**Treas:* Jose R Garcia
**VP:* Nicolas Mendizabel
Genl Mgr: Carlos Duran

D-U-N-S 13-925-5913
LEJEUNE INVESTMENT INC
CAROUSEL AUTOMOBILES
9393 Wayzata Blvd, Minneapolis, MN 55426-1862
Tel (763) 744-9393 *Founded/Ownrshp* 1981
Sales 70.1MM^E *EMP* 200
Accts Wipfli Llp Minneapolis Minn
SIC 5511 Automobiles, new & used; Automobiles, new & used
Ch Bd: Laurence F Le Jeune
**Ch Bd:* Laurence F Lejeune
**Pr:* Jon Hansen
**VP:* Tom Studer
Sls Mgr: Lynn Daleiden
Sls Mgr: Charlie Fick
Sales Asso: Jason Boers
Sales Asso: Jiten Trevdi

LEJEUNE LINCOLN MERCURY ISUZU
See LEJEUNE MOTOR CO

D-U-N-S 02-464-6788
LEJEUNE MOTOR CO
LEJEUNE LINCOLN MERCURY ISUZU
2215 N Marine Blvd, Jacksonville, NC 28546-6916
Tel (910) 455-1551 *Founded/Ownrshp* 1952
Sales 37.2MM^E *EMP* 85
SIC 5511 5571 Automobiles, new & used; Motorcycles; Automobiles, new & used; Motorcycles
Pr: Jerry S Stevenson
**Treas:* John O Stevenson
Genl Mgr: Frank Odrobina

D-U-N-S 80-957-2381
LEK CONSULTING LLC
75 State St Ste 1901, Boston, MA 02109-1864
Tel (617) 737-1725 *Founded/Ownrshp* 1983
Sales 73.7MM^E *EMP* 375
Accts O Connor And Drew Pc Cpas B
SIC 8742 Business consultant; Business consultant
COO: Jean Concannon
**CFO:* Michael Clabault
Bd of Dir: Jim Lawrence
VP: David Barrow
VP: Troy Norris
VP: Robert Rourke
VP: Susan Sure
VP: John Thomas
Mng Dir: Wiley Bell
Mng Dir: Robert Haslehurst
Mng Dir: Peter McKelvey

D-U-N-S 00-903-9389
LEKTRO INC
1190 Se Flightline Dr, Warrenton, OR 97146-9393
Tel (503) 861-2288 *Founded/Ownrshp* 1945
Sales 24.6MM^E *EMP* 68
Accts Geffin Messher
SIC 4581 Aircraft maintenance & repair services
Pr: Eric Paulson
CFO: Grant North
Ex VP: Jesse Long
Genl Mgr: Kurtis Long
IT Man: Todd Milliren
Sfty Dirs: Jason Mathews

Opers Mgr: Paul Davis
Manager: Scott Adams

D-U-N-S 16-819-2438
LELAND MANAGEMENT INC
6972 Lake Gloria Blvd, Orlando, FL 32809-3200
Tel (407) 447-9955 *Founded/Ownrshp* 1997
Sales 35.5MME *EMP* 289E
SIC 8741 Management services
CEO: Rebecca M Furlow
**CFO:* David A Furlow
Off Admin: Sara Munawar

D-U-N-S 00-921-4214
LELAND STANFORD JUNIOR UNIVERSITY (CA)
STANFORD LNEAR ACCELERATOR CTR
2575 Sand Hill Rd, Menlo Park, CA 94025-7015
Tel (650) 723-2300 *Founded/Ownrshp* 1891
Sales 3.0MMME *EMP* 15,000
Accts Pricewaterhousecoopers Llp Sa
SIC 8221 8069 8062 University; Children's hospital; General medical & surgical hospitals; University; Children's hospital; General medical & surgical hospitals
Pr: John Hennessy
**CFO:* Randall S Livingston
Chf Inves: Harry Turner
Top Exec: Britt Hedman
Top Exec: John Schmerge
VP: Bill Clebsch
**VP:* Debra Zumwalt
Dir Lab: Jonathan Dorfan
Assoc Dir: M Allen
Mng Dir: Nneka Rimmer
Mng Dir: Wafa WEI

D-U-N-S 04-211-5170
LELAND-POWELL FASTENERS LLC (TN)
(*Suby of* ELGIN FASTENER GROUP LLC) ★
8160 Highway 45 S, Martin, TN 38237-5614
Tel (731) 587-3106 *Founded/Ownrshp* 1967, 2012
Sales 20.1MME *EMP* 50
SIC 3452 3965 Screws, metal; Fasteners
Ch Bd: Joseph R Exum
**Pr:* Donald R Danner
Dir IT: Larry Stringfield

D-U-N-S 06-213-0687
LEM CONSTRUCTION CO INC (TX)
10849 Kinghurst St # 150, Houston, TX 77099-3404
Tel (281) 495-9550 *Founded/Ownrshp* 1971
Sales 35.9MME *EMP* 125
Accts Benton Duroy & Ivey Pc Ho
SIC 1629 Waste disposal plant construction; Waste disposal plant construction
Ch Bd: Larry W Laird II
**VP:* Herman Myers
VP: Ken Stringer
Sfty Mgr: Mike Harris
Board of Directors: Larry W Laird, Rosemary K Laird

D-U-N-S 18-480-5166
▲ LEMAITRE VASCULAR INC
43 2nd Ave, Burlington, MA 01803
Tel (781) 221-2266 *Founded/Ownrshp* 1983
Sales 71.1MM *EMP* 341E
Tkr Sym LMAT *Exch* NGM
SIC 3841 Surgical & medical instruments; Surgical & medical instruments
Ch Bd: George W Lemaitre
Pr: David B Roberts
CFO: Joseph P Pellegrino Jr
Bd of Dir: Russell D Hays
Sr VP: Trent G Kamke
Sr VP: Trent Kamkee
Sr VP: Jim Russell
VP: Laurie A Churchill
VP: Drew Enamait
VP: Peter Y Lee
VP: Wolfgang Meichelboeck
VP: David Ngau
VP: Michael Wijas
Board of Directors: Lawrence J Jasinski, John J O'-connor, John A Roush, Michael H Thomas

D-U-N-S 79-367-0030
LEMAN MANHATTAN PREPARATORY SCHOOL LLC
41 Broad St, New York, NY 10004-2513
Tel (212) 232-0266 *Founded/Ownrshp* 2003
Sales 20.0MME *EMP* 190
SIC 8211 Private elementary & secondary schools; Private elementary & secondary schools
Comm Man: Brylee Maxfield
Mng Dir: Gerard Witter

D-U-N-S 15-730-6903 IMP
LEMAN USA INC
(*Suby of* LEMAN - INTERNATIONAL SYSTEM TRANSPORT A/S)
1860 Renaissance Blvd, Sturtevant, WI 53177-1745
Tel (262) 884-4700 *Founded/Ownrshp* 1985
Sales 65.6MM *EMP* 108
SIC 4731 4225 Freight forwarding; General warehousing & storage; Freight forwarding; General warehousing & storage
Pr: Mikael Olesen
CFO: Randy Fortel
VP: Torben Caesius

D-U-N-S 02-327-2776 IMP
LEMANS CORP (WI)
PARTS UNLIMITED
3501 Kennedy Rd, Janesville, WI 53545-8884
Tel (608) 758-1111 *Founded/Ownrshp* 1967
Sales 809.8MME *EMP* 1,000
SIC 5013 Motor vehicle supplies & new parts; Motorcycle parts; Motor vehicle supplies & new parts; Motorcycle parts
Ch Bd: Fred Fox
**Pr:* Jeffrey Fox
**CFO:* Mark Scharenbroch
VP: Mike Collins
**VP:* Roger Dolan
**VP:* Arlene Grzelinski
VP: Robert Maynard
Exec: Cindy Amundson

Prgrm Mgr: Brian Sherry
**Genl Mgr:* Lynne Severson
Sftwr Eng: Tim Ledger

D-U-N-S 06-187-1125
LEMATIC INC
2410 W Main St, Jackson, MI 49203-1099
Tel (517) 787-3301 *Founded/Ownrshp* 1970
Sales 23.7MME *EMP* 60
SIC 3556 Bakery machinery
CEO: Dale J Le Crone
**Pr:* John Hamilton
**CFO:* Tammy Sanford
Off Mgr: Marcia King
Plnt Mgr: Chad Paquin

D-U-N-S 00-178-0758
LEMBERG ELECTRIC CO INC (WI)
4085 N 128th St Ste 100, Brookfield, WI 53005-1812
Tel (262) 373-0163 *Founded/Ownrshp* 1954
Sales 33.1MME *EMP* 130
SIC 1731 1799 General electrical contractor; Communications specialization; Fiber optic cable installation; Sign installation & maintenance; General electrical contractor; Communications specialization; Fiber optic cable installation; Sign installation & maintenance
Pr: David M Washebek
Bd of Dir: Gregg Eisenhardt
**VP:* Timothy W Scheid
Genl Mgr: Melissa Glenz
Sfty Dirs: Marty Schulz
Sls Mgr: Robert Kruesel

D-U-N-S 78-978-3685
LEMBI GROUP INC
2101 Market St, San Francisco, CA 94114-1321
Tel (415) 861-1111 *Founded/Ownrshp* 1990
Sales 15.9MME *EMP* 1,510E
SIC 6531 Real estate managers; Real estate managers
Pr: Frank Lembi
**VP:* Walter Lembi

D-U-N-S 04-141-5605
LEMCO MILLS INC
766 Koury Dr, Burlington, NC 27215-6721
Tel (336) 226-5548 *Founded/Ownrshp* 1988
Sales 22.7MME *EMP* 190E
Accts Stoutstuartburlingtonmc
SIC 2251 Women's hosiery, except socks; Women's hosiery, except socks
Pr: Chester Mayer
**Ex VP:* Joseph Weinstein

D-U-N-S 12-417-3860
LEMEK LLC
PANERA BREAD
8184 Lark Brown Rd # 101, Elkridge, MD 21075-3403
Tel (443) 552-0700 *Founded/Ownrshp* 1998
Sales 77.2MME *EMP* 2,200
SIC 5812 Fast-food restaurant, chain; Fast-food restaurant, chain
Sr VP: Thomas Kish

D-U-N-S 01-679-6542
LEMMEN OIL CO
13 E Randall St, Coopersville, MI 49404-1422
Tel (616) 837-6531 *Founded/Ownrshp* 1948
Sales 22.9MME *EMP* 33
SIC 5171 5083 5511 Petroleum bulk stations; Farm & garden machinery; Automobiles, new & used
Pr: Helene Lemmen
**Pr:* Doug Lemmen

D-U-N-S 14-758-9907
LEMNA CORP
LEMNA INFRASTRUCTURE FIN ENTP
4215 White Bear Pkwy # 200, Saint Paul, MN 55110-7541
Tel (612) 253-2000 *Founded/Ownrshp* 1983
Sales 79.0MME *EMP* 550
SIC 5074 Water purification equipment; Water purification equipment
Pr: Viet Ngo
**CFO:* Brien Johnson
**VP:* Poldi Gerard

LEMNA INFRASTRUCTURE FIN ENTP
See LEMNA CORP

D-U-N-S 06-656-6969
LEMO USA INC
(*Suby of* INTERLEMO USA INC) ★
635 Park Ct, Rohnert Park, CA 94928-7940
Tel (707) 206-3700 *Founded/Ownrshp* 1986
Sales 85.8MME *EMP* 100
SIC 5065 3678 Connectors, electronic; Electronic connectors; Connectors, electronic; Electronic connectors
CEO: Dinshaw Pohwala
Genl Mgr: Win Baerthel
Genl Mgr: Tim Hassett
CTO: Michael Grieco
Dir IT: Michael Greco
Natl Sales: Carol Taylor-Lueck
Sls&Mrk Ex: Dave Ennis
Sls Mgr: Charles Fixa
Sls Mgr: Jim Giovanovitch

D-U-N-S 01-640-2765
LEMOINE CO L L C
214 Jefferson St Ste 200, Lafayette, LA 70501-7050
Tel (337) 896-7720 *Founded/Ownrshp* 1995
Sales 146.7MME *EMP* 266
SIC 1542 Nonresidential construction; Nonresidential construction
CEO: Leonard K Lemoine
COO: Van Champagne
**CFO:* Donald H Broussard Jr
CFO: Donald Broussard
Div Mgr: William Lemoine
Off Mgr: Shelly Schexnayder
Sfty Mgr: Aaron Vincent
Opers Mgr: Tim Burdette
Sls Mgr: Belinda Rhodes
Snr PM: J Miranda
Snr PM: Scott Penton

LEMON GRASS
See WORLD OF GOOD TASTES INC

D-U-N-S 01-163-4027
LEMON GROVE ULTRA MART INC (CA)
KANO FOODS
2913 Stonefield Dr, Jamul, CA 91935-1660
Tel (619) 729-3729 *Founded/Ownrshp* 1998
Sales 25.0MM *EMP* 250E
SIC 5541 7215 Gasoline service stations; ; Laundry, coin-operated; Gasoline service stations; Laundry, coin-operated
Pr: Sam Charry
**CFO:* Bill Charry

D-U-N-S 07-273-9949 IMP/EXP
LEMON-X CORP (NY)
BEVOLUTION GROUP
(*Suby of* BEVOLUTION GROUP) ★
168 Railroad St, Huntington Station, NY 11746-1540
Tel (631) 424-2850 *Founded/Ownrshp* 1972, 2015
Sales 80.0MME *EMP* 1E
SIC 2087 Cocktail mixes, nonalcoholic; Cocktail mixes, nonalcoholic
CEO: James Grassi
**Sec:* Sonia Grassi
Ex VP: Jerry Desmond
VP: Darren Krantz
Rgnl Mgr: Mark Hanna
Opers Mgr: Billy Giddens

D-U-N-S 07-955-1320
LEMONIS FISCHER ACQUISTION CO LLC
250 Parkway Dr Ste 270, Lincolnshire, IL 60069-4346
Tel (847) 808-3000 *Founded/Ownrshp* 2014
Sales 8.8MME *EMP* 400
SIC 6799 Investors; Investors

D-U-N-S 01-252-5127
LEMOORE UNION ELEMENTARY SCHOOL DISTRICT
100 Vine St, Lemoore, CA 93245-3418
Tel (559) 924-6800 *Founded/Ownrshp* 1970
Sales 21.5MME *EMP* 360
SIC 8211 Public elementary & secondary schools; Public elementary & secondary schools
Comm Man: Pamela Barker
Ex Dir: Angela Sorrentino
Dir IT: Laura Sasaki

D-U-N-S 07-462-8934
LEMOORE UNION HIGH SCHOOL DISTRICT
KINGS COUNTY SCHOOLS
5 Powell Ave, Lemoore, CA 93245-2856
Tel (559) 924-6610 *Founded/Ownrshp* 1924
Sales 23.2MM *EMP* 200
Accts Borchardt Corona & Faeth Fre
SIC 8211 Public elementary & secondary schools; Public senior high school; Public elementary & secondary schools; Public senior high school

D-U-N-S 78-448-2080
LEN MAYER & CO LLC
848 Brickell Ave Ste 900, Miami, FL 33131-2996
Tel (305) 358-7720 *Founded/Ownrshp* 2005
Sales 40.6MME *EMP* 454
SIC 6799 Real estate investors, except property operators; Real estate investors, except property operators

LEN STOLER FORD
See LEN STOLER INC

D-U-N-S 04-415-1389 EXP
LEN STOLER INC
LEN STOLER FORD
11275 Reisterstown Rd, Owings Mills, MD 21117-1997
Tel (410) 581-7000 *Founded/Ownrshp* 1968
Sales 171.3MME *EMP* 410
SIC 5511 Automobiles, new & used; Automobiles, new & used
Pr: Barry Stoler
**CFO:* David Leibowitz
CFO: Dave Liebowitz
**VP:* James Berg
**Prin:* Len Stoler
Sls Mgr: Edward Caster
Sls Mgr: Allan Talmadge
Sls Mgr: Armon Tuscani
Sales Asso: Chelsea Jefferson
Sales Asso: Joe Michalski
Board of Directors: Roslyn Stoler

D-U-N-S 10-826-9358 IMP
LEN-TEX CORP
LEN-TEX WALLCOVERINGS
18 Len Tex Ln, North Walpole, NH 03609-1140
Tel (603) 445-2342 *Founded/Ownrshp* 1983
Sales 39.2MME *EMP* 108
SIC 2679 Wallpaper; Wallpaper
Pr: Don Lennon
**Treas:* Charles Lennon
Natl Sales: Steve Andrews

LEN-TEX WALLCOVERINGS
See LEN-TEX CORP

D-U-N-S 02-916-2450 IMP
LENACO CORP
BLUE RIBBON SUPPLY COMPANY BRS
451 E Jamie Ct, South San Francisco, CA 94080-6204
Tel (650) 873-3500 *Founded/Ownrshp* 1958
Sales 32.1MME *EMP* 45
SIC 5085 5087 Industrial supplies; Laundry equipment & supplies
CEO: Daisy Dilena
**Treas:* Carolyn Dilena
**VP:* John Dilena

D-U-N-S 03-258-5549
LENAPE REGIONAL HIGH SCHOOL DISTRICT
93 Willow Grove Rd, Shamong, NJ 08088-8961
Tel (609) 268-2588 *Founded/Ownrshp* 1954
Sales 155.5MM *EMP* 1,200
Accts Holman Frenia Allison Pc M
SIC 8211 High school, junior or senior; High school, junior or senior

Ofcr: Lee Pinkerton
Ex Dir: James Crowley
MIS Dir: Mike Haas
Teacher Pr: Paige Macgregor
Instr Medi: John Donaldson

D-U-N-S 07-550-0231
LENAPE VALLEY FOUNDATION
500 N West St, Doylestown, PA 18901-2366
Tel (215) 345-5300 *Founded/Ownrshp* 1957
Sales 14.6MM *EMP* 400E
Accts Detweiler Hershey & Associates
SIC 8093 Mental health clinic, outpatient; Mental health clinic, outpatient
CEO: Alan Hartl
**CFO:* Walter Wolaniuk
Treas: Catherine Forkin
Exec: Traci Gorman
Psych: Marjorie Rubin

D-U-N-S 16-098-2930
LENAR DETECTIVE AGENCY INC
COLONIAL SECURITY SERVICE
23 N Michigan Ave, Kenilworth, NJ 07033-1750
Tel (908) 298-0012 *Founded/Ownrshp* 1982
Sales 8.2MME *EMP* 300
SIC 7381 Private investigator; Security guard service; Private investigator; Security guard service
Pr: Eugene Pendyke
**VP:* Clifford Deckman

D-U-N-S 03-870-5794
LENAWEE INTERMEDIATE SCHOOL DISTRICT INC
4107 N Adrian Hwy, Adrian, MI 49221-9309
Tel (517) 265-2119 *Founded/Ownrshp* 1975
Sales 32.9MME *EMP* 400E
Accts Gross Puckey Gruel & Roof P
SIC 8211 Public elementary & secondary schools; Public elementary & secondary schools
**Pr:* Howard Keller
**Treas:* Richard Germond
**VP:* Victor Hogue
Sls&Mrk Ex: Kyle Hoffman

D-U-N-S 18-798-4265 IMP
LENAWEE STAMPING CORP
VAN ROB TECUMSEH
(*Suby of* VAN-ROB INC)
1200 E Chicago Blvd, Tecumseh, MI 49286-8605
Tel (517) 404-9796 *Founded/Ownrshp* 2006
Sales 127.3MME *EMP* 330
SIC 3465 Body parts, automobile: stamped metal; Body parts, automobile: stamped metal
Pr: Allan Power
Mfg Mgr: Greg Darling

D-U-N-S 10-200-1906
LENBROOK SQUARE FOUNDATION INC
3747 Peachtree Rd Ne Ofc, Brookhaven, GA 30319-1381
Tel (404) 264-3386 *Founded/Ownrshp* 1980
Sales 28.9MM *EMP* 150
Accts Smith & Howard Pc Atlanta Ga
SIC 8059 Rest home, with health care; Rest home, with health care
CEO: Becky Webster
**CFO:* Chris Keysor
CFO: Christopher Keysor
VP: Mike McDaniel
VP Mktg: Felicia Sveda

LENCO ARMORED VEHICLES
See LENCO INDUSTRIES INC

D-U-N-S 17-610-8418
LENCO DIAGNOSTIC LABORATORIES INC
1857 86th St, Brooklyn, NY 11214-3108
Tel (718) 232-1515 *Founded/Ownrshp* 2001
Sales 30.0MM *EMP* 250
SIC 8071 Medical laboratories
CEO: Lenny Tilman
**Pr:* Irina Tylman
Ex VP: Sal Cumella
VP: Thomas Asher
Genl Mgr: Dennis Yurovsky
Off Mgr: Deanna Cruz
**CIO:* Felix Sandler

D-U-N-S 96-819-3060 IMP
LENCO INC - PMC
(*Suby of* PMC GROUP INC) ★
10240 Deer Park Rd, Waverly, NE 68462-1499
Tel (402) 786-2000 *Founded/Ownrshp* 1997
Sales 32.9MME *EMP* 150
SIC 3089 Injection molding of plastics; Injection molding of plastics
Pr: Paritosh Chakrabarti
VP: David Tolly
Genl Mgr: Daryl Chapelle

D-U-N-S 05-195-0293 IMP/EXP
LENCO INDUSTRIES INC
LENCO ARMORED VEHICLES
10 Betnr Industrial Dr, Pittsfield, MA 01201-7831
Tel (413) 443-7359 *Founded/Ownrshp* 1981
Sales 23.6MME *EMP* 60
SIC 3711 Cars, armored, assembly of
Pr: Leonard W Light
VP: Diane Light
Off Mgr: Christi Marchetto
IT Man: Carrie Mackinnon
Tech Mgr: Steve Mix

LEND LEASE
See RABO AGRIFINANCE INC

D-U-N-S 62-235-2490 IMP
LEND LEASE (US) CONSTRUCTION HOLDINGS INC
(*Suby of* LEND LEASE CONSTRUCTION HOLDINGS (EMEA) LIMITED)
200 Park Ave Fl 9, New York, NY 10166-0999
Tel (212) 592-6800 *Founded/Ownrshp* 1999
Sales 547.1MME *EMP* 730

SIC 1542 1541 8742 Commercial & office building, new construction; Industrial buildings, new construction; Construction project management consultant; Commercial & office building, new construction; Industrial buildings, new construction; Construction project management consultant
CEO: Robert McNamara
**Pr:* Jeffrey L Arfsten
COO: Ron Clarkson
**COO:* Dan Labbad
**CFO:* Tony Lombardo
**Treas:* Brad Robinson
Sr Cor Off: Suzn Head
Top Exec: Ray Dardenne
Ex VP: Jeff Arfsten
Ex VP: Jeff Riemer
Ex VP: Linda Sjogren
Ex VP: Thomas Tether
Sr VP: Bruce Berardi
Sr VP: Rick Wehmeier
VP: Kelly Benedict
VP: Kevin Bowen
VP: Richard Caster
VP: Mary Costello
VP: Majid Fanik
VP: Brian Fleming
VP: Marie Halloran

D-U-N-S 00-892-4029
LEND LEASE (US) CONSTRUCTION INC
(*Suby of* LEND LEASE (US) CONSTRUCTION HOLDINGS INC) ★
200 Park Ave Fl 9, New York, NY 10166-0999
Tel (212) 592-6700 *Founded/Ownrshp* 1987
Sales 547.1MM^E *EMP* 661
SIC 1541 1542 1522 8741 8742 Industrial buildings, new construction; Hospital construction; Commercial & office building, new construction; Shopping center construction; Religious building construction; Hotel/motel, new construction; Construction management; Construction project management consultant; Industrial buildings, new construction; Hospital construction; Commercial & office building, new construction; Shopping center construction; Religious building construction; Hotel/motel, new construction; Construction management; Construction project management consultant
Pr: Jeff Arfsten
CFO: Alex Cockerton
**Treas:* Brad Robinson
Ex VP: Michael M Feigin
Sr VP: Nick Grecco
VP: William Connor
VP: Dennis Sawyer
VP: Gerry Stern
Exec: Chuck Richmond
**Prin:* George Keppler
**Prin:* Gary Rutledge
Board of Directors: Dale Connor

D-U-N-S 82-775-6771
LEND LEASE (US) CONSTRUCTION INC
(*Suby of* LEND LEASE (US) INC) ★
800 W 6th St Ste 1600, Los Angeles, CA 90017-2719
Tel (213) 430-4660 *Founded/Ownrshp* 1983
Sales 36.6MM^E *EMP* 80
SIC 6552 8741 Land subdividers & developers, residential; Management services
CEO: Steve McCann
Ex VP: Todd C Pennington
Sr VP: Simon Muir
IT Man: Jules Jeanmard
Snr PM: Donald Robb

D-U-N-S 09-698-1824 IMP
LEND LEASE (US) CONSTRUCTION LMB INC (NY)
(*Suby of* M/L BOVIS HOLDINGS LTD) ★
200 Park Ave Fl 9, New York, NY 10166-0999
Tel (212) 592-6700 *Founded/Ownrshp* 1979, 1999
Sales 119.1MM^E *EMP* 465^E
SIC 1522 1541 1542 8741 8742 Residential construction; Industrial buildings, new construction; Nonresidential construction; Management services; Management consulting services; Residential construction; Industrial buildings, new construction; Nonresidential construction; Management services; Management consulting services
Pr: Ralph Esposito
**Treas:* Brad Robinson
VP: John Anania
Mng Dir: Daniel Labbad
IT Man: Dennis Griffeth

D-U-N-S 00-759-5861
LEND LEASE (US) INC
(*Suby of* LEND LEASE CONSTRUCTION HOLDINGS (EMEA) LIMITED)
250 Civic Center Dr, New York, NY 10166
Tel (212) 592-6700 *Founded/Ownrshp* 1992
Sales 288.4MM^E *EMP* 3,097
SIC 6799 6552 Investors; Subdividers & developers; Investors; Subdividers & developers
Pr: Peter A Marchetto

D-U-N-S 08-722-2936
LEND LEASE (US) PUBLIC PARTNERSHIPS LLC
(*Suby of* LENDLEASE CORPORATION LIMITED)
1801 West End Ave # 1700, Nashville, TN 37203-2526
Tel (615) 324-8800 *Founded/Ownrshp* 1999
Sales 143.3MM^E *EMP* 399
SIC 1522 Residential construction; Residential construction
Ex VP: Bruce Anderson
**CFO:* Simon Benson
**Treas:* Brad Robinson
Mng Dir: Peter Brecht
Mng Dir: Murray Coleman
Mng Dir: Eduardo Sposito
Genl Mgr: Ann Arnold
QC Dir: Tim Kelley
Sfty Mgr: James Steinke

D-U-N-S 02-750-0848
LEND LEASE AMERICAS INC
200 Park Ave Fl 9, New York, NY 10166-0999
Tel (212) 592-6700 *Founded/Ownrshp* 1997
Sales 152.1MM^E *EMP* 450
SIC 1542 1541 Nonresidential construction; Industrial buildings & warehouses; Nonresidential construction; Industrial buildings & warehouses

D-U-N-S 17-858-2347
LEND LEASE APARTMENT MANAGEMENT LLC
(*Suby of* WINNRESIDENTIAL LIMITED PARTNERSHIP) ★
6 Faneuil Hall Market Pl, Boston, MA 02109-6115
Tel (617) 742-4500 *Founded/Ownrshp* 2005
Sales 176.6M^E *EMP* 474^E
SIC 7513 Truck leasing, without drivers
Pr: Samuel Ross

D-U-N-S 12-780-7704 IMP
LENDERLIVE NETWORK INC
710 S Ash St Ste 200, Denver, CO 80246-1989
Tel (303) 226-8000 *Founded/Ownrshp* 1999
Sales 121.6MM^E *EMP* 376^E
SIC 4813 6163 ; Loan brokers; ; Loan brokers
CEO: Rick Seehausen
COO: Dick Solheim
CFO: Adam Nichols
Chf Mktg O: Kim Starley
Sr VP: Donna Clayton
Sr VP: Steve Crawford
Sr VP: Len Franco
Sr VP: Bob Fulton
Sr VP: Richard R Holsclaw
Sr VP: Kevin Kelley
Sr VP: Jan Kidder
Sr VP: Karen Morehart
Sr VP: Reid Nelson
Sr VP: Eric Prosperi
Sr VP: Chris Sabbe
Sr VP: Richard Sauerwein
Sr VP: Mitch Tanenbaum
VP: Pete Butler
VP: Bob Crittenden
VP: Tom Hecker
VP: Eric Seabrook

D-U-N-S 00-302-8953
LENDERS GROUP LLC
3160 Camino Del Rio S # 103, San Diego, CA 92108-3813
Tel (619) 574-4880 *Founded/Ownrshp* 1997
Sales NA *EMP* 3^E
SIC 6163 Mortgage brokers arranging for loans, using money of others; Mortgage brokers arranging for loans, using money of others
**Bd of Dir:* Patricia Moore

D-U-N-S 60-758-3978
■ **LENDERS TITLE CO INC**
(*Suby of* IBERIA FINANCIAL SERVICES) ★
1 Allied Dr Ste 1710, Little Rock, AR 72202-2069
Tel (501) 225-3519 *Founded/Ownrshp* 2007
Sales NA *EMP* 138
SIC 6411 Insurance agents
CEO: L Duncan Miller

D-U-N-S 88-353-4281
LENDING SOLUTIONS INC
2200 Point Blvd Ste 110, Elgin, IL 60123-7868
Tel (847) 844-2200 *Founded/Ownrshp* 1994
Sales NA *EMP* 400
SIC 6153 7389 Short-term business credit; Short-term business credit; Financial services
Ch: Mark E Johnson
**Pr:* Lee Kolquist
Pr: Robert Macari
**CEO:* David Kushner
Sr Cor Off: Kathleen Burgess
**Ex VP:* Dave Brooke
VP: Jeff Frantz
**VP:* Mike Karst
VP: Jim Milano
**VP:* Thomas R Zak
Brnch Mgr: Joseph Provenzano

D-U-N-S 80-122-0836
▲ **LENDINGCLUB CORP**
71 Stevenson St Ste 300, San Francisco, CA 94105-2985
Tel (415) 632-5600 *Founded/Ownrshp* 2006
Sales NA *EMP* 843^E
Accts Deloitte & Touche Llp San Fra
Tkr Sym LC *Exch* NYS
SIC 6163 Loan brokers; Loan brokers
CEO: Renaud Laplanche
Pr: Avia Kay
Pr: Kolya Klimenko
CFO: Carrie Dolan
Bd of Dir: Lorien Gabel
Chf Mktg O: Scott Sanborn
Sr VP: Darin Cline
Sr VP: Bruce Marcellus
Sr VP: Zhi Zhou
VP: Jeffrey Barlow
VP: Darrell Davis
VP: Andrew Deringer
VP: Roger Dickerson
VP: Tom Green
VP: Beth Haiken
VP: Mitchel Harad
VP: Kal Majmundar
VP: Mike Norris
VP: Paul Rosenfeld
Dir Risk M: Chaomei Chen
Dir Risk M: Ed Tang
Board of Directors: Daniel Ciporin, Jeffrey Crowe, Rebecca Lynn, John J Mack, Mary Meeker, John C Morris, Lawrence Summers, Simon Williams

D-U-N-S 82-818-4429
▲ **LENDINGTREE INC**
11115 Rushmore Dr, Charlotte, NC 28277-3442
Tel (704) 541-5351 *Founded/Ownrshp* 2008
Sales NA *EMP* 218^E
Tkr Sym TREE *Exch* NGM
SIC 6163 6531 Loan brokers; Real estate brokers & agents; Loan brokers; Real estate brokers & agents
Ch Bd: Douglas R Lebda
Treas: Keith B Hall
Chf Mktg O: Gabriel Dalporto
VP: Bruce Cook
VP: Teri Didjurgis
VP: Julie Hackett
VP: Lowell Orelup
VP: Victor Vaca
VP: Brian Walby
Board of Directors: Neal Dermer, Robin Henderson, Peter Horan, Steven Ozonian, Craig Troyer

D-U-N-S 03-647-5671
■ **LENDINGTREE LLC**
(*Suby of* LENDINGTREE INC) ★
11115 Rushmore Dr, Charlotte, NC 28277-3442
Tel (704) 541-5351 *Founded/Ownrshp* 1996, 2008
Sales NA *EMP* 190^E
SIC 6163 Loan brokers; Loan brokers
CEO: Dough Lebda
**Pr:* Gabriel Dalporto
**CFO:* Alex Mandel
**Sr VP:* Claudette Hampton
Sr VP: Sam Mischner
**Sr VP:* Katharine Pierce
Sr VP: Fred Saunders
VP: Paul Huckabone
Prgrm Mgr: Zeal Shah
Off Admin: Chelsea Usack
Mktg Mgr: Rich Finch
Board of Directors: Michael Devico, Richard Field, Robert Kennedy, Daniel Lieber, Robert A Spass, W James Tozer Jr

D-U-N-S 95-848-3414
LENDMARK FINANCIAL SERVICES LLC
2118 Usher St Nw, Covington, GA 30014-2434
Tel (678) 625-6500 *Founded/Ownrshp* 2013
Sales NA *EMP* 500
SIC 6162 Loan correspondents; Loan correspondents
CEO: Robert W Aiken
Pr: Melanie Henry
Pr: Vincent Kelley
**CFO:* Wayne Taylor
Chf Cred: Al Appelman
Chf Mktg O: Ethan Andelman
Sr VP: Robert Greenhaw
VP: Rick Clayton
VP: Richard Davis
VP: Becky Hewison
VP: Zaheer Khan
VP: Steve Marousek
VP: Chris McKinley
VP: Daren Thomas
VP: Brian Waichunas
VP: Kerry Ward

D-U-N-S 62-214-2834
■ **LENEL SYSTEMS INTERNATIONAL INC**
(*Suby of* UNITED TECHNOLOGIES CORP) ★
1212 Pittsford Victor Rd, Pittsford, NY 14534-3820
Tel (585) 248-9720 *Founded/Ownrshp* 1991
Sales 20.7MM^E *EMP* 120
SIC 7382 Fire alarm maintenance & monitoring
Pr: Joe Kirmser
**Pr:* Luis Oreeboso
VP: Paul Dipeso
VP: Louis Jordan
VP: Johnathan Marcioli
VP: Michael Regelski
VP: Jamile Track
VP: Dante Volpe
Exec: Laura Cameron
Exec: William Herring
Prgrm Mgr: Brian Gregory

LENEXA
See TALLGRASS TECHNOLOGIES LLC

D-U-N-S 06-575-6868
LENEXA HOTEL LP
CROWNE PLZ HTL KS-OVRLND PK
730 New Hampshire St # 206, Lawrence, KS 66044-2736
Tel (785) 841-3100 *Founded/Ownrshp* 1979
Sales 22.1MM^E *EMP* 644
SIC 7011 Hotel, franchised; Hotel, franchised
Pr: Stephen J Craig

D-U-N-S 12-658-7059
LENFEST GROUP L L C
300 Barr Harbor Dr # 460, Conshohocken, PA 19428-2984
Tel (610) 940-0815 *Founded/Ownrshp* 1999
Sales 37.1MM^E *EMP* 400
SIC 5065 5963 7371 Electronic parts & equipment; Direct sales, telemarketing; Computer software development; Electronic parts & equipment; Direct sales, telemarketing; Computer software development

LENIHAN JEEP
See LENIHAN OLDSMOBILE JEEP INC

D-U-N-S 02-250-8043
LENIHAN OLDSMOBILE JEEP INC
LENIHAN JEEP
451 Route 73 S, Marlton, NJ 08053-9698
Tel (856) 983-3800 *Founded/Ownrshp* 1970
Sales 21.1MM^E *EMP* 70
SIC 5511 Automobiles, new & used; Automobiles, new & used
Pr: Thomas Lenihan
Exec: Joe Lenihan

D-U-N-S 14-878-9626 EXP
LENIX OFFICE & GENERAL SUPPLIES LLC
(*Suby of* BADAFI, S.A. DE C.V.)
6400 S 28th St, McAllen, TX 78503-8516
Tel (956) 971-9545 *Founded/Ownrshp* 2003
Sales 71.8MM^E *EMP* 500
SIC 5943 Office forms & supplies; Office forms & supplies
Owner: Alfredo Bada
**Genl Mgr:* Karina Castro

D-U-N-S 00-450-0575 EXP
LENMORE INC (PA)
WIMCO METALS
401 Penn Ave, Pittsburgh, PA 15221-2135
Tel (412) 243-8000 *Founded/Ownrshp* 1915
Sales 120.3MM *EMP* 30
Accts Lally Co Pittsburgh Pa
SIC 5093 Nonferrous metals scrap; Nonferrous metals scrap
CEO: Glen S Gross
**Pr:* Morris E Gross

LENNAR BUILDERS
See LENNAR HOMES OF CALIFORNIA INC

D-U-N-S 06-126-0857
■ **LENNAR CAROLINA LLC**
(*Suby of* LENNAR CORP) ★
11230 Carmel Commons Blvd, Charlotte, NC 28226-3920
Tel (704) 542-8300 *Founded/Ownrshp* 1997
Sales 20.4MM^E *EMP* 67
SIC 1521 Single-family housing construction
Genl Mgr: Mark Taylor
Off Mgr: Christina Thurman
Sls Mgr: Tim Samuels

D-U-N-S 14-012-9474
LENNAR COLORADO LLC
9781 S Meridian Blvd, Englewood, CO 80112-5934
Tel (303) 754-0600 *Founded/Ownrshp* 2003
Sales 24.1MM^E *EMP* 130
SIC 1521 New construction, single-family houses; New construction, single-family houses
Opers Mgr: Mark Chapman
VP Sls: Michael Veliz

D-U-N-S 05-537-8061 EXP
▲ **LENNAR CORP**
700 Nw 107th Ave Ste 400, Miami, FL 33172-3154
Tel (305) 559-4000 *Founded/Ownrshp* 1954
Sales 7.7MMM *EMP* 6,825^E
Tkr Sym LEN *Exch* NYS
SIC 1531 6552 6163 Operative builders; Condominium developers; Townhouse developers; Subdividers & developers; Loan brokers; Operative builders; Condominium developers; Townhouse developers; Subdividers & developers; Loan brokers
CEO: Stuart A Miller
Pr: Richard Beckwitt
Pr: Tim Kent
COO: Jonathan M Jaffe
CFO: Bruce E Gross
Treas: Diane J Bessette
Ex VP: Tom Lytle
Ex VP: Robert Santos
VP: Mark Bacon
VP: Marc Chasman
VP: Erland K Horner
VP: John Jessup
VP: Dan Raatjes
VP: Anita Reynoso
VP: Glenn Richmond
VP: Eric Sergi
Dir Risk M: Jessica Rodriguez
Comm Man: Courtney Lee
Board of Directors: Irving Bolotin, Steven L Gerard, Theron I Gilliam, Sherrill W Hudson, R Kirk Landon, Sidney Lapidus, Teri P McClure, Armando Olivera, Jeffrey Sonnenfeld

D-U-N-S 96-674-4091
LENNAR CORP SEVERANCE VEBA TR
700 Nw 107th Ave Ste 400, Miami, FL 33172-3154
Tel (305) 229-6400 *Founded/Ownrshp* 2011
Sales 23.7MM *EMP* 2^E
SIC 6733 Trusts; Trusts
Prin: Alberto Furmanski

D-U-N-S 60-734-2284
■ **LENNAR FINANCIAL SERVICES LLC**
(*Suby of* US HOME) ★
700 Nw 107th Ave Ste 400, Miami, FL 33172-3139
Tel (305) 559-4000 *Founded/Ownrshp* 2002
Sales NA *EMP* 2,000^E
SIC 6162 6153 6361 6411 7382 Mortgage bankers; Short-term business credit; Title insurance; Insurance agents, brokers & service; Security systems services; Mortgage bankers; Short-term business credit; Title insurance; Insurance agents, brokers & service; Security systems services
Pr: David McCain
**CFO:* Nancy Kaminsky
**Ch:* Allan Pekor
**Treas:* Janice Munoz
**Ex VP:* Linda Reed
VP: Diane Bessette
VP: John Jessup
IT Man: Brian Seveland

D-U-N-S 03-249-7497 EXP
■ **LENNAR HOMES INC**
(*Suby of* LENNAR CORP) ★
730 Nw 107th Ave Ste 300, Miami, FL 33172-3104
Tel (305) 559-4000 *Founded/Ownrshp* 1969
Sales 414.9MM^E *EMP* 600
SIC 1531 Operative builders; Operative builders
Pr: Stuart A Miller
**Pr:* Rick Beckwitt
Pr: Ric Rojas
**COO:* Jonathan M Jaffe
COO: Samantha Thompson
CFO: Miguel Avila
**VP:* Diane J Bessette
**VP:* Bruce Gross
**VP:* Janice Munoz
Mktg Dir: Tim Farley
Mktg Dir: Nury Rodriguez

D-U-N-S 12-947-5534 IMP
■ **LENNAR HOMES LLC**
(*Suby of* LENNAR CORP) ★
700 Nw 107th Ave Ste 400, Miami, FL 33172-3139
Tel (305) 559-4000 *Founded/Ownrshp* 1954
Sales 168.4MM^E *EMP* 325^E
SIC 1531 Operative builders; Operative builders
Treas: Jacqui Desouza
VP: Bruce Ramsey
IT Man: Joe Timme
Sales Asso: Kathy Eller
Nrsg Dir: Teri Lytel

D-U-N-S 94-951-9342
■ **LENNAR HOMES OF CALIFORNIA INC**
LENNAR BUILDERS
(*Suby of* LENNAR HOMES INC) ★
25 Enterprise Ste 400, Aliso Viejo, CA 92656-2712
Tel (949) 349-8000 *Founded/Ownrshp* 1996
Sales 56.5MM^E *EMP* 311
SIC 6531 6552 Appraiser, real estate; Subdividers & developers; Appraiser, real estate; Subdividers & developers
CEO: Stuart Miller
Genl Mgr: Caroline Koschel
VP Opers: Bob Tummolo
Manager: Fiona Didomenico

LENNAR MULTI FAMILY COMMUNITY
See LMC HOLLYWOOD HIGHLAND HOLDINGS LLC

LENNOX
See INNOVATIVE HEARTH PRODUCTS LLC

D-U-N-S 00-528-8840 IMP/EXP
■ **LENNOX INDUSTRIES INC**
(*Suby of* LENNOX INTERNATIONAL INC) ★
2100 Lake Park Blvd, Richardson, TX 75080-2254
Tel (972) 497-5000 *Founded/Ownrshp* 1904
Sales 560.2MM^E *EMP* 5,500
SIC 3585

D-U-N-S 13-956-4538 EXP
▲ **LENNOX INTERNATIONAL INC**
2100 Lake Park Blvd, Richardson, TX 75080-2254
Tel (972) 497-5000 *Founded/Ownrshp* 1895
Sales 3.3MMM *EMP* 9,800
Accts Kpmg Llp Dallas Texas
Tkr Sym LII *Exch* NYS
SIC 3585 3621 Refrigeration & heating equipment; Furnaces, warm air: electric; Air conditioning units, complete: domestic or industrial; Refrigeration equipment, complete; Coils, for electric motors or generators; Refrigeration & heating equipment; Furnaces, warm air: electric; Air conditioning units, complete: domestic or industrial; Refrigeration equipment, complete; Coils, for electric motors or generators
Ch Bd: Todd M Bluedorn
CFO: Susan Carter
CFO: Joseph W Reitmeier
Sr Cor Off: Daniel Scssa
Ofcr: William F Stoll
Ex VP: Prakash Bedapudi
Ex VP: Scott J Boxer
VP: David Dorsctt
VP: Les Gibson
VP: Kevin Harsey
VP: Otis Hayes
VP: Andrea Heaberg
VP: Tim Macguire
VP: Rick Marrale
VP: Gary McGuire
VP: Luanna Millot
VP: Rick Pclini
VP: Roy A Rumbough Jr
Board of Directors: Todd J Teske, Janet K Cooper, Richard L Thompson, C L Henry, John E Major, John W Morris III, Karen H Quintos, Kim K W Rucker, Paul W Schmidt, Terry D Stinson, Gregory T Swienton

D-U-N-S 06-381-5955
■ **LENNOX NATIONAL ACCOUNT SERVICES LLC**
INDUSTRIAL BUILDING SERVICES
(*Suby of* LENNOX INDUSTRIES INC) ★
3511 Ne 22nd Ave Ste 300, Fort Lauderdale, FL 33308-6261
Tel (954) 537-5544 *Founded/Ownrshp* 1982
Sales 28.6MM^E *EMP* 170
SIC 8721 Accounting services, except auditing; Accounting services, except auditing
CFO: David Silko
Opers Mgr: Dave Hansen

D-U-N-S 01-265-7227
LENNOX SCHOOL DISTRICT
10319 Firmona Ave, Inglewood, CA 90304-1419
Tel (310) 330-4950 *Founded/Ownrshp* 1945
Sales 36.4MM^E *EMP* 585
SIC 8211 Public elementary & secondary schools; Public elementary & secondary schools
Bd of Dir: Marisol Cruz
Bd of Dir: Veronica Renteria
Bd of Dir: Jerardo Usquiano
Bd of Dir: Maria Verduzco-Smith

D-U-N-S 83-867-2202
LENNY & VINNYS INC
533 S Howard Ave Ste 3, Tampa, FL 33606-2063
Tel (813) 254-3929 *Founded/Ownrshp* 1991
Sales 5.2MM^E *EMP* 350
SIC 5812 Pizza restaurants; Pizza restaurants
Pr: Paul Samson

D-U-N-S 82-871-8846
LENOIR CITY FORD INC
775 Highway 321 N, Lenoir City, TN 37771-6547
Tel (865) 988-0003 *Founded/Ownrshp* 2006
Sales 20.2MM^E *EMP* 45
SIC 5511 Automobiles, new & used
Pr: Jim Allen
Sls Mgr: Breck Davis
Sls Mgr: Wayne Minor

D-U-N-S 00-969-0264
LENOIR CITY UTILITIES BOARD
LCUB
200 Depot St, Lenoir City, TN 37771-2917
Tel (865) 376-4421 *Founded/Ownrshp* 1938
Sales 109.6MM^E *EMP* 134
SIC 4911 Distribution, electric power; Distribution, electric power
Genl Mgr: Freddie Nelson
VP: Jinni Redmond
Brnch Mgr: Richard Martin

LENOIR COUNTY
See COUNTY OF LENOIR

D-U-N-S 07-557-9847
LENOIR COUNTY BOARD OF EDUCATION INC
2017 W Vernon Ave, Kinston, NC 28504-3329
Tel (252) 527-1109 *Founded/Ownrshp* 1920
Sales 56.1MM^E *EMP* 1,400
SIC 8211 Public elementary & secondary schools; School board; Public elementary & secondary schools; School board

D-U-N-S 07-979-8926
LENOIR COUNTY PUBLIC SCHOOLS
2017 W Vernon Ave, Kinston, NC 28504-3329
Tel (252) 527-1109 *Founded/Ownrshp* 2015
Sales 34.1MM^E *EMP* 1,128^E
SIC 8211 Public elementary & secondary schools
MIS Dir: Sheila Heath
Pr Dir: Patrick Holmes
Teacher Pr: Robin Roberson

D-U-N-S 07-201-0093
LENOIR MEMORIAL HOSPITAL INC
DOWN EAST MEDICAL SUPPLY
100 Airport Rd, Kinston, NC 28501-1634
Tel (252) 522-7000 *Founded/Ownrshp* 1950
Sales 94.8MM *EMP* 811
SIC 8062 General medical & surgical hospitals; General medical & surgical hospitals
Pr: Gary Black
Chf Path: Michael Haddad
**CFO:* Sarah Mayo
**Treas:* Mary Cauley
Dir Risk M: Donna Floyd
Dir Rad: Mark Adkins
Dir Rad: Andrej Hnatov
Dir Rx: Dale Hardy
Prac Mgr: Debora Kilmer
CIO: Karl Vanderstouw
Dir IT: Jeff Hastings

D-U-N-S 00-315-6213
LENOIR MIRROR CO (NC)
401 Kincaid St, Lenoir, NC 28645-9476
Tel (828) 728-3271 *Founded/Ownrshp* 1929
Sales 27.8MM^E *EMP* 155
SIC 3231 Mirrored glass; Furniture tops, glass: cut, beveled or polished; Doors, glass: made from purchased glass; Mirrored glass; Furniture tops, glass: cut, beveled or polished; Doors, glass: made from purchased glass
Ch Bd: A G Jonas Jr
**Pr:* Drew Mayberry
**Treas:* Myron L Moore Jr
IT Man: Bill Austin
IT Man: Jack Beve
Trfc Mgr: Terry Simmons
Mktg Dir: Reginald Greene

D-U-N-S 06-630-0153
LENOIR-RHYNE UNIVERSITY (NC)
625 7th Ave Ne, Hickory, NC 28601-3984
Tel (828) 328-1741 *Founded/Ownrshp* 1891
Sales 45.6MM^E *EMP* 400
Accts Mcgladrey Llp Greensboro Nc
SIC 8221 Colleges universities & professional schools; Colleges universities & professional schools
Pr: Dr Wayne B Powell
**Ex VP:* Larry M Hall
VP: Brent Heaberlin
**VP:* Peter Kendall
VP: Scott Shrode
Exec: Ann Blackmon
Ex Dir: Debbie Punch
CIO: Ben Talley
Mktg Dir: Mike Langford

D-U-N-S 02-912-2207 IMP
LENORE JOHN & CO
1250 Delevan Dr, San Diego, CA 92102-2437
Tel (619) 232-6136 *Founded/Ownrshp* 1966
Sales 143.9MM^E *EMP* 270
SIC 5149 5182 5181 Soft drinks; Mineral or spring water bottling; Wine; Liquor; Beer & other fermented malt liquors; Soft drinks; Mineral or spring water bottling; Wine; Liquor; Beer & other fermented malt liquors
CEO: John G Lenore
**Pr:* Jamie Lenore
Dir IT: Greg Aprahamian

D-U-N-S 15-334-5173 IMP
LENOVO (UNITED STATES) INC
LENOVO INTERNATIONAL
(*Suby of* LENOVO GROUP LIMITED)
1009 Think Pl, Morrisville, NC 27560-9002
Tel (919) 294-2500 *Founded/Ownrshp* 2005
Sales 777.2MM^E *EMP* 1,968
SIC 3571 Electronic computers; Electronic computers
Ch: Yang Yuanqing
Ch Bd: Liu Chuanzhi
Pr: Liu Jun
Pr: Gianfranco Lanci
Pr: Peter Schrady
CFO: Wong W Ming
CFO: Zhou Qingtong
Chf Mktg O: Deepak Advani
Ofcr: David Roman
Sr VP: Van Duijl
Sr VP: Rory Reed
Sr VP: Gerry P Smith
Sr VP: Milko Van Duijl
VP: WEI Guan
VP: Charlie Mulgrove
Exec: John Mayr
Exec: Virginia McAfee
Comm Man: Stephanie Shi

D-U-N-S 07-909-8933
LENOVO HOLDING CO INC
1009 Think Pl, Morrisville, NC 27560-9002
Tel (919) 294-0600 *Founded/Ownrshp* 2007
Sales 137.7MM^E *EMP* 315^E
SIC 3571 Personal computers (microcomputers)
Sls Mgr: Sean Chua
Sls Mgr: Stewart Wheeler
Sales Asso: Benjamin Smith
Snr Mgr: Michel Fisher

D-U-N-S 01-097-2387 IMP
LENOVO INC
6540 Franz Warner Pkwy, Whitsett, NC 27377-9215
Tel (336) 449-9144 *Founded/Ownrshp* 2007
Sales 20.5MM^E *EMP* 32^E
SIC 3571 Electronic computers
CEO: Yang Yuanqing
**Sr VP:* Peter Hortensius
**Sr VP:* Milko Van Duijl
**Sr VP:* Chen Xudong
**Sr VP:* He Zhiqiang

LENOVO INTERNATIONAL
See LENOVO (UNITED STATES) INC

D-U-N-S 07-876-5314 IMP
LENOVO US FULFILLMENT CENTER LLC
(*Suby of* LENOVO HOLDING CO INC) ★
6540 Franz Warner Pkwy, Whitsett, NC 27377-9215
Tel (919) 294-0477 *Founded/Ownrshp* 2007
Sales 137.7MM^E *EMP* 266^E
SIC 3571 Electronic computers
Chf Mktg O: Joel Mondshane
Sr VP: David Roman
Sr VP: H Zhiqiang
VP: Timothy Carroll
VP: John Egan
VP: Paul Leslie
VP: Wilfredo Sotolongo
Ex Dir: Bill Perez
Prgrm Mgr: Robert Graziano
Sls Dir: John Veit
Snr Mgr: Kristen Iadanza

LENOX
See AMERICAN SAW & MFG CO

LENOX COLLECTIONS
See CERAMIC ART CO INC

D-U-N-S 83-002-6741
LENOX CORP
DANSK
(*Suby of* CLARION CAPITAL PARTNERS LLC) ★
1414 Radcliffe St Fl 2, Bristol, PA 19007-5418
Tel (267) 525-7800 *Founded/Ownrshp* 2009
Sales 214.3MM^E *EMP* 1,098
Accts Deloitte & Touche Llp Philadel
SIC 3229 3161 5719 5948 Tableware, glass or glass ceramic; Luggage; Briefcases; Traveling bags; China; Glassware; Luggage & leather goods stores; Tableware, glass or glass ceramic; Luggage; Briefcases; Traveling bags; China; Glassware; Luggage & leather goods stores
Pr: Lester Gribetz
Pr: Robert Bishop
**CEO:* Peter B Cameron
**COO:* Jerome Ciszewskiis
CFO: Steve Oaconnell
**Ch:* Barry Bramley
**Treas:* Stephen O'Connell
Ofcr: William Robedee
Ex VP: Bill Wieland
**Sr VP:* James Wilson
VP: Diane Bezak
VP: Julia Bunk
VP: Erin Carachilo
VP: Timothy Carder
VP: Mario Castano
VP: Robert Cohen
VP: Sherri Crisenbery
VP: David Desiderio
VP: Glenn Destefano
**VP:* David Enright
VP: Mike Lubka

D-U-N-S 10-574-6874
LENOX FINANCIAL MORTGAGE CORP
WESLEND FINANCIAL
200 Sandpointe Ave # 800, Santa Ana, CA 92707-5783
Tel (949) 428-5100 *Founded/Ownrshp* 1999
Sales NA *EMP* 105
SIC 6162 Mortgage bankers & correspondents; Mortgage bankers & correspondents
CEO: Wesley C Hoaglund

LENOX HILL HOSPITAL
See LHH CORP

LENOX HOSPITALITY
See PROCACCIANTI GROUP LLC

D-U-N-S 01-128-2977
■ **LENS REPLACEMENT INC**
SPECIALTY INSURANCE MKTG AGCY
(*Suby of* RLI CORP) ★
9025 N Lindbergh Dr, Peoria, IL 61615-1499
Tel (309) 692-1000 *Founded/Ownrshp* 1969
Sales NA *EMP* 400
SIC 6411 Insurance claim adjusters, not employed by insurance company; Insurance claim adjusters, not employed by insurance company
Pr: Gerald D Stephens
**CFO:* Joseph E Dondanville
Chf Mktg O: Brian Hoover
**Ex VP:* Jonathan E Michael
VP: Brent Flanigan
VP: Christopher Gleason
**VP:* Kim J Hensey
VP: Jeff Myers
VP: Piyush Singh
Dir IT: Carl Flower
Mktg Mgr: Charlie May

D-U-N-S 82-968-2355 IMP
LENS VISION-EASE CORP
VISION-EASE LENS
7000 Sunwood Dr Nw, Ramsey, MN 55303-5160
Tel (763) 576-3930 *Founded/Ownrshp* 2014
Sales 188.6MM^E *EMP* 1,200
SIC 3851 Eyeglasses, lenses & frames; Eyeglasses, lenses & frames
CEO: John Weber
COO: Karen Hoyt
**CFO:* Richard G Faber
**Ch:* Doug Hepper
**Treas:* Bradley D Carlson
VP: Cass Lundgren
VP: Cindy Mark
VP: Jeffrey McCurrach

IT Man: Nick George
IT Man: Todd Norman
Opers Mgr: Dennis McMahon

LENSEC
See PROGRESSIVE SYSTEMS LLC

D-U-N-S 00-700-1696 IMP
LENSING WHOLESALE INC
ARCHITECTURAL SALES DIV
600 N 6th Ave, Evansville, IN 47710-1442
Tel (812) 423-6891 *Founded/Ownrshp* 1948
Sales 40.0MM *EMP* 140
SIC 5031 5023

D-U-N-S 00-234-5502 IMP
LENTZ MILLING CO (PA)
2045 N 11th St, Reading, PA 19604-1201
Tel (610) 921-0666 *Founded/Ownrshp* 1941
Sales 112.5MM^E *EMP* 150
SIC 5149 5142 Baking supplies; Flour; Yeast; Sugar, refined; Bakery products, frozen; Baking supplies; Flour; Yeast; Sugar, refined; Bakery products, frozen
Pr: Edward T Lentz
Ofcr: Scott Gullo
**VP:* James H Lentz
VP: Ted Lentz
IT Man: Edward Himmelberger
IT Man: Justin Sherwood

D-U-N-S 03-734-0247
LENZ INC
1180 Highway 7 E, Hutchinson, MN 55350-5637
Tel (320) 587-4030 *Founded/Ownrshp* 1979
Sales 46.7MM^E *EMP* 60
SIC 5083 3523 2752 5943 7359 Farm & garden machinery; Farm machinery & equipment; Commercial printing, lithographic; Office forms & supplies; Equipment rental & leasing
Pr: Craig Lenz
**VP:* Paul Lenz
Prin: Dan Debenham

D-U-N-S 10-124-0984 IMP
LENZE AC TECH CORP
LENZE POWER TRANSMISSION
(*Suby of* LENZE OPERATIONS GMBH)
630 Douglas St, Uxbridge, MA 01569-2001
Tel (508) 278-9100 *Founded/Ownrshp* 2001
Sales 32.3MM^E *EMP* 150
SIC 7699 5085 Industrial equipment services; Power transmission equipment & apparatus; Industrial equipment services; Power transmission equipment & apparatus
CEO: Allen E Ottoson
**Pr:* Charles W Edwards
**CFO:* David Cybulski
**Treas:* Jeffrey L Donaldson
Area Mgr: Cliff Alberts
**Genl Mgr:* Gene Wood
Mktg Mgr: Deb Kling
Mktg Mgr: Merrill Martin
Mktg Mgr: Jim Spann
Manager: Larry Costigan
Manager: Jake Henry

D-U-N-S 83-125-8343 IMP
LENZE AMERICAS CORP
630 Douglas St, Uxbridge, MA 01569-2001
Tel (508) 278-9100 *Founded/Ownrshp* 2008
Sales 53.5MM^E *EMP* 59
SIC 5085 Industrial supplies
Pr: Charles W Edwards
**Pr:* Steven J Smidler
**Treas:* David Cybulski
Sr VP: Dirk Watzke
VP: Ken Mueck
Area Mgr: Gurmukh Dhadda
Dir IT: Mark Collins
Dir IT: Doug Poirier
Manager: Andre Drouin
Sls Mgr: Danny McDonald
Snr Mgr: Daniel Ducharme

LENZE POWER TRANSMISSION
See LENZE AC TECH CORP

D-U-N-S 11-950-0556 IMP/EXP
LENZING FIBERS INC
(*Suby of* LENZING AKTIENGESELLSCHAFT)
12950 Highway 43 N, Axis, AL 36505-4324
Tel (251) 679-2200 *Founded/Ownrshp* 2004
Sales 66.8MM^E *EMP* 128^E
SIC 2823 Cellulosic manmade fibers; Cellulosic manmade fibers
Ch: Michael Junghans
**Pr:* Mark Lejman
**CEO:* Kevin J Allen
**Sec:* John M Patterson
Div Mgr: Kurt Stangl
Sls Mgr: Walter Petermaier
Sls Mgr: Gerhard Soriat

LEO A DALY
See LEO A DALY CO

D-U-N-S 00-728-4011
LEO A DALY CO
LEO A DALY
8600 Indian Hills Dr, Omaha, NE 68114-4039
Tel (808) 521-8889 *Founded/Ownrshp* 1915
Sales 139.4MM *EMP* 750
Accts Bkd Llp Omaha Nebraska
SIC 8712 Architectural engineering; Architectural engineering
Ch Bd: Leo A Daly III
Pr: Dennis W Petersen
VP: Daniel Dellovechio
VP: Terry Holmes
VP: Brian Rice
Dir Bus: Christopher Johnson
Dir Bus: Cheri Pavlik
Prgrm Mgr: Owen Miyamoto
Dir IT: Edward Ockerman II
IT Man: Brian Compton
IT Man: Brooke Grammier

D-U-N-S 05-625-8379
LEO A DALY CO
LOCKWOOD, ANDREWS & NEWNAM
(*Suby of* LEO A DALY) ★
2925 Briarpark Dr Ste 400, Houston, TX 77042-3746
Tel (713) 266-6900 *Founded/Ownrshp* 1991
Sales 45.0MM^E *EMP* 284
SIC 8711 8712 Consulting engineer; Architectural engineering; Consulting engineer; Architectural engineering
Pr: Dennis Peterson
**CEO:* Leo A Daly III
**Sec:* John J Chrostek
**Sr VP:* George R Jumonville
**Sr VP:* James C Williamson
VP: J Anthony Boyd
VP: Arnie Cohen
VP: Drew Hardin
VP: W E Merrill
VP: T N Turk
VP: Joe Waterfield
Exec: Brenda Mayes

D-U-N-S 83-038-0015
LEO A DALY/BURNS & MCCONNELL JOINT VENTURE
8600 Indian Hills Dr, Omaha, NE 68114-4039
Tel (402) 391-8111 *Founded/Ownrshp* 2009
Sales 29.0MM^E *EMP* 3,000
SIC 8712 8711 Architectural services; Architectural engineering; Architectural engineering; Engineering services; Consulting engineer
Prin: Randy Pope

D-U-N-S 00-692-8956
LEO BURNETT CO INC
A R C
(*Suby of* PUBLICIS GROUPE S A)
35 W Wacker Dr Fl 21, Chicago, IL 60601-1755
Tel (312) 220-5959 *Founded/Ownrshp* 1999, 2002
Sales 202.7MM^E *EMP* 2,000^E
SIC 7311 3993 Advertising agencies; Signs & advertising specialties; Advertising agencies; Signs & advertising specialties
CEO: Thomas L Bernardin
**Pr:* Bob Raidt
**Pr:* Richard Stoddart
CEO: Leo Burnett Milan
COO: Maher Achi
**CFO:* Patrick Dumouchel
CFO: Robert Maloney
Ofcr: Miguel A Furones
**Ex VP:* Jim Carlton
**Ex VP:* Amy Cheronis
**Ex VP:* Michelle Kristula Green
Ex VP: Nick Jones
Ex VP: Jim Mikol
Sr VP: Tony Booth
VP: Anne Rockey
Assoc Dir: Jessica Harold
Creative D: Maria Bernal
Creative D: Amanda Butts
Creative D: Kent Carmichael
Creative D: Dean Casagrande
Creative D: Bill Dillard

D-U-N-S 13-700-3153
LEO BURNETT DETROIT INC
(*Suby of* PUBLICIS GROUPE S A)
3310 W Big Beaver Rd # 107, Troy, MI 48084-2807
Tel (248) 458-8300 *Founded/Ownrshp* 1978
Sales 28.9MM^E *EMP* 155
SIC 7311 Advertising agencies; Advertising agencies
Pr: James Moore
Sr VP: Tony Booth
VP: Galen Chandler
VP: Steve Lyons
VP: Mike Muscat
VP: Paul Serra
VP: Erik Zaar
Creative D: Steve Chavez
Creative D: Jack Crifasi
Telecom Ex: Carol Biernat
Art Dir: Ron Alexander

D-U-N-S 00-590-4578 IMP
LEO D BERNSTEIN & SONS INC (NY)
BERNSTEIN DISPLAY
151 W 25th St Frnt 1, New York, NY 10001-7204
Tel (212) 337-9578 *Founded/Ownrshp* 1965
Sales 24.0MM^E *EMP* 150
SIC 3999 2541 5046 7389 Forms: display, dress & show; Store & office display cases & fixtures; Store fixtures; Store equipment; Design services; Forms: display, dress & show; Store & office display cases & fixtures; Store fixtures; Store equipment; Design services
Ch Bd: Roger Friedman
**Pr:* Anthony Tripoli
**COO:* Mitchell Bernstein
**Ch:* Edmund Bernstein
Trfc Mgr: Steve Jones

D-U-N-S 01-873-4046
LEO E KARL INC
KARL CHEVROLET COMPANY, THE
261 Elm St Ste 1, New Canaan, CT 06840-5310
Tel (203) 966-9508 *Founded/Ownrshp* 1927
Sales 24.1MM^E *EMP* 50
SIC 5511 Automobiles, new & used; Automobiles, new & used
Ch Bd: Leo E Karl Jr
**Pr:* Leo Karl III
**Treas:* Edward J Karl
Sls Mgr: Scott Sams

D-U-N-S 09-430-3310
LEO GENTRY WHOLESALE NURSERY INC
11251 Se 232nd Ave, Damascus, OR 97089-6172
Tel (503) 658-5181 *Founded/Ownrshp* 1977
Sales 53.2MM^E *EMP* 315^E
SIC 5193 Nursery stock; Nursery stock
Pr: Leo E Gentry
**VP:* Brian Gentry
**VP:* Leo Gentry II

D-U-N-S 02-801-8786
LEO HOFFMAN CHEVROLET INC
PUENTE HILLS CHEVROLET
15432 Nelson Ave, City of Industry, CA 91744-4416
Tel (626) 968-8411 *Founded/Ownrshp* 1944
Sales 49.8MM^E *EMP* 158
SIC 5511 7515 Automobiles, new & used; Passenger car leasing; Automobiles, new & used; Passenger car leasing
Pr: Thomas L Hoffman
**Treas:* Kurt Hoffman
**VP:* Gary A Campbell

D-U-N-S 00-483-9338
LEO J ROTH CORP
841 Holt Rd Ste 1, Webster, NY 14580-9200
Tel (585) 872-0220 *Founded/Ownrshp* 1955
Sales 55.4MM^E *EMP* 150
SIC 1761 1711 7699 7623 3444 Roofing contractor; Mechanical contractor; Boiler & heating repair services; Air conditioning repair; Awnings & canopies; Roofing contractor; Mechanical contractor; Boiler & heating repair services; Air conditioning repair; Awnings & canopies
Pr: Thomas Roth
**Ch Bd:* Robert Lroth
**Treas:* Donald A Fella
Ex VP: John Buren
**VP:* John C Van Buren
IT Man: Mark Easton

D-U-N-S 00-744-1777
LEO JOURNAGAN CONSTRUCTION CO INC
JOURNAGAN CNSTR & AGGREGATES
3003 E Chestnut Expy, Springfield, MO 65802-2580
Tel (417) 869-7222 *Founded/Ownrshp* 1950
Sales 86.2MM^E *EMP* 147
SIC 1422 1611 1623 Crushed & broken limestone; Highway & street construction; Sewer line construction; Crushed & broken limestone; Highway & street construction; Sewer line construction
Ch: Leo Journagan
**Pr:* Allen Journagan
**Treas:* John View
**VP:* Dale Popejoy

LEO MARTIN USED CARS
See MARTIN LEO CHEVROLET INC

D-U-N-S 83-269-2615 IMP
LEO PHARMA INC
(*Suby of* LEO PHARMA A/S)
1 Sylvan Way Ste 1, Parsippany, NJ 07054-3880
Tel (973) 637-1690 *Founded/Ownrshp* 2009
Sales 89.1MM^E *EMP* 180
SIC 5122 Pharmaceuticals; Pharmaceuticals
Pr: John Koconis
Pr: Barbara J Osborne
VP: Mitch Johnson
VP: George Padden

D-U-N-S 04-081-8718
LEO YASSENOFF JEWISH COMMUNITY CENTER OF GREATER COLUMBUS
1125 College Ave, Columbus, OH 43209-7802
Tel (614) 231-2731 *Founded/Ownrshp* 1945
Sales 11.0MM^E *EMP* 308
Accts Mcgladrey & Pullen Llp Columb
SIC 8641 8699 Social club, membership; Recreation association; Charitable organization; Social club, membership; Recreation association; Charitable organization
Ex Dir: Carol Folkerth
**CFO:* Louise Young
Bd of Dir: Julie Saar
Art Dir: Jared Saltman

D-U-N-S 80-136-9369 IMP
LEOCH BATTERY CORP
19751 Descartes Unit A, Foothill Ranch, CA 92610-2620
Tel (949) 588-5853 *Founded/Ownrshp* 2003
Sales 30.9MM^E *EMP* 11,000^E
SIC 3621 Storage battery chargers, motor & engine generator type; Storage battery chargers, motor & engine generator type
Pr: Hui Peng
Sls Dir: John Stanphill
Sls Mgr: Crystal He
Sls Mgr: Kelly Liu
Sls Mgr: Amy Yang

D-U-N-S 06-992-0528
LEOMINSTER CREDIT UNION
20 Adams St, Leominster, MA 01453-5668
Tel (978) 537-8021 *Founded/Ownrshp* 1954
Sales NA *EMP* 140
SIC 6062 6163 State credit unions, not federally chartered; Loan brokers; State credit unions, not federally chartered; Loan brokers
Ch Bd: Anthony A Gasbarro
Pr: Brenda Bujnevicie
**Pr:* John R Caulfield
Pr: Thomas Clancy
Pr: Heather Dumais
**Pr:* John J Obrien
**CEO:* Terry B Lisle
**CFO:* Gary M Abrams
**Treas:* Giulio G Greco
**V Ch Bd:* Henry Lisciotti Jr
Ofcr: Diane Farnsworth
Ofcr: June Navalany
Ofcr: Timothy Oleary
**Sr VP:* Craig S Madonia
**Sr VP:* Barbara A Mahoney
**Sr VP:* Maria Menzaro
**VP:* Donald Notaro
VP: Oscar O'Connor
**VP:* Michael J Sauvageau

D-U-N-S 83-241-8425
LEOMINSTER PUBLIC SCHOOLS
24 Church St, Leominster, MA 01453-3102
Tel (978) 534-7700 *Founded/Ownrshp* 2009
Sales 10.7MM^E *EMP* 866^E
SIC 8299 Educational services

LEON AUTOMOTIVE INTERIORS
See LEON INTERIORS INC

D-U-N-S 08-193-6650
LEON COUNTY SCHOOL BOARD
2757 W Pensacola St, Tallahassee, FL 32304-2907
Tel (850) 487-7100 *Founded/Ownrshp* 1924
Sales 198.6MM^E *EMP* 5,030
Accts David W Martin Cpa Tallahas
SIC 8211 8249 8222 Public elementary & secondary schools; Technical institute; Vocational schools; Aviation school; Public elementary & secondary schools; Vocational schools; Aviation school; Technical institute
Bd of Dir: Alva Striplin
Exec: V I Dennis
Ex Dir: Belinda Kelly
Dept Mgr: Jo Wenger
IT Man: Dale Joiner
IT Man: Tom Vogelgesang
Psych: Megan Davis
Psych: Robert Grandal

D-U-N-S 00-492-9688
LEON COUNTY SCHOOL DISTRICT
2757 W Pensacola St, Tallahassee, FL 32304-2907
Tel (850) 487-7100 *Founded/Ownrshp* 1981
Sales 129.8MM^E *EMP* 4,000^E
SIC 8211 Elementary & secondary schools; Public elementary school; Public junior high school; Public senior high school; Elementary & secondary schools; Public elementary school; Public junior high school; Public senior high school
V Ch: Dee Crumpler
CFO: Merrill Wimberley
CIO: Bill Nimmons
MIS Dir: Chris Petley
IT Man: Justin Williamson
Teacher Pr: VI Dennis

D-U-N-S 00-241-2096
LEON D DEMATTEIS CONSTRUCTION CORP
DE MATTEIS ORGANIZATION
820 Elmont Rd, Elmont, NY 11003-4026
Tel (516) 285-5500 *Founded/Ownrshp* 1946
Sales 22.0MM^E *EMP* 50
SIC 1542 1522 Nonresidential construction; Residential construction
Ch Bd: Richard De Matteis
**Sec:* Steve Mezick
**Ex VP:* Al Di Meo
VP: Steve Tartaro
**Exec:* Scott De Matteis
Snr PM: Paul Nardone

D-U-N-S 06-979-0863
LEON E WINTERMYER INC
(*Suby of* LEW HOLDING CO INC) ★
220 Yocumtown Rd, Etters, PA 17319-9006
Tel (717) 938-1468 *Founded/Ownrshp* 1968
Sales 20.1MM^E *EMP* 120
SIC 1794 Excavation work; Excavation work
Pr: Leon E Wintermyer

D-U-N-S 03-349-9666
LEON FARMER AND CO
100 Rail Ridge Rd, Athens, GA 30607-1337
Tel (706) 353-1166 *Founded/Ownrshp* 1983
Sales 52.6MM^E *EMP* 180
SIC 5181 Beer & other fermented malt liquors; Beer & other fermented malt liquors
CEO: H Leon Farmer Jr
**Pr:* H Leon Farmer III
**Treas:* Tim Mackey
**Ex VP:* Victoria P Farmer
Sr VP: Mickey Register
VP: Herb Brackin
Sales Exec: Randy Dover
Mktg Mgr: Sierra Sandusky

D-U-N-S 07-844-0875
LEON FLAGLER HOLDINGS LLC
LEON MEDICAL CENTER
(*Suby of* LEON MEDICAL CENTERS INC) ★
7950 Nw 5th Ct, Miami, FL 33150-2833
Tel (305) 631-3900 *Founded/Ownrshp* 2008
Sales 30.3MM^E *EMP* 1,892^E
SIC 8011 Offices & clinics of medical doctors
Pharmcst: Luis Marquez

D-U-N-S 11-872-3170 IMP
LEON INTERIORS INC
LEON AUTOMOTIVE INTERIORS
(*Suby of* MOTUS INTEGRATED TECHNOLOGIES) ★
4901 Clay Ave Sw, Grand Rapids, MI 49548-3074
Tel (616) 531-7970 *Founded/Ownrshp* 2015
Sales 271.3MM^E *EMP* 600
SIC 3089 3714 3086 Molding primary plastic; Motor vehicle parts & accessories; Plastics foam products; Molding primary plastic; Motor vehicle parts & accessories; Plastics foam products
CEO: Ed McAvoy
CFO: Mike Rondeau
**Treas:* Chris Afendoulis

D-U-N-S 00-174-9845 IMP
LEON KOROL CO
2050 E Devon Ave, Elk Grove Village, IL 60007-6037
Tel (847) 725-2200 *Founded/Ownrshp* 1959
Sales 41.0MM^E *EMP* 64
SIC 5099 Novelties, durable; Novelties, durable
Pr: Steve Korol
**VP:* Gary Korol
VP: Al Silcroft

D-U-N-S 03-824-5733
LEON LEVINE PROPERTIES LTD
6000 Fairview Rd Ste 1525, Charlotte, NC 28210-2212
Tel (704) 817-6506 *Founded/Ownrshp* 2010
Sales 21.5MM *EMP* 2^E
SIC 6512 Nonresidential building operators
Prin: Leon Levine

D-U-N-S 07-850-3015
LEON MANAGEMENT INTERNATIONAL INC (FL)
11501 Sw 40th St Fl 2, Miami, FL 33165-3313
Tel (305) 642-5366 *Founded/Ownrshp* 2012
Sales 160.8MM^E *EMP* 1,904^E
SIC 8741 Business management
Pr: Benjamin Leon III
Ch: Benjamin J Leon
Treas: Silvia Leon
VP: Silvia J Maury

LEON MEDICAL CENTER
See LEON FLAGLER HOLDINGS LLC

D-U-N-S 94-723-7210 EXP
LEON MEDICAL CENTERS INC
(*Suby of* LEON MANAGEMENT INTERNATIONAL INC) ★
11501 Sw 40th St, Miami, FL 33165-3313
Tel (305) 559-2881 *Founded/Ownrshp* 1986
Sales 160.8MM^E *EMP* 1,900
SIC 8011 Offices & clinics of medical doctors; Medical centers; Offices & clinics of medical doctors; Medical centers
Pr: Benjamin Leon Jr
**Pr:* Benjamin I Leon
**Treas:* Silvia Leon
**Sec:* Lourdes Leon
VP: Marcus Gomez Sr
VP: Carlos Nuez Sr
Off Mgr: Clara Aragno

D-U-N-S 00-248-9375
LEON N WEINER & ASSOCIATES INC
1 Fox Pt Ctr 4 Denny Rd, Wilmington, DE 19809
Tel (302) 656-1354 *Founded/Ownrshp* 1961
Sales 52.4MM^E *EMP* 220
SIC 6552 1521 1542 Subdividers & developers; New construction, single-family houses; Commercial & office building, new construction
Pr: Kevin P Kelly
**Treas:* Christopher Bartges
**Ex VP:* David Curtis
**Sr VP:* Glenn Brooks
**VP:* William Demarco
**VP:* John Gorlich
VP: Himanshu Patel
**VP:* Thomas Perkins
Dir IT: William Marco
Sales Exec: Joe Cimino
Sales Exec: Jillian Raczkowski

LEONA GROUP ARIZONA
See SMITH ACADEMY FOR EXCELLENCE INC

LEONA GROUP ARIZONA
See LEONA GROUP L L C

D-U-N-S 01-545-2535
LEONA GROUP L L C
2125 University Park Dr # 250, Okemos, MI 48864-5903
Tel (517) 333-9030 *Founded/Ownrshp* 1996
Sales 115.1MM^E *EMP* 1,200^E
SIC 8742 Management consulting services; Management consulting services
CEO: William Coats

D-U-N-S 87-623-7012
LEONA GROUP L L C
LEONA GROUP ARIZONA
7878 N 16th St Ste 150, Phoenix, AZ 85020-4470
Tel (480) 726-9536 *Founded/Ownrshp* 1997
Sales 68.8MM^E *EMP* 1,600
SIC 8211 Private junior high school; Private junior high school
CEO: Dr Bill Coats
**COO:* Michele Kaye
Ex VP: Derrick Shelton
Comm Dir: Madalyn Kaltz
Off Mgr: Kathy Thommasson
Off Admin: Vanessa Roman

D-U-N-S 96-795-6033
LEONA M AND HARRY B HELMSLEY CHARITABLE TRUST
230 Park Ave, New York, NY 10169-0005
Tel (212) 679-3600 *Founded/Ownrshp* 2011
Sales 175.4MM *EMP* 16^E
SIC 6733 Trusts; Trusts
CEO: John R Ettinger
CFO: Leigh Bonney
Ofcr: Rachel Norman
Genl Couns: Sarah E Paul

D-U-N-S 00-814-3372
LEONARD & HARRAL PACKING CO
L&H PACKING
(*Suby of* LEONARD FAMILY CORP) ★
647 Steves Ave, San Antonio, TX 78210-3819
Tel (210) 532-3241 *Founded/Ownrshp* 1994
Sales 78.2MM^E *EMP* 365
SIC 2011 5147 2077 2048 Meat by-products from meat slaughtered on site; Meats, fresh; Animal & marine fats & oils; Prepared feeds; Meat by-products from meat slaughtered on site; Meats, fresh; Animal & marine fats & oils; Prepared feeds
Ch Bd: K E Leonard
Pr: Justin Still
CEO: Kenneth E Leonard
COO: Neal Leonard
CFO: Russell Faldik
Sec: Marvin Eggleston

D-U-N-S 04-294-9172
LEONARD ALUMINUM UTILITY BUILDINGS INC
LEONARD BUILDING & TRCK COVERS
566 Holly Springs Rd, Mount Airy, NC 27030-8081
Tel (304) 425-7141 *Founded/Ownrshp* 1967
Sales 83.5MM^E *EMP* 150
SIC 5531 3448 Truck equipment & parts; Prefabricated metal buildings; Carports: prefabricated metal; Truck equipment & parts; Prefabricated metal buildings
Pr: Sandra P Leonard
**CEO:* David Oneal

*COO: Bruce Strohl
*VP: Michael J Leonard
Dir IT: Scott Muller
Sfty Mgr: Eddie Long
Genl Couns: Rick Pepin

D-U-N-S 96-951-4525
LEONARD AND BERYL BUCK FOUNDATION
600 California St, San Francisco, CA 94108-2704
Tel (415) 396-3737 Founded/Ownrshp 2011
Sales 49.1MM EMP 3E
Accts Burr Pilger Mayer Inc San F
SIC 8641 Civic social & fraternal associations; Civic social & fraternal associations

LEONARD BUILDING & TRCK COVERS
See LEONARD ALUMINUM UTILITY BUILDINGS INC

D-U-N-S 06-378-7337
LEONARD BUS SALES INC
4 Leonard Way, Deposit, NY 13754-1240
Tel (607) 467-3100 Founded/Ownrshp 1965
Sales 36.8MME EMP 120
SIC 5012 Buses; Buses
Pr: Michael Leonard
COO: Gina Dubois
*VP: Edward Joyce
*VP: Barbara R Leonard
Genl Mgr: Dave Rindo
Opers Mgr: Bill Harvey
Sls Dir: Rick Pranitis

D-U-N-S 00-279-1317
LEONARD E BELCHER INC (MA)
L E BELCHER
615 Saint James Ave, Springfield, MA 01109-3833
Tel (413) 736-8324 Founded/Ownrshp 1933, 1951
Sales 56.9MME EMP 30
SIC 5172 5541 Petroleum products; Gasoline service stations
Pr: Edward C Hough
*CFO: Christine C Devin
*CFO: David F Ryan
*VP: Michael Natale
IT Man: Kristopher Gobeille
Sls Mgr: Jonathon Barber
Sls Mgr: Jimmy Gianfelice

D-U-N-S 83-542-0001
LEONARD FAMILY CORP
647 Steves Ave, San Antonio, TX 78210-3819
Tel (210) 532-3241 Founded/Ownrshp 1994
Sales 163.4MME EMP 605
SIC 5147 Meats, fresh; Meats, fresh
Pr: Kenneth E Leonard
CFO: Russell Saldik
VP: Neal Leonard

LEONARD FLRENCE CTR FOR LIVING
See CHELSEA JEWISH GREEN HOUSE INC

D-U-N-S 61-680-5719 IMP
LEONARD GREEN & PARTNERS LP
11111 Santa Monica Blvd # 2000, Los Angeles, CA 90025-3354
Tel (310) 954-0444 Founded/Ownrshp 1989
Sales 4.3MMME EMP 14,266
SIC 6211 Investment bankers; Investment bankers
Pt: Jonathan D Sokoloff
*Pt: John M Baumer
*Pt: John G Danhakl
*Pt: James Halper
*Pt: Peter J Nolan
*Pt: Jonathan A Sciffer
*COO: Lily W Chang
*CFO: Cody L Franklin
Ofcr: Reginald Holden
VP: Jeffrey Suer
CIO: Lynn Cicalo

D-U-N-S 09-328-1400
LEONARD INSURANCE SERVICES AGENCY INC
(Suby of DAWSON INSURANCE INC) ★
4244 Mount Pleasant St Nw, Canton, OH 44720-5469
Tel (330) 266-1904 Founded/Ownrshp 2014
Sales NA EMP 58E
SIC 6411 Insurance agents, brokers & service
Pr: W Fred Kloots Jr
Sr VP: Todd Witham
VP: Paul Cruciani
VP: John Fink
VP: Richard Martindale
VP: Perry Schlabach
VP: Jon Smith
VP: W Todd Witham
Doctor: Marsha Dunn

D-U-N-S 00-309-7425
LEONARD PAPER CO (MD)
725 N Haven St, Baltimore, MD 21205-2903
Tel (410) 563-0800 Founded/Ownrshp 1940
Sales 74.0MM EMP 140
Accts Stegman & Company Baltimore
SIC 5113 5087 Disposable plates, cups, napkins & eating utensils; Towels, paper; Janitors' supplies; Disposable plates, cups, napkins & eating utensils; Towels, paper; Janitors' supplies
Pr: Daniel Leonard
*Sec: John Leonard
VP: Dan Leonard Jr
*VP: Michael E Leonard
*VP: Robert Leonard
Sls Mgr: Paul Baumann

D-U-N-S 00-514-5511
LEONARD PETERSON & CO INC
400 Webster Rd, Auburn, AL 36832-4243
Tel (334) 821-6832 Founded/Ownrshp 1890
Sales 24.6MME EMP 102
SIC 3821 Laboratory furniture; Laboratory furniture
Ch Bd: Roger D Lethander
*Treas: Anne Garrett
VP: Randy Jensen
*VP: Todd Lethander
Exec: Scott Couch
Plnt Mgr: Carvin Morris

D-U-N-S 00-285-7555
LEONARD S FIORE INC (PA)
5506 6th Ave Rear, Altoona, PA 16602-1295
Tel (814) 946-3686 Founded/Ownrshp 1954
Sales 117.9MME EMP 250
Accts Harry K Sickler Associates T
SIC 1542 Commercial & office building, new construction; Commercial & office building, new construction
Pr: Richard F Fiore Sr
*Ch: Leonard S Fiore Jr
*Ex VP: Michael A Fiore
*VP: Richard F Fiore Jr
*VP: Joseph Irwin
Mtls Mgr: William Gunnett

D-U-N-S 13-063-3225
LEONARD STREET & DEINARD PROFESSIONAL ASSOCIATION
STINSON LEONARD STREET
150 S 5th St Ste 2300, Minneapolis, MN 55402-4223
Tel (612) 335-1500 Founded/Ownrshp 1922
Sales 47.2MME EMP 400
SIC 8111 General practice law office; General practice law office
Pr: Lowell Stortz
Sr Pt: Daniel McInerney
Pr: Paula Benson
Pr: Sue May
Pr: Barbara McCoy
Pr: Angelique Sherman
COO: Michael Taylor
*CFO: Wayne Schertler
IT Man: Victoria Jaffray
Counsel: Sidney Kaplan
Counsel: Richard Pepin

D-U-N-S 04-262-2779 IMP/EXP
LEONARD T VERRASTRO INC
700 Moosic Rd, Old Forge, PA 18518-2031
Tel (570) 343-2454 Founded/Ownrshp 1973
Sales 46.4MME EMP 95
SIC 5181 5149 Beer & other fermented malt liquors; Soft drinks; Beer & other fermented malt liquors; Soft drinks
Pr: Leonard T Verrastro Jr

D-U-N-S 18-366-2787
LEONARD TERRACE APARTMENTS
GRAND RAPIDS HOUSING COMMISION
1315 Leonard St Ne Ofc, Grand Rapids, MI 49505-5568
Tel (616) 235-2890 Founded/Ownrshp 2005
Sales 23.4MME EMP 4
Accts Rehmann Robson Grand Rapids
SIC 6513 Apartment building operators; Apartment building operators

D-U-N-S 11-887-6692
LEONARD TOYOTA INC
TOYOTA OF HACKENSACK
278 River St, Hackensack, NJ 07601-7503
Tel (201) 488-7777 Founded/Ownrshp 1999
Sales 43.2MME EMP 100
SIC 5511 Automobiles, new & used; Automobiles, new & used
Pr: Frank Holtham Jr
*Genl Mgr: Fred Radulic
Sls Mgr: Tony Munoz
Sls Mgr: Mario Puente
Sales Asso: Edwin Alvarado
Sales Asso: Adel Atta
Sales Asso: Walter Chacon
Sales Asso: William Coll
Sales Asso: Joe Giglio
Sales Asso: Antonio Gualpa
Sales Asso: Marino Hernandez

LEONARDO LO CASCIO SELECTIONS
See WINEBOW INC

D-U-N-S 16-959-2003
LEONARDS AUTO INC
26 W New Haven Ave, Melbourne, FL 32901-4406
Tel (321) 727-1931 Founded/Ownrshp 1963
Sales 27.0MM EMP 13
SIC 5521 Used car dealers; Used car dealers
Pr: Robert Tibbetts

D-U-N-S 04-364-9482 IMP
LEONARDS CARPET SERVICE INC
XGRASS TURF DIRECT
1121 N Red Gum St, Anaheim, CA 92806-2582
Tel (714) 630-1930 Founded/Ownrshp 1970
Sales 39.3MME EMP 150
SIC 2541 1771 1799 Drapery & upholstery stores; Carpet laying; Floor covering stores; Home furnishings; Table or counter tops, plastic laminated; Flooring contractor; Artificial turf installation
Pr: Leonard Nagel
*CEO: Joel Nagel
Genl Mgr: Pete Segaar
IT Man: Roberta Papke
Mktg Mgr: Robert Cozart

D-U-N-S 06-385-1567
LEONARDS EXPRESS INC (NY)
6070 Collett Rd Bldg 2, Farmington, NY 14425-9531
Tel (585) 924-8140 Founded/Ownrshp 2000
Sales 28.7MME EMP 40E
SIC 4731 4213 Freight transportation arrangement; Trucking, except local
Ch Bd: Kenneth F Johnson
*Ch Bd: Patricia H Johnson
*Pr: Kent L Johnson
*VP: Michael Riccio

D-U-N-S 79-387-1232
■ **LEONARDS METAL INC**
VERSAFORM
(Suby of LEONARDS METALS) ★
3030 N Highway 94, Saint Charles, MO 63301-5323
Tel (636) 949-1532 Founded/Ownrshp 1998
Sales 79.5MME EMP 500
SIC 3728 Aircraft parts & equipment; Aircraft parts & equipment
Pr: Ronald Saks
*Treas: Lawrence E Dickinson
VP: Duane Hahn
IT Man: Robert Collumbien

LEONARD'S METALS
See LMI AEROSPACE INC

D-U-N-S 09-477-4630
LEONARDTOWN SCHOOL DISTRICT
P.O. Box 641 (20650-0641)
Tel (301) 475-4250 Founded/Ownrshp 2001
Sales 12.1MME EMP 1,400
SIC 8211 Public elementary & secondary schools; Public elementary & secondary schools
Prin: Joan Kozlovsky

LEONA'S NEIGHBORHOOD PLACE
See LEONAS PIZZERIA INC

D-U-N-S 01-346-6727
LEONAS PIZZERIA INC (IL)
LEONA'S NEIGHBORHOOD PLACE
3931 S Leavitt St, Chicago, IL 60609-2203
Tel (773) 843-0050 Founded/Ownrshp 1967
Sales 32.7MME EMP 1,100
SIC 5812 5813 Pizzeria, independent; Italian restaurant; Caterers; Drinking places; Pizzeria, independent; Italian restaurant; Caterers; Drinking places
Pr: Leon Toia
*CFO: Doug Quinn
*VP: Salvatore P Toia
CTO: Tina Niera

D-U-N-S 79-720-4633
LEONE & KEEBLE INC
108 W Boone Ave, Spokane, WA 99201-2310
Tel (509) 327-4451 Founded/Ownrshp 1992
Sales 27.3MME EMP 62
SIC 1542 Commercial & office building, new construction; Commercial & office buildings, renovation & repair
Pr: Craig Leone
*VP: Paul Keeble
*VP: Thomas Mercer

D-U-N-S 04-271-7686 IMP/EXP
LEONE INDUSTRIES INC
(Suby of ARDAGH GROUP SA)
443 S East Ave, Bridgeton, NJ 08302-3498
Tel (856) 455-2000 Founded/Ownrshp 2012
Sales 64.3MME EMP 350
SIC 3221 Glass containers; Glass containers
Pr: Peter Leone
CFO: Clay Martin
CFO: Jeff Patterson
*VP: David J Leone
CTO: Stephanie Ojeda
MIS Dir: Bill Carroll
Sls Mgr: John Orr

D-U-N-S 05-677-0803
LEONHARDT MANUFACTURING CO INC
800 High St, Hanover, PA 17331-1736
Tel (717) 632-4150 Founded/Ownrshp 1970
Sales 22.3MME EMP 90
SIC 3498 3599 7692 3471 Tube fabricating (contract bending & shaping); Machine shop, jobbing & repair; Welding repair; Plating & polishing
CEO: Robert H Jacobs
*Pr: Jason D Jacobs
*CFO: Jarrod M Klunk
*Treas: Midge Leonhardt
*VP: Hans J Leonhardt
VP Sls: John Dell
Sales Asso: Jonathan Burke

D-U-N-S 62-163-6448 IMP
LEONI WIRE INC
(Suby of LEONISCHE HOLDING INC) ★
301 Griffith Rd, Chicopee, MA 01022-2129
Tel (413) 593-1352 Founded/Ownrshp 2005
Sales 40.3MME EMP 92
SIC 3351 3315 Wire, copper & copper alloy; Steel wire & related products; Wire, copper & copper alloy; Steel wire & related products
Pr: Neville Crabbe
Ofcr: Sven Schmidt
VP: Claude Burlot
Mng Dir: Pushpendra Singh
Mng Dir: Markus Thoma
Rgnl Mgr: Cristian Bleotu
Dept Mgr: Sue Watts
Genl Mgr: Rolf Reidinger
IT Man: Elizabeth Fox
IT Man: John Hassall
Plnt Mgr: David Adamcik
Board of Directors: Klaus Probst

D-U-N-S 87-686-1881 IMP/EXP
LEONI WIRING SYSTEMS INC
(Suby of LEONISCHE HOLDING INC) ★
2861 N Flowing Wells Rd # 121, Tucson, AZ 85705-9397
Tel (520) 741-0895 Founded/Ownrshp 2005
Sales 707.7MME EMP 2,100
SIC 3643 8741 5063 Harness assemblies for electronic use: wire or cable; Management services; Wire & cable; Current-carrying wiring devices; Management services; Wire & cable
CEO: Martin Gloesslein
*Pr: Juergen Linhard
*CFO: Larry Finkenthal
*CFO: Jay Meridew
IT Man: Lisa Reed

D-U-N-S 07-057-3829
LEONIA BOARD OF EDUCATION
570 Grand Ave, Leonia, NJ 07605-2102
Tel (201) 302-5200 Founded/Ownrshp 1915
Sales 13.6MME EMP 280
SIC 8211 Public elementary & secondary schools; Public elementary & secondary schools

D-U-N-S 07-980-6911
LEONIA PUBLIC SCHOOLS
570 Grand Ave, Leonia, NJ 07605-2102
Tel (201) 302-5200 Founded/Ownrshp 2015
Sales 5.1MME EMP 351E
SIC 8211 Public elementary & secondary schools

D-U-N-S 18-250-5466
LEONIE INDUSTRIES LLC
17383 W Sunset Blvd # 420, Pacific Palisades, CA 90272-5100
Tel (310) 573-9505 Founded/Ownrshp 2004
Sales 25.6MME EMP 208E
SIC 8732 Business research service; Business research service
Pr: Rema Chidiacdupontm
Ofcr: Carlos Guerra
Ofcr: Tim Neumann
Ofcr: Troy Nienow
Dir Bus: John Landry
Dir Bus: Aaron Mallin
Prgrm Mgr: Ashlea Adelegan
Prgrm Mgr: Bruce Barr
Prgrm Mgr: Shane Keane
Prgrm Mgr: Mytran Lam
Prgrm Mgr: Charles Owens

D-U-N-S 83-186-8109
LEONISCHE HOLDING INC
(Suby of LEONI BORDNETZ-SYSTEME GMBH)
2861 N Flowing Wells Rd, Tucson, AZ 85705-9397
Tel (520) 741-0895 Founded/Ownrshp 2010
Sales 757.4MME EMP 176E
SIC 3679 Harness assemblies for electronic use: wire or cable
Prin: Martin Gloesslein

D-U-N-S 00-735-0721
LEONS FINE FOODS INC (TX)
LEON'S TEXAS CUISINE
2100 Redbud Blvd, McKinney, TX 75069-8215
Tel (972) 529-5050 Founded/Ownrshp 1945, 1975
Sales 47.8MME EMP 245
SIC 2099 2013 Food preparations; Sausages & other prepared meats; Food preparations; Sausages & other prepared meats
Pr: Robert L Clements
Sr VP: John Vroman
VP: Allen Dillon

LEON'S TEXAS CUISINE
See LEONS FINE FOODS INC

D-U-N-S 09-678-6447
LEOPARDO COMPANIES INC (IL)
LEOPARDO CONSTRUCTION
5200 Prairie Stone Pkwy, Hoffman Estates, IL 60192-3709
Tel (847) 783-3000 Founded/Ownrshp 1979
Sales 105.3MME EMP 300E
SIC 1542 8741 Commercial & office building, new construction; Commercial & office buildings, renovation & repair; Construction management
CEO: James A Leopardo
*Pr: Rick Mattioda
*CFO: John Ward
*Sr VP: Mike Behm
*Sr VP: Pierre Cowart
*Sr VP: Rick Dupraw
*Sr VP: Mike Leopardo
VP: Scott Higgins
VP: Anthony Iannessa
VP: Gary Leopardo
*VP: Sal T Leopardo
VP: Matt Miller
Exec: Christopher Novak
Exec: Rory Tihinen

LEOPARDO CONSTRUCTION
See LEOPARDO COMPANIES INC

D-U-N-S 00-342-8216 EXP
LEOS VACATION CENTER INC
729 State Route 3 N, Gambrills, MD 21054-1398
Tel (410) 987-4793 Founded/Ownrshp 1972
Sales 25.0MM EMP 40
SIC 5561 Motor homes; Travel trailers: automobile, new & used; Recreational vehicle parts & accessories; Motor homes; Travel trailers: automobile, new & used; Recreational vehicle parts & accessories
Pr: Greg Merkel
*VP: Jacki Merkel

LEP SPECIAL FASTENERS
See FONTANA FASTENERS INC

D-U-N-S 00-110-5741
■ **LEPAGE BAKERIES INC**
COUNTRY KITCHEN
(Suby of FLOWERS FOODS INC) ★
11 Adamian Dr, Auburn, ME 04210-8304
Tel (207) 783-9161 Founded/Ownrshp 2012
Sales 118.7MME EMP 525
SIC 2051 5461 Bread, cake & related products; Bread, all types (white, wheat, rye, etc): fresh or frozen; Doughnuts, except frozen; Rolls, bread type: fresh or frozen; Bakeries; Bread, cake & related products; Bread, all types (white, wheat, rye, etc): fresh or frozen; Doughnuts, except frozen; Rolls, bread type: fresh or frozen; Bakeries
Pr: Andy Barowsky

LEPCO
See LAWN EQUIPMENT PARTS CO

D-U-N-S 80-096-6772
LEPERCQ DE NEUFLIZE / TOCQUEVILLE SECURITIES LP
40 W 57th St Fl 19, New York, NY 10019-4010
Tel (212) 698-0800 Founded/Ownrshp 1987
Sales 54.0MM EMP 85
SIC 6799 Investors; Investors
Pt: Francois Sicart
*Pt: John Cassidy
*Pt: Roger Cotta
*Pt: Robert Kleinschmidt
Mng Dir: Stephen Cate
Mng Dir: Bruno Desforges

D-U-N-S 09-528-8684
LEPIER OIL CO INC
(Suby of LE PIERS INC) ★
320 1st St E, Fosston, MN 56542-1326
Tel (218) 435-1040 Founded/Ownrshp 1983
Sales 25.0MM EMP 5
SIC 5172 Petroleum products; Petroleum products

CEO: Larry Le Pier
**Pr:* Tami Hemmesch

D-U-N-S 00-848-1757
LEPORT EDUCATIONAL INSTITUTE INC
LEPORT SCHOOLS
1 Technology Dr Bldg A, Irvine, CA 92618-2350
Tel (914) 374-8860 *Founded/Ownrshp* 2000
Sales 23.5MM^E *EMP* 255
SIC 8211 Elementary & secondary schools; Elementary & secondary schools
CEO: Ramandeep S Girn
IT Man: Alexandria Negron

LEPORT SCHOOLS
See LEPORT EDUCATIONAL INSTITUTE INC

LEPPINK'S FOOD CENTER
See LEPPINKS INC

D-U-N-S 06-587-8225
LEPPINKS INC
LEPPINK'S FOOD CENTER
303 W Main St, Belding, MI 48809-1675
Tel (616) 794-3660 *Founded/Ownrshp* 1961
Sales 55.9MM^E *EMP* 450
SIC 5411 5251 5945 Grocery stores; Hardware; Toys & games; Grocery stores; Hardware; Toys & games
Pr: John Leppink
**Sec:* Richard Cole

LEPPO EQUIPMENT
See LEPPO INC

D-U-N-S 01-834-2063
LEPPO INC (OH)
LEPPO EQUIPMENT
176 West Ave, Tallmadge, OH 44278-2145
Tel (330) 633-3999 *Founded/Ownrshp* 1945, 1962
Sales 58.8MM *EMP* 128
Accts Houston Fearer Ltd Akron O
SIC 5082 7353 7629 General construction machinery & equipment; Heavy construction equipment rental; Business machine repair, electric; General construction machinery & equipment; Heavy construction equipment rental; Business machine repair, electric
CEO: Dale Leppo
**Pr:* Glenn Leppo
**Treas:* Joanne Sweeney
VP Sls: Dan Lebeau
Sales Asso: Kirk Laps
Sales Asso: Sam Page

D-U-N-S 00-707-6664 EXP
LEPRINO FOODS CO
1830 W 38th Ave, Denver, CO 80211-2200
Tel (303) 480-2600 *Founded/Ownrshp* 1955, 1965
Sales 1.9MMM^E *EMP* 3,700
SIC 2022 Cheese, natural & processed; Cheese, natural & processed
CEO: James G Leprino
**Pr:* Larry J Jensen
Treas: Dan Alonzi
Sr VP: Mike Cureton
**Sr VP:* Michael L Reidy
VP: David J Kielsmeier
VP: Edith A Quartey
VP: Rob Schwartz
VP: Daniel A Vecchiarelli
Exec: Julia Lambert
Exec: Kylan Linney
Dir Risk M: Steven Levine
Assoc Dir: Brian Erickson
Assoc Dir: Jason Mounts
Board of Directors: Michael Leprino

D-U-N-S 78-878-1123
LEPRINO FOODS DAIRY PRODUCTS CO
(*Suby of* LEPRINO FOODS CO) ★
1830 W 38th Ave, Denver, CO 80211-2225
Tel (303) 480-2600 *Founded/Ownrshp* 2006
Sales 74.1MM^E *EMP* 350
SIC 5143 Dairy products, except dried or canned; Dairy products, except dried or canned
Ch Bd: James G Leprino
**Pr:* Larry Jansen
**Sr VP:* Ronald Clump
Dir IT: Simon Drummond

LERCH BATES
See BATES LERCH INC

D-U-N-S 11-402-6941
LERDAHL BUSINESS INTERIORS INC
7182 Us Highway 14 # 502, Middleton, WI 53562-4265
Tel (608) 831-1010 *Founded/Ownrshp* 1984
Sales 20.8MM^E *EMP* 25
SIC 5021 5046 Office & public building furniture; Partitions
Pr: Jeff Lerdahl
**VP:* Tim Lerdahl
Mktg Dir: Tonya Zurfluh

D-U-N-S 83-223-0804
LERETA LLC
1123 Park View Dr, Covina, CA 91724-3748
Tel (800) 537-3821 *Founded/Ownrshp* 2009
Sales 229.6MM^E *EMP* 450
SIC 6211 6541 6361 Tax certificate dealers; Title search companies; Real estate title insurance; Tax certificate dealers; Title search companies; Real estate title insurance
Pr: John Walsh
Pr: Glenn McCarthy
**COO:* James V Micali
CFO: Sharon Yokoyama
**Ex VP:* Chris Masten
Sr VP: Lily Akimoff
Sr VP: Richard Yonis
VP: Mike Blaha
VP: Kevin Brown
VP: Mark Bruce
VP: Jonnine Eras
VP: Dominique Froesch
VP: Linda Johnson
VP: Bronson Quon
VP: Ted Smith
VP: Adrienne Williams
VP: Dave Wilson

D-U-N-S 09-490-0339
LERNER CORP
2000 Tower Oaks Blvd Fl 8, Rockville, MD 20852-4284
Tel (301) 284-6000 *Founded/Ownrshp* 1994
Sales 27.6MM^E *EMP* 200
SIC 6531 Real estate agents & managers; Real estate agents & managers
Pr: Theodore N Lerner
**COO:* Allan Gottlied

D-U-N-S 07-482-6496
LERNER LAND INVESTMENT CORP
LERNER MARK
2000 Tower Oaks Blvd Fl 8, Rockville, MD 20852-4284
Tel (301) 284-6000 *Founded/Ownrshp* 1954
Sales 15.4MM^E *EMP* 600
SIC 6531 Real estate managers; Real estate managers
Pr: Theodore N Lerner
**Treas:* Edward L Cohen
**Ex VP:* Mark D Lerner
**Sr VP:* Lori Creasy

LERNER MARK
See LERNER LAND INVESTMENT CORP

D-U-N-S 14-925-4182 IMP
■ **LERNER NEW YORK HOLDING INC**
(*Suby of* NEW YORK & CO INC) ★
450 W 33rd St Bsmt 3, New York, NY 10001-2637
Tel (212) 736-1222 *Founded/Ownrshp* 2002
Sales 67.8MM^E *EMP* 2,100
SIC 5621 Women's clothing stores; Women's clothing stores
Pr: Richard Crystal
Dist Mgr: Tony Lynch
IT Man: Greg England
IT Man: Anthony Rizzo
Snr Mgr: Joann Fassett

D-U-N-S 00-698-6814 IMP
■ **LERNER NEW YORK INC** (DE)
(*Suby of* NEW YORK & CO INC) ★
330 W 34th St Fl 7, New York, NY 10001-2406
Tel (212) 884-2000 *Founded/Ownrshp* 1985, 2002
Sales 208.6MM^E *EMP* 2,100
SIC 5621 Women's clothing stores; Women's clothing stores
Ch Bd: Gregory Scott
**Ch Bd:* Richard Crystal
**CFO:* Sheamus Toal
Ex VP: Jackie Corso
**Ex VP:* John E Dewolf III
Ex VP: Mathew Gluckson
**Ex VP:* Leslie Goldmann
Ex VP: Hope Grey
**Ex VP:* Sandra Brooslin Viviano
VP: Jinn Chung
VP: Susan Reiss

D-U-N-S 00-645-1702 IMP
LERNER PUBLISHING GROUP INC (MN)
RUNESTONE PRESS
1251 Washington Ave N, Minneapolis, MN 55401-1036
Tel (612) 332-3344 *Founded/Ownrshp* 1959
Sales 33.2MM^E *EMP* 210
SIC 2731 Book publishing; Book publishing
CEO: Adam Lerner
CFO: Margaret Wunderlich
Assoc Ed: Anna Cavallo

D-U-N-S 05-072-5910
LERNER SAMPSON & ROTHFUSS A LEGAL PROFESSIONAL ASSOCIATION (OH)
L S R
120 E 4th St, Cincinnati, OH 45202-4070
Tel (513) 241-3100 *Founded/Ownrshp* 1975
Sales 43.6MM^E *EMP* 360
SIC 8111 General practice law office; General practice law office
Pr: Richard M Rothfuss
COO: Teresa Miller
CFO: Janis Dorgan
**Prin:* Donald M Lerner
Sftwr Eng: Joanna Shaffer

D-U-N-S 00-784-3535
LEROY COOPERATIVE ASSOCIATION INC
505 E 6th St, Le Roy, KS 66857-9668
Tel (620) 964-2225 *Founded/Ownrshp* 1960
Sales 53.7MM *EMP* 32
Accts Lindburg Vogel Pierce Faris M
SIC 5153 5191 5531 5541 2875 Grain elevators; Farm supplies; Automotive tires; Gasoline service stations; Fertilizers, mixing only; Grain elevators; Farm supplies; Automotive tires; Gasoline service stations; Fertilizers, mixing only
Pr: Rick Crooks

LEROY SELMON'S RESTAURANT
See OS SOUTHERN INC

D-U-N-S 03-282-3528 EXP
LEROY SMITH INC
4776 Old Dixie Hwy, Vero Beach, FL 32967-1239
Tel (772) 567-3421 *Founded/Ownrshp* 1945
Sales 36.3MM^E *EMP* 85
SIC 5148 Fruits, fresh; Fruits, fresh
Pr: Elson R Smith Jr

LEROY SOMER NA DIV EMERSON ELC
See LEROY-SOMER INC

D-U-N-S 07-452-2723
LEROY SPRINGS & CO INC
2201 Old Nation Rd, Fort Mill, SC 29715
Tel (803) 547-1000 *Founded/Ownrshp* 1938
Sales 43.3MM *EMP* 363
Accts The Springs Company Lancaster
SIC 7997 7011 Golf club, membership; Resort hotel; Golf club, membership; Resort hotel
Pr: Tim Patterson
Genl Mgr: Crystal Ray

LEROY WILLIAMS JR
See IMPORT FRONT ENDS & PARTS

D-U-N-S 79-052-5752 EXP
■ **LEROY-SOMER INC**
LEROY SOMER NA DIV EMERSON ELC
(*Suby of* EMERSON ELECTRIC CO) ★
669 Natchez Trace Dr, Lexington, TN 38351-4125
Tel (731) 967-3000 *Founded/Ownrshp* 1999
Sales 160.2MM^E *EMP* 800^E
SIC 3621 Motors & generators; Power generators; Motors & generators; Power generators
Pr: Dan Ray

LES
See LOYDS ELECTRIC SUPPLY INC

LES
See LINCOLN ELECTRIC SYSTEM

D-U-N-S 06-127-3215
LES FILE DRYWALL INC
116 Industrial Ave Ne, Albuquerque, NM 87107-2229
Tel (505) 345-8283 *Founded/Ownrshp* 1955
Sales 32.5MM^E *EMP* 250
SIC 1742 Drywall; Drywall
Pr: Jason File
**Sec:* Leslie C File
Snr PM: Ramon Sandoval

D-U-N-S 03-537-6441
LES OLSON CO
3244 S 300 W, Salt Lake City, UT 84115-3411
Tel (435) 586-2345 *Founded/Ownrshp* 1956
Sales 119.6MM^E *EMP* 170
SIC 5044 Office equipment; Office equipment
Ch Bd: L Ray Olson
Pr: Larry G Olson
Treas: James Robert Olson Jr
Treas: Lisa Olson Thaller
VP: Aaron Mehrley
VP: Richard Moore
VP: Larry Troy Olson
IT Man: Eric Swink
Opers Mgr: Clayton Olson
Sls Mgr: Gary Facer
Sls Mgr: Chris Gale

D-U-N-S 10-396-3539
LES ROGERS INC
ROGERS & ROGERS TOYOTA
2351 Us Highway 86, Imperial, CA 92251-9780
Tel (760) 353-9300 *Founded/Ownrshp* 1998
Sales 27.7MM^E *EMP* 70
SIC 5511 Automobiles, new & used; Automobiles, new & used
Pr: Leslie F Rogers III
Sls Mgr: Armando Murillo

LES SCHWAB EQUIPMENT
See MIDWAY EQUIPMENT & SUPPLY CO

LES SCHWAB TIRE CENTERS
See LES SCHWAB WAREHOUSE CENTER INC

D-U-N-S 06-878-9445
LES SCHWAB TIRE CENTERS OF BOISE INC
(*Suby of* LES SCHWAB TIRE CENTERS) ★
20900 Cooley Rd, Bend, OR 97701-3406
Tel (541) 447-4136 *Founded/Ownrshp* 1952
Sales 55.0MM^E *EMP* 307
SIC 5531 Automotive tires; Automotive accessories; Automotive tires; Automotive accessories
Pr: Dick Borgman
**Pr:* John Britton
**Treas:* Jim A Goad
Mktg Dir: John Maloney

D-U-N-S 78-767-1411
LES SCHWAB TIRE CENTERS OF CALIFORNIA INC
(*Suby of* LES SCHWAB TIRE CENTERS) ★
646 Nw Madras Hwy, Prineville, OR 97754-1444
Tel (541) 447-4136 *Founded/Ownrshp* 1989
Sales 64.1MM^E *EMP* 283
SIC 5531 Automotive tires; Automotive accessories; Automotive tires; Automotive accessories
Ch: Margaret Denton
**Treas:* Dianna S Tomseth

D-U-N-S 02-776-6617
LES SCHWAB TIRE CENTERS OF IDAHO INC
(*Suby of* LES SCHWAB TIRE CENTERS) ★
646 Nw Madras Hwy, Prineville, OR 97754-1444
Tel (541) 447-4136 *Founded/Ownrshp* 1959
Sales 191.2MM^E *EMP* 990
SIC 5531 Automotive tires; Automotive accessories; Automotive tires; Automotive accessories
Pr: John M Britton
**Ch Bd:* Margaret S Denton
Pr: G Phillip Wick
CFO: John Cuniff
Treas: Gerald V Darnell
Treas: James A Goad
Chf Mktg O: Dale Thompson
Ex VP: Richard W Priday
VP: Brian Capp
VP: Ken Edwards
Exec: Tom Freedman

D-U-N-S 02-776-7110 IMP
LES SCHWAB TIRE CENTERS OF OREGON INC (OR)
(*Suby of* LES SCHWAB TIRE CENTERS) ★
20900 Cooley Rd, Bend, OR 97701-3406
Tel (541) 416-5427 *Founded/Ownrshp* 1952
Sales 35.6MM^E *EMP* 322
SIC 3011 Truck or bus inner tubes; Truck or bus inner tubes
Ch: Dick Borgman
**Ch Bd:* Margaret Schwab Denton
**Ch Bd:* Leslie B Schwab
**Pr:* John Britton
**CFO:* John Cuniff
**Treas:* Gerald V Darnell
**Ex VP:* Richard W Priday
**Sr VP:* Tom Freedman
**Prin:* G Phillip Wick
Off Mgr: Pat Dean
Sls Mgr: Steven J Boekholder

D-U-N-S 07-072-3986
LES SCHWAB TIRE CENTERS OF PORTLAND INC
(*Suby of* LES SCHWAB TIRE CENTERS) ★
20900 Cooley Rd, Bend, OR 97701-3406
Tel (541) 447-4136 *Founded/Ownrshp* 1973
Sales 279.9MM^E *EMP* 1,552
SIC 5531 Automotive tires; Automotive tires; Automotive accessories
Ch Bd: Margaret Schwab Denton
Pr: John Britton
Pr: G Phillip Wick
CFO: Thomas Freedman
Treas: Gerald V Darnell
Ex VP: Richard W Priday

D-U-N-S 17-440-1997
LES SCHWAB TIRE CENTERS OF UTAH INC
(*Suby of* LES SCHWAB TIRE CENTERS) ★
20900 Cooley Rd, Bend, OR 97701-3406
Tel (541) 447-4136 *Founded/Ownrshp* 2001
Sales 60.0MM *EMP* 300
SIC 5531 Automotive tires; Automotive accessories; Automotive tires; Automotive accessories
Pr: John Britton

D-U-N-S 04-978-9522 IMP
LES SCHWAB TIRE CENTERS OF WASHINGTON INC
(*Suby of* LES SCHWAB TIRE CENTERS) ★
20900 Cooley Rd, Bend, OR 97701-3406
Tel (541) 447-4136 *Founded/Ownrshp* 1976
Sales 400.0MM^E *EMP* 400^E
SIC 5531 Automotive tires; Automotive accessories; Automotive tires; Automotive accessories
Ch: Richard Borgman
**Pr:* John Britton
CFO: Jack Cuniff
CFO: Gery Darnell
**CFO:* James Goad Jr
Ex VP: Richard W Priday
**Ex VP:* Dan Roberts
**VP:* Corey J Parks
**Prin:* CAM Durrell
Brnch Mgr: Mike Crakes
Telecom Mg: Rich Knight

LES SCHWAB TIRES
See SHAUB-ELLISON CO INC

D-U-N-S 04-126-9697 IMP
LES SCHWAB WAREHOUSE CENTER INC
LES SCHWAB TIRE CENTERS
20900 Cooley Rd, Bend, OR 97701-3406
Tel (541) 447-4136 *Founded/Ownrshp* 1958
Sales 2.5MMM^E *EMP* 5,680
SIC 5014 7534 5531 Automobile tires & tubes; Tire recapping; Automotive & home supply stores; Automobile tires & tubes; Tire recapping; Automotive & home supply stores
CEO: Richard Borgman
**Pr:* John Britton
**CFO:* Tom Freedman
**Treas:* Gerald V Darnell
Trst: Steven Bjorvik
Chf Mktg O: Dale Thompson
Ex VP: Ray Compton
**VP:* Dick Borgman
VP: Jerry Darnielle
**VP:* Larry Henderson
**VP:* Phil Powell
**VP:* Dan Roberts
**VP:* Doug Smith
Board of Directors: Denny Denton, Alan L Schwab, Diana Tomseth, Matthew S Tomseth

LES STANFORD AUTO WORLD
See LES STANFORD CHEVROLET INC

D-U-N-S 04-496-4641
LES STANFORD CHEVROLET INC (MI)
LES STANFORD AUTO WORLD
21730 Michigan Ave, Dearborn, MI 48124-2350
Tel (313) 565-6000 *Founded/Ownrshp* 1947
Sales 41.8MM^E *EMP* 100
SIC 5511 5561 5521 New & used car dealers; Motor homes; Used car dealers
Pr: Paul Stanford
Store Mgr: Brian Greiner
CTO: Dianne Pierce
Sls&Mrk Ex: Scott Montgomery
Sls Mgr: Eric Hibbert

LES STUMPF FORD
See STUMPF MOTOR CO INC

D-U-N-S 78-331-0097
LES STUMPF FORD INC
L AND S TRUCK CENTER
3030 W College Ave, Appleton, WI 54914-2909
Tel (800) 236-8899 *Founded/Ownrshp* 1921
Sales 60.8MM^E *EMP* 160
SIC 5511 7513 7515 7532 5531 5521 Automobiles, new & used; Truck leasing, without drivers; Passenger car leasing; Top & body repair & paint shops; Automotive & home supply stores; Used car dealers; Automobiles, new & used; Truck leasing, without drivers; Passenger car leasing; Top & body repair & paint shops; Automotive & home supply stores; Used car dealers
Pr: Leslie F Stumpf
**VP:* Darlene Stumpf
VP: Jon Stumpf
Advt Dir: John Larson
Pr Dir: Russ Pierce
Sls Mgr: Erick Gafner

D-U-N-S 09-950-9846
LES TROIS PETITS COCHONS INC
4223 1st Ave Fl 2, Brooklyn, NY 11232-3313
Tel (212) 219-1230 *Founded/Ownrshp* 1975
Sales 22.4MM^E *EMP* 67
SIC 5147 Meats & meat products
Ch Bd: Alain Sinturel

D-U-N-S 00-280-2874
LES WILSON INC
205 Industrial Ave, Carmi, IL 62821-2211
Tel (618) 382-4667 *Founded/Ownrshp* 1942, 1958

Sales 49.1MM^E *EMP* 150
Accts Botsch & Associates Cpa S Ll
SIC 1381 Drilling oil & gas wells; Drilling oil & gas wells
Pr: Robert L Wilson
**Treas:* Stephanie L Wilson

D-U-N-S 61-856-0601 IMP/EXP
LESAFFRE INTERNATIONAL CORP
(*Suby of* LESAFFRE ET COMPAGNIE)
7475 W Main St, Milwaukee, WI 53214-1552
Tel (414) 615-3300 *Founded/Ownrshp* 1977
Sales 218.1MM^E *EMP* 596
SIC 2099 Yeast; Yeast
Ch Bd: Denise Lesaffre
**Pr:* John Riesch
**CFO:* Geoffrey O'Connor
**Treas:* Cary Levinson
**VP:* Chris Kaltenbach
**VP:* Chris Katenbach
Natl Sales: Sandi Cazalet
Manager: Detlef Werner

D-U-N-S 17-683-9009 IMP/EXP
LESAFFRE YEAST CORP
RED STAR YEAST COMPANY
(*Suby of* LESAFFRE INTERNATIONAL CORP) ★
7475 W Main St, Milwaukee, WI 53214-1552
Tel (414) 615-3300 *Founded/Ownrshp* 1994
Sales 197.7MM^E *EMP* 448
SIC 5149 Groceries & related products; Groceries & related products
Ch Bd: Lucien Lesaffre
**Pr:* John Riesch
COO: George Parry
**CFO:* Geoff O'Connor
Treas: Geoffrey O Connor
Exec: Laura Collins
Area Mgr: Stan Denton
CIO: Bryan Jocques
QA Dir: Carole Paasch-Homan
Dir IT: Ken Massey
Sls Dir: David Lewis

D-U-N-S 12-252-3061 IMP
LESAINT LOGISTICS INC
(*Suby of* LESAINT LOGISTICS LLC) ★
4487 Le Saint Ct, West Chester, OH 45014-2229
Tel (513) 874-3900 *Founded/Ownrshp* 2005
Sales 46.5MM^E *EMP* 232
SIC 4225 4212 General warehousing & storage; Local trucking, without storage; General warehousing & storage; Local trucking, without storage
Pr: Jeff Pennington
Sfty Dirs: Patrick Wong

D-U-N-S 11-872-9917 IMP/EXP
LESAINT LOGISTICS LLC
868 W Crossroads Pkwy, Romeoville, IL 60446-4332
Tel (630) 243-5950 *Founded/Ownrshp* 2006
Sales 103.7MM^E *EMP* 232
SIC 4731 4225 8742 Freight transportation arrangement; General warehousing & storage; Materials mgmt. (purchasing, handling, inventory) consultant; Freight transportation arrangement; General warehousing & storage; Materials mgmt. (purchasing, handling, inventory) consultant
Pr: Jeff Pennington
CFO: Lon Purdy
Ex VP: Dino Moler
VP: Bill Lansaw
Exec: Jennifer Russo
VP Opers: Dan Harmon

D-U-N-S 12-182-4163 IMP/EXP
LESCHACO INC
(*Suby of* LEXZAU, SCHARBAU GMBH & CO. KG)
15355 Vantage Pkwy W # 195, Houston, TX 77032-1965
Tel (281) 590-2515 *Founded/Ownrshp* 1978
Sales 66.3MM *EMP* 55
Accts Pannell Kerr Forster Of Texas
SIC 4731 4783 Foreign freight forwarding; Customhouse brokers; Containerization of goods for shipping
Pr: Mark C Malambri
VP: Gary Haverkorn
VP: Raymond Lin
VP: Tom Villacampa
Brnch Mgr: Kelly Bruening
Brnch Mgr: Scott Mazza

D-U-N-S 94-598-9937
LESCO DISTRIBUTING INC
1203 E Industrial Dr, Orange City, FL 32763-7108
Tel (386) 775-7244 *Founded/Ownrshp* 1996
Sales 30.0MM^E *EMP* 57
SIC 5064 3678 Radios; Electronic connectors
Pr: Greg M Kacarab
**Sec:* Tammy L Kacarab
**VP:* Dough Maresse
**VP:* Richard D Marrese
Genl Mgr: Debra Soliz
Merch Mgr: Neil Brookmyer
Sls Mgr: Scott Austin

D-U-N-S 00-445-3825 EXP
■ **LESCO INC** (OH)
(*Suby of* DEERE & CO) ★
1385 E 36th St, Cleveland, OH 44114-4114
Tel (216) 706-9250 *Founded/Ownrshp* 1962, 2007
Sales 195.5MM^E *EMP* 1,122
SIC 5191 5083 5261 Grass seed; Lawn machinery & equipment; Mowers, power; Nurseries; Lawn & garden equipment; Lawn & garden supplies; Grass seed; Lawn machinery & equipment; Mowers, power; Nurseries; Lawn & garden equipment; Lawn & garden supplies
Pr: Jeffrey L Rutherford
Ch Bd: J Martin Erbaugh
COO: Bruce K Thorn
CFO: Michael A Weisbarth
Sr VP: Steven Cochran
Sr VP: Richard Doggett
VP: Mark Hradil
VP: Amy McGahan
VP: Kathleen M Minahan
VP: Lisa Zone
Exec: Cristy Cote

D-U-N-S 13-077-2395
LESCO RESTORATIONS INC
1341 Nazareth Church Rd, Spartanburg, SC 29301-5999
Tel (864) 439-8031 *Founded/Ownrshp* 1976
Sales 22.9MM^E *EMP* 130
SIC 1799 1761 Waterproofing; Roofing, siding & sheet metal work
Pr: Jim Marley
VP: Doug Marrese
VP: Scott Smith
Brnch Mgr: Ken Johnson
IT Man: Mike Brewer
IT Man: David Maiorana

D-U-N-S 61-516-7541
LESCONCIERGES INC
77 Maiden Ln Fl 6, San Francisco, CA 94108-5420
Tel (415) 905-6088 *Founded/Ownrshp* 2001
Sales 46.2MM^E *EMP* 199^E
SIC 7363 Help supply services; Help supply services
Ch Bd: Linda Jenkinson
**Pr:* Ramesh Patel

D-U-N-S 06-157-6252
LESEA BROADCASTING CORP
WHME TV 46
61300 Ironwood Rd, South Bend, IN 46614-9019
Tel (574) 291-8200 *Founded/Ownrshp* 1972
Sales 75.0MM^E *EMP* 240
SIC 4833 4832 Television broadcasting stations; Gospel; Religious; Television broadcasting stations; Gospel; Religious
Pr: Peter Sumrall
**Treas:* David E Sumrall
Ex VP: Michael Young
**VP:* Andrew Sumrall
Ex Dir: Chuck Huffman
Genl Mgr: Keith Passon
Genl Mgr: Lisa Slayton
Genl Mgr: Mike Swinehart
Off Mgr: Idell Stelly
Opers Mgr: Swinehart Mike

D-U-N-S 09-397-2644
LESIKAR HOLDINGS INC (TX)
CYCLONE STEEL
4950 W Greens Rd, Houston, TX 77066-4852
Tel (713) 635-5555 *Founded/Ownrshp* 1978, 1984
Sales 42.0MM^E *EMP* 55
SIC 5051 Steel
Pr: Steve Lesikar
Sec: Ladonna Lesikar

D-U-N-S 80-823-5477
LESLEY HOLDING CO INC
432 Mcneely Rd, Piedmont, SC 29673-9420
Tel (864) 295-1760 *Founded/Ownrshp* 1992
Sales 22.0MM *EMP* 163
SIC 3441 Fabricated structural metal; Fabricated structural metal
Pr: James Lesley
**VP:* Donald Lesley

D-U-N-S 00-176-8910
LESLEY UNIVERSITY
29 Everett St, Cambridge, MA 02138-2702
Tel (617) 868-9600 *Founded/Ownrshp* 1942
Sales 104.6MM *EMP* 800
Accts Mayer Hoffman Mccann Pc Bosto
SIC 8221 College, except junior; College, except junior
Pr: Joseph B Moore
**COO:* Charles Gilroy
COO: Edmund Toomey
**Treas:* Robert Sage
VP: Lori Ayotte
CIO: Karen Boudreaushea
Pgrm Dir: Linda Grisham
Pgrm Dir: Prudence King
Pgrm Dir: Elizabeth Stringer

D-U-N-S 00-128-4959 IMP
■ **LESLIE CONTROLS INC** (NJ)
(*Suby of* CIRCOR INTERNATIONAL INC) ★
12501 Telecom Dr, Temple Terrace, FL 33637-0903
Tel (813) 978-1000 *Founded/Ownrshp* 1900
Sales 34.7MM^E *EMP* 225
SIC 3491 3433 3822 3593 3494 3492 Automatic regulating & control valves; Valves, automatic control; Pressure valves & regulators, industrial; Solenoid valves; Steam heating apparatus; Auto controls regulating residntl & coml environmt & applncs; Fluid power cylinders & actuators; Valves & pipe fittings; Fluid power valves & hose fittings; Automatic regulating & control valves; Valves, automatic control; Pressure valves & regulators, industrial; Solenoid valves; Steam heating apparatus; Auto controls regulating residntl & coml environmt & applncs; Fluid power cylinders & actuators; Valves & pipe fittings; Fluid power valves & hose fittings
Pr: David A Bloss Sr
**VP:* Alan R Carlsen
VP: Leslie Cryolab
VP: Fabrizio Decandia
VP: Jeff Helbling
Exec: Steve Zdawczynski
CIO: Richard Rochford
Netwrk Eng: Shawn Harrison
Prd Mgr: Joseph Scalise
Mktg Dir: Carolyn Franklin
Mktg Dir: Tina Ware

D-U-N-S 03-984-9450
LESLIE COUNTY BOARD OF EDUCATION
27 Eagle Ln, Hyden, KY 41749
Tel (606) 672-2397 *Founded/Ownrshp* 1878
Sales 16.9MM^E *EMP* 360
SIC 8211 Public elementary & secondary schools; High school, junior or senior; School board; Public elementary & secondary schools; High school, junior or senior; School board

D-U-N-S 04-573-9182
■ **LESLIE COUNTY TELEPHONE CO**
(*Suby of* TDS TELECOMMUNICATIONS CORP) ★
22076 Main St, Hyden, KY 41749-8568
Tel (606) 672-2303 *Founded/Ownrshp* 1988
Sales 279.0MM^E *EMP* 2,700
SIC 4813 Local telephone communications; Local telephone communications
CEO: David A Wittwer

D-U-N-S 14-351-5323
LESLIE DIGITAL IMAGING LLC
LDI
50 Jericho Quadrangle # 115, Jericho, NY 11753-2726
Tel (516) 877-9100 *Founded/Ownrshp* 1999
Sales 55.0MM *EMP* 240
SIC 5044 7379 Photocopy machines; Computer related consulting services; Photocopy machines; Computer related consulting services
Pr: Fuchs Avery
COO: Paul Schwartz
**CFO:* Barry Bunsis
Sr VP: Mark Marturano
Sr VP: Stephen Uresk
VP: Doug Cassetta
VP: Jay Feldman
VP: B Williams
Sales Exec: Carol Vojt
VP Sls: Romano Ray
Mktg Dir: Brian Gertler

D-U-N-S 04-557-8929 IMP
LESLIE EQUIPMENT CO
JOHN DEERE
6248 Webster Rd, Cowen, WV 26206-8723
Tel (304) 226-3299 *Founded/Ownrshp* 1973
Sales 75.0MM^E *EMP* 250
SIC 5082

D-U-N-S 01-968-1435
LESLIE H WEXNER
8000 Walton Pkwy, New Albany, OH 43054-7073
Tel (614) 939-6000 *Founded/Ownrshp* 2008
Sales 42.1MM *EMP* 9^E
SIC 8641 Civic social & fraternal associations
Prin: Leslie H Wexner
Bd of Dir: Erica Brown

D-U-N-S 62-783-7842
LESLIE KNOTT LETCHER PERRY COMMUNITY ACTION COUNCIL INC
398 Roy Campbell Dr, Hazard, KY 41701-9486
Tel (606) 642-3310 *Founded/Ownrshp* 1965
Sales 38.5MM *EMP* 100
SIC 8322 Individual & family services; Individual & family services
Ex Dir: Rick Baker
Ofcr: Cena Stacy
Pgrm Dir: Renee Sexton

D-U-N-S 02-870-6307
LESLIE MOTORS
VICTORY TOYOTA
5 Heitzinger Plz, Seaside, CA 93955-3613
Tel (831) 393-3020 *Founded/Ownrshp* 1969
Sales 45.8MM^E *EMP* 100
SIC 5511 Automobiles, new & used; Automobiles, new & used
Pr: Peter E Blackstock
Sls Mgr: George Czechowski
Sls Mgr: Tracy Tate
Sales Asso: Mpowell Victorytoyota

D-U-N-S 13-041-0467
LESLIE RESOURCES INC
1021 Tori Dr, Hazard, KY 41701-6670
Tel (606) 439-0946 *Founded/Ownrshp* 2007
Sales 184.9MM^E *EMP* 3,991
SIC 1221 Surface mining, bituminous; Surface mining, bituminous
Ch Bd: Larry Addington

D-U-N-S 79-386-5697 IMP
LESLIES HOLDINGS INC
3925 E Broadway Rd # 100, Phoenix, AZ 85040-2966
Tel (602) 366-3999 *Founded/Ownrshp* 2007
Sales 1.6MMM^E *EMP* 3,200
SIC 5999 Swimming pool chemicals, equipment & supplies; Swimming pool chemicals, equipment & supplies
CEO: Larry Hayward
**Pr:* Michael L Hatch
**CFO:* Steven L Ortega
Sr VP: Janet I McDonald
CIO: Janet Macdonald
CTO: Lon Weiss
MIS Dir: Sherry Porter

D-U-N-S 05-010-6095 IMP
LESLIES POOLMART INC
LESLIE'S POOLS
(*Suby of* LESLIES HOLDINGS INC) ★
2005 E Indian School Rd, Phoenix, AZ 85016-6113
Tel (602) 366-3999 *Founded/Ownrshp* 2007
Sales 1.6MMM^E *EMP* 3,200^E
SIC 5091 Swimming pools, equipment & supplies; Swimming pools, equipment & supplies
Ch Bd: Lawrence H Hayward
Pr: Michael L Hatch
CFO: Steven L Ortega
CFO: Steven Ortega
Sr VP: Brian P Agnew
Sr VP: Brian Agnew
Sr VP: Stephen Blakeslee
Sr VP: Kory Klecker
VP: Sean Cope
VP: Kean Corrigan
VP: Bill Hicks
VP: Bill Rutherford
VP: Len Tamboer
Board of Directors: Edward C Agnew, John M Baumer, John G Danhakl, Michael J Fourticq

LESLIE'S POOLS
See LESLIES POOLMART INC

D-U-N-S 02-563-5228
LESMAN INSTRUMENT CO (IL)
135 Bernice Dr, Bensenville, IL 60106-3366
Tel (630) 595-8400 *Founded/Ownrshp* 1962, 1980
Sales 24.0MM *EMP* 33
SIC 5084 5085

D-U-N-S 00-821-3688
LESON CHEVROLET CO INC
LESON MEDIUM DUTY TRUCKS
1501 Westbank Expy, Harvey, LA 70058-4491
Tel (504) 366-4381 *Founded/Ownrshp* 1948
Sales 48.7MM^E *EMP* 110
SIC 5511 7532 7515 5521 Automobiles, new & used; Top & body repair & paint shops; Passenger car leasing; Used car dealers; Automobiles, new & used; Top & body repair & paint shops; Passenger car leasing; Used car dealers
Pr: Donald R Trapp
**Sec:* Simon Savoie
**VP:* June W Trapp
Sls Mgr: Terry Chauvin
Sls Mgr: Andrew Navarre
Sls Mgr: Reed Prestenbach
Sls Mgr: Paul Rodrigue
Sls Mgr: James Shaheen
Sales Asso: Gerald Lieteau

LESON MEDIUM DUTY TRUCKS
See LESON CHEVROLET CO INC

LESPORTSAC
See BRAND SCIENCE LLC

LESSING'S
See LESSINGS INC

D-U-N-S 01-211-3718
LESSINGS INC
LESSING'S
3500 Sunrise Hwy Ste 100, Great River, NY 11739-1001
Tel (631) 567-8200 *Founded/Ownrshp* 1961
Sales 16.0MM^E *EMP* 350
SIC 5812 Contract food services; Restaurant, family: independent; Contract food services; Restaurant, family: independent
Ch Bd: John S Lessing
**Ex VP:* John S Lessing Jr
**Ex VP:* Mark Lessing
**VP:* Lawrence Lessing III
Board of Directors: Robert Ferguson, Steve Lessing, Christopher Ryan

D-U-N-S 14-466-1188
LESSORS INC
1056 Gemini Rd, Eagan, MN 55121-2205
Tel (651) 789-9270 *Founded/Ownrshp* 1983
Sales 73.9MM^E *EMP* 403
SIC 4213 Trucking, except local; Trucking, except local
CEO: James R Shapiro

D-U-N-S 08-187-0479
LESTER A DRENK BEHAVIORAL HEALTH CENTER INC
DRENK CENTER , THE
1289 Route 38 Ste 203, Hainesport, NJ 08036-2730
Tel (609) 267-5656 *Founded/Ownrshp* 1955
Sales 20.6MM *EMP* 320
Accts Bowman & Company Llp Voorhees
SIC 8093 Mental health clinic, outpatient; Mental health clinic, outpatient
CEO: Harry J Marmorstein
**CFO:* David M Thompson
MIS Dir: Wayne Harrison

D-U-N-S 06-847-5623
LESTER AND ROSALIE ANIXTER CENTER
CHICAGO HEARING SOCIETY - DIV
2001 N Clybourn Ave Fl 3, Chicago, IL 60614-4036
Tel (773) 973-7900 *Founded/Ownrshp* 1919
Sales 21.7MM *EMP* 300
Accts Ss&G Inc Des Plaines Il
SIC 8322 Social services for the handicapped; Social services for the handicapped
CEO: Teresa Garate
**Ch Bd:* Joanna Horsnail
**CFO:* James Noga
Off Mgr: Martin Goertel

LESTER BUILDING SUPPLY
See LESTER GROUP INC

D-U-N-S 08-364-5130
LESTER BUILDING SYSTEMS LLC
1111 2nd Ave S, Lester Prairie, MN 55354-1003
Tel (320) 395-5212 *Founded/Ownrshp* 2004
Sales 100.4MM^E *EMP* 300
SIC 2452 Prefabricated buildings, wood; Prefabricated buildings, wood
Dir Soc: Stephanie Beste
Area Mgr: Craig Nieland
Genl Mgr: Craig Loger
IT Man: Bruce Minor
Plnt Mgr: Marty Schermann
Mktg Mgr: Jeannette Raufeisen
Sls Mgr: Butch Boehler
Sls Mgr: Steven Gustafson
Sls Mgr: Brad Hovden
Snr Mgr: Glenn Maesse

D-U-N-S 16-845-7443
LESTER BUILDINGS LLC
(*Suby of* LESTER BUILDING SYSTEMS LLC) ★
1111 2nd Ave S, Lester Prairie, MN 55354-1007
Tel (320) 395-5343 *Founded/Ownrshp* 2004
Sales 27.0MM *EMP* 120
SIC 1542 Nonresidential construction; Nonresidential construction
VP Sls: Mike Kelly

D-U-N-S 03-644-5448
LESTER E COX MEDICAL CENTER
COX HEALTH
305 S National Ave # 500, Springfield, MO 65802-3420
Tel (417) 269-6000 *Founded/Ownrshp* 1906
Sales 206.1MM^E *EMP* 6,000

SIC 8011 Medical centers; Medical centers
Pr: Robert Bezanson
**CEO:* Steve Edwards
**CFO:* Jake McWay
**VP:* John Duff
Dir Rad: Joseph Blamey
Ex Dir: Darren Bass
Brnch Mgr: John Carlile
Brnch Mgr: Carl Davis
Nurse Mgr: Marcy Estes
Nurse Mgr: Cindy Potts
Nurse Mgr: Lorinda Rehagen

D-U-N-S 07-303-7343
LESTER E COX MEDICAL CENTERS
COXHEALTH
1423 N Jefferson Ave, Springfield, MO 65802-1917
Tel (417) 269-3000 *Founded/Ownrshp* 1906
Sales 898.4MM *EMP* 9,100
SIC 8062 8069 General medical & surgical hospitals; General medical & surgical hospitals; Drug addiction rehabilitation hospital
CEO: Steven D Edwards
Chf Rad: Bryan Hall
Dir Vol: Barbara Frogue
COO: John Hursh
**CFO:* Jacob McWay
CFO: David Strong
Ofcr: Tracy Mitchell
Ofcr: Ron Prenger
VP: John Duff
VP: Laurie Duff
VP: Robert L Ferguson
VP: John Fry
VP: Karen Kramer
VP: Pete Leer
VP: Dan Sontheimer
Exec: Cindy Covington
Dir Risk M: Steven Brown
Dir Risk M: Charity Elmer
Dir Lab: Phyllis Finnell
Comm Dir: Yvette Williams

D-U-N-S 01-177-3322
LESTER GLENN BUICK INC
LESTER GLENN ISUZU
230 Rte 37 E, Toms River, NJ 08753-5589
Tel (732) 349-4200 *Founded/Ownrshp* 1972
Sales 38.6MM^E *EMP* 80^E
SIC 5511

LESTER GLENN ISUZU
See LESTER GLENN BUICK INC

D-U-N-S 00-312-0821
LESTER GROUP INC (VA)
LESTER BUILDING SUPPLY
101 Commonwealth Blvd E, Martinsville, VA 24112-2082
Tel (276) 638-8834 *Founded/Ownrshp* 1917
Sales 53.6MM^E *EMP* 175
Accts Dixon Hughes Goodman Llp Roan
SIC 5211 2491 6552 0811 Millwork & lumber; Wood preserving; Subdividers & developers; Timber tracts; Millwork & lumber; Wood preserving; Subdividers & developers; Timber tracts
CEO: George W Lester II
**Pr:* James O' Brien
COO: Terri Richardson
**Treas:* Tim Joyce
**Ex VP:* James Farrell
Genl Mgr: Brian Whitlow
Genl Mgr: Brian Witlow
CIO: Obstler Neal
CTO: Georgew Lester
IT Man: Kendall Preskitt

LESTER R SUMMERS HAULING
See LESTER R SUMMERS INC

D-U-N-S 00-278-9931
LESTER R SUMMERS INC (PA)
LESTER R SUMMERS HAULING
40 Garden Spot Rd Ste 100, Ephrata, PA 17522-9803
Tel (717) 733-6556 *Founded/Ownrshp* 1945
Sales 22.6MM *EMP* 111
Accts Simon Lever Llp Lancaster Pa
SIC 4213 4212 Building materials transport; Local trucking, without storage; Building materials transport; Local trucking, without storage
Pr: J Harold Summers
**Sec:* Lester R Summers Jr
**VP:* Kenneth R Summers

D-U-N-S 07-888-1489
LESTER SCHWAB KATZ & DWYER LLP
LSK&D
120 Broadway Fl 38, New York, NY 10271-3999
Tel (212) 964-6611 *Founded/Ownrshp* 1999
Sales 26.1MM^E *EMP* 160
SIC 8111 General practice law office; General practice law office
Mng Pt: Michael Mc Donagh
Pt: Richard Granofsky
Pt: Lawrence Green
Pt: Steven Prystowsky
Pt: Harold L Schwab
Mng Pt: Michael Donagh
Pr: Jasmine Rupnarain
Ofcr: Marcus Pincus
Ofcr: Vera Saks
Dir IT: Tony Lee
Counsel: Jennifer Kelly

D-U-N-S 83-125-8962
LESTERS OF GREENVALE INC
2411 Coney Island Ave, Brooklyn, NY 11223-5021
Tel (718) 645-4501 *Founded/Ownrshp* 1948
Sales 41.7MM^E *EMP* 700
SIC 2389 Apparel for handicapped; Apparel for handicapped
Pr: Perry Shcorr

D-U-N-S 03-106-1336
LETA ENTERPRISES INC
FRANK LETA ACURA
1177 Tesson Ferry Rd, Saint Louis, MO 63128
Tel (314) 291-2332 *Founded/Ownrshp* 1966
Sales 61.8MM^E *EMP* 110
SIC 5511 Automobiles, new & used; Automobiles, new & used
Pr: Frank S Leta
**VP:* Jeff Conrad
**VP:* Antoinette Leta
Sales Asso: Christopher Ruppert

D-U-N-S 03-007-3068
LETCHER COUNTY PUBLIC SCHOOL DIST
224 Parks St, Whitesburg, KY 41858-7538
Tel (606) 633-4455 *Founded/Ownrshp* 1900
Sales 30.9MM^E *EMP* 639
SIC 8211 Public elementary school; Public elementary school
Teacher Pr: Denise Yonts

D-U-N-S 15-034-7268 IMP
LETCO GROUP LLC
LIVING EARTH
1901 Cal Crossing Rd, Dallas, TX 75220-7005
Tel (972) 506-8575 *Founded/Ownrshp* 2007
Sales 76.6MM^E *EMP* 230
SIC 2875 Compost; Potting soil, mixed; Compost; Potting soil, mixed
Pr: Mark Rose
Brnch Mgr: Paul Tomaso
Genl Mgr: Jeff Robnett

D-U-N-S 04-926-6976 IMP/EXP
LETICA CORP
52585 Dequindre Rd, Rochester Hills, MI 48307-2321
Tel (248) 652-0557 *Founded/Ownrshp* 1968
Sales 810.4MM^E *EMP* 1,800
SIC 2656 3089 Sanitary food containers; Plastic containers, except foam; Sanitary food containers; Plastic containers, except foam
Ch Bd: Ilija Letica
**Treas:* Gudrun Letica
VP: Charles Dorger
**VP:* Albert J Gustafson
VP: Anton Letica
VP: Tim Nelson
VP: Brian Vautaw
Off Mgr: June Phillips
CIO: Bob Stone
QA Dir: Richard Leonard
IT Man: Cosentino Andy

LETIGRE
See LT2 LLC

LETNER ROOFING COMPANY
See DANNY LETNER INC

D-U-N-S 07-762-8493
LETNES RESTAURANT INC
BONANZA RESTAURANT
137 2nd Ave S, Waite Park, MN 56387-1323
Tel (320) 253-4092 *Founded/Ownrshp* 1975
Sales 19.7MM^E *EMP* 600
SIC 5812 Steak restaurant; Steak restaurant
Pr: Steven Letnes
**CEO:* Curtis Letnes

D-U-N-S 05-598-3522 EXP
■ LETOURNEAU TECHNOLOGIES AMERICA INC (TX)
(*Suby of* JOY GLOBAL LONGVIEW OPERATIONS LLC) ★
2400 Macarthur St, Longview, TX 75602-5300
Tel (903) 237-7000 *Founded/Ownrshp* 1956, 1970
Sales 20.9MM^E *EMP* 53
SIC 5082 5084 3531 General construction machinery & equipment; Industrial machinery & equipment; Construction machinery
CEO: Thomas P Burke
**Pr:* Robert Chesnik
**CEO:* Dan Eckermann
**VP:* Anniken Hoelsaeter
**VP:* Jack McElroy
Genl Mgr: Lowry Wood

D-U-N-S 01-047-3718
LETOURNEAU UNIVERSITY
2100 S Mobberly Ave, Longview, TX 75602-3564
Tel (903) 233-3000 *Founded/Ownrshp* 1946
Sales 64.2MM *EMP* 814
Accts Bkd Llp Fort Wayne In
SIC 8221 University; University
Pr: Dale A Lunsford
**CFO:* Mike Hood
Treas: Ben Burleson
Ofcr: Barnabas Bridgman
Ofcr: Leigh Dufrene
Ofcr: Rachel Fox
Assoc VP: Alan Clipperton
Ex VP: Aaron Lorson
VP: Katie Carvalho
VP: Melanie Dittmer
VP: Michael Koreis

D-U-N-S 14-289-1048 IMP
LETS DO LUNCH
INTEGRATED FOOD SERVICE
310 W Alondra Blvd, Gardena, CA 90248-2423
Tel (310) 523-3664 *Founded/Ownrshp* 1991
Sales 33.8MM^E *EMP* 80
SIC 2099 Sandwiches, assembled & packaged: for wholesale market
Pr: Paul G Giuliano
VP: Lisa Durkin
**VP:* Jon Sugimoto

D-U-N-S 80-000-0705
LETS GO INC
(*Suby of* HARVARD STUDENT AGENCIES INC) ★
67 Mount Auburn St, Cambridge, MA 02138-4961
Tel (617) 495-9659 *Founded/Ownrshp* 1960
Sales 41.5MM^E *EMP* 1,000
SIC 2741 Miscellaneous publishing; Miscellaneous publishing
Genl Mgr: Anne Chisholm
**Snr Sftwr:* David Powers
Dir IT: Doug Hoffman
IT Man: Mark Ting
Prd Mgr: Jansen Thurmer
Mktg Mgr: Caitlin Loveitt

D-U-N-S 12-487-3055
LETSTALK.COM INC
201 Mission St Ste 3000, San Francisco, CA 94105-1884
Tel (415) 357-7600 *Founded/Ownrshp* 1999
Sales 22.2MM^E *EMP* 100
SIC 4812 4813 Cellular telephone services; Telephone communication, except radio
Pr: Delly Tamer
COO: Lance Frey
COO: Ruth Yankoupe

D-U-N-S 02-661-8207
LETSOS CO
8435 Westglen Dr, Houston, TX 77063-6311
Tel (713) 783-3200 *Founded/Ownrshp* 1953
Sales 152.7MM^E *EMP* 325
SIC 1711 7623 Mechanical contractor; Plumbing contractors; Warm air heating & air conditioning contractor; Air conditioning repair; Mechanical contractor; Plumbing contractors; Warm air heating & air conditioning contractor; Air conditioning repair
Pr: James N Letsos III
**CFO:* Mark Letsos
**Ex VP:* John G Letsos
CIO: Jason Feng
Snr PM: Ronald Lavoi
Snr PM: David Laws
Snr PM: Alan Mikulenka

D-U-N-S 01-901-8035
LETTER SYSTEMS INC
J S MCCARTHY PRINTING
15 Darin Dr, Augusta, ME 04330-7815
Tel (207) 622-7126 *Founded/Ownrshp* 1978
Sales 39.9MM^E *EMP* 207
SIC 2752 Commercial printing, offset; Commercial printing, offset
Pr: Richard Tardiff
COO: Bill White
**CFO:* Conrad Ayotte
Dir IT: Judi Hanson
VP Opers: Jon Tardiff
Opers Mgr: Tedd Giroux

D-U-N-S 15-186-8536
LETTERHEAD PRESS INC
LPI
16800 W Ryerson Rd, New Berlin, WI 53151-3522
Tel (262) 787-1717 *Founded/Ownrshp* 1984
Sales 22.4MM^E *EMP* 125
SIC 2759 Embossing on paper
Pr: Michael Graf
**CFO:* Kevin Webb
VP: Dick Reindl
Dir IT: Evan Howard
Plnt Mgr: Joe Miller
Ql Cn Mgr: Jon Young

D-U-N-S 96-949-0478
LETTIE PATE WHITEHEAD FOUNDATION INC
191 Peachtree St Ne # 3540, Atlanta, GA 30303-1799
Tel (404) 522-6755 *Founded/Ownrshp* 2011
Sales 52.0MM *EMP* 2^E
SIC 8322 Community center; Community center
Prin: P Hardin

D-U-N-S 10-114-7676
LETTIRE CONSTRUCTION CORP
334 E 110th St 336, New York, NY 10029-3105
Tel (212) 996-6640 *Founded/Ownrshp* 1984
Sales 150.0MM *EMP* 90
SIC 1531 Operative builders
Pr: Nicholas Lettire
**VP:* Gerard Lettire
Snr PM: Daniel Hlavac

D-U-N-S 07-686-4396
LETTUCE ENTERTAIN YOU ENTERPRISES INC
5419 N Sheridan Rd # 116, Chicago, IL 60640-1964
Tel (773) 878-7340 *Founded/Ownrshp* 1971
Sales 131.9MM^E *EMP* 3,500
SIC 5812 8741 Eating places; Restaurant management; Eating places; Restaurant management
CEO: Kevin Brown
Pt: Perry H Fuselier
Pt: Michael Rotolo
Mng Pt: Perry Fuselier
Mng Pt: Jerrod Melman
**Pr:* Manford Joast
**Pr:* Robert Wattel
**Ch:* Richard Melman
Ex VP: Sue Chernoff
VP: Susie Southgate-Fox
**VP:* Jay Stieber
Exec: Juan Diaz
Exec: Daniel Espinoza
Exec: Moreno Espinoza
Exec: Ben Goodnick
Exec: Marcelo Han
Exec: Matt Holmes
Exec: Anthony Martin
Exec: Andrew Shedden
Exec: Thierry Tritsch
Exec: Chico Valchez

D-U-N-S 03-594-3984
LETTUCE ENTERTAIN YOU TOO INC
5419 N Sheridan Rd # 116, Chicago, IL 60640-1900
Tel (773) 878-7340 *Founded/Ownrshp* 1976
Sales 121.5MM^E *EMP* 5,000
SIC 5812 5813 Restaurant, family: independent; Cocktail lounge; Restaurant, family: independent; Cocktail lounge
Pr: Richard Melman
**V Ch Bd:* Charles Haskell
Ex VP: Jay Stieber
**VP:* Robert Wattell
Exec: Chris Morvis
Genl Mgr: Adam Murphy

D-U-N-S 05-526-9534
LETTUCE FEED YOU INC
MCDONALD'S
120 Washington St Ste 201, Watertown, NY 13601-3330
Tel (315) 782-8030 *Founded/Ownrshp* 1977
Sales 11.1MM^E *EMP* 500
SIC 5812 Fast-food restaurant, chain; Fast-food restaurant, chain
Pr: James O'Donnell

D-U-N-S 04-525-6922
▲ LEUCADIA NATIONAL CORP (NY)
520 Madison Ave Bsmt A, New York, NY 10022-4357
Tel (212) 460-1900 *Founded/Ownrshp* 1968
Sales 12.3MMM *EMP* 13,082^E
Accts Pricewaterhousecoopers Llp Ne
Tkr Sym LUK *Exch* NYS
SIC 6798 6211 1382 2011 2426 Real estate investment trusts; Investment certificate sales; Investment bankers; Liquefied petroleum gases (natural) production; Real estate investment trusts; Investment certificate sales; Investment bankers; Oil & gas exploration services; Boxed beef from meat slaughtered on site; Dimension, hardwood
CEO: Richard B Handler
**Ch Bd:* Joseph S Steinberg
**Pr:* Brian P Friedman
CFO: Teresa S Gendron
Treas: Rocco J Nittoli
Treas: Rocco Nittoli
Bd of Dir: Paul Dougan
Ex VP: Thomas Mara
Ex VP: Michael J Sharp
VP: Barbara L Lowenthal
VP: Barbara Lowenthal
VP: Joseph Oconnor
VP: Cullen Schaar
Board of Directors: Linda L Adamany, Robert D Beyer, Francisco L Borges, W Patrick Campbell, Robert E Joyal, Jeffery C Keil, Michael T O'kane, Stuart H Reese

D-U-N-S 07-520-9510
LEUKEMIA & LYMPHOMA SOCIETY INC
LLS
1311 Mnroneck Ave Ste 310, White Plains, NY 10605
Tel (914) 949-5213 *Founded/Ownrshp* 1949
Sales 290.3MM *EMP* 825
SIC 8699 8399 8322 8011 8733 8621

D-U-N-S 03-965-8448
LEUNER INC
NORTHEAST GREAT DANE
315 Sunnymeade Rd, Hillsborough, NJ 08844-4638
Tel (908) 359-9599 *Founded/Ownrshp* 1945
Sales 52.7MM^E *EMP* 160
SIC 5012 5013 7539 Trailers for trucks, new & used; Trailer parts & accessories; Truck parts & accessories; Trailer repair; Trailers for trucks, new & used; Trailer parts & accessories; Truck parts & accessories; Trailer repair
Ch Bd: Thomas Leuner
VP: John Gendelman

D-U-N-S 04-577-6796 IMP
LEUPOLD & STEVENS INC
14400 Nw Greenbrier Pkwy, Beaverton, OR 97006-5791
Tel (503) 526-1400 *Founded/Ownrshp* 1944
Sales 107.6MM^E *EMP* 500^E
SIC 3827 Telescopic sights; Lens mounts; Binoculars; Telescopic sights; Lens mounts; Binoculars
Pr: Calvin S Johnston
**Ch Bd:* Jim Clark
Pr: Fritz Kaufman
**Pr:* Howard Werth
VP: Kimberly King
VP: Kevin Trepa
VP: Wayne Waycloud
Exec: Kathy McCallister
CTO: Skip Lingle
QA Dir: Martha Figueroa
QA Dir: Tram Nguyen
Board of Directors: Don R Kania, Dennis Spindler

D-U-N-S 79-879-3469 IMP/EXP
LEVANTINA USA INC
(*Suby of* LEVANTINA Y ASOCIADOS DE MINERALES SOCIEDAD ANONIMA)
11180 Zodiac Ln, Dallas, TX 75229-4721
Tel (972) 488-2800 *Founded/Ownrshp* 1992
Sales 23.7MM^E *EMP* 54^E
SIC 5032 Brick, stone & related material
CEO: Frank De Haan
**COO:* Joseph K Dobbins
CFO: Ken Dobbins
Genl Mgr: Brandon Fish
Genl Mgr: John Mitchell
Sales Asso: Anna Miller
Sales Asso: Joe Nelson

LEVATOY
See LEVCO SALES INC

D-U-N-S 10-785-6648
LEVCO SALES INC
LEVATOY
465 W Main St Ste 3, Wyckoff, NJ 07481-1452
Tel (201) 820-3030 *Founded/Ownrshp* 1971
Sales 23.0MM^E *EMP* 6
SIC 5199 5092 General merchandise, non-durable; Toys; General merchandise, non-durable; Toys
Pr: George Schwartz
**VP:* Joshua Schwartz

D-U-N-S 07-833-0696
LEVEL 10 CONSTRUCTION LP
1050 Entp Way Ste 250, Sunnyvale, CA 94089
Tel (408) 747-5000 *Founded/Ownrshp* 2011
Sales 200.0MM *EMP* 220
Accts Lautze
SIC 1542 Commercial & office buildings, renovation & repair; Commercial & office buildings, renovation & repair
Pr: Dennis Giles
CFO: Jim Evans
Off Mgr: Pauline Flores

VP Opers: Mike Conroy
Sfty Dirs: Rick Siefert
Mktg Dir: Jill Lonergan

D-U-N-S 10-372-8239
LEVEL 10 LLC
TEKSERVE POS
2495 Pembroke Ave, Hoffman Estates, IL 60169-2010
Tel (847) 805-9050 *Founded/Ownrshp* 2001
Sales 48.0MM *EMP* 95
SIC 7389 5044 7629 Field warehousing; Cash registers; Electronic equipment repair; Field warehousing; Cash registers; Electronic equipment repair

D-U-N-S 96-746-1567
LEVEL 3 AUDIO VISUAL LLC
955 E Javelina Ave # 106, Mesa, AZ 85204-6632
Tel (480) 892-1071 *Founded/Ownrshp* 1996
Sales 39.0MM^E^ *EMP* 53
SIC 5065 7539 Electronic parts & equipment; Automotive sound system service & installation
CEO: Robert Bradley Peterson
COO: Jeremy Elsesser
Ofcr: Lisa Hale

D-U-N-S 00-697-0263
▲ **LEVEL 3 COMMUNICATIONS INC** (DE)
1025 Eldorado Blvd, Broomfield, CO 80021-8254
Tel (720) 888-1000 *Founded/Ownrshp* 1988
Sales 6.7MMM *EMP* 10,040^E^
Accts Kpmg Llp Denver Colorado
Tkr Sym LVLT *Exch* NYS
SIC 4813 7373 7374 Telephone communication, except radio; Computer integrated systems design; Data processing & preparation; Telephone communication, except radio; Computer integrated systems design; Data processing & preparation
Pr: Jeffrey K Storey
Pr: Michael Buchner
**CFO:* Sunit S Patel
CFO: S Sunit
**Ofcr:* Laurinda Y Pang
Ex VP: Neil Hobbs
**Sr VP:* Eric J Mortensen
Exec: Jodi Ashley
Exec: Melissa Benton
Ex Dir: Stan Lake
**CTO:* John F Waters Jr
Board of Directors: Kevin P Chilton, Steven T Clontz, Irene M Esteves, T Michael Glenn, Spencer B Hays, Peter Seah Lim Huat, Michael J Mahoney, Kevin W Mooney, Peter Van Oppen

D-U-N-S 07-309-0917
■ **LEVEL 3 COMMUNICATIONS LLC**
(*Suby of* LEVEL 3 FINANCING INC) ★
1025 Eldorado Blvd, Broomfield, CO 80021-8254
Tel (720) 888-1000 *Founded/Ownrshp* 1998
Sales 1.4MMM^E^ *EMP* 5,300
Accts Kpmg Llp Denver Co
SIC 4813 7373 Telephone communication, except radio; Computer integrated systems design; Telephone communication, except radio; Computer integrated systems design
Pr: Jeff Storey
CFO: Sunit A Patel
**Ex VP:* Sunit Patel
**Ex VP:* Thomas C Stortz
**Sr VP:* Robin Grey
VP: Edward Macatee
**Prin:* Charles C Miller III
Snr Mgr: Tim Day

D-U-N-S 78-350-2458
■ **LEVEL 3 FINANCING INC**
(*Suby of* LEVEL 3 COMMUNICATIONS INC) ★
1025 Eldorado Blvd, Broomfield, CO 80021-8254
Tel (720) 888-1000 *Founded/Ownrshp* 1990
Sales 1.4MMM^E^ *EMP* 5^E^
SIC 4813 Telephone communication, except radio
CEO: James Crowe
**Pr:* Kevin O'Hara
**CFO:* Sunit Patel
**Ex VP:* Thomas Stortz
**Sr VP:* Eric Mortensen

D-U-N-S 10-715-8677
■ **LEVEL 3 HOLDINGS INC**
(*Suby of* LEVEL 3 FINANCING INC) ★
1025 Eldorado Blvd 2000, Broomfield, CO 80021-8254
Tel (720) 888-1000 *Founded/Ownrshp* 1996
Sales 29.8MM^E^ *EMP* 200^E^
SIC 1241 Coal mining services; Coal mining services
Pr: Douglas Bradbury
**VP:* Neil J Eckstein
**VP:* Matthew J Johnson
**VP:* Thomas C Stortz

D-U-N-S 14-489-4172
LEVEL 5 LLC
2018 Powers Ferry Rd Se # 750, Atlanta, GA 30339-7201
Tel (404) 761-0008 *Founded/Ownrshp* 2003
Sales 34.5MM^E^ *EMP* 52
SIC 1542 Bank building construction; Design & erection, combined: non-residential
CEO: Brad Eller
**Ch:* J F Kassler
**Sr VP:* John Hyche
**VP:* Michael Colvin
VP: Robert Quarles

LEVEL 99
See PHOENIX TEXTILE INC

D-U-N-S 02-644-0842
LEVEL FOOD CENTER INC
8509 Western Hills Blvd # 200, Fort Worth, TX 76108-3410
Tel (817) 246-5578 *Founded/Ownrshp* 1964
Sales 22.5MM^E^ *EMP* 320
SIC 5411 Supermarkets, chain; Supermarkets, chain
Pr: James Level
**Treas:* Craig Level
**VP:* Richard Level
**VP:* Ruth Level

D-U-N-S 80-864-8336
LEVEL ONE BANCORP INC
LEVEL ONE BANK
32991 Hamilton Ct, Farmington Hills, MI 48334-3330
Tel (248) 737-0300 *Founded/Ownrshp* 2006
Sales NA *EMP* 65^E^
SIC 6021 National commercial banks; National commercial banks
Pr: Patrick Fehring
**CFO:* David C Walker
Ofcr: Jacqueline Gismondi
Ofcr: Jacob Hachey
Ofcr: Sara Rusea
Ofcr: David Watkins
Assoc VP: Matthew Thompson
**Ex VP:* Gregory A Wernette
Sr VP: Fred Fordon
**Sr VP:* Leslie Geupel
Sr VP: Violet Gintsis
Sr VP: Timothy Mackay
**Sr VP:* Eva Scurlock
VP: Charles Borders
VP: Brenda Brandom
VP: Holly Dapolito
VP: Brad Donnelly
VP: Curtis King
VP: Michelle Kirsten
VP: Keith Lublin
VP: Ryan Oliver
Board of Directors: Barbara Allushuski, Stefan Wanczyk

LEVEL ONE BANK
See LEVEL ONE BANCORP INC

LEVEL SOLAR
See SUNCREST SOLAR INC

D-U-N-S 15-451-1757
LEVEL STUDIOS INC
(*Suby of* ROSETTA LLC) ★
4800 Morabito Pl, San Luis Obispo, CA 93401-8748
Tel (805) 781-0546 *Founded/Ownrshp* 2010
Sales 22.3MM^E^ *EMP* 215
SIC 8742 Marketing consulting services; Marketing consulting services
CEO: Tom Adamski
Pr: Dan Connolly
COO: Paul Rappoport
Chf Cred: Alexander Mahernia
Sr VP: Michael Phillips
VP: Patrick Dahl
VP: Tom Kotlarek
VP: Rebecca Lee
VP: Peter Tax
VP: Curt Van Inwegen
Comm Man: Brittany Slattery

D-U-N-S 02-542-7907
LEVELLAND INDEPENDENT SCHOOL DISTRICT (TX)
704 11th St, Levelland, TX 79336-5400
Tel (806) 894-6355 *Founded/Ownrshp* 1923
Sales 33.4MM *EMP* 375
SIC 8211 Public elementary school; Public junior high school; Public senior high school; Public elementary school; Public junior high school; Public senior high school

LEVELUP
See SCVNGR INC

D-U-N-S 14-291-3396
LEVELWING MEDIA LLC
260 W 35th St Ste 802, New York, NY 10001-2577
Tel (646) 216-8320 *Founded/Ownrshp* 2002
Sales 49.0MM *EMP* 40
SIC 8742 Marketing consulting services; Marketing consulting services

D-U-N-S 07-443-6940
LEVENFELD PEARLSTEIN LLC
LP
2 N La Salle St Ste 1300, Chicago, IL 60602-3709
Tel (312) 346-8380 *Founded/Ownrshp* 1999
Sales 25.6MM^E^ *EMP* 135
SIC 8111 Corporate, partnership & business law; Corporate, partnership & business law

D-U-N-S 17-575-3300 IMP
LEVENGER CO
420 S Congress Ave, Delray Beach, FL 33445-4696
Tel (561) 276-2436 *Founded/Ownrshp* 1990
Sales 33.3MM^E^ *EMP* 150^E^
SIC 5961 Catalog & mail-order houses; Furniture & furnishings, mail order; Catalog & mail-order houses; Furniture & furnishings, mail order
Pr: Steven Leveen
Pr: Wanda Cieri
VP: Lori Granger Leveen
VP Mktg: Brian Dean
Mktg Dir: Dana Leake
Mktg Dir: Daniel Marshall
Mktg Mgr: Kristine Cucurello
Art Dir: Ilene Stern

LEVENSON AND HILL
See LEVENSON LEVENSON & HILL INC

D-U-N-S 03-533-4689
LEVENSON LEVENSON & HILL INC
LEVENSON AND HILL
717 N Harwood St Ste 800, Dallas, TX 75201-6579
Tel (214) 932-6000 *Founded/Ownrshp* 1981
Sales 31.3MM^E^ *EMP* 100
SIC 7311 8743 Advertising agencies; Public relations & publicity; Advertising agencies; Public relations & publicity
Pr: Barbara Levenson
**CEO:* Stanley R Levenson
Ex VP: Saira Haleem
Ex VP: Robert N McEnany
Sr VP: Faithe Nicholson
VP: Dara Dobbins
VP: Saira Hill
VP: Katie Martin
VP: Melissa Renner
Creative D: Charles Paris

LEVENTHAL BROS & CO
See LEVENTHAL LTD

D-U-N-S 00-122-6471
LEVENTHAL LTD
LEVENTHAL BROS & CO
P.O. Box 564, Fayetteville NC (28302-0564)
Tel (516) 365-9540 *Founded/Ownrshp* 1996
Sales 23.2MM^E^ *EMP* 250
SIC 2337 5136 2326 5137 Uniforms, except athletic: women's, misses' & juniors'; Uniforms, men's & boys'; Work uniforms; Uniforms, women's & children's; Uniforms, except athletic: women's, misses' & juniors'; Uniforms, men's & boys'; Work uniforms; Uniforms, women's & children's
Sec: Danny Shamdasani

D-U-N-S 80-759-6051
LEVERAGE INFORMATION SYSTEMS INC
FEDERAL NETWORK SERVICES
18815 139th Ave Ne Ste B, Woodinville, WA 98072-3565
Tel (425) 482-9200 *Founded/Ownrshp* 1993
Sales 26.4MM^E^ *EMP* 75
SIC 7373 5045 Computer integrated systems design; Computers
Pr: Douglas Chesler
**VP:* Terry Woodruff
Netwrk Eng: Louis Goscinski
Opers Mgr: Rosie Sineros
Natl Sales: Jim Portugal
Sls&Mrk Ex: Len Fager
Mktg Dir: Kevin Flynn
Sls Dir: Dawn Isaac
Sls Mgr: Don Hedges
Sls Mgr: Bob Herold
Sls Mgr: Ray Leblond

LEVEREDGE, THE
See SOLAR CITY INC

D-U-N-S 03-753-4484
LEVERING MANAGEMENT INC
MARION MANOR
201 N Main St, Mount Vernon, OH 43050-2400
Tel (740) 397-3897 *Founded/Ownrshp* 1956
Sales 29.8MM^E^ *EMP* 500
SIC 8741 Management services; Management services
Pr: William B Levering

D-U-N-S 03-840-9868
LEVI RAY & SHOUP INC
LRS
2401 W Monroe St, Springfield, IL 62704-1439
Tel (217) 793-3800 *Founded/Ownrshp* 1979
Sales 205.6MM *EMP* 603
Accts Mcgladrey Llp Springfield I
SIC 7371 5045 7379 Custom computer programming services; Computer software development; Computers, peripherals & software; Computer related consulting services; Custom computer programming services; Computer software development; Computers, peripherals & software; Computer related consulting services
Pr: Richard H Levi
**Sr VP:* John Howerter
**VP:* Pam Benad
**VP:* Max Dillahunty
**VP:* Brian Huggins
VP: Kevin Huxley
VP: Ken Ratliff
VP: Roger Ray
VP: Harvey Thomas
Prac Mgr: Jim Krug
MIS Dir: Scott Richardson

D-U-N-S 00-910-9273 IMP/EXP
LEVI STRAUSS & CO
1155 Battery St, San Francisco, CA 94111-1264
Tel (415) 501-6000 *Founded/Ownrshp* 1850
Sales 4.7MMM *EMP* 16,000
Accts Pricewaterhousecoopers Llp Sa
SIC 2325 2339 2321 2331 2337 2329 Jeans: men's, youths' & boys'; Slacks, dress: men's, youths' & boys'; Jeans: women's, misses' & juniors'; Slacks: women's, misses' & juniors'; Athletic clothing: women's, misses' & juniors'; Men's & boys' furnishings; Shirts, women's & juniors': made from purchased materials; T-shirts & tops, women's: made from purchased materials; Skirts, separate: women's, misses' & juniors'; Jackets (suede, leatherette, etc.), sport: men's & boys'; Athletic (warmup, sweat & jogging) suits: men's & boys'; Jeans: men's, youths' & boys'; Slacks, dress: men's, youths' & boys'; Jeans: women's, misses' & juniors'; Slacks: women's, misses' & juniors'; Athletic clothing: women's, misses' & juniors'; Men's & boys' furnishings; Shirts, women's & juniors': made from purchased materials; T-shirts & tops, women's: made from purchased materials; Skirts, separate: women's, misses' & juniors'; Jackets (suede, leatherette, etc.), sport: men's & boys'; Athletic (warmup, sweat & jogging) suits: men's & boys'
Pr: Charles V Bergh
**Ch Bd:* Stephen C Neal
Pr: Roy Bagattini
Pr: Seth Ellison
Pr: Anne Rohosy
CFO: Harmit Singh
Chf Cred: Kelly McGinnis
Bd of Dir: Gokul Krishna
Ex VP: Lillian Jin
Ex VP: Susan Kilgore
Ex VP: Rich Lack
Ex VP: Steve Levandowski
Ex VP: John Quandt
Ex VP: Daryl Thomas
Ex VP: Jeff Turner
Sr VP: Seth R Jaffe
Sr VP: David Love
Sr VP: Fred Paulenich
Exec: Howard Beger
Exec: Nare Jagroop
Exec: Pamela Strazadas
Board of Directors: Patricia Salas Pineda, Troy Alstead, Jill Beraud, Vanessa J Castagna, Robert A Eckert, Spencer Fleischer, Mimi L Haas, Peter E Haas Jr, Robert D Haas, Jenny Ming

D-U-N-S 00-880-0542
LEVIN MORRIS AND SON
MORRIS LEVIN RENTL & PARTS CTR
1816 S K St, Tulare, CA 93274-6842
Tel (559) 686-8665 *Founded/Ownrshp* 1981
Sales 47.5MM^E^ *EMP* 125
SIC 5251 1711 7359 Lumber & other building materials; Plumbing, heating, air-conditioning contractors; Rental store, general; Hardware; Plumbing, heating, air-conditioning contractors; Rental store, general
Pr: Paul Atlas
CFO: Tom Colesberry
**VP:* David Atlas
**VP:* Marilyn Atlas

D-U-N-S 09-359-6005
LEVIN PAPANTONIO THOMAS MITCHELL ECHSNER & PROCTOR PA
316 S Baylen St Ste 600, Pensacola, FL 32502-5996
Tel (850) 435-7169 *Founded/Ownrshp* 1969
Sales 22.7MM^E^ *EMP* 141
SIC 8111 General practice attorney, lawyer; General practice attorney, lawyer
Pr: Mark Proctor
**Sec:* Leo Thomas
**VP:* M Robert Blanchard
**VP:* Virginia M Buchanan
VP: Shane Lincke
Ex Dir: Martin Levin
Dir IT: Greg Rawson
Sls&Mrk Ex: Robert Blanchard

D-U-N-S 15-363-0694
LEVIN PROFESSIONAL SERVICES INC
WASHINGTON PROF SYSTEMS
11242 Grandview Ave, Wheaton, MD 20902-4632
Tel (301) 942-6800 *Founded/Ownrshp* 1986
Sales 28.7MM^E^ *EMP* 43
SIC 5099 Video & audio equipment
VP: Alan Levin
**CFO:* Brett Schneider
**Treas:* Abbe Levin
VP: Greg Lukens
Snr PM: Kris Emery

D-U-N-S 05-321-2478
LEVIN TIRE CENTER INC
9500 Indianapolis Blvd, Highland, IN 46322-2616
Tel (219) 924-1710 *Founded/Ownrshp* 1969
Sales 35.2MM^E^ *EMP* 99
SIC 5531 7538 Automotive tires; General automotive repair shops
Pr: Barry Levin
Mktg Dir: Daniel Trzeciak

D-U-N-S 07-829-6043
LEVINDALE HEBREW GERIATRIC CENTER AND HOSPITAL INC (MD)
(*Suby of* LIFEBRIDGE HEALTH INC) ★
2434 W Belvedere Ave # 1, Baltimore, MD 21215-5267
Tel (410) 601-2400 *Founded/Ownrshp* 1927
Sales 84.7MM *EMP* 461
Accts Kpmg Llp Mc Lean Va
SIC 8069 8051 Specialty hospitals, except psychiatric; Geriatric hospital; Skilled nursing care facilities; Specialty hospitals, except psychiatric; Geriatric hospital; Skilled nursing care facilities
CEO: Ronald Rothstein
**Pr:* Aric Spitulnik
COO: Idriz Limaj
CFO: Raul Lujuan
**VP:* Cathy Gallo
**VP:* David Krajewski
VP: Jennifer Labute
**VP:* Susan Levy
VP: John Robison
Dir Rad: Bradley Jones
Pharmcst: Robin Franklin

D-U-N-S 04-834-8663 IMP
LEVINDI
(*Suby of* VIVENDI HOLDING I LLC) ★
800 3rd Ave, New York, NY 10022-7649
Tel (212) 572-7000 *Founded/Ownrshp* 1995
Sales 8.0MM^E^ *EMP* 478^E^
SIC 2085 2084 5182 2033 2086 2037 Distilled & blended liquors; Neutral spirits, except fruit; Bourbon whiskey; Cocktails, alcoholic; Brandy; Wines; Wine coolers (beverages); Wine & distilled beverages; Fruit juices: packaged in cans, jars, etc.; Fruit drinks (less than 100% juice): packaged in cans, etc.; Fruit juice concentrates, frozen
Pr: Gean Fourtou Jr
CFO: Jacque Espinasse
Div Pres: Anita Larson
Ofcr: Kathy Chalmers
VP: George E Bushnell III
VP: Kevin Conway
VP: Rosanna M Duruthy
VP: Tereasa Harris
VP: Gary Minck
Genl Mgr: Tina Scalise

LEVINE BUILDERS
See JE LEVINE BUILDER INC

LEVINE CHILDREN'S HOSPITAL
See CAROLINAS MEDICAL CENTER AT HOME LLC

D-U-N-S 18-858-0922
LEVINE LEICHTMAN CAPITAL PARTNERS INC
LLCP
335 N Maple Dr Ste 240, Beverly Hills, CA 90210-5198
Tel (310) 275-5335 *Founded/Ownrshp* 1994
Sales 332.3MM^E^ *EMP* 966
SIC 6799 Investors; Investors
CEO: Lauren B Leichtman
**Pr:* Arthur E Levine
CFO: Steve Hogan
Assoc Dir: Peter Deschner
Assoc Dir: Nathan Lemmerman
Assoc Dir: Matthew Rich
Mng Dir: Monica Holec
Mng Dir: Brad Parish
Mng Dir: Kimberly Pollack
Mng Dir: Lee Stern

D-U-N-S 07-418-9747
LEVINGSTON GROUP LLC
210 Teal Dr, Sulphur, LA 70665-6410
Tel (337) 527-3806 Founded/Ownrshp 1961
Sales 29.7MM^E EMP 218
SIC 8711 Engineering services; Engineering services
Pr: Mark G Nixon
*COO: Dan Leveque
*Treas: Sharon Thomas
Mktg Dir: Mark Leblanc
Mktg Dir: Donna Smith

LEVIN'S FURNITURE
See SAM LEVIN INC

D-U-N-S 92-854-2703 IMP/EXP
LEVIS ONLY STORES INC
LEVI'S OUTLET
(Suby of LEVI STRAUSS & CO) ★
1155 Battery St, San Francisco, CA 94111-1203
Tel (415) 501-6000 Founded/Ownrshp 1995
Sales 67.2MM^E EMP 700
SIC 5651 Jeans stores; Jeans stores
CEO: Chip Bergh
*Pr: Catherine Byron
*Pr: Seth Jaffe
*CFO: Harmit Singh
Bd of Dir: Peter E Haas Sr
Ofcr: Jill Nash
*Ex VP: James Curleigh
VP: Babu Goi
*VP: Marion White
Dir Surg: Nancy Shyer
Assoc Dir: Cynthia Koster

LEVI'S OUTLET
See LEVIS ONLY STORES INC

D-U-N-S 00-123-3089 IMP/EXP
LEVITON MANUFACTURING CO INC
201 N Service Rd, Melville, NY 11747-3138
Tel (631) 812-6000 Founded/Ownrshp 1990
Sales 1.5MMM^E EMP 6,095
SIC 3643 3613 3357 3674 3694 3678 Current-carrying wiring devices; Caps & plugs, electric: attachment; Connectors, electric cord; Sockets, electric; Fuses, electric; Nonferrous wiredrawing & insulating; Building wire & cable, nonferrous; Diodes, solid state (germanium, silicon, etc.); Transistors; Engine electrical equipment; Electronic connectors; Current-carrying wiring devices; Caps & plugs, electric: attachment; Connectors, electric cord; Sockets, electric; Fuses, electric; Nonferrous wiredrawing & insulating; Building wire & cable, nonferrous; Diodes, solid state (germanium, silicon, etc.); Transistors; Engine electrical equipment; Electronic connectors
CEO: Donald J Hendler
*Pr: Daryoush Larizadeh
COO: Ron Kotwica
*CFO: Mark Baydarian
*V Ch Bd: Stephen Sokolow
VP: John Lamontagne
Exec: Gina De Burgo
Dir Bus: Jason Kim
Prin: Brian Groenig
Genl Mgr: Cesar Monroy
Sftwr Eng: Kenny Cheung
Board of Directors: Shirley Leviton

D-U-N-S 03-705-4566 IMP
LEVITTOWN FISH MARKET INC
LEVITTOWN SEAFOOD
137 Marine St, Farmingdale, NY 11735-5609
Tel (631) 420-8639 Founded/Ownrshp 1980
Sales 30.0MM EMP 40
SIC 5146 Fish, fresh; Fish, frozen, unpackaged
Pr: Robert Tuccillo

LEVITTOWN PUBLIC SCHOOL
See LEVITTOWN UNION FREE SCHOOL DISTRICT

LEVITTOWN SEAFOOD
See LEVITTOWN FISH MARKET INC

D-U-N-S 06-593-1701
LEVITTOWN UNION FREE SCHOOL DISTRICT
LEVITTOWN PUBLIC SCHOOL
150 Abbey Ln, Levittown, NY 11756-4042
Tel (516) 520-8300 Founded/Ownrshp 1950
Sales 27.2MM^E EMP 330
Accts Rs Abrams & Co Llp Island
SIC 8211 Public elementary & secondary schools; Public elementary & secondary schools
Pr: Michael Pappas
Bd of Dir: Kenneth E Auer
Trst: Frank Ward
Ofcr: Marie Donnelly
VP: Diane Byrnes
VP: Tom Carriero
*VP: Peter Porrazzo
Exec: Patricia Schultz
Adm Dir: Vicki Riley
Schl Brd P: Peggy Marenghi
Board of Directors: Kenneth Auer Sr, George S Bruno Jr, Gary M Fisch, Ronald L Kinberg, James Moran, Michael D Moriarity, Diane Shapiro

D-U-N-S 04-432-4515 IMP
LEVITZ FURNITURE CORP
(Suby of LEVITZ HOME FURNISHINGS, INC.)
300 Crossways Park Dr, Woodbury, NY 11797-2035
Tel (516) 682-0481 Founded/Ownrshp 1936
Sales 229.1MM^E EMP 2,700
SIC 5712 Furniture stores; Bedding & bedsprings
Ch Bd: Larry Zigerelli
*CFO: Kathy Guinnessey
*Sr VP: Jane Gilmartin
VP: William Kelly
*Prin: Tom Baumlin
S&M/VP: Joanne Jacobs
Board of Directors: Tom Baumlin

D-U-N-S 07-624-5109 IMP
LEVLAD LLC
(Suby of NATURAL PRODUCTS GROUP LLC) ★
9200 Mason Ave, Chatsworth, CA 91311-6005
Tel (818) 882-2951 Founded/Ownrshp 2006
Sales 109.0MM^E EMP 215^E
SIC 5047 5122

LEVY COUNTY BD COMMISSIONERS
See COUNTY OF LEVY

D-U-N-S 07-979-9681
LEVY COUNTY SCHOOL DISTRICT
480 Marshburn Dr, Bronson, FL 32621-6221
Tel (352) 486-5231 Founded/Ownrshp 2015
Sales 7.5MM^E EMP 788^E
SIC 8211 Public elementary & secondary schools
Bd of Dir: Angela Johnson
Pr Dir: Barb Rivers
Teacher Pr: Candy Dean
HC Dir: Rosalind Hall

D-U-N-S 87-940-6627
LEVY COUNTY SCHOOLS FOUNDATION INC
4 W Park Ave Ste 8, Chiefland, FL 32626-0500
Tel (352) 493-6056 Founded/Ownrshp 1989
Sales 42.0MM^E EMP 900
Accts Beauchamp & Edwards Cpa S Ch
SIC 8399 Elementary & secondary schools; County supervisors' & executives' offices; Fund raising organization, non-fee basis
Pr: Denny George
Exec: Lori Lott
Dir Lab: Tina Berger
Off Mgr: Angie Jordan

D-U-N-S 00-137-9288 IMP
LEVY GROUP INC (NY)
LIZ CLAIBORNE COATS
512 7th Ave Fl 4, New York, NY 10018-0867
Tel (212) 398-0707 Founded/Ownrshp 1995
Sales 100.0MM^E EMP 250
SIC 2337 2385 Women's & misses' suits & coats; Jackets & vests, except fur & leather: women's; Raincoats, except vulcanized rubber: purchased materials; Women's & misses' suits & coats; Jackets & vests, except fur & leather: women's; Raincoats, except vulcanized rubber: purchased materials
Ch Bd: Jack Arthur Levy
*Ch: Donald Levy
VP: Russ Caputo
*VP: Lawrence Levy
*VP: Richard Levy
MIS Dir: Max Norman
MIS Dir: Gary Seagobind
Ql Cn Mgr: Rich Albom
VP Sls: Larry Leeder

D-U-N-S 61-716-8034
LEVY R & H LIMITED PARTNERSHIP
980 N Michigan Ave # 400, Chicago, IL 60611-4501
Tel (312) 664-8200 Founded/Ownrshp 1989
Sales 190.0MM^E EMP 7,000
SIC 5812 Contract food services; Contract food services
Pt: Lawrence F Levy
Pt: Andrew Lansing
Pt: Robert Seiffert
VP: Alison Weber

D-U-N-S 08-534-3861
LEVY SECURITY CORP
8750 W Bryn Mawr Ave # 1000, Chicago, IL 60631-3554
Tel (773) 867-9204 Founded/Ownrshp 1979
Sales 17.1MM^E EMP 900
SIC 7381 Security guard service; Security guard service
Ch Bd: Deborah G Levy
*Pr: Abe Barkin
Pr: Patty Hoppenstedt
Dir Sec: Eric J Swanson

D-U-N-S 00-107-9136
LEW A CUMMINGS CO INC (NH)
CUMMINGS PRINTING COMPANY
4 Peters Brook Dr, Hooksett, NH 03106-1822
Tel (603) 625-6901 Founded/Ownrshp 1959
Sales 20.7MM EMP 106
SIC 2752 Publication printing, lithographic; Publication printing, lithographic
Pr: John L Cummings
COO: Mark Hamel
*Treas: Norma J Shea
IT Man: Mark Ingoldsby

D-U-N-S 93-834-0585
LEW HOLDING CO INC
220 Yocumtown Rd, Etters, PA 17319-9006
Tel (717) 938-1468 Founded/Ownrshp 1984
Sales 50.2MM^E EMP 170
SIC 1611 1794 7353 4522 Surfacing & paving; Excavation work; Heavy construction equipment rental; Flying charter service; Surfacing & paving; Excavation work; Heavy construction equipment rental; Flying charter service
Pr: Leon E Wintermyer
Opers Mgr: Keith Moyer

LEW WEBB'S IRVINE NISSAN
See WEBBS LEW IRVINE NISSAN INC

D-U-N-S 83-290-0984
LEWA ACQUISITION CORP
500 Lake Cook Rd Ste 430, Deerfield, IL 60015-5268
Tel (847) 940-3535 Founded/Ownrshp 2009
Sales 3.1MM^E EMP 480
SIC 0272 2353 Horses & other equines; Hats: cloth, straw & felt; Horses & other equines; Hats: cloth, straw & felt
Pr: D H Carroll
Treas: Gary J Minta

D-U-N-S 19-324-2401
LEWA INC
LEWA STABLES
500 Lake Cook Rd Ste 400, Deerfield, IL 60015-5269
Tel (847) 940-3535 Founded/Ownrshp 1977
Sales 8.7MM^E EMP 514
SIC 0272 Horses & other equines; Horses & other equines
Pr: D H Carroll
*Treas: Gary J Minta
Board of Directors: D H Carroll

LEWA STABLES
See LEWA INC

D-U-N-S 04-705-9126 IMP/EXP
LEWA-NIKKISO AMERICA INC
(Suby of LEWA GMBH)
132 Hopping Brook Rd, Holliston, MA 01746-1455
Tel (508) 429-7403 Founded/Ownrshp 2005
Sales 41.3MM^E EMP 92
SIC 5084 3586 3561 Pumps & pumping equipment; Measuring & dispensing pumps; Pumps & pumping equipment; Pumps & pumping equipment; Measuring & dispensing pumps; Pumps & pumping equipment
Pr: Peter Castellanos
Chf Mktg O: Stefan Glasmeyer
*VP: Ray Ruddy
Mng Dir: Sylvain Latuilerie
Sls Dir: Aslam Parvez
Manager: Glenn Haneberg
Manager: Michael Libbey
Manager: Bob Limper
Sls Mgr: Bob Fletcher

D-U-N-S 05-926-0604
■ **LEWAN & ASSOCIATES INC**
(Suby of GLOBAL IMAGING SYSTEMS INC) ★
1400 S Colo Blvd Ste 500, Denver, CO 80222
Tel (303) 759-5440 Founded/Ownrshp 1999
Sales 58.7MM^E EMP 385
SIC 7629 5734 5112 5999 7359 7379 Business machine repair, electric; Personal computers; Photocopying supplies; Photocopy machines; Facsimile equipment; Equipment rental & leasing; Computer related consulting services; Business machine repair, electric; Personal computers; Photocopying supplies; Photocopy machines; Facsimile equipment; Equipment rental & leasing; Computer related consulting services
Pr: Fred Cannataro
*Ch Bd: Tom Johnson
Ex VP: Steve John
Exec: Vicki Mares
*Prin: Jim Arnold
Brnch Mgr: Karen Arnold
Brnch Mgr: Joe Grassello
VP Sls: David Coffman
Sls Mgr: Bryan Cox
Sls Mgr: Van Hartley
Sls Mgr: Julian Heron

D-U-N-S 05-339-5786
LEWARE CONSTRUCTION CO OF FLORIDA INC
925 Thomas Ave, Leesburg, FL 34748-3628
Tel (352) 787-1616 Founded/Ownrshp 1988
Sales 52.1MM^E EMP 220
SIC 1622 Bridge construction; Bridge construction
Pr: James F Leware Jr
*VP: Andrew M Clark
*VP: Scott M Leware

D-U-N-S 01-830-1028 IMP
LEWCO INC
706 Lane St, Sandusky, OH 44870-3846
Tel (419) 625-4014 Founded/Ownrshp 1967
Sales 55.1MM^E EMP 104
SIC 3535 3567 Bulk handling conveyor systems; Industrial furnaces & ovens; Bulk handling conveyor systems; Industrial furnaces & ovens
Pr: Ronald Guerra
COO: Lou Schaefer
*VP: Gerald Guerra
Exec: Ruth Bodyke
Ex Dir: Bob Berry
Opers Mgr: Mark Parker
Mktg Dir: Troy Lewis
Manager: Kim Gill
Manager: John Ryals

D-U-N-S 16-179-8053 IMP/EXP
LEWCO SPECIALTY PRODUCTS INC
6859 Renoir Ave, Baton Rouge, LA 70806-2184
Tel (225) 924-3221 Founded/Ownrshp 1986
Sales 27.4MM EMP 51
SIC 2299

D-U-N-S 06-795-3240
LEWER AGENCY INC
4534 Wornall Rd, Kansas City, MO 64111-3236
Tel (816) 753-4390 Founded/Ownrshp 1956
Sales NA EMP 100
SIC 6411 Insurance brokers
Pr: Mike Lewer
COO: Rodney Vallejo
Sr VP: Mike Dlugolecki
VP: Melissa Grann
VP Opers: Julie Lewer
Sales Exec: Erin Bennett
Mktg Dir: Johnathan Greenleaf
Mktg Mgr: Renee Higgins

D-U-N-S 01-568-6591
LEWES BAY CO LLC
DIVER C P CHEVROLET-O
17861 Coastal Hwy, Lewes, DE 19958-4935
Tel (302) 645-6221 Founded/Ownrshp 2000
Sales 28.0MM^E EMP 50
SIC 5511 Automobiles, new & used

D-U-N-S 19-732-5277
■ **LEWIN GROUP INC**
(Suby of OPTUMINSIGHT INC) ★
3130 Frview Pk Dr Ste 500, Falls Church, VA 22042
Tel (703) 269-5500 Founded/Ownrshp 2007
Sales 26.2MM^E EMP 150
SIC 8742 Hospital & health services consultant; Hospital & health services consultant
Pr: William J Miller
Treas: Robert Worth Oberrender
Ex VP: Lisa Chimento
Sr VP: Charlie Bruetman
Sr VP: Yvonne Powell
Sr VP: Kimberlee Tripoli
VP: John W Kelly
VP: Ann Osborn
VP: Robert Page
VP: Jim Van Erden
VP: Paul J Wallace

D-U-N-S 00-941-8286
LEWIS & CLARK COLLEGE (OR)
0615 Sw Palatine Hill Rd, Portland, OR 97219-7879
Tel (503) 768-7000 Founded/Ownrshp 1867
Sales 115.8MM EMP 800
Accts Moss Adams Llp Portland Oreg
SIC 8221 College, except junior; Professional schools; College, except junior; Professional schools
Pr: Thomas J Hochstettler
Sr Pt: Portland John Jr
*Pr: Barry Glassner
Treas: Bonny Rice
Trst: James Gardner
Trst: John Howard
Trst: Frederick Jubitz
Trst: Randy Massengale
Trst: Owen Panner
Trst: Edward Perkins
Trst: Ronald Ragen
Trst: Robert Ridgley
Trst: Joan Smith
Trst: Charles Spalding
Trst: Ann Swindells
Trst: John Wright
Ex VP: Peter Chang
VP: Hal Abrams
*VP: Jane Monnig Atkinson
VP: Richard J Bettega
*VP: David Ellis

D-U-N-S 08-439-8981
LEWIS & CLARK MARINE INC
2801 Rock Rd Ste 3, Granite City, IL 62040-6863
Tel (618) 876-1116 Founded/Ownrshp 1986
Sales 22.2MM^E EMP 220
SIC 4492 Towing & tugboat service; Towing & tugboat service
Pr: Paul Wellhausen

D-U-N-S 09-426-0593
LEWIS & LAMBERT LLLP
5936 Eden Dr, Fort Worth, TX 76117-6121
Tel (817) 834-7146 Founded/Ownrshp 1997
Sales 33.9MM^E EMP 150
Accts Wood Stephens & O Neil Llp
SIC 1711 3444 3545 Ventilation & duct work contractor; Ducts, sheet metal; Angle rings; Ventilation & duct work contractor; Ducts, sheet metal; Angle rings
Pr: Alfred Leidner
*CFO: Mike Tankersley
*VP: Larry Brady
*VP: Dennis Hacic
*VP: Bill Morrow
Natl Sales: Josh Crichton

D-U-N-S 07-210-7220
LEWIS - SMITH CORP
LEWIS-SMITH SUPPLY
1306 Columbia Hwy, Dothan, AL 36301-1828
Tel (334) 793-5088 Founded/Ownrshp 1974
Sales 24.5MM EMP 69
Accts Mcdaniel & Associates Pc D
SIC 5074 5075 5087 Plumbing & hydronic heating supplies; Heating equipment (hydronic); Air conditioning equipment, except room units; Sprinkler systems; Plumbing & hydronic heating supplies; Heating equipment (hydronic); Air conditioning equipment, except room units; Sprinkler systems
Pr: Mark Smith
*Ch Bd: Carolyn Smith
*VP: Benny Buchanan

D-U-N-S 84-071-7990 IMP
LEWIS ACQUISITION CORP
LEWIS PLASTICS
712 W Winthrop Ave, Addison, IL 60101-4311
Tel (773) 486-5660 Founded/Ownrshp 2001
Sales 22.3MM^E EMP 67^E
SIC 3089 Injection molding of plastics
Pr: William Lacek
Genl Mgr: Bob Vanhoegarden

D-U-N-S 07-199-6722
LEWIS AND CLARK COMMUNITY COLLEGE
5800 Godfrey Rd, Godfrey, IL 62035-2426
Tel (618) 468-7000 Founded/Ownrshp 1971
Sales 20.4MM EMP 604
Accts Cj Schlosser & Company Llc
SIC 8222 Community college; Community college
Pr: Dale T Chapman
Pr: Joey Gibbs
VP: Mary Schulte
Off Admin: Noelle Balandi

D-U-N-S 03-392-1719
LEWIS AND RAULERSON INC
1759 State St, Waycross, GA 31501-6714
Tel (912) 283-5951 Founded/Ownrshp 1939
Sales 100.3MM^E EMP 50
SIC 5171 Petroleum bulk stations; Petroleum bulk stations
Pr: Bill F Raulerson
*Ex VP: David Turner
*Sr VP: Clay Parker
*VP: Carl Lewis
Off Mgr: Phylis Dixon
MIS Dir: William Woodard

D-U-N-S 06-353-6304
LEWIS AND TIBBITTS INC
1470 Indl Ave, San Jose, CA 95112
Tel (408) 925-0220 Founded/Ownrshp 1973
Sales 27.8MM EMP 104
SIC 1623

D-U-N-S 03-140-9956
LEWIS AUTO PLAZA INC
LEWIS TOYOTA
2951 Sw Fairlawn Rd, Topeka, KS 66614-1525
Tel (785) 273-2220 Founded/Ownrshp 1991
Sales 30.4MM^E EMP 67
SIC 5511 Automobiles, new & used; Automobiles, new & used
Pr: Rod Lewis

Exec: Paula Ylinging
Dir IT: Rodney Deters
IT Man: Leanne Anderson
Sls Mgr: Brad Harms
Sls Mgr: Jeff Kulick
Sales Asso: Doug Carter
Sales Asso: Richard Harmon
Sales Asso: Gary Prough

D-U-N-S 00-692-3387 IMP
LEWIS BEAR CO INC (FL)
6120 Enterprise Dr, Pensacola, FL 32505-1858
Tel (850) 434-8612 *Founded/Ownrshp* 1876
Sales 58.6MM^E *EMP* 170
SIC 5181 Beer & ale; Beer & ale
Pr: Lewis Bear Jr
Treas: Joseph Bonner
**Treas:* Stephen E Cox
**VP:* Joseph C Bonner
Brnch Mgr: Sid Taylor
VP Sls: Ed Koontz
Board of Directors: Cindi Bear, David Bear, Lewis Bear III

D-U-N-S 00-625-0427 IMP
LEWIS BOLT & NUT CO (MN)
30105 6th Ave, La Junta, CO 81050-9502
Tel (719) 384-5400 *Founded/Ownrshp* 1992
Sales 90.0MM^E *EMP* 150
SIC 3452 Bolts, nuts, rivets & washers; Bolts, nuts, rivets & washers
Pr: Mark Paper
**VP:* Dave Barry
**VP:* Cheryl Masias
**VP:* Cheryl McIntosh
VP: Jeremy Soden
**VP Mfg:* Carl Zimmerman
Plnt Mgr: Brett McIntosh
Sls Mgr: Robert Fiorio

D-U-N-S 09-642-7059
LEWIS BRISBOIS BISGAARD & SMITH LLP
633 W 5th St Ste 4000, Los Angeles, CA 90071-2074
Tel (213) 250-1800 *Founded/Ownrshp* 1979
Sales 170.6MM^E *EMP* 775
SIC 8111 General practice law office; General practice law office
Mng Pt: Robert F Lewis
Pt: Christopher P Bisgaard
Pt: Roy M Brisbois Vcard
Mng Pt: Duane Musfelt
Mng Pt: Bob Smith
COO: William Pon
CFO: Patricia Williamson
Off Mgr: Dana Trevers
Off Admin: Pat Elliott
IT Man: Jocelyn Julian
Mgr Info S: Michael Yu

D-U-N-S 00-629-7113 IMP
LEWIS BROTHERS BAKERIES INC
500 N Fulton Ave, Evansville, IN 47710-1571
Tel (812) 425-4642 *Founded/Ownrshp* 1925
Sales 697.6MM^E *EMP* 2,500
SIC 2051 5149 Bread, all types (white, wheat, rye, etc): fresh or frozen; Groceries & related products; Bread, all types (white, wheat, rye, etc): fresh or frozen; Buns, bread type: fresh or frozen; Rolls, sweet: except frozen; Doughnuts, except frozen; Groceries & related products
Pr: R Jack Lewis Jr
Treas: Rodger Lesh
**Treas:* Jeffery J Sankovitch
Ofcr: Chris Frano
VP: Dan Coyle
VP: Eustace Denton
VP: Dean Short
VP: Carol Stratman
Genl Mgr: Carl Finfrock
Dir IT: Jim Hudock
Plnt Mgr: Nathan Ponder

D-U-N-S 05-066-7054
LEWIS BROTHERS BAKERIES INC OF TENNESSEE (TN)
BUNNY BREAD
(*Suby of* LEWIS BROTHERS BAKERIES INC) ★
855 Scott St, Murfreesboro, TN 37129-2735
Tel (615) 893-6041 *Founded/Ownrshp* 1964
Sales 49.6MM^E *EMP* 340
SIC 2051 Bread, all types (white, wheat, rye, etc): fresh or frozen; Buns, bread type: fresh or frozen; Bread, all types (white, wheat, rye, etc): fresh or frozen; Buns, bread type: fresh or frozen
Pr: R Jack Lewis Jr
**Chf Mktg O:* Rick Hardesty
Exec: Paul Alexander

LEWIS CENTER FOR EDUCTL RES
See HIGH DESERT PARTNERSHIP IN ACADEMIC EXCELLENCE FOUNDATION INC

D-U-N-S 19-614-2004
LEWIS CHRYSLER DODGE
LEWIS CHRYSLER PLYMOUTH DODGE
(*Suby of* LEWIS MANAGEMENT INC) ★
3311 N College Ave, Fayetteville, AR 72703-3816
Tel (479) 442-7552 *Founded/Ownrshp* 1988
Sales 25.0MM^E *EMP* 99
SIC 5511 5521 New & used car dealers; Automobiles, used cars only; New & used car dealers; Automobiles, used cars only
Owner: Tom Lewis Jr
IT Man: Missy Tarsley

LEWIS CHRYSLER PLYMOUTH DODGE
See LEWIS CHRYSLER DODGE

LEWIS COMPANY
See J LEWIS PARTNERS LP

D-U-N-S 06-090-9660
LEWIS CO SCHOOL DISTRICT
96 Plummers Ln, Vanceburg, KY 41179-7681
Tel (606) 796-2811 *Founded/Ownrshp* 1902
Sales 21.4MM *EMP* 159^E
Accts Reynolds & Company Cpa S Port
SIC 8211 Public elementary school; Public senior high school; School board; Public elementary school; Public senior high school; School board

D-U-N-S 06-617-4871
LEWIS COMPANIES
1156 N Mountain Ave, Upland, CA 91786-3633
Tel (909) 985-0971 *Founded/Ownrshp* 1973
Sales 54.0MM^E *EMP* 380
SIC 1531 Operative builders; Operative builders
Pr: Richard A Lewis
VP: William Francke
VP: Robert Martin
**Prin:* Goldy S Lewis
**Prin:* Randall W Lewis
Off Mgr: Edna Johnson
Mktg Mgr: Chris Johnson

D-U-N-S 93-186-4250
LEWIS CONTRACTORS INC
7300 Ranch Road 2243, Georgetown, TX 78628-7142
Tel (512) 355-9094 *Founded/Ownrshp* 1995
Sales 22.0MM^E *EMP* 81
Accts Brown Graham & Company Pc
SIC 1794 1623 Excavation work; Water, sewer & utility lines; Excavation work; Water, sewer & utility lines
Pr: Ronald Lewis
**VP:* Justine Lewis
**VP:* Matthew Lewis
Mtls Mgr: Chris Chapman
Sfty Mgr: Tommy Lauderdale
Snr Mgr: Dave Clark

D-U-N-S 10-158-0637
LEWIS COUNTY BOARD OF EDUCATION
LEWIS COUNTY SCHOOLS
514 Main Ave, Weston, WV 26452-2049
Tel (304) 269-8300 *Founded/Ownrshp* 1933
Sales 21.1MM^E *EMP* 515
SIC 8211 Public elementary & secondary schools; Public elementary & secondary schools
**Treas:* Monika Weldon
HC Dir: Carol Williams

LEWIS COUNTY FAMILY HEALTH CEN
See LEWIS COUNTY PRIMARY CARE CENTER

LEWIS COUNTY FOREST PRODUCTS
See LONG BELL VENTURES LLC

D-U-N-S 06-305-9364
LEWIS COUNTY GENERAL HOSPITAL EMPLOYEES ASSOCIATION INC
BEAVER RIVER HEALTH CENTER
7785 N State St, Lowville, NY 13367-1297
Tel (315) 376-5200 *Founded/Ownrshp* 1932
Sales 37.0M *EMP* 400
SIC 8062 8051 8011 General medical & surgical hospitals; Skilled nursing care facilities; Offices & clinics of medical doctors; General medical & surgical hospitals; Skilled nursing care facilities; Offices & clinics of medical doctors
Pr: Mark J Rappaport
Chf Path: Robert Coffin
Dir Vol: Polly Schell
CFO: Jeffery Hellinger
CFO: Richard Lang
Dir Lab: Sindy Pomimbille
Dir Rx: Diane Loftuf
Off Mgr: Sandra Sulliavn
IT Man: Trista Mullin
Surgeon: Vivian Chang
Obsttrcn: Cynthia Fraser

D-U-N-S 10-947-4759
LEWIS COUNTY PRIMARY CARE CENTER
LEWIS COUNTY FAMILY HEALTH CEN
211 Ky 59, Vanceburg, KY 41179-7647
Tel (606) 796-3029 *Founded/Ownrshp* 1983
Sales 22.2MM *EMP* 102^E
Accts Embr Services Llc Maysville
SIC 8011 Medical centers; Medical centers
Pr: Jerry Ugrin
VP Mktg: Michelle Mc Cane
Doctor: Jeff Parker

D-U-N-S 10-007-3089
LEWIS COUNTY SCHOOL SYSTEM
206 S Court St, Hohenwald, TN 38462-1736
Tel (931) 796-2375 *Founded/Ownrshp* 1927
Sales 9.2MM^E *EMP* 350
SIC 8211 9411 Public elementary school; Public junior high school; Public senior high school; School board; Administration of educational programs; Public elementary school; Public junior high school; Public senior high school; School board; Administration of educational programs

LEWIS COUNTY SCHOOLS
See LEWIS COUNTY BOARD OF EDUCATION

D-U-N-S 07-982-7383
LEWIS COUNTY SCHOOLS
96 Plummers Ln, Vanceburg, KY 41179-7681
Tel (606) 796-2811 *Founded/Ownrshp* 2015
Sales 10.6MM^E *EMP* 316^E
SIC 8211 Public elementary & secondary schools

D-U-N-S 07-967-6528
LEWIS COUNTY SCHOOLS
514 Main Ave, Weston, WV 26452-2049
Tel (304) 269-8300 *Founded/Ownrshp* 2015
Sales 3.1MM^E *EMP* 287^E
SIC 8211 Public elementary & secondary schools

D-U-N-S 00-894-2088 IMP
LEWIS DRUGS INC
LEWIS FAMILY DRUGS
2701 S Minn Ave Ste 1, Sioux Falls, SD 57105-4787
Tel (605) 367-2800 *Founded/Ownrshp* 1942
Sales 146.8MM^E *EMP* 675
SIC 5311 5912 Department stores, non-discount; Drug stores; Department stores, non-discount; Drug stores
Pr: Mark Griffin
Pr: Doug Gravning
Pr: Bill Ladwig
COO: Neilsen David
**COO:* David Nielson
**CFO:* Scott Cross
VP: Dave Nielsen
Dir Rx: Jim Rasmussen
CTO: Naomi Graves
IT Man: Matthew Newman
IT Man: Kevin Riley

LEWIS ENERGY GROUP
See LEWIS RESOURCE MANAGEMENT LLC

D-U-N-S 85-911-8379
LEWIS ENERGY GROUP LP
10101 Reunion Pl Ste 1000, San Antonio, TX 78216-4157
Tel (210) 384-3200 *Founded/Ownrshp* 1998
Sales 988.3MM *EMP* 1,000
Accts Bkd Llp San Antonio Texas
SIC 1311 Crude petroleum & natural gas; Crude petroleum & natural gas
Pr: Rod Lewis
COO: Bret Jameson
Ofcr: Craig Rosenstein
VP: Alfred Holcomb
VP: Stan Jumper
VP: Mike Loudermilk
VP: Chad McGuffin
VP: Rick Smart
IT Man: Lisa Damuth
IT Man: Paul Gray
IT Man: Charlene Trevino

D-U-N-S 96-139-4806
LEWIS ENVIRONMENTAL GROUP INC
155 Railroad Plz Ste 1, Royersford, PA 19468-1953
Tel (610) 792-5595 *Founded/Ownrshp* 1996
Sales 43.2MM^E *EMP* 60^E
SIC 4959 1799 Toxic or hazardous waste cleanup; Decontamination services
Pr: Richard D Lewis
**Owner:* Neil Lewis
**Ch:* Richard Lewis
**Treas:* Donna Lewis
VP: David Lindenmuth
VP: Steve Ohrwaschel
**VP:* Steven Orhwaschel
Exec: Mara Tammaro
Opers Mgr: Jim Gould
Mktg Mgr: Rebecca Note
Snr Mgr: A J Bero

LEWIS FAMILY DRUGS
See LEWIS DRUGS INC

D-U-N-S 85-962-5287
LEWIS FOOD TOWN INC
3131 Pawnee St, Houston, TX 77054-3302
Tel (713) 746-3600 *Founded/Ownrshp* 1994
Sales 224.8MM^E *EMP* 1,700
SIC 5411 Supermarkets, chain; Supermarkets, chain
Pr: Ross Lewis
**Sec:* Billy G Drews

D-U-N-S 06-986-2100
LEWIS FOODS INC (CT)
6 Thorndal Cir Ste 5, Darien, CT 06820-5415
Tel (203) 656-3661 *Founded/Ownrshp* 1973
Sales 11.0MM^E *EMP* 300
SIC 5812 4522 Fast-food restaurant, chain; Air passenger carriers, nonscheduled; Fast-food restaurant, chain; Air passenger carriers, nonscheduled
Pr: James R Lewis

D-U-N-S 03-673-9006
LEWIS GALE PHYSICIANS LLC
1802 Braeburn Dr, Salem, VA 24153-7357
Tel (540) 772-3530 *Founded/Ownrshp* 2005
Sales 36.2MM^E *EMP* 580^E
SIC 8011 General & family practice, physician/surgeon; General & family practice, physician/surgeon

D-U-N-S 60-420-6664
LEWIS LEASE CRUTCHER WA LLC
HOLYOKE FINE HOMES
(*Suby of* W LEASE LEWIS CO) ★
2200 Western Ave, Seattle, WA 98121-1921
Tel (206) 264-1985 *Founded/Ownrshp* 1989
Sales 151.8MM^E *EMP* 275
SIC 1542 1521 Commercial & office building, new construction; Single-family housing construction; Commercial & office building, new construction; Single-family housing construction
CEO: Bart Ricketts
COO: Lonny Collins
CFO: Berger Dodge
CFO: J Philo Hall
CFO: John Hall
Ch: Bill Lewis
VP: Jeff Cleator
Admn Mgr: Jan Van
Admn Mgr: Jan Vancourt
Off Mgr: Gary Smith
Mktg Dir: Carey Smith

D-U-N-S 00-327-6912 EXP
LEWIS M CARTER MANUFACTURING CO INC
LMC
615 Hwy 84 W, Donalsonville, GA 39845
Tel (229) 524-2197 *Founded/Ownrshp* 1939
Sales 44.2MM^E *EMP* 157^E
SIC 3523 3556 3535 Hulling machinery, agricultural; Cleaning machines for fruits, grains & vegetables; Food products machinery; Conveyors & conveying equipment; Hulling machinery, agricultural; Cleaning machines for fruits, grains & vegetables; Food products machinery; Conveyors & conveying equipment
CEO: Lewis M Carter Jr
CFO: Gordon Carpenter
**Treas:* Joann Kelley
VP: Marcus Carter
Prgrm Mgr: Michael Montgomery
IT Man: Ronald Donalson
Netwrk Mgr: Wendell Craft
Prd Mgr: Mike Woodall
Ql Cn Mgr: Frankie Taylor

D-U-N-S 18-050-6982
LEWIS MANAGEMENT INC
3373 N College Ave, Fayetteville, AR 72703-3816
Tel (479) 442-5301 *Founded/Ownrshp* 1983
Sales 58.6MM^E *EMP* 299
Accts Duell & Allred Cpa
SIC 5511 5551 6512 5734 Automobiles, new & used; Boat dealers; Nonresidential building operators; Computer & software stores; Automobiles, new & used; Boat dealers; Nonresidential building operators; Computer & software stores
Pr: Thomas Lewis Sr

D-U-N-S 03-227-9499 EXP
LEWIS MARINE SUPPLY INC (FL)
220 Sw 32nd St, Fort Lauderdale, FL 33315-3388
Tel (954) 523-5403 *Founded/Ownrshp* 1956, 1970
Sales 74.2MM^E *EMP* 150
SIC 5088 Marine supplies; Marine supplies
CEO: Stephen R Lewis
**Pr:* Carolyn Coleman
**Treas:* Cassels Melissa
**Treas:* Betty Reyher
**VP:* Lisa D Evans
**VP:* John Penn
**VP:* John E Stephens
Sales Exec: Justin Heaps

D-U-N-S 00-792-0630
LEWIS MERIWETHER ELECTRIC COOPERATIVE (TN)
1625 Highway 100, Centerville, TN 37033-1023
Tel (931) 729-3558 *Founded/Ownrshp* 1939
Sales 80.7MM *EMP* 71
Accts Winnett Associates Pllc Shel
SIC 4911 Distribution, electric power; Distribution, electric power
CEO: Hal Womble
**Ch Bd:* Sam Fussell
**CFO:* Randy James
**V Ch Bd:* Johnnie Ruth Elrod
Dist Mgr: Jason Graves
VP Opers: Ed Greenwell

D-U-N-S 09-659-0757
LEWIS OIL CO INC (FL)
621 Se Depot Ave, Gainesville, FL 32601-7086
Tel (352) 376-3293 *Founded/Ownrshp* 1971
Sales 25.3MM^E *EMP* 70
SIC 5171 5411 5541

D-U-N-S 07-280-9924
LEWIS P C JACKSON
JACKSON LEWIS
1133 Weschester Ave, White Plains, NY 10604
Tel (914) 872-8060 *Founded/Ownrshp* 1958
Sales 267.0MM^E *EMP* 1,160
SIC 8111 General practice law office; General practice law office
Prin: Ana C Shields
Pt: Brooks R Amiot
Pt: Richard J Hafets
Pt: Emmett F McGee
Pt: Larry R Seegull
Mng Pt: Kevin Lashus
Mng Pt: Mickey Silberman
CFO: Diana Ferreira
Ch: Vincent Cino
Sr VP: Leighton Dawkins
VP: Thomas Alexander
VP: Patty Archambault
VP: Loretta Mitchell
Adv Bd Mbr: Tamara Branch

D-U-N-S 79-909-0159
LEWIS PALMER SCHOOL DISTRICT
EL PASO COUNTY SCHL DISTRIC 38
146 E Jefferson St, Colorado Springs, CO 80907-6908
Tel (719) 488-4705 *Founded/Ownrshp* 2007
Sales 54.7MM *EMP* 800
Accts Swanhorst & Company Llc Green
SIC 8211 Public elementary & secondary schools; Public elementary & secondary schools
Pr: Jeff Ferguson
**CFO:* Cheryl Wangeman
Dir IT: Lance Nozot

D-U-N-S 13-120-4059
LEWIS PAPER INTERNATIONAL INC
LEWIS PAPER PLACE
1400 S Wolf Rd Ste 100, Wheeling, IL 60090-6524
Tel (847) 520-3386 *Founded/Ownrshp* 1980
Sales 76.7MM^E *EMP* 158
SIC 5111 Printing paper; Printing paper
CEO: Miriam W Lewis
Pr: Robert J Zessis
Sr VP: Yvonne M Jewson
Genl Mgr: Rob Erwin
Dir IT: Shari F Necheles
IT Man: Shari Necheles

LEWIS PAPER PLACE
See LEWIS PAPER INTERNATIONAL INC

LEWIS PLASTICS
See LEWIS ACQUISITION CORP

LEWIS RAIL SERVICE COMPANY
See HOLLAND LP

D-U-N-S 07-842-7294
LEWIS RESOURCE MANAGEMENT LLC
LEWIS ENERGY GROUP
(*Suby of* LEWIS ENERGY GROUP LP) ★
10101 Reunion Pl Ste 1000, San Antonio, TX 78216-4157
Tel (210) 384-3200 *Founded/Ownrshp* 2012
Sales 559.4MM *EMP* 250
Accts Bkd Llp San Antonio Texas
SIC 4924 Natural gas distribution; Natural gas distribution
Pr: Rodney R Lewis
**VP:* Rick Price

D-U-N-S 08-302-8308
LEWIS RICE LLC
600 Washington Ave # 2500, Saint Louis, MO 63101-1311
Tel (314) 444-7600 *Founded/Ownrshp* 1994

Sales 35.0MM[E] *EMP* 360
SIC 8111 General practice law office; General practice law office
Pt: John K Pruellage
**Pt:* Brian Bouquet
**Pt:* Thomas Cardonna
**Pt:* Duane Coleman
**Pt:* Steven Drapekin
**Pt:* Robert Golterman
**Pt:* John Hall
**Pt:* Ronald Norwood
**Pt:* Robert Will
Pr: Jenna Conway
Pr: Devona Howard
Pr: Cathy Murphy
CFO: Chris Buckley
Bd of Dir: Thomas L Caradonna
Bd of Dir: Jonathan F Dalton
Bd of Dir: Peter K Hartweger
Bd of Dir: Thomas M Martin

D-U-N-S 02-011-5796
LEWIS ROCA ROTHGERBER LLP
201 E Washington St # 1200, Phoenix, AZ 85004-4446
Tel (602) 262-5311 *Founded/Ownrshp* 1994
Sales 72.1MM[E] *EMP* 347
SIC 8111 General practice law office; General practice law office
Pt: Jose A Cardenas
Pt: Ann-Martha Andrews
Pt: Timothy Blakeley
Pt: Douglas Irish
Pt: Joye Gilsinger
COO: Chris Anderson
COO: Bob McCormick
CFO: Dean Mannen
Off Admin: Renee Galgano
CTO: Neil Ferguson
Netwrk Mgr: Steven Stringham

D-U-N-S 03-126-6018
LEWIS SEED & FERTILIZER INC (KS)
HOME CITY GRAIN
208 2nd St, Home, KS 66438-9766
Tel (785) 799-3321 *Founded/Ownrshp* 1940
Sales 29.8MM[E] *EMP* 12
Accts Kickhaefer & Associate Pa
SIC 5153 5191 Grains; Chemicals, agricultural; Grains; Chemicals, agricultural
Pr: James L Schramm
**Ch Bd:* Leo James Schramm
**Sec:* Patricia A Schramm
Ex Dir: Julie Hackenmiller

D-U-N-S 00-330-4417
LEWIS STEEL WORKS INC (GA)
613 S Main St, Wrens, GA 30833-4534
Tel (706) 547-6561 *Founded/Ownrshp* 1896
Sales 35.8MM[E] *EMP* 140
SIC 3443 Dumpsters, garbage; Dumpsters, garbage
CEO: R Bryan Lewis
**Sec:* Tony Garin

D-U-N-S 07-488-9379
LEWIS THOMASON KING KRIEG & WALDROP PC
620 Market St Ste 500, Knoxville, TN 37902-2237
Tel (865) 246-3873 *Founded/Ownrshp* 1988
Sales 25.4MM[E] *EMP* 183
SIC 8111 General practice attorney, lawyer; General practice attorney, lawyer
Ch: Richard W Krieg
Pr: Deborah Stevens
CFO: William Kunkel
Chf Mktg O: Ellen Robinson
Prin: Lars E Schuller
Counsel: Dale Bay

LEWIS TOYOTA
See LEWIS AUTO PLAZA INC

D-U-N-S 00-740-1003
LEWIS TRANSPORT INC (KY)
506 Burkesville St, Columbia, KY 42728-1610
Tel (270) 384-4132 *Founded/Ownrshp* 1952, 1966
Sales 28.4MM *EMP* 50
SIC 4213 Liquid petroleum transport, non-local; Liquid petroleum transport, non-local
Pr: Pamela Scott
**Treas:* Lisa R Lewis
**VP:* Carol S Lewis
Off Mgr: Shelly Wilson
Mtls Mgr: Anicia Mendez

D-U-N-S 06-792-1775
LEWIS TREE SERVICE INC
300 Lucius Gordon Dr, West Henrietta, NY 14586-9686
Tel (585) 436-3208 *Founded/Ownrshp* 2000
Sales 349.9MM[E] *EMP* 2,950
SIC 0783 7699 Tree trimming services for public utility lines; Cleaning services; Tree trimming services for public utility lines; Cleaning services
Ch Bd: A C Fred Engelfried
**Pr:* Richard C Alt
**Pr:* Thomas R Rogers
**CFO:* Joseph L Redman
**CFO:* James W Stenger
**Sr VP:* R Douglas Roof
**VP:* Daniel Oberlies
VP: Greg Reitz
Area Mgr: Joshua Pinto
Div Mgr: David Boyd
Div Mgr: Steven Gould

D-U-N-S 06-996-4104
LEWIS UNIVERSITY
1 University Pkwy, Romeoville, IL 60446-1832
Tel (815) 838-0500 *Founded/Ownrshp* 1960
Sales 169.4MM *EMP* 500
Accts Selden Fox Ltd Cpas Oak Bro
SIC 8221 University; University
Pr: Brother James Gaffney
CFO: Rhonda Y Pilgrim
Treas: Gregory Maruszak
**Ex VP:* Wayne J Draudt
**Sr VP:* Robert C Derose
**Sr VP:* Joseph T Falese
**Sr VP:* Raymond Kennelly
VP: Robert De Rose
VP: Barbara Reidy
Comm Man: Samuel Enyia
Snr Ntwrk: Kimberly Jupiter-King
Board of Directors: A Board of Directors

D-U-N-S 07-663-0623
LEWIS-CLARK STATE COLLEGE FOUNDATION INC
LCSC
500 8th Ave, Lewiston, ID 83501-2698
Tel (208) 792-5272 *Founded/Ownrshp* 1893
Sales 23.5MM[E] *EMP* 500
Accts Moss Adams Llp Eugune Oregon
SIC 8221 5942 College, except junior; College book stores; College, except junior; College book stores
Pr: J Anthony Fernandez
**VP:* Carmen Simone
**VP:* Lori Stinson
Exec: Michael Benke
Assoc Dir: Carol Martin

D-U-N-S 02-611-2081
■ **LEWIS-GALE HOSPITAL INC**
LEWIS-GALE MEDICAL CENTER
(*Suby of* HCA INC) ★
1900 Electric Rd, Salem, VA 24153-7494
Tel (540) 772-3680 *Founded/Ownrshp* 1998
Sales 285.2MM *EMP* 1,400[E]
SIC 8062 General medical & surgical hospitals; General medical & surgical hospitals
CEO: Victor Giovanetti
**Pr:* James Thweatt Jr
**COO:* Charlotte Tyson
CFO: Angela Bainter
CFO: William Bainter
**CFO:* Angela Reynolds
Dir Lab: Bob Lindsey
Dir Rx: Joe Ciezkowski
Off Mgr: Rick Harmon
MIS Dir: Beth Cole
Mktg Dir: Nancy May

LEWIS-GALE MEDICAL CENTER
See LEWIS-GALE HOSPITAL INC

LEWIS-GOETZ & CO - CORP HDQTR
See LEWIS-GOETZ AND CO INC

D-U-N-S 00-253-0335 IMP/EXP
LEWIS-GOETZ AND CO INC (PA)
LEWIS-GOETZ & CO - CORP HDQTR
(*Suby of* ERIKS N.V.)
650 Washington Rd Ste 500, Pittsburgh, PA 15228-2714
Tel (800) 937-9070 *Founded/Ownrshp* 1935, 1991
Sales 650.0MM[E] *EMP* 1,039
SIC 5085 Rubber goods, mechanical; Rubber goods, mechanical
Pr: Jeffrey T Crane
COO: David A Chrnock
**COO:* George R Fox
**CFO:* Michael J Kulmoski
Ex VP: Joann Capan
VP: Gary Giallonardo
VP: Rich Holderman
**VP:* Hanne Van Elsen
Dir Bus: Jeremy Lloyd
Brnch Mgr: Mark Deangelo
Brnch Mgr: Lynda Eborn

D-U-N-S 02-209-4213
LEWIS-PALMER SCHOOL DISTRICT NO 38
LPSD
146 Jefferson St, Monument, CO 80132-9200
Tel (719) 488-4700 *Founded/Ownrshp* 1883
Sales 55.2MM *EMP* 800
Accts Swanhorst & Company Llc Gree
SIC 8211 Public elementary school; Public junior high school; Public senior high school; Public elementary school; Public junior high school; Public senior high school
**CFO:* Cheryl Wangeman
MIS Dir: Chris Mack
Schl Brd P: Mark Pfoff
Psych: Char Armstrong

LEWIS-SMITH SUPPLY
See LEWIS - SMITH CORP

D-U-N-S 08-395-7969
LEWIS-WATKINS-FARMER AGENCY INC (TX)
WATKINS INSURANCE GROUP
3834 Spicewood Springs Rd, Austin, TX 78759-8976
Tel (512) 452-8877 *Founded/Ownrshp* 1949
Sales NA *EMP* 85
SIC 6411 Insurance agents, brokers & service
Pr: Patrick Watkins
VP: Hal Cromwell
VP: Brent Howell
**VP:* Michael Mosley
VP: Michael R Mosley
VP: Eddie Tisdale
**VP:* Rodney Watkins
**VP:* Matthew Womack
Exec: Herschel Cone
Sls Mgr: Cherie Wilson

D-U-N-S 05-392-8958
LEWISBURG AREA SCHOOL DISTRICT
1951 Wash Ave Dept Co, Lewisburg, PA 17837
Tel (570) 522-3334 *Founded/Ownrshp* 1950
Sales 16.5MM *EMP* 358
Accts Forgett & Kerstetter Pc Cpa S
SIC 8211 Public elementary & secondary schools; Public elementary & secondary schools
IT Man: Robert Tickering

D-U-N-S 00-723-6359 IMP
LEWISBURG CONTAINER CO
(*Suby of* PRATT PROPERTIES INC) ★
275 W Clay St, Lewisburg, OH 45338-8107
Tel (937) 962-2681 *Founded/Ownrshp* 2005
Sales 51.5MM[E] *EMP* 250
SIC 2653 Boxes, corrugated: made from purchased materials; Display items, corrugated: made from purchased materials; Boxes, corrugated: made from purchased materials; Display items, corrugated: made from purchased materials
Pr: Anthony Pratt
**CFO:* David Wiser
**Sec:* Davis Kyles
Trfc Mgr: Craig Petry

D-U-N-S 00-404-6918
LEWISBURG PRINTING INC
LPC
135 Legion Ave, Lewisburg, TN 37091-2800
Tel (931) 359-1526 *Founded/Ownrshp* 2009
Sales 28.8MM[E] *EMP* 100[E]
SIC 2752 2759 2721 Commercial printing, lithographic; Commercial printing; Periodicals; Commercial printing, lithographic; Commercial printing; Periodicals
Pr: Thomas H Hawkins IV
**Sec:* Genie Hawkins Kelso
Off Mgr: Fran Callahan
Dir IT: Matthew Hopkins
VP Sls: Kirk Kelso
Snr Mgr: Hale Hawkins

LEWISGALE HOSP AT MONTGOMERY
See MONTGOMERY REGIONAL HOSPITAL INC

D-U-N-S 02-284-5788
LEWISTON AUTO CO INC
300 Debra Dr, Lewiston, MN 55952-2102
Tel (507) 523-2861 *Founded/Ownrshp* 1995
Sales 21.0MM *EMP* 25
SIC 5511 7532 7538 Automobiles, new & used; Bump shops, automotive repair; General automotive repair shops; Automobiles, new & used; Bump shops, automotive repair; General automotive repair shops
Pr: Lyle J Nienow
Sales Asso: Brent Anderson

LEWISTON HIGH SCHOOL KEY CLUB
See LEWISTON SCHOOL DEPARTMENT

D-U-N-S 06-004-8634
LEWISTON INDEPENDENT SCHOOL DISTRICT NO1
LEWISTON PUBLIC SCHOOLS
3317 12th St, Lewiston, ID 83501-5308
Tel (208) 748-3000 *Founded/Ownrshp* 1880
Sales 30.5MM[E] *EMP* 800
Accts Hayden & Ross Pa
SIC 8211 Public combined elementary & secondary school; Public junior high school; Public senior high school; Public combined elementary & secondary school; Public junior high school; Public senior high school
Pr: Brenda Forge
VP: Sheri Allen
Psych: Annie Bynum
Psych: Katlin Kammers

LEWISTON PUBLIC SCHOOLS
See LEWISTON INDEPENDENT SCHOOL DISTRICT NO1

D-U-N-S 06-939-0387
LEWISTON SCHOOL DEPARTMENT
LEWISTON HIGH SCHOOL KEY CLUB
36 Oak St, Lewiston, ME 04240-7190
Tel (207) 795-4104 *Founded/Ownrshp* 2011
Sales 14.6MM[E] *EMP* 490[E]
SIC 8211 Elementary & secondary schools
Prin: Hillary Poussard
Snr Mgr: Elizabeth Dulac

D-U-N-S 17-732-8226
LEWISTOWN HEALTH CARE FOUNDATION
400 Highland Ave, Lewistown, PA 17044-1167
Tel (717) 248-5411 *Founded/Ownrshp* 1985
Sales 4.1MM *EMP* 953
Accts Parentebeard Llc Philadelphia
SIC 6512 5912 Nonresidential building operators; Drug stores; Nonresidential building operators; Drug stores
Pr: Kay Hamilton
**Pr:* Phylis Palm
**CFO:* Randy Tewksbury

D-U-N-S 01-058-3649
LEWISTOWN HOSPITAL
400 Highland Ave, Lewistown, PA 17044-1198
Tel (717) 248-5411 *Founded/Ownrshp* 1905
Sales 97.3MM *EMP* 900[E]
SIC 8062 8221

D-U-N-S 04-353-9290
LEWISVILLE AUTOPLEX LLC
LEWISVILLE MITSUBISHI
1515 S Stemmons Fwy, Lewisville, TX 75067-6312
Tel (972) 436-3104 *Founded/Ownrshp* 2002
Sales 31.5MM[E] *EMP* 50
SIC 5511 Automobiles, new & used
Genl Mgr: Doug Baum
Store Mgr: Antonio Sanchez
Sales Exec: Michael Baum
Sales Asso: Terry Gray
Sales Asso: Damon Green
Sales Asso: Jeremy Smalley

D-U-N-S 07-137-2338
LEWISVILLE INDEPENDENT SCHOOL DISTRICT
1800 Timber Creek Rd, Flower Mound, TX 75028-1146
Tel (469) 713-5200 *Founded/Ownrshp* 1877
Sales 597.0MM *EMP* 4,500
SIC 8211

LEWISVILLE MITSUBISHI
See LEWISVILLE AUTOPLEX LLC

D-U-N-S 12-443-5855
LEWISVILLE VOLKSWAGEN LLC
HENDRICK
893 S Stemmons Fwy, Lewisville, TX 75067-5351
Tel (214) 838-1090 *Founded/Ownrshp* 2001
Sales 33.9MM[E] *EMP* 80
SIC 5511 Automobiles, new & used

LEX BRODIE'S TIRES CO
See LBTC HOLDINGS LLC

LEX BUSINESS SOLUTIONS
See LEX INC

D-U-N-S 88-441-6348
LEX INC
LEX BUSINESS SOLUTIONS
1912 Woodford Rd Ste 100, Vienna, VA 22182-3795
Tel (703) 254-6100 *Founded/Ownrshp* 1994
Sales 10.9MM[E] *EMP* 350
SIC 8111 General practice law office; General practice law office
Pr: David Tomashefski

D-U-N-S 78-969-4825 IMP
LEX PRODUCTS LLC
15 Progress Dr, Shelton, CT 06484-6218
Tel (203) 363-3738 *Founded/Ownrshp* 1989
Sales 57.2MM[E] *EMP* 180
SIC 3829 3315 3643 3613 Measuring & controlling devices; Cable, steel: insulated or armored; Circuit boards, television & radio printed; Measuring & controlling devices; Cable, steel: insulated or armored; Current-carrying wiring devices; Switchboards & parts, power
CEO: Robert R Luther
Pr: Vin Bove
Sales Asso: Mike Reilly
Sales Asso: Blake Whilden

LEX TV
See LEXINGTON INSURANCE CO

D-U-N-S 00-166-4465 IMP
LEXA INTERNATIONAL CORP (DE)
1 Landmark Sq Ste 407, Stamford, CT 06901-2601
Tel (203) 326-5200 *Founded/Ownrshp* 1920
Sales 465.8MM[E] *EMP* 1,204
Accts Citrin Cooperman & Company Ll
SIC 5171 3822 Petroleum bulk stations & terminals; Auto controls regulating residntl & coml environmt & applncs; Petroleum bulk stations & terminals; Auto controls regulating residntl & coml environmt & applncs
Ch Bd: Antonia Axson Johnson
V Ch: Goeran P Ennerfelt
V Ch Bd: P Goeran Ennerfelt
VP: John Pascale
VP: Charles W Seitz

D-U-N-S 11-873-0472
LEXAMAR CORP
(*Suby of* DECOMA ADMARK) ★
100 Lexamar Dr, Boyne City, MI 49712-9799
Tel (231) 582-3163 *Founded/Ownrshp* 1987
Sales 166.1MM[E] *EMP* 325
SIC 3089 Injection molded finished plastic products; Injection molded finished plastic products
Pr: Al Powers
Dir Lab: Ken Bradley
Genl Mgr: Grahame Burrow
IT Man: Curt Reynolds
IT Man: Tom Schlueter
Trfc Mgr: Cheryl Savoix
Sls Mgr: Tom Stewart

D-U-N-S 01-295-1872 IMP
LEXANI WHEEL CORP
2380 Railroad St Ste 101, Corona, CA 92880-5471
Tel (951) 808-4220 *Founded/Ownrshp* 1996
Sales 41.0MM[E] *EMP* 120
SIC 5013 Wheels, motor vehicle; Wheels, motor vehicle
CEO: Frank Hodges
Genl Mgr: Michael Kim
Mktg Dir: Aaron Dewitt
Sls Mgr: John Wallace
Board of Directors: Harold C Taber Jr

D-U-N-S 80-143-8677
LEXAS COMPANIES LLC
8275 S Eastrn Ave Ste 200, Las Vegas, NV 89123
Tel (702) 385-6000 *Founded/Ownrshp* 2005
Sales 25.0MM *EMP* 16[E]
SIC 6531 6513 Condominium manager; Apartment building operators
CFO: Tom George

LEXAS TOYOTA OF MELBOURNE
See TOYOTA OF MELBOURNE

D-U-N-S 62-792-3501 IMP
LEXEL IMAGING SYSTEMS INC
FOSTER SOLUTIONS
(*Suby of* CITIDAL PARTNERS, LLC)
1500 Bull Lea Rd Ste 150, Lexington, KY 40511-1266
Tel (859) 243-5500 *Founded/Ownrshp* 2014
Sales 37.6MM[E] *EMP* 275
SIC 3671 Electron tubes; Electron tubes
CEO: Rod Way
**Pr:* William Frohoff
**CFO:* Steven Lalonde
Mng Dir: John Morris
CTO: Scott Dansky
IT Man: Bill Frohoff
IT Man: Carol Simpson
Snr Mgr: Troy Horne

D-U-N-S 82-834-6630
LEXIA LLC
(*Suby of* SHINSEI BANK, LIMITED)
8742 Lucent Blvd Ste 300, Highlands Ranch, CO 80129-2386
Tel (720) 241-7200 *Founded/Ownrshp* 2008
Sales NA *EMP* 310
SIC 6719 Investment holding companies, except banks; Investment holding companies, except banks

D-U-N-S 05-179-2836 IMP
■ **LEXICON INC**
HARMAN SPECIALTY GROUP
(*Suby of* HARMAN INTERNATIONAL INDUSTRIES INC) ★
1718 W Mishawaka Rd, Elkhart, IN 46517-9439
Tel (203) 328-3500 *Founded/Ownrshp* 1993
Sales 24.2MM[E] *EMP* 130
SIC 3651 Audio electronic systems; Audio electronic systems
Pr: John Batliner
Sr VP: Scott Robbins
Sftwr Eng: Clint Herron
VP Mfg: Larry Bender

Opers Mgr: Wayne Hall
Sls Dir: Beth High
Manager: Troy Bornman
Manager: Steve Zhu
Snr Mgr: Nils Lahr

D-U-N-S 15-423-7234 IMP
LEXICON INC
SCHUECK STEEL
8900 Fourche Dam Pike, Little Rock, AR 72206-3806
Tel (501) 490-4200 *Founded/Ownrshp* 1996
Sales 456.1MM^E *EMP* 1,300
Accts Frost Pllc Little Rock Arkan
SIC 1791 3441 3444 1796 1761 3533 Structural steel erection; Fabricated structural metal; Sheet metalwork; Machinery installation; Sheet metalwork; Oil field machinery & equipment; Structural steel erection; Fabricated structural metal; Sheet metalwork; Machinery installation; Sheet metalwork; Oil field machinery & equipment
Pr: Patrick T Schueck
**Treas:* Jeff D Weatherly
**Ex VP:* Eugene Riley Jr
**VP:* John Bailey
VP: Phillip Connor
**VP:* Mark A Davis
**VP:* Gary Loyd
**VP:* Brian Rutherford
Genl Mgr: Bryant Givens
Dir IT: Jason Richmond
Opers Mgr: Chris Reynolds
Board of Directors: Thomas Schueck

D-U-N-S 87-702-4000
LEXICON MARKETING (USA) INC
640 S San Vicente Blvd, Los Angeles, CA 90048-4654
Tel (323) 782-8282 *Founded/Ownrshp* 2003
Sales 58.6MM^E *EMP* 500^E
SIC 5049 5999 School supplies; Education aids, devices & supplies; School supplies; Education aids, devices & supplies
Pr: Valeria Rico
CFO: Rob Ro
VP: Rosa Hernandez
Creative D: Jorge Azpiazu
Mng Dir: Adrian Aguirre
MIS Dir: Fernando Gonzalez
Dir IT: Pablo Ianni
Telecom Mg: Erwin Gamez
Opers Mgr: Cristina Atilio
Prd Mgr: Marsiol Zumaeta

D-U-N-S 60-691-2413
LEXICON MARKETING LLC
6380 Wilshire Blvd # 1400, Los Angeles, CA 90048-5018
Tel (323) 782-7400 *Founded/Ownrshp* 2005
Sales 26.3MM^E *EMP* 500
SIC 5963 Direct selling establishments; Direct selling establishments
COO: Cristina Atilio
**CFO:* Robert Ro
IT Man: Stella McCarty
VP Opers: Rosa Hernandez

D-U-N-S 83-817-9638
▲ LEXICON PHARMACEUTICALS INC
8800 Technology Forest Pl, The Woodlands, TX 77381-1160
Tel (281) 863-3000 *Founded/Ownrshp* 1995
Sales 22.8MM *EMP* 106^E
Tkr Sym LXRX *Exch* NGS
SIC 2834 Pharmaceutical preparations
Pr: Lonnel Coats
Owner: Lance K Ishimoto
**Ch Bd:* Raymond Debbane
CFO: Julia P Gregory
CFO: Jeffrey L Wade JD
Ex VP: Tamar D Howson
Ex VP: Pablo Lapuerta
Ex VP: Alan J Main
VP: William Heydorn
VP: Hartmuth Kolb
VP: Randall Riggs
VP: Paul Strumph
VP: James Tessner
VP: Suman Wason
VP: Alan Wilson
VP Bus: Randy Riggs
Board of Directors: Philippe J Amouyal, Samuel L Barker, Robert J Lefkowitz, Alan S Nies, Frank P Palantoni, Christopher J Sobecki, Judith L Swain

D-U-N-S 02-199-7863
LEXIDAN FOODS LLC (KY)
WAFFLE HOUSE
2901 Richmond Rd, Lexington, KY 40509-1771
Tel (803) 760-2711 *Founded/Ownrshp* 2008
Sales 6.1MM^E *EMP* 300
SIC 5812 Restaurant, family: chain; Restaurant, family: chain

D-U-N-S 12-835-5372
LEXINGTON ACQUISITION INC
12660 Branford St, Pacoima, CA 91331-3451
Tel (818) 768-5768 *Founded/Ownrshp* 2001
Sales 30.8MM^E *EMP* 145
SIC 3441 Fabricated structural metal; Fabricated structural metal
Pr: Richard Bencivengo
COO: Dave Piper
CFO: Mike Santiago
Ofcr: Christopher Jordan
Ofcr: Dale Utiger
VP: Patti Drum
VP: Ron Hubbard
IT Man: Richard Dencivengo
Snr PM: Jeff Lewis

D-U-N-S 07-786-4346
LEXINGTON CENTER CORP
RUPP ARENA
430 W Vine St, Lexington, KY 40507
Tel (859) 233-4567 *Founded/Ownrshp* 1972
Sales 22.0MM *EMP* 460
SIC 6531

D-U-N-S 14-593-0749
LEXINGTON CENTER DEAF SERVICES
30th & 75th St, Jackson Heights, NY 11372
Tel (718) 350-3056 *Founded/Ownrshp* 1983
Sales 8.9MM^E *EMP* 450
Accts Rs Abrams & Co Llp Islandi
SIC 8093 Specialty outpatient clinics; Specialty outpatient clinics
Pr: Kevin Keane
Ch Bd: Martin Sternburg
CEO: Oscar Cohen
Treas: Joy Taylor
VP: Laura Hines
VP: Albert Hliback

D-U-N-S 03-472-6067
LEXINGTON CHEVROLET INC (TN)
JONES CHEVROLET
515 S Broad St, Lexington, TN 38351-2210
Tel (731) 968-2527 *Founded/Ownrshp* 1930, 1993
Sales 25.0MM *EMP* 24
SIC 5511 7515 Automobiles, new & used; Passenger car leasing; Automobiles, new & used; Passenger car leasing
Pr: Jim Essary
**VP:* Benny Washburn
Sls Dir: Chester Singleton
Sales Asso: Billy Perry

D-U-N-S 10-005-8742
LEXINGTON CITY BOARD OF EDUCATION
LEXINGTON CITY SCHOOLS
1010 Fair St, Lexington, NC 27292-1665
Tel (336) 242-1527 *Founded/Ownrshp* 1901
Sales 32.4MM *EMP* 506
SIC 8211 Public elementary & secondary schools; Public elementary & secondary schools
Bd of Dir: Sandra Reynolds
Schl Brd P: Scott Biesecker
HC Dir: Jennifer Brown

LEXINGTON CITY SCHOOLS
See LEXINGTON CITY BOARD OF EDUCATION

D-U-N-S 07-979-8789
LEXINGTON CITY SCHOOLS
1010 Fair St, Lexington, NC 27292-1665
Tel (336) 242-1527 *Founded/Ownrshp* 2015
Sales 4.3MM^E *EMP* 471^E
SIC 8211 Public elementary & secondary schools
Pr Dir: Nicole Piggott
Teacher Pr: Dave Fairall

D-U-N-S 16-603-5548
LEXINGTON COMMUNITY COLLEGE
KCTCS-BLUEGRASS DISTRICT
(*Suby of* KCTCS) ★
215 Oswald Bldg, Lexington, KY 40506-0001
Tel (859) 257-4872 *Founded/Ownrshp* 2004
Sales 6.4MM^E *EMP* 500
SIC 8222 Community college; Community college
CEO: Jim Kerley PHD

D-U-N-S 10-994-3865
LEXINGTON COMMUNITY SERVICES INC
127 E State St, Gloversville, NY 12078-1204
Tel (518) 773-7931 *Founded/Ownrshp* 1986
Sales 2.3MM *EMP* 300
SIC 8322 Social services for the handicapped; Social services for the handicapped
Ex Dir: Paul Nigra

D-U-N-S 78-667-5111
LEXINGTON CORPORATE ENTERPRISES INC
17725 Volbrecht Rd, Lansing, IL 60438-4542
Tel (708) 418-0700 *Founded/Ownrshp* 2005
Sales 106.1MM^E *EMP* 200
SIC 5075 1711 Warm air heating & air conditioning; Warm air heating & air conditioning contractor; Warm air heating & air conditioning; Warm air heating & air conditioning contractor
Pr: Raymond Mungo
**Ex VP:* David Yanow
**VP:* Timothy M Scott

LEXINGTON COUNTY HEALTH SERVIC
See LEXINGTON MEDICAL CENTER

D-U-N-S 14-484-6250
LEXINGTON COUNTY HEALTH SERVICES DISTRICT INC
2720 Sunset Blvd, West Columbia, SC 29169-4810
Tel (803) 791-2000 *Founded/Ownrshp* 1988
Sales 811.2MM^E *EMP* 6,000^E
Accts Kpmg Llp Atlanta Ga
SIC 8062 8011 8299 8051 General medical & surgical hospitals; Clinic, operated by physicians; Educational service, nondegree granting: continuing educ.; Skilled nursing care facilities; General medical & surgical hospitals; Clinic, operated by physicians; Educational service, nondegree granting: continuing educ.; Skilled nursing care facilities
Pr: Michael Biediger
**COO:* Tod Augsburger
**VP:* Melinda P Kruzner
Dir IT: Donna Lyles

LEXINGTON COUNTY SCHOOL DISTRI
See BOOKLAND CAYCE SCHOOL DISTRICT NO 2

D-U-N-S 01-179-7404
LEXINGTON COUNTY SCHOOL DISTRICT 3
338 W Columbia Ave, Batesburg, SC 29006-2028
Tel (803) 532-4423 *Founded/Ownrshp* 1953
Sales 23.5MM^E *EMP* 383
Accts Mccregor & Company Llp Columb
SIC 8211 Public elementary & secondary schools; Public elementary & secondary schools
**Ch:* Cheryl A Burgess
Trst: Stacey Derrick
Dir IT: Michael Powell
IT Man: Lu Bickley
IT Man: Debra Mitchell
Pr Dir: Judith Turner-Fox
HC Dir: Oren Meetze

D-U-N-S 10-007-1471
LEXINGTON COUNTY SCHOOL DISTRICT ONE EDUCATIONAL FOUNDATION
100 Tarrar Springs Rd, Lexington, SC 29072-3835
Tel (803) 821-1000 *Founded/Ownrshp* 1952
Sales 437.6M *EMP* 3,500
Accts Burkett Burkett & Burkett Cpa
SIC 8211 Public elementary & secondary schools; Public elementary & secondary schools
**CFO:* John Butler
Treas: Byron Sistare
Trst: Edwin Harmon
Ofcr: Chris Ellisor
Exec: Daniel Powell
Adv Bd Mbr: Michael Gunter
Dir IT: Harriet Zwart
Psych: Cameron Anderson
Psych: Amy Long

D-U-N-S 11-327-9132
LEXINGTON FOUR INC
WEB:WWW.ALTOONAHOSPITAL.ORG
(*Suby of* LEXINGTON HOLDINGS INC) ★
620 Howard Ave, Altoona, PA 16601-4804
Tel (814) 946-2204 *Founded/Ownrshp* 1996
Sales 10.1MM *EMP* 332
SIC 8741 Management services; Management services
Pr: Neil Port

D-U-N-S 96-744-0897
LEXINGTON FOUR NINETY INC
BABCOCK CENTER
2725 Banny Jones Ave, West Columbia, SC 29170-2109
Tel (803) 799-1970 *Founded/Ownrshp* 2011
Sales 27.4MM *EMP* 99
Accts Sheheen Hancock & Godwin Llp C
SIC 6513 Apartment building operators
Dist Mgr: Phillip Crocker

D-U-N-S 18-770-3574 IMP/EXP
LEXINGTON FURNITURE INDUSTRIES INC
LEXINGTON HOME BRANDS
1300 National Hwy, Thomasville, NC 27360-2318
Tel (336) 474-5300 *Founded/Ownrshp* 2002
Sales 621.7MM^E *EMP* 3,000
SIC 2512 Upholstered household furniture; Upholstered household furniture
Pr: Phil Haney
CFO: Scott Richardson
VP: Kelly Cain
VP: Robert Stamper
VP Sls: Doug Hartzog
VP Sls: Art Negrin
Mktg Mgr: Jennifer Ledford
Mktg Mgr: Samantha Peloquin

D-U-N-S 82-686-7801
LEXINGTON GROUP INTERNATIONAL INC
9200 W Sunset Blvd # 820, West Hollywood, CA 90069-3603
Tel (310) 385-1071 *Founded/Ownrshp* 2005
Sales 67.0MM^E *EMP* 800^E
SIC 8051 Convalescent home with continuous nursing care
CEO: Lee C Samson
**COO:* Lawrence E Feigen

D-U-N-S 06-832-4037
■ LEXINGTON H-L SERVICES INC (KY)
KENTUCKY CONNECT
(*Suby of* MCCLATCHY CO) ★
100 Midland Ave, Lexington, KY 40508-1943
Tel (859) 231-3100 *Founded/Ownrshp* 1953, 1973
Sales 51.2MM^E *EMP* 277
SIC 2711 2752 Newspapers, publishing & printing; Commercial printing, lithographic; Newspapers, publishing & printing; Commercial printing, lithographic
Pr: Rufus Friday
**Pr:* Timothy M Kelly
Pr: Kim Woods
**CFO:* Elaine Lintecum
CFO: Michael McCord
Bd of Dir: Fran Elsen
**VP:* Peter Baniak
**VP:* Chris Christian
VP: James Green
**VP:* Robert Weil
IT Man: Brenda Holder
Board of Directors: Kathy Aldridge, Rita S Gatton, Larry D Keeling, Jamie Lucke, Jim Niemi, Joel Pett

LEXINGTON HEALTH NETWORK
See ROYAL MANAGEMENT CORP

D-U-N-S 11-246-0964
LEXINGTON HOLDINGS INC
WEB:WWW.ALTOONAHOSPITAL.ORG
620 Howard Ave, Altoona, PA 16601-4804
Tel (814) 946-2204 *Founded/Ownrshp* 2008
Sales 2.2MM *EMP* 1,575
SIC 8741 Hotel or motel management; Hotel or motel management
CEO: James W Barner
**Treas:* David J Duncan

LEXINGTON HOME BRANDS
See LEXINGTON FURNITURE INDUSTRIES INC

D-U-N-S 16-668-8874
LEXINGTON HOMES INC
100 Lexington Cir, Lexington, MS 39095-7061
Tel (662) 834-0292 *Founded/Ownrshp* 2004
Sales 26.5MM^E *EMP* 170
SIC 2451 Mobile homes; Mobile homes
Pr: Harold Weaver
**VP:* Gene Rogers
**VP:* Mike Sullivan

D-U-N-S 12-060-5621
■ LEXINGTON HOSPITAL CORP
HENDERSON COUNTY CMNTY HOSP
(*Suby of* COMMUNITY HEALTH SYSTEMS INC) ★
200 W Church St, Lexington, TN 38351-2038
Tel (731) 968-3646 *Founded/Ownrshp* 2003
Sales 21.2MM^E *EMP* 157
SIC 8062 8082 General medical & surgical hospitals; Home health care services
CEO: Hooly Clark
Pr: Linda Brewer
CFO: Chris Hendren
Treas: Deborah Roberts
Exec: Gail Dyer
Doctor: Damon Owens
Nrsg Dir: Charlene Morgan

LEXINGTON INDUSTRIES
See FULTON COUNTY A R C

D-U-N-S 00-695-2519
■ LEXINGTON INSURANCE CO
LEX TV
(*Suby of* NATIONAL UNION FIRE INSURANCE CO OF PITTSBURGH PA) ★
99 High St Fl 23, Boston, MA 02110-2378
Tel (212) 770-7000 *Founded/Ownrshp* 1965, 1975
Sales NA *EMP* 312
SIC 6331 Fire, marine & casualty insurance; Fire, marine & casualty insurance
Pr: Jeremy Johnson
Pr: Max Palladino
**Treas:* Robert Jacobson
Treas: Dean Owens
Ex VP: Erik Nikodem
Sr VP: Sharyl Bales
Sr VP: Frank Douglas
Sr VP: George R Statts
VP: Stephen Andrick
VP: Nick Anselmo
VP: Bradley Cox
VP: Ed Croak
VP: Tom Grandmaison
VP: Shawn Homand
VP: Meredith King
VP: Ken Morrison
VP: Fred Owen
VP: Stephen Paris
VP: Keith Peacock
VP: Douglas Story

D-U-N-S 02-684-5347
LEXINGTON LINCOLN-MERCURY INC
GREEN'S SUZUKI
608 E New Circle Rd, Lexington, KY 40505-2904
Tel (859) 254-2391 *Founded/Ownrshp* 1978
Sales 31.0MM *EMP* 70
SIC 5511 Automobiles, new & used; Automobiles, new & used
Pr: Curtis Clay Green I
**Treas:* Curtis Clay Green II

D-U-N-S 05-459-8339
LEXINGTON LOCAL SCHOOL DISTRICT
103 Clever Ln, Lexington, OH 44904-1269
Tel (419) 884-2132 *Founded/Ownrshp* 1890
Sales 23.2MM *EMP* 275
Accts Sam Stamm Support Systems Gro
SIC 8211 9411 Public elementary & secondary schools; High school, junior or senior; School board; Administration of educational programs; Public elementary & secondary schools; High school, junior or senior; School board; Administration of educational programs
Dir IT: Levi Mowery
Schl Brd P: Robert Whitney
Instr Medi: Michelle Olecki

D-U-N-S 96-871-2245
LEXINGTON LOGISTICS LLC
TRIENDA
N7660 Industrial Rd, Portage, WI 53901-9451
Tel (608) 742-9451 *Founded/Ownrshp* 2011
Sales NA *EMP* 349
SIC 4731 Freight transportation arrangement

D-U-N-S 80-979-6050
LEXINGTON MACHINING LLC
677 Buffalo Rd, Rochester, NY 14611-2014
Tel (585) 235-0880 *Founded/Ownrshp* 2007
Sales 25.9MM *EMP* 187
SIC 3451 Screw machine products; Screw machine products
Pr: Warren Delano
Ch Bd: Michael Lubin

D-U-N-S 06-744-0453
LEXINGTON MEDICAL CENTER
LEXMEDICAL
(*Suby of* DAVIDSON HEALTH CARE INC) ★
250 Hospital Dr, Lexington, NC 27292-6792
Tel (336) 248-5161 *Founded/Ownrshp* 1986
Sales 79.5MM^E *EMP* 550
SIC 8062 General medical & surgical hospitals; General medical & surgical hospitals
Pr: Williams James
COO: Dennis Ayers
CFO: Danny Squires
**VP:* Danny Squares
**Prin:* Donnie Lambeth
**Prin:* Bret Nicks
Off Mgr: Lori Sickelbaugh
CIO: Kevin Buchanan
QA Dir: Karen Grigg
Doctor: George Azar
Doctor: Marc F Fedder MD

D-U-N-S 06-933-3797
LEXINGTON MEDICAL CENTER (SC)
LEXINGTON COUNTY HEALTH SERVIC
(*Suby of* LEXINGTON COUNTY HEALTH SERVICES DISTRICT INC) ★
2720 Sunset Blvd, West Columbia, SC 29169-4810
Tel (803) 791-2000 *Founded/Ownrshp* 1971, 1988
Sales 781.7MM *EMP* 5,616^E
SIC 8062 General medical & surgical hospitals; General medical & surgical hospitals
Pr: Michael J Biediger
Chf Rad: Layne Clemenz
**COO:* Todd Augsburger
**CFO:* Melinda Kruzner
Dir Lab: Lois Cassidy
Assoc Dir: Pam Free
Assoc Dir: Janet Smoak
Prac Mgr: Ginger Dubose
CIO: Kathleen Herald

MIS Dir: Nolan Hennesse
IT Man: Melinda Krezner

D-U-N-S 08-411-0865 IMP
LEXINGTON MFG INC (MN)
1330 115th Ave Nw, Minneapolis, MN 55448-3133
Tel (763) 772-9740 *Founded/Ownrshp* 1957, 1993
Sales 31.0MM^E *EMP* 125
Accts Froehling Anderson Minneapoli
SIC 2499 Decorative wood & woodwork; Decorative wood & woodwork
CEO: Robert G Dimke
COO: Steve McKoskey
CFO: Steve Giebler
**VP:* John Dimke
Genl Mgr: Steve McKoskeey
IT Man: Bob Sunfdahl
Mtls Mgr: Larry Michelson
Ql Cn Mgr: Ryan Brotzel
Sls Dir: Bill Dewitt
Snr Mgr: Paul Werner

D-U-N-S 08-248-1433
LEXINGTON NURSING HOME INC
632 Se 3rd St, Lexington, OK 73051-9902
Tel (405) 527-6531 *Founded/Ownrshp* 1977
Sales 158.3MM *EMP* 61
SIC 8052 Intermediate care facilities; Intermediate care facilities
Pr: Gerald Lawson

D-U-N-S 07-979-9285
LEXINGTON PUBLIC SCHOOLS
146 Maple St, Lexington, MA 02420-2504
Tel (781) 861-2550 *Founded/Ownrshp* 2015
Sales 9.2MM^E *EMP* 589^E
SIC 8211 Public elementary & secondary schools

D-U-N-S 80-834-0954
LEXINGTON REALTY TRUST
1 Penn Plz Ste 4015, New York, NY 10119-4015
Tel (212) 692-7200 *Founded/Ownrshp* 1993
Sales 424.3MM *EMP* 48^E
SIC 6798 Real estate investment trusts; Real estate investment trusts
Pr: T Wilson Eglin
**Ch Bd:* E Robert Roskind
CFO: Patrick Carroll
**V Ch Bd:* Richard J Rouse
Ex VP: Nabil Andrawis
Ex VP: Joseph S Bonventre
Ex VP: Beth Boulerice
Ex VP: Lara Johnson
VP: Michael Costello
VP: James Dudley
VP: George Wilson
Exec: Irfan Butt
Board of Directors: Richard S Frary, James Grosfeld, Claire A Koeneman, Kevin W Lynch, Harold First

D-U-N-S 04-091-3477 IMP
LEXINGTON REGIONAL HEALTH CENTER
LEXINGTON REGIONAL HEALTH CTR
1201 N Erie St, Lexington, NE 68850-1560
Tel (308) 324-5651 *Founded/Ownrshp* 1976
Sales 23.3MM *EMP* 180
Accts Seim Johnson Llp Omaha Nebr
SIC 8062 General medical & surgical hospitals; General medical & surgical hospitals
Pr: Kerry Teetor
Chf Rad: John Ford
**COO:* Jim Hain
**CFO:* Wade Eschenbrenner
**Treas:* Jerry Brown
**VP:* Kathy Neil
Exec: Jill John
Dir Lab: Cathy Sarnes
Dir Rad: Jo Swartz
Dir Rx: Donna Soflin
**Prin:* Robb Hanna

LEXINGTON REGIONAL HEALTH CTR
See LEXINGTON REGIONAL HEALTH CENTER

D-U-N-S 60-821-3187 IMP
LEXINGTON RUBBER GROUP INC
QSR
(*Suby of* Q HOLDING CO) ★
1700 Highland Rd, Twinsburg, OH 44087-2221
Tel (330) 425-8472 *Founded/Ownrshp* 1988
Sales 84.0MM^E *EMP* 410
SIC 3069 Hard rubber & molded rubber products; Hard rubber & molded rubber products
CEO: Randy Ross
CFO: Dennis Welhouse

D-U-N-S 10-004-8412
LEXINGTON SCHOOL DISTRICT 001
300 S Washington St, Lexington, NE 68850-2442
Tel (308) 324-4681 *Founded/Ownrshp* 1885
Sales 15.4MM^E *EMP* 305
Accts Contryman Associates Pc Le
SIC 8211 Public elementary & secondary schools; Public elementary & secondary schools

D-U-N-S 07-979-8951
LEXINGTON SCHOOL DISTRICT 01
100 Tarrar Springs Rd, Lexington, SC 29072-3835
Tel (803) 321-1002 *Founded/Ownrshp* 2015
Sales 66.4MM^E *EMP* 2,879^E
SIC 8211 Public elementary & secondary schools

D-U-N-S 10-007-1497
LEXINGTON SCHOOL DISTRICT 4
GASTON SWANSAE SCHOOL DISTRICT
607 E 5th St, Swansea, SC 29160-9702
Tel (803) 568-1000 *Founded/Ownrshp* 1941
Sales 34.3MM *EMP* 480
Accts Mcgregor & Company Llp Orange
SIC 8211 Public elementary & secondary schools; Public elementary & secondary schools
Ex Dir: Kaye Shaw

D-U-N-S 80-756-2181
LEXINGTON SCHOOL DISTRICT 5
MAINTENANCE DEPARTMENT
1020 Dutchfork Rd, Ballentine, SC 29002
Tel (803) 732-8011 *Founded/Ownrshp* 2000
Sales 193.7MM *EMP* 13
SIC 8211 Public elementary & secondary schools; Public elementary & secondary schools

D-U-N-S 07-851-2027
LEXINGTON SCHOOL FOR DEAF / CENTER FOR DEAF
30Th Ave 75Th St, East Elmhurst, NY 11370
Tel (718) 899-8800 *Founded/Ownrshp* 1869
Sales 868.3M *EMP* 400
SIC 8211 School for physically handicapped; School for physically handicapped
CEO: Dr Rigina Carroll
**CEO:* Kevin Keane
VP: Gregory Hlibok

D-U-N-S 86-699-8131
LEXINGTON SCHOOL FOR DEAF INC
2626 75th St, East Elmhurst, NY 11370-1497
Tel (718) 350-3300 *Founded/Ownrshp* 1869
Sales 22.1MM *EMP* 217^E
Accts Loeb & Troper Llp New York N
SIC 8211 School for physically handicapped; School for physically handicapped
CEO: Donald Galloway
Brnch Mgr: Manuel Mosquera

D-U-N-S 04-422-5241
LEXINGTON STEEL CORP
1400 16th St Ste 250, Oak Brook, IL 60523-8800
Tel (708) 594-9200 *Founded/Ownrshp* 1990
Sales 74.6MM^E *EMP* 85
SIC 5051 3312 Steel; Blast furnaces & steel mills; Steel; Blast furnaces & steel mills
CEO: Robert S Douglass
**Pr:* Timothy M McFarland

D-U-N-S 02-042-8777
LEXINGTON-FAYETTE URBAN COUNTY GOVERNMENT
LFUCG
200 E Main St, Lexington, KY 40507-1310
Tel (859) 258-3386 *Founded/Ownrshp* 1775
Sales NA *EMP* 2,772
Accts Dean Dorton Allen Ford Pllc
SIC 9121 9111 ; ; Executive offices; ; ; Executive offices
Ofcr: James Fawcett
Ofcr: Sally Hamilton
Ofcr: Ryan Holland
Ofcr: Gary Warner
Comm Dir: Susan Straub
Mng Ofcr: Brad Stone
Adm Dir: Rick Curtis
Adm Dir: David Loney
Ex Dir: Stephanie Hong
Brnch Mgr: Anthony Wright
Plng Mgr: Jim Rebmann

D-U-N-S 16-200-7871
LEXISNEXIS GROUP
(*Suby of* REED ELSEVIER INC) ★
9443 Springboro Pike, Miamisburg, OH 45342-5490
Tel (937) 865-6800 *Founded/Ownrshp* 2008
Sales 566.5MM^E *EMP* 3,507^E
SIC 7375 Data base information retrieval; Data base information retrieval
CEO: Kurt Sanford
Pr: Michael Lamb
CEO: Doug Kaplan
CFO: Rebecca Schmitt
Bd of Dir: Floyd Clarke
Ofcr: Mike Higgins
Ex VP: Ian McDougall
Ex VP: Jeff Reihl
Ex VP: Doreen Tyburski
Ex VP: Alex Watson
Sr VP: Lisa Agona
Sr VP: Christopher Ainsley
Sr VP: Carol Dibattiste
Sr VP: Kate Holden
Sr VP: Mark Norman
Sr VP: Joanna Stone
Sr VP: Donald Welsko
VP: Lisa Baumgarten
VP: John Birch
VP: Jim Christiansen
VP: Robert Hall

D-U-N-S 15-293-0061
LEXISNEXIS RISK ASSETS INC
CHOICEPOINT
(*Suby of* REED ELSEVIER US HOLDINGS INC) ★
1105 N Market St Ste 501, Wilmington, DE 19801-1253
Tel (770) 752-6000 *Founded/Ownrshp* 1997
Sales NA *EMP* 5,000
SIC 6411 7375 8721 7323 Information bureaus, insurance; Information retrieval services; Accounting, auditing & bookkeeping; Credit reporting services; Information bureaus, insurance; Information retrieval services; Accounting, auditing & bookkeeping; Credit reporting services
Ch Bd: Derek V Smith
**Pr:* Douglas C Curling
**CFO:* Kenneth Fogarty
**CFO:* David E Trine
**Ex VP:* David T Lee
Ex VP: Dan H Rocco
**Ex VP:* Steven W Surbaugh
VP: Alton Adams
VP: Donald Welsko
Snr Sftwr: Ahsan Ul-Haque
Tech Mgr: Mark Sulimirski

D-U-N-S 06-011-7244
LEXISNEXIS RISK SOLUTIONS INC
(*Suby of* CHOICEPOINT) ★
1000 Alderman Dr, Alpharetta, GA 30005-4101
Tel (678) 694-6000 *Founded/Ownrshp* 1975
Sales 593.4MM^E *EMP* 5,000
SIC 8748 Business consulting; Business consulting
CEO: Bill Madison
**Ch Bd:* Derek V Smith
**Pr:* Douglas C Curling
Pr: Keith Moore
Ofcr: Judy Mar
**Ex VP:* David T Lee
**Ex VP:* Vijay Raghavan
Ex VP: Doreen Tyburski
**Ex VP:* Donald Welsko
**Sr VP:* Lisa Agona
Sr VP: Matt Pruitt
**Sr VP:* Scott Sessler
Sr VP: Jennifer Williams
VP: Jennifer Lemming

D-U-N-S 61-208-4517 IMP/EXP
LEXJET LLC
1605 Main St Ste 400, Sarasota, FL 34236-5853
Tel (941) 330-1210 *Founded/Ownrshp* 1994
Sales 77.0MM^E *EMP* 100
SIC 5045 5112 5111 2672 5043 Computers, peripherals & software; Computer paper; Printing & writing paper; Thermoplastic coated paper: made from purchased materials; Cameras & photographic equipment; Computers, peripherals & software; Computer paper; Printing & writing paper; Thermoplastic coated paper: made from purchased materials; Cameras & photographic equipment
Pr: Ronald T Simkins
**VP:* Author Lambert
Mktg Mgr: Kelly Price
Sales Asso: Joshua Crissman

D-U-N-S 61-301-4695
LEXMAR DISTRIBUTION INC
200 Erie St, Pomona, CA 91768-3327
Tel (909) 620-7001 *Founded/Ownrshp* 1990
Sales 25.0MM *EMP* 170
SIC 4214 Local trucking with storage
Pr: Alex Kole
**VP:* Alex Kolesnikov
Genl Mgr: Marlin Brover

D-U-N-S 83-442-9078 IMP
LEXMARK CARPET MILLS INC
285 Kraft Dr, Dalton, GA 30721-1502
Tel (706) 277-3000 *Founded/Ownrshp* 1993
Sales 94.5MM^E *EMP* 245^E
SIC 2273 Carpets & rugs; Carpets & rugs
Pr: Todd White
CFO: James Butler
VP: Scott Austin
VP: Justin Cash
VP: Tom Mathis
Natl Sales: Paul Pauluzzi
Mktg Dir: Tammy Horn

D-U-N-S 18-064-1441
■ **LEXMARK ENTERPRISE SOFTWARE LLC**
PERCEPTIVE SOFTWARE LLC
(*Suby of* LEXMARK INTERNATIONAL INC) ★
8900 Renner Blvd, Lenexa, KS 66219-3049
Tel (913) 422-7525 *Founded/Ownrshp* 2004
Sales 324.5MM^E *EMP* 1,140
SIC 7371 7372 Computer software development; Prepackaged software; Computer software development; Prepackaged software
CEO: Scott Coons
**COO:* Darren Knipp
**VP:* Cary Decamp
**VP:* David Lintz
Creative D: Kevin Potts
Prgrm Mgr: Joshua Mochel
Genl Mgr: David Wadler
Off Mgr: Judy Hegarty
Dir IT: Balaji Vatsavaya
Dir IT: Bruce Wang
IT Man: Marcus Gilbert

D-U-N-S 62-333-1717 IMP
▲ **LEXMARK INTERNATIONAL INC**
740 W New Circle Rd, Lexington, KY 40511-1876
Tel (859) 232-2000 *Founded/Ownrshp* 1990
Sales 3.7MMM *EMP* 12,700
Tkr Sym LXK *Exch* NYS
SIC 3577 Printers, computer; Printers, computer
Pr: Paul A Rooke
Pr: Paul A Rooke
CFO: David Reeder
VP: Robert J Patton
Admn Mgr: Sylvia Vincent
Counsel: Greg Anderson
Board of Directors: Kathi P Seifert, Jared L Cohon, J Edward Coleman, W Roy Dunbar, William R Fields, Ralph E Gomory, Stephen R Hardis, Sandra L Helton, Robert Holland Jr, Michael J Maples

D-U-N-S 07-372-2878
LEXMED INC
LMC EXTENDED CARE
(*Suby of* LEXINGTON COUNTY HEALTH SERVICES DISTRICT INC) ★
815 Old Cherokee Rd, Lexington, SC 29072-9041
Tel (803) 359-5181 *Founded/Ownrshp* 1989
Sales 98.3MM^E *EMP* 2,653
Accts Kpmg Llp Atlanta Ga
SIC 8051 Skilled nursing care facilities; Skilled nursing care facilities
Pr: Mike Biediger
Phys Thrpy: Janet Haltiwanger
Board of Directors: Mary Ball, Ken Shelton

LEXMEDICAL
See LEXINGTON MEDICAL CENTER

D-U-N-S 07-860-3893
LEXOLUTION HOLDINGS LLC
75 Broad St Rm 610, New York, NY 10004-3211
Tel (212) 370-9400 *Founded/Ownrshp* 2001
Sales 35.0MM^E *EMP* 24
SIC 6719 Public utility holding companies; Public utility holding companies

D-U-N-S 82-738-7668
LEXON INSURANCE CO
12890 Lebanon Rd, Mount Juliet, TN 37122-2870
Tel (615) 553-9500 *Founded/Ownrshp* 2008
Sales NA *EMP* 105
SIC 6351 Surety insurance; Surety insurance
Pr: David Campbell
**COO:* Craig Hunt Krahl
**CFO:* Philip Gregory Lauer
**Ch:* Thomas Dieruf
**Ex VP:* Carol Lynn Fritz
**Sr VP:* Jeremy Sentman
**Sr VP:* Jeffrey Smalling
**VP:* Michael Bruce
**VP:* Rose Culbertson
**VP:* Gregory Semrow
Dir IT: Kelly Schwartz
Board of Directors: David Campbell, Rose Culbertson, Thomas Dieruf, Philip Lauer, Matthew Semeraro, Gregory Semrow

LEXON SURETY GROUP
See BOND SAFEGUARD INSURANCE CO

LEXTRON ANIMAL HEALTH
See ANIMAL HEALTH INTERNATIONAL INC

LEXUS DE SAN JUAN
See HVPH MOTOR CORP

LEXUS KEARNEY MESA
See RENLENTLESS PRUSUITS INC

LEXUS OF ANNAPOLIS
See BAY MOTOR CAR CO LLC

LEXUS OF AUSTIN
See JOHN ROBERTS AUSTIN INC

LEXUS OF BELLEVUE
See HO INC

LEXUS OF BROOKFIELD
See BLUEMOUND IMPORTS INC

LEXUS OF CERRITOS
See BARGAIN RENT-A-CAR

LEXUS OF CHARLESTON
See GENE REED TOYOTA INC

LEXUS OF CHATTANOOGA
See CAPITAL MOTOR SALES INC

LEXUS OF CHERRY HILL
See RICHARDSON IMPORTS INC

LEXUS OF CONCORD
See CONCORD AUTOMOBILE DEALERSHIP LLC

LEXUS OF ENGLEWOOD
See AUTOLAND OF ENGLEWOOD INC

LEXUS OF FT MYERS
See FORT MYERS LINCOLN MERCURY INC

LEXUS OF GREENVILLE
See TOYOTA OF GREENVILLE INC

LEXUS OF GREENWICH
See GRIFFIN MANAGEMENT CO INC

LEXUS OF JACKSONVILLE
See S D S AUTOS INC

LEXUS OF KNOXVILLE
See T & W OF KNOXVILLE INC

LEXUS OF LANSING
See SPARTAN AUTOS INC

LEXUS OF LEHIGH VALLEY
See T C MOTOR CAR CO

LEXUS OF MANHATTAN
See MANHATTAN LUXURY AUTOMOBILES INC

LEXUS OF MASSAPEQUA
See MASSAPEQUA IMPORTS 1 LTD

LEXUS OF MEMPHIS
See AVENIR PARTNERS INC

LEXUS OF NAPERVILLE
See DAN WOLF MOTORS OF NAPERVILLE INC

LEXUS OF NASHVILLE
See PERFORMANCE PETROPLEX INC

D-U-N-S 78-301-9078
LEXUS OF NEW ORLEANS
LEBLANC AUTOMOBILES
8811 Veterans Memorial Bl, Metairie, LA 70003-5236
Tel (504) 207-3285 *Founded/Ownrshp* 1990
Sales 33.3MM^E *EMP* 75
SIC 5511 Automobiles, new & used; Automobiles, new & used
Pr: V Price Leblanc Jr
**Treas:* Clifton Leblanc
Exec: Sheila Seawright
IT Man: Canfill Karlan
Sales Exec: Mark McCoy
Sales Asso: Jennifer Taylor

LEXUS OF NORTHBOROUGH
See M/H NORTHBOROUGH INC

LEXUS OF NORWOOD
See HERB CHAMBERS ROUTE 1 INC

LEXUS OF OMAHA
See TALMAR ENTERPRISES INC

LEXUS OF ORLAND
See KOWALIS MOTOR CAR INC

LEXUS OF ORLANDO
See WINTER PARK IMPORTS INC

LEXUS OF PALM BEACH
See LUXURY IMPORTS OF PALM BEACH INC

LEXUS OF PEMBROKE PINES
See COUNTYLINE AUTO CENTER INC

LEXUS OF PLEASANTON
See LOP AUTOMOTIVE CO LLC

LEXUS OF PORTLAND
See KUNI WEST SLOPE MOTORS LLC

LEXUS OF RENO
See THOMAS S DOLAN ENTERPRISES INC

LEXUS OF RIVERSIDE
See DAVIDSON MOTORS INC

LEXUS OF ROCKVILLE
See SONIC-ROCKVILLE MOTORS INC

LEXUS OF SACRAMENTO
See RPM LUXURY AUTO SALES INC

LEXUS OF SEATTLE
See F B W INC

LEXUS OF SOUTH ATLANTA
See SOUTH ATLANTA AUTOMOTIVE GROUP LLC

LEXUS OF TAMPA BAY
See GULF MANAGEMENT INC

LEXUS OF THOUSAND OAKS
See TOPA MOTORS INC

LEXUS OF TOLEDO
See JIM WHITE CO INC

LEXUS OF TULSA
See DON THORNTON AUTOMOTIVE LLC

D-U-N-S 07-849-5642
■ LEXUS OF WARWICK
(*Suby of* PENSKE AUTOMOTIVE GROUP INC) ★
1095 Centerville Rd, Warwick, RI 02886-4230
Tel (401) 821-1510 *Founded/Ownrshp* 2012
Sales 33.3MM^E *EMP* 13^E
SIC 5511 New & used car dealers
Genl Mgr: Phillip Driscoll
Sls Mgr: Ray West

D-U-N-S 61-007-7711
LEXUS OF WATERTOWN INC
(*Suby of* FOREIGN AUTO IMPORTS INC) ★
330 Arsenal St, Watertown, MA 02472-2721
Tel (617) 393-1000 *Founded/Ownrshp* 1989
Sales 22.1MM^E *EMP* 40
SIC 5511 Automobiles, new & used
Pr: Murray Patkin
Genl Mgr: Vincent Liuzzi
Sls Dir: Phillip Gregoire
Sls Mgr: Michael Espey
Sls Mgr: Bob Gelin
Sls Mgr: Ken Mulstay
Sls Mgr: Garvin Pavlosky
Sales Asso: John Barstow
Sales Asso: Steven Batsinelas
Sales Asso: Michael Berube
Sales Asso: Casey Bierer

LEXUS OF WAYZATA
See VILLAGE LUXURY IMPORTS INC

LEXUS OF WESTMINSTER
See RRL CORP

LEXUS SANTA MONICA
See VOLKSWAGEN SANTA MONICA INC

D-U-N-S 06-611-1795
LEXXIOM INC
7945 Cartilla Ave A, Rancho Cucamonga, CA 91730-3069
Tel (909) 481-2536 *Founded/Ownrshp* 2000
Sales 24.0MM^E *EMP* 360
SIC 8741 Administrative management; Administrative management
Pr: Robert Lemelin
**COO:* Brian Lemelin
**CFO:* Leo Lemelin

D-U-N-S 07-962-6640
■ LEYARD AMERICAN CORP
(*Suby of* LEYARD OPTOELECTRONIC CO., LTD)
1692 Barclay Blvd, Buffalo Grove, IL 60089-4523
Tel (847) 385-4146 *Founded/Ownrshp* 2014
Sales 179.0MM^E *EMP* 312^E
SIC 5199 General merchandise, non-durable
Pr: Zach Zhang
Manager: Rafa Ran

D-U-N-S 05-100-1030
LEYDEN COMMUNITY HIGH SCHOOL DISTRICT 212 (INC)
EAST LEYDEN HIGH SCHOOL
3400 Rose St, Franklin Park, IL 60131-2155
Tel (847) 451-3000 *Founded/Ownrshp* 1924
Sales 35.0MM^E *EMP* 426
Accts Mathieson Moyski Celer & Co Ll
SIC 8211 Public elementary & secondary schools; Public senior high school; Public elementary & secondary schools; Public senior high school
Netwrk Eng: Keith Rogers

D-U-N-S 06-859-5685
LEYDIG VOIT & MAYER LTD (IL)
180 N Stetson Ave 4900, Chicago, IL 60601-6708
Tel (312) 616-5600 *Founded/Ownrshp* 1971, 1991
Sales 31.1MM^E *EMP* 190
SIC 7389 Copyright protection service; Copyright protection service
Pr: John Kilyk
**Treas:* Steven T Peterson
**VP:* Robert F Green
Counsel: Berton S Sheppard

D-U-N-S 94-505-4658 EXP
LEYEN FOOD LLC
14328 Lomitas Ave, City of Industry, CA 91746-3016
Tel (626) 333-8812 *Founded/Ownrshp* 1992
Sales 59.2MM^E *EMP* 80^E
SIC 5147 5144 Meats & meat products; Poultry & poultry products; Meats & meat products; Poultry & poultry products
Genl Mgr: Michael Ng

LEYMAN LIFTGATES
See LEYMAN MANUFACTURING CORP

D-U-N-S 00-423-8804 IMP
LEYMAN MANUFACTURING CORP (OH)
LEYMAN LIFTGATES
10900 Kenwood Rd, Blue Ash, OH 45242-2893
Tel (513) 891-6210 *Founded/Ownrshp* 1940
Sales 23.2MM^E *EMP* 90
SIC 3713 Truck & bus bodies
Pr: John Mc Henry
**VP:* Robert Drews Jr
**VP:* Raymond B Leyman
**VP:* William Margroum
Prd Mgr: Bruce Stewart
Natl Sales: Jeff Morgan
Sls Mgr: Brian Herbert

D-U-N-S 92-805-8101
LEZK CORP
MIDAMERICAN BUILDING SERVICES
6682 W Greenfield Ave # 109, Milwaukee, WI 53214-4960
Tel (414) 475-2600 *Founded/Ownrshp* 1995
Sales 8.9MM^E *EMP* 300
SIC 7349 Janitorial service, contract basis; Janitorial service, contract basis
Pr: Edward Aprahamian

D-U-N-S 01-400-7462
LEZZER HOLDINGS INC
LEZZER LUMBER
311 Schofield St, Curwensville, PA 16833-1433
Tel (814) 236-0220 *Founded/Ownrshp* 1954
Sales 85.8MM^E *EMP* 142
SIC 5211 Bathroom fixtures, equipment & supplies; Millwork & lumber; Insulation material, building; Bathroom fixtures, equipment & supplies; Millwork & lumber; Insulation material, building
CEO: Michael F Lezzer
**Pr:* David M Lezzer
**Treas:* Margaret Lezzer
**Treas:* Julie A Seighman
**Ex VP:* Kenneth C Lezzer
**VP:* Elizabeth Lezzer

LEZZER LUMBER
See LEZZER HOLDINGS INC

D-U-N-S 10-158-5990
LEZZER LUMBER INC
(*Suby of* LEZZER HOLDINGS INC) ★
311 Schofield St, Curwensville, PA 16833-1433
Tel (814) 236-0220 *Founded/Ownrshp* 1983
Sales 76.3MM^E *EMP* 382^E
SIC 5211 Lumber & other building materials
Pr: Maurice Lezzer
**Pr:* Dave Lezzer
**COO:* John Lloyd
**CFO:* Jay Lee
CFO: Tom Peters
**Treas:* Julie Seighman
Store Mgr: George Mandel
Store Mgr: Jim Vasil
Manager: Josh Ritchie
Sales Asso: Dave Heisey
Sales Asso: Ted Loose

LF
See LA FERIA INDEPENDENT SCHOOL DISTRICT

D-U-N-S 84-599-5158
LF HARRELSON INC
HARRELSON TOYOTA
2574 Cherry Rd, Rock Hill, SC 29732-2173
Tel (803) 328-2886 *Founded/Ownrshp* 1991
Sales 20.4MM^E *EMP* 70
SIC 5511 Automobiles, new & used; Automobiles, new & used
Pr: Louis F Harrelson
**VP:* Bob Harrelson
Sls Mgr: Harrelson Louis

D-U-N-S 80-011-6766
LF KRUPP CONSTRUCTION INC
415 Old State Rd, Ellisville, MO 63021-5927
Tel (636) 391-8844 *Founded/Ownrshp* 1992
Sales 30.0MM *EMP* 100^E
SIC 1611 1622 1794 General contractor, highway & street construction; Bridge construction; Excavation work; General contractor, highway & street construction; Bridge construction; Excavation work
CEO: Mark J Reizer
**CFO:* Dan Hyland
**VP:* Dan Belzines
**VP:* Larry Hudson
**VP:* John Miener
**VP:* Mark Nelson

D-U-N-S 96-225-3592
LF LOGISTICS USA LLC
23019 International Airpo, Jamaica, NY 11413
Tel (212) 827-3308 *Founded/Ownrshp* 2004
Sales 50.0MM *EMP* 35
SIC 4731 Freight transportation arrangement; Freight transportation arrangement
Pr: David Levinson
VP: Matthew Haffler

D-U-N-S 96-474-1784 IMP
LF MENS GROUP LLC
(*Suby of* GBG USA INC) ★
1359 Broadway Fl 21, New York, NY 10018-7824
Tel (646) 839-7000 *Founded/Ownrshp* 2011
Sales 131.7MM^E *EMP* 200^E
SIC 5136 Men's & boys' clothing; Men's & boys' clothing
Ex VP: Tony Kim

D-U-N-S 06-188-2820
LFC ENTERPRISES INC
SIX L'S PACKING
315 New Market Rd E, Immokalee, FL 34142-3509
Tel (239) 657-3117 *Founded/Ownrshp* 2001
Sales 82.7MM^E *EMP* 369^E
SIC 5431 Fruit stands or markets
Pr: Kent Shoemaker
**VP:* Darren Micelle
**VP:* Gerry Odell

D-U-N-S 00-814-5203 IMP
LFD LLC
L F D HOME FURNISHINGS
1500 Commerce Dr, Mission, TX 78572-1657
Tel (956) 584-4500 *Founded/Ownrshp* 1953
Sales 70.9MM^E *EMP* 310
Accts Burton Mccumber & Cortez Llp
SIC 5712 5722 Furniture stores; Household appliance stores; Furniture stores; Household appliance stores
Ch: Jules Gosseaux
CFO: Aaron Heller

D-U-N-S 02-993-6460
LFG EMPLOYEES GROUP LLC
5424 Rufe Snow Dr Ste 502, Fort Worth, TX 76180-9045
Tel (817) 428-9736 *Founded/Ownrshp* 2001
Sales NA *EMP* 285
Accts Lane Gorman Trubitt Pllc Dal
SIC 6159 Truck finance leasing; Truck finance leasing
Pr: Gerald Chunn
**Treas:* Dan Chase
**VP:* Dick Corley

D-U-N-S 05-869-9836 EXP
LFI WIND DOWN INC
LANE FURNITURE
(*Suby of* HERITAGE HOME GROUP LLC) ★
5380 Highway 145 S, Tupelo, MS 38801-0811
Tel (662) 566-7211 *Founded/Ownrshp* 1998
Sales 645.0MM^E *EMP* 3,600
SIC 2512 Recliners: upholstered on wood frames; Couches, sofas & davenports: upholstered on wood frames; Recliners: upholstered on wood frames; Couches, sofas & davenports: upholstered on wood frames
Pr: Greg Roy
**CFO:* Vance Johnston
**Treas:* Steven G Rolls
**Sr VP:* Meridith Graham
**VP:* Jon D Botsford
VP: Skip Holliman
VP: Randy Porter
VP: Michael Weece

LFNY
See LYCEE FRANCAIS DE NEW YORK (INC)

D-U-N-S 07-869-0545
LFP BROADCASTING LLC
8484 Wilshire Blvd # 900, Beverly Hills, CA 90211-3227
Tel (323) 852-5020 *Founded/Ownrshp* 2004
Sales 55.4MM^E *EMP* 192^E
SIC 7822 Distribution for television: motion picture; Distribution for television: motion picture

D-U-N-S 06-167-3836 IMP
LFS INC
LUMMI FISHERIES SUPPLIES
(*Suby of* TRIDENT SEAFOODS CORP) ★
851 Coho Way Ste 200, Bellingham, WA 98225-2070
Tel (360) 734-3336 *Founded/Ownrshp* 1988
Sales 21.4MM^E *EMP* 60
SIC 5091 5941 3731 Fishing equipment & supplies; Fishing equipment; Trawlers, building & repairing
Pr: Phil Kolody
Genl Mgr: Patricia Bartz
Sls Mgr: Tony Wallace

LFUCG
See LEXINGTON-FAYETTE URBAN COUNTY GOVERNMENT

D-U-N-S 19-465-5882 IMP/EXP
LG CHEM AMERICA INC
(*Suby of* LG CHEM. LTD.)
910 Sylvan Ave, Englewood Cliffs, NJ 07632-3306
Tel (201) 816-2000 *Founded/Ownrshp* 2009
Sales 600.0MM^E *EMP* 35
SIC 5099 5169 5199 Containers: glass, metal or plastic; Detergents & soaps, except specialty cleaning; General merchandise, non-durable; Containers: glass, metal or plastic; Detergents & soaps, except specialty cleaning; General merchandise, non-durable
Pr: Richard Do
CFO: Chun Park
VP: Paul Lee
**Prin:* Jay Kim
Genl Mgr: Young Pyo
Snr Mgr: Peter Kim
Snr Mgr: Gyeong Ryoo

D-U-N-S 60-312-8195 IMP
LG CHEM MICHIGAN INC
LGCMI
(*Suby of* LG CHEM. LTD.)
1 Lg Way, Holland, MI 49423-8574
Tel (616) 494-7196 *Founded/Ownrshp* 2006
Sales 34.0MM *EMP* 330^E
Accts Kpmg Llp New York Ny
SIC 3691 Battery testers, electrical; Storage batteries
CEO: Prabhakar Patil
**Pr:* Nicholas Kassanos
**CFO:* Jang Woo Park
**Treas:* Beomgi Lee
Off Mgr: Jill Miller

D-U-N-S 01-716-1358 IMP
LG CHEM POWER INC
LGCPI
(*Suby of* LG CHEM. LTD.)
1857 Technology Dr, Troy, MI 48083-4244
Tel (248) 307-1800 *Founded/Ownrshp* 2010
Sales 25.2MM^E *EMP* 101^E
SIC 3691 Storage batteries
CEO: Prabhakar Patil
CFO: Kookrho Lee
Prgrm Mgr: Mark Slagh
Prgrm Mgr: Mike Stebner
Off Mgr: Julie Burke
**IT Man:* Mohamed Alamgir
Snr Mgr: Pam Frink
Snr Mgr: Satish Ketkar
Snr Mgr: Ken Oswandel

D-U-N-S 80-825-9811
LG CNS AMERICA INC
(*Suby of* LG CNS CO.,LTD)
920 Sylvan Ave, Englewood Cliffs, NJ 07632-3301
Tel (201) 816-2010 *Founded/Ownrshp* 2003
Sales 34.9MM^E *EMP* 79^E
SIC 7373 Systems software development services
CEO: Kim Dae Hoon
VP: Kim Jisook
Genl Mgr: Paul Jeong
Genl Mgr: Harry Kim
Genl Mgr: Charles Yoon
Netwrk Mgr: Billy Choe
Sftwr Eng: Jay Yoon
Sls Dir: Shin Koo
Snr Mgr: Patrick Lee
Snr Mgr: Eun Park

D-U-N-S 10-304-4686 IMP
LG DISPLAY AMERICA INC
(*Suby of* LG DISPLAY CO., LTD.)
2540 N 1st St Ste 400, San Jose, CA 95131-1016
Tel (408) 350-0190 *Founded/Ownrshp* 2013
Sales 64.1MM^E *EMP* 120
SIC 5065 Modems, computer; Modems, computer
Pr: Chris Min
**Pr:* Davis Lee
**CFO:* James Jeong
**Sr VP:* Yong Kee Huang
**Prin:* Cheol D Ong Jeong
**Prin:* Sang Deog Yeo
VP Sls: Tim Park
Sls Mgr: Angella Yoon
Snr Mgr: Ho Kang

D-U-N-S 02-904-9590 IMP
LG ELECTRONICS ALABAMA INC
(*Suby of* LG ELECTRONICS USA INC) ★
201 James Record Rd Sw, Huntsville, AL 35824-1513
Tel (256) 772-0623 *Founded/Ownrshp* 2004
Sales 98.9MM^E *EMP* 600
SIC 3651 3695 5064 5085 5065 4225 Television receiving sets; Video recording tape, blank; Microwave ovens, non-commercial; Industrial supplies; Tapes, audio & video recording; General warehousing & storage; Television receiving sets; Video recording tape, blank; Microwave ovens, non-commercial; Industrial supplies; Tapes, audio & video recording; General warehousing & storage
Pr: SOO M Kim
**Pr:* Bon-Joon Koo
**CFO:* Michael Woo
Ex VP: Dermot J Boden
Ex VP: Reginald J Bull
VP: Rick Calacci
VP: John Riddle
VP: Scott Williams
VP: Richard Wingate
Exec: Jerry Stewart
**Prin:* Havis Kwon

D-U-N-S 94-171-6508 IMP
LG ELECTRONICS MOBILECOMM USA INC
LG INFOCOMM U.S.A.
(*Suby of* LG ELECTRONICS USA INC) ★
10225 Willow Creek Rd, San Diego, CA 92131-1639
Tel (858) 635-5300 *Founded/Ownrshp* 1996
Sales 130.7MM^E *EMP* 150
SIC 5065 3663 Mobile telephone equipment; Radio & TV communications equipment; Mobile telephone equipment; Radio & TV communications equipment
CEO: Wayne Park
**Pr:* Kyung Joo Hwang
**Treas:* Jae Dong Han
Ofcr: Sarah Knight
VP: Eric Ley
VP: M Ehtisham Rabbani
VP: Jay Vandenbree
CTO: Woo Paik
IT Man: Bruce Bean
IT Man: Ross Joseph
Software D: Erick Gonzaalez

D-U-N-S 07-009-4818 IMP
LG ELECTRONICS USA INC
LG GROUP AIC
(*Suby of* LG ELECTRONICS INC.)
1000 Sylvan Ave, Englewood Cliffs, NJ 07632-3318
Tel (201) 816-2000 *Founded/Ownrshp* 1975
Sales 9.7MMM *EMP* 2,500
Accts Kpmg Llp
SIC 5064 3651 Electrical appliances, television & radio; Electrical appliances, major; Electrical entertainment equipment; Air conditioning appliances; Household audio & video equipment; Electrical appliances, television & radio; Electrical appliances, major; Electrical entertainment equipment; Air conditioning appliances; Household audio & video equipment
Pr: William Cho
Pr: Yasser Nafei
**CFO:* Soohan Bae
CFO: Byeong Choi
CFO: Jonh Ho Park
Sr VP: Rick Calacci
Sr VP: James Fishler
Sr VP: Kevin McNamara
Sr VP: John Riddle
Sr VP: Jay Vandenbree
VP: Jeff Dowell
VP: Kevin Holian
VP: Ehtisham Rabbani
VP: Kevin Shin
VP: Laurence Smith

LG FULFILLMENT
See MDM COMMERCIAL ENTERPRISES INC

LG GROUP AIC
See LG ELECTRONICS USA INC

D-U-N-S 14-912-0367 IMP/EXP
LG HAUSYS AMERICA INC
(*Suby of* LG HAUSYS, LTD.)
900 Circle 75 Pkwy Se # 15, Atlanta, GA 30339-3035
Tel (877) 842-8372 *Founded/Ownrshp* 1988
Sales 87.1MM^E *EMP* 250^E
SIC 2541 Counter & sink tops; Counter & sink tops
CFO: Yuku Kang
Ex VP: David Thoresen
**Prin:* Bongsoo Kim
**Prin:* Anthony Rivera
**Prin:* Cathy Scutier
Tech Mgr: Chul Jung
Opers Mgr: Antonio Kim
Plnt Mgr: J E Moon
Natl Sales: Michelle Wheeler
Mktg Mgr: Lee Heemun
Sls Mgr: Kevin Braun

D-U-N-S 05-185-4511
LG INC
LION BROTHERS
10246 Reisterstown Rd, Owings Mills, MD 21117-3606
Tel (410) 363-1000 *Founded/Ownrshp* 1978
Sales 69.2MM^E *EMP* 400^E
SIC 2395 Emblems, embroidered; Emblems, embroidered
CEO: Susan Ganz
**Ch Bd:* Elinor C Ganz
Pr: David F Paulus

LG INFOCOMM U.S.A.
See LG ELECTRONICS MOBILECOMM USA INC

D-U-N-S 14-585-9398 IMP
LG INNOTEK USA INC
(*Suby of* LG INNOTEK CO., LTD.)
2540 N 1st St Ste 400, San Jose, CA 95131-1016
Tel (408) 955-0364 *Founded/Ownrshp* 1994
Sales 26.4MM^E *EMP* 200
SIC 3679 Antennas, receiving; Antennas, receiving
Pr: Sung IL Yang
**Mktg Mgr:* Harry Kang

LG SEED
See AGRELIANT GENETICS LLC

D-U-N-S 62-110-1484 IMP
■ **LG&E AND KU ENERGY LLC**
(*Suby of* PPL CORP) ★
220 W Main St Ste 1400, Louisville, KY 40202-5301
Tel (502) 627-2000 *Founded/Ownrshp* 2010
Sales 3.1MMM *EMP* 3,482
SIC 4911 4931 4932 4924 Generation, electric power; Transmission, electric power; Distribution, electric power; Natural gas distribution; Gas & other services combined; Generation, electric power; Transmission, electric power; Distribution, electric power; Electric & other services combined; Gas & other services combined; Natural gas distribution
Ch Bd: Victor A Staffieri
Pr: Keith Fowley
CFO: Kent W Blake
Treas: Bruce Raque
Ex VP: Carol Hardison
Sr VP: Paula Pottinger
VP: Ralph Bowling
VP: Nathanael Esposito
VP: Chris Hermann
VP: Tom Jessee
VP: Nancy Kitchen
VP: John McCall
VP: Dorothy O'Brien
Board of Directors: S Bradford Rives, Vincent Sorgi, William H Spence, Paul W Thompson

D-U-N-S 00-610-3696
■ **LG&E AND KU SERVICES CO**
(*Suby of* LG&E AND KU ENERGY LLC) ★
220 W Main St Ste 1400, Louisville, KY 40202-5301
Tel (502) 627-2000 *Founded/Ownrshp* 2000
Sales 4.3MMM^E *EMP* 1,000
SIC 4911 Electric services; Electric services
CEO: Victor Staffieri
**CFO:* Kent Blake
**Treas:* Dan Arbough
VP: John Malloy
Prgrm Mgr: Thembi Tillman
Dir IT: Kathy Butler
Corp Couns: Jay Warren

D-U-N-S 78-761-0898
■ **LG&E CAPITAL CORP**
(*Suby of* LG&E AND KU ENERGY LLC) ★
220 W Main St Ste 1400, Louisville, KY 40202-5301
Tel (502) 627-2000 *Founded/Ownrshp* 1991
Sales 68.3MM^E *EMP* 525
SIC 6719 Investment holding companies, except banks; Investment holding companies, except banks
Ch Bd: Roger W Hale
Pr: Richard Aitken-Davies
VP: George W Basinger
VP: Frederick J Newton III
VP: S Bradford Rives
VP: Victon A Staffieri
Dir IT: Joan Ferch
Dir IT: Michael Miller

LG-TEK
See LINGUAL INFORMATION SYSTEM TECHNOLOGIES INC

LGC PROPERTY LIABILITY TRUST
See LOCAL GOVERNMENT CENTER PROPERTY-LIABILITY TRUST LLC

D-U-N-S 96-882-8723 IMP
LGC WIRELESS INC
(*Suby of* TE CONNECTIVITY NETWORKS INC) ★
541 E Trimble Rd, San Jose, CA 95131-1224
Tel (408) 952-2400 *Founded/Ownrshp* 2007
Sales 27.0MM^E *EMP* 227
SIC 3663 Carrier equipment, radio communications; Carrier equipment, radio communications
Pr: Ian Sugarbroad
Genl Pt: Howard Lee
**CFO:* John Niedermaier
**Sr VP:* Michael Frausing
**VP:* Dermot Conlon
VP: Daniel Weinblatt
Genl Mgr: Paul Chang
Genl Mgr: Thomas Jacob
Genl Mgr: Marcio Neubauer
Dir IT: John Georges

LGCMI
See LG CHEM MICHIGAN INC

LGCPI
See LG CHEM POWER INC

D-U-N-S 17-477-6273
LGD MANAGEMENT LP
1390 E Bitters Rd, San Antonio, TX 78216-2914
Tel (210) 564-0100 *Founded/Ownrshp* 2005
Sales 9.5MM^E *EMP* 2,300
SIC 8741 Management services
Prin: Dave Sheffield

D-U-N-S 01-662-0881
LGE COMMUNITY CREDIT UNION
430 Commerce Park Dr Se, Marietta, GA 30060-2710
Tel (770) 424-0060 *Founded/Ownrshp* 2008
Sales NA *EMP* 76^E
SIC 6062 State credit unions; State credit unions
CEO: Chris Ledgett
**COO:* Hank Branch
**CFO:* Candace Bracewell
Ex VP: Richard W Hampton
VP: Susan Tillery
CTO: Laura King

D-U-N-S 18-865-1327
LGE ELECTRICAL SALES INC
INDEPENDENT PWR SYSTEMS & LGE
(*Suby of* INDEPENDENT ELECTRIC SUPPLY INC) ★
650 University Ave # 218, Sacramento, CA 95825-6726
Tel (916) 563-2737 *Founded/Ownrshp* 1994
Sales 91.9MM^E *EMP* 325
SIC 5063 Communication equipment; Electrical apparatus & equipment
Pr: Gerald W Gierke
**Sec:* Raymond G Landgraf
**VP:* David E Evans
Sales Asso: Jim Keys
Sales Asso: Mike McQuiddy
Sales Asso: Mike Vanderhurst

LGH
See LANCASTER GENERAL HOSPITAL

LGH
See LIFTING GEAR HIRE CORP

LGH
See LAFAYETTE GENERAL HEALTH SYSTEM INC

LGI
See LUIS GARRATON INC

LGI HOMES & DEVELOPMENT.
See LGI SERVICES LLC

D-U-N-S 07-912-8694
▲ **LGI HOMES INC**
1450 Lake Robbins Dr # 430, The Woodlands, TX 77380-3294
Tel (281) 362-8998 *Founded/Ownrshp* 2003
Sales 383.2MM *EMP* 390
Accts Ernst & Young Llp Houston Te
Tkr Sym LGIH *Exch* NGS
SIC 1531 Subdividers & developers; Land subdividers & developers, residential; Operative builders; Speculative builder, single-family houses
Ch Bd: Eric T Lipar
Pr: Michael Snider
CFO: Charles Merdian
Chf Mktg O: Rachel Eaton
Ofcr: Margaret Britton
Ex VP: Jack Lipar
Board of Directors: Ryan Edone, Duncan Gage, Bryan Sansbury, Steven Smith, Robert Vaharadian

D-U-N-S 00-976-0948
■ **LGI INTERNATIONAL INC**
(*Suby of* LIBERTY GLOBAL INC) ★
12300 Liberty Blvd, Englewood, CO 80112-7009
Tel (720) 875-5800 *Founded/Ownrshp* 2013
Sales 338.2MM^E *EMP* 1,510
SIC 4841 Cable television services; Cable television services
Ch Bd: John C Malone
**Treas:* Graham Hollis
**V Ch Bd:* Robert Bennett
**Sr VP:* Miranda Curtis
**Sr VP:* Bernard Dvorak
**Sr VP:* David Koff
**Sr VP:* David Leonard

D-U-N-S 13-714-1904
LGI SERVICES LLC
LGI HOMES & DEVELOPMENT.
1450 Lake Robbins Dr # 430, The Woodlands, TX 77380-3294
Tel (281) 362-8998 *Founded/Ownrshp* 1995
Sales 35.0MM^E *EMP* 170
SIC 6552 Land subdividers & developers, residential
VP: Brad Locke

D-U-N-S 04-468-7424
▲ **LGL GROUP INC**
2525 Shader Rd, Orlando, FL 32804-2721
Tel (407) 298-2000 *Founded/Ownrshp* 1928
Sales 23.0MM *EMP* 153
Accts Mcgladrey Llp Orlando Florid
Tkr Sym LGL *Exch* ASE
SIC 3679 3559 Electronic circuits; Electronic component making machinery; Electronic circuits; Electronic component making machinery
CEO: Michael J Ferrantino Sr
COO: Robert Mamazza
CFO: Patti A Smith
Bd of Dir: Patrick Guarino
Dir IT: Michael Montgomery
Mktg Dir: Param Nampoothiri

LGM PHARMA
See IBS PHARMA LLC

LGS
See LITTLE GENERAL STORE INC

D-U-N-S 78-943-4953
LGS INNOVATIONS LLC
13665 Dulles Technology D, Herndon, VA 20171-4639
Tel (703) 793-3383 *Founded/Ownrshp* 2006
Sales 226.2MM^E *EMP* 650
SIC 4813 Communication signal enhancement network system; Telephone communication, except radio
CEO: Kevin L Kelly
Pr: Edward M Eldridge Jr
CFO: Debra Pfaff
Treas: Michael Slane
Sr VP: Daniel Bigbie
VP: Marc Beacken
VP: Robert Farr
VP: John Fitzgerald
Snr Sftwr: Joe Beissel
Snr Sftwr: Ryan Wallach
Snr Ntwrk: Alvaro Garcia

D-U-N-S 92-979-9575
LGS INTEGRATED SOLUTIONS INC
13665 Dulles Tech Dr, Herndon, VA 20171-4607
Tel (866) 547-4243 *Founded/Ownrshp* 1992
Sales 20.9MM^E *EMP* 492
SIC 8711 Engineering services; Engineering services
Pr: Richard Leeuwen
**CFO:* Debra Pfaff

D-U-N-S 62-098-6042 IMP
LGS SPECIALTY SALES LTD
1 Radisson Plz Fl 10, New Rochelle, NY 10801-5767
Tel (718) 542-2200 *Founded/Ownrshp* 1990
Sales 156.8MM *EMP* 15
Accts Rogoff & Company Pc New York
SIC 5141 5148 Food brokers; Fresh fruits & vegetables; Food brokers; Fresh fruits & vegetables
Pr: Luke Sears

LH
See LIQUIDHUB INC

D-U-N-S 83-828-2457
LH BRAZOS OPERATING LP
DRISKILL HOTEL, THE
604 Brazos St, Austin, TX 78701-3212
Tel (512) 391-7162 *Founded/Ownrshp* 1889
Sales 23.0MM *EMP* 250
SIC 7011 5812 7389 7991 6512 5813 Hotels; Eating places; Convention & show services; Physical fitness facilities; Nonresidential building operators; Drinking places; Hotels; Eating places; Convention & show services; Physical fitness facilities; Nonresidential building operators; Drinking places
Genl Pt: Sergio Ortiz
Ofcr: Joe Gallagher
Mktg Dir: Brett Boering
Mktg Mgr: Jenna Reed
Sls Mgr: Claire Aronis
Sls Mgr: Heather Boyle

D-U-N-S 01-887-8637 IMP
LH GAULT & SON INC
11 Ferry Ln W, Westport, CT 06880-5808
Tel (203) 227-5181 *Founded/Ownrshp* 1932
Sales 33.4MM^E *EMP* 65
SIC 1411 5032 3441 5211 1629 3531 Granite dimension stone; Building stone; Granite building stone; Marble building stone; Gravel; Fabricated structural metal; Sand & gravel; Drainage system construction; Pavers
Pr: Samuel M Gault
**Ch:* William L Gault
**VP:* James Donaher
Mktg Dir: Megan Gill
Mktg Dir: Megan Smith
Sls Dir: Clay Bassett
Sls Mgr: John Dehler
Sls Mgr: Chris Wood
Sales Asso: Christopher Domagala

D-U-N-S 80-789-4295
LH UNIVERSAL OPERATING LLC
SHERATON UNIVERSAL HOTEL
333 Universal Hollywood Dr, Universal City, CA 91608-1001
Tel (818) 980-1212 *Founded/Ownrshp* 2007
Sales 30.0MM *EMP* 280
SIC 7011 Hotels; Hotels
Dir Sec: Sean Waldron
Genl Mgr: Ryan Laskey
Genl Mgr: Randy Player
Off Mgr: Sherry Samanon
IT Man: Mort Heydari
Sls Mgr: Gloria Poon
Sls Mgr: Richard Reeves

D-U-N-S 02-049-3789
LHB INC
21 W Superior St Ste 500, Duluth, MN 55802-2085
Tel (218) 727-8446 *Founded/Ownrshp* 1964
Sales 33.4MM^E *EMP* 157
Accts Bhz Minneapolis Mn
SIC 8711 8712 Consulting engineer; Architectural services; Consulting engineer; Architectural services
CEO: William Bennett
**Treas:* Richard Carter
Ofcr: Geoff Lang
**VP:* Jay Bergman
VP: David Bjerknes
**VP:* Michael Fischer
**VP:* Joseph Litman
**VP:* Steve McNeill
Genl Mgr: Dan Heldt
IT Man: Charles Bouschor
Sls&Mrk Ex: Joellyn Gum
Board of Directors: David Williams, Evan Aljoe, Bill Zerfas, Jay Bergman, Dave Bjerkness, Jim Brew, K C Lim, Joseph Litman, Jerry Putnam, Phil Rolle, Karl M Ruthenbeck

LHB INDUSTRIES
See LIGHTHOUSE FOR BLIND

D-U-N-S 01-038-6472
▲ **LHC GROUP INC**
901 Hugh Wallis Rd S, Lafayette, LA 70508-2511
Tel (337) 233-1307 *Founded/Ownrshp* 1994
Sales 733.6MM *EMP* 10,866
Accts Kpmg Llp Baton Rouge Louisia
Tkr Sym LHCG *Exch* NGS
SIC 8082 8322 Home health care services; Rehabilitation services; Home health care services; Rehabilitation services
Ch Bd: Keith G Myers
Dir Recs: Ann Faile
Pr: Donald D Stelly
COO: Kevin Frank
CFO: Anna Noack
CFO: Dionne E Viator
Ex VP: Joshua L Proffitt
Ex VP: Barry Stewart
Sr VP: Jeffrey M Kreger
VP: Melanie Kuehn
VP: Marcus D Macip
Dir Risk M: Jean Hall

D-U-N-S 07-104-5397 IMP
LHH CORP
LENOX HILL HOSPITAL
(*Suby of* NORTH SHORE - LONG ISLAND JEWISH HEALTH SYSTEM INC) ★
100 E 77th St, New York, NY 10075-1850
Tel (212) 434-2000 *Founded/Ownrshp* 2010
Sales 340.8MM^E *EMP* 2,955
Accts Ernst & Young Us Llp Indianap
SIC 8062 General medical & surgical hospitals; General medical & surgical hospitals
Ex Dir: Franck Danza
Ofcr: Debora Marsden
Ofcr: Rosanne Raso
VP: John Connolly
Dir Teleco: Bart Lavore
Dir Rad: Kristin Byrne
Dir Rad: Evan Dillon
Dir Rx: Paul Nowierski
Adm Dir: Ann Oswald
Ex Dir: Dennis Connors
Ex Dir: Gus Costalas

D-U-N-S 00-407-6313
LHHN MEDICAL PC
MANHATTAN'S PHYSICIAN GROUP
440 9th Ave Fl 9, New York, NY 10001-1656
Tel (917) 510-2800 *Founded/Ownrshp* 2010
Sales 23.5MM^E *EMP* 375
SIC 8011 Offices & clinics of medical doctors; Offices & clinics of medical doctors
Ch Bd: J Hank Duffy
**CEO:* Howard Tepper
**COO:* Lynn Lang
**CFO:* Stephen Giasi

LHI
See LOGISTICS HEALTH INC

D-U-N-S 83-047-3380
LHI ENTERPRISES INC
(*Suby of* SUN CAPITAL PARTNERS INC) ★
5200 Town Center Cir # 470, Boca Raton, FL 33486-1015
Tel (561) 394-0550 *Founded/Ownrshp* 2009
Sales 38.8MM^E *EMP* 225^E
SIC 6719 Investment holding companies, except banks; Investment holding companies, except banks
Co-CEO: Marc Leder
**Co-CEO:* Rodger Krouse
**Mng Dir:* C Deryl Couch

D-U-N-S 07-408-7552
LHI LIGHTING SALES INC (KY)
3943 Central Ave, Louisville, KY 40218-2648
Tel (502) 964-9661 *Founded/Ownrshp* 1960, 1975
Sales 50.0MM *EMP* 25
SIC 5063 Lighting fixtures, residential; Lighting fixtures, commercial & industrial; Lighting fixtures, residential; Lighting fixtures, commercial & industrial
Pr: Charles Lanham
**VP:* Jeff Boone
**VP:* Ron Catron
**VP:* Thad Lanham
**VP:* Ron Williams

D-U-N-S 15-525-0749
LHM CORP TCD
LARRY H. MILLER CHRYSLER DODGE
(*Suby of* LARRY H MILLER TOYOTA) ★
1800 W 104th Ave, Denver, CO 80234-3602
Tel (303) 469-1931 *Founded/Ownrshp* 2014
Sales 25.0MM^E *EMP* 85
SIC 5511 Automobiles, new & used
Genl Mgr: Brent Wood
Sls Mgr: Brian Tyson
Board of Directors: John Watt

D-U-N-S 07-986-2705
LHM CORP TDR
LARRY H MLLER DODGE RAM TUCSON
9350 S 150 E Ste 1000, Sandy, UT 84070-2721
Tel (520) 745-7901 *Founded/Ownrshp* 2013
Sales 23.8MM^E *EMP* 137^E
SIC 5511 New & used car dealers
Pr: Karen G Miller
Sec: Gregory S Miller
VP: Stephen F Miller

D-U-N-S 14-201-0607
LHO LEESBURG ONE LESSEE INC
LANSDOWNE RESORT
44050 Woodridge Pkwy, Leesburg, VA 20176-5103
Tel (703) 729-8400 *Founded/Ownrshp* 2011
Sales 15.3MM^E *EMP* 600
SIC 7011 Hotels; Hotels
Pr: Michael Barnello
**CFO:* Bruce A Riggins
**Ex VP:* Alfred L Young Jr
**VP:* Ian Gaum
**VP:* Robert K Hagan

D-U-N-S 15-154-9649 IMP
LHOIST NORTH AMERICA INC
(*Suby of* LIME HOLDING INC) ★
3700 Hulen St, Fort Worth, TX 76107-6816
Tel (817) 732-8164 *Founded/Ownrshp* 1985
Sales 413.1MM^E *EMP* 450
SIC 3274

D-U-N-S 00-330-9630 IMP
LHOIST NORTH AMERICA OF ALABAMA LLC (AL)
(*Suby of* LHOIST NORTH AMERICA INC) ★
3700 Hulen St, Fort Worth, TX 76107-6816
Tel (817) 732-8164 *Founded/Ownrshp* 1989
Sales 36.1MM^E *EMP* 196
SIC 3274 1422 Lime; Crushed & broken limestone; Lime; Crushed & broken limestone
CEO: Ron Thompson
**CFO:* Kyle Colde
**Treas:* Bob Nordin

D-U-N-S 16-085-8601 IMP
LHOIST NORTH AMERICA OF ARIZONA INC
HEADQUARTERS
(*Suby of* LHOIST NORTH AMERICA INC) ★
3700 Hulen St, Fort Worth, TX 76107-6816
Tel (817) 732-8164 *Founded/Ownrshp* 1975
Sales 72.6MM^E *EMP* 432
SIC 3274 Dolomitic lime, dead-burned dolomite; Quicklime; Dolomitic lime, dead-burned dolomite; Quicklime
CEO: Ludwig De Mot
**Treas:* Bob Nordin
Plnt Mgr: Russ Curtis
Sls Mgr: Brett Tanner

D-U-N-S 03-483-0794 IMP
LHOIST NORTH AMERICA OF TENNESSEE INC
EAST REGIONAL OFFICE
(*Suby of* LHOIST NORTH AMERICA INC) ★
750 Old Hickory Blvd 200-2, Brentwood, TN 37027-4592
Tel (615) 259-4222 *Founded/Ownrshp* 2006
Sales 137.9MM^E *EMP* 250
SIC 1422 Crushed & broken limestone; Crushed & broken limestone
CEO: Ludwig De Mot
VP: Jim West
Sls Mgr: Barry Collins

D-U-N-S 07-840-5005 IMP
LHOIST NORTH AMERICA OF TEXAS LTD
(*Suby of* LHOIST NORTH AMERICA INC) ★
3700 Hulen St, Fort Worth, TX 76107-6816
Tel (817) 732-8164 *Founded/Ownrshp* 1991
Sales 73.0MM^E *EMP* 164^E
SIC 1422 Crushed & broken limestone
CEO: Ludwig De Mot

D-U-N-S 18-171-1151
LHOIST NORTH AMERICA OF VIRGINIA INC
VIRGINIA PLANT US80 & US81
(*Suby of* LHOIST NORTH AMERICA INC) ★
2093 Big Stony Creek Rd, Ripplemead, VA 24150-3036
Tel (540) 626-7163 *Founded/Ownrshp* 1966
Sales 33.0MM^E *EMP* 119
SIC 3274 1422 Lime; Crushed & broken limestone
Pr: Mot Ludwig De
**Treas:* Bob Nordin
**VP:* Kyle Kolde
**Prin:* Jon Passic
**Plnt Mgr:* Mike Anderson
Plnt Mgr: Joseph Ferrell
Ql Cn Mgr: Barry Kast

D-U-N-S 09-320-2471
LHOSPICE SAINT ANTOINE DE WOONSOCKET R I
SAINT ANTOINE RESIDENCE
10 Rhodes Ave, North Smithfield, RI 02896-6987
Tel (401) 767-3500 *Founded/Ownrshp* 1913
Sales 22.8MM *EMP* 350^E
SIC 8051 Convalescent home with continuous nursing care; Convalescent home with continuous nursing care
Exec: Jeff Aubin
Dir Soc: Laurie-Ann Oliveria
Ex Dir: Wendy Fargnoli
Ex Dir: Mary A Ltrui
Sls&Mrk Ex: Melissa Decosta
Mktg Dir: Paula Davis
Mktg Dir: Isabel Pestana
Nrsg Dir: Joyce Corsi

D-U-N-S 80-541-0953
LHP HOSPITAL GROUP INC
2400 Dallas Pkwy Ste 450, Plano, TX 75093-4373
Tel (972) 943-1700 *Founded/Ownrshp* 2008
Sales 202.2MM^E *EMP* 1,210^E
SIC 8062 General medical & surgical hospitals; General medical & surgical hospitals
CEO: John F Holland
CFO: John W Ehrie
CFO: David Nosacka
Div Pres: Paul A Kappelman
Bd of Dir: Brian Lasater
Ex VP: Tom Frazier
Ex VP: Rebecca Hurley
Sr VP: Larry Schunder
VP: Patricia Ball
VP: Mary Bessinger
VP: Ed Davidson
VP: Edward T Davidson Jr
VP: Edward Davidson
VP: Don Fentem
VP: Lonnie Garrison
VP: Andrew Montgomery
VP: Shane Olivier
VP: Brian Padgett
VP: Maureen Potter
VP: Dawn Tosner
Board of Directors: Frederick A Hessler

D-U-N-S 08-321-6429
LHP SOFTWARE LLC
1888 Poshard Dr, Columbus, IN 47203-1897
Tel (812) 373-0870 *Founded/Ownrshp* 2001
Sales 32.2MM^E *EMP* 237
SIC 7371 3999 Custom computer programming services; Stage hardware & equipment, except lighting; Custom computer programming services; Stage hardware & equipment, except lighting
COO: Jean Hou
Ofcr: David Redding
VP: Lyle Shuey
VP: Zachary Warrner
Dir Bus: Michael Humphrey
Off Mgr: Sally James
CTO: David Foley
Software D: Yuvati Kurmude

D-U-N-S 08-076-0593 IMP/EXP
LHV INC
SUPERMERCADO ECONO LARES
Carretera 670 Km 1 0 St Carrete, Manati, PR 00674
Tel (787) 621-3220 *Founded/Ownrshp* 1997
Sales 59.2MM^E *EMP* 600
SIC 5411 Supermarkets, independent
Pr: Lino Hernandez
**Sec:* Dulce Vazquez

LI TONG INTERNATIONAL
See JC HORIZON LTD

LI WATER
See NEW YORK AMERICAN WATER CO INC

LI-COR BIO SCIENCES
See LI-COR INC

D-U-N-S 06-223-7961
LI-COR INC
LI-COR BIO SCIENCES
4647 Superior St, Lincoln, NE 68504-1357
Tel (402) 467-3576 *Founded/Ownrshp* 1971
Sales 100.0MM *EMP* 335
SIC 3826 Analytical instruments; Analytical instruments
Pr: William W Biggs
**Treas:* Craig A Jessen
**Ex VP:* Martin Hansen
**Sr VP:* Lyle Middendorf
VP: Greg Biggs
VP: Dan Hile
VP: Dr Mike Olive
VP: Kerry Petersen
IT Man: Anthony Banks

D-U-N-S 62-757-0021
LI-WAY TRANSFER & STORAGE INC
55 Chamisa Rd, Covington, GA 30016-1109
Tel (770) 787-8113 *Founded/Ownrshp* 1990
Sales 20.0MM^E *EMP* 90
SIC 4213 4214 Trucking, except local; Local trucking with storage
CEO: E Wayne Pugh
**VP:* Lisa Pugh
Brnch Mgr: Billy Sanders
Off Mgr: Wayne Pugh
Off Mgr: Regina Stewart

D-U-N-S 78-436-7273
LIA AUTO GROUP INC
LIA HONDA
1258 Central Ave, Albany, NY 12205-5201
Tel (518) 438-4555 *Founded/Ownrshp* 2003
Sales 28.5MM^E *EMP* 78^E
SIC 5511 Automobiles, new & used
Ch Bd: William Lia
Genl Mgr: Richard Taylor
IT Man: Mike Calicchia
Mktg Dir: Theresa Lazzari
Mktg Dir: George Michaelides
Sls Mgr: Raoul Gouin
Sls Mgr: Jim Wester

D-U-N-S 09-190-5869
LIA GROUP INC
ALBANY CITY HONDA
1258 Central Ave, Albany, NY 12205-5201
Tel (866) 883-3481 *Founded/Ownrshp* 1995
Sales 33.8MM^E *EMP* 85
SIC 5511 Automobiles, new & used; Automobiles, new & used
Ch Bd: William Lia

LIA HONDA
See LIA AUTO GROUP INC

LIA SOPHIA
See ACT II JEWELRY LLC

LIA TOYOTA OF COLONIE
See COLONIE IMPORT DISTRIBUTORS LTD

D-U-N-S 78-114-0827
LIAISON INTERNATIONAL INC
311 Arsenal St Ste 15, Watertown, MA 02472-2784
Tel (617) 612-2000 *Founded/Ownrshp* 1996
Sales 22.2MM^E *EMP* 50^E
SIC 7371 7379 Computer software development; Computer related consulting services
Pr: George Haddad
CFO: James Pluntze
Assoc VP: Tom Anderson
Sr VP: Jessica Finnefrock
Ex Dir: Hilda Abreu
Off Mgr: Brianne Costello
Snr Sftwr: Daniel Buttig
Snr Sftwr: Rob Jones
QA Dir: Alok Balakrishnan
Software D: Benjamin Kanouse
Software D: Alex Pennace

D-U-N-S 83-985-7344
LIAISON TECHNOLOGIES INC
3157 Royal Dr Ste 200, Alpharetta, GA 30022-2484
Tel (770) 642-5000 *Founded/Ownrshp* 2000
Sales 154.1MM^E *EMP* 328
SIC 7373 Systems integration services; Systems integration services
CEO: Robert A Renner
Pr: Sanjiv Bhalodai
CFO: Larry Mieldezis
Ofcr: Manish Gupta
Ofcr: Hmong Vang
Ex VP: Bruce Chen
Ex VP: Jaymie Forrest
Sr VP: Rob Consoli
VP: Ehi Binitie
VP: Chris Hale
VP: Mark Malis
VP: Barry Nelson
VP: Alice Westerfield
Board of Directors: Jon Duke, Clark Golestani

D-U-N-S 15-284-5202 IMP/EXP
■ **LIBBEY GLASS INC**
(*Suby of* LIBBEY INC) ★
300 Madison Ave Fl 4, Toledo, OH 43604-2634
Tel (419) 325-2100 *Founded/Ownrshp* 1993
Sales 393.5MM^E *EMP* 2,172
SIC 3229 3231 Tableware, glass or glass ceramic; Products of purchased glass; Tableware, glass or glass ceramic; Products of purchased glass
CEO: Stephanie A Streeter
**CFO:* Richard Reynolds
**Treas:* Ken Boerger
VP: L Frederick Ashton
VP: Brenda Bennett
**VP:* Daniel P Ibele
**VP:* Susan A Kovach
VP: Timothy T Paige
VP: John A Zarb
MIS Dir: Dave Johnson
Prd Mgr: Mike Rounds
Board of Directors: Carlos V Duno, William A Foley, Peter C McC Howell, Deborah G Miller, Carol B Moerdyk, John C Orr, Terence P Stewart

D-U-N-S 80-598-3335 EXP
▲ **LIBBEY INC**
300 Madison Ave, Toledo, OH 43604-1561
Tel (419) 325-2100 *Founded/Ownrshp* 1888
Sales 855.8MM *EMP* 6,553
Tkr Sym LBY *Exch* ASE
SIC 3229 3262 Glass furnishings & accessories; Tableware, glass or glass ceramic; Bowls, glass; Ashtrays, glass; Tableware, vitreous china; Glass furnishings & accessories; Tableware, glass or glass ceramic; Bowls, glass; Ashtrays, glass; Tableware, vitreous china
CEO: Stephanie A Streeter
**Ch Bd:* William A Foley
COO: James White
COO: Jim White
CFO: Sherry L Buck
Chf Cred: Anthony W Gardner Jr
Ofcr: Annunciata Cerioli
VP: Jay Achenbach
VP: Jonathon S Freeman
VP: Susan A Kovach
VP: Roberto Rubio
VP: John A Zarb
Exec: Rich Hoover
Board of Directors: Carlos V Duno, Peter C McC Howell, Ginger M Jones, Theo Killion, Deborah G Miller, Carol B Moerdyk, John C Orr

LIBBY FARMS
See WOOLCO FOODS INC

D-U-N-S 02-459-4392 IMP
LIBBY HILL SEAFOOD RESTAURANTS INC (NC)
4517 W Market St Ste B, Greensboro, NC 27407-1541
Tel (336) 294-0505 *Founded/Ownrshp* 1955
Sales 24.6MM *EMP* 125
SIC 5146 5812

D-U-N-S 10-856-5409
LIBBY PERSZYK KATHMAN HOLDINGS INC
L P K
19 Garfield Pl Fl 5, Cincinnati, OH 45202-4391
Tel (513) 241-6330 *Founded/Ownrshp* 1983
Sales 34.1MM^E *EMP* 400^E
SIC 7336 Package design; Package design
Pr: Jerome Kathman
**Pr:* John Recker
**COO:* Phil Best
**CFO:* Dennis Geiger

D-U-N-S 08-742-6268
LIBERAL SCHOOL DISTRICT
401 N Kansas Ave, Liberal, KS 67901-3329
Tel (620) 604-1010 *Founded/Ownrshp* 1964
Sales 38.5MM^E *EMP* 700
Accts Byron Bird & Associates Chtd
SIC 8211 Public elementary & secondary schools; High school, junior or senior; Vocational high school; Public elementary & secondary schools; High school, junior or senior; Vocational high school
Pr Dir: Jason McAfee

D-U-N-S 01-523-3392
LIBERATION GROUP INC
FISHER PRECIOUS METALS
2151 W Hillsboro Blvd, Deerfield Beach, FL 33442-1200
Tel (800) 390-8576 *Founded/Ownrshp* 2010
Sales 25.0MM *EMP* 5
SIC 5944 Jewelry, precious stones & precious metals
Pr: John S Fisher
**VP:* Lynn A Fisher

D-U-N-S 06-324-4409
▲ **LIBERATOR MEDICAL HOLDINGS INC**
2979 Se Gran Park Way, Stuart, FL 34997-6715
Tel (772) 287-2414 *Founded/Ownrshp* 2007
Sales 81.6MM *EMP* 319
Tkr Sym LBMH *Exch* ASE
SIC 5999 8082 Medical apparatus & supplies; Home health care services; Medical apparatus & supplies; Home health care services
Pr: Mark A Libratore
COO: John Leger
CFO: Robert J Davis
VP: Hannah Perez
IT Man: Jason Bretz
Mktg Mgr: David Baird
Snr Mgr: John Wooldridge
Snr Mgr: Erick Zingg

D-U-N-S 17-761-2967
■ **LIBERATOR MEDICAL SUPPLY INC**
(*Suby of* LIBERATOR MEDICAL HOLDINGS INC) ★
2979 Se Gran Park Way, Stuart, FL 34997-6715
Tel (772) 287-2414 *Founded/Ownrshp* 1987
Sales 57.9MM^E *EMP* 300
SIC 5999 7352 5047 Medical apparatus & supplies; Incontinent care products; Medical equipment rental; Medical equipment & supplies; Medical apparatus & supplies; Incontinent care products; Medical equipment rental; Medical equipment & supplies
Pr: Mark Libratore
**COO:* John Leger
**CFO:* Robert Davis
IT Man: Jennifer Libratore
VP Mktg: Paul Levett

D-U-N-S 05-645-1214
LIBERMAN BROADCASTING INC
1845 W Empire Ave, Burbank, CA 91504-3402
Tel (818) 729-5300 *Founded/Ownrshp* 1988
Sales 265.0MM^E *EMP* 830
SIC 4832 Radio broadcasting stations; Radio broadcasting stations
CEO: Lenard D Liberman
**Pr:* Jose Liberman
**CFO:* Frederic T Boyer
Ex VP: John Heffron
**VP:* Winter Horton
**VP:* Eduardo Leon
**VP:* Blima Tuller
Mktg Dir: Amy Stephenson
Sls Mgr: Ozzie Mendoza
Sls Mgr: Daisy Ortiz
Pgrm Dir: Cristian Garcia

D-U-N-S 07-832-6764 IMP
LIBERTAS COPPER LLC
HUSSEY COPPER
100 Washington St, Leetsdale, PA 15056-1000
Tel (724) 251-4200 *Founded/Ownrshp* 1848, 2011
Sales 248.2MM^E *EMP* 575
SIC 3366 3351 Copper foundries; Copper rolling & drawing; Copper foundries; Copper rolling & drawing
CEO: John Harrington
**CFO:* Brian Benjamin

D-U-N-S 02-704-0443 EXP
LIBERTO SPECIALTY CO INC
RICOS PRODUCTS
830 S Presa St, San Antonio, TX 78210-1375
Tel (210) 222-1415 *Founded/Ownrshp* 1909
Sales 86.9MM^E *EMP* 140
SIC 5046 5145 Commercial cooking & food service equipment; Confectionery; Commercial cooking & food service equipment; Confectionery
CEO: Frank G Liberto
**Pr:* Tony Liberto
CFO: Jeremy Poledge
**CFO:* Jeremy Powledge
VP: Charlie Gomez
VP: Joe Sain
Creative D: Michelle Scott
VP Mktg: Mark Bagley
VP Mktg: Sameera Hashme
Mktg Mgr: Enrico Falanga
Sls Mgr: John Sajewich

D-U-N-S 13-157-5961
LIBERTY 53 SCHOOL DISTRICT
LIBERTY PUBLIC SCHOOL
8 Victory Ln Ste 100, Liberty, MO 64068-2371
Tel (816) 736-5300 *Founded/Ownrshp* 1885
Sales 141.1MM *EMP* 2,200
Accts Westrbook & Co Pc Richmon
SIC 8211 Public combined elementary & secondary school; Public combined elementary & secondary school
**CFO:* Carol Embree
Exec: Colleen Jones
Dir Sec: Gary Majors
Pr Dir: Eleen Stewart
Psych: Kathy Alagna
HC Dir: Kathy Ellermeier

D-U-N-S 11-867-2732
LIBERTY AMBULANCE SERVICE INC
1626 Atlantic Univ Cir, Jacksonville, FL 32207-2227
Tel (904) 721-0008 *Founded/Ownrshp* 1984
Sales 27.3MM^E *EMP* 180
SIC 4119 Ambulance service
Pr: Michael Assaf
**CEO:* Robert Assaf
**VP:* Jackie Assaf
Exec: Clinton Randolph

D-U-N-S 96-636-8987
LIBERTY ANALYTICAL CORP
COMPUCHEM
501 Madison Ave, Cary, NC 27513-4404
Tel (919) 379-4100 *Founded/Ownrshp* 1996
Sales 23.1MM^E *EMP* 65^E
SIC 8734 Testing laboratories
Pr: Keith Scott
VP: Kenneth Grzybowski
**VP:* Robert E Meierer
**VP:* Mark S Ross
Exec: Mike Pearce
**Prin:* Willaim Waring
IT Man: Harold Cray
Software D: Bobby Bowden
Ql Cn Mgr: James Feldhaus
Sales Asso: Bob Starling

D-U-N-S 02-559-2155 IMP
LIBERTY AUTO CITY INC
LIBERTY SUBARU
1000 E Park Ave, Libertyville, IL 60048-2900
Tel (888) 346-7082 *Founded/Ownrshp* 1965
Sales 25.0MM *EMP* 150
SIC 5511 Automobiles, new & used; Automobiles, new & used
Pr: Joseph M Massarelli
VP: Joe Massarelli
Sls Mgr: Kathie Frisch
Sls Mgr: Ben Jacobs

D-U-N-S 86-787-1423
LIBERTY AUTO GROUP
LIBERTY FORD MAPLE HEIGHT
5500 Warrensville Ctr Rd, Maple Heights, OH 44137-3126
Tel (216) 662-3673 *Founded/Ownrshp* 2002
Sales 80.4MM^E *EMP* 400^E
SIC 5511 New & used car dealers; Automobiles, new & used
Pr: Jim Herrick

D-U-N-S 11-922-0127
LIBERTY AUTOMOTIVE LTD
LIBERTY TOYOTA
4397 Route 130 S, Burlington, NJ 08016-2249
Tel (609) 386-6300 *Founded/Ownrshp* 1984
Sales 39.1MM^E *EMP* 107^E
SIC 5511 Automobiles, new & used; Automobiles, new & used
Pr: Jim Richardson
**VP:* John Richard Mee
Genl Mgr: Rich Mee
Sls Mgr: Christopher Bennett
Sls Mgr: Tori Delano
Sls Mgr: David Keegan
Sales Asso: James Fitzgerald

Sales Asso: Tito Martinez
Sales Asso: Doug Phillips

LIBERTY AV SOLUTIONS
See LIBERTY WIRE & CABLE INC

D-U-N-S 03-954-3975
■ LIBERTY AVEX INC
(*Suby of* BENCHMARK ELECTRONICS INC) ★
3000 Technology Rd, Angleton, TX 77515-2524
Tel (979) 849-6550 *Founded/Ownrshp* 2000
Sales 20.2MM^E *EMP* 492^E
SIC 3672 Printed circuit boards; Printed circuit boards
Pr: Donald E Nigbor
Ex VP: Steven A Barton
Ex VP: Cary T Fu

D-U-N-S 01-823-3432
LIBERTY BANCORP INC
1410 Saint Georges Ave, Avenel, NJ 07001-1158
Tel (732) 499-7200 *Founded/Ownrshp* 1991
Sales NA *EMP* 70^E
SIC 6035 Federal savings banks
Pr: John Bowen
VP Opers: Lucille Capece

D-U-N-S 80-845-0100
▲ LIBERTY BANCORP INC
16 W Franklin St, Liberty, MO 64068-1637
Tel (816) 781-4822 *Founded/Ownrshp* 2006
Sales NA *EMP* 111^E
Tkr Sym LBCP *Exch* OTC
SIC 6035 Savings institutions, federally chartered; Federal savings & loan associations; Savings institutions, federally chartered; Federal savings & loan associations
Pr: Brent M Giles
**CFO:* Marc J Weishaar
VP: Roger Hamblin
VP: Barbara Murray
VP: Martin Weishaar
Brnch Mgr: Joe Pickett
Dir IT: Connie Koosman

D-U-N-S 16-855-3506
■ LIBERTY BANCSHARES INC
(*Suby of* HOME BANCSHARES INC) ★
2901 E Highland Dr, Jonesboro, AR 72401-6224
Tel (870) 934-9000 *Founded/Ownrshp* 2013
Sales NA *EMP* 500
SIC 6712 6022 Bank holding companies; State commercial banks; Bank holding companies; State commercial banks
Pr: John Freeman

D-U-N-S 00-691-7579
LIBERTY BANK
315 Main St, Middletown, CT 06457-3338
Tel (860) 344-7200 *Founded/Ownrshp* 1825
Sales NA *EMP* 512
SIC 6036 6163 6022 Savings institutions, not federally chartered; Loan brokers; State commercial banks; Savings institutions, not federally chartered; Loan brokers; State commercial banks
Pr: Chandler J Howard
COO: Robin Fujio
CFO: Thomas J Pastorello
Treas: Nicholas Sabetta
Chf Mktg O: Sue Murphy
Ofcr: Gerard M Kusinski
Ofcr: Cynthia Sheehan
Ex VP: Deborah C Bochain
Ex VP: Ronald J Catrone
Ex VP: Richard Hagarty
Ex VP: Thomas Hylinski
Sr VP: Barry J Abramowitz
Sr VP: Stephen Barlow
Sr VP: Patricia D Jatkevicius
Sr VP: Don Peruta
VP: Edward Amato
VP: Thomas A Ballachino
VP: Eric Bernard
VP: Donna Flynn
VP: Nancy Gates
VP: Brian Hedge
Board of Directors: Michael Helfgott, David E A Carson, Grace Sawyer Jones, David G Carter, Lawrence McHugh, William T Christopher, Timothy Ryan, Jean M D'aquila, Richard W Tomc, David Director, Mark R Gingras, Winona S Goings, Gary Gomola, Steve J Gorss

D-U-N-S 03-633-3482
LIBERTY BANK
318 E Main St, Siloam Springs, AR 72761-3232
Tel (479) 524-8101 *Founded/Ownrshp* 1960
Sales NA *EMP* 60
SIC 6022 State commercial banks; State commercial banks
Pr: Art Morris
VP: Kim Morris
Board of Directors: D E Allen Jr, Roderick Allen, Robert Brown, Hank Harrison, Charles Jones, Mark Simmons, Dr Duane Thomas

D-U-N-S 79-077-7028
■ LIBERTY BANK
SFNC
(*Suby of* SFNC) ★
4625 S National Ave, Springfield, MO 65810-2772
Tel (417) 888-3000 *Founded/Ownrshp* 2007
Sales NA *EMP* 3^E
SIC 6712 Bank holding companies; Bank holding companies
VP: Petiford David
Ofcr: J J Zind
Ex VP: Garry Robinson
Sr VP: David Petiford
Sr VP: Bob Ward
VP: Kris Nau

D-U-N-S 06-549-6283
LIBERTY BANK AND TRUST CO
(*Suby of* LIBERTY FINANCIAL SERVICES, INC.)
6600 Plaza Dr Ste 310, New Orleans, LA 70127-7916
Tel (504) 240-5100 *Founded/Ownrshp* 1972
Sales NA *EMP* 30^E
SIC 6022 State commercial banks; State commercial banks
Pr: Alden J Mc Donald Jr
**Ch Bd:* Norman Francis
COO: Gregory St Etienne
**CFO:* Leroy Watts
Bd of Dir: Pat Sechler
Ofcr: Todd McDonald
Sr VP: Lee Kennedy
**Sr VP:* Edward Wood
VP: Mysheka Battiste
VP: Westley Christopher
VP: Roger Reese
VP: Sheila Thomas
Exec: Dawn Dixon

D-U-N-S 02-096-5752
LIBERTY BANK FOR SAVINGS (INC) (IL)
2392 N Milwaukee Ave, Chicago, IL 60647-2951
Tel (773) 384-4000 *Founded/Ownrshp* 1898, 1960
Sales NA *EMP* 166
SIC 6036 Savings & loan associations, not federally chartered; Savings & loan associations, not federally chartered
CEO: William J Smigiel
CFO: Kane Connell
**CFO:* Joseph Moravecek
Sr VP: Cary Tengel
Sr VP: Kevin Tynan
VP: Kathleen Julkowski
QA Dir: Monica Lesny
IT Man: Goran Brnic
IT Man: Eric David
IT Man: Ivelisse Rodriguez
IT Man: Tony Rosado

D-U-N-S 05-272-4569
LIBERTY BANK FSB
6601 Westown Pkwy Ste 140, West Des Moines, IA 50266-7731
Tel (515) 222-0731 *Founded/Ownrshp* 1998
Sales NA *EMP* 300
SIC 6163 6035 Loan brokers; Savings institutions, federally chartered; Loan brokers; Savings institutions, federally chartered
Pr: Russ Olsen

D-U-N-S 60-829-2384
LIBERTY BANK OF ARKANSAS
2901 E Highland Dr, Jonesboro, AR 72401-6224
Tel (870) 934-9000 *Founded/Ownrshp* 2003
Sales NA *EMP* 500
SIC 6022

D-U-N-S 02-505-1738
LIBERTY BANKERS LIFE
1605 L B Johnson Fwy # 710, Dallas, TX 75234-6099
Tel (469) 522-4400 *Founded/Ownrshp* 2011
Sales NA *EMP* 54^E
SIC 6411 Insurance agents, brokers & service
Prin: Bradford A Phillips
Snr Mgr: Van Vaughan

D-U-N-S 01-463-9389 EXP
■ LIBERTY BELL EQUIPMENT CORP
MEDCO
(*Suby of* ESSENDANT CO) ★
3201 S 76th St, Philadelphia, PA 19153-3215
Tel (215) 492-6700 *Founded/Ownrshp* 2014
Sales 247.3MM^E *EMP* 165^E
SIC 5013 Automobile service station equipment; Tools & equipment, automotive; Body repair or paint shop supplies, automotive; Automobile service station equipment; Tools & equipment, automotive; Body repair or paint shop supplies, automotive
Pr: Andrew A Keim
**Sec:* Don Bernhardt
Area Mgr: Rick Britton
Telecom Mg: Steve Koung

D-U-N-S 07-955-9539
LIBERTY BROADBAND CORP
12300 Liberty Blvd, Englewood, CO 80112-7009
Tel (720) 875-5400 *Founded/Ownrshp* 2014
Sales 69.0MM *EMP* 11^E
Tkr Sym LBRDK *Exch* NGS
SIC 4841 Cable & other pay television services

D-U-N-S 03-586-3307
LIBERTY BUICK INC
8737 W Bell Rd, Peoria, AZ 85382-3709
Tel (623) 933-5000 *Founded/Ownrshp* 1987
Sales 45.3MM^E *EMP* 120^E
SIC 5511 Automobiles, new & used; Automobiles, new & used
Pr: Dana Moore
**CFO:* Barry Libersin
**VP:* Louis Sands IV
Exec: Sherri Masterson
Genl Mgr: Autumn Henderson
Off Mgr: Janell Eichen
Sls&Mrk Ex: Mike Moline
Sls Mgr: Rusty Lemmon
Sls Mgr: Jerry Wood

D-U-N-S 61-437-3822 IMP
■ LIBERTY CABLEVISION OF PUERTO RICO LLC
(*Suby of* LEO CABLE LP)
Urb Indl Tres Monjitas 1, San Juan, PR 00918
Tel (787) 766-0909 *Founded/Ownrshp* 2012
Sales 151.5MM^E *EMP* 350^E
SIC 4841 Cable television services; Cable television services
CEO: Ron Dorchester
**CFO:* Jorge Hernandez
Mng Dir: Naji Khoury
Genl Mgr: Edward Hernandez
Dir IT: Francisco Herrero
IT Man: Lisabeth Nieves

D-U-N-S 79-339-8728 IMP
LIBERTY CABLEVISION OF PUERTO RICO LLC
Urb Industrial Tres Monj, San Juan, PR 00919
Tel (787) 657-3050 *Founded/Ownrshp* 2005
Sales NA *EMP* 1,500
SIC 4841 Cable television services

D-U-N-S 19-897-6888
LIBERTY CAPITAL INC
2251 Rombach Ave, Wilmington, OH 45177-1995
Tel (937) 382-1000 *Founded/Ownrshp* 1985
Sales NA *EMP* 700
SIC 6035 Federal savings & loan associations; Federal savings & loan associations
Pr: James R Powell
**Sr VP:* Suzan Kranjc
VP: Isabelle Cochrane
VP: Jeanna Francis
VP: Deborah Lauer
VP: Rick Loechler
VP: Laurissa Manning
VP: Nita Nelson
VP: Amanda Ping
VP: Denise Puskaric
VP: Larysa Rudak
VP: Mahjabeen Shirazi
VP: Anita Toth
VP: Martin Varghese
VP: Edel Walsh
VP: Lance West
VP: Christi Young

LIBERTY CARE RECYCLING
See LAUREL MOUNTAIN PARTNERS LLC

D-U-N-S 00-647-8234 IMP
LIBERTY CARTON CO (MN)
(*Suby of* LIBERTY DIVERSIFIED INTERNATIONAL INC) ★
870 Louisiana Ave S, Golden Valley, MN 55426-1672
Tel (763) 540-9600 *Founded/Ownrshp* 1932
Sales 110.6MM^E *EMP* 1,000
SIC 2653 Boxes, corrugated: made from purchased materials; Display items, corrugated: made from purchased materials; Boxes, corrugated: made from purchased materials; Display items, corrugated: made from purchased materials
Ch Bd: Michael Fiterman
**COO:* Daniel Zdon
**CFO:* Byron Wieberdink
**Ex VP:* David Lenzen
**VP:* Ronda Bayer
**VP:* Michael Snowball
Genl Mgr: Craig Musselman
Ql Cn Mgr: Amy Frana

D-U-N-S 95-942-5539 IMP
LIBERTY CARTON CO -TEXAS INC
(*Suby of* LIBERTY DIVERSIFIED INTERNATIONAL INC) ★
5100 Glenview Dr, Fort Worth, TX 76117-1304
Tel (817) 577-6100 *Founded/Ownrshp* 1991
Sales 60.7MM^E *EMP* 200
SIC 2653 Boxes, corrugated: made from purchased materials; Boxes, corrugated: made from purchased materials
Ch Bd: Michael B Fiterman
**COO:* Daniel Zdon
**CFO:* Byron Wieberdink
**Ex VP:* David Lenzen
**VP:* Ronda Bayer
Sls Dir: Ralph Nolan

D-U-N-S 13-860-4769
LIBERTY CASTING CO LLC
550 Liberty Rd, Delaware, OH 43015-8670
Tel (740) 363-1941 *Founded/Ownrshp* 2003
Sales 33.5MM^E *EMP* 125
SIC 3321 Gray iron castings; Ductile iron castings; Gray iron castings; Ductile iron castings
**CFO:* Viera Maruli
VP: Rick Vaught
S&M/VP: Terry Geisen

D-U-N-S 00-512-9853
LIBERTY CENTRAL SCHOOL DISTRICT
115 Buckley St, Liberty, NY 12754-1601
Tel (845) 292-6171 *Founded/Ownrshp* 1941
Sales 17.0MM^E *EMP* 326^E
SIC 8211 Public elementary & secondary schools; Public elementary & secondary schools
Bd of Dir: Michael McGuire
**Prin:* Jeri Finnegan
**Prin:* Jack Stressman
Schl Brd P: Andrew Kavleski
Teacher Pr: Christine Klein

D-U-N-S 36-269-2662
LIBERTY CHEVROLET INC
30400 Lyon Center Dr E, New Hudson, MI 48165-8900
Tel (248) 486-1900 *Founded/Ownrshp* 2003
Sales 39.3MM^E *EMP* 85
SIC 5511 Automobiles, new & used; Automobiles, new & used
Pr: Jay Feldman
CFO: Val Van Note
Ofcr: J C Cramer
Natl Sales: Ben Brown

D-U-N-S 60-324-3049 EXP
LIBERTY CHEVROLET INC
90 Bay State Rd Ste 2, Wakefield, MA 01880-1093
Tel (781) 246-1919 *Founded/Ownrshp* 1988
Sales 27.2MM^E *EMP* 70
SIC 5511 5561 Automobiles, new & used; Recreational vehicle dealers; Automobiles, new & used; Recreational vehicle dealers
Pr: John Knopf
**Treas:* Jeffrey Manning

D-U-N-S 07-456-3628
LIBERTY COACH INC (IL)
1400 Morrow Ave, North Chicago, IL 60064-3220
Tel (847) 578-4600 *Founded/Ownrshp* 1972
Sales 20.5MM^E *EMP* 68
SIC 3711 Motor buses, except trackless trollies, assembly of
Pr: Frank Konigseder
**Owner:* Tom Williams
**Sec:* Kurt Konigseder

D-U-N-S 16-281-1538
LIBERTY CONSTRUCTION SERVICES LLC
350 Granite St Ste 2306, Braintree, MA 02184-4963
Tel (617) 602-4001 *Founded/Ownrshp* 2004
Sales 30.0MM^E *EMP* 80
SIC 1389 Construction, repair & dismantling services
Pr: Kevin Chin
**VP:* Marshall Felix

D-U-N-S 60-326-9879
LIBERTY CONTRACTING CORP
2531 94th St, North Bergen, NJ 07047-1411
Tel (201) 488-9300 *Founded/Ownrshp* 1989
Sales 21.2MM^E *EMP* 150^E
SIC 1795 Wrecking & demolition work; Wrecking & demolition work
Pr: Frank Cali
**VP:* Dominic Bullaro
**VP:* George Fotiadis
VP: George Fotiados
Prin: Mike Hellis
MIS Dir: Mike Hillis

D-U-N-S 04-493-5542
LIBERTY CORP
(*Suby of* RAYCOM MEDIA INC) ★
135 S Main St Ste 1000, Greenville, SC 29601-2781
Tel (864) 609-8111 *Founded/Ownrshp* 2005
Sales 74.9MM^E *EMP* 1,400
SIC 4833 Television broadcasting stations; Television broadcasting stations
Ch Bd: W Hayne Hipp
**Pr:* James M Keelor
**CFO:* Howard L Schrott
Bd of Dir: John H Mullin
Bd of Dir: Eugene E Stone
**VP:* Martha G Williams
Netwrk Mgr: Kevin Flynn

LIBERTY COUNTRY PLACE
See NORTHWEST COUNTRY PLACE INC

D-U-N-S 07-248-0783
LIBERTY COUNTY
LIBERTY COUNTY BOARD OF COMMIS
112 N Main St, Hinesville, GA 31313-3216
Tel (912) 876-2164 *Founded/Ownrshp* 1777
Sales NA *EMP* 382
Accts Carr Riggs & Ingram Llc T
SIC 9111 County supervisors' & executives' offices;
Ch: John D McIve
CFO: Kim McGlothlin
Dir IT: Clint Stanley
Sfty Dirs: Tom Burris

LIBERTY COUNTY BOARD OF COMMIS
See LIBERTY COUNTY

D-U-N-S 10-064-6173
LIBERTY COUNTY BOARD OF EDUCATION
200 Bradwell St, Hinesville, GA 31313-2706
Tel (912) 876-2162 *Founded/Ownrshp* 1900
Sales 99.9MM^E *EMP* 1,800
Accts Russell W Hinton-State Audito
SIC 8211 Public elementary & secondary schools; School board
Ch Bd: Lily Baker

D-U-N-S 10-384-9089
LIBERTY COUNTY OF TEXAS
1923 Sam Houston St, Liberty, TX 77575-4800
Tel (936) 336-4665 *Founded/Ownrshp* 1800
Sales NA *EMP* 350
SIC 9111 Executive offices; ; Executive offices;
Pr: Craig McNair
**Prin:* Logan Pickett
CIO: Dean Hendrix
IT Man: James Carson
IT Man: Ralph Fuller
IT Man: Kim Harris

D-U-N-S 07-979-9718
LIBERTY COUNTY SCHOOL SYSTEM
200 Bradwell St, Hinesville, GA 31313-2706
Tel (912) 876-2161 *Founded/Ownrshp* 2015
Sales 12.1MM^E *EMP* 1,629^E
SIC 8211 Public elementary & secondary schools
Pr Dir: Patricia Crane
HC Dir: Mary Alexander
HC Dir: Carol Darcy

D-U-N-S 78-086-4406
LIBERTY DENTAL PLAN OF CALIFORNIA INC
340 Commerce Ste 100, Irvine, CA 92602-1358
Tel (949) 223-0007 *Founded/Ownrshp* 2001
Sales NA *EMP* 300
SIC 6324 Dental insurance; Dental insurance
Pr: Amir Hossein Neshat
**CFO:* Maja Kapic

D-U-N-S 00-976-0930
LIBERTY DEVELOPMENT CORP
295 W Crgville Rd Ste 630, Roswell, GA 30075
Tel (678) 336-1395 *Founded/Ownrshp* 1996
Sales 27.0MM *EMP* 20
SIC 6531 Real estate agents & managers; Real estate agents & managers
Pr: Spurgeon Richardson
**CFO:* Kevin Olson

D-U-N-S 13-165-3805
LIBERTY DIALYSIS LLC
(*Suby of* FRESENIUS MEDICAL CARE AG & CO. KGAA)
7650 Se 27th St Ste 200, Mercer Island, WA 98040-3060
Tel (206) 236-5001 *Founded/Ownrshp* 2012
Sales 41.5MM^E *EMP* 850
SIC 8092 Kidney dialysis centers; Kidney dialysis centers
Off Mgr: Natalie Hodges
IT Man: Adrian Sellhorn

D-U-N-S 60-524-4797
LIBERTY DISTRIBUTION CO LLC
290 E El Prado Ct, Chandler, AZ 85225-0995
Tel (602) 437-4246 *Founded/Ownrshp* 2007
Sales 33.4MM^E *EMP* 140
SIC 5962 Candy & snack food vending machines
VP: Steve Lewis
Board of Directors: Art J Wain

D-U-N-S 17-782-9900
LIBERTY DISTRIBUTORS INC
Rr 40 Box E, Triadelphia, WV 26059
Tel (304) 547-0414 *Founded/Ownrshp* 1987
Sales 44.8MM^E *EMP* 55
SIC 5113 5199 5169 5112 5111 Industrial & personal service paper; Packaging materials; Chemicals & allied products; Stationery & office supplies; Printing & writing paper
Pr: F Mark Peluchette
CFO: Jim Lightner
**Sec:* Paul Peluchetti
**VP:* Dave Peluchetti
VP Sls: Paul Peluchette
Sales Asso: Dan Messinger
Sales Asso: Nathan Peluchette

D-U-N-S 06-145-6489 IMP/EXP
LIBERTY DIVERSIFIED INTERNATIONAL INC
5600 Highway 169 N, Minneapolis, MN 55428-3096
Tel (763) 536-6600 *Founded/Ownrshp* 1972
Sales 657.7MM^E *EMP* 1,820
SIC 2653 2631 5112 2542 3089 5961 Boxes, corrugated: made from purchased materials; Paperboard mills; Stationery & office supplies; Fixtures, office: except wood; Fixtures, store: except wood; Partitions for floor attachment, prefabricated: except wood; Shelving, office & store: except wood; Plastic containers, except foam; Plastic kitchenware, tableware & houseware; Plastic processing; Injection molding of plastics; Mail order house; Boxes, corrugated: made from purchased materials; Paperboard mills; Stationery & office supplies; Fixtures, office: except wood; Fixtures, store: except wood; Partitions for floor attachment, prefabricated: except wood; Shelving, office & store: except wood; Plastic containers, except foam; Plastic kitchenware, tableware & houseware; Plastic processing; Injection molding of plastics; Mail order house
Ch Bd: Michael Fiterman
**Pr:* Mark S Schumacher
**CFO:* Byron Wieberdink
CFO: Byron Wiedredink
**Ex VP:* David Lenzen
**VP:* Ronda Bayer
**VP:* Sally Bredehoft
VP: Bill Hack
**VP:* Michael Snowball
Dir Risk M: Scott Towne
Genl Mgr: Todd Gardner

D-U-N-S 92-669-0087
LIBERTY EDUCATIONAL MINISTRIES
1301 S Us Highway 377, Argyle, TX 76226-7744
Tel (940) 294-2000 *Founded/Ownrshp* 2007
Sales 23.3MM *EMP* 1
Accts Freemon Shapard & Story Wichi
SIC 8661 Religious organizations; Religious organizations
Prin: Craig Martin

D-U-N-S 87-627-3637
LIBERTY ELECTRONICS
191 Howard St, Reno, PA 16343
Tel (814) 676-0600 *Founded/Ownrshp* 2007
Sales 21.7MM^E *EMP* 275
SIC 3679 Harness assemblies for electronic use: wire or cable; Harness assemblies for electronic use: wire or cable
Pr: John Dumot

D-U-N-S 13-118-8997 IMP
LIBERTY ELECTRONICS INC
189 Howard St, Franklin, PA 16323-2347
Tel (814) 432-7505 *Founded/Ownrshp* 1985
Sales 94.3MM^E *EMP* 295
SIC 3679 5051 Harness assemblies for electronic use: wire or cable; Miscellaneous nonferrous products; Harness assemblies for electronic use: wire or cable; Miscellaneous nonferrous products
Pr: John Dumot
**Treas:* John Smith
**Treas:* Linda Wolbert
**VP:* Scott Anderson
Prgrm Mgr: Eric Rhoads
Prgrm Mgr: Terry West
Plnt Mgr: Rex Phillips
Ql Cn Mgr: Robert Nestor

LIBERTY ELEMENTARY
See SALLISAW PUBLIC SCHOOL DISTRICT

LIBERTY ELEMENTARY SCHOOL
See UNION COUNTY SCHOOL DISTRICT

D-U-N-S 17-917-2416
LIBERTY ELEVATOR CORP
63 E 24th St, Paterson, NJ 07514-2021
Tel (973) 279-1390 *Founded/Ownrshp* 1987
Sales 42.9MM^E *EMP* 65
SIC 5084 7699 1796 Elevators; Elevators: inspection, service & repair; Elevator installation & conversion
Pr: Douglas J Muttart
**Sec:* Janet N Muttart
**VP:* Darren G Muttart
Genl Mgr: Tina Cortina

LIBERTY ENERGY
See ALGONQUIN POWER AND UTILITIES CORP

LIBERTY ENERGY
See LIBERTY UTILITIES (CALPECO ELECTRIC) LLC

D-U-N-S 07-851-5476
LIBERTY ENERGY UTILITIES (NEW HAMPSHIRE) CORP
LIBERTY UTILITIES
(*Suby of* LIBERTY UTILITIES CO) ★
15 Buttrick Rd, Londonderry, NH 03053-3305
Tel (905) 287-2061 *Founded/Ownrshp* 2011
Sales 340.6MM^E *EMP* 655^E
SIC 1311 Crude petroleum & natural gas; Crude petroleum & natural gas
Pr: Victor Del Vecchio
Opers Mgr: Deon Scott

LIBERTY ENGINEERING
See DELAWARE ELECTRO INDUSTRIES INC

LIBERTY ENTERPRISES
See MONTGOMERY COUNTY CHAPTER NYSARC INC

D-U-N-S 80-145-3577
■ **LIBERTY ENTERTAINMENT INC**
(*Suby of* DIRECTV GROUP HOLDINGS LLC) ★
2230 E Imperial Hwy, El Segundo, CA 90245-3504
Tel (310) 964-5000 *Founded/Ownrshp* 2009
Sales 88.7MM^E *EMP* 252^E
SIC 4841 Cable & other pay television services

D-U-N-S 79-351-2856
LIBERTY FINANCIAL CORP
4201 Westown Pkwy Ste 320, West Des Moines, IA 50266-6720
Tel (515) 226-0500 *Founded/Ownrshp* 1985
Sales NA *EMP* 12
SIC 6712 Bank holding companies; Bank holding companies
Ch Bd: W A Krause
**Pr:* Russ Olson
**VP:* Doug Pullin

D-U-N-S 05-800-8418
LIBERTY FINANCIAL SERVICES INC
LIBERTY INSURANCE AGENCY
1910 Cochran Rd Ste 800, Pittsburgh, PA 15220-1224
Tel (412) 571-5700 *Founded/Ownrshp* 1985
Sales NA *EMP* 70^E
SIC 6411 Insurance agents
Pr: Kevin Heher
VP: Michael Courtad
VP: Steve Horvath
VP: Gary Wobb
Sales Exec: Mary Duffy

D-U-N-S 80-913-0193
LIBERTY FINANCIAL SERVICES INC
4425 Singing Hills Blvd, Sioux City, IA 51106-9536
Tel (712) 224-4425 *Founded/Ownrshp* 2008
Sales NA *EMP* 222
SIC 6712 Bank holding companies
Prin: Robert A Mullen

LIBERTY FLAGS
See SEASONAL DESIGNS INC

LIBERTY FORD LINCOLN MERCURY
See JIM HERRICK MOTORS INC

D-U-N-S 05-725-5572
LIBERTY FORD LINCOLN MERCURY INC
LIBERTY FORD VERMILLION
(*Suby of* JIM HERRICK MOTORS INC) ★
4215 Liberty Ave, Vermilion, OH 44089-2132
Tel (440) 967-6191 *Founded/Ownrshp* 1982
Sales 36.5MM^E *EMP* 114
SIC 5511 Automobiles, new & used; Automobiles, new & used
Pr: James R Herrick
Genl Mgr: Jerry Draga

LIBERTY FORD MAPLE HEIGHT
See LIBERTY AUTO GROUP

LIBERTY FORD VERMILLION
See LIBERTY FORD LINCOLN MERCURY INC

D-U-N-S 05-407-6583 IMP
LIBERTY FRUIT CO INC
1247 Argentine Blvd, Kansas City, KS 66105-1508
Tel (913) 238-4606 *Founded/Ownrshp* 1965
Sales 103.3MM^E *EMP* 351
Accts Mayer Hoffman Mccann Pc Le
SIC 5148 Fruits, fresh; Vegetables, fresh; Fruits, fresh; Vegetables, fresh
CEO: Arnold Caviar
**Pr:* Allen Caviar
**Ex VP:* Reade Sievert
VP: Allen Cavier
**VP Opers:* Mike Logan
Ql Cn Mgr: Ana Deshpande
Ql Cn Mgr: Sarah Mann
VP Mktg: John Nelson

D-U-N-S 07-940-0414
■ **LIBERTY FUELS CO LLC**
MISSISSIPPI LIGNITE MINING
(*Suby of* NORTH AMERICAN COAL CORP) ★
1000 Mcintire Rd, Ackerman, MS 39735-4524
Tel (601) 737-7000 *Founded/Ownrshp* 2014
Sales 24.7MM *EMP* 20^E
SIC 1221 Bituminous coal & lignite-surface mining; Bituminous coal & lignite-surface mining
Ch: Alfred M Rankin Jr
**CEO:* Robert L Benson
**CFO:* JP Sullivan Jr
**Sr VP:* J C Butler Jr
**VP:* Michael J Gregory

D-U-N-S 96-756-4779
■ **LIBERTY FUELS CO LLC**
(*Suby of* NORTH AMERICAN COAL CORP) ★
4707 Highway 493, De Kalb, MS 39328-7789
Tel (601) 737-7000 *Founded/Ownrshp* 2008
Sales 38.7MM^E *EMP* 259^E
SIC 1221 Bituminous coal & lignite-surface mining

D-U-N-S 07-203-8938
LIBERTY FUND INC
8335 Allison Pointe Trl # 300, Indianapolis, IN 46250-1684
Tel (317) 842-0880 *Founded/Ownrshp* 1960
Sales 24.7MM *EMP* 47
SIC 6732 Educational trust management; Educational trust management
Ch Bd: T Alan Russell
Pr: Chris L Talley
Sec: Sandra J Schaller
Bd of Dir: Richard Duesenberg
Bd of Dir: Joseph Johnston
Ex VP: Emilio J Pacheco
VP: Patricia Gallagher
VP: Douglas J Den Uyl
Dir IT: James Cote

D-U-N-S 82-487-4036 IMP/EXP
LIBERTY FURNITURE INDUSTRIES INC
6021 Greensboro Dr Sw A, Atlanta, GA 30336-2873
Tel (404) 629-1003 *Founded/Ownrshp* 1992
Sales 80.5MM *EMP* 125
Accts Moore Colon & Company Pc Ma
SIC 5021 Furniture; Furniture
Pr: Ricky Brian
**CFO:* Shanda Davis
VP: Jonathan Cowles
**VP:* Russell Jacks
VP: Jason Wagy
S&M/VP: Meho Tepic

D-U-N-S 12-600-6647
LIBERTY GENEVA STEEL LTD
GENMAK GENEVA LIBERTY
947 Martin Luther King Jr, Youngstown, OH 44502-1106
Tel (330) 740-0103 *Founded/Ownrshp* 2002
Sales 44.1MM^E *EMP* 84
SIC 3316 7389 Strip steel, flat bright, cold-rolled: purchased hot-rolled; Scrap steel cutting; Strip steel, flat bright, cold-rolled: purchased hot-rolled; Scrap steel cutting
Pt: David T McLeroy
CFO: Enzo Dechellis
Exec: Barb McLeroy
Manager: David Bauschard

D-U-N-S 78-463-3906
■ **LIBERTY GLOBAL INC**
(*Suby of* LIBERTY GLOBAL PLC)
12300 Liberty Blvd, Englewood, CO 80112-7009
Tel (303) 220-6600 *Founded/Ownrshp* 2013
Sales 4.9MMM^E *EMP* 22,000^E
SIC 4841 4813 Cable & other pay television services;
Pr: Michael T Fries
Pr: Michelle Keist
Pr: William Warga
COO: Marceau Caby
CFO: Charles H R Bracken
Bd of Dir: Paul Gould
Ex VP: Bernard G Dvorak
Ex VP: Bryan H Hall
Ex VP: Bryan Hall
Sr VP: Amy M Blair
Sr VP: Bernard Dovorak
Sr VP: Bob Leighton
Sr VP: Albert Rosenthaler
Sr VP: Jim Ryan
Sr VP: Andrea Salvato
Sr VP: Rick Westerman
VP: Marcel Van Den Berg
VP: Timothy Burke
VP: Jim Clark
VP: Phil Colby
VP: Valerie Cover

LIBERTY GLOVE & SAFETY CO
See LIBERTY GLOVE INC

D-U-N-S 60-305-5088 IMP
LIBERTY GLOVE INC
LIBERTY GLOVE & SAFETY CO
433 Cheryl Ln, City of Industry, CA 91789-3023
Tel (909) 595-2992 *Founded/Ownrshp* 1988
Sales 52.8MM^E *EMP* 50
SIC 5099 Safety equipment & supplies
Pr: Michael Young
CFO: Vicki Lin
Brnch Mgr: Oscar Mejia
IT Man: Joe Young

LIBERTY GRAPHICS
See LIBERTY LITHOGRAPHERS INC

D-U-N-S 94-930-4430
LIBERTY HAMPSHIRE CO LLC
(*Suby of* GUGGENHEIM PARTNERS LLC) ★
227 W Monroe St, Chicago, IL 60606-5055
Tel (312) 827-0100 *Founded/Ownrshp* 2011
Sales NA *EMP* 535^E
SIC 6141 Personal credit institutions; Personal credit institutions
Pt: Thomas Irvin
Mng Dir: Pam Berger
CIO: Sean P Connelly

D-U-N-S 00-134-3870 IMP/EXP
■ **LIBERTY HARDWARE MFG CORP**
(*Suby of* MASCO CORP) ★
140 Business Park Dr, Winston Salem, NC 27107-6539
Tel (336) 769-4077 *Founded/Ownrshp* 1942, 1997
Sales 360.2MM^E *EMP* 393
SIC 5072 Hardware; Hardware
Pr: Rick Roetken
VP: Robert Buck
**VP:* Ronnie Murray
**VP:* Mark Stull
Comm Dir: Chris Lemnios
Web Dev: Steven Tisdale
Natl Sales: Courtnee Miller
VP Mktg: Dianne Pisarek
Board of Directors: Rick Roetken

D-U-N-S 36-430-2489 IMP
LIBERTY HARDWOODS INC
3900 N Kentucky Ave, Kansas City, MO 64161-8303
Tel (816) 231-0852 *Founded/Ownrshp* 1997
Sales 26.6MM^E *EMP* 75
SIC 5031 5211 Lumber: rough, dressed & finished; Lumber & other building materials
Pr: Larry Sumner
CFO: Michelle Blodgett
**CFO:* Mike Henry
**VP:* Larry Chambers
**VP:* Gary Gaulter
**VP:* Dwayne Jones
**VP:* Kevin Sickel
Sales Asso: Robb Goodwin
Sales Asso: Allen Green

D-U-N-S 14-244-9771
■ **LIBERTY HEALTHCARE GROUP INC**
LIBERTY MEDICAL SUPPLY
(*Suby of* POLYMEDICA CORPORATION)
8881 Liberty Ln, Port Saint Lucie, FL 34952-3477
Tel (772) 398-7257 *Founded/Ownrshp* 1997
Sales 71.8MM^E *EMP* 2,037
SIC 5961 Pharmaceuticals, mail order; Pharmaceuticals, mail order
Pr: Joan Dp Kennedy
Pr: Harvey Frank A
Pr: Frank A Harvey
Pr: Bob Mark
COO: Peter McKenzie
COO: Arlene Rodriguez
COO: Frank Schulte
CFO: Johnathan Star
Treas: Peter Gaylord
VP: Kelly Ellis
VP: Marc Lamrouex
VP: Henrik Sandell
VP: Ivette Zuniga
Exec: Devin Anderson

D-U-N-S 78-979-1428
LIBERTY HEALTHCARE GROUP LLC
LIBERTY HLTH RHBILITATION SVCS
2334 S 41st St, Wilmington, NC 28403-5502
Tel (800) 438-1115 *Founded/Ownrshp* 2006
Sales 24.9MM^E *EMP* 120^E
SIC 8059 Convalescent home

D-U-N-S 78-733-6817
LIBERTY HEALTHCARE SYSTEM INC
LIBERTYHEALTH
(*Suby of* SAINT BARNABAS CORP) ★
355 Grand St, Jersey City, NJ 07302-4321
Tel (318) 251-9458 *Founded/Ownrshp* 2014
Sales 370.6MM^E *EMP* 2,600
SIC 8062 General medical & surgical hospitals; General medical & surgical hospitals
CEO: Stephen Kirby
Pr: Joseph F Scott
Sr VP: Paul Goldberg
Sr VP: Dan Murray
VP: Paul Murphy
VP: Brenda Thompson
Dir Rad: Maria Saguil
Ex Dir: Bill Cook
Prgrm Mgr: Jenna Whiteside
CIO: Arne Larsen
Dir IT: Craig Scudieri

D-U-N-S 08-515-4227
LIBERTY HILL INDEPENDENT SCHOOL DISTRICT
301 Forrest St, Liberty Hill, TX 78642-4337
Tel (512) 260-5580 *Founded/Ownrshp* 1884
Sales 18.7MM^E *EMP* 344
SIC 8211 Public elementary & secondary schools; Public junior high school; Public senior high school; School board; Public elementary & secondary schools; Public junior high school; Public senior high school; School board

LIBERTY HLTH RHBILITATION SVCS
See LIBERTY HEALTHCARE GROUP LLC

D-U-N-S 80-660-7453
LIBERTY HOMECARE AND HOSPICE LLC
2334 S 41st St, Wilmington, NC 28403-5502
Tel (910) 332-0170 *Founded/Ownrshp* 2006
Sales 18.7MM^E *EMP* 500
SIC 8082 Home health care services; Home health care services

D-U-N-S 82-812-5463
LIBERTY HOMECARE GROUP LLC
2334 S 41st St, Wilmington, NC 28403-5502
Tel (910) 815-3122 *Founded/Ownrshp* 2002
Sales 37.5MM^E *EMP* 3,500
SIC 8082 Home health care services; Home health care services
CFO: Joe Calcutt

D-U-N-S 95-927-1727
LIBERTY HOMES INC
9075 S 1300 E Ste 201, Sandy, UT 84094-3174
Tel (801) 561-2525 *Founded/Ownrshp* 1994
Sales 48.0MM *EMP* 12
SIC 1521 Mobile home repair, on site; Mobile home repair, on site
Pr: David Clark

LIBERTY HONDA
See J B J ASSOCIATES INC

LIBERTY IMPORT CENTER
See UNITED MOTORS LTD

D-U-N-S 05-066-7195
LIBERTY INDEPENDENT SCHOOL DISTRICT
1600 Grand Ave, Liberty, TX 77575-4725
Tel (936) 336-7213 *Founded/Ownrshp* 1917
Sales 27.6MM^E *EMP* 450
SIC 8211 Public elementary & secondary schools; School board; Public elementary & secondary schools; School board
**CFO:* Julie Hebert
Teacher Pr: Lannise Reidland
Teacher Pr: Annette Taylor
Psych: Cassandra Myers
Psych: Karole Seay

LIBERTY INSURANCE AGENCY
See LIBERTY FINANCIAL SERVICES INC

D-U-N-S 15-518-3924
LIBERTY INSURANCE CORP
LIBERTY MUTUAL
(*Suby of* LIBERTY MUTUAL HOLDING CORP) ★
175 Berkeley St, Boston, MA 02116-5066
Tel (617) 357-9500 *Founded/Ownrshp* 1988
Sales NA *EMP* 15
SIC 6331 Fire, marine & casualty insurance; Property damage insurance; Fire, marine & casualty insurance; Property damage insurance
Pr: Edmund Francis Kelly
**Treas:* Julianna Coyle
VP: Christine Lahey

D-U-N-S 79-065-7378
▲ LIBERTY INTERACTIVE CORP
12300 Liberty Blvd, Englewood, CO 80112-7009
Tel (720) 875-5300 Founded/Ownrshp 1991
Sales 10.5MMM EMP 20,078
Tkr Sym QVCA Exch NGS
SIC 4841 5961 Cable & other pay television services; Television, home shopping; Cable & other pay television services; Television, home shopping
Pr: Gregory B Maffei
*Ch Bd: John C Malone
CFO: Christopher W Shean
Sr VP: Richard N Baer
Sr VP: Albert E Rosenthaler
Board of Directors: Michael A George, M Ian G Gilchrist, Evan D Malone, David E Rapley, M Lavoy Robison, Larry E Romrell, Andrea L Wong

D-U-N-S 87-481-9428 IMP/EXP
■ LIBERTY INTERACTIVE LLC
(Suby of LIBERTY INTERACTIVE CORP) ★
12300 Liberty Blvd, Englewood, CO 80112-7009
Tel (720) 875-5400 Founded/Ownrshp 1994
Sales 10.2MMM^E EMP 22,075
SIC 5961 4841 7819 4813 Television, home shopping; Cable & other pay television services; Services allied to motion pictures; Telephone communication, except radio; Television, home shopping; Cable & other pay television services; Services allied to motion pictures; Telephone communication, except radio
Pr: Gregory B Maffei
*CFO: David J A Flowers
*Sr VP: Christopher W Shean

D-U-N-S 84-742-7960
LIBERTY INTERNATIONAL HOLDINGS INC
(Suby of LIBERTY MUTUAL INSURANCE CO) ★
175 Berkeley St, Boston, MA 02116-5066
Tel (617) 357-9500 Founded/Ownrshp 1994
Sales NA EMP 3,684
SIC 6331 Fire, marine & casualty insurance; Fire, marine & casualty insurance
Pr: David Long
*Ch Bd: Thomas Ramey
*CFO: Paul Condrin
IT Man: Jennifer Fernald
Board of Directors: Gary L Countryman, Robert Gruhl, Edmond Kelly, Chris Mansfield, Stewart Steffey

D-U-N-S 09-205-8783
LIBERTY INTERNATIONAL TRUCKS OF NEW HAMPSHIRE LLC
1400 S Willow St, Manchester, NH 03103-4024
Tel (603) 623-8873 Founded/Ownrshp 2000
Sales 33.7MM^E EMP 73^E
Accts Bornstein & Sweatt Pc Manche
SIC 5511 5531 Trucks, tractors & trailers: new & used; Truck equipment & parts; Trucks, tractors & trailers: new & used; Truck equipment & parts
*Treas: Anthony Sinacore
Genl Mgr: Jeffrey Nicholas
Sls Mgr: John Larochelle
Sales Asso: Jim Ramsay

D-U-N-S 01-336-6260
LIBERTY INTERNATIONAL UNDERWRITERS USA
LIBERTY INTL UNDERWRITERS USA
(Suby of LIBERTY MUTUAL INSURANCE CO) ★
55 Water St Fl 23, New York, NY 10041-0024
Tel (212) 208-4100 Founded/Ownrshp 1811, 1999
Sales NA EMP 450
SIC 6331 Fire, marine & casualty insurance; Fire, marine & casualty insurance
Pr: David Cohen
Pr: John Atherton
Pr: Ray Cliett
Pr: Jose Crespo
Pr: Dwight Davis
Pr: Patrick Doherty
Pr: Paul Hartley
Pr: Peter Hartog
Pr: Ron Howson
Pr: Tommy Laurendine
Pr: Johnathan Lee
Pr: Kevin Lee
Pr: Marcia Nolan
Pr: Arturo Posada
CFO: Michelle Smith
Ofcr: Sandra Chu
*Ofcr: Michael Finnegan
*Ofcr: Jessica Rogin
Ex VP: Frank O'Connor
Sr VP: Valoree Celona
Sr VP: Tony Glenn

LIBERTY INTL UNDERWRITERS USA
See LIBERTY INTERNATIONAL UNDERWRITERS USA

D-U-N-S 80-358-9568
LIBERTY IRON & METAL HOLDINGS LLC
(Suby of SCHOLZ HOLDING GMBH)
2144 W Mcdowell Rd, Phoenix, AZ 85009-3011
Tel (602) 254-2154 Founded/Ownrshp 2007
Sales 34.7MM^E EMP 500
SIC 5093 4953 Nonferrous metals scrap; Nonferrous metals scrap; Ferrous metal scrap & waste; Recycling, waste materials
CEO: Marc Olgin
*Ch: Gerald Jerry Olgin
Brnch Mgr: Jory Greenfield

D-U-N-S 01-408-7498
LIBERTY IRON & METAL LLC
(Suby of SCHOLZ HOLDING GMBH)
1431 East Ave, Erie, PA 16503-1568
Tel (814) 453-6758 Founded/Ownrshp 2007
Sales 36.8MM^E EMP 50
SIC 5093 Metal scrap & waste materials
*Ex VP: Steven Olgin
*VP: Joe Diamond
Genl Mgr: Michael Bobry
IT Man: Christine Hammer

D-U-N-S 00-353-4084 IMP
LIBERTY IRON & METAL SOUTHWEST LLC
(Suby of LIBERTY IRON & METAL HOLDINGS LLC) ★
2144 W Mcdowell Rd, Phoenix, AZ 85009-3011
Tel (602) 254-2154 Founded/Ownrshp 2007
Sales 22.4MM^E EMP 45
SIC 4953 Recycling, waste materials
COO: Mike Diamond
Ex VP: Steve Olgin
*Genl Mgr: Daniel Sumberg

D-U-N-S 01-370-4482 EXP
LIBERTY KENWORTH HINO TRUCK SALES
LIBERTY KENWORTH SOUTH JERSEY
2160 Route 322, Swedesboro, NJ 08085-3630
Tel (856) 803-1700 Founded/Ownrshp 1990
Sales 45.0MM EMP 42
SIC 5012 Truck bodies; Truck bodies
Pr: Don Metzger

LIBERTY KENWORTH SOUTH JERSEY
See LIBERTY KENWORTH HINO TRUCK SALES

D-U-N-S 17-052-7378
LIBERTY LIFE ASSURANCE CO OF BOSTON
MYLIBERTYCLAIM
(Suby of LIBERTY MUTUAL HOLDING CORP) ★
175 Berkeley St, Boston, MA 02116-3350
Tel (617) 357-9500 Founded/Ownrshp 1996
Sales NA EMP 173
SIC 6311 6321 6324 Life insurance; Life insurance carriers; Disability health insurance; Hospital & medical service plans; Life insurance; Life insurance carriers; Disability health insurance; Hospital & medical service plans
Pr: Edmund Kelly
*COO: Jean Scarrow
*COO: Mortin Spitzer
*Treas: Elliott Williams
Sr VP: John Watkins
VP: James Hinchley
*VP: Merrill Mack
IT Man: Kevin Tompkins
Sls Mgr: Paul Cunningham
Sls Mgr: Lampai Vongmany
Sales Asso: David Messinger

LIBERTY LINEN
See AT WORK SALES CORP

D-U-N-S 04-932-2647
LIBERTY LINES TRANSIT INC
475 Saw Mill River Rd, Yonkers, NY 10701-4993
Tel (914) 969-6900 Founded/Ownrshp 1953
Sales 20.3MM^E EMP 800
SIC 4111 Bus line operations
Pr: Gerry D'Amore
*VP: George Bernacchia
VP: Brian Berwacchia

D-U-N-S 00-555-1684
LIBERTY LITHOGRAPHERS INC
LIBERTY GRAPHICS
18625 West Creek Dr, Tinley Park, IL 60477-6247
Tel (708) 633-7450 Founded/Ownrshp 1964
Sales 30.0MM^E EMP 102^E
SIC 2752 Commercial printing, offset
Pr: Angela L Hipelius
VP: Angela Hipelius
Creative D: Sue Rasmussen
Genl Mgr: Thomas Miskovic
Sls Mgr: John Hipelius

D-U-N-S 15-083-4562
LIBERTY LOYDS HOMES INC
(Suby of NATIONAL MENTOR INC) ★
2540 W Shaw Ln Ste 111, Fresno, CA 93711-2700
Tel (559) 226-5611 Founded/Ownrshp 1991
Sales 7.6MM^E EMP 500
SIC 8059 8331 8361 Home for the mentally retarded, exc. skilled or intermediate; Vocational training agency; Residential care; Home for the mentally retarded, exc. skilled or intermediate; Vocational training agency; Residential care
VP: Nancy Bargman

D-U-N-S 92-954-5119
LIBERTY MANAGEMENT GROUP CORP
19 Spear Rd Ste 304, Ramsey, NJ 07446-1223
Tel (201) 236-8880 Founded/Ownrshp 2003
Sales 65.5MM^E EMP 855
SIC 8741 Hospital management; Hospital management
Pr: William J Hartigan
*Pr: Gay Hartigan
VP: Robert Eustis
VP: Christopher Smith
Exec: Jenna Bongermino
Dir Sec: Carl Kuhlmeier
Telecom Ex: Joann Kennedy
Info Man: Mary Rowland
Mktg Dir: Mike Kettle
Orthpdst: Jackie Federici

D-U-N-S 18-857-1616
LIBERTY MARITIME CORP
1979 Marcus Ave Ste 200, New Hyde Park, NY 11042-1059
Tel (516) 488-8800 Founded/Ownrshp 1988
Sales 40.6MM^E EMP 300
SIC 4731 Agents, shipping; Agents, shipping
Ch Bd: Philip J Shapiro
*Pr: Dale B Moses
*VP: David Hussey
*VP: Thomas Keenan

D-U-N-S 02-061-0924
LIBERTY MATERIALS INC
18214 E River Rd, Conroe, TX 77302-5754
Tel (281) 572-4003 Founded/Ownrshp 1989
Sales 39.9MM^E EMP 72
SIC 1442 Sand mining
Pr: James E Welch
*Treas: Evelyn Welch
*VP: Paul Welch

D-U-N-S 93-272-8488
LIBERTY MECHANICAL CONTRACTORS LLC
550 Brush Ave Frnt 1, Bronx, NY 10465-1881
Tel (718) 409-1444 Founded/Ownrshp 1994
Sales 24.0MM^E EMP 175
SIC 1711 Plumbing contractors; Plumbing contractors
CEO: Michael Contillo

LIBERTY MEDIA
See STARZ MEDIA LLC

D-U-N-S 07-865-9157
▲ LIBERTY MEDIA CORP
12300 Liberty Blvd, Englewood, CO 80112-7009
Tel (720) 875-5400 Founded/Ownrshp 2006
Sales 4.4MMM EMP 2,327^E
Accts Kpmg Llp Denver Colorado
Tkr Sym LMCA Exch NGS
SIC 4841 Cable & other pay television services; Cable & other pay television services
Pr: Gregory B Maffei
CFO: Christopher W Shean
*Sr VP: Richard N Baer
Sr VP: Albert Rosenthaler
VP: Pamela Coe
VP: Todd Griffin
VP: Wade Haufschild
VP: Tim Lenneman
VP: Chris Olsen
VP: Connie Rosengarten
VP: Leonard Stegman
VP: William Warga
Exec: Sheryl Shelton
Dir Risk M: Jenny Hill

D-U-N-S 80-854-2401
LIBERTY MEDICAL SPECIALTIES INC
612 Jefferson St Ste 10, Whiteville, NC 28472-3708
Tel (910) 642-2250 Founded/Ownrshp 1993
Sales 23.4MM^E EMP 105
SIC 5912 5999 7352 Proprietary (non-prescription medicine) stores; Medical apparatus & supplies; Medical equipment rental
VP: Mary Hooks
*Pr: John A McNeill Jr
*Sec: Joseph M Hooks

LIBERTY MEDICAL SUPPLY
See LIBERTY HEALTHCARE GROUP INC

D-U-N-S 18-949-6037
LIBERTY MOTORS INC
600 Westwood Dr, North Liberty, IA 52317-9694
Tel (559) 896-5000 Founded/Ownrshp 1989
Sales 25.2MM^E EMP 120
SIC 5511 Automobiles, new & used; Pickups, new & used; Vans, new & used; Automobiles, new & used; Pickups, new & used; Vans, new & used
CEO: Dwight Nelson

D-U-N-S 08-006-3662 IMP
LIBERTY MOUNTAIN SPORTS LLC (OR)
ADVANCED BASE CAMP
9816 S Jordan Gtwy, Sandy, UT 84070-9509
Tel (801) 307-9200 Founded/Ownrshp 1950, 1997
Sales 63.7MM^E EMP 150
SIC 5091 Sporting & recreation goods; Sporting & recreation goods
Comm Man: Rich Morris

LIBERTY MUTUAL
See EMPLOYERS INSURANCE OF WAUSAU A MUTUAL CO

LIBERTY MUTUAL
See LIBERTY INSURANCE CORP

LIBERTY MUTUAL
See HELMSMAN MANAGEMENT SERVICES LLC

LIBERTY MUTUAL AGENCY MARKETS
See LIBERTY-USA CORP

D-U-N-S 61-977-8269
LIBERTY MUTUAL EQUITY CORP
(Suby of LIBERTY MUTUAL INSURANCE CO) ★
175 Berkeley St, Boston, MA 02116-5066
Tel (617) 357-9500 Founded/Ownrshp 1990
Sales NA EMP 220
SIC 6331 Fire, marine & casualty insurance; Fire, marine & casualty insurance
Pr: Edmund F Kelly
Treas: Juliana M Coyle
Treas: Robert H Gruhl
Treas: Robert H Grul
Ex VP: Davey S Scoon
Sr VP: James Haynie
Sr VP: John Lennon
VP: Tom Robbins
VP: Jan Sharp
MIS Dir: Karl Bletzer
Snr Mgr: Nathan Zangerle

D-U-N-S 00-695-2527
LIBERTY MUTUAL FIRE INSURANCE CO INC
(Suby of LIBERTY MUTUAL GROUP INC) ★
175 Berkeley St, Boston, MA 02116-5066
Tel (617) 357-9500 Founded/Ownrshp 1908
Sales NA EMP 1,503
SIC 6331 Fire, marine & casualty insurance; Fire, marine & casualty insurance
Ch Bd: Gary L Countryman
*Pr: Edmund F Kelly
*CFO: J Paul Chondrin
CFO: James Condrin
Sr VP: Christopher C Mansfield
Sftwr Eng: Rob Clarke
Sls Mgr: Kerry Goss

D-U-N-S 96-714-1727
LIBERTY MUTUAL FOUNDATION INC
175 Berkeley St, Boston, MA 02116-5066
Tel (617) 357-9500 Founded/Ownrshp 2011
Sales 30.4MM EMP 2^E
SIC 8699 Charitable organization; Charitable organization
Prin: Melissa Macdonnell

D-U-N-S 07-832-0916
LIBERTY MUTUAL GROUP ASSET MANAGEMENT INC
(Suby of LIBERTY MUTUAL GROUP INC) ★
175 Berkeley St, Boston, MA 02116-5066
Tel (617) 357-9500 Founded/Ownrshp 2011
Sales 20.2MM^E EMP 250
SIC 6282 Investment advisory service; Investment advisory service
Ch Bd: David Long
*Pr: A Alexander Fontanes
*Treas: David Hayter
Sr Inv Off: Stephen Whalen
VP: Helen O'Rourke

D-U-N-S 10-834-9981
LIBERTY MUTUAL GROUP INC
(Suby of LMHC MASSACHUSETTS HOLDINGS INC) ★
175 Berkeley St, Boston, MA 02116-5066
Tel (617) 357-9500 Founded/Ownrshp 2001
Sales NA EMP 41,165
SIC 6331 6321 6351 7389 Fire, marine & casualty insurance; Workers' compensation insurance; Automobile insurance; Burglary & theft insurance; Accident insurance carriers; Health insurance carriers; Reinsurance carriers, accident & health; Liability insurance; Fidelity or surety bonding; Fidelity responsibility insurance; Financial services; Fire, marine & casualty insurance; Workers' compensation insurance; Automobile insurance; Burglary & theft insurance; Accident insurance carriers; Health insurance carriers; Reinsurance carriers, accident & health; Liability insurance; Fidelity or surety bonding; Fidelity responsibility insurance; Financial services
Ch Bd: Edmund F Kelly
*Pr: David H Long
Pr: Timothy Zepnick
COO: Kirk Maddern
*Treas: Laurance H S Yahia
VP: Christopher Mansfield
Dir Risk M: John McCabe
Genl Mgr: Martin Bourlot
IT Man: Denise Riopel
Opers Mgr: Todd Reimer
Sls Dir: John Lemire

D-U-N-S 06-721-5793 IMP/EXP
LIBERTY MUTUAL HOLDING CO INC
175 Berkeley St, Boston, MA 02116-5066
Tel (617) 357-9500 Founded/Ownrshp 2001
Sales NA EMP 50,000
Accts Ernst & Young Llp Boston Ma
SIC 6331 6321 6351 7389 Fire, marine & casualty insurance; Workers' compensation insurance; Automobile insurance; Burglary & theft insurance; Accident insurance carriers; Health insurance carriers; Reinsurance carriers, accident & health; Liability insurance; Fidelity or surety bonding; Fidelity responsibility insurance; Financial services; Fire, marine & casualty insurance; Workers' compensation insurance; Automobile insurance; Burglary & theft insurance; Accident insurance carriers; Health insurance carriers; Reinsurance carriers, accident & health; Liability insurance; Fidelity or surety bonding; Fidelity responsibility insurance; Financial services
Pr: David H Long
*Ch Bd: Edmund F Kelly
COO: Matthew D Nickerson
COO: Jean M Scarrow
CFO: James Dore
CFO: Shannon Griepsma
*CFO: Dennis J Langwell
*Treas: Laurance H S Yahia
*Ex VP: J Paul Condrin III
Ex VP: A A Fontanes
Sr VP: Edward J Gramer
*Sr VP: Christopher C Mansfield
Sr VP: James M McGlennon
Sr VP: Robert T Muleski
Sr VP: Helen E Sayles
VP: John D Doyle
VP: Al Kappleman
*VP: Dexter R Legg
Comm Dir: Paul Hunsanger
Board of Directors: Thomas J May, Michael J Babcock, Stephen F Page, Gary C Butler, Ellen A Rudnick, Charles I Clough Jr, Martin P Slark, Gary L Countryman, William C Van Faasen, Nicholas M Donofrio, Annette M Verschuren, Francis A Doyle III, John P Hamill, Marian L Heard, John P Manning

D-U-N-S 78-770-4162
LIBERTY MUTUAL HOLDING CORP
(Suby of LIBERTY MUTUAL INSURANCE CO) ★
175 Berkeley St, Boston, MA 02116-5066
Tel (617) 357-9500 Founded/Ownrshp 1999
Sales NA EMP 250
SIC 6331 Fire, marine & casualty insurance; Fire, marine & casualty insurance
Pr: Edmund Kelly

D-U-N-S 00-695-2535
LIBERTY MUTUAL INSURANCE CO
(Suby of LIBERTY MUTUAL GROUP INC) ★
175 Berkeley St, Boston, MA 02116-5066
Tel (617) 357-9500 Founded/Ownrshp 1912
Sales NA EMP 33,750
SIC 6331 6321 6351 7389 Fire, marine & casualty insurance; Workers' compensation insurance; Automobile insurance; Burglary & theft insurance; Accident insurance carriers; Health insurance carriers; Reinsurance carriers, accident & health; Liability insurance; Fidelity or surety bonding; Fidelity responsibility insurance; Personal service agents, brokers & bureaus; Fire, marine & casualty insurance; Workers' compensation insurance; Automobile insurance; Burglary & theft insurance; Accident insurance carriers; Health insurance carriers; Reinsurance carriers, accident & health; Liability insurance; Fidelity or surety bonding; Fidelity responsibility insurance; Personal service agents, brokers & bureaus
Pr: Edmund F Kelly
V Ch: Martin Slark
Pr: Constance Bayne
Pr: Francisco Campos

Pr: Derek Sproule
CFO: James P Condrin
**CFO:* Dennis J Langwell
Treas: Juliana M Coyle
Treas: Laurance Hs Yahia
Bd of Dir: Matthew Coyle
Bd of Dir: Francis Doyle
Bd of Dir: Marian Heard
Bd of Dir: John Manning
Bd of Dir: Annette Verschuren
Ex VP: Mike Martin
Sr VP: Eric J Brosius
Sr VP: Douglas Cauti
Sr VP: Melanie M Foley
**Sr VP:* Christopher C Mansfield
Sr VP: Stuart McGuigan
VP: Michael Hurley

D-U-N-S 96-352-5675
LIBERTY N & R CTR OF MECKLENBURG
3700 Shamrock Dr, Charlotte, NC 28215-3218
Tel (704) 940-8367 *Founded/Ownrshp* 2010
Sales 1.2MMM *EMP* 10^E
SIC 8051 Skilled nursing care facilities; Skilled nursing care facilities
Prin: Ronald McNeill

D-U-N-S 06-552-9794
LIBERTY NATIONAL BANK INC
629 Sw C Ave Ste B, Lawton, OK 73501-4302
Tel (580) 492-4136 *Founded/Ownrshp* 1983
Sales NA *EMP* 52
SIC 6022 State commercial banks
Pr: Chuck Henson
COO: T C Miller
Ofcr: Kip Ackley
Sr VP: Chris Graham
**VP:* Patrick Schibi

D-U-N-S 00-690-0385
■ **LIBERTY NATIONAL LIFE INSURANCE CO**
(*Suby of* TORCHMARK CORP) ★
100 Cncourse Pkwy Ste 350, Hoover, AL 35244
Tel (205) 325-2722 *Founded/Ownrshp* 1900
Sales NA *EMP* 1,090
SIC 6321 6311 Accident insurance carriers; Life insurance carriers; Accident insurance carriers; Life insurance carriers
Pr: Roger Smith
Sr Cor Off: Kenneth Hunt
Sr Cor Off: James Sedgwick
**Chf Mktg O:* Andrew W King
**Ex VP:* Steve Dichiaro
Ex VP: Vurl Duce
**Sr VP:* C Fletcher
Sr VP: Wester A Gray
**Sr VP:* Jack A Kelley Jr
VP: G Burns
VP: Chou H Ceng
**VP:* Chou Hung Cheng
**VP:* John Chou
**VP:* Robert Dobbs
**VP:* West Graves
VP: Michael Hadder
Div/Sub He: Scot Ferguson

D-U-N-S 07-787-2679
LIBERTY NORTHWEST INSURANCE CORP
(*Suby of* LIBERTY MUTUAL INSURANCE CO) ★
650 Ne Holladay St, Portland, OR 97232-2045
Tel (503) 239-5800 *Founded/Ownrshp* 1983
Sales NA *EMP* 950
SIC 6331 Workers' compensation insurance; Workers' compensation insurance
Pr: Julie Burnett
**VP:* Mary Augustyn
VP: Gary Hubbard
VP: James Scott
Rgnl Mgr: Heidi Nelson
Dir IT: Robert Mills
Software D: Lance Poehler
VP Opers: Mark Backstrom
Snr Mgr: Denise Demarre

D-U-N-S 96-950-7206 IMP
LIBERTY OILFIELD SERVICES LLC
950 17th St Ste 2000, Denver, CO 80202-2801
Tel (303) 515-2800 *Founded/Ownrshp* 2011
Sales 279.1MM^E *EMP* 150
SIC 1382 Oil & gas exploration services; Oil & gas exploration services
CEO: Scott Tiedgen
**CFO:* Michael Stock
Dir Bus: Tom Riebel
Tech Mgr: Ruben Alba
Sls Mgr: Ron Rafferty

D-U-N-S 15-287-0932 IMP
LIBERTY PACKING CO LLC
MORNING STAR COMPANY THE
724 Main St, Woodland, CA 95695-3491
Tel (209) 826-7100 *Founded/Ownrshp* 2001
Sales 119.8MM^E *EMP* 120^E
SIC 5148 Vegetables; Vegetables
Ex Dir: Kim Higgs

LIBERTY PAPER
See D D OFFICE PRODUCTS INC

D-U-N-S 83-487-7797
LIBERTY PAPER INC
DREAMWORKS COATING SOLUTIONS
(*Suby of* LIBERTY DIVERSIFIED INTERNATIONAL INC) ★
13500 Liberty Ln, Becker, MN 55308-4623
Tel (763) 261-6100 *Founded/Ownrshp* 1993
Sales 48.9MM^E *EMP* 96
SIC 2679 4953 2631 Corrugated paper: made from purchased material; Recycling, waste materials; Paperboard mills; Corrugated paper: made from purchased material; Recycling, waste materials; Paperboard mills
Ch Bd: Michael Fiterman
**COO:* Daniel Zdon
**CFO:* Byron Wieberdink
**Ex VP:* David Lenzen
**VP:* Ronda Bayer
**VP:* Michael Snowball
Exec: Gail Landowski
Sales Exec: Dean Flicker
Sls Mgr: Andrew O'Brien
Sls Mgr: Andrew Obrien
Snr Mgr: Lance Moe

D-U-N-S 18-592-8574 IMP
LIBERTY PARTS TEAM INC
3517 W Beltline Hwy, Madison, WI 53713-2838
Tel (608) 268-7600 *Founded/Ownrshp* 2005
Sales 31.7MM^E *EMP* 70
SIC 5045 Computers, peripherals & software; Computer peripheral equipment; Printers, computer
CEO: David Reinke
IT Man: Shawn Heil
Mktg Mgr: Robert Reinke

D-U-N-S 80-903-6614
LIBERTY PAYROLL & BENEFIT SOLUTIONS LLC
2152 S Vineyard Ste 117, Mesa, AZ 85210-6881
Tel (480) 962-1580 *Founded/Ownrshp* 2007
Sales 21.0MM *EMP* 7
SIC 8721 Payroll accounting service; Payroll accounting service

D-U-N-S 16-062-5450
LIBERTY PENN BANK
(*Suby of* LIBERTY PENN FINANCIAL CORP) ★
724 W Lancaster Ave # 210, Wayne, PA 19087-2558
Tel (610) 535-4500 *Founded/Ownrshp* 2004
Sales NA *EMP* 50^E
SIC 6022

D-U-N-S 01-514-8878
LIBERTY PENN FINANCIAL CORP
20 Harvey Ln, Malvern, PA 19355-2944
Tel (610) 889-2033 *Founded/Ownrshp* 2010
Sales 24.6MM *EMP* 2
Accts Parentebeard Llc Malvern Pen
SIC 6282 Investment advice; Investment advice
Prin: Patrick J Ward

D-U-N-S 80-297-3813
LIBERTY PENN FINANCIAL CORP
353 W Lancaster Ave, Wayne, PA 19087-3907
Tel (610) 254-8600 *Founded/Ownrshp* 2008
Sales NA *EMP* 86^E
Accts Bdo Llp Philadelphia Pennsyl
SIC 6712 Bank holding companies; Bank holding companies
Pr: Brian C Zwaan
Ex VP: Albert L Jones
**Prin:* Patrick Ward

LIBERTY PHOTO PRODUCTS
See LIBERTY SYNERGISTICS INC

D-U-N-S 10-094-6768 IMP/EXP
LIBERTY POLYGLAS INC
LIBERTY PULTRUSIONS WEST
1575 Lebanon School Rd, West Mifflin, PA 15122-3433
Tel (412) 466-8611 *Founded/Ownrshp* 2002
Sales 24.5MM^E *EMP* 60
SIC 3089 Molding primary plastic
Pr: David Grisfith
Info Man: Dale Peters

D-U-N-S 78-297-7920
LIBERTY PONTIAC-GMC TRUCK LLC
9028 E Independence Blvd, Matthews, NC 28105-4506
Tel (704) 708-8000 *Founded/Ownrshp* 1991
Sales 29.6MM^E *EMP* 48
SIC 5511 7538 5531 Automobiles, new & used; General automotive repair shops; Automotive parts
**VP:* Jim Keffer
Genl Mgr: Navid Azadi
**Genl Mgr:* Brad McCorkle
Sls Mgr: Brad Mc Mc Corkle
Sls Mgr: Greg Mongelli

D-U-N-S 79-066-1040
LIBERTY PORT LLC
7020 Prof Pkwy E Ste 101, Sarasota, FL 34240
Tel (941) 552-9515 *Founded/Ownrshp* 2003
Sales 30.0MM *EMP* 110
SIC 8748 Telecommunications consultant; Telecommunications consultant
CFO: Tony Turner
VP: Justin Turner
Board of Directors: Parker Turner

D-U-N-S 11-236-1204
LIBERTY POWER CORP LLC
1901 W Cypress Creek Rd # 501, Fort Lauderdale, FL 33309-1826
Tel (866) 769-3799 *Founded/Ownrshp* 2001
Sales 62.2MM^E *EMP* 65^E
SIC 4925 Gas production and/or distribution; Gas production and/or distribution
CEO: David Hernandez
**Pr:* Alberto Daire
Sr VP: Richard Rathvon
VP: Terri Doerschuck
VP: Jennifer Hansard
VP: Harris Rosen
VP: Guy Souheaver
VP: Ignacio Taveras
VP: Derik Viner
IT Man: Steve Martinez
IT Man: Matthew Stasium

D-U-N-S 78-408-7293
LIBERTY POWER HOLDINGS LLC
(*Suby of* LIBERTY POWER CORP LLC) ★
1901 W Cypress Creek Rd # 501, Fort Lauderdale, FL 33309-1826
Tel (954) 489-7148 *Founded/Ownrshp* 2005
Sales 29.6MM^E *EMP* 65^E
SIC 4911 Distribution, electric power; Distribution, electric power
CEO: David Hernandez
**Pr:* Alberto Daire

D-U-N-S 05-852-6278
LIBERTY PROPANE OPERATIONS LLC
JENKINS GAS
1305 Us Highway 70 E, New Bern, NC 28560-6609
Tel (252) 633-5560 *Founded/Ownrshp* 2005
Sales 38.3MM^E *EMP* 320
SIC 5984 5983 5541 Liquefied petroleum gas, delivered to customers' premises; Fuel oil dealers; Filling stations, gasoline; Liquefied petroleum gas, delivered to customers' premises; Fuel oil dealers; Filling stations, gasoline
IT Man: John Proctor

D-U-N-S 02-061-9175
LIBERTY PROPERTY LIMITED PARTNERSHIP
(*Suby of* LIBERTY PROPERTY TRUST) ★
500 Chesterfield Pkwy, Malvern, PA 19355-8707
Tel (610) 648-1700 *Founded/Ownrshp* 1994
Sales 792.6MM *EMP* 433
SIC 6512 Nonresidential building operators; Nonresidential building operators
Ch Bd: William P Hankowsky
Genl Pt: Liberty Property Trust
CFO: George J Alburger Jr
VP: Albert J Kraft III
VP: Anthony Nichols Jr

D-U-N-S 06-571-9254
LIBERTY PROPERTY TRUST
500 Chesterfield Pkwy, Malvern, PA 19355-8707
Tel (610) 648-1700 *Founded/Ownrshp* 1972
Sales 794.6MM^E *EMP* 453^E
SIC 6798 Real estate investment trusts; Real estate investment trusts
CEO: William P Hankowsky
**COO:* Robert E Fenza
**CFO:* George J Alburger Jr
**Treas:* George F Congdon
**Ex VP:* Thomas C Deloach Jr
**Ex VP:* Daniel P Garton
**Ex VP:* Michael T Hagan
**Sr VP:* Frederick F Buchholz
Sr VP: John Gattuso
Sr VP: Robert Kiel
Sr VP: James J Mazzarelli
Sr VP: Joe Trinkle
VP: Mike Alderman
VP: Peter Balitsaris
VP: Howard Buzzard
VP: Brian Cohen
VP: Amy Field
VP: Mary Morrissey
VP: Sue Petruno
VP: Andy Petry
VP: Erin Plourde
Board of Directors: Frederick F Buchholz, Thomas C Deloach Jr, Katherine Elizabeth Dietze, Daniel P Garton, M Leanne Lachman, David L Lingerfelt

LIBERTY PUBLIC SCHOOL
See LIBERTY 53 SCHOOL DISTRICT

LIBERTY PULTRUSIONS WEST
See LIBERTY POLYGLAS INC

D-U-N-S 00-213-3445 IMP/EXP
LIBERTY PUMPS INC (NY)
7000 Appletree Ave, Bergen, NY 14416-9446
Tel (585) 494-1817 *Founded/Ownrshp* 1965, 1975
Sales 78.3MM *EMP* 130
Accts Freed Maxick Cpa S Pc
SIC 3561 Pumps, domestic: water or sump; Pumps, domestic: water or sump
Ch Bd: Charles E Cook
**CFO:* Dennis Burke
**VP:* Allan Davis
VP: Rebecca Evangelista
VP: Gary Volk
**VP:* Randy Waldron
Dir IT: Bill Wu
Ql Cn Mgr: Chuck Johnson
Ql Cn Mgr: Mike Schuff
Natl Sales: Chuck Schwabe
Manager: Steve Ritsema

D-U-N-S 07-948-6581
■ **LIBERTY QVC HOLDINGS LLC**
(*Suby of* LIBERTY INTERACTIVE CORP) ★
12300 Liberty Blvd, Englewood, CO 80112-7009
Tel (484) 701-3777 *Founded/Ownrshp* 2003
Sales 8.8MMM^E *EMP* 17,500^E
SIC 4841 5961 Cable & other pay television services; Television, home shopping
Pr: Gregory B Maffei

D-U-N-S 83-254-0384
■ **LIBERTY RC INC**
YONKERS EAST DIALYSIS CENTER
(*Suby of* DAVITA HEALTHCARE PARTNERS INC) ★
5 Odell Plz Ste 131, Yonkers, NY 10701-1406
Tel (914) 376-0296 *Founded/Ownrshp* 1997
Sales 6.5MM^E *EMP* 326^E
SIC 8092 Kidney dialysis centers

D-U-N-S 04-068-7121
LIBERTY REGIONAL MEDICAL CENTER INC
HOSPITAL AUTHORITY OF LIBERTY
462 Elma G Miles Pkwy, Hinesville, GA 31313-4000
Tel (912) 369-9400 *Founded/Ownrshp* 1994
Sales 47.7MM *EMP* 485
SIC 8062 General medical & surgical hospitals; General medical & surgical hospitals
CEO: Scott Kroell
**CEO:* Hugh Scott Kroell Jr
**CFO:* Martha Traylor
**Ch:* Jon Long
**Treas:* Will Darsey
**VP:* James Rogers
VP: Elise Stafford
Dir Rad: Leon Douglas
Dir Rad: Carrie Strickland
Dir Rx: Ed Zwick
Dir Env Sv: Gina Kurbin

D-U-N-S 15-740-9558
LIBERTY RESOURCES INC
714 Market St Ste 100, Philadelphia, PA 19106-2337
Tel (215) 634-2000 *Founded/Ownrshp* 1983
Sales 24.7MM^E *EMP* 300
Accts Robin Kramer & Green Llp Fort
SIC 8322 Social services for the handicapped; Social services for the handicapped
CEO: Thomas H Earle
**Ch:* Marsha Thrower
**Treas:* Joe Nolan
Ofcr: Fady Sahhar
VP: Patrick Kilgallon
**Prin:* Mary Ellen Caffrey
Sls&Mrk Ex: Lisa Brody

D-U-N-S 16-653-4891 IMP
LIBERTY RESOURCES INC
1045 James St Ste 100, Syracuse, NY 13203-2758
Tel (315) 425-1004 *Founded/Ownrshp* 1979
Sales 37.2MM *EMP* 700
SIC 8322 8361 Individual & family services; Crisis intervention center; Home for the mentally handicapped; Rehabilitation center, residential: health care incidental; Group foster home; Individual & family services; Crisis intervention center; Home for the mentally handicapped; Rehabilitation center, residential: health care incidental; Group foster home
CEO: Carl M Coyle
**Pr:* Michael Sayles
**CFO:* Kim Prior
CFO: Joanna Viggiano
**Treas:* Jim Getman
VP: Mary Sorensen
VP: Kimberly Sullivan
VP: Kimberly Sullivan-Dec
IT Man: Mike Ryan

D-U-N-S 82-695-1837
LIBERTY RESTAURANT GROUP
24 Bridge St, Metuchen, NJ 08840-2276
Tel (732) 494-4300 *Founded/Ownrshp* 2006
Sales 14.5MM^E *EMP* 350
SIC 5812 Fast-food restaurant, chain; Fast-food restaurant, chain
Pr: Jay E Amarosa
Admn Mgr: Tracy Amarosa

D-U-N-S 18-512-1167 IMP/EXP
LIBERTY RICHTER INC
(*Suby of* WORLD FINER FOODS LLC) ★
1455 Broad St Ste 4, Bloomfield, NJ 07003-3039
Tel (973) 338-0300 *Founded/Ownrshp* 1926
Sales 45.0MM *EMP* 11^E
SIC 5149 5499 Specialty food items; Gourmet food stores; Specialty food items; Gourmet food stores
Pr: Frank Muchel

D-U-N-S 19-638-1842 IMP
■ **LIBERTY SAFE AND SECURITY PRODUCTS INC**
(*Suby of* COMPASS DIVERSIFIED HOLDINGS) ★
1199 W Utah Ave, Payson, UT 84651-9749
Tel (801) 925-1000 *Founded/Ownrshp* 1988
Sales 90.9MM^E *EMP* 350^E
SIC 3499 Safes & vaults, metal; Safes & vaults, metal
Pr: Kim Waddoups
**COO:* Steve Allred
**CFO:* Greg Clements
**Ch:* David Heidecorn
Trfc Dir: Ron Bell
Mktg Dir: James Skousen
Board of Directors: Todd Atkinson

D-U-N-S 06-092-7936
LIBERTY SAVINGS BANK
(*Suby of* LIBERTY CAPITAL INC) ★
3435 Airborne Rd Ste B, Wilmington, OH 45177-8951
Tel (937) 382-1000 *Founded/Ownrshp* 1984
Sales NA *EMP* 125
SIC 6035 Federal savings banks; Federal savings banks
Ch Bd: James R Powell
Pr: Joe Hoskins
Pr: Robert E Reed
COO: John Glaser
COO: James Towell
CFO: Susan Kranjc
V Ch Bd: John H Powell
Ofcr: Jenny Davis
Ofcr: Andy Powell
Sr VP: Pamela W Brooks
Sr VP: Tony Massara
VP: William Beal
VP: Beth Breihan
VP: Bruce Clapp
VP: Carie Elston
VP: Lisa Felker
VP: Timothy Fiedler
VP: Andy Germann
VP: Karl Koett
VP: Jean Manly
VP: Mary J McNulty

LIBERTY SCHOOL
See SALINE AREA SCHOOLS

D-U-N-S 62-607-7267
LIBERTY SHARES INC
300 S Main St, Hinesville, GA 31313-3222
Tel (912) 368-3332 *Founded/Ownrshp* 1986
Sales NA *EMP* 300^E
SIC 6712 Bank holding companies; Bank holding companies
Pr: James M Floyd Jr
**CFO:* Philip F Resch

D-U-N-S 07-961-4050
LIBERTY SPAIN INSURANCE GROUP LLC
(*Suby of* LIBERTY MUTUAL HOLDING CO INC) ★
175 Berkeley St, Boston, MA 02116-5066
Tel (617) 357-9500 *Founded/Ownrshp* 2004
Sales NA *EMP* 1,200^E
SIC 6311 Life insurance; Life insurance

D-U-N-S 05-500-4720
LIBERTY STEEL FABRICATION INC
1861 Main St, Fyffe, AL 35971-3487
Tel (256) 623-3027 *Founded/Ownrshp* 1998
Sales 29.6MM^E *EMP* 60
SIC 3441 Fabricated structural metal
Pr: Kelly Pittman
**Sr VP:* Steven Mitchell

*VP: Mark Campbell
Exec: Cary Hearn
Exec: Holly Swords

D-U-N-S 07-973-8807
LIBERTY STEEL INDUSTRIES INC (OH)
900 Dietz Rd Ne, Warren, OH 44483-2755
Tel (330) 372-6363 Founded/Ownrshp 2015
Sales 21.8MM^E EMP 104
SIC 3469 Metal stampings
Pr: James T Weller
*CFO: Phil Latmardo
Plnt Mgr: Phil Henry
Plnt Mgr: Mike Hildack

D-U-N-S 04-409-4134 IMP
LIBERTY STEEL PRODUCTS INC
11650 Mahoning Ave, North Jackson, OH 44451-9688
Tel (330) 538-2236 Founded/Ownrshp 1965
Sales 67.3MM^E EMP 100
Accts Packer Thomas Canfield Ohio
SIC 5051 Steel; Steel
Ch Bd: James T Weller Sr
*CEO: Andrew J Weller Jr
*CFO: James M Grasso
VP: Samuel Cannell
Rgnl Mgr: John Clarke
Dir IT: Edward Springer
Dir IT: John Vigorito
IT Man: Tony Labbiento
QC Dir: Scott Peters
Plnt Mgr: Rick Phillips
VP Sls: Joseph Mazias

LIBERTY SUBARU
See LIBERTY AUTO CITY INC

D-U-N-S 13-123-6036 IMP
LIBERTY SYNERGISTICS INC
LIBERTY PHOTO PRODUCTS
1041 Calle Trepadora, San Clemente, CA 92673-6204
Tel (949) 361-1100 Founded/Ownrshp 1984
Sales 22.7MM^E EMP 55
SIC 5085 3861

D-U-N-S 07-847-6518
▲ LIBERTY TAX INC
1716 Corp Landing Pkwy, Virginia Beach, VA 23454-5681
Tel (757) 493-8855 Founded/Ownrshp 2010
Sales 162.1MM EMP 1,026
Accts Kpmg Llp Norfolk Virginia
Tkr Sym TAX Exch NGM
SIC 7291 Tax return preparation services; Tax return preparation services
Ch Bd: John T Hewitt
CFO: Kathleen E Donovan
VP: Richard G Artese
VP: Mark F Baumgartner
VP: Chris Carroll
VP: Chuck Lovelace
VP: James J Wheaton
Prgrm Mgr: Nathalie Sauvaire
Dist Mgr: Fermin Aguilera
Genl Mgr: Michelle Cox
Genl Mgr: Robert Donica
Board of Directors: Gordon D'angelo, John R Garel, Steven Ibbotson, Ross N Longfield, Ellen M McDowell, George T Robson

LIBERTY TAX SERVICE
See JTH TAX INC

D-U-N-S 36-164-0282
LIBERTY TIRE RECYCLING LLC
(Suby of LAUREL MOUNTAIN PARTNERS LLC) ★
625 Liberty Ave Ste 3100, Pittsburgh, PA 15222-3115
Tel (412) 562-1700 Founded/Ownrshp 2008
Sales 31.4MM^E EMP 30
SIC 5093 Scrap & waste materials
CEO: Jeffrey Kendall
CFO: Dale Van Steenberg
Sr VP: Kurt C Meyer
VP: Doug Carlson
Dir Bus: Jonathan Stein
Genl Mgr: Rahni Behr
Genl Mgr: Jim Kington
Genl Mgr: George Woodward
Off Mgr: Sharon Jones
Off Mgr: Toni Matthews
CIO: John Graham

D-U-N-S 96-490-6007
LIBERTY TIRE RECYCLING LLC
1251 Waterfront Pl # 400, Pittsburgh, PA 15222-4261
Tel (412) 562-1700 Founded/Ownrshp 2005
Sales 346.0MM^E EMP 1,100^E
SIC 5093 4953 8744 Scrap & waste materials; Recycling, waste materials;
CEO: Jeffrey D Kendall
COO: Thomas Womble
CFO: Dale Van Steenberg
Sr VP: Ronald B Carlson
VP: Gregory Cummings
VP: Dan Drakulich
VP: Peter Ellis
VP: John Fuller
VP: Robert Pahanich
VP: Andrew C Russell
Brnch Mgr: Peter Sinclair

D-U-N-S 16-885-4177
LIBERTY TITLE & ESCROW CO
275 W Natick Rd Ste 1000, Warwick, RI 02886-1162
Tel (401) 751-8090 Founded/Ownrshp 1997
Sales NA EMP 75
SIC 6361 Title insurance
Pr: Gary D Marinosci
Mng Pt: Phillip Norman
CFO: William C Tsonos
Treas: Steven Autieri
VP: Kim Davis
VP: Kristen Gabriele
VP: Michelle Haas
VP Opers: Katie McNamara
Sales Exec: John Colitz
Snr Mgr: Kim Coleman

LIBERTY TOYOTA
See LIBERTY AUTOMOTIVE LTD

LIBERTY TOYOTA
See LARRY H MILLER OF COLORADO SPRINGS

D-U-N-S 11-912-3792
LIBERTY TRANSPORTATION INC
(Suby of LIBERTY DISTRIBUTION, INC)
838 Croft Rd, Greensburg, PA 15601-8861
Tel (724) 668-2772 Founded/Ownrshp 1984
Sales 28.2MM^E EMP 150
SIC 4213 4225 Trucking, except local; General warehousing & storage; Trucking, except local; General warehousing & storage
Pr: Charles Runzo
*Pr: Chuck Runzo
*Sr VP: Nickie M Doran
Sr VP: Brad Forsyth
*Sr VP: Mark Palla
*Sr VP: Lori M Runzo
*Sr VP: Ken Snoots
Sfty Dirs: Jackie Calisti

LIBERTY TRAVEL
See FC USA INC

D-U-N-S 07-946-8907
▲ LIBERTY TRIPADVISOR HOLDINGS INC
12300 Liberty Blvd, Englewood, CO 80112-7009
Tel (720) 875-5200 Founded/Ownrshp 2014
Sales 1.3MMM EMP 2,400^E
Tkr Sym LTRPB Exch NGS
SIC 7374 Data processing & preparation
Pr: Gregory B Maffei
*Ch Bd: John C Malone
CFO: Christopher W Shean
Sr VP: Richard N Baer
*Sr VP: Albert E Rosenthaler

D-U-N-S 60-547-2638
LIBERTY TRUCK CENTER INC
LIBERTY TRUCK STOPS
1492 Oliver Rd, New Milford, PA 18834-7591
Tel (570) 434-2330 Founded/Ownrshp 1989
Sales 47.4MM^E EMP 60
SIC 5172 5541 Engine fuels & oils; Truck stops; Engine fuels & oils; Truck stops
Pr: Amrit Kaur
*VP: Simrat Aulakh
VP Opers: Gerald Danniel

LIBERTY TRUCK STOPS
See LIBERTY TRUCK CENTER INC

D-U-N-S 07-326-8039
LIBERTY TULLETT INC
(Suby of TULLETT PREBON AMERICAS CORP) ★
199 Water St Fl 17, New York, NY 10038-3539
Tel (212) 208-2000 Founded/Ownrshp 1999
Sales NA EMP 165
Accts Ernst & Young Llp New York N
SIC 6099 6221 Foreign currency exchange; Futures brokers & dealers, commodity; Foreign currency exchange; Futures brokers & dealers, commodity
Pr: Louis Scotto
*CFO: Mark Downey
Sr VP: Bruce Ballaban
Ex Dir: Michael Fallon
CTO: Darren Coombes
Dir IT: Leon Fischer
*Snr Mgr: Vinayek Singh

LIBERTY UNION HIGH SCHOOL
See LIBERTY UNION SCHOOL DISTRICT

D-U-N-S 07-856-2263
LIBERTY UNION SCHOOL DISTRICT
LIBERTY UNION HIGH SCHOOL
20 Oak St, Brentwood, CA 94513-1379
Tel (925) 634-2166 Founded/Ownrshp 1908
Sales 27.6MM^E EMP 295
Accts Stephen Roatch Accountancy Cor
SIC 8211 Public elementary & secondary schools; Public elementary & secondary schools
Bd of Dir: Daron Spears
Dir Sec: Jim Estinson

D-U-N-S 06-600-1074
LIBERTY UNIVERSITY INC
1971 University Blvd, Lynchburg, VA 24515-0002
Tel (434) 582-2000 Founded/Ownrshp 1972
Sales 668.3MM^E EMP 7,200
Accts Dixon Hughes Goodman Llp Glen
SIC 8221 University; University
Pr: Jerry Lamon Falwell Jr
CFO: Ronald Kennedy
CFO: Don Moon
Sr VP: Mark Hine
VP: Ronald E Hawkins
VP: Johnnie Moore Jr
Assoc Dir: Sarah Dean
Assoc Dir: Rod Dempsey
Assoc Dir: Rena Lindevaldsen
Assoc Dir: Tory Lucas
Assoc Dir: Rachel McQuigg
Assoc Dir: Amy Teer

D-U-N-S 07-942-1883
■ LIBERTY USA HOLDINGS LLC
(Suby of LIBERTY INTERACTIVE CORP) ★
12300 Liberty Blvd, Englewood, CO 80112-7009
Tel (720) 875-5300 Founded/Ownrshp 2007
Sales 8.4MMM^E EMP 18,210^E
SIC 4841 Cable & other pay television services

D-U-N-S 01-437-2809 IMP
LIBERTY USA INC
VENDOR FRIENDS
920 Irwin Run Rd, West Mifflin, PA 15122-1092
Tel (412) 461-2700 Founded/Ownrshp 1987
Sales 110.6MM^E EMP 100
SIC 5194 5145 5122 5141 Cigarettes; Cigars; Candy; Chewing gum; Cosmetics, perfumes & hair products; Groceries, general line; Cigarettes; Cigars; Candy; Chewing gum; Cosmetics, perfumes & hair products; Groceries, general line
Pr: Gary McGuirk
*Pr: Gary F McGuirk Sr
*VP: Brian McGuirk
CIO: Brian McGinty

LIBERTY UTILITIES
See LIBERTY ENERGY UTILITIES (NEW HAMPSHIRE) CORP

D-U-N-S 96-625-1832
LIBERTY UTILITIES (CALPECO ELECTRIC) LLC
LIBERTY ENERGY
933 Eloise Ave, South Lake Tahoe, CA 96150-6470
Tel (530) 543-5288 Founded/Ownrshp 2009
Sales 55.0MM^E EMP 60
SIC 4911 Distribution, electric power
*Pr: Mike Smart

D-U-N-S 83-040-8873
LIBERTY UTILITIES (ENERGYNORTH NATURAL GAS) CORP
ENERGYNORTH NATURAL GAS, INC.
(Suby of LIBERTY ENERGY UTILITIES (NEW HAMPSHIRE) CORP) ★
15 Buttrick Rd, Londonderry, NH 03053-3305
Tel (603) 328-2700 Founded/Ownrshp 2012
Sales 165.1MM^E EMP 300
SIC 4924 Natural gas distribution; Natural gas distribution
Pr: Victor Del Vecchio

D-U-N-S 00-695-2261
LIBERTY UTILITIES (GRANITE STATE ELECTRIC) CORP
GRANITE STATE ELECTRIC COMPANY
(Suby of LIBERTY ENERGY UTILITIES (NEW HAMPSHIRE) CORP) ★
15 Buttrick Rd, Londonderry, NH 03053-3305
Tel (603) 328-2700 Founded/Ownrshp 1912, 2012
Sales 21.5MM^E EMP 58
SIC 4911 Electric services; Electric services
Pr: Daniel Saad
Area Mgr: Robert Blank

D-U-N-S 04-402-2287
LIBERTY UTILITIES (NEW ENGLAND NATURAL GAS CO) CORP
(Suby of ALGONQUIN POWER & UTILITIES CORP)
36 5th St, Fall River, MA 02721-2846
Tel (774) 627-2901 Founded/Ownrshp 2013
Sales 21.3MM^E EMP 140
SIC 4925 Gas production and/or distribution
Pr: James M Sweeny
*CFO: Ian Robertson
*Treas: David Bronicheski

D-U-N-S 07-831-3643
LIBERTY UTILITIES CO
(Suby of ALGONQUIN POWER & UTILITIES CORP)
12725 W Indian School Rd, Avondale, AZ 85392-9520
Tel (905) 465-4500 Founded/Ownrshp 2010
Sales 353.3MM^E EMP 658^E
SIC 4939 Combination utilities; Combination utilities
Pr: David Pasieka
VP: Andy Ling
Opers Mgr: David Jacobsmeier
Opers Mgr: Beecher Vaillancourt

D-U-N-S 17-789-9655
LIBERTY WASTE SERVICES LIMITED LLC
625 Liberty Ave Ste 3100, Pittsburgh, PA 15222-3115
Tel (412) 562-0148 Founded/Ownrshp 2006
Sales 80.2MM^E EMP 230
SIC 4953 Non-hazardous waste disposal sites; Non-hazardous waste disposal sites

D-U-N-S 92-833-8607
LIBERTY WEST UNIVERSITY
208 University Dr, West Liberty, WV 26074-1082
Tel (304) 336-8053 Founded/Ownrshp 1965
Sales 29.6MM EMP 280
Accts Cliftonlarsonallen Llp Plymou
SIC 8221 9411 College, except junior; ; College, except junior;
Pr: Robin C Capehart
Pr: John McCullough
*COO: Patrick Henry
COO: David Wright
*CFO: John Wright III
Treas: Steve Bohach
Ex VP: John Davis
VP: Mallory Clegg
VP: Donna Lukich
Prin: Robert Strong
Ex Dir: Scott Cook

D-U-N-S 55-671-7916 IMP
■ LIBERTY WIRE & CABLE INC
LIBERTY AV SOLUTIONS
(Suby of C S C) ★
11675 Ridgeline Dr, Colorado Springs, CO 80921-3904
Tel (719) 388-7500 Founded/Ownrshp 2006
Sales 67.4MM^E EMP 119
SIC 5063 Electronic wire & cable; Electronic wire & cable
Pr: John Dace
Pr: Cameron Smith
*CFO: Sheldon B Saidman
*Ch: Gary A Michelson
*VP: Mike Brown
VP: Sydney Chou
*VP: Jerry Dixon
VP: Ed Jankowski
Off Mgr: Martha Friedrickh
Sales Exec: Jesse Carson
Mktg Dir: Becky McWilliams

D-U-N-S 01-327-2620
LIBERTY-EYLAU INDEPENDENT SCHOOL DISTRICT
2901 Leopard Dr, Texarkana, TX 75501-7817
Tel (903) 832-1535 Founded/Ownrshp 1974
Sales 26.7MM EMP 1,153
Accts Thomas & Thomas Llp Texarkana
SIC 8211 Public elementary & secondary schools; School board; Public elementary & secondary schools; School board
Teacher Pr: Leronda Graff

D-U-N-S 02-126-7588
LIBERTY-USA CORP
LIBERTY MUTUAL AGENCY MARKETS
(Suby of LIBERTY MUTUAL INSURANCE CO) ★
62 Maple Ave, Keene, NH 03431-1625
Tel (603) 352-3221 Founded/Ownrshp 1999
Sales NA EMP 400
SIC 6411 Property & casualty insurance agent; Property & casualty insurance agent
Pr: Gary Gregg

LIBERTYHEALTH
See JERSEY CITY MEDICAL CENTER INC

LIBERTYHEALTH
See LIBERTY HEALTHCARE SYSTEM INC

D-U-N-S 03-949-2238
LIBERTYTOWN USA 2 INC
13131 Dairy Ashford Rd # 230, Sugar Land, TX 77478-4396
Tel (832) 295-5024 Founded/Ownrshp 2007
Sales 108.5MM^E EMP 675
SIC 6719 Investment holding companies, except banks
CEO: Philip Morrison
Sec: Gregory Rossmiller

D-U-N-S 92-702-7136
■ LIBERTYVILLE BANK & TRUST CO
(Suby of WINTRUST FINANCIAL CORP) ★
507 N Milwaukee Ave, Libertyville, IL 60048-2000
Tel (847) 367-6800 Founded/Ownrshp 1995
Sales NA EMP 135
SIC 6022 State commercial banks; State commercial banks
CEO: Bert Carstens
*Pr: Edward Werdell
Ofcr: Jenny Winquist
Ofcr: Ryan Zicco
Assoc VP: Kimberly Swider
Ex VP: Bill Westerman
*Ex VP: William Westerman
*Sr VP: Nicholas Begley
Sr VP: Dan Lawlor
Sr VP: Michael Murphy
Sr VP: Christopher Piazzi
Sr VP: Ursula Schuebel
VP: Karen Bouas
*VP: Joan Derango
VP: Bruce Greenberg
*VP: Brian Mikaelian
VP: Timothy Notaro
VP: Karen Schmidt
VP: Cindy Tysland
VP: Rachel Vincent
*VP: Lynn Wiacek

D-U-N-S 14-478-9500
LIBERTYVILLE BUICK GMC
1120 S Milwaukee Ave, Libertyville, IL 60048-3717
Tel (847) 680-5000 Founded/Ownrshp 1984
Sales 22.9MM^E EMP 85
SIC 5511 5521 Automobiles, new & used; Vans, new & used; Pickups, new & used; Used car dealers; Automobiles, new & used; Vans, new & used; Pickups, new & used; Used car dealers
Prin: Garrett Gioulos

D-U-N-S 02-559-1488
LIBERTYVILLE CHEVROLET INC
1001 S Milwaukee Ave, Libertyville, IL 60048-3294
Tel (847) 362-1400 Founded/Ownrshp 1982
Sales 51.5MM^E EMP 92
SIC 5511 Automobiles, new & used; Automobiles, new & used
Pr: James Spellman
VP: Joe Bosco

D-U-N-S 60-542-5214
LIBERTYVILLE SCHOOL DISTRICT 70
1381 Lake St, Libertyville, IL 60048-1729
Tel (847) 362-8393 Founded/Ownrshp 1870
Sales 39.9MM EMP 340^E
Accts Evoy Kamschulte Jacobs & Co
SIC 8211 Public elementary school; Public elementary school
Pr: Maryann Ovassapian
*VP: Tom Vickers
*Prin: Julie Dementi
*Prin: Chris Kennedy
Instr Medi: Dr Jill Gilbea

LIBERTYVILLE TOYOTA
See VILLAGE MOTORS LLC

LIBERTYWORKS
See ROLLS-ROYCE NORTH AMERICAN TECHNOLOGIES INC

D-U-N-S 00-546-3997 IMP
LIBMAN CO (IL)
220 N Sheldon St, Arcola, IL 61910-1616
Tel (217) 268-4200 Founded/Ownrshp 1898, 1968
Sales 59.4MM^E EMP 250^E
SIC 3991 2392 Brooms & brushes; Mops, floor & dust
Pr: Robert Libman
*Sec: William Libman
CIO: Paul Shearer
Software D: Brian Pressler
Sftwr Eng: Keith Fuller
Ql Cn Mgr: Floyol Fu
Sls Mgr: Andrew Libman
Art Dir: Michael Robey

D-U-N-S 60-362-7139
LIBOR MANAGEMENT LLC
701 Carlson Pkwy, Minnetonka, MN 55305-5240
Tel (763) 212-5400 Founded/Ownrshp 2005
Sales 15.0MM^E EMP 444^E
SIC 7011 Hotels
VP: Steve Hedberg
VP: John M Diracles

D-U-N-S 17-794-0517 IMP/EXP
LIBRA INC
3310 N 2nd St, Minneapolis, MN 55412-2604
Tel (612) 522-2600 Founded/Ownrshp 1987

Sales 26.3MM^E EMP 30
SIC 5199 General merchandise, non-durable
Pr: Ziv S Liberman
COO: James Zelina
VP: Gustavo Gonzalez
*VP: Lee Liberman
Genl Couns: Bert Diaz

D-U-N-S 01-902-9511
LIBRA INDUSTRIES INC (OH)
7770 Division Dr, Mentor, OH 44060-4860
Tel (440) 974-7770 Founded/Ownrshp 1980
Sales 39.7MM^E EMP 120^E
SIC 3699 Printed circuit boards; Electrical equipment & supplies; Electronic connectors; Current-carrying wiring devices; Metal stampings; Nonferrous wire-drawing & insulating; Electrical equipment & supplies
CEO: Rod Howell
*COO: Albert Catani
COO: Patrick Leber
CFO: Robert Hanzie
VP: Brian Bukovec
Prgrm Mgr: Adrienne Clark
Prgrm Mgr: Veronica Heim
Prgrm Mgr: Janet Meyer
CTO: Ronda Reese
QA Dir: Robert Thibodeau
IT Man: Roy Starks

D-U-N-S 06-247-5637 IMP/EXP
LIBRA INDUSTRIES INC (IL)
LIBRA SAFETY PDT RECYCLABLES
1951 Arthur Ave, Elk Grove Village, IL 60007-6004
Tel (224) 265-8500 Founded/Ownrshp 1945, 1972
Sales 23.3MM^E EMP 69
SIC 5085 5136 5137 7218 Industrial supplies; Gloves, men's & boys'; Work clothing, men's & boys'; Women's & children's clothing; Gloves, women's & children's; Industrial clothing launderers; Industrial supplies; Gloves, men's & boys'; Work clothing, men's & boys'; Women's & children's clothing; Gloves, women's & children's; Industrial clothing launderers
CEO: William Maki
Genl Mgr: Jennifer Gillette
Plnt Mgr: Tom Sokol

D-U-N-S 06-186-5754
LIBRA INDUSTRIES INC OF MICHIGAN
WORK APPAREL DIVISION
1435 N Blackstone St, Jackson, MI 49202-2227
Tel (517) 787-5675 Founded/Ownrshp 1969
Sales 75.7MM^E EMP 90
SIC 5084 3559 1741 Recycling machinery & equipment; Recycling machinery; Tuckpointing or restoration
Pr: Beth Yoxheimer
VP Sls: Tim Lightner
Manager: Stan Balkema
Sales Asso: Todd Parshall

LIBRA SAFETY PDT RECYCLABLES
See LIBRA INDUSTRIES INC

D-U-N-S 18-687-5076
LIBRARY ASSOCIATES INC
LAC GROUP
10390 Santa Monica Blvd # 230, Los Angeles, CA 90025-5093
Tel (323) 852-1083 Founded/Ownrshp 1989
Sales 34.1MM^E EMP 300
SIC 8742 7361 8231 Management consulting services; Employment agencies; Library services; Management consulting services; Employment agencies; Library services
CEO: Deborah L Schwarz
*COO: Robert F Corrao Jr
*CFO: Kristen E Kneussl
Ex VP: Tyler Leshney
VP: Keith Gurtzweiler
Dir Bus: Jim Dieterle

D-U-N-S 10-898-9799
LIBRARY CORP
1 Research Park, Inwood, WV 25428-9733
Tel (304) 229-0100 Founded/Ownrshp 1975
Sales 31.5MM EMP 220
Accts Smith Elliot Kearns & Company
SIC 7371 7373 7372 Computer software development & applications; Turnkey vendors, computer systems; Value-added resellers, computer systems; Prepackaged software; Computer software development & applications; Turnkey vendors, computer systems; Value-added resellers, computer systems; Prepackaged software
Pr: Annette Harwood Murphy
*Sec: Calvin Whittington
*VP: Gary W Kirk
Mng Dir: Paul Leppert
CTO: Jabe Bloom
CTO: Megan Derrick
QA Dir: Craig Alford
QA Dir: Wade Torbenson
Dir IT: Simon Marcus
Web Dev: Ryan Mann
Web Dev: Ed Tryon

D-U-N-S 78-879-0434
■ **LIBRARY OF CONGRESS**
(Suby of CONGRESS UNITED STATES) ★
101 Independence Ave Se, Washington, DC 20540-0002
Tel (202) 707-5000 Founded/Ownrshp 1800
Sales 125.7MM^E EMP 4,213
SIC 8231 9121 Libraries; Legislative bodies; ; Libraries; Legislative bodies;
Bd of Dir: Jane Gilchrist
Ofcr: Beatriz Haspo
Ofcr: Stephanie Marcus
Top Exec: Constance Carter
Exec: Jay Miller
Exec: Littlejohn Tom
Assoc Dir: Bessie Alkisswani
Comm Dir: Gayle Osterberg
Adm Dir: Eugenie Duncan
Adm Dir: Pauline Herbert
Adm Dir: Joanne Kitching

D-U-N-S 61-209-3500
LIBRARY SYSTEMS & SERVICES LLC
12850 Middlebrook Rd # 400, Germantown, MD 20874-5281
Tel (301) 540-5100 Founded/Ownrshp 1996
Sales 61.7MM^E EMP 700
SIC 8742 Management consulting services; Management consulting services
CEO: Brad King
Pr: Ron Dubberly
CFO: Steve Field
VP: George Bateman
VP: Judy CM
VP: C M Judy
Genl Mgr: Janice Anderson

D-U-N-S 07-882-3310
LICENSALE INC
900 Bush St Apt 205, San Francisco, CA 94109-6379
Tel (604) 681-6888 Founded/Ownrshp 2013
Sales 25.0MM EMP 100
SIC 6794 8748 Patent buying, licensing, leasing; Business consulting; Patent buying, licensing, leasing; Business consulting
Pr: Benjamin Arazy
*CFO: Mingsheng Qiu

LICENSED AS CLEAR CHANNEL
See IN-TER-SPACE SERVICES INC

D-U-N-S 96-175-0965
LICENSING AND REGULATION SOUTH CAROLINA DEPARTMENT OF LABOR
(Suby of STATE OF SOUTH CAROLINA) ★
110 Centerview Dr, Columbia, SC 29210-8432
Tel (803) 896-4300 Founded/Ownrshp 2000
Sales NA EMP 373^E
SIC 9651 Labor regulatory agency; ; Labor regulatory agency;
Ex Dir: Holly Pisarik
*Prin: Adrienne R Youmans
CIO: Matt Faile
Art Dir: Laura J Pace

D-U-N-S 12-319-4313
LICHTY BROS CONSTRUCTION INC
22 Hillwood Cir, Newnan, GA 30263-5856
Tel (770) 254-1313 Founded/Ownrshp 1992
Sales 21.0MM EMP 8
SIC 1521 Single-family housing construction; Single-family housing construction
Pr: Galen Lichty
*VP: Dan Lichty
Off Mgr: Becky Moore

LICK WILMERDING HIGH SCHOOL
See CALIFORNIA SCHOOL OF MECHANICAL ARTS

LICKING COUNTY COMMISSIONERS
See COUNTY OF LICKING

D-U-N-S 05-588-6584
LICKING HEIGHTS LOCAL SCHOOL DISTRICT
6539 Summit Rd Sw, Summit Station, OH 43073
Tel (740) 927-9046 Founded/Ownrshp 1956
Sales 15.5MM^E EMP 282
Accts Mary Taylor Cpa Columbus Oh
SIC 8211 Public elementary & secondary schools; High school, junior or senior; School board; Public elementary & secondary schools; High school, junior or senior; School board
*Pr: Rudy Shaffer
*VP: Michael O'Neil
Exec: Kimberly Jonker
Prin: Ron Stephens
IT Man: Chris Cashtoller

D-U-N-S 78-675-9134
LICKING MEMORIAL HEALTH SYSTEMS
1320 W Main St, Newark, OH 43055-1822
Tel (740) 348-4000 Founded/Ownrshp 1984
Sales 209.7MM EMP 1,700
Accts Mountjoy Chilton Medley Llp C
SIC 8741 6411 Hospital management; Insurance agents, brokers & service; Hospital management; Insurance agents, brokers & service
CFO: Rob Montagnese
*Pr: Robert Montagnese
*VP: Sallie Arnett
Dir Rx: Jeff Smith
Off Mgr: Kathy Watters
CIO: Debra Heldman
QI Cn Mgr: Brian Thatcher
Mktg Dir: Tom Argyle
Pr Dir: Carol Hutchison
Pr Mgr: Mike Andrews
Surgeon: Victor Ferrini

LICKING MEMORIAL HLTH SYSTEMS
See LICKING MEMORIAL HOSPITAL

D-U-N-S 04-642-4750
LICKING MEMORIAL HOSPITAL (OH)
LICKING MEMORIAL HLTH SYSTEMS
(Suby of LICKING MEMORIAL HEALTH SYSTEMS) ★
1320 W Main St, Newark, OH 43055-3699
Tel (740) 348-4137 Founded/Ownrshp 1898, 1986
Sales 189.7MM EMP 1,143^E
SIC 8062 General medical & surgical hospitals; General medical & surgical hospitals
Pr: Robert A Montagnese
Chf OB: Janae Davis
Ofcr: Colette Dollison
*VP: Sallie Arnett
VP: Sally Arnett
*VP: Craig Cairns
VP: J Fisher
VP: Ann Hubbuch
*VP: Veronica Link
*VP: Christine McGee
VP: Ann Peterson
*VP: Cynthia L Webster
VP: Debboe Yooung
VP: Debbie Young
Dir OR: Greg Wallis
Dir Risk M: Paula Alexander
Dir Lab: Lorei Reinhard

D-U-N-S 00-805-2075
LICKING MEMORIAL PROFESSIONAL CORP
1272 W Main St Ste 5n, Newark, OH 43055-2058
Tel (740) 348-1805 Founded/Ownrshp 1994
Sales 36.6MM EMP 3
Accts Mountjoy Chilton Medley Louis
SIC 8011 8049 Offices & clinics of medical doctors; Nurses, registered & practical; Offices & clinics of medical doctors; Nurses, registered & practical
Ch: Gordon Wilken
*Sec: John Hinderer

D-U-N-S 01-051-4541
LICKING RIVER RESOURCES INC
(Suby of US COAL CORP) ★
6301 Old Richmond Rd, Lexington, KY 40515-9730
Tel (859) 223-8820 Founded/Ownrshp 2001
Sales 108.0MM^E EMP 180
SIC 1241 Coal mining services; Coal mining services
Pr: John A Collins
*VP: Chris Lacy
*VP: Kenneth Whitt

D-U-N-S 82-975-6795
LICKING RURAL ELECTRIFICATION
1500 Granville Rd, Newark, OH 43055-1536
Tel (740) 344-2102 Founded/Ownrshp 2009
Sales 52.0MM EMP 19^E
SIC 4911 Electric services
Prin: Charles Manning

D-U-N-S 00-893-1198
LICKING RURAL ELECTRIFICATION INC
11339 Mount Vernon Rd, Utica, OH 43080-7703
Tel (740) 892-2071 Founded/Ownrshp 1936
Sales 52.0MM EMP 190
SIC 4911 Distribution, electric power; Distribution, electric power
Pr: Charles Manning
COO: George Charles Manning
Ch: Dave Mussard
*Sec: Arland K Rogers
VP: Neil Buxton
Board of Directors: Frank Anderson, Donald Bowman, Neil Buxton, Dan Mc Kee, Ned Staas, Robert Swick

D-U-N-S 08-443-6245
LICKING VALLEY LOCAL SCHOOLS
1379 Licking Valley Rd, Newark, OH 43055-9450
Tel (740) 763-3396 Founded/Ownrshp 1957
Sales 21.4MM EMP 465
SIC 8211 Public elementary & secondary schools; High school, junior or senior; School board; Public elementary & secondary schools; High school, junior or senior; School board
Pr: Jackie Caughenbaugh

D-U-N-S 00-502-1159
LICKING VALLEY RURAL ELECTRIC COOPERATIVE CORP (KY)
271 Main St, West Liberty, KY 41472-1009
Tel (606) 743-3179 Founded/Ownrshp 1940
Sales 29.7MM EMP 38
SIC 4911 Electric services; Electric services
Genl Mgr: Kerry Howard
CFO: Sandra Bradley
Sales Exec: Bill Kimelton

D-U-N-S 07-055-8747
LICKING-KNOX GOODWILL INDUSTRIES INC
65 S 5th St, Newark, OH 43055-5404
Tel (740) 345-9861 Founded/Ownrshp 1977
Sales 13.0MM EMP 325
Accts Clark Schaefer Hackett Spring
SIC 8331 8741 5932 Community service employment training program; Sheltered workshop; Vocational training agency; Management services; Used merchandise stores; Community service employment training program; Sheltered workshop; Vocational training agency; Management services; Used merchandise stores
CEO: Timothy J Young
*CFO: Vicki M Osborn

D-U-N-S 60-303-2769
LICO INC
AUTOMATIC SYSTEMS
9230 E 47th St, Kansas City, MO 64133-1801
Tel (816) 356-0660 Founded/Ownrshp 1981
Sales 44.2MM^E EMP 250
SIC 1791 1542 1521 3448 3535 1796 Structural steel erection; Institutional building construction; General remodeling, single-family houses; Buildings, portable: prefabricated metal; Conveyors & conveying equipment; Installing building equipment; Structural steel erection; Institutional building construction; General remodeling, single-family houses; Buildings, portable: prefabricated metal; Conveyors & conveying equipment; Installing building equipment
CEO: Robert A Hoehn
Board of Directors: William D Thomas

LICR FUND
See LUDWIG INSTITUTE FOR CANCER RESEARCH

D-U-N-S 61-856-7630
LICT CORP
401 Theodore Fremd Ave, Rye, NY 10580-1422
Tel (914) 921-7601 Founded/Ownrshp 1989
Sales 973.2MM^E EMP 2,885
Accts Kpmg Llp New York Ny
SIC 4813 4841 4833 Telephone communication, except radio; Cable & other pay television services; Television broadcasting stations; Telephone communication, except radio; Cable & other pay television services; Television broadcasting stations
Ch Bd: Mario J Gabelli
*CEO: Robert E Dolan
*COO: James Dabramo
*Sr VP: Evelyn Jerden
VP: Stephen Moore
*VP Admn: Thomas J Hearity

D-U-N-S 61-670-2366
LIDDELL BROTHERS INC
600 Industrial Dr, Halifax, MA 02338-1255
Tel (781) 293-2100 Founded/Ownrshp 2001
Sales 21.1MM^E EMP 63^E
SIC 1611 4911 1623 1622 1791 1711 Highway & street construction; Electric services; Water, sewer & utility lines; Bridge, tunnel & elevated highway; Structural steel erection; Plumbing, heating, air-conditioning contractors
Pr: Gary Liddell
*VP: Jacob Liddell
Off Mgr: Michelle Ingrom
Sls Mgr: Craig Barnard
Sales Asso: Wendy Orwig

D-U-N-S 00-805-7445 IMP
LIDE INDUSTRIES LLC
(Suby of PERMIAN TANK & MANUFACTURING INC) ★
1618 W Highway 84, Mexia, TX 76667-4558
Tel (254) 562-0233 Founded/Ownrshp 2008
Sales 37.0MM^E EMP 150^E
SIC 3795 3443 Tanks & tank components; Fabricated plate work (boiler shop); Tanks & tank components; Fabricated plate work (boiler shop)
*CFO: Howard Seely
Psych: Justin Day

D-U-N-S 14-467-0841
LIDESLAMBOUS INC
CAPTAIN GEORGES SEAFOOD REST
5363 Richmond Rd, Williamsburg, VA 23188-2061
Tel (757) 565-2323 Founded/Ownrshp 1985
Sales 9.8MM^E EMP 500^E
SIC 5812 5813 Seafood restaurants; Tavern (drinking places); Seafood restaurants; Tavern (drinking places)
Pr: George Pitsilides
Exec: Marcy Jahn
Genl Mgr: Tom Long

LIDESTRI FOOD & BEVERAGE
See LIDESTRI FOODS INC

D-U-N-S 09-440-5503 IMP
LIDESTRI FOODS INC
LIDESTRI FOOD & BEVERAGE
815 Whitney Rd W, Fairport, NY 14450-1030
Tel (201) 944-1233 Founded/Ownrshp 1998
Sales 285.4MM^E EMP 750
SIC 2033 Spaghetti & other pasta sauce: packaged in cans, jars, etc.; Spaghetti & other pasta sauce: packaged in cans, jars, etc.
CEO: John Lidestri
*CFO: John Veterer
VP: Tony Bash
VP: Carmen Gianni
VP: David Labudde
VP: Santi Lidestri
*VP: Edward Salzano
VP: Mark Scoville
*VP: Donna Yanicky
VP Bus Dev: Alan Davis
*Prin: Joe Ferrigno

D-U-N-S 01-720-6202
LIDO LIGHTING INC (NY)
966 Grand Blvd, Deer Park, NY 11729-5790
Tel (631) 595-2000 Founded/Ownrshp 1975
Sales 20.8MM^E EMP 23
SIC 5063 Lighting fixtures, commercial & industrial; Lighting fixtures, residential
Pr: William G Pierro Jr
*Treas: Anne M Pierro
VP: Ed Grimaldi
Genl Mgr: Susan Garrahan

D-U-N-S 95-604-1339 IMP
■ **LIDS CORP**
(Suby of GENESCO INC) ★
7555 Woodland Dr, Indianapolis, IN 46278-2705
Tel (888) 564-4287 Founded/Ownrshp 2004
Sales 383.4MM^E EMP 2,730
SIC 5699 Sports apparel; Sports apparel
Pr: Jack Ladsey
Mng Pt: Casey Walts
*Pr: Kenneth J Kocher
*COO: Joseph Glenn Campbell
*CFO: Richard E Cramer
CFO: Richard E Cramr
Treas: Brooke Nichols
VP: Robert J Dennis
Comm Man: Tracy Brink
Brnch Mgr: Brian Brewer
Brnch Mgr: Nikki Cadell

LIDS SPORTS GROUP
See HAT WORLD INC

D-U-N-S 15-276-0567 IMP
LIEBEL-FLARSHEIM CO LLC
2111 E Galbraith Rd, Cincinnati, OH 45237-1624
Tel (513) 761-2700 Founded/Ownrshp 1986
Sales 37.4MM^E EMP 258
SIC 3841 3844 5047 Surgical & medical instruments; Surgical instruments & apparatus; Operating tables; X-ray apparatus & tubes; Fluoroscopic X-ray apparatus & tubes; Radiographic X-ray apparatus & tubes; Hospital equipment & furniture; Medical equipment & supplies; Surgical & medical instruments; Surgical instruments & apparatus; Operating tables; X-ray apparatus & tubes; Fluoroscopic X-ray apparatus & tubes; Radiographic X-ray apparatus & tubes; Hospital equipment & furniture; Medical equipment & supplies
Pr: Bradley Fercho
*Treas: John E Teufel
VP: Dane Battiato
*VP: Roger A Keller
*VP: David Morra
VP: Edwin Sohngen
*VP: Joseph Wuestner
CIO: Joseph Rhorer
Opers Mgr: Dennis Abraham
Opers Mgr: Caren Ante
Opers Mgr: Gustavo Ferreira

D-U-N-S 00-886-2898 IMP
LIEBERMAN COMPANIES INC
VIKING VENDING
9549 Penn Ave S Ste 100, Bloomington, MN 55431-2596
Tel (952) 887-5299 *Founded/Ownrshp* 1946
Sales 20.2MM^E *EMP* 80
SIC 5087 7699 Vending machines & supplies; Vending machine repair; Vending machines & supplies; Vending machine repair
Pr: Harold Lieberman
CFO: Hal Lieberman
**Ch:* Stephen E Lieberman
Genl Mgr: Tim Zahn

D-U-N-S 11-083-0239
LIEBERMAN MANAGEMENT SERVICES INC
25 Northwest Point Blvd # 330, Elk Grove Village, IL 60007-1056
Tel (847) 459-0000 *Founded/Ownrshp* 1971
Sales 29.7MM^E *EMP* 160^E
SIC 6514 Residential building, four or fewer units: operation
Ch Bd: Stanley B Lieberman
**Pr:* James I Pio
**CEO:* Carla Young Kennedy
**CFO:* Kevin Adam
**VP:* Don Kekstadt
**VP:* John Santoro
Dir Bus: Charles Perry
Dist Mgr: Brian Butler

D-U-N-S 06-992-7648
LIEBERMAN RESEARCH WORLDWIDE INC (CA)
1900 Ave Of The Sts 160 Ste 1600, Los Angeles, CA 90067
Tel (310) 553-7721 *Founded/Ownrshp* 1973
Sales 41.0MM^E *EMP* 200
SIC 8732 Market analysis or research; Market analysis or research
Pr: David Sackman
**Ch Bd:* Arnold Fishman
VP: Frank Chipman
VP: Chris Elsbury
VP: Laura Latshaw
VP: Elena Morales
VP: Matthew Parsons
VP: Charles Swann

D-U-N-S 00-430-9647 IMP/EXP
■ LIEBERT CORP
EMERSON NETWORK POWER
(*Suby of* EECO INC) ★
1050 Dearborn Dr, Columbus, OH 43085-4709
Tel (614) 888-0246 *Founded/Ownrshp* 1987
Sales 1.0MMM^E *EMP* 2,999
SIC 3613 3585 7629 Regulators, power; Air conditioning equipment, complete; Electronic equipment repair; Regulators, power; Air conditioning equipment, complete; Electronic equipment repair
Pr: Steve Hassell
Pr: Robert P Bauer
Pr: Robert Yopko
Treas: Thomas Vennemeyer
Ex VP: Ed Feeney
Ex VP: W Odell
Ex VP: Earl Weaver
Sr VP: James Good
VP: Joe Jones
VP: Bob Kinross
VP: Fred Lancia
VP: Gorie Lapointe
VP: Steve Madara
VP: Peter Panfil

D-U-N-S 14-108-1930
■ LIEBERT NORTH AMERICA INC
(*Suby of* EMERSON NETWORK POWER) ★
1050 Dearborn Dr, Columbus, OH 43085-4709
Tel (614) 888-0246 *Founded/Ownrshp* 1999
Sales 201.2MM^E *EMP* 1,800
SIC 3699 3585 Electrical equipment & supplies; Refrigeration & heating equipment; Electrical equipment & supplies; Refrigeration & heating equipment
Pr: Robert P Bauer
VP: James Good

D-U-N-S 78-435-0675
LIEBHERR AEROSPACE SALINE INC
(*Suby of* LIEBHERR-AEROSPACE & TRANS SAS)
1465 Woodland Dr, Saline, MI 48176-1627
Tel (734) 429-7225 *Founded/Ownrshp* 2005
Sales 43.7MM^E *EMP* 145
SIC 4581 Aircraft maintenance & repair services; Aircraft maintenance & repair services
Pr: Alex Vlielander
CFO: Martin Stein
Ofcr: Wilhelm Kohler
Ex VP: Charles Thoyerrozat
Mng Dir: Christoph Kleiner
Tech Mgr: Mark Sobol
Opers Mgr: Derek Hampel
Ql Cn Mgr: Jim Will
VP Sls: Kevin Heise
VP Sls: Steve Whisenhunt
Manager: John Hartford

LIEBHERR AUTOMATION SYSTEMS CO
See LIEBHERR GEAR TECHNOLOGY INC

D-U-N-S 14-384-9011 IMP/EXP
LIEBHERR CRANES INC
(*Suby of* LIEBHERR-INTERNATIONAL S.A.)
4100 Chestnut Ave, Newport News, VA 23607-2420
Tel (757) 928-2505 *Founded/Ownrshp* 2003
Sales 69.4MM^E *EMP* 140
SIC 5082 Cranes, construction; Cranes, construction
Pr: Georg Diesch
**Pr:* Daniel Pitzer
**Ex VP:* Lena Hogue
Ex VP: Paul Robson
VP: Scott Moreland
VP: Josef Steigmiller
Exec: Carrington Hughes
**Exec:* Ingo Schiller
**Exec:* Ralf Vieten
Brnch Mgr: Mike Clark
Brnch Mgr: Nathan Kavanaugh

D-U-N-S 17-705-4173 IMP/EXP
LIEBHERR GEAR TECHNOLOGY INC
LIEBHERR AUTOMATION SYSTEMS CO
(*Suby of* LIEBHERR-INTERNATIONAL S.A.)
1465 Woodland Dr, Saline, MI 48176-1627
Tel (734) 429-7225 *Founded/Ownrshp* 1987
Sales 33.1MM^E *EMP* 55
SIC 5084 Industrial machinery & equipment
Pr: Peter Wiedemann
**Ex VP:* Lena Hogue
Sls Mgr: Scott Kilberg

D-U-N-S 05-404-2296 IMP
LIEBHERR MINING & CONSTRUCTION EQUIPMENT INC
(*Suby of* LIEBHERR-INTERNATIONAL S.A.)
4100 Chestnut Ave, Newport News, VA 23607-2420
Tel (757) 245-5251 *Founded/Ownrshp* 1970
Sales 368.0MM^E *EMP* 950
SIC 5082 5084 3532 Construction & mining machinery; Excavating machinery & equipment; Cranes, construction; Road construction & maintenance machinery; Machine tools & accessories; Mining machinery; Construction & mining machinery; Excavating machinery & equipment; Cranes, construction; Road construction & maintenance machinery; Machine tools & accessories; Mining machinery
Pr: Lena Hogue
Ex VP: Cheri Cooke
Ex VP: Georg Diesch
Assoc Dir: Tim Petersen
Genl Mgr: Ulrich Hamme
Sftwr Eng: Douglas Rilee
VP Opers: Jochen Faber
Opers Mgr: David Bennett
Trfc Mgr: Angela Fizzano
Manager: Reinhold Cordella
Sls Mgr: Derek Alband

D-U-N-S 00-597-2443
■ LIEBOVICH BROS INC (IL)
(*Suby of* RELIANCE STEEL & ALUMINUM CO) ★
2116 Preston St, Rockford, IL 61102-1975
Tel (815) 987-3200 *Founded/Ownrshp* 1940
Sales 300.1MM^E *EMP* 559
SIC 5051 Ferrous metals; Ferrous metals
Pr: Michael J Tulley
IT Man: David Corirossi

D-U-N-S 02-530-8318
■ LIEBOVICH STEEL & ALUMINUM CO
(*Suby of* LIEBOVICH BROS INC) ★
2116 Preston St, Rockford, IL 61102-1975
Tel (815) 987-3200 *Founded/Ownrshp* 1989
Sales 300.0MM *EMP* 559^E
SIC 5051 Metals service centers & offices; Metals service centers & offices
Pr: Michael Shanley
Pr: Greg Liebovich
Pr: Michael P Shanley

D-U-N-S 01-750-7302
LIECHTY INC
(*Suby of* KENN-FELD GROUP LLC) ★
1701 S Defiance St, Archbold, OH 43502-9798
Tel (419) 445-1565 *Founded/Ownrshp* 2011
Sales 21.7MM^E *EMP* 100
SIC 5083 Agricultural machinery & equipment; Agricultural machinery & equipment
Pr: Orval Jay Beck

D-U-N-S 08-386-9164
LIEFF CABRASER HEIMANN & BERNSTEIN LLP
275 Battery St Fl 29, San Francisco, CA 94111-3339
Tel (415) 788-0245 *Founded/Ownrshp* 1972
Sales 22.5MM^E *EMP* 128
SIC 8111 Antitrust & trade regulation law; Environmental law; Labor & employment law; Securities law; Antitrust & trade regulation law; Environmental law; Labor & employment law; Securities law
Pt: Robert L Lieff
Pt: William Bernstein
Pt: Elizabeth J Cabraser
Pt: James M Finberg
Pt: Richard M Heimann
Dir Soc: Lin Corrently
IT Man: John Gersten
Counsel: David Rudolph
Counsel: Nigel Taylor

D-U-N-S 00-734-7372
LIEUTENANT GOVERNOR LOUISIANA STATE OFFICE OF
(*Suby of* EXECUTIVE OFFICE OF STATE OF LOUISIANA) ★
2020 Saint Charles Ave, New Orleans, LA 70130-5319
Tel (225) 342-7009 *Founded/Ownrshp* 2007
Sales NA *EMP* 539^E
SIC 9111 Executive offices;
Prin: Judy Morse

D-U-N-S 19-548-6105
LIF INDUSTRIES INC
5 Harbor Park Dr Ste 1, Port Washington, NY 11050-4698
Tel (516) 390-6800 *Founded/Ownrshp* 1986
Sales 25.7MM^E *EMP* 120
SIC 3442 5031 Metal doors; Window & door frames; Door frames, all materials; Metal doors; Window & door frames; Door frames, all materials
Pr: Joseph Gallo Jr
**Ch Bd:* Vincent Gallo
**VP:* Anthony Gallo

LIFE
See LIVING INTENTIONALLY FOR EXCELLENCE LLLP LIMITED PARTNERSHIP

D-U-N-S 18-335-4083
LIFE ALERT EMERGENCY RESPONSE INC
16027 Ventura Blvd # 400, Encino, CA 91436-2728
Tel (800) 247-0000 *Founded/Ownrshp* 1987
Sales 42.7MM^E *EMP* 600
SIC 7382 5731 Confinement surveillance systems maintenance & monitoring; Consumer electronic equipment; Confinement surveillance systems maintenance & monitoring; Consumer electronic equipment
Pr: Isaac Shepher
**CFO:* Felix Leung
**Sr VP:* Miriam Shepher
VP: Richard Chen
CTO: Yasha Sigal
Dir IT: Russ States

D-U-N-S 14-446-6869
LIFE AMBULANCE SERVICE INC
729 6th St, Portsmouth, OH 45662-4030
Tel (740) 354-6169 *Founded/Ownrshp* 1985
Sales NA *EMP* 833^E
SIC 4119

D-U-N-S 78-366-0074
LIFE AND SPECIALTY VENTURES LLC
LSV
17500 Chenal Pkwy Ste 500, Little Rock, AR 72223-9059
Tel (501) 378-2910 *Founded/Ownrshp* 2005
Sales 232.1MM^E *EMP* 1,200^E
SIC 6719 Personal holding companies, except banks; Personal holding companies, except banks
CEO: Jason Mann
**CFO:* Mark Langston
IT Man: Brandy Stults

LIFE BOSTON INSURANCE COMPANY
See LONDEN INSURANCE INC

D-U-N-S 84-816-7003
LIFE BRIDGES INC
674 Old Chattanooga Pike, Cleveland, TN 37311-8517
Tel (423) 339-0811 *Founded/Ownrshp* 1978
Sales 15.3MM *EMP* 477
Accts Harting Bishop & Arrendale Pll
SIC 8322 Social services for the handicapped; Social services for the handicapped
CEO: Lucas Queen
**COO:* Diana Jackson
**CFO:* Ginger Davis

LIFE CARE CENTER OF HILO
See HILO MEDICAL INVESTORS LTD

D-U-N-S 03-067-1002
LIFE CARE CENTERS OF AMERICA INC
3570 Keith St Nw, Cleveland, TN 37312-4309
Tel (423) 472-9585 *Founded/Ownrshp* 1975
Sales 1.6MMM^E *EMP* 29,000
SIC 8051 8052 Skilled nursing care facilities; Intermediate care facilities; Skilled nursing care facilities; Intermediate care facilities
Ch Bd: Forrest L Preston
Pr: Bryan A Cook
**Pr:* Beecher Hunter
Ex VP: Mohney Ralph
Sr VP: Norma Cooper
Sr VP: Terry Henry
Sr VP: Carol Hulgan
Sr VP: Carson Mike
Sr VP: Don Provonsha
VP: Bobby Holder
**VP:* Lisa Lay
VP: Rick Mountz
VP: Dick Odenthal
VP: Tyler Owens
VP: Sue Payne
VP: Mary Pfeifer
VP: Pamela Rau
VP: James Sanner
VP: Rick Starke
VP: David Starrett
VP: Richard Swanker

D-U-N-S 18-795-5141
LIFE CARE HOME HEALTH SERVICES CORP
4723 W Atl Ave Ste 21, Delray Beach, FL 33445
Tel (561) 272-5866 *Founded/Ownrshp* 1988
Sales 30.2MM^E *EMP* 1,500
SIC 8082 7361 Home health care services; Nurses' registry; Home health care services; Nurses' registry
VP: Mary Harrison
**VP:* Debbie Dacus
Exec: Kevin Meyer

D-U-N-S 18-201-1262
LIFE CARE PONTE VEDRA INC
VICAR'S LANDING
1000 Vicars Landing Way, Ponte Vedra Beach, FL 32082-3151
Tel (904) 273-1700 *Founded/Ownrshp* 1983
Sales 20.2MM *EMP* 198
Accts Harbeson Fletcher & Bateh Llp
SIC 8361 8052 8051 Geriatric residential care; Intermediate care facilities; Skilled nursing care facilities; Geriatric residential care; Intermediate care facilities; Skilled nursing care facilities
Ex Dir: Raymond M Johnson
**Pr:* Milton Fulton
**Treas:* Guy Nix

D-U-N-S 10-734-1711
LIFE CARE SERVICES CORP
LCS
(*Suby of* L C S) ★
400 Locust St Ste 820, Des Moines, IA 50309-2334
Tel (515) 875-4500 *Founded/Ownrshp* 1986
Sales 27.0MM^E *EMP* 200
SIC 6513 Retirement hotel operation
Pr: Stan Thurston
COO: Joel Nelson
Ch: Ed Kenny
Ex VP: Diane Bridgewater
Ex VP: Rick Exline
Ex VP: Kent Larson
VP: Joe Brucella
VP: Bruce Cannon
VP: Scott Doherty
VP: Laura Franco
VP: Richard Funk
VP: Mary Harrison
VP: Brett Logan
VP: Lee Lyles
VP: Warren Naviasky
VP: Michael Page
VP: Rich Seibert
Dir Risk M: Dennis Tabor

D-U-N-S 07-350-0514
LIFE CARE SERVICES LLC
L C S
(*Suby of* LCS HOLDINGS INC) ★
400 Locust St Ste 820, Des Moines, IA 50309-2334
Tel (515) 875-4500 *Founded/Ownrshp* 1971
Sales 45.7MM^E *EMP* 350
SIC 8322

LIFE CHARTER SCHOOL
See LIFESCHOOL OF DALLAS

LIFE CHOICE HOSPICE
See SPECIAL CARE HOSPICE LLC

LIFE CHRISTIAN SCHOOL
See FIRST ASSEMBLY OF GOD LIFE CENTER OF TACOMA WASHINGTON

LIFE CHURCH
See LIFE COVENANT CHURCH INC

D-U-N-S 04-421-1365
LIFE CONCEPTS INC
QUEST
500 E Colonial Dr, Orlando, FL 32803-4504
Tel (407) 218-4300 *Founded/Ownrshp* 1980
Sales 29.1MM *EMP* 550
Accts Moore Stephens Lovelace Pa
SIC 8361 Rehabilitation center, residential: health care incidental; Rehabilitation center, residential: health care incidental
Pr: John Gill
**Ch Bd:* David Canora
**V Ch:* Greg Rodeghier
**COO:* Karenne Levy
**CFO:* Todd Thrasher
**Treas:* Suzanne Bennett
**VP:* Eb Blakely
VP: Carol Debauche
**VP:* John Dogaer
Ex Dir: Verna Morris
Mktg Dir: Tikisha Ousley-Hughes

D-U-N-S 08-699-8382
LIFE COVENANT CHURCH INC
LIFE CHURCH
4600 E 2nd St, Edmond, OK 73034-7550
Tel (405) 680-5433 *Founded/Ownrshp* 1997
Sales 89.6MM *EMP* 120^E
Accts Cole & Reed Pc Oklahoma Cit
SIC 8661 Non-denominational church; Non-denominational church
Pr: Craig Groeschel
**CFO:* Cathi Linch
**VP:* Bobby Gruenewald
**VP:* Jerry Hurley
CTO: Kellian Schneider
Opers Mgr: David Summers
Snr Mgr: Mark Allen
Snr Mgr: Luke Guevara
Snr Mgr: Davey Rumsey

D-U-N-S 08-863-0264
LIFE CYCLE ENGINEERING INC
L C E
4360 Corporate Rd Ste 100, North Charleston, SC 29405-7439
Tel (843) 744-7110 *Founded/Ownrshp* 1976
Sales 91.1MM *EMP* 600
SIC 7371 7373 7376 7379 8711 Electrical or electronic engineering; Industrial engineers; Marine engineering; Mechanical engineering; Custom computer programming services; Computer integrated systems design; Computer facilities management; Computer related maintenance services; Engineering services
CEO: Robert Fei
Ch Bd: James Fei
CFO: Robert Bendetti
Sr VP: Bill Guin
Sr VP: Dave Johnson
Sr VP: Manuel Lovgren
VP: Martin Baker
VP: Edward S Godfrey
VP: Larry Hargrove
VP: Jerry Vevon
Prgrm Mgr: Andy Rowe
Board of Directors: James R Fei, Robert F Fei

D-U-N-S 02-104-3732
LIFE E M S INC (MI)
LIFE EMERGENCY MEDICAL SVCS
1275 Cedar St Ne, Grand Rapids, MI 49503-1353
Tel (616) 395-5433 *Founded/Ownrshp* 1979
Sales 41.1MM^E *EMP* 300
SIC 4119 Ambulance service; Ambulance service
Pr: Mark Meijer
**VP:* Ken Morris

LIFE EMERGENCY MEDICAL SVCS
See LIFE E M S INC

LIFE EXT QLTY SPPLMNTS VTAMINS
See LIFE EXTENSION FOUNDATION INC

D-U-N-S 05-265-7798
LIFE EXTENSION FOUNDATION BUYERS CLUB INC (NV)
3600 W Commercial Blvd, Fort Lauderdale, FL 33309-3338
Tel (954) 766-8433 *Founded/Ownrshp* 1980
Sales 39.6MM^E *EMP* 400
SIC 8399 5499 5942 Fund raising organization, non-fee basis; Health & dietetic food stores; Book stores; Fund raising organization, non-fee basis; Health & dietetic food stores; Book stores
CEO: Paul Gilner
**CFO:* James Murray
Genl Couns: Jason Greenstein
Board of Directors: William Faloon

D-U-N-S 13-839-2407
LIFE EXTENSION FOUNDATION INC
LIFE EXT QLTY SPPLMNTS VTAMINS
3600 W Coml Blvd Ste 100, Fort Lauderdale, FL 33309
Tel (954) 766-8433 *Founded/Ownrshp* 1977
Sales 200.0MM^E *EMP* 350
SIC 8733 Medical research; Medical research
CEO: Paul Gilner
VP: Luke Huber
VP: Steven Joyal
VP Mktg: Rey Searles
Mktg Dir: Audrey Garrett
Manager: Gary Kleinman
Manager: Mitch Levy
Manager: Chad Thomas
Genl Couns: Jason Greenstein

LIFE FLEET
See ATLANTIC AMBULANCE SERVICE ACQUISITION INC

D-U-N-S 96-227-0901
LIFE FOR RELIEF AND DEVELOPMENT INC
17300 W 10 Mile Rd, Southfield, MI 48075-2930
Tel (248) 424-7493 *Founded/Ownrshp* 1992
Sales 34.0MM *EMP* 20
Accts Kaszubski Al-Hassan Sadapscpa
SIC 8322 Crisis intervention center; Disaster service; Crisis intervention center; Disaster service
Pr: Mujahid H Alfayadh
COO: Mohammed Alomari

D-U-N-S 04-665-2421
LIFE GENERATIONS HEALTHCARE LLC
20371 Irvine Ave Ste 210, Newport Beach, CA 92660-0251
Tel (714) 241-5600 *Founded/Ownrshp* 1998
Sales 61.9MM^E *EMP* 700
SIC 8051 Skilled nursing care facilities; Skilled nursing care facilities
Pr: Thomas Olds Jr
**CFO:* Lois A Mastrocola
Dir Risk M: Teresa Green
Dir Bus: Tim Miller
Dir IT: Paul Haider
Opers Mgr: Walter Cline
Sls&Mrk Ex: Myla Palicious

LIFE IN THE WORD
See JOYCE MEYER MINISTRIES INC

D-U-N-S 62-415-4803
LIFE INC
2609 Royall Ave, Goldsboro, NC 27534-8615
Tel (919) 273-4390 *Founded/Ownrshp* 1977
Sales 18.8MM^E *EMP* 690
SIC 8361 Residential care; Residential care
Pr: Beatris Lamb
**Sec:* Sharon Raynor
Ex VP: Samuel King
**VP:* Tommy Lamb
Doctor: Renne Hill

D-U-N-S 05-157-6783
LIFE INSURANCE CO OF ALABAMA
LIFE OF ALABAMA
302 Broad St, Gadsden, AL 35901-3716
Tel (256) 543-2022 *Founded/Ownrshp* 1952
Sales NA *EMP* 70^E
SIC 6321 6311 Accident insurance carriers; Health insurance carriers; Reinsurance carriers, accident & health; Life insurance carriers; Life reinsurance
Pr: Clarence W Daugette III
**Ex VP:* M Lynn Lowe
**Ex VP:* Ray Renfow
VP: Hoyt Casey
VP: Mark Hayes

D-U-N-S 00-791-3957
■ **LIFE INSURANCE CO OF NORTH AMERICA** (PA)
(*Suby of* CIGNA) ★
1601 Chestnut St, Philadelphia, PA 19192-0003
Tel (215) 761-1000 *Founded/Ownrshp* 1956, 2001
Sales NA *EMP* 1,500
SIC 6321 6311 Accident insurance carriers; Life insurance carriers; Accident insurance carriers; Life insurance carriers
Sr VP: Joseph M Fitzgerald
**CFO:* Jean Walker
**Treas:* Paul Bergsteinsson
**Sr VP:* Richard A Brownmiller
**Sr VP:* Gregory Deming
**Sr VP:* Kevin Gravatt
**Sr VP:* Kathleen McEndy
**Sr VP:* Eric M Reisenwitz
**Sr VP:* Julian Romeu
**Sr VP:* Jerold H Rosenblum
VP: Steven G Mellas

D-U-N-S 00-936-8084
LIFE IS GOOD
15 Hudson Park Dr, Hudson, NH 03051-3989
Tel (603) 204-5020 *Founded/Ownrshp* 1994
Sales 25.0MM^E *EMP* 150^E
SIC 2759 Screen printing
CEO: Albert Jacobs
Dir IT: Sean Manners
Pr Dir: Cathy Cantwell
Snr Mgr: Bert Jacobs

D-U-N-S 19-555-4998
LIFE IS GOOD CO
51 Melcher St Ste 901, Boston, MA 02210-1500
Tel (617) 867-8900 *Founded/Ownrshp* 1997
Sales 2.2MM *EMP* 340
SIC 5651 Family clothing stores; Family clothing stores
Pr: Albert A Jacobs
CFO: Bob Ramano
**Treas:* John Jacobs
VP: Kerrie Gross
Off Mgr: Samantha Denette
Mktg Mgr: Bree Oates
Mktg Mgr: Karin Piscitelli

D-U-N-S 96-040-2766
LIFE LINE SCREENING OF AMERICA LTD
6150 Oak Tree Blvd, Independence, OH 44131-6917
Tel (216) 581-6556 *Founded/Ownrshp* 1996
Sales 57.8MM^E *EMP* 700
SIC 8099 Health screening service; Health screening service
CEO: Sean Schultz
Ch: Colin Scully
Ex VP: Timothy Phillips
Sr VP: Jack Smith
VP: Eric Greenberg
VP: Susan Stevie
Prin: Andy Manganaro
Netwrk Mgr: Keven Sipsock
Web Dev: Shannon Kish

LIFE LINK III
See CRITICAL CARE SERVICES INC

D-U-N-S 07-759-7615
LIFE MANAGEMENT CENTER OF NORTHWEST FLORIDA INC
525 E 15th St, Panama City, FL 32405-5412
Tel (850) 769-9481 *Founded/Ownrshp* 1954
Sales 15.9MM *EMP* 300
Accts Segers Sowell Stewart Johnson
SIC 8093 8063 Mental health clinic, outpatient; Psychiatric hospitals; Mental health clinic, outpatient; Psychiatric hospitals
CEO: Ned Ailes
**COO:* Deborah Mobley
**CFO:* Wesley Berry
Exec: Susan Langford
CIO: Renee Davis
Dir QC: Steve Wilkie
Snr Mgr: Julie Kitzerow

LIFE OF ALABAMA
See LIFE INSURANCE CO OF ALABAMA

LIFE PITTSBURGH INC
See LIVING INDEPENDENTLY FOR ELDERLY

LIFE PLANS
See BURNHAM BENEFITS INSURANCE SERVICES

LIFE PLUS
See EURARK LLC

LIFE PLUS
See PRO-LYCO

D-U-N-S 04-438-1739
LIFE PLUS INTERNATIONAL
MULTI-WAY LIFE PLUS
267 E Main St, Batesville, AR 72501-5512
Tel (870) 698-2311 *Founded/Ownrshp* 1982
Sales 51.1MM^E *EMP* 158
SIC 5122 Vitamins & minerals; Vitamins & minerals
Pt: Ed Danskin
Snr Mgr: Rick Land

D-U-N-S 10-763-4354
LIFE QUOTES INC
8205 Cass Ave Ste 102, Darien, IL 60561-5319
Tel (630) 515-0170 *Founded/Ownrshp* 1984
Sales NA *EMP* 106^E
SIC 6411 Insurance agents & brokers
CEO: Robert Bland
**COO:* William V Thoms
CFO: Phillip A Perillo
Treas: William V Thomas
Bd of Dir: Robert Williams
Ex VP: Robert Goss
Sr VP: William L Hemsworth II
VP: Eric A Bergquist
VP: Cindy Mulvihill
VP: Michelle Zieba
Dir IT: Josh Harris
Board of Directors: Jeremiah A Denton Jr, Richard F Gretsch, John B Hopkins, Bruce J Rueben, Timothy J Shannon

D-U-N-S 79-782-8092
LIFE RE CORP
(*Suby of* SR CORPORATE SOLUTIONS AMERICA HOLDING CORP) ★
175 King St, Armonk, NY 10504-1606
Tel (914) 828-8500 *Founded/Ownrshp* 1988
Sales NA *EMP* 946
SIC 6311 6321 Life reinsurance; Reinsurance carriers, accident & health; Life reinsurance; Reinsurance carriers, accident & health
Ch Bd: Rodney A Hawes Jr
**COO:* Jacques E Dubois
**Ex VP:* W Weldon Wilson
**VP:* Patricia Harrigan

D-U-N-S 01-541-6696
LIFE SAFETY DESIGNS INC
3038 Lenox Ave, Jacksonville, FL 32254-4204
Tel (904) 388-1700 *Founded/Ownrshp* 1992
Sales 22.4MM^E *EMP* 35
SIC 5063 Electrical apparatus & equipment
Pr: Darryl Elksnis
**COO:* Steve Platt
**VP:* Grant Gardner
Off Mgr: Shannon Wheat

D-U-N-S 10-991-3587
LIFE SCIENCES RESEARCH INC
(*Suby of* LION HOLDINGS INC) ★
Mettlers Rd, East Millstone, NJ 08875
Tel (732) 649-9961 *Founded/Ownrshp* 2001
Sales 67.5MM^E *EMP* 1,648^E
SIC 8731 Commercial physical research; Biological research; Commercial physical research; Commercial research laboratory; Commercial physical research; Biological research; Commercial physical research; Commercial research laboratory
CEO: Andrew Baker
**Pr:* Brian Cass
CFO: Richard Michaelson
CFO: Richard A Michelson
Dir Bus: David Halverson
Dir Bus: Melanie Hann
Dir IT: Don Wagner
VP Opers: Julian Griffiths

LIFE SFETY SLTIONS INTEGRATORS
See GARDEN & ASSOCIATES INCT L

LIFE SKILLS CENTER
See HAT WHITE MANAGEMENT LLC

LIFE SOURCE
See UPPER MIDWEST ORGAN PROCUREMENT ORGANIZATION INC

D-U-N-S 83-221-6878
LIFE SPICE AND INGREDIENTS LLC
300 Cherry Ln, Palm Beach, FL 33480-3419
Tel (708) 301-0447 *Founded/Ownrshp* 2009
Sales 23.0MM *EMP* 23
SIC 2099 Seasonings & spices
S&M/VP: Lisa Stern

D-U-N-S 02-408-0477
LIFE ST FRANCIS
1435 Liberty St, Trenton, NJ 08629-2220
Tel (609) 599-5433 *Founded/Ownrshp* 2009
Sales 26.7MM *EMP* 12
Accts Deloitte Tax Llp Philadelphia
SIC 8082 Home health care services
Prin: Jill Ann Viggiano
Nrsg Dir: Marianne Gerace

D-U-N-S 62-794-9522
LIFE STEPS FOUNDATION INC
5839 Green Valley Cir # 204, Culver City, CA 90230-6963
Tel (310) 306-4746 *Founded/Ownrshp* 1984
Sales 3.9MM *EMP* 450
Accts Vasquez & Co Llp Los Angeles
SIC 8322 Individual & family services; Individual & family services
CEO: Virginia Franco
Ex Dir: Rachael Pritz
Prgrm Mgr: Luz Martir
Prgrm Mgr: Lisa Tapia

D-U-N-S 00-785-3983
LIFE STORAGE CENTERS LLC (IL)
777 Lake Zurich Rd # 200, Barrington, IL 60010-3118
Tel (847) 381-1911 *Founded/Ownrshp* 2008
Sales 22.5MM^E *EMP* 344^E
SIC 4225 General warehousing & storage

D-U-N-S 18-215-8873 IMP
■ **LIFE TECHNOLOGIES CORP**
(*Suby of* THERMO FISHER SCIENTIFIC INC) ★
5791 Van Allen Way, Carlsbad, CA 92008-7321
Tel (760) 603-7200 *Founded/Ownrshp* 2014
Sales 2.4MMM^E *EMP* 10,000
SIC 2836 2835 Biological products, except diagnostic; In vitro & in vivo diagnostic substances; Biological products, except diagnostic; In vitro & in vivo diagnostic substances
CEO: Seth Hoogasian
Pr: Mark P Stevenson
CEO: Seth H Hoogasian
Ofcr: John A Cottingham
Ex VP: John Gerace
VP: Paul Grossman
VP: Cheri Walker
VP: R Wimalaratane
CTO: Willard Woods
Sales Asso: Arthur Cheung
Snr Mgr: Vernon Ameen
Board of Directors: Seth H Hoogasian

LIFE TIME CONSTRUCTION
See LTF CONSTRUCTION CO LLC

D-U-N-S 78-430-7084 IMP
LIFE TIME FITNESS INC
(*Suby of* LTF HOLDINGS INC) ★
2902 Corporate Pl, Chanhassen, MN 55317-4773
Tel (952) 229-7543 *Founded/Ownrshp* 2015
Sales 1.2MMM^E *EMP* 22,500
SIC 7997 Health club; Membership sports & recreation clubs
Pr: Bahram Akradi
COO: Jeffrey G Zwiefel
CFO: Eric J Buss
Ex VP: Jess R Elmquist
Ex VP: Tami A Kozikowski
Ex VP: Tami Kozikowski
Sr VP: John M Hugo
Off Mgr: Brooke Rymer

LIFE UNIFORM
See SCRUBS & BEYOND LLC

LIFE UNIFORM
See HEALTHCARE UNIFORM CO INC

D-U-N-S 17-489-3024 IMP/EXP
LIFE UNIFORM CO
2132 Kratky Rd, Saint Louis, MO 63114-1704
Tel (314) 824-2900 *Founded/Ownrshp* 2004
Sales NA *EMP* 916
SIC 5699 5661

D-U-N-S 07-592-0041
LIFE UNIVERSITY INC
1269 Barclay Cir Se, Marietta, GA 30060-2903
Tel (770) 426-2600 *Founded/Ownrshp* 1974
Sales 55.6MM *EMP* 330
Accts Bdo Usa Atlanta Ga
SIC 8221 Professional schools; Professional schools
Pr: Guy Reikeman
Pr: Cynthia Boyd
**Pr:* Guy Riekeman
COO: Paul Ketcham
**CFO:* William D Jarr
VP: William Jarr
Ex Dir: Christie Kwon
Rgnl Mgr: Dan Carlton
Dir IT: Thorton Muir
Opers Mgr: Scott Earley
Mktg Dir: Brenda Boone

D-U-N-S 14-841-8577
LIFE-LINE EMERGENCY VEHICLES INC
1 Lifeline Dr, Sumner, IA 50674-9003
Tel (563) 578-3317 *Founded/Ownrshp* 1985
Sales 35.2MM *EMP* 185
SIC 3713 Ambulance bodies; Ambulance bodies

Pr: Connie Leicher
**Sec:* Peggy Becker
IT Man: Karman Nilges

D-U-N-S 17-559-1379
LIFEBANC
4775 Richmond Rd, Cleveland, OH 44128-5919
Tel (216) 752-5433 *Founded/Ownrshp* 1986
Sales 25.3MM *EMP* 81
Accts Ss&G Inc Solon Oh
SIC 8099 Organ bank; Organ bank
Ex Dir: Gordon Bowen
QA Dir: Valerie Horvath

LIFEBLOOD
See MID SOUTH REGIONAL BLOOD CENTER

D-U-N-S 00-479-8299
■ **LIFEBOAT DISTRIBUTION INC**
(*Suby of* WAYSIDE TECHNOLOGY GROUP INC) ★
1157 Shrewsbury Ave, Shrewsbury, NJ 07702-4321
Tel (800) 847-7078 *Founded/Ownrshp* 1995
Sales 33.1MM^E *EMP* 45
SIC 5045 7379 Computers; Computer related maintenance services
Pr: Simon F Nynens
COO: Russ Betts
**VP:* Daniel Jamieson
Sales Exec: Donald Gries
Sls Mgr: Michael Byrnes
Sls Mgr: Nicole Cignarella
Sales Asso: Manoj Nair

D-U-N-S 13-148-0618
LIFEBRIDGE HEALTH INC
2401 W Belvedere Ave, Baltimore, MD 21215-5216
Tel (410) 601-5653 *Founded/Ownrshp* 1985
Sales 120.1MM *EMP* 6,000^E
Accts Kpmg Llp Baltimore Md
SIC 8062 General medical & surgical hospitals; General medical & surgical hospitals
CEO: Neil M Meltzer
**Ch Bd:* Howard Weiss
COO: Jeff Watson
**CFO:* David Krajewski
**Sr VP:* Aric Spitulnik
Dir Rx: John D Bona
Dir IT: Chris Boortz
IT Man: Steven Sandler
Ansthlgy: Mark Coleman
Ansthlgy: Sukhjit Sandhu
Ansthlgy: William Su

LIFECARE ASSURANCE COMPANY
See 21ST CENTURY LIFE AND HEALTH CO INC

D-U-N-S 60-470-7935
LIFECARE ASSURANCE CO INC
(*Suby of* 21ST CENTURY LIFE AND HEALTH CO INC) ★
21600 Oxnard St Fl 16, Woodland Hills, CA 91367-4976
Tel (818) 887-4436 *Founded/Ownrshp* 1988
Sales NA *EMP* 246
SIC 6321 6411 6311 Accident & health insurance; Insurance agents, brokers & service; Life insurance; Accident & health insurance; Insurance agents, brokers & service; Life insurance
Pr: James Glickman
**COO:* Alan S Hughes
**CFO:* Daniel J Disipio
**VP:* Peter Diffley
**VP:* Gwen D Franklin
**VP:* Jay R Peters
**VP:* Jim Rogers
**VP:* Kirk R Shearburn
**VP Admn:* Dick Sato
Dir IT: Ivan Banev

LIFECARE FAMILY OF HOSPITALS
See LIFECARE HOLDINGS INC

LIFECARE FAMILY OF HOSPITALST
See LIFECARE HOSPITALS OF PITTSBURGH INC

LIFECARE HEALTH PARTNERS
See HCL OF NORTH CAROLINA LLC

D-U-N-S 10-123-0931 IMP
LIFECARE HOLDINGS INC
LIFECARE FAMILY OF HOSPITALS
(*Suby of* LCI HOLDCO LLC) ★
5340 Legacy Dr Ste 150, Plano, TX 75024-3131
Tel (469) 241-2100 *Founded/Ownrshp* 1993
Sales 448.8MM^E *EMP* 4,500^E
SIC 8069 8051 Specialty hospitals, except psychiatric; Skilled nursing care facilities; Specialty hospitals, except psychiatric; Skilled nursing care facilities
Ch Bd: Phillip B Douglas
**COO:* Stuart Archer
**COO:* Frank J Battafarano
**CFO:* Stuart A Walker
Ofcr: Pat A Denney
Ofcr: Erik Pahl
**Ex VP:* Grant B Asay
Ex VP: Grant Asay
**Sr VP:* Catherine A Conner
Sr VP: Greg Floyd
Sr VP: Leroy F Thompson Jr
Sr VP: Audrey Wathen
**VP:* Maegan Bowman
VP: Diane H Partridge
Board of Directors: Karen H Bechtel, William Hamburg, William P Johnston, William H McMullan Jr, Stephen H Wise

D-U-N-S 78-498-0729
LIFECARE HOSPITAL OF SHREVEPORT
(*Suby of* LIFECARE FAMILY OF HOSPITALS) ★
2550 Kings Hwy, Shreveport, LA 71103-3922
Tel (318) 212-6960 *Founded/Ownrshp* 2006
Sales 18.3MM^E *EMP* 362^E
SIC 8062 General medical & surgical hospitals

LIFECARE HOSPITALS
See ABC HCL LLC

LIFECARE HOSPITALS OF DALLAS
See NORTH TEXAS HCL LP

D-U-N-S 00-697-4948
LIFECARE HOSPITALS OF PITTSBURGH INC
LIFECARE FAMILY OF HOSPITALST
(*Suby of* LIFECARE FAMILY OF HOSPITALS) ★
225 Penn Ave, Wilkinsburg, PA 15221-2148
Tel (412) 247-2424 *Founded/Ownrshp* 1999
Sales 48.1MM *EMP* 500^E
SIC 8062 General medical & surgical hospitals; General medical & surgical hospitals
Pr: W Earl Reed III
**CFO:* Harry Peterson
**Treas:* Leroy F Thompson Jr
**Treas:* Chris Walker
Trst: William Donaldson
Trst: John Rangos
Ofcr: Elaine Hatfield
Dir Risk M: Carolyn Griffin
Dir Rad: Sally Miller
Dir Rx: Thanh Le
Dir Env Sv: Kerry Bush

D-U-N-S 55-553-6866
LIFECARE HOSPITALS OF SOUTH TEXAS
(*Suby of* LIFECARE FAMILY OF HOSPITALS) ★
2001 S M St, McAllen, TX 78503-1551
Tel (956) 630-4303 *Founded/Ownrshp* 2005
Sales 31.1MM *EMP* 1
SIC 8062 General medical & surgical hospitals; General medical & surgical hospitals
CEO: Mike Adams
Dir Inf Cn: Janie Ituarte
Dir Case M: Martin Acosta
Dir Rx: Anita Ramirez
HC Dir: Cheryl Dennis

LIFECARE HOSPITALS WISCONSIN
See NEW LIFECARE HOSPITALS OF MILWAUKEE LLC

D-U-N-S 13-174-2959
LIFECARE INC
2 Armstrong Rd Ste 301, Shelton, CT 06484-4735
Tel (203) 226-2680 *Founded/Ownrshp* 1984
Sales 22.5MM^E *EMP* 300
SIC 8322 8741 General counseling services; Referral service for personal & social problems; Management services; General counseling services; Referral service for personal & social problems; Management services
CEO: Peter G Burki
Mng Pt: Chris Burki
**Pr:* Gary Guiser
**CFO:* Pat Lamarco
**Treas:* John B Bourke
**Sr VP:* Peggy Macmannis
**Sr VP:* Scott Spencer
**Sr VP:* Roberta Wachtelhausen
VP: Bryce Breen
**Dir Sec:* Jeffrey A Burki
CIO: Michael Wattenbarger

D-U-N-S 93-752-5376
LIFECARE MANAGEMENT SERVICES LLC
(*Suby of* LIFECARE FAMILY OF HOSPITALS) ★
5340 Legacy Dr, Plano, TX 75024-3178
Tel (469) 241-2100 *Founded/Ownrshp* 1995
Sales 122.0MM^E *EMP* 678
SIC 8062 8069 General medical & surgical hospitals; Chronic disease hospital; General medical & surgical hospitals; Chronic disease hospital
Ch: Phillip B Douglasm
**COO:* Stuart Archer
COO: Bryan Burklow
Sr VP: Bridget Gallagher
Sr VP: Timothy L Hunt
**VP:* Maegan Bowman
**VP:* Stephanie Carpenter
**VP:* Ann Corrigan
VP: Jake Socha
Dir Rx: Lori Breckheimer
QA Dir: Susan Weaver

D-U-N-S 11-287-3526
LIFECARE MEDICAL CENTER
715 Delmore Dr, Roseau, MN 56751-1599
Tel (218) 463-2500 *Founded/Ownrshp* 1994
Sales 37.5MM *EMP* 240^E
Accts Eide Badly Llp Minneapolis M
SIC 8062 8052 8051 General medical & surgical hospitals; Intermediate care facilities; Skilled nursing care facilities; General medical & surgical hospitals; Intermediate care facilities; Skilled nursing care facilities
Pr: Keith Okeson
Chf Path: David Brett
V Ch: Bill Wagner
CFO: Cathy Huss
QA Dir: Marilyn Grashtrom
Surgeon: Luis Jain
Pharmcst: Judy Mattson

D-U-N-S 80-979-7517
LIFECARE MEDICAL TRANSPORTS INC
1170 International Pkwy, Fredericksburg, VA 22406-1126
Tel (540) 286-6991 *Founded/Ownrshp* 1993
Sales 25.9MM^E *EMP* 235
SIC 4119 Ambulance service; Ambulance service
Pr: Kevin Dillard
**VP:* Daniel Wildman

D-U-N-S 15-722-4205 IMP
LIFECELL CORP
(*Suby of* CHIRON HOLDINGS INC) ★
1 Millennium Way, Branchburg, NJ 08876-3876
Tel (908) 947-1100 *Founded/Ownrshp* 2011
Sales 428.0MM *EMP* 600^E
SIC 2836 Biological products, except diagnostic; Biological products, except diagnostic
CEO: Joe Woody
CFO: Steve Sovieski
Sr VP: Lisa N Collera
Sr VP: Bruce Lamb
VP: Kristina Reyes
Dir IT: Andrew Calovich
Dir IT: Christian Natale
Dir IT: Antoinette Serafino
Dir IT: Jennifer Texer
Dir IT: Leah Whiteley
Dir IT: Kathi Wilson
Board of Directors: Timothy E Guertin

D-U-N-S 17-626-3259
LIFECENTER NORTHWEST
LCNW
3650 131st Ave Se Ste 200, Bellevue, WA 98006-1395
Tel (425) 201-6563 *Founded/Ownrshp* 1996
Sales 27.1MM *EMP* 90^E
Accts Clark Nuber Ps Bellevue Wa
SIC 8099 Organ bank; Organ bank
Pr: Kevin O'Connor
**Ch Bd:* Ernesta Ballard
**Pr:* Kevin O Connor
**CFO:* John Klein
CFO: John H Klein
**Treas:* Jim Young

LIFECHEK DRUG
See LIFECHEK INC

D-U-N-S 61-943-9888 IMP
LIFECHEK INC
LIFECHEK DRUG
1100 Jackson St Ste B, Richmond, TX 77469-3320
Tel (281) 232-3940 *Founded/Ownrshp* 1988
Sales 62.9MM^E *EMP* 310
SIC 5912 Drug stores; Drug stores
Pr: Bruce Gingrich
CFO: William Bohn
**Prin:* Valerie Gingrich

D-U-N-S 08-535-8869
■ LIFECORE BIOMEDICAL INC
(*Suby of* LANDEC CORP) ★
3515 Lyman Blvd, Chaska, MN 55318-3051
Tel (952) 368-4300 *Founded/Ownrshp* 2010
Sales 54.0MM^E *EMP* 255
SIC 3842 2833 3841 Implants, surgical; Medicinal chemicals; Surgical & medical instruments; Implants, surgical; Medicinal chemicals; Surgical & medical instruments
Pr: Larry D Hiebert
CFO: Scott Collins
VP: James G Hall
VP: John Heinmiller
VP: Kipling Thacker
Dir Lab: Douglas Doster
Dir Lab: Angel Rayller
CIO: Teri Kidd
QA Dir: Tony Hanson
QA Dir: Feona Hasselbalch
Dir IT: Thomas Garrett

D-U-N-S 96-175-4269
■ LIFECORE BIOMEDICAL LLC
(*Suby of* LIFECORE BIOMEDICAL INC) ★
3515 Lyman Blvd, Chaska, MN 55318-3051
Tel (952) 368-4300 *Founded/Ownrshp* 2008
Sales 24.4MM^E *EMP* 76^E
SIC 3842 2833 Implants, surgical; Medicinal chemicals
Pr: Larry Hiebert
**CEO:* Dennis J Allingham
CFO: Scott Collins
VP: Richard Curtis
**VP:* Kipling Thacker
Pgrm Dir: William Taylor

D-U-N-S 18-432-5173
LIFEDESIGNS INC
200 E Winslow Rd, Bloomington, IN 47401-8657
Tel (812) 332-9615 *Founded/Ownrshp* 1982
Sales 11.2MM *EMP* 330^E
Accts Crowe Horwath Llp Indianapoli
SIC 8361 Residential care for the handicapped; Residential care for the handicapped
CEO: Susan Rinne
Ofcr: Stephanie Shelton
Adm Dir: Cindy Fleetwood
Off Mgr: Vern Hageman
IT Man: Jeremiah Rieke
Pr Dir: Janessa Gerber
HC Dir: Renee Clevenger
Snr Mgr: Kemberly Johnson

D-U-N-S 19-566-4701
LIFEGIFT ORGAN DONATION CENTER
2510 Westridge St, Houston, TX 77054-1508
Tel (713) 523-4438 *Founded/Ownrshp* 1987
Sales 36.5MM *EMP* 174
Accts Weaver And Tidwell Llp Housto
SIC 8099 8322 Medical help service; Medical services organization; Social service center
Pr: Kevin A Myer
**Ch:* Joseph Deleon
**Treas:* Sharyn Ivory
**Sr VP:* Patricia A Rubin
**Comm Dir:* Laura Frnka
Mng Dir: Kimberly Davis
Mng Dir: Jessica Leibold
Mng Dir: Rhonda Young
Mng Dir: Joanna Zaman
IT Man: Diane Blom

D-U-N-S 08-310-4542
LIFEGUARD TRANSPORTATION SERVICE INC
4211 Jerry L Maygarden Rd, Pensacola, FL 32504-5029
Tel (850) 473-6776 *Founded/Ownrshp* 1998
Sales 32.0MM *EMP* 2
SIC 4119 Local passenger transportation; Ambulance service; Local passenger transportation; Ambulance service
Pr: John Roche
CFO: Bryan Karson

D-U-N-S 82-646-2319
LIFEHME INC
DURABLE MEDICAL EQUIPMENT
454 Berryhill Rd, Columbia, SC 29210-6447
Tel (803) 254-8775 *Founded/Ownrshp* 1974
Sales 28.6MM^E *EMP* 90
SIC 5999 7352 5912 5047 Medical apparatus & supplies; Medical equipment rental; Drug stores; Hospital equipment & furniture
Pr: Dewey Roof

LIFELINE
See AMERIVISION COMMUNICATIONS INC

D-U-N-S 83-125-8863 IMP/EXP
LIFELINE ENERGY INTERNATIONAL INC
2150 Town Square Pl # 200, Sugar Land, TX 77479-1465
Tel (713) 266-9216 *Founded/Ownrshp* 2008
Sales 25.8MM^E *EMP* 88
SIC 5074 Heating equipment & panels, solar
Pr: Jarrod Erwin
**COO:* Graeme Critchley
**Ex VP:* Ryan Erwin
**VP:* Bob Eaton
**CTO:* Ron Johnson
**Opers Mgr:* Patrick Brady

D-U-N-S 02-511-5275 IMP
LIFELINE FOODS LLC
2811 S 11th Street Rd, Saint Joseph, MO 64503-3461
Tel (816) 279-1651 *Founded/Ownrshp* 2001
Sales 61.2MM^E *EMP* 140
SIC 2869 2041 Ethyl alcohol, ethanol; Grain mills (except rice); Ethyl alcohol, ethanol; Grain mills (except rice)
CEO: Robin Venn
COO: Mike Sobetski
**CFO:* Jay Lang
VP: Matt Gibson
**VP:* Matthew Gibson
Dir Lab: Eric Collop
IT Man: June Ichikawa
Mill Mgr: Kyle Hamm
Opers Mgr: Chris Scherer
Secur Mgr: Ruben Bulgin
Sls Mgr: Alycia Nelson

D-U-N-S 02-574-7101
LIFELINE HEALTH CARE INC
LIFELINE HOME HEALTH CARE
(*Suby of* LIFELINE HOME HEALTH CARE) ★
600 Clifty St, Somerset, KY 42503-1733
Tel (606) 679-4100 *Founded/Ownrshp* 1984
Sales 8.5MM^E *EMP* 435
SIC 8082 Home health care services; Home health care services
CEO: James T Wilson
**Pr:* James Frazer
**VP:* Steward Framer
**VP:* James Randall
VP: Steve Snowden

LIFELINE HOME HEALTH CARE
See LIFELINE HEALTH CARE INC

D-U-N-S 15-451-4921
LIFELINE HOME HEALTH CARE
600 Clifty St, Somerset, KY 42503-1790
Tel (606) 679-4100 *Founded/Ownrshp* 1992
Sales 30.4MM^E *EMP* 800^E
SIC 8082 7352 Home health care services; Medical equipment rental; Home health care services; Medical equipment rental
Ch: James Wilson

LIFELINE HOSPITAL
See LTAC INVESTORS LLC

LIFELINE KENTUCKY
See PRESBYTERIAN HOMES AND SERVICES OF KENTUCKY

D-U-N-S 00-861-6760
LIFELINE MEDICAL ASSOCIATES LLC
99 Cherry Hill Rd Ste 220, Parsippany, NJ 07054-1102
Tel (973) 316-6760 *Founded/Ownrshp* 1998
Sales 17.4MM^E *EMP* 300
SIC 8011 Gynecologist; Gynecologist

D-U-N-S 78-995-5890 EXP
LIFELINE PHARMACEUTICALS LLC
MEDICAL SUPPLY DEPOT, THE
1301 Nw 84th Ave Ste 101, Doral, FL 33126-1516
Tel (305) 643-8841 *Founded/Ownrshp* 2006
Sales 25.6MM *EMP* 24
SIC 5122 Pharmaceuticals; Pharmaceuticals
IT Man: Rick Nielsen
Sr VP: Ben Rivera
VP: Veronica Nielsen
Mng Dir: Ania Leyva
Snr Mgr: Anthony Pimpinelli

D-U-N-S 08-003-0042 IMP
LIFELINE SYSTEMS CO
PHILIPS LIFELINE
(*Suby of* PHILIPS CONSUMER LIFESTYLE) ★
111 Lawrence St, Framingham, MA 01702-8171
Tel (508) 988-1000 *Founded/Ownrshp* 2014
Sales 192.9MM^E *EMP* 897
SIC 3669 Emergency alarms; Emergency alarms
Pr: Kimberly O'Laughlin
Pr: Gerard Van Spaendonck
Ch: L D Shapiro
Treas: James Mark Mattern II
Sr VP: Edward M Bolesky
Sr VP: Richard M Reich
Sr VP: Donald G Strange
VP: Paul Cavanaugh
VP: John D Giannetto
VP: Nick Padula
VP: Mark T Rutherford
VP: Leonard E Wechslen
Exec: Patricia Lamonte
Dir Surg: Leverda Wallace

D-U-N-S 15-080-2932
LIFELINK FOUNDATION INC
LIFELINK TISSUE BANK
9661 Delaney Creek Blvd, Tampa, FL 33619-5121
Tel (813) 253-2640 *Founded/Ownrshp* 1982
Sales 88.0MM *EMP* 500
Accts Lewis Birch & Ricardo Llc Cle
SIC 8099 Medical services organization; Medical services organization
Ch Bd: Dana L Shires Jr
**Pr:* Dennis F Heinrichs
**CFO:* Bryan Mc Donald
Sr VP: John Rhon
VP: Donna Becker
VP: Ruth Bell
VP: Jay Campbell
VP: Mich Eggsware
VP: Beth Horn-Brinson
VP: Bobbie Pierson
Exec: Florell Barron
Dir Risk M: Lynn Smith
Dir Rx: Robert Adikes
Comm Man: Carl Weller

D-U-N-S 05-364-5099
LIFELINK HOUSING CORP
1900 Spring Rd Ste 300, Oak Brook, IL 60523-1480
Tel (630) 368-0817 *Founded/Ownrshp* 1987
Sales 11.2MM^E *EMP* 1,000
SIC 6513 Retirement hotel operation; Retirement hotel operation
CEO: Rev Carl A Zimmerman

LIFELINK TISSUE BANK
See LIFELINK FOUNDATION INC

D-U-N-S 36-070-9336
▲ LIFELOCK INC
60 E Rio Salado Pkwy # 400, Tempe, AZ 85281-9129
Tel (480) 682-5100 *Founded/Ownrshp* 2005
Sales 476.0MM *EMP* 669^E
Tkr Sym LOCK *Exch* NYS
SIC 7382 Protective devices, security; Protective devices, security
Ch Bd: Todd Davis
Pr: Hilary A Schneider
COO: Cristine Vieira
CFO: Chris G Power
Chf Mktg O: Ty Shay
Sr VP: Don Beck
VP: Ed Lacasse
VP: Kymber Lowe
VP: Jamison Manwaring
VP: Eric Rosado
VP: Marco Wirasinghe
Exec: Magesh Varadharajan
Board of Directors: Gary Briggs, David Cowan, Roy A Guthrie, Albert A Pimentel, Thomas J Ridge, Jaynie Miller Studenmund

D-U-N-S 19-049-4849
LIFELONG AIDS ALLIANCE
210 S Lucile St, Seattle, WA 98108
Tel (206) 957-1600 *Founded/Ownrshp* 1983
Sales 24.8MM *EMP* 132
Accts Jacobson Jarvis & Co Pllc Se
SIC 8399 Community development groups; Advocacy group; Fund raising organization, non-fee basis; Health & welfare council; Community development groups; Advocacy group; Fund raising organization, non-fee basis; Health & welfare council
Ex Dir: Barbara Ebert
Ofcr: BJ Cavnor
Ofcr: Tabitha Jensen
Ofcr: Scott Warnock
Ex Dir: David Richart

D-U-N-S 17-772-6908
LIFELONG MEDICAL CARE
OVER 60 HEALTH CENTER
2344 6th St, Berkeley, CA 94710-2412
Tel (510) 704-6010 *Founded/Ownrshp* 1976
Sales 35.6MM^E *EMP* 260
Accts Marcum Llp San Francisco Ca
SIC 8011 General & family practice, physician/surgeon; General & family practice, physician/surgeon
CEO: Marty A Lynch
**COO:* Brenda Shipp
**CFO:* Rick Clark
Ofcr: Jacquelin Poon
Dir IT: Betsy AMI
IT Man: Philip Klatt
Netwrk Eng: John Kelly
Site Mgr: Tim Zenor-Davis
Psych: Catherine Lee
Podiatrist: Alison Cook
Pgrm Dir: Wing Wong

D-U-N-S 13-445-3281
LIFEMAP ASSURANCE CO
(*Suby of* REGENCE BLUECROSS BLUESHIELD OF OREGON) ★
200 Sw Market St Fl 14, Portland, OR 97201-5715
Tel (503) 220-6126 *Founded/Ownrshp* 1966
Sales NA *EMP* 107
SIC 6321 Accident & health insurance; Disability health insurance
CEO: Bill Barr
**Ch:* Dudley Slater
**Treas:* Andreas Ellis
**Treas:* Daniel Mallea

D-U-N-S 60-264-3934
■ LIFEMARK HOSPITALS OF FLORIDA INC
PALMETTO GENERAL HOSPITAL
(*Suby of* TENET HEALTHCARE CORPORATION)
2001 W 68th St, Hialeah, FL 33016-1801
Tel (305) 823-5000 *Founded/Ownrshp* 1985
Sales 195.7MM^E *EMP* 1,400
SIC 8062 General medical & surgical hospitals; General medical & surgical hospitals
CEO: Ana Mederos
Chf Rad: Jose Becerra
**COO:* Gina C Diaz
**CFO:* Oscar Vicente
Dir Inf Cn: Norma Montalban
Dir Rx: Mary Ibarra-Diaz
Dir Rx: Mary Ibarradiaz
Dir Bus: Vilma H Medio
Dir Bus: Yvonne Odette
Mng Dir: Ricardo Dominguez
Dir IT: Pedro Nevarez

D-U-N-S 79-557-3401
■ LIFEMARK HOSPITALS OF LOUISIANA INC
(*Suby of* LIFEMARK HOSPITALS, INC)
880 W Commerce Rd Ste 111, New Orleans, LA 70123-3371
Tel (504) 736-8606 *Founded/Ownrshp* 1984
Sales 4.0MM^E *EMP* 400

SIC 8062 General medical & surgical hospitals; General medical & surgical hospitals
Pr: Don Steigman
**VP:* Thomas Sabatino

LIFEMATTERS
See LM1 LLC

D-U-N-S 12-182-8156
LIFENET HEALTH
1864 Concert Dr, Virginia Beach, VA 23453-1903
Tel (757) 464-4761 *Founded/Ownrshp* 1982
Sales 210.9MM *EMP* 500
Accts Kpmg Llp Mc Lean Va
SIC 8099 Organ bank; Organ bank
CEO: Rony Thomas
CFO: Don Berkstreer
CFO: Gordon Berkstresser
CFO: Gordon Berkstressor
Ex VP: Douglas Wilson
VP: David Adamson
VP: Arthur Brame
VP: Donald Brandenburg
VP: Thomas Brewer
VP: Tim Jankiewicz
VP: Terry Joe
VP: Perry Lange
VP: Christina Pierce
VP: Michael Plew
VP: Michael Poole
VP: Don Pritchard
VP: Alan Smith
VP: Patrick Thompson
Dir Lab: Miranda Malone

D-U-N-S 82-646-2152
LIFENET INC
6225 Saint Michael Dr, Texarkana, TX 75503-2690
Tel (903) 832-8531 *Founded/Ownrshp* 1993
Sales 24.2MM *EMP* 290
SIC 4119 4522

D-U-N-S 06-188-1853
LIFEPATH HOSPICE
12470 Telecom Dr Ste 300, Temple Terrace, FL 33637-0904
Tel (813) 877-2200 *Founded/Ownrshp* 2011
Sales 86.3MM *EMP* 40^E^
SIC 8052 Personal care facility
Prin: George H Wallace

D-U-N-S 08-079-6428
LIFEPATH INC (PA)
3500 High Point Blvd, Bethlehem, PA 18017-7803
Tel (610) 866-1930 *Founded/Ownrshp* 1974
Sales 41.7MM^E^ *EMP* 625
Accts Geiger & Associates Allentown
SIC 8093 8059 8052 Specialty outpatient clinics; Home for the mentally retarded, exc. skilled or intermediate; Intermediate care facilities; Specialty outpatient clinics; Home for the mentally retarded, exc. skilled or intermediate; Intermediate care facilities
CEO: Paul Coleman
**Pr:* Mark Henry
VP: Karen Clarke
Exec: Missy Maxwell
Exec: Roxanne Torrence
Dir Risk M: Angie Rothrock
Assoc Dir: Felicia Zimmerman
Brnch Mgr: Pat Brelsford
MIS Dir: Mark Goldstein

LIFEPATH SYSTEMS
See COLLIN COUNTY MENTAL HEALTH MENTAL RETARDATION CENTER INC

D-U-N-S 78-540-2541
LIFEPOINT CORPORATE SERVICES GENERAL PARTNERSHIP
103 Powell Ct Ste 200, Brentwood, TN 37027-5079
Tel (615) 372-8500 *Founded/Ownrshp* 1999
Sales 41.6MM^E^ *EMP* 400
SIC 8742 Management consulting services; Management consulting services
Prin: David Ingram
Genl Pt: Lifepoint Csgp
Pt: Lifepoint Cs LP

D-U-N-S 19-805-4350
▲ **LIFEPOINT HEALTH INC**
330 Seven Springs Way, Brentwood, TN 37027-5098
Tel (615) 920-7000 *Founded/Ownrshp* 1997
Sales 4.4MMM *EMP* 38,000
Tkr Sym LPNT *Exch* NGS
SIC 8062 8742 General medical & surgical hospitals; Hospital, medical school affiliated with nursing & residency; Hospital & health services consultant; General medical & surgical hospitals; Hospital, medical school affiliated with nursing & residency; Hospital & health services consultant
Ch Bd: William F Carpenter III
Chf Rad: Amir Ibrahim
Chf Rad: Austin Jones
Pr: Donald J Bivacca
Pr: David M Dill
Pr: R Scott Raplee
Pr: Jeffrey G Seraphine
CFO: James Barbuat
CFO: James Gory
CFO: Leif M Murphy
CFO: Penny Westmorland
CFO: Forrest Whichard
Ofcr: Chris Bangerter
Ofcr: Russell L Holman
Ofcr: Patrick Kowalski
Ofcr: Steve Womack
Sr VP: Michael S Coggin
VP: Becky Janssen
Board of Directors: Gregory T Bier, Richard H Evans, Dewitt Ezell Jr, Michael P Haley, Marguerite W Kondracke, John E Maupin Jr, Reed V Tuckson, Owen G Shell Jr

D-U-N-S 94-436-0908
■ **LIFEPOINT OF LAKE CUMBERLAND LLC**
DUKE LIFEPOINT HEALTHCARE
(*Suby of* HISTORIC LIFEPOINT HOSPITALS INC) ★
305 Langdon St, Somerset, KY 42503-2750
Tel (606) 679-7441 *Founded/Ownrshp* 2002
Sales 100.5MM^E^ *EMP* 1,100
SIC 8062 8082 General medical & surgical hospitals; Home health care services; General medical & surgical hospitals; Home health care services
CFO: Steve Frenatz
Dir Lab: Dorothy Skidmore
Dir Rx: Kevin Crabtree
Dir Pat Ac: Kevin Albert
QC Dir: Diann Vanhook
Pharmcst: Amanda Wesley
Pharmcst: Ron Wright
HC Dir: Patty Ruckel

D-U-N-S 55-619-6210 EXP
■ **LIFEPORT INC**
SIKORSKY
(*Suby of* SIKORSKY AIRCRAFT CORP) ★
1610 Heritage St, Woodland, WA 98674-9581
Tel (360) 225-3738 *Founded/Ownrshp* 2010
Sales 38.2MM^E^ *EMP* 235
SIC 3841 3728 Surgical & medical instruments; Aircraft parts & equipment; Surgical & medical instruments; Aircraft parts & equipment
Pr: David Adler
**Pr:* Jeffrey Jannito
**Pr:* William Weaver
CFO: Jamie Halliwell
**Ch:* Jeff Jannitto
**Treas:* Edward Beyer
Treas: Cecelia Henderson
Ex VP: Frank Graham
**VP:* Jason K Darley
**VP:* Corliss Montesi
VP: Ken Ward
**VP:* Noah Zuckerman
Dir Bus: Andrew Rukliss

LIFEPROOF
See TREEFROG DEVELOPMENTS INC

D-U-N-S 14-840-5988
LIFEQUEST
2460 John Fries Hwy, Quakertown, PA 18951-2259
Tel (215) 536-6152 *Founded/Ownrshp* 1983
Sales 29.1MM^E^ *EMP* 323
Accts Grant Thornton Philadelphia
SIC 8741 8351 8361 8051 Nursing & personal care facility management; Child day care services; Residential care; Extended care facility; Nursing & personal care facility management; Child day care services; Residential care; Extended care facility
Pr: Roger B Hiser
CFO: Sam Arena
**CFO:* Hank Kussay
CFO: Nancy Merriweather
Nrsg Dir: Amy Durnin

D-U-N-S 15-227-2667
LIFERAY INC
1400 Montefino Ave # 100, Diamond Bar, CA 91765-5501
Tel (877) 543-3729 *Founded/Ownrshp* 2006
Sales 71.2MM^E^ *EMP* 200^E^
SIC 7373 Systems software development services; Systems software development services
CEO: Bryan Cheung
Pr: Jorge Ferrer
CFO: Scott Tachiki
**Chf Mktg O:* Paul Hinz
VP: Brian Endo
Genl Mgr: Ross Kennedy
Genl Mgr: Franck Verbeke
QA Dir: Charles Austin
QA Dir: Ken Duenwald
QA Dir: Evan Nagayama
QA Dir: Kristoffer Onias

LIFE'S WORC
See W LIFES O R C INC

D-U-N-S 80-143-8487 IMP
LIFES2GOOD INC
(*Suby of* LIFES 2 GOOD LIMITED)
355 N Canal St, Chicago, IL 60606-1207
Tel (312) 454-6167 *Founded/Ownrshp* 2007
Sales 30.7MM^E^ *EMP* 70
SIC 5122 Cosmetics, perfumes & hair products
Ch: Giora Zucker
**Pr:* James Murphy
**CFO:* Tom Tierney
**VP:* Mark Holland

D-U-N-S 15-340-9313
■ **LIFESCAN INC**
(*Suby of* JOHNSON & JOHNSON) ★
965 Chesterbrook Blvd, Chesterbrook, PA 19087-5614
Tel (800) 227-8862 *Founded/Ownrshp* 1986
Sales 238.9MM^E^ *EMP* 1,500
SIC 2835 3841 Blood derivative diagnostic agents; Medical instruments & equipment, blood & bone work; Blood derivative diagnostic agents; Medical instruments & equipment, blood & bone work
CFO: James Buschmeier
**Pr:* Asbury Valerie
VP: Glenn Johnson
**VP:* Lee Ty
Dir Bus: Anthony Delizza
Dir Bus: Mark Zenz
Dir Bus: Mark T Zenz
Prgrm Mgr: Rita Ducharme
Prgrm Mgr: Robert Guillou
CIO: Madeline Fackler
DP Dir: Damyanti Patel

D-U-N-S 83-119-6733
■ **LIFESCAN PRODUCTS LLC**
(*Suby of* JOHNSON & JOHNSON) ★
1000 Gibraltar Dr, Milpitas, CA 95035-6312
Tel (408) 719-8443 *Founded/Ownrshp* 2006
Sales 45.3MM^E^ *EMP* 500^E^
SIC 3841 3845 Surgical & medical instruments; Ultrasonic scanning devices, medical; Surgical & medical instruments; Ultrasonic scanning devices, medical
Ch Bd: Eric Milledge
CFO: Louis Caro
Dir Bus: Jim Parent
IT Man: Lisa Lapp
Mktg Dir: Natasha Shaw
Sales Asso: Debby Kilby
Snr PM: Eugene Melewski
Snr Mgr: Mike Matthews

D-U-N-S 17-588-6261
LIFESCHOOL OF DALLAS
LIFE CHARTER SCHOOL
950 S Interstate 35 E, Lancaster, TX 75146-3304
Tel (972) 274-7950 *Founded/Ownrshp* 1996
Sales 41.8MM *EMP* 49^E^
Accts Hankins Eastup Deaton Tonn
SIC 8211 Elementary & secondary schools; Elementary & secondary schools
Pr: Brent Wilson
**CFO:* Scott Fuller
**Treas:* Ruben Martinez
IT Man: Megan Harrison

D-U-N-S 96-984-2181
LIFESCHOOL OF DALLAS
945 S Interstate 35 E, Lancaster, TX 75146
Tel (972) 274-7919 *Founded/Ownrshp* 1996
Sales 32.4MM *EMP* 3^E^
Accts Freemon Shapard & Story Windt
SIC 8641 Civic social & fraternal associations; Civic social & fraternal associations
CEO: Barry West

D-U-N-S 16-066-8526
LIFESCRIPT INC
4000 Macarthur Blvd # 800, Newport Beach, CA 92660-2544
Tel (949) 454-0422 *Founded/Ownrshp* 1999
Sales 29.7MM^E^ *EMP* 110
SIC 2741 Information retrieval services
CEO: Ronald Caporale
**COO:* Brian J Hogan
**CFO:* James L Stock
Bd of Dir: John Sklare
**Chf Mktg O:* Edward C Geehr
Sr VP: Alan Adams
Sr VP: Robert Cecere
Sr VP: Dan Felter
VP: Laurie Berger
VP: Eric Darby
VP: Jennifer Harold
VP: Jeoff Micalizzi
VP: Vani Rangachar
VP: Gary Rizo

D-U-N-S 08-959-3255
LIFESECURE INSURANCE CO
(*Suby of* BLUE CROSS AND BLUE SHIELD OF MICHIGAN) ★
10559 Citation Dr Ste 300, Brighton, MI 48116-8399
Tel (810) 220-7700 *Founded/Ownrshp* 2006
Sales NA *EMP* 40
SIC 6311 Life insurance carriers
Pr: Tiffany Albert
**CFO:* Stephen H Kellar
VP: Hamm Douglas
**VP:* Brian Vestergaard
Sls Mgr: Mindy Zaborowski

D-U-N-S 96-289-2613
LIFESERVE BLOOD CENTER
431 E Locust St, Des Moines, IA 50309-1909
Tel (515) 288-0276 *Founded/Ownrshp* 2010
Sales 40.0MM *EMP* 350
SIC 8099 3842 Medical services organization; Surgical appliances & supplies; Medical services organization; Surgical appliances & supplies
CEO: Stacey Sime
**CFO:* Cheryl Ritter
VP: Katie Marchik
VP: Tracy Sipma
Dir Lab: Gregg Hawkins
Dir Lab: Paulette Hice
CIO: Terri Jensen
MIS Dir: Dan Downs
Info Man: Linda Barnum
Pr Dir: Christine Hayes

D-U-N-S 02-061-1554
LIFESHARE BLOOD CENTERS
8910 Linwood Ave, Shreveport, LA 71106-6508
Tel (318) 222-7770 *Founded/Ownrshp* 1942
Sales 46.0MM *EMP* 450
Accts Heard Mcelroy & Vestal Llc
SIC 8099 2836 Blood bank; Biological products, except diagnostic; Blood derivatives; Blood bank; Biological products, except diagnostic; Blood derivatives
Pr: Margaret E Wallace
**Ch Bd:* Walter M Sanchez
**CFO:* Linda N Allsup
**Treas:* Gary J Levy MD
**VP:* Marie Sanders
Dir Risk M: Randy Hufstetler
Dir Lab: Wendell Jones
**Prin:* Robert D Hoepner
**Prin:* Ric Jones
Ex Dir: Ron Hein
Brnch Mgr: Robert Taylor

D-U-N-S 07-407-5730
LIFESKILLS INC
380 Suwannee Trail St, Bowling Green, KY 42103-7956
Tel (270) 901-5000 *Founded/Ownrshp* 1972
Sales 44.5MM *EMP* 435
Accts Bkd Llp Bowling Green Ky
SIC 8063 8069 8051 8331 Hospital for the mentally ill; Substance abuse hospitals; Mental retardation hospital; Job training & vocational rehabilitation services; Hospital for the mentally ill; Substance abuse hospitals; Mental retardation hospital; Job training & vocational rehabilitation services
Pr: Alice Simpson
Ofcr: Scott Bell
**VP:* Patty Harrison
IT Man: Joe Beavers
IT Man: Arthur Stockton
Ql Cn Mgr: Linda Carter
Doctor: P Reddy

LIFESMART
See SOURCE NETWORK SALES AND MARKETING LLC

D-U-N-S 17-310-1668
LIFESOURCE BLOOD SERVICES
(*Suby of* INSTITUTE FOR TRANSFUSION MEDICINE) ★
5505 Pearl St, Rosemont, IL 60018-5317
Tel (877) 543-3768 *Founded/Ownrshp* 1987
Sales 27.3MM^E^ *EMP* 625
SIC 8099 Blood related health services; Blood bank; Blood donor station; Blood related health services; Blood bank; Blood donor station
Pr: Jim Covert
COO: Kent Oestreich
**CFO:* Mark Gequinto
VP: Roxanne Tata

D-U-N-S 08-509-1726
LIFESOUTH COMMUNITY BLOOD CENTERS INC
4039 W Newberry Rd, Gainesville, FL 32607-2342
Tel (352) 224-1600 *Founded/Ownrshp* 1974
Sales 81.5MM *EMP* 527
Accts James Moore & Co Pl Gainesvil
SIC 8099 Blood bank; Blood bank
CEO: Nancy Eckert
**Treas:* Willard Shafer
Rgnl Mgr: Colleen Coleman
Rgnl Mgr: Dawn Prestwood
Rgnl Mgr: Lauren Russell
Rgnl Mgr: Lorrie Woods
CIO: William Wurzbach
Dir IT: Timothy Markwordt
Tech Mgr: Holly Davis
Software D: Scott Bevington
Software D: Jason Strauch

D-U-N-S 08-713-2502
LIFESPACE COMMUNITIES INC
100 E Grand Ave Ste 200, Des Moines, IA 50309-1835
Tel (515) 288-5805 *Founded/Ownrshp* 1976
Sales 210.6MM *EMP* 1,875
Accts Cliftonlarsonallen Llp Minnea
SIC 8059 Rest home, with health care; Rest home, with health care
CEO: Scott M Harrison
COO: Jay Biere
CFO: Larry Smith
Treas: Larry M Smith
Dir Risk M: Harold Kavan
Ex Dir: Tim Smith
Mktg Dir: Jason Buls
Mktg Dir: Richard Burke
Mktg Dir: Mark Zulo
Snr Mgr: Krista Maeder

D-U-N-S 87-816-3674
LIFESPAN CORP
167 Point St Ste 170, Providence, RI 02903-4771
Tel (401) 444-3500 *Founded/Ownrshp* 1986
Sales 143.4MM^E^ *EMP* 8,000
Accts Kpmg Llp Boston Ma
SIC 8011 Hospital management; Clinic, operated by physicians; Internal medicine, physician/surgeon; Physical medicine, physician/surgeon
CEO: Timothy J Babineau MD
Dir Vol: Eleanor Merchant
Pr: August Cordeiro
Treas: Marianne Kennedy
Bd of Dir: Carol Lewis
Ex VP: Boyd King
Ex VP: Frederick J Macri
Ex VP: Eva Owens
Sr VP: Kenneth E Arnold
Sr VP: Karen Rosene Montella
Sr VP: Peter Snyder
VP: Maria Pina
Dir Risk M: Cheryl Chandler
Dir Risk M: Joan Flynn
Dir Lab: Rolf Carlson
Dir Bus: Armand Boulanger

D-U-N-S 12-593-8894
LIFESPAN INC
200 Clanton Rd Ste B, Charlotte, NC 28217-1447
Tel (704) 523-1010 *Founded/Ownrshp* 1973
Sales 15.4MM *EMP* 526
Accts Langdon & Company Llp Garner
SIC 8211 8361 School for the retarded; Self-help group home; School for the retarded; Self-help group home
CEO: Davan Claniger
CFO: Stacy Roddy
**Treas:* Ralph Adams
VP: Christopher White
Pgrm Dir: Ruth Edwards
Pgrm Dir: Beth Southern

D-U-N-S 12-614-8704
LIFESPAN RECYCLING CO INC
LIFESPAN TECHNOLOGY RECYCLING
275 Grove St Ste 2-400, Auburndale, MA 02466-2273
Tel (781) 239-8154 *Founded/Ownrshp* 2002
Sales 26.2MM^E^ *EMP* 2^E^
SIC 4953 7389 Recycling, waste materials; Document & office record destruction
Pr: Dag Adamson
**CFO:* Brooks Hoffman
Opers Mgr: Marshall Smith

LIFESPAN TECHNOLOGY RECYCLING
See LIFESPAN RECYCLING CO INC

D-U-N-S 04-007-4742
LIFESPIRE INC (NY)
A.C.R.M.D
1 Whitehall St Fl 9, New York, NY 10004-2141
Tel (212) 741-0100 *Founded/Ownrshp* 1951
Sales 98.8MM *EMP* 1,600
Accts Mbaf Cpas Llc Valhalla Ny
SIC 8322 Individual & family services; Individual & family services
CEO: Mark Van Voorst
Pr: Peter Valvo
**CFO:* Keith Lee
Ex VP: Kamelia Kameli

LIFESPRING HEALTH SYSTEMS
See LIFESPRING INC

D-U-N-S 07-409-4442
LIFESPRING INC
LIFESPRING HEALTH SYSTEMS
460 Spring St, Jeffersonville, IN 47130-3452
Tel (812) 280-2080 *Founded/Ownrshp* 1964
Sales 17.6MM *EMP* 300
Accts Blue & Co Llc Indianapolis
SIC 8093 Mental health clinic, outpatient; Mental health clinic, outpatient
CEO: Terry L Stawar
Pr: David Fowler
CFO: Nick Clark
VP: Wanda Booker
VP: Asad Ismail
VP: Karen Jones
VP: Jana Kixmiller
VP: Christian Rice
IT Man: Beth Keeney
Psych: Sheryl Schneider

D-U-N-S 82-481-5708
LIFESTAR RESPONSE CORP
(*Suby of* FALCK USA INC) ★
3710 Commerce Dr Ste 1006, Halethorpe, MD 21227-1653
Tel (631) 289-1100 *Founded/Ownrshp* 2011
Sales 55.6MM^E^ *EMP* 1,606^E^
SIC 4119 Ambulance service
CEO: Jon Colin
Pr: Daniel Platt
CFO: James T Buonincontri
VP: Claire Ringham
VP: Doug Tisdale
Opers Mgr: Dennis Poole
Mktg Dir: Daniel Brown

D-U-N-S 05-274-5572
LIFESTAR RESPONSE OF MARYLAND INC
(*Suby of* LIFESTAR RESPONSE CORP) ★
3710 Commerce Dr Ste 1006, Baltimore, MD 21227-1653
Tel (410) 720-6060 *Founded/Ownrshp* 2000
Sales 17.8MM^E^ *EMP* 525
SIC 4119 Ambulance service; Ambulance service
Ch Bd: Charles Maymon
Ch Bd: Jon Colin
Pr: Danny Platt
Ofcr: Charles Boone
VP: Claire R Ringham

D-U-N-S 03-896-5927
LIFESTEPS INC (PA)
383 New Castle Rd, Butler, PA 16001-1743
Tel (724) 283-1010 *Founded/Ownrshp* 1954
Sales 24.6MM *EMP* 429
Accts Maher Duessel Cpa S Pittsburg
SIC 8093 8351 8322 Rehabilitation center, outpatient treatment; Child day care services; Individual & family services; Rehabilitation center, outpatient treatment; Child day care services; Individual & family services
Pr: Karen Sue Owens
CFO: John Eyth
VP: Joan Miller
VP: Michael Smith
Mng Ofcr: Jim Schellhammer
Dir IT: Doug Maley
IT Man: Lisa Steiner
HC Dir: Jill Wilson

LIFESTREAM
See BLOOD BANK OF SAN BERNARDINO AND RIVERSIDE COUNTIES

D-U-N-S 07-758-9612
LIFESTREAM BEHAVIORAL CENTER INC
2020 Talley Rd, Leesburg, FL 34748-3426
Tel (352) 360-6575 *Founded/Ownrshp* 1971
Sales 36.1MM *EMP* 550
Accts Greenlee Kurras Rice & Brown
SIC 8011 8361 8063 Psychiatric clinic; Residential care; Psychiatric hospitals; Psychiatric clinic; Residential care; Psychiatric hospitals
Ch: Timothy Morris
CEO: Jonathan M Cherry
CFO: Carol Dozier
Treas: Michael Sleaford
Sr VP: Jill Baird
Sr VP: Rick Hankey
Sr VP: K Howard Wiener
Brnch Mgr: John Fitzgerald
CTO: Chad Heim
Software D: Susan Gregory

D-U-N-S 01-960-9874
LIFESTREAM COMPLETE SENIOR LIVING INC
BAPTIST VILLAGE
11555 W Peoria Ave, Youngtown, AZ 85363-1640
Tel (623) 933-3333 *Founded/Ownrshp* 1975
Sales 3.5MM *EMP* 300
SIC 8051 6513 8059

D-U-N-S 17-815-6055
LIFESTREAM INC
444 Myrtle St, New Bedford, MA 02746-1682
Tel (508) 993-1991 *Founded/Ownrshp* 1995
Sales 19.6MM *EMP* 400
Accts Meyer Regan & Wilner Llp Fa
SIC 8361 8331 Home for the mentally handicapped; Job training & vocational rehabilitation services; Home for the mentally handicapped; Job training & vocational rehabilitation services
Pr: John Latawiec
Ch: Robert Dowd
Treas: Calvin Siegal
Treas: David Westgate
Sr VP: Paul Correia
Sr VP: Robert W Desrosiers
Sr VP: Bonnie Mello
VP: Cornelia Burrtarrant
VP: Robert Defrofierf
Ex Dir: Kathleen Cardenas

D-U-N-S 01-528-3377
LIFESTYLE COMMUNITIES LTD
230 West St Ste 200, Columbus, OH 43215-2655
Tel (614) 918-2000 *Founded/Ownrshp* 1996
Sales 22.0MM^E^ *EMP* 53^E^
SIC 1522 Multi-family dwellings, new construction
Pt: Michael J Deasecentis Jr
Pt: Michael J Deasecentis Sr
COO: Brent Miller
CFO: Richard Miller
VP: Rob Zelina
Dist Mgr: Megan Tackett
Genl Mgr: Justin Pendergrass
Genl Mgr: Alexis Webb
Opers Mgr: Kirk Nail
Mktg Dir: Russell Boiarsky
Mktg Mgr: Shannon Walker

LIFESTYLE FAMILY FITNESS CTRS
See LIFESTYLE FAMILY FITNESS II INC

D-U-N-S 05-408-6301
LIFESTYLE FAMILY FITNESS II INC
LIFESTYLE FAMILY FITNESS CTRS
1511 N West Shore Blvd, Tampa, FL 33607-4543
Tel (949) 255-7200 *Founded/Ownrshp* 1985
Sales NA *EMP* 775
SIC 7991 Health club

D-U-N-S 07-876-5750
LIFESTYLE HEARING CORP (USA) INC
AUDIOLOGY MANAGEMENT GROUP
(*Suby of* LIFESTYLE HEARING CORPORATION)
1101 Brickell Ave N401, Miami, FL 33131-3105
Tel (786) 563-4010 *Founded/Ownrshp* 2012
Sales 30.0MM *EMP* 150
SIC 5999 Hearing aids
Pr: Michael Tease
VP: Dave Dutson

D-U-N-S 61-524-7095
LIFESTYLE OPTIONS INC
475 N Martingale Rd # 260, Schaumburg, IL 60173-2405
Tel (847) 240-7330 *Founded/Ownrshp* 1989
Sales 10.6MM^E^ *EMP* 450
SIC 8082 Home health care services; Home health care services
CEO: Molly Miceli
COO: Laura Debruin
Off Mgr: Barbara Teschner

D-U-N-S 80-808-0915 IMP/EXP
LIFESTYLE SOLUTIONS INC
5555 Auto Mall Pkwy, Fremont, CA 94538-5128
Tel (510) 249-9301 *Founded/Ownrshp* 1991
Sales 45.7MM^E^ *EMP* 50
SIC 5021 Beds & bedding
CEO: Sean Pathiratne
COO: Johann Abeyesinhe
CIO: Bhavik Jhavari
VP Sls: Ana Padgaokar
Sls Mgr: J C Gholston
Nutrtnst: Lisa Kuklis

LIFESTYLES DIABETES CENTER
See GIBSON GENERAL HOSPITAL INC

D-U-N-S 05-693-7659 IMP
LIFESTYLES STORES INC
LIGHTING ONE
1801 W 33rd St, Edmond, OK 73013-3816
Tel (405) 348-7420 *Founded/Ownrshp* 1971
Sales 20.5MM^E^ *EMP* 125
SIC 5719 5063 Lighting fixtures; Lighting fixtures; Lighting fixtures; Lighting fixtures
Pr: Gregg Tunison
Pr: David Howl

D-U-N-S 09-166-2924
LIFETIME ASSISTANCE INC
LAICO INDUSTRIES
425 Paul Rd, Rochester, NY 14624-4721
Tel (585) 247-2255 *Founded/Ownrshp* 1978
Sales 64.8MM^E^ *EMP* 1,300
Accts Bonadio & Co Llp Pittsford N
SIC 8322 6512 Association for the handicapped; Nonresidential building operators; Association for the handicapped; Nonresidential building operators
CEO: James Branciforte
CFO: Kevin Judge
Assoc Dir: Jennifer Fiacco
Mng Dir: Pearl Nettles
Genl Mgr: Ronnie Urquhart
QA Dir: Rebecca Ziobrowski
Pgrm Dir: Dennis Brown

D-U-N-S 11-521-3613 EXP
▲ LIFETIME BRANDS INC
1000 Stewart Ave, Garden City, NY 11530-4814
Tel (516) 683-6000 *Founded/Ownrshp* 1945
Sales 586.0MM *EMP* 1,425^E^
Tkr Sym LCUT *Exch* NGS
SIC 3421 5023 5719 Cutlery; Home furnishings; Kitchen tools & utensils; Stainless steel flatware; Kitchenware; Cutlery; Glassware; Cutlery; Home furnishings; Kitchen tools & utensils; Stainless steel flatware; Kitchenware; Cutlery; Glassware
Ch Bd: Jeffrey Siegel
Pr: Steven Lizak
Pr: Daniel Siegel
COO: Ronald Shiftan
CFO: Laurence Winoker
Chf Mktg O: Allison Hickey
Sr VP: Charles Ellis
Sr VP: Craig Phillips
VP: Tony Arancio
VP: Hugh Biber
VP: Jeff Cobb
VP: Anna Dee
VP: Tim Dixon
VP: Joan Foley
VP: Matthew Kamenstein
VP: Paul Kanter
VP: Linda Levine
VP: Tom Mirabile
VP: Bill Olohan
VP: Sid Ramnarace
VP: Michele Seder
Board of Directors: David E R Dangoor, Michael J Jeary, John Koegel, Cherrie Nanninga, Craig Phillips, Dennis E Reaves, Michael J Regan, William U Westerfield

LIFETIME CARE
See GENESEE REGION HOME CARE ASSOCIATION INC

LIFETIME COMPOSITES
See WOODBRIDGE CORP

D-U-N-S 10-330-5082
LIFETIME ENTERTAINMENT SERVICES LLC
LIFETIME TELEVISION
(*Suby of* A&E TELEVISION NETWORKS LLC) ★
235 E 45th St Fl 14, New York, NY 10017-3305
Tel (212) 424-7000 *Founded/Ownrshp* 2009
Sales 174.1MM^E^ *EMP* 720
SIC 4841 Cable television services; Cable television services
Pr: Andrea Wong
CFO: James Wesley
Ex VP: Rick Haskins
Ex VP: Jane Tollinger
Sr VP: Nina Lederman
Sr VP: Linda Rein
VP: Richard Basso
VP: Cathy Christiano
VP: Alan Gabay
VP: David Hillman
VP: Andie Kallinger
VP: Ann Kenny
VP: Mike Malone
VP: Andrew Morris
VP: Pete Sgro
VP: Evan Silverman
VP: Sandy Varo
VP: Richard Zehner

D-U-N-S 62-402-3248
■ LIFETIME FILTER INC
(*Suby of* BAKER DISTRIBUTING CO LLC) ★
1005 Katyland Dr, Katy, TX 77493-2531
Tel (281) 391-8060 *Founded/Ownrshp* 1990
Sales 44.5MM^E^ *EMP* 420
SIC 3564 Filters, air: furnaces, air conditioning equipment, etc.; Filters, air: furnaces, air conditioning equipment, etc.
Prin: Jimmy Cagle
CFO: Richard Oleary
VP: Vincent Maresca
VP: Maresca Anthony R
VP: Alex Trevino
Genl Mgr: David Pemberton

D-U-N-S 03-710-1813
LIFETIME FINANCIAL MANAGEMENT INC
LIFETIME MEDICAL SUPPORT SVCS
235 Lonsdale Ave, Pawtucket, RI 02860-2717
Tel (401) 333-8900 *Founded/Ownrshp* 1979
Sales 9.1MM^E^ *EMP* 300
SIC 7363 8082 Medical help service; Home health care services; Medical help service; Home health care services
Pr: Marie Issa

LIFETIME HEALTH
See GENESEE VALLEY GROUP HEALTH ASSOCIATION

LIFETIME HEALTH COMPANIES, THE
See LIFETIME HEALTHCARE INC

D-U-N-S 18-000-4629
LIFETIME HEALTHCARE INC
LIFETIME HEALTH COMPANIES, THE
165 Court St, Rochester, NY 14647-0001
Tel (585) 454-1700 *Founded/Ownrshp* 1997
Sales NA *EMP* 7,000^E^
SIC 6324 6321 Group hospitalization plans; Accident & health insurance; Group hospitalization plans; Accident & health insurance
CEO: David H Klein
Ch Bd: Mary A Bellardini
V Ch: Randall Clark
Pr: Philip Puchalski
Ofcr: Susan Emhof
VP: Julia Flack
VP: Jonathan Kaplan
VP: Tom Luce
VP: Michael McGreevy
VP: Stephen Sloan
VP: Geoff Taylor

D-U-N-S 14-541-1034 IMP/EXP
LIFETIME LLC
LIFETIME PRODUCTS
Freeport Ctr Bldg D-11, Clearfield, UT 84016
Tel (801) 776-1532 *Founded/Ownrshp* 2003
Sales 154.1MM^E^ *EMP* 1,200^E^
SIC 3089 Plastic processing; Plastic processing
Genl Mgr: Heidi Moulton
CIO: John Bowden

LIFETIME MEDICAL SUPPORT SVCS
See LIFETIME FINANCIAL MANAGEMENT INC

LIFETIME PRODUCTS
See LIFETIME LLC

D-U-N-S 14-845-5041 IMP
LIFETIME PRODUCTS INC
Freeport Ctr Bldg D-11, Clearfield, UT 84016
Tel (801) 776-1532 *Founded/Ownrshp* 1986
Sales 676.2MM^E^ *EMP* 1,708
SIC 2519 3949 2531 2511 Garden furniture, except wood, metal, stone or concrete; Basketball equipment & supplies, general; Public building & related furniture; Wood household furniture; Garden furniture, except wood, metal, stone or concrete; Basketball equipment & supplies, general; Public building & related furniture; Wood household furniture
Pr: Richard Hendrickson
Pr: Jo Healy
Sec: Mark E Whiting
Sr VP: Clinton Morris
Sr VP: Vince Rhoton
VP: Bob Adams
VP: Brent Allen
VP: Brett Horstmann
CIO: John Bowden
Opers Mgr: Amanda Steed
Plnt Mgr: Mark Cole
Board of Directors: Kathy Mower

LIFETIME TELEVISION
See LIFETIME ENTERTAINMENT SERVICES LLC

D-U-N-S 05-437-5308
LIFETOUCH CHURCH DIRECTORIES AND PORTRAITS INC
UNITED CHURCH DIRECTORIES
(*Suby of* LIFETOUCH INC) ★
11000 Viking Dr Ste 400, Eden Prairie, MN 55344-7242
Tel (952) 826-4000 *Founded/Ownrshp* 1995
Sales 39.9MM^E^ *EMP* 1,424
SIC 7221 2741 Photographic studios, portrait; Directories: publishing & printing; Photographic studios, portrait; Directories: publishing & printing
CEO: Paul Harmel
CFO: Randy Pladson

D-U-N-S 00-696-2351
LIFETOUCH INC (MN)
11000 Viking Dr, Eden Prairie, MN 55344-7242
Tel (952) 826-4000 *Founded/Ownrshp* 1936, 1977
Sales 752.0MM^E^ *EMP* 26,175
SIC 7221 7812 2741 Photographer, still or video; School photographer; Video tape production; Yearbooks: publishing & printing; Photographer, still or video; School photographer; Video tape production; Yearbooks: publishing & printing
Ch Bd: Paul Harmel
Pr: Jake Barker
Pr: Tim Flanagan
CFO: Randolph J Pladson
Ofcr: Nikki Bechtel
VP: Glenn Elo
VP: Kelvin W Miller
VP: Thomas Wargolet
Area Mgr: Kevin Green
Dist Mgr: Mark Devine
Dist Mgr: Brandin McColm

D-U-N-S 13-073-3546
LIFETOUCH NATIONAL SCHOOL STUDIOS INC
(*Suby of* LIFETOUCH INC) ★
11000 Viking Dr Ste 300, Eden Prairie, MN 55344-7242
Tel (952) 826-4000 *Founded/Ownrshp* 1946
Sales 279.6MM^E^ *EMP* 5,000
SIC 7221 School photographer; School photographer
CEO: Paul Harmel
Treas: Randolph J Pladson
VP: Jim Haeg
VP: Dale Knudsen
VP: Ted L Koenecke
VP: Mark Schoenrock
VP: George M Ward
MIS Dir: Scott Kimball
Manager: Mark Fandel
Manager: Jan Younce
Sls Mgr: Rhonda Smith

D-U-N-S 05-516-3604
LIFETOUCH PORTRAIT STUDIOS INC
(*Suby of* LIFETOUCH INC) ★
11000 Viking Dr, Eden Prairie, MN 55344-7235
Tel (952) 826-4335 *Founded/Ownrshp* 1983
Sales 80.0MM^E^ *EMP* 2,200
SIC 7221 Photographer, still or video; Photographer, still or video
Ch Bd: Richard P Erickson
CEO: Paul Harmel
Treas: James V O'Halloran Jr
VP: Gail Thurmer
Prin: John Anderson
Prin: James Campbell
Prin: Ted Koenecke
Prin: Randolph Pladson
Brnch Mgr: Andrea Parmer
Mktg Mgr: Amie Mayo
Board of Directors: Donald Goldfus, Richard A Hassel, Robert Larson, John L Reid, Phillip Samper

D-U-N-S 96-540-4069
LIFETOUCH SERVICES INC
(*Suby of* LIFETOUCH INC) ★
11000 Viking Dr, Eden Prairie, MN 55344-7242
Tel (952) 826-4000 *Founded/Ownrshp* 2010
Sales 21.2MM^E^ *EMP* 700^E^
SIC 7221 Photographic studios, portrait; Photographic studios, portrait
CEO: Paul Harmel
Treas: Dale Garton

D-U-N-S 04-350-4058 IMP
LIFETREE MANUFACTURING LLC
2401 W 1st St, Tempe, AZ 85281-2329
Tel (480) 477-9075 *Founded/Ownrshp* 2013
Sales 28.3MM^E^ *EMP* 72
SIC 2834 Vitamin, nutrient & hematinic preparations for human use
CEO: Dave Prechel
Pr: Brandon Martin
Ofcr: Trevor Martin
Board of Directors: Scott Brooks, Brandon Martin, Trevor Martin

D-U-N-S 96-300-2795
■ LIFETRUST AMERICA INC
(*Suby of* FIVE STAR QUALITY CARE INC) ★
113 Seaboard Ln Ste 150a, Franklin, TN 37067-8296
Tel (615) 342-0601 *Founded/Ownrshp* 2004
Sales 26.9MM^E^ *EMP* 1,000
SIC 8361 8051 8052 8059 Residential care; Skilled nursing care facilities; Intermediate care facilities; Nursing home, except skilled & intermediate care facility; Rest home, with health care; Residential care; Skilled nursing care facilities; Intermediate care facilities; Nursing home, except skilled & intermediate care facility; Rest home, with health care
CEO: Pat Mulloy
CFO: Jim Bauchiero

D-U-N-S 55-705-3266
▲ LIFEVANTAGE CORP
9785 S Monroe St Ste 300, Sandy, UT 84070-4292
Tel (801) 432-9000 *Founded/Ownrshp* 2004
Sales 190.3MM *EMP* 166^E^
Accts Eks&H Llp Denver Colorado
Tkr Sym LFVN *Exch* NAS

SIC 2834 Pharmaceutical preparations; Pharmaceutical preparations
Pr: Darren Jensen
**Ch Bd:* Garry Mauro
Pr: David Brown
COO: Robert Urban
CFO: Mark Jaggi
**V Ch Bd:* Dave Manovich
Chf Mktg O: Ryan Goodwin
Ofcr: Justin Rose
Sr VP: Ryan Thompson
VP: Kyle Burdash
VP: Anthony Del Vicario
VP: John Genna
VP: Calli Mott
Board of Directors: Michael A Beindorff, Darren Jensen, George E Metzger,richard O, Dave Toole

D-U-N-S 80-126-6201
LIFEWATCH CORP
(*Suby of* LIFEWATCH AG)
10255 W Higgins Rd # 100, Rosemont, IL 60018-5608
Tel (847) 720-2100 *Founded/Ownrshp* 2006
Sales 159.9MM^E *EMP* 601
Accts Pricewaterhousecoopers Llp
SIC 8099 5047 3845 Physical examination & testing services; Patient monitoring equipment; Electro-medical equipment; Electrocardiographs; Physical examination & testing services; Patient monitoring equipment; Electro-medical equipment; Electrocardiographs
Pr: Brent Cohen
**CFO:* Kobi Ben Efraim
CFO: Francis J Leonard
Ex VP: Jake Mendelsohn
VP: George Michelson
VP: Dan Pawlik
VP: Michael Turchi
Snr Sftwr: Yuriy Savytskyy
**CIO:* Jake Mehndelson
Sls Dir: Leigh Kelly

D-U-N-S 05-316-6711
LIFEWATCH INC
CARD GUARD
10255 W Higgins Rd # 100, Rosemont, IL 60018-5608
Tel (847) 720-2100 *Founded/Ownrshp* 2006
Sales 20.6MM^E *EMP* 350
SIC 3845 Heart-lung machine; Heart-lung machine
Pr: Frederick Mindermann
CFO: Francis J Leonard
VP: George Michelson
**VP:* Roger Richardson

D-U-N-S 79-793-6734
LIFEWATCH SERVICES INC
(*Suby of* LIFEWATCH CORP) ★
10255 W Higgins Rd # 100, Rosemont, IL 60018-5608
Tel (847) 720-2100 *Founded/Ownrshp* 2000
Sales 149.0MM^E *EMP* 600
SIC 5047 8099 3845 8071 Patient monitoring equipment; Electro-medical equipment; Physical examination service, insurance; Health screening service; Physical examination & testing services; Electrocardiographs; Testing laboratories; Patient monitoring equipment; Electro-medical equipment; Physical examination service, insurance; Health screening service; Physical examination & testing services; Electrocardiographs; Testing laboratories
CEO: Stephan Rietiker
**Pr:* Roger K Richardson
**CFO:* Kobi Ben Efraim
**CFO:* Mike Turchi
**Prin:* Yacov Geva

D-U-N-S 00-404-0010 IMP
LIFEWAY CHRISTIAN RESOURCES OF SOUTHERN BAPTIST CONVENTION (TN)
B & H PUBLISHERS
1 Lifeway Plz, Nashville, TN 37234-1001
Tel (615) 251-2000 *Founded/Ownrshp* 1891
Sales 500.2MM *EMP* 2,477
Accts Ernst & Young Llp
SIC 5942 5963 2731 5999 5735 5947 Books, religious; Direct selling establishments; Book publishing; Religious goods; Compact discs; Records; Gift shop; Books, religious; Direct selling establishments; Book publishing; Religious goods; Compact discs; Records; Gift shop
CEO: Thom S Rainer
**Pr:* Sam S Rainer III
Assoc VP: Bruce Grubbs
**Ex VP:* Brad Waggoner
VP: Bill Crayton
**VP:* Eric Geiger
VP: Tim Hill
**VP:* Jerry Rhyne
**VP:* Ed Stetzer
**VP:* Tim Vineyard
**VP:* Selma Wilson

D-U-N-S 15-303-2214 IMP
▲ LIFEWAY FOODS INC
6431 Oakton St, Morton Grove, IL 60053-2727
Tel (847) 967-1010 *Founded/Ownrshp* 1986
Sales 118.9MM *EMP* 360^E
Accts Crowe Horwath Llp Oak Brook
Tkr Sym LWAY *Exch* NGM
SIC 2023 2026 Dry, condensed, evaporated dairy products; Fluid milk; Kefir; Yogurt; Fermented & cultured milk products; Dry, condensed, evaporated dairy products; Fluid milk; Kefir; Yogurt; Fermented & cultured milk products
Pr: Julie Smolyansky
COO: Edward P Smolyansky
Art Dir: Stephanie Salvatore
Board of Directors: Renzo Bernardi, Paul Lee, Mariano Lozano, Jason Scher

D-U-N-S 11-375-0418
LIFEWELL BEHAVIORAL WELLNESS
DESERT ESPERANZA
202 E Earll Dr Ste 200, Phoenix, AZ 85012-2647
Tel (602) 441-5307 *Founded/Ownrshp* 1974
Sales 22.7MM *EMP* 360
Accts Henry & Horne Llp Tempe Az
SIC 8361 8093 Rehabilitation center, residential: health care incidental; Drug clinic, outpatient; Rehabilitation center, residential: health care incidental; Drug clinic, outpatient
Ch Bd: Thomas C Williams
**CEO:* Thomas K McKelvey
**CFO:* Doris Vaught
IT Man: David Anderson

D-U-N-S 96-191-1224
LIFEWISE HEALTH PLAN OF OREGON
(*Suby of* PREMERA BLUE CROSS) ★
2020 Sw 4th Ave Ste 1000, Portland, OR 97201-4965
Tel (503) 295-6707 *Founded/Ownrshp* 2008
Sales NA *EMP* 2^E
SIC 6321 Accident & health insurance
Pr: Majd El-Azma
Ex VP: Kent Marquardt
VP: Sharon Sitton
Comm Dir: Jodi Coffey
Off Mgr: Ann Condon
IT Man: Scott Rossow
Manager: Cathy Harber
Sls Mgr: Majd Elazma

D-U-N-S 11-415-2077
LIFEWORKS NW
TUALATIN VALLEY CENTERS
14600 Nw Cornell Rd, Portland, OR 97229-5442
Tel (503) 645-3581 *Founded/Ownrshp* 1961
Sales 33.7MM *EMP* 125
Accts Hoffman Stewart & Schmidt Pc
SIC 8322 8093 Individual & family services; Specialty outpatient clinics; Mental health clinic, outpatient; Individual & family services; Specialty outpatient clinics; Mental health clinic, outpatient
Pr: Mary Monnat
V Ch: John Wagner

D-U-N-S 11-622-6259
LIFEWORKS SERVICES INC
2965 Lone Oak Dr Ste 160, Eagan, MN 55121-3019
Tel (651) 454-2732 *Founded/Ownrshp* 1966
Sales 56.2MM *EMP* 195
SIC 8322 Social services for the handicapped; Social services for the handicapped
Ch Bd: Steve Wexler
**Pr:* Judy Lysne
Ofcr: Jamie Ehlert
VP: Tony Saputo-Swanson
Prgrm Mgr: Connie Giles
IT Man: Don Becchetti
S&M/VP: Frederick Urch
Mktg Dir: Tony Saputo
Sales Asso: Sharon Allen

D-U-N-S 00-308-4209 IMP
■ LIFOAM INDUSTRIES LLC (MD)
(*Suby of* JARDEN CORP) ★
121 Bata Blvd Ste D, Belcamp, MD 21017-1435
Tel (410) 889-1023 *Founded/Ownrshp* 1954, 2012
Sales 125.5MM^E *EMP* 500
SIC 3086 Plastics foam products; Plastics foam products
CEO: John Cantlin
**CFO:* Cris Keller
IT Man: Dale Bargar
IT Man: Illya Suhoy
Tech Mgr: Dan Buffo
QC Dir: Sam Martin
Sls Mgr: Brian Stiefel

D-U-N-S 06-387-5967
LIFT INC
3745 Hempland Rd, Mountville, PA 17554-1545
Tel (717) 295-1800 *Founded/Ownrshp* 2003
Sales 99.1MM^E *EMP* 220
SIC 5084 7353 Lift trucks & parts; Cranes & aerial lift equipment, rental or leasing; Lift trucks & parts; Cranes & aerial lift equipment, rental or leasing
Pr: Donald G Herman
**VP:* Kirk W Sears
Genl Mgr: Gayle Velky
Sales Exec: Dave Corey
Sales Asso: Stephen Sanger

D-U-N-S 01-706-0647
LIFT KIDS INC
12424 Research Blvd 109, Austin, TX 78759-2315
Tel (651) 298-9200 *Founded/Ownrshp* 2008
Sales 34.4MM *EMP* 2^E
Accts H Michael Blair Cpa Rosemou
SIC 8699 Charitable organization; Charitable organization
Pr: Joseph Barrett

D-U-N-S 00-808-1416
LIFT MOORE INC
7810 Pinemont Dr, Houston, TX 77040-6516
Tel (713) 688-5533 *Founded/Ownrshp* 1961
Sales 22.5MM^E *EMP* 48
SIC 3537 Cranes, industrial truck
Pr: Herb Koenig Jr
**Sec:* Mary Koenig
Exec: Billy Cardwell
Sfty Mgr: Neil Koenig
Prd Mgr: Jody Miller
Natl Sales: Steve Coffee
Manager: Ed Morris
Manager: Terry Soots
Sales Asso: Navied Sadeghi
Doctor: John Strempfer

D-U-N-S 82-523-7675
LIFT OFF DISTRIBUTION LLC
7077 Oakland Mills Rd, Columbia, MD 21046-1620
Tel (301) 490-5542 *Founded/Ownrshp* 2000
Sales 72.9MM *EMP* 126
Accts Mcgladrey Llp Baltimore Mary
SIC 5149 Beverages, except coffee & tea
Pr: Ann Keith
**CEO:* David Keith
Sls Mgr: Thomas Alter

D-U-N-S 05-534-4253 EXP
LIFT POWER INC
6801 Suemac Pl, Jacksonville, FL 32254-2723
Tel (904) 783-0250 *Founded/Ownrshp* 2010
Sales 26.6MM *EMP* 74
SIC 5084 7538 7513

D-U-N-S 06-865-0498 IMP
LIFT SOLUTIONS INC
14616 Shepard St, Omaha, NE 68138-4315
Tel (402) 330-1690 *Founded/Ownrshp* 1999
Sales 38.5MM^E *EMP* 75
SIC 5084 Lift trucks & parts
Pr: Steven G Buehler
Mtls Mgr: Tim McSorley
Opers Mgr: Jeff Fuller

D-U-N-S 02-547-6185 IMP/EXP
LIFT SOURCE INC
ATLAS TOYOTA MATERIAL HANDLING
5050 River Rd, Schiller Park, IL 60176-1092
Tel (847) 678-3450 *Founded/Ownrshp* 2011
Sales 97.5MM^E *EMP* 330
SIC 5999 5084

D-U-N-S 60-369-8643 IMP
LIFT SYSTEMS INC
1505 7th St, East Moline, IL 61244-2112
Tel (309) 764-9842 *Founded/Ownrshp* 2005
Sales 20.1MM^E *EMP* 72^E
SIC 3536 Hoists, cranes & monorails
Pr: Bruce Forster
**VP:* Ray Shuman
**VP:* Brian Wagner
Prd Mgr: Tim Faccio

D-U-N-S 12-136-1641 IMP
LIFT TECHNOLOGIES INC
LIFT-TEK ELECAR
7040 S Highway 11, Westminster, SC 29693-3915
Tel (864) 647-1119 *Founded/Ownrshp* 1998
Sales 88.0MM^E *EMP* 200
SIC 3537 Industrial trucks & tractors; Industrial trucks & tractors
CEO: Conrad Ostermier
**CFO:* David McBride
Ofcr: Bill Keeter
**VP:* Greg Smith
Telecom Ex: Charles Long
CTO: Mark Dawley
Sls&Mrk Ex: Mark Friday
S&M/VP: David Hahn

D-U-N-S 06-768-3896
LIFT TRUCK SERVICE CENTER INC
JC B OF AR
12829 Interstate 30, Little Rock, AR 72209-7011
Tel (501) 568-3330 *Founded/Ownrshp* 1973
Sales 31.6MM^E *EMP* 70
Accts George L Mallory Iii D/B/A M
SIC 5084 7699 5087 Lift trucks & parts; Industrial machinery & equipment repair; Floor machinery, maintenance
Pr: Carl Morehead
**VP:* Mark Morehead
Brnch Mgr: Brad Pittman
Sls Mgr: Bill Schroeder

D-U-N-S 78-246-6981 IMP
LIFT-TECH INC
1909 Mcfarland Dr, Landisville, PA 17538-1810
Tel (717) 898-6615 *Founded/Ownrshp* 1982
Sales 22.5MM^E *EMP* 250
SIC 3315 2298 Wire & fabricated wire products; Ropes & fiber cables; Wire & fabricated wire products; Ropes & fiber cables
Pr: Jeffrey M Klibert
**Sec:* Charles T Anton
**VP:* John D Roberts
Dir IT: Greg Bebinchak

LIFT-TEK ELECAR
See LIFT TECHNOLOGIES INC

D-U-N-S 08-198-5467 IMP
LIFTEC INC
124 Sylvania Pl, South Plainfield, NJ 07080-1448
Tel (908) 769-0034 *Founded/Ownrshp* 1997
Sales 24.5MM^E *EMP* 50
SIC 5084 7359 Materials handling machinery; Equipment rental & leasing
Pr: Steve Panek
**VP:* Tom Sylvester

D-U-N-S 19-397-8368
LIFTECH EQUIPMENT COMPANIES INC
6847 Ellicott Dr Ste 1, East Syracuse, NY 13057-1140
Tel (315) 463-6971 *Founded/Ownrshp* 1987
Sales 72.2MM^E *EMP* 156
SIC 5084 7699 7359 Materials handling machinery; Industrial truck repair; Industrial truck rental; Materials handling machinery; Industrial truck repair; Industrial truck rental
Pr: Joseph Verzino
CFO: Mike Vaughan
VP: Gerald Maywright
Natl Sales: Mike Yezzi
Manager: Paul Maher
Sls Mgr: Ryan Curtis
Sls Mgr: Eric Vreeland

D-U-N-S 06-912-8655 IMP/EXP
LIFTED RESEARCH GROUP INC
L R G
7 Holland, Irvine, CA 92618-2506
Tel (949) 581-1144 *Founded/Ownrshp* 1999
Sales 99.7MM^E *EMP* 100^E
SIC 5136 Men's & boys' clothing; Men's & boys' clothing
Pr: Robert D Wright
VP: Mike Schillmoeller
VP: Zach Wright
Prd Mgr: Amy Davis
Ql Cn Mgr: Keith Romero
Mktg Mgr: Kevin Delaney
Mktg Mgr: Mike Posner
Sls Mgr: Paul Hauke
Sls Mgr: Nick Terrio

D-U-N-S 08-264-2237 IMP
LIFTEX CORP
48 Vincent Cir Ste D, Warminster, PA 18974-1538
Tel (800) 478-4651 *Founded/Ownrshp* 1999
Sales 38.7MM^E *EMP* 200^E
SIC 3536 Hoisting slings; Hoisting slings
CEO: Paul E Keating
Pr: Greg Crain
**Pr:* Derek W McNab
COO: Mark Kowalick
**Treas:* Paul Keating
**Sec:* John Fleming
Off Mgr: Maria Terchi

D-U-N-S 62-533-2713
LIFTING GEAR HIRE CORP
LGH
9925 Industrial Dr, Bridgeview, IL 60455-1982
Tel (708) 598-4727 *Founded/Ownrshp* 1990
Sales 43.0MM *EMP* 191
SIC 7359 Equipment rental & leasing; Equipment rental & leasing
Ch: William B Parkinson
**Pr:* Tony Fiscelli
IT Man: Tom Beasley
Opers Mgr: Brian Ward
Mktg Mgr: Christina Czeszewski
Sales Asso: Don Johnson

LIFTMASTER
See CHAMBERLAIN GROUP INC

D-U-N-S 14-878-9923 IMP
LIFTONE LLC
(*Suby of* CAROLINA TRACTOR & EQUIPMENT CO INC) ★
440 E Westinghouse Blvrd, Charlotte, NC 28273
Tel (704) 588-1300 *Founded/Ownrshp* 2012
Sales 239.4MM^E *EMP* 560^E
SIC 5084 Materials handling machinery; Materials handling machinery
Pr: Bill Ryan
Brnch Mgr: Don Welch
IT Man: Glenda Karriker
S&M/VP: Scott Alexander

D-U-N-S 09-039-9106
LIGA PUERTORRIQUENA CONTRA EL CANCER INC
HOSPITAL ONCOLOGICO ISAAC GONZ
Cond Centro Plz, San Juan, PR 00909-2110
Tel (787) 763-4149 *Founded/Ownrshp* 1938
Sales 13.1MM *EMP* 300
SIC 8069 Cancer hospital
Ex Dir: Felix Ortiz Baez
**Pr:* Ruben Eli Matos
**Prin:* Jorge Perez
Board of Directors: Milagros Vargas

D-U-N-S 18-410-5260
▲ LIGAND PHARMACEUTICALS INC
11119 N Torrey Pines Rd, La Jolla, CA 92037-1046
Tel (858) 550-7500 *Founded/Ownrshp* 1987
Sales 64.5MM *EMP* 19^E
Tkr Sym LGND *Exch* NGM
SIC 2834 Pharmaceutical preparations; Pharmaceutical preparations
CEO: John L Higgins
**Ch Bd:* John W Kozarich
Pr: Matthew W Foehr
CFO: Matthew Korenberg
Sr VP: William A Pettit
VP: Charles S Berkman
VP: Keith Marschke
VP: Andre Negro-Vilar
VP: Lin Zhi

D-U-N-S 00-128-8463 IMP
■ LIGGETT GROUP LLC
(*Suby of* VGR HOLDING LLC) ★
100 Maple Ln, Mebane, NC 27302-8160
Tel (919) 304-7700 *Founded/Ownrshp* 2006
Sales 101.6MM^E *EMP* 449
SIC 2111 Cigarettes; Cigarettes
CEO: Ronald J Bernstein
Pr: Greg Sulin
**Ex VP:* James A Taylor
**VP:* Lynda Amey
**VP:* Steven H Erikson
**VP:* Jerry R Loftin
**VP:* John R Long
VP Opers: Tim Jackson
VP Opers: Bill Turner
Opers Mgr: Richard Spaugh
Ql Cn Mgr: Paul Derby

LIGHT BULBS UNLIMITED
See LBU INTERNATIONAL INC

D-U-N-S 17-829-6976 IMP
LIGHT CORP INC
14800 172nd Ave, Grand Haven, MI 49417-8969
Tel (616) 842-5100 *Founded/Ownrshp* 1986
Sales 33.0MM^E *EMP* 150^E
SIC 3646 Commercial indusl & institutional electric lighting fixtures; Desk lamps, commercial; Commercial indusl & institutional electric lighting fixtures; Desk lamps, commercial
CEO: Gary Verplank
**Pr:* Bradley Davis
**Treas:* Lurelle J Verplank
**VP:* Budd Brink
Sls Mgr: Tom Ruggiero

D-U-N-S 08-085-1595 IMP
LIGHT FANTASTIC REALTY INC
FRAQTIR
114 Boston Post Rd, West Haven, CT 06516-2043
Tel (203) 934-3441 *Founded/Ownrshp* 1977
Sales 25.6MM^E *EMP* 125
SIC 3647 3645 Dome lights, automotive; Residential lighting fixtures; Dome lights, automotive; Residential lighting fixtures
CEO: Allison K Schieffelin
Pr: David R Pfund
**CFO:* Cynthia Hoboken
**Ex VP:* Suzanne Carroll
VP: Paul R Ford
**VP:* Joseph R Zaharewicz
VP Sls: Russell Suppies

D-U-N-S 80-833-2261
■ **LIGHT GROUP LLC**
LIGHT LAS VEGAS
(*Suby of* MORGANS HOTEL GROUP CO) ★
6385 S Rainbow Blvd # 800, Las Vegas, NV 89118-3201
Tel (702) 247-6611 *Founded/Ownrshp* 2011
Sales 44.3MM[E] *EMP* 900
SIC 7929 5812 7011 Entertainment service; Eating places; Casino hotel; Entertainment service; Eating places; Casino hotel
CEO: Andy Masi
VP: Beth Bartolini
VP: Melanie James
**VP:* Russell Jones
VP: Norman Ly
VP: Susie McDaniel
Exec: Chris Conlon
Dir Soc: Brandon Nusbaum
Dir Soc: Josh Ouzer
Dir Soc: Diego Pineda
Dir Soc: Scott Warren
Creative D: Nick Gold

LIGHT HOUSE POINT CASINO
See GREENVILLE RIVERBOAT LLC

LIGHT LAS VEGAS
See LIGHT GROUP LLC

D-U-N-S 00-601-1720 EXP
LIGHT METALS CORP (MI)
L M C
2740 Prairie St Sw, Wyoming, MI 49519-6098
Tel (616) 538-3030 *Founded/Ownrshp* 1944
Sales 57.3MM[E] *EMP* 270
SIC 3354 3444 Aluminum extruded products; Sheet metalwork; Aluminum extruded products; Sheet metalwork
Pr: George T Boylan
**VP:* Jeff Boylan
Prd Dir: John Filush
QC Dir: Bill Grant
Ql Cn Mgr: George Wagner

LIGHT MINISTRIES
See NEW LIGHT CHURCH WORLD OUTREACH AND WORSHIP CENTERS INC

D-U-N-S 07-505-8495 IMP
LIGHT SOURCES INC
L S I
37 Robinson Blvd, Orange, CT 06477-3623
Tel (203) 799-7877 *Founded/Ownrshp* 1983
Sales 36.5MM[E] *EMP* 230[E]
SIC 3641 Ultraviolet lamps; Lamps, fluorescent, electric; Ultraviolet lamps; Lamps, fluorescent, electric
Pr: Christian Sauska
VP: Gino Ciancanelli
VP: Arpad Pirovic
Dir IT: Bruce Danton
Dir IT: Robert Huber
IT Man: Jose Cordeno
Mfg Dir: Graham Foster
Sfty Mgr: Bob Miske

D-U-N-S 78-443-4784
LIGHT TOWER FIBER LLC
LIGHTOWER FIBER NETWORKS
80 Central St Ste 240, Boxborough, MA 01719-1245
Tel (978) 264-6000 *Founded/Ownrshp* 2007
Sales 136.0MM[E] *EMP* 223
SIC 4899 Data communication services; Data communication services
Pr: Rob Shanahan
CEO: Robert J Shanahan
COO: Jason Campbell
CFO: Eric Sandman
Ex VP: David Mayer
VP: Anthony Barone
VP: Mark Legere
VP: Rob Poulton
VP: Eric Swanholm
Dir Risk M: Doug Dalissandro
CIO: Bruce Dyke

D-U-N-S 93-382-5325
LIGHT TOWER RENTALS INC
L T R
2330 E I20 S Service Rd, Odessa, TX 79764
Tel (432) 530-3330 *Founded/Ownrshp* 1994
Sales 91.5MM[E] *EMP* 326
SIC 7359 Equipment rental & leasing; Equipment rental & leasing
Pr: Theodore Hogan
**CFO:* Keith Muncy
**Sec:* John C Avary
Brnch Mgr: Jayson Braim
Brnch Mgr: Jeremy Nuckolls
Brnch Mgr: Ralph Slavey
Brnch Mgr: Ronnie Woodard
Netwrk Mgr: Nathan Billingsley
Sales Asso: Daniel Nitche

D-U-N-S 83-568-6148
LIGHTBOUND LLC
731 W Henry St Ste 201, Indianapolis, IN 46225-1116
Tel (317) 259-5050 *Founded/Ownrshp* 2000
Sales 25.0MM[E] *EMP* 50
SIC 7373 4813 Computer integrated systems design;
CEO: Jack Carr
**COO:* John J Carr
Sls Mgr: Ron Pirau

D-U-N-S 07-851-2353
LIGHTBRIDGE COMMUNICATIONS CORP
7900 Westpark Dr Ste A300, Mc Lean, VA 22102-4240
Tel (703) 873-2000 *Founded/Ownrshp* 2010
Sales 41.9MM[E] *EMP* 150[E]
SIC 8748 Telecommunications consultant; Telecommunications consultant
Pr: Kenneth Young
CFO: Rebecca Stahl
VP: Nancy O Feeney

D-U-N-S 07-944-1199
LIGHTCO INC
636 Ramona St, Palo Alto, CA 94301-2545
Tel (908) 403-7815 *Founded/Ownrshp* 2013
Sales 30.0MM *EMP* 45
SIC 3827 Optical instruments & lenses
CEO: Dave Grannan
**Sr VP:* Harpuneet Singh
**VP:* Bradley Lautenbach
**VP:* Prashant Velagaleti
**CTO:* Rajiv Laroia

D-U-N-S 95-865-7298
LIGHTEDGE SOLUTIONS INC
215 10th St Ste 1000, Des Moines, IA 50309-3616
Tel (515) 471-1000 *Founded/Ownrshp* 1996
Sales 34.3MM[E] *EMP* 75
SIC 4813
CEO: Jeffrey Springborn
**Pr:* Jeff Springborn
**CFO:* Steve Denherder
Treas: Matthew Kinley
**VP:* T J Bangs
VP: Brenden Bryan
VP: Jay Devers
VP: Kent Kunkel
**VP:* Mike McHenry
VP: Jared Stanley
Dir IT: Jeff Kingland

D-U-N-S 13-318-7695
LIGHTEN UP LLC
3350 Riverwood Pkwy Se # 2220, Atlanta, GA 30339-3362
Tel (770) 693-1508 *Founded/Ownrshp* 2001
Sales 36.8MM[E] *EMP* 180[E]
SIC 5031 Doors & windows; Molding, all materials; Doors & windows; Molding, all materials
CFO: Allen Bryan

LIGHTER LEASH
See BAR PRODUCTS.COM INC

LIGHTERA
See LUMINUS INC

LIGHTFORM
See FORMS AND SURFACES CO LLC

LIGHTHOUSE, THE
See TRUCK LIGHTHOUSE

D-U-N-S 60-199-8219
LIGHTHOUSE ACADEMIES
1780 Sloan Ave, Indianapolis, IN 46203-3640
Tel (317) 351-1534 *Founded/Ownrshp* 2005
Sales 32.7MM[E] *EMP* 22
Accts Fitzgerald Isaac Llc Indianap
SIC 8211 Private elementary & secondary schools; Private elementary & secondary schools
Pr: Michael B Ronan

D-U-N-S 84-523-5477
LIGHTHOUSE BAPTIST CHURCH
2577 Us Highway 441 S, Sylva, NC 28779-7654
Tel (828) 586-3884 *Founded/Ownrshp* 2011
Sales 6.6MM[E] *EMP* 325
SIC 8661 Baptist Church; Baptist Church

LIGHTHOUSE CAFE
See HENNESSEYS TAVERN INC

D-U-N-S 95-973-3556
LIGHTHOUSE COLLISION SERVICES INC
1009 Zelda Loop Rd, Fallsburg, KY 41230
Tel (606) 686-1297 *Founded/Ownrshp* 2008
Sales 75.1MM *EMP* 8
SIC 8999 Artists & artists' studios; Artists & artists' studios
Pr: Kenny Aldrich
**Treas:* Anna Aldrich
**VP:* Joshua Aldrich

D-U-N-S 87-836-5626
LIGHTHOUSE COMPUTER SERVICES INC
6 Blackstone Valley Pl # 205, Lincoln, RI 02865-1112
Tel (401) 334-0799 *Founded/Ownrshp* 1995
Sales 24.7MM[E] *EMP* 105[E]
SIC 5734 7379 Computer software & accessories; Computer related consulting services
Pr: Thomas Mrva
**CFO:* Tony Fiore
**Ex VP:* Jeanne Mrva
VP: Brook Lovatt
**VP:* Michael A Mespelli
VP: Eugene Stakhov
Exec: Steve Nelson
CTO: Ernie Yanke
IT Man: Jim Brooks
VP Opers: Richard Unsworth
Mktg Dir: Mike Adams

LIGHTHOUSE COUNTY COMMONS APTS
See RICHLIEU ASSOCIATES

D-U-N-S 92-697-4403
LIGHTHOUSE DOCUMENT TECHNOLOGIES INC
51 University St Ste 400, Seattle, WA 98101-3614
Tel (206) 223-9690 *Founded/Ownrshp* 2007
Sales 27.3MM[E] *EMP* 90
SIC 7379 8111 Computer related consulting services; Specialized legal services
CEO: Brian McManus J D
Adv Bd Mbr: Heng-Pin Kiang

D-U-N-S 11-342-1309
LIGHTHOUSE ELECTRIC CO INC
1957 Route 519, Canonsburg, PA 15317-5128
Tel (724) 873-3500 *Founded/Ownrshp* 1984
Sales 149.2MM[E] *EMP* 400
Accts Stelmack Dobransky & Eannace L
SIC 1731 General electrical contractor; General electrical contractor
CEO: Anthony Mikec
**Pr:* Todd A Mikec
Treas: Doug Brock
**Sec:* P Douglas Brock
VP: Joshua Eckenrode
**VP:* Mark A Mikec

D-U-N-S 00-282-5289 IMP
LIGHTHOUSE ELECTRIC COOPERATIVE (TX)
Hwy 70 E, Floydada, TX 79235
Tel (806) 983-2814 *Founded/Ownrshp* 1938
Sales 34.4MM *EMP* 40
Accts Bolinger Segars Gilbert And Mo
SIC 4911 Distribution, electric power; Transmission, electric power
Pr: Don Dean
**Sec:* Gaylord Groce
**Ex VP:* Bill Harbin
**VP:* Tom Cope
Board of Directors: Thomas Cope, J W Jackson, Tom Johnson, Ronald Mullins, Jerrold Vinson

LIGHTHOUSE FOR THE BLIND
See TRAVIS ASSOCIATION FOR BLIND

D-U-N-S 05-173-1214
LIGHTHOUSE FOR BLIND
LHB INDUSTRIES
10440 Trenton Ave, Saint Louis, MO 63132-1223
Tel (314) 423-7955 *Founded/Ownrshp* 1933
Sales 24.1MM *EMP* 82
Accts Botz Deal & Co Saint Charles
SIC 5047 2842 5087 Medical equipment & supplies; Specialty cleaning preparations; Janitors' supplies; Medical equipment & supplies; Specialty cleaning preparations; Janitors' supplies
Pr: John Thompson
**CFO:* Joseph Hull

D-U-N-S 00-928-2278
LIGHTHOUSE FOR BLIND INC
SKILLCRAFT
2501 S Plum St, Seattle, WA 98144-4711
Tel (206) 322-4200 *Founded/Ownrshp* 1918
Sales 72.8M *EMP* 400
Accts Trout Ebersole & Groff Llp L
SIC 8331 3444 Job training & vocational rehabilitation services; Job training services; Sheet metalwork; Job training & vocational rehabilitation services; Job training services; Sheet metalwork
CEO: Kirk Adams
**CFO:* Mary Cabrian
**Sr VP:* Robert S Johnson
VP: Emil Dupuy
**VP:* Constance Englestad
**VP:* Paula Hoffman
**VP:* Bob Johnson
VP: Pat O'Hara
**VP:* Pat Ohara
Dir: Kirk Laughlin
IT Man: Pegi Brumett

D-U-N-S 00-837-6060
LIGHTHOUSE HOSPICE
(*Suby of* HARDEN HEALTHCARE SERVICES LLC) ★
100 College St, Round Rock, TX 78664-4415
Tel (866) 678-0505 *Founded/Ownrshp* 2011
Sales 3.7MM[E] *EMP* 962[E]
SIC 8052 Personal care facility

D-U-N-S 06-471-7816
LIGHTHOUSE HOSPICE
(*Suby of* HARDEN HEALTHCARE SERVICES LLC) ★
305 Coke Ave Ste 140, Hillsboro, TX 76645-2685
Tel (254) 710-9800 *Founded/Ownrshp* 2011
Sales 1.8MM[E] *EMP* 962[E]
SIC 8082 8069 Home health care services; Specialty hospitals, except psychiatric
Prin: Celeste McCraw

D-U-N-S 94-293-1478 EXP
LIGHTHOUSE IMPORTS LLC
TOYOTA OF ST AUGUSTINE
200 S Biscayne Blvd # 1818, Miami, FL 33131-2310
Tel (386) 677-7300 *Founded/Ownrshp* 2007
Sales 24.9MM[E] *EMP* 67
SIC 5511 Automobiles, new & used; Automobiles, new & used
Genl Mgr: Dan Johnson
Genl Mgr: Tim Peeler
Sls Dir: Alex Fischer
Sls Mgr: Steve Pawelski

D-U-N-S 12-753-2539
LIGHTHOUSE INSURANCE GROUP INC
AUSTIN-POWELL-LANKES AGENCY
877 E 16th St, Holland, MI 49423-9130
Tel (616) 392-6900 *Founded/Ownrshp* 1960
Sales NA *EMP* 145
SIC 6411 6331 6321 6311 Insurance agents, brokers & service; Fire, marine & casualty insurance; Accident & health insurance; Life insurance
Pr: Pam Allard
**Pr:* Thomas Helmstter
**Sec:* James C Schippers
Dir Risk M: Gene Reed
**Prin:* Kathleen Andersen
Brnch Mgr: Kerri Woolverton
IT Man: Bruce Bos
Mktg Mgr: Jeff Beyer

D-U-N-S 06-344-5562
LIGHTHOUSE INSURANCE GROUP LLC
6150 Oak Tree Blvd # 210, Independence, OH 44131-6976
Tel (216) 503-2439 *Founded/Ownrshp* 2011
Sales NA *EMP* 80
SIC 6411 Insurance agents, brokers & service
CEO: Jason Farro
**Prin:* Charles Farro

D-U-N-S 07-327-2486
LIGHTHOUSE INTERNATIONAL
111 E 59th St, New York, NY 10022-1264
Tel (212) 821-9601 *Founded/Ownrshp* 1906
Sales 20.0MM *EMP* 343
Accts Grant Thornton Llp New York
SIC 8322 8331 Association for the handicapped; Job training & vocational rehabilitation services; Association for the handicapped; Job training & vocational rehabilitation services
Ch Bd: James M Dubin
Pr: Mark Ackermann
CEO: Alan R Morse
V Ch Bd: Joseph Ripp
Sr VP: Robert Hoak
Sr VP: Peter Minichiello
Sr VP: Cynthia Stuen
Assoc Dir: Phyllis Farmer
Assoc Dir: Melissa Shorey
Off Mgr: Wanda Rivera
Off Mgr: Juliet Serapio
Board of Directors: Fred Gainer, Ellen M Mello, Eric Widing, Sal Argento, Arlene Gordon, Charles G Meyer Jr, Mrs Robert I Williams, Lee D Arning, Carolyn Halk, Barbara A Munder, Harold P Wilmerding, Joseph G Beck, Charles G Horn, David Paton MD, Adele Block, Richard L Intrator, Dr Dorothy M Philips, Ed Blodgett, Maria Kalnay, Mrs A T Pouch Jr, Lloyd H Dalzell, Lloyd Kaufman Phd, Rennie Roberts, Mrs Robert P Devecchi, Arthur H Keeney MD, Hope G Solinger

D-U-N-S 13-513-4364
LIGHTHOUSE MASONRY INC
150 John Vertente Blvd, New Bedford, MA 02745-1207
Tel (508) 995-0192 *Founded/Ownrshp* 2002
Sales 23.4MM *EMP* 130
SIC 1741 Masonry & other stonework; Masonry & other stonework
Pr: Paul M Alves
**Prin:* Heidi Freitas

LIGHTHOUSE NURSING CARE CENTER
See LIGHTHOUSE OF REVERE INC

D-U-N-S 09-107-9041
LIGHTHOUSE OF REVERE INC
LIGHTHOUSE NURSING CARE CENTER
3575 Piedmont Rd Ne 15-930, Atlanta, GA 30305-1623
Tel (404) 233-6500 *Founded/Ownrshp* 1995
Sales 13.4MM *EMP* 395
Accts Mayer Hoffman Mccann Pc Ply
SIC 8742 Management consulting services; Management consulting services
Pr: Gregory K Grove
VP: C Willis Bass
VP: William Roew III
Off Mgr: Karen Cheek

D-U-N-S 19-622-8753
LIGHTHOUSE WORLDWIDE SOLUTIONS INC
47300 Kato Rd, Fremont, CA 94538-7334
Tel (510) 438-0500 *Founded/Ownrshp* 1988
Sales 30.1MM[E] *EMP* 175[E]
SIC 3823

D-U-N-S 08-186-1585
LIGHTHOUSE YOUTH SERVICES INC
401 E Mcmillan St, Cincinnati, OH 45206-1922
Tel (513) 221-3350 *Founded/Ownrshp* 1969
Sales 25.1MM *EMP* 300
Accts Clark Schaefer Hacket Cincinn
SIC 8322 Child related social services; Child related social services
Pr: Robert C Mecum
Dir Vol: Lauren Frooman
CFO: Judith Oakman
**CFO:* Judy Oakman
**VP:* Jean Sepate
Off Mgr: Merry Paul
Opers Supe: Eric Cavey
Pgrm Dir: Victoria Burke
Pgrm Dir: Jenna Krysiak
Pgrm Dir: Sidney Taylor
Pgrm Dir: Calvin Williams

D-U-N-S 17-521-8296 IMP
LIGHTING & SUPPLIES INC
SUNSHINE LIGHTING
744 Clinton St, Brooklyn, NY 11231-2104
Tel (718) 522-2243 *Founded/Ownrshp* 1981
Sales 40.7MM[E] *EMP* 80
SIC 5063 Lighting fixtures; Light bulbs & related supplies
Ch Bd: Mordechai Kohn
Genl Mgr: Mendy Greenberger
Genl Mgr: Nina Yeret
Genl Mgr: Hillel Zafir
Mktg Dir: Lea Benashen

LIGHTING AND BATH
See FARREYS WHOLESALE HARDWARE CO INC

D-U-N-S 00-403-0177
LIGHTING AND LAMP CORP (AL)
AUDIO-VIDEO ENVIRONMENTS
2552 Pelham Pkwy, Pelham, AL 35124-1329
Tel (205) 271-1423 *Founded/Ownrshp* 1953
Sales 24.5MM[E] *EMP* 100
Accts Cork Hill & Company Llc
SIC 5063 5719 Lighting fixtures; Lighting fixtures; Lighting fixtures; Lighting fixtures
CEO: Randall W Calhoun
**Ch Bd:* Patricia W Burks

LIGHTING DOT COM.COM
See AMERICAN DE ROSA LAMPARTS LLC

LIGHTING GALLERY BY BROWN'S
See BROWNS ELECTRICAL SUPPLY CO INC

D-U-N-S 17-445-4678 IMP/EXP
LIGHTING HOLDINGS INTERNATIONAL LLC
4 Manhattanville Rd, Purchase, NY 10577-2139
Tel (845) 306-1850 *Founded/Ownrshp* 1985
Sales 77.2MM[E] *EMP* 1,400
SIC 3641 5719 5063 4225 3643 3229 Electric lamps & parts for generalized applications; Lamps & lamp shades; Lighting fixtures; General warehousing; Current-carrying wiring devices; Lamp sockets & receptacles (electric wiring devices); Pressed & blown glass; Electric lamps & parts for generalized applications; Lamps & lamp shades; Lighting fixtures; General warehousing; Current-carrying wiring devices; Lamp sockets & receptacles (electric wiring devices); Pressed & blown glass
CEO: Dionne Gadsden
CEO: Steve Imgham
CFO: William Drexles
Ex VP: Jan Germis
Ex VP: Tom Mullally

Ex VP: Marcos Paganini
Dir IT: Gary Belios
Dir IT: Cheryl Page
VP Opers: Gregory Barry

D-U-N-S 02-661-8637 IMP
LIGHTING INC
4179 Telephone Rd, Houston, TX 77087
Tel (713) 623-6500 *Founded/Ownrshp* 1940
Sales 29.6MM^E *EMP* 102
SIC 5719 5251 5063 Lighting fixtures; Builders' hardware; Lighting fixtures
Pr: Brad Bailey
**Treas:* Tim Bailey
**VP:* Donald S Bailey

LIGHTING ONE
See LIFESTYLES STORES INC

D-U-N-S 79-041-3074 IMP
LIGHTING RESOURCES LLC
1919 Williams St Ste 350, Simi Valley, CA 93065-2855
Tel (909) 923-7252 *Founded/Ownrshp* 1989
Sales 25.2MM^E *EMP* 38
SIC 4953 Recycling, waste materials
CFO: Tina Mintz
CFO: Steven Seckar
Brnch Mgr: Michelle Brown
Brnch Mgr: Thomas Slattery
Opers Mgr: Jose Ascencio
Opers Mgr: Jamie Shortt
Manager: Susan Richard
Sls Mgr: Pete Septoski

D-U-N-S 18-368-7664 IMP
▲ LIGHTING SCIENCE GROUP CORP
1830 Penn St, Melbourne, FL 32901-2617
Tel (321) 779-5520 *Founded/Ownrshp* 2005
Sales 91.2MM *EMP* 85^E
Tkr Sym LSCG *Exch* OTO
SIC 3646 3648 Commercial indusl & institutional electric lighting fixtures; Street lighting fixtures; Commercial indusl & institutional electric lighting fixtures; Street lighting fixtures
CEO: Edward D Bednarcik
**Ch Bd:* Craig Cogut
COO: Wayne Nesbit
VP: Al Aylsworth
VP: Mike Maskwa
VP: Jim McKenzie
**CTO:* Fredric Maxik
Mktg Dir: Sean Harris
Snr Mgr: Steve Faber
Board of Directors: Seth Bernstein, Sanford Climan, Richard H Davis Jr, Donald Harkleroad, James L Jones, Fredric Maxik, Dennis McGill, Jonathan Rosenbaum, Leon Wagner

D-U-N-S 80-514-0634
LIGHTING UNLIMITED LLC
4211 Richmond Ave, Houston, TX 77027-6813
Tel (713) 626-0729 *Founded/Ownrshp* 2007
Sales 24.3MM^E *EMP* 43
SIC 5063 Lighting fixtures
Genl Mgr: Craig Frank
Sales Exec: Darlene Fautt

LIGHTINGUNIVERSE.COM
See ALLIED TRADE GROUP INC

D-U-N-S 01-849-3531
■ LIGHTLAB IMAGING INC (DE)
(*Suby of* ST JUDE MEDICAL CARDIOVASCULAR DIVISION) ★
4 Robbins Rd, Westford, MA 01886-4113
Tel (978) 577-3400 *Founded/Ownrshp* 1998, 2010
Sales 9.7MM^E *EMP* 283
SIC 8732 3841 Research services, except laboratory; Catheters
CEO: Daniel J Starks
VP: Nathan Harris
VP: Doug Woodruff
Dir Surg: Nathaniel Wallis
CTO: Joseph M Schmitt

D-U-N-S 09-744-4491 IMP
LIGHTLIFE FOODS INC
100 Grandview Rd Ste 400, Braintree, MA 02184-2686
Tel (413) 774-9000 *Founded/Ownrshp* 2013
Sales 74.8MM^E *EMP* 249^E
SIC 2099 2034 2032 Food preparations; Dehydrated fruits, vegetables, soups; Canned specialties; Food preparations; Dehydrated fruits, vegetables, soups; Canned specialties
Pr: Roy Lubetkin
CFO: Michael Morin

D-U-N-S 80-961-6142
LIGHTNING FLUID SERVICES INC
1310 Southwood St, Alice, TX 78332
Tel (361) 396-0801 *Founded/Ownrshp* 2007
Sales 458.7MM^E *EMP* 12
SIC 1389 7389 Oil field services;
Pr: William Starns

D-U-N-S 78-909-7623
LIGHTNING HOCKEY LP
TAMPA BAY LIGHTNING, THE
(*Suby of* TAMPA BAY SPORTS ENTERTAINMENT LLC) ★
401 Channelside Dr, Tampa, FL 33602-5400
Tel (813) 301-6500 *Founded/Ownrshp* 2010
Sales 54.7MM^E *EMP* 1,200
SIC 7941 Ice hockey club; Ice hockey club
Pr: Steve Griggs
CEO: Tod Leiweke
Ch: Jeff Vinik
Ex VP: Jarrod Dillon
Ex VP: Jim Shimberg
Ex VP: Bill Wickett
VP: Bill Abercrombie
VP: David Andreychuk
VP: Eric Blankenship
VP: Elizabeth Frazier
VP: Keith Harris
VP: Doug Riefler

D-U-N-S 06-066-6832
LIGHTNING HYBRIDS LLC
319 Cleveland Ave, Loveland, CO 80537-5505
Tel (970) 624-6220 *Founded/Ownrshp* 2012
Sales 33.1MM^E *EMP* 40
SIC 5511 New & used car dealers
CEO: Dan Johnson
Pr: Tim Reeser
VP Sls: David Brosky

LIGHTNING MOTORS
See BERGEN COUNTY AUTO GROUP LLC

D-U-N-S 79-334-8280
LIGHTNING PROTECTION SYSTEMS LLC
VFC
90 Cutler Dr, North Salt Lake, UT 84054-2901
Tel (801) 292-2956 *Founded/Ownrshp* 2006
Sales 32.0MM^E *EMP* 120^E
SIC 1799 Lightning conductor erection
Off Mgr: Kimberly Mount

D-U-N-S 00-790-4998
LIGHTNING ROD MUTUAL INSURANCE CO (INC)
1685 Cleveland Rd, Wooster, OH 44691-2335
Tel (330) 262-9060 *Founded/Ownrshp* 1906
Sales NA *EMP* 275
SIC 6331 Fire, marine & casualty insurance & carriers; Fire, marine & casualty insurance & carriers
Pr: John P Murphy
**CFO:* Kenneth B Stockman
**V Ch Bd:* F Emerson Logee
Ex VP: Kevin Day
VP: Greg Owen
IT Man: Kim Thompson
VP Mktg: Greg Brunn

D-U-N-S 84-021-5961 IMP/EXP
LIGHTNING SOURCE INC
(*Suby of* INGRAM INDUSTRIES INC) ★
1246 Heil Quaker Blvd, La Vergne, TN 37086-3515
Tel (615) 213-5815 *Founded/Ownrshp* 1997
Sales 61.0MM^E *EMP* 221^E
SIC 2732 Book printing; Book printing
Ch Bd: John R Ingram
**Pr:* Philip C Ollila
**COO:* Shawn D Morin
**Sr VP:* Brian Dauphin
**Sr VP:* David Roland
**Sr VP:* John F Secrest
VP: John Campbell
VP: Jeff Crawford
VP: Stacy Rawls
VP: Andrew Weinstein
Exec: April Beeler
Board of Directors: Mary Cavarra, John R Ingram, Orrin H Ingram

D-U-N-S 07-973-1830
LIGHTNING TRANSPORTATION LOGISTICS LLC
LIGHTNING TRNSP LOGISTICS
840 Nw 144th St, Miami, FL 33168-3024
Tel (813) 444-5144 *Founded/Ownrshp* 2011
Sales 27.5MM^E *EMP* 22^E
SIC 4789 Cargo loading & unloading services

LIGHTNING TRNSP LOGISTICS
See LIGHTNING TRANSPORTATION LOGISTICS LLC

D-U-N-S 00-569-0446 IMP/EXP
LIGHTOLOGY LLC
1718 W Fullerton Ave, Chicago, IL 60614-1922
Tel (773) 883-6111 *Founded/Ownrshp* 2001
Sales 23.9MM^E *EMP* 75
SIC 5719 Lighting fixtures

LIGHTOWER FIBER NETWORKS
See LIGHTTOWER FIBER LLC

D-U-N-S 87-648-4593
LIGHTOWER FIBER NETWORKS II LLC
80 Central St, Boxborough, MA 01719-1245
Tel (978) 264-6000 *Founded/Ownrshp* 2012
Sales 29.5MM^E *EMP* 300
SIC 4813 Local & long distance telephone communications; Local & long distance telephone communications
CEO: Robert Shanahan
**COO:* Jason Campbell
**CFO:* Eric Sandman
**Ex VP:* Doug Dalissandro
Mktg Mgr: John Sullivan

D-U-N-S 15-672-4010
LIGHTRIVER TECHNOLOGIES INC
2150 John Glenn Dr, Concord, CA 94520-5671
Tel (925) 363-9000 *Founded/Ownrshp* 2001
Sales 23.2MM^E *EMP* 50
Accts Wmshb
SIC 4899 Communication signal enhancement network system
Pr: Glenn A Johansen
**CFO:* Garrett Grunewald
VP: Matt Briley
**VP:* Mike Jonas
Rgnl Mgr: Doug Forrester
CTO: Dean Campbell
Netwrk Mgr: Morries Merchant
Netwrk Eng: Muhammed Javaid

D-U-N-S 05-278-3065
■ LIGHTRON CORP
WESTERN SYNTHETIC FELT
(*Suby of* GRIFFON CORP) ★
100 Jericho Quadrangle, Jericho, NY 11753-2708
Tel (516) 938-5544 *Founded/Ownrshp* 1969
Sales 40.2MM *EMP* 3
SIC 3429 3585 Manufactured hardware (general); Cold drink dispensing equipment (not coin-operated); Manufactured hardware (general); Cold drink dispensing equipment (not coin-operated)
VP: Allen R Kaden
**Pr:* Robert Balemian

LIGHTS FANTASTIC
See FLECO INDUSTRIES INC

D-U-N-S 09-142-7708 IMP
LIGHTS OF AMERICA INC
611 Reyes Dr, Walnut, CA 91789-3098
Tel (909) 594-7883 *Founded/Ownrshp* 1977
Sales 303.9MM^E *EMP* 1,200
SIC 3645 3646 7629 3641 Fluorescent lighting fixtures, residential; Fluorescent lighting fixtures, commercial; Electrical repair shops; Electric lamps; Fluorescent lighting fixtures, residential; Fluorescent lighting fixtures, commercial; Electrical repair shops; Electric lamps
CEO: Usman Vakil
**Ex VP:* Farooq Vakil
VP: Ryan Nicholson
Genl Mgr: Anjum Rokerya
VP Mfg: Woo Park
Opers Mgr: Kamran Mirza
VP Sls: Brian Halliwell

D-U-N-S 01-267-5257
■ LIGHTSHIP TANKERS LLC
(*Suby of* SEABULK INTERNATIONAL INC) ★
7200 Highway 87, Port Arthur, TX 77642-0324
Tel (409) 962-0201 *Founded/Ownrshp* 2001
Sales 7.9MM^E *EMP* 340^E
SIC 4412 4424 Deep sea foreign transportation of freight; Deep sea domestic transportation of freight
Pr: Steve Willrich

D-U-N-S 04-715-6026
■ LIGHTSHIP TANKERS V LLC
(*Suby of* SEABULK INTERNATIONAL INC) ★
2200 Eller Dr, Fort Lauderdale, FL 33316-3069
Tel (954) 523-2200 *Founded/Ownrshp* 1999
Sales 9.2MM^E *EMP* 408^E
SIC 4492 Towing & tugboat service
Pr: J Erik Hvide

LIGHTSONLINE.COM
See PROGRESSIVE LIGHTING INC

D-U-N-S 00-365-2906
LIGHTSOURCE CREATIVE SERVICES INC
121 La Porte Ave, Fort Collins, CO 80524-4379
Tel (970) 224-2806 *Founded/Ownrshp* 1996
Sales 150.0MM *EMP* 10
SIC 7336 Commercial art & graphic design; Commercial art & graphic design
Pr: Matt Faye
**VP:* Lisa Malmquist

D-U-N-S 80-734-9803
LIGHTSPEED ONLINE RESEARCH LLC
LIGHTSPEED RESEARCH
(*Suby of* THE KANTAR GROUP LIMITED)
3 Mountainview Rd Ste 3, Warren, NJ 07059-6704
Tel (908) 605-4500 *Founded/Ownrshp* 2000
Sales 52.3MM^E *EMP* 650^E
SIC 8732 Market analysis or research; Market analysis or research
CEO: David Day
Pr: Mark Ridick
**COO:* Andrew Cayton
**CFO:* Mich McCauley
CFO: T M McCauley
Treas: Tom Lobene
Sr VP: James Brooks
Sr VP: Francesco Colbertaldo
Sr VP: Cheryl Harris
Sr VP: Thomas O Neuman
VP: Nancy Kienzler
VP: Sejal Patel
VP: James Riley
VP: Barbara Taylor
Exec: Christina Swatton

LIGHTSPEED RESEARCH
See LIGHTSPEED ONLINE RESEARCH LLC

D-U-N-S 13-108-6001
LIGHTSQUARED INC
(*Suby of* HARBINGER CAPITAL PARTNERS GP LLC) ★
10802 Parkridge Blvd, Reston, VA 20191-4334
Tel (703) 390-1899 *Founded/Ownrshp* 2010
Sales 107.6MM^E *EMP* 330^E
SIC 4899 Data communication services; Data communication services
Ch: Douglas Smith
CFO: Scott Macleod
CFO: Marc Montagner
Treas: Jamie Kase
Treas: Scott G Macleod
Ex VP: Gary Epstein
Sr VP: Terry Neal
Sr VP: Tom Purcell
Sr VP: Randy S Segal
VP: Maqbool Aliani
VP: Joe Berenato
VP: Brendan Boughton
VP: Santanu Dutta
VP: Matthew Foosaner
VP: Bryan Hartin
VP: Blair Kutrow
VP: John Pappajohn
VP: Ajay Parikh
VP: Geoff Stearn
VP: Scott Wiener
VP: James A Wiseman

D-U-N-S 03-963-1542
LIGHTSQUARED INC OF VIRGINIA
10802 Parkridge Blvd, Reston, VA 20191-4334
Tel (703) 390-2700 *Founded/Ownrshp* 2001
Sales 35.0MM *EMP* 350
SIC 3663 Satellites, communications; Satellites, communications
CEO: Sanjiv Ahuja

D-U-N-S 10-252-3391
LIGHTSQUARED LP
(*Suby of* LIGHTSQUARED INC) ★
10802 Parkridge Blvd, Reston, VA 20191-4334
Tel (703) 390-2700 *Founded/Ownrshp* 2007
Sales 25.3MM^E *EMP* 110
SIC 4812 Radio telephone communication
Pt: Sanjiv Ahuja
V Ch: H Good
Pr: Carson Agnew
Pr: John H Mattingly

COO: Mark Faris
COO: Marc Montagner
COO: Doug Smith
Treas: Eric Swank
Sec: Kurt Haufler
Ofcr: Drew Caplan
Sr VP: Randy Segal
VP: Ray S Baxter
VP: James Corry
VP: Larry D Haughey
VP: Peter Karabinis
VP: Ines Lebow
VP: Steve Soroka
VP: James A Wiseman
Board of Directors: Philip A Falcone

D-U-N-S 14-940-0819
LIGHTSTONE GROUP LLC
460 Park Ave Rm 1300, New York, NY 10022-1861
Tel (212) 616-9969 *Founded/Ownrshp* 2002
Sales 645.7MM^E *EMP* 10,780
SIC 6531 Real estate agents & managers; Real estate agents & managers
CEO: David Lichtenstein
Pr: Christian Gabrielsen
**Pr:* Mitchell C Hochberg
**CFO:* Donna Brandin
**Ex VP:* Arvind K Bajaj
**Ex VP:* Pamela Z Meadows
Sr VP: Bruno De Vinck
VP: John Coon
VP: Guy Crawford
VP: Akiva Elazary
VP: Joshua Kornberg
VP: Jonathan Rabinow
VP: Josh Rubinger
VP: Rich Westlund
VP: Peter Zucco

D-U-N-S 82-945-8715
LIGHTSTONE VALUE PLUS REIT INC
1985 Cedarbridge Ave # 1, Lakewood, NJ 08701-7031
Tel (732) 367-0129 *Founded/Ownrshp* 2009
Sales 93.5MM *EMP* 15^E
SIC 6798 Real estate investment trusts; Real estate investment trusts
Pr: Mark Gatto
**Pr:* Michael A Reisner
**Ex VP:* Douglas Crossman

D-U-N-S 00-312-1170
LIGHTWELL INC
565 Metro Pl S Ste 220, Dublin, OH 43017-5380
Tel (614) 310-2700 *Founded/Ownrshp* 1998
Sales 21.4MM^E *EMP* 75^E
SIC 7379 Computer related consulting services
Ch: Michelle Kerr
**Ch Bd:* Michelle Abreu
Sr VP: Chad Young
VP: John Porten
Dir IT: John Massie
Info Man: John Flor
Sales Exec: Tony Donatelli
VP Mktg: Lori Angalich
Mktg Mgr: Amy Heeter
Board of Directors: Chad Mead

D-U-N-S 96-461-9605
LIGHTWERKS COMMUNICATION SYSTEMS INC
CCS PRESENTATION SYSTEMS
3331 Jack Northrop Ave, Hawthorne, CA 90250-4426
Tel (323) 954-7754 *Founded/Ownrshp* 1996
Sales 21.0MM^E *EMP* 54
Accts Warfield & Company Cpa S Scot
SIC 5999 1731 7377 7389 Audio-visual equipment & supplies; Communications specialization; Computer peripheral equipment rental & leasing; Office facilities & secretarial service rental; Audio-visual equipment & supplies; Communications specialization; Computer peripheral equipment rental & leasing; Office facilities & secretarial service rental
CEO: Gina M Riberi
**Pr:* Gina Riberi
VP: Stephanie Roese
Dir IT: Melissa Dancer
Sls Mgr: Ben Pickrel

LIGHTWORKS OF STEAMBOAT
See ASPEN ELECTRIC AND SUPPLY INC

D-U-N-S 17-592-5866
LIGHTWORKS OPTICS INC
14192 Chambers Rd, Tustin, CA 92780-6908
Tel (714) 247-7100 *Founded/Ownrshp* 2012
Sales 24.8MM *EMP* 60
SIC 3827 7389 8748

D-U-N-S 07-935-8600
LIGHTYEAR ACQUISITION CO LLC
13900 Lincoln Park Dr # 101, Herndon, VA 20171-3254
Tel (703) 991-1464 *Founded/Ownrshp* 2011
Sales 43.2MM^E *EMP* 250^E
SIC 7373 Investment holding companies, except banks; Systems integration services

D-U-N-S 05-123-8835
LIGHTYEAR CAPITAL LLC
9 W 57th St, New York, NY 10019-2701
Tel (212) 328-0555 *Founded/Ownrshp* 2001
Sales 151.1MM^E *EMP* 966
SIC 6726 Investment offices; Investment offices
CFO: Ellan Ben-Hayon
Ex VP: Lori Forlano
Ex VP: Julie Miller
VP: David Cynn
VP: Kevin Doldan
VP: Daniel Freyman
**Prin:* David W Glenn
Mng Dir: Chris Casciato
Mng Dir: Michael Doppelt
Mng Dir: Thierry Ho
Mng Dir: Dharanjay Pai

D-U-N-S 14-326-1449
LIGHTYEAR FUND L P
(*Suby of* LIGHTYEAR CAPITAL LLC) ★
51 W 52nd St Fl 21, New York, NY 10019-6117
Tel (212) 882-5600 *Founded/Ownrshp* 2003

Sales 62.1MM[E] *EMP* 804
SIC 6726 5065 5999 Management investment funds, closed-end; Electronic parts & equipment; Telephone & communication equipment; Management investment funds, closed-end; Electronic parts & equipment; Telephone & communication equipment
Pt: Donald Marron
Assoc VP: Renee Lenzy
VP: Daniel Freyman
VP: Tomas Kasenchak
VP: Dominick Messana
VP: Richard Murphy
VP: Jack Railey
VP: Smita Sahu
VP: Debora Winfree
Mng Dir: Stewart Gross

D-U-N-S 83-040-9764
LIGHTYEAR NETWORK SOLUTIONS INC
1901 Eastpoint Pkwy, Louisville, KY 40223-4145
Tel (502) 244-6666 *Founded/Ownrshp* 1997
Sales 66.4MM *EMP* 140[E]
SIC 4813

D-U-N-S 80-754-6916
LIGHTYEAR NETWORK SOLUTIONS LLC
1901 Eastpoint Pkwy, Louisville, KY 40223-4145
Tel (502) 244-1174 *Founded/Ownrshp* 2010
Sales 48.3MM[E] *EMP* 140[E]
SIC 4813 Long distance telephone communications; Long distance telephone communications
CEO: Stephen M Lochmueller
Pr: Randy Ammon
COO: Rena Phillips
Sr VP: Ed Wampler
VP: Kevin Shady
VP: Bruce Widener
Mng Dir: Mark Sajer
Dir IT: David Corral
VP Opers: Kevin Hayes
VP Sls: Kevin B Parker
Board of Directors: Gary R Donahee, Jeffrey T Hardesty, W Bruce Lunsford

D-U-N-S 05-709-7818 IMP/EXP
LIGNOTECH USA INC
BORREGAARD LIGNOTECH
(*Suby of* SARPSFOSS LIMITED)
100 Grand Ave, Rothschild, WI 54474-1198
Tel (715) 359-6544 *Founded/Ownrshp* 1991
Sales 21.7MM[E] *EMP* 96
SIC 2861 Gum & wood chemicals; Gum & wood chemicals
Pr: Paul J La Vanway
**Pr:* Paul Romberg
**VP:* Attilio Caruso
**VP:* Ray Douglass
**VP:* Russel A Erickson

D-U-N-S 00-786-2600
LIGON ELECTRIC SUPPLY CO INC OF NC
(*Suby of* SESCO) ★
2010 2nd Ave, Huntington, WV 25703-1108
Tel (304) 523-7491 *Founded/Ownrshp* 2003
Sales 22.1MM[E] *EMP* 100
SIC 5063 Electrical supplies; Electrical supplies
Pr: John Spoor
**VP:* Jim Lathan

D-U-N-S 08-573-2852
LIGON INDUSTRIES LLC
1927 1st Ave N Ste 500, Birmingham, AL 35203-4000
Tel (205) 322-3302 *Founded/Ownrshp* 1998
Sales 645.5MM[E] *EMP* 2,155
SIC 3365 3593 3325 3471 3714 3446 Aluminum foundries; Fluid power cylinders & actuators; Alloy steel castings, except investment; Chromium plating of metals or formed products; Cylinder heads, motor vehicle; Architectural metalwork; Aluminum foundries; Fluid power cylinders & actuators; Alloy steel castings, except investment; Chromium plating of metals or formed products; Cylinder heads, motor vehicle; Architectural metalwork

D-U-N-S 94-179-0867
LIGONIER CONSTRUCTION CO
1350 Route 30, Laughlintown, PA 15655-1018
Tel (724) 238-4782 *Founded/Ownrshp* 1995
Sales 20.9MM *EMP* 60
Accts Ken Bridgeman
SIC 1623 Water, sewer & utility lines; Water, sewer & utility lines
Pr: David Herroltz
**Sec:* Cathy Herrholtz

D-U-N-S 03-007-9644
LIGONIER VALLEY SCHOOL DISTRICT AUTHORITY
339 W Main St, Ligonier, PA 15658-1131
Tel (724) 238-5696 *Founded/Ownrshp* 1966
Sales 12.7MM[E] *EMP* 345
SIC 8211 Public elementary & secondary schools; Public elementary & secondary schools

D-U-N-S 80-982-4639
LIGURIA FOODS INC
1515 15th St N, Humboldt, IA 50548-1017
Tel (515) 332-4121 *Founded/Ownrshp* 2008
Sales 70.0MM *EMP* 113
SIC 2013 Sausages & related products, from purchased meat; Sausages & related products, from purchased meat
Pr: Lance Chamber
**CFO:* Paul Sinkus
**Treas:* Dennis Pyle
**VP:* Gary Piearson
**Prin:* Jehan Saulnier
Manager: Richard Walker

LIIF
See LOW INCOME INVESTMENT FUND

D-U-N-S 05-992-8101
LIL CRICKET FOOD STORES INC
(*Suby of* CENAMA INC) ★
2271 S Pine St, Spartanburg, SC 29302-4339
Tel (864) 582-7199 *Founded/Ownrshp* 2008
Sales 35.5MM[E] *EMP* 500
SIC 5411 Convenience stores, chain; Convenience stores, chain
Pr: Gordon D Zuber

D-U-N-S 09-310-3646 IMP
LIL DRUG STORE PRODUCTS INC
1201 Continental Pl Ne, Cedar Rapids, IA 52402-2025
Tel (319) 393-0454 *Founded/Ownrshp* 1978
Sales 93.5MM[E] *EMP* 65[E]
SIC 5122 Drugs, proprietaries & sundries; Drugs & drug proprietaries; Drugs, proprietaries & sundries; Drugs & drug proprietaries
Pr: Chris Dewolf
CFO: Jeff Pitz
VP: Donald Chizek
IT Man: Michael Wenthe
Ql Cn Mgr: Chris Waters
Mktg Dir: Steve R Bosking
Mktg Mgr: Erin Dougherty
Manager: Dennis Betzler
Sls Mgr: Ben Pinti

LIL' DUTCH MAID COOKIES
See ABIMAR FOODS INC

D-U-N-S 06-529-1361
LIL THRIFT FOOD MARTS INC
1007 Arsenal Ave, Fayetteville, NC 28305-5329
Tel (910) 433-4490 *Founded/Ownrshp* 1971
Sales 88.6MM[E] *EMP* 300
Accts Cherry Bekaert & Holland Llp
SIC 5541 5411 Filling stations, gasoline; Convenience stores, chain; Filling stations, gasoline; Convenience stores, chain
CEO: Chris Neal
**Pr:* Vance B Neal

LILA DOYLE NURSING CARE FCILTY
See OCONEE MEDICAL CENTER

D-U-N-S 00-949-7686
LILE INTERNATIONAL COMPANIES INC
AMERICAN MOVERS
8060 Sw Pfaffle St # 200, Tigard, OR 97223-8489
Tel (503) 691-3500 *Founded/Ownrshp* 1959
Sales 89.9MM[E] *EMP* 350
Accts Mcgladrey & Pullen Llp Tacom
SIC 4214 4213 4225 4731 Local trucking with storage; Household goods moving & storage, local; Trucking, except local; Household goods transport; General warehousing & storage; Truck transportation brokers; Local trucking with storage; Household goods moving & storage, local; Trucking, except local; Household goods transport; General warehousing & storage; Truck transportation brokers
Pr: Diane Deautremont
VP: Donald Connelly
**VP:* Barbara L Duzsik
Dir Bus: Kim Hickman
Brnch Mgr: Carole Miller
Trfc Dir: Peter Valdez
Opers Mgr: Noah Quinton

D-U-N-S 96-369-9546
LILI UNITED WHOLESALE
2260 S Archibald Ave E, Ontario, CA 91761-8571
Tel (909) 438-6625 *Founded/Ownrshp* 2005
Sales 22.9MM *EMP* 25
SIC 5092

D-U-N-S 36-418-8979
■ **LILIEN SYSTEMS**
(*Suby of* SYSOREX GLOBAL HOLDINGS CORP) ★
17 E Sir Francis Drake Bl, Larkspur, CA 94939-1708
Tel (415) 389-7500 *Founded/Ownrshp* 2013
Sales 30.6MM[E] *EMP* 173[E]
SIC 7373 Computer integrated systems design
CEO: Nadir Ali
Ex VP: Dhruv Gulati
Exec: Rick Rutledge
IT Man: Bill Becker
IT Man: Tom Tao
VP Sls: Kevin Garrison
VP Sls: Bret Osborn
Mktg Mgr: John Galbraith
Sales Asso: Philip Dapaah

D-U-N-S 08-098-7712
LILIUOKALANI TRUST (HI)
QUEEN LLIUOKALANI CHILD CENTRE
1300 Halona St, Honolulu, HI 96817-2796
Tel (808) 847-1302 *Founded/Ownrshp* 1909
Sales 33.5MM[E] *EMP* 165
SIC 6732 Charitable trust management; Charitable trust management
Ex Dir: Benjamin Henderson
**Ch Bd:* Thomas Kaulukukui Jr

D-U-N-S 87-825-1966
LILJA CORP
229 Rickenbacker Cir, Livermore, CA 94551-7616
Tel (925) 454-9544 *Founded/Ownrshp* 1992
Sales 92.4MM[E] *EMP* 240
SIC 1541 Industrial buildings & warehouses; Industrial buildings & warehouses
CEO: Walter Bowe
**Pr:* William Field
**COO:* Mike Simmons
**CFO:* Matt Costenbader
**VP:* Michael Simmons

D-U-N-S 02-486-2484
LILLEY INTERNATIONAL INC
103 East Blvd, Williamston, NC 27892-2657
Tel (252) 792-4192 *Founded/Ownrshp* 1953
Sales 33.4MM[E] *EMP* 72
SIC 5511 5999

LILLIAN AUGUST COLLECTION
See LILLIAN AUGUST DESIGNS INC

D-U-N-S 18-169-9752 IMP
LILLIAN AUGUST DESIGNS INC
LILLIAN AUGUST COLLECTION
32 Knight St, Norwalk, CT 06851-4707
Tel (203) 847-3314 *Founded/Ownrshp* 1980
Sales 40.4MM[E] *EMP* 160
Accts Jh Cohn Llp Roseland New
SIC 5719 Housewares; Housewares
Ch Bd: Dan Weiss
**COO:* John Weiss
Board of Directors: Robert Grayson

LILLIAN VERNON
See CURRENT USA INC

D-U-N-S 14-711-5414
LILLIBRIDGE HEALTH CARE REAL ESTATE TRUST
LILLIBRIDGE HEALTH CARE SVCS
5308 W Plano Pkwy, Plano, TX 75093-4821
Tel (972) 248-9100 *Founded/Ownrshp* 2005
Sales 33.9MM[E] *EMP* 200
SIC 6552 Land subdividers & developers, commercial; Land subdividers & developers, commercial
Pr: Todd Lilibridge
VP: Sonya Brizzolara
VP: Dwight Jones
VP: Stephen Owen
Genl Mgr: Carla Cabral
Genl Mgr: George Cochran
Genl Mgr: Cindy Edward
Genl Mgr: Amanda Heismann
Genl Mgr: Rachel McMahon
Genl Mgr: Teresa Wall
Genl Mgr: Kristian Watkins

LILLIBRIDGE HEALTH CARE SVCS
See LILLIBRIDGE HEALTH CARE REAL ESTATE TRUST

D-U-N-S 60-936-0123
■ **LILLIBRIDGE HEALTHCARE SERVICES INC**
(*Suby of* VENTAS INC) ★
353 N Clark St Ste 3300, Chicago, IL 60654-4708
Tel (312) 408-1370 *Founded/Ownrshp* 2010
Sales 23.5MM[E] *EMP* 225
SIC 8082 8399 8062 6798 Home health care services; Health systems agency; General medical & surgical hospitals; Real estate investment trusts; Home health care services; Health systems agency; General medical & surgical hospitals; Real estate investment trusts
CEO: Todd W Lillibridge
Ex VP: Chuck Fendrich
Ex VP: Kevin Geraghty
Ex VP: Michael Lincoln
Ex VP: Mike Lincoln
Ex VP: Carla M Lyons
Ex VP: James E Mendelson
Ex VP: John Montgomery
Sr VP: Jack Dudick
Sr VP: Margie McHugh
Sr VP: Phil Taylor
VP: Timothy Fecker

D-U-N-S 06-181-1311
LILLISTON FORD INC
833 N Delsea Dr, Vineland, NJ 08360-2701
Tel (856) 691-2020 *Founded/Ownrshp* 1983
Sales 29.0MM *EMP* 67
SIC 5511 5531 7515 7513 5521 Automobiles, new & used; Trucks, tractors & trailers: new & used; Automotive parts; Passenger car leasing; Truck rental & leasing, no drivers; Used car dealers; Automobiles, new & used; Trucks, tractors & trailers: new & used; Automotive parts; Passenger car leasing; Truck rental & leasing, no drivers; Used car dealers
Pr: John Lilliston

D-U-N-S 00-701-8377 IMP
LILLY CO
3613 Knight Arnold Rd, Memphis, TN 38118-2729
Tel (901) 363-6000 *Founded/Ownrshp* 1919
Sales 119.3MM[E] *EMP* 183
Accts Reynolds Bone & Griesbeck Plc
SIC 5084 7699 7359 5046 Lift trucks & parts; Materials handling machinery; Industrial truck repair; Equipment rental & leasing; Shelving, commercial & industrial; Lift trucks & parts; Materials handling machinery; Industrial truck repair; Equipment rental & leasing; Shelving, commercial & industrial
Pr: Thomas J Clark III
**COO:* Eric Wisher
Mtls Mgr: John Wofford
Sls Mgr: Brad Gregory
Sls Mgr: David Overall

LILLY DEL CARIBE
See ELI LILLY INDUSTRIES INC

D-U-N-S 02-755-9074
LILLY ENTERPRISES INC
MCDONALD'S
216 E Corsicana St, Athens, TX 75751-2504
Tel (903) 677-4806 *Founded/Ownrshp* 1997
Sales 15.7MM[E] *EMP* 450
SIC 5812 Fast-food restaurant, chain; Fast-food restaurant, chain
Pr: Kevin Lilly
**VP:* Jeaneane Lilly

LILLY LIBRARY
See WABASH COLLEGE

LILLY PULITZER
See SUGARTOWN WORLDWIDE LLC

LILLY SOFTWARE ASSOCIATES
See INFOR (US) INC

D-U-N-S 96-304-9908
LILY CARES FOUNDATION INC
Lilly Corporate Center, Indianapolis, IN 46285-0001
Tel (317) 277-9109 *Founded/Ownrshp* 2010
Sales 503.3MM *EMP* 2
SIC 8699 Charitable organization; Charitable organization

D-U-N-S 01-922-7354
LILY TRANSPORTATION CORP
145 Rosemary St Ste D3, Needham, MA 02494-3251
Tel (781) 247-1300 *Founded/Ownrshp* 1958
Sales 98.9MM[E] *EMP* 500
SIC 7513 Truck leasing, without drivers; Truck leasing, without drivers
CEO: John Simourian II
**Ch Bd:* John A Simourian
**CFO:* Stephen Dmohowski
CFO: Derica Rice
CFO: Vern Sherman
**Ex VP:* James E Walker
Sr VP: Jim Lavery
**VP:* Jonathan L Baldi
**VP:* Jack Poor
VP: David Powell
Genl Mgr: Tim Ahearn

D-U-N-S 01-811-6038
LIMA AUTO MALL INC (OH)
LIMA CDLLAC PNTIAC OLDS NISSAN
2200 N Cable Rd, Lima, OH 45807-1792
Tel (419) 993-6000 *Founded/Ownrshp* 1921
Sales 40.4MM[E] *EMP* 100
SIC 5511 7538 7532 7515 Automobiles, new & used; General automotive repair shops; Top & body repair & paint shops; Passenger car leasing; Automobiles, new & used; General automotive repair shops; Top & body repair & paint shops; Passenger car leasing
Pr: William C Timmermeister
**Sec:* Susan B Timmermeister
**VP:* Rodger L Mc Clain
Sls Mgr: Ryan Swaney

LIMA CDLLAC PNTIAC OLDS NISSAN
See LIMA AUTO MALL INC

D-U-N-S 09-479-7743
LIMA CITY SCHOOL SYSTEM
515 Calumet Ave, Lima, OH 45804-1405
Tel (419) 998-2400 *Founded/Ownrshp* 1835
Sales 34.4MM[E] *EMP* 750
Accts Jim Petro Dayton Ci
SIC 8211 Public elementary school; Public junior high school; Public senior high school; Public elementary school; Public junior high school; Public senior high school
MIS Dir: Beth Jokinen

LIMA MEMORIAL HEALTH SYSTEM
See LIMA MEMORIAL HOSPITAL

D-U-N-S 01-292-1818
LIMA MEMORIAL HOSPITAL
LIMA MEMORIAL HEALTH SYSTEM
(*Suby of* LIMA MEMORIAL JOINT OPERATING CO) ★
1001 Bellefontaine Ave, Lima, OH 45804-2899
Tel (419) 228-3335 *Founded/Ownrshp* 1984
Sales 158.3MM *EMP* 1,500[E]
SIC 8062 General medical & surgical hospitals; General medical & surgical hospitals
Pr: Michael Swick
**VP:* Bob Armstrong
Ansthlgy: Samantha Linden
Ansthlgy: Kyung Park
Doctor: Richard Gordon
HC Dir: Deb Barnes

D-U-N-S 07-980-7440
LIMA MEMORIAL JOINT OPERATING CO
1001 Belelfontaine Ave, Lima, OH 45804
Tel (419) 228-5165 *Founded/Ownrshp* 1998
Sales 13.8MM[E] *EMP* 1,500
SIC 8062 General medical & surgical hospitals
Pr: Michael Swick
**CFO:* Eric Pohjala

D-U-N-S 19-962-3414 IMP
LIMA REFINING CO
(*Suby of* HUSKY ENERGY INC)
1150 S Metcalf St, Lima, OH 45804-1145
Tel (419) 226-2300 *Founded/Ownrshp* 2007
Sales 157.8MM[E] *EMP* 400[E]
SIC 2911 Petroleum refining; Petroleum refining
CEO: William Kalsse
**Pr:* Gregory King
Sr VP: Todd Neu

D-U-N-S 00-791-5960
LIMBACH CO LLC
(*Suby of* LIMBACH ENGRG & DESIGN SVCS) ★
31 35th St, Pittsburgh, PA 15201-1917
Tel (412) 359-2100 *Founded/Ownrshp* 1901
Sales 235.4MM[E] *EMP* 850
SIC 1711 Plumbing, heating, air-conditioning contractors; Plumbing, heating, air-conditioning contractors
CEO: Charles A Bacon III
**Pr:* Craig Sasser
**CFO:* Dennis Sacco
Sr VP: David R Leathes
Exec: Matt Corrigan
Off Mgr: Olivia Gonzalez
Plng Mgr: Rich Miller
CTO: Robert Wilder
IT Man: Padraic McGrath
Opers Mgr: Dan Dailey
Opers Mgr: Kevin Mirlisena

D-U-N-S 92-649-5037
LIMBACH CO LP
WESTERN AIR & REFRIGERATION
(*Suby of* LIMBACH CO LLC) ★
12442 Knott St, Garden Grove, CA 92841-2832
Tel (714) 653-7000 *Founded/Ownrshp* 2002
Sales 37.3MM[E] *EMP* 167
SIC 1711 8711 Mechanical contractor; Engineering services; Mechanical contractor; Engineering services
CEO: Charlie Bacon
**VP:* Robert C Morgan
Off Mgr: Olivia Gonzales

LIMBACH ENGRG & DESIGN SVCS
See LIMBACH FACILITY SERVICES LLC

D-U-N-S 10-157-9738
LIMBACH FACILITY SERVICES LLC
LIMBACH ENGRG & DESIGN SVCS
(*Suby of* LIMBACH HOLDINGS LLC) ★
31 35th St, Pittsburgh, PA 15201-1917
Tel (412) 359-2200 *Founded/Ownrshp* 2002
Sales 292.4MM[E] *EMP* 1,011

SIC 1711 8741 Plumbing, heating, air-conditioning contractors; Administrative management; Plumbing, heating, air-conditioning contractors; Administrative management
CEO: Charles A Bacon III
COO: Kristopher Thorne
CFO: John Jordan
VP: Mike Balistreri
VP: David R Leathers
Brnch Mgr: Robert Morgan

D-U-N-S 88-447-1509
LIMBACH HOLDINGS LLC
31 35th St, Pittsburgh, PA 15201-1917
Tel (412) 359-2226 *Founded/Ownrshp* 1994
Sales 292.4MM^E *EMP* 1,066
SIC 1711 Plumbing, heating, air-conditioning contractors; Plumbing, heating, air-conditioning contractors
Ch: Charles A Bacon
*Sr VP: Thom Barry
*Sr VP: Marc Hoogstraten
*Sr VP: Kevin Labrecque
*Sr VP: David R Leathers

D-U-N-S 08-374-2460
LIMBAUGH MOTORS INC (AL)
LIMBAUGH TOYOTA
2200 Avenue T, Birmingham, AL 35218-2942
Tel (205) 780-0500 *Founded/Ownrshp* 1989
Sales 34.1MM^E *EMP* 77
SIC 5511 Automobiles, new & used; Automobiles, new & used
Pr: Limbaugh J Bruce
*Sec: Kathy Mc Donald
VP: Richard Bond
Exec: Kay McKenzie
Off Mgr: Pam Hamaker
Sls Mgr: Dion Bell

LIMBAUGH TOYOTA
See LIMBAUGH MOTORS INC

D-U-N-S 01-380-7144 IMP
LIMCO AIREPAIR INC
(*Suby of* LIMCO-PIEDMONT INC) ★
5304 S Lawton Ave, Tulsa, OK 74107-9428
Tel (918) 445-4300 *Founded/Ownrshp* 2009
Sales 25.2MM^E *EMP* 140
SIC 3443 7699 3585 3444 3398 Heat exchangers, condensers & components; Aircraft & heavy equipment repair services; Refrigeration & heating equipment; Sheet metalwork; Metal heat treating; Heat exchangers, condensers & components; Aircraft & heavy equipment repair services; Refrigeration & heating equipment; Sheet metalwork; Metal heat treating
CFO: Mary Dowdy
Exec: Nina Schmiege
Genl Mgr: Brad Beall
Genl Mgr: Pam Godfrey
QA Dir: Stan Grzelak
IT Man: Mike Dunne
IT Man: Cheryl Noris
IT Man: Keith Selensky
Sfty Mgr: Bill Frankenberger
Prd Mgr: Tony Manuel
Mktg Dir: Bob McDonanld

D-U-N-S 80-613-8629
LIMCO-PIEDMONT INC
(*Suby of* TATTECHNOLOGIES LTD.)
5304 S Lawton Ave, Tulsa, OK 74107-9428
Tel (918) 445-4300 *Founded/Ownrshp* 2007
Sales 27.7MM^E *EMP* 275^E
SIC 4581 3728 Aircraft maintenance & repair services; Aircraft parts & equipment; Aircraft maintenance & repair services; Aircraft parts & equipment
Ch Bd: Shmuel Fledel
Pr: Yair Raz
CFO: Mary Dowdy

D-U-N-S 03-147-4096
▲ LIME ENERGY CO
4 Gateway Ctr, Newark, NJ 07102-4062
Tel (704) 892-4442 *Founded/Ownrshp* 1997
Sales 58.8MM *EMP* 164
Accts Bdo Usa Llp Chicago Illinoi
Tkr Sym LIME *Exch* NAS
SIC 1711 8711 Mechanical contractor; Energy conservation engineering; Mechanical contractor; Energy conservation engineering
Pr: C Adam Procell
*Ch Bd: Richard P Kiphart
CFO: Mary Colleen Brennan
Sr VP: Stephen Guthrie
VP: Richard Fish
VP: Richard Vaillencourt
VP: Don White
VP Bus Dev: Larry Ostema
Genl Mgr: Jim Ealahan
Pgrm Dir: Arjun Saroya

D-U-N-S 60-246-6088 IMP
LIME HOLDING INC
(*Suby of* KDM HOLDING INC.)
3700 Hulen St, Fort Worth, TX 76107-6816
Tel (817) 732-8164 *Founded/Ownrshp* 1981
Sales 413.1MM^E *EMP* 500
SIC 3274 Lime; Quicklime; Hydrated lime; Dolomitic lime, dead-burned dolomite; Lime; Quicklime; Hydrated lime; Dolomitic lime, dead-burned dolomite
CEO: Ludwig De Mot
IT Man: Chip McClellan

LIME INSTRUMENT
See SUPREME ELECTRICAL SERVICES INC

D-U-N-S 96-503-4312
LIME ROCK PARTNERS II LP
274 Riverside Ave Ste 3b, Westport, CT 06880-4823
Tel (203) 293-2750 *Founded/Ownrshp* 2010
Sales 64.0MM^E *EMP* 130^E
SIC 6733 6211 Private estate, personal investment & vacation fund trusts; Security brokers & dealers
Prin: Donna Pruner
VP: Gary Sernovitz

D-U-N-S 61-673-3197
LIME ROCK RESOURCES
1111 Bagby St Ste 4600, Houston, TX 77002-2559
Tel (713) 292-9510 *Founded/Ownrshp* 2005
Sales 33.7MM^E *EMP* 30
SIC 1382 Oil & gas exploration services
CEO: Eric Mullins
*Pt: C Tim Miller
*CEO: Charles Adcock
*COO: Tim Miller
CFO: Tray Black
*CFO: Morrow Evans
*Sr VP: Chris Butta
VP: Dawn Smajstrla
IT Man: Thomas Owen
Prd Mgr: Steven Hunter

D-U-N-S 02-955-1756
▲ LIMELIGHT NETWORKS INC
222 S Mill Ave Ste 800, Tempe, AZ 85281-2899
Tel (602) 850-5000 *Founded/Ownrshp* 2001
Sales 162.2MM *EMP* 482^E
Accts Ernst & Young Llp Phoenix Ar
Tkr Sym LLNW *Exch* NGS
SIC 7372 7375 Application computer software; Business oriented computer software; Information retrieval services; On-line data base information retrieval; Application computer software; Business oriented computer software; Information retrieval services; On-line data base information retrieval
Pr: Robert A Lento
CFO: Peter J Perrone
Chf Mktg O: Charles Kirby Wadsworth
Ofcr: Philip C Maynard
Ofcr: George E Vonderhaar
VP: Dan Boncel
VP: Sara Buttle
VP: William Charnock
VP: Jason Clement
VP: Jeff Freund
VP: Barb King
VP: Paul Louden
VP: Kevin Odden
Dir Bus: Jacob Cross
Dir Bus: Andy Knutson
Board of Directors: Walter D Amaral, Jeffrey T Fisher, Joseph H Gleberman, Gray Hall, Fredric W Harman, David C Peterschmidt

D-U-N-S 07-371-7597
LIMESTONE COLLEGE
1115 College Dr, Gaffney, SC 29340-3799
Tel (864) 489-7151 *Founded/Ownrshp* 1845
Sales 50.3MM *EMP* 320
Accts Cherry Bekaert Llp Greenville
SIC 8221 College, except junior; College, except junior
Pr: Walt Griffin
*CFO: David Rilling
Ofcr: Franklin Mitchell
*Ex VP: Karen Gainey
Ex VP: Stephen Jennings
*VP: William Baker
*VP: Mike Cerino
*VP: C R Horton
*VP: Robert Overton
*VP: Chris Phenicie
Comm Dir: Charles Wyatt

D-U-N-S 07-210-6628
LIMESTONE COUNTY BOARD OF EDUCATION
300 S Jefferson St, Athens, AL 35611-2549
Tel (256) 232-5353 *Founded/Ownrshp* 1900
Sales 107.8MM^E *EMP* 1,200
SIC 8211 Public elementary & secondary schools; School board
Pr: Brett McGill
IT Man: Kim Emerson
Board of Directors: Dr William Berry, John Blankenship, Joel Glaze, Mike Poff, Fred Robertson Jr, Shelly Towe

D-U-N-S 07-979-8750
LIMESTONE COUNTY SCHOOL DISTRICT
300 S Jefferson St, Athens, AL 35611-2549
Tel (256) 232-5353 *Founded/Ownrshp* 2015
Sales 9.3MM^E *EMP* 1,038^E
SIC 8211 Public elementary & secondary schools
CFO: Jonathan Craft
Bd of Dir: Anthony Hilliard
Bd of Dir: Darin Russell
Bd of Dir: Charles Shoulders
Exec: Nancy Allfrey
Schl Brd P: Marty Adams
Teacher Pr: Pam Malone
Psych: Doug Warner
HC Dir: Rhonda Gibbs

LIMEVILLE QUARRY
See MARTIN LIMESTONE INC

LIMITED
See L BRANDS STORE DESIGN & CONSTRUCTION INC

D-U-N-S 13-858-2361
■ LIMITED BRANDS LOGISTICS SERVICES INC
MAST GLOBAL LOGISTICS
(*Suby of* L BRANDS INC) ★
2 Limited Pkwy, Columbus, OH 43230-1445
Tel (614) 415-7500 *Founded/Ownrshp* 1986
Sales 87.2MM^E *EMP* 62^E
SIC 5113 Shipping supplies
Pr: Rick Jackson

D-U-N-S 04-231-5093 IMP/EXP
LIMITED STORES LLC
(*Suby of* SUN CAPITAL PARTNERS INC) ★
7775 Walton Pkwy Ste 400, New Albany, OH 43054-8203
Tel (614) 289-2200 *Founded/Ownrshp* 2007
Sales 1.7MMM^E *EMP* 18,000
SIC 5621 5941 5632 Ready-to-wear apparel, women's; Apparel accessories; Sporting goods & bicycle shops; Ready-to-wear apparel, women's; Sporting goods & bicycle shops; Apparel accessories
CFO: Stuart Burgdoerfer
VP: Jenn Jong
VP: Martyn Redgrave
Dist Mgr: Darlene Blair-Wade
Dist Mgr: Misty Brown
Dist Mgr: Mareatha Hornsby
Dist Mgr: Vicki Leavitt
Dist Mgr: Kevin Schrock
Plng Mgr: Chris Bichsel
Store Mgr: Sharon Cahill
Store Mgr: Stephanie Haley

LIMITED SVC HLTH ORGANIZATION
See CARE PLUS DENTAL PLAN

D-U-N-S 07-747-8639
■ LIMITED TECHNOLOGY SERVICES INC
(*Suby of* L BRANDS INC) ★
3 Limited Pkwy, Columbus, OH 43230-1467
Tel (614) 415-7000 *Founded/Ownrshp* 1999
Sales 76.1MM^E *EMP* 800
SIC 7374 Data processing & preparation; Data processing & preparation
Pr: Jon Ricker
Dir IT: Tom Danzeisen

D-U-N-S 07-834-8412
■ LIMON WIND III LLC
(*Suby of* NEXTERA ENERGY INC) ★
700 Universe Blvd, Juno Beach, FL 33408-2657
Tel (561) 691-7171 *Founded/Ownrshp* 2011
Sales 28.4MM^E *EMP* 68^E
SIC 4911 Electric services
Prin: Tj Tuscai

D-U-N-S 00-691-4105 IMP/EXP
▲ LIMONEIRA CO
1141 Cummings Rd Ofc, Santa Paula, CA 93060-9783
Tel (805) 525-5541 *Founded/Ownrshp* 1893
Sales 103.4MM *EMP* 331^E
Accts Ernst & Young Llp Los Angeles
Tkr Sym LMNR *Exch* NGM
SIC 0723 0174 0179 6531 6799 Fruit (fresh) packing services; Citrus fruits; Lemon grove; Orange grove; Avocado orchard; Real estate agents & managers; Real estate leasing & rentals; Commodity investors; Fruit (fresh) packing services; Citrus fruits; Lemon grove; Orange grove; Avocado orchard; Real estate agents & managers; Real estate leasing & rentals; Commodity investors
Pr: Harold S Edwards
*Ch Bd: Gordon E Kimball
CFO: Joseph D Rumley
*V Ch Bd: John W Blanchard
*V Ch Bd: Robert M Sawyer
Ofcr: Jocelyn Hernandez
Ofcr: Frances Martinez
Sr VP: Alex M Teague
Genl Mgr: Lee Nesbitt
Genl Mgr: Mark Spencer
Sls Dir: John Carter
Board of Directors: John W H Merriman, Ronald Michaelis, Keith W Renken, Donald R Rudkin, Scott S Slater

D-U-N-S 01-626-2043 IMP
LIMOSS US LLC
LINEAR MOTION SYSTEMS
964 Highway 45, Baldwyn, MS 38824-8593
Tel (662) 365-2200 *Founded/Ownrshp* 2009
Sales 28.1MM *EMP* 26
SIC 3625 Actuators, industrial; Actuators, industrial
CFO: Benjie Gray
COO: Preben Petersen
*VP: Damon Fisher
Opers Mgr: Dave Dye

D-U-N-S 06-552-8077
LIMRA INTERNATIONAL INC
300 Day Hill Rd, Windsor, CT 06095-4761
Tel (860) 688-3358 *Founded/Ownrshp* 1917
Sales 42.1MM^E *EMP* 234
SIC 8611 2721

D-U-N-S 08-526-1308 IMP/EXP
LIMSON TRADING INC
1300 Gezon Pkwy Sw, Grand Rapids, MI 49509-9300
Tel (616) 530-3110 *Founded/Ownrshp* 1998
Sales 126.9MM *EMP* 13
SIC 5141 Food brokers; Food brokers
Pr: David Lee Gray
VP: Barbara Kuiper
Genl Mgr: Jagtar Nijjar
QA Dir: Steve Brunsting
Ql Cn Mgr: Katie Kolarik

D-U-N-S 00-380-3772
■ LIN BROADCASTING INC
WISH-TV
(*Suby of* MEDIA GENERAL INC) ★
1950 N Meridian St, Indianapolis, IN 46202-1304
Tel (317) 956-8576 *Founded/Ownrshp* 1954, 1987
Sales 29.8MM^E *EMP* 234
SIC 4833 Television broadcasting stations; Television broadcasting stations
Genl Mgr: Jeff White
Pr: Les Vann
*VP: Scott Blumenthal

D-U-N-S 36-260-2237 IMP
LIN ENGINEERING INC
16245 Vineyard Blvd, Morgan Hill, CA 95037-7123
Tel (408) 919-0200 *Founded/Ownrshp* 1987
Sales 27.5MM^E *EMP* 125
SIC 3621 Motors, electric; Motors, electric
Pr: Ted T Lin
*CFO: Rouyu Loughry
*Sec: Cynthia Lin
Sls Dir: Dave Housel
Sls Mgr: Alice Diaz
Snr Mgr: Richard Badgerow

D-U-N-S 11-852-5831
LIN R ROGERS ELECTRICAL CONTRACTORS INC
2050 Marconi Dr Ste 200, Alpharetta, GA 30005-5202
Tel (770) 772-3400 *Founded/Ownrshp* 1983
Sales 131.4MM *EMP* 1,100
Accts Moore Stephens Tiller Llc Dul
SIC 1731 General electrical contractor; General electrical contractor
Ch: Lin R Rogers
*Pr: Chris Rogers
*CEO: Christoper L Rogers
*VP: Jamal Chehimi
*VP: Benedict Cramer
*VP: Jason Hayes
*VP: Lindsey Rogers Schoultz
*VP: Ken Sisson
*Prin: Linda Chaney
VP Sls: Ron Gilcrease

D-U-N-S 79-143-1067
■ LIN TELEVISION CORP
(*Suby of* MEDIA GENERAL INC) ★
701 Brazos St Ste 800, Austin, TX 78701-2556
Tel (512) 774-6110 *Founded/Ownrshp* 2014
Sales 679.4MM^E *EMP* 5,300^E
SIC 4833 Television broadcasting stations; Television broadcasting stations
Pr: Vincent L Sadusky
CFO: Richard J Schmaeling

D-U-N-S 92-789-4402
LIN TELEVISION OF TEXAS LP
KNVA TELEVISION
908 W Martin Luther King, Austin, TX 78701-1018
Tel (512) 478-5400 *Founded/Ownrshp* 1994
Sales 41.4MM^E *EMP* 164
SIC 4833 Television broadcasting stations; Television broadcasting stations
Pt: Eric Lassberg
Mktg Mgr: Deidre Conley
Sls Mgr: Scott Nelson
Snr Mgr: Jim Spencer

D-U-N-S 10-320-3431
LIN TV CORP
1 W Exchange St Ste 305, Providence, RI 02903-1095
Tel (401) 454-2880 *Founded/Ownrshp* 1966
Sales 553.4MM *EMP* 2,558^E
SIC 4833 7311

D-U-N-S 07-889-0119
LINA GALE INC (CA)
230 S 9th Ave, City of Industry, CA 91746-3309
Tel (909) 595-8898 *Founded/Ownrshp* 1991
Sales 47.0MM^E *EMP* 100
SIC 5122 Cosmetics
CEO: John Chen
*CFO: Lina Chen

D-U-N-S 02-138-8649
LINAMAR FORGINGS CAROLINA INC
LINAMAR FORGINGS, INC.
(*Suby of* LINAMAR HOLDING NEVADA INC) ★
2401 Stantonsburg Rd Se, Wilson, NC 27893-8414
Tel (252) 237-8181 *Founded/Ownrshp* 2014
Sales 55.0MM *EMP* 100
SIC 3566 3562 Gears, power transmission, except automotive; Ball bearings & parts; Gears, power transmission, except automotive; Ball bearings & parts

LINAMAR FORGINGS, INC.
See LINAMAR FORGINGS CAROLINA INC

D-U-N-S 14-618-8789
LINAMAR HOLDING NEVADA INC
(*Suby of* LINAMAR CORPORATION)
25300 Telg Rd 450, Southfield, MI 48034
Tel (248) 355-3533 *Founded/Ownrshp* 1998
Sales 61.4MM^E *EMP* 100^E
SIC 3545 Precision measuring tools
CEO: Linda Hasenfratz
*Pr: Jim Jarrell
*Treas: Dale Schneider

D-U-N-S 00-115-9425 IMP/EXP
LINATEX CORP OF AMERICA
WEIR MINERALS LINATEX-GALLATIN
(*Suby of* WEIR MINERALS NORTH AMERICA) ★
1550 Airport Rd, Gallatin, TN 37066-3792
Tel (615) 230-2100 *Founded/Ownrshp* 1982, 2010
Sales 48.2MM^E *EMP* 70
SIC 5084 3479 Processing & packaging equipment; Coating of metals & formed products
Pr: Peter Atkinson
*Ch Bd: Scott Smith
*Treas: Andi Simon
Exec: Elaine Gore
Exec: Sherrill Legnon
Genl Mgr: Pat Warchol
IT Man: Gracie Philip
Plnt Mgr: Esteban Dominguez
Plnt Mgr: Russ Sterzer
Board of Directors: Peter Atkinson, Kenny Brooks

D-U-N-S 00-289-5597
LINBECK GROUP LLC
(*Suby of* AQUINAS CORP) ★
3900 Essex Ln Ste 1200, Houston, TX 77027-5486
Tel (713) 621-2350 *Founded/Ownrshp* 1964
Sales 268.3MM^E *EMP* 500
SIC 1542 Commercial & office building, new construction; Shopping center construction; Hospital construction; Commercial & office building, new construction; Shopping center construction; Hospital construction
Ch Bd: Chuck Greco
CEO: David Stueckler
CFO: Bill Riegler
Ex VP: Bill Scott
Off Admin: Cheris Oller
Snr PM: Tom Hale
Board of Directors: Allen Nagel, Edwin H Wingate

D-U-N-S 04-214-9755
LINC ENERGY OPERATIONS INC
1000 La St Ste 1500, Houston, TX 77002
Tel (713) 580-6600 *Founded/Ownrshp* 2011
Sales 22.8MM^E *EMP* 46^E
SIC 3533 Oil & gas field machinery
Ch: Ken Dark

LINC GROUP
See ABM FACILITY SOLUTIONS GROUP LLC

D-U-N-S 80-057-4019
■ LINC LOGISTICS CO
(Suby of UNIVERSAL TRUCKLOAD SERVICES INC) ★
12755 E 9 Mile Rd, Warren, MI 48089-2621
Tel (586) 467-1500 Founded/Ownrshp 2012
Sales 98.1MM^E EMP 1,500
SIC 8742 Transportation consultant; Transportation consultant
V Ch: Manuel J Moroun
IT Man: Barry Denning
Opers Mgr: Jonathan Jansons

D-U-N-S 92-899-1256 IMP
LINC SYSTEMS INC
16540 Southpark Dr, Westfield, IN 46074-8436
Tel (317) 399-3200 Founded/Ownrshp 1995
Sales 73.4MM^E EMP 67
SIC 5085 5199 Fasteners, industrial: nuts, bolts, screws, etc.; Packaging materials; Fasteners, industrial: nuts, bolts, screws, etc.; Packaging materials
Pr: Ted Azar
*Sec: William Dennis
Sls Mgr: Brian Caudill

D-U-N-S 62-220-4774
LINCARE HOLDINGS INC
(Suby of LINDE AG)
19387 Us Highway 19 N, Clearwater, FL 33764-3102
Tel (727) 530-7700 Founded/Ownrshp 2012
Sales 508.8MM^E EMP 10,841^E
SIC 8082 8093 Home health care services; Specialty outpatient clinics; Home health care services; Specialty outpatient clinics
CEO: John P Byrnes
*Pr: Shawn S Schabel
*CFO: Paul G Gabos
Dist Mgr: Tarrah Filo-Loos
Dist Mgr: Nan Pearson
Genl Mgr: Chris Morgan

D-U-N-S 08-642-1534
LINCARE INC
(Suby of LINCARE HOLDINGS INC) ★
19387 Us Highway 19 N, Clearwater, FL 33764-3102
Tel (727) 530-7700 Founded/Ownrshp 1990
Sales 496.6MM^E EMP 10,841
SIC 8082 5999 Home health care services; Hospital equipment & supplies; Home health care services; Hospital equipment & supplies
CEO: Kristen Hoefer
Pr: Vanessa Hager
*COO: Greg McCarthy
CFO: Jim Emmanuel
CFO: Morris Kunofsky
*CFO: Crispin Teufel
Ofcr: Jenna Pedersen
Ofcr: Jenna Petersen
Comm Dir: Brian Jennings
Area Mgr: Peter Butkevitch
Area Mgr: Will Reynold

D-U-N-S 36-257-6431
LINCHRIS HOTEL CORP
269 Hanover St Ste 2, Hanover, MA 02339-2245
Tel (781) 826-8824 Founded/Ownrshp 1985
Sales 73.6MM^E EMP 1,219
SIC 7011 Hotels & motels; Hotels & motels
CEO: Christopher Gistis
*Pr: Michael Sullivan
*CFO: Glenn Gistis
Sr VP: Janine Hodge
*Sr VP: Dennis Jakubowski
*Sr VP: Robb M Moskowitz
*VP: Liz Jobin
VP Opers: Nicholas Pancoast

D-U-N-S 00-801-0738 IMP
LINCO-ELECTROMATIC INC
CAMERON MEASUREMENT SYSTEMS
4580 W Wall St, Midland, TX 79703-7624
Tel (432) 694-9644 Founded/Ownrshp 1965
Sales 20.4MM^E EMP 120
SIC 5084 3613 3625

LINCOLN
See MARION FORD INC

LINCOLN ADVERTISING COMPANY
See LINCOLN PROPERTY CO CSE INC

D-U-N-S 80-002-6176
LINCOLN BANCORP
508 Main St, Reinbeck, IA 50669-1052
Tel (319) 788-6441 Founded/Ownrshp 2007
Sales NA EMP 225^E
SIC 6022 State commercial banks
Prin: Cordell Q Peterson
Ofcr: Renee Vandenakker
VP: Cathy Schuler
VP: Jessie Schunk
VP: Julie Versluis
CIO: Jeff Becker
VP Mktg: Angela Ewoldt

LINCOLN BENEFIT LIFE CO.
See ALLSTATE FINANCIAL SERVICES LLC

D-U-N-S 04-230-5052
LINCOLN BLOOMINGTON MERCURY
WALZER QUALITY MAZDA
1001 Clover Dr S, Minneapolis, MN 55420-1040
Tel (952) 888-5880 Founded/Ownrshp 2004
Sales 31.3MM^E EMP 84
SIC 5511 Automobiles, new & used; Automobiles, new & used
Prin: Andrew Walzer
Treas: Rich Hage
Exec: Carol Lehr

D-U-N-S 00-806-0170
LINCOLN BUILDERS INC
1910 Farmerville Hwy, Ruston, LA 71270-3008
Tel (318) 255-3822 Founded/Ownrshp 1962
Sales 104.4MM EMP 85
Accts The Robinette Firm Apac Monr
SIC 1542 Commercial & office building, new construction; Commercial & office buildings, renovation & repair; Commercial & office building, new construction; Commercial & office buildings, renovation & repair
CEO: Danny Graham
*Sec: Lynn Hutchinson
Dir Bus: Ayres Bradford

D-U-N-S 87-260-1088
LINCOLN BUILDERS OF BATON ROUGE INC
11567 Mercantile Dr, Baton Rouge, LA 70809-4914
Tel (225) 706-5038 Founded/Ownrshp 2007
Sales 35.0MM EMP 20
SIC 1522 1771 Residential construction; Concrete work
Pr: Ronnie Myers
*CFO: Lynn V Hutchinson
*VP: Keith Keller
*VP: Daryll Williams

D-U-N-S 04-542-2722 IMP
LINCOLN CENTER FOR PERFORMING ARTS INC (NY)
AVERY FISHER HALL
10 Lincoln Center Plz, New York, NY 10023-6912
Tel (212) 875-5000 Founded/Ownrshp 1956
Sales 54.1MM^E EMP 525
Accts Kpmg Llp New York Ny
SIC 7922 Theatrical producers & services; Theatrical producers & services
Pr: Reynold Levy
Pr: Robert Arning
V Ch: William Rhodes
V Ch: Peter White
CFO: Joseph Lozito
*CFO: Daniel Rubin
Sr VP: Tracy Johnson
Sr VP: Andre Mirabelli
VP: Cecelia Gilchriest
VP: Jerry Hastings
VP: Sarah Kerman
VP: Greg Shepps
VP: Hassett Timothy
Exec: Clare Avery
Exec: Jennifer Berry
Exec: Eileen McMahon
Exec: Kamal Sookram
Assoc Dir: Wendy Mazo

LINCOLN CENTER THEATER
See BEAUMONT VIVIAN THEATER INC

LINCOLN CENTRE
See MARION CITY SCHOOLS

LINCOLN COLLEGE
See LINCOLN UNIVERSITY (INC)

D-U-N-S 05-773-8726
LINCOLN COMMUNITY FOUNDATION
215 Centennial Mall S, Lincoln, NE 68508-1895
Tel (402) 474-2345 Founded/Ownrshp 1959
Sales 27.6MM EMP 9
SIC 8399 8111 Health & welfare council; Legal services
Pr: Dawson Dowty
VP: Paula Metcalf
*VP: Chandler Tyrrell

D-U-N-S 12-581-5589
LINCOLN COMMUNITY HEALTH CENTER INC
1301 Fayetteville St, Durham, NC 27707-2398
Tel (919) 956-4000 Founded/Ownrshp 1972
Sales 28.2MM EMP 165^E
Accts Simmons Richey & Company Pc L
SIC 8011 Medical centers; Medical centers
CEO: Philip A Harewood
CFO: William Seagroves

LINCOLN COMMUNITY HOME HEALTH
See LINCOLN COMMUNITY HOSPITAL AND NURSING HOME

D-U-N-S 08-038-7715
LINCOLN COMMUNITY HOSPITAL AND NURSING HOME (CO)
LINCOLN COMMUNITY HOME HEALTH
111 6th St, Hugo, CO 80821-2002
Tel (719) 743-2421 Founded/Ownrshp 1959
Sales 27.1MM^E EMP 173
SIC 8051 8062 Skilled nursing care facilities; General medical & surgical hospitals
CEO: Herman Schreivogel
Dir Lab: Gwen Schroeder
Dir IT: Michael Gaskins
IT Man: Linda Messer
Sfty Mgr: Steve Young

LINCOLN COMPOSITES
See LINCOLN HEXAGON INC

D-U-N-S 08-547-2256
LINCOLN CONSOLIDATED SCHOOL DISTRICT
LINCOLN CONSOLIDATED SCHOOLS
8970 Whittaker Rd, Ypsilanti, MI 48197-9440
Tel (734) 484-7001 Founded/Ownrshp 1924
Sales 27.9MM^E EMP 600
Accts Rehmann Robson Jackson Mi
SIC 8211 Public elementary school; Public junior high school; Public senior high school; Public elementary school; Public junior high school; Public senior high school
MIS Dir: Andrew Hahn
Dir IT: Jona Ramey
Teacher Pr: Heshimu Green
HC Dir: Kitty Heiss

LINCOLN CONSOLIDATED SCHOOLS
See LINCOLN CONSOLIDATED SCHOOL DISTRICT

D-U-N-S 05-535-6471
LINCOLN CONSTRUCTION INC
4790 Shuster Rd, Columbus, OH 43214-1997
Tel (614) 457-6015 Founded/Ownrshp 1976
Sales 40.0MM EMP 50
SIC 1542

D-U-N-S 07-498-2570
LINCOLN CONTRACTING & EQUIPMENT CO INC
(Suby of RIGGS INDUSTRIES INC) ★
2478 Lincoln Hwy, Stoystown, PA 15563-7821
Tel (814) 629-6641 Founded/Ownrshp 1973
Sales 25.2MM EMP 100
SIC 7353 3441 1241 Heavy construction equipment rental; Fabricated structural metal; Mine preparation services; Heavy construction equipment rental; Fabricated structural metal; Mine preparation services
Pr: Harold Walker
*CFO: William B Friedline
*Treas: David F Lowry
*VP: C Daniel Riggs
Genl Mgr: Jim Cunningham
Sfty Dirs: Kevin Macy

D-U-N-S 00-643-6364
LINCOLN CONTRACTORS SUPPLY INC (WI)
11111 W Hayes Ave, Milwaukee, WI 53227-1918
Tel (414) 541-1327 Founded/Ownrshp 1956
Sales 26.3MM EMP 85
Accts Tushaus & Associates Llc Mil
SIC 5082 7359 General construction machinery & equipment; Equipment rental & leasing; General construction machinery & equipment; Equipment rental & leasing
Pr: Norman C Knief
VP: Dale Guenther
VP: Keith Turtenwald
Brnch Mgr: Bryan Rieckman
IT Man: Aaron Knief
Manager: Phil Thomasen
Sls Mgr: Dan Gust

D-U-N-S 08-686-9336
LINCOLN COUNTY
COUNTY OF LINCOLN
115 W Main St, Lincolnton, NC 28092-2611
Tel (704) 736-8488 Founded/Ownrshp 1779
Sales NA EMP 540
Accts Martin Starnes & Associates C
SIC 9111 Executive offices; ; Executive offices;
*Prin: W Tracy Jackson
CIO: Doug Jones
Opers Supe: Bruce Mashburn
Opers Supe: Carol Mecimore

D-U-N-S 07-507-5804
LINCOLN COUNTY BOARD OF EDUCATION
233 E Monticello St, Brookhaven, MS 39601-3328
Tel (601) 835-0011 Founded/Ownrshp 1890
Sales 6.4MM^E EMP 350
SIC 8211 Public elementary & secondary schools; Public elementary & secondary schools

D-U-N-S 08-552-4213
LINCOLN COUNTY BOARD OF EDUCATION
10 Marland Ave Ste 100, Hamlin, WV 25523-1058
Tel (304) 824-3033 Founded/Ownrshp 1900
Sales 20.4MM^E EMP 405
SIC 8211 Public elementary school; Public junior high school; Public senior high school; Public elementary school; Public junior high school; Public senior high school
Pr: Stephen Priestley
*CFO: Birdie Gandy

D-U-N-S 07-824-5164
LINCOLN COUNTY HEALTH SYSTEM FOUNDATION
LINCOLN MEDICAL CENTER
106 Medical Center Blvd, Fayetteville, TN 37334-2684
Tel (931) 438-1100 Founded/Ownrshp 1917
Sales 52.4MM^E EMP 544
SIC 8062 8051 8059 8082 4119 General medical & surgical hospitals; Skilled nursing care facilities; Convalescent home; Home health care services; Ambulance service; General medical & surgical hospitals; Skilled nursing care facilities; Convalescent home; Home health care services; Ambulance service
CEO: Jamie Guin
*CFO: David Groce
*CFO: Mike Harbor
Sr Cor Off: Linda Jackson
Off Mgr: Carla Doss
Off Mgr: Patsy Shields
CIO: Bobby Neeley
Dir IT: Don Lavender
Mktg Mgr: Jennifer Wolaver

D-U-N-S 07-183-4923
LINCOLN COUNTY PUBLIC HOSPITAL DISTRICT 3
LINCOLN HOSPITAL
10 Nicholls St, Davenport, WA 99122-9729
Tel (509) 725-7501 Founded/Ownrshp 1963
Sales 34.2MM^E EMP 270
SIC 8062 8051 General medical & surgical hospitals; Convalescent home with continuous nursing care; General medical & surgical hospitals; Convalescent home with continuous nursing care
Ch: Gerald Krause
*CFO: Tyson Lacy
Treas: Brian Madison
Dir Rad: Jean Riendeau
IT Man: Annette Edwards
QC Dir: Cheryl Nelson
Mktg Mgr: Kyp Graber
Surgeon: Deanna Davidson

LINCOLN COUNTY PUBLIC SCHOOLS
See LINCOLN COUNTY SCHOOL DISTRICT

D-U-N-S 62-128-0564
LINCOLN COUNTY R-III SCHOOL DISTRICT BUILDING CORP
TROY R-III SCHOOL DISTRICT
951 W College St, Troy, MO 63379-1112
Tel (636) 462-3739 Founded/Ownrshp 1992
Sales 60.7MM EMP 750
Accts Larson Allen Weishair Company
SIC 8211 Public adult education school; Public adult education school
*Pr: Eric Hood
Pr Dir: April Bryant
Teacher Pr: Barb Furrer

D-U-N-S 19-301-6540
LINCOLN COUNTY SCHOOL DISTRICT
LINCOLN COUNTY PUBLIC SCHOOLS
353 N Generals Blvd, Lincolnton, NC 28092-3558
Tel (704) 732-2261 Founded/Ownrshp 1994
Sales 73.3MM^E EMP 1,600
SIC 8211 Public elementary & secondary schools; Public elementary & secondary schools
IT Man: Peggy Lafferty
Pr Dir: Sandra Andrews
Schl Brd P: Candi Burgin
Schl Brd P: Carl Robinson

D-U-N-S 09-289-6588
LINCOLN COUNTY SCHOOL DISTRICT (INC)
459 Sw Coast Hwy, Newport, OR 97365-4978
Tel (541) 265-9211 Founded/Ownrshp 1923
Sales 35.2MM^E EMP 500
SIC 8211 Public elementary & secondary schools; Public elementary & secondary schools
V Ch: Karen Bondley
Genl Mgr: Susan Graves
IT Man: Mark Bartnick
Netwrk Mgr: Ardis Christensen
Sys Mgr: Laurie Urquhart
Sls Mgr: Sharon Rogers
Schl Brd P: Liz Martin
Psych: Vicky Roller

D-U-N-S 05-062-2778
LINCOLN COUNTY SCHOOL DISTRICT 2
222 E 4th Ave, Afton, WY 83110-1010
Tel (307) 885-7146 Founded/Ownrshp 1976
Sales 21.4MM^E EMP 290
SIC 8211 Public elementary & secondary schools; Public elementary & secondary schools
MIS Dir: Kyle Webber
HC Dir: Skyla Hamilton

D-U-N-S 07-409-4707
LINCOLN COUNTY SCHOOLS
305 Danville Ave, Stanford, KY 40484-1205
Tel (606) 365-1333 Founded/Ownrshp 1930
Sales 42.1MM^E EMP 650
Accts Pauly Rogers & Co Pc Tig
SIC 8211 Public elementary & secondary schools; High school, junior or senior; Public elementary & secondary schools; High school, junior or senior
MIS Dir: Darren Yaden
Pr Dir: Pam Hart
HC Dir: Eva Stone

D-U-N-S 07-979-8790
LINCOLN COUNTY SCHOOLS
206 Davidson St E, Fayetteville, TN 37334-3502
Tel (931) 433-3565 Founded/Ownrshp 2014
Sales 3.8MM^E EMP 300^E
SIC 8211 Public elementary & secondary schools
MIS Dir: Brad Luna
HC Dir: Carmen Smith
HC Dir: Linda Tallman

D-U-N-S 07-979-9694
LINCOLN COUNTY SCHOOLS
Lincoln County Schools, Hamlin, WV 25523
Tel (304) 824-3033 Founded/Ownrshp 2015
Sales 5.3MM^E EMP 395^E
SIC 8211 Public elementary & secondary schools
HC Dir: Teresa Ryan

D-U-N-S 08-764-8879
LINCOLN COUNTY SCHOOLS
231 E Monticello St, Brookhaven, MS 39601-3328
Tel (601) 835-3448 Founded/Ownrshp 1900
Sales 11.6MM^E EMP 420
SIC 8211 Public elementary & secondary schools; Public elementary & secondary schools
CFO: Cheryl Shelby

D-U-N-S 80-045-6787
LINCOLN CRST SALES INC
(Suby of CRST INTERNATIONAL INC) ★
3930 16th Ave Sw, Cedar Rapids, IA 52404-2332
Tel (319) 396-4400 Founded/Ownrshp 2005
Sales 38.0MM^E EMP 180
SIC 4731 Transportation agents & brokers; Transportation agents & brokers
CEO: John Smith
*Pr: David L Rusch
*Sec: Wesley L Brackey

D-U-N-S 87-958-0306
LINCOLN DODGE INC
PERFORMANCE JEEP DODGE
6601 Telluride Dr, Lincoln, NE 68521-8974
Tel (402) 477-3777 Founded/Ownrshp 1993
Sales 31.3MM^E EMP 90
SIC 5511 Automobiles, new & used; Automobiles, new & used
Pr: F Mickey Anderson
*CEO: Talton K Anderson
Off Mgr: Crystal Henning

D-U-N-S 96-574-3776
LINCOLN EASTERN MANAGEMENT CORP
LPC
2000 Mckinney Ave Ste 950, Dallas, TX 75201-2011
Tel (214) 740-3300 Founded/Ownrshp 1991
Sales 6.5MM^E EMP 300
SIC 6531 Real estate managers; Real estate managers
Ch Bd: Mack Pogue
*Pr: Tim Byrne
Treas: Nancy Davis
*VP: James Richard Anderson
*VP: Dan Jacks
*Exec: Fred E Chaney
*Exec: William J Grant Jr
*Exec: Jay Helm
*Exec: Kevin J Keane
*Exec: Blake J Pogue
Dist Mgr: Stacy Martinez

D-U-N-S 18-995-3891
▲ LINCOLN EDUCATIONAL SERVICES CORP
200 Executive Dr Ste 340, West Orange, NJ 07052-3303
Tel (973) 736-9340 *Founded/Ownrshp* 1946
Sales 325.0MM *EMP* 2,572
Tkr Sym LINC *Exch* NGS
SIC 8222 Technical institute; Technical institute
Pr: Scott M Shaw
CFO: Brian K Meyers
Ex VP: Kenneth M Swisstack
Sr VP: Peter Tahinos
Sr VP: Valerian J Thomas
VP: Stephen Ace
VP: Susan English
VP: Steve Lee
VP: Tayfun Selen
VP: Rajat Shah
Prgrm Mgr: Nagar Vishwanath

D-U-N-S 07-178-3596 IMP/EXP
■ LINCOLN ELECTRIC CO
(*Suby of* LINCOLN ELECTRIC HOLDINGS INC) ★
22801 Saint Clair Ave, Euclid, OH 44117-1199
Tel (216) 481-8100 *Founded/Ownrshp* 1895
Sales 1.0MMM^E *EMP* 3,500
SIC 3548 Arc welding generators, alternating current & direct current; Electrodes, electric welding; Arc welding generators, alternating current & direct current; Electrodes, electric welding
Sr VP: Frederick G Stueber
Pr: Steven B Hedlund
Treas: Marsha Anderson
**Ofcr:* Anthony Battle
**VP:* Jennifer Ansberry
VP: Michael S Mintun
VP: Steven R Summer
VP: Steven R Sumner
Brnch Mgr: H Elliott
IT Man: Henry Batushin
Sfty Dirs: Frank Conroy

D-U-N-S 00-419-9048 IMP/EXP
▲ LINCOLN ELECTRIC HOLDINGS INC (OH)
22801 Saint Clair Ave, Cleveland, OH 44117-2524
Tel (216) 481-8100 *Founded/Ownrshp* 1998
Sales 2.8MMM *EMP* 10,150^E
Accts Ernst & Young Llp Cleveland
Tkr Sym LECO *Exch* NGS
SIC 3548 Welding apparatus; Welding & cutting apparatus & accessories; Arc welding generators, alternating current & direct current; Welding apparatus; Welding & cutting apparatus & accessories; Arc welding generators, alternating current & direct current
CEO: Christopher Mapes
Pr: George Blankenship
Pr: Tom Flohn
Pr: Mathias Hallmann
Pr: David Leblanc
**CFO:* Vincent K Petrella
Bd of Dir: David Lincoln
**Ofcr:* Gretchen A Farrell
**Ex VP:* Gabriel Bruno
**Ex VP:* Frederick G Stueber
**Sr VP:* Geoffrey P Allman
Sr VP: George D Blankenship
Sr VP: Doug Lance
Dir Risk M: John Hach

D-U-N-S 78-598-5248 IMP
■ LINCOLN ELECTRIC INTERNATIONAL HOLDING CO
(*Suby of* LINCOLN ELECTRIC HOLDINGS INC) ★
22801 Saint Clair Ave, Euclid, OH 44117-2524
Tel (216) 481-8100 *Founded/Ownrshp* 2000
Sales 395.4MM^E *EMP* 9,000^E
SIC 3548 Welding apparatus; Welding apparatus
Ch: John Stropki
Admn Mgr: Kerry Ochaba
Off Mgr: Doug Bull
Off Mgr: John Hach
Software D: Timnit Ghebreyesus
Software D: David Kempert
Software D: Timothy Rowan
Software D: Randy Skedel
Ql Cn Mgr: Don Moffett
Sales Exec: Mary Beck
Natl Sales: David Mazak

D-U-N-S 82-959-7348
LINCOLN ELECTRIC SYSTEM
LES
1040 O St, Lincoln, NE 68508-3609
Tel (402) 475-4211 *Founded/Ownrshp* 1966
Sales 394.0MM^E *EMP* 453^E
SIC 4911 Electric services; Electric services
CEO: Kevin Wailes
CFO: Keith Brown
VP: Jason Fortik
VP: Douglas Friendt
VP: Lisa Hale
VP: Russ Reno
Prgrm Mgr: Janet Chung
Genl Mgr: James Fischer
Dir IT: William Lang
IT Man: Aaron Anderson
IT Man: Mary Hunhoff

LINCOLN FINANCIAL
See LINCOLN LIFE & ANNUNITY CO OF NEW YORK

LINCOLN FINANCIAL
See LINCOLN NATIONAL INSURANCE ASSOCIATES INC

LINCOLN FINANCIAL
See LINCOLN NATIONAL (CHINA) INC

LINCOLN FINANCIAL
See LINCOLN NATIONAL INVESTMENT COMPANIES INC

D-U-N-S 18-753-9218
■ LINCOLN FINANCIAL ADVISORS CORP
(*Suby of* LINCOLN NATIONAL LIFE INSURANCE CO) ★
1300 S Clinton St, Fort Wayne, IN 46802-3506
Tel (800) 237-3813 *Founded/Ownrshp* 1968
Sales NA *EMP* 354
SIC 6311 6282 8748 8742 Life insurance carriers; Investment advisory service; Business consulting; Management consulting services; Life insurance carriers; Investment advisory service; Business consulting; Management consulting services
Pr: Robert W Dineen
**CEO:* Dennis R Glass
**COO:* Lucy Gafe
**Treas:* Jeffrey Coutts
VP: Duane Bernt
VP: Thomas Kaeher
VP: Susan Stalteri
**VP:* Ronald W Turpin
VP: Kenneth Wagner
**Prin:* Bob Dineen

D-U-N-S 79-884-2683
LINCOLN FINANCIAL GROUP LLC
100 N Greene St Ste M, Greensboro, NC 27401-2551
Tel (336) 691-3000 *Founded/Ownrshp* 2012
Sales 31.2MM^E *EMP* 20^E
SIC 6289 Financial reporting
CEO: Dennis R Glass
Pr: Robert D Benson
COO: Randal J Freitag
VP: John Barber
VP: Richard Millard
VP: Joy Mulcahy
Exec: Alisa Henderson
Mng Dir: Michael Williams
Netwrk Mgr: Jeff Sides
VP Mktg: Bradley Mendenhall

D-U-N-S 02-749-8042
■ LINCOLN FINANCIAL SECURITIES CORP
(*Suby of* LINCOLN NATIONAL CORP) ★
1 Granite Pl, Concord, NH 03301-3258
Tel (603) 226-5000 *Founded/Ownrshp* 2007
Sales 110.0MM *EMP* 480
SIC 6722 Mutual fund sales, on own account; Mutual fund sales, on own account
Pr: Christopher Flint
CFO: Keith Ryan
**Treas:* Jack Westen
Ex VP: Andrew A McElwee Jr
Ex VP: Harold L Morrison Jr
VP: Lisa S Clifford
VP: Dave Furman
VP: Margaret A Salamy

LINCOLN FINANCIAL SPORTS, INC.
See RAYCOM SPORTS NETWORK INC

D-U-N-S 00-507-0966 IMP
■ LINCOLN FOODSERVICE PRODUCTS LLC
(*Suby of* MANITOWOC CO INC) ★
1333 E 179th St, Cleveland, OH 44110-2501
Tel (260) 459-8200 *Founded/Ownrshp* 1957, 2009
Sales 54.3MM^E *EMP* 340^E
SIC 3556 Ovens, bakery; Slicers, commercial, food; Biscuit cutters (machines); Ovens, bakery; Slicers, commercial, food; Biscuit cutters (machines)
Pr: Charlie Kingdon
**VP:* Steve Deidering
**VP:* Thomas Kurgan
VP: Effie Lee
**VP:* James Silcox
**VP:* Duane Yoder
MIS Dir: Elizabeth Witmer

LINCOLN GENERAL INSURANCE CO
See WALSHIRE ASSURANCE CO

D-U-N-S 08-673-1593
LINCOLN GENERAL INSURANCE CO (PA)
(*Suby of* KINGSWAY FINANCIAL SERVICES INC)
3501 Concord Rd Ste 120, York, PA 17402-8606
Tel (717) 757-0000 *Founded/Ownrshp* 1977
Sales NA *EMP* 465
SIC 6331 Fire, marine & casualty insurance; Fire, marine & casualty insurance
Pr: Gary J Orndorff
**Pr:* Scott D Wollney
IT Man: Kelly Dale
IT Man: Steve Sarne

D-U-N-S 07-271-1054
LINCOLN HALL
LINCOLN HALL - IVES SCHOOL
Rr 202, Lincolndale, NY 10540
Tel (914) 248-9450 *Founded/Ownrshp* 1863
Sales 21.5MM *EMP* 380
Accts Bdo Usa Llp New York Ny
SIC 8361 Halfway home for delinquents & offenders; Halfway home for delinquents & offenders
Ex Dir: Jack Flavin
**Ch:* James G Nugent
**Treas:* Martin J McNamara
**VP:* William J Collier Jr
Board of Directors: John Michael Chiaravalloti

LINCOLN HALL - IVES SCHOOL
See LINCOLN HALL

D-U-N-S 06-219-6485
LINCOLN HARRIS LLC
4725 Piedmont Row Dr, Charlotte, NC 28210-4270
Tel (704) 331-0917 *Founded/Ownrshp* 1998
Sales 104.5MM^E *EMP* 658
SIC 6531 6552 Real estate agents & managers; Subdividers & developers; Real estate agents & managers; Subdividers & developers
CEO: John W Harris III
COO: Denise Dexter
Ex VP: Ronald Steen
Ex VP: Chris Wasko
Sr VP: David Connor
Sr VP: Jubal Early
Sr VP: Donna Gravely
Sr VP: Carter Houchins
Sr VP: Dave Oddo
Sr VP: Javier Osuna
Sr VP: Brett Phillips
Sr VP: Chris Vasbinder
Sr VP: Campbell Walker
VP: Tracy Dodson
VP: Brett Kennedy
VP: Tim Kirksey
VP: Matt Larson
VP: Betsy McIntyre
VP: Patrick Stark
VP: Mike Stiene
VP: Chris Swart

D-U-N-S 07-106-6724
LINCOLN HEALTH SYSTEM
200 Gamble Dr, Lincolnton, NC 28092-4413
Tel (704) 735-3071 *Founded/Ownrshp* 1969
Sales 24.0MM^E *EMP* 500
SIC 8741 Hospital management; Nursing & personal care facility management; Hospital management; Nursing & personal care facility management
Pr: Peter Acker
Dir IT: Lisa Sykes
IT Man: Todd Greene
Board of Directors: Hilda Costner, John McLaughlin, Dr Robert Reid, L D Warlick Jr

D-U-N-S 04-130-2506
LINCOLN HERITAGE LIFE INSURANCE CO
(*Suby of* LONDEN INSURANCE GROUP INC) ★
4343 E Camelback Rd # 400, Phoenix, AZ 85018-2705
Tel (800) 750-6404 *Founded/Ownrshp* 1975
Sales NA *EMP* 100
SIC 6311 6411 Life insurance carriers; Insurance agents, brokers & service; Life insurance carriers; Insurance agents, brokers & service
CEO: Jack W Londen
**Pr:* Thomas Londen
**CFO:* Larry Schuneman
**Treas:* Dean Lathrop
**Sr VP:* Mary Johnson
**VP:* James Jerome
**VP:* Keith Perkins
**VP:* Doug Turner
Brnch Mgr: Ryan Farnsworth
VP Mktg: Norman Beazer
Snr Mgr: Bret Davis

D-U-N-S 18-528-3772 IMP
LINCOLN HEXAGON INC
LINCOLN COMPOSITES
(*Suby of* HEXAGON COMPOSITES ASA)
5117 Nw 40th St, Lincoln, NE 68524-2221
Tel (402) 464-8211 *Founded/Ownrshp* 2005
Sales 143.4MM^E *EMP* 300
SIC 3714 Gas tanks, motor vehicle; Gas tanks, motor vehicle
Pr: John D Schimenti
CFO: George Siedlecki
VP: Frank Haeberli
Dir Bus: Chet Dawes
Dir Bus: Marc Meyer
IT Man: Norman Newhouse
Ql Cn Mgr: Nancy Ballard

D-U-N-S 96-215-0335 IMP
LINCOLN HOLDINGS LLC
MONUMENTAL SPORTS & ENTRMT
627 N Glebe Rd Ste 850, Arlington, VA 22203-2144
Tel (202) 266-2200 *Founded/Ownrshp* 1999
Sales 59.7MM^E *EMP* 1,668^E
SIC 7941 Sports clubs, managers & promoters; Sports clubs, managers & promoters
CFO: Peter Biche
Manager: Letitia Petrillo

LINCOLN HOSPITAL
See LINCOLN COUNTY PUBLIC HOSPITAL DISTRICT 3

LINCOLN HOUSING AUTHORITY
See HOUSING AUTHORITY OF CITY OF LINCOLN

D-U-N-S 00-446-8161 IMP/EXP
LINCOLN INDUSTRIAL CORP
(*Suby of* SKF MOTION TECHNOLOGIES) ★
1 Lincoln Way, Saint Louis, MO 63120-1508
Tel (314) 679-4200 *Founded/Ownrshp* 1912
Sales 93.6MM^E *EMP* 415
SIC 3569 3559 3561 3714 Lubricating equipment; Lubricating systems, centralized; Lubrication equipment, industrial; Lubrication machinery, automatic; Automotive related machinery; Automotive maintenance equipment; Pumps & pumping equipment; Industrial pumps & parts; Motor vehicle parts & accessories; Lubricating equipment; Lubricating systems, centralized; Lubrication equipment, industrial; Lubrication machinery, automatic; Automotive related machinery; Automotive maintenance equipment; Pumps & pumping equipment; Industrial pumps & parts; Motor vehicle parts & accessories
Pr: Robert Law
VP: Phil Cernuto
Dist Mgr: Brian Miller
Dist Mgr: Jerry Robinson
QA Dir: Phil Balbi
IT Man: Mike Gargac
IT Man: Bhavdip Shah
Ql Cn Mgr: Matthew Maidlow
Manager: Rich Putignano
Snr Mgr: Yvonne Simmons

D-U-N-S 15-454-8507 IMP
LINCOLN INDUSTRIES INC
LINCOLN PLATING
600 W E St Ste 100, Lincoln, NE 68522-1399
Tel (402) 473-2124 *Founded/Ownrshp* 1952
Sales 18.1MM^E *EMP* 340
SIC 3471 3441 Electroplating & plating; Fabricated structural metal; Electroplating & plating; Fabricated structural metal
CEO: Marc Le Baron
**Pr:* Thomas Hance
Pr: Scott Weishaar
**CFO:* Andy Hunzeker
Treas: Wayne Pape
Dir Bus: Clint Boothe
Comm Man: Kylie Ensrud
Telecom Ex: Norma Hardle
CIO: Slavic Stepanyuk
IT Man: Lori Saale
VP Opers: Tim Carpenter

D-U-N-S 07-283-5903
LINCOLN INTERMEDIATE UNIT 12
65 Billerbeck St, New Oxford, PA 17350-9375
Tel (717) 624-4616 *Founded/Ownrshp* 1971
Sales 39.7MM^E *EMP* 1,700
SIC 8299 Public elementary & secondary schools; Educational services
Ex Dir: Dr Leeann Zeroth
HC Dir: Patricia McVicker

D-U-N-S 15-984-2020
LINCOLN INTERNATIONAL LLC
500 W Madison St Ste 3900, Chicago, IL 60661-4595
Tel (312) 580-8339 *Founded/Ownrshp* 2015
Sales 87.8MM^E *EMP* 190
SIC 6211 Investment bankers; Investment bankers
CEO: Robert B Barr
Sr VP: Robert Horak
VP: Greg Alkhas
VP: Matthew Buck
VP: Jeffrey Corum
VP: Anthony Crisman
VP: Aude Doyen
VP: Michael Fisch
VP: Brian Garfield
VP: Ross Gordon
VP: Scott Hebbeler
VP: Mark Jones-Pritchard
VP: Harry Kalmanowicz
VP: Phillip Knotts
VP: Chaim Lubin
VP: Natalie Marjancik
VP: Saurin Mehta
VP: Gaurang Shastri
VP: Chris Stradling
VP: Curtis Tatham
VP: Christine Tiseo

D-U-N-S 06-573-2406
LINCOLN INVESTMENT PLANNING INC
218 Glenside Ave, Wyncote, PA 19095-1534
Tel (215) 887-8111 *Founded/Ownrshp* 1969
Sales 85.0MM^E *EMP* 220
SIC 6211 6282 Mutual funds, selling by independent salesperson; Brokers, security; Investment advice; Mutual funds, selling by independent salesperson; Brokers, security; Investment advice
Ch Bd: Edward S Forst Sr
**Pr:* Edward S Forst Jr
CFO: N Marr
**Treas:* Harry Forst
Chf Mktg O: Neil D Wernick
Ofcr: Matthew Attanucci
Ofcr: Daniel Auriemma
Ofcr: Raymond Donnelly
Ofcr: Michael La Monda
Ofcr: Cyndi Leventhal
Ofcr: Gina Martin
Ofcr: Barry Rawls
Ofcr: Stanley Startzell
Sr VP: Denis Houser
Sr VP: Steve Quickel
VP: Joyce Calderone
**VP:* Thomas Forst
VP: Dierdre Koerick

D-U-N-S 07-143-8204
LINCOLN LAND COMMUNITY COLLEGE FOUNDATION
5250 Shepherd Rd, Springfield, IL 62703-5402
Tel (217) 786-2200 *Founded/Ownrshp* 1967
Sales 15.0MM *EMP* 505
Accts Sikich Llp Springfield Illin
SIC 8222 Junior college; Junior college
Pr: Charlotte J Warren
VP: Richard Bertrees
**VP:* Eileen Tepatti
DP Exec: Barry Lamb

LINCOLN LAND OIL COMPANY
See CHRONISTER OIL CO

D-U-N-S 00-374-1527
■ LINCOLN LIFE & ANNUNITY CO OF NEW YORK (NY)
LINCOLN FINANCIAL
(*Suby of* LINCOLN NATIONAL LIFE INSURANCE CO) ★
100 Madison St Ste 1860, Syracuse, NY 13202-2707
Tel (315) 428-8400 *Founded/Ownrshp* 1997
Sales NA *EMP* 540^E
SIC 6311 6411 Life insurance; Insurance agents, brokers & service; Life insurance; Insurance agents, brokers & service
Pr: Lorry J Stensrud
CFO: Troy Panning
VP: Jim Gutosky
VP: Karen Ritgert
**Prin:* Joanne B Collins
Sys/Dir: Gary Kern
Snr Mgr: Robert Sheppard

D-U-N-S 03-506-8758
LINCOLN LUMBER CO
932 N 23rd St, Lincoln, NE 68503-2494
Tel (402) 474-4488 *Founded/Ownrshp* 1963
Sales 56.2MM^E *EMP* 150
SIC 5031 5211 Lumber, plywood & millwork; Lumber & other building materials; Lumber, plywood & millwork; Lumber & other building materials
Pr: Donald Hamill
**Sec:* Beverly Hamill

D-U-N-S 80-564-4494
LINCOLN LUMBER LP
1390 Fm 1314, Conroe, TX 77301
Tel (936) 539-4421 *Founded/Ownrshp* 1975
Sales 60.0MM *EMP* 100
SIC 2421 5031 Building & structural materials, wood; Lumber: rough, dressed & finished; Building & structural materials, wood; Lumber: rough, dressed & finished
Genl Pt: Edwin M Blazek
Pt: Cynthia Blazek

D-U-N-S 07-383-0788
LINCOLN LUTHERAN COMMUNITY CARE CORP
2000 Domanik Dr, Racine, WI 53404-2910
Tel (262) 633-0500 *Founded/Ownrshp* 1990
Sales 6.0MM *EMP* 400
SIC 8051 Skilled nursing care facilities; Skilled nursing care facilities

D-U-N-S 05-873-9632
LINCOLN LUTHERAN OF RACINE WISCONSIN INC
2000 Domanik Dr Stop 1, Racine, WI 53404-2984
Tel (262) 633-0500 *Founded/Ownrshp* 1954
Sales 23.0MM[E] *EMP* 400
SIC 8051 7021 6513 Convalescent home with continuous nursing care; Rooming & boarding houses; Retirement hotel operation; Convalescent home with continuous nursing care; Rooming & boarding houses; Retirement hotel operation
CEO: Rev Daniel Risch
CFO: Jerry Apple
CFO: Rick Bova Jr
Sr VP: Carolyn Seeger

D-U-N-S 08-225-1133
LINCOLN MANUFACTURING INC
198 Meadowlands Blvd, Washington, PA 15301-8961
Tel (724) 222-2700 *Founded/Ownrshp* 2003
Sales 20.0MM[E] *EMP* 35
SIC 5082 7699 Mining machinery & equipment, except petroleum; Hydraulic equipment repair
Pr: Jason W Piatt
Off Mgr: Peggy Stewart

D-U-N-S 16-201-1647 IMP/EXP
LINCOLN MANUFACTURING INC
31209 Fm 2978 Rd, Magnolia, TX 77354-2388
Tel (281) 252-9494 *Founded/Ownrshp* 1997
Sales 163.0MM[E] *EMP* 400
Accts David B Saba Cpa
SIC 3533 5082 Oil & gas field machinery; Oil field equipment; Oil & gas field machinery; Oil field equipment
Pr: Eric Ward
**Treas:* David S Carnahan
Dir Bus: Barry Beard
Genl Mgr: John Burns
Dir IT: James Dampier
IT Man: Rex Hebert
Opers Mgr: Tyler Coates
Ql Cn Mgr: Eric Norton
Sales Exec: Tammy Walker
Sls Mgr: Jose Negrete
Sales Asso: Cari Mielsch

D-U-N-S 94-378-5733 IMP
LINCOLN MANUFACTURING USA LLC
102 Industrail Park Rd, Stanford, KY 40484-8804
Tel (606) 365-3016 *Founded/Ownrshp* 1996
Sales 25.2MM *EMP* 120
Accts Hotta Liesenberg Saito Indian
SIC 3465 5085 3469 Automotive stampings; Industrial tools; Metal stampings; Automotive stampings; Industrial tools; Metal stampings
COO: Wayne Vanwinkle
Plnt Mgr: Ivan Price
Ql Cn Mgr: Chris Cummings

D-U-N-S 19-570-1081 EXP
LINCOLN MARGATE INC
MARGATE VOLVO
(*Suby of* HOLMAN ENTERPRISES INC) ★
2250 N State Road 7, Margate, FL 33063-5716
Tel (954) 978-2277 *Founded/Ownrshp* 1988
Sales 26.3MM[E] *EMP* 65
SIC 5511 5531 5013 7538 5521 Automobiles, new & used; Automotive parts; Automotive supplies & parts; General automotive repair shops; Automobiles, used cars only; Automobiles, new & used; Automotive parts; Automotive supplies & parts; General automotive repair shops; Automobiles, used cars only
Pr: Glen Gardner
**Pr:* Ken Loisseau
**VP:* Ken Loiseau
Exec: Stephen Smith
Sls Mgr: Fred Carson
Sales Asso: Alan Koppel

D-U-N-S 00-281-0229
LINCOLN MARTI COMMUNITY AGENCY INC (FL)
2700 Sw 8th St, Miami, FL 33135-4619
Tel (305) 643-4888 *Founded/Ownrshp* 1990
Sales 21.1MM *EMP* 557[E]
Accts Grau & Company Miami Fl
SIC 8322 2732 8211 5812 Individual & family services; Book printing; Specialty education; Contract food services; Individual & family services; Book printing; Specialty education; Contract food services
Pr: Arminda Espinosa
**VP:* Dominica Alcantara
Board of Directors: Maria Vasallo

D-U-N-S 00-468-2203
LINCOLN MEDICAL AND MENTAL HEALTH CENTER
(*Suby of* NEW YORK CITY HEALTH AND HOSPITALS CORP) ★
234 E 149th St, Bronx, NY 10451-5504
Tel (718) 579-5000 *Founded/Ownrshp* 2011
Sales 331.4MM[E] *EMP* 512[E]
SIC 8062 General medical & surgical hospitals
Ex Dir: Milton Nunez
Exec: Mildred Santiago
Dir Rx: Michael Thomas
Nurse Mgr: Debra Glenn
Psych: Bonnie Chwast
Psych: Sandra Runes
Surgeon: Rushi Shah
Ansthlgy: Jean Maurice
Doctor: Vihren Dimitrov
Doctor: Harriet Jones
Doctor: Lin Kin

LINCOLN MEDICAL CENTER
See LINCOLN COUNTY HEALTH SYSTEM FOUNDATION

D-U-N-S 04-946-7251
LINCOLN MEMORIAL UNIVERSITY
6965 Cumberland Gap Pkwy, Harrogate, TN 37752-8231
Tel (423) 869-3611 *Founded/Ownrshp* 1897
Sales 96.2MM *EMP* 400[E]
Accts Rodefer Moss & Co Pllc Knoxvi
SIC 8221 University; University
Pr: B James Dawson
**VP:* Cynthia Whitt
VP: Parham Williams
CIO: Richard Lewallen
HC Dir: Lisa Travis
HC Dir: Emily Weyant

LINCOLN MERCURY
See JOHN DEERY MOTORS INC

LINCOLN MERCURY
See JACK FORD GRIFFIN INC

LINCOLN MERCURY
See SIOUX FALLS FORD INC

LINCOLN MERCURY
See PAUL CERAME AUTO GROUP INC

LINCOLN MERCURY
See FORD ROGERS SALES INC

LINCOLN MERCURY
See JIM FORD BASS INC

LINCOLN MERCURY
See MARSTALLER MOTORS INC

LINCOLN MERCURY
See MIKE KEHOE FORD INC

LINCOLN MERCURY
See DON BOHN FORD

LINCOLN MERCURY
See ROBINSON BROTHERS INC

LINCOLN MERCURY
See WEST HERR FORD OF AMHERST LLC

LINCOLN MERCURY
See PREMIER FORD INC

LINCOLN MERCURY
See HEISER FORD INC

LINCOLN MERCURY
See BALLENTINE GEORGE FORD INC

LINCOLN MERCURY
See SUTTON FORD INC

LINCOLN MERCURY
See IMLAY CITY FORD INC

LINCOLN MERCURY
See NORTH POINT FORD INC

LINCOLN MERCURY DEALER
See ZIEMS FORD CORNERS INC

D-U-N-S 01-767-8863
LINCOLN MERCURY OF KINGS AUTO MALL
MONTGOMERY JEEP EAGLE
9600 Kings Auto Mall Rd, Cincinnati, OH 45249-8240
Tel (513) 683-3800 *Founded/Ownrshp* 1954
Sales 47.9MM[E] *EMP* 163
SIC 5511 7514 7538 7515 5521 Automobiles, new & used; Passenger car rental; General automotive repair shops; Passenger car leasing; Used car dealers; Automobiles, new & used; Passenger car rental; General automotive repair shops; Passenger car leasing; Used car dealers
Pr: Robert C Reichert
**Sec:* Lou Galbraith
**VP:* Gerald M Car Michael
**VP:* Mark Pittman

LINCOLN MERCURY OF WAYNE
See WAYNE MOTORS INC

D-U-N-S 06-954-9376 IMP/EXP
LINCOLN MOVING & STORAGE CO INC
8420 S 190th St, Kent, WA 98031-1200
Tel (425) 251-5900 *Founded/Ownrshp* 1986
Sales 26.4MM[E] *EMP* 125
SIC 4213 4214 Trucking, except local; Household goods moving & storage, local; Trucking, except local; Household goods moving & storage, local
Pr: Chris Di Julio
VP: Chris Dijulio
**VP:* Danny Dijulio
VP: Ron Prideaux

D-U-N-S 87-665-6364
■ LINCOLN NATIONAL (CHINA) INC
LINCOLN FINANCIAL
(*Suby of* LINCOLN NATIONAL CORP) ★
1300 S Clinton St, Fort Wayne, IN 46802-3506
Tel (260) 455-2000 *Founded/Ownrshp* 1994
Sales NA *EMP* 2,000
SIC 6411 Insurance agents, brokers & service; Insurance agents, brokers & service
CEO: Dennis Glass
VP: Kristi J Harkenrider
VP: Don Mockler
VP: Rick Nelson

D-U-N-S 04-640-0180
▲ LINCOLN NATIONAL CORP
150 N Rad Chester Rd A305 Ste A, Radnor, PA 19087
Tel (484) 583-1400 *Founded/Ownrshp* 1968
Sales NA *EMP* 9,627[E]
Accts Ernst & Young Llp Philadelphi
Tkr Sym LNC *Exch* NYS
SIC 6311 6321 6371 6722 6411 6282 Life insurance; Health insurance carriers; Reinsurance carriers, accident & health; Pensions; Pension funds; Welfare pensions; Management investment, open-end; Insurance agents, brokers & service; Insurance agents & brokers; Property & casualty insurance agent; Investment advisory service; Life insurance; Health insurance carriers; Reinsurance carriers, accident & health; Pensions; Pension funds; Welfare pensions; Management investment, open-end; Insurance agents, brokers & service; Insurance agents & brokers; Property & casualty insurance agent; Investment advisory service
Pr: Dennis R Glass
Pr: Mary Carruth
Pr: Byron Champlin
Pr: Naxine Chang
Pr: Bryon Cooper
Pr: Belinda Fairbanks
Pr: Deana Friedt
Pr: John Gruning
Pr: Daniel Herr
Pr: Brad Jeffrey
Pr: Marty Kennedy
Pr: Julie Macdonald
Pr: Brian Moody
Pr: Christopher Potochar
Pr: Jim Rooney
Pr: Lance Schulz
Pr: Jennifer Sheriff
Pr: Paul Spurr
Pr: James Tierney
Pr: Crystal Tucker
Pr: David Vachon
Board of Directors: Isaiah Tidwell, William J Avery, William H Cunningham, George W Henderson III, Eric G Johnson, Gary C Kelly, M Leanne Lachman, Michael F Mee, William Porter Payne, Patrick S Pittard

D-U-N-S 96-629-5565
LINCOLN NATIONAL CORP VOLUNTARY EMPLOYEE BENEFICIARY ASSN
150 N Radnor Chester Rd, Radnor, PA 19087-5252
Tel (484) 583-1669 *Founded/Ownrshp* 2011
Sales 118.5MM *EMP* 2
SIC 8699 Membership organizations; Membership organizations
VP: Steven Brody

D-U-N-S 06-066-9876
■ LINCOLN NATIONAL INSURANCE ASSOCIATES INC
LINCOLN FINANCIAL
(*Suby of* LINCOLN NATIONAL LIFE INSURANCE CO) ★
350 Church St Fl 9, Hartford, CT 06103-1139
Tel (860) 466-1000 *Founded/Ownrshp* 1967
Sales 67.4MM[E] *EMP* 310
SIC 6282 6211 Investment advisory service; Security brokers & dealers; Investment advisory service; Security brokers & dealers
Pr: Robert Dineen
CFO: Diane McCarthy
Sr VP: Michael Wright
VP: Patrice Calnen
VP: Patrick Caulfield
VP: Katie Dunnington
VP: Ryan Lommel
VP: Stephen Rahn
VP: Joe Spada
VP: Ron Williams
Dir IT: Justin George
Board of Directors: Frederick J Crawfo, Mike Gilliland

D-U-N-S 92-621-8652
■ LINCOLN NATIONAL INVESTMENT COMPANIES INC
LINCOLN FINANCIAL
(*Suby of* LINCOLN NATIONAL CORP) ★
200 E Berry St, Fort Wayne, IN 46802-2731
Tel (260) 455-2000 *Founded/Ownrshp* 1995
Sales 172.5MM[E] *EMP* 4,000
SIC 6282 6722 Investment advice; Management investment, open-end; Investment advice; Management investment, open-end
Pr: Jon Boscia

D-U-N-S 00-693-7163
■ LINCOLN NATIONAL LIFE INSURANCE CO
(*Suby of* LINCOLN NATIONAL CORP) ★
1300 S Clinton St, Fort Wayne, IN 46802-3506
Tel (260) 455-2000 *Founded/Ownrshp* 1998
Sales NA *EMP* 3,470
SIC 6411 6321 6211 6282 Insurance agents, brokers & service; Accident & health insurance; Disability health insurance; Security brokers & dealers; Investment advice; Insurance agents, brokers & service; Accident & health insurance; Disability health insurance; Security brokers & dealers; Investment advice
Pr: Dennis Glass
Pr: Paul E Gibson
Pr: John H Gotta
Pr: Eric Patterson
**CFO:* Frederick Crawford
Treas: Rise Taylow
**Ex VP:* Charles Cornelio
Sr VP: John Addison
Sr VP: Michael Burns
Sr VP: Sandra Callahan
Sr VP: Donald Dibble
Sr VP: Robert Dineen
Sr VP: Charles Elam II
Sr VP: Randal Freitag
Sr VP: Mark Konen
Sr VP: Marvin Maynard
Sr VP: Douglas Miller
Sr VP: William Seawell II
Sr VP: Kenneth Solon
Sr VP: Richard Stange
VP: Richard Corwin
Board of Directors: Keith Ryan

D-U-N-S 00-699-6763
■ LINCOLN NATIONAL LIFE INSURANCE CO
(*Suby of* LINCOLN NATIONAL CORP) ★
100 N Greene St, Greensboro, NC 27401-2547
Tel (336) 691-3000 *Founded/Ownrshp* 2007
Sales NA *EMP* 8,000
SIC 6411 6321 6324 Insurance agents, brokers & service; Accident insurance carriers; Health insurance carriers; Hospital & medical service plans; Insurance agents, brokers & service; Accident insurance carriers; Health insurance carriers; Hospital & medical service plans
Pr: Dennis R Glass
**CFO:* Randal J Freitag
**Ex VP:* Adam G Ciongoli
Board of Directors: George William Henderson I

D-U-N-S 80-130-5913
■ LINCOLN NATIONAL RISK MANAGEMENT INC
(*Suby of* LINCOLN NATIONAL CORP) ★
1670 Magnavox Way, Fort Wayne, IN 46804-1536
Tel (260) 455-2000 *Founded/Ownrshp* 1998
Sales NA *EMP* 3,650
SIC 6411 Insurance agents, brokers & service; Insurance agents, brokers & service
Pr: Jon Boscia
**VP:* Lowry Scensrud
VP: Russell Sviever

LINCOLN OFFICE
See BAKER AVENUE INVESTMENTS INC

D-U-N-S 02-559-4284
LINCOLN OFFICE LLC
(*Suby of* BAKER AVENUE INVESTMENTS INC) ★
205 Eastgate Dr, Washington, IL 61571-9238
Tel (309) 427-2500 *Founded/Ownrshp* 2000
Sales 54.8MM[E] *EMP* 52[E]
SIC 5021 7389 1799 2522 Office & public building furniture; Interior design services; Home/office interiors finishing, furnishing & remodeling; Office furniture installation; Office furniture, except wood; Tables, office: except wood; Panel systems & partitions, office: except wood; Office cabinets & filing drawers: except wood
Pr: William E Pape
**CFO:* Jerry Sweet

D-U-N-S 80-793-8928 IMP/EXP
LINCOLN PAPER AND TISSUE LLC
50 Katadin Ave, Lincoln, ME 04457-1307
Tel (207) 794-0600 *Founded/Ownrshp* 2004
Sales 198.7MM[E] *EMP* 400
SIC 2621 Tissue paper; Tissue paper
CFO: John Wimann
CFO: John Wissman
CFO: John Wissmann
Dir IT: Jay Krishnamurthy
Manager: John Rather

D-U-N-S 10-065-0431
LINCOLN PARISH SCHOOL BOARD
410 S Farmerville St, Ruston, LA 71270-4655
Tel (318) 255-1430 *Founded/Ownrshp* 1880
Sales 73.7MM *EMP* 1,104
Accts Allen Green & Williamson Llp
SIC 8211 Public elementary & secondary schools; School board
Pr: Otha Anders
CFO: Yoland Dade
Adm Dir: Ronny Volentine
Psych: Marilyn Rushing

D-U-N-S 07-922-8212
LINCOLN PARISH SCHOOLS
410 S Farmerville St, Ruston, LA 71270-4655
Tel (318) 255-1430 *Founded/Ownrshp* 2013
Sales 6.1MM[E] *EMP* 794[E]
SIC 8211 Public elementary & secondary schools

D-U-N-S 02-011-5192
LINCOLN PARK CITY OF (INC)
1355 Southfield Rd, Lincoln Park, MI 48146-2380
Tel (313) 386-1800 *Founded/Ownrshp* 1925
Sales NA *EMP* 406
Accts Plante & Moran Pllc Southfie
SIC 9111 County supervisors' & executives' offices; County supervisors' & executives' offices
Exec: Scott Kaiser
Brnch Mgr: Donald Mandernach
DP Dir: Gary Higgins

LINCOLN PARK MEDICAL CENTER
See HOPEWELL HEALTH CENTERS INC

LINCOLN PARK PUBLIC SCHOOLS
See SCHOOL DISTRICT OF CITY OF LINCOLN PARK

D-U-N-S 03-023-9263
LINCOLN PARK SUBACUTE & REHAB CENTER TWO
499 Pine Brook Rd, Lincoln Park, NJ 07035-1804
Tel (973) 317-7500 *Founded/Ownrshp* 2001
Sales 7.1MM[E] *EMP* 529
SIC 8051 Convalescent home with continuous nursing care; Convalescent home with continuous nursing care
CEO: Mimi Feliciano
Dir IT: John Manuel

D-U-N-S 06-863-4179
LINCOLN PARK ZOOLOGICAL SOCIETY
2001 N Clark St, Chicago, IL 60614-4757
Tel (312) 742-2000 *Founded/Ownrshp* 1959
Sales 45.0MM *EMP* 175[E]
Accts Plante & Moran Pllc Chicago
SIC 8422 Zoological garden, noncommercial; Zoological garden, noncommercial
Pr: Kevin Bell
Pr: Christine Zrinsky
**CFO:* Troy Baresel
VP: Bryan Anderson
VP: Neal David
VP: Marybeth Johnson
VP: Steven Thompson
Exec: Donna Curtis

CTO: Brooke Wiles
Dir IT: Phil Beckert
Sls Mgr: Jennie Fiala

LINCOLN PLATING
See LINCOLN INDUSTRIES INC

LINCOLN PROPERTY CO
See LPC COMMERCIAL SERVICES INC

D-U-N-S 00-295-3008
LINCOLN PROPERTY CO
LP
2000 Mckinney Ave # 1000, Dallas, TX 75201-1954
Tel (214) 740-3300 *Founded/Ownrshp* 1965
Sales 246.6MM^E *EMP* 3,985
SIC 6531 Real estate managers; Real estate managers
Pr: A Mack Pogue
Pt: Brian Byrne
Pt: Jeffery B Franzen
Pr: Tim Byrne
Pr: Jerry Grove
COO: Gregory S Courtwright
COO: Jeffrey T Courtwright
CFO: William A Macneil
CFO: Dennis Streit
Ex VP: Webber Beall
Ex VP: Reggie D Delponte
Ex VP: Robert Dozier
Ex VP: John Grissim
Ex VP: John S Herr
Ex VP: David Pettle
Ex VP: Ellis L Shamburger
Ex VP: Scott Wilder
Sr VP: Tony Bartlett
Sr VP: Tony R Bartlett
Sr VP: Greg Cahill
Sr VP: Scott Caldwell

D-U-N-S 10-893-5040
LINCOLN PROPERTY CO CSE INC
LINCOLN ADVERTISING COMPANY
2000 Mckinney Ave Ste 950, Dallas, TX 75201-2011
Tel (214) 740-3300 *Founded/Ownrshp* 1979
Sales 52.5MM^E *EMP* 362
SIC 1541 Industrial buildings & warehouses; Industrial buildings & warehouses
Ch Bd: Mack Pogue
**Pr:* William C Duvall
CFO: Eric Law
**CFO:* Ken Mooder
Sr Ex VP: William Hickey
Ex VP: Webber Beall
Ex VP: John Herr
Ex VP: David Krumwiede
Sr VP: John Grissim
VP: Kevin Brown
VP: Scott Caldwell
VP: Adriano Calvanese
VP: John Cappellano
VP: Sean Chrisom
VP: Jeffry Courtwright
VP: Mike Crockett
VP: Rodger Dean
VP: Rick Genthe
VP: Matt George
VP: Charlie Giammalva
VP: Mark Glagola

D-U-N-S 13-936-3295 IMP/EXP
LINCOLN PROVISION INC
CHICAGO GOURMET STEAKS
824 W 38th Pl, Chicago, IL 60609-1415
Tel (773) 254-2400 *Founded/Ownrshp* 1985
Sales 132.4MM^E *EMP* 125
SIC 5142 5147 Packaged frozen goods; Meats & meat products; Packaged frozen goods; Meats & meat products
Pr: James J Stevens
**Pr:* Jim J Stevens Jr
CFO: Niteen Joshi
**VP:* Mark Stevens
IT Man: Jon Schaffner

D-U-N-S 07-979-9469
LINCOLN PUBLIC SCHOOLS
1624 Lonsdale Ave, Lincoln, RI 02865-1840
Tel (401) 721-3313 *Founded/Ownrshp* 2015
Sales 4.5MM^E *EMP* 409^E
SIC 8211 Public elementary & secondary schools

D-U-N-S 07-289-8737
LINCOLN PUBLIC SCHOOLS INC
LANCASTER CNTY SCHL DISTRCT 1
5905 O St, Lincoln, NE 68510-2235
Tel (402) 436-1000 *Founded/Ownrshp* 1854
Sales 417.5MM *EMP* 6,950
Accts Hsmc-Orizon Kansas City Omah
SIC 8211 Public senior high school; Public senior high school; Public junior high school; Public elementary school
Bd of Dir: Katie Stephenson
Ofcr: Gary Reber
VP: Lance Francisco
Dir Sec: Joe Wright
CIO: Wade Gibson
DP Exec: Lisa Bogus
Dir IT: Rosemary Engel
Instr Medi: Cara Lucas-Richt
Psych: Jennifer Bass
Psych: Tim Ernst
Psych: Kathy Fergen

D-U-N-S 88-385-5355
LINCOLN SANDERSON MERCURY INC
2121 W Bell Rd, Phoenix, AZ 85023-3311
Tel (602) 375-7500 *Founded/Ownrshp* 1995
Sales 38.5MM^E *EMP* 144
SIC 5511 5521 Automobiles, new & used; Used car dealers; Automobiles, new & used; Used car dealers
Pr: David Kimmerle
**Treas:* Stephen Wendt
Exec: John Epperson
Sls Mgr: Joe Cavaretta
Sls Mgr: Duane Fleet
Sls Mgr: Jim Landeros
Sls Mgr: Todd Roth

D-U-N-S 00-798-9254
LINCOLN SAVINGS BANK
(*Suby of* LINCOLN BANCORP) ★
508 Main St, Reinbeck, IA 50669-1052
Tel (319) 788-6441 *Founded/Ownrshp* 1902, 1986
Sales NA *EMP* 150
SIC 6022 State commercial banks; State commercial banks
Ch Bd: Cordell Q Peterson
**Pr:* Steve Tscherter
Trst Ofcr: Nathaniel Tagtow
Sr VP: Angela Timp
VP: Jerry Fannon
VP: Chris Frischmeyer
VP: Gary Lorenz
VP: Chad Scieszinski
VP: Julie Versluis
IT Man: Randy Clark
Snr Mgr: Emily Girsch

LINCOLN SCHOOL
See ANSONIA SCHOOL DISTRICT

D-U-N-S 19-001-9609
LINCOLN SQUARE HOTEL LLC
600 Bellevue Way Ne, Bellevue, WA 98004-5011
Tel (425) 450-1535 *Founded/Ownrshp* 2005
Sales 25.0MM *EMP* 200
SIC 7011 Hotels; Hotels

D-U-N-S 03-513-8510
■ LINCOLN SYSCO INC
(*Suby of* SYSCO CORP) ★
900 King Bird Rd, Lincoln, NE 68521-3009
Tel (402) 423-1031 *Founded/Ownrshp* 1959
Sales 272.1MM^E *EMP* 460
SIC 5148 5142 5143 5141 5087 5113 Fresh fruits & vegetables; Soup, frozen; Dairy products, except dried or canned; Cheese; Groceries, general line; Restaurant supplies; Industrial & personal service paper; Cups, disposable plastic & paper; Napkins, paper; Towels, paper; Fresh fruits & vegetables; Soup, frozen; Dairy products, except dried or canned; Cheese; Groceries, general line; Restaurant supplies; Industrial & personal service paper; Cups, disposable plastic & paper; Napkins, paper; Towels, paper
Pr: Bill Delaney
**Pr:* Kim B Brown
CFO: Fred Schmidt
**Sr VP:* Brian Beach
VP: Thomas Donlan
VP: Justin Kenney
MIS Dir: Michael Chase
Dir IT: Ken Waltke
Sfty Mgr: Suraya Kamelian
Sfty Mgr: Jesse Keebler
Opers Mgr: Shari Hupka

D-U-N-S 07-754-9285
■ LINCOLN TECHNICAL INSTITUTE INC
(*Suby of* LINCOLN EDUCATIONAL SERVICES CORP) ★
200 Executive Dr Ste 340, West Orange, NJ 07052-3397
Tel (718) 246-4001 *Founded/Ownrshp* 1999
Sales 75.0MM^E *EMP* 1,200
Accts Deloitte & Touche Llp Parsipp
SIC 8222 Technical institute; Technical institute
Ch Bd: Shaun Mc Alamt
Pr: Alexandra Luster
CFO: Cesar Riveiro
**Treas:* Nicholas Raspa
VP: Brian Meyers
IT Man: Bill Fottis
VP Opers: Stephen Buchenot
VP Opers: Deborah Ramentol
Mktg Mgr: Frank Galindo

LINCOLN TOWERS COMMUNITY
See AKAM ASSOCIATES INC

D-U-N-S 07-570-1920
LINCOLN TOWN OF (INC) (RI)
100 Old River Rd, Lincoln, RI 02865-1342
Tel (401) 333-0780 *Founded/Ownrshp* 1871, 1970
Sales NA *EMP* 513
Accts Bacon & Company Cpa S Llc W
SIC 9111 City & town managers' offices; ; City & town managers' offices;

D-U-N-S 08-660-5318
LINCOLN UNIFIED SCHOOL DISTRICT
2010 W Swain Rd, Stockton, CA 95207-4055
Tel (209) 953-8700 *Founded/Ownrshp* 1878
Sales 68.1MM^E *EMP* 994
SIC 8211 Public elementary school; Public junior high school; Public senior high school; Public elementary school; Public junior high school; Public senior high school
CEO: Donald Ruhstaller
Prgrm Mgr: Phillip Edmond
Psych: Kristin Ruffoni
Psych: Emily Smith

LINCOLN UNIVERSITY, THE
See LINCOLN UNIVERSITY

D-U-N-S 07-197-0164
LINCOLN UNIVERSITY
820 Chestnut St, Jefferson City, MO 65101-3500
Tel (573) 681-5000 *Founded/Ownrshp* 1866
Sales 12.4MM *EMP* 475^E
Accts Bkd Llp Springfield Mo
SIC 8221 College, except junior; College, except junior
Pr: Kevin D Rome Sr PHD
Ofcr: Robert Clay
Top Exec: Cynthia Chapel
Ex VP: Jim Marcantonio
VP: Ann Harris
**Prin:* Connie B Hamacher
IT Man: T Mangold

D-U-N-S 07-547-7331
LINCOLN UNIVERSITY
LINCOLN UNIVERSITY, THE
1570 Baltimore Pike, Lincoln University, PA 19352-9141
Tel (484) 365-8000 *Founded/Ownrshp* 2000
Sales 52.8MM *EMP* 425
SIC 8221 University; University
Pr: Valerie I Harrison
Pr: Diane Brown
CFO: Cesar Ribeiro
Treas: Clifton Thomas
Ofcr: Craig Chapman
Ofcr: Christopher Golder
Ofcr: Kevin Thompson
Ofcr: Donna Tyre-Draper
VP: Maureen Stokes
Exec: Debbie Bullock
Admn Mgr: Tanya Bynum

D-U-N-S 07-141-9733
LINCOLN UNIVERSITY (INC)
LINCOLN COLLEGE
300 Keokuk St, Lincoln, IL 62656-1630
Tel (217) 735-5050 *Founded/Ownrshp* 1865
Sales 29.7MM *EMP* 200
Accts Jm Abbott & Associates Ltd Li
SIC 8222 Junior college; Junior college
Pr: John D Blackburn
**VP:* A Gigi Fansler
VP: Gigi Fansler
**Ex Dir:* Vance Laine
Store Mgr: Donna Hutchinson
CTO: Tony Schilling
Doctor: Debora Vanhoorn

D-U-N-S 86-743-5133 IMP
LINCOLN VARSITY INC
49251 Grand River Ave, Novi, MI 48374-1206
Tel (248) 305-5300 *Founded/Ownrshp* 1994
Sales 45.0MM^E *EMP* 130
SIC 5511 7538 Automobiles, new & used; Vans, new & used; General automotive repair shops; Automobiles, new & used; Vans, new & used; General automotive repair shops
Pr: Louis C Stanford
VP: Michael Stanford
Genl Mgr: Jerry Law
Sls Mgr: Deborah Adams
Sales Asso: Michael Cash
Sales Asso: Gina Papia
Sales Asso: John Treharne

LINCOLN WINDOWS
See LINCOLN WOOD PRODUCTS INC

D-U-N-S 00-613-6048
LINCOLN WOOD PRODUCTS INC (WI)
LINCOLN WINDOWS
1400 W Taylor St, Merrill, WI 54452-2916
Tel (715) 536-2461 *Founded/Ownrshp* 1947
Sales 47.6MM^E *EMP* 300
SIC 2431 Window frames, wood; Doors, wood; Window frames, wood; Doors, wood
Pr: Rick Bliese
**Prin:* Steve Kahle
**Prin:* Mark Knorr
**Prin:* Dennis Krueger
**Prin:* Todd Metz
MIS Mgr: Dale Kryzanowski
Plnt Mgr: Tim Diels
Plnt Mgr: John Heldt
Trfc Mgr: Virgil Kleinschmidt

LINCOLN YMCA
See YOUNG MENS CHRISTIAN ASSOCIATION OF LINCOLN NEBRASKA

LINCOLN-MERCURY DARIEN
See MILLER AUTOMOBILE CORP

D-U-N-S 08-338-0071
LINCOLN-SUDBURY REGIONAL HIGH SCHOOL
390 Lincoln Rd, Sudbury, MA 01776-1409
Tel (781) 259-9527 *Founded/Ownrshp* 1956
Sales 34.8MM *EMP* 43^E
Accts Powers & Sullivan Llc Wakefi
SIC 8211 Public senior high school; School board; Public senior high school; School board
Prin: Scott Carpenter
**Treas:* Pauline Paste
Off Mgr: Nancy Carbutt
Psych: Stephanie Kunst
Psych: Rebecca Platt
Psych: Muriel Riseman

D-U-N-S 96-779-8414
LINCOLN-WAY AREA SPECIAL EDUCATION DISTRICT 843
PIONEER GROVE EDUCATIONAL CTR
601 Willow St, Frankfort, IL 60423-1140
Tel (815) 806-4685 *Founded/Ownrshp* 1975
Sales 13.9MM^E *EMP* 380^E
SIC 8211 Specialty education; Specialty education
Exec: Tammy Pitts
DP Exec: Mike Frantini

D-U-N-S 07-746-8650
LINCOLNHEALTH
ST ANDREWS HOSPITAL
(*Suby of* LINCOLNHEALTH GROUP) ★
35 Miles St, Damariscotta, ME 04543-4047
Tel (207) 563-1234 *Founded/Ownrshp* 1955
Sales 67.9MM *EMP* 205
Accts Mainehealth Portland Me
SIC 8062 General medical & surgical hospitals; General medical & surgical hospitals
CEO: James Donovan
Sr VP: Cindy Leavitt
Prgrm Mgr: Cassandra Cote
Prgrm Mgr: Donna Levi
Prgrm Mgr: Richard Veilleux
Pharmcst: Patrice Carter

D-U-N-S 80-809-1990
LINCOLNHEALTH GROUP
6 Saint Andrews Ln, Boothbay Harbor, ME 04538-1731
Tel (207) 633-1901 *Founded/Ownrshp* 2009
Sales 10.7MM *EMP* 800^E
Accts Mainehealth Portland Me
SIC 8741 Home health care services; General medical & surgical hospitals; Hospital management; Hospital management
Pr: James Donovan
Prgrm Mgr: Nicole Cooley

D-U-N-S 15-399-6012
LINCOLNSHIRE MANAGEMENT INC
780 3rd Ave Rm 4000, New York, NY 10017-2173
Tel (212) 319-3633 *Founded/Ownrshp* 1987
Sales 160.7MM^E *EMP* 400
SIC 6211 7389 3599 Investment bankers; Automobile recovery service; Catapults; Investment bankers; Automobile recovery service; Catapults
Pr: Thomas J Maloney
COO: Allen Weinstein
Comm Man: Bill Buttrick
Prin: W A Shea
Mng Dir: James Binch
Mng Dir: C K Clay
Mng Dir: Richard Huo
Mng Dir: Philip Kim
Mng Dir: Pieter Kodde
Mng Dir: Thomas Ley
Mng Dir: James McLaughlin

D-U-N-S 18-403-0468
LINCOLNSHIRE PRAIRIEVIEW SCHOOLS DISTRICT 103
1370 N Riverwoods Rd, Lincolnshire, IL 60069-2402
Tel (847) 295-4030 *Founded/Ownrshp* 1904
Sales 21.4MM^E *EMP* 300
SIC 8211 Public elementary & secondary schools; Public elementary & secondary schools
Exec: Carey Murphy
Cmptr Lab: Ann Blomberg
Sls&Mrk Ex: Darryl Johnson

D-U-N-S 04-745-6306
LINCOLNWAY COMMUNITY HIGH SCHOOL DISTRICT 210
1801 E Lincoln Hwy, New Lenox, IL 60451-3801
Tel (815) 462-2345 *Founded/Ownrshp* 1954
Sales 74.1MM^E *EMP* 900
SIC 8211 Public senior high school; Public senior high school
DP Exec: John Pehle
Mktg Mgr: Stacy Holland

D-U-N-S 15-287-1591
LINCOLNWAY ENERGY LLC
59511 Lincoln Hwy, Nevada, IA 50201-7992
Tel (515) 232-1010 *Founded/Ownrshp* 2006
Sales 147.3MM *EMP* 41
Accts Mcgladrey Llp Des Moines Iow
SIC 2869 2861 Ethyl alcohol, ethanol; Ethanolamines; Ethyl acetate, natural; Ethyl alcohol, ethanol; Ethanolamines; Ethyl acetate, natural
Pr: Eric Hakmiller
**Ch Bd:* Jeff Taylor
CFO: Rick Ogle
**Treas:* Terrill Wycoff
**V Ch Bd:* Brian Conrad
Off Mgr: Kay Gammon
Opers Mgr: Matt Lenning
Snr Mgr: Randy Retleff

D-U-N-S 08-536-0147 IMP
LIND ELECTRONIC DESIGN CO INC
LIND ELECTRONICS
6414 Cambridge St, Minneapolis, MN 55426-4427
Tel (952) 927-6303 *Founded/Ownrshp* 1975
Sales 23.0MM *EMP* 54
SIC 3629 3691 3825 Battery chargers, rectifying or nonrotating; Power conversion units, a.c. to d.c.: static-electric; Batteries, rechargeable; Test equipment for electronic & electrical circuits; Battery chargers, rectifying or nonrotating; Power conversion units, a.c. to d.c.: static-electric; Batteries, rechargeable; Test equipment for electronic & electrical circuits
Pr: Leroy Lind
Pr: Tom Martin
**Sec:* Patricia Lind
Ofcr: Eugene Tomasevich
VP: Karen Dong
**VP:* Dave Murphy
Sls Mgr: Josh Mueller

LIND ELECTRONICS
See LIND ELECTRONIC DESIGN CO INC

D-U-N-S 02-868-5634 IMP
LINDA CASA FURNITURE INC
4815 Whittier Blvd, Los Angeles, CA 90022-3023
Tel (888) 783-0632 *Founded/Ownrshp* 1974
Sales 34.0MM *EMP* 180
SIC 5712 5731 5722 Furniture stores; Television sets; High fidelity stereo equipment; Electric household appliances; Furniture stores; Television sets; High fidelity stereo equipment; Electric household appliances
Pr: Ben Liberman

D-U-N-S 03-855-8805
LINDA CONSTRUCTION CO INC
1801 N Tryon St Ste A, Charlotte, NC 28206-2786
Tel (704) 333-7120 *Founded/Ownrshp* 1977
Sales 20.4MM^E *EMP* 50
SIC 1542 Commercial & office buildings, renovation & repair
Pr: Linda Holden
**Ex VP:* Gary Olnowich

D-U-N-S 06-794-9933
LINDA HALL LIBRARY
5109 Cherry St, Kansas City, MO 64110-2498
Tel (816) 363-4600 *Founded/Ownrshp* 1942
Sales 20.5MM *EMP* 90
SIC 8231 Libraries; Libraries
Ch Bd: Dwight D Sutherland
**Pr:* C Lee Jones
Ofcr: Bruce Bradley
Top Exec: Julie Brinkman
VP: Angela Tangen

D-U-N-S 03-855-6754
LINDA SILVESTRI
YMCA
1 Sewall St, Salem, MA 01970-3405
Tel (978) 740-9622 *Founded/Ownrshp* 2001

Sales 35.9MM *EMP* 90
SIC 8641 7991 8351 7032 8322 Youth organizations; Physical fitness facilities; Child day care services; Youth camps; Individual & family services
Ex Dir: Deborah Amaral

D-U-N-S 80-852-8728
LINDA YORBA REDEVELOPMENT AGENCY
4845 Casa Loma Ave, Yorba Linda, CA 92886-3364
Tel (714) 961-7100 *Founded/Ownrshp* 2007
Sales 21.1MM *EMP* 1
Accts Lance Soll & Lunghard Llp B
SIC 8748 Urban planning & consulting services; Urban planning & consulting services
Ex Dir: Steven K Harris

D-U-N-S 04-365-9580 IMP
LINDA YORBA WATER DISTRICT INC
1717 E Miraloma Ave, Placentia, CA 92870-6785
Tel (714) 701-3000 *Founded/Ownrshp* 1959
Sales 29.6MM *EMP* 76ᴱ
Accts White Nelson Diehl Evans Llp
SIC 4941 4952 Water supply; Sewerage systems; Water supply; Sewerage systems
Genl Mgr: Ken Vecchiarelli
Bd of Dir: Gary Melton
VP: Phil Hawkins
Genl Mgr: Marc Marcantonio
Genl Mgr: Michael Payne
IT Man: Anh Nguyen

LINDAL BUILDING PRODUCTS
See LINDAL CEDAR HOMES INC

D-U-N-S 00-949-8429 IMP
LINDAL CEDAR HOMES INC
LINDAL BUILDING PRODUCTS
4300 S 104th Pl, Seattle, WA 98178-2093
Tel (206) 725-0900 *Founded/Ownrshp* 1990
Sales 56.5MMᴱ *EMP* 190
SIC 2452 1751 Prefabricated wood buildings; Prefabricated buildings, wood; Window & door (prefabricated) installation; Prefabricated wood buildings; Prefabricated buildings, wood; Window & door (prefabricated) installation
Pr: Michael Harris
**Ch Bd:* Sir Walter Lindal
**Pr:* Douglas F Lindal
**CFO:* Dennis Greg
**VP:* Martin J Lindal
IT Man: Tricia Froiland
VP Mktg: Signe Benson

D-U-N-S 07-837-6969
LINDALE INDEPENDENT SCHOOL DISTRICT
505 Pierce St, Lindale, TX 75771-3336
Tel (903) 881-4000 *Founded/Ownrshp* 1946
Sales 26.9MMᴱ *EMP* 500
SIC 8211 Public combined elementary & secondary school; Public elementary & secondary schools
Dir Sec: Joey King
Pr Dir: Lauren Loyless

D-U-N-S 36-226-9086
LINDAMOOD-BELL LEARNING PROCESSES
406 Higuera St Ste 120, San Luis Obispo, CA 93401-6131
Tel (805) 541-3836 *Founded/Ownrshp* 1987
Sales 45.3MMᴱ *EMP* 750
SIC 8093 Specialty outpatient clinics; Specialty outpatient clinics
Pr: Nanci Bell
**Treas:* Patricia Lindamood
Comm Dir: Erin Bell
Ex Dir: Carl Marcin
Off Mgr: Kileigh Donoghue
Off Mgr: Fl McNicoll
Off Mgr: Jenny Painter
Off Mgr: Kate Sands
Off Mgr: Michelle Strand
IT Man: Rod Bell
Site Mgr: Ben Moffatt

D-U-N-S 03-122-4124
LINDBERGH SCHOOL DISTRICT
4900 S Lindbergh Blvd, Saint Louis, MO 63126-3235
Tel (314) 729-2400 *Founded/Ownrshp* 1949
Sales 108.6M *EMP* 304
SIC 8211 Public elementary school; Public junior high school; Public senior high school; Public elementary school; Public junior high school; Public senior high school
Prgrm Mgr: Bill Hopkins
CTO: Jim Denner
IT Man: Victor Lenz
Netwrk Mgr: Mariano Marin
Sls&Mrk Ex: Patrick Lanane

D-U-N-S 80-423-1467
LINDBERGH SCHOOLS
4900 S Lindbergh Blvd, Saint Louis, MO 63126-3235
Tel (314) 729-2400 *Founded/Ownrshp* 2008
Sales 67.8MM *EMP* 224
Accts Kerber Eck & Braeckel Llp St
SIC 8211 Public elementary & secondary schools; Public elementary & secondary schools
Pr Dir: Beth Johnston
HC Dir: Wami Singora

D-U-N-S 00-283-1824
LINDBLAD CONSTRUCTION CO OF JOLIET INC
717 E Cass St, Joliet, IL 60432-3003
Tel (815) 726-6251 *Founded/Ownrshp* 1989
Sales 48.0MM *EMP* 50
Accts Cliftonlarsonallen Llp Oak Br
SIC 1541 Industrial buildings, new construction; Industrial buildings, new construction
Pr: Thomas J Lind
Sr VP: Gary Proffitt
VP: Denielle Hrusosky
**VP:* Mark Stadalsky
Snr Mgr: Brian Long

D-U-N-S 96-730-4309
▲ LINDBLAD EXPEDITIONS HOLDINGS INC
509 7th St Nw, Washington, DC 20004-1600
Tel (202) 654-7060 *Founded/Ownrshp* 2010
Sales 21.8MMᴱ *EMP* 72ᴱ
Tkr Sym LIND *Exch* NAS
SIC 6799 Investors
Ch Bd: Mark D Ein
**CFO:* L Dyson Dryden

D-U-N-S 10-113-8014
■ LINDBLAD EXPEDITIONS LLC
(*Suby of* LINDBLAD EXPEDITIONS HOLDINGS INC) ★
96 Morton St Fl 9, New York, NY 10014-3326
Tel (212) 765-7740 *Founded/Ownrshp* 2015
Sales 21.8MMᴱ *EMP* 70
SIC 4481 4725 Deep sea passenger transportation, except ferry; Tour operators
CEO: Sven Olof Lindblad
COO: Ian Rogers
Chf Mktg O: Rich Fontaine
Ofcr: Trey Byus
VP: Lesa Bain
Prgrm Mgr: Daniel Gutierrez
Mktg Mgr: Amy Harrigan
Mktg Mgr: Elissa Marton
Mktg Mgr: Darlene Salzer
Mktg Mgr: Rebecca Wolf
Snr Mgr: Orion Purser

D-U-N-S 80-626-9713
LINDE CORP
118 Armstrong Rd, Pittston, PA 18640-9628
Tel (570) 299-5700 *Founded/Ownrshp* 2006
Sales 47.7MMᴱ *EMP* 250
Accts Mcgrail Merkel Quinn & Associa
SIC 1623 1389 Underground utilities contractor; Oil field services; Gas field services; Underground utilities contractor; Oil field services; Gas field services
Pr: Scott F Linde
**Treas:* Robert Hessling
**VP:* Christopher Langel
Assoc Dir: Stefano Innocenzi
Opers Mgr: Dave Walsh

D-U-N-S 06-542-3485 IMP/EXP
LINDE ENGINEERING NORTH AMERICA INC
LINDE ENGINEERING US
(*Suby of* LINDE HOLDINGS LLC) ★
5 Sentry Pkwy E Ste 300, Blue Bell, PA 19422-2312
Tel (610) 834-0300 *Founded/Ownrshp* 1982
Sales 127.1MMᴱ *EMP* 260
SIC 3567 8711 Incinerators, metal: domestic or commercial; Industrial engineers; Incinerators, metal: domestic or commercial; Industrial engineers
Pr: Joerg Linsenmaier
**Pr:* Samir J Serhan
CFO: Linde AG
**Treas:* Gabriela Redondo
**VP:* Emerson Rhodes
Mng Dir: Christian Bruch
Mng Dir: Juergen Nowicki
Off Mgr: Irene Tarloski
IT Man: Vipul Desai
VP Opers: Carl Rentschler
Snr PM: James A Deisinger

LINDE ENGINEERING US
See LINDE ENGINEERING NORTH AMERICA INC

D-U-N-S 01-422-4836
LINDE ENTERPRISES INC
9 Collan Park, Honesdale, PA 18431-7654
Tel (570) 299-5700 *Founded/Ownrshp* 1965
Sales 20.1MMᴱ *EMP* 130
Accts Parente Beard Llc Wilkes-Barn
SIC 1629 1623 Earthmoving contractor; Gas main construction; Water main construction; Sewer line construction; Earthmoving contractor; Gas main construction; Water main construction; Sewer line construction
Pr: Scott Linde
Treas: Robert Hessling
VP: Paul Fedor
**VP:* Christopher A Langel
VP: Robert McGraw
VP: John Padavan

D-U-N-S 80-556-8339 IMP
LINDE GAS NORTH AMERICA LLC
(*Suby of* LINDE NORTH AMERICA INC) ★
575 Mountain Ave, New Providence, NJ 07974-2097
Tel (908) 464-8100 *Founded/Ownrshp* 2006
Sales 887.8MMᴱ *EMP* 3,700
SIC 2813 Oxygen, compressed or liquefied; Nitrogen; Argon; Hydrogen; Oxygen, compressed or liquefied; Nitrogen; Argon; Hydrogen
CEO: Dr Wolfgang Reitzle
**Pr:* Patrick F Murphy
**Ch:* Mark D Weller
VP: Philippe D Brunet
**Prin:* Mike Walsh

D-U-N-S 00-417-4819
LINDE GAS USA LLC
(*Suby of* LINDE AG)
575 Mountain Ave, New Providence, NJ 07974-2097
Tel (908) 464-8100 *Founded/Ownrshp* 2007
Sales 100.7MMᴱ *EMP* 600ᴱ
SIC 2813 5084 Oxygen, compressed or liquefied; Nitrogen; Acetylene; Hydrogen; Welding machinery & equipment; Oxygen, compressed or liquefied; Nitrogen; Acetylene; Hydrogen; Welding machinery & equipment
Pr: Patrick Murphy
**Treas:* Jonathan Hoy
Top Exec: Satish Tamhankar
**Ex VP:* Mark Weller
**Sr VP:* John Brull
VP: Gene Allen
VP: David Johnston
Mfg Mgr: Glen Radomski
Snr PM: Naresh Suchak
Snr Mgr: Kevin Prisk

D-U-N-S 07-851-8054 IMP/EXP
LINDE GLOBAL HELIUM
575 Mountain Ave, New Providence, NJ 07974-2097
Tel (908) 464-8100 *Founded/Ownrshp* 2012
Sales 26.4MMᴱ *EMP* 99
SIC 2813 Oxygen, compressed or liquefied; Oxygen, compressed or liquefied
Pr: Joe Horn
Brnch Mgr: Edward Ribar
Netwrk Mgr: Marryann Sicola
Sales Asso: Larry Biegel
Sales Asso: Mike Browne
Snr Mgr: Louie Chabarria

D-U-N-S 13-160-2331
LINDE HOLDINGS LLC
(*Suby of* LINDE NORTH AMERICA INC) ★
6100 S Yale Ave Ste 1200, Tulsa, OK 74136-1905
Tel (918) 477-1200 *Founded/Ownrshp* 2005
Sales 213.2MMᴱ *EMP* 389
SIC 8711 Engineering services; Engineering services
Prin: Larry Hoose
IT Man: Ben Beckham
Sls Mgr: Joe Galbraith

D-U-N-S 00-136-8141 IMP/EXP
LINDE LLC
(*Suby of* LINDE NORTH AMERICA INC) ★
575 Mountain Ave, New Providence, NJ 07974-2097
Tel (908) 464-8100 *Founded/Ownrshp* 2006
Sales 676.6MMᴱ *EMP* 3,700
SIC 2813 3569 3561 3823 Oxygen, compressed or liquefied; Nitrogen; Argon; Hydrogen; Gas separators (machinery); Pumps & pumping equipment; Industrial flow & liquid measuring instruments; Oxygen, compressed or liquefied; Nitrogen; Argon; Hydrogen; Gas separators (machinery); Pumps & pumping equipment; Industrial flow & liquid measuring instruments
Mng Pt: Robert Mullaney
COO: Fred Kinkin
Top Exec: Valerie Egan
Top Exec: Susan Ross
Dir Bus: Thomas Armitt
Mng Dir: Sanjiv Lamba
Area Mgr: Don Smiley
Brnch Mgr: Joe Doucet
Brnch Mgr: Gary Grove
Brnch Mgr: John Hanam
Brnch Mgr: Pablo Pacheco

D-U-N-S 10-624-8008 IMP/EXP
LINDE NORTH AMERICA INC
(*Suby of* LINDE AG)
575 Mountain Ave, New Providence, NJ 07974-2097
Tel (908) 464-8100 *Founded/Ownrshp* 1983
Sales 1.7MMMᴱ *EMP* 3,700ᴱ
SIC 2813 3569 3559 3561 3511 3823 Industrial gases; Oxygen, compressed or liquefied; Nitrogen; Argon; Gas producers, generators & other gas related equipment; Cryogenic machinery, industrial; Pumps & pumping equipment; Turbines & turbine generator sets; Flow instruments, industrial process type; Industrial gases; Oxygen, compressed or liquefied; Nitrogen; Argon; Gas producers, generators & other gas related equipment; Cryogenic machinery, industrial; Pumps & pumping equipment; Turbines & turbine generator sets; Flow instruments, industrial process type
Pr: Pat Murphy
Pr: Frederic Jagush
Pr: Kevin Kilroy
Top Exec: Carlos Nulman
Ex VP: Kenneth Linde
CIO: Konstantin Fiedler
Dir IT: Bruce Turnbull
Plnt Mgr: Al Espy
Plnt Mgr: Kristie Hawkins
Plnt Mgr: Daniel Kahan
Plnt Mgr: Jodi Lund

D-U-N-S 05-594-0043 IMP
LINDE PROCESS PLANTS INC
(*Suby of* LINDE HOLDINGS LLC) ★
6100 S Yale Ave Ste 1200, Tulsa, OK 74136-1905
Tel (918) 477-1200 *Founded/Ownrshp* 2002
Sales 86.1MMᴱ *EMP* 389
SIC 3444 8711 1629 Sheet metalwork; Engineering services; Chemical plant & refinery construction; Sheet metalwork; Engineering services; Chemical plant & refinery construction
Pr: Steve Bertone
Pr: Shawn Quinton
**VP:* Jody Black
**VP:* Juergen Fuchs
**VP:* Ron Key
VP: Klaus Poganski
**VP:* Don Worman
IT Man: Tony Pryor
Snr PM: Ali Jangi
Snr Mgr: David Duval
Snr Mgr: John Scott
Board of Directors: Steve Bertone, Juergen Nowicki

D-U-N-S 00-696-7848
LINDELL BANK & TRUST (MO)
(*Suby of* FIRST ILLINOIS BANCORP INC)
6900 Clayton Ave, Saint Louis, MO 63139-3739
Tel (314) 645-7700 *Founded/Ownrshp* 1923
Sales NA *EMP* 55
SIC 6022 State commercial banks; State commercial banks
Ch Bd: Melvin L Hall
**CFO:* James Seitz
**Sr VP:* Joseph Fix
Sr VP: David Hall
VP: Russell Greenleaf
VP: Lisa Mitchell
**VP:* Janice M Walton
VP: Tricia Whelan
Sls&Mrk Ex: Joseph Fixx

D-U-N-S 12-214-6996 IMP/EXP
LINDEN BULK TRANSPORTATION CO INC
4200 Tremley Point Rd, Linden, NJ 07036-6536
Tel (908) 862-3883 *Founded/Ownrshp* 1981
Sales 35.3MMᴱ *EMP* 140
SIC 4213 Trucking, except local; Trucking, except local
Pr: Sanford Salz
**Pr:* Paul Defalco
VP: Lou Dinicola
**VP:* Michael Doctro
VP: Richard Miller
**VP:* Debra Salz
**VP:* Michael Salz
**VP:* Jared Stadlin
Genl Mgr: Stacy Defalco
IT Man: Eric Pufahl
Trfc Mgr: Kathy Arnold

D-U-N-S 17-305-1272
LINDEN CAPITAL PARTNERS II LP
111 S Wacker Dr Ste 4000, Chicago, IL 60606-4309
Tel (312) 506-5600 *Founded/Ownrshp* 2008
Sales 63.7MMᴱ *EMP* 450ᴱ
SIC 6799 Investment clubs; Investment clubs

D-U-N-S 05-535-9848
LINDEN CITY OF INC
301 N Wood Ave Ste 1, Linden, NJ 07036-7218
Tel (908) 474-8479 *Founded/Ownrshp* 1925
Sales NA *EMP* 561
SIC 9111 Mayors' offices; ; Mayors' offices;
**Pr:* Robert Bunk
Snr Mgr: Barbara Jones

D-U-N-S 05-310-8908
LINDEN COMMUNITY SCHOOLS (MI)
BOARD OF EDUCATION
7205 Silver Lake Rd, Linden, MI 48451-8710
Tel (810) 591-0980 *Founded/Ownrshp* 1950
Sales 17.8MMᴱ *EMP* 300
Accts Yeo & Yeo Pc
SIC 8211 Public elementary school; Public junior high school; Public senior high school; Public elementary school; Public junior high school; Public senior high school
V Ch: Nancy Smitz
Bd of Dir: Cindy Day
Bd of Dir: Shirley Green
Bd of Dir: Steve Murphy

LINDEN LAB
See LINDEN RESEARCH INC

D-U-N-S 09-282-9055
LINDEN LLC
111 S Wacker Dr Ste 3350, Chicago, IL 60606-4306
Tel (312) 506-5657 *Founded/Ownrshp* 1998
Sales 40.4MMᴱ *EMP* 18ᴱ
SIC 6726 Management investment funds, closed-end
**Pt:* Richard U De Schutter
**Pt:* Gary A Kagan
**Pt:* Chris M Kolber
**Pt:* Charles Mamrak
Mng Pt: Eric Larson
**CFO:* Douglass W Vandegrift
VP: Kam Shah
Off Mgr: Laura Swajkowski

D-U-N-S 82-623-7963 IMP/EXP
LINDEN LUMBER LLC
23741 Us Highway 43, Linden, AL 36748-4380
Tel (334) 295-8751 *Founded/Ownrshp* 2009
Sales 31.8MMᴱ *EMP* 160
SIC 2421 Lumber: rough, sawed or planed; Lumber: rough, sawed or planed
Pr: Hugh Overmyer
**VP:* Alan Lewis

LINDEN OAKS HOSPITAL
See NAPERVILLE PSYCHIATRIC VENTURES

D-U-N-S 14-755-6398
LINDEN PONDS INC
300 Linden Ponds Way, Hingham, MA 02043-3791
Tel (781) 337-2255 *Founded/Ownrshp* 2002
Sales 55.1MM *EMP* 50
Accts Rsm Mcgladrey Inc Baltimore
SIC 8059 Nursing home, except skilled & intermediate care facility; Nursing home, except skilled & intermediate care facility
Ch: Mary Helen Lorenz
**Pr:* Wayne Craig
**Treas:* Willow Pasley
**Ex Dir:* Ian Lee Brown
Ex Dir: Brenda Harrington

D-U-N-S 07-931-9497
LINDEN PUBLIC SCHOOLS
2 E Gibbons St, Linden, NJ 07036-2951
Tel (908) 486-7157 *Founded/Ownrshp* 1930
Sales 33.5MMᴱ *EMP* 655
SIC 8211 Public elementary & secondary schools; Public elementary & secondary schools
Nrsg Dir: Susan Fegan
HC Dir: Stephen Yesinko

D-U-N-S 16-933-2371
LINDEN RESEARCH INC
LINDEN LAB
945 Battery St, San Francisco, CA 94111-1305
Tel (415) 243-9000 *Founded/Ownrshp* 1999
Sales 54.8MMᴱ *EMP* 330ᴱ
Accts Kpmg Llp San Francisco Ca
SIC 7371 Computer software development; Computer software development
CEO: Ebbe Altberg
Pt: Bill Gurley
**COO:* Bob Komin
**CFO:* Malcolm Dunne
**CFO:* John Zdanowski
Ofcr: Tom Hale
Ofcr: Leanne Hoang
Sr VP: Frank Ambrose
Sr VP: Howard Look
**VP:* Robin Ducot
VP: Robin Harper
**VP:* Lori Medeiros
VP: Brian Michon
VP: Joe Miller
**VP:* Jeff Peterson
**VP:* Lee Senderov
VP: Cyn Skyberg
VP: Judy Wade
VP: Ginsu Yoon

D-U-N-S 10-629-9076
LINDEN STREET CAPITAL CORP
4010 Pilot Dr Ste 103, Memphis, TN 38118-6916
Tel (901) 842-7110 *Founded/Ownrshp* 1977
Sales 23.9MM^E *EMP* 220
SIC 4581 3674 Aircraft maintenance & repair services; Fuel cells, solid state; Aircraft maintenance & repair services; Fuel cells, solid state
Ch: John C Stanley IV
**Pr:* Fred Tavoleti

D-U-N-S 01-402-0283
LINDEN UNIFIED SCHOOL DISTRICT
18527 E Highway 26, Linden, CA 95236-9584
Tel (209) 887-3894 *Founded/Ownrshp* 1965
Sales 45.0MM^E *EMP* 1,006
SIC 8211 Public elementary & secondary schools; School board; Public elementary & secondary schools; School board
Schl Brd P: Marvin Vaccarezza

D-U-N-S 08-566-1130 IMP
LINDEN WAREHOUSE AND DISTRIBUTION CO INC
1300 Lower Rd, Linden, NJ 07036-6523
Tel (908) 474-0543 *Founded/Ownrshp* 1963
Sales 20.1MM^E *EMP* 85^E
SIC 4226 Special warehousing & storage
Ch: Sanford Salz
**Ex VP:* Louis Salz
**VP:* Debra Salz
**VP:* Michael Salz
**VP:* Jared Stadlin
Genl Mgr: Arthur Calvani
IT Man: Joe Adornetto
Netwrk Mgr: Anthony Grieco
Sfty Mgr: Johnathan Womack
Opers Mgr: Lou Di Nicola

D-U-N-S 15-731-2620
LINDENGROVE INC
LINDENGROVE PHARMACY
13700 W National Ave # 9, New Berlin, WI 53151-9503
Tel (262) 797-4600 *Founded/Ownrshp* 1987
Sales 51.0MM *EMP* 1,000
Accts Wipfli Llp Milwaukee Wi
SIC 8051 5912 Convalescent home with continuous nursing care; Drug stores; Convalescent home with continuous nursing care; Drug stores
CEO: Linda Joel
**CFO:* Mark Sperka
Dir Rx: Kareen Schmidtknecht
**Prin:* Robert Schaefer
Ex Dir: Dave Rindfleisch
Pharmcst: Gary Gaszak
Pharmcst: Debbie Peterson
Pharmcst: Scott Treland

D-U-N-S 96-351-7201
LINDENGROVE MUKWONAGO
837 County Road Nn E, Mukwonago, WI 53149-1013
Tel (262) 363-6830 *Founded/Ownrshp* 2010
Sales 505.1MM *EMP* 25^E
SIC 8051 Skilled nursing care facilities; Skilled nursing care facilities
Prin: Lynn Lang

LINDENGROVE PHARMACY
See LINDENGROVE INC

LINDENHURST PUBLIC SCHOOL
See LINDENHURST UNION FREE SCHOOL DISTRICT

D-U-N-S 06-594-8036
LINDENHURST UNION FREE SCHOOL DISTRICT
LINDENHURST PUBLIC SCHOOL
350 Daniel St, Lindenhurst, NY 11757-3547
Tel (631) 226-6441 *Founded/Ownrshp* 1930
Sales 41.4MM^E *EMP* 1,000
SIC 8211 Public elementary & secondary schools; Public elementary & secondary schools
VP: Edward J Murphy Jr
Dir IT: Kelly Waters
IT Man: Edward Salina
Pr Dir: Alison De Maria
Board of Directors: Cathy Donato Sectry Bussin

LINDENMEYR CENTRAL
See CENTRAL NATIONAL-GOTTESMAN INC

D-U-N-S 10-060-4461
LINDENWOLD SCHOOL DISTRICT INC
801 Egg Harbor Rd, Lindenwold, NJ 08021-1327
Tel (856) 784-4071 *Founded/Ownrshp* 1930
Sales 15.8MM^E *EMP* 500
Accts Deloitte By Fax On November 6
SIC 8211 Public elementary & secondary schools; Kindergarten; Elementary school; Public elementary & secondary schools; Kindergarten; Elementary school
Pr: Cathy Moncrief
Pr: Kathy Moncries
Treas: Bonnie Jackson
VP: Kevin Mc Gahey
Dir IT: Sam Delfino

D-U-N-S 07-696-4410
LINDENWOOD UNIVERSITY
209 S Kingshighway St, Saint Charles, MO 63301-1695
Tel (636) 949-2000 *Founded/Ownrshp* 2006
Sales 185.0MM *EMP* 1,200
Accts Kpmg Llp Columbus Oh
SIC 8221 University; University
Pr: James D Evans
Dir Recs: Adam Ulrich
**CFO:* David Kandel
CFO: David Kandle
Treas: John Hammond
VP: Alyssa Entwistle
VP: John Oldani
Comm Dir: Scott Queen
Comm Dir: Bill Vahle
Ex Dir: Brian Rivolta
CTO: Jann Weitdel

LINDER CENTER OF HOPE
See CRAIG & FRANCES LINDNER CENTER OF HOPE

D-U-N-S 02-955-4532 IMP
LINDER EQUIPMENT CO
311 E Kern Ave, Tulare, CA 93274-4107
Tel (559) 685-5000 *Founded/Ownrshp* 1947
Sales 25.8MM *EMP* 50
Accts Sciacca & Company Visalia Ca
SIC 5999 7699 Farm machinery repair; Farm equipment & supplies; Farm machinery repair
Pr: Frances Linder
Treas: Robert Linder
Sec: Troy D Allen
VP: Francine Linder
Mktg Dir: Jim Dokken

D-U-N-S 00-411-2884 IMP/EXP
LINDER INDUSTRIAL MACHINERY CO
(*Suby of* SUMITOMO CORP OF AMERICAS) ★
1601 S Frontage Rd # 100, Plant City, FL 33563-2004
Tel (813) 754-2727 *Founded/Ownrshp* 1953
Sales 161.3MM^E *EMP* 470
SIC 5082 7353 Construction & mining machinery; Heavy construction equipment rental; Construction & mining machinery; Heavy construction equipment rental
Pr: John L Coughlin
**CFO:* Peggy H Smith
Ex VP: Bob Olejniczak
VP: Chet Miller
VP: Eric Teague
Exec: Kim Shaw
Rgnl Mgr: Steve Ricker
Brnch Mgr: Chris Wilkes
Off Mgr: Ann Moore
Netwrk Mgr: Don Knox
Mktg Dir: Melissa Hancock

D-U-N-S 01-625-5852 IMP/EXP
LINDER INDUSTRIAL MACHINERY CO
SUMIQUIP
(*Suby of* SUMITOMO CORPORATION)
1601 S Frontage Rd Ste 2, Plant City, FL 33563-2004
Tel (813) 754-2000 *Founded/Ownrshp* 2007
Sales 324.9MM^E *EMP* 1,004^E
SIC 5082 General construction machinery & equipment; General construction machinery & equipment
Ch: Jeff Cox
**Pr:* Hitoshi Kai
**CFO:* Peggy Smith
VP: Vincent Aguayo
**VP:* Max Kobyashi
**VP:* Masanori Osada
Brnch Mgr: Scott McDougle
Dir IT: Don Knox
Dir IT: Eric Stride
Mtls Mgr: Bo Ross
Manager: Rob Leavel

LINDERHOUSE
See GEORGIA NUT CO

D-U-N-S 07-149-1344
LINDQUIST & VENNUM PLLP
80 S 8th St Ste 4200, Minneapolis, MN 55402-2274
Tel (612) 371-3211 *Founded/Ownrshp* 1968
Sales 32.8MM^E *EMP* 363
SIC 8111 General practice law office; General practice law office
Genl Pt: Dennis O'Malley
Pt: J Christopher Cuneo
Pt: Thomas F Dougherty
Pt: James M Lockhart
Pt: Tiffanie Stasiak
VP: John Laravuso
Off Mgr: Linda Gavel
CIO: Suzette Allaire
IT Man: Celia Thomas

LINDSAY CADILLAC OF ALEXANDRIA
See LINDSAY MOTOR CAR CO

LINDSAY CHEVROLET & ISUZU
See LINDSAY CHEVROLET LLC

D-U-N-S 05-171-9573
LINDSAY CHEVROLET INC
285 W Elm St, Lebanon, MO 65536-3519
Tel (417) 532-3114 *Founded/Ownrshp* 1970
Sales 21.9MM^E *EMP* 54
SIC 5511 Automobiles, new & used
Pr: Larry Lindsay
**Sec:* Desselle Lindsey
**VP:* Darrell D Lindsay

D-U-N-S 02-397-8570
LINDSAY CHEVROLET LLC
LINDSAY CHEVROLET & ISUZU
(*Suby of* LINDSAY CADILLAC OF ALEXANDRIA) ★
15605 Jefferson Davis Hwy, Woodbridge, VA 22191-4114
Tel (703) 670-8181 *Founded/Ownrshp* 1998
Sales 37.4MM^E *EMP* 80
SIC 5511 5012 Automobiles, new & used; Pickups, new & used; Automobiles; Trucks, noncommercial; Automobiles, new & used; Pickups, new & used; Automobiles; Trucks, noncommercial
**Genl Mgr:* Paul Smyth
Store Mgr: David Burzynski
Sls Mgr: Alfonso Brooks
Sls Mgr: Frankie Brunette
Sls Mgr: Johnnan Johnson
Sls Mgr: Yogi Sharma
Sales Asso: Tom Lagrave
Sales Asso: Adia Robinson
Sales Asso: Lyndsey Selwaeh
Sales Asso: Allison Shine
Sales Asso: Stephen Zolnowski

D-U-N-S 06-864-5696 EXP
▲ LINDSAY CORP
2222 N 111th St, Omaha, NE 68164-3817
Tel (402) 829-6800 *Founded/Ownrshp* 1955
Sales 617.9MM *EMP* 1,202^E
Tkr Sym LNN *Exch* NYS
SIC 3523 3599 3443 Irrigation equipment, self-propelled; Machine & other job shop work; Pipe, standpipe & culverts; Irrigation equipment, self-propelled; Machine & other job shop work; Pipe, standpipe & culverts
Pr: Richard W Parod
Pr: Steven Cotariu
CFO: James C Raabe
Treas: Mark A Roth
Bd of Dir: Howard Buffett
VP: Eric R Arneson
VP: James Shearer
Rgnl Mgr: Luis Mendez
CIO: Eric Talmadge
QA Dir: Sheik Ramessar
IT Man: Greg Oswald
Board of Directors: Robert E Brunner, Howard G Buffet, Michael N Christodolou, W Thomas Jagodinski, Michael C Nahl, David B Rayburn, Michael D Walter, William F Welsh II

D-U-N-S 02-269-0515
LINDSAY FORD LLC
(*Suby of* LINDSAY CADILLAC OF ALEXANDRIA) ★
11250 Veirs Mill Rd, Wheaton, MD 20902-2525
Tel (301) 933-8165 *Founded/Ownrshp* 2005
Sales 57.6MM^E *EMP* 115
SIC 5511 7538 7533 Automobiles, new & used; Pickups, new & used; General automotive repair shops; Muffler shop, sale or repair & installation; Automobiles, new & used; Pickups, new & used; General automotive repair shops; Muffler shop, sale or repair & installation
CFO: John Smallwood
Mktg Dir: Jodi Onoffrey
Sls Mgr: Bill Godley
Sales Asso: Tom Lagrave
Sales Asso: Shawn Powell

LINDSAY GOLDBERG
See GOLDBERG LINDSAY & CO LLC

D-U-N-S 02-620-0256 IMP
■ LINDSAY MANUFACTURING LLC
(*Suby of* LINDSAY CORP) ★
2222 N 111th St, Omaha, NE 68164-3817
Tel (402) 829-6800 *Founded/Ownrshp* 2006
Sales 89.5MM^E *EMP* 500
SIC 3523 3599 3499 3443 Irrigation equipment, self-propelled; Machine & other job shop work; Barricades, metal; Pipe, standpipe & culverts; Irrigation equipment, self-propelled; Machine & other job shop work; Barricades, metal; Pipe, standpipe & culverts
Pr: Richard W Parod
Pr: Scott Marion
CFO: Jim Raabe
Treas: David B Downing
VP: Eric R Arneson
VP: James Raabe
VP: Mark A Roth
VP: Reuben P Srinivasan
VP: Randy Wood
Rgnl Mgr: Richard Hall
IT Man: Greg Oswald

D-U-N-S 02-362-9355 IMP
LINDSAY MOTOR CAR CO
LINDSAY CADILLAC OF ALEXANDRIA
1525 Kenwood Ave, Alexandria, VA 22302-2319
Tel (703) 998-6600 *Founded/Ownrshp* 1953
Sales 170.4MM^E *EMP* 150
SIC 5511 Automobiles, new & used; Automobiles, new & used
CEO: Danny Niblett
**VP:* Charles T Lindsay Jr
VP: Michael Lindsay
**Prin:* Chris Lindsay
Dir IT: Paul Moline
Sls Mgr: Anthony Cancel
Sales Asso: Frank Passarelli

D-U-N-S 01-756-9021 EXP
LINDSAY PRECAST INC (OH)
6845 Erie Ave Nw, Canal Fulton, OH 44614-8509
Tel (330) 854-6282 *Founded/Ownrshp* 1968
Sales 23.0MM^E *EMP* 118
SIC 3272 3699 Septic tanks, concrete; Manhole covers or frames, concrete; Security devices; Septic tanks, concrete; Manhole covers or frames, concrete; Security devices
Pr: Roland Lindsay Sr
**Treas:* Linda Lindsay
**VP:* Timothy Gesaman
Plnt Mgr: Matt Blind
Plnt Mgr: Chuck Kelley

D-U-N-S 00-617-5772
LINDSAY SASH INC (MN)
LINDSAY WINDOW & DOOR
1995 Commerce Ln, North Mankato, MN 56003-1701
Tel (507) 625-4278 *Founded/Ownrshp* 1947
Sales 25.2MM^E *EMP* 150
SIC 2431 5211 Door sashes, wood; Door screens, wood frame; Doors, wood; Lumber & other building materials; Door sashes, wood; Door screens, wood frame; Doors, wood; Lumber & other building materials
Pr: John C Roise
**VP:* Geoff Roise
**VP:* Sue Roise
Plnt Mgr: Steve Simpson

D-U-N-S 14-415-4630 IMP
■ LINDSAY TRANSPORTATION SOLUTIONS INC
BARRIER SYSTEMS SALES & SVC
(*Suby of* LINDSAY CORP) ★
180 River Rd, Rio Vista, CA 94571-1208
Tel (707) 374-6800 *Founded/Ownrshp* 2006
Sales 63.1MM^E *EMP* 354^E
SIC 3272 3559 Concrete products, precast; Concrete products machinery; Concrete products, precast; Concrete products machinery
CEO: Richard W Parod
**Pr:* David B Downing
**COO:* Chris Sanders
**Treas:* Mark A Roth
VP: Eric Arneson
VP: Gerrit Dyke
**VP:* James Raabe
Rgnl Mgr: Ron Vititoe
Opers Mgr: Darrell Hubbard
S&M/VP: Michael Dreznes
S&M/VP: J D Sobol

D-U-N-S 07-862-1387
■ LINDSAY TRANSPORTATION SOLUTIONS SALES & SERVICE LLC
LINDSAY TRNSP SOLUTIONS
(*Suby of* BARRIER SYSTEMS SALES & SVC) ★
180 River Rd, Rio Vista, CA 94571-1208
Tel (707) 374-6800 *Founded/Ownrshp* 2007
Sales 33.8MM^E *EMP* 250
SIC 5084 Safety equipment; Safety equipment
Pr: Bill Cooley

LINDSAY TRNSP SOLUTIONS
See LINDSAY TRANSPORTATION SOLUTIONS SALES & SERVICE LLC

D-U-N-S 03-733-3341
LINDSAY UNIFIED SCHOOL DISTRICT
WASHINGTON ELEMENTARY SCHOOL
371 E Hermosa St, Lindsay, CA 93247-2172
Tel (559) 562-5111 *Founded/Ownrshp* 1890
Sales 32.7MM^E *EMP* 540^E
SIC 8211 Public elementary school; Public junior high school; Public senior high school; Public elementary school; Public junior high school; Public senior high school

LINDSAY WINDOW & DOOR
See LINDSAY SASH INC

D-U-N-S 18-985-4966 IMP/EXP
LINDSAYCA INC
14350 Chrisman Rd, Houston, TX 77039-1509
Tel (713) 467-9560 *Founded/Ownrshp* 2003
Sales 25.0MM *EMP* 104
SIC 1389 8711 Oil field services; Engineering services; Oil field services; Engineering services
Pr: Jorge Santos
**Pr:* Hector Fuentes
**Sr VP:* Jesus Fuentes
VP: Willian Rodriguez

D-U-N-S 83-749-8443
LINDSEY CONTRACTORS INC
701 S Loop 340, Waco, TX 76706-4154
Tel (254) 752-3391 *Founded/Ownrshp* 1994
Sales 22.8MM^E *EMP* 225
SIC 1611 1623 1771 General contractor, highway & street construction; Water main construction; Sewer line construction; Driveway, parking lot & blacktop contractors; Blacktop (asphalt) work; Driveway contractor; Parking lot construction; General contractor, highway & street construction; Water main construction; Sewer line construction; Driveway, parking lot & blacktop contractors; Blacktop (asphalt) work; Driveway contractor; Parking lot construction
Pr: Claude Lindsey
**VP:* Rebecca Lindsey

D-U-N-S 07-869-4701
LINDSEY CUNNINGHAM GROUP LTD
3030 N Rocky Point Dr W # 530, Tampa, FL 33607-5803
Tel (813) 830-7100 *Founded/Ownrshp* 2012
Sales 1.2MMM^E *EMP* 7,000^E
SIC 6719 Personal holding companies, except banks
Pr: Philippe Bes
**COO:* David Radcliff
**CFO:* Ed Mullen
VP: Oded Schneider
Brnch Mgr: David Haft
Brnch Mgr: Coralee Harder
Genl Mgr: Bryan Hill
Snr Mgr: Damon Bennett
Snr Mgr: Mark Thompson
Snr Mgr: Jane Tutoki

LINDSEY INTERNATIONAL CO.
See LINDSEY MANUFACTURING CO

LINDSEY LEXUS OF ALEXANDRIA
See ALEXANDRIA MOTOR CARS INC

D-U-N-S 79-330-7166
LINDSEY MANAGEMENT CO INC
1200 E Joyce Blvd, Fayetteville, AR 72703-5189
Tel (479) 521-6686 *Founded/Ownrshp* 1985
Sales 17.2MM *EMP* 400
SIC 6531 Real estate managers; Real estate managers
Pr: Scott Rogerson
**Ch Bd:* Jim Lindsey
Pr: Dustin Douglas
**VP:* Job Branch
**VP:* Richard Parker
Genl Couns: Anne Mourney

D-U-N-S 00-850-5547 IMP
LINDSEY MANUFACTURING CO
LINDSEY INTERNATIONAL CO.
760 N Georgia Ave, Azusa, CA 91702-2249
Tel (626) 969-3471 *Founded/Ownrshp* 1947
Sales 47.9MM^E *EMP* 110
SIC 3463 3644 Pole line hardware forgings, nonferrous; Noncurrent-carrying wiring services; Pole line hardware forgings, nonferrous; Noncurrent-carrying wiring services
Pr: Keith E Lindsey
**CFO:* Frederick Findley
CTO: Rick Zonneville
Dir IT: Luke Walker
VP Opers: Steve Scholfield

D-U-N-S 08-505-3411
LINDSEY WILSON COLLEGE INC (KY)
L W C
210 Lindsey Wilson St, Columbia, KY 42728-1298
Tel (270) 384-2126 *Founded/Ownrshp* 1903
Sales 62.3MM *EMP* 375^E
Accts Strothman And Company Louisvl
SIC 8221 5942 College, except junior; Book stores; College, except junior; Book stores
Pr: William T Luckey Jr
Pr: Harriet Gold

Ofcr: Ben Martin
Ex VP: John Begley
**VP:* Dean Adams
**VP:* Roger Drake
**VP:* Denise Fudge
**VP:* Bettie Starr
Genl Mgr: Joann Panko
Off Mgr: Brittany Pike
Store Mgr: Tammy Adamson

D-U-N-S 03-076-0375
LINDSTROM AIR CONDITIONING INC (FL)
3581 W Mcnab Rd, Pompano Beach, FL 33069-4810
Tel (954) 420-5300 *Founded/Ownrshp* 1975, 1999
Sales 24.4MM^E *EMP* 101
SIC 1711 Warm air heating & air conditioning contractor
Pr: Jeffrey Lindstrom
**Treas:* Douglas Lindstrom
Genl Mgr: Joseph Canosa
Opers Mgr: Chris Adanti
Snr Mgr: Lisa Nelson

D-U-N-S 02-345-4853 IMP/EXP
LINDSTROM EQUIPMENT INC
S927 Cty Rd J, Mondovi, WI 54755
Tel (715) 946-3168 *Founded/Ownrshp* 1975
Sales 36.2MM *EMP* 30
SIC 5083

D-U-N-S 10-227-3422 IMP
LINDSTROM LLC
(*Suby of* HARBOUR GROUP LTD) ★
2950 100th Ct Ne, Blaine, MN 55449-5100
Tel (864) 877-7200 *Founded/Ownrshp* 2011
Sales 74.6MM^E *EMP* 200
SIC 5072 Miscellaneous fasteners; Miscellaneous fasteners
CEO: Virgil Lindstrom
**CFO:* Greg Wilson
**Sr VP:* Mike French
Genl Mgr: Bernie Longen

D-U-N-S 13-239-1327 IMP
LINDT & SPRUNGLI (USA) INC
(*Suby of* CHOCOLADEFABRIKEN LINDT & SPRUNGLI AG)
1 Fine Chocolate Pl, Stratham, NH 03885-2592
Tel (603) 778-8100 *Founded/Ownrshp* 1987
Sales 194.9MM^E *EMP* 650
SIC 2066 5149 5441 Chocolate; Chocolate; Candy; Chocolate; Chocolate; Candy
Pr: Thomas Linemayr
Treas: Markus Gasser
VP: Daniel Studer
Exec: Karen Ferrari
Mng Dir: Jaques Amey MD
Area Mgr: Michaela Scarpatetti
Off Mgr: Mica Magee
CTO: Leesa Daw
QA Dir: Steve Valliere
Dir IT: Stephen Scapicchio
IT Man: John Walter

D-U-N-S 09-472-6692
LINDY OFFICE PRODUCTS
1247 W Grove Ave, Orange, CA 92865-4118
Tel (714) 921-5600 *Founded/Ownrshp* 1979
Sales 22.3MM^E *EMP* 38
SIC 5112 Stationery & office supplies
Pr: Nancy Lindauer
**Ex VP:* Norman Lindauer
IT Man: Seth Lindauer
VP Mktg: Ken Golemo
Sls Mgr: Wilson Yu

D-U-N-S 10-366-3865
LINDYS HOMEMADE LLC
920 Black Satchel Rd A, Charlotte, NC 28216-3401
Tel (704) 391-7994 *Founded/Ownrshp* 1998
Sales 23.4MM^E *EMP* 25
SIC 5143 Ice cream & ices

D-U-N-S 15-444-4210 IMP
LINE 6 INC
(*Suby of* YAMAHA CORPORATION)
26580 Agoura Rd, Calabasas, CA 91302-1921
Tel (818) 575-3600 *Founded/Ownrshp* 1985
Sales 34.5MM^E *EMP* 215
SIC 3931 Musical instruments; Musical instruments
Pr: Paul Foeckler
**CFO:* Mary Ellen Broganer
CFO: Mary Broganer
Sr VP: David Froker
VP: Carol Bartholemy
VP: Adam Castillo
VP: Steve De Furia
VP: Doug Provisor
**VP Admn:* Susan Wolf
Prgrm Mgr: Don Cook
**CTO:* Michel Doidic

D-U-N-S 00-545-4251
LINE CRAFT TOOL CO INC
AMSTADT INDUSTRIES
10 W North Ave, Lombard, IL 60148-1263
Tel (630) 932-1182 *Founded/Ownrshp* 1976
Sales 25.0MM^E *EMP* 170
SIC 3599 5251 5084 3714 Machine shop, jobbing & repair; Tools; Machine tools & accessories; Motor vehicle parts & accessories; Machine shop, jobbing & repair; Tools; Machine tools & accessories; Motor vehicle parts & accessories
Pr: Jakob Amstadt
**Pr:* Jack W Amstadt

D-U-N-S 10-066-9431
LINE MOUNTAIN SCHOOL DISTRICT INC
185 Line Mountain Rd, Herndon, PA 17830-7325
Tel (570) 758-2640 *Founded/Ownrshp* 1966
Sales 23.3MM^E *EMP* 382
Accts Jones & Co Pc
SIC 8211 Public elementary & secondary schools; Public elementary & secondary schools
Treas: Florian J Gutkowski
Board of Directors: Alyce T Bostwick, Hilda M Klock, Dean E Raker, David E Reiner, Glenn L Schreffler, Maurice E Wilkinson

LINE PIPE INTERNATIONAL
See KELLY PIPE CO LLC

D-U-N-S 09-029-1365
LINE-X ACQUISITION LLC
1862 Sparkman Dr Nw, Huntsville, AL 35816-1122
Tel (256) 721-1331 *Founded/Ownrshp* 1999
Sales 31.5MM^E *EMP* 700
SIC 7532 Customizing services, non-factory basis; Customizing services, non-factory basis
CEO: Kevin Heronimus
Ofcr: John Q Wesley II

D-U-N-S 07-854-5588
LINEAGE LOGISTICS HOLDINGS LLC
17911 Von Karman Ave # 400, Irvine, CA 92614-6261
Tel (800) 678-7271 *Founded/Ownrshp* 2011
Sales 1.5MMM^E *EMP* 3,000^E
SIC 4222 Warehousing, cold storage or refrigerated; Warehousing, cold storage or refrigerated
Pr: Greg Lehmkuhl
**Pr:* Timothy Dayton
**Pr:* Paul Hendricksen
**Pr:* Mike McClendon
**CEO:* Bill Hendricksen
CFO: Jeremy Breaux
**CFO:* Todd Nelson
Ofcr: Allen Merrill
**Ex VP:* Tim Smith
**Sr VP:* Scott Chapman
**VP:* Calvin Austin
**VP:* Marcus Lester
**VP:* Patrick Stimpert

D-U-N-S 07-909-2447
LINEAGE LOGISTICS LLC
(*Suby of* LINEAGE LOGISTICS HOLDINGS LLC) ★
17911 Von Karman Ave # 400, Irvine, CA 92614-6261
Tel (800) 678-7271 *Founded/Ownrshp* 2013
Sales 88.1MM^E *EMP* 150^E
SIC 4222 Cheese warehouse; Warehousing, cold storage or refrigerated
CEO: Bill Hendricksen
CFO: Jeremy Breaux
Ex VP: Tim Smith
Sr VP: Jason Burnett
Sr VP: John Dittrick
VP: Ken Hudson
Genl Mgr: Willie Ashford
Genl Mgr: Ryan Axman
Genl Mgr: Greg Blaufuss
Genl Mgr: Reginald Burke
Genl Mgr: Tony Caetano

D-U-N-S 96-243-7096
■ **LINEAGE POWER HOLDINGS INC**
GE CRITICAL POWER
(*Suby of* GENERAL ELECTRIC CO) ★
601 Shiloh Rd, Plano, TX 75074-7210
Tel (974) 244-9288 *Founded/Ownrshp* 2007
Sales 171.6MM^E *EMP* 2,300^E
SIC 6719 Investment holding companies, except banks; Investment holding companies, except banks
CEO: Craig Witsoe
**CFO:* Skip Sorenson
IT Man: Jeffry Ruff
Tech Mgr: Jerry Strunk
Opers Mgr: Steven McCauley
VP Mktg: Trent Waterhouse
Snr Mgr: Ed Wiest

D-U-N-S 06-871-8196
■ **LINEAL INDUSTRIES INC**
(*Suby of* WILLBROS T&D SERVICES LLC) ★
350 Presto Sygan Rd, Bridgeville, PA 15017-1327
Tel (412) 914-5910 *Founded/Ownrshp* 1971
Sales 94.5MM^E *EMP* 250
SIC 1623 Oil & gas pipeline construction; Oil & gas pipeline construction
Pr: Lee Robbins
**Ex VP:* Johnny Priest

D-U-N-S 94-507-5976 IMP
■ **LINEAL TECHNOLOGIES INC**
PLYGEM INDUSTRIES
(*Suby of* MW MANUFACTURERS INC) ★
350 State St, Rocky Mount, VA 24151-1178
Tel (540) 484-6783 *Founded/Ownrshp* 1999
Sales 41.1MM^E *EMP* 90
SIC 3089 3442 Extruded finished plastic products; Window frames & sash, plastic; Window screening, plastic; Windows, plastic; Metal doors, sash & trim
CEO: Kerry Robinet
**Pr:* Earl Dodson

D-U-N-S 96-508-1180
LINEAR CONTROLS INC
107 1/2 Commission Blvd, Lafayette, LA 70508-3514
Tel (337) 839-9702 *Founded/Ownrshp* 2004
Sales 136.8MM^E *EMP* 200
SIC 5063 Electrical apparatus & equipment; Electrical apparatus & equipment
CEO: Andre Clemons
CFO: Dawn Quibodeaux

D-U-N-S 00-599-1468 IMP
LINEAR INDUSTRIES LTD
1850 Enterprise Way, Monrovia, CA 91016-4271
Tel (626) 303-1130 *Founded/Ownrshp* 1960
Sales 24.1MM^E *EMP* 62^E
SIC 5085 3625 5065 5072 3568 3545 Bearings; Positioning controls, electric; Electronic parts; Hardware; Power transmission equipment; Machine tool accessories; Bearings; Positioning controls, electric; Electronic parts; Hardware; Power transmission equipment; Machine tool accessories
Pr: Anthony Dell Angelica
**Treas:* Jean Cade
**VP:* Savonia Angelica
VP: Perry Priestley

LINEAR INTERNATIONAL
See LINEAR MOLD & ENGINEERING INC

D-U-N-S 03-864-8119
LINEAR LIGHTING CORP
3130 Hunters Point Ave, Long Island City, NY 11101-3132
Tel (718) 361-7552 *Founded/Ownrshp* 1965
Sales 32.2MM^E *EMP* 150
SIC 3646 5063 Commercial indusl & institutional electric lighting fixtures; Electrical apparatus & equipment; Commercial indusl & institutional electric lighting fixtures; Electrical apparatus & equipment
CEO: Larry Deutsch
**Pr:* Stanley Deutsch
MIS Dir: Andrew Okuboyhejo
VP Sls: Michael Deutsch
Sls Mgr: Scott Anderson
Sls Mgr: James Duplessie

D-U-N-S 06-126-5372
■ **LINEAR MOLD & ENGINEERING INC**
LINEAR INTERNATIONAL
(*Suby of* MOOG INC) ★
12926 Stark Rd, Livonia, MI 48150-1526
Tel (734) 422-6060 *Founded/Ownrshp* 2015
Sales 37.1MM^E *EMP* 120
SIC 3743 Locomotives & parts
Pr: John Tenbusch

D-U-N-S 13-133-1253 IMP
LINEAR MOTION LLC
THOMSON AEROSPACE & DEFENSE
(*Suby of* MEGGITT-USA INC) ★
628 N Hamilton St, Saginaw, MI 48602-4301
Tel (989) 759-8300 *Founded/Ownrshp* 2011
Sales 43.2MM^E *EMP* 170
SIC 3728 Aircraft parts & equipment; Aircraft parts & equipment
Pr: Nathan Hendrix
Pr: Craig Palmer
Pr: Patrick Scott

LINEAR MOTION SYSTEMS
See LIMOSS US LLC

D-U-N-S 03-253-3788 IMP
▲ **LINEAR TECHNOLOGY CORP**
1630 Mccarthy Blvd, Milpitas, CA 95035-7487
Tel (408) 432-1900 *Founded/Ownrshp* 1981
Sales 1.4MMM *EMP* 4,661
Tkr Sym LLTC *Exch* NGS
SIC 3674 Integrated circuits, semiconductor networks, etc.; Integrated circuits, semiconductor networks, etc.
CEO: Lothar Maier
**Ch Bd:* Robert H Swanson Jr
Pr: Bob Reay
COO: Alexander R McCann
CFO: Paul Cauglin
CFO: Paul Coghlan
Sr Cor Off: Kay Rhind
VP: Don Paulus
VP: Steve Pietkiewicz
Area Mgr: Kevin Swanson
IT Man: Rahul Pandey
Board of Directors: Arthur C Agnos, John J Gordon, David S Lee, Richard M Moley, Thomas S Volpe

D-U-N-S 19-714-9797
LINEAR TITLE & CLOSING LTD
127 John Clarke Rd Ste 1, Middletown, RI 02842-7632
Tel (401) 841-9991 *Founded/Ownrshp* 2004
Sales NA *EMP* 220
Accts Muto Volluci & Co Ltd War
SIC 6361 Title insurance; Title insurance
Pr: Nick Liuzza
Pr: Ryan Goodman
**COO:* Nathan Chandler
**CFO:* Todd Costa
Ex VP: Mark Selbee
Sr VP: Rudy Krupka
Sr VP: Brian Reseigh
Sr VP: Adam Wubbena
VP: Richard Ardoin
VP: Jessica Kauffman
CTO: Lloyd Knower

D-U-N-S 03-093-3881
LINEBARGER GOGGAN BLAIR & SAMPSON LLP (TX)
2700 Via Fortuna Ste 400, Austin, TX 78746-7997
Tel (512) 447-6675 *Founded/Ownrshp* 1976, 2009
Sales 139.4MM^E *EMP* 1,500
SIC 8111

D-U-N-S 01-375-4549
LINEDATA SERVICES INC
(*Suby of* LINEDATA SERVICES)
260 Franklin St Ste 1300, Boston, MA 02110-3127
Tel (617) 912-4700 *Founded/Ownrshp* 2003
Sales 20.2MM^E *EMP* 51^E
SIC 7371 Computer software development
Pr: Anvaraly Jiva
**CFO:* Denis Bley
**CFO:* Jack Wiener
**Treas:* Arnaud Allmang
Ex VP: Deb Biswas
VP: Toby Battell
VP: Kara Benedetto
VP: Terry Brennan
VP: Eric Hamilton
**VP:* Peter Muldoon
VP: Dan Pagano
VP: Bob Proctor
VP: Randy Stafford
VP: Jon Symonds
VP: Michael Underwood

LINEL SIGNATURE
See SIGNATURE SKYLIGHTS LLC

D-U-N-S 14-700-7330 IMP
LINEMARK PRINTING INC
501 Prince Georges Blvd, Upper Marlboro, MD 20774-7415
Tel (301) 925-9000 *Founded/Ownrshp* 1985
Sales 35.6MM^E *EMP* 90
SIC 2752 2791 Commercial printing, offset; Typesetting; Commercial printing, offset; Typesetting
Pr: Steve Bearden
Treas: Patricia Bearden

**Sec:* Colleen Pattee
**VP:* Dave Ashton
Prd Mgr: Joe Dodson
Mktg Dir: Eric Grainger

D-U-N-S 00-115-3923 IMP
LINEMASTER SWITCH CORP (CT)
29 Plaine Hill Rd, Woodstock, CT 06281-2913
Tel (860) 630-4920 *Founded/Ownrshp* 1952
Sales 45.3MM^E *EMP* 160
SIC 3625 Switches, electric power; Switches, electric power
Pr: Joseph J Carlone Jr
QA Dir: Richard Oellers
IT Man: Keith Worthington
Mfg Mgr: John Palazzo
Ql Cn Mgr: Jeremy Kaplan

LINEN HOLDINGS
See HARBOR LINEN LLC

LINENS OF THE WEEK
See ALSCO INC

LINENS OF THE WEEK
See PALACE LAUNDRY INC

D-U-N-S 01-768-2928
LINER LLP
1100 Glendon Ave Fl 14, Los Angeles, CA 90024-3518
Tel (310) 500-3500 *Founded/Ownrshp* 1996
Sales 23.8MM^E *EMP* 100^E
SIC 8111 Legal services
Pt: Heather H Gilhooly
Pt: Gerald Scott Janoff
Pt: Mitchell C Regenstreif
Pt: Randall J Sunshine
CFO: Cody Cluff
IT Man: Jill Striff
Counsel: Marc Nurik
Counsel: Alison Raddock
Counsel: Robert Shore
Snr Mgr: Robert Kaufman

D-U-N-S 60-633-0967
LINER SOURCE INC
21102 State Road 44, Eustis, FL 32736-5330
Tel (352) 357-3500 *Founded/Ownrshp* 1985
Sales 52.0MM^E *EMP* 100^E
SIC 5193 Flowers & florists' supplies
Pr: James L Langford

D-U-N-S 02-152-7512
LINES BUILDER CO LLC
9525 Queens Blvd Fl 10, Rego Park, NY 11374-4566
Tel (914) 921-8240 *Founded/Ownrshp* 2008
Sales 200.4M^E *EMP* 500
SIC 1521 New construction, single-family houses
Pr: Alex Katsman

D-U-N-S 19-947-0878
■ **LINETEC**
(*Suby of* APOGEE ENTERPRISES INC) ★
7500 Stewart Ave, Wausau, WI 54401-9064
Tel (715) 843-4100 *Founded/Ownrshp* 1983
Sales 83.6MM^E *EMP* 430
SIC 3442 Metal doors, sash & trim; Metal doors, sash & trim
Co-Ownr: Rick Marshall
Co-Ownr: Andy Joswiak
VP: Terri Dayan
VP: Rob Houchens
Plnt Mgr: Paul Bratz
Sls Mgr: Wendy Taylor

D-U-N-S 05-596-8317
LINFIELD COLLEGE
900 Se Baker St Unit A512, McMinnville, OR 97128-6894
Tel (503) 883-2200 *Founded/Ownrshp* 1898
Sales 65.2MM *EMP* 577
Accts Kpmg Llp Portland Or
SIC 8221 College, except junior; College, except junior
Pr: Thomas Hellie
Treas: Owen Fritz
Ofcr: Jacob Blair
Ofcr: Kathryn Karr
Ofcr: Marty Ransier
Ofcr: Irving Wiswall
VP: Bruce Wyatt
Exec: Nova Bekofsky
Ex Dir: Gordon Kroemer
Genl Mgr: Jason Briles
Dir IT: Shay Dakan

LINFINITY MICROELECTRONICS
See MICROSEMI CORP - ANALOG MIXED SIGNAL GROUP

D-U-N-S 00-618-6183
LINFOR INC (MN)
15600 32nd Ave N, Minneapolis, MN 55447-1456
Tel (763) 559-2911 *Founded/Ownrshp* 1962
Sales 23.7MM^E *EMP* 75
SIC 3492 Hose & tube fittings & assemblies, hydraulic/pneumatic
Pr: Jonathan Lindfors
**Ex VP:* Robin Lindfors

D-U-N-S 79-897-7059
LINFORD CONTRACT GLAZING LLC
LCG FACADES
1211 S 700 W, Salt Lake City, UT 84104-1546
Tel (801) 975-0281 *Founded/Ownrshp* 2007
Sales 24.5MM *EMP* 192
SIC 1793 3448 Glass & glazing work; Panels for prefabricated metal buildings; Glass & glazing work; Panels for prefabricated metal buildings
CFO: Kris Standiford
COO: Ted Derby
Prd Mgr: Kevin French

D-U-N-S 15-694-6196
■ **LINGER LONGER DEVELOPMENT CO**
REYNOLDS PLANTATION
(*Suby of* METLIFE INC) ★
100 Linger Longer Rd, Greensboro, GA 30642-7427
Tel (888) 298-3119 *Founded/Ownrshp* 2012
Sales 270.2MM^E *EMP* 600

SIC 6552 7997 Land subdividers & developers, residential; Golf club, membership; Tennis club, membership; Swimming club, membership; Land subdividers & developers, residential; Golf club, membership; Tennis club, membership; Swimming club, membership
CEO: Dan Dupree
Pt: Bill Dewitt
**CEO:* Dan Dupree
**CEO:* Rob Mitchel
**CFO:* Rex Rohm
VP: Tim Hong
VP: Glenn Winslette
Exec: Jere Mills
Exec: Micki Tanner
Prgrm Mgr: Julie House
Dept Mgr: Michael Raymond
Board of Directors: Dan Dupree

D-U-N-S 05-318-0373
LINGO CONSTRUCTION SERVICES INC
123 Nw 8th St, Oklahoma City, OK 73102-5804
Tel (405) 602-2100 *Founded/Ownrshp* 1998
Sales 20.4MM^E *EMP* 80
SIC 1799 Service station equipment installation, maintenance & repair
Pr: Stanley L Lingo

LING'S
See OUT OF SHELL LLC

D-U-N-S 17-613-5283
LINGUAL INFORMATION SYSTEM TECHNOLOGIES INC
LG-TEK
6865 Deerpath Rd Ste 300, Elkridge, MD 21075-6254
Tel (410) 953-0300 *Founded/Ownrshp* 1997
Sales 29.7MM^E *EMP* 200
SIC 7371 Software programming applications; Software programming applications
CEO: Elizabeth Rendon
**Pr:* Mark Lewis
Ex VP: Larry Evans
VP: Alan Kersey
VP: Milton Rendn
**VP:* Milton Rendon
VP: Peter Walsh
Prgrm Mgr: Mary Hopkins
VP Opers: Scott Snyder
Sls Dir: Richard Brown
Snr Mgr: Elizabeth Rendon-Sherman

LINGUASYS
See ASPECT SOFTWARE INC

D-U-N-S 13-636-3749
LINIUM LLC
187 Wolf Rd Ste 210, Albany, NY 12205-1348
Tel (518) 689-3100 *Founded/Ownrshp* 2000
Sales 62.1MM^E *EMP* 362
Accts Arthur Place & Company Pc
SIC 8742 Management consulting services; Management consulting services
CEO: Joseph P Burke
Mng Pt: Curtis Grajeda
Mng Pt: Dave Howard
Mng Pt: Mike Monda
Pr: Martha Burke
CFO: Tracie McGill
Sr VP: Don Brandt
VP: Rajesh Chopra
VP: Julie Jacobs
VP: Tae Kim
VP: Sandra Martin
Dir Bus: Steve George

D-U-N-S 83-565-6224
LINK AMERICA LLC
3002 Century Dr, Rowlett, TX 75088-7542
Tel (972) 463-0050 *Founded/Ownrshp* 1994
Sales 179.0MM^E *EMP* 26
SIC 8748

D-U-N-S 09-652-4731
LINK ASSOCIATES FOUNDATION INC
1452 29th St, West Des Moines, IA 50266-1306
Tel (515) 262-8888 *Founded/Ownrshp* 1956
Sales 1.0MM *EMP* 348
SIC 8361 8331 Home for the mentally handicapped; Sheltered workshop; Home for the mentally handicapped; Sheltered workshop
Exec: Robin Stewart
Ex Dir: Linda Dunshee
Prgrm Mgr: Carol Franke
Prgrm Mgr: Lisa Green
Prgrm Mgr: Janell Head
Pgrm Dir: Jay Bruns

D-U-N-S 15-199-5284
LINK CLEAR TECHNOLOGIES LLC
5202 W Douglas Ste 300, Salt Lake City, UT 84116
Tel (801) 424-0018 *Founded/Ownrshp* 2004
Sales 28.6MM^E *EMP* 200
SIC 7374 Computer graphics service; Computer graphics service
CEO: Phil Hansen
COO: Ben Henderson
CFO: Sam Funk
Chf Mktg O: Ted Roxbury
Ex VP: Ty Christensen
Ex VP: Mauri Love
Ex VP: Gary McCalla
Ex VP: Adam Mergist
Ex VP: Jason Webster
Snr Sftwr: Brandon Johnson

D-U-N-S 11-911-5509
LINK COMPUTER CORP
Stadium Dr, Bellwood, PA 16617
Tel (814) 742-7700 *Founded/Ownrshp* 1980
Sales 82.4MM^E *EMP* 90
SIC 5045 7371 7373 1731 7378 7361 Computers, peripherals & software; Custom computer programming services; Computer integrated systems design; Computer installation; Computer maintenance & repair; Employment agencies; Computers, peripherals & software; Custom computer programming services; Computer integrated systems design; Computer installation; Computer maintenance & repair; Employment agencies
Pr: Timothy Link
VP: Jack Collins
**VP:* Brian Link
VP: Joe Merilli
VP: Suann Spencer
Snr Ntwrk: Adam Guise
Snr Ntwrk: Robert Stewart
IT Man: Art Sauerland
Software D: Mary Shirey
S&M/VP: Mac Rosenbaum
S&M/VP: Mark Williams

D-U-N-S 07-724-5848 IMP
LINK CONSTRUCTION GROUP INC
5350 Nw 77th Ct, Doral, FL 33166-4110
Tel (305) 665-9826 *Founded/Ownrshp* 2001
Sales 26.8MM^E *EMP* 54
SIC 1542 Commercial & office building contractors
Pr: Guillermo Fernandez
**VP:* Miguel Cerra
VP: Maria Martinez
VP: Reno Stapleton
Exec: Nestor Castellon
Mktg Mgr: Heidi Pabon
Snr PM: Neil Jurado
Snr PM: Amany Solan
Snr Mgr: Felix Martinez

LINK ENGINEERING COMPANY
See LINK MANUFACTURING INC

LINK ENGINEERING COMPANY
See LINK GROUP INC

D-U-N-S 96-758-0957 IMP
LINK GROUP INC
LINK ENGINEERING COMPANY
43855 Plymouth Oaks Blvd, Plymouth, MI 48170-2539
Tel (734) 453-0800 *Founded/Ownrshp* 2010
Sales 97.1MM^E *EMP* 377
SIC 5013 Truck parts & accessories; Truck parts & accessories
CEO: Roy Link
**CFO:* Derek Stoneburg
VP: Warren Brown
Genl Mgr: Matthew Link
Genl Mgr: Jeff Veryser
CTO: Jerry Curtis
Software D: Tyler Odom
Sftwr Eng: David Showalter
Sls Dir: Mike Crosby

D-U-N-S 02-781-1590
LINK HILLS COUNTRY CLUB INC
1325 E Allens Bridge Rd, Greeneville, TN 37743-5112
Tel (423) 638-3114 *Founded/Ownrshp* 1954
Sales 706.8M *EMP* 360
Accts David M Ellis Cpa Greeneville
SIC 7997 Country club, membership; Country club, membership

LINK HOSP HLTHCARE PRFSSIONALS
See LINK OIL & GAS PROFESSIONALS INC

D-U-N-S 00-532-0486 IMP
LINK MANUFACTURING INC
LINK ENGINEERING COMPANY
(*Suby of* LINK ENGINEERING CO) ★
43855 Plymouth Oaks Blvd, Plymouth, MI 48170-2539
Tel (734) 453-0800 *Founded/Ownrshp* 1934
Sales 62.7MM^E *EMP* 325^E
SIC 3829 Physical property testing equipment; Testing equipment: abrasion, shearing strength, etc.; Physical property testing equipment; Testing equipment: abrasion, shearing strength, etc.
Ch Bd: Roy Link
**CFO:* Derek Stoneburg
**VP:* Warren Brown
**VP:* Timothy Olex
Genl Mgr: Aaron Marks

D-U-N-S 03-627-0692 IMP
LINK MFG LTD (IA)
223 15th St Ne, Sioux Center, IA 51250-2120
Tel (712) 722-4868 *Founded/Ownrshp* 1981
Sales 25.6MM^E *EMP* 180
SIC 3714 Motor vehicle parts & accessories; Motor vehicle body components & frame; Motor vehicle wheels & parts; Shock absorbers, motor vehicle; Motor vehicle parts & accessories; Motor vehicle body components & frame; Motor vehicle wheels & parts; Shock absorbers, motor vehicle
Ch Bd: Arlan Van Wyk
**Pr:* Dennis Michaels
Ql Cn Mgr: Dan Frederick
Manager: Jimmy Winslett

D-U-N-S 08-452-0043
LINK OIL & GAS PROFESSIONALS INC
LINK HOSP HLTHCARE PRFSSIONALS
11000 Equity Dr Ste 250, Houston, TX 77041-8240
Tel (281) 596-8900 *Founded/Ownrshp* 1996
Sales 19.9MM^E *EMP* 400
SIC 7361

D-U-N-S 07-246-6915
LINK REC INC
Hwy 53, Minong, WI 54859
Tel (715) 466-2272 *Founded/Ownrshp* 1947, 1999
Sales 29.6MM^E *EMP* 125
SIC 5551 Motor boat dealers; Outboard motors; Marine supplies
Owner: Robert Steinway
IT Man: John Ericson

D-U-N-S 18-898-4827 IMP
LINK SNACKS INC
JACK LINK BEEF JERKY
1 Snack Food Ln, Minong, WI 54859-4405
Tel (715) 466-2234 *Founded/Ownrshp* 1987
Sales 92.4MM^E *EMP* 320
SIC 2013

D-U-N-S 16-959-9656
LINK THEORY HOLDINGS (US) INC
(*Suby of* FAST RETAILING USA INC) ★
38 Gansevoort St, New York, NY 10014-1502
Tel (212) 300-0800 *Founded/Ownrshp* 2003
Sales 20.5MM^E *EMP* 163
SIC 5651 Family clothing stores
Pr: Andrew Rosen
Co-CEO: Ricky C Sasaki

D-U-N-S 15-451-4814 IMP/EXP
LINK-BELT CONSTRUCTION EQUIPMENT CO LP LLLP
LINK-BELT CRANES
(*Suby of* SUMITOMO HEAVY INDUSTRIES, LTD.)
2651 Palumbo Dr, Lexington, KY 40509-1233
Tel (859) 263-5200 *Founded/Ownrshp* 1986
Sales 184.7MM^E *EMP* 796
SIC 3531 Cranes; Cranes
Pr: Chuck Martz
VP: John Claflin
VP: Russ Hopper
VP: Don Moore
VP: Melvin Porter
VP: Dan Quinn
VP: Bill Stramer
Dist Mgr: Kyle Nape
MIS Dir: Mike Neal
Sls Mgr: Scott Dighans

LINK-BELT CRANES
See LINK-BELT CONSTRUCTION EQUIPMENT CO LP LLLP

D-U-N-S 17-221-7437
LINK2HEALTH SOLUTIONS INC
50 Broadway Fl 19, New York, NY 10004-3814
Tel (212) 614-6303 *Founded/Ownrshp* 2004
Sales 24.8MM *EMP* 7
Accts Rsm Mcgladrey Inc New York N
SIC 8322 Individual & family services
Pr: Robert Borsody

D-U-N-S 03-535-7776
LINKAMERICA CORP
1939 S Memorial Dr, Tulsa, OK 74112-7044
Tel (817) 799-0998 *Founded/Ownrshp* 2011
Sales NA *EMP* 750
SIC 4212 4213

D-U-N-S 12-913-3893
▲ LINKEDIN CORP
2029 Stierlin Ct Ste 200, Mountain View, CA 94043-4655
Tel (650) 687-3600 *Founded/Ownrshp* 2003
Sales 2.2MMM *EMP* 6,897^E
Accts Deloitte & Touche Llp San Jos
Tkr Sym LNKD *Exch* NYS
SIC 7375 On-line data base information retrieval; On-line data base information retrieval
CEO: Jeffrey Weiner
**Ch Bd:* Reid Hoffman
CFO: Steven Sordello
Sr VP: Michael Gamson
Sr VP: J Kevin Scott
Sr VP: Kevin Scott
VP: Michael Callahan
Dir Bus: Jorge Tapias
Sftwr Eng: Riccardo Ferretti
Board of Directors: A George Battle, Leslie Kilgore, Stanley J Meresman, Michael J Moritz, David Sze

D-U-N-S 12-780-4867
■ LINKEX INC
(*Suby of* SAIA INC) ★
2230 Lyndon B Johnson Fwy # 300, Dallas, TX 75234-7331
Tel (972) 481-9900 *Founded/Ownrshp* 2015
Sales 20.4MM^E *EMP* 54
SIC 4731 Freight forwarding
Pr: Neil Plunkett
**COO:* Jamie Wyatt
VP: Sunny Parks
VP: Gayla Plunkett
VP: James Robertson
Dir Bus: Pierre Fuentes
IT Man: Bob Bybee

D-U-N-S 11-260-0853
LINKOUS CONSTRUCTION CO INC
1661 Aaron Brenner Dr # 207, Memphis, TN 38120-1466
Tel (901) 754-0700 *Founded/Ownrshp* 1983
Sales 38.1MM^E *EMP* 100
SIC 1542 1541 Commercial & office building, new construction; Shopping center construction; Warehouse construction; Industrial buildings, new construction; Commercial & office building, new construction; Shopping center construction; Warehouse construction; Industrial buildings, new construction
CEO: R E Linkous
**Pr:* Rusty Linkous
**Sec:* Clare Linkous
**VP:* Michael Brewer
Snr PM: Kevin Scott

D-U-N-S 92-702-1076
LINKS INSURANCE SERVICES LLC
1821 State Route 71, Belmar, NJ 07719-3227
Tel (732) 449-4200 *Founded/Ownrshp* 2001
Sales NA *EMP* 27
SIC 6411 Insurance agents, brokers & service; Insurance agents, brokers & service

LINKS SIGN LANGUAGE INTERPRETI
See GOODWILL SERVING PEOPLE OF SOUTHERN LOS ANGELES COUNTY

D-U-N-S 02-256-0820
LINKS TECHNOLOGY SOLUTIONS INC
440 E State Pkwy Ste 220, Schaumburg, IL 60173-6414
Tel (847) 252-7600 *Founded/Ownrshp* 1999
Sales 20.1MM^E *EMP* 150
SIC 7379 7374 Computer related consulting services; Computer graphics service; Computer related consulting services; Computer graphics service
Pr: Brian H Burke
COO: Patrick McManamon
Off Mgr: Patty Errera
Software D: Joe Lutz
Software D: Sean Rios

D-U-N-S 96-457-3422 IMP
LINKS UNLIMITED INC
7050 Links Dr, Cincinnati, OH 45237
Tel (513) 842-6500 *Founded/Ownrshp* 1996
Sales 37.9MM^E *EMP* 35
SIC 5091 Golf equipment
CEO: Scott Kooken
**CFO:* Matt Cookin
**VP:* Bret Williams
Comm Dir: Cheryl Davis
Prgrm Mgr: Megan Sykora
Dir IT: Brian Schank
Sls Dir: Corey Wolfe
Sales Asso: Tony Ceja

LINKS2CARE
See LOVING CARE AGENCY INC

D-U-N-S 07-545-5878
LINKSCORP LLC
2801 Lakeside Dr Ste 207, Bannockburn, IL 60015-1200
Tel (847) 405-6700 *Founded/Ownrshp* 1998
Sales 7.6MM^E *EMP* 700
SIC 7992 Public golf courses; Public golf courses

D-U-N-S 19-510-8220 IMP
LINKSYS LLC
131 Theory, Irvine, CA 92617-3045
Tel (949) 823-3000 *Founded/Ownrshp* 2013
Sales 507.3MM^E *EMP* 630^E
SIC 5065 Electronic parts & equipment; Communication equipment; Electronic parts & equipment; Communication equipment
Ex VP: J Pocock
Rgnl Mgr: David Boyd
Rgnl Mgr: Michael Peters
Genl Mgr: Andrew Tay
Sls Mgr: Jeff Cortez

D-U-N-S 84-315-4258
LINKUS ENTERPRISES LLC
18631 Lloyd Ln, Anderson, CA 96007-8459
Tel (530) 229-9197 *Founded/Ownrshp* 2000
Sales 140.7MM^E *EMP* 650^E
SIC 1623 5731 4813 Telephone & communication line construction; Antennas, satellite dish; ;Telephone & communication line construction; Antennas, satellite dish;
CEO: Horacio Guzman
**COO:* John Daily
**VP:* Dant Morris
Dir IT: George Mize
Mktg Dir: George Simpson
Mktg Dir: John Trotter

D-U-N-S 07-988-6378
■ LINN ACQUISITION CO LLC
(*Suby of* LINN ENERGY LLC) ★
600 Travis St Ste 4900, Houston, TX 77002-3017
Tel (281) 840-4000 *Founded/Ownrshp* 2013
Sales 1.4MMM^E *EMP* 3^E
SIC 1311 Crude petroleum production

D-U-N-S 05-096-5961
LINN BENTON COMMUNITY COLLEGE FACULTY ASSOCIATION
6500 Pacific Blvd Sw, Albany, OR 97321-3755
Tel (541) 917-4999 *Founded/Ownrshp* 1967
Sales 38.6MM *EMP* 930
Accts Kenneth Kuhns & Co Salem Or
SIC 8222 Community college; Community college
Pr: Joseph Paris
**Pr:* Greg Hamann
Sfty Dirs: David Wienecke
Secur Mgr: Bruce Thompson
Psych: Larry Anderson
Psych: Tiffany Castillo
Nrsg Dir: Faye Melius

D-U-N-S 00-787-2237
LINN CO-OPERATIVE OIL CO
325 35th St, Marion, IA 52302-3815
Tel (319) 377-4881 *Founded/Ownrshp* 1930
Sales 150.0MM *EMP* 72
SIC 5153 5171 5191

D-U-N-S 78-765-2684
LINN CONTRACTING COMPANIES INC
309 S Green St, Chicago, IL 60607-3501
Tel (312) 454-0200 *Founded/Ownrshp* 1919
Sales 23.2MM^E *EMP* 120
SIC 1522 1542 1521 Remodeling, multi-family dwellings; Multi-family dwellings, new construction; Commercial & office buildings, renovation & repair; Commercial & office building, new construction; Institutional building construction; Single-family housing construction
Pr: Brad Mathes
**VP:* Robert Mathes

D-U-N-S 05-597-7508
LINN COUNTY BOARD OF COMMISSIONERS
300sw 4th Ave Rm 115, Albany, OR 97321
Tel (541) 967-3825 *Founded/Ownrshp* 1847
Sales NA *EMP* 744
Accts Pauly Rogers And Co Pc Tig
SIC 9121 County commissioner; ; County commissioner;
Ch: Roger Nyquist
**Prin:* John Lindsey
**Prin:* Cliff Wooten

LINN COUNTY REC
See LINN COUNTY RURAL ELECTRIC COOP ASSOCIATION

D-U-N-S 00-582-6128
LINN COUNTY RURAL ELECTRIC COOP ASSOCIATION
LINN COUNTY REC
5695 Rec Dr, Marion, IA 52302-6218
Tel (319) 377-1587 *Founded/Ownrshp* 1938
Sales 54.3MM *EMP* 60
Accts Larsonallen Llp Austin Mn
SIC 4911 Distribution, electric power; Distribution, electric power
CEO: Kim Colberg
**Pr:* Gary Schropp
**Treas:* Roger Krug
**VP:* Lisa Rose
Opers Mgr: Lenny Tow
Board of Directors: Kirk Hiland, Kenneth Squires, Elmer Vanorny, Dan Wille

D-U-N-S 13-212-1125
▲ LINN ENERGY LLC
600 Travis St Ste 5100, Houston, TX 77002-3092
Tel (281) 840-4000 *Founded/Ownrshp* 2003
Sales 4.9MMM *EMP* 1,800ᴱ
Tkr Sym LINE *Exch* NGS
SIC 1311 Crude petroleum & natural gas; Crude petroleum & natural gas
Ch Bd: Mark E Ellis
COO: Arden L Walker Jr
CFO: David B Rottino
Treas: Steven Sellers
Sr VP: Jamin B McNeil
VP: Karen Dickson
VP: Abdon Rangel
VP: Tanya Smith
VP: Candice J Wells
CIO: Tony Williams
IT Man: Tom Marshioni
Board of Directors: David D Dunlap, Stephen J Hadden, Michael C Linn, Joseph P McCoy, Jeffrey C Swoveland

D-U-N-S 05-685-6222
LINN GEAR CO
100 N 8th St, Lebanon, OR 97355-2213
Tel (541) 259-1211 *Founded/Ownrshp* 1965
Sales 41.3MMᴱ *EMP* 120
SIC 3568 Power transmission equipment; Sprockets (power transmission equipment); Couplings, shaft: rigid, flexible, universal joint, etc.; Collars, shaft (power transmission equipment); Power transmission equipment; Sprockets (power transmission equipment); Couplings, shaft: rigid, flexible, universal joint, etc.; Collars, shaft (power transmission equipment)
Pr: Gill Hartl
**VP:* Brian Hartl
Admn Mgr: Ron Bloom
Sales Asso: Stan McCann
Board of Directors: John Hainz, Jeannette Hartl, Raymond Hartl, Gary Jones

LINN HOUSE
See AIDS HEALTHCARE FOUNDATION

D-U-N-S 80-781-9573
■ LINN OPERATING INC
(*Suby of* LINN ENERGY LLC) ★
600 Travis St Ste 5100, Houston, TX 77002-3092
Tel (713) 227-1868 *Founded/Ownrshp* 2007
Sales 293.2MMᴱ *EMP* 400ᴱ
SIC 1382 Oil & gas exploration services; Oil & gas exploration services
Pr: Michael Linn
**COO:* Mark Ellis
**CFO:* Kolja Rockov
**Sr VP:* Lisa Anderson
**Sr VP:* Roland Keddie
**Sr VP:* Charlene Ripley
**Sr VP:* Arden Walker

D-U-N-S 83-727-1782
LINN RETAIL CENTERS INC
PARAMOUNT AUTO SERVICE
1789 Woodlane Dr Ste A, Saint Paul, MN 55125-3910
Tel (651) 731-0515 *Founded/Ownrshp* 1964
Sales 76.7MMᴱ *EMP* 200
SIC 5541 5531 Gasoline service stations; Filling stations, gasoline; Automotive accessories; Automotive parts; Gasoline service stations; Filling stations, gasoline; Automotive accessories; Automotive parts
Pr: Stephen Linn
**VP:* Amy Dumonceaux
VP: Clarence Linn
**VP:* Jeffrey Linn

D-U-N-S 62-005-7273
LINN STAR TRANSFER INC
9440 Wright Bros Ct Sw, Cedar Rapids, IA 52404-8005
Tel (319) 247-7160 *Founded/Ownrshp* 1998
Sales 29.6MMᴱ *EMP* 130
SIC 4212 7538 Local trucking, without storage; General truck repair
Pr: Dennis Munson
**VP:* Jana Munson
Genl Mgr: Todd Frigstad
Genl Mgr: Earl Leroy
Genl Mgr: Gary Rossier
VP Opers: David Dunek
Opers Mgr: Ben Bandurraga

D-U-N-S 96-700-1496
LINN WEST PAPER CO
(*Suby of* BELGRAVIA INVESTMENTS INC) ★
4800 Mill St, West Linn, OR 97068-3396
Tel (503) 557-6500 *Founded/Ownrshp* 2011
Sales 70.7MMᴱ *EMP* 250
SIC 2621 Catalog, magazine & newsprint papers; Catalog, magazine & newsprint papers
Pr: Ron Stern
**COO:* Brian Konan
**CFO:* Brad Mongrain
VP: Kim Burt
VP: Stewart Deindorfer
VP: Jay Droge
VP: Penny Machinski
VP: Penny Mashinski
Dir IT: Christopher Corrigan
IT Man: John Manning
IT Man: Bob Ohnstad

D-U-N-S 09-871-6285
LINN-MAR COMMUNITY SCHOOL
3333 10th St, Marion, IA 52302-5435
Tel (319) 377-5543 *Founded/Ownrshp* 1947
Sales 30.7MMᴱ *EMP* 635
SIC 8211 Public elementary school; Public junior high school; Public senior high school; School board; Public elementary school; Public junior high school; Public senior high school; School board
Treas: Trish Peddicord

D-U-N-S 07-864-9152
▲ LINNCO LLC
600 Travis St Ste 5100, Houston, TX 77002-3092
Tel (281) 840-4000 *Founded/Ownrshp* 2012
Sales 97.4MMᴱ *EMP* 1,800ᴱ
Tkr Sym LNCO *Exch* NGS
SIC 1311 Crude petroleum & natural gas; Natural gas production; Crude petroleum & natural gas; Natural gas production
Ch Bd: Mark E Ellis
COO: Arden L Walker Jr
CFO: Kolja Rockov
CFO: David B Rottino
Sr VP: Thomas E Emmons
Sr VP: Jamin B McNeil
VP: Candice J Wells
Board of Directors: Stephen J Hadden, Terrence S Jacobs, Michael C Linn, Joseph P McCoy, Linda M Stephens

LINO LAKES
See MOLIN CONCRETE PRODUCTS CO INC

D-U-N-S 79-459-8912 IMP/EXP
LINON HOME DECOR PRODUCTS INC
22 Jericho Tpke Ste 200, Mineola, NY 11501-2949
Tel (516) 699-1000 *Founded/Ownrshp* 1991
Sales 24.4MMᴱ *EMP* 53
SIC 5023 5021 Floor coverings; Household furniture
Pr: Demetrios Ziozis
CFO: Florence Vasilikas
VP: Steve Mazarakis
VP: Dimitrios Papadopoul
VP Opers: Dimitrios Papadopoulos
VP Sls: Frank Derasmo
VP Sls: John Micaelides

LINPAC
See ORBIS CORP

LINPAC ROPAK PACKAGING CENTRAL
See ROPAK CENTRAL INC

D-U-N-S 14-038-9763
LINQUEST CORP
5140 W Goldleaf Cir # 400, Los Angeles, CA 90056-1299
Tel (323) 924-1600 *Founded/Ownrshp* 2003
Sales 94.0MMᴱ *EMP* 440
SIC 8711 Aviation &/or aeronautical engineering; Aviation &/or aeronautical engineering
CEO: Leon Biederman
Pr: Mark Sturza
**COO:* Ronald Gorda
**CFO:* Matthew Lyons
**VP:* John Alexovich
**VP:* Pravin Jain
**VP:* James Light
**VP:* Scott Sharp
**VP:* Scott Stowe
**VP:* Greg Young
Snr Sftwr: Terry Ferguson

D-U-N-S 62-393-1557
LINROC COMMUNITY SERVICES CORP
Linden Blvd At Brookdale, Brooklyn, NY 11212
Tel (718) 240-5656 *Founded/Ownrshp* 1985
Sales 53.1MMᴱ *EMP* 2,000
SIC 8741 Nursing & personal care facility management; Hospital management; Nursing & personal care facility management; Hospital management
Pr: Frank Maddalena
**CFO:* Jeff Davis

D-U-N-S 03-530-5309
LINS SUPERMARKETS INC
LIN'S THRIFTWAY
(*Suby of* ASSOCIATED FOOD STORES INC) ★
1850 W 2100 S, Salt Lake City, UT 84119-1304
Tel (801) 973-4400 *Founded/Ownrshp* 1999
Sales 44.9MMᴱ *EMP* 610
Accts Deloitte & Touche
SIC 5411 Grocery stores; Grocery stores
Pr: Richard A Parkinson
**VP:* Brian Duff

LIN'S THRIFTWAY
See LINS SUPERMARKETS INC

D-U-N-S 78-407-6809
LINSALATA CORP
(*Suby of* TRANSTAR HOLDING CO) ★
5900 Landerbrook Dr # 280, Cleveland, OH 44124-4029
Tel (440) 684-1400 *Founded/Ownrshp* 2005
Sales 531.9MMᴱ *EMP* 2,300ᴱ
SIC 5013 Automotive supplies & parts; Automotive supplies & parts
Pr: Monte Ahuja
**Pr:* Eric V Bacon
**Pr:* Daniel L Desantis
**Pr:* Stephen B Perry
**Pr:* Gregory L Taber
**CFO:* Jeffrey R Marshall
**VP:* Mark A Kirk

D-U-N-S 07-497-8321 IMP
LINT LARRY J FLOOR & WALL COVERING CO
LINT, LARRY J FLOOR & WALL CVG
111 Notch Ln, Wendel, PA 15691
Tel (724) 446-0480 *Founded/Ownrshp* 1968
Sales 25.2MMᴱ *EMP* 68
SIC 5023 5032 Floor coverings; Ceramic wall & floor tile
Pr: Larry J Lint
Genl Mgr: Edward Lint
Off Mgr: Michele Smith

LINT, LARRY J FLOOR & WALL CVG
See LINT LARRY J FLOOR & WALL COVERING CO

D-U-N-S 61-677-0988
LINTEC USA HOLDING INC
(*Suby of* LINTEC CORPORATION)
64 Industrial Pkwy, Woburn, MA 01801-1969
Tel (781) 935-7850 *Founded/Ownrshp* 1990
Sales 30.7MMᴱ *EMP* 174
Accts Ernst & Young Llp
SIC 3083 2295 Plastic finished products, laminated; Window sheeting, plastic; Laminating of fabrics; Plastic finished products, laminated; Window sheeting, plastic; Laminating of fabrics
Pr: H Kainose
Treas: Hitoshi Asai

D-U-N-S 62-069-8571
LINTECH COMPONENTS CO INC
710 Union Pkwy Ste 8, Ronkonkoma, NY 11779-7428
Tel (631) 580-9500 *Founded/Ownrshp* 1990
Sales 38.0MMᴱ *EMP* 32
SIC 5065 Electronic parts & equipment
Pr: Ken Linden
**VP:* J Linden
VP Mktg: Victoria Archer
VP Mktg: Donna Devita
Sls Mgr: Dan Semon

D-U-N-S 86-812-7168 IMP
LINTECH INTERNATIONAL LLC
7705 Ne Industrial Blvd, Macon, GA 31216-7745
Tel (478) 781-3705 *Founded/Ownrshp* 2007
Sales 93.0MMᴱ *EMP* 60
SIC 5169 Chemicals, industrial & heavy; Chemicals, industrial & heavy
CEO: Julie Hinson-Vanbrunt
**Mng Pt:* Randy Griffin
**Mng Pt:* Thomas Hinson
Ex VP: Julie Van Brunt
**VP:* Randy Waldman
Exec: Roger Shaw
Sls Mgr: Rick Diener

D-U-N-S 61-874-2571 IMP
LINTEX LINENS INC
295 5th Ave Ste 1702, New York, NY 10016-7160
Tel (212) 679-8046 *Founded/Ownrshp* 1990
Sales 31.2MMᴱ *EMP* 450
SIC 2299 5023 Fabrics: linen, jute, hemp, ramie; Linens, table; Fabrics: linen, jute, hemp, ramie; Linens, table
Pr: Kurt Hamburger
**VP:* Rae Ellen Blum

LINTONS FOOD MANAGEMENT SVCS
See FOOD MANAGEMENT SERVICES INC

D-U-N-S 79-881-4534
LINUX FOUNDATION
660 York St Ste 102, San Francisco, CA 94110-2102
Tel (415) 723-9709 *Founded/Ownrshp* 2007
Sales 23.1MM *EMP* 9
Accts Hoffman Stewart & Schmidt Pc
SIC 8641 Civic social & fraternal associations
Pr: Jim Zemlin
VP Bus: Mike Woster
Comm Dir: Jennifer Cloer
Genl Mgr: Clyde Seepersad
IT Man: Lisa Smiley-Gillis
Software D: Andy Hidalgo
Sftwr Eng: Jeff Licquia

D-U-N-S 00-443-1185 IMP
■ LINVATEC CORP (FL)
CONMED LINVATEC
(*Suby of* CONMED CORP) ★
11311 Concept Blvd, Largo, FL 33773-4908
Tel (727) 392-6464 *Founded/Ownrshp* 1963, 1997
Sales 146.6MMᴱ *EMP* 900
SIC 3842 3841 2821 Surgical appliances & supplies; Surgical instruments & apparatus; Elastomers, nonvulcanizable (plastics); Surgical appliances & supplies; Surgical instruments & apparatus; Elastomers, nonvulcanizable (plastics)
Pr: Joseph Darling
Pr: Brett Thompson
**Treas:* Terence M Berge
VP: Brad Bailey
**VP:* Andy Matyk
**VP:* Luke A Pomilio
VP: Bret Poole
VP: Mark Snyder
Prgrm Mgr: William Mazurek
DP Exec: Dave Estes
MIS Dir: David Jenkins

D-U-N-S 00-327-7089
LINXX GLOBAL SOLUTIONS INC
LINXX SECURITY
272 Bendix Rd Ste 220, Virginia Beach, VA 23452-1367
Tel (757) 222-0300 *Founded/Ownrshp* 1990
Sales 23.4MM *EMP* 377
SIC 8331 Work experience center; Work experience center
CEO: Marty Strong
**CFO:* Adam Burke
Ofcr: Marcus Boggs
**VP:* Sydney Beem
Prgrm Mgr: Brian Wubker
IT Man: Susan Brink

LINXX SECURITY
See LINXX GLOBAL SOLUTIONS INC

LINZER PRODUCTS
See AHI INVESTMENT INC

D-U-N-S 00-136-7739 IMP
LINZER PRODUCTS CORP (NY)
(*Suby of* AHI INVESTMENT INC) ★
248 Wyandanch Ave, West Babylon, NY 11704-1506
Tel (631) 253-3333 *Founded/Ownrshp* 1892, 1988
Sales 77.0MMᴱ *EMP* 284ᴱ
SIC 5199 3991 Broom, mop & paint handles; Paint brushes
Pr: Brent Swenson
**Treas:* Mark Saji
VP: Tony Hazantonis
Manager: Tim Grant
Sls Mgr: John Reimer

D-U-N-S 19-388-1190 IMP
LIOCHEM INC
(*Suby of* TOYO INK INTERNATIONAL CORP) ★
2145 E Park Dr Ne, Conyers, GA 30013-5743
Tel (770) 760-7226 *Founded/Ownrshp* 1988
Sales 32.3MMᴱ *EMP* 75
SIC 2899 2821 2891 Ink or writing fluids; Acrylic resins; Adhesives & sealants; Ink or writing fluids; Acrylic resins; Adhesives & sealants
CEO: Naoto Sumiya
**CFO:* Bonney W J
**Sec:* William J Bonney
IT Man: Ronnie Robertson

D-U-N-S 00-424-4083 EXP
LION APPAREL INC (OH)
(*Suby of* LION GROUP INC) ★
7200 Poe Ave Ste 400, Dayton, OH 45414-2798
Tel (937) 898-1949 *Founded/Ownrshp* 1930
Sales 255.4MMᴱ *EMP* 760
SIC 2311 Firemen's uniforms: made from purchased materials; Military uniforms, men's & youths': purchased materials; Policemen's uniforms: made from purchased materials; Firemen's uniforms: made from purchased materials; Military uniforms, men's & youths': purchased materials; Policemen's uniforms: made from purchased materials
CEO: Steve Schwartz
Pr: John Fisher
**Pr:* Stephen A Schwartz
Treas: Richard Musick
Ofcr: Linda Lewis
Sr VP: William Gillingham
VP: Cathy Bennett
VP: John Granby
VP: Andrew Smith
Exec: Bill Rhinehimer
**Prin:* Mark Berliant

LION BRAND YARN
See ORCHARD YARN AND THREAD CO INC

D-U-N-S 00-303-2810 IMP
LION BREWERY INC (PA)
GIBBONS BREWING CO
700 N Pennsylvania Ave, Wilkes Barre, PA 18705-2451
Tel (570) 823-8801 *Founded/Ownrshp* 1905
Sales 30.6MMᴱ *EMP* 135
SIC 2082 2086 Beer (alcoholic beverage); Ale (alcoholic beverage); Porter (alcoholic beverage); Malt liquors; Soft drinks: packaged in cans, bottles, etc.; Beer (alcoholic beverage); Ale (alcoholic beverage); Porter (alcoholic beverage); Malt liquors; Soft drinks: packaged in cans, bottles, etc.
CEO: W Smulowitz
**Pr:* Charles Lawson Jr
CFO: Michael Clarke
**CFO:* Betty Dennis
**Sec:* W Ciolek
Off Mgr: Jerry Shinal
QA Dir: Courtney Sperger
QC Dir: Rebecca Brandenburg
Ql Cn Mgr: Bernie Mushinsky
Snr Mgr: Daniel Yerkes

LION BROTHERS
See LG INC

D-U-N-S 09-488-3550 IMP
LION BROTHERS CO INC
(*Suby of* LG INC) ★
10246 Reisterstown Rd, Owings Mills, MD 21117-3606
Tel (410) 363-1000 *Founded/Ownrshp* 1978
Sales 69.2MMᴱ *EMP* 400
SIC 2395 Emblems, embroidered; Emblems, embroidered
Ch Bd: Elinor C Ganz
**Pr:* Susan Ganz
Treas: Mickie Holden
Dir IT: Warren Klug
IT Man: Warren Koug
Sales Exec: Eric Aist
Sales Exec: Joe Zeoli

D-U-N-S 80-260-0507 IMP/EXP
LION COPOLYMER GEISMAR LLC
(*Suby of* LION COPOLYMER HOLDINGS LLC) ★
36191 Highway 30, Geismar, LA 70734-3526
Tel (225) 673-8871 *Founded/Ownrshp* 2007
Sales 97.1MMᴱ *EMP* 224
SIC 2822 Synthetic rubber; Synthetic rubber
Pr: Jesse Zeringue
Cmptr Lab: Randy Moran
IT Man: David Norton
Sfty Mgr: Keith Bergseid
Sfty Mgr: Sam Colon
Plnt Mgr: Bobby Rikhoff
Plnt Mgr: Philip Spillane
Mktg Mgr: Yuka Kimoto

D-U-N-S 80-205-5579 EXP
LION COPOLYMER HOLDINGS LLC
36191 Highway 30, Geismar, LA 70734-3526
Tel (225) 673-8871 *Founded/Ownrshp* 2007
Sales 234.6MMᴱ *EMP* 474
SIC 2822 Synthetic rubber; Synthetic rubber

LION COUNTRY SAFARI - FLORIDA
See LION COUNTRY SAFARI INC-FLORIDA

D-U-N-S 10-447-7914
LION COUNTRY SAFARI INC-FLORIDA
LION COUNTRY SAFARI - FLORIDA
2003 Lion Cntry Safari Rd, Loxahatchee, FL 33470-3977
Tel (561) 793-1084 *Founded/Ownrshp* 1967
Sales 22.1MMᴱ *EMP* 170
SIC 0971 Wildlife management
Pr: Leon Unterhalter
**Treas:* Stanley Franks
**VP:* Harold Kramer

*VP: Marc Unterhalter
Dir IT: Jean Levy

D-U-N-S 07-963-6182
LION ELASTOMER HOLDINGS LLC
(Suby of LION COPOLYMER HOLDINGS LLC) ★
36191 Highway 30, Geismar, LA 70734-3526
Tel (225) 673-8871 Founded/Ownrshp 2014
Sales 135.7MM^E EMP 251
SIC 2822 Synthetic rubber; Synthetic rubber
Pr: Jesse Zeringue

D-U-N-S 13-571-7622 EXP
LION ELASTOMERS LLC
(Suby of LION ELASTOMER HOLDINGS LLC) ★
1615 Main St, Port Neches, TX 77651-3039
Tel (409) 722-8321 Founded/Ownrshp 2014
Sales 135.7MM^E EMP 250
SIC 2822 Synthetic rubber
Pr: Jesse Zeringue
*CFO: Neil Jurkovic
Tech Mgr: Zamin Shuh

D-U-N-S 07-871-9479
LION EQUITY HOLDINGS LLC
(Suby of LION EQUITY PARTNERS LLC) ★
3003 E 3rd Ave Ste 201, Denver, CO 80206-5120
Tel (303) 847-4100 Founded/Ownrshp 2010
Sales 64.9MM^E EMP 300^E
SIC 6719 Investment holding companies, except banks; Investment holding companies, except banks
Dir Bus: Aaron Polack

D-U-N-S 96-200-3997
LION EQUITY PARTNERS LLC
3003 E 3rd Ave Ste 201, Denver, CO 80206-5120
Tel (303) 847-4100 Founded/Ownrshp 2007
Sales 64.9MM^E EMP 304^E
SIC 6799 Investors
Prin: Michael Porricelli

D-U-N-S 80-779-0600
LION GABLES REALTY LIMITED PARTNERSHIP
3399 Peachtree Rd Ne, Atlanta, GA 30326-1120
Tel (404) 923-5500 Founded/Ownrshp 1993
Sales 100.2MM^E EMP 1,251^E
SIC 6531 Real estate managers; Real estate managers
CEO: David D Finch

D-U-N-S 07-986-8052
LION GROUP INC
7200 Poe Ave Ste 400, Dayton, OH 45414-2798
Tel (937) 898-1949 Founded/Ownrshp 2014
Sales 79.8MM^E EMP 760
SIC 6719 Investment holding companies, except banks
*Treas: James Disanto
*Treas: Richard Musick

D-U-N-S 83-289-2215
LION HOLDINGS INC
Mettlers Rd, East Millstone, NJ 08875
Tel (732) 649-9961 Founded/Ownrshp 2009
Sales 148.5MM^E EMP 1,648^E
SIC 8731 Commercial physical research; Commercial physical research; Biological research; Commercial physical research; Commercial research laboratory
CEO: Andrew H Baker
*CFO: Richard Michaelson

LION OIL CO
See RONALD C LA FRANCHI

D-U-N-S 13-122-5211
■ **LION OIL CO**
(Suby of DELEK US HOLDINGS INC) ★
7102 Commerce Way, Brentwood, TN 37027-2896
Tel (615) 771-6701 Founded/Ownrshp 2011
Sales 44.6MM^E EMP 600
SIC 2911 4612 Gasoline blending plants; Diesel fuels; Jet fuels; Asphalt or asphaltic materials, made in refineries; Crude petroleum pipelines; Gasoline blending plants; Diesel fuels; Jet fuels; Asphalt or asphaltic materials, made in refineries; Crude petroleum pipelines
Pr: Lee Lampton
Sec: Kathy Stone
VP: George Ishee
VP: Ronnie Jackson
VP: William W Lampton
VP: John Wallace
VP Mfg: Don Davis

LION PACKING CO
See LION RAISINS INC

D-U-N-S 04-601-3306 IMP/EXP
LION RAISINS INC
LION PACKING CO
9500 S De Wolf Ave, Selma, CA 93662-9534
Tel (559) 834-6677 Founded/Ownrshp 1944
Sales 84.3MM^E EMP 400
SIC 2034 Raisins; Raisins
Pr: Alfred Lion Jr
VP: Al Lion
*VP: Bruce Lion
*Prin: Isabel Lion
*Prin: Larry Lion
CTO: Doug Snyder
Sfty Mgr: Raul Gomez
Sales Exec: Dennis Vartan

D-U-N-S 94-271-0211 EXP
LION-VALLEN LIMITED PARTNERSHIP
L V I
7200 Poe Ave Ste 400, Dayton, OH 45414-2798
Tel (937) 898-1949 Founded/Ownrshp 1996
Sales 72.4MM^E EMP 300^E
SIC 5136 5137 Uniforms, men's & boys'; Uniforms, women's & children's; Uniforms, men's & boys'; Uniforms, women's & children's
Pt: Stephen Schwartz
Sr VP: Terry Smith
VP: Mark Boyed
VP: Dennis Dudek
VP: Alan Nash

Dir IT: Larry Tieman
Sales Asso: John Gambrino

D-U-N-S 09-690-0907
LIONAKIS (CA)
1919 19th St, Sacramento, CA 95811-6714
Tel (916) 558-1901 Founded/Ownrshp 1909
Sales 58.2MM^E EMP 255
SIC 8711 7389 8712 Engineering services; Interior design services; Architectural services; Engineering services; Interior design services; Architectural services
Pr: Tim Fry
CFO: Andy Deeble
Treas: Jeff Farley
Dir Soc: Etienne Louw
Dir Soc: Kerry Volker
Dir: Anita Williams
Dir Bus: Charles Hack
Mng Dir: Jack Curson
Brnch Mgr: Mike Navarro
Off Mgr: Susan Boutelle
Off Mgr: Susan Wells

D-U-N-S 00-467-1400
▲ **LIONBRIDGE TECHNOLOGIES INC**
1050 Winter St Ste 2300, Waltham, MA 02451-1407
Tel (781) 434-6000 Founded/Ownrshp 1996
Sales 490.6MM EMP 5,560^E
Accts Pricewaterhousecoopers Llp B
Tkr Sym LIOX Exch NGM
SIC 7389 7374 7371 Translation services; Data processing & preparation; Computer software development & applications; Translation services; Data processing & preparation; Computer software development & applications
Ch Bd: Rory J Cowan
COO: Satish Maripuri
CFO: Donald M Muir
Ofcr: Myriam Martin-Kail
Ofcr: Paula Barbary Shannon
Top Exec: Rohit Rana
Sr VP: Henri Broekmate
Sr VP: Harish Joshy
Sr VP: Marc Osofsky
Sr VP: Paula Shannon
Sr VP: Richard Tobin
VP: Robin Lloyd
VP: Allison McDougall
VP: Clint Poole
VP: Don Scott
VP: Margaret A Shukur
VP: Jay Sitaram
VP: Larry Wade
Exec: Monish Parekh
Board of Directors: Edward A Blechschmidt, Michael G Dallas, Guy L De Chazal, Steven R Fisher, Paul Kavanagh, Jack Noonan, James Quella, Claude Sheer

D-U-N-S 14-423-5652 IMP
LIONEL LLC
6301 Performance Dr Sw, Concord, NC 28027-3426
Tel (704) 454-4200 Founded/Ownrshp 2013
Sales 50.0MM EMP 120
SIC 3944 Trains & equipment, toy: electric & mechanical; Trains & equipment, toy: electric & mechanical
CFO: Chris Elrod

D-U-N-S 08-404-4064
LIONETTI ASSOCIATES LLC
LORCO PETROLEUM SERVICES
450 S Front St, Elizabeth, NJ 07202-3009
Tel (908) 820-8800 Founded/Ownrshp 1957
Sales 50.0MM^E EMP 100
SIC 5093 7699 Oil, waste; Tank truck cleaning service; Oil, waste; Tank truck cleaning service
Pt: John Lionetti
Pt: Frank Lo Bello Jr
Sfty Mgr: Terry Tyndall
Sales Asso: Mark Johnson

D-U-N-S 18-784-3706
LIONHEART HOLDINGS LLC
LIONHEART VENTURES
54 Friends Ln Ste 125, Newtown, PA 18940-3403
Tel (215) 283-8400 Founded/Ownrshp 2003
Sales 64.8MM^E EMP 210
SIC 3724 3561 3594 3433 3255 3823 Aircraft engines & engine parts; Pumps & pumping equipment; Fluid power pumps & motors; Heating equipment, except electric; Clay refractories; Industrial instrmnts msrmnt display/control process variable; Aircraft engines & engine parts; Pumps & pumping equipment; Fluid power pumps & motors; Heating equipment, except electric; Clay refractories; Industrial instrmnts msrmnt display/control process variable
CEO: David Bovenizer
Ex VP: Patrick Laphen

D-U-N-S 94-331-2546
LIONHEART TECHNOLOGIES INC
BIO-TEK INSTRUMENTS
100 Tigan St, Winooski, VT 05404-1356
Tel (802) 655-4040 Founded/Ownrshp 1996
Sales 50.4MM^E EMP 240
SIC 3845 Electromedical equipment; Electromedical equipment
Pr: Briar L Alpert
CFO: Claus Deutscher
Area Mgr: Cindy Jiang
Off Admin: Kate Ll
Mfg Mgr: Deanie Dinick
Sales Exec: Mike Bryles
Natl Sales: Craig Abrahams
Mktg Mgr: Dongping Guo
Sls Mgr: Sam Chueh
Sls Mgr: Zach Hsieh

LIONHEART VENTURES
See LIONHEART HOLDINGS LLC

LIONMARK CNSTR COMPANIES
See LIONMARK CONSTRUCTION COMPANIES LLC

D-U-N-S 00-383-3290
LIONMARK CONSTRUCTION COMPANIES LLC (MO)
LIONMARK CNSTR COMPANIES
1620 Woodson Rd, Saint Louis, MO 63114-6129
Tel (314) 991-2180 Founded/Ownrshp 1932
Sales 228.1MM^E EMP 334
SIC 1611 2951 1622 General contractor, highway & street construction; Resurfacing contractor; Asphalt & asphaltic paving mixtures (not from refineries); Bridge construction; General contractor, highway & street construction; Asphalt & asphaltic paving mixtures (not from refineries); Bridge construction
Pr: Edward Gomes Jr
*CFO: Thomas Feldmann
*VP: Gene Allen
*VP: Roy Burns
VP: Henry Schmitt
MIS Dir: Todd Ledbetter
Sfty Mgr: Joseph Reichmuth

LION'S CHOICE
See RED LION BEEF CORP

LIONS CLUBS INTERNATIONAL
See INTERNATIONAL ASSOCIATION OF LIONS CLUBS INC

D-U-N-S 82-875-9568
LIONS CLUBS INTERNATIONAL FOUNDATION
300 W 22nd St, Oak Brook, IL 60523-8806
Tel (630) 571-5466 Founded/Ownrshp 2008
Sales 71.2MM EMP 49^E
Accts Mcgladrey Llp Chicago Il
SIC 8699 Charitable organization; Charitable organization
Ex Dir: Peter Lynch
Treas: Jeff Hendricks
VP: Gary Kemp
Dept Mgr: Tamara Ivetic
Dept Mgr: Matthew Kiefer
Dept Mgr: Patricia Luce

D-U-N-S 06-125-0531
■ **LIONS GATE ENTERTAINMENT INC**
(Suby of LIONS GATE ENTERTAINMENT CORP)
2700 Colorado Ave Ste 200, Santa Monica, CA 90404-5502
Tel (310) 449-9200 Founded/Ownrshp 2006
Sales 2.4MMM EMP 536
Accts Ernst & Young Llp Los Angeles
Tkr Sym LGF Exch NYS
SIC 7812 Motion picture production & distribution; Motion picture production & distribution
Ch Bd: Jon Feltheimer
V Ch: Michael Burns
Pr: Steven Beeks
Pr: Joseph Drake
Pr: Erik Feig
Pr: Sarah Greenberg
Pr: Tim Palen
CFO: James Keegan
CFO: Jim Keegan
Ex VP: Gillian Bohrer
Ex VP: John Dellaverson
Ex VP: Julie Fontaine
Ex VP: B Gladstone
Ex VP: Gary Goodman
Ex VP: Jennifer Hollingsworth
Ex VP: Patricia Laucella
Ex VP: Wayne Levin
Ex VP: Robert Melnik
Ex VP: David Nonaka
Ex VP: Ross Pollack
Ex VP: Anne Ross
Board of Directors: Gordon Crawford

D-U-N-S 15-084-4025
LIONS QUICK MARTS INC
1307 Woodman Rd, Janesville, WI 53545-1068
Tel (608) 754-1159 Founded/Ownrshp 1983
Sales 25.2MM EMP 78
SIC 5411 5541 Convenience stores; Filling stations, gasoline; Convenience stores; Filling stations, gasoline
Pr: James L Johnson
*VP: Ann P Johnson

D-U-N-S 07-450-1891
LIONS SERVICES INC
4600 N Tryon St Ste A, Charlotte, NC 28213-7058
Tel (704) 921-1527 Founded/Ownrshp 1975
Sales 27.6MM^E EMP 150
Accts J Ronald Martin Pa Charlo
SIC 2392 7389 8331 Mops, floor & dust; Ironing board pads: made from purchased materials; Pillowcases: made from purchased materials; Packaging & labeling services; Job training & vocational rehabilitation services
CEO: Jim Cranford

D-U-N-S 00-640-2820 IMP/EXP
LIPARI FOODS OPERATING CO LLC
26661 Bunert Rd, Warren, MI 48089-3650
Tel (586) 447-3500 Founded/Ownrshp 2011
Sales 379.3MM^E EMP 700^E
SIC 5147 5141 5143

D-U-N-S 07-855-9200
LIPHAM CONSTRUCTION CO INC (TX)
400 N Broadway St, Aspermont, TX 79502
Tel (940) 989-3503 Founded/Ownrshp 1964
Sales 31.3MM^E EMP 145
Accts Phillips & Associates Cpa S
SIC 1611 4214 Highway & street paving contractor; Local trucking with storage; Highway & street paving contractor; Local trucking with storage
Pr: Chris Lipham

D-U-N-S 00-311-4964
LIPHART STEEL CO INC
3308 Rosedale Ave, Richmond, VA 23230-4290
Tel (804) 355-7481 Founded/Ownrshp 1938
Sales 33.3MM EMP 83
Accts Keiter Glen Allen Virginia
SIC 3441 1791 Building components, structural steel; Iron work, structural; Building components, structural steel; Iron work, structural
Pr: Edwin C Jennings Jr
Pr: Mike Teachey
Ex VP: R N Ruby
VP: Rob Kerr
Exec: Sue Rasmussen
Genl Mgr: Lee Parker
Snr Mgr: Butch Swecker

D-U-N-S 60-853-0713 IMP
LIPHATECH INC
(Suby of DE SANGOSSE)
3600 W Elm St, Milwaukee, WI 53209-3108
Tel (888) 331-7900 Founded/Ownrshp 1989
Sales 43.2MM^E EMP 250
SIC 2819 2879 Industrial inorganic chemicals; Agricultural chemicals; Industrial inorganic chemicals; Agricultural chemicals
CEO: Carl Tanner

D-U-N-S 06-230-3029
LIPINSKI LANDSCAPE & IRRIGATION INC (NJ)
100 Sharp Rd, Marlton, NJ 08053-5547
Tel (856) 797-8000 Founded/Ownrshp 1976, 1978
Sales 18.6MM^E EMP 400
SIC 0782 1629 0781 Landscape contractors; Irrigation system construction; Landscape counseling services; Landscape contractors; Irrigation system construction; Landscape counseling services
Pr: Doug Cook
CFO: Thomas Donnelly
Genl Mgr: April Zalusky

LIPMAN
See FARM-OP INC

D-U-N-S 00-886-8127 IMP
LIPMAN BROTHERS LLC (TN)
411 Great Circle Rd, Nashville, TN 37228-1403
Tel (615) 244-2230 Founded/Ownrshp 1939, 1987
Sales 346.0MM^E EMP 170
SIC 5182 Wine & distilled beverages; Wine & distilled beverages
CEO: Robert S Lipman
*Sec: Stefan Banks
*Sec: Ken Howell
*VP: Greg Naiser
*VP: Richard Thibus
Off Mgr: Janet Pruitt
Dir IT: John Pamplin
Opers Mgr: Tremayne Wade
Natl Sales: Scott Gstell
VP Mktg: Paul Grand
Sls Dir: Charlie Jackson

D-U-N-S 05-190-2096
LIPMAN INSURANCE ADMINISTRATORS INC
39420 Liberty St Ste 260, Fremont, CA 94538-2297
Tel (510) 796-4676 Founded/Ownrshp 1987
Sales NA EMP 100
SIC 6371 Union welfare, benefit & health funds
Pr: Frederic J Lipman
CFO: Melinda De Campo
*CFO: Janet Sylvester
Dir IT: Noah Hart

LIPMAN PRODUCE
See LIPMAN-TEXAS LLC

LIPMAN PRODUCE
See CUSTOM-PAK INC

D-U-N-S 07-831-8182
LIPMAN-TEXAS LLC (FL)
LIPMAN PRODUCE
315 New Market Rd E, Immokalee, FL 34142-3509
Tel (239) 657-4421 Founded/Ownrshp 1930
Sales 129.2MM^E EMP 251^E
SIC 5148 Fruits, fresh; Fruits, fresh
Pr: Kent Shoemaker
*VP: Darren Micelle

D-U-N-S 01-222-0914
■ **LIPOSCIENCE INC**
(Suby of LABCORP OF AMERICA) ★
2500 Sumner Blvd, Raleigh, NC 27616-3235
Tel (919) 212-1999 Founded/Ownrshp 2014
Sales 52.3MM EMP 239
SIC 8071 2835 Medical laboratories; In vitro & in vivo diagnostic substances; Enzyme & isoenzyme diagnostic agents; Medical laboratories; In vitro & in vivo diagnostic substances; Enzyme & isoenzyme diagnostic agents
Pr: Howard B Doran
*CFO: Lucy G Martindale
*Ofcr: William C Cromwell
*Ex VP: James D Otvos
VP: Chuck Jackson
VP: Ray Pourfarzib
VP: Peter Riefenhauser
VP: Timothy Williams
Sys Mgr: Roger Keim
Sftwr Eng: Ryan Laytham
Sftwr Eng: Michael Pack

D-U-N-S 00-720-5198
LIPPERT BROS INC
2211 E I 44 Service Rd, Oklahoma City, OK 73111-8217
Tel (405) 478-3301 Founded/Ownrshp 1920
Sales 52.3MM EMP 90
Accts Van Wieren & Jones Inc Okla
SIC 1542 1629 1541 Commercial & office building, new construction; Hospital construction; School building construction; Dams, waterways, docks & other marine construction; Industrial buildings, new construction; Commercial & office building, new construction; Hospital construction; School building construction; Dams, waterways, docks & other marine construction; Industrial buildings, new construction
Pr: Rick Lippert
*Treas: Tolly Payne
*Sec: Tolley Payne
*Sr VP: Bruce Barta
*Sr VP: Tom Lippert
*VP: Joel Lippert

Prin: Don E Lippert Jr
Off Mgr: Myra Windexter

D-U-N-S 04-322-2470 IMP
■ LIPPERT COMPONENTS INC
HOME-STYLE INDUSTRIES
(*Suby of* DREW INDUSTRIES INC) ★
3501 County Road 6 E, Elkhart, IN 46514-7663
Tel (800) 551-9149 *Founded/Ownrshp* 1956, 1997
Sales 1.1MMM^E *EMP* 5,109
SIC 3711 3469 3444 3714 Chassis, motor vehicle; Stamping metal for the trade; Metal roofing & roof drainage equipment; Motor vehicle parts & accessories; Chassis, motor vehicle; Stamping metal for the trade; Metal roofing & roof drainage equipment; Motor vehicle parts & accessories
CEO: Jason Lippert
**Ch Bd:* L Douglas Lippert
**Pr:* Shane Duncan
**Pr:* Scott Mereness
**CFO:* Todd Blyly
**CFO:* Joshua Lippert
VP: Jim Chamberlain
VP: Jason Falk
VP: Conny Holcombe
VP: John Ries
VP: Josh Roan
VP: Ryan Smith

LIPPINCOTT WILLIAMS & WILKIN
See WOLTERS KLUWER HEALTH INC

D-U-N-S 08-049-7845 IMP
LIPPMANN - MILWAUKEE INC
3271 E Van Norman Ave, Cudahy, WI 53110-1047
Tel (414) 744-2565 *Founded/Ownrshp* 2011
Sales 49.2MM^E *EMP* 100
SIC 3532 Crushing, pulverizing & screening equipment; Washers, aggregate & sand; Crushing, pulverizing & screening equipment; Washers, aggregate & sand
Ch: Diane Gabriel
**Pr:* Robert Turner
**Exec:* Gina Dathe
Sfty Mgr: Alex Silvasi
Manager: Morris Holly
Manager: Jack Koontz
Manager: Steve Phillips
Sales Asso: Mel Weeks

D-U-N-S 07-353-9876
LIPSCOMB & PITTS INSURANCE LLC
2670 Union Avenue Ext # 200, Memphis, TN 38112-4434
Tel (901) 321-1000 *Founded/Ownrshp* 1954
Sales NA *EMP* 120
SIC 6411 Insurance agents; Life insurance agents
COO: Blaine Means
Sr VP: Craig Wright
VP: Jay Harvill
VP: Bo Midgett
VP: Daniel Roberson
Dir IT: Iain Sutcliffe

D-U-N-S 09-211-8215
LIPSCOMB OIL CO INC (MS)
1010 N Broadway St, Greenville, MS 38701-2004
Tel (662) 332-7500 *Founded/Ownrshp* 1978
Sales 78.9MM *EMP* 300
Accts Horne Llp Ridgeland Mississi
SIC 5541 5171 Gasoline service stations; Petroleum bulk stations; Gasoline service stations; Petroleum bulk stations
Pr: James H Lipscomb III
**Sec:* Mary Lynn Lipscomb

D-U-N-S 07-538-1186
LIPSCOMB UNIVERSITY (TN)
DAVID LIPSCOMB CAMPUS SCHOOL
1 University Park Dr, Nashville, TN 37204-3956
Tel (615) 966-1000 *Founded/Ownrshp* 1891
Sales 157.0MM *EMP* 550^E
Accts Lattimore Black Morgan & Cain
SIC 8221 8211 Colleges universities & professional schools; Private combined elementary & secondary school; Colleges universities & professional schools; Private combined elementary & secondary school
Pr: L Randolph Lowry III
Pr: Chris Taylor
Pr: Carrie Thompson
**CFO:* Danny Taylor
VP: Larry Cochran
VP: Michael Hammond
VP: Walt Leaver
Assoc Dir: Karin Hensley
Dir Soc: Aaron Fiant
Genl Mgr: Wolcott Fary
Opers Mgr: Dennis Hood

D-U-N-S 78-856-1442
LIPSEY COMMUNICATIONS LLC
CONNECTIVITY SOURCE
7155 Old Katy Rd, Houston, TX 77024-2134
Tel (713) 861-3332 *Founded/Ownrshp* 1999
Sales 40.4MM^E *EMP* 215
SIC 5999 Telephone equipment & systems; Telephone equipment & systems
Pr: Scott Aronstein
**Ch:* Richard A Lipsey

D-U-N-S 02-719-4315 IMP
LIPSITZ MANAGEMENT CO INC
M. LIPSITZ & CO
100 Elm St, Waco, TX 76704-2507
Tel (254) 756-6661 *Founded/Ownrshp* 1895
Sales 38.7MM^E *EMP* 150
SIC 5093 Ferrous metal scrap & waste; Nonferrous metals scrap; Ferrous metal scrap & waste; Nonferrous metals scrap
Pr: Tommy G Salome Jr
Treas: Thelma Lipsitz
VP: Charles Johnson
**VP:* Melvin A Lipsitz Jr

D-U-N-S 06-734-7294
LIPTEN CO LLC
28054 Center Oaks Ct A, Wixom, MI 48393-3363
Tel (248) 374-8910 *Founded/Ownrshp* 1969
Sales 26.6MM^E *EMP* 36
SIC 5084 1796 1711 Pollution control equipment, air (environmental); Power plant machinery; Pollution control equipment installation; Boiler & furnace contractors
CEO: James Spencer
**Pr:* Jim Marshall
**CFO:* Frances Dorland
**VP:* John Ingraham
Dir Bus: Ron Johnston
Off Mgr: Caryn Robinson
Off Admin: Victoria Ricci
Off Admin: Natasha Young
Natl Sales: Steve Johnson

D-U-N-S 06-649-3292 IMP
LIPTIS PHARMACEUTICALS USA INC
110 Red Schoolhouse Rd, Spring Valley, NY 10977-7032
Tel (845) 627-0260 *Founded/Ownrshp* 1995
Sales 129.2MM^E *EMP* 1,022
SIC 2834 Pharmaceutical preparations; Pharmaceutical preparations
CEO: Sherin Awad
**Pr:* Dick Klaus
**VP:* Jenny Avalos

LIPTON ENERGY
See LIPTON INC

D-U-N-S 00-255-2065
LIPTON INC (MA)
LIPTON ENERGY
458 South St, Pittsfield, MA 01201-8217
Tel (413) 443-9198 *Founded/Ownrshp* 1910
Sales 22.8MM^E *EMP* 50
SIC 5172 5983 5541 5411 5999 Fuel oil; Lubricating oils & greases; Fuel oil dealers; Filling stations, gasoline; Convenience stores; Plumbing & heating supplies; Fuel oil; Lubricating oils & greases; Fuel oil dealers; Filling stations, gasoline; Convenience stores; Plumbing & heating supplies
Pr: Sanford Lipton
**Pr:* Leonard S Lipton
Pr: Mike Lipton
Treas: Alan Lipton
**Sec:* Michael Lipton

LIPTON TOYOTA
See ROBERT L LIPTON INC

D-U-N-S 84-720-5382
■ LIQUENT INC
(*Suby of* PAREXEL INTERNATIONAL CORP) ★
101 Gibraltar Rd Ste 200, Horsham, PA 19044-2362
Tel (215) 957-6401 *Founded/Ownrshp* 2012
Sales 29.5MM^E *EMP* 220
SIC 7372 7373 Prepackaged software; Systems software development services; Prepackaged software; Systems software development services; Systems integration services
CEO: Rick Riegel
**CFO:* Karl Jaegr
**CFO:* David Pincus
VP: Odile L Roy Des Barres
**VP:* Kate Courter
**VP:* Jeff Huntsman
VP: Shylendra Kumar
**VP:* Marybeth Thompson
**CTO:* Hugh Tamassia
IT Man: Lauren Brooks
IT Man: Norman Phengvath

D-U-N-S 00-194-2499 IMP/EXP
LIQUI-BOX CORP (OH)
901 E Byrd St Ste 1105, Richmond, VA 23219-4068
Tel (804) 325-1400 *Founded/Ownrshp* 1963, 2015
Sales 386.1MM^E *EMP* 1,100
SIC 2673 3585 3089 3081 5149 Plastic bags: made from purchased materials; Soda fountain & beverage dispensing equipment & parts; Plastic containers, except foam; Blow molded finished plastic products; Injection molded finished plastic products; Plastic film & sheet; Mineral or spring water bottling; Plastic bags: made from purchased materials; Soda fountain & beverage dispensing equipment & parts; Plastic containers, except foam; Blow molded finished plastic products; Injection molded finished plastic products; Plastic film & sheet; Mineral or spring water bottling
Pr: Ken Swanson
CFO: Lou Marmo
Sr VP: Greg Gard
Sr VP: Anthony Rizzo
VP: Dave Klopp

D-U-N-S 07-874-8033
LIQUI-BOX CORP
480 Schrock Rd Ste G, Columbus, OH 43229-1092
Tel (614) 888-9280 *Founded/Ownrshp* 1963
Sales 50.0MM^E *EMP* 97^E
SIC 2631 5084 Container, packaging & boxboard; Processing & packaging equipment
CEO: Roszann Graham
**COO:* Stewart Graves
CFO: Lou Marmo
Sr VP: Anthony Rizzo
Sfty Mgr: Linda Cline
Prd Mgr: Joseph Callueng
Sls Mgr: Kevin Griffin

LIQUI-GROW
See TWIN STATE INC

LIQUID CONTROL
See GRACO OHIO INC

D-U-N-S 00-525-1061 IMP
■ LIQUID CONTROLS LLC
(*Suby of* IDEX CORP) ★
105 Albrecht Dr, Lake Bluff, IL 60044-2252
Tel (847) 295-1050 *Founded/Ownrshp* 2001
Sales 33.1MM^E *EMP* 190^E
SIC 3824 Positive displacement meters; Positive displacement meters
Dir Bus: Teck Yap
Rgnl Mgr: Rob Rose
Genl Mgr: Fred Niemeier
MIS Mgr: Mark Stokes

D-U-N-S 12-985-3151
LIQUID DISTRIBUTORS INC
33 Rockland Rd, Norwalk, CT 06854-4607
Tel (203) 853-1500 *Founded/Ownrshp* 1992
Sales 37.3MM^E *EMP* 70
SIC 5172 Gases, liquefied petroleum (propane); Gases, liquefied petroleum (propane)
Pr: David Gable

D-U-N-S 09-143-5276
LIQUID ENVIRONMENTAL SOLUTIONS OF TEXAS LLC
7651 Esters Blvd Ste 200, Irving, TX 75063-4034
Tel (866) 694-7327 *Founded/Ownrshp* 2002
Sales 95.1MM^E *EMP* 100
SIC 4953 Liquid waste, collection & disposal
VP: Alan Viterbi
**Sr VP:* Dana King
VP: Alan Gohlke
**VP:* Bob Goldberg
Exec: John Clague
Dir Lab: Danielle Messer
Natl Sales: Michelle Besterfeldt
Natl Sales: Kerrie Crimmins
Mktg Dir: Crystal Garcia

LIQUID FILTER DIVISION
See GRAVER TECHNOLOGIES LLC

D-U-N-S 07-253-2471 IMP
LIQUID GRAPHICS INC
17822 Gillette Ave Ste C, Irvine, CA 92614-0534
Tel (949) 486-3588 *Founded/Ownrshp* 2000
Sales 21.3MM^E *EMP* 85
SIC 2329 Men's & boys' sportswear & athletic clothing
Pr: Josh Merrell
**CFO:* Bryan Renner

D-U-N-S 06-915-7287 IMP
LIQUID INVESTMENTS INC (CA)
3840 Via De La Valle # 300, Del Mar, CA 92014-4268
Tel (858) 509-8510 *Founded/Ownrshp* 1981
Sales 167.5MM^E *EMP* 629
Accts Robert R Redwitz & Co Irvin
SIC 5181 5145 5182 Beer & other fermented malt liquors; Fountain supplies; Wine; Beer & other fermented malt liquors; Fountain supplies; Wine
CEO: Ron L Fowler
**Ex VP:* Mark Herculson
VP: Earl Kight
Snr Mgr: Josh Pava

D-U-N-S 07-119-8089 IMP
LIQUID METRONICS INC (MA)
L M I
(*Suby of* MILTON ROY AMERICAS) ★
8 Post Office Sq Ste 1, Acton, MA 01720-3948
Tel (978) 263-9800 *Founded/Ownrshp* 1984, 1991
Sales 20.1MM^E *EMP* 140
SIC 3586 3823 Measuring & dispensing pumps; Industrial instrmnts msrmnt display/control process variable; Measuring & dispensing pumps; Industrial instrmnts msrmnt display/control process variable
Pr: Jean-Claude Pharmont
**Treas:* Thomas Rogan
Genl Mgr: Diane Laverty
MIS Mgr: Carmen Patuto
Sfty Dirs: Samuel Nbi

D-U-N-S 14-496-7424 IMP
LIQUID PACKAGING LLC
9300 S Sangamon St, Chicago, IL 60620-2733
Tel (773) 341-7700 *Founded/Ownrshp* 2004
Sales 40.7MM^E *EMP* 300
SIC 2844 2841 Cosmetic preparations; Soap & other detergents; Cosmetic preparations; Soap & other detergents
COO: Mark Wozniak
COO: Mark Woznik
CFO: David Wood

D-U-N-S 00-380-3897
LIQUID TRANSPORT CORP (IN)
8470 Allison Pointe Blvd # 400, Indianapolis, IN 46250-4365
Tel (317) 841-4200 *Founded/Ownrshp* 1949, 2006
Sales 99.1MM^E *EMP* 300
SIC 4213 Contract haulers; Contract haulers
Ch Bd: Ronald B Dana
**Pr:* Keith Lewis
VP: Bob Bianchi
VP: Pete Legere
Genl Mgr: Steve Shipley
Off Mgr: Mardea Erwin
CIO: Nick Crider
Dir IT: Chuck Applequist
IT Man: Chuck Appelquist
Mktg Mgr: Mary Wilhelm

D-U-N-S 00-589-5664 IMP
LIQUID WEB INC
2703 Ena Dr, Lansing, MI 48917-8585
Tel (517) 322-0434 *Founded/Ownrshp* 1997
Sales 57.0MM *EMP* 4
Accts Uhy Llp Farmington Hills Mic
SIC 4813 ;
Pr: Matthew Hill
COO: Chris Strandt
**CFO:* Terry Flood
**Sec:* Gregg Hill
VP: James Robinson
Mng Dir: Scott Haraburda
Mng Dir: Adam Kaminski
Mng Dir: John Xie
QA Dir: David Barnett
QA Dir: Steven Collins
Web Dev: Todd Wilson

D-U-N-S 13-583-5531
LIQUIDAGENTS HEALTHCARE LLC
6900 Dallas Pkwy Ste 450, Plano, TX 75024-4338
Tel (972) 543-5200 *Founded/Ownrshp* 2000
Sales 11.1MM^E *EMP* 300
SIC 7361 Executive placement; Executive placement
**CFO:* Jenny Hanlon
CTO: Amy Crowder
Manager: Jennifer Neice

LIQUIDATION CHANNEL
See JEWELRY CHANNEL INC

D-U-N-S 02-813-1535
LIQUIDHUB INC
LH
(*Suby of* LIQUIDHUB INDIA PRIVATE LIMITED)
500 E Swedesford Rd # 300, Wayne, PA 19087-1614
Tel (610) 688-6531 *Founded/Ownrshp* 2001
Sales 117.0MM^E *EMP* 562^E
SIC 8748 Business consulting; Business consulting
Pr: Jonathan A Brassington
COO: Stephen Racioppo
Ofcr: Sean Narayanan
Exec: Arvind Kumar
Dir Bus: Sira Cormier
Mng Dir: Jeffrey Branagh
Mng Dir: John Gresko
Mng Dir: David Hastings
Mng Dir: Saikumar Kasi
Mng Dir: David Weinberg
Mng Dir: Ajay Yeluri

D-U-N-S 93-335-1611
▲ LIQUIDITY SERVICES INC
1920 L St Nw Ste 600, Washington, DC 20036-5017
Tel (202) 467-6868 *Founded/Ownrshp* 2000
Sales 397.1MM *EMP* 1,049
Accts Ernst & Young Llp Mclean Vi
Tkr Sym LQDT *Exch* NGS
SIC 7389 Auction, appraisal & exchange services; Auction, appraisal & exchange services
Ch Bd: William P Angrick III
Mng Pt: Moji Malek
Pr: Gardner Dudley
Pr: Roger Gravley
Pr: Cayce Roy
CFO: Jorge A Celaya
CFO: James M Rallo
Ex VP: Thomas Burton
Ex VP: Tom Burton
Ex VP: Holger Schwarz
Sr VP: Asad Haroon
VP: Ram Aikat
VP: Johnson Brian
VP: Chad Farrell
VP: Timothy Hwu
VP: Pradheep Sampath
VP: James E Williams
Board of Directors: Philip A Clough, George H Ellis, Patrick W Gross, Beatriz Infante, Jaime Mateus-Tique

D-U-N-S 10-936-8998
LIQUIDNET HOLDINGS INC
498 Fashion Ave Fl 15, New York, NY 10018-6753
Tel (646) 674-2000 *Founded/Ownrshp* 1999
Sales 71.3MM^E *EMP* 164
SIC 6211 Brokers, security; Brokers, security
CEO: Seth Merrin
COO: John Kelly
CFO: Bill Maw
VP: Mike Lazar
QA Dir: Lin Zhang
Software D: Derek Kusiak
Board of Directors: Lawrence S Bacow, Jim Brown, Nathan Gantcher, Michael Price, Lady Barbara Thomas Judge, Lawrence Zicklin

D-U-N-S 09-004-3548
LIQUILUX GAS CORP
215 Del Muelle Final Ave, Ponce, PR 00731
Tel (787) 842-3320 *Founded/Ownrshp* 1954, 2000
Sales 39.8MM^E *EMP* 45
SIC 5171 5541 Petroleum bulk stations; Gasoline service stations
Pr: Angel Rivera

D-U-N-S 11-596-3621
LIQUOR BARN INC
(*Suby of* LIQUOR STORES N.A. LTD)
9920 Corporate Campus Dr, Louisville, KY 40223-4051
Tel (502) 815-4280 *Founded/Ownrshp* 1989
Sales 37.1MM^E *EMP* 245
SIC 5921 5947 5411 Beer (packaged); Wine; Hard liquor; Party favors; Grocery stores; Beer (packaged); Wine; Hard liquor; Party favors; Grocery stores
Pr: Rob Rosenstein
Site Mgr: Brad Williams

LIQUOR BARN ULTMATE PTY SOURCE
See LIQUOR STORES USA SOUTH INC

D-U-N-S 96-339-9774
LIQUOR STORES USA SOUTH INC
LIQUOR BARN ULTMATE PTY SOURCE
(*Suby of* LIQUOR STORES GP INC)
921 Beaumont Centre Pkwy, Lexington, KY 40513-9009
Tel (859) 223-1400 *Founded/Ownrshp* 2008
Sales 33.3MM^E *EMP* 300
SIC 5921 Liquor stores; Liquor stores
Pr: Rick Crook
**COO:* Scott Morrow

LIQUORS DIVISION
See V SUAREZ & CO INC

D-U-N-S 00-716-7914 IMP
LIRO ENGINEERS INC
3 Aerial Way, Syosset, NY 11791-5501
Tel (516) 938-5476 *Founded/Ownrshp* 1984
Sales 153.3MM^E *EMP* 475
Accts Marc L Montaruli Cpa Pc
SIC 1522 Hotel/motel & multi-family home construction; Hotel/motel & multi-family home construction
CEO: Rocco Trotta
**Ch Bd:* Luis Tormenta
**Sr VP:* Michael Burton
**Sr VP:* Lawrence S Roberts
**VP:* Michael Bailey
**VP:* Peter Gerbasi
**VP:* Michael Rennard
IT Man: Nancy Malicki
Snr PM: Henry Zappulla

LIRO GROUP, THE
See LIRO PROGRAM AND CONSTRUCTION MANAGEMENT PE PC

D-U-N-S 11-822-8840
LIRO PROGRAM AND CONSTRUCTION MANAGEMENT PE PC
LIRO GROUP, THE
3 Aerial Way, Syosset, NY 11791-5501
Tel (516) 938-5476 *Founded/Ownrshp* 1983
Sales 38.4MM^E *EMP* 200
Accts Marc L Montaruli Cpapc
SIC 8741 Construction management; Construction management
Ch Bd: Rocco L Trotta PC
**CEO:* Luis Tormenta
**CFO:* Lawrence Roberts
Bd of Dir: John Lekstutis
Chf Mktg O: Andrew Weinberg
**Sr VP:* Michael Burton
VP: Brant Aidikoff
VP: Gene Bifilco
VP: Jerrold Cohen
VP: James Eckhoff
**VP:* Edward Frysztacki
**VP:* Michael Mascaro
VP: Joseph Massa
VP: Michael Rennard
Exec: Rocco Trotta

D-U-N-S 01-344-4732
LIS CUSTOM DESIGNS INC
LONG ISLAND STOVE
999 S Oyster Bay Rd # 407, Bethpage, NY 11714-1044
Tel (516) 484-6262 *Founded/Ownrshp* 1929
Sales 67.8MM^E *EMP* 65
SIC 5031 5064 Kitchen cabinets; Electrical appliances, television & radio; Kitchen cabinets; Electrical appliances, television & radio
Ch Bd: Gene Spivak
**CFO:* Lawrence Teicher

D-U-N-S 06-144-4662 IMP
LISA AND DOUGLAS GOLDMAN FUND
1 Daniel Burnham Ct Bsmt, San Francisco, CA 94109-5474
Tel (415) 771-1717 *Founded/Ownrshp* 2001
Sales 38.0MM *EMP* 2
SIC 8049 Offices of health practitioner; Offices of health practitioner
Pr: Douglas E Goldman

D-U-N-S 11-030-2908
LISA L RUSSELL
EDUCATIONAL TUTORIAL SERVICES
272 Pine Ave, Indiana, PA 15701-9032
Tel (724) 910-1007 *Founded/Ownrshp* 1995
Sales 475.0M *EMP* 576
SIC 8299 Educational services; Educational services
Owner: Lisa L Russell

D-U-N-S 05-561-9944
LISA MOTOR LINES INC
GREAT WESTERN EXPRESS
(*Suby of* FROZEN FOOD EXPRESS INDUSTRIES INC) ★
3400 Stonewall St, Lancaster, TX 75134-1536
Tel (817) 698-3110 *Founded/Ownrshp* 1990
Sales 23.0MM^E *EMP* 503
SIC 4213 Refrigerated products transport; Refrigerated products transport
Ch Bd: Stoney Stubbs
**CEO:* John Stites
**Ex VP:* Charles Robertson
**Sr VP:* F Dixon McElwee

D-U-N-S 83-968-7399
LISA SHAW
CROWN FOODS
242 Constant Ave, Severn, MD 21144-3403
Tel (410) 305-0099 *Founded/Ownrshp* 1991
Sales 500.0M *EMP* 300
SIC 5812 Concessionaire; Concessionaire
Pr: Lisa Shaw

D-U-N-S 02-811-3042
LISA WALTERS ACUITY
2800 S Taylor Dr, Sheboygan, WI 53081-8474
Tel (800) 242-7666 *Founded/Ownrshp* 2010
Sales NA *EMP* 144^E
SIC 6411 Insurance agents, brokers & service
Prin: Karl Graf
Pr: Michael Falk
Ofcr: Kevin Adolphson
VP: Laura Conklin
VP: Marcus Knuth
VP: Wally Waldhart
VP: Ed Warren
Genl Mgr: Mike Kieckhafer
Genl Mgr: Debbie Kretschmann
Genl Mgr: Brian Peacock
Genl Mgr: Melissa Winter

LISAC TIRE
See LISACS TIRE OF BUTTE

D-U-N-S 03-522-4468 IMP
LISACS TIRE OF BUTTE
LISAC TIRE
2200 Yale Ave, Butte, MT 59701-3875
Tel (406) 782-4294 *Founded/Ownrshp* 1953
Sales 36.7MM^E *EMP* 50
SIC 5014 5599 Automobile tires & tubes; Dunebuggies
Pr: Mark Lisac
**Sec:* Linda Carlson
**VP:* Greg Carlson

D-U-N-S 79-346-5840
LISANN PARTY CORP
PARTY CITY
2024 W Henrietta Rd 2c, Rochester, NY 14623-1357
Tel (585) 292-6170 *Founded/Ownrshp* 1992
Sales 27.5MM^E *EMP* 300
SIC 5947 Gifts & novelties; Gifts & novelties
Ch Bd: Gary R Blum
**VP:* Mary Jane Blum

LISBON THRIFT STORE
See OPEN DOOR CENTER

D-U-N-S 17-254-8187
LISBON VALLEY MINING CO LLC
755 N Mn St Ste B, Moab, UT 84532
Tel (435) 686-9950 *Founded/Ownrshp* 1997
Sales 89.2MM^E *EMP* 109
SIC 1021 Copper ores; Copper ores
CEO: Robert M Frayser
**CFO:* Tom Chilcott

LISC
See LOCAL INITIATIVES SUPPORT CORP

D-U-N-S 93-818-8059
LISCIOS ITALIAN BAKERY INC
128 Delsea Dr S 130, Glassboro, NJ 08028-2605
Tel (856) 863-0100 *Founded/Ownrshp* 1994
Sales 24.8MM^E *EMP* 120
SIC 5461 Bakeries
Pr: James Liscio
**VP:* Charles L Vilotti

LISD
See LUFKIN INDEPENDENT SCHOOL DISTRICT

D-U-N-S 19-567-4551 IMP/EXP
LISEGA INC
(*Suby of* LISEGA SE)
370 E Dumplin Valley Rd, Kodak, TN 37764-1351
Tel (865) 940-5200 *Founded/Ownrshp* 1987
Sales 47.0MM *EMP* 209
SIC 3494 3441 8711 Valves & pipe fittings; Fabricated structural metal; Mechanical engineering; Valves & pipe fittings; Fabricated structural metal; Mechanical engineering
Pr: Dr Georg Friberg
**CFO:* William Hoffler
**Ch:* Hans Hardtke
**Prin:* Milton E Corbin
Admn Mgr: Bill Hoffler
Genl Mgr: Robert Beldyk
IT Man: John Kupski
Opers Mgr: Johnny Bible
Manager: William Reid
Sls Mgr: Curt Aronson
Sls Mgr: Fritz Hornbogen

LISI AEROSPACE
See MONADNOCK CO

D-U-N-S 10-343-1300
LISI INC
1600 W Hillsdale Blvd # 100, San Mateo, CA 94402-3770
Tel (650) 348-4131 *Founded/Ownrshp* 1976
Sales NA *EMP* 140
SIC 6411 Insurance agents
Ch Bd: Philip Lebherz
**CEO:* Becky Patel
**VP:* Tamara Henderson
**Ex Dir:* Ken Doyle
**Ex Dir:* Hadley Weiler
Mktg Mgr: Shannon Carboni
Mktg Mgr: Frank Estrada
Mktg Mgr: Jeff Hoss
Mktg Mgr: Michele Isaly
Mktg Mgr: Peter Mehta
Manager: Sandra Bealu

D-U-N-S 07-907-1494
LISK TRUCKING INC
6975 Nc 742 N, Wadesboro, NC 28170-8740
Tel (704) 272-7641 *Founded/Ownrshp* 1973
Sales 21.8MM^E *EMP* 150
SIC 4213 4212 Contract haulers; Local trucking, without storage; Contract haulers; Local trucking, without storage
Pr: Howard Lisk Jr
**Pr:* Bruce Lisk
**Treas:* Stacie L Stoker
VP: Daniel Lisk
**VP:* Jerry Lisk
Genl Mgr: Deborah Moss

D-U-N-S 07-260-4218
LISKOW & LEWIS A PROFESSIONAL LAW CORP
701 Poydras St Ste 5000, New Orleans, LA 70139-5000
Tel (504) 581-7979 *Founded/Ownrshp* 1974
Sales 27.9MM^E *EMP* 200
SIC 8111 General practice attorney, lawyer; General practice attorney, lawyer
Pr: Robert Angelico
**Pr:* R Keith Jarrett
**Pr:* Gene W Lafitte
**Sec:* William W Pugh
**Sec:* K Todd Wallace

D-U-N-S 00-727-6900 IMP
LISLE CORP
807 E Main St, Clarinda, IA 51632-2342
Tel (712) 542-5101 *Founded/Ownrshp* 1903
Sales 61.3MM^E *EMP* 230
SIC 3423 3714 Hand & edge tools; Mechanics' hand tools; Wrenches, hand tools; Motor vehicle parts & accessories; Hand & edge tools; Mechanics' hand tools; Wrenches, hand tools; Motor vehicle parts & accessories
Ch: John C Lisle
**Pr:* Frederick Lisle
**Treas:* Marty Williams
**VP:* Mary Landhuis
Board of Directors: John Arthur, Nancy Bakehouse, William Brown, Marcia Folsom, Philip E Lisle, Samuel Lisle

D-U-N-S 00-506-3854 IMP
LIST INDUSTRIES INC
401 Jim Moran Blvd, Deerfield Beach, FL 33442-1781
Tel (954) 429-9155 *Founded/Ownrshp* 1936
Sales 74.1MM^E *EMP* 200^E
SIC 2542 Lockers (not refrigerated): except wood; Lockers (not refrigerated): except wood
Pr: Herbert A List Jr
Ofcr: Thomas Champa
VP: Greg Louden
Exec: Diego Bentacur
Rgnl Mgr: Bob Geurtze
Rgnl Mgr: Jeff Lovelace
Genl Mgr: Dan Fay
VP Mfg: Dave Cole
VP Mfg: David Kole
Sfty Dirs: Jorge Carrasquilla
Opers Mgr: John Camadeca

D-U-N-S 36-180-5166
LIST PLYMOUTH LLC
STORAGE CRAFT
401 Jim Moran Blvd, Deerfield Beach, FL 33442-1781
Tel (954) 429-9155 *Founded/Ownrshp* 2007
Sales 30.0MM *EMP* 50
SIC 2542 Lockers (not refrigerated): except wood; Lockers (not refrigerated): except wood

D-U-N-S 06-274-2044
LISTEN UP INC
5295 E Evans Ave, Denver, CO 80222-5221
Tel (303) 744-1179 *Founded/Ownrshp* 1972
Sales 20.5MM *EMP* 100
Accts Eks&H Lllp Denver Colorado
SIC 5731 1731 5065 High fidelity stereo equipment; Consumer electronic equipment; Radios, two-way, citizens' band, weather, short-wave, etc.; Television sets; Sound equipment specialization; Electronic parts & equipment; High fidelity stereo equipment; Consumer electronic equipment; Radios, two-way, citizens' band, weather, short-wave, etc.; Television sets; Sound equipment specialization; Electronic parts & equipment
Pr: Walton L Stinson III
**Sec:* Mary Stinson
**Ex VP:* Michael P Dixon
**Sr VP:* Steven Weiner
Genl Mgr: Dave Jackson
Opers Mgr: Jane Gnoit
Sales Asso: Craig Congdon
Sales Asso: Jim Kearns
Sales Asso: Bill Rollin
Sales Asso: Kevin Russell
Sales Asso: Justin Sander

LISTENING EAR CRISIS CENTER
See CRISIS CENTER INC

LISTER HILL
See HEALTH SERVICES (INC)

D-U-N-S 08-494-5468
LISTERHILL CREDIT UNION
4790 2nd St, Muscle Shoals, AL 35661-1285
Tel (256) 383-9204 *Founded/Ownrshp* 1952
Sales NA *EMP* 245
SIC 6062 State credit unions, not federally chartered; State credit unions, not federally chartered
Ch: Cyril B Mann
Pr: Johnathan Gray
**CFO:* Clay Morgan
**VP:* Joyce Bates
VP: Paula Coburn
**VP:* Ivan Fike
VP: Ivan Fikes
**VP:* Daryl McMinn
Exec: Marsha Moore
Brnch Mgr: Denise Baker
Brnch Mgr: Debi Bretherick
Board of Directors: Franklin Brown, Otis Dickerson, James Holiday, Mark Lender, Bob Little, Mark Massey

D-U-N-S 00-507-7581 IMP/EXP
LITANIA SPORTS GROUP INC (IL)
GILL ATHLETICS
601 Mercury Dr, Champaign, IL 61822-9675
Tel (217) 367-8438 *Founded/Ownrshp* 1918, 1987
Sales 27.4MM^E *EMP* 135
SIC 3949 Track & field athletic equipment; Track & field athletic equipment
Pr: C David Hodge
**CFO:* Jason Norton
**VP:* Steve Vogelsang
Div Mgr: Mike Cunningham
VP Mfg: Dan Shenck

D-U-N-S 14-820-0939
LITCHFIELD CAVO LLP
303 W Madison St Ste 300, Chicago, IL 60606-3300
Tel (312) 236-7657 *Founded/Ownrshp* 1998
Sales 28.4MM^E *EMP* 145
SIC 8111 Legal services; Legal services
Pt: Alan I Becker
Mng Pt: William Catto
Mng Pt: Stephanie Dykeman
Mng Pt: David Gold
Mng Pt: Kearney Kilens
Mng Pt: Bethany Minich
Mng Pt: H Twining
Ofcr: Jason Hunter
Off Admin: Mary Gaudette
Counsel: Robert Lammie
Counsel: Richard Martin

LITCHFIELD COMPANY THE
See LITCHFIELD CO OF SC LTD PTRSHP

D-U-N-S 00-586-7213
LITCHFIELD CO OF SC LTD PTRSHP
LITCHFIELD COMPANY THE
14240 Ocean Hwy 17n, Pawleys Island, SC 29585-4829
Tel (843) 237-4000 *Founded/Ownrshp* 1956
Sales 54.0MM^E *EMP* 155
SIC 6552 6531 Subdividers & developers; Real estate agents & managers
Mng Pt: Douglas M Mahon
Pt: Rusty Phillips
Mng Pt: Douglas G Mahon
VP: Barbara Ruble
Exec: Judy Lucas
IT Man: Amy Mitchell
Sales Exec: Hector Alvarez
Sales Exec: Betsy Harper
Sales Exec: Courtney Koonce
Sales Exec: Catherine Nel
Sales Exec: Ryan Schubiger

D-U-N-S 79-372-3516
LITCHFIELD ELEM SCH DIST 79
BARBARA ROBEY ELEMENTARY SCH
272 E Sagebrush St, Litchfield Park, AZ 85340-4934
Tel (623) 547-1400 *Founded/Ownrshp* 2007
Sales 17.4MM^E *EMP* 600
SIC 8211 Elementary & secondary schools; Elementary & secondary schools
Pr: Dr Julie Ann Lein
Prin: Melissa Wisner
Teacher Pr: Monica Sanders

D-U-N-S 00-290-1676
LITCHFIELD ELEMENTARY SCHOOL DISTRICT 79 (AZ)
272 E Sagebrush St, Litchfield Park, AZ 85340-4934
Tel (623) 535-6000 *Founded/Ownrshp* 1924
Sales 39.3MM^E *EMP* 1,000
Accts Cronstrom Osuch & Company Sc
SIC 8211 Public elementary school; Public junior high school; School board; Public elementary school; Public junior high school; School board
Dir IT: Paul Clark
Dir IT: Brad Cruz
Dir IT: John Miller

LITCHFIELD PUBLIC SCHOOLS
See INDEPENDENT SCHOOL DISTRICT 465

D-U-N-S 04-664-1825
LITCO PETROLEUM INC
EXPRESS SHOPS
323 Highway 72 W, Corinth, MS 38834-5408
Tel (662) 287-1471 *Founded/Ownrshp* 1988
Sales 196.9MM^E *EMP* 600
Accts Nail Mckinney Professional Ass
SIC 5541 5172 5411 Filling stations, gasoline; Gasoline; Convenience stores; Filling stations, gasoline; Gasoline; Convenience stores
Pr: Taft Little

LITE CONTROL
See LITECONTROL CORP

D-U-N-S 15-065-4049
LITE-ON AUTOMOTIVE NORTH AMERICA INC
3221 W Big Beaver Rd # 104, Troy, MI 48084-2803
Tel (248) 792-6187 *Founded/Ownrshp* 2003
Sales 39.8MM^E *EMP* 720
SIC 5064 Electrical appliances, television & radio; Electrical appliances, television & radio
Pr: Victor Evjen
CEO: Arian Vantenberg

D-U-N-S 02-560-1741 IMP
LITE-ON INC
LITE-ON U S A
(*Suby of* LITE-ON TECHNOLOGY CORPORATION)
720 S Hillview Dr, Milpitas, CA 95035-5455
Tel (408) 946-4873 *Founded/Ownrshp* 2006
Sales 24.5MM^E *EMP* 62
SIC 5065 Electronic parts & equipment; Semiconductor devices; Electronic parts & equipment; Semiconductor devices
Pr: Sonny Hsuen-Ching Chao
COO: Tom Tang
VP: Jerry Basham
Snr Sftwr: Jing Shao
CTO: Nancy Chow
Sls Mgr: Ken Mackenzie
Counsel: Erik Chen

LITE-ON U S A
See LITE-ON INC

D-U-N-S 00-101-8118 IMP
■ **LITECONTROL CORP**
LITE CONTROL
(*Suby of* NEWCO LIGHTING INC) ★
65 Spring St, Plympton, MA 02367-1701
Tel (781) 294-0100 *Founded/Ownrshp* 2014
Sales 45.7MM^E *EMP* 205
SIC 3646 Fluorescent lighting fixtures, commercial; Ceiling systems, luminous; Fluorescent lighting fixtures, commercial; Ceiling systems, luminous
Pr: Brian Golden
COO: Adrian R Grundy
VP: Anthony J Caruso
VP: Brian G Connors
VP: Paul L Duane
Exec: Kathleen Plath
CTO: Dee Oliverio
Sfty Mgr: Michael Cornaglia
Ql Cn Mgr: Charles Moylan
Manager: Brian McNeil
Manager: Jeffrey Niedermaier

D-U-N-S 05-117-1130 IMP
LITEHOUSE INC
LITEHOUSE SPECIALTY FOODS
100 Litehouse Dr, Sandpoint, ID 83864-0528
Tel (208) 920-2000 *Founded/Ownrshp* 1977
Sales 153.9MM *EMP* 450
SIC 2035 2033 Dressings, salad: raw & cooked (except dry mixes); Jams, including imitation: packaged in cans, jars, etc.; Dressings, salad: raw & cooked (except dry mixes); Jams, including imitation: packaged in cans, jars, etc.
CEO: Jim Frank
**CEO:* Edward Hawkins Jr
**CFO:* Kelly Prior
Treas: Betty Menser
VP: Maria Emmer-Aanes
**VP:* Paul Kusche
**VP:* Dan Munson
**VP:* Daren Parsons
**VP:* David Rich
Plnt Mgr: Susan Serne
Mktg Mgr: Margi Gunter

LITEHOUSE POOLS & SPAS
See LITEHOUSE PRODUCTS LLC

D-U-N-S 01-778-9801 IMP
LITEHOUSE PRODUCTS LLC
LITEHOUSE POOLS & SPAS
11052 Pearl Rd, Strongsville, OH 44136-3308
Tel (440) 238-7300 *Founded/Ownrshp* 2004
Sales 37.1MM^E *EMP* 100
SIC 5091 3949 5999 5712

LITEHOUSE SPECIALTY FOODS
See LITEHOUSE INC

D-U-N-S 07-403-8084 IMP
LITELAB CORP
251 Elm St, Buffalo, NY 14203-1603
Tel (716) 856-4300 Founded/Ownrshp 1975
Sales 27.0MM^E EMP 140
SIC 3646 3645 Commercial indusl & institutional electric lighting fixtures; Residential lighting fixtures; Commercial indusl & institutional electric lighting fixtures; Residential lighting fixtures
CEO: Frederick A Spaulding
Pr: Jacob Levin
*COO: Lawrence Christ
*Sec: Dawn M Casati
Mfg Dir: Michael Heaverlo
Opers Mgr: Rob White
Sls Mgr: Peter Zopp

D-U-N-S 11-227-4951
■ LITEPOINT CORP
(Suby of TERADYNE INC) ★
965 W Maude Ave, Sunnyvale, CA 94085-2802
Tel (408) 456-5000 Founded/Ownrshp 2011
Sales 34.4MM^E EMP 44
SIC 8711 Electrical or electronic engineering
Pr: Benny Madsen
*COO: Brad Robbins
*Sr VP: Spiros Bouas
*Sr VP: Dana McCarty
VP: Rob Brownstein
*VP: Faruq Palla
*VP: Luc Schoups
VP: Karsten Vandrup
*VP: Niels Vinggaard
Dir Lab: Jose Gonsalez
Dir Bus: Toni Asuncion

LITESPEED-MERLIN-QUINTANA ROO
See AMERICAN BICYCLE GROUP LLC

D-U-N-S 02-952-5789 IMP/EXP
LITEX INDUSTRIES LIMITED
3401 Trinity Blvd, Grand Prairie, TX 75050-4239
Tel (972) 871-4350 Founded/Ownrshp 1980
Sales 139.2MM^E EMP 344
SIC 5064 5063 Fans, household: electric; Lighting fixtures; Fans, household: electric; Lighting fixtures
Pt: Mike Miller
Pt: John Mares
VP: Harold Wolfson Hwolf
VP: Peter WEI
IT Man: Kevin Sullivan
Natl Sales: Greg Pronti
Natl Sales: David Rauschuber
Sls Mgr: Tom Gray
Sls Mgr: Sharon Martinez

LITHCHEM
See RETRIEV TECHNOLOGIES INC

D-U-N-S 15-696-1518
■ LITHIA ACDM INC
LITHIA ACURA OF JOHNSTON
(Suby of LITHIA MOTORS INC) ★
5200 Merle Hay Rd, Johnston, IA 50131-1205
Tel (515) 253-0333 Founded/Ownrshp 2007
Sales 20.6MM^E EMP 70
SIC 5511 Automobiles, new & used; Automobiles, new & used
VP: Richard Schulte
*Treas: Kari Schulte
Store Mgr: Kevin Lovell

LITHIA ACURA OF JOHNSTON
See LITHIA ACDM INC

LITHIA AUTO CENTER OF MISSOULA
See LITHIA OF MISSOULA INC

D-U-N-S 06-148-4754
LITHIA AUTOMOTIVE GROUP INC
LITHIA TOYOTA
163 S 9th St, Springfield, OR 97477-4736
Tel (541) 747-3374 Founded/Ownrshp 1980
Sales 21.5MM^E EMP 130
SIC 5511 Automobiles, new & used; Pickups, new & used
Pr: Sid Debore
Sls Mgr: Mark Aggson

D-U-N-S 00-797-8059
■ LITHIA CB INC
(Suby of LITHIA MOTORS INC) ★
8853 W Fairview Ave, Boise, ID 83704-8211
Tel (208) 323-5000 Founded/Ownrshp 1999
Sales 20.5MM^E EMP 133
SIC 5511 Automobiles, new & used; Pickups, new & used; Vans, new & used; Automobiles, new & used; Pickups, new & used; Vans, new & used
Pr: Sid Deboer
*VP: Bryan Deboer
*VP: R Bradford Gray
*VP: M L Dick Heimann

LITHIA CHEVROLET
See LITHIA OF SIOUX FALLS INC

D-U-N-S 02-906-7105
LITHIA CHEVROLET OF SALINAS
RICHARDSON CHEVROLET
366 Abbott St, Salinas, CA 93901-4354
Tel (831) 758-6464 Founded/Ownrshp 1923
Sales 32.0MM^E EMP 60
SIC 5511 Automobiles, new & used; Automobiles, new & used
CEO: Sidney Deboer
Pt: William E Quinlan III
Pt: George E Richardson Jr

LITHIA CHRYSLER JEEP DODGE
See PISCHKE MOTORS OF LACROSSE INC

LITHIA CHRYSLER JEEP DODGE
See LITHIA DODGE OF ROSEBURG INC

LITHIA DODGE OF BILLINGS
See LITHIA OF BILLINGS INC

LITHIA DODGE OF CORPUS CHRISTI
See LITHIA GP OF TEXAS LLC

LITHIA DODGE OF FRESNO
See LITHIA OF CALIFORNIA INC

D-U-N-S 06-876-1733
■ LITHIA DODGE OF ROSEBURG INC
LITHIA CHRYSLER JEEP DODGE
(Suby of LITHIA MOTORS INC) ★
1600 Ne Airport Rd, Roseburg, OR 97470-1555
Tel (541) 672-6555 Founded/Ownrshp 1973
Sales 33.2MM^E EMP 170
SIC 5511 New & used car dealers; New & used car dealers
Ch Bd: Sidney Deboyer
*Treas: Kim Gordon

LITHIA DODGE OF SANTA ROSA
See LITHIA OF SANTA ROSA INC

D-U-N-S 03-950-6415
■ LITHIA FOOTHILLS CHRYSLER INC
AUTOPLUS SUPERSTORE
(Suby of LITHIA MOTORS INC) ★
3835 S College Ave, Fort Collins, CO 80525-3013
Tel (970) 226-5340 Founded/Ownrshp 1986
Sales 20.8MM^E EMP 103
SIC 5511 5531 7538 7515 5521 Automobiles, new & used; Automotive parts; General automotive repair shops; Passenger car leasing; Used car dealers; Automobiles, new & used; Automotive parts; General automotive repair shops; Passenger car leasing; Used car dealers
Pr: Sidney Deboer
Genl Mgr: Brent Hall

LITHIA FORD LINCOLN MERCURY
See LITHIA ROSE FT INC

LITHIA FORD LNCOLN MRCURY BISE
See LITHIA FORD OF BOISE INC

D-U-N-S 03-394-2780
■ LITHIA FORD OF BOISE INC
LITHIA FORD LNCOLN MRCURY BISE
(Suby of LITHIA MOTORS INC) ★
8853 W Fairview Ave, Boise, ID 83704-8211
Tel (208) 342-6811 Founded/Ownrshp 1963
Sales 42.9MM^E EMP 150
SIC 5511 7538 7515 7513 5521 Automobiles, new & used; Trucks, tractors & trailers: new & used; Pickups, new & used; General automotive repair shops; Passenger car leasing; Truck rental & leasing, no drivers; Used car dealers; Automobiles, new & used; Trucks, tractors & trailers: new & used; Pickups, new & used; General automotive repair shops; Passenger car leasing; Truck rental & leasing, no drivers; Used car dealers
Pr: Sidney Deboer
Genl Mgr: Douglas Orr
Sls Mgr: Randy Price

D-U-N-S 02-616-4871
■ LITHIA GP OF TEXAS LLC (TX)
LITHIA DODGE OF CORPUS CHRISTI
(Suby of LITHIA MOTORS INC) ★
4313 S Staples St, Corpus Christi, TX 78411-2703
Tel (361) 992-8000 Founded/Ownrshp 1945, 2005
Sales 28.2MM^E EMP 88
SIC 5511 Automobiles, new & used; Pickups, new & used; Automobiles, new & used; Pickups, new & used
Genl Mgr: Wayne Lidell

D-U-N-S 05-221-3907
▲ LITHIA MOTORS INC
150 N Bartlett St, Medford, OR 97501-6015
Tel (541) 776-6401 Founded/Ownrshp 1946
Sales 5.3MMM EMP 8,827^E
Tkr Sym LAD Exch NYS
SIC 5511 5531 5013 7539 Automobiles, new & used; Automotive parts; Automotive supplies & parts; Automotive repair shops; Automobiles, new & used; Automotive parts; Automotive supplies & parts; Automotive repair shops
Pr: Bryan B Deboer
CFO: Christopher Holzshu
Sr VP: Jeffrey B Deboer
Sr VP: Jeffrey B Deoer
Sr VP: Scott A Hillier
Sr VP: Scott Hillier
VP: Mark Dundon
VP: Martin Mindling
VP: Bryan Osterhout
VP: Mark Smith
VP: Ken Wright
Board of Directors: Thomas Becker, Susan O Cain, Kenneth E Roberts, William J Young

D-U-N-S 07-960-2973
■ LITHIA NC INC
LITHIA NISSAN OF CLOVIS
(Suby of LITHIA MOTORS INC) ★
370 W Herndon Ave, Clovis, CA 93612-0242
Tel (888) 569-9785 Founded/Ownrshp 2014
Sales 27.0MM^E EMP 150^E
SIC 5511 Automobiles, new & used
Pr: Bryan Deboer
CFO: Christopher Holzshu

LITHIA NISSAN OF CLOVIS
See LITHIA NC INC

D-U-N-S 03-521-3263
■ LITHIA OF BILLINGS INC
LITHIA DODGE OF BILLINGS
(Suby of LITHIA MOTORS INC) ★
2229 King Ave W, Billings, MT 59102-6421
Tel (406) 652-2200 Founded/Ownrshp 2003
Sales 21.7MM^E EMP 68
SIC 5511 Automobiles, new & used; Pickups, new & used; Automobiles, new & used; Pickups, new & used
Pr: Alan Cawthen
Genl Mgr: Dan Chumney

D-U-N-S 05-168-1732
■ LITHIA OF CALIFORNIA INC
LITHIA DODGE OF FRESNO
(Suby of LITHIA MOTORS INC) ★
360 E Jackson St, Medford, OR 97501-5825
Tel (559) 431-1661 Founded/Ownrshp 2006
Sales 26.9MM^E EMP 115
SIC 5511 Automobiles, new & used; Pickups, new & used; Vans, new & used; Automobiles, new & used; Pickups, new & used; Vans, new & used
Pr: Norman K Harris
*Sec: Margaret Harris
*VP: John J Harris
Off Mgr: Diane Cox

D-U-N-S 18-853-2407
■ LITHIA OF FAIRBANKS INC
CHEVROLET CADILLAC FAIRBANKS
(Suby of LITHIA MOTORS INC) ★
3300 S Cushman St, Fairbanks, AK 99701-7520
Tel (907) 452-8211 Founded/Ownrshp 2005
Sales 21.6MM^E EMP 167^E
SIC 5511 Automobiles, new & used
Pr: Bryan Osterhout
IT Man: Kathy Koerner

D-U-N-S 02-647-2713
■ LITHIA OF HONOLULU-BGMCC LLC
HONOLULU BUICK GMC CADILLAC
(Suby of LITHIA MOTORS INC) ★
2945 N Nimitz Hwy, Honolulu, HI 96819-1903
Tel (808) 836-7007 Founded/Ownrshp 2014
Sales 26.4MM^E EMP 149^E
SIC 5511 Automobiles, new & used
Genl Mgr: Charlie Wong
Opers Mgr: Eric Hiramoto
Sls Mgr: Mark Sherlock

D-U-N-S 04-978-1185
■ LITHIA OF MISSOULA INC
LITHIA AUTO CENTER OF MISSOULA
(Suby of LITHIA MOTORS INC) ★
5001 Grizzly Ct, Missoula, MT 59808-8672
Tel (406) 721-5000 Founded/Ownrshp 2003
Sales 29.1MM^E EMP 150^E
SIC 5511 Automobiles, new & used
Pr: Bryan Osterhout
Exec: Chris Kakos

D-U-N-S 06-612-3480
■ LITHIA OF SANTA ROSA INC
LITHIA DODGE OF SANTA ROSA
(Suby of LITHIA MOTORS INC) ★
2727 Dowd Dr, Santa Rosa, CA 95407-7818
Tel (707) 542-3331 Founded/Ownrshp 2003
Sales 21.1MM^E EMP 70
SIC 5511 Automobiles, new & used; Pickups, new & used; Trucks, tractors & trailers: new & used; Vans, new & used; Automobiles, new & used; Pickups, new & used; Trucks, tractors & trailers: new & used; Vans, new & used
Pr: Sidney Deboer

D-U-N-S 05-684-8088
■ LITHIA OF SIOUX FALLS INC
LITHIA CHEVROLET
(Suby of LITHIA MOTORS INC) ★
4200 W 12th St, Sioux Falls, SD 57107-0238
Tel (605) 336-1700 Founded/Ownrshp 2000
Sales 27.7MM^E EMP 125
SIC 5511 Automobiles, new & used; Automobiles, new & used
Ch Bd: Sidney B De Boer
Genl Mgr: Bill Termaat

LITHIA RENO HYUNDAI
See LITHIA SALMIR INC

D-U-N-S 15-236-6097
■ LITHIA ROSE FT INC
LITHIA FORD LINCOLN MERCURY
(Suby of LITHIA MOTORS INC) ★
1650 Ne Stephens St, Roseburg, OR 97470-5615
Tel (541) 440-1412 Founded/Ownrshp 1999
Sales 22.6MM^E EMP 100
SIC 5511 Automobiles, new & used; Automobiles, new & used
Pr: Bryan Osterhout

D-U-N-S 17-934-3470
■ LITHIA SALMIR INC
LITHIA RENO HYUNDAI
(Suby of LITHIA MOTORS INC) ★
2620 Kietzke Ln, Reno, NV 89502-4321
Tel (775) 823-5500 Founded/Ownrshp 1997
Sales 20.0MM^E EMP 60
SIC 5511 7538 Automobiles, new & used; General automotive repair shops; Automobiles, new & used; General automotive repair shops
Pr: Sidney B Deboer
*VP: Manfred Heimann
Genl Mgr: Dylan Clunie
Store Mgr: Marty Biegler
Sls Mgr: Tony Mazzone

LITHIA TOYOTA
See LITHIA AUTOMOTIVE GROUP INC

D-U-N-S 12-350-3877
LITHIUM TECHNOLOGIES INC
225 Bush St Fl 15, San Francisco, CA 94104-4249
Tel (510) 653-6800 Founded/Ownrshp 2001
Sales 80.0MM^E EMP 155
SIC 7372 Prepackaged software; Prepackaged software
CEO: Robert Tarkoff
CFO: Carlton Baab
*CFO: Mark Culhane
CFO: Mike Dinsdale
Ofcr: Sanjay Dholakia
*Ofcr: Ravi Kumaraswami
*Ofcr: Misha Logvinov
*Sr VP: Jim Drill
*Sr VP: Joe Fernandez
Sr VP: Charles Hough
Sr VP: Doug Jones
*Sr VP: Sunil Rajasekar
*Sr VP: Jennifer Trzepacz
*Sr VP: Ed Van Siclen
VP: Dave Evans
VP: Iain Grant
VP: Ron Rasmussen
VP: Chris Simoes
*VP: Bruno Teuber
Exec: Shannon Murphy
Board of Directors: Peter Fenton, Joe Fernandez, Jeffrey A Miller, Ravi Mohan, Geoffrey Moore, Gordon Ritter, Brooke Seawell, Pete Sonsini

D-U-N-S 09-671-9125
LITHKO CONTRACTING INC (OH)
5353 Hmlton Middletown Rd, Liberty Twp, OH 45011-2407
Tel (513) 539-4290 Founded/Ownrshp 1994
Sales 121.2MM^E EMP 450
SIC 1771 Concrete work; Foundation & footing contractor; Flooring contractor; Concrete repair; Concrete work; Foundation & footing contractor; Flooring contractor; Concrete repair
Pr: Robert Strobel
COO: Matt Ahlquist
*VP: Perry Hausfeld
*VP: Johnnie Tong
*Prin: Scott E Wiegand
Off Mgr: Phillis Clontz
Off Mgr: Kim Haller
Off Admin: Courtney Ferrell
Dir IT: Chris Doll
VP Opers: Jeffrey Sullivan
Sfty Dirs: Aaron Shaffer

D-U-N-S 00-625-1300
LITHO TECHNICAL SERVICES
(Suby of COMMERCIAL PRINT GROUP INC) ★
1600 W 92nd St, Minneapolis, MN 55431-2322
Tel (952) 888-7945 Founded/Ownrshp 1977
Sales 30.1MM^E EMP 115
Accts Schreier Kosbab Cornell Kah
SIC 2752 Commercial printing, lithographic; Commercial printing, lithographic
Pr: Bill Cahill
*VP: Bob Johnson
*Prin: Robert Gallivan Jr
*Prin: Leonard W Gehlhar
*Prin: Harlan L Moore
*Prin: Wesley Rasmussen
Opers Mgr: Darik Aho

LITHOCRAFT CO
See MAN-GROVE INDUSTRIES INC

D-U-N-S 07-822-2528
LITHOGRAPHICS INC (TN)
1835 Air Lane Dr, Nashville, TN 37210-3838
Tel (615) 889-1200 Founded/Ownrshp 1975
Sales 31.3MM^E EMP 230
SIC 2759 Commercial printing; Commercial printing
CEO: David M Bailey Sr
*Pr: David Bailey Jr
COO: Mike Clark
VP: Christina Adams
*VP: Judy Hardison
*VP: Ron Martin
*VP: Mike Rutherford
IT Man: Peter Abouaravong
Web Prj Mg: Terry Zimmerman

D-U-N-S 00-833-0946 IMP
LITHOGRAPHIX INC
12250 Crenshaw Blvd, Hawthorne, CA 90250-3332
Tel (323) 770-1000 Founded/Ownrshp 1979
Sales 159.9MM^E EMP 325
SIC 2752 2759 Commercial printing, lithographic; Commercial printing; Commercial printing, lithographic; Commercial printing
Pr: Herbert Zebrack
*CFO: Victor Wolfe
*Sec: Jeffrey Zebrack
VP: Layne Morey
VP: George Wolden
Software D: James Cox
Sales Exec: Jeff Campbell
Sales Exec: Charlotte Lee
Sls Mgr: Rick Manarino

LITHONIA LIGHTING
See ACUITY BRANDS LIGHTING INC

D-U-N-S 00-917-5647 IMP
LITHOTYPE CO INC
333 Point San Bruno Blvd, South San Francisco, CA 94080-4917
Tel (650) 871-1750 Founded/Ownrshp 1966
Sales 39.0MM EMP 100
SIC 2752 Wrappers, lithographed
Pr: Aphos Ikonomou
*CEO: Penelope Rich
*CFO: Linda Sartori
*VP: Carl Haynes
*VP: Robert Shoreen
Genl Mgr: Lynn Davis
Netwrk Mgr: Julian Fernandez
*VP Mfg: Greg Edwall
Opers Mgr: Jeff Aubin
Plnt Mgr: Mirk Hines
Prd Mgr: Vlad Gites

D-U-N-S 79-972-0289
LITHUANIAN FOUNDATION INC
14911 E 127th St, Lemont, IL 60439-7417
Tel (630) 257-1616 Founded/Ownrshp 1962
Sales 20.2MM EMP 2^E
Accts Deraimo Abendrotn Associates
SIC 8733 Noncommercial research organizations
Pr: Paul Killius
Pr: Paul Kilius
*Pr: Ruta Staniulis

D-U-N-S 14-422-1959
LITIGATION MANAGEMENT INC
6000 Parkland Blvd # 100, Mayfield Heights, OH 44124-6120
Tel (440) 484-2000 Founded/Ownrshp 1984
Sales 42.0MM^E EMP 452
SIC 8111 Legal aid service; Legal aid service
Pr: Elizabeth Juliano
VP: Matt Gengich

VP: Matthew Gingrich
IT Man: John Weigand

LITITZ MUTUAL INSURANCE CO
See PENN CHARTER MUTUAL INSURANCE CO

D-U-N-S 00-791-2306
LITITZ MUTUAL INSURANCE CO INC (PA)
2 N Broad St, Lititz, PA 17543-1005
Tel (800) 626-4751 *Founded/Ownrshp* 1888
Sales NA *EMP* 70
SIC 6331 Fire, marine & casualty insurance: mutual
Pr: Henry H Gibbel
Treas: Glenn Shelly
VP: Mark Crutcher
VP: Robert D Dodds
VP: John R Gibbel
Mktg Mgr: Bonnie Kratts

LITMAN EXCAVATING & CNSTR
See LITMAN EXCAVATING INC

D-U-N-S 94-974-2662
LITMAN EXCAVATING INC
LITMAN EXCAVATING & CNSTR
836 1st St, New Martinsville, WV 26155-1502
Tel (304) 455-1050 *Founded/Ownrshp* 1994
Sales 31.5MM^E *EMP* 135^E
SIC 1794 3531 Excavation work; Backhoes, tractors, cranes, plows & similar equipment; Excavation work; Backhoes, tractors, cranes, plows & similar equipment
Pr: Robert B Litman
**Prin:* Ronald M Musser
Off Mgr: Dana Martin

LITSCO
See LONG ISLAND TINSMITH SUPPLY CORP

LITTAU HARVESTER ACCEPTANCE
See LITTAU HARVESTER INC

D-U-N-S 80-977-3146
LITTAU HARVESTER INC
LITTAU HARVESTER ACCEPTANCE
855 Rogue Ave, Stayton, OR 97383-9421
Tel (503) 769-5953 *Founded/Ownrshp* 2000
Sales 37.7MM^E *EMP* 110
SIC 5083 4213 Harvesting machinery & equipment; Trucking, except local; Harvesting machinery & equipment; Trucking, except local
Pr: Willard Norman Johnson
Off Mgr: Joy Jenkins
Sales Exec: Norm Johnson
Sls Mgr: Brian Thompson

D-U-N-S 07-959-2116
LITTEL MITZUL INC (IL)
4723 S Seeley Ave Apt 2, Chicago, IL 60609-4039
Tel (773) 540-8147 *Founded/Ownrshp* 2014
Sales 28.0MM *EMP* 1
SIC 4789 Cargo loading & unloading services; Cargo loading & unloading services
Pr: Miguel Angel Herrera

D-U-N-S 00-521-2246 IMP
▲ LITTELFUSE INC
8755 W Higgins Rd Ste 500, Chicago, IL 60631-2701
Tel (773) 628-1000 *Founded/Ownrshp* 1927
Sales 852.0MM *EMP* 7,400
Accts Grant Thornton Llp Chicago
Tkr Sym LFUS *Exch* NGS
SIC 3613 3679 Fuses & fuse equipment; Electronic circuits; Fuses & fuse equipment; Electronic circuits
Ch Bd: Gordon Hunter
COO: David W Heinzmann
COO: Mark Hubbard
COO: Jan La Hayne
CFO: Philip G Franklin
Ex VP: Ralph Brandi
Sr VP: Matthew J Cole
Sr VP: Ian Highley
VP: F S Daniel
VP: Dal Ferbert
VP: Deepak Nayar
VP: Michael P Rutz
VP: Ryan Stafford
VP: Daniel Stanek
Exec: Paul Dickinson
Board of Directors: Cary T Fu, Anthony Grillo, John E Major, William P Noglows, Ronald L Schubel

D-U-N-S 07-347-9284 IMP
■ LITTELFUSE MEXICO HOLDING LLC
(*Suby of* LITTELFUSE INC) ★
612 E Lake St, Lake Mills, WI 53551-1737
Tel (920) 648-3000 *Founded/Ownrshp* 2013
Sales 39.8MM^E *EMP* 187^E
SIC 3625 Switches, electronic applications; Switches, electronic applications
CEO: Greg Heald
COO: Neil Hamlin
Prgrm Mgr: Guillermo Ymay
QA Dir: Shirley Hofer
Plnt Mgr: Dave York

D-U-N-S 01-760-2681
LITTER DISTRIBUTING CO INC
CLASSIC BRANDS CHILLICOTHE
(*Suby of* LITTER INDUSTRIES INC) ★
656 Hospital Rd, Chillicothe, OH 45601-9030
Tel (740) 775-2063 *Founded/Ownrshp* 1938
Sales 30.3MM^E *EMP* 88
SIC 5181 Beer & other fermented malt liquors; Beer & other fermented malt liquors
Pr: Robert W Litter

D-U-N-S 82-559-7529
LITTER INDUSTRIES INC
524 Eastern Ave, Chillicothe, OH 45601-3471
Tel (740) 773-2196 *Founded/Ownrshp* 1987
Sales 36.1MM^E *EMP* 100
SIC 5984 5571 5181 7359 6512 Propane gas, bottled; Liquefied petroleum gas, delivered to customers' premises; Motorcycle dealers; Beer & ale; Equipment rental & leasing; Commercial & industrial building operation; Propane gas, bottled; Liquefied petroleum gas, delivered to customers' premises; Motorcycle dealers; Beer & ale; Equipment rental & leasing; Commercial & industrial building operation
Pr: Robert W Litter

LITTLE AMERICA HOTEL COMPANY
See LITTLE AMERICA HOTELS & RESORTS INC

D-U-N-S 78-502-4360
LITTLE AMERICA HOTELS & RESORTS INC
LITTLE AMERICA HOTEL COMPANY
(*Suby of* GRAND AMERICA HOTEL) ★
500 S Main St, Salt Lake City, UT 84101-2405
Tel (801) 258-6000 *Founded/Ownrshp* 2005
Sales 54.7MM^E *EMP* 700
SIC 7011 Hotels & motels; Hotels & motels
Pr: Earl Holding
VP: Bruce Fery
Genl Mgr: Frank Cherrif
IT Man: Darrel Cruz

D-U-N-S 17-497-8346
LITTLE ANITAS MEXICAN FOOD INC
3041 University Blvd Se, Albuquerque, NM 87106-5040
Tel (505) 888-0104 *Founded/Ownrshp* 1974
Sales 12.1MM^E *EMP* 300
SIC 5812 Mexican restaurant; Mexican restaurant
Pr: Larry Gutierrez

D-U-N-S 10-818-6016
LITTLE BAY LOBSTER LLC
158 Shattuck Way, Newington, NH 03801-7880
Tel (603) 431-3170 *Founded/Ownrshp* 2006
Sales 32.3MM^E *EMP* 90
SIC 5146 Seafoods; Seafoods
CFO: Bill Blackett

D-U-N-S 04-808-2747 IMP
LITTLE CAESAR ENTERPRISES INC
LITTLE CAESAR'S
(*Suby of* ILITCH HOLDINGS INC) ★
2211 Woodward Ave, Detroit, MI 48201-3400
Tel (313) 983-6000 *Founded/Ownrshp* 1959
Sales 270.1MM^E *EMP* 6,000
SIC 5812 6794 5141 5046 8741 Pizzeria, chain; Franchises, selling or licensing; Groceries, general line; Cooking equipment, commercial; Restaurant equipment & supplies; Management services; Pizzeria, chain; Franchises, selling or licensing; Groceries, general line; Cooking equipment, commercial; Restaurant equipment & supplies; Management services
Ch Bd: Michael Ilitch
Pr: William Crystler
Pr: Karen Cullen
Pr: Greg Martino
Pr: David Scrivano
CEO: Christopher Ilitch
CFO: Scott Fischer
Treas: Matthew Greenough
Sr VP: Michael Scruggs
VP: John Beasley
VP: Ed Gleich
VP: Rick Muse
VP: Darrell Snygg
Comm Dir: Kathryn Oldham

D-U-N-S 13-757-8795
LITTLE CAESAR OF SAN ANTONIO INC
LITTLE CAESAR'S
925 Coronado Blvd Ste 100, Universal City, TX 78148-3237
Tel (210) 658-0998 *Founded/Ownrshp* 1984
Sales 24.3MM^E *EMP* 900
SIC 5812 Pizzeria, chain; Pizzeria, chain
Pr: Lee R Hotchkiss
**CFO:* Jason Hotchkiss
**Treas:* Kathleen Hotchkiss

LITTLE CAESAR'S
See LITTLE CAESAR ENTERPRISES INC

LITTLE CAESAR'S
See BAYOFF ENTERPRISES INC

LITTLE CAESAR'S
See ENTERPRISE FOOD SERVICES INC

LITTLE CAESAR'S
See MAGNUM FOODS INC

LITTLE CAESAR'S
See LITTLE CAESAR OF SAN ANTONIO INC

LITTLE CAESAR'S
See LITTLE CAESARS OF INDIANA INC

LITTLE CAESAR'S
See SEVEN IS INC

LITTLE CAESAR'S
See ILITCH HOLDINGS INC

D-U-N-S 12-129-2072
LITTLE CAESARS OF INDIANA INC
LITTLE CAESAR'S
9111 Broadway Ste Mm, Merrillville, IN 46410-7011
Tel (708) 452-3197 *Founded/Ownrshp* 1983
Sales 25.0MM^E *EMP* 260
SIC 6794 5812 Franchises, selling or licensing; Pizzeria, chain
Prin: Ronald Bernacchi
**Pr:* Donald Bernacchi
**Treas:* Steven Bernacchi

D-U-N-S 13-949-8752
LITTLE CAESARS WEST INC
2211 Woodward Ave, Detroit, MI 48201-3467
Tel (313) 983-6000 *Founded/Ownrshp* 1983
Sales 9.2MM^E *EMP* 600
SIC 5812 Pizzeria, chain; Pizzeria, chain
Pr: Mike Ilitch Jr
**Sec:* Marian Ilitch
IT Man: Andre Davis

D-U-N-S 06-996-2314
LITTLE CITY FOUNDATION
1760 W Algonquin Rd, Palatine, IL 60067-4791
Tel (847) 358-5510 *Founded/Ownrshp* 1957
Sales 25.6MM *EMP* 450
Accts Mcgladrey Llp Chicago Illin
SIC 8211 School for the retarded; School for the retarded
Doctor: Karen Larsen

LITTLE COMPANY MARY SVC AREA
See PROVIDENCE LITTLE CO OF MARY MEDICAL CENTER-TORRANCE

LITTLE CO MARY- SAN PEDRO HOSP
See SAN PEDRO PENINSULA HOSPITAL

D-U-N-S 04-702-2827
LITTLE CO OF MARY HOSPITAL AND HEALTH CARE CENTERS
2800 GIFT SHOP, THE
2800 W 95th St, Evergreen Park, IL 60805-2701
Tel (708) 422-6200 *Founded/Ownrshp* 1893
Sales 156.9MM^E *EMP* 2,000
SIC 8062 Hospital, AMA approved residency; Hospital, AMA approved residency
Pr: Dennis Riley
Chf OB: Robert M Bonaminio
Chf Rad: Irving L Fuld
**COO:* Mary Freyer
CFO: Carl Carrier
**CFO:* Raymond Snowden
Treas: Dennis Kelly
**Treas:* Thomas Sahey
Bd of Dir: John Hanlon
VP: Mary Quick
VP: Kevin Rehder
VP: Randy Ruther
Exec: Carol Martinez
Comm Man: Karen Perrino

D-U-N-S 96-959-1861
LITTLE CO OF MARY HOSPITAL INC
2800 W 95th St, Evergreen Park, IL 60805-2795
Tel (708) 229-5688 *Founded/Ownrshp* 2011
Sales 173.2MM *EMP* 2,200
SIC 8062 General medical & surgical hospitals; General medical & surgical hospitals
CEO: Dennis Reilly
**COO:* Mary Freyer
Ofcr: Marcus Schausele
Exec: Susan Arnold
Exec: Jim Denvir
Dir Risk M: Gina Knox
Comm Man: Cheryl Conroy
Ex Dir: Marilyn Daley
Dir IT: Gary Nalley
Opers Supe: Rebecca Karr
Opers Mgr: Jill Fuggett

D-U-N-S 07-785-6029 EXP
LITTLE CO OF MARY HOSPITAL OF INDIANA INC
MEMORIAL HOSP & HLTH CARE CTR
800 W 9th St, Jasper, IN 47546-2514
Tel (812) 996-2345 *Founded/Ownrshp* 1951
Sales 169.9MM *EMP* 950
Accts Blue & Co Llc Indianapolis I
SIC 8062 General medical & surgical hospitals; General medical & surgical hospitals
Pr: Raymond W Snowden
COO: John Dillon
Bd of Dir: Adrian Davis
Ofcr: Rosemary Woerner
VP: Tonya Heim
VP: Gary Light
VP: Ronald Salyk
Chf Nrs Of: Amy Weisman
Dir QC: Denise Kaetzel
Dir IT: Jan Renner
IT Man: Sean Kluemper

LITTLE CO OF MARYS HOSPITAL
See PHYSICIAN MATCH

LITTLE COLORADO MEDICAL CENTER
See WINSLOW MEMORIAL HOSPITAL INC

D-U-N-S 06-935-0363
LITTLE COLORADO MEDICAL CENTER
1501 N Williamson Ave, Winslow, AZ 86047-2735
Tel (928) 289-4691 *Founded/Ownrshp* 2011
Sales 29.6MM *EMP* 62^E
SIC 8011 Offices & clinics of medical doctors; Offices & clinics of medical doctors
CEO: Jack Dempsey
COO: Randy Glassman
CFO: John Dempsey
CFO: Randal Glassman
Dir OR: Jackie Hartman
Dir Rad: Dawna Lewis
Dir Rx: Tammy Bird
CIO: Michael Howard
QA Dir: Sonia Ybarra
Dir IT: Kathy Softley
Surgeon: Dilip Parikh

D-U-N-S 07-390-0722
LITTLE CYPRESS-MAURICEVILLE CISD INC
6586 Fm 1130, Orange, TX 77632-3723
Tel (409) 883-2232 *Founded/Ownrshp* 1968
Sales 30.6MM *EMP* 516
Accts Wathen Deshong & Juncker Llp
SIC 8211 Public senior high school; Public senior high school
Schl Brd P: Rex Peveto
Instr Medi: Roy Mazzagate

LITTLE DEALER-LITTLE PRICES
See ARIZONA STATE TRAILER SALES INC

D-U-N-S 06-255-6725
LITTLE DIVERSIFIED ARCHITECTURAL CONSULTING INC
5815 Westpark Dr, Charlotte, NC 28217-3554
Tel (704) 525-6350 *Founded/Ownrshp* 1966
Sales 50.2MM^E *EMP* 200^E
SIC 8711 Engineering services; Engineering services
CEO: Phil Kuttner
**Pr:* John Komisin
**CFO:* James L McGarry
**Ch:* William B Little
**Ch:* W Edwin McMahan
Prin: Scott Brideu
IT Man: Terry Bradshaw
Tech Mgr: Doug Andrews
Snr PM: Douglas Engel
Snr PM: Ramon Santos
Snr PM: Mary Sullivan

D-U-N-S 09-545-3171
LITTLE DIXIE COMMUNITY ACTION AGENCY INC
209 N 4th St, Hugo, OK 74743-3809
Tel (580) 326-3351 *Founded/Ownrshp* 1966
Sales 21.8MM *EMP* 200
SIC 8093 8399 Specialty outpatient clinics; Antipoverty board; Specialty outpatient clinics; Antipoverty board
Ex Dir: Bob Yandell
Sls&Mrk Ex: Johnny Robinson
Pgrm Dir: Johnna Ballenger
Pgrm Dir: Linda Byrd
Pgrm Dir: Joan Edge
Pgrm Dir: Lynette O'Dell
Pgrm Dir: Stacie Pluhatsch
Pgrm Dir: Dennis Smith
Pgrm Dir: Steve Tucker
Pgrm Dir: Dennis Willeford
Pgrm Dir: Johnna Yow

D-U-N-S 07-302-1263
LITTLE DUTCH BOY BAKERIES INC
12349 S 970 E, Draper, UT 84020-9357
Tel (801) 571-3800 *Founded/Ownrshp* 1973
Sales 36.0MM *EMP* 90
SIC 2052

D-U-N-S 07-983-7696
LITTLE ELM INDEPENDENT SCHOOL DISTRICT
LITTLE ELM ISD
300 Lobo Ln, Little Elm, TX 75068-5216
Tel (972) 947-9340 *Founded/Ownrshp* 1970
Sales 46.9MM^E *EMP* 737
Accts Hankins Eastup Deaton Tonn
SIC 8211 Public elementary school; Public junior high school; Public senior high school; Public elementary school; Public junior high school; Public senior high school
CFO: Grant Anderson
Dir IT: John Atchison
Dir IT: David Sons
Snr Mgr: Dale McKendrick

LITTLE ELM ISD
See LITTLE ELM INDEPENDENT SCHOOL DISTRICT

D-U-N-S 09-283-0103
LITTLE ENTERPRISES INC
STONE COLD MASONRY
416 W Lone Cactus Dr, Phoenix, AZ 85027-2910
Tel (623) 385-7110 *Founded/Ownrshp* 1999
Sales 33.4MM^E *EMP* 105^E
SIC 1541 Industrial buildings & warehouses; Industrial buildings & warehouses
Pr: Lance Little
CEO: April Cheeseman

LITTLE FALLS COMMUNITY SCHOOLS
See INDEPENDENT SCHOOL DISTRICT 482

D-U-N-S 08-930-3627
LITTLE FALLS CORN POOL
17936 Heron Rd, Little Falls, MN 56345-6579
Tel (320) 632-1614 *Founded/Ownrshp* 2001
Sales 32.9MM *EMP* 1
SIC 8641 Civic social & fraternal associations; Civic social & fraternal associations
Pr: Mike Barrett

D-U-N-S 07-582-2965
LITTLE FALLS HOSPITAL
MOHAWK VALLEY NETWORK
(*Suby of* MOHAWK VALLEY HEALTH SYSTEM) ★
140 Burwell St, Little Falls, NY 13365-1794
Tel (315) 823-5262 *Founded/Ownrshp* 1893
Sales 25.6MM *EMP* 30
Accts Fust Charles Chambers Llp Syr
SIC 8062 General medical & surgical hospitals
CEO: Michael Ogden
CFO: Mark Mornielli
**CFO:* James Vielkind
Dir Lab: Stephanie Dyer
IT Man: Joann Weiner
Mktg Dir: Kate Reese
Nrsg Dir: Joan S Conboy
HC Dir: Lori Usyk

D-U-N-S 01-139-7221
LITTLE FALLS SHOP RITE MARKET INC
171 Browertown Rd Ste 2, Little Falls, NJ 07424-1718
Tel (973) 256-0909 *Founded/Ownrshp* 1987
Sales 20.6MM^E *EMP* 282
SIC 5411 5912 7384 5992 2052 2051 Supermarkets, chain; Drug stores; Photofinish laboratories; Florists; Cookies & crackers; Bread, cake & related products; Supermarkets, chain; Drug stores; Photofinish laboratories; Florists; Cookies & crackers; Bread, cake & related products
Pr: Charles M Infusino
**Sec:* Carol Tokar

D-U-N-S 06-596-3506
LITTLE FLOWER CHILDREN AND FAMILY SERVICES OF NEW YORK
2450 N Wading River Rd, Wading River, NY 11792-1402
Tel (631) 929-6200 *Founded/Ownrshp* 1929
Sales 17.7MM *EMP* 500
Accts Baker Tilly Virchow Krause Ll
SIC 8361 8322 Residential care; Individual & family services; Residential care; Individual & family services
CEO: Grace Logrande
**CFO:* Kevin Kundmueller

CFO: Kathleen Reiss
Ex Dir: Camille Lucarini

D-U-N-S 61-204-7167
LITTLE FLOWER MANOR OF DIOCESE OF SCRANTON
200 S Meade St, Wilkes Barre, PA 18702-6221
Tel (570) 823-6131 *Founded/Ownrshp* 1974
Sales 8.4MM^E *EMP* 286
Accts Kronick Kalada Berdy & Co Ki
SIC 8051 Skilled nursing care facilities; Skilled nursing care facilities
Pr: Bishop James Timlin

D-U-N-S 06-950-4363
LITTLE FRIENDS INC
140 N Wright St, Naperville, IL 60540-4748
Tel (630) 355-6533 *Founded/Ownrshp* 1965
Sales 15.2MM *EMP* 380
Accts Frost Ruttenberg & Rothblatt P
SIC 8361 8331 Home for the mentally handicapped; Vocational rehabilitation agency; Home for the mentally handicapped; Vocational rehabilitation agency
Pr: Kristi Landorf
**CFO:* Cindy Romine
**Treas:* William Cordes
Ex VP: Patti Boheme
VP: Susan Iona
VP: Wayne Pearce
**Ex Dir:* Jack Ryan
Sales Asso: Maureen Reichelt

LITTLE GANT FRMRS MKT RVERDALE
See LITTLE GIANT FARMERS MARKET CORP

D-U-N-S 08-225-3063
LITTLE GENERAL STORE INC
LGS
4036 Robert C. Byrd Dr, Beckley, WV 25801
Tel (304) 253-9592 *Founded/Ownrshp* 1975
Sales 129.9MM^E *EMP* 650
SIC 5411 Convenience stores; Convenience stores
CEO: Greg Darby
**CEO:* Corey Beasley
**Prin:* Gloria Tolbert
Site Mgr: Della Blankenship
Site Mgr: Steve Nunley
Site Mgr: Renee Webb

LITTLE GIANT
See BRENNAN EQUIPMENT AND MANUFACTURING INC

D-U-N-S 10-863-8669
LITTLE GIANT FARMERS MARKET CORP
LITTLE GANT FRMRS MKT RVERDALE
399 Upper Riverdale Rd, Jonesboro, GA 30236-1006
Tel (770) 997-8865 *Founded/Ownrshp* 1983
Sales 23.3MM^E *EMP* 160^E
SIC 5431 5411 5421 Fruit stands or markets; Vegetable stands or markets; Grocery stores; Meat markets, including freezer provisioners
Ch Bd: R Bruce Dixon
**Pr:* Michael Lynn Dixon

LITTLE GIANT LADDERS
See WING ENTERPRISES INC

D-U-N-S 00-718-9699
■ **LITTLE GIANT PUMP CO LLC** (OK)
(*Suby of* FRANKLIN ELECTRIC CO INC) ★
301 N Macarthur Blvd, Oklahoma City, OK 73127-6616
Tel (405) 947-2511 *Founded/Ownrshp* 1940, 2006
Sales 88.2MM^E *EMP* 500
SIC 3561 Pumps, domestic: water or sump; Cylinders, pump; Pumps, domestic: water or sump; Cylinders, pump
Pr: Norman Heidebrecht
Treas: James Nicholson
VP: Ted Foti

D-U-N-S 06-094-6415
LITTLE HAVANA ACTIVITIES & NUTRITION CENTERS OF DADE COUNTY INC
700 Sw 8th St Fl 1, Miami, FL 33130-3300
Tel (305) 858-0887 *Founded/Ownrshp* 1973
Sales 34.8MM *EMP* 206
Accts Glsc & Company Pllc Miami Fl
SIC 8322 8742 8351 7361 Individual & family services; Management consulting services; Child day care services; Employment agencies; Individual & family services; Management consulting services; Child day care services; Employment agencies
Pr: Ramon Perez-Dorrbecker
MIS Dir: Andy Lopez
**Nutrtnst:* Elisa Juara

D-U-N-S 15-111-8275
LITTLE HILLS HEALTHCARE LLC
CENTERPOINTE HOSPITAL
4801 Weldon Spring Pkwy, Weldon Spring, MO 63304-9101
Tel (636) 441-7300 *Founded/Ownrshp* 2003
Sales 46.7MM *EMP* 150^E
SIC 8063 Psychiatric hospitals
CEO: Azfar Malik
Pr: Chris Lhotak
CFO: Steve Frantz
CFO: Ron Moore
Treas: Susan Mathis
Dept Mgr: Victoria Saali
IT Man: Michael Solom
Sfty Dirs: Sequoyah Primeau
Mktg Mgr: Connie McDonald

D-U-N-S 07-526-8631
LITTLE LAKE CITY SCHOOL DISTRICT
10515 Pioneer Blvd, Santa Fe Springs, CA 90670-3703
Tel (562) 868-8241 *Founded/Ownrshp* 1882
Sales 26.1MM^E *EMP* 350
SIC 8211 Public elementary school; Public elementary school
Bd of Dir: Lynn Berg
Bd of Dir: Heidi McDonald
Bd of Dir: Janet Rock

LITTLE LEAG BASBAL & SOFTBALL
See LITTLE LEAGUE POLAND FOUNDATION

D-U-N-S 06-960-3215
LITTLE LEAGUE POLAND FOUNDATION (PA)
LITTLE LEAG BASBAL & SOFTBALL
539 Us Route 15 Hwy, Williamsport, PA 17702-8541
Tel (570) 326-3607 *Founded/Ownrshp* 1939, 1993
Sales 25.9MM *EMP* 98
Accts Pricewaterhousecoopers Llp H
SIC 8699 Athletic organizations; Athletic organizations
Pr: Stephen Keener
**CFO:* David Houseknecht
**Treas:* Melissa Singer
VP: Chris Bean
VP: Wayne Devine
VP: George Hockenbury
VP: Joe Shurites

D-U-N-S 03-872-1395
LITTLE MIAMI LOCAL SCHOOL DISTRICT
7247 Zoar Rd, Maineville, OH 45039-8098
Tel (513) 899-2264 *Founded/Ownrshp* 1954
Sales 23.3MM^E *EMP* 350
SIC 8211 Public elementary school; Public senior high school; School board; Public elementary school; Public senior high school; School board
Pr: Bobbie Grice
Treas: Terry Gonda
VP: Michael Cremeans
VP: Mary Hamburg
Adm Dir: Kathy Bullock

D-U-N-S 00-797-5956
LITTLE OCMULGEE ELECTRIC MEMBERSHIP CORP (GA)
26 W Railroad Ave, Alamo, GA 30411
Tel (912) 568-7171 *Founded/Ownrshp* 1938
Sales 24.4MM *EMP* 43
Accts Nichols Cauley & Associates Ll
SIC 4911 8699 Distribution, electric power; Distribution, electric power; Athletic organizations
Pr: Carey Locke
**Sec:* Fred Gilder
**VP:* Jim Knight
Genl Mgr: Lewis Sheffield
Opers Mgr: Keith Couey

D-U-N-S 00-613-2294 IMP/EXP
LITTLE RAPIDS CORP (WI)
GRAHAM PROFESSIONAL PRODUCTS
2273 Larsen Rd, Green Bay, WI 54303-4809
Tel (920) 490-5400 *Founded/Ownrshp* 1925
Sales 77.4MM^E *EMP* 460
SIC 2621

D-U-N-S 13-146-8787
LITTLE RED SERVICES INC
(*Suby of* ARCTIC SLOPE REGIONAL CORP) ★
3900 C St Ste 302, Anchorage, AK 99503-5965
Tel (907) 349-2931 *Founded/Ownrshp* 2014
Sales 27.4MM^E *EMP* 170
SIC 1381 1382 Reworking oil & gas wells; Oil & gas exploration services; Reworking oil & gas wells; Oil & gas exploration services
Pr: Douglas L Smith
VP Opers: Joe Curgus

D-U-N-S 07-739-3783
LITTLE ROCK DIAGNOSTIC CLINIC
10001 Lile Dr, Little Rock, AR 72205-6299
Tel (501) 227-8000 *Founded/Ownrshp* 1961
Sales 49.4MM^E *EMP* 170
Accts Hart Chandler & Associates P
SIC 8011 Clinic, operated by physicians
CEO: Gregory Campbell
**Pr:* Elizabeth Berry
**Pr:* Dr William Morton
**Pr:* Richard Rapp
**Sec:* Mark Dyer
**VP:* Terence Angtuaco
**VP:* Robert Paul Svoboda
Exec: Derek Johnston
Off Mgr: Lynn Coren
Sls&Mrk Ex: Lynn Claud
Doctor: Shun Zhong Bao

D-U-N-S 05-196-1712
LITTLE ROCK DODGE INC
5809 S University Ave, Little Rock, AR 72209-2153
Tel (501) 562-7200 *Founded/Ownrshp* 1970
Sales 46.6MM^E *EMP* 285
SIC 5511 Automobiles, new & used; Automobiles, new & used
Pr: Gerald Martindill Sr
**Treas:* Dorothy Martindill
**VP:* Gerald F Martindill Jr
VP: Gerald F Butch Martindill Jr

D-U-N-S 08-257-1951
LITTLE ROCK MUNICIPAL AIRPORT COMMISSION
BILL HILLARY CLINTON NAT ARPRT
1 Airport Dr Little Rock, Little Rock, AR 72202
Tel (501) 372-3439 *Founded/Ownrshp* 1951
Sales 25.6MM^E *EMP* 165
SIC 4581 Airport
Ex Dir: Bryan Malinowski
Ex Dir: Ronald F Mathieu
Ex Dir: Ronald Mathieu
IT Man: Jones Justin

LITTLE ROCK PUBLIC SCHOOLS
See LITTLE ROCK SCHOOL DISTRICT

D-U-N-S 04-064-4007
LITTLE ROCK SCHOOL DISTRICT
LITTLE ROCK PUBLIC SCHOOLS
810 W Markham St, Little Rock, AR 72201-1306
Tel (501) 447-1000 *Founded/Ownrshp* 1875
Sales 332.6MM *EMP* 4,000
Accts Hudson Cisne & Co Llp Littl
SIC 8211 Public elementary & secondary schools; Public elementary & secondary schools
Bd of Dir: Jody Carreiro
Bd of Dir: Katherine Mitchell
Bd of Dir: Kate Runder
VP: Keith Richardson
VP: Amanda Warren
Exec: David Bernard
Exec: Donna Muldrew
Exec: Summer Young
Comm Dir: Tiffany Hoffman
Schl Brd P: Greg Adams
Teacher Pr: Robert Robinson

D-U-N-S 12-020-0217
LITTLE ROCK WASTE WATER UTILITY
11 Clearwater Dr, Little Rock, AR 72204-8009
Tel (501) 376-2903 *Founded/Ownrshp* 1935
Sales 51.2MM *EMP* 214
Accts Bkd Llp Little Rock Ar
SIC 4952 Sewerage systems; Sewerage systems
CEO: Greg Ramon
**Prin:* Pete Hornibrook
**Prin:* Marilyn Perryman

LITTLE SCHOLARS LEARNING CTR
See PROFESSIONAL EDUCATORS INSTITUTE

LITTLE SIOUX CORN PROCESSORS
See LSCP LLLP

D-U-N-S 02-255-0177
LITTLE SIOUX CORN PROCESSORS LLC
LSCP
4808 F Ave, Marcus, IA 51035-7070
Tel (712) 376-2800 *Founded/Ownrshp* 2000
Sales 350.0MM *EMP* 45^E
Accts Christianson & Associates Pll
SIC 2869 Ethyl alcohol, ethanol; Ethyl alcohol, ethanol
Ch Bd: Ron Wetherell
**CFO:* Gary Grotjohn
**V Ch Bd:* Myron Pingel
**Genl Mgr:* Steve Roe

D-U-N-S 07-493-5800 IMP
LITTLE SISTERS OF POOR BALTIMORE INC
601 Maiden Choice Ln, Baltimore, MD 21228-3630
Tel (410) 744-9367 *Founded/Ownrshp* 1854
Sales 3.4MM *EMP* 460
SIC 8059

D-U-N-S 00-388-1678
LITTLE SIX CASINO
2354 Sioux Trl Nw, Prior Lake, MN 55372-9077
Tel (952) 445-6000 *Founded/Ownrshp* 2007
Sales 8.9MM^E *EMP* 400
SIC 7999 Gambling establishment; Gambling establishment

D-U-N-S 07-862-2520
LITTLE SPROUTS LLC
354 Merrimack St Ste 270, Lawrence, MA 01843-1755
Tel (978) 291-0256 *Founded/Ownrshp* 2012
Sales 10.4MM^E *EMP* 400^E
SIC 8351 Child day care services; Child day care services
CEO: Mark Anderegg
CFO: Melissa Leger

LITTLE STORE , THE
See BEST OIL CO

D-U-N-S 04-270-4692 IMP/EXP
LITTLE TIKES CO
(*Suby of* MGA ENTERTAINMENT INC) ★
2180 Barlow Rd, Hudson, OH 44236-4199
Tel (330) 650-3000 *Founded/Ownrshp* 2006
Sales 220.8MM^E *EMP* 2,100
SIC 3944 2519

LITTLE TREES
See CAR-FRESHNER CORP

LITTLE YANKEE
See ASSOCIATED GROCERS OF MAINE INC

LITTLEDIKE
See ALPARK PETROLEUM INC

D-U-N-S 03-392-1743
LITTLEFIELD CONSTRUCTION CO (GA)
1518 Albany Ave, Waycross, GA 31503-4907
Tel (912) 283-8181 *Founded/Ownrshp* 1955, 1976
Sales 21.0MM *EMP* 50
SIC 1611 General contractor, highway & street construction; General contractor, highway & street construction
Pr: David Littlefield Jr
**Sec:* Kathleen Littlefield
**VP:* Dan S Littlefield

D-U-N-S 03-544-9099
LITTLEFIELD OIL CO (AR)
3403 Cavanaugh Rd, Fort Smith, AR 72908-7870
Tel (479) 646-0595 *Founded/Ownrshp* 1992
Sales 43.2MM^E *EMP* 90
SIC 5171

D-U-N-S 95-682-1326 IMP/EXP
▲ **LITTLEJOHN & CO LLC**
8 Sound Shore Dr Ste 303, Greenwich, CT 06830-7254
Tel (203) 552-3500 *Founded/Ownrshp* 1996
Sales 3.1MMM^E *EMP* 6,860
SIC 6799 Investors; Investors
Pr: Michael I Klein
**Pr:* Brian Ramsay
**Ch:* Angus C Littlejohn Jr
VP: Andrew Goodrich
**VP:* Drew Greenwood
**VP:* Steven B Kalter
**VP:* Gentry Klein
**VP:* Brian W Michaud

D-U-N-S 78-630-5938
LITTLEJOHN ENGINEERING ASSOCIATES INC
1935 21st Ave S, Nashville, TN 37212-3801
Tel (423) 928-3500 *Founded/Ownrshp* 1989
Sales 25.6MM^E *EMP* 95
SIC 8711 0781 Civil engineering; Landscape counseling & planning
Pr: James H Littlejohn
VP: Jeffrey D Heinze
IT Man: Mark Myers
Snr PM: Chuck Downham

D-U-N-S 00-582-4297
LITTLEJOHN GRAIN INC (IL)
8801 E Us Hwy 40, Martinsville, IL 62442
Tel (217) 382-4158 *Founded/Ownrshp* 1945, 1986
Sales 61.9MM *EMP* 69
Accts Clifton Gunderson Llp Dixon
SIC 5153 5191 Grain elevators; Fertilizer & fertilizer materials; Feed; Grain elevators; Fertilizer & fertilizer materials
Pr: Kent O Littlejohn
**Treas:* Brenda K Littlejohn
**VP:* Greg Littlejohn

D-U-N-S 00-605-8242
LITTLER DIECAST CORP
500 W Walnut St, Albany, IN 47320-1028
Tel (765) 789-4456 *Founded/Ownrshp* 1954, 1977
Sales 23.4MM^E *EMP* 90
SIC 3363 5084 Aluminum die-castings; Machinists' precision measuring tools
Pr: John D Littler
**Sec:* Douglas R Littler
**VP:* Mark D Littler
**VP:* Marie Vaughn

D-U-N-S 07-875-8919
LITTLER MENDELSON PC
650 California St Fl 20, San Francisco, CA 94108-2693
Tel (415) 433-1940 *Founded/Ownrshp* 1956
Sales 311.9MM^E *EMP* 1,500
SIC 8111 General practice law office; General practice law office
CEO: Thomas J Bender
**Ch Bd:* Robert Millman
Pr: Sandy McNeely
**Pr:* Marko Mrkonich
Pr: Sarah Rachal
CFO: Mat Rosswood
**Treas:* Steven R Mc Cown
VP: Scott Hultsman
Off Admin: Melissa Machado
CIO: Jennifer Dunn
CTO: Apo Hagopian
Board of Directors: Wesley J Fastiff, Wendy Wallner

D-U-N-S 01-058-2633
LITTLESTOWN AREA SCHOOL DISTRICT
162 Newark St, Littlestown, PA 17340-1208
Tel (717) 334-7094 *Founded/Ownrshp* 1970
Sales 22.4MM^E *EMP* 300
Accts Greenawalt & Company Pc Cpa
SIC 8211 Public elementary school; Public junior high school; Public senior high school; Public elementary school; Public junior high school; Public senior high school
**Pr:* John L Warhime Jr
**Treas:* Thomas Taholsky
Dir Sec: Jeffrey Laux
MIS Dir: Lori Stollar

D-U-N-S 01-892-9653 IMP
LITTLETON COIN CO LLC (NH)
1309 Mount Eustis Rd, Littleton, NH 03561-3735
Tel (800) 645-3122 *Founded/Ownrshp* 1945, 1991
Sales 67.7MM^E *EMP* 325
SIC 5961 Coins, mail order; Coins, mail order
Pr: David M Sundman
**CFO:* Edward Hennessey
Opers Mgr: Yvonne Burlock
Mktg Mgr: Kierstin Egan

D-U-N-S 00-290-1684
LITTLETON ELEMENTARY SCHOOL DISTRICT 65
1600 S 107th Ave, Avondale, AZ 85323-2209
Tel (623) 478-5600 *Founded/Ownrshp* 1920
Sales 38.1MM^E *EMP* 600
SIC 8211 Elementary school; Elementary school
Pr Dir: Sue Garrison
HC Dir: Tina Kauffmann

LITTLETON GROUP
See HUEYT LITTLETON CLAIMS SERVICE OF WEST TEXAS INC

D-U-N-S 06-990-5735
LITTLETON HOSPITAL ASSOCIATION
LITTLETON REGIONAL HOSPITAL
600 Saint Johnsbury Rd, Littleton, NH 03561-3442
Tel (603) 444-9000 *Founded/Ownrshp* 1906
Sales 81.7MM *EMP* 320
SIC 8062 General medical & surgical hospitals; General medical & surgical hospitals
CEO: Warren K West
COO: Peter Wright
CFO: Nick Braccino
CFO: Bob Fotter
Ofcr: Linda Gilmore
Dir Lab: Kim Miller
Dir Rad: Rob Mach
Dir Pat Ac: Ron Ness
Snr Ntwrk: Eric Perkins
Dir IT: Cindy Richards
Dir IT: Scott Vachon

LITTLETON LUMBER
See CONCORD LUMBER CORP

D-U-N-S 04-070-6798
LITTLETON PUBLIC SCHOOLS FOUNDATION
5776 S Crocker St, Littleton, CO 80120-2012
Tel (303) 347-3478 *Founded/Ownrshp* 1930
Sales 824.1M^E *EMP* 402
Accts Jds Professional Group Englew
SIC 8211 Public elementary & secondary schools; Public elementary & secondary schools
Pr: Mary McGlone
CFO: Scott Myers
**Treas:* Matt Dell
Bd of Dir: Sue Chandler
VP: Lindsey Thomas
Admn Mgr: Amber Prescott
IT Man: Peggy Hester
Netwrk Mgr: Mike Zehner
Pr Dir: Diane Leiker
Pr Dir: Mark Lindstone
Psych: Carla C Baca

LITTLETON REGIONAL HOSPITAL
See LITTLETON HOSPITAL ASSOCIATION

D-U-N-S 19-160-5237
LITTON LOAN SERVICING LP
4828 Loop Central Dr # 104, Houston, TX 77081-2193
Tel (713) 960-9676 Founded/Ownrshp 2011
Sales NA EMP 1,190
SIC 6162

D-U-N-S 05-874-2453
LITURGICAL PUBLICATIONS INC
2875 S James Dr, New Berlin, WI 53151-3667
Tel (262) 785-1188 Founded/Ownrshp 1972
Sales 53.1MM^E EMP 300
SIC 2721

D-U-N-S 07-800-6681
LITZENBERG MEMORIAL COUNTY HOSPITAL
MERRICK COUNTY
1715 26th St, Central City, NE 68826-9501
Tel (308) 946-3015 Founded/Ownrshp 1959
Sales 20.0MM^E EMP 159
SIC 8062 General medical & surgical hospitals
Ch: Darrell Widman
Pr: Jeanette Kleve
*CEO: Julie Murray
Ofcr: Helen Foulk
Cmptr Lab: Jean Kennedy
IT Man: Joyce Rodriguez
Nrsg Dir: Diane Schoch
Phys Thrpy: Rob Schnitzler

LIUNA
See LABORERS INTERNATIONAL UNION OF NORTH AMERICA

D-U-N-S 12-358-2111
LIVA DISTRIBUTORS INC
3173 Iris Ave, San Diego, CA 92173-1234
Tel (619) 423-9997 Founded/Ownrshp 1998
Sales 20.8MM^E EMP 30
SIC 5141 5147 Groceries, general line; Meats & meat products
Pr: Amanda Limon

LIVE INTERNATIONAL
See ARTISAN PICTURES INC

D-U-N-S 61-415-2143
▲ LIVE NATION ENTERTAINMENT INC
9348 Civic Center Dr Lbby, Beverly Hills, CA 90210-3642
Tel (310) 867-7000 Founded/Ownrshp 2005
Sales 6.8MMM EMP 7,900
Tkr Sym LYV Exch NYS
SIC 7922 7389 7941 Entertainment promotion; Theatrical production services; Theatrical companies; Promoters of shows & exhibitions; Sports clubs, managers & promoters; Entertainment promotion; Theatrical production services; Theatrical companies; Promoters of shows & exhibitions; Sports clubs, managers & promoters
Pr: Michael Rapino
Ch Bd: Arthur Fogel
Pr: Ron Bension
Pr: Mark Campana
Pr: Morgan McGrath
Pr: John Reid
Pr: Alan Ridgeway
Pr: Bob Roux
Pr: Jared Smith
Pr: Russell Wallach
Pr: Mark Yovich
Pr: David Zedeck
COO: Joe Berchtold
COO: Jim Cornett
CFO: Chonda Chenoweth
CFO: Kathy Willard
Bd of Dir: Ariel Emanuel
Ofcr: Carrie Davis
Ex VP: John Hopmans
VP: Kelsey Hession
Board of Directors: Randall Mays, Mark Carleton, Mark Shapiro, Jonathan Dolgen, Ari Emanuel, Ted Enloe, Jeff Hinson, Jimmy Iovine, Peggy Johnson, Jim Kahan, Greg Maffei

D-U-N-S 80-676-9758 IMP
■ LIVE NATION MERCHANDISE INC
SIGNATURES SNI
(Suby of LIVE NATION ENTERTAINMENT INC) ★
2 Bryant St Fl 3, San Francisco, CA 94105-1641
Tel (415) 247-7400 Founded/Ownrshp 2002
Sales 50.5MM^E EMP 80
SIC 5199 Advertising specialties; Advertising specialties
Pr: Michael Rapino
Sr VP: Carl Walter
Sr VP: Pete Weber
VP: Rick Fish
Comm Man: Myles Silton

D-U-N-S 18-122-8891
LIVE NATION MUSIC GROUP TEXAS INC
2000 West Loop S Ste 1300, Houston, TX 77027-3512
Tel (713) 693-8152 Founded/Ownrshp 2005
Sales 6.4MMM EMP 250
Accts Ernst & Young Llp Los Angeles
SIC 7922 6512 Theatrical producers & services; Theater building, ownership & operation; Theatrical producers & services; Theater building, ownership & operation
CEO: Michael Rapino
Ex VP: Beckye Levin
*Sr VP: Michael Sanchez
*VP: David Cheadle
VP: Michael McGaw

D-U-N-S 00-819-0576
■ LIVE NATION WORLDWIDE INC
(Suby of LIVE NATION ENTERTAINMENT INC) ★
220 W 42nd St, New York, NY 10036-7200
Tel (917) 421-5100 Founded/Ownrshp 2007
Sales 147.6MM^E EMP 3,000
SIC 7922 Theatrical producers & services; Theatrical producers & services
Pr: Brian Becker
*CFO: Ed Stacey
*Ex VP: Steve Smith
*VP: Leeann Gliha
*Genl Couns: Dale Head

D-U-N-S 07-992-0050
LIVE OAK BANCSHARES INC (NC)
1741 Tiburon Dr, Wilmington, NC 28403-6244
Tel (910) 790-5867 Founded/Ownrshp 2008
Sales NA EMP 263^E
Tkr Sym LOB Exch NGS
SIC 6022 State commercial banks
Ch Bd: James S Mahan III
Pr: Neil L Underwood
CFO: S Brett Caines
V Ch Bd: William L Williams III
Ofcr: David G Lucht
Board of Directors: William H Cameron, Diane B Glossman, Glen F Hoffsis, Don W Jackson, Howard K Landis III, Jerald L Pullins

D-U-N-S 82-963-5999
LIVE OAK BANKING CO
1741 Tiburon Dr, Wilmington, NC 28403-6244
Tel (910) 790-5867 Founded/Ownrshp 2008
Sales NA EMP 30
SIC 6021 National commercial banks; National commercial banks
CEO: Chip Mahan
*Ch Bd: James S Mahan III
*Pr: David Lucht
*Pr: Neil L Underwood
CFO: Lawrence Brobst
CFO: Lawrence S Brobt
*CFO: Brett Caines
Chf Cred: Caroline Esmond
Mktg Dir: Micah Davis
Pr Mgr: Jessica Trichel

LIVE OAK ELEMENTARY
See CASTAIC UNION SCHOOL DISTRICT 130

LIVE OAK HOMES
See WMT HOUSING LLC

D-U-N-S 78-013-4276
■ LIVE OAK PERRY AND SOUTH GEORGIA RAILWAY CO
(Suby of NORFOLK SOUTHERN RAILWAY CO) ★
3 Commercial Pl, Norfolk, VA 23510-2108
Tel (757) 629-2600 Founded/Ownrshp 1991
Sales 19.2MM^E EMP 1,360^E
SIC 4011 Railroads, line-haul operating
Pr: Paul R Rudder

D-U-N-S 36-195-7207
LIVE WELL FINANCIAL INC
830 E Main St Ste 1000, Richmond, VA 23219-2700
Tel (804) 201-4409 Founded/Ownrshp 2005
Sales NA EMP 400
SIC 6162 Mortgage companies, urban; Mortgage companies, urban
Pr: Michael C Hild
CFO: Eric Rohr
*VP: Donna Edwards
*VP: Lisa Girardi
*VP: Brett Ludden

LIVE-RITE PRODUCTS
See CONTINENTAL VITAMIN CO INC

D-U-N-S 15-984-9327 IMP/EXP
LIVEDO USA INC
(Suby of LIVEDO CORPORATION)
4925 Livedo Dr, Wilson, NC 27893-9403
Tel (252) 237-1373 Founded/Ownrshp 2004
Sales 24.0MM^E EMP 55
SIC 2676 Sanitary paper products
Pr: Tadashi Hoshikawa
*VP: Keiichi Ishikawa
QA Dir: Leslie Williams

D-U-N-S 05-963-2170
LIVEFYRE INC
360 3rd St Ste 700, San Francisco, CA 94107-2164
Tel (415) 800-0900 Founded/Ownrshp 2009
Sales 28.4MM^E EMP 105^E
SIC 7371 Computer software development
CEO: Jordan Kretchmer
Sr VP: Kenneth Grosso
Sr VP: David Rodriguez
Sr VP: Scott Sorochak
Sr VP: Nate Underwood
VP: Bruce Ableson
VP: Jonathan Carroll
VP: Jenna Langer
VP: Sankar Patel
VP: Colby Teller
Creative D: Michelle Haft
Dir Bus: Matt Cantieri

D-U-N-S 04-228-7912
LIVELY CADILLAC GMC CO INC
400 N Spur 63, Longview, TX 75601-5007
Tel (903) 757-6600 Founded/Ownrshp 1967
Sales 27.3MM^E EMP 65
SIC 5511 Automobiles, new & used; Automobiles, new & used
Pr: Gordon Lively Jr
*Pr: Gordon Lively Sr
Off Mgr: Calva James
Sales Asso: Ron Navara

D-U-N-S 17-555-6158
LIVELY DISTRIBUTING INC
2633 W Cypress St, Phoenix, AZ 85009-2697
Tel (602) 253-8990 Founded/Ownrshp 1973
Sales 22.0MM EMP 40
SIC 5143 5141 Dairy products, except dried or canned; Groceries, general line
Pr: Bernard W Lively
*VP: Jody Lively
IT Man: Janet Jones

D-U-N-S 02-675-3426
LIVENGOOD FEEDS INC
300 N Colorado St, Lockhart, TX 78644-2162
Tel (512) 398-2351 Founded/Ownrshp 1971
Sales 32.3MM^E EMP 55
SIC 5191 5621 2048 Feed; Fertilizer & fertilizer materials; Insecticides; Seeds: field, garden & flower; Ready-to-wear apparel, women's; Prepared feeds
Pr: Burt R Livengood
*VP: Gail Livengood

D-U-N-S 02-415-1403
LIVEONNY INC (NY)
460 W 34th St Fl 15, New York, NY 10001-2320
Tel (646) 291-4444 Founded/Ownrshp 2009
Sales 32.0MM^E EMP 2
SIC 8099 Medical services organization; Medical services organization
CEO: Helen Irving
*Prin: Jim Aranda

D-U-N-S 06-517-7763
LIVEOPS INC
555 Twin Dolphin Dr # 400, Redwood City, CA 94065-2132
Tel (650) 453-2700 Founded/Ownrshp 2003
Sales 73.2MM^E EMP 300^E
SIC 7363 Help supply services; Help supply services
CEO: Vasili Triant
Pr: Marty Beard
Pr: Suresh Duddi
Pr: Mark Westover
CFO: Bill Slakely
CFO: William Slakey
Sr Cor Off: Douglas Feirstein
Chf Mktg O: Ann Sung Ruckstuhl
Ex VP: Murray Demo
Ex VP: Olivier Gachot
Ex VP: Jeremy King
Sr VP: Steven Griset
Sr VP: Karl Gustafson
Sr VP: Karl W Gustafson
Sr VP: Marie Amoruso Jackson
Sr VP: Norma Jean Lane
Sr VP: Sanjay Mathur
Sr VP: Terry Murphy
Sr VP: John Nai
Sr VP: Aaron Ridgway
Sr VP: Jeff Thompson
Board of Directors: James Beer, RT Bradley, Steve Capelli, Geoff Eisenberg, Robert Enslin, Joseph F Hoffman, Jeffrey D Jordan

D-U-N-S 94-615-9233
▲ LIVEPERSON INC
475 10th Ave Fl 5, New York, NY 10018-9722
Tel (212) 609-4200 Founded/Ownrshp 1995
Sales 209.9MM EMP 1,058^E
Tkr Sym LPSN Exch NAS
SIC 7371 4813 Computer software development & applications; ; Computer software development & applications;
Ch Bd: Robert P Locascio
CFO: Daniel R Murphy
Ex VP: Dustin Dean
Ex VP: Monica L Greenberg
Ex VP: Peter K Phillips
Sr VP: Daryl Carlough
Sr VP: Michael Montour
Sr VP: Jeremy Sokolic
Sr VP: Jackson L Wilson
Exec: Jason Roberts
Dir Bus: Brad Bernstein
Board of Directors: Peter Block, Kevin C Lavan, David Vaskevitch, William G Wesemann

D-U-N-S 07-959-4591
LIVER AND PANCREAS CENTER UNIVERSITY OF MARYLAND ST JOSEPH MEDICAL CENTER
HODES LIVER & PANCREAS CENTER
(Suby of UNIVERSITY MD ST JSEPH MED CTR) ★
7505 Osler Dr Ste 303, Towson, MD 21204-7738
Tel (410) 427-2024 Founded/Ownrshp 2014
Sales 199.6M^E EMP 839^E
SIC 8062 Hospital, medical school affiliation
Prin: Deborah Hartley

LIVERMORE HONDA
See ARBM INC

LIVERMORE VALLEY CHARTER SCHL
See TRI-VALLEY LEARNING CORP

D-U-N-S 07-015-9694
LIVERMORE VALLEY JOINT UNIFIED SCHOOL DISTRICT
NORTH QUINCY
685 E Jack London Blvd, Livermore, CA 94551-1855
Tel (925) 606-3200 Founded/Ownrshp 1966
Sales 84.8MM^E EMP 1,600
Accts Nigro & Nigro Pc Marrieta Ca
SIC 8211 Public senior high school; Public junior high school; Public elementary school; Public adult education school; Public senior high school; Public junior high school; Public elementary school; Public adult education school
*CEO: Anders W Lundberg
Bd of Dir: Julie Elfin

LIVERNOIS MOTORSPORTS
See LIVERNOIS VEHICLE DEVELOPMENT LLC

D-U-N-S 83-217-1024
LIVERNOIS VEHICLE DEVELOPMENT LLC
LIVERNOIS MOTORSPORTS
2500 S Gulley Rd, Dearborn Heights, MI 48125-1152
Tel (313) 561-5500 Founded/Ownrshp 2000
Sales 36.8MM^E EMP 245
SIC 8711 Engineering services; Engineering services
CEO: Norma Wallis
Mktg Dir: Rachel Tousignant
Sales Asso: Miles Potter

D-U-N-S 05-098-2958
LIVERPOOL CENTRAL SCHOOL DISTRICT
195 Blackberry Rd, Liverpool, NY 13090-3047
Tel (315) 622-7148 Founded/Ownrshp 1950
Sales 146.5MM EMP 1,300
Accts Ciaschi Dietershagen Little
SIC 8211 Public elementary school; Public junior high school; Public senior high school; Public elementary school; Public junior high school; Public senior high school
*Ex Dir: Katherine Phillips
Dir Sec: Michael McCarthy
Dir IT: Tillotson Lind
IT Man: James Chrisfield
Netwrk Mgr: Ronald Richardson
Schl Brd P: Patricia Rosier

D-U-N-S 05-116-3434
LIVERPOOL ENTERPRISES INC
10924 Van Jacksn Rd # 306, San Antonio, TX 78230-2559
Tel (210) 696-6072 Founded/Ownrshp 1971
Sales 35.4MM^E EMP 70
SIC 5065 Electronic parts & equipment; Electronic parts & equipment
Pr: Leonard Holzman
VP: Lazaro Geidishman

D-U-N-S 79-132-0984 IMP
LIVESCRIBE INC
7677 Oakport St Ste 1200, Oakland, CA 94621-1975
Tel (510) 777-0071 Founded/Ownrshp 2007
Sales 42.2MM^E EMP 50
SIC 5045 Computer software
CEO: Gilles Bouchard
*CFO: Ken Cucarola
*CFO: Paul Machle
Ex VP: Sasha Pesic
*Sr VP: Brett Halle
VP: Marc Thomas
Creative D: Chris Cast
Snr Sftwr: Gurmeet Kalra
Snr Sftwr: Marcel Weiher
Dir IT: John Shearer
Mktg Mgr: Summer Nashif

LIVESTOCK FEDERATION
See FEDERACION DE ASOCIACIONES PECUARIAS DE PUERTO RICO INC

D-U-N-S 10-420-8496
LIVESTOCK NUTRITION CENTER LLC
LNC
5860 Ridgeway Center Pkwy, Memphis, TN 38120-4030
Tel (901) 763-7055 Founded/Ownrshp 2006
Sales 25.7MM^E EMP 35^E
SIC 0751 Cattle services
Pr: Baer Ben
COO: Andy Gaines

D-U-N-S 11-038-2731
LIVESTRONG FOUNDATION
2201 E 6th St, Austin, TX 78702-3456
Tel (512) 236-8820 Founded/Ownrshp 1997
Sales 23.3MM^E EMP 50
SIC 8641

D-U-N-S 13-588-0388
LIVETV LLC
(Suby of THALES HOLDING CORP) ★
700 S Babcock St, Melbourne, FL 32901-1406
Tel (321) 308-3900 Founded/Ownrshp 2014
Sales 72.5MM^E EMP 497^E
SIC 8748 3663 3651 Telecommunications consultant; Television broadcasting & communications equipment; Television receiving sets; Music distribution apparatus; Telecommunications consultant; Television broadcasting & communications equipment; Television receiving sets; Music distribution apparatus
CEO: Nate Quigley
Pr: Bill Clifton
Pr: Glenn Latta
COO: Christopher L Collins
Bd of Dir: Jeff Frisco
VP: Karen Hawkins
VP: Jason Lundstrom
Exec: Ashley Rooks
Prgrm Mgr: Livio Campos
Prgrm Mgr: Patty Foy
Prgrm Mgr: Nancy Walker

D-U-N-S 61-489-9305
LIVEVOX INC
450 Sansome St Fl 9, San Francisco, CA 94111-3317
Tel (415) 671-6000 Founded/Ownrshp 1998
Sales 34.6MM^E EMP 150^E
SIC 8748 Telecommunications consultant; Telecommunications consultant
CEO: Louis Summe
COO: Larry Siegel
CFO: Michael Leraris
VP: Chris Pigott
VP: Rich Riley
QA Dir: Julian Jaramillo
Board of Directors: C Douglas Bauer

D-U-N-S 10-116-4879
LIVEWIRE MOBILE INC
55 Merrick Way Ste 220, Coral Gables, FL 33134-5126
Tel (978) 742-3100 Founded/Ownrshp 1983
Sales 33.1MM^E EMP 168^E
SIC 7373 Computer integrated systems design; Computer integrated systems design
Pr: Matthew Stecker
Sr VP: Steve Gladstone
VP: Paul J Deeley
VP: Eugene J Didonato
VP: Eugene Didonato
VP: Harold Klett
VP: Charles Lynam
VP: Keith Maffiore
VP: Timothy Walsh
Exec: Dale Reed
Assoc Dir: Lauri Cagnassola
Board of Directors: Patrick Bennett, Thomas Dusenberry, Alan Howe, W Frank King, Robert M Pons, Pamela D A Reeve, Jill C Thoerle

D-U-N-S 17-605-1662
▲ LIVEWORLD INC
4340 Stevens Creek Blvd, San Jose, CA 95129-1147
Tel (408) 564-6286 Founded/Ownrshp 1996
Sales 26.6MM^E EMP 73^E
Accts Stonefield Josephson Inc Sa
Tkr Sym LVWD Exch OTO
SIC 4813
CEO: Peter H Friedman

CFO: David Houston
Ex VP: Chris N Christensen
Ex VP: Jenna Woodul
VP: Martin Bishop
VP: Mike Dosik
Sftwr Eng: Anu Shah
VP Mktg: Jason Kapler
Sls Dir: Leanna Schultz
Mktg Mgr: Gregg Turek
Snr Mgr: Sonia Hill
Board of Directors: Jeffrey Hayzlett

D-U-N-S 08-648-0865
LIVHOME INC
5670 Wilshire Blvd # 500, Los Angeles, CA 90036-5682
Tel (323) 933-5880 *Founded/Ownrshp* 1999
Sales 54.6MM^E *EMP* 1,329
SIC 8322 Geriatric social service; Geriatric social service
Ch Bd: Mike Nicholson
CFO: Danny Gampe
**Ofcr:* Cody D Legler
VP: Melissa Beck-Hamidi
VP: Maureen Kehan
MIS Dir: Terrance Scotton

LIVIN INTERACTIVE
See WAS SERVICES LLC

D-U-N-S 04-843-9731
LIVING BRANCHES
275 Dock Dr, Lansdale, PA 19446-6232
Tel (215) 368-4438 *Founded/Ownrshp* 1978
Sales 2.7MM *EMP* 640^E
Accts Parentebeard Llc Philadelphia
SIC 6513 8052 8051 Retirement hotel operation; Personal care facility; Skilled nursing care facilities; Retirement hotel operation; Personal care facility; Skilled nursing care facilities
Pr: Edward D Brubaker
**CFO:* Steven Myers
Ofcr: Melissa Groff
Dir Risk M: Bruce Alder
Sales Asso: Amanda Lesuer

D-U-N-S 96-961-4440
LIVING CITIES INC
NATIONAL COMMUNITY DEVELOPMENT
1040 Avenue Of The Americ, New York, NY 10018-3717
Tel (646) 442-2200 *Founded/Ownrshp* 2011
Sales 27.1MM *EMP* 26
Accts Bdo Usa Llp Bethesda Md
SIC 8699 Charitable organization
Pr: Ben Hecht

D-U-N-S 06-524-2674 IMP
LIVING DIRECT INC
COMPACTAPPLIANCE.COM
500 N Capital Of Texa, Austin, TX 78746-3302
Tel (512) 467-7170 *Founded/Ownrshp* 2001
Sales 41.4MM^E *EMP* 116^E
SIC 5963 Appliance sales, house-to-house
Pr: Richard Lundbom
**Pr:* Scott Madison
**Pr:* Jason Roussos
**COO:* Drew Leakey
**CFO:* Danny Wilbanks
**VP:* Dave Jenkins
Manager: Chris Balderas
Mktg Mgr: Fred Hopkins
Mktg Mgr: Titus Lam
Sls Mgr: Ryan Pontius

LIVING DOLL
See LDLA CLOTHING LLC

LIVING EARTH
See LETCO GROUP LLC

LIVING ESSENTIALS
See INNOVATION VENTURES LLC

LIVING HOPE PHYSIOTHERAPY
See PHYSIOTHERAPY ASSOCIATES INC

D-U-N-S 04-539-9735
LIVING INDEPENDENTLY FOR ELDERLY
LIFE PITTSBURGH INC
681 Andersen Dr Ste 550, Pittsburgh, PA 15220-2766
Tel (412) 388-8042 *Founded/Ownrshp* 1998
Sales 42.0MM *EMP* 40
SIC 8051 Skilled nursing care facilities
Ex Dir: Joann Gago
COO: Bridget Hartnett

D-U-N-S 17-635-8398
LIVING INNOVATIONS SUPPORT SERVICES INC
273 Locust St 2c, Dover, NH 03820-4009
Tel (603) 422-7308 *Founded/Ownrshp* 1997
Sales 17.9MM^E *EMP* 360
SIC 8322 Individual & family services; Association for the handicapped; Individual & family services; Association for the handicapped
Pr: Neal Ouellett

D-U-N-S 04-116-1999
LIVING INTENTIONALLY FOR EXCELLENCE LLLP LIMITED PARTNERSHIP
LIFE
200 Commonwealth Ct # 200, Cary, NC 27511-2431
Tel (810) 600-3425 *Founded/Ownrshp* 2011
Sales 50.0MM *EMP* 33
SIC 2759 Publication printing; Publication printing
Pt: Robert Hallstrand

D-U-N-S 04-717-9072
LIVING RESOURCES CORP
300 Washington Avenue Ext, Albany, NY 12203-7303
Tel (518) 218-0000 *Founded/Ownrshp* 1974
Sales 33.3MM *EMP* 680
SIC 8361 8322 Home for the mentally retarded; Individual & family services; Home for the mentally retarded; Individual & family services
CEO: Fredrick W Erlich
IT Man: Bonnie Rush

D-U-N-S 02-250-0606
LIVING SOCIAL INC
1445 New York Ave Nw # 200, Washington, DC 20005-2157
Tel (877) 521-4191 *Founded/Ownrshp* 2007
Sales 808.0MM^E *EMP* 4,900^E
SIC 5961 ;
Pr: Gautam Thakar
**Treas:* Dan Frederico
Sr VP: Nick Macey
Sr VP: Mitch Spolan
Exec: Jessica Lipschutz
Exec: Carly Webb
Exec: Alexandria Whaley
**Prin:* Timothy O'Shaughnessy
Genl Mgr: Travis Connell
Genl Mgr: Michael Moore
Genl Mgr: David Strauss
Board of Directors: Paul Guyardo

D-U-N-S 12-966-7825 IMP
LIVING SPACES FURNITURE LLC
14501 Artesia Blvd, La Mirada, CA 90638-5805
Tel (714) 523-2000 *Founded/Ownrshp* 2003
Sales 78.6MM^E *EMP* 200^E
SIC 5712 5021 Furniture stores; Furniture; Furniture stores; Furniture
VP: Rene Interiano
VP: George Kavorkian
VP: Luke Parker
Exec: Ryan Nagy
Genl Mgr: Jeff Seabrook
Software D: Kylan Swank
Opers Mgr: Jay Martinez

LIVING STONE PRECIOUS METALS
See LSPM LLC

D-U-N-S 07-926-6427
LIVING WATER INTEGRA TRADE INC
1000 Jorie Blvd Ste 365, Oak Brook, IL 60523-4512
Tel (630) 560-4521 *Founded/Ownrshp* 2013
Sales 80.0MM^E *EMP* 5
SIC 6221 Commodity traders, contracts; Commodity traders, contracts
Pr: Zheliang Wang

D-U-N-S 07-717-7918 IMP
LIVING WATER INTERNATIONAL
4001 Greenbriar Dr # 200, Stafford, TX 77477-4029
Tel (281) 207-7800 *Founded/Ownrshp* 1990
Sales 25.2MM *EMP* 54
Accts Blazek & Vettering Houston T
SIC 1781 Water well drilling; Water well drilling
CEO: Mike Mantel
**Pr:* Jerry Wiles
**Treas:* Richard Lewis
**VP:* Emison Lewis
**Ex Dir:* Gary Evans

LIVINGSTON & HAVEN
See PARK HYDE PARTNERS INC

D-U-N-S 83-104-2820
LIVINGSTON & HAVEN LLC
AEG INTERNATIONAL
(*Suby of* LIVINGSTON & HAVEN) ★
11529 Wilmar Blvd, Charlotte, NC 28273-6448
Tel (704) 588-3670 *Founded/Ownrshp* 1947
Sales 29.1MM^E *EMP* 180
SIC 5084 3594 4911 Hydraulic systems equipment & supplies; Fluid power pumps & motors; Hydraulic systems equipment & supplies; Fluid power pumps & motors;
CEO: Clifton B Vann III
**Pr:* Clifton B Vann IV
**Treas:* Anne Q Woody
Manager: Rich Arnold

D-U-N-S 05-489-4985
LIVINGSTON BOARD OF EDUCATION (INC)
LIVINGSTON PUBLIC SCHOOL DST
11 Foxcroft Dr, Livingston, NJ 07039-2699
Tel (973) 535-8000 *Founded/Ownrshp* 1894
Sales 48.8MM^E *EMP* 900
SIC 8211 9111 Public elementary & secondary schools; Mayors' offices; Public elementary & secondary schools; Mayors' offices
**Pr:* Ronnie Spring
**VP:* Barry Funt
**Prin:* Pam Chirls
Prin: Deborah Cook
**Prin:* David Jasin
Prin: Bernadette Pilchman
Prin: Jeffrey Truppo
**Prin:* Leslie Winograd
IT Man: Kathleen Pizzano

D-U-N-S 07-560-1773
LIVINGSTON COUNTY
844 W Lincoln St, Pontiac, IL 61764-2325
Tel (815) 844-6378 *Founded/Ownrshp* 1837
Sales NA *EMP* 300
Accts Clifton Larson Allen Llp Peor
SIC 9111 County supervisors' & executives' offices; ; County supervisors' & executives' offices;
Ch Bd: John T Jacobson
**Ch Bd:* Jeanne Wrapp

D-U-N-S 10-003-6854
LIVINGSTON EDUCATIONAL SERVICE AGENCY
1425 W Grand River Ave, Howell, MI 48843-1916
Tel (517) 546-5550 *Founded/Ownrshp* 1962
Sales 23.9MM^E *EMP* 400
SIC 8211 Specialty education; Specialty education

D-U-N-S 05-711-5722
LIVINGSTON HEALTH CARE SYSTEM INC
111 Clara Barton St, Dansville, NY 14437-9503
Tel (585) 335-6001 *Founded/Ownrshp* 1993
Sales 10.3MM^E *EMP* 505
SIC 8011 Clinic, operated by physicians; Clinic, operated by physicians
Pr: James Wissler
**VP:* Jay Maslyn

D-U-N-S 09-870-3820
LIVINGSTON HEALTHCARE
LIVINGSTON MEMORIAL HOSPITAL
504 S 13th St, Livingston, MT 59047-3727
Tel (406) 222-3541 *Founded/Ownrshp* 1944
Sales 33.0MM *EMP* 320
SIC 8062 8082 General medical & surgical hospitals; Home health care services; General medical & surgical hospitals; Home health care services
CEO: Bren Lowe
CFO: Ryan Speas
**Treas:* Larry Blakely
Dir Rad: Laura Caes
Dir Rx: Deb Anczak
Dir Rx: Laine Loberg
Comm Man: Rebekah Stoner
Off Mgr: Heather Chavez
Dir IT: Jody Duron
IT Man: Mark Figelski
Sfty Dirs: Lori Goodman

D-U-N-S 10-007-5514
LIVINGSTON INDEPENDENT SCHOOL DISTRICT
1412 S Houston Ave, Livingston, TX 77351-4212
Tel (936) 328-2100 *Founded/Ownrshp* 1920
Sales 38.7MM^E *EMP* 630
SIC 8211 Public elementary & secondary schools; High school, junior or senior; Public elementary & secondary schools; High school, junior or senior
Bd of Dir: Henry Ager
Bd of Dir: Jami Alexander
Bd of Dir: Stephanie Bond
Bd of Dir: Marion Burden
Bd of Dir: Denise David
Bd of Dir: Jettie Dewalt
Bd of Dir: Sarah Dickens
Bd of Dir: Deana Evans
Bd of Dir: Linda Harris
Bd of Dir: Debra Jones
Bd of Dir: Chad Lilley
Bd of Dir: Jana McLendon
Bd of Dir: Shelly Moore
Bd of Dir: Karen Morris
Bd of Dir: Tracy Nettles
Bd of Dir: Mylinda Proctor
Bd of Dir: Lucy Puntes
Bd of Dir: Angela Stanley
Bd of Dir: Viki Stifflemire
Bd of Dir: Norris Taff
Bd of Dir: Marilyn Taylor

D-U-N-S 00-513-3874
LIVINGSTON INTERNATIONAL INC
(*Suby of* LIVINGSTON INTERNATIONAL INC)
670 Young St, Tonawanda, NY 14150-4103
Tel (716) 692-3100 *Founded/Ownrshp* 1945, 2013
Sales 178.1MM^E *EMP* 900
SIC 4731 Customhouse brokers; Customhouse brokers
CEO: Steven C Preston
**Pr:* Roy Coburn
**Pr:* Peter Luit
**CFO:* Chris McMullen
**Sr VP:* Victor Dsouza
**VP:* Wendy Archambault
**VP:* Cora Di Pietro
**VP:* Stephane Ethier

D-U-N-S 02-416-0452
LIVINGSTON INTERNATIONAL INC
(*Suby of* LIVINGSTON INTERNATIONAL INC)
150 E Pierce Rd Ste 500, Itasca, IL 60143-1228
Tel (630) 766-0202 *Founded/Ownrshp* 1986
Sales 90.8MM^E *EMP* 389^E
SIC 7389 Brokers' services
CEO: Steve Preston
**Pr:* Roy Coburn
Pr: Matt Goodman
**Pr:* Christopher Logan
**CFO:* Chris McMullen
**CFO:* Sharon Sritong
**Ofcr:* Craig E Conway
**Sr VP:* Victor Dsouza
**VP:* Wendy Archambault
**VP:* Stephane Ethier
**VP:* Bob Perkins
**VP:* David Schulingkamp
**VP:* Catherine Townsend

D-U-N-S 79-282-6687
■ **LIVINGSTON INTERNATIONAL TECHNOLOGY SERVICES CORP**
JPMORGAN CHASE VASTERA INC.
(*Suby of* JPMORGAN CHASE BANK NATIONAL ASSOCIATION) ★
45025 Aviation Dr Ste 200, Dulles, VA 20166-7526
Tel (703) 661-9006 *Founded/Ownrshp* 2005
Sales 35.0MM^E *EMP* 590
Accts Kpmg Llp Mclean Virginia
SIC 7373 7379 Systems software development services; Computer related consulting services; Systems software development services; Computer related consulting services
Pr: Brian D Henderson
CFO: Chris Paton
VP: Gregory Stock
VP: Jonathan Vaughters
VP: George Weise
VP: Ravin Yadav
Exec: Jane Derrick
Mng Dir: Gerardo Duran

D-U-N-S 16-832-2720
LIVINGSTON LENDING LLC
120 W Grand River Ave, Brighton, MI 48116-1650
Tel (810) 229-6669 *Founded/Ownrshp* 2004
Sales NA *EMP* 10
SIC 6163 Loan brokers; Loan brokers
Off Mgr: Kim Bullinger

D-U-N-S 17-776-9924
LIVINGSTON MACHINERY CO
5201 S Highway 81, Chickasha, OK 73018-9613
Tel (405) 224-5056 *Founded/Ownrshp* 1987
Sales 88.7MM *EMP* 127
SIC 5083 5999 7699 5261 Agricultural machinery; Farm equipment parts & supplies; Farm machinery; Agricultural equipment repair services; Lawnmowers & tractors; Agricultural machinery; Farm equipment parts & supplies; Farm machinery; Agricultural equipment repair services; Lawnmowers & tractors
Pr: Earl Livingston
**COO:* Shawn Skaggs
IT Man: Jeremy Owens
IT Man: Mark Stephens
Sls Dir: Michael Boyd

LIVINGSTON MEMORIAL HOSPITAL
See LIVINGSTON HEALTHCARE

LIVINGSTON MEMORIAL VISITING N
See LIVINGSTON MEMORIAL VNA HEALTH CORP

D-U-N-S 79-118-8071
LIVINGSTON MEMORIAL VNA HEALTH CORP
LIVINGSTON MEMORIAL VISITING N
1996 Eastman Ave Ste 101, Ventura, CA 93003-5768
Tel (805) 642-0239 *Founded/Ownrshp* 1947
Sales 16.6MM *EMP* 292
Accts Kellogg & Andelson Accountancy
SIC 8741 8082 Hospital management; Nursing & personal care facility management; Home health care services; Hospital management; Nursing & personal care facility management; Home health care services
Pr: Lanyard K Dial MD
**Ch Bd:* Charles Hair MD
**Pr:* Judy Hecox
**Treas:* Jeffrey Paul
Dir Soc: Stephanie Montenegro
Off Mgr: Janis Hedden
Dir IT: Maddy Hazard

D-U-N-S 08-874-6458
LIVINGSTON OAKLAND HUMAN SERVICE AGENCY
196 Cesar E Chavez Ave, Pontiac, MI 48342-1094
Tel (248) 209-2600 *Founded/Ownrshp* 1964
Sales 25.7MM *EMP* 500
Accts Herbert & Associates Pc Roche
SIC 8399 8351 8322 Community action agency; Head start center, except in conjunction with school; Individual & family services; Community action agency; Head start center, except in conjunction with school; Individual & family services
CEO: Ronald B Borngesser
**CFO:* Natalie M Hargett
CFO: Brad Michaud
Assoc Dir: Linda Waal

D-U-N-S 09-490-9413
LIVINGSTON PARISH SCHOOL DISTRICT
13909 Florida Blvd, Livingston, LA 70754-6340
Tel (225) 686-7044 *Founded/Ownrshp* 2005
Sales 108.5MM^E *EMP* 2,404
SIC 8211 Public elementary & secondary schools; Public elementary & secondary schools
**Pr:* Keith Martin
Bd of Dir: James Watson
Exec: Lloyd Degeneres
Exec: Dennis Delee
Exec: Stacey Milton
Exec: Stacey Wise
Dir Sec: Wendy Gill
Admn Mgr: Patricia Davis
Cmptr Lab: Cindy Bergeron
Cmptr Lab: Heather Wheeler
IT Man: Lonnie Luce

D-U-N-S 08-938-2717
LIVINGSTON PIPE & TUBE INC
1612 Route 4, Staunton, IL 62088-4073
Tel (618) 635-8700 *Founded/Ownrshp* 1996
Sales 49.1MM^E *EMP* 60
SIC 5051 Pipe & tubing, steel; Pipe & tubing, steel
Pr: Ronald Mueller
VP: Randy Anderson
**VP:* Keith Klobnak

D-U-N-S 09-871-0908
LIVINGSTON PUBLIC SCHOOL DISTRICT
132 S B St, Livingston, MT 59047-2612
Tel (406) 222-0861 *Founded/Ownrshp* 1965
Sales 7.1MM^E *EMP* 300
SIC 8211 Public elementary school; Public junior high school; Public senior high school; Public special education school; Public elementary school; Public junior high school; Public senior high school; Public special education school
Schl Brd P: Ted Madden

LIVINGSTON PUBLIC SCHOOL DST
See LIVINGSTON BOARD OF EDUCATION (INC)

D-U-N-S 07-979-9148
LIVINGSTON PUBLIC SCHOOLS
11 Foxcroft Dr, Livingston, NJ 07039-2613
Tel (973) 535-8000 *Founded/Ownrshp* 2015
Sales 5.6MM^E *EMP* 553^E
SIC 8211 Public elementary & secondary schools
Pr Dir: Marilyn Lehren
Teacher Pr: Susan Burman

LIVINGSTON REGIONAL HOSPITAL
See HOSPITAL CORP OF SMITH AND OVERTON COUNTY

D-U-N-S 19-321-1638
LIVINGSTON UNION SCHOOL DISTRICT
922 B St, Livingston, CA 95334-1150
Tel (209) 394-5400 *Founded/Ownrshp* 1954
Sales 16.3MM^E *EMP* 300
SIC 8211 9411 Public elementary & secondary schools; Administration of educational programs; Public elementary & secondary schools; Administration of educational programs
Psych: Suzann Rockholt
Psych: Dennis Saller

D-U-N-S 79-116-5566
LIVINGSTON-WYOMING COUNTY CHAPTER NYSARC
(*Suby of* NYSARC INC) ★
18 Main St, Mount Morris, NY 14510-1036
Tel (585) 658-2828 *Founded/Ownrshp* 1998
Sales 11.7MM^E *EMP* 350
Accts Bonadio & Co Llp Pittsford
SIC 8331 8322 Sheltered workshop; Individual & family services; Sheltered workshop; Individual & family services
Ex Dir: Cindy Huether
Sfty Mgr: Penny Cartwright

D-U-N-S 07-106-3440
LIVINGSTONE COLLEGE INC
701 W Monroe St, Salisbury, NC 28144-5298
Tel (704) 216-6000 *Founded/Ownrshp* 1879
Sales 29.5MM *EMP* 140
Accts Murphy And Company Pc Conyers
SIC 8221 College, except junior; College, except junior
Pr: Jimmy R Jentine
Ofcr: William Moody
**VP:* Louis Chambers
VP: Herman Felton
VP: Lisa Geogory
VP: Orlando Lewis
**VP:* Peta Gaye Shaw
VP: Lelia Vickers
Brnch Mgr: Jerome Funderburk
MIS Dir: Rudolph Harrison
Pr Dir: Carl Locus

D-U-N-S 10-066-4069
LIVONIA CENTRAL SCHOOL DISTRICT INC
40 Spring St, Livonia, NY 14487-9703
Tel (585) 346-4000 *Founded/Ownrshp* 1938
Sales 32.1MM *EMP* 330
Accts Raymond F Wager Cpa Pc H
SIC 8211 Public elementary & secondary schools; Public elementary & secondary schools
**Pr:* Dave Woodruff
**Treas:* Kathy Morsch
**VP:* Andy Mattle

D-U-N-S 07-423-6662
LIVONIA PUBLIC SCHOOL DISTRICT
LIVONIA PUBLIC SCHOOLS
15125 Farmington Rd, Livonia, MI 48154-5413
Tel (734) 744-2500 *Founded/Ownrshp* 1918
Sales 190.4MM *EMP* 2,100
Accts Plante & Moran Pllc Auburn H
SIC 8211 Public elementary & secondary schools; Public senior high school; Public junior high school; Public elementary school; Public elementary & secondary schools; Public senior high school; Public junior high school; Public elementary school
Bd of Dir: Lynda L Scheel
Trst: Tammy Bonifield
IT Man: Steven Mezzadri
Netwrk Mgr: Jim Seay
Pr Dir: Mary Benoit
Pr Dir: Donna McDowell
Schl Brd P: Mark Johnson
Teacher Pr: Phil Francis
HC Dir: Jennifer Taiariol
Pgrm Dir: Jay Young

LIVONIA PUBLIC SCHOOLS
See LIVONIA PUBLIC SCHOOL DISTRICT

D-U-N-S 07-886-4640
LIZ BUNNY LLC
TOYOTA SERVICES
(*Suby of* TOYOTA FINANCIAL SERVICES) ★
16427 N Scottsdale Rd, Scottsdale, AZ 85254-8197
Tel (424) 558-6454 *Founded/Ownrshp* 2013
Sales 52.0MM *EMP* 45
SIC 5511 Automobiles, new & used; Automobiles, new & used

LIZ CLAIBORNE COATS
See LEVY GROUP INC

LIZ CLAIBORNE SWIMWEAR
See SWIMWEAR ANYWHERE INC

LIZARD INCENT EVENTS COMPANY
See NEW WORLD TRAVEL INC

D-U-N-S 08-637-3768
LIZARDS THICKET INC
1036 Market St, Columbia, SC 29201-4741
Tel (803) 799-5016 *Founded/Ownrshp* 1977
Sales 28.6MM *EMP* 600
Accts Jw Hunt And Company Llp Co
SIC 5812 American restaurant; American restaurant
Pr: Mark Williams
**Ch:* Robert E Williams Jr
**Sec:* Clayton Tapp
**VP:* James Lloyd Williams
Pr Mgr: Sara Krisnow

D-U-N-S 10-889-9501
LJ ASSOCIATES INC
L J AVIATION
125 Aviation Ln Ste 112, Latrobe, PA 15650-5101
Tel (724) 537-0520 *Founded/Ownrshp* 1980
Sales 20.1MM^E *EMP* 100
SIC 4522 Flying charter service
Pr: Edward M Kilkeary
CFO: Barb Gabelt
Sr VP: Shelly Duncan
Snr Mgr: Don Allen
Snr Mgr: Ted Moss

LJ MELODY
See CBRE CAPITAL MARKETS INC

D-U-N-S 82-841-4008
LJ ROGERS INC
7723 Oakwood Street Ext, Mebane, NC 27302-9293
Tel (919) 304-8782 *Founded/Ownrshp* 1987
Sales 25.1MM^E *EMP* 150^E
SIC 4213 4212 Investment holding companies, except banks; Trucking, except local; Local trucking, without storage
Pr: Ronald W Rogers
**VP:* Linwood J Rogers

D-U-N-S 01-183-3068
LJ ZUCCA INC
760 S Delsea Dr, Vineland, NJ 08360-4613
Tel (856) 692-7425 *Founded/Ownrshp* 1947
Sales 25.8MM^E *EMP* 70
SIC 5194 5145

D-U-N-S 96-803-3576
LJ/HAH HOLDINGS CORP
8 Sound Shore Dr Ste 303, Greenwich, CT 06830-7254
Tel (248) 553-5300 *Founded/Ownrshp* 2010
Sales 400.8MM^E *EMP* 3,168
SIC 2891 3714 Adhesives & sealants; Motor vehicle parts & accessories; Adhesives & sealants; Motor vehicle parts & accessories
CEO: Robert Depierre

D-U-N-S 02-547-5513
LJA ENGINEERING INC
LJA SURVEYING
2929 Briarpark Dr Ste 600, Houston, TX 77042-3768
Tel (713) 953-5200 *Founded/Ownrshp* 1997
Sales 77.4MM^E *EMP* 280
SIC 8711 Professional engineer; Professional engineer
Pr: Calvin T Ladner
Treas: Toff McCullough
**Sr VP:* Jeff P Collins
**Sr VP:* James E Moehlman
VP: Daniel Copps
VP: Alan McKee
Div Mgr: Steven Gonzales
Off Mgr: Debbie Hooker
VP Mktg: Barbara Foss
Mktg Mgr: Maria Lucio
Snr PM: Bob Devillier

LJA SURVEYING
See LJA ENGINEERING INC

D-U-N-S 08-474-9910
LJB INC
2500 Newmark Dr, Miamisburg, OH 45342-5407
Tel (937) 259-5000 *Founded/Ownrshp* 1966
Sales 25.7MM^E *EMP* 200
SIC 8712

D-U-N-S 05-992-8346
LJC DISMANTLING CORP
415a Meacham Ave, Elmont, NY 11003-3246
Tel (516) 488-3883 *Founded/Ownrshp* 1999
Sales 33.6MM *EMP* 15
Accts Jay Fox Island Park New York
SIC 1795 Demolition, buildings & other structures
Pr: Michael Ragno
**VP:* Benedict Versaci

LJG
See LA JOLLA GROUP INC

D-U-N-S 84-705-9169
LJK COMPANIES INC
TRAVELLIANCE
10225 Yellow Circle Dr # 200, Minnetonka, MN 55343-4668
Tel (952) 944-5462 *Founded/Ownrshp* 1989
Sales 29.4MM^E *EMP* 200
SIC 7011 Hotels; Hotels
CEO: Lisa Wing
**Ch Bd:* Larry Gehl
Pr: Andrew Claude
**Pr:* Dirk Draayer
**Ofcr:* Scott Dunlop
VP: Laxmi Govindan
VP: Brant Marklund
VP: Brant Merklind
Dir IT: Trent Boonis

D-U-N-S 96-945-0097
LJT & ASSOCIATES INC
9881 Brokenlnd Pkwy # 400, Columbia, MD 21046-3025
Tel (443) 283-2550 *Founded/Ownrshp* 1994
Sales 70.0MM *EMP* 432
SIC 8711 Business consulting; Engineering services
Pr: Robert Conrad
**CFO:* Andrew Fleischer
**Sr VP:* Jim Bishop

D-U-N-S 14-315-5369
LJT TENNESSEE LLC
(*Suby of* L JT) ★
600 River Terminal Rd, Chattanooga, TN 37406-1731
Tel (423) 697-7051 *Founded/Ownrshp* 2002
Sales 25.4MM^E *EMP* 100
SIC 3317 3498 Welded pipe & tubes; Boiler tubes (wrought); Fabricated pipe & fittings; Welded pipe & tubes; Boiler tubes (wrought); Fabricated pipe & fittings
Exec: Mike Ahrens

D-U-N-S 17-314-0356
LK COMSTOCK & CO INC
A RAILWORKS COMPANY
(*Suby of* RAILWORKS TRANSIT SYSTEMS INC) ★
83 Central Ave, Farmingdale, NY 11735-6901
Tel (631) 592-5867 *Founded/Ownrshp* 2003
Sales 33.8MM^E *EMP* 90
SIC 1731 Access control systems specialization
Pr: Ben D'Alessandro
**Pr:* Mark N Patterson
**CEO:* Jeffrey M Levy

LK INDUSTRIES
See KING LOAD MANUFACTURING CO

LK JORDAN & ASSOCIATES
See LKJ DELAWARE INC

D-U-N-S 62-788-6849
LKJ DELAWARE INC
LK JORDAN & ASSOCIATES
321 Texan Trl Ste 100, Corpus Christi, TX 78411-1825
Tel (361) 814-9700 *Founded/Ownrshp* 1990
Sales 24.4MM *EMP* 51
Accts Tranbarger & Company Llp C
SIC 7361 Employment agencies
Pr: Linda K Jordan
**VP:* Leslie Jordan
Snr Mgr: Nancy Collins

D-U-N-S 03-920-3534
LKL ASSOCIATES INC
3437 W Norris View Ln, West Jordan, UT 84088-8816
Tel (801) 225-3830 *Founded/Ownrshp* 1979
Sales 32.2MM^E *EMP* 80
SIC 5031 5251

D-U-N-S 13-920-1818 IMP
LKM FOODS INC
C W DUNNET & CO
3200 S Lawrence St, Philadelphia, PA 19148-5620
Tel (215) 271-9029 *Founded/Ownrshp* 1985
Sales 22.4MM^E *EMP* 26
SIC 5143 5149 5142 Cheese; Butter; Margarine; Packaged frozen goods
Pr: Ralph F Marta
**Sec:* Leonard D Kallman
Ex VP: Rosemary Fidacaro
**VP:* Kallman Leonard
IT Man: Marc Kallman

D-U-N-S 79-785-9832
LKN COMMUNICATIONS INC
ACN INC
134 Medical Park Rd # 105, Mooresville, NC 28117-8527
Tel (704) 260-3323 *Founded/Ownrshp* 1992
Sales 451.8MM^E *EMP* 1,110
SIC 4813 Local & long distance telephone communications;

LKQ AUTO PARTS OF SOUTH TEXAS
See LKQ BEST AUTOMOTIVE CORP

D-U-N-S 16-081-5247 IMP
■ **LKQ BEST AUTOMOTIVE CORP**
LKQ AUTO PARTS OF SOUTH TEXAS
(*Suby of* LKQ CORP) ★
1710 W Mount Houston Rd, Houston, TX 77038-3812
Tel (281) 820-9184 *Founded/Ownrshp* 1999
Sales 29.3MM^E *EMP* 105
SIC 5015 5531 Automotive supplies, used; Automotive parts; Automotive supplies, used; Automotive parts
CEO: Joseph M Holsten
**Sr VP:* Victor M Casini
**VP:* Michael S Clark
**VP:* John S Quinn

D-U-N-S 02-811-7104 IMP
▲ **LKQ CORP**
500 W Madison St Ste 2800, Chicago, IL 60661-2506
Tel (312) 621-1950 *Founded/Ownrshp* 1998
Sales 6.7MMM *EMP* 29,909^E
Accts Deloitte & Touche Llp Chicago
Tkr Sym LKQ *Exch* NGS
SIC 5093 5015 Automotive wrecking for scrap; Motor vehicle parts, used; Automotive parts & supplies, used; Automotive wrecking for scrap; Motor vehicle parts, used; Automotive parts & supplies, used
Pr: Robert L Wagman
Ch Bd: Joseph M Holsten
CEO: John S Quinn
CFO: Dominick P Zarcone
Chf Mktg O: Don Unrau
Ex VP: Mark Spears
Sr VP: Robert A Alberico
Sr VP: Victor M Casini
Sr VP: Steven Greenspan
VP: Michael S Clark
VP: Brandon Gee
Exec: Bradley Willen
Board of Directors: A Clinton Allen, Ronald G Foster, Robert M Hanser, Blythe J McGarvie, Paul M Meister, John F O'brien, William M Webster IV

D-U-N-S 01-749-4253
■ **LKQ TRIPLETTASAP INC**
TRIPLETT ASAP
(*Suby of* LKQ CORP) ★
1435 Triplett Blvd, Akron, OH 44306-3303
Tel (330) 733-6333 *Founded/Ownrshp* 1998
Sales 40.2MM^E *EMP* 160
SIC 5015 5521 Automotive parts & supplies, used; Used car dealers; Automotive parts & supplies, used; Used car dealers
Pr: Stuart Willen
VP: Brad Willen
VP: Todd Willen

D-U-N-S 78-498-0240 IMP
LL BEAN INTERNATIONAL
(*Suby of* L L BEAN INC) ★
15 Casco St, Freeport, ME 04033-0002
Tel (207) 865-4761 *Founded/Ownrshp* 2000
Sales 1.5MM *EMP* 1,000
SIC 5961 Catalog & mail-order houses; Catalog & mail-order houses
Ch Bd: Shawn Gorman
**VP:* Kierston Vansoest

D-U-N-S 07-881-2177 IMP
LL BUILDING PRODUCTS INC
G A F
(*Suby of* GAF CORP) ★
295 Mckoy Rd, Burgaw, NC 28425-4421
Tel (910) 259-6374 *Founded/Ownrshp* 1998
Sales 67.2MM^E *EMP* 1^E
SIC 2952 Roofing materials
CEO: Todd Christiansen
Dir IT: Brent Coats

D-U-N-S 00-638-4404
LL GLOBAL INC
(*Suby of* LIMRA INTERNATIONAL INC) ★
300 Day Hill Rd, Windsor, CT 06095-1783
Tel (860) 298-3848 *Founded/Ownrshp* 2009
Sales NA *EMP* 209^E
SIC 6411 Advisory services, insurance
Pr: Robert A Kerzner
**VP:* Gary R Aluise

D-U-N-S 02-414-3582
LL GLOBAL INC OF CONNECTICUT
300 Day Hill Rd, Windsor, CT 06095-1783
Tel (860) 298-3848 *Founded/Ownrshp* 2009
Sales 42.9MM *EMP* 1^E
Accts Pershing Yoakley & Associates
SIC 7389 Financial services; Financial services
Prin: Robert A Kerzner

D-U-N-S 19-729-2121 IMP
LL INDUSTRIES INC
DAVIS KITCHEN
4750 S Park Ave, Tucson, AZ 85714-1636
Tel (520) 889-4949 *Founded/Ownrshp* 1988
Sales 22.1MM^E *EMP* 85
SIC 5031 5211 Kitchen cabinets; Cabinets, kitchen
Pr: L L Mulcahy
Mktg Dir: Mike Mulcahy

D-U-N-S 00-590-2655 IMP
LLADRO USA INC (NJ)
(*Suby of* LLADRO SA.)
40 Enterprise Ave N, Secaucus, NJ 07094-2500
Tel (201) 527-3156 *Founded/Ownrshp* 1988
Sales 35.8MM^E *EMP* 85
SIC 5199 Gifts & novelties; Leather, leather goods & furs
CEO: Rick Fencel
**Pr:* Jose Llardo
CFO: Abgelo Dipalo
VP: Ruth Considine
Div Mgr: Jose Perez
IT Man: Roy Brasse
**VP Sls:* Glenn Conciatori
Manager: Enrique Campos
Sales Asso: Claudia Lopez

D-U-N-S 08-944-2289
LLAMAS PLASTICS INC
12970 Bradley Ave, Sylmar, CA 91342-3851
Tel (818) 362-0371 *Founded/Ownrshp* 1977
Sales 26.7MM^E *EMP* 105
SIC 3728 3089 3083 Aircraft parts & equipment; Plastic containers, except foam; Laminated plastics plate & sheet; Aircraft parts & equipment; Plastic containers, except foam; Laminated plastics plate & sheet
CEO: Ricardo M Llamas
**Pr:* Oswald Llamas
**Sec:* Jeff Mabry
Prgrm Mgr: Peter Delgado
Off Mgr: Carol Dorhorty
Board of Directors: V Scott Borison

D-U-N-S 61-148-7708
LLAMASOFT INC
201 S Main St Ste 400, Ann Arbor, MI 48104-2113
Tel (734) 418-3119 *Founded/Ownrshp* 1998
Sales 63.9MM^E *EMP* 196^E
SIC 7373 Custom computer programming services; Systems software development services
Pr: Donald A Hicks
**Owner:* Julie Whells
**COO:* Dale Erker
**CFO:* John Ternes
**Sr VP:* John Ames Jr
Sr VP: Alejandro Nieto
Sr VP: Llamasoft Nieto
**VP:* Toby Brzoznowski
VP: Greg Grindey
VP: Nejat Karabakal
VP: Simon McCluskey
VP: Jeff Metersky
VP: Tony Mirra
VP: Chris Schneider
Dir Bus: Ken Germain

D-U-N-S 08-628-2266
LLANO COUNTY HOSPITAL AUTHORITY (TX)
200 W Ollie St, Llano, TX 78643-2628
Tel (325) 247-5040 *Founded/Ownrshp* 1958
Sales 21.6MM^E *EMP* 300
SIC 8062 Hospital, affiliated with AMA residency; Hospital, affiliated with AMA residency
CEO: Kevin Leeper
COO: Linda Meredith
Dir Case M: Karen Carney
Orthpdst: Gordon Marshall
Dir Health: Kim Beasley

D-U-N-S 02-154-7815
LLANO IND SCHOOL DISTRICT
1400 Oatman St, Llano, TX 78643-2734
Tel (325) 247-4747 *Founded/Ownrshp* 1867
Sales 40.6MM *EMP* 280
Accts Patillo Brown & Hill Llp
SIC 8211 Public elementary school; Public junior high school; Public senior high school; Public elementary school

D-U-N-S 05-284-2617
LLANO LOGISTICS INC
(*Suby of* UNITED SUPERMARKETS LLC) ★
5801 Martin L King Blvd, Lubbock, TX 79404-5507
Tel (806) 472-5900 *Founded/Ownrshp* 1996, 2013
Sales 31.1MM^E *EMP* 300^E
SIC 4789 4731 Freight car loading & unloading; Freight forwarding; Freight car loading & unloading; Freight forwarding
CEO: Robert Taylor
Genl Mgr: Carlos Mendoza

LLC, CARL ZEISS NTS
See CARL ZEISS MICROSCOPY LLC

LLC, FORCE AMERICA DISTRG
See FORCE AMERICA INC

D-U-N-S 07-951-9376
LLC INVESTOR MEMBER LLC
448 Depot St Ne, Christiansburg, VA 24073-2050
Tel (540) 382-2002 *Founded/Ownrshp* 2014
Sales 3.8MM^E *EMP* 300
SIC 6513 Apartment building operators; Apartment building operators
Pr: Janaka Casper
Treas: Jeffrey Reed

D-U-N-S 14-621-2373 IMP
LLC PRITCHARD BROWN
6501 Erdman Ave, Baltimore, MD 21205-3510
Tel (410) 483-5600 *Founded/Ownrshp* 2003
Sales 26.6MM^E *EMP* 105
SIC 3444 Metal housings, enclosures, casings & other containers
COO: Sigurd Jensen

LLC, RESIDENT CARE CONSULTING
See HEALTHCARE FACILITY MANAGEMENT LLC

D-U-N-S 04-531-5694 IMP
■ **LLC SHIELD PACK**
(*Suby of* BEMIS CO INC) ★
411 Downing Pines Rd, West Monroe, LA 71292-8009
Tel (318) 387-4743 *Founded/Ownrshp* 2011
Sales 26.7MM^E *EMP* 99
SIC 2671 2673 2656 Paper coated or laminated for packaging; Plastic film, coated or laminated for packaging; Bags: plastic, laminated & coated; Sanitary food containers
Pr: Don E Nimus
**Treas:* Jerry S Krempa
Opers Mgr: Terri Brinson
Plnt Mgr: Raymond Self

D-U-N-S 07-205-9830
LLC SOUTHERN LIGHT
107 Saint Francis St # 1800, Mobile, AL 36602-3318
Tel (251) 445-1048 *Founded/Ownrshp* 1998
Sales 31.7MM^E *EMP* 50
SIC 1731 Communications specialization
**COO:* Eric Daniels
VP: Andru Bramblett
VP: Christopher Jones
Dir Bus: Scott McMahan
CTO: Jack De La Garza
IT Man: Paul Imperado
Netwrk Eng: Jeff Etheridge
Opers Mgr: Gabe Watson
Sls Dir: Jim Sfakianos

LLCP
See LEVINE LEICHTMAN CAPITAL PARTNERS INC

D-U-N-S 07-838-3402 IMP/EXP
LLFLEX LLC
1225 W Burnett Ave, Louisville, KY 40210-1879
Tel (502) 635-6331 *Founded/Ownrshp* 2011
Sales 100.0MM *EMP* 141
SIC 2672 Coated & laminated paper; Coated & laminated paper
CEO: James Squatrito
**CFO:* Jon Heard
VP Mfg: Kevin Hughes

D-U-N-S 62-186-2390
LLK CORP
SATURN
5550 N Keystone Ave, Indianapolis, IN 46220-3458
Tel (317) 293-1551 *Founded/Ownrshp* 1990
Sales 28.4MM^E *EMP* 150
SIC 5511 Automobiles, new & used; Automobiles, new & used
Ch Bd: Freda Lockhart
**Pr:* Lynn Kimmel
**VP:* Gregory Mark Lockhart

D-U-N-S 09-946-9983
LLL SALES CO LLC
GARDENA HONDA
(*Suby of* DCH NORTH AMERICA INC.)
15541 S Western Ave, Gardena, CA 90249-4320
Tel (310) 515-5700 *Founded/Ownrshp* 2002
Sales 35.1MM^E *EMP* 140
SIC 5511 7538 Automobiles, new & used; General automotive repair shops; Automobiles, new & used; General automotive repair shops
Prin: Shauwai Lam
Sls Mgr: Mike Hansen
Sls Mgr: Brian Santos
Sales Asso: Yumiko Morikawa

D-U-N-S 07-682-9597
■ **LLNS INC** (NY)
(*Suby of* OMNICOM GROUP INC) ★
488 Madison Ave, New York, NY 10022-5702
Tel (212) 771-3000 *Founded/Ownrshp* 1972, 2006
Sales 27.8MM^E *EMP* 185
SIC 7311 Advertising agencies; Advertising agencies
Ch: Anne Devereux
**Pr:* Janet Donnelly
**CEO:* Sharon Callahan
**CFO:* Stephen Weiss
**Ofcr:* Steve Hamburg
Sr VP: Harriet Perdikaris
Sr VP: Melissa Weiss
VP: Perry Kolber

D-U-N-S 14-193-3494 IMP
LLOG EXPLORATION CO LLC
1001 Ochsner Blvd Ste 200, Covington, LA 70433-8152
Tel (504) 833-7700 *Founded/Ownrshp* 2002
Sales 1.0MMM *EMP* 75^E
Accts Ernst & Young Llp New Orleans
SIC 1311 1382 Oil & gas exploration services; Crude petroleum & natural gas; Oil & gas exploration services
CEO: Scott Gutterman
CFO: Kem Ducote
**Sr VP:* Tim Lindsey
VP: Michael Altobelli
**VP:* Mike Altobelli
**VP:* Jay Cole
**VP:* Bruce Cooley
VP: Malloy French
VP: Philip Lejeune
VP: Bob McMann
Exec: John Doughtie

D-U-N-S 05-391-4094
LLOG EXPLORATION OFFSHORE LLC (LA)
1001 Ochsner Blvd Ste 200, Covington, LA 70433-8152
Tel (985) 801-4300 *Founded/Ownrshp* 1996
Sales 180.8MM^E *EMP* 100
SIC 1382 Oil & gas exploration services; Oil & gas exploration services
**Ch Bd:* Gerald A Boelte
**Ex VP:* Kevin P Guilbeau

D-U-N-S 02-906-2445
LLOYD APPLING INC
SALINAS HYUNDAI
700 Auto Center Cir, Salinas, CA 93907-2504
Tel (831) 444-9000 *Founded/Ownrshp* 1965
Sales 23.1MM^E *EMP* 49
SIC 5511 5521 Automobiles, new & used; Used car dealers; Automobiles, new & used; Used car dealers
Pr: Emma Sue Jamiesson
Exec: Suzanne Powers
Genl Mgr: Nathen Hughes
Sls Mgr: Simon Bashir
Sls Mgr: Jorge Ramirez

D-U-N-S 02-974-9892
LLOYD BELT GMC TRUCK
2007 Buss Hwy 54 S, Eldon, MO 65026
Tel (573) 392-3333 *Founded/Ownrshp* 1965
Sales 22.1MM^E *EMP* 58
SIC 5511 Automobiles, new & used; Pickups, new & used
Pr: Lloyd Belt
**VP:* Gregory Belt

D-U-N-S 06-327-7263
LLOYD CONSTRUCTION CO INC
2180 N Wilmot Rd, Tucson, AZ 85712-3015
Tel (520) 884-9821 *Founded/Ownrshp* 1971
Sales 20.5MM^E *EMP* 44
Accts Beach Fleischman Pc Tucson
SIC 1542 School building construction; Commercial & office building, new construction; Hospital construction; School building construction; Commercial & office building, new construction; Hospital construction
Pr: William E Lloyd
**VP:* Bradlee Lloyd
**VP:* Brian Lloyd
Off Mgr: Clarie Pemberton
Sfty Mgr: Robby Garvey
Mktg Dir: Bonnie Dana
Snr PM: Paul Pena

LLOYD CREATIVE TEMPORARIES
See LLOYD STAFFING INC

D-U-N-S 01-546-0846
LLOYD DEAN
185 Berry St Ste 300, San Francisco, CA 94107-1773
Tel (415) 438-5756 *Founded/Ownrshp* 2011
Sales 55.0MM *EMP* 50^E
SIC 8742 Hospital & health services consultant; Hospital & health services consultant
Prin: Catholic Healthcare West
Sr VP: Elizabeth Shih
Snr Mgr: Connie Clemmons-Brown

D-U-N-S 83-741-1768
LLOYD MARTHA COMMUNITY RESIDENTIAL FACILITY INC
66 Lloyd Ln, Troy, PA 16947-1502
Tel (570) 297-2185 *Founded/Ownrshp* 1928
Sales 6.3MM *EMP* 291
SIC 8211 Private special education school; School for the retarded; Private special education school; School for the retarded
**Pr:* Richard Macintire

D-U-N-S 02-912-2900
LLOYD PEST CONTROL CO
935 Sherman St, San Diego, CA 92110-4092
Tel (619) 298-9865 *Founded/Ownrshp* 1931
Sales 23.7MM^E *EMP* 250
SIC 7342 Exterminating & fumigating; Exterminating & fumigating
Pr: James A Ogle III
CFO: Ken Keith
**VP:* Herb Field
Sls Mgr: Aaron Frost
Sls Mgr: David Hinrichs

D-U-N-S 00-499-8134
LLOYD PLYLER CONSTRUCTION LLP
PLYLER FABRICATION
3505 Texoma Pkwy, Sherman, TX 75090-1917
Tel (903) 893-6393 *Founded/Ownrshp* 2001
Sales 30.1MM *EMP* 90
SIC 1541 1796 3441

D-U-N-S 15-390-4243
LLOYD PRO GROUP INC
2675 Breckinridge Blvd # 100, Duluth, GA 30096-8953
Tel (770) 497-1200 *Founded/Ownrshp* 2001
Sales NA *EMP* 100
SIC 6311 Life insurance
Pr: James C Lloyd
**CFO:* Linda Grant

D-U-N-S 10-585-2016
LLOYD STAFFING INC
LLOYD CREATIVE TEMPORARIES
445 Broadhollow Rd # 119, Melville, NY 11747-3631
Tel (631) 777-7600 *Founded/Ownrshp* 1971
Sales 66.0MM^E *EMP* 1,500
SIC 7363 Temporary help service; Temporary help service
CEO: Merrill Banks
**Pr:* Keith Banks
**CFO:* Vincent J Albanese
CFO: Russell Owens
**VP:* Jason Banks
**VP:* Donna Caputo
**VP:* Carolyn Doyle
**VP:* Marc Lester
**VP:* Nancy Schuman
CIO: Joseph R Brennskag
Opers Mgr: Christine Panzella

D-U-N-S 84-534-0231
LLOYD STOKES
MCDONALD'S
3515 E Race Ave, Searcy, AR 72143-6202
Tel (501) 268-3105 *Founded/Ownrshp* 1997
Sales 4.8MM^E *EMP* 280
SIC 5812 Fast-food restaurant, chain; Fast-food restaurant, chain
Owner: Lloyd Stokes

D-U-N-S 04-739-0992
LLOYD W AUBRY CO INC
2148 Dunn Rd, Hayward, CA 94545-2204
Tel (510) 732-9038 *Founded/Ownrshp* 1988
Sales 32.3MM *EMP* 79
Accts Jones Henle & Schunck Danvil
SIC 1796 8711 Machinery installation; Mechanical engineering; Machinery installation; Mechanical engineering
Pr: Robert Butler
**CFO:* Jay Butler
VP: John Butler
Genl Mgr: Robert Havens
Snr PM: Barrett Randick

D-U-N-S 14-737-1335
LLOYDS ILLINOIS INC
(*Suby of* LLOYD'S MARKET ASSOCIATION)
131 W Madison St Ste 3870, Chicago, IL 60602-4541
Tel (312) 407-6200 *Founded/Ownrshp* 2004
Sales NA *EMP* 15
SIC 6411 Insurance information & consulting services; Insurance information & consulting services
Pr: Maryanne Swaim
**CFO:* John W O'Hara
CFO: Sue Winger
VP: Keith Wenckowski

D-U-N-S 96-704-8521 IMP/EXP
LLOYDS MATERIAL SUPPLY CO INC
1462 E 9th St, Pomona, CA 91766-3833
Tel (909) 623-8781 *Founded/Ownrshp* 1993
Sales 79.9MM^E *EMP* 412
SIC 3999 5091 Hot tubs; Hot tubs; Spa equipment & supplies; Hot tubs; Hot tubs; Spa equipment & supplies
Pr: Casey Loyd
CFO: Steve Graham

D-U-N-S 86-762-0457
LLOYDS REGISTER AMERICAS INC
(*Suby of* LLOYD'S REGISTER OF SHIPPING TRUST CORPORATION LIMITED)
1330 Enclave Pkwy Ste 200, Houston, TX 77077-2578
Tel (281) 675-3100 *Founded/Ownrshp* 2000
Sales 80.0MM^E *EMP* 205
SIC 7389 Safety inspection service; Industrial & commercial equipment inspection service; Inspection & testing services; Safety inspection service; Industrial & commercial equipment inspection service; Inspection & testing services
Pr: Paul Huber
**Treas:* David Arneson
Sr VP: Simon Reeve
Exec: Nitin Mangale
Exec: Jessica Mendieta
Comm Man: Andrew Foulkes
Mng Dir: Iain Carmichael
Genl Mgr: W Adlard
Off Mgr: Alicja Suska
Tech Mgr: Bruce McDonald
Tech Mgr: Robert Tustin
Board of Directors: David Corbett, Paul Huber, Alastair Marsh, Timothy Protheroe, Andrew Smith

D-U-N-S 07-914-1492
LLOYDS REGISTER DRILLING INTEGRITY SERVICES INC
1330 Enclave Pkwy Ste 200, Katy, TX 77449
Tel (281) 675-3100 *Founded/Ownrshp* 2002
Sales 6.3MM^E *EMP* 276
SIC 1389 Servicing oil & gas wells; Servicing oil & gas wells
Pr: Paul Huber
Sr VP: Teril Smith

D-U-N-S 02-036-1767
LLOYDS REGISTER NORTH AMERICA INC
(*Suby of* LLOYDS REGISTER AMERICAS INC) ★
1330 Enclave Pkwy Ste 200, Houston, TX 77077-2578
Tel (281) 675-3100 *Founded/Ownrshp* 2000
Sales 64.0MM *EMP* 75
Accts Berson & Corrado Llp New York
SIC 7389 Safety inspection service; Safety inspection service
Pr: Timothy Protheroe
**Pr:* Andrew Smith
**Treas:* David Arneson
Ofcr: Anne Cowne
Ofcr: Becky Walton
Sr VP: Paul Phyall
VP: Simon Batters
VP: Zahid Rahman
VP: Dorrith Thomas
Dir Bus: David Hadlet
Comm Man: Wesley Blake

D-U-N-S 07-789-1224
LLP BUTLER SNOW
1020 Highland Colony Pkwy # 1400, Ridgeland, MS 39157-2139
Tel (601) 853-1930 *Founded/Ownrshp* 2013
Sales 58.7MM^E *EMP* 350
SIC 8111 General practice law office; General practice law office
Pr: Melinda Etheridge
Bd of Dir: Bob Anderson
Dir IT: Kevin Rutledge

D-U-N-S 06-815-6215
LLP ROBINS KAPLAN
ROBINS KAPLAN MILLER & CIRESI
800 Lasalle Ave Ste 2800, Minneapolis, MN 55402-2039
Tel (612) 349-8500 *Founded/Ownrshp* 1938
Sales 99.5MM^E *EMP* 600
SIC 8111 Legal services; Legal services
Ch: Martin R Lueck
Genl Pt: Dick Nigon
Pt: Robert Auchter
Pt: V R Denham Jr
Pt: Keith Styles
Mng Pt: Cole Fauver
Mng Pt: Kenneth Freeling
Mng Pt: Steven A Schumeister
Exec: Kelly McLain
IT Man: Michael Tanner
Counsel: Richard Gill

LLR EQUITY PARTNERS
See LLR PARTNERS INC

D-U-N-S 09-524-8865
LLR PARTNERS INC
LLR EQUITY PARTNERS
2929 Arch St Ste 1650, Philadelphia, PA 19104-2864
Tel (215) 717-2900 *Founded/Ownrshp* 1999
Sales 71.4MM^E *EMP* 212
SIC 6282 Investment advisory service; Investment advisory service
Prin: Howard Ross
Pt: Gregory M Case
VP: Jack Slye
Dir Bus: Wm C Bullitt
Prin: Seth Lehr
Prin: Ira Lubert
Prin: Todd J Morrissey
Prin: Scott A Perricelli
Prin: David J Reuter
Prin: David A Stienes

LLS
See LEUKEMIA & LYMPHOMA SOCIETY INC

LLU
See LOMA LINDA UNIVERSITY

LLUMC
See LOMA LINDA UNIVERSITY MEDICAL CENTER

LM
See LATVA MACHINE INC

D-U-N-S 10-733-0698
LM ASSOCIATES
300 Monroeville Mall, Pittsburgh, PA 15219
Tel (412) 261-1500 *Founded/Ownrshp* 1979
Sales 73.0MM^E *EMP* 443
SIC 6552 6512 Land subdividers & developers, commercial; Commercial & industrial building operation; Land subdividers & developers, commercial; Commercial & industrial building operation
Mng Pt: Edward J Lewis
Genl Pt: Mark E Mason
Pt: Steve Guy
Pt: David Matter
Pt: Frank A Molinero
Pt: Richard I Miller
Pt: George Whalen
CTO: Steve Starinsky
VP Opers: Scott Bergstein

D-U-N-S 03-206-2827
LM HEAVY CIVIL CONSTRUCTION LLC
L M H
100 Hancock St Ste 901, Quincy, MA 02171-1745
Tel (617) 845-8000 *Founded/Ownrshp* 2005
Sales 24.0MM^E *EMP* 51^E
SIC 1611 1622 General contractor, highway & street construction; Bridge, tunnel & elevated highway
CEO: Max Marino
**Pr:* Michele Massari
**Treas:* Robert Macri
**VP:* Steve Harrington
VP: Steven Harrington
VP: John Pastore
**VP:* Peter Williamson
Mtls Mgr: Paul Sena
Sfty Mgr: Jeffrey Clarke

D-U-N-S 07-866-0332 IMP
LM SAFETY PLUS
Pilkington, Denver, CO 80014
Tel (419) 247-4585 *Founded/Ownrshp* 1975
Sales 841.0M *EMP* 640
SIC 3714 Windshield frames, motor vehicle; Windshield frames, motor vehicle
Genl Mgr: Moises Sotelo

D-U-N-S 00-824-7710 EXP
LM SCOFIELD CO (CA)
6533 Bandini Blvd, Commerce, CA 90040-3182
Tel (323) 720-3000 *Founded/Ownrshp* 1915, 1970
Sales 31.0MM^E *EMP* 109
SIC 2899 2816 Concrete curing & hardening compounds; Inorganic pigments; Concrete curing & hardening compounds; Inorganic pigments
CEO: Phillip J Arnold
**Pr:* Phillip Arnold
CFO: David Wardenaar
**VP:* John Watson

D-U-N-S 01-206-0535 IMP/EXP
LM WIND POWER BLADES (ARKANSAS) INC
LM WIND POWER USA
(*Suby of* LM WIND POWER A/S)
7400 Scott Hamilton Dr, Little Rock, AR 72209-3175
Tel (501) 801-6300 *Founded/Ownrshp* 2014
Sales 43.7MM^E *EMP* 200
SIC 3089 Thermoformed finished plastic products; Thermoformed finished plastic products
Pr: Soren Hoffer
**Treas:* Bruce Mitchell

D-U-N-S 05-288-5311 IMP/EXP
LM WIND POWER BLADES (ND) INC (ND)
LM WIND POWER LITTLE ROCK
(*Suby of* LM WIND POWER HOLDING A/S)
1580 S 48th St, Grand Forks, ND 58201-3808
Tel (701) 780-9910 *Founded/Ownrshp* 1998
Sales 301.7MM^E *EMP* 880^E
SIC 3511 3621 Turbines & turbine generator sets & parts; Motors & generators; Turbines & turbine generator sets & parts; Motors & generators
CEO: Roland M Sunden
**CFO:* Dominique Yates
**Treas:* Sean R O Leary
**VP:* Randy L Fox
VP: Kenneth Kaser
VP: Christopher Springham
Exec: Dan Gordon
Exec: Gerald Muizelaar

CTO: Frank V Nielsen
IT Man: Travis Allen

LM WIND POWER LITTLE ROCK
See LM WIND POWER BLADES (ND) INC

LM WIND POWER USA
See LM WIND POWER BLADES (ARKANSAS) INC

LM WIRELESS
See LMEG WIRELESS LLC

LM&O ADVERTISING
See LAUGHLIN MARINACCIO & OWENS INC

D-U-N-S 18-412-9679
LM1 LLC
LIFEMATTERS
7768 Woodmont Ave Ste 200, Bethesda, MD 20814-6034
Tel (301) 652-7212 *Founded/Ownrshp* 2004
Sales 8.3MM *EMP* 650[E]
SIC 8082 Home health care services; Home health care services
CFO: Gary Reburn
VP: Carolyn Sweeney

LMAERO
See LOCKHEED MARTIN AERONAUTICAL CO

LMASSC
See LOCKHEED MARTIN AERONAUTICAL SYSTEMS SUPPORT CO

LMC
See LEWIS M CARTER MANUFACTURING CO INC

LMC
See LUMBERMENS MERCHANDISING CORP

D-U-N-S 06-379-8714
LMC ENTERPRISES
CHEMCO PRODUCTS COMPANY
6401 Alondra Blvd, Paramount, CA 90723-3758
Tel (562) 602-2116 *Founded/Ownrshp* 1962
Sales 25.2MM[E] *EMP* 120
SIC 2842 Cleaning or polishing preparations; Floor waxes; Cleaning or polishing preparations; Floor waxes
CEO: Elaine S Cooper
**Pr:* Janis Utz
**COO:* John D Grimes
CFO: Shawn Carroll
Ex VP: David McCullough
Dir IT: Justin Foster
Sls Mgr: Russell Gaston

LMC EXTENDED CARE
See LEXMED INC

D-U-N-S 07-872-5649
LMC HOLLYWOOD HIGHLAND HOLDINGS LLC
LENNAR MULTI FAMILY COMMUNITY
95 Enterprise Ste 200, Aliso Viejo, CA 92656-2611
Tel (949) 448-1600 *Founded/Ownrshp* 2013
Sales 20.9MM[E] *EMP* 500
SIC 1542 Commercial & office building contractors
CEO: Todd Farrell

LMC INDUSTRIES
See LAKEMARY CENTER INC

D-U-N-S 00-629-1314 IMP
LMC INDUSTRIES INC
100 Manufacturers Dr, Arnold, MO 63010-4727
Tel (636) 282-8080 *Founded/Ownrshp* 1945
Sales 44.9MM[E] *EMP* 250[E]
SIC 3089 3469 3465 Injection molding of plastics; Stamping metal for the trade; Automotive stampings; Injection molding of plastics; Stamping metal for the trade; Automotive stampings
Ch Bd: Allan Suellentrop
**Pr:* Craig Morton
**CFO:* Keith Suellentrop
**VP:* Steven Suellentrop
Ql Cn Mgr: Jeff Eberle

LMC INSURANCE
See LA MAIR-MULOCK-CONDON CO

D-U-N-S 03-277-0963
LMC INSURANCE & RISK MANAGEMENT INC
4200 University Ave # 200, West Des Moines, IA 50266-5945
Tel (515) 244-0166 *Founded/Ownrshp* 2010
Sales NA *EMP* 200[E]
SIC 6411 Insurance agents, brokers & service; Insurance agents, brokers & service
Pr: Greg Lamair
CFO: Mark Lyons
Sales Exec: Karen Cooper

D-U-N-S 83-098-5714 IMP
■ **LMC RIGHT START INC**
(*Suby of* LIBERTY MEDIA CORP) ★
4643 S Ulster St Ste 1200, Denver, CO 80237-2868
Tel (720) 974-8198 *Founded/Ownrshp* 2012
Sales 20.3MM[E] *EMP* 80[E]
SIC 5999 Baby carriages & strollers
Pr: Michael Wagner
**VP:* Gigi Healy
**VP:* Scott Henry
Snr Sftwr: John Fowler
Snr Sftwr: Eric Mitkowski
IT Man: Justin Davis

D-U-N-S 14-907-8771
LMD INTEGRATED LOGISTICS SERVICES INC
3136 E Victoria St, Compton, CA 90221-5618
Tel (310) 605-5100 *Founded/Ownrshp* 2003
Sales 28.5MM[E] *EMP* 67
SIC 4225 General warehousing & storage
CEO: Louis M Diblosi Jr
**CFO:* Marilyn Zakis
VP Opers: Miguel Estrella

LMDSI
See LOCKHEED MARTIN DESKTOP SOLUTIONS INC

D-U-N-S 79-120-4550
LMEG WIRELESS LLC
LM WIRELESS
303 Louisiana Ave, Brooklyn, NY 11207-8206
Tel (718) 832-0700 *Founded/Ownrshp* 2003
Sales 75.0MM[E] *EMP* 160
SIC 5961 5065 Electronic kits & parts, mail order; Telephone equipment
Mktg Mgr: Aron Brown
Sls Mgr: Mike Ash

LMF
See LAUREL MACHINE AND FOUNDRY CO

D-U-N-S 17-270-2789
LMG INC
2350 Investors Row, Orlando, FL 32837-8331
Tel (407) 850-0505 *Founded/Ownrshp* 1984
Sales 46.3MM[E] *EMP* 190[E]
SIC 7359 7373 Audio-visual equipment & supply rental; Systems integration services; Audio-visual equipment & supply rental; Systems integration services
Pr: Leslie M Goldberg
**COO:* David M John
**CFO:* Rick A Perry
VP: Ronald D Avey
Dir Bus: Rich Tate
Mng Dir: Wazza Bray
Dir IT: Rob Lee
Opers Supe: David Cherepy
Opers Mgr: Gabrielle Justice
Opers Mgr: Shane Purvenas
Sales Exec: Jon Byler

LMH
See LAWRENCE MEMORIAL HOSPITAL ENDOWMENT ASSOCIATION

D-U-N-S 10-854-4672
LMHC MASSACHUSETTS HOLDINGS INC
(*Suby of* LIBERTY MUTUAL HOLDING CO INC) ★
175 Berkeley St, Boston, MA 02116-5066
Tel (617) 357-9500 *Founded/Ownrshp* 2001
Sales NA *EMP* 41,208
SIC 6331 6321 6351 7389 Fire, marine & casualty insurance; Workers' compensation insurance; Automobile insurance; Burglary & theft insurance; Accident insurance carriers; Health insurance carriers; Reinsurance carriers, accident & health; Liability insurance; Fidelity or surety bonding; Fidelity responsibility insurance; Financial services; Fire, marine & casualty insurance; Workers' compensation insurance; Automobile insurance; Burglary & theft insurance; Accident insurance carriers; Health insurance carriers; Reinsurance carriers, accident & health; Liability insurance; Fidelity or surety bonding; Fidelity responsibility insurance; Financial services
Ch Bd: Edmund F Kelly
IT Man: Cindy Wood

LMI
See MUSICIANS FRIEND INC

LMI AEROSPACE
See D3TECHNOLOGIES INC

D-U-N-S 04-129-7664
▲ **LMI AEROSPACE INC**
LEONARD'S METALS
411 Fountain Lakes Blvd, Saint Charles, MO 63301-4352
Tel (636) 946-6525 *Founded/Ownrshp* 1948
Sales 387.8MM *EMP* 1,970
Tkr Sym LMIA *Exch* NGS
SIC 3728 Aircraft parts & equipment; Aircraft parts & equipment
Pr: Daniel G Korte
Pr: Jay Inman
COO: Joseph Demartino
CFO: Clifford C Stebe Jr
Chf Cred: Renee Skonier
Ofcr: Jennifer L Alfaro
Ofcr: Jennifer Alfaro
VP: David A Fillmore
VP: Bob Grah
VP: Reiner Rix
VP: Keith Schrader
VP: Keith M Schrader
VP: Scott Underwood
Comm Dir: Amy Horton
Dir Bus: Kenneth Scherwinski
Board of Directors: Gerald E Daniels, John S Eulich, Sanford S Neuman, Judith W Northup, John M Roeder, Ronald S Saks, Gregory L Summe

D-U-N-S 04-193-1697
LMI CUSTOM MIXING LLC
(*Suby of* LAUREN INTERNATIONAL LTD) ★
804 Byesville Rd, Cambridge, OH 43725-9327
Tel (740) 435-0444 *Founded/Ownrshp* 1997
Sales 30.2MM[E] *EMP* 74
SIC 2891 Rubber cement
CFO: David Gingrich
Sls Mgr: Greg Mealer

D-U-N-S 18-713-1560
LMI LANDSCAPES INC
1437 Halsey Way, Carrollton, TX 75007-4410
Tel (303) 294-9000 *Founded/Ownrshp* 1987
Sales 59.1MM[E] *EMP* 204
SIC 0781 Landscape architects; Landscape architects
Pr: Jody O'Donnell
Genl Mgr: Darrin Stricklen
VP Opers: Frank Kynkor

D-U-N-S 12-156-1559
LMI LEGACY HOLDINGS II INC
LANDAUER-METROPOLITAN, INC.
1 Bradford Rd, Mount Vernon, NY 10553-1260
Tel (914) 663-3200 *Founded/Ownrshp* 1984
Sales NA *EMP* 470[E]
SIC 7352 5047

LMI SOLUTIONS
See LASERMASTERS LLC

D-U-N-S 87-901-9008 IMP
LMI SYSTEMS INC
LMI TECHNOLOGY GROUP
4680 N Royal Atlanta Dr, Tucker, GA 30084-3801
Tel (770) 491-0343 *Founded/Ownrshp* 1993
Sales 27.0MM *EMP* 170
SIC 1731 7382 7629 7359

LMI TECHNOLOGY GROUP
See LMI SYSTEMS INC

D-U-N-S 00-751-0308
LMK AUTO GROUP LIMITED (TX)
MC KAIG CHEVROLET GEO
1110 Broadway Ave, Gladewater, TX 75647-2503
Tel (903) 845-2132 *Founded/Ownrshp* 1931, 1995
Sales 47.0MM *EMP* 32
SIC 5511 5531 7538 Automobiles, new & used; Automotive & home supply stores; General automotive repair shops; Automobiles, new & used; Automotive & home supply stores; General automotive repair shops
Pr: Mark Abernathy
**Treas:* Kent Abernathy
**VP:* Larry Aaron

D-U-N-S 94-946-8284
LMK TECHNOLOGIES LLC
1779 Chessie Ln, Ottawa, IL 61350-9687
Tel (815) 433-1530 *Founded/Ownrshp* 2012
Sales 20.6MM[E] *EMP* 73
SIC 3552 Spindles, textile
CEO: Michael J Reardon
**Pr:* Larry W Kiest Jr
VP: Shain Cheney
**VP:* James A Gordon
**VP:* Todd M Hamilton
Genl Mgr: Bruce Kamin

LML EXPRESS
See LOADMATCH LOGISTICS INC

D-U-N-S 18-188-7816
LMN DEVELOPMENT LLC
KALAHARI WATERPARK RESORT
7000 Kalahari Dr, Sandusky, OH 44870-8628
Tel (419) 433-7200 *Founded/Ownrshp* 2003
Sales 83.1MM[E] *EMP* 1,000[E]
SIC 7011 7996 5091 Resort hotel; Amusement parks; Water slides (recreation park); Resort hotel; Amusement parks; Water slides (recreation park)
Pr: Todd Nelson
CFO: Mary Bonte-Stath
CFO: Mary Spath
Genl Mgr: Brian Shanle
IT Man: Matthew Dick
Mktg Mgr: Kristann Hartley
Sls Mgr: Mike Thatcher

LMP STEEL & WIRE COMPANY
See NUCOR-LMP INC

D-U-N-S 08-134-6124
LMR INC
TRAVEL LEADERS
6445 Poplar Ave Ste 200, Memphis, TN 38119-4811
Tel (901) 761-1708 *Founded/Ownrshp* 1976
Sales 45.0MM *EMP* 25
SIC 4724 Travel agencies; Travel agencies
Pr: Linda Bourgeois
VP Opers: Warwick Garner
VP Sls: Mickey Michelle Rooker

LMR TRANSPORTATION
See DALKO RESOURCES INC

LMS
See LOGISTICS MANAGEMENT SOLUTIONS LC

LMS BUILDING SERVICES
See LAWYER MECHANICAL SERVICES INC

D-U-N-S 78-370-2590
LMS INTELLIBOUND INC
6525 The Corners Pkwy, Norcross, GA 30092-3344
Tel (770) 724-0564 *Founded/Ownrshp* 1998
Sales 95.0MM[E] *EMP* 1,600
SIC 4225 General warehousing & storage; General warehousing & storage
CEO: Steve Taylor
**Pr:* William Harper
Genl Mgr: William Davis
Site Mgr: Michael Adams
Opers Mgr: Mike Henleben

D-U-N-S 09-950-0907 IMP
LMT ONSRUD LP
(*Suby of* LMT TOOL SYSTEMS GMBH)
1081 S Northpoint Blvd, Waukegan, IL 60085-8215
Tel (847) 473-1933 *Founded/Ownrshp* 1998
Sales 28.6MM *EMP* 107
Accts Miller Cooper & Co Ltd Cpas
SIC 3423 3545 Hand & edge tools; Machine tool accessories; Hand & edge tools; Machine tool accessories
Pr: Robert Ostroga
**VP:* Leslie Banduch
**VP:* Robert Wallwin
Mktg Mgr: Jennifer Neubauer
Manager: Tom Cornwell

D-U-N-S 00-922-4163 IMP
LN CURTIS AND SONS
L. N. CURTIS & SONS L.N. CURT
1800 Peralta St, Oakland, CA 94607-1609
Tel (510) 839-5111 *Founded/Ownrshp* 1971
Sales 53.2MM[E] *EMP* 115
SIC 5087 5099 Firefighting equipment; Safety equipment & supplies; Firefighting equipment; Safety equipment & supplies
CFO: Paul F Curtis
**Treas:* John Viboch
**VP:* Jeff Curtis
**VP:* Tim Henderson
VP: Brandon Winters
Brnch Mgr: Troy Garside
Off Admin: Kaylene Holman

Dir IT: Tim White
Mktg Mgr: Tracy Henderson
Sales Asso: Sheldon Castain
Sales Asso: Aaron Clough

D-U-N-S 11-814-0037
LNB BANCORP INC
457 Broadway, Lorain, OH 44052-1739
Tel (440) 244-6000 *Founded/Ownrshp* 1984
Sales NA *EMP* 267[E]
SIC 6022 State commercial banks

LNC
See LIVESTOCK NUTRITION CENTER LLC

D-U-N-S 03-006-1886
LNF DISTRIBUTORS LTD
BUDWEISER BEER
3900 N Mccoll Rd, McAllen, TX 78501-9160
Tel (956) 687-6206 *Founded/Ownrshp* 1991
Sales 25.2MM[E] *EMP* 250
SIC 5181 Beer & ale; Beer & ale
Pt: Joseph Lamantia
Genl Mgr: Bobby Casso
Genl Mgr: Steve Lamantia
IT Man: John Beagla

D-U-N-S 14-078-7743 IMP
LNG FREEPORT DEVELOPMENT L P
333 Clay St Ste 5050, Houston, TX 77002-4101
Tel (713) 980-2888 *Founded/Ownrshp* 2002
Sales 80.2MM[E] *EMP* 99
Accts Ernst & Young Llp Houston Tx
SIC 4922 Natural gas transmission; Natural gas transmission
CEO: Michael S Smith
Pr: Charles Reimer
Pr: Jody Sumrall
Bd of Dir: Robert Heitmann
Ex VP: Mike Quilty
VP: Bobby Gaspard
VP: Keith Little
VP: John Tobola
Genl Couns: John Tabola
Snr Mgr: Steve Chafin

D-U-N-S 03-815-4464
LNK INTERNATIONAL INC
60 Arkay Dr, Hauppauge, NY 11788-3708
Tel (631) 435-3500 *Founded/Ownrshp* 1980
Sales 48.6MM[E] *EMP* 200[E]
SIC 2834

D-U-N-S 00-302-1078
LNP MEDIA GROUP INC
BUSINESS INTELLHGENCER JOURNAL
8 W King St, Lancaster, PA 17603-3824
Tel (717) 291-8811 *Founded/Ownrshp* 1928
Sales 121.8MM[E] *EMP* 550[E]
SIC 2711 2752

D-U-N-S 02-682-5807
LNR PROPERTY LLC
(*Suby of* STARWOOD PROPERTY TRUST INC) ★
1601 Washington Ave # 600, Miami Beach, FL 33139-3165
Tel (305) 695-5500 *Founded/Ownrshp* 2010
Sales 158.8MM[E] *EMP* 480
SIC 6513 Apartment building operators; Apartment building operators
VP: Shahram M Siddiqui
**Pr:* Jeffrey P Krasnoff
COO: Matthias Schlueter
**COO:* Ronald E Schrager
CFO: Steve Ferguson
Chf Mktg O: Yesenia Marcos
Sr VP: Elizabeth Alonso
Sr VP: Tom Creasy
Sr VP: Jennifer Fernandez
Sr VP: Kevin Hanson
Sr VP: Ken Kristofek
Sr VP: Rina Paniry
Sr VP: Arne Shulkin
VP: Brett Birkeland
VP: Tillie Borchers
VP: Bjorn Borgenhard
VP: Natan Bresler
**VP:* Robert Cherry
**VP:* Zena M Dickstein
VP: Hector Gomez
VP: Nicola Hudson

D-U-N-S 11-622-8537 IMP
LNS AMERICA INC
(*Suby of* LNS SA)
4621 E Tech Dr, Cincinnati, OH 45245-1044
Tel (513) 528-5674 *Founded/Ownrshp* 1980
Sales 40.0MM *EMP* 77[E]
SIC 5084 Industrial machinery & equipment
CEO: John Tolasky
**Pr:* Eve Scemama
VP: Sraj Frank
Rgnl Mgr: John Stone
Dir IT: Damien Wenisch

LNV ENGINEERING
See LNV INC

D-U-N-S 05-077-2461
LNV INC
LNV ENGINEERING
801 Navigation Blvd # 300, Corpus Christi, TX 78408-2600
Tel (361) 866-2127 *Founded/Ownrshp* 2000
Sales 22.5MM[E] *EMP* 55
SIC 8711 Engineering services
Pr: Dan S Leyendecker
**VP:* Derek E Naiser
VP: Derek Naiser
**VP:* Eric A Trejo
**VP:* Robert M Viera
IT Man: Clifton Kuecker
Sfty Dirs: Roy Montemayor
Snr Mgr: Randal Martin

LNVA
See LOWER NECHES VALLEY AUTHORITY INDUSTRIAL DEVELOPMENT CORP

LNVA
See LOWER NECHES VALLEY AUTHORITY

D-U-N-S 02-838-6522 IMP/EXP
LO BUE BROS INC
LOBUE CITRUS
201 S Sweetbriar Ave, Lindsay, CA 93247-2422
Tel (559) 562-2548 *Founded/Ownrshp* 1934
Sales 48.0MM *EMP* 200
SIC 0723

LO LO CHICKEN AND WAFFLES
See CUTCHALL MANAGEMENT CO INC

D-U-N-S 60-304-3753
LO NIDY CO INC
GOPHER RESOURCE
2900 Lone Oak Pkwy, Eagan, MN 55121-1929
Tel (651) 454-3310 *Founded/Ownrshp* 1987
Sales 41.1MM^E *EMP* 150
SIC 3341 3339 Lead smelting & refining (secondary); Antimony refining (primary); Lead smelting & refining (secondary); Antimony refining (primary)
Pr: Irving L Kutoff
**CEO:* Mark Kutoff

D-U-N-S 82-618-9904 IMP/EXP
LO TRADING CORP
10800 Nw 21st St Ste 250, Miami, FL 33172-2061
Tel (305) 477-7630 *Founded/Ownrshp* 1993
Sales 35.7MM *EMP* 18
SIC 5085 5169 4731 Industrial supplies; Chemicals, industrial & heavy; Freight forwarding; Industrial supplies; Chemicals, industrial & heavy; Freight forwarding
Pr: Luis Oberndorfer
**COO:* Johnnatan Mery
**VP:* Ana C Oberndorfer
Exec: Karen Guzman
Opers Mgr: Christian Hans

D-U-N-S 06-753-1665
LO VULLO ASSOCIATES INC
6450 Transit Rd, Depew, NY 14043-1033
Tel (716) 681-5201 *Founded/Ownrshp* 1950
Sales NA *EMP* 85
SIC 6411 Insurance agents; Insurance brokers
Pr: Leonard T Lo Vullo
CFO: Phillip Rapini
Sr VP: Paul Lovullo
**Sr VP:* Paul Lo Vullo
**VP:* Dave Pietrowski
Info Man: Bob Mihalski

LOAD BANKS FOR RENT
See COMRENT INTERNATIONAL LLC

D-U-N-S 00-897-3396
LOAD DELIVERED LOGISTICS LLC
750 N Orleans St Ste 100, Chicago, IL 60654-5051
Tel (877) 930-5623 *Founded/Ownrshp* 2007
Sales 42.3MM^E *EMP* 75^E
SIC 4213 Trucking, except local
CEO: Robert Nathan
**Pr:* Michelon Jon
**VP:* Simon Danny
**VP:* J Kevin Green

D-U-N-S 13-547-4406
LOAD ONE LLC
13221 Inkster Rd, Taylor, MI 48180-4427
Tel (734) 947-9440 *Founded/Ownrshp* 2003
Sales 47.9MM^E *EMP* 170
SIC 4212 Local trucking, without storage; Local trucking, without storage
CEO: John Elliott
Pr: Cindy Schuck
Admn Mgr: Becky Kennedy
Dir IT: Matt George
VP Opers: Mike Johnson
Trfc Dir: Matthew Baisden
Trfc Dir: Robert Falzon
Trfc Dir: Sara Ferguson
Trfc Dir: Dave Floyd
Trfc Dir: Kristen Hellems
Trfc Dir: Lisa Jasina

D-U-N-S 94-811-6207 IMP
LOAD TRAIL LLC
220 Farm Road 2216, Sumner, TX 75486-4648
Tel (903) 784-8719 *Founded/Ownrshp* 1996
Sales 107.5MM *EMP* 410^E
SIC 3799 Trailers & trailer equipment; Trailers & trailer equipment
IT Man: Shane Richard
Sfty Dirs: Greg Friesen
Sls&Mrk Ex: Abe Harms

D-U-N-S 17-165-2485 EXP
LOADCRAFT INDUSTRIES LTD
3811 N Bridge St, Brady, TX 76825
Tel (325) 597-2911 *Founded/Ownrshp* 2004
Sales 129.1MM^E *EMP* 365^E
SIC 3533 Oil & gas field machinery; Oil & gas field machinery
Mng Pt: Terry McIver
**Pt:* Donald Barley
**Pt:* Cary Brown
**Pt:* Dale Brown
**Pt:* Ray Jones
**Pt:* Grady McIver
CFO: Luis Collazo

LOADMASTER INDUSTRIES
See DERRICK LOADMASTER & EQUIPMENT INC

D-U-N-S 96-231-0574
LOADMASTER UNIVERSAL RIGS INC
6935 Brittmoore Rd, Houston, TX 77041-3807
Tel (281) 598-7240 *Founded/Ownrshp* 2004
Sales 50.0MM *EMP* 100
SIC 8711 Structural engineering
Pr: Roger M Barnes
**VP:* Gary Jiang
**VP:* Guozhang Jiang
Sales Asso: Douglas Hortvet

D-U-N-S 80-560-0454
LOADMATCH LOGISTICS INC
LML EXPRESS
1013 Ashes Dr Ste 200, Wilmington, NC 28405-8304
Tel (910) 344-0700 *Founded/Ownrshp* 2006
Sales 29.0MM *EMP* 57
SIC 4212 4731 Local trucking, without storage; Lumber (log) trucking, local; Lumber & timber trucking; Freight transportation arrangement
Pr: Gary Winstead
Pr: Jimmy Foster
**VP:* Scott Anderson
**Genl Mgr:* Keith Hanson

D-U-N-S 16-204-9501
LOADSPRING SOLUTIONS INC
187 Ballardvale St B210, Wilmington, MA 01887-1053
Tel (978) 685-9715 *Founded/Ownrshp* 1999
Sales 22.0MM^E *EMP* 48
SIC 4813
Pr: Eric Leighton
Ex VP: Al Marshall
Ex VP: Jim Smith
VP: Warren Krueger
VP: Stan Sturges
VP: Cameron Vixie
Mng Dir: Ron Willome
Off Mgr: Dianne Niemczyk
Sftwr Eng: Christopher Granzella
Sftwr Eng: Zac Shapleigh
Sftwr Eng: Can Yegen

LOAF 'N JUG
See MINI MART INC

LOANCARE
See FNF SERVICING INC

D-U-N-S 83-022-5707
LOANDEPOT.COM LLC
26642 Towne Centre Dr, Foothill Ranch, CA 92610-2808
Tel (949) 474-1322 *Founded/Ownrshp* 2010
Sales NA *EMP* 5,000
SIC 6162 Mortgage bankers; Mortgage bankers
CEO: Anthony Hsieh
Pr: David Norris
CFO: Jon Frojen
Ofcr: Diana Harvey
Ex VP: Peter Macdonald
Ex VP: Chad Smith
Ex VP: Bryan Sullivan
Sr VP: Michael H Wilson
CTO: Dominick Marchetti

D-U-N-S 06-188-1524
LOANLOGICS INC
4800 E Street Rd Ste 50, Feasterville Trevose, PA 19053-6658
Tel (215) 367-5500 *Founded/Ownrshp* 2006
Sales 59.2MM^E *EMP* 49^E
SIC 5045 Computer software
CEO: Howard H Conyack Jr
Pt: Douglas R Sheridan
**CEO:* Brian K Fitzpatrick
**CFO:* Jl John Alarcon
Chf Cred: Gerard Gerry Glavey
Ofcr: Craig Riddell
Ofcr: Michael Vitali
**Ex VP:* Joseph A Helfrich
Sr VP: Mary Anne Ahmer
Sr VP: Ira Artman
Sr VP: Terese L Campbell
Sr VP: Terese Campbell
Sr VP: Griff Durham
Sr VP: Leah Fox
Sr VP: Gerry Glavey
Sr VP: Les Parker
Sr VP: Jessica Price
Creative D: Justin Brindisi
Board of Directors: Howard Conyack Jr

LOANS 4 HOMES
See LANDLOVERS LLC

LOANSTAR ELECTRIC SUPPLY
See 1155 DISTRIBUTOR PARTNERS LLC

D-U-N-S 78-706-0920
LOBAR ASSOCIATES INC
4 Barlo Cir, Dillsburg, PA 17019-1621
Tel (717) 432-3429 *Founded/Ownrshp* 1995
Sales 31.9MM *EMP* 140
SIC 1541 1542 Industrial buildings, new construction; Commercial & office building, new construction; Industrial buildings, new construction; Commercial & office building, new construction
Pr: Lee E Eichelberger
**COO:* Marvin Diller
Treas: William Scott Gash
S&M/VP: Scarlette Lastoskie
Snr PM: Ike Sholley

D-U-N-S 05-291-7143
LOBAR INC (PA)
1 Old Mill Rd, Dillsburg, PA 17019-1620
Tel (717) 432-9728 *Founded/Ownrshp* 1967
Sales 94.4MM^E *EMP* 175^E
SIC 1541 1542 8741 1629 1731 7371

LOBBY GIFT SHOP
See WOMENS AUXILARY OF W A FOOTE MEMORIAL HOSPITAL

D-U-N-S 09-471-9705
LOBEL FINANCIAL CORP (CA)
1150 N Magnolia Ave, Anaheim, CA 92801-2605
Tel (714) 995-3333 *Founded/Ownrshp* 1979
Sales NA *EMP* 80^E
SIC 6141 Automobile loans, including insurance
CEO: Harvey Lobel
**Sec:* Gary Lobel
**VP:* David Lobel
Brnch Mgr: Karen Richards

LOBO DISTRIBUTING
See PHOENIX BEVERAGES INC

D-U-N-S 17-063-6893 IMP
LOBO TORTILLA FACTORY INC
7777 Hines Pl, Dallas, TX 75235-3312
Tel (972) 388-8000 *Founded/Ownrshp* 2004
Sales 23.5MM^E *EMP* 160
SIC 2099 Tortillas, fresh or refrigerated; Tortillas, fresh or refrigerated
**CFO:* Tom Rowell
VP: Ron King
Prd Mgr: Francisco Munoz

LOBSTER HOUSE, THE
See COLD SPRINGS FISH & SUPPLY CO

LOBSTER SHANTY RESTAURANTS
See CHEFS INTERNATIONAL INC

LOBUE CITRUS
See LO BUE BROS INC

D-U-N-S 06-557-4683 IMP/EXP
LOC PERFORMANCE PRODUCTS INC
13505 N Haggerty Rd, Plymouth, MI 48170-4251
Tel (734) 453-2300 *Founded/Ownrshp* 1971
Sales 88.8MM^E *EMP* 225
SIC 3541 Machine tools, metal cutting type; Machine tools, metal cutting type
CEO: Victor Vojcek
**Pr:* Lou Burr
**COO:* Jason Atkinson
**CFO:* Thomas Horne
VP: Mike Lassila
Prgrm Mgr: Jerry Bryant
Prgrm Mgr: Paul Menosky
Genl Mgr: Jeff Hanson
Dir IT: Jasper Recto
IT Man: J B Pergeau
IT Man: Jessica Segarra

D-U-N-S 02-626-4713
LOCAL & WESTERN OF TEXAS INC
5445 La Sierra Dr Ste 100, Dallas, TX 75231-3463
Tel (214) 750-6633 *Founded/Ownrshp* 1986
Sales 147.2MM *EMP* 12
SIC 5142

D-U-N-S 96-909-3736
LOCAL 1 HEALTH FUND
1211 W 22nd St, Oak Brook, IL 60523-2109
Tel (630) 288-6868 *Founded/Ownrshp* 2011
Sales 40.8MM *EMP* 3
Accts Bansley And Kiener Llp Chicag
SIC 8631 Labor unions & similar labor organizations; Labor unions & similar labor organizations
Pr: Tom Balanoff

D-U-N-S 79-701-7766
LOCAL 1102 RETIREMENT TRUST
311 Crossways Park Dr, Woodbury, NY 11797-2041
Tel (516) 683-1102 *Founded/Ownrshp* 2007
Sales 21.1MM *EMP* 2
SIC 6733 Trusts; Trusts
Prin: Frank Bail

D-U-N-S 96-660-3628
LOCAL 150 IUOE VACATION SAVINGS PLAN
6150 Joliet Rd, Countryside, IL 60525-3994
Tel (708) 482-7300 *Founded/Ownrshp* 2011
Sales 22.5MM *EMP* 3
Accts Graff Ballauer & Blanski Pc N
SIC 8631 Labor unions & similar labor organizations; Labor unions & similar labor organizations
Prin: William Dugan

LOCAL 169
See BOILERMAKERS AFL CIO

D-U-N-S 96-922-7557
LOCAL 191 HEALTH SVCE & INS PLAN AND INSURANCE PLAN
1139 Fairfield Ave Ste 1, Bridgeport, CT 06605-1190
Tel (203) 366-5849 *Founded/Ownrshp* 2011
Sales NA *EMP* 2^E
Accts Sm Esposito & Co Pc Hamden C
SIC 6411 Insurance agents, brokers & service; Insurance agents, brokers & service

LOCAL 2000 AIRLINE ATTENDANTS
See TEAMSTERS LOCAL 2000

D-U-N-S 04-754-6858
LOCAL 25 SEIU WELFARE FUND
SEIU LOCAL 25 WELFARE FUND
111 E Wacker Dr Ste 2500, Chicago, IL 60601-4200
Tel (312) 240-1600 *Founded/Ownrshp* 1968
Sales NA *EMP* 19
Accts Bansley And Kiener Llp Chicag
SIC 6371 Pension, health & welfare funds; Pension, health & welfare funds

D-U-N-S 96-656-8797
LOCAL 272 WELFARE FUND
220 E 23rd St Ste 805, New York, NY 10010-4685
Tel (212) 726-9730 *Founded/Ownrshp* 2011
Sales NA *EMP* 3
Accts Abrams Herde And Merkel Llp N
SIC 6371 Pension, health & welfare funds; Pension, health & welfare funds
Prin: Marc Goodman

LOCAL 282
See BUFFALO PROFESSIONAL FIRE FIGHTERS ASSOCIATION INC

LOCAL 29
See SPOKANE FIRE FIGHTERS UNION

D-U-N-S 07-327-0696
LOCAL 32B-32J SEIU SERVICE EMPLOYEE INTERNATIONAL UNION
SEIU LOCAL 32BJ
25 W 18th St, New York, NY 10011-4677
Tel (215) 627-7358 *Founded/Ownrshp* 1934
Sales 41.6MM^E *EMP* 350
Accts Salibello & Broder Llp
SIC 8631 Trade union; Trade union
Pr: Michael Fishman

Comm Man: Lynsey Kryzwick
Sfty Dirs: Ben Andrews

D-U-N-S 96-723-4472
LOCAL 338 HEALTH AND WELFARE FUND
1505 Kellum Pl, Mineola, NY 11501-4811
Tel (516) 294-1338 *Founded/Ownrshp* 2011
Sales NA *EMP* 3^E
Accts Buchbinder Tunick & Co Llp Ne
SIC 6371 Pension, health & welfare funds; Pension, health & welfare funds
Prin: John Durso

D-U-N-S 96-456-4657
LOCAL 342 HEALTH CARE FUND
166 E Jericho Tpke, Mineola, NY 11501-2098
Tel (516) 747-5980 *Founded/Ownrshp* 2010
Sales 21.1MM *EMP* 3
Accts Novak Francella Llc Bala Cynw
SIC 8631 Labor unions & similar labor organizations; Labor unions & similar labor organizations

LOCAL 342-50 UFCW
See AMALGAMATED MEATCUTTERS & RETAIL FD STORE EMP LOC 342 WEL A&P FUND

D-U-N-S 96-726-9858
LOCAL 351 IBEW HEALTH AND WELFARE FUND
830 Bear Tavern Rd, Ewing, NJ 08628-1020
Tel (609) 718-1323 *Founded/Ownrshp* 2011
Sales 33.7MM *EMP* 12^E
Accts le Shaffer & Co West Trenton
SIC 8631 Labor unions & similar labor organizations; Labor unions & similar labor organizations

LOCAL 371
See AMALGAMATED WELFARE TRUST FUND

D-U-N-S 07-524-3527
LOCAL 371 SOCIAL SERVICE EMPLOYEES UNION INC
817 Broadway Fl 14, New York, NY 10003-4709
Tel (212) 598-7040 *Founded/Ownrshp* 1967
Sales 27.1MM *EMP* 40
SIC 8631 Labor union; Labor union
Pr: Charles Ensley
**Pr:* Farice Moore
**Pr:* Yolanda Pamarejo
**Sec:* Joe Nazario
**VP:* Beverly Brown
**VP:* Lawrence Glickson
**VP:* Ira Williams
Board of Directors: Michael Baolesteros, Robert Baxter, Mary Lewis

D-U-N-S 96-674-2517
LOCAL 400 UNITED FOOD AND COMMERCIAL WORKERS AND EMPLOYER HEALTH AND WELFARE FUND
600 D St Ste 250, Charleston, WV 25303-3118
Tel (304) 343-7682 *Founded/Ownrshp* 2011
Sales 21.6MM *EMP* 2^E
Accts Dennis G Jenkins Cpa Llc Kenn
SIC 8611 Business associations

D-U-N-S 84-132-3017
LOCAL 580 INSURANCE FUNDS
501 W 42nd St Fl 2, New York, NY 10036-6205
Tel (212) 695-5206 *Founded/Ownrshp* 1946
Sales NA *EMP* 13
SIC 6371 Union trust funds; Union trust funds

D-U-N-S 96-783-7423
LOCAL 705 IBOFT HEALTH AND WELFARE FUND
1645 W Jackson Blvd 700, Chicago, IL 60612-3276
Tel (312) 738-2800 *Founded/Ownrshp* 2011
Sales NA *EMP* 3^E
Accts Bansley And Kiener Llp Chicag
SIC 6371 Pension, health & welfare funds; Pension, health & welfare funds

D-U-N-S 17-084-2652
LOCAL 804 WELFARE TRUST FUND
3421 Review Ave, Long Island City, NY 11101-3218
Tel (718) 786-4205 *Founded/Ownrshp* 1950
Sales 71.5MM *EMP* 20
Accts Buchbinder Tunick & Company N
SIC 6733 Trusts, except educational, religious, charity: management; Trusts, except educational, religious, charity: management

D-U-N-S 02-328-9581
LOCAL 812 HEALTH FUND
445 Northern Blvd Ste 30, Great Neck, NY 11021-4804
Tel (516) 303-1455 *Founded/Ownrshp* 2008
Sales 45.9MM *EMP* 2
Accts Saxbst Llp New York Ny
SIC 8099 Health & allied services

LOCAL 863 PENSION FUND
See TEAMSTERS LOCAL 863

D-U-N-S 07-937-9133
LOCAL 888 HEALTH FUND
160 E Union Ave, East Rutherford, NJ 07073-2124
Tel (800) 223-1503 *Founded/Ownrshp* 2014
Sales 26.2MM *EMP* 2
SIC 6722 Money market mutual funds

D-U-N-S 96-780-7053
LOCAL 888 HEALTH FUND
6 Gramatan Ave Ste 600, Mount Vernon, NY 10550-3223
Tel (914) 668-8881 *Founded/Ownrshp* 2011
Sales 20.7MM *EMP* 3
Accts Armao Costa & Ricciardi Cpa S
SIC 8631 Labor unions & similar labor organizations; Labor unions & similar labor organizations
Pr: Max Bruny

D-U-N-S 80-044-2654
LOCAL 888 U F C W
6 Gramatan Ave Ste 600, Mount Vernon, NY 10550-3223
Tel (914) 668-8881 *Founded/Ownrshp* 2007

Sales 26.2MM *EMP* 2
Accts Armao Costa & Ricciardi Cpa
SIC 8631 Collective bargaining unit; Collective bargaining unit
Pr: Max Bruny

D-U-N-S 02-645-6199
LOCAL 9 IBEW AND OUTSIDE CONTRACTORS HEALTH & WELFARE
4415 Harrison St Ste 330, Hillside, IL 60162-1905
Tel (708) 449-9004 *Founded/Ownrshp* 1896
Sales 21.6MM *EMP* 3
Accts Calibre Cpa Group Pllc Chica
SIC 8631 Labor unions & similar labor organizations; Labor unions & similar labor organizations

D-U-N-S 96-780-7319
LOCAL 94 94A 94B HEALTH & BENEFIT TRUST FUND IUOE AFL-CIO
331 W 44th St 337, New York, NY 10036-5402
Tel (212) 541-9880 *Founded/Ownrshp* 2011
Sales 106.5MM *EMP* 13E
Accts Schultheis & Panettieri Llp H
SIC 8631 Labor unions & similar labor organizations; Labor unions & similar labor organizations
Pr: Kuba Brown
CFO: Bill Faranda

D-U-N-S 07-966-2289
▲ LOCAL CORP
LOCAL.COM
7555 Irvine Center Dr, Irvine, CA 92618-2930
Tel (949) 784-0800 *Founded/Ownrshp* 1999
Sales 83.1MM *EMP* 93E
Tkr Sym LOCM *Exch* NAS
SIC 7311 Advertising agencies; Advertising agencies
Ch Bd: Frederick G Thiel
CFO: Kenneth S Cragun
Ofcr: Scott Reinke
Sr VP: Erick Herring
Sr VP: Peter Hutto
Sr VP: George Kellerman
VP: Peter Chang
VP: Eileen Licitra
VP: Joe Lindsay
VP: Mark Wallin
Exec: Jean Fairchild
Board of Directors: Norman K Farra Jr, Philip K Fricke, David M Hughes, John M Payne, John E Rehfeld

LOCAL FEVER
See JEANS WAREHOUSE INC

LOCAL GOVERNMENT
See COUNTY OF COCHISE

D-U-N-S 04-867-0822
LOCAL GOVERNMENT CENTER INC
NEW HMPSHIRE LCAL GVRNMENT CTR
25 Triangle Park Dr, Concord, NH 03301-5799
Tel (603) 224-7447 *Founded/Ownrshp* 1941
Sales 26.2MME *EMP* 120E
SIC 8611 Trade associations
Ex Dir: John B Andrews
**CFO:* Sandal R Keeffe
Dir IT: Dan Bartlett
IT Man: Sherri Ames

D-U-N-S 14-347-8795
LOCAL GOVERNMENT CENTER PROPERTY-LIABILITY TRUST LLC
LGC PROPERTY LIABILITY TRUST
(*Suby of* LOCAL GOVERNMENT CENTER INC) ★
25 Triangle Park Dr, Concord, NH 03301-5799
Tel (603) 224-7447 *Founded/Ownrshp* 1985
Sales NA *EMP* 119
SIC 6331 Property damage insurance; Fire, marine & casualty insurance & carriers
Bd of Dir: Gloria Lacasse

D-U-N-S 79-038-6478
LOCAL GOVERNMENT COMMISSION INC
980 9th St Ste 1700, Sacramento, CA 95814-2736
Tel (916) 448-1198 *Founded/Ownrshp* 1980
Sales 22.3MM *EMP* 26
Accts Gilbert Associates Inc Sacr
SIC 8651 Political action committee; Political action committee
Ex Dir: Kate Meis
Assoc Dir: Paul Zykofsky
Mng Dir: Linda Cloud
Plng Mgr: Steve Tracy
Pgrm Dir: Kif Scheuer
Pgrm Dir: Michele Warren

D-U-N-S 60-825-0635
LOCAL GOVERNMENT FEDERAL CREDIT UNION
323 W Jones St Ste 600, Raleigh, NC 27603-1369
Tel (919) 755-0534 *Founded/Ownrshp* 1983
Sales NA *EMP* 97
SIC 6061 Federal credit unions; Federal credit unions
Pr: Maurice R Smith
VP: Garland Avent
VP: Jeanne Couchois
VP: Deborah Isenhour
VP: Eric Johnson
VP: Phelps Terry
VP Mktg: Ashley Ruffin

D-U-N-S 93-184-9285
LOCAL INITIATIVE HEALTH AUTHORITY FOR LOS ANGELES COUNTY
L A CARE HEALTH PLAN
1055 W 7th St Fl 11, Los Angeles, CA 90017-2751
Tel (213) 694-1250 *Founded/Ownrshp* 1995
Sales NA *EMP* 900
Accts Deloitte & Touche Llp Los Ang
SIC 6324 Hospital & medical service plans; Hospital & medical service plans
CEO: Howard A Kahn
**COO:* John Wallace
**CFO:* Tim Reilly
Bd of Dir: Andrea Van Hook
**Chf Mktg O:* Gertrude Carter
Ofcr: Denise Corley
Exec: Elaine Batchlor
Dir Rx: Duane Asao
Prgrm Mgr: Ben Tysch
CIO: Tom Schwaninger
CTO: Cat Ellen

D-U-N-S 03-821-8772
LOCAL INITIATIVES SUPPORT CORP
LISC
501 Fashion Ave Fl 7, New York, NY 10018-5970
Tel (212) 455-9800 *Founded/Ownrshp* 1979
Sales 44.1MME *EMP* 420E
Accts Kpmg Llp New York Ny
SIC 8399 Community development groups; Community development groups
Pr: Michael Rubinger
COO: Michael Tierney
CFO: Elizabeth Pugh
Ofcr: Maria Canton
Ofcr: Beth Dufek
Ofcr: Chase Gordon
Ofcr: Nancy Howard
Ofcr: Ashley Jones
Ofcr: Kathleen Kovacs
Ofcr: Jay Paget
Ofcr: Joe Vaughan
Ex VP: Tina Brooks
Ex VP: Tobin Levy
VP: Evelyn Brown
VP: Dorene Conlon
VP: Maria Gutierrez
VP: Mindy Leiterman
VP: Richard Manson
VP: Fred Mason
VP: Vince Odonnell
VP: Stephanie Okeefe
Board of Directors: Greg Belinfanti, Kelly Caffarelli, Kathryn E Merchant, Karen Parkhill, Nilda Ruiz

D-U-N-S 18-753-3302
LOCAL INSIGHT YELLOW PAGES INC
(*Suby of* BERRY)
100 Executive Pkwy, Hudson, OH 44236-1630
Tel (330) 650-7100 *Founded/Ownrshp* 1984, 2007
Sales 21.4MME *EMP* 175
SIC 2741

D-U-N-S 00-202-6797
■ LOCAL MEDIA GROUP INC (NY)
(*Suby of* NEW MEDIA INVESTMENT GROUP INC) ★
40 Mulberry St, Middletown, NY 10940-6302
Tel (845) 341-1100 *Founded/Ownrshp* 1936, 2013
Sales 225.4MME *EMP* 2,900
SIC 2711 7313 Newspapers: publishing only, not printed on site; Newspaper advertising representative; Newspapers: publishing only, not printed on site; Newspaper advertising representative
Pr: John Wilcox
**COO:* William T Kennedy
**CFO:* Jonathan Kahan
**CFO:* William A Zurilla
**Ch:* Patrick Purcell
**Sr VP:* Kurt Lozier
**VP:* Patricia Gatto
VP: Joan Harrington
Dir IT: David Foglia
Dir IT: David Laders
IT Man: Gregory Bryant

D-U-N-S 08-191-3519 IMP
LOCAL MOTION INC
D.VA
(*Suby of* MINAMI CORP US) ★
870 Kawaiahao St, Honolulu, HI 96813-5208
Tel (808) 523-7873 *Founded/Ownrshp* 1991
Sales 33.4MME *EMP* 107
SIC 5136 5699 5941 5091 Beachwear, men's & boys'; Marine apparel; Surfing equipment & supplies; Surfing equipment & supplies; Beachwear, men's & boys'; Marine apparel; Surfing equipment & supplies; Surfing equipment & supplies
Pr: Koji Minami
Pr: Carolyn Chu

D-U-N-S 84-951-9814
LOCAL MOTION INC
LOCAL MOTION OF BOSTON
66b Rocsam Park Rd, Braintree, MA 02184-6706
Tel (781) 535-6344 *Founded/Ownrshp* 1993
Sales 25.8MME *EMP* 185E
Accts Bonanno Savino & Davies Pc
SIC 4151 4119 School buses; Limousine rental, with driver; School buses; Limousine rental, with driver
Pr: Bill Carragher
**Treas:* Bruce Barrowors

LOCAL MOTION OF BOSTON
See LOCAL MOTION INC

D-U-N-S 07-945-0299
LOCAL NO 9 IBEW AND OUTSIDE CONTRACTORS
1 Westbrook Corporate Ctr # 430, Westchester, IL 60154-5710
Tel (708) 449-9004 *Founded/Ownrshp* 2014
Sales NA *EMP* 3E
SIC 6371 Pension funds

D-U-N-S 07-843-6788
■ LOCAL STAFF LLC
MEDSTAFF HEALTHCARE SOLUTIONS
(*Suby of* CROSS COUNTRY HEALTHCARE INC) ★
6551 Pk Of Commerce Blvd, Boca Raton, FL 33487-8218
Tel (800) 347-2264 *Founded/Ownrshp* 2003
Sales 7.7MME *EMP* 500
SIC 8011 Offices & clinics of medical doctors; Offices & clinics of medical doctors

D-U-N-S 79-508-5401
■ LOCAL TV LLC
(*Suby of* TRIBUNE MEDIA CO) ★
1 Riverfront Pl Ste 505, Newport, KY 41071-4520
Tel (859) 448-2700 *Founded/Ownrshp* 2013
Sales 205.0MME *EMP* 800
SIC 4833 Television broadcasting stations; Television broadcasting stations
**CFO:* Ted Kuhlman

LOCAL UNION 478 ACDE
See INTERNATIONAL UNION OF OPERATING ENGINEERS

LOCAL WINE TOURS
See TERLATO WINE GROUP LTD

LOCAL.COM
See LOCAL CORP

D-U-N-S 16-150-6894
■ LOCATING INC
(*Suby of* DYCOM INDUSTRIES INC) ★
2575 Westside Pkwy # 100, Alpharetta, GA 30004-6410
Tel (678) 461-3900 *Founded/Ownrshp* 1984
Sales 33.3MME *EMP* 205
SIC 8711 Engineering services; Engineering services
Pr: Dennis Tarosky
**Ch:* Steven Nielsen
**Treas:* H Deferrari
**Sec:* Richard B Vilsoet
**Ex VP:* Terry L Fordham

D-U-N-S 86-717-8915
LOCATOR SERVICES GROUP LTD
TLSG CONSULTING
280 Summer St Ste 701, Boston, MA 02210-1131
Tel (617) 859-0600 *Founded/Ownrshp* 1994
Sales 30.2MM *EMP* 28
SIC 7389 Financial services; Financial services
Pr: Kim S Sawyer
Counsel: Steven Barry

LOCCITANE EN PROVENCE
See LOCCITANE INC

D-U-N-S 07-944-7092
LOCCITANE INC
120 Herrod Blvd, Dayton, NJ 08810-1528
Tel (212) 696-9098 *Founded/Ownrshp* 2014
Sales 62.1MME *EMP* 1,400
SIC 5999 Toiletries, cosmetics & perfumes; Toiletries, cosmetics & perfumes
Sr VP: Benoit Mennegand

D-U-N-S 87-826-8200 EXP
LOCCITANE INC
LOCCITANE EN PROVENCE
(*Suby of* L'OCCITANE INTERNATIONAL SA)
1430 Broadway Fl 2, New York, NY 10018-9227
Tel (212) 333-4880 *Founded/Ownrshp* 1995
Sales 259.1MME *EMP* 600
SIC 5122 5999 5961 Drugs, proprietaries & sundries; Perfumes; Toiletries, cosmetics & perfumes; Cosmetics & perfumes, mail order; Drugs, proprietaries & sundries; Perfumes; Toiletries, cosmetics & perfumes; Cosmetics & perfumes, mail order
Pr: Reinold Geiger
**CFO:* Francois Cambours
Treas: Wilfrid Poisnel
VP: Stephanie Guinard
Mng Dir: Leela Petrakis

LOCHBRIDGE
See CW PROFESSIONAL SERVICES LLC

D-U-N-S 80-857-1363
LOCHEARN NURSING HOME LLC
FUTURECARE
(*Suby of* FUTURE CARE HEALTH AND MANAGEMENT OF HOMEWOOD INC) ★
4800 Seton Dr, Baltimore, MD 21215-3210
Tel (410) 358-3410 *Founded/Ownrshp* 2005
Sales 21.2MM *EMP* 250
SIC 8741 Nursing & personal care facility management; Nursing & personal care facility management
Pr: Gary Attman

D-U-N-S 02-280-8901
LOCHER BROS INC
18098 365th Ave, Green Isle, MN 55338-2137
Tel (507) 326-5471 *Founded/Ownrshp* 1939
Sales 20.1MME *EMP* 55
Accts Schad Lindstrand And Company
SIC 5181 Beer & other fermented malt liquors
Ch Bd: Alfred W Locher
**Pr:* Robert Utendorfer
**VP:* Tim Hukreide

D-U-N-S 84-792-5666 IMP/EXP
■ LOCHINVAR LLC
(*Suby of* A O SMITH CORP) ★
300 Maddox Simpson Pkwy, Lebanon, TN 37090-5366
Tel (615) 889-8900 *Founded/Ownrshp* 2011
Sales 89.6MME *EMP* 375
SIC 3639 3443 5074 Hot water heaters, household; Boilers: industrial, power, or marine; Plumbing & hydronic heating supplies; Hot water heaters, household; Boilers: industrial, power, or marine; Plumbing & hydronic heating supplies
Pr: William L Vallett Jr
**Pr:* Bill Vallett Jr
**Ex VP:* Jeff Vallett
VP: Barbara Gatlin
VP: Robert Lancaster
VP: Jack Myers
VP: Bret Thompson
Exec: Ken Blackburn
Rgnl Mgr: David Olson
Genl Mgr: Dana Scharping
CTO: Warren Brandon

D-U-N-S 04-640-3515
LOCHMANDY MOTOR SALES INC
LOCHMANDY MOTORS
920 N Nappanee St, Elkhart, IN 46514-1248
Tel (574) 264-1174 *Founded/Ownrshp* 1964
Sales 41.1MME *EMP* 100
SIC 5511 7538 7532 5521 Automobiles, new & used; Pickups, new & used; Vans, new & used; General automotive repair shops; Top & body repair & paint shops; Used car dealers; Automobiles, new & used; Pickups, new & used; Vans, new & used; General automotive repair shops; Top & body repair & paint shops; Used car dealers
Pr: Craig S Lochmandy
**Sec:* Dennis Lochmandy
Store Mgr: Mike Deposltar
Sales Exec: Michael Lowery
VP Sls: Gary Struble
Sls Mgr: Abbigail Lochmandy

LOCHMANDY MOTORS
See LOCHMANDY MOTOR SALES INC

D-U-N-S 02-719-4364
LOCHRIDGE-PRIEST INC
2901 E Industrial Blvd, Waco, TX 76705-1899
Tel (254) 772-0670 *Founded/Ownrshp* 2007
Sales 57.3MME *EMP* 340
SIC 1711

LOCK HAVEN HOSPITAL
See CLINTON HOSPITAL CORP

LOCK HAVEN MEDICAL CENTER
See CLINTON HOSPITAL CORP

D-U-N-S 17-250-8103
LOCK HAVEN UNIVERSITY OF PENNSYLVANIA
STATE SYSTEM OF HIGHER EDUC
(*Suby of* STATE SYSTEM HIGHER EDUCATN PA) ★
401 N Fairview St, Lock Haven, PA 17745-2390
Tel (570) 484-2010 *Founded/Ownrshp* 1982
Sales 48.7MME *EMP* 413
SIC 8221 9411 University; ; University;
Pr: Craig Dean Willis PHD
VP: Jenn Barnes
VP: Deborah Erickson
VP: William N Hall Jr
VP: William Hanelly
**VP:* Linda D Koch PHD
**VP:* Robert Little
**VP:* Dr Roy T Stewart
**VP:* Jerry Updegraff
Pr Dir: Daniel Hanson
Pr Dir: Collins Morgan

D-U-N-S 78-279-5827 IMP
LOCK JOINT TUBE LLC
L J T
(*Suby of* LERMAN HOLDING CO. INC.)
515 W Ireland Rd, South Bend, IN 46614-3805
Tel (574) 299-5326 *Founded/Ownrshp* 1991
Sales 40.2MME *EMP* 230
SIC 3317 Welded pipe & tubes; Tubes, wrought: welded or lock joint; Welded pipe & tubes; Tubes, wrought: welded or lock joint
CEO: David Lerman
**Pr:* Ted Lerman
Dir IT: David Haghiri
Netwrk Mgr: Joe Pairitz
Tech Mgr: Ron Adamczyk
Plnt Mgr: Mark Richner
Sales Asso: Marcia Deal
Sales Asso: Melissa Demetz
Sales Asso: Ingrid Horne
Sales Asso: Darrell Johnson
Sales Asso: Matt Taylor

LOCKARD COMPANY, THE
See WAYNE S LOCKARD & SONS INC

D-U-N-S 06-487-4712 IMP
LOCKE INSULATORS INC
(*Suby of* NGK NORTH AMERICA INC) ★
2525 Insulator Dr, Baltimore, MD 21230-5098
Tel (410) 752-8020 *Founded/Ownrshp* 1965
Sales 21.2MME *EMP* 130
SIC 3264 Insulators, electrical: porcelain; Insulators, electrical: porcelain
Pr: John Dippold
**Sec:* Minoru Akiyama

D-U-N-S 07-843-2044
LOCKE LORD LLP
2200 Ross Ave Ste 2200, Dallas, TX 75201-2748
Tel (214) 740-8000 *Founded/Ownrshp* 1916
Sales 291.9MME *EMP* 1,150
SIC 8111 General practice law office; General practice law office
Ch: Jerry K Clements
Pt: Kay W McCurdy
Mng Pt: Balbir Bindra
Mng Pt: Robert D Miller
CFO: Mary Ann Jay
Ch: Don M Glendenning
Treas: Leldon Walenta
VP: Shonn Brown
Exec: Philip Cooper
Ex Dir: Miles Holsworth
CIO: Jerry McEachern

D-U-N-S 00-720-5206 IMP
LOCKE SUPPLY CO
LOCKE WHOLESALE HTG & COOLG
1300 Se 82nd St, Oklahoma City, OK 73149-4400
Tel (405) 635-3230 *Founded/Ownrshp* 1955
Sales 360.0MM *EMP* 900
SIC 5063 5074 5075 1711

LOCKE WHOLESALE HTG & COOLG
See LOCKE SUPPLY CO

D-U-N-S 06-280-0826
LOCKHART AUTOMOTIVE GROUP INC
LOCKHART CADILLAC SOUTH
1287 Us Highway 31 S C, Greenwood, IN 46143-2464
Tel (317) 253-1551 *Founded/Ownrshp* 1965, 1973
Sales 50.9MME *EMP* 120
SIC 5511 Automobiles, new & used; Automobiles, new & used
VP: Gregory M Lockhart
**VP:* Lynn Kimmel

LOCKHART CADILLAC SOUTH
See LOCKHART AUTOMOTIVE GROUP INC

D-U-N-S 05-907-9509 IMP/EXP
LOCKHART CHEMICAL CO
2873 W Hardies Rd, Gibsonia, PA 15044-8209
Tel (724) 444-1900 *Founded/Ownrshp* 1972
Sales 21.8MME *EMP* 125

SIC 2819 8731 2899 2865 Chemicals, high purity: refined from technical grade; Commercial physical research; Chemical preparations; Cyclic crudes & intermediates; Chemicals, high purity: refined from technical grade; Commercial physical research; Chemical preparations; Cyclic crudes & intermediates
Pr: Raj Minhas
**Ch Bd:* Thomas Gillespie Jr
**Treas:* Charles J Frasca
VP: Brian K Benjamin
**VP:* Larry Burkestrom
**VP:* Rajinder Minhas

D-U-N-S 05-541-7968
LOCKHART GEOPHYSICAL CO
1600 Broadway Ste 1660, Denver, CO 80202-4915
Tel (303) 592-5220 *Founded/Ownrshp* 1981
Sales 191.3MM^E *EMP* 150^E
SIC 1382

D-U-N-S 02-154-9639
LOCKHART INDEPENDENT SCHOOL DISTRICT
105 S Colorado St, Lockhart, TX 78644-2730
Tel (512) 398-0000 *Founded/Ownrshp* 1925
Sales 54.0MM *EMP* 660^E
Accts West Davis & Company Llp Au
SIC 8211 Public elementary & secondary schools; Public elementary & secondary schools
Pr: Susan K Brooks
CFO: Tina Knudsen
Bd of Dir: Carl Cisneros
Trst: Charles Kelly
Adm Dir: Roland Ortiz
Schl Brd P: Tim Juarez

D-U-N-S 00-334-0874
LOCKHART POWER CO (SC)
(*Suby of* MILLIKEN & CO) ★
420 River St, Lockhart, SC 29364
Tel (864) 545-2211 *Founded/Ownrshp* 1912
Sales 28.1MM^E *EMP* 39^E
SIC 4911 Generation, electric power; Transmission, electric power; Distribution, electric power
Pr: B E Corbett
COO: Bryan Stone
Genl Mgr: Leslie S Anderson
Sys Mgr: Paul McCutchon

D-U-N-S 10-664-6813
LOCKHEED GEORGIA EMPLOYEES FEDERAL CREDIT UNION
430 Commerce Park Dr Se, Marietta, GA 30060-2710
Tel (770) 421-2640 *Founded/Ownrshp* 1951
Sales NA *EMP* 178
SIC 6061 Federal credit unions; Federal credit unions
Pr: Ed Collins
**Ch Bd:* Sandra Walls
**CFO:* Candy Bracewell
**Ex VP:* Richard Hampton

D-U-N-S 94-858-6433
■ **LOCKHEED MARTIN AERONAUTICAL CO**
LMAERO
(*Suby of* LOCKHEED MARTIN CORP) ★
86 S Cobb Dr Se, Marietta, GA 30063-0001
Tel (770) 494-4411 *Founded/Ownrshp* 1951
Sales 228.8MM^E *EMP* 7,600
SIC 3721 3812 7699 3769 Aircraft; Search & navigation equipment; Aircraft & heavy equipment repair services; Guided missile & space vehicle parts & auxiliary equipment; Aircraft; Search & navigation equipment; Aircraft & heavy equipment repair services; Guided missile & space vehicle parts & auxiliary equipment
Pr: Ralph Heath
**VP:* Larry J McQuien
Genl Mgr: Lee Ryant
Snr Ntwrk: Mike Gibson
Corp Couns: Tressa Q Deandrade

D-U-N-S 14-976-9754
■ **LOCKHEED MARTIN AERONAUTICAL SYSTEMS SUPPORT CO**
LMASSC
(*Suby of* LOCKHEED MARTIN CORP) ★
86 S Cobb Dr Se, Marietta, GA 30063-0001
Tel (770) 494-2011 *Founded/Ownrshp* 1996
Sales 21.3MM^E *EMP* 200^E
SIC 4581 Airports, flying fields & services; Aircraft servicing & repairing; Aircraft maintenance & repair services; Airports, flying fields & services; Aircraft servicing & repairing; Aircraft maintenance & repair services
Pr: Michael Caim
VP: David L Haines
VP: Michael Terry
VP Opers: Mac Stevenson

D-U-N-S 18-181-4575
■ **LOCKHEED MARTIN AEROPARTS INC**
(*Suby of* LOCKHEED MARTIN CORP) ★
211 Industrial Park Rd, Johnstown, PA 15904-1961
Tel (814) 262-3000 *Founded/Ownrshp* 1987
Sales 24.6MM^E *EMP* 107
SIC 3724 3728 3444 Aircraft engines & engine parts; Aircraft parts & equipment; Sheet metalwork; Aircraft engines & engine parts; Aircraft parts & equipment; Sheet metalwork
Pr: Rebeca Z Styles
**Treas:* Kenneth R Possenriede
**VP:* Richard F Horvath
Dept Mgr: Craig Deemer
CTO: Ernest Lee Jr

D-U-N-S 11-917-3318 IMP
■ **LOCKHEED MARTIN AIRCRAFT CENTER**
(*Suby of* LOCKHEED MARTIN CORP) ★
244 Terminal Rd, Greenville, SC 29605-5508
Tel (864) 422-6262 *Founded/Ownrshp* 1984
Sales 502.2MM^E *EMP* 8,200
SIC 3721 4581 Aircraft; Motorized aircraft; Airport hangar rental; Aircraft cleaning & janitorial service
CEO: Raymond A Burick
**Pr:* Steven Kreger

D-U-N-S 04-430-6348
■ **LOCKHEED MARTIN ASPEN SYSTEMS CORP**
(*Suby of* LOCKHEED MARTIN CORP) ★
700 N Frederick Ave, Gaithersburg, MD 20879-3328
Tel (301) 240-7000 *Founded/Ownrshp* 2006
Sales 71.5MM^E *EMP* 1,651
SIC 7374 7379 7389 Data processing service; Computer related consulting services; Financial services; Data processing service; Computer related consulting services; Financial services
Pr: Albert Lampert
**Treas:* Linda J Dybiec
**Ex VP:* Eugene Brannock

D-U-N-S 87-893-3951
■ **LOCKHEED MARTIN ASPENMED SERVICES INC**
(*Suby of* LOCKHEED MARTIN ASPEN SYSTEMS CORP) ★
700 N Frederick Ave, Gaithersburg, MD 20879-3328
Tel (301) 240-7000 *Founded/Ownrshp* 2001
Sales 19.1MM *EMP* 485
SIC 7363 5047 Labor resource services; Medical equipment & supplies; Labor resource services; Medical equipment & supplies
Pr: David Shinton
Treas: Linda Dybiec
VP: Gregory Shomo

D-U-N-S 12-545-6652
LOCKHEED MARTIN COMMERCIAL ENGINE SOLUTIONS
3523 General Hudnell Dr, San Antonio, TX 78226-2030
Tel (210) 928-5000 *Founded/Ownrshp* 2002
Sales 12.5MM^E *EMP* 450
SIC 7699 Aircraft & heavy equipment repair services; Aircraft & heavy equipment repair services
Pt: Ed Bergin

D-U-N-S 07-873-4856
LOCKHEED MARTIN CORP
MISSION SYSTEMS AND TRAINING
32 Miles W Kaumualii Bldg 328, Kekaha, HI 96752
Tel (808) 335-8020
Sales NA *EMP* 90,720^E
SIC 3761

D-U-N-S 83-495-1691 IMP/EXP
▲ **LOCKHEED MARTIN CORP**
6801 Rockledge Dr, Bethesda, MD 20817-1877
Tel (301) 897-6000 *Founded/Ownrshp* 1995
Sales 45.6MMM *EMP* 120,735
Tkr Sym LMT *Exch* NYS
SIC 3761 3721 3663 3764 3812 3728 Space vehicles, complete; Guided missiles, complete; Ballistic missiles, complete; Guided missiles & space vehicles, research & development; Aircraft; Research & development on aircraft by the manufacturer; Satellites, communications; Propulsion units for guided missiles & space vehicles; Guided missile & space vehicle engines, research & devel.; Warfare counter-measure equipment; Missile guidance systems & equipment; Sonar systems & equipment; Radar systems & equipment; Aircraft parts & equipment; Research & dev by manuf., aircraft parts & auxiliary equip; Space vehicles, complete; Guided missiles, complete; Ballistic missiles, complete; Guided missiles & space vehicles, research & development; Aircraft; Research & development on aircraft by the manufacturer; Satellites, communications; Propulsion units for guided missiles & space vehicles; Guided missile & space vehicle engines, research & devel.; Warfare counter-measure equipment; Missile guidance systems & equipment; Sonar systems & equipment; Radar systems & equipment; Aircraft parts & equipment; Research & dev by manuf., aircraft parts & auxiliary equip
Ch Bd: Marillyn A Hewson
CFO: Bruce L Tanner
Treas: Kenneth R Possenriede
Ex VP: Dale P Bennett
Ex VP: Rob Weiss
Sr VP: Kenneth J Disken
Sr VP: Maryanne R Lavan
Sr VP: Paul Lemmo
Sr VP: Rodney A Makoske
Sr VP: Ronald T Rand
VP: Brian P Colan
VP: Gerry Fasano
VP: Andrea Greenan
VP: Gordon Johndroe
VP: Chandra McMahon
VP: Dan Nelson
VP: Jessica Nielsen
Board of Directors: Joseph W Ralston, Daniel F Akerson, Anne Stevens, Nolan D Archibald, Rosalind G Brewer, David B Burritt, Bruce A Carlson, James O Ellis Jr, Thomas J Falk, Gwendolyn S King, James M Loy

D-U-N-S 15-324-9859
■ **LOCKHEED MARTIN DESKTOP SOLUTIONS INC**
LMDSI
(*Suby of* LOCKHEED MARTIN CORP) ★
2700 Prosperity Ave # 200, Fairfax, VA 22031-4339
Tel (703) 206-0030 *Founded/Ownrshp* 1997
Sales 37.6MM^E *EMP* 222
SIC 5045 7371 Computers, peripherals & software; Computer software development; Computers, peripherals & software; Computer software development
IT Man: Jack Bleacher

D-U-N-S 12-054-9840
■ **LOCKHEED MARTIN ENERGY RESEARCH CORP**
(*Suby of* LOCKHEED MARTIN CORP) ★
1 Bethel Valley Rd, Oak Ridge, TN 37830-8050
Tel (865) 574-1000 *Founded/Ownrshp* 1996
Sales 98.4MM^E *EMP* 4,000
SIC 8733 Noncommercial research organizations; Noncommercial research organizations
Pr: Alvin W Trivelpiece
IT Man: David Rose

D-U-N-S 03-722-5935
■ **LOCKHEED MARTIN ENGINEERING & SCIENCES CO**
(*Suby of* LOCKHEED MARTIN CORP) ★
700 N Frederick Ave, Gaithersburg, MD 20879-3328
Tel (301) 240-7000 *Founded/Ownrshp* 1979
Sales 22.2MM^E *EMP* 640
SIC 8711 7374 Electrical or electronic engineering; Mechanical engineering; Industrial engineers; Data processing & preparation; Electrical or electronic engineering; Mechanical engineering; Industrial engineers; Data processing & preparation
Pr: Jay Huneycutt
**VP:* Christopher A Minton

D-U-N-S 07-011-0937
■ **LOCKHEED MARTIN FEDERAL HEALTHCARE INC**
(*Suby of* LOCKHEED MARTIN CORP) ★
700 N Frederick Ave, Gaithersburg, MD 20879-3328
Tel (301) 240-7000 *Founded/Ownrshp* 2004
Sales 10.6MM^E *EMP* 500
SIC 8742 Hospital & health services consultant; Hospital & health services consultant
Pr: Paul Ryan
**Treas:* Nancy P Vineyard
**VP:* William L Deckelman Jr
Plnt Mgr: Paul Sherman

D-U-N-S 17-019-7748
■ **LOCKHEED MARTIN GLOBAL TELECOMMUNICATIONS INC**
(*Suby of* BT LATAM HOLDINGS ONE, INC.)
1600 Tysons Blvd Ste 550, Mc Lean, VA 22102-4892
Tel (703) 556-9500 *Founded/Ownrshp* 2002
Sales 166.6MM^E *EMP* 927
SIC 4813 1731 Local & long distance telephone communications; ; Fiber optic cable installation; Local & long distance telephone communications; ; Fiber optic cable installation
Pr: Kenneth Possenriede
**Pr:* George Kappaz
**CFO:* Ian Gerrard
**Ch:* Brian Thompson
**Ex VP:* Philip Walker
VP: Jennifer Hill
**VP:* David C Preiss
**VP:* Rena H Whitney
Ex Dir: Arlan Stehney

D-U-N-S 12-050-5032
LOCKHEED MARTIN GLOBAL TELECOMMUNICATIONS LLC
(*Suby of* SULLIVAN UNIVERSITY SYSTEM INC) ★
6560 Rock Spring Dr, Bethesda, MD 20817-1145
Tel (301) 571-7135 *Founded/Ownrshp* 1963
Sales 267.6MM^E *EMP* 1,000^E
SIC 4813 Telephone communication, except radio; Telephone communication, except radio
CEO: Marillyn A Hewson
Treas: Wesley D Minami
Chf Inves: Christopher Ll
VP: Steven F Bell
VP: Jerome W Breslow
VP: Peter Clyne
VP: Robert Coutts
VP: Susan Miller
VP: Susan L Sallet
VP: Christophe Wallers
VP: Warren Y Zeger
Exec: Bruce L Crockett

D-U-N-S 05-860-5858
■ **LOCKHEED MARTIN GOVERNMENT SERVICES INC**
(*Suby of* LOCKHEED MARTIN CORP) ★
700 N Frederick Ave, Gaithersburg, MD 20879-3328
Tel (856) 486-5156 *Founded/Ownrshp* 1968
Sales 80.8MM^E *EMP* 4,873
SIC 7379 7373 7374 7372 Computer related consulting services; Computer integrated systems design; Computer systems analysis & design; Data processing service; Data entry service; Application computer software; Computer related consulting services; Computer integrated systems design; Computer systems analysis & design; Data processing service; Data entry service; Application computer software
Pr: Harvey Braswell
**Pr:* Don Thorpe
**Pr:* Bob Woods
**Plnt Mgr:* Marty Smith

D-U-N-S 14-508-4211
■ **LOCKHEED MARTIN GOVERNMENT SERVICES INC**
(*Suby of* LOCKHEED MARTIN CORP) ★
700 N Frederick Ave, Gaithersburg, MD 20879-3328
Tel (301) 240-7000 *Founded/Ownrshp* 2006
Sales 130.6MM^E *EMP* 5,000
SIC 8741 Management services; Management services
Pr: Gene Loftus
VP: Stephen W Brinch

D-U-N-S 13-577-6545
■ **LOCKHEED MARTIN GYROCAM SYSTEMS LLC**
(*Suby of* LOCKHEED MARTIN CORP) ★
5600 W Sand Lake Rd Mp-265, Orlando, FL 32819-8907
Tel (407) 356-6500 *Founded/Ownrshp* 2009
Sales 23.2MM^E *EMP* 100
SIC 3812 Search & navigation equipment; Search & navigation equipment
CEO: Jay Pitman
Prgrm Mgr: James Francis
**Opers Mgr:* Dan Kiehl
Sls Mgr: Jeremy Myers

D-U-N-S 04-291-3165
■ **LOCKHEED MARTIN INDUSTRIAL DEFENDER INC**
VERANO
(*Suby of* LOCKHEED MARTIN CORP) ★
225 Foxboro Blvd, Foxboro, MA 02035-2854
Tel (508) 543-4812 *Founded/Ownrshp* 1996
Sales 31.4MM^E *EMP* 95
SIC 7371 Custom computer programming services
Pr: Brian M Ahern
**Sec:* James L Gennari
**Sr VP:* John Shaw
Snr Sftwr: Otto Fowler
Snr Sftwr: Ehab Kashkash
Snr Sftwr: Mark Shmulevich
Dir IT: David Rowbotham
Info Man: Scott Abrants
Sftwr Eng: Phil Foster
Sftwr Eng: Darin Morse
Sftwr Eng: Steve Quinn

D-U-N-S 14-623-6315
■ **LOCKHEED MARTIN INFORMATION TECHNOLOGY COMMERCIAL CORP**
(*Suby of* LOCKHEED MARTIN CORP) ★
3114 Lord Baltimore Dr # 200, Baltimore, MD 21244-2872
Tel (443) 436-7800 *Founded/Ownrshp* 1998
Sales 12.3MM^E *EMP* 601
SIC 8742 Management consulting services; Management consulting services
Pr: Kay Kapoor
IT Man: Renee Higgs

D-U-N-S 09-306-1914
■ **LOCKHEED MARTIN INTEGRATED SYSTEMS INC**
(*Suby of* LOCKHEED MARTIN CORP) ★
1210 Massillon Rd, Akron, OH 44315-0001
Tel (330) 796-2800 *Founded/Ownrshp* 1999
Sales 22.5MM^E *EMP* 99
SIC 3699 3769 3728 3812 Electrical equipment & supplies; Guided missile & space vehicle parts & auxiliary equipment; Aircraft parts & equipment; Search & navigation equipment; Electrical equipment & supplies; Guided missile & space vehicle parts & auxiliary equipment; Aircraft parts & equipment; Search & navigation equipment
Prin: Ken Kiley
Sys Mgr: Nicole Castro
Sftwr Eng: Michael Bennett
VP Mktg: Bob Lowry

D-U-N-S 83-619-6972
■ **LOCKHEED MARTIN INTEGRATED SYSTEMS INC**
(*Suby of* LOCKHEED MARTIN SERVICES INC) ★
6801 Rockledge Dr, Bethesda, MD 20817-1803
Tel (856) 486-5000 *Founded/Ownrshp* 1996
Sales 786.2MM^E *EMP* 5,668
SIC 3812 Search & navigation equipment; Search & navigation equipment
CEO: Marillyn A Hewson
**Pr:* Richard J Masi
**Ex VP:* Richard F Ambrose
**Ex VP:* Dale P Bennett
**VP:* Sondra L Barbour
**VP:* Bruce L Tanner

D-U-N-S 04-803-5351
■ **LOCKHEED MARTIN INTEGRATED TECHNOLOGY LLC**
(*Suby of* LOCKHEED MARTIN GOVERNMENT SERVICES INC) ★
700 N Frederick Ave, Gaithersburg, MD 20879-3328
Tel (301) 240-7000 *Founded/Ownrshp* 2005
Sales 130.6MM^E *EMP* 5,000
SIC 8741 Management services; Management services

D-U-N-S 02-311-0377
■ **LOCKHEED MARTIN LOGISTIC SERVICES INC**
LOCKHEED MARTIN LOGISTIC SVCS
(*Suby of* LOCKHEED MARTIN CORP) ★
244 Terminal Rd, Greenville, SC 29605-5508
Tel (864) 236-3552 *Founded/Ownrshp* 1997
Sales 69.4MM^E *EMP* 3,000
SIC 4581 Aircraft servicing & repairing; Aircraft servicing & repairing
Pr: Edward J Bergin
CFO: Connie Mearkle
**VP:* Thomas Barthel

LOCKHEED MARTIN LOGISTIC SVCS
See LOCKHEED MARTIN LOGISTIC SERVICES INC

D-U-N-S 11-439-4778
■ **LOCKHEED MARTIN MANAGEMENT SYSTEMS DESIGNERS INC**
(*Suby of* LOCKHEED MARTIN CORP) ★
700 N Frederick Ave, Gaithersburg, MD 20879-3328
Tel (301) 240-7000 *Founded/Ownrshp* 2007
Sales 15.9MM^E *EMP* 590
SIC 7374 7373 Data processing service; Systems integration services; Data processing service; Systems integration services
Treas: Marcia Desmond
VP: James Iannuzzi
VP: Thomas Martwinski
IT Man: Sam Stevens
VP Sls: Jeffery Beyer
Mktg Mgr: Beth Wingate

D-U-N-S 02-022-5678
■ **LOCKHEED MARTIN ORINCON CORP**
(*Suby of* LOCKHEED MARTIN CORP) ★
10325 Meanley Dr, San Diego, CA 92131-3011
Tel (858) 455-5530 *Founded/Ownrshp* 1973, 2003
Sales 42.0MM^E *EMP* 350
SIC 7371 8731 Computer software development & applications; Commercial physical research; Computer software development & applications; Commercial physical research
Ch Bd: Daniel Alspach

CFO: Thomas P O'Hara
Netwrk Eng: Sean Harris
Board of Directors: Charles H Black, Leon Edney, James Forrester, Robert Kogler, William D Lowery, Jeff Nash, Jay Rains, Dr John T Rickard, Larry Shantz

D-U-N-S 80-525-8373
■ LOCKHEED MARTIN SERVICES INC
(*Suby of* LOCKHEED MARTIN CORP) ★
700 N Frederick Ave, Gaithersburg, MD 20879-3328
Tel (301) 240-7669 *Founded/Ownrshp* 1993
Sales 826.1MM^E *EMP* 20,000
SIC 8711 8741 8742 Engineering services; Management services; Management consulting services; Engineering services; Management services; Management consulting services
CEO: Marillyn A Hewson
**Treas:* Mike Mittrione
**Ex VP:* Bruce L Tanner

D-U-N-S 03-204-6666 IMP
■ LOCKHEED MARTIN SIPPICAN INC
(*Suby of* LOCKHEED MARTIN CORP) ★
7 Barnabas Rd, Marion, MA 02738-1421
Tel (508) 748-3399 *Founded/Ownrshp* 2004
Sales 106.6MM^E *EMP* 450
SIC 3812 3826 3499 3672 3829 3845 Warfare counter-measure equipment; Environmental testing equipment; Target drones, for use by ships: metal; Printed circuit boards; Physical property testing equipment; Electromedical equipment; Warfare counter-measure equipment; Environmental testing equipment; Target drones, for use by ships: metal; Printed circuit boards; Physical property testing equipment; Electromedical equipment
Pr: Latisha Rourke
**Pr:* William E Walsh Jr
**CFO:* James J Hickey
**VP:* Douglas J Dapprich
**VP:* Lawrence C Hall
**VP:* Thomas L Jarbeau
**VP:* James Langenheim
**VP:* Bernard Mitchell
**VP:* Donna M O'Connor
**VP:* Kenneth R Possenriede
Exec: Donna Hogan
Board of Directors: Richard I Arthur, Thomas Corcoran, Alan Holt, George E Melton, William E Walsh Jr, Claudius Watts

D-U-N-S 13-930-7151
■ LOCKHEED MARTIN SPACE OPERATIONS CO
(*Suby of* LOCKHEED MARTIN CORP) ★
700 N Frederick Ave, Gaithersburg, MD 20879-3328
Tel (301) 240-7000 *Founded/Ownrshp* 1994
Sales 241.4MM^E *EMP* 19,000^E
SIC 4789 Space flight operations, except government; Space flight operations, except government
Pr: Jay Honeycutt
**Sr VP:* Ken Reightler
**VP:* J R Kline

D-U-N-S 61-737-9607
■ LOCKHEED MARTIN TECHNICAL SERVICES INC
(*Suby of* LOCKHEED MARTIN CORP) ★
700 N Frederick Ave, Gaithersburg, MD 20879-3328
Tel (301) 240-7000 *Founded/Ownrshp* 1988
Sales 89.3MM^E *EMP* 20,000
SIC 8731 Electronic research; Electronic research
Pr: Linda Renfro
Ch: Richard G Adamson
Treas: Janet L Mc Gregor
Treas: Robert W Powell Jr
Ex VP: Michael F Camardo
VP: Philip J Duke
VP Bus: Kenneth F Morton
Board of Directors: Valerie C French

D-U-N-S 18-294-9776 IMP/EXP
■ LOCKHEED MARTIN TRAINING SOLUTIONS INC
(*Suby of* LOCKHEED MARTIN CORP) ★
100 Global Innovation Cir, Orlando, FL 32825-5003
Tel (407) 306-4000 *Founded/Ownrshp* 1995
Sales 159.5MM^E *EMP* 506^E
SIC 3728 Military aircraft equipment & armament; Military aircraft equipment & armament
Pr: Nick Ali
Pr: Doug Greenlaw
**CEO:* Marillyn A Hewson
**CFO:* Bruce L Tanner
Treas: John C McCarthy
VP: Glenn Brown
**VP:* Harold Browning
VP: William Carithers
VP: James Craig
VP: Thomas Dorsey
VP: Leonard Hicks
VP: Debra Palmer

D-U-N-S 55-721-6512
■ LOCKHEED MARTIN UNMANNED INTEGRATED SYSTEMS INC
(*Suby of* LOCKHEED MARTIN CORP) ★
133 W Park Loop Nw, Huntsville, AL 35806-1745
Tel (256) 722-0175 *Founded/Ownrshp* 2012
Sales 28.3MM^E *EMP* 150
SIC 7373 7371 Computer systems analysis & design; Custom computer programming services; Computer systems analysis & design; Custom computer programming services
Pr: Jesse D May
**CFO:* Joel Key
**VP:* Jay Chandler
Exec: Tom McKee
Dir Bus: Jay McConville
**Genl Mgr:* Ken Young

D-U-N-S 06-389-2830
LOCKHEED WINDOW CORP
925 S Main St, Pascoag, RI 02859-3521
Tel (401) 568-3061 *Founded/Ownrshp* 1956
Sales 42.2MM^E *EMP* 100
SIC 3442 1751 1542 Screens, window, metal; Window & door installation & erection; Commercial & office buildings, renovation & repair; Screens, window, metal; Window & door installation & erection; Commercial & office buildings, renovation & repair
Pr: Jeffrey Kosiver
Genl Mgr: Bob Gregoire
Off Mgr: Pam Terman

LOCKING FLOORS
See KEITH MANUFACTURING CO

D-U-N-S 60-594-7014
LOCKMASTERS INC
LOCKMASTERS SECURITY INSTITUTE
2101 John C Watts Dr, Nicholasville, KY 40356-2597
Tel (859) 885-6041 *Founded/Ownrshp* 2005
Sales 25.9MM^E *EMP* 47
SIC 5072 8221 5087 3429 Hardware; Security devices, locks; Colleges universities & professional schools; Service establishment equipment; Keys, locks & related hardware
Pr: Mark Miller
IT Man: John Jeffers
Mfg Mgr: Ed Deja
Mktg Mgr: Ricki Keaton
Sales Asso: Scott Said

LOCKMASTERS SECURITY INSTITUTE
See LOCKMASTERS INC

LOCKPORT CITY SCHOOL DISTRICT
See CITY SCHOOL DISTRICT OF CITY OF LOCKPORT

LOCKPORT PRESBYTERIAN HOMES
See PRESBYTERIAN SENIOR CARE OF WESTERN NEW YORK INC

D-U-N-S 04-089-0758
LOCKPORT SCHOOL DISTRICT 205
1323 E 7th St, Lockport, IL 60441-3823
Tel (815) 588-8000 *Founded/Ownrshp* 1909
Sales 45.0MM *EMP* 488
SIC 8211 Public senior high school; Public senior high school
Prin: Robert M Meader
Prin: Peter M Sullivan
Dir Sec: Frank Desandre

D-U-N-S 96-476-8563
LOCKPORT STEEL FABRICATORS LLC
3051 S State St, Lockport, IL 60441-5024
Tel (815) 726-6281 *Founded/Ownrshp* 2004
Sales 31.3MM^E *EMP* 80
SIC 3449 Bars, concrete reinforcing: fabricated steel
Pr: Greg Radecki
**CFO:* Dan Wiesbrock
VP Opers: Dirk Pfeil
QI Cn Mgr: Mathew Yingling

LOCKREY MANUFACTURING
See RAKA CORP

D-U-N-S 79-142-6109
LOCKTON AFFINITY LLC
LOCKTON RISK SERVICES, INC.
(*Suby of* LOCKTON INC) ★
7300 College Blvd Ste 500, Overland Park, KS 66210-1884
Tel (913) 652-7500 *Founded/Ownrshp* 1987
Sales NA *EMP* 180
SIC 6411 Insurance brokers; Insurance brokers
COO: Joseph Ziegler
Mng Pt: Sean Vandermaas
CEO: Steven Egnoire
Ex VP: Jacques Dufresne
Ex VP: Marianne K Sears
Sr VP: Karen Espinosa
Sr VP: Michael Owen
Sr VP: Ray Pallett
Sr VP: Robert L Smith
Sr VP: James Stevens
Sr VP: Monica Wilkens
Sr VP: Shannon Wilson
Sr VP: Richard Woods
VP: Daniel Binette
VP: Jeffrey Jacobs
VP: Nikki Pealer
VP: Bob Smith
VP: Susan Vance

LOCKTON COMPANIES
See SELECT ADVANTAGE EMPLOYERS GROUP

LOCKTON COMPANIES, INC.
See LOCKTON COMPANIES LLC

D-U-N-S 79-142-6323
LOCKTON COMPANIES LLC
LOCKTON COMPANIES, INC.
(*Suby of* LOCKTON INC) ★
444 W 47th St Ste 900, Kansas City, MO 64112-1906
Tel (816) 960-9000 *Founded/Ownrshp* 1999
Sales NA *EMP* 35
SIC 6411 Insurance agents, brokers & service
COO: Glenn A Spencer
Pr: Chris Keith
Ex VP: Rex Jennings
Sr VP: Chris Bartnik
Sr VP: Matthew Gooda
Sr VP: Eric Hirschberg
Sr VP: Bill Wright
VP: Chad Phillips
VP: Stacy Pocrass
Exec: Michael Hopson
**Prin:* Rick Kahle

D-U-N-S 80-953-8825
LOCKTON COMPANIES LLC
2100 Ross Ave Ste 1400, Dallas, TX 75201-6706
Tel (214) 969-6748 *Founded/Ownrshp* 2006
Sales NA *EMP* 100^E
SIC 6411 Insurance agents, brokers & service
Pr: John L Lumelieau
Treas: Alax L Salts

D-U-N-S 15-345-5555
LOCKTON COMPANIES LLC-PACIFIC SERIES
LOCKTON INSURANCE BROKERS
(*Suby of* LOCKTON INC) ★
725 S Figueroa St Fl 35, Los Angeles, CA 90017-5435
Tel (213) 689-0500 *Founded/Ownrshp* 2006
Sales NA *EMP* 350
SIC 6411 Insurance brokers; Insurance brokers
COO: Leonard Fodemski
Pt: Philip Hurrle
Mng Pt: Debbie Day
Pr: Timothy J Noonan
Pr: Mark Pastorius
CFO: Leonard G Fodemski
Ofcr: Kate Chan
Assoc VP: Shelly Noble-Seavall
Ex VP: Mark Carlin
Ex VP: Mark Cwizkel
Ex VP: Richard Roderick
Sr VP: Karle Kern
Sr VP: Keli Tomack
Sr VP: Viesha Treadwell
VP: Kathy Gazlay
VP: Donald Glazier
VP: Joyce Hans
VP: Robert L Johnson
VP: Matthew McFall
VP: CIC Noonan
VP: Lindsey Phillips

LOCKTON DUNNING BENEFITS
See LOCKTON-DUNNING SERIES OF LOCKTON COMPANIES LLC

D-U-N-S 16-137-3857
LOCKTON INC
444 W 47th St Ste 900, Kansas City, MO 64112-1906
Tel (816) 960-9000 *Founded/Ownrshp* 1966
Sales NA *EMP* 1,355
SIC 6411 Property & casualty insurance agent; Insurance agents; Life insurance agents; Property & casualty insurance agent; Insurance agents; Life insurance agents
Ch: David M Lockton
Pr: Joe Agnello
Pr: Bob Irvin
Pr: Chris Keith
Pr: Thomas J Schaffler
CEO: Tony Gusmao
CEO: John Lumelleau
COO: Mark Henderson
COO: Ross Reda
COO: Jason Richardson
COO: Glenn Spencer
CFO: Henry Bond
V Ch Bd: Ron Lockton
Ex VP: Michael Andler
Ex VP: Jim Caldwell
Ex VP: Kevin Cummings
Sr VP: David Bachrach
Sr VP: Chris Bartnik
Sr VP: Ray Beegle
Sr VP: Mickey Brown
Sr VP: William Butler

LOCKTON INSURANCE BROKERS
See LOCKTON COMPANIES LLC-PACIFIC SERIES

LOCKTON RISK SERVICES, INC.
See LOCKTON AFFINITY LLC

D-U-N-S 12-930-9720
LOCKTON-DUNNING SERIES OF LOCKTON COMPANIES LLC
LOCKTON DUNNING BENEFITS
(*Suby of* LOCKTON INC) ★
2100 Ross Ave Ste 1200, Dallas, TX 75201-7943
Tel (214) 969-6100 *Founded/Ownrshp* 1977
Sales NA *EMP* 118^E
SIC 6411 Insurance agents
COO: Steve Bohannon
Ch Bd: Mike Brewer
Pr: Judy Cole
Pr: Roger E Lambourn
Ex VP: Sheri Pixley
Ex VP: Bruce Sammis
Ex VP: Charles Vilder
Sr VP: Robert Allday
Sr VP: David Altimont
Sr VP: Steve Brooks
Sr VP: Diane Childress
Sr VP: Larry Childress
Sr VP: Kenneth Dowell
Sr VP: Todd Leveridge
Sr VP: Jeffrey Miller
Sr VP: Lynn Palmer
Sr VP: Donna Pankotai
VP: Gregory R Alperstein
VP: Culley Barragan
VP: George Brown
VP: Kim Foerster

LOCKTOOTH DIVISION
See HODELL-NATCO INDUSTRIES INC

D-U-N-S 14-751-9375 IMP
LOCKUP DEVELOPMENT CORP
800 W Frontage Rd, Northfield, IL 60093-1205
Tel (847) 441-4682 *Founded/Ownrshp* 1984
Sales 36.4MM^E *EMP* 90
SIC 1541 6512 8741 Industrial buildings & warehouses; Warehouse construction; Nonresidential building operators; Management services
Pr: Robert Soudan
CFO: Bill Gerber
IT Man: Judy Righter

LOCKWOOD, ANDREWS & NEWNAM
See LEO A DALY CO

D-U-N-S 00-969-4555
LOCKWOOD INDUSTRIES INC
FRALOCK DIVISION
28525 Industry Dr, Valencia, CA 91355-5424
Tel (661) 702-6999 *Founded/Ownrshp* 1971
Sales 69.8MM^E *EMP* 136
SIC 2672 2821 3644 Adhesive backed films, foams & foils; Polyimides (skybond, kaplon); Insulators & insulation materials, electrical; Adhesive backed films, foams & foils; Polyimides (skybond, kaplon); Insulators & insulation materials, electrical
CEO: Scott Tucker
**COO:* Marcelo Norona
**CFO:* Bobby Booher
CFO: Bobbi Rose
Sls Mgr: Rich Orstad

D-U-N-S 09-194-5261 IMP
LOCKWOOD INTERNATIONAL INC
TY VALVE
10203 Wallisville Rd, Houston, TX 77013-4115
Tel (713) 674-9610 *Founded/Ownrshp* 1977
Sales 253.1MM^E *EMP* 200
SIC 5085 Valves & fittings; Valves & fittings
Pr: Mike Lockwood
**VP:* Tom Lockwood
VP: Pat Murphy
Dist Mgr: Dennis Hough
Dir IT: Chris Beard
IT Man: Allen Walls
Opers Mgr: Darren Frederick
QI Cn Mgr: Terry Choi
Sls Mgr: Tim Burress
Sls Mgr: Brenden Lackey
Sls Mgr: CAM Wowk

D-U-N-S 03-082-8651
LOCKWOOD MC KINNON CO INC
TACO BELL
79 N Main St, Mansfield, MA 02048-2229
Tel (508) 339-2075 *Founded/Ownrshp* 1974
Sales 21.3MM^E *EMP* 600
SIC 5812 7832 Fast-food restaurant, chain; Motion picture theaters, except drive-in; Fast-food restaurant, chain; Motion picture theaters, except drive-in
Pr: Roger Lockwood
**VP:* David Lockwood
**VP:* Alexander G Mc Kinnon

D-U-N-S 06-275-1805
LOCO INC
2249 Broadway Ste 10, Grand Junction, CO 81507-1157
Tel (970) 242-5857 *Founded/Ownrshp* 1972
Sales 71.8MM^E *EMP* 75
SIC 5541 5411 5172 Filling stations, gasoline; Convenience stores; Engine fuels & oils; Filling stations, gasoline; Convenience stores; Engine fuels & oils
CEO: Robert L Lipson III

D-U-N-S 07-422-0542
LOCOMOTIVE ENGINEERS AND CONDUCTORS MUTUAL PROTECTIVE ASSOCIATION
LE & CMPA
4000 Town Ctr Ste 1250, Southfield, MI 48075-1407
Tel (313) 962-1512 *Founded/Ownrshp* 1910
Sales NA *EMP* 11
SIC 6321 6411 Fraternal accident & health insurance organizations; Insurance agents, brokers & service; Fraternal accident & health insurance organizations; Insurance agents, brokers & service
Pr: William L Davis
**Treas:* Christine Brayanis

D-U-N-S 61-383-6357
LOCOMOTIVE SERVICE INC
200 Union Blvd Ste 415, Lakewood, CO 80228-1832
Tel (720) 898-8577 *Founded/Ownrshp* 1995
Sales 72.3MM^E *EMP* 100
SIC 5172 3743 Diesel fuel; Railroad locomotives & parts, electric or nonelectric
Pr: Ryan Gilmer
**VP:* Michael Kester

D-U-N-S 07-913-8183
■ LOCUM LEADERS INC (MO)
(*Suby of* ONWARD HEALTHCARE INC) ★
64 Danbury Rd, Wilton, CT 06897-4429
Tel (203) 834-3000 *Founded/Ownrshp* 2013
Sales 25.0MM *EMP* 43
SIC 7361 Employment agencies; Employment agencies
Pr: Kevin Clark
Treas: Michael Dylag
VP: Stephen Saville

D-U-N-S 60-316-1134
LOCUS TELECOMMUNICATIONS INC
CALLPLUS
(*Suby of* KDDI AMERICA INC) ★
2200 Fletcher Ave Ste 6, Fort Lee, NJ 07024-5016
Tel (201) 585-3600 *Founded/Ownrshp* 1993
Sales 59.4MM^E *EMP* 160
SIC 4813 Telephone communication, except radio; Telephone communication, except radio
Pr: Satoru Manabe
**COO:* Yasunori Matsuda
**CFO:* John Chough
VP: Henry Park
VP: Jack Woo

LOCUST GROVE PUBLIC SCHOOLS
See GROVE LOCUST PUBLIC SCHOOLS

LOCUST RIDGE QUARRY
See HAINES AND KIBBLEHOUSE INC

D-U-N-S 06-803-4321
LOCUST VALLEY CENTRAL SCHOOL DISTRICT
22 Horse Hollow Rd, Locust Valley, NY 11560-1118
Tel (516) 277-5000 *Founded/Ownrshp* 1960
Sales 41.3MM^E *EMP* 600
SIC 8211 Public elementary & secondary schools; Public elementary & secondary schools
Pr: Yao Chu
Comm Dir: Pam Kaplan
Dir IT: Judy Marino
Netwrk Mgr: David Dutra
Schl Brd P: Suzanne Sgueglia
Pgrm Dir: Monica Cagney

D-U-N-S 07-023-9124
LODAN ELECTRONICS INC
3311 N Kennicott Ave, Arlington Heights, IL 60004-1429
Tel (847) 398-5311 *Founded/Ownrshp* 1999
Sales 60.0MM^E *EMP* 200
SIC 3496 Miscellaneous fabricated wire products; Miscellaneous fabricated wire products
Pr: Raymond A Kedzior
**Pr:* Thomas Cornhoff
**CFO:* Patricia Bonner
**VP:* Brett Kedzior

D-U-N-S 02-280-3639
LODERMEIERS INC
103 N 3rd St, Goodhue, MN 55027-9136
Tel (651) 923-4441 *Founded/Ownrshp* 1947
Sales 23.9MM *EMP* 65
Accts Smith Schafer & Associates Lt
SIC 1542 5083 Farm building construction; Farm implements; Farm building construction; Farm implements
Pr: Richard Lodermeier

D-U-N-S 14-219-5648 IMP
LODERS CROKLAAN USA LLC
(*Suby of* LODERS CROKLAAN B.V.)
24708 W Durkee Rd, Channahon, IL 60410-5249
Tel (815) 730-5200 *Founded/Ownrshp* 2002
Sales 90.5MM^E *EMP* 180
SIC 2079 Edible oil products, except corn oil; Edible oil products, except corn oil
Prin: Julian Veitch
CFO: Mike Molenkamp
**Prin:* Yeow Seng Lee
**Prin:* William Troy
IT Man: Clay Bonham
IT Man: Jian Ming
Opers Mgr: Craig Nelson
Plnt Mgr: Flavio Libralesso

LODGE AT KOELE
See LANAI RESORTS LLC

LODGE CASINO AT BLACK HAWK.
See BLACK HAWK / JACOBS ENTERTAINMENT LLC

D-U-N-S 02-661-9494 IMP
LODGE LUMBER CO INC
5001 Oates Rd, Houston, TX 77013-2817
Tel (713) 672-6679 *Founded/Ownrshp* 1940
Sales 23.1MM *EMP* 42
SIC 5031 Lumber, plywood & millwork; Lumber, plywood & millwork
Pr: John W Lodge III
**Treas:* Walter W Luck
**VP:* Janet Lodges
Dir IT: Doug Rodermund
Sls Mgr: Bob Exum

D-U-N-S 03-703-6928
LODGE MANAGEMENT CORP
LODGE MGT GROUP ENTRMT ENTPS
8 W Division St Ste 200, Chicago, IL 60610-2217
Tel (312) 664-6656 *Founded/Ownrshp* 1977
Sales 21.9MM^E *EMP* 250
SIC 5813 6512 Bar (drinking places); Commercial & industrial building operation; Bar (drinking places); Commercial & industrial building operation
CEO: Paul Risolia
**Pr:* Lynda Z McKeaney
**Pr:* F Owen McKerney
Mktg Dir: Matt Kubinski

LODGE MGT GROUP ENTRMT ENTPS
See LODGE MANAGEMENT CORP

LODGE OF FOUR SEASONS
See CHASE RESORTS INC

D-U-N-S 05-074-8180
LODGEWORKS LP (KS)
8100 E 22nd St N Bldg 500, Wichita, KS 67226-2305
Tel (316) 681-5100 *Founded/Ownrshp* 2000
Sales 39.0MM^E *EMP* 300
SIC 7011 Hotels & motels; Hotels & motels
Pt: Roy R Baker
Pt: Tony Isaac
Sr VP: Royr Baker
VP: Chris Gebert
VP: Cheryl Gilliam
Brnch Mgr: Chris Shelton
Genl Mgr: Tracie Caudle
VP Sls: Liz Thompson
S&M/VP: Barry White
Sls Dir: Peggy Kahler

D-U-N-S 04-313-5698
LODGIAN INC
(*Suby of* LSREF LODGING INVESTMENTS LLC) ★
2002 Summit Blvd Ste 300, Brookhaven, GA 30319-6403
Tel (404) 364-9400 *Founded/Ownrshp* 1998, 2010
Sales 145.4MM^E *EMP* 3,046
SIC 7011 5813 Hotels & motels; Drinking places; Hotels & motels; Drinking places
Pr: Daniel E Ellis
COO: Michael W Amaral
**CFO:* James A Maclennan
**Sr VP:* Bryan Esposito
**Sr VP:* Thomas Rosati
**VP:* Donna B Cohen
VP: Joseph F Kelly
**VP:* James R McGrath
Brnch Mgr: Charito Monis
Brnch Mgr: Michael Patel
Genl Mgr: Jack Bhakta
Board of Directors: W Blair Allen, John W Allison, Stewart J Brown, Paul J Garity, Stephen P Grathwohl, Michael J Grondahl, Alex R Lieblong, Mark S Oei

D-U-N-S 15-723-9450
LODGING DEVELOPMENT AND MANAGEMENT INC
DAYS INN
2001 Wheeler Ave, West Memphis, AR 72301-2239
Tel (870) 735-4243 *Founded/Ownrshp* 1984
Sales 13.0MM^E *EMP* 370
SIC 7011 8741 Hotels & motels; Motels; Hotel or motel management; Hotels & motels; Motels; Hotel or motel management
Pr: James O House
**Sec:* Danny Miller
**VP:* Jeff House

D-U-N-S 84-212-7289
LODGING DYNAMICS HOSPITALITY GROUP LLC
5314 N Riv Ste 310, Provo, UT 84604
Tel (801) 375-7800 *Founded/Ownrshp* 2008
Sales 13.6MM^E *EMP* 300
SIC 6531 6513 Real estate agents & managers; Apartment hotel operation; Real estate agents & managers; Apartment hotel operation
Prin: Joel Sybrowsky
**Prin:* D Keith Wilson

D-U-N-S 15-409-2068
LODGING ENTERPRISES LLC
OAKTREE INN
(*Suby of* AMERICAN HOTEL INCOME PROPERTIES REIT INC.)
8080 E Central Ave # 180, Wichita, KS 67206-2371
Tel (316) 630-6300 *Founded/Ownrshp* 2013
Sales 82.8MM^E *EMP* 1,010
SIC 7011 8741 6552 Hotels & motels; Management services; Subdividers & developers; Hotels & motels; Management services; Subdividers & developers
Pr: William Burgess
**Treas:* David Mitchell
Dir IT: Dan Carpentier
VP Opers: Michael Martin

D-U-N-S 96-842-0468
LODGING RLJ TRUST L P
(*Suby of* RLJ LODGING TRUST) ★
3 Bethesda Metro Ctr # 1000, Bethesda, MD 20814-5330
Tel (301) 280-7777 *Founded/Ownrshp* 2011
Sales 1.1MMM *EMP* 9^E
Accts Pricewaterhousecoopers Llp Mc
SIC 7011 Vacation lodges; Vacation lodges
Pr: Thomas Baltimore
CFO: Leslie D Hale
VP: Susan Sloan
VP Admn: Anita Wells

D-U-N-S 16-288-5193
LODGING SOLUTIONS LLC
265 Broadhollow Rd Fl 3, Melville, NY 11747-4833
Tel (516) 307-3000 *Founded/Ownrshp* 2004
Sales 27.0MM^E *EMP* 90
SIC 7389 Hotel & motel reservation service; Hotel & motel reservation service

D-U-N-S 07-321-8554
LODGING UNLIMITED INC
344 Willowbrook Ln, West Chester, PA 19382-5578
Tel (610) 436-8400 *Founded/Ownrshp* 1970
Sales 10.1MM^E *EMP* 350
SIC 8741 8742 Hotel or motel management; Industry specialist consultants; Hotel or motel management; Industry specialist consultants
CEO: Morris E Lasky

D-U-N-S 80-750-1754
LODGING/HOSPITALITY MANAGEMENT CORP
L H M
111 West Port Plz Ste 500, Saint Louis, MO 63146-3015
Tel (314) 434-9500 *Founded/Ownrshp* 1991
Sales 36.9MM^E *EMP* 365
SIC 7011 Hotels & motels; Hotels & motels
CEO: Robert F O Loughlin
**Pr:* Stephen M O'Loughlin
**CFO:* Joseph Mooney
**Sr VP:* Cathy J Raftery
**VP:* Craig R Cobler
**VP:* Sherry Lappe
**VP:* Tom Lyons
Rgnl Mgr: Darlene Balzano
VP Opers: Craig Cobler
Sls Mgr: Corey McCarthy

D-U-N-S 02-000-4552
LODI CITY OF INC
CITY HALL
221 W Pine St, Lodi, CA 95240-2019
Tel (209) 333-6700 *Founded/Ownrshp* 1906
Sales NA *EMP* 450
Accts Macias Gini & O Connell Llp
SIC 9111 City & town managers' offices; ; City & town managers' offices;
Genl Mgr: Stephen Schwabauer
Plng Mgr: Craig Hoffman
Sls Mgr: Wendy Dowhower

D-U-N-S 02-356-6060
LODI HONDA MOTORS INC
1700 S Cherokee Ln, Lodi, CA 95240-7802
Tel (209) 473-3100 *Founded/Ownrshp* 1980
Sales 29.8MM^E *EMP* 90
SIC 5511 Automobiles, new & used; Automobiles, new & used
Pr: S Robert Zamora
**VP:* Paul Wondries

D-U-N-S 07-467-3807
LODI MEMORIAL HOSPITAL ASSOCIATION INC
975 S Fairmont Ave, Lodi, CA 95240-5118
Tel (209) 334-3411 *Founded/Ownrshp* 1945
Sales 174.9MM *EMP* 1,050
Accts Moss Adams Llp Sacramento Ca
SIC 8062 General medical & surgical hospitals; Medical equipment rental; Hospital equipment & supplies; General medical & surgical hospitals
CEO: Joseph P Harrington
Chf OB: Jane M Maloney
Dir Recs: Ellen M Donald
Dir Vol: Sarah Beasley
Pr: Jana Van Os
COO: Jim Russell
**CFO:* Terrence Deak
CFO: Ron Kreitner
CFO: Ron Kreutner
Ofcr: David Mack
**VP:* Debbe Moreno
Exec: Mark Wallace
Dir OR: Ron Ligsay
Dir Inf Cn: Schyerle Beal
Dir Inf Cn: Altino McKelvey
Dir Inf Cn: Donna Salvi
Dir Inf Cn: Gerg Woolf
Dir Risk M: Daleen Marie
Dir Lab: Karla Theis
Dir Rad: Erik Yasumoto
Dir Rx: Sandy Atwater

LODI POLICE DEPARTMENT
See BOROUGH OF LODI

D-U-N-S 18-421-3882
LODI SCHOOL DISTRICT
8 Hunter St, Lodi, NJ 07644-2925
Tel (973) 778-4620 *Founded/Ownrshp* 1895
Sales 10.6MM^E *EMP* 300
SIC 8211 9411 Public elementary & secondary schools; Administration of educational programs; Public elementary & secondary schools; Administration of educational programs

D-U-N-S 08-244-8093
LODI UNIFIED SCHOOL DISTRICT
1305 E Vine St, Lodi, CA 95240-3179
Tel (209) 331-7000 *Founded/Ownrshp* 1967
Sales 297.0MM *EMP* 3,516
Accts Gilbert Associates Inc Sacr
SIC 8211 Public elementary & secondary schools; Public elementary & secondary schools
**Pr:* Mr Ron Heberle
Ofcr: Douglas Barge
**VP:* Mr Joe Nava
Prgrm Mgr: Josephine Fierro
Trfc Dir: Virginia Connolly
Trfc Dir: Ranee Cunningham
Trfc Dir: Margie Duran
Trfc Dir: Sandy Torris
Opers Supe: Andi Kutlik
Instr Medi: Gabriela Vazquez
HC Dir: Kristen Elgen

D-U-N-S 07-293-4193
LOEB & LOEB LLP
10100 Santa Monica Blvd # 2200, Los Angeles, CA 90067-4120
Tel (310) 282-2000 *Founded/Ownrshp* 1909
Sales 46.9MM^E *EMP* 268
SIC 8111 General practice law office; General practice law office
Ch: Barry I Slotnick
Pt: Kenneth B Anderson
Pt: Daniel D Frohling
Pt: Elizabeth L Majers
Pt: Mickey Mayerson
Pt: Benny Pang
Pt: David S Schaefer
Pr: Yolanda Bacote
COO: Alan Cutler
COO: Jerry Post
Ch: Stan Johnson
Ch: Michael A Mayerson
Ch: Robert A Meyer

D-U-N-S 00-196-4451 IMP
LOEB ELECTRIC CO (OH)
UNISTRUT-COLUMBUS
1800 E 5th Ave Ste A, Columbus, OH 43219-2592
Tel (614) 294-6351 *Founded/Ownrshp* 1911
Sales 176.7MM^E *EMP* 155
SIC 5063 Electrical apparatus & equipment; Lighting fixtures; Circuit breakers; Wire & cable; Electrical apparatus & equipment; Lighting fixtures; Circuit breakers; Wire & cable
Pr: Charles A Loeb
**CFO:* Jeff Blunt
Ex VP: Robert Richards
**Prin:* M J Walsh
Brnch Mgr: Bill Gannon
Opers Mgr: Guy Blauser
Sales Asso: Jacob Bringardner
Sales Asso: Steve Bruns
Sales Asso: Kartra Johnson
Sales Asso: Emily Kershaw
Sales Asso: Tina Weis

LOEB OIL
See HERMAN L LOEB LLC

LOEC, INC.
See FONTEM US INC

D-U-N-S 10-401-2463
LOEFFEL STEEL PRODUCTS INC
14100 S Loeffel Steel Dr, Riverdale, IL 60827-1947
Tel (847) 382-6770 *Founded/Ownrshp* 1983
Sales 29.3MM^E *EMP* 55
SIC 5051 Steel
Pr: Maurice F Loeffel
**VP:* Matthew Loeffel
**VP:* Timothy K Loeffel Sr

D-U-N-S 00-184-0644
LOEHMANN-BLASIUS CHEVROLET INC (CT)
90 Scott Rd, Waterbury, CT 06705-3203
Tel (203) 753-9261 *Founded/Ownrshp* 1929, 1971
Sales 70.7MM^E *EMP* 140
SIC 5511 Automobiles, new & used; Automobiles, new & used
Pr: Frederickw Blasius Sr
**Treas:* Juan Rodriguez
**VP:* Frederick W Blasius Jr
IT Man: Andrew Pape
Sls Mgr: Christopher Minerly

D-U-N-S 60-180-7183 IMP
LOEHMANNS HOLDINGS INC
(*Suby of* ISTITHMAR WORLD)
2500 Halsey St Frnt 1, Bronx, NY 10461-3692
Tel (718) 409-2000 *Founded/Ownrshp* 2006
Sales 185.0MM^E *EMP* 1,784
SIC 5621 5661 3171 Ready-to-wear apparel, women's; Women's shoes; Women's handbags & purses; Ready-to-wear apparel, women's; Women's shoes; Women's handbags & purses
CEO: Steven Newman
**Pr:* Robert N Friedman
**COO:* Robert Glass
**Co-Ch Bd:* William J Fox
**Co-Ch Bd:* Joseph Nusim
Sr VP: Frank Lamolino
CTO: Ramona Horibata

D-U-N-S 00-787-4563 IMP
LOEHMANNS INC (DE)
(*Suby of* LOEHMANNS HOLDINGS INC) ★
2500 Halsey St, Bronx, NY 10461-3637
Tel (718) 409-2000 *Founded/Ownrshp* 1921, 2000
Sales 185.0MM^E *EMP* 1,700
SIC 5621 Ready-to-wear apparel, women's
Pr: Robert N Friedman
**Ch Bd:* Steven Newman
**COO:* Robert Glass
Sr VP: Marvin Gardner
Sr VP: Tim Palmieri
VP: Tony D'Annibale
Plng Mgr: Gladys Fernandez
Store Mgr: Carole Benis
Dir IT: Mark Tipton

D-U-N-S 60-400-3129
LOEKS STAR PARTNERS
STAR THEATRES
920 Main St, Kansas City, MO 64105-2017
Tel (816) 471-2090 *Founded/Ownrshp* 2002
Sales 3.0MM^E *EMP* 362^E
SIC 7832 Motion picture theaters, except drive-in
Pt: Loews Cineplex Entertainment C
Pt: Oaktree C LLC

LOEWS CORONADO BAY RESORT
See 51ST ST & 8TH AVE CORP

D-U-N-S 00-698-6905
▲ LOEWS CORP
667 Madison Ave Fl 7, New York, NY 10065-8087
Tel (212) 521-2000 *Founded/Ownrshp* 1946
Sales NA *EMP* 17,510
Accts Deloitte & Touche Llp New Yor
Tkr Sym L *Exch* NYS
SIC 6331 6311 1381 4922 7011 Property damage insurance; Fire, marine & casualty insurance: stock; Life insurance carriers; Drilling oil & gas wells; Pipelines, natural gas; Hotels; Property damage insurance; Fire, marine & casualty insurance: stock; Life insurance carriers; Drilling oil & gas wells; Pipelines, natural gas; Hotels
Pr: James S Tisch
**Ch Bd:* Andrew H Tisch
V Ch: Paul W Whetsell
CFO: David B Edelson
Treas: Andrew Stegen
Ex VP: Troy Furbay
Ex VP: Sharleotte Saint-Martin
Sr VP: Constantine S Dimas
Sr VP: Gary W Garson
Sr VP: Jonathan Kantor
Sr VP: Peter Keegan
Sr VP: Michael Palmeri
Sr VP: Richard W Scott
Sr VP: Marc Shapiro
Sr VP: Jimmy Suh
VP: Jason Boxer
VP: Brian Byrne
VP: Elizabeth Harlow
VP: Mary Skafidas
VP: Ramu Venkatachalam
VP: Debbie Walker
Board of Directors: Ken Miller, Lawrence S Bacow, Anthony Welters, Ann E Berman, Joseph L Bower, Charles D Davidson, Charles M Diker, Jacob A Frenkel, Paul J Fribourg, Walter L Harris, Philip A Laskawy

D-U-N-S 00-373-2509
■ LOEWS HOLLYWOOD HOTEL LLC
(*Suby of* LOEWS CORP) ★
1755 N Highland Ave, Hollywood, CA 90028-4403
Tel (323) 450-2235 *Founded/Ownrshp* 2012
Sales 15.8MM^E *EMP* 375
SIC 7011 Hotels; Hotels
Ch Bd: Jonathan Tisch
Genl Mgr: Dan Shaughnessy
Natl Sales: Gigi Cabrera
Natl Sales: Cristina Godwin
Sls Dir: Danny Benaderet
Sls Dir: Hedy Varga
Sls Mgr: Paulene Kawasjee

LOEWS HOTELS & RESORTS
See LOEWS HOTELS HOLDING CORP

D-U-N-S 12-157-0840 IMP
■ LOEWS HOTELS HOLDING CORP
LOEWS HOTELS & RESORTS
(*Suby of* LOEWS CORP) ★
667 Madison Ave, New York, NY 10065-8029
Tel (212) 521-2000 *Founded/Ownrshp* 1983
Sales 500.0M *EMP* 2,723
SIC 7011 Hotels; Hotels
CEO: S Kirk Kinsell
Pr: Jonathan Nathanson
Pr: Glenn Zarin
COO: Jack W Bernsmeier
**CFO:* Vincent Dunleavy
**Ch:* Jonathan M Tisch
Chf Mktg O: Bruce Himelstein
Ex VP: Kenneth Siegel
Sr VP: Jim Cone
Sr VP: Thomas Staab
VP: Elif Bali
VP: Brian Byrne
**VP:* Gary Garson
VP: Zack Miller-Murphy
VP: Jonathan Mohraz
VP: Alan Momeyer
VP: Audrey Rampinelli
VP: Marc Soucy
VP: Jeffrey Stewart
Exec: Carl Schaubhut
Exec: Olivier Senoussaoui

LOEWS HTELS AT UNVRSAL ORLANDO
See UCF HOTEL VENTURE

LOEWS L'ENFANT PLAZA HOTEL
See LOEWS WASHINGTON HOTEL CORP

LOEW'S MIAMI BEACH
See LOEWS MIAMI BEACH HOTEL OPERATING CO INC

D-U-N-S 04-638-9867
■ LOEWS MIAMI BEACH HOTEL OPERATING CO INC
LOEW'S MIAMI BEACH
(*Suby of* LOEWS HOTELS & RESORTS) ★
1601 Collins Ave, Miami Beach, FL 33139-3112
Tel (305) 604-5427 *Founded/Ownrshp* 1996
Sales NA *EMP* 900
SIC 7011 Hotels & motels; Hotels & motels
Ch Bd: Jonathan M Tisch
**Rgnl VP:* John Thacher
**VP:* Gary W Garson
**VP:* Charlotte St Martin
Info Man: Bill Kreuter
Natl Sales: Christopher Baran
Natl Sales: Rory Mullen
Natl Sales: Nyki Tevini
Mktg Dir: Kathleen Bernesby
Pr Dir: Jeff Abbaticchio
Sls Dir: Chse Gerson

LOEWS PHILADELPHIA HOTEL
See TWELFTH STREET HOTEL ASSOCIATES LP

LOEWS REGENCY HOTEL
See 61ST & PARK AVE CORP

LOEWS SANTA MONICA BEACH HOTEL
See DTRS SANTA MONICA LLC

D-U-N-S 13-058-3834
LOEWS TUCSON HOTEL INC
LOEWS VENTANA CANYON RESORT
7000 N Resort Dr, Tucson, AZ 85750-1341
Tel (520) 299-6832 *Founded/Ownrshp* 1983
Sales 33.4MM^E *EMP* 500
SIC 7011 5812 Resort hotel; Eating places; Resort hotel; Eating places
Pr: Brian Johnson
CFO: Christopher Thullen
Dir Soc: Sheila Bourque
Ex Dir: Nick Smith
Dir IT: Kurt Neuberg
Natl Sales: Alisha Jackson
Mktg Dir: Mike Domingas
Mktg Dir: Marcia Kleiman
Pr Mgr: Sarah J Beal
Snr Mgr: Victoria Cote
Snr Mgr: Joan Le Fevre

LOEWS VENTANA CANYON RESORT
See LOEWS TUCSON HOTEL INC

LOEWS VENTANA CANYON RESORT
See VENTANA CANYON HOTEL ASSOCIATES

D-U-N-S 93-787-1747
■ LOEWS WASHINGTON HOTEL CORP
LOEWS L'ENFANT PLAZA HOTEL
(*Suby of* LOEWS HOTELS & RESORTS) ★
3340 Players Club Pkwy # 200, Memphis, TN 38125-8942
Tel (901) 821-4146 *Founded/Ownrshp* 1973
Sales 51.4M^E *EMP* 280
SIC 7011 7991 5813 5812 Hotels & motels; Physical fitness facilities; Drinking places; Eating places
CEO: Johnathan M Tish
Dir IT: Jae Sung

D-U-N-S 78-758-2469
LOEWY ENTERPRISES
SUNRISE PRODUCE COMPANY
500 Burning Tree Rd, Fullerton, CA 92833-1400
Tel (323) 726-3838 *Founded/Ownrshp* 1991
Sales 69.5MM^E *EMP* 90
SIC 5148 Fresh fruits & vegetables; Fresh fruits & vegetables
Pr: Paul Carone
VP: Danny Calvejo
Mfg Dir: Bruce Dauer
Ql Cn Mgr: John Akin

LOFFLER BUSINESS SYSTEMS
See LOFFLER COMPANIES INC

D-U-N-S 17-360-7987
LOFFLER COMPANIES INC
LOFFLER BUSINESS SYSTEMS
1101 E 78th St Ste 200, Bloomington, MN 55420-1405
Tel (952) 925-6800 *Founded/Ownrshp* 1986
Sales 43.0MM *EMP* 315
SIC 5734 Printers & plotters: computers; Printers & plotters: computers
CEO: James S Loffler
CFO: Neil Lee
Bd of Dir: Jerry Beeskow
Sr VP: Kevin Motl
VP: Jeff Rehbein
VP: Gordy Running
Rgnl Mgr: Katie Peterson
Admn Mgr: Chuck Ernst
CTO: Randy Olson
Software D: Brian Steckling
Netwrk Eng: Luke Bruun
Board of Directors: John Finch, Julie Koch

LOFFREDO FRESH PRODUCE CO
See LOFFREDO GARDENS INC

D-U-N-S 04-704-9580
LOFFREDO GARDENS INC
LOFFREDO FRESH PRODUCE CO
4001 Sw 63rd St, Des Moines, IA 50321-1607
Tel (816) 421-7480 *Founded/Ownrshp* 1970
Sales 127.1MM^E *EMP* 330
SIC 5148 Vegetables, fresh; Fruits, fresh; Vegetables, fresh; Fruits, fresh
Pr: Gene Loffredo
**COO:* Steve Winders
**CFO:* Mark Zimmerman
**Treas:* Larry E Loffredo
**VP:* John J Loffredo
Brnch Mgr: Bill Winn
Off Mgr: Bob Gordon
IT Man: Tina Epperson
IT Man: Ryan Meier
IT Man: Ryan Meir
Opers Mgr: John Davis

D-U-N-S 62-164-1844
LOFTCO INC
1832 E Deer Valley Rd, Phoenix, AZ 85024-5605
Tel (602) 445-4000 *Founded/Ownrshp* 1993
Sales 40.8MM^E *EMP* 300^E
SIC 1751 1521 Framing contractor; New construction, single-family houses; Framing contractor; New construction, single-family houses
CEO: Michael A Lofton
**Pr:* Mark R Sippola
VP: Michael Loften
**VP:* Sandra K Lofton
IT Man: Cody Peters
Sfty Dirs: Gustaco Rios
Sls&Mrk Ex: Jim Raptis

D-U-N-S 16-723-5063 IMP
LOFTEX USA LLC
58 W 40th St Fl 10, New York, NY 10018-2639
Tel (212) 302-1162 *Founded/Ownrshp* 2004
Sales 70.0MM^E *EMP* 7
SIC 5023 Towels; Towels
Sls Dir: Luis Hernandez

D-U-N-S 88-487-8034 IMP
■ LOFTHOUSE BAKERY PRODUCTS INC
RALCORP FROZEN BAKERY PRODUCTS
(*Suby of* RALCORP HOLDINGS INC) ★
215 N 700 W Ste A10, Ogden, UT 84404-1342
Tel (801) 776-3500 *Founded/Ownrshp* 2007
Sales 190.2MM^E *EMP* 550^E
SIC 5149 Bakery products; Bakery products
Pr: K J Hunt
**Pr:* David P Skarie
COO: Steven Smith
**VP:* S K Harris
Genl Mgr: Mark Stoner
Sfty Mgr: Jerine Price

D-U-N-S 03-591-6907
LOFTIN EQUIPMENT CO
2111 E Highland Ave # 255, Phoenix, AZ 85016-4795
Tel (602) 272-9466 *Founded/Ownrshp* 1976
Sales 137.8MM^E *EMP* 100^E
SIC 5063 5084 5999 Generators; Engines & parts, diesel; Electronic parts & equipment; Generators; Engines & parts, diesel; Electronic parts & equipment
Pr: Mark Loftin
**VP:* John Haney
**VP:* Charles Loftin
Tech Mgr: Jon Uber

D-U-N-S 82-826-4973 IMP
LOFTIS STEEL & ALUMINUM INC
4204 Charlotte Ave, Nashville, TN 37209-3605
Tel (615) 463-9191 *Founded/Ownrshp* 2000
Sales 30.9MM^E *EMP* 30
SIC 5051 Steel
Pr: Donald Loftis

LOFTNESS SPCIALIZED EQUIPMENTS
See LOFTNESS SPECIALIZED FARM EQUIPMENT INC

D-U-N-S 08-023-0147 IMP
LOFTNESS SPECIALIZED FARM EQUIPMENT INC
LOFTNESS SPCIALIZED EQUIPMENTS
650 S Main St, Hector, MN 55342
Tel (320) 848-6266 *Founded/Ownrshp* 1975
Sales 25.8MM *EMP* 95
Accts Conwat Deuth & Schmiesing Pl
SIC 3523 3531 Farm machinery & equipment; Forestry related equipment; Farm machinery & equipment; Forestry related equipment
Pr: Gloria Nelson
**Sr VP:* Dave Nelson
**VP:* Jerry Sechler
Off Mgr: Kerry Kadelbach

D-U-N-S 61-932-6254
LOFTON CO LLC
1832 E Deer Valley Rd, Phoenix, AZ 85024-5605
Tel (602) 445-4000 *Founded/Ownrshp* 1999
Sales 14.3MM^E *EMP* 430
SIC 1522 Apartment building construction; Apartment building construction
CFO: Ildie Schmidth
VP: Barbara Phillips

D-U-N-S 06-933-6832
LOFTON CORP (LA)
LOFTON STAFFING SERVICES
9414 Interline Ave, Baton Rouge, LA 70809-1911
Tel (225) 924-0200 *Founded/Ownrshp* 1979
Sales 119.7MM^E *EMP* 5,800
SIC 7361

D-U-N-S 01-039-2314
LOFTON LABEL INC
6290 Claude Way, Inver Grove Heights, MN 55076-4465
Tel (651) 457-8118 *Founded/Ownrshp* 1981
Sales 29.3MM^E *EMP* 101
SIC 2672 5084 Labels (unprinted), gummed: made from purchased materials; Printing trades machinery, equipment & supplies; Labels (unprinted), gummed: made from purchased materials; Printing trades machinery, equipment & supplies
CEO: Richard Gajewski
**VP:* William Garens
MIS Dir: Andy Mosca
IT Man: Jimmy Rana
VP Opers: Mike Gaughan
Mtls Mgr: Bud Kowalski
Prd Mgr: Joe Burger
Sales Asso: Brian Lutcavish

D-U-N-S 82-886-2990
LOFTON SECURITY SERVICE INC
9405 Interline Ave, Baton Rouge, LA 70809-1912
Tel (225) 906-2200 *Founded/Ownrshp* 2003
Sales 13.5MM *EMP* 1,300
SIC 7381 Guard services; Guard services
Pr: T Bret Lofton
**Treas:* G Bart Lofton
IT Man: John Babin

LOFTON STAFFING SERVICES
See LOFTON CORP

D-U-N-S 78-051-9943
LOFTWARE HOLDINGS INC
249 Corporate Dr, Portsmouth, NH 03801-6885
Tel (603) 766-3630 *Founded/Ownrshp* 2005
Sales 22.0MM *EMP* 75^E
SIC 7371 7372 Computer software development; Prepackaged software; Computer software development; Prepackaged software
Ch: Dana Anderson
CEO: Robert Oconnor Jr
CFO: Brian Collin
**VP:* Eric Anderson
**VP:* Ed Irwin
VP: Robert Rae Jr
VP: Josh Roffman
VP: Jim Thompson
VP: Mark Wick

D-U-N-S 60-458-3211
LOFTWARE INC
(*Suby of* LOFTWARE HOLDINGS INC) ★
249 Corporate Dr, Portsmouth, NH 03801-6885
Tel (603) 766-3630 *Founded/Ownrshp* 2006
Sales 20.2MM^E *EMP* 75^E
SIC 7371 Computer software development & applications
Pr: Robert O Connor Jr
CFO: Brian Collin
**CFO:* Brian Collin
Sr VP: Michael Rennell
**VP:* Robert Rae Jr
VP: Jim Thompson
**VP:* Mark Wick
Mng Dir: John Bradshaw
Snr Sftwr: Lynn Lamontagne
IT Man: Duane Oconner
Sftwr Eng: Owen McKone
Board of Directors: Eric Anderson

D-U-N-S 02-282-4676
LOG HOUSE FOODS INC
700 Berkshire Ln N, Minneapolis, MN 55441-5499
Tel (763) 546-8395 *Founded/Ownrshp* 1982
Sales 26.7MM^E *EMP* 35
SIC 5149 2052 Bakery products; Zwieback
Ch: Alan Kasdan
**Pr:* Josh Kasdan
COO: Michelle Strand
Site Mgr: Tom Olson
Sfty Mgr: Pat Peterson
Trfc Mgr: Cris Lewis
Sales Exec: Paul Brown
Sales Exec: Larry Phillips
Natl Sales: Tony D'Agosta

LOG ON A MAILING SERVICES
See LOG ON COMPUTER & MAILING SERVICES INC

D-U-N-S 19-730-9669
LOG ON COMPUTER & MAILING SERVICES INC
LOG ON A MAILING SERVICES
520 8th Ave Fl 14, New York, NY 10018-6507
Tel (212) 279-4567 *Founded/Ownrshp* 1987
Sales 23.8MM^E *EMP* 145
SIC 7331 7374 Mailing service; Computer processing services; Mailing service; Computer processing services
Ch Bd: Sherman Arnowitz
**Pr:* Evan Cohen
**CEO:* Daniel Arnowitz
Ex VP: Dan Cantelmo
IT Man: Melinda French
Sls Mgr: Jonathan Korn

D-U-N-S 13-040-0799 IMP/EXP
LOGAN ALUMINUM INC
200 Gate Two Rd 2rd, Russellville, KY 42276
Tel (270) 755-6000 *Founded/Ownrshp* 1985
Sales 228.8MM^E *EMP* 960
SIC 3355 Aluminum rolling & drawing; Aluminum rolling & drawing
Pr: Randy Schumaker
**COO:* Dan Minwell
**CFO:* Gary Grohovsky
Ex VP: Charlie Richardson
Exec: Curtis Whistle
Telecom Ex: Roy Whittaker
QA Dir: Dayna Chapman
IT Man: Glenn Baugh
IT Man: Jeff France
IT Man: Daryl Simpson
IT Man: Curtis Wilson

LOGAN CAMPUS
See SOUTHERN WEST VIRGINIA COMMUNITY AND TECHNICAL COLLEGE

D-U-N-S 07-093-5598
LOGAN CITY CORP
LOGAN CITY HALL
72 E 700 N, Logan, UT 84321
Tel (435) 716-9002 *Founded/Ownrshp* 1866
Sales NA *EMP* 600
Accts Hansen Bradshaw Malmrose & E
SIC 9111 City & town managers' offices; ; City & town managers' offices;
**CFO:* Rich Anderson
**Prin:* Jay Larsen

LOGAN CITY HALL
See LOGAN CITY CORP

D-U-N-S 09-466-9827
LOGAN CITY SCHOOL DISTRICT
101 W Center St, Logan, UT 84321-4520
Tel (435) 755-2300 *Founded/Ownrshp* 1872
Sales 38.8MM^E *EMP* 800
Accts Jones Simkins Pc Logan Ut
SIC 8211 Public elementary & secondary schools; Public elementary & secondary schools
Bd of Dir: Ann Geary
VP: Fred Duersch Jr
Netwrk Eng: Rik Stallings
Schl Brd P: Kristie Cooley
Psych: Grant Calverley
Psych: Rayann Hansen

LOGAN COLLEGE OF CHIROPRACTIC
See LOGAN UNIVERSITY INC

D-U-N-S 61-157-9160
LOGAN CONTRACTORS SUPPLY INC
4101 106th St, Urbandale, IA 50322-7949
Tel (515) 253-9048 *Founded/Ownrshp* 1990
Sales 97.9MM^E *EMP* 90
SIC 5082 General construction machinery & equipment; Road construction equipment; General construction machinery & equipment; Road construction equipment
Pr: Bruce Logan
**CEO:* Jerry L Logan
**VP:* Jeff Logan
Brnch Mgr: Scott Dyvad
Sls Mgr: Scott Mouw
Sales Asso: George Goad
Sales Asso: Matt Melichar

D-U-N-S 00-794-5116 IMP
LOGAN CORP (WV)
20 Mcjunkin Rd, Nitro, WV 25143-2506
Tel (304) 526-4700 *Founded/Ownrshp* 1904
Sales 60.4MM^E *EMP* 90
SIC 5082 5085 5084 7359 7353 5051 General construction machinery & equipment; Mining machinery & equipment, except petroleum; Industrial supplies; Industrial machinery & equipment; Equipment rental & leasing; Heavy construction equipment rental; Metals service centers & offices; General construction machinery & equipment; Mining machinery & equipment, except petroleum; Industrial supplies; Industrial machinery & equipment; Equipment rental & leasing; Heavy construction equipment rental; Metals service centers & offices
CEO: C McD England III
**Pr:* Dachary M Taylor
Ex VP: John Horn
Sr VP: Doug Barker
VP: Debbie Adkins
**VP:* C Randolph Holbrook
VP: Gary Kraft
Genl Mgr: Zach Taylor
MIS Mgr: Howard Adkins
Opers Mgr: Jamie Kelly
Natl Sales: David Sullender

D-U-N-S 07-680-9854
LOGAN COUNTY BOARD OF EDUCATION
506 Holly Ave, Logan, WV 25601-3306
Tel (304) 792-2060 *Founded/Ownrshp* 1865
Sales 76.5MM *EMP* 950
Accts Perry And Associates Marietta
SIC 8211 Public junior high school; Public senior high school; Public elementary school; School board
Pr: Jim Frye

D-U-N-S 07-966-3845
LOGAN COUNTY BOARD OF EDUCATION
2222 Bowling Green Rd, Russellville, KY 42276-9629
Tel (270) 726-2436 *Founded/Ownrshp* 1920
Sales 32.0MM *EMP* 517
Accts Carr Riggz & Ingram Llc Bow
SIC 8211 Public elementary & secondary schools; Public elementary & secondary schools
**CFO:* Danny L Harris CPA

D-U-N-S 07-979-8977
LOGAN COUNTY SCHOOLS
506 Holly Ave, Logan, WV 25601-3306
Tel (304) 792-2060 *Founded/Ownrshp* 2015
Sales 5.5MM^E *EMP* 1,297^E
SIC 8211 Public elementary & secondary schools
Dir Sec: David Thompson

D-U-N-S 96-344-5213
LOGAN COUNTY SCHOOLS
2222 Bowling Green Rd, Russellville, KY 42276-9602
Tel (270) 726-2436 *Founded/Ownrshp* 2010
Sales 30.7MM *EMP* 1^E
Accts Carr Riggs & Ingram Llc Russ
SIC 7389 Financial services; Financial services
Prin: Danny Harris
HC Dir: Barry Goley

LOGAN ELM BOARD OF EDUCATION
See LOGAN ELM LOCAL SCHOOL DISTRICT

D-U-N-S 60-703-0061
LOGAN ELM HEALTH CARE CENTER
370 Tarlton Rd, Circleville, OH 43113-9136
Tel (614) 837-1938 *Founded/Ownrshp* 1973
Sales 17.5MM^E *EMP* 320
SIC 8051 Skilled nursing care facilities; Skilled nursing care facilities
Pr: James Farley
**Ex VP:* Michael Scharfenberger
HC Dir: Mary Molan

D-U-N-S 04-860-3708
LOGAN ELM LOCAL SCHOOL DISTRICT
LOGAN ELM BOARD OF EDUCATION
9579 Tarlton Rd, Circleville, OH 43113-9448
Tel (740) 474-7501 *Founded/Ownrshp* 1953
Sales 21.7MM *EMP* 255
SIC 8211 Public elementary school; Public junior high school; Public senior high school; School board; Public elementary school; Public junior high school; Public senior high school; School board
Schl Brd P: Deborah Shaw

D-U-N-S 11-045-6469
■ LOGAN GENERAL HOSPITAL LLC
LOGAN REGIONAL MEDICAL CENTER
(*Suby of* HISTORIC LIFEPOINT HOSPITALS INC) ★
20 Hospital Dr, Logan, WV 25601-3452
Tel (304) 831-1101 *Founded/Ownrshp* 2002
Sales 88.4MM *EMP* 1
SIC 8011 Medical centers; Medical centers
CEO: John Walker
Chf OB: Suthipan Chevy
Chf Rad: Marsha Anderson
COO: Tim Harclerode
VP: Meridith Moody
Dir OR: Lisa Fordyce
Dir Inf Cn: Dawn Vandal
Dir Risk M: Michael Meadows
Dir Lab: Willie Viars
**Prin:* Med Records
Sfty Dirs: Kent Bragg

D-U-N-S 03-753-1209
LOGAN HOCKING LOCAL SCHOOL DISTRICT
2019 E Front St, Logan, OH 43138-9678
Tel (740) 385-8517 *Founded/Ownrshp* 1973
Sales 21.1MM^E *EMP* 400
Accts Jim Petro Athens Oh
SIC 8211 Public elementary school; Public senior high school; Public elementary school; Public senior high school
IT Man: Karen Walton
Schl Brd P: Ed Penrod

D-U-N-S 03-125-0149
LOGAN HOLDINGS INC
LOGAN OIL TOOLS
11027 Lucerne St, Houston, TX 77016-1919
Tel (281) 617-5300 *Founded/Ownrshp* 2009
Sales NA *EMP* 320
SIC 6719 Investment holding companies, except banks; Investment holding companies, except banks

D-U-N-S 07-839-0244
LOGAN LAVELLE HUNT INSURANCE AGENCY LLC
11420 Bluegrass Pkwy, Louisville, KY 40299-2348
Tel (502) 499-6880 *Founded/Ownrshp* 2012
Sales NA *EMP* 64^E
SIC 6411 Insurance agents, brokers & service
Prin: James Trent Hunt

LOGAN LOGISTICS
See W L LOGAN TRUCKING CO

D-U-N-S 01-898-7570
LOGAN MANAGEMENT INC
125 Wood Lake Dr Unit 312, Athens, GA 30606-8361
Tel (404) 219-8043 *Founded/Ownrshp* 2014
Sales 55.0MM *EMP* 2
SIC 3711 Motor vehicles & car bodies
Pr: Eric Logan

D-U-N-S 96-376-2687
■ LOGAN MEMORIAL HOSPITAL AUXILIARY INC
(*Suby of* HISTORIC LIFEPOINT HOSPITALS INC) ★
1625 Nashville St, Russellville, KY 42276-8853
Tel (270) 726-4011 *Founded/Ownrshp* 2002
Sales 22.1MM *EMP* 220
SIC 8062 General medical & surgical hospitals; General medical & surgical hospitals
CEO: Jim Bills
Dir OR: Heather Martin
Comm Man: Linda Isakson
MIS Dir: Paul Storms
Software D: Joyce Noe
Surgeon: Steve Reese

LOGAN OIL TOOLS
See LOGAN HOLDINGS INC

D-U-N-S 12-826-4111 IMP/EXP
LOGAN OIL TOOLS INC
11006 Lucerne St, Houston, TX 77016-1920
Tel (281) 219-6613 *Founded/Ownrshp* 1999
Sales 160.4MM^E *EMP* 330
SIC 5082 Oil field equipment; Oil field equipment
CEO: Gerald Hage
**CEO:* David Barr
CFO: David Jones
**CFO:* Larry Kelster
Ex VP: Paul Deutch
VP: Daniel Craig
VP: Jeff Ferguson
Dist Mgr: Jerry Branum
Dist Mgr: Guy Lee
QA Dir: Raphael Abili
QA Dir: Robert Ausman

LOGAN REGIONAL MEDICAL CENTER
See LOGAN GENERAL HOSPITAL LLC

D-U-N-S 12-513-4999
LOGAN ROGERSVILLE R 8 SCHOOL DISTRICT
LOGAN ROGERSVILLE SCHOOL
100 E Front St, Rogersville, MO 65742-9236
Tel (417) 753-2891 *Founded/Ownrshp* 1900
Sales 15.8MM^E *EMP* 280
SIC 8211 9411 Public junior high school; Public senior high school; School board; Administration of educational programs; Public junior high school; Public senior high school; School board; Administration of educational programs

LOGAN ROGERSVILLE SCHOOL
See LOGAN ROGERSVILLE R 8 SCHOOL DISTRICT

D-U-N-S 00-433-7148
LOGAN SIMPSON DESIGN INC
51 W 3rd St Ste 450, Tempe, AZ 85281-2883
Tel (480) 967-1343 *Founded/Ownrshp* 1990
Sales 42.5MM^E *EMP* 105
SIC 0781 Landscape architects
Pr: Diane Simpson Colebank
Ofcr: Julie Andersen
**VP:* Wayne Colebank
**Rgnl Mgr:* Tom Keith
Rgnl Mgr: Richard Remington
Dir IT: Robert French

D-U-N-S 08-307-9566 IMP
LOGAN SQUARE ALUMINUM SUPPLY INC
REMODELERS SUPPLY CENTER
2500 N Pulaski Rd, Chicago, IL 60639-2107
Tel (773) 235-2500 *Founded/Ownrshp* 1979
Sales 76.0MM^E *EMP* 400
SIC 5211 3089 Lumber & other building materials; Windows, plastic; Lumber & other building materials; Windows, plastic
Pr: Louis Silver
Brnch Mgr: Dave Lambert
IT Man: Chaim Dissen
IT Man: Arek Martin
Sls Mgr: Arthur Lukaszka
Sales Asso: David Pukas

D-U-N-S 07-588-7430
LOGAN UNIVERSITY INC
LOGAN COLLEGE OF CHIROPRACTIC
1851 Schoettler Rd, Chesterfield, MO 63017-5597
Tel (636) 227-2100 *Founded/Ownrshp* 1935
Sales 24.5MM *EMP* 250
Accts Uhy Advisors Mo Inc Saint Lou
SIC 8221 8041 Professional schools; Offices & clinics of chiropractors; Professional schools; Offices & clinics of chiropractors
Pr: J Clay McDonald
**Pr:* George Goodman DC
**CFO:* Patricia Marcella
CIO: Brad Hough
Acupntre: Andrea Faucett

D-U-N-S 79-179-5412 IMP
LOGANS ROADHOUSE INC
(*Suby of* LRI HOLDINGS INC) ★
3011 Armory Dr Ste 300, Nashville, TN 37204-3721
Tel (615) 885-9056 *Founded/Ownrshp* 2010
Sales 303.2MM^E *EMP* 7,000^E
SIC 5812 Steak restaurant; Steak restaurant
Pr: Sam Borgese
**Ch Bd:* Mike Andres
**CFO:* James J Hagan
Sr VP: Maria Rivera
VP: Stephen Anderson
**VP:* Amy Bertauski
VP: Karen Davis
Info Man: Scott Devor

D-U-N-S 07-890-7540
LOGANSPORT COMMUNITY SCHOOL CORP FOUNDATION INC
2829 George St, Logansport, IN 46947-3902
Tel (574) 722-2911 *Founded/Ownrshp* 1965
Sales 28.0MM^E *EMP* 685
SIC 8211 Public elementary & secondary schools; Public elementary school; Public junior high school; School board; Public elementary & secondary schools; Public elementary school; Public junior high school; School board

LOGANSPORT MEMORIAL HOSPITAL
See MEMORIAL HOSPITAL

D-U-N-S 07-339-3894
LOGANSPORT MUNICIPAL UTILITIES
601 E Broadway Ste 101, Logansport, IN 46947-3146
Tel (574) 753-6231 *Founded/Ownrshp* 1978
Sales 40.9MM *EMP* 120
SIC 4931 8741 4971 Electric & other services combined; Management services; Irrigation systems; Electric & other services combined; Management services; Irrigation systems
Board of Directors: Richard Dilling, Todd Miller, Thomas Slusser, Tom Smith, C Forrest Spencer

D-U-N-S 10-419-0561
LOGE GROUP LLC
4150 Intl Plz Ste 900, Fort Worth, TX 76109
Tel (800) 824-3882 *Founded/Ownrshp* 2004
Sales NA *EMP* 523
SIC 6411 Medical insurance claim processing, contract or fee basis; Medical insurance claim processing, contract or fee basis

D-U-N-S 07-993-4819
LOGENIX INTERNATIONAL LLC
5285 Shawnee Rd Ste 320, Alexandria, VA 22312-2328
Tel (703) 256-4885 *Founded/Ownrshp* 1998
Sales 23.0MM *EMP* 15^E
SIC 4731 Freight forwarding
Ofcr: David Aleman
Sr VP: Geoff Speck
IT Man: Steve Collatz

D-U-N-S 11-887-4254
LOGFRET INC
6801 W Side Ave, North Bergen, NJ 07047-6441
Tel (201) 817-1140 *Founded/Ownrshp* 1984
Sales 21.9MM^E *EMP* 57
Accts Metis Group Basking Ridge Nj
SIC 4731 Freight forwarding; Customs clearance of freight
Ch: Jean Francois Millet
**CEO:* Christian Millet
**CFO:* Ken Mistri
**Ex VP:* Elio Levy
Sales Exec: Alexandre Millet
Sales Exec: Martha Nevins
Doctor: Tom Webb MD

D-U-N-S 02-716-2502
LOGGINS MEAT CO INC
1908 E Erwin St, Tyler, TX 75702-6413
Tel (903) 595-1011 *Founded/Ownrshp* 1942
Sales 21.3MM^E *EMP* 61^E
SIC 5142 2011 Frozen fish, meat & poultry; Meat packing plants
Ch Bd: Bobby G Loggins

LOGIC
See WIELAND DESIGNS INC

LOGIC ELECTRONIC MFG SVCS
See LOGIC PD INC

D-U-N-S 04-433-6162
LOGIC INC (KS)
890 N Martway Ct, Olathe, KS 66061-7065
Tel (913) 764-4400 *Founded/Ownrshp* 1981
Sales 24.0MM *EMP* 39
SIC 5084 5045

D-U-N-S 07-257-7059 IMP
LOGIC PD INC
LOGIC ELECTRONIC MFG SVCS
6201 Bury Dr, Eden Prairie, MN 55346-1720
Tel (952) 646-1191 *Founded/Ownrshp* 1981
Sales 170.6MM^E *EMP* 490
SIC 3672 8711 Printed circuit boards; Engineering services; Printed circuit boards; Engineering services
Pr: Bruce Dewitt
**CFO:* Sandy Bell
**Chf Cred:* Jason Voiovich
**VP:* Lorri Anderson
VP: Paul Fabian
**VP:* Mona Phaff
VP: Jackie Torfin
**VP:* Eric Wilkowske
Prgrm Mgr: David Beck
IT Man: Gail Hubertus
Sftwr Eng: Mark Herscher

D-U-N-S 05-762-2408 IMP
LOGIC TECHNOLOGY DEVELOPMENT LLC
2004 Nw 25th Ave, Pompano Beach, FL 33069-5222
Tel (954) 780-8540 *Founded/Ownrshp* 2010
Sales 60.0MM *EMP* 50
SIC 5194 Cigarettes
Pr: Miguel Martin
**CFO:* Larry Yellin
Treas: Michael Nete
**Chf Cred:* Tony Gaines
Manager: Jon Thomson

D-U-N-S 87-818-2401
LOGICAL CHOICE TECHNOLOGIES INC
1045 Progress Cir, Lawrenceville, GA 30043-4646
Tel (770) 564-1044 *Founded/Ownrshp* 1994
Sales 37.1MM^E *EMP* 200
SIC 7373 5045 7378 Computer integrated systems design; Computers, peripherals & software; Computer maintenance & repair; Computer integrated systems design; Computers, peripherals & software; Computer maintenance & repair
Pr: Cynthia B Kaye
**COO:* Kevin Shupenia
**Ofcr:* N Ronald Kaye
**Sr VP:* Shelly Raymond Dejesus
**VP:* Sherry Lofgren
Sales Asso: Jim Rosenmoser

D-U-N-S 14-825-4915
LOGICAL SYSTEMS INC
L S I
2756 Appling Center Cv # 101, Memphis, TN 38133-5079
Tel (901) 377-5574 *Founded/Ownrshp* 1985
Sales 33.9MM *EMP* 60
Accts Watkins Uiberall Pllc Memphis
SIC 7373 8742 Systems engineering, computer related; Automation & robotics consultant; Systems engineering, computer related; Automation & robotics consultant
CEO: Larry Bailey
**Pr:* Dan Miller
**CFO:* Lentz Gatlin
**VP:* Larry Baker
**Prin:* Jim Gavigan
**Prin:* David Jackson
Brnch Mgr: Dennie Lott
Manager: Mary Deshields
Sls Mgr: Gregory Henderson

D-U-N-S 80-764-3150
LOGICALIS INC
(*Suby of* LOGICALIS LIMITED)
1 Penn Plz Ste 5130, New York, NY 10119-5160
Tel (212) 596-7160 *Founded/Ownrshp* 1999
Sales 386.3MM *EMP* 700
Accts Deloitte & Touche Llp Detroit
SIC 5045 Computers, peripherals & software; Computers, peripherals & software
CEO: Vince Deluca
COO: Mark Rogers
**COO:* Michael Souders
**Ex VP:* Eric Tilds
**Sr VP:* Mike Martin
Sr VP: Jim Reichwein
**Sr VP:* Dan Sytsma
Mng Dir: Stuart Hendry
Mng Dir: Andreas Riepen
Prgrm Mgr: Stephen Thompson
Area Mgr: Shannon Wainright

D-U-N-S 96-856-7060
LOGICALIS US HOLDINGS INC
(*Suby of* LOGICALIS INC) ★
34505 W 12 Mile Rd, Farmington Hills, MI 48331-3258
Tel (248) 957-5600 *Founded/Ownrshp* 2000
Sales 422.3MM *EMP* 2
Accts Deloitte & Touche Llp Detroit
SIC 5045 Computers, peripherals & software; Computers, peripherals & software
CEO: Vince Deluca
**COO:* Michael Souders
**CFO:* Rich Pirrotta
**Ex VP:* Eric Tilds
**Sr VP:* Dan Sytsma
VP: Jim Cook
VP: Brandon Harris
VP: Mike Martin
VP: Bob Verhan
Dir IT: Terry Strobecker
Netwrk Eng: Michael Bowyer

D-U-N-S 03-548-2287 IMP
LOGICDATA NORTH AMERICA INC
UNITED LOGIC
1525 Gezon Pkwy Sw Ste C, Grand Rapids, MI 49509-9548
Tel (616) 328-8841 *Founded/Ownrshp* 2011
Sales 40.0MM *EMP* 10
SIC 5063 Control & signal wire & cable, including coaxial; Motor controls, starters & relays: electric
Pr: Steven D Jones
**Pr:* Johannes Sauer
Tech Mgr: Vincent Mates

D-U-N-S 93-922-6965
LOGICOR INC
1236 N Spencer Ste 3, Mesa, AZ 85203-4350
Tel (480) 857-7900 *Founded/Ownrshp* 1995
Sales 38.0MM *EMP* 28
SIC 7371 Computer software development; Computer software development
Pr: Gary Deutsch
**VP:* Brenda Deutsch

D-U-N-S 80-620-5571
LOGICWORKS CORP
155 Ave Of The Ameri Fl 5, New York, NY 10013-1507
Tel (212) 625-5300 *Founded/Ownrshp* 1993
Sales 25.2MM^E *EMP* 65
SIC 4813
CEO: George Kerns
**Ch Bd:* S Carter Burden III
**Pr:* Kenneth Ziegler

D-U-N-S 01-027-2008
LOGIK PRECISION INC (TX)
5007 Steffani Ln, Houston, TX 77041-7819
Tel (713) 939-0061 *Founded/Ownrshp* 1995, 1998
Sales 20.0MM^E *EMP* 40
SIC 3599 Machine & other job shop work
Pr: Carlos M Sierra
IT Man: Robert Peck

D-U-N-S 17-183-4203
■ LOGILITY INC
(*Suby of* AMERICAN SOFTWARE INC) ★
470 E Paces Ferry Rd Ne, Atlanta, GA 30305-3301
Tel (404) 261-9777 *Founded/Ownrshp* 2009
Sales 22.8MM^E *EMP* 141^E
SIC 7371 7372 Computer software development & applications; Prepackaged software; Business oriented computer software; Computer software development & applications; Prepackaged software; Business oriented computer software
CEO: J Michael Edenfield
**Ch Bd:* James C Edenfield
**Pr:* H Allan Dow
COO: Tony Gordon
**CFO:* Vincent C Klinges
Sr VP: Geoffrey W Cobleigh
**Sr VP:* Ed Thompson
**VP:* Mark A Balte
VP: Joan Brendel
**VP:* Karin L Bursa
VP: Len Sherwinski
VP: Josh Stephens
**VP:* Donald L Thomas
VP: Andrew G White
VP: Norm Williams

D-U-N-S 00-470-0303
LOGISCO MANAGEMENT CO INC
3100 Reeves Rd, Plainfield, IN 46168-7926
Tel (317) 837-7007 *Founded/Ownrshp* 1998
Sales 34.7MM^E *EMP* 350
SIC 4225 General warehousing; General warehousing
Pr: Chuck Cline
CFO: Mark Monroe
Genl Mgr: Shelli Austin

D-U-N-S 79-937-6645
LOGISOURCE INC
SOURCE TRANSPORT
700 Matthews Mint Hill Rd, Matthews, NC 28105-2891
Tel (704) 815-1660 *Founded/Ownrshp* 1995
Sales 20.0MM^E *EMP* 25
SIC 4731 4225 Freight transportation arrangement; Freight forwarding; Freight consolidation; General warehousing & storage
Pr: Jim Lloyd
**Ex VP:* Steve Brown
VP: John Flowers
Opers Mgr: Bill Gaut
Manager: Bill Calafiura
Manager: Chris Lawson
Manager: Don Peebles
Sls Mgr: Stein Ray
Sales Asso: George Cowles

LOGISTA
See OFFICE MANAGEMENT SYSTEMS INC

D-U-N-S 07-633-1375 IMP
LOGISTEC USA INC
225 Newcastle St, Brunswick, GA 31520-8571
Tel (912) 267-9086 *Founded/Ownrshp* 1988
Sales 25.5MM^E *EMP* 140^E
SIC 3731 Shipbuilding & repairing; Shipbuilding & repairing
CEO: Serge Dubreuil
**CFO:* Micahel Vasaturo

D-U-N-S 14-187-6248
LOGISTIC DYNAMICS INC
L D I
1140 Wehrle Dr, Buffalo, NY 14221-7748
Tel (716) 250-3477 *Founded/Ownrshp* 2003
Sales 68.9MM^E *EMP* 100^E
SIC 4731 Freight transportation arrangement; Freight transportation arrangement
CEO: Dennis Brown
**Pr:* Dana Frost
**CFO:* Jad Maouad
Genl Mgr: Jeff Gelner

D-U-N-S 09-659-8248
LOGISTIC SERVICES INTERNATIONAL INC (FL)
L S I
6111 Technology Ct, Jacksonville, FL 32221-8104
Tel (904) 771-2100 *Founded/Ownrshp* 1978, 2006
Sales 63.6MM *EMP* 475
Accts Dixon Hughes Goodman Llp Jac

SIC 8299 8331 9411 Airline training; Job training & vocational rehabilitation services; Administration of educational programs; Airline training; Job training & vocational rehabilitation services; Administration of educational programs
CEO: Charles A Johns
**Pr:* Warren Rosander
Pr: Dennis Vonburg
**CFO:* Warren S Rosander
**VP:* Michael S French
**VP:* Mike Griffin
VP: Ed Turner
Prgrm Mgr: Christopher Elwood
Prgrm Mgr: Lee Steele

D-U-N-S 82-487-9951
LOGISTIC SOLUTIONS INC
216 Stelton Rd Ste C2, Piscataway, NJ 08854-3284
Tel (732) 457-0015 *Founded/Ownrshp* 1990
Sales 26.0MM^E *EMP* 250
SIC 7371 Computer software development; Computer software development
Ch Bd: Tanuja Desai
**Pr:* Amit Limaye
Dir Bus: Shirley Handa

D-U-N-S 07-307-4577
LOGISTIC SPECIALTIES INC
1530 Layton Hills Pkwy # 201, Layton, UT 84041-5710
Tel (801) 525-5300 *Founded/Ownrshp* 1973
Sales 31.3MM *EMP* 180
Accts Heb Business Solutions Salt L
SIC 8742 Marketing consulting services; Marketing consulting services
Ch Bd: Jerry Slatter
Pr: G Degrauw
**Pr:* Sean M Slatter
VP: Josh Johnson
VP: Rick Lee
VP: Angie Tymofichuk
Site Mgr: Allen Reagan

D-U-N-S 93-252-1776
■ **LOGISTICARE SOLUTIONS LLC**
(*Suby of* PROVIDENCE SERVICE CORP) ★
1275 Peachtree St Ne Fl 6, Atlanta, GA 30309-3580
Tel (404) 888-5800 *Founded/Ownrshp* 1999
Sales 884.2MM *EMP* 2,000
SIC 4731 Transportation agents & brokers; Transportation agents & brokers
CEO: Herman Schwarz
CFO: Thomas E Oram
Ex VP: Steven Linowes
Sr VP: Chuck Dezearn
VP: Kirk Gonzales
Rgnl Mgr: Rita Preble
Genl Mgr: Allen Davis
CIO: Rob Cornell
IT Man: Vance Hendley
Sfty Mgr: Gordon McInnis

D-U-N-S 06-807-0817
LOGISTICS & DISTRIBUTION SERVICES CORPOR
1755 Purina Way, Sparks, NV 89431-6524
Tel (775) 356-1992 *Founded/Ownrshp* 2001
Sales 30.0MM^E *EMP* 88
SIC 4213 4212 Trucking, except local; Local trucking, without storage
Pr: Ross A Kline
**Treas:* Theresa Gruppo
Sfty Dirs: Truman Mathews

D-U-N-S 17-879-9370
LOGISTICS & TECHNOLOGY SERVICES INC
L T S
305 Church St Sw Ste 810, Huntsville, AL 35801-4907
Tel (256) 489-5311 *Founded/Ownrshp* 2005
Sales 28.5MM *EMP* 310
SIC 8742 Maintenance management consultant; Maintenance management consultant
Pr: Roweana E Hale
COO: Hobie Frady
Prgrm Mgr: Kyle Smith

LOGISTICS GROUP
See BADGLEY WETJEN HOLDING LLC

D-U-N-S 13-146-8071
■ **LOGISTICS HEALTH INC**
LHI
(*Suby of* SPECIALTY BENEFITS LLC) ★
328 Front St S, La Crosse, WI 54601-4023
Tel (866) 284-8788 *Founded/Ownrshp* 1999
Sales 65.0MM^E *EMP* 900^E
SIC 8011 Health maintenance organization; Health maintenance organization
CEO: Donald J Weber
Pr: Jon Lewis
**COO:* Brian D Hafner
**Chf Mktg O:* David Tornberg MD
VP: Brian Hafner
VP: Tom Hamilton
**VP:* Armagan Islamoglu
**VP:* Tom Walch
Exec: Denise Thompson
Rgnl Mgr: Tricia Parker
QA Dir: Sandra Elsen

D-U-N-S 15-767-7076
LOGISTICS HOLDINGS LLC
M33 INTEGRATED SOLUTIONS
(*Suby of* TRANSPLACE TEXAS LP) ★
511 Rhett St, Greenville, SC 29601-2413
Tel (864) 672-2862 *Founded/Ownrshp* 2015
Sales 44.3MM^E *EMP* 66
Accts Dixon Hughes Goodman Llp Gree
SIC 4731 Freight transportation arrangement
Sr Pt: Sammy Riddle
Pr: Jay Baker
VP: Beth Smith
Dir Bus: Terry Setzer
CTO: Warren Patterson
Dir IT: Silviu Necula
Opers Mgr: Robert Saffioti
Manager: Dave Lane

D-U-N-S 07-966-8583
LOGISTICS HOLLINGSWORTH GROUP LLC
14225 W Warren Ave, Dearborn, MI 48126-1456
Tel (313) 768-1400 *Founded/Ownrshp* 1999
Sales 183.1MM *EMP* 700^E
SIC 7389 Packaging & labeling services; Packaging & labeling services
CEO: Stephen Barr
**Pr:* R James Lapointe
**COO:* Michael T McNamara
**VP:* Martha Chalifoux

D-U-N-S 87-721-4569
■ **LOGISTICS INSIGHT CORP**
OAKLAND LOGISTICS SERVICE INC
(*Suby of* LINC LOGISTICS CO) ★
12755 E 9 Mile Rd, Warren, MI 48089-2621
Tel (586) 467-1500 *Founded/Ownrshp* 1992
Sales 96.5MM^E *EMP* 1,000
SIC 8742 Transportation consultant; Transportation consultant
CEO: H E Wolfe
**CFO:* David Crittenden
**Sr VP:* M Akkanen
Sr VP: Don Berquist
Comm Dir: Peter Spata
Rgnl Mgr: Samuel Gentile
Genl Mgr: Chuck Downing
Genl Mgr: Mark Gillette
Genl Mgr: Jim Kelly
Genl Mgr: Seth Kohman
Genl Mgr: Denny Roland

D-U-N-S 79-705-5840
LOGISTICS INTERNATIONAL LLC
TRANS GROUP
1150 Gateway Dr W, Shakopee, MN 55379-3819
Tel (952) 697-4900 *Founded/Ownrshp* 2007
Sales 38.5MM^E *EMP* 77
SIC 4731 Freight transportation arrangement
VP: Kevin Lemke
Sales Exec: Noel Ringold

D-U-N-S 05-338-5738 IMP
LOGISTICS MANAGEMENT INSTITUTE
L M I
7940 Jones Branch Dr, Mc Lean, VA 22102-3381
Tel (703) 917-9800 *Founded/Ownrshp* 1961
Sales 251,5MM *EMP* 841
SIC 8742

D-U-N-S 78-042-7449
LOGISTICS MANAGEMENT RESOURCES INC
13853 Perkins Rd, Baton Rouge, LA 70810-3436
Tel (225) 755-1388 *Founded/Ownrshp* 1989
Sales 29.9MM^E *EMP* 60
SIC 4731 Transportation agents & brokers
Pr: Terry W Hodges
Admn Mgr: Chelette Gautreau
VP Opers: Sean Gautreaux
Trfc Dir: Sharon Patterson
Opers Mgr: Roy Drez

D-U-N-S 92-827-8415
LOGISTICS MANAGEMENT RESOURCES INC
4300 Crossings Blvd, Prince George, VA 23875-1452
Tel (804) 541-6193 *Founded/Ownrshp* 1994
Sales 28.3MM^E *EMP* 275
SIC 7379 7374 7373 7371 Computer related maintenance services; Data processing & preparation; Computer integrated systems design; Custom computer programming services; Computer related maintenance services; Data processing & preparation; Computer integrated systems design; Custom computer programming services
Pr: David S Weisman
**COO:* Michael Williams
CFO: Bob Stansky
**CFO:* Bob Stransky
VP: Paul Self
**Prin:* Kenneth Briggs

D-U-N-S 06-987-6519
LOGISTICS MANAGEMENT SOLUTIONS LC
LMS
(*Suby of* TRANSPLACE TEXAS LP) ★
1 Cityplace Dr Ste 415, Saint Louis, MO 63141-7066
Tel (314) 692-8886 *Founded/Ownrshp* 2014
Sales 57.2MM^E *EMP* 146
SIC 4731 Freight consolidation; Freight consolidation
CEO: Dennis Schoemehl
**CFO:* Scott Hunt
VP Sls: Robert Morrey

LOGISTICS ONE
See INTELOCO

LOGISTICS PLANNING SERVICES
See HALL ENTERPRISES INC

D-U-N-S 12-569-4591
LOGISTICS PLUS INC
1406 Peach St Ste 3, Erie, PA 16501-1879
Tel (814) 461-7600 *Founded/Ownrshp* 1996
Sales 63.4MM^E *EMP* 100^E
SIC 4731 Truck transportation brokers; Truck transportation brokers
Pr: Jim Berlin
**Pr:* Fred Rizzuto
**CFO:* Debra Peterson
Ofcr: Rini Angelina
Ofcr: Moosa Bahrani
Ex VP: Bruce Kennedy
**Sr VP:* Gretchen Seth
**Sr VP:* Arthur Whelan
Exec: Cynthia Garza
Exec: Elena Martinez
Mng Dir: Dhafir Aldouri

D-U-N-S 15-796-0787
LOGISTICS SOLUTIONS GROUP INC
4701 Owens Way Ste 100, Prince George, VA 23875-2366
Tel (804) 452-4403 *Founded/Ownrshp* 1999
Sales 30.2MM *EMP* 450
SIC 7379 4731 Computer related consulting services; Transportation agents & brokers; Computer related consulting services; Transportation agents & brokers
Pr: Ramon Navarro
Pr: Peggy Hughes
**Ex VP:* Donna Navarro
VP: Joe Frazer
Sfty Mgr: David J Adams
Board of Directors: Ramon Navarro

D-U-N-S 09-287-6015
LOGISTICS SUPPORT INC (VA)
2611 Jefferson Davis Hwy # 12000, Arlington, VA 22202-4016
Tel (703) 412-4892 *Founded/Ownrshp* 2001
Sales 21.6MM *EMP* 280
Accts Cohn Reznick Llp Vienna Virg
SIC 8742 Management consulting services; Management consulting services
Pr: David Dean Compton
**CFO:* Joseph Sciacca
**Sr VP:* Victoria M Brown
**VP:* Lora Adams
**VP:* Rich Hansen
VP: Victoria Williamson
Exec: Kathleen Martin
IT Man: Jim Snuggs

D-U-N-S 13-190-3333 EXP
LOGISTICS SYSTEMS INC
1100 G St Nw Ste 410, Washington, DC 20005-7426
Tel (202) 347-0821 *Founded/Ownrshp* 2001
Sales 24.8MM *EMP* 215
Accts Bdo Usa Llp Mclean Va
SIC 4225 7373 7376 8744 General warehousing & storage; Computer integrated systems design; Computer facilities management; Base maintenance (providing personnel on continuing basis); General warehousing & storage; Computer integrated systems design; Computer facilities management; Base maintenance (providing personnel on continuing basis)
Pr: Lawrence Wilkerson
Pr: Jarvis Newsome
Sales Exec: Marcell Lewis

LOGISTICS TEAM
See AMERIFREIGHT INC

LOGISTICS TEAM
See I3PL LLC

D-U-N-S 16-967-7221
LOGISTICSFINANCE
32325 Coast Hwy Ste 201, Laguna Beach, CA 92651-6777
Tel (949) 715-5070 *Founded/Ownrshp* 2000
Sales NA *EMP* 9
SIC 6153 Direct working capital financing; Direct working capital financing
Pr: Kevin Lynch
Bd of Dir: Ed Collins

D-U-N-S 02-423-7877 IMP
■ **LOGITECH INC** (CA)
(*Suby of* LOGITECH INTERNATIONAL S.A.)
7700 Gateway Blvd, Newark, CA 94560-1046
Tel (510) 795-8500 *Founded/Ownrshp* 1982
Sales NA *EMP* 5,000
Tkr Sym LOGI *Exch* NGS
SIC 3577 Computer peripheral equipment; Input/output equipment, computer; Computer peripheral equipment; Input/output equipment, computer
Pr: Bracken P Darrell
**Ch Bd:* Guerrino De Luca
COO: Patricia Landauer
CFO: Michael Lovell
VP: Nikki Montgomery
Exec: Kristen Onken
Dir Bus: D J Garner
Snr Sftwr: Ji Yang
Snr Ntwrk: Jeff Eisenman
Dir IT: Tony Henson
IT Man: Scott Cameron

D-U-N-S 12-941-1836
LOGIX COMMUNICATIONS LP
2950 North Loop W Fl 8, Houston, TX 77092-8846
Tel (713) 862-2000 *Founded/Ownrshp* 2002
Sales 97.4MM *EMP* 315
Accts Hein & Associates Llp Housto
SIC 4813 Local & long distance telephone communications; Local & long distance telephone communications
Ch Bd: Ron Henriksen
CEO: Matt Asmus
CFO: Craig Sheetz
VP: Ken Bonvillian
VP: Anthony Brown
VP: Terry Burnside
VP: John Skidmore
VP: Glenn Taylor
VP: Michael Watson
Sls Dir: Landon Dick

D-U-N-S 07-527-6931
LOGIX FEDERAL CREDIT UNION
2340 N Hollywood Way, Burbank, CA 91505-1124
Tel (818) 718-5328 *Founded/Ownrshp* 1937
Sales NA *EMP* 350
SIC 6061 Federal credit unions; Federal credit unions
Pr: David Styler
COO: Phil Hart
**COO:* Dave Styler
**CFO:* Ana Fonseca
Ofcr: Maria Beltran
Ofcr: Sean Brown
Ofcr: Kara Buss
Ofcr: Ariel Cabrera
Ofcr: Anthony Carusa
Ofcr: Jeff Chen
Ofcr: Orlando Duque
Ofcr: Nuvia Espana
Ofcr: Irma Heffner
Ofcr: Staci Hermann II
Ofcr: Gabriel Mann
Ofcr: Donna Matthews
Ofcr: Shawn McKendry
Ofcr: Tina Orellana
Ofcr: Jason Pelletier
Ofcr: Lisa Perez
Ofcr: Carol Salgado

D-U-N-S 17-589-5205
▲ **LOGMEIN INC**
320 Summer St Ste 100, Boston, MA 02210-1701
Tel (781) 638-9050 *Founded/Ownrshp* 2003
Sales 221.9MM *EMP* 804^E
Tkr Sym LOGM *Exch* NGS
SIC 7372 7379 Prepackaged software; Computer related consulting services; Prepackaged software; Computer related consulting services
Ch Bd: Michael K Simon
Pr: William R Wagner
CFO: Edward K Herdiech
Chf Mktg O: W Sean Ford
Sr VP: Michael J Donahue
Dir Bus: Mario Finocchiaro
Off Admin: Kaylyn Grange
IT Man: Michael Natale
Netwrk Eng: Oliver Hunermund
Sales Exec: Jeff Cozzaglio
Sales Exec: Robin Linehan
Board of Directors: Steven J Benson, Steven G Chambers, Michael J Christenson, Edwin J Gillis, Gregory W Hughes, Marilyn Matz

D-U-N-S 03-034-7137 IMP
LOGO CHAIR INC (TN)
117 Se Parkway, Franklin, TN 37064-3925
Tel (615) 261-2100 *Founded/Ownrshp* 2000
Sales 28.9MM^E *EMP* 43
SIC 5021 5999 3086 2392 Outdoor & lawn furniture; Tents; Ice chests or coolers (portable), foamed plastic; Blankets, comforters & beddings
Pr: Matthew McCauley
Pr: Jason Potts
CFO: Craig Billingsley
CFO: Jenny East
**Sec:* Jonathan Pope
**VP:* Kris Talley
Opers Mgr: Cameron Stewart

LOGO EXPRESSIONS
See DENNIS FOLAND INC

D-U-N-S 19-519-8788
LOGO HOLDINGS I CORP
626 W Main St, Louisville, KY 40202-2972
Tel (502) 637-5443 *Founded/Ownrshp* 2012
Sales 247.2MM^E *EMP* 2,410^E
SIC 3577 Graphic displays, except graphic terminals; Graphic displays, except graphic terminals
Pr: Hank Baughman
IT Man: Bobbi Adams

D-U-N-S 04-219-7289
LOGO HOLDINGS II CORP
(*Suby of* LOGO HOLDINGS I CORP) ★
626 W Main St, Louisville, KY 40202-2972
Tel (502) 637-5443 *Founded/Ownrshp* 2012
Sales 125.2MM^E *EMP* 2,405^E
SIC 6719 7336 Investment holding companies, except banks; Graphic arts & related design; Investment holding companies, except banks; Graphic arts & related design
Pr: Hank Baughman

D-U-N-S 07-938-3882
LOGO HOLDINGS III LLC
626 W Main St Ste 500, Louisville, KY 40202-4269
Tel (502) 637-5443 *Founded/Ownrshp* 2012
Sales 16.5MM^E *EMP* 350^E
SIC 2796 Platemaking services; Platemaking services

LOGOED MERCHANDISE
See IMPERIAL MARKETING INC

D-U-N-S 82-997-8766 IMP
LOGOMARK INC
1201 Bell Ave, Tustin, CA 92780-6420
Tel (714) 675-6100 *Founded/Ownrshp* 1992
Sales 166.4MM^E *EMP* 250
SIC 5199 Advertising specialties; Advertising specialties
Pr: Trevor Gnesin
Pr: Maggie Wheeler
CFO: Gardnar O'Brien
Sr VP: Brian P Padian
IT Man: Vernon Eintracht
Prd Mgr: Tony Mirabella
Mktg Dir: Leon Lazarus
Mktg Dir: Leon Lezarus
Manager: Dave Atlas
Manager: Dana Bonanne
Manager: Erich Braun

D-U-N-S 07-831-6141 IMP
LOGOPLASTE USA INC
(*Suby of* LOGOPLASTE INVESTIMENTO, SGPS, S.A.)
14420 N Van Dyke Rd, Plainfield, IL 60544-5867
Tel (815) 230-6961 *Founded/Ownrshp* 2006
Sales 100.0MM *EMP* 200
SIC 3085 Plastics bottles; Plastics bottles
CEO: Filipe De Botton
Opers Mgr: Stephanie Johnson
Prd Mgr: Tim Morgan

LOGOS BIBLE SOFTWARE
See FAITHLIFE CORP

LOGOS ROME
See LOGOS TECHNOLOGIES INC

D-U-N-S 02-881-5111
LOGOS TECHNOLOGIES INC
LOGOS ROME
2701 Prosperity Ave # 400, Fairfax, VA 22031-4313
Tel (703) 229-0180 *Founded/Ownrshp* 1996
Sales 47.9MM^E *EMP* 127^E
SIC 8711 7389 Engineering services; ; Engineering services;
Pr: Greg Poe
**COO:* Mike Fagan
**CFO:* Michael Haddad
VP: Michael Pagels
Dir Sec: Shawna Brown
Prgrm Mgr: Deborah Althoff

Prgrm Mgr: Thomas Hunter
Prgrm Mgr: Dave Luber
Off Mgr: Diana Fortner
Dir IT: Juan Rosas
IT Man: Jessica Flores

D-U-N-S 17-938-9650
LOGRHYTHM INC
4780 Pearl East Cir, Boulder, CO 80301-2472
Tel (303) 245-9074 *Founded/Ownrshp* 2005
Sales 171.1MM^E *EMP* 250^E
SIC 7372 Business oriented computer software; Business oriented computer software
CEO: Andy Grolnick
CFO: Mark Vellequette
Ch: Chris Petersen
Sr VP: Bill Smith
VP: David Anthony
VP: Ross Brewer
VP: James Carder
VP: Mike Reagan
VP: Nancy Reynolds
Prgrm Mgr: Beth Petersen
Off Mgr: Christine Sznip
Board of Directors: Karen Blasing, Todd Headley, Robert Lentz, Dick Williams

LOGS FINANCIAL SERVICES
See LOGS GROUP L L C

D-U-N-S 94-130-9833
LOGS GROUP L L C
LOGS FINANCIAL SERVICES
2121 Waukegan Rd Ste 300, Bannockburn, IL 60015-1831
Tel (847) 374-0437 *Founded/Ownrshp* 1998
Sales 80.7MM^E *EMP* 550^E
SIC 8741 Financial management for business; Financial management for business
Ch Bd: Gerald Shapiro
Mng Pt: Penny Daigrepont
**Pr:* Gerald Alt
**Pr:* Jamie Zelvin
**COO:* David Van Ess
**CFO:* Lawrence Rosenbaum
Ex VP: Karen L Pattuo
**Ex VP:* Kay Schinker
**Ex VP:* Daniel C Schmidt
**VP:* Janet Bennett
Comm Dir: Michelle Spellerberg

D-U-N-S 15-067-0404
LOGTEC INC
(*Suby of* SERCO SERVICES INC) ★
1818 Library St Ste 1000, Reston, VA 20190-6276
Tel (703) 939-6000 *Founded/Ownrshp* 2007
Sales 30.2MM^E *EMP* 365
SIC 8748 Business consulting; Business consulting
Pr: Michael E Zettler
Pr: Bill Kivlan
VP: Edward Becker
VP: John Bradunas
VP: Phillip Cagigas
VP: Gary A Kowl
VP: Mary Sherman
Prgrm Mgr: Arthur Petrini
Genl Mgr: Patricia Silvestri
IT Man: Patricia Femia
Sftwr Eng: Brion Bunn

LOGUE INDUSTRIES, INC.
See CREATION TECHNOLOGIES CALEXICO INC

D-U-N-S 04-022-8389 IMP
■ LOHMANN ANIMAL HEALTH INTERNATIONAL INC
BIOLOGICS PRODUCTION
(*Suby of* LOHMANN ANIMAL HEALTH GMBH)
375 China Rd, Winslow, ME 04901-0632
Tel (207) 859-9400 *Founded/Ownrshp* 1997
Sales 33.9MM^E *EMP* 112
SIC 2836 Vaccines; Vaccines
CEO: David Zacek
**Pr:* Frank Sterner
**Sec:* Crystal Olsen
Ofcr: Erin Burnham
VP: Carlos Artigas
**VP:* Dianna Rafue
IT Man: Jeff Hastings
Netwrk Mgr: Charles Sumrell

D-U-N-S 62-791-7685
LOHMILLER & CO
CARRIER WEST
4800 Osage St Ste 100, Denver, CO 80221-7816
Tel (303) 825-4328 *Founded/Ownrshp* 1990
Sales 44.5MM^E *EMP* 100
SIC 5075 1711 Air conditioning & ventilation equipment & supplies; Warm air heating equipment & supplies; Plumbing, heating, air-conditioning contractors; Air conditioning & ventilation equipment & supplies; Warm air heating equipment & supplies; Plumbing, heating, air-conditioning contractors
CEO: Roger Lee
**Pr:* Chuck Lohmiller
Sls Mgr: Jimayne Dutton

D-U-N-S 03-106-2771 IMP
LOHR DISTRIBUTING CO INC
LOHR FINE WINES SPIRITS
1100 S 9th St, Saint Louis, MO 63104-3597
Tel (314) 436-8299 *Founded/Ownrshp* 1964
Sales 88.7MM^E *EMP* 120
SIC 5181 Beer & other fermented malt liquors; Beer & other fermented malt liquors
Pr: Ronald K Lohr
CFO: Chris Dipasqua
VP: Kurt Leinauer
VP: Steven E Lohr
Rgnl Mgr: Nino Razzi
Sales Exec: Marty Sheahan
Sls Mgr: Robert Gassoff

LOHR FINE WINES SPIRITS
See LOHR DISTRIBUTING CO INC

LOISE TOWN HLTHCARE FOUNDATION
See LOUISE TOWN HOSPITAL

D-U-N-S 15-774-1414
LOJAC ENTERPRISES INC
1401 Toshiba Dr, Lebanon, TN 37087-2588
Tel (615) 449-1401 *Founded/Ownrshp* 1986
Sales 80.2MM^E *EMP* 250
SIC 1611 1794 5032 Highway & street paving contractor; Excavation & grading, building construction; Asphalt mixture; Highway & street paving contractor; Excavation & grading, building construction; Asphalt mixture
Ch Bd: B F Jack Lowery
**Pr:* Donald G Chambers
CFO: Kellie Mires
Dir IT: Nic Morris
Board of Directors: W C Bill Marks

D-U-N-S 10-175-7557
LOJAC INC
1401 Toshiba Dr, Lebanon, TN 37087-2588
Tel (615) 449-1401 *Founded/Ownrshp* 1983
Sales 47.5MM^E *EMP* 125
SIC 1611 3271 3993 General contractor, highway & street construction; Blocks, concrete or cinder: standard; Signs & advertising specialties; General contractor, highway & street construction; Blocks, concrete or cinder: standard; Signs & advertising specialties
CEO: B F Jack Lowery
**Pr:* Donald G Chambers
CFO: Kelly Chambers
**CFO:* Kellie Mires
**VP:* Glenn Chambers
Div Mgr: Russ Williams
Sfty Dirs: Lanny Thomas
Sls Mgr: Bill Tabeling

D-U-N-S 04-893-0218 IMP
▲ LOJACK CORP
40 Pequot Way, Canton, MA 02021-2306
Tel (781) 302-4200 *Founded/Ownrshp* 1978
Sales 133.5MM *EMP* 685^E
Accts Grant Thornton Llp Boston Ma
Tkr Sym LOJN *Exch* NGS
SIC 3699 Security devices; Security control equipment & systems; Security devices; Security control equipment & systems
Pr: Randy L Ortiz
CFO: Kenneth L Dumas
Bd of Dir: Gary Dilts
Bd of Dir: Marcia Hooper
Chf Mktg O: Brian Boyce
Sr VP: Harold E Dewsnap
Sr VP: Emad Isaac
Sr VP: Jose M Oxholm
VP: Joe Castelli
VP: Torsten Gruenzig
Genl Mgr: Elia De Leon
Board of Directors: David J Shea, Alan L Bazaar, Rory J Cowan, Edward Davis, Gary E Dilts, Marcia J Hooper, Philip Horlock, John A Janitz, John H Mackinnon, Robert J Murray

D-U-N-S 62-497-6924 EXP
LOKEY AUTOMOTIVE GROUP INC
LOKEY NISSAN
27850 Us Highway 19 N, Clearwater, FL 33761-4902
Tel (727) 789-8100 *Founded/Ownrshp* 1990
Sales 91.3MM^E *EMP* 300
SIC 5511 7532 Automobiles, new & used; Collision shops, automotive; Automobiles, new & used; Collision shops, automotive
Pr: Paul B Lokey
**COO:* Tb Staton
**CFO:* Angel Aaron
Genl Mgr: Glenn Jones
Dir IT: Tracy Slusser
Sls Dir: Eric Cohen
Sls Mgr: David Hampson
Sls Mgr: Rick Rizzo
Sales Asso: Paul Pavletic

LOKEY MERCEDES
See LOKEY MOTOR GROUP INC

LOKEY METALS
See BILL LOKEY CO INC

D-U-N-S 18-372-6595 EXP
LOKEY MOTOR GROUP INC
LOKEY MERCEDES
19820 Us Highway 19 N, Clearwater, FL 33764-5016
Tel (727) 530-1661 *Founded/Ownrshp* 1957
Sales 90.9MM^E *EMP* 260
SIC 5511 Automobiles, new & used; Automobiles, new & used
Pr: Philip E Lokey
**VP:* Sharon Boraski

LOKEY NISSAN
See LOKEY AUTOMOTIVE GROUP INC

D-U-N-S 03-221-0775
LOKEY OLDSMOBILE INC
27850 Us Highway 19 N, Clearwater, FL 33761-4902
Tel (727) 799-2151 *Founded/Ownrshp* 1952
Sales 26.3MM^E *EMP* 116
SIC 5511 Automobiles, new & used; Automobiles, new & used
Pr: Paul Lokey
Sls Mgr: George Gowen

D-U-N-S 62-126-0855 IMP
LOKRING TECHNOLOGY LLC
38376 Apollo Pkwy, Willoughby, OH 44094-7724
Tel (440) 942-0880 *Founded/Ownrshp* 2003
Sales 38.2MM^E *EMP* 73^E
SIC 3312 Pipes & tubes
Pr: Bill Lennon
CTO: Dave Schatz
IT Man: Lisa Fleming
IT Man: Michael Vaughn
Mtls Mgr: Vijay Mudambi
Ql Cn Mgr: Vincent Traina

LOLLICUP TEA ZONE
See LOLLICUP USA INC

D-U-N-S 00-971-3582 IMP/EXP
LOLLICUP USA INC (CA)
LOLLICUP TEA ZONE
6185 Kimball Ave, Chino, CA 91708-9126
Tel (626) 965-8882 *Founded/Ownrshp* 2000
Sales 60.0MM *EMP* 33
SIC 5113 5149 Cups, disposable plastic & paper; Coffee & tea; Cups, disposable plastic & paper; Coffee & tea
CEO: Alan Yu
**VP:* Marvin Cheng
VP: Joanne Wang
CTO: Candy Yu
Sls Mgr: Jerome Tung

D-U-N-S 00-590-4107 IMP/EXP
LOLLYTOGS LTD
FRENCH TOAST
100 W 33rd St Ste 1012, New York, NY 10001-2914
Tel (212) 502-6000 *Founded/Ownrshp* 1948
Sales 73.3MM^E *EMP* 220
SIC 2369 5137 Girls' & children's outerwear; Sportswear, women's & children's

D-U-N-S 14-131-2947 IMP
LOLOI INC
LOLOI RUGS
4501 Spring Valley Rd, Dallas, TX 75244-3706
Tel (972) 503-5656 *Founded/Ownrshp* 2003
Sales 103.1MM^E *EMP* 180
Accts Firooznia & Mekul Cpa S Pc S
SIC 5023 Rugs; Rugs
Pr: Amir Loloi
VP: Valerie Jacobs
**VP:* Sussan Loloi
IT Man: Jonathan Shipley
Opers Mgr: Tammy Holcomb
Prd Mgr: Anibal Soto
Manager: Craig Rieger
Sls Mgr: Tim Ward

LOLOI RUGS
See LOLOI INC

D-U-N-S 04-723-3382 IMP
■ LOMA INTERNATIONAL INC
LOMA SYSTEMS
(*Suby of* ILLINOIS TOOL WORKS INC) ★
550 Kehoe Blvd, Carol Stream, IL 60188-1838
Tel (630) 588-0900 *Founded/Ownrshp* 2008
Sales 49.7MM^E *EMP* 80
SIC 5065 3535 5084 Electronic parts & equipment; Conveyors & conveying equipment; Industrial machinery & equipment; Electronic parts & equipment; Conveyors & conveying equipment; Industrial machinery & equipment
Pr: Hugh Zentmyer
VP: Kristina Benassi
Genl Mgr: Pradeep Rochliani
CTO: Anthony Divito
Sls&Mrk Ex: Art Malinowski
Mktg Mgr: James Chrismas
Manager: Bob Borsellino
Manager: Todd Fletcher
Sales Asso: Ginger Vaicius

D-U-N-S 93-288-4711
LOMA LINDA ACADEMY
10656 Anderson St, Loma Linda, CA 92354-2104
Tel (909) 796-0161 *Founded/Ownrshp* 1920
Sales 20.5MM^E *EMP* 140
SIC 8211 Private elementary & secondary schools
Prin: L Roo McKenzie
Prin: Bob Dennis
Off Admin: Patricia Inostroza
Psych: Lorraine Thompson

LOMA LINDA INTL HEART INST
See LOMA LINDA UNIVERSITY ANESTHESIOLOGY MEDICAL GROUP INC

D-U-N-S 00-965-6273
LOMA LINDA UNIVERSITY
LLU
11060 Anderson St, Loma Linda, CA 92350-1736
Tel (909) 558-4540 *Founded/Ownrshp* 1909
Sales 713.7MM^E *EMP* 7,000
SIC 8221 University; University
Pr: Richard H Hart
**Ex VP:* Ruthita J Fike
**Ex VP:* H Roger Hadley
**Ex VP:* Kevin J Lang
**Sr VP:* Rachelle B Bussell
**Sr VP:* Verlon Strauss
Exec: Kevin Boggs
Ex Dir: Nellie Killion
Ex Dir: Janelle Pyke

D-U-N-S 04-994-3319
LOMA LINDA UNIVERSITY ANESTHESIOLOGY MEDICAL GROUP INC (CA)
LOMA LINDA INTL HEART INST
11234 Anderson St Rm 2532, Loma Linda, CA 92354-2804
Tel (909) 558-4475 *Founded/Ownrshp* 1974
Sales 23.1MM^E *EMP* 38
Accts Soren Mcadam Christenson Llp
SIC 8011 Cardiologist & cardio-vascular specialist; Cardiologist & cardio-vascular specialist
Pr: Robert D Martin MD
**CFO:* Stanley D Brauer MD
Surgeon: OK Ojogho

D-U-N-S 78-668-1007
LOMA LINDA UNIVERSITY DENTAL GROUP INC
LOMA LINDA UNIVERSITY SCHOOL O
(*Suby of* LVI ENVIRONMENTAL SERVICES) ★
11092 Anderson St, Loma Linda, CA 92350-1706
Tel (909) 558-4675 *Founded/Ownrshp* 1989
Sales 410.1M *EMP* 350
Accts E Eugene Platt & Assoc Cpa S
SIC 8221 Colleges universities & professional schools; Colleges universities & professional schools
Pr: Richard H Hart
**VP:* Kevin J Lang
HC Dir: Sylvia Davis

D-U-N-S 09-224-6990
LOMA LINDA UNIVERSITY HEALTH CARE
(*Suby of* LLU) ★
11370 Anderson St # 3900, Loma Linda, CA 92350-1715
Tel (909) 558-2806 *Founded/Ownrshp* 1967
Sales 713.7MM^E *EMP* 4,836^E
SIC 8062 8011 8051 5999 Physicians' office, including specialists; Hospital, medical school affiliated with residency; Medical centers; Extended care facility; Convalescent equipment & supplies
Pr: Richard Hart
**CEO:* Rosita Fike
Ex Dir: Rhodes Rigsby
Off Mgr: Terry Merrick
Nurse Mgr: Debbie Clausen
Pathlgst: Mia Perez
Obsttrcn: Kathleen M Lau
Opthamlgy: Shyun Jeng
Plas Surg: Byron Bailey
Doctor: Evelyn Choo
Doctor: Jesse Dovich MD

D-U-N-S 83-754-7017
LOMA LINDA UNIVERSITY HEALTH CARE
11175 Campus St, Loma Linda, CA 92350-1700
Tel (909) 558-4985 *Founded/Ownrshp* 1989
Sales 158.3MM *EMP* 1,100
SIC 8011 Offices & clinics of medical doctors; Offices & clinics of medical doctors
Pr: Roger Hadley MD
**V Ch:* David B Hinshaw Jr
VP: James Pappas

D-U-N-S 07-688-6571
LOMA LINDA UNIVERSITY MEDICAL CENTER
LLUMC
(*Suby of* LOMA LINDA UNIVERSITY HEALTH CARE) ★
11234 Anderson St, Loma Linda, CA 92354-2871
Tel (909) 558-4000 *Founded/Ownrshp* 1980
Sales 713.7MM^E *EMP* 4,676
SIC 8062 8011 8051 5999 Hospital, medical school affiliated with residency; Medical centers; Extended care facility; Medical apparatus & supplies; Hospital, medical school affiliated with residency; Medical centers; Extended care facility; Medical apparatus & supplies
V Ch: Richard H Hart
V Ch: Richard H Hart
**Pr:* James Jesse
**Treas:* Noni Patchett
Ofcr: Judith Storfjell
**VP:* Richard Catalano
VP: Lyndon Edwards
VP: Daniel W Giang
VP: Mark Reeves
Adm Dir: Kenneth Breyer
Adm Dir: Paul B Simms

LOMA LINDA UNIVERSITY SCHOOL O
See LOMA LINDA UNIVERSITY DENTAL GROUP INC

LOMA SYSTEMS
See LOMA INTERNATIONAL INC

D-U-N-S 00-624-7696 EXP
LOMANCO INC (AR)
2101 W Main St, Jacksonville, AR 72076-4247
Tel (501) 982-6511 *Founded/Ownrshp* 1946
Sales 26.2MM^E *EMP* 215
SIC 3444 3634 3089 3442 Metal ventilating equipment; Fans, exhaust & ventilating, electric: household; Plastic hardware & building products; Metal doors, sash & trim; Metal ventilating equipment; Fans, exhaust & ventilating, electric: household; Plastic hardware & building products; Metal doors, sash & trim
Pr: Chris Grimes
**Sec:* Jim Byrd
**VP:* Dennis Belden
CIO: Scott Webb
MIS Dir: Vernon Oberle
Plnt Mgr: Michael Taylor
Natl Sales: Mike Nichols
Sls Mgr: Mike Mitchell
Sales Asso: Mary Carroll
Snr Mgr: Jim Green

D-U-N-S 02-212-4796
LOMAR DISTRIBUTING INC
(*Suby of* HY-VEE FOOD AND DRUG) ★
5820 Westown Pkwy, West Des Moines, IA 50266-8223
Tel (515) 244-3105 *Founded/Ownrshp* 1990
Sales 169.5MM^E *EMP* 100
SIC 5143 5149 Cheese; Specialty food items; Cheese; Specialty food items
Pr: Brandon Lampkin
**Treas:* Michael Skokan
Sr VP: Katie Graham
**VP:* William E Sales Jr
VP: Bruce Way

D-U-N-S 08-120-7276
LOMAR MACHINE & TOOL CO
135 Main St, Horton, MI 49246-9540
Tel (517) 563-8136 *Founded/Ownrshp* 1976
Sales 27.4MM^E *EMP* 105
SIC 3549 3544 Assembly machines, including robotic; Special dies & tools; Jigs & fixtures
CEO: James L Geisman
**Pr:* Ronald E Geisman
CFO: Todd Pelton
**Treas:* Mary L Geisman
**VP:* Charles Murphy
VP: Steve White
Prgrm Mgr: Matt Murphy
Dir IT: Charlie Bryant
IT Man: Randy Hunter
Opers Mgr: Jack Vincent
Plnt Mgr: Mark Gladstone

LOMBARD ELEMENTARY SCHL DST 44
See BOARD OF EDUCATION SCHOOL DISTRICT 44

D-U-N-S 01-888-9139
LOMBARD FORD INC (CT)
Rr 44, Winsted, CT 06098
Tel (860) 379-3301 Founded/Ownrshp 1961, 1982
Sales 20.1MM^E EMP 47
SIC 5511 Automobiles, new & used
Pr: Robert Lombard
*Treas: Patricia Lombard

D-U-N-S 07-973-7292
LOMBARD TOYOTA INC
725 W Roosevelt Rd, Lombard, IL 60148-4215
Tel (630) 629-3900 Founded/Ownrshp 1975
Sales 30.2MM^E EMP 70
SIC 5511 7539 Automobiles, new & used; Automotive repair shops; Automobiles, new & used; Automotive repair shops
Owner: Ron Postma
Genl Mgr: John Lipinski
Sales Asso: Gene Scardine

LOMBARDI DESIGN & MFG
See ANNA YOUNG ASSOC LTD

D-U-N-S 07-831-3823
LOMBARDO HOMES OF SE MICHIGAN LLC
51237 Danview Tech Ct, Shelby Township, MI 48315
Tel (586) 781-7900 Founded/Ownrshp 2008
Sales 60.0MM EMP 80
SIC 1521 Single-family housing construction; Single-family housing construction
VP: Cathy Jaraczewski

D-U-N-S 15-292-2456
LOMBARDY HOLDINGS INC
3166 Hrseless Carriage Rd, Norco, CA 92860-3612
Tel (951) 808-4550 Founded/Ownrshp 1996
Sales 85.0MM EMP 400
SIC 1623 5211 Telephone & communication line construction; Cable television line construction; Electrical construction materials; Telephone & communication line construction; Cable television line construction; Electrical construction materials
CEO: Marc Laulhere

D-U-N-S 09-742-0376 IMP/EXP
LOMBART BROTHERS INC
LOMBART INSTRUMENT
5358 Robin Hood Rd, Norfolk, VA 23513-2430
Tel (757) 853-8888 Founded/Ownrshp 1979
Sales 75.0MM^E EMP 130
SIC 5048 Optometric equipment & supplies; Lenses, ophthalmic; Optometric equipment & supplies; Lenses, ophthalmic
Pr: Richard B Lombart
*VP: Kenneth A Lombart
Admn Mgr: Linda Mahon
VP Opers: Lance Pashia
Opers Mgr: Hillarene Donovan
Sls&Mrk Ex: Philip Gordon
Sls Mgr: Peter Leadem
Sls Mgr: Gordon Siteman

LOMBART INSTRUMENT
See LOMBART BROTHERS INC

LOMONT MOLDING IMT
See LOMONT MOLDING INC

D-U-N-S 10-231-9852 EXP
LOMONT MOLDING INC
LOMONT MOLDING IMT
1516 E Mapleleaf Dr, Mount Pleasant, IA 52641-3117
Tel (319) 385-1528 Founded/Ownrshp 1982
Sales 21.4MM^E EMP 152
SIC 3089 3086

LOMPOC SKILLED CARE CENTER
See LOMPOC VALLEY MEDICAL CENTER

D-U-N-S 07-020-6800
LOMPOC UNIFIED SCHOOL DISTRICT
1301 N A St, Lompoc, CA 93436-3516
Tel (805) 742-3300 Founded/Ownrshp 1960
Sales 65.7MM^E EMP 1,300
SIC 8211 Public elementary & secondary schools; Public elementary school; Public senior high school; Public adult education school; Public elementary & secondary schools; Public elementary school; Public senior high school; Public adult education school
Trst: Marianne Kugler
Pr Dir: Art Diaz

D-U-N-S 07-532-9003
LOMPOC VALLEY MEDICAL CENTER
LOMPOC SKILLED CARE CENTER
1515 E Ocean Ave, Lompoc, CA 93436-7092
Tel (805) 737-3300 Founded/Ownrshp 1947
Sales 95.4MM^E EMP 675
SIC 8062 8051 General medical & surgical hospitals; Skilled nursing care facilities; General medical & surgical hospitals; Skilled nursing care facilities
CEO: Jim Raggio
*COO: Naishadh Buch
Bd of Dir: Roger McConnell
Ofcr: Neil Imano
Dir Lab: Robert Lingl
*Prin: Jayne Scalise
QA Dir: Linda Everly
Software D: Michael Despres
Ansthlgy: Toni Horton
Doctor: Cedric Kwon
Diag Rad: Duard Enoch

D-U-N-S 00-901-7823
LONDEN INSURANCE GROUP INC
4343 E Camelback Rd # 400, Phoenix, AZ 85018-2705
Tel (602) 957-1650 Founded/Ownrshp 1963
Sales NA EMP 150
SIC 6311 6321 8741 Life insurance carriers; Accident insurance carriers; Health insurance carriers; Administrative management; Life insurance carriers; Accident insurance carriers; Health insurance carriers; Administrative management
Ch Bd: Jack W Londen
Pr: Marce Boersma
Pr: Thomas Londen
CFO: Larry Schuneman
Sr VP: Dean Lathrop
VP: Judith Pettit
VP: Monica Sole
Mktg Mgr: Fran McGovern
Pgrm Dir: Paula Rodriguez

D-U-N-S 07-382-0599
LONDEN INSURANCE INC
LIFE BOSTON INSURANCE COMPANY
(Suby of LINCOLN HERITAGE LIFE INSURANCE CO) ★
4343 E Camelback Rd # 400, Phoenix, AZ 85018-2705
Tel (602) 957-1650 Founded/Ownrshp 1991
Sales NA EMP 75
SIC 6311 Life insurance
Ch Bd: Jack W Londen
*Pr: Thomas Londen
*Treas: Dean Lathrop
*V Ch Bd: Doris Londen

D-U-N-S 80-913-3197
LONDON BAY -T S S ACQUISITION CO LLC
(Suby of LONDON BAY CAPITAL LLC) ★
49 Moraga Ave, San Francisco, CA 94129-1122
Tel (415) 814-7781 Founded/Ownrshp 2007
Sales 51.0MM^E EMP 250
SIC 8742 Marketing consulting services; Marketing consulting services
CEO: Sam Humphreys

D-U-N-S 80-123-9752
LONDON BAY CAPITAL LLC
5 Funston Ave Ste B, San Francisco, CA 94129-5266
Tel (415) 292-1700 Founded/Ownrshp 2005
Sales 51.0MM^E EMP 254
SIC 6799 8742 Venture capital companies; Marketing consulting services; Venture capital companies; Marketing consulting services
CEO: Sam Humphreys

D-U-N-S 14-696-9092
LONDON BRIDGE TRADING CO LTD
585 London Bridge Rd, Virginia Beach, VA 23454-5226
Tel (757) 498-0207 Founded/Ownrshp 1985
Sales 54.6MM^E EMP 260
SIC 7389 2399 5139 3069 5091 Design services; Boots; Camping equipment & supplies; Rubber coated fabrics & clothing; Belting & belt products; Design services; Belting & belt products; Boots; Rubber coated fabrics & clothing; Camping equipment & supplies
CEO: Harold Douglas McDougal
*Pr: David M Bohannon II
Pr: Vince Moran
*CFO: Kevin P Moran
*Sec: Linda Hunt Cdougal
Ex VP: Ken Beasley
VP: Steve Thayer
IT Man: Steve Cauffiel
IT Man: Craig Tilden

D-U-N-S 01-419-7333 IMP
LONDON BROADCASTING CO INC
15455 Dallas Pkwy Ste 100, Addison, TX 75001-6739
Tel (214) 730-0151 Founded/Ownrshp 2007
Sales 82.7MM^E EMP 350
SIC 4833 Television broadcasting stations; Television broadcasting stations
Pr: Terry London
*CFO: Carl Kornmeyer

D-U-N-S 05-750-7485
LONDON FRUIT INC
9010 S Cage Blvd, Pharr, TX 78577-9769
Tel (956) 781-7799 Founded/Ownrshp 1981
Sales 33.9MM EMP 50^E
Accts Long Chilton Llp Mcallen Tex
SIC 5148 Fresh fruits & vegetables; Fresh fruits & vegetables
Pr: Barry London
*Treas: Nora London
*VP: Gerardo L Garcia

D-U-N-S 07-980-0231 IMP
■ **LONDON HARRY CANDIES INC**
HARRY LONDON CHOCOLATES
(Suby of FANNIE MAY CONFECTIONS BRANDS INC) ★
5353 Lauby Rd, North Canton, OH 44720-1572
Tel (330) 494-0833 Founded/Ownrshp 2006
Sales 37.9MM^E EMP 250^E
SIC 2066 5441 Chocolate & cocoa products; Candy; Chocolate & cocoa products; Candy
Pr: Terry Michell
*CFO: Matthew J Anderson
*VP: Ed Seibolt
Dir IT: Mike Arshinkoff

D-U-N-S 96-168-1603 IMP
LONDON LUXURY LLC
270 North Ave Ste C, New Rochelle, NY 10801-5106
Tel (914) 636-2100 Founded/Ownrshp 2002
Sales 29.0MM^E EMP 48
SIC 5023 Bedspreads
CEO: Marc Jason
*CFO: Sanjay Tillu
Chf Mktg O: Moshe Abehsera
Sr VP: Lee Dubin
Sr VP: Dubin Lee
CTO: Gary Blaine

D-U-N-S 09-750-9996 IMP
LONDON MAGGY INTERNATIONAL LTD
MAGGY LONDON BLOUSE DIV
530 Fashion Ave Fl 16, New York, NY 10018-4896
Tel (212) 944-7199 Founded/Ownrshp 1979
Sales 38.8MM^E EMP 200
SIC 2331 Women's & misses' blouses & shirts; Women's & misses' blouses & shirts
Ch Bd: Larry Lefkowitz
*Ch: Milton Cahn
Ex VP: Lee Polsky
Sr VP: Jerry Sholtz
VP: Devin Fitzpatrick
IT Man: Joy Bongioni
VP Sls: Glenn Phillips

D-U-N-S 07-396-0718
LONDONDERRY SCHOOL DISTRICT
268 Mammoth Rd, Londonderry, NH 03053-3003
Tel (603) 432-6920 Founded/Ownrshp 1972
Sales 35.2MM^E EMP 650
SIC 8211 Public elementary & secondary schools; Public junior high school; Public senior high school; Public elementary & secondary schools; Public junior high school; Public senior high school
Bd of Dir: George Herrmann
Bd of Dir: Kim Lindley-Soucy
Dir IT: Shawn Coe

D-U-N-S 00-691-0624
LONE CYPRESS CO LLC
PEBBLE BEACH RESORTS
2700 17 Mile Dr, Pebble Beach, CA 93953-2668
Tel (831) 647-7500 Founded/Ownrshp 1999
Sales 110.7MM^E EMP 1,700^E
SIC 7011 7992 5941 7991 Resort hotel; Public golf courses; Golf goods & equipment; Tennis goods & equipment; Physical fitness facilities; Resort hotel; Public golf courses; Golf goods & equipment; Tennis goods & equipment; Physical fitness facilities
CEO: Bill Perocchi
*Pr: Cody Plott
*CFO: Dave Heuck
*Ex VP: Paul Spengler
*Ex VP: Mark Stilwell
VP: Dominic Vannes
Natl Sales: Michael Parker
Snr Mgr: Dave Rankin

D-U-N-S 00-811-0322 IMP
LONE STAR BAKERY INC
6905 Us Highway 87 E, China Grove, TX 78263-6029
Tel (210) 648-6400 Founded/Ownrshp 1880
Sales 121.9MM^E EMP 400
SIC 2053 Frozen bakery products, except bread; Frozen bakery products, except bread
Pr: Mac S Morris Jr
*VP: Tracy Fletcher
*VP: Mandy Morris
VP: Don Wilson
Dir IT: Jerome Neuhoff
Dir IT: Tom Oatman
Manager: Christina Zavala

D-U-N-S 01-597-0056 EXP
LONE STAR BEEF PROCESSORS LP
2150 E 37th St, San Angelo, TX 76903-3415
Tel (325) 658-5555 Founded/Ownrshp 1997
Sales 39.9MM^E EMP 200
SIC 2011 Meat packing plants; Meat packing plants
Pt: John Cross
Pt: Burley Smith
VP: Debbie Farr

D-U-N-S 02-493-2477
LONE STAR CAFE INC
9811 Anderson Mill Rd, Austin, TX 78750-2262
Tel (512) 331-5444 Founded/Ownrshp 1980, 1999
Sales 11.6MM^E EMP 800
SIC 5812 American restaurant; American restaurant
Pr: Rick Redmond DDS

D-U-N-S 14-006-8821
LONE STAR CIRCLE OF CARE
A.W. GRIMES MEDICAL OFFICES
205 E University Ave # 200, Georgetown, TX 78626-6814
Tel (512) 686-0523 Founded/Ownrshp 2001
Sales 66.9MM EMP 420
Accts Bkd Llp Springfield Missour
SIC 8062 8011 General medical & surgical hospitals; Primary care medical clinic; General medical & surgical hospitals; Primary care medical clinic
Pr: Rhonda Mundhenk
*CFO: Jon Calvin
*Ch: Jack Hunnicutt
VP: Marlo Fisher
Comm Dir: Rebekah Haynes
Genl Couns: Sarah Churchill
Genl Couns: Marshall Preddy
Genl Couns: Tillery Stout
Snr Mgr: Tracy Angelocci

LONE STAR CIVIL CONSTRUCTION
See FELIX ASSOCIATES OF FLORIDA INC

D-U-N-S 04-032-5706
LONE STAR COLLEGE SYSTEM
LSC SYSTEM OFFICE
5000 Research Forest Dr, The Woodlands, TX 77381-4356
Tel (832) 813-6500 Founded/Ownrshp 1972
Sales 176.1MM^E EMP 5,137
Accts Mcconnell & Jones Llp Houston
SIC 8222 Junior college; Junior college
VP: Lawrence Brandyburg
VP: Christine Williams
Ex Dir: Greg Nelson
Prgrm Mgr: Michael Sellers
Off Admin: Susan Myers
Off Admin: Danny Osburn
CTO: Richard Fitzmaurice
MIS Dir: Allen Rice
Dir IT: Oscar Ramos
Dir IT: Kenneth Smith
IT Man: Carolyn Poe

D-U-N-S 06-410-7956 IMP
LONE STAR CONSOLIDATED FOODS LLC
LONE STAR DONUT
1727 N Beckley Ave, Dallas, TX 75203-1007
Tel (214) 946-2185 Founded/Ownrshp 1950
Sales 87.1MM^E EMP 150
SIC 5142 Bakery products, frozen; Bakery products, frozen
CEO: Dolores Burdine
*Pr: Kathy Burdine
*Ex VP: Calvin Burdine
*VP: Kevin Murray
Ql Cn Mgr: Olga Pryor
Sls Mgr: Chuck Barrett

D-U-N-S 14-146-8475
LONE STAR CORROSION SERVICES INC
9220 Taub Rd, Houston, TX 77064-6614
Tel (281) 955-1313 Founded/Ownrshp 2003
Sales 45.2MM^E EMP 80
SIC 5169 3471 Chemicals & allied products; Finishing, metals or formed products; Chemicals & allied products; Finishing, metals or formed products
Pr: James G Cronin Jr
*CFO: Tonya T Cronin
VP Opers: Mike Lacaze
Opers Mgr: Howard Salge

D-U-N-S 00-733-7025 IMP
LONE STAR CORRUGATED CONTAINER CORP
SAV WAY CARTON FORMS
700 N Wildwood Dr, Irving, TX 75061-8832
Tel (972) 721-0238 Founded/Ownrshp 1959
Sales 24.3MM EMP 135
SIC 2653 3993 2759 Boxes, corrugated: made from purchased materials; Signs & advertising specialties; Commercial printing; Boxes, corrugated: made from purchased materials; Signs & advertising specialties; Commercial printing
Pr: John W Mc Leod Jr
CFO: John McLeod
*Sec: Lorene Cash
*VP: Richard Ward
Sls Mgr: Steve Devries

LONE STAR DONUT
See LONE STAR CONSOLIDATED FOODS LLC

LONE STAR FARM & HOME CENTER
See TEXAS FARM PRODUCTS CO

D-U-N-S 16-826-1175 IMP
LONE STAR FASHIONS INC
GOODWISH INDUSTRIES
2830 Produce Row, Houston, TX 77023-5822
Tel (713) 674-7247 Founded/Ownrshp 1999
Sales 29.7MM^E EMP 140^E
SIC 5136 5137 Men's & boys' clothing; Women's & children's clothing; Men's & boys' clothing; Women's & children's clothing
Pr: Saleem Gagai
*VP: Mirza N Baig
Off Admin: Norma Pineda

D-U-N-S 07-219-3683 IMP/EXP
LONE STAR FASTENERS LP
(Suby of LS PRECISION MANUFACTURING INC) ★
24131 W Hardy Rd, Spring, TX 77373-5769
Tel (281) 353-1191 Founded/Ownrshp 2003
Sales 32.8MM^E EMP 200
SIC 3452 Bolts, nuts, rivets & washers; Bolts, nuts, rivets & washers
Pt: Peter Stein
Pt: Steve Cabral
Pt: Gregory A David
Pt: Jim Stersik
VP: Don Marshall
IT Man: Bobby Baker
IT Man: Adam Barrilleaux
IT Man: Mark Hutchison
IT Man: Don Perry
Sls Mgr: Amanda Barton

LONE STAR FORD
See SONIC AUTOMOTIVE OF TEXAS LP

D-U-N-S 62-537-4731 IMP
LONE STAR FORK LIFT INC
4213 Forest Ln, Garland, TX 75042-6820
Tel (972) 494-5438 Founded/Ownrshp 1991
Sales 44.5MM^E EMP 107
SIC 5084 7699 7359 Lift trucks & parts; Industrial truck repair; Industrial truck rental
Pr: Josh McSwain
*Pr: Don Mc Swain
*CFO: Gerard McEvoy
*VP: Bridget Mc Swain

D-U-N-S 06-028-6759
LONE STAR FUND IV (US) LP
2711 N Haskell Ave, Dallas, TX 75204-2911
Tel (214) 754-8300 Founded/Ownrshp 2001
Sales 3.6MMM^E EMP 47,026^E
SIC 6726 Investment offices; Investment offices
Pr: Andre Collin
Prin: Len Allen
Prin: John Grayken
Mktg Dir: Brad Haga

D-U-N-S 80-913-0482
LONE STAR FUND V (US) LP
(Suby of LONE STAR PARTNERS V, L. P.)
717 N Harwood St Ste 2200, Dallas, TX 75201-6515
Tel (214) 754-8300 Founded/Ownrshp 2004
Sales 12.9MMM^E EMP 2,350
SIC 6799 5812 Real estate investors, except property operators; Steak & barbecue restaurants; Steak restaurant; Real estate investors, except property operators; Steak & barbecue restaurants; Steak restaurant
Ch Bd: John Grayken
VP: Jeffrey Kert
VP: Leigh REA

D-U-N-S 83-158-4672
LONE STAR FUNDS
2711 N Haskell Ave # 1700, Dallas, TX 75204-2922
Tel (214) 754-8300 Founded/Ownrshp 2008
Sales 100.6MM^E EMP 200^E
SIC 6211 Investment firm, general brokerage
Pr: Andre Collin
VP: Kevin Barner
VP: Kevin Carlson
Mng Dir: Bob Ricci
Mng Dir: Hugh Ward
Off Admin: Kim Roberts

D-U-N-S 09-136-9264
LONE STAR HMA LP
MESQUITE COMMUNITY HOSPITAL
3500 Interstate 30 Frnt, Mesquite, TX 75150-2651
Tel (972) 698-3300 Founded/Ownrshp 1978
Sales 32.2MM^E EMP 800

SIC 8062 8011 General medical & surgical hospitals; Offices & clinics of medical doctors; General medical & surgical hospitals; Offices & clinics of medical doctors
Ch Bd: Joseph Vumbacco
CFO: Chris Stuart
Phys Thrpy: Cheryl Watson
HC Dir: Mary McCormick

D-U-N-S 62-211-7521
LONE STAR HOLDINGS LLC
LONE STAR OVERNIGHT
6500 River Place Blvd # 2, Austin, TX 78730-1155
Tel (512) 873-8067 *Founded/Ownrshp* 2002
Sales 113.1MM^E *EMP* 600
SIC 4215 4513 4212 Package delivery, vehicular; Parcel delivery, vehicular; Package delivery, private air; Delivery service, vehicular; Package delivery, vehicular; Parcel delivery, vehicular; Package delivery, private air; Delivery service, vehicular
CEO: Rick Jones
Genl Pt: Gary Gunter
Pt: Keith Jaeger
Pt: George Stephens
Pr: Richard Jones
VP: David Galante
Opers Mgr: Chavies Fisher
Opers Mgr: Jason Fletcher
Opers Mgr: Michael Pokluda
Mktg Dir: Mark Scholz

D-U-N-S 00-126-5321 IMP
LONE STAR INDUSTRIES INC
BUZZI UNICHEM
(*Suby of* BUZZI UNICEM USA) ★
10401 N Meridian St # 400, Indianapolis, IN 46290-1154
Tel (317) 706-3314 *Founded/Ownrshp* 1919, 1999
Sales 152.7MM^E *EMP* 751
SIC 3241 3273 Portland cement; Ready-mixed concrete; Portland cement; Ready-mixed concrete
Pr: David A Nepereny
**CFO:* Nancy Krial
**VP:* David S Rifkind

D-U-N-S 11-972-9254
LONE STAR INFRASTRUCTURE LLC
108 Mcnutt Rd, Hutto, TX 78634
Tel (512) 681-6000 *Founded/Ownrshp* 2001
Sales 16.5MM^E *EMP* 400
SIC 1611 Highway & street construction; Highway & street construction
Prin: Dan Zollinger
CFO: Eduardo Garcia

D-U-N-S 01-140-3465
LONE STAR INSTRUMENTATION & ELECTRIC CORP
2222 W 42nd St, Odessa, TX 79764-6305
Tel (432) 368-7827 *Founded/Ownrshp* 2009
Sales 36.5MM^E *EMP* 164^E
SIC 3699 Electrical equipment & supplies
Pr: Ronnie Hobbs
Sfty Dirs: Tina Polson
Opers Mgr: Israel Ramirez
Opers Mgr: Skylar Smith

D-U-N-S 78-370-2843
LONE STAR INVESTMENT ADVISORS LLC
LS NEW MARKETS INV ADVISORS
4455 L B Johnson Fwy 30, Dallas, TX 75244
Tel (972) 702-7390 *Founded/Ownrshp* 2006
Sales 78.6MM^E *EMP* 375
SIC 6282 Investment advisory service; Investment advisory service
Mng Pt: Arthur W Hollingsworth
**CFO:* Scott Billings

D-U-N-S 14-815-9296
LONE STAR LUBRICATION INC
JIFFY LUBE
3059 W 15th St, Plano, TX 75075-7633
Tel (972) 867-7544 *Founded/Ownrshp* 1987
Sales 17.4MM^E *EMP* 650
SIC 7549 Lubrication service, automotive; Lubrication service, automotive
Pr: William Bandy

LONE STAR MARINE SHELTERS
See MARINE SHELTERS HOLDINGS LLC

D-U-N-S 10-720-3346
LONE STAR MILK PRODUCERS INC
2716 Commerce St, Wichita Falls, TX 76301-8051
Tel (817) 781-1194 *Founded/Ownrshp* 1997
Sales 163.9MM^E *EMP* 135^E
SIC 5143 Milk; Milk
Pr: James G Baird
**COO:* Sonia Fabian
**Sec:* Felice M Baird
**VP:* W C Barton
Off Mgr: Felice Baired

LONE STAR NATIONAL BANCSHARES-
See LONE STAR NATIONAL BANK

LONE STAR NATIONAL BANCSHARES-
See LONE STAR NATIONAL BANK SHARES NEVEDA

D-U-N-S 00-924-7144
LONE STAR NATIONAL BANCSHARES—TEXAS INC (TX)
LONE STAR NATIONAL BANK
4500 N 10th St Ste 305, McAllen, TX 78504-2969
Tel (956) 781-4321 *Founded/Ownrshp* 1995
Sales NA *EMP* 643
Accts Smith Fankhauser Voigt & Watso
SIC 6712 6021 Bank holding companies; National commercial banks; Bank holding companies; National commercial banks
Ch: Alonzo Cantu
V Ch: Oscar Gonzalez
**Pr:* S David Deanda
**CFO:* George R Carruthers
CFO: George Carruthers
Ofcr: Ed Borges
Ex VP: Tony Gorman
Ex VP: Kevin Pilgrim
Ex VP: Angie Vera-Oliva
VP: Abrana Gonzalez
VP: Marco Perez
VP: Leticia Zavala

LONE STAR NATIONAL BANK ,
See LONE STAR NATIONAL BANCSHARES—TEXAS INC

D-U-N-S 10-275-6954
LONE STAR NATIONAL BANK
LONE STAR NATIONAL BANCSHARES-
(*Suby of* LONE STAR NATIONAL BANCSHARES-) ★
520 E Nolana Ave Ste 110, McAllen, TX 78504-2681
Tel (956) 781-4321 *Founded/Ownrshp* 1998
Sales NA *EMP* 143
SIC 6021 National commercial banks; National commercial banks
Ch Bd: Alonzo Cantu
**Ch Bd:* Oscar R Gonzalez
**Pr:* S David De Anda
**CEO:* A Javier Rodriguez
**CFO:* David Penoli
Sr Cor Off: Velma Garcia
Ofcr: Sochi Guerra
Ex VP: Valerie Cardenas
**Ex VP:* George R Carruthers
Ex VP: Raymond Cisneros
**Ex VP:* Sam De La Garza
**Ex VP:* Angie Vera-Oliva
Sr VP: Tom Bynum
Sr VP: Martinez Cfsa
Sr VP: Kenneth Grams
Sr VP: Gloria Guerra
Sr VP: Sameer Saxena
VP: Roberto Contreras
VP: Jaime Gorina
VP: Eva Markum

D-U-N-S 12-675-7983
LONE STAR NATIONAL BANK SHARES NEVEDA
LONE STAR NATIONAL BANCSHARES-
(*Suby of* LONE STAR NATIONAL BANCSHARES—TEXAS INC) ★
100 W Ferguson St, Pharr, TX 78577-9517
Tel (956) 781-4321 *Founded/Ownrshp* 1998
Sales NA *EMP* 143
SIC 6021 National commercial banks; National commercial banks
CEO: A Jabier Rodriguez
V Ch: Oscar Gonzalez
CFO: George Carrruthers

D-U-N-S 96-823-1550
■ **LONE STAR NGL LLC**
(*Suby of* ENERGY TRANSFER PARTNERS LP) ★
800 E Sonterra Blvd # 400, San Antonio, TX 78258-3940
Tel (210) 403-7300 *Founded/Ownrshp* 2011
Sales 189.3MM^E *EMP* 200
SIC 1321 Natural gas liquids; Natural gas liquids
CEO: Kelcy L Warren
**Pr:* Marshall S McCrea III
**CFO:* Martin Salinas
**Sr VP:* Thomas P Mason

D-U-N-S 80-952-1516
■ **LONE STAR NGL PIPELINE LP**
(*Suby of* LONE STAR NGL LLC) ★
1300 Main St 10, Houston, TX 77002-6803
Tel (210) 403-7300 *Founded/Ownrshp* 2011
Sales 112.2MM^E *EMP* 200^E
SIC 4924 1321 Natural gas distribution; Natural gas liquids
Pt: Kelcy L Warren
Pt: Marshall S McCrea III
Pt: Martin Salinas Jr
VP: Brad Burmaster
Dir Surg: Josie Castrejana

LONE STAR OVERNIGHT
See LONE STAR HOLDINGS LLC

LONE STAR PARK AT GRND PRAIRIE
See LONE STAR RACE PARK LTD

LONE STAR PERIODICALS
See NEWS GROUP INC

D-U-N-S 00-833-5171
LONE STAR PLASTICS INC (TX)
(*Suby of* AMTOPP DIV) ★
2875 Market St Ste 100, Garland, TX 75041-2466
Tel (972) 271-9410 *Founded/Ownrshp* 1995, 2010
Sales 36.6MM^E *EMP* 200
SIC 2673 Food storage & trash bags (plastic); Trash bags (plastic film): made from purchased materials; Plastic bags: made from purchased materials; Food storage & trash bags (plastic); Trash bags (plastic film): made from purchased materials; Plastic bags: made from purchased materials
Pr: Webster F Stickney
Pr: Mark Bailey
**COO:* Joe Chen
**Treas:* Lee Seidel
VP: Jscott Atherley
**VP:* Gerald E Casteel
Plnt Mgr: Jill Bonneau
VP Sls: Jason Duane
Manager: Allen Wilson

D-U-N-S 86-844-8671
LONE STAR RACE PARK LTD
LONE STAR PARK AT GRND PRAIRIE
1000 Lone Star Pkwy, Grand Prairie, TX 75050-7941
Tel (972) 263-7223 *Founded/Ownrshp* 2013
Sales 23.2MM^E *EMP* 700^E
SIC 7948 Racing, including track operation; Racing, including track operation
Pt: Bob Kaminski
Ex VP: Caren McGratty
VP: Michael Shamburg
Genl Mgr: Gregg Driggers
Sfty Dirs: Eddie Rodriguez

D-U-N-S 80-307-6645
LONE STAR RAILROAD CONTRACTORS INC
4201 S Interstate Hwy 45, Ennis, TX 75119-0883
Tel (972) 878-9500 *Founded/Ownrshp* 1993
Sales 33.1MM *EMP* 130
Accts Anderson Marx & Bohl Pc C
SIC 1629 Railroad & railway roadbed construction; Railroad & railway roadbed construction
Pr: Paul Newman
**Treas:* Susan Hamm
**VP:* Josh Newman

D-U-N-S 83-320-9047
LONE STAR REAL ESTATE FUND (US) LP
2711 N Haskell Ave, Dallas, TX 75204-2911
Tel (214) 754-8300 *Founded/Ownrshp* 2007
Sales 365.2MM^E *EMP* 3,050^E
SIC 6733 Private estate, personal investment & vacation fund trusts; Private estate, personal investment & vacation fund trusts
Pt: Louis Paletta

D-U-N-S 85-945-7348
LONE STAR ROAD CONSTRUCTION LTD
10333 Windfern Rd, Houston, TX 77064-5288
Tel (281) 477-0515 *Founded/Ownrshp* 1999
Sales 41.5MM *EMP* 45
Accts Wrinkle Gardner & Company Pc
SIC 1611 Highway & street construction; Highway & street construction
CEO: Dwane Hubble

D-U-N-S 83-261-6432 IMP/EXP
LONE STAR SPECIALTIES LLC
6412 Us Highway 259 S, Lone Star, TX 75668-3100
Tel (903) 656-2536 *Founded/Ownrshp* 2009
Sales 25.0MM^E *EMP* 20
SIC 5172 Petroleum products

D-U-N-S 87-987-2344
LONE STAR STATE BANCSHARES INC
6220 Milwaukee Ave, Lubbock, TX 79424-0604
Tel (806) 771-7717 *Founded/Ownrshp* 2007
Sales NA *EMP* 60^E
SIC 6021 National commercial banks
Prin: Alan Lackey

D-U-N-S 82-663-7725
LONE STAR STATE BANK OF WEST TEXAS
(*Suby of* LONE STAR STATE BANCSHARES INC) ★
6220 Milwaukee Ave, Lubbock, TX 79424-0604
Tel (806) 771-7717 *Founded/Ownrshp* 2006
Sales NA *EMP* 48^E
SIC 6022 State commercial banks; State commercial banks
CEO: Alan Lackey
**Pr:* Kirk Thomas
**COO:* Lestie Glover
**CFO:* Edmund McGee
Ofcr: Sherolyn Castleman
Sr VP: Amanda Chacon
**Sr VP:* Nanette Deso
Sr VP: Clay Mercer
Sr VP: Jon Ruth
Sr VP: Steven Yandell
VP: Ashlee Thompson
VP: Megan White

LONE STAR STEAKHOUSE & SALOON
See LONE STAR STEAKS INC

LONE STAR STEAKHOUSE & SALOON
See LONE STAR STEAKHOUSE OF RICHMOND INC

D-U-N-S 78-618-1792
LONE STAR STEAKHOUSE & SALOON OF KANSAS INC
5055 W Park Blvd Ste 500, Plano, TX 75093-2587
Tel (972) 295-8600 *Founded/Ownrshp* 2006
Sales 464.7MM^E *EMP* 19,750
SIC 5812 Steak & barbecue restaurants; Steak & barbecue restaurants
Ch Bd: William Greene
**CEO:* Jamie B Coulter
COO: Jan Dietrich
**COO:* Mark Mednansky
**CFO:* John D White
**Sr VP:* Gerald T Aaron

D-U-N-S 80-027-8603
LONE STAR STEAKHOUSE & SALOON OF LOUISIANA INC
(*Suby of* LONE STAR STEAKHOUSE & SALOON OF KANSAS INC) ★
125 N Market St Ste 1300, Wichita, KS 67202-1713
Tel (316) 264-8888 *Founded/Ownrshp* 1992
Sales 16.3MM^E *EMP* 525
SIC 5812 Steak & barbecue restaurants; Steak & barbecue restaurants
Pr: Patrick Droesth
CFO: Jon Howie

D-U-N-S 03-427-5227
LONE STAR STEAKHOUSE & SALOON OF OHIO INC (OH)
(*Suby of* LONE STAR STEAKHOUSE & SALOON OF KANSAS INC) ★
224 E Douglas Ave Ste 700, Wichita, KS 67202-3424
Tel (316) 558-5100 *Founded/Ownrshp* 2001
Sales 27.1MM^E *EMP* 1,375
SIC 5812 Steak restaurant
Prin: Louie Elliot
Genl Mgr: Pratt Shirly
VP Opers: Mark Mednansky

D-U-N-S 78-376-7262
LONE STAR STEAKHOUSE OF RICHMOND INC
LONE STAR STEAKHOUSE & SALOON
(*Suby of* LONE STAR STEAKHOUSE & SALOON OF KANSAS INC) ★
5055 W Park Blvd Ste 500, Plano, TX 75093-2587
Tel (804) 272-0391 *Founded/Ownrshp* 1990
Sales 4.6MM^E *EMP* 310
SIC 5812 5813 Steak restaurant; Saloon; Steak restaurant; Saloon
Pr: Jamie B Coulter

D-U-N-S 03-411-6785
LONE STAR STEAKS INC (NC)
LONE STAR STEAKHOUSE & SALOON
(*Suby of* LONE STAR STEAKHOUSE & SALOON OF KANSAS INC) ★
5055 W Park Blvd Ste 500, Plano, TX 75093-2587
Tel (972) 295-8600 *Founded/Ownrshp* 1989
Sales 42.6MM^E *EMP* 1,300
SIC 5812 Steak restaurant; Steak restaurant

D-U-N-S 00-750-5464 IMP/EXP
■ **LONE STAR TECHNOLOGIES INC**
(*Suby of* UNITED STATES STEEL CORP) ★
15660 Dallas Pkwy Ste 500, Dallas, TX 75248-3354
Tel (972) 770-6401 *Founded/Ownrshp* 1942
Sales 303.7MM^E *EMP* 2,699
SIC 3317 3312 Steel pipe & tubes; Welded pipe & tubes; Well casing, wrought: welded, lock joint or heavy riveted; Seamless pipes & tubes; Sheet or strip, steel, hot-rolled; Steel pipe & tubes; Welded pipe & tubes; Well casing, wrought: welded, lock joint or heavy riveted; Seamless pipes & tubes; Sheet or strip, steel, hot-rolled
CEO: Rhys J Best
**Pr:* Joseph Alvarado
**CFO:* Charles J Keszler
VP: Nikhil Amin
**VP:* Robert F Spears

D-U-N-S 80-012-0383
■ **LONE STAR TRANSMISSION LLC**
(*Suby of* NEXTERA ENERGY INC) ★
700 Universe Blvd, West Palm Beach, FL 33408-2657
Tel (561) 691-7171 *Founded/Ownrshp* 2007
Sales 53.9MM^E *EMP* 129^E
SIC 4911 Electric services

D-U-N-S 18-746-3781 IMP
LONE STAR TRANSPORTATION LLC
(*Suby of* DASEKE LONE STAR INC) ★
1100 Northway Dr, Fort Worth, TX 76131-1425
Tel (817) 306-1000 *Founded/Ownrshp* 2014
Sales 122.5MM^E *EMP* 456
SIC 4213 Heavy machinery transport; Heavy machinery transport
CEO: Tex Robbins
VP: Jim Cortese
**VP:* David Ferebee
VP: Doug Miller
VP: Aubrey Scully
VP: Pete Trosky
Dir IT: Joel Hartley
Sfty Dirs: Butch Burnett
Trfc Dir: Conley Ligon
Opers Mgr: James Hester
Opers Mgr: Brandon Livingston

D-U-N-S 13-609-8519
LONE STAR US ACQUISITIONS LLC
2711 N Haskell Ave, Dallas, TX 75204-2911
Tel (214) 754-8300 *Founded/Ownrshp* 1998
Sales 8.4MM^E *EMP* 416^E
SIC 6799 Real estate investors, except property operators

D-U-N-S 18-370-8309
■ **LONESOURCE INC**
(*Suby of* STAPLES INC) ★
114 Mackenan Dr Ste 300, Cary, NC 27511-7920
Tel (919) 466-8615 *Founded/Ownrshp* 2013
Sales 20.7MM^E *EMP* 182
SIC 5943 Office forms & supplies; Office forms & supplies
CEO: Bradley P King
COO: Stacey King
CFO: David L Ryan
Ex VP: Alex Sossaman
Sr VP: Bennt Thomas

LONESTAR
See DOUGLASS DISTRIBUTING RETAIL CO INC

LONESTAR ENERGY FABRICATION
See LS ENERGY FABRICATION LLC

D-U-N-S 02-026-9952
LONESTAR FREIGHTLINER GROUP LLC (TX)
WICHITA FALLS FREIGHTLINER
2051 Hughes Rd, Grapevine, TX 76051-7317
Tel (817) 428-9736 *Founded/Ownrshp* 2001
Sales 374.8MM *EMP* 580
Accts Lane Gorman Trubitt Pllc Dall
SIC 5511 7538 General truck repair; Trucks, tractors & trailers: new & used; Truck equipment & parts; Trucks, tractors & trailers: new & used; General truck repair
COO: Dan Steven
**Pt:* Clay Corley
**Pt:* Jay Simmons
**Pr:* Vic Corley
**CFO:* James Bennie
Genl Mgr: Kent Noble

D-U-N-S 05-422-8015
LONESTAR PETROLEUM LP
HIDDEN MEADOWS SHELL PLAZA
6161 Savoy Dr Ste 904, Houston, TX 77036-3316
Tel (713) 266-3481 *Founded/Ownrshp* 1992
Sales 22.0MM^E *EMP* 28
SIC 5172 5541 Gasoline; Filling stations, gasoline
Pr: Abdul R Zakaria
**VP:* Mohemmed Zakaria

D-U-N-S 01-480-1261
LONESTAR PROSPECTS LTD
VISTA SAND
3549 Monroe Hwy, Granbury, TX 76049-2715
Tel (817) 279-1660 *Founded/Ownrshp* 2011
Sales 57.6MM^E *EMP* 130
SIC 1446 Silica sand mining
Pt: Roger Sikes
CFO: Bill Lorimer

LONESTAR RANCH AND OUTDOORS
See 4C LONESTAR RANCH & OUTDOORS INC

D-U-N-S 12-230-9131
LONG & FOSTER COMPANIES INC
14501 George Carter Way # 1, Chantilly, VA 20151-1788
Tel (888) 462-9111 *Founded/Ownrshp* 1968
Sales NA *EMP* 2,500
SIC 6531 6794 Real estate brokers & agents; Real estate brokers & agents; Franchises, selling or licensing
CEO: P Wesley Foster Jr
**Treas:* Betty F Foster
VP: Alan Simon
Exec: Mary Plonka
Comm Man: Leslie Loges
Brnch Mgr: Tina Buckley
Brnch Mgr: Joe Deluca
Brnch Mgr: Dottie Faust
Brnch Mgr: Denise Jasinski
Brnch Mgr: Betsy Matz
Brnch Mgr: Michael Murphy

D-U-N-S 04-838-5512
LONG & FOSTER INSTITUTE OF REAL ESTATE INC
KEMPER INSURANCE
(*Suby of* LONG & FOSTER COMPANIES INC) ★
14501 George Carter Way, Chantilly, VA 20151-1787
Tel (703) 877-7600 *Founded/Ownrshp* 1982
Sales NA *EMP* 165
SIC 6411 Insurance agents, brokers & service
Pr: P Wesley Foster
**Treas:* Betty Foster
**VP:* George T Eastment III
VP: Bruce Enger
Genl Couns: Debra Brletic

D-U-N-S 18-055-6912 IMP
LONG AFFAIR CARPET AND RUG INC
LA CARPET & RUG
8775 Research Dr, Irvine, CA 92618-4217
Tel (714) 734-8501 *Founded/Ownrshp* 1987
Sales 22.3MM^E *EMP* 100
SIC 5713 Carpets
Pr: Ghaffar Khalaj Hedayati
**VP:* Mohammed Ghods

LONG AUTOMOTIVE
See R H LONG MOTOR SALES CO

D-U-N-S 92-788-2167
LONG BEACH ACCEPTANCE CORP
801 Cherry St Ste 3500, Fort Worth, TX 76102-6854
Tel (817) 302-7000 *Founded/Ownrshp* 1995
Sales NA *EMP* 398
SIC 6141 Automobile loans, including insurance

LONG BEACH CITY COLLEGE
See LONG BEACH COMMUNITY COLLEGE DISTRICT

D-U-N-S 08-939-7889
LONG BEACH CITY SCHOOL DISTRICT
LONG BEACH PUBLIC SCHOOLS
239 Lido Blvd, Lido Beach, NY 11561-5092
Tel (516) 897-2104 *Founded/Ownrshp* 1912
Sales 55.2MM^E *EMP* 939
Accts Cullen & Danowski Llp Port Je
SIC 8211 Public elementary & secondary schools; Public elementary school; Public junior high school; Public senior high school; Public elementary & secondary schools; Public elementary school; Public junior high school; Public senior high school
Adm Dir: Bob Sambo
Teacher Pr: Randy Berger

D-U-N-S 14-508-7321
LONG BEACH COMMUNITY COLLEGE DISTRICT
LONG BEACH CITY COLLEGE
4901 E Carson St, Long Beach, CA 90808-1706
Tel (562) 938-5020 *Founded/Ownrshp* 1928
Sales 389.0MM *EMP* 2,812^E
SIC 8222 Community college
Pr: Eloy Ortiz Oakley
**Pr:* Mark Bowen
**Pr:* Roberto Uranga
CFO: Eloy Oakley
Treas: Doni Bois
VP: Lou Bynum
**VP:* Dr Thomas J Clark
**VP:* Jeffrey A Kellogg
**VP:* Douglas W Otto
VP: Greg Peterson
Exec: Dean Hopkins

LONG BEACH HONDA CARS
See LONG BEACH MOTORS INC

D-U-N-S 80-778-6223
LONG BEACH LINCOLN MERCURY INC
PACIFIC FORD
3500 Cherry Ave, Long Beach, CA 90807-4914
Tel (562) 426-3301 *Founded/Ownrshp* 1992
Sales 64.9MM^E *EMP* 200
SIC 5511 Automobiles, new & used; Automobiles, new & used
Pr: Henry J Caruso
**Sec:* Harry Stevenson

D-U-N-S 06-196-1207
LONG BEACH MEDICAL CENTER
455 E Bay Dr, Long Beach, NY 11561-2301
Tel (516) 897-1000 *Founded/Ownrshp* 1925
Sales 54.2MM *EMP* 830
SIC 8062

D-U-N-S 13-346-2556
LONG BEACH MEMORIAL MEDICAL CENTER
MILLER CHILDREN'S HOSPITAL
(*Suby of* MEMORIAL CARE MEDICAL CENTERS) ★
2801 Atlantic Ave Fl 2, Long Beach, CA 90806-1701
Tel (562) 933-2000 *Founded/Ownrshp* 1907
Sales 650.8MM^E *EMP* 6,000
Accts Pricewaterhousecoopers Llp L
SIC 8062 General medical & surgical hospitals
CEO: John Bishop
**Pr:* Barry Arbuckle PHD
**COO:* Tamra Kaplan
**COO:* Suize Reinsvold
COO: Susie Reinsvold
Treas: Michael Trainotti
Bd of Dir: David Brown
Bd of Dir: James Craig
Bd of Dir: John Dameron
Bd of Dir: Peter Knudson
Bd of Dir: Sean Miller
Bd of Dir: Kenneth Walker
**Sr VP:* Judy Fix
**Sr VP:* Scott Joslyn
**VP:* Thomas Poole
Exec: Susie Gonzalez
Dir Risk M: Rachel Nealeigh
Dir Rad: John Azaren
Dir Rad: Hosam Moustafa

D-U-N-S 07-965-3970
LONG BEACH MEMORIAL NURSING HOME INC
(*Suby of* SOUTH NASSAU COMMUNITIES HOSPITAL INC) ★
375 E Bay Dr, Long Beach, NY 11561-2350
Tel (516) 897-1000 *Founded/Ownrshp* 2014
Sales 16.7MM *EMP* 300
SIC 8051 Convalescent home with continuous nursing care; Convalescent home with continuous nursing care
Pr: Bernard Kennedy
CFO: Barry Stan
Treas: Michael Tribush
Ex VP: Martin Nester Jr
Ex Dir: Doug Meltzer

D-U-N-S 06-774-6909
LONG BEACH MOTORS INC (CA)
LONG BEACH HONDA CARS
1500 E Spring St, Signal Hill, CA 90755-1843
Tel (562) 426-4444 *Founded/Ownrshp* 1983
Sales 28.8MM^E *EMP* 74
SIC 5511

LONG BEACH PAIN CENTER
See HEALTHSMART PACIFIC INC

LONG BEACH PUBLIC SCHOOLS
See LONG BEACH CITY SCHOOL DISTRICT

LONG BEACH PUBLIC TRANSIT
See LONG BEACH PUBLIC TRANSPORTATION CO INC

D-U-N-S 05-012-5194
LONG BEACH PUBLIC TRANSPORTATION CO INC
LONG BEACH PUBLIC TRANSIT
1963 E Anaheim St, Long Beach, CA 90813-3907
Tel (562) 591-8753 *Founded/Ownrshp* 1963
Sales 37.0MM^E *EMP* 650
Accts Kpmg Llp Los Angeles Ca
SIC 4111 Bus line operations; Bus line operations
Pr: Laurence W Jackson
Bd of Dir: Sarah Miller
Sr VP: Robyn Peterson
VP: Vince Rouzaud
Genl Mgr: Chris Liapis
Off Admin: Jocelyn Alvarez
QA Dir: Rick Operchuck
QA Dir: Branden Spalding
Tech Mgr: Dennis Elefante
Opers Supe: Roderick Bell
Opers Supe: Chaka Garbutt
Board of Directors: Laverne David

D-U-N-S 04-673-6062
LONG BEACH SCHOOL DISTRICT
19148 Commission Rd, Long Beach, MS 39560-2311
Tel (228) 864-1146 *Founded/Ownrshp* 1953
Sales 29.5MM *EMP* 425
SIC 8211 Public elementary & secondary schools; Public elementary & secondary schools
Prin: Billy Moore
**Prin:* Carolyn Hamilton
**Prin:* Veronica Sprinkle
Dir IT: Matthew Ely

D-U-N-S 07-294-8854
LONG BEACH UNIFIED SCHOOL DISTRICT
LBUSD
1515 Hughes Way, Long Beach, CA 90810-1865
Tel (562) 997-8000 *Founded/Ownrshp* 1945
Sales 677.3MM^E *EMP* 15,000
Accts Vicenti Lloyd Stutzman Llp
SIC 8211 Public elementary school; Public junior high school; Public senior high school; Public elementary school; Public junior high school; Public senior high school
CFO: Lawrence Bozanich
Ofcr: Juan Luna
Exec: Leticia Rodriguez
Dir Sec: Thomas Hickman
Off Mgr: Betty Ortiz
Off Admin: Aimee Daez
DP Exec: Tanya Robertson
Dir IT: Raymond Martens
Opers Mgr: Trina Kelm
Pr Dir: Chris Eftychiou
Instr Medi: Joyce Kuroiwa

D-U-N-S 13-073-1511 IMP
LONG BELL VENTURES LLC
LEWIS COUNTY FOREST PRODUCTS
154 Hale Rd E, Winlock, WA 98596
Tel (360) 785-3915 *Founded/Ownrshp* 2003
Sales 40.0MM *EMP* 300
SIC 5031 Lumber, plywood & millwork; Lumber, plywood & millwork

D-U-N-S 02-452-2963 IMP
LONG BEVERAGE INC (NC)
10500 World Trade Blvd, Raleigh, NC 27617-4246
Tel (919) 232-2100 *Founded/Ownrshp* 1950, 1976
Sales 106.2MM^E *EMP* 195
SIC 5181 5149 Beer & other fermented malt liquors; Soft drinks; Beer & other fermented malt liquors; Soft drinks
Pr: Rodney M Long
**VP:* David N Long
Exec: Ryan Swift
Opers Mgr: Jeff Brown
Opers Mgr: Dylon Graham

D-U-N-S 08-198-1193
LONG BRANCH CITY OF (INC)
344 Broadway, Long Branch, NJ 07740-6994
Tel (732) 222-7000 *Founded/Ownrshp* 1904
Sales NA *EMP* 350
SIC 9111 Mayors' offices; Mayors' offices
Ofcr: Gregory May
IT Man: Jason Roebuck
IT Man: Charles Shirley

LONG BROTHERS BAG CO DIV
See CINCINNATI DRUM SERVICE INC

LONG BUILDING ENVIRONMENTS
See LONG BUILDING TECHNOLOGIES INC

D-U-N-S 06-274-4495
LONG BUILDING TECHNOLOGIES INC
LONG BUILDING ENVIRONMENTS
5001 S Zuni St, Littleton, CO 80120-1071
Tel (303) 975-2100 *Founded/Ownrshp* 1992
Sales 197.2MM^E *EMP* 279
SIC 5075 1711 Air conditioning & ventilation equipment & supplies; Heating & air conditioning contractors; Air conditioning & ventilation equipment & supplies; Heating & air conditioning contractors
CEO: Jeff Long
**Pr:* Mark A Balent
**VP:* Jeffrey C Long
Assoc Dir: Scott Papay
Brnch Mgr: Joe Moran
Opers Mgr: Eric Nelson
Opers Mgr: Peter Samuelson
Sls Mgr: Brent Garrison
Sales Asso: Ginger Reed

D-U-N-S 19-331-1289
LONG COUNTY BOARD OF EDUCATION
LONG COUNTY SCHOOL SYSTEM
468 S Mcdonald St, Ludowici, GA 31316-6028
Tel (912) 545-2367 *Founded/Ownrshp* 1918
Sales 26.2MM *EMP* 300
Accts Department Of Audits And Accou
SIC 8211 Public elementary & secondary schools; High school, junior or senior; Public elementary & secondary schools; High school, junior or senior
Ch Bd: Bensy Golden
Psych: Melissa Bragg
Psych: Jessica Ehrlich

LONG COUNTY SCHOOL SYSTEM
See LONG COUNTY BOARD OF EDUCATION

D-U-N-S 06-281-6913
LONG ELECTRIC CO INC
6902 Hawthorn Park Dr, Indianapolis, IN 46220-3911
Tel (317) 356-2455 *Founded/Ownrshp* 1972
Sales 59.3MM^E *EMP* 300
SIC 1731 General electrical contractor; General electrical contractor
Pr: Jerry Chlystun
**CFO:* Michael Chlystun
**VP:* William Chlyftun
Sfty Dirs: David Svir

D-U-N-S 00-283-1667
LONG FENCE CO INC (DC)
8545 Edgeworth Dr, Capitol Heights, MD 20743-3790
Tel (301) 350-2400 *Founded/Ownrshp* 1938
Sales 85.7MM^E *EMP* 440
SIC 1799

D-U-N-S 13-104-7052
LONG FOUNDATION DRILLING CO
3014 Brandau Rd, Hermitage, TN 37076-3501
Tel (615) 885-5664 *Founded/Ownrshp* 1985
Sales 26.9MM^E *EMP* 120
SIC 1799 Boring for building construction
Pr: Robert Bruce Long
**Treas:* Vicky Hinesley
**VP:* Shelby Cook
**VP:* Chris Long
VP: Christopher W Long
VP: Keith Miller
VP: Fred Porter
Mktg Dir: Bruce Long

D-U-N-S 19-626-4576
LONG HAUL TRUCKING INC
6600 Jansen Ave Ne, Albertville, MN 55301-9686
Tel (763) 497-3727 *Founded/Ownrshp* 1985
Sales 74.6MM^E *EMP* 300
SIC 4213 Trucking, except local
Pr: John S Daniels
**CFO:* Tiffani Steinke
CTO: Paul Wederath
Sfty Dirs: Sue Brown

D-U-N-S 84-764-7708
LONG INDUSTRIES INC
105 Private Road 413, Buffalo, TX 75831-6858
Tel (903) 389-3263 *Founded/Ownrshp* 1992
Sales 46.4MM^E *EMP* 150^E
Accts Janes Reitmeter Boyd & Therrel
SIC 1629 1799 Petroleum storage tank installation, underground; Power plant construction; Power plant construction; Petroleum storage tanks, pumping & draining; Petroleum storage tank installation, underground
Pr: Columbus Wayne Long
**VP:* June Long
Opers Mgr: Danny Crocker
VP Sls: Jody Day

LONG ISLAND AQAR EXHIBITION CTR
See ATLANTIS MARINE WORLD LLC

D-U-N-S 01-157-3740
LONG ISLAND AUTO FIND INC
1201 Montauk Hwy, Copiague, NY 11726-4907
Tel (631) 592-9012 *Founded/Ownrshp* 2006
Sales 30.0MM *EMP* 34
Accts Nicholas Agnone & Co Llc Cp
SIC 5521 Used car dealers; Used car dealers
CEO: Brian Keegan

D-U-N-S 93-838-6232
LONG ISLAND AUTOMOTIVE GROUP INC
SATURN PARTS DEPOT
(*Suby of* MARUBENI AUTO & CONSTRUCTION MACHINERY (AMERICA) INC) ★
124 Greene Ave, Amityville, NY 11701-2931
Tel (631) 264-2244 *Founded/Ownrshp* 1995
Sales 19.6MM^E *EMP* 280
SIC 7538 5511 General automotive repair shops; New & used car dealers; General automotive repair shops; New & used car dealers
Pr: Masuyuki Hirmatsu
CFO: Michael Minella
Sls Mgr: Kevin Sweeny
Snr Mgr: John Kipp

LONG ISLAND BEEF
See J A O MEAT PACKING CO INC

LONG ISLAND BLOOD SERVICES
See NEW YORK BLOOD CENTER INC

LONG ISLAND BUS
See METROPOLITAN SUBURBAN BUS AUTH

D-U-N-S 05-935-2799
LONG ISLAND COLLEGE HOSPITAL INC
(*Suby of* SUNY DOWNSTATE MEDICAL CENTER) ★
450 Clarkson Ave, Brooklyn, NY 11203-2012
Tel (718) 780-1000 *Founded/Ownrshp* 2010
Sales 76.5MM^E *EMP* 2,500
SIC 8092 8062 9199 Kidney dialysis centers; General medical & surgical hospitals; ; Kidney dialysis centers; ; General medical & surgical hospitals
Pr: Rita Battles
Dir Recs: Dawn Maynard
**CFO:* Thomas Pfeiffer
Off Mgr: Denise Lisita
Off Mgr: Debbie Salliey
Opers Mgr: Leon ABO
Surgeon: Steven Herman
Obsttrcn: Sanford Lederman
Doctor: Maxine Orris MD
Diag Rad: Mercedes Washington

LONG ISLAND COMMUNITY FOUNDATI
See NEW YORK COMMUNITY TRUST AND COMMUNITY FUNDS INC

D-U-N-S 07-917-1134
LONG ISLAND ELECTRIC UTILITY SERVCO LLC
333 Earle Ovington Blvd, Uniondale, NY 11553-3610
Tel (516) 719-9810 *Founded/Ownrshp* 2012
Sales 4.3MMM^E *EMP* 2,500
SIC 4911 Electric services; Electric services
Pr: Dave Daly

D-U-N-S 04-204-2788 IMP
LONG ISLAND FIREPROOF DOOR INC
5 Harbor Park Dr Ste 1, Port Washington, NY 11050-4698
Tel (516) 390-6800 *Founded/Ownrshp* 1969
Sales 29.0MM^E *EMP* 85
SIC 5031 3442 Doors; Building materials, exterior; Building materials, interior; Fire doors, metal; Doors; Building materials, exterior; Building materials, interior; Fire doors, metal
Pr: Vincent Gallo
CFO: John Hart
**VP:* Joseph Gallo
Sls Mgr: David Kanner

LONG ISLAND HEAD START
See L I CHILD AND FAMILY DEVELOPMENT SERVICES INC

D-U-N-S 06-474-4014
LONG ISLAND HOME (NY)
NSLIJ
(*Suby of* NORTH SHORE - LONG ISLAND JEWISH HEALTH SYSTEM INC) ★
400 Sunrise Hwy, Amityville, NY 11701-2508
Tel (631) 264-4000 *Founded/Ownrshp* 2012
Sales 93.4MM *EMP* 1,112
Accts Ernst & Young Llp New York N
SIC 8063 8051 Psychiatric hospitals; Skilled nursing care facilities; Psychiatric hospitals; Skilled nursing care facilities
CEO: Robert E Detor
**CFO:* Patricia A Porter
Dir Rx: Warren Drezen
Admn Mgr: Annamaria Digrigoli
MIS Dir: Douglas Simpson
Dir QC: Ken Corbin
Dir IT: Pam Coroga
Dir IT: Pamela Cucugliello
Nrsg Dir: Christine Moran

D-U-N-S 06-472-7027 IMP/EXP
LONG ISLAND JEWISH MEDICAL CENTER
NSLIJ
(*Suby of* NORTH SHORE - LONG ISLAND JEWISH HEALTH SYSTEM INC) ★
27005 76th Ave, New Hyde Park, NY 11040-1496
Tel (516) 465-2600 *Founded/Ownrshp* 1949
Sales 1.4MMM *EMP* 214
SIC 8062 8063 8069 General medical & surgical hospitals; Psychiatric hospitals; Children's hospital; General medical & surgical hospitals; Psychiatric hospitals; Children's hospital
CEO: Michael J Dowling
COO: Charles M Trunz
CFO: Robert S Shapiro
Ofcr: John Sandhusen
Sr VP: Joseph Cabral
Sr VP: Donna Drummond
VP: John Dicapua
VP: John Fantasia
**VP:* George Raptis
Dir OR: Veronica Petersen
Dir Soc: Nancy Geller

D-U-N-S 01-282-9669 IMP
LONG ISLAND PANELING CENTERS INC
LONG ISLAND PNLING CLNGS FLORS
69 Sunrise Hwy, Lindenhurst, NY 11757-2585
Tel (631) 888-7664 *Founded/Ownrshp* 1964
Sales 23.1MM^E *EMP* 60

SIC 5031 5211 5251 5046 5039 1752 Building materials, interior; Paneling, wood; Molding, all materials; Lumber & other building materials; Paneling; Flooring, wood; Hardware; Store fixtures; Ceiling systems & products; Floor laying & floor work
Sec: Phyllis Sternberg
**Pr:* Frank Sternberg
VP: Jay Osman
**VP:* Robert Sternberg

D-U-N-S 04-446-6035
LONG ISLAND PIPE SUPPLY INC
586 Commercial Ave, Garden City, NY 11530-6418
Tel (516) 222-8008 *Founded/Ownrshp* 1979
Sales 59.7MM[E] *EMP* 120
SIC 3498 5074 Fabricated pipe & fittings; Plumbing fittings & supplies; Fabricated pipe & fittings; Plumbing fittings & supplies
Pr: Robert Moss

D-U-N-S 60-386-2520
LONG ISLAND PIPE SUPPLY INC
586 Commercial Ave, Garden City, NY 11530-6418
Tel (516) 222-8008 *Founded/Ownrshp* 1965
Sales 24.7MM[E] *EMP* 40[E]
SIC 3569 Sprinkler systems, fire: automatic
CEO: Robert Moss
Brnch Mgr: Gregory Jarvis
Brnch Mgr: Thomas Munroe
IT Man: Nick Pomponio
Sales Asso: Malory Jahrmarkt

LONG ISLAND PNLING CLNGS FLORS
See LONG ISLAND PANELING CENTERS INC

D-U-N-S 13-355-1270
LONG ISLAND POWER AUTHORITY
PSEGLI AS AGENT FOR LIPA
333 Earle Ovington Blvd # 403, Uniondale, NY 11553-3606
Tel (516) 222-7700 *Founded/Ownrshp* 1986
Sales 117.0MM[E] *EMP* 100[E]
Accts Kpmg Llp Melville Ny
SIC 4911 Generation, electric power; Transmission, electric power; Generation, electric power; Transmission, electric power
CEO: Michael D Hervey
COO: John McMahon
CFO: Thomas Falcone
**CFO:* Herbert L Hogue
**VP:* Michael Deering
**VP:* Kenneth Kane
Dir Risk M: Corey Horowitz
Counsel: Justin Bell
Counsel: Joseph Wiener

D-U-N-S 00-699-2929
LONG ISLAND RAIL ROAD CO (NY)
MTA LONG ISLAND RAIL ROAD
(*Suby of* M T A) ★
9027 Sutphin Blvd, Jamaica, NY 11435-3647
Tel (718) 558-7597 *Founded/Ownrshp* 1834, 1966
Sales 571.0MM[E] *EMP* 7,000
SIC 4111 Commuter rail passenger operation; Commuter rail passenger operation
Pr: Helena Williams
CFO: Nicholas Di Mola
CFO: Nicholas Mola
Ex VP: Albert Cosenza
VP: Lockhart Bailey
VP: Thomas Prendergast
VP: Kurt Sobina
Snr Mgr: Denis Mahon

LONG ISLAND STOVE
See LIS CUSTOM DESIGNS INC

D-U-N-S 01-239-4557 IMP
LONG ISLAND TINSMITH SUPPLY CORP
LITSCO
7611 88th St, Glendale, NY 11385-7829
Tel (718) 846-0400 *Founded/Ownrshp* 1918
Sales 37.0MM[E] *EMP* 36
SIC 5033 1761 Roofing & siding materials; Roofing, asphalt & sheet metal; Roofing, siding & sheet metal work
CEO: Harvey C Lucks
**Treas:* Susan D Lucks
**VP:* Stuart A Lucks

D-U-N-S 62-238-1499
LONG ISLAND UK AUTO INC
LAND ROVER OF SMITHTOWN
124 Greene Ave, Amityville, NY 11701-2931
Tel (631) 264-2244 *Founded/Ownrshp* 2003
Sales 31.8MM[E] *EMP* 154
SIC 5511 6159 Automobiles, new & used; Finance leasing, vehicles: except automobiles & trucks; Automobiles, new & used; Finance leasing, vehicles: except automobiles & trucks
Pr: Bryan A Lazarus
**VP:* Michael Lazarus

D-U-N-S 06-593-3103
LONG ISLAND UNIVERSITY
700 Northern Blvd, Greenvale, NY 11548-1327
Tel (516) 299-2535 *Founded/Ownrshp* 1926
Sales 501.6MM *EMP* 3,300
Accts Kpmg Llp New York Ny
SIC 8221 University; University
Pr: Dr Kimberly R Cline
Pr: Kitty Rockett
**Pr:* David Steinberg PHD
**CFO:* Robert Altholz
Ch: Thomas Pulling
Treas: Robert N Altholz
Ofcr: Peggy Riggs
VP: Lucille Ambrosio
VP: Michael Arons
VP: George Baroudi
VP: Christopher Fevola
VP: Melodee A Gandia
VP: Jennifer Goodwin
VP: Salvatore Greco
VP: Jeffrey Kane
VP: Benjamin Moore
VP: Jackie Nealon
VP: George Sutton
VP: Christopher Williams
Exec: Nancy Sissons
Exec: Keith Walcott
Board of Directors: Susanne Flower, James Newell, Patricia Stephens, David Sterling

LONG JOHN SILVER'S
See AMERICAN SEAFOOD PARTNERS LP

LONG JOHN SILVER'S
See NELLIS MANAGEMENT CO LLC

LONG JOHN SILVER'S
See TAVERN RESTAURANT GROUP INC

LONG JOHN SILVER'S
See JAK FOODS INC

LONG JOHN SILVER'S
See TREASURE ISLES HC INC

LONG JOHN SILVER'S
See TAJAY RESTAURANTS INC

D-U-N-S 00-651-5118
LONG JOHN SILVERS RESTAURANT INC
(*Suby of* YORKSHIRE GLOBAL RESTAURANTS INC) ★
1441 Gardiner Ln, Louisville, KY 40213-1914
Tel (502) 874-3000 *Founded/Ownrshp* 1946
Sales 71.8MM[E] *EMP* 10,000
SIC 5812 6794 Fast-food restaurant, chain; Franchises, selling or licensing; Fast-food restaurant, chain; Franchises, selling or licensing
Pr: David Deno
**CFO:* Mark Plummer
Treas: Cheri Leistner
**Sr VP:* Forrest Ragsdale
Exec: Sheryl Baker
Site Mgr: Roland Brink
Site Mgr: Jordan Carnahan
Site Mgr: Beverly Cooney
Site Mgr: Shelly Huber

LONG LIVE HOLDINGS
See TOTAL PRODUCT DESTRUCTION LLC

D-U-N-S 07-925-9241
LONG METALS CO LLC
1106 E Seymour St Ste 6, Muncie, IN 47302-2500
Tel (765) 313-7801 *Founded/Ownrshp* 2013
Sales 22.4MM[E] *EMP* 72[E]
SIC 3444 Sheet metalwork
Pr: Henry Long

D-U-N-S 04-803-0779 IMP
LONG MOTOR CORP
VICTORIA BRITISH
14600 W 107th St, Lenexa, KS 66215-4015
Tel (913) 541-1525 *Founded/Ownrshp* 2008
Sales 63.6MM[E] *EMP* 350
SIC 5961 5013 Automotive supplies & equipment, mail order; Automotive supplies & parts; Automotive supplies & equipment, mail order; Automotive supplies & parts
Pr: Rebecca Hanrahan
CFO: Travis Morash
VP: Becky Hanrahan
**VP:* Janet Long
Exec: Aaron Hammond
IT Man: Deborah Denton
VP Sls: Daryll Malnicof
Mktg Mgr: Susan Berkowitz

D-U-N-S 03-720-4930
LONG MOTORS INC
VOLVO
2931 Us Highway 1, Lawrenceville, NJ 08648-2403
Tel (609) 882-0600 *Founded/Ownrshp* 1982
Sales 25.2MM[E] *EMP* 58
SIC 5511 7538 Automobiles, new & used; General automotive repair shops; Automobiles, new & used; General automotive repair shops
Owner: David J Long Jr
V Ch: Chris Long
**Treas:* Matthew C Long
Genl Mgr: Laurence Long
Sales Asso: Nils Falk
Sales Asso: Russell Sabine

D-U-N-S 04-403-6747
LONG PAINTING CO
21414 68th Ave S Main, Kent, WA 98032-2412
Tel (253) 234-8050 *Founded/Ownrshp* 1998
Sales 28.8MM *EMP* 300
Accts Bernston Porter & Company Pll
SIC 1721 Commercial painting; Industrial painting; Commercial painting; Industrial painting
Ch Bd: Michael Cassidy
**Pr:* John Fisher
**Sec:* Denica Bucklin
VP: Rob Webster
Admn Mgr: Sue Fauver
Sfty Dirs: Mike Wilkinson
Prd Mgr: Roy Mueller
Sales Exec: Bill Carver

D-U-N-S 10-920-5562
LONG POINT CAPITAL
747 3rd Ave Rm 2200, New York, NY 10017-2845
Tel (212) 593-1800 *Founded/Ownrshp* 1998
Sales 61.8MM[E] *EMP* 585
SIC 6211 Investment bankers; Investment bankers
Prin: Ira Starr
**Prin:* Gerard Boylan
**Prin:* William C Uhgetta Jr
Mng Dir: John Morgan

D-U-N-S 00-420-5732
LONG POINT DEVELOPMENT LLC
TERRANEA RESORT
100 Terranea Way, Rancho Palos Verdes, CA 90275-1013
Tel (310) 265-2800 *Founded/Ownrshp* 2004
Sales 49.4MM[E] *EMP* 1,000
SIC 7011 Resort hotel; Resort hotel

D-U-N-S 18-506-7733
LONG PONTIAC/HYUNDAI INC
6035 International Dr, Chattanooga, TN 37421-1617
Tel (423) 855-5664 *Founded/Ownrshp* 1988
Sales 29.7MM[E] *EMP* 72
SIC 5511 Automobiles, new & used; Automobiles, new & used
Pr: H Nelson Long
Plnt Mgr: Nelson Long

LONG PRAIRIE PACKING
See ROSENS DIVERSIFIED INC

D-U-N-S 04-671-2444
LONG PRAIRIE PACKING CO INC
(*Suby of* LONG PRAIRIE PACKING) ★
100 Bridgepoint Curv # 249, South Saint Paul, MN 55075
Tel (651) 552-8230 *Founded/Ownrshp* 1975
Sales 108.0MM[E] *EMP* 1,462
SIC 2011 Meat packing plants; Beef products from beef slaughtered on site; Meat packing plants; Beef products from beef slaughtered on site
CEO: Thomas J Rosen
**Pr:* Greg Benedict
**Treas:* Robert Hovde

D-U-N-S 11-953-2906
LONG RANGE MUSIC INC
(*Suby of* THORN EMI NORTH AMERICA INC)
101 Winners Cir N, Brentwood, TN 37027-5352
Tel (615) 371-6800 *Founded/Ownrshp* 2011
Sales 8.5MM[E] *EMP* 463[E]
SIC 2741 Music books: publishing & printing

D-U-N-S 07-483-2445
LONG RAP INC
UP AGAINST THE WALL
1420 Wisconsin Ave Nw, Washington, DC 20007-2827
Tel (202) 337-6610 *Founded/Ownrshp* 2009
Sales 23.9MM[E] *EMP* 300
Accts Gaytan Kallman & Co Los Ang
SIC 5611 5621 Men's & boys' clothing stores; Women's clothing stores; Men's & boys' clothing stores; Women's clothing stores
Pr: Charles Rendelman
**Sec:* Stuart Ezrailson
**VP:* Paul Donnellan

D-U-N-S 96-860-0841
LONG TERM CARE GROUP INC
LTCG
(*Suby of* STONE POINT CAPITAL LLC) ★
11000 Prairie Lakes Dr, Eden Prairie, MN 55344-3885
Tel (952) 516-6800 *Founded/Ownrshp* 2014
Sales NA *EMP* 1,000
SIC 6411 Insurance agents & brokers; Insurance agents & brokers
CEO: Peter Goldstein
Pr: Peter Levine
COO: Rob Frederick
CFO: Dean Miller
Chf Mktg O: Stephen K Holland
Chf Mktg O: Mark Regan
Ex VP: Patrick Yount
Sr VP: Colleen Huberman
Sr VP: Keith Jasper
Sr VP: Paul Kay
Sr VP: Kelly Lundgren
Sr VP: Eileen Tell
VP: Chad Bellin
VP: Jim Bruha
VP: Doug Foote
VP: Adam Hoffman
VP: David McGuire
VP: Bradley Schumacher

D-U-N-S 78-443-9338
LONG VIEW SYSTEMS CORP (USA)
(*Suby of* LONG VIEW SYSTEMS CORPORATION)
555 17th St Ste 1600, Denver, CO 80202-3916
Tel (303) 226-5655 *Founded/Ownrshp* 1999
Sales 34.6MM[E] *EMP* 130
SIC 7379 Computer related consulting services; Computer related consulting services
Pr: Donald Bialik
CFO: Peter Przybylski
**VP:* Kent Mitchell
CTO: Robin Bell
Sftwr Eng: Tyrel Diekmann
Mktg Dir: Tannis Ebbels

D-U-N-S 93-314-4263
LONG WAVE INC
115 E California Ave # 400, Oklahoma City, OK 73104-2456
Tel (405) 235-2217 *Founded/Ownrshp* 1995
Sales 24.0MM[E] *EMP* 110
SIC 8711 Consulting engineer; Consulting engineer
CEO: Philip Miller
**Pr:* David Miller
Chf Mktg O: Chris Lozano
Sr VP: John Major
**VP:* Jeffrey Miller
**VP:* Jack Sprague
Prgrm Mgr: Kelley Smith
Dir IT: Michael Walker
IT Man: Mark Johnson
IT Man: Lauren Teter
Software D: Justin Halstead
Board of Directors: David Miller, Jeffrey Miller, Phillip Miller, Jack Sprague

D-U-N-S 03-328-3839
LONG WHOLESALE DISTRIBUTORS INC
201 N Fulton Dr, Corinth, MS 38834-4621
Tel (662) 287-2421 *Founded/Ownrshp* 1943
Sales 43.8MM[E] *EMP* 200
SIC 5141 5194 5072 5122 5142

D-U-N-S 03-339-5906
LONG WHOLESALE INC (MS)
5173 Pioneer Rd, Meridian, MS 39301-8834
Tel (601) 482-3144 *Founded/Ownrshp* 1905, 1963
Sales 43.5MM[E] *EMP* 110[E]
SIC 5141 5194 5145 5122

LONG-LEWIS FORD
See LONG-LEWIS INC

D-U-N-S 00-690-0088 IMP
LONG-LEWIS INC (AL)
LONG-LEWIS FORD
2551 Highway 150, Hoover, AL 35244-3533
Tel (205) 989-3673 *Founded/Ownrshp* 1906, 1986
Sales 164.9MM[E] *EMP* 350
SIC 5511 5072

D-U-N-S 36-192-5381 IMP
■ **LONGABERGER CO**
(*Suby of* CVSL INC) ★
1 Markt Sq 1500 E Main, Newark, OH 43058
Tel (740) 322-5000 *Founded/Ownrshp* 1990
Sales 34.4MM[E] *EMP* 200[E]
SIC 2499 3269

LONGBOAT KEY CLUB
See KEY CLUB ASSOCIATES LIMITED PARTNERSHIP

D-U-N-S 84-380-8619 IMP
LONGCHAMP U S A INC
4 Applegate Dr B, Robbinsville, NJ 08691-2342
Tel (609) 581-5555 *Founded/Ownrshp* 1994
Sales 45.8MM[E] *EMP* 120
SIC 5199 5948 Leather, leather goods & furs; Luggage & leather goods stores; Leather, leather goods & furs; Luggage & leather goods stores
Pr: Stephanie Disegni
**Genl Mgr:* Jean Cassegrain
Dir IT: Chuck Potalivo
IT Man: Charles Potalivo
Mktg Dir: Cheryl Napiorkowski

LONGCHAMPS COMMUNICATION SYSTS
See LONGCHAMPS ELECTRIC INC

D-U-N-S 06-675-7972
LONGCHAMPS ELECTRIC INC
LONGCHAMPS COMMUNICATION SYSTS
700 Harvey Rd, Manchester, NH 03103-3312
Tel (603) 625-5954 *Founded/Ownrshp* 1975
Sales 21.5MM[E] *EMP* 75
SIC 1731 Electrical work
Pr: Robert O Longchamps
COO: Glenn Trowbridge
**VP:* Kevin M Duffy

D-U-N-S 09-993-1222
LONGHORN BUILDING MATERIALS INC
(*Suby of* G M S) ★
4025 Mint Way, Dallas, TX 75237-1603
Tel (214) 330-0423 *Founded/Ownrshp* 1979
Sales 30.0MM *EMP* 35
SIC 5031

D-U-N-S 05-654-1519
LONGHORN DODGE INC
LONGHORN DODGE SALES & SERVICE
4500 South Fwy, Fort Worth, TX 76115-3513
Tel (817) 926-2681 *Founded/Ownrshp* 1971
Sales 50.0MM *EMP* 78
SIC 5511 Automobiles, new & used; Pickups, new & used; Vans, new & used; Automobiles, new & used; Pickups, new & used; Vans, new & used
Ch: Richard L Adams
**Pr:* Vickie Gibson
**CFO:* Brian Gibson
**VP:* Robert Adams
**VP:* Gary Gibson
Board of Directors:

LONGHORN DODGE SALES & SERVICE
See LONGHORN DODGE INC

D-U-N-S 87-841-5710
LONGHORN EXCAVATORS INC
1819 Frst Oaks St Ste 140, Richmond, TX 77406
Tel (281) 344-0074 *Founded/Ownrshp* 1993
Sales 39.1MM[E] *EMP* 175
Accts Morris Ligon & Rodriguez Sug
SIC 1794 1629 Excavation work; Land preparation construction
Pr: John Parker
Genl Mgr: Sandy Aguilar
Genl Mgr: Lisa Landin
Mtls Mgr: Conrad Jorchen

D-U-N-S 00-569-4687 IMP
LONGHORN GLASS MANUFACTURING LP
(*Suby of* ANHEUSER-BUSCH COMPANIES LLC) ★
4202 Fidelity St, Houston, TX 77029-3550
Tel (713) 679-7500 *Founded/Ownrshp* 2001
Sales 53.8MM[E] *EMP* 150
SIC 3221 Bottles for packing, bottling & canning: glass; Bottles for packing, bottling & canning: glass
Pr: Patrick Stokes

D-U-N-S 04-179-6160 IMP/EXP
LONGHORN INC
2640 Tarna Dr, Dallas, TX 75229-2221
Tel (972) 406-0222 *Founded/Ownrshp* 1982
Sales 43.8MM[E] *EMP* 80
SIC 5083 5085 5084 Irrigation equipment; Industrial supplies; Valves & fittings; Industrial machinery & equipment; Irrigation equipment; Industrial supplies; Valves & fittings; Industrial machinery & equipment
Pr: Loyd H Evans Jr
**CFO:* Tom Swor
**VP:* Luke Evans
**VP:* Lynn Evans

D-U-N-S 07-048-6576
LONGHORN INTERNATIONAL TRUCKS LTD
JOHN DEERE
(*Suby of* INTERNATIONAL TRUCKS OF HOUSTON LLC) ★
4711 E 7th St, Austin, TX 78702-5016
Tel (512) 389-1111 *Founded/Ownrshp* 1976
Sales 43.3MM[E] *EMP* 95
SIC 5012 5013 Trucks, commercial; Truck parts & accessories; Trucks, commercial; Truck parts & accessories
Pr: Duane Kyrish
Pt: Ed A Kyrish
Genl Mgr: Wayne McCoy
Sales Asso: James Michelson

LONGHORN STEAK HOUSE
See RESTAURANTS OPERATORS INC

D-U-N-S 19-358-5080
LONGHORN STEEL & FLAMECUTTING INC
(*Suby of* JOINT HOLDINGS/BASIC METAL INDUSTRIES INC) ★
12229 Fm 529 Rd, Houston, TX 77041-2805
Tel (713) 896-7988 *Founded/Ownrshp* 1988
Sales 49.5MM^E *EMP* 65
SIC 5051 3599 3312 3441 Metals service centers & offices; Machine shop, jobbing & repair; Structural shapes & pilings, steel; Fabricated structural metal; Metals service centers & offices; Machine shop, jobbing & repair; Structural shapes & pilings, steel; Fabricated structural metal
CEO: Gerald D Hodge
**COO:* Thomas G Viele

D-U-N-S 14-436-2076
LONGISTICS TRANSPORTATION INC
10900 World Trade Blvd, Raleigh, NC 27617-4202
Tel (919) 281-2510 *Founded/Ownrshp* 1984
Sales 25.3MM^E *EMP* 150
SIC 4213 4214 8742 Trucking, except local; Local trucking with storage; Transportation consultant; Trucking, except local; Local trucking with storage; Transportation consultant
Pr: Duane Long
Pr: Tony Copeland
**VP:* H Berry Petty Jr
**VP:* Lou Tapper

D-U-N-S 00-225-5503
LONGLEY JONES ASSOCIATES INC
1010 James St Ste 1, Syracuse, NY 13203-2706
Tel (315) 424-0200 *Founded/Ownrshp* 1961, 1966
Sales 11.8MM^E *EMP* 400
SIC 6531 Real estate brokers & agents; Real estate managers; Real estate brokers & agents; Real estate managers
Pr: E Carlyle Smith
**CFO:* Barry Peck
**Treas:* Sherwood Finn

D-U-N-S 00-346-0144
LONGLEY SUPPLY CO
2018 Oleander Dr, Wilmington, NC 28403-2336
Tel (910) 762-7793 *Founded/Ownrshp* 1946
Sales 83.9MM^E *EMP* 100
SIC 5074 5063 5075 Plumbing fittings & supplies; Electrical supplies; Warm air heating & air conditioning; Plumbing fittings & supplies; Electrical supplies; Warm air heating & air conditioning
Pr: Emily Longley
Treas: Henry Longley Jr
Brnch Mgr: Allen Broome
Brnch Mgr: Chuck Giles
IT Man: Joey Clark
Sls Mgr: Mark Matz
Sales Asso: Brent Bunn
Sales Asso: Sam McKenzie
Sales Asso: David Pigott

D-U-N-S 08-147-4470
LONGMONT CLINIC PC
SONUS-USA
1925 Mountain View Ave, Longmont, CO 80501-3128
Tel (720) 494-3130 *Founded/Ownrshp* 1906
Sales 33.5MM^E *EMP* 310
SIC 8011 5999 Clinic, operated by physicians; Hearing aids; Clinic, operated by physicians; Hearing aids
Pr: John Stathis
**CFO:* Tony Heatherton
VP: Warren Laughlin
Surgeon: John D Douthit
Surgeon: Natalie S Weger
Plas Surg: Jeffrey T Swail
Doctor: Abby Emdur
Doctor: Bruce Grossman
Doctor: Irina Robinson

D-U-N-S 05-683-3833 IMP
LONGMONT UNITED HOSPITAL
1950 Mountain View Ave, Longmont, CO 80501-9865
Tel (303) 651-5111 *Founded/Ownrshp* 1971
Sales 189.7MM *EMP* 1,100
Accts Eks&H Lllp Denver Co
SIC 8062 General medical & surgical hospitals; General medical & surgical hospitals
CEO: Mitchell Carson
Pr: Darleen Savage
**CFO:* Neil W Bertrand
CFO: Mona McCarthy
Treas: Patti Rosquist
Ofcr: Johnathan Bradley
Ofcr: Dan Palmquist
VP: Becky Herman
VP: Carol Smith
Exec: Warren Laughlin
Dir Rx: John Ives

D-U-N-S 09-116-1067
LONGO DE PUERTO RICO INC (NJ)
1018 Ashford Ave Ste 3a9, San Juan, PR 00907
Tel (787) 721-5268 *Founded/Ownrshp* 1980
Sales 25.0MM *EMP* 104
SIC 1623

D-U-N-S 06-748-5672 IMP
LONGO ELECTRICAL-MECHANICAL INC
LONGO INDUSTRIES
1 Harry Shupe Blvd, Wharton, NJ 07885-1646
Tel (973) 537-0400 *Founded/Ownrshp* 1946
Sales 23.0MM *EMP* 99^E
SIC 5063 5084 7694 3621 3462 Electrical apparatus & equipment; Generators; Motors, electric; Pumps & pumping equipment; Armature rewinding shops; Motors & generators; Iron & steel forgings
Ch Bd: Joseph M Longo
**Treas:* Richard Dewalk

D-U-N-S 14-716-0873
LONGO ENTERPRISES INC
5728 Hood St, Houston, TX 77023-5918
Tel (713) 928-2355 *Founded/Ownrshp* 1984
Sales 21.8MM^E *EMP* 170
SIC 1743 5032 Terrazzo work; Tile installation, ceramic; Marble installation, interior; Marble building stone; Terrazzo work; Tile installation, ceramic; Marble installation, interior; Marble building stone
Pr: Victor Longo
**Sec:* Ann Longo

LONGO INDUSTRIES
See LONGO ELECTRICAL-MECHANICAL INC

LONGO LEXUS
See EL MONTE AUTOMOTIVE GROUP INC

LONGO SCION
See D LONGO LLC

D-U-N-S 02-387-9005
LONGROAD ASSET MANAGEMENT LLC
177 Sound Beach Ave Ste 1, Old Greenwich, CT 06870-1740
Tel (203) 967-1400 *Founded/Ownrshp* 2001
Sales 65.5MM^E *EMP* 508
SIC 6726 Investment offices; Investment offices
Bd of Dir: Steve Zambito
VP: Jamie Kennedy
VP: Ross Sealfon
Mng Dir: George Szele

D-U-N-S 78-326-3551 IMP
■ **LONGS DRUG STORES CALIFORNIA INC**
(*Suby of* LONGS DRUG STORES CORP) ★
1 Cvs Dr, Woonsocket, RI 02895-6146
Tel (925) 937-1170 *Founded/Ownrshp* 1938
Sales 1.3MMM^E *EMP* 18,999
SIC 5912 Drug stores; Proprietary (non-prescription medicine) stores; Drug stores; Proprietary (non-prescription medicine) stores
Pr: Harold Somerset

D-U-N-S 00-691-0004
■ **LONGS DRUG STORES CORP**
(*Suby of* CVS HEALTH CORP) ★
1 Cvs Dr, Woonsocket, RI 02895-6146
Tel (401) 770-1830 *Founded/Ownrshp* 1938, 2008
Sales 1.4MMM^E *EMP* 21,900
SIC 5912 5961 Drug stores; Proprietary (non-prescription medicine) stores; Pharmaceuticals, mail order; Drug stores; Proprietary (non-prescription medicine) stores; Pharmaceuticals, mail order
Ch Bd: Warren F Bryant
**COO:* Todd J Vasos
**CFO:* Steven F McCann
**Treas:* Roger L Chelemedos
**Sr VP:* William J Rainey
VP: Charles Armstrong
VP: Lee Klein
VP: Brian T McAndrews
VP: Brad McTeer
VP: Bruce Mentch
VP: Alan Pope
VP: Larry Prato

D-U-N-S 03-446-6359 IMP
LONGS PRODUCTS LLC
2630 Broadway Ave, Alexandria, LA 71302-4831
Tel (318) 443-0451 *Founded/Ownrshp* 2015
Sales 20.4MM^E *EMP* 15
SIC 5087 2851 Cleaning & maintenance equipment & supplies; Removers & cleaners
Pr: Jillian Donaghey
VP: Ryan Donaghey

LONGSTREET
See STRETCH-O-RAMA INC

D-U-N-S 93-394-8820 IMP
LONGSTREET CLINIC P C
NORTHEAST GA INPATIENT SVCS
725 Jesse Jewell Pkwy Se, Gainesville, GA 30501-3834
Tel (770) 718-1122 *Founded/Ownrshp* 1994
Sales 59.2MM^E *EMP* 634
SIC 8011 Clinic, operated by physicians; Clinic, operated by physicians
CEO: Amelia Mimi Collins
**COO:* T Loren Funk
**CFO:* J Allen Butts
Opers Mgr: Kimberlee Joyce
Obsttrcn: Michael P Connor
Obsttrcn: Karen D Dillard
Obsttrcn: Karen D Illar
Obsttrcn: Ross Jacobson
Doctor: Janet G Boone
Doctor: Philip R Male
Doctor: Holmes B Marchman MD

D-U-N-S 13-109-1340 IMP
LONGSTRETH SPORTING GOODS LLC
LONGSTRETH WOMEN'S SPORTS
78 Wells Rd, Spring City, PA 19475-8628
Tel (610) 495-7022 *Founded/Ownrshp* 2007
Sales 22.2MM^E *EMP* 60^E
SIC 5091 5961 Athletic goods; Fitness & sporting goods, mail order

LONGSTRETH WOMEN'S SPORTS
See LONGSTRETH SPORTING GOODS LLC

D-U-N-S 00-901-0471 IMP
LONGUST DISTRIBUTING INC (AZ)
2432 W Birchwood Ave, Mesa, AZ 85202-1064
Tel (480) 820-6244 *Founded/Ownrshp* 1975, 2005
Sales 114.1MM^E *EMP* 165
SIC 5023 Floor coverings; Resilient floor coverings: tile or sheet; Carpets; Wood flooring; Floor coverings; Resilient floor coverings: tile or sheet; Carpets; Wood flooring
Pr: Steve Wallace
**CFO:* William Bobertz
**Sr VP:* John Laird
**Sr VP:* Drew Mittelstaedt
Mktg Mgr: Debbie Hendy

D-U-N-S 79-213-4996
LONGVIEW ASSISTED LIVING
311 Sicomac Ave, Wyckoff, NJ 07481-2100
Tel (201) 848-5855 *Founded/Ownrshp* 1999
Sales 5.9MM^E *EMP* 625
SIC 8052 Intermediate care facilities; Intermediate care facilities
Off Mgr: Jamie Robinson

D-U-N-S 60-680-5984
LONGVIEW BRIDGE AND ROAD LTD
792 Skinner Ln, Longview, TX 75605-7352
Tel (903) 663-0264 *Founded/Ownrshp* 1989
Sales 145.9MM^E *EMP* 400^E
SIC 1611 1622 1794 General contractor, highway & street construction; Bridge construction; Excavation work; General contractor, highway & street construction; Bridge construction; Excavation work
Pt: Larry Johnson
Genl Pt: Lb R LLC
Pt: Alan Woods
Mtls Mgr: Larry Stone

D-U-N-S 09-537-7177
LONGVIEW DISTRIBUTION I LLC
GULF COAST IGNITION & CONTROLS
6650 Roxburgh Dr Ste 100, Houston, TX 77041-5212
Tel (832) 467-4600 *Founded/Ownrshp* 1997
Sales 43.9MM^E *EMP* 180
SIC 5084 3625 Instruments & control equipment; Relays & industrial controls; Instruments & control equipment; Relays & industrial controls
CEO: Jack Maley
**COO:* Tim Smith
**CFO:* Mitce Maples
Rgnl Mgr: Scott Easterling
Off Mgr: Leslee Macygin
DP Exec: Chad Tucker
Sls&Mrk Ex: Jay Cervenka
Sls&Mrk Ex: Ivan Soto
Sls&Mrk Ex: Raymond Stanley
VP Sls: Mike Bolton

D-U-N-S 00-904-1443 IMP/EXP
■ **LONGVIEW FIBRE PAPER AND PACKAGING INC**
KAPSTONE
(*Suby of* KAPSTONE PAPER AND PACKAGING CORP) ★
300 Fibre Way, Longview, WA 98632-1199
Tel (360) 425-1550 *Founded/Ownrshp* 2013
Sales 375.6MM^E *EMP* 999
SIC 2621 Corrugated & solid fiber boxes; Paperboard mills; Pulp mills; Paper mills; Paper mills
CEO: Roger W Stone
**Pr:* Matthew Kaplan
**CFO:* Andrea K Tarbox
Sr VP: Robert Arkell
Sr VP: Frank McShane
VP: Ken Gettman
VP: Philip Herold
**VP:* Lou Loosbrock
VP: Ivan Olsen
**Prin:* Randy Nebel
Genl Mgr: Ed Hendrix

D-U-N-S 80-775-6598
LONGVIEW HOLDING CORP
(*Suby of* ROCKWOOD SERVICE CORP) ★
43 Arch St, Greenwich, CT 06830-6512
Tel (203) 869-6734 *Founded/Ownrshp* 2005
Sales 217.7MM^E *EMP* 2,600
SIC 6719 1389 Personal holding companies, except banks; Testing, measuring, surveying & analysis services; Personal holding companies, except banks; Testing, measuring, surveying & analysis services
Pr: Peter O Scannell
**CFO:* John P Lockwood
**VP:* Harald B Findlay

LONGVIEW I S D
See LONGVIEW INDEPENDENT SCHOOL DISTRICT

D-U-N-S 01-047-6513
LONGVIEW INDEPENDENT SCHOOL DISTRICT
LONGVIEW I S D
1301 E Young St, Longview, TX 75602-2251
Tel (903) 753-0206 *Founded/Ownrshp* 1909
Sales 96.1MM *EMP* 1,302
Accts Karen A Jacks & Associates P
SIC 8211 Public elementary & secondary schools; Public elementary & secondary schools
Bd of Dir: John Preston
Prin: Bonnie Bogue
Prin: Sarah Bridges
Prin: Carl Briley
Prin: Jacqueline Burnett
Prin: Linda Dorsey
Prin: Vernessa Gentry
Prin: Linda Lister
Prin: Lola Moore
Prin: Mary L Reed
Prin: Nancy Welch

D-U-N-S 10-579-5301
LONGVIEW INSPECTION INC
99 Miller Trunk Hwy, Duluth, MN 55811
Tel (218) 393-8599 *Founded/Ownrshp* 1979
Sales 40.0MM *EMP* 7
SIC 7389 Building inspection service; Building inspection service
Pr: Micheal Crech

D-U-N-S 62-695-0393
LONGVIEW INTERNATIONAL TECHNOLOGY SOLUTIONS INC
FIRSTVIEW FEDERAL TS
11950 Democracy Dr # 275, Reston, VA 20190-5692
Tel (703) 657-5488 *Founded/Ownrshp* 2005
Sales 23.4MM^E *EMP* 82^E
SIC 7373 Systems engineering, computer related
Pr: Albert B Long
**Pr:* Ben Long
**COO:* Mike Robbins

D-U-N-S 18-791-5277
■ **LONGVIEW MEDICAL CENTER LP**
CHS
(*Suby of* COMMUNITY HEALTH SYSTEMS INC) ★
2901 4th St, Longview, TX 75605-5128
Tel (903) 758-1818 *Founded/Ownrshp* 2007
Sales 113.2MM^E *EMP* 676
SIC 8062 8099 General medical & surgical hospitals; Medical services organization; General medical & surgical hospitals; Medical services organization
Genl Pt: Jim Kendrick
Pt: Jill Bayless
Pt: Todd Johnson
COO: Roy Finch
Prin: Vicki Briggs
S&M/VP: Stacey Newman
Mktg Dir: Libby Bryson
Pr Mgr: Kelly Sneed
Nrsg Dir: Stephanie Foster
HC Dir: Wendy Hill

LONGVIEW NEWS JOURNAL
See TEXAS COMMUNITY MEDIA LLC

D-U-N-S 08-097-1930
LONGVIEW PUBLIC SCHOOLS
2715 Lilac St, Longview, WA 98632-3526
Tel (360) 575-7000 *Founded/Ownrshp* 1923
Sales 49.9MM^E *EMP* 933
SIC 8211 Public senior high school; Public elementary school; Public junior high school; Public senior high school; Public elementary school; Public junior high school
Pr: Jennifer Leach
**VP:* Ted Thomas
CTO: Sandra Catt
Opers Mgr: Julie Watson
Instr Medi: Bill Ofstun
Psych: Patrick Kelley
Psych: Christine Kelly

D-U-N-S 95-818-6371
LONGVIEW RECREATIONAL VEHICLES INC
LONGVIEW RV
30 Lawnacre Rd, Windsor Locks, CT 06096-2837
Tel (413) 247-9314 *Founded/Ownrshp* 1959
Sales 22.5MM^E *EMP* 100
SIC 5561 Recreational vehicle dealers
Pr: Frances Roberts
Genl Mgr: John Psilos

LONGVIEW RV
See LONGVIEW RECREATIONAL VEHICLES INC

D-U-N-S 94-798-5974 IMP
LONGWALL - ASSOCIATES INC
212 Kendall Ave, Chilhowie, VA 24319-5713
Tel (276) 646-2004 *Founded/Ownrshp* 1996
Sales 69.4MM^E *EMP* 175
SIC 3532 Mining machinery; Mining machinery
Pr: Paul Campbell
**Ch:* E S Tony Campbell
**Treas:* Josie Campbell
Sales Exec: John Melkowski
Sls Mgr: Mike Cook

D-U-N-S 62-446-8880
LONGWOOD AT OAKMONT INC
500 Route 909, Verona, PA 15147-3863
Tel (412) 826-5800 *Founded/Ownrshp* 1990
Sales 22.5MM *EMP* 184
SIC 8361 Geriatric residential care; Geriatric residential care
CEO: Paul Winkler
Ex Dir: Mike Haye
HC Dir: Karen Dolan

D-U-N-S 06-803-1921
LONGWOOD CENTRAL SCHOOL DISTRICT
35 Yaphank Middle Is, Middle Island, NY 11953-2369
Tel (631) 345-2793 *Founded/Ownrshp* 1946
Sales 41.3MM^E *EMP* 716
SIC 8211 Public elementary & secondary schools; Public elementary & secondary schools
**Pr:* Daniel Tomaszewski
**VP:* William K Miller
VP: William Miller
Pr Dir: Pamela Donovan
HC Dir: Gina Curiale

D-U-N-S 61-280-2256
LONGWOOD COMMUNITY LIVING CENTER
200 Long St, Booneville, MS 38829-4306
Tel (662) 728-6234 *Founded/Ownrshp* 1992
Sales 402.1MM *EMP* 72
SIC 8051 Skilled nursing care facilities; Skilled nursing care facilities
Pr: Douglas Wright Jr
Board of Directors: Dewitt Crawford

D-U-N-S 78-701-0297 IMP
■ **LONGWOOD ELASTOMERS INC**
LONGWOOD INDUSTRIES
(*Suby of* LONGWOOD INDUSTRIES INC) ★
706 Green Valley Rd # 410, Greensboro, NC 27408-7046
Tel (336) 272-3710 *Founded/Ownrshp* 1995
Sales 81.3MM^E *EMP* 422
SIC 3069 3081 Molded rubber products; Unsupported plastics film & sheet; Molded rubber products; Unsupported plastics film & sheet
Pr: Dana S Waterman
**CFO:* Kim Thompson

D-U-N-S 02-161-3975
LONGWOOD FOUNDATION INC
100 W 10th St Ste 1109, Wilmington, DE 19801-1694
Tel (302) 654-2477 *Founded/Ownrshp* 1937
Sales 35.7MM *EMP* 3
Accts Cover & Rossiter Pa Wilmin
SIC 8641 Civic social & fraternal associations; Civic social & fraternal associations
Pr: There Du Pont
Treas: Stephen Martinenza
**Prin:* H R Sharp III

D-U-N-S 07-707-7477 IMP
LONGWOOD GARDENS INC
1001 Longwood Rd, Kennett Square, PA 19348-1913
Tel (610) 388-1000 *Founded/Ownrshp* 1924
Sales 21.8MM *EMP* 448
Accts Cover & Rossiter Wilmington
SIC 8422 Botanical garden; Botanical garden
Pr: Nathan Hayward III
Dir Vol: Sally Kutyla
**CFO:* Dennis Fisher

**VP:* Irenee Du Pont
**VP:* Peg Stabler
Comm Man: Patricia Evans
**Ex Dir:* Paul Redman
IT Man: John Page
IT Man: John Reid
Snr Mgr: Jim Harbage
Snr Mgr: Shawn Kister
Board of Directors: Ann C Rose, Matthew Brown, C Porter Schutt III, Benjamin F Dupont, Valerie J Sill C F A, Steven B Hutton, Cynthia Du Pont Tobias, Margaret L Laird, Thomas K Whitford, Richard Lighty, Robin W Morgan, Robert Peck, Jane G Pepper, Blaine T Phillips Jr

LONGWOOD INDUSTRIES
See LONGWOOD ELASTOMERS INC

D-U-N-S 78-398-2739 IMP
■ LONGWOOD INDUSTRIES INC
(*Suby of* WABTEC) ★
706 Green Valley Rd # 212, Greensboro, NC 27408-7038
Tel (336) 272-3710 *Founded/Ownrshp* 2013
Sales 81.3MM^E *EMP* 450
SIC 3069 3081 Molded rubber products; Unsupported plastics film & sheet; Molded rubber products; Unsupported plastics film & sheet
Sr VP: Kimberly L Rice
**Ex VP:* James J McDonnell
**Sr VP:* Joseph E Mihalick
VP: Joseph Mihalick
VP: Kimberly Rice

D-U-N-S 06-197-7427 EXP
LONGWOOD LINCOLN-MERCURY INC
DE LAND TOYOTA
3505 N Us Highway 17 92, Longwood, FL 32750-3771
Tel (407) 322-4884 *Founded/Ownrshp* 1979
Sales 88.4MM^E *EMP* 307^E
SIC 5511 Automobiles, new & used; Automobiles, new & used
Pr: Stephen R Parks
**Sec:* Greg Corless
Dir IT: Andy Harris
Sls Mgr: Tom Lewis

D-U-N-S 08-008-0831
LONGWOOD MANAGEMENT CORP
LONGWOOD MANOR SANITARIUM
4032 Wilshire Blvd Fl 6, Los Angeles, CA 90010-3425
Tel (213) 389-6900 *Founded/Ownrshp* 1964
Sales 154.0MM^E *EMP* 2,000
SIC 8742 6513 General management consultant; Retirement hotel operation; General management consultant; Retirement hotel operation
CEO: David Friedmand
**Pr:* Jacob Friedman
**Treas:* Lea Friedman
**VP:* Irving Friedman
VP Opers: Kevin Bruso

LONGWOOD MANOR SANITARIUM
See LONGWOOD MANAGEMENT CORP

D-U-N-S 17-817-4801
LONGWOOD SECURITY SERVICES INC
429 Newbury St, Boston, MA 02115-1801
Tel (617) 735-0600 *Founded/Ownrshp* 1986
Sales 11.0MM^E *EMP* 285^E
SIC 7381 8748 Security guard service; Business consulting; Security guard service; Business consulting
Pr: John T Connelly
Ofcr: Noel O'Laoghaire

D-U-N-S 16-792-2525
LONGWOOD UNIVERSITY
201 High St, Farmville, VA 23909-1801
Tel (434) 395-2000 *Founded/Ownrshp* 1849
Sales 76.9MM^E *EMP* 700
SIC 8221 Colleges universities & professional schools; Colleges universities & professional schools
Pr: Patricia Cormier
**Pr:* W Taylor Reveley IV
Bd of Dir: Lori Mitchell
Ofcr: Ray Ostrander
Ofcr: Quincy Steele
Ofcr: Tony Williams
VP: Richard Bratcher
VP: Sabrina Brown
VP: Victoria Kindon
VP: Jennifer Kingsley
VP: Melissa Pelletier
Dir Lab: Raymond Vadeboncoeur

D-U-N-S 07-169-1457
LONGWORTH ENTERPRISES INC
8050 Beckett Center Dr, West Chester, OH 45069-5017
Tel (513) 738-4663 *Founded/Ownrshp* 2009
Sales 2.5MM^E *EMP* 300
SIC 7299 Home improvement & renovation contractor agency
CEO: Marc Longworth IL

D-U-N-S 83-156-6187
LONGYEAR HOLDINGS INC
(*Suby of* BOART LONGYEAR LIMITED)
2340 W 1700 S, Salt Lake City, UT 84104
Tel (801) 972-6430 *Founded/Ownrshp* 2005
Sales 2.7MM^E *EMP* 9,500
SIC 1481 3532 3559 Test boring for nonmetallic minerals; Drills & drilling equipment, mining (except oil & gas); Concrete products machinery; Test boring for nonmetallic minerals; Drills & drilling equipment, mining (except oil & gas); Concrete products machinery
Ch Bd: Michael Moore
**Ch Bd:* David McLemore
**Pr:* Paul Brunner
**Pr:* Blake Cavit
**Sr VP:* Fab Rasetti
Dir IT: Kevin Vaughan
Tech Mgr: Jessi Pettey
Manager: Sharon Condrat

D-U-N-S 07-739-7859
LONOKE COUNTY CO-OP INC
5406 Hwy 70 E, Lonoke, AR 72086
Tel (501) 676-3130 *Founded/Ownrshp* 1975
Sales 30.3MM *EMP* 35
Accts Robert D Ferguson Fayettevil
SIC 5191 Feed; Seeds: field, garden & flower; Chemicals, agricultural; Fertilizer & fertilizer materials; Feed; Seeds: field, garden & flower; Chemicals, agricultural; Fertilizer & fertilizer materials
Genl Mgr: Phillip Murray

LONZ WINERY
See PARAMOUNT DISTILLERS INC

D-U-N-S 07-887-4294
LONZA AMERICA INC (DE)
(*Suby of* LONZA GROUP AG)
90 Boroline Rd Ste 1, Allendale, NJ 07401-1629
Tel (201) 316-9200 *Founded/Ownrshp* 1980
Sales 390.3MM^E *EMP* 2,201
SIC 8731 Biotechnical research, commercial; Biotechnical research, commercial
CEO: Stephan Borgas
**Ch Bd:* Werner J Bauer
**Ch Bd:* Rolf Soiron
CFO: Raymond French
Chf Mktg O: Michael Frizberg
VP: James Coletta
Comm Man: Teri McCarthy
Mktg Dir: Christian Rose
Mktg Mgr: Kim Yang

D-U-N-S 00-840-1668
LONZA BIOLOGICS INC
(*Suby of* LONZA GROUP AG)
101 International Dr, Portsmouth, NH 03801-2815
Tel (603) 334-6100 *Founded/Ownrshp* 2008
Sales 62.4MM^E *EMP* 96
SIC 2834 Pharmaceutical preparations; Pharmaceutical preparations
VP: Anthony Rottuno
**Pr:* Stephan Kutzer
VP: Juerg Burger
**VP:* Alexander Hoy
**VP:* Scott Waldman
Dir IT: Michael Dennis
QI Cn Mgr: Ann Farnsworth

D-U-N-S 09-314-9750 EXP
LONZA BIOLOGICS INC
(*Suby of* LONZA AMERICA INC) ★
101 International Dr, Portsmouth, NH 03801-2815
Tel (603) 610-4500 *Founded/Ownrshp* 1993
Sales 196.3MM^E *EMP* 476
SIC 2834 Pharmaceutical preparations; Pharmaceutical preparations
Pr: Stephan Kutzer
CFO: Rob Schauder
CFO: Roland Waibel
**Treas:* Alexander Hoy
VP: Joe Garni
VP: Mailet Minassian
Assoc Dir: John Morse
Genl Mgr: Randy Beightol
Telecom Ex: Randall Spayd
CIO: Thomas Salvetti
Cmptr Lab: Jim Brooks

D-U-N-S 00-164-3170 IMP
LONZA INC (NY)
(*Suby of* LONZA AMERICA INC) ★
90 Boroline Rd Ste 1, Allendale, NJ 07401-1629
Tel (201) 316-9200 *Founded/Ownrshp* 1958
Sales 168.5MM^E *EMP* 549
SIC 2899 2869 2819 Chemical preparations; Industrial organic chemicals; Industrial inorganic chemicals; Chemical preparations; Industrial organic chemicals; Industrial inorganic chemicals
CEO: Jeanne Thomas
CFO: Waibel Basel
CFO: Andrea Dybove
CFO: Toralf Haag
CFO: Andrew Hoy
VP: Allan M Kushins
VP: Marcel A Olbrecht
VP: Scott Waldman
Exec: Jasmine Dsouza
Dir Risk M: Patrick Boylan
Dir Lab: Gaetano La Delfa
Assoc Dir: Kent Beech
Assoc Dir: Jessica Jean
Assoc Dir: Erin Murdach
Assoc Dir: Annette Wagner
Dir Bus: John Kokai-Kun
Dir Bus: Anahita Lion
Comm Man: Melanie Disa
Comm Man: Pia Schaefer
Board of Directors: Roland Waibel

D-U-N-S 13-115-4267
LONZA ROCKLAND INC
(*Suby of* LONZA AMERICA INC) ★
191 Thomaston St, Rockland, ME 04841-2130
Tel (207) 594-3400 *Founded/Ownrshp* 1998
Sales 25.3MM^E *EMP* 65
SIC 2836 Biological products, except diagnostic
CEO: Stephan Borgas
Mfg Mgr: David Cowan
Snr Mgr: Hugh White

D-U-N-S 60-909-5955
LONZA WALKERSVILLE INC
(*Suby of* LONZA GROUP AG)
8830 Biggs Ford Rd, Walkersville, MD 21793-8415
Tel (301) 898-7025 *Founded/Ownrshp* 2007
Sales 117.8MM^E *EMP* 480
SIC 2836 Biological products, except diagnostic; Biological products, except diagnostic
Pr: Shawn Cavanagh
CFO: Ralf Geier
CFO: Andy Long
Ofcr: Edward Flynn
Exec: Stephani Mauzy
Dir Bus: Richard Giles
Prgrm Mgr: Andrew Durdock
Prgrm Mgr: Jack Harvey
CTO: Daniel Marshak
IT Man: Cathy Boyd
QI Cn Mgr: Christine Quigley

D-U-N-S 09-942-0713
LOOKING UPWARDS INC
438 E Main Rd Ste 101, Middletown, RI 02842-5264
Tel (401) 293-5790 *Founded/Ownrshp* 1977
Sales 14.0MM *EMP* 340
Accts Kahn Litwin Renza & Co Ltd Pr
SIC 8322 Association for the handicapped; Association for the handicapped
Ex Dir: Carrie Miranda

LOOKOUT RIDGE
See AGSTAR FINANCIAL SERVICES ACA

D-U-N-S 00-196-4196 IMP
LOOMCRAFT TEXTILE & SUPPLY CO (IL)
2516 Tucker St, Burlington, NC 27215-8885
Tel (336) 222-0515 *Founded/Ownrshp* 1950, 1955
Sales 41.8MM^E *EMP* 99
SIC 5131 5714 5719 2221 Upholstery fabrics, woven; Drapery & upholstery stores; Upholstery materials; Window furnishings; Broadwoven fabric mills, manmade; Upholstery fabrics, woven; Drapery & upholstery stores; Upholstery materials; Window furnishings; Broadwoven fabric mills, manmade
Pr: Ronald Frankel
**Treas:* Robert Meroney

D-U-N-S 05-637-0109
LOOMIS ARMORED US LLC
2500 Citywest Blvd # 900, Houston, TX 77042-3000
Tel (713) 435-6700 *Founded/Ownrshp* 2006
Sales 687.0MM *EMP* 8,000
SIC 7381 4789 Armored car services; Cargo loading & unloading services; Armored car services; Cargo loading & unloading services
Pr: Lars Blecko
**COO:* Chuck Obrien
**CFO:* Marcus Hagegard
**CFO:* Patrick Otero
VP: Mark Clark
**VP:* Shirley R Jefferies
**VP:* Sarah Kattapong
Exec: Blake Spurrier
Brnch Mgr: Phil Aitken
Brnch Mgr: Jim Anderson
Brnch Mgr: Keith Beezhold

LOOMIS CHAFFEE SCHOOL
See LOOMIS INSTITUTE INC

D-U-N-S 10-167-6310
LOOMIS CO
850 N Park Rd, Wyomissing, PA 19610-1307
Tel (610) 374-4040 *Founded/Ownrshp* 1982
Sales NA *EMP* 375
SIC 6411 8742 Insurance agents, brokers & service; Policyholders' consulting service; Management consulting services; Insurance agents, brokers & service; Policyholders' consulting service; Management consulting services
Pr: James R Loomis
**Treas:* Kathy Schlegel
VP: Joe Reedy
Opers Mgr: Eric Sandoe

D-U-N-S 06-924-6825
LOOMIS INSTITUTE INC (CT)
LOOMIS CHAFFEE SCHOOL
4 Batchelder Rd, Windsor, CT 06095-3028
Tel (860) 687-6000 *Founded/Ownrshp* 1874
Sales 43.3MM *EMP* 195
Accts Blum Shapiro & Company Pc Cpa
SIC 8211 Private senior high school; Private senior high school
Ch Bd: Chris Norton
**Pr:* Sheila Culbert
**CFO:* Christopher Wejchert

D-U-N-S 02-692-6816
LOOMIS INTERNATIONAL INC
100 N Richey St, Pasadena, TX 77506-1055
Tel (713) 477-7148 *Founded/Ownrshp* 1996
Sales 93.5MM^E *EMP* 100
SIC 1389 Testing, measuring, surveying & analysis services; Gas field services; Pipe testing, oil field service
Pr: Larry C Johnson
**CFO:* Ryan McMinn
Dist Mgr: Jose Espinoza
Dist Mgr: Lothario Pratt
Sfty Mgr: Kathy Nouis
Sls&Mrk Ex: Kent Padgett

D-U-N-S 00-695-2568
LOOMIS SAYLES & CO LP (MA)
(*Suby of* NATIXIS GLOBAL ASSET MANAGEMENT LP) ★
1 Financial Ctr Fl 34, Boston, MA 02111-2660
Tel (617) 482-2451 *Founded/Ownrshp* 1926, 1968
Sales 207.8MM^E *EMP* 525
SIC 6282 Investment counselors; Investment counselors
CEO: Robert J Blanding
Pr: Keith Beaudin
Pr: Kevin Charleston
Treas: Paul Scherber
Chf Inves: Jae Park
Ofcr: Jean Loewenberg
Ofcr: Jeff Meyer
Ofcr: Don Ryan
Ex VP: John Gallagher
VP: David Beach
VP: John Bell
VP: Michael Braiewa
VP: Neil Burke
VP: Frank Caparrotta
VP: Dana Chamberlain
VP: David Cohen
VP: Heather Folino
VP: Dozier Gardner
VP: Daniel Garuti
VP: Anthony Generelli
VP: Kevin Gribben
Board of Directors: Paul Sherba, David Waldman

D-U-N-S 80-873-7964
LOOMIS SERVICES US LLC
(*Suby of* LOOMIS ARMORED US LLC) ★
2500 Citywest Blvd # 900, Houston, TX 77042-3000
Tel (713) 435-6700 *Founded/Ownrshp* 1997
Sales 71.7MM^E *EMP* 148^E
SIC 7381 Armored car services
Pr: Lars Blecko
COO: Bill Barthelemy
**COO:* Chuck Obrien
**CFO:* Marcus Hagegrd
Ex VP: Kenneth Hgman
**Sr VP:* Pat Otero
**Sr VP:* Danny Pack
VP: Bruce Magelky
Exec: Elizabeth Calloway
Genl Mgr: Tom Harper
IT Man: Magnus Kerlind

D-U-N-S 17-343-9808
LOONEY RICKS KISS LRK INC
80 Preservation Ct, Eads, TN 38028-8006
Tel (901) 853-1513 *Founded/Ownrshp* 2004
Sales 30.0MM *EMP* 75
SIC 8712 Architectural services
VP: James Looney
**Pr:* Frank Ricks

D-U-N-S 79-999-2755
LOOP CAPITAL MARKETS LLC
111 W Jacks Blvd Ste 1901, Chicago, IL 60604
Tel (312) 913-4900 *Founded/Ownrshp* 1997
Sales 52.0MM^E *EMP* 128
Accts Mc Gladrey & Pullen
SIC 6211 Investment bankers; Investment bankers
CFO: Tasha Henderson
Ofcr: Stephen Berkeley
Sr VP: Patrick Coleman
Sr VP: Gail Gallagher
Sr VP: Andrew Heilig
Sr VP: Patrick Knoell
Sr VP: Frank Paul
Sr VP: Eileen Piechocki
Sr VP: John Rutherford
Sr VP: Cary Schulz
Sr VP: Rohit Syal
VP: Anna Hsu
VP: Shaan Kapoor
VP: Ani Tchaghlasian
VP: Martin Trekas

D-U-N-S 09-418-1633 IMP/EXP
LOOP LLC
LOUISIANA OFFSHORE OIL PORT
137 Northpark Blvd, Covington, LA 70433-5071
Tel (985) 632-6970 *Founded/Ownrshp* 1972
Sales 163.8MM^E *EMP* 128
SIC 1389 Oil field services; Oil field services
Pr: Robert Thompson
**Treas:* Philip J Simoneaux
VP: Happie Ledet
**VP:* Thomas V Mc Cauley
VP: Jill Shane
IT Man: Greg Galliano
Netwrk Eng: John Chilton

D-U-N-S 09-039-7410 IMP
LOOP PAPER RECYCLING INC
2401 S Laflin St, Chicago, IL 60608-5005
Tel (312) 942-0042 *Founded/Ownrshp* 1998
Sales 42.0MM^E *EMP* 114
SIC 4953 Recycling, waste materials
Pr: Frank Ward Jr
CFO: Jeff Goffrey
**Prin:* George Ward

D-U-N-S 13-932-8660
LOOPER REED & MCGRAW A PROFESSIONAL CORP
1300 Post Oak Blvd # 2000, Houston, TX 77056-8000
Tel (713) 986-7000 *Founded/Ownrshp* 1985
Sales 28.3MM^E *EMP* 195
SIC 8111 General practice attorney, lawyer; General practice attorney, lawyer
Pr: J Cary Gray
Pr: Melissa Khan
Bd of Dir: Ben L Aderholt
Chf Mktg O: Cary J Gray
Ofcr: Mark Gargiulo
**VP:* Donald R Looper
**VP:* Randall B Wilhite
IT Man: Jason Rodriguez
Counsel: Gayla Crain
Counsel: Jack Rains

D-U-N-S 94-451-6715
■ LOOPNET INC
(*Suby of* COSTAR GROUP INC) ★
101 California St # 4300, San Francisco, CA 94111-5889
Tel (415) 243-4200 *Founded/Ownrshp* 2012
Sales 17.5MM^E *EMP* 300^E
SIC 6531 Real estate agents & managers; Real estate agent, commercial; Real estate agents & managers; Real estate agent, commercial
CEO: Richard J Boyle Jr
Pr: Thomas Byrne
CFO: Brent Stumme
Sr VP: Jason Greenman
Sr VP: Wayne Warthen
Sr VP: Wayne B Warthen
VP: Richard Boyle
Rgnl Mgr: Nichja Dryg
Rgnl Mgr: Jennifer Whitney
Off Mgr: Andrea Kay
QA Dir: Mousumi Panda

D-U-N-S 05-310-8122 IMP/EXP
LOOPS NURSERY & GREENHOUSES INC
2568 Old Middleburg Rd N, Jacksonville, FL 32210-3598
Tel (904) 772-0880 *Founded/Ownrshp* 1949
Sales 27.6MM^E *EMP* 80
SIC 5193 Flowers & florists' supplies; Plants, potted
Pr: David Wayne Loop
**Sec:* Ruth Loop
VP: Jonathan Corbin
VP: Matthew Weaver
Exec: Marie Smith

LOOPTEX MILLS & PHENIX CARPETS
See PHENIX FLOORING LLC

D-U-N-S 00-453-4657 IMP
LOOS & CO INC (CT)
WIRE ROPE DIV
Rr 101, Pomfret, CT 06258
Tel (860) 928-7981 *Founded/Ownrshp* 1989
Sales 60.0MM *EMP* 450
SIC 3315 3357 5051 2298 Wire, ferrous/iron; Nonferrous wiredrawing & insulating; Cable, wire; Cordage & twine; Wire, ferrous/iron; Nonferrous wiredrawing & insulating; Cable, wire; Cordage & twine
Pr: William Loos
*Pr: Richard Griswold
VP: Russ Cox
Exec: Joan Fortin
Dir IT: Brian Budney
IT Man: Jeffrey Richmond
IT Man: Brent Tuttle
VP Opers: Alan Jaaskela
Ql Cn Mgr: Steve Fairfield

D-U-N-S 00-893-7948
LOOS & DILWORTH INC (PA)
PETRO CHOICE
(*Suby of* PETRO CHOICE) ★
1300 Virginia Dr, Fort Washington, PA 19034-3221
Tel (215) 785-3591 *Founded/Ownrshp* 1893, 2009
Sales 21.0MM^E^ *EMP* 25
SIC 5172 Lubricating oils & greases
Pr: Richard G Campbell
*CFO: Michael Monahan
VP: Mike Gawlinski
*Genl Mgr: Winifred Hutchison

D-U-N-S 14-424-1031
LOOSE PLASTICS INC
1016 E 1st St, Gladwin, MI 48624-1268
Tel (989) 246-1880 *Founded/Ownrshp* 1985
Sales 34.8MM^E^ *EMP* 120
SIC 3083 Laminated plastics plate & sheet
CEO: Scott C Loose
*Treas: Jamie A Loose
*VP: Joshua Loose
Sfty Mgr: Jeff Walker
Ql Cn Mgr: Cody Allen
Sales Asso: Bryant Brandel

D-U-N-S 07-840-8153
LOP AUTOMOTIVE CO LLC
LEXUS OF PLEASANTON
4345 Rosewood Dr, Pleasanton, CA 94588-3003
Tel (925) 847-0678 *Founded/Ownrshp* 1996
Sales 26.8MM^E^ *EMP* 130
SIC 5511 Automobiles, new & used; Automobiles, new & used

D-U-N-S 02-766-4478 IMP/EXP
LOPAREX LLC
EASY MASK
(*Suby of* LOPAREX HOLDING B.V.)
1255 Crescent Green # 400, Cary, NC 27518-8132
Tel (919) 678-7700 *Founded/Ownrshp* 2005
Sales 248.2MM^E^ *EMP* 732
SIC 2672 Coated paper, except photographic, carbon or abrasive; Coated paper, except photographic, carbon or abrasive
CEO: Michael Apperson
*COO: Jack Taylor
CFO: John Mays
VP: Mike Werner
Tech Mgr: Chip Sheeran
Tech Mgr: Bruce Unruh
Software D: Tammy Martin

D-U-N-S 00-697-2556
LOPEZ FOODS INC
6016 Nw 120th Ct, Yukon, OK 73099
Tel (405) 499-0181 *Founded/Ownrshp* 2009
Sales 35.5MM^E^ *EMP* 500
SIC 3556 Meat processing machinery; Meat processing machinery
Pr: Jimmy English

D-U-N-S 09-476-8702
LOPEZ FOODS INC
6016 Nw 120th Ct, Oklahoma City, OK 73162-1729
Tel (405) 603-7500 *Founded/Ownrshp* 1992
Sales 400.0MM *EMP* 1,564
SIC 2013 2011 Prepared beef products from purchased beef; Sausages from purchased meat; Bacon, side & sliced: from purchased meat; Meat packing plants; Prepared beef products from purchased beef; Sausages from purchased meat; Bacon, side & sliced: from purchased meat; Meat packing plants
CEO: Ed Sanchez
*Ch Bd: John C Lopez
*COO: James D English
VP: John Schaller
Exec: Michelle Wagner
Opers Mgr: Alan Nance
Opers Mgr: Eric Underwood
Sls Dir: Raj Srinivas
Sls Mgr: Brenda Gomez

D-U-N-S 80-528-5871
LOPEZ HEALTH SYSTEMS INC
2209 N Highway 83, Crystal City, TX 78839-1756
Tel (830) 374-3525 *Founded/Ownrshp* 1990
Sales 21.1MM^E^ *EMP* 1,300
SIC 8082 Home health care services; Home health care services
Pr: Amparo Lopez
CFO: Raul Flores
*VP: Victor Lopez

LOPEZ HOUSTON METALS
See LOPEZ SCRAP METAL INC

D-U-N-S 19-030-5599 IMP
LOPEZ NEGRETE COMMUNICATIONS INC
3336 Richmond Ave Ste 200, Houston, TX 77098-3022
Tel (713) 877-8777 *Founded/Ownrshp* 1985
Sales 38.1MM^E^ *EMP* 135^E^
SIC 7311 Advertising agencies; Advertising agencies
Pr: Alex L Negrete
*COO: Cathy L Negrete
CFO: Cathryn Negrete
VP: Michelle McLeod
VP: Crystal Monteleone
VP: Jochi Quijano
Exec: Rochelle Lopez
Creative D: Rodrigo Alonso
Creative D: John Castrillon
Creative D: Jonathan Diaz
Creative D: Eduardo Duran
Creative D: Iliana Escalona
Creative D: Santiago Garces
Creative D: Jaime Gonzalez
Creative D: Javier Gonzalez-Herba
Creative D: Hernan Ibanez
Creative D: Rafa Juarez
Creative D: Vicent Llopis
Creative D: Juan Quintana
Creative D: Nestor Rivera
Creative D: Francisco Sanchez

D-U-N-S 07-508-7528 IMP
LOPEZ SCRAP METAL INC
LOPEZ HOUSTON METALS
351 N Nevarez Rd, El Paso, TX 79927-4120
Tel (915) 859-0770 *Founded/Ownrshp* 1970
Sales 103.3MM *EMP* 52
Accts Pena Briones Mcdaniel & Co E
SIC 5093 3341 Ferrous metal scrap & waste; Nonferrous metals scrap; Secondary nonferrous metals; Ferrous metal scrap & waste; Nonferrous metals scrap; Secondary nonferrous metals
Pr: Isidro Lopez
*Treas: Hector E Lopez

LOPI
See TRAVIS INDUSTRIES INC

D-U-N-S 09-030-2365
LOPITO ILEANA & HOWIE INC
1st St Ste 13, Guaynabo, PR 00968
Tel (787) 783-1160 *Founded/Ownrshp* 1972
Sales 25.0MM *EMP* 80
SIC 7311 Advertising agencies; Advertising agencies
Pr: Carlos J Rodriguez
Pt: Jos Luis Alvarez

D-U-N-S 11-377-5795
LOQUERCIO AUTOMOTIVE INC
NORTHWEST VALLEY DODGE
881 E Chicago St, Elgin, IL 60120-6818
Tel (847) 888-8222 *Founded/Ownrshp* 2005
Sales 23.1MM^E^ *EMP* 50
SIC 5511 Automobiles, new & used
Pr: Robert P Loquercio

D-U-N-S 06-148-8144
LOR INC
ROLLINS RANCHES
2170 Piedmont Rd Ne, Atlanta, GA 30324-4135
Tel (404) 486-5600 *Founded/Ownrshp* 1978
Sales 164.1MM^E^ *EMP* 1,426
SIC 6799 5084 3443 Investors; Pumps & pumping equipment; Fabricated plate work (boiler shop); Investors; Pumps & pumping equipment; Fabricated plate work (boiler shop)
CEO: R Randall Rollins
Pr: Gary W Rollins
CEO: Randall Rollins

D-U-N-S 00-361-6786
LOR-MAR MECHANICAL SERVICES INC (PA)
6710 Westfield Ave Ste A, Pennsauken, NJ 08110-1502
Tel (856) 910-8144 *Founded/Ownrshp* 1997, 2010
Sales 33.3MM *EMP* 85
Accts Haefele Flanagan & Co Pc
SIC 1711 Plumbing contractors; Warm air heating & air conditioning contractor; Plumbing contractors; Warm air heating & air conditioning contractor
Pr: Eugene J Pint
*VP: Thomas Marcinek
*VP: Daniel J Wilson
Off Mgr: Gene Pinto
Manager: Jim Markowski

D-U-N-S 13-173-6985 IMP
■ **LORAD CORP**
LORAD MEDICAL SYSTEMS
(*Suby of* HOLOGIC INC) ★
36 Apple Ridge Rd, Danbury, CT 06810-7301
Tel (203) 790-5544 *Founded/Ownrshp* 2000
Sales 34.0MM^E^ *EMP* 200
SIC 3844 3841 Radiographic X-ray apparatus & tubes; Biopsy instruments & equipment; Radiographic X-ray apparatus & tubes; Biopsy instruments & equipment
VP: Raymond Calvo
CIO: Glen Kretkowski

LORAD MEDICAL SYSTEMS
See LORAD CORP

LORAIN BOARD OF EDUCATION
See LORAIN CITY SCHOOL DISTRICT

D-U-N-S 08-332-1083
LORAIN CITY OF (INC) (OH)
200 W Erie Ave Ste 714, Lorain, OH 44052-1606
Tel (440) 204-2090 *Founded/Ownrshp* 1896
Sales NA *EMP* 540
Accts Dave Yost Columbus Ohio
SIC 9111 City & town managers' offices; ; City & town managers' offices;
Ofcr: Ritenauer Chase
Ex VP: Heidi Gedling
VP: R J Budway
Exec: Robert Gilchrist
MIS Dir: Dave Comer
Snr Mgr: Richard Klinar

D-U-N-S 07-675-5412
LORAIN CITY SCHOOL DISTRICT
LORAIN BOARD OF EDUCATION
2350 Pole Ave, Lorain, OH 44052-4301
Tel (440) 233-2232 *Founded/Ownrshp* 1900
Sales 58.4MM^E^ *EMP* 1,500
SIC 8211 Public elementary & secondary schools; Public elementary & secondary schools
*Treas: Dale Weber
IT Man: Diana Miglets
Schl Brd P: Timothy Williams
Teacher Pr: Carol Gottschling

D-U-N-S 19-146-5491 IMP
LORAIN COUNTY AUTOMOTIVE SYSTEMS INC
LCAS
(*Suby of* CHEMICAL) ★
7470 Industrial Pkwy Dr, Lorain, OH 44053-2070
Tel (440) 960-7470 *Founded/Ownrshp* 1996
Sales 196.1MM^E^ *EMP* 1,718
SIC 3714 Motor vehicle engines & parts; Motor vehicle engines & parts
CEO: Arvind Pradhan
*CFO: Tom Rockwell
Rgnl Mgr: Desiree Cutright
Mtls Mgr: Sherri Ulich

D-U-N-S 07-778-0674
LORAIN COUNTY COMMUNITY COLLEGE DISTRICT
L C C C
1005 Abbe Rd N, Elyria, OH 44035-1613
Tel (440) 365-5222 *Founded/Ownrshp* 1961
Sales 145.7MM^E^ *EMP* 1,400^E^
Accts Balestra Harr & Scherer Cpas
SIC 8221 Colleges universities & professional schools; Colleges universities & professional schools
Pr: Roy A Church
V Ch: Andy Gurd
Treas: David Strittmather
Ofcr: Debbie Richter
*VP: Quentin Potter
VP: Karen Wells
Off Admin: D Corn
Dir IT: Jeff Traxler
IT Man: Kim Bilancini
IT Man: Laurie Carlberg
Info Man: Andy Dovci

D-U-N-S 01-085-4313
LORAIN COUNTY JOINT VOCATIONAL SCHOOL
15181 State Route 58, Oberlin, OH 44074-9753
Tel (440) 774-1051 *Founded/Ownrshp* 1971
Sales 20.0MM *EMP* 303^E^
Accts Costin & Company North Ridgev
SIC 8211 Public vocational/technical school; Public vocational/technical school
Cmptr Lab: Tim Reeves
Dir IT: Gary McLntyre
Schl Brd P: Rex Engle
HC Dir: Linda Mahar

LORAIN COUNTY TREASURER
See COUNTY OF LORAIN

D-U-N-S 00-790-3446
■ **LORAIN NATIONAL BANK**
(*Suby of* NORTHWEST BANCSHARES INC) ★
457 Broadway, Lorain, OH 44052-1769
Tel (440) 244-6000 *Founded/Ownrshp* 2015
Sales NA *EMP* 239
SIC 6021 National trust companies with deposits, commercial; National trust companies with deposits, commercial
Ch Bd: James R Herrick
CEO: Dan Klimas
COO: Kevin W Nelson
CFO: Gregory D Friedman
CFO: James Nicholson
Treas: Thomas P Ryan
V Ch Bd: James F Kidd
Chf Cred: Mike Bickerton
Ofcr: Sandra Dubell
Trst Ofcr: Nancy Noga
Ex VP: Debra Brown
Sr VP: Kevin Ball
Sr VP: Robert Cox
Sr VP: Michael D Ireland
Sr VP: Emma N Mason
Sr VP: Frank Soltis
Sr VP: James H Weber
VP: Lisa Arnoczky
VP: Christian Athey
VP: Kris Barker
VP: Diane Depould

D-U-N-S 94-681-6212
▲ **LORAL SPACE & COMMUNICATIONS INC**
565 5th Ave, New York, NY 10017-2413
Tel (212) 697-1105 *Founded/Ownrshp* 2005
Sales 869.9MM^E^ *EMP* 441
Tkr Sym LORL *Exch* NGS
SIC 3663 4899 Satellites, communications; Satellite earth stations; Data communication services; Satellites, communications; Satellite earth stations; Data communication services
Pr: AVI Katz
CFO: John Capogrossi
Sr VP: Paul Estey
VP: Jeanette H Clonan
CTO: David N Wendling
Sftwr Eng: Brent Goodale

D-U-N-S 13-384-6969
■ **LORAL SPACECOM CORP**
(*Suby of* LORAL SPACE & COMMUNICATIONS INC) ★
888 7th Ave 40, New York, NY 10106-0001
Tel (212) 697-1105 *Founded/Ownrshp* 1997
Sales 869.4MM *EMP* 2,000
Accts Deloitte & Touche Llp New Yor
SIC 3663 Satellites, communications; Satellites, communications
CEO: Michael Targoff
*Treas: Richard Mastoloni
Sr VP: Arnold Friedman

D-U-N-S 01-034-5452 IMP/EXP
LORAM MAINTENANCE OF WAY INC
3900 Arrowhead Dr, Hamel, MN 55340-9529
Tel (763) 478-6014 *Founded/Ownrshp* 1954
Sales 300.0MM *EMP* 1,100
SIC 3743 Railway maintenance cars; Railway maintenance cars
CEO: Philip J Homan
CFO: Lois Sietsma
Ofcr: James Perkins
*VP: Joe Carlin
*VP: Don Cherrey
*VP: Tom Dejoseph
*VP: Jim Perkins
IT Man: Lisa Lindquist
Sftwr Eng: Steve Dercks
Sfty Dirs: Matthew Rossing
Opers Mgr: Jason Holt

D-U-N-S 36-168-8042
LORAM RAIL SERVICES LLC
(*Suby of* LORAM MAINTENANCE OF WAY INC) ★
3900 Arrowhead Dr, Hamel, MN 55340-9529
Tel (763) 478-6014 *Founded/Ownrshp* 2004
Sales 6.9MM^E^ *EMP* 400
SIC 4789 Railroad maintenance & repair services; Railroad maintenance & repair services
Pr: Paul V Wilson
IT Man: Peter Hauer

D-U-N-S 93-864-2808
LORANGE HOLDING CO
TELEVERDE
4636 E University Dr # 150, Phoenix, AZ 85034-7418
Tel (480) 967-1402 *Founded/Ownrshp* 1992
Sales 25.7MM^E^ *EMP* 170
SIC 7389 Telemarketing services; Telemarketing services
Pr: James H Hooker
Bd of Dir: Shawn Dyer
Chf Mktg O: Ray Kemper
*VP: Vince Barsolo
VP: April Brown
VP: Robert Clark
VP: Bryan Ehrenfreund
VP: Aaron Johnson
VP: Karen Schweitzer
VP: Ken Simonelic
VP: Cody Young
Dir Bus: Joan Barnes
Dir Bus: Molly Burns
Dir Bus: Justin Vogel

D-U-N-S 06-324-7514
LORAS COLLEGE
1450 Alta Vista St, Dubuque, IA 52001-4399
Tel (563) 588-7100 *Founded/Ownrshp* 1839
Sales 36.0MM *EMP* 400
Accts Baker Tilly Virchow Krause Ll
SIC 8221 College, except junior; College, except junior
Pr: James E Collins
Ex VP: John Burney
*VP: Omar Correa
*VP: Michael Doyle
*VP: David Eisinger
VP: Jacob Shireman
*VP: Arthur Sunleaf
Tech Mgr: Robert Schoofs

D-U-N-S 10-298-6981
LORBER INDUSTRIES OF CALIFORNIA
LORBER INDUSTRIES OF CLAIF
823 N Roxbury Dr, Beverly Hills, CA 90210-3017
Tel (310) 275-1568 *Founded/Ownrshp* 1969
Sales 28.0MM^E^ *EMP* 435
SIC 2261 2262 2253 2257 Screen printing of cotton broadwoven fabrics; Bleaching cotton broadwoven fabrics; Shrinking cotton cloth; Napping of cotton broadwoven fabrics; Screen printing: manmade fiber & silk broadwoven fabrics; Bleaching: manmade fiber & silk broadwoven fabrics; Shrinking: manmade fiber & silk cloth; Napping: manmade fiber & silk broadwoven fabrics; Knit outerwear mills; Weft knit fabric mills; Screen printing of cotton broadwoven fabrics; Bleaching cotton broadwoven fabrics; Shrinking cotton cloth; Napping of cotton broadwoven fabrics; Screen printing: manmade fiber & silk broadwoven fabrics; Bleaching: manmade fiber & silk broadwoven fabrics; Shrinking: manmade fiber & silk cloth; Napping: manmade fiber & silk broadwoven fabrics; Knit outerwear mills; Weft knit fabric mills
Pr: Tom Lorber
*CFO: John Robertson
*VP: Michael Gruener
*VP: Greg Lorber
*VP: Michael Painter

LORBER INDUSTRIES OF CLAIF
See LORBER INDUSTRIES OF CALIFORNIA

D-U-N-S 36-450-2922
LORCH INC
BURGER KING
655 Lakeshore Dr W, Hebron, OH 43025-9733
Tel (740) 929-2337 *Founded/Ownrshp* 1983
Sales 5.6MM^E^ *EMP* 300
SIC 5812 Fast-food restaurant, chain
Pr: Frank Lorch

LORCO PETROLEUM SERVICES
See LIONETTI ASSOCIATES LLC

D-U-N-S 07-945-3874
LORD & SON CONSTRUCTION INC
19 David St, Fort Walton Beach, FL 32547-2510
Tel (850) 863-5158 *Founded/Ownrshp* 1975
Sales 24.8MM^E^ *EMP* 50
SIC 1542 Commercial & office building, new construction
Pr: Leven D Lord
*VP: Anthony J Klumpp

D-U-N-S 62-340-2687 IMP
LORD & TAYLOR LLC
(*Suby of* HUDSON'S BAY COMPANY)
424 5th Ave, New York, NY 10018-2771
Tel (212) 391-3344 *Founded/Ownrshp* 2006
Sales 1.3MMM^E^ *EMP* 9,000
SIC 5621 5611 5632 5999 Women's clothing stores; Men's & boys' clothing stores; Women's accessory & specialty stores; Cosmetics; Women's clothing stores; Men's & boys' clothing stores; Women's accessory & specialty stores; Cosmetics
CEO: Russ Hardin
*CFO: Michael Culhane

CFO: Don Perinchies
**Treas:* Lucas Evans
**Chf Mktg O:* Amy Avitabile
Sr VP: Roger W Adams
Sr VP: Bruce Kelso
**VP:* John Manos
VP: Carol Rudo
Area Mgr: Lorraine Auerbach
Area Mgr: Therese Ayoub

D-U-N-S 01-212-2123
LORD ABBETT & CO LLC
90 Hudson St Fl 10, Jersey City, NJ 07302-3900
Tel (201) 827-2000 *Founded/Ownrshp* 1950
Sales 299.9MM^E *EMP* 509
SIC 6282 Investment advisory service; Investment advisory service
Pt: Daria L Foster
**Pt:* Stacy P Allen
**Pt:* Zane Brown
**Pt:* Daria L Foster
**Pt:* Paul Hilstad
**Pt:* WT Hudson
**Pt:* Robert G Morris
**Pt:* Robert Noelke
COO: Joan A Binstock
VP: Kenneth Cutler
VP: John Walsh
Exec: Apparao Avancha
Exec: Robert Coyne
Exec: Joseph Desimone
Exec: Joseph Leonti
Comm Dir: Chris Finn
Comm Man: Jason Farago

D-U-N-S 96-383-1581
LORD ABBETT & CO LLC
(*Suby of* LORD ABBETT & CO LLC) ★
90 Hudson St, Jersey City, NJ 07302-3900
Tel (888) 522-2388 *Founded/Ownrshp* 1993
Sales 21.3MM^E *EMP* 500
SIC 6211 6722 Security brokers & dealers; Management investment, open-end; Security brokers & dealers; Management investment, open-end
**Mng Pt:* Daria Foster

D-U-N-S 07-539-2233
LORD CHAMBERLAIN INC
(*Suby of* RYDERS HEALTH MANAGEMENT INC) ★
7003 Main St, Stratford, CT 06614-1397
Tel (203) 375-5894 *Founded/Ownrshp* 1968
Sales 20.3MM *EMP* 380
SIC 8051 Skilled nursing care facilities; Skilled nursing care facilities
CEO: Martin Sbriglio
**Pr:* Robert Sbriglio Sr
Ofcr: Robert Whipple
**VP:* Margaret Sbriglio
HC Dir: Gail Hudak

D-U-N-S 07-540-3626
LORD CHAMBERLAIN REALTY LIMITED LIABILITY CO
PARK GARDEN APARTMENTS
Ryders Lndg, Stratford, CT 06497
Tel (203) 381-1327 *Founded/Ownrshp* 1974
Sales 9.9MM^E *EMP* 300
SIC 6513 8069 Apartment building operators; Specialty hospitals, except psychiatric; Apartment building operators; Specialty hospitals, except psychiatric
Pt: Dr Robert Sbriglio
Pt: Margaret Sbriglio
Pt: Martin Sbriglio
Exec: Helen Dickerson
Dir IT: John Vournelis
HC Dir: Gail Devine
HC Dir: Gail Hudak

D-U-N-S 00-503-1281 IMP/EXP
LORD CORP (PA)
111 Lord Dr, Cary, NC 27511-7923
Tel (814) 868-3180 *Founded/Ownrshp* 1940, 1992
Sales NA *EMP* 3,256
SIC 2891 3724 3728 2851

D-U-N-S 09-009-5324
LORD ELECTRIC CO OF PUERTO RICO INC
8 Ave Simon Madera, San Juan, PR 00924-2231
Tel (787) 758-4040 *Founded/Ownrshp* 1959, 1989
Sales 55.0MM^E *EMP* 531
SIC 1731 1711 Electrical work; Mechanical contractor; Electrical work; Mechanical contractor
Pr: Cesar Roman
**Pr:* Manuel Rosabal

D-U-N-S 05-734-4079 IMP/EXP
LOREAL CARIBE INC
(*Suby of* LOREAL USA INC) ★
B7 Calle Pbonuco Ste 1700, Guaynabo, PR 00968
Tel (787) 625-5000 *Founded/Ownrshp* 1984
Sales 24.7MM^E *EMP* 70
SIC 5122 2844 Cosmetics, perfumes & hair products; Perfumes & colognes
Pr: Aljandro Eastman

D-U-N-S 00-213-6794 IMP/EXP
LOREAL USA INC
L'OREAL USA PRODUCTS
(*Suby of* L'OREAL)
575 5th Ave, New York, NY 10017-2446
Tel (212) 984-4000 *Founded/Ownrshp* 1953, 1994
Sales 6.1MMM^E *EMP* 18,860
SIC 5122 2844

L'OREAL USA PRODUCTS
See LOREAL USA INC

D-U-N-S 02-592-4770
LOREN BUICK & PONTIAC INC (IL)
PONTIAC IN GLENVIEW
1610 Waukegan Rd, Glenview, IL 60025-2108
Tel (847) 729-8900 *Founded/Ownrshp* 1947
Sales 114.9MM *EMP* 80
SIC 5511 5521 Automobiles, new & used; Used car dealers; Automobiles, new & used; Used car dealers
CEO: Irving Segeal
**Pr:* Paula Segal

D-U-N-S 06-020-9947
LOREN COMMUNICATIONS INTERNATIONAL LIMITED
48 Wall St Ste 1100, New York, NY 10005-2903
Tel (212) 752-4900 *Founded/Ownrshp* 1975
Sales 14.5MM^E *EMP* 500
SIC 8731 Medical research, commercial; Medical research, commercial
Ch Bd: Pamela Loren
**Pr:* Madeline Winters
**Treas:* Adriana Pell

D-U-N-S 00-445-6729 IMP
LOREN COOK CO (OH)
2015 E Dale St, Springfield, MO 65803-4637
Tel (417) 869-6474 *Founded/Ownrshp* 1941
Sales 161.1MM^E *EMP* 700
SIC 3564 Exhaust fans: industrial or commercial; Ventilating fans: industrial or commercial; Blowing fans: industrial or commercial; Exhaust fans: industrial or commercial; Ventilating fans: industrial or commercial; Blowing fans: industrial or commercial
Ch Bd: Gerald A Cook
Pr: Steve Burney
Pr: Bob Valbracht
Treas: Gerald A Cook Jr
VP: Mannie Brahman
VP: Victor Colwell
VP: Loren Cook II
Sales Exec: Ron Michael

D-U-N-S 00-415-9336
LOREN HYUNDAI INC
1620 Waukegan Rd, Glenview, IL 60025-2108
Tel (224) 766-7185 *Founded/Ownrshp* 1987
Sales 24.0MM^E *EMP* 80^E
SIC 5511 Automobiles, new & used; Automobiles, new & used
Pr: Paula Segal
**Pr:* William F Napleton
**VP:* Irving Segal
IT Man: Marcia Rast

D-U-N-S 00-961-8448
LORENTZ BRUUN CO INC
LORENTZ BRUUN CONSTRUCTION
3611 Se 20th Ave Ste 300, Portland, OR 97202-2967
Tel (503) 232-7106 *Founded/Ownrshp* 1946
Sales 23.4MM^E *EMP* 50
SIC 1541 1542 Industrial buildings, new construction; Commercial & office building, new construction
Pr: Mark C Bruun
VP: Kurt Bruun
Div Mgr: Jeff Blize
Opers Mgr: Scott McDilda

LORENTZ BRUUN CONSTRUCTION
See LORENTZ BRUUN CO INC

D-U-N-S 96-800-2824 IMP
LORENZ INC
KAREL MANUFACTURING
280 Campillo St Ste G, Calexico, CA 92231-3200
Tel (760) 356-1019 *Founded/Ownrshp* 1993
Sales 110.8MM^E *EMP* 400
SIC 3699 Electrical equipment & supplies; Electrical equipment & supplies
Pr: Zaven Arakelian
IT Man: Isabel Garcia
IT Man: Sergio Vargas
Mtls Mgr: Victgr Delgado
Opers Mgr: Fernando Preza

D-U-N-S 01-243-1458
LORENZ SCHNEIDER CO INC (NY)
2000 Plaza Ave Ste 4, New Hyde Park, NY 11040-4903
Tel (516) 328-1400 *Founded/Ownrshp* 1915, 1936
Sales 25.8MM^E *EMP* 100
SIC 5145 Potato chips; Pretzels; Potato chips; Pretzels
Pr: Anthony Gerbino
**CEO:* Bruce D Brown
Area Mgr: Mirla Fee

LORENZO USA
See SIMON GOLUB & SONS INC

D-U-N-S 16-060-4802
LORETTO HEALTH AND REHABILITATION CENTER
700 E Brighton Ave, Syracuse, NY 13205-2201
Tel (315) 469-1991 *Founded/Ownrshp* 2003
Sales 57.6MM *EMP* 2,000
Accts Fust Charles Chambers Llp Syr
SIC 8322 Rehabilitation services; Rehabilitation services
Ch Bd: J Andrew Breuer
**Sec:* John A Cirando
IT Man: Angela Newcomb

D-U-N-S 02-520-9461
LORETTO HOSPITAL (IL)
645 S Central Ave, Chicago, IL 60644-5016
Tel (773) 854-5567 *Founded/Ownrshp* 1939
Sales 65.0MM *EMP* 550
SIC 8063 8062 8069 Psychiatric hospitals; Hospital, affiliated with AMA residency; Drug addiction rehabilitation hospital; Psychiatric hospitals; Hospital, affiliated with AMA residency; Drug addiction rehabilitation hospital
CEO: Dr Sonia Mehta
Ch Bd: Edward M Hogan
CFO: Kenneth McGhee
VP: Tina Chambers
Dir Case M: Deanna Read
Dir Lab: Don Lindaman
Dir Lab: Donald Lindeman
Dir Lab: Don Wendaman
Dir Rad: Mary Rinder
Chf Nrs Of: Kathy Donahue
CIO: Suresh Kirshnan

D-U-N-S 60-974-9309
LORETTO INDEPENDENT LIVING SERVICES INC
100 Malta Ln, North Syracuse, NY 13212-2375
Tel (315) 469-5570 *Founded/Ownrshp* 2005
Sales 38.4MM *EMP* 2
Accts Fust Charles Chambers Llp Syr
SIC 8322 Old age assistance; Old age assistance
CFO: Kathe Callon
**Pr:* Michael J Solovon
Treas: Chirstine Reilly
**VP:* Penny Adulevcia

D-U-N-S 07-230-9966
LORIG CONSTRUCTION CO
250 E Touhy Ave, Des Plaines, IL 60018-2658
Tel (847) 298-0360 *Founded/Ownrshp* 1986
Sales 99.4MM^E *EMP* 300
SIC 1622 Bridge construction; Viaduct construction; Highway construction, elevated; Bridge construction; Viaduct construction; Highway construction, elevated
Ch: Max Lorig
**Pr:* David H Lorig
Snr PM: Kevin May

D-U-N-S 61-737-9169 EXP
LORILLARD TOBACCO CO LLC
714 Green Valley Rd, Greensboro, NC 27408-7018
Tel (336) 335-6600 *Founded/Ownrshp* 1989
Sales NA *EMP* 2,700
SIC 2111 Cigarettes

D-U-N-S 00-603-1785 IMP
LORIN INDUSTRIES INC
COIL ANODIZING
1960 Roberts St, Muskegon, MI 49442-6087
Tel (231) 722-1631 *Founded/Ownrshp* 1943
Sales 34.0MM^E *EMP* 90^E
SIC 3471 Anodizing (plating) of metals or formed products
Ch Bd: Robert L Kersman
**CEO:* Park Kersman
**Sec:* L Philip Kelly
VP: John Montague
VP: Randy Straka
QA Dir: Barb Laus
Sfty Dirs: Tom Achterhoff
Opers Mgr: Jason Locke
Opers Mgr: Tom Tian
Mktg Mgr: Edward Doza

D-U-N-S 07-370-6277
LORIS COMMUNITY HOSPITAL DISTRICT
LORIS COMMUNITY HOSPITAL DST
3655 Mitchell St, Loris, SC 29569-2827
Tel (843) 716-7000 *Founded/Ownrshp* 1950
Sales 55.1MM^E *EMP* 650
Accts Larson Allen Llp Cpas
SIC 8062 8051 8741 General medical & surgical hospitals; Skilled nursing care facilities; Management services; General medical & surgical hospitals; Skilled nursing care facilities; Management services
CEO: Edward Tinsley
Chf Rad: Scott Lackey
**COO:* Arnold Green
**CFO:* Fred O Todd
Dir Lab: Karen Gore
Mktg Dir: Celeste Bondurant-Bell

LORIS COMMUNITY HOSPITAL DST
See LORIS COMMUNITY HOSPITAL DISTRICT

D-U-N-S 03-971-3409
LORIS GIFTS INC
LORI'S HOSPITAL GIFT SHOPS
2125 Chenault Dr Ste 100, Carrollton, TX 75006-4936
Tel (972) 759-5000 *Founded/Ownrshp* 1997
Sales 180.4MM^E *EMP* 1,400
SIC 5947

LORI'S HOSPITAL GIFT SHOPS
See LORIS GIFTS INC

D-U-N-S 92-807-9354
LORIS MCLEOD SEACOAST HOSPITAL
3655 Mitchell St, Loris, SC 29569-2827
Tel (843) 716-7000 *Founded/Ownrshp* 2012
Sales 99.0MM *EMP* 52^E
SIC 8062 General medical & surgical hospitals; General medical & surgical hospitals
Sr VP: Arnold Green
Dir Lab: Karen Williams
Mktg Dir: Christy Allsbrook

LOROM WEST
See CABLE CONNECTION INC

D-U-N-S 96-402-5415
LORRAINE ENTERPRISES LC
IHOP
4801 Wentworth Ct, Fort Worth, TX 76132-2029
Tel (817) 292-4467 *Founded/Ownrshp* 1994
Sales 10.0MM *EMP* 350
SIC 5812 Restaurant, family: chain; Restaurant, family: chain
Pr: Anthony Paduano
**VP:* F W Burnett
**VP:* John Stuart

LORTS MANUFACTURING
See A F LORTS CO INC

D-U-N-S 00-783-0631
LORTSCHER AGRI SERVICE INC (KS)
310 Railroad St, Bern, KS 66408-8069
Tel (785) 336-6171 *Founded/Ownrshp* 1948, 1975
Sales 25.7MM^E *EMP* 50
SIC 5153 5191 2048

D-U-N-S 03-059-9302
■ **LOS ALAMITOS MEDICAL CENTER INC**
(*Suby of* TENET HEALTHCARE CORPORATION)
3751 Katella Ave, Los Alamitos, CA 90720-3113
Tel (714) 826-6400 *Founded/Ownrshp* 1970
Sales 25.4M *EMP* 1,105
Accts Stan Diliberto Cpa Cfp Inc Se
SIC 8062 General medical & surgical hospitals
CEO: Michele Finney
Chf Path: Azar Daneshbod
**Pr:* Alice Livingood
**Pr:* Margaret Watkins
Dir Rad: Sherrie Fernandez
Dir Rx: Karen Milligan
QA Dir: Maureen Kochen
Mtls Mgr: Wendy Roberts
Doctor: Juan Rodriguez
Phys Thrpy: Theresa Arnold

LOS ALAMITOS RACE TRACK
See QUARTER HORSE RACING INC

D-U-N-S 10-312-3121
LOS ALAMITOS UNIFIED SCHOOL DISTRICT
10293 Bloomfield St, Los Alamitos, CA 90720-2264
Tel (562) 799-4700 *Founded/Ownrshp* 1980
Sales 49.3MM^E *EMP* 900^E
SIC 8211 Public elementary & secondary schools; Public elementary & secondary schools
CEO: Megan Cutuli
VP: Bianka Kelley

D-U-N-S 07-929-5470
LOS ALAMOS MEDICAL CENTER
3917 West Rd Ste 105, Los Alamos, NM 87544-5305
Tel (505) 662-4201 *Founded/Ownrshp* 2013
Sales 39.2MM^E *EMP* 300
SIC 8062 General medical & surgical hospitals; General medical & surgical hospitals
CEO: Feliciano Jiron
Obsttrcn: Benjamin Neal
Doctor: Greg King
Doctor: Cynthia Rossi

D-U-N-S 04-299-2875
LOS ALAMOS NATIONAL BANK
LANB
(*Suby of* TRINITY CAPITAL CORP) ★
1200 Trinity Dr, Los Alamos, NM 87544-3286
Tel (505) 662-5171 *Founded/Ownrshp* 1963, 1975
Sales NA *EMP* 315
SIC 6021 National commercial banks; National commercial banks
Pr: Steve Wells
COO: Tim Doyle
CFO: Daniel Bartholomew
Ofcr: Karen Easton
Sr VP: Mark French
Sr VP: Fidel Gutierrez
VP: Liz Cavasos
Dir IT: Tim Ickes

D-U-N-S 09-383-8014
LOS ALAMOS NATIONAL LABORATORY FOUNDATION
LANL FOUNDATION
1112 Plaza Del Norte, Espanola, NM 87532-3216
Tel (505) 753-8890 *Founded/Ownrshp* 1997
Sales 4.7MM *EMP* 10,751
Accts Cliftonlarsonallen Llp Albuqu
SIC 8699 Charitable organization; Charitable organization
CEO: Jenny Parks
**CFO:* Mihaela Popa Simil
**Treas:* Wayne Kennedy
Bd of Dir: Jeffrey Howlel
**VP:* Rich Marquez
**VP:* Libbie Martinez
Exec: Rhonda Overbay
Prgrm Mgr: Mark Shepard
QA Dir: Walter Elliott
Netwrk Eng: Kyle Lamb
Snr Mgr: Keith Lindsay

D-U-N-S 17-525-2894
LOS ALAMOS NATIONAL SECURITY LLC
105 Central Park Sq, Los Alamos, NM 87544-4019
Tel (877) 723-4101 *Founded/Ownrshp* 2006
Sales 601.7MM^E *EMP* 11,000^E
SIC 8748 Business consulting; Business consulting
Admn Mgr: Mike Barr

D-U-N-S 07-338-7409
LOS ALAMOS PUBLIC SCHOOLS
2075 Trinity Dr Ste 100, Los Alamos, NM 87544-3093
Tel (505) 663-2222 *Founded/Ownrshp* 1947
Sales 144.5M *EMP* 635
Accts Griego Professional Services
SIC 8211 Public combined elementary & secondary school; Public combined elementary & secondary school
Bd of Dir: Jody Benson
Bd of Dir: David Foster
Bd of Dir: Nancyann Holmes
Bd of Dir: Matt Williams
Dir IT: Dean Obermeyer
Sys Mgr: Ellen Lewis
Schl Brd P: Steve Girrens
Psych: Jennifer Neil
Psych: Kimberly Wheeler
Psych: Georgina Williams

D-U-N-S 08-941-6002
LOS ALAMOS TECHNICAL ASSOCIATES INC
LATA
999 Central Ave Ste 300, Los Alamos, NM 87544-3328
Tel (505) 662-9080 *Founded/Ownrshp* 1975
Sales 72.7MM^E *EMP* 237
SIC 8711 4959 Industrial engineers; Industrial engineers; Environmental cleanup services
Ofcr: L Phillip Reinig
**Pr:* William Vantine
**Ofcr:* William Enloe
**Ofcr:* Robert Kingsbury
**Ofcr:* Robert Wilson
**Ofcr:* Raymond Ziler
VP: Rob Gamble
VP: Mark Harenberg
**VP:* Rees Lattimer
VP: Rob Pfendler
**VP:* Robert Pfendler
**VP:* Dina Quintana
**VP:* Orge Rasmussen
**VP:* Mae Wright
Comm Man: Ben Privitt

D-U-N-S 60-406-1895
LOS ALTOS FOOD PRODUCTS INC
450 Baldwin Park Blvd, City of Industry, CA 91746-1407
Tel (626) 330-6555 *Founded/Ownrshp* 1988
Sales 139.9MM^E *EMP* 105
Accts Sotomayor & Associates Llp P

SIC 5143 Cheese; Cheese
Pr: Raul Andrade
VP: Alin Andrade
**VP:* Gloria Andrade

D-U-N-S 01-094-2142
LOS ALTOS SCHOOL DISTRICT
201 Covington Rd, Los Altos, CA 94024-4096
Tel (650) 947-1100 *Founded/Ownrshp* 1909
Sales 52.2MM *EMP* 350
SIC 8211 9111 Public elementary & secondary schools; Mayors' offices; Public elementary & secondary schools; Mayors' offices
**Prin:* Jeff Baier
**Prin:* Randall Kenyon
MIS Dir: Jackie Sigua
Teacher Pr: Marlene Revelo
Psych: Judy Rothenberg

D-U-N-S 82-930-5460
LOS ANGELES AIRPORT PEACE OFFICERS ASSOCIATION
LAAPOA
6080 Center Dr Fl 6, Los Angeles, CA 90045-9205
Tel (310) 242-5218 *Founded/Ownrshp* 1983
Sales 823.8M *EMP* 425
SIC 8641 Civic social & fraternal associations; Civic social & fraternal associations
Pr: Marshall E McClain
**Treas:* Rodney Rouzan
**VP:* Julius Levy

LOS ANGELES ANGELS OF ANAHEIM
See ANGELS BASEBALL LP

D-U-N-S 83-956-4051
LOS ANGELES BIO MEDICAL RESEARCH INSTITUTE
1124 W Carson St Rm 512, Torrance, CA 90502-2006
Tel (310) 222-3604 *Founded/Ownrshp* 1996
Sales 75.0MM *EMP* 50
Accts Yh Advisors Inc Huntington Be
SIC 8732 Research services, except laboratory; Research services, except laboratory
Prin: Eli Ipp

D-U-N-S 06-992-6962
LOS ANGELES BIOMEDICAL RESEARCH INSTITUTE AT HARBOR-UCLA MEDICAL CENTER
LA BIOMED
1124 W Carson St, Torrance, CA 90502-2006
Tel (877) 452-2674 *Founded/Ownrshp* 1952
Sales 73.3MM *EMP* 800
SIC 8733

D-U-N-S 04-745-1117
LOS ANGELES BOARD MILLS INC
LOS ANGELES PPR BOX & BD MILLS
6027 S Eastern Ave, Commerce, CA 90040-3413
Tel (323) 685-8900 *Founded/Ownrshp* 1901
Sales 32.5MM^E *EMP* 150
SIC 2631 2652 2653 5113 2657 Folding boxboard; Packaging board; Setup boxboard; Setup paperboard boxes; Boxes, corrugated: made from purchased materials; Industrial & personal service paper; Folding paperboard boxes; Folding boxboard; Packaging board; Setup boxboard; Setup paperboard boxes; Boxes, corrugated: made from purchased materials; Industrial & personal service paper; Folding paperboard boxes
Pr: William H Kewell III
**Sec:* Carol A Kewell
CIO: Kacey Broqust
Sls Mgr: Robert Apeloni

D-U-N-S 12-693-9607
LOS ANGELES CAPITAL MANAGEMENT AND EQUITY RESEARCH INC
LA CAPITAL
11150 Santa Monica Blvd, Los Angeles, CA 90025-3380
Tel (310) 479-9998 *Founded/Ownrshp* 2002
Sales 57.7MM *EMP* 46^E
Accts Grant Thornton Llp Los Angele
SIC 6726 Investment offices; Investment offices
Pr: Thomas D Stevens
CFO: Jennifer Reynolds
**Treas:* Hal Reynolds
Chf Invest: Reynolds Hal
**VP:* David Borger
Mng Dir: Linda Barker
Mng Dir: Lara Clarke
Mng Dir: Lara Lundstrom
Mng Dir: Chuck Morris
Off Mgr: Charlotte Perry
Dir IT: Steve Oetomo

D-U-N-S 04-093-0096
LOS ANGELES CITY COLLEGE
(*Suby of* LOS ANGELES COMMUNITY COLLEGE DISTRICT) ★
855 N Vermont Ave, Los Angeles, CA 90029-3588
Tel (323) 953-4000 *Founded/Ownrshp* 2005
Sales 166.9MM^E *EMP* 1^E
SIC 8222 Junior college
VP: Art Taylor
Ex VP: Heidi Johnson
Dir IT: Beau Blaser
Dir IT: Bo Ser
Opers Mgr: Ronda Guess
Pgrm Dir: Juan Alvarez

LOS ANGELES CNTY TAX COLLECTR
See COUNTY OF LOS ANGELES

LOS ANGELES COLD STORAGE CO
See STANDARD-SOUTHERN CORP

D-U-N-S 07-226-6174
LOS ANGELES COMMUNITY COLLEGE DISTRICT
770 Wilshire Blvd, Los Angeles, CA 90017-3719
Tel (213) 891-2000 *Founded/Ownrshp* 1929
Sales 347.8MM^E *EMP* 8,500
Accts Kpmg Llp Irvine Ca
SIC 8222 Community college; Community college
**Pr:* Scott J Svonkin
Trst: Rodney Robinson
Ofcr: Shawn Gordon
Ofcr: Lynn Gross
Ex VP: Adriana Barrera
VP: Carol Justiniano
VP: Tina Park
VP: Nancy Pearlman
**VP:* Steve Veres
Off Admin: Wanda Lewis
CTO: Kenneth Takeda

D-U-N-S 16-192-8122
LOS ANGELES CONSERVATION CORPS INC
605 W Olympic Blvd # 450, Los Angeles, CA 90015-1400
Tel (213) 362-9000 *Founded/Ownrshp* 1985
Sales 20.4MM *EMP* 115^E
Accts Singerlewak Llp Los Angeles
SIC 7363 Temporary help service; Temporary help service
Pr: Mercedes Morton
**CEO:* Wendy Butts
**Treas:* Albert Chavez
Prgrm Mgr: Deborah Fryman

D-U-N-S 13-940-4529
LOS ANGELES CONVENTION AND EXHIBITION CENTER AUTHORITY (INC)
CONVENTION CENTER LOS ANGELES
1201 S Figueroa St, Los Angeles, CA 90015-1308
Tel (213) 741-1151 *Founded/Ownrshp* 1999
Sales 21.5MM *EMP* 288
SIC 6512 Commercial & industrial building operation; Property operation, auditoriums & theaters
Genl Mgr: Brad Gessner
Pr: Annie Bebber
CFO: John Hyde
Bd of Dir: Estella Flores
VP: Kathleen Clariett
VP: Carisa Malanum
Dir Soc: Dan Federoff
Dir Soc: Lacc Gossman
Dir Soc: Adrienne Hall
Dir Soc: Frank Keefer
Dir Soc: Stefanie Tomlin
Dir Soc: Deanna Valencia
Comm Dir: Tom Drew

D-U-N-S 11-312-1024
LOS ANGELES COUNTY DEVELOPMENTAL SERVICES FOUNDATION
FRANK D LANTERMAN REGIONAL CEN
3303 Wilshire Blvd # 700, Los Angeles, CA 90010-1704
Tel (213) 383-1300 *Founded/Ownrshp* 1979
Sales 135.4MM *EMP* 180
SIC 8099 8322 8093 Medical services organization; Individual & family services; Mental health clinic, outpatient; Medical services organization; Individual & family services; Mental health clinic, outpatient
Ex Dir: Dianne Anand
Bd of Dir: Frank Lanterman
VP: Marjorie Heller
Brnch Mgr: John Walker
Opers Mgr: Martha Aguirre
Opers Mgr: Claudia Ayala
Pr Dir: Karen Ingram

D-U-N-S 08-302-0297
LOS ANGELES COUNTY EMPLOYEES RETIREMENT ASSOCIATION
LACERA
300 N Lake Ave Ste 720, Pasadena, CA 91101-5674
Tel (626) 564-6000 *Founded/Ownrshp* 1938
Sales NA *EMP* 340
Accts Brown Armstrong Accountancy Co
SIC 6371 Pension funds; Pension funds
CEO: Gregg Rademather
V Ch: John Barger
Pr: Fred Whiting
Bd of Dir: Bonnie Nolley
Bd of Dir: Richard Wirth
Ofcr: Ted Granger
Sr Inv Off: James Rice
VP: Margaret Shuler
Exec: Renee Henry
Dir Risk M: Cynthia Guider
Prin: Lisa Mazzocco

D-U-N-S 07-192-1746
LOS ANGELES COUNTY FAIR ASSOCIATION
FAIRPLEX RV PARK
1101 W Mckinley Ave, Pomona, CA 91768-1639
Tel (909) 623-3111 *Founded/Ownrshp* 1922
Sales 28.2MM^E *EMP* 300
Accts Vavrinektrineday & Co Llp Ran
SIC 7999 8412 Fair; Museums & art galleries; Fair; Museums & art galleries
CEO: James Henwood
Bd of Dir: Thelma M De Santa
**VP:* Micheal Seder
Dir Soc: Tim Long
Mktg Dir: Michael Chee

D-U-N-S 16-930-8129
LOS ANGELES COUNTY FIRE FIGHTERS LOCAL 1014 INC
3460 Fletcher Ave, El Monte, CA 91731-3002
Tel (310) 639-1014 *Founded/Ownrshp* 1949
Sales 65.5MM *EMP* 27
SIC 8631 Labor unions & similar labor organizations; Labor unions & similar labor organizations
Pr: David Gillotte
Admn Mgr: Al Cain

D-U-N-S 96-528-6185
LOS ANGELES COUNTY FIREMENS RELIEF ASSOCIATION
815 Colorado Blvd Fl 4, Los Angeles, CA 90041-1745
Tel (714) 996-4046 *Founded/Ownrshp* 2010
Sales 79.7MM *EMP* 26
Accts Harrington Group Cpas Llp Pas
SIC 8211 Public elementary & secondary schools
Pr: John Jacobsen

LOS ANGELES COUNTY HOSPITAL
See LAC USC MEDICAL CENTER

D-U-N-S 04-405-5523
LOS ANGELES COUNTY METROPOLITAN TRANSPORTATION AUTHORITY
1 Gateway Plz Fl 25, Los Angeles, CA 90012-3745
Tel (323) 466-3876 *Founded/Ownrshp* 1964
Sales 699.1MM^E *EMP* 9,800
SIC 4111 Bus line operations; Subway operation; Bus line operations; Subway operation
CEO: Arthur Leahy
**CEO:* Rick Thorpe
**COO:* Carolyn Flowers
COO: Robert Holland
COO: Lonnie Mitchell
**CFO:* Nalini Ahuja
Bd of Dir: Steven Carnevale
Ofcr: Violeta Aguilos
Ofcr: Patricia Torres Bruno
Ofcr: Martha Welborne
Ofcr: Zipporah Yamamoto
Ex VP: Cynthia Gibson
Exec: Brian Mahaffey
Board of Directors: Yvonne B Burke, Doug Failing, John Fasana, David Fleming, Richard Katz, Bonnie Lowenthal, Pam O'conner, Bernard Parks, Zev Yaroslavsky

D-U-N-S 07-968-6976
LOS ANGELES COUNTY MUSEUM OF NATURAL HISTORY FOUNDATION
900 Exposition Blvd, Los Angeles, CA 90007-4057
Tel (213) 763-3437 *Founded/Ownrshp* 1965
Sales 43.9MM *EMP* 37^E
SIC 8412 Museum
CEO: Jane G Pisano

D-U-N-S 60-288-0189
LOS ANGELES COUNTY OFFICE OF EDUCATION
LACOE
9300 Imperial Hwy, Downey, CA 90242-2813
Tel (562) 922-6111 *Founded/Ownrshp* 1852
Sales 747.3MM *EMP* 4,000
Accts Vavrinek Trine Day & Co Ll
SIC 8211 Specialty education; Specialty education
CEO: Rudell S Freer
**Pr:* Rebecca J Turrentine
CFO: Scott Price
Bd of Dir: Douglas Boyd
Bd of Dir: Myra Demeter
Bd of Dir: Alex Johnson
Bd of Dir: Maria Yepes
Ofcr: Chris Burdy
Ofcr: Jeff Young
**VP:* Katie Braude
Exec: Margo Minecki
Dir Bus: Debbie Simons

D-U-N-S 10-387-2516
LOS ANGELES DEPARTMENT OF WATER AND POWER
LADWP
111 N Hope St, Los Angeles, CA 90012-2607
Tel (213) 367-4211 *Founded/Ownrshp* 1902
Sales 3.1MMM *EMP* 9,000^E
Accts Kpmg Llp Los Angeles Ca
SIC 4941 4911 Water supply; Electric services; Water supply; Electric services
Pr: Thomas Sayles
**CFO:* Philip Leiver
Bd of Dir: John Burmahln
Ofcr: Armando Parra
Ofcr: David H Wiggs Jr
Ofcr: Gary Wong
Sr Inv Off: Jeremy Wolfson
Genl Mgr: Marcie Edwards
Genl Mgr: Cindy Montanez
CIO: Matt Lampe
Cmptr Lab: Can Nguyen

D-U-N-S 18-578-4014
LOS ANGELES ENGINEERING INC
633 N Barranca Ave, Covina, CA 91723-1229
Tel (626) 869-1400 *Founded/Ownrshp* 1987
Sales 24.3MM^E *EMP* 110
Accts Schlotzhauer & West Cpas Yor
SIC 1795 1629 1611 8711 1623 Demolition, buildings & other structures; Earthmoving contractor; Concrete construction: roads, highways, sidewalks, etc.; Engineering services; Water, sewer & utility lines; Demolition, buildings & other structures; Earthmoving contractor; Concrete construction: roads, highways, sidewalks, etc.; Engineering services; Water, sewer & utility lines
Pr: Henry Angus O'Brien
Pr: Jeff Geist
VP: Kim Zuccaro

D-U-N-S 07-334-9818
LOS ANGELES FILM SCHOOLS LLC
6363 W Sunset Blvd Fl 5, Los Angeles, CA 90028-7317
Tel (323) 860-0789 *Founded/Ownrshp* 1999
Sales 24.8MM^E *EMP* 350
SIC 8299 Music & drama schools; Music & drama schools
CEO: Diana Derycz Kessler
**VP:* Kenna Langer
**Ex Dir:* Amber Chaib
Opers Mgr: Paul Balbirnie

D-U-N-S 16-514-3348
LOS ANGELES FIREMAN RELIEF ASSOCIATION INC
WIDOWS, ORPHANS AND DIS
2900 W Temple St, Los Angeles, CA 90026-4516
Tel (800) 244-3439 *Founded/Ownrshp* 1906
Sales 79.7MM *EMP* 41
Accts Harrington Group Cpas Llp S
SIC 8322 Emergency social services
Pr: Barry G Hedberg
**VP:* John Kitchens

D-U-N-S 07-018-9998
LOS ANGELES FREE CLINIC
SABAN COMMUNITY CLINIC
8405 Beverly Blvd, Los Angeles, CA 90048-3401
Tel (323) 653-8622 *Founded/Ownrshp* 1967
Sales 17.8MM *EMP* 300
Accts Rbz Llp Los Angeles Ca
SIC 8742 Management consulting services; Management consulting services
CEO: Jeffrey Bujer
CFO: Muriel Nouwezem
Treas: Eric Jung
Ofcr: Johni Robinson
Dir Soc: Chuck Sawyer
Dir IT: Phillip Velasco
IT Man: Martin Perez
Surg Cl Rc: Rahim Kanji

D-U-N-S 08-377-1246
LOS ANGELES HOTEL-RESTAURANT EMPLOYER-UNION WELFARE FUND
130 S Alvarado St Fl 2, Los Angeles, CA 90057-2202
Tel (213) 484-8480 *Founded/Ownrshp* 1952
Sales NA *EMP* 30
SIC 6371 Union funds; Union funds
Prin: Irving K Baldwin
Prin: Miguel Contreras

D-U-N-S 07-724-3368
LOS ANGELES JEWISH HOME FOR AGING
GRANCELL VILLAGE
7150 Tampa Ave, Reseda, CA 91335-3700
Tel (818) 774-3000 *Founded/Ownrshp* 1915
Sales 22.7MM *EMP* 760
Accts Moss Adams Llp Stockton Ca
SIC 8051 8361 Skilled nursing care facilities; Residential care; Skilled nursing care facilities; Residential care
Ch Bd: Arthur A Greenberg
**CEO:* Molly Forrest
**COO:* John Graham
COO: Larissa Stepanians
**Ch:* Jeffrey Glassman
Ofcr: Laurie Manners
Sr VP: Ira Schreck
**VP:* Sherri B Cunningham
**VP:* Shelly J Ryan
VP: Corey Slavin
Ex Dir: Haya Berci

D-U-N-S 07-723-5034
LOS ANGELES LGBT CENTER
L.A. GAY & LESBIAN CENTER
1625 Schrader Blvd, Los Angeles, CA 90028-6213
Tel (323) 993-7618 *Founded/Ownrshp* 1972
Sales 66.2MM *EMP* 240
Accts Bdo Usa Llp Los Angeles Ca
SIC 8399 Community development groups; Community development groups
CEO: Lorri L Jean
CFO: Randy Hogan
**CFO:* Michael Holtzman
CFO: Mike Holtzman
Ofcr: Darrel Cummings
Dir Soc: Lorri Jean
Prgrm Mgr: Anthony Gutierrez
Off Mgr: George Hernandez
MIS Dir: Kevin Powers
MIS Dir: Valerie Wagner
IT Man: Hilary Hanft

LOS ANGELES MARRIOTT DOWNTOWN
See LA HOTEL VENTURE LLC

D-U-N-S 04-608-0243
LOS ANGELES MEMORIAL COLISEUM ASSOCIATION
3911 S Figueroa St, Los Angeles, CA 90037-1207
Tel (213) 765-6357 *Founded/Ownrshp* 1996
Sales 3.5MM *EMP* 500
SIC 5812 Concessionaire; Caterers; Concessionaire; Caterers
**Ch Bd:* Don Knabe
**Treas:* Greg Hellmold

D-U-N-S 07-293-3336
LOS ANGELES MEMORIAL COLISEUM COMMISSION
LA SPORTS ARENA
3911 S Figueroa St, Los Angeles, CA 90037-1207
Tel (213) 747-7111 *Founded/Ownrshp* 1923
Sales NA *EMP* 500
Accts Mcgladrey Llp Los Angeles Ca
SIC 9199 ;
Pr: Don Knabe
**CFO:* Gregory Hellmold
Dir IT: Leo Caudillo

D-U-N-S 11-281-8604 IMP
LOS ANGELES OPERA CO
135 N Grand Ave Ste 327, Los Angeles, CA 90012-3018
Tel (213) 972-7219 *Founded/Ownrshp* 1966
Sales 52.8MM *EMP* 500
SIC 7922

D-U-N-S 05-922-2430
LOS ANGELES PHILHARMONIC ASSOCIATION
L A PHILHARMONIC
151 S Grand Ave, Los Angeles, CA 90012-3034
Tel (213) 972-7300 *Founded/Ownrshp* 1934
Sales 124.8MM *EMP* 2,000
Accts Singerlewak Llp Los Angeles
SIC 7929 Entertainers & entertainment groups; Entertainers & entertainment groups
CEO: Deborah Borda
**Ch:* David C Bohnett
Bd of Dir: Doris Christy
Bd of Dir: Rafael G Mendez
Bd of Dir: Mona Patel
Ofcr: Sheri Broedlow
VP: Emily Laskin
Dir: Emily Tung
Art Dir: Gretchen Citrin
Snr Mgr: Malorie Barbee

D-U-N-S 96-988-8671
LOS ANGELES POLICE COMMAND OFFICERS ASSOCIATION
100 W 1st St, Los Angeles, CA 90012-4112
Tel (877) 275-5273 *Founded/Ownrshp* 2011
Sales 258.0M *EMP* 405^E
Accts Robert Moore Accountancy Corpo

SIC 8699 Membership organizations
Prin: Deborah A Gonzales

D-U-N-S 08-007-3703
LOS ANGELES POLICE CREDIT UNION
L A P F C U
16150 Sherman Way, Van Nuys, CA 91406-3938
Tel (818) 787-6520 *Founded/Ownrshp* 1936
Sales NA *EMP* 111
SIC 6062 6061 State credit unions; Federal credit unions; State credit unions; Federal credit unions
Ch Bd: Tyler E Izen
**Pr:* G Michael Padgett
CFO: Michael Padgett
**Treas:* Warren D Spayth
Ofcr: Ibrahim Abusway
VP: Norma Feder-Dong
VP: Ron Guzman
VP: Evany Perkins
VP: Luann Smith
IT Man: Norma Dong
IT Man: Sal Miranda

D-U-N-S 12-215-0431
LOS ANGELES POLICE RELIEF ASSOCIATION INC
600 N Grand Ave, Los Angeles, CA 90012-2212
Tel (213) 674-3701 *Founded/Ownrshp* 1939
Sales 203.6MM *EMP* 23E
Accts Romberger Wilson & Beeson Inc
SIC 8641 Fraternal associations; Fraternal associations

LOS ANGELES PPR BOX & BD MILLS
See LOS ANGELES BOARD MILLS INC

D-U-N-S 10-387-7569
LOS ANGELES REGIONAL FOOD BANK
1734 E 41st St, Vernon, CA 90058-1502
Tel (323) 234-3030 *Founded/Ownrshp* 1977
Sales 78.3MM *EMP* 120
Accts Singerlewak Llp Los Angeles
SIC 8322 Meal delivery program; Meal delivery program
Pr: Michael Flood
Dir Vol: Eli Beltran
Dir Vol: May Duong
Pr: Cece Forrester
**CFO:* Czarina Luna
Treas: Christina Carroll
VP: Marisela Licea
Comm Dir: Jennifer Errico
Manager: Wesley Mayorga
Pr Mgr: Marie Carpenter

D-U-N-S 00-838-2004 IMP
LOS ANGELES RUBBER CO
MECHANICAL DRIVES AND BELTING
2915 E Washington Blvd, Los Angeles, CA 90023-4218
Tel (323) 263-4131 *Founded/Ownrshp* 1898
Sales 33.2MME *EMP* 55E
SIC 5063 Power transmission equipment, electric
CEO: Carol A Durst
**VP:* David Durst
**VP:* Wayne Roberts
Brnch Mgr: Tom Shelton
Sls Mgr: Salvador Guardado
Sales Asso: Paula Gonzales
Sales Asso: Kevin Malone
Sales Asso: Fenton Menzies
Sales Asso: Dee Spickler
Sales Asso: James Staffa

D-U-N-S 00-838-2400 IMP
■ **LOS ANGELES TIMES COMMUNICATIONS LLC**
(*Suby of* TRIBUNE MEDIA CO) ★
202 W 1st St Ste 500, Los Angeles, CA 90012-4401
Tel (213) 237-3700 *Founded/Ownrshp* 2000
Sales 1.1MMME *EMP* 4,285E
SIC 2711 Newspapers, publishing & printing; Newspapers, publishing & printing
CEO: Austin Beutner
Ofcr: Don Reis
Ofcr: David Rosales
Ex VP: Kathy Thomson
VP: Jack Kemp
VP: Crane Kenney
VP: Johanna Maska
CTO: Scott Sullivan

D-U-N-S 08-433-7823
LOS ANGELES TOURISM & CONVENTION BOARD (CA)
333 S Hope St Ste 1800, Los Angeles, CA 90071-1430
Tel (213) 624-7300 *Founded/Ownrshp* 1971
Sales 38.3MM *EMP* 77
Accts Bdo Usa Llp Coast Mesa Ca
SIC 7389 Convention & show services; Tourist information bureau; Convention & show services; Tourist information bureau
CEO: Ernest Wooden Jr
Mng Pt: Bob Graziano
**Ch Bd:* Alan I Rothenberg
**CFO:* Stefan J Dietrich
Ex VP: Don Orris
Sr VP: Tom Conley
Sr VP: Lucienne Hassler
Sr VP: Mitch Huberman
Sr VP: Stacey Luchs
Sr VP: Emily Simonitsch
VP: Branden Chapman
VP: Erik Dahlerbruch
VP: John Semcken
VP: Matt Wikstrom
Exec: James D Brubaker

D-U-N-S 08-591-9843
LOS ANGELES TRUCK CENTERS LLC
VELOCITY VEHICLE GROUP
2429 Peck Rd, Whittier, CA 90601-1605
Tel (562) 447-1200 *Founded/Ownrshp* 1998
Sales 72.5MME *EMP* 650
SIC 7538 5012 5013 7532

D-U-N-S 00-690-3959 IMP
LOS ANGELES TURF CLUB INC (CA)
SANTA ANITA PARK
(*Suby of* MAGNA CARTOP SYSTEMS OF AMERICA INC) ★
285 W Huntington Dr, Arcadia, CA 91007-3439
Tel (626) 574-6330 *Founded/Ownrshp* 1964, 2011
Sales 25.7MME *EMP* 450
SIC 7948 Horse race track operation; Horse race track operation
CEO: Gregory C Avioli
Ch Bd: Frank Stronach
Pr: George Haines II
VP: Frank Demarco Jr

D-U-N-S 07-528-4901
LOS ANGELES UNIFIED SCHOOL DISTRICT
LAUSD
333 S Beaudry Ave Ste 209, Los Angeles, CA 90017-5141
Tel (213) 241-1000 *Founded/Ownrshp* 1853
Sales 3.1MMME *EMP* 65,231
SIC 8211 Public elementary & secondary schools; Public elementary & secondary schools
CFO: Chuck Burbridge
Bd of Dir: Marquerite Lamotte
Bd of Dir: Jon Lauritzen
Bd of Dir: David Tokofsky
Bd of Dir: Maria Ventura
Admn Mgr: Susan Babit
Admn Mgr: Ellen Chambers
DP Exec: Joyce Edelson
DP Exec: Maria Solis
Dir IT: Randy Singh
IT Man: Michael Mah

D-U-N-S 96-480-7361
LOS ANGELES UNIFIED SCHOOL DISTRICT EDUCATION FOUNDATION
333 S Beaudry Ave Fl 23, Los Angeles, CA 90017-1468
Tel (213) 241-6989 *Founded/Ownrshp* 2002
Sales 7.4MMM *EMP* 15E
Accts Simpson & Simpson Los Angeles
SIC 8399 Fund raising organization, non-fee basis; Fund raising organization, non-fee basis
Prin: Melissa Infusino

D-U-N-S 15-029-7385
LOS ANGELES UNIVERSAL PRESCHOOL
888 S Figueroa St Ste 800, Los Angeles, CA 90017-5306
Tel (213) 416-1200 *Founded/Ownrshp* 2004
Sales 73.6MM *EMP* 200
Accts Vasquez & Co Llp Los Angeles
SIC 8351 Preschool center; Preschool center
CEO: Celia C Ayala
COO: Celia Ayala
CFO: Elsa Luna
Sr VP: Maria Veloz
VP: Fernando Almodovar
VP: Peter Chacko

D-U-N-S 02-038-5711
LOS ANGELES WORLD AIRPORTS
1 World Way, Los Angeles, CA 90045-5803
Tel (855) 463-5252 *Founded/Ownrshp* 2010
Sales 66.0MME *EMP* 391E
SIC 4581 Airport
**Prin:* Michael Cummings
Mng Dir: Grady Mary

LOS ANGLES ARPRT HILTON TOWERS
See FORTUNA ENTERPRISES LP

D-U-N-S 01-300-7430
LOS BANOS UNIFIED SCHOOL DISTRICT
1717 S 11th St, Los Banos, CA 93635-4800
Tel (209) 826-3801 *Founded/Ownrshp* 1890
Sales 63.0MME *EMP* 900
SIC 8211 Public elementary & secondary schools; Public elementary school; Public junior high school; Public senior high school; Public elementary & secondary schools; Public elementary school; Public junior high school; Public senior high school
Bd of Dir: Andree Soares

LOS CABOS MEXICAN FOODS
See M C I FOODS INC

D-U-N-S 06-944-8736
LOS FRESNOS CONSOLIDATED INDEPENDENT SCHOOL DISTRICT
600 N Mesquite St, Los Fresnos, TX 78566-3634
Tel (956) 233-4407 *Founded/Ownrshp* 1920
Sales 110.2MM *EMP* 1,600
Accts Pattillo Brown & Hill Llp
SIC 8211 Public elementary & secondary schools; Public elementary & secondary schools
**CFO:* David Young
Bd of Dir: Kristy Atkinson
Bd of Dir: Leonel Garza
Bd of Dir: Juan Mendoza
Bd of Dir: Ruben Trevino
VP: Rey Farias
CTO: Carlos Santillana
IT Man: Jesse Gonzalez
Schl Brd P: Sandra Garcia
HC Dir: Denise Davis

D-U-N-S 10-000-6980
LOS GATOS UNION SCHOOL DISTRICT
17010 Roberts Rd, Los Gatos, CA 95032-4510
Tel (408) 335-2000 *Founded/Ownrshp* 1863
Sales 16.6MME *EMP* 300
SIC 8211 Public elementary school; Public elementary school
Prin: Dr Diana G Abbati
Trst: Tina Orsi-Hartigan

D-U-N-S 08-146-6427
LOS LUNAS SCHOOL DISTRICT
119 Luna St Se, Los Lunas, NM 87031-6814
Tel (505) 865-9636 *Founded/Ownrshp* 1920
Sales 56.0MME *EMP* 980
SIC 8211 Public elementary & secondary schools; School board; Public elementary & secondary schools; School board
Ofcr: Mark Garcia
Ofcr: Meghan Sanchez
Dir IT: John Schaaf
Teacher Pr: Andrew Saiz
HC Dir: David Jimenez

D-U-N-S 07-155-3739 IMP
LOS RIOS COMMUNITY COLLEGE DISTRICT (CA)
1919 Spanos Ct, Sacramento, CA 95825-3981
Tel (916) 568-3041 *Founded/Ownrshp* 1964
Sales 92.2MM *EMP* 7,000
Accts Gilbert Associates Inc Sacr
SIC 8222 Community college; Community college
Bd of Dir: Mary Leland
Ofcr: Daniel Broussard
Ofcr: Kenneth Quirarte
Ofcr: Jeremy Rogers
Assoc VP: Jerome Countee
Exec: Ryan Cox
Store Mgr: Maria Hyde
IT Man: Kevin Flash
Psych: Mary Allred
Psych: Imelda Farias
Psych: Gomez Martin

D-U-N-S 80-621-4680 IMP/EXP
■ **LOS ROBLES HOSPITAL & MEDICAL CENTER**
(*Suby of* HCA INC) ★
215 W Janss Rd, Thousand Oaks, CA 91360-1899
Tel (805) 497-2727 *Founded/Ownrshp* 1978
Sales 356.2MM *EMP* 35E
SIC 8062 General medical & surgical hospitals; General medical & surgical hospitals
CEO: Greg Angle
Trst: Alan Mintz
Dir Sec: Patrick Smith
MIS Dir: Alex Bryar
Mktg Dir: Kris Carraway
Psych: Sonny Bui
Pathlgst: Robin Rawson
Pathlgst: Wayne Schultheis
Nrsg Dir: Samin Shanidz

LOS TIOS MEXICAN RESTAURANTS
See UNCLES ACQUISITION CORP

LOSS AND RISK ADVISORS
See BARNEY & BARNEY INC

D-U-N-S 01-171-5836
LOSURDO FOODS INC
BEL-CAPRI
20 Owens Rd, Hackensack, NJ 07601-3297
Tel (201) 343-6680 *Founded/Ownrshp* 1959
Sales 91.7MME *EMP* 150
SIC 5141 2022 2033 2045 Groceries, general line; Natural cheese; Tomato sauce: packaged in cans, jars, etc.; Pizza doughs, prepared: from purchased flour; Groceries, general line; Natural cheese; Tomato sauce: packaged in cans, jars, etc.; Pizza doughs, prepared: from purchased flour
Pr: Marc Jx Losurdo
**Pr:* Bjorn Hermann
**Treas:* Maria Losurdo
**Ex VP:* Marc Losurdo
Mktg Dir: Vincenza Circelto

D-U-N-S 00-892-7345
LOTH INC
ASSET SOLUTIONS
3574 E Kemper Rd, Cincinnati, OH 45241-2009
Tel (513) 769-9700 *Founded/Ownrshp* 1994
Sales 127.6MME *EMP* 150E
SIC 5021 5712 Office & public building furniture; Office furniture; Office & public building furniture; Office furniture
CEO: JB Buse Jr
**Pr:* Rick Naber
**CFO:* Eric Roach
Dept Mgr: Bryan Taulbee

D-U-N-S 00-383-5006 IMP
LOTSPEICH CO INC (FL)
16101 Nw 54th Ave, Hialeah, FL 33014-6151
Tel (305) 624-7777 *Founded/Ownrshp* 1925
Sales 47.9MME *EMP* 150
SIC 1542 Commercial & office building, new construction; Commercial & office building, new construction; Specialized public building contractors
Treas: Jay W Lotspeich
**Pr:* Scott Masson
**CEO:* James M Mandich
**CFO:* Larry Wheeler
Ex VP: John Dusnik
**VP:* Craig Gordon
**VP:* Joaquin Riera
Opers Mgr: Craig Wall

D-U-N-S 04-274-6495
LOTSPEICH CO OF FLORIDA INC
6351 Nw 28th Way Unit A, Fort Lauderdale, FL 33309-1739
Tel (954) 978-2388 *Founded/Ownrshp* 1966
Sales 47.6MME *EMP* 220
SIC 1742 1799 1752 5251 Drywall; Acoustical & ceiling work; Home/office interiors finishing, furnishing & remodeling; Access flooring system installation; Hardware; Drywall; Acoustical & ceiling work; Home/office interiors finishing, furnishing & remodeling; Access flooring system installation; Hardware
CEO: David H Fee
CFO: Paul Keenan
**CFO:* Marvin Yit
Bd of Dir: Michael Fee
VP: Craig Gordon
**VP:* Jerrell Ligon
Genl Mgr: David Ceccofiglio
Dir IT: Steve Wolfron
Snr PM: Bianca Bayser
Snr PM: Carlos Yepes
Snr Mgr: Len Kern

D-U-N-S 87-748-0272
LOTT CLEAN WATER ALLIANCE
500 Adams St Ne, Olympia, WA 98501-6911
Tel (360) 664-2333 *Founded/Ownrshp* 2000
Sales 24.0MM *EMP* 67
Accts Brian Sonntag Cgfm
SIC 1629 4941 Waste water & sewage treatment plant construction; Water supply; Waste water & sewage treatment plant construction; Water supply
Ex Dir: Michael D Strub
**Pr:* Cynthia Pratt
**Treas:* Justin Long
**VP:* Sandra Romero
**VP:* Bruce Zeller
Genl Mgr: Rick Hughes
Snr Mgr: Terri Prather
Board of Directors: Steve Langer, Tom Oliva, Cynthia Pratt, Sandra Romero

LOTT CONTRACTORS
See LOTT SURPLUS MATERIALS INC

D-U-N-S 09-791-4931
LOTT ENTERPRISES INC
PURE AIR FILTER
204 Eastman St, Greenwood, MS 38930-7000
Tel (662) 453-0034 *Founded/Ownrshp* 1978
Sales 32.4MME *EMP* 151
Accts Taylor Powell Wilson & Hartf
SIC 3564 Filters, air: furnaces, air conditioning equipment, etc.; Filters, air: furnaces, air conditioning equipment, etc.
Pr: Timmy Lott III
**Pr:* T W Lott Jr
**COO:* James H Lott
Off Mgr: Robin Thornton
Manager: Gary Welch

D-U-N-S 15-416-8306
LOTT INDUSTRIES INC
3350 Hill Ave, Toledo, OH 43607-2937
Tel (419) 534-4980 *Founded/Ownrshp* 1955
Sales 9.0MM *EMP* 1,001
SIC 8331 8741 Sheltered workshop; Management services; Sheltered workshop; Management services
CEO: Jeff Holland

D-U-N-S 05-110-0741
LOTT MARKETING INC
1328 S Loop W Ste 102, Houston, TX 77054-4092
Tel (713) 799-9394 *Founded/Ownrshp* 1969
Sales 22.4MME *EMP* 79
SIC 5141 Food brokers; Food brokers
Pr: Tommy W Lott
COO: Morris Hancock
**VP:* Ron Lott
Exec: Gerry Hall

D-U-N-S 03-435-7772
LOTT OIL CO INC
1855 South Dr, Natchitoches, LA 71457-2658
Tel (318) 356-5858 *Founded/Ownrshp* 1963
Sales 77.5MME *EMP* 194
SIC 5171 Petroleum bulk stations; Petroleum bulk stations
Pr: Luther W Lott Jr
**Sec:* Daniel J Broderick
**VP:* John W Dewitt
Dist Mgr: Mike Howard
Prd Dir: Mark Massia
Sls Mgr: David Dollar

D-U-N-S 12-070-3103
LOTT SURPLUS MATERIALS INC
LOTT CONTRACTORS
15798 Wise Rd, Hamshire, TX 77622
Tel (409) 243-2229 *Founded/Ownrshp* 1995
Sales 33.6MME *EMP* 420
SIC 1623 Pipeline construction; Pipeline construction
Pr: Robert Lott

D-U-N-S 04-507-9873
LOTTERY COMMISSION OHIO
(*Suby of* EXECUTIVE OFFICE STATE OF OHIO) ★
615 W Superior Ave Fl 4, Cleveland, OH 44113-1879
Tel (800) 589-6446 *Founded/Ownrshp* 1974
Sales NA *EMP* 351
SIC 9311 Lottery control board, government; ; Lottery control board, government;
Telecom Mg: Thomas Rakowsky
Counsel: Kathleen Weiss

D-U-N-S 09-117-3117
LOTTERY COMMISSION TEXAS
(*Suby of* EXECUTIVE OFFICE OF STATE OF TEXAS) ★
611 E 6th St, Austin, TX 78701-3715
Tel (512) 344-5000 *Founded/Ownrshp* 1999
Sales NA *EMP* 304
Accts Maxwell Locke & Ritter Llp A
SIC 9311 Lottery control board, government; ; Lottery control board, government;
Prin: Gary Grief
Ch: C Clowe

D-U-N-S 00-477-0459
LOTUS COMMUNICATIONS CORP (CA)
3301 Barham Blvd Ste 200, Los Angeles, CA 90068-1358
Tel (323) 512-2225 *Founded/Ownrshp* 1959
Sales 111.0MME *EMP* 391
SIC 4832 Radio broadcasting stations; Radio broadcasting stations
Pr: Howard Kalmenson
**Treas:* William H Shriftman
**Sr VP:* Jim Kalmenson
**Sr VP:* Jerry Roy
**VP:* Jasmin Dorismond
Genl Mgr: Kevin O'Rorke

D-U-N-S 01-185-0484
■ **LOTUS DEVELOPMENT CORP**
(*Suby of* IBM) ★
55 Cambridge Pkwy, Cambridge, MA 02142-1234
Tel (617) 577-8500 *Founded/Ownrshp* 1995
Sales 143.9MME *EMP* 7,909
SIC 7372 7379 Application computer software; Computer related consulting services; Application computer software; Computer related consulting services
Genl Mgr: Mike Rhodin
Mng Dir: Takayuki Takeda
DP Dir: Michael Hoffler

D-U-N-S 92-763-7355 IMP
LOTUS INTERNATIONAL CO
6880 Commerce Blvd, Canton, MI 48187-4457
Tel (734) 245-0140 *Founded/Ownrshp* 1995
Sales 281.9MM *EMP* 520
SIC 8711 3651 1221 Television receiving sets; Bituminous coal & lignite-surface mining; Consulting engineer; Consulting engineer; Television receiving sets; Bituminous coal & lignite-surface mining
Pr: Madan M Sharma
**CFO:* Sam Venkat
Sales Exec: Prasad Koppolu

LOU ANA FOODS
See VENTURA FOODS LLC

LOU BACDRODT CHEVY MAZDA
See B C S S LTD

D-U-N-S 02-578-8183
LOU BACHRODT CHEVROLET CO
7070 Cherryvale N Blvd, Rockford, IL 61112-1002
Tel (815) 332-3000 *Founded/Ownrshp* 1953
Sales 71.5MM^E^ *EMP* 98
SIC 5511 7515 7513 5531 5521 Automobiles, new & used; Pickups, new & used; Vans, new & used; Passenger car leasing; Truck leasing, without drivers; Automotive & home supply stores; Used car dealers; Automobiles, new & used; Pickups, new & used; Vans, new & used; Passenger car leasing; Truck leasing, without drivers; Automotive & home supply stores; Used car dealers
Pr: Patrick M Bachrodt
**CFO:* Kim Clark
Genl Mgr: George Schaffner
Genl Mgr: John Widiger
Sales Asso: Lothan Henry

D-U-N-S 03-267-7932
LOU BACHRODT CHEVROLET INC
1801 W Atlantic Blvd, Pompano Beach, FL 33069-2799
Tel (954) 971-3000 *Founded/Ownrshp* 1983
Sales 64.6MM^E^ *EMP* 135
SIC 5511 Automobiles, new & used; Automobiles, new & used
Pr: Louis C Bachrodt III
**VP:* Louis C Bachrodt Jr
**VP:* Sean Bachrodt
**VP:* Mark Rhoades
Exec: Kathryn Bradeis
Dir IT: Mark Rhodes

D-U-N-S 18-693-3933
■ **LOU FORD GRUBB INC**
(*Suby of* AUTONATION INC) ★
8555 E Frk Llyd Wrt Pkwy, Scottsdale, AZ 85260
Tel (480) 991-3333 *Founded/Ownrshp* 1998
Sales 40.3MM^E^ *EMP* 215
SIC 5511 Automobiles, new & used; Trucks, tractors & trailers: new & used; Automobiles, new & used; Trucks, tractors & trailers: new & used
Pr: Lou S Grubb
**Sec:* George Hudock
**Ex VP:* Daniel L Grubb
Board of Directors: Evelyn F Grubb

D-U-N-S 62-394-3586
LOU FUSZ AUTOMOTIVE NETWORK INC
925 N Lindbergh Blvd, Saint Louis, MO 63141-5934
Tel (314) 997-3400 *Founded/Ownrshp* 1988
Sales 399.0MM^E^ *EMP* 900
SIC 5511 5531 5521 Automobiles, new & used; Automotive parts; Automobiles, used cars only; Automobiles, new & used; Automotive parts; Automobiles, used cars only
Pr: Randy Fusz
**Pr:* Louis Fusz Jr
COO: Jim Shelton
Treas: Martha Fusz
**Sec:* Peter Ramey
Bd of Dir: Pete Fusz
Sales Exec: Rick Schwab
Mktg Dir: Ted Stranz
Sls Mgr: Tom Capstick
Sls Mgr: Jim Davies
Sls Mgr: Ryan Mager

D-U-N-S 82-968-5387
LOU FUSZ CHEVROLET INC
FUSZ LOU USED CARS
(*Suby of* LOU FUSZ MOTOR CO) ★
5120 N Service Rd, Saint Peters, MO 63376-3960
Tel (636) 397-2000 *Founded/Ownrshp* 1991
Sales 37.0MM^E^ *EMP* 100
SIC 5511 Automobiles, new & used; Automobiles, new & used
Pr: Louis Fusz Jr
COO: Jim Shelton
**Sec:* Peter Ramey
Sls Mgr: Rita Thompson
Sales Asso: Jerry Calvert
Sales Asso: Tony Iannicola
Sales Asso: Joe Redmond

D-U-N-S 82-677-7823 EXP
LOU FUSZ FORD INC
LOU FUSZ USED CARS
(*Suby of* LOU FUSZ AUTOMOTIVE NETWORK INC) ★
2 Caprice Dr, Chesterfield, MO 63005-1309
Tel (636) 532-9955 *Founded/Ownrshp* 1990
Sales 25.8MM^E^ *EMP* 60
SIC 5511 5521 Automobiles, new & used; Automobiles, used cars only; Automobiles, new & used; Automobiles, used cars only
Pr: Lou Fusz Jr
Genl Mgr: Gary Romeo
Sales Asso: Darryl Herndon

D-U-N-S 03-103-6858
LOU FUSZ MOTOR CO
LOU FUSZ PONTIAC
(*Suby of* LOU FUSZ AUTOMOTIVE NETWORK INC) ★
10329 Old Olive Street Rd, Saint Louis, MO 63141-5921
Tel (314) 994-1500 *Founded/Ownrshp* 1990
Sales 300.0MM *EMP* 400
SIC 5511 7514 Automobiles, new & used; Rent-a-car service; Automobiles, new & used; Rent-a-car service
Ch Bd: Louis J Fusz Sr
**Pr:* Louis Fusz Jr
**Treas:* Martha Fusz
Store Mgr: Mark Linneman
Dir IT: John Bissell
Sls Mgr: Ron Franklin
Sls Mgr: Rick Schildknecht

LOU FUSZ PONTIAC
See LOU FUSZ MOTOR CO

LOU FUSZ USED CARS
See LOU FUSZ FORD INC

D-U-N-S 05-204-3718
LOU LARICHE CHEVROLET INC
40875 Plymouth Rd, Plymouth, MI 48170-4294
Tel (734) 453-4600 *Founded/Ownrshp* 1970
Sales 31.9MM^E^ *EMP* 70
SIC 5511 Automobiles, new & used; Pickups, new & used; Vans, new & used; Automobiles, new & used; Pickups, new & used; Vans, new & used
Pr: Louis La Riche
**Sec:* Sharon Rowe
Div Mgr: Ronald Chaudoin

D-U-N-S 04-471-6322 IMP
LOU SALLY FASHIONS CORP
S L FASHIONS
1400 Broadway Rm 601, New York, NY 10018-0728
Tel (212) 354-9670 *Founded/Ownrshp* 1974
Sales 35.0MM *EMP* 40^E^
SIC 2335 Women's, juniors' & misses' dresses; Women's, juniors' & misses' dresses
CEO: Mitchell Grabow

D-U-N-S 87-823-5779 IMP
LOU SOBH CERRITOS SATURN INC
18400 Studebaker Rd, Cerritos, CA 90703-5345
Tel (562) 860-2424 *Founded/Ownrshp* 2002
Sales 25.7MM^E^ *EMP* 95
SIC 5511 Automobiles, new & used; Automobiles, new & used
Pr: Lou Sobh

D-U-N-S 10-203-5037
LOU SOBH FORD INC
2473 Pleasant Hill Rd, Duluth, GA 30096-4325
Tel (770) 232-0099 *Founded/Ownrshp* 2001
Sales 26.1MM^E^ *EMP* 110
SIC 5511 Automobiles, new & used; Automobiles, new & used
Pr: Lou M Sobh
CFO: M L Sobh
Store Mgr: Kenny Barnes

D-U-N-S 19-750-6566 IMP
LOU-RICH INC
EXACT MANUFACTURING
(*Suby of* INNOVANCE INC) ★
505 W Front St, Albert Lea, MN 56007-2795
Tel (507) 377-8910 *Founded/Ownrshp* 2003
Sales 56.0MM *EMP* 300
SIC 3599 3544 3469 Machine shop, jobbing & repair; Special dies, tools, jigs & fixtures; Metal stampings; Machine shop, jobbing & repair; Special dies, tools, jigs & fixtures; Metal stampings
CEO: Mike Larson
VP: Kevin Davis
Prgrm Mgr: Bruce Mullenbach
Genl Mgr: Roger Paul
IT Man: Dan Clausses
Plnt Mgr: Galen Berg
Prd Mgr: Lowell Nelson
Ql Cn Mgr: Tony Blakstad
Sls Mgr: Tim Kaasa

D-U-N-S 19-464-0272 IMP/EXP
LOUD TECHNOLOGIES INC
(*Suby of* SUN MACKIE LLC) ★
16220 Wood Red Rd Ne, Woodinville, WA 98072-9061
Tel (425) 892-6500 *Founded/Ownrshp* 1988
Sales 114.8MM^E^ *EMP* 533
SIC 3651 Household audio & video equipment; Audio electronic systems; Loudspeakers, electrodynamic or magnetic; Music distribution apparatus; Household audio & video equipment; Audio electronic systems; Loudspeakers, electrodynamic or magnetic; Music distribution apparatus
Pr: Rodney E Olson
**Pr:* Mark Graham
**COO:* James Stewart
COO: Jim Stewart
**CFO:* Case Kuehn
Treas: William A Garrard
Ex VP: Kenton Forsythe
Ex VP: Robert A McDonald
Ex VP: Paul Rice
Sr VP: Ken Berger
Sr VP: Kenneth P Berger
Sr VP: Shawn C Powers
VP: Scott T King
**VP:* Mark E Kuchenrither
**VP:* Jason H Neimark
**VP:* Clarence E Terry
Dir Rx: Christopher Mael
Board of Directors: Kevin J Calhoun, Jon W Gacek, C Daryl Hollis, George R Rea, R Lynn Skillen, Thomas V Taylor

D-U-N-S 11-039-7432
LOUDERDALE COUNTY VOLUNTEER FIRE SERVICE
1319 23rd Ave, Meridian, MS 39301-4025
Tel (601) 482-9856 *Founded/Ownrshp* 2009
Sales NA *EMP* 403
SIC 9224 Fire department, volunteer; Fire department, volunteer
Prin: Clarence Butler

D-U-N-S 01-805-3012
LOUDON COUNTY CENTRAL GARAGE
(*Suby of* LOUDOUN COUNTY) ★
42000 Loudoun Center Pl, Leesburg, VA 20175-8953
Tel (703) 771-6485 *Founded/Ownrshp* 1991
Sales 9.9MM^E^ *EMP* 500
SIC 7538 General automotive repair shops; General automotive repair shops

D-U-N-S 10-067-0900
LOUDON COUNTY SCHOOL DISTRICT
100 River Rd Ste 113, Loudon, TN 37774-1042
Tel (865) 458-5411 *Founded/Ownrshp* 1880
Sales 15.1MM^E^ *EMP* 447
SIC 8211 Public elementary & secondary schools; School board; Public elementary & secondary schools; School board
IT Man: Chip Miller
Pr Dir: Maria Warren
Psych: Donna Yeaney

D-U-N-S 18-351-3092
LOUDON STEEL INC
8208 Ellis Rd, Millington, MI 48746-9402
Tel (989) 871-9353 *Founded/Ownrshp* 1984
Sales 24.9MM^E^ *EMP* 80
SIC 3441 3535 3537 3496 2542 Fabricated structural metal; Conveyors & conveying equipment; Industrial trucks & tractors; Miscellaneous fabricated wire products; Partitions & fixtures, except wood
Pr: Gregg Loudon

D-U-N-S 03-032-0832
LOUDOUN COUNTY
1 Harrison St Se Fl 1, Leesburg, VA 20175-3102
Tel (703) 777-0100 *Founded/Ownrshp* 1757
Sales NA *EMP* 6,999
Accts Cherry Bekaert Llp Tysons Cor
SIC 9199 ; General government administration; ; General government administration
Treas: Tamra Spink
**Treas:* H Roger Zurn Jr
Ofcr: Matthew Bisgaier
Ofcr: Lance Kelley
Ofcr: Mark Lauzier
Ofcr: Virginia Newsome
Ofcr: Wayne Promisel
Ofcr: Heather Rosenberg
Ofcr: Steven Schochet
Ofcr: Kara Staskel
Ofcr: David Street
Ofcr: Kraig Troxell

D-U-N-S 18-872-7911 IMP
LOUDOUN COUNTY PUBLIC SCHOOL DISTRICT
LCPS
21000 Education Ct, Broadlands, VA 20148-5526
Tel (571) 252-1000 *Founded/Ownrshp* 1757
Sales 629.2M *EMP* 10,000
SIC 8211 Public elementary & secondary schools; Public elementary & secondary schools
Adm Dir: Michael J Lunsford
HC Dir: Nancy Markley
Snr PM: Scott Klose

D-U-N-S 07-035-6605
LOUDOUN COUNTY SANITATION AUTHORITY INC
LOUDOUN WATER
44865 Loudoun Water Way, Ashburn, VA 20147-6109
Tel (571) 291-7700 *Founded/Ownrshp* 1959
Sales 79.0MM *EMP* 200
Accts Yount Hyde & Barbour Pc W
SIC 4952 4941 Sewerage systems; Water supply; Sewerage systems; Water supply
Prin: Pravin Gandhi
**Ch:* Fred Jennings
**Treas:* Dale Hammes
Ofcr: Lenny McDonald
Exec: Jan Chase
**Prin:* Mark Koblos
Prgrm Mgr: Karen Arnold
CIO: Edward Burrell
Mtls Mgr: Marty Graham

D-U-N-S 18-051-0281
LOUDOUN HEALTHCARE INC
INOVA LOUDOUN HOSPITAL
(*Suby of* INOVA HEALTH SYSTEM) ★
44045 Riverside Pkwy, Leesburg, VA 20176-5101
Tel (703) 777-3300 *Founded/Ownrshp* 2005
Sales 44.9MM^E^ *EMP* 1,300
SIC 8062 8059 General medical & surgical hospitals; Nursing home, except skilled & intermediate care facility; General medical & surgical hospitals; Nursing home, except skilled & intermediate care facility
Pr: J Knox Singleton
**CEO:* Rodney Huebbers
**CFO:* Glenn Zirbfer
Off Mgr: Karen Evans

D-U-N-S 06-936-5807
LOUDOUN HOSPITAL CENTER (VA)
INOVA LOUDOUN HOSPITAL
(*Suby of* INOVA FAIRFAX HOSPITAL) ★
44045 Riverside Pkwy, Leesburg, VA 20176-5101
Tel (703) 858-6000 *Founded/Ownrshp* 1912, 1985
Sales 210.6MM^E^ *EMP* 1,000^E^
SIC 8062 General medical & surgical hospitals; General medical & surgical hospitals
Pr: Randall Kelley
Chf Rad: Allen Joseph
**Pr:* J Knox Singleton
**CFO:* Glenn Zirbser
**Ch:* Patrick Rhodes
Dir Rad: Deborah Blair
Dir Rad: Afarin Ghadi
**Prin:* Rhonda Kohnen
Nurse Mgr: Cindy Andrejasich
Pathlgst: Nahla Acoury
Obsttrcn: Chauncey Stokes

D-U-N-S 80-445-7039
LOUDOUN MEDICAL GROUP PC
224d Cornwall St Nw, Leesburg, VA 20176-2700
Tel (703) 777-1146 *Founded/Ownrshp* 2000
Sales 63.5MM^E^ *EMP* 1,000
SIC 8011 Medical centers; Medical centers
CEO: Marybeth Tamasy
**Ch:* Kevin Oconnnor
**Treas:* John Andrew
Exec: Karen Feely
Exec: Marybeth Tamsay
Doctor: John Cook

D-U-N-S 00-794-1990
LOUDOUN MUTUAL INSURANCE CO INC (VA)
15609 High St, Waterford, VA 20197-1522
Tel (540) 579-4101 *Founded/Ownrshp* 1849
Sales NA *EMP* 30
Accts Mitchell & Co Pc Leesburg
SIC 6331 Fire, marine & casualty insurance: mutual; Fire, marine & casualty insurance: mutual
Pr: Christopher Shipe
**Treas:* Loyd Hutchinson
VP: April Bridgeman
VP: Timothy J Koppenhaver
Ex Dir: Richard Oliyer
IT Man: Kim Dorman
VP Mktg: J David King

LOUDOUN WATER
See LOUDOUN COUNTY SANITATION AUTHORITY INC

LOUIS A WEISS MEMORIAL HOSP
See VHS ACQUISITION SUBSIDIARY NUMBER 3 INC

D-U-N-S 07-169-3183
LOUIS BERGER AIRCRAFT SERVICES INC
125 The Pkwy Ste 250, Greenville, SC 29615-6626
Tel (864) 640-4077 *Founded/Ownrshp* 1996
Sales 22.0MM *EMP* 70^E^
SIC 8748 Business consulting; Business consulting
Pr: Bill McLendon
**CEO:* Steve Townes
**VP:* Jack Gundrum
VP: Keith Moncrief

D-U-N-S 14-332-3439
LOUIS BERGER AND ASSOCIATES INC
412 Mount Kemble Ave, Morristown, NJ 07960-6666
Tel (973) 407-1000 *Founded/Ownrshp* 2005
Sales 58.8MM^E^ *EMP* 3,000
SIC 8711 Consulting engineer; Consulting engineer
Pr: Nicolas Masucci
**VP:* Gul Khan

D-U-N-S 08-727-7190
LOUIS BERGER GROUP DOMESTIC INC (NJ)
(*Suby of* LOUIS BERGER GROUP INC) ★
412 Mount Kemble Ave, Morristown, NJ 07960-6666
Tel (973) 407-1000 *Founded/Ownrshp* 1972, 1994
Sales 28.2MM^E^ *EMP* 67
SIC 8711 8712 8732 Consulting engineer; Architectural services; Economic research; Consulting engineer; Architectural services; Economic research
Pr: Thomas Lewis
**Treas:* Luke McKinnon
**Prin:* Larry D Walker

D-U-N-S 04-388-1093
LOUIS BERGER GROUP INC
(*Suby of* BERGER GROUP HOLDINGS INC) ★
412 Mount Kemble Ave, Morristown, NJ 07960-6666
Tel (973) 407-1000 *Founded/Ownrshp* 1963
Sales 176.8MM^E^ *EMP* 534
SIC 8748 8712 8711 Consulting engineer; Economic consultant; Architectural services; Economic consultant; Architectural services; Consulting engineer
Ch Bd: Fredric S Berger
Pr: Anatoly Hochstein
Pr: Meg Lassarat
Pr: Thomas Lewis
COO: James G Bach
CFO: Simon Hemming
CFO: Luke McKinnon
Treas: Horacio Alvarez
Ex VP: Rick Falconio
Ex VP: Larry D Walker
Sr VP: Bob Schmidt
VP: Charles Bell
VP: Ed Garvey
VP: Daniel Grey
VP: Jack Gundrum
VP: Thomas Nicastro
VP: John Nicolay
VP: Charlie Raubacher
VP: D Stamatis

D-U-N-S 01-376-1783
LOUIS BERGER LOGISTICS SERVICES INC
(*Suby of* LOUIS BERGER SERVICES INC) ★
125 The Pkwy Ste 150, Greenville, SC 29615-6629
Tel (864) 385-7500 *Founded/Ownrshp* 2009
Sales 11.2MM^E^ *EMP* 550
SIC 7549 Automotive maintenance services; Automotive maintenance services
Pr: Chuck Swannack
**CEO:* Steve Townes
**VP:* Tim Jones

D-U-N-S 96-209-9425
LOUIS BERGER SERVICES INC
(*Suby of* BERGER GROUP HOLDINGS INC) ★
125 The Pkwy Ste 250, Greenville, SC 29615-6626
Tel (864) 385-7500 *Founded/Ownrshp* 2012
Sales 98.5MM^E^ *EMP* 1,000^E^
SIC 6719 Investment holding companies, except banks; Investment holding companies, except banks
CEO: Steve Townes
CFO: Jeffrey Hartman
VP: Paul Chamberlain
VP: Nancy Grigsby
DP Exec: Klaffky Richard
VP Opers: Keith Moncrief
VP Opers: Suzanne Mueller

D-U-N-S 00-896-4546 IMP/EXP
LOUIS BERKMAN CO
MEYER PRODUCTS
600 Grant St Ste 3230, Pittsburgh, PA 15219-2713
Tel (740) 283-3722 *Founded/Ownrshp* 1931
Sales 90.2MM^E^ *EMP* 188
SIC 3711 5085 Snow plows (motor vehicles), assembly of; Industrial supplies; Snow plows (motor vehicles), assembly of; Industrial supplies
Ch: Robert A Paul
**Prin:* Raphael J Omerza
MIS Dir: Joyce Calvarese

D-U-N-S 61-316-7431
LOUIS COUNTY HOSPITAL DISTRICT NUMBER 1
MORTON GENERAL HOSPITAL
521 Adams St, Morton, WA 98356-9323
Tel (360) 496-5112 *Founded/Ownrshp* 2006
Sales 35.3MM^E *EMP* 200
SIC 8062 General medical & surgical hospitals; General medical & surgical hospitals
CEO: Ron Dearth
**Ch Bd:* Sheri Hendricks
Sr VP: Don Allison
Dir Lab: Carl Lian
Sfty Dirs: Brian Williams
QC Dir: Jerri Andersen
Mktg Dir: Diane Evans
Nrsg Dir: Trish Frady

D-U-N-S 07-480-3180
LOUIS CREATIVE HAIRDRESSERS INC
RATNER COMPANY
1577 Spring Hill Rd # 600, Vienna, VA 22182-2223
Tel (703) 698-7090 *Founded/Ownrshp* 1950
Sales 10.4MM^E *EMP* 304
SIC 7231 Beauty shops; Beauty shops
CEO: Jean Ratner
Treas: Ronald G Sieel
**VP:* Warren Ratner

D-U-N-S 04-157-5283
LOUIS DIAMOND GLICK CORP
LOUIS GLICK AND COMPANY
1271 Ave Of The Amrcs 4, New York, NY 10020-1302
Tel (212) 259-0315 *Founded/Ownrshp* 1945
Sales 90.6MM *EMP* 55
Accts Morris Teichman & Co Pc
SIC 5094 3911 Diamonds (gems); Precious stones & metals; Jewelry, precious metal; Diamonds (gems); Precious stones & metals; Jewelry, precious metal
Pr: Louis Glick
**CFO:* Aaron Cohen
CIO: Pinchus Menche

D-U-N-S 83-140-1463
LOUIS DREYFUS BIOFUELS HOLDINGS LLC
(*Suby of* LD COMMODITIES GRAINS AND OILSEEDS HOLDINGS LLC) ★
4800 Main St Ste 600, Kansas City, MO 64112-2509
Tel (574) 566-2100 *Founded/Ownrshp* 2006
Sales 48.9MM^E *EMP* 3^E
SIC 6221 Commodity traders, contracts

D-U-N-S 96-511-0190 IMP/EXP
LOUIS DREYFUS CITRUS INC
(*Suby of* LD COMMODITIES CITRUS HOLDINGS LLC) ★
355 9th St, Winter Garden, FL 34787-3651
Tel (407) 656-1000 *Founded/Ownrshp* 1996
Sales 85.2MM^E *EMP* 425
SIC 2037 2033 Fruit juice concentrates, frozen; Canned fruits & specialties; Fruit juice concentrates, frozen; Canned fruits & specialties
Pr: Peter R Hahn
**Pr:* Scott Hogan
COO: Ciro Echesortu
**Treas:* Luciano Cocito
**Sr VP:* Randal G Freeman
VP: Bill Ballenden
VP: Gabriela S Ldcommodities
**VP:* Jeffrey Zanchelli
Mng Dir: Miguel Catella
Sls Dir: Jeff Graham

D-U-N-S 07-847-6878
LOUIS DREYFUS COMMODITIES COTTON STORAGE LLC
(*Suby of* LOUIS DREYFUS COMMODITIES LLC) ★
40 Danbury Rd, Wilton, CT 06897-4441
Tel (203) 761-2000 *Founded/Ownrshp* 2005, 2009
Sales 20.5MM^E *EMP* 300
SIC 6221 Commodity contracts brokers, dealers; Commodity contracts brokers, dealers

D-U-N-S 82-855-8861
LOUIS DREYFUS COMMODITIES GRAND JUNCTION LLC
(*Suby of* LOUIS DREYFUS NORFOLK LLC) ★
1149 U Ave, Grand Junction, IA 50107-8562
Tel (515) 738-2800 *Founded/Ownrshp* 2007
Sales 46.5MM^E *EMP* 65
SIC 6221 Commodity traders, contracts
Pr: Sean W Martin
Treas: Serge A Stepanov
VP: Bruce R Chapin
VP: H Thomas Hayden Jr
VP: Bradley A Johannes
VP: Hal Wolkin
VP: Jeffrey Zanchelli

D-U-N-S 01-015-5372
LOUIS DREYFUS COMMODITIES LLC
SANGAMON TRANSPORTATION
(*Suby of* LDC HOLDING INC) ★
40 Danbury Rd, Wilton, CT 06897-4441
Tel (203) 761-2000 *Founded/Ownrshp* 1940, 2006
Sales 13.0MM^E *EMP* 2,000
SIC 6221 Commodity contracts brokers, dealers; Commodity contracts brokers, dealers
Ch: Serge Schoen
COO: Mikael Morn
**CFO:* Robert G Eckert
**CFO:* Claude Ehlinger
**Treas:* Sean Colvin
**Treas:* Serge A Stepanov
Ofcr: Reina Barcan
**Sr VP:* Hal Wolkin
**VP:* Mr Don Carlson
**VP:* Mark Gerardi
VP: Sean Martin
VP: Andrea Maserati

D-U-N-S 96-543-4793
LOUIS DREYFUS COMMODITIES LLC
(*Suby of* LDC HOLDING INC) ★
40 Danbury Rd, Wilton, CT 06897-4441
Tel (203) 761-2000 *Founded/Ownrshp* 2010
Sales 884.7MM^E *EMP* 1,300
Accts Ernst & Young Llp Stamford C
SIC 6221 Commodity contracts brokers, dealers; Commodity contracts brokers, dealers
CEO: Mayo Schmidt
**CFO:* Robert Eckert
**Genl Couns:* Cornelius Grealy

D-U-N-S 60-258-2764
LOUIS DREYFUS GAS DEVELOPMENT LP
2200 Atlantic St Ste 800, Stamford, CT 06902-6834
Tel (203) 761-8100 *Founded/Ownrshp* 2005
Sales 35.5MM^E *EMP* 149^E
SIC 6552 Land subdividers & developers, commercial
Pr: Timothy Stuart
Genl Pt: Louis Dreyfus Resources
Ltd Pt: Louis Dreyfus LP Asset Holding
VP: Alfonso Madrid
VP: Joseph Rothbauer
IT Man: Jason Delainey
Plnt Mgr: David Selig

D-U-N-S 60-899-0552
LOUIS DREYFUS HOLDING CO INC
(*Suby of* IMPALA SAS)
10 Westport Rd Ste 200, Wilton, CT 06897-4548
Tel (203) 761-2000 *Founded/Ownrshp* 1976
Sales 140.7MM^E *EMP* 1,749
SIC 6221 5153 6512 6531 1311 Commodity traders, contracts; Grains; Commercial & industrial building operation; Real estate managers; Natural gas production
Pr: Hal Wolkin
Treas: Richard D Gray

D-U-N-S 82-855-9265
LOUIS DREYFUS NORFOLK LLC
(*Suby of* LOUIS DREYFUS BIOFUELS HOLDINGS LLC) ★
3002 N Victory Rd, Norfolk, NE 68701-0833
Tel (402) 844-2680 *Founded/Ownrshp* 2006
Sales 46.9MM^E *EMP* 72^E
SIC 6221 Commodity traders, contracts
Prin: Bruce R Chapin

D-U-N-S 04-568-7431
LOUIS FORD LAKIS INC
LAKIS FORD
2201 W Main St, Galesburg, IL 61401-3262
Tel (309) 342-1121 *Founded/Ownrshp* 1968
Sales 25.6MM^E *EMP* 75
SIC 5511 Automobiles, new & used; Automobiles, new & used
Pr: Steven Lakis
**Treas:* Joann Lakis
Sls Mgr: Mike Glasnovich
Sls Mgr: Gene Stull
Sales Asso: Ricardo Sandoval

LOUIS FUSZ MAZDA
See FUSZ LOUIS NISSAN- MAZDA INC

LOUIS GLICK AND COMPANY
See LOUIS DIAMOND GLICK CORP

D-U-N-S 02-513-9783 IMP
LOUIS GLUNZ BEER INC (IL)
7100 N Capitol Dr Ste 2, Lincolnwood, IL 60712-2740
Tel (847) 676-9500 *Founded/Ownrshp* 1888, 1992
Sales 43.5MM^E *EMP* 75
SIC 5181 Beer & other fermented malt liquors; Beer & other fermented malt liquors
Pr: John P Glunz
Treas: Louis Glunz III
**Sec:* Janet Bischoff
**VP:* Patricia Glunz
**VP:* Malcolm Harvey
Sls Mgr: Jane Delaney

D-U-N-S 02-298-7283
LOUIS INDUSTRIES INC
222 Indl L Loop St W, Paynesville, MN 56362
Tel (320) 243-3696 *Founded/Ownrshp* 1940
Sales 25.7MM^E *EMP* 34
SIC 5051 3544 3312 Sheets, metal; Rods, metal; Tubing, metal; Special dies, tools, jigs & fixtures; Blast furnaces & steel mills
Ch Bd: Kevin Wall
**CEO:* Leo Louis
**CFO:* Lance Louis
**VP:* Cecil Louis

D-U-N-S 02-244-7825
LOUIS J GRASMICK LUMBER CO INC
6715 Quad Ave, Baltimore, MD 21237-2499
Tel (410) 325-9663 *Founded/Ownrshp* 1950
Sales 43.3MM *EMP* 60
SIC 5031 2448

D-U-N-S 00-277-9684
LOUIS J KENNEDY TRUCKING CO
KENNEDY LOGISTICS
342 Schuyler Ave, Kearny, NJ 07032-4003
Tel (201) 998-4142 *Founded/Ownrshp* 1949
Sales NA *EMP* 500
SIC 4213

D-U-N-S 01-901-3457
LOUIS J PARADIS INC (ME)
PARADIS FAMILY SUPERMARKETS
62 W Main St Ste 101, Fort Kent, ME 04743-1264
Tel (207) 834-3020 *Founded/Ownrshp* 1946
Sales 36.4MM^E *EMP* 300
SIC 5411 Grocery stores, independent; Grocery stores, independent
Pr: Kathy Roy
**Treas:* Craig Paradis
**VP:* Denis Paradis

D-U-N-S 07-028-3416
LOUIS L BORICK FOUNDATION
2707 Kipling St, Houston, TX 77098-1214
Tel (213) 278-0855 *Founded/Ownrshp* 2001
Sales 66.7MM *EMP* 3^E
SIC 8641 Civic social & fraternal associations
Prin: Louis L Borick

D-U-N-S 00-100-0363 IMP/EXP
LOUIS M GERSON CO INC
16 Commerce Blvd Ste D, Middleboro, MA 02346-1085
Tel (508) 947-4000 *Founded/Ownrshp* 1945
Sales 21.4MM^E *EMP* 150
SIC 3842 Respiratory protection equipment, personal; Respiratory protection equipment, personal
Ch Bd: Ronald L Gerson
**CFO:* Christopher Nazar
CFO: Richard Turicelli
VP: Linda Kruger
Ql Cn Mgr: Robert Brunell
Natl Sales: Bill Petres
Natl Sales: Steve Walley
Sls&Mrk Ex: Richard Magnant

D-U-N-S 00-509-8926
LOUIS MESKAN BRASS FOUNDRY INC
MESKAN FOUNDRY
2007 N Major Ave 13, Chicago, IL 60639-2951
Tel (773) 237-7662 *Founded/Ownrshp* 1907
Sales 22.5MM *EMP* 102
Accts Goettche Tranen Winter & Rus
SIC 3366 3365 Castings (except die): brass; Aluminum & aluminum-based alloy castings; Castings (except die): brass; Aluminum & aluminum-based alloy castings
Pr: David Meskan
**Ex VP:* Allen Meskan
Sls&Mrk Ex: Bruce Mell

D-U-N-S 01-105-3931
LOUIS P CANUSO INC
401 Crown Point Rd, West Deptford, NJ 08086-2143
Tel (215) 334-4700 *Founded/Ownrshp* 1965
Sales 52.7MM^E *EMP* 45
SIC 5085 Valves & fittings
Ch Bd: Louis P Canuso
**Pr:* Joseph Canuso
**VP:* Gerald Canuso
MIS Dir: Grace Freni
Sales Asso: Paul Ambrose

D-U-N-S 00-890-1928 EXP
LOUIS PADNOS IRON AND METAL CO
185 W 8th St, Holland, MI 49423-3107
Tel (616) 396-6521 *Founded/Ownrshp* 1905
Sales 138.9MM^E *EMP* 450
SIC 5093 4491 3599

LOUIS RAPHAEL
See KIZAN INTERNATIONAL INC

LOUIS SHANKS OF AUSTIN
See LOUIS SHANKS OF TEXAS INC

D-U-N-S 02-602-9454 IMP
LOUIS SHANKS OF TEXAS INC
LOUIS SHANKS OF AUSTIN
2930 W Anderson Ln, Austin, TX 78757-1123
Tel (512) 451-6501 *Founded/Ownrshp* 1945
Sales 55.2MM^E *EMP* 250
SIC 5712 5713 5719 Furniture stores; Office furniture; Carpets; Bedding (sheets, blankets, spreads & pillows); Furniture stores; Office furniture; Carpets; Bedding (sheets, blankets, spreads & pillows)
CEO: Amor Forwood
**Pr:* Michael Amor Forwood
**Sec:* Suzanne Forwood
**VP:* Becky Warner

LOUIS SHIFFMAN ELECTRIC
See REDLYN ELECTRIC CORP

D-U-N-S 01-702-8713
LOUIS T OLLESHEIMER & SON INC
605 E 12 Mile Rd, Madison Heights, MI 48071-2568
Tel (248) 544-3900 *Founded/Ownrshp* 1999
Sales 144.3MM^E *EMP* 74
SIC 5033 5082 Roofing & siding materials; Construction & mining machinery; Roofing & siding materials; Construction & mining machinery
Treas: Barbara Ollesheimer
**Pr:* James R Ollesheimer

D-U-N-S 00-448-0083
■ **LOUIS TRAUTH DAIRY LLC**
(*Suby of* DEAN FOODS CO) ★
16 E 11th St, Newport, KY 41071-2110
Tel (859) 431-7553 *Founded/Ownrshp* 1920
Sales 56.0MM^E *EMP* 350
SIC 5143 5149 2033 2026 2024 Dairy products, except dried or canned; Milk & cream, fluid; Ice cream & ices; Butter; Beverages, except coffee & tea; Mineral or spring water bottling; Tea; Canned fruits & specialties; Fluid milk; Ice cream & frozen desserts; Dairy products, except dried or canned; Milk & cream, fluid; Ice cream & ices; Butter; Beverages, except coffee & tea; Mineral or spring water bottling; Tea; Canned fruits & specialties; Fluid milk; Ice cream & frozen desserts
Prin: Rachael A Gonzalez
**CEO:* Greg Engles
**Sr VP:* Gary Sparks
**VP:* Dan Smith
**Prin:* Steven J Kemps

D-U-N-S 18-511-8684 IMP
LOUIS VUITTON NORTH AMERICA INC
(*Suby of* LVMH MOET HENNESSY LOUIS VUITTON INC) ★
1 E 57th St, New York, NY 10022-2561
Tel (212) 931-2000 *Founded/Ownrshp* 1999
Sales 33.6MM^E *EMP* 182
SIC 5948 5099 Luggage & leather goods stores; Luggage; Luggage & leather goods stores; Luggage
CEO: Antonio Belloni
V Ch: Pierre Gode
**Pr:* Felix Rohatyn
**Ex VP:* Bruce Ingram
VP: Jean Christophe
VP: Denise Garrigan
VP: Patty McMahon
VP: John Mulliken
VP: Charly Nixon
VP: Gena Smith
Comm Dir: Marissa Cortes

D-U-N-S 06-031-2219
LOUIS WEISS MEM HOSP
VANGUARD HEALTH SYSTEMS
4646 N Marine Dr, Chicago, IL 60640-5759
Tel (773) 564-7085 *Founded/Ownrshp* 2010
Sales 53.2MM^E *EMP* 950
SIC 8062 General medical & surgical hospitals; General medical & surgical hospitals
CEO: Tony Tedeschi
**CFO:* Jeff Wright

D-U-N-S 00-411-4690
LOUIS WOHL & SONS INC (FL)
11101 N 46th St, Tampa, FL 33617-2009
Tel (813) 985-8870 *Founded/Ownrshp* 1897, 1977
Sales 21.1MM^E *EMP* 43
SIC 5046 Hotel equipment & supplies; Restaurant equipment & supplies
VP: Tony Deriso
**VP:* Steven Paver

D-U-N-S 07-813-4616 IMP/EXP
LOUIS WURTH AND CO (CA)
(*Suby of* WURTH GROUP OF NORTH AMERICA INC) ★
895 Columbia St, Brea, CA 92821-2917
Tel (714) 529-1771 *Founded/Ownrshp* 1975
Sales 117.0MM^E *EMP* 305
SIC 5072 5198 Furniture hardware; Stain; Furniture hardware; Stain
Pr: Vito Mancini
**Pr:* Tom Mauss
**CFO:* Ed McGraw
VP: Bob Shine
CTO: Becky Gentle
Dir IT: Gary McElligatt
Mfg Dir: Jeff Debozy
Opers Mgr: Andy Gette
Opers Mgr: Paul Wilson
VP Sls: Don Scardami
Mktg Dir: Kathy Greene

D-U-N-S 10-086-3455
LOUISA COUNTY PUBLIC SCHOOLS
L C
953 Davis Hwy, Mineral, VA 23117-4149
Tel (540) 894-5115 *Founded/Ownrshp* 1742
Sales 37.1MM^E *EMP* 700
Accts Robinson Farmer Cox Associate
SIC 8211 Public elementary & secondary schools; Public elementary & secondary schools

D-U-N-S 04-349-9169
LOUISA FOOD PRODUCTS INC (MO)
1918 Switzer Ave, Saint Louis, MO 63136-3779
Tel (314) 868-3000 *Founded/Ownrshp* 1964
Sales 21.8MM^E *EMP* 90
SIC 2038 5142 2098 2035 2033 2013 Ethnic foods, frozen; Packaged frozen goods; Macaroni & spaghetti; Pickles, sauces & salad dressings; Canned fruits & specialties; Sausages & other prepared meats
Pr: Thomas J Baldetti
COO: Pete Baldetti
Exec: Mary Binz
**Prin:* John Baldetti
Ql Cn Mgr: John Engelhard
Sales Exec: Rob Foskett
Natl Sales: Rachel Gaertner

LOUISANA FODS GLOBL SFOOD SRCE
See SYSCO LOUISIANA SEAFOOD LLC

LOUISANA SCRETARY STATE OFFICE
See DEPARTMENT OF STATE LOUISIANA

D-U-N-S 07-202-8376
LOUISBURG COLLEGE INC
501 N Main St, Louisburg, NC 27549-2399
Tel (919) 496-2521 *Founded/Ownrshp* 1857
Sales 20.3MM *EMP* 120
Accts Mcgladrey Llp Rocky Mount Nc
SIC 8222 Junior college; Junior college
Pr: Mark David La Branche
Pr: Brandy Gupton
**CFO:* Belinda Faulkner
Ofcr: Jermaine Thomas
**VP:* Jim Eck
VP: Stephanie Tolbert
Off Admin: Robin Johannesen
Mktg Dir: Amy McManus
Mktg Dir: Anne Strickland
Snr Mgr: Vicki Reid

LOUISE ET CIE
See VINCENT CAMUTO LLC

D-U-N-S 07-793-4461
LOUISE OBICI MEMORIAL HOSPITAL INC
OBICI HEALTH SYSTEMS
2800 Godwin Blvd, Suffolk, VA 23434-8038
Tel (757) 934-4000 *Founded/Ownrshp* 1950
Sales 81.7MM^E *EMP* 1,272
Accts Boyce Spady & Moore Plc Suffo
SIC 8062 General medical & surgical hospitals; General medical & surgical hospitals
Pr: William C Giermak
Pr: David Bernd
CFO: William A Carpenter
Off Mgr: Terry Christovich
Pharmcst: Angela Kang
Diag Rad: Andrew Zasada

D-U-N-S 05-324-2009 IMP
LOUISE PARIS LTD (NY)
ME-JANE
1407 Broadway Rm 1405, New York, NY 10018-2843
Tel (212) 719-9300 *Founded/Ownrshp* 1977
Sales 46.3MM^E *EMP* 45
SIC 5137 Women's & children's clothing
Ch Bd: Salomon Barnathan
**VP:* Albert Barnathan
VP Sls: Sindi Blaur

D-U-N-S 62-380-4775
LOUISE SAINT REGIONAL HOSPITAL
9460 N Name Uno Ste 225, Gilroy, CA 95020-3532
Tel (408) 848-8640 *Founded/Ownrshp* 1997
Sales 82.3MM *EMP* 10

Accts Grant Thornton Llp San Franci
SIC 8062 General medical & surgical hospitals
Pr: Theodore P Fox
Pharmcst: Art Weybright

D-U-N-S 10-720-8220
LOUISE TOWN HOSPITAL
LOISE TOWN HLTHCARE FOUNDATION
400 Highland Ave, Lewistown, PA 17044-1167
Tel (717) 242-7200 *Founded/Ownrshp* 1950
Sales 11.2MM^E *EMP* 900
SIC 8062 8011 General medical & surgical hospitals; Offices & clinics of medical doctors; General medical & surgical hospitals; Offices & clinics of medical doctors
CEO: Kay A Hamilton

D-U-N-S 04-746-1306
LOUISE W EGGLESTON CENTER INC
EGGLESTON SERVICES
1161 Ingleside Rd, Norfolk, VA 23502-5608
Tel (757) 858-8011 *Founded/Ownrshp* 1955
Sales 23.0MM *EMP* 560
Accts Pbmares Llp Norfolk Virgini
SIC 8331 Vocational rehabilitation agency; Vocational rehabilitation agency
Pr: Paul J Atkinson
**CFO:* Rick Briggs
CFO: Kenny White
Treas: Carol Denning
VP: Garrat Cooper
VP: Michelle Flynn
Prgrm Mgr: Michael Johnson
IT Man: Rick Biggs

LOUISE'S TRATTORIA
See LT ACQUISITION CORP

LOUISVILLE
See LOUISVILLE LADDER INC

LOUISEVILLE PAVING
See LPX INC

D-U-N-S 00-805-6202
LOUISIANA ASSOCIATION FOR BLIND
1750 Claiborne Ave, Shreveport, LA 71103-4189
Tel (318) 635-6471 *Founded/Ownrshp* 1927
Sales 26.3MM *EMP* 139
Accts James K Mcclelland Cpa Llc
SIC 2678 5044 1731 2675 8322 Tablets & pads, book & writing: from purchased materials; Office equipment; Safety & security specialization; Index cards, die-cut: made from purchased materials; Rehabilitation services; Tablets & pads, book & writing: from purchased materials; Office equipment; Safety & security specialization; Index cards, die-cut: made from purchased materials; Rehabilitation services
CEO: Shelly Taylor
**Pr:* Elaine M Taylor
Treas: James Batte
**VP:* Tom Tyler
**VP:* Doug Young

D-U-N-S 60-507-6090
LOUISIANA BAPTIST CONVENTION
1250 Macarthur Dr, Alexandria, LA 71303-3124
Tel (318) 448-3402 *Founded/Ownrshp* 1983
Sales 22.0MM *EMP* 80
SIC 4841 Cable television services; Cable television services
Ex Dir: David Hankins
Ofcr: Michelle Rhodes
VP: Richard Blue
Assoc Dir: Wayne Sheppard
Ex Dir: Wayne Taylor
Netwrk Eng: John Bordelon
Snr Mgr: Randy Turner

D-U-N-S 78-704-7901
LOUISIANA BOARD OF REGENTS
1201 N 3rd St Ste 6-200, Baton Rouge, LA 70802-5243
Tel (225) 342-4253 *Founded/Ownrshp* 1974
Sales NA *EMP* 6,983
SIC 9411 Administration of educational programs; ; Administration of educational programs;
Ofcr: Kimberly Small
Dir IT: Slava Sereda

D-U-N-S 86-015-3295
■ **LOUISIANA CASINO CRUISES INC**
CASINO ROUGE
(*Suby of* PENN NATIONAL GAMING INC) ★
1717 River Rd N, Baton Rouge, LA 70802-5134
Tel (225) 709-7777 *Founded/Ownrshp* 2001
Sales 36.6MM^E *EMP* 960
SIC 7999 5813 5812 Card & game services; Drinking places; Eating places; Card & game services; Drinking places; Eating places
Pr: Kevin Desanctis
**Pr:* Peter M Carlino
**Treas:* Robert S Ippolito
**VP:* Thomas P Burke
**VP:* James Rigot
Genl Mgr: Jon Zimmerman
CIO: Warren Miller

D-U-N-S 96-576-7838
LOUISIANA CHILDRENS MEDICAL CENTER INC
CHILDREN'S HOSPITAL
200 Henry Clay Ave, New Orleans, LA 70118-5720
Tel (504) 896-9581 *Founded/Ownrshp* 1997
Sales 926.4MM *EMP* 6,100^E
Accts Laporte Apac Metairie La
SIC 8069 Specialty hospitals, except psychiatric; Children's hospital
Pr: Mary Perrin
Mngd Care: Cindy Nuesslein

D-U-N-S 83-027-2360
LOUISIANA CITIZENS PROPERTY INSURANCE CORP
1 Galleria Blvd Ste 720, Metairie, LA 70001-7514
Tel (888) 568-6455 *Founded/Ownrshp* 2009
Sales NA *EMP* 91
SIC 6331 Property damage insurance
CEO: David E Thomas
VP: Quin Netzel

D-U-N-S 00-818-7494
■ **LOUISIANA COCA-COLA BOTTLING CO LIMITED**
(*Suby of* COCA-COLA REFRESHMENTS USA INC) ★
5601 Citrus Blvd, New Orleans, LA 70123-5508
Tel (504) 818-7000 *Founded/Ownrshp* 1986
Sales 98.7MM^E *EMP* 1,700
SIC 2086 5962 Soft drinks: packaged in cans, bottles, etc.; Merchandising machine operators; Soft drinks: packaged in cans, bottles, etc.; Merchandising machine operators
VP: Lowry Kline
Treas: Joyce Lavinder
VP: Bernard Bommier
VP: Paul Gordon
VP: Pamela Kimmet
Genl Mgr: Rick Kehr
Sls Mgr: Kelsie Boylan

D-U-N-S 07-067-5699
LOUISIANA COLLEGE
1140 College Dr, Pineville, LA 71359-1000
Tel (318) 487-7011 *Founded/Ownrshp* 1906
Sales 20.8MM *EMP* 143
Accts Payne Moore & Herrington Llp
SIC 8221 College, except junior; College, except junior
Pr: Dr Argile Smith
**CFO:* Randall Hargis
Ofcr: David Barnard
Ofcr: Linde Wyser
VP: Janet Austin
VP: Brandon Bannon
VP: Cheryl Clark
**VP:* Tim Johnson
**VP:* Dr Peggy Pack
VP: Travis Wright
Dir IT: Shane Davis

LOUISIANA COMMUNITY & TECH
See DELGADO COMMUNITY COLLEGE

D-U-N-S 07-100-3094
LOUISIANA COMMUNITY & TECHNICAL COLLEGE SYSTEM
LCTCS
265 S Foster Dr, Baton Rouge, LA 70806-4104
Tel (225) 922-2800 *Founded/Ownrshp* 1999
Sales 38.5MM^E *EMP* 810
SIC 8249 Vocational schools; Vocational schools
Ch Bd: Steven Smith
**Pr:* Joseph May
Ex VP: Monty Sullivan
Sr VP: Jan Jackson
Sr VP: Tarie Roberson
VP: Jimmy Sawtelle
Ex Dir: Stephanie Ercolini
Ex Dir: Sean Martin

D-U-N-S 13-177-8354
LOUISIANA CRANE & CONSTRUCTION LLC
1045 Highway 190, Eunice, LA 70535-2947
Tel (337) 550-6217 *Founded/Ownrshp* 2001
Sales 243.0MM *EMP* 130
SIC 7389 7353 1623 Crane & aerial lift service; Cranes & aerial lift equipment, rental or leasing; Oil & gas line & compressor station construction; Crane & aerial lift service; Cranes & aerial lift equipment, rental or leasing; Oil & gas line & compressor station construction
CEO: Logan Fournerat
**CFO:* Douglas Marbantel

D-U-N-S 80-992-6843
LOUISIANA DEPARTMENT OF AGRICULTURE AND FORESTRY
LDAF
(*Suby of* EXECUTIVE OFFICE OF STATE OF LOUISIANA) ★
5825 Florida Blvd # 1140, Baton Rouge, LA 70806-4259
Tel (225) 922-1234 *Founded/Ownrshp* 1812
Sales NA *EMP* 600
SIC 9641 Regulation of agricultural marketing; ; Regulation of agricultural marketing;

D-U-N-S 80-992-7429
LOUISIANA DEPARTMENT OF CHILDREN AND FAMILY SERVICES
(*Suby of* EXECUTIVE OFFICE OF STATE OF LOUISIANA) ★
627 N 4th St, Baton Rouge, LA 70802-5343
Tel (225) 342-4220 *Founded/Ownrshp* 1989
Sales NA *EMP* 4,700
SIC 9441 Administration of social & manpower programs; ; Administration of social & manpower programs;
IT Man: Martina Stribling
Genl Couns: Steve Mayer

D-U-N-S 80-992-6850
LOUISIANA DEPARTMENT OF CULTURE RECREATION AND TOURISM
(*Suby of* EXECUTIVE OFFICE OF STATE OF LOUISIANA) ★
1051 N 3rd St, Baton Rouge, LA 70802-5239
Tel (225) 342-8100 *Founded/Ownrshp* 1976
Sales NA *EMP* 600^E
SIC 9111 ;

D-U-N-S 80-992-6868
LOUISIANA DEPARTMENT OF ECONOMIC DEVELOPMENT
L E D
(*Suby of* EXECUTIVE OFFICE OF STATE OF LOUISIANA) ★
1051 N 3rd St, Baton Rouge, LA 70802-5239
Tel (225) 342-3000 *Founded/Ownrshp* 1988
Sales NA *EMP* 350
SIC 9611 Administration of general economic programs; ; Administration of general economic programs;

D-U-N-S 80-992-6884
LOUISIANA DEPARTMENT OF ELECTIONS AND REGISTRATION
ELECTIONS & REGISTRATION DEPT
(*Suby of* EXECUTIVE OFFICE OF STATE OF LOUISIANA) ★
4888 Constitution Ave, Baton Rouge, LA 70808-3323
Tel (225) 922-0900 *Founded/Ownrshp* 1949
Sales NA *EMP* 300
SIC 9199 General government administration;

D-U-N-S 80-992-7056
LOUISIANA DEPARTMENT OF ENVIRONMENTAL QUALITY
OFFICE OF THE SECRETARY
(*Suby of* EXECUTIVE OFFICE OF STATE OF LOUISIANA) ★
602 N 5th St, Baton Rouge, LA 70802-5312
Tel (225) 219-3953 *Founded/Ownrshp* 1984
Sales NA *EMP* 1,000
SIC 9511 Air, water & solid waste management; Air, water & solid waste management;
Pr: Peggy Hatch
Exec: Jean Kelly

D-U-N-S 80-992-7064
LOUISIANA DEPARTMENT OF HEALTH AND HOSPITALS
(*Suby of* EXECUTIVE OFFICE OF STATE OF LOUISIANA) ★
628 N 4th St, Baton Rouge, LA 70802-5342
Tel (225) 342-9500 *Founded/Ownrshp* 1975
Sales NA *EMP* 4,000
SIC 9431 Administration of public health programs; ; Administration of public health programs;
**CFO:* Pam Diaz
CFO: Janet O'Dell
Dir Inf Cn: Edna Clark
Dir Rx: Philip McCrory
Chf Nrs Of: Mary Fontenelle
**Prin:* Courtney N Phillips
**Prin:* Jerry Phillips
Prgrm Mgr: Bill Perkins
Prgrm Mgr: Ross Pottschmidt
Off Admin: Tammy Brumfield
Telecom Mg: Chris Parish

D-U-N-S 80-992-7072
LOUISIANA DEPARTMENT OF INSURANCE
(*Suby of* EXECUTIVE OFFICE OF STATE OF LOUISIANA) ★
1702 N 3rd St, Baton Rouge, LA 70802-5143
Tel (225) 342-5423 *Founded/Ownrshp* 1812
Sales NA *EMP* 640
SIC 9651 Insurance commission, government; ; Insurance commission, government;
Ofcr: Jana Braud
Exec: Laura Landry
Ex Dir: Rosanne Prats
Prgrm Mgr: Angela Lawson
Area Mgr: Clinton Phillips
Mktg Mgr: Stephanie Roussell
Snr Mgr: Donald Couvillion

D-U-N-S 80-992-7080
LOUISIANA DEPARTMENT OF JUSTICE
OFFICE OF THE ATTORNEY GENERAL
(*Suby of* EXECUTIVE OFFICE OF STATE OF LOUISIANA) ★
1885 N 4th St, Baton Rouge, LA 70802-5159
Tel (225) 326-6705 *Founded/Ownrshp* 1812
Sales NA *EMP* 524
SIC 9222 Attorney General's office; ; Attorney General's office;

D-U-N-S 94-199-3305
LOUISIANA DEPARTMENT OF MILITARY AFFAIRS
(*Suby of* EXECUTIVE OFFICE OF STATE OF LOUISIANA) ★
6400 Saint Claude Ave, New Orleans, LA 70117-1456
Tel (504) 278-8071 *Founded/Ownrshp* 1812
Sales NA *EMP* 2,600
SIC 9711 9451 National Guard; ; Administration of veterans' affairs; ; National Guard; ; Administration of veterans' affairs;
**Pr:* Bennett C Landreneau

D-U-N-S 09-468-6487
LOUISIANA DEPARTMENT OF MOTOR VEHICLES
(*Suby of* LOUISIANA DEPARTMENT OF PUBLIC SAFETY & CORRECTIONS) ★
7979 Independence Blvd, Baton Rouge, LA 70806-6409
Tel (225) 925-6335 *Founded/Ownrshp* 2007
Sales NA *EMP* 750
SIC 9621 Motor vehicle licensing & inspection office, government; Motor vehicle licensing & inspection office, government;

D-U-N-S 80-992-7387
LOUISIANA DEPARTMENT OF NATURAL RESOURCES
(*Suby of* EXECUTIVE OFFICE OF STATE OF LOUISIANA) ★
617 N 3rd St Ste A, Baton Rouge, LA 70802-5432
Tel (225) 342-1446 *Founded/Ownrshp* 1976
Sales NA *EMP* 600
SIC 9111 Executive offices; Executive offices

D-U-N-S 93-892-0949
LOUISIANA DEPARTMENT OF PUBLIC EDUCATION
(*Suby of* EXECUTIVE OFFICE OF STATE OF LOUISIANA) ★
1201 N 3rd St, Baton Rouge, LA 70802-5243
Tel (225) 342-3836 *Founded/Ownrshp* 1974
Sales NA *EMP* 1,000
SIC 9411 Administration of educational programs; ; Administration of educational programs;
Exec: Gwendolyn Scott
DP Exec: Rizwan Ahmed
IT Man: Janet Broussard

D-U-N-S 09-366-9286
LOUISIANA DEPARTMENT OF PUBLIC SAFETY & CORRECTIONS
(*Suby of* EXECUTIVE OFFICE OF STATE OF LOUISIANA) ★
7919 Independence Blvd, Baton Rouge, LA 70806-6409
Tel (225) 925-6006 *Founded/Ownrshp* 2000
Sales NA *EMP* 3,000
SIC 9221 State police; ; State police;
IT Man: Rexford McDonald
IT Man: Wayne Narcisse

D-U-N-S 80-992-7403
LOUISIANA DEPARTMENT OF PUBLIC SAFETY AND CORRECTIONS
(*Suby of* EXECUTIVE OFFICE OF STATE OF LOUISIANA) ★
504 Mayflower St, Baton Rouge, LA 70802-6419
Tel (225) 342-6740 *Founded/Ownrshp* 1983
Sales NA *EMP* 8,224^E
SIC 9229 9223 Public order & safety statistics centers; ; Correctional institutions;
Dist Mgr: Michael Hoffpauir
Dir IT: Terence Clair
IT Man: Thomas Bickham

D-U-N-S 80-992-7411
LOUISIANA DEPARTMENT OF REVENUE AND TAXATION
REVENUE AND TAXATION DEPT
(*Suby of* EXECUTIVE OFFICE OF STATE OF LOUISIANA) ★
617 N 3rd St Ste B, Baton Rouge, LA 70802-5432
Tel (225) 219-5500 *Founded/Ownrshp* 1976
Sales NA *EMP* 924
SIC 9311 Taxation department, government; ; Taxation department, government;
Ch: Senator Conrad Appel
**Prin:* Dan Claitor
**Prin:* Jack Donahue
**Prin:* Elbert L Guillory
Snr Mgr: Travis Fossett

D-U-N-S 80-992-7759
LOUISIANA DEPARTMENT OF TRANSPORTATION AND DEVELOPMENT
(*Suby of* EXECUTIVE OFFICE OF STATE OF LOUISIANA) ★
1201 Capitol Access Rd, Baton Rouge, LA 70802-4438
Tel (225) 379-1232 *Founded/Ownrshp* 1977
Sales NA *EMP* 5,500
SIC 9111 Executive offices; Executive offices
IT Man: Ben Spears
IT Man: Lesha Woods

D-U-N-S 94-213-4594
LOUISIANA DEPARTMENT OF VETERANS AFFAIRS
(*Suby of* EXECUTIVE OFFICE OF STATE OF LOUISIANA) ★
602 N 5th St, Baton Rouge, LA 70802-5312
Tel (225) 247-6057 *Founded/Ownrshp* 1966
Sales NA *EMP* 500
SIC 9111 Executive offices; Executive offices
Prin: David Lacerte

D-U-N-S 80-992-7783
LOUISIANA DEPARTMENT OF WILDLIFE AND FISHERIES
(*Suby of* EXECUTIVE OFFICE OF STATE OF LOUISIANA) ★
2000 Quail Dr, Baton Rouge, LA 70808-9038
Tel (225) 765-2623 *Founded/Ownrshp* 1872
Sales NA *EMP* 792
SIC 9512 Fish & wildlife conservation agency, government; ; Fish & wildlife conservation agency, government;
Ofcr: Teri Larose

D-U-N-S 09-365-6432
LOUISIANA DIVISION OF ADMINISTRATION
(*Suby of* EXECUTIVE OFFICE OF STATE OF LOUISIANA) ★
1201 N 3rd St Ste 7-20, Baton Rouge, LA 70802-5243
Tel (225) 342-7000 *Founded/Ownrshp* 1960
Sales NA *EMP* 1,500
SIC 9199 ;
CEO: Mark Drennon
Ofcr: Lydia Herman

D-U-N-S 12-732-6911
LOUISIANA DOCK CO LLC
(*Suby of* ACL TRANSPORTATION SERVICES LLC) ★
1701 Utica Pike, Jeffersonville, IN 47130-4747
Tel (812) 288-0100 *Founded/Ownrshp* 2007
Sales 741.0MM *EMP* 18^E
SIC 7389 Personal service agents, brokers & bureaus; Personal service agents, brokers & bureaus
Off Mgr: Kristin Rubino

LOUISIANA DOT COMPANY
See ACL TRANSPORTATION SERVICES LLC

D-U-N-S 10-402-3692
LOUISIANA ENERGY & POWER AUTHORITY
L E P A
210 Venture Way, Lafayette, LA 70507-5319
Tel (337) 237-8439 *Founded/Ownrshp* 1979
Sales 72.9MM *EMP* 55
Accts Wright Moore Dehart Dupuis
SIC 4911 Distribution, electric power; Distribution, electric power
Ch: Hyram Copeland
Bd of Dir: Robert Bergeron
Sr VP: Jennifer Dupuis
**Genl Mgr:* Cordell Grand
Plnt Mgr: Larry Noland

D-U-N-S 13-663-1004 IMP
LOUISIANA ENERGY SERVICES LLC
L E S
(*Suby of* URENCO LIMITED)
275 Andrews Hwy, Eunice, NM 88231
Tel (575) 394-4646 *Founded/Ownrshp* 2004
Sales 229.6MM[E] *EMP* 301[E]
SIC 1094 Uranium-radium-vanadium ores; Uranium-radium-vanadium ores
CEO: Gregory O D Smith
**CFO:* Paul Mason
**Sec:* Perry Robinson
Dir Risk M: Dwight Besada

D-U-N-S 15-075-9678
LOUISIANA EXTENDED CARE CENTERS INC
SENIOR VILLAGE NURSING HOME
763 Avery Blvd N, Ridgeland, MS 39157-5218
Tel (601) 956-8884 *Founded/Ownrshp* 1983
Sales 520.0MM *EMP* 487
SIC 8051 8052 Skilled nursing care facilities; Intermediate care facilities; Skilled nursing care facilities; Intermediate care facilities
Pr: Glynn Beebe
**CEO:* David Stallard
**VP:* Lansing Kolb
**VP:* Joe Sadler

D-U-N-S 06-021-2974
LOUISIANA FARM BUREAU CASUALTY INSURANCE CO (LA)
FARM BUREAU INSURANCE
(*Suby of* FARM BUREAU INSURANCE) ★
9516 Airline Hwy, Baton Rouge, LA 70815-5501
Tel (225) 922-6200 *Founded/Ownrshp* 1981
Sales NA *EMP* 240
SIC 6411 Insurance agents, brokers & service; Insurance agents, brokers & service
CEO: Gerald Garnett
**Pr:* Ronald Roy Anderson
**Treas:* Dennis Griffin
Ex VP: Wynne Jacobs
**VP:* Jack Anderson
VP: Gail Chisum
**VP:* Steven Walter Ingram
**VP:* H Wynne Jacobs
**VP:* Mickey Nugent
**VP:* John Stenmark
VP: Bob Warner
**VP:* Thomas Young
**VP:* Linda Zaunbrecher
Board of Directors: David Hillman, Carl Loop Jr, Donald Patman, David Waide, David Winkles Jr

D-U-N-S 06-009-3895
LOUISIANA FARM BUREAU MUTUAL INSURANCE CO INC)
FARM BUREAU INSURANCE
9516 Airline Hwy, Baton Rouge, LA 70815-5501
Tel (225) 922-6200 *Founded/Ownrshp* 1957
Sales NA *EMP* 289
SIC 6411 Insurance agents, brokers & service; Insurance agents, brokers & service
Pr: Ronald Anderson
**Sec:* Jackie J Theriot
**Ex VP:* H Wynne Jacobs
Ex VP: Wynne H Jacobs
**VP:* Gail Chisum
Creative D: Lauren Thom
Pr Dir: Michael Danna

D-U-N-S 06-263-1809 IMP
■ **LOUISIANA GENERATING LLC**
(*Suby of* NRG ENERGY INC) ★
10719 Airline Hwy, Baton Rouge, LA 70816-4213
Tel (609) 524-4500 *Founded/Ownrshp* 2000
Sales 215.2MM[E] *EMP* 463
SIC 4911 Generation, electric power; Transmission, electric power; Generation, electric power; Transmission, electric power
Pr: Jeff Baudier

D-U-N-S 19-181-2429
LOUISIANA GUEST HOUSE LLC
JENNINGS GUEST HOUSE
4333 Shreveport Hwy, Pineville, LA 71360-3828
Tel (318) 445-6470 *Founded/Ownrshp* 1987
Sales 21.1MM[E] *EMP* 600[E]
SIC 8051 Skilled nursing care facilities; Skilled nursing care facilities
CEO: James E Richardson
**Ch Bd:* Donna McPherson
Pr: Jerrine Harrell
CFO: Nicole Howard

LOUISIANA HEALTH CARE REVIEW
See EQHEALTH SOLUTIONS INC

LOUISIANA HEALTH PLAN
See LOUISIANA HIGH RISK HEALTH POOL INC

D-U-N-S 06-951-7761
LOUISIANA HEALTH SERVICE AND INDEMNITY CO (LA)
BLUE CROSS
5525 Reitz Ave, Baton Rouge, LA 70809-3802
Tel (225) 295-3307 *Founded/Ownrshp* 1934
Sales NA *EMP* 1,500
Accts Neal D King Cpa-King Lejeune
SIC 6321 6324 6411 Health insurance carriers; Group hospitalization plans; Insurance agents, brokers & service; Health insurance carriers; Group hospitalization plans; Insurance agents, brokers & service
Pr: Mike Reitz
**CFO:* Adam Short
Ofcr: Michele Calandro
Ofcr: Anthony Tardugno
Sr VP: Brian Keller
Sr VP: Tej Shah
VP: Jacqueline Addison
VP: Robert Drelick
VP: Milam Ford
VP: Charles Landreneau
VP: Rodney Rone
VP: Mary Saporito
VP: Dean Simon
VP: Brian Small
VP: Tony Wittman

LOUISIANA HEART HOSPITAL
See LOUISIANA MEDICAL CENTER AND HEART HOSPITAL LLC

D-U-N-S 87-480-9452
LOUISIANA HIGH RISK HEALTH POOL INC
LOUISIANA HEALTH PLAN
9947 Trendale Dr, Greenwell Springs, LA 70739-4953
Tel (225) 926-6245 *Founded/Ownrshp* 1991
Sales 22.8MM *EMP* 5
SIC 8621 Health association
Ch Bd: Catherine Sullivan
IT Man: Diane Brunecke

D-U-N-S 87-801-5858
LOUISIANA I GAMING LP
BOOMTOWN BELLE CASINO
4132 Peters Rd, Harvey, LA 70058-1805
Tel (504) 366-7711 *Founded/Ownrshp* 1994
Sales 26.8MM[E] *EMP* 1,200
SIC 7999 Gambling establishment; Gambling establishment
Prin: Michael Kosnett
Advt Dir: Erica Blanchard

D-U-N-S 00-694-7204 IMP/EXP
LOUISIANA MACHINERY CO LLC
CATERPILLAR
3799 W Airline Hwy, Reserve, LA 70084-5717
Tel (985) 536-1121 *Founded/Ownrshp* 1960
Sales 195.1MM[E] *EMP* 400
SIC 5082 7699 7353

D-U-N-S 13-303-7627
LOUISIANA MEDICAL CENTER AND HEART HOSPITAL LLC
LOUISIANA HEART HOSPITAL
64030 Highway 434, Lacombe, LA 70445-3456
Tel (985) 690-7500 *Founded/Ownrshp* 2011
Sales 58.9MM *EMP* 350
SIC 8062 General medical & surgical hospitals; General medical & surgical hospitals
CEO: Roy Wright
**CEO:* Steve Blades
**VP:* Glenda Dobson

LOUISIANA MILLWORK
See MASONITE CORP

D-U-N-S 11-277-8691 IMP
LOUISIANA NURSERY OUTLET INC
8680 Perkins Rd, Baton Rouge, LA 70810-1026
Tel (225) 766-0300 *Founded/Ownrshp* 1983
Sales 24.1MM[E] *EMP* 150
SIC 5261 Nursery stock, seeds & bulbs; Lawn & garden supplies
Pr: Mitch A Mayes
**Sec:* Marilyn Mayes

D-U-N-S 94-212-3795
LOUISIANA OFFICE OF GROUP BENEFITS
(*Suby of* DEPARTMENT OF TREASURY LOUISIANA) ★
7389 Florida Blvd Ste 124, Baton Rouge, LA 70806-4657
Tel (225) 925-6625 *Founded/Ownrshp* 2000
Sales NA *EMP* 500
SIC 9311 9651 Finance, taxation & monetary policy; ; Regulation, miscellaneous commercial sectors; ; Finance, taxation & monetary policy; ; Regulation, miscellaneous commercial sectors;
**CEO:* Kip Wall
IT Man: Brad Townsend

D-U-N-S 11-742-0661
LOUISIANA OFFICE OF STUDENT FINANCIAL ASSISTANCE
602 N 5th St, Baton Rouge, LA 70802-5312
Tel (225) 219-1012 *Founded/Ownrshp* 1973
Sales 252.1MM *EMP* 133
SIC 9411 ;
Ex Dir: Melanie Amrhein
CFO: Jack Hart

LOUISIANA OFFSHORE OIL PORT
See LOOP LLC

D-U-N-S 80-915-4958 IMP
LOUISIANA PIGMENT CO LP
3300 Bayou Dinde Rd, Westlake, LA 70669-8102
Tel (337) 882-7000 *Founded/Ownrshp* 1993
Sales 226.2MM[E] *EMP* 500
SIC 2816 Titanium dioxide, anatase or rutile (pigments); Titanium dioxide, anatase or rutile (pigments)
Plnt Mgr: Greg Godfrey
Genl Mgr: Doug Weaver
CTO: John Hammond
Cmptr Lab: Greg Cooper
Cmptr Lab: John Parigi
Sfty Dirs: John Dubose
Sfty Dirs: Allen Himel
Sfty Dirs: Walt Nolen
Sfty Mgr: Lou Lacock
Sfty Mgr: Gene Stevens
Plnt Mgr: Tim J Hall

D-U-N-S 84-481-7390
LOUISIANA PLASTIC CONVERTING CORP
LPCC
503 Downing Pines Rd, West Monroe, LA 71292-8010
Tel (318) 387-5490 *Founded/Ownrshp* 1985
Sales 21.1MM[E] *EMP* 121
SIC 4953 Refuse systems; Refuse systems
Pr: John Mark Wilhite
Sales Exec: Pat Smith

D-U-N-S 00-377-4002
LOUISIANA PUBLIC HEALTH INST
LPHI
1515 Poydras St Ste 1200, New Orleans, LA 70112-4536
Tel (504) 301-9800 *Founded/Ownrshp* 1997
Sales 29.7MM *EMP* 86
Accts Laporte Apac Metairie La
SIC 8399 Health systems agency; Health systems agency
CEO: Joseph Kimbrell
Comm Man: Lauren Conrad

D-U-N-S 07-320-0334 EXP
LOUISIANA RICE MILL LLC
4 S Avenue D, Crowley, LA 70526-5657
Tel (337) 783-9777 *Founded/Ownrshp* 2003
Sales 280.6MM *EMP* 100
SIC 2044 Rice milling; Rice milling
Sfty Mgr: Janice Cart

D-U-N-S 80-855-8662
LOUISIANA RIVERBOAT GAMING PARTNERSHIP
DIAMOND JACKS CASINO & RESORT
711 Diamondjacks Blvd, Bossier City, LA 71111-5046
Tel (318) 678-7633 *Founded/Ownrshp* 1993
Sales 37.3MM[E] *EMP* 1,200
SIC 7999 Gambling establishment; Gambling establishment
Pt: G Dan Marshall
Pt: Joe Collings
Pr: Raymond Cook
Secur Mgr: Greg Jackson
Secur Mgr: Sean McCloud

D-U-N-S 10-402-4476
LOUISIANA SAFETY SYSTEMS INC
2505 Se Evangeline Trwy, Lafayette, LA 70508-2167
Tel (337) 237-8211 *Founded/Ownrshp* 1983
Sales 48.2MM[E] *EMP* 70
SIC 5085 7699 Valves & fittings; Valve repair, industrial
CEO: H Brooks Bernard
Pr: Jerry Domec
**VP:* Richard Maloney
Plnt Mgr: Darrel Boulet
Ql Cn Mgr: Harold Gerac
Sales Exec: Bruce Smotherman
Sales Asso: Doug Sealy

D-U-N-S 12-323-2949
LOUISIANA SCHOOL FOR DEAF
LSD
2888 Brightside Dr, Baton Rouge, LA 70820-3509
Tel (225) 757-3481 *Founded/Ownrshp* 2002
Sales 27.4MM[E] *EMP* 360
SIC 8211 School for physically handicapped; School for physically handicapped
Netwrk Mgr: Susan Blackwell
Psych: Amanda Scobel

D-U-N-S 02-678-1026
LOUISIANA STATE BOARD OF ELECTROLYSIS EXAMINERS
(*Suby of* EXECUTIVE OFFICE OF STATE OF LOUISIANA) ★
711 Mahlon St, Deridder, LA 70634-4253
Tel (337) 463-6180 *Founded/Ownrshp* 2001
Sales NA *EMP* 385[E]
SIC 9199 General government administration;
Ch: Cheri Miller

D-U-N-S 07-877-0585
LOUISIANA STATE PENITENTIARY
ANGOLA STATE PENITENTIARY
17544 Tunica Trce, Angola, LA 70712-3029
Tel (225) 655-4411 *Founded/Ownrshp* 1901
Sales NA *EMP* 1,500
SIC 9223 ;
Genl Mgr: Burl Cain
**Prin:* Pamela Mincin

D-U-N-S 07-505-0765 IMP/EXP
LOUISIANA STATE UNIVERSITY
LOUISIANA STATE UNIVERSITY A&M
(*Suby of* LOUISIANA STATE UNIVERSITY) ★
202 Himes Hall, Baton Rouge, LA 70803-0001
Tel (225) 578-2760 *Founded/Ownrshp* 1860
Sales 1.0MMM[E] *EMP* 26,000
SIC 8221

D-U-N-S 94-005-0792
LOUISIANA STATE UNIVERSITY
3810 W Lkshore Dr Ste 111, Baton Rouge, LA 70808
Tel (225) 578-2760 *Founded/Ownrshp* 1970
Sales 1.7MMM *EMP* 26,000
SIC 8221

LOUISIANA STATE UNIVERSITY A&M
See LOUISIANA STATE UNIVERSITY

D-U-N-S 06-952-8735
LOUISIANA SUGAR CANE COOPERATIVE INC (LA)
6092 Resweber Hwy, Saint Martinville, LA 70582-6804
Tel (337) 394-3255 *Founded/Ownrshp* 1973
Sales 65.7MM[E] *EMP* 80
SIC 2061 Raw cane sugar; Blackstrap molasses made from sugar cane; Raw cane sugar; Blackstrap molasses made from sugar cane
Pr: Michael G Melancon
**Treas:* Dane Berard
**Treas:* Kenny Laperouse
**VP:* Ross Harper
IT Man: Corey Verret
Snr Mgr: Antonio Avila

D-U-N-S 00-498-7925
LOUISIANA SUGAR REFINING LLC
1230 S 5th St, Gramercy, LA 70052-3174
Tel (225) 869-6990 *Founded/Ownrshp* 2010, 2005
Sales 79.2MM[E] *EMP* 300
SIC 2062 Cane sugar refining; Cane sugar refining
CEO: Larry Faucheux
CFO: Hal Merchler

D-U-N-S 01-430-7750
LOUISIANA SW TRANSPORTATION INC (LA)
13097 Highway 308, Larose, LA 70373-2001
Tel (985) 693-6266 *Founded/Ownrshp* 1992
Sales 21.1MM[E] *EMP* 50
SIC 4731 Truck transportation brokers
Pr: Bryan Arceneaux

D-U-N-S 06-974-6725
LOUISIANA TECH UNIVERSITY
1100 Hull Ave, Ruston, LA 71270
Tel (318) 257-3267 *Founded/Ownrshp* 1894
Sales 125.9MM[E] *EMP* 1,230
SIC 8221 University; University
Pr: Daniel D Reneau
**VP:* Dr Kenneth W REA
**VP:* Joseph R Thomas Jr

D-U-N-S 12-028-2330
LOUISIANA UNITED METHODIST CHILDREN AND FAMILY SERVICES INC
LA METHODIST CHILDREN'S HOME
904 Deville Ln, Ruston, LA 71270-6313
Tel (318) 255-5020 *Founded/Ownrshp* 1902
Sales 16.4MM *EMP* 320[E]
Accts Robinson Gardner Langston & Br
SIC 8361 Orphanage; Orphanage
Pr: Terrel Deville
**CFO:* Howard Ingram Jr
**Ex VP:* John Allen
Pgrm Dir: Rebecca Hutchinson

D-U-N-S 87-937-0815 EXP
LOUISIANA VALVE SOURCE LLC
101 Metals Dr, Youngsville, LA 70592-5812
Tel (337) 856-9100 *Founded/Ownrshp* 2005
Sales 65.6MM[E] *EMP* 129
SIC 5084 Industrial machinery & equipment; Industrial machinery & equipment
Pr: Jory L Bernard
**CFO:* Susan Guidry
**Treas:* Corin Vincent
**VP:* Malcolm D Ardoin
Exec: Kerry Landry
VP Opers: David Ardoin
Opers Mgr: Mike Owens
Sls Mgr: Mike Gilliland
Sales Asso: Kevin Bigot
Sales Asso: Stacy Clark
Sales Asso: Louis Falgout

D-U-N-S 09-859-6901
LOUISIANA WHOLESALE DRUG CO INC
GOOD NEIGHBOR PHARMACY
2085 I 49 S Service Rd, Sunset, LA 70584
Tel (337) 662-1040 *Founded/Ownrshp* 1979
Sales 350.0MM *EMP* 75
Accts John S Dowling & Company Ope
SIC 5122 Drugs & drug proprietaries; Druggists' sundries; Drugs & drug proprietaries; Druggists' sundries
Pr: Gayle R White
CFO: Ricky Ducote
**VP:* Carl Savoie
Sales Exec: Buddy Ryder

D-U-N-S 78-995-0326
LOUISIANA WORKERS COMPENSATION CORP
LWCC
2237 S Acadian Thruway, Baton Rouge, LA 70808-2371
Tel (225) 924-7788 *Founded/Ownrshp* 1991
Sales NA *EMP* 250[E]
SIC 6331 Workers' compensation insurance; Workers' compensation insurance
CEO: Kristin W Wall
**Pr:* Stephen W Cavanaugh
**Pr:* Christian Wall
**Ch:* Donald T Boysie Bollinger
Bd of Dir: Hampton Johnson
Assoc VP: Sandra Mayfield
Sr VP: William B Bangs
**Sr VP:* Paul Buffone
**Sr VP:* Mike De Laat
**Sr VP:* John Hawie
**Sr VP:* Jeffrey H Skagg
Sr VP: Jeffrey Skaggs
**Sr VP:* Michael Stiltner
**VP:* Michel J Stiltner

D-U-N-S 06-150-0534 EXP
▲ **LOUISIANA-PACIFIC CORP** (OR)
414 Union St Ste 2000, Nashville, TN 37219-1711
Tel (615) 986-5600 *Founded/Ownrshp* 1972
Sales 1.9MMM *EMP* 4,500
Tkr Sym LPX *Exch* NYS
SIC 2493 2436 2435 2421 2431 Strandboard, oriented; Particleboard products; Fiberboard, other vegetable pulp; Hardboard, tempered; Panels, softwood plywood; Panels, hardwood plywood; Veneer stock, hardwood; Lumber: rough, sawed or planed; Moldings & baseboards, ornamental & trim; Strandboard, oriented; Particleboard products; Fiberboard, other vegetable pulp; Hardboard, tempered; Panels, softwood plywood; Panels, hardwood plywood; Veneer stock, hardwood; Lumber: rough, sawed or planed; Moldings & baseboards, ornamental & trim
CEO: Curtis M Stevens
**Ch Bd:* E Gary Cook
CFO: Sallie B Bailey
Treas: Mark G Tobin
Ex VP: Richard S Olszewski
VP: Dave Crowe
VP: Jeff F Duncan
VP: Craig Sichling
VP: Don Walker
VP: Walter M Wirfs
Exec: Bo Adams
Exec: Lazere Chris
Exec: Brian Daley
Exec: Dee Graham
Exec: Doggett John
Exec: Tim Johnson
Exec: Aaron Kluger
Exec: Wiggs Thompson
Exec: Conchuratt Tom
Board of Directors: Daniel K Frierson, Kurt M Landgraf, Colin D Watson, John W Weaver

D-U-N-S 94-450-3122
■ **LOUISIANA-PACIFIC CORP**
(*Suby of* LOUISIANA-PACIFIC CORP) ★
805 Sw Broadway, Portland, OR 97205-3339
Tel (503) 821-5000 *Founded/Ownrshp* 1986
Sales 31.9MM[E] *EMP* 440

SIC 8741 Administrative management; Administrative management
Ch Bd: Mark A Suwyn
**Treas:* Curtis M Stevens
**VP:* William L Hebert
Dir IT: Jim Scott
IT Man: John Bowden
IT Man: Dave Kramer
IT Man: Randy Thompson
Genl Couns: Christopher Keyes

LOUISIANA'S PREMIER PRODUCTS
See CHEF JOHN FOLSE & CO LLC

D-U-N-S 09-538-1984 IMP
LOUISVILLE & JEFFERSON COUNTY METROPOLITAN SEWER DISTRICT
700 W Liberty St, Louisville, KY 40203-1911
Tel (502) 540-6000 *Founded/Ownrshp* 1946
Sales 477.0MME *EMP* 608
Accts Crowe Horwath Llp Louisville
SIC 4952 Sewerage systems; Sewerage systems
Ex Dir: Herbert Scharttein
CFO: Tony Ralston
Ex Dir: Becky Bennett
IT Man: Chad Collier
IT Man: Maria Mullaney
Opers Mgr: Alex Novak

D-U-N-S 96-827-1564
LOUISVILLE ARENA AUTHORITY INC
1 Arena Plz, Louisville, KY 40202-1363
Tel (502) 367-5107 *Founded/Ownrshp* 2006
Sales 26.4MM *EMP* 15
SIC 7941 Stadium event operator services
Ch Bd: Jim Host

D-U-N-S 00-637-1926 IMP/EXP
LOUISVILLE BEDDING CO INC
10400 Bunsen Way, Louisville, KY 40299-2500
Tel (502) 491-3370 *Founded/Ownrshp* 1889
Sales 184.7MME *EMP* 750
SIC 2392 3949 Mattress pads; Sporting & athletic goods; Mattress pads; Sporting & athletic goods
Pr: Stephen Elias
Ch Bd: Steve Elias
COO: Mary Jo Kissel
Ex VP: Eric Besner
Genl Mgr: Kevin O'Connell
Genl Mgr: Damon Roberts
Dir IT: Kevin Crafton
Web Dev: Thomas Robertson
VP Mktg: Kim Robertson
VP Sls: Denise Matlack
Board of Directors: Prentice E Brown, Thomas Buetow, Robert Hill, John Minihan, Michael Seago, Gary Sterling, Alice Walter

D-U-N-S 09-469-5913
LOUISVILLE CARE CENTER
410 W 5th St, Louisville, NE 68037-6006
Tel (402) 234-2125 *Founded/Ownrshp* 1972
Sales 412.0MM *EMP* 65
SIC 8059 Nursing home, except skilled & intermediate care facility; Nursing home, except skilled & intermediate care facility
Nrsg Dir: Cindy Shera
HC Dir: Britany Knispel
HC Dir: Cheryl Taylor
Board of Directors: Robert Keyes, Mark Leibman, James Schleuter, Darlene Zaloudek

D-U-N-S 00-637-6248
LOUISVILLE FIRE BRICK WORKS
4500 Louisville Ave, Louisville, KY 40209-1410
Tel (502) 363-2656 *Founded/Ownrshp* 1889
Sales 35.5MME *EMP* 50
SIC 3255 5085 Brick, clay refractory; Industrial supplies; Refractory material
Pr: Bill C Shuck
Genl Mgr: Greg Shuck
Sales Asso: Kevin Webb

LOUISVILLE FORGE & GEAR WORKS
See AICHI FORGE USA INC

D-U-N-S 07-404-9941
LOUISVILLE FREE PUBLIC LIBRARY INC
301 York St, Louisville, KY 40203-2205
Tel (502) 574-1600 *Founded/Ownrshp* 1903
Sales 4.7MME *EMP* 325
SIC 8231 Public library; Public library
**Prin:* Jefferson C Govt
**Prin:* City of Louisville
Off Mgr: Sandra Murphy

D-U-N-S 00-694-5505 IMP
■ **LOUISVILLE GAS AND ELECTRIC CO** (KY)
(*Subsy of* LG&E AND KU ENERGY LLC) ★
220 W Main St Ste 1400, Louisville, KY 40202-5301
Tel (502) 627-2000 *Founded/Ownrshp* 1913, 2010
Sales 1.5MMM *EMP* 1,029E
Accts Ernst & Young Llp Louisville
SIC 4931 4911 4924 Electric & other services combined; Generation, electric power; Transmission, electric power; Distribution, electric power; Natural gas distribution; Electric & other services combined; Generation, electric power; Transmission, electric power; Distribution, electric power; Natural gas distribution
Ch Bd: Victor A Staffieri
**COO:* Paul W Thompson
CFO: Kent W Blake
Chf Mktg O: Martyn Gallus
VP: DOT Brien
Prgrm Mgr: Shirley Campbell
Prgrm Mgr: Bill Cooper
CIO: Eric Slavinsky
QA Dir: Abby Hedges
IT Man: Eric Peek
Netwrk Eng: Jason Hamm
Board of Directors: S Bradford Rives, Vincent Sorgi, William H Spence

D-U-N-S 12-099-0457
LOUISVILLE HOSPITAL
JOSEPH GILENE, PRESIDENT
217 E Chestnut St, Louisville, KY 40202-1821
Tel (502) 587-1100 *Founded/Ownrshp* 2002
Sales 856.0ME *EMP* 3,500
SIC 8062 General medical & surgical hospitals
Pr: Joseph Gilene

D-U-N-S 03-761-8217 IMP/EXP
LOUISVILLE LADDER INC
LOUISEVILLE
7765 National Tpke # 190, Louisville, KY 40214-4803
Tel (502) 636-2811 *Founded/Ownrshp* 2005
Sales 182.4MME *EMP* 850
SIC 2499 Ladders, wood; Metal ladders; Construction & mining machinery; Ladders, wood
Pr: Ricardo Clausse
**VP:* Florinda E Altamirano
IT Man: Stephen Dean
Natl Sales: Jay Howard
Sls Dir: Robert Zimmerman
Mktg Mgr: John McDaniel
Sls Mgr: Luis Pastrana

LOUISVILLE METRO
See LOUISVILLE-JEFFERSON COUNTY METRO GOVERNMENT

D-U-N-S 55-742-5642
LOUISVILLE METRO HOUSING AUTHORITY
420 S 8th St, Louisville, KY 40203-1906
Tel (502) 569-3400 *Founded/Ownrshp* 1935
Sales NA *EMP* 401
SIC 9531 ;
Exec: Wavid Ray
IT Man: Mike Loughmiller

D-U-N-S 00-799-2795 IMP
LOUISVILLE MILL SUPPLY CO (KY)
520 S 15th St, Louisville, KY 40203-1722
Tel (502) 583-0050 *Founded/Ownrshp* 1934, 2011
Sales 34.1MME *EMP* 30
SIC 5085 Industrial supplies; Mill supplies
Pr: Craig Shellmaker
**Sec:* Michele Shellhamer
Sales Exec: Denise Davis

D-U-N-S 10-003-9965
LOUISVILLE MUNICIPAL SCHOOL DISTRICT
112 S Columbus Ave, Louisville, MS 39339-2934
Tel (662) 773-3411 *Founded/Ownrshp* 1872
Sales 20.8MME *EMP* 450
Accts Watkins Ward & Stafford Pllc
SIC 8211 Public elementary & secondary schools; Public elementary & secondary schools
**Pr:* W Mort Donald

D-U-N-S 02-407-0997
LOUISVILLE PAVING CO INC
TENNI-TRAC SPORTS SURFACES
(*Subsy of* LOUISEVILLE PAVING) ★
1801 Payne St, Louisville, KY 40206-1999
Tel (502) 471-1130 *Founded/Ownrshp* 1949
Sales 43.2MME *EMP* 150E
Accts Mountjoy Chilton Medley Llp L
SIC 1611 2951 2851 Surfacing & paving; Asphalt paving mixtures & blocks; Paints & allied products; Surfacing & paving; Asphalt paving mixtures & blocks; Paints & allied products
Pr: William B Dougherty
**CEO:* John T Doughtery Jr
Treas: Edward Miller
**VP:* Joseph W Dougherty
VP: John T Doughery Jr
VP: Douglas Wood
Dir Bus: Larry Hobson
IT Man: Debbie Wilson
QC Dir: Kevin Klain
Opers Mgr: Jason Grace
Opers Mgr: Jason Schmidt

D-U-N-S 06-297-3128
LOUISVILLE REGIONAL AIRPORT AUTHORITY
700 Administration Dr, Louisville, KY 40209-1537
Tel (502) 368-6524 *Founded/Ownrshp* 1928
Sales 72.7MM *EMP* 200
Accts Crowe Horwath Llp Louisville
SIC 4581 Airport; Airport
Pr: CT Miller
CFO: Michael Burris
Sec: Robert L Knust
Ofcr: Michael Sims
Dir IT: Janet Barrow

LOUISVILLE SLUGGER
See HILLERICH & BRADSBY CO

D-U-N-S 02-407-1110 IMP
LOUISVILLE TILE DISTRIBUTORS INC (KY)
CAMEO MARBLE
4520 Bishop Ln, Louisville, KY 40218-4508
Tel (502) 452-2037 *Founded/Ownrshp* 1955
Sales 146.4MME *EMP* 280
SIC 5032 5211 1743 Cut stone & stone products; Tile, ceramic; Ceramic wall & floor tile; Terrazzo, tile, marble, mosaic work; Marble building stone; Ceramic wall & floor tile; Tile, ceramic; Terrazzo, tile, marble, mosaic work
Ch Bd: Aubrey J Wilcox
**Pr:* Robert Deangelis
**Pr:* Jerry G Short
CFO: Bob Knabel
CFO: Howard Passamanack
Ex VP: Don Kincaid
**Ex VP:* Carolyn Wilcox
**VP:* Robert Knabel
Admn Mgr: Travis Wilcox
IT Man: Beth Wilhite
Manager: Patti Smith-Connelly

D-U-N-S 00-637-9374 IMP
LOUISVILLE TIN & STOVE CO (KY)
COZY HEATERS
(*Subsy of* BRINLY-HARDY CO) ★
737 S 13th St, Louisville, KY 40210-1007
Tel (502) 589-5380 *Founded/Ownrshp* 1981, 2014
Sales 22.1MME *EMP* 100
SIC 3433 Wall heaters, except electric
Pr: Richard A Mudd
Sfty Mgr: Steve Lincoln
Sls Mgr: Robert Busby

D-U-N-S 02-027-5319
LOUISVILLE TITLE AGENCY FOR NW OH INC (OH)
626 Madison Ave Ste 100, Toledo, OH 43604-1106
Tel (419) 248-4611 *Founded/Ownrshp* 1948
Sales NA *EMP* 91
SIC 6411
Pr: John W Martin
Ex VP: William Lewis
Exec: Marrianne Cappiello
CIO: Edwin Martin
VP Mktg: Bill Dwyer
Genl Couns: Jim Lindsay

D-U-N-S 04-117-2545
LOUISVILLE WATER CO
550 S 3rd St, Louisville, KY 40202-1839
Tel (502) 569-3600 *Founded/Ownrshp* 1854
Sales 330.2MME *EMP* 447
Accts Crowe Howart Llp Louisville
SIC 4941 Water softener service; Water supply
Pr: James H Brammell
Pr: Dawn Czajka
COO: Helena Dahman
CFO: Robert Miller
Treas: Amber Halloran
VP: Spencer Bruce
VP: Barbara Dickens
VP: Karla Teasley
VP: David Vogel
Exec: Jim Smith
Dir Risk M: Don McKay
Comm Man: Barbara Crow

D-U-N-S 07-313-5584
LOUISVILLE-JEFFERSON COUNTY METRO GOVERNMENT
LOUISVILLE METRO
527 W Jefferson St, Louisville, KY 40202-2814
Tel (502) 574-2003 *Founded/Ownrshp* 1779
Sales NA *EMP* 6,500
Accts Crowe Horwath Llp Louisville
SIC 9111 Executive offices; ; Executive offices;
Dir Vol: Andrew Brooks
CFO: Jane Driskell
**CFO:* Daniel Frockt
Ofcr: John Marshall
Ofcr: Heather Palmer
Ofcr: Pamela Windsor
Exec: Tina Lentz
Mng Dir: Angela Wilson
Brnch Mgr: Dolores Delahanty
Brnch Mgr: Ted Pullen
IT Man: Amit Sarkar

D-U-N-S 11-429-7534
LOUNORA INDUSTRIES INC
1402 Waterworks Rd, Columbus, MS 39701-2757
Tel (662) 328-1685 *Founded/Ownrshp* 1986
Sales 38.1MME *EMP* 300E
Accts Te Lott & Company Cpa S Col
SIC 2511 2599 Wood household furniture; Hotel furniture; Wood household furniture; Hotel furniture
Prin: Reau Berry
**Pr:* J Reau Berry
**CFO:* Judy Griffith
**VP:* Kelli Berry

LOUP CITY HEALTH
See ROSE LANE HOME

LOUP POWER DISTRICT
See LOUP RIVER PUBLIC POWER DISTRICT

D-U-N-S 06-863-9764
LOUP RIVER PUBLIC POWER DISTRICT
LOUP POWER DISTRICT
2404 15th St, Columbus, NE 68601-5021
Tel (402) 564-3171 *Founded/Ownrshp* 1933
Sales 97.7MME *EMP* 132
Accts Dana F Cole & Company Llp G
SIC 4911 ; Generation, electric power; Distribution, electric power; Transmission, electric power; ; Generation, electric power; Distribution, electric power; Transmission, electric power
Pr: Neal Suess
**Pr:* Ron Ziola
**CFO:* Kim Grubaugh
Bd of Dir: Rich Aerni
Bd of Dir: Larry Zach
**VP:* David Bell
**VP:* Kendall Christensen
IT Man: Les Hardesty

LOURDES HEALTH NETWORK
See OUR LADY OF LOURDES HOSPITAL AT PASCO

LOURDES HEALTH SYSTEM
See LOURDES MEDICAL CENTER OF BURLINGTON COUNTY

LOURDES HOSPITAL
See OUR LADY OF LOURDES MEMORIAL HOSPITAL INC

LOURDES HOSPITAL
See MERCY HEALTH PARTNERS - LOURDES INC

D-U-N-S 87-766-8814
LOURDES HOSPITAL
169 Riverside Dr, Binghamton, NY 13905-4198
Tel (607) 798-5111 *Founded/Ownrshp* 1987
Sales 14.6MME *EMP* 1,800
SIC 8062 General medical & surgical hospitals; General medical & surgical hospitals
Pr: John Oneil
**CFO:* Brian Regan
**VP:* Kathlyn Appler

D-U-N-S 83-935-5513
LOURDES MEDICAL ASSOCIATES PA
HMSO
500 Grove St Ste 100, Haddon Heights, NJ 08035-1761
Tel (856) 796-9390 *Founded/Ownrshp* 1995
Sales 21.5MME *EMP* 179E
SIC 8011 Offices & clinics of medical doctors
Pr: Steven Fox
**Ex VP:* Pierre Scott
**VP:* Denise Cortland
**VP:* Joseph Egan
**VP:* Linda O'Donnell

D-U-N-S 79-987-9569 EXP
LOURDES MEDICAL CENTER OF BURLINGTON COUNTY
LOURDES HEALTH SYSTEM
(*Subsy of* OUR LADY OF LOURDES MEDICAL CENTER INC) ★
218 Sunset Rd, Willingboro, NJ 08046-1110
Tel (609) 835-2900 *Founded/Ownrshp* 1998
Sales 122.9MM *EMP* 530E
SIC 8062 General medical & surgical hospitals
CEO: Alexander Hatala
Podiatrist: Ira Silverman
Pharmcst: Lisa Dinoto
Pharmcst: Elizabeth Lash

D-U-N-S 79-649-0857
LOURDES MEDICAL CENTER OF BURLINGTON COUNTY A NEW JERSEY NONPROFIT CORP
(*Subsy of* CATHOLIC HEALTH EAST) ★
218 Sunset Rd, Willingboro, NJ 08046-1110
Tel (609) 835-2900 *Founded/Ownrshp* 2007
Sales 59.4MM *EMP* 3,440E
Accts Deloitte Tax Llp Philadelphia
SIC 8062 General medical & surgical hospitals; General medical & surgical hospitals
Prin: Randall Maguire

D-U-N-S 83-140-6798
LOURDES UNIVERSITY
6832 Convent Blvd Unit 2, Sylvania, OH 43560-4891
Tel (419) 885-3211 *Founded/Ownrshp* 1958
Sales 37.0MM *EMP* 223
SIC 8221 Colleges & universities; Colleges & universities
Pr: Robert C Helmer
Assoc Dir: Shawn Bussell
Store Mgr: Ann Morris
CTO: Andrea Domachowski
Psych: Rebecca Kim
Genl Couns: B Ahluwalia
Snr Mgr: Mary McPeak
Snr Mgr: James O'Brien
Snr Mgr: Andy Rogers

D-U-N-S 09-852-8243
LOURDES-NOREEN MCKEEN RESIDENCE FOR GERIATIC CARE INC
315 S Flagler Dr, West Palm Beach, FL 33401-5677
Tel (561) 655-8544 *Founded/Ownrshp* 1962
Sales 14.9MM *EMP* 300
SIC 8059 8052 6513 Nursing home, except skilled & intermediate care facility; Intermediate care facilities; Apartment building operators; Nursing home, except skilled & intermediate care facility; Intermediate care facilities; Apartment building operators
**Pr:* De Loudes Veilleux
Off Mgr: Gail Luciano
Mktg Dir: Edith Pecan

D-U-N-S 01-016-6403
LOUREIRO ENGINEERING ASSOCIATES INC (CT)
100 Northwest Dr, Plainville, CT 06062-1559
Tel (860) 747-6181 *Founded/Ownrshp* 1975
Sales 57.6MME *EMP* 115
SIC 8711 Consulting engineer; Consulting engineer
CEO: Jeffrey J Loureiro
**CFO:* Brian Fox
VP: Margaret Averill
VP: Kevin Vidmar
Snr PM: Jeremy Paradis

D-U-N-S 15-280-1796
LOUTEX CONTRACTORS INC
13086 Us Highway 84 E, Joaquin, TX 75954-2526
Tel (936) 269-4791 *Founded/Ownrshp* 2003
Sales 59.9MME *EMP* 160
SIC 1623 Oil & gas pipeline construction; Oil & gas pipeline construction
Pr: Anthony Harvey
**VP:* Michael Harvey

D-U-N-S 19-848-9122
LOVCO CONSTRUCTION INC
1300 E Burnett St, Signal Hill, CA 90755-3512
Tel (562) 595-1601 *Founded/Ownrshp* 1988
Sales 22.9MME *EMP* 125
SIC 1794 1771 1611 Excavation work; Concrete work; Highway & street construction; General contractor, highway & street construction; Excavation work; Concrete work; Highway & street construction; General contractor, highway & street construction
Pr: Terry C Lovingier
**Treas:* Katie Lovingier
**VP:* Steve Barnett
**VP:* Matt Lovinger
**VP:* Mike McGougan

LOVE & QUICHES DESSERTS
See LOVE & QUICHES LTD

D-U-N-S 07-579-6441 EXP
LOVE & QUICHES LTD
LOVE & QUICHES DESSERTS
178 Hanse Ave, Freeport, NY 11520-4698
Tel (516) 623-8800 *Founded/Ownrshp* 1974
Sales 73.6MME *EMP* 250
SIC 2053 Frozen bakery products, except bread; Frozen bakery products, except bread
CEO: Irwin Axelrod
**Pr:* Andrew Axelrod
Pr: Larry Lamarr
CFO: Jeffrey Appleman
CFO: Corey M Aronin
**Ch:* Susan Axelrod
Ex VP: Karen Sullivan
VP: Joan Axelrod
VP: Michael Goldstein
VP: Michael Goldstien
VP: Aaron Heisler
VP: Bonnie Warstadt

D-U-N-S 87-312-3848 EXP
LOVE A CHILD INC
12411 Commerce Lakes Dr, Fort Myers, FL 33913-8663
Tel (239) 210-6107 *Founded/Ownrshp* 1985
Sales 34.5MM *EMP* 12
Accts Dixon Hughes Goodman Llp Ashe
SIC 8661 Non-denominational church; Non-denominational church
Pr: Sharyn Burnette
**Prin:* Jennifer Whitis
**Ex Dir:* Bobby Burnette
Ex Dir: Robert Burnette
**Ex Dir:* Sandra Smith

D-U-N-S 00-387-5135
LOVE ADVERTISING INC (TX)
770 S Post Oak Ln Ste 101, Houston, TX 77056-1913
Tel (713) 552-1055 *Founded/Ownrshp* 1979
Sales 42.0MM *EMP* 48
SIC 7311 Advertising agencies
Pr: Brenda Love
CFO: Ken Ramage
Ex VP: Billie Vanslyke
VP: Shannon Moss

D-U-N-S 00-228-3430 IMP
LOVE AUTO GROUP INC (SC)
LOVE AUTOMOTIVES
1255 Knox Abbott Dr, Cayce, SC 29033-3325
Tel (803) 407-4800 *Founded/Ownrshp* 1939, 1961
Sales 58.5MM^E *EMP* 128
SIC 5511 7515 Automobiles, new & used; Passenger car leasing; Automobiles, new & used; Passenger car leasing
Ch Bd: Nathan J Love
**Pr:* Michael E Love
**VP:* Steve Hyatt
Store Mgr: Robbie Bedwell
Sls Mgr: Michael Corley
Sls Mgr: Micky Fox
Sls Mgr: Craig Willis
Sales Asso: Gary Ellis
Sales Asso: Dennis Rowe

LOVE AUTOMOTIVES
See LOVE AUTO GROUP INC

D-U-N-S 00-721-7573
LOVE BOTTLING CO (OK)
3200 S 24th St W, Muskogee, OK 74401-8222
Tel (918) 682-3434 *Founded/Ownrshp* 1919
Sales 32.0MM *EMP* 120
SIC 5149 5145 Soft drinks; Snack foods; Soft drinks; Snack foods
CEO: William Barry Love
**VP:* James Gully
Plnt Mgr: James Gulley
Mktg Mgr: Joe Harrison
Sls Mgr: Willard Perry

D-U-N-S 00-724-0740 EXP
LOVE BOX CO LLC
(*Suby of* PRATT INDUSTRIES (USA) INC) ★
700 E 37th St N, Wichita, KS 67219-3510
Tel (316) 838-0851 *Founded/Ownrshp* 2005
Sales 13.9MM^E *EMP* 1,400
SIC 2653 2448 4213

D-U-N-S 61-038-7813
LOVE CHRYSLER INC
4401 S Padre Island Dr, Corpus Christi, TX 78411-4409
Tel (361) 991-5683 *Founded/Ownrshp* 1989
Sales 27.8MM^E *EMP* 70
SIC 5511 Automobiles, new & used; Automobiles, new & used
Pr: Marion Luna Brem
**Sec:* A G Noaman

D-U-N-S 79-196-8378 IMP
LOVE CULTURE INC
2423 E 23rd St, Los Angeles, CA 90058-1201
Tel (614) 625-4781 *Founded/Ownrshp* 2007
Sales 166.9MM^E *EMP* 1,000^E
SIC 5621 Women's clothing stores; Women's clothing stores
Pr: Jai Rhee
CFO: David Griffith
Treas: Myong Kim

D-U-N-S 61-316-9023
LOVE HEALTHCARE LLC
2830 S Redwood Rd Ste A, West Valley City, UT 84119-5626
Tel (801) 973-0900 *Founded/Ownrshp* 2005
Sales 4.3MM^E *EMP* 300
SIC 8082 Home health care services; Home health care services

LOVE LEXUS TOYOTA
See C & O MOTORS INC

D-U-N-S 80-799-8901
LOVE LEXUS TOYOTA INC
C & M MOTORS
1433 Maccorkle Ave, Saint Albans, WV 25177-1826
Tel (304) 727-7777 *Founded/Ownrshp* 1994
Sales 47.0MM^E *EMP* 200
SIC 5511 7538 7515 5531 Automobiles, new & used; General automotive repair shops; Passenger car leasing; Automotive & home supply stores; Automobiles, new & used; General automotive repair shops; Passenger car leasing; Automotive & home supply stores
Pr: James Love
VP: Mary Love

D-U-N-S 79-315-5870
LOVE SAVINGS HOLDING CO
212 S Central Ave Ste 201, Saint Louis, MO 63105-3545
Tel (314) 512-8500 *Founded/Ownrshp* 1985
Sales NA *EMP* 305
SIC 6719 Investment holding companies, except banks; Investment holding companies, except banks
Ch Bd: Andrew S Love
**Pr:* Laurence A Schiffer
**VP:* John Wiest

D-U-N-S 92-685-6266 IMP
LOVETREE FASHION INC
1053 Towne Ave, Los Angeles, CA 90021-2053
Tel (213) 747-3755 *Founded/Ownrshp* 2009
Sales 32.9MM *EMP* 30
SIC 2335 Women's, juniors' & misses' dresses; Women's, juniors' & misses' dresses
CEO: Dong Sheng Ning
Off Mgr: John Kang

D-U-N-S 06-195-2268
LOVED ONES IN HOME CARE LLC
144 7th Ave, South Charleston, WV 25303-1452
Tel (304) 744-4081 *Founded/Ownrshp* 1999
Sales 15.0MM *EMP* 1,200
SIC 8082 Visiting nurse service
CEO: Donna Skeen
COO: Jenna Skeen
Genl Mgr: Ronald Locke

D-U-N-S 00-625-8438
LOVEGREEN INDUSTRIAL SERVICES INC (MN)
2280 Sibley Ct, Saint Paul, MN 55122-1998
Tel (651) 707-9560 *Founded/Ownrshp* 1948
Sales 21.9MM^E *EMP* 60
SIC 1796 3599 3537 Machinery installation; Machine shop, jobbing & repair; Industrial trucks & tractors
Pr: Vernon J Lovegreen III
**VP:* Gerald Johnson
**VP:* Kevin Lovegreen
Snr PM: Chuck Oestreich

D-U-N-S 00-509-3620 IMP
LOVEJOY INC (IL)
2655 Wisconsin Ave, Downers Grove, IL 60515-4299
Tel (630) 852-0500 *Founded/Ownrshp* 1900, 1989
Sales 60.0MM^E *EMP* 280
SIC 3568 Couplings, shaft: rigid, flexible, universal joint, etc.; Pulleys, power transmission; Couplings, shaft: rigid, flexible, universal joint, etc.; Pulleys, power transmission
Pr: M W Hennessy
**VP:* James Krejci
Genl Mgr: Jim Lovejoy
Genl Mgr: Oscar Sitkowski

D-U-N-S 02-967-4694
LOVEJOY INDEPENDENT SCHOOL DISTRICT
259 Country Club Rd, Allen, TX 75002-7643
Tel (469) 742-8000 *Founded/Ownrshp* 1940
Sales 50.2MM *EMP* 530
Accts Hankins Eastup Deaton Tonn
SIC 8211 Public elementary & secondary schools; School board; Public elementary & secondary schools; School board
**CFO:* Shay Adams
Schl Brd P: Ann Casey

D-U-N-S 01-824-2412
LOVEJOY INDUSTRIES INC
194 S Main St, Versailles, KY 40383-1214
Tel (859) 873-6828 *Founded/Ownrshp* 1982
Sales 48.9MM^E *EMP* 400
SIC 3364 3363 3544 Zinc & zinc-base alloy die-castings; Aluminum die-castings; Special dies, tools, jigs & fixtures; Zinc & zinc-base alloy die-castings; Aluminum die-castings; Special dies, tools, jigs & fixtures
Ch Bd: Walter R Lovejoy
**Pr:* Matthew Lovejoy
**CFO:* Mark Kepf
VP: Daniel Crea
Off Mgr: Anna Ward

LOVELACE BIOMEDICAL
See LOVELACE RESPIRATORY RESEARCH INSTITUTE

D-U-N-S 04-591-1138
LOVELACE BIOMEDICAL & ENVIRONMENTAL RESEARCH INSTITUTE
INHALATION TOXICOLOGY RES INST
(*Suby of* LOVELACE BIOMEDICAL) ★
2425 Ridgecrest Dr Se, Albuquerque, NM 87108-5127
Tel (505) 348-9400 *Founded/Ownrshp* 1975
Sales 114.7MM *EMP* 465
Accts Moss Adams Llp Albuquerque N
SIC 8733 Medical research; Medical research
**Pr:* Ross Leclaire
**Treas:* Richard McGivney
Board of Directors: Robert Rubin

D-U-N-S 60-279-1881
LOVELACE HEALTH SYSTEM INC
(*Suby of* AHS NEW MEXICO HOLDINGS, INC.)
4101 Indian School Rd Ne # 110, Albuquerque, NM 87110-3991
Tel (800) 808-7363 *Founded/Ownrshp* 2003
Sales 297.2MM^E *EMP* 3,183^E
SIC 8062 General medical & surgical hospitals; General medical & surgical hospitals
Pr: Ron Stern
**CFO:* Stephen Forney
Ofcr: Tobey Merlin
**VP:* Clint Adams
VP: Carole Henry
VP: Bob Skinner
Dir Case M: Vicki Broshious
Off Mgr: Brenda Yantorn
Netwrk Eng: Rene Ruiz
S&M/VP: Nanci George
Mktg Dir: Serena Lyons

D-U-N-S 07-576-9000
LOVELACE RESPIRATORY RESEARCH INSTITUTE
LOVELACE BIOMEDICAL
2425 Ridgecrest Dr Se, Albuquerque, NM 87108-5127
Tel (505) 348-9400 *Founded/Ownrshp* 1947
Sales 82.6MM *EMP* 555
Accts Moss Adams Llp Albuquerque N
SIC 8733 8731 Scientific research agency; Commercial physical research; Scientific research agency; Commercial physical research
Pr: Robert W Rubin
CFO: Richard McGivney
**CFO:* Shannon Toma
Bd of Dir: John Shelton
Exec: Lorraine Vigil
Assoc Dir: Jane Maestas
MIS Dir: Larry Padgett
IT Man: Kendall Hanson
IT Man: Ruth Kief
Site Mgr: Alicia Gonzales
Board of Directors: Joe Fulcher, Melvin Twiest MD, W Phelps Anderson, Major General Retired, Frank Bond, Jackie Lovelace-Johnson, Sara Esterson-Bond, Judy Jones, Augustine Choi MD, Jack McCarthy MD, Norm Corzine, Barbara Rogers, Jane Delgado Phd, Robert Rubin Phd, John Doesburg, John Shelton, Gregory Downey MD, Pam Sullivan, David Durgin, James Swenberg

D-U-N-S 07-288-9421
LOVELAND CITY SCHOOL DISTRICT
757 S Lebanon Rd, Loveland, OH 45140-9308
Tel (513) 683-5600 *Founded/Ownrshp* 1930
Sales 27.3MM^E *EMP* 417
Accts Mary Taylor Cpa Auditor Of St
SIC 8211 Public elementary & secondary schools; High school, junior or senior; School board; Public elementary & secondary schools; High school, junior or senior; School board
VP: Dave Blumberg
VP: Lisa Schmidt
VP: Heidi Weber
**Prin:* James Kolp
**Prin:* Judy McClanahan
**Prin:* Linda Pennington
**Prin:* Gary Waits
Dir IT: Nancy Glasgow
Dir IT: David Knapp
Psych: Sarah Ninnemann
Psych: Robin Schneider

D-U-N-S 02-391-2736 IMP
LOVELAND DISTRIBUTING CO INC
2290 Dabney Rd, Richmond, VA 23230-3344
Tel (804) 355-4943 *Founded/Ownrshp* 1951
Sales 37.4MM^E *EMP* 165
SIC 5181

D-U-N-S 03-211-5206
LOVELAND FORD LINCOLN INC
999 E Eisenhower Blvd, Loveland, CO 80537-3923
Tel (970) 667-2220 *Founded/Ownrshp* 1956
Sales 25.6MM^E *EMP* 60
SIC 5511 7538 5531 Automobiles, new & used; General automotive repair shops; Automobile & truck equipment & parts; Automobiles, new & used; General automotive repair shops; Automobile & truck equipment & parts
Pr: Daniel Zwisler
Genl Mgr: Josh Ingrim

D-U-N-S 04-780-3051 IMP
LOVELAND PRODUCTS INC
PLATTE CHEMICAL CO
(*Suby of* CROP PRODUCTION SERVICES INC) ★
3005 Rocky Mountain Ave, Loveland, CO 80538-9001
Tel (970) 356-8920 *Founded/Ownrshp* 1970
Sales 105.8MM^E *EMP* 340
SIC 2879 Agricultural chemicals; Agricultural chemicals
Pr: Richard Gearheard
**VP:* Robert Boyce
VP: Warren Hammerbeck
**VP:* Debra Keith
**VP:* Brent Smith
Genl Mgr: Pat Payne

D-U-N-S 05-133-3257
LOVEN SYSTEMS LLC
(*Suby of* DATAFACTZ) ★
22260 Haggerty Rd Ste 285, Northville, MI 48167-8971
Tel (248) 504-6870 *Founded/Ownrshp* 2014
Sales 8.8MM^E *EMP* 330
SIC 7379 Computer related consulting services

LOVERING VOLVO OF CONCORD
See ALCO MOTORS INC

D-U-N-S 04-433-2005
LOVES BAKERY INC (HI)
(*Suby of* FIRST BAKING CO.,LTD.)
911 Middle St, Honolulu, HI 96819-2317
Tel (808) 841-2088 *Founded/Ownrshp* 1851, 1981
Sales 45.9MM^E *EMP* 310
SIC 2051 Bread, cake & related products; Bread, cake & related products
Pr: Michael J Walters
**Ch Bd:* Masahide Hosokai
**Treas:* Ed Sunahara
**Treas:* Alan Hideo Yamada
**VP:* Byron James Masaru Chong

D-U-N-S 03-304-0353
LOVES TRAVEL STOPS & COUNTRY STORES INC
10601 N Pennsylvania Ave, Oklahoma City, OK 73120-4108
Tel (405) 302-6500 *Founded/Ownrshp* 1964
Sales 5.1MMM^E *EMP* 10,600
SIC 5541 5411 5947 Truck stops; Convenience stores, independent; Gift, novelty & souvenir shop; Truck stops; Convenience stores, independent; Gift, novelty & souvenir shop
Ch Bd: Tom E Love
Pr: Reg Kennerty
**Pr:* Frank Love
**CFO:* Doug Stussi
**Ex VP:* Kevin Asbury
**Ex VP:* Tom Edwards
**Ex VP:* Shane Wharton
VP: Jenny Meyer
**VP:* Terry Ross
**VP:* Jim Xenos
Genl Mgr: Shane Anderson

LOVE'S TRVL STOPS CNTRY STORES
See MUSKET CORP

LOVESAC
See SAC ACQUISITION LLC

D-U-N-S 14-397-1484
LOVETT CUSTOM HOMES INC
INTOWN HOMES
1520 Oliver St Ste 270, Houston, TX 77007-6035
Tel (713) 961-3877 *Founded/Ownrshp* 2004
Sales 26.0MM^E *EMP* 125
SIC 8741 Construction management
Prin: Frank Liu
VP Sls: David Foor

D-U-N-S 07-810-7992
LOVETT SCHOOL
4075 Paces Ferry Rd Nw, Atlanta, GA 30327-3099
Tel (404) 231-8744 *Founded/Ownrshp* 1926
Sales 56.5MM *EMP* 450
Accts Metcalf Davis Cpas Atlanta G
SIC 8211 Preparatory school; Preparatory school
**CFO:* Thomas A Avery
Bd of Dir: Lucy Barry
Bd of Dir: Mary Battle
Bd of Dir: Howard Boyd
Bd of Dir: Brooks Cowles
Bd of Dir: Lauren Gearon
Bd of Dir: Linda Gray
Bd of Dir: Kurt Hohlstein
Bd of Dir: Kathy Hunsinger
Bd of Dir: Jane Maddox
Bd of Dir: Heather Metzger
Bd of Dir: Wright Mitchell
Bd of Dir: Allison Peavy
Trst: John Williams
Assoc Dir: Janie Coleman
Assoc Dir: Jamar Jeffers

D-U-N-S 03-970-7385 IMP
LOVIN ENTERPRISES INC
DREAMGIRL INTERNATIONAL
5548 Lindbergh Ln, Bell, CA 90201-6410
Tel (323) 268-0220 *Founded/Ownrshp* 2003
Sales 29.8MM *EMP* 75
SIC 5137 2389 2329

D-U-N-S 95-887-5205
LOVING CARE AGENCY INC
LINKS2CARE
(*Suby of* EPIC HEALTH SERVICES INC) ★
611 Rte 46 W Ste 200, Hasbrouck Heights, NJ 07604
Tel (201) 403-9300 *Founded/Ownrshp* 2015
Sales 294.8MM^E *EMP* 6,500
SIC 8011 8082 Home health care services; Pediatrician; Home health care services
Pr: Glen R Cavallo
**CFO:* Patrick Patton
Sr VP: Karen Dargo-Mullahey
**Sr VP:* George Herchenroether
VP: Cathy Anwyl
VP: David Cwiertnia
Brnch Mgr: Alma Phillips
Brnch Mgr: Madeline Presz
Brnch Mgr: Deb Smolko
CTO: Stacey Evanuik

LOVING HANDS HM HLTH CARE SVCS
See LOVING HANDS LTD

D-U-N-S 12-228-2460
LOVING HANDS LTD
LOVING HANDS HM HLTH CARE SVCS
676 Winters Ave Ste 1, Paramus, NJ 07652-3913
Tel (201) 265-3523 *Founded/Ownrshp* 1984
Sales 25.1MM^E *EMP* 1,200
SIC 7363 8082 Medical help service; Home health care services; Medical help service; Home health care services
CFO: Paul Provost
**VP:* Nick Provost

D-U-N-S 12-351-4762
LOVINGTON MUNICIPAL SCHOOLS
18 W Washington Ave, Lovington, NM 88260-4023
Tel (575) 739-2200 *Founded/Ownrshp* 1918
Sales 18.2MM^E *EMP* 450
SIC 8211 Public elementary & secondary schools; School board; Public elementary & secondary schools; School board
Ofcr: Christy Stinson
Prin: Cliff Burch

D-U-N-S 02-011-6729
LOVITT & TOUCHE INC
7202 E Rosewood St # 200, Tucson, AZ 85710-1368
Tel (520) 722-3000 *Founded/Ownrshp* 1969
Sales NA *EMP* 200
SIC 6411 Insurance agents & brokers; Insurance agents & brokers
Pr: Steven D Touche
**CFO:* Denise Birger
**VP:* Joseph C Dhuey
**VP:* Mary Katherine Krugman
VP: Matthew Nelson
**VP:* John L Shearman
**VP:* David Mark Wilder

D-U-N-S 83-010-4386
LOW BOOK SALES & LEASING INC
3371 S State St, Salt Lake City, UT 84115-4526
Tel (801) 467-4576 *Founded/Ownrshp* 1993
Sales 50.9MM^E *EMP* 138
SIC 5521 Automobiles, used cars only
Pr: Dave Nielson
**Sec:* Charles G Felt
**VP:* Jarrod Clarke
VP: Kevin Gallagher
Sls Mgr: CAM Bennee
Sls Mgr: Cash Brown
Sls Mgr: Justin Evens

LOW COST POWER
See VERDE ENERGY USA INC

LOW COUNTRY FOOD BANK
See LOWCOUNTRY FOOD BANK INC

LOW COUNTRY HARLEY
See S II S LLC

D-U-N-S 36-133-8312
LOW INCOME INVESTMENT FUND
LIIF
50 California St Ste 2900, San Francisco, CA 94111-4708
Tel (415) 772-9094 *Founded/Ownrshp* 1984
Sales 23.2MM *EMP* 42
Accts Grant Thornton Llp San Franci
SIC 8399 Community development groups
Pr: Nancy O Andrews
V Ch: Ellen Seidman
**COO:* Kimberly Latimer-Nelligan
CFO: Larry Liederman
**CFO:* Donald P Lofe Jr
Treas: Byron Phillips
Ofcr: Eve Siegel
**Sr VP:* Brian Prater

D-U-N-S 07-888-3748
LOW T CENTER LLC
1920 E State Highway 114, Southlake, TX 76092-6510
Tel (817) 410-3800 *Founded/Ownrshp* 2009
Sales 28.6MM^E *EMP* 200
SIC 8011 Offices & clinics of medical doctors
CTO: Ferny Espinoza
Opers Mgr: Addison Alm
Mktg Dir: Holly Krebs
Mktg Dir: Eric Sardina
Surgeon: William Reilly
Med Dir: Lawrence Huber

D-U-N-S 00-327-8264 IMP/EXP
LOW TEMP INDUSTRIES INC (GA)
L T I
9192 Tara Blvd, Jonesboro, GA 30236-4913
Tel (678) 379-0913 *Founded/Ownrshp* 1947
Sales 48.7MM^E *EMP* 150
SIC 3589 Food warming equipment, commercial; Food warming equipment, commercial
Pr: Benjamin E Casey
**CEO:* William E Casey
**CFO:* Richard V Priegel
**Prin:* David W Pearson
Dist Mgr: Bill Steadman
Mfg Dir: Mike Bell
Sls Dir: Greg Chance
Mktg Mgr: David Pearson

D-U-N-S 07-646-2480
LOW VOLTAGE WIRING LTD
L V W ELECTRONICS
1540 Quail Lake Loop, Colorado Springs, CO 80906-4652
Tel (719) 540-8900 *Founded/Ownrshp* 1972
Sales 21.8MM^E *EMP* 75
SIC 1731 3661 3663 Cable television installation; Fiber optic cable installation; Sound equipment specialization; Fire detection & burglar alarm systems specialization; Telephone & telegraph apparatus; Radio & TV communications equipment
CEO: Rusty Griffith
**Pr:* John Borchert
**VP:* Patricia Lewis
**VP:* Kendall Mangun
**VP:* Anwyn Sather

D-U-N-S 00-749-6391
LOW-TEMP INSULATIONS INC (NE)
L T I CONTRACTING
22631 N 18th Ave, Phoenix, AZ 85027-1352
Tel (623) 516-9100 *Founded/Ownrshp* 1958
Sales 25.6MM^E *EMP* 100
SIC 1541 1742

D-U-N-S 16-591-4102
LOWCOUNTRY FOOD BANK INC
LOW COUNTRY FOOD BANK
2864 Azalea Dr, Charleston, SC 29405-8216
Tel (843) 747-8146 *Founded/Ownrshp* 1983
Sales 36.4MM *EMP* 24
Accts Elliott Davis Llc/Pllc Colum
SIC 8322 Social service center
Ch: H Scott Blue
Dir Vol: Mary McLernon
**COO:* Jarmaine Husser
Bd of Dir: Shawn A Jenkins
VP: Scott Blue

D-U-N-S 01-845-0452
LOWE & YOUNG INC
7058 E Lincoln Way, Wooster, OH 44691-8614
Tel (330) 262-6111 *Founded/Ownrshp* 1947
Sales 21.0MM *EMP* 23
Accts Long Cook & Samsa Inc Woos
SIC 5083 Farm & garden machinery; Farm & garden machinery
Pr: Bill Hartzler
Treas: Stephanie Luginbuhl
**VP:* Jason Steiner
Off Admin: Teeka Hartzler
Sls Mgr: Dave Colvin

D-U-N-S 13-182-3630 EXP
■ **LOWE BOATS INC**
(*Suby of* BRUNSWICK CORP) ★
2900 Industrial Dr, Lebanon, MO 65536-4521
Tel (417) 532-9101 *Founded/Ownrshp* 2004
Sales 76.7MM^E *EMP* 325
SIC 3732 Boat building & repairing; Boat building & repairing
Pr: Les Crawford
VP: Terry Goodrich
**VP:* John Metcalf
Sfty Dirs: Carl Rader
Mtls Mgr: Mark Mathis
Mtls Mgr: Jim Mooney
Ql Cn Mgr: Dave Hagen
VP Sls: Keith Yunger
Mktg Dir: Beverly Ramsey

LOWE BUICK-OLDS-PONTIAC-GMC
See LOWE DEVAN INC

D-U-N-S 03-160-2261
LOWE DEVAN INC
LOWE BUICK-OLDS-PONTIAC-GMC
1151 Gault Ave S, Fort Payne, AL 35967-4973
Tel (256) 845-0922 *Founded/Ownrshp* 1974
Sales 31.2MM^E *EMP* 90
SIC 5511 5015 7538 7532 New & used car dealers; Automotive supplies, used; General automotive repair shops; Body shop, automotive
Pr: Devan Lowe
**VP:* Kendall Hamilton

D-U-N-S 00-331-6700
LOWE ELECTRIC SUPPLY CO (GA)
1525 Forsyth St, Macon, GA 31201-1442
Tel (478) 743-8661 *Founded/Ownrshp* 1903, 1997
Sales 67.1MM^E *EMP* 70
SIC 5063 5074 Electrical supplies; Lighting fixtures; Plumbing & hydronic heating supplies; Electrical supplies; Lighting fixtures; Plumbing & hydronic heating supplies
CEO: James W Kinman Jr
**CFO:* Brenda S Lord
**CFO:* James D McKinnon
Brnch Mgr: Bo Southers
IT Man: Angela Fogle
IT Man: Micah Mole
Sls Mgr: John Davis
Sls Mgr: Wyatt Griffies
Sales Asso: Greg Brewer
Sales Asso: Ian Johnson
Sales Asso: Enoch Lake

D-U-N-S 10-389-0356
LOWE ENTERPRISES INC
LEI AG SEATTLE
11777 San Vicente Blvd # 900, Los Angeles, CA 90049-6615
Tel (310) 820-6661 *Founded/Ownrshp* 2011
Sales 750.1MM^E *EMP* 5,000
SIC 6531 6552 Real estate managers; Subdividers & developers; Real estate managers; Subdividers & developers
Pr: Robert J Lowe
V Ch: Brian T Prinn
Pr: Joseph Heredia
Pr: Michael H Lowe
Pr: Rachel Pederson
Pr: Grant Rickhoff
Pr: James Sabatier
Pr: Rick Swagerty
COO: Lisa Annaheim
COO: Dick Poladian
CFO: William Raphae
CFO: William T Wethe
Ex VP: Jeffrey Allen
Ex VP: Jeffrey L Allen
Ex VP: Janice Diehl
Ex VP: Terri Haack
Ex VP: Thomas P Luersen
Ex VP: Peter O'Keeffe
Ex VP: Matthew H Walker
Sr VP: Jeffery Allen
Sr VP: Lynda S Cook

D-U-N-S 05-967-3103
LOWE MANUFACTURING CO INC
18903 High Point Rd, Viola, WI 54664-8916
Tel (608) 538-4000 *Founded/Ownrshp* 1983
Sales 24.6MM^E *EMP* 90
SIC 3531 3423 Posthole diggers, powered; Entrenching machines; Hand & edge tools
Pr: Richard Lowe
**VP:* Mary Lowe

D-U-N-S 86-906-2901
LOWELL AREA SCHOOL DISTRICT
LOWELL AREA SCHOOLS
300 High St, Lowell, MI 49331-1478
Tel (616) 897-1470 *Founded/Ownrshp* 1887
Sales 40.2MM *EMP* 450
Accts Hungerford Aldrin Nichols &
SIC 8211 Public elementary school; Public junior high school; Public senior high school; Public elementary school; Public junior high school; Public senior high school

LOWELL AREA SCHOOLS
See LOWELL AREA SCHOOL DISTRICT

D-U-N-S 07-952-1928
LOWELL CITY OF (INC)
375 Merrimack St Rm 27, Lowell, MA 01852-5939
Tel (978) 970-4200 *Founded/Ownrshp* 1826
Sales NA *EMP* 3,000
SIC 9311 ;
**CFO:* Thomas Moses
CIO: Mir N Fernandez

D-U-N-S 10-739-6520
LOWELL COMMUNITY HEALTH CENTER INC
161 Jackson St, Lowell, MA 01852-2103
Tel (978) 937-9700 *Founded/Ownrshp* 1985
Sales 29.1MM *EMP* 285
Accts Alexander Aronson Finning Wes
SIC 8011 Offices & clinics of medical doctors; Offices & clinics of medical doctors
Pr: Dorcas-Grigg Saito
**COO:* Henry Och
**CFO:* Robert Ebersole
Dir IT: Mark Conway
Dir IT: Richard Naples
IT Man: Robin Licata
Doctor: Hamid Danesh MD
Nrsg Dir: Christine Isabelle
Pgrm Dir: Sidney Liang

LOWELL ENGINEERING
See MAGNA MIRRORS NORTH AMERICA LLC

D-U-N-S 00-695-4895
LOWELL FIVE CENT SAVINGS BANK (MA)
55 Technology Dr Ste 1, Lowell, MA 01851-5203
Tel (978) 452-1300 *Founded/Ownrshp* 1854
Sales NA *EMP* 180
SIC 6036 State savings banks, not federally chartered; State savings banks, not federally chartered
Pr: David E Wallace
**Ch:* Robert A Caruso
Ofcr: Chris Geaghan
Ofcr: Normand Zarella
VP: Thomas Boucher
VP: Jimmie Denwiddie
VP: Thomas Hosey
VP: Mara Sweeney
Sls&Mrk Ex: Amy B Werner

LOWELL FOODS
See LOWELL INTERNATIONAL CO

D-U-N-S 01-944-1377
LOWELL GENERAL HOSPITAL
L G H
295 Varnum Ave, Lowell, MA 01854-2193
Tel (978) 937-6000 *Founded/Ownrshp* 1891
Sales 405.4MM *EMP* 3,000^E
SIC 8062 Hospital, professional nursing school; Hospital, professional nursing school
Pr: Normand E Deschene
Chf Rad: Jonas Berman
**Ch Bd:* Clemintine Alexis
**COO:* Joseph White
**CFO:* Susan Green
**CFO:* Richard Jeffcote
Treas: Thomas Rubricki
**Ex VP:* Joseph Jody White III
**VP:* Amy Hoey
**VP:* Wayne E Pasanen
Dir Lab: Leslie Davis
Dir Rad: Judy Canal
Dir Rad: Michelle O'Brien

D-U-N-S 01-529-0331 IMP
LOWELL INTERNATIONAL CO
LOWELL FOODS
9234 Belmont Ave, Franklin Park, IL 60131-2808
Tel (847) 260-5018 *Founded/Ownrshp* 1993
Sales 40.7MM^E *EMP* 50
SIC 5141 5192 Food brokers; Magazines
Pr: Conrad J Lowell

D-U-N-S 02-073-8837
LOWELL JOINT SCHOOL DISTRICT
11019 Valley Home Ave, Whittier, CA 90603-3098
Tel (562) 943-0211 *Founded/Ownrshp* 1902
Sales 25.1MM *EMP* 300
SIC 8211 Public elementary school; Public junior high school; Public elementary school; Public junior high school
CEO: Patricia Howell
Prin: Kathy Jabuka
Prin: Kim Likert
Prin: Tara Ryan
Schl Brd P: Fred Schambeck
Instr Medi: Sarah Ornelas

LOWELL SR HIGH SCHOOL
See TRI-CREEK SCHOOL CORP

D-U-N-S 14-474-1881
LOWELL WOLF INDUSTRIES INC
WOLF PAVING
612 N Sawyer Rd, Oconomowoc, WI 53066-9231
Tel (262) 965-2121 *Founded/Ownrshp* 1983
Sales 83.2MM^E *EMP* 301
SIC 1611 1794 General contractor, highway & street construction; Surfacing & paving; Excavation & grading, building construction; General contractor, highway & street construction; Surfacing & paving; Excavation & grading, building construction
Pr: Lowell Wolf
**VP:* Devin Wolf
Ql Cn Mgr: Mark Sweeting
Sls Mgr: Julie Messmer

LOWELL'S PAINT PLUS
See ZITCO INC

D-U-N-S 61-988-7367
LOWEN CORP
LOWEN SIGN COMPANY
1111 Airport Rd, Hutchinson, KS 67501-1983
Tel (620) 663-2161 *Founded/Ownrshp* 1984
Sales 76.3MM^E *EMP* 300
SIC 2759 3993 5999 2679 2752 Commercial printing; Signs & advertising specialties; Decals; Labels, paper: made from purchased material; Commercial printing, lithographic; Commercial printing; Signs & advertising specialties; Decals; Labels, paper: made from purchased material; Commercial printing, lithographic
Pr: Matt T Lowen
CFO: Linda Daniels
**Treas:* Linda L Daniels
Sr VP: Doug Cook
Dir Bus: Sean Carlson
Prgrm Mgr: Darren Keller
CTO: Geryl Hendrix
Dir IT: Kristin Wolfe
Sfty Mgr: Debra Lizalde
Plnt Mgr: Mary Purdue
Plnt Mgr: Gene Schierling
Board of Directors: Matt Lowen

LOWEN SIGN COMPANY
See LOWEN CORP

D-U-N-S 04-075-0317
LOWENSTEIN SANDLER LLP
65 Livingston Ave Ste 2, Roseland, NJ 07068-1725
Tel (973) 597-2500 *Founded/Ownrshp* 1978
Sales 109.0MM^E *EMP* 568
SIC 8111 General practice law office; General practice law office
CEO: Gary M Wingens
Pt: Michele J Alexander
Pt: David M Banker
Pt: Daniel J Barkin
Pt: Nicole Denise Bearce
V Ch: Herschel S Weinstein
CFO: William B Farrell
Treas: Robert G Minion
Sec: Bruce D Shoulson
Bd of Dir: Gina Buccellato
Bd of Dir: Diane Estevez
Bd of Dir: Laurie Pami

LOWEPRO
See DAYMEN US INC

D-U-N-S 14-609-9668
LOWER BRULE SIOUX TRIBE
187 Oyate Cir, Lower Brule, SD 57548-8500
Tel (605) 473-5561 *Founded/Ownrshp* 1934
Sales NA *EMP* 368^E
SIC 9131 Indian reservation; ; Indian reservation;
Genl Mgr: Annalisa Estes
IT Man: Trish Lundell
Snr Mgr: Steve Sievert

D-U-N-S 07-145-4888
LOWER BUCKS HOSPITAL (PA)
(*Suby of* PRIME HEALTHCARE SERVICES INC) ★
501 Bath Rd, Bristol, PA 19007-3190
Tel (215) 785-9200 *Founded/Ownrshp* 1954, 2012
Sales 71.7MM *EMP* 1,400
SIC 8062 General medical & surgical hospitals; General medical & surgical hospitals
CEO: Peter Adamo
**COO:* Matt Shelak
**CFO:* Courtney Coffman
Dir OR: Karen Bucy
**Prin:* Pete Caldwell
IT Man: Jason Wayne
Surgeon: Karl Helmold
Snr Mgr: Ranga RAO

D-U-N-S 04-408-9829
LOWER CAMDEN COUNTY REGIONAL EDUCATION ASSOCIATION
LOWER CAMDEN HIGH SCHOOL DST 1
200 Coopers Folly Rd, Atco, NJ 08004
Tel (856) 767-2850 *Founded/Ownrshp* 1939
Sales 59.5MM *EMP* 27
Accts Bowman & Company Llp
SIC 8211 School board; School board
**Pr:* Aurthur L Oppmann
**Treas:* Lois F Tigro
**VP:* Linda Geary
MIS Dir: Donato De Santis

LOWER CAMDEN HIGH SCHOOL DST 1
See LOWER CAMDEN COUNTY REGIONAL EDUCATION ASSOCIATION

D-U-N-S 14-437-2620
LOWER CAPE FEAR HOSPICE INC
1414 Physicians Dr, Wilmington, NC 28401-7335
Tel (800) 207-6908 *Founded/Ownrshp* 1978
Sales 34.8MM *EMP* 400
Accts Earney & Company Llp Wilming
SIC 8069 Specialty hospitals, except psychiatric; Specialty hospitals, except psychiatric
Pr: Lauren Myles-Bystron
V Ch: Charles Long
**CFO:* Deborah Pressley
**VP:* Mary McKenna
**VP:* Kimberly Paul
**VP:* Karen Reichow
**VP:* Laurie Taylor
VP: Gwen Whitley
Comm Man: Stacey Manning
Dir IT: Rob Stumpf
IT Man: Rebecca Peirce

D-U-N-S 10-060-4545
LOWER CAPE MAY REGIONAL SCHOOL DISTRICT
687 Route 9, Cape May, NJ 08204-4637
Tel (609) 884-3475 *Founded/Ownrshp* 1961
Sales 22.0MM^E *EMP* 300
Accts Inverso & Stewart Llc Marlto
SIC 8211 Public elementary & secondary schools; Public elementary & secondary schools

D-U-N-S 04-322-6885
LOWER COLORADO RIVER AUTHORITY
LCRA
3700 Lake Austin Blvd, Austin, TX 78703-3504
Tel (512) 473-3200 *Founded/Ownrshp* 1934
Sales 316.5M^E *EMP* 1,800
SIC 4911 4941 1629 Distribution, electric power; Water supply; Waste water & sewage treatment plant construction; Distribution, electric power; Water supply; Waste water & sewage treatment plant construction
Ch: Timothy Timmerman
V Ch: Hughes G Abell
CFO: John Miesmer
Bd of Dir: John H Mathews
VP: Bobby R Phillips
Area Supr: Bobby Fohn
Area Supr: Michael Moyer
Dist Mgr: Melinda Armbuster
**Genl Mgr:* Becky Motal
Genl Mgr: Ross Phillips
Software D: Michael Motal

D-U-N-S 09-535-9816
LOWER DAUPHIN SCHOOL DISTRICT INC
291 E Main St, Hummelstown, PA 17036-1799
Tel (717) 566-3721 *Founded/Ownrshp* 1966
Sales 60.0MM *EMP* 527
Accts Brown Schultz Sheridan & Fritz
SIC 8211 Public combined elementary & secondary school; School board; Public combined elementary & secondary school; School board
VP: Cindy Morris
Pr Dir: James Hazen
Teacher Pr: Angela Hepner
HC Dir: Andrew McCrea

LOWER FLORENCE COUNTY HOSPITAL
See LAKE CITY COMMUNITY HOSPITAL

D-U-N-S 02-267-5461
LOWER GREAT LAKES KENWORTH INC
WHITEFORD KENWORTH
4625 W Western Ave, South Bend, IN 46619-2303
Tel (574) 234-9007 *Founded/Ownrshp* 2000
Sales 71.6MM^E *EMP* 170
SIC 5511 5012 Trucks, tractors & trailers: new & used; Trucks, commercial; Trucks, tractors & trailers: new & used; Trucks, commercial
Pr: Ronald Whiteford II
Sls Mgr: Brad Burton

D-U-N-S 78-647-4049
■ **LOWER KEYS MEDICAL CENTER**
HMA
(*Suby of* HEALTH MANAGEMENT ASSOCIATES INC) ★
5900 College Rd, Key West, FL 33040-4342
Tel (305) 294-5531 *Founded/Ownrshp* 1989
Sales 107.4MM *EMP* 487
SIC 8062 General medical & surgical hospitals; General medical & surgical hospitals
CEO: Nicki Will
Nrsg Dir: Kim Bassett Rn

D-U-N-S 08-625-3507
LOWER KUSKOKWIM SCHOOL DISTRICT
1004 Ron Edwards Way, Bethel, AK 99559
Tel (907) 543-4824 *Founded/Ownrshp* 1977
Sales 23.7MM^E *EMP* 362
SIC 8211 Public elementary & secondary schools; Public elementary & secondary schools
Schl Brd P: Susan Murphy
Teacher Pr: Joshua Gill
HC Dir: Aaron Shock

D-U-N-S 83-101-5818
LOWER NECHES VALLEY AUTHORITY
LNVA
7850 Eastex Fwy, Beaumont, TX 77708-2815
Tel (409) 892-4011 *Founded/Ownrshp* 1933
Sales 33.9MM^E *EMP* 112
Accts Wathen Deshong & Juncker Llp
SIC 4941 Water supply; Water supply
Genl Mgr: Scott Hall
Treas: Jordan Reese

D-U-N-S 07-420-4991
LOWER NECHES VALLEY AUTHORITY INDUSTRIAL DEVELOPMENT CORP (TX)
LNVA
7850 Eastex Fwy, Beaumont, TX 77708-2815
Tel (409) 892-4011 *Founded/Ownrshp* 1933
Sales 23.5MM *EMP* 100
Accts Wathen Deshong & Juncker Llp
SIC 4941 Water supply; Water supply
**CFO:* Lewis Michael Daws
**Genl Mgr:* Scott Hall

D-U-N-S 12-162-4373
LOWER PIONEER VALLEY EDUCATIONAL COLLABORATIVE
LPVEC
174 Brush Hill Ave, West Springfield, MA 01089-1204
Tel (413) 735-2200 *Founded/Ownrshp* 1975
Sales 1.2MM *EMP* 300
SIC 8211 8249 Specialty education; Vocational schools; Specialty education; Vocational schools
Ex Dir: Anne S McKenzie
Cmptr Lab: Mary Schaller-Race

D-U-N-S 13-410-8310
LOWER RIO GRANDE VALLEY WORKFORCE DEVELOPMENT BOARD
WORKFORCE SOLUTIONS
3101 W Us Highway 83, McAllen, TX 78501-8247
Tel (956) 928-5000 *Founded/Ownrshp* 1999
Sales 49.0MM *EMP* 35^E
SIC 7361 Employment agencies; Employment agencies
CEO: Yvonne Gonzalez
CFO: Patrick Mele
VP: Nancy Reed

D-U-N-S 18-828-7122
LOWER TOWNSHIP BOARD OF EDUCATION
LOWER TOWNSHIP ELEMENTARY
905 Seashore Rd, Cape May, NJ 08204-4312
Tel (609) 884-9400 *Founded/Ownrshp* 1920
Sales 20.0MM^E *EMP* 265
SIC 8211 Public elementary & secondary schools; Public elementary & secondary schools

LOWER TOWNSHIP ELEMENTARY
See LOWER TOWNSHIP BOARD OF EDUCATION

D-U-N-S 07-979-9150
LOWER TOWNSHIP SCHOOL DISTRICT
834 Seashore Rd, Cape May, NJ 08204-4650
Tel (609) 884-9400 *Founded/Ownrshp* 2015
Sales 3.2MM^E *EMP* 289^E
SIC 8211 Public elementary & secondary schools

D-U-N-S 05-720-1667
LOWER VALLEY ENERGY INC
236 N Washington, Afton, WY 83110
Tel (307) 885-3175 *Founded/Ownrshp* 1937
Sales 55.6MM *EMP* 65
Accts Decoria Maichel & Teague Ps
SIC 4911 4924 Distribution, electric power; Transmission, electric power; Natural gas distribution; Distribution, electric power; Transmission, electric power; Natural gas distribution
Ch: Rod R Jensen
**CEO:* James R Webb
**Prin:* Peter Cook

D-U-N-S 07-575-3095
LOWER VALLEY HOSPITAL ASSOCIATION
FAMILY HEALTH WEST NURSING HM
228 N Cherry St, Fruita, CO 81521-2101
Tel (970) 858-9871 *Founded/Ownrshp* 1946
Sales 39.5MM *EMP* 435
SIC 8051 8059 8062 Skilled nursing care facilities; Personal care home, with health care; General medical & surgical hospitals; Skilled nursing care facilities; Personal care home, with health care; General medical & surgical hospitals
CEO: Mark Francis
**CFO:* Jason McCormick
Dir OR: Tarji Bond
Dir Lab: John Silva
Dir Rad: Michelle Angelo
Dir Rx: Melody White
QA Dir: Lynn Finley
IT Man: Cheryl Dean
IT Man: Patrick Yount

D-U-N-S 05-841-5662
LOWER YUKON SCHOOL DISTRICT INC
IGNACIOUS BEAN MEMORIAL SCHOOL
100 Main St, Mountain Village, AK 99632
Tel (907) 591-2411 *Founded/Ownrshp* 1976
Sales 26.0MM^E *EMP* 460^E
Accts Mikunda Cottrell & Co Anchor
SIC 8211 Public combined elementary & secondary school; Public combined elementary & secondary school
Bd of Dir: Caroline Ulak
Schl Brd P: Kate Thompson

D-U-N-S 12-248-3238
LOWERMYBILLS INC
LOWERMYBILLS.COM
(*Suby of* CORE DIGITAL MEDIA) ★
12181 Bluff Creek Dr, Playa Vista, CA 90094-2627
Tel (310) 348-6800 *Founded/Ownrshp* 2014
Sales 41.6MM^E *EMP* 200^E
SIC 7375 Information retrieval services; Information retrieval services
Pr: Steve Krazer
Bd of Dir: Nancyjane Goldston
VP: Jeff Hughes
VP: David Razavi
VP: Patricia Tobin
Exec: Aaron Wilson
QA Dir: Aldo Marinero
Software D: Ricardo Espergue
Sftwr Eng: Sharmila Velamur
Opers Mgr: Noah Staitman
Mktg Mgr: Yvette Garcia

LOWERMYBILLS.COM
See LOWERMYBILLS INC

D-U-N-S 15-193-5590
LOWERY CORP
APPLIED IMAGING
5282 East Paris Ave Se, Grand Rapids, MI 49512-9634
Tel (616) 554-5200 *Founded/Ownrshp* 1986
Sales 56.0MM *EMP* 225
SIC 5044 7379 Copying equipment;
Pr: John Lowery
Sec: Sandra Lowery
VP: Joe Green
VP: John Konyonbelt
Off Mgr: Janet Langerak
Manager: Gabe Price
Prd Mgr: Allen Husted
Sales Exec: Randy Magner
Sls Mgr: Victor Edgar
Sls Mgr: Jason Hartman
Sls Mgr: Brad Kelly

D-U-N-S 00-699-7142 IMP/EXP
▲ **LOWES COMPANIES INC** (NC)
1000 Lowes Blvd, Mooresville, NC 28117-8520
Tel (704) 758-1000 *Founded/Ownrshp* 1946
Sales 56.2MMM *EMP* 266,000
Tkr Sym LOW *Exch* NYS
SIC 5211 5031 5722 5064 Lumber & other building materials; Building materials, exterior; Building materials, interior; Household appliance stores; Electrical appliances, television & radio; Lumber & other building materials; Building materials, exterior; Building materials, interior; Household appliance stores; Electrical appliances, television & radio
Ch Bd: Robert A Niblock
COO: Rick D Damron
CFO: Robert F Hull Jr
Treas: Tiffany L Mason
Chf Cred: Ross W McCanless
Chf Mktg O: Marci P Grebstein
Ofcr: Maureen K Ausura
Ofcr: Michael A Jones
Ex VP: Michael K Brown
Ex VP: Bob Gfeller
Ex VP: J Michael Mabry Jr
Sr VP: Maureen Ausura
Sr VP: Cedric T Coco
Sr VP: Ronnie E Damron
Sr VP: Matthew V Hollifield
Sr VP: Dennis R Knowles
Sr VP: Richard D Maltsbarger
Sr VP: Brian N Peace
VP: Richard Elledge
Exec: Sarah Miller
Board of Directors: Bertram L Scott, Raul Alvarez, Eric C Wiseman, David W Bernauer, Angela F Braly, Laurie Z Douglas, Richard W Dreiling, Robert L Johnson, Marshall O Larsen, Richard K Lochridge, James H Morgan

D-U-N-S 04-451-5187
LOWES FOOD STORES INC
JUST SAVE
(*Suby of* ALEX LEE INC) ★
1381 Old Mill Cir Ste 200, Winston Salem, NC 27103-1497
Tel (336) 659-2429 *Founded/Ownrshp* 1984
Sales 759.1MM^E *EMP* 8,000
Accts Stocks Smith Campbell & Dend
SIC 5411 Supermarkets, chain; Supermarkets, chain
Ch Bd: Boyd Lee George
**Pr:* Steve Hall
**Sec:* Ron W Knedlik
VP: Dwight Beane
VP: Michael Moore
Store Dir: Kate Allred
Prac Mgr: Donna Cline
Genl Mgr: Pat Fraser
Store Mgr: Frank Locicero
CIO: Mark McSwain
Advt Dir: Lisa Selip
Board of Directors:

D-U-N-S 01-881-0275 EXP
■ **LOWES HOME CENTERS LLC**
(*Suby of* LOWES COMPANIES INC) ★
1605 Curtis Bridge Rd, Wilkesboro, NC 28697-2263
Tel (336) 658-4000 *Founded/Ownrshp* 1958
Sales 31.3MMM^E *EMP* 209,850
SIC 5211 5031 5722 5064 Lumber & other building materials; Building materials, exterior; Building materials, interior; Household appliance stores; Electrical appliances, television & radio; Lumber & other building materials; Building materials, exterior; Building materials, interior; Household appliance stores; Electrical appliances, television & radio
CEO: Robert Niblock
**Pr:* Larry D Stone
**CFO:* Robert F Hull Jr
**Treas:* James A Cook III
**Ex VP:* Gregory M Bridgeford
**Ex VP:* Micheal K Brown
**Ex VP:* Joesph M Mabry Jr
**Sr VP:* Maureen K Ausura
Sr VP: Rick Damron
**Sr VP:* Matthew V Hollifield
Sr VP: Kevin Skidmore

LOWE'S MARKET
See PAY AND SAVE INC

LOWES MOTOR SPEEDWAY
See CHARLOTTE MOTOR SPEEDWAY LLC

LOWGRADE LUMBER
See SILVARIS CORP

D-U-N-S 87-859-3102
LOWMAN HOME INC
2101 Fortress Dr, White Rock, SC 29177
Tel (803) 732-3000 *Founded/Ownrshp* 1911
Sales 19.0MM^E *EMP* 400
SIC 8051 6513 6514 Skilled nursing care facilities; Apartment building operators; Residential building, four or fewer units: operation; Skilled nursing care facilities; Apartment building operators; Residential building, four or fewer units: operation
Ofcr: Melissa Yetter
Nrsg Dir: Lynn Avery
Nrsg Dir: Dee Longno
HC Dir: Victoria Geronimakis

LOWNDES BOARD OF SUPERVISORS
See COUNTY OF LOWNDES

D-U-N-S 18-386-0444
LOWNDES CO SCHOOL DISTRICT
BOARD OF EDUCATION
80 Commerce St, Hayneville, AL 36040-2788
Tel (334) 548-2131 *Founded/Ownrshp* 1900
Sales 16.0MM^E *EMP* 443
SIC 8211 Public elementary & secondary schools; Public elementary & secondary schools
IT Man: Donald Dotson

D-U-N-S 19-301-1335
LOWNDES CO SCHOOL DISTRICT
1053 Highway 45 S, Columbus, MS 39701-8601
Tel (662) 244-5000 *Founded/Ownrshp* 1985
Sales 35.7MM^E *EMP* 835
SIC 8211 Public elementary & secondary schools; School board; Public elementary & secondary schools; School board
HC Dir: Donna Manning

LOWNDES COUNTY BOARD OF COMMIS
See COUNTY OF LOWNDES

D-U-N-S 15-338-2205
LOWNDES COUNTY BOARD OF EDUCATION INC
1592 Norman Dr, Valdosta, GA 31601-3581
Tel (229) 245-2250 *Founded/Ownrshp* 1871
Sales 98.1MM *EMP* 1,002
Accts Greg S Griffin Atlanta Geor
SIC 8211 Public elementary & secondary schools; Public elementary & secondary schools
CFO: Susan S Swader

D-U-N-S 96-339-3710
LOWNDES COUNTY SCHOOL DISTRICT
1053 Highway 45 S, Columbus, MS 39701-8601
Tel (662) 244-5000 *Founded/Ownrshp* 2010
Sales 18.1MM^E *EMP* 603^E
SIC 8211 Elementary & secondary schools
Pr: Jane Kilgore
**VP:* Robert Barksdale

D-U-N-S 07-979-9733
LOWNDES COUNTY SCHOOLS
1592 Norman Dr, Valdosta, GA 31601-3581
Tel (229) 245-2250 *Founded/Ownrshp* 2015
Sales 11.5MM^E *EMP* 1,088^E
SIC 8211 Public elementary & secondary schools
Area Mgr: Libby Peters

D-U-N-S 08-472-9094
LOWNDES DROSDICK DOSTER KANTOR & REED PROFESSIONAL ASSOCIATION (FL)
215 N Eola Dr, Orlando, FL 32801-2095
Tel (407) 843-4600 *Founded/Ownrshp* 1969
Sales 22.2MM^E *EMP* 200
SIC 8111 General practice attorney, lawyer; General practice attorney, lawyer
CEO: John F Lowndes
**Pr:* Nicholas A Pope
**Treas:* Hal H Kantor
**VP:* William E Doster

D-U-N-S 09-354-3205
LOWNDES MEDICAL CLINIC
(*Suby of* HOSPITAL-NORTH MISSISSIPPI MED) ★
56 Dutch Ln, Columbus, MS 39702-5500
Tel (662) 329-3808 *Founded/Ownrshp* 1970
Sales 72.9MM^E *EMP* 12
SIC 8011 General & family practice, physician/surgeon; General & family practice, physician/surgeon
Dir Lab: Robbye Adams

D-U-N-S 00-792-9268
LOWRIE BRUCE CHEVROLET INC (TX)
711 Sw Loop 820, Fort Worth, TX 76134-1299
Tel (817) 293-5811 *Founded/Ownrshp* 1915, 1966
Sales 65.5MM^E *EMP* 128
SIC 5511 Automobiles, new & used; Pickups, new & used; Automobiles, new & used; Pickups, new & used
Prin: Bruce Lowrie

**Treas:* Karen Peterson
**Sec:* Karen Teames
**VP:* Maurine Lowrie
**VP:* Roddy Lowrie
**VP:* Randy Shapiro
Sls Dir: Terry Powell
Sls Mgr: Scott Dreyer
Sls Mgr: Mike Ross
Board of Directors: Ernest L Allen Jr

D-U-N-S 08-674-5452 EXP
LOWRY HOLDING CO INC
LOWRY SOLUTIONS
9420 Maltby Rd, Brighton, MI 48116-8801
Tel (810) 229-7200 *Founded/Ownrshp* 1979
Sales 150.2MM^E *EMP* 135^E
SIC 5045 2672 8742 7373 5044 5734 Computers, peripherals & software; Coated & laminated paper; Management consulting services; Systems integration services; Office equipment; Computer & software stores; Computers, peripherals & software; Coated & laminated paper; Management consulting services; Systems integration services; Office equipment; Computer & software stores
CEO: Michael Lowry
**CFO:* Mark Muehlenbeck
**Ex VP:* Steven R Lowry
VP: Steve Ellis
VP: Dale Karolak
VP: Paul Rakowicc

D-U-N-S 03-625-6469
LOWRY OIL CO INC
311 Old Salem Rd, Seneca, SC 29672-2330
Tel (864) 882-2441 *Founded/Ownrshp* 1991
Sales 21.4MM^E *EMP* 29
Accts Gary T Duncan Cpa
SIC 5171 5983 5172 Petroleum bulk stations; Fuel oil dealers; Petroleum products
Pr: Roy E Adams

D-U-N-S 18-611-3122
LOWRY PARK ZOOLOGICAL SOCIETY OF TAMPA INC
1101 W Sligh Ave, Tampa, FL 33604-5958
Tel (813) 935-8552 *Founded/Ownrshp* 1988
Sales 17.0MM *EMP* 333
Accts Cbiz Mhm Llc Clearwater Fl
SIC 7999 Zoological garden, commercial; Zoological garden, commercial
Pr: Craig Pugh
COO: Tony Moore
**CFO:* Elizabeth Hennig
**Treas:* Susan Touchton
Bd of Dir: Heather Henry
**Ex VP:* David Zimmerman
**VP:* Larry Killmar
**VP:* Jennifer McLachlan

LOWRY SOLUTIONS
See LOWRY HOLDING CO INC

D-U-N-S 05-146-6845
LOWRYS INC
8501 Telfair Ave, Sun Valley, CA 91352-3928
Tel (818) 768-4661 *Founded/Ownrshp* 1997
Sales 55.0MM *EMP* 60
Accts Lodgen Lacher Golditch Sard
SIC 5085 5169 Industrial supplies; Sealants; Industrial supplies; Sealants
Pr: Keith D Musante
**VP:* Mike Musante

LOWVILLE ACADEMY & CENTRAL SCH
See LOWVILLE CENTRAL SCHOOL DISTRICT

D-U-N-S 07-730-8757
LOWVILLE CENTRAL SCHOOL DISTRICT
LOWVILLE ACADEMY & CENTRAL SCH
7668 N State St, Lowville, NY 13367-1353
Tel (315) 376-9001 *Founded/Ownrshp* 1808
Sales 26.2MM *EMP* 250^E
Accts Poulsen & Podvin Cpa Pc W
SIC 8211 Public elementary & secondary schools; High school, junior or senior; Public elementary & secondary schools; High school, junior or senior
**CFO:* Sandra Rivers
**Prin:* Cheryl Steckly
Dir IT: Ron Gingerich
Schl Brd P: Thomas Schneeberger

D-U-N-S 00-333-9157 IMP
LOXCREEN CO INC
(*Suby of* M-D BUILDING PRODUCTS INC) ★
1630 Old Dunbar Rd, West Columbia, SC 29172-1936
Tel (803) 822-1600 *Founded/Ownrshp* 1947, 2012
Sales 102.6MM^E *EMP* 600
SIC 3354 3442 3089 Aluminum extruded products; Screen doors, metal; Storm doors or windows, metal; Screens, window, metal; Extruded finished plastic products; Aluminum extruded products; Screen doors, metal; Storm doors or windows, metal; Screens, window, metal; Extruded finished plastic products
CEO: John Parrish
**COO:* Joe T Comitale
**VP:* Howard McClure
**VP:* Ronald B Rhymer
**VP:* Fred Vermeer
**VP:* Rick Wheeler
Exec: Laraine Whitfield
Opers Mgr: Ronald Clayton

D-U-N-S 00-378-1424
■ **LOY CLARK PIPELINE CO** (OR)
(*Suby of* MDU CONSTRUCTION SERVICES GROUP INC) ★
19020 Sw Cipole Rd Ste A, Tualatin, OR 97062-8362
Tel (503) 644-2137 *Founded/Ownrshp* 1957, 1999
Sales 54.6MM^E *EMP* 350
SIC 1623 Pipeline construction; Pipeline construction
Pr: Michael Bass
VP: Vernon Raile
Ex Dir: Douglas Kane
Div Mgr: Roger Johnson
Dir IT: Steve Klepak
Netwrk Mgr: John Paist

D-U-N-S 07-194-4649
■ **LOYAL AMERICAN LIFE INSURANCE CO**
(*Suby of* CIGNA HEALTH AND LIFE INSURANCE CO) ★
250 E 5th St Fl 8, Cincinnati, OH 45202-4119
Tel (800) 633-6752 *Founded/Ownrshp* 2012
Sales NA *EMP* 235
SIC 6311 Life insurance
Pr: Charles Scheper
**Ch Bd:* Robert A Adams
**COO:* Jane Rollinson
**CFO:* W Randolph Samples
**Ex VP:* Mark Muething
**Sr VP:* Edward C Dahmer Jr
**Sr VP:* Linda McGhee

LOYAL ORDER OF THE MOOSE
See MOOSE INTERNATIONAL INC

D-U-N-S 83-101-7848
LOYAL SOURCE GOVERNMENT SERVICES LLC
3680 Avalon Park E Blvd, Orlando, FL 32828-9372
Tel (407) 306-8441 *Founded/Ownrshp* 2011
Sales 56.0MM *EMP* 1,000
SIC 8062 General medical & surgical hospitals; General medical & surgical hospitals
Prgrm Mgr: Jeff Henderson

D-U-N-S 02-969-9840
LOYDS ELECTRIC SUPPLY INC
LES
838 Stonetree Dr Hghrd Pl Highroad, Branson, MO 65615
Tel (417) 334-2171 *Founded/Ownrshp* 1961
Sales 51.5MM^E *EMP* 85
SIC 5063 5719 Electrical supplies; Lighting fixtures; Electrical supplies; Lighting fixtures
Pr: Phillip D Loyd
**VP:* Edith M Loyd
**VP:* Gary W Loyd
Opers Mgr: Daryl Froeschle
Mktg Mgr: Mike Martinez

D-U-N-S 06-858-9936
LOYOLA ACADEMY
1100 Laramie Ave, Wilmette, IL 60091-1089
Tel (847) 256-1100 *Founded/Ownrshp* 1909
Sales 38.2MM^E *EMP* 240
SIC 8211 7929 Catholic junior high school; Catholic senior high school; Entertainers & entertainment groups; Catholic junior high school; Catholic senior high school; Entertainers & entertainment groups
Pr: Patrick E McGrath
VP: Bob Miller
CIO: Jim Jackimiec
CTO: Faye Ryan
Psych: Nancy Menendezcollege

D-U-N-S 08-433-9308
LOYOLA HIGH SCHOOL OF LOS ANGELES
1901 Venice Blvd, Los Angeles, CA 90006-4401
Tel (213) 381-5121 *Founded/Ownrshp* 1865
Sales 21.8MM^E *EMP* 120
SIC 8211 Private senior high school
CEO: Gregory Moen Goethals
**Pr:* Father Robert Walsh
CFO: Jim Rich
**VP:* Robert Walsh
Psych: Darylanne Crowley
Psych: Geoffrey Joy
Psych: Dele Varga
Psych: Thomas Vavra

D-U-N-S 07-294-6239
LOYOLA MARYMOUNT UNIVERSITY INC
1 Lmu Dr Ste 100, Los Angeles, CA 90045-2677
Tel (310) 338-2700 *Founded/Ownrshp* 1911
Sales 338.6MM *EMP* 1,449
Accts Pricewaterhousecoopers Llp Lo
SIC 8221 University; University
Pr: Timothy Law Snyder
Pr: Barbara Busse
Bd of Dir: Kyle Studebaker
Sr VP: Joseph Hellige
VP: Christopher Chapple
VP: Kathleen Flanagan
**VP:* Victor J Gold
VP: Dennis Slon
Comm Man: Mike Andrick
Comm Man: Tonya Weger
Netwrk Eng: Christian Swan

D-U-N-S 08-598-8517
LOYOLA RECOVERY FOUNDATION INC
1159 Pittsford Victor Rd # 240, Pittsford, NY 14534-3827
Tel (585) 203-1005 *Founded/Ownrshp* 1917
Sales 5.0MM *EMP* 450
Accts Bonadio & Co Llp Pittsford
SIC 8093 8322 Specialty outpatient clinics; Substance abuse counseling; Specialty outpatient clinics; Substance abuse counseling
Pr: Christopher Wilkins Sr
**Pr:* Gerry Icenhower
**CFO:* Zach Fuller

D-U-N-S 07-492-7740
LOYOLA UNIVERSITY MARYLAND INC
4501 N Charles St, Baltimore, MD 21210-2601
Tel (410) 617-2000 *Founded/Ownrshp* 1852
Sales 285.5MM *EMP* 2,066
SIC 8221 College, except junior; College, except junior
Pr: Bryan Linnane
Pr: Jare Allen
Pr: John McKiernan
Pr: Jim Paquette
CFO: Christopher Murphy
**Treas:* John A Palmucci
Bd of Dir: Erin O'Keefe
Ofcr: Julie Ryder
**VP:* Susan Donovan
VP: Megan Gillick
**VP:* David Sears
Assoc Dir: David Alexander
Assoc Dir: Maureen Finnegan
Assoc Dir: Almarie Wood

D-U-N-S 96-391-0265
LOYOLA UNIVERSITY MEDICAL CENTER
2160 S 1st Ave Rm 255, Maywood, IL 60153-3328
Tel (708) 327-3300 *Founded/Ownrshp* 2010
Sales 1.0MMM *EMP* 19
SIC 8011 Physicians' office, including specialists
Prin: Patrick Stiff MD
Ofcr: William Cannon
VP: Leonard Vertuno
Dir Risk M: Kathleen Ostrowski
Assoc Dir: Joel Super
Adm Dir: Krista Curley
Adm Dir: Rose Lach
Off Mgr: Marie Chemik
Off Mgr: Sheila Fiala
Off Mgr: Rich Novotny
Pathlgst: Valdas Gasilionis

D-U-N-S 00-820-3309 IMP
LOYOLA UNIVERSITY NEW ORLEANS INC
6363 Saint Charles Ave, New Orleans, LA 70118-6195
Tel (504) 865-2011 *Founded/Ownrshp* 1912
Sales 120.1MM *EMP* 1,000
Accts Deloitte & Touche Llp New Or
SIC 8221 University; University
Pr: Rev Kevin W Wildes S J
CFO: Rhonda Cartwright
CFO: Linda Richard
VP: James Bradley
VP: John Calamia
VP: Ana Morales
Ex Dir: Bret Jacobs
Off Mgr: Amelia Vitt
Off Admin: Deborah Stansbury
CTO: Vicki McNeil
Mktg Mgr: Nathan Martin

D-U-N-S 07-436-8911 IMP/EXP
LOYOLA UNIVERSITY OF CHICAGO INC
820 N Michigan Ave Fl 1, Chicago, IL 60611-2196
Tel (312) 915-6000 *Founded/Ownrshp* 1870
Sales 540.0MM *EMP* 10,500
Accts Deloitte & Touche Llp Chicag
SIC 8221 University; University
Pr: Michael J Garanzini
**CFO:* Robert A Munson
Treas: Susan Bodin
Bd of Dir: Katherine Kaufka
Trst: John F Cuneo
Trst: Frank W Hogan
Trst: Robert L Parkinson
Trst: Joseph A Power
VP: Mark Feiereisel
VP: Philip Hale
VP: Susan Malisch
Assoc Dir: Kristi Hodges

LOZANO ENTERPRISES
See LA OPINION LP

D-U-N-S 00-725-9484 IMP/EXP
LOZIER CORP (NE)
6336 John J Pershing Dr, Omaha, NE 68110-1122
Tel (402) 457-8000 *Founded/Ownrshp* 1937
Sales 437.9MM *EMP* 2,490
Accts Mcgladrey Llp Omaha Ne
SIC 2541 2542 Store fixtures, wood; Partitions & fixtures, except wood; Store fixtures, wood; Partitions & fixtures, except wood
Pr: Sheri L Andrews
**CFO:* Steve Franz
**Ch:* Allan Lozier
**Treas:* Jan Muller
**Bd of Dir:* Dianne Lozier
Ex VP: Troy Wilhelm
VP: Monty Allgood
VP: Bob Braun
VP: Jay Daily
**VP:* Dave Gnuse
VP: Bill Naidenovich
VP: Neil Sherman
Dir Bus: Jason Uhl

D-U-N-S 79-119-5949 EXP
LOZIER FOUNDATION
6336 John J Pershing Dr, Omaha, NE 68110-1100
Tel (402) 457-8000 *Founded/Ownrshp* 2007
Sales 35.6MM *EMP* 8^E
SIC 3088 Plastics plumbing fixtures; Plastics plumbing fixtures
CEO: Cherry Andrews

D-U-N-S 09-578-4666
LOZIER OIL CO INC
1 S Sunny St, Farmington, IL 61531-1187
Tel (309) 245-4846 *Founded/Ownrshp* 1962
Sales 40.2MM^E *EMP* 25
SIC 5172 Petroleum products
Pr: Martin Lozier
**Pr:* Martine Lozier
**Sec:* Marjorie Lozier

D-U-N-S 12-194-6362
LOZIER STORE FIXTURES INC
(*Suby of* LOZIER CORP) ★
6336 John J Pershing Dr, Omaha, NE 68110-1100
Tel (402) 457-8000 *Founded/Ownrshp* 2013
Sales 76.9MM^E *EMP* 300
SIC 5046 Store machines; Shelving, commercial & industrial
Pr: Sheri Andrews
Treas: Jan Muller
Sales Asso: Dustin Murphy

LP
See LINCOLN PROPERTY CO

LP
See LEVENFELD PEARLSTEIN LLC

LP ACQUISITION CORP
See PULITZER INC

D-U-N-S 96-701-2852
LP COLUMBIA LLC
SIGNATURE HEALTHCARE COLUMBIA
1410 Trotwood Ave, Columbia, TN 38401-4901
Tel (931) 388-6443 *Founded/Ownrshp* 2011
Sales 950.0M *EMP* 11,375
SIC 8051 Skilled nursing care facilities; Skilled nursing care facilities
Prin: Deirdre M McManus
Sls&Mrk Ex: Kelly McGuire

D-U-N-S 84-103-3855 IMP/EXP
■ **LP EVANS MOTORS WPB INC**
MERCEDES BENZ OF MIAMI
(*Suby of* AUTONATION INC) ★
1200 Nw 167th St, Miami, FL 33169-5310
Tel (305) 707-0147 *Founded/Ownrshp* 1998
Sales 53.0MM^E *EMP* 160
SIC 5511 Automobiles, new & used; Automobiles, new & used
Pr: Mike Maroone
Genl Mgr: Joel Moskow
Sls Mgr: Jose Vallverdu

D-U-N-S 07-936-0241
LP HARRODSBURG LLC
HARRODSBURG HEALTH & REHAB CTR
853 Lexington Rd, Harrodsburg, KY 40330-1260
Tel (859) 734-7791 *Founded/Ownrshp* 2014
Sales 107.7MM^E *EMP* 13,957
SIC 8051 Skilled nursing care facilities; Skilled nursing care facilities
Prin: E Joseph Steier
Prin: John Harrison
Prin: Rafael Ramos
Nrsg Dir: Maureen Curtsinger

D-U-N-S 05-881-4021
LPA GROUP INC
(*Suby of* MICHAEL BAKER INTERNATIONAL HOLDCO CORP) ★
700 Huger St, Columbia, SC 29201-3663
Tel (803) 254-2211 *Founded/Ownrshp* 2010
Sales 32.8MM^E *EMP* 475
SIC 8711 Engineering services; Engineering services
Pr: Arthur E Parrish
**Pr:* Bradley Mallory
**CFO:* Richard Schwab
**Ch:* R Glen Lott
**VP:* Elham Farzam
**VP:* Amir Fouladgar
**VP:* Paul A Holt
**VP:* R K Holt
**VP:* Harold E Linnenkohl
**VP:* Mohsen Mohammadi
**VP:* Dain A Pe
**VP:* Paul A Pe
**VP:* Robert J Probst
**VP:* Dennis J Wiehl

D-U-N-S 02-782-8867
LPA INC
L P A
5161 California Ave # 100, Irvine, CA 92617-8002
Tel (949) 261-1001 *Founded/Ownrshp* 1971
Sales 56.4MM^E *EMP* 240
SIC 8712 8711 0781 Architectural services; Engineering services; Landscape counseling & planning; Architectural services; Engineering services; Landscape counseling & planning
Pr: Robert O Kupper
**Pr:* Dan Heinfeld
**CFO:* Charles Pruitt
**VP:* James Kelly
Off Mgr: Pat Delaney
CTO: Linda Gor
MIS Dir: John Robeson
Dir IT: Robert Kupper
IT Man: Albert Villa
IT Man: Jason Willis
Sys Mgr: Jason Whitesel

D-U-N-S 13-233-2466
LPA INVESTMENT LLC
LA PETITE ACADEMY
21333 Haggerty Rd Ste 300, Novi, MI 48375-5537
Tel (866) 244-5384 *Founded/Ownrshp* 1998
Sales 420.0MM *EMP* 12,800^E
SIC 8351 Child day care services; Child day care services
Pr: Graves Gary
**Pr:* Gary Graves
Off Mgr: Dan Knight

LPC
See LEWISBURG PRINTING INC

LPC
See LINCOLN EASTERN MANAGEMENT CORP

D-U-N-S 62-337-6605
LPC COMMERCIAL SERVICES INC
LINCOLN PROPERTY CO
2000 Mckinney Ave # 1000, Dallas, TX 75201-1954
Tel (202) 513-6710 *Founded/Ownrshp* 1990
Sales 159.4MM^E *EMP* 565
SIC 6552 Land subdividers & developers, commercial; Land subdividers & developers, residential; Land subdividers & developers, commercial; Land subdividers & developers, residential
Ch: William C Duvall
**Ch:* Mack Pogue
**Treas:* Nancy A Davis
**Ofcr:* William Hickey
**VP:* John Paul Price
Dir IT: Anthony Hernandez
IT Man: Todd Hawkins
IT Man: Jay Kenney

D-U-N-S 10-561-9212
LPC CRUDE OIL INC
408 W Wall St Ste B, Midland, TX 79701-4460
Tel (432) 682-8555 *Founded/Ownrshp* 2002
Sales 90.5MM^E *EMP* 100
SIC 5172 Crude oil; Crude oil
Pr: Steve Mills
COO: Tim Kohn
CFO: Chance Fletcher
VP: Daniel Carter

LPCC
See LOUISIANA PLASTIC CONVERTING CORP

D-U-N-S 00-378-6555
LPCIMINELLI CONSTRUCTION CORP (NY)
(*Suby of* LPCIMINELLI INC) ★
2421 Main St, Buffalo, NY 14214-2393
Tel (716) 855-1200 *Founded/Ownrshp* 1961
Sales 38.4MM^E *EMP* 150
SIC 1541 1542 Commercial & office building, new construction; Commercial & office buildings, renovation & repair; Industrial buildings, new construction; Renovation, remodeling & repairs: industrial buildings; Industrial buildings, new construction; Commercial & office building, new construction
Ch Bd: Louis P Ciminelli
**Pr:* Dar Alemeter
**Sec:* Amy Clifton
**Ex VP:* Joseph A Mannarino
**Sr VP:* Frank L Ciminelli II
VP: Joe Mannarino
VP: Michael Trachtenberg
**VP:* John Walker
Sfty Mgr: Robert Overoff
Snr Mgr: Dudley West

D-U-N-S 96-237-8071
LPCIMINELLI INC
(*Suby of* LPCIMINELLI INTERESTS, INC.)
2421 Main St Ste 1, Buffalo, NY 14214-2393
Tel (716) 855-1200 *Founded/Ownrshp* 2003
Sales 42.7MM^E *EMP* 170
SIC 8741 Construction management; Construction management
CEO: Louis P Ciminelli
Ex VP: Eugene Partridge
**Sr VP:* Frank L Ciminelli II
VP: Anthony Cimino
VP: Steve Giordano
VP: Christopher J Hogan
VP: Dudley West
Admn Mgr: Joanne Reinhold
Sfty Mgr: Danielle Zientek
Snr PM: Douglas Blobner
Snr PM: Patrick Bubb

LPD VIDEO JOURNAL EDUCATION
See SCHOOL IMPROVEMENT NETWORK LLC

D-U-N-S 12-062-2055
LPG ENTERPRISES INC
MCDONALD'S
12854 Eastridge Dr Ne, Albuquerque, NM 87112-4715
Tel (505) 299-4155 *Founded/Ownrshp* 1980
Sales 30.5MM^E *EMP* 1,000
Accts Horne Cpas & Business Advisors
SIC 5812 Fast-food restaurant, chain; Fast-food restaurant, chain
Pr: Larry Garcia
**VP:* Pearlene Garcia

D-U-N-S 96-176-7142 EXP
LPG VENTURES INC
971 N Jefferson St, Kearney, MO 64060-8301
Tel (816) 737-1306 *Founded/Ownrshp* 1995
Sales 39.0MM^E *EMP* 49^E
SIC 5084 Tanks, storage
Pr: August Baanders
Prd Mgr: Jared Grimsley
Sls Dir: Colin Rogers
Manager: Jerry Russell

LPGA
See LADIES PROFESSIONAL GOLF ASSOCIATION

LPHI
See LOUISIANA PUBLIC HEALTH INST

LPI
See LETTERHEAD PRESS INC

D-U-N-S 03-496-3751 IMP
■ **LPL FINANCIAL CORP**
L P L FINANCIAL SERVICES
(*Suby of* LPL HOLDINGS INC) ★
75 State St Ste 2401, Boston, MA 02109-1823
Tel (617) 423-3644 *Founded/Ownrshp* 1989
Sales 467.9MM^E *EMP* 986
SIC 6211 Brokers, security; Brokers, security
Ch Bd: Todd A Robinson
Pr: Kim Ashcraft
**Pr:* Mark Casady
**COO:* Esther Stearns
CFO: Jeni Bahr
CFO: William Maher
**CFO:* Becky S Shulman
**V Ch Bd:* David H Butterfield
Ofcr: Paul Middlemiss
Ex VP: David Akellian
**Ex VP:* Gina Cannella
Ex VP: David Reich
**Sr VP:* Jeffrey Kleintop
Sr VP: Chris Paul
Sr VP: Michael Watson
VP: Shaun Christensen

D-U-N-S 03-971-2984
■ **LPL FINANCIAL CORP**
(*Suby of* LPL HOLDINGS INC) ★
4707 Executive Dr, San Diego, CA 92121-3091
Tel (800) 877-7210 *Founded/Ownrshp* 2002
Sales 60.9MM^E *EMP* 75
SIC 6211 Security brokers & dealers
Pr: Mark Casady
Mng Pt: Rodney Medina
Ex VP: Mimi Bock
Ex VP: James Shorris
Sr VP: Patrick Cox
Sr VP: Aaron Gordon
VP: Andrew Blake
VP: Anthony Henry
VP: Kristine Koczajowski

D-U-N-S 78-882-3016
▲ **LPL FINANCIAL HOLDINGS INC**
75 State St Ste 2401, Boston, MA 02109-1823
Tel (617) 423-3644 *Founded/Ownrshp* 2005
Sales 4.3MMM *EMP* 3,185
Tkr Sym LPLA *Exch* NGS

SIC 6211 6282 6091 Security brokers & dealers; Investment advisory service; Investment counselors; Nondeposit trust facilities; Security brokers & dealers; Investment advisory service; Investment counselors; Nondeposit trust facilities
Ch Bd: Mark S Casady
Pr: Dan H Arnold
CFO: Matthew J Audette
Ofcr: Sallie R Larsen
Dir Risk M: Michelle Oroschakoff
Mng Dir: David Bergers
Mng Dir: Victor P Fetter
Mng Dir: Tom Gooley
Mng Dir: J Andrew Kalbaugh
Mng Dir: William Morrissey
Mng Dir: Ryan Parker

D-U-N-S 60-315-8502
■ LPL HOLDINGS INC
(*Suby of* LPL FINANCIAL HOLDINGS INC) ★
4707 Executive Dr, San Diego, CA 92121-3091
Tel (858) 450-9606 *Founded/Ownrshp* 2005
Sales 567.2MM^E *EMP* 1,200^E
SIC 6211 Brokers, security; Dealers, security; Brokers, security; Dealers, security
CEO: Mark Casady
Sr Pt: Stephen Molinelli
Ofcr: April Sinicrope
Ex VP: Robert Comfort
Ex VP: Caroline Delaney
Ex VP: Melanie Hardin
Ex VP: Bruce Miller
Sr VP: Kimberly Sweet
VP: Cheryl Brown
VP: Allison Harris
VP: Scott McCaffrey
VP: Michael Sims
VP: Joe Sovcik

D-U-N-S 01-947-7488
LPM HOLDING CO INC
EPICUREAN FEAST
24 Main St, Maynard, MA 01754-2506
Tel (978) 897-0660 *Founded/Ownrshp* 1990
Sales 16.9MM^E *EMP* 300
SIC 5812 Cafeteria; Cafeteria
Pr: Robert J Watson
**CFO:* Tim Sheehan
VP: Jim Sinatra
Mktg Mgr: Jared Bars

D-U-N-S 03-951-1696
LPR CONSTRUCTION CO
1171 Des Moines Ave, Loveland, CO 80537-5106
Tel (800) 577-1844 *Founded/Ownrshp* 1979
Sales 158.5MM^E *EMP* 350
Accts Bauerle And Company Pc Den
SIC 1791 Structural steel erection; Structural steel erection
Pr: Charles Rockwell Turner
CFO: Grant Thayer
Treas: Sheila Ehasz
**Sec:* Diahan Ehasz
**VP:* G Louis Carner Jr
**VP:* Mike Charley
Exec: Dana Hohn
Dir IT: Gary Byers
IT Man: Dana Hahn
Site Mgr: Charlie Anstaett
QI Cn Mgr: Dan Welch

LPS
See LAGNIAPPE PHARMACY SERVICES LLC

D-U-N-S 00-215-7097 IMP
LPS INDUSTRIES INC (GA)
LAWRENCE PACKAGING
10 Caesar Pl, Moonachie, NJ 07074-1701
Tel (201) 438-3515 *Founded/Ownrshp* 1959
Sales 40.1MM^E *EMP* 250
SIC 2671 5046 3081 2673 2754 2621 Packaging paper & plastics film, coated & laminated; Scales, except laboratory; Packing materials, plastic sheet; Plastic bags: made from purchased materials; Labels: gravure printing; Packaging paper; Bag paper; Packaging paper & plastics film, coated & laminated; Scales, except laboratory; Packing materials, plastic sheet; Plastic bags: made from purchased materials; Labels: gravure printing; Packaging paper; Bag paper
CEO: Madeleine D Robinson
CFO: Mary Barbarisi
VP: Tim Fletcher
VP Opers: Robert Gow
VP Mktg: Charles Ardman
Sls Mgr: Tom Leonard

D-U-N-S 11-899-7266
LPS INTEGRATION INC
230 Great Circle Rd # 218, Nashville, TN 37228-1706
Tel (615) 254-0581 *Founded/Ownrshp* 2002
Sales 87.2MM *EMP* 72
Accts Horne Llp Ridgeland Mississi
SIC 5045 7379 Computers, peripherals & software; Computer related consulting services; Computers, peripherals & software; Computer related consulting services
CEO: Todd Sanford
**Pr:* Chris McMillen
**CEO:* David Linzy
**COO:* Frank Pulliza
**CFO:* Theresa Chester
VP: Gregg Ambulos
VP: Bill McClanahan
Snr Ntwrk: Blake Arnold
Snr Ntwrk: Matt Lang
Netwrk Eng: Terry Bentley
Netwrk Eng: David Hill

D-U-N-S 83-174-3179
■ LPS REAL ESTATE GROUP INC
(*Suby of* BLACK KNIGHT INFOSERV LLC) ★
2050 Main St Ste 400, Irvine, CA 92614-8270
Tel (949) 681-4700 *Founded/Ownrshp* 2006
Sales 30.1MM^E *EMP* 792^E
SIC 7374 Data processing & preparation
Pr: Jay Gaskill

LPSD
See LEWIS-PALMER SCHOOL DISTRICT NO 38

LPVEC
See LOWER PIONEER VALLEY EDUCATIONAL COLLABORATIVE

D-U-N-S 06-083-9961
LPX INC
LOUISEVILLE PAVING
1801 Payne St, Louisville, KY 40206-1942
Tel (502) 583-1726 *Founded/Ownrshp* 1996
Sales 63.9MM *EMP* 175
SIC 1611 1771 1629 General contractor, highway & street construction; Driveway contractor; Tennis court construction; General contractor, highway & street construction; Driveway contractor; Tennis court construction
Pr: William B Dougherty
**Sec:* Joseph W Dougherty
**VP:* John T Dougherty

D-U-N-S 06-118-9981
■ LQ MANAGEMENT LLC
LA QUINTA INN
(*Suby of* LA QUINTA HOLDINGS INC.)
909 Hidden Rdg Ste 600, Irving, TX 75038-3822
Tel (214) 492-6600 *Founded/Ownrshp* 2005
Sales 961.8MM^E *EMP* 7,600
SIC 7011 Hotels & motels; Hotels & motels
Pr: Wayne B Goldberg
COO: Angelo Lambardi
COO: William McCalmont
CFO: Keith Cline
Bd of Dir: Francis Cash
Ex VP: Julie M Cary
Ex VP: Mark La Bissoniere
Ex VP: Angelo J Lombardi
Ex VP: Rajiv K Trivedi
Sr VP: Stephen T Parker
VP: Henry Cope
VP: Vicki Cutwright
VP: Ivonne Laboy
VP: James Marshall
VP: Hoang Nguyen
VP: David Sims
VP: Gary Zodrow

D-U-N-S 84-817-5019
LR DEVELOPMENT CO LLC
RELATED MIDWEST
(*Suby of* RELATED COMPANIES L P) ★
350 W Hubbard St Ste 301, Chicago, IL 60654-6901
Tel (312) 595-7400 *Founded/Ownrshp* 2000
Sales 51.6MM^E *EMP* 100
SIC 6552 6531 1542 Land subdividers & developers, commercial; Real estate brokers & agents; Commercial & office building, new construction
Pr: Curt Bailey
Sr VP: Kerry Dickson
Sr VP: Ann Thompson
Snr PM: Amy Mayer

D-U-N-S 03-977-3163
LRA WORLDWIDE INC
5 Walnut Grove Dr Ste 280, Horsham, PA 19044-2282
Tel (215) 830-1240 *Founded/Ownrshp* 1980
Sales 45.0MM^E *EMP* 280
SIC 8742 Business consultant; Business consultant
Pr: Stan Lashner
**Pr:* Robert M Rush
Ofcr: Rob Lusch
**Ex VP:* John Roberto
VP: Ben Flournoy
VP: Rick Reilly
CTO: Jonathan Emanuele
QA Dir: Shannon Becraft
QA Dir: Keith Bliss
QA Dir: Camie Costanzo
QA Dir: Bree Davis

LRCSC
See LAKES REGION COMMUNITY SERVICES COUNCIL INC

D-U-N-S 78-514-7786
LRE GROUND SERVICES INC
1115 S Main St, Brooksville, FL 34601-5667
Tel (352) 796-0229 *Founded/Ownrshp* 2000
Sales 31.9MM^E *EMP* 130
SIC 1799 1771 1741 Building site preparation; Concrete pumping; Foundation building; Building site preparation; Professional instrument repair services; Foundation building
CEO: Susan L Woolever
**Pr:* Rachel D Vitale
COO: Gary Carr
Ex VP: Rachel Vitale
**VP:* Frank V Vitale
Genl Mgr: Frank Vitale
Opers Mgr: Jesse Miller
Mktg Mgr: Jim Flynn

D-U-N-S 10-420-2713
LRES CORP
765 The City Dr S Ste 300, Orange, CA 92868-6916
Tel (714) 520-5737 *Founded/Ownrshp* 2002
Sales 27.0MM *EMP* 96
SIC 6531 Real estate managers; Real estate managers
Pr: Roger Beane
**COO:* Paul Abbamonto
**COO:* Alice Sorenson
**CFO:* Susheel Mantha
Ofcr: Donald Mask
**Sr VP:* Richard Cimino
Sr VP: Nick Grant
VP: Candice Merriweather
VP: Greg Musso
VP: Damon Paxson
VP: Chris Pitts
VP: Ed Skornik
VP: Ann Song

D-U-N-S 07-396-8455
LRGHEALTHCARE
HEALTHLINK
80 Highland St, Laconia, NH 03246-3298
Tel (603) 524-3211 *Founded/Ownrshp* 1898
Sales 168.9MM *EMP* 1,600
Accts Baker Newman & Noyes Llc Manc
SIC 8062 General medical & surgical hospitals; General medical & surgical hospitals
CEO: Thomas A Clairmont
Ofcr: Thomas Podawiltz
**Ex VP:* Henry Lipman
**Sr VP:* Ellen Wolff
Comm Dir: Ron Blackey
Dir Pat Ac: Joyce Bluhm
Off Mgr: Brenda Ford
CTO: Carole Domin
IT Man: Nicholas Grenon
IT Man: Scott Vachon
Netwrk Eng: Bruce Veilleux

D-U-N-S 79-042-5610
LRI HOLDINGS INC
(*Suby of* ROADHOUSE PARENT INC) ★
3011 Armory Dr Ste 300, Nashville, TN 37204-3721
Tel (615) 885-9056 *Founded/Ownrshp* 2010
Sales 614.3MM *EMP* 14,885^E
Accts Grant Thornton Llp Atlanta G
SIC 5812 6794 Steak restaurant; Franchises, selling or licensing; Steak restaurant; Franchises, selling or licensing
Pr: Samuel N Borgese
CFO: Edmund J Schwartz
Chf Mktg O: Len A Van Popering
Sr VP: Mariahilda Rivera
CIO: John C Laporte

LRMC
See LAKEWAY REGIONAL MEDICAL CENTER LLC

LRMC
See LAKELAND REGIONAL MEDICAL CENTER INC

D-U-N-S 62-493-7132
LRN CORP
1100 Glendon Ave Ste 800, Los Angeles, CA 90024-3512
Tel (310) 209-5400 *Founded/Ownrshp* 2000
Sales 47.0MM^E *EMP* 220
SIC 8111 Corporate, partnership & business law; Corporate, partnership & business law
CEO: Dov Seidman
Pt: Sue Darow
Pt: Carla Schoonderbeek
**Pr:* Jean-Marc Levy
**CFO:* Ron Charow
Treas: Trent Derosia
Ex VP: Alister Christopher
**Ex VP:* David Greenberg
Ex VP: David Greenburg
**Ex VP:* Kal Patel
VP: Donald Hoffman
Comm Dir: Bernadette Blaze

D-U-N-S 94-294-8613
LRP MAGAZINE GROUP
AXON MAGAZINE GROUP
(*Suby of* L R P) ★
747 Dresher Rd Ste 500, Dresher, PA 19025
Tel (215) 784-0860 *Founded/Ownrshp* 1986
Sales 15.9MM^E *EMP* 300
SIC 2721 Magazines: publishing only, not printed on site; Magazines: publishing only, not printed on site
Pr: Ken Kahn
IT Man: Vic Votsch

D-U-N-S 08-569-8900
LRP PUBLICATIONS INC
L R P
360 Hiatt Dr, Palm Beach Gardens, FL 33418-7106
Tel (215) 784-0860 *Founded/Ownrshp* 1975
Sales 79.4MM^E *EMP* 350
SIC 2721 Trade journals: publishing & printing; Trade journals: publishing & printing
Pr: Kenneth Kahn
**CFO:* Todd Lutz
Mktg Dir: Angela Hazuda
Mktg Mgr: John McNeff

D-U-N-S 96-855-5362
LRR ENERGY LP
1111 Bagby St Ste 4600, Houston, TX 77002-2559
Tel (713) 292-9510 *Founded/Ownrshp* 2011
Sales 187.9MM *EMP* 153^E
Tkr Sym LRE *Exch* NYS
SIC 1311 Crude petroleum & natural gas; Crude petroleum & natural gas
CEO: Scott W Smith
CFO: Angelique Brou
CFO: Richard A Robert
VP: Christopher A Butta
VP: Jaime Casas
VP: Britt Pence

D-U-N-S 01-702-5115
LRR FOOD INC
850 76th St Sw, Grand Rapids, MI 49518
Tel (810) 629-1383 *Founded/Ownrshp* 1960
Sales 144.1MM^E *EMP* 2,000
SIC 5411 5921 Supermarkets, independent; Beer (packaged); Wine; Supermarkets, independent; Beer (packaged); Wine
Ch Bd: Russell V Gilder Jr
**Pr:* Lisa Van Gilder

LRS
See LEVI RAY & SHOUP INC

D-U-N-S 84-015-9318 EXP
LS ENERGIA INC
1200 S Pine Island Rd # 420, Plantation, FL 33324-9907
Tel (954) 628-3059 *Founded/Ownrshp* 1995
Sales 300.0MM *EMP* 100
SIC 1731 Energy management controls; Energy management controls
Pr: Jose Tamayo

D-U-N-S 07-841-1138
LS ENERGY FABRICATION LLC
LONESTAR ENERGY FABRICATION
8120 Mchard Rd, Houston, TX 77053-5259
Tel (281) 573-9500 *Founded/Ownrshp* 2009
Sales 23.6MM^E *EMP* 100^E
SIC 3533 Oil & gas drilling rigs & equipment; Oil & gas drilling rigs & equipment
CEO: Darryl A Schroeder
**Pr:* Brian Shanklin
VP Opers: Scott Schroeder

D-U-N-S 36-196-3528
LS FARMS LLC
29794 Schuster Rd, Mc Farland, CA 93250-9784
Tel (661) 792-3192 *Founded/Ownrshp* 1998
Sales 9.4MM *EMP* 500
Accts Barbich Hooper King Dill Hoffm
SIC 0191 General farms, primarily crop; General farms, primarily crop

D-U-N-S 09-007-7983 IMP
LS HOLDING INC
JEWELS AND LITTLE SWITZERLAND
(*Suby of* NXP CORPORATION LTD)
5195 Dronningens Gade # 3, St Thomas, VI 00802-6497
Tel (248) 809-5560 *Founded/Ownrshp* 1953, 2009
Sales 23.8MM^E *EMP* 200
SIC 5944 5947 5999 3442 Jewelry stores; Watches; Gift shop; Perfumes & colognes; Metal doors, sash & trim; Jewelry stores; Watches; Gift shop; Perfumes & colognes; Metal doors, sash & trim
CEO: Hal Tayler
**Pr:* Robert Baumgardner

LS NEW MARKETS INV ADVISORS
See LONE STAR INVESTMENT ADVISORS LLC

D-U-N-S 03-330-5215
LS POWER DEVELOPMENT LLC
(*Suby of* LS POWER EQUITY PARTNERS LP) ★
1 Tower Center Blvd Fl 21, East Brunswick, NJ 08816-1145
Tel (732) 249-6750 *Founded/Ownrshp* 2001
Sales 72.6MM^E *EMP* 100
SIC 4911 Generation, electric power; Generation, electric power

D-U-N-S 62-253-5107
LS POWER EQUITY PARTNERS LP
1700 Broadway Fl 35, New York, NY 10019-5905
Tel (212) 615-3456 *Founded/Ownrshp* 2004
Sales 74.8MM^E *EMP* 100
SIC 3568 1796 Power transmission equipment; Power generating equipment installation; Power transmission equipment; Power generating equipment installation
Ch Bd: Mike Segal
**Ex VP:* Mark Brennan
**Ex VP:* Shimon Edelstein
**Ex VP:* John King
**Ex VP:* David Nanus
**VP:* Joe Fontana
**VP:* Allyn Salpeter

D-U-N-S 61-843-4950
LS PRECISION MANUFACTURING INC
24131 W Hardy Rd, Spring, TX 77373-5769
Tel (281) 353-1191 *Founded/Ownrshp* 2008
Sales 32.8MM^E *EMP* 235^E
SIC 3452 Bolts, nuts, rivets & washers; Bolts, nuts, rivets & washers
Pr: Charles Wolley
**CFO:* Dwayne Clark

D-U-N-S 11-821-6084
LS RUBBER INDUSTRIES INC
(*Suby of* BANKS BROS CORP) ★
24 Federal Plz, Bloomfield, NJ 07003-5636
Tel (973) 680-4488 *Founded/Ownrshp* 1969
Sales 14.3MM^E *EMP* 292
SIC 3069 3714 3053 Foam rubber; Motor vehicle parts & accessories; Gaskets, packing & sealing devices; Foam rubber; Motor vehicle parts & accessories; Gaskets, packing & sealing devices
Pr: Lawrence Banks
**Sec:* Stanley F Banks

D-U-N-S 00-103-8103
LS TECHNOLOGIES LLC
LST
2750 Prosperity Ave # 400, Fairfax, VA 22031-4312
Tel (703) 205-9146 *Founded/Ownrshp* 2000
Sales 32.3MM *EMP* 203^E
Accts Pbmares Llp Fairfax Virgini
SIC 8711 8999 8741 Consulting engineer; Communication services; Management services; Consulting engineer; Communication services; Management services
CEO: Keith A Wallace
**Pr:* Tom J Loftus
**CFO:* Derek Bigelow
**VP:* Stephen R Dash
VP: Richard Jehlen
**VP:* Richard A Thoma
VP: Ken Treadwell
Dir IT: Paul Robinson
IT Man: Sasha Tabib
VP Mktg: Dale Olpin

D-U-N-S 01-117-4516 IMP
LS TRACTOR USA LLC
(*Suby of* LS MTRON LTD.)
6900 Corporation Pkwy, Battleboro, NC 27809-9272
Tel (252) 984-0700 *Founded/Ownrshp* 2008
Sales 25.9MM^E *EMP* 31
SIC 5083 4212 Tractors, agricultural; Local trucking, without storage
CEO: Derek Johannes
Info Man: Anand Bhansali
Plnt Mgr: Raymond Bullock

LS TRAVEL RETAIL NORTH AMERICA
See HDS RETAIL NORTH AMERICA LP

D-U-N-S 08-374-2403
LS1 LLC (AL)
RITE WAY SERVICE
331 1st Ave N, Birmingham, AL 35204-4904
Tel (205) 251-9249 *Founded/Ownrshp* 2014
Sales NA *EMP* 2,200
SIC 7349 Janitorial service, contract basis

LS3P ARCHITECTS
See LS3P ASSOCIATES LTD

D-U-N-S 05-207-1545
LS3P ASSOCIATES LTD
LS3P ARCHITECTS
205 1/2 King St, Charleston, SC 29401-3129
Tel (843) 577-4444 *Founded/Ownrshp* 1964
Sales 22.6MM^E *EMP* 201
SIC 8712 7389

D-U-N-S 12-258-8510 IMP/EXP
■ LSB CHEMICAL LLC
(*Suby of* LSB INDUSTRIES INC) ★
16 S Pennsylvania Ave, Oklahoma City, OK 73107-7024
Tel (405) 235-4546 *Founded/Ownrshp* 1983
Sales 120.0MM^E *EMP* 364
SIC 2819 2873 2892 Sulfuric acid, oleum; Nitric acid; Ammonium nitrate, ammonium sulfate; Explosives; Sulfuric acid, oleum; Nitric acid; Ammonium nitrate, ammonium sulfate; Explosives
Pr: Paul Rydlund
**VP:* Larry D Fitzwater
**VP:* Brian Lewis
**VP:* Dallas C Robinson

D-U-N-S 03-365-3770
■ LSB CORP
(*Suby of* PEOPLES UNITED FINANCIAL INC) ★
30 Massachusetts Ave # 8, North Andover, MA 01845-3458
Tel (978) 725-7500 *Founded/Ownrshp* 2010
Sales NA *EMP* 2,015^E
SIC 6022 State commercial banks
CEO: Gerald T Mulligan
**CFO:* Diane L Walker
Bd of Dir: Kathleen Reynolds
VP: Teresa Flynn
Creative D: Wendy Reynolds

D-U-N-S 80-692-1453
LSB FINANCIAL
62 Pleasant St, Laconia, NH 03246-3420
Tel (603) 524-1212 *Founded/Ownrshp* 2007
Sales NA *EMP* 250^E
SIC 6712 Bank holding companies; Bank holding companies
Prin: Linda Normandin

D-U-N-S 04-686-0979 IMP
▲ LSB INDUSTRIES INC
16 S Pennsylvania Ave, Oklahoma City, OK 73107-7024
Tel (405) 235-4546 *Founded/Ownrshp* 1968
Sales 732.5MM *EMP* 1,949
Accts Ernst & Young Llp Oklahoma Ci
Tkr Sym LXU *Exch* NYS
SIC 3822 3585 3567 2873 Hydronic controls; Heat pumps, electric; Heating units & devices, industrial: electric; Ammonium nitrate, ammonium sulfate; Anhydrous ammonia; Fertilizers: natural (organic), except compost; Urea; Hydronic controls; Heat pumps, electric; Heating units & devices, industrial: electric; Ammonium nitrate, ammonium sulfate; Anhydrous ammonia; Fertilizers: natural (organic), except compost; Urea
CEO: Daniel D Greenwell
**Ch Bd:* Jack E Golsen
Pr: Richard Aldridge
CFO: Mark T Behrman
**CFO:* Tony M Shelby
**V Ch Bd:* Barry H Golsen
Ex VP: David R Goss
Ex VP: Brian Lewis
Ex VP: Richard Sanders
Sr VP: Phil Gough
Sr VP: Paul Rydlund
Sr VP: David M Shear
Sr VP: Michael D Tepper
VP: Robert Porter
VP: Harold Rieker
Board of Directors: Lynn F White, Webster L Benham, Charles A Burtch, Robert A Butkin, Daniel D Greenwell, Louis S Massimo, Andrew K Mittag, William F Murdy, Richard W Roedel, Richard S Sanders Jr

LSC SYSTEM OFFICE
See LONE STAR COLLEGE SYSTEM

LSCP
See LITTLE SIOUX CORN PROCESSORS LLC

D-U-N-S 11-415-0548 IMP/EXP
LSCP LLLP
LITTLE SIOUX CORN PROCESSORS
(*Suby of* LITTLE SIOUX CORN PROCESSORS LLC) ★
4808 F Ave, Marcus, IA 51035-7070
Tel (712) 376-2800 *Founded/Ownrshp* 2001
Sales 274.5MM *EMP* 45
Accts Christianson & Associates Pll
SIC 4925 0115 Gas production and/or distribution; Manufactured gas, production & distribution; Corn; Gas production and/or distribution; Manufactured gas, production & distribution; Corn

LSD
See LOUISIANA SCHOOL FOR DEAF

LSE
See LAFAYETTE STEEL ERECTOR INC

LSF INTERACTIVE
See GEARY LSF GROUP INC

D-U-N-S 02-692-5465
LSF5 BI-LO HOLDINGS LLC
WINN-DIXIE
(*Suby of* LONE STAR FUND V (US) LP) ★
5050 Edgewood Ct, Jacksonville, FL 32254-3601
Tel (904) 783-5000 *Founded/Ownrshp* 2005
Sales 12.6MMM^E *EMP* 180,526^E
SIC 5411 Convenience stores, chain
Pr: R Randall Onstead Jr

D-U-N-S 80-828-3910
LSF5 CAVALIER INVESTMENTS LLC
VIRGINIA OIL COMPANY
1410 Commwl Dr Ste 202, Wilmington, NC 28403
Tel (434) 979-1380 *Founded/Ownrshp* 2007
Sales 17.5MM^E *EMP* 280
SIC 5411 Convenience stores; Convenience stores

D-U-N-S 07-856-8804
LSF5 WAGON HOLDINGS LLC
2711 N Haskell Ave # 1700, Dallas, TX 75204-2911
Tel (214) 515-6824 *Founded/Ownrshp* 2007
Sales 64.3MM^E *EMP* 6,890
SIC 5812 5813 Eating places; Drinking places; Eating places; Drinking places
CEO: John P Grayken

D-U-N-S 07-927-8795
LSF8 GYPSUM HOLDINGS LP
2711 N Haskell Ave, Dallas, TX 75204-2911
Tel (703) 480-3800 *Founded/Ownrshp* 2013
Sales 33.7MM^E *EMP* 504
SIC 3275 Gypsum products; Gypsum board; Wallboard, gypsum; Gypsum plaster; Gypsum products; Gypsum board; Wallboard, gypsum; Gypsum plaster
Prin: Isaac Preston

D-U-N-S 08-826-6093
LSG LUFTHANSA SERVICE INC
LSG SKY SHAFT
505 Detroit Metro Airport, Detroit, MI 48242-1011
Tel (734) 942-3914 *Founded/Ownrshp* 1995
Sales 15.6MM^E *EMP* 700
SIC 5812 Caterers; Caterers
Genl Mgr: John Willan

LSG SKY CHEFS
See SKY CHEFS INC

D-U-N-S 15-467-9252 IMP
LSG SKY CHEFS USA INC
(*Suby of* LSG LUFTHANSA SERVICE HOLDING AG)
6191 N State Highway 161 # 100, Irving, TX 75038-2290
Tel (972) 793-9000 *Founded/Ownrshp* 2001
Sales 539.5MM^E *EMP* 7,321
Accts Price Waterhousecoopers Llp D
SIC 5812 5962 Caterers; Contract food services; Coffee shop; Merchandising machine operators; Caterers; Contract food services; Coffee shop; Merchandising machine operators
Ch: Hanns R Rech
CFO: Jens Theuerkorn
**CFO:* Patrick Tolbertp
Treas: Jamie Rafftesaeth
**Sr VP:* Pat Berkelbaugh
Web Dev: Ben Galaviz
Netwrk Eng: Joel Nola

LSG SKY SHAFT
See LSG LUFTHANSA SERVICE INC

LSI
See LASER SPINE INSTITUTE LLC

D-U-N-S 01-244-4253 IMP
LSI CORP
(*Suby of* AVAGO TECHNOLOGIES LIMITED)
1320 Ridder Park Dr, San Jose, CA 95131-2313
Tel (408) 433-8000 *Founded/Ownrshp* 1980, 2014
Sales 1.5MMM^E *EMP* 5,272
SIC 3674 Microcircuits, integrated (semiconductor); Microcircuits, integrated (semiconductor)
Pr: Abhijit Y Talwalkar
**COO:* D Jeffrey Richardson
**CFO:* Bryon Look
Ex VP: Jeff Hoogenboom
**Ex VP:* Jean F Rankin
Ex VP: Frank A Tornghi
**Sr VP:* Gautam Srivastava
VP: Phil Bullinger
**CTO:* Gregory L Huff
Sls Mgr: Stephannie Rodgers

D-U-N-S 04-316-8426 EXP
LSI CORP OF AMERICA INC
(*Suby of* COBE CAPITAL LLC) ★
2100 Xenium Ln N, Minneapolis, MN 55441-3697
Tel (763) 559-4664 *Founded/Ownrshp* 2013
Sales 45.4MM^E *EMP* 186^E
SIC 2541 2434 Wood kitchen cabinets; Partitions for floor attachment, prefabricated: wood; Partitions for floor attachment, prefabricated: wood; Wood kitchen cabinets
CEO: Omar Haque
**VP:* Daniel Brown
**Prin:* Darryl Rosser

LSI GRAPHIC SOLUTIONS PLUS
See LSI INTEGRATED GRAPHICS LP

D-U-N-S 00-607-7606
LSI INC
(*Suby of* JACK LINK BEEF JERKY) ★
200 Industrial Dr, New Glarus, WI 53574-9635
Tel (608) 527-2131 *Founded/Ownrshp* 2000
Sales 28.6MM^E *EMP* 200
SIC 2013 Sausages from purchased meat; Smoked meats from purchased meat; Sausages from purchased meat; Smoked meats from purchased meat
Pr: Michael McDonald
**CEO:* Troy Link
**COO:* Jay Link
QC Dir: Mark Huntimer
Plnt Mgr: Doug Draper
Plnt Mgr: Lee Stearns

D-U-N-S 08-093-4375 IMP/EXP
▲ LSI INDUSTRIES INC
10000 Alliance Rd, Blue Ash, OH 45242-4706
Tel (513) 793-3200 *Founded/Ownrshp* 1976
Sales 307.8MM *EMP* 1,579^E
Accts Grant Thornton Llp Cincinnati
Tkr Sym LYTS *Exch* NGS
SIC 3648 3993 3663 Lighting equipment; Floodlights; Public lighting fixtures; Area & sports luminaries; Electric signs; Light communications equipment; Lighting equipment; Floodlights; Public lighting fixtures; Area & sports luminaries; Electric signs; Light communications equipment
Pr: Dennis W Wells
**Ch Bd:* Gary P Kreider
Pr: John A Bagwell
Pr: Sylvia Bilban
Pr: Jeff A Croskey
Pr: Fred Jalbout
Pr: David McCauley
CFO: Ronald S Stowell
Ex VP: Andrew J Foerster
Ex VP: Paul T Foster
Ex VP: Jeff Ginder
Ex VP: James P Sferra
Sr VP: John Page
VP: Jeff Bastian
VP: Tom Cantrell
VP: Jeff Ehret
VP: Joanne Horn
VP: Scott Manley
VP: Sharon Martin
VP: We Mayo
VP: Bob O'Neil
Board of Directors: Robert P Beech, Dennis B Meyer, Wilfred T O'gara, Mark A Serrianne, James P Sferra

D-U-N-S 36-444-6039
■ LSI INTEGRATED GRAPHICS LP
LSI GRAPHIC SOLUTIONS PLUS
(*Suby of* LSI INDUSTRIES INC) ★
14902 Sommermeyer St # 120, Houston, TX 77041-5306
Tel (713) 744-4100 *Founded/Ownrshp* 1988
Sales 44.5MM^E *EMP* 200
SIC 2759 3993 3613 2851 2752 2671 Screen printing; Signs & advertising specialties; Switchgear & switchboard apparatus; Paints & allied products; Commercial printing, lithographic; Packaging paper & plastics film, coated & laminated; Screen printing; Signs & advertising specialties; Switchgear & switchboard apparatus; Paints & allied products; Commercial printing, lithographic; Packaging paper & plastics film, coated & laminated
CFO: Ronald S Stowell
COO: Steven Estep
VP: Robin Hood
VP: Stephen Rundall
Creative D: Matt Pentifallo
VP Sls: Andrew Harey
Snr PM: Vicki Mancill

D-U-N-S 12-227-3303 IMP
■ LSI LIGHTRON INC
(*Suby of* LSI INDUSTRIES INC) ★
500 Hudson Valley Ave, New Windsor, NY 12553-4744
Tel (845) 562-5500 *Founded/Ownrshp* 2000
Sales 183.9MM^E *EMP* 1,000
SIC 3646 5063 Commercial indusl & institutional electric lighting fixtures; Electrical apparatus & equipment; Commercial indusl & institutional electric lighting fixtures; Electrical apparatus & equipment
CEO: Gene Littman
**Pr:* Barry White

D-U-N-S 60-342-0183
LSI SOLUTIONS INC
7796 Victor Mendon Rd, Victor, NY 14564-8966
Tel (585) 586-4509 *Founded/Ownrshp* 1986
Sales 26.4MM^E *EMP* 111
SIC 8731 Commercial physical research; Medical research, commercial; Commercial physical research; Medical research, commercial
Pr: Jude S Sauer MD
**Treas:* Eva P Sauer MD
Prgrm Mgr: Mark Keyser
Rgnl Mgr: Darren Davis
IT Man: Glen Metz
Mktg Dir: Bob Bartz

D-U-N-S 61-179-2334
■ LSI TITLE CO
L S I
(*Suby of* BLACK KNIGHT INFOSERV LLC) ★
1400 Cherrington Pkwy, Coraopolis, PA 15108-4356
Tel (412) 299-4000 *Founded/Ownrshp* 2008
Sales 19.4MM^E *EMP* 525
SIC 6531 Appraiser, real estate; Appraiser, real estate
V Ch: C William Griffin
**Pr:* Ron Frazier
**Ex VP:* Doug Ashe
**Ex VP:* W Patrick Lawrence II
**Sr VP:* David Ashley
**Sr VP:* Shari Ferline
**Sr VP:* Patricia Kendrick
**Sr VP:* Michelle Wilkes
Exec: Diane Book

D-U-N-S 05-543-1836 IMP
LSIS USA INC
2000 Millbrook Dr, Lincolnshire, IL 60069-3630
Tel (847) 941-8240 *Founded/Ownrshp* 2012
Sales 221.8MM^E *EMP* 23,000
SIC 5063 Power wire & cable; Power wire & cable
Pr: Min Dokko
Genl Mgr: Eric Chung
Mktg Mgr: Mehran Mohsenian

LSK&D
See LESTER SCHWAB KATZ & DWYER LLP

LSL HEALTH CARE
See LSL INDUSTRIES INC

D-U-N-S 04-670-3096 IMP
LSL INDUSTRIES INC
LSL HEALTH CARE
5535 N Wolcott Ave, Chicago, IL 60640-1019
Tel (773) 878-1100 *Founded/Ownrshp* 1981
Sales 31.4MM^E *EMP* 84
SIC 3841 3842 Surgical & medical instruments; Surgical appliances & supplies
Pr: Ashok Luthra
IT Man: Mark Brezinski
Sfty Mgr: Tony Huffman
Opers Mgr: Nisar Ahmed
Natl Sales: Mark Simmons

LSO
See CRI 2000 LP

D-U-N-S 06-313-5636 IMP
LSP PRODUCTS GROUP INC
TECH SPECIALTY
(*Suby of* CHEMSEARCH DIVISION) ★
3689 Arrowhead Dr, Carson City, NV 89706-2008
Tel (775) 884-4242 *Founded/Ownrshp* 1998
Sales 26.9MM^E *EMP* 120^E
SIC 3089 Plastic hardware & building products
Pr: Rick Mejia
Pr: David Bacon
CFO: Ben Decarlo
Treas: Irena Kildisas
VP: Tim Doyle
VP: Jeri Mitchell
VP: Rich Robinson
VP: Glen Scivally
VP: Susan Staples
Off Mgr: Graciela Alvizo
Dir IT: Claude Cognian

D-U-N-S 78-842-0425
LSPM LLC
LIVING STONE PRECIOUS METALS
606 S Hill St Ste 603, Los Angeles, CA 90014-1761
Tel (213) 622-4653 *Founded/Ownrshp* 2007
Sales 45.0MM *EMP* 2
SIC 3911 5094 Jewelry, precious metal; Precious metals; Jewelry, precious metal; Precious metals

D-U-N-S 94-987-5884
LSQ FUNDING GROUP LC
(*Suby of* LSQ GROUP LLC) ★
2600 Lucien Way Ste 100, Maitland, FL 32751-7064
Tel (407) 206-0022 *Founded/Ownrshp* 1996
Sales NA *EMP* 55
SIC 6153 Factoring services
Ch Bd: Max Eliscu
Pr: Joe Kiefer
Pr: Alexa Ragsdale
COO: Roger Allen
CFO: Terry Ragsdale
Ofcr: Stan Carpenter
Ex VP: Tyler Grady
Ex VP: Tanya Plotnikoff
Sr VP: Larry Stephenson
VP: Tanya Boczek
VP: Tom Harris
VP: Bob Reagen
Exec: Matt Durfee
Creative D: Damien Wolf

D-U-N-S 07-984-3614
LSQ GROUP LLC
2600 Lucien Way Ste 100, Maitland, FL 32751-7064
Tel (407) 206-0022 *Founded/Ownrshp* 2015
Sales NA *EMP* 55^E
SIC 6153 Factoring services

D-U-N-S 96-250-6437
LSREF LODGING INVESTMENTS LLC
(*Suby of* LONE STAR REAL ESTATE FUND (US) LP) ★
2711 N Haskell Ave, Dallas, TX 75204-2911
Tel (214) 754-8300 *Founded/Ownrshp* 2010
Sales 183.4MM^E *EMP* 3,046^E
SIC 6798 Real estate investment trusts; Real estate investment trusts
Pt: Louis Paletta

D-U-N-S 80-867-8262
LSRI HOLDINGS INC
(*Suby of* LANDRYS INC) ★
1510 West Loop S, Houston, TX 77027-9505
Tel (713) 850-1010 *Founded/Ownrshp* 1993
Sales 1.2MMM^E *EMP* 16,000
SIC 5812 Seafood restaurants; Steak & barbecue restaurants; Seafood restaurants; Steak & barbecue restaurants
Ch Bd: Tilman J Fertitta
**CFO:* Rick Lim
**Ex VP:* Richard E Ervin
Ex VP: Richard E Rvin
**Ex VP:* Steve Scheinthal

LST
See LS TECHNOLOGIES LLC

LSU HCSD
See LSU HEALTH SYSTEM HEALTH CARE SERVICES DIVISION

LSU HEALTH
See W O MOSS REGIONAL HOSPITAL FOUNDATION INC

D-U-N-S 12-386-5677
LSU HEALTH SCIENCE CENTER
JOHN A MATA MD
1501 Kings Hwy, Shreveport, LA 71103-4228
Tel (318) 675-4679 *Founded/Ownrshp* 1980
Sales 34.1MM^E *EMP* 40
SIC 8011 Urologist
Ch: Dennis D Venable MD
Treas: Xiao C Wu
Ofcr: Jameson Jordan
IT Man: Derrick Thomas
IT Man: Arin Whit
Pathlgst: Patrick Adegboyega
Obsttrcn: Destin R Black
Obsttrcn: Glenn G Brooks
Obsttrcn: Rose M Brouillette
Obsttrcn: Danielle B Cooper
Obsttrcn: Lynn J Groome

D-U-N-S 13-673-6662
LSU HEALTH SYSTEM HEALTH CARE SERVICES DIVISION
LSU HCSD
5429 Airline Hwy, Baton Rouge, LA 70805-1712
Tel (225) 354-4870 *Founded/Ownrshp* 1994
Sales 24.5MM^E *EMP* 277
SIC 8741 Hospital management; Nursing & personal care facility management
CEO: Lanette Buie

LSV
See LIFE AND SPECIALTY VENTURES LLC

LT
See LABORATORY TESTING INC

D-U-N-S 00-903-1530
LT ACQUISITION CORP
LOUISE'S TRATTORIA
15335 Morrison St Ste 240, Sherman Oaks, CA 91403-6701
Tel (818) 788-0500 *Founded/Ownrshp* 1998

Sales 14.9MM^E *EMP* 350
SIC 5812 Italian restaurant; Caterers; Italian restaurant; Caterers
Pr: Robert Serritella
**CFO:* Corrie Oekawa
**VP:* Marc Buckhantz

LT FOODS AMERICA
See KUSHA INC

D-U-N-S 60-754-1989
LT2 LLC
LETIGRE
250 Park Ave S Fl 10, New York, NY 10003-1402
Tel (212) 684-1510 *Founded/Ownrshp* 2003
Sales 25.0MM *EMP* 25
SIC 2321 2331 Men's & boys' furnishings; Women's & misses' blouses & shirts
CFO: Paul Pagano

D-U-N-S 01-862-6495
LTAC INVESTORS LLC
LIFELINE HOSPITAL
200 School St, Steubenville, OH 43953-9610
Tel (740) 346-2600 *Founded/Ownrshp* 2005
Sales 20.4MM^E *EMP* 150
SIC 8062 General medical & surgical hospitals
**CEO:* Susan Tournay Colpo
Dir Lab: Janet Cipullo
Mtls Dir: Mark McKinnon

LTC
See LEBANON TOOL CO INC

LTC
See LEADING TECHNOLOGY COMPOSITES INC

D-U-N-S 19-702-6024
LTC EDDY INC
NORTH EAST HOUSE
315 S Manning Blvd, Albany, NY 12208-1707
Tel (518) 271-5000 *Founded/Ownrshp* 1984
Sales 1.5MM *EMP* 385
Accts Kpmg Peat Marwick Llp Albany
SIC 8741 6513 Nursing & personal care facility management; Apartment building operators; Nursing & personal care facility management; Apartment building operators
Pr: James Reed
**CEO:* Jo Ann Constantino
**Prin:* Norman Dascher

D-U-N-S 17-006-1340
LTC GLOBAL INC
6201 Presidential Ct, Fort Myers, FL 33919-3524
Tel (800) 362-8837 *Founded/Ownrshp* 2004
Sales NA *EMP* 87
SIC 6411 Insurance agents, brokers & service
Pr: Thomas Skiff
Chf Mktg O: Deborah Skiff

D-U-N-S 79-528-4793
▲ LTC PROPERTIES INC
2829 Townsgate Rd Ste 350, Westlake Village, CA 91361-3019
Tel (805) 981-8655 *Founded/Ownrshp* 1992
Sales 118.9MM *EMP* 19^E
Tkr Sym LTC *Exch* NYS
SIC 6798 Real estate investment trusts; Real estate investment trusts
Ch Bd: Wendy L Simpson
COO: Nick Cafferillo
CFO: Pamela J Shelley-Kessler
Treas: Caroline L Chikhale
Ex VP: Clint B Malin
Sr VP: Brent P Chappell
VP: Christophe Ishihawa
VP: T Andrew Stokes
Dir IT: Sam Yellen
Snr Mgr: Joe Conner

D-U-N-S 96-240-0151
LTCCORP GOVERNMENT SERVICES INC
250 S Wacker Dr Ste 600, Chicago, IL 60606-5837
Tel (313) 875-4115 *Founded/Ownrshp* 2011
Sales NA *EMP* 865
SIC 8711 6719

D-U-N-S 04-730-6055 IMP/EXP
LTCCORP GOVERNMENT SERVICES-OH INC
TOLTEST
1480 Ford St, Maumee, OH 43537-1731
Tel (419) 794-3500 *Founded/Ownrshp* 2010
Sales NA *EMP* 300
SIC 1542 8744

LTCG
See LONG TERM CARE GROUP INC

D-U-N-S 02-519-5116 IMP
LTD COMMODITIES LLC
L-T-D COMMODITIES
2800 Lakeside Dr, Bannockburn, IL 60015-1280
Tel (847) 295-6058 *Founded/Ownrshp* 2001
Sales 357.7MM^E *EMP* 1,500^E
SIC 5961 5947 Catalog & mail-order houses; Gift, novelty & souvenir shop; Catalog & mail-order houses; Gift, novelty & souvenir shop
Pr: Sheldon Leibowitz
CEO: Michael Hara
COO: Dion Bell
Genl Mgr: Rick Disclafani
Dir IT: Katherine Liolis
IT Man: Tim Christoff

D-U-N-S 06-392-5913
LTD CONSTRUCTION SERVICES GP
WALTON CONSTRUCTION
358 E Fthill Blvd Ste 100, San Dimas, CA 91773
Tel (909) 267-7777 *Founded/Ownrshp* 2004
Sales 57.0MM *EMP* 45
SIC 1542 1522 Commercial & office building contractors; Apartment building construction
Pr: Thomas W Gibson
Pr: Rick Moses

D-U-N-S 86-930-4923
LTD DIRECT MARKETING INC
1013 Centre Rd Ste 400, Wilmington, DE 19805-1265
Tel (302) 633-3000 *Founded/Ownrshp* 1994
Sales 13.9MM^E *EMP* 600
SIC 7389 8742 Telemarketing services; Marketing consulting services; Telemarketing services; Marketing consulting services
Pr: Tom Drake
**CFO:* Walter Kern

D-U-N-S 80-987-8507
LTD FINANCIAL SERVICES LP
7322 Southwest Fwy # 1600, Houston, TX 77074-2010
Tel (713) 414-2100 *Founded/Ownrshp* 1993
Sales 28.3MM^E *EMP* 500^E
Accts Buffington & Company Pc
SIC 7322 Collection agency, except real estate; Collection agency, except real estate
Pr: Jim Glaus
Exec: Maria Charping
VP Mktg: Jamie Campise

LTD HOSPITALITY GROUP
See LTD MANAGEMENT CO LLC

D-U-N-S 02-397-8620
LTD INC
LUSTINE TOYOTA-DODGE
14227 Jefferson Davis Hwy, Woodbridge, VA 22191-2108
Tel (703) 494-1800 *Founded/Ownrshp* 1978
Sales 64.5MM^E *EMP* 146
SIC 5511 Automobiles, new & used; Automobiles, new & used
VP: Noble Steven P
**Ch Bd:* Burton Lustine
**Pr:* Lowell Kairys
**Pr:* Kairys Lowell N
**VP:* Giddings James
Sls Mgr: Matt Lepage
Sls Mgr: Amine Rezki

D-U-N-S 80-007-1920
LTD MANAGEMENT CO LLC
LTD HOSPITALITY GROUP
1564 Crossways Blvd, Chesapeake, VA 23320-2841
Tel (757) 420-0900 *Founded/Ownrshp* 1991
Sales 93.5MM^E *EMP* 800^E
SIC 8741 8721 Hotel or motel management; Accounting, auditing & bookkeeping; Hotel or motel management; Accounting, auditing & bookkeeping
Pr: Dilip Desai
Mng Pt: Neel Desai
Mng Pt: Kush Thakkar
**Pr:* Bharat Shah
Sr VP: Prakash Rajamani
**Sr VP:* Kimberly Schlick
Dir IT: Tony Parrow
Sls Dir: Dawn Anderson
Sls Dir: Mandy Bashore
Sls Dir: Lori Lowry
Sls Mgr: Stephanie Eckes

LTD PARTS
See BBB INDUSTRIES LLC

D-U-N-S 03-329-8162
LTE OLDCO LLC
LAYTON TRUCK EQUIPMENT
2425 Platte Pl, Colorado Springs, CO 80909-6041
Tel (719) 597-0400 *Founded/Ownrshp* 2010
Sales 26.4MM^E *EMP* 100^E
SIC 5012 5084 5251 5531

D-U-N-S 02-365-2170
LTF CONSTRUCTION CO LLC
LIFE TIME CONSTRUCTION
(*Suby of* LIFE TIME FITNESS INC) ★
2902 Corporate Pl, Chanhassen, MN 55317-4560
Tel (952) 229-7521 *Founded/Ownrshp* 1998
Sales 46.2MM^E *EMP* 120
SIC 1611 General contractor, highway & street construction; General contractor, highway & street construction
CEO: Bahram Akradi

D-U-N-S 07-988-1824
LTF HOLDINGS INC
2902 Corporate Pl, Chanhassen, MN 55317-4560
Tel (952) 380-0303 *Founded/Ownrshp* 2015
Sales 703.2MM^E *EMP* 22,500^E
SIC 6719 Investment holding companies, except banks
Ch Bd: Bahram Akradi

D-U-N-S 02-594-0156
LTG LONESTAR TRUCK GROUP EAST LLC
SHREVEPORT TRUCK CENTER
2051 Hughes Rd, Grapevine, TX 76051-7317
Tel (817) 428-9736 *Founded/Ownrshp* 2007
Sales 127.6MM *EMP* 215^E
SIC 5531

D-U-N-S 80-742-2469
LTG SHREVEPORT TRUCK CENTER LP
7300 Greenwood Rd, Shreveport, LA 71119-8902
Tel (318) 938-9955 *Founded/Ownrshp* 2007
Sales 22.0MM *EMP* 65
SIC 5511

D-U-N-S 36-077-0981
LTHM DALLAS - OPERATIONS LLC
SOUTH HAMPTON COMMUNITY HOSP
2929 S Hampton Rd, Dallas, TX 75224-3026
Tel (214) 623-4400 *Founded/Ownrshp* 2012
Sales NA *EMP* 300
SIC 8062 General medical & surgical hospitals

D-U-N-S 83-261-7026
LTHM HOUSTON - OPERATIONS LLC
RENAISSANCE HOSPITAL-HOUSTON
1221 Mckinney St Ste 2850, Houston, TX 77010-2028
Tel (713) 697-7777 *Founded/Ownrshp* 2009
Sales 47.3MM^E *EMP* 350^E
SIC 8062 General medical & surgical hospitals; General medical & surgical hospitals
CEO: Kirk Soileau

VP: Cathy McCue
Chf Nrs Of: Tina Baggett
IT Man: Charles Boan
Mtls Mgr: Amanda Montemayor
Mtls Mgr: Stephanie Myles

LTHRN CMNTY SVCS SOUTHERN NENG
See LUTHERAN COMMUNITY SERVICES INC

LTI
See LAVALLE TRANSPORTATION INC

LTI
See ECLI PRODUCTS LLC

D-U-N-S 07-960-2058
LTI HOLDINGS INC
27 W Mohler Church Rd, Ephrata, PA 17522-9029
Tel (717) 738-3044 *Founded/Ownrshp* 1983
Sales 25.3MM^E *EMP* 375
SIC 3281 3083

D-U-N-S 61-574-5168 IMP
LTI HOLDINGS INC
BOYD
(*Suby of* SNOW PHIPPS GROUP LLC) ★
600 S Mcclure Rd, Modesto, CA 95357-0520
Tel (209) 236-1111 *Founded/Ownrshp* 2013
Sales 581.9MM^E *EMP* 2,664
SIC 3069 2822 Gaskets, all materials; Hard rubber & molded rubber products; Rubber automotive products; Synthetic rubber
Pr: Mitch Aiello
**CFO:* Kurt Wetzel
Dir IT: Thom McGehee
VP Sls: Roger Malmrose

D-U-N-S 10-286-5839
LTI INC
MILKY WAY
(*Suby of* LYNDEN INC) ★
8631 Depot Rd, Lynden, WA 98264-9301
Tel (360) 757-1968 *Founded/Ownrshp* 1946
Sales 58.4MM^E *EMP* 587
SIC 4213 Trucking, except local; Trucking, except local
Pr: Brad Williamson
**Ch:* Guy A Jansen
Treas: Dick Korpela
**VP:* Bob Griggs
VP: Don Guthie
**VP:* Kalise E Hastings
Genl Mgr: Len Kilmer
Trfc Dir: Greg Tolle
Board of Directors: Brad Williamson

D-U-N-S 12-885-9472
LTI TRUCKING SERVICES INC
1024 Eagle Park Rd, National Stock Yards, IL 62071
Tel (618) 274-3000 *Founded/Ownrshp* 2005
Sales 28.5MM^E *EMP* 150
SIC 4213 Trucking, except local
Pr: Nicholas Civello
CFO: Phil Hamel
Sr VP: Dan Allison
Off Mgr: Paula Naugle

D-U-N-S 60-743-2106
LTI TRUCKING SERVICES INC
411 N 10th St Ste 500, Saint Louis, MO 63101-1320
Tel (314) 932-6970 *Founded/Ownrshp* 2005
Sales 40.0MM *EMP* 50
SIC 4731 Freight forwarding
Pr: Nicholas Civello
**VP:* Bob Brendel
VP Opers: Kevin Boeckmann
Sls Mgr: Paula Hubbard

D-U-N-S 15-397-7970
LTK CONSULTING SERVICES INC
LTK ENGINEERING SERVICES
100 W Butler Ave, Ambler, PA 19002-5703
Tel (215) 542-0700 *Founded/Ownrshp* 1984
Sales 65.7MM^E *EMP* 285
SIC 8711 Consulting engineer; Consulting engineer
Ch Bd: George N Dorshimer
**CFO:* Christopher M Lawlor
**Sec:* Catherine M Schmidt
Bd of Dir: Eloy Martinez
VP: Bill Frandsen
**VP:* Tom Furmaniak
**VP:* Frederick H Landell
VP: Cliffo Woodbury
Prgrm Mgr: Jim Herzog
Prgrm Mgr: Bill Whitbred
Area Mgr: Lloyd Mack

LTK ENGINEERING SERVICES
See LTK CONSULTING SERVICES INC

D-U-N-S 07-967-4723
LTL COLOR COMPOUNDERS LLC
INFINITY LTL
(*Suby of* AMERICHEM INC) ★
20 Progress Dr, Morrisville, PA 19067-3702
Tel (215) 736-1126 *Founded/Ownrshp* 2014
Sales 24.0MM *EMP* 53
SIC 2295 3087 Resin or plastic coated fabrics; Custom compound purchased resins
Pr: Carlos Carreno
CFO: Robert Bissinger
Genl Mgr: James Figaniak

D-U-N-S 96-805-5236
LTL HOLDINGS LTD LLP
2728 Agnes St, Corpus Christi, TX 78405-2208
Tel (361) 882-3311 *Founded/Ownrshp* 1995
Sales 25.3MM^E *EMP* 30^E
SIC 5172 5541 6519 4213 Aircraft fueling services; Diesel fuel; Gasoline service stations; Real property lessors; Trucking, except local
Pr: Garnett T Brooks
**VP:* Patsy Brooks

D-U-N-S 18-948-7580 IMP
LTL WHOLESALE INC
L T L HOME PRODUCTS
125 Route 61 S, Schuylkill Haven, PA 17972-1000
Tel (570) 385-5470 *Founded/Ownrshp* 1984
Sales 20.0MM^E *EMP* 70
SIC 5031 5072 Doors; Builders' hardware

Pr: Malcolm Groff
**VP:* Walter Furer
**VP:* John McGowan

D-U-N-S 08-261-9222
■ LTM INC
KNIFE RIVER MATERIALS
(*Suby of* KNIFE RIVER COAL MINING) ★
3770 Kirtland Rd, Central Point, OR 97502-9316
Tel (541) 779-6304 *Founded/Ownrshp* 2007
Sales 20.3MM^E *EMP* 125
SIC 3273 5032 1611 1521 Ready-mixed concrete; Concrete mixtures; Paving mixtures; Aggregate; Concrete construction: roads, highways, sidewalks, etc.; Highway & street paving contractor; Single-family home remodeling, additions & repairs; Ready-mixed concrete; Concrete mixtures; Paving mixtures; Aggregate; Concrete construction: roads, highways, sidewalks, etc.; Highway & street paving contractor; Single-family home remodeling, additions & repairs
VP: Dale Lininger
**Pr:* David S Bull
COO: Bob Vaughan

D-U-N-S 93-289-9784
LTM INC
925 E Main St Ste 66, Havelock, NC 28532-2375
Tel (252) 444-6881 *Founded/Ownrshp* 1994
Sales 23.7MM^E *EMP* 300
Accts Frye & Wolcott Cpas Manassa
SIC 8711 Engineering services; Engineering services
Pr: David W Baldwin
**COO:* Lee Ann Baldwin
COO: Lee A Bldwin
**CFO:* Thomas J Debenedetto
VP: Jackie Baber
VP: Ray Brassley

D-U-N-S 61-354-3636
LTP MANAGEMENT GROUP INC
4411 Cleveland Ave, Fort Myers, FL 33901-9011
Tel (239) 275-6339 *Founded/Ownrshp* 1985
Sales 20.6MM^E *EMP* 205
SIC 8741 Restaurant management; Restaurant management
CEO: David L Lageschulte
**Pr:* Terry K Brawner
**Treas:* Paul Lynch

LTR
See LUNDAY-THAGARD CO

D-U-N-S 83-235-8683 IMP
LTS LLC
11932 Brittmoore Park Dr, Houston, TX 77041-7225
Tel (832) 467-4040 *Founded/Ownrshp* 1993
Sales 22.3MM^E *EMP* 50
SIC 5049 Engineers' equipment & supplies

D-U-N-S 78-766-0513 IMP/EXP
LTS LOHMANN THERAPY SYSTEMS CORP
(*Suby of* LTS LOHMANN THERAPIE-SYSTEME AG)
21 Henderson Dr, West Caldwell, NJ 07006-6607
Tel (973) 575-5170 *Founded/Ownrshp* 2009
Sales 228.8MM^E *EMP* 1,000
SIC 2834 Pharmaceutical preparations; Pharmaceutical preparations
CEO: Wolfgang Hartwig
**CFO:* H Werner Lscher
**CFO:* Gregory Webink
**Chf Mktg O:* Tim Schlange
Ofcr: Peter Schwarz
VP: Salvatore Fascetta
**VP:* Kenneth Rogers
**VP:* Dave Sacks
**VP:* Salvatore Sascatta
VP: Wolfgang Schaefer
**VP:* Wolfgang Schafer
Exec: Patricia Zailo

D-U-N-S 04-485-0758
LTS RENTALS LLC
927 Black Diamond Way, Lodi, CA 95240-0738
Tel (209) 334-4100 *Founded/Ownrshp* 1957
Sales 36.6MM *EMP* 110
Accts Degregori Gormsen & Ringer Ll
SIC 7513 4212 Truck rental, without drivers; Local trucking, without storage; Truck rental, without drivers; Local trucking, without storage
Ex VP: Jim Musgrave

D-U-N-S 03-770-9361
LTV REAL ESTATE CORP
P.O. Box 267176 (33326-7176)
Tel (954) 304-6291 *Founded/Ownrshp* 2011
Sales 30.0MM *EMP* 25
SIC 6531 Real estate brokers & agents
CEO: Bill Fernandez

D-U-N-S 00-507-1313
LTX CREDENCE CORP
CREDENCE SYSTEMS
1355 California Cir, Milpitas, CA 95035-3021
Tel (408) 635-4300 *Founded/Ownrshp* 2010
Sales 57.9MM^E *EMP* 199^E
SIC 3674 Semiconductors & related devices
Prin: Timothy Wrye
**Pr:* Warren Necoechea
**Pr:* Peter Rood
COO: David Ranhoff
CFO: Kevin Eichler
CFO: Mark Gallenberger
Sr VP: Carlos Lazalde
**VP:* Scott Aldridge
VP: Tim Coffey
VP: Doug Cutsforth
VP: Michael Goldbach
VP: Tim Hallock
VP: Tony Miola
VP: Steve Wigley
Exec: Jill Barres

D-U-N-S 18-730-4951
LTX INC
LAWRENCE TRANSPORTATION
1515 Industrial Dr Nw, Rochester, MN 55901-0792
Tel (507) 282-6715 *Founded/Ownrshp* 1987
Sales 79.3MM^E *EMP* 456

SIC 4213 Refrigerated products transport; Refrigerated products transport
Ch Bd: Steve Lawrence
*Pr: George C Wilson
*CFO: Jayson Crell

D-U-N-S 60-155-8492
LUANA BANCORPORATION
P.O. Box 68 (52156-0068)
Tel (563) 539-2166 Founded/Ownrshp 2005
Sales NA EMP 41E
SIC 6022 State commercial banks
Pr: Robert A Schultz

D-U-N-S 00-531-0685
LUANA SAVINGS BANK (IA)
(Suby of LUANA BANCORPORATION) ★
100 Harvest Dr, Luana, IA 52156-4700
Tel (563) 539-2166 Founded/Ownrshp 1908
Sales NA EMP 24
SIC 6036 6163 State savings banks, not federally chartered; Loan brokers; State savings banks, not federally chartered; Loan brokers
Pr: David Schultz
Ofcr: Josh Williams
*VP: Larry Fritz
IT Man: Joe Kriener

D-U-N-S 08-548-4384
LUBAR & CO INC
700 N Water St Ste 1200, Milwaukee, WI 53202-4259
Tel (414) 291-9000 Founded/Ownrshp 1977
Sales 236.5MME EMP 511E
SIC 6722 Management investment, open-end; Management investment, open-end
*Pr: David Lubar
*Pt: Vince Shiely
Pr: Tiffany Johnston
*CFO: David Bauer
*Ch: Sheldon Lubar
Bd of Dir: John Becker
*Prin: David Kuehl

D-U-N-S 03-120-5750
LUBBERS BROTHERS INC
944 N Main St, Cheney, KS 67025-9139
Tel (316) 540-3103 Founded/Ownrshp 1985
Sales 32.2MM EMP 60
SIC 5511 Automobiles, new & used; Automobiles, new & used
Pr: Denny Lubbers
*Treas: Alan Lubbers
*VP: Larry Lubbers

D-U-N-S 09-143-6766
LUBBERS CHEVROLET INC
914 N Main St, Cheney, KS 67025-9139
Tel (316) 540-0011 Founded/Ownrshp 1988
Sales 38.5MM EMP 100E
SIC 5511 Automobiles, new & used; Automobiles, new & used
Pr: Lawrence Lubbers
*Treas: James Lubbers
*VP: Alan Lubbers
Sls Mgr: Bryon Hull

LUBBOCK AERO
See ABILENE AERO INC

LUBBOCK CASH REGISTER
See TRUNO RETAIL TECHNOLOGY SOLUTIONS

D-U-N-S 07-166-0492
LUBBOCK COUNTY HOSPITAL DISTRICT
UNIVERSITY MEDICAL CENTER
602 Indiana Ave, Lubbock, TX 79415-3364
Tel (806) 775-8200 Founded/Ownrshp 1978
Sales 322.0MME EMP 2,000
SIC 8062 Hospital, medical school affiliation; Hospital, medical school affiliation
Pr: David Allison
VP: Adrienne Cozart
Dir Case M: Joyce Timmons
Dir IT: Shane Terrell
Obsttrcn: Sharon Shoulders
Pharmcst: Debbie Condra

D-U-N-S 14-003-7487
LUBBOCK HEART HOSPITAL LP
4810 N Loop 289, Lubbock, TX 79416-3025
Tel (806) 687-7777 Founded/Ownrshp 2003
Sales 71.4MM EMP 350
SIC 8062 General medical & surgical hospitals; General medical & surgical hospitals
CEO: Roy Vinson
CFO: William E Woolsey
Dir OR: Suzanne Nolen
Surgeon: Robert Carr
Surgeon: Stephen Cord
Surgeon: Jeff Headrick
Surgeon: Garry Pollock
Doctor: W Brogan
HC Dir: Chrissy Rister

D-U-N-S 83-071-3694
LUBBOCK HERITAGE HOSPITAL LLC
GRACE MEDICAL CENTER
(Suby of GRACE AMBULATORY SURGERY CTR) ★
2412 50th St, Lubbock, TX 79412-2504
Tel (806) 785-0077 Founded/Ownrshp 2009
Sales 42.8MME EMP 225
SIC 8062 General medical & surgical hospitals; General medical & surgical hospitals
CEO: Dana Rains
*COO: Randy Nichols
COO: David Weil
CFO: Vanessa Reasoner
Dir Risk M: Carol Livingston
Dir Rx: Tim Oursbourn
CIO: Jason Deroun
QA Dir: Patsy Anderson
Mktg Dir: Dick Wright
Pathlgst: Tom Mattison
Nrsg Dir: Everette Smith

D-U-N-S 02-033-3878
LUBBOCK INDEPENDENT SCHOOL DISTRICT
1628 19th St, Lubbock, TX 79401-4832
Tel (806) 766-1000 Founded/Ownrshp 1907
Sales 295.4MM EMP 3,300
Accts Bolinger Segars Gilbert & Mo
SIC 8211 Public adult education school; Public elementary school; Public junior high school; Public senior high school; Public adult education school; Public elementary school; Public junior high school; Public senior high school
COO: Jennifer Walden
Exec: Bill Tarro
Dir Sec: Jody Scifers
Genl Mgr: Michael Cochrane
Genl Mgr: Mark Hayes
IT Man: Carolyn Jordan
Sales Asso: Anush Gharibyan
Psych: Lea Brown
HC Dir: Paulette Rozneck

D-U-N-S 01-845-0044
■ **LUBBOCK MOTORS-GM LTD**
(Suby of GROUP 1 AUTOMOTIVE INC) ★
6000 19th St, Lubbock, TX 79407-1616
Tel (806) 793-2727 Founded/Ownrshp 1987
Sales 86.1MME EMP 500
SIC 5511 5531 Automobiles, new & used; Automotive parts; Automobiles, new & used; Automotive parts
Genl Mgr: Scott George
Exec: Mack Owen
Sls Mgr: Herman Knorr

D-U-N-S 09-320-1556
LUBBOCK NATIONAL BANK (TX)
(Suby of COMMERCE NATIONAL FINANCIAL SERVICES INC) ★
4811 50th St, Lubbock, TX 79414-3418
Tel (806) 792-1000 Founded/Ownrshp 1977, 1989
Sales 39.9MM EMP 160E
SIC 7389 Financial services; Financial services
Pr: Keith A Mann
Ofcr: Kerri Johnson
*Ex VP: Benny Martin
*Ex VP: Denise W Thomas
Sr VP: Christopher Robinson
Sr VP: Lee Wilson
VP: Kim Koontz
VP: Kyle McNeese
VP: Drew Smith

D-U-N-S 09-878-6460
LUBBOCK REGIONAL MENTAL HEALTH MENTAL RETARDATION CENTER
LUBBOCK REGIONAL MHMR
904 Avenue O, Lubbock, TX 79401-3924
Tel (806) 766-0310 Founded/Ownrshp 1967
Sales 25.9MME EMP 500
SIC 8093 Specialty outpatient clinics; Mental health clinic, outpatient; Drug clinic, outpatient; Alcohol clinic, outpatient; Specialty outpatient clinics; Mental health clinic, outpatient; Drug clinic, outpatient; Alcohol clinic, outpatient
Pr: Danett Castle
V Ch: Robert B Kazee Jr
Dir IT: Daniel Smith
IT Man: Cindy Holtman
Pr Dir: Roger Karr
Snr Mgr: Beth Lawson

LUBBOCK REGIONAL MHMR
See LUBBOCK REGIONAL MENTAL HEALTH MENTAL RETARDATION CENTER

D-U-N-S 10-067-1486
LUBBOCK-COOPER INDEPENDENT SCHOOL DISTRICT
16302 Loop 493, Lubbock, TX 79423-7805
Tel (806) 863-7100 Founded/Ownrshp 1940
Sales 46.8MM EMP 425E
Accts Terry & King Cpas Pc Lubb
SIC 8211 Elementary & secondary schools; Finishing school, secondary; Elementary & secondary schools; Finishing school, secondary
Trst: Daniel Castro
Ofcr: Chris Alderson
Sr VP: Paul Ehlers
MIS Dir: Donna Hanfeld
Pr Dir: Sadie Alderson
Teacher Pr: Darla Heinrich
Psych: Laura Burrescia
Psych: Siles Langston
Psych: Langston Siles
HC Dir: Kristy Rose

D-U-N-S 03-861-7700 IMP
LUBE - POWER INC
50146 Utica Dr, Shelby Township, MI 48315-3293
Tel (586) 247-6500 Founded/Ownrshp 2007
Sales 48.7MME EMP 83
SIC 3569 5084 8711 Lubrication equipment, industrial; Hydraulic systems equipment & supplies; Consulting engineer; Lubrication equipment, industrial; Hydraulic systems equipment & supplies; Consulting engineer
Pr: Dale McNeill
*Treas: Dan Hodder
*VP: Brian Lightcap
Ex Dir: Kim Bachand
Opers Mgr: Amy Kot
Sls Mgr: Keith Chene

D-U-N-S 82-676-3737
LUBE HOLDINGS INC
(Suby of LUBE AGGREGATOR INC)
101 Chestnut Ave, Sharon, PA 16146-1751
Tel (724) 981-3123 Founded/Ownrshp 2004
Sales 86.3MME EMP 512E
SIC 6719 Investment holding companies, except banks
CEO: Greg Lippert

D-U-N-S 83-449-7559
LUBE MANAGEMENT CORP
JIFFY LUBE
7430 S Creek Rd Ste 200, Sandy, UT 84093-6160
Tel (801) 569-8800 Founded/Ownrshp 1999
Sales 23.7MME EMP 500
SIC 7549 Lubrication service, automotive; Lubrication service, automotive
Pr: Kirk Umphrey

LUBE-TECH
See LUBRICATION TECHNOLOGIES INC

LUBEMASTER
See DEVELOPMENTAL SYSTEMS INC

D-U-N-S 10-315-0074 IMP
LUBERSKI INC
HIDDEN VILLA RANCH
310 N Harbor Blvd Ste 205, Fullerton, CA 92832-1954
Tel (714) 680-3447 Founded/Ownrshp 1991
Sales 260.0MME EMP 261
SIC 5144 5143 Eggs; Milk; Cheese; Eggs; Milk; Cheese
CEO: Timothy Luberski
CFO: Don Lawson
*Ex VP: Robert J Kelly
*Ex VP: Greg Schneider
*Ex VP: Michael Sencer
*VP: Tim Clausen
VP: Robert Kelly
Off Mgr: Michelle Baello
IT Man: Robert Sencer
Opers Mgr: Kyle Kilcher
VP Mktg: Nick Jioras

D-U-N-S 86-720-5866 IMP
LUBERSKI INC
HIDDEN VILLA RANCH
(Suby of HIDDEN VILLA RANCH) ★
310 N Harbor Blvd Ste 205, Fullerton, CA 92832-1954
Tel (714) 680-3447 Founded/Ownrshp 1987
Sales 260.0MM EMP 261E
SIC 5144 Eggs; Milk cooling stations; Eggs
Pr: Tim E Luberski
*CFO: Don Lawson
*Ex VP: Robert J Kelly
*Ex VP: Greg Schneider
*Ex VP: Michael Sencer

LUBERT ADLER PARTNERS
See LUBERT-ADLER MANAGEMENT CO LP

D-U-N-S 01-135-9002
LUBERT-ADLER MANAGEMENT CO LP
LUBERT ADLER PARTNERS
2929 Arch St Ste 1650, Philadelphia, PA 19104-2868
Tel (215) 972-2200 Founded/Ownrshp 1997
Sales 90.8MME EMP 275
SIC 6798 Real estate investment trusts; Real estate investment trusts
CEO: Dean Adler
Pt: Patrick Lee
Pr: Gerald A Ronon
CFO: Eric Emrich
Ch: Ira Lubert
Bd of Dir: Jeff Keil
VP: John Buck
VP: David Lorry
VP: Alexander Popovich
Prin: Neill Faucett
Prin: Stuart Margulies

D-U-N-S 95-941-3774 IMP
LUBO USA LLC
360 Dr Mrtn Lthr Kg Jr Dr Martin, Norwalk, CT 06854
Tel (203) 967-1140 Founded/Ownrshp 1996
Sales 50.0MM EMP 60
SIC 5084 Screening machinery & equipment; Screening machinery & equipment
Pr: Pieter Van Djk
*VP: Erik Van Djk

LUBRICANT ADDITIVES
See LUBRIZOL CORP

D-U-N-S 15-989-8493
LUBRICAR INC
JIFFY LUBE
3520 Calle Cuervo Nw, Albuquerque, NM 87114-9220
Tel (505) 897-6701 Founded/Ownrshp 1997
Sales 28.0MM EMP 425
SIC 7549 Lubrication service, automotive; Lubrication service, automotive
Pr: Keith Mortensen
*Ch Bd: Bevon Mortensen
*CFO: Richard Jones
*VP: Robert Mortensen

D-U-N-S 04-442-2632 IMP/EXP
LUBRICATING SPECIALTIES CO
TECHNOLUBE PRODUCTS CO
8015 Paramount Blvd, Pico Rivera, CA 90660-4811
Tel (562) 776-4000 Founded/Ownrshp 1998
Sales 73.3MME EMP 170
SIC 2992 Lubricating oils & greases; Lubricating oils; Oils & greases, blending & compounding; Lubricating oils & greases; Lubricating oils; Oils & greases, blending & compounding
Pr: Stephen Milam
CFO: Sydney Thwaites
*VP: Rob Kress
*VP: Steve Miller
VP: Mark Negast
Sls Mgr: Jose Blanco

D-U-N-S 00-801-9119 EXP
LUBRICATION ENGINEERS INC
300 Bailey Ave, Fort Worth, TX 76107-1856
Tel (817) 834-6321 Founded/Ownrshp 1951
Sales 22.4MME EMP 100
SIC 2992 Oils & greases, blending & compounding; Oils & greases, blending & compounding
Pr: Scott A Schwindaman
*CEO: Randall L Kressler
*Treas: Patrick J Kraus
*Ex VP: Jeffrey Turner
*VP: Darren G Booth
*VP: John Sander
Mng Dir: Danny Roberts

IT Man: Shelly King
*VP Sls: Vincent M Tofani
Sls Mgr: Clay Calk
Sls Mgr: Paul Llewellyn

D-U-N-S 05-625-4808 IMP/EXP
■ **LUBRICATION SYSTEMS CO OF TEXAS LLC**
TOTAL LUBRICATION MGT CO
(Suby of COLFAX CORP) ★
1740 Stebbins Dr, Houston, TX 77043-2807
Tel (713) 464-6266 Founded/Ownrshp 2007
Sales 22.4MME EMP 90
SIC 1796 3569 Machinery installation; Lubricating systems, centralized; Filters
CEO: Clay H Kiefaber
*CFO: C Scott Brannan
*VP: William Flexon

D-U-N-S 06-652-5163 IMP
LUBRICATION TECHNOLOGIES INC
LUBE-TECH
900 Mendelssohn Ave N, Minneapolis, MN 55427-4387
Tel (763) 545-0707 Founded/Ownrshp 1993
Sales 164.7MME EMP 165
SIC 5172 5169 Lubricating oils & greases; Chemicals & allied products; Lubricating oils & greases; Chemicals & allied products
CEO: Christian Bame
COO: Eric Jackson
VP: Steve Danker
VP: Dan Gregg
Genl Mgr: Matt Finley
Genl Mgr: Dave Stascavage
CIO: Dave Morris
Dir IT: Todd Matvick
Dir IT: Brian Miller
IT Man: Bob Brandenburg
IT Man: Andrew Ellinghausen

LUBRICORP, LLC
See RPI HOLDINGS LLC

LUBRIPLATE LUBRICANTS
See FISKE BROTHERS REFINING CO INC

D-U-N-S 13-047-0016
■ **LUBRIQUIP INC**
OTHER STYLES - SEE OPERATION
(Suby of IDEX CORP) ★
18901 Cranwood Pkwy, Cleveland, OH 44128-4041
Tel (216) 581-2000 Founded/Ownrshp 1988
Sales 31.9MME EMP 300
SIC 3714 Lubrication systems & parts, motor vehicle; Lubrication systems & parts, motor vehicle
Pr: Rick Morgan
*VP: Jeff Gacka

D-U-N-S 01-237-6732 EXP
■ **LUBRIZOL ADVANCED MATERIALS INC**
(Suby of LUBRICANT ADDITIVES) ★
9911 Brecksville Rd, Cleveland, OH 44141-3201
Tel (216) 447-6129 Founded/Ownrshp 1870
Sales 712.4MME EMP 2,780
SIC 2899 2891 Chemical preparations; Adhesives & sealants; Chemical preparations; Adhesives & sealants
CEO: James L Hambrick
*Pr: Donald W Bogus
*CFO: Daniel R Welly
Treas: Charles P Cooley III
*Sr VP: Andrew Auvil
*Sr VP: Thomas J Malafronte
*Sr VP: Julian M Steinberg
*VP: Suzanne F Day
*VP: John J King
*VP: Eric R Schnur
*VP: Gregory D Taylor
*VP: Mike Vaughn

D-U-N-S 00-417-2565 IMP/EXP
■ **LUBRIZOL CORP**
LUBRICANT ADDITIVES
(Suby of BERKSHIRE HATHAWAY INC) ★
29400 Lakeland Blvd, Wickliffe, OH 44092-2298
Tel (440) 943-4200 Founded/Ownrshp 2011
Sales 13.7MMME EMP 14,043
SIC 2899 2869 Oil treating compounds; Industrial organic chemicals; Oil treating compounds; Industrial organic chemicals
Pr: James L Hambrick
*COO: Stephen F Kirk
*CFO: Charles P Cooley
*CFO: Suzanne F Day
*CFO: Brian A Valentine
VP: Donald W Bogus
VP: Yannick Couedic
VP: Stephen A Di Biase
*VP: John J King
*VP: Larry D Norwood
*VP: Eric R Schnur
VP: Gregory D Taylor
VP: Mike Vaughn
Exec: Karl Scott
Creative D: Terry Pacifico
Comm Man: Cathy Kopanski

D-U-N-S 19-021-7737 IMP
■ **LUBRIZOL SPECIALTY PRODUCTS INC**
PSPI
(Suby of BERKSHIRE HATHAWAY INC) ★
2000 W Sam Houston Pkwy S # 320, Houston, TX 77042-3615
Tel (713) 339-8703 Founded/Ownrshp 2014
Sales 28.1MME EMP 80E
SIC 2819 3533 Industrial inorganic chemicals; Oil & gas field machinery
Pr: Steve Sementcuk
*Pr: Mike Brown

LUBY EQUIPMENT SERVICES
See MACHINE MAINTENANCE INC

D-U-N-S 02-701-4984 IMP
▲ **LUBYS INC**
13111 Nw Fwy Ste 600, Houston, TX 77040-6392
Tel (713) 329-6800 Founded/Ownrshp 1947
Sales 394.0MM EMP 8,352

Accts Grant Thornton Llp Houston T
Tkr Sym LUB *Exch* NYS
SIC 5812 Family restaurants; Family restaurants
Pr: Christopher J Pappas
**Ch Bd:* Gasper Mir III
**COO:* Peter Tropoli
CFO: K Scott Gray
**V Ch Bd:* Judith B Craven
Board of Directors: Arthur Rojas Emerson, Jill Griffin, J S B Jenkins, Frank Markantonis, Joe C McKinney, Harris J Pappas

D-U-N-S 60-390-8950
■ LUBYS RESTAURANTS LIMITED PARTNERSHIP
(*Suby of* LUBYS INC) ★
13111 Nw Fwy Ste 600, Houston, TX 77040-6392
Tel (713) 329-6800 *Founded/Ownrshp* 1996
Sales 204.4MM^E *EMP* 7,320
SIC 5812 Cafeteria; Cafeteria
Ch: Gasper Mir III
**Pr:* Chris Pappas
**Pr:* Christopher J Pappas
Pr: Dan J Rathmell
**COO:* Peter Tropoli
Treas: Roland Gonzalez
**Sr VP:* Benjamin T Coutee
**Sr VP:* K Scott Gray
VP: Ron Bass
Genl Mgr: Greg Eatchel
Genl Mgr: Julie Humphrey

D-U-N-S 01-012-9310
LUCAS ASSOCIATES INC (GA)
LUCAS GROUP
950 E Paces Ferry Rd Ne # 2300, Atlanta, GA 30326-1385
Tel (404) 239-5620 *Founded/Ownrshp* 1970
Sales 60.3MM^E *EMP* 339
SIC 7361 7363 Employment agencies; Temporary help service; Employment agencies; Temporary help service
Pr: Andrea Jennings
Sr Pt: Elaine Beagle
Sr Pt: Erica Dawley
Sr Pt: Steve Dawson
Sr Pt: Katherine Franklin
Sr Pt: Emily Gransky
Sr Pt: Charles Herman
Sr Pt: Mike Kahn
Sr Pt: Chris Kehl
Sr Pt: Tamara Klein
Sr Pt: Dan McCall
Sr Pt: Christian Montagliani
Sr Pt: Brook Monticello
Sr Pt: Hank Park
Sr Pt: Alison Parry
Sr Pt: Brian Rains
Sr Pt: Courtney Sapire
Pt: Lisa Decker
Pt: Barry Dolgow
Pt: Brett Duarte
Pt: Dave Haberman

D-U-N-S 07-914-0606
LUCAS BUILDING MAINENANCE LLC
323 Mastin Ave, Ironton, OH 45638-2432
Tel (740) 479-1800 *Founded/Ownrshp* 1993
Sales 200.0M *EMP* 740
SIC 7349 Building cleaning service; Building cleaning service

D-U-N-S 03-460-4777
LUCAS CHEVROLET-CADILLAC INC (TN)
101 S James Campbell Blvd, Columbia, TN 38401-4323
Tel (615) 244-2555 *Founded/Ownrshp* 1965
Sales 21.0MM^E *EMP* 50
SIC 5511 5521 Automobiles, new & used; Pickups, new & used; Vans, new & used; Used car dealers
Ch: Harold W Lucas
**Pr:* H Thomas Lucas
**Sec:* Allison G Lucas
**VP:* Tonya Lucas
Genl Mgr: Wade Allen
Sales Asso: Randy Drane

LUCAS CO HEALTH CENTER COUNSEL
See LUCAS COUNTY HEALTH CENTER FOUNDATION

LUCAS CO PRE-SCHOOL UNIT
See EDUCATIONAL SERVICE CENTER OF LAKE ERIE WEST

D-U-N-S 07-839-0319
LUCAS COUNTY DEPARTMENT OF JOB & FAMILY SERVICES
(*Suby of* AUDITOR OFFICE) ★
3210 Monroe St, Toledo, OH 43606-7738
Tel (419) 213-8999 *Founded/Ownrshp* 2012
Sales NA *EMP* 441^E
SIC 9441 Social security administration, government;

D-U-N-S 07-349-3371
LUCAS COUNTY HEALTH CENTER FOUNDATION
LUCAS CO HEALTH CENTER COUNSEL
1200 N 7th St, Chariton, IA 50049-1210
Tel (641) 774-3000 *Founded/Ownrshp* 1960
Sales 46.5MM^E *EMP* 180
Accts Denman & Company Llp West De
SIC 8062 General medical & surgical hospitals
CEO: Veronica Fuhs
Chf Rad: Robert Filippone
**CEO:* Dan Minkos
**CFO:* Larry Brown
**Treas:* Randy Westman
Dir Inf Cn: Tonya Dyson
Dir Lab: Keith Rickman
Chf Nrs Of: Jo Lawless
**Prin:* Betty Hansen
Obsttrcn: Fred Margolin
Podiatrist: Mark Wetzel

LUCAS GROUP
See LUCAS ASSOCIATES INC

LUCAS, HONDA OF JACKSONVILLE
See LUCAS INVESTMENTS INC

D-U-N-S 12-299-6999
LUCAS INC
11800 Lewis Rd, Chester, VA 23831-3735
Tel (804) 748-5823 *Founded/Ownrshp* 2000
Sales 36.8MM^E *EMP* 250^E
SIC 1794 1611 4953 Excavation & grading, building construction; Highway & street construction; Sanitary landfill operation; Excavation & grading, building construction; Highway & street construction; Sanitary landfill operation
Pr: Tony Lucas
**Sec:* Elizabeth S Barefoot
**VP:* Paul Swenson

D-U-N-S 03-238-2459
LUCAS INVESTMENTS INC
LUCAS, HONDA OF JACKSONVILLE
7801 Blanding Blvd, Jacksonville, FL 32244-5115
Tel (904) 737-0804 *Founded/Ownrshp* 1964
Sales 29.4MM^E *EMP* 66
SIC 5511 7538 Automobiles, new & used; General automotive repair shops; Automobiles, new & used; General automotive repair shops
Pr: Scott E Boyles
CFO: Darris Davis
**Sec:* Rosemary J Rose
Sls Dir: James Macdonald
Sls Mgr: Jim Wessels

D-U-N-S 01-113-7338
LUCAS MOTOR CO INC (NJ)
N Columbus Rd Rr 130, Burlington, NJ 08016
Tel (609) 386-3100 *Founded/Ownrshp* 1916, 1946
Sales 25.4MM^E *EMP* 55
SIC 5511 Automobiles, new & used; Pickups, new & used; Vans, new & used; Automobiles, new & used; Pickups, new & used; Vans, new & used
Pr: Francis J Lucas Jr
**VP:* Eileen Lucas

D-U-N-S 62-273-1073 IMP/EXP
LUCAS OIL PRODUCTS INC
302 N Sheridan St, Corona, CA 92880-2067
Tel (951) 270-0154 *Founded/Ownrshp* 1989
Sales 20.5MM^E *EMP* 48
SIC 2992 5169 Lubricating oils & greases; Oil additives
CEO: Forrest Lucas
**VP:* Charlotte Lucas
Dir Sec: Joseph Ganino
Genl Mgr: Robert Patison
IT Man: Bill Binckes
IT Man: Rhoda Binckes
VP Opers: Brian Nichols
Sfty Dirs: Aaron Daugherty
Opers Mgr: Michael Shugrue
Sales Exec: Marty Martin
Natl Sales: Mark Sromalla

LUCAS OIL STADIUM
See CAPITAL IMPROVEMENT BOARD OF MANAGERS

D-U-N-S 00-608-6425 IMP
■ LUCAS-MILHAUPT INC
(*Suby of* HANDY & HARMAN) ★
5656 S Pennsylvania Ave, Cudahy, WI 53110-2453
Tel (414) 769-6000 *Founded/Ownrshp* 1942
Sales 75.8MM^E *EMP* 328^E
SIC 3356 Nonferrous rolling & drawing; Nonferrous rolling & drawing
Pr: John Whitenack
Pr: David Jordan
COO: Jessica Megna
CFO: Jim Barthel
VP: Chuck Fuerstenau
VP: Pam King
CTO: John Gapinski
CTO: Brian Hughes
CTO: Joseph Shapiro
IT Man: Jeff Bieringer
IT Man: Kim Parker

LUCASFILM COML PRODUCTIONS
See LUCASFILM LTD LLC

D-U-N-S 96-712-3535
LUCASFILM FOUNDATION
1 Letterman Dr Ste 216, San Francisco, CA 94129-1495
Tel (415) 623-1000 *Founded/Ownrshp* 2005
Sales 26.0MM *EMP* 2
SIC 7829 Motion picture distribution services; Motion picture distribution services
Pr: George W Lucas

D-U-N-S 06-013-9946 IMP
■ LUCASFILM LTD LLC
LUCASFILM COML PRODUCTIONS
(*Suby of* WALT DISNEY CO) ★
1110 Gorgas Ave Bldg C-Hr, San Francisco, CA 94129-1406
Tel (415) 623-1000 *Founded/Ownrshp* 2012
Sales 76.0MM^E *EMP* 750
SIC 7812 6794 Motion picture production & distribution; Television film production; Patent owners & lessors; Motion picture production & distribution; Television film production; Patent owners & lessors
Pr: Kathleen Kennedy
CFO: Steve Condiotti
CFO: Harriette Helmer
Top Exec: Blaire Chaput
Top Exec: Mike Vollman
Ex VP: Howard Roffman
VP: Lori Aultman
VP: Steve Candiotti
VP: Doug Chiang
VP: Jeff Ruggels
VP: Lisa Ullmann
Exec: Richard Dunn

D-U-N-S 62-035-8387
LUCASVARITY AUTOMOTIVE HOLDING CO
(*Suby of* TRW AUTOMOTIVE INC) ★
12001 Tech Center Dr, Livonia, MI 48150-2122
Tel (734) 855-2600 *Founded/Ownrshp* 2003
Sales 77.7MM^E *EMP* 1,752^E
SIC 3714 Motor vehicle parts & accessories

D-U-N-S 19-417-8794
LUCCAS FREEZER & COLD STORAGE INC
(*Suby of* AGRO MERCHANTS GROUP) ★
2321 Industrial Way, Vineland, NJ 08360-1551
Tel (856) 690-9000 *Founded/Ownrshp* 2014
Sales 51.4MM^E *EMP* 225
Accts Romano Hearing Testa & Knorr
SIC 4222 Storage, frozen or refrigerated goods; Warehousing, cold storage or refrigerated; Storage, frozen or refrigerated goods; Warehousing, cold storage or refrigerated
Pr: Russell Lucca

LUCCHESE BOOT CO
See LUCCHESE INC

D-U-N-S 18-530-2072 IMP
LUCCHESE INC
LUCCHESE BOOT CO
(*Suby of* ARENA BRANDS INC) ★
40 Walter Jones Blvd, El Paso, TX 79906-5301
Tel (915) 778-8585 *Founded/Ownrshp* 1998
Sales 64.4MM^E *EMP* 450
SIC 3143 3144 Boots, dress or casual: men's; Boots, canvas or leather: women's; Boots, dress or casual: men's; Boots, canvas or leather: women's
Pr: Doug Kindy
Pr: Fred Gibbon
VP: Tom Hough
Brnch Mgr: Carlos Armendariz
IT Man: Edward Walsh
Sls&Mrk Ex: Mario Vega
VP Sls: Cindy Moore

D-U-N-S 07-329-4647
LUCE HENRY FOUNDATION INC
51 Madison Ave Fl 30, New York, NY 10010-1621
Tel (212) 251-0130 *Founded/Ownrshp* 1936
Sales 47.7MM *EMP* 20
SIC 8699 Charitable organization; Charitable organization
Ch: Margaret Fitzgerald
**Pr:* Michael Gilligan
CFO: John Daley
**Prin:* John Evans
IT Man: Liz Brennan

D-U-N-S 04-301-9470
LUCE PRESS CLIPPINGS INC (MO)
BURRELLE'S/LUCE
(*Suby of* BURRELLES INFORMATION SERVICES LLC) ★
44 W 1st Ave, Mesa, AZ 85210-1356
Tel (480) 649-3070 *Founded/Ownrshp* 1948, 2003
Sales 11.4MM^E *EMP* 350
SIC 7389 Press clipping service; Press clipping service
Pr: John P French
**VP:* David J French
Exec: Dane Stewart

D-U-N-S 00-177-7655 IMP
LUCE SCHWAB & KASE INC (NJ)
9 Gloria Ln, Fairfield, NJ 07004-3358
Tel (973) 227-4840 *Founded/Ownrshp* 1957
Sales 38.7MM *EMP* 47
SIC 5075 Warm air heating & air conditioning
CEO: James F Luce
Mktg Dir: Rebecca Tuttle
Sales Asso: Steve Critelli

D-U-N-S 07-963-6302
LUCENT HEALTH SOLUTIONS INC
1826 Elm Hill Pike, Nashville, TN 37210-3710
Tel (612) 940-0141 *Founded/Ownrshp* 2014
Sales 34.6MM^E *EMP* 75^E
SIC 8741 Hospital management
CEO: Brett Rodewald
Chf Cred: Alex Arnet

D-U-N-S 13-438-8524
LUCENT JEWELERS INC
1200 Ave Of Americas, New York, NY 10036
Tel (212) 869-2820 *Founded/Ownrshp* 1999
Sales 169.4MM^E *EMP* 1,100
SIC 5094 Diamonds (gems); Diamonds (gems)
Pr: Harry Savalia
VP: Mark Grinfeld
**VP:* Nilesh Savalia
VP Sls: Kuntesh Desai

LUCENT POLYMERS ACQUISITION
See LUCENT POLYMERS INC

D-U-N-S 96-943-0958 EXP
■ LUCENT POLYMERS INC
LUCENT POLYMERS ACQUISITION
(*Suby of* CITADEL PLASTICS HOLDINGS INC) ★
1700 Lynch Rd, Evansville, IN 47711-2848
Tel (812) 421-2216 *Founded/Ownrshp* 2013
Sales 154.7MM^E *EMP* 100
SIC 5162 Resins; Plastics resins; Resins; Plastics resins
Pr: Kevin Kuhnash
Pr: Dennis Straub
**Treas:* Tracy Ripple
Sfty Mgr: Brian Edge
Opers Mgr: Dana Elpers
Ql Cn Mgr: Deb Carnahan-Wilson

D-U-N-S 01-826-3301 IMP
LUCENT TECHNOLOGIES INTERNATIONAL INC
(*Suby of* ALCATEL-LUCENT USA INC) ★
600 Mountain Ave 700, New Providence, NJ 07974-2008
Tel (908) 582-8500 *Founded/Ownrshp* 1996
Sales 152.3MM *EMP* 400
SIC 5065 Communication equipment; Communication equipment
Pr: Janet O'Rourke
CFO: Scott Ashby
Assoc VP: Brian Witt
VP: Tom Finnegan
VP: Jeff Jaffe
VP: Thomas Miller
CTO: Peter Busschbach
CTO: Ruell Levesque
Tech Mgr: Priscilla Doyle
Tech Mgr: Richard Osullivan
VP Sls: Alain Penel

D-U-N-S 79-830-0851
LUCENT TECHNOLOGIES WORLD SERVICES INC
(*Suby of* LUCENT TECHNOLOGIES INTERNATIONAL INC) ★
600 Mountain Ave, New Providence, NJ 07974-2008
Tel (908) 582-3000 *Founded/Ownrshp* 1995
Sales 69.5MM^E *EMP* 200
SIC 5065 7622 3674 3663 3661 3577 Electronic parts & equipment; Communication equipment repair; Semiconductors & related devices; Radio & TV communications equipment; Telephone & telegraph apparatus; Computer peripheral equipment; Electronic parts & equipment; Communication equipment repair; Semiconductors & related devices; Radio & TV communications equipment; Telephone & telegraph apparatus; Computer peripheral equipment
VP: Dave Bolka
CFO: Bill Stenger
**Treas:* Meg Walsh
Chf Mktg O: Charles Bahr
Chf Inves: Jean Grisi
Ex VP: Ahmed Nawaz
**VP:* Gil Harris
VP: Brenda Le
Exec: Vin Kaminski
Comm Dir: Dave Rodewald
Dir Bus: Tom Friar
Dir Bus: Mike McLaren

D-U-N-S 09-261-1466 IMP
LUCERO CABLES INC (CA)
193 Stauffer Blvd, San Jose, CA 95125-1042
Tel (408) 536-0340 *Founded/Ownrshp* 1978, 1982
Sales 22.9MM^E *EMP* 110
SIC 3679 3571 Harness assemblies for electronic use: wire or cable; Electronic computers
CEO: Madeline Eliasnia
**Pr:* Surendra Gupta
**Ch:* Art Eliasnia
**Treas:* Iraj Pessian
**VP:* Serjik Avanes
Manager: Karen Schultz

D-U-N-S 08-434-8143
LUCIA MAR UNIFIED SCHOOL DISTRICT
LUCIA MAR USD
602 Orchard Ave, Arroyo Grande, CA 93420-4000
Tel (805) 474-3000 *Founded/Ownrshp* 1966
Sales 61.0MM^E *EMP* 1,000
Accts Vavrinek Trine Day & Co Ll
SIC 8211 Public elementary & secondary schools; Public elementary & secondary schools
Prin: Bob Mistele
Pr Dir: Amy Jacobs
Schl Brd P: Mark Millis

LUCIA MAR USD
See LUCIA MAR UNIFIED SCHOOL DISTRICT

D-U-N-S 05-264-1446 IMP
LUCIFER LIGHTING CO
3750 N Panam Expy, San Antonio, TX 78219-2223
Tel (210) 227-7329 *Founded/Ownrshp* 1979
Sales 29.7MM^E *EMP* 100
SIC 3646 Commercial indusl & institutional electric lighting fixtures
Pr: Gilbert Lang Mathews
CFO: Kathleen Maxfield
Bd of Dir: Thomas Sweeney
VP: Nora AP
VP: Drew Placido
Mfg Dir: Leigh Lathrop
Prd Mgr: Darryl Harlos
Ql Cn Mgr: Adrian Martinez
Sls Dir: Brooke Ford
Sls Dir: Claire Gleed
Manager: Rich Boughton
Board of Directors: Suzanne Mathews, Thomas J Sweeney

D-U-N-S 12-283-3119
LUCILE PACKARD FOUNDATION FOR CHILDRENS HEALTH
400 Hamilton Ave Ste 240, Palo Alto, CA 94301-1834
Tel (650) 497-8365 *Founded/Ownrshp* 1998
Sales 79.1MM *EMP* 44
Accts Kpmg Llp San Francisco Ca
SIC 8322 Child related social services; Child related social services
Pr: Steven Peets
CFO: Kathy Coulbourne
Bd of Dir: James Mitchell
Bd of Dir: George A Pavlov
Ofcr: Dewi Faulkner
Sr VP: Linda Collier
Sr VP: Brian Perronne
Info Man: Robin Consunto
Info Man: Foust Regan
Board of Directors: Manuel A Henriquez

D-U-N-S 06-912-5441 IMP
LUCILE SALTER PACKARD CHILDRENS HOSPITAL AT STANFORD
725 Welch Rd, Palo Alto, CA 94304-1601
Tel (650) 736-7398 *Founded/Ownrshp* 1919
Sales 1.1MMM *EMP* 1,100^E
SIC 8069 8082 5912 Children's hospital; Home health care services; Drug stores & proprietary stores; Children's hospital; Home health care services; Drug stores & proprietary stores
Pr: Christopher Dawes
**CFO:* Timothy W Carmack
VP: Barbara Ralston
Chf Nrs Of: Paul Shuttleworth
Off Mgr: Laurie Jones
Pharmcst: Diane Stanton
Board of Directors: Susan Bostrom, John Levin

LUCILLE ROBERTS FITNES DIET PL
See ROBERTS LUCILLE HEALTH SPA INC

D-U-N-S 17-459-6783
LUCILLES FLOWER SHOP
LUCILLE'S FLOWERS
411 N Wilson St, Vinita, OK 74301-2432
Tel (918) 256-6187 *Founded/Ownrshp* 1999
Sales 27.8MM *EMP* 4
SIC 5992 Florists; Florists
Owner: Brenda Lauchner

LUCILLE'S FLOWERS
See LUCILLES FLOWER SHOP

D-U-N-S 00-626-6563 IMP/EXP
LUCITE INTERNATIONAL INC
(*Suby of* MITSUBISHI RAYON LUCITE GROUP LIMITED)
7275 Goodlett Farms Pkwy, Cordova, TN 38016-4909
Tel (901) 381-2000 *Founded/Ownrshp* 1999
Sales 52.0MM^E *EMP* 350
SIC 2821

D-U-N-S 15-642-5915 IMP
■ **LUCIX CORP**
(*Suby of* HEICO CORP) ★
800 Avenida Acaso Ste E, Camarillo, CA 93012-8758
Tel (805) 987-6645 *Founded/Ownrshp* 1999
Sales 31.5MM *EMP* 140
SIC 3679 8731 Microwave components; Commercial physical research; Microwave components; Commercial physical research
Pr: Mark Shahriary
**CFO:* Cheryl Johnson
**VP:* D Ick Fanucchi

D-U-N-S 08-046-8879
LUCK BROS INC (NY)
73 Trade Rd, Plattsburgh, NY 12901-6219
Tel (518) 561-4321 *Founded/Ownrshp* 1950
Sales 27.0MM *EMP* 100
Accts Martindale Keysor & Co Pllc
SIC 1623 Water main construction; Sewer line construction; Water main construction; Sewer line construction
Pr: Theodore J Luck
**Treas:* James K Luck
VP: Jamie Hemingway
**VP:* Christopher Luck
CTO: Jim McCarthy

LUCK STONE CENTRAL SERVICES
See LUCK STONE CORP

D-U-N-S 00-287-5227 IMP
LUCK STONE CORP (VA)
LUCK STONE CENTRAL SERVICES
515 Stone Mill Dr, Manakin Sabot, VA 23103-3261
Tel (804) 784-3383 *Founded/Ownrshp* 1923
Sales 754.0MM^E *EMP* 750
SIC 1423 2899 3281 5211 8741 Crushed & broken granite; Chemical preparations; Cut stone & stone products; Masonry materials & supplies; Management services; Crushed & broken granite; Chemical preparations; Cut stone & stone products; Masonry materials & supplies; Management services
Pr: Charles S Luck IV
**Ch Bd:* Charles S Luck III
**CFO:* Roy B Goodman
Ex VP: Wayne Feigenbutz
VP: Richard Hart
VP: John Legore
VP: Jim H Ness
VP: Luck Stone
Exec: Bill Chenault
Dir Bus: Matthew Schiefer
Genl Mgr: Joe Carnahan

D-U-N-S 00-541-8462
LUCKEY FARMERS INC (OH)
1200 W Main St, Woodville, OH 43469-9701
Tel (419) 849-2711 *Founded/Ownrshp* 1918
Sales 145.0MM^E *EMP* 115
SIC 5153 Grain elevators; Grain elevators
CEO: Daniel Walski
Dir Risk M: Bill Wensink
IT Man: Andrew Gladden

D-U-N-S 06-233-4578
LUCKEY LOGISTICS LLC
29988 N 00 East Rd, Streator, IL 61364-8762
Tel (815) 672-2931 *Founded/Ownrshp* 1970
Sales 25.2MM^E *EMP* 170
SIC 4213

D-U-N-S 94-425-1537
LUCKIE & CO LLC
600 Luckie Dr Ste 150, Birmingham, AL 35223-2448
Tel (205) 879-2121 *Founded/Ownrshp* 1983
Sales 59.1MM *EMP* 125^E
SIC 7311 Advertising agencies; Advertising agencies
Pr: Tom Luckie
Pr: Brian Wright
**COO:* Ed Mizzell
**CFO:* Chris Statt
**Ch:* Robert E Luckie III
Chf Mktg O: John Heenan
Ex VP: Brian Pia
Sr VP: Mike Murphy
Sr VP: Linda Roundtree
VP: Eunice Carter
VP: Laura Doumont
VP: Mike Knowles
VP: Ronnie Roberts
VP: Dana Williams
Exec: Brian Conley
Creative D: Rich Albright
Creative D: White Brad
Creative D: Bob Harrison
Creative D: Stephanie Naman

D-U-N-S 00-979-1047 IMP
LUCKINBILL INC
MECHANICAL CONTRACTORS
304 E Broadway Ave, Enid, OK 73701-4102
Tel (580) 233-2026 *Founded/Ownrshp* 1945
Sales 52.8MM^E *EMP* 160
SIC 1711 1623 7692 Plumbing contractors; Oil & gas pipeline construction; Welding repair; Plumbing contractors; Warm air heating & air conditioning contractor; Refrigeration contractor; Oil & gas pipeline construction; Sewer line construction; Water main construction; Underground utilities contractor; Welding repair
Pr: Dennis Luckinbill
**Sec:* Anna Sue Luckinbill
VP: JC Vincent
Dir Risk M: Cindy Cooley
Sfty Dirs: Hector Covarrubias

D-U-N-S 79-495-8165
LUCKMARR PLASTICS INC
L M GROUP
35735 Stanley Dr, Sterling Heights, MI 48312-2661
Tel (586) 978-8498 *Founded/Ownrshp* 1983
Sales 21.8MM^E *EMP* 65
SIC 3089 3544 3469 Injection molded finished plastic products; Special dies, tools, jigs & fixtures; Metal stampings
Pr: Luciano Pierobon
CFO: Jerry Kolb
**VP:* Marco Pierobon
Genl Mgr: Kurt Hahn
Genl Mgr: Nick Nicaise
Plnt Mgr: Virgil Nacaisse

D-U-N-S 00-194-6409 IMP
LUCKS CO (WA)
LUCKS FOOD DECORATING COMPANY
3003 S Pine St, Tacoma, WA 98409-4793
Tel (253) 383-4815 *Founded/Ownrshp* 1953
Sales 23.1MM^E *EMP* 150
SIC 2087 Food colorings; Food colorings
Pr: Richard Ellison
**CFO:* Carl Lucks
**Treas:* William G Lucks
**Sr VP:* Dan Elliott
**VP:* John E Lantz

LUCKS FOOD DECORATING COMPANY
See LUCKS CO

LUCKY 32
See QUAINTANCE-WEAVER INC

LUCKY BRAND
See TREBBIANNO LLC

D-U-N-S 61-472-9275 IMP/EXP
LUCKY BRAND DUNGAREES LLC
540 S Santa Fe Ave, Los Angeles, CA 90013-2233
Tel (213) 443-5700 *Founded/Ownrshp* 2013
Sales 614.6MM^E *EMP* 477
SIC 2325 2339 Dungarees: men's, youths' & boys'; Jeans: men's, youths' & boys'; Jeans: women's, misses' & juniors'; Dungarees: men's, youths' & boys'; Jeans: men's, youths' & boys'; Jeans: women's, misses' & juniors'
Pr: Timothy Mack
CFO: Nigel Kershaw
Bd of Dir: Meghan Kelly
Sr VP: David Chiovetti
Sr VP: Courtney Lynch
VP: Connie Cartmill
VP: Kelly Robuck
VP: Lisa Young
Exec: Alexia Henderson
Dist Mgr: Cindy Flores
Dist Mgr: Jan Gallo

D-U-N-S 12-309-9082 IMP
LUCKY BRAND DUNGAREES STORES LLC
(*Suby of* LUCKY BRAND DUNGAREES LLC) ★
1441 Broadway Fl 29, New York, NY 10018-1905
Tel (212) 354-4900 *Founded/Ownrshp* 2000
Sales 34.5MM^E *EMP* 420
SIC 5651 Family clothing stores; Family clothing stores
Ch: Paul Charron

D-U-N-S 79-072-1732
LUCKY CAB CO (INC)
LUCKY LIMOUSINE
4195 W Diablo Dr, Las Vegas, NV 89118-2357
Tel (702) 732-4400 *Founded/Ownrshp* 1990
Sales 18.8MM^E *EMP* 287
SIC 4121 Taxicabs; Taxicabs
Pr: Jason Awad

LUCKY CHANCES CASINO
See LUCKY CHANCES INC

D-U-N-S 01-668-6441
LUCKY CHANCES INC
LUCKY CHANCES CASINO
1700 Hillside Blvd, Colma, CA 94014-2801
Tel (650) 758-2237 *Founded/Ownrshp* 1998
Sales 28.6MM^E *EMP* 650
SIC 7999 Card rooms; Card rooms
CEO: Rommel R Medina
**Pr:* Ruell Medina
Exec: Lida Chatman
Genl Mgr: Art Van Loon
Dir IT: Martin Cruz

D-U-N-S 02-247-7137
LUCKY CONVENIENCE MARKETS INC
LUCKY'S
2406 Mountain Rd, Pasadena, MD 21122-1212
Tel (410) 255-3427 *Founded/Ownrshp* 1976
Sales 25.0MM *EMP* 6
SIC 5411 Convenience stores, chain; Delicatessens; Convenience stores, chain; Delicatessens
Pr: Charles A Lynch
**VP:* Judith Anne Lynch

D-U-N-S 92-986-5251
LUCKY EAGLE CASINO
(*Suby of* CHEHALIS TRIBE) ★
12888 188th Ave Sw, Rochester, WA 98579-9643
Tel (360) 273-2000 *Founded/Ownrshp* 1995
Sales 44.7MM^E *EMP* 700
SIC 5812 5947 American restaurant; Gift, novelty & souvenir shop; American restaurant; Gift, novelty & souvenir shop
Ch: David Burnett
Ex VP: Rodney Youckton
Sr VP: Kendreah Bodman
Sr VP: Nicole McMaster
Exec: Kevin Bray
Admn Mgr: David Rodewald
Genl Mgr: Sally Roque
Genl Mgr: John Setterstrom
Dir IT: Pablo Bellon
Sales Exec: Duncan McLeod
VP Mktg: John Straus
Board of Directors: David Youckton

LUCKY LIL'S
See TOWN PUMP INC

LUCKY LIMOUSINE
See LUCKY CAB CO (INC)

D-U-N-S 78-625-8488
LUCKY STRIKE ENTERTAINMENT INC
15260 Ventura Blvd # 1110, Sherman Oaks, CA 91403-5346
Tel (818) 933-3752 *Founded/Ownrshp* 2004
Sales 301.0MM^E *EMP* 1,712
SIC 3949 5812 5813 Bowling alleys & accessories; American restaurant; Bar (drinking places); Bowling alleys & accessories; American restaurant; Bar (drinking places)
Pr: Steven Foster
Sr VP: Gail Stoltze
VP: Bill Ginsburg
VP: Jim Parker
Genl Mgr: Maureen Doheny
Genl Mgr: Cory Gallant
Genl Mgr: Tiffany Newsome
Genl Mgr: Justin Rosenberg
Genl Mgr: Eric Wills
IT Man: Jonathan Bloom
VP Sls: Derek Duronslet

D-U-N-S 13-722-0195
LUCKY STRIKE ENTERTAINMENT LLC
LUCKY STRIKE LANES
(*Suby of* LUCKY STRIKE ENTERTAINMENT INC) ★
15260 Ventura Blvd # 1110, Sherman Oaks, CA 91403-5346
Tel (323) 467-7776 *Founded/Ownrshp* 2002
Sales 57.9MM^E *EMP* 1,662
SIC 7933 Ten pin center; Ten pin center
CTO: Chris Logan
Sls Mgr: Kimberly Adams

LUCKY STRIKE LANES
See LUCKY STRIKE ENTERTAINMENT LLC

LUCKY'S
See LUCKY CONVENIENCE MARKETS INC

D-U-N-S 03-439-0934
LUCKYS FARMERS MARKET HOLDING CO LLC
LUCKYS MARKET
6328 Monarch Park Pl # 100, Niwot, CO 80503-6101
Tel (303) 530-0782 *Founded/Ownrshp* 2012
Sales 18.8MM^E *EMP* 284^E
SIC 5812 5411 Eating places; Supermarkets

LUCKYS MARKET
See LUCKYS FARMERS MARKET HOLDING CO LLC

D-U-N-S 80-748-1999
LUCOR INC
JIFFY LUBE
790 Pershing Rd, Raleigh, NC 27608-2712
Tel (919) 828-9511 *Founded/Ownrshp* 1998
Sales 92.6MM^E *EMP* 2,011
SIC 7549 Lubrication service, automotive; Lubrication service, automotive
Ch Bd: Stephen P Conway
**Pr:* Jerry B Conway
**CFO:* Kendall A Carr
VP: Brady R Thompson
Mktg Mgr: Barbara Wallen

D-U-N-S 11-387-1487
LUCWORK ENTERPRISES INC
TACO BELL
7211 N Knoxville Ave # 3, Peoria, IL 61614-2077
Tel (309) 691-6686 *Founded/Ownrshp* 1982
Sales 11.4MM^E *EMP* 300
SIC 5812 Fast-food restaurant, chain; Fast-food restaurant, chain
Pr: Harold L Jenkins
**VP:* Janet Jenkins

LUCY CORR VILLAGE
See HEALTH CENTER COMMISSION FOR COUNTY OF CHESTERFIELD VIRGINIA

D-U-N-S 07-590-9465
■ **LUCY LEE HOSPITAL INC**
NORTH CAMPUS
(*Suby of* HEALTH MANAGEMENT ASSOCIATES INC) ★
2620 N Westwood Blvd, Poplar Bluff, MO 63901-3396
Tel (573) 785-7721 *Founded/Ownrshp* 2003
Sales 38.3MM^E *EMP* 1,300
SIC 8062 General medical & surgical hospitals; General medical & surgical hospitals
CEO: Bruce Eady
COO: Cliff Yeager
COO: Mike Youngmann
CFO: John Erickson
CFO: Paul Peiffer
**Ex VP:* John Bollmer

D-U-N-S 07-482-8344
LUCY W HAYES TRAINING SCHOOL FOR DECONESSES & MISSIONARIES INC
SIBLEY MEMORIAL HOSPITAL
(*Suby of* JOHNS HOPKINS HEALTH SYS CORP) ★
5255 Loughboro Rd Nw, Washington, DC 20016-2633
Tel (202) 537-4257 *Founded/Ownrshp* 2012
Sales 206.1MM^E *EMP* 1,500
SIC 8062 General medical & surgical hospitals; General medical & surgical hospitals
Pr: Richard O Davis
Ofcr: Henry Haywood
VP: Tera Eaton
VP: Gem Henry
VP: Mary Lethbridge
VP: Christine Lewis
Nurse Mgr: Marianne Durgavich
IT Man: Ron Evans
Opthamlgy: Sarah Merrill
Doctor: Kim Cox
Doctor: Michelle Divito

D-U-N-S 09-961-8696
LUDECA INC
1425 Nw 88th Ave, Doral, FL 33172-3017
Tel (305) 591-8935 *Founded/Ownrshp* 1979
Sales 23.6MM^E *EMP* 42
SIC 5084 5085 Industrial machinery & equipment; Industrial supplies
Pr: Heinz Luedeking
**Treas:* Marianne Luedeking
**VP:* Dieter Seidenthal
IT Man: Frank Seidenthal

D-U-N-S 05-310-4733
LUDINGTON AREA SCHOOL DISTRICT
809 E Tinkham Ave, Ludington, MI 49431-1536
Tel (231) 845-7303 *Founded/Ownrshp* 1900
Sales 22.3MM *EMP* 290
SIC 8211 Public senior high school; Public senior high school
**Pr:* Susan Peterson
**Treas:* Shawn McDonald
**VP:* Timothy Heinrich
Dir IT: Andy Klevorn

D-U-N-S 11-826-2054 IMP/EXP
LUDLOW COMPOSITES CORP
CROWN MATS & MATING
2100 Commerce Dr, Fremont, OH 43420-1048
Tel (419) 332-5531 *Founded/Ownrshp* 2000
Sales 50.3MM^E *EMP* 180
SIC 3089 3081 Mats or matting, rubber; Latex, foamed; Vinyl film & sheet; Mats or matting, rubber; Latex, foamed; Vinyl film & sheet
Pr: Vincent J Dephillips
**Pr:* B Randall Dobbs
Ex VP: Randy Dobbs
VP: Allen Boedeker
VP: Barry Payne
DP Dir: Robert Critchet
Dir IT: Kerry Laird
IT Man: Bob Critchet
Sales Exec: Chris Pricozzi
Natl Sales: Dennis Knapp
Natl Sales: Alison Minnich

D-U-N-S 96-772-6030 IMP
LUDLOW CORP
LUDLOW JUTE COMPANY LIMITED
(*Suby of* MALLINCKRODT LLC) ★
15 Hampshire St, Mansfield, MA 02048-1113
Tel (508) 261-8000 *Founded/Ownrshp* 2012
Sales 23.4MM^E *EMP* 300^E
SIC 2834 Druggists' preparations (pharmaceuticals); Druggists' preparations (pharmaceuticals)
Pr: Matthew Harbaugh
**Treas:* Kevin Dasilva
**VP:* John Kapples

LUDLOW JUTE COMPANY LIMITED
See LUDLOW CORP

D-U-N-S 14-982-5585 IMP
LUDLOW MANUFACTURING INC
3821 Hawthorn Ct, Waukegan, IL 60087-3221
Tel (847) 263-4248 *Founded/Ownrshp* 2000
Sales 25.4MM^E *EMP* 15
SIC 5051 Tin & tin base metals, shapes, forms, etc.
Pr: Jenny Ludlow
**VP:* Todd Ludlow

D-U-N-S 07-979-9244
LUDLOW PUBLIC SCHOOLS
63 Chestnut St, Ludlow, MA 01056-3404
Tel (413) 583-8372 *Founded/Ownrshp* 2015
Sales 4.4MM^E *EMP* 376^E
SIC 8211 Public elementary & secondary schools

D-U-N-S 10-003-2069
LUDLOW SCHOOL DISTRICT
63 Chestnut St, Ludlow, MA 01056-3404
Tel (413) 583-8372 *Founded/Ownrshp* 1983
Sales 18.3MM^E *EMP* 701
SIC 8211 9411 Public elementary & secondary schools; School board; Administration of educational programs; Public elementary & secondary schools; School board; Administration of educational programs

D-U-N-S 00-802-5447 IMP
LUDLUM MEASUREMENTS INC
501 Oak St, Sweetwater, TX 79556-3209
Tel (325) 235-5494 *Founded/Ownrshp* 1962
Sales 60.5MM^E *EMP* 500
SIC 3829 3826 3824 3823 Nuclear radiation & testing apparatus; Analytical instruments; Fluid meters & counting devices; Industrial instrmnts msrmnt display/control process variable; Nuclear radiation & testing apparatus; Analytical instruments; Fluid meters & counting devices; Industrial instrmnts msrmnt display/control process variable
Pr: Donald G Ludlum
CFO: Ed Emerson
**CFO:* Jeanie McPherson
**VP:* Larry M Ludlum
VP: Jamie Witt
Genl Mgr: Charles Hurlbut
Genl Mgr: Larry Place
Genl Mgr: John Spaulding
DP Exec: Patrick Brand
IT Man: Richard Smola
IT Man: Tony Tillman

LUDMAN INDUSTRIES
See LUDMAN MACHINE CO LLC

D-U-N-S 04-803-3765
LUDMAN MACHINE CO LLC (WI)
LUDMAN INDUSTRIES
4810 N 124th St, Milwaukee, WI 53225-3601
Tel (414) 431-3500 *Founded/Ownrshp* 1968, 2011
Sales 30.0MM *EMP* 40
SIC 3532 Stamping mill machinery (mining machinery)
CFO: Jeff Butcher
VP: Ken Skarlupka
Off Mgr: Mary Matusik
Opers Mgr: Walter Schaeffer
Opers Mgr: Walter Schaffer
S&M/VP: Mark Ferge

D-U-N-S 03-744-4122
LUDVIK ELECTRIC CO
3900 S Teller St, Lakewood, CO 80235-2213
Tel (303) 781-9601 *Founded/Ownrshp* 1980
Sales 62.5MM *EMP* 340ᴱ
Accts Mayer Hoffman Mccann Pc Den
SIC 1731 General electrical contractor; General electrical contractor
Pr: James Ludvik
**CFO:* Richard B Giles
**VP:* Larvin Franklin
VP: Robert Hadley
**VP:* Joseph Miller
**VP:* Donald Reinstein
IT Man: Bob Hadley
Snr Mgr: Tom Spackman

D-U-N-S 04-775-9683
LUDWIG BUILDINGS INC
521 Time Saver Ave, New Orleans, LA 70123-3132
Tel (504) 733-6260 *Founded/Ownrshp* 1923
Sales 24.3MMᴱ *EMP* 100
SIC 3448 Prefabricated metal buildings
Pr: Edward B Ludwig III
**Treas:* Edward B Ludwig Jr

D-U-N-S 03-824-3465 IMP/EXP
LUDWIG HOLDINGS CORP
WOLF-TEC
20 Kieffer Ln, Kingston, NY 12401-2209
Tel (845) 340-9727 *Founded/Ownrshp* 1977
Sales 22.2MMᴱ *EMP* 85
SIC 3556 8742 Food products machinery; Meat, poultry & seafood processing machinery; Industry specialist consultants; Food & beverage consultant
CEO: Ralf Ludwig
**Owner:* Peter Ludwig
**CFO:* Don Tegeler
Mtls Mgr: Peter Paulsen
Manager: Nick Zellmer

D-U-N-S 00-469-3565
LUDWIG INSTITUTE FOR CANCER RESEARCH
LICR FUND
666 3rd Ave Fl 28, New York, NY 10017-4030
Tel (212) 450-1500 *Founded/Ownrshp* 1973
Sales 227.2MM *EMP* 703
Accts Kpmg Ag
SIC 8733 Medical research; Medical research
Ch: John L Notter
**Pr:* Edward A McDermott Jr
Ofcr: Jonathan Skipper
Adm Dir: Dario Florean
IT Man: Elisa Plante

D-U-N-S 00-447-8038
LUDY GREENHOUSE MFG CORP
122 Railroad St, New Madison, OH 45346-5016
Tel (800) 255-5839 *Founded/Ownrshp* 1953
Sales 20.4MMᴱ *EMP* 62
Accts Ault Henderson & Lewis Cpa
SIC 1542 3448 Greenhouse construction; Greenhouses: prefabricated metal
Pr: Stephan A Scantland
**VP:* Deborah Scantland
Manager: Becky Yount

D-U-N-S 00-287-3883
LUEDER CONSTRUCTION CO
LUEDER SERVICE CENTER
9999 J St Ste B, Omaha, NE 68127-1125
Tel (402) 339-1000 *Founded/Ownrshp* 1986
Sales 64.2MM *EMP* 65
Accts Blackman & Associates Pc Cpa
SIC 1542 Commercial & office building, new construction; Commercial & office building, new construction
Pr: R Brad Von Gillern
**CFO:* David J Hanus
**VP:* Andrew Bailey
Dir Bus: Greg Key
Snr Mgr: Brian Cieslik

LUEDER SERVICE CENTER
See LUEDER CONSTRUCTION CO

D-U-N-S 06-653-3316
LUEKENS FOOD STORES INC
LUEKEN'S VILLAGE FOODS, NORTH
1171 Paul Bunyan Dr Nw, Bemidji, MN 56601-4199
Tel (218) 444-3663 *Founded/Ownrshp* 1969
Sales 48.9MMᴱ *EMP* 355
SIC 5411 Supermarkets, independent; Supermarkets, independent
CEO: Karla Parenteau
**Pr:* Joseph A Lueken
**Sec:* Betty Dirk
**VP:* Bill Foley
**VP:* Janice E Lueken
Exec: Carla Parenteau
Store Dir: Matt Sconce

LUEKEN'S VILLAGE FOODS, NORTH
See LUEKENS FOOD STORES INC

D-U-N-S 11-413-3317 IMP
LUEMME INC
COSABELLA
12186 Sw 128th St, Miami, FL 33186-5230
Tel (305) 253-9904 *Founded/Ownrshp* 1983
Sales 27.2MMᴱ *EMP* 60
SIC 5137 Lingerie; Underwear: women's, children's & infants'; Sportswear, women's & children's
Pr: Valeria Campello
CFO: Mike Bernstein
**VP:* Guido Campello
**VP:* Silvia Campello
**VP:* Ugo Campello
VP: Sergio Oxman
Dir IT: Anthony De Abreu
IT Man: Mark Chin
IT Man: Anthony Deabreu
Sales Asso: Shanequa Watt

D-U-N-S 00-808-0194
LUFKIN COCA COLA BOTTLING CO
DR PEPPER OF LUFKIN
704 Webber St, Lufkin, TX 75904-2612
Tel (936) 639-2355 *Founded/Ownrshp* 1962
Sales 22.9MMᴱ *EMP* 80
SIC 2086 Soft drinks: packaged in cans, bottles, etc.
Pr: Lynne D Haney
**Sec:* Jim Watkins
**VP:* James A Watkins
CTO: Cecil Muckelroy
Plnt Mgr: Bobby Slaughter
Sls Mgr: Mike Stokes

LUFKIN DAILY NEWS
See COX TEXAS PUBLICATIONS INC

D-U-N-S 08-356-4492
LUFKIN INDEPENDENT SCHOOL DISTRICT
LISD
101 N Cotton Sq, Lufkin, TX 75904-2925
Tel (936) 634-6696 *Founded/Ownrshp* 1935
Sales 61.6MMᴱ *EMP* 27ᴱ
Accts Alexander Lankford & Hiers I
SIC 8211 Public elementary & secondary schools; Public elementary & secondary schools
**Pr:* Dr Keven Ellis
**CFO:* Charlotte Bynum
**VP:* Scott Skelton
IT Man: Carolyn Beavers
Pr Dir: Sheila Adams
Schl Brd P: Stanley New
HC Dir: Jan Fullbright

D-U-N-S 00-809-0375 IMP/EXP
■ **LUFKIN INDUSTRIES LLC**
(*Suby of* GENERAL ELECTRIC CO) ★
601 S Raguet St, Lufkin, TX 75904-3951
Tel (936) 634-2211 *Founded/Ownrshp* 2013
Sales 977.9MMᴱ *EMP* 4,700ᴱ
SIC 3561 3321 3462 Pumps & pumping equipment; Pumps, oil well & field; Gray iron castings; Ductile iron castings; Iron & steel forgings; Pump, compressor & turbine forgings; Pumps & pumping equipment; Pumps, oil well & field; Gray iron castings; Ductile iron castings; Iron & steel forgings; Pump, compressor & turbine forgings
Pr: John F Glick
**CFO:* Christopher L Boone
**Chf Cred:* Alejandro Cestero
Ex VP: Serena Fanucchi
VP: C D Hay
VP: Larry Hoes
**VP:* Scott Semlinger
Genl Mgr: Raymond Hawkins
Off Mgr: Marc Boulet
Off Admin: Leighanne McDonald
Mfg Dir: Rickie Gilley

D-U-N-S 00-429-3077 IMP
LUFTHANSA TECHNIK LOGISTIK OF AMERICA LLC
(*Suby of* LUFTHANSA TECHNIK LOGISTIK GMBH)
1640 Hempstead Tpke, East Meadow, NY 11554-1096
Tel (516) 296-9429 *Founded/Ownrshp* 1999, 2000
Sales 27.0MMᴱ *EMP* 68
SIC 4731 8742 Domestic freight forwarding; Foreign freight forwarding; Materials mgmt. (purchasing, handling, inventory) consultant; Domestic freight forwarding; Foreign freight forwarding; Materials mgmt. (purchasing, handling, inventory) consultant
Board of Directors: Birgit Kathmeyer

D-U-N-S 00-784-9169
LUHR BROS INC (IL)
250 W Sand Bank Rd, Columbia, IL 62236-1044
Tel (618) 281-4106 *Founded/Ownrshp* 1939
Sales 134.7MM *EMP* 400
SIC 1629 Dams, waterways, docks & other marine construction; Dams, waterways, docks & other marine construction
Ch Bd: Twyla Luhr
**Pr:* Michael Luhr
COO: Steve Glenn
Treas: Sheryl Metzger
Ofcr: Lloyd Miller
**VP:* William R Gardner
**VP:* Jay Luhr
**VP:* William G Shaw
CTO: John Bergman
Dir IT: Tammy Duffy
Dir IT: Tammy Lefever

D-U-N-S 96-564-2148
LUI CHE WOO CHARITY
433 California St, San Francisco, CA 94104-2016
Tel (415) 982-7777 *Founded/Ownrshp* 2010
Sales 43.3MM *EMP* 2
SIC 8699 Charitable organization
Prin: Lawrence Y Lui

LUIGI'S FAMILY RESTAURANT
See JACKIES INTERNATIONAL INC

D-U-N-S 02-461-5924 IMP
LUIHN FOOD SYSTEMS INC (NC)
KFC
2950 Gateway Centre Blvd, Morrisville, NC 27560-9615
Tel (919) 850-0558 *Founded/Ownrshp* 1966
Sales 45.7MMᴱ *EMP* 1,200
SIC 5812 Fast-food restaurant, chain; Fast-food restaurant, chain
Pr: S Allan Luihn
**VP:* Allan J Luihn
Genl Mgr: Tammy Flower
Dir IT: Mark McLoughlin
Mktg Dir: Sheila Branch
Mktg Dir: Theresa Eberwein
Snr Mgr: Chip Davis

D-U-N-S 09-001-4978
LUIS A AYALA COLON SUCRES INC
AYACOL
3091 Santiago De Los C, Ponce, PR 00716
Tel (787) 848-9000 *Founded/Ownrshp* 1968
Sales 27.8MM *EMP* 115
Accts Uhy Del Valle & Nieves Psc Sa
SIC 4491 4729 Stevedoring; Steamship ticket offices; Stevedoring; Steamship ticket offices
Ch: Luis A Ayala-Parsi
**Pr:* Hernan F Ayala-Parsi
**Treas:* Nelson Riollano

D-U-N-S 80-076-5752
LUIS ESPARZA SERVICES INC
183 Hwy 33, Maricopa, CA 93252
Tel (661) 766-2344 *Founded/Ownrshp* 1988
Sales 8.6MMᴱ *EMP* 500
SIC 7361 8631 Labor contractors (employment agency); Labor unions & similar labor organizations; Labor contractors (employment agency); Labor unions & similar labor organizations
Pr: Luis Esparza

LUIS FREIRE
See KMA ASSOCIATES OF PUERTO RICO INC

D-U-N-S 09-002-0777 IMP
LUIS GARRATON INC
LGI
Luchetti Ind Park Rd 28 C, Bayamon, PR 00961
Tel (787) 788-6100 *Founded/Ownrshp* 1948
Sales 85.9MM *EMP* 250
Accts Falcon Sanchez & Associates P
SIC 5122 5141 Pharmaceuticals; Cosmetics, perfumes & hair products; Groceries, general line; Pharmaceuticals; Cosmetics, perfumes & hair products; Groceries, general line
Pr: Raul Rodriguez Font
CFO: Maria Leon
**Treas:* Maria Victoria Leon Freire
VP: Elizabeth Garraton
**VP:* Rafael Rodriguez

D-U-N-S 00-203-3710 IMP
LUITPOLD PHARMACEUTICALS INC (NY)
(*Suby of* DAIICHI SANKYO COMPANY, LIMITED)
5 Ramsey Rd, Shirley, NY 11967-4701
Tel (631) 924-4000 *Founded/Ownrshp* 1946, 1970
Sales 157.3MMᴱ *EMP* 800
SIC 2834 Pharmaceutical preparations; Pharmaceutical preparations
Ch Bd: Mary Jane Helenek
Genl Mgr: William Berger
QA Dir: Mark Carroll
QA Dir: Gina Curcio
QA Dir: John Maiero
IT Man: Darrin Turner
Netwrk Mgr: Greg Miller
Netwrk Eng: Kenneth Kinkead
Opers Supe: Jennifer Karagjozi
Sfty Mgr: Liz Tilton
Natl Sales: Kent Harris

LUJACK'S NORTHPARK AUTO PLAZA
See QUAD CITY AUTOMOTIVE GROUP LLC

D-U-N-S 08-665-5198 IMP
LUK CLUTCH SYSTEMS LLC
(*Suby of* LUK USA LLC) ★
3401 Old Airport Rd, Wooster, OH 44691-9544
Tel (330) 264-4383 *Founded/Ownrshp* 2004
Sales 104.0MMᴱ *EMP* 1,000ᴱ
SIC 3714 3563 3566 Motor vehicle parts & accessories; Clutches, motor vehicle; Power transmission equipment; Speed changers, drives & gears; Motor vehicle parts & accessories; Clutches, motor vehicle; Power transmission equipment; Speed changers, drives & gears
VP: David Marlar
Genl Mgr: Mike Simon
MIS Mgr: Hans Peter Seiter
Board of Directors: Siegfried Kronmueller

D-U-N-S 15-212-2359 IMP/EXP
LUK TRANSMISSION SYSTEMS LLC
(*Suby of* LUK USA LLC) ★
3401 Old Airport Rd, Wooster, OH 44691-9544
Tel (330) 264-4383 *Founded/Ownrshp* 2004
Sales 228.8MMᴱ *EMP* 640
SIC 3714 3566 Motor vehicle parts & accessories; Speed changers, drives & gears; Motor vehicle parts & accessories; Speed changers, drives & gears

D-U-N-S 17-094-9692 IMP
LUK USA LLC
(*Suby of* SCHAEFFLER GROUP USA INC) ★
3401 Old Airport Rd, Wooster, OH 44691-9544
Tel (330) 264-4383 *Founded/Ownrshp* 2009
Sales 332.9MMᴱ *EMP* 1,000ᴱ
SIC 3714 Motor vehicle parts & accessories; Motor vehicle parts & accessories
CEO: Klaus Rosenfeld
**Pr:* Marc McGrath
COO: Oliver Jung
**VP:* Ashi Uppal
Exec: Steven Bushman
Exec: Greg Tinnell
Prgrm Mgr: Patrick Lindemann
CIO: Tom Miller
Dir IT: Shoukat Bhamani
Plnt Mgr: Al McAfoos
Prd Mgr: Jeff Hemphill

D-U-N-S 16-165-0929
LUKA INC
MCDONALD'S
4010 Technology Way Ste E, Carson City, NV 89706-2012
Tel (775) 883-1097 *Founded/Ownrshp* 1996
Sales 11.2MMᴱ *EMP* 300
SIC 5812 Fast-food restaurant, chain; Fast-food restaurant, chain
Pr: Christopher Kassity
VP: Sharon Kassity

D-U-N-S 14-030-2188
LUKE & ASSOCIATES INC
375 Commerce Pkwy Ste 103, Rockledge, FL 32955-4201
Tel (321) 452-4601 *Founded/Ownrshp* 2004
Sales 19.5MMᴱ *EMP* 310
SIC 7363 Medical help service; Medical help service
Pr: Jim Barfield
**CFO:* Rich Hall
Chf Mktg O: Serena Brock
**VP:* Sherri Scott
IT Man: Frank Hines
IT Man: Carol Taylor

D-U-N-S 04-891-5359
LUKE FRUIA INVESTMENTS INC
LUKE FRUIA MOTORS
2645 Barnard Rd, Brownsville, TX 78520-8628
Tel (956) 541-3141 *Founded/Ownrshp* 1987
Sales 46.2MMᴱ *EMP* 98
SIC 5511 7538 Automobiles, new & used; Pickups, new & used; General automotive repair shops; Automobiles, new & used; Pickups, new & used; General automotive repair shops
Pr: Luke Fruia Jr
**Sec:* Rosalinda Fruia
**VP:* Felicia Lu
Genl Mgr: John Edge
Pr Mgr: Yolanda Morales
Sales Asso: Maurilio Alaniz
Sales Asso: Rudy Buitureira
Sales Asso: Mauricio Cordero
Sales Asso: Ernesto Delgado
Sales Asso: Israel Gutierrez
Sales Asso: Miguel Rodriguez

LUKE FRUIA MOTORS
See LUKE FRUIA INVESTMENTS INC

D-U-N-S 00-737-2233
LUKE MOTOR CO II LP
VANDERGRIFF HONDA
1104 W Interstate 20, Arlington, TX 76017-5830
Tel (817) 275-3371 *Founded/Ownrshp* 1999
Sales 27.9MMᴱ *EMP* 80
SIC 5511 5521 Automobiles, new & used; Used car dealers; Automobiles, new & used; Used car dealers
Treas: Bob Holcomb
Treas: Bob Morford
VP: John Morford
VP: Victor Vandergriff
Sls Mgr: Sterling Carter
Sales Asso: Anna Lane

D-U-N-S 04-422-6116
LUKE OIL CO INC
3592 N Hobart Rd, Hobart, IN 46342-1442
Tel (219) 962-7676 *Founded/Ownrshp* 1967
Sales 32.2MMᴱ *EMP* 20
SIC 5172 7549 Petroleum products; Gasoline; Lubrication service, automotive
Ch Bd: Ralph Luke
**Pr:* Thomas M Collins
Dist Mgr: B loz
Genl Mgr: Rick Enright

D-U-N-S 12-665-2010 IMP
■ **LUKE PAPER CO**
NEWPAGE
(*Suby of* VERSO CORP) ★
300 Pratt St, Luke, MD 21540-1015
Tel (301) 359-3311 *Founded/Ownrshp* 2015
Sales 161.4MMᴱ *EMP* 1,000ᴱ
SIC 2621 Paper mills; Paper mills
Pr: George F Martin
Sr VP: Stacy Mazza
IT Man: Jon Evans

D-U-N-S 03-261-9616
LUKE SAINT HOME CARE
190 E Bannock St, Boise, ID 83712-6241
Tel (208) 381-2138 *Founded/Ownrshp* 1984
Sales 28.8MM *EMP* 4
SIC 8082 Home health care services
Pr: Edwin Dahlbert
CFO: Jeff Taylor
Pharmcst: Gayla Bollinger
Pharmcst: Julie Eiefle
Pharmcst: Mark Hofstetter
Pharmcst: Lisa Mathis

LUKE THEIS CONTRACTORS
See LUKE THEIS ENTERPRISES INC

D-U-N-S 10-863-3561
LUKE THEIS ENTERPRISES INC
LUKE THEIS CONTRACTORS
14120 State Route 568, Findlay, OH 45840-9428
Tel (419) 422-2040 *Founded/Ownrshp* 1969
Sales 122.0MM *EMP* 57
SIC 1542 1541 1521 Nonresidential construction; Industrial buildings & warehouses; New construction, single-family houses; Nonresidential construction; Industrial buildings & warehouses; New construction, single-family houses
Pr: Luke Theis

D-U-N-S 03-808-7920
LUKES LANDSCAPING INC
LUKES-SAWGRASS LANDSCAPE
(*Suby of* FIRST SERVICE RESIDENTIAL FLORIDA INC) ★
2200 N 30th Rd, Hollywood, FL 33021-3737
Tel (954) 925-8200 *Founded/Ownrshp* 1970
Sales 56.0MMᴱ *EMP* 3,370ᴱ
SIC 0781 0782 Landscape planning services; Lawn care services
Pr: Jerome Palazzolo
**Treas:* Robert Rabin
**VP:* Kennith Kuznik
Off Mgr: Joanne Dottin

LUKES-SAWGRASS LANDSCAPE
See LUKES LANDSCAPING INC

D-U-N-S 00-445-7826
LUKJAN METAL PRODUCTS INC (OH)
645 Industry Rd, Conneaut, OH 44030-3045
Tel (440) 599-8127 Founded/Ownrshp 1964
Sales 26.7MM^E EMP 160
SIC 3444 3312 Ducts, sheet metal; Blast furnaces & steel mills; Ducts, sheet metal; Blast furnaces & steel mills
Pr: Anatol Lukjanczuk
*VP: Elena Kelly
*VP: Dan Korda
Sls Dir: Lou Dangelico

D-U-N-S 01-229-6021
LUKOIL AMERICAS CORP
(Suby of LUKOIL, PAO)
505 5th Ave Fl 9, New York, NY 10017-4921
Tel (212) 421-4141 Founded/Ownrshp 1997
Sales 87.5MM^E EMP 624
SIC 1311 Crude petroleum & natural gas; Crude petroleum & natural gas
Ch Bd: Vadim Guzman
*CEO: Robert Ferluga

D-U-N-S 03-926-1576
LUKOIL NORTH AMERICA LLC
(Suby of LUKOIL-VOLGOGRADENERGO, OOO)
505 5th Ave Fl 9, New York, NY 10017-4921
Tel (212) 421-4141 Founded/Ownrshp 2011
Sales 21.0MM^E EMP 24^E
SIC 1381 5541 Drilling oil & gas wells; Filling stations, gasoline
CEO: Vadim Gulzman

D-U-N-S 00-682-3801 IMP
LUKOIL OVERSEAS OFFSHORE PROJECTS INC
3 Greenway Plz Ste 1200, Houston, TX 77046-0332
Tel (713) 877-8544 Founded/Ownrshp 1951
Sales 80.5MM^E EMP 100^E
SIC 1382 Oil & gas exploration services; Oil & gas exploration services
CEO: Kevin Black
*CFO: Maxim Kobyakov
CFO: John Malone
Ex VP: John Gorman
VP: Ron Wallace
VP Opers: Edward Hare
Opers Mgr: Robert Banks
*Genl Couns: Lui Chambers
Snr Mgr: Juan Salinas

D-U-N-S 11-108-8691 IMP/EXP
LUKOIL PAN AMERICAS LLC
(Suby of LITASCO SA)
1095 Ave Of The Americas, New York, NY 10036-6797
Tel (646) 562-3600 Founded/Ownrshp 2008
Sales 59.7MM^E EMP 12
SIC 5172 2999 Petroleum products; Crude oil; Coke
*Pr: Vagit Alekperov
Treas: Rich Wahlers
Off Mgr: Tom Brown

D-U-N-S 17-596-9054 IMP
LULA-WESTFIELD LLC
451 Hwy 1005, Paincourtville, LA 70391
Tel (985) 369-6450 Founded/Ownrshp 1997
Sales 45.7MM^E EMP 225
SIC 2061 Raw cane sugar; Blackstrap molasses made from sugar cane; Raw cane sugar; Blackstrap molasses made from sugar cane
Pr: Michael Daigle
*VP: Charles Savoie

LULULEMON ATHLETICA USA
See LULULEMON USA INC

D-U-N-S 01-206-0918
LULULEMON USA INC
LULULEMON ATHLETICA USA
(Suby of LULULEMON ATHLETICA CANADA INC)
2201 140th Ave E, Sumner, WA 98390-9711
Tel (604) 732-6124 Founded/Ownrshp 2002
Sales 4.0MM EMP 5,000^E
SIC 5137 5331 Sharpeners, sporting goods; Variety stores; Women's & children's sportswear & swimsuits; Variety stores
Pr: Laurent Potdevin

LUMANAIR AVIATION SERVICES
See LUMANAIR INC

D-U-N-S 00-284-9545
LUMANAIR INC (DE)
LUMANAIR AVIATION SERVICES
43 W 752 Rr 30, Sugar Grove, IL 60554
Tel (630) 466-4866 Founded/Ownrshp 1961
Sales 25.8MM^E EMP 25
SIC 5172 4581 8299 Aircraft fueling services; Aircraft servicing & repairing; Flying instruction
Pr: Robert F Luman Jr
*Sec: Josephine Luman
*VP: Mike S Luman
Exec: Kathy Vandeveir
Snr Mgr: Bob Eckhoff

D-U-N-S 00-629-1405 IMP
■ **LUMARA HEALTH INC**
(Suby of AMAG PHARMACEUTICALS INC) ★
1100 Winter St Fl 3, Waltham, MA 02451-1473
Tel (617) 498-3300 Founded/Ownrshp 1971, 2014
Sales 36.4MM^E EMP 214^E
SIC 2834 Pharmaceutical preparations; Pharmaceutical preparations
Pr: Gregory Divis
*Pr: Gregory J Divis Jr
Pr: Gregg Raybuck
*CFO: Thomas S McHugh
*VP: Patrick J Christmas
VP: Cynthia Kirk
VP: Mary Mullen
Sls&Mrk Ex: Andrea Keith

D-U-N-S 05-504-1706
■ **LUMARA HEALTH SERVICES LTD** (MO)
(Suby of LUMARA HEALTH INC) ★
1 Corporate Woods Dr, Bridgeton, MO 63044-3807
Tel (314) 646-3700 Founded/Ownrshp 1998
Sales 27.8MM^E EMP 76^E
SIC 5122 Pharmaceuticals
Pr: Jerald Wenker
Sls Mgr: Monica Pierre

D-U-N-S 09-497-2973
LUMASENSE TECHNOLOGIES INC
3301 Leonard Ct, Santa Clara, CA 95054-2054
Tel (408) 727-1600 Founded/Ownrshp 2003
Sales 109.3MM^E EMP 421
SIC 3823 3845 3829 3825 Industrial instrmnts msrmnt display/control process variable; Temperature instruments: industrial process type; Industrial process control instruments; Electromedical equipment; Measuring & controlling devices; Instruments to measure electricity; Industrial instrmnts msrmnt display/control process variable; Temperature instruments: industrial process type; Industrial process control instruments; Electromedical equipment; Measuring & controlling devices; Instruments to measure electricity
CEO: Steve Abely
*Pr: Vivek Joshi
Pr: Steve Uhlir
*VP: Subra Sankar
VP: Brett Sargent
*VP: Ronald Sutton
VP: Victor Wong
*VP: Diane Wotus
Mng Dir: Anke John
Area Mgr: Bob Mintz
Off Admin: Sayali Gawali

D-U-N-S 06-109-5071
LUMBEE RIVER ELECTRIC MEMBERSHIP CORP
605 E 4th Ave, Red Springs, NC 28377-1668
Tel (910) 843-7932 Founded/Ownrshp 1940
Sales 126.6MM EMP 121
Accts Dixon Hughes Goodman Llp Danv
SIC 4911 Distribution, electric power; Distribution, electric power
*CEO: Perry Cummings
*VP: Carmen Dietrich
VP: Chris Locklear
*VP: Angela Revels-Bullard
*VP: Robert Strickland
*Genl Mgr: Ronnie Hunt
Genl Mgr: Misha Melvin
Sfty Mgr: Ernest Chavis

D-U-N-S 05-802-9658 IMP
LUMBER AND THINGS INDUSTRIES INC
Keyser Industrial Park, Keyser, WV 26726
Tel (304) 788-5600 Founded/Ownrshp 1997
Sales 29.0MM^E EMP 200
SIC 2448 Wood pallets & skids; Wood pallets & skids
Pr: Jack E Amoruso
CFO: Karen Leaf
Dir IT: Jack Ambrosio
Natl Sales: Victor Knight

D-U-N-S 00-599-1641 IMP
LUMBER CITY CORP (CA)
NEIMAN-REED LUMBER CO
20525 Nordhoff St Ste 210, Chatsworth, CA 91311-6135
Tel (818) 407-3888 Founded/Ownrshp 1948, 1986
Sales 108.9MM^E EMP 550
SIC 5211 5031 Lumber & other building materials; Lumber, plywood & millwork; Lumber & other building materials; Lumber, plywood & millwork
Pr: Jesse A Ruf
*CFO: John Lyons

D-U-N-S 09-570-8566
LUMBER GROUP INC
WHOLESALE WOOD PRODUCTS
819 Cowarts Rd, Dothan, AL 36303-6323
Tel (334) 793-6028 Founded/Ownrshp 1979
Sales 25.0MM^E EMP 55
SIC 5031 2421 5211 Lumber: rough, dressed & finished; Sawmills & planing mills, general; Lumber products; Lumber: rough, dressed & finished; Sawmills & planing mills, general; Lumber products
Pr: George C Harris
*VP: James C Stuckey

D-U-N-S 16-178-4095 IMP
LUMBER INVESTORS LLC
MARTIN DISTRIBUTORS
3401 Eddie Williams Ave, Alexandria, LA 71302-4758
Tel (318) 448-0590 Founded/Ownrshp 1986
Sales 45.4MM^E EMP 90
Accts Rozier Harrington & Mckay Al
SIC 5031 5211 Lumber: rough, dressed & finished; Building materials, exterior; Building materials, interior; Lumber & other building materials; Lumber: rough, dressed & finished; Building materials, exterior; Building materials, interior; Lumber & other building materials
CEO: H Allen Wiggins
CFO: Kendall Cox
CFO: Kenneth E Cox
VP: Floyd T Andries
VP: Walter Clarence Melcher
Opers Mgr: Don Tassin

D-U-N-S 96-197-6698
▲ **LUMBER LIQUIDATORS HOLDINGS INC**
3000 John Deere Rd, Toano, VA 23168-9332
Tel (757) 259-4280 Founded/Ownrshp 1994
Sales 1.0MMM EMP 1,891
Tkr Sym LL Exch NYS
SIC 5211 Lumber & other building materials; Lumber & other building materials
CEO: Thomas D Sullivan
*Ch Bd: John M Presley
CFO: Daniel E Terrell
CFO: Gregory A Whirley Jr
Treas: H F Marcus Jr
Ofcr: Marco Q Pescara
Ofcr: William K Schlegel
Sr VP: Rick A Boucher
Sr VP: Ray Cotton
Sr VP: Carl Daniels
Sr VP: Robert W Morrison
Sr VP: Charles Schwartz
VP: Tyler C Greenan
Board of Directors: Macon F Brock Jr, Douglas T Moore, Peter B Robinson, Martin F Roper, Thomas D Sullivan, Nancy M Taylor, Jimmie L Wade

D-U-N-S 94-901-2280 IMP/EXP
■ **LUMBER LIQUIDATORS INC**
HUSKY HARDWOOD FLOORS
(Suby of LUMBER LIQUIDATORS HOLDINGS INC) ★
3000 John Deere Rd, Toano, VA 23168-9332
Tel (757) 259-4280 Founded/Ownrshp 1994
Sales NA EMP 788
SIC 5031 5211 Hardboard; Lumber products; Hardboard; Lumber products
CEO: Robert Lynch
CFO: Everett T Daniel
CFO: Daniel E Terrell
Ofcr: John Kauzlarich
Ofcr: Sandra C Whitehouse
Sr VP: Carl Daniels
Sr VP: Alison Lantz
Sr VP: E Jean Matherne
Sr VP: Robert Morrison
VP: James J Costa
VP: Andy Grosse
VP: Jay Quickel
VP: Ken Strohschein
VP: Jeffrey Stubbs
VP: Chuck Weigand
Creative D: Angel Gonzalez
Board of Directors: Macon F Brock Jr, Douglas T Moore, John M Presley, Martin F Roper, Thomas D Sullivan, Richard D Tadler

D-U-N-S 02-271-3911
LUMBER ONE AVON INC
101 2nd St Nw, Avon, MN 56310-9507
Tel (320) 356-7342 Founded/Ownrshp 1940
Sales 30.6MM EMP 55
SIC 5211 1521 1522 Lumber & other building materials; New construction, single-family houses; Multi-family dwelling construction; Lumber & other building materials; New construction, single-family houses; Multi-family dwelling construction
CEO: Barbara Brandes
*COO: Ted Schmid
*CFO: Judith C Schmid
*VP: Charles Brandes
Board of Directors: Marne Schmid

D-U-N-S 01-419-3511
LUMBER ONE HOME CENTER INC
682 Highway 365, Mayflower, AR 72106-9630
Tel (501) 470-1122 Founded/Ownrshp 2005
Sales 22.5MM^E EMP 30
SIC 5031 5211 Lumber, plywood & millwork; Lumber & other building materials
Owner: John Pam Morton
*CFO: Terry Butler
*Sec: Pamela D Morton
*VP: Rodney Persons

LUMBER PDTS HOLDINGS & MGT CO
See LUMBER PRODUCTS AN OREGON CORP

D-U-N-S 00-790-8759 IMP/EXP
LUMBER PRODUCTS AN OREGON CORP
LUMBER PDTS HOLDINGS & MGT CO
19855 Sw 124th Ave, Tualatin, OR 97062-8007
Tel (503) 692-3322 Founded/Ownrshp 1938, 1986
Sales 96.6MM^E EMP 540
SIC 5031 Lumber: rough, dressed & finished; Plywood; Doors; Lumber: rough, dressed & finished; Plywood; Doors
Pr: Peter J Hall
*Pr: Edward C Hostmann
*COO: Craig Hall
*CFO: Bart Walker
Admn Mgr: Carla Singler
Opers Mgr: A Swindlehurst
Sales Exec: John McMains
Sales Exec: Larry Nelson

D-U-N-S 60-331-3701
LUMBER SPECIALISTS INC
NEWS GAZETTE
15 E Main St, Champaign, IL 61820-3625
Tel (217) 351-5252 Founded/Ownrshp 1988
Sales 51.4MM^E EMP 400
SIC 2711 Newspapers, publishing & printing; Newspapers, publishing & printing
Pr: John Foreman
*CFO: John Reed
Genl Mgr: Tim Evans
IT Man: Darren Holt
Prd Mgr: Bob Brown
Prd Mgr: Bob Shelton
Mktg Dir: Amy George
Mktg Dir: Cassandra Schowengerdt
Sls Mgr: Jackie Martin

D-U-N-S 10-233-6633
LUMBER SPECIALTIES - US LBM LLC
LUMBER SPECIALTIES, LTD.
(Suby of US LBM HOLDINGS LLC) ★
1700 Beltline Rd, Dyersville, IA 52040-2210
Tel (563) 875-2858 Founded/Ownrshp 2014
Sales 60.8MM^E EMP 200
SIC 2439 Trusses, wooden roof; Trusses, wooden roof
Pr: Dennis Westhoff

LUMBER SPECIALTIES, LTD.
See LUMBER SPECIALTIES - US LBM LLC

D-U-N-S 01-116-3565
LUMBERJACK BUILDING CENTERS INC (MI)
ACE HARDWARE
3470 Pointe Tremble Rd, Algonac, MI 48001-4642
Tel (810) 794-4921 Founded/Ownrshp 1948, 1964
Sales 25.0MM^E EMP 113
SIC 5251 Hardware
Ch Bd: Gordon Birgbauer Jr
VP: Shawn Martin
Store Mgr: Belinda Schrader
IT Man: Sam Kauffman
Sfty Mgr: Jeff Fahs
Sls Mgr: Randy Bonacorsi

D-U-N-S 06-181-2087
LUMBERMEN ASSOCIATES INC
2101 Hunter Rd, Bristol, PA 19007
Tel (215) 785-4600 Founded/Ownrshp 1961, 1979
Sales 107.0MM EMP 65
Accts Bbd Philadelphia Pa
SIC 5031 Lumber: rough, dressed & finished
Pr: Thomas J Deegan
*CFO: Brian R Cassel
*Treas: Timothy M Deegan
*Ex VP: Thomas C Coleman

D-U-N-S 00-983-5794 IMP
LUMBERMENS BRICK & SUPPLY CO
LUMBERMEN'S NATURAL STONE & BR
13709 Industrial Rd, Omaha, NE 68137-1129
Tel (402) 894-2222 Founded/Ownrshp 1932
Sales 23.6MM EMP 60
Accts Lutz & Company Pc
SIC 5032 5719 Brick, except refractory; Fireplace equipment & accessories; Brick, except refractory; Fireplace equipment & accessories
Ch: Dale Funk
*Pr: Jeffery D Funk
*Treas: David Modlin
Sales Exec: Wes Vawser
VP Sls: John Rutkowski

D-U-N-S 04-708-7812
LUMBERMENS BUYING SERVICE CO
1290 Pearl St, Eugene, OR 97401-3540
Tel (541) 687-1535 Founded/Ownrshp 1966
Sales 40.0MM EMP 4
SIC 5031 Lumber: rough, dressed & finished
Pr: Craig Soderberg
*Sec: Dale Blomberg
*VP: Todd Bradshaw

D-U-N-S 00-656-7465
LUMBERMENS INC (MI)
ROSEWOOD WORKS
4433 Stafford Ave Sw, Grand Rapids, MI 49548-4124
Tel (616) 261-3200 Founded/Ownrshp 1955, 1986
Sales 263.3MM^E EMP 270
SIC 5033 5031 5198 Roofing, asphalt & sheet metal; Shingles, except wood; Insulation, thermal; Doors & windows; Windows; Paneling, wood; Molding, all materials; Stain; Roofing, asphalt & sheet metal; Shingles, except wood; Insulation, thermal; Doors & windows; Windows, Paneling, wood; Molding, all materials; Stain
Pr: Roger Vanderheide
*Ex VP: Douglas Rathbun
VP: Dave Mulder
*VP: Steve Petersen
VP: Steve Peterson
Sales Asso: Jeff Brown
Sales Asso: John Ruthkowski

D-U-N-S 00-893-9803 EXP
LUMBERMENS MERCHANDISING CORP
LMC
137 W Wayne Ave, Wayne, PA 19087-4018
Tel (610) 293-3678 Founded/Ownrshp 1935
Sales 221.8MM^E EMP 200
SIC 5031 5072 Lumber: rough, dressed & finished; Millwork; Plywood; Wallboard; Builders' hardware; Lumber: rough, dressed & finished; Millwork; Plywood; Wallboard; Builders' hardware
Pr: John Somerville Jr
*Treas: Anthony J Decarlo
Top Exec: Christopher Hart
*Sr VP: John L Broomell
*Sr VP: David J Gonze
Sr VP: David Gonze
*VP: Kathleen M Butcosk
*VP: Vern Dando
*VP: John Keeley
*VP: Andrew J Toombs
Board of Directors: Douglas R Kuiken, Douglas E Ashy Sr, Kenneth L Lawson Jr, W A Bissette, Kenneth J Lehman, Jeffrey B Brown, Michael F Lezzer, David M Campbell, David Majeski, C Christopher Cluss, Joel C Robinson Jr, Farrell L Goble, Steven C Steinman, George W Hodges, Alfred J Torrisi, Thomas J Hughes, Charles L Kirchner

LUMBERMEN'S NATURAL STONE & BR
See LUMBERMENS BRICK & SUPPLY CO

D-U-N-S 07-628-0528
LUMBERMENS UNDERWRITING ALLIANCE
L U A
1905 Nw Corporate Blvd, Boca Raton, FL 33431-7315
Tel (561) 994-1900 Founded/Ownrshp 1973
Sales NA EMP 226
SIC 6331 6411 6311 Fire, marine & casualty insurance & carriers; Insurance agents, brokers & service; Life insurance; Fire, marine & casualty insurance & carriers; Insurance agents, brokers & service; Life insurance
Ch Bd: Christine Lynn
*Pr: Bill Broich
*CEO: Jan Carlsson
CFO: William Broich
*CFO: Jeff Poirier
VP: Kathy Antonello
*VP: Mindy Appel
*VP: Mary Moore
*VP: Wil Nance
VP: Michael North
VP: Craig Smith

D-U-N-S 15-298-1155
LUMBERTON CELLULOSE LLC
(Suby of BUCKEYE TECHNOLOGIES INC) ★
1000 Noir St, Lumberton, NC 28358-6660
Tel (910) 737-3200 Founded/Ownrshp 1968
Sales 22.3MM^E EMP 27
SIC 2611 Pulp produced from non-wood fiber base; Pulp produced from wood base; Pulp produced from non-wood fiber base; Pulp produced from wood base
Pr: Patrick Boushka
IT Man: Melody Hager
Sfty Mgr: Mark Griffin

LUMBERTON CITY CLERK
See CITY OF LUMBERTON

D-U-N-S 01-919-1204
LUMBERTON INDEPENDENT SCHOOL DISTRICT
LUMBERTON ISD
121 S Main St, Lumberton, TX 77657-7368
Tel (409) 923-7580 *Founded/Ownrshp* 1957
Sales 40.3MM^E *EMP* 575
Accts Jr Edwards & Associates Llc
SIC 8211 Public elementary & secondary schools; Public elementary & secondary schools
Bd of Dir: Kenny Burkhalter
VP: Harry Roberts
Secur Mgr: Russell Brown
Schl Brd P: James Glenn

LUMBERTON ISD
See LUMBERTON INDEPENDENT SCHOOL DISTRICT

D-U-N-S 02-574-3238 IMP
LUMBERYARD SUPPLIERS INC
SERVICE WHOLESALE
300 Pinecrest Dr, East Peoria, IL 61611-1598
Tel (309) 694-4356 *Founded/Ownrshp* 2001
Sales 30.9MM *EMP* 130
SIC 5033 5031 Roofing, siding & insulation; Roofing & siding materials; Doors & windows; Roofing, siding & insulation; Roofing & siding materials; Doors & windows
Pr: Troy Reed
**CFO:* Daniel Schumacher
Sls Mgr: Kevin Boyer
Sales Asso: Mike Brownfield
Sales Asso: Vaughn Kumlander

D-U-N-S 14-242-3826
LUMENATE TECHNOLOGIES LP
16633 Dallas Pkwy Ste 450, Addison, TX 75001-6811
Tel (972) 248-8999 *Founded/Ownrshp* 2003
Sales 109.3MM^E *EMP* 240
SIC 7379 Computer related consulting services; Computer related consulting services
Pt: Reagan Dixon
Pt: Chad Hodges
Pt: Collin Miles
Pt: Jeff Stoll
Pr: David Deyoung
Pr: Chris Harrington
VP: Denisa Bravenec
VP: Gary Derheim
VP: Ethan Simmons
Exec: Amy Densberger
Mktg Dir: Tim Barto

D-U-N-S 88-362-4843 IMP
LUMENIS INC
(*Suby of* LUMENIS LTD.)
2033 Gateway Pl Ste 200, San Jose, CA 95110-3714
Tel (408) 764-3000 *Founded/Ownrshp* 1992
Sales 231.2MM^E *EMP* 600
SIC 5047 Therapy equipment; Therapy equipment
CEO: Tzipi Ozer Armon
**Ch Bd:* Harel Beit-On
**Pr:* Abner Ray
COO: Zivi Nedivisioni
CFO: Laurie Hanover
**CFO:* Kevin Morano
**CFO:* Ophir Yakovian
**Ex VP:* Mono Grencel
**VP:* Elad Benjamin
**VP:* Hadas Padan
**VP:* Roy Ramati

D-U-N-S 13-411-3146 IMP/EXP
LUMENS
LUMENS LIGHT & LIVING
2028 K St, Sacramento, CA 95811-4217
Tel (916) 444-5585 *Founded/Ownrshp* 2003
Sales 29.2MM^E *EMP* 52^E
SIC 5063 5712 Lighting fixtures; Furniture stores
Pr: Ken Plumlee
Ofcr: Denise Armstrong
Ofcr: Charles Holdredge
VP: Donald Wolf
Area Mgr: Steve Ott
Snr Sftwr: Brian Del Vecchio
Dir IT: Thomas Armbruster
Web Dev: Jeff Medich
Mktg Dir: Kathy Van Velzer
Sls Dir: B J Kalay

LUMENS LIGHT & LIVING
See LUMENS

D-U-N-S 80-946-5594
LUMENSION SECURITY INC
8660 E Hartford Dr # 300, Scottsdale, AZ 85255-2580
Tel (888) 725-7828 *Founded/Ownrshp* 1991
Sales 46.8MM^E *EMP* 150^E
SIC 7371 7379 Computer software development; Computer related consulting services; Computer software development; Computer related consulting services
CEO: Pat Clawson
**Pr:* Michael Wittig
VP: Chris Andrew
VP: Nick Squire
Dir Bus: Russell Eddleman
Dir Bus: Ken Wilson
Prin: Ming Fu
Off Admin: Meghan Shields
Snr Sftwr: Thomas Bernhard
Snr Sftwr: Adam Johnson
Snr Sftwr: Pero Matic
Board of Directors: Jeffrey Banks, Gerard Lopez, Rory O'driscoll

D-U-N-S 07-981-7523
▲ LUMENTUM HOLDINGS INC
400 N Mccarthy Blvd, Milpitas, CA 95035-5112
Tel (408) 546-5483 *Founded/Ownrshp* 2014
Sales 225.5MM^E *EMP* 1,550^E
Tkr Sym LITE *Exch* NGS
SIC 3669 3674 3826 Emergency alarms; Semiconductors & related devices; Optical isolators; Analytical instruments; Laser scientific & engineering instruments
Pr: Alan Lowe
**Ch Bd:* Martin Kaplan
CFO: Aaron Tachibana
Sr VP: Craig Cocchi
Sr VP: Jason Reinhardt
Sr VP: Vincent Retort
Sr VP: Shreyas Shah
VP: Chris Pfistner
Board of Directors: Harold Covert, Penelope Herscher, Brian Lillie, Samuel Thomas

LUMERIS
See ESSENCE GROUP HOLDINGS CORP

D-U-N-S 01-600-2486
LUMERIS SOLUTIONS CO LLC
13900 Riverport Dr, Maryland Heights, MO 63043-4831
Tel (314) 344-2000 *Founded/Ownrshp* 1999
Sales 21.7MM^E *EMP* 84^E
SIC 7372 8742 Application computer software; Hospital & health services consultant
CEO: W Michael Long
CFO: James L Starr
Ex VP: Deb Gribble
Sr VP: Terry L Snyder
VP: Brian Caldwell
VP: Lou A Gilmore
Dir IT: Aaron Pantazo
Mktg Mgr: Jennifer Smith

D-U-N-S 03-850-7976
■ LUMEX INC
SUN OPTO
(*Suby of* ILLINOIS TOOL WORKS INC) ★
425 N Gary Ave, Carol Stream, IL 60188-1823
Tel (630) 315-2150 *Founded/Ownrshp* 2004
Sales 53.1MM^E *EMP* 650
SIC 3679

D-U-N-S 06-954-9228 IMP/EXP
LUMICOR INC (WA)
SCHOBER
1400 Monster Rd Sw Ste A, Renton, WA 98057-2902
Tel (425) 255-4000 *Founded/Ownrshp* 1972
Sales 20.0MM^E *EMP* 80
SIC 3728 3089 Aircraft parts & equipment; Laminating of plastic
Pr: Dan Lessard
Sales Exec: Kit Elliott
VP Sls: Pete Placido
Sls Dir: Brad Ralns

D-U-N-S 12-499-8217 IMP
LUMILEDS LLC
PHILIPS LUMILEDS LIGHTING CO
370 W Trimble Rd, San Jose, CA 95131-1008
Tel (408) 964-2900 *Founded/Ownrshp* 2013
Sales 146.1MM^E *EMP* 470^E
SIC 3825 Electrical energy measuring equipment; Electrical energy measuring equipment
CEO: Pierre Yves Lesaicherre
**COO:* Ajay Marathe
**Sr VP:* Klemens Brunner
**Sr VP:* Mircea-Irimia Buzgar-Nazare
Sr VP: Emmanuel Dieppedalle
Sr VP: Pascal Popis
**VP:* Alex Kirk
VP: Paul Van Der Plas

D-U-N-S 79-878-3288
LUMINA FOUNDATION FOR EDUCATION INC
30 S Meridian St Ste 700, Indianapolis, IN 46204-3568
Tel (317) 951-5300 *Founded/Ownrshp* 1990
Sales NA *EMP* 48
SIC 6111 Student Loan Marketing Association
Ch: Jamie P Merisotis
COO: David Maas
CFO: J Maas
**CFO:* J David Mass
Treas: Allan Bufferd
Ofcr: Jeanna Berdel
Ofcr: Susan Johnson
Ofcr: Jeanna Keller
Ofcr: Nicole McDonald
Ofcr: Amber Moliring
Ofcr: Tina Smith
**Ex VP:* Susan O Conner
VP: Danette Howard
VP: Kiko Suarez
Comm Dir: Teresa Detrich
Board of Directors: Wm R Neale, Rev E Wm Beauchamp, J Bonnie Newman, Gerald Bepko, Richard J Ramsden, Susan M Boyle, Edward R Schmidt, Norris Darrell Jr, Randolph Waterfield Jr, Martha Lamkin, James C Lintzenich, Edward McCabe, Marie V McDemmond, John M Mutz

D-U-N-S 06-914-5589 IMP
LUMINAIRE INC (FL)
8950 Nw 33rd St, Doral, FL 33172-1223
Tel (305) 437-7975 *Founded/Ownrshp* 2002
Sales 21.6MM^E *EMP* 84
SIC 5712 5719 Furniture stores; Housewares
Pr: Nasir Kassamali
**VP:* Nargis Kassamali
Exec: Erica Bryant
IT Man: Daryl Altenhof
Sales Asso: Katrin Lieske

D-U-N-S 60-625-2393
LUMINANT ENERGY CO LLC
(*Suby of* ENERGY FUTURE HOLDINGS CORP) ★
1601 Bryan St, Dallas, TX 75201-3401
Tel (214) 812-4600 *Founded/Ownrshp* 2007
Sales 23.6MM^E *EMP* 170
SIC 4924 Natural gas distribution; Natural gas distribution

D-U-N-S 10-950-6043 IMP
LUMINANT GENERATION CO LLC
T X U
(*Suby of* TEXAS COMPETITIVE ELECTRIC HOLDINGS CO LLC) ★
1601 Bryan St, Dallas, TX 75201-3401
Tel (214) 812-4600 *Founded/Ownrshp* 2001
Sales 868.0MM^E *EMP* 2,000^E
SIC 4925 4911 Gas production and/or distribution; Electric services; Gas production and/or distribution; Electric services
CEO: Mac McFarland
**Pr:* Brian Dickie
**CFO:* Robert Frenzel

D-U-N-S 04-463-2834
LUMINANT MINING CO LLC (TX)
TXU
(*Suby of* TXU ENERGY INDUSTRIES CO) ★
1601 Bryan St, Dallas, TX 75201-3401
Tel (214) 812-4600 *Founded/Ownrshp* 1952, 2002
Sales 673.7MM^E *EMP* 653
SIC 1221 Bituminous coal & lignite-surface mining; Bituminous coal & lignite-surface mining
**Mng Pt:* Paul M Keglevic
**Pr:* David A Campbell
**CFO:* Paul Keglevic
**V Ch Bd:* Mike Greene
**Ex VP:* M A McFarland
**Sr VP:* Richard R Federwisch
**Sr VP:* Robert C Frenzel

D-U-N-S 01-061-8542
LUMINANT POWER
3708 Charles Mrtn Hall Rd, Rockdale, TX 76567-3080
Tel (512) 314-6628 *Founded/Ownrshp* 2010
Sales 43.7MM^E *EMP* 163
SIC 4911 Generation, electric power

LUMINATOR AIRCRAFT PARTS DIV
See LUMINATOR HOLDING LP

D-U-N-S 96-624-2521 IMP
LUMINATOR HOLDING LP
LUMINATOR AIRCRAFT PARTS DIV
(*Suby of* LUMINATOR TECHNOLOGY GROUP LLC) ★
900 Klein Rd, Plano, TX 75074-3712
Tel (972) 424-6511 *Founded/Ownrshp* 2010
Sales 37.3MM^E *EMP* 203
SIC 3613 3643 3646 3647 3621 Switchgear & switchboard apparatus; Current-carrying wiring devices; Commercial indusl & institutional electric lighting fixtures; Aircraft lighting fixtures; Control equipment for electric buses & locomotives; Switchgear & switchboard apparatus; Current-carrying wiring devices; Commercial indusl & institutional electric lighting fixtures; Aircraft lighting fixtures; Control equipment for electric buses & locomotives
Pr: AVI Zisman
Pr: Nick Moolenijzer
Pr: Ramin Safavi
Pr: Rodney Wallace
**CFO:* Rich Rosselet
VP: Steven Boyd
VP: Kelly Hansen
VP: Rick Swanson
Mng Dir: Andrew Murray
Rgnl Mgr: Brian Stark
QA Dir: Charles Maddox

D-U-N-S 07-829-6029 IMP
LUMINATOR TECHNOLOGY GROUP LLC
900 Klein Rd, Plano, TX 75074-3712
Tel (972) 424-6511 *Founded/Ownrshp* 2014
Sales 79.8MM^E *EMP* 400
SIC 3613 3643 3646 3647 Switchgear & switchboard apparatus; Current-carrying wiring devices; Commercial indusl & institutional electric lighting fixtures; Aircraft lighting fixtures; Switchgear & switchboard apparatus; Current-carrying wiring devices; Commercial indusl & institutional electric lighting fixtures; Aircraft lighting fixtures
Pr: AVI Zisman
**CFO:* Rich Rosselet
**VP:* Steven Boyd
VP: Nick Moolenijzer
VP Sls: Dan Kelleher
VP Sls: Riko Yap
Sls Mgr: Thomas Jacobsson

D-U-N-S 14-156-2020
LUMINENT MORTGAGE CAPITAL INC
1 Commerce Sq, Philadelphia, PA 19103-1415
Tel (215) 564-5900 *Founded/Ownrshp* 2003
Sales 520.8MM *EMP* 26^E
SIC 6798 Real estate investment trusts; Real estate investment trusts
Pr: Zachary H Pashel
**Ch Bd:* Craig A Cohen
CFO: Karen Chang
Sr VP: Dimitri Papatheoharis

D-U-N-S 82-823-4661
■ LUMINENTOIC INC
(*Suby of* MRV COMMUNICATIONS INC) ★
20550 Nordhoff St, Chatsworth, CA 91311-6113
Tel (818) 773-9044 *Founded/Ownrshp* 2000
Sales 50.2MM^E *EMP* 996
SIC 3674 Semiconductors & related devices; Semiconductors & related devices
Ch Bd: Noah Lotan
**Pr:* Aaron Levy
Ofcr: Yu-Heng Jan
VP: Chen Genossar
VP: Gordon Li
VP: Jan Yu
Ex Dir: Rob Goldman
**CTO:* Mark Heimbuch
S&M/VP: James S Locke
Board of Directors: Dan Avida, Richard S Hill, Dr Shlomo Margalit, Amos Wilnai

D-U-N-S 17-814-0935
■ LUMINESCENT SYSTEMS INC
L S I
(*Suby of* ASTRONICS CORP) ★
130 Commerce Way, East Aurora, NY 14052-2191
Tel (716) 655-0800 *Founded/Ownrshp* 1968
Sales 58.1MM^E *EMP* 412
SIC 3647 3646 3648 3577 Aircraft lighting fixtures; Commercial indusl & institutional electric lighting fixtures; Lighting equipment; Computer peripheral equipment; Aircraft lighting fixtures; Commercial indusl & institutional electric lighting fixtures; Lighting equipment; Computer peripheral equipment
Pr: Peter Gundermann
**CFO:* Dave Burner
CFO: David Burney
**VP:* Frank Johns
**VP:* James Kramer
**VP:* Richard Miller
Exec: Jill Draper
IT Man: Stevenson Nate

D-U-N-S 96-547-6641
▲ LUMINEX CORP
12212 Technology Blvd, Austin, TX 78727-6100
Tel (512) 219-8020 *Founded/Ownrshp* 1995
Sales 226.9MM *EMP* 741^E
Tkr Sym LMNX *Exch* NGS
SIC 3841 8731 Diagnostic apparatus, medical; Commercial physical research; Biological research; Diagnostic apparatus, medical; Commercial physical research; Biological research
Pr: Nachum Shamir
Pr: Jeremy Bridgecook
Pr: Carrano C John
CFO: Harriss T Currie
Sr VP: Russell W Bradley
Sr VP: Jeremy Bridge-Cook
Sr VP: Nancy M Fairchild
Sr VP: Richard W Rew II
Sr VP: Richard Rew
VP: Nancy M Capezzuti
VP: Nancy Krunic
Exec: Mark Chandler
Exec: Edwin Chien
Exec: Cora Lahey
Assoc Dir: John Geddes
Board of Directors: Robert J Cresci, Thomas W Erickson, Fred C Goad Jr, Jay B Johnston, Jim D Kever, G Walter Loewenbaum II, Kevin M McNamara, Edward A Ogunro

D-U-N-S 14-248-8597 IMP
LUMINUS DEVICES INC
(*Suby of* LIGHTERA) ★
175 New Boston St, Woburn, MA 01801-6203
Tel (978) 528-8000 *Founded/Ownrshp* 2013
Sales 34.1MM^E *EMP* 120
SIC 3648 Lighting equipment; Lighting equipment
CEO: Decai Sun
**Pr:* Keith Ward
**CFO:* Kevin Shih
**Ex VP:* Jim Miller
**Ex VP:* Ellen Richstone
**VP:* Mark Pugh
**VP:* Tony Tong
Board of Directors: Charles F Jerabek

D-U-N-S 07-916-5801
LUMINUS INC
LIGHTERA
1145 Sonora Ct, Sunnyvale, CA 94086-5384
Tel (408) 708-7000 *Founded/Ownrshp* 2012
Sales 34.1MM^E *EMP* 200
SIC 3646 Fluorescent lighting fixtures, commercial; Fluorescent lighting fixtures, commercial
CEO: Decai Sun

D-U-N-S 03-720-5312
LUMITE INC
1515 N County Line Rd, Alto, GA 30510-2511
Tel (770) 869-1700 *Founded/Ownrshp* 2004
Sales 45.6MM^E *EMP* 99^E
SIC 5083 Tractors, agricultural; Tractors, agricultural
CEO: Ron Rooks

D-U-N-S 10-863-1797 IMP
LUMITEX INC
8443 Dow Cir, Strongsville, OH 44136-1796
Tel (440) 243-8401 *Founded/Ownrshp* 1992
Sales 24.4MM^E *EMP* 150
SIC 3646 3641 3648 3845 Commercial indusl & institutional electric lighting fixtures; Electric lamps; Lighting equipment; Electromedical equipment; Commercial indusl & institutional electric lighting fixtures; Electric lamps; Lighting equipment; Electromedical equipment
Pr: Peter W Broer
**CFO:* Thomas E Walden

LUMMI FISHERIES SUPPLIES
See LFS INC

D-U-N-S 02-024-5247
LUMMI INDIAN BUSINESS COUNCIL INC
LUMMI TRIBE LUMMI RESERVATION
2665 Kwina Rd, Bellingham, WA 98226-9291
Tel (360) 312-2200 *Founded/Ownrshp* 1969
Sales NA *EMP* 800
SIC 9131 Indian reservation; ; Indian reservation
Ch: Tim Ballew II
V Ch: Candice Wilson
**Treas:* Darrell Hillaire
**Treas:* Sheryl Jones
Ex Dir: David Bunton
Genl Mgr: Ted Wright
IT Man: Kate Clark
IT Man: Elden Hillaire

LUMMI TRIBE LUMMI RESERVATION
See LUMMI INDIAN BUSINESS COUNCIL INC

D-U-N-S 80-269-5015 IMP/EXP
LUMMUS CORP
225 Bourne Blvd, Savannah, GA 31408-9586
Tel (912) 447-9000 *Founded/Ownrshp* 1987
Sales 56.1MM^E *EMP* 200
SIC 3559 3552 3542 Cotton ginning machinery; Textile machinery; Machine tools, metal forming type; Cotton ginning machinery; Textile machinery; Machine tools, metal forming type
Ch Bd: Dikran Izmirlian
**Pr:* Stephen Marbut
**CFO:* Martin Amlung
Board of Directors: Michael Wagner

D-U-N-S 00-698-7028
LUMMUS OVERSEAS CORP
CB & I LUMMUS GLOBAL INC
(*Suby of* CHICAGO BRIDGE & IRON CO (DELAWARE)) ★
1515 Broad St, Bloomfield, NJ 07003-3002
Tel (973) 893-1515 *Founded/Ownrshp* 1907, 2007

Sales 233.3MM^E *EMP* 4,000
SIC 8711 1629 8741 Engineering services; Industrial plant construction; Construction management; Engineering services; Industrial plant construction; Construction management
Pr: Martin W Gross
**Ex VP:* K Farid
**VP:* M Duplantier
**VP:* M J Ford Jr
VP: Jules Lerner
Genl Mgr: Helion Sardina

D-U-N-S 03-354-1319 IMP
LUMMUS SUPPLY CO
1554 Bolton Rd Nw, Atlanta, GA 30331-1099
Tel (404) 794-1501 *Founded/Ownrshp* 1946
Sales 30.4MM *EMP* 73
Accts Larry W Nichols Pc Atlant
SIC 5211 2431 Lumber & other building materials; Millwork; Lumber & other building materials; Millwork
Pr: William L Lummus
**CFO:* R H Lummus III
Genl Mgr: Phil Tyson
Dir IT: Brandon Underwood

D-U-N-S 80-548-8686
LUMMUS TECHNOLOGY INC
(*Suby of* CHICAGO BRIDGE & IRON COMPANY N.V.)
1515 Broad St Ste A110, Bloomfield, NJ 07003-3054
Tel (973) 338-0702 *Founded/Ownrshp* 1930
Sales 68.1MM^E *EMP* 500^E
SIC 8711 Engineering services; Engineering services
CEO: Philip K Asherman
**Pr:* Dan McCarthy
**CFO:* Ronald A Ballschmiede
Sr VP: Ronald D Dawson
VP: Fred Gardner
VP: Patrick Mullen
**VP:* Luke V Scorsone
IT Man: Kandasamy Sundaram
Snr Mgr: Jaroslav Cervenka

D-U-N-S 07-834-4519
▲ LUMOS NETWORKS CORP
1 Lumos Plz, Waynesboro, VA 22980-4549
Tel (540) 946-2000 *Founded/Ownrshp* 2011
Sales 201.4MM *EMP* 579^E
Tkr Sym LMOS *Exch* NGS
SIC 4813 Telephone communication, except radio; ; Telephone communication, except radio;
Pr: Timothy G Biltz
CFO: Johan G Broekhuysen
Ofcr: Joseph E McCourt Jr
Sr VP: Diego B Anderson
Sr VP: Craig M Drinkhall
Sr VP: Mary McDermott
VP: John Lewis
IT Man: Wendy Batts
Sfty Mgr: Scott Wellborn
VP Mktg: Joti Balani
VP Sls: Glenn Lytle
Board of Directors: Robert E Guth, Michael K Robinson, Brian V Rosenberg, Michael T Sicoli, Jerry E Vaughn

D-U-N-S 83-985-4382
■ LUMOS NETWORKS LLC
(*Suby of* NTELOS HOLDINGS CORP) ★
1200 Greenbrier St, Charleston, WV 25311-1002
Tel (304) 720-2100 *Founded/Ownrshp* 2010
Sales 82.8MM^E *EMP* 145
SIC 4813 8748 Local & long distance telephone communications; Telecommunications consultant; Local & long distance telephone communications; Telecommunications consultant
Dir IT: Darius Walker
Netwrk Mgr: Jack Belcher
Opers Mgr: Glen Keaton
Sls Mgr: Russell King

D-U-N-S 96-905-1833
LUMOS NETWORKS OPERATING CO INC
1 Lumos Plz, Waynesboro, VA 22980-4549
Tel (540) 946-3500 *Founded/Ownrshp* 2011
Sales 35.0MM^E *EMP* 500
SIC 4813 Telephone communication, except radio; Telephone communication, except radio
Pr: Michael B Moneymaker
COO: Frank L Berry
Sr VP: Jeffrey Miller
VP: William Davis
VP: Thomas Ferry
VP: Celia Kovac

D-U-N-S 07-979-9731
LUMPKIN COUNTY SCHOOL SYSTEM
56 Indian Dr, Dahlonega, GA 30533-3871
Tel (706) 864-3611 *Founded/Ownrshp* 2015
Sales 4.5MM^E *EMP* 339^E
SIC 8211 Public elementary & secondary schools
Pr Dir: Anne Davis
HC Dir: Sharon Head

D-U-N-S 08-243-6932 IMP
LUMSDEN CORP
HOYT WIRE CLOTH DIV
10 Abraso St, Lancaster, PA 17601-3104
Tel (717) 394-6871 *Founded/Ownrshp* 1977
Sales 25.6MM^E *EMP* 130
SIC 3496 3535 Screening, woven wire: made from purchased wire; Belt conveyor systems, general industrial use; Screening, woven wire: made from purchased wire; Belt conveyor systems, general industrial use
CEO: Glenn P Farrell
**Pr:* Arthur Lumsden
**Treas:* Alexander D Lumsden
**VP:* Tom Boaman
**VP:* Gina Mitchell
Sls Mgr: Peter Moore
Sales Asso: Connie Clayton
Sales Asso: Karen Devine
Sales Asso: Robin Horner
Sales Asso: Kim Le

D-U-N-S 06-491-1670
LUNA CASEY FORD MERCURY INC
CASEY LOS LUNAS AUTO MART
499 Emelio Lopez Rd, Los Lunas, NM 87031
Tel (505) 866-3100 *Founded/Ownrshp* 1973
Sales 21.7MM^E *EMP* 62
SIC 5511 7538 Automobiles, new & used; General automotive repair shops; Automobiles, new & used; General automotive repair shops
Pr: Brad Francis
**Pr:* Casey Luna

LUNA COMMERCIAL
See PONCE CASH & CARRY INC

D-U-N-S 62-713-2913
▲ LUNA INNOVATIONS INC
301 1st St Sw Ste 200, Roanoke, VA 24011-1921
Tel (540) 769-8400 *Founded/Ownrshp* 1990
Sales 21.2MM *EMP* 244^E
Tkr Sym LUNA *Exch* NAS
SIC 8731 3827 7372 3841 Commercial physical research; Optical instruments & lenses; Prepackaged software; Surgical & medical instruments; Commercial physical research; Optical instruments & lenses; Prepackaged software; Surgical & medical instruments
Pr: My E Chung
Pr: Aaron Hullman
CFO: Dale E Messick
Treas: Scott A Graeff
VP: Talfourd H Kemper Jr
Dir IT: Marc Hrovatic
Sls Mgr: Mark Huggard
Board of Directors: Ed J Coringrato Jr, Donald Pastor, Richard W Roedel, Gary Spiegel, John B Williamson III, Michael M Wise

LUNA PARK AT CONEY ISLAND
See CENTRAL AMUSEMENT INTERNATIONAL LLC

D-U-N-S 11-806-0342
LUNA VALLE INC
VALLE LUNA MEXICAN FOOD
3336 W Bell Rd, Phoenix, AZ 85053-2925
Tel (602) 993-3108 *Founded/Ownrshp* 1983
Sales 10.3MM^E *EMP* 300
Accts Tull Forsberg & Olson
SIC 5812 5813 Mexican restaurant; Drinking places; Mexican restaurant; Drinking places
Pr: William L Riddle III
**Treas:* Jane Ann Riddle
**VP:* Donald W Stamper

D-U-N-S 05-056-3808
LUNAN CORP
414 N Orleans St Ste 402, Chicago, IL 60654-8002
Tel (312) 645-9898 *Founded/Ownrshp* 1967
Sales 46.7MM^E *EMP* 1,000^E
Accts Crowe Chizek Oak Brook II
SIC 5812 Fast-food restaurant, chain; Fast-food restaurant, chain
Pr: Gregory Schulson
**Ch Bd:* Michael Schulson
**CFO:* Steve Ganek
**VP:* Brendan Casey
VP Opers: Jeff Winograd
Mktg Dir: Janet Broline

D-U-N-S 05-461-1322 IMP/EXP
LUNARDIS SUPER MARKET INC
432 N Canal St Ste 22, South San Francisco, CA 94080-4666
Tel (650) 588-7507 *Founded/Ownrshp* 1972
Sales 38.0MM^E *EMP* 300
SIC 5411 Supermarkets; Supermarkets
Pr: Alfred Lunardi
**VP:* Paul Lunardi

LUNARPAGES
See ADD2NET INC

LUNAS CONSTRUCTION CLEAN UP
See LUNAS CONSTRUCTION INC

D-U-N-S 79-485-5072
LUNAS CONSTRUCTION INC
LUNAS CONSTRUCTION CLEAN UP
4830 E Cartier Ave, Las Vegas, NV 89115-4509
Tel (702) 644-6840 *Founded/Ownrshp* 1992
Sales 27.0MM^E *EMP* 99
SIC 4953 4212 3011 5093 Refuse collection & disposal services; Non-hazardous waste disposal sites; Recycling, waste materials; Garbage: collecting, destroying & processing; Hazardous waste transport; Retreading materials, tire; Rubber scrap
Pr: Manuel Madrigal
**Treas:* Norberto Madrigal
**VP:* Victor Madrigal
Mktg Dir: Maria Juarez

LUNCH PROGRAM
See FOUNDATION HEALTH SERVICES INC

D-U-N-S 00-289-0999
LUNCHTIME SOLUTIONS INC (SD)
717 N Derby Ln Ste C, North Sioux City, SD 57049-3186
Tel (605) 235-0939 *Founded/Ownrshp* 1997
Sales 15.0MM^E *EMP* 350
SIC 8322 Meal delivery program; Meal delivery program
Pr: Michael Cranny
VP: Chris Goeb
Exec: Deni Brown
Rgnl Mgr: Elliott Warshaw

D-U-N-S 04-294-5715
LUND BROWN ENTERPRISES LLC
7490 Clubhouse Rd Ste 200, Boulder, CO 80301-3720
Tel (303) 530-2900 *Founded/Ownrshp* 2010
Sales 229.9MM^E *EMP* 6,000
SIC 6794 Franchises, selling or licensing; Franchises, selling or licensing
Owner: Dewey R Brown

LUND CADILLAC COMPANY
See LUND CADILLAC LLC

D-U-N-S 15-367-0039
LUND CADILLAC LLC
LUND CADILLAC COMPANY
1311 E Bell Rd Ste 1, Phoenix, AZ 85022-2724
Tel (888) 713-8103 *Founded/Ownrshp* 1999
Sales 39.2MM^E *EMP* 130
SIC 5511 Automobiles, new & used; Automobiles, new & used
CIO: Jay Alverez
Dir IT: Mike Ellis
Dir IT: Matt McDermott
Sls Mgr: Frank Barela
Sls Mgr: Tim Kielhman
Sls Mgr: Matt Kinder
Sls Mgr: Ken Schwagerman
Sls Mgr: Tom Williams

D-U-N-S 96-156-6502
LUND FOOD HOLDINGS INC
LUNDS
4100 W 50th St Ste 100, Minneapolis, MN 55424-1272
Tel (952) 927-3663 *Founded/Ownrshp* 1997
Sales 555.6MM^E *EMP* 4,500
SIC 5411 Supermarkets, chain; Supermarkets, chain
CEO: Russell T Lund III
**Pr:* Russell Lund
CFO: Von Martin
VP: Kevin Baartman
VP: James Geisler
Genl Mgr: Heather Wicklander
Store Mgr: Steve Carda
Store Mgr: Brian Glaser
Store Mgr: Mike Schwartz
Off Admin: Shelly Sunde
QA Dir: Chris Gindorff

D-U-N-S 14-851-0928 IMP
LUND INC
DEFLECTA SHIELD
(*Suby of* LUND INTERNATIONAL HOLDING CO) ★
4325 Hamilton Mill Rd # 400, Buford, GA 30518-8848
Tel (678) 804-3767 *Founded/Ownrshp* 2007
Sales 153.2MM^E *EMP* 500
SIC 3714 Motor vehicle parts & accessories; Bumpers & bumperettes, motor vehicle; Sun roofs, motor vehicle; Wind deflectors, motor vehicle; Motor vehicle parts & accessories; Bumpers & bumperettes, motor vehicle; Sun roofs, motor vehicle; Wind deflectors, motor vehicle
CEO: George Scherff
**Pr:* Mitch Fogle
**COO:* Bob Chapman
**CFO:* Glenn A Hollis
**CFO:* Bill White
**VP:* Tammy Gracek
VP: Harry Samp
**VP:* Matt Stanesic
**VP:* Joe Thompson
Exec: Stephen Treichel
VP Sls: Ken Robinson

D-U-N-S 96-880-5536
LUND INTERNATIONAL HOLDING CO
TRADESMAN TRUCK ACCESSORIES
4325 Hamilton Mill Rd, Buford, GA 30518-8835
Tel (678) 804-3767 *Founded/Ownrshp* 2007
Sales 251.1MM^E *EMP* 500^E
SIC 3714 Motor vehicle parts & accessories; Bumpers & bumperettes, motor vehicle; Sun roofs, motor vehicle; Wind deflectors, motor vehicle; Motor vehicle parts & accessories; Bumpers & bumperettes, motor vehicle; Sun roofs, motor vehicle; Wind deflectors, motor vehicle
Pr: Mitch Fogle
**COO:* Tammy Gracek
**CFO:* Mark Stanko
**Sr VP:* Joe Thompson
VP: William Toms

D-U-N-S 00-583-2613
■ LUNDA CONSTRUCTION CO (WI)
(*Suby of* TUTOR PERINI CORP) ★
620 Gebhardt Rd, Black River Falls, WI 54615-9152
Tel (715) 284-2322 *Founded/Ownrshp* 1938, 2011
Sales 389.0MM *EMP* 1,785
Accts Deloitte & Touche Llp Los Ang
SIC 1622 8711 Bridge construction; Engineering services; Bridge construction; Engineering services
Pr: Larry Lunda
**CFO:* Carl Holmquist
Ofcr: Chris Fox
VP: Dennis L Behnke
**VP:* Tom Braun
**VP:* Richard Slifka
Off Admin: Lisa Braun
IT Man: Michael Haun

D-U-N-S 13-810-3192
■ LUNDA CONSTRUCTION CO
(*Suby of* LUNDA CONSTRUCTION CO) ★
15601 Clanton Ave S, Rosemount, MN 55068
Tel (651) 437-9666 *Founded/Ownrshp* 1968
Sales 31.5MM^E *EMP* 650
SIC 1622 Bridge construction; Bridge construction
Pr: Larry Lunda
**CEO:* Milton Lunda

D-U-N-S 00-834-5464
LUNDAY-THAGARD CO
LTR
(*Suby of* WORLD OIL MARKETING CO) ★
9302 Garfield Ave, South Gate, CA 90280-3805
Tel (562) 928-7000 *Founded/Ownrshp* 1982
Sales 56.3MM^E *EMP* 475
SIC 2952 2951 2911 Roof cement: asphalt, fibrous or plastic; Asphalt paving mixtures & blocks; Petroleum refining; Roof cement: asphalt, fibrous or plastic; Asphalt paving mixtures & blocks; Petroleum refining
Ch Bd: Bernard B Roth
**Pr:* Robert Roth
**Pr:* Peter Stockhausen
**COO:* Austin Miller
VP: Jim Gravatt
**VP:* Larry Mori
**VP:* Steve Roth
**VP:* Bert Wootan
Sfty Mgr: Craig Caskey

D-U-N-S 01-834-3595
LUNDBECK LLC (IL)
(*Suby of* H. LUNDBECK A/S)
4 Parkway N, Deerfield, IL 60015-2502
Tel (847) 282-1000 *Founded/Ownrshp* 2000, 2009
Sales 168.1MM^E *EMP* 687^E
SIC 2834 5122 Pharmaceutical preparations; Pharmaceuticals
CEO: Sean Nolan
Pr: Erik Allikmets
**CFO:* Curtis Rhine
Treas: Nicolaj Kofoed
VP: Peter Anastasiou
VP: Anders Buur
VP: Eric Floyd
VP: Thomas Forrester
VP: Charles R Krikorian
VP: Patroski Lawson
VP: Brian McCarthy
VP: Dierck Schoch
Assoc Dir: Anna Eramo
Dir Bus: Bradon Kashfian

D-U-N-S 18-510-7935 IMP
LUNDBECK RESEARCH USA INC
(*Suby of* LUNDBECK LLC) ★
215 College Rd Ste 100, Paramus, NJ 07652-1419
Tel (201) 261-1331 *Founded/Ownrshp* 2003
Sales 27.1MM^E *EMP* 99
SIC 5122

LUNDBERG FAMILY FARMS
See WEHAH FARM INC

D-U-N-S 03-181-6614
LUNDE LINCOLN-MERCURY INC
140 40th St Sw, Fargo, ND 58103-1152
Tel (701) 282-7600 *Founded/Ownrshp* 1986
Sales 25.3MM *EMP* 83^E
SIC 5511 New & used car dealers; Automobiles, new & used; Pickups, new & used; New & used car dealers; Automobiles, new & used; Pickups, new & used
Pr: Andrew Boen
**Sec:* Norin Hegney

D-U-N-S 09-231-5498 IMP
LUNDELL MANUFACTURING CORP (MN)
2700 Ranchview Ln N, Minneapolis, MN 55447-1907
Tel (763) 559-4114 *Founded/Ownrshp* 1978
Sales 27.4MM^E *EMP* 85
SIC 3069 Hard rubber & molded rubber products
Pr: Thomas Lundell
**CFO:* David Brown
**VP:* Timothy Lundell
Netwrk Mgr: Troy Nichols
VP Sls: Steve Wittwer
Sls Mgr: Jim Grover
Sls Mgr: Schuehle Randy

LUNDGREN HONDA
See RICHARD LUNDGREN INC

LUNDS
See LUND FOOD HOLDINGS INC

D-U-N-S 06-902-0774 IMP
LUNDS FISHERIES INC
997 Ocean Dr, Cape May, NJ 08204-1899
Tel (609) 884-7600 *Founded/Ownrshp* 1928
Sales 83.4MM^E *EMP* 100
SIC 5146 Fish, fresh; Fish, frozen, unpackaged; Fish, fresh; Fish, frozen, unpackaged
Pr: Jeff Reichle
**VP:* Wayne Reichle

D-U-N-S 02-291-6134
LUNDS INC
4100 W 50th St Ste 100, Minneapolis, MN 55424-1272
Tel (952) 927-3663 *Founded/Ownrshp* 1961
Sales 182.2MM^E *EMP* 1,709
SIC 5411 Supermarkets, chain; Supermarkets, chain
Pr: Russell T Lund III
**Treas:* Von Martin
**VP:* Jim Geisler
Store Mgr: Steve Bishop

D-U-N-S 18-549-4515
LUNDY SERVICES LLC
4050 Black Gold Dr, Dallas, TX 75247-6304
Tel (214) 951-8181 *Founded/Ownrshp* 1988
Sales 53.5MM^E *EMP* 377
SIC 1799 Home/office interiors finishing, furnishing & remodeling; Home/office interiors finishing, furnishing & remodeling
Ofcr: Liz Hardy
Exec: Kelly Beers
MIS Dir: Tom Heicken

LUNENBURG BOARD OF EDUCATION
See LUNENBURG COUNTY SCHOOL DISTRICT

D-U-N-S 01-360-1547
LUNENBURG COUNTY SCHOOL DISTRICT
LUNENBURG BOARD OF EDUCATION
1009 Main St, Kenbridge, VA 23944-3531
Tel (434) 676-2467 *Founded/Ownrshp* 1994
Sales 11.3MM^E *EMP* 375
SIC 8211 Public elementary & secondary schools; Public elementary & secondary schools
Schl Brd P: Donald Carnes

D-U-N-S 10-003-2077
LUNENBURG PUBLIC SCHOOLS
1025 Mass Ave, Lunenburg, MA 01462-1432
Tel (978) 582-4100 *Founded/Ownrshp* 1950
Sales 21.7MM^E *EMP* 455
SIC 8211 Public elementary & secondary schools; Public elementary & secondary schools
**Prin:* Michael Barney
**Prin:* Cynthia Daukantas
**Prin:* Keith Hochstein

D-U-N-S 82-999-9221 IMP
LUNERA LIGHTING INC
1615 Wyatt Dr, Santa Clara, CA 95054-1587
Tel (650) 241-3875 *Founded/Ownrshp* 2009
Sales 23.0MM *EMP* 30^E
SIC 5063 Lighting fixtures, commercial & industrial
CEO: Douglas Schendt

VP: Don Barnetson
VP: Tom Quinn
Manager: Lori Endara
Sales Asso: Saldy Suriben

D-U-N-S 05-466-9676
LUNGHAMER BUICK GMC INC
5825 Highland Rd, Waterford, MI 48327-1828
Tel (248) 461-1000 *Founded/Ownrshp* 1974, 2004
Sales 25.2MM^E *EMP* 60
SIC 5511 5521 Automobiles, new & used; Pickups, new & used; Used car dealers; Automobiles, new & used; Pickups, new & used; Used car dealers
Pr: Joseph Lunghamer Jr
Genl Mgr: Dave Snelling
Genl Mgr: Scott Ziegler
Off Mgr: Kathy Marquette
Store Mgr: Tony Tinnin
Sls Mgr: Mike Porter
Sales Asso: Kati Rola

D-U-N-S 00-384-3851 IMP
LUNSETH PLUMBING AND HEATING CO (ND)
1710 N Washington St, Grand Forks, ND 58203-1426
Tel (701) 772-6631 *Founded/Ownrshp* 1935, 2004
Sales 24.0MM^E *EMP* 102
SIC 1711 Plumbing contractors; Warm air heating & air conditioning contractor
Pr: David Kvidt
VP: Reginold C Jehart
**VP:* Phil Kraemer

LUPIENT & CHEVROLET
See LUPIENT CHEVROLET OF BLOOMINGTON

D-U-N-S 02-290-1011
LUPIENT CHEVROLET OF BLOOMINGTON
LUPIENT & CHEVROLET
1601 Southtown Dr, Minneapolis, MN 55431-1431
Tel (952) 884-3333 *Founded/Ownrshp* 1967
Sales 29.5MM^E *EMP* 85
SIC 5511 7538 7532 Automobiles, new & used; General automotive repair shops; Body shop, automotive; Automobiles, new & used; General automotive repair shops; Body shop, automotive
Ch Bd: James Lupient
Genl Mgr: Pam Guilford
Genl Mgr: Tom Schmitz
Sales Exec: Tim Redfield
Sls Dir: Greg Pomish
Sls Mgr: Pete Thom
Sales Asso: Jeremiah Steffens

D-U-N-S 04-952-9126
LUPIENT OLDSMOBILE CO (INC)
JIM LUPIENT OLDS CO
7100 Wayzata Blvd, Minneapolis, MN 55426-1674
Tel (763) 546-2222 *Founded/Ownrshp* 1969
Sales 62.8MM^E *EMP* 240
SIC 5511 7538 5521 Automobiles, new & used; General automotive repair shops; Used car dealers; Automobiles, new & used; General automotive repair shops; Used car dealers
Pr: James Lupient
DP Exec: Michelle Notch
Sls Mgr: Greg Pomish

D-U-N-S 08-915-3071 IMP
LUPIN PHARMACEUTICALS INC
(*Suby of* LUPIN LIMITED)
111 S Calvert St Ste 2150, Baltimore, MD 21202-6116
Tel (410) 576-2000 *Founded/Ownrshp* 2003
Sales 221.8MM^E *EMP* 220
SIC 5122 Drugs & drug proprietaries; Drugs & drug proprietaries
CEO: Vinita Gupta
**Pr:* Paul McGarty
**CFO:* William Gileza
Ex VP: Dhananjay Bakhle
Sr VP: Gary Deeb
Sr VP: Nilesh Gupta
Sr VP: Xian-Ming Zeng
VP: Rangnath Deshpande
VP: Ganadhish Kamat
VP: Mickey Proctor
VP: Nitin Vadia

D-U-N-S 17-011-6409
LUPTON VENTURES INC
1405 14th St, Fort Lupton, CO 80621-2718
Tel (303) 659-9767 *Founded/Ownrshp* 2004
Sales 93.2MM^E *EMP* 170
SIC 3353 Aluminum sheet, plate & foil; Aluminum sheet, plate & foil
CEO: Jeff Frim

LURCAT
See DAMICO & PARTNERS INC

D-U-N-S 09-607-0123 IMP
LURGI INC
(*Suby of* AIR LIQUIDE GLOBAL E&C SOLUTIONS GERMANY GMBH)
6750 Poplar Ave Ste 720, Memphis, TN 38138-7421
Tel (901) 756-8250 *Founded/Ownrshp* 2007
Sales 34.2MM^E *EMP* 200
SIC 1541 8741 8711

D-U-N-S 07-135-6521
LURIE BESIKOF LAPIDUS & CO LLP
2501 Wayzata Blvd, Minneapolis, MN 55405-2197
Tel (612) 377-4404 *Founded/Ownrshp* 1952
Sales 22.7MM^E *EMP* 100^E
SIC 8721 Certified public accountant
Pt: Beth Kieffer Leonard
Pt: Marshall J Besikof
Pt: David D Brauer
Pt: Neil N Lapidus
Pt: Joel Lebewitz
Mng Pt: Farley Kaufmann
Ex VP: Patricia Darke
Ex Dir: Jeff Wold
Off Admin: Ashley Reyes
Mktg Mgr: Shana Karle

D-U-N-S 15-264-8564
LURIE CHILDRENS MEMORIAL FOUNDATION
CHILDREN'S MEMORIAL HOSPITAL
225 E Chicago Ave, Chicago, IL 60611-2991
Tel (312) 227-7500 *Founded/Ownrshp* 1984
Sales 65.0MM *EMP* 80
SIC 8399 Fund raising organization, non-fee basis; Fund raising organization, non-fee basis
Pr: Francia Harrington
**Pr:* Margaret Devine

D-U-N-S 02-406-3877 IMP
LUSAMERICA FOODS INC
16480 Railroad Ave, Morgan Hill, CA 95037-5210
Tel (408) 294-6622 *Founded/Ownrshp* 1976
Sales 117.1MM^E *EMP* 150^E
SIC 5146 5142 Fish, fresh; Fish, frozen, unpackaged; Packaged frozen goods; Fish, fresh; Fish, frozen, unpackaged; Packaged frozen goods
CEO: Fernando Luis Frederico
VP: Anna Frederico
MIS Dir: Paula Silva
Sls Mgr: Randy Fairbanks

D-U-N-S 00-958-5464
LUSARDI CONSTRUCTION CO
1570 Linda Vista Dr, San Marcos, CA 92078-3880
Tel (760) 744-3133 *Founded/Ownrshp* 1947
Sales 117.6MM^E *EMP* 250
SIC 1542 1541

D-U-N-S 12-771-2789
LUSE HOLDINGS INC
3990 Enterprise Ct, Aurora, IL 60504-8132
Tel (630) 862-2600 *Founded/Ownrshp* 2002
Sales 38.7MM^E *EMP* 150^E
Accts Callero
SIC 1799 Insulation of pipes & boilers; Asbestos removal & encapsulation
Pr: Steven T Luse
**CFO:* John A Lorenz
Ex VP: Joshua Shaw
VP: James Markham
VP: James McGoldrick
Genl Mgr: James Cholke
IT Man: Bill Hansen
IT Man: Justin Wright
Snr PM: John Provencher

LUSHER CHARTER SCHOOL
See ADVOCATES FOR ARTS-BASED EDUCATION CORP

D-U-N-S 08-336-8428 IMP
LUSID TECHNOLOGIES INC
NORTHSTAR COATINGS
5195 W 4700 S, Salt Lake City, UT 84118-6109
Tel (801) 966-5300 *Founded/Ownrshp* 1999
Sales 36.3MM^E *EMP* 48
SIC 5198 2851 Paints; Paints & allied products
Pr: Labree Truesdale
Manager: Marc Sloven

D-U-N-S 05-256-6932
LUSK DISPOSAL SERVICE INC (WV)
Rr 460 Box E, Princeton, WV 24740
Tel (304) 425-9338 *Founded/Ownrshp* 1966
Sales 46.7MM^E *EMP* 70
SIC 4953 4212 Rubbish collection & disposal; Local trucking, without storage
Pr: Gordon Lusk
**Sec:* Betty Lusk

LUSK GROUP, THE
See LUSK MECHANICAL CONTRACTORS INC

D-U-N-S 78-532-9293
LUSK MECHANICAL CONTRACTORS INC
LUSK GROUP, THE
820 S Dixie Hwy, Muldraugh, KY 40155-1210
Tel (502) 942-6966 *Founded/Ownrshp* 1991
Sales 44.3MM^E *EMP* 250
Accts Bechtler Parker & Watts Loui
SIC 1711 Mechanical contractor; Mechanical contractor
Pr: Judy Lusk
**VP:* Harry L Lusk
**VP:* Leighann Lusk

LUST BUICK
See STEVEN LUST AUTOMOTIVE INC

D-U-N-S 00-521-9290 IMP/EXP
LUSTER PRODUCTS INC (IL)
1104 W 43rd St, Chicago, IL 60609-3342
Tel (773) 579-1800 *Founded/Ownrshp* 1955
Sales 82.8M *EMP* 401
SIC 2844 Hair preparations, including shampoos; Shampoos, rinses, conditioners: hair; Hair preparations, including shampoos; Shampoos, rinses, conditioners: hair
Ch Bd: Blondell Luster
**Pr:* Jory Luster
**VP:* Fred Luster II
**VP:* Sonia Luster
Dir IT: Tony Giovingo
IT Man: Ellen Burris
Opers Mgr: Cory Luster
Plnt Mgr: Ramesh Sharan
Ql Cn Mgr: Joe Fox
Mktg Dir: Ann Anthony
Mktg Dir: Tracey Bell

LUSTINE TOYOTA-DODGE
See LTD INC

D-U-N-S 19-518-5272
LUTCO INC
677 Cambridge St Ste 1, Worcester, MA 01610-2664
Tel (508) 756-6296 *Founded/Ownrshp* 1945
Sales 23.5MM^E *EMP* 135
SIC 3562 Ball bearings & parts; Ball bearings & parts
Pr: John C Stowe
MIS Dir: Richard Hallorian
IT Man: John Pattison
Sls Dir: Linda Mura

LUTE RILEY HONDA
See SONIC - LUTE RILEY LP

D-U-N-S 01-827-6303
LUTE SUPPLY INC (OH)
3920 Us Highway 23, Portsmouth, OH 45662-6468
Tel (740) 353-2112 *Founded/Ownrshp* 1952
Sales 84.5MM^E *EMP* 65
SIC 5074 5075 5031 5087 5085 Plumbing fittings & supplies; Air conditioning & ventilation equipment & supplies; Warm air heating equipment & supplies; Kitchen cabinets; Service establishment equipment; Tools; Plumbing fittings & supplies; Air conditioning & ventilation equipment & supplies; Warm air heating equipment & supplies; Kitchen cabinets; Service establishment equipment; Tools
Pr: Christopher H Lute
**Treas:* Jason C Lute
VP: Dave Fleming
**VP:* Brian Hancock
Brnch Mgr: Chris Shupert
Sls Mgr: Roger McKenzie
Sls Mgr: Bob Williams

LUTGERT COMPANIES
See SCOTTSDALE CO

D-U-N-S 10-626-4633
LUTH RESEARCH INC
SURVEYSAVVY.COM
1365 4th Ave, San Diego, CA 92101-4208
Tel (619) 234-5884 *Founded/Ownrshp* 1977
Sales 55.9MM^E *EMP* 335
SIC 8732 Market analysis or research; Market analysis or research
Pr: Roseanne Luth
**Ex VP:* Charles Rosen
VP: Marcos Gill
VP: Becky Wu
VP Bus Dev: Candice Rab
Mng Dir: Sean Miller
Snr Sftwr: Khoa Nguyen
QA Dir: Scott Hill
Web Dev: Alexandra Peak
Mktg Dir: Janeen Hazel
Sls Dir: Jason Chadwick

LUTHER ACRES MANOR
See LUTHERCARE

LUTHER BROOKDALE
See BROOKLYN CENTER MOTORS LLC

D-U-N-S 80-041-0602
LUTHER BURBANK CORP
816 4th St, Santa Rosa, CA 95404-4505
Tel (707) 523-9898 *Founded/Ownrshp* 2007
Sales 134.9MM^E *EMP* 134^E
SIC 8211 Elementary & secondary schools
CEO: George Mancini

D-U-N-S 04-110-0918
LUTHER COLLEGE
700 College Dr, Decorah, IA 52101-1041
Tel (563) 387-1372 *Founded/Ownrshp* 1865
Sales 80.2MM *EMP* 550
Accts Baker Tilly Virchow Krause Ll
SIC 8221 College, except junior; College, except junior
Pr: Paula J Carlson
**Pr:* Richard Torgerson
Trst: M Miller
**VP:* Pete Christensen
**VP:* Diane Tacke
Exec: Pam Torresdal
Ex Dir: Chris Barth
Ex Dir: Sheila Radford
Opers Supe: Marcia Jensen

LUTHER FAMILY FORD
See CC MOTORS LLC

D-U-N-S 78-794-8876
LUTHER HOLDING CO
3701 Alabama Ave S, Minneapolis, MN 55416-5156
Tel (763) 593-5755 *Founded/Ownrshp* 1989
Sales 243.8MM^E *EMP* 700
SIC 5511 7515 7513 6512 6552 5611 Automobiles, new & used; Pickups, new & used; Vans, new & used; Passenger car leasing; Truck leasing, without drivers; Commercial & industrial building operation; Subdividers & developers; Men's & boys' clothing stores; Automobiles, new & used; Pickups, new & used; Vans, new & used; Passenger car leasing; Truck leasing, without drivers; Commercial & industrial building operation; Subdividers & developers; Men's & boys' clothing stores
Pr: David Luther
**Pr:* R Daniel Luther
CFO: Barb Hillbert
**Treas:* C David Luther
VP: Mike Gallagher
Genl Mgr: Carlos Garcia
Dir IT: Brian Kenny
IT Man: Dan Johnson

D-U-N-S 08-456-7320
LUTHER HOME OF MERCY
WILLISTON LUTHER HOME OF MERCY
5810 N Main St, Williston, OH 43468
Tel (419) 836-3918 *Founded/Ownrshp* 1928
Sales 21.2MM *EMP* 499
Accts Gilmore Jasion & Mahler Ltd M
SIC 8052 Intermediate care facilities; Intermediate care facilities
Ex Dir: Rev Donald Wukotich
COO: Theresa Cousino
Dir IT: Mark Bly
HC Dir: Tony Lompis

D-U-N-S 84-180-1186
LUTHER HOSPITAL
HEALTHWORKS
733 W Clairemont Ave, Eau Claire, WI 54701-6101
Tel (715) 838-3060 *Founded/Ownrshp* 1986
Sales 230.8MM *EMP* 5
SIC 8011 Occupational & industrial specialist, physician/surgeon; Occupational & industrial specialist, physician/surgeon

D-U-N-S 09-704-7872
LUTHER KING CAPITAL MANAGEMENT CORP
301 Commerce St Ste 1600, Fort Worth, TX 76102-4190
Tel (817) 429-6256 *Founded/Ownrshp* 1979
Sales 676.9MM^E *EMP* 1,314
SIC 6282 Investment counselors; Investment counselors
Pr: John Luther King Jr
**COO:* Michael Yeager
**Treas:* Lisa Rettew
**VP:* David L Dowler
**VP:* Paul Greenwell
VP: John Gunthorp
VP: Craig Hester
**VP:* Scot C Hollmann
**VP:* Mark Johnson
**VP:* Bryan King
**VP:* Trisha Kroutil
**VP:* Jim Krrigan
VP: David Lehmann
**VP:* Allan Marshall
**VP:* Joan Maynard
VP: Greg McCoy
**VP:* Vince Melashenko
**VP:* Jim Orser
**VP:* Steve Purvis
**VP:* Jacob Smith
**VP:* Bill Uhlemeyer

LUTHER MANOR
See UNITED LUTHERAN PROGRAM FOR AGING INC

D-U-N-S 07-134-0608
LUTHER MIDELFORT MAYO HEALTH SYSTEM
733 W Clairemont Ave, Eau Claire, WI 54701-6101
Tel (715) 838-5353 *Founded/Ownrshp* 1992
Sales NA *EMP* 1,076
SIC 6324 8011 Health maintenance organization (HMO), insurance only; Clinic, operated by physicians; Health maintenance organization (HMO), insurance only; Clinic, operated by physicians
CEO: Randall Linton
Off Mgr: Betty Savall

D-U-N-S 01-458-5863
LUTHER P MILLER INC
641 S Edgewood Ave, Somerset, PA 15501-2560
Tel (814) 445-6569 *Founded/Ownrshp* 2001
Sales 25.0MM^E *EMP* 60
SIC 5171 5411 Petroleum bulk stations; Grocery stores, independent; Petroleum bulk stations; Grocery stores, independent
Ch: Alan Miller
**Pr:* Troy Miller
**Treas:* Lana Miller

D-U-N-S 07-817-0545
LUTHER SC SER OF METRO NY INC
LUTHERAN SOCIAL SERVICES NY
475 Riverside Dr Ste 1244, New York, NY 10115-0046
Tel (212) 870-1100 *Founded/Ownrshp* 1972
Sales 25.6MM^E *EMP* 400
SIC 8322 8361 Adoption services; Orphanage; Adoption services; Orphanage
Pr: Ronald S Drews
CFO: Paul H Crumb
**CFO:* John Heidgerd
VP: Christine Connell
Comm Dir: Sharon Ross
Off Admin: Muriel Edwards
Info Man: Gladys Wilds
Site Mgr: Teresa Outlaw-Johnson
Site Mgr: Lizette Singh
Pgrm Dir: Ayla Colella

D-U-N-S 02-295-2642
LUTHER WESTSIDE VOLKSWAGON INC
2370 Highway 100 S, Minneapolis, MN 55416-1703
Tel (952) 377-4100 *Founded/Ownrshp* 2002
Sales 30.0MM *EMP* 100
SIC 5511 Automobiles, new & used; Automobiles, new & used
Pr: David Luther
CFO: C Luther
Exec: Julie Hose
Exec: Kris Lamere
Genl Mgr: Steve Hendricks
Sls Mgr: Marc Carden
Sales Asso: Carole Anderson

LUTHERAN CARE
See KATHERINE LUTHER RESIDENTIAL HEALTH CARE & REHABILITATION CENTER INC

D-U-N-S 07-086-3501
LUTHERAN CARE CHARITABLE NETWORK INC
110 Utica Rd, Clinton, NY 13323-1548
Tel (315) 853-5515 *Founded/Ownrshp* 1972
Sales 10.0MM^E *EMP* 450
SIC 8051 Skilled nursing care facilities; Skilled nursing care facilities
Pr: Andrew Peterson

D-U-N-S 36-413-2480
LUTHERAN CARE MINISTRIES NETWORK INC
108 Utica Rd, Clinton, NY 13323-1548
Tel (315) 235-7104 *Founded/Ownrshp* 1998
Sales 15.4MM^E *EMP* 400
Accts Price Waterhouse & Coopers
SIC 8051 Skilled nursing care facilities; Skilled nursing care facilities
Pr: Andrew Peterson
MIS Dir: Rob Morehouse

D-U-N-S 02-212-7091
LUTHERAN CENTER AT POUGHKEEPSIE
965 Dutchess Tpke, Poughkeepsie, NY 12603-1551
Tel (845) 486-9494 *Founded/Ownrshp* 1995
Sales 23.4MM *EMP* 225
SIC 8361 Home for the aged; Home for the aged
CFO: Jonathan Immordino
VP: Debra Lipsen

D-U-N-S 07-867-5154
LUTHERAN CHARITY ASSOCIATION
JAMESTOWN HOSPITAL
2422 20th St Sw, Jamestown, ND 58401-6201
Tel (701) 252-1050 *Founded/Ownrshp* 1935
Sales 39.4MM *EMP* 230ᴱ
Accts Wipfli Llp Minneapolis Mn
SIC 8062 General medical & surgical hospitals; General medical & surgical hospitals
CFO: Brandon Vaughan
CFO: Alan Oneil
Exec: Ricki Ramlo
Dir OR: Carolyn Janssen
CIO: Sheri Schweitzer
CTO: Nicole Oster
MIS Dir: Jeremey Fehiele
Pr Dir: Jan Barnes
Surgeon: Michael Dean
Podiatrist: Manuel Harris

D-U-N-S 08-104-4786
LUTHERAN CHILD AND FAMILY SERVICES OF ILLINOIS
LCFS
7620 Madison St, River Forest, IL 60305-2193
Tel (708) 771-7180 *Founded/Ownrshp* 1873
Sales 31.9MM *EMP* 400
SIC 8322 Family (marriage) counseling; Child guidance agency; Adoption services; Family (marriage) counseling; Child guidance agency; Adoption services
Pr: Gene L Svebakken
**CFO:* Paul S Karl
**CFO:* Lynn Murakami
**VP:* Mike Bertrand
VP: Ann Ferguson
**VP:* Beverly Jones
**VP:* Dave Roth
Ex Dir: Craig Hjorth
Dir IT: Doug Cablk
Opers Supe: Maria Potter
Pr Dir: Deborah Al-Waraqi

D-U-N-S 06-855-0441
LUTHERAN CHURCH - MISSOURI SYNOD
1333 S Kirkwood Rd, Saint Louis, MO 63122-7226
Tel (314) 965-9000 *Founded/Ownrshp* 1847
Sales 145.2MM *EMP* 325ᴱ
Accts Brown Smith Wallace Llc St
SIC 8661 Lutheran Church; Lutheran Church
Pr: Matthew Harrison
Pr: Peter Meier
**COO:* Ron Schultz
**CFO:* Jerald Wulf
VP: Dorothy Kaestner
**VP:* Herbert Miller
Off Mgr: Diane Grimm

D-U-N-S 11-438-3461
LUTHERAN CHURCH-MISSOURI SYNOD
NEBRASKA LUTHERAN DISTRICT OFF
152 S Columbia Ave, Seward, NE 68434-2204
Tel (402) 643-2961 *Founded/Ownrshp* 1991
Sales 44.7MM *EMP* 14ᴱ
SIC 8661 Lutheran Church; Lutheran Church
Pr: Russell Sommerfeld
CFO: Paul Pettit

D-U-N-S 96-735-1599
LUTHERAN COMMUNITY AT TELFORD
12 Lutheran Home Dr, Telford, PA 18969-1728
Tel (215) 723-9819 *Founded/Ownrshp* 2011
Sales 20.8MM *EMP* 70ᴱ
Accts Kreischer Miller Horsham Pa
SIC 8361 Home for the aged; Home for the aged
Prin: Terry Colath

D-U-N-S 04-207-0701
LUTHERAN COMMUNITY FOUNDATION (MN)
625 4th Ave S Ste 1500, Minneapolis, MN 55415-1624
Tel (612) 844-4110 *Founded/Ownrshp* 1994
Sales 29.8MM *EMP* 15
SIC 8322 Social service center; Social service center
Pr: Chris D Andersen
Off Admin: Kelly Klukas

LUTHERAN COMMUNITY SERVICE
See INTERNATIONAL COUNSELING SERVICES

D-U-N-S 12-152-4099
LUTHERAN COMMUNITY SERVICES INC
LTHRN CMNTY SVCS SOUTHERN NENG
(*Suby of* ASCENTRIA CARE ALLIANCE) ★
14 E Worcester St Ste 300, Worcester, MA 01604-3612
Tel (774) 243-3900 *Founded/Ownrshp* 2001
Sales 29.7MM *EMP* 3ᴱ
SIC 8399 Community development groups; Community development groups
CEO: Angela Bovill
**Pr:* David Forsberg
**COO:* Dana Ramish
**CFO:* Lisa Cohen
**Treas:* Nick Russo
VP: Jodie Justofin
**VP:* Angela Wallilngford
**Prin:* Alana Geary

D-U-N-S 00-741-7702
LUTHERAN COMMUNITY SERVICES NORTHWEST
4040 S 188th St Ste 300, Seatac, WA 98188-5070
Tel (206) 816-3253 *Founded/Ownrshp* 1997
Sales 30.3MM *EMP* 520
Accts Clark Nuber Ps Bellevue Wa
SIC 8322 Adoption services; Adoption services
CEO: Roberta Nestaas
**CFO:* Kay Harvey
Ofcr: Jaime Schilling
**VP:* Richard Hutchins
Pgrm Dir: Michelle Madsen

D-U-N-S 08-441-6601
LUTHERAN COMMUNITY SERVICES NORTHWEST INC (OR)
605 Se Csar E Chavez Blvd, Portland, OR 97214-3216
Tel (503) 231-7480 *Founded/Ownrshp* 1926
Sales 26.3MM *EMP* 700
SIC 8322 Family service agency; Family service agency
CEO: Roberta Nestass
**COO:* Bruce Strade
CFO: John Hamilton
**CFO:* Kay Harvey
Off Mgr: Donna Grady
Sls&Mrk Ex: Kay Reed
HC Dir: Roberta Nestaas

D-U-N-S 09-855-9024
LUTHERAN COUMMUNITY SERVICES NORTH WEST
4040 S 188th St Ste 300, Seatac, WA 98188-5070
Tel (206) 901-1685 *Founded/Ownrshp* 1978
Sales 9.2MMᴱ *EMP* 420
Accts Clark Nuber Cpa Bellevue Wa
SIC 8322 Individual & family services; General counseling services; Adoption services; Crisis center; Individual & family services; General counseling services; Adoption services; Crisis center
Pr: Roberta Nestaas
**VP:* Kay Harvey

D-U-N-S 03-278-1148
LUTHERAN FAMILY SERVICES IN CAROLINAS
LUTHERAN SERVICES CAROLINAS
1416 S Martin Luther King, Salisbury, NC 28144-5592
Tel (919) 832-2620 *Founded/Ownrshp* 1976
Sales 14.6MM *EMP* 375
Accts Langdon & Company Llp Garner
SIC 8322 Family service agency; Family service agency
Pr: Ted Goins
VP: Ronald Rau
Ex Dir: Laura Benson
Ex Dir: Jeffrey Demagistris
Ex Dir: Ronnie Huffman

D-U-N-S 60-814-5199
LUTHERAN FAMILY SERVICES OF NEBRASKA INC
124 S 24th St Ste 230, Omaha, NE 68102-1226
Tel (402) 342-7038 *Founded/Ownrshp* 1895
Sales 19.9MM *EMP* 300
Accts Seim Johnson Llp Omaha Nebr
SIC 8322 General counseling services; General counseling services
Pr: Ruth Henrichs
COO: Kerry Kernen
**CFO:* Richard Henrichs
**VP:* Steve Peterson

D-U-N-S 19-799-1078
LUTHERAN FAMILY SERVICES OF VIRGINIA INC
HEALTH SERVICE/ HUMAN SERVICES
2609 Mcvitty Rd, Roanoke, VA 24018-3513
Tel (540) 774-7100 *Founded/Ownrshp* 1982
Sales 26.2MM *EMP* 160
Accts Cherry Bekaert & Holland Llp
SIC 8322 Adoption services; Child related social services; Family service agency; Adoption services; Child related social services; Family service agency
CEO: Julie Swanson
**Treas:* Pastor Jim Larsen
**VP:* Doris Cook

LUTHERAN GENERAL HEALTH PLAN
See LUTHERAN GENERAL HEALTH PRACTICE ORGANIZATION INC

D-U-N-S 19-623-9008
LUTHERAN GENERAL HEALTH PRACTICE ORGANIZATION INC
LUTHERAN GENERAL HEALTH PLAN
1661 Feehanville Dr # 200, Mount Prospect, IL 60056-6087
Tel (847) 298-6000 *Founded/Ownrshp* 1983
Sales NA *EMP* 75
SIC 6324 Hospital & medical service plans
**Pr:* Steven J King
**VP:* Lee B Sacks MD
Med Dir: Scott Sarran

D-U-N-S 60-331-2331
LUTHERAN GENERAL MEDICAL GROUP S C
1775 Dempster St Ste 10, Park Ridge, IL 60068-1143
Tel (847) 795-2800 *Founded/Ownrshp* 1906
Sales 55.0MMᴱ *EMP* 1,000
SIC 8093 Specialty outpatient clinics

D-U-N-S 62-067-9688
■ **LUTHERAN HEALTH NETWORK OF INDIANA LLC**
(*Suby of* QUORUM HEALTH RESOURCES LLC) ★
2123 Lincolnway Ct, Fort Wayne, IN 46819-2140
Tel (260) 479-3550 *Founded/Ownrshp* 2001
Sales 101.9MMᴱ *EMP* 1,060
SIC 6719 Investment holding companies, except banks; Investment holding companies, except banks
Pr: Brian Bauer
COO: Bernard A Niezer
Ofcr: Tracy Burdine
Ofcr: Thomas Pitzen
VP: Krista Quinones
Snr Ntwrk: Jason Whiteaker

LUTHERAN HOME, THE
See LUTHERAN HOME FOR AGED

D-U-N-S 08-233-9458
LUTHERAN HOME
2116 Dover Center Rd, Cleveland, OH 44145-3154
Tel (440) 871-0090 *Founded/Ownrshp* 1932
Sales 22.1MMᴱ *EMP* 280
SIC 8052 8051 Intermediate care facilities; Skilled nursing care facilities; Intermediate care facilities; Skilled nursing care facilities
CEO: Charles H Rinne
**COO:* Greg Wiechert
**CFO:* Carolyn Nyikes
VP: Rod Braye
Exec: Chris Hope
Dir Soc: Jamie Woods
IT Man: Matt Walling

D-U-N-S 80-964-5182
LUTHERAN HOME ALBEMARLE PROPERTY INC
24724 S Business 52, Albemarle, NC 28001-8179
Tel (704) 982-8191 *Founded/Ownrshp* 2004
Sales 219.1M *EMP* 1,000
Accts Langdon & Company Llp Garneer
SIC 6531 Real estate managers; Real estate managers
CEO: Ted W Goins Jr
**Treas:* Annette S Conrad

D-U-N-S 08-869-1324
LUTHERAN HOME ASSOCIATION
337 S Meridian St, Belle Plaine, MN 56011-1919
Tel (414) 256-3888 *Founded/Ownrshp* 1898
Sales 3.2MM *EMP* 550
SIC 8059 8322 8082 Nursing home, except skilled & intermediate care facility; Home for the mentally retarded, exc. skilled or intermediate; Social services for the handicapped; Adult day care center; Home health care services
Pr: Michael R Klatt
IT Man: Doyle Voss

D-U-N-S 06-990-0918
LUTHERAN HOME AT MOORESTOWN INC
255 E Main St, Moorestown, NJ 08057-2999
Tel (856) 235-1214 *Founded/Ownrshp* 1946
Sales 20.7MM *EMP* 300
Accts Parentebeard Llc Philadelphia
SIC 8051 8361 8052 Skilled nursing care facilities; Geriatric residential care; Intermediate care facilities; Skilled nursing care facilities; Geriatric residential care; Intermediate care facilities

LUTHERAN HOME FOR THE AGED
See LUTHERAN LIFE COMMUNITIES

D-U-N-S 08-439-8601
LUTHERAN HOME FOR AGED
LUTHERAN HOME, THE
2825 Bloomfield Rd, Cape Girardeau, MO 63703-6398
Tel (573) 986-6341 *Founded/Ownrshp* 1967
Sales 19.0MM *EMP* 500
Accts The Luthern Home For The Aged
SIC 8051 8059 Skilled nursing care facilities; Nursing home, except skilled & intermediate care facility; Skilled nursing care facilities; Nursing home, except skilled & intermediate care facility

D-U-N-S 05-432-1823
LUTHERAN HOME FOR AGED INC
800 W Oakton St, Arlington Heights, IL 60004-4600
Tel (847) 253-3710 *Founded/Ownrshp* 1892
Sales 51.2MM *EMP* 700
SIC 8051 8052 8059

D-U-N-S 07-893-1748
LUTHERAN HOME INC
7500 W North Ave, Milwaukee, WI 53213-1717
Tel (414) 258-4192 *Founded/Ownrshp* 1906
Sales 23.4MM *EMP* 515
SIC 8051 Skilled nursing care facilities; Skilled nursing care facilities
Pr: Marina Rosenberg
CFO: Brian Blank
CFO: Richard Love
**Treas:* Mark S Krueger
**Ex VP:* Paul A Schreiber
VP: Mary Swoboda
IT Man: Mary Shimek
Nrsg Dir: Kerri Livermore
HC Dir: Rebecca Kloss

LUTHERAN HOME-RIVER FALLS
See WISCONSIN LUTHERAN HOME MINISTRIES INC

D-U-N-S 07-432-6208
LUTHERAN HOMES INC
6701 S Anthony Blvd, Fort Wayne, IN 46816-2035
Tel (260) 447-0800 *Founded/Ownrshp* 1978
Sales 11.2MM *EMP* 450
Accts Bkd Llp Fort Wayne In
SIC 8051 8052 Extended care facility; Intermediate care facilities; Extended care facility; Intermediate care facilities
CEO: Alex Kiefer
**Pr:* Mark Franke
CFO: Donna Scanlon
**Treas:* Nate Fink
**VP:* Troy Panning
**VP:* Lisa Troxel
**Ex Dir:* Rev Dwight Anderson
Off Mgr: Karl Kostoff
IT Man: Greg Ernest
Nrsg Dir: Sarah Knight
Nrsg Dir: Sarah Merriman

D-U-N-S 06-151-6688
LUTHERAN HOMES OF MICHIGAN INC
LUTHERAN HOMES OF MONROE
9710 Junction Rd, Frankenmuth, MI 48734-9502
Tel (989) 652-3470 *Founded/Ownrshp* 1893
Sales 34.8MM *EMP* 900
Accts Plante & Moran Pllc Southfiel
SIC 8051 8322 8082 Extended care facility; Old age assistance; Home health care services; Extended care facility; Old age assistance; Home health care services
Pr: David M Gehm
COO: Linda Reinbold
VP Opers: Robert Rice
Snr Mgr: Todd Seibt

LUTHERAN HOMES OF MONROE
See LUTHERAN HOMES OF MICHIGAN INC

D-U-N-S 09-302-6391
LUTHERAN HOMES OF OCONOMOWOC INC
SHOREHAVEN HEALTH CENTER
1305 W Wisconsin Ave, Oconomowoc, WI 53066-2646
Tel (262) 567-8341 *Founded/Ownrshp* 1939
Sales 18.4MM *EMP* 360
SIC 8051 6513 Skilled nursing care facilities; Retirement hotel operation; Skilled nursing care facilities; Retirement hotel operation
Ex Dir: Tim Thiele
Off Mgr: Donna Grugel
IT Man: Ed Somers
Manager: Butch Gartzke
Doctor: Martin Crull

D-U-N-S 07-614-7818
LUTHERAN HOMES OF OSHKOSH INC
225 N Eagle St, Oshkosh, WI 54902-4125
Tel (920) 235-3454 *Founded/Ownrshp* 1963
Sales 5.0MM *EMP* 350
Accts Larsonallen Llp Minneapolis
SIC 8051 6513 Skilled nursing care facilities; Apartment building operators; Skilled nursing care facilities; Apartment building operators
Pr: Craig Ubbelohde
**VP:* Allen Abraham
VP: Gerard Bodalski

D-U-N-S 96-915-1823
LUTHERAN HOMES OF SOUTH CAROLINA INC
300 Ministry Dr, Irmo, SC 29063-2366
Tel (803) 749-5110 *Founded/Ownrshp* 2011
Sales 70.7MM *EMP* 58ᴱ
Accts Cliftonlarsonallen Llp Charlo
SIC 8661 Lutheran Church; Lutheran Church
Prin: Melissa Yetter
CFO: Deedee White
Trst: Richard Campbell
VP: Robert Coon
VP: Denise Dickinsen
Exec: Lynnette Webb

LUTHERAN HOSPITAL
See LUTHERAN MEDICAL CENTER (INC)

LUTHERAN HOSPITAL - LA CROSSE
See GUNDERSEN LUTHERAN MEDICAL CENTER INC

D-U-N-S 08-527-7044
LUTHERAN HOSPITAL ASSOCIATION OF SAN LUIS VALLEY
SAN LUIS VLY REGIONAL MED CTR
106 Blanca Ave, Alamosa, CO 81101-2340
Tel (719) 589-2511 *Founded/Ownrshp* 1928
Sales 21.3MMᴱ *EMP* 380
Accts Bkd Llp Colorado Springs Co
SIC 8062 General medical & surgical hospitals; General medical & surgical hospitals
Ch Bd: Robert Hagadorn
Chf Rad: Edward Carter
Pr: Svetlana Bresnitz
**CEO:* Konnie Martin
Treas: Russell Achatz
Trst: Karla Hardesty
Trst: Kendal Knaus
Dir Risk M: Leonard Snow
Dir Lab: Mary Rice
CIO: Chuck Laufle
Dir IT: Margie Clemmer

LUTHERAN HOSPITAL OF INDIANA
See IOM HEALTH SYSTEM LP

D-U-N-S 02-429-8938
■ **LUTHERAN HOSPITAL OF INDIANA LP**
(*Suby of* COMMUNITY HEALTH SYSTEMS INC) ★
7950 W Jefferson Blvd, Fort Wayne, IN 46804-4160
Tel (260) 479-3434 *Founded/Ownrshp* 2009
Sales 35.0MMᴱ *EMP* 5,000
SIC 8062 General medical & surgical hospitals
CEO: Byan Bauer

LUTHERAN HOUR MINISTRIES
See INTERNATIONAL LUTHERAN LAYMENS LEAGUE

D-U-N-S 61-792-5789
LUTHERAN IMMIGRATION & REFUGEE SERVICE
700 Light St, Baltimore, MD 21230-3850
Tel (410) 230-2700 *Founded/Ownrshp* 1940
Sales 50.3MM *EMP* 75
SIC 8322 Individual & family services
VP: Annie Wilson
**Pr:* Linda Hartke
VP: Susan Krehbiel
CIO: Bill Bisbee
CTO: Kim Lehner
IT Man: Jane Anthon
IT Man: Deborah Flavin

D-U-N-S 16-449-4291
LUTHERAN LIFE COMMUNITIES
LUTHERAN HOME FOR THE AGED
800 W Oakton St, Arlington Heights, IL 60004-4602
Tel (847) 368-7400 *Founded/Ownrshp* 1984
Sales 55.6MMᴱ *EMP* 1,200
SIC 8052 Intermediate care facilities; Intermediate care facilities
CEO: Roger Paulsberg
CEO: Tim Leone
CFO: Carl Moellenkamp
HC Dir: Marlette Borland
HC Dir: Deanna Orsi

LUTHERAN MEDICAL CENTER
See SHORE PARK PROPERTIES INC

D-U-N-S 07-690-3129
LUTHERAN MEDICAL CENTER (INC)
LUTHERAN HOSPITAL
(*Suby of* CLEVELAND CLINIC FOUNDATION) ★
1730 W 25th St, Cleveland, OH 44113-3108
Tel (216) 696-4300 *Founded/Ownrshp* 1895
Sales 91.9MM *EMP* 800
SIC 8062 8011 8069 General medical & surgical hospitals; Offices & clinics of medical doctors; Specialty hospitals, except psychiatric; General medical & surgical hospitals; Offices & clinics of medical doctors; Specialty hospitals, except psychiatric
CEO: David Pesre MD
Dir Recs: Pat Koch

*CFO: Christopher Winters
Dir OR: Amyu Boone
Dir Case M: Cathleen Lawley
Off Mgr: Virginia R Tipton
Doctor: Leslie J Gilbert MD
Doctor: Michelle Rader
Diag Rad: J Bradley Burns
Diag Rad: Howard S Cahn
Diag Rad: Andrea L Desberg

D-U-N-S 10-175-2137
LUTHERAN RETIREMENT MINISTRIES OF ALAMANCE COUNTY NORTH CAROLINA
TWIN LAKES CENTER
3701 Wade Coble Dr, Burlington, NC 27215-9743
Tel (336) 538-1400 Founded/Ownrshp 1983
Sales 25.8MM EMP 291
Accts Gilliam Coble & Moser Llp Bur
SIC 8051 8052 8059 Skilled nursing care facilities; Intermediate care facilities; Rest home, with health care; Skilled nursing care facilities; Intermediate care facilities; Rest home, with health care
*CFO: Jennings Chandler II

D-U-N-S 07-502-3663
LUTHERAN SENIOR CITY INC
LUTHERAN VILLAGE COURTYARD
(Suby of LUTHERAN SOCIAL SERVICES OF CENTRAL OHIO) ★
935 N Cassady Ave, Columbus, OH 43219-2283
Tel (614) 228-5200 Founded/Ownrshp 1962
Sales 13.2MM EMP 300
SIC 8051 Skilled nursing care facilities; Skilled nursing care facilities
Ch: Rev Thomas Hudson
*Pr: Larry Crowell
*CFO: Phil Helser
CIO: Thomas Stofac
DP Exec: Terry Beichtel

D-U-N-S 16-027-8776
LUTHERAN SENIOR SERVICES
1600 S Brentwd Blvd # 300, Saint Louis, MO 63144-1307
Tel (314) 968-9313 Founded/Ownrshp 1985
Sales 183.2MM EMP 2,254
Accts Cliftonlarsonallen Llp St Lo
SIC 8361 Geriatric residential care; Geriatric residential care
Pr: John Kotovsky
Pr: Carla Baum
Pr: Michael Raso
COO: Jake Bell
*COO: Linda M Detring
*CFO: Paul Ogier
CFO: Gary Winchell
CFO: Gary M Winschel
CFO: Gary Winshel
Ofcr: Ellen Harmon
VP: Gary Anderson
VP: Lea A Coates
VP: Linda Detring
VP: Sue Duncan
VP: Mary Lazare
Exec: Renee Brumfield
Dir Soc: Sally Best
Creative D: Kathi Bell

D-U-N-S 15-375-5517
LUTHERAN SENIORLIFE
191 Scharberry Ln, Mars, PA 16046-2429
Tel (724) 776-1100 Founded/Ownrshp 1986
Sales 7.7MM EMP 800^E
Accts Baker Tilly Virchow Krause Llp
SIC 8741 Hospital management; Nursing & personal care facility management; Hospital management; Nursing & personal care facility management
Pr: V Gregory Hughes
*CFO: Susan Q Digirolamo
*Sr VP: Barbara Marte
*VP: David Hamm
VP: Renee Pekor
VP: Donna Vankirk
*Prin: David Fenoglietto
*Prin: Renee M Pekor
Ex Dir: Karen Russell
Natl Sales: George McWilliams

LUTHERAN SERVICES CAROLINAS
See LUTHERAN FAMILY SERVICES IN CAROLINAS

D-U-N-S 13-967-6936
LUTHERAN SERVICES FLORIDA INC
3627a W Waters Ave, Tampa, FL 33614-2783
Tel (813) 868-4438 Founded/Ownrshp 1982
Sales 150.8MM EMP 565
Accts Lewis Birch & Ricardo Llc C
SIC 8322 Social service center; Social service center
Pr: Samuel M Sipes
*Pr: Christopher J Card
Ofcr: Angie Henderson
VP: Angela W Combs
VP: Afinney MPA
*VP: Michael Seeraj
*VP: George Wallace
*VP: David Yarborough
Ex Dir: Fred Tausig
Prgrm Mgr: Marcia Thompson
Prgrm Mgr: Audrey Williams

D-U-N-S 07-106-3077
LUTHERAN SERVICES FOR AGING INC
1416 S Martin Luther, Salisbury, NC 28144
Tel (704) 637-2870 Founded/Ownrshp 1960
Sales 75.6MM EMP 1,400
Accts Langdon & Company Llp Garner
SIC 8051 8052 8059 Convalescent home with continuous nursing care; Intermediate care facilities; Rest home, with health care; Convalescent home with continuous nursing care; Intermediate care facilities; Rest home, with health care
Pr: Ted W Grins Jr
*CFO: Kirby Nickerson
VP: Ted Hakala

D-U-N-S 08-712-4665
LUTHERAN SERVICES IN IOWA INC
LUTHERAN SOCIAL SERVICES
3125 Cottage Grove Ave, Des Moines, IA 50311-3809
Tel (515) 271-7333 Founded/Ownrshp 1939
Sales 34.7MM EMP 800
SIC 8322 Individual & family services; Individual & family services
Pr: Doug Johnson
*VP: Micheal Bucks

D-U-N-S 07-144-6041
LUTHERAN SERVICES NORTHEAST
(Suby of DIAKON LUTHERAN SOCIAL MINISTRIES) ★
1 S Home Ave, Topton, PA 19562-1317
Tel (610) 682-2145 Founded/Ownrshp 2001
Sales 16.2MM^E EMP 700
SIC 8361 8082 8322 Home for the aged; Home health care services; Adoption services; Child related social services; Meal delivery program; Family counseling services; Home for the aged; Home health care services; Adoption services; Child related social services; Meal delivery program; Family counseling services
Pr: Rev Daun E McKee PHD

D-U-N-S 96-735-2167
LUTHERAN SOCIAL MINISTRIES AT CRANES MILL INC
3 Manhattan Dr, Burlington, NJ 08016-4119
Tel (609) 386-7171 Founded/Ownrshp 2011
Sales 28.2MM EMP 2
Accts Parentebeard Llc Philadelphia
SIC 8322 Individual & family services; Individual & family services
CEO: Roger Arnholt

D-U-N-S 07-548-1846
LUTHERAN SOCIAL MINISTRIES OF NEW JERSEY INC
3 Manhattan Dr, Burlington, NJ 08016-4119
Tel (609) 386-7171 Founded/Ownrshp 1904
Sales 92.5MM EMP 650
Accts Parentebeard Llc Philadelphia
SIC 8322 8361 Social service center; Rest home, with health care incidental; Social service center; Rest home, with health care incidental
Pr: Jerry Nugent
*CFO: Francis J Kardos
Exec: Jennifer Larocca

D-U-N-S 07-972-8721
LUTHERAN SOCIAL SERVICE OF MINNESOTA (MN)
2485 Como Ave, Saint Paul, MN 55108-1469
Tel (651) 642-5990 Founded/Ownrshp 1865
Sales 89.3MM EMP 2,300
Accts Cliftonlarsonallen Llp Minnea
SIC 8322 Individual & family services; Individual & family services
CEO: Jodi Harpstead
*Pr: Mark A Peterson
*CFO: Ken Borle
*CFO: Patrick Thueson
*VP: Joyce Norals
Comm Man: Jacqueline Nelson
Prgrm Mgr: Gwendolyn Dunkin
Prgrm Mgr: Jen Fairbourne
Prgrm Mgr: Lynn Gerlach-Collard
Prgrm Mgr: Tara Giese
Prgrm Mgr: Duncan Gregory

LUTHERAN SOCIAL SERVICES
See SPIRITRUST LUTHERAN

LUTHERAN SOCIAL SERVICES
See LUTHERAN SERVICES IN IOWA INC

D-U-N-S 07-404-2433
LUTHERAN SOCIAL SERVICES FOUNDATION OF UPSTATE NEWYORK INC
715 Falconer St, Jamestown, NY 14701-1935
Tel (716) 665-4905 Founded/Ownrshp 1886
Sales 2.3MM EMP 600
SIC 8361 Children's home; Rest home, with health care incidental; Residential care for the handicapped; Children's home; Rest home, with health care incidental; Residential care for the handicapped
Ch: Eric Livengood
*Pr: Thomas E Holt
*Treas: Wiliam Myott
Prgrm Mgr: Samantha Vanstrom
Telecom Ex: Carolyn Murray
CIO: Rick Shick
MIS Mgr: Jonathan Price
Mktg Mgr: Patty Eckwahl
Board of Directors: Isabelle Jackson, Paul Sandberg, Norma Anderson, Herbert Larson, Doreen Sixbey, Pauline Bouckhuyt, J Eric Livengood, John Bylund, Timothy Magnuson, Jon Castle, Dr Lee M Miller, Roger Edborg, Marshall Nelson, Michael Goldman, Durand Peterson, Rev Wesley Hamlin, Karen Rine, Frederick Heft, Juliet Rosch, Richard Holt, Raymond Samuelson

D-U-N-S 82-998-3787
LUTHERAN SOCIAL SERVICES HOUSING INC
3911 20th Ave S, Fargo, ND 58103-4719
Tel (701) 271-3207 Founded/Ownrshp 2009
Sales 9.0MM EMP 360
Accts Eide Bailly Llp Fargo Nd
SIC 8322 6513 Individual & family services; Apartment building operators; Individual & family services; Apartment building operators
Pr: Jessica Thomasson
*CEO: Robert Sanderson
*CFO: Joan Penner
Sr VP: Janell Regimbal

LUTHERAN SOCIAL SERVICES NY
See LUTHER SC SER OF METRO NY INC

D-U-N-S 12-320-0214
LUTHERAN SOCIAL SERVICES OF CENTRAL OHIO
500 W Wilson Bridge Rd, Worthington, OH 43085-2238
Tel (419) 289-3523 Founded/Ownrshp 1914
Sales 42.2MM EMP 500
Accts Plante & Moran Pllc Columbus
SIC 8322 Outreach program; Outreach program
Pr: Larry Crowell
CFO: Dan Damon
*CFO: Philip D Helser
*VP: Rose Craig
*VP: Rick Davis
*VP: Heather McCracken
Comm Dir: Jennifer Hamilton
Ex Dir: Susan Villilo
Off Mgr: Denise Horn
QA Dir: Marilyn Justice
Dir IT: Terry Betchel

D-U-N-S 07-685-5626
LUTHERAN SOCIAL SERVICES OF ILLINOIS
1001 E Touhy Ave Ste 50, Des Plaines, IL 60018-5817
Tel (847) 635-4600 Founded/Ownrshp 1965
Sales 97.7MM EMP 2,014
Accts Baker Tilly Virchow Krause Llp
SIC 8322 6514 6513 Social service center; Senior citizens' center or association; Social services for the handicapped; Dwelling operators, except apartments; Apartment building operators; Social service center; Senior citizens' center or association; Social services for the handicapped; Dwelling operators, except apartments; Apartment building operators
CEO: Mark A Stutrud
Dir Vol: Diane Bergquist
V Ch: Paul Olson
*Pr: Rev Frederick Aigner
*CFO: Gerald E Noonan
CFO: Gerald Noonan
Ofcr: Mary Jensen
*VP: Susan E Gregory
*VP: Gean M Johnson
VP: Larry Lutey
VP: David Novak
Exec: Wanda Sabbs
Dir Soc: Megan Condon

D-U-N-S 06-984-0817
LUTHERAN SOCIAL SERVICES OF MICHIGAN
8131 E Jefferson Ave, Detroit, MI 48214-2691
Tel (313) 823-7700 Founded/Ownrshp 1934
Sales 101.5MM EMP 1,250
Accts Bdo Usa Llp Grand Rapids Mi
SIC 8051 8322 Skilled nursing care facilities; Individual & family services; Skilled nursing care facilities; Individual & family services
Pr: Mark Stutrud
*CFO: Gerald Benjamin
VP: Dave Barcus
*VP: Jerald W Benjamin
*VP: Sean De Four
*VP: Robert Louis
*VP: Vickie Thompson
Comm Dir: Barbara Lewis
Prgrm Mgr: Trish Harris
Off Mgr: Patty McKenna
Dir IT: Frank Sellgren

D-U-N-S 13-257-0219
LUTHERAN SOCIAL SERVICES OF NORTH DAKOTA
3911 20th Ave S Ste A, Fargo, ND 58103-4799
Tel (701) 235-7341 Founded/Ownrshp 1936
Sales 43.4MM EMP 325
Accts Eide Bailly Llp Fargo Nd
SIC 8322 Geriatric social service; Geriatric social service
VP: Jessica Thomasson
*CEO: Robert Sanderson
*CFO: Joan Penner
*Sr VP: Janell Regimbal
*VP: Mary J Weiler
Telecom Ex: Mark Chamberlain

D-U-N-S 04-410-8785
LUTHERAN SOCIAL SERVICES OF NORTHEAST FLORIDA INC
4615 Phillips Hwy, Jacksonville, FL 32207-7265
Tel (904) 448-5995 Founded/Ownrshp 1979
Sales 30.0MM EMP 100
Accts Lba Certified Public Accountan
SIC 8322 Family service agency; Refugee service; Multi-service center; Family service agency; Refugee service; Multi-service center
CEO: R Wayne Rieley
*COO: Paul Bussell
*VP: Jeanne Maszy
*Prin: Marie Friedsam

D-U-N-S 04-237-4876
LUTHERAN SOCIAL SERVICES OF SOUTH DAKOTA
705 E 41st St Ste 200, Sioux Falls, SD 57105-6048
Tel (605) 357-0100 Founded/Ownrshp 1920
Sales 21.2MM EMP 300
Accts Eide Bailly Llp Sioux Falls
SIC 8322 Social service center; Social service center
Pr: Betty Oldenkamp
*Pr: Joanne E Negstad
*VP: Steve Anderson
VP: Rebecca Knudsen
VP: Bill Peterson
VP: Heidi Schultz
*VP: Tom Walsh
Ex Dir: Shireen Ranschau
IT Man: Nathan Beyer

D-U-N-S 06-945-8149
LUTHERAN SOCIAL SERVICES OF SOUTH INC (TX)
8305 Cross Park Dr, Austin, TX 78754-5154
Tel (512) 454-4611 Founded/Ownrshp 1926
Sales 62.6MM EMP 784
Accts Holtzman Partners Llp Austin
SIC 8051 8361 8322 Convalescent home with continuous nursing care; Residential care; Child related social services; Convalescent home with continuous nursing care; Residential care; Child related social services
CEO: Kurt Senske
*Pr: Betsy Guthrie
*Pr: Sam Sipes
*CFO: Michael Loo
*Sr VP: David Kahle
*Sr VP: Mark Minick
VP: Scott Carroll
IT Man: Mary Castillo
IT Man: Rex Davila

D-U-N-S 14-901-8905
LUTHERAN SOCIAL SERVICES OF SOUTHWEST
10201 S 51st St Ste 180, Phoenix, AZ 85044-5235
Tel (520) 748-2300 Founded/Ownrshp 1970
Sales 12.8MM EMP 450
Accts Lumbard & Associates Pllc Ph
SIC 8661 Churches, temples & shrines; Churches, temples & shrines
CEO: Charles E Monroe
VP: Carol Ybarra

D-U-N-S 06-046-0730
LUTHERAN SOCIAL SERVICES OF WISCONSIN AND UPPER MICHIGAN INC
647 W Virginia St Ste 200, Milwaukee, WI 53204-1535
Tel (262) 896-3446 Founded/Ownrshp 1882
Sales 56.5MM EMP 2,300
Accts Baker Tilly Virchow Krause Llp
SIC 8322 8082 Social service center; Home health care services; Social service center; Home health care services
Pr: David N Larson
Ofcr: Walt Zimmermann
Ex VP: Larry Lutey
VP: Christy Brown
VP: Edward Cole
Prgrm Mgr: Gregory Duncan
Genl Mgr: Renee Devine
Dir IT: James Fisher
Dir IT: Daniel Mertz
IT Man: Amanda Holland

D-U-N-S 80-286-3852
LUTHERAN TRUST INC
(Suby of GUIDEONE INC) ★
1500 Wall St, Saint Charles, MO 63303-3500
Tel (636) 724-3418 Founded/Ownrshp 2000
Sales NA EMP 62
SIC 6411 Insurance agents, brokers & service; Insurance agents, brokers & service
Pr: Jan Beckstrom
VP: Lorri Cowger
VP: Bill Deyke
Sales Exec: Kermit Starnes
VP Mktg: Kim Fielder

D-U-N-S 10-234-8315
LUTHERAN UNIVERSITY ASSOCIATION INC
VALPARAISO UNIVERSITY
1700 Chapel Dr, Valparaiso, IN 46383-4520
Tel (219) 464-5000 Founded/Ownrshp 1925
Sales 144.1MM^E EMP 1,000
SIC 8221 University; University
Pr: Mark A Heckler
COO: Donna Patterson
CFO: Charley Gillispie
Assoc VP: Kerry Hutchinson
Assoc VP: Jason Petrovich
VP: Gillispie Charley
*VP: Charley E Gillispie
VP: Bonnie Hunter
VP: Michael Joseph
VP: Chelsea Kiehl
Exec: Laurie Eberhardt
Assoc Dir: Jill Clark
Assoc Dir: Bart Harvey
Assoc Dir: Kristi Rensberger

LUTHERAN VILLAGE COURTYARD
See LUTHERAN SENIOR CITY INC

D-U-N-S 79-903-5613
LUTHERAN WORLD RELIEF INC
700 Light St, Baltimore, MD 21230-3850
Tel (410) 230-2800 Founded/Ownrshp 1945
Sales 45.1MM EMP 40
Accts Mcgladrey Llp Baltimore Mary
SIC 8322 Individual & family services; Individual & family services
Pr: Daniel V Speckhard
VP: Kevin Sanderson
VP: Cherri Waters
Prin: Joann Theys
Ex Dir: Rafael Padilla
Ex Dir: MAI Pham
IT Man: Hugh Wiegel

D-U-N-S 07-119-2405
LUTHERCARE (PA)
LUTHER ACRES MANOR
600 E Main St, Lititz, PA 17543-2299
Tel (717) 626-1171 Founded/Ownrshp 1949
Sales 49.9MM EMP 500
Accts Parentebeard Llc Lancaster P
SIC 8052 8361 8051 Personal care facility; Residential care; Skilled nursing care facilities; Personal care facility; Residential care; Skilled nursing care facilities
Pr: Carl R McAloose
*Ch: Robert A Brandt Jr
*Treas: William Kiely
Ofcr: Lisa Garman
*VP: Beth Brennan
VP: Elizabeth Brennan
*VP: Blake S Daub
*VP: Curtis B Evans
*VP: William C Snyder
Comm Man: Amy Kenn
Ex Dir: Stacy Lewis

LUTHERN AFFILIATED SERVICES
See PASSAVANT RETIREMENT & HEALTH CENTER

D-U-N-S 17-764-8482 EXP
LUTHERS BAR-B-Q INC
2611 Cypress Creek Pkwy, Houston, TX 77068-3731
Tel (281) 537-8895 *Founded/Ownrshp* 1975
Sales 14.1MM^E *EMP* 800
Accts Coopers & Lybrand Llp Houston
SIC 5812 Barbecue restaurant; Barbecue restaurant
Pr: Mike Jolley
CFO: Kirby Gorton
Rgnl Mgr: Laurie A Johnson
Genl Mgr: Brandon Acres

D-U-N-S 07-175-6530
LUTHERS RUDY GMC TRUCK & MOTOR HOME CENTER INC
RUDY LUTHER TOYOTA
(*Suby of* LUTHER HOLDING CO) ★
8805 Wayzata Blvd, Golden Valley, MN 55426-1397
Tel (763) 544-4450 *Founded/Ownrshp* 1974
Sales 29.4MM^E *EMP* 75
SIC 5511 Automobiles, new & used; Pickups, new & used; Automobiles, new & used; Pickups, new & used
Pr: Luke Luther
Genl Mgr: Mark Beithon
Genl Mgr: Monte Bion
Sls Mgr: Miranda Guptill
Sales Asso: Anastasia Albert
Sales Asso: Jay Bernards
Sales Asso: Lon Blumenberg
Sales Asso: Kurt Daugherty
Sales Asso: Bill Devries
Sales Asso: Rich Eiss
Sales Asso: Michael Gallob

LUTHI MACHINERY COMPANY
See ATLAS PACIFIC ENGINEERING CO

D-U-N-S 00-239-0912 EXP
LUTRON ELECTRONICS CO INC (PA)
7200 Suter Rd, Coopersburg, PA 18036-1249
Tel (610) 282-3800 *Founded/Ownrshp* 1959
Sales 569.4MM^E *EMP* 1,500^E
SIC 3625 Control equipment, electric; Control equipment, electric
Ch Bd: Susan Hakkarainen
**Pr:* Michael W Pessina
CFO: Frank Parrillo
VP: Stephanie Deutsch
VP: Gail Jancsics
VP: Paul Lobo
**VP:* John Longenderfer
VP: Oscar Mendez
**VP:* Walter S Peake
Exec: Eric Lind
Exec: Mark Rose

D-U-N-S 82-977-7999
LUTRON SERVICES CO INC
(*Suby of* LUTRON ELECTRONICS CO INC) ★
7200 Suter Rd, Coopersburg, PA 18036-1249
Tel (610) 282-3800 *Founded/Ownrshp* 1992
Sales 23.6MM^E *EMP* 99
SIC 8744 1799 Facilities support services; Bowling alley installation
Owner: Joel Spira
**Pr:* Michael W Pessina
Sec: Mollissa Reid
**Prin:* Ruth Spira
Rgnl Mgr: Brenden Van Kamp
Dist Mgr: Rob Roland
Sftwr Eng: Brian Pinto
Sfty Dirs: Scott Fatzinger
Opers Mgr: Todd Spangler
Prd Mgr: Conrad Wiederman
Manager: Drew Vaughn

D-U-N-S 09-422-5166
LUTZ FREY CORP
1195 Ivy Dr, Lancaster, PA 17601-1123
Tel (717) 394-4635 *Founded/Ownrshp* 1997
Sales 39.0MM *EMP* 150
Accts Reinsel Kuntz Lesher Llp York
SIC 1711 1761 3446 3444 3441 Plumbing contractors; Warm air heating & air conditioning contractor; Sheet metalwork; Architectural metalwork; Sheet metalwork; Fabricated structural metal; Plumbing contractors; Warm air heating & air conditioning contractor; Sheet metalwork; Architectural metalwork; Sheet metalwork; Fabricated structural metal
CEO: Richard Donnelly Jr
**Pr:* Scott P Rhoads
**Treas:* Nancy Daub
**VP:* Robert W Wagner
IT Man: Phil Weaver

D-U-N-S 06-733-0415
LUTZ ROOFING CO INC
4721 22 Mile Rd, Shelby Township, MI 48317-1515
Tel (586) 739-1148 *Founded/Ownrshp* 1982
Sales 36.7MM *EMP* 150
SIC 1761 Roofing contractor; Roofing contractor
CEO: William Borgiel
VP Sls: Don Sekula

D-U-N-S 01-249-2761
LUTZ SURGICAL PARTNERS LLC
19105 N Us Highway 41 # 300, Lutz, FL 33549-4206
Tel (813) 866-1959 *Founded/Ownrshp* 2007
Sales 27.3MM^E *EMP* 12^E
SIC 8011 Surgeon
**VP:* Bruce Curran

D-U-N-S 10-892-6288
LUV N CARE LTD
NUBY
3030 Aurora Ave Ste 200, Monroe, LA 71201-7259
Tel (318) 388-4916 *Founded/Ownrshp* 1984
Sales 77.7MM^E *EMP* 400
SIC 5999 Infant furnishings & equipment; Infant furnishings & equipment
Pr: Joseph Hakim
**VP:* Jack Hakim
**Prin:* Edward Hakim

D-U-N-S 10-663-5055 IMP
LUVATA APPLETON LLC
553 Carter Ct, Kimberly, WI 54136-2201
Tel (920) 749-3820 *Founded/Ownrshp* 1965
Sales 27.1MM^E *EMP* 245
SIC 3351

D-U-N-S 00-701-5050
LUVATA ELECTROFIN TEXAS INC
(*Suby of* LUVATA OY)
1423 W Ormsby Ave, Louisville, KY 40210-1815
Tel (502) 634-9458 *Founded/Ownrshp* 1966
Sales 47.5MM^E *EMP* 200
SIC 2851 1799 7699 4953 3479 Paints & allied products; Corrosion control installation; Machinery cleaning; Industrial equipment cleaning; Hazardous waste collection & disposal; Refuse collection & disposal services; Coating of metals & formed products; Paints & allied products; Corrosion control installation; Machinery cleaning; Industrial equipment cleaning; Hazardous waste collection & disposal; Refuse collection & disposal services; Coating of metals & formed products
Pr: John Peter Leesi
**Pr:* Dennis Appel
**CFO:* Jyrki Vesaluoma
**Ex VP:* Mike Powell
**Ex VP:* Hannu Wahlroos
**Sr VP:* Bob Kickham
**Sr VP:* Justin Roux
Plnt Mgr: Pieter Keyzer

D-U-N-S 14-713-0058 IMP/EXP
LUVATA GRENADA LLC
(*Suby of* NORDIC CAPITAL SVENSKA AB)
3984 Highway 51 S, Grenada, MS 38901-9318
Tel (662) 226-3421 *Founded/Ownrshp* 2005
Sales 757.1MM^E *EMP* 4,000
SIC 3621 3585 Coils, for electric motors or generators; Refrigeration equipment, complete; Coils, for electric motors or generators; Refrigeration equipment, complete
Ch: John Peter Leesi
**Ch Bd:* Hannu Wahlroos
**Pr:* Dennis Appel
**CFO:* Ron Beal
**CFO:* Jyrki Vesaluoma
**Treas:* Scott Neece
VP: Mike Schwartz
Genl Mgr: Brenda Gleaton
IT Man: Dave Anderson
Opers Mgr: Kathy Brazil
Opers Mgr: Chris Wagner

D-U-N-S 60-408-1786 IMP
LUVATA WATERBURY INC
(*Suby of* AURUBIS BUFFALO INC) ★
2121 Thomaston Ave Ste 1, Waterbury, CT 06704-1037
Tel (203) 753-5215 *Founded/Ownrshp* 2012
Sales 58.0MM^E *EMP* 66
SIC 3357 Magnet wire, nonferrous; Magnet wire, nonferrous
Pr: James C Lajewski
Opers Mgr: Robert Schaedler

D-U-N-S 00-817-7685
LUVEL DAIRY PRODUCTS INC
(*Suby of* PRAIRIE FARMS DAIRY INC) ★
926 Veterans Memorial Dr, Kosciusko, MS 39090-3856
Tel (662) 289-2511 *Founded/Ownrshp* 2007
Sales 44.5MM^E *EMP* 225
SIC 2026 2024 Fluid milk; Ice cream & ice milk; Fluid milk; Ice cream & ice milk
Pr: James Briscoe
**Sec:* Charles Terry
**VP:* Richard Briscoe

LUVERNE S W M N FARMER'S CO-OP
See MAGNOLIA FARMERS CO-OPERATIVE ELEVATOR & LUMBER INC

D-U-N-S 00-621-8978 IMP
LUVERNE TRUCK EQUIPMENT INC (MN)
RE-TRAC
1200 E Birch St, Brandon, SD 57005-2001
Tel (605) 582-7200 *Founded/Ownrshp* 1963, 1979
Sales 36.6MM^E *EMP* 200
SIC 3714 3231 Motor vehicle parts & accessories; Bumpers & bumperettes, motor vehicle; Motor vehicle body components & frame; Ice scrapers & window brushes, motor vehicle; Mirrors, truck & automobile: made from purchased glass; Motor vehicle parts & accessories; Bumpers & bumperettes, motor vehicle; Motor vehicle body components & frame; Ice scrapers & window brushes, motor vehicle; Mirrors, truck & automobile: made from purchased glass
Pr: John Schulzetenberg
**Treas:* Shawn Mann
**VP:* Steve Lempelius
**VP:* Charles Madison
Exec: Maria Kelly
Dir IT: Sean Fields
Sls&Mrk Ex: Deb Wilson
Manager: John Joustra
Board of Directors: Ron Bach

LUX ACCESSORIES
See INTERNATIONAL INSPIRATIONS LTD

D-U-N-S 00-252-7067
LUX HOME INC (NJ)
PELLA WINDOWS & DOORS
4 Dedrick Pl, West Caldwell, NJ 07006-6303
Tel (973) 575-0200 *Founded/Ownrshp* 1953, 1993
Sales 50.7MM^E *EMP* 211
SIC 5031 Doors & windows; Doors & windows
Pr: David Sidman
**Sr VP:* Alan Wechsler
VP: Jack Goldman
Dir IT: Sharon Meshel

D-U-N-S 03-109-5912 IMP
LUXCO INC
DAVID SHERMAN
5050 Kemper Ave, Saint Louis, MO 63139-1106
Tel (314) 772-2626 *Founded/Ownrshp* 1958
Sales 43.9MM^E *EMP* 165^E
SIC 2085 5182 Distilled & blended liquors; Wine & distilled beverages; Distilled & blended liquors; Wine & distilled beverages
Pr: Donn Lux
**COO:* David Bratcher
COO: Eric Henning
**Ex VP:* Dan Streepy
**VP:* Steve Soucy
Dir IT: Amel Pasagic
Mktg Mgr: Sara Downard
Mktg Mgr: Ashley Ulkus
Sales Asso: Heather Leek

LUXFER GAS CYLINDER
See LUXFER INC

D-U-N-S 06-448-3704 IMP/EXP
LUXFER INC
LUXFER GAS CYLINDER
(*Suby of* BA HOLDINGS INC) ★
3016 Kansas Ave Bldg 1, Riverside, CA 92507-3445
Tel (336) 578-4515 *Founded/Ownrshp* 1973, 1996
Sales 88.8MM^E *EMP* 370
SIC 3728 3354 Aircraft parts & equipment; Shapes, extruded aluminum; Aircraft parts & equipment; Shapes, extruded aluminum
Pr: John Rhodes
Pr: Anthony Barnes
Ex VP: Michael J Reynolds
Sr VP: Hendy Holrowd
Sr VP: William Schuler
VP: Micheal Edwards
Exec: Andy Beaden
Mng Dir: David Rix
Genl Mgr: Kathy McDogall
Dir IT: John Dibble
IT Man: Richard Lintin

D-U-N-S 80-020-8949 EXP
LUXI GROUP LLC
545 Broadway Ste 3, Brooklyn, NY 11206-2962
Tel (212) 813-1111 *Founded/Ownrshp* 2007
Sales 21.9MM^E *EMP* 235^E
SIC 5712 5961 5944 Furniture stores; Catalog & mail-order houses; Watches; Furniture stores; Catalog & mail-order houses; Watches

D-U-N-S 02-140-3992
LUXOR GRAND LODGE 44 CROWN & SCEPTER GRAND CHAPTER OES
MODERN FREE NORTH CAROLINA
8735 Broomsage Ln Apt J, Charlotte, NC 28217-5861
Tel (704) 759-6430 *Founded/Ownrshp* 2007
Sales 11.7MM^E *EMP* 500
SIC 8641 Civic social & fraternal associations; Civic social & fraternal associations
VP: Harry Smith
**V Ch:* Steven Reese
**Pr:* Charles Griffin
**Treas:* Johnnie Tabron
**Trst:* Joyce Allen
**Trst:* Clara Spivey
**VP:* Jaye Goode

LUXOR HOTEL & CASINO
See RAMPARTS INC

LUXOTICA SERVICE CENTER
See LUXOTTICA RETAIL NORTH AMERICA INC

LUXOTTICA GROUP
See LUXOTTICA US HOLDINGS CORP

D-U-N-S 14-158-3190 IMP
LUXOTTICA RETAIL
SUNGLASS HUT
(*Suby of* LUXOTICA SERVICE CENTER) ★
4000 Luxottica Pl, Mason, OH 45040-8114
Tel (513) 765-6000 *Founded/Ownrshp* 2003
Sales 78.5MM^E *EMP* 229^E
SIC 5995 Eyeglasses, prescription
Prin: Carlo Priviteira
CFO: Steve Pattison
Ex VP: Frank A Bynhm
Sr VP: Mildred Curtis
VP: Rick Hayes
Exec: Jim Bettner
Ex Dir: Jim Ackner
Brnch Mgr: Ron Caruthers
Brnch Mgr: Susan Craib
Brnch Mgr: Mario Delacruz
Brnch Mgr: Trevor Denny

D-U-N-S 79-101-3642 IMP
LUXOTTICA RETAIL NORTH AMERICA INC
LUXOTICA SERVICE CENTER
(*Suby of* LUXOTTICA GROUP) ★
4000 Luxottica Pl, Mason, OH 45040-8114
Tel (513) 765-6000 *Founded/Ownrshp* 1998
Sales 1.9MMM^E *EMP* 14,000
SIC 5995 Optical goods stores; Optical goods stores
Prin: Thomas L Buehler
Pr: Larry Norton
COO: Frank Baynham
**COO:* Kerry Bradley
**CFO:* Jack Dennis
Assoc VP: Peter Grimes
Assoc VP: Jeanine McHugh
Ex VP: Tom Coleman
**Ex VP:* Valeric Giacobbi
Ex VP: Seth McLaughlin
Sr VP: Paula Donnelly
VP: Michael Braine
VP: John Decaprio
VP: Kathy Drury
**VP:* Vito Giannola
VP: Erwin Hinteregger
VP: Frank Kudlac
Exec: Mark Foutch

D-U-N-S 07-486-7966
LUXOTTICA US HOLDINGS CORP
LUXOTTICA GROUP
(*Suby of* LUXOTTICA GROUP SPA)
44 Harbor Park Dr, Port Washington, NY 11050-4652
Tel (516) 484-3800 *Founded/Ownrshp* 2003
Sales 2.7MMM^E *EMP* 35,000
SIC 5048 5099 5995 5999 Frames, ophthalmic; Lenses, ophthalmic; Sunglasses; Eyeglasses, prescription; Sunglasses; Frames, ophthalmic; Lenses, ophthalmic; Sunglasses; Eyeglasses, prescription; Sunglasses
CEO: Andrea Guerra
**Ch Bd:* Vito Giannola
Treas: Vito Giannnola
**Treas:* Vito Gianolla
Assoc VP: Emma Horn
Assoc VP: Jennifer Ziza
Ex VP: Andrea Dorigo
Ex VP: Pierre Fay
Sr VP: Luca Biondolillo
Sr VP: Uguzzoni Fabrizio
Sr VP: Jack Roddy
Sr VP: Holly Rush
**VP:* Michael Boxer
VP: Jack Dampier
VP: Susan Eyvazzadeh
VP: Nicola Perini
VP: Henry Sand
**VP:* Dan Socci

D-U-N-S 02-295-9717
LUXTERA INC
2320 Camino Vida Roble # 100, Carlsbad, CA 92011-1562
Tel (760) 448-3520 *Founded/Ownrshp* 2001
Sales 21.3MM^E *EMP* 60^E
SIC 3674 Semiconductors & related devices
Pr: Greg Young
**Pr:* Peter De Dobbelaere
**CFO:* Van Holland
Bd of Dir: Eli Yablonovitch
Sr VP: Edward P Holtaway
**VP:* Joseph Balardeta
**VP:* Christopher Bergey
VP: Brad Byk
**VP:* Samus Daly
VP: Peter Dobbelaere
**VP:* Cary Gunn
**VP:* Ron Horan
**VP:* Roger Merel
VP: James Perrott
**VP:* Gabriele Sartori
VP: Marek Tlalka
VP: Bob Twomey
**VP:* Hadi Yazdanmehr
Board of Directors: Martin Colombatto, Alex Dickinson, Lanny Ross

LUXURY APPAREL GROUP
See PETER MILLAR LLC

D-U-N-S 01-856-1159
LUXURY BRAND HOLDINGS INC
ROSS-SIMONS
(*Suby of* FREEMAN SPOGLI & CO LLC) ★
9 Ross Simons Dr, Cranston, RI 02920-4581
Tel (401) 463-3100 *Founded/Ownrshp* 2002
Sales 62.2MM^E *EMP* 350
Accts Deloitte & Touche Llp Hartfor
SIC 5944 Jewelry stores; Jewelry stores
Pr: Darrell Ross
Pr: Terry Matthews
**COO:* Robert J Simone
CFO: Robert Pulciani
VP: Larry Davis
VP: Terry Matthies
**VP:* David Pawlak
Genl Mgr: Chris Temple
IT Man: Barbara Darling
Sls Mgr: Robin McAlpine

D-U-N-S 07-886-1745 IMP
LUXURY BRAND PARTNERS LLC
4141 Ne 2nd Ave Ste 205, Miami, FL 33137-3592
Tel (305) 600-1305 *Founded/Ownrshp* 2002
Sales 52.7MM^E *EMP* 88^E
SIC 5122 Cosmetics
Chf Inves: Deva Finger
VP: Lyndsey Bardnell

D-U-N-S 60-318-1389
LUXURY IMPORTS OF PALM BEACH INC
LEXUS OF PALM BEACH
5700 Okeechobee Blvd, West Palm Beach, FL 33417-4320
Tel (561) 291-6004 *Founded/Ownrshp* 1988
Sales 27.2MM^E *EMP* 90
SIC 5511 Automobiles, new & used; Automobiles, new & used

D-U-N-S 18-291-5900
■ **LUXURY LINENS (INC)**
BURLINGTON COAT FACTORY
(*Suby of* BURLINGTON COAT FACTORY WAREHOUSE CORP) ★
1830 N Route 130, Burlington, NJ 08016-3017
Tel (609) 387-7800 *Founded/Ownrshp* 1987
Sales 39.2MM^E *EMP* 1,000
SIC 5719 Linens; Linens
Pr: Jack Moore
**VP:* Richard Rynda

D-U-N-S 93-980-8283 IMP/EXP
LUXURY MOTORS INC
BENTLEY DOWNERS GROVE
330 Ogden Ave, Downers Grove, IL 60515-3141
Tel (630) 324-6547 *Founded/Ownrshp* 1993
Sales 21.1MM^E *EMP* 60^E
SIC 5511 Automobiles, new & used; Automobiles, new & used
Pr: Joe Abbas

D-U-N-S 78-021-5104
LUXURY OPTICAL HOLDINGS CO
(*Suby of* CIRCLE PEAK CAPITAL MANAGEMENT LLC) ★
2651 N Crim Ste 200, Las Vegas, NV 89128
Tel (702) 798-8638 *Founded/Ownrshp* 2006
Sales 46.9MM^E *EMP* 250^E
SIC 5995 Eyeglasses, prescription; Eyeglasses, prescription
Pr: Glenn Reisch
**Treas:* Susan Schnabel
Dist Mgr: Jodi Dyhrkopp

LUXVERA VIRGINIA BEACH CI
See REGENT UNIVERSITY

D-U-N-S 06-051-3058
LUZERNE COUNTY
200 N River St, Wilkes Barre, PA 18711-1004
Tel (570) 825-1500 *Founded/Ownrshp* 1900

Sales NA *EMP* 2,087
Accts Zelenkofske Axelrod Llc Harri
SIC 9111 Executive offices; ; Executive offices;
V Ch: Edward Brominski
**Ch:* Gregory Skrepnak

D-U-N-S 07-599-5522
LUZERNE COUNTY COMMUNITY COLLEGE FOUNDATION
1333 S Prospect St, Nanticoke, PA 18634-3814
Tel (570) 740-0200 *Founded/Ownrshp* 1967
Sales 1.6MM *EMP* 895
Accts Parentebeard Llc Philadelphia
SIC 8222 8221 Community college; Colleges universities & professional schools; Community college; Colleges universities & professional schools
Ch: Barry H Williams
**Pr:* Thomas P Leary
Ofcr: Michael Dana-Shatley
Ofcr: Keith Frederick
Ofcr: Lawrence Hahn
Ofcr: Lynn Salamon
VP: Dana Clark
VP: Ronald Strothers
VP: Mary Yerke
Netwrk Mgr: Sandra Norton
Tech Mgr: Doris Slavitsko

D-U-N-S 12-563-3177
LUZERNE COUNTY CONVENTION CENTER AUTHORITY
WACHOVIA ARENA AT CASEY PLAZA
255 Highland Park Blvd, Wilkes Barre, PA 18702-6769
Tel (570) 825-5601 *Founded/Ownrshp* 1999
Sales 35.2MM^E *EMP* 500
SIC 7389 Convention & show services; Tourist information bureau; Convention & show services; Tourist information bureau
Ch Bd: Patrick Judge
**Ex Dir:* Rebecca Bonnevier

D-U-N-S 07-916-5106
LUZERNE INTERMEDIATE UNIT 18
368 Tioga Ave, Kingston, PA 18704-5117
Tel (570) 287-9681 *Founded/Ownrshp* 1971
Sales 23.5MM^E *EMP* 289^E
SIC 8211 Public elementary & secondary schools; Public elementary & secondary schools
Ex Dir: Michael Ostrowski
**Pr:* Ernest Ashbridge Jr
**Treas:* John Williams
Ofcr: Matt Bonawits
**VP:* Karen Whipple
Ex Dir: Anthony Grieco
Admn Mgr: Chuck Williams
MIS Dir: Don Shelarski
IT Man: Tara Pisano
Pr Dir: Joe Delvecca

D-U-N-S 06-960-3637
LUZERNE OPTICAL LABORATORIES LTD (PA)
180 N Wilkes Barre Blvd, Wilkes Barre, PA 18702-5341
Tel (570) 822-3183 *Founded/Ownrshp* 1973
Sales 29.1MM^E *EMP* 185
SIC 3851 Ophthalmic goods; Ophthalmic goods
Pr: John Dougherty
**CFO:* Lorraine Dougherty
**Genl Mgr:* Neil J Dougherty

LUZIANNE
See REILY FOODS CO

D-U-N-S 79-153-1655
LV CASINO LLC
(*Suby of* LAKE TAHOE HORZN CASINO RESORT) ★
160 E Flamingo Rd, Las Vegas, NV 89109-4574
Tel (702) 836-5990 *Founded/Ownrshp* 2007
Sales 84.7M^E *EMP* 762^E
SIC 7999 Gambling establishment
Genl Mgr: Sig Ortloff

D-U-N-S 96-856-6377
LV GAMING VENTURES LLC
M RESORT SPA CASINO, THE
12300 Las Vegas Blvd S, Henderson, NV 89044-9506
Tel (702) 797-1000 *Founded/Ownrshp* 2011
Sales 34.8MM^E *EMP* 1,600
SIC 7011 7991 Casino hotel; Resort hotel; Spas

D-U-N-S 03-244-6122
LV HIERS INC
253 Florida Ave, Macclenny, FL 32063-2419
Tel (904) 259-2314 *Founded/Ownrshp* 2004
Sales 118.6MM *EMP* 12
SIC 5171

D-U-N-S 07-957-2711
LV LOMAS INC
(*Suby of* L.V. LOMAS LIMITED)
11850 Sw 67th Ave Ste 110, Portland, OR 97223-8963
Tel (503) 404-2501 *Founded/Ownrshp* 1999
Sales 40.0MM *EMP* 15
SIC 5169 Food additives & preservatives; Food additives & preservatives
Pr: Kevin J Russell
CFO: Ross Clark
VP: Spence Morris

D-U-N-S 05-667-5531
LV VENTURES INC
233 S Wacker Dr Ste 2150, Chicago, IL 60606-6370
Tel (312) 993-1800 *Founded/Ownrshp* 1982
Sales 32.3MM^E *EMP* 282
SIC 3544 3568 3519 Special dies, tools, jigs & fixtures; Railroad car journal bearings; Diesel, semi-diesel or duel-fuel engines, including marine; Special dies, tools, jigs & fixtures; Railroad car journal bearings; Diesel, semi-diesel or duel-fuel engines, including marine
Pr: William Farley
**CFO:* Todd Sluzas
**VP:* Martin Pajor

D-U-N-S 14-409-9079
LV2 EQUITY PARTNERS LLC
1618 Denver St, Midland, MI 48640-2703
Tel (989) 631-2687 *Founded/Ownrshp* 2003
Sales NA *EMP* 132
SIC 6159 Small business investment companies; Small business investment companies

D-U-N-S 80-637-5411
LVB ACQUISITION HOLDING LLC
56 E Bell Dr, Warsaw, IN 46582-6989
Tel (574) 267-6639 *Founded/Ownrshp* 2006
Sales NA *EMP* 9,279
SIC 3842 3841 3845 Implants, surgical; Medical instruments & equipment, blood & bone work; Electromedical apparatus

D-U-N-S 80-638-1773
■ **LVB ACQUISITION INC**
(*Suby of* ZIMMER BIOMET HOLDINGS INC) ★
56 E Bell Dr, Warsaw, IN 46582-6989
Tel (574) 267-6639 *Founded/Ownrshp* 2015
Sales 3.2MMM^E *EMP* 9,279
SIC 3842 3841 3845 Implants, surgical; Supports: abdominal, ankle, arch, kneecap, etc.; Surgical appliances & supplies; Medical instruments & equipment, blood & bone work; Surgical instruments & apparatus; Suction therapy apparatus; Electromedical apparatus; Ultrasonic medical equipment, except cleaning; Implants, surgical; Supports: abdominal, ankle, arch, kneecap, etc.; Surgical appliances & supplies; Medical instruments & equipment, blood & bone work; Surgical instruments & apparatus; Suction therapy apparatus; Electromedical apparatus; Ultrasonic medical equipment, except cleaning
Co-Pr: Stephen Ko
Co-Pr: Michael Dal Ballo
Co-Pr: Andrew Rhee
Co-Pr: Jeffrey Rhodes

D-U-N-S 88-423-7892
LVC ACQUISITION CORP
2655 S Maryland Pkwy # 201, Las Vegas, NV 89109-1645
Tel (702) 734-8944 *Founded/Ownrshp* 1991
Sales 22.7MM^E *EMP* 460
SIC 7991 Athletic club & gymnasiums, membership; Athletic club & gymnasiums, membership
Ch Bd: Rudy Smith
**Pr:* Andrew J Palluck
CFO: Tom White

D-U-N-S 00-655-1229
LVDE CORP
INDIAN CREEK HYDRO
5100 San Felipe St 244e, Houston, TX 77056-3600
Tel (713) 840-1489 *Founded/Ownrshp* 2010, 2014
Sales 100.0MM *EMP* 20
SIC 4911 Distribution, electric power; Distribution, electric power
Ch Bd: Robert Klein
**CEO:* Daneil Dygert

D-U-N-S 07-864-1443
■ **LVGV LLC**
M RESORT SPA CASINO
(*Suby of* PENN NATIONAL GAMING INC) ★
12300 Las Vegas Blvd S, Henderson, NV 89044-9506
Tel (702) 797-1000 *Founded/Ownrshp* 2013
Sales 160.0MM *EMP* 1,600
SIC 7011 7991 Casino hotel; Resort hotel; Spas
Pr: Bob Sheldon

LVH-LAS VEGAS HOTEL & CASINO
See COLONY RESORTS LVH ACQUISITIONS LLC

LVI ENVIRONMENTAL SERVICES
See NORTHSTAR DEMOLITION AND REMEDIATION LP

LVI FACILITY SERVICES
See NORTHSTAR CONTRACTING GROUP INC

D-U-N-S 18-772-3577
LVI PARENT CORP
(*Suby of* NORTHSTAR GROUP HOLDINGS LLC) ★
150 W 30th St Fl 8, New York, NY 10001-4151
Tel (212) 951-3660 *Founded/Ownrshp* 2002
Sales 371.8MM *EMP* 3,500
Accts Grant Thornton Llp New York
SIC 1795 Demolition, buildings & other structures; Demolition, buildings & other structures
Pr: Scott E State
CFO: Paul S Cutrone

D-U-N-S 12-156-5709 IMP
LVMH FRAGRANCE BRANDS US LLC
(*Suby of* GIVENCHY)
80 State St, Albany, NY 12207-2541
Tel (212) 931-2600 *Founded/Ownrshp* 2007
Sales 38.0MM^E *EMP* 95
SIC 5122 2844 Perfumes; Toilet preparations
Ch Bd: Alain Chevret
**Pr:* Camille A McDonald
Sr VP: Michael Feuling
VP: Nicolas Morineaux
VP: Elizabeth Rose
CTO: Dan Delvecchio
VP Sls: Debra Nuzzo
VP Pub Rls: Linn Tanzman

D-U-N-S 14-471-6771 IMP
LVMH MOET HENNESSY LOUIS VUITTON INC
(*Suby of* SOFIDIV)
19 E 57th St, New York, NY 10022-2506
Tel (212) 931-2700 *Founded/Ownrshp* 2005
Sales 1.3MMM^E *EMP* 5,000
SIC 5948 5199 Luggage, except footlockers & trunks; Anatomical specimens & research material; Luggage, except footlockers & trunks; Anatomical specimens & research material
CEO: Mark Weber
COO: Gary Hahn
VP: George Blainski
VP: Robert Mihin
Exec: Richard Vela
Dir IT: Patrick Giraudeau
Dir IT: Bob Swierczek
VP Opers: George Goeller
Mktg Dir: Matt Space
Mktg Mgr: Thomas Abramowicz
Mktg Mgr: Janine Vanacore

LVMH MOET HNNSSY LOUIS VUITTON
See BENEFIT COSMETICS LLC

D-U-N-S 05-244-3132 IMP
LVMH WATCH & JEWELRY USA INC
TAG HEUER DIVISION
(*Suby of* LVMH MOET HENNESSY LOUIS VUITTON)
966 S Springfield Ave, Springfield, NJ 07081-3556
Tel (973) 467-1890 *Founded/Ownrshp* 2000
Sales 32.8MM^E *EMP* 89
SIC 5094 Watches & parts; Watches & parts
Pr: Fred Reffsin
Chf Mktg O: Matt Space

D-U-N-S 01-353-6051
■ **LVP ACQUISITIONS CORP**
(*Suby of* EXTENDED STAY HOTELS) ★
100 Dunbar St, Spartanburg, SC 29306-5186
Tel (864) 573-1600 *Founded/Ownrshp* 2007
Sales 84.2M^E *EMP* 9,150^E
SIC 7011 Hotel, franchised
COO: Wade Ballard

LVPG
See LEHIGH VALLEY PHYSICIANS GROUP

D-U-N-S 36-321-5208
LW INTEGRITY FUNDING LLC
1127 Wehrle Dr Ste 10, Buffalo, NY 14221-7700
Tel (716) 873-3500 *Founded/Ownrshp* 2004
Sales NA *EMP* 1
SIC 6162 Mortgage bankers & correspondents; Mortgage bankers & correspondents

D-U-N-S 10-272-3137
LW MILLER TRANSPORTATION INC
1050 W 200 N, Logan, UT 84321-8255
Tel (435) 753-8350 *Founded/Ownrshp* 1982
Sales 26.5MM^E *EMP* 191
SIC 4213 7699 Contract haulers; Aircraft & heavy equipment repair services; Contract haulers; Aircraft & heavy equipment repair services
Pr: Larry W Miller
**Sec:* Kent D Stratford
**VP:* Rex Miller
Div Mgr: Dennis Shaw

D-U-N-S 12-172-3050 IMP/EXP
LWB HOLDING CO
425 S Salem Church Rd, York, PA 17408-5955
Tel (717) 792-3611 *Founded/Ownrshp* 1984
Sales 59.6MM^E *EMP* 464
SIC 1422 3297 Dolomite, crushed & broken-quarrying; Dolomite or dolomite-magnesite brick & shapes; Dolomite, crushed & broken-quarrying; Dolomite or dolomite-magnesite brick & shapes
VP: Paul A Dydek
VP: Ian Taylor
Rgnl Mgr: Lloyd Widener
Dir IT: Brian Mengel
Tech Mgr: Lloyd West
Sfty Mgr: Gary Bartkowski
Sfty Mgr: Keith Hoke
Opers Mgr: Sujoy Sen
Plnt Mgr: Rick Gladfelter
Plnt Mgr: Kevin Newton
Snr PM: Terry Mee

LWCC
See LEISURE WORLD OF MARYLAND CORP

LWCC
See LOUISIANA WORKERS COMPENSATION CORP

D-U-N-S 61-682-3282
LWHS LTD
BATA PLASTICS
1001 40th St Se, Grand Rapids, MI 49508-2401
Tel (616) 452-5300 *Founded/Ownrshp* 2000
Sales 27.4MM^E *EMP* 55
SIC 5093 Plastics scrap
Pr: W Lee Hammond
**CFO:* Barbara Hammond

D-U-N-S 04-181-3077 IMP
LWIN FAMILY CO
HISSHO SUSHI
11949 Steele Creek Rd, Charlotte, NC 28273-3773
Tel (704) 504-4667 *Founded/Ownrshp* 1998
Sales 100.4MM^E *EMP* 100
SIC 5146 Fish & seafoods; Fish & seafoods
CEO: Hissho Sushi
**Pr:* Philip Maung
**Treas:* Kristina Tong
**VP:* Tom Yap
Opers Mgr: Naing Lin
Opers Mgr: Lily Wang
Opers Mgr: Yuan Wang
Sales Exec: Daniel Rutherford
Mktg Dir: Vanessa Curry

D-U-N-S 06-286-5159 IMP
LWO ACQUISITIONS CO LLC
CIRCUITRONICS
1920 Hurd Dr, Irving, TX 75038-4312
Tel (972) 573-1140 *Founded/Ownrshp* 2015
Sales 20.5MM^E *EMP* 50
SIC 3672 3678 3679 Printed circuit boards; Electronic connectors; Electronic circuits; Electronic crystals; Electronic loads & power supplies; Electronic switches
Pr: Jordan Bastable
VP: Alok Patel
Prd Mgr: Trey Johnson

D-U-N-S 07-837-7284
LWP LESSEE LLC
15445 Innovation Dr, San Diego, CA 92128-3432
Tel (858) 521-3370 *Founded/Ownrshp* 2010
Sales 358.4MM^E *EMP* 691
SIC 4911 Generation, electric power; Generation, electric power

LXG
See SUTTERS MILL SPECIALTIES INC

LXR LUXURY RESORTS & HOTELS
See WHM LLC

D-U-N-S 01-368-4122
LXR TRAVEL LLC
5140 Main St Ste 303, Williamsville, NY 14221-5265
Tel (716) 568-7094 *Founded/Ownrshp* 2007
Sales 40.0MM *EMP* 20
SIC 4724 Travel agencies; Travel agencies
CFO: Beth Brown

D-U-N-S 02-925-0727 IMP
LY BROTHERS CORP
SUGAR BOWL BAKERY
1963 Sabre St, Hayward, CA 94545-1021
Tel (510) 782-2118 *Founded/Ownrshp* 1984
Sales 81.0MM^E *EMP* 260
SIC 2051 Bakery: wholesale or wholesale/retail combined
Pr: Andrew A Ly
CFO: John Ying
**Ch:* Tom Ly
**Treas:* Paul Ly
**Ex VP:* Sam Ly
**VP:* Binh Ly

D-U-N-S 08-039-7847
LYALL LEN CHEVROLET INC
14500 E Colfax Ave, Aurora, CO 80011-6998
Tel (303) 344-3100 *Founded/Ownrshp* 1976
Sales 38.4MM^E *EMP* 95
SIC 5511 Automobiles, new & used; Automobiles, new & used
Pr: Jim Lyall
Genl Mgr: Dan Johnson
Store Mgr: Jon Hall
Sls Mgr: Manuel Banderas
Sls Mgr: Ryan Johnson
Sls Mgr: Tom Marsh

D-U-N-S 09-433-7920
LYBARGER OIL INC
704 N Maple St, Garnett, KS 66032-1077
Tel (785) 448-5512 *Founded/Ownrshp* 1998
Sales 42.4MM *EMP* 19
SIC 5171 Petroleum bulk stations; Petroleum bulk stations
Pr: David Lybarger
**CFO:* Dennis Swartz
**Sec:* Betty J Lybarger

D-U-N-S 02-038-7858
LYCEE FRANCAIS DE NEW YORK (INC) (NY)
LFNY
505 E 75th St, New York, NY 10021-3462
Tel (212) 369-1400 *Founded/Ownrshp* 1935
Sales 41.3MM *EMP* 215
Accts Marks Paneth Llp New York Ny
SIC 8211 Private combined elementary & secondary school; Private combined elementary & secondary school
CFO: Evelyne Estey
Comm Man: Cecile Gregoriades
Dir IT: Jeremie Bourdon
Dir IT: Tony Tanael
IT Man: Harriet Weitzman
Info Man: Rosanna Beck

D-U-N-S 07-083-3884
LYCEE FRANCAIS LA PEROUSE
755 Ashbury St, San Francisco, CA 94117-4013
Tel (415) 661-5232 *Founded/Ownrshp* 1967
Sales 20.3MM *EMP* 180
SIC 8211 Private combined elementary & secondary school; Private elementary & secondary schools; Private combined elementary & secondary school; Private elementary & secondary schools
CFO: Emmanuel Poulain
Ofcr: Elizabeth Chaponot
HC Dir: Isabelle Desmole

D-U-N-S 01-700-7925
LYCESS FRANCAIS DE SAN FRANCISCO
1201 Ortega St, San Francisco, CA 94122-4411
Tel (415) 566-1685 *Founded/Ownrshp* 2006, 2008
Sales 22.8MM *EMP* 3
SIC 8731 Environmental research
Prin: Marc Rossano

D-U-N-S 06-348-9538 IMP
LYCO MANUFACTURING INC
115 Commercial Dr, Columbus, WI 53925-1008
Tel (920) 623-4152 *Founded/Ownrshp* 1972
Sales 23.3MM^E *EMP* 70
SIC 3556 3444 Food products machinery; Sheet metalwork
Pr: David R Zittel
**CEO:* Steve Hughes
**CFO:* Cindy Abendschein
Area Mgr: Jeff Zittel
VP Opers: Bill Zittel
Plnt Mgr: Doug Spangler
Sls Mgr: Tom Surmiak
Snr Mgr: Ron Kennedy

D-U-N-S 05-844-6105
LYCOMING COLLEGE
LYCOMING COLLEGE BOOKSTORE
700 College Pl, Williamsport, PA 17701-5192
Tel (570) 321-4000 *Founded/Ownrshp* 1812
Sales 36.6MM *EMP* 370
Accts Baker Tilly Virchow Krause Ll
SIC 8221 College, except junior; College, except junior
Pr: James Evans Douthat PHD
COO: Nicole Franquet
**CFO:* Robert Griesemer
**Ch:* Robert L Shangraw
VP: Barbara Carlin
VP: Loni Kline
Exec: Jackie Bilger
Exec: Anne Landon
**Prin:* Peter Lynn
CIO: Rob Dunkleberger

LYCOMING COLLEGE BOOKSTORE
See LYCOMING COLLEGE

D-U-N-S 80-309-4929
LYCOMING COMMUNITY CARE INC
VALLEY VIEW NURSING CENTER
2140 Warrensville Rd, Montoursville, PA 17754-9621
Tel (570) 433-3161 *Founded/Ownrshp* 1990
Sales 13.9MM *EMP* 280
Accts Larson Kellett & Associates Pc
SIC 8361 8051 Home for the aged; Skilled nursing care facilities; Home for the aged; Skilled nursing care facilities
CFO: Steve Fry
Exec: Wendy Fogleman

D-U-N-S 06-049-5488
LYCOMING-CLINTON COUNTIES COMMISSION FOR COMMUNITY ACTION INC
STEP
2138 Lincoln St, Williamsport, PA 17701-5549
Tel (570) 327-5495 *Founded/Ownrshp* 1966
Sales 32.6MM *EMP* 250E
SIC 8399 Community action agency; Community action agency
Ex Dir: Janet Alling
**Ch Bd:* Harold C Yost
**Pr:* Larry Chilson
COO: Jim Plankenhorn
**Sec:* Carolyn Bullock
**Prin:* Russell Reitz
Prgrm Mgr: Dan Merk
Prgrm Mgr: Cathy Stopper
Prgrm Mgr: Teresa Way
CIO: Phillip Good
Snr Mgr: Rachelle Abbott

D-U-N-S 61-317-5327 IMP
LYCORED CORP
LYCORED USA
(*Suby of* LYCORED LTD)
377 Crane St, Orange, NJ 07050-2602
Tel (973) 882-0322 *Founded/Ownrshp* 2005
Sales 35.0MM *EMP* 49
SIC 2023 Dietary supplements, dairy & non-dairy based
Ch: Rony Patishi-Chillim
Pr: Doug Lynch
**CFO:* Benjamin Regev
**Ch:* Morris Zelkha
Sr VP: Scott Larkin
VP: Yonatan Brenner
VP: Joost Overeem
VP: Golan Raz
VP: Liat Simha
Dir IT: Elaine Brzezowski
Prd Mgr: Sarah Pullen

LYCORED USA
See LYCORED CORP

D-U-N-S 09-882-5706
LYDA SWINERTON BUILDERS INC
(*Suby of* SWINERTON INC) ★
805 Las Cimas Pkwy # 130, Austin, TX 78746-6527
Tel (210) 684-1770 *Founded/Ownrshp* 2002
Sales 26.5MME *EMP* 157
SIC 1521 Single-family housing construction; Single-family housing construction
Ch: Gary Rafferty
**Pr:* Michael RE
**CFO:* Keith T Schnell
Treas: Dan Beyer
**VP:* Luke P Argilla
**VP:* Frederick A Brown
**VP:* W J Dysart
**VP:* Jeffrey C Hoopes
**VP:* Paul G Pruitt
**VP:* Leland Rocchio
**VP:* Linda G Schowalter

D-U-N-S 00-113-9963 IMP
▲ LYDALL INC
1 Colonial Rd, Manchester, CT 06042-2307
Tel (860) 646-1233 *Founded/Ownrshp* 1969
Sales 535.8MM *EMP* 2,100
Accts Pricewaterhousecoopers Llp Ha
Tkr Sym LDL *Exch* NYS
SIC 2297 3053 2899 2631 3714 3564 Nonwoven fabrics; Gaskets, all materials; Insulating compounds; Automobile board; Filters: oil, fuel & air, motor vehicle; Oil strainers, motor vehicle; Filters, air: furnaces, air conditioning equipment, etc.; Nonwoven fabrics; Gaskets, all materials; Insulating compounds; Automobile board; Filters: oil, fuel & air, motor vehicle; Oil strainers, motor vehicle; Filters, air: furnaces, air conditioning equipment, etc.
Pr: Dale G Barnhart
COO: Franck Valton
CFO: Scott M Deakin
Treas: James V Laughlan
Treas: Suzanne L Moore
Sr VP: Michael Barnes
VP: Chad McDaniel
VP: Jim Posa
VP: Erika H Turner
VP Bus Dev: David Glenn
Prgrm Mgr: Brian Porter
Board of Directors: Kathleen Burdett, W Leslie Duffy, Matthew T Farrell, Marc T Giles, William D Gurley, Suzanne Hammett, S Carl Soderstrom Jr

D-U-N-S 61-543-6011 IMP
■ LYDALL PERFORMANCE MATERIALS INC
(*Suby of* LYDALL INC) ★
134 Chestnut Hill Rd, Rochester, NH 03867-5182
Tel (603) 332-4600 *Founded/Ownrshp* 1970
Sales 21.2MME *EMP* 110
SIC 3569 Filters; Filters
Pr: David Williams
**CFO:* Robert Julian
**Treas:* James Laughlan
VP: Bill Feld
Prgrm Mgr: Gary Riches
IT Man: Matthew Greenberg
Plnt Mgr: Jeff Miller
Ql Cn Mgr: Jeffrey Milem
Ql Cn Mgr: Donnie White
Sls Dir: Ming-Teh Huang
Sls Dir: Greg Wool

D-U-N-S 08-543-8430 IMP
■ LYDALL THERMAL/ACOUSTICAL INC
METALS
(*Suby of* LYDALL INC) ★
1243 Buck Shoals Rd, Hamptonville, NC 27020-7624
Tel (336) 468-8522 *Founded/Ownrshp* 1977
Sales 104.8MME *EMP* 618
SIC 3441 Fabricated structural metal; Fabricated structural metal
Sr VP: Joe Abbruzzi

D-U-N-S 87-490-8010 IMP
LYDEN OIL CO
30692 Tracy Rd, Walbridge, OH 43465-9775
Tel (419) 666-1948 *Founded/Ownrshp* 2000
Sales 140.7MM *EMP* 167
Accts Rehmann Robson Llc Toledo Oh
SIC 5172 Lubricating oils & greases; Lubricating oils & greases
Pr: Breen Lyden
**VP:* Paul Lyden

LYDIA HEALTHCARE CENTER
See LYDIA HEALTHCARE INC

D-U-N-S 17-342-5752
LYDIA HEALTHCARE INC
LYDIA HEALTHCARE CENTER
203 Mallard Ln, Bloomingdale, IL 60108-5406
Tel (708) 385-8700 *Founded/Ownrshp* 1987
Sales 24.7MME *EMP* 250
SIC 8062 8051 General medical & surgical hospitals; Convalescent home with continuous nursing care; General medical & surgical hospitals; Convalescent home with continuous nursing care
Pr: Arnold Simonsen
**Ex Dir:* Susan Simonsen

D-U-N-S 78-107-1022
LYDIA SECURITY MONITORING INC
C.O.P.S. MONITORING
1041 Glassboro Rd Ste F2, Williamstown, NJ 08094-3546
Tel (856) 629-1111 *Founded/Ownrshp* 1989
Sales 28.1MME *EMP* 300
SIC 7382 Security systems services; Security systems services
CEO: Ira Riklis
**Pr:* James McMullen
COO: Colleen Engler
**CFO:* Robert Martino
**Ex VP:* Dan Barbera
**Ex VP:* Don Maden
VP: Sarah Brooks
**VP:* Elle Daley
VP: Heather Sparks
VP: Kristen Tierno
**Prin:* Ira D Riklas

D-U-N-S 00-942-4680
LYDIG CONSTRUCTION INC
11001 E Montgomery Dr, Spokane Valley, WA 99206-4714
Tel (509) 534-0451 *Founded/Ownrshp* 1996
Sales 241.2MME *EMP* 130
Accts Moss Adams Llp Spokane Washi
SIC 1542 1541 Commercial & office building, new construction; Industrial buildings, new construction; Commercial & office building, new construction; Industrial buildings, new construction
CEO: Larry Swartz
**CFO:* Mark Bray
Ofcr: Taylor Brown
**VP:* William Gottschalk
**VP:* Kenneth Schwartz
CTO: Jon Edwards
Sfty Dirs: Paul Moorman
Mktg Mgr: Won Moc
Snr PM: Andrew Johnson
Snr PM: Lori Porath

D-U-N-S 04-614-8029
LYF-TYM BUILDING PRODUCTS CO INC
4601 Corp Dr Nw Ste 105, Concord, NC 28027
Tel (704) 886-1555 *Founded/Ownrshp* 1976
Sales 29.7MME *EMP* 59
SIC 5031 3444 3089 Lumber, plywood & millwork; Gutters, sheet metal; Downspouts, sheet metal; Windows, plastic
Pr: Curt Corder
**Treas:* Tim Brooks Sr
**VP:* Lisa Corder
Sales Asso: James Frisco
Sales Asso: Xeng Yang

D-U-N-S 04-922-2193
LYFORD CONSOLIDATED INDEPENDENT SCHOOL DISTRICT INC
8204 Simon Gomez Rd, Lyford, TX 78569
Tel (956) 347-3900 *Founded/Ownrshp* 1911
Sales 20.3MM *EMP* 300
Accts Buffo & Berkman Raymondville
SIC 8211 Public elementary & secondary schools; Public elementary & secondary schools
Ofcr: Lupe Reyna
Psych: Olivia Rincones
Psych: Rosie Salazar
Psych: Jennifer Zamorano

D-U-N-S 83-261-5574
LYFT INC
2300 Harrison St, San Francisco, CA 94110-2013
Tel (855) 946-7433 *Founded/Ownrshp* 2007
Sales 39.9MME *EMP* 200
SIC 4119 Local rental transportation; Local rental transportation
CEO: Logan Green
**Pr:* John Zimmer
**VP:* David Estrada
CTO: Chris Lambert
Sftwr Eng: Liz Neu
Mktg Dir: Adam Fishman
Snr Mgr: Max Giella
Board of Directors: Jonathan Christodoro

D-U-N-S 06-689-4478
LYKE CORP
RIPON PRINTERS
656 S Douglas St, Ripon, WI 54971-9044
Tel (920) 748-3136 *Founded/Ownrshp* 1919
Sales 50.8MM *EMP* 330
SIC 2752

D-U-N-S 00-409-3472
LYKES BROS INC (FL)
400 N Tampa St Ste 1900, Tampa, FL 33602-4776
Tel (813) 223-3911 *Founded/Ownrshp* 1875
Sales 85.1MME *EMP* 250
SIC 0174 6331 Citrus fruits; Agricultural insurance; Citrus fruits; Agricultural insurance
Ch Bd: Howell L Ferguson
**Pr:* Carl J Bauman
**Pr:* Charles P Lykes Jr
**CEO:* Michael L Carrere
COO: Angela J Whitaker
**CFO:* Fred Bennett
CFO: Frederick J Bennett
**Ex VP:* Hiram P Hampton
VP: Bill Barber
**VP:* Joe Collins
VP: Mark E Jackson
VP: Richard P Russo
VP: William P Taulbee II
**VP:* Elizabeth A Waters
VP: Thomas A Webster

D-U-N-S 01-823-0573
LYKINS COMPANIES INC
LYKINS ENERGY SOLUTIONS
5163 Wlfpn Plsnt Hl Rd, Milford, OH 45150-9632
Tel (513) 831-8820 *Founded/Ownrshp* 1952
Sales 205.7MME *EMP* 235
SIC 4213 5172 5411 Gasoline; Diesel fuel; Fuel oil; Trucking, except local; Convenience stores, chain; Trucking, except local; Gasoline; Diesel fuel; Fuel oil; Convenience stores, chain
CEO: Jeff Lykins
**CFO:* Robert J Manning
Brnch Mgr: Mike Hamm
Div Mgr: Diana Brown
Div Mgr: Mike Schmid
CIO: Larry Owens
MIS Dir: Julie Jump
Mktg Dir: Mary Gray
Sls Mgr: Joe Suttmiller

LYKINS ENERGY SOLUTIONS
See LYKINS COMPANIES INC

D-U-N-S 09-062-9395
LYKINS OIL CO
(*Suby of* LYKINS COMPANIES INC) ★
5163 Wlfpn Plsnt Hl Rd, Milford, OH 45150-9632
Tel (513) 831-8820 *Founded/Ownrshp* 1948
Sales 183.1MME *EMP* 125
SIC 5172 5983 Gasoline; Diesel fuel; Fuel oil; Lubricating oils & greases; Fuel oil dealers; Gasoline; Diesel fuel; Fuel oil; Lubricating oils & greases; Fuel oil dealers
Pr: D Jeff Lykins
**CFO:* Robert J Manning
**VP:* Ronald Lykins

LYLE ANDERSON CO., THE
See LYLE ANDERSON FINANCIAL CO LLC

D-U-N-S 62-273-9399
LYLE ANDERSON FINANCIAL CO LLC
LYLE ANDERSON CO., THE
8777 N Gainey Center Dr # 205, Scottsdale, AZ 85258-2133
Tel (480) 443-2630 *Founded/Ownrshp* 1991
Sales 32.8MME *EMP* 600
SIC 6531 Real estate managers; Real estate managers

D-U-N-S 05-333-7572
LYLE INDUSTRIES
(*Suby of* THERMOFORMING TECHNOLOGY GROUP LLC)
4144 Lyle Rd, Beaverton, MI 48612-8603
Tel (989) 435-7717 *Founded/Ownrshp* 2014
Sales 28.1MME *EMP* 77E
SIC 3559 Plastics working machinery
Pr: Brian Redmond
**VP:* Brian Crawford
**VP:* Sandra Schwartz

D-U-N-S 01-953-4114 IMP
LYLE INDUSTRIES INC
1800 Kimberly Park Dr, Dalton, GA 30720-7058
Tel (706) 278-2500 *Founded/Ownrshp* 1981
Sales 28.1MME *EMP* 100E
SIC 2273 3714 Finishers of tufted carpets & rugs; Motor vehicle parts & accessories
Pr: Lamar G Lyle
**Sec:* Loutrelle Lyle

D-U-N-S 95-912-1393
LYLE MACHINERY CO
650 Highway 49 S, Jackson, MS 39218-9443
Tel (601) 939-4000 *Founded/Ownrshp* 1995
Sales 36.5MME *EMP* 70
SIC 5082 Construction & mining machinery; Construction & mining machinery
Pr: John Lyle Jr
**Pr:* Daniel A Lyle
Ex VP: Dan Lyle
**VP:* Susan R Hester
VP: Jim King
**VP:* James Lyle
Area Mgr: Jonathan McKinley
Info Man: Andrew Thompson
Info Man: Seth Whitehead
Opers Mgr: Chris Shelton
VP Sls: Jim Luther

D-U-N-S 00-625-3306
LYLE SIGNS INC (MN)
6294 Bury Dr, Eden Prairie, MN 55346-1718
Tel (952) 934-7653 *Founded/Ownrshp* 1905, 1990
Sales 21.7MME *EMP* 100
SIC 3993 Signs & advertising specialties; Signs & advertising specialties
Pr: Peter F Pierce Jr
**VP:* Jeffrey Edson
VP Mfg: Larry Beck
Sls Dir: Mike Russell

D-U-N-S 00-690-4023
LYLES DIVERSIFIED INC (CA)
WM LYLES CO
1210 W Olive Ave, Fresno, CA 93728-2816
Tel (559) 441-1900 *Founded/Ownrshp* 1946
Sales 31.9MM *EMP* 200
SIC 1623 1629 1611 3494 6513 Water & sewer line construction; Water main construction; Sewer line construction; Power plant construction; Highway & street paving contractor; Sprinkler systems, field; Apartment building operators; Water & sewer line construction; Water main construction; Sewer line construction; Power plant construction; Highway & street paving contractor; Sprinkler systems, field; Apartment building operators
CEO: William Lyles IV
**CEO:* William M Lyles
**CFO:* Michael F Elkins
Sr VP: Stan Simmons
**VP:* Gerald V Lyles
VP: Sheller Todd
Dir IT: John Driscoll
IT Man: Steve Stambach
Snr PM: Grant Gourley

D-U-N-S 79-246-2947
LYMAN GARRIGAN GROUP INC
GARRIGAN LYMAN
1524 5th Ave Ste 400, Seattle, WA 98101-1654
Tel (206) 223-5548 *Founded/Ownrshp* 1993
Sales 20.2MME *EMP* 50E
SIC 8742 Marketing consulting services
Pr: Tim Garrigan
**Pr:* Rebecca Lyman
**Treas:* Cheronne Wong
**VP:* Bryan Cummings
**VP:* Chris Geiser
Creative D: Kalie Kimball-Malone
Creative D: James Nesbitt
Creative D: Kurt Reifschneider
Ex Dir: Karen Burke
Off Mgr: Aly Crystal
Off Mgr: Aly Prestel

D-U-N-S 02-802-1061 IMP
LYMAN GROUP INC
201 East St, Woodland, CA 95776-3523
Tel (530) 662-5442 *Founded/Ownrshp* 1963
Sales 88.8MME *EMP* 63
SIC 5191 Chemicals, agricultural; Fertilizer & fertilizer materials; Chemicals, agricultural; Fertilizer & fertilizer materials
Ch: Leslie F Lyman
**Pr:* Johnny Council
**CFO:* Scott Mansell
**VP:* Walt Johnson

LYMAN LUMBER COMPANY
See BEP/LYMAN LLC

D-U-N-S 08-831-7292 IMP/EXP
LYMAN PRODUCTS CORP (CT)
RAYTECH INDUSTRIES DIV
475 Smith St, Middletown, CT 06457-1529
Tel (860) 632-2020 *Founded/Ownrshp* 1876, 1977
Sales 21.0MME *EMP* 115
SIC 3559 Ammunition & explosives, loading machinery; Metal finishing equipment for plating, etc.; Ammunition & explosives, loading machinery; Metal finishing equipment for plating, etc.
Pr: Richard Ranzinger
**Treas:* Luke Fichthorn III
**VP:* Thomas Andersen

D-U-N-S 00-891-0622
LYMAN-RICHEY CORP
(*Suby of* ASH GROVE CEMENT CO) ★
4315 Cuming St, Omaha, NE 68131-1014
Tel (402) 556-3600 *Founded/Ownrshp* 1884, 1935
Sales 118.1MME *EMP* 400
SIC 3273 1442 3271 5211 5032 Ready-mixed concrete; Construction sand & gravel; Construction sand mining; Gravel mining; Concrete block & brick; Lumber & other building materials; Brick, stone & related material; Ready-mixed concrete; Construction sand & gravel; Construction sand mining; Gravel mining; Concrete block & brick; Lumber & other building materials; Brick, stone & related material
Pr: Patrick J Gorup
**Pr:* Kevin D Schmidt
CFO: Mark Osborn
**Treas:* Mark F Osborn
Ex VP: Kevin Schmidt
Exec: Gordon Wellensiek
Brnch Mgr: John Stueve
Genl Mgr: Doug Harrison
IT Man: Al Miller
Sls&Mrk Ex: Norman Nelson
VP Sls: Mark Deetz

D-U-N-S 14-476-3067 IMP
LYME COMPUTER SYSTEMS INC
18 On The Cmn, Lyme, NH 03768
Tel (603) 795-4000 *Founded/Ownrshp* 1999
Sales 58.0MM *EMP* 27
SIC 5045 Computers, peripherals & software; Computer peripheral equipment; Computer software
Pr: Curt M Vinson
**CEO:* Judy Vinson
VP: Josh Longacre
Exec: Bill McCarthey
Mktg Dir: Colin Nicol
Sls Dir: Nancy Stanley
Sales Asso: Richard Hussey

D-U-N-S 04-643-5491 IMP
LYN-LAD GROUP LTD
20 Boston St, Lynn, MA 01904-2527
Tel (781) 598-6010 *Founded/Ownrshp* 1981
Sales 59.1MME *EMP* 275E

SIC 2499 5082 5251 7359 Ladders, wood; Ladders; Scaffolding; Hardware; Equipment rental & leasing; Ladders, wood; Ladders; Scaffolding; Hardware; Equipment rental & leasing
Pr: Frank Koughan
**CFO:* Susan Kline
Dept Mgr: Tom Fitzgerald

D-U-N-S 01-356-3556
LYNBROOK GLASS & ARCHITECTURAL METALS CORP
941 Motor Pkwy, Hauppauge, NY 11788-5281
Tel (631) 582-3060 *Founded/Ownrshp* 1997
Sales 29.1MM^E *EMP* 140
SIC 1793 1542 Glass & glazing work; Store front construction; Glass & glazing work; Store front construction
Pr: Joseph Torsiello
**Sec:* Lisa Torsiello
**VP:* Laurence Torsiello
Dir IT: Joseph Fortosiello
Plnt Mgr: Keith Leonard

D-U-N-S 06-189-9340
LYNBROOK UNION FREE SCHOOL DISTRICT 20 INC
111 Atlantic Ave, Lynbrook, NY 11563-3437
Tel (516) 887-8065 *Founded/Ownrshp* 1892
Sales 28.6MM^E *EMP* 676
SIC 8211 Public elementary & secondary schools; Public elementary & secondary schools
Pr: Joan Hines
**VP:* Charlene Faustmann
HC Dir: Arlene Mishanie
Board of Directors: George Berch, Harry L Leonard, Michael McLean, Michael Rehns

LYNCH BUICK-PONTIAC
See LYNCH MOTORS INC

D-U-N-S 03-148-8901
LYNCH CHEVROLET-CADILLAC OF AUBURN INC
LYNCH NISSAN
154 W Creek Pkwy, Auburn, AL 36830-7007
Tel (334) 821-4888 *Founded/Ownrshp* 2005
Sales 38.7MM^E *EMP* 100
SIC 5511 7389 Automobiles, new & used; Automobile recovery service; Automobiles, new & used; Automobile recovery service
Pr: William Lynch
**VP:* David T Mills
Genl Mgr: Paul Brockwell
Genl Mgr: James Kite
Sls Mgr: Alan Cox
Sls Mgr: Scott Frizzell
Sls Mgr: Don Riggins
Sls Mgr: Kevin Wheat
Sales Asso: James Arnold
Sales Asso: Marcus Durrell
Sales Asso: Bobby Harris

D-U-N-S 02-226-1051
LYNCH FORD - MT VERNON INC
410 Highway 30 Sw, Mount Vernon, IA 52314-1564
Tel (319) 895-8500 *Founded/Ownrshp* 1994
Sales 34.2MM^E *EMP* 85
SIC 5511 5521 Automobiles, new & used; Used car dealers; Automobiles, new & used; Used car dealers
Pr: Dan Lynch
**VP:* Joseph Kirby
Sls Mgr: Greg Schafer

D-U-N-S 10-231-5769
LYNCH HOLDCO INC
7702 S 168th St, Omaha, NE 68136-1160
Tel (402) 289-8356 *Founded/Ownrshp* 1983
Sales 57.1MM^E *EMP* 50^E
SIC 5031

LYNCH INDUSTRIES
See DUBLIN MANAGEMENT ASSOCIATES OF NEW JERSEY INC

D-U-N-S 06-961-9625
LYNCH LIVESTOCK INC (IA)
WAUCOMA TIRE CO
331 3rd St Nw, Waucoma, IA 52171-9448
Tel (563) 776-3311 *Founded/Ownrshp* 1977
Sales 78.0MM^E *EMP* 220
SIC 5154 Hogs; Hogs
Pr: Gerald Lynch
**VP:* Ruth A Lynch
Sls Mgr: Matt Haywood

D-U-N-S 07-646-1433
LYNCH MATERIAL HANDLING CO INC
2360 Industrial Ln, Broomfield, CO 80020-1612
Tel (303) 466-2323 *Founded/Ownrshp* 1968
Sales 26.5MM^E *EMP* 80^E
SIC 5046 Shelving, commercial & industrial
Ch Bd: Erma M Mantey
**Pr:* Norman E Ooms
**VP:* Donald A Rutkowski
IT Man: Kay Hill
IT Man: Connie Tendler

D-U-N-S 80-409-2153 IMP
■ **LYNCH METALS INC**
(*Suby of* METALS USA INC) ★
1075 Lousons Rd, Union, NJ 07083-5029
Tel (908) 686-8401 *Founded/Ownrshp* 2007
Sales 38.9MM^E *EMP* 61
SIC 5051 Metals service centers & offices; Metals service centers & offices
Pr: Clinton D Lynch
Mtls Mgr: Donna Fulco
Sales Asso: Melissa Garvey
Sales Asso: Dee Santi

D-U-N-S 05-254-2503
LYNCH MOTORS INC
LYNCH BUICK-PONTIAC
500 W Center St, Manchester, CT 06040-4735
Tel (860) 646-4321 *Founded/Ownrshp* 2001
Sales 36.2MM^E *EMP* 110
SIC 5511 7538 Automobiles, new & used; Trucks, tractors & trailers: new & used; General automotive repair shops; Automobiles, new & used; Trucks, tractors & trailers: new & used; General automotive repair shops
Pr: Michael B Lynch Jr
VP: Thomas Carpenter
VP: Frank M Lynch
Genl Mgr: Bonnie Holt

LYNCH NISSAN
See LYNCH CHEVROLET-CADILLAC OF AUBURN INC

D-U-N-S 05-595-2832
LYNCH OIL CO INC
1244 E Carroll St, Kissimmee, FL 34744-1453
Tel (321) 639-8198 *Founded/Ownrshp* 1969
Sales 40.6MM^E *EMP* 37
SIC 5171 Petroleum bulk stations
Pr: Bradley C Lynch
Sls Mgr: Jim Wells

D-U-N-S 03-394-7714
LYNCH OIL INC (ID)
411 Overland Ave, Burley, ID 83318-1026
Tel (208) 678-9009 *Founded/Ownrshp* 1923, 1987
Sales 24.6MM^E *EMP* 44
Accts Westfall & West Fall Cpa Bur
SIC 5172 Petroleum brokers; Petroleum brokers
Pr: James C Lynch Jr
Dist Mgr: Scott Lynch

LYNCH TELEPHONE
See CENTRAL UTAH TELEPHONE INC

D-U-N-S 78-780-0861
LYNCH TELEPHONE CORP III
(*Suby of* LICT CORP) ★
401 Theodore Fremd Ave, Rye, NY 10580-1422
Tel (914) 921-8821 *Founded/Ownrshp* 1998
Sales 43.5MM^E *EMP* 590
SIC 4813 Telephone communication, except radio; Telephone communication, except radio
CEO: Robert Dolan
Sr VP: Evelyn C Jerden

LYNCH TRUCK CENTER
See JOHN LYNCH CHEVROLET-PONTIAC SALES INC

D-U-N-S 12-070-8805
LYNCHBURG CITY SCHOOLS
915 Court St, Lynchburg, VA 24504-1603
Tel (434) 847-1420 *Founded/Ownrshp* 1871
Sales 35.3MM^E *EMP* 499
Accts Brown Edwards & Company Llp
SIC 8211 Public elementary & secondary schools; Public elementary & secondary schools
Bd of Dir: Jenny Poore
Off Mgr: Kathie Stoner
Trfc Dir: Daryl Conner
Pr Dir: Lee Forester
Psych: Brenda Colinger
Psych: Tamara Jamerson
Psych: Katrina Johnson
Psych: Corlett Keefer
Psych: Santina Knight
Psych: Dawn Kuminski
Psych: Karl Loos

D-U-N-S 07-475-5265
LYNCHBURG COLLEGE
1501 Lakeside Dr, Lynchburg, VA 24501-3113
Tel (434) 544-8100 *Founded/Ownrshp* 1917
Sales 63.5MM *EMP* 1,077
Accts Brown Edwards & Company Ll
SIC 8221 College, except junior; College, except junior
Pr: Kenneth R Garren
Pr: Shannon Brennan
Ofcr: Cheryl Murphy-Anderson
Ofcr: John Stafford
VP: Denise M McDonald
VP: Edward A Polloway
Dir IT: Richard Hill
Advt Dir: Betty McKinney
HC Dir: Mandi Dolan

D-U-N-S 79-009-3538
LYNCHBURG NURSING CENTER
(*Suby of* CHATTANOOGA MEDICAL INVESTORS LIMITED PARTNERSHIP) ★
40 Nursing Home Rd, Lynchburg, TN 37352-7098
Tel (931) 759-6000 *Founded/Ownrshp* 1992
Sales 11.5MM^E *EMP* 302
SIC 8051 8093 Skilled nursing care facilities; Rehabilitation center, outpatient treatment; Skilled nursing care facilities; Rehabilitation center, outpatient treatment
Ex Dir: Jane Edwards
Off Mgr: Kathy Barfield

D-U-N-S 01-596-5155
LYNCHBURG STEEL & SPECIALTY CO (VA)
275 Francis Ave, Monroe, VA 24574-2758
Tel (434) 929-0951 *Founded/Ownrshp* 1970, 2010
Sales 23.5MM^E *EMP* 75
SIC 1791 3441 Structural steel erection; Fabricated structural metal
Pr: C V Anderson Jr
**Pr:* Douglas B Anderson
**CEO:* Geraldine K Anderson
CFO: Sonny Morris
**VP:* Samuel McConaghy
VP: Clarence Roakes
VP: Jim Woods
Sfty Mgr: Jay Mann

D-U-N-S 07-971-1704
LYNCHES RIVER CONTRACTING INC
1104 W Mcgregor St, Pageland, SC 29728-2016
Tel (843) 675-4285 *Founded/Ownrshp* 2014
Sales 35.0MM *EMP* 95
SIC 1611 Airport runway construction
Pr: Thad Preslar

D-U-N-S 00-894-1494
LYNCHES RIVER ELECTRIC COOPERATIVE INC
707 S Arant St, Pageland, SC 29728-8224
Tel (843) 672-6111 *Founded/Ownrshp* 1939
Sales 46.1MM *EMP* 50^E
SIC 4911 Transmission, electric power; Transmission, electric power
VP: John C Barr Jr
Treas: Steve Chewning
Ex Dir: James Taylor
Dir IT: Matt Smith

D-U-N-S 94-195-8394 IMP
LYNCO DISTRIBUTION INC
LYNCO PRODUCTS
1410 11th St W, Milan, IL 61264-2264
Tel (309) 787-2300 *Founded/Ownrshp* 2002
Sales 134.8MM^E *EMP* 150
SIC 5199 Variety store merchandise
Pr: Edward Lampo
Pr: Jerry Follette
CFO: John Mitchell
**VP:* Anthony J Alexander
VP: Bill Bone
CIO: Bill Hintz
VP Opers: Christopher Cartelli
VP Sls: Rich Stapf
Mktg Mgr: Lizabeth Wilson
Sales Asso: Alex Kiel

D-U-N-S 05-199-5363 IMP
LYNCO FLANGE & FITTING INC
5114 Steadmont Dr, Houston, TX 77040-6526
Tel (713) 690-3034 *Founded/Ownrshp* 1981
Sales 20.3MM^E *EMP* 21
SIC 5051 Pipe & tubing, steel
Pr: Lynn Vanover
**VP:* Michael F Galland

LYNCO PRODUCTS
See LYNCO DISTRIBUTION INC

D-U-N-S 09-639-4697
LYND CO
8000 W Interstate 10 # 1200, San Antonio, TX 78230-3872
Tel (210) 798-8114 *Founded/Ownrshp* 1979
Sales 98.2MM^E *EMP* 787
SIC 6513 6512 Apartment hotel operation; Commercial & industrial building operation; Apartment hotel operation; Commercial & industrial building operation
CEO: Michael Lynd
**Pt:* Samuel J Kasparek
**CFO:* Sean Kiehne
**Ex VP:* Jeffrey Weissman
**VP:* Randy Brown
**VP:* Lucille Hebert
**VP:* Michael J Lynd Jr
**VP:* Patricia A Lynd
VP: Garrett Swaldi
**VP:* Paul Valdez
Ql Cn Mgr: Jane Neesham

D-U-N-S 00-921-0613
■ **LYNDA.COM INC**
(*Suby of* LINKEDIN CORP) ★
6410 Via Real, Carpinteria, CA 93013-2925
Tel (805) 477-3900 *Founded/Ownrshp* 2012, 2015
Sales 30.0MM^E *EMP* 375
SIC 8244 4813 Software training, computer; Commercial school;
CEO: Eric Robison
Pr: Andrew Wait
CFO: Elaine Kitagawa
CFO: Ning Yang
Sr VP: Tanya Staples
VP: Michael Lydon
VP: Shveta Mujumdar
VP: Michael Ninness
VP: Ken Sandy
Dir Bus: Jennifer Ames
Dir Bus: Jennifer Ames-Gore
Dir Bus: Chery Foy
Dir Bus: Karen Graves
Dir Bus: Ryan McGinnis

D-U-N-S 00-696-1734
LYNDALE TERMINAL CO (MN)
HOLIDAY STATION STORES
4567 American Blvd W, Minneapolis, MN 55437-1123
Tel (952) 830-8700 *Founded/Ownrshp* 1932, 1969
Sales 295.6MM^E *EMP* 4,500
SIC 5311 5411 5541 Department stores; Supermarkets, chain; Convenience stores; Gasoline service stations; Department stores; Supermarkets, chain; Convenience stores; Gasoline service stations
Pr: Ronald Erickson
**VP:* Gerald Erickson

D-U-N-S 19-357-7665
LYNDE AND HARRY BRADLEY FOUNDATION INC
1241 N Franklin Pl, Milwaukee, WI 53202-2901
Tel (414) 291-9915 *Founded/Ownrshp* 1942
Sales 42.9MM *EMP* 18
SIC 8399 Fund raising organization, non-fee basis; Fund raising organization, non-fee basis
Pr: Michael Grebbe
V Ch: David V Uihlein Jr
Pr: Michael Joyce
Ch: Terry Considine
Ch: T Rhodes
Ex VP: William Armstrong
Sr VP: William Schambra
VP: Daniel Schmidt

D-U-N-S 79-630-3501
LYNDEN AIR CARGO LLC
(*Suby of* LYNDEN INC) ★
6441 S Airpark Pl, Anchorage, AK 99502-1809
Tel (907) 243-6150 *Founded/Ownrshp* 1996
Sales 28.7MM^E *EMP* 160
SIC 4522 Air cargo carriers, nonscheduled; Air cargo carriers, nonscheduled
CEO: Jon Burdick
**Pr:* Rick Zerkel
QC Dir: Jeff Pull
Opers Mgr: Dani Camden

D-U-N-S 05-932-0788 IMP
LYNDEN AIR FREIGHT INC
LYNDEN INTERNATIONAL
(*Suby of* LYNDEN INC) ★
18000 Intl Blvd Ste 800, Seatac, WA 98188-4263
Tel (206) 777-5300 *Founded/Ownrshp* 1970
Sales 114.2MM^E *EMP* 354
SIC 4731

D-U-N-S 06-277-4674
LYNDEN INC (WA)
18000 Intl Blvd Ste 800, Seatac, WA 98188-4263
Tel (206) 241-8778 *Founded/Ownrshp* 1947
Sales 844.8MM^E *EMP* 2,000
SIC 4213 4731 4424 Trucking, except local; Domestic freight forwarding; Coastwide transportation, freight; Trucking, except local; Domestic freight forwarding; Coastwide transportation, freight
Pr: Jonathan Burdick
Ch Bd: Jim Jansen
COO: Alex McKallor
CFO: Brad McKeown
VP: Everett H Billingslea
VP: Christine Heitzig
VP: John Kaloper
VP: Ji Kim
VP: Richard Korpela
VP: Stephanie Littleton
VP: Rick Pollock
Dir Bus: Ladonna Blackwell

LYNDEN INTERNATIONAL
See LYNDEN AIR FREIGHT INC

D-U-N-S 09-287-3777
LYNDEN SCHOOL DISTRICT
1203 Bradley Rd, Lynden, WA 98264-9514
Tel (360) 354-4443 *Founded/Ownrshp* 1941
Sales 18.2MM^E *EMP* 300
SIC 8211 Public elementary & secondary schools; Public junior high school; Public senior high school; Public elementary & secondary schools; Public junior high school; Public senior high school
**VP:* Teresa Camfield
Adm Dir: Roger Gates
MIS Dir: Kim Olson
Dir IT: Jeff Leischner
Teacher Pr: Mandi Lenaburg

D-U-N-S 00-279-9260
LYNDEN TRANSPORT INC (WA)
(*Suby of* LYNDEN INC) ★
18000 Intl Blvd Ste 600, Seatac, WA 98188-4263
Tel (206) 575-9575 *Founded/Ownrshp* 1927
Sales 31.0MM^E *EMP* 200
SIC 4213 Trucking, except local; Trucking, except local
Pr: Paul Grimaldi
Sec: Sylvia Chew
VP: Michael W Oliver
Prin: James E Beck
Sls Mgr: Gabriel Omat

D-U-N-S 09-646-3963 IMP
LYNDEX-NIKKEN INC
(*Suby of* NIKKEN KOSAKUSHO WORKS LTD.)
1468 Armour Blvd, Mundelein, IL 60060-4404
Tel (847) 367-4800 *Founded/Ownrshp* 1979
Sales 47.9MM^E *EMP* 63
SIC 5084 Machine tools & accessories
Pr: Masahiro Kashiwakura
**CFO:* James F Gould
VP: Frank Fullone
VP: Preben Hansen
VP: Jun Hayashi
VP: Chidong Xie
Natl Sales: Carl Figgins
Manager: Bob Berongi
Manager: Duke Dang
Manager: Dan O'Connor
Sales Asso: Cindy Tillinghast

D-U-N-S 09-821-5494
LYNDHURST BOARD OF EDUCATION
420 Fern Ave, Lyndhurst, NJ 07071-2252
Tel (201) 372-0223 *Founded/Ownrshp* 1804
Sales 25.6MM^E *EMP* 400
SIC 8211 School board; Public elementary school
Pr: Christopher Musto
VP: Joseph Abruscato
IT Man: Valerie Troncone

D-U-N-S 06-222-3011
LYNDHURST FOUNDATION INC
517 E 5th St, Chattanooga, TN 37403-1826
Tel (423) 756-0767 *Founded/Ownrshp* 1977
Sales 20.0MM *EMP* 5
SIC 8699 Charitable organization; Charitable organization
Pr: Jack Murrah
Ofcr: Sarah Morgan
VP: M C Benic III
**VP:* Benic Clark
Assoc Dir: Macon Toledano

D-U-N-S 02-155-6808
LYNDON BAINES JOHNSON FOUNDATION
2313 Red River St, Austin, TX 78705-5737
Tel (512) 232-2266 *Founded/Ownrshp* 1969
Sales 24.7MM *EMP* 26
Accts Midwikis & Granger Pc Austin
SIC 6732 Charitable trust management
**Ch Bd:* Lyndon Olson
V Ch: Ben Barnes
**Pr:* Elizabeth Christian
**Ch:* Larry Temple

D-U-N-S 78-690-6743
LYNDON PROPERTY INSURANCE CO
(*Suby of* PROTECTIVE LIFE INSURANCE CO) ★
14755 North Outer 40 Rd, Chesterfield, MO 63017-6050
Tel (636) 536-5600 *Founded/Ownrshp* 2000
Sales NA *EMP* 400
SIC 6411 Insurance agents, brokers & service; Insurance agents, brokers & service
CFO: Greg Cariolano

D-U-N-S 88-490-1588
LYNDON STATE COLLEGE
LYNDON STATE COLLEGE AMER
(*Suby of* JOHNSON STATE COLLEGE) ★
1001 College Rd, Lyndonville, VT 05851
Tel (802) 626-6200 *Founded/Ownrshp* 1961
Sales 113.6MM *EMP* 220
Accts Berry Dunn Mcneil & Parker
SIC 8221 College, except junior; College, except junior
Pr: Carol Moore
Store Mgr: Raymond Dubois
Dir IT: Michael Dente
Snr Mgr: Jason Ryan

LYNDON STATE COLLEGE AMER
See LYNDON STATE COLLEGE

D-U-N-S 06-031-2634
LYNDON STEEL CO LLC (NC)
(*Suby of* FABSOUTH LLC) ★
1947 Union Cross Rd, Winston Salem, NC 27107-6448
Tel (336) 785-0848 *Founded/Ownrshp* 1977
Sales 46.5MM[E] *EMP* 250
SIC 3441 Fabricated structural metal; Fabricated structural metal
Pr: David R Morgan
**Pt:* Mike Carcieri
**Pt:* Sam Winters
CFO: Thomas Craver
VP: Larry Whicker
Mng Dir: Scott Macdonald
Dir IT: Derwin Williams
VP Prd: Michael Carcieri
Snr PM: Brinkley Ferguson
Snr PM: Dan Manross

D-U-N-S 05-351-0459 IMP
LYNE LABORATORIES INC
PHARMACEUTICAL RESOURCES
10 Burke Dr, Brockton, MA 02301-5505
Tel (508) 583-8700 *Founded/Ownrshp* 1979
Sales 27.3MM[E] *EMP* 68
Accts William Steele & Associates P
SIC 2834 8731 Pharmaceutical preparations; Commercial physical research
Pr: Stephen Tarallo
**Treas:* Philip J Tarallo
VP: Linda Buckley
**VP:* Top Linda
VP: Linda Top
**VP:* Robert J Walker
VP Sls: Phil Tarello

D-U-N-S 62-161-0989
LYNESS CONSTRUCTION LP
1501 S Main St Ste B, Cleburne, TX 76033-6854
Tel (817) 558-0612 *Founded/Ownrshp* 1987
Sales 29.2MM[E] *EMP* 60
SIC 1542 Commercial & office building contractors
Genl Pt: Tim Lyness
Pr: Ryan Lyness

D-U-N-S 79-453-3976
LYNGBLOMSTEN
1415 Almond Ave, Saint Paul, MN 55108-2507
Tel (651) 646-2941 *Founded/Ownrshp* 1976
Sales 1.9MM *EMP* 340
Accts Larson Allen Weishair Company
SIC 8059 8361 8322 8082 8051 Personal care home, with health care; Residential care; Individual & family services; Home health care services; Skilled nursing care facilities; Personal care home, with health care; Residential care; Individual & family services; Home health care services; Skilled nursing care facilities
Pr: Paul Mikelson
Nrsg Dir: Greg Wainman

D-U-N-S 02-909-3846 IMP
LYNGSO GARDEN MATERIALS INC
345 Shoreway Rd, San Carlos, CA 94070-2708
Tel (650) 364-1730 *Founded/Ownrshp* 1950
Sales 24.7MM[E] *EMP* 45
SIC 5191 5032 5261 5211 3273 1442 Garden supplies; Greenhouse equipment & supplies; Soil, potting & planting; Brick, stone & related material; Garden supplies & tools; Lumber & other building materials; Ready-mixed concrete; Construction sand & gravel
Pr: Linda Dent
**CFO:* Theresa Lyngso
VP Opers: James Kolter
S&M/VP: Vic Thomas
Sls Mgr: Daniel Garcia
Board of Directors: John H Lyngso, Mary Lyngso

D-U-N-S 84-404-4078
LYNGSOE SYSTEMS INC
(*Suby of* LYNGSOE SYSTEMS HOLDING A/S)
7470 New Tech Way Ste P, Frederick, MD 21703-9461
Tel (301) 360-0910 *Founded/Ownrshp* 1999
Sales 26.4MM[E] *EMP* 200
SIC 7373 8231 Computer system selling services; Library services; Computer system selling services; Library services
Pr: Finn Mathissen
VP: Torben Madsen
**VP:* Torben Mathissen

D-U-N-S 80-470-6190
LYNN AMIEE INC
29 PALMS
366 5th Ave Fl 11, New York, NY 10001-2232
Tel (212) 268-4747 *Founded/Ownrshp* 1993
Sales 71.8MM[E] *EMP* 100
SIC 5137 2389 Women's & children's accessories; Disposable garments & accessories; Women's & children's accessories; Disposable garments & accessories
Ch Bd: Steven Spolansky
**VP:* Michael Spolansky
CTO: John Devito

D-U-N-S 07-952-5606
LYNN CITY OF (INC)
3 City Hall Sq, Lynn, MA 01901-1020
Tel (781) 598-4000 *Founded/Ownrshp* 1631
Sales NA *EMP* 775
Accts Melanson Heath & Company Pc A
SIC 9111 Mayors' offices; ; Mayors' offices;
COO: John Pace
Treas: Richard Fortucci
Ofcr: Keith Sheppard
Dir IT: Peter Efstratios

LYNN COMMUNITY HEALTH CENTER
See LYNN COMMUNITY HEALTH INC

D-U-N-S 03-083-4915
LYNN COMMUNITY HEALTH INC
LYNN COMMUNITY HEALTH CENTER
269 Union St, Lynn, MA 01901-1314
Tel (781) 581-3900 *Founded/Ownrshp* 1972
Sales 74.2MM *EMP* 375[E]
Accts Feeley & Driscoll Pc Bosto
SIC 8093 Specialty outpatient clinics; Specialty outpatient clinics
Ex Dir: Lori Abrams Berry
COO: Ronald Doncaster
Prac Mgr: Ana Bakhshyan
Off Admin: Velia Minero
Dir IT: Jacob Bush
IT Man: AMR Mostafa
Psych: Sara Alexakos
Psych: James Conway
Obsttrcn: Rosa Diaz
Doctor: Toryalai Amiri
Doctor: Rachelle Darout

LYNN COUNCIL ON AGING
See GREATER LYNN SENIOR SERVICES INC

D-U-N-S 14-558-9086
LYNN INVESTMENT CORP
235 Saint Nicholas Ave, South Plainfield, NJ 07080-1809
Tel (908) 753-2200 *Founded/Ownrshp* 2004
Sales 25.0MM *EMP* 40
SIC 7389 5051 Metal cutting services; Metals service centers & offices; Metal cutting services; Metals service centers & offices
Pr: William Lynch Jr

D-U-N-S 00-103-8439 IMP
LYNN LADDER AND SCAFFOLDING CO INC (MA)
(*Suby of* LYN-LAD GROUP LTD) ★
20 Boston St 24, Lynn, MA 01904-2527
Tel (781) 598-6010 *Founded/Ownrshp* 1946
Sales 30.8MM[E] *EMP* 120
SIC 5082 2499 3499 7359 5531 7532 Ladders; Ladders, wood; Metal ladders; Equipment rental & leasing; Automobile & truck equipment & parts; Customizing services, non-factory basis; Ladders; Ladders, wood; Metal ladders; Equipment rental & leasing; Automobile & truck equipment & parts; Customizing services, non-factory basis
CEO: Susan Kline
**Pr:* Alan Kline
Genl Mgr: Tony Doucette
Board of Directors: Susan Kline

LYNN LAYTON CADILLAC
See LYNN LAYTON OLDSMOBILE-CADILLAC-NISSAN

D-U-N-S 10-208-9760
LYNN LAYTON CHEVROLET INC
2416 6th Ave Se, Decatur, AL 35601-6516
Tel (205) 252-6410 *Founded/Ownrshp* 1983
Sales 34.2MM[E] *EMP* 80
SIC 5511 5531 7538 5521 Automobiles, new & used; Pickups, new & used; Automobile & truck equipment & parts; General automotive repair shops; Used car dealers; Automobiles, new & used; Pickups, new & used; Automobile & truck equipment & parts; General automotive repair shops; Used car dealers
Pr: Bradford L Layton
Off Mgr: Alta Brown

D-U-N-S 03-156-8280
LYNN LAYTON OLDSMOBILE-CADILLAC-NISSAN (AL)
LYNN LAYTON CADILLAC
2402 6th Ave Se, Decatur, AL 35601-6516
Tel (256) 353-8150 *Founded/Ownrshp* 1951
Sales 21.4MM[E] *EMP* 47
SIC 5511 Automobiles, new & used
Pr: Bradford Lynn Layton
Sales Asso: Will Frederick
Sales Asso: Kyle Looney

D-U-N-S 01-074-9158
LYNN MANAGEMENT CO INC
MCDONALD'S
2896 Crescent Ave Ste 105, Eugene, OR 97408-7422
Tel (541) 431-0885 *Founded/Ownrshp* 1997
Sales 10.6MM[E] *EMP* 430
SIC 5812 Fast-food restaurant, chain; Fast-food restaurant, chain
Pr: Patricia Sanders
CTO: Steve Long
CTO: Gerald Nakamura
CTO: Eileen Traylor

D-U-N-S 14-718-3818 IMP
LYNN PRODUCTS INC
PUREFORMANCE CABLES
2645 W 237th St, Torrance, CA 90505-5269
Tel (310) 530-5966 *Founded/Ownrshp* 1982
Sales 155.6MM[E] *EMP* 1,000
SIC 3577 3357 Computer peripheral equipment; Fiber optic cable (insulated); Computer peripheral equipment; Fiber optic cable (insulated)
Pr: Hsinyu Lin
**Treas:* Chun MEI Shei
**VP:* Eric Tseng
Off Mgr: Hoover Liao
IT Man: Hugh Jass
Sls Mgr: Dan Miller

D-U-N-S 80-363-7297
LYNN PUBLIC SCHOOLS
100 Bennett St, Lynn, MA 01905-3004
Tel (781) 593-1680 *Founded/Ownrshp* 1647
Sales 11.5MM *EMP* 2,000
SIC 8211 Public elementary & secondary schools; Public elementary & secondary schools
VP: Cathy Carmody
Area Mgr: Ben Johnson
IT Man: Christine Kaczorowski
Teacher Pr: Barbara Rafuse
Psych: Daniel Dill
HC Dir: Kathleen McNulty
HC Dir: Dennis Thompson

LYNN REGIONAL CANCER INSTITUTE
See BACO RATON COMMUNITY HOSPITAL INC

LYNN RGNAL CNCER CTR BOCA RTON
See BOCA RATON REGIONAL HOSPITAL INC

D-U-N-S 07-131-0197
LYNN UNIVERSITY INC (FL)
3601 N Military Trl, Boca Raton, FL 33431-5598
Tel (561) 237-7000 *Founded/Ownrshp* 1963, 1971
Sales 87.3MM *EMP* 500
Accts Crowe Horwath Llp Fort Lauder
SIC 8221 College, except junior; College, except junior
Pr: Donald E Ross
**Treas:* John Mortimer
**Chf Mktg O:* Sherrie Weldon
**Ex VP:* Jack Sites
**VP:* Anthony Casale
**VP:* Kathleen Cheek-Milby
**VP:* Jan Glitz
**VP:* Gregory Malfitano
Dir Sec: Mike McMurry
HC Dir: Brett Ormandy

D-U-N-S 03-251-8693
LYNNCO SUPPLY CHAIN SOLUTIONS INC
2448 E 81st St Ste 2600, Tulsa, OK 74137-4212
Tel (918) 664-5540 *Founded/Ownrshp* 2000
Sales 20.7MM[E] *EMP* 100[E]
SIC 4731 Freight transportation arrangement
Owner: Anisya Fritz
**Pr:* Wendy A Buxton
**Ch:* Lynn Fritz
Genl Mgr: Ron Hefty
Opers Mgr: Doug Milroy

D-U-N-S 01-111-2786
LYNNES AUTOMOTIVE GROUP
318 Bloomfield Ave, Bloomfield, NJ 07003-4805
Tel (973) 743-2111 *Founded/Ownrshp* 1959
Sales 29.5MM[E] *EMP* 60
SIC 5511 Automobiles, new & used; Automobiles, new & used
Pr: Dominick Tozzo
CFO: Victor Pita
**VP:* Guy Kooman
IT Man: Stella Kelly

D-U-N-S 01-175-6624 IMP
LYNNES NISSAN WEST INC
(*Suby of* LYNNES AUTOMOTIVE GROUP) ★
59 Us Highway 206, Stanhope, NJ 07874-3262
Tel (973) 347-2200 *Founded/Ownrshp* 1984
Sales 21.9MM[E] *EMP* 56
SIC 5511 7539 5531 Automobiles, new & used; Automotive repair shops; Automotive parts; Automobiles, new & used; Automotive repair shops; Automotive parts
Pr: Dominic Tozzo
**Treas:* Julie Tozzo
**VP:* Steven Tozzo

D-U-N-S 09-745-2676
■ **LYNNFIELD DRUG INC**
FREEDOM DRUG
(*Suby of* CURASCRIPT SPECIALTY DIST) ★
12 Kent Way Ste 120, Byfield, MA 01922-1221
Tel (978) 499-1400 *Founded/Ownrshp* 2001
Sales 165.0MM *EMP* 100
SIC 5912 5961 Drug stores; Pharmaceuticals, mail order; Drug stores; Pharmaceuticals, mail order
Pr: Kim Rondeau
VP: Keith Ebling
VP: Chris Houston
Pharmcst: Frank Seamster

D-U-N-S 07-850-2000
LYNNFIELD PUBLIC SCHOOLS
525 Salem St, Lynnfield, MA 01940-2359
Tel (781) 334-5806 *Founded/Ownrshp* 2012
Sales 23.7MM[E] *EMP* 596
SIC 8211 Public elementary & secondary schools; Public elementary & secondary schools

D-U-N-S 07-950-8297
LYNNFIELD TOWN OF (INC)
55 Summer St, Lynnfield, MA 01940-1861
Tel (781) 334-7663 *Founded/Ownrshp* 1814
Sales NA *EMP* 743
Accts Melanson Heath & Company Pc
SIC 9111 8211 City & town managers' offices; Elementary & secondary schools; City & town managers' offices; Elementary & secondary schools
Ex Dir: Dennis Roy
Cmptr Lab: Grayce Kushmerek
Sales Exec: Scott Holloway
Nrsg Dir: Sandra Wilson

D-U-N-S 04-568-1665
LYNNHAVEN LINCOLN MERCURY INC
SOUTHERN KIA LYNNHAVEN
(*Suby of* GREENBRIER OF VIRGINIA INC) ★
2375 Virginia Beach Blvd, Virginia Beach, VA 23454-4007
Tel (757) 340-0800 *Founded/Ownrshp* 1968
Sales 23.4MM[E] *EMP* 63
SIC 5511 Automobiles, new & used; Automobiles, new & used
Pr: Bradley Hunt
**Pr:* Bob Flather
**Pr:* William Sheppard
**Treas:* Dorothy L Clement
**Treas:* Elizabeth Kruger
**VP:* Charles T Odum

D-U-N-S 09-121-7323
LYNNHAVEN MARINE BOATEL INC (VA)
2150 W Great Neck Rd, Virginia Beach, VA 23451-1504
Tel (757) 481-0700 *Founded/Ownrshp* 1977, 1997
Sales 28.7MM[E] *EMP* 75
SIC 5551 4493 7699 5091 3732 Boat dealers; Marine supplies & equipment; Marinas; Boat repair; Marine engine repair; Boat accessories & parts; Boat building & repairing
Pr: Charles Guthrie
**VP:* Marion Goodman
Sfty Mgr: Donnie Washburn

D-U-N-S 01-293-5966
LYNNHAVEN XII LLC (GA)
WOODLAWN NURSING HOME
206 Southgate Dr, Boone, NC 28607-6250
Tel (828) 265-0080 *Founded/Ownrshp* 1997
Sales 6.2MM[E] *EMP* 320
SIC 8099 Medical services organization; Medical services organization
Ex VP: Sara Massey
**Prin:* Ruth Henson

LYNN'S HALLMARK
See CARD PLACE INC

LYNNWOOD CYCLE BARN
See CYCLE BARN INC

D-U-N-S 18-801-9251
LYNNWOOD MOTOR CO INC
ACURA OF LYNNWOOD
21515 Highway 99, Lynnwood, WA 98036-7339
Tel (425) 775-2925 *Founded/Ownrshp* 1987
Sales 32.7MM[E] *EMP* 75
SIC 5511 Automobiles, new & used; Automobiles, new & used
Pr: Eero Tetri
**Sec:* Jim Morino
Sales Asso: Raj Khanna
Sales Asso: Anthony Mickelsen
Sales Asso: Dave Moreno
Sales Asso: Ben Philipose

D-U-N-S 00-793-7147
LYNTEGAR ELECTRIC COOPERATIVE INC (TX)
1807 Main St, Tahoka, TX 79373
Tel (806) 561-4588 *Founded/Ownrshp* 1938
Sales 76.3MM *EMP* 103
Accts Bolinger Segars Gilbert & Mo
SIC 4911 Electric services; Electric services
CEO: Greg Henley
**Ch Bd:* Earl J Brown Jr
Genl Mgr: Sue Dawson
IT Man: Scottie Olivan
Snr Mgr: Helen Fuentes

D-U-N-S 07-527-8630
LYNWOOD UNIFIED SCHOOL DISTRICT
11321 Bullis Rd, Lynwood, CA 90262-3600
Tel (310) 639-5627 *Founded/Ownrshp* 1950
Sales 103.3MM[E] *EMP* 1,700
Accts Nigro Nigro & White Pc Mur
SIC 8211 Public elementary & secondary schools; Public elementary & secondary schools
Ofcr: Bennetta Jones
VP: Oscar Espinoza
Instr Medi: David Washington
HC Dir: Kavin Dobson

LYNX
See CENTRAL FLORIDA REGIONAL TRANSPORTATION AUTHORITY

D-U-N-S 00-372-3434 IMP
LYNX ENTERPRISES INC (OH)
2184 Schlichter Dr, Hamilton, OH 45015-1345
Tel (513) 856-9161 *Founded/Ownrshp* 1995
Sales 70.0MM *EMP* 20[E]
SIC 5169 Chemicals & allied products
Pr: William Schmidt

LYNX POWER SYSTEMS
See SIGNAL POINT SYSTEMS INC

D-U-N-S 16-006-2634
■ **LYNX SERVICES LLC**
(*Suby of* CLAIMS SERVICES GROUP LLC) ★
6351 Bayshore Rd Ste 18, Fort Myers, FL 33917-3172
Tel (412) 995-6500 *Founded/Ownrshp* 2014
Sales 41.1MM[E] *EMP* 650
SIC 8742 6411 Marketing consulting services; Medical insurance claim processing, contract or fee basis; Marketing consulting services; Medical insurance claim processing, contract or fee basis
Pr: John Wysseier
VP: Richard Palmer
VP: Chris Umble
IT Man: Lee A Dorn
Sls Mgr: Peter Masci

D-U-N-S 00-144-8414
LYON & BILLARD CO
CENTER HARDWARE
38 Gypsy Ln, Meriden, CT 06451-7910
Tel (203) 235-4487 *Founded/Ownrshp* 1847
Sales 38.7MM[E] *EMP* 160
SIC 5211 Lumber & other building materials; Lumber products; Masonry materials & supplies; Millwork & lumber; Lumber & other building materials; Lumber products; Masonry materials & supplies; Millwork & lumber
Pr: Edward R Goralnik
**Treas:* Mildred Goralnik
**VP:* Alan Goralnik

LYON & DITTRICH HOLDING CO
See L & D GROUP INC

D-U-N-S 14-367-2918 IMP
LYON BAKERY INC
135 R St Sw, Washington, DC 20024-3418
Tel (202) 484-2100 *Founded/Ownrshp* 2000
Sales 21.8MM[E] *EMP* 88
SIC 5149 Breads, rolls & buns
Pr: Gerardo Del Cerro
**VP:* Alidad Hakimi

D-U-N-S 07-124-8355
LYON COLLEGE
2300 Highland Rd, Batesville, AR 72501-3699
Tel (870) 793-9813 Founded/Ownrshp 2005
Sales 26.0MM EMP 160
Accts Williamskeepers Llc Columbia
SIC 8221 College, except junior; College, except junior
Pr: Donald V Weatherman
*VP: David L Heringer
VP: David Heringer
VP: F Johnston
*VP: John Jones
*VP: Kenneth J Rueter
Exec: Robert Richard
Genl Mgr: Sandy Harbison
CTO: Amy Foree
MIS Dir: Charles Neal
Pr Dir: Bob R Qualls

LYON COMMUNITIES
See LYON MANAGEMENT GROUP INC

D-U-N-S 09-300-8118 IMP
LYON CONKLIN & CO INC
(Suby of FERGUSON ENTERPRISES INC) ★
4501 Hollins Ferry Rd # 140, Baltimore, MD 21227-4623
Tel (410) 540-4880 Founded/Ownrshp 2001
Sales 69.2MM[E] EMP 250
SIC 5075 5051 Warm air heating & air conditioning; Air conditioning & ventilation equipment & supplies; Warm air heating equipment & supplies; Sheets, metal; Warm air heating & air conditioning; Air conditioning & ventilation equipment & supplies; Warm air heating equipment & supplies; Sheets, metal
CEO: Frank Roach
*Pr: David Brown
VP Mktg: George Tilghman

D-U-N-S 07-625-0679
LYON COUNTY
LYON COUNTY COURT HOUSE
430 Commercial St, Emporia, KS 66801-4013
Tel (620) 341-3270 Founded/Ownrshp 1862
Sales NA EMP 299
SIC 9211 ;
Ch: Scott A Briggs
Pr: Sue Stephens

LYON COUNTY COURT HOUSE
See LYON COUNTY

D-U-N-S 80-050-3919
LYON COUNTY SCHOOL DISTRICT
25 Joe Parr Way, Yerington, NV 89447-2315
Tel (775) 463-3006 Founded/Ownrshp 2007
Sales 64.6MM[E] EMP 1,125
Accts Schettler Macy & Silva Llc Re
SIC 8211 Public elementary & secondary schools; Public elementary & secondary schools
Ofcr: Alvin McNeil
Dir Sec: Shani Bues
MIS Dir: Allen Mederios
IT Man: Julie Gibbs
Teacher Pr: Tim Logan

D-U-N-S 07-882-8502 IMP
LYON LLC
(Suby of ECHELON CAPITAL LLC) ★
420 N Main St, Montgomery, IL 60538-1367
Tel (630) 892-8941 Founded/Ownrshp 2013
Sales 104.1MM[E] EMP 267[E]
SIC 2542 Shelving, office & store: except wood
CEO: Louise E Berg
*CFO: Robert Miller
*Ex VP: William Guo
*Ex VP: Matthew Zakaras

D-U-N-S 60-224-0566
LYON MANAGEMENT GROUP INC
LYON COMMUNITIES
4901 Birch St Frnt, Newport Beach, CA 92660-2114
Tel (949) 252-9101 Founded/Ownrshp 1989
Sales 33.8MM[E] EMP 300
SIC 6513 Apartment building operators; Apartment building operators
Ch: Frank T Suryan Jr
*Pr: Cheryl A Martin
*COO: Trent D Brooks
CFO: Diane Murphy
*Sr VP: John E Townsend
*Sr VP: Peter D Zak

LYON REAL ESTATE
See L LYON WILLIAM & ASSOCIATES INC

LYON SHEET METAL WORKS DIV
See CORRIGAN BROTHERS INC

D-U-N-S 00-317-7003
LYON SHIPYARD INC (VA)
1818 Brown Ave, Norfolk, VA 23504-4458
Tel (757) 622-4661 Founded/Ownrshp 1928, 1971
Sales 57.9MM[E] EMP 190
SIC 3731 Shipbuilding & repairing; Shipbuilding & repairing
Pr: George C Lyon Jr
*VP: Thomas Ackiss
*VP: Johnny E Gaskins
*VP: Ken Kimball
QA Dir: Jim Thomas
Sfty Mgr: Douglas Boss
Sfty Mgr: Barker Steve

D-U-N-S 00-511-9474 IMP
LYON WORKSPACE PRODUCTS LLC
420 N Main St, Montgomery, IL 60538-1367
Tel (630) 892-8941 Founded/Ownrshp 2015
Sales 79.4MM[E] EMP 500
SIC 2542 Shelving, office & store: except wood; Lockers (not refrigerated): except wood; Cabinets: show, display or storage: except wood; Shelving, office & store: except wood; Lockers (not refrigerated): except wood; Cabinets: show, display or storage: except wood
COO: Douglas M Harrison
Dist Mgr: Robert Brossell
Dist Mgr: Lyon Countryman
Dist Mgr: Jeremy Dennis
Dist Mgr: Bryan Lenz
Dist Mgr: Jeff Majnarich
Dist Mgr: Bryan Miller
Dist Mgr: Jeff Shuler
Dist Mgr: Mike Wilgus
IT Man: Margi Washington
Mtls Mgr: Kim Renninger

D-U-N-S 19-412-3154 IMP/EXP
LYONDELL CHEMICAL CO
(Suby of LYONDELLBASELL INDUSTRIES INC) ★
Lyondell Bas Twr Ste 700, Houston, TX 77010
Tel (713) 309-7200 Founded/Ownrshp 2007
Sales 2.3MMM[E] EMP 7,340
SIC 2869 2911 Industrial organic chemicals; Olefins; Ethylene; Propylene, butylene; Gasoline blending plants; Oils, fuel; Jet fuels; Oils, lubricating; Industrial organic chemicals; Olefins; Ethylene; Propylene, butylene; Gasoline blending plants; Oils, fuel; Jet fuels; Oils, lubricating
Pr: Morris Gelb
Pr: Dave Prilutski
CFO: Alan S Bigman
CFO: Robert Blakley
CFO: Karyn Ovelmen
Ofcr: Craig B Glidden
Ofcr: Michael Hopkins
Ofcr: Georgia Smith
Ex VP: Charlie Graham
Sr VP: Kevin W Brown
Sr VP: C Bart De Jong
Sr VP: Edward J Dineen
Sr VP: Cees Los
Sr VP: Timothy D Roberts
Sr VP: Karen Swindler
Sr VP: Jackie Wolf
VP: John Beard
VP: Russell T Crockett Jr
VP: Kevin Denicola
VP: Earl Ehlers
VP: J R Fontenot

D-U-N-S 18-184-3095
LYONDELL CHEMICAL WORLDWIDE INC
1221 Mckinney St Ste 1600, Houston, TX 77010-2006
Tel (713) 652-7200 Founded/Ownrshp 2009
Sales NA EMP 6,892[E]
SIC 2869 Propylene, butylene

LYONDELLBASELL
See HOUSTON REFINING LP

D-U-N-S 62-392-8645 IMP
LYONDELLBASELL ADVANCED POLYOLEFINS USA INC
(Suby of SOLVAY SA)
1200 Harmon Rd, Auburn Hills, MI 48326-1550
Tel (817) 792-1400 Founded/Ownrshp 1997
Sales 17.2MM[E] EMP 348
SIC 3087 Custom compound purchased resins; Custom compound purchased resins
CEO: Jim Gallogly
*Pr: Frederick Young

D-U-N-S 80-155-0802 IMP
LYONDELLBASELL INDUSTRIES INC
(Suby of LYONDELLBASELL INDUSTRIES HOLDINGS B.V.)
1221 Mckinney St Ste 700, Houston, TX 77010-2045
Tel (713) 309-7200 Founded/Ownrshp 2007
Sales 2.3MMM[E] EMP 7,340
SIC 2821 Polymethyl methacrylate resins (plexiglass); Polymethyl methacrylate resins (plexiglass)
CEO: Jim Gallogly
CFO: Bill Wright
Chf Inves: Jim Newgard
*Ex VP: Craig Glidden
*Ex VP: Karyn Ovelmen
*Ex VP: Bob Patele
*Ex VP: Tim Roberts
*VP: Morris Gelb
Dir Risk M: Gerald Obrien
Admn Mgr: Linda Adams
CIO: Robert Tolblert

D-U-N-S 05-419-2569
LYONESS AMERICA INC
(Suby of LYONESS INTERNATIONAL AG)
350 5th Ave Ste 2710, New York, NY 10118-2710
Tel (212) 967-3814 Founded/Ownrshp 2010
Sales 40.0MM[E] EMP 130
SIC 7375 Information retrieval services; Data base information retrieval
CEO: Mario D Hoffmann
*COO: Angela Schadl
Ex VP: Stefano Baldesi

D-U-N-S 07-857-7612
LYONESS MANAGEMENT AMERICAS INC
(Suby of LYONESS AMERICA INC) ★
1450 Brickell Ave # 1700, Miami, FL 33131-3444
Tel (786) 220-7822 Founded/Ownrshp 2010
Sales 40.0MM EMP 75
SIC 8699 Personal interest organization
CEO: Iain Bratt
COO: Angela Schadl
CFO: Efrain Vega

D-U-N-S 00-639-9497 IMP/EXP
LYONS COMPANIES LLC
11401 Electron Dr, Louisville, KY 40299-3857
Tel (502) 267-0087 Founded/Ownrshp 2007
Sales 21.8MM EMP 160
SIC 3441

D-U-N-S 04-648-6478
LYONS ELEMENTARY SCHOOL DISTRICT 103
4100 Joliet Ave, Lyons, IL 60534-1513
Tel (708) 783-4100 Founded/Ownrshp 1887
Sales 21.9MM[E] EMP 568
SIC 8211 Public elementary school; Public elementary school

D-U-N-S 62-375-4876
LYONS GROUP LTD
800 Boylston St Ste 1400, Boston, MA 02199-8052
Tel (617) 262-2605 Founded/Ownrshp 1980
Sales 86.3MM EMP 1,000[E]
SIC 8741 Restaurant management
Pr: Patrick T Lyons
*Treas: Edward J Sparks

D-U-N-S 04-639-9069 EXP
LYONS INDUSTRIES INC
30000 M 62 W, Dowagiac, MI 49047-9348
Tel (269) 782-3404 Founded/Ownrshp 1968
Sales 29.1MM[E] EMP 115
SIC 3088 Plastics plumbing fixtures; Bathroom fixtures, plastic; Shower stalls, fiberglass & plastic; Tubs (bath, shower & laundry), plastic; Plastics plumbing fixtures; Bathroom fixtures, plastic; Shower stalls, fiberglass & plastic; Tubs (bath, shower & laundry), plastic
Ch Bd: Donald D Lyons
*Pr: Lance Lyons
*CFO: Richard Xouris

D-U-N-S 04-166-1042 IMP/EXP
LYONS MAGNUS INC
3158 E Hamilton Ave, Fresno, CA 93702-4163
Tel (559) 268-5966 Founded/Ownrshp 1967
Sales 218.5MM[E] EMP 600
SIC 2033 2026 2087 Jams, including imitation: packaged in cans, jars, etc.; Jellies, edible, including imitation: in cans, jars, etc.; Preserves, including imitation: in cans, jars, etc.; Fruit pie mixes & fillings: packaged in cans, jars, etc.; Yogurt; Syrups, flavoring (except drink); Extracts, flavoring; Jams, including imitation: packaged in cans, jars, etc.; Jellies, edible, including imitation: in cans, jars, etc.; Preserves, including imitation: in cans, jars, etc.; Fruit pie mixes & fillings: packaged in cans, jars, etc.; Yogurt; Syrups, flavoring (except drink); Extracts, flavoring
Pr: Robert E Smittcamp
Pr: Jon Parker
CFO: Phil James
*Sec: Muriel Smittcamp
Sr VP: Shannon Hernandez
Off Mgr: Melinda Ingram
QA Dir: Sean Graham
QA Dir: Tess Jones
QA Dir: David Vargas
Tech Mgr: Jose Perez
VP Prd: Kris Porter

LYONS MEDICAL CENTER
See HUTCHINSON CLINIC PA

D-U-N-S 00-891-6223
LYONS NATIONAL BANK
35 William St, Lyons, NY 14489-1544
Tel (315) 946-4871 Founded/Ownrshp 1865
Sales NA EMP 67
SIC 6021 National commercial banks; National commercial banks
Pr: Robert Schick
Pr: Todd Juffs
Ofcr: Chad Proper
Ex VP: C J Britt
Ex VP: Diana Johnson
VP: Jeff Friend
*VP: Bruce Hodgman
VP: Jim King
VP: Pamela Lee
VP: Robert Macdonell
VP: Tom Muller
VP: Mike Rusinko
VP: Gavitt Saxon

D-U-N-S 62-238-2778
LYONS SALT CO
CENTRAL SALT
(Suby of BSC HOLDING INC) ★
1660 Avenue N, Lyons, KS 67554-9201
Tel (620) 257-5626 Founded/Ownrshp 1990
Sales 27.7MM[E] EMP 75
SIC 1479 Salt (common) mining
Pr: Ken Grimm
*Treas: Judy Samayoa
*VP: Peter Powell

D-U-N-S 07-944-8018
LYONS SCHOOL DISTRICT 103
4100 Joliet Ave, Lyons, IL 60534-1513
Tel (708) 783-4100 Founded/Ownrshp 2014
Sales 12.4MM[E] EMP 368[E]
SIC 8211 Elementary & secondary schools
Prin: Raymond Lauk
HC Dir: Melissa Seabrooks

D-U-N-S 00-821-4074
LYONS SPECIALTY CO LLC
A A VENDING SERVICE DIV
2800 La Highway 1 N, Port Allen, LA 70767-3417
Tel (225) 356-1319 Founded/Ownrshp 1923
Sales 123.5MM EMP 80
SIC 5194 5145 5149 Tobacco & tobacco products; Confectionery; Groceries & related products; Tobacco & tobacco products; Confectionery; Groceries & related products
COO: Raetzsch Hugh
VP: Davis Aquin
Genl Mgr: Charles Schimmel
VP Sls: Ali Momenzadeh
Manager: Allison Chapman

D-U-N-S 79-458-0761
LYONS TIRE & AUTO CENTERS INC
210 Lexington St, Waltham, MA 02452-4612
Tel (781) 894-4900 Founded/Ownrshp 1992
Sales 24.3MM[E] EMP 75
SIC 5014 Tires & tubes
Pr: Stephen Garzone
*Treas: Ann Garzone

D-U-N-S 16-066-9586
LYONS TOWNSHIP HIGH SCHOOL PARENT TEACHER COUNCIL
DISTRICT 204
100 S Brainard Ave, La Grange, IL 60525-2100
Tel (708) 579-6300 Founded/Ownrshp 1888
Sales 37.3MM[E] EMP 527
SIC 8211 Public senior high school; Public senior high school
Bd of Dir: Ann Dudek
VP: Alexis Gutierrez
Dir IT: Ken Smith

LYONS TOYOTA DODGE
See BILL LYONS CARS INC

D-U-N-S 07-587-3562
LYRASIS (INC) (LA)
1438 W Peachtree St Nw, Atlanta, GA 30309-2955
Tel (404) 892-0943 Founded/Ownrshp 1936, 2009
Sales 74.4MM EMP 100
Accts Carr Riggs & Ingram Llc Atla
SIC 8611 Business associations; Business associations
Ex Dir: Kate F Nevins
CFO: Vern Ritter
CIO: Dee Anderson
IT Man: Carol Smith

D-U-N-S 84-448-4704
LYRIC HEALTH CARE LLC
7150 Columbia Gateway Dr J, Columbia, MD 21046-2972
Tel (443) 539-2369 Founded/Ownrshp 1998
Sales NA EMP 4,300
SIC 8059 Personal care home, with health care

D-U-N-S 06-858-4846 IMP
LYRIC OPERA OF CHICAGO
20 N Wacker Dr Ste 860, Chicago, IL 60606-2899
Tel (312) 332-2244 Founded/Ownrshp 1954
Sales 90.5MM EMP 100
SIC 7922 Opera company; Opera company
Treas: Joe Dunn
IT Man: Rene Calvo
Prd Mgr: April Busch
Mktg Dir: Tracy Galligher
Mktg Dir: Susan Mathieson
Mktg Dir: Lisa Middleton
Mktg Mgr: Emily Lange
Mktg Mgr: Kira Lowe

D-U-N-S 55-728-2261
▲ LYRIS INC
401 Congress Ave Ste 2650, Austin, TX 78701-3708
Tel (512) 201-8287 Founded/Ownrshp 2007
Sales 31.2MM EMP 140
Accts Burr Pilger Mayer Inc San J
Tkr Sym LYRI Exch OTO
SIC 7372 Prepackaged software; Prepackaged software
Pr: John Philpin
*Ch Bd: William T Comfort III
COO: Deborah Eudaley
VP: Cindy Sherrett
VP: Nav Singh
Sftwr Eng: Jenny Kazarina
VP Mktg: Alex Lustberg

D-U-N-S 02-838-0306
LYTLE CONSTRUCTION INC
1100 Se Hamblen Rd, Lees Summit, MO 64081-2938
Tel (816) 524-7275 Founded/Ownrshp 2001
Sales 25.7MM[E] EMP 95
SIC 1542 Hospital construction; Hospital construction
Pr: Robert Lytle
*VP: Craig Brandon
Site Mgr: Robert Volz

D-U-N-S 09-228-1229
LYTLE ENTERPRISES LLC
10500 Ne 8th St Ste 1700, Bellevue, WA 98004-4326
Tel (425) 463-1200 Founded/Ownrshp 1972
Sales 37.5MM[E] EMP 400
SIC 6719 Investment holding companies, except banks; Investment holding companies, except banks
Sr VP: Jill Ashton

D-U-N-S 04-390-7203
LYTLE PHILLIPS LLP
1 Canalside 125 Main St, Buffalo, NY 14203
Tel (716) 847-8400 Founded/Ownrshp 1997
Sales 60.4MM[E] EMP 465
SIC 8111 General practice law office; General practice law office
Mng Pt: Morgan G Graham
Pt: William J Brown
Pt: Thomas Burns
Pt: Morgan G Graham
Pt: Robert M Greene
Pt: Edward M Griffith Jr
Pt: Martin Idzik
Pt: Annabelle Irey
Pt: Gary Kotaska
Pt: James A Locke
Pt: Kenneth Manning
Pt: Claude Montgomery
Pt: David J Murray
Pt: Martha L Salzman
Pt: Raymond H Seitz
Pt: Paul Stecker
Pt: James W Whitcomb
Pt: Thomas Wiswall
Pt: Paul Zuydhoek
COO: Lisa McDougall

D-U-N-S 80-901-0510 IMP
LYTRO INC
1300 Terra Bella Ave, Mountain View, CA 94043-1850
Tel (650) 316-8888 Founded/Ownrshp 2006
Sales 31.2MM[E] EMP 80
SIC 5946 Cameras
CEO: Jason Rosenthal
COO: Omer Cohen
VP: Stan Jirman
Snr Sftwr: Grant Yoshida
Opers Mgr: Kathy Lee
VP Mktg: Kira Wampler
Snr Mgr: Ariel Braunstein

D-U-N-S 00-100-7558 IMP
LYTRON INC (MA)
55 Dragon Ct, Woburn, MA 01801-1039
Tel (781) 933-7300 Founded/Ownrshp 1958
Sales 36.0MM[E] EMP 210[E]
SIC 3585 3443

D-U-N-S 92-676-5017
LYTTON RANCHERIA
CASINO SAN PABLO
13255 San Pablo Ave, San Pablo, CA 94806-3907
Tel (510) 215-7888 *Founded/Ownrshp* 2003
Sales 20.2MM^E *EMP* 547
SIC 7999 Gambling & lottery services; Gambling & lottery services
Genl Mgr: Michael Gorczynski
Prin: Cathi Hamel
Secur Mgr: Felipe Guzman

D-U-N-S 02-649-9454
LYTX INC
9785 Towne Centre Dr, San Diego, CA 92121-1968
Tel (858) 430-4000 *Founded/Ownrshp* 1998
Sales 85.2MM^E *EMP* 300
SIC 3812 Search & navigation equipment; Search & detection systems & instruments; Search & navigation equipment; Search & detection systems & instruments
CEO: Brandon Nixon
CFO: Paul J Pucino
CFO: Kelli Richard
Chf Mktg O: Kara Kerker
Ex VP: Drew Martin
Ex VP: David Riordan
Sr VP: Shelley Bennett
Sr VP: Julie Cunningham
Sr VP: Eliot Feldstein
VP: Bryon Cook
VP: Tonya Cross
VP: Tom Fisher
VP: Sue Greenway
VP: Kris Hanson
VP: Patrick Shipley
Comm Dir: Greg Lund
Board of Directors: Thomas Darcy, Marco Thompson

D-U-N-S 80-859-0413 IMP/EXP
■ **LZB MANUFACTURING INC**
LA-Z-BOY
(*Suby of* LA-Z-BOY INC) ★
1 Lazboy Dr, Monroe, MI 48162-5138
Tel (734) 242-1444 *Founded/Ownrshp* 2004
Sales 144.8MM^E *EMP* 801
SIC 2512 Upholstered household furniture; Upholstered household furniture
Pr: Mark S Bacon Sr
**CFO:* Louis M Riccio
**Treas:* Greg A Brinks
**VP:* R Rand Tucker

M

M & A AUTO
See MID COLUMBIA BUS CO INC

D-U-N-S 07-567-6072
M & A DISTRIBUTING CO INC
M & A DISTRIBUTION
31031 Diamond Pkwy, Solon, OH 44139-5463
Tel (440) 703-4580 *Founded/Ownrshp* 1981
Sales 53.7MM^E *EMP* 135^E
SIC 5182 5181 Wine & distilled beverages; Beer & other fermented malt liquors; Wine & distilled beverages; Beer & other fermented malt liquors
Pr: John M Antonucci
CFO: Joe McHenry
Mktg Mgr: Jason Edwards

M & A DISTRIBUTION
See M & A DISTRIBUTING CO INC

D-U-N-S 00-890-7735
M & A ELECTRIC POWER CO-OPERATIVE
4169 Highway Pp, Poplar Bluff, MO 63901-3968
Tel (573) 785-9651 *Founded/Ownrshp* 1948
Sales 20.7MM *EMP* 46
SIC 4911

D-U-N-S 08-312-4862
M & A MORTGAGE INC
1600 N Broadway Ste 1020, Santa Ana, CA 92706-3930
Tel (714) 560-1970 *Founded/Ownrshp* 1997
Sales NA *EMP* 75
SIC 6163 Mortgage brokers arranging for loans, using money of others; Mortgage brokers arranging for loans, using money of others
Pr: Maria Avalos
**CFO:* Martin Alvarado

D-U-N-S 05-651-5745
M & A SCOTT CORP
MCDONALD OFFICE
218 W Ash St, Piqua, OH 45356-2202
Tel (937) 773-7200 *Founded/Ownrshp* 1979
Sales 17.7MM^E *EMP* 500
SIC 5812 Fast-food restaurant, chain; Fast-food restaurant, chain
Pr: Benjamin P Scott

D-U-N-S 04-700-5293
M & A SUPPLY CO INC
7000 Executive Center Dr # 200, Brentwood, TN 37027-3299
Tel (615) 399-5324 *Founded/Ownrshp* 1969
Sales 56.8MM^E *EMP* 140
SIC 5075 5074 Warm air heating & air conditioning; Plumbing & hydronic heating supplies; Warm air heating & air conditioning; Plumbing & hydronic heating supplies
Ch Bd: Charles E Anderson
**Pr:* Edwin Anderson
**Sec:* Donna Anderson
**VP:* Roger Yates
Opers Mgr: Ed Adcock
Opers Mgr: Billy Salyer
Sls Mgr: Dan Cartin
Sls Mgr: Tommy Lamb
Sls Mgr: Mike Mann

D-U-N-S 04-107-2349
M & B ASPHALT CO INC
1525 W Seneca Cnty Rd 42, Tiffin, OH 44883
Tel (419) 992-4235 *Founded/Ownrshp* 1958
Sales 85.7MM^E *EMP* 38
SIC 1429 2951 1611 2952 1771

D-U-N-S 04-732-6210
M & B PAUL INC
CENTRAL CITY TOYOTA
4800 Chestnut St, Philadelphia, PA 19139-3513
Tel (215) 476-1200 *Founded/Ownrshp* 1969
Sales 40.6MM^E *EMP* 115
SIC 5511 Automobiles, new & used; Automobiles, new & used
Pr: Maxwell Paul
**VP:* Joseph Newell
Genl Mgr: Brad Paul
VP Mktg: Ryan Pesin
Sls Mgr: Ted Daddario
Sls Mgr: Martin Fusselman
Sls Mgr: Frank Miksit
Sales Asso: Calvin Jones
Sales Asso: Lewis Strand
Sales Asso: Tim Woodard

D-U-N-S 84-023-2904
M & B SEA PRODUCTS INC
110 Herman Melville Blvd, New Bedford, MA 02740-7344
Tel (508) 979-1020 *Founded/Ownrshp* 1993
Sales 22.3MM^E *EMP* 37
SIC 5146 Fish & seafoods
Pr: John Murray

M & B WINDOW FASHIONS
See HD WINDOW FASHIONS INC

M & C
See MURCHISON & CUMMING LLP

D-U-N-S 00-229-7232 IMP
■ **M & C SPECIALTIES CO** (PA)
(*Suby of* ILLINOIS TOOL WORKS INC) ★
90 James Way, Southampton, PA 18966-3825
Tel (215) 322-7441 *Founded/Ownrshp* 1962
Sales 65.0MM^E *EMP* 400
SIC 2672 Tape, pressure sensitive: made from purchased materials; Tape, pressure sensitive: made from purchased materials
Pr: Donald Rauch
**Pr:* Sevan Demirdogden
**Treas:* Felix L Rodriguez Jr
**Sec:* Daniel Cistone
**VP:* Mark W Croll
Plnt Mgr: Joel Villavicencio
Prd Mgr: Joe Benincasa

M & D ACE HARDWARE
See M & D SUPPLY INC

M & D DISTRIBUTORS
See MAGNETO & DIESEL INJECTOR SERVICE INC

D-U-N-S 62-521-2212
M & D FRAGRANCES & COSMETICS INC
3 Taylor Rd, Edison, NJ 08817-2510
Tel (732) 339-1100 *Founded/Ownrshp* 1990
Sales 34.6MM^E *EMP* 61
SIC 5122 5999 Cosmetics; Perfumes; Cosmetics
Pr: Dalip Malhotra
**VP:* Neetu Malhotra

D-U-N-S 02-071-1438 IMP
M & D INDUSTRIES CORP (OK)
SONIC DRIVE-IN
2701 W I 44 Service Rd # 102, Oklahoma City, OK 73112-3775
Tel (405) 942-2936 *Founded/Ownrshp* 1975
Sales 75.0MM *EMP* 1,800
SIC 5812 Drive-in restaurant; Drive-in restaurant
Pr: Dan Winters
**VP:* Marvin D Jirous

D-U-N-S 08-655-0860
M & D MECHANICAL CONTRACTORS INC
1810 Sherman St Se, Decatur, AL 35601-3440
Tel (256) 353-1444 *Founded/Ownrshp* 1992
Sales 25.0MM *EMP* 165
Accts Dent Baker & Company Llp Bir
SIC 1711 Mechanical contractor; Warm air heating & air conditioning contractor; Ventilation & duct work contractor; Process piping contractor; Mechanical contractor; Warm air heating & air conditioning contractor; Ventilation & duct work contractor; Process piping contractor
Pr: Allan Schollian
**COO:* Bobby L Allfrey
**Treas:* Rodney Ferguson
Prd Mgr: Greg Broadway

M & D PRINTING DIV
See KINGERY PRINTING CO

D-U-N-S 02-605-5269
M & D SUPPLY INC
M & D ACE HARDWARE
4580 College St, Beaumont, TX 77707-3910
Tel (409) 842-2731 *Founded/Ownrshp* 1972
Sales 23.2MM^E *EMP* 85
SIC 5251

D-U-N-S 02-614-6175
M & E BRAZOS LTD
BRAZOS M & E
622 Commerce St, Clute, TX 77531-5612
Tel (979) 233-2841 *Founded/Ownrshp* 1988
Sales 47.7MM *EMP* 300
Accts Grant Thornton Llp Houston
SIC 7699 1629 Industrial machinery & equipment repair; Earthmoving contractor; Industrial machinery & equipment repair; Earthmoving contractor
Prin: Mark Monical
Genl Pt: Harold E Monical
Genl Pt: Jerry Monical
Sec: Tammi Blevins

D-U-N-S 60-496-3058 IMP
M & E COMPONENTS INC
M&E GROUP
1828 Mound Rd, Rockdale, IL 60436-9325
Tel (815) 730-0555 *Founded/Ownrshp* 2004
Sales 23.9MM^E *EMP* 23
SIC 5085 5063 Fasteners, industrial: nuts, bolts, screws, etc.; Electrical apparatus & equipment
Pr: Brad Cain
Pr: David Cirak
**VP:* Vicki Bender
Plnt Mgr: Jim Wisnieski
VP Sls: Brian Okeeffe

D-U-N-S 80-123-1093
■ **M & F FINANCIAL SERVICES INC**
MERCHANTS & FARMERS BANK
(*Suby of* MERCHANTS AND FARMERS BANK) ★
134 W Washington St, Kosciusko, MS 39090-3633
Tel (662) 289-5121 *Founded/Ownrshp* 1895
Sales NA *EMP* 415
SIC 6141 Automobile & consumer finance companies; Automobile & consumer finance companies
Pr: Scott Wiggers
VP: Andy McMillan

D-U-N-S 03-908-7705
M & F FIRST CORP
134 W Washington St, Kosciusko, MS 39090-3633
Tel (662) 289-5121 *Founded/Ownrshp* 1890
Sales NA *EMP* 456^E
SIC 6022

D-U-N-S 05-438-8533 IMP
M & F WESTERN PRODUCTS INC
1303 Holiday Dr, Sulphur Springs, TX 75482-4703
Tel (903) 885-8646 *Founded/Ownrshp* 1977
Sales 40.1MM^E *EMP* 150
SIC 5137 5136 Women's & children's accessories; Caps, men's & boys'; Women's & children's accessories; Caps, men's & boys'
Pr: Mickey F Eddins
**Treas:* Paul Eddins
**VP:* David L Eddins
Netwrk Mgr: John Eddins
Sales Exec: Lyn Burnett
Natl Sales: Gene House

D-U-N-S 88-398-3413
M & F WORLDWIDE CORP
(*Suby of* MACANDREWS & FORBES HOLDINGS INC) ★
35 E 62nd St, New York, NY 10065-8014
Tel (212) 572-8600 *Founded/Ownrshp* 2011
Sales 2.6MMM^E *EMP* 9,000
SIC 5149 8741 2782 Flavourings & fragrances; Business management; Checkbooks; Flavourings & fragrances; Business management; Checkbooks
Pr: Barry F Schwartz
**Pr:* Christine M Taylor
**Treas:* Alison M Horowitz
Ofcr: Steven Fasman
Board of Directors: Stephen G Taub, Philip E Beekman, Carl B Webb, William C Bevins, Martha L Byorum, Charles T Dawson, Theo W Folz, John M Keane, Paul M Meister, Ronald O Perelman, Bruce Slovin

D-U-N-S 07-042-7489 EXP
M & G ELECTRONICS CORP
889 Seahawk Cir, Virginia Beach, VA 23452-7809
Tel (757) 468-6000 *Founded/Ownrshp* 1976
Sales 113.5MM^E *EMP* 700
SIC 3613 3694 3699 3643 3357 Panelboards & distribution boards, electric; Harness wiring sets, internal combustion engines; Electrical equipment & supplies; Current-carrying wiring devices; Nonferrous wiredrawing & insulating; Panelboards & distribution boards, electric; Harness wiring sets, internal combustion engines; Electrical equipment & supplies; Current-carrying wiring devices; Nonferrous wiredrawing & insulating
Pr: Mark F Garcea
Treas: Larry Holleman
CIO: Don Feazelle
Dir IT: Don Schlotterbeck
Sfty Mgr: Edward Noble
Plnt Mgr: Cheryl Underwood
Prd Mgr: Jeremy White
Sls Mgr: Rick Futrell

D-U-N-S 14-440-9307
M & G INVESTMENTS INC
DISHMAN-DODGE
7700 E Sprague Ave, Spokane Valley, WA 99212-2935
Tel (509) 924-3250 *Founded/Ownrshp* 1995
Sales 33.2MM^E *EMP* 100
SIC 5511 Automobiles, new & used; Automobiles, new & used
Pr: Marlene Hollenback
**VP:* Mark Waltermire
Store Mgr: Mike Kahabka
Sls&Mrk Ex: Robert Bear

D-U-N-S 02-617-0675 EXP
M & G PARTNERS LLP (WI)
FASHION ANGELS ENTERPRISES
306 N Milwaukee St Fl 1, Milwaukee, WI 53202-5832
Tel (414) 961-9200 *Founded/Ownrshp* 1994
Sales 68.5MM^E *EMP* 94
SIC 5094 5092 Beads; Educational toys; Arts & crafts equipment & supplies; Beads; Toys & hobby goods & supplies; Arts & crafts equipment & supplies; Educational toys
CEO: Mark Miller
**Pt:* Goldi Miller
**Pt:* Myra Mouloudji
Ex VP: Jonathan Victor
VP: Chris Dresselhuys
VP: Steve Jackson
Exec: John Lee
VP Sls: Jaimie Dow
Mktg Mgr: Kaeti Lindquist
Sls Mgr: Roger Pollack

D-U-N-S 16-071-2522 IMP/EXP
M & G POLYMERS USA LLC
(*Suby of* M&G USA CORP) ★
27610 Huntington Rd, Apple Grove, WV 25502-8121
Tel (304) 576-2041 *Founded/Ownrshp* 2005
Sales 77.4MM^E *EMP* 275^E
SIC 2821 Polyesters; Polyethylene resins; Polyesters; Polyethylene resins
Pr: Marko Ghisolfi
VP Opers: Guido Ghisolfi
Opers Mgr: Jeff Black
Plnt Mgr: Jeff Shay
Pr Dir: Chuck Kern
Snr PM: Dave Sayer

M & H
See MUSSELMAN AND HALL CONTRACTORS LLC

D-U-N-S 09-946-8688
M & H BUILDING SPECIALTIES INC
3084 S Highland Dr Ste E, Las Vegas, NV 89109-1056
Tel (702) 385-3168 *Founded/Ownrshp* 1978
Sales 12.6MM *EMP* 500^E
Accts Fair Anderson & Langerman La
SIC 1742 1542 Acoustical & ceiling work; Commercial & office buildings, renovation & repair; Acoustical & ceiling work; Commercial & office buildings, renovation & repair
Pr: Jerrad Martin
**VP:* Bonnie Martin

D-U-N-S 15-473-8157
M & H ENTERPRISES INC
19450 State Highway 249 # 600, Houston, TX 77070-3058
Tel (281) 664-7222 *Founded/Ownrshp* 1977
Sales 44.2MM^E *EMP* 250
SIC 8711 Engineering services; Engineering services
Pr: David Costello
VP: Chris Morris
Mktg Mgr: Heidi Hochstrasser
Snr PM: Brian Coates
Snr PM: Charles Turner

M & H GAS
See MILLER & HOLMES INC

M & I TRUST
See MARSHALL & ILSLEY TRUST CO NATIONAL ASSOCIATION

D-U-N-S 05-131-6495
M & J BUS LINES INC
130 Ingham Hill Rd, Old Saybrook, CT 06475-4115
Tel (860) 388-0263 *Founded/Ownrshp* 1995
Sales 21.2MM^E *EMP* 330
SIC 4151 School buses; School buses
Pr: Michael Beebe
**VP:* Michael Collins

M & J BUTTON
See M & J TRIMMING CO INC

D-U-N-S 01-836-2253
M & J ENERGY GROUP LLC
5431 Highway 90 E, Broussard, LA 70518-5906
Tel (337) 237-8024 *Founded/Ownrshp* 2010
Sales 27.8MM^E *EMP* 29^E
SIC 5172 Petroleum brokers
CEO: Marlon Haynes
Pr: Leroy Charles
Genl Mgr: Andy Landry
Sales Asso: Gwen Viator

D-U-N-S 14-676-1270
M & J FOODS LLC
4100 I 55 S, Jackson, MS 39212-5519
Tel (601) 594-1085 *Founded/Ownrshp* 2004
Sales 30.0MM *EMP* 14
SIC 5141 Groceries, general line; Groceries, general line

D-U-N-S 10-158-9620
M & J MANAGEMENT CORP
MCDONALD'S
147 Delta Dr, Pittsburgh, PA 15238-2805
Tel (412) 963-6550 *Founded/Ownrshp* 1968
Sales 45.4MM^E *EMP* 1,000
Accts Horovitz Rudoy & Roteman Llc
SIC 5812 Fast-food restaurant, chain; Fast-food restaurant, chain
Pr: Michael J Delligatti
**Treas:* Daniel Hubert
**VP:* Daniel T Deligatti

D-U-N-S 11-478-9238
M & J SEAFOOD CO INC
6859 Walthall Way, Paramount, CA 90723-2028
Tel (562) 529-2786 *Founded/Ownrshp* 2001
Sales 21.1MM^E *EMP* 30
SIC 5146 Seafoods
CEO: J Jesus Rodriguez
COO: Wendy McDonalds
Off Mgr: Wendy Medino

D-U-N-S 01-283-1901 IMP
M & J SHOES LLC
MARTY SHOES
121 Carver Ave, Westwood, NJ 07675-2602
Tel (201) 497-6634 *Founded/Ownrshp* 2009
Sales 46.7MM^E *EMP* 100
Accts Traphagen & Traphagen Llc
SIC 5139 Shoes

D-U-N-S 01-212-6082 IMP
M & J TRIMMING CO INC
M & J BUTTON
1008 6th Ave, New York, NY 10018-5495
Tel (212) 391-6200 *Founded/Ownrshp* 1964
Sales 52.4MM^E *EMP* 140
SIC 5131 5949

D-U-N-S 00-808-3362 IMP
■ **M & J VALVE**
SPX FLOW CONTROL
(*Suby of* SPX CORP) ★
19191 Hempstead Hwy, Houston, TX 77065
Tel (281) 469-0550 *Founded/Ownrshp* 1977

Sales 31.1MM^E *EMP* 200
SIC 3491 Automatic regulating & control valves; Pressure valves & regulators, industrial; Process control regulator valves; Valves, automatic control; Automatic regulating & control valves; Pressure valves & regulators, industrial; Process control regulator valves; Valves, automatic control
Pr: Don Cantra

M & K QUALITY TRUCK SALES
See M & K TRUCK AND TRAILER INC

M & K QUALITY TRUCK SALES
See CM LIQUIDATION INC

D-U-N-S 79-042-0632 EXP
M & K TRUCK AND TRAILER INC
M & K QUALITY TRUCK SALES
8800 Byron Commerce Dr Sw, Byron Center, MI 49315-8491
Tel (616) 878-4981 *Founded/Ownrshp* 1988
Sales 88.4MM^E *EMP* 166^E
SIC 5511 4212 Trucks, tractors & trailers: new & used; Local trucking, without storage; Trucks, tractors & trailers: new & used; Local trucking, without storage
Pr: Ron Meyering
VP: Russ Raine
Genl Mgr: Brian Cary
Genl Mgr: Bob Devink
Genl Mgr: Ted Pilecki
Opers Mgr: Tim Behrens
Sls Mgr: Tim Schimmel

M & L CHRYSLER JEEP DODGE RAM
See M AND L MOTOR CO INC

M & L FOODS
See M & L FROZEN FOODS INC

D-U-N-S 08-304-1715
M & L FROZEN FOODS INC
M & L FOODS
1320 S Broadway, Saint Louis, MO 63104-4402
Tel (314) 231-8055 *Founded/Ownrshp* 1974
Sales 24.1MM^E *EMP* 29
SIC 5141 Groceries, general line
CEO: Pete Tocco
**Pr:* Tony Tocco
**Sec:* Barry Pass
**VP:* Frankie Tocco
**VP:* Leonard Tocco

M & L TRUCKING SERVICES
See M AND L TRUCKING INC

D-U-N-S 95-854-5337
M & M ASPHALT MAINTENANCE INC
1180 Sw 10th St, Delray Beach, FL 33444-1243
Tel (561) 588-0949 *Founded/Ownrshp* 2009
Sales 28.6MM^E *EMP* 75
SIC 1611 1771 Surfacing & paving; Blacktop (asphalt) work
Pr: Ken Goldberg
**Treas:* David Goldberg
Off Mgr: Tina Gladden

D-U-N-S 14-756-2441
M & M AUTOMOTIVE GROUP INC
BROADWAY VOLKSWAGEN
2740 Broadway, Oakland, CA 94612-3110
Tel (510) 834-7711 *Founded/Ownrshp* 1996
Sales 25.7MM^E *EMP* 42
SIC 5511 Automobiles, new & used
CEO: Michael Murphy
**Pr:* Mike Murphy
Exec: Joe Haddade
Genl Mgr: Sean Driver
Genl Mgr: Samir Rohayem
IT Man: Stephen Day
Sls Mgr: Tony Rohayem

D-U-N-S 02-975-9904
M & M AUTOMOTIVE INC
KARL MALONE TOYOTA
11453 S Lone Peak Pkwy, Draper, UT 84020-6872
Tel (801) 553-5800 *Founded/Ownrshp* 1997
Sales 125.0MM *EMP* 175
SIC 5511 Automobiles, new & used; Automobiles, new & used
Pr: Karl A Malone
**VP:* Andrew Madsen
**VP:* Gregory S Miller
Genl Mgr: Jon May

M & M B B
See MINISTERS AND MISSIONARIES BENEFIT BOARD OF AMERICAN BAPTIST CHURCHES

D-U-N-S 09-809-5680
M & M CARTAGE CO INC
4106 Eastmoor Rd, Louisville, KY 40218-3002
Tel (502) 456-4586 *Founded/Ownrshp* 1974
Sales 46.3MM^E *EMP* 150
SIC 4212 4213 Light haulage & cartage, local; Contract haulers; Light haulage & cartage, local; Contract haulers
Pr: Donald Hayden
**Sec:* Frances Jane Hayden
Trfc Dir: George Lewis
Opers Mgr: Rob Birk

D-U-N-S 11-255-9539
M & M CONTRACTING OF TEXAS INC
4660 Boldt Rd, San Antonio, TX 78222-3803
Tel (210) 648-4010 *Founded/Ownrshp* 1993
Sales 22.6MM^E *EMP* 85
SIC 1542 1794 1795 Commercial & office buildings, renovation & repair; Excavation & grading, building construction; Demolition, buildings & other structures; Commercial & office buildings, renovation & repair; Excavation & grading, building construction; Demolition, buildings & other structures
Pr: Mark Cuppetilli
Treas: Jim Harris
VP: Tommy Hanson
Snr Mgr: John Adams

M & M DISTRIBUTING
See SHAR PRODUCTS CO

M & M DISTRIBUTORS
See WIEMAR DISTRIBUTORS INC

D-U-N-S 15-472-2698 IMP/EXP
M & M INDUSTRIES INC
316 Corporate Pl, Chattanooga, TN 37419-2339
Tel (423) 821-3302 *Founded/Ownrshp* 1986
Sales 70.7MM^E *EMP* 115
SIC 3089 3411 Injection molding of plastics; Metal cans; Injection molding of plastics; Metal cans
Pr: Glenn H Morris Sr
CFO: Bettina Johnson

D-U-N-S 00-253-0772
M & M LIGHTING LP
5620 S Rice Ave, Houston, TX 77081-2196
Tel (713) 667-5611 *Founded/Ownrshp* 1961
Sales 30.0MM *EMP* 58^E
SIC 5063 5719 3646 Lighting fixtures, commercial & industrial; Lighting fixtures, residential; Lighting fixtures; Commercial indusl & institutional electric lighting fixtures; Lighting fixtures, commercial & industrial; Lighting fixtures, residential; Lighting fixtures; Commercial indusl & institutional electric lighting fixtures
Genl Pt: Allan Margolin
Pt: Renee Margolin
Manager: Joe Fallas

D-U-N-S 09-946-7144
M & M MANAGEMENT CO
176 W Main St, Ventura, CA 93001-2510
Tel (805) 648-6925 *Founded/Ownrshp* 1965
Sales 33.0MM^E *EMP* 413
SIC 8742 8741 General management consultant; Business management; General management consultant; Business management
CEO: Joseph Mark Ellison
**CFO:* Marty Lavere
**Treas:* Nick T Ananais
**Sec:* Sue Ellison

D-U-N-S 15-144-6366
M & M MARKETING INC
26 Highland Cir, Needham, MA 02494-3012
Tel (781) 444-0313 *Founded/Ownrshp* 1985
Sales 61.6MM^E *EMP* 11
Accts Cowan Bolduc Doherty North An
SIC 5141 Groceries, general line; Groceries, general line
Pr: Kevin C Mc Carthy
VP: Stephen Copp

M & M MARS
See MARS CHOCOLATE NORTH AMERICA LLC

D-U-N-S 00-805-7796 IMP/EXP
M & M MERCHANDISERS INC
1923 Bomar Ave, Fort Worth, TX 76103-2102
Tel (817) 339-1400 *Founded/Ownrshp* 1976
Sales 30.5MM^E *EMP* 78
SIC 5046 5099 5065 Display equipment, except refrigerated; Musical instruments; Sound equipment, electronic; Closed circuit television; Display equipment, except refrigerated; Musical instruments; Sound equipment, electronic; Closed circuit television
CEO: Marty Stenzler
Pr: Todd Ordway
**COO:* Chuck Franklin
**CFO:* Kirk Wensel
Exec: Amy Odle
Brnch Mgr: Wayne Williams

D-U-N-S 06-034-0312
M & M MOLDING CORP (NY)
250 Creative Dr, Central Islip, NY 11722-4404
Tel (631) 582-1900 *Founded/Ownrshp* 1977
Sales 28.9MM^E *EMP* 200
SIC 3089 Injection molded finished plastic products; Injection molded finished plastic products
Pr: Mathias Meinzinger
**CFO:* John McLaughlin
CFO: Ron Sacker
**Treas:* Gunther Bartsch
Info Man: Steve Walsh

M & M RESTAURANT SUPPLY
See KEYSTONE FOODS LLC

D-U-N-S 11-594-3193
M & M ROOFING INC
3488 Eagle Nest Dr, Crete, IL 60417-1287
Tel (708) 756-7800 *Founded/Ownrshp* 1976
Sales 32.5MM^E *EMP* 109
SIC 1521 1541 1761 1751 General remodeling, single-family houses; Renovation, remodeling & repairs: industrial buildings; Roofing & gutter work; Roofing contractor; Siding contractor; Window & door installation & erection; General remodeling, single-family houses; Renovation, remodeling & repairs: industrial buildings; Roofing & gutter work; Roofing contractor; Siding contractor; Window & door installation & erection
Pr: Michael E Yadron
Sales Asso: Mike Peters

D-U-N-S 00-687-0612
M & M SERVICE CO INC
130 N Chiles St, Carlinville, IL 62626-1684
Tel (217) 854-4516 *Founded/Ownrshp* 1931
Sales 294.4MM *EMP* 165
Accts Cliftonlarsonallen Llp Normal
SIC 5153 5191 5171 Grain elevators; Feed; Fertilizer & fertilizer materials; Petroleum bulk stations; Grain elevators; Feed; Fertilizer & fertilizer materials; Petroleum bulk stations
Pr: Gary Meyers
VP: Emmet Bennett
Genl Mgr: Brad Klaus
Opers Mgr: Steve Mullink

D-U-N-S 02-644-1498
M & M TRANSPORT SERVICES INC (MA)
643 Manley St, West Bridgewater, MA 02379-1002
Tel (617) 769-9370 *Founded/Ownrshp* 1990
Sales 90.9MM^E *EMP* 400
SIC 4213 4212 Trucking, except local; Local trucking, without storage; Trucking, except local; Local trucking, without storage
Pr: Mark Warsofsky

D-U-N-S 05-861-0163
M & M WELDING & FABRICATORS INC
8100 Cessna Ave, Gaithersburg, MD 20879-4177
Tel (301) 948-9330 *Founded/Ownrshp* 1972
Sales 20.4MM^E *EMP* 55
SIC 1711 1799 7692 3444 Boiler setting contractor; Petroleum storage tank installation, underground; Welding repair; Sheet metalwork
CEO: Russell Mullican
**Pr:* Carey M Dove
**Sec:* Ethel F Mullican
**Ex VP:* David Poe

D-U-N-S 60-849-9328
M & N FOODS LLC
CARL'S JR.
1355 Grand Ave Ste 101, San Marcos, CA 92078-2453
Tel (760) 744-2550 *Founded/Ownrshp* 1999
Sales 50.9MM^E *EMP* 550
SIC 2043 Infants' foods, cereal type
Pr: Michael Borchard
CFO: Doug Sommer

D-U-N-S 09-123-6802
M & O AGENCIES INC (AZ)
MAHONEY GROUP, THE
(*Suby of* SOUTHWESTERN FINANCIAL CORPORATION)
1835 S Extension Rd, Mesa, AZ 85210-5942
Tel (480) 730-4920 *Founded/Ownrshp* 1960, 2001
Sales NA *EMP* 195
SIC 6411 Insurance agents, brokers & service; Insurance agents, brokers & service
Ch: Glendon D Nelson
**Pr:* Steven Goble
VP: Glen Luglan
Brnch Mgr: Richard Perry
Snr Mgr: Yanira Roman

D-U-N-S 06-998-3104
M & O INSULATION CO
17217 Ashland Ave, East Hazel Crest, IL 60429-1822
Tel (708) 389-3800 *Founded/Ownrshp* 2008
Sales 34.8MM^E *EMP* 225
SIC 1742 5033 Insulation, buildings; Insulation, thermal; Insulation, buildings; Insulation, thermal
Pr: Kevin Doherty
**CEO:* Peter Castellarin
Exec: Jay Schunk
Snr Mgr: Bob Geary

D-U-N-S 10-154-9053
M & O MARKETING INC
4000 Town Ctr Ste 1100, Southfield, MI 48075-1406
Tel (248) 784-1400 *Founded/Ownrshp* 1977
Sales NA *EMP* 66
SIC 6411 Insurance information & consulting services
Pr: Timothy J Otto
VP: Charlot Bewersdorff
**VP:* Dennis Brown
VP: Nancy Turnquist
Dir IT: Brian Canfield
Software D: Jimmy Wu
VP Opers: Maria Prichard
Sls Dir: Doug Roberts
Sales Asso: Brenda Chandler
Sales Asso: Kristine Martin
Sales Asso: Kim Yaldoo

D-U-N-S 09-873-2753 IMP
M & Q PACKAGING CORP
(*Suby of* M & Q PLASTIC PRODUCTS CO) ★
3 Earl Ave, Schuylkill Haven, PA 17972-8961
Tel (570) 385-4991 *Founded/Ownrshp* 1979
Sales 20.3MM^E *EMP* 100
SIC 3089 Plastic processing
Pr: Michael Schmal
**Pr:* William H Menges
**Sec:* Joseph Mallozzi
**Sec:* Francis S Quinn
**VP:* Timothy Blucher
IT Man: Chris Duplisea
Mtls Mgr: Joe Juritsch
Plnt Mgr: Ernie Bachert
Prd Mgr: Ernie Bacherat
Ql Cn Mgr: Debra Demcher

D-U-N-S 00-217-2401 IMP
M & Q PLASTIC PRODUCTS CO
PAN SAVER
542 N Lewis Rd Ste 206, Limerick, PA 19468-3521
Tel (484) 369-8906 *Founded/Ownrshp* 1956
Sales 44.6MM^E *EMP* 350
SIC 3089 Blow molded finished plastic products; Blow molded finished plastic products
Pr: Iiichael Schmal
**CFO:* Joseph Mallozzi
**Treas:* Blaise Mazzoni
**VP:* Ernie Bachert
**VP:* Tim Blucher
**VP:* John Menges
**Prin:* Curt Rubenstein
Rgnl Mgr: Carl Hackett
Dir IT: Ernie Frey
IT Man: Chris Duplisea
Sls&Mrk Ex: George Telford

D-U-N-S 84-389-1354
M & R CO
M&R
33 E Tokay St, Lodi, CA 95240-4149
Tel (209) 941-2631 *Founded/Ownrshp* 1961
Sales 60.0MM *EMP* 65
SIC 5148 Fresh fruits & vegetables; Fresh fruits & vegetables
Prin: Donald Reynolds

D-U-N-S 07-833-8806
M & R HIGH POINT HOLDINGS INC
402 High Point Dr Ste 101, Cocoa, FL 32926-6602
Tel (321) 631-0245 *Founded/Ownrshp* 2011
Sales 580.3MM *EMP* 2
Accts James Moore & Co Pl Gaine
SIC 6719 Holding companies; Holding companies
Prin: Mahesh R Shah

D-U-N-S 15-175-1161 IMP
M & R PRINTING EQUIPMENT INC
M & R SALES AND SERVICE
(*Suby of* M&R HOLDINGS INC) ★
1n372 Main St, Glen Ellyn, IL 60137-3576
Tel (630) 858-6101 *Founded/Ownrshp* 1993
Sales 111.0MM^E *EMP* 400
SIC 3555 3552 5084 Printing trades machinery; Printing machinery, textile; Printing trades machinery, equipment & supplies; Printing trades machinery; Printing machinery, textile; Printing trades machinery, equipment & supplies
CEO: Richard Hoffman
**Pr:* Ronnie Riggs
CFO: Howard Bloom
**VP:* Richard Nesladek
VP: Dave Zimmer
CIO: Clarence Rupert
IT Man: Perry Boyce
Netwrk Eng: Patryk Wasilewski
Plnt Mgr: Larry Iaccino

M & R SALES AND SERVICE
See M & R PRINTING EQUIPMENT INC

D-U-N-S 87-855-1167
M & R SALES AND SERVICE INC
M&R
(*Suby of* M & R PRINTING EQUIPMENT INC) ★
1n 372 Main St, Glen Ellyn, IL 60137
Tel (630) 858-6101 *Founded/Ownrshp* 1994
Sales 25.5MM^E *EMP* 400
SIC 8743 Sales promotion; Sales promotion
Pr: Richard Hoffman
**CFO:* Howard Bloom
VP: Bob Greenleaf
**VP:* Michael Hoffman
Rgnl Mgr: John Carroll
Rgnl Mgr: Tyler Kimball
Genl Couns: Roger Herdrich

D-U-N-S 15-100-8331
M & R UNITED INC
DAIRY QUEEN
402 High Point Dr Ste 101, Cocoa, FL 32926-6602
Tel (321) 631-0245 *Founded/Ownrshp* 1985
Sales 94.4MM *EMP* 30
SIC 5812 5411 Ice cream stands or dairy bars; Convenience stores, independent; Ice cream stands or dairy bars; Convenience stores, independent
Pr: Mahesh R Shah
**VP:* Rashmi Shah

D-U-N-S 80-094-6295
M & S AUTOMOBILE SALES INC
MC KENNY-SLNAS HNDA MITSUBISHI
4295 Wilkinson Blvd, Gastonia, NC 28056-7213
Tel (704) 824-8844 *Founded/Ownrshp* 1990
Sales 31.6MM *EMP* 51^E
SIC 5511 5012 Automobiles, new & used; Automobiles & other motor vehicles; Automobiles, new & used; Automobiles & other motor vehicles
Pr: Salvador Salinas
Off Mgr: Tammy Livingston
Sls Mgr: Marvin Reid
Sales Asso: David Craig

D-U-N-S 10-722-3695
M & S EQUIPMENT INC
7810 N Highway 87, Coolidge, AZ 85128-9208
Tel (520) 723-4181 *Founded/Ownrshp* 1983
Sales 21.7MM^E *EMP* 30
SIC 5083 Agricultural machinery & equipment; Farm equipment parts & supplies
Pr: Thomas M Scott
**Sec:* Bradly Scott
**VP:* Brent Scott

D-U-N-S 05-580-2987
M & S FOODS OF IOWA INC
MCDONALD'S
4726 N Brady St Ste B, Davenport, IA 52806-3977
Tel (563) 332-1148 *Founded/Ownrshp* 1971
Sales 15.1MM^E *EMP* 629
SIC 5812 8741 Fast-food restaurant, chain; Management services; Fast-food restaurant, chain; Management services
Pr: Harold E Steinke
**Prin:* Sandra Mohr

D-U-N-S 01-258-9701
M & V PROVISION CO INC
1827 Flushing Ave, Ridgewood, NY 11385-1040
Tel (718) 456-7070 *Founded/Ownrshp* 1975
Sales 25.5MM^E *EMP* 35
SIC 5147 5143 5142 5149 Meats, fresh; Cheese; Packaged frozen goods; Condiments
Pr: Paul Vallario
**Pr:* Anthony F Ciuffo
**Ex VP:* Michael Ciuffo
**VP:* Joseph Castrogiovanni
**VP:* Joseph Vallario

D-U-N-S 18-050-4359
M & W CONTRACTORS INC
400 S Stewart St, Creve Coeur, IL 61610-4100
Tel (309) 694-8220 *Founded/Ownrshp* 1990
Sales 25.0MM *EMP* 250
SIC 1541 Industrial buildings, new construction; Renovation, remodeling & repairs: industrial buildings; Industrial buildings, new construction; Renovation, remodeling & repairs: industrial buildings
Pr: Terry Kull
**VP:* Dave Schlachter

D-U-N-S 10-176-4249
M & W TRANSPORTATION CO INC
1110 Pumping Station Rd, Nashville, TN 37210-2219
Tel (615) 256-5755 *Founded/Ownrshp* 1983
Sales 26.1MM^E *EMP* 110
Accts Carr Riggs & Ingram Nashvill
SIC 4213 4731 4212 Trucking, except local; Freight transportation arrangement; Local trucking, without storage
CEO: J Michael McFarlin

**Ex VP:* Mark Boyette
Snr Mgr: Shelby Payne

D-U-N-S 11-521-0379 IMP
M &Y TRADING CORP
HELBY IMPORT COMPANY
37 Hayward Ave, Carteret, NJ 07008-3154
Tel (732) 969-5300 *Founded/Ownrshp* 1983
Sales 23.3MM^E *EMP* 65
SIC 5092 Arts & crafts equipment & supplies
Ch Bd: S Weiss
CTO: Ronnie Weinblut
Opers Mgr: Devin Gannon

D-U-N-S 02-414-2036
M & Z CORP
DRY RIDGE TOYOTA
9 Taft Hwy, Dry Ridge, KY 41035-8123
Tel (859) 824-9200 *Founded/Ownrshp* 1989
Sales 22.8MM^E *EMP* 50
SIC 5511 5521 5012 Automobiles, new & used; Used car dealers; Automobiles & other motor vehicles
Pr: Robert G Marshall II
Store Mgr: Randy Wells
Sls Mgr: Scott Bryant
Sls Mgr: Randy Moore
Sls Mgr: Matt Sensel
Sales Asso: Jared Asher
Sales Asso: Steven Begley

M 3
See M3 INSURANCE SOLUTIONS INC

M 7 AEROSPACE
See FAIRCHILD AIRCRAFT INC

D-U-N-S 07-767-2772
M 75 INC
MAUI TOYOTA
320 Hana Hwy, Kahului, HI 96732-2317
Tel (808) 877-2781 *Founded/Ownrshp* 1975
Sales 47.0MM *EMP* 51
SIC 5511 5521 Automobiles, new & used; Vans, new & used; Pickups, new & used; Used car dealers; Automobiles, new & used; Vans, new & used; Pickups, new & used; Used car dealers
CEO: Damien J Farias
**Pr:* Kathleen Hee
CFO: Chad Llanes
**Treas:* Aaron Hee
Board of Directors: Damien J K Farias, Joyce Lacno

M A A C PROJECT
See METROPOLITAN AREA ADVISORY COMMITTEE ON ANTI-POVERTY OF SAN DIEGO COUNTY INC

M A C
See MAGNETIC ANALYSIS CORP

M A C
See MAC VALVES INC

M A C
See MIKUNI AMERICAN CORP

M A F
See MISSION AVIATION FELLOWSHIP

D-U-N-S 00-526-4775
M A FORD MFG CO INC (IA)
7737 Northwest Blvd, Davenport, IA 52806-1077
Tel (563) 391-6220 *Founded/Ownrshp* 1919, 1941
Sales 38.9MM^E *EMP* 300
SIC 3545

M. A. I.
See MIDWEST ACOUST-A-FIBER INC

D-U-N-S 00-890-4385 IMP
M A MORTENSON CO
MORTENSON CONSTRUCTION
(*Suby of* M A MORTENSON COMPANIES INC) ★
700 Meadow Ln N, Minneapolis, MN 55422-4837
Tel (763) 522-2100 *Founded/Ownrshp* 1954
Sales 1.7MMM^E *EMP* 1,730
Accts Pricewaterhousecoopers Llp Mi
SIC 1542 1629 Institutional building construction; Commercial & office building, new construction; Industrial plant construction; Power plant construction; Waste water & sewage treatment plant construction; Institutional building construction; Commercial & office building, new construction; Industrial plant construction; Power plant construction; Waste water & sewage treatment plant construction
CEO: M A Mortenson Jr
Pr: Daniel L Johnson
CEO: Thomas F Gunkel
COO: Tom Wacker
CFO: Sandra G Sponem
Ch: David Mortenson
Sr VP: Bob Hansen
Sr VP: John Ohman
Sr VP: Paul I Cossette
Sr VP: Sandy Sponem
Sr VP: John V Wood
Sr VP: John Wood
VP: William Patt
Dir Risk M: Krista Twesme

D-U-N-S 13-073-1797 IMP
M A MORTENSON COMPANIES INC
700 Meadow Ln N, Minneapolis, MN 55422-4837
Tel (763) 522-2100 *Founded/Ownrshp* 1983
Sales 1.7MMM^E *EMP* 2,000
Accts Pricewaterhousecoopers Llp Mi
SIC 1542 1629 Institutional building construction; Commercial & office building, new construction; Industrial plant construction; Power plant construction; Waste water & sewage treatment plant construction; Institutional building construction; Commercial & office building, new construction; Industrial plant construction; Power plant construction; Waste water & sewage treatment plant construction
CEO: M A Mortenson Jr
**Pr:* Tom Gunkel
**CFO:* Peter A Conzemius
CFO: Sandy Sponem
VP: Bill Patt
Snr PM: Rob Weise

D-U-N-S 03-403-4447 IMP
M A NORDEN CO INC (AL)
6955 Cary Hamilton Rd, Theodore, AL 36582-2001
Tel (251) 653-0003 *Founded/Ownrshp* 1939
Sales 42.6MM^E *EMP* 140
SIC 5093 2611 5111 Scrap & waste materials; Pulp mills; Printing & writing paper; Scrap & waste materials; Pulp mills; Printing & writing paper
Pr: Martin A Norden III

M A O
See MID-AMERICA OVERSEAS INC

D-U-N-S 00-817-2157 IMP
M A PATOUT & SON LIMITED
3512 J Patout Burns Rd, Jeanerette, LA 70544-7122
Tel (337) 276-4592 *Founded/Ownrshp* 1825
Sales 360.8MM *EMP* 413
Accts Broussard Poche Lewis And Brea
SIC 2061 Raw cane sugar; Blackstrap molasses made from sugar cane; Cane syrup made from sugar cane; Raw cane sugar; Blackstrap molasses made from sugar cane; Cane syrup made from sugar cane
Ch Bd: Frank W Patout
**CEO:* Craig Caillier
**CFO:* Randall K Romero
**Treas:* J Jared Patout
Board of Directors: William Patout III

M A T
See MIDWEST AIR TECHNOLOGIES INC

D-U-N-S 00-680-4058
M ALFIERI CO INC
399 Thornall St Ste 15, Edison, NJ 08837-2240
Tel (732) 548-2200 *Founded/Ownrshp* 1955
Sales 55.8MM^E *EMP* 150
SIC 1541 1542 Industrial buildings & warehouses; Commercial & office building, new construction; Industrial buildings & warehouses; Commercial & office building, new construction
Pr: Dominick Alfieri
**VP:* Michael Alfieri
Dir IT: David Klein

D-U-N-S 02-467-6546 EXP
M AND L MOTOR CO INC (NC)
M & L CHRYSLER JEEP DODGE RAM
406 Piedmont Dr, Lexington, NC 27295-2410
Tel (336) 248-5191 *Founded/Ownrshp* 1960
Sales 24.9MM *EMP* 48
SIC 5511 Automobiles, new & used; Automobiles, new & used
Prin: William McNulty
**VP:* Hazel Fritts
Sls Mgr: Dick Foster
Sls Mgr: Justin McNulty

D-U-N-S 19-531-6799
M AND L TRUCKING INC
M & L TRUCKING SERVICES
1 Revere Park, Rome, NY 13440-5568
Tel (315) 339-2550 *Founded/Ownrshp* 1988
Sales 42.2MM^E *EMP* 73^E
SIC 4731 4213 Truck transportation brokers; Trucking, except local
Ch Bd: Joseph F Mammone
**VP:* David Skinner
Off Mgr: Camille Vanwie
IT Man: Tami Beckwith
Opers Supe: John Dyer
Opers Supe: Michele Nicoletta
Manager: Mike Barrilo
Manager: Roland Lamantia
Sls Mgr: Peter Frappolli
Sls Mgr: Jodie Greene

D-U-N-S 04-739-2741
M ARTHUR GENSLER JR & ASSOCIATES INC
2 Harrison St Fl 4, San Francisco, CA 94105-6127
Tel (415) 433-3700 *Founded/Ownrshp* 1965
Sales 915.3MM *EMP* 3,500
Accts Burr Pilger Mayer Inc San Fra
SIC 8712 Architectural services; Architectural services
Co-CEO: Andy Cohen
**Ch Bd:* Robin Klehr Avia
**CFO:* Karen Draper
**Co-CEO:* Diane Hoskins
VP: Christopher P Johnson
VP: Jimmy Mejia
VP: Joe Turi
Prin: Joseph Brancato
Prin: David J Calkins
Prin: Scott Dunlap
Prin: Lamar Johnson

M B
See MARQUEZ BROTHERS INTERNATIONAL INC

M B C
See MAVERICK BOAT CO INC

M B C I
See NCI GROUP INC

D-U-N-S 10-200-4306
M B FAYETTE SPECIALISTS INC
FAYETTE IMPORT
1588 Highway 85 N, Fayetteville, GA 30214-4054
Tel (770) 461-3784 *Founded/Ownrshp* 2001
Sales 113.2MM *EMP* 15
SIC 7538 General automotive repair shops; General automotive repair shops
Pr: Ronnie Taylor
**VP:* Douglas Horgen

M B I
See MBI ENERGY LOGISTICS LLC

M B I
See MANHATTAN BUSINESS INTERIORS INC

M B I
See MBI DIRECT MAIL INC

D-U-N-S 02-068-7208 IMP/EXP
M B K INC
CACTUS STONE & TILE
401 S 50th St, Phoenix, AZ 85034-2013
Tel (602) 220-1685 *Founded/Ownrshp* 1973
Sales 24.9MM^E *EMP* 80
SIC 5032 Ceramic wall & floor tile
Pr: Kirk M Butler
COO: Kelly M Upton
**VP:* Lloyd C Butler

D-U-N-S 00-791-9442
M B KAHN CONSTRUCTION CO INC (SC)
101 Flintlake Rd, Columbia, SC 29223-7851
Tel (803) 736-2950 *Founded/Ownrshp* 1927
Sales 225.9MM *EMP* 429
Accts Elliott Davis Decosimo Llc C
SIC 1542 8742 Nonresidential construction; Construction project management consultant; Nonresidential construction; Construction project management consultant
Pr: William H Neely
Pr: Danny Owens
COO: Dave Petty
Ex VP: Timothy C Cullum
Ex VP: James Heard
Ex VP: Michael Satterwhite
VP: Chuck Saylors
VP Opers: L Davis Petty
Site Mgr: Don Beres
Site Mgr: Andy Finley
VP Sls: Jack Brown
Board of Directors: Alan B Kahn, Charles B Kahn, Ronald L McCall

D-U-N-S 09-223-9557 EXP
M B LEASING CORP
BILL USSERY MTRS MERCEDES BENZ
(*Suby of* BILL USSERY MOTORS BODY SHOP INC) ★
300 Almeria Ave, Coral Gables, FL 33134-5812
Tel (305) 445-8593 *Founded/Ownrshp* 1971
Sales 6.3MM^E *EMP* 300
SIC 7515 Passenger car leasing; Passenger car leasing
Pr: Bob Brockway

M B S
See MANITOWOC BEVERAGE SYSTEMS INC

M B S
See MANNING BUILDING SUPPLIES INC

M B S
See MBS INSIGHT INC

D-U-N-S 61-895-5152
M BAR C CONSTRUCTION INC
674 Rancheros Dr, San Marcos, CA 92069-3005
Tel (760) 744-4131 *Founded/Ownrshp* 2005
Sales 38.8MM^E *EMP* 85
SIC 1791 1623 Structural steel erection; Electric power line construction
CEO: Jason Ianni
VP: Erik Krivokopich
VP Opers: Drew Lippert

D-U-N-S 00-512-1181 IMP
M BLOCK & SONS INC
BLOCK HOUSE
5020 W 73rd St, Bedford Park, IL 60638-6612
Tel (708) 728-8400 *Founded/Ownrshp* 1970
Sales 188.0MM^E *EMP* 400
SIC 5064 5023 Electrical appliances, television & radio; Home furnishings; Electrical appliances, television & radio; Home furnishings
Pr: Bruce Levy
**CFO:* Edward C Roels
**VP:* David Dewes
**VP:* Jody Fellows
**VP:* Mark McManus

D-U-N-S 06-283-2845
M BRADY & ASSOCIATES
9753 Independence Ave, Chatsworth, CA 91311-4318
Tel (818) 700-8813 *Founded/Ownrshp* 1979
Sales 130.0MM *EMP* 15
SIC 5082 General construction machinery & equipment; General construction machinery & equipment
Pr: Michael E Brady

D-U-N-S 00-983-9341
■ M BRUENGER & CO INC
(*Suby of* BRUENGER TRUCKING CO) ★
6250 N Broadway St, Park City, KS 67219-1197
Tel (316) 744-0494 *Founded/Ownrshp* 1975
Sales 26.1MM^E *EMP* 150
SIC 4213 Trucking, except local; Trucking, except local
Pr: Wick Hollingsworth
**VP:* Joseph Diekemper

M C
See MUIR-CHASE PLUMBING CO INC

M C
See MORGAN ADVANCED CERAMICS INC

M C A
See MAIL CONTRACTORS OF AMERICA INC

M C A
See MERCHANDISING CORP OF AMERICA INC

M C ASSEMBLY
See M C TEST SERVICE INC

M C C
See MERCURY CASUALTY CO

D-U-N-S 00-890-0508
M C GUTHERIE LUMBER CO
12152 Merriman Rd, Livonia, MI 48150-1914
Tel (734) 513-5777 *Founded/Ownrshp* 1925
Sales 31.1MM *EMP* 71
SIC 5031 5211 Lumber: rough, dressed & finished; Hardboard; Plywood; Millwork; Millwork & lumber; Lumber: rough, dressed & finished; Hardboard; Plywood; Millwork; Millwork & lumber
Pr: Melvin C Gutherie III
**Ch Bd:* Melvin C Gutherie Jr
**Sec:* Sharon R Gutherie

**Ex VP:* Michael Mahoney
**VP:* Kenneth Scrimger
Genl Mgr: William Gutherie
Genl Mgr: Dave Pompa

M C H C
See MITSUBISHI PLASTICS COMPOSITES AMERICA INC

D-U-N-S 06-788-6625
M C HOLDINGS INC
MCMM
5709 Education Dr Apt 205, Cheyenne, WY 82009-6308
Tel (307) 514-1510 *Founded/Ownrshp* 2005
Sales 40.0MMM *EMP* 15,600
SIC 6719 Personal holding companies, except banks
Pr: Erich Lynch

D-U-N-S 00-953-7929
M C I FOODS INC
LOS CABOS MEXICAN FOODS
13013 Molette St, Santa Fe Springs, CA 90670-5521
Tel (310) 635-5664 *Founded/Ownrshp* 1970
Sales 37.1MM^E *EMP* 140
SIC 2038 Ethnic foods, frozen; Ethnic foods, frozen
Ch Bd: Alberta Southard
**Pr:* Daniel Southard
**VP:* Chris Hakmiller
**VP:* John M Southard
Plnt Mgr: Javier Moscoso
Plnt Mgr: Fred Puglia
Ql Cn Mgr: Ashish Belekevich
Ql Cn Mgr: Ashish Goyal
Sls Mgr: Diane Martin

M C L CAFETERIAS
See MCL INC

D-U-N-S 80-867-4774
M C M HARVESTERS INC
1585 Lirio Ave, Ventura, CA 93004-3227
Tel (805) 659-6833 *Founded/Ownrshp* 1992
Sales 10.4MM^E *EMP* 300
SIC 7361 Labor contractors (employment agency); Labor contractors (employment agency)
Pr: Dennis Mc Murray

D-U-N-S 00-592-1978 IMP
M C PACKAGING CORP
200 Adams Blvd, Farmingdale, NY 11735-6615
Tel (631) 414-7840 *Founded/Ownrshp* 1966
Sales 22.9MM^E *EMP* 135
SIC 2679 Cardboard products, except die-cut; Cardboard products, except die-cut
Ch Bd: Robert M Silverberg
**Pr:* Marc Silverberg

M C R
See MCR FEDERAL LLC

D-U-N-S 00-448-0794
M C TANK TRANSPORT INC
10134 Mosteller Ln, West Chester, OH 45069-3872
Tel (513) 771-8667 *Founded/Ownrshp* 1971
Sales 21.5MM^E *EMP* 75
SIC 4212 Local trucking, without storage
Pr: Timothy Anderson
**Treas:* Cindy Anderson
Sfty Mgr: Jeff Lewis

D-U-N-S 14-705-1874 IMP
M C TEST SERVICE INC
M C ASSEMBLY
(*Suby of* MC ASSEMBLY HOLDINGS INC) ★
425 North Dr, Melbourne, FL 32934-9209
Tel (321) 956-3052 *Founded/Ownrshp* 2007
Sales 243.1MM^E *EMP* 1,600^E
SIC 3672 8734 Printed circuit boards; Testing laboratories; Printed circuit boards; Testing laboratories
Pr: George W Moore
Pr: Jay Sing
**COO:* Luis Ramirez
**CFO:* Mark McReynolds
CFO: Mark McReynolds
**VP:* Vicki Cooke
**VP:* Jake Kulp
Prgrm Mgr: Ann Holmes
Prgrm Mgr: Daniel Prina
Prgrm Mgr: Arthur Waters
IT Man: Michael Lamaster

D-U-N-S 01-426-1069
M C TRUCKING CO INC
400 Keck St, Seward, PA 15954
Tel (814) 446-4441 *Founded/Ownrshp* 1946
Sales 25.2MM^E *EMP* 165
SIC 4213 4212 Trucking, except local; Local trucking, without storage; Trucking, except local; Local trucking, without storage
Pr: John P Muchesko
**Sec:* Eleanor Muchesko

D-U-N-S 09-594-4575
M C VAN KAMPEN TRUCKING INC
5841 Clay Ave Sw, Grand Rapids, MI 49548-5759
Tel (616) 531-9931 *Founded/Ownrshp* 1976
Sales 41.4MM^E *EMP* 150
SIC 4213 Refrigerated products transport; Refrigerated products transport
Owner: Marvin Van Kampen
**Sec:* Sue Vankampen
VP: David Wozniak

M C W
See MCW SOLUTIONS LLC

D-U-N-S 06-717-9739
M CAMPBELL & CO INC
CAMPBELL AND CO
2828 W Irving St, Pasco, WA 99301-4595
Tel (509) 545-9848 *Founded/Ownrshp* 1983
Sales 27.5MM^E *EMP* 115
SIC 1711 Heating & air conditioning contractors; Heating & air conditioning contractors
Pr: Michael G Campbell
Exec: Shari Pitzer
Genl Mgr: Sherry Erickson

D-U-N-S 07-849-5998
M CASPERSON ENTERPRISE LLC (UT)
MICHAEL CASPERSON
220 S 100 E, St George, UT 84770-3425
Tel (800) 275-8802 *Founded/Ownrshp* 2011
Sales 43.5MM^E *EMP* 1,099
SIC 5063 1731 Burglar alarm systems; Fire detection & burglar alarm systems specialization; Burglar alarm systems; Fire detection & burglar alarm systems specialization

M CATERING BY MICHAEL'S
See M CULINARY CONCEPTS LLC

M CHRISTOPHER AND COMPANY
See M CHRISTOPHER CUSTOM HOMES LLC

D-U-N-S 82-625-1162
M CHRISTOPHER CUSTOM HOMES LLC
M CHRISTOPHER AND COMPANY
630 Oakmont Ct, McKinney, TX 75069-8500
Tel (214) 288-9456 *Founded/Ownrshp* 2006
Sales 73.2MM *EMP* 9
Accts Pitts & Pitts Allen Texas
SIC 1521 Single-family home remodeling, additions & repairs; New construction, single-family houses; Single-family home remodeling, additions & repairs; New construction, single-family houses

D-U-N-S 78-171-6360
M CO OF SHREVEPORT INC
8889 Linwood Ave, Shreveport, LA 71106-6505
Tel (318) 687-7777 *Founded/Ownrshp* 1990
Sales 53.5MM^E *EMP* 65
SIC 5014 7534 Truck tires & tubes; Rebuilding & retreading tires

D-U-N-S 00-231-6149 IMP/EXP
M COHEN AND SONS INC (PA)
IRON SHOP, THE
400 Reed Rd, Broomall, PA 19008-4001
Tel (610) 544-7100 *Founded/Ownrshp* 1931
Sales 34.0MM *EMP* 230
SIC 3446

D-U-N-S 00-892-6669
M CONLEY CO
1312 4th St Se, Canton, OH 44707-3243
Tel (330) 456-8243 *Founded/Ownrshp* 1901
Sales 77.0MM^E *EMP* 110
SIC 5113 5087 5084 Industrial & personal service paper; Paper & products, wrapping or coarse; Janitors' supplies; Safety equipment; Industrial & personal service paper; Paper & products, wrapping or coarse; Janitors' supplies; Safety equipment
CEO: Robert Stuart III
**Pr:* Eric Conley
COO: Robert H Stewart III
COO: Robert Stewart
CFO: Doug Marianek
VP: Robert Geisinger
**Prin:* Michael Conley
**Prin:* Ernest A Gerber
Opers Mgr: Paul Ratliff
Sls Mgr: Jim Haupt
Sales Asso: Christopher Hoover
Board of Directors: Craig Conley, Eric Conley, Robert Stewart

M. COOPER WINSUPPLY
See GOODE INDUSTRIES INC

D-U-N-S 05-271-0076 IMP
■ **M CUBED TECHNOLOGIES INC**
(*Suby of* II-VI INC) ★
31 Pecks Ln Ste 8, Newtown, CT 06470-5312
Tel (203) 304-2941 *Founded/Ownrshp* 2012
Sales 45.1MM^E *EMP* 150
SIC 3444 5051 3599 Machine shop, jobbing & repair; Sheet metalwork; Metals service centers & offices; Sheet metalwork; Metals service centers & offices; Machine shop, jobbing & repair
Pr: Randall Price Sr
**CFO:* William J Lauricella
**Ex VP:* Jai Singh
VP: Michael Aghajanian
VP: Jai R Singh
Admn Mgr: Elmer Miller
Genl Mgr: John McInerney
Genl Mgr: Brian Monti
Sls Mgr: Shinji Ishii

D-U-N-S 10-225-1480
M CULINARY CONCEPTS LLC
M CATERING BY MICHAEL'S
20645 N 28th St, Phoenix, AZ 85050-4627
Tel (602) 200-5757 *Founded/Ownrshp* 1999
Sales 19.7MM^E *EMP* 600
SIC 5812 Caterers; Caterers

D-U-N-S 07-245-1966
M CUTONE MUSHROOM CO INC
CUTONE, M & CO
145 Market St, Chelsea, MA 02150-1702
Tel (617) 889-1122 *Founded/Ownrshp* 1981
Sales 35.5MM^E *EMP* 140
SIC 5148 Vegetables, fresh; Vegetables, fresh
Pr: Mario C Cutone Jr
**VP:* Mario Cutone III
Telecom Ex: Butch Cutone

M D A
See MISSISSIPPI DEVELOPMENT AUTHORITY

M D ANDERSON CANCER CENTER ORL
See ORLANDO CANCER CENTER

D-U-N-S 18-949-5281
M D ANDERSON SERVICES CORP
MD ANDERSON CANCER CENTER
(*Suby of* MD ANDERSON CANCER CENTER) ★
7505 Main St Ste 500, Houston, TX 77030-4524
Tel (713) 745-9692 *Founded/Ownrshp* 1989
Sales 32.6MM *EMP* 16
Accts Deloitte Tax Llp Houston Tx
SIC 8082 Home health care services; Home health care services
CEO: Leon J Leach
Assoc VP: Donna Hemphill

D-U-N-S 83-491-4277
■ **M D C BROOKLYN**
(*Suby of* BUREAU OF PRISONS) ★
80 29th St, Brooklyn, NY 11232-1503
Tel (718) 840-4200 *Founded/Ownrshp* 2003
Sales NA *EMP* 305
SIC 9223 Prison, government; ; Prison, government;
Prin: Calvin Morton
Info Man: Raoul Watson

M D C RESEARCH
See MARKET DECISIONS CORP

D-U-N-S 86-873-5424 IMP
M D DISTRIBUTORS INC
ALCOME USA
(*Suby of* M & D FRAGRANCES & COSMETICS INC) ★
40 Brunswick Ave Ste 207, Edison, NJ 08817-2589
Tel (732) 339-1100 *Founded/Ownrshp* 1991
Sales 34.6MM^E *EMP* 60^E
SIC 5122 Perfumes; Cosmetics
Pr: Dalip Malhotra
CFO: Shakti Chadra

M D H A
See METROPOLITAN DEVELOPMENT & HOUSING AGENCY

D-U-N-S 05-097-7099 IMP/EXP
M D HENRY CO INC
MPU POWER GROUP
120 Clark St, Pelham, AL 35124-1906
Tel (205) 967-2893 *Founded/Ownrshp* 1970
Sales 28.2MM^E *EMP* 75
SIC 1623 Electric power line construction
CEO: Julia Henry
**Pr:* Patrick Henry
**CFO:* Tanya Lawley
CFO: Pat Toomey
**Sr VP:* Hal Lockhart

M D I
See MATERIAL DISTRIBUTORS INC

M D I
See MERCHANTS DISTRIBUTORS LLC

M D L
See MERYL DIAMOND LTD

D-U-N-S 96-563-6525
M D LOGISTICS INC
MD EXPRESS
1301 Perry Rd Ste 101, Plainfield, IN 46168-7613
Tel (317) 838-8700 *Founded/Ownrshp* 1996
Sales 21.4MM^E *EMP* 70
SIC 4731 Freight forwarding
Pr: Mark Sell
VP: Christine Downs
VP: Jeff Luthman
VP: John Sell
VP: Bob Witney
Area Mgr: Scott Hawley
Area Mgr: Michael Nicholas
QA Dir: Robert Grange
Dir IT: John Frances
Dir IT: Jonathan Francis
Opers Supe: Michael Williams

M D P
See MADISON DEARBORN PARTNERS LLC

M D PRUITTS HOME FURNISHINGS
See SENSING ENTERPRISES INC

M D S
See MORRISTOWN DRIVERS SERVICE INC

M D S
See MANUFACTURED DUCT & SUPPLY CO

D-U-N-S 11-153-2524
M D WISE INC
1200 Madison Ave Ste 400, Indianapolis, IN 46225-1616
Tel (317) 822-7300 *Founded/Ownrshp* 2002
Sales 457.5MM *EMP* 48
SIC 8621 Health association
Pr: Charlotte Macbeth
Pr: Gary Phillips
CFO: Susan Overton
VP: Maggie Moss
Dir Rx: Henry Johnson
Off Mgr: Kim Graves
CIO: Julie Sample
Software D: C J Nasser
Sls Mgr: Caroline Doebbeling
Snr Mgr: Jamie Bruce

D-U-N-S 01-103-2653 IMP
M DAVIS & SONS INC
19 Germay Dr, Wilmington, DE 19804-1104
Tel (302) 998-3385 *Founded/Ownrshp* 1948
Sales 65.6MM^E *EMP* 330^E
SIC 1711 1731 1791 Plumbing contractors; Mechanical contractor; Ventilation & duct work contractor; General electrical contractor; Iron work, structural; Plumbing contractors; Mechanical contractor; Ventilation & duct work contractor; General electrical contractor; Iron work, structural
CEO: Margaret D Del Fabbro
**Ch Bd:* Charles R Davis
**Pr:* John S Bonk

D-U-N-S 60-569-6889 IMP
M DOHMEN USA INC
25 Ellwood Ct, Greenville, SC 29607-5340
Tel (864) 676-1669 *Founded/Ownrshp* 1989
Sales 26.3MM *EMP* 23
SIC 5169 Dyestuffs; Dyestuffs
Pr: Jim McCall
Off Mgr: Lou Caulk

D-U-N-S 80-626-9056
M DOTTAVIO PRODUCE INC
1088 N Main Rd 86, Vineland, NJ 08360-2539
Tel (856) 692-3311 *Founded/Ownrshp* 1991
Sales 36.2MM *EMP* 10
Accts Fabietti Hale Hammerstedt &
SIC 5141 Food brokers; Food brokers
Pr: Michael D'Ottavio

M E A
See MATANUSKA ELECTRIC ASSOCIATION INC

M E A
See MICHIGAN EDUCATION ASSOCIATION - NEA

M E A N
See MUNICIPAL ENERGY AGENCY OF NEBRASKA (INC)

D-U-N-S 60-299-2349
M E B A MEDICAL AND BENEFITS PLAN
1007 Eastern Ave, Baltimore, MD 21202-4652
Tel (410) 539-5635 *Founded/Ownrshp* 1955
Sales 39.9MM *EMP* 55
Accts Buchbinder Tunick & Company Ll
SIC 6733 Vacation funds for employees
MIS Dir: Ron Simmons
IT Man: Michael Rattray

D-U-N-S 04-902-1405
M E DEY & CO INC
700 W Virginia St Ste 300, Milwaukee, WI 53204-1549
Tel (414) 747-7000 *Founded/Ownrshp* 1994
Sales 27.5MM *EMP* 55
SIC 4731 Customhouse brokers; Freight forwarding; Customhouse brokers; Freight forwarding
Pr: Robert Gardenier
**Ex VP:* Sandi Siegel
**VP:* Randy Kupfer
IT Man: Bruce Siegel
**VP Opers:* Jane Meyer
Opers Mgr: Lynn Kucharas
Opers Mgr: Sheila Richards
Opers Mgr: Lauren Worthy
**VP Sls:* Carrie Fix

M E F A
See MASSACHUSETTS EDUCATIONAL FINANCING AUTHORITY

M E G
See MILLER ENVIRONMENTAL GROUP INC

D-U-N-S 94-330-7058
M E H INC
HAAS METAL ENGINEERING
2828 Nw Button Rd, Topeka, KS 66618-1456
Tel (785) 235-1524 *Founded/Ownrshp* 1994
Sales 34.2MM^E *EMP* 92
SIC 3441 Fabricated structural metal; Fabricated structural metal
Pr: Jonny Haas
Prd Mgr: Travis Schreiner

D-U-N-S 11-973-4242
M E H INVESTMENTS INC
BURGER KING
11020 N Ttum Blvd Ste 103, Phoenix, AZ 85028
Tel (602) 569-6100 *Founded/Ownrshp* 1983
Sales 500.0M^E *EMP* 290
SIC 5812 Fast-food restaurant, chain; Fast-food restaurant, chain
Pr: Dennis W Hitzeman

M E I
See MEL CHEMICALS INC

M E I
See CRANE PAYMENT INNOVATIONS INC

M E I
See MAINTENANCE ENTERPRISES II INC

M E N A
See MITSUBISHI ENGINE NORTH AMERICA INC

M E P
See MISSION ESSENTIAL PERSONNEL LLC

D-U-N-S 92-978-3587
■ **M E S HOLDING CORP**
EMCOR CONSTRUCTION SERVICES
(*Suby of* EMCOR GROUP INC) ★
301 Merritt 7, Norwalk, CT 06851-1070
Tel (203) 849-7800 *Founded/Ownrshp* 1994
Sales 155.2MM^E *EMP* 700^E
SIC 1711 1731 Plumbing, heating, air-conditioning contractors; Electrical work
Pr: Tony Guzzi
**VP:* Leicle Chesser

D-U-N-S 05-670-2707
M EAGLES TOOL WAREHOUSE INC
178 Sherman Ave Ste 192, Newark, NJ 07114-1739
Tel (973) 824-6951 *Founded/Ownrshp* 1971
Sales 62.1MM^E *EMP* 61^E
SIC 5013 Tools & equipment, automotive
Pr: George Gering
**VP:* Steven Gering
Genl Mgr: Mike Gering
Sales Asso: Sam Cochran
Sales Asso: Michael Small

M F A TRUE VALUE HARDWARE
See FARMERS PRODUCE EXCHANGE (INC)

D-U-N-S 08-333-1249 IMP
M F CACHAT CO LLC
M.F. CACHAT COMPANY, THE
(*Suby of* IMCD N.V.)
14725 Detroit Ave Ste 300, Lakewood, OH 44107-4124
Tel (216) 228-8900 *Founded/Ownrshp* 2015
Sales 133.0MM^E *EMP* 90
SIC 5169 Chemicals & allied products; Chemicals & allied products
Pr: John Mastrantoni
CFO: Bruce Jarosz
Mtls Mgr: Ryan Jones
VP Sls: Alison M Azar
Mktg Mgr: Mark Walter
Manager: Alison Azar
Manager: Kevin Trainor
Sls Mgr: Janeen Dolinar
Sls Mgr: Jeanine Hill-Jacob
Sls Mgr: Tim Koetters

D-U-N-S 00-799-7257 IMP
M F FOLEY CO (MA)
FOLEY FRESH
24 W Howell St, Boston, MA 02125-1108
Tel (508) 997-0773 *Founded/Ownrshp* 1918, 1986
Sales 49.3MM^E *EMP* 65
SIC 5146 Fish, fresh; Seafoods; Fish, fresh; Seafoods
Owner: Peter Ramsden
**Pr:* Michael F Foley
Exec: Nick Martin
Off Mgr: Maria Demelo
Sales Exec: John Williams
S&M/VP: Laura Ramsden

M F I
See MITSUI FOODS INC

M F I
See MODUS FURNITURE INTERNATIONAL

M F I INTERNATIONAL
See MFI INTERNATIONAL MANUFACTURING LLC

M F S
See MASSACHUSETTS FINANCIAL SERVICES CO

M FINANCIAL GROUP
See M FINANCIAL HOLDINGS INC

D-U-N-S 04-581-5359
M FINANCIAL HOLDINGS INC
M FINANCIAL GROUP
1125 Nw Couch St Ste 900, Portland, OR 97209-4129
Tel (503) 232-6960 *Founded/Ownrshp* 1995
Sales 58.3MM^E *EMP* 250
SIC 7389 Financial services; Financial services
Pr: Fred Jonske
COO: Bruce Fuller
CFO: Phyllis Kloak
**Treas:* Kevin Kukar
Ofcr: Steven Chang
Ofcr: Frank Day
Ofcr: Laura Hoey
Ofcr: Jennifer Tucker
**Sr VP:* Daniel F Byrne
**Sr VP:* Randall M O Connor
**Sr VP:* Donald H Friedman
**Sr VP:* Connie K Morrison
Sr VP: Randall O'Connor
VP: Dan Byrne
VP: Carrie Fleisher
VP: Rodger Hergenrader
VP: Jim Hilliker
VP: Stephen Michael
VP: Susan O'Sullivan
VP: Curt Rynties
VP: Craig Shigeno
Board of Directors: Grace Vandecruze, James A Cheney, David J Coyle, David J Downey, Richard D Mack, John W Meisenbach, Lawton M Nease, Victor H Palmieri, Gabriel L Shaheen, Mark I Solomon

D-U-N-S 03-717-7284
M FREDRIC & CO
28024 Dorothy Dr, Agoura Hills, CA 91301-2610
Tel (818) 597-0212 *Founded/Ownrshp* 1980
Sales 25.1MM^E *EMP* 200
SIC 5621 5611 5641

D-U-N-S 85-904-8944 IMP/EXP
M FRIED STORE FIXTURES INC
101 Varick Ave, Brooklyn, NY 11237-1216
Tel (718) 624-2999 *Founded/Ownrshp* 1990
Sales 35.6MM^E *EMP* 72
Accts Saul N Friedman & Company Br
SIC 5046 2542 5078 Store fixtures & display equipment; Shelving, office & store: except wood; Garment racks: except wood; Counters or counter display cases: except wood; Refrigeration equipment & supplies; Store fixtures & display equipment; Shelving, office & store: except wood; Garment racks: except wood; Counters or counter display cases: except wood; Refrigeration equipment & supplies
**Pr:* M Fried
**VP:* Jacob Brauner
Dir IT: Abe Klein
IT Man: Joseph Grunhut
Mktg Mgr: Esther Friedman
Sales Asso: Ben Honig
Sales Asso: Moshe Loffler
Board of Directors: Abraham Klein

M G A
See METROPOLITAN GRAPHIC ARTS INC

D-U-N-S 15-469-0879 IMP
M G BRYAN EQUIPMENT CO LP
1906 S Great Sw Pkwy, Grand Prairie, TX 75051-3503
Tel (972) 623-4300 *Founded/Ownrshp* 1986
Sales 22.3MM^E *EMP* 19
SIC 5084 3561 5082 3531 Engines & parts, diesel; Engines, gasoline; Industrial pumps & parts; Pump jacks & other pumping equipment; Pumps, oil well & field; Cranes, construction; Backhoes, tractors, cranes, plows & similar equipment
Genl Pt: Mike Bryan
Pr: Matt Bryan
IT Man: Andrew Rhett
Mfg Mgr: George Camarillo
Opers Mgr: Brian Dempsuy
Opers Mgr: Al Valdes
Sls Dir: Robert Esparza

D-U-N-S 11-759-5892
M G DYESS INC
7159 Highway 35, Bassfield, MS 39421-9678
Tel (601) 943-6663 *Founded/Ownrshp* 1992
Sales 40.4MM^E *EMP* 60
Accts Horne Llp Ridgeland Mississi
SIC 1623 Pipeline construction; Pipeline construction
CEO: Glynn Dyess
**Pr:* Grant Dyess
Treas: Jena Dyess
**VP:* Michael Dyess
**VP:* Ricky Dyess
Snr Mgr: Nathan Tansel

D-U-N-S 00-555-4068 IMP
M G ELECTRIC SERVICE CO (IL)
7 W Campbell St, Arlington Heights, IL 60005-1448
Tel (847) 439-7500 *Founded/Ownrshp* 1951
Sales 20.6MM^E *EMP* 60
Accts Haran & Associates Ltd Wilme
SIC 1731 1542 1541 General electrical contractor; Commercial & office building contractors; Industrial buildings & warehouses; General electrical contractor; Commercial & office building contractors; Industrial buildings & warehouses
Pr: Ronald Desideri
**VP:* Thomas Desideri

D-U-N-S 80-984-9870
M G EXPORT-IMPORT INTERNATIONAL INC
160 Tamarack Ave, Carlsbad, CA 92008-4059
Tel (760) 729-6892 *Founded/Ownrshp* 1986
Sales 45.0MM *EMP* 25
SIC 5122 5084 Cosmetics; Industrial machinery & equipment; Cosmetics; Industrial machinery & equipment
Pr: Bernard Goldstein
VP: Marina Goldstein

M G H
See MGH INC

D-U-N-S 79-346-6632 IMP
M G H HEALTH SERVICES CORP
GENERAL HOSPITAL
55 Fruit St, Boston, MA 02114-2696
Tel (617) 724-0567 *Founded/Ownrshp* 1986
Sales 18.4MM^E *EMP* 1,400^E
SIC 8082 8059 8071 8062 Home health care services; Personal care home, with health care; Medical laboratories; General medical & surgical hospitals; Home health care services; Personal care home, with health care; Medical laboratories; General medical & surgical hospitals
Pr: James Mongan
**VP:* Jay Pieper

D-U-N-S 79-142-4385
■ **M G I C MORTGAGE INSURANCE CORP**
(*Suby of* MGIC INVESTMENT) ★
250 E Kilbourn Ave, Milwaukee, WI 53202-3102
Tel (414) 347-6480 *Founded/Ownrshp* 1987
Sales NA *EMP* 900
SIC 6351 Mortgage guarantee insurance; Mortgage guarantee insurance
Pr: Kurt Culver
**CFO:* J Michael Lauer
**Sr VP:* Joseph J Ziino
**VP:* Mike Mead
**VP:* Patrick Sinks

M G K
See MCLAUGHLIN GORMLEY KING CO

M G M
See MGM HOLDINGS INC

D-U-N-S 13-154-1815 IMP
M G MCGRATH INC
1387 Cope Ave E, Maplewood, MN 55109-2602
Tel (651) 704-0300 *Founded/Ownrshp* 1985
Sales 47.4MM^E *EMP* 115
SIC 1761 Architectural sheet metal work
CEO: Michael G McGrath
**Pr:* Mike P McGrath
CFO: Patrick Kolb
**VP:* Jeanne McGrath
Genl Mgr: Greg Matthews
Genl Mgr: Tim Sauro
Off Mgr: Charlee Anderson
Sfty Dirs: Thomas Schoenecker
Mktg Dir: Kelly McGrath
Snr PM: Mark Lasalle

D-U-N-S 84-385-7736 IMP/EXP
M G NEWYORK INC
14 E 60th St Ste 400, New York, NY 10022-7146
Tel (212) 371-5566 *Founded/Ownrshp* 1983
Sales 28.8MM *EMP* 10
SIC 3172 5122 Cosmetic bags; Drugs, proprietaries & sundries; Cosmetic bags; Drugs, proprietaries & sundries
Pr: Marlyse Gros

D-U-N-S 00-352-0210
M G NEWELL CORP (NC)
301 Citation Ct, Greensboro, NC 27409-9027
Tel (502) 459-7475 *Founded/Ownrshp* 1885, 1984
Sales 69.4MM^E *EMP* 84
SIC 5084 5199 Industrial machinery & equipment; Food product manufacturing machinery; Dairy products manufacturing machinery; Packaging materials; Industrial machinery & equipment; Food product manufacturing machinery; Dairy products manufacturing machinery; Packaging materials
Pr: J Michael Sherrill
**VP:* Julie Hart
Opers Mgr: Karen McDaniel
S&M/Dir: Mimi Cartee
Sales Asso: Margie Staley

M G P
See MOONEY GENERAL PAPER CO INC

M G STRAILERS
See MGS INC

D-U-N-S 00-923-6381 IMP
M G WEST CO
2 Shaw Aly Fl 3, San Francisco, CA 94105-0904
Tel (415) 284-4800 *Founded/Ownrshp* 1985
Sales 20.7MM^E *EMP* 20
SIC 5021 4225 7641 Office furniture; Desks; Chairs; Filing units; General warehousing & storage; Furniture refinishing
CEO: Donald W Sullivan
**Pr:* Andrew L Sullivan
**CFO:* Lile Hu
**Treas:* Maureen Sullivan
**VP:* Nancy West
VP Opers: Dolores Freudenberg

D-U-N-S 02-224-0865
M GERVICH & SONS INC
901 E Nevada St, Marshalltown, IA 50158-3009
Tel (641) 753-3178 *Founded/Ownrshp* 1947
Sales 21.6MM^E *EMP* 30
SIC 5051 5093 4953 3341 3312 Steel; Metal scrap & waste materials; Refuse systems; Secondary nonferrous metals; Blast furnaces & steel mills
Pr: Douglas Gervich
Opers Mgr: Kurt Jackson

D-U-N-S 00-791-1829
M GLOSSER & SONS INC (PA)
72 Messenger St, Johnstown, PA 15902-2189
Tel (814) 533-2800 *Founded/Ownrshp* 1899
Sales 32.5MM^E *EMP* 80
SIC 5051 3443

D-U-N-S 12-136-1179
M GRIECO ENTERPRISES INC
METRO FORD
1651 New State Hwy, Raynham, MA 02767-5444
Tel (508) 822-1000 *Founded/Ownrshp* 2001
Sales 26.8MM^E *EMP* 60
SIC 5511 Automobiles, new & used; Automobiles, new & used
Pr: Michael Grieco
Genl Mgr: Dominic Grieco
**Genl Mgr:* Kelly McMullen
**Genl Mgr:* Dominic Trieco

D-U-N-S 09-534-6482
M H C INC
CROPP METCALF HEATING & AIR CO
8421 Hilltop Rd, Fairfax, VA 22031-4301
Tel (703) 698-8855 *Founded/Ownrshp* 1979
Sales 54.3MM^E *EMP* 210
SIC 1711 Warm air heating & air conditioning contractor; Warm air heating & air conditioning contractor
Pr: Mitchell P Cropp
**Sec:* William Metcalfe
**VP:* Judy Blare
**VP:* Brian Matthew Cropp

D-U-N-S 06-386-9846 IMP/EXP
M H EBY INC
MH EBY TRAILERS
1194 Main St, Blue Ball, PA 17506
Tel (717) 354-4971 *Founded/Ownrshp* 1974
Sales 100.0MM *EMP* 375
SIC 3713 5012 Truck bodies (motor vehicles); Trailers for trucks, new & used; Truck bodies (motor vehicles); Trailers for trucks, new & used
Pr: Mennoh EBY Jr
**Pr:* N Travis EBY
**VP:* Nicholas A EBY
VP: Travis EBY
Mfg Mgr: Luray Horst
Plnt Mgr: Gary Musselman

M H EQUIPMENT COMPANY
See MH LOGISTICS CORP

M H M
See METHODIST HEALTHCARE MINISTRIES OF SOUTH TEXAS INC

M H M R AUTHORIY HARRIS COUNTY
See MENTAL HEALTH AND MENTAL RETARDATION AUTHORITY OF HARRIS COUNTY

M H TECHNOLOGIES
See WALKER ENGINEERING INC

M H V
See MID-HUDSON VALLEY FEDERAL CREDIT UNION

D-U-N-S 00-192-7300 IMP
M HIDARY & CO INC (NY)
10 W 33rd St Rm 900, New York, NY 10001-3317
Tel (212) 736-6540 *Founded/Ownrshp* 1948
Sales 24.2MM^E *EMP* 100
SIC 2369 2311 2325 2329 5136 5137 Girls' & children's outerwear; Men's & boys' suits & coats; Men's & boys' trousers & slacks; Men's & boys' sportswear & athletic clothing; Men's & boys' clothing; Women's & children's clothing
Ch: Morris Hidary
CFO: Richard Levine
**Treas:* David Hidary
VP: Jack A Hidary
Mng Dir: Margie Valverde
IT Man: Russ Salvatore
Mktg Dir: Max Shalom
Sales Asso: Amy Jacobson

D-U-N-S 00-543-4766 IMP/EXP
M HOLLAND CO
400 Skokie Blvd Ste 600, Northbrook, IL 60062-7906
Tel (847) 272-7370 *Founded/Ownrshp* 1948
Sales 436.0MM^E *EMP* 150
SIC 5162 Plastics resins; Plastics resins
Pr: Edward J Holland
**CFO:* Patrick McKune
VP: J D Barry
VP: J Bourgeois
VP: Rudy Bourgeois
VP: Dwight Morgan
VP: Mike Ojile
Exec: Rob Donaldson
DP Dir: Joaan Guy
Dir IT: Douglas Goldstein
IT Man: Bob Fredriksen

M I
See MASON INDUSTRIES INC

M I
See MEASUREMENT INC

M I B
See MISSISSIPPI INDUSTRIES FOR BLIND (INC)

M I C
See MITSUBISHI INTERNATIONAL CORP

M I C
See MOTORS INSURANCE CORP

M I C GROUP
See MAGNETIC INSTRUMENTS CORP

D-U-N-S 96-680-0021
M I CASA PERSONAL ASSISTANCE SERVICES
440 N Fm 1110, Clint, TX 79836
Tel (915) 851-4663 *Founded/Ownrshp* 1996
Sales 3.2MM^E *EMP* 300
SIC 8082 Home health care services; Home health care services
Pr: Manuel Gonzalez

M I G
See MANUFACTURERS INDUSTRIAL GROUP LLC

M I G
See MOORE IACOFANO GOLTSMAN INC

M I I
See MARVAL INDUSTRIES INC

D-U-N-S 62-166-7062
M I I INC
(*Suby of* BCBSM INC) ★
3535 Blue Cross Rd, Saint Paul, MN 55122-1154
Tel (952) 456-8972 *Founded/Ownrshp* 1984
Sales NA *EMP* 112
SIC 6321 Accident & health insurance
Pr: Christopher Aasland

M I L
See MAGNETIC INSPECTION LABORATORY INC

M I P
See MITSUBISHI INTERNATIONAL POLYMER-TRADE CORP

M I R
See MIDWEST INDUSTRIAL RUBBER INC

M IT INTERNATIONAL
See DISTRIBUTION INTERNATIONAL SOUTHWEST INC

D-U-N-S 08-769-8833
M INTERNATIONAL INC (VA)
1301 Dolley Madison Blvd, Mc Lean, VA 22101-3912
Tel (703) 448-4400 *Founded/Ownrshp* 1977
Sales 24.9MM^E *EMP* 70
SIC 5088 7538 7699 Aircraft & parts; General truck repair; Aircraft & heavy equipment repair services
Pr: Richard D McConn
**Pr:* Robert Ruck
**CFO:* Mehdi Protzuk
**VP:* Tom Duncan
IT Man: Leslie McConn
Sales Exec: Ed Newell

D-U-N-S 07-495-7168
M J BRUNNER INC
11 Stanwix St Fl 5, Pittsburgh, PA 15222-1312
Tel (412) 995-9500 *Founded/Ownrshp* 1975
Sales 28.9MM^E *EMP* 180
SIC 7311 7331 8743 Advertising consultant; Mailing service; Public relations & publicity; Advertising consultant; Mailing service; Public relations & publicity
CEO: Michael Brunner
**Pr:* Scott Morgan
**CEO:* Michael Brunner
Sr VP: Katie Bicknell
**Sr VP:* Rick Gardinier
**Sr VP:* Tracy Gross
Sr VP: David Sladack
VP: Matt Blackburn
**VP:* Rick Booth
VP: John Gatesman
VP: Dan Gbur
VP: Lindy Gross
**VP:* Celeste Jones
VP: Michelle Latta
VP: Jackie Murray
VP: George Potts
VP: Gordon Robertson
VP: Louis Sawyer
VP: Erin Stoner
VP: Dave Vissat
Creative D: Dan Magdich
Board of Directors: Michael Brunner

D-U-N-S 12-421-9382 IMP
M J CELCO INC
3900 Wesley Ter, Schiller Park, IL 60176-2132
Tel (847) 671-1900 *Founded/Ownrshp* 1999
Sales 50.0MM *EMP* 185
SIC 3469 Metal stampings; Metal stampings
Pr: Michael Cielak
CFO: Tom Meyers
**Sec:* Stanley Cielak
Genl Mgr: Tom Sikorski
Mfg Dir: Don Mayo
Sales Exec: Andy Kluczny

D-U-N-S 78-643-9885
M J DEAN CONSTRUCTION INC
M J DEAN DRYWALL
5055 W Patrick Ln Ste 101, Las Vegas, NV 89118-2840
Tel (702) 873-1947 *Founded/Ownrshp* 1989
Sales 79.9MM^E *EMP* 500^E
SIC 1542 Commercial & office building, new construction; Commercial & office building, new construction
Pr: Michael Dean
CFO: Chris Flanagan
**Ex VP:* Roland Kent
**VP:* Michael Cherwin
Dir IT: Tommy Glidewell
Ql Cn Mgr: Dave Steelefox

M J DEAN DRYWALL
See M J DEAN CONSTRUCTION INC

D-U-N-S 04-930-7705
M J KELLNER CO INC
MJ KELLNER FOODSERVICE
5700 International Pkwy, Springfield, IL 62711-4052
Tel (217) 483-1700 *Founded/Ownrshp* 1922
Sales 47.0MM^E *EMP* 72
SIC 5141

D-U-N-S 13-106-6248
M J LATHERN CO INC
METALS 2 GO
1300 Old Hewitt Rd, Waco, TX 76712-6651
Tel (254) 235-7700 *Founded/Ownrshp* 2002
Sales 44.9MM^E *EMP* 35
SIC 5051 Aluminum bars, rods, ingots, sheets, pipes, plates, etc.
Pr: Michael Jay Lathern
**VP:* Mary Ann Lathern

D-U-N-S 92-794-6103
M J PETERSON LP
PEPPER TREE HEIGHTS ASSOCIATES
501 J James Adbn Pkwy 100, Amherst, NY 14228
Tel (716) 689-6006 *Founded/Ownrshp* 1978
Sales 30.0MM *EMP* 19
SIC 6531 Real estate agents & managers; Real estate agents & managers
Pt: Stephen M Ross
CFO: Patrick Finucane

D-U-N-S 18-892-6844
M J SHERIDAN OF TEXAS INC
9015 Sweetbrush Dr, Houston, TX 77064-1599
Tel (281) 469-5810 *Founded/Ownrshp* 1988
Sales 62.6MM^E *EMP* 225
SIC 1623

M J SULLIVAN AUTOMOTIVE CORNER
See SULLYS AUTO SALES & SERVICE INC

D-U-N-S 00-890-0623 IMP
M JACOB & SONS
SPRAYCO
35601 Veronica St, Livonia, MI 48150-1203
Tel (734) 744-4900 *Founded/Ownrshp* 1885
Sales 51.9MM^E *EMP* 60
SIC 5085 5149 7389 Commercial containers; Crowns & closures, metal; Plastic bottles; Glass bottles; Health foods; Packaging & labeling services; Commercial containers; Crowns & closures, metal; Plastic bottles; Glass bottles; Health foods; Packaging & labeling services
Pr: David Lubin
**Pr:* Martin S Jacob
**CEO:* Kenneth Weir
**Ex VP:* Robert J Stieler
Sr VP: Neil Bloomberg
**Sr VP:* Paul Stieler
VP: Timothy King
VP: Eric Seidel
Off Mgr: Ronni Majewski
Off Mgr: Sharon White
IT Man: Ryan Barnes

D-U-N-S 19-721-3168
M K G ENTERPRISES INC
MCDONALD'S
2800 Electric Rd Ste 100, Roanoke, VA 24018-3549
Tel (540) 989-1707 *Founded/Ownrshp* 1983
Sales 7.1MM^E *EMP* 293
SIC 5812 Fast-food restaurant, chain; Fast-food restaurant, chain
Pr: Michael Grimm
VP: Grimm J M

D-U-N-S 00-446-2032 IMP/EXP
M K MORSE CO
1101 11th St Se, Canton, OH 44707-3400
Tel (330) 453-8187 *Founded/Ownrshp* 1963, 2001
Sales 91.5MM^E *EMP* 450^E
SIC 3425 Saw blades for hand or power saws; Saw blades for hand or power saws
CEO: Nancy Sonner
**Owner:* Sally Dale
**Pr:* James Batchelder
**CFO:* Thomas Herrick Jr
**Treas:* George Briercheck
VP: Philip Metz
VP: Chip Tomlinson
Off Mgr: Teidre Lazarides
Off Mgr: Sameer Marde
QA Dir: Dave Vlacovsky
Dir IT: Dave Strickland
Board of Directors: Sally Dale

D-U-N-S 04-365-9770 IMP
M K PRODUCTS INC
MK MANUFACTURING
16882 Armstrong Ave, Irvine, CA 92606-4975
Tel (949) 798-1425 *Founded/Ownrshp* 1966
Sales 22.1MM^E *EMP* 81
SIC 3548 Electric welding equipment
Pr: Chris Westlake
**CFO:* Joseph J Lapaglia
VP: Paco Perez
Exec: Lou Cantieri
MIS Dir: Scott Zickefoose
IT Man: Loc Trang
Sftwr Eng: Eric Kajdas
Sfty Mgr: Hector Rivera
Mfg Mgr: Mark Bell
VP Sls: Paul Miller
VP Sls: Karen Zahner

D-U-N-S 02-801-0957
M K SMITH CHEVROLET
12845 Central Ave, Chino, CA 91710-4120
Tel (909) 628-8961 *Founded/Ownrshp* 1984
Sales 70.0MM *EMP* 120
SIC 5511 7549 5531 Automobiles, new & used; Automotive maintenance services; Automotive parts; Automobiles, new & used; Automotive maintenance services; Automotive parts
Pr: Robert W Smith
**CEO:* Marc Smith
**Treas:* Carolyn Coble
Sales Asso: George Chavez
Sales Asso: George Modlin
Sales Asso: George Monarrez
Sales Asso: Alex Tercero

M L B
See MLB ADVANCED MEDIA LP

M L B
See MAJOR LEAGUE BASEBALL ENTERPRISES INC

D-U-N-S 80-741-6842
M L E HOLDINGS INC
1301 W 400 N, Orem, UT 84057-4442
Tel (801) 224-0589 *Founded/Ownrshp* 2007
Sales 35.6MM^E *EMP* 398^E
SIC 2531 2522 2521 Public building & related furniture; Office desks & tables: except wood; Panel systems & partitions, office: except wood; Chairs, office: padded or plain, except wood; Tables, office: except wood; Wood office furniture; Wood office chairs, benches & stools; Chairs, office: padded, upholstered or plain: wood; Panel systems & partitions (freestanding), office: wood
Ch: Gregory Wilson

D-U-N-S 14-455-9069
M L PARTNERSHIP
MARSH LANDING COUNTRY CLUB
25655 Marsh Landing Pkwy, Ponte Vedra Beach, FL 32082-1919
Tel (904) 285-6514 *Founded/Ownrshp* 2005
Sales 55.0MM^E *EMP* 150^E
SIC 6552 7997 Subdividers & developers; Golf club, membership
Prin: Steven Loveland
Genl Mgr: Bruno Couturier
Dir IT: Dana Kasler
Dir IT: Jared Nielsen

D-U-N-S 06-901-6657
M L RUBERTON CONSTRUCTION CO
1512 Mays Landing Rd, Hammonton, NJ 08037-2857
Tel (609) 561-3800 *Founded/Ownrshp* 1975
Sales 23.7MM^E *EMP* 60
SIC 1611 1799 General contractor, highway & street construction; Petroleum storage tank installation, underground
Pr: Elizabeth Pitale
**Pr:* Andrew G Berenato Jr
CFO: Michael Lerner
**VP:* Andrea Berenato
**VP:* Richard Berenato
Genl Mgr: Rick Bernardo
Opers Mgr: John Thomas

D-U-N-S 11-331-0379
M L SMITH JR LLC
2338 Highway 33, Ruston, LA 71270-3294
Tel (318) 255-4474 *Founded/Ownrshp* 1990
Sales 28.1MM *EMP* 100
Accts Donald Tucker Betts & Fuller
SIC 3291 1741 Abrasive metal & steel products; Refractory or acid brick masonry; Abrasive metal & steel products; Refractory or acid brick masonry
Tech Mgr: Mike Blackford

D-U-N-S 03-955-7962
■ **M L STERN & CO LLC**
(*Suby of* HILLTOP SECURITIES HOLDINGS LLC) ★
8350 Wilshire Blvd Fl 1, Beverly Hills, CA 90211-2324
Tel (323) 658-4400 *Founded/Ownrshp* 2008
Sales 46.4MM^E *EMP* 210
SIC 6211 Brokers, security; Brokers, security
Assoc VP: Jennifer Huey
Sr VP: Greg Flack
Sr VP: Don Lewis
Sr VP: Stacy Stern
VP: Phil Borenstein
VP: Richard Dimino
VP: Alicia Kitz
VP: Leonard Laub
VP: John Madonna
VP: Jeff Margolis
VP: Cliff Milleman
VP: Justin Parker
VP: Steve Powell
VP: Erick Renderos
VP: Andrew Rudy

M L WISMER
See WISMER DISTRIBUTING CO LTD

D-U-N-S 01-474-2027 IMP
M LEVIN & CO INC
6700 Essington Ave H5, Philadelphia, PA 19153-3403
Tel (215) 336-2900 *Founded/Ownrshp* 1906
Sales 40.5MM^E *EMP* 65
SIC 5148 Fresh fruits & vegetables; Fresh fruits & vegetables
Pr: Michael Levin
**Treas:* Joel Siegel
**VP:* Mark Levin
Genl Mgr: Tracie Levin
Off Mgr: Dolores Dougherty

M. LIPSITZ & CO
See LIPSITZ MANAGEMENT CO INC

D-U-N-S 02-456-2292
M LIPSITZ & CO LTD (TX)
100 Elm St, Waco, TX 76704-2507
Tel (254) 756-6661 *Founded/Ownrshp* 1963
Sales 41.0MM^E *EMP* 113^E
SIC 5093 Ferrous metal scrap & waste
Pr: Tom Salome Jr
COO: Charles Johnson
VP: Melvin Lipsitz Jr
Opers Mgr: David Romero

M LUIS CONSTRUCTION CO
See MANUEL LUIS CONSTRUCTION CO INC

M M & M ELECTRICAL SUPPLY
See GUND CO INC

M M & P HEALTH & BENEFIT PLANS
See MASTERS MATES AND PILOTS HEALTH & BENEFIT PLANS

M M C
See MAGAN MEDICAL CLINIC INC

D-U-N-S 05-388-7741
M M C INC
(*Suby of* NEW-COM INC) ★
6600 Amelia Earhart Ct B, Las Vegas, NV 89119-3535
Tel (702) 642-3332 *Founded/Ownrshp* 1984
Sales 41.1MM^E *EMP* 215
SIC 1623 Water main construction; Sewer line construction; Water main construction; Sewer line construction
Pr: Greg J Paulk
**Treas:* Brady Stevens

D-U-N-S 94-901-3445
M M DIRECT MARKETING INC
(*Suby of* MM ADVERTISING) ★
14271 Corporate Dr, Garden Grove, CA 92843-4937
Tel (714) 265-4100 *Founded/Ownrshp* 1998
Sales 9.8MM^E *EMP* 300
SIC 7331 6794 Mailing service; Franchises, selling or licensing; Mailing service; Franchises, selling or licensing
Pr: Godfred P Otueye

D-U-N-S 19-631-8505 IMP
M M FAB INC
SOUTH SEAS IMPORTS
2300 E Gladwick St, Compton, CA 90220-6208
Tel (310) 763-3800 *Founded/Ownrshp* 1988
Sales 29.4MM^E *EMP* 85
SIC 5131 Piece goods & other fabrics
Pr: Richard Friedman
Sales Exec: Sergio Garcia

M M I
See MONEY MANAGEMENT INTERNATIONAL INC

M M I
See MARKETING MANAGEMENT INC

M M I INTERNATIONAL
See SCHNITZER STEEL INTERNATIONAL

D-U-N-S 96-485-2136
M M MANUFACTURING LLC
65 Infantry Ave 109 S, Lajas, PR 00667
Tel (787) 899-1707 *Founded/Ownrshp* 2010
Sales 390.0M *EMP* 340
SIC 2311 Military uniforms, men's & youths': purchased materials; Military uniforms, men's & youths': purchased materials
Pr: Maria I Colon Melendez

D-U-N-S 13-146-6765
M M NORTHWEST HARVEST/E
711 Cherry St, Seattle, WA 98104-1924
Tel (206) 625-0755 *Founded/Ownrshp* 1967
Sales 53.2MM *EMP* 70
Accts Clark Nuber Ps Bellevue Wa
SIC 8322 Individual & family services; Individual & family services
CEO: Shelley Rotondo

M M O
See MEDICAL MANAGEMENT OPTIONS LLC

M M POST FOUNDATION
See HILLWOOD MUSEUM & GARDENS FOUNDATION

M M S D
See MILWAUKEE METROPOLITAN SEWERAGE DISTRICT

M M SUSPENSIONS
See MAGNETI MARELLI OF TENNESSEE LLC

M M W E C
See MASSACHUSETTS MUNICIPAL WHOLESALE ELECTRIC CO

D-U-N-S 01-432-9106 IMP
M M WEAVER AND SONS INC
169 N Groffdale Rd, Leola, PA 17540-9000
Tel (717) 656-2321 *Founded/Ownrshp* 1936
Sales 54.0MM *EMP* 44
Accts Martin Accounting Service Mye
SIC 5083 7699 Farm implements; Farm machinery repair; Farm implements; Farm machinery repair
Pr: Eujene Hurst
**Treas:* Ervin Weaver
**Sec:* Curtis Weaver
**VP:* Edward Weaver

D-U-N-S 07-865-1078
M MICRO TECHNOLOGIES INC
MICROTECHNOLOGIES
2901 Gateway Dr, Pompano Beach, FL 33069-4326
Tel (954) 973-6166 *Founded/Ownrshp* 2003
Sales 53.6MM^E *EMP* 500
SIC 3629 3699 Electronic generation equipment; Electrical equipment & supplies; High-energy particle physics equipment; Electronic generation equipment; Electrical equipment & supplies; High-energy particle physics equipment
Prin: Michele Hamilton
Treas: Antonio Bossiello
Tech Mgr: Magda Posada

M MODAL
See MMODAL INC

M N A
See OHIO MODULE MANUFACTURING CO LLC

D-U-N-S 01-456-6715 IMP
M N GOLDSTEIN CO (PA)
GOLDSTEINS FURNITURE
1340 N Hermitage Rd, Hermitage, PA 16148-3107
Tel (724) 981-1136 *Founded/Ownrshp* 1900, 1999
Sales 32.5MM^E *EMP* 140
SIC 5712

D-U-N-S 82-556-9312
M N ONE INC
HONDA OF SEATTLE
(*Suby of* HONDA OF SEATTLE) ★
1015 Olive Way, Seattle, WA 98101-1826
Tel (206) 382-8800 *Founded/Ownrshp* 1992
Sales 35.6MM^E *EMP* 135
SIC 5511 Automobiles, new & used; Automobiles, new & used
Pr: Brad Miller
**CFO:* Stuart Lund
Genl Mgr: Ryan Jupiter

M O C
See UNIVERSITY OF MOUNT OLIVE INC

M O C INSURANCE SERVICES
See MAROEVICH OSHEA & COGHLAN INSURANCE INC

D-U-N-S 04-643-4676
M O DION & SONS INC (CA)
1543 W 16th St, Long Beach, CA 90813-1210
Tel (714) 540-5535 *Founded/Ownrshp* 1930, 1986
Sales 159.6MM *EMP* 115
Accts Windes Inc Long Beach Cali
SIC 5172 Gasoline; Diesel fuel; Lubricating oils & greases; Gasoline; Diesel fuel; Lubricating oils & greases
CEO: Pat Cullen
**Pr:* Matt Cullen
**CEO:* Patrick B Cullen
**CFO:* Bill Frank

M P
See MP TECHNOLOGIES LLC

M P A
See MP ASSOCIATES INC

M P C LOUISVILLE PROMOTIONS
See MPC PROMOTIONS LLC

M P ENVIRONMENTAL SERVICES
See M P VACUUM TRUCK SERVICE

M P G
See MEDIA PLANNING GROUP USA LLC

M P G TRUCK & TRACTOR
See MAINE POTATO GROWERS INC

M P I
See MICRO-PROBE INC

M P I
See MICROBOARD PROCESSING INC

M P I
See MIDWEST PERISHABLES INC

M P I LABEL SYSTEMS
See MILLER PRODUCTS INC

D-U-N-S 77-997-2017 IMP
M P N INC
ACTIVE RADIATOR
3675 Amber St, Philadelphia, PA 19134-2730
Tel (215) 289-9480 *Founded/Ownrshp* 1953
Sales 32.0MM^E *EMP* 205
SIC 3714 Radiators & radiator shells & cores, motor vehicle; Radiators & radiator shells & cores, motor vehicle
Pr: Martin Newell Jr
**COO:* Paul Luff
**Treas:* Regina Newell
VP: Tom Mourer
Sls Mgr: Mike Stoehr

D-U-N-S 10-794-2948
M P O INC
(*Suby of* OBAGI MEDICAL PRODUCTS INC) ★
3760 Kilroy Airport Way # 5, Long Beach, CA 90806-2443
Tel (562) 628-1007 *Founded/Ownrshp* 2004
Sales 27.5MM^E *EMP* 199
SIC 5122 Cosmetics; Cosmetics
Pr: Al Hummel
**CFO:* Preston Romm
**Ex VP:* David Goldstein
VP: Nasim Glaubitz
VP: James Hartman
VP: Laura Hunter
VP: Ronald Lapre
**Prin:* Albert F Hummel

D-U-N-S 80-003-0421 IMP
M P PUMPS INC
(*Suby of* LIONHEART HOLDINGS LLC) ★
34800 Bennett, Fraser, MI 48026-1694
Tel (586) 293-8240 *Founded/Ownrshp* 2008
Sales 28.3MM^E *EMP* 90
SIC 3594 3561 Fluid power pumps & motors; Pumps & pumping equipment; Fluid power pumps & motors; Pumps & pumping equipment
Pr: Greg Peabody
VP: Nancy Mohan
Exec: Dorothy Hunter
Genl Mgr: John Farrell
Prd Mgr: Mark Storks
S&M/VP: Joe Keine
Manager: Joseph Ash

M P S
See MEDICAL PLUS SUPPLIES INC

M P S
See MILWAUKEE PUBLIC SCHOOLS

M P S
See MACMILLAN HOLDINGS LLC

M P U
See MANITOWOC PUBLIC UTILITIES (INC)

D-U-N-S 06-457-5012
M P VACUUM TRUCK SERVICE
M P ENVIRONMENTAL SERVICES
3400 Manor St, Bakersfield, CA 93308-1451
Tel (661) 393-1151 *Founded/Ownrshp* 1958, 1991
Sales 34.7MM^E *EMP* 175
SIC 4953 Hazardous waste collection & disposal; Hazardous waste collection & disposal
Pr: Dawn Calderwood

D-U-N-S 17-410-1204
M PETE MCNABB INC
ARTHUR RUTENBERG HOMES
9415 Town Center Pkwy, Lakewood Ranch, FL 34202-5134
Tel (941) 907-6771 *Founded/Ownrshp* 1987
Sales 20.5MM *EMP* 57
SIC 1521 Single-family housing construction; Single-family housing construction
Pr: M Pete McNabb

**CFO:* Ron Gratz
**VP:* Kevin Garcia
**VP:* Stephen Gaston
**VP:* Derek Nelson

M Q B
See MCQUADE AND BANNIGAN INC

M R
See MARC REALTY LLC

M R C
See LABARGE PIPE AND STEEL CO

M R C
See CALUMET MONTANA REFINING LLC

M R H
See MARLETTE REGIONAL HOSPITAL

M R L
See MONTANA RAIL LINK INC

D-U-N-S 00-621-3339 IMP
M R L EQUIPMENT CO INC
5379 Southgate Dr, Billings, MT 59101-4638
Tel (877) 788-2907 *Founded/Ownrshp* 1993
Sales 32.9MM^E *EMP* 95
SIC 5082 3531 Contractors' materials; Construction machinery; Contractors' materials; Construction machinery
CEO: John Gonitzke
Sr VP: Joe Meick
**VP:* James Stielman
VP Sls: Steve Shinners

D-U-N-S 88-400-7980
M R M ENTERPRISES INC
STARR HOME HEALTH AGENCY
410 W 2nd St Ste B2, Rio Grande City, TX 78582-3608
Tel (956) 487-0597 *Founded/Ownrshp* 1995
Sales 7.1MM^E *EMP* 320
SIC 8082 Home health care services; Home health care services
**CFO:* Mario Guerra Sr
VP: Guerra Rosa Maria

M R P C
See MOLDED RUBBER & PLASTIC CORP

M R S
See MIDWEST REFRIGERATED TRANSPORT INC

M R S I
See MARKETING RESEARCH SERVICES INC

M R SHEET METAL
See MASON ROAD SHEET METAL INC

D-U-N-S 02-461-7193
M R WILLIAMS INC (NC)
235 Raleigh Rd, Henderson, NC 27536-4977
Tel (252) 438-8104 *Founded/Ownrshp* 1948, 1976
Sales 66.9MM^E *EMP* 125^E
SIC 5141

M RESORT
See MARNELL SHER GAMING LLC

M RESORT SPA CASINO
See LVGV LLC

M RESORT SPA CASINO, THE
See LV GAMING VENTURES LLC

M S
See MAU-SHERWOOD SUPPLY CO

M S
See NATIONAL MULTIPLE SCLEROSIS SOCIETY

M S
See MARK SCOTT CONSTRUCTION INC

M S A D 47
See RSU 18

D-U-N-S 10-076-1923
M S A D 52
TURNER ELEMENTARY SCHOOL
91 Matthews Way, Turner, ME 04282-3929
Tel (207) 225-3406 *Founded/Ownrshp* 1977
Sales 18.5MM^E *EMP* 400
SIC 8211 Elementary & secondary schools; Public elementary school; Elementary & secondary schools; Public elementary school
Prin: Cynthia Alexander

D-U-N-S 02-098-5792
M S AMTEX-N INC
SOUTHEAST MODULAR MFG
(*Suby of* AMTEX-NMS HOLDINGS INC) ★
2500 Industrial St, Leesburg, FL 34748-3609
Tel (352) 326-9729 *Founded/Ownrshp* 1999
Sales 38.7MM^E *EMP* 150
SIC 3448 Prefabricated metal buildings; Prefabricated metal buildings
Ch: David Meyer
Pr: Jim Ginas
COO: Les Berczy
Opers Mgr: Mike Jones
Plnt Mgr: Dave Mathis

M S C
See METALS SUPPLY CO LTD

M S C
See MEISTER SUPPLY CO

M S C INDUSTRIAL SUPPLY
See SID TOOL CO INC

M S C INDUSTRIAL SUPPLY
See ASIDCO INC

D-U-N-S 94-467-8267
M S C LLC
CHARNEY MARKETING SERVICES
1800 Walt Whitman Rd # 140, Melville, NY 11747-3099
Tel (516) 799-1892 *Founded/Ownrshp* 1996
Sales NA *EMP* 44^E
SIC 6411 Insurance brokers

D-U-N-S 05-018-2841
M S D WAYNE TOWNSHIP
1220 S High School Rd, Indianapolis, IN 46241-3127
Tel (317) 243-8251 Founded/Ownrshp 2010
Sales NA EMP 1,318E
SIC 9111 City & town managers' offices
CFO: Dennis Tackitt
Dir Sec: Doug Scheffel
MIS Dir: Pete Just
Dir IT: Mark Lutey
IT Man: Kayanne Klinker
Pr Dir: Mary Lang
Schl Brd P: Shirley Deckard
Schl Brd P: Stan Ellis
Teacher Pr: Shenia Suggs

M S F
See MSF ELECTRIC INC

D-U-N-S 02-401-8942
M S FOSTER & ASSOCIATES INC
1866 N Country Ln, Michigan City, IN 46360-9386
Tel (219) 879-9225 Founded/Ownrshp 1997, 1999
Sales 51.0MM EMP 2
SIC 5131 Net goods; Net goods
Pr: Michael Foster
Sls Mgr: Annette Foster

M S G
See MANNIK & SMITH GROUP INC

M S I
See MARKING SYSTEMS INC

D-U-N-S 07-098-7227 IMP/EXP
M S INTERNATIONAL INC
MSI
2095 N Batavia St, Orange, CA 92865-3101
Tel (714) 685-7500 Founded/Ownrshp 1983
Sales 414.8MME EMP 750
SIC 5032 Brick, stone & related material; Brick, stone & related material
CEO: Manahar Shah
*Pr: Rajesh Shah
*Sec: Chandrika Shah
Ofcr: Marlene Ramirez
VP: Kishor Panchani
VP: Sanjay Sanghvi
*VP: Rupesh Shah
Ex Dir: Steve Rowe
Mng Dir: Shamin Patel
Sls Dir: David Harris
Sls Mgr: Mark Mehta

D-U-N-S 83-128-0016
M S IOWA INC
(Suby of MECHANICAL SALES INC) ★
11009 Aurora Ave, Des Moines, IA 50322-7902
Tel (515) 276-9005 Founded/Ownrshp 2003
Sales 27.5MM EMP 48
SIC 3585 Heating & air conditioning combination units; Heating & air conditioning combination units
Pr: Jerry Cook
*Treas: Mark Morris
*VP: Timothy Grossman
Off Mgr: Jeanette Dimauro

D-U-N-S 05-586-3492
M S KENNEDY CORP
(Suby of ANAREN INC) ★
6635 Kirkville Rd, East Syracuse, NY 13057-9672
Tel (315) 701-6751 Founded/Ownrshp 2008
Sales 4.8MME EMP 450
SIC 3679

M S MANAGEMENT
See MORRIS SILVERMAN MANAGEMENT CORP

D-U-N-S 84-441-5039
M S N B C INTERACTIVE NEWS L L C
MSNBC.COM
1 Microsoft Way Bldg 25, Redmond, WA 98052-8300
Tel (425) 703-6397 Founded/Ownrshp 1996
Sales 22.3MME EMP 706
SIC 7383 News syndicates; News syndicates
CFO: Rick Causey
Creative D: Marc Greenstein
Genl Mgr: Charlie Tillinghast
Dir IT: Travis McElfresh

D-U-N-S 14-416-8390 IMP
M S ROUSE CO
1611 Kona Dr, Rancho Dominguez, CA 90220-5413
Tel (310) 764-4695 Founded/Ownrshp 1985
Sales 24.8MME EMP 100
Accts Gary L Wysocky Santa Rosa C
SIC 1752 Carpet laying; Resilient floor laying; Wood floor installation & refinishing
CEO: Mark S Rouse
*Pr: Scott Rouse
*COO: Jeffrey Lasher
*VP: Brian Davison
Snr Mgr: Trisha Pantera

M S S
See MOVERS SPECIALTY SERVICE INC

D-U-N-S 96-029-5343
■ **M S W INC**
MAIN STREET STATION HOTEL
(Suby of CALIFORNIA HOTEL AND CASINO) ★
2950 Industrial Rd, Las Vegas, NV 89109-1100
Tel (702) 792-7200 Founded/Ownrshp 1993
Sales 19.0MME EMP 900
Accts Deloitte & Touche Llp
SIC 7011 Hotels & motels; Hotels & motels
Pr: William S Boyd
Pr: Stan Salter
VP: Tom Ballance
VP: William Boyd
VP: Richard Darnold
*VP: Ellis Landau
VP: Michael Mathis
MIS Mgr: Jon Richardson

D-U-N-S 00-102-0718 IMP
M S WALKER INC (MA)
20 3rd Ave, Somerville, MA 02143-4404
Tel (617) 776-6700 Founded/Ownrshp 1931, 1949
Sales 129.2MME EMP 200
SIC 5182 Liquor; Liquor
Pr: Harvey Allen
Treas: Richard A Sandler
VP: Michael Allen
VP: Steve Blanchard
VP: Doug Shaw
Dir Soc: Christine Bono
Info Man: William Livingstone
Opers Mgr: Jeffrey Walsh
Mktg Dir: Ken Anderson
Mktg Mgr: Justin Shaw
Sls Mgr: Jeff Allen

M S X INTERNATIONAL
See MSX INTERNATIONAL PLATFORM SERVICES LLC

M SCHNOLL & SONS
See SCHNOLL PAINTING CORP

D-U-N-S 84-915-5882 EXP
M SEGUE CORP
25862 Commercentre Dr A, Lake Forest, CA 92630-8877
Tel (949) 382-2080 Founded/Ownrshp 1994
Sales 29.6MME EMP 49
SIC 5045 Computers, peripherals & software
Pr: Steve Vertun
Pr: Michelle Vilchuck
*CFO: Derek Stout
VP: Mark Dunlap
*VP: Lyle Peterson
Dir Bus: Melvin Simpson
Opers Mgr: Riley Schmitten
Sls Dir: Richard Pawlak

D-U-N-S 06-119-8305
M SHANKEN COMMUNICATIONS INC
825 8th Ave Fl 33, New York, NY 10019-8872
Tel (212) 684-4224 Founded/Ownrshp 1972
Sales 36.7MME EMP 135
SIC 2721 Magazines: publishing & printing; Magazines: publishing & printing
Ch Bd: Marvin R Shanken
Ch: Janice McManus-Genverino
*V Ch Bd: Michael Moaba
Sr VP: Tonnie McGilvary
Sr VP: Frank Walters
VP: Samantha Shanken Baker
VP: Alison Cohen
VP: Donald Gatterdam
VP: Liz McGuire
VP: Laura Sandy
VP: Laura Zandi

D-U-N-S 09-452-3248
M SHANNON INC
MCDONALD'S
5055 N 12th St Ste 200, Phoenix, AZ 85014-3346
Tel (602) 266-2994 Founded/Ownrshp 1978
Sales 8.3MME EMP 420
SIC 5812 Fast-food restaurant, chain; Fast-food restaurant, chain
Pr: Marion M Magruder Jr
*VP: Sandra Magruder

D-U-N-S 01-422-6351 IMP/EXP
M SIMON ZOOK CO
ZOOK MOLASSES CO
4960 Horseshoe Pike, Honey Brook, PA 19344-1361
Tel (610) 273-3776 Founded/Ownrshp 1970
Sales 128.5MME EMP 170
SIC 5149 2048 4013 Molasses, industrial; Prepared feeds; Railroad terminals; Molasses, industrial; Prepared feeds; Railroad terminals
Pr: Sally L Martin
*COO: Larry E Martin
*CFO: Dean Johnson
Genl Mgr: Paul Leininger
Dir IT: Kyle Stoltzfus
Plnt Mgr: Ron Smoker
Sales Exec: Ron Glessner

D-U-N-S 01-265-0214
M SLAVIN & SONS LTD (NY)
SALVIN, M & SONS
800 Food Center Dr # 37, Bronx, NY 10474-0013
Tel (718) 495-2800 Founded/Ownrshp 1925
Sales 65.0MM EMP 300
SIC 5146 Fish, fresh; Fish, fresh
Ch Bd: Stanley Slavin
*Pr: Herbie Slavin
CFO: John Lavin
*Sec: Cindy Slavin
*VP: Mitchell Slavin
*Prin: Barry Slavin

D-U-N-S 13-960-9585
M SPACE HOLDINGS LLC
629 Parkway Dr Ste A, Park City, UT 84098-5738
Tel (435) 659-2345 Founded/Ownrshp 2000
Sales 26.4MME EMP 55
SIC 1796 Installing building equipment
Pr: Jeff Deutschendorf
*COO: Dale Goebel
*CFO: Marshall Minor
Genl Couns: Christopher Orlovsky

D-U-N-S 01-285-1705
M SPIEGEL & SONS OIL CORP (NY)
S O S FUELS DIV
10 E Village Rd, Tuxedo Park, NY 10987-4512
Tel (845) 351-4700 Founded/Ownrshp 1964
Sales 136.7MM EMP 38
Accts Weiser Mazars Llp Woodbury N
SIC 5172 5983 Gasoline; Fuel oil; Diesel fuel; Fuel oil dealers; Gasoline; Fuel oil; Diesel fuel; Fuel oil dealers
CEO: Richard Spiegel
*Treas: Robert Spiegel

D-U-N-S 11-215-3940
M SQUARED CONSULTING INC
(Suby of SOLOMEDWARDS) ★
111 Sutter St Ste 900, San Francisco, CA 94104-4523
Tel (415) 391-1038 Founded/Ownrshp 2013
Sales 27.9MME EMP 240
SIC 8742 Business consultant; Business consultant
CEO: John Kunzweiler
CFO: Dirk Sodestrom
Sr VP: Lance Lennier
VP: Sondra Kiss
VP: Anita Kratka
VP: Colleen Lingane
VP: Scott Lininger
VP: Charlie Vezzali
VP Bus Dev: Bob Sottile
Dir Bus: Fiona McFarlane
IT Man: Pedro Sermeno

M SYSTEMS SUPER MARKETS CO.
See J C PACE & CO

M T A
See MASS TRANSPORTATION AUTHORITY INC

M T A
See METROPOLITAN TRANSPORTATION AUTHORITY

M T A
See MATANUSKA TELEPHONE ASSOCIATION INC

M T A
See MIDWEST TRANSATLANTIC LINES INC

M T A
See MASSACHUSETTS TEACHERS ASSOCIATION STAFF ORGANIZATION INC

M T C
See MUTUAL TRADING CO INC

M T C
See MANAGEMENT AND TRAINING CORP

M T C
See METROPOLITAN TRANSPORTATION COMMISSION

M T C
See MICRO-TECHNOLOGY CONCEPTS INC

D-U-N-S 00-157-5716
■ **M T C HOLDINGS**
(Suby of PORTS AMERICA INC) ★
3 Embarcadero Ctr Ste 550, San Francisco, CA 94111-4048
Tel (912) 651-4000 Founded/Ownrshp 2000
Sales 44.4MME EMP 380
SIC 4491 Stevedoring; Marine terminals; Loading vessels; Unloading vessels; Stevedoring; Marine terminals; Loading vessels; Unloading vessels
Pr: Michael Hassing
*CFO: Gail Parris
*Ch: Christopher Redlich Jr

D-U-N-S 05-985-4455 IMP
M T DEASON CO INC
2820 Commerce Blvd, Irondale, AL 35210-1216
Tel (205) 956-2266 Founded/Ownrshp 1982
Sales 35.7MME EMP 34E
SIC 4924 5074 5085 Natural gas distribution; Pipes & fittings, plastic; Plumbing & heating valves; Industrial supplies
CEO: Mike Deason
*Pr: Barbara McCauley
VP: Suzette Armatas

M T E
See MONROE TRUCK EQUIPMENT INC

M T F
See MUSCULOSKELETAL TRANSPLANT FOUNDATION INC

M T G
See MODERN TECHNOLOGIES GROUP INC

M T I
See MANAGEMENT TECHNOLOGY INC

M T I
See MAINTHIA TECHNOLOGIES INC

D-U-N-S 62-442-0048
M T LANEY CO INC
5400 Enterprise St, Eldersburg, MD 21784-9322
Tel (410) 795-1761 Founded/Ownrshp 1997
Sales 50.0MM EMP 165
SIC 1771 1794 1629 Blacktop (asphalt) work; Excavation work; Tennis court construction; Blacktop (asphalt) work; Excavation work; Tennis court construction
Pr: Mel Laney
Treas: Ryan Laney
*VP: Mike Laney

M T M
See MEDICAL TRANSPORTATION MANAGEMENT INC

M T O
See MUROTECH OHIO CORP

M T S
See MARTIN TRANSPORTATION SYSTEMS INC

M T S
See MTS TECHNOLOGIES INC

M T W
See MISSION TO WORLD (PCA) INC

M T X
See MITEK CORP

D-U-N-S 15-376-9831
M TIMM DEVELOPMENT INC
233 E Carrillo St Ste D, Santa Barbara, CA 93101-2186
Tel (805) 963-0358 Founded/Ownrshp 1984
Sales 27.4MME EMP 110
SIC 6552 Land subdividers & developers, commercial; Land subdividers & developers, residential
Pr: Milan Timm
*VP: Matt Easter
Off Mgr: Julie Joe

M TUCKER
See SINGER NY LLC

M TUCKER COMPANY
See M TUCKER CO INC

D-U-N-S 01-228-1697 IMP
M TUCKER CO INC
M TUCKER COMPANY
(Suby of M TUCKER) ★
1200 Madison Ave, Paterson, NJ 07503-2813
Tel (800) 688-2537 Founded/Ownrshp 2011
Sales 24.0MME EMP 100
SIC 5113 5046 Disposable plates, cups, napkins & eating utensils; Restaurant equipment & supplies; Disposable plates, cups, napkins & eating utensils; Restaurant equipment & supplies
Pr: Stephen Tucker
*COO: Mark Fuchs
Treas: Debra Raymond
VP: Bruce Klein

M U B
See MORGANTOWN UTILITY BOARD

M U D
See METROPOLITAN UTILITIES DISTRICT

M V A I C
See MOTOR VEHICLE ACCIDENT INDEMNIFICATION CORP

M V L A
See MOUNTAIN VIEW-LOS ALTOS UNION HIGH SCHOOL DISTRICT

D-U-N-S 03-804-9532
M V M INC
44620 Guilford Dr Ste 150, Ashburn, VA 20147-6063
Tel (571) 223-4500 Founded/Ownrshp 1979
Sales 197.2MME EMP 4,100
SIC 7381 8741 Detective & armored car services; Management services; Detective & armored car services; Management services
Pr: Dario O Marquez
*COO: David Westrate
*CFO: Joseph D Stanton
*Ex VP: Kevin P Marquez
*Sr VP: Louie T McKinney
*VP: Maria Campos
Admn Mgr: Margie Cebrian
Off Admin: Parwin Karimi
IT Man: Imad Samha
IT Man: Shun Zhang

M V R B C
See MISSISSIPPI VALLEY REGIONAL BLOOD CENTER INC

D-U-N-S 02-126-2183
M W B LEASING CORP
1 Penn Plz Fl 49, New York, NY 10119-0033
Tel (212) 594-5300 Founded/Ownrshp 1973
Sales 9.9MME EMP 300
SIC 6531 Real estate managers; Real estate managers
Pr: David Bershad
*VP: Patricia Hynes
*VP: William Lerach
*VP: Melvin Weiss

D-U-N-S 62-189-6661
M W BUILDERS INC
(Suby of MW BUILDERS GROUP INC) ★
10955 Lowell Ave Ste 300, Shawnee Mission, KS 66210-2368
Tel (913) 469-0101 Founded/Ownrshp 2002
Sales 78.3MME EMP 310
SIC 1542 Specialized public building contractors; Commercial & office building contractors; Specialized public building contractors; Commercial & office building contractors
CEO: William McDermott
*Pr: Jason Evelyn
*Pr: Peter Kelley
*CFO: David Cimpl
*Treas: David Burt
IT Man: Darrin Brillhuart

M W E
See MCDERMOTT WILL & EMERY LLP INC

M W M
See MIDWEST MANUFACTURING AND MECHANICAL INC

M W SERVICES
See MOUNT WHEELER POWER INC

D-U-N-S 01-898-8725
M W SEWALL & CO INC
259 Front St, Bath, ME 04530-2633
Tel (207) 442-7994 Founded/Ownrshp 1887
Sales 54.3MME EMP 165
SIC 5172 5983 5541 5411 Gasoline; Lubricating oils & greases; Diesel fuel; Fuel oil; Fuel oil dealers; Gasoline service stations; Convenience stores, independent; Gasoline; Lubricating oils & greases; Diesel fuel; Fuel oil; Fuel oil dealers; Gasoline service stations; Convenience stores, independent
Ch Bd: Edward Sewall Jr
*Pr: Edward Sewall III

M X R
See MERRY X-RAY CHEMICAL CORP

M ZT
See MACRO-Z-TECHNOLOGY CO

D-U-N-S 17-564-6611 IMP
M&A TECHNOLOGY INC
EDUBUYERS
2045 Chenault Dr, Carrollton, TX 75006-5021
Tel (972) 490-5803 Founded/Ownrshp 1985
Sales 160.4MME EMP 140
SIC 5045 7373 Computers, peripherals & software; Systems integration services; Computers, peripherals & software; Systems integration services
Pr: Magdy S Elwany
*Sr VP: Donna Shepard
Sr VP: Donna Zweback
VP: Shahab Azmoudeh
*VP: Tom Garrett
VP: Jihad Jubran
VP: Victor Mux
Prgrm Mgr: Christie Hite
CTO: Val Overbey

Mktg Mgr: Herb Emerson
Manager: Debi Cooper

D-U-N-S 78-802-1681
M&C HOTEL INTERESTS INC
RICHFIELD TECHNICAL SERVICES
(*Suby of* RICHFIELD HOLDINGS, INC.)
6560 Greenwood Plaza Blvd # 300, Greenwood Village, CO 80111-4980
Tel (303) 779-2000 *Founded/Ownrshp* 1991
Sales 64.0MM^E *EMP* 2,300
SIC 8741 8712 6321 6331 7389 Hotel or motel management; Architectural services; Accident & health insurance carriers; Workers' compensation insurance; Purchasing service; Hotel or motel management; Architectural services; Accident & health insurance carriers; Workers' compensation insurance; Purchasing service
Pr: Paul T Underhill
**Sr VP:* Lyle L Boll

D-U-N-S 84-165-5538
M&C MANAGEMENT SERVICES (USA) INC
MILLENNIUM HOTELS & RESORTS
(*Suby of* MILLENNIUM & COPTHORNE HOTELS PLC)
7600 E Orchard Rd 230s, Greenwood Village, CO 80111-2518
Tel (303) 779-2000 *Founded/Ownrshp* 2000
Sales 330.4MM^E *EMP* 5,000
SIC 7011 Hotels; Hotels
CEO: John Arnett
**Pr:* Robert Morse
VP: Janlyn Mahlman
VP: Augustine Silva
Dir IT: John Edwards
IT Man: Justin Griswold
IT Man: Mike Motyl
Sls Mgr: Lindsey Sullivan

D-U-N-S 18-888-5540 IMP
M&D WHOLESALE DISTRIBUTORS INC
CIGARS INTERNATIONAL
(*Suby of* SCANDINAVIAN TOBACCO GROUP A/S)
1911 Spillman Dr Dept 26, Bethlehem, PA 18015-2029
Tel (484) 285-0400 *Founded/Ownrshp* 2007
Sales 32.6MM^E *EMP* 150
SIC 5993 Cigar store
Pr: Craig Reynolds
**CEO:* Keith Meier
COO: Willie Murphy
**VP:* John Demarco
Store Mgr: Brock Williard
IT Man: Dave Delphia
Mktg Mgr: Sarah Santos

D-U-N-S 13-462-6113
M&E CONTRACTORS INC
9001a Hermitage Rd, Richmond, VA 23228
Tel (804) 353-6007 *Founded/Ownrshp* 2003
Sales 54.3MM^E *EMP* 250
SIC 1731 1711 Electrical work; Mechanical contractor; Electrical work; Mechanical contractor
Pr: Robert P Norton
**COO:* Irvin B Prude
**VP:* Richard K Adams
VP: David Minter
**VP:* J David Minter
**VP:* Thomas W Peabody
Snr PM: Alex Ray
Snr PM: Gary Wright

M&E GROUP
See M & E COMPONENTS INC

M&F
See MACHINERY & FACTORY INDUSTRIAL SUPPLY INC

D-U-N-S 02-281-2697 IMP
M&G DURAVENT INC
(*Suby of* M & G GROUP EUROPE B.V.)
877 Cotting Ct, Vacaville, CA 95688-9354
Tel (707) 446-1786 *Founded/Ownrshp* 2010
Sales 106.1MM^E *EMP* 400
SIC 3444 Metal ventilating equipment; Metal ventilating equipment
Pr: Brooks Sherman
**VP:* Victor Lambert

D-U-N-S 01-990-9607
M&G USA CORP
(*Suby of* MOSSI & GHISOLFI SPA)
27610 Huntington Rd, Apple Grove, WV 25502-8121
Tel (304) 576-4652 *Founded/Ownrshp* 2012
Sales 79.2MM^E *EMP* 293^E
SIC 3089 Plastic processing
Pr: Vittorio Ghisolfi

D-U-N-S 14-925-3366 IMP
M&H PLASTICS INC
(*Suby of* MAYNARD & HARRIS PLASTICS)
485 Brooke Rd, Winchester, VA 22603-5764
Tel (540) 504-0030 *Founded/Ownrshp* 2003
Sales 43.0MM^E *EMP* 115
SIC 3085 3089 Plastics bottles; Plastic containers, except foam
CEO: Kurt Nyberg
**CFO:* Edward J Adams Jr
Comm Dir: N J Smith
Dir IT: Gene Fletcher

D-U-N-S 08-190-5135
M&I DEALER FINANCE INC
(*Suby of* HARRIS BMO BANK NATIONAL ASSOCIATION) ★
11548 W Thdore Trcker Way, Milwaukee, WI 53214-1142
Tel (414) 302-3457 *Founded/Ownrshp* 1982
Sales NA *EMP* 90
SIC 6022 State commercial banks; State commercial banks
Pr: Thomas Oneill
Treas: Scott Sheaffer
Board of Directors: Robert A Schaefer, Joseph F Schoendorf Jr

D-U-N-S 04-630-8961 IMP
■ M&I ELECTRIC INDUSTRIES INC (TX)
(*Suby of* AMERICAN ELECTRIC TECHNOLOGIES INC) ★
1250 Wood Branch Park Dr # 600, Houston, TX 77079-1233
Tel (713) 644-8182 *Founded/Ownrshp* 1963, 2007
Sales 55.4MM^E *EMP* 300
SIC 3613 7694 1731 3825 3625 3612 Switchgear & switchgear accessories; Electric motor repair; General electrical contractor; Instruments to measure electricity; Relays & industrial controls; Transformers, except electric; Switchgear & switchgear accessories; Electric motor repair; General electrical contractor; Instruments to measure electricity; Relays & industrial controls; Transformers, except electric
Pr: James Steffek
**Ch Bd:* Arthur G Dauber
**COO:* Bill Miller
**CFO:* John H Untereker
**Treas:* Joseph F McGuire
**Sr VP:* Charles M Dauber
VP: Dave Grove
VP: Glenn Guy
VP: Rick Thompson
Dir Bus: Frank Davis
IT Man: Gordon Walker
Board of Directors: Paul N Katz, Howard W Kelley, Peter Menikoff, Lamar Nash, Hoke Peacock II, Stuart Schube J

D-U-N-S 03-427-5685
M&L INDUSTRIES LLC
KUBOTA
1210 Saint Charles St, Houma, LA 70360-2774
Tel (985) 876-2280 *Founded/Ownrshp* 1953
Sales 40.3MM^E *EMP* 107
SIC 5084 5083 Materials handling machinery; Tractors, agricultural; Materials handling machinery; Tractors, agricultural
VP: Todd McBroom
Genl Mgr: Sharon Adams
**Genl Mgr:* Steven Marmande

D-U-N-S 06-917-2294 EXP
■ M&M AEROSPACE HARDWARE INC (FL)
KLX AEROSPACE SOLUTIONS
(*Suby of* KLX AEROSPACE SOLUTIONS) ★
10000 Nw 15th Ter, Doral, FL 33172-2754
Tel (305) 925-2600 *Founded/Ownrshp* 1974, 2014
Sales 221.8MM^E *EMP* 300
SIC 5088 Aircraft equipment & supplies; Aircraft equipment & supplies
CEO: Amin J Khoury
**Pr:* Werner Lieberherr
**Pr:* Bob Marchetti
Sr VP: Terry Bond
Sr VP: Randy Heathcock
**Sr VP:* Thomas P McCaffrey
**VP:* Sean Cromie
Genl Mgr: James Ricketts
QA Dir: Ed Kubek
QA Dir: Daniel Tuttle
Mktg Dir: Jeff Horsager

D-U-N-S 96-778-2942
M&M GAMING LLC
SIENA HOTEL SPA & CASINO
1 S Lake St, Reno, NV 89501-1556
Tel (775) 682-3900 *Founded/Ownrshp* 2010
Sales NA *EMP* 350
SIC 7011

D-U-N-S 06-124-4831 IMP/EXP
M&M INDUSTRIAL SERVICES INC (TX)
7064 Patillo Rd, Beaumont, TX 77705-0418
Tel (409) 729-9488 *Founded/Ownrshp* 1999
Sales 42.3MM^E *EMP* 57
SIC 5085 Commercial containers
Pr: Terry Metreyeon
Ofcr: Pauline Morgan
**Prin:* Jeff Newton

M&M MANUFACTURING COMPANY
See M&M MANUFACTURING LLC

D-U-N-S 00-802-5355 IMP
■ M&M MANUFACTURING LLC
M&M MANUFACTURING COMPANY
(*Suby of* MITEK INDUSTRIES INC) ★
4001 Mark Iv Pkwy, Fort Worth, TX 76106-4129
Tel (817) 336-2311 *Founded/Ownrshp* 2015
Sales 126.0MM^E *EMP* 480
SIC 3444 Ducts, sheet metal; Ducts, sheet metal
CEO: Rob Felton
**Pr:* Roderick D Stepp
COO: Robert Felton
**VP:* Melvin Nobles
**VP:* Steve Priester
**VP:* Michael D Stepp
**VP:* Jim Strong
Sales Asso: Brandon Stepp

D-U-N-S 96-824-3688
M&M PIPELINE ACQUISITION LLC
M&M PIPELINE SERVICES
274 Mount Moriah Rd, Eupora, MS 39744-3346
Tel (662) 258-7101 *Founded/Ownrshp* 2010
Sales 24.8MM^E *EMP* 450
SIC 1623 Pipeline construction; Pipeline construction
Pr: Joe Marlar

M&M PIPELINE SERVICES
See M&M PIPELINE ACQUISITION LLC

D-U-N-S 04-636-7892
M&M PUMP & SUPPLY INC
(*Suby of* DN PARTNERS LLC) ★
1125 Olivette Executive P, Saint Louis, MO 63132-3250
Tel (314) 395-8122 *Founded/Ownrshp* 1967, 1979
Sales 38.9MM^E *EMP* 73
SIC 5084 Oil well machinery, equipment & supplies; Oil well machinery, equipment & supplies
Pr: Philip D Buerster
**Pr:* John Ollech
**Ex VP:* Scott Buerster
Sales Asso: Allen Berry
Sales Asso: Mark Judge

D-U-N-S 04-993-5919 IMP
M&M REFRIGERATION INC
412 Railroad Ave Ste 1, Federalsburg, MD 21632-1451
Tel (410) 754-8005 *Founded/Ownrshp* 2005
Sales 33.4MM^E *EMP* 80
SIC 3585 Refrigeration equipment, complete
Pr: Dufferin McConnell
**CFO:* Pamela M Schertz
VP: Ole Christensen
VP: Greg Robison
VP Sls: Dave Odum

D-U-N-S 07-956-5256
M&N DEALERSHIPS XII LLC
METRO FORD OF OKC
2800 W I 44 Service Rd, Oklahoma City, OK 73112-3722
Tel (405) 928-5454 *Founded/Ownrshp* 2014
Sales 39.1MM^E *EMP* 100
SIC 5511 7538 Automobiles, new & used; General automotive repair shops

M&R
See M & R CO

M&R
See M & R SALES AND SERVICE INC

D-U-N-S 87-855-0516 IMP
M&R HOLDINGS INC
M&R PRINTING
1n372 Main St, Glen Ellyn, IL 60137-3576
Tel (630) 858-6101 *Founded/Ownrshp* 1993
Sales 111.0MM^E *EMP* 400
SIC 3552 Printing machinery, textile; Printing machinery, textile
Pr: Richard Hoffman
**VP:* Howard Bloom
**VP:* Richard Nesladek
Manager: Tim Foreman

M&R PRINTING
See M&R HOLDINGS INC

M&S COMPAINES
See ALTERNATE NUMBER FIVE INC

D-U-N-S 14-468-1140
M&S TECHNOLOGIES INC
14175 Proton Rd, Dallas, TX 75244-3604
Tel (214) 420-5801 *Founded/Ownrshp* 2004
Sales 48.6MM *EMP* 32
SIC 7382 Protective devices, security
Pr: Sean Stenovitch
**VP:* Mark Miller

M&T
See MANUFACTURERS AND TRADERS TRUST CO

D-U-N-S 07-279-6022
▲ M&T BANK CORP
1 M&T Plz, Buffalo, NY 14203
Tel (716) 842-5445 *Founded/Ownrshp* 1969
Sales NA *EMP* 15,782
Tkr Sym MTB *Exch* NYS
SIC 6022 State commercial banks; State commercial banks
CEO: Robert G Wilmers
Ch Bd: Robert J Bojdak
Pr: Susan Bell
Pr: Deanna Benvenuto
Pr: Mark J Czarnecki
Pr: Chris Nehmsmann
Pr: Melissa Pinkerton
Pr: Veronika Steen II
Pr: Michael Weinstock
Pr: Mike Wolf
Pr: Amy Zawadzki
CFO: Rene F Jones
Ofcr: Stephen Nalawadi
Ofcr: Abdul Sissoko
Ofcr: George Smilanich
Ex VP: Richard S Gold
Ex VP: Michele D Trolli
VP: Nicholas Athineos
VP: Kimberly Barker
VP: Renee Bellagamba
VP: Jason Bishop

D-U-N-S 14-738-8748
■ M&T BANK CORP
(*Suby of* M&T) ★
255 East Ave Ste 100, Rochester, NY 14604-2624
Tel (585) 258-8204 *Founded/Ownrshp* 1969
Sales NA *EMP* 300
SIC 6022 State trust companies accepting deposits, commercial; State trust companies accepting deposits, commercial
Pr: Daniel Burn
**Treas:* Gary S Paul
**VP:* Richard A Lammert
Exec: Richard Morabito

D-U-N-S 93-974-4819
■ M&T BANK NATIONAL ASSOCIATION
(*Suby of* M&T BANK CORP) ★
48 Main St, Oakfield, NY 14125-1044
Tel (800) 528-6532 *Founded/Ownrshp* 1995
Sales 227.3MM *EMP* 45^E
SIC 6211 Investment bankers; Investment bankers
Ch: Robert G Wilmers
**Pr:* Robert E Sadler Jr
Ex VP: Harry R Stainrook
Sr VP: James A Gately
Sr VP: Richard A Lammert
Sr VP: Alfred F Luhr III
Sr VP: William H Mabee

D-U-N-S 78-848-8336
■ M&TMORTGAGE CORP
(*Suby of* M&T) ★
1 Fountain Plz, Buffalo, NY 14203-1420
Tel (716) 842-5445 *Founded/Ownrshp* 1991
Sales NA *EMP* 1,050
SIC 6162 Mortgage bankers; Mortgage brokers, using own money; Mortgage bankers; Mortgage brokers, using own money
Sr VP: Michael Drury
Ofcr: Sandra Casewell
Ofcr: Rosemarie Gott
**Sr VP:* Michael Todaro
VP: Sam Adolph
VP: Amy Audetat
VP: Phil Battaglia
VP: Robert Doust
VP: Rich Gold
VP: Gary Hutchings
Mng Dir: Richard Rickli
Board of Directors: Emerson L Brumback, Michael P Pinto, Robert E Sadler Jr

D-U-N-S 12-982-1018
M+W AMERICAS INC
(*Suby of* M+W FACILITY ENGINEERING GMBH)
1001 Klein Rd Ste 400, Plano, TX 75074-3751
Tel (972) 535-7300 *Founded/Ownrshp* 1990
Sales 305.5MM^E *EMP* 920
SIC 3433 Personal holding companies, except banks; Solar heaters & collectors
Pr: Richard Whitney
**COO:* Gary C Baughman
CFO: Hannes Rosenthaler
Ex VP: Ralf Graber
Ex VP: Rudolf Simon
**VP:* Jose Rivas
Dir Bus: Dave Perez
Mng Dir: Herbert Blaschitz
Mng Dir: Ralf Schmid
Brnch Mgr: Rich Schwarzbeck
Dir IT: Martin Boekeloo

D-U-N-S 62-114-7255 IMP
M+W US INC
(*Suby of* M+W GROUP GMBH)
125 Monroe St, Watervliet, NY 12189-4019
Tel (518) 266-3400 *Founded/Ownrshp* 2005
Sales 185.2MM^E *EMP* 400
SIC 1542 8711 Nonresidential construction; Engineering services; Nonresidential construction; Engineering services
Pr: Rick Whitney
COO: Ron Oakley
Ex VP: Ralf Gr Ber
**VP:* Alan Asadoorian
**VP:* Ralf Graber
**VP:* Jose M Rivas
Exec: Virginia Riggione
Rgnl Mgr: Michael Bennett
Snr PM: Peter Hypnar

D-U-N-S 05-950-5065 IMP
M-B COMPANIES INC
1200 Park St, Chilton, WI 53014-1647
Tel (920) 849-2313 *Founded/Ownrshp* 1974
Sales 26.7MM^E *EMP* 100
SIC 3531 Road construction & maintenance machinery; Road construction & maintenance machinery
Pr: Terrence Cosgrove
Genl Mgr: Steve Karlin
Genl Mgr: Steven Muellenbach
Opers Mgr: Doug Blada
Plnt Mgr: William Hoff
Plnt Mgr: Ron Magargle
Mktg Dir: Bryan Peters
Sls Dir: Rob Miller
Sls Mgr: Kurt Schallmo
Sales Asso: Dave Kabat
Snr Mgr: Jim Steiner

D-U-N-S 95-990-9540 IMP
M-B COMPANIES INC
1615 Wisconsin Ave, New Holstein, WI 53061-1339
Tel (920) 898-4203 *Founded/Ownrshp* 1974
Sales 35.5MM^E *EMP* 100
SIC 3531 3711 1721 Pavers; Motor vehicles & car bodies; Pavement marking contractor; Pavers; Motor vehicles & car bodies; Pavement marking contractor
Pr: Terence Cosgrove
Brnch Mgr: Steve Karlin
DP Exec: Pat Gill

D-U-N-S 05-516-7324 IMP
M-B INDUSTRIES INC
SUNBELT SPRING & STAMPING
9205 Rosman Hwy, Rosman, NC 28772
Tel (828) 862-4263 *Founded/Ownrshp* 1971
Sales 78.5MM^E *EMP* 225
Accts Greene Smith Roddy & Co P
SIC 3495 3469 3552 3496 3648 3398 Wire springs; Stamping metal for the trade; Textile machinery; Miscellaneous fabricated wire products; Street lighting fixtures; Metal heat treating; Wire springs; Stamping metal for the trade; Textile machinery; Miscellaneous fabricated wire products; Street lighting fixtures; Metal heat treating
Pr: Edwin E Morrow
Prd Mgr: Tim Petit
Mktg Mgr: Robert Reid

D-U-N-S 09-826-6802
M-C FABRICATION INC
15612 S Keeler Ter, Olathe, KS 66062-3510
Tel (913) 764-5454 *Founded/Ownrshp* 1979
Sales 28.8MM^E *EMP* 79
SIC 3441 3599 Fabricated structural metal; Machine shop, jobbing & repair
Pr: Don L Mitchell
Sec: Janice Mitchell
VP: Brad Mitchell
Genl Mgr: Dave Gibson
IT Man: Mike Allen

D-U-N-S 00-718-8063 IMP/EXP
M-D BUILDING PRODUCTS INC
4041 N Santa Fe Ave, Oklahoma City, OK 73118-8512
Tel (405) 528-4411 *Founded/Ownrshp* 2000
Sales 269.6MM^E *EMP* 600
SIC 3442 Weather strip, metal; Moldings & trim, except automobile: metal; Weather strip, metal; Moldings & trim, except automobile: metal
CEO: Loren A Plotkin
CFO: Kathryn McKinney
Ch: Richard Gaugler
Ex VP: Larry Sanford
Ex VP: Steve Wright
Plnt Mgr: Tom Stark
Manager: Sandy Britt
Board of Directors: Brent Gooden, Rick Moore

M-DCPS SCHOOL BOARD
See SCHOOL BOARD OF MIAMI-DADE COUNTY

D-U-N-S 11-598-0286
M-E ENGINEERS INC
ME ENGINEERS
14143 Denver West Pkwy # 300, Lakewood, CO 80401-3269
Tel (303) 421-6655 *Founded/Ownrshp* 1981
Sales 48.2MM^E *EMP* 240
SIC 8711 Consulting engineer; Consulting engineer
CEO: Mike Hart
**Pr:* Martin Ed Ragain
**Pr:* Frank Stefan
**Ch:* Ed Ragain
**VP:* Scott Gerard
**VP:* Allan Tochihara
Exec: Trish Lovato
Genl Mgr: Drew Depalma
IT Man: Ramon Martin
Mktg Mgr: Alexandrea Merrell
Snr PM: Roger Loomis

D-U-N-S 00-145-7241 IMP
M-F ATHLETIC CO INC (RI)
EVERYTHING TRACK & FIELD
1600 Division Rd, West Warwick, RI 02893-7504
Tel (401) 942-9363 *Founded/Ownrshp* 1960
Sales 36.8MM^E *EMP* 55
SIC 5091 5961 Sporting & recreation goods; Fitness & sporting goods, mail order
Pr: Eric Falk
**Treas:* Grace Falk
Genl Mgr: Jaime Harvie
IT Man: Sabrina Mimnaugh

M-G FEED
See M-G INC

D-U-N-S 06-507-5749
M-G INC
M-G FEED
1201 County Rd, Weimar, TX 78962-3311
Tel (979) 725-8581 *Founded/Ownrshp* 1975
Sales 39.6MM *EMP* 80
SIC 5144 2048 5191

D-U-N-S 07-867-7128
M-I LLC
M-I SWACO
(*Suby of* M-I LLC) ★
8045 Dixie Hwy, Florence, KY 41042-2963
Tel (859) 283-8400 *Founded/Ownrshp* 2001
Sales 47.1MM^E *EMP* 285
SIC 3559 Ammunition & explosives, loading machinery; Ammunition & explosives, loading machinery
Brnch Mgr: Tim Richardson
Dist Mgr: Justin Iburg
Sfty Dirs: Boe Bryan

D-U-N-S 16-080-1585 IMP/EXP
M-I LLC
M-I SWACO A SCHLUMBERGER CO
(*Suby of* SCHLUMBERGER) ★
5950 N Course Dr, Houston, TX 77072-1626
Tel (281) 561-1300 *Founded/Ownrshp* 1994
Sales 3.1MMM^E *EMP* 3,500
SIC 1389 2865 2869 8711 8741 Oil field services; Mud service, oil field drilling; Cyclic crudes & intermediates; Industrial organic chemicals; Engineering services; Management services; Oil field services; Mud service, oil field drilling; Cyclic crudes & intermediates; Industrial organic chemicals; Engineering services; Management services
CEO: Paal Kibsgaard
Pr: Joe Bacho
Ex VP: Simon Ayat
Ex VP: Ashok Belani
Ex VP: J-F Poupeau
Sr VP: Bryan Dudman
VP: Richard Chandler
VP: Bertrand Chavignon
VP: Stephanie Cox
VP: Bill Kirby
VP: Alan McLean

M-I SWACO
See M-I LLC

M-I SWACO A SCHLUMBERGER CO
See M-I LLC

D-U-N-S 08-193-1958
M-K-D DISTRIBUTORS INC
DREYERS GRAND ICE CREAM NW
18404 72nd Ave S, Kent, WA 98032-1010
Tel (425) 251-0809 *Founded/Ownrshp* 1979
Sales 28.5MM^E *EMP* 200
SIC 5143 2024 Ice cream & ices; Ice cream & frozen desserts; Ice cream & ices; Ice cream & frozen desserts
Pr: David Mutzel
**Sec:* Kenneth Mutzel
Admn Mgr: Shari Cornett

D-U-N-S 02-849-2770 IMP/EXP
M-L HOLDINGS CO
4601 Washington Blvd, Baltimore, MD 21227-4460
Tel (410) 242-6500 *Founded/Ownrshp* 1997
Sales 118.2MM^E *EMP* 165
SIC 5082 6719 Crushing, pulverizing & screening machinery; Investment holding companies, except banks; Crushing, pulverizing & screening machinery; Investment holding companies, except banks
Prin: Tom Logan
**Prin:* John Logan
**Prin:* Robert Matz

M-OESC
See MONMOUTH OCEAN EDUCATIONAL SERVICES COMMISSION

D-U-N-S 88-437-4521
M-PLAN INC
(*Suby of* THE HEALTH CARE GROUP LLC)
8802 N Meridian St # 100, Indianapolis, IN 46260-5318
Tel (317) 963-9700 *Founded/Ownrshp* 1989
Sales NA *EMP* 255
SIC 6324 6411 Health maintenance organization (HMO), insurance only; Insurance agents, brokers & service; Health maintenance organization (HMO), insurance only; Insurance agents, brokers & service
Pr: Alex Slabosky
**CFO:* Connie Brown
Ex Dir: Ceresa Beason
Board of Directors: Chuck Mihalik, Kathleen Shook, Alex Slabosky

D-U-N-S 04-052-4852 IMP
M-S CASH DRAWER CORP (CA)
2085 E Foothill Blvd B, Pasadena, CA 91107-6400
Tel (626) 792-2111 *Founded/Ownrshp* 1974, 1988
Sales 24.5MM^E *EMP* 64
SIC 5044 Cash registers
Pr: Paul R Masson
VP: Michael Rees
Tech Mgr: Geoff Addison
Mktg Dir: Laura Hamilton
Sls Mgr: Amar Chauhan

D-U-N-S 17-433-2072 IMP/EXP
M-TEK INC
(*Suby of* KASAI KOGYO CO., LTD.)
1020 Volunteer Pkwy, Manchester, TN 37355-6461
Tel (931) 728-4122 *Founded/Ownrshp* 1986
Sales 452.0MM^E *EMP* 2,422
SIC 3089 3714 3429 Injection molded finished plastic products; Motor vehicle parts & accessories; Manufactured hardware (general); Injection molded finished plastic products; Motor vehicle parts & accessories; Manufactured hardware (general)
CEO: Masaki Sugisawa
**Pr:* N Onedara
Treas: Tatsuo Kase
**Treas:* Shinichi Yasukawa
**Sr VP:* Koichi Yoshida
VP: Kazuhiro Kobayashi
Dept Mgr: R L Walker
Genl Mgr: Jim Leyhew
IT Man: Kenneth Chaffin
Software D: Johnathon Cotner
Software D: Douglas Mertz

D-U-N-S 18-385-2615
M-TEX INDUSTRIAL SUPPLY CO INC
925 Lavon Cir, Lavon, TX 75166-1876
Tel (214) 414-1070 *Founded/Ownrshp* 1987
Sales 22.5MM^E *EMP* 40
SIC 5085 Valves & fittings
Pr: Danny B McCartney
**Treas:* Patti McCartney
**VP:* Jim Martin

D-U-N-S 11-740-0325
M-TRON COMPONENTS INC
1891 Lakeland Ave, Ronkonkoma, NY 11779-7416
Tel (631) 467-5100 *Founded/Ownrshp* 1984
Sales 26.9MM^E *EMP* 19
SIC 5065 Electronic parts & equipment; Electronic parts
Pr: Mark Kealey
**Sec:* Michael D Kealey
Opers Mgr: Stacey Kay
Mktg Dir: Anthony Cestari
Sls Mgr: John Zaita

D-U-N-S 00-749-8371
■ **M-TRON INDUSTRIES INC**
MTRONPTI
(*Suby of* LGL GROUP INC) ★
1703 E Highway 50, Yankton, SD 57078-4134
Tel (605) 665-9321 *Founded/Ownrshp* 2000
Sales 23.0MM^E *EMP* 153
SIC 3679 Quartz crystals, for electronic application; Oscillators
CEO: Greg P Anderson
**CFO:* Laduane Clifton
**Treas:* Linda Biles
Plng Mgr: Jennifer Arden
Off Admin: Juliet De Shazer
Dir IT: Jason Eskew
Ql Cn Mgr: James Kotalik
Mktg Mgr: Julie Holt

D-U-N-S 96-338-9726
▲ **M/A-COM TECHNOLOGY SOLUTIONS HOLDINGS INC**
100 Chelmsford St, Lowell, MA 01851-2694
Tel (978) 656-2500 *Founded/Ownrshp* 2009
Sales 420.6MM *EMP* 918^E
Tkr Sym MTSI *Exch* NGS
SIC 3674 Semiconductors & related devices; Semiconductors & related devices
Pr: John Croteau
Ch Bd: John Ocampo
CFO: Robert McMullan
Sr VP: Robert Dennehy
Sr VP: Thomas Hwang
Sr VP: Michael Murphy
Sr VP: Preetinder Virk
VP: Suja Ramnath
Board of Directors: Charles Bland, Peter Chung, Stephen G Daly, Susan Ocampo, Gil Van Lunsen

D-U-N-S 82-776-9154
■ **M/A-COM TECHNOLOGY SOLUTIONS INC**
(*Suby of* M/A-COM TECHNOLOGY SOLUTIONS HOLDINGS INC) ★
100 Chelmsford St, Lowell, MA 01851-2694
Tel (978) 656-2500 *Founded/Ownrshp* 1999
Sales 237.5MM^E *EMP* 915
SIC 3663 3679 Radio & TV communications equipment; Radio & TV communications equipment; Microwave components
Pr: John Croteau
CFO: Robert Mc Mullan
Sr VP: Robert Dennehy
Sr VP: Thomas Hwang
VP: Greg Marshall
VP: Bill Van Anglen
Genl Mgr: Ron Karfelt
Plng Mgr: Barbara Clement
Off Admin: Patti Macdonald
Mfg Mgr: Brian Robertson
Opers Mgr: Paul Bovaird

D-U-N-S 01-617-4096
■ **M/A/R/C INC**
DMSP
(*Suby of* OMNICOM GROUP INC) ★
2800 Story Rd W 200, Irving, TX 75038-5267
Tel (800) 884-6272 *Founded/Ownrshp* 1999
Sales 45.9MM^E *EMP* 500
SIC 8742 8732 Marketing consulting services; Market analysis or research; Marketing consulting services; Market analysis or research
CEO: Merrill Dubrow
**Ch Bd:* David Scholes
Pr: Lori Taylor
**COO:* Billy Sewell
**CFO:* Greg Horvath
Ex VP: Rob Arnett
Ex VP: Randy Wahl
Ex VP: Kimberley Walsh
Ex VP: Mark Wright
Sr VP: Susan Hurry
Sr VP: John Pehrson
Sr VP: Hurry Susan
VP: Ann Barrick
VP: Kevin Bishop
VP: Ron Bose
VP: Trae Clevenger
VP: Bill Cole
VP: Peter Dannenfelser
VP: Barron Evans
VP: Gene Ferruzza
VP: Chris Godfrey

D-U-N-S 13-201-3405 EXP
M/H NORTHBOROUGH INC
LEXUS OF NORTHBOROUGH
14 Belmont St 24, Northborough, MA 01532-2417
Tel (508) 870-3222 *Founded/Ownrshp* 2003
Sales 24.0MM^E *EMP* 58
SIC 5511 7538 5531 New & used car dealers; General automotive repair shops; Automotive parts
Pr: Mitch Cook
Sales Asso: David Richmann
Sales Asso: Qaadir Williams

D-U-N-S 07-164-9743
▲ **M/I HOMES INC** (OH)
3 Easton Oval Ste 500, Columbus, OH 43219-6011
Tel (614) 418-8000 *Founded/Ownrshp* 1973
Sales 1.2MMM *EMP* 927
Tkr Sym MHO *Exch* NYS
SIC 1531 6162 Speculative builder, single-family houses; Townhouse developers; Mortgage bankers & correspondents; Speculative builder, single-family houses; Townhouse developers; Mortgage bankers & correspondents
Ch Bd: Robert H Schottenstein
Pr: Audrey Cangialosi
**CFO:* Phillip G Creek
CFO: Peter Provenzano
Chf Mktg O: Bill McDonough
Ofcr: Jason Ellis
Div VP: Brad Nelson
**Ex VP:* J Thomas Mason
VP: Ana Ainz
VP: Edward G Boyle
VP: Ann Marie W Hunker
VP: Matthew Pagoria
VP: George Young
Exec: Robin Stephens
Board of Directors: Joseph A Alutto, Friedrich K M Bohm, William H Carter, Michael P Glimcher, Thomas D Igoe, Norman L Traeger, Sharen Jester Turney

D-U-N-S 02-310-9150
M/I HOMES OF MINNEAPOLIS/ST PAUL LLC
941 Hillwind Rd Ne # 300, Minneapolis, MN 55432-5965
Tel (763) 586-7200 *Founded/Ownrshp* 2015
Sales 42.0MM *EMP* 22^E
SIC 1521 Single-family housing construction
Pr: Hans T Hagen Jr
**Treas:* Dan Mosow
**VP:* Ted Hagen
VP: Doug Smith
Sys Mgr: Jason Beack
Sls Mgr: Kristine Bofferding

D-U-N-S 10-630-8729
■ **M/K EXPRESS CO**
(*Suby of* MARMON/KEYSTONE LLC) ★
780 E Butler Rd, East Butler, PA 16029
Tel (724) 283-4500 *Founded/Ownrshp* 1984
Sales 21.4MM^E *EMP* 90
SIC 4731 4213 4212 Truck transportation brokers; Trucking, except local; Local trucking, without storage
Pr: Norman E Gottschalk Jr
**Treas:* Robert C Gluth
**VP:* Robert A Pritzker

D-U-N-S 14-786-0761
M/L BOVIS HOLDINGS LTD
(*Suby of* LENDLEASE CORPORATION LIMITED)
200 Park Ave Fl 9, New York, NY 10166-0999
Tel (212) 592-6700 *Founded/Ownrshp* 1988
Sales 119.1MM^E *EMP* 600
SIC 1522 1541 1542 8741 8742 Residential construction; Industrial buildings & warehouses; Nonresidential construction; Management services; Management consulting services; Residential construction; Industrial buildings & warehouses; Nonresidential construction; Management services; Management consulting services
Pr: Dale Connor
Ex VP: Charlie Woodman
VP: Tom Carroll

M13 AUTO AND TRUCK REPAIR
See CLIO CHRYSLER DODGE JEEP INC

D-U-N-S 03-498-3175
M2 ASSOCIATES INC
MICROSCOPES SYSTEMS
668 N Coast Hwy 76-3995a, Laguna Beach, CA 92651-1513
Tel (775) 336-8601 *Founded/Ownrshp* 2011
Sales 25.0MM *EMP* 75
SIC 2842 Cleaning or polishing preparations; Cleaning or polishing preparations
CFO: Jack Mehoffe

D-U-N-S 08-901-0321
M2 LOGISTICS INC
2413 Hazelwood Ln, Green Bay, WI 54304-1905
Tel (920) 569-8800 *Founded/Ownrshp* 2003
Sales 20.1MM^E *EMP* 34
SIC 8742 Transportation consultant
Owner: Paul Anderson
VP: Lilli Schaefer
**VP:* Mike Sullivan
Genl Mgr: Brian Hopewell

M2 SERVICES
See SUNRISE BEACH CORP

D-U-N-S 12-544-0375
M2 TECHNOLOGY INC
21702 Hardy Oak Blvd # 100, San Antonio, TX 78258-4834
Tel (210) 566-3773 *Founded/Ownrshp* 2000
Sales 31.2MM *EMP* 32
SIC 7373 Value-added resellers, computer systems; Value-added resellers, computer systems
CEO: Mark S Martinez
**COO:* Sue McElyea
Genl Mgr: Curt Veteikis
Software D: Randy Blackmond
Sls Mgr: Tyler Thompson

M2GEN
See MOFFITT GENETICS CORP

D-U-N-S 96-875-6556
M3 APPALACHIA GATHERING LLC
1099 Main Ave Ste 210, Durango, CO 81301-5157
Tel (970) 247-4423 *Founded/Ownrshp* 2011
Sales 28.0MM *EMP* 8
SIC 4932 Gas & other services combined
Pr: Frank Tsuru
COO: Brant Baird
CFO: George Francisco
Ch: Bill Pritchard

D-U-N-S 01-560-4197
M3 CAPITAL PARTNERS LLC
150 S Wacker Dr Ste 3100, Chicago, IL 60606-4224
Tel (312) 499-8500 *Founded/Ownrshp* 2001
Sales 28.5MM^E *EMP* 110
SIC 6799 Venture capital companies
Admn Mgr: Donald Suter
VP: Rishi Patel
Off Mgr: Christine Mao
IT Man: Gregory Van Den Ham

D-U-N-S 15-156-7427
M3 ENGINEERING & TECHNOLOGY CORP
2051 W Sunset Rd Ste 101, Tucson, AZ 85704-1722
Tel (520) 293-1488 *Founded/Ownrshp* 1986
Sales 143.8MM *EMP* 470
Accts Beachfleischman Pc Tucson Az
SIC 8741 8712 8711 Construction management; Architectural services; Consulting engineer; Construction management; Architectural services; Consulting engineer
Pr: Daniel H Neff
**Sr VP:* Douglas Austin
**Sr VP:* Thomas L Drielick
**Sr VP:* Dennis Mulligan
**VP:* Lee Becker
**VP:* Patrick W Dugan
**VP:* Peter A Erath
**VP:* Conrad E Huss
**VP:* David E Sitterud
Genl Mgr: Don Griswold
CIO: Stan Neff

M3 GLASS TECHNOLOGIES
See JOHNNY AND LORENE INC

D-U-N-S 09-854-8159
M3 INSURANCE SOLUTIONS INC
M 3
828 John Nolen Dr, Madison, WI 53713-1424
Tel (608) 273-0655 *Founded/Ownrshp* 1970
Sales NA *EMP* 200
SIC 6411 Insurance agents; Insurance agents
CEO: Mike Victorson
Pt: Christine Kenyon
Pr: Ed Rapee III
Pr: Michael E Victorson
Ex VP: Dale Dam
Ex VP: Thomas Golden
Ex VP: Richard F Kekula
Ex VP: Michael J Moore
Ex VP: Mike Moore
VP: Chris Halverson
VP: James Lutcf
VP: Jim Yeager
Dir Risk M: Maureen Anderson
Dir Risk M: Randall Beier
Dir Soc: Traci Mandell
Dir Bus: Claire Flitcroft

D-U-N-S 05-856-5857
M3 MIDSTREAM LLC
600 Travis St Ste 5600, Houston, TX 77002-2909
Tel (713) 783-3000 *Founded/Ownrshp* 2010
Sales 123.3MM^E *EMP* 180
SIC 1311 Natural gas production; Natural gas production
CEO: Frank Tsuru
Pr: Chris Pearce
**COO:* Brant Baird
**Ch:* Bill Pritchard
**VP:* George Francisco

M3 TECHNOLOGY
See J&K ELECTRONICS INC

M33 INTEGRATED SOLUTIONS
See LOGISTICS HOLDINGS LLC

D-U-N-S 04-456-7623
M5 MOTORS INC
MERCEDES BENZ OF FORT MITCHELL
2100 Dixie Hwy, Ft Mitchell, KY 41011-2669
Tel (859) 331-1500 *Founded/Ownrshp* 2012
Sales 23.0MM *EMP* 55

SIC 5511 Automobiles, new & used; Automobiles, new & used
Pr: Bernardo F Moreno

D-U-N-S 12-652-5976
M7 AEROSPACE LLC
(*Suby of* ELBIT SYSTEMS OF AMERICA LLC) ★
10823 Ne Entrance Rd, San Antonio, TX 78216-6001
Tel (210) 391-4098 *Founded/Ownrshp* 2010
Sales 59.0MM^E *EMP* 380
SIC 4581 5088 Aircraft servicing & repairing; Aircraft & parts; Aircraft; Aircraft servicing & repairing; Aircraft & parts
VP: Mike Henry
Pr: Raanan Horowitz
Ofcr: Harold Williams
Sr VP: Barry Eccleston
VP: Tom Carter
VP: Brett Cohen
VP: Phil Fletcher
VP: Emory Kilgore
VP: Mike McClain
VP: Edmund Self
VP: Brian Waechter

D-U-N-S 96-380-3536
MA ACQUISITION CO LLC
501 Galveston St, Wichita Falls, TX 76301-5906
Tel (940) 397-2100 *Founded/Ownrshp* 2010
Sales 83.5MM^E *EMP* 251
SIC 6733 Personal investment trust management; Personal investment trust management
CEO: Ron Duncan

D-U-N-S 78-291-6936
MA ANGELIADES INC
544 47th Ave, Long Island City, NY 11101-5415
Tel (718) 786-5555 *Founded/Ownrshp* 1991
Sales 32.4MM^E *EMP* 180^E
Accts J H Cohn Llp Eatontown Ne
SIC 1542 8741 Specialized public building contractors; Commercial & office building contractors; Construction management; Specialized public building contractors; Commercial & office building contractors; Construction management
Pr: Mike Angeliades
**VP:* Manny Angeliades
**VP:* Dimitri Malajidis

D-U-N-S 07-925-8385
MA DEATLEY CONSTRUCTION INC
829 Evans Rd, Clarkston, WA 99403-9701
Tel (509) 751-1428 *Founded/Ownrshp* 1998
Sales 36.2MM^E *EMP* 100^E
SIC 5082 1794 Construction & mining machinery; Excavation work; Construction & mining machinery; Excavation work
Pr: Mark A Deatley
**VP:* Scott Palmer
VP: Donald Ruchert
Exec: Deedee Pearson
Mtls Mgr: Andy Schrock

D-U-N-S 94-240-8766
MA FEDERAL INC
IGOV.COM
12030 Sunrise Valley Dr # 300, Reston, VA 20191-3447
Tel (703) 356-1160 *Founded/Ownrshp* 1996
Sales 162.7MM^E *EMP* 100^E
Accts Cherry Bekaert & Holland Ll
SIC 5045 Computers, peripherals & software; Computers, peripherals & software
CEO: Patrick A Neven
**Pr:* Michael Tyrrell
**CFO:* Steven Hamric
**Sr VP:* Walter Hupalo
**VP:* Chuck Reiche
VP: Tom Walsh
VP Bus Dev: Sean Thompson
Dir Bus: Peter Davis
Dir Bus: Charlie Phillips
Prgrm Mgr: Mary Gordner
Snr Ntwrk: Josh Hughes

D-U-N-S 00-615-8828 IMP
MA GEDNEY CO
GEDNEY FOODS COMPANY
2100 Stoughton Ave, Chaska, MN 55318-2200
Tel (952) 448-2612 *Founded/Ownrshp* 1881
Sales 20.6MM^E *EMP* 125
SIC 2035 Pickles, vinegar; Pickles, vinegar
CEO: Charles Weil
**Pr:* Barry Stecter
**VP:* James R Cook
**VP:* Carl Tuttle
Exec: Merrill Ayers
Dir Lab: Nadya Messer
Board of Directors: Frank Gleeson, Joseph Goggin, Horace E Hitch, Jefferson Jones, Dean Thomas

D-U-N-S 08-001-8421
▲ **MA INDUSTRIAL JV LLC**
5683 Hines Dr, Ann Arbor, MI 48108-7901
Tel (734) 585-9500 *Founded/Ownrshp* 2015
Sales 724.4MM^E *EMP* 5,800^E
SIC 3585 3679 6719 Parts for heating, cooling & refrigerating equipment; Hermetic seals for electronic equipment; Investment holding companies, except banks
CEO: Gregory L Christopher

D-U-N-S 04-581-9810
MA INDUSTRIES INC
303 Dividend Dr, Peachtree City, GA 30269-1907
Tel (770) 487-7761 *Founded/Ownrshp* 1969
Sales 30.2MM^E *EMP* 190
SIC 3089 3559 3554 3053 Molding primary plastic; Recycling machinery; Paper industries machinery; Gaskets, all materials; Molding primary plastic; Recycling machinery; Paper industries machinery; Gaskets, all materials
CEO: Thomas Windham
**Pr:* Bobbie Don Peacock
**CFO:* Mike Glynn
VP: Tom Fleming
VP: Bill Martin
Opers Mgr: Mark Atkinson
Opers Mgr: Tom Howlak
Natl Sales: Ken Chlopecki

D-U-N-S 15-509-3172 IMP/EXP
MA LABORATORIES INC
MA LABS
2075 N Capitol Ave, San Jose, CA 95132-1009
Tel (408) 941-0808 *Founded/Ownrshp* 1988
Sales 164.8MM^E *EMP* 600
SIC 5045

MA LABS
See MA LABORATORIES INC

D-U-N-S 07-909-2662
MAACO FRANCHISING LLC
(*Suby of* DRIVEN BRANDS INC) ★
440 S Church St Ste 700, Charlotte, NC 28202-2059
Tel (704) 377-8855 *Founded/Ownrshp* 2013
Sales 18.8MM^E *EMP* 366^E
SIC 8741 Management services; Management services

D-U-N-S 18-534-8935
MAALI RESTAURANT INC
PONDEROSA STEAKHOUSE
7932 W Sand Lake Rd # 301, Orlando, FL 32819-7230
Tel (407) 345-9200 *Founded/Ownrshp* 1985
Sales 10.7MM^E *EMP* 340
Accts Downtown Business Services Or
SIC 5812 Steak restaurant; Steak restaurant
Pr: Amjad Maali
**VP:* Mike Maali

D-U-N-S 16-850-0127
MAALT LP
MAALT TRANSPORT
4413 Carey St, Fort Worth, TX 76119-4219
Tel (817) 205-0460 *Founded/Ownrshp* 2004
Sales 118.6MM^E *EMP* 400
SIC 4225 4731 General warehousing & storage; Truck transportation brokers
Pt: Martin Robertson
Pt: Gary Humphreys
CFO: Craig Mackey
VP: Steve McCarley
IT Man: Carlyle Lockhart
Plnt Mgr: Daniel Flaherty

MAALT TRANSPORT
See MAALT LP

MAAMECH
See MID-ATLANTIC AIR INC

D-U-N-S 78-322-5428
MAAS HOLDING INC
1349 S Broadway, Los Angeles, CA 90015-3037
Tel (213) 746-4853 *Founded/Ownrshp* 1991
Sales 25.0MM *EMP* 14
SIC 5094 5064 6531 Watches & parts; Radios; Real estate agent, commercial; Watches & parts; Radios; Real estate agent, commercial
Pr: Anil Lalwani
**Treas:* Kishin Lalwani
**VP:* Sunil Lalwani

D-U-N-S 08-381-7221 IMP
■ **MAAX SPAS (ARIZONA) INC**
(*Suby of* BROOKFIELD ASSET MANAGEMENT INC)
25605 S Arizona Ave, Chandler, AZ 85248-7964
Tel (480) 895-0598 *Founded/Ownrshp* 1976
Sales 42.7MM^E *EMP* 150
SIC 5074 Plumbing & hydronic heating supplies; Plumbing & hydronic heating supplies
Pr: John Johnson
**VP:* Terry Rake
Dir IT: Michael Rogers
Dir IT: Cliff Russell
IT Man: Amadeo Aguirre
IT Man: Bill Canotti
Mtls Mgr: Gary Latimer
Manager: George Seamans
Sls Mgr: Mary Van De Walle
Sales Asso: Nancy Kemna

D-U-N-S 96-171-8181 EXP
■ **MAAX SPAS INDUSTRIES CORP**
(*Suby of* BROOKFIELD ASSET MANAGEMENT INC)
25605 S Arizona Ave, Chandler, AZ 85248-7964
Tel (480) 895-0598 *Founded/Ownrshp* 2008
Sales 53.0MM^E *EMP* 150
SIC 3088 Plastics plumbing fixtures; Hot tubs, plastic or fiberglass; Bathroom fixtures, plastic; Hot tubs, plastic or fiberglass
Pr: John Johnson
**CFO:* Jose G Suarezz-Cabrera
CFO: Russell Suchon
VP: Paul Christosoro
**VP:* Emil Hygaard
Exec: Sue Tetreault

D-U-N-S 84-800-4248
MAAX US CORP
(*Suby of* MAAX BATH INC)
7767 Elm Creek Blvd N # 310, Maple Grove, MN 55369-7041
Tel (877) 438-6229 *Founded/Ownrshp* 2009
Sales 135.1MM^E *EMP* 1,200
SIC 3088 Whirlpool baths, hydrotherapy equipment; Tubs (bath, shower & laundry), plastic; Tubs (bath, shower & laundry), plastic
CEO: Mark Gold
VP: David Lipkin
**Prin:* Paul Golden
Rgnl Mgr: Paul Langlois
Manager: Jeffrey Strabala
Sales Asso: Melanie Grenier

MABANE TEMPORARY SERVICES
See PREMIER STAFFING INC

D-U-N-S 03-746-2488
MABANK INDEPENDENT SCHOOL DISTRICT
310 E Market St, Mabank, TX 75147-2311
Tel (903) 880-1300 *Founded/Ownrshp* 1900
Sales 35.8MM *EMP* 1,107
Accts Smith Lambright & Associates
SIC 8211 Public elementary & secondary schools; Public elementary & secondary schools
HC Dir: Pam Odom

MABAR
See TOTAL TRUCK & TRAILER INC

D-U-N-S 78-820-5821
MABE TRUCKING CO INC
1603 Mill Ave, Eden, NC 27288-3919
Tel (336) 635-2283 *Founded/Ownrshp* 1988
Sales 36.4MM^E *EMP* 150
SIC 4212 4213 Local trucking, without storage; Contract haulers; Local trucking, without storage; Contract haulers
Pr: Roger D Mabe Sr
Sfty Mgr: Dwight Loftis

MABEE GYMNASIUM
See UNIVERSITY OF OZARKS

D-U-N-S 17-190-2265
MABEY INC
(*Suby of* MABEY BRIDGING (AMERICAS) LIMITED)
6770 Dorsey Rd, Elkridge, MD 21075-6205
Tel (410) 379-5317 *Founded/Ownrshp* 1989
Sales 36.6MM^E *EMP* 195
SIC 7359 Equipment rental & leasing; Equipment rental & leasing
CEO: Robert Aylward
**CFO:* Nicholas Yancich
VP: Patrick Sweeney
IT Man: Tim O'Keefe
Sales Asso: Dawn Richardson
Board of Directors: Bob Aylward, David Murray, Nicholas Yancich

D-U-N-S 78-838-7231
MABIE MARKETING GROUP INC
CALIFORNIA MARKETING
8352 Clairemont Mesa Blvd, San Diego, CA 92111-1302
Tel (858) 279-5585 *Founded/Ownrshp* 1984
Sales 21.3MM^E *EMP* 200
SIC 7389 Telemarketing services; Telemarketing services
Pr: John Mabie
Ex VP: Samantha Galarneau
Ex VP: Samantha Tremble
IT Man: Donald Kirchner
Prd Dir: Heather Tremble

D-U-N-S 61-881-3406
MABREY BANCORPORATION INC
101 E 6th St, Okmulgee, OK 74447-4603
Tel (918) 756-7910 *Founded/Ownrshp* 1968
Sales NA *EMP* 250
SIC 6021 6022 National commercial banks; State commercial banks; National commercial banks; State commercial banks
Pr: W Carlisle Mabrey III
**Ch:* Lurline R Mubrey
**Treas:* David R Carder
**Ex VP:* Bruce R Mabrey
**VP:* John Mabrey
**VP:* Marilyn Sullivan

D-U-N-S 03-635-1336
MABREY BANK
CITIZEN SECURITY BANK AND TRUS
(*Suby of* CITIZEN SECURITY BANK AND TR) ★
14821 S Memorial Dr, Bixby, OK 74008-3743
Tel (918) 366-4000 *Founded/Ownrshp* 1924, 1979
Sales NA *EMP* 100
SIC 6035 Federal savings & loan associations; Federal savings & loan associations
Ch Bd: Lurline Mabrey
**CEO:* Carlisle Mabrey III

D-U-N-S 93-397-2242
MABRY BROTHERS INC
5731 Halifax Ave, Fort Myers, FL 33912-4404
Tel (239) 482-1122 *Founded/Ownrshp* 1995
Sales 22.0MM^E *EMP* 112
SIC 1731 1711 Electrical work; Heating & air conditioning contractors; Electrical work; Heating & air conditioning contractors
Pr: Jimmie G Mabry
**VP:* Michael W Mabry

MABSC
See MEGGITT AIRCRAFT BRAKING SYSTEMS CORP

MAC
See MOTOR APPLIANCE CORP

MAC
See METROPOLITAN AIRPORTS COMMISSION

MAC
See MANUFACTURED ASSEMBLIES CORP

D-U-N-S 02-488-8972
■ **MAC ACQUISITION OF KANSAS LLC** (KS)
(*Suby of* IGNITE RESTAURANT GROUP INC) ★
6750 Lyndon B Johnson Fwy, Dallas, TX 75240-6512
Tel (972) 674-4300 *Founded/Ownrshp* 2008, 2013
Sales 205.1MM^E *EMP* 10,000
SIC 5812 Italian restaurant; Italian restaurant
CEO: Norman Abdallah
Pr: David Catalano
CFO: Carey Carrington
VP: Drew Stafford
Genl Mgr: Tom Cook
Snr Sftwr: Jon Tryzbiac

D-U-N-S 00-620-7005
MAC ARTHUR CO (MN)
WEEKES FOREST PRODUCTS
2400 Wycliff St, Saint Paul, MN 55114-1268
Tel (651) 646-2773 *Founded/Ownrshp* 1913, 2004
Sales 700.0M *EMP* 1,000
SIC 5033 3448

D-U-N-S 15-497-1340
MAC ATTACK INC
MCDONALD'S
156 State St, Macon, GA 31206-1068
Tel (478) 742-5200 *Founded/Ownrshp* 2005
Sales 9.6MM^E *EMP* 300
SIC 5812 Fast-food restaurant, chain; Fast-food restaurant, chain
CEO: John Folsom
**Prin:* Paul Salinas

D-U-N-S 96-535-0692
MAC AUTO TEAM LLC
CHRYSLER ON NICHOLASVILLE
1010 Elizabeth St, Nicholasville, KY 40356-8710
Tel (859) 887-2400 *Founded/Ownrshp* 2008
Sales 33.5MM^E *EMP* 100
SIC 5511 Automobiles, new & used; Automobiles, new & used

D-U-N-S 02-921-4632 IMP
MAC BEATH HARDWOOD CO (CA)
2150 Oakdale Ave, San Francisco, CA 94124-1516
Tel (415) 647-0782 *Founded/Ownrshp* 1954
Sales 25.0MM *EMP* 90
Accts Shea Labagh Debberstein Cpa
SIC 5031 5211 Hardboard; Millwork & lumber; Hardboard; Millwork & lumber
CEO: Carter Rothrock
Pr: Pete Bernthal
**Pr:* George C Rothrock
**CFO:* Jonathan Macbeath
**VP:* Rick McDaniel
**VP:* Alan Ross
Genl Mgr: Doug Mahoskey
Sales Exec: Jon Mac Beath

D-U-N-S 01-720-4652
MAC BHUPINDER SINGH
MAC CHEVRON-CANOGA
5960 Canoga Ave, Woodland Hills, CA 91367-5042
Tel (818) 710-8212 *Founded/Ownrshp* 1981
Sales 50.0MM *EMP* 45
SIC 5541 Filling stations, gasoline; Filling stations, gasoline
Owner: Bhupinder Singh Mac

D-U-N-S 60-995-0084
MAC BUSINESS SOLUTIONS INC
9057 Gaither Rd, Gaithersburg, MD 20877-1424
Tel (301) 590-2555 *Founded/Ownrshp* 1990
Sales 25.0MM *EMP* 25^E
SIC 5734 7378 Computer software & accessories; Computer peripheral equipment; Computer maintenance & repair
Pr: Sunita Tohan
CEO: Surinder Tohan
Opers Mgr: Robby Ghimire

D-U-N-S 00-947-0873
MAC CAL CO
MAC CAL MANUFACTURING
1737 Junction Ave, San Jose, CA 95112-1010
Tel (408) 441-1435 *Founded/Ownrshp* 1983
Sales 21.6MM^E *EMP* 80
SIC 3444 3479 7336 Sheet metalwork; Housings for business machines, sheet metal; Name plates: engraved, etched, etc.; Silk screen design
Pr: Michael Hall
**CEO:* Renee Hall
**CFO:* Cathy McDonald

MAC CAL MANUFACTURING
See MAC CAL CO

MAC CHEVRON-CANOGA
See MAC BHUPINDER SINGH

MAC CHURCHILL ACURA
See MAC CHURCHILL INC

D-U-N-S 04-581-4642 EXP
MAC CHURCHILL INC
MAC CHURCHILL ACURA
3125 Ne Loop 820, Fort Worth, TX 76137-2469
Tel (817) 806-0500 *Founded/Ownrshp* 2000
Sales 62.5MM^E *EMP* 60
SIC 5511 Automobiles, new & used; Automobiles, new & used
Pr: Mac Churchill
Dir IT: Paul Garmer
Sales Asso: Robert Cassell
Sales Asso: Carlo Guerrera

D-U-N-S 03-785-7976
MAC CONSTRUCTION & EXCAVATING INC
1908 Unruh Ct, New Albany, IN 47150-6948
Tel (812) 284-4250 *Founded/Ownrshp* 1980
Sales 96.3MM^E *EMP* 200
Accts Mountjoy Chilton Medley Llp
SIC 1623 1622 1794 Water main construction; Sewer line construction; Highway construction, elevated; Bridge construction; Excavation & grading, building construction; Water main construction; Sewer line construction; Highway construction, elevated; Bridge construction; Excavation & grading, building construction
CEO: Chad Unruh
**Pr:* Travis Unruh
**Pr:* Victor O Unruh
**CEO:* Jean M Unruh
**COO:* Darlene Cochran
CFO: Christopher Bane
Dir IT: Brian Barfield
Mtls Mgr: Mike Hawn
Sfty Mgr: Neal Biggs
VP Sls: Michael Lyttle
Sls Dir: Rusty Crosier

D-U-N-S 04-571-1827
MAC CORP OF KANSAS
900 Nw Hunter Dr Ste 2s, Blue Springs, MO 64015-7706
Tel (816) 229-6090 *Founded/Ownrshp* 1979
Sales 21.7MM *EMP* 21^E

SIC 1541 1542 Industrial buildings & warehouses; Commercial & office building, new construction; Industrial buildings & warehouses; Commercial & office building, new construction
Pr: Robert W Andrew
**VP:* Carolyn Davis
Dir Bus: Lloyd Black
**Off Mgr:* Brenda Andrew

MAC DONALD
See DOUBLE K VENTURES INC

MAC DONALD'S SHELL 1-9
See P K M CORP

MAC FIRE SYSTEMS
See MAC SYSTEMS INC

MAC FOOD MART
See MCINTOSH ENERGY CO INC

MAC GROUP
See MAMIYA AMERICA CORP

D-U-N-S 00-538-5786
MAC GROUP INTERNATIONAL INC (MI)
METROPOLITAN ALLOYS OF DETROIT
17385 Ryan Rd, Detroit, MI 48212-1115
Tel (313) 366-4443 *Founded/Ownrshp* 1941
Sales 34.7MM^E *EMP* 60
SIC 5051 Zinc; Anode metal; Zinc; Anode metal
Pr: Murray Spilman
**COO:* Gilbert Spilman
**VP:* Jeffrey Spilman

D-U-N-S 05-248-7840
MAC HAIK CHEVROLET LTD (TX)
11711 Katy Fwy, Houston, TX 77079-1739
Tel (281) 497-6600 *Founded/Ownrshp* 1982
Sales 65.2MM^E *EMP* 151^E
SIC 5511 Automobiles, new & used; Pickups, new & used; Vans, new & used; Automobiles, new & used; Pickups, new & used; Vans, new & used
Genl Pt: Mac Haik
Genl Pt: Lonnie Sabbath
VP: Pam Gardner
Genl Mgr: Peter Wink
Sls Mgr: Corey Echols
Sls Mgr: Hussein Hylton
Sls Mgr: Horace Manuel
Sales Asso: Micah Marks
Sales Asso: Don Yarnal

MAC HAIK CHRYSLER JEEP
See HOUSTON MAC HAIK DODGE CHRYSLER JEEP LTD

D-U-N-S 08-356-0490
MAC HAIK ENTERPRISES
11757 Katy Fwy Ste 1500, Houston, TX 77079-1794
Tel (281) 496-7788 *Founded/Ownrshp* 1974
Sales 99.8MM^E *EMP* 720
SIC 6531 5511 Real estate managers; Automobiles, new & used; Pickups, new & used; Vans, new & used; Real estate managers; Automobiles, new & used; Pickups, new & used; Vans, new & used
Owner: Mac Haik
CFO: Bill Blackwell
Treas: Ian Smith
Sr VP: Ron Marshall
Sr VP: Brandon Poynter
VP: Amy Jankowski
VP: Christina Logan
VP: Rachel Schipul
Dir Risk M: Nathan Walker
Sls Dir: Chris Ferguson

MAC HAIKS SOUTHWAY FORD
See SOUTHWAY MAC HAIK FORD LTD

MAC HEATERS
See MAC INC

D-U-N-S 01-853-3070
■ **MAC INC**
MAC HEATERS
(*Suby of* GENERAC MOBILE PRODUCTS LLC) ★
2106 E Indiana Ave, Bismarck, ND 58504-5924
Tel (701) 222-4328 *Founded/Ownrshp* 1997
Sales 53.3MM^E *EMP* 200
SIC 3585 Heating equipment, complete
CEO: Michael Seifert
Pr: Paul Christinson
VP: Tom Roehrich
IT Man: Eric Veidel
S&M/VP: Craig Primiani
Bus Dev Di: Joe Volk

MAC INTYRE OLDSMOBILE
See BILL MACINTYRE CHEVROLET INC

MAC KENZIE WAREHOUSE
See S F AUTOMOTIVE PARTS WAREHOUSE INC

MAC LIQUID TANK TRAILER
See MAC LTT INC

D-U-N-S 96-978-7907
MAC LTT INC
MAC LIQUID TANK TRAILER
(*Suby of* MAC TRAILER MANUFACTURING INC) ★
1400 Fairchild Ave, Kent, OH 44240-1818
Tel (330) 474-3795 *Founded/Ownrshp* 2011
Sales 154.6MM^E *EMP* 116^E
SIC 3569 Assembly machines, non-metalworking
Pr: Jim Maiorana
Mtls Mgr: Kenneth Buler
Plnt Mgr: Ken Grosswiller

D-U-N-S 79-118-2850
MAC MANAGEMENT INC
5929 Baker Rd Ste 420, Minnetonka, MN 55345-5940
Tel (952) 937-8033 *Founded/Ownrshp* 1992
Sales 29.5MM^E *EMP* 200
SIC 1611 2951 5032 Highway & street paving contractor; Resurfacing contractor; Road materials, bituminous (not from refineries); Sand, construction; Gravel; Limestone; Highway & street paving contractor; Resurfacing contractor; Road materials, bituminous (not from refineries); Sand, construction; Gravel; Limestone
Pr: Blair B Bury
**Treas:* Maynard Schuldt
**VP:* Blaine M Johnson

D-U-N-S 80-382-5939 IMP
MAC MANUFACTURING INC
14599 Commerce St Ne, Alliance, OH 44601-1003
Tel (330) 823-9900 *Founded/Ownrshp* 1995
Sales 343.1MM^E *EMP* 1,300
SIC 3715 5012 Truck trailers; Trailers for trucks, new & used; Truck bodies
Pr: Michael A Conny
**Sec:* Jenny Conny
Ex VP: Diana Austin
**VP:* Dan Tubbs

D-U-N-S 18-866-0844 IMP
MAC MEDICAL INC
820 S Mulberry St, Millstadt, IL 62260-2076
Tel (618) 476-3550 *Founded/Ownrshp* 1998
Sales 24.8MM^E *EMP* 61
SIC 5047 Medical & hospital equipment
Pr: Dennis W Cooper
Rgnl Mgr: Dragan Veljkovic

D-U-N-S 10-011-6016
MAC MOTORS INC
HARTFORD TOYOTA SUPERSTORE
158 Weston St, Hartford, CT 06120-1512
Tel (860) 278-5411 *Founded/Ownrshp* 2001
Sales 23.3MM^E *EMP* 65
SIC 5511 Automobiles, new & used; Automobiles, new & used
Pr: Richard McAllister

D-U-N-S 04-253-1533
■ **MAC NEAL MEMORIAL HOSPITAL ASSOCIATION**
(*Suby of* VANGUARD HEALTH SYSTEMS INC) ★
3249 Oak Park Ave, Berwyn, IL 60402-3429
Tel (708) 783-9100 *Founded/Ownrshp* 1931
Sales 438.9M^E *EMP* 1,053
SIC 8062 General medical & surgical hospitals; General medical & surgical hospitals
Pr: Mr Michael P Kenahan W
**Pr:* Brian Lemon
**CFO:* Brooks Turkel
Pgrm Dir: Jenny Wasielewski

D-U-N-S 60-820-8773 IMP/EXP
MAC NEIL AUTOMOTIVE PRODUCTS LIMITED
WEATHERTECH
1 Macneil Ct, Bolingbrook, IL 60440-4903
Tel (630) 769-1500 *Founded/Ownrshp* 1989
Sales 110.9MM^E *EMP* 130^E
SIC 5531 5013 Automotive accessories; Automotive supplies
CEO: David Mac Neil
Pr: David Iverson
**Pr:* Allan Thom
**CFO:* Les Veatch
VP: Michael Bishop
VP: Al Thom
Manager: Steve Meyn
Opers Mgr: Thomas Virzi
Plnt Mgr: Jeremy Simkowski
Prd Mgr: Jorge Cisneros
Ql Cn Mgr: Aaron Rosenstock

D-U-N-S 04-113-6029
MAC PAPER CONVERTERS INC
MAC PAPERS ENVELOPE CONVERTERS
8370 Philips Hwy, Jacksonville, FL 32256-8204
Tel (800) 334-7026 *Founded/Ownrshp* 1964
Sales 61.6MM^E *EMP* 213
SIC 2677 Envelopes; Envelopes
CEO: David S McGehee
**Pr:* Sutton McGehee
**Treas:* Jonathan Y Rogers
**Sr VP:* Thomas R McGehee
**VP:* Darnell M Babbit
VP: John Brent
**VP:* Robert Tees
VP Sls: Bob Thole

MAC PAPERS ENVELOPE CONVERTERS
See MAC PAPER CONVERTERS INC

D-U-N-S 00-407-9141 IMP/EXP
MAC PAPERS INC
3300 Phillips Hwy, Jacksonville, FL 32207-4312
Tel (904) 396-5312 *Founded/Ownrshp* 1964
Sales 873.3MM^E *EMP* 870
SIC 5112 5111 Envelopes; Fine paper; Envelopes; Fine paper
Ch Bd: Frank S McGehee
Pr: David S McGehee
CEO: Sutton McGehee
CFO: John W Brent
Sec: Jonathan Y Rogers
Sr VP: Jerry Shane
VP: Darnell M Babbit
VP: Steve Bethea
VP: Dave Boynton
VP: Stephen L Collins
**VP:* Thomas R McGehee Jr
Board of Directors: Ann Mc Gehee, Delia Mc Gehee, Delia Mc Gehee II, Ann M Riley

D-U-N-S 80-003-2112
MAC PARENT LLC
ROMANO'S MACARONI GRILL
(*Suby of* REDROCK PARTNERS LLC) ★
3100 S Gessner Rd Ste 125, Houston, TX 77063-3744
Tel (832) 649-2260 *Founded/Ownrshp* 2015
Sales 272.5MM^E *EMP* 7,500^E
SIC 5812 6794 Grills (eating places); Grills (eating places); Franchises, selling or licensing
Pr: John Gilbert
Pr: John Gilbert
Ex VP: Craig Rawls
Sr VP: John McLaughlin
Dir Soc: Dave Cranston
Genl Mgr: Daryl Askins
Genl Mgr: Jeff Bender
Genl Mgr: Lindsey Crowley
Genl Mgr: Raul Macias
Genl Mgr: Kent Mastainich
Genl Mgr: Karna Patel

D-U-N-S 18-355-3312
MAC PIZZA MANAGEMENT INC
DOMINO'S PIZZA
3104 Texas Ave S, College Station, TX 77845-5050
Tel (979) 693-5200 *Founded/Ownrshp* 1985
Sales 25.5MM^E *EMP* 750
SIC 5812 Pizzeria, chain; Pizzeria, chain
Pr: Michael Cunningham
**VP:* Cindy Cunningham
VP: Tom Moyes

D-U-N-S 07-889-1451
MAC PROPERTY MANAGEMENT INC
32 N Dean St, Englewood, NJ 07631-2807
Tel (201) 408-7387 *Founded/Ownrshp* 2005
Sales 20.2MM^E *EMP* 280
SIC 8741 Management services; Management services

D-U-N-S 36-429-3175
MAC RESTAURANT CORP
MC ALLISTER'S
100 Old Cherokee Rd Ste F, Lexington, SC 29072-7959
Tel (803) 772-0976 *Founded/Ownrshp* 1997
Sales 10.5MM *EMP* 450
SIC 5812 6794 Eating places; Patent owners & lessors; Eating places; Patent owners & lessors
Pr: George Mc Laughlin

D-U-N-S 01-643-0790
MAC SOURCE COMMUNICATIONS INC
(*Suby of* MERIDIAN GROUP) ★
509 Erie Blvd W, Syracuse, NY 13204-2422
Tel (315) 432-1642 *Founded/Ownrshp* 1997
Sales 30.5MM^E *EMP* 111
SIC 8748 Telecommunications consultant; Telecommunications consultant
Ch Bd: Ian Pye
**Pr:* Timothy McDermott
**CFO:* Mike Brannan
**Sr VP:* Rochelle Slater
**VP:* Bill Flaherty
VP: Wayne Ianuario
**VP:* Donald Norkett
Netwrk Eng: Ankit Badani
Site Mgr: Tom Donahue
Natl Sales: Greg Carswell
Natl Sales: Odila Roman

D-U-N-S 36-060-4813
MAC SYSTEMS INC
MAC FIRE SYSTEMS
1010 E 2nd St, Tulsa, OK 74120-2006
Tel (918) 582-3736 *Founded/Ownrshp* 1989
Sales 21.7MM *EMP* 124
Accts Fisher & Company Tulsa Oklah
SIC 1711 1731 7382 Fire detection & burglar alarm systems specialization; Access control systems specialization; Fire sprinkler system installation; Security control equipment & systems; Fire sprinkler system installation; Fire detection & burglar alarm systems specialization; Access control systems specialization; Security systems services
Pr: Drake McDannold
Div Mgr: Thomas Detar
IT Man: Roy McDannold
Opers Mgr: Matt Cravens
Sls&Mrk Ex: Scott Frazier
Sls Mgr: Scott Simpson
Sales Asso: Brennen Carr

D-U-N-S 79-821-8780 IMP
MAC TRAILER MANUFACTURING INC
(*Suby of* MAC MANUFACTURING INC) ★
14599 Commerce St Ne, Alliance, OH 44601-1003
Tel (330) 823-9900 *Founded/Ownrshp* 1992
Sales 154.9MM^E *EMP* 400^E
SIC 3715 5012 5013 5015 7539 Truck trailers; Trailers for trucks, new & used; Truck bodies; Motor vehicle supplies & new parts; Motor vehicle parts, used; Trailer repair; Truck trailers; Trailers for trucks, new & used; Truck bodies; Motor vehicle supplies & new parts; Motor vehicle parts, used; Trailer repair
Pr: Mike Conny
COO: John Raymond
CFO: Diana Austin
**CFO:* Bill Ogden
**Treas:* Jenny Conny
**VP:* Ben Childers
VP: Tay Griffith
**VP:* David Sandor
IT Man: Dennis Postiy
IT Man: Dennis Posty
Ql Cn Mgr: Greg Utley

D-U-N-S 00-535-4295 IMP
MAC VALVES INC (MI)
M A C
30569 Beck Rd, Wixom, MI 48393-2842
Tel (248) 624-7700 *Founded/Ownrshp* 1948, 1959
Sales 159.1MM^E *EMP* 890
SIC 3492 3494 3491 Control valves, fluid power: hydraulic & pneumatic; Valves & pipe fittings; Industrial valves; Control valves, fluid power: hydraulic & pneumatic; Valves & pipe fittings; Industrial valves
Pr: Robert Neff
**Treas:* Martha C Welch
**VP:* Douglas Mc Cuiston
Genl Mgr: Jim Knudson
IT Man: Bradley McMahon
Mfg Mgr: Jay Diehl
Plnt Mgr: John Haar
VP Sls: Douglas McCuiston
VP Sls: Matt Neff
Sls Dir: Joseph Richardson

D-U-N-S 01-814-4832
MAC-CLARK RESTAURANTS INC (NY)
MCDONALD'S
185 Genesee St Ste 1505, Utica, NY 13501-2109
Tel (315) 735-1240 *Founded/Ownrshp* 1978
Sales 26.5MM^E *EMP* 750
SIC 5812 Fast-food restaurant, chain; Fast-food restaurant, chain
Pr: Harold T Clark

D-U-N-S 01-930-0060
MAC-GRAY CORP
(*Suby of* SPIN HOLDCO INC) ★
35 Corporate Dr Ste 220, Burlington, MA 01803-4244
Tel (781) 487-7600 *Founded/Ownrshp* 2014
Sales 58.8MM^E *EMP* 804^E
SIC 7215 5087 Laundry, coin-operated; Laundry equipment & supplies; Laundry, coin-operated; Laundry equipment & supplies
Pr: Bob Doyle
Pr: George Rionda
**CEO:* Robert Doyle
**CFO:* Gary Dailey
Ex VP: Todd Burger
**Ex VP:* Phil Emma
**Ex VP:* Ray Loser
Ex VP: Neil F Maclellan
VP: Dennis Collins
VP: Brian Larson
**VP:* Linda Serafini

D-U-N-S 19-713-7177
MAC-LAD CORP
4195 Middle Country Rd, Calverton, NY 11933-1172
Tel (631) 727-0165 *Founded/Ownrshp* 1988
Sales 21.8MM^E *EMP* 26
SIC 5031 Lumber, plywood & millwork; Building materials, interior
CEO: Ray Macalpine

D-U-N-S 06-264-2756
MAC-LAFF INC (LA)
MCDONALD'S
106 Oak Way Ln, Lafayette, LA 70506-3900
Tel (337) 981-4800 *Founded/Ownrshp* 1972
Sales 10.4MM^E *EMP* 325
SIC 5812 Fast-food restaurant, chain; Fast-food restaurant, chain
Pr: Edward J Krampe Jr

D-U-N-S 07-858-5982 IMP
MACADAMIA BEAUTY LLC
MACADAMIA NATURAL OIL
5850 Granite Pkwy Ste 370, Plano, TX 75024-6751
Tel (818) 859-7870 *Founded/Ownrshp* 2012
Sales 24.0MM *EMP* 30
SIC 5999 Cosmetic preparations; Hair care products
CFO: Saurabh Nayyar

MACADAMIA NATURAL OIL
See MACADAMIA BEAUTY LLC

D-U-N-S 09-960-4985
MACADOS OF BECKLEY LLC
120 Church Ave Sw Ste B, Roanoke, VA 24011-1919
Tel (540) 342-7231 *Founded/Ownrshp* 1978
Sales 22.4MM^E *EMP* 750
SIC 5812 Delicatessen (eating places); Delicatessen (eating places)
Pr: Richard H Macher
**Treas:* Shakie Macher
Genl Mgr: Chris Arnold

D-U-N-S 10-345-0347
MACALAN GROUP INC
5825 Mark Dabling Blvd, Colorado Springs, CO 80919-2233
Tel (719) 634-5523 *Founded/Ownrshp* 2002
Sales 38.7MM^E *EMP* 162
SIC 8748 Business consulting; Business consulting
CEO: Bruce J Parkman
**CFO:* Andy Woglom
Comm Dir: Bonnie Moss

D-U-N-S 01-340-5901
MACALESTER COLLEGE
200 Amherst St, Saint Paul, MN 55105-1912
Tel (651) 698-8650 *Founded/Ownrshp* 1874
Sales 97.7MM *EMP* 1^E
SIC 8299 Educational services; Educational services
Pr: Brian C Rosenberg
**Prin:* Carleton Macy

D-U-N-S 07-762-6778
MACALESTER COLLEGE
1600 Grand Ave, Saint Paul, MN 55105-1899
Tel (651) 696-6000 *Founded/Ownrshp* 1874
Sales 166.0MM *EMP* 750
Accts Cliftonlarsonallen Llp Waite
SIC 8221 College, except junior; College, except junior
Pr: Brian Rosenberg
**CFO:* David Wheaton
Treas: Kenneth Tivey
Assoc VP: Kathleen Abbott
Assoc Dir: Daymond Dean
Assoc Dir: Coco Du
Assoc Dir: Paul Odegaard
Off Mgr: Deanna Brabant
CIO: Gary Martin
Sls Mgr: Paula Paul-Wagner
Pgrm Dir: Sarah Sargent

D-U-N-S 09-931-2340
MACALJON/SCL INC
4524 Ogeechee Rd, Savannah, GA 31405-1208
Tel (912) 236-9333 *Founded/Ownrshp* 2001
Sales 31.3MM *EMP* 250
Accts Pedrick & Company Llc Savann
SIC 1711 Mechanical contractor; Mechanical contractor
Pr: Ben Macmillan
**CFO:* Andrew Dyer
**CFO:* Corey Fountain
**VP:* Chris Rowland
Sales Asso: Justin Martin
Snr PM: Craig Macmillan

MACALLISTER ENGINE POWER
See MACALLISTER MACHINERY CO INC

D-U-N-S 00-693-8419 IMP
MACALLISTER MACHINERY CO INC
MACALLISTER ENGINE POWER
7515 E 30th St, Indianapolis, IN 46219-1192
Tel (317) 545-2151 *Founded/Ownrshp* 1941
Sales 1.3MMM *EMP* 1,850

SIC 5082 5013 7699 Tractors, construction; General construction machinery & equipment; Construction equipment repair; Automotive supplies & parts; Tractors, construction; General construction machinery & equipment; Automotive supplies & parts; Construction equipment repair
Ch Bd: Pershing E Macallister
Pr: Christopher E Macallister
CFO: David Baldwin
Treas: John Deckard
VP: Mike Alte
Genl Mgr: Mike Doyle
Dir IT: Garry Buechler
IT Man: Dan Zachary
Software D: Robert Jordan
Mtls Mgr: Billy Campbell
Opers Mgr: Mason Keiffer

D-U-N-S 00-695-8573 IMP/EXP
MACALLISTER MACHINERY CO INC
MICHIGAN CAT
24800 Novi Rd, Novi, MI 48375-2414
Tel (248) 349-4800 *Founded/Ownrshp* 1943, 2011
Sales 497.6MM *EMP* 648
SIC 5082 General construction machinery & equipment; General construction machinery & equipment
Pr: Chris Macallister
**COO:* Bill Hodges
**CFO:* Dave Baldwin
VP: Arnold Strouse
Netwrk Mgr: Jeremy Parkinson
Snr Mgr: Mark Brohl

D-U-N-S 87-830-4849 IMP/EXP
MACANDREWS & FORBES HOLDINGS INC
35 E 62nd St, New York, NY 10065-8014
Tel (212) 572-8600 *Founded/Ownrshp* 1993
Sales 5.3MMME *EMP* 60,637
SIC 7819 Film processing, editing & titling: motion picture; Film processing, editing & titling: motion picture
Ch Bd: Ronald O Perelman
Sr Ex VP: William C Bevins
Ex VP: Steven M Cohen
Ex VP: Steven L Fasman
Ex VP: Gavin Isaacs
Ex VP: Paul G Savas
Ex VP: Edward Taibi
Ex VP: Frances F Townsend
Sr VP: James Chin
Sr VP: Evan Knisely
Sr VP: Debbie Perelman
Sr VP: Christine Taylor
VP: William Buccella
VP: Geoffrey Chow
VP: Floyd Clarke
VP: Michelle Galdos
VP: Timothy Murphy
VP: Audrey Rosinberg
VP: Cali Tran

D-U-N-S 11-291-9956 IMP/EXP
MACANDREWS & FORBES INC
(*Suby of* MACANDREWS & FORBES HOLDINGS INC) ★
38 E 63rd St, New York, NY 10065-8027
Tel (212) 688-9000 *Founded/Ownrshp* 1991
Sales 1.7MMME *EMP* 25,000E
SIC 2844 2087 2121 7819 2721 2731

D-U-N-S 02-784-0974
MACATAC INC
MCDONALD'S
4175 State Route 34, Hurricane, WV 25526-9771
Tel (304) 757-7778 *Founded/Ownrshp* 1980
Sales 11.8MME *EMP* 350
SIC 5812 Fast-food restaurant, chain; Fast-food restaurant, chain
Pr: Frederick Haughey
**VP:* Linda Haughey

D-U-N-S 96-953-5152 IMP
■ MACATAWA BANK
(*Suby of* MACATAWA BANK CORP) ★
815 E Main Ave, Zeeland, MI 49464-1387
Tel (616) 748-9847 *Founded/Ownrshp* 1998
Sales NA *EMP* 190E
SIC 6021 National commercial banks; National commercial banks
Pr: Phillip Koning
Ofcr: Laura Wolters
**Ex VP:* Ronald L Haan
**Sr VP:* Richard Wieringa
VP: Lynn Bobeldyk
**VP:* Vicki Denboer
VP: Krista Geyer
**VP:* Collette Neumann
VP: Sandy Siedlecki
VP: John Simonds
Site Mgr: Ben Overway
Board of Directors: Michael K Le Roy

D-U-N-S 04-708-6918
▲ MACATAWA BANK CORP
10753 Macatawa Dr, Holland, MI 49424-9578
Tel (616) 820-1444 *Founded/Ownrshp* 1997
Sales NA *EMP* 395E
Accts Bdo Usa Llp Grand Rapids Mi
Tkr Sym MCBC *Exch* NGS
SIC 6022 State commercial banks; State commercial banks
CEO: Ronald L Haan
**Ch Bd:* Richard L Postma
Pr: Ron Buit
CFO: Jon W Swets
Chf Cred: Craig A Hankinson
Ofcr: Jorge Gonzalez
Ofcr: Curt Stuck
Sr VP: Matthew D Hoeksema
Sr VP: Jill A Walcott
VP: Christine Bart
VP: Jason Coney
VP: Ryan Ed
VP: Linda Elenbaas
VP: Stephanie Jamrog
VP: Frederick Lake
VP: James Lilly
VP: Rhonda Romatz
VP: Jodi Sevigny

Board of Directors: Thomas J Wesholski, Mark Bugge, Wayne J Elhart, Charles A Geene, Robert L Herr, Birgit Klohs, Michael K Le Roy, Arend D Lubbers, Douglas B Padnos, Thomas P Rosenbach

D-U-N-S 96-626-8513
MACAULAY BROWN INC
MACB
2933 Bunker Hill Ln # 220, Santa Clara, CA 95054-1124
Tel (937) 426-3421 *Founded/Ownrshp* 2011
Sales 2.5MME *EMP* 1,500
SIC 8711 Engineering services
Ex Dir: Vicki Summers
VP: John Graziano

D-U-N-S 07-925-3831
MACAULAY-BROWN INC
1951 Polaris Rd, Finksburg, MD 21048-2070
Tel (937) 426-3421 *Founded/Ownrshp* 2014
Sales 27.2MME *EMP* 1,900
SIC 8711 Electrical or electronic engineering; Electrical or electronic engineering
VP: Victoria Summers

D-U-N-S 09-650-0483
MACAULAY-BROWN INC (OH)
MACB
4021 Executive Dr, Beavercreek, OH 45430-1062
Tel (937) 426-3421 *Founded/Ownrshp* 1979, 2002
Sales 444.9MME *EMP* 2,000
SIC 8711 8733 Engineering services; Research institute; Engineering services; Research institute
Pr: Sidney E Fuchs
Pr: Bob Mazze
CEO: Sid Fuchs
**CFO:* Michael C Zeiser
Ofcr: Mark Demoreski
**Ofcr:* Mike Ritter
Sr VP: Mike Beauchamp
**Sr VP:* Mark P Chadason
Sr VP: Mark Chadason
Sr VP: Tim Lawrence
Sr VP: Fred Norman
Sr VP: William Pratt
Sr VP: Donald Raines
Sr VP: Jim Soos
**VP:* Dave Bramlage
VP: Brian Brown
VP: John Graziano
VP: Dan Gutierrez
VP: Mia Kerivan
**VP:* Mia Kerivan-Omalley
VP: Troy Kohler
Board of Directors: Bruce Lesser, Kevin Soder

MACAYO MEXICAN RESTAURANT
See MACAYO VEGAS INC

D-U-N-S 94-970-8598
MACAYO RESTAURANTS LLC
1480 E Bethany Home Rd # 130, Phoenix, AZ 85014-2022
Tel (602) 200-1780 *Founded/Ownrshp* 1946
Sales 46.5MME *EMP* 1,000
SIC 5812 5149 5813 Mexican restaurant; Bar (drinking places); Groceries & related products; Mexican restaurant; Groceries & related products; Bar (drinking places)
Genl Mgr: Juan Gonzales
CIO: Lee Schnoor
Mktg Dir: Sharon Banta

D-U-N-S 03-493-9868
MACAYO VEGAS INC
MACAYO MEXICAN RESTAURANT
1480 E Bethany Home Rd, Phoenix, AZ 85014-2003
Tel (602) 264-1831 *Founded/Ownrshp* 1959
Sales 12.3MME *EMP* 393
SIC 5812 5813 Mexican restaurant; Drinking places; Mexican restaurant; Drinking places
Pr: Stephen Johnson
**Sec:* Edmond Haddad
**VP:* Victoria Johnson
VP: Jason Petzke
CIO: Lee Schnoor

MACB
See MACAULAY-BROWN INC

MACB
See MACAULAY BROWN INC

D-U-N-S 08-445-3315
MACBER INC
JAX MARKET
401 N East St, Anaheim, CA 92805-3338
Tel (714) 778-2461 *Founded/Ownrshp* 1977
Sales 21.8MME *EMP* 280
SIC 5411 Grocery stores, independent; Grocery stores, independent
CEO: Willard R Macaloney

MACC ENERGY BASIN CLINIC
See MEMORIAL HOSPITAL OF CARBON COUNTY

D-U-N-S 86-100-4844
MACCALL MANAGEMENT LLC
185 Suth State St Ste 202, Salt Lake City, UT 84111
Tel (801) 320-7200 *Founded/Ownrshp* 1994
Sales 17.8MME *EMP* 400E
SIC 8741 Hotel or motel management; Hotel or motel management

MACCO JIM & SONS CARPET WHSE
See MACCOS FLOOR COVERING CENTER INC

D-U-N-S 18-312-4197
MACCOR INC
4322 S 49th West Ave, Tulsa, OK 74107-6100
Tel (918) 446-1874 *Founded/Ownrshp* 1987
Sales 23.0MME *EMP* 72
SIC 3825 Battery testers, electrical
Pr: Andrew Mackay
Pr: Mike Sandoval
Ofcr: Greg Jenkins
VP: Douglas McKinney
VP: Deonn Odell

D-U-N-S 03-019-2553
MACCOS FLOOR COVERING CENTER INC
MACCO JIM & SONS CARPET WHSE
2035 Larsen Rd, Green Bay, WI 54303-4805
Tel (920) 432-5501 *Founded/Ownrshp* 1969
Sales 27.0MME *EMP* 120
SIC 5713 Floor covering stores; Carpets; Linoleum
Pr: Jeff Macco
**Treas:* James J Macco
VP: Jim Walters
Ex Dir: Kathy Baier

D-U-N-S 60-894-2124
MACCRAY IND SCHOOL DIST 2180
711 Wolverine Dr, Clara City, MN 56222
Tel (320) 847-3401 *Founded/Ownrshp* 1990
Sales 20.5MME *EMP* 472
SIC 8211 Elementary & secondary schools; Elementary & secondary schools
V Ch: Scott Ruiter
Bd of Dir: Tate Mueller
Instr Medi: Diane Holien

D-U-N-S 18-884-3981
MACCURRACH GOLF CONSTRUCTION INC
3501 Faye Rd, Jacksonville, FL 32226-2379
Tel (904) 646-1581 *Founded/Ownrshp* 1988
Sales 23.7MME *EMP* 120
SIC 1629 Golf course construction; Golf course construction
Pr: Allan I Maccurrach

D-U-N-S 14-465-9299 IMP
MACDERMID COLORSPAN INC
(*Suby of* MACDERMID PRINTING SOLUTIONS LLC) ★
11311 K Tel Dr, Hopkins, MN 55343-8869
Tel (952) 944-9457 *Founded/Ownrshp* 2000
Sales 31.4MME *EMP* 263
SIC 5085 3555 5045 3577 Industrial supplies; Typesetting machines: linotype, monotype, intertype, etc.; Computers, peripherals & software; Computer peripheral equipment; Industrial supplies; Typesetting machines: linotype, monotype, intertype, etc.; Computers, peripherals & software; Computer peripheral equipment
Pr: Rick Bigauette
**VP:* Rinnie Dicenzo
MIS Dir: Paul Kielty

D-U-N-S 00-116-4599 IMP/EXP
MACDERMID INC (CT)
(*Suby of* PLATFORM SPECIALTY PRODUCTS CORP) ★
245 Freight St, Waterbury, CT 06702-1818
Tel (203) 575-5700 *Founded/Ownrshp* 1922, 2007
Sales 401.6MME *EMP* 1,500E
SIC 2899 2842 2874 2992 2752 3577 Chemical preparations; Plating compounds; Rust resisting compounds; Stencil correction compounds; Cleaning or polishing preparations; Phosphates; Lubricating oils; Offset & photolithographic printing; Printers & plotters; Chemical preparations; Plating compounds; Rust resisting compounds; Stencil correction compounds; Cleaning or polishing preparations; Phosphates; Lubricating oils; Offset & photolithographic printing; Printers & plotters
Ch Bd: Daniel H Leever
**Pr:* Scot Benson
**CFO:* Frank J Monteiro
Ex VP: Peter Kukanskis
Ex VP: John Malfettone
**VP:* John L Cordani
Sfty Mgr: Sherrie Gillis

D-U-N-S 87-802-8430 IMP/EXP
MACDERMID PRINTING SOLUTIONS LLC
(*Suby of* MACDERMID INC) ★
5210 Phillip Lee Dr Sw, Atlanta, GA 30336-2217
Tel (404) 472-0072 *Founded/Ownrshp* 1994
Sales 249.9MME *EMP* 1,131
SIC 3555 Printing plates; Printing plates
Ch Bd: David Beckerman
CFO: Gerry Miller
**Ex VP:* Gerard Loeb
Brnch Mgr: John P Brice O

D-U-N-S 06-046-8733
MACDONALD & OWEN VENEER AND LUMBER CO INC
1900 Riley Rd, Sparta, WI 54656-1481
Tel (608) 269-4417 *Founded/Ownrshp* 1968
Sales 26.7MME *EMP* 50E
SIC 5031 Lumber: rough, dressed & finished
Pr: David Twite
**CFO:* Tammy Cuda
Sls Mgr: Adam Hyer
Sales Asso: Mike McGlinn

MACDONALD MACHINERY COMPANY
See RPM MACHINERY LLC

D-U-N-S 96-806-9968
MACDONALD MOTT INC
(*Suby of* MOTT MACDONALD INTERNATIONAL LIMITED)
111 Wood Ave S Ste 410, Iselin, NJ 08830-2700
Tel (973) 379-3400 *Founded/Ownrshp* 2001
Sales 30.0MM *EMP* 140
SIC 8742 8711 Civil engineering; House designer; Management consulting services; Management consulting services; Civil engineering
Pr: Keith Howells
**Treas:* Craig Velasquez
**VP:* Martin Hornsby

D-U-N-S 13-163-7956
MACDONALD-MILLER FACILITY SOLUTIONS INC
7717 Detroit Ave Sw, Seattle, WA 98106-1903
Tel (206) 763-9400 *Founded/Ownrshp* 2002
Sales 98.0MME *EMP* 300
SIC 1731 1711 Electronic controls installation; Heating & air conditioning contractors; Electronic controls installation; Heating & air conditioning contractors
Pr: Derrick Simonds

CFO: Stephanie Gebhardt
CFO: James Macdonald
**Sec:* Tyler Kopet
**Sec:* Steve Nicholes
Sr VP: Reagan Perry
**VP:* Steven Lovely
**Prin:* Frederic J Sigmond
**Prin:* Gus Simonds
IT Man: Lilay Gebreigziabher
Sfty Dirs: Lee Pyfrom

MACDOUGALL OIL COMPANY
See REX OIL CO INC

D-U-N-S 07-070-7104
MACDOUGALL PIERCE CONSTRUCTION INC
12720 Ford Dr, Fishers, IN 46038-2893
Tel (317) 596-6371 *Founded/Ownrshp* 1976
Sales 28.9MME *EMP* 56
Accts Jeff Mullen Cpa
SIC 1542 Commercial & office building, new construction
CEO: G Robert Macdougall
**Pr:* James A Gundlach
**CFO:* Scott Stull
VP: Robert Kemper
**VP:* Mark Tichenor
Snr Mgr: Derek Isaac

D-U-N-S 18-576-9312 IMP/EXP
▲ MACE SECURITY INTERNATIONAL INC
4400 Carnegie Ave, Cleveland, OH 44103-4342
Tel (440) 424-5321 *Founded/Ownrshp* 1993
Sales 26.8MME *EMP* 164E
Tkr Sym MACE *Exch* OTO
SIC 3699 3999 Security devices; Self-defense sprays; Security devices; Self-defense sprays
Pr: John J McCann
CFO: Gregory Krzemien
Div Pres: John O'Leary
**Sr VP:* Carl R Smith
**VP:* Eric Crawford
VP: Garnett Meador
CTO: Sarah Butterfield
Board of Directors: Denis J Amato, Richard A Barone, Terrance W Gainer, Suzanne M Hopgood, Daniel V Perella, Larry Pollock

D-U-N-S 02-016-5585
▲ MACERICH CO (MD)
401 Wilshire Blvd Ste 700, Santa Monica, CA 90401-1452
Tel (310) 394-6000 *Founded/Ownrshp* 1964
Sales 1.1MMM *EMP* 1,117
Accts Kpmg Llp Los Angeles Califor
Tkr Sym MAC *Exch* NYS
SIC 6798 Real estate investment trusts; Real estate investment trusts
Ch Bd: Arthur M Coppola
**Pr:* Edward C Coppola
Pr: Lorina Escudero
Pr: Laura Lloyd
Pr: Cassie Malayil
CFO: Thomas E O'Hern
**V Ch Bd:* Dana K Anderson
Ofcr: Thomas J Leanse
Ofcr: Thomas Ohern
Ex VP: Richard Bayer
Sr VP: Jamie Bourbeau
Sr VP: Douglas Healey
Sr VP: Melanie Balfour Heywood
Sr VP: John Perry
VP: Sue Martinez
VP: Mike Nevins
VP: Jeanne Phares
VP: Nancy Rendos
VP: Madonna Shannon
VP: Timothy Steffan
Board of Directors: Douglas D Abbey, Fred S Hubbell, Diana M Laing, Stanley A Moore, Mason G Ross, William P Sexton, Steven L Soboroff, Andrea M Stephen, John Sullivan

D-U-N-S 80-821-9836
■ MACERICH PARTNERSHIP LP
CHESTERFIELD TOWNE CENTER
(*Suby of* MACERICH CO) ★
11500 Midlothian Tpke # 578, North Chesterfield, VA 23235-4780
Tel (804) 794-4661 *Founded/Ownrshp* 1994
Sales 21.1MME *EMP* 165
SIC 6798 Real estate investment trusts; Real estate investment trusts
Secur Mgr: James Toney
Mktg Dir: Becky Valenti
Mktg Mgr: Noelynn Koo

MACEY'S FOOD & DRUG
See MACEYS INC

D-U-N-S 03-537-1723
MACEYS INC
MACEY'S FOOD & DRUG
(*Suby of* ASSOCIATED FOOD STORES INC) ★
7850 S 1300 E, Sandy, UT 84094-0746
Tel (801) 255-4888 *Founded/Ownrshp* 1999
Sales 25.4MME *EMP* 200
SIC 5411 Supermarkets, chain; Supermarkets, chain
VP: John Allen
Store Dir: Tony Macey

D-U-N-S 60-932-1344
MACFADDEN & ASSOCIATES INC
8403 Colesville Rd # 400, Silver Spring, MD 20910-6331
Tel (301) 588-5900 *Founded/Ownrshp* 1986
Sales 31.6MME *EMP* 225
SIC 4813 7373 7299 7374 Telephone communication, except radio; Computer integrated systems design; Personal document & information services; Data processing & preparation; Telephone communication, except radio; Computer integrated systems design; Personal document & information services; Data processing & preparation
Pr: Russell Hall
**Pr:* David M Binns
COO: Michael Sears

Info Man: Janet Kim
Mktg Dir: Janet Kemp

MACFARLANE CSTA HSING PARTNERS
See HIGHRIDGE COSTA INVESTORS LLC

D-U-N-S 55-626-9579
■ MACGREGOR GROUP INC
(*Suby of* ITG SOLUTIONS NETWORK INC) ★
321 Summer St Fl 1, Boston, MA 02210-1725
Tel (978) 561-1330 *Founded/Ownrshp* 2006
Sales 22.6MM^E *EMP* 295
SIC 7379 7372 Computer related consulting services; Prepackaged software
Pr: Steven Levy
**COO:* Rob Flatley
**CFO:* John O Brian
**Ex VP:* Deirdre Noonan
**CTO:* Rolando Rabines
Mktg Mgr: Paul Wigglesworth

D-U-N-S 19-428-5904
MACH 1 GLOBAL SERVICES INC
MACH1
1530 W Broadway Rd, Tempe, AZ 85282-1131
Tel (480) 921-3900 *Founded/Ownrshp* 1988
Sales 142.4MM^E *EMP* 210
SIC 4731 4212 Freight forwarding; Local trucking, without storage; Freight forwarding; Local trucking, without storage
CEO: Jamie Fletcher
COO: Eric Bond
**COO:* Rob Lively
VP: Rick Batia
VP: Justin Panasewicz
VP: David Scappe
Admn Mgr: Chris Beaudoin
Dist Mgr: Edward Garcia
Dist Mgr: Jared Licata
Dist Mgr: Kari Thomsen
Dist Mgr: Peggy Weaver
Board of Directors: Kathleen Entzminger, Michael Entzminger, Jamie Fletcher

D-U-N-S 07-928-7530 IMP
MACH SPEED HOLDINGS LLC
APOLLO BRANDS
(*Suby of* TRANSITION CAPITAL PARTNERS LP) ★
7200 Bishop Rd Ste 280, Plano, TX 75024-3639
Tel (214) 978-3800 *Founded/Ownrshp* 2011
Sales 125.0MM^E *EMP* 75
SIC 5091 5065 3679

MACH1
See MACH 1 GLOBAL SERVICES INC

MACHACKEMACH APARTMENTS
See PJ HOUSING PRESERVATION LP

D-U-N-S 80-073-9232
MACHIAS BANCORP MHC
4 Center St, Isle Au Haut, ME 04645
Tel (207) 255-3347 *Founded/Ownrshp* 2007
Sales NA *EMP* 98^E
SIC 6712 Bank holding companies

D-U-N-S 04-146-0569
MACHIAS SAVINGS BANK
(*Suby of* MACHIAS BANCORP MHC) ★
4 Center St, Machias, ME 04654-1110
Tel (207) 255-3347 *Founded/Ownrshp* 1969
Sales NA *EMP* 215
SIC 6036 6163 State savings banks, not federally chartered; Loan brokers; State savings banks, not federally chartered; Loan brokers
Ch Bd: Donald Foster
**Pr:* Larry Barker
Ofcr: Catherine Betz
Ofcr: Sean Daye
Ofcr: Jeanine Mallar
Ofcr: Paul Rudd
**Ex VP:* Donald E Reynolds
Sr VP: Whitney Scott
**Sr VP:* J Scott Whitney
VP: Kelli Emery
VP: Chris Fitzpatrick
VP: Ben Ketchen
**VP:* Steven M Leackfeldt
Exec: Danielle Caricofe
Board of Directors: Richard H Bagley, Gregory R Coffin, Clyde R Crane, Charles A Dinsmore, Donald A Foster, Robert W Foster, Patrick C Jordan

D-U-N-S 06-530-0535
MACHINE & WELDING SUPPLY CO
ARC3 GASES SOUTH
(*Suby of* ARC3 GASES INC) ★
1660 Us Highway 301 S, Dunn, NC 28334-6791
Tel (910) 892-4016 *Founded/Ownrshp* 2013
Sales 120.8MM^E *EMP* 260
SIC 5084 5169 Welding machinery & equipment; Industrial gases; Welding machinery & equipment; Industrial gases
Pr: Emmett C Aldredge Jr
**VP:* Emmett C Aldredge III
**VP:* Jeff Johnson
Exec: Scott Coats
Brnch Mgr: Daryl Bass
Brnch Mgr: Mitch Dees
Brnch Mgr: Jan McLamb
Store Mgr: Keith Benfield
Manager: Steve Browning
Sales Asso: Ray Adams

MACHINE CLOTHING COMPANY
See BILLION TOWER INTL LLC

D-U-N-S 00-716-5186 IMP
MACHINE LABORATORY LLC (MO)
(*Suby of* TECH INVESTMENTS LLC) ★
8040 Bond St, Lenexa, KS 66214-1591
Tel (913) 825-7400 *Founded/Ownrshp* 1957
Sales 78.2MM^E *EMP* 250
SIC 3599 3451 Machine shop, jobbing & repair; Screw machine products; Machine shop, jobbing & repair; Screw machine products
CEO: James E Finley
CFO: Mark Deuel
Exec: Darryl Cochran
**Genl Mgr:* Delena Haefner
Plnt Mgr: Marty Stout

D-U-N-S 07-591-3996
MACHINE MAINTENANCE INC
LUBY EQUIPMENT SERVICES
2300 Cassens Dr, Fenton, MO 63026-2503
Tel (636) 343-9970 *Founded/Ownrshp* 1977
Sales 49.7MM^E *EMP* 91
SIC 5082 7699 5084 7359 General construction machinery & equipment; Mining machinery & equipment, except petroleum; Construction equipment repair; Drilling equipment, excluding bits; Equipment rental & leasing; General construction machinery & equipment; Mining machinery & equipment, except petroleum; Construction equipment repair; Drilling equipment, excluding bits; Equipment rental & leasing
Pr: Robert Luby
VP Sls: Ted Rose
Sls Mgr: Elbert Cook
Sls Mgr: Greg Dennis
Sls Mgr: Ken Steffens
Sales Asso: Jason Harmon

D-U-N-S 02-548-8081 IMP/EXP
MACHINE OLDCO LIQUIDATION LLC (IL)
1961 Edgewater Dr, North Pekin, IL 61554-7831
Tel (309) 382-3045 *Founded/Ownrshp* 1950, 1997
Sales 35.6MM^E *EMP* 150
SIC 3599 Machine shop, jobbing & repair; Machine shop, jobbing & repair
**Pr:* Mark Markovich
CFO: Rich Johnson

D-U-N-S 00-612-5140 IMP
MACHINE SERVICE INC (WI)
1000 Ashwaubenon St, Green Bay, WI 54304-5604
Tel (920) 339-3000 *Founded/Ownrshp* 1948
Sales 54.3MM *EMP* 150
Accts Patrickus & Jones Sc Green
SIC 3714 3568 3599 3594 5013 Motor vehicle parts & accessories; Power transmission equipment; Machine shop, jobbing & repair; Fluid power pumps & motors; Truck parts & accessories; Motor vehicle parts & accessories; Power transmission equipment; Machine shop, jobbing & repair; Fluid power pumps & motors; Truck parts & accessories
CEO: Edward L Fowles
**Sec:* Michael Anderson
Brnch Mgr: Randy Smith
Genl Mgr: Bryan Schultz
Dir IT: Chad Sylvester
Sfty Dirs: Ryan Landry
Sfty Mgr: David Ninnemann
Mktg Dir: Bill Renier
Sales Asso: Larry Collier

D-U-N-S 11-041-5317 IMP
MACHINE SOLUTION PROVIDERS INC
MSP
2659 Wisconsin Ave, Downers Grove, IL 60515-4244
Tel (630) 717-7040 *Founded/Ownrshp* 2002
Sales 23.1MM^E *EMP* 55
SIC 3531 Roofing equipment
Pr: William A Novak
**VP:* Michael P O'Brien

D-U-N-S 05-174-1452
MACHINE SPECIALTIES INC
6511 Franz Warner Pkwy, Whitsett, NC 27377-9215
Tel (336) 603-1919 *Founded/Ownrshp* 1969
Sales 29.5MM *EMP* 160
Accts Breslow Starling Frost Warner
SIC 3599 Machine shop, jobbing & repair; Machine shop, jobbing & repair
Pr: Robert Simmons
**CFO:* Brent Allen
Exec: Patrick Stone
Ql Cn Mgr: Marc Libertore
Ql Cn Mgr: Travis Nance
Sls Mgr: Tommy Dowling

D-U-N-S 11-278-2362
MACHINE SPECIALTY & MANUFACTURING INC
215 Rousseau Rd, Youngsville, LA 70592-5252
Tel (337) 837-0020 *Founded/Ownrshp* 1984
Sales 34.0MM *EMP* 125
SIC 3463 Flange, valve or pipe fitting forgings, nonferrous; Flange, valve or pipe fitting forgings, nonferrous
CEO: Anna Lois Vige
**Pr:* Andrew S Vige
**VP:* Colette Vige
Sfty Dirs: Brandon Biessenberger

D-U-N-S 13-082-9828
MACHINE TOOL & GEAR INC
MTG
(*Suby of* BAY CITY DIVISION) ★
1021 N Shiawassee St, Corunna, MI 48817-1151
Tel (989) 743-3936 *Founded/Ownrshp* 2002
Sales 150.0M *EMP* 500
SIC 3714 5051 3089 Iron or steel flat products; Motor vehicle parts & accessories; Motor vehicle parts & accessories; Iron or steel flat products; Automotive parts, plastic
Ch Bd: David Segal

MACHINE TOOL DIVISION
See GROB SYSTEMS INC

D-U-N-S 02-291-6720
MACHINE TOOL SUPPLY CORP
3150 Mike Collins Dr, Eagan, MN 55121-2292
Tel (651) 405-6314 *Founded/Ownrshp* 1952
Sales 32.4MM^E *EMP* 35
SIC 5085 5084 Industrial supplies; Machine tools & accessories
CEO: Todd A Kerin
**VP:* Troy Kerin
Sales Asso: Kevin Goplen

MACHINE TOOLS SUPPLY
See MT SUPPLY INC

MACHINED PRODUCTS
See FABRICATED METALS CO

D-U-N-S 02-351-4631
MACHINERY & FACTORY INDUSTRIAL SUPPLY INC
M&F
1021 6th St, Racine, WI 53403-1101
Tel (262) 634-5533 *Founded/Ownrshp* 1951
Sales 22.1MM^E *EMP* 38
SIC 5085 Industrial supplies; Welding supplies
Pr: Charles W Gray
IT Man: Tim Foster
Sales Asso: Chris Mosey

D-U-N-S 19-268-1807 EXP
MACHINERY CORP OF AMERICA INC
1983 Nw 88th Ct Ste 301, Doral, FL 33172-2630
Tel (305) 593-2005 *Founded/Ownrshp* 1986
Sales 70.3MM^E *EMP* 48
SIC 5082 General construction machinery & equipment; Masonry equipment & supplies
Pr: Jefferson Powell
**VP:* Richard Lucy
**VP:* Jefferson Norman Powell
Genl Mgr: Carlos Fernandes
Trfc Mgr: Miriam Callejas

D-U-N-S 11-928-2861 IMP
MACHINERY EXCHANGE CORP
3700 Massillon Rd Ste 350, Uniontown, OH 44685-9591
Tel (330) 896-0585 *Founded/Ownrshp* 1983
Sales 30.0MM *EMP* 9
SIC 5084 Industrial machinery & equipment; Industrial machinery & equipment
Pr: Robert C Thompson

MACHINERY RENTAL COMPANY
See REYNOLDS FAMILY HOLDING CO

D-U-N-S 08-981-9312 EXP
MACHINERY SYSTEMS INC (IL)
SYSTEMS FINANCIAL CREDIT
614 E State Pkwy, Schaumburg, IL 60173-4533
Tel (847) 490-7939 *Founded/Ownrshp* 1977
Sales 31.2MM^E *EMP* 70
SIC 5084 Machine tools & metalworking machinery
Ch Bd: Joseph Romanowski
**Pr:* Ronald J Mager
**Sr VP:* Mike Cekanor
**VP:* Erik Cook
Mktg Dir: Dorothea Rynearson
Sls Mgr: Mike Bielfeldt
Sls Mgr: Tim Cirone
Sls Mgr: Steve Nehls
Sls Mgr: Ken Sofolo

D-U-N-S 02-471-7618
MACHINERY TOOLING & SUPPLY LLC (WI)
614 E State Pkwy, Schaumburg, IL 60173-4533
Tel (847) 882-8085 *Founded/Ownrshp* 1998
Sales 27.9MM^E *EMP* 33
SIC 5084 5085 Industrial machinery & equipment; Industrial supplies
CEO: Bob Cuthbertson
Sales Asso: Christine Bauer

MACHINING AND FRAME DIVISION
See MASS PRECISION INC

D-U-N-S 19-872-0351 IMP
MACHINING TECHNOLOGIES INC
MATECH
510 Naylor Mill Rd, Salisbury, MD 21801-1192
Tel (410) 548-1627 *Founded/Ownrshp* 1988
Sales 55.2MM^E *EMP* 123
SIC 3599 Machine & other job shop work; Custom machinery; Machine shop, jobbing & repair; Machine & other job shop work; Custom machinery; Machine shop, jobbing & repair
Pr: Rafael Correa
**CEO:* George Mokhiber
CFO: Roseane Adamo
CFO: Martin Rosenhaft
**CFO:* Roger Young
**Ex VP:* Daniel E Seman
Prgrm Mgr: Benito Calderon
Prgrm Mgr: William Corner
Prgrm Mgr: Phil Villella
CIO: Thomas Crawford
QA Dir: Fred Silva
Board of Directors: Cecilia Seman

D-U-N-S 00-924-4112
MACHINISTS INC
7600 5th Ave S, Seattle, WA 98108-4116
Tel (206) 763-0990 *Founded/Ownrshp* 1971
Sales 32.3MM *EMP* 200
SIC 3599 1799 Machine & other job shop work; Sandblasting of building exteriors; Machine & other job shop work; Sandblasting of building exteriors
Pr: Hugh La Bossier
IT Man: Sherrill Sandmire
Plnt Mgr: Nick Cole

MACHLINK-MUSCATINE POWER & WAT
See MUSCATINE POWER & WATER (INC)

D-U-N-S 07-852-8310
MACHOL & JOHANNES LLC
700 17th St Ste 200, Denver, CO 80202-3558
Tel (303) 830-0075 *Founded/Ownrshp* 2009
Sales 21.3MM^E *EMP* 175
SIC 8111 Debt collection law; Debt collection law
Admn Mgr: Ana Stephens
Dir IT: Son Nguyen

MACI
See MICHIGAN AUTOMOTIVE COMPRESSOR INC

D-U-N-S 80-516-3342
MACIAS GINI & OCONNELL LLP
3000 S St Ste 300, Sacramento, CA 95816-7014
Tel (916) 928-4600 *Founded/Ownrshp* 1992
Sales 33.4MM *EMP* 220
SIC 8721 Accounting, auditing & bookkeeping; Accounting, auditing & bookkeeping
Pt: Kenneth A Macias
**Pt:* Ernest Gini
**Pt:* Jim Godsey
**Pt:* Rick Green
**Pt:* Scott Hammon
**Pt:* Cynthia Pon
**Pt:* Jan Rosati
**Mng Pt:* Kevin O Connell
CFO: Amy Sanatkar
Off Mgr: Crystal Powell
IT Man: Sam Ellison

MACK AND PARKER
See HUB INTERNATIONAL OF ILLINOIS LIMITED

D-U-N-S 02-443-8103 EXP
MACK BROWN INC
2705 Us Highway 421 N, Boone, NC 28607-7654
Tel (828) 264-9051 *Founded/Ownrshp* 1971
Sales 24.9MM^E *EMP* 60
SIC 5511 7515 7514 7513 5521 5012 Automobiles, new & used; Passenger car leasing; Passenger car rental; Truck rental & leasing, no drivers; Used car dealers; Automobiles & other motor vehicles; Automobiles, new & used; Passenger car leasing; Passenger car rental; Truck rental & leasing, no drivers; Used car dealers; Automobiles & other motor vehicles
Pr: Kent Brown
**Treas:* Jason K Brown
Dir IT: Brian Miller

D-U-N-S 08-772-7186 EXP
MACK CLEVELAND SALES INC
PERFORMANCE TRUCK
1263 Us Highway 59 N, Cleveland, TX 77327-2877
Tel (281) 593-8888 *Founded/Ownrshp* 1977
Sales 117.1MM^E *EMP* 270
SIC 5012 Trucks, commercial; Truck tractors; Trailers for trucks, new & used; Trucks, commercial; Truck tractors; Trailers for trucks, new & used
Pr: RC Sweeten
**VP:* Skipper Martin
Off Mgr: Sondra McGuire
Sales Exec: Mike Herbert
Manager: Albert Chapa
Sls Mgr: Chase Robinson
Sales Asso: Joshua Cunningham

D-U-N-S 11-536-7773
MACK ENERGY CO
(*Suby of* JATH OIL CO) ★
1202 N 10th St, Duncan, OK 73533-3832
Tel (580) 252-5580 *Founded/Ownrshp* 1980
Sales 33.6MM^E *EMP* 125
SIC 1311 1382 Crude petroleum production; Natural gas production; Oil & gas exploration services; Crude petroleum production; Natural gas production; Oil & gas exploration services
Pr: T H McCasland III
**Treas:* Noble Means
**VP:* Chris Fowler
**VP:* Randy Smith
Board of Directors: James Garis, Marlyn Hugon, Mark McCasland, Gil Messersmith

D-U-N-S 80-489-3105
MACK ENERGY CORP
PIPE & SUPPLY
11352 Lovington Hwy, Artesia, NM 88210-9634
Tel (575) 748-1288 *Founded/Ownrshp* 1990
Sales 533.6MM^E *EMP* 500
SIC 1311 2911 Crude petroleum & natural gas; Oils, fuel; Oils, lubricating; Crude petroleum & natural gas; Oils, fuel; Oils, lubricating
Pr: Mack C Chase
**CFO:* Brad Bartek
**VP:* Robert Chase
Off Admin: Crissa Carter
Dir IT: Rodney Carter

D-U-N-S 05-409-6466 IMP
MACK FARMS INC
28501 Hwy 60 E, Lake Wales, FL 33898
Tel (863) 692-1200 *Founded/Ownrshp* 1976
Sales 34.8MM^E *EMP* 125
SIC 0161 Vegetables & melons
Pr: Arnold H Mack

D-U-N-S 05-022-7250 IMP
MACK GROUP INC
608 Warm Brook Rd, Arlington, VT 05250-8570
Tel (802) 375-2511 *Founded/Ownrshp* 1997
Sales 437.9MM^E *EMP* 1,400
Accts Gallagher Flynn & Company Ll
SIC 3089 3577 6719 Plastic processing; Injection molding of plastics; Injection molded finished plastic products; Computer peripheral equipment; Investment holding companies, except banks; Plastic processing; Injection molding of plastics; Injection molded finished plastic products; Computer peripheral equipment; Investment holding companies, except banks
Pr: Donald S Kendall III
**CFO:* Florence Belnap
**Sec:* Randy Boduch
Comm Dir: Julie Horst
Plnt Mgr: Marc Colety
Board of Directors: Raymond E Burns, William H Cooley, Jane Gardner, Nancy Kendall, William S Kendell

D-U-N-S 02-212-0851
MACK HOUSBY INC
4747 Ne 14th St, Des Moines, IA 50313-2010
Tel (515) 266-2666 *Founded/Ownrshp* 1969
Sales 70.9MM^E *EMP* 100
SIC 5511 Automobiles, new & used; Automobiles, new & used
Pr: Kelly J Housby
**VP:* Kevin J Housby
Admn Mgr: Lisa Freerksen
Natl Sales: Jared Modlin

D-U-N-S 06-535-0399
MACK II INC
POPEYES CHICKEN & BISCUITS
3421 Dogwood Dr, Atlanta, GA 30354-1415
Tel (404) 768-9977 *Founded/Ownrshp* 1972
Sales 23.2MM *EMP* 160

Accts Vanetta Stringfield Keyes Cpa
SIC 5812 Fast-food restaurant, chain; Fast-food restaurant, chain
CEO: Mack Wilbourn
**VP:* Cassandra Harmon

D-U-N-S 78-897-0903
MACK INDUSTRIES
(*Suby of* MACK INDUSTRIES INC) ★
507 Derby Ave, Bowling Green, OH 43402-3973
Tel (419) 353-7081 *Founded/Ownrshp* 1910
Sales 20.4MM^E *EMP* 173
SIC 3272 5211 1711 Burial vaults, concrete or precast terrazzo; Masonry materials & supplies; Septic system construction; Burial vaults, concrete or precast terrazzo; Masonry materials & supplies; Septic system construction
Pr: Betsie Mack
Oper/Mgr: Jeff Colvin

D-U-N-S 00-421-4466
MACK INDUSTRIES INC (OH)
MACK TRANSPORT
1321 Industrial Pkwy N # 500, Brunswick, OH 44212-6358
Tel (330) 460-7005 *Founded/Ownrshp* 1932, 1958
Sales 163.9MM^E *EMP* 500
SIC 3272 1771 Burial vaults, concrete or precast terrazzo; Septic tanks, concrete; Manhole covers or frames, concrete; Concrete work; Burial vaults, concrete or precast terrazzo; Septic tanks, concrete; Manhole covers or frames, concrete; Concrete work
Sec: Betsy Mack Nespeca
**Pr:* Betsy Mack-Nespeca
VP: Sean McNulty

D-U-N-S 92-671-2027
MACK INDUSTRIES OF MICHIGAN INC
8265 White Lake Rd, White Lake, MI 48386-1157
Tel (248) 620-7400 *Founded/Ownrshp* 1993
Sales 22.9MM^E *EMP* 173
SIC 3272 Concrete products; Concrete products
Pr: Howard J Mack
**VP:* Richard W Mack
Off Mgr: Nancy Benton

D-U-N-S 00-446-9987
MACK INDUSTRIES OF PENNSYLVANIA INC
(*Suby of* MACK INDUSTRIES INC) ★
201 Columbia Rd, Valley City, OH 44280-9706
Tel (330) 483-3111 *Founded/Ownrshp* 1976
Sales 28.5MM^E *EMP* 173
SIC 3272 Concrete products, precast; Concrete products, precast
Pr: Betsy Mack
CFO: Lee Disterhof
**Treas:* Barbara Mack
VP: Howard Mack
Sls Dir: Tom Setzer

D-U-N-S 11-862-0871
MACK MACK AND WALTZ INSURANCE GROUP INC
1211 S Military Trl # 100, Deerfield Beach, FL 33442-7619
Tel (954) 640-6225 *Founded/Ownrshp* 1993
Sales NA *EMP* 50
SIC 6411 Insurance agents
CEO: Jay Mack
Pr: Brad Lubin
**Pr:* Paul Mack
CFO: Deborah Powers
**VP:* Jacqueline Mack
**Prin:* Gregory Waltz

D-U-N-S 00-643-9814
MACK MILWAUKEE SALES INC
MILWAUKEE TRUCK SALES
4444 W Blue Mound Rd, Milwaukee, WI 53208-3670
Tel (414) 258-8484 *Founded/Ownrshp* 1951
Sales 115.6MM^E *EMP* 230
SIC 5511 New & used car dealers; Trucks, tractors & trailers: new & used; New & used car dealers; Trucks, tractors & trailers: new & used
Ch: Roger H Kriete
**Pr:* David Kriete
**VP:* George Pavin
Sls Mgr: Diana Sirovina

D-U-N-S 00-206-8096 IMP/EXP
MACK MOLDING CO INC
(*Suby of* MACK GROUP INC) ★
608 Warm Brook Rd, Arlington, VT 05250-8570
Tel (802) 375-2511 *Founded/Ownrshp* 1997
Sales 249.8MM^E *EMP* 1,000
SIC 3089 3577 Plastic processing; Computer peripheral equipment; Plastic processing; Computer peripheral equipment
Pr: Donald S Kendall III
Pr: Jeff Somple
**Pr:* Jeffrey Somple
**VP:* Randy Boduch
Prgrm Mgr: Tom McMahon
Dept Mgr: Martin Drobek
Genl Mgr: Don Boucher
QA Dir: Fan Cruickshank
Plnt Mgr: Marc Colety
Ql Cn Mgr: Nate James
Ql Cn Mgr: Sherman McNeil

D-U-N-S 00-790-5656
MACK OIL CO
1202 N 10th St, Duncan, OK 73533-3800
Tel (580) 252-5580 *Founded/Ownrshp* 1946
Sales 33.2MM^E *EMP* 5
SIC 6799 Investors; Investors
Ch Bd: T H Mc Casland III
**Treas:* Noble Means
**Sec:* J R Braught
**VP:* Chris Fowler
**VP:* Randy Smith

MACK SALES SOUTHERN CALIFORNIA
See TEC OF CALIFORNIA INC

D-U-N-S 14-276-4203 IMP
MACK TECHNOLOGIES FLORIDA INC
(*Suby of* MACK TECHNOLOGIES INC) ★
7505 Technology Dr, Melbourne, FL 32904-1574
Tel (321) 725-6993 *Founded/Ownrshp* 2002
Sales 45.5MM^E *EMP* 103
SIC 3672 Printed circuit boards; Printed circuit boards
Pr: John Kovach
Pr: Larry Walk
**Treas:* Randy Boduch
IT Man: Greg Pancratv
IT Man: Rick Pancratz
Board of Directors: William Kendall

D-U-N-S 80-789-5362 IMP
MACK TECHNOLOGIES INC
(*Suby of* MACK GROUP INC) ★
27 Carlisle Rd, Westford, MA 01886-3644
Tel (978) 392-5500 *Founded/Ownrshp* 1997
Sales 181.9MM^E *EMP* 700
SIC 3577 3571 Computer peripheral equipment; Electronic computers; Computer peripheral equipment; Electronic computers
Pr: John Kovach
**Sec:* Florence M Belnap
VP: Steve Barbera
Prgrm Mgr: Thomas Farias
Sls&Mrk Ex: Peter McDonald
Board of Directors: Jeffrey T Somple

MACK TRANSPORT
See MACK INDUSTRIES INC

D-U-N-S 07-970-3640
MACK TRUCK INC
VOLVO
900 National Service Rd, Greensboro, NC 27409
Tel (901) 734-6697 *Founded/Ownrshp* 2015
Sales 36.6MM^E *EMP* 150
SIC 5511 Automobiles, new & used

D-U-N-S 79-693-5930
MACK TRUCK SALES OF CHARLOTTE INC
SOUTHEASTERN LEASING & RENTAL
3609 Trailer Dr, Charlotte, NC 28269-4496
Tel (704) 599-5720 *Founded/Ownrshp* 1996
Sales 47.7MM^E *EMP* 60
SIC 5511 5531 7538 Trucks, tractors & trailers: new & used; Truck equipment & parts; General truck repair; Trucks, tractors & trailers: new & used; Truck equipment & parts; General truck repair
Pr: Ray Mason III
**Pr:* Michael P McMahon
**Treas:* John Kunkel
**VP:* Brad McMahon
Brnch Mgr: William Thomas
Sls Mgr: Don Krom

D-U-N-S 04-232-1117 IMP/EXP
MACK TRUCKS INC
(*Suby of* AB VOLVO)
7825 National Service Rd, Greensboro, NC 27409-9667
Tel (336) 393-4100 *Founded/Ownrshp* 2001
Sales 1.4MMM^E *EMP* 4,500
SIC 3711 3714 5012 6141 6153 7538 Motor trucks, except off-highway, assembly of; Truck tractors for highway use, assembly of; Motor vehicle parts & accessories; Truck tractors; Financing: automobiles, furniture, etc., not a deposit bank; Installment sales finance, other than banks; Financing of dealers by motor vehicle manufacturers organ.; General truck repair; Truck engine repair, except industrial; Motor trucks, except off-highway, assembly of; Truck tractors for highway use, assembly of; Motor vehicle parts & accessories; Truck tractors; Financing: automobiles, furniture, etc., not a deposit bank; Installment sales finance, other than banks; Financing of dealers by motor vehicle manufacturers organ.; General truck repair; Truck engine repair, except industrial
Pr: Stephen Roy
**Pr:* Dennis Slagel
**CEO:* Paul Vikner
**Treas:* Stephen Polzer
**Treas:* David Smith
Treas: Richard Welch
Sr Cor Off: Catherine Ragobert
Ex VP: Guy Clabeau
Ex VP: Dennis R Slagle
Ex VP: Sam Torrence
Ex VP: Mike Werth
Ex VP: Kevin Flaherty
**Sr VP:* Stan Janis
Sr VP: Bruno Linsolas
**Sr VP:* Frank Meehan
Sr VP: Harold W Wiegel
VP: Chad Cross
VP: Jason Hardy
**VP:* Bruce Hollenback
VP: Martin Kleker
VP: Mike Maddox

D-U-N-S 07-514-3230
▲ MACK-CALI REALTY CORP
343 Thornall St, Edison, NJ 08837-2206
Tel (732) 590-1000 *Founded/Ownrshp* 1994
Sales 636.8MM *EMP* 635^E
Tkr Sym CLI *Exch* NYS
SIC 6798 Real estate investment trusts; Real estate investment trusts
CEO: Mitchell E Rudin
**Ch Bd:* William L Mack
Pr: Michael J Demarco
Pr: Michael A Grossman
CEO: Mitchell E Rudin
CFO: Anthony Krug
Chf Inves: Ricardo Cardoso
Ex VP: Christopher Delorenzo
VP: Anthony P Decaro Jr
VP: Bill Donaleski
VP: Frank Shea
VP: Daniel Wagner
Board of Directors: Alan S Bernikow, Kenneth M Duberstein, Nathan Gantcher, Jonathan Litt, David S Mack, Alan G Philibosian, Irvin D Reid, Vincent Tese, Roy J Zuckerberg

D-U-N-S 78-424-2518
MACK-CALI REALTY L P
4 Becker Farm Rd Ste 104, Roseland, NJ 07068-1734
Tel (973) 577-2472 *Founded/Ownrshp* 1998
Sales 636.8MM *EMP* 2
SIC 6798 Real estate investment trusts; Real estate investment trusts
CEO: Mitchell Hersh
Pr: Mitchell E Hersh

D-U-N-S 16-149-5775 IMP
MACKAY COMMUNICATIONS INC
MACKAY MARINE
3691 Trust Dr, Raleigh, NC 27616-2955
Tel (919) 850-3000 *Founded/Ownrshp* 1895
Sales 61.5MM^E *EMP* 140
Accts Dixon Hughes Pllc
SIC 5088 7699 Navigation equipment & supplies; Nautical & navigational instrument repair; Navigation equipment & supplies; Nautical & navigational instrument repair
Pr: Ben Pratt
**Pr:* Jeff Schlacks
**CFO:* David Eckstine
**VP:* David Lemoine
**VP:* John Marra
IT Man: Kevin Aycock
VP Opers: Karen Harris
Mktg Mgr: Sue Rosen

D-U-N-S 80-315-5365
MACKAY JOINT SCHOOL DIST 182
JOINT SCHOOL DIST 128
411 Rose Ave, Mackay, ID 83251-7702
Tel (208) 588-2896 *Founded/Ownrshp* 1996
Sales 121.2MM *EMP* 36
Accts Balukoff Lindstrom & Co Pa
SIC 8211 Public elementary & secondary schools; Public elementary & secondary schools
Prin: Brandon Farris

MACKAY MARINE
See MACKAY COMMUNICATIONS INC

D-U-N-S 00-625-6317 EXP
MACKAY MITCHELL ENVELOPE CO LLC (MN)
2100 Elm St Se, Minneapolis, MN 55414-2533
Tel (612) 331-9311 *Founded/Ownrshp* 1959, 2000
Sales 124.3MM^E *EMP* 350
SIC 2677 Envelopes; Envelopes
CFO: Tim Chesiak
VP: Michael Becker
VP: Lee Bjerke
VP: Brian Bomberger
VP: Joseph Claeys
VP: Jack Easton
CIO: Kathy Hawkins
Dir IT: Shawn Foley
IT Man: Joan Samuelson
Web Prj Mg: Mark Larson
VP Opers: Reid Anderson

D-U-N-S 07-522-7934
MACKAY SHIELDS LLC
(*Suby of* NYLIFE LLC) ★
1345 Avenue Of The Americ, New York, NY 10105-3101
Tel (212) 303-6360 *Founded/Ownrshp* 1984
Sales 54.1MM^E *EMP* 136^E
SIC 6282 Investment advisory service; Investment advisory service
CEO: Jeffrey Phlegar
Ch Bd: Ravi Akhoury
Ofcr: Lucille Protas
Assoc Dir: Steven Caiazzo
Assoc Dir: Ryan Downey
Assoc Dir: Patrick Fennessey
Assoc Dir: Michael Griz
Assoc Dir: Sharon Manza
Assoc Dir: Nunzia Mazzoccoli
Assoc Dir: Bernardo Mesa
Assoc Dir: Brian Nelan
Assoc Dir: Brenda Rippe
Assoc Dir: Greg Schellenberg

MACKENTHUN'S COUNTY MARKET
See KM SUPERMARKETS INC

MACKENZIE DOOR COMPANY
See MACKENZIE GROUP INC

MACKENZIE ENVIRONMENTAL SVCS
See ET MACKENZIE CO

MACKENZIE FORD
See MACKENZIE MOTOR CO

D-U-N-S 00-253-1929
MACKENZIE GROUP INC (NY)
MACKENZIE DOOR COMPANY
4900 W Side Ave, North Bergen, NJ 07047-6411
Tel (212) 619-1885 *Founded/Ownrshp* 1944
Sales 23.1MM^E *EMP* 108
Accts Mcgrath Doyly And Phair
SIC 1751 1731 Window & door (prefabricated) installation; Electronic controls installation
Pr: Roger Soucek
**Treas:* John Hoopingarner
**VP:* Scott Mackenzie
VP: Hal Ottenstein
Opers Mgr: Ron Roeder

MACKENZIE KECK CONSTRUCTION
See MACKENZIE KECK INC

D-U-N-S 83-886-0708
MACKENZIE KECK INC
MACKENZIE KECK CONSTRUCTION
434 Sand Shore Rd Ste 2, Hackettstown, NJ 07840-5520
Tel (973) 298-8000 *Founded/Ownrshp* 1992
Sales 33.8MM^E *EMP* 65
SIC 1542 Nonresidential construction
CEO: Daniel Keck
**Pr:* Vikram K Reddi
**Pr:* Mike Stanley
VP: Dennis Collinson
Ex Dir: Seth Cubbage

D-U-N-S 02-765-5562
MACKENZIE MOTOR CO
MACKENZIE FORD
4151 Se Tualatin Vly Hwy, Hillsboro, OR 97123-7951
Tel (503) 693-1133 *Founded/Ownrshp* 1987
Sales 94.9MM^E *EMP* 250
SIC 5511 5521 Automobiles, new & used; Used car dealers; Automobiles, new & used; Used car dealers
Off Mgr: Lisa Bishops
Dir IT: Dave Leslie
Sls Mgr: Bill Huff
Sls Mgr: Shaun Weber

D-U-N-S 11-689-5173 IMP/EXP
MACKENZIE-CHILDS LLC
3260 State Route 90, Aurora, NY 13026-9769
Tel (315) 364-7567 *Founded/Ownrshp* 2008
Sales 40.1MM^E *EMP* 165
SIC 3263 2512 2511 Cookware, fine earthenware; Upholstered household furniture; Wood household furniture; Cookware, fine earthenware; Upholstered household furniture; Wood household furniture
CEO: Lee Feldman
**CFO:* Howard Cohen
CFO: John Vale
Exec: Brian Parent
Creative D: Rebecca Proctor
Dir IT: Shannon O'Brien
IT Man: Sarah Vaivoda
Web Dev: Josh Nacman
Sfty Dirs: Kevin Grish
Sales Exec: Jennifer Ellsworth

D-U-N-S 10-867-7444
MACKIN BOOK CO
MACKIN LIBRARY MEDIA
3505 County Road 42 W, Burnsville, MN 55306-3803
Tel (952) 895-9540 *Founded/Ownrshp* 1985
Sales 173.6MM^E *EMP* 350^E
SIC 5192 Books; Books
CEO: Randal Heise
**VP:* Kay M Heise
Comm Dir: Troy Mikell
Telecom Ex: Todd Ballwig
Sftwr Eng: Meyers Gordon
Mfg Dir: Paul Duncan
Natl Sales: Ryan C Thomas
Sales Asso: Mark Caldwell
Sales Asso: Susan Dalton
Sales Asso: Bob Dearen
Sales Asso: Jennifer Maydole

MACKIN LIBRARY MEDIA
See MACKIN BOOK CO

MACKINAC FINANCIAL
See MBANK

D-U-N-S 01-028-7548
▲ MACKINAC FINANCIAL CORP
130 S Cedar St, Manistique, MI 49854-1438
Tel (888) 343-8147 *Founded/Ownrshp* 1974
Sales NA *EMP* 133^E
Accts Plante & Moran Pllc Auburn H
Tkr Sym MFNC *Exch* NAS
SIC 6022 State commercial banks; State commercial banks
Ch Bd: Paul D Tobias
**Pr:* Kelly W George
CFO: Ernie R Krueger
VP: Laura Garvin
VP: Jennifer Stempki

D-U-N-S 03-017-9253
MACKINAC STRAITS HEALTH SYSTEM INC (MI)
MACKINAC STRAITS HOSPITAL AND
1140 N State St Ste 1762, Saint Ignace, MI 49781-1048
Tel (906) 643-8585 *Founded/Ownrshp* 2006
Sales 31.4MM *EMP* 280
SIC 8062 8051 Skilled nursing care facilities; General medical & surgical hospitals; General medical & surgical hospitals; Skilled nursing care facilities
CEO: Rod Nelson

MACKINAC STRAITS HOSPITAL AND
See MACKINAC STRAITS HEALTH SYSTEM INC

MACKINNON EQUIPMENT & SERVICES
See ADM VENTURES INC

D-U-N-S 03-238-4018
MACKOUL DISTRIBUTORS INC
MACKOUL FOODS
3425 N Main St, Jacksonville, FL 32206-2107
Tel (904) 355-2721 *Founded/Ownrshp* 1910
Sales 29.5MM^E *EMP* 82
SIC 5145 5411 5122 5113 5149 5194

MACKOUL FOODS
See MACKOUL DISTRIBUTORS INC

D-U-N-S 04-342-7855
MACKS OIL INC
577 Belle Acres Ln, Bastian, VA 24314-5335
Tel (276) 688-3902 *Founded/Ownrshp* 1962
Sales 27.9MM *EMP* 5
SIC 5172 Petroleum products; Petroleum products
Pr: Malcolm C Saunders
**Sec:* Richard Saunders
**VP:* Robert Saunders

MACK'S PRAIRIE WINGS
See MACKS SPORT SHOP LLLP

D-U-N-S 03-564-5522
MACKS SPORT SHOP LLLP (AR)
MACK'S PRAIRIE WINGS
2335 Highway 63 N, Stuttgart, AR 72160-3048
Tel (870) 673-6969 *Founded/Ownrshp* 1944, 1973
Sales 32.3MM^E *EMP* 115
SIC 5941 5961

MACL
See MID AMERICA CLINICAL LABORATORIES LLC

D-U-N-S 02-456-6710
MACLASKEY OIL FIELD SERVICES
12600 Cleburne Hwy, Weatherford, TX 76086
Tel (817) 594-8073 *Founded/Ownrshp* 2012

Sales 31.5MM^E *EMP* 73
SIC 5172 Crude oil
CEO: Kelly Maclaskey
**Sec:* Stacy Maclaskey

MACLEAN - DIXIE
See MACLEAN POWER LLC

MACLEAN CURTIS
See CURTIS L MACLEAN L C

MACLEAN FASTENERS
See MACLEAN-FOGG CO

D-U-N-S 01-866-8392
MACLEAN FIBERGLASS
(*Suby of* MACLEAN FASTENERS) ★
101 Park Ave, Newberry, SC 29108-1773
Tel (803) 276-4462 *Founded/Ownrshp* 1981, 1995
Sales 24.6MM^E *EMP* 74
SIC 3089 3082 Vulcanized fiber plates, sheets, rods or tubes; Unsupported plastics profile shapes
Pr: Dominic Diflippo
**VP:* Jerry Lysaght

MACLEAN, HEATHER CNM NP
See NORTH BEND MEDICAL CENTER INC

D-U-N-S 80-818-8903 IMP
MACLEAN POWER LLC
MACLEAN - DIXIE
(*Suby of* MACLEAN FASTENERS) ★
481 Munn Rd E Ste 300, Fort Mill, SC 29715-8462
Tel (847) 455-0014 *Founded/Ownrshp* 1998
Sales 119.3MM^E *EMP* 409^E
SIC 3493 Helical springs, hot wound: railroad equipment etc.
Pr: Tom Smith
Pdt Mgr: Steve Petres

MACLEAN POWER SYSTEMS
See MACLEAN POWER TN LLC

D-U-N-S 07-866-9547 IMP
MACLEAN POWER TN LLC
MACLEAN POWER SYSTEMS
(*Suby of* MACLEAN FASTENERS) ★
1465 Industrial Park Dr, Trenton, TN 38382-3937
Tel (847) 566-0010 *Founded/Ownrshp* 2012
Sales 197.0MM^E *EMP* 1,000
SIC 3679 Electronic loads & power supplies; Electronic loads & power supplies
Genl Mgr: Dhruva Mandal

MACLEAN VEHICLE SYSTEMS
See MACLEAN-FOGG COMPONENT SOLUTIONS LLC

D-U-N-S 00-508-6376 IMP
MACLEAN-FOGG CO
MACLEAN FASTENERS
1000 Allanson Rd, Mundelein, IL 60060-3804
Tel (847) 566-0010 *Founded/Ownrshp* 1925
Sales 1.4MMM^E *EMP* 4,500
SIC 3678 3452 3089 3061 3492 3451 Electronic connectors; Nuts, metal; Bolts, metal; Screws, metal; Plastic processing; Automotive rubber goods (mechanical); Fluid power valves & hose fittings; Screw machine products; Electronic connectors; Nuts, metal; Bolts, metal; Screws, metal; Plastic processing; Automotive rubber goods (mechanical); Fluid power valves & hose fittings; Screw machine products
**Pr:* Duncan A L Maclean
**CFO:* George H Cook
Ex VP: Gary Sullo
VP: Tom Macdonald
VP: Rob Whitney
Prgrm Mgr: Christian Muehlich
**Off Admin:* Brian Duffy
Ql Cn Mgr: Pratik Shah
Board of Directors: Andrew Silvernail, Paul F Anderson, Dean Gestal, Stanford J Goldblatt, Stephen M Gordon, Juergen Harnisch, Thomas R Hodgson, Barry L Maclean, David B Maclean, Duncan Maclean

D-U-N-S 13-329-3287 IMP
MACLEAN-FOGG COMPONENT SOLUTIONS LLC
MACLEAN VEHICLE SYSTEMS
(*Suby of* MACLEAN FASTENERS) ★
1000 Allanson Rd, Mundelein, IL 60060-3804
Tel (847) 566-0010 *Founded/Ownrshp* 2000
Sales 47.9MM^E *EMP* 130
SIC 5531 Automotive parts
VP: Duncan Maclean
**VP:* George Pazdirek

D-U-N-S 79-455-8390 IMP
MACLEAN-FOGG COMPONENT SOLUTIONS LLC
(*Suby of* MACLEAN FASTENERS) ★
1000 Allanson Rd, Mundelein, IL 60060-3804
Tel (248) 280-0880 *Founded/Ownrshp* 1998
Sales 62.9MM^E *EMP* 125^E
SIC 5085 Fasteners, industrial: nuts, bolts, screws, etc.; Fasteners, industrial: nuts, bolts, screws, etc.

MACLELLAN INDUSTRIAL SERVICE
See MACLELLAN INTEGRATED SERVICES INC

D-U-N-S 88-436-2302
MACLELLAN INTEGRATED SERVICES INC
MACLELLAN INDUSTRIAL SERVICE
3120 Wall St Ste 100, Lexington, KY 40513-1833
Tel (859) 219-5400 *Founded/Ownrshp* 2001
Sales 70.1MM^E *EMP* 500
SIC 7349 Cleaning service, industrial or commercial; Cleaning service, industrial or commercial
Pr: Jeffrey K Betzoldt
CFO: Jessica Green
**CFO:* Dwight E Hannah
**Sec:* Sanjay Singh
Comm Man: Ken Ruiz
VP Opers: John Evans
Site Mgr: Brent Hilley

D-U-N-S 83-103-1737
MACLEOD CONSTRUCTION INC
CONCRETE PUMPING BY MACLEOD
4293 Racing Dr, Denver, NC 28037-6241
Tel (704) 483-3580 *Founded/Ownrshp* 1987
Sales 38.7MM^E *EMP* 270
SIC 3273 1611 Ready-mixed concrete; Grading; Ready-mixed concrete; Grading
Pr: Robert Macleod
**Sec:* Judith Macleod
**VP:* Lorne Macleod
Off Mgr: Sue Werth

MACMILLAN
See HOLTZBRINCK PUBLISHERS LLC

D-U-N-S 95-973-7925 IMP/EXP
MACMILLAN HOLDINGS LLC
M P S
(*Suby of* HOLTZBRINCK PUBLISHERS HOLDINGS LIMITED)
175 5th Ave, New York, NY 10010-7703
Tel (646) 307-5151 *Founded/Ownrshp* 1998
Sales 418.0MM^E *EMP* 1,668
SIC 2721 2731

D-U-N-S 03-233-7594 IMP/EXP
MACMILLAN OIL CO OF FLORIDA INC
2955 E 11th Ave, Hialeah, FL 33013-3599
Tel (305) 691-7814 *Founded/Ownrshp* 1995
Sales 106.9MM^E *EMP* 45
SIC 5172 Petroleum products; Petroleum products
Pr: Amancio Alonso
VP: Frank Saldana
Genl Mgr: Danny Alonso
Genl Mgr: William Putnam

D-U-N-S 11-850-3549 IMP
MACMILLAN PUBLISHERS INC
(*Suby of* MACMILLAN LIMITED)
175 5th Ave Ste 400, New York, NY 10010-7726
Tel (646) 307-5151 *Founded/Ownrshp* 1982
Sales 136.2MM^E *EMP* 1,200
Accts Ernst & Young Llp
SIC 2731 5192 Books: publishing only; Books; Books: publishing only; Books
CEO: John Sargent
CFO: Libby Marenco
**Treas:* Mike Ross
Ofcr: Tammie Davis
Ofcr: Dinah Spence
Sr VP: Jamie Demas
Sr VP: Stephanie Liang
VP: Jaime Ariza
VP: Erin Coffey
VP: Devin Luna
VP: Tom Stouras
**VP:* Philip Swartz
VP: Cathrin Vischer
Board of Directors: Nicholas G Beam Shaw

D-U-N-S 05-018-1098 IMP/EXP
MACMILLAN-PIPER INC
1762 6th Ave S, Seattle, WA 98134-1609
Tel (206) 624-5135 *Founded/Ownrshp* 1969
Sales 20.4MM^E *EMP* 104
SIC 4783

D-U-N-S 01-892-2427
MACMILLIN CO INC
NEW ENGLAND CRANE SERVICE
(*Suby of* DEW) ★
17 Elm St Ste 2, Keene, NH 03431-3417
Tel (603) 352-3070 *Founded/Ownrshp* 2012
Sales 21.4MM *EMP* 45
Accts Blake Hurley Mccallum & Conley
SIC 1542 1541 Commercial & office building, new construction; Commercial & office buildings, renovation & repair; Hospital construction; Industrial buildings, new construction; Renovation, remodeling & repairs: industrial buildings; Commercial & office building, new construction; Commercial & office buildings, renovation & repair; Hospital construction; Industrial buildings, new construction; Renovation, remodeling & repairs: industrial buildings
CEO: William C Walker
**Pr:* Tad M Schrantz
**Treas:* Jane Stabler
**VP:* Steven Horton
**VP:* Arthur J Lagois
**VP:* Peter Tremblay
IT Man: Larry Woolson

D-U-N-S 01-894-9354 EXP
MACMULKIN CHEVROLET INC
3 Marmon Dr, Nashua, NH 03060-5205
Tel (603) 888-1121 *Founded/Ownrshp* 1980
Sales 32.2MM^E *EMP* 80
SIC 5511 Automobiles, new & used; Automobiles, new & used
Pr: Bernard J Thompson Sr
**Treas:* Nicholas Saykaly
**VP:* Bernard J Thompson Jr
**VP:* Jean M Thompson
**VP:* Jeffrey P Thompson

MACMURRAY PACIFIC
See WILDENRADT-MCMURRAY INC

MACNEAL HOSPITAL
See VHS OF ILLINOIS INC

D-U-N-S 07-389-2267
MACNEILL GROUP INC
(*Suby of* TEAM FOCUS INSURANCE GROUP LLC) ★
1300 Sawgrs Corp Pkwy, Sunrise, FL 33323-2826
Tel (954) 331-4800 *Founded/Ownrshp* 2000
Sales 30.0MM *EMP* 213
Accts Plante & Moran Pllc Chicago
SIC 8741 6411 Management services; Insurance agents, brokers & service; Management services; Insurance agents, brokers & service
Ch: Douglas W Bullington
**Pr:* Kevin M Tromer
**COO:* Michael Steinman
**CFO:* James Blake
Sr VP: Laura Decespedes
Sr VP: John Soutar
**VP:* Suzanne Brauer
**VP:* Nanette Brunson
**VP:* Bradford Budd
**VP:* Gustavo Frenandez
VP: Brian Harrison
Board of Directors: Douglas Bullington, Kevin Tromer

D-U-N-S 00-221-1613 IMP
MACO BAG CORP (NY)
412 Van Buren St, Newark, NY 14513-9205
Tel (315) 226-1000 *Founded/Ownrshp* 1929
Sales 37.6MM^E *EMP* 140
SIC 3081 2673 Plastic film & sheet; Plastic & pliofilm bags; Plastic film & sheet; Plastic & pliofilm bags
Ch Bd: J Scott Miller
**Pr:* Craig Miller
**Sec:* Susan Miller
Sfty Dirs: Bob Finley
Opers Mgr: Doug Kirchoff
Ql Cn Mgr: Ernest Cole
Ql Cn Mgr: Karen Marcus
Sls Mgr: Theresa Hinckley

MACO DEVELOPMENT COMPANY
See MACO MANAGEMENT CO INC

D-U-N-S 19-827-0076
MACO MANAGEMENT CO INC
MACO DEVELOPMENT COMPANY
111 N Main St, Clarkton, MO 63837-9241
Tel (573) 448-3000 *Founded/Ownrshp* 1977
Sales 21.3MM^E *EMP* 500
SIC 6513 Apartment building operators; Apartment building operators
Pr: James K Maddox
**Sec:* Sheila Cobb
**VP:* John W Maddox

MACOM
See MINDSPEED TECHNOLOGIES INC

D-U-N-S 06-189-0612
MACOMB COMMUNITY COLLEGE
14500 E 12 Mile Rd, Warren, MI 48088-3896
Tel (586) 445-7306 *Founded/Ownrshp* 1954
Sales 126.0MM *EMP* 2,000^E
SIC 8221 College, except junior; College, except junior
Pr: James Jacobs
Pr: Jill Little
COO: Christine Guarino
CFO: Arthur Knapp
**VP:* Elizabeth Argiri
VP: James Sawyer
VP: Charles Thomas
Assoc Dir: Holger Ekanger
CIO: Norman Schlafmann
CTO: Sus Jondreau
IT Man: Richard McMillan

D-U-N-S 02-265-9916
MACOMB COMMUNITY UNIT SCHOOL DISTRICT 185
323 W Washington St, Macomb, IL 61455-2118
Tel (309) 833-4161 *Founded/Ownrshp* 2001
Sales 24.8MM *EMP* 250
Accts Wermer Rogers Doran & Ruzon
SIC 8211 Public elementary & secondary schools; Public elementary & secondary schools
Treas: Liz Provine

MACOMB DAILY
See 21ST CENTURY NEWSPAPERS INC

D-U-N-S 08-394-2607 IMP
MACOMB GROUP INC (MI)
MACOMB PIPE & SUPPLY
6600 15 Mile Rd, Sterling Heights, MI 48312-4512
Tel (586) 274-4100 *Founded/Ownrshp* 1977, 1991
Sales 129.9MM *EMP* 307
Accts Gordon Advisors Pc Troy Mi
SIC 5085 Industrial supplies; Valves & fittings; Industrial supplies; Valves & fittings
CEO: William McGivern Jr
**Ex VP:* Keith Schatko
**VP:* Dick Dixon
**VP:* Steve Dixon
**VP:* James Tucker
Brnch Mgr: Zackariah Cook
Brnch Mgr: Scott Geiger
Brnch Mgr: Gary Phillips
Genl Mgr: Selena Carli
IT Man: Doug Okamoto
Opers Mgr: Michael Smith

D-U-N-S 07-841-7169
MACOMB INTERMEDIATE SCHOOL DISTRICT
MISD
44001 Garfield Rd, Clinton Township, MI 48038-1100
Tel (586) 228-3479 *Founded/Ownrshp* 1951
Sales 349.4MM^E *EMP* 14,000
SIC 8211 Public combined elementary & secondary school; Public special education school; School for the retarded; School for physically handicapped; Public combined elementary & secondary school; Public special education school; School for the retarded; School for physically handicapped
CEO: Paul Bodiya
Bd of Dir: Gus Demas
Bd of Dir: Ruth Green
Bd of Dir: Elaine Martin
Bd of Dir: Michael Scott
Bd of Dir: Mark Titus
Bd of Dir: Jennifer White
Exec: Henry Anderson
Exec: Victor Balaj
Exec: Sherry Kenward
Exec: Joseph McDonald

D-U-N-S 95-901-4556
MACOMB OAKLAND REGIONAL CENTER INC
16200 19 Mile Rd, Clinton Township, MI 48038-1103
Tel (586) 263-8700 *Founded/Ownrshp* 1972
Sales 198.2MM *EMP* 300
SIC 8093 Mental health clinic, outpatient; Mental health clinic, outpatient
CEO: Gerald Provencal
COO: Dennis Buildiong
**CFO:* Richard Stone
VP: Carrie Gerdeman
VP: John Torrone
CIO: Dan Manzardo
IT Man: Debbie Conway
IT Man: Mark Morehouse
Psych: Hugh Ransley

MACOMB PIPE & SUPPLY
See MACOMB GROUP INC

D-U-N-S 03-377-9497
MACON CIGAR & TOBACCO CO
MCT WHOLESALE
575 12th St, Macon, GA 31201-3537
Tel (478) 743-2236 *Founded/Ownrshp* 1946
Sales 56.7MM^E *EMP* 50
Accts Mcnair Mclemore Middlebrooks
SIC 5194 5141 5145 Tobacco & tobacco products; Cigars; Groceries, general line; Confectionery; Tobacco & tobacco products; Cigars; Groceries, general line; Confectionery
Pr: Thomas Alfred Sams Jr
**VP:* Kenneth Sams

D-U-N-S 02-990-2194
MACON CONSUMERS INC
C&R SUPERMARKET
206 N Rollins St, Macon, MO 63552-1589
Tel (660) 385-2151 *Founded/Ownrshp* 1967
Sales 56.4MM^E *EMP* 412^E
SIC 5411 Grocery stores, chain; Grocery stores, chain
Pr: Richard Ramsey
**Treas:* Jerry Edwards
**VP:* Mark Thomas

D-U-N-S 11-803-8777
MACON COUNTY GREYHOUND PARK INC
VICTORYLAND
8680 County Road 40, Shorter, AL 36075-4403
Tel (334) 727-0540 *Founded/Ownrshp* 1983
Sales 13.9MM^E *EMP* 400
SIC 7948 Dog racing; Dog racing
Pr: Milton E McGregor
**CFO:* Lee Yates
**VP:* Monte Russell
Genl Mgr: James Baker
Genl Mgr: Jim Gartland

D-U-N-S 07-979-8909
MACON COUNTY SCHOOL DISTRICT
31 Buck Creek Bypass Rd, Oglethorpe, GA 31068
Tel (478) 472-8188 *Founded/Ownrshp* 2015
Sales 11.2MM^E *EMP* 357^E
SIC 8211 Public elementary & secondary schools

D-U-N-S 10-007-3113
MACON COUNTY SCHOOL DISTRICT
501 College St, Lafayette, TN 37083-1706
Tel (615) 666-2125 *Founded/Ownrshp* 1950
Sales 15.7MM^E *EMP* 500
SIC 8211 8351 Public elementary & secondary schools; Child day care services; Public elementary & secondary schools; Child day care services

D-U-N-S 19-301-6565
MACON COUNTY SCHOOL DISTRICT
1202 Old Murphy Rd, Franklin, NC 28734-9111
Tel (828) 524-8771 *Founded/Ownrshp* 1840
Sales NA *EMP* 700
SIC 9411 8211 ; Elementary & secondary schools; ; Elementary & secondary schools
Bd of Dir: Stephanie McCall
Info Man: Bonnylin Covey
Info Man: Chanda Wilson
HC Dir: Jennifer Garrett

D-U-N-S 83-966-9181
MACON DEMPSEY ASSOCIATES LLC
DEMPSEY MACON ASSOCIATES
268 Summer St Fl 4, Boston, MA 02210-1188
Tel (617) 482-5500 *Founded/Ownrshp* 1997
Sales 10.4MM^E *EMP* 350
SIC 6512 6513 Nonresidential building operators; Apartment building operators; Nonresidential building operators; Apartment building operators
Ch: Mel Barkan
**Pr:* Bill Dischino

D-U-N-S 00-696-6642
MACON ELECTRIC COOP INC (MO)
31571 Business Route 36 E, Macon, MO 63552-3806
Tel (660) 385-3157 *Founded/Ownrshp* 1938
Sales 24.3MM *EMP* 46
Accts Schmidt & Company Llc Blue Sp
SIC 4911 1731 Distribution, electric power; Electrical work; Distribution, electric power; Electrical work
Genl Mgr: Wayne Hackman
Sr VP: Angela Hughes
Comm Man: Kami Mohn
Genl Mgr: Doug Drake
Opers Mgr: Bruce Wieberg

MACON INVESTMENT SERVICES
See ENTEGRA BANK

D-U-N-S 08-217-4129
MACON STATE COLLEGE FOUNDATION INC
BOARD OF REGNTS OF THE UNVRSTY
(*Suby of* BOARD OF REGENTS OF UNIVERSITY SYSTEM OF GEORGIA) ★
100 University Pkwy, Macon, GA 31206-5100
Tel (478) 471-2800 *Founded/Ownrshp* 1968
Sales 26.5MM^E *EMP* 303
SIC 8221 8222 Colleges universities & professional schools; Junior college; Colleges universities & professional schools; Junior college
CEO: Sue Chipman
**CFO:* Dewayne Foskey
CFO: Levy Youmans Jr
Assoc VP: Jeff Stewart III
VP: Nancy Stroud
Dir IT: Jackie McCann
Psych: Ruth Hagemann

D-U-N-S 03-002-4681
MACON SUPPLY INC (MT)
2730 Gabel Rd, Billings, MT 59102-7334
Tel (406) 245-5107 *Founded/Ownrshp* 1976
Sales 33.0MM^E *EMP* 48
SIC 5082 5211 Contractors' materials; Lumber & other building materials; Contractors' materials; Lumber & other building materials
Pr: Thomas Moffet
VP Opers: Blake Moffet

D-U-N-S 00-327-5500
■ **MACON TELEGRAPH PUBLISHING CO INC**
(*Suby of* MCCLATCHY CO) ★
487 Cherry St Ste 100, Macon, GA 31201-7992
Tel (478) 743-4130 *Founded/Ownrshp* 2006
Sales 49.9MM^E *EMP* 270
SIC 2711 Newspapers; Newspapers
Pr: Pamela Browning
**CEO:* George McCanless
VP: Terry Geiger
**VP:* Sherrie Marshall

D-U-N-S 02-745-6656
MACON WATER AUTHORITY
790 2nd St, Macon, GA 31201-6800
Tel (478) 464-5600 *Founded/Ownrshp* 1966
Sales 136.5MM^E *EMP* 200
Accts Mauldin And Jenkins Llc Maco
SIC 4941 4952 Water supply; Sewerage systems; Water supply; Sewerage systems
Ch Bd: Frank C Amerson Jr
CFO: Guy Boyle
Sr VP: Pat Topping
Snr Mgr: Joel Herndon

D-U-N-S 09-458-4273
MACONAQUAH SCHOOL DISTRICT
7932 S Strawtown Pike, Bunker Hill, IN 46914-9667
Tel (765) 689-9131 *Founded/Ownrshp* 1963
Sales 69.0MM *EMP* 300
SIC 8211 9411 Public elementary & secondary schools; School board; Administration of educational programs; Public elementary & secondary schools; School board; Administration of educational programs
Bd of Dir: Greg Bevington
Bd of Dir: Shelly Leary
Bd of Dir: David Scheblo
Ofcr: Keith Dinn
MIS Dir: Steve Grate
Netwrk Eng: Chris Percival
Schl Brd P: Robert Harkema

D-U-N-S 04-012-9142
MACOUPIN ENERGY LLC
1 Metropolitan Sq # 2600, Saint Louis, MO 63102-2723
Tel (314) 932-6112 *Founded/Ownrshp* 2008
Sales 29.0MM^E *EMP* 115^E
SIC 1241 Coal mining services

D-U-N-S 01-837-2990
MACPHERSON ENERGY CORP
100 Wilshire Blvd Ste 800, Santa Monica, CA 90401-1141
Tel (310) 452-3880 *Founded/Ownrshp* 1994
Sales 28.0MM^E *EMP* 30
SIC 1382 Oil & gas exploration services
Pr: Donald Macpherson Jr
**VP:* Scott Macpherson

D-U-N-S 00-633-5210
MACPHERSON OIL CO (CA)
(*Suby of* MACPHERSON ENERGY CORP) ★
100 Wilshire Blvd Ste 800, Santa Monica, CA 90401-1141
Tel (310) 452-3880 *Founded/Ownrshp* 1981, 1994
Sales 28.0MM^E *EMP* 30
SIC 1382 Oil & gas exploration services
CEO: Donald R Macpherson
**CFO:* Steve Wilson
**Sr VP:* Scott Macpherson
**VP:* Brad Williams

D-U-N-S 04-184-1057
MACPHERSON WESTERN TOOL & SUPPLY CO INC
203 Lawrence Dr Ste D, Livermore, CA 94551-5152
Tel (925) 443-8665 *Founded/Ownrshp* 1966
Sales 67.5MM^E *EMP* 190
SIC 5251 5085 5084 Tools; Tools; Industrial machinery & equipment; Tools; Tools; Industrial machinery & equipment
Pr: Jerry L Gerardot
**Sec:* Judy Gerardot
Brnch Mgr: Tim Bicha
Brnch Mgr: Connie Cottrell
Brnch Mgr: Randy Stanfield
IT Man: Mike Hagan
IT Man: Kevin Young
Opers Mgr: Bryan Meyers
Sls Mgr: Donna Byrd
Sales Asso: Don Ackerman
Sales Asso: Paul Aquilina

MACPHERSON'S
See ART SUPPLY ENTERPRISES INC

D-U-N-S 19-017-5427
MACPIE LLC
AVONDALE TOYOTA
10005 W Papago Fwy, Avondale, AZ 85323-5308
Tel (623) 936-7700 *Founded/Ownrshp* 2005
Sales 24.1MM^E *EMP* 70
SIC 5511 Automobiles, new & used; Automobiles, new & used
Mktg Dir: John Rondeau
Sls Mgr: Chris Hughes

D-U-N-S 82-812-2064
MACQUARIE BARNETT LLC
(*Suby of* MACQUARIE HOLDINGS (USA) INC) ★
500 Dallas St Ste 3100, Houston, TX 77002-4711
Tel (713) 275-6200 *Founded/Ownrshp* 2007
Sales 48.3MM^E *EMP* 623^E
SIC 6211 Security brokers & dealers

D-U-N-S 80-950-1823
MACQUARIE CAPITAL (USA) INC
MACQUARIE CAPITAL FUNDS
(*Suby of* MACQUARIE GROUP LIMITED)
1345 Ave Of The Americas, New York, NY 10105-0302
Tel (212) 231-1000 *Founded/Ownrshp* 2008
Sales 77.5MM^E *EMP* 160^E
SIC 6282 Investment advisory service; Investment advisory service
Pr: Murray Bleach
Sr VP: Natalie Ings
Sr VP: Marc Rosa
VP: Marie Galocha
VP: Guillermo Marroquin
Assoc Dir: Ashok Vishnubhakta
Dir Soc: Gwen Shusterman
Mng Dir: Sean Miller
Brnch Mgr: Brenda Kuhn

D-U-N-S 88-443-9795
MACQUARIE CAPITAL (USA) INC
(*Suby of* MACQUARIE GROUP LIMITED)
125 W 55th St Frnt 3, New York, NY 10019-5936
Tel (212) 231-1537 *Founded/Ownrshp* 2007
Sales 144.0MM^E *EMP* 600^E
SIC 6211 Security brokers & dealers; Security brokers & dealers
Ch Bd: Robert Redmond
V Ch: Rob Redmond
**Pr:* Michael McLauchlan
Sr VP: Saulo Almeida
Sr VP: David Blackford
Sr VP: Sung Chun
Sr VP: Peter Finn
Sr VP: Richard Gordon
Sr VP: Keith Kitagawa
Sr VP: Christina Lee
Sr VP: Heidi Muccifori
Sr VP: Tad Nacheff
Sr VP: Todd Narter
Sr VP: Charles Nuttall-Smith
Sr VP: Francisco Pozo
Sr VP: Andrea Sotgiu
VP: Oliver Bradley
VP: Bill Carcache
VP: William Demas
VP: Sandeep Gopalan
VP: Ray Iardella

MACQUARIE CAPITAL FUNDS
See MACQUARIE CAPITAL (USA) INC

D-U-N-S 79-884-6036
MACQUARIE ENERGY LLC
(*Suby of* MACQUARIE GROUP LIMITED)
500 Dallas St 31, Houston, TX 77002-4800
Tel (713) 275-6100 *Founded/Ownrshp* 2005
Sales 399.2MM^E *EMP* 265
SIC 6221 Natural gas transmission; Commodity traders, contracts; Commodity traders, contracts
CEO: Nicholas O'Kane
**Pr:* Tim Bourn
**Treas:* Trent Byerley
VP: Allan Bounds
**VP:* Matthew D'Agostino
**VP:* David Louw
Assoc Dir: Nathan Salisbury
Mng Dir: Bryan Frey
Dir IT: David Poston

D-U-N-S 92-984-9404
MACQUARIE HOLDINGS (USA) INC
125 W 55th St Fl 8, New York, NY 10019-5369
Tel (212) 231-1000 *Founded/Ownrshp* 2000
Sales 839.6MM^E *EMP* 1,500^E
SIC 6211 Security brokers & dealers; Security brokers & dealers
CEO: Oliver Yates
**Ch Bd:* Nicholas James Butcher
**Pr:* Alyssa Bonebrake
COO: Sarosh Irani
Sr VP: Jaime Gualy
VP: Meredith Gordon
VP: Samant Jain
Sls Mgr: Bob Richardson

D-U-N-S 17-748-7654 IMP
▲ **MACQUARIE INFRASTRUCTURE CORP**
125 W 55th St, New York, NY 10019-5369
Tel (212) 231-1000 *Founded/Ownrshp* 2004
Sales 1.3MMM *EMP* 3,200^E
Accts Kpmg Llp Dallas Texas
Tkr Sym MIC *Exch* NYS
SIC 5172 4581 4785 7521 4932 Petroleum products; Aircraft maintenance & repair services; Airports & flying fields; Toll road operation; Automobile parking; Outdoor parking services; Indoor parking services; Gas & other services combined; Petroleum products; Aircraft maintenance & repair services; Airports & flying fields; Toll road operation; Automobile parking; Outdoor parking services; Indoor parking services; Gas & other services combined
CEO: James Hooke
**Ch Bd:* Martin Stanley
V Ch: Ray Cosman
CFO: David Mitchell
CFO: Todd Weintraub
Sr VP: Roberta Konicki
VP: Drew Allen
VP: Benjamin Dixon
VP: Scott Elliott
VP: Terry Embury
VP: Scoff Hayduk
VP: Martha Jones
VP: David Light
VP: Dominic Magnabosco
VP: Frank Ross
VP: David Simpson
VP: Gary Underwood
VP: Jesse Ushewokunze
VP: Nandha Visvanathan
VP: Rodney Woodhouse-Gully
Assoc Dir: Matthew Dagostino
Board of Directors: Norman H Brown Jr, George W Carmany III, Henry E Lentz, William H Webb

D-U-N-S 07-965-4048
MACQUARIE INFRASTRUCTURE PARTNERS II INTERNATIONAL LP
125 W 55th St, New York, NY 10019-5369
Tel (212) 231-1310 *Founded/Ownrshp* 2008
Sales 724.0MM^E *EMP* 1,076^E
SIC 6282 Investment advisory service
CEO: Christopher J Leslie

D-U-N-S 60-358-4905 IMP
MACRO PLASTICS INC
2250 Huntington Dr, Fairfield, CA 94533-9732
Tel (707) 437-1200 *Founded/Ownrshp* 1991
Sales 40.2MM^E *EMP* 100
SIC 3089 Injection molding of plastics; Injection molding of plastics
Ch: David A Williams
**Pr:* Warren McDonald
**CFO:* Steve Moya
CFO: Paul Saubolle
Bd of Dir: Dan Jakubiak
**VP:* Jeff Mitchell
**VP:* Peter Piccioli
**VP:* Wendell Smith
Sls Mgr: Rob Crawford
Sls Mgr: Michael Ulrich

D-U-N-S 36-157-2394 IMP
MACRO RETAILING INC
SUPER SHOE STORES
601 Dual Hwy, Hagerstown, MD 21740-5901
Tel (301) 722-6563 *Founded/Ownrshp* 2005
Sales 36.3MM^E *EMP* 500^E
SIC 5661 Shoe stores; Shoe stores
Pr: Hary Tierney
**VP:* Ed Kelly

D-U-N-S 83-596-4461 IMP
■ **MACRO RETAILING LLC**
H. H. BROWN RETAIL, INC.
(*Suby of* B H SHOE HOLDINGS INC) ★
10365 Mount Savage Rd Nw, Cumberland, MD 21502-4925
Tel (301) 722-6563 *Founded/Ownrshp* 1994
Sales 86.0MM *EMP* 500
SIC 5661 Shoe stores
Pr: James Issler
**VP:* Marc Hamburg
Opers Mgr: Karen Emerick

D-U-N-S 60-589-7420
MACRO-Z-TECHNOLOGY CO
M Z T
841 E Washington Ave, Santa Ana, CA 92701-3878
Tel (714) 564-1130 *Founded/Ownrshp* 1989
Sales 43.3MM^E *EMP* 100
SIC 1611 1542 8711 Concrete construction: roads, highways, sidewalks, etc.; Commercial & office building contractors; Construction & civil engineering; Concrete construction: roads, highways, sidewalks, etc.; Commercial & office building contractors; Construction & civil engineering
CEO: Bryan J Zatica

D-U-N-S 01-062-6351
▲ **MACROGENICS INC**
9640 Medical Center Dr, Rockville, MD 20850-3368
Tel (301) 251-5172 *Founded/Ownrshp* 2000
Sales 47.8MM *EMP* 166
Accts Ernst & Young Llp Mclean Vir
Tkr Sym MGNX *Exch* NGS
SIC 2834 Pharmaceutical preparations; Pharmaceutical preparations
Pr: Scott Koenig
**Ch Bd:* Paulo Costa
COO: Michael Richman
CFO: James Karrels
Treas: Lynn Cilinski
Bd of Dir: Kenneth Galbraith
Sr VP: Ezio Bonvini
Sr VP: Anastasia Daifotis
Sr VP: Jennie Mather
Sr VP: Kathryn Stein
Sr VP: Jon Wigginton
VP: Randy Bradshaw
VP: Rob Dallimore
VP: Bob Obst
VP: Joseph Panigot
VP: Stanford Stewart
VP: Ronald L Wilder
VP Bus: Eric Risser
Dir Lab: Young Wang
Assoc Dir: Ralph Alderson
Assoc Dir: Mark Bowe
Board of Directors: Matthew Fust, Kenneth Galbraith, Edward Hurwitz, David Stump

D-U-N-S 06-034-5451
■ **MACROLEASE CORP**
CYBEX LEASING SERVICE DIV
(*Suby of* BANK RHODE ISLAND) ★
185 Express St Ste 100, Plainview, NY 11803-2406
Tel (516) 576-9000 *Founded/Ownrshp* 2005
Sales NA *EMP* 44
SIC 6159 Machinery & equipment finance leasing
Pr: Daniel W West
**Ex VP:* Deborah J Lange-Fifer
Ex VP: Salvatore Venuto
**VP:* Barbara Kearon
**VP:* Debbie J Lange
**VP:* Sal Venuto

D-U-N-S 01-069-4602
■ **MACROLINK INC** (CA)
(*Suby of* B/E AEROSPACE INC) ★
25 Scouting Blvd Ste 1, Medford, NY 11763-2243
Tel (631) 924-8265 *Founded/Ownrshp* 1975
Sales 20.0MM^E *EMP* 50
SIC 3823 3577 Computer interface equipment for industrial process control; Computer peripheral equipment
CEO: Mark Cordivari
**Pr:* David Vendor
**VP:* William Goodale
Genl Mgr: Marco Cordibari
IT Man: Pegi Marecek
IT Man: Chris Petersen

Sftwr Eng: Jim English
Mtls Mgr: Dan Genin

D-U-N-S 00-128-3845
MACROMEDIA INC
150 River St, Hackensack, NJ 07601-7110
Tel (201) 646-4000 *Founded/Ownrshp* 1921
Sales 289.5MM^E *EMP* 1,521^E
SIC 2711 2721 Newspapers, publishing & printing; Periodicals; Newspapers, publishing & printing; Periodicals
Ch Bd: Malcolm A Borg
**Treas:* Charles W Gibney
**VP:* Stephen A Borg
Board of Directors: Sandra A Borg, David L Cohen Esq

D-U-N-S 92-608-7735
MACROSOFT INC
2 Sylvan Way Ste 300, Parsippany, NJ 07054-3809
Tel (973) 889-0500 *Founded/Ownrshp* 1992
Sales 26.1MM^E *EMP* 150
Accts Connolly & Company Pc Warr
SIC 7371 8742 4813 7375 Computer software development & applications; Marketing consulting services; ; information retrieval services; Computer software development & applications; Marketing consulting services; ; Information retrieval services
CEO: Dr Ronald Mueller
**Pr:* Dr Edward G Sable
**VP:* Muhammad Basit
**VP:* Basit Qari
VP: G N Shah
Dir IT: Tariq Zamir
Sys Eng: Ruru Rai
Netwrk Eng: Art Sussman

MACS CHESTERFIELD CO
See MID-ATLANTIC CONVENIENCE STORES LLC

MAC'S CONVENIENCE STORES
See SHERMAN V ALLEN INC

D-U-N-S 11-318-1585
MACS CONVENIENCE STORES LLC
DAIRY MART CONVENIENCE STORE
(*Suby of* ALIMENTATION COUCHE-TARD INC)
4080 W Jnathan Moore Pike, Columbus, IN 47201-8667
Tel (812) 379-9227 *Founded/Ownrshp* 2012
Sales 616.6MM^E *EMP* 3,773
SIC 5411 Convenience stores, chain; Convenience stores, chain

MAC'S IGA FOODS
See MCDANIEL FOOD MANAGEMENT INC

D-U-N-S 00-622-3390 IMP
MACS INC
5970 50th Ave S, Moorhead, MN 56560-6011
Tel (218) 233-4600 *Founded/Ownrshp* 1932
Sales 37.2MM^E *EMP* 120
Accts Kevin L Campbell
SIC 5251 5072 Hardware; Hardware
Pr: Chuck McWethy
**Sec:* Marvin Faul
**VP:* Mary McWethy
**Prin:* Mike McWethy

D-U-N-S 04-265-6723
MACS MINIT MART INC
MIDSTATES PETROLEUM
8596 Highway 18, Vernon, AL 35592-5821
Tel (205) 695-0018 *Founded/Ownrshp* 1990
Sales 29.7MM^E *EMP* 61
SIC 5172 Petroleum products
Pr: Richard Mayers
CFO: Lanita Mayers

MAC'S SNACKS
See EVANS FOODS INC

MAC'S STEAK IN THE ROUGH
See FRESQUEZ INC

MACTAC
See MORGAN ADHESIVES CO LLC

MACU
See MID AMERICA CHRISTIAN UNIVERSITY

D-U-N-S 00-330-3633
MACUCH STEEL PRODUCTS INC (GA)
1527 Augusta Ave, Augusta, GA 30901-3465
Tel (706) 823-2420 *Founded/Ownrshp* 1948
Sales 34.9MM^E *EMP* 180
SIC 3441 Fabricated structural metal; Fabricated structural metal
CEO: William L Macuch
**Pr:* Gary L Cowart
VP: Gary Cowart
VP: Mary Hill
VP: Kelly May
Genl Mgr: Lori Kitchens
Genl Mgr: Kevin Pruett
Opers Mgr: Danny Herndon

MACVALLEY OIL COMPANY
See VALLEY FUEL SUPPLY INC

MACY'S
See MACYS.COM INC

D-U-N-S 03-718-3790
■ **MACYS CORPORATE SERVICES INC**
BLOOMINGDALE'S
(*Suby of* MACYS INC) ★
7 W 7th St Ste 1100, Cincinnati, OH 45202-2419
Tel (513) 579-7000 *Founded/Ownrshp* 2006
Sales 112.2MM^E *EMP* 620^E
SIC 5311 Department stores, non-discount; Department stores, non-discount
CEO: Terry J Lundgren
**Pr:* Jeffrey Gennette
**CFO:* Karen M Hoguet
Sls Mgr: Joni Skoglund

D-U-N-S 83-231-1906
■ MACYS CREDIT AND CUSTOMER SERVICES INC
(*Suby of* MACYS RETAIL HOLDINGS INC) ★
9111 Duke Blvd, Mason, OH 45040-8999
Tel (513) 398-5221 *Founded/Ownrshp* 1994
Sales 108.7MM^E *EMP* 3,000
SIC 7389 7322 6141 Credit card service; Adjustment & collection services; Personal credit institutions; Credit card service; Adjustment & collection services; Personal credit institutions
Pr: Michael Gatio
VP: Stephen Avila
VP: Karen Foos
VP: Lisa Goines
VP: Cynthia Walker
VP: Amy Wiandt
Genl Couns: Dennis Broderick

D-U-N-S 60-249-4650 IMP
■ MACYS FLORIDA STORES LLC
(*Suby of* MACYS RETAIL HOLDINGS INC) ★
7 W 7th St Fl 17, Cincinnati, OH 45202-2468
Tel (513) 579-7000 *Founded/Ownrshp* 2008
Sales 560.2MM^E *EMP* 8,273
SIC 5311 Department stores, non-discount; Department stores, non-discount

D-U-N-S 00-698-7135 IMP/EXP
▲ MACYS INC
7 W 7th St, Cincinnati, OH 45202-2424
Tel (513) 579-7000 *Founded/Ownrshp* 1830
Sales 28.1MMM *EMP* 166,900
Tkr Sym M *Exch* NYS
SIC 5311 Department stores, non-discount; Department stores
Ch Bd: Terry J Lundgren
Pr: Jeffrey Gennette
CFO: Karen M Hoguet
Chf Mktg O: Martine Reardon
Ofcr: William S Allen
Ofcr: Timothy Baxter
Ofcr: Robert B Harrison
Ofcr: Jeffrey A Kantor
Ofcr: Molly Langenstein
Ex VP: Joel A Belsky
Ex VP: Dennis J Broderick
Board of Directors: Annie Young-Scrivner, Francis S Blake, Paul C Varga, Stephen F Bollenbach, Craig E Weatherup, John A Bryant, Marna C Whittington, Deirdre P Connelly, Meyer Feldberg, Leslie D Hale, Sara Levinson, Joseph Neubauer, Joyce M Roche

D-U-N-S 83-108-3055
■ MACYS MERCHANDISING CORP
(*Suby of* MACYS RETAIL HOLDINGS INC) ★
7 W 7th St, Cincinnati, OH 45202-2424
Tel (513) 579-7000 *Founded/Ownrshp* 2009
Sales 82.3MM^E *EMP* 1,003
SIC 5311 Department stores, non-discount; Department stores, non-discount
Ch Bd: Jeffrey A Kantor
**Pr:* Terry J Lundgren
Pr: Cathy Rano
VP: Tom Papatoni
**VP:* Susan Robinson
Snr Mgr: Frances Velluzzi

D-U-N-S 36-127-7069 IMP
■ MACYS MERCHANDISING GROUP INC
(*Suby of* MACYS INC) ★
11 Penn Plz Fl 10, New York, NY 10001-2027
Tel (646) 429-6000 *Founded/Ownrshp* 2004
Sales 106.5MM^E *EMP* 1,155^E
SIC 5699 Western apparel; Western apparel
Pr: Leonard Marcus
Sr VP: Jay Gardner
VP: June Defabio
Mktg Mgr: Doug Kondrath
Mktg Mgr: Lisa Siragusa

D-U-N-S 13-071-2321 IMP
■ MACYS MERCHANDISING GROUP INTERNATIONAL LLC
(*Suby of* MACYS MERCHANDISING GROUP INC) ★
11 Penn Plz Fl 5, New York, NY 10001-2003
Tel (646) 429-6000 *Founded/Ownrshp* 2005
Sales 29.7MM^E *EMP* 494^E
SIC 5399 Army-Navy goods; Army-Navy goods
Pr: Janet Grove

D-U-N-S 87-796-0807 IMP/EXP
■ MACYS RETAIL HOLDINGS INC
(*Suby of* MACYS INC) ★
7 W 7th St Ste 1100, Cincinnati, OH 45202-2419
Tel (513) 579-7000 *Founded/Ownrshp* 1994
Sales 8.4MMM^E *EMP* 111,000
SIC 5311 Department stores, non-discount; Department stores, non-discount
CEO: Terry Lundgren
**Pr:* Jeffrey Gennette
**CFO:* Karen Hoguet
Sr VP: Michael Zorn
Dir Risk M: Ronald E Godfry

D-U-N-S 93-787-2620 IMP/EXP
■ MACYS SYSTEMS AND TECHNOLOGY INC
(*Suby of* MACYS RETAIL HOLDINGS INC) ★
5985 State Bridge Rd, Duluth, GA 30097-8208
Tel (678) 474-2000 *Founded/Ownrshp* 1994
Sales 229.7MM^E *EMP* 740
SIC 7374 Data processing & preparation; Data processing & preparation
Ch Bd: Thomas L Cole
**Pr:* Larry Lewark
**CFO:* Faye Glance
**Treas:* Karen Hoguet
Ex VP: Dave Seeley
Sr VP: Mike Manougian
Sr VP: Phil Stevens
VP: Mitch Borger
**VP:* Dennis Broderick
VP: Gian Cacioppo
VP: Robert Dickey
VP: Dan Gibson
VP: Andrew Koller
**VP:* Gary Nay
VP: Dave Seely
**VP:* Robert Seppelt
**VP:* John R Sims
VP: Joe Tirocke

D-U-N-S 78-652-3790 IMP/EXP
■ MACYS WEST STORES INC
(*Suby of* MACYS INC) ★
7 W 7th St Fl 17, Cincinnati, OH 45202-2468
Tel (513) 579-7000 *Founded/Ownrshp* 1999
Sales 2.2MMM^E *EMP* 34,000
SIC 5311

D-U-N-S 01-178-0678
■ MACYS.COM INC
MACY'S
(*Suby of* MACYS RETAIL HOLDINGS INC) ★
7 W 7th St, Cincinnati, OH 45202-2424
Tel (513) 579-7000 *Founded/Ownrshp* 1997
Sales 6.2MMM^E *EMP* 111,000^E
SIC 5961 5311 Mail order house; Department stores; Mail order house; Department stores
Ch Bd: Peter R Sachse
VP: Stacy Goldberg
VP: Darren Stoll
VP: Patricia Stromberg
**Prin:* Kent Anderson
S&M/VP: Gary Ostrager

D-U-N-S 06-167-9650
MAD ANTHONYS INC
ANTHONYS SEAFOOD
10502 Ne 37th Cir Bldg 8, Kirkland, WA 98033-7920
Tel (425) 455-0732 *Founded/Ownrshp* 1995
Sales 72.8MM^E *EMP* 1,500
SIC 5812 5813 Seafood restaurants; Chicken restaurant; Cocktail lounge; Seafood restaurants; Chicken restaurant; Cocktail lounge
Pr: Herbert M Gould III
CFO: Dave Fogle
VP: Jeff Arnot
**VP:* Herbert Milton Gould IV
Genl Mgr: Andrew Miller
Genl Mgr: Mary Nance
Genl Mgr: Vicki Westberg
Mktg Mgr: Lisa Jones

D-U-N-S 04-738-1962
MAD BAG INC
110 E 9th St Ste A813, Los Angeles, CA 90079-1813
Tel (213) 891-1526 *Founded/Ownrshp* 1996
Sales 30.0MM *EMP* 3
SIC 5137 Women's & children's clothing; Women's & children's clothing
Pr: Bruce A Gardner
**VP:* Marla Gardner

D-U-N-S 93-231-6565 IMP
MAD CATZ INC
(*Suby of* MAD CATZ INTERACTIVE, INC)
10680 Treena St Ste 500, San Diego, CA 92131-2447
Tel (858) 790-5008 *Founded/Ownrshp* 1999
Sales 70.6MM^E *EMP* 250
Accts Kpmg Llp San Diego Californ
SIC 3577 5734 Computer peripheral equipment; Software, computer games; Computer peripheral equipment; Software, computer games
Pr: Darren Richardson
**COO:* Brian Andersen
CFO: Stewart Halpern
**CFO:* Karen McGinnis
VP: Jeff Biglete
**VP:* Whitney Peterson
VP: Thomas Roberts
**VP:* Andrew Young
CTO: Thomas Cirrilo
Dir IT: Bret Stateham

D-U-N-S 94-636-3090 IMP/EXP
MAD DOGG ATHLETICS INC
SPINNING
2111 Narcissus Ct, Venice, CA 90291-4818
Tel (310) 823-7008 *Founded/Ownrshp* 1992
Sales 49.2MM^E *EMP* 120^E
SIC 5137 5122 7812 Sportswear, women's & children's; Vitamins & minerals; Video tape production; Sportswear, women's & children's; Vitamins & minerals; Video tape production
Pr: John R Baudhuin
**COO:* Aerin Shaw
Dir Soc: Ben Rippe
CTO: Vania Ballo
IT Man: Rhona Atwater
Prd Mgr: Michele McDonnell
Mktg Dir: Rhona Attwater

D-U-N-S 18-760-8005 IMP
MAD ENGINE INC
6740 Cobra Way Ste 100, San Diego, CA 92121-4102
Tel (858) 558-5270 *Founded/Ownrshp* 1987
Sales 73.5MM^E *EMP* 180^E
Accts Smith Mandel & Associates Llp
SIC 2261 Screen printing of cotton broadwoven fabrics; Screen printing of cotton broadwoven fabrics
CEO: Danish Gajiani
**Pr:* Alby Amato
**Ex VP:* Faizan Bakali
**VP:* Carolyn Foreman
**VP:* Clarinda Orng

D-U-N-S 07-955-5912
■ MAD MIMI LLC
(*Suby of* GO DADDY OPERATING CO LLC) ★
1562 1st Ave 205-6464, New York, NY 10028-4004
Tel (877) 960-6464 *Founded/Ownrshp* 2007, 2014
Sales 77.5M^E *EMP* 4,286^E
SIC 7371 8742 Computer software development & applications; Marketing consulting services
CEO: Dean Levitt

D-U-N-S 07-834-0293 IMP
MAD PROJECTS INDUSTRIES LLC
15 W 34th St Fl 8, New York, NY 10001-3015
Tel (212) 714-9300 *Founded/Ownrshp* 2010
Sales 500.0MM *EMP* 7
SIC 5136 Underwear, men's & boys'; Underwear, men's & boys'

MAD RIVER COMMUNITY HOSPITAL
See AMERICAN HOSPITAL MANAGEMENT CORP

D-U-N-S 08-159-3253
MAD RIVER LOCAL SCHOOL DISTRICT
801 Old Harshman Rd, Dayton, OH 45431-1238
Tel (937) 259-6606 *Founded/Ownrshp* 1900
Sales 42.0MM *EMP* 525
Accts Clark Schaefer Hackett Spring
SIC 8211 School board; Public junior high school; Public elementary & secondary schools; School board; Public junior high school; Public elementary & secondary schools
**Treas:* Jerry Ellender
Pr Dir: Jennifer Alexander

MAD WINGS
See SIMMONS PREPARED FOODS INC

D-U-N-S 04-841-1862 IMP/EXP
MADA MEDICAL PRODUCTS INC
625 Washington Ave, Carlstadt, NJ 07072-2901
Tel (201) 460-0454 *Founded/Ownrshp* 2006
Sales 24.3MM^E *EMP* 90
SIC 5047 Medical equipment & supplies; Dental equipment & supplies; Dentists' professional supplies
Pr: Jeffrey Adam
CFO: Robert Chasmar
Advt Dir: Louis Queralt

MADAME TUSSAUDS NEW YORK
See MERLIN ENTERTAINMENTS GROUP US LLC

MADD
See MOTHERS AGAINST DRUNK DRIVING INC

D-U-N-S 18-885-0333 IMP
MADDEN BOLT CORP
13420 Hempstead Rd, Houston, TX 77040-5813
Tel (713) 939-9999 *Founded/Ownrshp* 1989
Sales 30.2MM^E *EMP* 80
SIC 3452 Bolts, metal; Bolts, metal
Pr: David Madden
**VP:* Brian Madden
Opers Mgr: David Gray
Sls Mgr: Erik Falk

D-U-N-S 06-849-7080 IMP/EXP
MADDEN COMMUNICATIONS INC
901 Mittel Dr, Wood Dale, IL 60191-1118
Tel (630) 787-2200 *Founded/Ownrshp* 1960
Sales 173.8MM *EMP* 340
Accts Deloitte & Touche Llp Chicago
SIC 2752 Commercial printing, offset; Commercial printing, offset
Ch Bd: James P Donahugh
Pr: John Fitzgibbon
Pr: Sean Madden
COO: John McMahon
CFO: Thomas Nickele
Sr VP: Larry Gundrum
VP: Kevin Heniff
Exec: Amy Sebastian
MIS Dir: Ken Myers

D-U-N-S 00-285-5955
MADDEN CONTRACTING CO LLC (LA)
11288 Hwy 371, Minden, LA 71055
Tel (318) 377-0927 *Founded/Ownrshp* 1955
Sales 93.5MM^E *EMP* 175
Accts Broussard & Company Cpas Llc
SIC 1611 2951 General contractor, highway & street construction; Asphalt & asphaltic paving mixtures (not from refineries); General contractor, highway & street construction; Asphalt & asphaltic paving mixtures (not from refineries)
**Pr:* James D Madden
**Treas:* Lyda Madden
**VP:* S Douglas Madden
Off Mgr: Bob Moorehead

D-U-N-S 11-323-0924 IMP
MADDEN CORP
WELCOME TO THE ISLANDS
94-411 Koaki St, Waipahu, HI 96797-2806
Tel (808) 564-8800 *Founded/Ownrshp* 1984
Sales 49.2MM^E *EMP* 160
SIC 5199 2759 Gifts & novelties; Stationery: printing; Gifts & novelties; Stationery: printing
Pr: Dale Madden
**CFO:* Lloyd Uyeda
**Ex VP:* E Lynne Madden
Ex VP: Lynne E Maddn
Ex VP: Lynne Pre
VP: Stacey Suyama
IT Man: Calvin Hui
IT Man: Kelvin Hui

D-U-N-S 10-123-1228
MADDOX ELECTRIC CO INC
1555 Dopey Dr, Lake Buena Vista, FL 32830-8420
Tel (407) 934-8084 *Founded/Ownrshp* 2001
Sales 31.7MM^E *EMP* 210
Accts Blue & Co Llc Carmel In
SIC 1731 7629 Electrical work; Fiber optic cable installation; Telecommunication equipment repair (except telephones); Electrical work; Fiber optic cable installation; Telecommunication equipment repair (except telephones)
Pr: Scott Maddox
**Sec:* Donna Maddox
**Ex VP:* Randy Maddox
**VP:* David King
**VP:* James A Maddox

MADDOX OIL COMPANY
See WORKMAN OIL CO

D-U-N-S 13-198-2667 IMP/EXP
MADE IN NATURE LLC
1708 13th St, Boulder, CO 80302-6226
Tel (720) 420-0686 *Founded/Ownrshp* 2003
Sales 60.0MM *EMP* 61
SIC 5149 Fruits, dried
VP Opers: Sven Martinsen

MADE IN PARADISE
See CGS INDUSTRIES INC

MADE IN WASHINGTON
See SEABEAR CO

MADE2MANAGE SYSTEMS
See APTEAN HOLDINGS INC

D-U-N-S 04-895-9167
MADEIRA CITY SCHOOL DISTRICT (INC)
7465 Loannes Dr, Cincinnati, OH 45243-1851
Tel (513) 891-8222 *Founded/Ownrshp* 1913
Sales 20.3MM *EMP* 200
SIC 8211 Public elementary school; Public junior high school; Public senior high school; Public elementary school; Public junior high school; Public senior high school
COO: Wes Woolard
**Treas:* Susan Crabill
Pr Dir: Diane Nichols
Instr Medi: Melissa Broome
Instr Medi: Stephanie Welt

D-U-N-S 02-029-6935
MADEIRA SCHOOL INC (VA)
8328 Georgetown Pike, Mc Lean, VA 22102-1200
Tel (703) 556-8241 *Founded/Ownrshp* 1906
Sales 33.7MM *EMP* 150
Accts Regardie Brooks & Lewis Beth
SIC 8211 Private senior high school; Private senior high school
Prin: Elizabeth Griffith
Treas: Ron Taylor
Bd of Dir: Loni Parent
Ofcr: Christine Huber
Ofcr: Isabel Yordan
Prgrm Mgr: Whitney Morgan
CTO: Bethane Stitsh
Prd Mgr: Elaine Randolph

D-U-N-S 10-887-5345 IMP/EXP
MADEIRA USA LTD
30 Bayside Ct, Laconia, NH 03246-2302
Tel (603) 528-2944 *Founded/Ownrshp* 1983
Sales 21.4MM^E *EMP* 65
SIC 5131 Thread
Pr: Ken Paige
**VP:* Michael Schmidt
**Prin:* Hans Joachim Voeller
Off Mgr: Sandra Dame
IT Man: Brenda Boutwell
Natl Sales: Arnie Korfine
Sls Dir: Shirley Clark
Sls Dir: Colleen Hartigan

MADELINE & CO
See PMN INC

D-U-N-S 11-878-7027
MADER CONSTRUCTION CO INC
970 Bullis Rd, Elma, NY 14059-9638
Tel (716) 655-3400 *Founded/Ownrshp* 2000
Sales 26.9MM *EMP* 125
Accts Chiampou Travis Besaw & Kershn
SIC 1799 1742 Home/office interiors finishing, furnishing & remodeling; Exterior insulation & finish (EIFS) applicator; Home/office interiors finishing, furnishing & remodeling; Exterior insulation & finish (EIFS) applicator
Pr: Kevin Biddle
**Treas:* James Biddle Jr
**Exec:* Harold Keller Jr

D-U-N-S 08-538-6498
MADER NEWS INC
913 Ruberta Ave, Glendale, CA 91201-2346
Tel (818) 551-5000 *Founded/Ownrshp* 1972
Sales 26.4MM^E *EMP* 100
SIC 5192 Newspapers
Pr: Avan Mader
Dir IT: Justin Wil
Opers Mgr: Rafael Sotomayor

MADER SOUTHEAST
See MSEI INC

D-U-N-S 07-018-0245
MADERA COMMUNITY HOSPITAL
MCH
1250 E Almond Ave, Madera, CA 93637-5696
Tel (559) 675-5555 *Founded/Ownrshp* 1975
Sales 75.9MM *EMP* 800
SIC 8062 General medical & surgical hospitals; General medical & surgical hospitals
CEO: Evan J Rayner
Pr: Mary Aguirre
CFO: Donna Tooley
Dir Rx: Dale Costantino
Adm Dir: Karen Paolinelli
Mktg Dir: Rae Gomes
Doctor: Victor Yanez
Pharmcst: Angelica Malagon

D-U-N-S 03-040-2853
MADERA CORP
MCDONALD'S
6025 Nicolle St Ste A, Ventura, CA 93003-7602
Tel (805) 656-1137 *Founded/Ownrshp* 1966
Sales 9.6MM^E *EMP* 400
SIC 5812 Fast-food restaurant, chain; Fast-food restaurant, chain
Pr: Dean Wood
**VP:* Christoper Wood
**Off Mgr:* Colleen Knight

D-U-N-S 03-885-6290
MADERA COUNTY OFFICE OF EDUCATION
1105 S Madera Ave, Madera, CA 93637-5576
Tel (559) 673-6051 *Founded/Ownrshp* 1898
Sales 49.6MM *EMP* 400
Accts Borchardt Corona & Faeth Fre
SIC 8211 Public elementary & secondary schools; Public elementary & secondary schools
DP Dir: Joseph Newcomb

MADERA PROPANE
See TESEI PETROLEUM INC

D-U-N-S 79-402-6807
MADERA UNIFIED SCHOOL DISTRICT
1902 Howard Rd, Madera, CA 93637-5167
Tel (559) 675-4500 *Founded/Ownrshp* 2011
Sales 128.2MM^E *EMP* 2,000
Accts Vavrinek Trine Day & Co Fres
SIC 8211 Public elementary & secondary schools; Public elementary & secondary schools
Ofcr: Isabel Barreras
Dir Sec: Brett Moglia
MIS Dir: Steve Alexander
Dir IT: Greg Johnson
Dir IT: Paul Parkey
Teacher Pr: Ken Alberson

D-U-N-S 17-752-3560 IMP
MADERAS 3C INC
FERRETERIAS MADERAS 3C
Marginal Ave Kennedy, San Juan, PR 00920
Tel (787) 783-8260 *Founded/Ownrshp* 1987
Sales 20.7MM *EMP* 100
Accts Ivan O Canabat Perez San Jua
SIC 5251 Hardware; Hardware
Pr: Carlos C Castro
**Pr:* Carlos Cuebas-Castro

MADHAVA NATURAL SWEETENERS
See HONEY MADHAVA LTD

D-U-N-S 10-885-4829 IMP
MADICO INC
(*Suby of* LINTEC USA HOLDING INC) ★
64 Industrial Pkwy Ste 1, Woburn, MA 01801-1990
Tel (781) 756-4142 *Founded/Ownrshp* 1989
Sales 26.6MM^E *EMP* 125^E
SIC 3081 2295 Unsupported plastics film & sheet; Laminating of fabrics; Metallizing of fabrics; Unsupported plastics film & sheet; Laminating of fabrics; Metallizing of fabrics
CEO: Robert Connelly
Ch Bd: H Kainose
Treas: Akiyoshi Ishihara
VP: Michael Wharton
IT Man: Mike Colletti
Mtls Mgr: Keith Nadeau
Snr Mgr: Paul Dixon

D-U-N-S 96-806-6659
MADIGAN ARMY MEDICAL CENTER
9040 Fitzsimmons Dr, Lewis McChord, WA 98431-1000
Tel (253) 968-2200 *Founded/Ownrshp* 2011
Sales 39.9MM^E *EMP* 348^E
SIC 8011 Medical centers
Owner: Dallas Homas
Chf Rad: Stephen Yoest
Dir Rad: Marc Cote
CIO: Craig Anderson
Mktg Dir: Sharon Ayala
Psych: Steven Parkison
Obsttrcn: Jason Pates
Doctor: Frederick Flynn
Pharmcst: Helen Booth
Pgrm Dir: Paul Benfanti
Snr Mgr: Dan Orr

MADISN-NIDA BD COOP EDCTL SVCS
See MADISON-ONEIDA COUNTY BOCES (INC)

D-U-N-S 00-778-2923
MADISON AMHERST INC
AMHERSTMADISON
(*Suby of* PORT AMHERST LTD) ★
2 Port Amherst Dr, Charleston, WV 25306-6637
Tel (304) 926-1100 *Founded/Ownrshp* 1915, 1983
Sales 48.4MM^E *EMP* 300
SIC 1629 4449 4491 Marine construction; River transportation, except on the St. Lawrence Seaway; Marine cargo handling; Marine construction; River transportation, except on the St. Lawrence Seaway; Marine cargo handling
Pr: Charles D Jones
**COO:* Robert McCoy
**Treas:* Jeremy Hodges

D-U-N-S 03-890-9347
MADISON AREA SPECIAL ED CO-OP
MAESSU
702 Elm St, Madison, IN 47250-3317
Tel (812) 265-3448 *Founded/Ownrshp* 1976
Sales 9.3MM^E *EMP* 325
SIC 8211 Public special education school; Public special education school
Ex Dir: Connie Griffith

D-U-N-S 07-384-9200
MADISON AREA TECHNICAL COLLEGE DISTRICT
MATC
(*Suby of* WISCONSIN TECHNICAL COLLEGE SYSTEM BOARD) ★
1701 Wright St, Madison, WI 53704-2599
Tel (608) 246-6100 *Founded/Ownrshp* 1938
Sales 133.2MM^E *EMP* 3,500
Accts Clifton Larson Allen Llp Milw
SIC 8222 Technical institute; Technical institute
Pr: Jack E Daniels III
VP: Roger Price
VP Admn: Jerry Collingwood
CIO: David Wallace
Pgrm Dir: Garilyn Truttschel

MADISON AREA YMCA
See YOUNG MENS CHRISTIAN ASSOCIATION OF MADISON NJ

D-U-N-S 05-233-2285
MADISON BLOCK & STONE INC
5813 Us Highway 51, Madison, WI 53704-6199
Tel (608) 249-5633 *Founded/Ownrshp* 2006
Sales 24.3MM^E *EMP* 40
SIC 5083 5032 3281 Landscaping equipment; Brick, stone & related material; Limestone, cut & shaped; Marble, building: cut & shaped; Granite, cut & shaped
Pr: Jayme T Anderson

D-U-N-S 10-759-4558
MADISON BOROUGH BOARD OF EDUCATION
MADISON SCHOOL DIST
359 Woodland Rd, Madison, NJ 07940-2400
Tel (973) 593-3100 *Founded/Ownrshp* 1803
Sales 18.6MM^E *EMP* 300
SIC 8211 Public elementary & secondary schools; High school, junior or senior; School board; Public elementary & secondary schools; High school, junior or senior; School board
Bd of Dir: Joanne Spigner
VP: Jeanie Devincenzo

D-U-N-S 05-292-6367 IMP
MADISON CABLE CORP
(*Suby of* TE CONNECTIVITY) ★
125 Goddard Memorial Dr, Worcester, MA 01603-1233
Tel (508) 752-2884 *Founded/Ownrshp* 2000
Sales 36.9MM^E *EMP* 213
SIC 3357 3643 3577 Nonferrous wiredrawing & insulating; Current-carrying wiring devices; Computer peripheral equipment; Nonferrous wiredrawing & insulating; Current-carrying wiring devices; Computer peripheral equipment
CFO: Nicolas Marinelarena
CFO: Charles Leykum
VP: Roger Temple
Sls Mgr: Harry Jarvis

D-U-N-S 08-547-8605
MADISON CAPITAL FUNDING LLC
(*Suby of* NEW YORK LIFE INSURANCE CO) ★
30 S Wacker Dr Ste 3700, Chicago, IL 60606-7462
Tel (312) 596-6900 *Founded/Ownrshp* 2001
Sales NA *EMP* 55
SIC 6163 Loan brokers; Loan brokers
CEO: Monica Kelesy
**Ofcr:* Andrew Bucolo
Sr VP: Marc Pressler
Sr VP: Timothy Schifer
Sr VP: Jeffrey Scott
VP: Adam Chalmers
VP: Jennifer Cotton
VP: Robert Douglass
VP: Drew Guyette
VP: Faraaz Kamran
VP: William Kindorf
VP: Chris Martin
VP: Justin May
VP: Jason Schryver
VP: Christopher Taylor

D-U-N-S 92-985-0949 IMP
MADISON CAPITAL PARTNERS CORP
500 W Madison St Ste 3890, Chicago, IL 60661-4593
Tel (312) 277-0323 *Founded/Ownrshp* 1994
Sales 181.6MM^E *EMP* 2,150
SIC 3542 8741 Machine tools, metal forming type; Management services; Machine tools, metal forming type; Management services
Pr: Larry W Gies
CFO: Brent Campbell
**CFO:* John E Udelhofen
CFO: John Udelhofen
**VP:* Aaron J Vangetson
Mng Dir: Christopher Domke
IT Man: Aaron Vangetson

D-U-N-S 00-638-2667
MADISON CHEMICAL CO INC
3141 Clifty Dr, Madison, IN 47250-1885
Tel (812) 273-6000 *Founded/Ownrshp* 1947
Sales 22.3MM *EMP* 68
SIC 7349

D-U-N-S 04-715-5523
MADISON CITY SCHOOL DISTRICT
211 Celtic Dr, Madison, AL 35758-1853
Tel (256) 464-8370 *Founded/Ownrshp* 1998
Sales 51.5MM^E *EMP* 950
SIC 8211 Public elementary & secondary schools; Public elementary & secondary schools
**Pr:* Ray White
**VP:* Terri Johnson
MIS Dir: Aaron New
HC Dir: Bonnie Davis

MADISON CNCRSE HT GVERNORS CLB
See CONCOURSE HOTEL INC

D-U-N-S 96-636-3132
MADISON COMMUNITY FOUNDATION INC
820 N Washington Ave, Madison, SD 57042-1735
Tel (605) 256-5693 *Founded/Ownrshp* 2011
Sales 23.2MM *EMP* 3^E
Accts Baker Tilly Virchow Krouse Ll
SIC 8641 Civic social & fraternal associations; Civic social & fraternal associations
Ch: Jac B Garner

D-U-N-S 11-410-6008
MADISON COMMUNITY HEALTH CENTER INC
ACCESS COMMUNITY HEALTH CENTER
2901 W Beltline Hwy # 120, Madison, WI 53713-4231
Tel (608) 443-5500 *Founded/Ownrshp* 1980
Sales 28.2MM *EMP* 150
SIC 8011 Offices & clinics of medical doctors; Offices & clinics of medical doctors
CEO: Ken Loving
**CFO:* Joanne Holland
Ofcr: Joann Holland
IT Man: Marnee O'Meara
Psych: Chantelle Thomas
Snr Mgr: Tammy Quall

D-U-N-S 02-314-7023
MADISON COMPANIES LLC
5619 Dtc Pkwy Ste 800, Greenwood Village, CO 80111-3139
Tel (303) 957-2000 *Founded/Ownrshp* 1996
Sales 21.0MM^E *EMP* 70
SIC 6282 Investment advice
VP: Leigh Colyer

MADISON CONCRETE CONSTRUCTION
See MADISON CONSTRUCTION CO

D-U-N-S 08-619-6862
MADISON CONSOLIDATED SCHOOLS
2421 Wilson Ave, Madison, IN 47250-2134
Tel (812) 273-8511 *Founded/Ownrshp* 1960
Sales 28.9MM^E *EMP* 400
SIC 8211 Public elementary & secondary schools; Public elementary & secondary schools
Off Mgr: Pam Smith
Psych: Betsy Sullivan
Board of Directors: Roger Allman, Linda Darnell, Andy Lytle, Gail Spalding

D-U-N-S 06-903-1417
MADISON CONSTRUCTION CO (PA)
MADISON CONCRETE CONSTRUCTION
130 Quaker Ln, Malvern, PA 19355-2479
Tel (610) 695-8800 *Founded/Ownrshp* 1969
Sales 30.0MM^E *EMP* 200
SIC 1771

D-U-N-S 14-399-8578
MADISON CONSTRUCTION CO
15657 S 70th Ct, Orland Park, IL 60462-5107
Tel (708) 535-7716 *Founded/Ownrshp* 2002
Sales 35.7MM^E *EMP* 30
Accts Weiss Sugar Dvorak & Dusek
SIC 1542 Commercial & office building contractors
Pr: Rob Ferrino
**CFO:* Fred Gonzalez
**Ex VP:* Harry L Walder
**VP:* Robert Kostelny
**VP:* Dan Mitchell

D-U-N-S 00-183-0645
MADISON COUNTY
100 E Main St Rm 302, Jackson, TN 38301-6249
Tel (731) 423-6020 *Founded/Ownrshp* 1821
Sales NA *EMP* 600
Accts Justin P Wilson Nashville T
SIC 9111 Executive offices; ; Executive offices;
Snr Mgr: Kevin Mills

MADISON COUNTY BD SUPERVISORS
See MADISON COUNTY JUVENILE DRUG COURT

D-U-N-S 10-000-0629
MADISON COUNTY BOARD OF EDUCATION
MCSS
1275f Jordan Rd, Huntsville, AL 35811-9378
Tel (256) 852-2557 *Founded/Ownrshp* 1908
Sales 110.4MM^E *EMP* 1,800
Accts Ronald L Jones
SIC 8211 9111 Public elementary & secondary schools; Vocational high school; County supervisors' & executives' offices; Public elementary & secondary schools; Vocational high school; County supervisors' & executives' offices

D-U-N-S 10-005-8783
MADISON COUNTY BOARD OF EDUCATION
MADISON COUNTY SCHOOLS
5738 Us 25/70 Hwy, Marshall, NC 28753-6364
Tel (828) 649-9276 *Founded/Ownrshp* 1851
Sales 22.2MM^E *EMP* 425
SIC 8211 Public junior high school; Public senior high school; Public junior high school; Public senior high school
Bd of Dir: Lori Massey

D-U-N-S 86-857-3692
MADISON COUNTY COMMISSIONS
SHARON JOHNSTON PARK RESV
783 Coleman Rd, New Market, AL 35761-9103
Tel (256) 379-2132 *Founded/Ownrshp* 1978
Sales 87.1MM *EMP* 5
SIC 7999 Recreation center; Recreation center

D-U-N-S 07-501-6709
MADISON COUNTY COMMUNITY HOSPITAL (OH)
MADISON COUNTY HOSPITAL
210 N Main St, London, OH 43140-1115
Tel (740) 845-7000 *Founded/Ownrshp* 1962
Sales 36.1MM *EMP* 340
SIC 8062

MADISON COUNTY HOSPITAL
See MADISON COUNTY COMMUNITY HOSPITAL

D-U-N-S 06-084-5179
MADISON COUNTY JUVENILE DRUG COURT
MADISON COUNTY BD SUPERVISORS
146 W Center St, Canton, MS 39046-3735
Tel (601) 859-1177 *Founded/Ownrshp* 1900
Sales NA *EMP* 385
SIC 9111 Executive offices; ; Executive offices;
Pr: Gerald Steen
**Prin:* Steve Dye
**Prin:* Andy Taylor
Prin: David Vincent
IT Man: Christy Gleason

D-U-N-S 14-658-9213
MADISON COUNTY SCHOOL BOARD
60 School Board Ct, Madison, VA 22727-3096
Tel (540) 948-6836 *Founded/Ownrshp* 1871
Sales 13.6MM^E *EMP* 289
SIC 8211 Elementary & secondary schools; Public junior high school; Public senior high school; School board; Elementary & secondary schools; Public junior high school; Public senior high school; School board

D-U-N-S 00-722-0387
MADISON COUNTY SCHOOL DISTRICT
476 Highland Colony Pkwy, Ridgeland, MS 39157-8727
Tel (601) 879-3000 *Founded/Ownrshp* 1957
Sales 69.4MM^E *EMP* 1,343
Accts Kimberly Alford Cpa
SIC 8211 Public elementary & secondary schools; Public elementary & secondary schools
COO: Willie Williams
VP: Karen Baker
Dir IT: Gavin Guynes
Pr Dir: Ellen Aregood
Teacher Pr: Stephanie Hobson
Teacher Pr: Shay Williamson

D-U-N-S 07-407-0632
MADISON COUNTY SCHOOL DISTRICT
550 S Keeneland Dr, Richmond, KY 40475-3232
Tel (859) 624-4500 *Founded/Ownrshp* 1932
Sales 75.8MM^E *EMP* 1,500
SIC 8211 Public senior high school; Public junior high school; Public elementary school; Public senior high school; Public junior high school; Public elementary school
Dir IT: Kevin Hub

D-U-N-S 08-217-3634
MADISON COUNTY SCHOOL DISTRICT
55 Mary Ellen Ct, Danielsville, GA 30633-6712
Tel (706) 795-2191 *Founded/Ownrshp* 2001
Sales 43.6MM^E *EMP* 725
Accts Department Of Audits And Accou
SIC 8211 Public elementary & secondary schools; Public elementary & secondary schools
Psych: Chris Dennis
HC Dir: Donna Perry

MADISON COUNTY SCHOOLS
See MADISON COUNTY BOARD OF EDUCATION

D-U-N-S 07-979-8863
MADISON COUNTY SCHOOLS
5738 Us 25/70 Hwy, Marshall, NC 28753-6364
Tel (828) 649-9276 *Founded/Ownrshp* 2015
Sales 4.7MM^E *EMP* 315^E
SIC 8211 Public elementary & secondary schools
Dir IT: Paul Barilovits

D-U-N-S 07-979-8996
MADISON COUNTY SCHOOLS
1275 Jordan Rd, Huntsville, AL 35811-9378
Tel (256) 852-2557 *Founded/Ownrshp* 2015
Sales 55.1MM^E *EMP* 2,002^E
SIC 8211 Public elementary & secondary schools
Dir Sec: Kerry Wilkerson
Pr Dir: Geraldine Tibbs
Teacher Pr: Ken Kubik
Instr Medi: Vickey Sullivan
HC Dir: Janice Ward

D-U-N-S 06-929-3868 EXP
MADISON COUNTY WOOD PRODUCTS INC
3311 Chouteau Ave, Saint Louis, MO 63103-2911
Tel (314) 772-1722 *Founded/Ownrshp* 1981
Sales 33.2MM^E *EMP* 245
SIC 2448 2449 2441 2421 Pallets, wood; Wood containers; Nailed wood boxes & shook; Sawmills & planing mills, general; Pallets, wood; Wood containers; Nailed wood boxes & shook; Sawmills & planing mills, general
Pr: James Kesting
**VP:* Douglas Gaines

D-U-N-S 60-359-2978
MADISON DEARBORN PARTNERS IV LP
70 W Madison St Ste 3800, Chicago, IL 60602-4342
Tel (312) 895-1000 *Founded/Ownrshp* 2000
Sales 951.3MM^E *EMP* 14,000
SIC 5031 8744 Building materials, exterior; Facilities support services; Building materials, exterior; Building materials, interior; Composite board products, woodboard; Lumber: rough, dressed & finished; Facilities support services
Mng Dir: Benjamin D Chereskin
VP: Michael Kreger
Mng Dir: Timothy M Hurd
CIO: Stephen Heinmiller

D-U-N-S 17-063-4286
▲ **MADISON DEARBORN PARTNERS LLC**
M D P
70 W Madison St Ste 4600, Chicago, IL 60602-4215
Tel (312) 895-1000 *Founded/Ownrshp* 1998
Sales 5.0MMM^E *EMP* 8,800
SIC 6282 Investment advice
CEO: Paul J Finnegan
Pt: Harry Kraemer
Treas: Francisco Isla
Co-CEO: Samuel Mencoff
VP: Vivek Pattipati
Off Admin: Brian Boykins
Off Admin: Corey Caporale
IT Man: Sal Arcos
IT Man: Jackie Stuba

D-U-N-S 00-695-8433
MADISON ELECTRIC CO
MADISON ELECTRONICS
31855 Van Dyke Ave, Warren, MI 48093-1047
Tel (586) 825-0200 *Founded/Ownrshp* 1914
Sales 89.4MM^E *EMP* 200
Accts Baker Tilly Virchow Krause Llp
SIC 5063 3679 Electrical construction materials; Electrical supplies; Lighting fixtures; Harness assemblies for electronic use: wire or cable; Electrical construction materials; Electrical supplies; Lighting fixtures; Harness assemblies for electronic use: wire or cable
Pr: Brett Schneider
**CFO:* Benjamin Rosenthal
**Treas:* Jordan Glass
**VP:* Scott Leemaster
**VP:* Richard Sonenklar
**VP:* Jon Waitz
Sales Asso: Dick Arjeski
Sales Asso: Greg Warman

MADISON ELECTRONICS
See MADISON ELECTRIC CO

D-U-N-S 00-794-6346
■ **MADISON GAS AND ELECTRIC CO** (WI)
(*Suby of* MGE ENERGY INC) ★
133 S Blair St, Madison, WI 53788-0002
Tel (608) 252-7000 *Founded/Ownrshp* 1896
Sales 619.9MM *EMP* 695^E
Accts Pricewaterhousecoopers Llp Ch

SIC 4931 Electric & other services combined; Electric & other services combined
Ch Bd: Gary J Wolter
CFO: Jeffrey C Newman
Bd of Dir: Jean M Biddick
Sr VP: Lynn K Hobbi
VP: James G Bidlingmaier
VP: Kristine A Euclide
VP: Mark T Maranger
VP: Peter J Waldron
Board of Directors: Mark D Bugher, F Curtis Hastings, Regina M Millner, John R Nevin, James L Possin, Thomas R Stolper

D-U-N-S 04-081-3792
MADISON GROVEPORT SCHOOLS
5940 Clyde Moore Dr Ste C, Groveport, OH 43125-2010
Tel (614) 492-2520 *Founded/Ownrshp* 1848
Sales NA *EMP* 600
Accts Mary Taylor Cpa Columbus Oh
SIC 8211 Public elementary & secondary schools; Public elementary & secondary schools
Treas: John Walsh
Exec: Mary Guiher
Prin: Christine Bowser

D-U-N-S 83-210-5324
MADISON HAYWOOD DEVELOPMENTAL SERVICES INC
38 Garland Dr, Jackson, TN 38305-3602
Tel (731) 664-0855 *Founded/Ownrshp* 1972
Sales 14.3MM *EMP* 400
SIC 8211 School for the retarded; School for the retarded

D-U-N-S 07-791-6781
■ **MADISON HMA INC**
(*Suby of* HEALTH MANAGEMENT ASSOCIATES INC) ★
1421 E Peace St, Canton, MS 39046-4938
Tel (601) 855-5760 *Founded/Ownrshp* 2003
Sales 14.7MM^E *EMP* 309
SIC 8062 General medical & surgical hospitals; General medical & surgical hospitals
Ex Dir: Darryl Weaver

D-U-N-S 96-956-2623
MADISON HMA LLC
MADISON RIVER OAKS MEDICAL CTR
161 River Oaks Dr, Canton, MS 39046-5375
Tel (601) 855-4000 *Founded/Ownrshp* 2008
Sales 38.8MM *EMP* 200^E
SIC 8062 General medical & surgical hospitals; General medical & surgical hospitals

MADISON HONDA
See VINCES AUTO SALES INC

D-U-N-S 04-320-2381
■ **MADISON HOTEL CORP**
MADISON LOEWS HOTEL
(*Suby of* LOEWS HOTELS & RESORTS) ★
1177 15th St Nw, Washington, DC 20005-2701
Tel (202) 862-1600 *Founded/Ownrshp* 1961, 2002
Sales NA *EMP* 300
SIC 7011 Hotels; Hotels
Genl Mgr: James Lobasko
Ex Dir: Elizabeth Yeampierre
IT Man: Jeff Steere
Pr Dir: Ellen Gale
Sls Dir: Brad Heller

D-U-N-S 05-579-1490
MADISON HOTEL LLC
MADISON RENAISSANCE HOTEL
(*Suby of* MADISON ASSOCIATES PARTNERSHIP)
515 Madison St, Seattle, WA 98104-1147
Tel (206) 583-0300 *Founded/Ownrshp* 1997
Sales 17.6MM^E *EMP* 446^E
SIC 7011 Hotels & motels
Bd of Dir: Frederick Garcia
Bd of Dir: James Weaver
Exec: Rodolfo Gonzalez
Dir Soc: Cristin Peters
Dir Soc: Karyn Tanaka
Brnch Mgr: Rene Neidhart
Genl Mgr: Karen Lang
Off Mgr: Stephanie Pray
Sls Mgr: Tania Ostronic
Assoc Ed: David Weiss

D-U-N-S 00-747-2756
MADISON INC OF OKLAHOMA (OK)
(*Suby of* JOHN S FREY ENTERPRISES) ★
8500 New Sapulpa Rd, Tulsa, OK 74131-3873
Tel (918) 224-6990 *Founded/Ownrshp* 1946, 1967
Sales 34.1MM^E *EMP* 67
SIC 3441 1541 3448 3444 Fabricated structural metal; Prefabricated building erection, industrial; Prefabricated metal buildings; Sheet metalwork
Pr: John Samuel Frey
**Sec:* Barbara Cruncleton
VP: Mike Davis
**VP:* Robert E Hansen
Genl Mgr: Joe Weigand

D-U-N-S 04-436-6847 IMP/EXP
MADISON INDUSTRIES INC
295 5th Ave Ste 512, New York, NY 10016-7103
Tel (212) 679-5110 *Founded/Ownrshp* 1967
Sales 115.3MM^E *EMP* 550
SIC 2392 5023 Household furnishings; Comforters & quilts: made from purchased materials; Pillowcases: made from purchased materials; Mattress protectors, except rubber; Home furnishings; Household furnishings; Comforters & quilts: made from purchased materials; Pillowcases: made from purchased materials; Mattress protectors, except rubber; Home furnishings
Ch Bd: Michael Schwartz

D-U-N-S 00-327-3208
MADISON INDUSTRIES INC OF GEORGIA
(*Suby of* JOHN S FREY ENTERPRISES) ★
1035 Iris Dr Sw, Conyers, GA 30094
Tel (770) 483-4401 *Founded/Ownrshp* 1977
Sales 135.0MM^E *EMP* 250
SIC 1541 3444 Industrial buildings, new construction; Sheet metalwork; Industrial buildings, new construction; Sheet metalwork
CEO: John S Frey Jr
**Treas:* Grace Lee
**VP:* H Michael Davis
Sls Mgr: Wesley Edwards
Sls Mgr: Gene Soden

D-U-N-S 05-329-7032
MADISON LOCAL SCHOOL DISTRICT
1324 Middletown Eaton Rd, Middletown, OH 45042-1525
Tel (513) 420-4750 *Founded/Ownrshp* 1937
Sales 36.4MM *EMP* 262
Accts Bastin & Company Llc Cincinn
SIC 8211 9411 Public senior high school; School board; Administration of educational programs; Public senior high school; School board; Administration of educational programs
**Treas:* William Richardson
Sls&Mrk Ex: Mark Zimov
Mktg Dir: A J Huff
Schl Brd P: Dave French
HC Dir: Mary Fose

D-U-N-S 07-675-4902
MADISON LOCAL SCHOOL DISTRICT
1379 Grace St, Mansfield, OH 44905-2742
Tel (419) 589-2600 *Founded/Ownrshp* 1905
Sales 24.2MM^E *EMP* 450
SIC 8211 8351 Public elementary school; Public junior high school; Public senior high school; School board; Child day care services; Public elementary school; Public junior high school; Public senior high school; School board; Child day care services
Pr: Jeff Meyers
Treas: Missy Parish

D-U-N-S 08-332-8815
MADISON LOCAL SCHOOL DISTRICT
6741 N Ridge Rd, Madison, OH 44057-2656
Tel (440) 428-2166 *Founded/Ownrshp* 1900
Sales 14.1MM^E *EMP* 350
Accts James G Zupka Cpa Inc Gar
SIC 8211 Public elementary school; Public elementary school
**Treas:* Michael Vaccariello
Dir IT: Matthew Smith
Schl Brd P: Rex Reigert
Psych: Robin Harpster
Psych: Tracy McDaniel

MADISON LOEWS HOTEL
See MADISON HOTEL CORP

D-U-N-S 80-709-0188
MADISON MECHANICAL INC
1539 Fannie Dorsey Rd, Sykesville, MD 21784-8214
Tel (410) 461-7301 *Founded/Ownrshp* 1993
Sales 23.1MM^E *EMP* 65
Accts Cohn Reznick Llp Bethesda Ma
SIC 1711 Plumbing contractors; Heating & air conditioning contractors; Mechanical contractor; Plumbing contractors; Heating & air conditioning contractors; Mechanical contractor
Pr: Glenn A Haslam
**CFO:* Bob Buczkowski
**Sec:* Robert Buczkowski
VP: Mark Gullickson
Off Mgr: Bev Moore

D-U-N-S 07-198-8265
MADISON MEDICAL CENTER
611 W Main St Ste A, Fredericktown, MO 63645-1120
Tel (573) 783-3341 *Founded/Ownrshp* 1961
Sales 17.3MM *EMP* 299
SIC 8062 8059 8051 General medical & surgical hospitals; Nursing home, except skilled & intermediate care facility; Skilled nursing care facilities; General medical & surgical hospitals; Nursing home, except skilled & intermediate care facility; Skilled nursing care facilities
CEO: Lisa Twidwell
Doctor: Eric K Davis
Snr Mgr: Jeffery Stackle

D-U-N-S 07-300-4673
MADISON MEMORIAL HOSPITAL
450 E Main St, Rexburg, ID 83440-2048
Tel (208) 359-6432 *Founded/Ownrshp* 1951
Sales 59.8MM *EMP* 530
SIC 8062 General medical & surgical hospitals; General medical & surgical hospitals
CEO: Rachel Gonzales
**CFO:* Troy Christensen
CFO: Cecil Ricks
**Ch:* Scott Dixon
**Chf Cred:* Terry Conrad
Bd of Dir: Bruce Barton
Ofcr: Luann Dixon
Ofcr: Luanne Walker-Dixon
VP: Linda Perrenoud
Dir Inf Cn: Luann Walker
Dir Risk M: Nolan Bybee
Dir Rx: Dorsie Sullenger

D-U-N-S 02-046-6561
MADISON METROPOLITAN SCHOOL DISTRICT
MMSD
545 W Dayton St, Madison, WI 53703-1995
Tel (608) 663-1879 *Founded/Ownrshp* 1963
Sales 173.7MM^E *EMP* 4,006
SIC 8211 Public elementary & secondary schools; Secondary school; Public elementary & secondary schools; Secondary school
Pr: James Howard
**Treas:* Beth Moss
**VP:* Marj Passman
Ex Dir: Marggie Banker
Ex Dir: Cynthia Green
Ex Dir: John Harper
Sls&Mrk Ex: Donna Auld
Snr Mgr: Michael Hertting

D-U-N-S 07-893-4403
MADISON METROPOLITAN SEWERAGE DISTRICT INC
1610 Moorland Rd, Madison, WI 53713-3324
Tel (608) 222-1201 *Founded/Ownrshp* 1930
Sales 28.7MM *EMP* 90
Accts Cliftonlarsonallen Llp Milwau
SIC 4952 Sewerage systems; Sewerage systems
Ex Dir: Michael Mucha
COO: Joseph Anderson
CFO: Jeff Brochtrop
Sr Cor Off: James Nemke
Exec: Theresa Calderon
Exec: Peter Hartman
Exec: Matthew Hendrickson
Exec: Stephen Hoffman
Exec: Kelly Lynaugh
Exec: Don Lythjohan
Exec: Mary Manthey
Exec: Mitch McGrath
Exec: Michael Northouse
Exec: Joan Peebles
Exec: Mikki Smith
Dir Lab: Rhonda Riedner

D-U-N-S 00-403-9723 EXP
MADISON MILL INC (TN)
4101 Charlotte Ave, Nashville, TN 37209-3705
Tel (615) 269-8969 *Founded/Ownrshp* 1940, 1959
Sales 23.3MM^E *EMP* 140
SIC 2499 Dowels, wood; Handles, wood; Dowels, wood; Handles, wood
Pr: Thomas L McKelvey Jr
**VP:* Julian C Scruggs III
Snr Mgr: Julian Scroggs

MADISON MINE SUPPLY CO
See WATERLOO COAL CO INC

D-U-N-S 07-713-9855
MADISON MUTUAL INSURANCE CO
ILLINOIS MADISON INSUR AGCY
1 Mutual Ct, Edwardsville, IL 62025-3798
Tel (618) 656-3410 *Founded/Ownrshp* 1920
Sales NA *EMP* 47
SIC 6331 6411 Property damage insurance; Insurance agents, brokers & service
Int Pr: Michael Wenos
**Ch Bd:* Clinton H Rogier
Dir IT: Ken Somogyi

D-U-N-S 07-617-6023
■ **MADISON NATIONAL LIFE INSURANCE CO**
(*Suby of* INDEPENDENCE HOLDING CO) ★
1241 John Q Hammons Dr # 400, Madison, WI 53717-1929
Tel (608) 830-2000 *Founded/Ownrshp* 1987
Sales NA *EMP* 87
SIC 6311 6321 Life insurance carriers; Health insurance carriers
Pr: Larry Graber
**CFO:* Mark A Musser
**CFO:* Dianne Schauer
**Sr VP:* James Balgord
**Sr VP:* Murray Klein
**VP:* Jim Kenneally
IT Man: David Zanesco

D-U-N-S 00-608-3232
■ **MADISON NEWSPAPERS INC**
CAPITAL NEWSPAPERS
(*Suby of* LEE ENTERPRISES INC) ★
1901 Fish Hatchery Rd, Madison, WI 53713-1248
Tel (608) 252-6200 *Founded/Ownrshp* 1948
Sales 53.5MM^E *EMP* 645
SIC 2711 2721 2741 Newspapers, publishing & printing; Magazines: publishing & printing; Shopping news: publishing & printing; Newspapers, publishing & printing; Magazines: publishing & printing; Shopping news: publishing & printing
Ch Bd: Clayton Frink
**Pr:* Phil Blake
**VP:* Michael Jameson
Dist Mgr: Arlene Corning
CIO: Karin Langsdorf
Dir IT: Roger Leland
IT Man: John Cramer
MIS Mgr: Brian Woolley
VP Opers: Paul Fanlund

D-U-N-S 13-579-5172 IMP/EXP
MADISON ONE HOLDINGS LLC
BOUMATIC
2001 S Stoughton Rd, Madison, WI 53716-2849
Tel (608) 222-3484 *Founded/Ownrshp* 2002
Sales 84.4MM^E *EMP* 350
SIC 3523 Dairy equipment (farm); Milking machines; Dairy equipment (farm); Milking machines
CFO: Allen Vail
Sr VP: Gerald Thain
Dir IT: Bob Schaefer
Opers Mgr: Terry Schaefer

MADISON PAPER INDUSTRIES
See MADISON UPM

D-U-N-S 06-973-6130
MADISON PARISH HOSPITAL SERVICE DISTRICT
900 Johnson St, Tallulah, LA 71282-4537
Tel (318) 574-2374 *Founded/Ownrshp* 1972
Sales 24.0MM^E *EMP* 120
SIC 8062 General medical & surgical hospitals
CEO: Wendell Alford
Dir Env Sv: Shirley Masters
Dir Sec: Phil Scurria
CIO: Charles Whitaker
Dir QC: Susie Gaines
Dir Health: Cindy Weeks
HC Dir: Willie Stevenson

D-U-N-S 10-002-8331
MADISON PARISH SCHOOL DISTRICT
301 S Chestnut St, Tallulah, LA 71282-4205
Tel (318) 574-3616 *Founded/Ownrshp* 1993
Sales 23.3MM^E *EMP* 408^E
SIC 8211 Public elementary & secondary schools; Public elementary & secondary schools
Dir IT: Teresa Johnson
IT Man: Ann Simien
Psych: Connie Wallace
HC Dir: Rodger Pockett
HC Dir: Rodger Puckett

MADISON PERFORMANCE GROUP
See 488 PERFORMANCE GROUP INC

D-U-N-S 19-665-1954 IMP
MADISON PRECISION PRODUCTS INC
(*Suby of* METTS CORPORATION)
94 E 400 N, Madison, IN 47250-9599
Tel (812) 273-4702 *Founded/Ownrshp* 2009
Sales 175.2MM^E *EMP* 500
SIC 3363 3365 Aluminum die-castings; Aluminum foundries; Aluminum die-castings; Aluminum foundries
Pr: Michihiko Kato
**Ex VP:* Ken Degler
**VP:* Randy Boyd
**VP:* David A Sutherland
**Prin:* Kazuyoshi Matsushita
Sfty Mgr: Vicky Georgiev
Sls Mgr: Masahiko Koto
Snr Mgr: Chub McNeeley
Snr Mgr: Sanjay Mittal

D-U-N-S 07-979-9155
MADISON PUBLIC SCHOOLS
359 Woodland Rd, Madison, NJ 07940-2400
Tel (973) 593-3100 *Founded/Ownrshp* 2015
Sales 4.5MM^E *EMP* 354^E
SIC 8211 Public elementary & secondary schools

D-U-N-S 04-056-5302
MADISON Q STAFFING INC
2501 Centennial Dr # 111, Arlington, TX 76011-6600
Tel (817) 649-8400 *Founded/Ownrshp* 2010
Sales 950.0M *EMP* 364
SIC 7361 Employment agencies; Employment agencies
VP: Jose Perez

MADISON RENAISSANCE HOTEL
See MADISON HOTEL LLC

D-U-N-S 19-264-4235
■ **MADISON RESEARCH CORP**
(*Suby of* KRATOS DEFENSE & ROCKET SUPPORT SERVICES INC) ★
4904 Research Dr Nw, Huntsville, AL 35805-5906
Tel (256) 327-0000 *Founded/Ownrshp* 2006
Sales 28.9MM^E *EMP* 400
SIC 8711 Engineering services; Engineering services
Pr: Eric M Demarco
CFO: Deanna H Lund
Treas: Laura L Siegal
VP: Michael Fink
VP: Dave Ludwa
VP: Troy Moore
VP: Richard Selvaggio

D-U-N-S 83-546-7986
MADISON RESOURCE FUNDING CORP
72 Mirona Rd Ste 4, Portsmouth, NH 03801-5366
Tel (603) 427-1070 *Founded/Ownrshp* 1994
Sales NA *EMP* 38
SIC 6153 Factoring services
Pr: L Leonard Tierney
**VP:* James Klein
Off Mgr: Joy Johnson
CTO: Corei Mello

MADISON RIVER OAKS MEDICAL CTR
See MADISON HMA LLC

D-U-N-S 95-984-0844 IMP/EXP
MADISON SALES INC
60 E 42nd St Ste 505, New York, NY 10165-0509
Tel (516) 883-1133 *Founded/Ownrshp* 1987
Sales 25.0MM *EMP* 25
SIC 5082 Construction & mining machinery; Construction & mining machinery
Pr: Barry Richter
**VP:* Mark Carlton

MADISON SCHOOL DIST
See MADISON BOROUGH BOARD OF EDUCATION

D-U-N-S 07-983-6512
MADISON SCHOOL DISTRICT
5601 N 16th St, Phoenix, AZ 85016-2903
Tel (602) 664-7900 *Founded/Ownrshp* 2015
Sales 9.0MM^E *EMP* 319^E
SIC 8211 Public elementary & secondary schools

D-U-N-S 10-064-6413
MADISON SCHOOL DISTRICT 321
60 W Main St, Rexburg, ID 83440-1825
Tel (208) 359-3300 *Founded/Ownrshp* 1948
Sales 36.8MM *EMP* 650
SIC 8211 9411 Public elementary & secondary schools; School board; Administration of educational programs; Public elementary & secondary schools; School board; Administration of educational programs
Netwrk Eng: Derik Davenport
Netwrk Eng: Ben Dummar
Pr Dir: Rick Croft

D-U-N-S 03-702-8813
MADISON SCHOOL DISTRICT 38
5601 N 16th St, Phoenix, AZ 85016-2999
Tel (602) 664-7900 *Founded/Ownrshp* 1890
Sales 59.2MM *EMP* 45
SIC 8299 Educational services

D-U-N-S 17-867-8863
MADISON SECURITY GROUP INC
31 Kirk St, Lowell, MA 01852-1028
Tel (978) 459-5911 *Founded/Ownrshp* 2004
Sales 62.0MM^E *EMP* 1,500
SIC 6289 Security custodians; Security custodians
Pr: Joan Fiore
Pr: James Doyle
**VP:* Tim Grover

Brnch Mgr: Al Medeiros
Off Mgr: Hillary Dimauro

D-U-N-S 14-771-9041
MADISON SERVICES INC
MADISON SERVICES MISSISSIPPI
2068 Main St, Madison, MS 39110-8353
Tel (601) 856-4346 *Founded/Ownrshp* 1984
Sales 23.2MM^E *EMP* 206
SIC 8744 7349 1799 Base maintenance (providing personnel on continuing basis); Building maintenance services; Home/office interiors finishing, furnishing & remodeling; Base maintenance (providing personnel on continuing basis); Building maintenance services; Home/office interiors finishing, furnishing & remodeling
Pr: John W Lange
**Sec:* Carl Robert Montgomery
**VP:* J S Harris

MADISON SERVICES MISSISSIPPI
See MADISON SERVICES INC

MADISON SHOE COMPANY
See BM USA INC

MADISON SQUARE GARDEN COMPANY
See MSG SPORTS & ENTERTAINMENT LLC

D-U-N-S 96-665-1218 IMP
MADISON STREET CAPITAL LLC
105 W Madison St Ste 1500, Chicago, IL 60602-4602
Tel (312) 499-5900 *Founded/Ownrshp* 1996
Sales 32.8MM^E *EMP* 114
SIC 6211 Investment bankers; Investment bankers
Pr: Andrew D Smith
Sr VP: Karl D'Cunha
VP: Stewart Smith
Mng Dir: Bruce Lohman
Mng Dir: Lester Rodgers

D-U-N-S 04-683-3278
MADISON TITLE AGENCY LLC
1125 Ocean Ave Ste 1, Lakewood, NJ 08701-4577
Tel (732) 905-9400 *Founded/Ownrshp* 1998
Sales NA *EMP* 150^E
SIC 6411
Pr: Joseph Rosenbaum
Ofcr: Rachel Baum
Ofcr: Patty Gillich
Ofcr: Dina Schwarzman
Ofcr: Julia Wheat
Ofcr: Dina Wolpin
VP: Bunny Escava
Mng Dir: Sol Kinraich
Off Mgr: Naomi Neuberger
S&M/VP: Alan Proctor
Mktg Dir: Leah Teichman

D-U-N-S 09-537-5598
MADISON TOOL & DIE CO
145 Orchard St, Richmond, KY 40475-1638
Tel (859) 623-2680 *Founded/Ownrshp* 1987
Sales 60.0MM *EMP* 10
SIC 3312 Tool & die steel & alloys; Tool & die steel & alloys
Pr: Gary Rose
**VP:* Marvena Rose
Exec: Jennifer Baugh

D-U-N-S 08-474-9571
MADISON TROTWOOD CITY SCHOOL DISTRICT
3594 N Snyder Rd, Trotwood, OH 45426-3835
Tel (937) 854-3050 *Founded/Ownrshp* 1900
Sales 43.3MM *EMP* 435
SIC 8211 Public elementary & secondary schools; Public elementary & secondary schools
Bd of Dir: Deborah Daniel
Schl Brd P: Adrienne Heard

D-U-N-S 00-312-3629 IMP
MADISON UPM
MADISON PAPER INDUSTRIES
1 Main St, Madison, ME 04950
Tel (207) 696-3307 *Founded/Ownrshp* 2007
Sales 200.0MM^E *EMP* 225
SIC 2621 Paper mills; Paper mills
Genl Mgr: Russell Drechsel
Mfg Dir: Spencer Drury

D-U-N-S 02-192-4150 IMP
MADISON VINEYARD HOLDINGS LLC
JAMIESON RANCH VINEYARDS
(*Suby of* MADISON COMPANIES LLC) ★
1 Kirkland Ranch Rd, American Canyon, CA 94503-9697
Tel (707) 254-8673 *Founded/Ownrshp* 2009
Sales 22.1MM^E *EMP* 40
SIC 5182 5921 Wine; Wine
Pr: Bill Leigon
**VP:* Eric Kroll

MADISON WAREHOUSING
See SARDO & SONS WAREHOUSING INC

D-U-N-S 18-329-5575
MADISON WILLIAMS INC
(*Suby of* PINNACLE SUMMER INVESTMENTS INC) ★
600 Travis St Ste 5800, Houston, TX 77002-3008
Tel (713) 224-3100 *Founded/Ownrshp* 2000
Sales 28.1MM^E *EMP* 310
Accts Grant Thornton Llp Houston T
SIC 6211 Investment bankers; Brokers, security; Investment bankers; Brokers, security
CEO: William Sprague
**Ch:* George Ball
Mng Dir: Ric Saalwachter
Genl Couns: Jeffrey Nalley

D-U-N-S 00-308-6360
MADISON WOOD PRESERVERS INC (VA)
216 Oak Park Rd, Madison, VA 22727-4202
Tel (540) 948-6801 *Founded/Ownrshp* 1959
Sales 69.2MM *EMP* 75
SIC 2491

D-U-N-S 00-607-1716 IMP
MADISON-KIPP CORP
201 Waubesa St, Madison, WI 53704-5728
Tel (608) 244-3511 *Founded/Ownrshp* 2015
Sales 110.5MM^E *EMP* 500^E
SIC 3363 Aluminum die-castings; Aluminum die-castings
Pr: Tony Koblinski
CFO: Mark Daniel
Mfg Mgr: Mike Dykstra
Opers Mgr: Mari Fuller
Opers Mgr: Dave Grebe
Prd Mgr: Matthew Mullen
Prd Mgr: Brian Strohmenger

D-U-N-S 01-078-1573
MADISON-ONEIDA COUNTY BOCES (INC)
MADISN-NIDA BD COOP EDCTL SVCS
4937 Spring Rd, Verona, NY 13478-3526
Tel (315) 361-5500 *Founded/Ownrshp* 1968
Sales 71.1MM^E *EMP* 750
Accts D Arcangelo & Co Llp Rome Ny
SIC 8249 8211 Vocational schools; Elementary & secondary schools; Vocational schools; Elementary & secondary schools
**Treas:* Sandra J Foley
IT Man: Rebecca Lewis
Opers Mgr: David Phelps

D-U-N-S 00-824-6316 IMP
■ **MADISON/GRAHAM COLOR GRAPHICS INC**
COLORGRAPHICS
(*Suby of* CENVEO CORP) ★
150 N Myers St, Los Angeles, CA 90033-2109
Tel (323) 261-7171 *Founded/Ownrshp* 1953
Sales 109.9MM^E *EMP* 380
SIC 2752 7336 2796 Commercial printing, lithographic; Graphic arts & related design; Platemaking services; Commercial printing, lithographic; Graphic arts & related design; Platemaking services
CEO: Cappy Childs
**Pr:* Chris Madison
CFO: Ralph Strong
**VP:* Arthur Bell
VP: Ken Stout
Trfc Mgr: Tony Hernandez

D-U-N-S 07-132-3489
MADISONVILLE CITY OF (INC) (KY)
MADISONVILLE MUNICPL UTILITIES
67 N Main St, Madisonville, KY 42431-1962
Tel (270) 824-2101 *Founded/Ownrshp* 1807
Sales NA *EMP* 300
Accts Berry & Kingston Psc Madison
SIC 9111 City & town managers' offices; ; City & town managers' offices;
**Treas:* Gina Munger

D-U-N-S 07-842-5279
MADISONVILLE CONSOLIDATED INDEPENDENT SCHOOL DISTRICT
718 Bacon St, Madisonville, TX 77864-2513
Tel (936) 348-2797 *Founded/Ownrshp* 1913
Sales 18.1MM^E *EMP* 290
Accts John R Pechacek Cpa Bell
SIC 8211 Public elementary & secondary schools; School board; Public elementary & secondary schools; School board
Prin: Keith West
Schl Brd P: Martin Bennett

MADISONVILLE MUNICPL UTILITIES
See MADISONVILLE CITY OF (INC)

D-U-N-S 00-731-8926 EXP
MADIX INC
500 Airport Rd, Terrell, TX 75160-5200
Tel (256) 839-6354 *Founded/Ownrshp* 1962
Sales 290.4MM^E *EMP* 1,100
Accts Jamison Money Farmer & Co Pc
SIC 2542 2541 Partitions & fixtures, except wood; Fixtures, store: except wood; Shelving, office & store: except wood; Wood partitions & fixtures; Display fixtures, wood; Partitions & fixtures, except wood; Fixtures, store: except wood; Shelving, office & store: except wood; Wood partitions & fixtures; Display fixtures, wood
Ch Bd: Alan H Sharaway
**Pr:* Thomas A Satterfield
**V Ch Bd:* Walter S Dowdle
CIO: Al Cantrel
Dir IT: Al Cantrell
Sfty Mgr: Stephen Ellis
Sfty Mgr: John Reighter

D-U-N-S 06-989-5837
MADLYN AND LEONARD ABRAMSON CENTER FOR JEWISH LIFE
ABRAMSON GERIATRIC CENTER
1425 Horsham Rd, North Wales, PA 19454-1320
Tel (215) 371-3000 *Founded/Ownrshp* 1891
Sales 50.0MM^E *EMP* 1,000
SIC 8051 8069 6513 Extended care facility; Geriatric hospital; Retirement hotel operation; Extended care facility; Geriatric hospital; Retirement hotel operation
CEO: Carol A Irvine
V Ch: Leonard Cantor
V Ch: Seth Lehr
V Ch: Saul Reibstein
Pr: Frank Podietz
COO: Valerie G Palmieri
CFO: Mark T Wasserman
VP: Andy Bronstein
VP: Michael B Steinberg
VP: Staci Warsaw
Exec: Karen Baldwin

D-U-N-S 96-480-3089
MADLYN AND LEONARD ABRAMSON CENTER FOR JEWISH LIFE AND SUBSIDIARIES
1425 Horsham Rd, North Wales, PA 19454-1320
Tel (215) 371-1800 *Founded/Ownrshp* 2010
Sales NA *EMP* 2^E
Accts Parentebeard Llc Philadelphia
SIC 6311 Life insurance; Life insurance

D-U-N-S 00-691-3768
MADONNA INN INC
100 Madonna Rd, San Luis Obispo, CA 93405-5489
Tel (805) 543-3000 *Founded/Ownrshp* 1951, 2003
Sales 28.3MM^E *EMP* 200
SIC 5947 5461 5812 5813 7991 7011 Gift, novelty & souvenir shop; Bakeries; Cafe; Steak restaurant; Steak & barbecue restaurants; Bar (drinking places); Tavern (drinking places); Gift, novelty & souvenir shop; Bakeries; Cafe; Steak restaurant; Steak & barbecue restaurants; Bar (drinking places); Tavern (drinking places); Spas; Inns
CEO: Phyllis Madonna
Ex VP: Clint Pearce
Exec: Connie Pearce
Off Mgr: Zina Puieuek
Software D: Pete Clarno
Opers Mgr: Susie Kelly

D-U-N-S 04-091-2479
MADONNA REHABILITATION HOSPITAL
PROACTIVE
5401 South St, Lincoln, NE 68506-2150
Tel (402) 413-3000 *Founded/Ownrshp* 1966
Sales 103.1MM *EMP* 1,400
SIC 8051 Skilled nursing care facilities; Skilled nursing care facilities
Pr: Marsha Lommel
Dir Recs: Charlene Dunbar
COO: Paul Dongilli
CFO: Victor Witkowicz
**Treas:* Rich Herink
Ofcr: Jodi Blowers
VP: John Glenn
Dir Rad: Elizabeth Edwards
Dir Rx: Ingrid Songster
Dir Rx: Marsha Wagner
Dir IT: Bob Heydon

D-U-N-S 07-277-3054
MADONNA UNIVERSITY
36600 Schoolcraft Rd, Livonia, MI 48150-1176
Tel (734) 432-5300 *Founded/Ownrshp* 1938
Sales 55.2MM *EMP* 768^E
SIC 8221 College, except junior; College, except junior
Pr: Sister Rose Mary Kujawa
COO: Judith Moslak
**Treas:* Sister Mary Van Overberghe
Ofcr: Louis Brohl
Ofcr: Katie Jamnik
**VP:* Leonard Wilhelm
Exec: Susan Toma
Genl Mgr: Rick Martin
Off Admin: Patricia Lovelace
Pgrm Dir: Hakim Shahid
Snr Mgr: Carol Hall

D-U-N-S 18-440-4978
MADRI INC
MCDONALD'S
9335 Chandler Blf, Alpharetta, GA 30022-6219
Tel (770) 751-9362 *Founded/Ownrshp* 1982
Sales 9.5MM *EMP* 325
SIC 5812 Fast-food restaurant, chain; Fast-food restaurant, chain
Pr: Frank Phalen
**VP:* Patti Phalen

D-U-N-S 18-405-0875
MADRON SERVICES INC
301 N Canal St, Carlsbad, NM 88220-5831
Tel (575) 887-5830 *Founded/Ownrshp* 2004
Sales 32.5MM^E *EMP* 99
SIC 1389 Oil field services; Gas field services
Pr: Phillip P Madron
Genl Mgr: Randy Holman
Off Mgr: Sophie Martinez

D-U-N-S 02-867-9769
MADRUGA IRON WORKS INC
305 Gandy Dancer Dr, Tracy, CA 95377-9083
Tel (209) 832-7003 *Founded/Ownrshp* 1974
Sales 20.2MM^E *EMP* 45
SIC 3441 3599 Fabricated structural metal; Machine shop, jobbing & repair
CEO: Joseph Raymond Madruga
**Pr:* Elizabeth Betsy Madruga
**Pr:* Raymond M Madruga
VP: Elizabeth Madruga

MADSEN ELECTRIC
See CARL T MADSEN INC

D-U-N-S 10-255-4946
MADSEN KNEPPERS AND ASSOCIATES INC
100 Pringle Ave Ste 340, Walnut Creek, CA 94596-3512
Tel (925) 934-3235 *Founded/Ownrshp* 1983
Sales 25.6MM^E *EMP* 120
SIC 8748

D-U-N-S 05-648-2052
MAE HOLDING CO
7290 Deaconsbench Ct, Cincinnati, OH 45244-3708
Tel (513) 751-2424 *Founded/Ownrshp* 1966
Sales 22.0MM^E *EMP* 225
SIC 5031 5072 Door frames, all materials; Hardware; Door frames, all materials; Hardware
Pr: George Thurner III

D-U-N-S 17-415-3627
MAEHAL ENTERPRISES INC
PIKES PEAK HARLEY DAVIDSON
5867 N Nevada Ave Ste 100, Colorado Springs, CO 80918-3517
Tel (719) 278-2300 *Founded/Ownrshp* 1986
Sales 36.8MM^E *EMP* 90
SIC 5571 Motorcycle dealers; Motorcycle parts & accessories; Motorcycle dealers; Motorcycle parts & accessories
Pr: Robert Brooks
**CEO:* Herb Aston
**VP:* Sunny Ilson Aston
IT Man: Victor Vickers

MAELI ROSE
See JUSTFAB INC

D-U-N-S 00-166-5322
MAERSK INC (NY)
MAERSK LINE
(*Suby of* A.P. MOLLER - MARSK A/S)
180 Park Ave Ste 105, Florham Park, NJ 07932-1054
Tel (973) 514-5000 *Founded/Ownrshp* 1943, 2005
Sales 650.0MM^E *EMP* 3,000
SIC 4731 4491 4412 Agents, shipping; Stevedoring; Deep sea foreign transportation of freight; Agents, shipping; Stevedoring; Deep sea foreign transportation of freight
CEO: Sren Skou
**Ch Bd:* Russell J Brunner
**COO:* Morten Engelstoft
**CFO:* Morten K Nicolaisen
**Treas:* Pat Arnesen
**Chf Cred:* Philip V Connors
Bd of Dir: William S Stavropoulos
**Sr VP:* Doug Ceva
**Sr VP:* Kurt Mc Elroy
VP: Michael Colangelo
VP: Kevin Denman
VP: Neil W Magargal
VP: James P Philbin
Exec: Eric Herman

MAERSK LINE
See MAERSK INC

D-U-N-S 04-099-0913
MAERSK LINE LIMITED
(*Suby of* MAERSK INC) ★
1 Commercial Pl Fl 20, Norfolk, VA 23510-2126
Tel (757) 857-4800 *Founded/Ownrshp* 1983
Sales 140.3MM^E *EMP* 900^E
SIC 4499 Steamship leasing; Steamship leasing
Pr: J Russell Bruner
Pr: Greg Moore
**CFO:* Steven Hadder
**Chf Cred:* William Kenwall
**Sr VP:* Michael Hopkins
VP: Richard F Boyle
VP: Richard Boyle
**VP:* Rick Boyle
VP: Edward F Hanley
VP: Edward Hanley
VP: R Gregory Moore
**Exec:* Stephen Carmel
Dir Risk M: Lina Fennig
Board of Directors: John P Clancey, charles T, Harold W Gehman, Joe L Roby

MAESSU
See MADISON AREA SPECIAL ED CO-OP

MAESTRO MOTORS
See MARSHALL MUSIC CO

D-U-N-S 60-702-0294 IMP
MAF INDUSTRIES INC
(*Suby of* MAF)
36470 Highway 99, Traver, CA 93673
Tel (559) 897-2905 *Founded/Ownrshp* 1989
Sales 20.7MM^E *EMP* 100
SIC 3565 5084 Packing & wrapping machinery; Food industry machinery; Packing & wrapping machinery; Food industry machinery
Pr: Thomas Blanc
**VP:* Philippe Blanc

D-U-N-S 79-101-2644
MAFCO CONSOLIDATED GROUP INC
(*Suby of* MACANDREWS & FORBES HOLDINGS INC) ★
35 E 62nd St, New York, NY 10065-8014
Tel (212) 572-8600 *Founded/Ownrshp* 1995
Sales 240.9MM^E *EMP* 4,500
SIC 2121 2131 2869 Cigars; Smoking tobacco; Flavors or flavoring materials, synthetic; Cigars; Smoking tobacco; Flavors or flavoring materials, synthetic
Ch Bd: Ronald O Perelman

MAFCO MAGNASWEET
See MAFCO WORLDWIDE CORP

D-U-N-S 10-501-2467 IMP/EXP
MAFCO WORLDWIDE CORP
MAFCO MAGNASWEET
(*Suby of* M & F WORLDWIDE CORP) ★
300 Jefferson St, Camden, NJ 08104-2113
Tel (856) 964-8840 *Founded/Ownrshp* 1980
Sales 52.2MM^E *EMP* 230
SIC 2064 Licorice candy; Licorice candy
Pr: Steven Taub
**Sr VP:* Peter Vora
VP: Lisa Armstrong
**VP:* Lee Collison
**VP:* Leon Gorgol
Ql Cn Mgr: Liz Hall

D-U-N-S 00-132-5836
MAFCOTE INC (DE)
MIAMI WABASH PAPER
108 Main St Ste 3, Norwalk, CT 06851-4640
Tel (203) 847-8500 *Founded/Ownrshp* 1975
Sales 109.3MM^E *EMP* 350
SIC 2631 2657 2679 2671

D-U-N-S 60-248-6391 IMP
MAG AEROSPACE INDUSTRIES INC
MONOGRAM SYSTEMS
(*Suby of* ZODIAC AEROSPACE CS20001)
1500 Glenn Curtiss St, Carson, CA 90746-4012
Tel (310) 631-3800 *Founded/Ownrshp* 1989
Sales 176.7MM^E *EMP* 350
SIC 3431 3728 Plumbing fixtures: enameled iron cast iron or pressed metal; Portable chemical toilets, metal; Aircraft parts & equipment; Plumbing fixtures: enameled iron cast iron or pressed metal; Portable chemical toilets, metal; Aircraft parts & equipment
Pr: Sebastien Weber
**CFO:* Mark Scott
Sr VP: Olivier Zarrouati
**VP:* Tim Birbeck
**VP:* Mike Nieves
Prgrm Mgr: Angela Smith

*VP Sls: David Conrad
Sls Mgr: Caryn Larks

D-U-N-S 07-886-3434
MAG AUTOMOTIVE LLC
(Suby of AUTOMOTIVE TECHNOLOGY LLC) ★
6015 Center Dr, Sterling Heights, MI 48312-2667
Tel (586) 446-7000 Founded/Ownrshp 2013
Sales 51.9MM^E EMP 179^E
SIC 3559 Automotive related machinery; Automotive related machinery
Pr: Brian Prina
Treas: Robert Dudek

D-U-N-S 83-165-0044
MAG DS CORP
13580 Groupe Dr Ste 300, Woodbridge, VA 22192-4170
Tel (703) 376-8993 Founded/Ownrshp 2009
Sales 27.4MM EMP 250
SIC 8742 Management consulting services
CEO: Joseph Fluet
*CFO: Mark Huber
*Ofcr: France Hoang
*Ex VP: Joe Paull

D-U-N-S 06-193-7319 IMP/EXP
MAG IAS HOLDINGS INC
1395 Brickell Ave Ste 630, Miami, FL 33131-3317
Tel (786) 871-2904 Founded/Ownrshp 2012
Sales 445.9MM^E EMP 4,919
SIC 5084 Machine tools & accessories; Machine tools & accessories
Pr: Moshe Meidar
Ex VP: Gregory Vereschagin
*VP: Liad Meidar
*VP: Hillit R Meidar-Alfi

D-U-N-S 05-285-3454 IMP
MAG INSTRUMENT INC
2001 S Hellman Ave, Ontario, CA 91761-8019
Tel (909) 947-1006 Founded/Ownrshp 1955
Sales 172.2MM^E EMP 910^E
SIC 3648 Flashlights; Flashlights
CEO: Anthony Maglica
COO: Mike Moore
VP: David Hefner
*VP: James Zecchini
MIS Dir: Cody Becker
Sfty Dirs: Sam Olauwoye
Sfty Dirs: Jim Smith
*VP Sls: Thomas K Richardson
Sls Dir: Ken Friedman
Board of Directors: Jennifer Cimaglia, Anthony S Maglica, Dorothy Maglica, John Maglica

D-U-N-S 06-695-2748
MAG MUTUAL INSURANCE AGENCY LLC
3525 Piedmont Rd Ne 8-600, Atlanta, GA 30305-1556
Tel (404) 842-5600 Founded/Ownrshp 1988
Sales NA EMP 300
SIC 6351 6411 Liability insurance; Insurance agents, brokers & service; Liability insurance; Insurance agents, brokers & service
Chf Mktg O: Mary G Gregg

D-U-N-S 00-444-7769 IMP
MAG-NIF INC
8820 East Ave, Mentor, OH 44060-4390
Tel (440) 946-4308 Founded/Ownrshp 1963
Sales 20.5MM^E EMP 100
Accts Maloney & Novotny Llc Clevel
SIC 3944 3089 Banks, toy; Puzzles; Injection molding of plastics
Ch Bd: William W Knox Jr
Pr: Ken Tinner
*COO: Dennis Delaat
*Treas: Jim Weiss
VP: Jay Knox
Art Dir: Jon Cox

D-U-N-S 05-981-4897 IMP
MAG-TEK INC
1710 Apollo Ct, Seal Beach, CA 90740-5617
Tel (562) 546-6400 Founded/Ownrshp 1972
Sales 76.0MM^E EMP 225
SIC 3577 3674 Readers, sorters or inscribers, magnetic ink; Encoders, computer peripheral equipment; Semiconductors & related devices; Readers, sorters or inscribers, magnetic ink; Encoders, computer peripheral equipment; Semiconductors & related devices
Pr: Ann Marie Hart
Pr: Kiran Gandhi
CFO: Mike Brierley
CFO: Danny Jensen
*Ex VP: Louis E Struett
VP: Adriano Canzi
VP: Tom Coduto
VP: Brian Davis
VP: Sean Gately
Mng Dir: Steve Novis
Prgrm Mgr: Emmanuel Limtao

D-U-N-S 06-188-2726 IMP
MAG-TROL LONG BEACH LLC
RHINO ELECTRIC SUPPLY
(Suby of THIS) ★
600 W 15th St Ste A, Long Beach, CA 90813-1508
Tel (562) 216-7140 Founded/Ownrshp 1981
Sales 23.2MM^E EMP 32
SIC 5063 Electrical apparatus & equipment; Motor controls, starters & relays: electric
IT Man: James Shanohan
Sls Mgr: Gary Moe
Sales Asso: Oz Aguirre

MAGAGNINI
See INTELLISWIFT SOFTWARE INC

D-U-N-S 02-806-5662
MAGAN MEDICAL CLINIC INC
M M C
420 W Rowland St, Covina, CA 91723-2943
Tel (626) 331-6411 Founded/Ownrshp 1975
Sales 38.1MM^E EMP 263
SIC 8011 Clinic, operated by physicians; Urologist; Internal medicine, physician/surgeon; Ophthalmologist; Clinic, operated by physicians; Urologist; Internal medicine, physician/surgeon; Ophthalmologist
Pr: Bradley J Rosenberg
*Ex VP: Howard Ort MD
VP: Miguel Garcia
Exec: Nan McKinley
Snr Ntwrk: Richard Fernandez
Dir IT: Kevin Potter
IT Man: Dao Tran
Opers Mgr: Debbie Hawkins
Sls&Mrk Ex: Georgette McCloud
Surgeon: Steven Bast
Doctor: Hani Hashem

D-U-N-S 10-796-6418 IMP
MAGAZINE EXCHANGE INC
2001 Ne Foothill Blvd E4, Grants Pass, OR 97526-4240
Tel (541) 479-7389 Founded/Ownrshp 1976
Sales 22.1MM EMP 9
Accts Kathleen M Kelly Cpa Gra
SIC 5092 Hobby supplies; Hobby supplies
Pr: Roger Barry
Opers Mgr: Trina Mustain

D-U-N-S 07-525-8202
MAGAZINE PUBLISHERS OF AMERICA
PUBLISHERS INFORMATION BUREAU
810 7th Ave Fl 24, New York, NY 10019-5873
Tel (212) 872-3700 Founded/Ownrshp 1919
Sales 91.9MM EMP 47
SIC 8611 Trade associations; Trade associations
Pr: Nina B Link
*Ex VP: Ellen Oppenheim
Ex VP: Julia Whitehead
Sr VP: Susan Russ
Opers Mgr: Dom Rossi
Assoc Ed: Eric Sullivan

MAGAZINELINE
See AMERICAN COLLEGIATE MARKETING INC

D-U-N-S 03-386-6880
MAGBEE BROS LUMBER AND SUPPLY CO INC (GA)
MAGBEE CONTRACTORS SUPPLY
1065 Bankhead Hwy, Winder, GA 30680-8415
Tel (678) 425-2600 Founded/Ownrshp 1954
Sales 97.9MM^E EMP 211
SIC 2431 5211 3531 2439 Millwork; Doors & door parts & trim, wood; Windows & window parts & trim, wood; Lumber & other building materials; Construction machinery; Structural wood members; Millwork; Doors & door parts & trim, wood; Windows & window parts & trim, wood; Lumber & other building materials; Construction machinery; Structural wood members
CEO: Robert G Magbee
*Sec: Base Haslam Grady

MAGBEE CONTRACTORS SUPPLY
See MAGBEE BROS LUMBER AND SUPPLY CO INC

D-U-N-S 07-066-3091
MAGEE BENEVOLENT ASSOCIATION INC
MAGEE GENERAL HOSPITAL
300 3rd Ave Se, Magee, MS 39111-3665
Tel (601) 849-5070 Founded/Ownrshp 1942
Sales 48.3MM^E EMP 230
SIC 8062 General medical & surgical hospitals; General medical & surgical hospitals
CEO: Althea Crumpton
Chf Rad: Joe Ferguson
Pr: Jack L Herring
CFO: Chanda Roberts
Sec: Lester R Terrell
VP: James O Stephens
Dir Inf Cn: Stephanie Sullivan
Dir Lab: Tanya Wade
Dir Rx: Nita Turner
Off Mgr: Gail Patrick
CIO: Kirby Craft

D-U-N-S 12-219-1810
MAGEE ENTERPRISES INC
EXPRESS PERSONNEL SERVICES
1333 Arapaho Ave Ste D1, Springdale, AR 72764-6948
Tel (479) 756-1255 Founded/Ownrshp 1973
Sales 15.2MM^E EMP 606
SIC 7363 Temporary help service; Temporary help service
CEO: Paul Magee
Mng Dir: Kim Eldridge
Off Admin: Kelly Greaves
Off Admin: Tiffaney Gutierrez
Off Admin: Melissa Heldman
Off Admin: Renee Priebe
Off Admin: Brittany Ready
Opers Mgr: Monica Magee

MAGEE GENERAL HOSPITAL
See MAGEE BENEVOLENT ASSOCIATION INC

D-U-N-S 06-885-5097
MAGEE PLASTICS CO
303 Brush Creek Rd, Warrendale, PA 15086-7595
Tel (724) 776-2220 Founded/Ownrshp 1969
Sales 25.9MM^E EMP 84
SIC 3083 7389 3743 3728 Plastic finished products, laminated; Design, commercial & industrial; Railroad equipment; Aircraft parts & equipment
Pr: Glen H Maus
*Pr: Marylou Magee
*COO: Sheridan L Kelly
CFO: Herb Bennet
*Sec: Kelly S Magee
*Sr VP: Sean Magee
*VP: Charles W Story
Dir IT: Ted Magee
IT Man: Ronald Ofinski
Info Man: Dan Hubert
QI Cn Mgr: Todd Fritz

D-U-N-S 06-904-2406
MAGEE REHABILITATION HOSPITAL (PA)
1513 Race St, Philadelphia, PA 19102-1177
Tel (215) 587-3000 Founded/Ownrshp 1958
Sales 64.7MM EMP 600
SIC 8069 Specialty hospitals, except psychiatric; Specialty hospitals, except psychiatric
CEO: Jack Carroll
CFO: Pat Underwood
*CFO: Patricia Underwood
*Ch: Joseph J Mc Laughlin
VP: Eileen Carroll
*VP: Ron Siggs
Exec: Edward Petka
Dir Risk M: Carol Vinci
Dir Soc: Christina Freeman
Dir Rx: Richard Pacitti
Rgnl Mgr: Michelle Goodjoines

D-U-N-S 07-215-9460 IMP/EXP
MAGEE-WOMENS HOSPITAL OF UPMC
(Suby of UNIVERSITY OF PITTSBURGH MEDICAL CENTER) ★
300 Halket St, Pittsburgh, PA 15213-3108
Tel (412) 641-1000 Founded/Ownrshp 1912
Sales 165.0MM^E EMP 2,300
SIC 8062 Hospital, affiliated with AMA residency; Hospital, affiliated with AMA residency
Pr: Leslie C Davis
*Ch Bd: William Pietragallo
COO: William Cook
COO: Ketul Patel
CFO: Ilene Simmons
*Treas: Peter Eisenbrandt
Chf Mktg O: Richard L Sweet
Dir Lab: Monica Daood
Dir Lab: Edward Smith
Dir Rx: Laura Jung
Adm Dir: Nicole Travis

D-U-N-S 11-913-2785
MAGEE-WOMENS RESEARCH INSTITUTE AND FOUNDATION
3339 Ward St, Pittsburgh, PA 15213-4430
Tel (412) 641-8932 Founded/Ownrshp 1984
Sales 53.3MM EMP 250
Accts Ernst & Young Llp
SIC 8731 Biological research; Biological research
Ch: David Kaplan
V Ch: David Smith
*Treas: Jason M Harrison
VP: Maribeth McLaughlin
*Ex Dir: Yoel Sadovsky
Sls&Mrk Ex: Lauren Jones
Obsttrcn: Kristiina Parviainen

D-U-N-S 15-106-5349 IMP
MAGELLAN AEROSPACE BETHEL INC
(Suby of MAGELLAN AEROSPACE CORPORATION)
159 Grassy Plain St, Bethel, CT 06801-2806
Tel (203) 798-9373 Founded/Ownrshp 1998
Sales 27.9MM^E EMP 125
SIC 3728 3599 3724 Aircraft assemblies, subassemblies & parts; Machine & other job shop work; Aircraft engines & engine parts; Aircraft assemblies, subassemblies & parts; Machine & other job shop work; Aircraft engines & engine parts
CEO: James Butyniec
Chf Mktg O: Tami Niemer
Sfty Dirs: Bob Gaffney
Plnt Mgr: Larry Papazoglou
Mktg Mgr: Charles Kasper

D-U-N-S 15-126-2938 IMP
MAGELLAN AEROSPACE HAVERHILL INC
MIDDLETON AEROSPACE
(Suby of MAGELLAN AEROSPACE USA INC) ★
20 Computer Dr, Haverhill, MA 01832-1236
Tel (978) 774-6000 Founded/Ownrshp 1996
Sales 20.9MM^E EMP 120
SIC 3724 Aircraft engines & engine parts; Aircraft engines & engine parts
Pr: James S Butyniec
*Treas: Elena Milantoni

D-U-N-S 00-150-2335
MAGELLAN AEROSPACE NEW YORK INC (NY)
(Suby of MAGELLAN AEROSPACE CORPORATION)
9711 50th Ave, Corona, NY 11368-2740
Tel (718) 699-4000 Founded/Ownrshp 1939, 1999
Sales 34.2MM^E EMP 280
SIC 3728 3812 3769 3489 Aircraft parts & equipment; Aircraft assemblies, subassemblies & parts; Wing assemblies & parts, aircraft; Gears, aircraft power transmission; Search & navigation equipment; Guided missile & space vehicle parts & auxiliary equipment; Ordnance & accessories; Aircraft parts & equipment; Aircraft assemblies, subassemblies & parts; Wing assemblies & parts, aircraft; Gears, aircraft power transmission; Search & navigation equipment; Guided missile & space vehicle parts & auxiliary equipment; Ordnance & accessories
Pr: James S Butyniec
*Ch Bd: N Murray Edwards
*Ch Bd: John Marcello
*CFO: John B Decker
*CFO: John Mansfield
*VP: Jo-Ann Ball
VP: Jim Stauffer
Exec: Gerardo Patino
Genl Mgr: Henry David
Plnt Mgr: Louie David

D-U-N-S 05-971-8465
MAGELLAN AEROSPACE USA INC
MIDDLETON AEROSPACE
(Suby of MAGELLAN AEROSPACE LIMITED)
20 Computer Dr, Haverhill, MA 01832-1236
Tel (978) 774-6000 Founded/Ownrshp 1996
Sales 25.0MM^E EMP 145
SIC 3724 Aircraft engines & engine parts; Aircraft engines & engine parts
CEO: James S Butyniec
Treas: Paul F Gilbert
Genl Mgr: Dan Chaisson
Genl Mgr: Michael Grimmer
Genl Mgr: Paul Heide
Dir IT: Ron Burgess
IT Man: Doug Macdonald
QI Cn Mgr: Lou Diamontopoulos
Sls&Mrk Ex: Kelly Woiden
Sls Mgr: John Gillis

D-U-N-S 09-824-4796 IMP
MAGELLAN AIRCRAFT SERVICES LLLP
(Suby of MAGELLAN AVIATION GROUP LLLP) ★
2345 Township Rd Ste B, Charlotte, NC 28273-0119
Tel (704) 504-9204 Founded/Ownrshp 1998
Sales 128.6MM EMP 100
Accts Bdo Usa Llp Charlotte North
SIC 5088 Aircraft equipment & supplies; Aircraft equipment & supplies
Pr: William Polyi
*Pt: Robert G Fessler
*CFO: Lawrence E Grogan

D-U-N-S 16-810-2445
MAGELLAN AVIATION GROUP LLLP
2345 Township Rd Ste B, Charlotte, NC 28273-0119
Tel (704) 504-9204 Founded/Ownrshp 2008
Sales 133.1MM EMP 100
Accts Bdo Usa Llp Charlotte Nc
SIC 5088 Aircraft engines & engine parts; Aircraft engines & engine parts
Pt: David G Fessler
Pt: Niall Duggan
Pt: Robert G Fessler
Pt: Jerry Gerry
Pt: Larry Grogan
Pt: John McDonnell
Pt: Willam Polyi
Pt: Declan Treacy
Pt: Peter Zutty
VP: Jon Lobello
QA Dir: Jason Burris

D-U-N-S 07-309-2199
■ **MAGELLAN BEHAVIORAL HEALTH SERVICE LLC**
(Suby of MAGELLAN HEALTH INC) ★
55 Nod Rd, Avon, CT 06001-3819
Tel (860) 507-1900 Founded/Ownrshp 1997
Sales 98.1MM^E EMP 5,100
SIC 8322 Referral service for personal & social problems; Referral service for personal & social problems
Pr: Renee Lerer MD
Chf Mktg O: Shareh Ghani
Ofcr: Edie Jardine
Sr VP: Chris Hause
Sr VP: Ralph Pisano
Sr VP: Sunil Sachdev
VP: Chris Derrick
VP: John Edwards
VP: Janet Maurer
VP: Riwan Sheaprio
Dir Lab: Heather Chadwick
Assoc Dir: Kari Erickson
Dir Bus: Justin Beck

D-U-N-S 15-513-3796 IMP
MAGELLAN CORP
1650 Lake Cook Rd 300a, Deerfield, IL 60015-4747
Tel (847) 205-1155 Founded/Ownrshp 1985
Sales 48.1MM^E EMP 41
SIC 5051 5031 Iron & steel (ferrous) products; Lumber, plywood & millwork
Pr: Robert P Arthur
*VP: Avia Eilon
VP: Keith H Weiss
Natl Sales: Heather Morris

D-U-N-S 82-745-3106
MAGELLAN DEVELOPMENT GROUP LLC
225 N Columbus Dr Ste 100, Chicago, IL 60601-5228
Tel (312) 642-2777 Founded/Ownrshp 2012
Sales 23.3MM^E EMP 51^E
SIC 6552 Subdividers & developers
CFO: John Dekker
Chf Mktg O: Robin L Berger
Sr VP: Brian Gordon
VP: Brian D Gordon
VP: Sean P Linnane
VP: Michael Perry
VP Mktg: Tricia Van Horn
Pr Dir: Larry Schaffel

D-U-N-S 04-969-3732
▲ **MAGELLAN HEALTH INC**
4800 N Scottsdale Rd, Scottsdale, AZ 85251-7630
Tel (602) 572-6050 Founded/Ownrshp 1969
Sales 3.7MMM EMP 6,600
Tkr Sym MGLN Exch NGS
SIC 8063 8011 5122 Psychiatric hospitals; Radiologist; Pharmaceuticals; Psychiatric hospitals; Radiologist; Pharmaceuticals
Ch Bd: Barry M Smith
CEO: Sam K Srivastava
CFO: Jonathan N Rubin
Ofcr: Caskie Lewis-Clapper
Ofcr: Michelle Riegler
Ex VP: Robert Lagalia
Sr VP: David W Carter
Sr VP: John Littel
Sr VP: Linton C Newlin
Sr VP: Melissa Rose
Psych: Sue Bauserman
Board of Directors: John O Agwunobi, Michael S Diament, Perry G Fine, Kay Coles James, Robert M Le Blanc, William J McBride, Michael P Ressner, Mary F Sammons

D-U-N-S 12-670-5347
■ **MAGELLAN HEALTHCARE INC**
(Suby of MAGELLAN HEALTH INC) ★
14100 Magellan Plz, Maryland Heights, MO 63043-4644
Tel (410) 953-1000 Founded/Ownrshp 1999
Sales NA EMP 100
SIC 6324 Health maintenance organization (HMO), insurance only
CEO: Henry Harbin
*Pr: Dan Messina
*Ex VP: Michael F Murphy
VP: Don Clair
VP: Daniel Jolivet

D-U-N-S 06-601-5611
■ **MAGELLAN MEDICAID ADMINISTRATION INC**
COMPUTER COMPANY, THE
(Suby of MAGELLAN HEALTH INC) ★
11013 W Broad St Ste 500, Glen Allen, VA 23060-6017
Tel (804) 548-0100 Founded/Ownrshp 1968
Sales 91.7MM^E EMP 1,100
SIC 7374 8093 6411 8741 Computer processing services; Specialty outpatient clinics; Substance abuse clinics (outpatient); Mental health clinic, outpatient; Insurance claim processing, except medical; Medical insurance claim processing, contract or fee basis; Administrative management; Computer processing services; Specialty outpatient clinics; Substance abuse clinics (outpatient); Mental health clinic, outpatient; Insurance claim processing, except medical; Medical insurance claim processing, contract or fee basis; Administrative management
Pr: Timothy Nolan
Treas: Irene Shapiro
*VP: James Council
VP: Richard A Holloway
VP: Mark Huntley
VP: Linton C Newlin
VP: Jonathan Rubin
VP: Joseph E Whitters
VP: Edward L Wristen
IT Man: Umakanth Pandurangaiah

D-U-N-S 13-009-0343
MAGELLAN MEDICAL TECHNOLOGY CONSULTANTS INC
120 S 6th St Ste 2150, Minneapolis, MN 55402-1846
Tel (612) 677-0000 Founded/Ownrshp 1995
Sales 22.0MM^E EMP 200
SIC 3841 8748 Surgical & medical instruments; Business consulting; Surgical & medical instruments; Business consulting
CEO: Susan L Johnson
Manager: Joel Schneider

D-U-N-S 13-912-2738
■ **MAGELLAN MIDSTREAM HOLDINGS GP LLC**
(Suby of MAGELLAN MIDSTREAM PARTNERS LP) ★
1 One Williams Ctr Bsmt 2, Tulsa, OK 74172-0172
Tel (918) 574-7000 Founded/Ownrshp 2003
Sales 69.5MM^E EMP 1,127
SIC 4613 Refined petroleum pipelines; Refined petroleum pipelines
Pt: Don R Wellendorf
Pt: John D Chandler
Pt: Lonny E Townsend
CFO: Aaron Milford
Dir IT: Fawn McWilliams
Dir IT: John Moriarty
IT Man: Larry Dukes
Opers Supe: Clifford Bryant
Opers Supe: John Deaton
Opers Supe: Brian Norman

D-U-N-S 16-015-8069 IMP
▲ **MAGELLAN MIDSTREAM PARTNERS LP**
1 Williams Ctr Bsmt 2, Tulsa, OK 74172-0172
Tel (918) 574-7000 Founded/Ownrshp 2000
Sales 2.3MMM EMP 1,565
Tkr Sym MMP Exch NYS
SIC 5171 4613 Petroleum bulk stations & terminals; Refined petroleum pipelines; Gasoline pipelines (common carriers); Petroleum bulk stations & terminals; Refined petroleum pipelines; Gasoline pipelines (common carriers)
Ch Bd: Michael N Mears
Genl Pt: Magellan GP
CFO: Aaron L Milford
Sr VP: Larry J Davied
Area Supr: Phil Simpson
CIO: Jerry Schwegler
Genl Couns: Lonny E Townsnd

D-U-N-S 07-940-5006
■ **MAGELLAN PARTNERS RX INC**
(Suby of MAGELLAN HEALTH INC) ★
55 Nod Rd, Avon, CT 06001-3819
Tel (860) 507-1900 Founded/Ownrshp 2013
Sales 25.2MM^E EMP 5,030^E
SIC 8063 Psychiatric hospitals; Psychiatric hospitals
CEO: Barry M Smith

D-U-N-S 00-718-7305 IMP
■ **MAGELLAN PIPELINE CO LP**
(Suby of MAGELLAN MIDSTREAM PARTNERS LP) ★
1 Williams Ctr, Tulsa, OK 74172-0140
Tel (918) 574-7000 Founded/Ownrshp 1930, 2003
Sales 142.9MM^E EMP 435
SIC 4613 Gasoline pipelines (common carriers); Gasoline pipelines (common carriers)
Pt: Don Wellendorf
Pt: Jeff Holman

D-U-N-S 11-205-9741
■ **MAGELLAN TERMINALS HOLDINGS LP**
(Suby of MAGELLAN MIDSTREAM PARTNERS LP) ★
1 One Williams Ctr Bsmt 2, Tulsa, OK 74172-0172
Tel (918) 574-7000 Founded/Ownrshp 2001
Sales 181.1MM^E EMP 174
SIC 5171 Petroleum terminals; Petroleum terminals
Pt: Don R Wellendorf
VP: Lisa Korner

D-U-N-S 02-058-8844
MAGEN DAVID YESHIVA (NY)
2130 Mcdonald Ave, Brooklyn, NY 11223-2940
Tel (718) 236-5905 Founded/Ownrshp 1943
Sales 19.7MM^E EMP 400
SIC 8299 Religious school; Religious school
Pr: Steve Shahmah
*Pr: Eddie Esses
*Treas: Jack Hidary
*VP: Aslan Bawabes
*VP: Joseph Harary
Prin: Shimon Herskovits
*Ex Dir: Harvey Ishofsky
Opers Mgr: Allan Douglas

D-U-N-S 93-333-5887
MAGENIC TECHNOLOGIES INC
1600 Utica Ave S Ste 800, St Louis Park, MN 55416-3688
Tel (763) 398-4800 Founded/Ownrshp 1995
Sales 32.6MM^E EMP 240
SIC 7371 Custom computer programming services; Custom computer programming services
CEO: Greg Frankenfield
*Pr: Paul Fridman
*CFO: Scott Gabbard
CFO: Thomas J Goodmanson
CTO: Derek Ferguson
CTO: James McKelvey
S&M/VP: Brian Snyder

D-U-N-S 00-309-9171
MAGENTA LLC (IL)
3800 N Milwaukee Ave, Chicago, IL 60641-2806
Tel (773) 777-5050 Founded/Ownrshp 2008
Sales 28.1MM^E EMP 96^E
SIC 3089 Injection molding of plastics
Pr: Russell A Steele
*Treas: Michael Powles
VP: Dan Rudolph
IT Man: Mark Beam
Mfg Mgr: Thom Dyer
Opers Mgr: Michael Witek
S&M/VP: Kevin Bajus
Mktg Dir: Rich Majka
Board of Directors: Schooley David

D-U-N-S 04-018-1120
■ **MAGGIANOS INC**
MAGGIANO'S LITTLE ITALY
(Suby of BRINKER INTERNATIONAL INC) ★
6820 Lyndon B Johnson Fwy, Dallas, TX 75240-6511
Tel (972) 980-9917 Founded/Ownrshp 1994
Sales 64.1MM^E EMP 1,555
SIC 5812 Italian restaurant; Italian restaurant
Pr: Roger Thomson
*CFO: Chuck Sonsteby
*Sr VP: David Doyle
Genl Mgr: Todd Houchin

MAGGIANO'S LITTLE ITALY
See MAGGIANOS INC

MAGGIE B SALMAN ELEMENTARY
See SEALY INDEPENDENT SCHOOL DISTRICT

D-U-N-S 19-972-3201
MAGGIES FARM LLC
DOODAD
7990 Scond Flags Dr Ste D, Austell, GA 30168
Tel (800) 521-5234 Founded/Ownrshp 2005
Sales 24.0MM^E EMP 200
SIC 2711 Newspapers, publishing & printing; Commercial printing & newspaper publishing combined; Newspapers, publishing & printing; Commercial printing & newspaper publishing combined
Dir IT: Jeff Robinson
Mfg Mgr: Tim Cherry
Plnt Mgr: Kurt Charette
Sales Exec: Sharon Poulos

MAGGIE'S FUND
See DUFFIELD FAMILY FOUNDATION

MAGGNUSON LEXUS OF FREMONT
See FREMONT MAGNUSSONS IMPORTS INC

MAGGY LONDON BLOUSE DIV
See LONDON MAGGY INTERNATIONAL LTD

D-U-N-S 96-697-0188
■ **MAGIC ACQUISITION CORP**
POWER FORD
(Suby of AUTONATION INC) ★
23920 Creekside Rd, Valencia, CA 91355-1701
Tel (661) 382-4700 Founded/Ownrshp 1996
Sales 71.8MM^E EMP 350
SIC 5511 7538 5531 Automobiles, new & used; General automotive repair shops; Automotive & home supply stores; Automobiles, new & used; General automotive repair shops; Automotive & home supply stores
Genl Mgr: Dennis Hawking
CTO: Janice Gregory

MAGIC AIRE
See UNITED ELECTRIC CO LP

D-U-N-S 03-125-9054
MAGIC CIRCLE CORP
6302 E County Road 100 N, Coatesville, IN 46121-9689
Tel (765) 246-7737 Founded/Ownrshp 1981
Sales 52.6MM^E EMP 168
SIC 3524 Lawnmowers, residential: hand or power
Pr: Gary Morgan
*CFO: Simon Wilson
*VP: Jeff Haltom
Genl Mgr: John Layne
IT Man: Bradley Craig
Natl Sales: Rebecca Butler
Manager: Jason Sentell
Sls Mgr: Dixie Chopper
Sls Mgr: Bill Hare
Sls Mgr: Brice Hill
Sls Mgr: Chip Moses

MAGIC CITY FORD
See MAGIC CITY MOTOR CORP

D-U-N-S 00-313-3410
MAGIC CITY MOTOR CORP (VA)
MAGIC CITY FORD
809 Williamson Rd Ne, Roanoke, VA 24016-1525
Tel (540) 345-0911 Founded/Ownrshp 1938, 1952
Sales 48.6MM^E EMP 100
SIC 5511 7515 Automobiles, new & used; Pickups, new & used; Passenger car leasing; Automobiles, new & used; Pickups, new & used; Passenger car leasing
Ch: W W Johnson
CFO: Peney Burch
*VP: Harry G Johnson Jr
*VP: C M Robertson
Off Mgr: Katie Wright

IT Man: Darren Yeatts
Sls Mgr: Glenn Griffin
Sls Mgr: Edward Hall
Sales Asso: John Stclair

D-U-N-S 12-668-3551
MAGIC COIL PRODUCTS LLC
4143 County Road 61, Butler, IN 46721-9562
Tel (260) 868-2645 Founded/Ownrshp 2002
Sales 81.5MM EMP 50
Accts Beene Garter Llp Grand Rapids
SIC 5051 Steel; Steel
*CFO: Steve Lent
Manager: John Turco
Sls Mgr: Todd Moughler
Sales Asso: Marta Brown

MAGIC FORD
See FORD VALENCIA POWER

MAGIC FUND
See KEYBANK EB MANAGED GUARANTEED INVESTMENT CONTRACT FUND

MAGIC HAT BREWING COMPANY
See INDEPENDENT BREWERS UNITED CORP

MAGIC HOMAX
See HOMAX PRODUCTS INC

MAGIC IMAGE
See KENTUCKY TEXTILES INC

D-U-N-S 07-852-8568
MAGIC JOHNSON ENTERPRISES INC
9100 Wilshire Blvd 700e, Beverly Hills, CA 90212-3423
Tel (310) 247-2033 Founded/Ownrshp 1991
Sales 502.8MM^E EMP 10,100^E
SIC 8743 7389 Promotion service; Music recording producer
CEO: Earvin Johnson Jr
COO: Kawanna Brown
VP Opers: Sheila Ewing
Genl Couns: Brad Young

MAGIC KITCH'N
See PITCO FRIALATOR INC

D-U-N-S 07-881-9314
MAGIC LEAP INC
1855 Griffin Rd Ste B454, Dania Beach, FL 33004-2247
Tel (954) 889-7010 Founded/Ownrshp 2011
Sales 77.1MM^E EMP 200^E
SIC 7371 Computer software development
Pr: Rony Abovitz
*CFO: Russell Burke
*CFO: Scott Henry
*Ofcr: Rio Caraeff
Sr VP: Yannick Pellet
VP: Graeme Devine

MAGIC MART
See AMMARS INC

D-U-N-S 14-441-3127 EXP
MAGIC METALS INC
3401 Bay St, Union Gap, WA 98903-1886
Tel (509) 453-1690 Founded/Ownrshp 1985
Sales 25.3MM EMP 168
Accts Moss Adams Llp Yakima Washin
SIC 7692 3444 Welding repair; Sheet metalwork; Welding repair; Sheet metalwork
Pr: Garry L Griggs
*CFO: Timothy W Lick
*VP: Brian Warren
Dir IT: Rich Mickelson

D-U-N-S 07-828-1500 IMP
■ **MAGIC MOUNTAIN LLC**
SIX FLAGS MAGIC MOUNTAIN
(Suby of SIX FLAGS ENTERTAINMENT CORP) ★
26101 Magic Mountain Pkwy, Valencia, CA 91355-1052
Tel (661) 255-4100 Founded/Ownrshp 2006
Sales 21.1MM^E EMP 300
SIC 7922 7996 Entertainment promotion; Theme park, amusement; Entertainment promotion; Theme park, amusement
VP: Sherrie Bang
VP: Tim Tim Burkhart
Genl Mgr: Del Holland
Opers Mgr: Donald Spiller

MAGIC ON HOLD
See SPECTRIO LLC

D-U-N-S 11-899-1595 IMP
MAGIC SEASONING BLENDS LLC
CHEF PAUL PRUDHOMME
720 Distributors Row, New Orleans, LA 70123-3208
Tel (504) 731-3590 Founded/Ownrshp 1982
Sales 35.5MM^E EMP 150
SIC 2099 Seasonings & spices; Seasonings & spices
Ch Bd: Paul Prudhomme
Pr: Shawn McBribe
CFO: Paula Lacour
CFO: Tiffanie Roppolo
VP: John McBribe
Mktg Dir: Lori Prudhomme

D-U-N-S 07-972-9720
MAGIC SOFTWARE INC
5 Penn Plz Fl 23, New York, NY 10001-1810
Tel (917) 853-0482 Founded/Ownrshp 2014
Sales 6.5MM^E EMP 440
SIC 7371 8299 Computer software development & applications; Educational services
CEO: Akhtar Kamdar

D-U-N-S 02-088-7949
MAGIC STEEL CORP
4242 Clay Ave Sw Ste 2, Grand Rapids, MI 49548-3034
Tel (616) 532-4071 Founded/Ownrshp 1974
Sales 170.0MM^E EMP 103
SIC 5051 3312

D-U-N-S 11-069-2956
MAGIC STEEL SALES LLC
(Suby of MAGIC STEEL CORP) ★
4242 Clay Ave Sw Ste 2, Grand Rapids, MI 49548-3034
Tel (616) 532-4071 Founded/Ownrshp 1999
Sales 170.0MM EMP 62
SIC 5051

MAGIC TOYOTA
See I N X S INC

D-U-N-S 13-144-4028
MAGIC TRANSPORT INC
Pepsi Ind Pk Pr 2 Km 19 5, TOA Baja, PR 00949
Tel (787) 780-4020 Founded/Ownrshp 1984
Sales 26.0MM^E EMP 80
SIC 4491 Marine cargo handling
Pr: Carlos Padial
*VP: Antonio Pabon
VP: Tony Pabon
Genl Mgr: Johana Guadalebe
Opers Mgr: Johana Guadalupe

D-U-N-S 00-895-1501
MAGIC VALLEY ELECTRIC COOPERATIVE INC
1 3/4 Mi W Hwy 83, Mercedes, TX 78570
Tel (866) 225-5683 Founded/Ownrshp 1937
Sales 201.9MM EMP 217^E
Accts Bolinger Segars Gilbert And Mo
SIC 4911 Electric services; Electric services
Pr: Martin E Garcia
*Treas: M G Dyers
*Sec: Barbara S Miller
*VP: Reynaldo L Lopez
*Genl Mgr: John W Herrera
Sfty Dirs: Vicente Macias

D-U-N-S 04-727-2542
MAGIC VALLEY FRESH FROZEN LLC
MAGIC VALLEY FROZEN, LLC
3701 W Military Hwy, McAllen, TX 78503-4403
Tel (956) 994-8947 Founded/Ownrshp 2014
Sales 223.1MM^E EMP 275
SIC 5142 Frozen vegetables & fruit products; Frozen vegetables & fruit products

MAGIC VALLEY FROZEN, LLC
See MAGIC VALLEY FRESH FROZEN LLC

D-U-N-S 96-897-1028
MAGIC WINDOW CO
MAJIC WINDOW COMPANY
30580 Beck Rd, Wixom, MI 48393-2831
Tel (248) 668-9090 Founded/Ownrshp 1996
Sales 24.0MM^E EMP 140
SIC 5211 Door & window products; Door & window products
Pr: Bart Rue

MAGICAL CRUISE COMPANY
See DISNEY CRUISE VACATIONS INC

D-U-N-S 00-518-1789 IMP
MAGID GLOVE & SAFETY MANUFACTURING CO LLC (IL)
1300 Naperville Dr, Romeoville, IL 60446-1043
Tel (773) 384-2070 Founded/Ownrshp 1946
Sales 162.5MM^E EMP 862
SIC 3151 2381 5699 3842 2326 Gloves, leather: work; Gloves, work: woven or knit, made from purchased materials; Work clothing; Surgical appliances & supplies; Men's & boys' work clothing; Gloves, leather: work; Gloves, work: woven or knit, made from purchased materials; Work clothing; Surgical appliances & supplies; Men's & boys' work clothing
VP: Matt Montanez
VP: Ron Podgurski
Dist Mgr: Ken Barrick
Dist Mgr: David Elner
Dist Mgr: Melanie Jemison
S&M/Dir: Marlyse Cohen
S&M/Dir: Michael Stevens
Sls Mgr: Clay Covington
Sls Mgr: Ian Quan
Sales Asso: Paul Kwiatkowski
Sales Asso: Marcy Ozawa

D-U-N-S 00-578-1117
MAGILL CONSTRUCTION CO INC
977 Koopman Ln, Elkhorn, WI 53121-2023
Tel (262) 723-2283 Founded/Ownrshp 1953
Sales 20.5MM^E EMP 55
SIC 1542 Commercial & office building, new construction; Institutional building construction
Pr: Robert K Magill
*COO: Steven Knudson
VP: Matt Magill

D-U-N-S 01-257-3333
MAGLEBY & GREENWOOD PC
DMI
400 Cabot Dr, Hamilton, NJ 08691-3388
Tel (718) 649-9203 Founded/Ownrshp 1957
Sales 340.4MM EMP 70
SIC 5064

D-U-N-S 00-539-2162 IMP/EXP
MAGLINE INC (MI)
1205 W Cedar St, Standish, MI 48658-9563
Tel (800) 624-5463 Founded/Ownrshp 1945, 1947
Sales 27.8MM^E EMP 125
SIC 3537 Trucks, tractors, loaders, carriers & similar equipment; Dollies (hand or power trucks), industrial except mining; Trucks, tractors, loaders, carriers & similar equipment; Dollies (hand or power trucks), industrial except mining
CEO: D Brian Law
*Pr: Michael A Kirby
*Treas: George Lehnerer
IT Man: Matt Laplant
Plnt Mgr: Jim Gage
Ql Cn Mgr: Terry Perkins
Sales Exec: Greg Ecker
Sales Exec: Shauna Schneider

MAGLIO & COMPANY
See FRESH GROUP LTD

D-U-N-S 01-030-4397
■ MAGMA DESIGN AUTOMATION INC
(*Suby of* SYNOPSYS INC) ★
1650 Tech Dr Ste 100, San Jose, CA 95110
Tel (408) 565-7500 *Founded/Ownrshp* 2012
Sales 37.3MM^E *EMP* 696
SIC 7371 7373 Computer software development; Computer integrated systems design; Computer software development; Computer integrated systems design
CEO: Rajeev Madhavan
Pr: Noriaki Kikuchi
CFO: Peter S Teshima
Sr VP: Gregory C Walker
VP: Milan Lazich
Prin: Roy E Jewell
Mng Dir: Sarah Xu
CTO: Amir Ajami
IT Man: David Berthelot
IT Man: Joshua Fielden
VP Sls: Charlie Shin

MAGNA
See NORPLAS INDUSTRIES INC

MAGNA
See COSMA AMERICA HOLDINGS INC

D-U-N-S 11-551-3702 IMP
MAGNA CAR TOP SYSTEMS OF AMERICA INC
(*Suby of* MAGNA INTERNATIONAL INC)
2725 Commerce Pkwy, Auburn Hills, MI 48326-1789
Tel (248) 836-4500 *Founded/Ownrshp* 1999
Sales 123.2MM^E *EMP* 673^E
SIC 2394 Convertible tops, canvas or boat: from purchased materials; Convertible tops, canvas or boat: from purchased materials
Genl Mgr: Shawn Bentley
Sls Dir: Jim Horaney
Sls Dir: Dave Noel

D-U-N-S 00-698-9255
MAGNA CARTA COMPANIES INC (DE)
1 Park Ave Fl 15, New York, NY 10016-5802
Tel (212) 591-9500 *Founded/Ownrshp* 1925
Sales NA *EMP* 706
SIC 6331 Fire, marine & casualty insurance; Fire, marine & casualty insurance
Ch Bd: A L Furgatch
**Pr:* John T Hill II
**Sr VP:* David A Lawless
VP: Mark Battistelli
**VP:* Larry Gaddy
**VP:* Louis Masucci
**VP:* Theodore Smyk
**VP:* Grace H Yang
DP Exec: David Peterson

D-U-N-S 83-118-9480 IMP
MAGNA COMPOSITES LLC
6701 Statesville Blvd, Salisbury, NC 28147-7486
Tel (704) 797-8744 *Founded/Ownrshp* 2009
Sales NA *EMP* 323
SIC 3714

MAGNA COSMA BDY CHASSIS GROUP
See EAGLE BEND MFG INC

MAGNA DRIVE AUTO AMER DIV
See DRIVE AUTOMOTIVE INDUSTRIES OF AMERICA INC

D-U-N-S 83-042-5117
MAGNA E-CAR SYSTEMS OF AMERICA INC
(*Suby of* MAGNA INTERNATIONAL INC)
600 Wilshire Dr, Troy, MI 48084-1625
Tel (248) 836-4500 *Founded/Ownrshp* 2010
Sales 45.9MM^E *EMP* 300
SIC 5013 Automotive engines & engine parts; Automotive engines & engine parts
Pr: Donald Walker
**VP:* Jason Wolkove

D-U-N-S 96-479-3348
MAGNA E-CAR USA LIMITED PARTNERSHIP
(*Suby of* MAGNA INTERNATIONAL INC)
1955 Enterprise Dr, Rochester Hills, MI 48309-3804
Tel (248) 606-0600 *Founded/Ownrshp* 2010
Sales 25.4MM^E *EMP* 190
SIC 3621 Motors & generators; Motors & generators
Pt: Ted Robertson
VP: Ken Wagner
Dir IT: Jim Kane

D-U-N-S 07-950-1492
MAGNA E-CAR USA LLC
(*Suby of* MAGNA INTERNATIONAL INC)
10456 N Holly Rd, Holly, MI 48442-9319
Tel (248) 606-0600 *Founded/Ownrshp* 2010, 2012
Sales 20.9MM^E *EMP* 99
SIC 3764 Guided missile & space vehicle propulsion unit parts

D-U-N-S 95-883-4210 IMP
MAGNA ELECTRONICS INC
(*Suby of* MAGNA MIRRORS OF AMERICA INC) ★
10410 N Holly Rd, Holly, MI 48442-9332
Tel (810) 606-0444 *Founded/Ownrshp* 1996
Sales 144.7MM^E *EMP* 350
SIC 3672 3679 Printed circuit boards; Electronic circuits; Printed circuit boards; Electronic circuits
Pr: Carlos Mazzorine
Dir Bus: Michael Manchester
Prgrm Mgr: Dan Schram
Genl Mgr: Jeff Gary
IT Man: Cheryll Welch
Sys Mgr: Axel Nix
Sftwr Eng: Reza Sahba
Sftwr Eng: Brian Tedesco
Mktg Mgr: Dennis Hamilton
Sfty Mgr: Bob Carmack
Plnt Mgr: Tom Beattie

D-U-N-S 00-988-6712
MAGNA ENERGY SERVICES LLC
23295 Us Highway 85, La Salle, CO 80645-5201
Tel (970) 284-5752 *Founded/Ownrshp* 2007
Sales 31.6MM^E *EMP* 57^E
SIC 1389

D-U-N-S 80-121-7972
MAGNA ENERGY SERVICES LLC
385 Interlocken Blvd # 250, Broomfield, CO 80021-8067
Tel (307) 682-4195 *Founded/Ownrshp* 2007
Sales 32.7MM^E *EMP* 199^E
SIC 1781 Water well servicing; Water well servicing
**CEO:* Dennis Douglas
**Ch:* Neville Vere Nicoll
**VP:* Allan Brownie
Off Mgr: Tonia Spruhan

D-U-N-S 18-205-5137 IMP/EXP
MAGNA EXTERIORS AND INTERIORS OF AMERICA INC
DECOMA ADMARK
(*Suby of* MAGNA INTERNATIONAL INC)
750 Tower Dr, Troy, MI 48098-2863
Tel (248) 631-1100 *Founded/Ownrshp* 1987
Sales 1.1MMM^E *EMP* 2,400
SIC 3714 3544 8711 Motor vehicle body components & frame; Forms (molds), for foundry & plastics working machinery; Engineering services; Motor vehicle body components & frame; Forms (molds), for foundry & plastics working machinery; Engineering services
CEO: Donald J Walker
**Pr:* Guenther Apfalter
**COO:* Tom J Skudutis
**CFO:* Vincent J Galifi
**Ex VP:* Jeffrey O Palmer
**VP:* William Frederiksen
VP: Joanne Horibe
VP: Katie Meilinger
**VP:* S Randall Smallbone
Ex Dir: John Bol
Prgrm Mgr: Julia Kendrick

MAGNA GLOBAL TRADING
See ORION TRADING WORLDWIDE LLC

D-U-N-S 04-540-8742
MAGNA HOSPITALITY GROUP LC
300 Cntrvlle Rd Ste 300e, Warwick, RI 02886
Tel (401) 886-4484 *Founded/Ownrshp* 1998
Sales 20.4MM^E *EMP* 120
SIC 7011 Hotels & motels
CEO: Robert Indeglia Jr

D-U-N-S 83-040-1456
MAGNA INTERNATIONAL OF AMERICA INC
(*Suby of* MAGNA INTERNATIONAL INC)
750 Tower Dr 7000, Troy, MI 48098-2863
Tel (248) 729-2400 *Founded/Ownrshp* 1987
Sales 1.7MMM^E *EMP* 2,803^E
SIC 3714 Motor vehicle parts & accessories
Pr: Donald Walker
**Pr:* Marc Neeb
**Ex VP:* Vincent J Galifi
**Ex VP:* Swamy Kotagiri
**Ex VP:* Jeffrey O Palmer
VP: Scott Paradise
Prgrm Mgr: Vince Harris
Genl Mgr: David O'Connell
QA Dir: Jim Vanderweel
Ql Cn Mgr: Branden Caldwell

D-U-N-S 00-423-8739
MAGNA MACHINE CO (OH)
11180 Southland Rd, Cincinnati, OH 45240-3202
Tel (513) 851-6900 *Founded/Ownrshp* 1953
Sales 28.4MM^E *EMP* 104
SIC 3556 3554 3599 Bakery machinery; Paper industries machinery; Machine shop, jobbing & repair; Bakery machinery; Paper industries machinery; Machine shop, jobbing & repair
Pr: Scott Kramer
**CFO:* Greg Bodenburg
CFO: Mark Wilson
Treas: Paul Kramer
**VP:* James Parker
Genl Mgr: Greg Kalenowski
Sls Mgr: Casie Qvick

D-U-N-S 00-603-1561
MAGNA MIRRORS NORTH AMERICA LLC
LOWELL ENGINEERING
(*Suby of* MAGNA INTERNATIONAL INC)
6151 Bancroft Ave Se, Alto, MI 49302-9313
Tel (616) 827-3712 *Founded/Ownrshp* 1954, 1990
Sales 220.4MM^E *EMP* 1,100
SIC 3231 3442 Mirrors, truck & automobile: made from purchased glass; Metal doors, sash & trim; Mirrors, truck & automobile: made from purchased glass; Metal doors, sash & trim

D-U-N-S 00-601-1936 EXP
MAGNA MIRRORS OF AMERICA INC (MI)
(*Suby of* MAGNA INTERNATIONAL OF AMERICA INC) ★
5085 Kraft Ave Se, Grand Rapids, MI 49512-9707
Tel (616) 942-0163 *Founded/Ownrshp* 1905, 2008
Sales 1.7MMM^E *EMP* 8,000
SIC 3231 3647 3827 Mirrors, truck & automobile: made from purchased glass; Windshields, glass: made from purchased glass; Dome lights, automotive; Automotive lighting fixtures; Optical instruments & lenses; Mirrors, truck & automobile: made from purchased glass; Windshields, glass: made from purchased glass; Dome lights, automotive; Automotive lighting fixtures; Optical instruments & lenses
CEO: James L Brodie
**Sr VP:* Niall R Lynam
Prgrm Mgr: Jeff Brach
Prgrm Mgr: Darrell Combs
Prgrm Mgr: Erik Fontaine
Prgrm Mgr: Bricia Grothaus
Prgrm Mgr: Craig Kendall
Prgrm Mgr: Brian McGuire
Prgrm Mgr: Kim Morris
Prgrm Mgr: Todd Rhoades
Prgrm Mgr: Jerry Smith

D-U-N-S 61-727-2898 IMP
MAGNA MODULAR SYSTEMS INC
MAGNA TEAM SYSTEMS
(*Suby of* DECOMA ADMARK) ★
1800 Nathan Dr, Toledo, OH 43611-1091
Tel (419) 324-3387 *Founded/Ownrshp* 2008
Sales 225.0MM^E *EMP* 350
Accts Ernst & Young Llp Toronto Ca
SIC 3714 Motor vehicle body components & frame; Motor vehicle body components & frame
CEO: Grahhame Burrow
**Genl Mgr:* Keith McMahon

MAGNA POWERTRAIN LANSING
See LANSING L MPT L C

D-U-N-S 84-915-9988 IMP
MAGNA POWERTRAIN OF AMERICA INC
(*Suby of* MAGNA INTERNATIONAL INC)
1870 Technology Dr, Troy, MI 48083-4232
Tel (248) 597-7811 *Founded/Ownrshp* 1992
Sales 92.4MM^E *EMP* 151
SIC 5013 Automotive supplies; Automotive supplies
CEO: Donald J Walker
Pr: Steven Rush
CFO: Michael Alexander
Bd of Dir: Eric Richardson
Dir Risk M: Robert Dubois
Ex Dir: Kim Buhl
Prgrm Mgr: Hector Castro
Prgrm Mgr: Bret Farmer
Prgrm Mgr: Alain Hadorn
Prgrm Mgr: Christopher Shaw
Brnch Mgr: Len Macneil

MAGNA POWERTRAIN TROY
See MAGNA POWERTRAIN USA INC

D-U-N-S 16-563-2527 IMP
MAGNA POWERTRAIN USA INC
MAGNA POWERTRAIN TROY
(*Suby of* MAGNA POWERTRAIN INC)
1870 Technology Dr, Troy, MI 48083-4232
Tel (248) 680-4900 *Founded/Ownrshp* 2004
Sales 442.9MM^E *EMP* 2,983
SIC 3714 Motor vehicle engines & parts; Motor vehicle engines & parts
Pr: Jake Hirsch
Opers Mgr: Teri Freeburn
Ql Cn Mgr: Rob Janis
Ql Cn Mgr: Samara Wiltse

D-U-N-S 78-301-6538 IMP
MAGNA SEATING OF AMERICA INC
INTIER AUTOMOTIVE SEATING
(*Suby of* MAGNA INTERNATIONAL INC)
39600 Lewis Dr Ste 216, Novi, MI 48377-2953
Tel (248) 553-8011 *Founded/Ownrshp* 1985
Sales 415.4MM^E *EMP* 2,377
SIC 3714 Motor vehicle parts & accessories; Motor vehicle parts & accessories
Pr: Joseph Pittel
**Pr:* Mike Bisson
Pr: John Oilar
Ex VP: Michael McCarthy
**VP:* Glen Copeland
Prgrm Mgr: Scott Lavoie
Prgrm Mgr: John Radford
Prgrm Mgr: Mark Sander
Genl Mgr: Simon Kew
IT Man: Mark Sobel
VP Opers: Burge Young

MAGNA TEAM SYSTEMS
See MAGNA MODULAR SYSTEMS INC

D-U-N-S 80-909-4803 IMP/EXP
MAGNA TECHFORM OF AMERICA INC
(*Suby of* MAGNA CLOSURES INC)
128 Davis St, Portland, TN 37148-2081
Tel (615) 323-8668 *Founded/Ownrshp* 2014
Sales 20.0MM^E *EMP* 84
SIC 3714 Motor vehicle body components & frame
Pr: John O'Hara
Ex VP: Larry Langley
VP: Phil Landry
Genl Mgr: Antonio Cesaria
Genl Mgr: William Gross

D-U-N-S 05-741-2959
MAGNA-POWER ELECTRONICS (INC)
39 Royal Rd, Flemington, NJ 08822-6001
Tel (908) 237-2200 *Founded/Ownrshp* 1981
Sales 20.0MM^E *EMP* 85
SIC 3629 Electronic generation equipment
Pr: Ira J Pitel
**VP:* Adam Pitel
Prd Mgr: Rick Rainey

D-U-N-S 07-884-2472 IMP
MAGNA-TECH MANUFACTURING LLC
(*Suby of* CAPITALWORKS LLC) ★
3416 S Hoyt Ave, Muncie, IN 47302-2081
Tel (765) 284-5050 *Founded/Ownrshp* 2015
Sales 22.5MM^E *EMP* 140^E
SIC 3479 Coating of metals with plastic or resins
Pr: Dan Irvin
COO: John Durkovich
**CFO:* Derek Roesener
VP: Dennis Oakes
VP: Darren Smith
Genl Mgr: Shane Williams
Off Mgr: Bonnie Hampshire
Opers Mgr: Stephen Ferris
Plnt Mgr: Jason Collins
Ql Cn Mgr: Scott Shepherd
S&M/VP: Chris Russell

D-U-N-S 03-245-4357 IMP
■ MAGNABLEND INC
(*Suby of* UNIVAR INC) ★
326 N Grand Ave, Waxahachie, TX 75165-2220
Tel (972) 938-2028 *Founded/Ownrshp* 2012
Sales 182.0MM^E *EMP* 420
SIC 2899 Oil treating compounds; Oil treating compounds
Pr: Scott Pendery
Pr: Dan Johnson
**CFO:* Stephen Barnish
**VP:* Darlene Pendery
Cmptr Lab: Kimberly Cook
Cmptr Lab: Marita Hartford
IT Man: Christopher Richie
Plnt Mgr: Jason Honrud
Plnt Mgr: Josh McDonald
Mktg Mgr: Lauren Campbell
Manager: Matt Jones

D-U-N-S 14-821-9962
MAGNACARE HOLDINGS INC
1 Penn Plz Ste 4630, New York, NY 10119-4632
Tel (516) 282-8000 *Founded/Ownrshp* 1998
Sales 52.2MM^E *EMP* 250^E
SIC 8742 Hospital & health services consultant; Hospital & health services consultant
Pr: Joseph Berardo Jr
Pr: Derek Moore
COO: Thomas B Considine
CFO: Jim Cusumano
Chf Mktg O: Catherine Marino
Sr VP: Janine Bliablias
Sr VP: Gregg Gordon
Sr VP: Steven Kokulak
Sr VP: Bernard Piccione
VP: Arun Bhatia
VP: Joseph Brennan
VP: Elizabeth Jennings
VP: Ashan Nilaweera
VP: Michael Tufo

MAGNAFLOW
See CAR SOUND EXHAUST SYSTEM INC

D-U-N-S 15-580-8285 EXP
■ MAGNATRAX CORP
(*Suby of* NUCOR CORP) ★
1220 Old Alpharetta Rd # 310, Alpharetta, GA 30005-3972
Tel (678) 455-3360 *Founded/Ownrshp* 2007
Sales 136.4MM^E *EMP* 1,800
SIC 3448 3442 3479 4213 3444 Prefabricated metal buildings; Prefabricated metal components; Metal doors; Coating of metals & formed products; Trucking, except local; Metal roofing & roof drainage equipment; Prefabricated metal buildings; Prefabricated metal components; Metal doors; Coating of metals & formed products; Trucking, except local; Metal roofing & roof drainage equipment
CEO: Harry R Lowe
**CFO:* James D Frias
**Ex VP:* Allen Capsuto

D-U-N-S 07-075-8651 EXP
MAGNECO/METREL INC (OH)
223 W Interstate Rd, Addison, IL 60101-4513
Tel (630) 543-6660 *Founded/Ownrshp* 1981
Sales 65.8MM *EMP* 145
Accts Mowery & Schoenfeld Llc Linc
SIC 3297 Nonclay refractories; Nonclay refractories
Pr: Charles W Connors Jr
**CFO:* Susan C Malloy
**Ch:* Charles W Connors
Treas: Susan Malloy
**VP:* Madjid Soofi
Genl Mgr: Dominic Pautler
VP Mktg: Albert Dzermejko
S&M/VP: James S Irwin
Mktg Mgr: James Daley

D-U-N-S 55-684-6835 IMP/EXP
MAGNELL ASSOCIATE INC
ABS COMPUTER TECHNOLOGIES
17560 Rowland St, City of Industry, CA 91748-1114
Tel (562) 695-8823 *Founded/Ownrshp* 2005
Sales NA *EMP* 900
SIC 5045 Computers & accessories, personal & home entertainment

D-U-N-S 96-176-4156
MAGNEMOTION INC
139 Barnum Rd, Devens, MA 01434-3509
Tel (978) 757-9100 *Founded/Ownrshp* 1996
Sales 25.0MM *EMP* 78
SIC 3535 Unit handling conveying systems
CEO: Todd Webber
**CEO:* Richard Thornton
**Sec:* Mike Hannon
VP: Peter Ashe
**VP:* Tracy Clark
**VP:* Peter Mattila
**VP:* Brian Perreault
VP: Jim Wieler
**VP:* Eric Wildi
Snr Sftwr: Keith Ruenheck
Snr Sftwr: Lenny Story

D-U-N-S 16-657-2615 IMP
■ MAGNEQUENCH INC
(*Suby of* MOLYCORP MINERALS CANADA ULC)
237 S Pendleton Ave Ste C, Pendleton, IN 46064-1187
Tel (765) 778-7809 *Founded/Ownrshp* 1999
Sales 148.1MM^E *EMP* 1,300
SIC 3499 Magnets, permanent: metallic; Magnets, permanent: metallic
Pr: Constantine Karayanno
**Ch Bd:* Hong Zhang
**Pr:* Archibald Cox Jr
**COO:* Gary Riley
**CFO:* K C Ashok
**Sr VP:* Shannon Song
Mng Dir: Doug McInnes
Genl Mgr: Bernd Grieb
Off Mgr: Missy Wilson

D-U-N-S 00-791-7966 IMP/EXP
MAGNESITA REFRACTORIES CO (PA)
(*Suby of* MAGNESITA REFRATARIOS S/A.)
425 S Salem Church Rd, York, PA 17408-5955
Tel (717) 792-3611 *Founded/Ownrshp* 1941, 2008
Sales 121.2MM^E *EMP* 500
SIC 3297 3274 1422 Dolomite or dolomite-magnesite brick & shapes; Lime; Dolomite, crushed & broken-quarrying; Dolomite or dolomite-magnesite brick & shapes; Lime; Dolomite, crushed & broken-quarrying
Pr: Otto Levy
CFO: Jose Beraldo
**Sec:* Kelly L Myers

Sr Cor Off: Grace Marrero
Ex VP: Jim Piraino
**VP:* Paul A Dydek
**Prin:* Ronaldo Iabrudi Dos Santos Per
Off Mgr: Lorie Baker
MIS Dir: Brian Mangel
Dir IT: Don Griffin
Dir IT: Brian Mengel
Board of Directors: Flavio Rezende Barbosa, David A Gregory, Ronaldo Iabrudi Dos Santos

D-U-N-S 82-967-3115
MAGNESIUM ALUMINUM MICHIGAN CORP
MAMC MANUFACTURING
(*Suby of* TALON HOLDING LLC) ★
3559 Kraft Ave Se, Grand Rapids, MI 49512-2033
Tel (616) 949-2002 *Founded/Ownrshp* 2013
Sales 22.5MM^E *EMP* 100^E
SIC 3363 5051 Aluminum die-castings; Aluminum bars, rods, ingots, sheets, pipes, plates, etc.
Pr: Michael Carr

D-U-N-S 80-787-6867 IMP
MAGNESIUM PRODUCTS OF AMERICA INC
MERIDIAN LIGHTWEIGHT TECH
(*Suby of* MLTH HOLDINGS INC)
47805 Galleon Dr, Plymouth, MI 48170-2434
Tel (517) 663-2700 *Founded/Ownrshp* 2008
Sales 143.4MM^E *EMP* 360
SIC 3364 3369 3714 Magnesium & magnesium-base alloy die-castings; Nonferrous foundries; Motor vehicle parts & accessories; Magnesium & magnesium-base alloy die-castings; Nonferrous foundries; Motor vehicle parts & accessories
Pr: Erick Showalter
**Treas:* Daniel C Hanson
Plnt Mgr: Rick Lumsden
Snr Mgr: Chad Jackson

D-U-N-S 02-495-6344
MAGNESS OIL CO
CIRCLE K
167 Tucker Cemetery Rd, Gassville, AR 72635-8701
Tel (870) 425-4353 *Founded/Ownrshp* 1960
Sales 92.3MM^E *EMP* 120
SIC 5171 5541 5411 Petroleum bulk stations; Filling stations, gasoline; Convenience stores, independent; Petroleum bulk stations; Filling stations, gasoline; Convenience stores, independent
Pr: Benny W Magness
CFO: Richard Simmons
**VP:* Jeffrey W Magness
Genl Mgr: Debra Jones

MAGNET GROUP
See MAGNET LLC

D-U-N-S 12-175-7835 IMP
MAGNET LLC
MAGNET GROUP
7 Chamber Dr, Washington, MO 63090-5258
Tel (800) 458-9457 *Founded/Ownrshp* 1997
Sales 81.9MM^E *EMP* 425
SIC 3499 3993 Magnets, permanent: metallic; Signs & advertising specialties; Magnets, permanent: metallic; Signs & advertising specialties
CFO: Annette Eckerle
CFO: David Peden
Sr VP: Dan Jellinek
VP: Alissa Baker
VP: Jessica Hiner
Rgnl Mgr: Andy Stilts
CIO: Jeff Myer
CIO: Jeff Myers
IT Man: Renee Whitcraft
Plnt Mgr: Dianna Elkins
Natl Sales: Larry Asay

MAGNET P I
See EASTBAY RETAIL VENTURES INC

D-U-N-S 00-967-8939 IMP
MAGNET SALES & MFG CO INC
INTEGRATED MAGNETICS
(*Suby of* INTEGRATED TECHNOLOGIES GROUP INC) ★
11248 Playa Ct, Culver City, CA 90230-6100
Tel (310) 391-7213 *Founded/Ownrshp* 1981
Sales 8.8MM^E *EMP* 350
SIC 3448 3264 3621 Magnets, permanent: metallic; Magnets, permanent: ceramic or ferrite; Servomotors, electric; Coils, for electric motors or generators; Torque motors, electric; Prefabricated metal buildings; Porcelain electrical supplies; Servomotors, electric; Coils, for electric motors or generators; Torque motors, electric
Pr: Anil Nanji
Pr: Alan Anderson
**VP:* Gary Hooper
Dir IT: Oscar Rios
Mktg Mgr: Shaheen Nanji

D-U-N-S 82-692-1970
MAGNET-SCHULTZ AMERICA HOLDING LLC
401 Plaza Dr, Westmont, IL 60559-1233
Tel (630) 789-0600 *Founded/Ownrshp* 2007
Sales 21.8MM^E *EMP* 125^E
SIC 3451 3625 3599 Screw machine products; Solenoid switches (industrial controls); Brakes, electromagnetic; Machine & other job shop work; Screw machine products; Solenoid switches (industrial controls); Brakes, electromagnetic; Machine & other job shop work
Ch: Wolfgang E Schultz
Pr: David Stockwell
CFO: Theodore D Gault
Mfg Mgr: Steve Tietjen

D-U-N-S 78-331-1582
MAGNET-SCHULTZ OF AMERICA INC
MSA
(*Suby of* MAGNET-SCHULTZ AMERICA HOLDING LLC) ★
401 Plaza Dr, Westmont, IL 60559-1233
Tel (630) 789-0600 *Founded/Ownrshp* 1990
Sales 21.8MM^E *EMP* 85
SIC 3451 3625 3599 Screw machine products; Solenoid switches (industrial controls); Brakes, electromagnetic; Machine & other job shop work
Pr: David L Stockwell
**CFO:* Theodore D Gault
**VP:* Albert Schultz
Board of Directors: Dieter Schultz

D-U-N-S 01-336-2625
MAGNETATION INC (MN)
(*Suby of* MAGNETATION LLC) ★
102 Ne 3rd St Ste 120, Grand Rapids, MN 55744-2868
Tel (218) 398-0079 *Founded/Ownrshp* 2006
Sales 21.0MM^E *EMP* 100^E
SIC 1011 Iron ore mining; Iron ore mining
CEO: Larry Lehtinen

D-U-N-S 96-996-7731 IMP
MAGNETATION LLC
102 Ne 3rd St Ste 120, Grand Rapids, MN 55744-2868
Tel (218) 999-5165 *Founded/Ownrshp* 2010
Sales 100.0MM *EMP* 475
SIC 1011 Iron ore mining
CFO: Joseph A Broking
**Ch Bd:* Larry Lehtinen
**Pr:* Matt Lehtinen
**CFO:* Joe Broking
**VP:* Danilo Bibancos
**VP:* David Chappie
Genl Mgr: Robb Bigelow
Genl Mgr: Todd Roth
IT Man: Justin Haar
Sfty Dirs: Gina Gould
Opers Supe: Ron Chambers

D-U-N-S 06-923-1934
■ **MAGNETEC CORP** (CT)
ITHACA PERIPHERALS DIV
(*Suby of* TRANSACT TECHNOLOGIES INC) ★
7 Laser Ln, Wallingford, CT 06492-1928
Tel (203) 949-9933 *Founded/Ownrshp* 1973, 1996
Sales 52.2MM^E *EMP* 100
SIC 3577 Printers, computer; Printers, computer
Pr: Bart C Shuldman
Pr: David Ritchie
CFO: Richard Cote
Treas: Steven De Martino
Sr VP: John Cygielnik
Sr VP: Michael Kumpf
Sr VP: Lucy H Staley
VP: Richard Brunet
VP: Joanne Draper
VP: Joanne Wist

D-U-N-S 14-166-0303 IMP
■ **MAGNETECH INDUSTRIAL SERVICES INC**
(*Suby of* IES SUBSIDIARY HOLDINGS INC) ★
800 Nave Rd Se, Massillon, OH 44646-9476
Tel (330) 830-3500 *Founded/Ownrshp* 2013
Sales 42.8MM^E *EMP* 200
SIC 7629 Electrical equipment repair services
Pr: Michael P Moore
CFO: Mike Topa
VP: Cullen Burdette
VP: Edward Matheny
**VP:* William Wisnieweski
IT Man: Kent Adams
IT Man: Clyde Bartow
IT Man: Susan Hallett
Opers Mgr: Kevin Tripp
Sls Dir: Jim Skaggs
Sales Asso: Robert McCracken

D-U-N-S 11-753-1954 IMP
■ **MAGNETEK INC**
MAGNETEK MATERIAL HANDLING
(*Suby of* COLUMBUS MCKINNON CORP) ★
N49w13650 Campbell Dr, Menomonee Falls, WI 53051-7051
Tel (262) 783-3500 *Founded/Ownrshp* 2015
Sales 110.2MM^E *EMP* 328
Tkr Sym MAG *Exch* NGM
SIC 3625 Relays & industrial controls; Control equipment, electric; Electric controls & control accessories, industrial; Relays & industrial controls; Control equipment, electric; Electric controls & control accessories, industrial
Pr: Peter M McCormick
CFO: Marty J Schwenner
Treas: John Colling
VP: Scott S Cramer
VP: Richard Heppe
VP: Hungsun S Hui
VP: Paul Lindhorst
VP: Peter McCormick
VP: Michael J Stauber
Rgnl Mgr: Dick Taralli
Area Mgr: James Mulleady

MAGNETEK MATERIAL HANDLING
See MAGNETEK INC

MAGNETI MARELLI HOLDG USA INC
See MAGNETI MARELLI HOLDING USA LLC

D-U-N-S 96-254-3109
MAGNETI MARELLI HOLDING USA LLC
MAGNETI MARELLI HOLDG USA INC
(*Suby of* MAGNETI MARELLI SPA)
3900 Automation Ave, Auburn Hills, MI 48326-1788
Tel (248) 418-3000 *Founded/Ownrshp* 2004
Sales 3.5MMM^E *EMP* 34,000^E
SIC 3714 Motor vehicle parts & accessories; Motor vehicle parts & accessories
Pr: E Razelli
**Ch Bd:* Eugenio Razelli
**Pr:* James Rosseau
**CFO:* Roger Moore
**Treas:* Renato Bampa Soares
VP: Steven P Eason
Mgr Info S: Joseph Liles

D-U-N-S 14-433-7748 IMP
MAGNETI MARELLI NORTH AMERICA INC
3900 Automation Ave, Auburn Hills, MI 48326-1788
Tel (248) 418-3000 *Founded/Ownrshp* 2008
Sales 44.8MM^E *EMP* 101
SIC 5013 3714 Springs, shock absorbers & struts; Motor vehicle body components & frame; Shock absorbers, motor vehicle
Pr: Edison Lino
Ofcr: Paolo Arrighi
**VP:* Jose Tavares
Prgrm Mgr: Matthew Fraser
Plnt Mgr: Delmr Patterson
Sls Mgr: Cindy Dang
Snr Mgr: Gabriele Ercole
Snr Mgr: Ronnie Neri

D-U-N-S 83-289-8469 IMP
MAGNETI MARELLI OF TENNESSEE LLC
M M SUSPENSIONS
(*Suby of* MAGNETI MARELLI SPA)
181 Bennett Dr, Pulaski, TN 38478-5209
Tel (931) 363-4535 *Founded/Ownrshp* 2009
Sales 42.3MM^E *EMP* 110
SIC 3446 Acoustical suspension systems, metal; Acoustical suspension systems, metal
CFO: Jose Roca
Plnt Mgr: Greg Galloway

D-U-N-S 03-829-1837 IMP
MAGNETI MARELLI POWERTRAIN USA LLC
(*Suby of* MAGNETI MARELLI SPA)
2101 Nash St, Sanford, NC 27330-6338
Tel (919) 775-6247 *Founded/Ownrshp* 1975
Sales 116.9MM^E *EMP* 500^E
SIC 3714 3592 Fuel systems & parts, motor vehicle; Carburetors, pistons, rings, valves; Fuel systems & parts, motor vehicle; Carburetors, pistons, rings, valves
CEO: Roberto Flora
CFO: Walter Doglio
CFO: Marco Manzi
VP: Earl Losey
VP: Marco Nassi
VP: Gene Spektor
Mng Dir: Roberto Dalla
Prgrm Mgr: Greg Doble
Prgrm Mgr: Fabrice Grellier
Prgrm Mgr: Glenn Purvis
Dir IT: Robin Olah

MAGNETIC
See MYBUYS INC

D-U-N-S 00-148-9756 IMP
MAGNETIC ANALYSIS CORP (NY)
M A C
103 Fairview Pk Dr Ste 2, Elmsford, NY 10523-1544
Tel (914) 530-2000 *Founded/Ownrshp* 1928
Sales 34.9MM^E *EMP* 140
SIC 3829 3825 Testing equipment: abrasion, shearing strength, etc.; Instruments to measure electricity; Testing equipment: abrasion, shearing strength, etc.; Instruments to measure electricity
Ch: William S Gould III
**Ch Bd:* Jl Vitulli
V Ch: Robert Gould
**CFO:* Thomas F Gannalo
VP: Paul Bebick
**VP:* Dudley Boden
VP: Donald Bugden
Dist Mgr: Fred Fundy
Dist Mgr: John Hobbs
Dist Mgr: William Hoffmann
Genl Mgr: Billy Beasley
Board of Directors: Phil Battaglino, Karl Bergstrand, Jay Carron, Deborah Meyers

D-U-N-S 06-845-1533
MAGNETIC INSPECTION LABORATORY INC
M I L
1401 Greenleaf Ave, Elk Grove Village, IL 60007-5536
Tel (847) 437-4488 *Founded/Ownrshp* 1942
Sales 21.1MM^E *EMP* 85
SIC 8734 7692 3471 2899 Metallurgical testing laboratory; Welding repair; Plating & polishing; Chemical preparations
Pr: Robert L Schiewe
COO: Mike Ulman
VP: Jay Gandhi
VP: Andy Johnson
**VP:* Tim Schiewe
Genl Mgr: Thomas Hackler
Ql Cn Mgr: William Roman
Mktg Dir: Brandon Holleran
Sls Mgr: Don Berg

D-U-N-S 00-810-2212
MAGNETIC INSTRUMENTS CORP
M I C GROUP
(*Suby of* J B POINDEXTER & CO INC) ★
3140 S Blue Bell Rd, Brenham, TX 77833-5153
Tel (979) 277-7800 *Founded/Ownrshp* 1992
Sales 63.0MM^E *EMP* 489
SIC 3599 Machine shop, jobbing & repair; Machine shop, jobbing & repair
Ch Bd: John B Poindexter
**Pr:* Nelson Byman
Pr: Stan Stafford
**Sec:* Stephen Magee
VP: James Horner
**VP:* Brad Leuschner
VP: Larry Mersmann
Dist Mgr: Beverley Aron
Genl Mgr: Chris Callahan
Genl Mgr: Howard Goman
CTO: Ervin Parker

D-U-N-S 00-233-4084 IMP
MAGNETIC METALS CORP
(*Suby of* INDEL INC) ★
1900 Hayes Ave, Camden, NJ 08105-3656
Tel (856) 964-7842 *Founded/Ownrshp* 1977
Sales 46.5MM^E *EMP* 300
SIC 3542 Magnetic forming machines; Magnetic forming machines
Ch Bd: Henry Rowan Jr
**Owner:* Frank Raneiro
IT Man: Karen Coffaro

D-U-N-S 06-358-5988
MAGNETIC SPRINGS WATER CO
1917 Joyce Ave, Columbus, OH 43219-1029
Tel (614) 421-1780 *Founded/Ownrshp* 1974
Sales 57.1MM^E *EMP* 75
SIC 5149 5499 Mineral or spring water bottling; Water: distilled mineral or spring
Ch: James E Allison
**Pr:* Jeffrey Allison
**Sec:* Beverly Allison
**VP:* Sherry Allison
VP: Tim Vansickle
Genl Mgr: Kim Vansickle

MAGNETIC TECHNOLOGY
See ARNOLD MAGNETIC TECHNOLOGIES CORP

D-U-N-S 02-353-6386
MAGNETIC TICKET & LABEL CORP
MT&L CARD PRODUCTS
(*Suby of* HFS HOLDING CORP) ★
8719 Diplomacy Row, Dallas, TX 75247-5401
Tel (214) 634-8600 *Founded/Ownrshp* 1982
Sales 97.6MM^E *EMP* 400
SIC 2679 Labels, paper: made from purchased material; Labels, paper: made from purchased material
Pr: Peter A Pyhrr
**Sr VP:* Stan Welker
VP: Rafael Alaniz
VP: Dominic Cinquepalmi
VP: Dave Fehrman
**VP:* Barbara Fulenwiter
VP: Michael Hale
VP: Dina Reijers
VP: Stanley Walker
MIS Mgr: Helmut Lilischkies
VP Sls: Reiner Vanooteghem

MAGNETICSGROUP
See NATIONAL MAGNETICS GROUP INC

D-U-N-S 10-817-0648
MAGNETIKA INC
2041 W 139th St, Gardena, CA 90249-2409
Tel (310) 527-8100 *Founded/Ownrshp* 1981
Sales 40.8MM^E *EMP* 121
SIC 5063 3612 Transformers, electric; Power transmission equipment, electric; Ballasts for lighting fixtures; Power transformers, electric; Transformers, electric; Power transmission equipment, electric; Ballasts for lighting fixtures; Power transformers, electric
Pr: Francis Ishida
**CEO:* Basil P Caloyeras
Genl Mgr: Nick Defalco
IT Man: Ieng Liu
Sls&Mrk Ex: Frank McMahon

D-U-N-S 04-892-8378
MAGNETIX CORP
3600 Ecommerce Pl, Orlando, FL 32808-1340
Tel (407) 926-2400 *Founded/Ownrshp* 1992
Sales 24.9MM^E *EMP* 175
SIC 3652 3695 Pre-recorded records & tapes; Magnetic & optical recording media; Pre-recorded records & tapes; Magnetic & optical recording media
Ch: Robert Lefort
**Pr:* William Hohns

D-U-N-S 00-808-4725
MAGNETO & DIESEL INJECTOR SERVICE INC
M & D DISTRIBUTORS
7902 Fm 1960 Bypass Rd W, Humble, TX 77338-4002
Tel (713) 928-5686 *Founded/Ownrshp* 1943
Sales 50.0MM *EMP* 125
SIC 5084 Engines & parts, diesel; Engines & parts, diesel
Pr: A Bruce Ingram Jr
**Sec:* Donna Ingram
**VP:* Steve Bertsch
**VP:* Bruce Ingram III
CIO: Vincent Stokely
Sls Mgr: Trey Ingram
Sls Mgr: Ben Sassani

D-U-N-S 08-982-4684 EXP
MAGNETROL INTERNATIONAL INC
705 Enterprise St, Aurora, IL 60504-8149
Tel (630) 723-6600 *Founded/Ownrshp* 1979
Sales 103.6MM^E *EMP* 364
SIC 3823 3812 3699 3643 3625 3541 Level & bulk measuring instruments, industrial process; Flow instruments, industrial process type; Search & navigation equipment; Electrical equipment & supplies; Current-carrying wiring devices; Relays & industrial controls; Machine tools, metal cutting type; Level & bulk measuring instruments, industrial process; Flow instruments, industrial process type; Search & navigation equipment; Electrical equipment & supplies; Current-carrying wiring devices; Relays & industrial controls; Machine tools, metal cutting type
Pr: Jeffrey K Swallow
Pr: John Benway
**COO:* John E Heiser
**CFO:* Marlin K Underwood
VP: Michael Flasza
Assoc Dir: Julie Bjorkman
QA Dir: Rich Forst
Dir IT: Greg Martis
IT Man: Darren Meyer
IT Man: Paul Rymek
IT Man: Brian Timm

MAGNI FAB & MAGNETIC
See MAGNI- POWER CO

D-U-N-S 15-126-6269 IMP
MAGNI GROUP INC
390 Park St Ste 300, Birmingham, MI 48009-3400
Tel (248) 647-4500 *Founded/Ownrshp* 1987
Sales 88.9MM^E *EMP* 170
SIC 2899 3479 Rust resisting compounds; Coating, rust preventive; Rust resisting compounds; Coating, rust preventive
Ch: David E Berry
**Pr:* Tim Berry
VP: Robert Keagy
VP: Kamlesh Passi

VP: Doug Paul
VP: Kirk Weaver
Dir IT: Laurel Emerick
IT Man: Thomas Devilbiss
Opers Mgr: Richard Misplay
VP Mktg: Thomas McIntosh
Sls Mgr: Ed Koneczny

D-U-N-S 00-421-7592
MAGNI- POWER CO (OH)
MAGNI FAB & MAGNETIC
5511 E Lincoln Way, Wooster, OH 44691-8607
Tel (330) 264-3637 *Founded/Ownrshp* 1948
Sales 20.4MM^E *EMP* 157
SIC 3441

D-U-N-S 09-541-3050 IMP
MAGNI-INDUSTRIES INC
(*Suby of* MAGNI GROUP INC) ★
2771 Hammond St, Detroit, MI 48209-1239
Tel (313) 843-7855 *Founded/Ownrshp* 1987
Sales 38.8MM^E *EMP* 170
SIC 2899 Rust resisting compounds; Rust resisting compounds
Ch Bd: David E Berry
VP: Jack Benson
VP: Peter Pelloski
Genl Mgr: Tim Ogonowski
Genl Mgr: Todd Palmer
Dir IT: Tom Haig
Opers Mgr: Todd Dunseith
Ql Cn Mgr: Mike Fronczak

D-U-N-S 18-920-6287 IMP
■ **MAGNIFIQUE PARFUMES AND COSMETICS INC**
PERFUMANIA
(*Suby of* PERFUMANIA INC) ★
5900 N Andrews Ave # 500, Fort Lauderdale, FL 33309-2370
Tel (954) 335-9100 *Founded/Ownrshp* 1987
Sales 150.5MM^E *EMP* 1,500
SIC 5999 Perfumes & colognes; Perfumes & colognes
Pr: Michael W Katz
VP: Bill Reger
VP: A M Young

D-U-N-S 07-918-5553
MAGNITUDE SOFTWARE INC
SILVERBACK ENTERPRISE GROUP II
8432 154th Ave Ne, Redmond, WA 98052-3800
Tel (425) 372-2699 *Founded/Ownrshp* 2013, 2014
Sales 47.6MM^E *EMP* 277^E
SIC 7372 Business oriented computer software; Business oriented computer software
Pr: Nigel Turner
**CEO:* Chris Ney
**CFO:* Doug Moore

D-U-N-S 00-423-2823
MAGNODE CORP
400 E State St, Trenton, OH 45067-1549
Tel (513) 988-6351 *Founded/Ownrshp* 1986
Sales 31.3MM^E *EMP* 225
SIC 3354 Aluminum extruded products; Aluminum extruded products
CEO: Arthur W Bidwell
**Pr:* Martin J Bidwell
**Treas:* Douglas J Howell
**VP:* Johnie Adams
**VP:* Ann F Bidwell
**VP:* Joseph Bidwell
**VP:* Richard Hinkle
VP: Harry Siegel
**VP:* Tony Walter
Dir Lab: Christopher Daughetee
IT Man: Mike Jones

MAGNOLIA AUDIO VIDEO
See MAGNOLIA HI-FI LLC

D-U-N-S 10-179-5453
MAGNOLIA BANKING CORP
FARMERS BANK AND TRUST
200 E Main St, Magnolia, AR 71753-3530
Tel (870) 836-5701 *Founded/Ownrshp* 1906
Sales NA *EMP* 130^E
SIC 6022 State commercial banks; State commercial banks
Pr: Steve Keith
COO: Bruce Mallock
CFO: Janna B Snider
Ofcr: Nora Bailey
Ofcr: Judi Castleberry
Ofcr: Jackie K Cook
Ofcr: Sheryl Edwards
Ofcr: Judi S Franks
Ofcr: Virginia C Glass
Ofcr: Betsy J Kilgore
Ofcr: Lairie L Kincaid
Ofcr: Sheri Newell
Ofcr: Becky Palmer
Ofcr: Billy W Pike
Ofcr: Neca L Reap
Ofcr: Janet Redfearn
Ofcr: Talesha Tatom
Ofcr: John Way
Ofcr: Jeff White
Trst Ofcr: Libby Pearce
Trst Ofcr: Jackie D Tarlton

D-U-N-S 01-124-0355
MAGNOLIA BEEF CO INC
1070 Magnolia Ave, Elizabeth, NJ 07201-1481
Tel (908) 352-9412 *Founded/Ownrshp* 1964
Sales 20.3MM^E *EMP* 29
SIC 5147 Meats & meat products
Pr: Alan Simberloff

D-U-N-S 96-183-3675 IMP
MAGNOLIA BENEKE INC
1 Tuffy Ln, Columbus, MS 39701-3838
Tel (662) 328-4000 *Founded/Ownrshp* 2011
Sales 81.3MM^E *EMP* 843^E
SIC 2499 Seats, toilet
Pr: Thomas Whitaker
VP: Sandra Sanderson

D-U-N-S 15-744-4902
MAGNOLIA COCA-COLA BOTTLING CO
11001 Gateway Blvd W, El Paso, TX 79935-5003
Tel (915) 593-2653 *Founded/Ownrshp* 1985
Sales 26.7MM^E *EMP* 300
SIC 2086 Soft drinks: packaged in cans, bottles, etc.; Soft drinks: packaged in cans, bottles, etc.
Ch Bd: J W Wolslager Sr
**Pr:* J W Wolslager Jr
**Treas:* Paula L Wolslager
Treas: Paula L Wosager

D-U-N-S 02-249-3178
MAGNOLIA CONSTRUCTION LLC
514 S Strtford Rd Ste 140, Winston Salem, NC 27103
Tel (336) 724-7202 *Founded/Ownrshp* 1999
Sales 20.2MM *EMP* 35
Accts Cannon & Company Llp Winston
SIC 1542 Commercial & office building contractors; Commercial & office building contractors
**Off Mgr:* Monnette Cook
Off Mgr: Melinie Reid

D-U-N-S 01-089-9876
MAGNOLIA EDUCATIONAL & RESEARCH FOUNDATION
13950 Milton Ave Ste 200b, Westminster, CA 92683-2939
Tel (714) 892-5066 *Founded/Ownrshp* 1997
Sales 32.3MM *EMP* 49^E
Accts Hill Morgan And Associates Llp
SIC 8399 Noncommercial research organizations; Fund raising organization, non-fee basis
CEO: Dr Suleyman Bahceci
**CFO:* Mekan Muhammedov
IT Man: Julian Lopez

D-U-N-S 00-696-4654
MAGNOLIA ELECTRIC POWER ASSOCIATION
3012 Highway 98 E, McComb, MS 39648-9463
Tel (601) 876-5671 *Founded/Ownrshp* 1938
Sales 87.3MM *EMP* 73
Accts Wilson & Biggs Pllc Ridgeland
SIC 4911 Distribution, electric power; Distribution, electric power
Pr: Hollis Alford
VP: Dennis Wilson
**Genl Mgr:* Darrell Smith
Dir IT: Lawrence Weems
Opers Mgr: Aaron Achord
Board of Directors: Noel Andrews, John P Ard, John Mc Cabe, Bruce McCaffrey, Jerry Sisco, Jewell H Smith

D-U-N-S 02-285-5365
MAGNOLIA FARMERS CO-OPERATIVE ELEVATOR & LUMBER INC
LUVERNE S W M N FARMER'S CO-OP
402 S Freeman Ave, Luverne, MN 56156-2006
Tel (507) 283-4418 *Founded/Ownrshp* 1995
Sales 25.0MM *EMP* 20
SIC 5153 5191 Grains; Farm supplies; Feed; Fertilizer & fertilizer materials; Chemicals, agricultural; Grains; Farm supplies; Feed; Fertilizer & fertilizer materials; Chemicals, agricultural
Genl Mgr: Marlyn Mammen

D-U-N-S 13-121-8877 EXP
MAGNOLIA FOREST PRODUCTS INC
13252 Interstate 55 S, Terry, MS 39170
Tel (601) 878-2581 *Founded/Ownrshp* 1976
Sales 38.8MM^E *EMP* 51^E
SIC 5031 Lumber: rough, dressed & finished; Plywood
Pr: Dennis Berry
**Treas:* Ed Lewis
**VP:* Steve Brent

D-U-N-S 96-373-8034
MAGNOLIA HEALTH SYSTEMS INC
9480 Prority W Dr, Indianapolis, IN 46240
Tel (317) 818-1240 *Founded/Ownrshp* 1997
Sales 61.2MM^E *EMP* 2,000
SIC 8099 Medical services organization; Medical services organization
Pr: Stuart Reed
**VP:* Michael Reed

D-U-N-S 83-725-0190
MAGNOLIA HEALTHCARE INC
AUTUMN LEAVES NURSING HOME
(*Suby of* FOUNDATION HEALTH SERVICES INC) ★
17617 S Harrells Ferry Rd, Baton Rouge, LA 70816-3532
Tel (225) 753-0864 *Founded/Ownrshp* 1995
Sales 11.6MM *EMP* 383
Accts Zelenkofske Azelrod & Co Cpa
SIC 8051 Skilled nursing care facilities; Skilled nursing care facilities
Pr: Richard T Daspit Sr
**CFO:* Laurence Daspit

D-U-N-S 02-744-9529 IMP
■ **MAGNOLIA HI-FI LLC**
MAGNOLIA AUDIO VIDEO
(*Suby of* BEST BUY MOBILE FAIRFAX CO) ★
7601 Penn Ave S, Minneapolis, MN 55423-8500
Tel (206) 371-0092 *Founded/Ownrshp* 2012
Sales 71.1MM^E *EMP* 600
SIC 5731 Video recorders, players, disc players & accessories; High fidelity stereo equipment; Consumer electronic equipment; Video recorders, players, disc players & accessories; High fidelity stereo equipment; Consumer electronic equipment
Pr: Jim Tweten
CFO: Kurt Frost
Treas: David Barnett
VP: Dale Anderson
VP: Allan Conrad
VP: Steven John
VP: Mark McDougall
Exec: Rick Moore
Dir Surg: Aaron Miller
Genl Mgr: Greg Dorrell
Genl Mgr: Reza Moodi

D-U-N-S 82-711-6612
■ **MAGNOLIA HILL LLC**
RIVERWALK CASINO HOTEL
(*Suby of* CHURCHILL DOWNS INC) ★
1046 Warrenton Rd, Vicksburg, MS 39180-5994
Tel (601) 634-0100 *Founded/Ownrshp* 2012
Sales 14.1MM^E *EMP* 450
SIC 7011 Casino hotel; Casino hotel
Genl Mgr: Rob Long

D-U-N-S 80-669-6766
MAGNOLIA INDEPENDENT SCHOOL DISTRICT
31141 Nichols Sawmill Rd, Magnolia, TX 77355-6032
Tel (281) 356-3571 *Founded/Ownrshp* 2007
Sales 65.3MM^E *EMP* 1,500^E
SIC 8211 Public elementary & secondary schools; Public elementary school; Public junior high school; Public senior high school; Public elementary & secondary schools; Public elementary school; Public junior high school; Public senior high school
**CFO:* Erich Morris
Adm Dir: John Roch
Dir Sec: Garrett Matej
Dir IT: Melissa Beale
Pr Dir: Marsha Little
Psych: Kim Ayres
Psych: Lisa Kennedy
Psych: Bonnie McCoy

MAGNOLIA LIQUORS
See N GOLDRING CORP

D-U-N-S 04-003-2773
MAGNOLIA LIVING CENTER
(*Suby of* HMR ADVANTAGE HEALTH SYSTEMS INC) ★
201 N Ellis Ave, Dunn, NC 28334-3806
Tel (910) 892-4021 *Founded/Ownrshp* 1996
Sales 487.9MM *EMP* 100
SIC 8051 8052 Convalescent home with continuous nursing care; Intermediate care facilities; Convalescent home with continuous nursing care; Intermediate care facilities

D-U-N-S 02-102-4872
MAGNOLIA MANAGEMENT CORP
763 Avery Blvd N, Ridgeland, MS 39157-5218
Tel (601) 956-8884 *Founded/Ownrshp* 1979
Sales 21.3MM^E *EMP* 1,300
SIC 8051

MAGNOLIA MANOR
See FUNDAMENTAL ADMINISTRATIVE SERVICES LLC

D-U-N-S 07-571-8649
MAGNOLIA MANOR INC (GA)
2001 S Lee St, Americus, GA 31709-4797
Tel (229) 924-9352 *Founded/Ownrshp* 1959
Sales 9.0MM *EMP* 600
Accts Mauldin & Jenkins Llc Macon
SIC 8059 6513 Nursing home, except skilled & intermediate care facility; Retirement hotel operation; Apartment hotel operation; Nursing home, except skilled & intermediate care facility; Retirement hotel operation; Apartment hotel operation
Pr: Mark Todd
**CFO:* Jerry Vick
VP: Willie Beasley

D-U-N-S 07-831-2185
MAGNOLIA MANOR OF COLUMBUS INC
(*Suby of* MAGNOLIA MANOR INC) ★
2010 Warm Springs Rd, Columbus, GA 31904
Tel (229) 931-5907 *Founded/Ownrshp* 2011
Sales 20.8MM *EMP* 10^E
Accts Mauldin & Jenkins Llc Macon
SIC 8051 Skilled nursing care facilities
CEO: Mark R Todd
**COO:* Phill Fort
**CFO:* Scott Adkins
**Prin:* Jeff Vick

D-U-N-S 05-063-9624
MAGNOLIA MARINE TRANSPORT CO INC (MS)
(*Suby of* ERGON INC) ★
2829 Lakeland Dr Ste 2000, Jackson, MS 39232-7611
Tel (601) 933-3000 *Founded/Ownrshp* 1960
Sales 26.0MM^E *EMP* 250
SIC 4449

D-U-N-S 87-765-2875
MAGNOLIA PLUMBING INC
600 Gallatin St Ne, Washington, DC 20017-2359
Tel (202) 829-8510 *Founded/Ownrshp* 1950
Sales 63.4MM^E *EMP* 280
SIC 1711

D-U-N-S 10-180-2189
MAGNOLIA PROCESSING INC
PRIDE OF THE POND
5255 Highway 4, Tunica, MS 38676-6136
Tel (662) 363-3600 *Founded/Ownrshp* 1983
Sales 20.0MM^E *EMP* 150
SIC 2092 Fish, fresh: prepared; Fish, fresh: prepared
Pr: William Gidden
Treas: Norma H Battle
**Treas:* Sterling W Owen III
**VP:* Paul Battle Jr
Board of Directors: John W Owen, Will W Owen, Sterling Withers

D-U-N-S 07-859-2417
MAGNOLIA REGIONAL HEALTH CENTER
611 Alcorn Dr, Corinth, MS 38834-9388
Tel (662) 293-1000 *Founded/Ownrshp* 1965
Sales 154.1MM^E *EMP* 928
SIC 8062 General medical & surgical hospitals; General medical & surgical hospitals
CEO: Rick Napper
Chf Path: Michael Todd
COO: Ronnie Humes
CFO: William Akers
CFO: Brian Craven
Chf Mktg O: John Prather
VP: Gene Combest
VP: Angela Nowlin
VP: David Parker
VP: Pam Wallis
Dir Inf Cn: Amy Gray
Dir Lab: Heather Rhodes
Dir Rx: Todd Cox

D-U-N-S 10-257-1502
MAGNOLIA REGIONAL MEDICAL CENTER
101 Hospital Dr, Magnolia, AR 71753-2415
Tel (870) 235-3000 *Founded/Ownrshp* 1939
Sales 47.1MM^E *EMP* 260
SIC 8062 General medical & surgical hospitals; General medical & surgical hospitals
CEO: Margaret West
**Ch Bd:* Mike Epley
**CFO:* Christopher Comer
**Ch:* Molly Burns
Dir OR: Robin Hennessy
**Prin:* Moises Menendez
**Prin:* Steve Nipper
Dir IT: Tina Marlar
Phys Thrpy: Glenn Watson

D-U-N-S 00-714-7536
MAGNOLIA RIVER SERVICES INC
408 Bank St Ne, Decatur, AL 35601-1604
Tel (256) 773-9420 *Founded/Ownrshp* 2000
Sales 24.4MM^E *EMP* 98^E
Accts Wear Howell Strickland Quinn &
SIC 8711 Engineering services
Pr: Kimberly T Hoff
**Ch:* Charlie Pecchio
**Ex VP:* Ronald S Hoff Jr
**VP:* Ronnie Hoff
Exec: Nikki Frost
Off Mgr: Kris Staudt
Snr Mgr: Jim Tilley

D-U-N-S 03-990-7811
MAGNOLIA SCHOOL DISTRICT
2705 W Orange Ave, Anaheim, CA 92804-3298
Tel (714) 761-5533 *Founded/Ownrshp* 1921
Sales 38.4MM^E *EMP* 700
SIC 8211 Public elementary & secondary schools; Public elementary & secondary schools
HC Dir: Annette Cleveland

D-U-N-S 02-060-0508
MAGNOLIA SCHOOL DISTRICT 14
1400 High School Dr, Magnolia, AR 71753-2203
Tel (870) 234-2610 *Founded/Ownrshp* 1898
Sales 20.7MM^E *EMP* 325
SIC 8211 9411 Public elementary & secondary schools; High school, junior or senior; School board; Administration of educational programs; Public elementary & secondary schools; High school, junior or senior; School board; Administration of educational programs
Pr Dir: Vanda Crank

D-U-N-S 00-339-9557
MAGNOLIA STEEL CO INC (MS)
17 17th Ave S, Meridian, MS 39301-5401
Tel (601) 693-4301 *Founded/Ownrshp* 1950, 2009
Sales 31.1MM *EMP* 108
Accts Swain & Collins Pa Meridian
SIC 3441 Fabricated structural metal; Building components, structural steel; Fabricated structural metal; Building components, structural steel
Pr: Christopher D Crowe
**VP:* Kathryn C Coleman
VP: Bobby Gibson
Plnt Mgr: Paul Grice
Sales Exec: Chris Crow
Board of Directors: Joey Beeman

D-U-N-S 03-530-4850
MAGNOLIA WINDOW AND DOOR CO
1000 Pyratich Dr, Baldwin, GA 30511-4006
Tel (706) 778-1200 *Founded/Ownrshp* 1998
Sales 25.3MM^E *EMP* 105
SIC 5031 Windows
Pr: Mike Johnson
Dir IT: Mike Horan
Prd Mgr: Tim Dragoo

MAGNUM COFFEE ROASTERY
See L & K COFFEE CO LLC

D-U-N-S 10-712-8159
MAGNUM FOODS INC
LITTLE CAESAR'S
7205 N Robinson Ave, Oklahoma City, OK 73116-7710
Tel (405) 767-3313 *Founded/Ownrshp* 1983
Sales 19.9MM^E *EMP* 750
SIC 5812 Pizzeria, chain; Pizzeria, chain
Ch Bd: Carl Messer
**Pr:* Jeff Welsh
**Sec:* Gary Welsh
**VP:* Ben Poliquin
**VP:* Arthur R Schell
**VP:* Roland Zilka

D-U-N-S 62-162-5883
▲ **MAGNUM HUNTER RESOURCES CORP**
909 Lake Carolyn Pkwy # 600, Irving, TX 75039-3926
Tel (832) 369-6986 *Founded/Ownrshp* 2005
Sales 391.4MM *EMP* 440^E
Tkr Sym MHR *Exch* NYS
SIC 1311 Crude petroleum & natural gas; Crude petroleum & natural gas production; Crude petroleum & natural gas; Crude petroleum & natural gas production
Ch Bd: Gary C Evans
COO: Keith Yankowsky
CFO: Joseph C Daches
Ex VP: Glenn Dawson
Ex VP: R Glenn Dawson
Ex VP: H C Ferguson III
Sr VP: Richard S Farrell
Sr VP: Paul M Johnston
Sr VP: Donald Kirkendall
Sr VP: Kirk J Trosclair
VP: Chris Benton
VP: Debbie Funderburg
VP: Charlie Gibson
VP: Chris Hewitt

VP: David Lipp
VP: Richard Vickery
Dir Bus: Darren Espey

MAGNUM INKS & COATINGS
See MAGNUM MAGNETICS CORP

D-U-N-S 11-360-8228
MAGNUM INSURANCE AGENCY CO INC
4259 N Western Ave, Chicago, IL 60618-2815
Tel (773) 539-2102 *Founded/Ownrshp* 1981
Sales NA *EMP* 200
SIC 6411 Insurance agents, brokers & service; Insurance agents, brokers & service
Ch Bd: Craig Lamm
**Pr:* Ericka Ariza
**Pr:* Ericka Ceballos
VP: Christopher Roman

D-U-N-S 10-851-0322
MAGNUM LTL INC
CNH INDUSTRIAL AMERICA
3000 7th Ave N Ste 1, Fargo, ND 58102-3064
Tel (701) 293-8082 *Founded/Ownrshp* 1990
Sales 56.4MM^E *EMP* 170
SIC 4213 Trucking, except local; Trucking, except local
Pr: Wayne Gadberry
**CFO:* Don Jemtrud
**Sec:* Roger Madson
**VP:* David Gadberry
**VP:* James Johannesson
Netwrk Eng: Justin Haugen

D-U-N-S 83-156-2350
MAGNUM MACHINING INC
20959 State Highway 6, Deerwood, MN 56444-8550
Tel (218) 534-3552 *Founded/Ownrshp* 1994
Sales 20.1MM^E *EMP* 98^E
SIC 3599 Machine & other job shop work; Machine & other job shop work
CEO: Jerry Bowman
**Pr:* Kevin Cook
**VP:* Mavis Bowman
Plnt Mgr: Jay Landree

D-U-N-S 78-369-3328 IMP/EXP
MAGNUM MAGNETICS CORP
MAGNUM INKS & COATINGS
801 Masonic Park Rd, Marietta, OH 45750-9357
Tel (740) 373-7770 *Founded/Ownrshp* 1991
Sales 28.0MM^E *EMP* 160^E
SIC 3499 Magnets, permanent: metallic; Magnets, permanent: metallic
Pr: Allen Love
VP: Tom Love
Genl Mgr: Bruce Dean
IT Man: Joe Stout
Prd Mgr: Doug Rummer
Sls&Mrk Ex: Neil Huck
Mktg Mgr: Ruth Wyckoff
Sls Mgr: Jim Hoblick

D-U-N-S 79-344-6006
■ **MAGNUM MANAGEMENT CORP**
CEDAR POINT
(*Suby of* CEDAR FAIR LP) ★
1 Cedar Point Dr, Sandusky, OH 44870-5259
Tel (419) 627-2334 *Founded/Ownrshp* 1983
Sales 86.2MM^E *EMP* 800^E
SIC 4785 6552 7996 Toll bridge operation; Subdividers & developers; Amusement parks; Toll bridge operation; Subdividers & developers; Amusement parks
CEO: Richard L Kinzel
VP: Robert Decker
VP: Craig Freeman
VP: James Rein
VP: Bob Wagner
VP: Brian Witherow
Exec: Leslie Bradshaw
Genl Mgr: Daryl Allison
Genl Mgr: Joel Peugeot
Off Mgr: Lois A Lawrence
Dir IT: Renae Weaver

D-U-N-S 78-323-5828
MAGNUM OIL TOOLS INTERNATIONAL LTD
5655 Bear Ln Ste 100, Corpus Christi, TX 78405-4407
Tel (361) 299-6333 *Founded/Ownrshp* 2008
Sales 38.2MM^E *EMP* 130^E
SIC 3291 Abrasive products
CEO: Lynn Frazier
Creative D: Mark Marquez
Brnch Mgr: Phillip Ewers
Mfg Mgr: Eric Shank
Mfg Mgr: Eric Shanks
Opers Mgr: Eic Duckett
Mktg Dir: Justin Brandt
Mktg Dir: Brian Fiscus
Mktg Dir: Garrett Frazier

D-U-N-S 60-292-9858 IMP
MAGNUM SEMICONDUCTOR INC
591 Yosemite Dr, Milpitas, CA 95035-5448
Tel (408) 934-3700 *Founded/Ownrshp* 2005
Sales 36.4MM^E *EMP* 230^E
SIC 3674 Semiconductors & related devices; Semiconductors & related devices
Pr: Gopal Solanki
Pt: Andy Rappaport
CEO: Dr Jack Guedj
**CFO:* Terry Griffin
VP: Mark Carrington
VP: Scott Cho
**VP:* Gal Garriek
**VP:* Fure-Ching Jeng
**VP:* Mike Milne
**VP:* Marcel Tromp
Prin: Andrew Flett

D-U-N-S 93-848-3815
MAGNUM STAFFING SERVICES INC
2900 Smith St Ste 250, Houston, TX 77006-3445
Tel (713) 658-0068 *Founded/Ownrshp* 1996
Sales 42.2MM^E *EMP* 1,250
SIC 7363 Manpower pools; Labor resource services; Manpower pools; Labor resource services
Pr: Caroline Brown
**CFO:* Darrel Brown

VP: Brenda Perez
Dir IT: Steve Bowen

MAGNUM VENUS PLASTICH
See VENUS MAGNUM PRODUCTS INC

D-U-N-S 10-675-7529 IMP/EXP
MAGNUMM CORP
3839 E 10 Mile Rd, Warren, MI 48091-1358
Tel (586) 427-9420 *Founded/Ownrshp* 1983
Sales 22.3MM^E *EMP* 133
SIC 3714 3599 Thermostats, motor vehicle; Bellows, industrial: metal
Ch: Joseph M Lane
**Pr:* Martin L Abel

D-U-N-S 02-804-2586 IMP
MAGNUS INTERNATIONAL GROUP INC
16533 Chillicothe Rd, Chagrin Falls, OH 44023-4327
Tel (216) 592-8355 *Founded/Ownrshp* 2007
Sales 61.2MM^E *EMP* 80
SIC 4953 2048 2992 Recycling, waste materials; Prepared feeds; Rust arresting compounds, animal or vegetable oil base
CEO: Eric Lofquist
**Pr:* Theresa M Paicic
Pr: Sharon Sunderman
**CFO:* John Malloy
**VP:* Scott Forster
**Prin:* Mark Allio

MAGNUS PACIFIC CORPORATION
See MAGNUS PACIFIC LLC

D-U-N-S 00-520-4892
■ **MAGNUS PACIFIC LLC**
MAGNUS PACIFIC CORPORATION
(*Suby of* GREAT LAKES DREDGE & DOCK CORP) ★
6558 Lonetree Blvd, Rocklin, CA 95765-5874
Tel (916) 462-6400 *Founded/Ownrshp* 2008, 2014
Sales 48.0MM^E *EMP* 175
SIC 8999 8748 1629 1795 Geophysical consultant; Environmental consultant; Land reclamation; Demolition, buildings & other structures
Pr: Louay M Owaidat
**CFO:* Bruce Diettert
Mtls Mgr: Ryan Swanson
Site Mgr: Valentino Martinez

D-U-N-S 15-373-6111
MAGNUSON ACQUISITION COMAPNY LLC
MAGNUSON PRODUCTS
1990 Knoll Dr Ste A, Ventura, CA 93003-7309
Tel (805) 642-8833 *Founded/Ownrshp* 2010
Sales 23.7MM^E *EMP* 49
SIC 3714 Motor vehicle parts & accessories
CEO: Kim Pendergast
Chf Mktg O: Bob Roese
Ex VP: Matt Hately
**Ex VP:* Tim Krauskopf
Prd Mgr: Bill Austin
Sales Exec: Cindy Hernandez
Sls Dir: Terry Peddicord

MAGNUSON PRODUCTS
See MAGNUSON ACQUISITION COMAPNY LLC

D-U-N-S 01-133-9434
MAGNUSSEN DEALERSHIP GROUP (CA)
YUBA SUTTER AUTO BODY
401 Burgess Dr Ste A, Menlo Park, CA 94025-3476
Tel (650) 327-4100 *Founded/Ownrshp* 1983
Sales 31.1MM^E *EMP* 100
SIC 5511 7532 New & used car dealers; Body shop, automotive; New & used car dealers; Body shop, automotive
Pr: Bernard Magnussen
Exec: Shelly Magpuri

D-U-N-S 61-870-3292
MAGNUSSEN DODGE
MAGNUSSEN DODGE-CHRYSLER-JEEP
1901 Grass Valley Hwy, Auburn, CA 95603-2852
Tel (530) 885-2900 *Founded/Ownrshp* 1997
Sales 20.8MM^E *EMP* 62
SIC 5511 Automobiles, new & used; Automobiles, new & used
Pr: Bernard Magnussen
**Genl Mgr:* Tony Toohey
Sls Mgr: Eric Henderson
Sls Mgr: Scott Jeske

MAGNUSSEN DODGE-CHRYSLER-JEEP
See MAGNUSSEN DODGE

D-U-N-S 04-923-4735
MAGNUSSEN IMPORTS INC
TOYOTA OF PALO ALTO
690 San Antonio Rd, Palo Alto, CA 94306-4711
Tel (650) 494-1759 *Founded/Ownrshp* 1990
Sales 35.8MM^E *EMP* 102
SIC 5511 Automobiles, new & used; Automobiles, new & used
Pr: Bernard L Magnussen
Exec: Anna Diep
Genl Mgr: Bill Mason
Opers Mgr: Sabrina Sanchez
Sls Mgr: Andre Kamali
Sls Mgr: Richard Skordas

MAGNUSSEN'S A TOYOTA
See AUBURN MAGNUSSENS IMPORTS INC

D-U-N-S 05-548-9397
MAGNUSSON KLEMENCIC ASSOCIATES INC
1301 5th Ave Ste 3200, Seattle, WA 98101-2614
Tel (206) 292-1200 *Founded/Ownrshp* 1947
Sales 26.1MM^E *EMP* 124^E
SIC 8711 Engineering services; Engineering services
Ch Bd: Jon D Magnusson
**Pr:* Ron Klemencic
**COO:* Brian McIntyre
**Sr VP:* Ad A Gouwerok
**Sr VP:* Tony Tschanz
Exec: Tschanz Tony
Prin: Adam Koczarski

D-U-N-S 14-719-2231
MAGOFFIN COUNTY SCHOOLS
109 Gardner Trl, Salyersville, KY 41465-9743
Tel (606) 349-6117 *Founded/Ownrshp* 1860
Sales 26.7MM^E *EMP* 418
SIC 8211 Public elementary & secondary schools; Public elementary & secondary schools
**Ch:* Judy C Isaac
Genl Mgr: Stacey Blanton
Schl Brd P: Caroline Isaac

D-U-N-S 06-583-5050 IMP/EXP
MAGOTTEAUX INC
(*Suby of* MAGOTTEAUX INTERNATIONAL SA)
2360 Industrial Loop Rd, Pulaski, TN 38478-9596
Tel (931) 363-7471 *Founded/Ownrshp* 1970
Sales 95.4MM^E *EMP* 450
SIC 3369 Castings, except die-castings, precision; Castings, except die-castings, precision
CEO: Bernard Goblet
**Pr:* Walter Mersch
Exec: M Devalckeneer
Exec: V Werbrouck

MAGOUIRK CHEVROLET & OLDS
See BRENT MAGOUIRK CHEVROLET-OLDS-CADILLAC INC

D-U-N-S 00-506-6126
MAGPIE INTERNET COMMUNICATIONS CORP (CA)
PLANETMAGPIE
2762 Bayview Dr, Fremont, CA 94538-6518
Tel (510) 344-1200 *Founded/Ownrshp* 1998
Sales 200.0MM *EMP* 15
SIC 4813 7379 7374 ; ; ; ; Computer graphics service
Pr: Robert Douglas
VP: Doreyne Douglas

D-U-N-S 08-506-6137
MAGPIE SYSTEMS INC
(*Suby of* T D WILLIAMSON INC) ★
369 N Billy Mitchell Rd, Salt Lake City, UT 84116-2802
Tel (801) 281-2226 *Founded/Ownrshp* 1997
Sales 17.7MM^E *EMP* 300
SIC 7389 Pipeline & power line inspection service; Pipeline & power line inspection service
CEO: D Bruce Binkley
**Ch Bd:* Richard B Williamson
**Sr VP:* Bruce Thames
**VP:* Robert D McGrew

D-U-N-S 07-692-5788 IMP
MAGPUL INDUSTRIES CORP
1812 Boxelder St, Louisville, CO 80027-3008
Tel (303) 828-5194 *Founded/Ownrshp* 1999
Sales 28.2MM^E *EMP* 100
SIC 3484 Small arms
Pr: Richard Fitzpatrick
COO: Doug Smith
**VP:* Barbara Fitzpatrick
Creative D: Jeff Keil
Mtls Mgr: Russ Roecker
Prd Mgr: Libardo Jimenez
Sls Mgr: Justin Beard
Sls Mgr: Magpul Beard

D-U-N-S 01-151-0542
MAGRUDER COLOR CO INC
14 Takolusa Dr, Holmdel, NJ 07733-1232
Tel (817) 837-3293 *Founded/Ownrshp* 1926
Sales 24.1MM^E *EMP* 200
SIC 2865 Dyes & pigments; Color pigments, organic; Dyes & pigments; Color pigments, organic
Ch Bd: Allan Weissglass
**Pr:* Abdul Saleh
**VP:* Jay R Weissglass

D-U-N-S 00-648-6898
MAGRUDER CONSTRUCTION CO INC (MO)
243 W Outer Rd, Eolia, MO 63344
Tel (573) 485-2161 *Founded/Ownrshp* 1950, 2012
Sales 36.9MM^E *EMP* 100
Accts Williams Keepers Llc Columbia
SIC 1622 Highway construction, elevated
Pr: Mark H Magruder
**VP:* Mark Games
**VP:* Merle McGlasson
Off Mgr: Cindy Browning
Prd Mgr: Ron Twellman

MAGRUDER HOSPITAL
See H B MAGRUDER MEMORIAL HOSPITAL

D-U-N-S 82-519-7577
MAGT LP
CHARLES MAUND TOYOTA
8400 Research Blvd, Austin, TX 78758-8350
Tel (512) 458-2222 *Founded/Ownrshp* 1993
Sales 32.2MM^E *EMP* 75
SIC 5511 5521 Automobiles, new & used; Used car dealers; Automobiles, new & used; Used car dealers
Pr: Doug Maund
VP: James Dimeo
**VP:* Charles Maund
Sls Mgr: Lindsey Leblanc
Sls Mgr: Chris Martinez
Sls Mgr: Matthew McCreight
Sls Mgr: Steve Soskins

D-U-N-S 96-322-6936
MAGUIRE FOUNDATION
25 British American Blvd, Latham, NY 12110-1405
Tel (518) 640-5000 *Founded/Ownrshp* 2010
Sales 69.1MM *EMP* 2^E
SIC 8699 Charitable organization; Charitable organization

D-U-N-S 06-437-8433
MAGUIRE INSURANCE AGENCY INC
VALLEY FORGE INSURANCE BRKG
(*Suby of* PHILADELPHIA CONSOLIDATED HOLDING CORP) ★
1 Bala Plz Ste LI34, Bala Cynwyd, PA 19004-1400
Tel (610) 617-7900 *Founded/Ownrshp* 2002
Sales NA *EMP* 1,374
SIC 6411 Insurance agents; Insurance agents

Pr: James J Maguire Jr
**COO:* Chris J Maguire
**CFO:* Craig P Keller
**Chf Mktg O:* Sean S Sweeney
Ex VP: Sean Sweeney

D-U-N-S 96-450-3671
MAGUIRE PROPERTIES - SAN DIEGO TECH CENTER LLC
355 S Grand Ave Ste 3300, Los Angeles, CA 90071-1592
Tel (213) 673-1421 *Founded/Ownrshp* 2005
Sales 36.4MM *EMP* 5
SIC 6798 Real estate investment trusts; Real estate investment trusts
Sr VP: Ed Mullaney

D-U-N-S 62-123-0528
■ **MAGYAR BANCORP INC**
(*Suby of* MAGYAR BANCORP MHC) ★
400 Somerset St, New Brunswick, NJ 08901-3265
Tel (732) 342-7600 *Founded/Ownrshp* 2005
Sales NA *EMP* 95^E
Tkr Sym MGYR *Exch* NGM
SIC 6035 Savings institutions, federally chartered; Savings institutions, federally chartered; Federal savings & loan associations; Federal savings banks
Pr: John S Fitzgerald
**Ch Bd:* Joseph J Lukacs Jr
CFO: Jon R Ansari
**V Ch Bd:* Thomas Lankey
Sr VP: Brian Stanley

D-U-N-S 62-122-9728
▲ **MAGYAR BANCORP MHC**
400 Somerset St, New Brunswick, NJ 08901-3265
Tel (732) 342-7600 *Founded/Ownrshp* 2005
Sales NA *EMP* 109
SIC 6036 State savings banks, not federally chartered; State savings banks, not federally chartered
Ofcr: John S Fitzgerald
**Ch Bd:* Joseph J Lukacs Jr
**CFO:* Jon R Ansari

D-U-N-S 00-252-8008
■ **MAGYAR BANK** (NJ)
(*Suby of* MAGYAR BANCORP INC) ★
400 Somerset St, New Brunswick, NJ 08901-3265
Tel (732) 342-7600 *Founded/Ownrshp* 1922, 2006
Sales NA *EMP* 80
SIC 6036 State savings banks, not federally chartered; State savings banks, not federally chartered
Pr: John S Fitzgerald
Ch Bd: Joseph J Lukacs Jr
CFO: Jon R Ansai
CFO: Jon R Ansari
Ofcr: Lillian Lund
VP: Peter Brown
VP: Linda Cenicola
VP: Donna Fleming
VP: Thomas Iorio
VP: Laura Irovando
VP: Pamela Jasones
VP: Diane Prongay
VP: Craig Sinon

D-U-N-S 08-753-5043 IMP
MAH MACHINE CO
3301 S Central Ave, Cicero, IL 60804-3986
Tel (708) 656-1826 *Founded/Ownrshp* 1977
Sales 35.0MM^E *EMP* 105
SIC 3599 7699 Machine shop, jobbing & repair; Printing trades machinery & equipment repair
CEO: Martin Hozjan
**Pr:* Robert Hozjan
**VP:* Christopher Hozjan
**VP:* Martina Hozjan Ruda
**Prin:* Anna Hozjan
Ql Cn Mgr: John Sinitean

MAHAFFEY FABRIC STRUCTURES
See MAHAFFEY TENT & AWNING CO INC

D-U-N-S 05-870-1541 IMP
MAHAFFEY TENT & AWNING CO INC
MAHAFFEY FABRIC STRUCTURES
4161 Delp St, Memphis, TN 38118-6927
Tel (901) 363-6511 *Founded/Ownrshp* 1924
Sales 23.5MM *EMP* 105
SIC 7359 Tent & tarpaulin rental; Tent & tarpaulin rental
Pr: William J Pretsch
**VP:* George Smith
Genl Mgr: Clint Sidle
Mktg Mgr: Beth Wilson
Sls Mgr: Kevin Ponder
Sales Asso: Susan Lee

MAHAR MEDICAL
See MAHAR TOOL SUPPLY CO INC

D-U-N-S 01-736-5420
MAHAR TOOL SUPPLY CO INC
MAHAR MEDICAL
112 Williams St, Saginaw, MI 48602-1441
Tel (989) 799-5530 *Founded/Ownrshp* 1978
Sales 79.8MM^E *EMP* 114
SIC 5085

D-U-N-S 00-167-0488 IMP
■ **MAHARAM FABRIC CORP** (NY)
(*Suby of* HERMAN MILLER INC) ★
45 Rasons Ct, Hauppauge, NY 11788-4238
Tel (631) 582-3434 *Founded/Ownrshp* 1932, 2013
Sales 198.4MM^E *EMP* 290
SIC 5131 7389 Textiles, woven; Styling of fashions, apparel, furniture, textiles, etc.; Textiles, woven; Styling of fashions, apparel, furniture, textiles, etc.
Ch Bd: Donald Maharam
VP: Manny Feldsohn
VP: Manny Feldson
**Prin:* Michael Maharam
Dir IT: Sal Deaugustino
Sls Mgr: Melanie Harbert

D-U-N-S 02-696-5129
MAHARD EGG FARM INC
410 E 1st St, Prosper, TX 75078-2975
Tel (972) 347-2421 *Founded/Ownrshp* 1930

Sales 65.0MM EMP 166
SIC 0252 Chicken eggs; Chicken eggs
Pr: Ernest Mahard Jr
*VP: Andy Mahard

D-U-N-S 06-962-3338
MAHARISHI UNIVERSITY OF MANAGEMENT (IA)
MUM
1000 N 4th St, Fairfield, IA 52557-0002
Tel (641) 472-7000 Founded/Ownrshp 1971
Sales 37.6MM EMP 450
Accts Td&T Cpas And Advisors Pc Osk
SIC 8221 University; University
Pr: Bevan Morris
V Ch: Tom Stanley
*Treas: Michael Spivak
Ofcr: Spencer Bright
Ofcr: Thomas Brooks
Ofcr: Joanie Romes
Ofcr: David Streid
*Ex VP: Craig Pearson
*VP: David Todt
Dir Teleco: Michael Goodleman
Mng Dir: Jeffrey Cohen

D-U-N-S 00-529-5266 EXP
MAHASKA BOTTLING CO (IA)
PEPSICO
1407 17th Ave E, Oskaloosa, IA 52577-3559
Tel (641) 673-3481 Founded/Ownrshp 1912, 1947
Sales 51.5MM^E EMP 200
SIC 2086 5149 Carbonated beverages, nonalcoholic: bottled & canned; Pasteurized & mineral waters, bottled & canned; Groceries & related products; Carbonated beverages, nonalcoholic: bottled & canned; Pasteurized & mineral waters, bottled & canned; Groceries & related products
Pr: Bradley G Muhl
CFO: Pamela Willard
Genl Mgr: Andy Davis

D-U-N-S 08-537-5764
MAHASKA COUNTY HOSPITAL INC
MAHASKA HEALTH PARTNERSHIP
1229 C Ave E, Oskaloosa, IA 52577-4298
Tel (641) 672-3100 Founded/Ownrshp 1908
Sales 108.7MM^E EMP 474
SIC 8062 General medical & surgical hospitals; General medical & surgical hospitals
CEO: Jay Christensen
COO: Erin Baldwin
Doctor: Sreedhar Somisetty
Nrsg Dir: Darlene Keuning
HC Dir: Paul Topliff

MAHASKA HEALTH PARTNERSHIP
See MAHASKA COUNTY HOSPITAL INC

D-U-N-S 01-060-4861
MAHASKA HOSPITAL FOUNDATION
1229 C Ave E, Oskaloosa, IA 52577-4246
Tel (641) 672-3100 Founded/Ownrshp 1908
Sales 630.4M EMP 300^E
Accts Gronewold Bell Kyhnn & Co Pc
SIC 8062 General medical & surgical hospitals; General medical & surgical hospitals
CEO: Jay Christenson

MAHEC
See MOUNTAIN AREA HEALTH EDUCATION CENTER INC

D-U-N-S 03-271-8751 EXP
MAHER CHEVROLET INC
MAHER TRUCK CENTER
2901 34th St N, Saint Petersburg, FL 33713-3636
Tel (727) 323-5000 Founded/Ownrshp 1988
Sales 66.7MM^E EMP 210
SIC 5511 Automobiles, new & used; Automobiles, new & used
Pr: Michael B Meagher
*Treas: Greg Soulliere
VP: Fritz Bickell
*VP: Christine Warren

D-U-N-S 06-203-0762 IMP
MAHER TERMINALS LLC
1210 Corbin St Ste 1, Elizabeth, NJ 07201-2946
Tel (908) 527-8200 Founded/Ownrshp 1949
Sales 72.2MM^E EMP 171
SIC 4491 Marine terminals; Marine terminals
Pr: Gary Cross
COO: Carlos Dossantos
Treas: Randall P Mosca
Treas: Paul L Shahbazian
Ofcr: Hank Kanarek
Ex VP: Anthony Ray
Sr VP: Gerard Crotty
Sr VP: Jay Ruble
VP: Lou Allora
VP: Don Gartner
VP: Nicholas Picinich
VP: Steve Rummel
Exec: Gary Gilbert

MAHER TRUCK CENTER
See MAHER CHEVROLET INC

D-U-N-S 92-685-0926 IMP
MAHINDRA USA INC
(Suby of MAHINDRA AND MAHINDRA LIMITED)
9020 Jackrabbit Rd # 600, Houston, TX 77095-3398
Tel (281) 449-7771 Founded/Ownrshp 1995
Sales 285.8MM EMP 100
Accts Kahanek Franke & Associates
SIC 5083 Tractors, agricultural; Tractors, agricultural
Ch: Pawan Goenka
*Pr: Mani Iyer
*CFO: Avinash Bapat
*CFO: Hetal Shah
*VP: Cleo Frankline
IT Man: Rajesh Tiwaskar
Mtls Mgr: Tracy Davis
Opers Mgr: Jerry Murillo
Snr Mgr: Rob Butcher

D-U-N-S 79-646-6303 IMP
MAHLE AFTERMARKET INC
(Suby of MAHLE INDUSTRIES INC) ★
23030 Mahle Dr, Farmington Hills, MI 48335-2606
Tel (248) 347-9700 Founded/Ownrshp 2007
Sales 138.0MM^E EMP 200^E
SIC 5013 Automotive engines & engine parts; Automotive engines & engine parts
Ch Bd: Arnd Franz
*Ch: Prof Dr LNG Heinz K Junker
Rgnl Mgr: Skip Albritton
Genl Mgr: Dan Moody
VP Sls: Ken Carter
Sls Mgr: Mike Stachelski

D-U-N-S 10-675-7271 IMP
MAHLE BEHR CHARLESTON INC
(Suby of MAHLE BEHR USA INC) ★
4500 Leeds Ave Ste 101, Charleston, SC 29405-8515
Tel (843) 745-1233 Founded/Ownrshp 1994
Sales 146.9MM^E EMP 1,000
SIC 3714 Radiators & radiator shells & cores, motor vehicle; Air conditioner parts, motor vehicle; Motor vehicle engines & parts; Radiators & radiator shells & cores, motor vehicle; Air conditioner parts, motor vehicle; Motor vehicle engines & parts
Pr: Hans Lange
Exec: Antoinette Barnes
Exec: Paula Horn
Exec: Brenda Moore
IT Man: Kenny Sanders
IT Man: Eric Wilson

D-U-N-S 36-286-6233 IMP/EXP
MAHLE BEHR DAYTON LLC
(Suby of MAHLE BEHR GMBH & CO. KG)
1600 Webster St, Dayton, OH 45404-1144
Tel (937) 369-2900 Founded/Ownrshp 2002
Sales 272.4MM^E EMP 1,120^E
SIC 3714 Thermal analysis instruments, laboratory type; Motor vehicle parts & accessories
Ch Bd: Ing Heinz K Junker
*CEO: Willm Uhlenbecker
*CFO: Milan Belans

D-U-N-S 06-835-6898 IMP
MAHLE BEHR TROY INC
BEHR CLIMATE SYSTEMS
(Suby of MAHLE BEHR USA INC) ★
2700 Daley Dr, Troy, MI 48083-1949
Tel (817) 624-7273 Founded/Ownrshp 1993
Sales 44.2MM^E EMP 354
SIC 3585 3714 Air conditioning, motor vehicle; Radiators & radiator shells & cores, motor vehicle; Air conditioning, motor vehicle; Radiators & radiator shells & cores, motor vehicle
Genl Mgr: Markus Gosse

D-U-N-S 62-281-5975 IMP
MAHLE BEHR USA INC
(Suby of MAHLE GMBH)
2700 Daley Dr, Troy, MI 48083-1949
Tel (248) 743-3700 Founded/Ownrshp 2013
Sales 995.7MM^E EMP 3,182
SIC 3714 Radiators & radiator shells & cores, motor vehicle; Air conditioner parts, motor vehicle; Motor vehicle engines & parts; Radiators & radiator shells & cores, motor vehicle; Air conditioner parts, motor vehicle; Motor vehicle engines & parts
Pr: Wilm Uhlenbecker
*VP: Dean Arneson
IT Man: Joe Bulka
VP Opers: Uwe Gerber

D-U-N-S 09-637-2883 IMP/EXP
MAHLE ENGINE COMPONENTS USA INC
(Suby of MAHLE GMBH)
1 Mahle Dr, Morristown, TN 37814
Tel (423) 581-6603 Founded/Ownrshp 1976
Sales 163.4MM^E EMP 1,000
SIC 3592 3443

D-U-N-S 18-201-4555 IMP
MAHLE FILTER SYSTEMS NORTH AMERICA INC
(Suby of MAHLE GMBH)
906 Butler Dr, Murfreesboro, TN 37127-6137
Tel (615) 895-5572 Founded/Ownrshp 2001
Sales 152.6MM^E EMP 500
SIC 3714 Motor vehicle engines & parts; Cleaners, air, motor vehicle; Filters: oil, fuel & air, motor vehicle; Motor vehicle engines & parts; Cleaners, air, motor vehicle; Filters: oil, fuel & air, motor vehicle
Ch: Wolf-Henning Scheider
Prgrm Mgr: Cynthia Clemens
Prgrm Mgr: Mark Kemp
Prgrm Mgr: Stacy Schaeffler
Prgrm Mgr: Navneet Vijayvargiya
Prgrm Mgr: Benjamin Weber
Dir IT: Herb Strandberg
IT Man: Greg Ireland
IT Man: Dario Valente
Sys Mgr: Iwan Kurniawan
Opers Mgr: Eddie Nelson

D-U-N-S 07-099-0762 IMP
MAHLE INDUSTRIAL THERMAL SYSTEMS AMERICA LP
(Suby of MAHLE INDUSTRIAL THERMAL SYSTEMS GMBH & CO. KG)
5858 Safety Dr Ne, Belmont, MI 49306-9788
Tel (616) 647-3490 Founded/Ownrshp 2000
Sales 24.0MM^E EMP 99
SIC 3585 Refrigeration & heating equipment; Refrigeration & heating equipment
Pt: Micheal Goerg
Mng Dir: Armin Hagenloch
IT Man: Mona Genrich

D-U-N-S 61-055-4433
MAHLE INDUSTRIES INC
(Suby of MAHLE INDUSTRIEBETEILIGUNGEN GMBH)
1 Mahle Dr, Morristown, TN 37814
Tel (615) 895-5572 Founded/Ownrshp 1998
Sales 178.4MM^E EMP 215
SIC 8711 Engineering services; Engineering services
Ch: Prof Dr Heinz Junker
Pr: Roland Zitt
Treas: Ralf R Roske
VP: Michael Cable
VP: Jennifer Collier
VP: Jerry W Dillard
VP: Mark Gogol
QA Dir: Ron Peyton
QA Dir: Jane Wilder
Dir IT: Strandberg Herb
IT Man: Massimo Cardelli

D-U-N-S 02-843-6343
MAHLE POWERTRAIN LLC
(Suby of MAHLE INDUSTRIES INC) ★
23030 Mahle Dr, Farmington Hills, MI 48335-2606
Tel (248) 305-8200 Founded/Ownrshp 1958
Sales 41.2MM^E EMP 211
SIC 8711 3825 3823 3625 Engineering services; Engine electrical test equipment; Industrial instrmnts msrmnt display/control process variable; Relays & industrial controls; Engineering services; Engine electrical test equipment; Industrial instrmnts msrmnt display/control process variable; Relays & industrial controls
VP Sls: Scott Ferriman

D-U-N-S 61-687-4327
MAHLER ENTERPRISES INC
600 N Broadway Ste 200, Milwaukee, WI 53202-5009
Tel (414) 347-1350 Founded/Ownrshp 1988
Sales 21.4MM^E EMP 400^E
SIC 7349 7361 Janitorial service, contract basis; Placement agencies; Janitorial service, contract basis; Placement agencies
Pr: Peter Mahler
VP: Andrea Woda
Mng Dir: Kevin Chase
Mng Dir: Pat Sullivan

D-U-N-S 01-142-9347 IMP
MAHOGANY CO OF MAYS LANDING INC (NJ)
5274 Cedarwood Blvd, Mays Landing, NJ 08330-2029
Tel (609) 476-6400 Founded/Ownrshp 1954, 1955
Sales 25.4MM^E EMP 60
SIC 5131 5113 Fiberglass fabrics; Paper tubes & cores
CEO: George M Aaron
Pr: Robert A Hamilton
Sec: George B Aaron
VP Opers: Michael Brennan
Manager: Gerald Dear

D-U-N-S 01-320-8702
MAHOMED SALES & WAREHOUSING LLC (IN)
MSW
8258 Zionsville Rd, Indianapolis, IN 46268-1627
Tel (317) 472-5800 Founded/Ownrshp 1997
Sales 100.0MM EMP 45
SIC 4225 3714 General warehousing & storage; Motor vehicle parts & accessories
CEO: Yousuf Mohamed
*Pr: James Brown
*VP: Keith Kanipe
VP: Keith Kanite

D-U-N-S 12-419-7054
MAHOMET-SEYMOUR COMMUNITY UNIT SCHOOL DISTRICT 3
101 N Division St, Mahomet, IL 61853-7032
Tel (217) 586-2161 Founded/Ownrshp 1948
Sales 76.4M EMP 350
Accts Clifton Gunderson Llc
SIC 8211 8741 Public elementary & secondary schools; Management services; Public elementary & secondary schools; Management services
VP: Vicki Niswander
HC Dir: Nita Bachman

D-U-N-S 03-939-2835
MAHONE INC
5184 Reidsville Rd, Walkertown, NC 27051-9770
Tel (336) 486-0635 Founded/Ownrshp 2015
Sales NA EMP 631
SIC 6719 Investment holding companies, except banks
CEO: Takeisha Mahone

D-U-N-S 04-757-7614
MAHONEY ENVIRONMENTAL INC
712 Essington Rd, Joliet, IL 60435-4912
Tel (815) 730-2087 Founded/Ownrshp 1953
Sales 52.3MM^E EMP 105
SIC 2079 Shortening & other solid edible fats; Shortening & other solid edible fats
Pr: John Mahoney
Pr: Rick Sabol
Ex VP: Dave Ciarlette
VP: Robert Amicon
VP: Timothy J Zak
S&M/VP: Tim Norman
Manager: Chris Amesquita
Manager: Victor Pedraza
Sls Mgr: Brad Schofield

MAHONEY GROUP, THE
See M & O AGENCIES INC

D-U-N-S 01-971-9830 IMP
MAHONEYS GARDEN CENTERS LLC
242 Cambridge St, Winchester, MA 01890-2342
Tel (781) 729-5900 Founded/Ownrshp 1959
Sales 100.5MM^E EMP 450
SIC 5261 Nurseries; Lawn & garden supplies; Nurseries; Lawn & garden supplies
CFO: Susan Covino
Genl Mgr: Lauren Danaher
Genl Mgr: Mike Mahoney
Sls Dir: Bob Rocco

D-U-N-S 83-818-4836
MAHONEYS SILVER NUGGET INC
OPERA HOUSE
2140 Las Vegas Blvd N, North Las Vegas, NV 89030-5841
Tel (702) 399-1111 Founded/Ownrshp 1989
Sales 7.8MM^E EMP 350
Accts Kafoury Armstrong & Co Las
SIC 7011 Casino hotel; Casino hotel
Pr: Gary Mahoney
*Treas: Gail Mahoney
VP: Eric Tischler
Genl Mgr: Ann Makhay
Genl Mgr: Darla Wright

D-U-N-S 02-064-3706
MAHONING COUNTY
BOARD MHNING CNTY CMMISSIONERS
21 W Boardman St Ste 200, Youngstown, OH 44503-1416
Tel (330) 740-2130 Founded/Ownrshp 1845
Sales NA EMP 1,500
SIC 9121 County commissioner; ; County commissioner;
Dir IT: Jake Williams

MAHONING VLY HMTOLOGY ONCOLOGY
See TRUMBULL MEMORIAL HOSPITAL FOUNDATION

D-U-N-S 00-891-6249
■ **MAHOPAC BANK**
(Suby of TOMPKINS FINANCIAL CORP) ★
1441 Route 22 Ste 1, Brewster, NY 10509-4358
Tel (845) 628-3500 Founded/Ownrshp 1927
Sales NA EMP 120
SIC 6021 National commercial banks; National commercial banks
Pr: Stephen S Romaine
Pr: John Friend
*Ofcr: Gerald J Klein Jr
*Sr VP: Rosemary Hyland
Sr VP: John Kraus
*VP: Kathleen Rooney
*VP: Edward Yuhas

D-U-N-S 04-483-5445
MAHOPAC CENTRAL SCHOOL DISTRICT
179 E Lake Blvd, Mahopac, NY 10541-1666
Tel (845) 628-3415 Founded/Ownrshp 1946
Sales 41.1MM^E EMP 900
Accts O Connor Davies Munns & Dobbin
SIC 8211 Public elementary & secondary schools; High school, junior or senior; Public elementary & secondary schools; High school, junior or senior
*CFO: David Chapman
Bd of Dir: Earle Bellows
Bd of Dir: Patricia Caputo
Bd of Dir: Lawrence Keane
Bd of Dir: Leslie Mancuso
Bd of Dir: Lucy Massafra
Bd of Dir: Marc Pekowsky
Bd of Dir: Michael Sclafani
Bd of Dir: Tilde Zimmerman
Schl Brd P: Michael Scalfani
Snr Mgr: Bill Siclari

D-U-N-S 00-120-5640 IMP
MAHR FEDERAL INC
(Suby of CARL MAHR HOLDING GMBH)
1144 Eddy St, Providence, RI 02905-4511
Tel (401) 784-3100 Founded/Ownrshp 1999
Sales 86.6MM^E EMP 300
SIC 5084 Instruments & control equipment; Instruments & control equipment
Pr: Tony Picone
Mng Pt: Ulrich Kaspar
*CFO: John Robinson
*VP: Kurt Braun
VP: Eddy Hochwart
Mng Dir: Anna Nagar
Dist Mgr: Peter Ahting
Dist Mgr: Sam Banerjea
Dist Mgr: John Buck
Dist Mgr: Pete Erins
Dist Mgr: Robert Knizner

D-U-N-S 62-392-9486
MAHROUQ ENTERPRISES INTERNATIONAL (MEI) INC
DOLLAR RENT A CAR SALES
610 N Collins St, Arlington, TX 76011-6945
Tel (817) 260-0269 Founded/Ownrshp 1993
Sales 27.4MM^E EMP 73
SIC 5511 6141 7514 Automobiles, new & used; Automobile & consumer finance companies; Passenger car rental; Automobiles, new & used; Automobile & consumer finance companies; Passenger car rental
Pr: Hussein K Mahroug
*Pr: Sam Mahrouq
*Treas: Nehad Dwikat
*VP: Rania Mahroug

D-U-N-S 09-391-5346
MAHTOMEDI PUBLIC SCHOOLS
1520 Mahtomedi Ave, Mahtomedi, MN 55115-1907
Tel (651) 407-2000 Founded/Ownrshp 1932
Sales 42.7MM EMP 300
Accts Malloy Montague Karnowski R
SIC 8211 Public elementary & secondary schools; Public elementary & secondary schools

MAHWAH HONDA
See C L F NORTHERN JERSEY AUTO SALES INC

D-U-N-S 08-443-0073 IMP
MAI-WEAVE LLC
1800 E Pleasant St, Springfield, OH 45505-3316
Tel (937) 322-1698 Founded/Ownrshp 1977, 2002
Sales 30.9MM^E EMP 75
SIC 3081 Packing materials, plastic sheet; Packing materials, plastic sheet
Sls Mgr: Jeff Wright

D-U-N-S 92-948-1521
■ **MAIC HOLDINGS INC**
(Suby of PROASSURANCE CORP) ★
100 Brookwood Pl, Birmingham, AL 35209-6811
Tel (205) 877-4400 Founded/Ownrshp 2001
Sales NA EMP 215
SIC 6351 Liability insurance; Liability insurance
Ch Bd: A D Crowe MD
CFO: Edward Raynd
Treas: James J Morello
VP: John O Bashant

VP: Jeffrey L Bowlby
VP: Howard H Friedman
VP: Frank B O'Neil
VP: William P Sabados
VP: Darryl K Thomas

MAICOM CONSTRUCTION SERVICES
See MAIURI ELECTRICAL CORP

MAID-RITESTEAKCO
See POLARIZED MEAT CO INC

D-U-N-S 07-948-9879
MAIDEN & NASSAU LLC
(*Suby of* FEDERAL RESERVE BANK OF NEWYORK) ★
33 Maiden Ln, New York, NY 10038-4518
Tel (212) 509-0064 *Founded/Ownrshp* 2012
Sales 44.1MM^E *EMP* 1^E
SIC 6512 Nonresidential building operators

D-U-N-S 07-849-4263
MAIDENFORM
485 Us Highway 1 S, Iselin, NJ 08830-3009
Tel (732) 621-2216 *Founded/Ownrshp* 2012
Sales 39.3MM^E *EMP* 1,200
SIC 2341 Women's & children's underwear; Women's & children's underwear
Rgnl Mgr: Diana Courtney

D-U-N-S 36-421-6445 IMP
■ MAIDENFORM BRANDS INC
(*Suby of* HANESBRANDS INC) ★
485 Us Highway 1 S, Iselin, NJ 08830-3009
Tel (888) 573-0299 *Founded/Ownrshp* 2013
Sales 139.1MM^E *EMP* 1,230^E
SIC 2341 2342 5621 Women's & children's underwear; Women's & children's undergarments; Bras, girdles & allied garments; Brassieres; Foundation garments, women's; Girdles & panty girdles; Women's specialty clothing stores; Ready-to-wear apparel, women's; Women's & children's underwear; Women's & children's undergarments; Bras, girdles & allied garments; Brassieres; Foundation garments, women's; Girdles & panty girdles; Women's specialty clothing stores; Ready-to-wear apparel, women's
CEO: Maurice S Reznik
Pr: Malcolm Robinson
COO: Christopher W Vieth
Ofcr: Anthony D'Onofrio
Ex VP: Patrick J Burns
Ex VP: Nanci Prado
Ex VP: Gayle Weibley Wolman
Sr VP: Steven Castellano
Sr VP: Patricia J Royak
VP: Gayle Webley
Netwrk Mgr: John Hascup
Board of Directors: Norman Axelrod, Harold F Compton, Barbara Eisenberg, Nomi Ghez, Richard Johnson, Karen Rose

D-U-N-S 00-146-7893 IMP
MAIDENFORM INC
TRUE FORM
485f Us Highway 1 S # 120, Iselin, NJ 08830-3055
Tel (732) 621-2500 *Founded/Ownrshp* 1999
Sales NA *EMP* 1,120
SIC 2341 2342

D-U-N-S 07-927-5610
■ MAIDENFORM LLC
(*Suby of* HANESBRANDS INC) ★
1000 E Hanes Mill Rd, Winston Salem, NC 27105-1384
Tel (336) 519-8080 *Founded/Ownrshp* 2013
Sales 195.4MM^E *EMP* 1,120^E
SIC 5137 Lingerie; Lingerie
Prin: Joia Johnson

MAIDSTONE COFFEE
See TIM HORTONS USA INC

MAIDWELL
See GLAMORISE FOUNDATIONS INC

MAIL AMERICA
See CREATIVE COMMUNICATIONS LIMITED LIABILITY CO

D-U-N-S 96-834-9811
MAIL AMERICA COMMUNICATIONS INC
(*Suby of* MAIL AMERICA HOLDING INC) ★
1174 Elkton Farm Rd, Forest, VA 24551-2128
Tel (434) 534-8000 *Founded/Ownrshp* 1997
Sales 61.3MM^E *EMP* 325
SIC 7331 2752 Direct mail advertising services; Commercial printing, lithographic; Direct mail advertising services; Commercial printing, lithographic
Pr: John A Rodewald
**Prin:* David Collins
**Prin:* Dan Reber

D-U-N-S 96-834-8086
MAIL AMERICA HOLDING INC
(*Suby of* INNOVAIRRE COMMUNICATIONS LLC) ★
1174 Elkton Farm Rd, Forest, VA 24551-2128
Tel (434) 534-8000 *Founded/Ownrshp* 2013
Sales 61.3MM^E *EMP* 369^E
SIC 7331 Direct mail advertising services; Direct mail advertising services
Pr: Daniel A Reber
**VP:* Pat Cronin
VP Sls: Daryl Collins

MAIL BOXES ETC
See UPS STORE INC

D-U-N-S 02-987-1167
MAIL CO
STRAHM AUTOMTN & MAILING SVC
1700 Broadway Blvd Fl 2, Kansas City, MO 64108-1210
Tel (816) 756-2733 *Founded/Ownrshp* 1995
Sales 20.2MM^E *EMP* 85
SIC 2752 7331 2791 2789 Commercial printing, offset; Mailing service; Mailing list brokers; Typesetting; Bookbinding & related work
Pr: Brian Dicker
Exec: Dave Connor

D-U-N-S 15-424-6623
MAIL CONTRACTORS OF AMERICA INC
M C A
3800 N Rodney Parham Rd # 301, Little Rock, AR 72212-2489
Tel (501) 280-0500 *Founded/Ownrshp* 1956
Sales 125.0MM^E *EMP* 1,200
SIC 4212 Mail carriers, contract; Mail carriers, contract
Pr: Don Salmon
CFO: Bryan Wilson
VP: Sheila McDonald
Genl Mgr: Carol Harris

D-U-N-S 82-530-4017
MAIL CONTRACTORS OF ARKANSAS INC
(*Suby of* M C A) ★
3800 N Rod Parm Rd # 301, Little Rock, AR 72212-2489
Tel (501) 280-0500 *Founded/Ownrshp* 1991
Sales 13.9MM^E *EMP* 290
SIC 4212 Mail carriers, contract; Mail carriers, contract
Pr: Randall Mourot
**Sec:* Cliff Ferren
CIO: Donna Larkin

D-U-N-S 08-238-3373
MAIL HANDLING INC
MAIL HANDLING SERVICES
7550 Corporate Way, Eden Prairie, MN 55344-2045
Tel (952) 975-5000 *Founded/Ownrshp* 2009
Sales 24.6MM^E *EMP* 120
SIC 2752 7331 7374 Commercial printing, offset; Mailing service; Data processing service; Commercial printing, offset; Mailing service; Data processing service
Pr: Brian Ostenso
**Prin:* Todd Tuma
Prd Mgr: Rob Wright

MAIL HANDLING SERVICES
See MAIL HANDLING INC

D-U-N-S 18-462-4349
MAIL TERMINAL SERVICES LLC
2700 S Commerce Pkwy # 105, Weston, FL 33331-3629
Tel (800) 608-7280 *Founded/Ownrshp* 2004
Sales 37.5MM^E *EMP* 900
SIC 7389 Post office contract stations; Post office contract stations
CFO: Richard M Schorr

MAILCHIMP
See ROCKET SCIENCE GROUP LLC

D-U-N-S 01-765-5705 IMP
MAILENDER INC
9500 Glades Dr, West Chester, OH 45011-9400
Tel (513) 942-5453 *Founded/Ownrshp* 1936
Sales 35.2MM^E *EMP* 62
SIC 5113 Industrial & personal service paper; Industrial & personal service paper
CEO: Ken Mailender
**Pr:* Andrew Abel
**Treas:* Bill Katz
Ex VP: Chris Kleck
**VP:* Chris Ward
Exec: Larry Wilson
Sales Asso: Mark Gordon
Sales Asso: John Zak

MAILERS SOFTWARE
See MELISSA DATA CORP

D-U-N-S 05-552-8848
MAILING SERVICES OF PITTSBURGH INC
MSP
155 Commerce Dr, Freedom, PA 15042-9202
Tel (724) 371-3461 *Founded/Ownrshp* 1956
Sales 69.6MM^E *EMP* 310
SIC 7331 Mailing service; Mailing service
Ch Bd: Richard E Bushee Jr
**Pr:* Richard Bushee III
**Treas:* Bruce C Driehorst
**Ex VP:* Bruce D Wilson
Sr VP: Doug Johnston
**VP:* Steven M Bushee
VP: Steven Bushee
CTO: Jim Young
Dir IT: Cheryl Christiana
Netwrk Mgr: Rick Holcomb
Board of Directors: Philip J Bushee, Sharon Bushee, Steven M Bushee, G Ashley Woolridge

D-U-N-S 08-152-1072 IMP
MAILMEN INC (NY)
15 Enter Ln, Islandia, NY 11749-4897
Tel (631) 582-6900 *Founded/Ownrshp* 1977
Sales 42.3MM^E *EMP* 300
SIC 7331 2759 Direct mail advertising services; Laser printing; Direct mail advertising services; Laser printing
Ch: William J Vignola
Opers Mgr: Robert Carleo

D-U-N-S 82-823-7391
MAILROOM HOLDING INC
(*Suby of* NEOPOST SA)
478 Wheelers Farms Rd, Milford, CT 06461-9105
Tel (203) 301-3400 *Founded/Ownrshp* 2008
Sales NA *EMP* 600^E
SIC 6159 Machinery & equipment finance leasing; Machinery & equipment finance leasing
Pr: Dennis P Lestrange
COO: Patrick Mingles

D-U-N-S 18-907-4727
MAILSOUTH INC
IMAGEWORKS
5901 Highway 52 E, Helena, AL 35080-9423
Tel (205) 620-6200 *Founded/Ownrshp* 2010
Sales 91.9MM^E *EMP* 700
SIC 7311 7331 Advertising agencies; Direct mail advertising services; Advertising agencies; Direct mail advertising services
CEO: Steve Mitzel

**Pr:* Tom Settle
**CEO:* Richard J Hanna
**COO:* William L Wann Jr
**CFO:* William Hunt
**Sr VP:* Gregori D Bogich
Sr VP: Anthony O McKinney
**Sr VP:* Steven B Neal
**VP:* Darrell W Edwards
VP: Kathleen Kennally
VP: Mike Kowalczyk
VP: Mangesh Wadegaonkar
VP: David Wright
Creative D: Brian Blackman
Dir Bus: Chris Fraziei

D-U-N-S 08-944-4905
MAIMONIDES ACADEMY
310 Huntley Dr, West Hollywood, CA 90048-1919
Tel (310) 659-2456 *Founded/Ownrshp* 1971
Sales 21.7MM *EMP* 120
Accts Ruslan Magidov Los Angeles C
SIC 8211 Academy; Academy
Pr: Allan Enigy
**Pr:* Moshe Sassover
**Ex Dir:* Baruch Kupfer
Dir IT: Jacob Shaw
Opers Mgr: Nancy Schiff

D-U-N-S 87-653-3704 IMP
MAIMONIDES HEALTH RESOURCES INC
MAIMONIDES MEDICAL CENTER
4802 10th Ave, Brooklyn, NY 11219-2916
Tel (718) 283-6000 *Founded/Ownrshp* 1990
Sales 38.4MM^E *EMP* 160
SIC 5912 8062 Drug stores; General medical & surgical hospitals
Ch Bd: Martin D Payson
**Pr:* Pamela Brier
**CFO:* Robert Naldi
**CFO:* Elaine Swiontak
**Ex VP:* David I Cohen
**Ex VP:* Dominick Stanzione

MAIMONIDES MEDICAL CENTER
See MAIMONIDES HEALTH RESOURCES INC

D-U-N-S 05-738-1535
MAIMONIDES MEDICAL CENTER INC
4802 10th Ave, Brooklyn, NY 11219-2916
Tel (718) 581-0598 *Founded/Ownrshp* 1906
Sales 1.0MMM *EMP* 6,382
SIC 8062 General medical & surgical hospitals; General medical & surgical hospitals
Ch Bd: Martin D Payson
Chf Path: Robert Kalter
Dir Vol: Alla Zats
**Ch Bd:* Martin D Payson
**Pr:* Pamela Brier
Pr: William Howe
Pr: Eileen Tynion
COO: Dominick Stanzione
**COO:* Dominque Stanzione
**CFO:* Robert Naldi
Ofcr: Thomas Smith
Assoc VP: John Scanlan
Assoc VP: Sylvia Semenskaya
VP: Thomas Doherty
VP: Walter J Fahey
Assoc Dir: Charusheela Andaz
Assoc Dir: Adrian Chesney

MAIN AUTO PARTS
See WAREHOUSE DISTRIBUTORS INC

D-U-N-S 04-564-8060
MAIN BROTHERS OIL CO INC
MAIN CARE ENERGY
1 Booth Ln, Albany, NY 12205-1403
Tel (518) 438-4195 *Founded/Ownrshp* 1954
Sales 68.1MM *EMP* 150
Accts Saxbst Llp Albany New York
SIC 5171 5074 5983 Petroleum terminals; Oil burners; Fuel oil dealers; Petroleum terminals; Oil burners; Fuel oil dealers
Pr: David Tarsa
**Ch Bd:* Matthew Mattaraso
Telecom Ex: Dave Nasner
IT Man: Richard Deming
Sales Exec: Wil Hebert
Sales Exec: Will Hebert
Sls Mgr: Andy Kuhnel

MAIN CARE ENERGY
See MAIN BROTHERS OIL CO INC

D-U-N-S 00-958-4996 IMP
MAIN ELECTRIC SUPPLY CO
3600 W Segerstrom Ave, Santa Ana, CA 92704-6408
Tel (949) 833-3052 *Founded/Ownrshp* 1985
Sales 318.9MM^E *EMP* 300
SIC 5063 Electrical apparatus & equipment; Electrical apparatus & equipment
Pr: Scott R Germann
**COO:* Paul Vowels
**CFO:* Karen Morris
Dept Mgr: Christine Baeza
Brnch Mgr: Carlos Balencia
Brnch Mgr: Josh Lajoie
Brnch Mgr: Maurice Orozco
Brnch Mgr: Rob Siler
Brnch Mgr: Carlos Valencia
Dir IT: Mark Arnold
Dir IT: Rod Knight

D-U-N-S 01-861-4263
MAIN ENTERPRISES INC
1180 Stratford Rd, Stratford, CT 06615-7694
Tel (203) 334-3419 *Founded/Ownrshp* 1919
Sales 38.6MM^E *EMP* 90
SIC 1711 Warm air heating & air conditioning contractor; Ventilation & duct work contractor; Mechanical contractor; Warm air heating & air conditioning contractor; Ventilation & duct work contractor; Mechanical contractor
CEO: Kenneth J Oppedisano
**CFO:* Gregory Cross
**Ex VP:* Ed Wolf
**VP:* Michael Lestinsky

D-U-N-S 06-122-0377
MAIN EVENT ENTERTAINMENT LP
6652 Pinecrest Dr Ste 100, Plano, TX 75024-2940
Tel (972) 406-2600 *Founded/Ownrshp* 1998
Sales 73.3MM^E *EMP* 1,000
SIC 7929 5813 5812 Entertainers; Drinking places; Eating places; Entertainers; Drinking places; Eating places
CEO: Charlie Keegan
CFO: Chandra McCormack
CFO: Dough Novak
VP Mktg: Sherri Landry
Sls Mgr: Jennifer Gustafson

MAIN EXECUTIVE OFFICE
See PARISH OF JEFFERSON

D-U-N-S 78-761-9477 IMP
MAIN INDUSTRIAL TIRES LTD
107 Audubon Rd Ste 2, Wakefield, MA 01880-1245
Tel (713) 676-0251 *Founded/Ownrshp* 1998
Sales 25.3MM^E *EMP* 358^E
SIC 3011 Tires & inner tubes; Tires & inner tubes
Pr: Terry Lindbergh

D-U-N-S 08-512-8452
MAIN INDUSTRIES INC
107 E St, Hampton, VA 23661-1226
Tel (757) 265-3859 *Founded/Ownrshp* 1976
Sales 33.2MM^E *EMP* 210
SIC 4499 3471 Ship cleaning; Plating & polishing; Ship cleaning; Plating & polishing
Pr: Mike Challoner
**Sec:* Caldwell Challoner
**Prin:* Meredith Challoner

D-U-N-S 00-815-7760 IMP
MAIN IRON WORKS LLC
148 Old Ferry Rd, Houma, LA 70364-1691
Tel (985) 876-6302 *Founded/Ownrshp* 1986
Sales 42.2MM^E *EMP* 130
SIC 3731 Commercial cargo ships, building & repairing; Commercial cargo ships, building & repairing

D-U-N-S 12-400-4503
MAIN LANE INDUSTRIES LTD
6902 Flintlock Rd, Houston, TX 77040-4325
Tel (713) 896-3141 *Founded/Ownrshp* 2002
Sales 23.4MM^E *EMP* 75
SIC 1611 Highway & street paving contractor
Pt: Anthony Colombo
Pt: Craig King

D-U-N-S 96-962-8143
MAIN LINE AFFILIATES
MAIN LINE HEALTH HOSPITAL OPER
(*Suby of* MAIN LINE HEALTH INC) ★
240 N Radnor Chstr Rd # 260, Wayne, PA 19087-2121
Tel (484) 337-1453 *Founded/Ownrshp* 1984
Sales 31.4MM *EMP* 1,069^E
SIC 8062 General medical & surgical hospitals
Prin: Janie Powers

D-U-N-S 84-846-5964
MAIN LINE BROADCASTING LLC
9 Anthony Dr, Malvern, PA 19355-1972
Tel (610) 825-8101 *Founded/Ownrshp* 2005
Sales 25.3MM^E *EMP* 175
SIC 4832 Radio broadcasting stations
CEO: Marc Guralnick
**CFO:* Jeff Cohen

D-U-N-S 80-738-8264
MAIN LINE ENDOSCOPY EAST
AMSURG
333 E Ln Ave 2 Bala Plz, Bala Cynwyd, PA 19004
Tel (610) 660-8470 *Founded/Ownrshp* 2007
Sales 23.3MM^E *EMP* 488^E
SIC 8062 General medical & surgical hospitals
Prin: Andrew Philips

MAIN LINE HEALTH HOSPITAL OPER
See MAIN LINE AFFILIATES

D-U-N-S 17-344-7855
MAIN LINE HEALTH INC
MAIN LINE HLTH HOSP OPERATIONS
(*Suby of* MAIN LINE HEALTH SYSTEM) ★
130 S Bryn Mawr Ave, Bryn Mawr, PA 19010-3121
Tel (484) 337-3000 *Founded/Ownrshp* 1985
Sales 1.4MMM *EMP* 5,840^E
SIC 8741 Administrative management; Administrative management
Pr: John J Lynch III
**CFO:* Mike Buongiorno
Sr VP: Donald C Arthur
**Sr VP:* Brian T Corbett
Sr VP: Kenneth Kirbey
**Sr VP:* Kenneth E Kirby
**Sr VP:* Joann M Magnatta
Sr VP: Joann Magnatta
Sr VP: Eileen McAnally
Sr VP: Andrew J Norton
Sr VP: Sarah A Peterson
**Sr VP:* Barbara Wadsworth
**Sr VP:* Paul Yakulis
VP: Betty Craig
VP: Denise Murphy
VP: Joel A Port
VP: Harm J Scherpbier
VP: Laura Tansey
VP: Karen Thomas
Dir Risk M: Sharon Dirienzo
Dir: Carolyn Goldman

D-U-N-S 96-401-4278
MAIN LINE HEALTH SYSTEM
259 N Radnor Chester Rd # 290, Radnor, PA 19087-5240
Tel (610) 225-6200 *Founded/Ownrshp* 1995
Sales 1.5MMM *EMP* 17,485
SIC 8082 Home health care services; Home health care services
Pr: Joseph Sebastianelli
**CFO:* Kirk E Gorman
Chf Mktg O: Stanton Smullens
**Sr VP:* Thomas Mendicino
Sr VP: Dianne Salter
**Sr VP:* David F Simon

CIO: James Hauck
CIO: Deborah Krau
Counsel: Matt Ballard

D-U-N-S 10-963-1929
MAIN LINE HEALTHCARE
2 Industrial Blvd Ste 400, Paoli, PA 19301-1645
Tel (610) 648-1644 *Founded/Ownrshp* 1985
Sales 189.2MM *EMP* 760
SIC 8099 8011 Medical services organization; Physicians' office, including specialists; Medical services organization; Physicians' office, including specialists
CEO: Michael Buongiorno
**Pr:* Eric Mankin MD
VP: Lynne Stilley
Ex Dir: Dawn Tice

MAIN LINE HLTH HOSP OPERATIONS
See MAIN LINE HEALTH INC

MAIN LINE HONDA
See SCOTT IMPORTS INC

D-U-N-S 07-548-4121
MAIN LINE HOSPITALS INC
BRYN MAWR HOSPITAL
130 S Bryn Mawr Ave, Bryn Mawr, PA 19010-3121
Tel (610) 526-3000 *Founded/Ownrshp* 1892
Sales 1.1MMM *EMP* 3,353
SIC 8062 General medical & surgical hospitals; General medical & surgical hospitals
CEO: Leland I White
**CEO:* Jack Lynch
**CFO:* Michael J Buongiorno
Sr VP: Donald Arthur
**Sr VP:* Brian T Corbett
Sr VP: Joann Magnatta
VP: Joel Port
VP: Harm J Scherpbier
VP: Chris Torres
Dir Risk M: Denise Murphy
Dir Risk M: Jeffrey Small
Dir Lab: Glen Bull
Dir Rad: Emma Simpson

D-U-N-S 96-939-9398
MAIN LINE SERVICES
950 E Haverford Rd # 110, Bryn Mawr, PA 19010-3851
Tel (484) 337-8480 *Founded/Ownrshp* 2011
Sales 116.1MM *EMP* 4^E
Accts Pricewaterhousecoopers Llp Ph
SIC 8011 Medical centers; Medical centers

D-U-N-S 07-960-3570
MAIN METHODIST HOSPITAL
7700 Floyd Curl Dr, San Antonio, TX 78229-3902
Tel (210) 575-4000 *Founded/Ownrshp* 2014
Sales 94.7MM^E *EMP* 486^E
SIC 8062 General medical & surgical hospitals
CEO: Gay Nord
COO: Michael Beaver
VP: Anne Hoessner
VP: Susan Kilgore
VP: James Willis
Exec: Lea Svobota
Dir Teleco: Matthew Braswell
Dir Case M: Janis Madewell
Dir Case M: Margarita Vipraio
Dir Lab: Michael Davis
Chf Nrs Of: Wanda Gibbons

D-U-N-S 02-270-6436
MAIN MOTOR SALES CO
MAIN MOTORS CHEVROLET
435 W Main St, Anoka, MN 55303-2019
Tel (763) 421-2700 *Founded/Ownrshp* 1966
Sales 39.1MM^E *EMP* 110
Accts V Dreyer
SIC 5511 5521 Automobiles, new & used; Used car dealers; Automobiles, new & used; Used car dealers
Pr: Mark Carlson
VP: William Carlson
Genl Mgr: Vickie Dreyer
Store Mgr: Tricia Hedberg
Sls Mgr: Jeremy McFarland
Sls Mgr: Robert Work
Sales Asso: Ron Herman
Sales Asso: Brian Rasmussen
Sales Asso: Josh Solle

MAIN MOTORS CHEVROLET
See MAIN MOTOR SALES CO

D-U-N-S 18-184-5306
MAIN ROBERT A & SONS HOLDING CO INC
555 Goffle Rd, Wyckoff, NJ 07481-2937
Tel (201) 447-3700 *Founded/Ownrshp* 1985
Sales 25.7MM^E *EMP* 200
SIC 3496 3535 3443 3441 3451 3469 Miscellaneous fabricated wire products; Conveyors & conveying equipment; Cylinders, pressure: metal plate; Tower sections, radio & television transmission; Screw machine products; Metal stampings; Miscellaneous fabricated wire products; Conveyors & conveying equipment; Cylinders, pressure: metal plate; Tower sections, radio & television transmission; Screw machine products; Metal stampings
Prin: Robert A Main Jr
**Sec:* Susan Main
**VP:* William Main

D-U-N-S 07-963-5712
MAIN STEEL LLC
2200 Pratt Blvd, Elk Grove Village, IL 60007-5917
Tel (847) 916-1220 *Founded/Ownrshp* 2014
Sales 139.6MM^E *EMP* 234
SIC 3312 Stainless steel; Stainless steel
CEO: Tom Modrowski
CFO: Paul Patek
VP: Ryan Stack
Plnt Mgr: Kenneth Hargrove
VP Sls: James Henry
Sls Mgr: Brian Byrne
Sls Mgr: Jeff Cerny
Sls Mgr: Ed Hace
Sls Mgr: Luke Stephens
Sales Asso: Darren Carroll
Sales Asso: Gwen Smith

MAIN STREET AMERICA GROUP, THE
See NGM INSURANCE CO

MAIN STREET AMERICA GROUP, THE
See MAIN STREET AMERICA GROUP INC

D-U-N-S 80-040-5289
MAIN STREET AMERICA GROUP INC
MAIN STREET AMERICA GROUP, THE
4601 Touchton Rd E # 3300, Jacksonville, FL 32246-4485
Tel (904) 642-3000 *Founded/Ownrshp* 2005
Sales NA *EMP* 983^E
SIC 6411 Insurance agents, brokers & service; Insurance agents, brokers & service
Pr: Thomas M Van Berkel
Pr: Chris Cox
Pr: Tiffany Daly
Pr: Joe Meholic
Pr: Dave Randle
COO: Melissa Kerwick
COO: Steve Peeters
CFO: Amy Frederick
Assoc VP: Deb Jansen
Assoc VP: Lisa Murman
Assoc VP: Ron Profaizer
Sr VP: Jeff Kusch
VP: Brian Beggs
VP: Mark Berger
VP: Dean Dorman
VP: Bruce Fox
VP: Tom Frazier
VP: Dan Gaynor
VP: Nancy Giordano-Ramos
VP: Rob Hetzel
VP: Mike Lancashire
Board of Directors: Chris Doerr

MAIN STREET BRANCH CO , THE
See ARNOLD LUMBER CO

MAIN STREET CAMBRITT COOKIES
See MAIN STREET GOURMET LLC

D-U-N-S 84-006-2905
▲ MAIN STREET CAPITAL CORP
1300 Post Oak Blvd, Houston, TX 77056-3043
Tel (713) 350-6000 *Founded/Ownrshp* 2007
Sales 140.7MM *EMP* 38
Tkr Sym MAIN *Exch* NYS
SIC 6211 Investment firm, general brokerage; Investment firm, general brokerage
Ch Bd: Vincent D Foster
COO: Dwayne L Hyzak
CFO: Brent D Smith
Bd of Dir: Joseph Canon
Ofcr: Pamela Kemp
Ex VP: Rodger A Stout
VP: Shannon D Martin
Mng Dir: Nicholas Meserve
Board of Directors: Michael Appling Jr, Joseph E Canon, Arthur L French, J Kevin Griffin, John E Jackson

D-U-N-S 10-914-5024
MAIN STREET CASINO BREWERY & HOTEL INC
MAIN STREET STATION
200 N Main St, Las Vegas, NV 89101-2910
Tel (702) 387-1896 *Founded/Ownrshp* 1993
Sales 19.5MM^E *EMP* 658
SIC 7011 Casino hotel; Casino hotel
Sr VP: Stephen Thompson

D-U-N-S 15-553-8358
MAIN STREET FIBERS INC
608 E Main St, Ontario, CA 91761-1711
Tel (909) 986-6310 *Founded/Ownrshp* 1984
Sales 46.0MM *EMP* 60
Accts Kushner Smith Joanou And Gre
SIC 4953 Recycling, waste materials; Recycling, waste materials
CEO: Gregory S Young
**Pr:* Wayne Young
**Sec:* Steve Young
VP: Greg Young

D-U-N-S 79-827-1292
MAIN STREET GOURMET LLC
MAIN STREET CAMBRITT COOKIES
170 Muffin Ln, Cuyahoga Falls, OH 44223-3358
Tel (330) 929-0000 *Founded/Ownrshp* 2011
Sales 64.6MM^E *EMP* 108
SIC 2053 2099 2052 2051 Frozen bakery products, except bread; Food preparations; Cookies & crackers; Bread, cake & related products; Frozen bakery products, except bread; Food preparations; Cookies & crackers; Bread, cake & related products
CFO: Robert Ecker
QA Dir: Beverly Stopera
Plnt Mgr: Karl Driggs

D-U-N-S 79-324-8241
MAIN STREET NATURAL GAS INC
104 Townpark Dr Nw, Kennesaw, GA 30144-5508
Tel (770) 590-1000 *Founded/Ownrshp* 2006
Sales 135.0MM *EMP* 50
SIC 4922 Natural gas transmission; Natural gas transmission
CEO: Arthur C Corbin
CFO: Susan G Reeves

D-U-N-S 13-105-6707
MAIN STREET OPERATING CO INC
(*Suby of* HARDAWAY GROUP INC) ★
615 Main St, Nashville, TN 37206-3603
Tel (615) 254-5461 *Founded/Ownrshp* 1986
Sales 108.7MM^E *EMP* 238
SIC 1542 1541 1521 6531 Commercial & office building, new construction; Industrial buildings & warehouses; New construction, single-family houses; Real estate managers; Commercial & office building, new construction; Industrial buildings & warehouses; New construction, single-family houses; Real estate managers
Ch Bd: Stan H Hardaway
**Sec:* Kerry P Sloan
VP: Linda Guinn CPA

D-U-N-S 79-166-6050
MAIN STREET PRODUCE INC
2165 W Main St, Santa Maria, CA 93458-9739
Tel (805) 349-7170 *Founded/Ownrshp* 1976
Sales 25.0MM *EMP* 13
SIC 5148

D-U-N-S 01-604-3190
MAIN STREET RENEWAL LLC
8300 N Mopac Expy Ste 200, Austin, TX 78759-8392
Tel (512) 851-8950 *Founded/Ownrshp* 2012
Sales 24.1MM^E *EMP* 240
SIC 6531 Real estate leasing & rentals; Real estate leasing & rentals
Ch Bd: Sean Dobson

MAIN STREET STATION
See MAIN STREET CASINO BREWERY & HOTEL INC

MAIN STREET STATION HOTEL
See M S W INC

D-U-N-S 18-985-8277 IMP/EXP
MAIN TAPE CO INC
1 Capital Dr Ste 101, Cranbury, NJ 08512-3264
Tel (609) 395-1704 *Founded/Ownrshp* 1988
Sales 31.1MM^E *EMP* 160
SIC 2672 Adhesive papers, labels or tapes: from purchased material; Adhesive papers, labels or tapes: from purchased material
Pr: Joseph Musanti
COO: Jay Nesbitt
**Treas:* Joseph Vanore
VP: James Boyle
VP: Elizabeth Vondrak
CIO: Adam Gwizdz
QA Dir: Annie Brown
QA Dir: Brian McGovern
IT Man: William Cerpa
QC Dir: Beth White
Ql Cn Mgr: Alan Decker

D-U-N-S 13-812-8546
MAINE & MARITIMES CORP
209 State St, Presque Isle, ME 04769-2655
Tel (207) 760-2499 *Founded/Ownrshp* 2003
Sales 60.7MM^E *EMP* 140
SIC 4911 7372 7539 Distribution, electric power; Transmission, electric power; Prepackaged software; Electrical services; Distribution, electric power; Transmission, electric power; Prepackaged software; Electrical services
Pr: Brent M Boyles
V Ch: Nathan L Grass
**CFO:* Michael I Williams
**VP:* Tim D Brown
**VP:* Patrick C Cannon
VP: Michael A Eaton
VP: John Havrilla
VP: Mark M Hovey
Exec: Felicia Oclair
Plng Mgr: Michael R Bake
Dir IT: Richard Watson

D-U-N-S 07-840-9581
■ MAINE ASSISTED LIVING LLC
(*Suby of* KINDRED HEALTHCARE OPERATING INC) ★
680 S 4th St, Louisville, KY 40202-2407
Tel (502) 596-7300 *Founded/Ownrshp* 2012
Sales 3.0MM^E *EMP* 289^E
SIC 8051 Skilled nursing care facilities
Prin: Joseph Landenwich

D-U-N-S 78-277-5092
■ MAINE BANK & TRUST
(*Suby of* PEOPLES UNITED BANK) ★
467 Congress St Ste 100, Portland, ME 04101-3533
Tel (207) 828-3000 *Founded/Ownrshp* 2008
Sales NA *EMP* 150
SIC 6021 National commercial banks; National commercial banks
Ch Bd: Wayne C McGarvey
**Pr:* Samual A Ladd III
Ex VP: Bert Pelletier
Sr VP: Michael Stoddard

D-U-N-S 10-544-6327
MAINE BEHAVIORAL HEALTHCARE
SPRING HARBOR HOSPITAL
(*Suby of* MAINEHEALTH) ★
78 Atlantic Pl, South Portland, ME 04106-2316
Tel (207) 842-7700 *Founded/Ownrshp* 1999
Sales 32.2MM *EMP* 1,100
Accts Mainehealth Portland Me
SIC 8011 Health maintenance organization; Psychiatric clinic; Health maintenance organization; Psychiatric clinic
Pr: Dennis King
CEO: Patrica Davis
COO: Mary Jane Krebs
CFO: Michael Abbatiello
CFO: Mike Abbatiello
Ex VP: Greg A Bowers
Dir Rx: Gary Roy
Nurse Mgr: DOT Aube
Nurse Mgr: Nancy Masteller
CIO: Robert Rague
CTO: Marjorie Wiggins

D-U-N-S 00-694-9333
MAINE CENTRAL RAILROAD CO (ME)
(*Suby of* PAN AM RAILWAYS INC) ★
1700 Iron Horse Park, North Billerica, MA 01862-1641
Tel (978) 663-1041 *Founded/Ownrshp* 1862, 1981
Sales 19.9MM^E *EMP* 330
SIC 4011 Railroads, line-haul operating; Railroads, line-haul operating
Pr: Thomas Steiniger
**CFO:* Eric Lawler
Sr VP: Phillip Kingman
VP: Robert Culliford
VP: Steve Ryan

MAINE COAST MEMORIAL HOSPITAL
See MAINE COAST REGIONAL HEALTH FACILITIES INC

D-U-N-S 07-174-4486
MAINE COAST REGIONAL HEALTH FACILITIES INC
MAINE COAST MEMORIAL HOSPITAL
50 Union St Ste 2, Ellsworth, ME 04605-1534
Tel (207) 664-5311 *Founded/Ownrshp* 1947
Sales 77.0MM *EMP* 658
SIC 8062 8011 General medical & surgical hospitals; Offices & clinics of medical doctors; General medical & surgical hospitals; Offices & clinics of medical doctors
Ch: Rich Malaby
**Pr:* Douglas T Jones
**CEO:* Charlie Therrien
**CFO:* Kevin Sedgwick
**Treas:* Debra A Ehrlenbach
Off Mgr: Deborah Preble

D-U-N-S 18-636-1127
MAINE COMMUNITY COLLEGE SYSTEM
MCCS
323 State St, Augusta, ME 04330-7131
Tel (207) 629-4000 *Founded/Ownrshp* 1986
Sales 72.3MM^E *EMP* 1,200
Accts Baker Newman & Noyes Portland
SIC 8222 Junior colleges & technical institutes; Junior colleges & technical institutes
Pr: John Fitzsimmons
**CFO:* David Daigler
IT Man: Mary Lapointe

D-U-N-S 17-575-3169
MAINE COMMUNITY FOUNDATION INC
245 Main St, Ellsworth, ME 04605-1613
Tel (207) 667-9735 *Founded/Ownrshp* 1983
Sales 48.3MM *EMP* 28
SIC 6732 8733 Charitable trust management; Noncommercial research organizations; Charitable trust management; Noncommercial research organizations
Pr: Steven Rowe
Bd of Dir: Sidney Thaxter
**VP:* James Geary

MAINE CONTROLS
See MECHANICAL SERVICES INC

D-U-N-S 12-889-4730
MAINE DENTAL SERVICE CORP
DELTA DENTAL PLAN OF MAINE
1 Delta Dr, Concord, NH 03301-7426
Tel (603) 223-1000 *Founded/Ownrshp* 1965
Sales NA *EMP* 180
SIC 6324 Dental insurance; Dental insurance
Pr: Thomas Raffilo
VP: Lisa Rousseau
Dir IT: Eric Sobel
Software D: Amy Yang
Sftwr Eng: Jim Jensen
Sales Exec: Bojan Grgic
Snr Mgr: Michel Couret

D-U-N-S 80-904-5214
MAINE DEPARTMENT OF ADMINISTRATIVE AND FINANCIAL SERVICES
(*Suby of* EXECUTIVE OFFICE OF STATE OF MAINE) ★
78 State House Sta, Augusta, ME 04333-0078
Tel (207) 624-7800 *Founded/Ownrshp* 1992
Sales NA *EMP* 800^E
SIC 9199 General government administration; ; General government administration;
Snr Mgr: Roberta Ashey
Snr Mgr: Cynthia Bertocci
Snr Mgr: Randal Manning

D-U-N-S 80-904-5586
MAINE DEPARTMENT OF ENVIRONMENTAL PROTECTION
(*Suby of* EXECUTIVE OFFICE OF STATE OF MAINE) ★
28 Tyson Dr, Augusta, ME 04333-0001
Tel (207) 287-2812 *Founded/Ownrshp* 1972
Sales NA *EMP* 477
SIC 9511 Air, water & solid waste management; ; Air, water & solid waste management;
Prin: David Littell

D-U-N-S 80-904-5594
MAINE DEPARTMENT OF HEALTH AND HUMAN SERVICES
(*Suby of* EXECUTIVE OFFICE OF STATE OF MAINE) ★
221 State St, Augusta, ME 04330-6846
Tel (207) 287-1716 *Founded/Ownrshp* 1975
Sales NA *EMP* 2,800
SIC 9441 9431 Administration of social & manpower programs; ; Administration of public health programs; ; Administration of social & manpower programs; Administration of public health programs
**CEO:* William Boeschenstein

D-U-N-S 80-904-5958
MAINE DEPARTMENT OF PUBLIC SAFETY
(*Suby of* EXECUTIVE OFFICE OF STATE OF MAINE) ★
104 State House Sta, Augusta, ME 04333-0104
Tel (207) 626-3800 *Founded/Ownrshp* 1971
Sales NA *EMP* 630
SIC 9221 9229 State police; ; Public order & safety statistics centers; ; State police; ; Public order & safety statistics centers;

D-U-N-S 80-904-5966
MAINE DEPARTMENT OF TRANSPORTATION
(*Suby of* EXECUTIVE OFFICE OF STATE OF MAINE) ★
16 State House Sta, Augusta, ME 04333-0016
Tel (207) 624-3000 *Founded/Ownrshp* 1972
Sales NA *EMP* 2,500
SIC 9621 Regulation, administration of transportation; ; Regulation, administration of transportation;

D-U-N-S 80-904-5636
MAINE DEPT OF INLAND FISHERIES AND WILDLIFE
(*Suby of* EXECUTIVE OFFICE OF STATE OF MAINE) ★
284 State St 41 State Hou, Augusta, ME 04333-0001
Tel (207) 657-4977 *Founded/Ownrshp* 1995

Sales NA *EMP* 323
SIC 9512 Wildlife conservation agencies; ; Wildlife conservation agencies;

D-U-N-S 82-834-4999
MAINE DIAMOND DRILLING INC
2200 S 4000 W, Salt Lake City, UT 84120-1292
Tel (801) 974-0645 *Founded/Ownrshp* 2005
Sales 11.0MM^E *EMP* 400
SIC 1799 Core drilling & cutting; Core drilling & cutting
CEO: Robert Morgan
**Pr:* Francis McGuire
CFO: Denis Larocque

D-U-N-S 01-898-4377 IMP
MAINE DISTRIBUTORS
5 Coffey St, Bangor, ME 04401-5757
Tel (207) 947-4563 *Founded/Ownrshp* 1969
Sales 21.6MM^E *EMP* 95
SIC 5181 5182 5149

D-U-N-S 01-901-5304 IMP
MAINE DRILLING AND BLASTING INC
544 Brunswick Ave, Gardiner, ME 04345-6026
Tel (207) 582-4300 *Founded/Ownrshp* 1966
Sales 124.9MM^E *EMP* 300
SIC 1629 Blasting contractor, except building demolition; Blasting contractor, except building demolition
Pr: William D Purington
CFO: Tim Maynard
**Treas:* Timothy R Maynard
**VP:* Ted Purington Jr
Div Mgr: Travis Martzall
Dir IT: Dale Thomas
IT Man: Ken Smith
Web Prj Mg: Bill Purrington
Sfty Mgr: Bruce Lawler
Opers Mgr: Mike Bell

D-U-N-S 96-960-4722
MAINE EDUCATION ASSOCIATION BENEFITS TRUST
35 Community Dr, Augusta, ME 04330-8005
Tel (207) 622-5866 *Founded/Ownrshp* 2011
Sales NA *EMP* 2^E
Accts Macdonald Page & Co Llc Augus
SIC 6321 Health insurance carriers

D-U-N-S 06-099-4258
■ **MAINE ELECTRIC POWER CO INC** (ME)
(*Suby of* C M P) ★
Edison Dr, Augusta, ME 04336-0001
Tel (207) 623-3521 *Founded/Ownrshp* 1966
Sales 61.5MM^E *EMP* 400
SIC 4911 Electric services; Electric services
Pr: Sarah Burns

D-U-N-S 79-806-2881
MAINE EMPLOYERS MUTUAL INSURANCE CO
MEMIC
261 Commercial St, Portland, ME 04101-4622
Tel (207) 791-3300 *Founded/Ownrshp* 1993
Sales NA *EMP* 250
Accts Pricewaterhousecoopers Llp Bo
SIC 6331 Workers' compensation insurance; Workers' compensation insurance
Pr: John T Leonard
**Sr VP:* Michael Bourque
Sr VP: Donald V Hale
**Sr VP:* Catherine Lamson
Sr VP: John Marr
**Sr VP:* Robert S Mc Mann
VP: Dan Cote
Snr Mgr: Rob Sylvester

D-U-N-S 07-581-3824
MAINE ENDWELL CENTRAL SCHOOL DISTRICT
712 Farm To Market Rd, Endwell, NY 13760-1128
Tel (607) 754-1400 *Founded/Ownrshp* 1930
Sales 24.3MM^E *EMP* 593
SIC 8211 Public combined elementary & secondary school; Public combined elementary & secondary school

D-U-N-S 12-135-1316
MAINE ENERGY RECOVERY CO LIMITED PARTNERSHIP
110 Main St Ste 1308, Saco, ME 04072-3516
Tel (207) 286-1668 *Founded/Ownrshp* 2001
Sales 22.3MM^E *EMP* 81
SIC 4911 Generation, electric power; Generation, electric power
Genl Mgr: Ken Robbins
Genl Pt: Casella Waste Systems

D-U-N-S 11-207-6513
MAINE GENERAL MEDICAL CENTER INC
149 North St, Waterville, ME 04901-4974
Tel (207) 872-4190 *Founded/Ownrshp* 1991
Sales 166.7MM^E *EMP* 3,000
SIC 8011 Medical centers; Medical centers
Pr: Scott Bullock
Snr Mgr: Michael Bushey

D-U-N-S 00-109-4929 IMP
MAINE MACHINE PRODUCTS CO (ME)
(*Suby of* GENNX360 CAPITAL PARTNERS, L.P.)
79 Prospect Ave, South Paris, ME 04281-1108
Tel (207) 743-6344 *Founded/Ownrshp* 1956
Sales 35.0MM^E *EMP* 130
SIC 3599 Machine & other job shop work; Machine & other job shop work
Pr: David Macmahon
COO: Roland L Sutton Jr
CFO: Larry Collins
Exec: David Sutton
Prgrm Mgr: Jason Richardson
Genl Mgr: Scott Bourget
CTO: Jeff Sutton
IT Man: Stephanie Grover
IT Man: Joe Trybus
IT Man: Marc Vanderwood
Prd Mgr: Bruce Fox

MAINE MALL HONDA
See MAINE MALL MOTORS INC

D-U-N-S 01-907-2933
MAINE MALL MOTORS INC (ME)
MAINE MALL HONDA
191 Riverside St, Portland, ME 04103-1039
Tel (207) 774-1429 *Founded/Ownrshp* 1955, 1986
Sales 27.5MM^E *EMP* 80
SIC 5511 5531 5013 7515 7513 5521 Automobiles, new & used; Automotive parts; Automotive supplies & parts; Passenger car leasing; Truck rental & leasing, no drivers; Used car dealers; Automobiles, new & used; Automotive parts; Automotive supplies & parts; Passenger car leasing; Truck rental & leasing, no drivers; Used car dealers
CEO: Bradford Stevens
Sales Asso: Keith Schram

D-U-N-S 80-005-0879 IMP
MAINE MANUFACTURING LLC
GVS NORTH AMERICA
63 Community Dr, Sanford, ME 04073-5809
Tel (207) 324-1754 *Founded/Ownrshp* 2006
Sales 33.7MM^E *EMP* 97
SIC 3089 Injection molded finished plastic products
Pr: Bill Emhiser

D-U-N-S 07-174-6630
MAINE MARITIME ACADEMY
1 Pleasant St, Castine, ME 04420-0001
Tel (207) 326-4311 *Founded/Ownrshp* 1941
Sales 40.2MM^E *EMP* 200
Accts Baker Newman & Noyes Llc Por
SIC 8221 Colleges universities & professional schools; Service academy; Colleges universities & professional schools; Service academy
Pr: William J Brennan
VP: Austin Bottorf
VP: Darrell Donahue
VP: David Gardner
VP: Jeff Loustaunau
CTO: Lisa Roy
Dir IT: Richard Allard
Web Dev: Brian Wolf
Mtls Mgr: Arnie Grindle
Snr Mgr: David Hassett

D-U-N-S 07-173-2663
MAINE MEDICAL CENTER (ME)
22 Bramhall St, Portland, ME 04102-3175
Tel (207) 662-0111 *Founded/Ownrshp* 1870
Sales 905.0MM *EMP* 5,000
SIC 8062 8071 6513 Hospital, AMA approved residency; Medical laboratories; Apartment building operators; Hospital, AMA approved residency; Medical laboratories; Apartment building operators
Pr: Richard Petersen
V Ch: Christopher W Emmons
VP: Barry Blumenfeld
VP: Wayne Clark
VP: George L Higgins
VP: Ann Keillor
Dir Risk M: Erin Graydon-Baker
Dir Lab: Marcia Waterman
Dir Soc: Cindy Tack
Dir Rx: Brian Marden
Dir Env Sv: Charlie Papa

D-U-N-S 17-193-7501
MAINE MEDICAL PARTNERS
(*Suby of* MAINEHEALTH) ★
301c Us Route 1, Scarborough, ME 04074-9701
Tel (207) 396-8600 *Founded/Ownrshp* 1995
Sales 27.5MM^E *EMP* 450
SIC 8742 Management consulting services; Management consulting services
Pr: Steve Kasabian
Obsttrcn: Peter Manning

D-U-N-S 08-318-1347
MAINE MUNICIPAL ASSOCIATION
60 Community Dr, Augusta, ME 04330-9486
Tel (207) 621-2645 *Founded/Ownrshp* 1936
Sales 127.6MM^E *EMP* 112
SIC 8611 Business associations; Business associations
CEO: Christopher Lockwood
**CFO:* Martin Hanish
CFO: Gordon Tibbetts
Treas: Pamela Griffith
Trst: Jolan Ippolito
Ex VP: Miles Theeman
Sr VP: Kenneth Payne
Dir Bus: Tamara Butts

MAINE MUTUAL GROUP
See MMG INSURANCE CO

D-U-N-S 06-705-3512 IMP
MAINE OXY-ACETYLENE SUPPLY CO
ATLANTIC SAFETY AND SUPPLY
22 Albiston Way, Auburn, ME 04210-4869
Tel (207) 784-5788 *Founded/Ownrshp* 1935
Sales 76.7MM^E *EMP* 146
SIC 5169 5084 Industrial gases; Welding machinery & equipment; Industrial gases; Welding machinery & equipment
CEO: Dan Guerin
CFO: Doug Cunnigham
**Prin:* Brent Bonzek
**Prin:* John Brockway
**Prin:* Mark Carpino
**Prin:* John Conrad
**Prin:* Carolyn Flanigan
Brnch Mgr: Andy Way
Store Mgr: Nick Dole
Store Mgr: Bill Gaherty
Store Mgr: Jason Goldrup

D-U-N-S 12-232-2811 EXP
MAINE PLASTICS INC
1817 Kenosha Rd, Zion, IL 60099-5142
Tel (847) 379-9100 *Founded/Ownrshp* 1983
Sales 52.6MM^E *EMP* 165
SIC 5162 5093

D-U-N-S 00-110-0213
MAINE POTATO GROWERS INC (ME)
M P G TRUCK & TRACTOR
56 Parsons St, Presque Isle, ME 04769-2157
Tel (207) 764-3131 *Founded/Ownrshp* 1932
Sales 37.8MM^E *EMP* 125
Accts Chester M Kearney Presque Is
SIC 5083 5148 5191 Farm equipment parts & supplies; Potatoes, fresh; Fertilizer & fertilizer materials; Farm equipment parts & supplies; Potatoes, fresh; Fertilizer & fertilizer materials
Ch Bd: Ned Berce
**CEO:* Pierre Patenaude
**CFO:* Jennifer Sonntag
VP: Gregory Smith
CTO: Art Crouse
IT Man: Rick Cheperd

D-U-N-S 00-694-9507
MAINE PUBLIC SERVICE CO INC
(*Suby of* MAINE & MARITIMES CORP) ★
209 State St, Presque Isle, ME 04769-2655
Tel (207) 760-2300 *Founded/Ownrshp* 1917
Sales 57.5MM^E *EMP* 140
SIC 4911 Distribution, electric power; Distribution, electric power
Pr: Brent M Boyles
Ch Bd: Richard Daigle
CFO: Michael Williams
**Treas:* Randi J Arthurs
VP: Tim D Brown
VP: Patrick Cannon
VP: Michael A Eaton
Ex Dir: Deborah Gallant
IT Man: Paula Sperrey

MAINE SCHOOL ADM DST
See SCHOOL ADMIN DISTRICT 34

D-U-N-S 15-914-4484
MAINE SCHOOL ADMINISRATIVE DISTRICT 54
196 W Front St, Skowhegan, ME 04976-5108
Tel (207) 474-9508 *Founded/Ownrshp* 1966
Sales 11.5MM^E *EMP* 334
Accts Runyon Kersteen Ouellette Sou
SIC 8211 Public elementary & secondary schools; Public elementary & secondary schools

D-U-N-S 18-399-4243
MAINE SCHOOL ADMINISTRATION DISTRICT 60
21 Main St, North Berwick, ME 03906-6793
Tel (207) 676-2234 *Founded/Ownrshp* 1967
Sales 33.0MM *EMP* 650
SIC 8211 Public elementary & secondary schools; Public elementary & secondary schools
Dir IT: Rick Mills
Teacher Pr: Eva Hammel

D-U-N-S 11-440-7872
MAINE SCHOOL ADMINISTRATION DISTRICT NO 75
50 Republic Ave, Topsham, ME 04086-1136
Tel (615) 467-1542 *Founded/Ownrshp* 2014
Sales 8.8MM^E *EMP* 600
SIC 8299 Educational services; Educational services
V Ch: Keri Tice
Ofcr: Susan Berman
**Prin:* Shelly Doody
Info Man: Jeanne Houde
Board of Directors: Bradley Smith

D-U-N-S 18-331-8666
MAINE SCHOOL ADMINISTRATIVE DISTRICT NO 6
94 Main St, Buxton, ME 04093-6105
Tel (207) 929-3837 *Founded/Ownrshp* 1959
Sales NA *EMP* 821
SIC 9411 Administration of educational programs; Administration of educational programs
Prin: Mel Sheridan
Dir IT: Bruce Rozett
Dir IT: Debbie Tarbox

D-U-N-S 01-901-0305 IMP
MAINE SHELLFISH CO INC (ME)
(*Suby of* IPSWICH SHELLFISH CO INC) ★
95 Water St, Ellsworth, ME 04605-2032
Tel (207) 667-5336 *Founded/Ownrshp* 1949
Sales 27.6MM^E *EMP* 66
SIC 5142 5146 Fish, frozen: packaged; Seafoods
Pr: Chrissi Pappas
Genl Mgr: James Markos

D-U-N-S 08-687-7115
MAINE STATE HOUSING AUTHORITY (ME)
353 Water St, Augusta, ME 04330-6113
Tel (207) 626-4600 *Founded/Ownrshp* 1969
Sales NA *EMP* 123
Accts Baker Newman & Noyes Llc Por
SIC 6162 Mortgage bankers; Mortgage bankers
Ex Dir: John Gallagher
Pt: Lisa Lavigne
**Treas:* Thomas Cary
Bd of Dir: Sheryl Gregory
Bd of Dir: Elizabeth Horning
Bd of Dir: David G Lemoine
Off Mgr: Eric Winne

MAINE SUNDAY TELEGRAM
See MAINETODAY MEDIA INC

D-U-N-S 01-058-8499
MAINE TOWNSHIP HIGH SCHOOL DISTRICT 207
1177 S Dee Rd, Park Ridge, IL 60068-4379
Tel (847) 696-3600 *Founded/Ownrshp* 1902
Sales 155.9MM *EMP* 975
Accts Mcgladrey Llp Chicago Illino
SIC 8211 High school, junior or senior; High school, junior or senior
**Pr:* Margaret McGrath
**VP:* Donna Pellar
Teacher Pr: Debra Liles
Psych: Ed Burda
Psych: Cynthia Perez
Psych: Nicole Rinaldi
Psych: Mieka Yochim

D-U-N-S 04-511-2679
MAINE TURNPIKE AUTHORITY
2360 Congress St Ste 1, Portland, ME 04102-1999
Tel (207) 842-4030 *Founded/Ownrshp* 1977
Sales 127.0MM *EMP* 340
Accts Macpage Llc South Portland M
SIC 4785 Toll road operation; Toll road operation
Pr: Paul E Violette
V Ch: James Cloutier
V Ch: Lucien Gosselin
Pr: William Yates
IT Man: Marc Milliard

D-U-N-S 10-119-1526
MAINE VETERANS HOMES
5 Community Dr Ste 3, Augusta, ME 04330-8088
Tel (207) 622-0075 *Founded/Ownrshp* 1977
Sales 92.2MM *EMP* 1,000
SIC 8052 Intermediate care facilities; Intermediate care facilities
CEO: Kelley Kash
**CFO:* Robert St Pierre
IT Man: Mark Pavitt
IT Man: Jeremy Storer
Snr Mgr: Mary Dyer

D-U-N-S 10-931-0545
MAINEGENERAL COMMUNITY CARE
10 Water St Ste 308, Waterville, ME 04901-6566
Tel (207) 861-3400 *Founded/Ownrshp* 1988
Sales 21.2MM *EMP* 40
SIC 8399 Health systems agency; Health systems agency
Pr: Nona Boyink
**CFO:* Mary Griswold
Exec: Brenda Bowden
IT Man: Jo Hassam

D-U-N-S 15-971-9582
MAINEGENERAL HEALTH
35 Medical Center Pkwy, Augusta, ME 04330-8160
Tel (207) 626-1000 *Founded/Ownrshp* 1997
Sales 423.2MM *EMP* 3,800
Accts Baker Newman Noyes Portland
SIC 8062 General medical & surgical hospitals; General medical & surgical hospitals
Pr: Charles Hays
**COO:* Paul Stein
**CFO:* Michael Koziol
CFO: Kenneth Payne
Sr VP: Kash Basavappa
VP: Wendy Manter
Exec: Tammy Pomerleau
Dir Risk M: Elliot Sarantakos
Comm Dir: Paul Tobey
CTO: Eileen Cummings
IT Man: Marcia Feaby

D-U-N-S 07-746-1754
MAINEGENERAL MEDICAL CENTER
(*Suby of* MAINEGENERAL HEALTH) ★
35 Medical Center Pkwy, Augusta, ME 04330-8160
Tel (207) 626-1289 *Founded/Ownrshp* 1997
Sales 378.7MM *EMP* 2,200
SIC 8062 General medical & surgical hospitals; General medical & surgical hospitals
CEO: Chuck Hays
Chf Rad: Jonathan Hallenbeck
Ofcr: Jane Belanye
**Ofcr:* Charles Hays
Ofcr: Georgia Kosciusko
Sr VP: Gail Evans
VP: Barbara Crowley
Exec: Stephen Walsh
Dir Risk M: Elliott Sarantakos
Dir Risk M: Elliot Sarantokos
Dir Risk M: Elliot Savantakos
Dir: Michelle Ayotte
Comm Dir: Paul Tobey
Comm Man: Barbara Martin

D-U-N-S 07-174-6994
MAINEGENERAL REHABILITATION & LONG TERM CARE
(*Suby of* MAINEGENERAL HEALTH) ★
37 Gray Birch Dr, Augusta, ME 04330-6105
Tel (207) 621-7100 *Founded/Ownrshp* 1987
Sales 20.2MM^E *EMP* 300
Accts Baker Newman & Noyes Portland
SIC 8052 Personal care facility; Personal care facility
Pr: Nona Boyink
Nrsg Dir: Ellen Fuller
HC Dir: Jeannie Kibbin

D-U-N-S 85-858-2372
MAINEHEALTH
110 Free St, Portland, ME 04101-3576
Tel (207) 661-7001 *Founded/Ownrshp* 1987
Sales 59.4MM *EMP* 2,100
Accts Mainehealth Rectortown Va
SIC 8741 Hospital management; Nursing & personal care facility management; Hospital management; Nursing & personal care facility management
Pr: William Caron
**Treas:* Frank G McGinty
Trst: Richard L Roy
Chf Inves: John Heye
Ex VP: Frank McGinty
Sr VP: Deborah Deatrick
VP: Paul Chausse
**VP:* Mark Harris
Prgrm Mgr: Nora Bowne
Prgrm Mgr: Sharon Foerster
Genl Mgr: Bobbi Shirley
Board of Directors: Hanson D Louis

D-U-N-S 04-802-2305
MAINELLI MECHANICAL CONTRACTORS INC
8701 N 29th St, Omaha, NE 68112-1848
Tel (402) 457-5501 *Founded/Ownrshp* 1969
Sales 35.0MM^E *EMP* 120
SIC 1711 Plumbing contractors; Warm air heating & air conditioning contractor; Plumbing contractors; Warm air heating & air conditioning contractor
Pr: Thomas J McNeil

Treas: Rena McNaboe
**VP:* Steven Bena
**VP:* Rena Macaboe
**VP:* Terrance McNeil

D-U-N-S 00-225-1197
MAINES PAPER & FOOD SERVICE INC (NY)
101 Broome Corporate Pkwy, Conklin, NY 13748-1507
Tel (607) 779-1200 *Founded/Ownrshp* 1919, 1960
Sales 2.2MMM^E *EMP* 1,000
SIC 5142 5113 5141 5087 5147 5146 Packaged frozen goods; Industrial & personal service paper; Groceries, general line; Janitors' supplies; Meats, fresh; Seafoods; Packaged frozen goods; Industrial & personal service paper; Groceries, general line; Janitors' supplies; Meats, fresh; Seafoods
Co-Ch Bd: David Maines
**Pr:* Christopher Mellon
**Co-Ch Bd:* William Maines
Sr VP: Steve Stoner
VP: Patrick Doyle
VP: Marissa Haight
VP: Bob Kranz
VP: Jeff Sault
VP: Bill Savier
VP: Guy Zehner
Dir Bus: Bradley Hurlburt
Dir Bus: Brooks Teeter

D-U-N-S 12-664-0981
MAINETODAY MEDIA INC
MAINE SUNDAY TELEGRAM
390 Congress St, Portland, ME 04101-3514
Tel (207) 791-6650 *Founded/Ownrshp* 2009
Sales 122.2MM^E *EMP* 720
SIC 2711 Newspapers, publishing & printing; Newspapers, publishing & printing
CEO: Charles Cochrane
CIO: Denise Beck
Mktg Dir: Pamela Cassidy

D-U-N-S 06-461-8572
MAINFREIGHT INC
(*Suby of* MAINFREIGHT LIMITED)
1400 Glenn Curtiss St, Carson, CA 90746-4030
Tel (310) 900-1974 *Founded/Ownrshp* 2007
Sales 175.4MM^E *EMP* 310
SIC 4731 Domestic freight forwarding; Foreign freight forwarding; Domestic freight forwarding; Foreign freight forwarding
Pr: John Hepworth
**CEO:* Christopher Coppersmith
**VP:* John Eshuis
Sls Mgr: Michelle Merino

D-U-N-S 02-795-9865 IMP
MAINGATE INC
7900 Rockville Rd, Indianapolis, IN 46214-3107
Tel (317) 243-2000 *Founded/Ownrshp* 1995
Sales 25.3MM^E *EMP* 100
SIC 2339 2396 2395 6794 Women's & misses' athletic clothing & sportswear; Screen printing on fabric articles; Embroidery & art needlework; Copyright buying & licensing
Pr: David I Moroknek
**CFO:* Robert Bell
CFO: Jim Hall
Sr VP: Ned Walliser
**VP:* Bruce K Lynch
VP: Dan Petty
Dir Soc: Keith Stein
Netwrk Mgr: Charles Randle
Mktg Dir: Mark Higdon
Merch Mgr: Pete Wibbenmeyer
Sls Mgr: Jesse Overman

MAINLAND MEDICAL CENTER
See CHCA CLEAR LAKE LP

D-U-N-S 05-422-8119
MAINLAND REGIONAL HIGH SCHOOL DISTRICT
1301 Oak Ave, Linwood, NJ 08221-1653
Tel (609) 927-8058 *Founded/Ownrshp* 1961
Sales 30.7MM *EMP* 225^E
Accts Ford Scott & Associates Llc-M
SIC 8211 Public elementary & secondary schools; Public elementary & secondary schools
V Ch: Joseph Silipena Jr
VP: Samantha Goldhagen
**Prin:* Robert L Blake

MAINLINE HOLLOWGRAPHIC
See MAINLINE PRINTING INC

D-U-N-S 62-691-6779
MAINLINE INFORMATION SYSTEMS INC
1700 Summit Lake Dr, Tallahassee, FL 32317-7942
Tel (850) 219-5000 *Founded/Ownrshp* 1989
Sales 479.8MM *EMP* 568
Accts Kpmg Llp Jacksonville Fl
SIC 7373 7379 7371 Value-added resellers, computer systems; Computer related consulting services; Computer software systems analysis & design, custom; Value-added resellers, computer systems; Computer related consulting services; Computer software systems analysis & design, custom
Pr: Richard Kearney
Pr: Mike Wheeler
Treas: Joseph P Elebash
Ofcr: Susan Sturza
Ex VP: John R McCarthy
Sr VP: Sherrie E Kishbaugh
VP: Sandy Carter
Admn Mgr: Charles Vianey
Snr Sftwr: Raymond Horton
Snr Ntwrk: Steve Slater
Dir IT: Susan Geiger

D-U-N-S 15-742-1462
MAINLINE METALS INC
21 Bala Ave Ste 201, Bala Cynwyd, PA 19004-3203
Tel (610) 668-0888 *Founded/Ownrshp* 1986
Sales 29.7MM^E *EMP* 26
SIC 5051 Steel
Pr: Robert Dubin
**Sec:* David Zigerman
**VP:* Andrew Geisler
Rgnl Mgr: Guillermo Flores

Trfc Mgr: Celeste Starita
Sls Mgr: Jesse Canizio

D-U-N-S 00-715-8074 IMP
MAINLINE PRINTING INC (KS)
MAINLINE HOLLOWGRAPHIC
3500 Sw Topeka Blvd, Topeka, KS 66611-2374
Tel (785) 233-2338 *Founded/Ownrshp* 1958, 1990
Sales 20.0MM^E *EMP* 90
SIC 2752 2759 Commercial printing, offset; Embossing on paper
Pr: John Parker
**VP:* Tim Neidow
VP: Martine Padilla
IT Man: George Parker

D-U-N-S 15-187-6448
MAINLINE SUPPLY CO INC
120 N Shorecrest Rd, Columbia, SC 29209-4545
Tel (803) 788-9800 *Founded/Ownrshp* 1986
Sales 42.2MM^E *EMP* 120
SIC 5051 5074 Pipe & tubing, steel; Cast iron pipe; Pipes & fittings, plastic; Pipe & tubing, steel; Cast iron pipe; Pipes & fittings, plastic
Pr: L Steve Windham
**CFO:* Elizabeth Rhodes

MAINSAIL LODGING & DEVELOPMENT
See MAINSAIL MANAGEMENT GROUP INC

D-U-N-S 04-466-8460
MAINSAIL MANAGEMENT GROUP INC
MAINSAIL LODGING & DEVELOPMENT
4602 Eisenhower Blvd, Tampa, FL 33634-6359
Tel (813) 243-2600 *Founded/Ownrshp* 1994
Sales 23.4MM^E *EMP* 150^E
SIC 6531 Real estate agents & managers
Pr: Joe Colier
**VP:* Julianne V Corlew
**VP:* Norwood Smith
Exec: Kirk Lynch
Genl Mgr: Neisja Jones

D-U-N-S 10-724-1895
MAINSCAPE INC
13418 Britton Park Rd, Fishers, IN 46038-3583
Tel (317) 577-3155 *Founded/Ownrshp* 1985
Sales 90.9MM^E *EMP* 500
SIC 0781 Landscape counseling & planning; Landscape counseling & planning
Pr: Mark W Forsythe
**Treas:* Bruce H Torrance
**VP:* Zygmunt Mazanowski III
Opers Mgr: Francisco Calles
Opers Mgr: Josh Fuqua

D-U-N-S 79-923-2855
MAINSL SERVICES INC
7000 78th Ave N, Brooklyn Park, MN 55445-2744
Tel (763) 494-4553 *Founded/Ownrshp* 1989
Sales 33.9MM^E *EMP* 999
SIC 8399 Health systems agency; Health systems agency
CEO: Teresa Williams
Prgrm Mgr: Ross Archer
Prgrm Mgr: Mamu Barry
Prgrm Mgr: Arlene Beach
Prgrm Mgr: Jenessa Blazejewski
Prgrm Mgr: Doug Busch
Prgrm Mgr: Cindy Halligan
Prgrm Mgr: Christian Heinsler
Prgrm Mgr: Lorna Misoi
Prgrm Mgr: Tracey Phillips
Prgrm Mgr: Cindy Rath

D-U-N-S 05-499-9933
■ **MAINSOURCE BANK**
(*Suby of* MAINSOURCE FINANCIAL GROUP INC) ★
201 N Broadway St, Greensburg, IN 47240-1701
Tel (812) 663-4711 *Founded/Ownrshp* 1991
Sales NA *EMP* 388
SIC 6035 Savings institutions, federally chartered; Savings institutions, federally chartered
Pr: Michael K Bauer
Pr: Daniel Cobb
**CFO:* Brian K Conley
**Treas:* Carmen L Glenn
Ofcr: Brenda McKinney
Sr VP: Bill Goodwin
VP: Ed Heflin
Dir IT: Philip Dickey

D-U-N-S 15-060-3892
▲ **MAINSOURCE FINANCIAL GROUP INC**
2105 N State Road 3 Byp, Greensburg, IN 47240-9539
Tel (812) 663-6734 *Founded/Ownrshp* 1982
Sales NA *EMP* 814^E
Tkr Sym MSFG *Exch* NGS
SIC 6022 State commercial banks; State trust companies accepting deposits, commercial; State commercial banks; State trust companies accepting deposits, commercial
Ch Bd: Archie M Brown Jr
CFO: James M Anderson
Chf Cred: William J Goodwin
Ofcr: John Clerkin
Ofcr: Josh Gearhardt
Ofcr: Elisabeth Grace
Sr VP: Chris M Harrison
VP: Kevin Koehne
CIO: Malcolm Myers
Dir IT: Philip Dickey
IT Man: Shannon Goss
Board of Directors: Kathleen L Bardwell, William G Barron, Brian J Crall, D J Hines, Thomas M O'brien, Lawrence R Rueff, John G Seale, Charles J Thayer

D-U-N-S 00-494-4212
MAINSTREAM ENERGY CORP (DE)
REC SOLAR
775 Fiero Ln Ste 200, San Luis Obispo, CA 93401-7904
Tel (805) 528-9705 *Founded/Ownrshp* 2005
Sales NA *EMP* 493
SIC 1711 5049

D-U-N-S 09-801-9326
MAINSTREAM LIVING INC
2012 E 13th St, Ames, IA 50010-5601
Tel (515) 232-3591 *Founded/Ownrshp* 1976
Sales 16.9MM *EMP* 400
SIC 8361 Rehabilitation center, residential: health care incidental; Rehabilitation center, residential: health care incidental
CEO: Reinhold Berg
**CFO:* Jon Zellweger
VP: Lu Wingfield
IT Man: Rich Sharpe
IT Man: Kevin Smith
Pgrm Dir: Amber Schaefer

D-U-N-S 04-339-1275
MAINSTREAM SWIMSUITS INC
610 Uhler Rd, Easton, PA 18040-7001
Tel (610) 253-4281 *Founded/Ownrshp* 1945
Sales 29.6MM^E *EMP* 87
SIC 5137 Swimsuits: women's, children's & infants'; Swimsuits: women's, children's & infants'
Pr: Mark Waldman
**Sec:* Bruce Waldman
VP: Rick D'Amato

D-U-N-S 55-686-9733
MAINSTREET MORTGAGE INC
FIFC
3916 Lawson Dr, Troy, MI 48084-1728
Tel (248) 729-7316 *Founded/Ownrshp* 1990
Sales NA *EMP* 10
SIC 6162 Mortgage brokers, using own money; Mortgage brokers, using own money
Pr: George Douroujalian
Exec: Gayla Kalp

D-U-N-S 07-801-5088 IMP
MAINTAINER CORP OF IOWA INC
1701 2nd Ave, Sheldon, IA 51201-8549
Tel (712) 324-5001 *Founded/Ownrshp* 1982
Sales 37.5MM^E *EMP* 130
SIC 3713 Truck bodies (motor vehicles); Truck bodies (motor vehicles)
Pr: Dennis Michels
Off Mgr: Terri Malenke
IT Man: Dean Koele
Manager: Jason Klatt
Sls Mgr: Kory Jacobsma

MAINTECH ACQUISITION
See TRIANGLE SERVICES INC

D-U-N-S 07-888-1555
■ **MAINTECH INC**
(*Suby of* VOLT INFORMATION SCIENCES INC) ★
14 Commerce Dr Ste 104, Cranford, NJ 07016-3514
Tel (800) 426-8324 *Founded/Ownrshp* 1999
Sales 41.3MM^E *EMP* 423^E
SIC 7379
Pr: Frank W D'Alessio
**COO:* Bob Coscia
VP: Tony Chirico
VP: William D'Alessio
VP: Joseph Marino
VP: Joseph Miller
VP: Bill Olohan
VP: Bill Rudowitz
VP: George Sarvey
Dist Mgr: John Messina
Genl Mgr: John Sapone

D-U-N-S 15-210-0111
MAINTENANCE ASSISTANCE PROGRAMS INC
WHEELS
(*Suby of* WHEELS INC) ★
666 Garland Pl, Des Plaines, IL 60016-4725
Tel (847) 699-7000 *Founded/Ownrshp* 1979
Sales 28.3MM^E *EMP* 450
SIC 7538 Engine repair; Engine repair
Pr: Jim Frank

D-U-N-S 79-064-7952
MAINTENANCE BUILDERS SUPPLY LTD
MBS INCOPORATED
1418 Brittmoore Rd, Houston, TX 77043-4006
Tel (713) 462-8213 *Founded/Ownrshp* 1992
Sales 39.7MM^E *EMP* 50^E
SIC 5099 Locks & lock sets
Pr: Mark Beatty
VP: Cindy Thomas

MAINTENANCE DEPARTMENT
See LEXINGTON SCHOOL DISTRICT 5

D-U-N-S 93-224-9253
MAINTENANCE ENTERPRISES II INC
M E I
(*Suby of* CROWN ENTERPRISES LLC) ★
52410 Clarke Rd, White Castle, LA 70788-4914
Tel (225) 545-3970 *Founded/Ownrshp* 1967
Sales 82.2MM^E *EMP* 400
SIC 1541 Renovation, remodeling & repairs: industrial buildings; Steel building construction; Renovation, remodeling & repairs: industrial buildings; Steel building construction
Pr: Mike Campesi
**Sec:* Patrick O Campesi
**VP:* Ross J Campesi Jr
Opers Mgr: Roy Knapp

D-U-N-S 04-102-0855 IMP
MAINTENANCE RESOURCE INC
FACILITIES RESOURCE GROUP
3404 Busch Dr Sw Ste E, Grandville, MI 49418-1000
Tel (616) 406-0004 *Founded/Ownrshp* 1999
Sales 36.8MM^E *EMP* 95^E
SIC 1541 Renovation, remodeling & repairs: industrial buildings
Pr: John N Weeber
**VP:* James C Faber

D-U-N-S 08-867-8933
MAINTENANCE SERVICE SYSTEMS INC
CARPET CARE
125 Valencia Dr Ne, Albuquerque, NM 87108-1738
Tel (505) 265-8095 *Founded/Ownrshp* 1977

Sales 13.7MM^E *EMP* 350
SIC 7349 7217 Janitorial service, contract basis; Carpet & upholstery cleaning; Janitorial service, contract basis; Carpet & upholstery cleaning
Pr: Don L Crismore
**VP:* Sharon Crismore

D-U-N-S 09-067-7436
MAINTENANCE STAFF INC
122 W 8th St, Long Beach, CA 90813-4371
Tel (562) 493-3982 *Founded/Ownrshp* 1994
Sales 18.7MM^E *EMP* 2,600
SIC 7349 Janitorial service, contract basis; Janitorial service, contract basis
Pr: Vivian M Frahm

D-U-N-S 01-786-9785
MAINTENANCE SUPPLY CO INC
MASSCO
1837 S Meridian Ave, Wichita, KS 67213-1923
Tel (316) 264-7929 *Founded/Ownrshp* 1982
Sales 30.0MM^E *EMP* 100
SIC 5087 5044 5112 3646

D-U-N-S 78-444-0484 IMP
MAINTENANCE SUPPLY HEADQUARTERS LP
12315 Parc Crest Dr # 100, Stafford, TX 77477-2408
Tel (281) 530-6300 *Founded/Ownrshp* 2006
Sales 107.9MM^E *EMP* 65^E
SIC 5072 Hardware
Mng Pt: Richard Penick
Pt: Terri Moll
Pt: David Ryle
Area Mgr: Ken Ward
Opers Mgr: Amy Holt
Natl Sales: Izzy Garza
Sls Mgr: Paul Brown
Sales Asso: Geoffrey Coon

D-U-N-S 17-597-6252
MAINTENX INTERNATIONAL SERVICE MANAGEMENT GROUP INC
2202 N Howard Ave, Tampa, FL 33607-3454
Tel (813) 254-1656 *Founded/Ownrshp* 2004
Sales 24.5MM *EMP* 150
SIC 1711 7629 7299 Plumbing, heating, air-conditioning contractors; Electrical equipment repair services; Handyman service; Plumbing, heating, air-conditioning contractors; Electrical equipment repair services; Handyman service
Pr: Patrick Ohara
**Sr VP:* Juan C Gonzalez
**VP:* William Schaphorst
Mktg Dir: Maria Bevilacqua

D-U-N-S 00-831-7307 IMP
MAINTEX INC (CA)
13300 Nelson Ave, City of Industry, CA 91746-1516
Tel (626) 961-1988 *Founded/Ownrshp* 1960, 1986
Sales 21.7MM^E *EMP* 150
SIC 2842 5087

D-U-N-S 96-356-9413
MAINTHIA TECHNOLOGIES INC
M T I
7055 Engle Rd Ste 502, Cleveland, OH 44130-8456
Tel (440) 816-0202 *Founded/Ownrshp* 1996
Sales 38.9MM^E *EMP* 230
SIC 8744 Facilities support services; Facilities support services
Pr: Hemant Mainthia
**CFO:* Gary Bowden
Prgrm Mgr: George Guzauskas
Brnch Mgr: Todd Lockhart
Off Mgr: Lisa Hodge

D-U-N-S 03-365-0576
MAIPF
17456 N Laurel Park Dr # 130, Livonia, MI 48152-3981
Tel (734) 464-1100 *Founded/Ownrshp* 2010
Sales NA *EMP* 4^E
SIC 6331 Automobile insurance
Prin: Terri Miller

D-U-N-S 04-241-3666
MAITA CHEVROLET GEO
MAITA OLDSMOBILE
9650 Auto Center Dr, Elk Grove, CA 95757-8706
Tel (877) 835-0729 *Founded/Ownrshp* 1991
Sales 61.4MM^E *EMP* 164
SIC 5511 Automobiles, new & used; Automobiles, new & used
Pr: Vince Maita
**VP:* Steve Maita
Dir IT: Rich Koplin
IT Man: Sabrina Cappo
Sls Mgr: Chris Walker

D-U-N-S 00-961-7622
MAITA ENTERPRISES INC
MAITA'S TOYOTA OF SACRAMENTO
2500 Auburn Blvd, Sacramento, CA 95821-1703
Tel (916) 481-0855 *Founded/Ownrshp* 1988
Sales 71.8MM^E *EMP* 200
SIC 5511 Automobiles, new & used; Automobiles, new & used
Pr: Vincent L Maita
**Sec:* Diane Nowalski
**VP:* Steve Maita
Netwrk Mgr: Khanh Chau
Sales Exec: Al Rosenbloom
Sls&Mrk Ex: Dave Klingensmith
Sls Mgr: Richard Fabella
Sls Mgr: Jim Neely

MAITA OLDSMOBILE
See MAITA CHEVROLET GEO

MAITA'S TOYOTA OF SACRAMENTO
See MAITA ENTERPRISES INC

D-U-N-S 62-094-0668 IMP/EXP
MAITLAND-SMITH FURNITURE INDUSTRIES INC
1925 Eastchester Dr, High Point, NC 27265-1404
Tel (336) 812-2400 *Founded/Ownrshp* 1996
Sales 32.6MM^E *EMP* 140

SIC 5023 5021 Home furnishings; Household furniture; Home furnishings; Household furniture
Pr: Seamus Bateson
*CFO: Daniel Zeddy
VP Opers: Jeff Wray

D-U-N-S 61-629-6315
MAIURI ELECTRICAL CORP
MAICOM CONSTRUCTION SERVICES
85 Flagship Dr Ste J, North Andover, MA 01845-6160
Tel (781) 760-3160 Founded/Ownrshp 1986
Sales 25.9MM^E EMP 65
SIC 1731 1522 General electrical contractor; Hotel/motel & multi-family home construction; Multi-family dwellings, new construction
Pr: Paul Maiuri
*VP: Paul Delucia

MAIZE PUBLIC SCHOOLS USD 266
See MAIZE UNIFIED SCHOOL DISTRICT 266

D-U-N-S 09-144-1162
MAIZE UNIFIED SCHOOL DISTRICT 266
MAIZE PUBLIC SCHOOLS USD 266
11611 W 49th St N, Maize, KS 67101
Tel (316) 722-0614 Founded/Ownrshp 1966
Sales 50.0MM EMP 625
SIC 8211 Public elementary school; Public junior high school; Public senior high school; Public elementary school; Public junior high school; Public senior high school
*CFO: Steve Williams
Prin: Tyler Ewert
Prin: Shelley Jonas
Prin: Jeannine Pfannenstiel
Prin: Ken Rickard
Dir Sec: Tom Flint
HC Dir: Joann Wheeler

D-U-N-S 18-629-0003 IMP
MAJCO INC
BIG BRAND TIRE COMPANY
805 Via Alondra, Camarillo, CA 93012-8046
Tel (805) 388-0223 Founded/Ownrshp 1970
Sales 81.4MM^E EMP 225
Accts Soares Sandall Bernacchi & P
SIC 5531 Automotive tires; Automotive tires
Pr: Thomas L Graham
*Sec: Greg Robinson
VP: Ron King

D-U-N-S 13-661-5692 IMP
▲ MAJESCO ENTERTAINMENT CO
4041 Hadley Rd Ste T, South Plainfield, NJ 07080-1111
Tel (732) 225-8910 Founded/Ownrshp 2003
Sales 34.3MM EMP 16^E
Accts Eisneramper Llp Iselin New J
Tkr Sym COOL Exch NAS
SIC 3944 7372 Video game machines, except coin-operated; Prepackaged software; Application computer software; Home entertainment computer software; Video game machines, except coin-operated; Prepackaged software; Application computer software; Home entertainment computer software
CEO: Jesse Sutton
*Ch Bd: Trent D Davis
CFO: Michael Vesey
Chf Mktg O: Jeffrey Perlman
Ex VP: Pat Flaherty
Ex VP: Patrick Flaherty
Ex VP: Dick Wnuk
Sr VP: Chris Gray
QI Cn Mgr: Eric Jezercak

D-U-N-S 80-011-9992
■ MAJESCO INC
(Suby of MASTEK LIMITED)
412 Mount Kemble Ave 110c, Morristown, NJ 07960-6675
Tel (646) 731-1000 Founded/Ownrshp 1968
Sales 47.7MM^E EMP 352
Tkr Sym MJCO Exch ASE
SIC 7371 Computer software development; Computer software development
CEO: Ketan Mehta
*COO: Edward Ossie
*CFO: Farid Kazani
*Ex VP: Prateek Kumar
Ex VP: Tilakraj Panjabi
*Ex VP: Manish Shah
Sr VP: Denise Garth

MAJESTIC ATHLETIC
See MAROCO LTD

MAJESTIC GLOVE
See U S GLOVE CO INC

D-U-N-S 83-036-1551
MAJESTIC HOLDCO LLC
1 Buffington Harbor Dr, Gary, IN 46406-3000
Tel (702) 388-2400 Founded/Ownrshp 1996
Sales 94.9MM^E EMP 2,750^E
SIC 7011 Casino hotel; Casino hotel
CEO: Peter M Liguori

MAJESTIC HOMES
See PRESTIGE HOME CENTERS INC

D-U-N-S 04-981-3996
MAJESTIC INDUSTRY HILLS LLC
PACIFIC PLMS CONFERENCE RESORT
1 Industry Hills Pkwy, City of Industry, CA 91744-5160
Tel (562) 692-9581 Founded/Ownrshp 1999
Sales 32.0MM EMP 550
SIC 8741 Hotel or motel management; Hotel or motel management
CFO: Pamela Golovkhin
Dir Soc: Rita Cruz
Dir IT: Larry Koester
Natl Sales: Nicole Choe

D-U-N-S 00-103-2346
MAJESTIC INTERIORS
3621 Grandview Cir, Shingle Springs, CA 95682-6803
Tel (530) 672-9433 Founded/Ownrshp 1997, 1976
Sales 36.0MM EMP 30
SIC 1742 Drywall; Drywall
Owner: William Falconer

D-U-N-S 13-812-7878 IMP/EXP
MAJESTIC INTERNATIONAL ELECTRONIC TECHNOLOGIES INC
MET INTERNATIONAL
1900 Surveyor Blvd, Carrollton, TX 75006-5110
Tel (972) 478-5641 Founded/Ownrshp 1995
Sales 35.0MM^E EMP 95
SIC 5045 Mainframe computers
Pr: Sashi Kejriwal
IT Man: Kenneth Huss
Sls Mgr: Hitesh Shah

D-U-N-S 02-644-2798
MAJESTIC LIQUOR STORES INC
ARLINGTON BOTTLE SHOP
(Suby of CENTENNIAL BEVERAGE GROUP LLC) ★
1111 Jacksboro Hwy, Fort Worth, TX 76107-1431
Tel (817) 335-5252 Founded/Ownrshp 2011
Sales 20.5MM^E EMP 170
SIC 5921 5182 Liquor stores; Wine & distilled beverages; Liquor stores; Wine & distilled beverages
Pr: Ben A Lanford Jr
*VP: John M Bratton
*VP: Kyle T Fair

D-U-N-S 09-573-8902
MAJESTIC METALS INC
7770 Washington St, Denver, CO 80229-6211
Tel (303) 288-6855 Founded/Ownrshp 1979
Sales 32.9MM^E EMP 120
SIC 3444 Sheet metalwork; Sheet metal specialties, not stamped
Pr: Karl Roberts
*Sec: Dorothea J Roberts

D-U-N-S 00-958-5050
MAJESTIC REALTY CO (CA)
13191 Crossroads Pkwy N # 600, City of Industry, CA 91746-3493
Tel (562) 692-9581 Founded/Ownrshp 1948, 1945
Sales 46.2MM^E EMP 169
SIC 6531 6552

MAJESTIC STAR CASINO
See BARDEN COMPANIES INC

D-U-N-S 07-883-9945
MAJESTIC STAR CASINO II LLC
(Suby of MAJESTIC STAR CASINO LLC) ★
1 Buffington Harbor Dr, Gary, IN 46406-3000
Tel (219) 977-7777 Founded/Ownrshp 1992
Sales 5.6MM^E EMP 404^E
SIC 7011 Casino hotel
Tech Mgr: Keith Chambers

D-U-N-S 83-798-0077
MAJESTIC STAR CASINO LLC
(Suby of MAJESTIC HOLDCO LLC) ★
5524 S Fort Apache Rd # 120, Las Vegas, NV 89148-7669
Tel (702) 386-0226 Founded/Ownrshp 2001
Sales 94.9MM^E EMP 2,700^E
SIC 7011 Casino hotel; Casino hotel
Ch Bd: Cezar Froelich
Mng Pt: John Risner
CEO: Peter Liguori
Exec: Jack Binion
Genl Mgr: David S Schugar
Board of Directors: Patrick R Cruzen, Michelle R Sherman Nicki, John A Obrien

D-U-N-S 96-174-1670
MAJESTIC STAR CASINO LLC
1 Buffington Harbor Dr, Gary, IN 46406-3000
Tel (888) 225-8259 Founded/Ownrshp 1993
Sales 36.9MM^E EMP 465^E
SIC 7011 Casino hotel
Pr: Don Barden
CFO: Jon Bennett
VP: Judson Boyer
Dir IT: Rand Wendorf
Advt Mgr: Nicole Anderson
Advt Mgr: Alex Salinas
Genl Couns: Rodney Phillipe

MAJESTIC STEEL SERVICE
See MAJESTIC STEEL USA INC

D-U-N-S 09-497-2056 IMP/EXP
MAJESTIC STEEL USA INC
MAJESTIC STEEL SERVICE
31099 Chagrin Blvd # 150, Cleveland, OH 44124-5930
Tel (440) 786-2666 Founded/Ownrshp 1979
Sales 351.0MM^E EMP 278
SIC 5051 Sheets, metal; Structural shapes, iron or steel; Sheets, metal; Structural shapes, iron or steel
*Pr: Todd Leebow
*CFO: Susan Suvak
Chf Mktg O: Steve Chiles
*Ex VP: Jonathan Leebow

MAJESTIC THEATER
See GETTYSBURG COLLEGE

D-U-N-S 00-563-5848 IMP
MAJESTIC WINE & SPIRITS USA LLC (PA)
ALLIED BEVERAGE
(Suby of ALLIED BEVERAGE GROUP LLC) ★
487 Devon Park Dr Ste 216, Wayne, PA 19087-1808
Tel (610) 902-9400 Founded/Ownrshp 1995
Sales 65.4MM^E EMP 187^E
SIC 5182 Liquor
Sls Mgr: Shannon McKnight
Sales Asso: Kaufmann Paul

D-U-N-S 17-198-7910
MAJESTY HOSPITALITY STAFFING INC
1720 Regal Row Ste 115, Dallas, TX 75235-2220
Tel (214) 634-7508 Founded/Ownrshp 1996
Sales 11.6MM^E EMP 500
SIC 7363 Help supply services; Help supply services
Pr: Andy Wimpee
VP: Erickson Charles

MAJIC WINDOW COMPANY
See MAGIC WINDOW CO

D-U-N-S 18-110-0470
MAJIDZADEH ENTERPRISES INC
RESOURCE INTERNATIONAL
6350 Presidential Gtwy, Columbus, OH 43231-7653
Tel (614) 823-4949 Founded/Ownrshp 1983
Sales 29.4MM^E EMP 150
SIC 8711 Consulting engineer; Consulting engineer
Ch Bd: Farah Majidzadeh
*Pr: Kamran Majidzadeh
*CFO: Dominic Maxwell
*VP: Steve Johnson
VP: Steven Johnson
*Ex Dir: Jeffrey Engram

D-U-N-S 78-738-3603
MAJILITE MANUFACTURING INC
(Suby of MERIDIAN INDUSTRIES INC) ★
1530 Broadway Rd, Dracut, MA 01826-2830
Tel (978) 441-6800 Founded/Ownrshp 1979
Sales 23.0MM EMP 66
SIC 2262 Chemical coating or treating: manmade broadwoven fabrics; Chemical coating or treating: manmade broadwoven fabrics
Pr: Michael Willewerth
*Treas: Douglas C Miller
Exec: John Kapeckas
Board of Directors: Mary Ellen

D-U-N-S 04-090-9066
MAJOR ACQUISITION CORP OF
(Suby of THE MAJOR AUTOMOTIVE COMPANIES INC)
77 Far Brook Dr, Short Hills, NJ 07078-3022
Tel (973) 376-0240 Founded/Ownrshp 2001
Sales 9.7MM^E EMP 373^E
SIC 6799

D-U-N-S 18-612-4954 IMP
MAJOR BRANDS INC
6701 Southwest Ave, Saint Louis, MO 63143-2623
Tel (314) 645-1843 Founded/Ownrshp 1988
Sales 197.6MM^E EMP 632
SIC 5182 5181 Wine & distilled beverages; Beer & ale; Wine & distilled beverages; Beer & ale
CEO: Susan B McCollum
*Pr: Robert N Epsten
*CFO: Jim Havel
*Treas: Thomas Schawang
Ex VP: Christy Bertelson
VP: Rau Danny
VP: Ron Snider
*VP: David Vittor
Exec: Cyndi Nelson
Exec: Michelle Reichardt
Div Mgr: Terry Joyce

D-U-N-S 84-722-4680 IMP
MAJOR DRILLING AMERICA INC
(Suby of MAJOR DRILLING GROUP INTERNATIONAL INC)
2200 S 4000 W, Salt Lake City, UT 84120-1292
Tel (801) 974-0645 Founded/Ownrshp 2005
Sales 22.5MM^E EMP 100
SIC 1799 Core drilling & cutting
Pr: Francis McGuire
*Treas: James Gibson
*Treas: Robert J Newburn
*Sec: Denis Larocque

D-U-N-S 00-790-8312
MAJOR EAGLE INC
MC DONALD WHOLESALE COMPANY
2350 W Broadway, Eugene, OR 97402-2704
Tel (541) 345-8421 Founded/Ownrshp 1927
Sales 188.4MM^E EMP 330
Accts Isler Cpa Eugene Or
SIC 5181 5141 5194 5142 Beer & other fermented malt liquors; Groceries, general line; Smoking tobacco; Packaged frozen goods; Beer & other fermented malt liquors; Groceries, general line; Smoking tobacco; Packaged frozen goods
Ch: Weir W Mc Donald
*Pr: Charles R Huey
*CFO: Gary Thomsen
*VP: Steve Hayes
*VP: Jack Willis
*Prin: Lote Mason
Sales Asso: Junior Lolgo

D-U-N-S 07-597-1689
MAJOR HOSPITAL
150 W Washington St, Shelbyville, IN 46176-1236
Tel (317) 392-3211 Founded/Ownrshp 1930
Sales 115.2MM EMP 950
SIC 8062 8011 General medical & surgical hospitals; Offices & clinics of medical doctors; General medical & surgical hospitals; Offices & clinics of medical doctors
Pr: Jack Horner
COO: Jeff Williams
*CFO: Ralph Mercuri
CFO: Robin Nichols
Bd of Dir: Nancy E Dayhoff
Chf Mktg O: Mary B Conners
Ofcr: Scott Miller
VP: Linda Wessic
Exec: Lloyd Lewis
Dir Inf Cn: Candy Oliger
Dir Lab: Mark Andrews
Dir Lab: Kimberly Six
Dir Rad: Mona Bernard
Dir Rx: Kelly Connolly
Board of Directors: Richard Bishopp, Nancy Dayhoff, Richard Hidy, Dorine Wolsiefer

D-U-N-S 09-994-0892
MAJOR INDUSTRIES INC
7120 Stewart Ave, Wausau, WI 54401-8410
Tel (715) 842-4616 Founded/Ownrshp 1993
Sales 22.1MM^E EMP 91
SIC 3211 Flat glass; Skylight glass
Pr: Wayne A Toenjes
DP Dir: Christopher Gitzlaff
Plnt Mgr: Gene Morrissey
Natl Sales: David Nyseth

D-U-N-S 07-685-1476
MAJOR LEAGUE BASEBALL ENTERPRISES INC
M L B
245 Park Ave Fl 31, New York, NY 10167-3000
Tel (212) 931-7800 Founded/Ownrshp 1915
Sales 2.9MM^E EMP 300
Accts Ernst & Young Us Llp Indianap
SIC 4833 8699 Television broadcasting stations; Athletic organizations; Television broadcasting stations; Athletic organizations
Pr: Robert A Dupuy
*COO: Robert D Manfred
*CFO: Jonathan Mariner
*Treas: Bob Clark
*Ex VP: Timothy J Brosnan
*Ex VP: Daniel Halem
Ex VP: Joe Torre
VP: Christopher Tully
Prd Mgr: Andrea Longueira
Pr Dir: Mike Herman
Snr Mgr: Dan Kelleher

D-U-N-S 02-040-7417
MAJOR LEAGUE BASEBALL PLAYERS ASSOCIATION
12 E 49th St Fl 24, New York, NY 10017-1028
Tel (212) 826-0808 Founded/Ownrshp 1960
Sales 39.6MM EMP 36
Accts Elliot Horowitz & Company Llp
SIC 8631 Trade union; Trade union
Ex Dir: Donald M Fehr
*Ex Dir: Tony Clark
*Ex Dir: Don Fehr

D-U-N-S 88-307-7141
MAJOR LEAGUE SOCCER LLC
420 5th Ave Fl 7, New York, NY 10018-0223
Tel (212) 450-1200 Founded/Ownrshp 1995
Sales 47.3MM^E EMP 580
SIC 7941 Soccer club; Soccer club
Pr: Mark Abbott
Pr: Michael Gandler
COO: Chris Canetti
CFO: John Giraldo
*CFO: Sean Prendergast
*Ex VP: Dan Courtemanche
*Ex VP: J Todd Durbin
Ex VP: Todd Durbin
*Ex VP: Nelson Rodriguez
Sr VP: Bill Ordower
VP: Jody Boyle
VP: Jeff Busch
VP: Rocky Harris
VP: Doug Hicks
VP: Dave Mosca

D-U-N-S 19-505-6379
MAJOR MARKET INC
845 S Main Ave, Fallbrook, CA 92028-3347
Tel (760) 723-7305 Founded/Ownrshp 1988
Sales 26.1MM^E EMP 250
SIC 5411 Supermarkets, independent; Supermarkets, independent
Pr: Samuel R Logan
Exec: Mike Oxford

MAJOR PHARMACEUTICALS
See HARVARD DRUG GROUP L L C

D-U-N-S 00-606-7078 IMP
MAJOR TOOL AND MACHINE INC
1458 E 19th St, Indianapolis, IN 46218-4289
Tel (317) 636-6433 Founded/Ownrshp 1949
Sales 60.3MM^E EMP 320
SIC 7692 3599 3769 3544 3537 3444 Welding repair; Machine & other job shop work; Guided missile & space vehicle parts & auxiliary equipment; Special dies, tools, jigs & fixtures; Industrial trucks & tractors; Sheet metalwork; Welding repair; Machine & other job shop work; Guided missile & space vehicle parts & auxiliary equipment; Special dies, tools, jigs & fixtures; Industrial trucks & tractors; Sheet metalwork
Ch Bd: J Stephen Weyreter
Sr VP: Bjorn Lissman
Prgrm Mgr: Dave McGowan
Prgrm Mgr: Jason Silvey
Prgrm Mgr: Mike Trosen
Genl Mgr: Mike Kramer
QA Dir: Jim Abbett
Dir IT: Mark Sweeney
Plnt Mgr: Dean Drury
Plnt Mgr: John Huter
Sls Dir: Roger Paulson

D-U-N-S 01-239-7170 IMP
MAJOR WORLD CHEVROLET LLC
4340 Northern Blvd, Long Island City, NY 11101-1020
Tel (718) 937-3700 Founded/Ownrshp 2014
Sales 81.9MM^E EMP 250^E
SIC 5511 7515 7538 5521 Passenger car leasing; Automobiles, new & used; General automotive repair shops; Truck rental & leasing, no drivers; Used car dealers; New & used car dealers; Passenger car leasing; General automotive repair shops; Used car dealers
Counsel: Eric Kelpz

D-U-N-S 07-432-4336
MAJORITY BUILDERS INC
62900 Us 31 S, South Bend, IN 46614-4831
Tel (574) 291-2091 Founded/Ownrshp 1973
Sales 36.4MM^E EMP 85
SIC 1542 1541 1522 1794 Commercial & office building, new construction; Institutional building construction; Industrial buildings, new construction; Multi-family dwellings, new construction; Excavation & grading, building construction; Commercial & office building, new construction; Institutional building construction; Industrial buildings, new construction; Multi-family dwellings, new construction; Excavation & grading, building construction
Pr: Rick E Slagle
*VP: Steven C Slagle
Dir Bus: Phil Damico

D-U-N-S 00-725-8262 IMP/EXP
MAJORS PLASTICS INC
10117 I St, Omaha, NE 68127-1109
Tel (402) 331-1660 Founded/Ownrshp 1953
Sales 67.5MM EMP 500
Accts Boyle Hess & Elliott Cpas P
SIC 3089 Plastic kitchenware, tableware & houseware; Plastic kitchenware, tableware & houseware
Pr: Tim Mc Connell
*VP: Mark Swanson

D-U-N-S 05-981-6541
MAK-TEL INC
1030 Clifton Ave, Clifton, NJ 07013-3522
Tel (973) 574-0011 Founded/Ownrshp 1998
Sales 25.0MM EMP 11
SIC 4813 Telephone communications broker; Telephone communications broker
Pr: Abdul Kareem Qattous
CFO: Ahmad Alkiswania
*VP: Abdel Razzaq Esbeitan

MAKALLON LA JOLLA PROPERTIES
See MAKAR PROPERTIES LLC

D-U-N-S 12-229-4028
MAKAR ANAHEIM LLC
ANAHEIM HILTON & TOWERS
777 W Convention Way, Anaheim, CA 92802-3425
Tel (714) 750-4321 Founded/Ownrshp 2007
Sales 27.1MM^E EMP 1,200
SIC 7011 Hotels; Hotels

D-U-N-S 03-838-9305
MAKAR PROPERTIES LLC
MAKALLON LA JOLLA PROPERTIES
4100 Macarthur Blvd # 150, Newport Beach, CA 92660-2063
Tel (949) 255-1100 Founded/Ownrshp 2001
Sales 360.7MM^E EMP 1,200^E
SIC 6552 1542 Land subdividers & developers, commercial; Commercial & office building, new construction; Land subdividers & developers, commercial; Commercial & office building, new construction
CEO: Paul P Makarechian
*Pr: Peter Ciaccia
*COO: Douglas Kiel
COO: Jana McCluskey
Ex VP: Sandy Weissbard
Mktg Dir: Laura Foster
Counsel: Ira Lebovic

D-U-N-S 05-514-2751
MAKE CORP
1 S 450 Smmit Ave Ste 165, Oakbrook Terrace, IL 60181
Tel (630) 376-0646 Founded/Ownrshp 1981
Sales 22.7MMM EMP 192^E
Accts Kutchins Robbins & Diamond Lt
SIC 7379 Computer related consulting services; Computer related consulting services
Pr: Karen Wilson
VP: Charlie Macconnachie

MAKE-A-WISH, AMERICA
See MAKE-A-WISH FOUNDATION OF AMERICA

D-U-N-S 62-475-9932
MAKE-A-WISH FOUNDATION OF AMERICA
MAKE-A-WISH, AMERICA
4742 N 24th St Ste 400, Phoenix, AZ 85016-4862
Tel (602) 279-9474 Founded/Ownrshp 1983
Sales 77.7MM EMP 118
SIC 8322 Children's aid society; Children's aid society
Pr: David Williams
Pt: Kevin O'Toole
V Ch: Suzanne Allen
COO: Dennis Covelli
*COO: Kurt Kroemer
CFO: Della Cherchia
CFO: Ed Kendall
*CFO: Paul Melhorne
CFO: John Stetner
Bd of Dir: Steven Hill
VP: Paul Allvin
VP: Phillip Arrington
VP: Pamela Clark
VP: Pete Finley
VP: Steven Henderson
VP: Sylvia Hopkins
VP: Paul Kirchgraber
VP: Suzanne Matsumori
VP: Paul Miles
VP: Caroline Schmidt
VP: Todd Shellenberger

D-U-N-S 83-300-9579
MAKENA BEACH & GOLF RESORT MAUI
5400 Makena Alanui, Kihei, HI 96753-8435
Tel (808) 874-1111 Founded/Ownrshp 2009
Sales 22.3MM^E EMP 318
SIC 8741 Hotel or motel management; Hotel or motel management
Prin: Kelly Lewis
Prin: Edith Goertz
Genl Mgr: Carmine Iommazzo

D-U-N-S 15-114-0910
MAKENA HOTEL LLC
MAUI PRINCE HOTEL & RESORT
5400 Makena Alanui, Kihei, HI 96753-8435
Tel (808) 875-5888 Founded/Ownrshp 1995
Sales 9.2MM^E EMP 340^E
SIC 7992 7011 5812 7299 Public golf courses; Resort hotel; Eating places; ; Public golf courses; Resort hotel; Eating places;
Genl Mgr: Ted McAneeley

D-U-N-S 06-284-7758
■ **MAKER STUDIOS INC**
(Suby of WALT DISNEY CO) ★
5877 Rodeo Rd, Los Angeles, CA 90016-4405
Tel (310) 606-2182 Founded/Ownrshp 2009
Sales 28.2MM^E EMP 295^E
SIC 7812 Video production; Video production
CEO: Danny Zappin
Pr: Ben Donovan
CFO: Lisa Donovan
Sr VP: David Sievers
VP: Caroline Dando
VP: Chad Sahley
VP: Drew Walkup
Snr Sftwr: Sean Charboneau
Snr Sftwr: Thomas Gibbons
QA Dir: Joe Pardo
Dir IT: Ken Park

D-U-N-S 01-596-7125 IMP
■ **MAKERBOT INDUSTRIES LLC**
(Suby of MOJO) ★
1 Metrotech Ctr Fl 21, Brooklyn, NY 11201-3949
Tel (347) 334-6800 Founded/Ownrshp 2013
Sales 74.2MM^E EMP 150
SIC 3621 3625 5084 Motors & generators; Actuators, industrial; Industrial machinery & equipment; Motors & generators; Actuators, industrial; Industrial machinery & equipment
CEO: Jenny Lawton
Exec: Stephanie Berzon
Exec: Michele Muniz
Creative D: Peter Ciccotto
Genl Mgr: David Neff
Snr Sftwr: Quynh Dinh
QA Dir: Ray Cheng
QA Dir: Kevin Chik
IT Man: Jason Friske
IT Man: Brendan Lauer
IT Man: Rich McCarthy

D-U-N-S 02-855-0564 IMP
■ **MAKERS OF KAL INC**
HEALTHWAY
(Suby of NUTRACEUTICAL INTERNATIONAL CORP) ★
1500 Kearns Blvd, Park City, UT 84060-7226
Tel (435) 655-6000 Founded/Ownrshp 1995
Sales 115.2MM^E EMP 450
SIC 5122 Vitamins & minerals; Vitamins & minerals
Pr: Bruce Hough
*CEO: Frank W Gay II
*CFO: Cory McQueen

D-U-N-S 01-074-1974 IMP
MAKESHOPNCOMPANY INC
MALLTAIL
704 Kingshill Pl, Carson, CA 90746-1219
Tel (213) 748-5118 Founded/Ownrshp 2007
Sales 22.8MM EMP 200
Accts Kpmg Llp Los Angeles Ca
SIC 4731 5122 Transportation agents & brokers; Vitamins & minerals; Transportation agents & brokers; Vitamins & minerals
CEO: Kirock Kim
Brnch Mgr: Ian Choi

D-U-N-S 78-588-6284 IMP/EXP
MAKHTESHIM AGAN OF NORTH AMERICA INC
ADAMA US
(Suby of ADAMA AGRICULTURE B.V.)
3120 Highwoods Blvd # 100, Raleigh, NC 27604-1035
Tel (919) 256-9300 Founded/Ownrshp 1991
Sales 200.0MM EMP 210
SIC 2879 Agricultural chemicals
Pr: Rob Williams
CFO: Craig Lupton-Smith
Snr Mgr: Hollie Altice
Snr Mgr: Mike Drinen
Snr Mgr: Holly Kerns
Snr Mgr: Ellen Mueller
Snr Mgr: Dario Narvaez
Snr Mgr: Austin Tinsley
Snr Mgr: Herb Young

D-U-N-S 00-677-8799
MAKI BUILDING CENTERS INC (MA)
(Suby of MAKI CORP) ★
160 Massachusetts Ave, Lunenburg, MA 01462-1215
Tel (978) 343-7422 Founded/Ownrshp 1949, 1985
Sales 20.4MM^E EMP 180
SIC 5231 5211 5251 3354 Paint, glass & wallpaper; Lumber & other building materials; Hardware; Aluminum extruded products; Paint, glass & wallpaper; Lumber & other building materials; Hardware; Aluminum extruded products
Pr: Glenn V Maki
Exec: Kay Salo

D-U-N-S 15-216-4299
MAKI CORP
160 Massachusetts Ave, Lunenburg, MA 01462-1215
Tel (978) 343-7422 Founded/Ownrshp 1985
Sales 36.3MM^E EMP 220
SIC 5211 5031 5231 5198 5251 2431 Lumber & other building materials; Building materials, exterior; Building materials, interior; Paint; Paints; Hardware; Doors & door parts & trim, wood; Windows & window parts & trim, wood; Lumber & other building materials; Building materials, exterior; Building materials, interior; Paint; Paints; Hardware; Doors & door parts & trim, wood; Windows & window parts & trim, wood
Pr: Glenn V Maki
CTO: Dave Nadzak

D-U-N-S 96-328-4695
MAKING WAVES FOUNDATION INC
3220 Blume Dr Ste 250, San Pablo, CA 94806-5741
Tel (510) 237-6027 Founded/Ownrshp 1989
Sales 30.7MM EMP 1
SIC 8299 Educational services; Educational services
Ex Dir: Glenn Holsclaw

D-U-N-S 00-423-4183 IMP/EXP
MAKINO INC
(Suby of MAKINO MILLING MACHINE CO., LTD.)
7680 Innovation Way, Mason, OH 45040-9695
Tel (513) 573-7200 Founded/Ownrshp 1887
Sales 143.8MM^E EMP 646
SIC 3541 Machine tools, metal cutting type; Machine tools, metal cutting type
Pr: Donald Lane
Pr: Robert Henry
*VP: Bob Henry
VP: Tom Slager
QC Dir: Joe Brown
Sales Asso: Jerry Fraley

D-U-N-S 18-810-0010 IMP/EXP
MAKITA CORP OF AMERICA
(Suby of MAKITA USA INC) ★
2650 Buford Hwy, Buford, GA 30518-6045
Tel (770) 932-2901 Founded/Ownrshp 1984
Sales 85.3MM^E EMP 400
SIC 3546 Power-driven handtools; Power-driven handtools
Pr: Minio Owzeki
*VP: Tim Donovan
Plnt Mgr: Larry Peck
Manager: Danny Guerrero
Manager: Darnell Nunez
Manager: Brett Rose

D-U-N-S 07-271-5428 IMP
MAKITA USA INC
(Suby of MAKITA CORPORATION)
14930 Northam St, La Mirada, CA 90638-5753
Tel (714) 522-8088 Founded/Ownrshp 1970
Sales 284.9MM^E EMP 560
SIC 5072 Power handtools; Relays & industrial controls; Power-driven handtools; Power handtools
CEO: Hiroshi Tsujimura
Pr: Alex Oliva
Sr VP: Richszrd Chapman
VP: Travis Makita
VP: Jonathan Speaks
VP: Mack Tokui
Comm Man: Wayne Hart
Dist Mgr: Matt Book
Natl Sales: Chris Lawford
Natl Sales: Phil Owen
Natl Sales: Theresa Westphal

D-U-N-S 17-523-9677
■ **MAKO SURGICAL CORP**
(Suby of STRYKER CORP) ★
2555 Davie Rd, Davie, FL 33317-7424
Tel (866) 647-6256 Founded/Ownrshp 2013
Sales 100.7MM^E EMP 436
SIC 3842 Orthopedic appliances; Trusses, orthopedic & surgical; Orthopedic appliances; Trusses, orthopedic & surgical
Pr: Maurice R Ferre
Pr: Benny Hagag
CFO: Fritz L Laporte
Sr VP: Ivan Delevic
Sr VP: Ivan Develic
Sr VP: Menashe R Frank
Sr VP: Richard Leparmentier
Sr VP: Christopher R Marrus
Sr VP: Duncan H Moffat
Sr VP: Steven J Nunes
VP: Louis Arata
VP: Robert Cohen
VP: Lawrence T Gibbons
Dir Bus: Robert Porter

D-U-N-S 13-924-6271
MAKOTEK INC
4390 35th St Ste B, Orlando, FL 32811-6516
Tel (407) 521-0402 Founded/Ownrshp 2002
Sales 41.0MM^E EMP 380^E
SIC 1623 Telephone & communication line construction; Telephone & communication line construction
Pr: Richard Rettstadt
*VP: Richard Beltz

D-U-N-S 00-509-5740 IMP
MAKRAY MANUFACTURING CO INC (IL)
4400 N Harlem Ave, Norridge, IL 60706-4774
Tel (708) 456-7100 Founded/Ownrshp 1943
Sales 27.6MM^E EMP 100
SIC 3089 3544 Injection molded finished plastic products; Special dies, tools, jigs & fixtures
Pr: Paul Makray Jr
MIS Dir: Peter Smith
Dir IT: Doug Wood
IT Man: Darin Lewis
Sls Mgr: Ron Ballantyne

D-U-N-S 08-852-8976
MAKRO TECHNOLOGIES INC
1 Washington Park # 1303, Newark, NJ 07102-3179
Tel (973) 481-0100 Founded/Ownrshp 1996
Sales 25.2MM^E EMP 250
SIC 8731 7371 Biotechnical research, commercial; Computer software development; Biotechnical research, commercial; Computer software development
Pr: Harish Malneedi
*VP: Mahesh Malneedi
Exec: Vijay Kumar
Comm Man: Shah Javid
Snr Ntwrk: Suresh Pachipala
IT Man: Allem Sridhar
Software D: Deepak Makkar
Mktg Mgr: Swapna Katakam

D-U-N-S 06-421-6823
MAL ENTERPRISES INC
LAWRENCE BROTHERS
300 Hailey St, Sweetwater, TX 79556-4774
Tel (325) 236-6351 Founded/Ownrshp 1972
Sales 130.3MM^E EMP 750
SIC 5411 Grocery stores, independent; Grocery stores, independent
Pr: Jay Lawrence
*Treas: Larry N Hoover
*Sec: Mildred A Lawrence
*VP: Kyle Lawrence
*VP: Tere L Lawrence
Genl Mgr: Penny Hernandez

D-U-N-S 13-051-4540
MALAGA BANK FSB
(Suby of MALAGA FINANCIAL CORP) ★
2514 Via Tejon, Palos Verdes Estates, CA 90274-1311
Tel (310) 375-9000 Founded/Ownrshp 2003
Sales NA EMP 55
SIC 6036 State savings banks, not federally chartered; State savings banks, not federally chartered
Pr: John Polen
*Ch Bd: Jerry Donahue
*CFO: Mary Roberts
Ex VP: Jasna Penich
*Ex VP: Debbie Richardson
*Sr VP: Sue Chandeler
Sr VP: Mark Smith
VP: Kelly Gilmore

D-U-N-S 13-429-1413
MALAGA FINANCIAL CORP
2514 Via Tejon, Palos Verdes Estates, CA 90274-1311
Tel (310) 375-9000 Founded/Ownrshp 2002
Sales NA EMP 55^E
SIC 6036 State savings banks, not federally chartered
Pr: Randy C Bowers
*Ch Bd: Jerry Donahue
*CFO: Jasna Penich
Sr VP: Mark Smith
*VP: Debbie Richardson

D-U-N-S 02-534-8462
MALARK LOGISTICS INC
9100 85th Ave N, Brooklyn Park, MN 55445-2124
Tel (763) 428-3564 Founded/Ownrshp 1998
Sales 34.3MM^E EMP 66
SIC 4231 1541 Trucking terminal facilities; Warehouse construction
CEO: Sheryl Malark
*VP: Douglas Malark
*VP: Mark Wills

MALARKEY ROOFING PRODUCTS
See HERBERT MALARKEY ROOFING CO

D-U-N-S 10-309-4538
MALCA-AMIT NORTH AMERICA INC
580 5th Ave Lbby 1, New York, NY 10036-4727
Tel (212) 840-8330 Founded/Ownrshp 1980
Sales 46.9MM EMP 180
Accts Harlib Grossman & Englard Cpa
SIC 4731 Foreign freight forwarding; Customhouse brokers; Foreign freight forwarding; Customhouse brokers
Pr: Shmuel Alon
*VP: Amit Eytan

D-U-N-S 60-362-7233
MALCO ENTERPRISES INC
BUDGET RENT-A-CAR
3085 E Valencia Rd, Tucson, AZ 85706-5922
Tel (520) 806-4560 Founded/Ownrshp 1981
Sales 46.4MM^E EMP 300
SIC 7514 5511 7515 Rent-a-car service; New & used car dealers; Passenger car leasing; Rent-a-car service; New & used car dealers; Passenger car leasing
Pr: John Mallo

D-U-N-S 61-891-3701
MALCO ENTERPRISES OF NEVADA INC
BUDGET RENT-A-CAR
7120 Haven St, Las Vegas, NV 89119-4102
Tel (702) 736-1212 Founded/Ownrshp 1989
Sales 94.9MM^E EMP 300
SIC 5521 7514 7513 Automobiles, used cars only; Passenger car rental; Truck rental, without drivers; Automobiles, used cars only; Passenger car rental; Truck rental, without drivers
*CFO: Steve Badilla
*VP: Larry Mallo
IT Man: Tim Stewart

D-U-N-S 00-446-7874 IMP/EXP
MALCO PRODUCTS INC (OH)
361 Fairview Ave, Barberton, OH 44203-2700
Tel (330) 753-0361 Founded/Ownrshp 1953
Sales 49.5MM^E EMP 270
SIC 2842 8742 2899 2841 2819

D-U-N-S 06-652-3044 IMP
MALCO PRODUCTS INC
14080 State Highway 55 Nw, Annandale, MN 55302-3457
Tel (320) 274-8246 Founded/Ownrshp 1950
Sales 21.3MM^E EMP 200
SIC 3423 3469 3545 5072 Hand & edge tools; Garden & farm tools, including shovels; Metal stampings; Tools & accessories for machine tools; Hardware; Hand & edge tools; Garden & farm tools, including shovels; Metal stampings; Tools & accessories for machine tools; Hardware
CEO: Paul Keymer
Pr: Bruce Berhow
*Pr: Paul Hansen
CFO: Jeannette Rieger-Borer
Chf Mktg O: Mary Ross
*Ex VP: Donald Schmidt
*VP: David Keymer
Genl Mgr: Rik Berkbigler
Snr Mgr: John Karlovich
Snr Mgr: Red Petersen
Snr Mgr: Eric Peterson

D-U-N-S 07-351-0794
MALCO THEATRES INC (AR)
5851 Ridgeway Center Pkwy, Memphis, TN 38120-4035
Tel (901) 761-3480 Founded/Ownrshp 1930, 1929
Sales 53.6MM^E EMP 700
SIC 7832 Motion picture theaters, except drive-in; Motion picture theaters, except drive-in
Pr: Steven Lightman
*Ch Bd: Richard L Lightman
Treas: Herbert R Levy
*Ex VP: Robert Levy
*Ex VP: Jimmy Tashie
*VP: Bill W Blackburn
VP: Larry Etter
*VP: Michael Thomson
Genl Mgr: Jason Kokenge

D-U-N-S 04-503-1267 IMP
MALCOLM DRILLING CO INC
92 Natoma St Ste 400, San Francisco, CA 94105-2685
Tel (415) 901-4400 Founded/Ownrshp 1968
Sales 745.3MM^E EMP 5,650^E
SIC 1799 Building site preparation; Boring for building construction; Building site preparation; Boring for building construction
CEO: John M Malcolm

Pr: Terry Tucker
COO: Douglas Cefali
Treas: Derek Yamashita
Sr VP: Chase Chappelle
**VP:* Heinrich Majewski
**VP:* John Roe
VP: Bruce Wilhelm
Dist Mgr: Roberto Lopez
Info Man: Seechai Kwan

D-U-N-S 03-368-3327
MALCOLM FORD CUNNINGHAM INC
5675 Peachtree Indus Blvd, Atlanta, GA 30341-2219
Tel (770) 621-0200 *Founded/Ownrshp* 1954
Sales 45.2MM^E^ *EMP* 98
SIC 5511 5531 New & used car dealers; Automobile & truck equipment & parts; New & used car dealers; Automobile & truck equipment & parts
Pr: Malcolm Cunningham
**CFO:* Marvin W Claborn
CFO: William Paul
**Sec:* Shirley Todd
Genl Mgr: Mike Long
Genl Mgr: David Quick
Genl Mgr: Berry Wolten
Off Mgr: Jackie Henderson
CIO: Marie Brown
Opers Mgr: Derric Terrentine
Sls Mgr: Darryl Davis

MALCOLM PIRNIE, INC.
See ARCADIS CE INC

MALDEN PUBLIC SCHOOLS
See MALDEN SCHOOL DISTRICT

D-U-N-S 10-003-2101
MALDEN SCHOOL DISTRICT
MALDEN PUBLIC SCHOOLS
200 Pleasant St Rm 215, Malden, MA 02148-4829
Tel (781) 397-7217 *Founded/Ownrshp* 1627
Sales 35.0MM^E^ *EMP* 850
SIC 8211 Public elementary & secondary schools; School board; Public elementary & secondary schools; School board
HC Dir: Karen Reynolds

D-U-N-S 60-165-9667 IMP
MALDONADO NURSERY & LANDSCAPING INC
16348 Nacogdoches Rd, San Antonio, TX 78247-1005
Tel (210) 599-1219 *Founded/Ownrshp* 1987
Sales 28.0MM *EMP* 400
Accts Sturm Cpa Pc San Antonio Te
SIC 5261 1711 Nurseries & garden centers; Irrigation sprinkler system installation; Nurseries & garden centers; Irrigation sprinkler system installation
Pr: Rogelio Maldonado
**CFO:* Neomal Ratnayeke
CFO: Pat Vrba
**Treas:* Roy Maldonado Jr
Ex VP: Diana Alcala
**VP:* Jerry Maldonado

D-U-N-S 04-975-2066
MALEK INC
2521 Antelope St, Corpus Christi, TX 78408-3703
Tel (361) 888-8281 *Founded/Ownrshp* 1970
Sales 25.3MM^E^ *EMP* 130
SIC 1711

MALETIS BEVERAGE
See RM BEVERAGE DELAWARE LLC

D-U-N-S 09-011-8530 IMP
MALGOR & CO INC
Road Number 5 Km 3 5 St Road Numb, Catano, PR 00962
Tel (787) 788-0303 *Founded/Ownrshp* 1926, 1984
Sales 25.5MM *EMP* 87
Accts Deloitte & Touche Llp San Ju
SIC 5182 4222 2084 Wine; Warehousing, cold storage or refrigerated; Wines; Wine; Warehousing, cold storage or refrigerated; Wines
Pr: Conrado Garcia Guerra
**Treas:* Ana Maria Garcia Mendez
**VP:* Antonio Garcia Mendez
**VP:* Conrado Garcia Mendez Jr
IT Man: Antonio Garcia

D-U-N-S 00-419-6192
MALHEUR COUNTY SCHOOL DISTRICT 8-C
ONTARIO SCHOOL DISTRICT 8-C
195 Sw 3rd Ave, Ontario, OR 97914-2723
Tel (541) 889-5374 *Founded/Ownrshp* 1907
Sales 21.3MM^E^ *EMP* 359
Accts Oster Professional Group Cpa
SIC 8211 Public elementary school; Public junior high school; Public senior high school; School board; Public elementary school; Public junior high school; Public senior high school; School board
Bd of Dir: Cliff Bentz

D-U-N-S 07-927-3485
▲ MALIBU BOATS INC
5075 Kimberly Way, Loudon, TN 37774-6469
Tel (865) 458-5478 *Founded/Ownrshp* 1982
Sales 228.6MM *EMP* 509
Accts Mcgladrey Llp Indianapolis I
Tkr Sym MBUU *Exch* NGM
SIC 3732 Boat building & repairing; Boat building & repairing
CEO: Jack D Springer
**Ch Bd:* Michael K Hooks
COO: Ritchie L Anderson
CFO: Wayne R Wilson
VP: Dan L Gasper
Board of Directors: James R Buch, Ivar S Chhina, Michael J Connolly, Phillip S Estes, Mark W Lanigan, Peter E Murphy, John E Stokely

D-U-N-S 05-136-7969 IMP
MALIBU BOATS LLC
5075 Kimberly Way, Loudon, TN 37774-6469
Tel (865) 458-5478 *Founded/Ownrshp* 1982
Sales 141.9MM^E^ *EMP* 600
SIC 3732 Boats, fiberglass: building & repairing; Boats, fiberglass: building & repairing
COO: Ritchie L Anderson
CFO: Wayne R Wilson
VP: Dan L Gasper
Exec: Holly Fiegle
Dir IT: Jay Gomes
Plnt Mgr: Lynn Little
Mktg Dir: Hugh Michael
Mktg Dir: Hugh Quinlan
Sls Dir: Scott Davenport
Mktg Mgr: Paul Singer

D-U-N-S 78-867-6955
MALIBU CONFERENCE CENTER INC
327 Latigo Canyon Rd, Malibu, CA 90265-2708
Tel (818) 889-6440 *Founded/Ownrshp* 1985
Sales 35.6MM^E^ *EMP* 500
SIC 6512 Commercial & industrial building operation; Commercial & industrial building operation
Pr: Glen Gerson
Dir IT: Pam Mertzel

D-U-N-S 14-437-5250 IMP
MALIBU DESIGN GROUP
OCEAN DREAM
5445 Jillson St, Commerce, CA 90040-2117
Tel (323) 271-1700 *Founded/Ownrshp* 1982
Sales 35.9MM^E^ *EMP* 57^E^
SIC 5137 Swimsuits: women's, children's & infants'
CEO: Tai Chung
**Pr:* Henry Fan
CFO: Ben Quan

D-U-N-S 78-248-4273
▲ MALIBU ENTERTAINMENT WORLDWIDE INC
717 N Harwood St Ste 1650, Dallas, TX 75201-6501
Tel (214) 210-8701 *Founded/Ownrshp* 1985
Sales 67.0MM^E^ *EMP* 1,100
Tkr Sym MBEW *Exch* OTO
SIC 1629 7999 Athletic & recreation facilities construction; Recreation center; Athletic & recreation facilities construction; Recreation center
Pr: Richard Beckert
**Ch Bd:* Richard N Beckert
**CFO:* Scott Wheeler
Sec: Eric Terry
**Sec:* Robert Whitman
VP: Kenneth R Grissom
Mfg Dir: Rebecca Henderson
Board of Directors: Daniel A Decker, Julia E Demerau, L Scott Demerau, James T Hands, William M Kearns Jr, Steven D Scheetz, Bert W Wasserman

MALIBU LIMOUSINE SERVICE
See EXECUTIVE NETWORK ENTERPRISES INC

D-U-N-S 84-300-1236
MALIN INTERGRATED HANDLING SOLUTIONS AND DESIGN
5050 Cranswick Rd, Houston, TX 77041-7726
Tel (713) 690-5050 *Founded/Ownrshp* 2001
Sales 24.6MM^E^ *EMP* 200^E^
SIC 3537 Forklift trucks; Forklift trucks
VP: James Wilcox
Genl Mgr: Chris Smith
IT Man: Gavin Rick
Mtls Mgr: Brian Hyde

D-U-N-S 00-415-2351 IMP
MALISH CORP (OH)
4260 Hamann Pkwy, Willoughby, OH 44094-5624
Tel (440) 951-5356 *Founded/Ownrshp* 1948
Sales 23.5MM^E^ *EMP* 115^E^
SIC 3991 3089 Brushes, household or industrial; Extruded finished plastic products; Brushes, household or industrial; Extruded finished plastic products
Pr: Jeffery J Malish
COO: Gordon Overs
CFO: Stacey Scott
**Treas:* Mark Ray
VP: Jack Krippel
**VP:* Fred Lombardi
VP: Ken Shary
Ql Cn Mgr: Bob Heineman
Mktg Dir: Jack Cripple
Mktg Mgr: Peter Parker

D-U-N-S 05-831-2273
MALKIN PROPERTIES LLC
1 Grand Central Terminal, New York, NY 10017-5743
Tel (212) 953-0888 *Founded/Ownrshp* 1996
Sales 20.2MM^E^ *EMP* 85
SIC 6799 7389 Investors; Financial services
Ch Bd: Peter L Malkin
**Pr:* Anthony E Malkin
**CFO:* Ignacio L Ceriani
**Ex VP:* Donald B Kaplan
**Sr VP:* Thomas P Durels
Mktg Dir: Maya Stanic

MALL BODY SHOP
See MALL CHEVROLET INC

D-U-N-S 01-117-0206
MALL CHEVROLET INC (DE)
MALL BODY SHOP
75 Haddonfield Rd, Cherry Hill, NJ 08002-1462
Tel (856) 662-7000 *Founded/Ownrshp* 1966
Sales 30.4MM^E^ *EMP* 65
SIC 5511 Automobiles, new & used; Automobiles, new & used
Pr: Charles W Foulke III
**VP:* Charles Falkenstein
**VP:* Charles W Foulke II

MALL CHRYSLER JEEP
See ZIMMER MOTOR INC

D-U-N-S 14-796-7509
MALL CITY MECHANICAL INC
7184 Douglas Ave, Kalamazoo, MI 49009-5217
Tel (269) 349-3661 *Founded/Ownrshp* 1985
Sales 26.0MM^E^ *EMP* 130
SIC 1711 Mechanical contractor; Mechanical contractor
Ch Bd: Dennis Dehaan
**Pr:* Greg Moerman
**CEO:* Derek Rowe
**COO:* Gary Miner
**Treas:* Pat Moerman
**VP:* Dennis J Dehaan

MALL OF AMERICA
See MOAC MALL HOLDINGS LLC

MALL OF GEORGIA FORD
See GAWVT MOTORS INC

D-U-N-S 87-978-3306 EXP
MALLARD CREEK POLYMERS INC
8901 Research Dr, Charlotte, NC 28262-8541
Tel (704) 547-0622 *Founded/Ownrshp* 1995
Sales 35.3MM^E^ *EMP* 81
SIC 2821 Plastics materials & resins; Plastics materials & resins
Pr: Aaron Parekh
VP: Thayne Hansen
**VP:* Dan Neri
VP: Mahendra Parekh
Admn Mgr: Jane Billingsley
Opers Mgr: Frank Samartino
Plnt Mgr: Scot Whyte
Ql Cn Mgr: Jim Brown
Sls Mgr: Bob Klein
Sls Mgr: Robert Sobieski
Doctor: Dan Neary MD

MALLARD FOOD SHOP
See MALLARD OIL CO

D-U-N-S 04-591-8182
MALLARD OIL CO
MALLARD FOOD SHOP
1502 Dr Martin Luther, Kinston, NC 28501
Tel (252) 527-0364 *Founded/Ownrshp* 1968
Sales 103.5MM^E^ *EMP* 250
SIC 5171 5983 5984 Petroleum bulk stations; Fuel oil dealers; Liquefied petroleum gas, delivered to customers' premises; Petroleum bulk stations; Fuel oil dealers; Liquefied petroleum gas, delivered to customers' premises
Ch Bd: Felix Harvey
**Pr:* Frank Famularo
Genl Mgr: Mickey Connor

D-U-N-S 01-779-3845 IMP
MALLEYS CANDIES INC
MALLEY'S CHOCOLATES
1685 Victoria Ave, Lakewood, OH 44107-4054
Tel (216) 362-8700 *Founded/Ownrshp* 1958
Sales 42.9MM^E^ *EMP* 300^E^
SIC 5441 5451 2064 2068 2024 2066 Candy; Nuts; Ice cream (packaged); Candy bars, including chocolate covered bars; Chocolate candy, except solid chocolate; Nuts: dried, dehydrated, salted or roasted; Ice cream & ice milk; Chocolate & cocoa products; Candy; Nuts; Ice cream (packaged); Candy bars, including chocolate covered bars; Chocolate candy, except solid chocolate; Nuts: dried, dehydrated, salted or roasted; Ice cream & ice milk; Chocolate & cocoa products
Pr: Mike Malley
**VP:* Daniel Malley
VP: William McConnville
Creative D: David Haney
IT Man: Kelly Perkowski
Mktg Mgr: David Eichman

MALLEY'S CHOCOLATES
See MALLEYS CANDIES INC

D-U-N-S 01-079-6097
MALLICK MECHANICAL CONTRACTORS INC (MD)
8010 Cessna Ave, Gaithersburg, MD 20879-4119
Tel (240) 683-4925 *Founded/Ownrshp* 1993, 1994
Sales 20.9MM^E^ *EMP* 50
SIC 1711 Plumbing contractors
Pr: Kenneth Mallick

MALLIN CASUAL FURNITURE
See MINSON CORP

D-U-N-S 16-383-7383 IMP
MALLINCKRODT HOSPITAL PRODUCTS INC
(*Suby of* MALLINCKRODT PUBLIC LIMITED COMPANY)
12481 High Bluff Dr, San Diego, CA 92130-3585
Tel (858) 436-1400 *Founded/Ownrshp* 2014
Sales 42.8MM^E^ *EMP* 206
SIC 2834 Pharmaceutical preparations; Pharmaceutical preparations
Pr: Kathleen A Schaefer
**Treas:* John E Einwalter
Sr VP: Hazel Aker
Sr VP: Malcolm Smith
VP: Bob Divasto
VP: Scott Garrett
VP: Marvin R Haselhorst
Dir Bus: Neil Berkley
Brnch Mgr: Richard Casey
CTO: Malvina Laudicina
QA Dir: Elizabeth Carbajal

D-U-N-S 04-702-1092 IMP/EXP
MALLINCKRODT LLC
MALLINCKRODT PHARMACEUTICALS
(*Suby of* MALLINCKRODT PUBLIC LIMITED COMPANY)
675 Jmes S Mcdonnell Blvd, Hazelwood, MO 63042-2379
Tel (314) 654-2000 *Founded/Ownrshp* 2011
Sales 1.7MMM^E^ *EMP* 5,500
SIC 3841 3829 2834 2833 Surgical & medical instruments; Catheters; Anesthesia apparatus; Medical diagnostic systems, nuclear; Pharmaceutical preparations; Analgesics; Codeine & derivatives; Opium derivatives; Surgical & medical instruments; Catheters; Anesthesia apparatus; Medical diagnostic systems, nuclear; Pharmaceutical preparations; Analgesics; Codeine & derivatives; Opium derivatives
Pr: Mark Trudeau
CFO: Matthew Harbaugh
Sr VP: Thomas Berry
Sr VP: Peter Edwards
Dir Risk M: Mark Huddleston
Dir Lab: Kyle Hayes
Assoc Dir: Larry Silva
Assoc Dir: Rick Telder
Comm Dir: Nancy Stauder
Dist Mgr: Jeff Yuska
CIO: Shrikant Ramachandran

MALLINCKRODT PHARMACEUTICALS
See MALLINCKRODT LLC

D-U-N-S 01-878-5717
MALLON CHEVROLET INC
MALLON, DON CHEVROLET
774 W Thames St, Norwich, CT 06360-7002
Tel (860) 889-3333 *Founded/Ownrshp* 1950, 2000
Sales 21.2MM^E^ *EMP* 50
SIC 5511 Automobiles, new & used; Pickups, new & used; Vans, new & used; Automobiles, new & used; Pickups, new & used; Vans, new & used
Pr: Donald Mallon Jr

MALLON, DON CHEVROLET
See MALLON CHEVROLET INC

D-U-N-S 80-142-5856
MALLORY & EVANS CONTRACTORS AND ENGINEERS LLC
625 Kentucky St, Scottdale, GA 30079-1123
Tel (404) 297-1000 *Founded/Ownrshp* 2006
Sales 44.0MM *EMP* 35
SIC 1711 Mechanical contractor; Mechanical contractor
Pr: Stephen C Plane
Sr VP: Timothy Sidwell

D-U-N-S 05-287-7409
MALLORY ALEXANDER INTERNATIONAL LOGISTICS LLC
MALLORY TRANSPORTATION SYSTEM
4294 Swinnea Rd, Memphis, TN 38118-6620
Tel (901) 367-9400 *Founded/Ownrshp* 1998
Sales 211.0MM^E^ *EMP* 510
SIC 4731 4225 4789 Freight transportation arrangement; General warehousing & storage; Customs clearance of freight; General warehousing; Pipeline terminal facilities, independently operated
Pr: W Neely Mallory III
VP: Mike Heaton

D-U-N-S 00-483-8850
MALLORY AND EVANS INC
646 Kentucky St, Scottdale, GA 30079-1106
Tel (404) 297-1000 *Founded/Ownrshp* 1956
Sales 20.7MM^E^ *EMP* 150^E^
SIC 1711

D-U-N-S 07-640-9390 IMP
MALLORY CO
RAIN OR SHINE
1040 Industrial Way, Longview, WA 98632-1039
Tel (360) 636-5750 *Founded/Ownrshp* 1975
Sales 179.6MM^E^ *EMP* 187
SIC 5099 Safety equipment & supplies; Safety equipment & supplies
CEO: Timothy Loy
Off Mgr: Kit Kittelson
Opers Mgr: Tisha Proudfit
Opers Mgr: Lorene Simmons
Opers Mgr: Andy Wick
Sls Mgr: Marc Maher
Sls Mgr: Ross Nightingale
Sls Mgr: Bruce Rosebrock
Snr Mgr: Calvin Bryant

D-U-N-S 00-385-3850
MALLORY GROUP INC
MALORY ALEXANDER INTE
4294 Swinnea Rd, Memphis, TN 38118-6620
Tel (901) 367-9400 *Founded/Ownrshp* 1925
Sales 71.6MM^E^ *EMP* 150
SIC 4731 Freight forwarding
Pr: W Neeley Mallory III
**Sec:* Michael R Niclosi
**Ex VP:* B Lee Mallory III
**Sr VP:* William L Wadsworth

D-U-N-S 96-584-5022
MALLORY SAFETY AND SUPPLY LLC
(*Suby of* MALLORY CO) ★
1040 Industrial Way, Longview, WA 98632-1039
Tel (360) 690-8200 *Founded/Ownrshp* 1999
Sales 179.6MM^E^ *EMP* 185^E^
SIC 5099 8331 Safety equipment & supplies; Job training & vocational rehabilitation services; Safety equipment & supplies; Job training & vocational rehabilitation services
Pr: Tim Loy
**COO:* Shawn Murray
VP: Michael Carmassi
Sls Mgr: Matt Carlson
Sls Mgr: Maureen Jacobson
Sls Mgr: Marc Maher
Sls Mgr: Bill Rosenberger
Sls Mgr: Carrie Sawvel
Sls Mgr: Scott Watkins

MALLORY TRANSPORTATION SYSTEM
See MALLORY ALEXANDER INTERNATIONAL LOGISTICS LLC

D-U-N-S 09-376-0718
MALLOY BROTHERS
ADVANCE METRO MOVERS
195 Bethpage Sweet Holw, Old Bethpage, NY 11804-1314
Tel (516) 396-8600 *Founded/Ownrshp* 1962
Sales 30.4MM^E^ *EMP* 375
SIC 4213 4214 4212 Contract haulers; Local trucking with storage; Local trucking, without storage; Contract haulers; Local trucking with storage; Local trucking, without storage
Pr: Thomas James Molloy
Sr VP: Robert Gutmann
Prin: Michael Silvesro

D-U-N-S 07-943-0421
MALLOY CHARLOTTESVILLE LLC
MALLOY FORD
1300 Richmond Rd, Charlottesville, VA 22911-3508
Tel (434) 977-7960 *Founded/Ownrshp* 2013
Sales 20.3MM^E^ *EMP* 71
SIC 5511 Automobiles, new & used

Pr: Geoffrey Malloy
Off Mgr: Heather Jamerson

MALLOY ELECTRIC BEARING & SUP
See D M G INC

MALLOY FORD
See MALLOY CHARLOTTESVILLE LLC

D-U-N-S 04-718-9097
MALLOY INC
EDWARDS BROTHERS MALLOY
5411 Jackson Rd, Ann Arbor, MI 48103-1865
Tel (734) 665-6113 *Founded/Ownrshp* 1930
Sales 72.3MM^E *EMP* 325
SIC 2732 2789 2752 Books: printing & binding; Books: printing only; Bookbinding & related work; Commercial printing, lithographic; Books: printing & binding; Books: printing only; Bookbinding & related work; Commercial printing, lithographic
CEO: John Edwards
**Ch Bd:* Herbert H Upton Jr
**Pr:* William Upton
**VP:* Ben Mattison
**VP:* Robert Scheible
**VP:* Joe Upton
MIS Dir: Steve Mattison
**VP Mfg:* Peter Shima

MALLOY LNCOLN MRCURY MTSUBISHI
See MALLOY MOTOR CO

D-U-N-S 80-150-5587
MALLOY MOTOR CO
MALLOY LNCOLN MRCURY MTSUBISHI
1880 Opitz Blvd, Woodbridge, VA 22191-3302
Tel (703) 494-9121 *Founded/Ownrshp* 1992
Sales 24.9MM^E *EMP* 60
SIC 5511 Automobiles, new & used
Pr: Geoffrey M Malloy
Genl Mgr: Michael McShane
Counsel: Donald Markle

MALLTAIL
See MAKESHOPNCOMPANY INC

D-U-N-S 80-566-2681
MALNATI ORGANIZATION INC
MALNATI'S, LOU PIZZERIA
3685 Woodhead Dr, Northbrook, IL 60062-1816
Tel (847) 562-1814 *Founded/Ownrshp* 1984
Sales 45.4MM^E *EMP* 950
SIC 5812 Pizzeria, independent; Pizzeria, independent
Pr: Stuart Cohen

MALNATI'S, LOU PIZZERIA
See MALNATI ORGANIZATION INC

D-U-N-S 78-812-0145 IMP/EXP
MALNOVE HOLDING CO INC
13434 F St, Omaha, NE 68137-1181
Tel (402) 330-1100 *Founded/Ownrshp* 1991
Sales 225.5MM^E *EMP* 622
SIC 2657 Folding paperboard boxes; Folding paperboard boxes
Ch: Paul Malnove
**CFO:* James K Belcher
VP: Lee Andrews
QA Dir: Emma Coy
Ql Cn Mgr: Darrin Finley
Sales Exec: Tom Budny

D-U-N-S 01-435-6125 EXP
MALNOVE INC OF FLORIDA (NE)
(*Suby of* MALNOVE HOLDING CO INC) ★
10500 Canada Dr, Jacksonville, FL 32218-4968
Tel (904) 696-1600 *Founded/Ownrshp* 1956, 1981
Sales 109.5MM^E *EMP* 622
SIC 2657 Folding paperboard boxes; Folding paperboard boxes
CEO: Paul Malnove
VP: Peter Hofmann
Dir IT: John Samuelson
Plnt Mgr: Jim Burrows

D-U-N-S 00-725-8213
MALNOVE INC OF NEBRASKA
(*Suby of* MALNOVE HOLDING CO INC) ★
13434 F St, Omaha, NE 68137-1181
Tel (402) 330-1100 *Founded/Ownrshp* 1947
Sales 75.0MM *EMP* 250
SIC 2657

D-U-N-S 13-976-0169 IMP
MALNOVE INC OF UTAH
(*Suby of* MALNOVE HOLDING CO INC) ★
Freeport Ctr Bldg A 16f, Clearfield, UT 84016
Tel (801) 773-7400 *Founded/Ownrshp* 1985
Sales 40.0MM^E *EMP* 145
SIC 2391 Curtains & draperies; Curtains & draperies
Ch Bd: Paul Malnove
Genl Mgr: William Malnove

D-U-N-S 09-525-1765
MALONE CENTRAL SCHOOL DISTRICT
42 Huskie Ln, Malone, NY 12953-2451
Tel (518) 483-7800 *Founded/Ownrshp* 1964
Sales 21.1MM^E *EMP* 350
SIC 8211 Public elementary school; Public junior high school; Public senior high school; Academy; Public elementary school; Public junior high school; Public senior high school; Academy
Treas: Cynthia Reyome
Ofcr: Stephen Ansari
Ofcr: Jerry Griffin
Schl Brd P: Wayne Rogers
HC Dir: Sheila Glinski

D-U-N-S 00-584-5573
MALONE CONSTRUCTION CO INC
700 Antone St Nw, Atlanta, GA 30318-7604
Tel (404) 351-3991 *Founded/Ownrshp* 1946
Sales 33.6MM^E *EMP* 125
SIC 1542

D-U-N-S 14-756-7635
MALONE FAMILY FOUNDATION
12300 Liberty Blvd, Englewood, CO 80112-7009
Tel (303) 913-2959 *Founded/Ownrshp* 1997
Sales 23.7MM *EMP* 1
SIC 6732 Trusts: educational, religious, etc.
Pr: Jon Malone

D-U-N-S 00-796-0354
MALONE FREIGHT LINES INC (DE)
CRST MALONE
(*Suby of* CRST INTERNATIONAL INC) ★
1901 Floyd Bradford Rd, Trussville, AL 35173-3140
Tel (205) 951-1900 *Founded/Ownrshp* 1928, 1984
Sales 66.5MM^E *EMP* 700
Accts Dale Leary Accountant
SIC 4789 4213 Cargo loading & unloading services; Heavy hauling; Cargo loading & unloading services; Heavy hauling
Ch Bd: John M Smith
**Pr:* Scott Shephard

D-U-N-S 07-988-7708
MALONE MEDIA GROUP INC
9806a Whithorn Dr, Houston, TX 77095-5001
Tel (832) 427-6420 *Founded/Ownrshp* 2010
Sales 50.0MM *EMP* 47
SIC 7311

D-U-N-S 07-777-8983
MALONE UNIVERSITY
2600 Cleveland Ave Nw, Canton, OH 44709-3897
Tel (330) 471-8264 *Founded/Ownrshp* 1892
Sales 33.6MM *EMP* 500^E
Accts Bkd Llp Fort Wayne In
SIC 8221 University; University
Pr: David A King
**CFO:* Joy E Brathwaite
Treas: Jack Rogers
**VP:* Dr Christopher Abrams
VP: Timothy Bryan
VP: Sharon Sirpilla
**VP:* Howard Taylor
Sales Exec: Joanna Taylor

MALONES COST PLUS SUPERMARKETS
See MALONES FOOD STORES LLC

D-U-N-S 03-014-9793
MALONES FOOD STORES LLC
MALONES COST PLUS SUPERMARKETS
7730 Forney Rd Ste 1, Dallas, TX 75227-2507
Tel (214) 388-4756 *Founded/Ownrshp* 1976
Sales 72.4MM^E *EMP* 450
SIC 5411 Grocery stores; Grocery stores
**VP:* Jane Malone
Sales Exec: Jesse Salazar

MALONE'S GRILL & BAR
See RESTAURANT MANAGEMENT GROUP INC

D-U-N-S 06-773-3121
MALONEY PROPERTIES INC
27 Mica Ln Ste 301, Wellesley, MA 02481-1741
Tel (617) 209-5212 *Founded/Ownrshp* 1981
Sales 14.7MM^E *EMP* 300
SIC 6531 1542 1522 Real estate managers; Real estate brokers & agents; Commercial & office buildings, renovation & repair; Hotel/motel & multi-family home renovation & remodeling; Real estate managers; Real estate brokers & agents; Commercial & office buildings, renovation & repair; Hotel/motel & multi-family home renovation & remodeling
Pr: Janet Frazier
**Treas:* Celeste Vezina
VP: Edmond Canti
VP: Lynn Delidow
**VP:* Michael Frazier
VP: Susan Johnson
**VP:* Diana Kelly
VP: Mark Kelly
**VP:* Kathleen T Luce
VP: Joseph Salvia
**VP:* Susan S Stockard
Exec: Gina Maloney

MALONEY TECHNICAL PRODUCTS
See S & B TECHNICAL PRODUCTS INC

D-U-N-S 04-878-1871
MALOOF CONTRACTING CO INC
MCC
1651 Crofton Blvd Ste 2, Crofton, MD 21114-1314
Tel (410) 451-9263 *Founded/Ownrshp* 1988
Sales 30.0MM *EMP* 9
SIC 1742 Drywall; Acoustical & ceiling work; Drywall; Acoustical & ceiling work
Pr: Robert Maloof

D-U-N-S 00-891-4178
MALOOF DISTRIBUTING LLC
JOE G MALOOF & CO
701 Comanche Rd Ne, Albuquerque, NM 87107-4105
Tel (505) 345-1218 *Founded/Ownrshp* 1946
Sales 181.3MM^E *EMP* 2,300
SIC 5181 5149 Beer & other fermented malt liquors; Tea; Water, distilled; Beer & other fermented malt liquors; Tea; Water, distilled
CFO: Keith Hartnett

MALORY ALEXANDER INTE
See MALLORY GROUP INC

D-U-N-S 17-219-8512
MALOUF CONSTRUCTION LLC
972 County Road 473, Sidon, MS 38954-5002
Tel (601) 856-1044 *Founded/Ownrshp* 2004
Sales 46.2MM^E *EMP* 96
Accts Carr Riggs & Ingram Llc R
SIC 1542 Commercial & office building, new construction
Sfty Dirs: Richard Dickard

D-U-N-S 17-372-8908
MALOUF CONSTRUCTION SERVICES INC
972 County Road 473, Sidon, MS 38954-5002
Tel (662) 455-6111 *Founded/Ownrshp* 1987
Sales 40.9MM^E *EMP* 150
Accts Carr Riggs Ingram Llc
SIC 1542 1541 1629 Commercial & office building, new construction; Industrial buildings, new construction; Industrial plant construction; Commercial & office building, new construction; Industrial buildings, new construction; Industrial plant construction
Pr: George F Malouf
**CFO:* Jamel Abraham
**VP:* Andy Holliday
**VP:* Kathy Malouf

D-U-N-S 10-965-9982
MALOUF FORD LINCOLN INC
Rr 1, North Brunswick, NJ 08902
Tel (732) 951-0300 *Founded/Ownrshp* 2002
Sales 36.0MM^E *EMP* 90
SIC 5511 Automobiles, new & used; Automobiles, new & used
CEO: Richard Malouf
Sales Asso: Dwvaughn Browne
Sales Asso: Jack Taormina

D-U-N-S 00-201-1179 EXP
MALT PRODUCTS CORP (NJ)
88 Market St, Saddle Brook, NJ 07663-4830
Tel (201) 845-4420 *Founded/Ownrshp* 1939, 1962
Sales 173.4MM^E *EMP* 650
SIC 2083 2087 Malt; Malt byproducts; Flavoring extracts & syrups; Malt; Malt byproducts; Flavoring extracts & syrups
Pr: Ronald G Targen
**Pr:* Amy Targen
**Treas:* Nathan Mandelbaum

MALT-O-MEAL
See MOM BRANDS CO

D-U-N-S 00-982-5308
MALTBY ELECTRIC SUPPLY CO INC
336 7th St, San Francisco, CA 94103-4092
Tel (415) 863-5000 *Founded/Ownrshp* 1955
Sales 33.0MM *EMP* 64
Accts Eckley Lombardi Llp San Jose
SIC 5063 Electrical apparatus & equipment; Electrical apparatus & equipment
Pr: John A Maltby
COO: Andy Kawamura
VP: Scheron Briones
**VP:* Broadney Jason
Brnch Mgr: Lisa Enis
Brnch Mgr: Alberto Lopez
Sales Asso: Jason Ng

D-U-N-S 18-176-6874 IMP/EXP
MALTEUROP NORTH AMERICA INC
(*Suby of* MALTEUROP GROUPE)
3830 W Grant St, Milwaukee, WI 53215-2355
Tel (414) 671-1166 *Founded/Ownrshp* 2008
Sales 33.3MM^E *EMP* 150^E
SIC 2083 Malt; Malt
Ch: Alain Le Floch
**Pr:* Ian Maccan
**CEO:* Daniel Faguer
**Treas:* Dale Bugajski
**Sec:* Dale West
**VP:* Chris Mulder
Genl Mgr: Uldarico Garcoa
CTO: Denis Julien
IT Man: Ronald Nehmey
Netwrk Eng: Dan Brunnquell

D-U-N-S 07-850-9059
MALVERN BANCORP INC
42 E Lancaster Ave, Paoli, PA 19301-1455
Tel (610) 644-9400 *Founded/Ownrshp* 2012
Sales NA *EMP* 30
SIC 6036 Savings institutions, not federally chartered; Savings institutions, not federally chartered
Pr: Anthony C Weagley
COO: Missy Orlando
CFO: Joseph Gangemi
Ch: George E Steinmetz
Sr VP: Richard Fuchs
Board of Directors: F Claire Hughes, Howard Kent, Michael D Moss

D-U-N-S 08-880-4885
MALVERN FEDERAL SAVINGS BANK
42 E Lancaster Ave # 101, Paoli, PA 19301-1455
Tel (610) 644-9400 *Founded/Ownrshp* 1887
Sales NA *EMP* 100
SIC 6035 Federal savings & loan associations; Federal savings & loan associations
Pr: Anthony C Weagley
Ch Bd: Claire Hughes
COO: Ronald Anderson
Ofcr: Dennis Boyle
Ofcr: William H Woolworth III
Sr VP: Richard Fuchs
Sr VP: Alexander Kroll
VP: Linda Laurent
Board of Directors: Edward P Shanaughy, Gretchen Byrne, George E Steinmetz, Kristin S Camp, Carol Weir, Bobbie Marovich, Joseph E Palmer, Stacey Poploskie, David R Prizer, Thomas F Robinson, Ron Russell, Cordine Scartozzi

D-U-N-S 12-162-4365
MALVERN INSTRUMENTS INC
(*Suby of* SPECTRIS INC) ★
117 Flanders Rd Ste 110, Westborough, MA 01581-1071
Tel (508) 768-6400 *Founded/Ownrshp* 1997
Sales 46.4MM^E *EMP* 83
SIC 5084 7629 8734 Instruments & control equipment; Electrical equipment repair services; Testing laboratories
Pr: Brian W Dutko
**Sec:* Dawn Sims
Ofcr: Sarah Paterson
Off Mgr: Christen Jones
CTO: Neil Lewis
IT Man: Kathy Carideo
Software D: Harry Nystrom
Sftwr Eng: Darrell Pittman
Sftwr Eng: James Wraight
Sftwr Eng: Tao WEI
Opers Mgr: Bruce Gay

D-U-N-S 07-161-3533
MALVERN PREPARATORY SCHOOL
418 S Warren Ave, Malvern, PA 19355-2707
Tel (484) 595-1100 *Founded/Ownrshp* 1922
Sales 22.2MM *EMP* 120
Accts O Connell & Company Llc Jenki
SIC 8211 Preparatory school; Preparatory school
Pr: James H Stewart
V Ch: Margaret Boova
Trst: Emanuel Del Pizzo
Trst: Fred Hilliard
Comm Dir: Frank Luzi

D-U-N-S 08-924-0642
MALVERN SCHOOL DISTRICT
1517 S Main St, Malvern, AR 72104-5231
Tel (501) 332-7500 *Founded/Ownrshp* 1940
Sales 17.5MM^E *EMP* 310
SIC 8211 9411 Public elementary & secondary schools; Administration of educational programs; Public elementary & secondary schools; Administration of educational programs
**Treas:* Margaret Baker
MIS Dir: Jace Roberts
Teacher Pr: Nina Johnson
Psych: Debbie Baker

D-U-N-S 04-047-0551
MALVERNE UNION FREE SCHOOL DISTRICT 12
HOWARD T HERBER MIDDLE SCHOOL
301 Wicks Ln, Malverne, NY 11565-2244
Tel (516) 887-6400 *Founded/Ownrshp* 1930
Sales 27.4MM *EMP* 212
Accts R S Abrams & Co Llp Island
SIC 8211 Public elementary school; Public junior high school; Public senior high school; Public elementary school; Public junior high school; Public senior high school

D-U-N-S 00-786-8615
MALYS INC
6014 Rochester Rd, Troy, MI 48085-1301
Tel (248) 813-8880 *Founded/Ownrshp* 1947
Sales 26.1MM^E *EMP* 225
SIC 5122 5087 Cosmetics; Beauty parlor equipment & supplies; Cosmetics; Beauty parlor equipment & supplies
Pr: John Petroff

D-U-N-S 83-488-1187
MALYS OF CALIFORNIA INC
28145 Harrison Pkwy, Valencia, CA 91355-4165
Tel (661) 295-8317 *Founded/Ownrshp* 2007
Sales NA *EMP* 500
SIC 5087 Barber shop equipment & supplies; Beauty parlor equipment & supplies

MAMA DELUCA'S PIZZA
See FRANCHISE BRANDS LLC

MAMA LUPE'S TORTILLA PRODUCTS
See KING TORTILLA INC

MAMA MARY'S
See SPARTAN FOODS OF AMERICA INC

MAMA NINFA'S
See NINFAS HOLDINGS LP

D-U-N-S 19-674-9159
MAMA ROSAS LLC
(*Suby of* HGGC LLC) ★
1910 Fair Rd, Sidney, OH 45365-8906
Tel (937) 498-4511 *Founded/Ownrshp* 2011
Sales 293.4MM^E *EMP* 300^E
SIC 5141 5142 Groceries, general line; Food brokers; Packaged frozen goods; Bakery products, frozen; Groceries, general line; Food brokers; Packaged frozen goods; Bakery products, frozen
CEO: Scott McNair
Off Mgr: Christi Jones
Sfty Mgr: David Haller

D-U-N-S 80-904-2281 IMP/EXP
MAMAMIA PRODUCE LLC
164 Madison St, East Rutherford, NJ 07073-1641
Tel (973) 773-9494 *Founded/Ownrshp* 2003
Sales 27.3MM^E *EMP* 32
Accts Hirsch Oelbaum Bram Hanover
SIC 5148 Fruits

D-U-N-S 05-021-3495
MAMARONECK UNION FREE SCHOOL DISTRICT
1000 W Boston Post Rd, Mamaroneck, NY 10543-3399
Tel (914) 220-3000 *Founded/Ownrshp* 1850
Sales 115.8MM^E *EMP* 821
SIC 8211 Public senior high school; Public junior high school; Public elementary school; Public senior high school; Public junior high school; Public elementary school

MAMA'S CAFE
See 1776 LTD

MAMC MANUFACTURING
See MAGNESIUM ALUMINUM MICHIGAN CORP

D-U-N-S 00-607-0155 IMP
MAMCO CORP (WI)
8630 Industrial Dr, Franksville, WI 53126-9342
Tel (262) 886-9069 *Founded/Ownrshp* 1923
Sales 43.3MM^E *EMP* 320
SIC 3621 3566 Motors, electric; Electric motor & generator auxiliary parts; Speed changers, drives & gears; Motors, electric; Electric motor & generator auxiliary parts; Speed changers, drives & gears
Pr: William H Meltzer
**Treas:* Florence Meltzer
**VP:* Curt Meltzer
Off Mgr: Barb Waltman
VP Opers: Jeff Behnke
**VP Sls:* Ronald Meltzer

D-U-N-S 92-703-8468
MAMCO INC
ALABBASI
764 Ramona Expy Ste C, Perris, CA 92571-9716
Tel (951) 776-9300 *Founded/Ownrshp* 2002
Sales 26.9MM^E *EMP* 120^E
Accts Preety Gupta Cpa-Gupta Acc
SIC 1611 General contractor, highway & street construction
CEO: Marwan Alabbasi
**Pr:* Elizabeth Alabbasi
**VP:* Rumzi Alabbasi

D-U-N-S 18-841-5566 IMP
MAMIYA AMERICA CORP
MAC GROUP
75 Virginia Rd Ste 1, White Plains, NY 10603-1431
Tel (914) 347-3300 *Founded/Ownrshp* 1987
Sales 25.9MM^E *EMP* 55
SIC 5043 Photographic cameras, projectors, equipment & supplies
Pr: Jan Lederman
VP: Barry Burstein
VP: Bob Higgins
Rgnl Mgr: Franklin McDaniel
Sftwr Eng: Brenda Hipsher
Opers Mgr: John Nicholas
VP Mktg: Ray Vitiello
Mktg Dir: Sara Roberts
Manager: Phillip Abel
Sls Mgr: Francis Westfield
Snr Mgr: Louie Lu

D-U-N-S 00-698-7200 IMP
MAMIYE BROTHERS INC (NJ)
MAMIYE SALES
1385 Brdwy Fl 18, New York, NY 10018
Tel (212) 279-4150 *Founded/Ownrshp* 1946, 2001
Sales 145.9MM^E *EMP* 410
SIC 5137 Coordinate sets: women's, children's & infants'; Sweaters, women's & children's
VP: Abe Mamiye
**Ch Bd:* Hyman Mamiye
**CEO:* Charles D Mamiye
VP: Linda Cola
VP: Stephen Mamiye
Dir IT: Emil Lavagno

MAMIYE SALES
See MAMIYE BROTHERS INC

D-U-N-S 96-157-4808
MAMMA CHIA LLC
5205 Avd Encinas Ste E, Carlsbad, CA 92008-4366
Tel (855) 588-2442 *Founded/Ownrshp* 2010
Sales 23.1MM^E *EMP* 40
SIC 5149 Beverage concentrates
CEO: Janie Hoffman
CFO: Bob Crumby
Ex VP: Matthew Buckley
VP: Sean Venus
Mng Dir: Michael Moss
Sls Dir: Andy Blacklidge
Mktg Mgr: Dasha Alekseyeva
Mktg Mgr: Juliet Kim
Manager: Brandon Cervelli
Manager: Chris Summers
Sls Mgr: Jen OH

D-U-N-S 06-508-7942
MAMMOET USA SOUTH INC
(*Suby of* MAMMOET HOLDING B.V.)
20525 Fm 521 Rd, Rosharon, TX 77583-8127
Tel (281) 369-2200 *Founded/Ownrshp* 1999
Sales 45.0MM^E *EMP* 115
SIC 4213 4412 4424 4449 Heavy machinery transport; Deep sea foreign transportation of freight; Deep sea domestic transportation of freight; Canal & intracoastal freight transportation; Heavy machinery transport; Deep sea foreign transportation of freight; Deep sea domestic transportation of freight; Canal & intracoastal freight transportation
Pr: Richard Thomas Miller Jr
COO: Jan Kleyn
CFO: Matthijs Wijk
**Treas:* Matthijs Van Wick Jr
**VP:* Petrus Nooren
**VP:* Johannes J Van Breurelen
Mng Dir: John Nelson
Mng Dir: Tom Vanderenden
Site Mgr: Donovane Montgomery
Opers Mgr: Guy Breton
Opers Mgr: Eddie Hunter

D-U-N-S 78-043-8024
MAMMOTH FIRE ALARMS INC
176 Walker St, Lowell, MA 01854-3126
Tel (978) 934-9130 *Founded/Ownrshp* 1991
Sales 26.8MM^E *EMP* 50
SIC 5063 Fire alarm systems
Pr: Diane Beaulieu
**Treas:* Charles Beaulieu
IT Man: Brian Jarvis
Mktg Dir: Bryan Mango

MAMMOTH HOSPITAL
See SOUTHERN MONO HEALTHCARE DISTRICT

D-U-N-S 18-997-2276 IMP/EXP
■ MAMMOTH INC
(*Suby of* NORTEK AIR SOLUTIONS LLC) ★
13200 Pioneer Trl Ste 150, Eden Prairie, MN 55347-4125
Tel (952) 358-6600 *Founded/Ownrshp* 1935
Sales 36.9M^E *EMP* 400
SIC 3585 3433 5075 Refrigeration & heating equipment; Heating equipment, except electric; Warm air heating equipment & supplies
Pr: Eric Roberts
**CFO:* Owen Golke
**Treas:* Edward Cooney
Software D: Bob Larranaga
Mfg Mgr: Tony Matrella
Ql Cn Mgr: Dale Stinson

D-U-N-S 94-648-5679
MAMMOTH MOUNTAIN LAKE CORP
(*Suby of* MAMMOTH MOUNTAIN SKI AREA LLC) ★
10001 Minaret Rd, Mammoth Lakes, CA 93546
Tel (760) 934-2571 *Founded/Ownrshp* 1954
Sales 2.6MM^E *EMP* 450
SIC 7032 Sporting & recreational camps; Sporting & recreational camps
CEO: Alan Gregory
Prin: Rusty Gregory

D-U-N-S 02-864-8061 IMP
MAMMOTH MOUNTAIN SKI AREA LLC
(*Suby of* STARWOOD CAPITAL GROUP LLC) ★
10001 Minaret Rd, Mammoth Lakes, CA 93546
Tel (760) 934-2571 *Founded/Ownrshp* 2005
Sales 137.9MM *EMP* 350
Accts Pricewaterhousecoopers Llp S
SIC 7011 5812 Ski lodge; Resort hotel; Eating places; Ski lodge; Resort hotel; Eating places
Pt: David Cummings
CFO: Mark Clausen
Treas: Nick Gunter
**Ofcr:* Erik Forsell
VP: Bruce Burton
VP: Bill Cockroft
VP: Tom Smith
Dir Risk M: Craig Lister
Genl Mgr: Luis Villanueva
Dir IT: Greg Dallas
IT Man: Stacey Crockett

MAMMOTONE
See DEVICOR MEDICAL PRODUCTS INC

D-U-N-S 04-553-4690
MAMOLOS CONTINENTAL & BAILEY BAKERIES INC
703 S Main St, Burbank, CA 91506-2528
Tel (818) 841-9347 *Founded/Ownrshp* 1966
Sales 20.0MM *EMP* 327
SIC 5461 Bakeries; Bakeries
Pr: Ugo Mamolo
**VP:* Roger Terzuolo

D-U-N-S 78-619-6840 IMP
MAN CAPITAL CORP
(*Suby of* MAN SE)
591 Sw 13th Ter, Pompano Beach, FL 33069-3519
Tel (732) 582-8220 *Founded/Ownrshp* 1980
Sales 60.0MM^E *EMP* 550
SIC 3519 Diesel, semi-diesel or duel-fuel engines, including marine; Diesel, semi-diesel or duel-fuel engines, including marine
Pr: Siejberd Rottach
**Treas:* Vin Ritraj
Treas: Vinoo Rotraj

D-U-N-S 03-822-2329 IMP
MAN DIESEL & TURBO NORTH AMERICA INC
(*Suby of* MAN DIESEL & TURBO SE)
2 Amboy Ave, Woodbridge, NJ 07095-2662
Tel (713) 780-4200 *Founded/Ownrshp* 1980
Sales 55.0MM^E *EMP* 245
SIC 5999 7538 7539 3621 Engines & parts, air-cooled; Engine repair; Automotive turbocharger & blower repair; Rotor retainers or housings; Electric motor & generator auxillary parts; Engines & parts, air-cooled; Engine repair; Automotive turbocharger & blower repair; Rotor retainers or housings; Electric motor & generator auxillary parts
Ch Bd: Robert Burger
**CFO:* Sven Feyer
Ex VP: Man Bw
Mng Dir: Wayne Jones
Mng Dir: Alan Marsh
Brnch Mgr: Paul Korsgaard
Genl Mgr: Chris Betts
**Genl Mgr:* David Finn
Genl Mgr: Philip Heathcote
Genl Mgr: Michael Madely
Genl Mgr: James West

D-U-N-S 01-176-2841 IMP/EXP
MAN ENGINES & COMPONENTS INC
(*Suby of* MAN CAPITAL CORP) ★
591 Sw 13th Ter, Pompano Beach, FL 33069-3519
Tel (954) 946-9092 *Founded/Ownrshp* 1997
Sales 60.0MM^E *EMP* 40
SIC 5088 3714 3519 Marine propulsion machinery & equipment; Motor vehicle transmissions, drive assemblies & parts; Diesel, semi-diesel or duel-fuel engines, including marine; Marine propulsion machinery & equipment; Motor vehicle transmissions, drive assemblies & parts; Diesel, semi-diesel or duel-fuel engines, including marine
Pr: Ricardo Barbosa
**Treas:* Max Heller
**Treas:* Emilio Vargas
**Prin:* Sven Von Saafeld
Prd Mgr: Spencer Brumfield
Manager: Brett Halavacs

MAN HEIN PITSBURG
See BUTLER AUTO AUCTION

MAN STORE, THE
See GAGS AND GAMES INC

D-U-N-S 10-665-9188
MAN-CAL INC
MCDONALD'S
711 W 17th St Ste B1, Costa Mesa, CA 92627-4342
Tel (949) 722-8625 *Founded/Ownrshp* 1967
Sales 11.9MM^E *EMP* 300
SIC 5812 Fast-food restaurant, chain; Fast-food restaurant, chain
CEO: Sam Mangione
**Pr:* Virginia Mangione

D-U-N-S 01-239-7568
MAN-DELL FOOD STORES INC
MAN-DELL SUPERMARKET
24110 Hillside Ave, Bellerose, NY 11426-1397
Tel (718) 343-3434 *Founded/Ownrshp* 1950
Sales 70.4MM^E *EMP* 600
SIC 5411 5921 Supermarkets, chain; Beer (packaged); Supermarkets, chain; Beer (packaged)
Pr: Ronald Schubert
**Sec:* Joel Mandell
**V Ch Bd:* Lawrence Mandell
VP: Thomas Anderson

MAN-DELL SUPERMARKET
See MAN-DELL FOOD STORES INC

D-U-N-S 06-445-7203
MAN-GROVE INDUSTRIES INC
LITHOCRAFT CO
1201 N Miller St, Anaheim, CA 92806-1933
Tel (714) 630-3020 *Founded/Ownrshp* 1973
Sales 20.1MM^E *EMP* 64
SIC 2752 Commercial printing, lithographic
Pr: Bradley L Thurman
Ofcr: Robert Riley
**VP:* Colleen Cosgrove
Genl Mgr: Walter Thurman
VP Opers: Robert Navarro
Sales Asso: Glenn Stout

D-U-N-S 19-321-1021
MANA DEVELOPMENT LLC
MANNA BREAD DEVELOPMENT
2339 11th St Ste 2339, Encinitas, CA 92024-6604
Tel (760) 944-1070 *Founded/Ownrshp* 2008
Sales 409.8MM^E *EMP* 3,000
SIC 5149 Bakery products; Bakery products
Pt: Patrick Rogers

D-U-N-S 07-887-0292 IMP
MANA PRODUCTS INC
YOUR NAME PROFESSIONAL BRAND
3202 Queens Blvd Fl 6, Long Island City, NY 11101-2341
Tel (718) 361-2550 *Founded/Ownrshp* 1975
Sales 238.2MM^E *EMP* 800^E
SIC 2844 5122 Cosmetic preparations; Cosmetics; Cosmetic preparations; Cosmetics
Ch: Nikos Mouyiaris
CFO: Larry Weinstock
**CFO:* Lawrence Weinstock
Ex VP: N Masturzo
VP: David Chan
**VP:* Edward Ewankov
VP: Bruce Meyer
**VP:* Barbara Novick
**VP:* Dennis Roberts
**VP:* Bob Salem
VP: John Szweda
VP: Debi Theis
VP: Claudia Torelli
Dir Lab: Marjana Lilaj
Creative D: Aloise Levesque
Dir Bus: Eleni Spencer

D-U-N-S 11-849-8844 IMP/EXP
MANAC TRAILERS USA INC
(*Suby of* GROUPE CANAM INC)
8593 State Highway 77, Oran, MO 63771-7102
Tel (573) 262-2166 *Founded/Ownrshp* 2002
Sales 29.7MM^E *EMP* 110^E
SIC 3715 Truck trailers; Truck trailers
Pr: Charles Dutil
CFO: Lisa Stearns
Dir IT: Brandon Kielhofner
Sfty Mgr: Chuck Holbrrok

D-U-N-S 01-879-4438
MANAFORT BROTHERS INC (CT)
414 New Britain Ave, Plainville, CT 06062-2065
Tel (860) 229-4853 *Founded/Ownrshp* 1922
Sales 126.1MM^E *EMP* 500
SIC 1794 1771 1622 1795 4953 Excavation work; Foundation & footing contractor; Bridge, tunnel & elevated highway; Wrecking & demolition work; Recycling, waste materials; Excavation work; Foundation & footing contractor; Bridge, tunnel & elevated highway; Wrecking & demolition work; Recycling, waste materials
Pr: James Manafort Jr
**CFO:* Robert King
**Sec:* Lauren Manafort
Bd of Dir: Ann Catelli
VP: Bill Manafort
**VP:* David Manafort
VP: Frank Manafort Jr
**VP:* Jon Manafort
**VP:* Michael Tarsi
IT Man: Charles Mercier
Info Man: Mike Daversa

D-U-N-S 80-271-3644
MANAGED CARE OF AMERICA INC
1910 Cochran Rd Ste 605, Pittsburgh, PA 15220-1213
Tel (412) 922-2803 *Founded/Ownrshp* 1992
Sales NA *EMP* 100
Accts Mckeever Varga & Senko Pittsb
SIC 6411 8011 8742 8741 6321 Insurance agents, brokers & service; Health maintenance organization; Compensation & benefits planning consultant; Administrative management; Reinsurance carriers, accident & health
Pr: Charles Davidson
**CEO:* Phyllis Shehab
CFO: Dennis A Casey
**CFO:* Patrick Forrest
**Ex VP:* John Riston

D-U-N-S 04-283-8008
MANAGED CARE OF NORTH AMERICA INC
MCNA DENTAL
200 W Cypress Creek Rd # 500, Fort Lauderdale, FL 33309-2338
Tel (954) 730-7131 *Founded/Ownrshp* 1992
Sales NA *EMP* 100
SIC 6324 5047 Hospital & medical service plans; Dental equipment & supplies
CEO: Jeffrey Feingold
Dir IT: Stephen Smith
Sftwr Eng: Eric Lavigne

D-U-N-S 60-121-7979
■ MANAGED HEALTH NETWORK
(*Suby of* HEALTH NET INC) ★
2370 Kerner Blvd, San Rafael, CA 94901-5546
Tel (415) 460-8168 *Founded/Ownrshp* 1990
Sales NA *EMP* 1,300
SIC 6324 8099 8093 8011 Hospital & medical service plans; Health maintenance organization (HMO), insurance only; Medical services organization; Specialty outpatient clinics; Offices & clinics of medical doctors; Hospital & medical service plans; Health maintenance organization (HMO), insurance only; Medical services organization; Specialty outpatient clinics; Offices & clinics of medical doctors
CEO: Jeffrey Bairstow
Pr: Jerry Coil
Pr: Steven Sell
COO: Linda Brisbane
COO: Jonathan Wormhoudt
CFO: John Volkober
Ofcr: Gidget Peddie
Ofcr: Alison South
VP: Danny Amos
VP: Steve Blake
VP: Al Gross
VP: Chris Hause
VP: Gerry Long
VP: Dena Maddox
VP: Julius Schillinger
Board of Directors: John Crockerin

D-U-N-S 79-552-0436
■ MANAGED HEALTH SERVICES INSURANCE CORP
(*Suby of* CENTENE CORP) ★
10700 W Res Dr Ste 300, Wauwatosa, WI 53226
Tel (414) 773-4000 *Founded/Ownrshp* 1993
Sales NA *EMP* 120
SIC 6324 Hospital & medical service plans
Pr: Sherry B Husa
**Ch Bd:* Kathleen R Crampton
VP: Kathleen Tordik
**Prin:* Michael Neidorff
Prin: Richard Nemitz
Board of Directors: Howard Cox Jr, Robert J Johannes

D-U-N-S 05-562-3377
MANAGED NETWORK SERVICES LLC
(*Suby of* TOLT SOLUTIONS INC) ★
3800 Bridge Pkwy, Redwood City, CA 94065-1171
Tel (650) 232-4287 *Founded/Ownrshp* 2014
Sales 2.6MM^E *EMP* 323^E
SIC 7374 5734 Data processing service; Computer & software stores

D-U-N-S 80-770-0443
MANAGED STAFFING PS INC
15770 Dallas Pkwy Ste 800, Dallas, TX 75248-6616
Tel (469) 759-7372 *Founded/Ownrshp* 2013
Sales 26.7MM^E *EMP* 350^E
SIC 7363 Temporary help service; Temporary help service
CEO: Abid H Abedi
**Pr:* Seema Abedi
VP: Ron Abell
**VP:* Ray Jaffrey

D-U-N-S 78-005-0811
MANAGEDCOMP INC
10 Presidential Way, Woburn, MA 01801-1053
Tel (781) 938-2000 *Founded/Ownrshp* 2002
Sales NA *EMP* 250
SIC 6331 8742 Workers' compensation insurance; Management consulting services; Workers' compensation insurance; Management consulting services
Pr: Nancy Froude

D-U-N-S 80-533-8977
MANAGEMENT & BUDGET DEPARTMENT OF TECHNOLOGY
D M B
(*Suby of* EXECUTIVE OFFICE OF STATE OF MICHIGAN) ★
111 S Capitol Ave, Lansing, MI 48933-1555
Tel (517) 373-1004 *Founded/Ownrshp* 1948
Sales NA *EMP* 800
SIC 9311

D-U-N-S 02-568-9824
MANAGEMENT & BUSINESS ASSOCIATES INC
RESTORATIVE HEALTHCARE
7330 San Pedro Ave # 800, San Antonio, TX 78216-6235
Tel (210) 737-8090 *Founded/Ownrshp* 1999
Sales 24.1MM^E *EMP* 351
SIC 8082 8049 Home health care services; Nurses & other medical assistants; Home health care services; Nurses & other medical assistants
Pr: Ron Sanchez
**COO:* Jason Sanchez
**CIO:* Elling Omenson
CIO: Juan Valadez

D-U-N-S 09-407-1511
MANAGEMENT ANALYSIS & UTILIZATION INC
MAU WORKFORCE SOLUTIONS
501 Greene St Ste 100, Augusta, GA 30901-4400
Tel (706) 722-6806 *Founded/Ownrshp* 1973
Sales 215.3MM^E *EMP* 175
Accts Cherrybekaert Llp Augusta Ge
SIC 7361 Employment agencies; Employment agencies
Ch Bd: William G Hatcher Sr
**Pr:* Randall Hatcher
COO: Timi Fletcher
Dir Risk M: Olivia Marvin
Opers Mgr: Zachary Brewster
Opers Mgr: Tradd Rodgers
Mktg Mgr: Lori Holley
Mktg Mgr: Brett Yardley
Snr Mgr: Phillip Coleman
Snr Mgr: Jennifer Dickerson
Snr Mgr: Tom Dixon

D-U-N-S 07-433-4264
MANAGEMENT AND ENGINEERING TECHNOLOGIES INTERNATIONAL INC
METI
8600 Boeing Dr, El Paso, TX 79925-1226
Tel (915) 772-4975 *Founded/Ownrshp* 1994
Sales 36.9MM^E *EMP* 200^E
SIC 8711

D-U-N-S 03-920-3740
MANAGEMENT AND TRAINING CORP
M T C
500 N Market Place Dr # 100, Centerville, UT 84014-1711
Tel (801) 693-2600 *Founded/Ownrshp* 1980
Sales 761.5MM *EMP* 9,500
Accts Kpmg Llp Salt Lake City Utah
SIC 7349 8331 8744 8741 8249 Building maintenance, except repairs; Job training services; Correctional facility; Jails, privately operated; Business management; Vocational schools; Civil service training school; Building maintenance, except repairs; Job training services; Correctional facility; Jails, privately operated; Business management; Vocational schools; Civil service training school
Pr: R Scott Marquardt
Pr: Dawn Call
**CFO:* Lyle J Parry
Ofcr: Sean Dunham
**Sr VP:* Sergio Molina
**Sr VP:* John Pedersen
**Sr VP:* Odie Washington
VP: Wendell Bosen
VP: J C Conner
VP: Lonnie Hall
VP: Jeff Henry
VP: Dean Hoffman
VP: Greg Niblett
Dir Risk M: Jerry Anderson
Dir Risk M: Robert Unwin
Comm Dir: Randy Grayston

MANAGEMENT CO
See DRURY HOTELS CO LLC

MANAGEMENT COMPANY
See FORD RESTAURANT GROUP INC

D-U-N-S 07-944-7496
MANAGEMENT CO INC
MONROE MANOR NURSING HOME
3842 Independence Dr, Alexandria, LA 71303-3533
Tel (318) 445-1635 *Founded/Ownrshp* 1981
Sales 2.5MM^E *EMP* 278^E
SIC 8052 Intermediate care facilities
Pr: June Peach

D-U-N-S 08-235-5652
MANAGEMENT CONCEPTS INC
8230 Leesburg Pike # 800, Tysons Corner, VA 22182-2641
Tel (703) 790-9595 *Founded/Ownrshp* 1973
Sales 23.8MM^E *EMP* 200
SIC 8299 8742 2721 2731 Educational services; Management consulting services; Periodicals; Book publishing; Educational services; Management consulting services; Periodicals; Book publishing
CEO: Thomas Dungan III
Dir Rx: Debbie Barnard
Dir Rx: Tamarind Johnson
CTO: Cheryl-Ann Cohen
IT Man: Jim Nash
Natl Sales: Evelyn E Apont-Sacks
Mktg Mgr: Alyson Craig
Mktg Mgr: Chelsea Stafilatos
Snr PM: Walter Kniffin

D-U-N-S 11-337-7659
MANAGEMENT CONSULTING INC
MANCON
1961 Diamond Springs Rd, Virginia Beach, VA 23455-2319
Tel (757) 460-0879 *Founded/Ownrshp* 1983
Sales 417.7MM^E *EMP* 1,400
SIC 8742 Management consulting services; Management consulting services
CEO: Mary J Clarke
**Pr:* Rick Clarke
VP: David Bibby
**VP:* David Meadows
Prgrm Mgr: Rex Allen
CIO: Randy Whitman
IT Man: Jim Trainor
Netwrk Eng: Justin Long
**Sls Mgr:* Bart Consford
Sls Mgr: Paul Sumner

D-U-N-S 78-755-9921
MANAGEMENT DATA SYSTEMS INTERNATIONAL INC
MDSI
6225 Shiloh Rd, Alpharetta, GA 30005-2206
Tel (813) 975-3830 *Founded/Ownrshp* 1990
Sales 65.0MM *EMP* 200
Accts Spence Marston Bunch Morris
SIC 5065 Communication equipment; Communication equipment
CEO: Lisa McDonald Jillson
CFO: Wayne Grubbs
**CFO:* Kim Russell
**VP:* Marc Fowler
**VP:* Steve Hyser
**VP:* Ron Lawler
**VP:* Shawn Nickel
**VP:* Shannon Payne

D-U-N-S 55-604-4618
MANAGEMENT DECISIONS - MDI INC
35 Technology Pkwy S # 150, Norcross, GA 30092-2945
Tel (770) 416-7949 *Founded/Ownrshp* 1994
Sales 38.0MM^E *EMP* 350
SIC 7363 Help supply services; Temporary help service; Help supply services; Temporary help service
CEO: Richey Brownfield
**Ch Bd:* Ella Koscik
**Pr:* Connie Chiasson
**CFO:* Rick Hayslip
Mng Dir: Jeff Dean
IT Man: Lyle Sawyer
Sales Exec: Debbie Hoecker
Sls Dir: Aarik Eberhardt

MANAGEMENT DW MCMILLAN HM HLTH
See D W MCMILLAN MEMORIAL HOSPITAL

D-U-N-S 80-809-5710
MANAGEMENT HEALTH SOLUTIONS INC
99 Hawley Ln Ste 1201, Stratford, CT 06614-1202
Tel (888) 647-4621 *Founded/Ownrshp* 1999
Sales 20.7MM^E *EMP* 135
SIC 7372 8742 Business oriented computer software; Materials mgmt. (purchasing, handling, inventory) consultant; Business oriented computer software; Materials mgmt. (purchasing, handling, inventory) consultant
CFO: Tim S Ledwick
Pr: Kishore Bala
**CEO:* Edward Murphy
**COO:* Brian Campbell
VP: Alan Anderson
Prd Mgr: Gail Hoffman
Sales Exec: Bill Bailey
Sls Mgr: Linda Burg
Sls Mgr: Melissa Horn
Snr Mgr: Cindy Jones

D-U-N-S 15-297-2600
MANAGEMENT HEALTH SYSTEMS INC
MEDPRO STAFFING
1580 Sawgrs Corp Pkwy # 100, Sunrise, FL 33323-2859
Tel (954) 739-4247 *Founded/Ownrshp* 1997
Sales 50.0MM *EMP* 550
SIC 7363 Medical help service; Medical help service
Ch: Michael Lemonier
**P.:* Elizabeth Tonkin
**COO:* Linda Doughty
**CFO:* Frank Forbes
**VP:* James Parker
Genl Mgr: Wayne Starks

D-U-N-S 04-408-6841
■ MANAGEMENT RECRUITERS INTERNATIONAL INC
MANAGEMENT RECRUITERS INTL
(*Suby of* CDI CORP) ★
1801 Market St Fl 13, Philadelphia, PA 19103-1607
Tel (866) 836-9890 *Founded/Ownrshp* 1972
Sales 22.1MM^E *EMP* 100
SIC 7361 6794 Executive placement; Franchises, selling or licensing
Pr: John McDonald
**Pr:* Michael W Jalbert
**Treas:* Mark A Kerschner
Sr VP: David Stephens
**Sr VP:* Gary Williams
**VP:* Nancy Halverson
**VP:* Michael Rhode
**VP:* Ann Santomas
**VP:* Thomas S Verratti
**Prin:* Robert K Romaine Jr
Mng Dir: Steve Palamara

MANAGEMENT RECRUITERS INTL
See MANAGEMENT RECRUITERS INTERNATIONAL INC

D-U-N-S 08-363-1606
MANAGEMENT RESOURCE SYSTEMS INC
1907 Baker Rd, High Point, NC 27263-2007
Tel (336) 861-1960 *Founded/Ownrshp* 1977
Sales 55.2MM^E *EMP* 65
SIC 1542

D-U-N-S 79-464-5101
■ MANAGEMENT RESOURCES GROUP INC
(*Suby of* EMERSON ELECTRIC CO) ★
1100 Buckingham St, Watertown, CT 06795-6602
Tel (203) 264-0500 *Founded/Ownrshp* 2014
Sales 23.0MM *EMP* 85
SIC 8711 8742 Consulting engineer; Management consulting services; Consulting engineer; Management consulting services
CEO: Robert Distefano
COO: Will Goetz-Vice
**COO:* Scott McWilliams
Sr VP: Jay Pasqualoni
VP: Will Vice
IT Man: Dennis Belanger
Mktg Dir: Joe Carolan
Pr Dir: Earl Wooster
Snr Mgr: Jerry Pinkard

D-U-N-S 06-874-6346
MANAGEMENT SCIENCE ASSOCIATES INC (PA)
6565 Penn Ave, Pittsburgh, PA 15206-4490
Tel (412) 362-2000 *Founded/Ownrshp* 1963
Sales 128.8MM^E *EMP* 750
SIC 8742 7371

D-U-N-S 07-171-3085
MANAGEMENT SCIENCES FOR HEALTH INC
200 Rivers Edge Dr, Medford, MA 02155-5479
Tel (617) 250-9500 *Founded/Ownrshp* 1971
Sales 321.4MM *EMP* 400
Accts Tonneson & Company Inc Wakefi
SIC 8742 Hospital & health services consultant; Hospital & health services consultant
Pr: Jonathan Quick
**COO:* Paul Auxila
CFO: Vickie Barrow-Klein
**CFO:* Vickie Barrow Klein
Ofcr: Babajide Aiyegbusi
Ofcr: Jane Andelman
Ofcr: Lily Bower
Ofcr: Lauren Corazzini
Ofcr: Betsie Frei
Ofcr: Colin Gilmartin
Ofcr: Kevin Gunter
Ofcr: Jeanne Hamon
Ofcr: Christele Josephpressat
Ofcr: Angie Lee
Ofcr: Jackie Lemlin
Ofcr: Rachel Lieber
Ofcr: Peter Mahoney
Ofcr: Malia Mayson
Ofcr: Sharon O'Daniel II
Ofcr: Megan Quinn-Mueller
Ofcr: Heather Rafey

MANAGEMENT SERVICES DIVISION
See JUDICIARY COURTS OF STATE OF NEW JERSEY

D-U-N-S 00-654-3826
MANAGEMENT SERVICES GROUP INC (GA)
GLOBAL TECHNICAL SYSTEMS
784 Lynnhaven Pkwy, Virginia Beach, VA 23452-7315
Tel (757) 468-8751 *Founded/Ownrshp* 1997
Sales 33.5MM^E *EMP* 74
SIC 7373 Computer integrated systems design
Pr: Yusun J Spitzer
**CEO:* Terry Spitzer
Ex VP: Scott Carlton
VP: Robert S Gordy
**VP:* Spitzer Terry L
VP: Kevin McTigue
VP: Anthony Pember
Prgrm Mgr: Dean Nohe
Dir IT: James Conkle
IT Man: John Upperman
Pgrm Dir: Donna Richardson

D-U-N-S 80-136-9617
MANAGEMENT SSS INC
MSSS
Roosevlt Av 145a Fl 3, San Juan, PR 00918
Tel (787) 758-7700 *Founded/Ownrshp* 2004
Sales 69.3MM^E *EMP* 2,000
SIC 8742

D-U-N-S 04-840-7589
MANAGEMENT SYSTEMS INTERNATIONAL INC
MSI
(*Suby of* COFFEY INTERNATIONAL LIMITED)
200 12th St S, Arlington, VA 22202-5400
Tel (703) 979-7100 *Founded/Ownrshp* 1981
Sales 138.7MM *EMP* 250^E
Accts Kpmg Llp Mclean Va
SIC 8742 General management consultant; General management consultant
Pr: Lawrence Cooley
COO: Laurie Flamholtz
CFO: Paul J Wise
Exec: Marina Fanning
IT Man: Ausaf Alavi

D-U-N-S 13-186-9935
MANAGEMENT TECHNOLOGY INC
M T I
7700 Old Branch Ave D201, Clinton, MD 20735-1640
Tel (301) 856-4840 *Founded/Ownrshp* 1984
Sales 34.0MM^E *EMP* 175
SIC 7376 7373 4813 8744 Computer facilities management; Computer integrated systems design; Telephone communication, except radio; Facilities support services; Computer facilities management; Computer integrated systems design; Telephone communication, except radio; Facilities support services
Pr: Pauline Brooks
IT Man: John Meyer

D-U-N-S 96-614-0704
MANAGEMENT TEMPORARY & CONTRACT EMPLOYMENT SERVICES INC
145 A Roosevelt Ave, San Juan, PR 00919
Tel (787) 758-7700 *Founded/Ownrshp* 2005
Sales 67.9MM^E *EMP* 1,000
Accts Robert John Santiago Cpa San
SIC 8742 Human resource consulting services
Pr: Alma I Acosta
Sls Mgr: Iillyak Negroni

D-U-N-S 80-978-8321
MANAGEMENT TRAVERSE LLC RIZVI
260 E Brown St Ste 380, Birmingham, MI 48009-6223
Tel (248) 594-4751 *Founded/Ownrshp* 2004
Sales 36.7MM^E *EMP* 129^E
SIC 6282 Investment advice; Investment advice
COO: John A Giampetroni
COO: John Giampetroni
VP: Karen Blanchard

MANAGEMENT TRUST, THE
See MANAGEMENT TRUST ASSOCIATION INC

D-U-N-S 82-550-2201
MANAGEMENT TRUST ASSOCIATION INC
MANAGEMENT TRUST, THE
15661 Red Hill Ave # 201, Tustin, CA 92780-7300
Tel (714) 285-2626 *Founded/Ownrshp* 2011
Sales 135.0MM^E *EMP* 550
SIC 6733 Trusts; Trusts
CEO: William B Sasser

D-U-N-S 96-733-8075
MANAGEMENT-ILA MANAGED HEALTH CARE TRUST FUND
111 Broadway Fl 5, New York, NY 10006-1901
Tel (212) 766-5700 *Founded/Ownrshp* 2011
Sales 491.6MM *EMP* 3
Accts Desena & Company Cpas East Ha
SIC 8741 Management services; Management services

MANAGERS FUNDS
See AMG FUNDS LLC

D-U-N-S 08-095-0181
MANALAPAN-ENGLISHTOWN REGIONAL SCHOOL DISTRICT
54 Main St, Englishtown, NJ 07726-1529
Tel (732) 786-2500 *Founded/Ownrshp* 1878
Sales 84.6MM *EMP* 535
Accts Jump Perry And Company Llp
SIC 8211 Public elementary & secondary schools; Public elementary & secondary schools
Adm Dir: Patricia Resnyk
MIS Dir: Maribeth Cruz
Schl Brd P: Dotty Porcaro
Teacher Pr: Joanne Monroe
Teacher Pr: Shunda Williams

D-U-N-S 83-173-7957 IMP
MANAN MEDICAL PRODUCTS INC
241 W Palatine Rd, Wheeling, IL 60090-5824
Tel (800) 424-6779 *Founded/Ownrshp* 1996
Sales 35.5MM^E *EMP* 200
SIC 3842 3841 Surgical appliances & supplies; Surgical & medical instruments; Surgical appliances & supplies; Surgical & medical instruments
Pr: Bill L Hunter
VP: Manfred Mittermeier
VP: John Pavelt
Genl Mgr: George Leondis
Sfty Dirs: Bob Sove

D-U-N-S 02-583-7865
MANAN TOOL & MANUFACTURING INC
241 W Palatine Rd, Wheeling, IL 60090-5824
Tel (847) 637-3333 *Founded/Ownrshp* 2006
Sales 109.3MM^E *EMP* 1,112
SIC 3541 3841 Machine tools, metal cutting type; Needles, suture; Machine tools, metal cutting type; Needles, suture
Prin: Werner Mittermeier

D-U-N-S 07-204-0207 IMP
MANAR INC
TENNPLASCO
905 S Walnut St, Edinburgh, IN 46124-2002
Tel (812) 526-2891 *Founded/Ownrshp* 1974
Sales 35.0MM *EMP* 250
Accts Blue & Co Llc Seymour Indi
SIC 3089 Molding primary plastic; Molding primary plastic
CEO: Eugene Nolen
**CFO:* Larry Johnson
**VP:* Allan Miller
Genl Mgr: Don Roberts
Mtls Mgr: Richard Kellems
Opers Mgr: Mark Lohr
Manager: Chris Hanley
Sls Mgr: Kevin Hardiman

D-U-N-S 02-077-8395
MANASQUAN SAVINGS BANK (NJ)
(*Suby of* MSB FINANCIAL INC.)
2221 Landmark Pl, Manasquan, NJ 08736-1051
Tel (732) 223-4450 *Founded/Ownrshp* 1874
Sales NA *EMP* 84
SIC 6022 State trust companies accepting deposits, commercial; State trust companies accepting deposits, commercial
Pr: Pete Brown
Treas: Pamela Bateman
Ofcr: Gregory Hunt
Ofcr: Ralph Tancredi
Ex VP: Catherine Franzoni
**Sr VP:* William Campbell
Sr VP: Jeffery Casten
Sr VP: Robert A Hart
VP: Mark Beriault
VP: Nancy Canary
VP: Rich Lanza
**VP:* Ann Slavick

D-U-N-S 07-957-8974
MANASSAS PUBLIC SCHOOLS
8700 Centreville Rd 40, Manassas, VA 20110-8430
Tel (571) 377-6000 *Founded/Ownrshp* 2012
Sales 15.5MM^E *EMP* 772^E
SIC 8211 Public elementary & secondary schools
Pr Dir: Ameta Radford
Teacher Pr: Billie Kay Winfield
HC Dir: Sandra B Thompson

D-U-N-S 12-077-7792
MANATEE COUNTY FAMILY YOUNG MENS CHRISTIAN ASSO
MANATEE COUNTY YMCA
3805 59th St W, Bradenton, FL 34209-6050
Tel (941) 792-7484 *Founded/Ownrshp* 1975
Sales 6.6MM *EMP* 400
Accts Cpa Associates Bradenton Flo
SIC 8399 8322 7997 Community development groups; Individual & family services; Membership sports & recreation clubs; Community development groups; Individual & family services; Membership sports & recreation clubs
Pr: Sean Allison
**VP:* Terry Rehfeldt

MANATEE COUNTY GOVERNMENT
See COUNTY OF MANATEE

D-U-N-S 15-281-7151
MANATEE COUNTY RURAL HEALTH SERVICES INC
PARRISH HEALTH CENTER
700 8th Ave W Ste 101, Palmetto, FL 34221-4737
Tel (941) 776-4000 *Founded/Ownrshp* 1977
Sales 63.3MM *EMP* 400
SIC 8011 Gynecologist; Internal medicine, physician/surgeon; Obstetrician; Pediatrician; Gynecologist; Internal medicine, physician/surgeon; Obstetrician; Pediatrician
Pr: Walter Lpresha
**Pr:* Jeff Zimmerman
**COO:* Ray Fusco
COO: Raymond Fusco
**CFO:* John Nash
**Ch:* Lowe Garry J
Bd of Dir: Marc Lazarus
Ex VP: Charlie Wells
Sr VP: George Van Buren II
Sr VP: George Vanburen
VP: Ellen Adams
VP: Paul Cindrich
VP: Wardell Jackson
**VP:* Lowery Juanine

MANATEE COUNTY SCHOOL BOARD
See SCHOOL BOARD OF MANATEE COUNTY

MANATEE COUNTY YMCA
See MANATEE COUNTY FAMILY YOUNG MENS CHRISTIAN ASSO

MANATEE GLENS HOSPITAL
See CENTERSTONE OF FLORIDA INC

D-U-N-S 06-025-9314
■ MANATEE MEMORIAL HOSPITAL
(*Suby of* UNIVERSAL HEALTH SERVICES INC) ★
206 2nd St E, Bradenton, FL 34208-1000
Tel (941) 746-5111 *Founded/Ownrshp* 1992
Sales 244.3MM *EMP* 1,450
SIC 8062 General medical & surgical hospitals; General medical & surgical hospitals
CEO: Kevin Dilallo
CFO: Karen Sullivan
**CFO:* Mark Tierney
Exec: Garry Grant
Prac Mgr: Anne Sirois
Nurse Mgr: Roma Bennett
Nurse Mgr: Rebecca Bouchard
Nurse Mgr: Priscilla Cooper
DP Exec: Troy Beaubien
Pathlgst: Hung-WEI Lee
Surgeon: Kathleen Cnor
Board of Directors: Bert Beard, Troy Beaubies, Betty Chambliss, Beth Heinz, Andrew Knoch, Mike Lorraine, Alberto Montalvo, Barbara Raney, Ron Walter

MANATI MEDICAL CENTER
See DORADO HEALTH INC

D-U-N-S 07-927-8305
■ MANATRON INC (MI)
(*Suby of* THOMSON REUTERS CORP) ★
510 E Milham Ave, Portage, MI 49002-1439
Tel (269) 567-2900 *Founded/Ownrshp* 1972
Sales 48.5MM^E *EMP* 447
SIC 7373 7371 6531 Turnkey vendors, computer systems; Computer software development; Appraiser, real estate; Turnkey vendors, computer systems; Computer software development; Appraiser, real estate
Pr: G William McKinzie
Ex VP: Early L Stephens
Ex VP: Kurt Wagner
VP: Lisa Hargiss
VP: Kevin Jackson
VP: Daniel P Muthard
VP Bus Dev: Marty Ulanski
Ex Dir: Patrick Alesandrini
CIO: Bruce High
Dir IT: David Ford
Tech Mgr: Nick Wolf

D-U-N-S 07-189-4505
MANATT PHELPS & PHILLIPS LLP
11355 W Olympic Blvd Fl 2, Los Angeles, CA 90064-1656
Tel (310) 312-4000 *Founded/Ownrshp* 1965
Sales 141.2MM^E *EMP* 850
SIC 8111

D-U-N-S 00-782-0491 IMP
MANATTS INC
1775 Old 6 Rd, Brooklyn, IA 52211-7731
Tel (641) 522-9206 *Founded/Ownrshp* 1948
Sales 274.0MM^E *EMP* 475
SIC 1611 1442 2951 3273 Highway & street paving contractor; Airport runway construction; Sand mining; Gravel mining; Concrete, asphaltic (not from refineries); Ready-mixed concrete; Highway & street paving contractor; Airport runway construction; Sand mining; Gravel mining; Concrete, asphaltic (not from refineries); Ready-mixed concrete
**Treas:* J C Miller
**VP:* Anthony J Manatt
**VP:* Gerald J Manatt Jr
**VP:* Michael J Manatt
Div Mgr: Dennis Gallagher

D-U-N-S 08-770-8756
MANCAN INC
48 1st St Nw, Massillon, OH 44647-5450
Tel (330) 832-4595 *Founded/Ownrshp* 1976
Sales 113.4MM^E *EMP* 5,000
SIC 7361 Employment agencies; Employment agencies
Pr: Jonathan P Mason
**Sec:* Bonnie Mason
VP: Amy King
**Prin:* F Stuart Wilkins
Brnch Mgr: Jerry Miller
Dir IT: Mike Morris

D-U-N-S 02-503-0172
MANCARIS CHRYSLER JEEP INC
4630 W 95th St, Oak Lawn, IL 60453-2514
Tel (708) 423-0910 *Founded/Ownrshp* 1981
Sales 38.3MM^E *EMP* 90^E
SIC 5511 Automobiles, new & used; Automobiles, new & used
Pr: Frank Mancari Sr

D-U-N-S 06-817-3608
MANCHA DEVELOPMENT CO
BURGER KING
2275 Sampson Ave Ste 201, Corona, CA 92879-3402
Tel (951) 271-4100 *Founded/Ownrshp* 1979
Sales 91.2MM^E *EMP* 2,000
SIC 5812 Fast-food restaurant, chain; Fast-food restaurant, chain
CEO: Vince F Eupierre
CFO: Brent Dunkin
**CFO:* Frank Velasco
Dir IT: Scott Nakamura
VP Opers: Ken Wells

D-U-N-S 78-945-7756
MANCHESTER BOARD OF EDUCATION
MANCHESTER PUBLIC SCHOOLS
45 N School St, Manchester, CT 06042-2010
Tel (860) 647-3442 *Founded/Ownrshp* 2006
Sales 60.7MM^E *EMP* 1,400^E
SIC 8211 Public elementary & secondary schools; Public elementary & secondary schools
Genl Mgr: Kathleen Ouellette
Schl Brd P: Christopher Pattacini
HC Dir: Mary J Quistorff

D-U-N-S 10-007-3139
MANCHESTER CITY SCH DISTRICT
215 E Fort St, Manchester, TN 37355-1556
Tel (931) 728-2316 *Founded/Ownrshp* 1905
Sales 13.7MM^E *EMP* 286
SIC 8211 Public elementary & secondary schools; High school, junior or senior; Public elementary & secondary schools; High school, junior or senior
Prin: Tom Rutledge
IT Man: Bill Holt

D-U-N-S 03-972-1373
MANCHESTER COMMUNITY COLLEGE
Great Path, Manchester, CT 06045
Tel (860) 512-3000 *Founded/Ownrshp* 1963
Sales 27.6MM^E *EMP* 400
SIC 8221 Colleges universities & professional schools; Colleges universities & professional schools
Pr: Gena Glickman PHD
Ofcr: Ivette Dreyer
Dir Lab: Chuck Russell

D-U-N-S 78-916-8069
■ MANCHESTER GRAND RESORTS LP
HYATT HOTEL
(*Suby of* HYATT CENTER) ★
1 Market Pl Fl 33, San Diego, CA 92101-7714
Tel (619) 232-1234 *Founded/Ownrshp* 1983
Sales 24.0MM^E *EMP* 900
SIC 7011 Hotels & motels; Hotels & motels
CEO: Mark S Hoplamazian
Pt: Richard V Gibbons
Pt: Douglas F Manchester
CFO: Gebhard F Rainer
Ex VP: H Charles Floyd
Ex VP: Peter Fulton
Ex VP: Stephen G Haggerty
Sls Dir: Kate Brennen
Sls Mgr: Thomas Anderson
Sls Mgr: Sandy Lauter
Sls Mgr: Logan Webster

MANCHESTER HARLEY DAVIDSON
See COCHINO VENTURES LLC

D-U-N-S 93-233-5417
MANCHESTER HEALTHCARE INC
71 Haynes St, Manchester, CT 06040-4131
Tel (860) 646-1222 *Founded/Ownrshp* 2000
Sales NA *EMP* 500
SIC 6324 Hospital & medical service plans; Hospital & medical service plans
Pr: Peter Karl

MANCHESTER HONDA
See MANCHESTER SPORTS CENTER INC

D-U-N-S 05-891-0548
MANCHESTER MARKETING INC
SEIBERT'S SERVICE STATIONS
642 W Southside Plaza St, Richmond, VA 23224-1721
Tel (804) 276-3728 *Founded/Ownrshp* 1975
Sales 25.4MM^E *EMP* 95
Accts Keiter Glen Allen Virginia
SIC 7538 General automotive repair shops; General automotive repair shops
Ch: John R Seibert
**Pr:* Randolph S Seibert
**CFO:* Bob Miles
**VP:* Elizabeth Van Ness

MANCHESTER MEMORIAL HOSPITAL
See MEMORIAL HOSPITAL INC

D-U-N-S 07-732-5645
MANCHESTER MEMORIAL HOSPITAL INC
71 Haynes St, Manchester, CT 06040-4188
Tel (860) 646-1222 *Founded/Ownrshp* 1919
Sales 178.0MM *EMP* 1,056
SIC 8062 General medical & surgical hospitals; General medical & surgical hospitals
Pr: Marc Lory
Chf Path: Dennis G O'Neill
Sr VP: Dennis Mc Conville
VP: Mary Powers
Dir Rad: Dan Delgallo
Dir Bus: Kevin Murphy
Adm Dir: Rosanne Williams
Genl Mgr: Yaa Addae
CIO: Charles Covin
IT Man: Dennis Martini
Ansthlgy: John W McCarrick

MANCHESTER METALS
See MM HOLDINGS I LLC

D-U-N-S 05-348-9188 IMP
■ MANCHESTER PARADIGM INC
PARADIGM PRECISION
(*Suby of* GE AVIATION SYSTEMS LLC) ★
967 Parker St, Manchester, CT 06042-2208
Tel (860) 646-4048 *Founded/Ownrshp* 2004
Sales 136.0MM^E *EMP* 575
SIC 3728 Aircraft assemblies, subassemblies & parts; Aircraft assemblies, subassemblies & parts
Pr: Michael Grunza
**Pr:* James Donahu
**VP:* William W Booth
**VP:* Steve Lindsey

MANCHESTER PUBLIC SCHOOLS
See MANCHESTER BOARD OF EDUCATION

D-U-N-S 10-036-3639
MANCHESTER SCHOOL DISTRICT
195 Mcgregor St Ste 201, Manchester, NH 03102-3749
Tel (603) 624-6300 *Founded/Ownrshp* 1900
Sales 35.9MM^E *EMP* 500
SIC 8211 Public elementary & secondary schools; Public elementary school; Public elementary & secondary schools; Public elementary school
Prin: Richard Norton
Pr: Jo-Ann Mulligan
Ofcr: Barbara Gagne
Prin: Bill Krantz
Prin: Shelly Larochelle
Prin: Maryellen McGorry
Prin: Ellie Murphy
Prin: Patricia Storm
Prin: Jan Thompson
Prin: Mary-Frances Tintle
Prin: Gail Westergren

D-U-N-S 80-948-8828
MANCHESTER SCHOOL DISTRICT
45 N School St, Manchester, CT 06042-2010
Tel (860) 647-3442 *Founded/Ownrshp* 2010
Sales 15.1MM^E *EMP* 1,100
SIC 8211 Elementary & secondary schools; Elementary & secondary schools
Dir Sec: Stephen Tonucci
Pr Dir: Suzanne Angeloni
Teacher Pr: Terri Smith
HC Dir: Sue Valade

D-U-N-S 01-870-5392
MANCHESTER SPORTS CENTER INC (CT)
MANCHESTER HONDA
24 Adams St, Manchester, CT 06042-1802
Tel (860) 645-3100 *Founded/Ownrshp* 1964
Sales 41.3MM^E *EMP* 100^E
SIC 5511 5531 5571 Automobiles, new & used; Automotive parts; Automotive tires; Motorcycles; Automobiles, new & used; Automotive parts; Automotive tires; Motorcycles
Pr: John T Larabee
Mktg Dir: Stephen Cohun
Sls Mgr: John Casey
Sales Asso: Erik Nielsen
Sales Asso: Charlie Williams
Sales Asso: Dan Yorgensen

D-U-N-S 14-846-5008 IMP/EXP
MANCHESTER TANK & EQUIPMENT CO INC
(*Suby of* MCWANE CAST IRON PIPE CO) ★
1000 Corporate Centre Dr # 300, Franklin, TN 37067-6206
Tel (615) 370-6104 *Founded/Ownrshp* 1945
Sales 221.9MM^E *EMP* 1,050
SIC 3443 Industrial vessels, tanks & containers; Fuel tanks (oil, gas, etc.): metal plate; Tanks, standard or custom fabricated: metal plate; Industrial vessels, tanks & containers; Fuel tanks (oil, gas, etc.): metal plate; Tanks, standard or custom fabricated: metal plate
CEO: Larry Whitehead
**Pr:* Robert Graumann
**VP:* Danny M Clymer
**VP:* Tom Freeland
VP: Steve Harris
**VP:* D Harrison Whitehead
Sfty Dirs: Brian Cline
Ql Cn Mgr: Jared Shutwell
VP Sls: Scott Viebranz
Sls Dir: Robin Kinnaman
Mktg Mgr: Lesley Shorter

D-U-N-S 10-235-7530
MANCHESTER TOOL & DIE INC
601 S Wabash Rd, North Manchester, IN 46962-8148
Tel (260) 982-8524 *Founded/Ownrshp* 1981
Sales 20.1MM^E *EMP* 95
Accts Naragon North Manchester In
SIC 3714 Air conditioner parts, motor vehicle
Pr: Barry Blocher
Genl Mgr: Chad Williams
Plnt Mgr: Jerry Phillips

D-U-N-S 07-826-8653
MANCHESTER TOWNSHIP BOARD OF EDUCATION
MANCHSTER TOWNSHIP PUB SCHOOLS
121 Route 539, Whiting, NJ 08759-1237
Tel (732) 350-5900 *Founded/Ownrshp* 1920
Sales 51.2M *EMP* 432
Accts A J & K By Fax On November 2
SIC 8211 Public elementary & secondary schools; Public elementary school; Public senior high school; School board; Public elementary & secondary schools; Public elementary school; Public senior high school; School board
VP: James Pate
Exec: Claire Weimmer
Dir IT: Mark Stanley

D-U-N-S 07-431-5573
MANCHESTER UNIVERSITY INC
604 E College Ave, North Manchester, IN 46962-1276
Tel (260) 982-5000 *Founded/Ownrshp* 1889
Sales 68.0MM *EMP* 300^E
SIC 8221 College, except junior; College, except junior
Ch Bd: Marshal Link
**Pr:* Jo Yong Switzer
**Treas:* Jack Gochenaur
VP: Laine Mello
Comm Dir: Sari Algharabeh
Pgrm Dir: Cheri Krueckeberg

MANCHESTER TOWNSHIP PUB SCHOOLS
See MANCHESTER TOWNSHIP BOARD OF EDUCATION

D-U-N-S 06-332-3026
MANCINI AND GROESBECK INC
MANCINI/MARKETING SPECIALISTS
164 E 3900 S, Salt Lake City, UT 84107-1529
Tel (801) 266-4453 *Founded/Ownrshp* 1962
Sales 22.1MM^E *EMP* 145
SIC 5141 Food brokers; Food brokers
Ch: V P Mancini
**Pr:* Tad Mancini
**Ex VP:* Chris Mancini
VP: John Berceau
Exec: Stacy Bogenschutz

MANCINI DUFFY
See HALSEY MCCORMACK & HELMER INC

MANCINI/MARKETING SPECIALISTS
See MANCINI AND GROESBECK INC

D-U-N-S 05-051-4678 IMP
MANCINIS SLEEPWORLD INC
599 Hawthorn Pl, Livermore, CA 94550-7190
Tel (925) 456-6400 *Founded/Ownrshp* 1969
Sales 32.6MM^E *EMP* 150
SIC 5712 Furniture stores; Mattresses; Furniture stores; Mattresses
Pr: Randy Mancini
CFO: Marie Higgins
**VP:* Marc Fey
VP: Marc Sey
Site Mgr: Gerald Grewats
Site Mgr: Robert Guiterrez

D-U-N-S 06-643-4903
MANCO STRUCTURES LTD
6106 Fm 3009, Schertz, TX 78154-3205
Tel (210) 690-1705 *Founded/Ownrshp* 1968
Sales 21.6MM^E *EMP* 90
SIC 3272 Concrete products
Pr: Carlos D Cerna
Ql Cn Mgr: Rick Thames

MANCON
See MANAGEMENT CONSULTING INC

D-U-N-S 60-292-6805 IMP
MANCONIX INC
8585 Commerce Park Dr 500d, Houston, TX 77036-7427
Tel (281) 879-8849 *Founded/Ownrshp* 2005
Sales 23.6MM^E *EMP* 100
SIC 3699 3672 Electrical welding equipment; Printed circuit boards
Pr: Minh Leba
Pr: Thu Pham
**COO:* Oanh Nguyen
**CFO:* John Leba
IT Man: Lieu Nguyen

D-U-N-S 83-066-1299
MANCOR OHIO INC
(*Suby of* MANCOR CANADA INC)
1008 Leonhard St, Dayton, OH 45404-1666
Tel (937) 228-6141 *Founded/Ownrshp* 2006
Sales 68.9MM^E *EMP* 220
SIC 3713 Truck bodies & parts; Truck bodies & parts
Ch Bd: Art Church
**Pr:* Dale Harper

D-U-N-S 18-565-0447 IMP
MANCOR-PA INC
(*Suby of* MANCOR-SC INC) ★
160 Olin Way, Allentown, PA 18106-9370
Tel (610) 398-2300 *Founded/Ownrshp* 1987
Sales 50.0MM^E *EMP* 72
SIC 3714 Motor vehicle body components & frame; Motor vehicle body components & frame
Ch Bd: Art Church
**COO:* Dale Harper
Treas: Alan Tribe

D-U-N-S 11-513-6012
MANCOR-SC INC
(*Suby of* MANCOR CANADA INC)
397a Highway 601 S, Lugoff, SC 29078-8921
Tel (803) 438-2428 *Founded/Ownrshp* 1984
Sales 92.3MM^E *EMP* 232^E
SIC 8741 3713 3369 Management services; Truck & bus bodies; Nonferrous foundries; Management services; Truck & bus bodies; Nonferrous foundries
Pr: Art Church
**CFO:* Allen Tribe
IT Man: Leah Oliver

MANDA FINE MEATS
See MANDA PACKING CO LLC

D-U-N-S 00-817-1183
MANDA PACKING CO LLC
MANDA FINE MEATS
2445 Sorrel Ave, Baton Rouge, LA 70802-4252
Tel (225) 344-7636 *Founded/Ownrshp* 1947
Sales 45.5MM^E *EMP* 225
SIC 2013 Sausages & other prepared meats; Sausages & other prepared meats
CEO: Robert V Yarborough
VP: Steven Yarborough
VP: Tommy Yarborough

MANDALA
See OCEANSIDE GLASSTILE CO

MANDALAY BAY RESORT & CASINO
See MANDALAY CORP

MANDALAY BAY RESORT AND CASINO
See MANDALAY RESORT GROUP

D-U-N-S 03-196-9277
■ MANDALAY CORP
MANDALAY BAY RESORT & CASINO
(*Suby of* MANDALAY BAY RESORT AND CASINO) ★
3950 Las Vegas Blvd S, Las Vegas, NV 89119-1005
Tel (702) 798-6171 *Founded/Ownrshp* 1998
Sales 48.3MM^E *EMP* 400
SIC 7011 7999 7996 7991 5813 5812 Casino hotel; Gambling & lottery services; Gambling establishment; Gambling machines, operation; Theme park, amusement; Physical fitness facilities; Drinking places; Eating places; Casino hotel; Gambling & lottery services; Gambling establishment; Gambling machines, operation; Theme park, amusement; Physical fitness facilities; Drinking places; Eating places
Pr: Chuck Bowling
**Treas:* Daniel D'Arrigo
**Prin:* Glenn W Schaeffer
Prd Mgr: Don Alves
VP Sls: Bill Monson

D-U-N-S 06-778-3738
■ MANDALAY RESORT GROUP
MANDALAY BAY RESORT AND CASINO
(*Suby of* MGM RESORTS INTERNATIONAL) ★
3950 Las Vegas Blvd S, Las Vegas, NV 89119-1005
Tel (702) 632-7777 *Founded/Ownrshp* 2005
Sales 599.5MM^E *EMP* 28,000
SIC 7011 7999 7996 Casino hotel; Gambling & lottery services; Gambling establishment; Gambling machines, operation; Theme park, amusement; Casino hotel; Gambling & lottery services; Gambling establishment; Gambling machines, operation; Theme park, amusement
CEO: Michael S Ensign

*Pr: James J Murren
*Pr: Glenn Schaeffer
COO: Felix Rapapport
CFO: James Murren
*Treas: Daniel J D'Arrigo
Sr VP: Tony Alamo
Sr VP: Steve Greathouse
Sr VP: Gregg Solomon
VP: Danielle Babillino
*VP: Yvette Landau
*VP: Les Martin
VP: Bill Monson
VP: Michael Starr
Exec: Gerald Chin
Exec: Benjamin Jenkins
Comm Dir: Rey Bouknight

D-U-N-S 10-005-9864
MANDAN PUBLIC SCHOOL DISTRICT
901 Division St Nw, Mandan, ND 58554-1641
Tel (701) 751-6500 Founded/Ownrshp 1900
Sales 15.9MME EMP 300
Accts Rath & Mehrer Pc
SIC 8211 Public elementary & secondary schools; School board; Public elementary & secondary schools; School board
Prin: Tom Conlon
Prin: D R Furaus
Prin: Harlan Haak
Prin: Bob Kemisch
Prin: Bob Klemisch
Prin: Sharon Mosbrucker
Prin: Shirley Reed
Prin: Owen Stockdill

D-U-N-S 14-626-5488 IMP
MANDARIN ORIENTAL (NEWYORK) INC
(Suby of MANDARIN ORIENTAL INTERNATIONAL LIMITED)
80 Columbus Cir, New York, NY 10023-5800
Tel (212) 805-8800 Founded/Ownrshp 1999
Sales 25.2MME EMP 550
SIC 7011 Hotels & motels; Hotels & motels
Ch Bd: Richard Baker
*Ch Bd: Wolfgang K Hultner

MANDARIN ORIENTAL HOTEL NY
See COLUMBUS ISTITHMAR CENTRE LLC

D-U-N-S 83-303-2985
MANDARIN ORIENTAL LAS VEGAS LLC
(Suby of MANDARIN ORIENTAL HOTEL GROUP LIMITED)
2766 Auchmull St, Henderson, NV 89044-0214
Tel (702) 590-8888 Founded/Ownrshp 2008
Sales 22.0MME EMP 400
SIC 7011 Hotel or motel management; Hotels
CEO: Edouard Ettedgui
*CFO: Stuart Dickie
*Chf Mktg O: Michael Hobson

D-U-N-S 17-584-4166
MANDARIN ORIENTAL MANAGEMENT (USA) INC
(Suby of MANDARIN ORIENTAL INTERNATIONAL LIMITED)
345 California St # 1250, San Francisco, CA 94104-2622
Tel (415) 276-9602 Founded/Ownrshp 1987
Sales 48.4MME EMP 620
SIC 7011 Hotels & motels; Hotels; Resort hotel; Hotels & motels; Hotels; Resort hotel
CEO: Jan D Goessing
CFO: Stuart Dickie
Comm Dir: Veronica Choo
Comm Dir: Rebecca Hui

MANDARIN ORIENTAL MIAMI
See SWIRE BRICKELL KEY HOTEL LTD

MANDARINE ORIENTAL
See CITYCENTER BOUTIQUE HOTEL HOLDINGS LLC

MANDEE
See A & M (2015) LLC

D-U-N-S 06-746-5526 IMP/EXP
MANDEL METALS INC
AMERICAN AEROSPACE MATERIAL
11400 Addison Ave, Franklin Park, IL 60131-1124
Tel (847) 455-6606 Founded/Ownrshp 1968
Sales 52.1MME EMP 108
SIC 5051 3353 Aluminum bars, rods, ingots, sheets, pipes, plates, etc.; Aluminum sheet, plate & foil; Aluminum bars, rods, ingots, sheets, pipes, plates, etc.; Aluminum sheet, plate & foil
Pr: Richard Mandel
*COO: Steve Fallon
*Sec: Barbara Lindstrom
VP: Bob Izenstark
Sls Dir: Kevin Overberger
Sls Mgr: Daniel Martin

D-U-N-S 96-987-5918
MANDEL SUPPORTING FOUNDATIONS JACK N AND LILYAN MANDEL FUND
25701 Science Park Dr, Cleveland, OH 44122-7302
Tel (216) 593-2900 Founded/Ownrshp 2011
Sales 65.4MM EMP 3
Accts Ss&G Financial Services Inc
SIC 8641 Civic social & fraternal associations; Civic social & fraternal associations

MANDERBACH FORD
See GEORGE D MANDERBACH INC

D-U-N-S 00-979-1328
MANDERS DECORATING CO INC
9141 Brookville Rd, Silver Spring, MD 20910-1829
Tel (301) 589-7600 Founded/Ownrshp 1932
Sales 21.5MME EMP 217
SIC 1721 1742 Painting & paper hanging; Plastering, plain or ornamental; Painting & paper hanging; Plastering, plain or ornamental
Pr: William E Manders
CFO: John Agrusti
*CFO: Michael Valenti
*VP: Michael K Manders

D-U-N-S 14-546-3787
■ MANDIANT LLC
(Suby of FIREEYE INC) ★
2318 Mill Rd Ste 500, Alexandria, VA 22314-6877
Tel (703) 683-3141 Founded/Ownrshp 2013
Sales 44.7MME EMP 150
SIC 7379 Computer related consulting services; Computer related consulting services
Pr: Travis Reese
CFO: Mel Wesley
VP: Gregory Enriquez
VP: Jeff Scheel
VP: Grady Summers
VP: Stephen L Surdu
Exec: Yanek Korff
Mng Dir: Justin Bajko
Prgrm Mgr: David Cowart
Snr Sftwr: Alexis Ledoux
Snr Sftwr: Alex Mulfinger

D-U-N-S 14-626-3897
MANDLIK & RHODES INFORMATION SYSTEMS INC
223 Applebee St, Barrington, IL 60010-3036
Tel (224) 655-2959 Founded/Ownrshp 2004
Sales 22.4MME EMP 9
SIC 7389 7379 8748 Coupon redemption service; Computer related consulting services; Business consulting; Coupon redemption service; Computer related consulting services; Business consulting
Pr: Pradeep Mandlik
*VP: Kevin Rhodes

D-U-N-S 92-942-6104 IMP
MANDO AMERICA CORP
(Suby of MANDO CORPORATION)
4201 N Park Dr, Opelika, AL 36801-9667
Tel (334) 364-3600 Founded/Ownrshp 1996
Sales 953.5MM EMP 700
SIC 3999 3714 Automotive supplies & parts; Atomizers, toiletry; Air brakes, motor vehicle
Ch Bd: Chung In-Yung
Brnch Mgr: Michael Gaertner
Genl Mgr: Michael S Gaertner
IT Man: Jim Kell
Ql Cn Mgr: Debbie Anderson
Ql Cn Mgr: Kogeun Kim
Ql Cn Mgr: Carl Slavick
Sls Mgr: Cuk Lee
Sls Mgr: Bruce Zane

D-U-N-S 11-203-2151 IMP
MANDUJANO BROTHERS
4955 Watermelon Row, Coyanosa, TX 79730
Tel (432) 448-7731 Founded/Ownrshp 1997
Sales 22.8MME EMP 120
SIC 0161 0131 Watermelon farm; Cotton
Pt: Armando Mandujano
Pt: Tony Mandujano

D-U-N-S 08-001-9389
MANDUKA HOLDINGS LLC
2121 Park Pl Ste 250, El Segundo, CA 90245-4705
Tel (310) 146-1495 Founded/Ownrshp 2007
Sales 29.3MM EMP 64E
Accts Tanner Llc Salt Lake City Ut
SIC 6719 Investment holding companies, except banks
CEO: Sky Meltzer

MANE CALAFORNIA
See MANE INC

D-U-N-S 03-288-9151 IMP
MANE INC (OH)
MANE CALAFORNIA
(Suby of MANE USA INC) ★
2501 Henkle Dr, Lebanon, OH 45036-7794
Tel (513) 248-9876 Founded/Ownrshp 1998
Sales 85.2MME EMP 340
SIC 2087 2099 Flavoring extracts & syrups; Food preparations; Flavoring extracts & syrups; Food preparations
Ch Bd: Jean Mane
*Pr: Ken Hunter
Sec: Stacie Bennison
Sr VP: J D Vora
VP: Joanne Ferrara
VP: Samantha Forgham
VP: David Haase
VP: Deborah Knighton
VP: Robert Motta
VP: Michael Walsh
CTO: James Abel

D-U-N-S 04-768-5581 IMP
MANE USA INC
(Suby of V MANE FILS)
60 Demarest Dr, Wayne, NJ 07470-6702
Tel (973) 633-5533 Founded/Ownrshp 1956
Sales 128.0MME EMP 526
SIC 2869 Perfumes, flavorings & food additives; Perfumes, flavorings & food additives
Pr: Michel Mane
CFO: Taphiana Remick
Sr VP: Robert Macdonald
VP: Anthony Cannone
VP: Wendy Diamond
VP: Frank Lucia
VP: Mohan Pradhan
VP: Virgil Williams
VP Opers: Larry Deraney
Sfty Mgr: Clay Persaud
VP Sls: Brad Ament

D-U-N-S 00-310-2563
MANEKIN LLC (DE)
8601 Robert Fulton Dr # 100, Columbia, MD 21046-2561
Tel (410) 290-1400 Founded/Ownrshp 1945, 1999
Sales 32.9MME EMP 150
SIC 6531 1542 6552 Real estate brokers & agents; Real estate managers; Commercial & office building, new construction; Land subdividers & developers, commercial
CEO: Richard Alter
*COO: Lou Lapenna
COO: Linda Lewis
CFO: Ed Kouneski
Treas: Didier Wojs
Ex VP: Alton Fryer
Sr VP: Sharon Caplan
Sr VP: Sior Fields
*Sr VP: Owen Rouse
*Sr VP: Cole Schnorf
Sr VP: Suzanne Warren
VP: Barbara Alden
VP: Richard Fields
VP: George Santos
VP: Dan Sharpe

D-U-N-S 03-358-1174
MANER BUILDERS SUPPLY CO LLC
3787 Martinez Blvd, Martinez, GA 30907-2665
Tel (706) 863-0558 Founded/Ownrshp 1998
Sales 55.0MM EMP 150
Accts Cherry Bekaert Llp Augusta G
SIC 5031 5211 Building materials, exterior; Building materials, interior; Lumber & other building materials; Building materials, exterior; Building materials, interior; Lumber & other building materials
Pr: James C Broome
CFO: F Frank Chandler
Treas: Bertram D Harbin Jr
VP: Robert E McCrary III
VP: William A Wren
Rgnl Mgr: Denise Adams
Genl Mgr: Barry Patterson
Sls Mgr: Terry Hyatt

D-U-N-S 05-627-2594
MANFREDI MOTORS INC
STATEN ISLAND TOYOTA SALES
1590 Hylan Blvd, Staten Island, NY 10305-1926
Tel (718) 979-0033 Founded/Ownrshp 1987
Sales 48.5MME EMP 130E
SIC 5511 7515 Automobiles, new & used; Passenger car leasing; Automobiles, new & used; Passenger car leasing
Pr: Corrado Manfredi
Sls Mgr: Miguel Rodriguez

D-U-N-S 04-199-4773 IMP
MANFROTTO DISTRIBUTION INC
(Suby of THE VITEC GROUP PLC.)
10 Montinview Rd Ste S320, Upper Saddle River, NJ 07458
Tel (201) 818-9500 Founded/Ownrshp 1993
Sales 32.6MME EMP 69
SIC 5043 Photographic equipment & supplies
Pr: Paul Wilde
*CFO: Stefan Romaniuk
Comm Man: Larry White
Mng Dir: Bill Drysdale
Off Admin: Bernadette Peterson
MIS Dir: William Grieco
IT Man: Carlo Cuman
Web Prj Mg: Holly Montalbano
Netwrk Mgr: Valentina Manfrotto
Opers Mgr: Stuart Ashton
Ql Cn Mgr: Paul Morley

D-U-N-S 78-437-7707
MANGAN INC
3901 Via Oro Ave, Long Beach, CA 90810-1800
Tel (310) 835-8080 Founded/Ownrshp 1991
Sales 63.9MME EMP 180
SIC 8711 Engineering services; Engineering services
Pr: Richard Mangan
*CEO: Amin Solehjou
*CFO: Russell Seward
Mng Dir: Leon Juckett
MIS Dir: Steve Kladouris
Software D: Henry Rodriguez
Sftwr Eng: Eric Evans
Opers Mgr: Angela Fusco
Opers Mgr: Dennis Hockenbury
Snr PM: Jeffrey E Norman

D-U-N-S 61-176-2733
MANGANARO INDUSTRIES INC
52 Cummings Park, Woburn, MA 01801-2123
Tel (781) 937-8880 Founded/Ownrshp 1982
Sales 34.5MME EMP 1,000
SIC 1742 1741 1799 1743 Drywall; Acoustical & ceiling work; Masonry & other stonework; Fireproofing buildings; Tile installation, ceramic; Drywall; Acoustical & ceiling work; Masonry & other stonework; Fireproofing buildings; Tile installation, ceramic
*Treas: David Manganaro

D-U-N-S 19-149-8943
MANGANARO MIDATLANTIC LLC
6405d Ammendale Rd, Beltsville, MD 20705-1203
Tel (301) 937-0580 Founded/Ownrshp 2003
Sales 112.4MME EMP 600
SIC 1741 1742 1799 Masonry & other stonework; Masonry & other stonework; Acoustical & ceiling work; Waterproofing
Pr: Tom Vagrin
Sfty Mgr: Mike Dihmes
Snr PM: Rich Barrett
Snr PM: Patrick Glomb

D-U-N-S 00-253-4058 IMP
MANGAR INDUSTRIES INC (PA)
MANGAR MEDICAL PACKAGING
97 Britain Dr, New Britain, PA 18901-5193
Tel (215) 230-0133 Founded/Ownrshp 1986
Sales 125.9MME EMP 225
Accts Spear Coyne & Company Ltd Do
SIC 2671 Packaging paper & plastics film, coated & laminated; Packaging paper & plastics film, coated & laminated
Pr: Donald A Coleman
CFO: Ann Buckley
*Treas: James Magarity
Genl Mgr: Jim Cimbalista
Off Mgr: Janet West
QA Dir: Matt Chao
QA Dir: Mary Fleming
QA Dir: David Wrigley
IT Man: Rob Gibbs
IT Man: Shawn Woods
Mfg Mgr: Duc Nguyen

D-U-N-S 14-841-3024 IMP
MANGAR MEDICAL INC
97 Britain Dr, New Britain, PA 18901-5186
Tel (215) 230-0300 Founded/Ownrshp 1980
Sales 28.1MME EMP 200
SIC 3841 2671 Surgical & medical instruments; Packaging paper & plastics film, coated & laminated; Surgical & medical instruments; Packaging paper & plastics film, coated & laminated
CEO: Don Coleman
*Ch Bd: John Coleman
*Sec: Donald K Hanson
Chf Mktg O: Harry Shaw
*Prin: Douglas Coleman

MANGAR MEDICAL PACKAGING
See MANGAR INDUSTRIES INC

MANGEL & CO
See GROVE LONG CONFECTIONERY CO

MANGELSDORF SEED CO
See SIEMER ENTERPRISES INC

D-U-N-S 17-225-4083
MANGEN GROUP INC
6099 Seabluff Dr, Playa Vista, CA 90094-2251
Tel (310) 417-8225 Founded/Ownrshp 2004
Sales 9.6MME EMP 350E
SIC 5812 Fast-food restaurant, chain; Fast-food restaurant, chain
Pr: Howard Mangen

D-U-N-S 18-658-1716
MANGINO HOLDING CORP
299 Market St Ste 300, Saddle Brook, NJ 07663-5312
Tel (973) 742-3000 Founded/Ownrshp 1987
Sales 61.3MME EMP 500
SIC 4213 7513 4731 Contract haulers; Truck rental & leasing, no drivers; Truck transportation brokers; Contract haulers; Truck rental & leasing, no drivers; Truck transportation brokers
Ch Bd: Joseph Mangino Jr

D-U-N-S 94-294-6112
MANGIONE ENTERPRISES OF TURF VALLEY LIMITED PARTNERSHIP
2700 Turf Valley Rd Ste A, Ellicott City, MD 21042-2047
Tel (410) 465-1500 Founded/Ownrshp 1978
Sales 9.2MME EMP 400
SIC 7997 7011 7299 Country club, membership; Golf club, membership; Swimming club, membership; Tennis club, membership; Hotels; Banquet hall facilities; Country club, membership; Golf club, membership; Swimming club, membership; Tennis club, membership; Hotels; Banquet hall facilities
Pr: Pete Mangione

D-U-N-S 78-686-7262 IMP
MANGROVE EQUITY PARTNERS
101 S Franklin St, Tampa, FL 33602-5312
Tel (813) 868-4500 Founded/Ownrshp 2006
Sales 38.9MME EMP 500
SIC 3479 Coating, rust preventive; Coating, rust preventive
Mng Dir: Glenn Oken
*Pt: Barry Korthuis
*Mng Dir: Matt Young

D-U-N-S 04-145-4273
MANGUM OIL AND GAS CO
MORTON COMPANIES
(Suby of ICAN ENERGY CO)
4200 Stone Rd, Kilgore, TX 75662-6935
Tel (903) 983-6200 Founded/Ownrshp 1986
Sales 34.1MME EMP 74
SIC 5171 4212 5541 5984 Petroleum bulk stations; Petroleum haulage, local; Filling stations, gasoline; Propane gas, bottled; Petroleum bulk stations; Petroleum haulage, local; Filling stations, gasoline; Propane gas, bottled
Pr: Caroll W Brooks
*Treas: Wes Skelton
*VP: R S Martin III
*VP: Don Neumeyr

D-U-N-S 09-407-5947
MANHARD CONSULTING LTD
ACCURATE-MANHARD
900 Woodlands Pkwy, Vernon Hills, IL 60061-3103
Tel (847) 634-5550 Founded/Ownrshp 1992
Sales 44.4MME EMP 145
SIC 8748 8712 Systems analysis & engineering consulting services; Architectural services; Systems analysis & engineering consulting services; Architectural services
Pr: Donald E Manhard Jr
COO: Steve Winnike
CFO: Tom Sherman
VP: James Frayn
VP: William Hupperich
*VP: Peter E Manhard
VP: Tracy Richard
VP: P E Winnike
Area Mgr: John Winn
Plng Mgr: Christopher Baker
Dir IT: Donald Willemarck

MANHASSET PUBLIC SCHOOLS
See MANHASSET UNION FREE SCHOOL DISTRICT

D-U-N-S 04-905-5031
MANHASSET UNION FREE SCHOOL DISTRICT
MANHASSET PUBLIC SCHOOLS
200 Memorial Pl, Manhasset, NY 11030-2320
Tel (516) 627-8000 Founded/Ownrshp 1978
Sales 32.6MME EMP 600
SIC 8211 Public elementary school; Public junior high school; Public senior high school; Public elementary school; Public junior high school; Public senior high school

D-U-N-S 82-871-3805
MANHATTAN AND BRONX SURFACE TRANSIT OPERATING AUTHORITY
PUBLIC TRANSPORTATION
(*Suby of* NEW YORK CITY TRANSIT AUTHORITY) ★
2 Broadway, New York, NY 10004-2207
Tel (718) 694-1000 *Founded/Ownrshp* 2008
Sales 1.1MMM *EMP* 5,021ᴱ
SIC 4111 Local & suburban transit; Local & suburban transit
Prin: Walter Weinert

D-U-N-S 78-548-4387
▲ MANHATTAN ASSOCIATES INC
2300 Windy Ridge Pkwy Se 1000n, Atlanta, GA 30339-5675
Tel (770) 955-7070 *Founded/Ownrshp* 1990
Sales 492.1MM *EMP* 2,770
Accts Ernst & Young Llp Atlanta Ge
Tkr Sym MANH *Exch* NGS
SIC 7373 7372 5045 Computer integrated systems design; Systems software development services; Prepackaged software; Computers, peripherals & software; Computer peripheral equipment; Printers, computer; Computers; Computer integrated systems design; Systems software development services; Prepackaged software; Computers, peripherals & software; Computer peripheral equipment; Printers, computer; Computers
Pr: Eddie Capel
COO: Yogesh Bhardwaj
CFO: Terry Gillis
CFO: Dennis B Story
Ex VP: Jeffrey B Cashman
Sr VP: Terry Geraghty
Sr VP: Steve Smith
Exec: Sanjay Suri
Dir Bus: Jason Benner
CIO: Michael Barrett
CTO: Kim Ross
Board of Directors: Brian J Cassidy, Ed Eger, John J Huntz Jr, Dan J Lautenbach, Thomas E Noonan, Peter F Sinisgalli

D-U-N-S 60-807-4845
MANHATTAN BAGEL CO INC
(*Suby of* EINSTEIN NOAH RESTAURANT GROUP INC) ★
555 Zang St Ste 300, Lakewood, CO 80228-1013
Tel (303) 568-8000 *Founded/Ownrshp* 1998
Sales 30.1MMᴱ *EMP* 326
SIC 5461 Bagels; Bagels
CFO: Richard Dutkiewicz
**Sec:* Jill Sisson
**Sr VP:* Paul Caroline
**Sr VP:* Geraldo Donatiello
**VP:* David Ammons
**VP:* Kevin Kruse

D-U-N-S 80-901-2003
■ MANHATTAN BANCORP
(*Suby of* CARPENTER FUND MANAGER GP LLC) ★
2141 Rosecrans Ave # 1100, El Segundo, CA 90245-4747
Tel (310) 606-8000 *Founded/Ownrshp* 2007
Sales NA *EMP* 187
Accts Mcgladrey Llp Los Angeles Ca
Tkr Sym MNHN *Exch* OTO
SIC 6021 National commercial banks; National commercial banks
CEO: Terry L Robinson
**Ch Bd:* J Grant Couch Jr
Pr: John A Nerland
CFO: Curt A Christianssen
Chf Cred: Shannon Millard
Ex VP: Richard L Sowers
Board of Directors: Chris W Caras Jr, Harry W Chenoweth, John D Flemming, James B Jones, Louis P Smaldino, Gary C Wallance, Stephen P Yost, Michael A Zoeller

D-U-N-S 19-260-2183
MANHATTAN BANKING CORP
KANSAS STATE BANK
1010 Westloop Pl, Manhattan, KS 66502-2836
Tel (785) 537-4400 *Founded/Ownrshp* 1986
Sales NA *EMP* 112
SIC 6022 State commercial banks; State commercial banks
CEO: Phil Howe
**Pr:* Mike Daniels
Ex VP: Steve Burr
Sr VP: Thad Hall
**VP:* Carolyn Gordon
VP: Marsha Jarvis
VP: Milt Karavites
VP: Deborah Townsend
Mktg Mgr: Jenny Pauls

D-U-N-S 01-266-1138
MANHATTAN BEACH CITY SCHOOL DISTRICT
MBUSD
325 S Peck Ave, Manhattan Beach, CA 90266-6946
Tel (310) 318-7345 *Founded/Ownrshp* 1913
Sales 53.3MMᴱ *EMP* 610
Accts Moss Levy & Hartzhelm Llp B
SIC 8211 Public elementary & secondary schools; Public elementary & secondary schools
Prin: Vanderpoorte
**VP:* Karen Komatinsky
IT Man: Norma Brunkhardt
Teacher Pr: Carolyn Seaton
Psych: Emily Allen
HC Dir: Megan Atkins

D-U-N-S 09-400-6814 IMP
MANHATTAN BEACHWEAR INC
10700 Valley View St, Cypress, CA 90630-4835
Tel (714) 892-7354 *Founded/Ownrshp* 2011
Sales 229.8MMᴱ *EMP* 400
SIC 2339 Bathing suits: women's, misses' & juniors'; Beachwear: women's, misses' & juniors'; Athletic clothing: women's, misses' & juniors'; Sportswear, women's; Bathing suits: women's, misses' & juniors'; Beachwear: women's, misses' & juniors'; Athletic clothing: women's, misses' & juniors'; Sportswear, women's
CEO: Allan Colvin
Pr: Brenda West
CFO: Michael Conway
Exec: Bonnie Wilks
Dir IT: Derrick Andrews
Netwrk Mgr: Jennifer Moh
VP Merchng: Howie Greller
VP Sls: Ron Russell
Merch Mgr: Doreen Brennan

D-U-N-S 14-718-3602 IMP
MANHATTAN BEACHWEAR LLC
6600 Katella Ave, Cypress, CA 90630-5104
Tel (714) 892-7354 *Founded/Ownrshp* 2005
Sales NA *EMP* 400
SIC 2339

D-U-N-S 09-297-2231 IMP
MANHATTAN BEER DISTRIBUTORS LLC
955 E 149th St, Bronx, NY 10455-5021
Tel (718) 292-9300 *Founded/Ownrshp* 1970
Sales 736.2MMᴱ *EMP* 1,400
SIC 5181 Beer & ale; Beer & ale
Plnt Mgr: Simon Bergson
COO: Bill Bessette
COO: John Vacanti
CFO: George Wertheimer
Sr VP: Bill Deluca
VP: Al Greco
VP: Rob Mitchell
VP: Damian Rippon
VP: Sal Rossi
Dir Bus: Ender Berrios
Dir IT: Ziad Eljamal

D-U-N-S 17-821-9903
MANHATTAN BUSINESS INTERIORS INC
M B I
48 W 37th St Fl 9, New York, NY 10018-7318
Tel (212) 376-4400 *Founded/Ownrshp* 1987
Sales 45.1MMᴱ *EMP* 96
Accts Raich Ende Malter Co Llp New
SIC 1542 Commercial & office buildings, renovation & repair; Commercial & office buildings, renovation & repair
Pr: Edward S Campanella
CFO: Klaus Kessler
Ex VP: Joseph Vicari
**Sr VP:* Christopher Smith
VP: Daniel Blackall
**VP:* Jason Chen
**VP:* Jean Greenlaw
VP: Kenneth Hass
**VP:* Vincent Manciamelli
**VP:* John Prendergast
VP: Morton Yang
Dir Bus: Theodore Hiotis
Dir Bus: Tamara D Perez

D-U-N-S 03-613-2454
MANHATTAN CAPITAL CORP (CA)
2641 River Ave, Rosemead, CA 91770-3301
Tel (626) 288-8530 *Founded/Ownrshp* 1952
Sales 65.3MMᴱ *EMP* 600
SIC 1623 6411 Oil & gas pipeline construction; Insurance agents, brokers & service; Oil & gas pipeline construction; Insurance agents, brokers & service
Ch Bd: Gregory Warde

D-U-N-S 07-104-0810
MANHATTAN COLLEGE CORP
4513 Mnhttan College Pkwy, Bronx, NY 10471-4004
Tel (718) 862-8000 *Founded/Ownrshp* 1853
Sales 135.6MMᴱ *EMP* 496ᴱ
SIC 8221 University; University
**Pr:* Brennan O'Donnell PHD
**CFO:* Matthew S McManness
Treas: Caitlin Applegate
Ex VP: William C Clyde
VP: William J Bisset Jr
VP: Jack Curran
VP: Andrew Ryan
Dir: Stephen White
Comm Man: Lydia Gray
Ex Dir: Harry Welsh
Off Mgr: Grace Cabrera
Board of Directors: John Lawler, Valentine A Lehr

D-U-N-S 04-546-1498
MANHATTAN CONSTRUCTION (FLORIDA) INC
MANHATTAN CONSTRUCTION COMPANY
(*Suby of* MANHATTAN CONSTRUCTION GROUP INC) ★
3705 Westview Dr Ste 1, Naples, FL 34104-4033
Tel (239) 643-6000 *Founded/Ownrshp* 2009
Sales 169.8MMᴱ *EMP* 500
SIC 1542 8712 1531 1521 8741 Commercial & office building, new construction; Architectural services; Operative builders; Single-family housing construction; Construction management; Commercial & office building, new construction; Architectural services; Operative builders; Single-family housing construction; Construction management
Pr: Robert Koenig
**Ch Bd:* Robert Carsello
**Pr:* Fred Pezeshkan
**Treas:* Jim Lawson
**Ex VP:* Thomas Williams
**Sr VP:* Thomas Abraham
**VP:* Bill Dean
VP: Bruce Fields
VP: Gordon Knapp
Exec: Paul Wharen
Mng Dir: Ray Atkinson

MANHATTAN CONSTRUCTION COMPANY
See MANHATTAN CONSTRUCTION (FLORIDA) INC

D-U-N-S 05-395-9755 IMP
MANHATTAN CONSTRUCTION CO
(*Suby of* ROONEY HOLDINGS INC) ★
5601 S 122nd East Ave, Tulsa, OK 74146-6912
Tel (918) 583-6900 *Founded/Ownrshp* 1984
Sales 574.0MMᴱ *EMP* 1,100
SIC 1542 Institutional building construction; Institutional building construction
Pr: John Reyhan
V Ch: Patrick Fogarty
COO: George Kolczun
**CFO:* Kevin Moore
CFO: Kevin P Moore
**Treas:* Jim Lawson
**Ex VP:* Robert Bowen
Ex VP: Frank Fralick
**Ex VP:* Bob Vecera
VP: Pat Cartwright
VP: Tom Kramer
VP: George Kreis
VP: Michael Lauder
VP: Bob Postma
Exec: Jon Clark
Exec: H Frost
Exec: Bob Jack
Dir Bus: B J Brundage
Dir Bus: David Hale
Comm Man: Brent Dostal

D-U-N-S 83-163-0673
MANHATTAN CONSTRUCTION GROUP INC
(*Suby of* ROONEY HOLDINGS INC) ★
5601 S 122nd East Ave, Tulsa, OK 74146-6912
Tel (918) 878-3341 *Founded/Ownrshp* 2009
Sales 169.8MMᴱ *EMP* 524
SIC 1542 Nonresidential construction; Nonresidential construction
Pr: Kevin Moore
Ex VP: Elmon Henry
Sfty Mgr: Julie Lovelace
Snr PM: Brian Travis

D-U-N-S 06-499-3389
MANHATTAN EYE EAR & THROAT HOSPITAL
(*Suby of* LENOX HILL HOSPITAL) ★
210 E 64th St, New York, NY 10065-7471
Tel (212) 702-7400 *Founded/Ownrshp* 1916
Sales 26.8MMᴱ *EMP* 350
SIC 8069 Eye, ear, nose & throat hospital; Eye, ear, nose & throat hospital
Ex Dir: Phillip Rosenthal

D-U-N-S 00-170-9310
MANHATTAN FORD LINCOLN INC
1 International Blvd # 1100, Mahwah, NJ 07495-0028
Tel (212) 549-2200 *Founded/Ownrshp* 1960
Sales 68.8MMᴱ *EMP* 195
SIC 5511 7538 5531 7514 Automobiles, new & used; Pickups, new & used; Trucks, tractors & trailers: new & used; Vans, new & used; General automotive repair shops; Automobile & truck equipment & parts; Passenger car rental; Automobiles, new & used; Pickups, new & used; Trucks, tractors & trailers: new & used; Vans, new & used; General automotive repair shops; Automobile & truck equipment & parts; Passenger car rental
Pr: Gary B Flom
**Sec:* Pam Allen

D-U-N-S 11-439-6468
MANHATTAN IMPORTED CARS INC
MANHATTAN LNCOLN MRCURY JAGUAR
11617 Old Georgetown Rd, Rockville, MD 20852-2797
Tel (301) 881-0912 *Founded/Ownrshp* 1969
Sales 46.5MMᴱ *EMP* 160
SIC 5511 Automobiles, new & used; Automobiles, new & used
Pr: Joseph Herson
Top Exec: Jerry Jaffe
CIO: Terry Dwyer
Sales Asso: Sean Williams

D-U-N-S 06-120-8450
MANHATTAN JEEP CHRYSLER DODGE INC (DE)
678 11th Ave, New York, NY 10019-7047
Tel (212) 765-6633 *Founded/Ownrshp* 1972, 1988
Sales 22.6MMᴱ *EMP* 65
SIC 5511 7538 Automobiles, new & used; General automotive repair shops; Automobiles, new & used; General automotive repair shops
Pr: John R Monninger
Sales Asso: Leif Johansson
Sales Asso: Homer Wright

D-U-N-S 00-698-7242
MANHATTAN LIFE INSURANCE CO
(*Suby of* MANHATTAN LIFE INSURANCE CO) ★
10777 Northwest Fwy # 100, Houston, TX 77092-7336
Tel (713) 529-0045 *Founded/Ownrshp* 2000
Sales NA *EMP* 115ᴱ
SIC 6311 Life insurance; Life insurance
CEO: David Harris
**Pr:* Daniel George
**CFO:* Kent Lamb
**VP:* Mary Rainey

D-U-N-S 11-048-0113
MANHATTAN LIFE INSURANCE CO
10777 Northwest Fwy # 100, Houston, TX 77092-7336
Tel (713) 529-0045 *Founded/Ownrshp* 1998
Sales NA *EMP* 200
SIC 6411 Advisory services, insurance; Advisory services, insurance
CEO: David Harris
**Pr:* Daniel George
**CFO:* Kent Lamb
Chf Mktg O: Todd Hayden
VP: Ann Blakey
VP: Jeffrey Gorton
VP: Teresa Moro
VP: David Parsons
S&M/VP: Jim Brown
Mktg Dir: John Penko
Mktg Dir: Alan Vala

D-U-N-S 11-287-2788
MANHATTAN LIFE INSURANCE CO
(*Suby of* MANHATTAN LIFE INSURANCE CO) ★
10777 Northwest Fwy # 100, Houston, TX 77092-7336
Tel (800) 669-9030 *Founded/Ownrshp* 2001
Sales NA *EMP* 1ᴱ
SIC 6311 Life insurance carriers
CEO: David Harris

MANHATTAN LNCOLN MRCURY JAGUAR
See MANHATTAN IMPORTED CARS INC

D-U-N-S 82-650-1058
MANHATTAN LUXURY AUTOMOBILES INC
LEXUS OF MANHATTAN
662 11th Ave, New York, NY 10036-2006
Tel (212) 977-4400 *Founded/Ownrshp* 1994
Sales 28.4MMᴱ *EMP* 80
SIC 5511 Automobiles, new & used; Automobiles, new & used
Pr: Carmelo Giuffre
CFO: Rich Velija
**VP:* John Iacono
Genl Mgr: Greg Rojek
Sls Mgr: Stephen Johnson
Sls Mgr: Jon Popper
Sales Asso: Jon Bloch
Sales Asso: Warren Newland

MANHATTAN MERCURY
See SEATON PUBLISHING CO INC

D-U-N-S 93-222-3225 IMP
MANHATTAN MOTORCARS INC
PORCHE OF MANHATTAN
270 11th Ave, New York, NY 10001-1215
Tel (212) 594-0937 *Founded/Ownrshp* 1996
Sales 27.2MMᴱ *EMP* 60
SIC 5511 New & used car dealers; New & used car dealers
Pr: Brian Miller
**VP:* John Kaufman
Off Mgr: Christine Ruggieri
Sls Mgr: Jeff Drajin
Sls Mgr: Lee McHugh
Sales Asso: Jaclyn Johnston

MANHATTAN PARKING GROUP
See MANHATTAN PARKING SYSTEMS GARAGE CORP

D-U-N-S 80-688-7311
MANHATTAN PARKING SYSTEMS GARAGE CORP
MANHATTAN PARKING GROUP
545 5th Ave Rm 600, New York, NY 10017-3644
Tel (212) 490-3460 *Founded/Ownrshp* 2000
Sales 12.5MMᴱ *EMP* 300
SIC 7521 Parking garage; Parking garage
Pr: Lawrence R Lipman
Ex VP: Greg Gonzalez
**VP:* Donna Lipman
Sls Mgr: Betty Martinez

D-U-N-S 60-352-1126
MANHATTAN PRIVATE MIDDLESCHOOL LEAGUE
BUCKLEY SCHOOL
113 E 73rd St, New York, NY 10021-3536
Tel (212) 535-8787 *Founded/Ownrshp* 2006
Sales 28.3MM *EMP* 90
SIC 8211 Private elementary & secondary schools; Private elementary & secondary schools
Pr: Pedro Morales
CFO: Tom Stanton
Treas: Per Von Scheele
HC Dir: Jo Lynch

D-U-N-S 15-135-0378
MANHATTAN PSYCHIATRIC CENTER
1 Wards Is Ofc 2, New York, NY 10035-6011
Tel (646) 672-6767 *Founded/Ownrshp* 1896
Sales 40.1MMᴱ *EMP* 1,400
SIC 8063 Psychiatric hospitals; Psychiatric hospitals
Ex Dir: Eileen Consilvio
**Ex Dir:* Steve Rebinowitz
Ex Dir: Yvette Wilson
CIO: Jeff Fox

D-U-N-S 09-826-3486
MANHATTAN RETIREMENT FOUNDATION INC
MEADOWLARK HILLS
2121 Meadowlark Rd, Manhattan, KS 66502-4521
Tel (785) 537-4610 *Founded/Ownrshp* 1979
Sales 21.9MM *EMP* 300
Accts Cliftonlarsonallen Llp St Lo
SIC 8051 Skilled nursing care facilities; Skilled nursing care facilities
COO: Lonnie Baker
Bd of Dir: Brenda Hoefler
VP: Clay Bowman
VP: Robert Dickson
Dir IT: Darin Pelfrey
Mktg Dir: Sarah Guge
Sales Asso: Becky Fitzgerald
Nrsg Dir: Pam Hastings
Nrsg Dir: Alana Johnston
Pgrm Dir: Michelle Haub
Snr Mgr: Jacqueline Brown

D-U-N-S 04-255-4782
MANHATTAN ROAD & BRIDGE CO
(*Suby of* ROONEY HOLDINGS INC) ★
5601 S 122nd East Ave, Tulsa, OK 74146-6912
Tel (918) 583-6900 *Founded/Ownrshp* 1956
Sales 117.4MMᴱ *EMP* 350ᴱ
SIC 1622 Bridge construction; Bridge construction
Pr: Mike Webb
**Ex VP:* Todd Saxton
VP: Kevin Petray
VP: Mark Windle
**Prin:* Kendall Adams
**Prin:* Bobby J Lee
**Prin:* Jack J Lee
Dir IT: Nick Hopper
IT Man: Robert Rains
Sfty Dirs: Nick Taylor
Mtls Mgr: Curt Smith

D-U-N-S 07-861-3684
MANHATTAN SCHOOL OF MUSIC INC
MICHAEL
120 Claremont Ave, New York, NY 10027-4698
Tel (212) 749-2802 *Founded/Ownrshp* 1917
Sales 45.2MM *EMP* 450
Accts Kpmg Llp New York Ny
SIC 8299 8221 Music school; Colleges universities & professional schools; Music school; Colleges universities & professional schools
Ch Bd: Peter Robbins
**Pr:* Robert Sirota
CFO: James Gandre
CFO: Joanne Mandry
**Ex VP:* Paul Kelleher
VP: Andrea Galan
Adm Dir: Elizabeth Young

D-U-N-S 13-191-1778
MANHATTAN SKYLINE MANAGEMENT CORP
103 W 55th St 2, New York, NY 10019-5306
Tel (212) 977-4813 *Founded/Ownrshp* 1984
Sales 20.8MM^E *EMP* 220
SIC 6531 Real estate managers; Real estate managers
Ch Bd: Donald Zucker

D-U-N-S 96-686-8556 IMP
MANHATTAN TELECOMMUNICATIONS CORP
METTEL
55 Water St Fl 32, New York, NY 10041-3299
Tel (212) 607-2000 *Founded/Ownrshp* 1996
Sales 70.0MM^E *EMP* 175
SIC 4813 Local telephone communications; Local telephone communications
CEO: Marshall Aronow
**Pr:* David Aronow
**COO:* Andoni Economou
Sr VP: Joe Held
VP: Edward J Fox III
VP: Edward Fox
VP: Ted Salame
VP: Lori Thomas
Genl Mgr: Christina Dovi
Snr Ntwrk: Dennis Migardos
CIO: Alex Citkin

D-U-N-S 07-328-2378
MANHATTAN THEATRE CLUB INC
311 W 43rd St Fl 9, New York, NY 10036-6446
Tel (212) 399-3000 *Founded/Ownrshp* 1970
Sales 25.8MM *EMP* 90
Accts Mbaf Cpas Llc New York Ny
SIC 7922 Theatrical producers & services; Theatrical producers & services
Ch Bd: David Hodgson
**Ch:* Peter J Solomon
Treas: David Dillon
**Treas:* Stephen Wilson
IT Man: Mendy Sudranski
Prd Mgr: Josh Helman

D-U-N-S 07-983-9980
MANHATTAN-OGDEN UNIFIED SCHOOL DISTRICT 383
2031 Poyntz Ave, Manhattan, KS 66502-3868
Tel (785) 587-2000 *Founded/Ownrshp* 2015
Sales 13.3MM^E *EMP* 716^E
SIC 8211 Public elementary & secondary schools
Pr Dir: Michele Jones
Teacher Pr: Larry Doll
Instr Medi: Lucas Loughmiller

MANHATTAN'S PHYSICIAN GROUP
See LHHN MEDICAL PC

D-U-N-S 07-543-3086
MANHATTANVILLE COLLEGE
2900 Purchase St, Purchase, NY 10577-2132
Tel (914) 694-2200 *Founded/Ownrshp* 1841
Sales 63.5MM *EMP* 420^E
Accts Grant Thornton Llp New York
SIC 8221 College, except junior; College, except junior
Pr: Jon Strauss
**COO:* Art Berke
VP: Jose Gonzalez
VP: Gail Simmons
VP: Marina Vasarhelyi
VP: Barry Ward
Assoc Dir: Barbara Shulman
Dir: Nancy Kingston
Off Mgr: Barbara Altizio
VP Opers: J G Palmer
Psych: Brenda Boatswain

D-U-N-S 08-673-2179 EXP
■ **MANHEIM AUCTIONS GOVERNMENT SERVICES LLC**
(*Suby of* MANHEIM INVESTMENTS INC) ★
6205 Pachtree Dunwoody Rd, Atlanta, GA 30328-4524
Tel (404) 843-5000 *Founded/Ownrshp* 1993
Sales 1,000.0M *EMP* 700
SIC 5012 Automobile auction; Automobile auction
COO: Darryl Ceccoli
CFO: Jo Lupino
**Treas:* Robert E Gartin
Mktg Mgr: Marya Sabesky

MANHEIM AUTO AUCTION
See MANHEIMS GREATER PENSACOLA AUTO AUCTION INC

D-U-N-S 09-873-3678
MANHEIM CENTRAL SCHOOL DISTRICT
71 N Hazel St, Manheim, PA 17545-1511
Tel (717) 665-3422 *Founded/Ownrshp* 1840
Sales 47.4M *EMP* 380
SIC 8211 Public elementary school; Public junior high school; Public senior high school; School board; Public elementary school; Public junior high school; Public senior high school; School board
CFO: George W Ioannidis
Bd of Dir: Kimberly Garner
VP: Seth Kensinger
Cmptr Lab: Steve Waddington
Schl Brd P: Ken Kowalski
Teacher Pr: Carolyn Duda

D-U-N-S 36-117-9323
■ **MANHEIM CORPORATE SERVICES INC**
(*Suby of* COX AUTOMOTIVE INC) ★
6325 Pachtree Dunwoody Rd, Atlanta, GA 30328-4545
Tel (678) 645-2067 *Founded/Ownrshp* 2000
Sales 21.5MM^E *EMP* 38^E
SIC 5012 Automobiles & other motor vehicles
Pr: Dean H Eisner

MANHEIM FREDERICKSBURG
See FREDERICKSBURG AUTO AUCTION INC

D-U-N-S 16-169-7347 EXP
■ **MANHEIM INVESTMENTS INC**
(*Suby of* COX AUTOMOTIVE INC) ★
6205 Pachtree Dunwoody Rd, Atlanta, GA 30328-4524
Tel (678) 645-0000 *Founded/Ownrshp* 1991
Sales 1.1MMM^E *EMP* 20,000
SIC 5012 Automobile auction; Automobile auction
CEO: Sanford H Schwartz
**Pr:* Dennis Berry
**Treas:* Robert E Gartin

MANHEIM KANSAS CITY
See AUTO AUCTIONS INC

MANHEIM PITTSBURGH
See MANHEIM REMARKETING INC

D-U-N-S 02-145-0549 EXP
■ **MANHEIM REMARKETING INC**
MANHEIM PITTSBURGH
(*Suby of* MANHEIM INVESTMENTS INC) ★
21095 Route 19, Cranberry Township, PA 16066-5907
Tel (724) 452-5555 *Founded/Ownrshp* 1968
Sales 221.8MM^E *EMP* 2,000
SIC 5012 Automobile auction; Automobile auction
Pr: Dean H Eisner
**Treas:* Richard J Jacobson
**VP:* Maria L Friedman
MIS Mgr: Jerry Stich

D-U-N-S 14-709-3582
■ **MANHEIM REMARKETING INC**
(*Suby of* COX AUTOMOTIVE INC) ★
6325 Pachtree Dunwoody Rd, Atlanta, GA 30328-4545
Tel (678) 645-2067 *Founded/Ownrshp* 1985
Sales 155.4MM^E *EMP* 293^E
SIC 5012 Automobile auction
Pr: Dean H Eisner
Exec: Debbie Harris

D-U-N-S 01-272-9737
MANHEIM TOWNSHIP SCHOOL DISTRICT
450a Candlewyck Rd, Lancaster, PA 17601-2877
Tel (717) 560-3085 *Founded/Ownrshp* 1924
Sales 80.3MM *EMP* 630
SIC 8211 Public elementary school; Public junior high school; Public senior high school; Public elementary school; Public junior high school; Public senior high school
CTO: Timothy Williams
Pr Dir: Marcie Brody
Schl Brd P: Bill Murray
Teacher Pr: Donna Prokay
Psych: Christina Ravert

D-U-N-S 15-321-3293 EXP
■ **MANHEIMS GREATER ORLANDO AUTO AUCTION INC**
CENTRAL FLORIDA AUTO AUCTION
(*Suby of* COX AUTOMOTIVE INC) ★
9800 Bachman Rd, Orlando, FL 32824-8005
Tel (407) 438-1000 *Founded/Ownrshp* 1997
Sales 73.7MM^E *EMP* 330
SIC 5531 5012 Automotive accessories; Automobile auction; Automotive accessories; Automobile auction
Pr: Dean Eisner
CFO: Dutch Herdegen
Brnch Mgr: Laura Woemmel

D-U-N-S 93-101-9053
■ **MANHEIMS GREATER PENSACOLA AUTO AUCTION INC**
MANHEIM AUTO AUCTION
(*Suby of* COX AUTOMOTIVE INC) ★
401 W Burgess Rd, Pensacola, FL 32503-7116
Tel (850) 474-3979 *Founded/Ownrshp* 1997
Sales 31.1MM^E *EMP* 210
SIC 5012 5531 Automobile auction; Automotive accessories; Automobile auction; Automotive accessories
Prin: Tom Holton
**VP:* Dewayne L Musick
**Prin:* Greg Price

D-U-N-S 04-906-2839
■ **MANHEIMS LOUISVILLE AUTO AUCTION**
TOTAL VEHICLE SOLUTIONS
(*Suby of* COX AUTOMOTIVE INC) ★
5425 Highway 31 E, Clarksville, IN 47129-9228
Tel (812) 283-0734 *Founded/Ownrshp* 1999
Sales 24.2MM^E *EMP* 160^E
SIC 5012 Automobile auction; Automobile auction

MANIFEST DIGITAL
See MANIFEST SOLUTIONS LLC

D-U-N-S 08-827-0710
MANIFEST SOLUTIONS LLC
MANIFEST DIGITAL
35 E Wacker Dr Ste 1000, Chicago, IL 60601-2108
Tel (312) 563-1945 *Founded/Ownrshp* 2007
Sales 19.5MM^E *EMP* 400^E
Accts Brown Cpa Group Ltd Northbr
SIC 8742 Marketing consulting services
CEO: James Benedict
Pr: Carryn Quibell
COO: David Barron
CFO: Mike Latiner
Ofcr: Simon Goodship
Ex VP: John Conmy
VP: Blake Allen
Mng Dir: Doug Jones
Dir Sec: Jamie Anderson
Off Admin: Katie Tolle
Dir IT: Trent Jurewicz
Board of Directors: Dan Wilhelm

D-U-N-S 08-833-9106
MANIFOLD SERVICES INC (MI)
6101 Newport Rd, Portage, MI 49002-9233
Tel (269) 323-9484 *Founded/Ownrshp* 1973
Sales 44.7MM^E *EMP* 400
SIC 6552 6531 Land subdividers & developers, commercial; Cooperative apartment manager; Land subdividers & developers, commercial; Cooperative apartment manager
Pr: Edward Ravitz
**Sec:* Kenneth Nothaft

D-U-N-S 08-192-3526
MANIILAQ ASSOCIATION
MANIILAQ HEALTH CENTER
733 2nd Ave Ferguson Bldg, Kotzebue, AK 99752
Tel (907) 442-3311 *Founded/Ownrshp* 1967
Sales 80.9MM *EMP* 620
Accts Altman Rogers & Company Ancho
SIC 8062 8741 General medical & surgical hospitals; Management services; General medical & surgical hospitals; Management services
Pr: Helen Bolen
CFO: Craig Moen
Bd of Dir: Brad Reich
**VP:* Barbara Janitscheck

D-U-N-S 15-962-7462
MANIILAQ ASSOCIATION CHILDRENS HOUSE INC
633 A Bison St, Kotzebue, AK 99752
Tel (907) 442-3157 *Founded/Ownrshp* 1979
Sales 80.9MM *EMP* 15
SIC 8351 Child day care services

MANIILAQ HEALTH CENTER
See MANIILAQ ASSOCIATION

D-U-N-S 09-656-2244
MANIKEN LLC
8621 Robert Fulton Dr # 100, Columbia, MD 21046-2620
Tel (410) 290-1400 *Founded/Ownrshp* 1971
Sales 125.0MM *EMP* 160
SIC 6512 Commercial & industrial building operation; Commercial & industrial building operation
Pt: Richard Alter
Pt: Louis Lapenna
CFO: Ed Kouneski
Sr VP: Owen J Rouse Jr
Dir IT: Barbara Plouff

MANILDRA MILLING
See HONAN HOLDINGS USA INC

D-U-N-S 07-304-3549 IMP/EXP
MANILDRA MILLING CORP
(*Suby of* HONAN HOLDINGS USA INC) ★
4210 Shawnee Mission Pkwy 312a, Fairway, KS 66205-2545
Tel (913) 362-0777 *Founded/Ownrshp* 1974
Sales 29.8MM^E *EMP* 35
SIC 5149 Groceries & related products
Ch: John T Honan
**Pr:* Neal Bassi
**Pr:* Gerry Degnan
**Treas:* Paul Mall
**VP:* Keval Bassi
Off Mgr: Dennis Kehne

D-U-N-S 06-007-8912
MANIN DISTRIBUTING CORP
21 Twosome Dr, Moorestown, NJ 08057-1367
Tel (856) 638-0707 *Founded/Ownrshp* 1976
Sales 25.0MM *EMP* 9
SIC 5064 Electrical entertainment equipment; Electrical appliances, major; Electrical entertainment equipment; Electrical appliances, major
Ch Bd: Martin L Manin
**Pr:* Scott Manin
**Treas:* Mark Manin

D-U-N-S 00-616-3422 IMP
MANIONS WHOLESALE BUILDING SUPPLIES INC
1300 Garfield Ave, Superior, WI 54880-2345
Tel (715) 394-6606 *Founded/Ownrshp* 1935
Sales 54.8MM^E *EMP* 170
SIC 5031

D-U-N-S 10-203-3925 IMP
MANIS LUMBER CO
WHEELER'S
2 Riverside Indus Park Ne, Rome, GA 30161-7301
Tel (706) 232-2400 *Founded/Ownrshp* 1986
Sales 88.2MM^E *EMP* 560
SIC 5031 5211 Lumber, plywood & millwork; Lumber & other building materials; Lumber, plywood & millwork; Lumber & other building materials
Pr: James T Manis
**CEO:* Mark W Manis
Sfty Dirs: Wayne White

D-U-N-S 00-219-3332 IMP
MANISCHEWITZ CO
HOROWITZ
(*Suby of* B MANISCHEWITZ CO) ★
80 Avenue K, Newark, NJ 07105-3803
Tel (201) 553-1100 *Founded/Ownrshp* 1998
Sales 65.7MM^E *EMP* 250
SIC 2052 2045 2032 2091 Matzos; Cake mixes, prepared: from purchased flour; Soups, except seafood: packaged in cans, jars, etc.; Fish: packaged in cans, jars, etc.; Matzos; Cake mixes, prepared: from purchased flour; Soups, except seafood: packaged in cans, jars, etc.; Fish: packaged in cans, jars, etc.
CEO: Paul Bensabat
Pr: Alain Bankier
Pr: Mark Weinsten
CFO: Brian W Duffy
CFO: Tanisha O'Neal
VP: Michael Schall
Dir IT: Jaroslaw Pirog
Dir IT: Dan Tannenbaum
IT Man: Jean Lebosky
Sls Dir: Marcia Wiener
Mktg Mgr: Deborah Sidney

MANISCHEWITZ SHELZER COMPANY
See DAYS BEVERAGE INC

D-U-N-S 05-109-6188
MANISTEE AREA PUBLIC SCHOOLS
52512 Maple St Ste 1, Manistee, MI 49660
Tel (231) 723-1521 *Founded/Ownrshp* 1867
Sales 9.8MM^E *EMP* 295
SIC 8211 Public elementary & secondary schools; Public senior high school; Public elementary & secondary schools
Prin: Ila M Prickett
Prin: Robert Riemersma
Dir IT: Roy Anciso

D-U-N-S 13-759-9593 IMP/EXP
■ **MANITEX INC**
(*Suby of* MANITEX INTERNATIONAL INC) ★
3000 S Austin Ave, Georgetown, TX 78626-7544
Tel (512) 942-3000 *Founded/Ownrshp* 1985
Sales 25.6MM^E *EMP* 140^E
SIC 3536 3537 Hoists, cranes & monorails; Cranes, industrial truck; Hoists, cranes & monorails; Cranes, industrial truck
CEO: David J Langevin
**Pr:* Bob Latchab
**COO:* Bob Litchev
**CFO:* David Gransee
VP: Gene Wallin
IT Man: Charles Carden
Manager: Paul Gibson

D-U-N-S 78-540-9392 IMP
▲ **MANITEX INTERNATIONAL INC**
9725 Industrial Dr, Bridgeview, IL 60455-2304
Tel (708) 430-7500 *Founded/Ownrshp* 1993
Sales 264.0MM *EMP* 663^E
Tkr Sym MNTX *Exch* NAS
SIC 3537 3536 Industrial trucks & tractors; Forklift trucks; Lift trucks, industrial: fork, platform, straddle, etc.; Hoists, cranes & monorails; Industrial trucks & tractors; Forklift trucks; Lift trucks, industrial: fork, platform, straddle, etc.; Hoists, cranes & monorails
Ch Bd: David J Langevin
Pr: Andrew M Rooke
CFO: David H Gransee
Bd of Dir: Terrence McKenna
Sr VP: Scott Rolston
VP: Peter L Seltzberg
VP Mfg: Bob Litchev
QC Dir: Ralph Fulwood
Board of Directors: Ronald M Clark, Robert S Gigliotti, Frederick B Knox, Marvin B Rosenberg, Stephen J Tober

D-U-N-S 14-441-2640
MANITO SUPER 1 FOODS INC
240 W Hayden Ave Ste F, Hayden Lake, ID 83835-8194
Tel (208) 772-5722 *Founded/Ownrshp* 1985
Sales 117.2MM^E *EMP* 800
SIC 5411 Supermarkets, independent; Supermarkets, independent
Pr: Ronald Mc Intire
Exec: Robbie Cornett
Dept Mgr: Laurie Jones

D-U-N-S 01-374-5237 IMP
MANITOBA CORP
130 Central Ave, Lancaster, NY 14086-1827
Tel (716) 685-7000 *Founded/Ownrshp* 1916
Sales 70.0MM *EMP* 46
SIC 5093

D-U-N-S 00-607-0031 IMP
MANITOU AMERICAS INC (WI)
GEHL COMPANY
(*Suby of* MANITOU BF)
1 Gehl Way, West Bend, WI 53095-3463
Tel (262) 334-9461 *Founded/Ownrshp* 1859, 2008
Sales 250.1MM^E *EMP* 848
SIC 3531 3523 Backhoes, tractors, cranes, plows & similar equipment; Dozers, tractor mounted: material moving; Cranes; Excavators: cable, clamshell, crane, derrick, dragline, etc.; Farm machinery & equipment; Haying machines: mowers, rakes, stackers, etc.; Balers, farm: hay, straw, cotton, etc.; Harvesters, fruit, vegetable, tobacco, etc.; Backhoes, tractors, cranes, plows & similar equipment; Dozers, tractor mounted: material moving; Cranes; Excavators: cable, clamshell, crane, derrick, dragline, etc.; Farm machinery & equipment; Haying machines: mowers, rakes, stackers, etc.; Balers, farm: hay, straw, cotton, etc.; Harvesters, fruit, vegetable, tobacco, etc.
Pr: Daniel Miller
**Ch Bd:* William D Gehl
COO: Malcolm F Moore
CFO: Thomas Rettler
Treas: James J Monnat
VP: Alain Becque
VP: Shannon Dyke
VP: James C Green
VP: Daniel Mier
VP: Daniel L Miller
VP: Michael J Mulcahy
Dir Rx: Stanislav Shulga
Board of Directors: John T Byrnes, Richard J Fotsch, John W Splude, Dr Hermann Viets

MANITOU BOATS
See TRITON INDUSTRIES INC

D-U-N-S 00-732-5483 IMP
MANITOU NORTH AMERICA INC (TX)
(*Suby of* MANITOU BF)
6401 Imperial Dr, Waco, TX 76712-6803
Tel (254) 799-0232 *Founded/Ownrshp* 1946
Sales 24.0MM^E *EMP* 86
SIC 3523 3537 3593 3524 Turf equipment, commercial; Forklift trucks; Lift trucks, industrial: fork, platform, straddle, etc.; Fluid power cylinders & actuators; Lawn & garden equipment
Pr: Serge Bosche
Ex VP: Herve Rochet
**VP:* M C Braud

Exec: Donna Machac
Genl Mgr: Stuart Walker
CIO: Clint Labonte
IT Man: Pascale Hudson

D-U-N-S 03-985-1944 IMP
■ **MANITOWOC BEVERAGE EQUIPMENT INC**
FLOMATIC INTERNATIONAL
(*Suby of* MANITOWOC CO INC) ★
2100 Future Dr, Sellersburg, IN 47172-1874
Tel (812) 246-7000 *Founded/Ownrshp* 1902
Sales 23.0MM^E *EMP* 200
SIC 3585 Ice making machinery; Cold drink dispensing equipment (not coin-operated); Ice making machinery; Cold drink dispensing equipment (not coin-operated)
Pr: Michael J Kachmer
**CEO:* Terry Growcock
**CFO:* Tim Wood
**Treas:* C J Laurino
Sr VP: Glen Tellock
**VP:* T G Musial
VP: Paul Rusk

D-U-N-S 06-162-7712 IMP/EXP
■ **MANITOWOC BEVERAGE SYSTEMS INC**
M B S
(*Suby of* MANITOWOC CO INC) ★
2100 Future Dr, Sellersburg, IN 47172-1874
Tel (419) 861-0800 *Founded/Ownrshp* 1998
Sales 290.9MM^E *EMP* 3,000
SIC 3585 Soda fountain & beverage dispensing equipment & parts; Soda fountain & beverage dispensing equipment & parts
Pr: Terry D Growcock
**CEO:* John Barber
**Treas:* Glenn E Tellock
VP: David Mosteller
**Prin:* Robert R Friedl
Opers Mgr: Mike Kascak
Ql Cn Mgr: Gary Herrmann

D-U-N-S 00-607-3183 IMP/EXP
▲ **MANITOWOC CO INC** (WI)
2400 S 44th St, Manitowoc, WI 54220-5846
Tel (920) 684-4410 *Founded/Ownrshp* 1902
Sales 3.8MMM *EMP* 12,300
Accts Pricewaterhousecoopers Llp Mi
Tkr Sym MTW *Exch* NYS
SIC 3536 3537 3531 3585 Hoists, cranes & monorails; Cranes, overhead traveling; Cranes, industrial plant; Trucks, tractors, loaders, carriers & similar equipment; Cranes; Excavators: cable, clamshell, crane, derrick, dragline, etc.; Ice making machinery; Refrigeration equipment, complete; Soda fountain & beverage dispensing equipment & parts; Ice boxes, industrial; Hoists, cranes & monorails; Cranes, overhead traveling; Cranes, industrial plant; Trucks, tractors, loaders, carriers & similar equipment; Cranes; Excavators: cable, clamshell, crane, derrick, dragline, etc.; Ice making machinery; Refrigeration equipment, complete; Soda fountain & beverage dispensing equipment & parts; Ice boxes, industrial
Pr: Kenneth W Krueger
CFO: Carl J Laurino
Treas: Therese C Houlahan
Ex VP: Benjamin Culbertson
Sr VP: Thomas J Angst
Sr VP: Eric Etchart
Sr VP: Maurice D Jones
Sr VP: Thomas G Musial
VP: Dave Hinton
Creative D: Mariella De La Torre
Brnch Mgr: Randy Broeckert
Board of Directors: Roy V Armes, Robert G Bown, Joan K Chow, Donald M Condon Jr, Cynthia M Egnotovich, Kenneth W Krueger, Keith D Nosbusch, James L Packard

D-U-N-S 83-243-0115
■ **MANITOWOC CRANE COMPANIES INC**
(*Suby of* MANITOWOC CO INC) ★
2400 S 44th St, Manitowoc, WI 54220-5846
Tel (920) 684-4410 *Founded/Ownrshp* 1996
Sales 147.3MM^E *EMP* 350^E
SIC 3536 Hoists, cranes & monorails
Ch: M Gusho
**Treas:* J P Sande III
**VP:* S St John

MANITOWOC CRANE GROUP
See GROVE US LLC

D-U-N-S 96-511-8755 IMP/EXP
■ **MANITOWOC CRANES LLC**
(*Suby of* MANITOWOC CRANE COMPANIES INC) ★
2401 S 30th St, Manitowoc, WI 54220-5919
Tel (920) 684-6621 *Founded/Ownrshp* 1996
Sales 156.3MM^E *EMP* 281^E
SIC 3531 Construction machinery
VP: Tom Musial
Treas: Therese Houlahan
Ex VP: Gilles Martin
Ex VP: Ronald Schad
VP: Chuck Maddox
VP: Lb Smith
VP: Tom Tetlow
VP Bus Dev: Paul A Boggs
Prgrm Mgr: Mark Harlacher
DP Dir: Dave Patrikus
IT Man: Christine Teh

D-U-N-S 96-752-3382 IMP
■ **MANITOWOC FOODSERVICE COMPANIES LLC**
(*Suby of* MANITOWOC CO INC) ★
2227 Welbilt Blvd, Trinity, FL 34655-5130
Tel (727) 375-7010 *Founded/Ownrshp* 2009
Sales 261.9MM^E *EMP* 1,500
SIC 3585 3448 1711 3632 8742 Refrigeration equipment, complete; Prefabricated metal components; Refrigeration contractor; Refrigerators, mechanical & absorption: household; Restaurant & food services consultants; Refrigeration equipment, complete; Prefabricated metal components; Refrigeration contractor; Refrigerators, mechanical & absorption: household; Restaurant & food services consultants
Ofcr: Denise Messiti
Ex VP: Mike Hicks
VP: Dennis O'Toole
Netwrk Mgr: Lee Cooper
Manager: Kenny Smith

D-U-N-S 83-243-0784 IMP
■ **MANITOWOC FSG HOLDINGS INC**
(*Suby of* MANITOWOC FOODSERVICE COMPANIES LLC) ★
2110 S 26th St, Manitowoc, WI 54220-6321
Tel (920) 682-0161 *Founded/Ownrshp* 1996
Sales 34.9MM^E *EMP* 264^E
SIC 3536 Hoists, cranes & monorails
Ch: M J Kachmer
**Pr:* M D Jones
**VP:* C J Laurino

D-U-N-S 83-243-0958 IMP
■ **MANITOWOC FSG OPERATIONS INC**
(*Suby of* MANITOWOC FSG HOLDINGS INC) ★
6100 Neil Rd, Reno, NV 89511-1132
Tel (775) 322-2277 *Founded/Ownrshp* 2007
Sales 34.9MM^E *EMP* 257^E
SIC 3536 Hoists, cranes & monorails
Ch: M J Kachmer
**Pr:* M D Jones
**VP:* C J Laurino

D-U-N-S 07-839-9945
MANITOWOC FSG OPERATIONS LLC
2400 S 44th St, Manitowoc, WI 54220-5846
Tel (920) 652-2222 *Founded/Ownrshp* 2010
Sales 6.4MM^E *EMP* 334^E
SIC 3589 Commercial cooking & foodwarming equipment
Prin: Mike Philipps
VP: Mark Richardson

D-U-N-S 05-221-7776
■ **MANITOWOC FSG SERVICES LLC**
(*Suby of* MANITOWOC CO INC) ★
2110 S 26th St, Manitowoc, WI 54220-6321
Tel (920) 682-0161 *Founded/Ownrshp* 2004
Sales 58.6MM^E *EMP* 122^E
SIC 3585 Ice making machinery
VP: Jason Suchomel
VP: George Vuduris
IT Man: Hal Armstrong
Mktg Mgr: Melissa Laabs

D-U-N-S 10-277-6015 IMP/EXP
■ **MANITOWOC ICE INC**
(*Suby of* MANITOWOC CO INC) ★
2110 S 26th St, Manitowoc, WI 54220-6321
Tel (920) 682-0161 *Founded/Ownrshp* 1996
Sales 45.2MM^E *EMP* 93^E
SIC 3585 Ice making machinery
VP: Robert Herre
VP: Maurice Jones
VP: Mark Kreple
VP: Tom Musial
VP: Susan Ribeiro
VP: Denny Romer
Mtls Mgr: David Williamson
Prd Mgr: Dan Brandl
Ql Cn Mgr: Bill Retzer
Mktg Mgr: Tom Huray
Counsel: Dean E Flynn

D-U-N-S 03-193-6974
MANITOWOC PUBLIC SCHOOL DISTRICT
2902 Lindbergh Dr, Manitowoc, WI 54220-3626
Tel (920) 686-4777 *Founded/Ownrshp* 1910
Sales 37.1MM^E *EMP* 800
SIC 8211 Public combined elementary & secondary school; Public combined elementary & secondary school
Teacher Pr: Lori Miron

D-U-N-S 07-479-8752 IMP
MANITOWOC PUBLIC UTILITIES (INC)
M P U
1303 S 8th St, Manitowoc, WI 54220-5313
Tel (920) 683-4600 *Founded/Ownrshp* 1889
Sales 75.3MM *EMP* 95
Accts Schenck Sc Green Bay Wiscon
SIC 4939 4941 4911 1623 Combination utilities; Water supply; Electric services; Water, sewer & utility lines; Combination utilities; Water supply; Electric services; Water, sewer & utility lines
Pr: Dan Hornung
Bd of Dir: Kevin Crawford
**Genl Mgr:* Nilaksh Kothari
MIS Mgr: Gary Heim
Opers Supe: Brian Fassbender

D-U-N-S 82-915-3662
MANITOWOC TOOL & MANUFACTURING LLC
MTM
4330 Expo Dr, Manitowoc, WI 54220-7304
Tel (920) 686-8232 *Founded/Ownrshp* 2008
Sales 47.1MM^E *EMP* 90
SIC 3441 Fabricated structural metal; Fabricated structural metal
Pr: Scott J Mertens

D-U-N-S 05-529-8384
MANITOWOC TOOL AND MACHINING LLC
MTM
4211 Clipper Dr, Manitowoc, WI 54220-4115
Tel (920) 682-8825 *Founded/Ownrshp* 1995
Sales 97.1MM^E *EMP* 300^E
SIC 3441 Fabricated structural metal; Fabricated structural metal
Pr: Scott J Mertens
Pr: Steve Schiller
**CFO:* Jean Hansen
Ex VP: Larry Jaeger
Ql Cn Mgr: Henry Butkovich
Sls Mgr: Jerry Shew

MANITWOC OVENS ADVNCED COOKING
See CLEVELAND RANGE LLC

MANKATO AREA PUBLIC SCHOOL
See INDEPENDENT SCHOOL DISTRICT NO 77

D-U-N-S 06-047-3790
MANKATO CLINIC LTD
1230 E Main St, Mankato, MN 56001-8001
Tel (507) 389-8680 *Founded/Ownrshp* 1962
Sales 73.9MM^E *EMP* 700
SIC 8011 Clinic, operated by physicians; Clinic, operated by physicians
CEO: Randall A Farrow
Dir IT: Cheryl Jones
Psych: Marsha Fields
Surgeon: Jeremy Berger
Surgeon: Bryan Wood
Obsttrcn: Heather Carlson
Obsttrcn: Tara Denke
Obsttrcn: Mark Taylor
Podiatrist: Lynn Gustafson DPM
Doctor: Andrew Miller
Doctor: Stephen Penkhus

D-U-N-S 06-144-5045
MANKATO FORD ACQUISITION CORP
1935 Madison Ave, Mankato, MN 56001-5414
Tel (507) 387-3454 *Founded/Ownrshp* 1997
Sales 26.7MM^E *EMP* 54
SIC 5511 Automobiles, new & used
Pr: Michael Rstom
**VP:* Gary Nelson
Genl Mgr: Barry Iia
Sls Mgr: Michael King
Sales Asso: Tom Tepley

D-U-N-S 00-696-1486
MANKATO MOTOR CO
(*Suby of* RYDELL MANAGEMENT CO LLC) ★
1815 Madison Ave, Mankato, MN 56001-5449
Tel (507) 625-5641 *Founded/Ownrshp* 2009
Sales 29.5MM^E *EMP* 66
SIC 5511 Automobiles, new & used; Automobiles, new & used
CEO: Dale Schmitt
**Pr:* Loren Holub
Off Mgr: Terri Price
Sls Mgr: Ted Evans
Sls Mgr: Justin Frauendienst
Sls Mgr: Jason Wenk
Sales Asso: Shea Aamot
Sales Asso: Dick Arndt
Sales Asso: Matthew Berg
Sales Asso: Joe Bidwell
Sales Asso: Marty Bode

D-U-N-S 06-816-1900
MANKATO REHABILITATION CENTER INC
MRCI WORKSOURCE
15 Map Dr, Mankato, MN 56001-8944
Tel (507) 386-5600 *Founded/Ownrshp* 1953
Sales 61.7MM *EMP* 375
Accts Cliftonlarsonallen Llp Mankat
SIC 8331 2671 Job training & vocational rehabilitation services; Packaging paper & plastics film, coated & laminated; Job training & vocational rehabilitation services; Packaging paper & plastics film, coated & laminated
Pr: Brian Benshoof
CFO: Jeff Call
Sr VP: Linda Leiding
VP: Brenda Rohlfing
VP: Bill Schwartz
Comm Man: Matthew Coulsey
Board of Directors: Brian Benshoof

D-U-N-S 00-949-1770
MANKE LUMBER CO INC
SUPERIOR WOOD TREATING
1717 Marine View Dr, Tacoma, WA 98422-4192
Tel (253) 572-6252 *Founded/Ownrshp* 1952
Sales 96.0MM^E *EMP* 450
SIC 2421 2491 2499 Lumber: rough, sawed or planed; Wood preserving; Poles & pole crossarms, treated wood; Posts, treated wood; Flooring, treated wood block; Mulch or sawdust products, wood; Lumber: rough, sawed or planed; Wood preserving; Poles & pole crossarms, treated wood; Posts, treated wood; Flooring, treated wood block; Mulch or sawdust products, wood
Pr: Charles Manke
Chf Mktg O: Randy Jordan
**VP:* James Manke

D-U-N-S 60-284-1488
MANKO WINDOW SYSTEMS INC
800 Hayes Dr, Manhattan, KS 66502-5087
Tel (785) 776-9643 *Founded/Ownrshp* 1989
Sales 86.5MM^E *EMP* 375
SIC 3442 1799 5039 Metal doors, sash & trim; Store fronts, prefabricated, metal; Glass tinting, architectural or automotive; Glass construction materials; Metal doors, sash & trim; Store fronts, prefabricated, metal; Glass tinting, architectural or automotive; Glass construction materials
Pr: Gary Jones
CFO: Bill Ulirch
**Sec:* Joe Jones
VP: Kevin Dix
**VP:* Steve Jones
Site Mgr: Kevin Bauer
Sfty Mgr: Greg Kohls
Plnt Mgr: Joe Modean
Sales Exec: Scott Leiker

D-U-N-S 13-019-3456
MANLEY DEAS & KOCHALSKI LLC
1400 Goodale Blvd Ste 200, Columbus, OH 43212-3777
Tel (614) 220-5611 *Founded/Ownrshp* 2003
Sales 40.9MM^E *EMP* 300
SIC 8111 Legal services; Legal services
Mng Pt: Brian T Deas
IT Man: Kate Vanderzee

MANLEY'S MIGHTY MART
See MANLEYS MIGHTY-MART LLC

D-U-N-S 83-911-8577
MANLEYS MIGHTY-MART LLC
MANLEY'S MIGHTY MART
1249 Upper Front St # 203, Binghamton, NY 13905-1125
Tel (607) 772-9131 *Founded/Ownrshp* 1995
Sales 21.9MM^E *EMP* 140
SIC 5411 Convenience stores

MANLY HONDA OF SANTA ROSA
See FOREIGN AUTOMOTIVE

D-U-N-S 18-628-4006
MANN & HUMMEL ADVANCED FILTRATION CONCEPTS INC
(*Suby of* MANN + HUMMEL INC) ★
7070 International Dr, Louisville, KY 40258-2864
Tel (502) 935-9333 *Founded/Ownrshp* 1987
Sales 21.3MM^E *EMP* 90
SIC 3569 5084 Filters, general line: industrial; Industrial machinery & equipment
Pr: Brian Pahl

D-U-N-S 16-025-7473 IMP
MANN + HUMMEL INC
(*Suby of* MANN + HUMMEL GMBH)
6400 S Sprinkle Rd, Portage, MI 49002-9706
Tel (269) 329-3900 *Founded/Ownrshp* 1996
Sales 1.1MMM^E *EMP* 1,000
SIC 3559 3585 Dehumidifiers electric, except portable; Plastics working machinery; Plastics working machinery; Dehumidifiers electric, except portable
Pr: Alfred Weber
COO: Ronald Randall
IT Man: Chris Lim
Opers Mgr: Sarka Neumannova
Ql Cn Mgr: Jonathan Kelly
Ql Cn Mgr: Ryan Stewart
Sales Exec: Jeffrey Chew
Sls&Mrk Ex: Donovan Chee
Sls Mgr: Leslie Lai

D-U-N-S 05-676-5001
MANN AND PARKER LUMBER CO
335 N Constitution Ave, New Freedom, PA 17349-9522
Tel (717) 235-4834 *Founded/Ownrshp* 1956
Sales 22.7MM^E *EMP* 55
SIC 5031 Lumber: rough, dressed & finished; Millwork
Ch Bd: Robert R Bushman Sr
**Pr:* Gregory V Lutter Sr
**VP:* Gary Johnston
Prd Mgr: David Bushman
Sales Exec: Brad Scarboroughr

MANN ENERGY SERVICES
See MANN ENTERPRISES LLC

D-U-N-S 07-714-1468
MANN ENTERPRISES LLC
MANN ENERGY SERVICES
109 N 4th St Ste 200, Bismarck, ND 58501-4003
Tel (701) 751-4315 *Founded/Ownrshp* 2009
Sales 21.7MM^E *EMP* 65
SIC 1382 Oil & gas exploration services

D-U-N-S 78-545-5767
MANN FINANCIAL INC
1220 Whitefish Stage B, Kalispell, MT 59901-2753
Tel (406) 751-6263 *Founded/Ownrshp* 1989
Sales NA *EMP* 123
SIC 6162 6163 Mortgage bankers; Loan brokers; Mortgage bankers; Loan brokers
Pr: Donald Mann
**Sec:* Tom Greiner
Sr Cor Off: Gene Cook
**VP:* Julie Krause

D-U-N-S 05-422-5776
MANN MECHANICAL CO
100 Pine St, Avondale Estates, GA 30002-1015
Tel (678) 681-6299 *Founded/Ownrshp* 1971
Sales 68.6MM^E *EMP* 150
SIC 1711 Mechanical contractor; Mechanical contractor
Pr: Martin W Mann
**CFO:* Coy M Mitcham
Snr PM: Billy Barnes

D-U-N-S 02-906-5273
MANN PACKING CO INC
1333 Schilling Pl, Salinas, CA 93901-4535
Tel (831) 422-7405 *Founded/Ownrshp* 1945
Sales 148.6MM^E *EMP* 500
SIC 0723 4783 0722 Vegetable packing services; Packing & crating; Crop harvesting; Vegetable packing services; Packing & crating; Crop harvesting
CEO: Lorri Koster
**Pr:* Michael Jarrod
COO: Debbie Tangonan
CFO: Bill Beaton
**CFO:* William Beaton
**Ch:* Richard Ramsey
Exec: Pat Reyes
CIO: Gina Nucci
Sls Mgr: Terence Billingsley
Board of Directors: Don Nucci, William Ramsey

D-U-N-S 78-101-4944 IMP
MANN+HUMMEL PUROLATOR FILTERS LLC
OE FILTERS
(*Suby of* MANN + HUMMEL INC) ★
3200 Natal St, Fayetteville, NC 28306-2845
Tel (910) 425-4181 *Founded/Ownrshp* 2006
Sales 1.0MMM *EMP* 1,000^E
SIC 3569 Filters
CEO: Alfred Weber
**CFO:* Frank B Jehle
CTO: Sommerlad Michael
QA Dir: Scott Gilchrist
Web Dev: Rod Watkins
Plnt Mgr: Michael Beauchamp

Ql Cn Mgr: Mahesh Sarangi
Mktg Mgr: Marianne Guldberg

D-U-N-S 11-282-7332 IMP
MANN+HUMMEL USA INC
(*Suby of* MANN + HUMMEL INC) ★
6400 S Sprinkle Rd, Portage, MI 49002-9706
Tel (269) 329-3900 *Founded/Ownrshp* 1983
Sales 106.8MM^E *EMP* 500
SIC 3089 3714 Injection molding of plastics; Motor vehicle parts & accessories; Injection molding of plastics; Motor vehicle parts & accessories
CEO: Alfred Weber
**Pr:* Frank B Jehle
Pr: Julie Thomas
**Pr:* Emese Weissenbacher
CFO: Bill Liacone
Treas: Dennis Ruiter
Prgrm Mgr: Jon Buddemeier
Prgrm Mgr: Ryo Kawabata
QC Dir: John Costin
Mtls Mgr: Brad Metzger
Mtls Mgr: Mathew Webster

MANNA BREAD DEVELOPMENT
See MANA DEVELOPMENT LLC

MANNA DISTRIBUTION SERVICES
See MANNA FREIGHT SYSTEMS INC

D-U-N-S 07-794-6218
MANNA ENTERPRISES INC
JACKS RESTAURANT
5065 Us Highway 78 W D, Oxford, AL 36203-6132
Tel (256) 835-5946 *Founded/Ownrshp* 1982
Sales 7.5MM^E *EMP* 400
SIC 5812 Fast-food restaurant, chain; Fast-food restaurant, chain
CEO: Wayne Reaves
**VP:* Brian Reaves
**VP:* Katie Reaves

D-U-N-S 16-298-7861
MANNA FOOD BANK INC
MANNA FOODBANK
627 Swannanoa River Rd, Asheville, NC 28805-2445
Tel (828) 299-3663 *Founded/Ownrshp* 1983
Sales 27.5MM *EMP* 52
Accts Carter Pc Asheville North C
SIC 8322 Individual & family services; Temporary relief service
Pr: Jim Mathews
**Pr:* Sheryl Williams
**CEO:* Cindy Threlkeld
**CFO:* Nancy Flippin
**VP:* Melody Dunlop

MANNA FOODBANK
See MANNA FOOD BANK INC

D-U-N-S 55-619-8265
MANNA FREIGHT SYSTEMS INC
MANNA DISTRIBUTION SERVICES
2440 Enterprise Dr, Mendota Heights, MN 55120-1143
Tel (651) 905-7560 *Founded/Ownrshp* 1991
Sales 41.3MM^E *EMP* 115
SIC 4731 Domestic freight forwarding; Foreign freight forwarding; Domestic freight forwarding; Foreign freight forwarding
Pr: Alan J Meehan
**COO:* Charles A Martin
**CFO:* Kate Pope
Genl Mgr: Justin Mann
Natl Sales: Jonathan Measells
Natl Sales: Rick Wylie
Mktg Mgr: Bob Frey
Sls Mgr: Clif Krause

D-U-N-S 14-766-6812 IMP/EXP
MANNA PRO PRODUCTS LLC
707 Spirit 40 Park Dr # 150, Chesterfield, MO 63005-1137
Tel (636) 681-1700 *Founded/Ownrshp* 2007
Sales 60.0MM^E *EMP* 200
SIC 2048 Livestock feeds; Livestock feeds
Pr: John Howe
**COO:* Roger Cagle
VP: Herb Andrews
Sftwr Eng: Andrew Bresler
Sales Exec: Steven Medeiros
Sales Exec: Kirk Moser
Natl Sales: Robert Bagley
Mktg Dir: Beth Rogers
Mktg Mgr: Carolyn Adams
Mktg Mgr: Libby Wilson
Sls Mgr: Natalie Bullock

D-U-N-S 84-055-6351 IMP
▲ MANNATECH INC
600 S Royal Ln Ste 200, Coppell, TX 75019-3828
Tel (972) 471-7400 *Founded/Ownrshp* 1993
Sales 190.0MM *EMP* 270^E
Tkr Sym MTEX *Exch* NGS
SIC 2833 Medicinals & botanicals; Medicinals & botanicals
Pr: Alfredo Bala
**Ch Bd:* J Stanley Fredrick
Pr: Yong Jae Park
Pr: Christopher J Simons
Treas: Ronald D Norman
**V Ch Bd:* Robert A Toth
Chf Mktg O: Joel R Bikman
VP: Ben Mayo
Creative D: Zoe Tennesen
Mktg Dir: Alan Boyd
Board of Directors: Linda K Ferrell, Gerald E Gilbert, Larry A Jobe, Marlin Ray Robbins, Eric W Schrier

D-U-N-S 19-338-2603 IMP
MANNED SPACE FLIGHT EDUCATION FOUNDATION INCORPORA
SPACE CENTER HOUSTON PROJECT
1601 Nasa Pkwy, Houston, TX 77058-3145
Tel (281) 244-2100 *Founded/Ownrshp* 1986
Sales 24.4MM *EMP* 250
Accts Blazek & Vetterling Houston
SIC 8412 Museum; Museum
Pr: Richard E Allen Jr
**Sec:* Janet L Brown
VP: Jim Reinhartsen
Opers Mgr: Anson Brantley

D-U-N-S 07-522-1564
MANNES COLLEGE OF MUSIC INC (NY)
55 W 13th St Bsmt, New York, NY 10011-7958
Tel (212) 580-0210 *Founded/Ownrshp* 1916, 1979
Sales 4.1MM *EMP* 300
Accts Ernst & Young
SIC 8299 Music school; Music school

D-U-N-S 00-702-6669
MANNHEIM SCHOOL DISTRICT 83
ENGER SCHOOL
10401 Grand Ave, Franklin Park, IL 60131-2294
Tel (847) 455-5299 *Founded/Ownrshp* 1869
Sales 29.3MM^E *EMP* 450
SIC 8211 Public elementary & secondary schools; Public elementary & secondary schools
Ex Dir: Dr Bruce A Lane
Bd of Dir: Humberto Chaidez
Bd of Dir: Octavio Cordero
Dir IT: Debbie Motycka
Teacher Pr: Wayne Spychala
HC Dir: Barbara Nielsen

D-U-N-S 05-416-8372
MANNIK & SMITH GROUP INC
M S G
1800 Indian Wood Cir, Maumee, OH 43537-4086
Tel (419) 891-2222 *Founded/Ownrshp* 1971
Sales 24.2MM *EMP* 205
Accts Gilmore Jasion & Mahler Ltd
SIC 8711 8748 Consulting engineer; Civil engineering; Business consulting; Consulting engineer; Civil engineering; Business consulting
Pr: C Michael Smith
**CFO:* Thomas Beshalske
CFO: Steven Vandenbossche
**Ch:* Jaan Mannik
Sr VP: Richard Bertz
**Sr VP:* Barry Buschmann
**Sr VP:* Dean Niese
VP: Russ Critelli
VP: Sean Kelley
Exec: Tim Isley
**Prin:* Mike Smith

D-U-N-S 87-920-6712
MANNING & KASS ELLROD RAMIREZ TRESTER LLP
801 S Figueroa St Fl 15, Los Angeles, CA 90017-5504
Tel (213) 624-6900 *Founded/Ownrshp* 1994
Sales 29.1MM^E *EMP* 200
SIC 8111 General practice attorney, lawyer; General practice attorney, lawyer
Mng Pt: Steven D Manning
DP Exec: Alice Napier
Dir IT: Robert Rantos

D-U-N-S 07-368-6594
MANNING & NAPIER ADVISORS LLC
290 Woodcliff Dr Ste 300, Fairport, NY 14450-4298
Tel (716) 639-9205 *Founded/Ownrshp* 1970
Sales 217.6MM^E *EMP* 425
SIC 6282 8742 7375 Investment advisory service; Management consulting services; On-line data base information retrieval; Investment advisory service; Management consulting services; On-line data base information retrieval
CEO: Patrick Cunningham
**Pr:* B Reuben Auspitz
**Pr:* Jeff Coons
CFO: Brian Foster
**CFO:* James Mikolaichik
**Treas:* William Manning
VP: Jason Badesha
VP: Julie Bagley
VP: Antony Desorbo
VP: Donna Dhont
VP: Kathleen Emert
VP: Chris Labounty
VP: Bill Logan
VP: Jeffrey McCormack
VP: Winston Nelson
VP: Michael Purcell
VP: Peter Reitmeyer
VP: Chris Roop
VP: Colin Schleifer
VP: George Stemerman

D-U-N-S 07-986-8650
■ MANNING & NAPIER ALTERNATIVE OPPORTUNITIES LLC
(*Suby of* MANNING & NAPIER INC) ★
290 Woodcliff Dr Ste 300, Fairport, NY 14450-4298
Tel (585) 325-6880 *Founded/Ownrshp* 2015
Sales 11.3MM^E *EMP* 432^E
SIC 6282 Investment advice

D-U-N-S 96-913-8333
▲ MANNING & NAPIER INC
290 Woodcliff Dr Ste 300, Fairport, NY 14450-4298
Tel (585) 325-6880 *Founded/Ownrshp* 1970
Sales 405.4MM *EMP* 507^E
Tkr Sym MN *Exch* NYS
SIC 6282 8742 6722 Investment advice; Investment advisory service; Management consulting services; Management investment, open-end; Investment advice; Investment advisory service; Management consulting services; Management investment, open-end
CEO: Patrick Cunningham
Ch Bd: William Manning
Pr: Jeffrey S Coons
CFO: James Mikolaichik
Ofcr: Richard B Yates
Ex VP: Charles H Stamey
VP: Jennifer Brockwell
VP: Cary Clayborn
VP: Stephanie Cochran
VP: Jim Hakewill
VP: Andrew Kirby
VP: Chris Labounty
VP: Frank Natale
VP: Julie A Nye
VP: Deanna Perry
VP: Scott Pilchard
VP: Aaron Pisani
VP: Michael Purcell
VP: Colin Schleifer
VP: Patrick White
Board of Directors: Richard Goldberg, Barbara Goodstein, Edward J Pettinella, Robert M Zak

D-U-N-S 12-262-7003
MANNING BUILDING SUPPLIES INC
M B S
10900 Philips Hwy, Jacksonville, FL 32256-1551
Tel (904) 268-7000 *Founded/Ownrshp* 1984
Sales 47.9MM^E *EMP* 220
SIC 5211 Lumber & other building materials; Millwork & lumber; Lumber & other building materials; Millwork & lumber
Pr: James H Cissel
**VP:* James H Cissel IV
**VP:* Stephen S Wiechens
Exec: Joy Driver
Genl Mgr: Dale Altenburg
Genl Mgr: John Blanchard
Genl Mgr: Bob Lavin
Genl Mgr: Gary Moore
Genl Mgr: Erik Olson
Sls Mgr: David Price
Sales Asso: Chris Vose

D-U-N-S 15-213-8913
MANNING MANAGEMENT CORP
680 Ben Franklin Hwy E, Birdsboro, PA 19508-1527
Tel (610) 385-6797 *Founded/Ownrshp* 2001
Sales 31.3MM^E *EMP* 40^E
SIC 5039 5082 Structural assemblies, prefabricated: non-wood; General construction machinery & equipment
Pr: Drew T Seibert
**Sec:* Stephen Kegerise
**VP:* Otis F Caldwell

D-U-N-S 09-694-2222
MANNING MENARD OIL CO INC (LA)
519 Jacqulyn St, Abbeville, LA 70510-8413
Tel (337) 893-2428 *Founded/Ownrshp* 1959
Sales 22.2MM *EMP* 13^E
Accts Kolder Champagne Slaven & Co
SIC 5172 Gasoline; Gasoline
Pr: Mona D Menard
**Treas:* John Menard
**VP:* Brenda Harman
VP: Brenda M Harmon

MANNING PERMIT
See KENTUCKY DIVISION OF MINE RECLAMATION & ENFORCEMENT

D-U-N-S 01-364-9868
MANNING-SQUIRES-HENNIG CO INC
8426 Seven Springs Rd, Batavia, NY 14020-9604
Tel (585) 343-5365 *Founded/Ownrshp* 1958
Sales 32.3MM^E *EMP* 130
SIC 1542 1541

D-U-N-S 05-965-4954
MANNINGS INC
MANNINGS MARKET PLACE
4720 Moffett Rd, Mobile, AL 36618-2226
Tel (251) 343-1485 *Founded/Ownrshp* 1971
Sales 35.4MM^E *EMP* 225
SIC 5411 Grocery stores; Grocery stores
CEO: Danny Manning
**CFO:* Dwan Manning
**VP:* Kamal Constantine
**VP:* Daphne Walters
IT Man: Francis Paul

MANNINGS MARKET PLACE
See MANNINGS INC

D-U-N-S 00-234-9256 EXP
MANNINGTON MILLS INC (NJ)
MANNINGTON RSILIENT FLOORS DIV
75 Mannington Mills Rd, Salem, NJ 08079-2009
Tel (856) 935-3000 *Founded/Ownrshp* 1915
Sales 804.0MM^E *EMP* 2,390
SIC 3996 3253 2273 2435 Hard surface floor coverings; Wall tile, ceramic; Floor tile, ceramic; Rugs, tufted; Carpets, hand & machine made; Veneer stock, hardwood; Hardwood plywood, prefinished; Panels, hardwood plywood; Plywood, hardwood or hardwood faced; Hard surface floor coverings; Wall tile, ceramic; Floor tile, ceramic; Rugs, tufted; Carpets, hand & machine made; Veneer stock, hardwood; Hardwood plywood, prefinished; Panels, hardwood plywood; Plywood, hardwood or hardwood faced
CEO: Russel Grizzel
**Ch Bd:* Keith S Campbell
**Pr:* Thomas S Davis
CFO: Debbie Freels
**Treas:* Francis J Norris
Treas: Kim Speakman
VP: Joe Amato
VP: Alonzo Burns
VP: Barbara Gallagher
VP: Mark Hollinger
VP: Dave Kitts
VP: Sean Moffet
VP: Paul Snyder
Comm Dir: Betsy Amoroso

MANNINGTON RSILIENT FLOORS DIV
See MANNINGTON MILLS INC

MANNIX
See INTERSTATE WINDOW CORP

D-U-N-S 12-857-6977
▲ MANNKIND CORP
25134 Rye Canyon Loop # 300, Valencia, CA 91355-5045
Tel (661) 775-5300 *Founded/Ownrshp* 1991
Sales 88.4MM^E *EMP* 287^E
Tkr Sym MNKD *Exch* NGM
SIC 8731 2834 Biotechnical research, commercial; Pharmaceutical preparations; Biotechnical research, commercial; Pharmaceutical preparations
Pr: Hakan S Edstrom
**Ch Bd:* Alfred E Mann
COO: Juergen A Martens
CFO: Matthew J Pfeffer
Sr VP: Anders Boss
VP: Dan Burns
VP: Howard Hoffman
VP: Diane M Palumbo
VP: David B Thomson
Assoc Dir: Michael Bergey
Assoc Dir: Rusty Cappadona
Assoc Dir: Mary Faris
Assoc Dir: Mark King
Assoc Dir: Uriel Malyankar
Assoc Dir: George Tonelli
Board of Directors: Ronald J Consiglio, Michael A Friedman, Kent Kresa, David H Maccallum, Henry L Nordhoff

MANN'S TIRE & WHEEL CONNECTION
See TIRE & WHEEL CONNECTION LP

MANOR AT SANTA TERESITA HOSPIT
See SANTA TERESITA INC

MANOR CARE
See HCR MANORCARE MEDICAL SERVICES OF FLORIDA LLC

D-U-N-S 78-398-3414
■ MANOR CARE INC
(*Suby of* CARLYLE GROUP L P) ★
333 N Summit St Ste 100, Toledo, OH 43604-2617
Tel (419) 252-5500 *Founded/Ownrshp* 2007
Sales 997.8MM^E *EMP* 1,500
SIC 8051 8082 8062 Convalescent home with continuous nursing care; Home health care services; Specialty outpatient clinics; Extended care facility; Home health care services; General medical & surgical hospitals
Pr: Paul A Ormond
**COO:* Stephen L Guillard
**CFO:* Steven M Cavanaugh
CFO: Kedon Shaw
VP: Nancy A Edwards
VP: John K Graham
VP: Lynn M Hood
VP: John I Remenar
**VP:* Spencer C Moler
VP: Linda E Neumann
VP: David B Parker
**VP:* Richard A Parr II
Exec: Doug Pearson

D-U-N-S 04-954-6781
■ MANOR CARE OF AMERICA INC
(*Suby of* MANOR CARE INC) ★
333 N Summit St Ste 103, Toledo, OH 43604-2617
Tel (419) 252-5500 *Founded/Ownrshp* 1998
Sales 101.5MM^E *EMP* 700
SIC 8051 8062 8082 Extended care facility; General medical & surgical hospitals; Home health care services; Extended care facility; General medical & surgical hospitals; Home health care services
Pr: Paul A Ormond
**COO:* M Keith Weikel
**CFO:* Geoffrey G Myers
VP: William Kinschner
**VP:* Muriy Mercier

D-U-N-S 87-752-6525
■ MANOR CARE OF BOYNTON BEACH INC
(*Suby of* HCR MANORCARE MEDICAL SERVICES OF FLORIDA LLC) ★
333 N Summit St Ste 103, Toledo, OH 43604-2617
Tel (419) 252-5500 *Founded/Ownrshp* 1982
Sales 7.7MM^E *EMP* 400
SIC 8051 Skilled nursing care facilities; Skilled nursing care facilities
Ch: Paul A Ormond
**CFO:* Steve Cavanaugh

D-U-N-S 17-784-4230
■ MANOR CARE OF KANSAS INC
(*Suby of* HCR MANORCARE MEDICAL SERVICES OF FLORIDA LLC) ★
333 N Summit St Ste 100, Toledo, OH 43604-2617
Tel (419) 252-5500 *Founded/Ownrshp* 1998
Sales 7.8MM^E *EMP* 350
SIC 8051 8093 Skilled nursing care facilities; Rehabilitation center, outpatient treatment; Skilled nursing care facilities; Rehabilitation center, outpatient treatment

D-U-N-S 17-448-3388
■ MANOR CARE OF NORTH OLMSTED INC
(*Suby of* HCR MANORCARE MEDICAL SERVICES OF FLORIDA LLC) ★
333 N Summit St Ste 100, Toledo, OH 43604-2617
Tel (419) 252-5500 *Founded/Ownrshp* 1976
Sales 4.0MM^E *EMP* 385
SIC 8051 Skilled nursing care facilities; Skilled nursing care facilities
Pr: Paul Ormond
**Pr:* Stewart Bainum Jr
**Pr:* Donald C Tomasso
**VP:* James A Maccutcheon

MANOR CRTTER CONVALESCENT CTR
See WILLAMETTE VIEW INC

D-U-N-S 14-807-9528
MANOR ESTATES INC
PRINCETON PLACE
500 Louisiana Blvd Ne, Albuquerque, NM 87108-2051
Tel (505) 255-1717 *Founded/Ownrshp* 1986
Sales 20.7MM^E *EMP* 340
SIC 8052 8051 Intermediate care facilities; Skilled nursing care facilities; Intermediate care facilities; Skilled nursing care facilities
Pr: Danny Prince
CFO: Jason Patterson
**VP:* Brenda Peterson

D-U-N-S 05-022-3239
MANOR INDEPENDENT SCHOOL DISTRICT
10335 Us Highway 290 E, Manor, TX 78653-4686
Tel (512) 278-4000 *Founded/Ownrshp* 1900
Sales 101.9MM *EMP* 1,200
Accts West Davis & Company Llp Au

SIC 8211 Public elementary school; Public junior high school; Public senior high school; Public elementary school; Public junior high school; Public senior high school
IT Man: Bert Sandoval
Schl Brd P: Marlin Thomas
HC Dir: Cindy Kobia

MANOR PARK
See PARK MANOR INC

MANOR PINES CONVALESCENT CTR
See MARRINSON GROUP INC

MANORCARE HLTH SRVCES- KENOSHA
See HEARTLAND-WASHINGTON MANOR OF KENOSHA WI LLC

MANORWOOD HOMES
See COMMODORE CORP

MANPOWER
See FAMOSO INC

MANPOWER
See RIGHT MANAGEMENT INC

MANPOWER
See HAT LIMITED PARTNERSHIP

MANPOWER
See TOPEKA SERVICES INC

MANPOWER
See CPM LTD INC

MANPOWER
See COLLIER INVESTMENTS

D-U-N-S 07-615-2776
■ **MANPOWER INC OF NEW YORK**
(*Suby of* MANPOWERGROUP INC) ★
100 W Manpower Pl, Milwaukee, WI 53212-4030
Tel (414) 961-1000 *Founded/Ownrshp* 1953
Sales NA *EMP* 700
SIC 9441 Administration of social & human resources; Administration of social & human resources
Pr: Jeff Joerres
Mng Pt: Ken Shelton
**Pr:* Jonas Prising
**VP:* Terry Hueneke
**VP:* James J Katte
**VP:* Walter Kozlowski
**VP:* Douglas Krueger
VP: Patti Puccinelli
Area Mgr: Ron Brinson
Brnch Mgr: Adam Bates
Brnch Mgr: Sharon Fields

D-U-N-S 96-336-1894
■ **MANPOWER WORLD HEAD QUARTERS**
(*Suby of* MANPOWERGROUP INC) ★
100 W Manpower Pl, Milwaukee, WI 53212-4030
Tel (414) 961-1000 *Founded/Ownrshp* 1947
Sales 20.5MM^E *EMP* 900
SIC 7363 Manpower pools; Manpower pools
Pr: Jeffrey A Joerres

D-U-N-S 78-201-5911
▲ **MANPOWERGROUP INC**
100 W Manpower Pl, Milwaukee, WI 53212-4030
Tel (414) 961-1000 *Founded/Ownrshp* 1948
Sales 20.7MMM *EMP* 26,000
Accts Deloitte & Touche Llp Milwauk
Tkr Sym MAN *Exch* NYS
SIC 7363 7361 Help supply services; Temporary help service; Office help supply service; Employment agencies; Executive placement; Help supply services; Temporary help service; Office help supply service; Employment agencies; Executive placement
CEO: Jonas Prising
**Ch Bd:* Jeffrey A Joerres
COO: Darryl Green
CFO: Michael J Van
Ex VP: Owen G Sullivan
Sr VP: Richard D Buchband
VP: Lisa Banner
VP: Bill Carollo
VP: Stacey Force
VP: Byrne Luft
Mng Dir: Erika Hendzel
Board of Directors: Gina R Boswell, William Downe, Patricia Hemingway Hall, Roberto Mendoza, Paul Read, Elizabeth P Sartain, John R Walter, Edward J Zore

D-U-N-S 00-215-1660 IMP
MANROLAND INC
MANROLAND WEBSYSTEMS
(*Suby of* MANROLAND SHEETFED GMBH)
800 E Oakhill Dr, Westmont, IL 60559-5587
Tel (630) 920-2000 *Founded/Ownrshp* 2012
Sales 36.0MM^E *EMP* 60
SIC 3555 5084 Printing trades machinery; Printing trades machinery, equipment & supplies; Printing trades machinery; Printing trades machinery, equipment & supplies
CEO: Michael Mugavero
CFO: Brian Gott
CFO: Thomas Harris
Treas: Mark Herman
VP: Ron Sams
VP: Jon Surch
Mng Dir: Franz Von Frstenberg
Trfc Dir: Frauke Bleyer-Ogilby
Sales Exec: Gary Day
Manager: Steve Landmann
Manager: George Newkirk

MANROLAND WEBSYSTEMS
See MANROLAND INC

MANS LUMBER AND MILL WORK
See N A MANS & SONS INC

MANSBACH METAL COMPANY
See PROGRESS METAL RECLAMATION CO

MANSCO
See MANUFACTURERS SUPPLY CO

D-U-N-S 60-253-2751 IMP
MANSFIELD - KING LLC
6501 Julian Ave, Indianapolis, IN 46219-6603
Tel (317) 788-0750 *Founded/Ownrshp* 2005
Sales 30.0MM^E *EMP* 75
SIC 2844 Toilet preparations
Pr: Charles Haywood
Prd Mgr: Jennifer Day

MANSFIELD BLANKING DIV
See SHILOH CORP

D-U-N-S 09-328-5286
MANSFIELD CITY SCHOOLS
124 N Linden Rd, Mansfield, OH 44906-2616
Tel (419) 525-6426 *Founded/Ownrshp* 1900
Sales 65.8MM *EMP* 900
SIC 8211 Public elementary school; Public junior high school; Public senior high school; Public special education school; Public elementary school; Public junior high school; Public senior high school; Public special education school
Sr VP: Patricia Robinson

D-U-N-S 96-869-1241
MANSFIELD ENERGY CORP
1025 Airport Pkwy, Gainesville, GA 30501-6813
Tel (678) 450-2000 *Founded/Ownrshp* 2010
Sales 7.7MMM *EMP* 450^E
Accts Smith & Howard Cpas Atlanta
SIC 5172 4212 1796 Petroleum products; Petroleum haulage, local; Pollution control equipment installation; Petroleum products; Petroleum haulage, local; Pollution control equipment installation
CEO: Michael F Mansfield
**Pr:* John Byrd
**Treas:* Mike Davino

D-U-N-S 18-295-6284 IMP/EXP
MANSFIELD ENGINEERED COMPONENTS INC
ASSEMBLEIS CO
1776 Harrington Mem Rd, Mansfield, OH 44903-8996
Tel (419) 524-1331 *Founded/Ownrshp* 1987
Sales 25.0MM^E *EMP* 160
SIC 3499

D-U-N-S 06-138-1935
MANSFIELD INDEPENDENT SCHOOL DISTRICT (TX)
605 E Broad St, Mansfield, TX 76063-1766
Tel (817) 299-6300 *Founded/Ownrshp* 1912
Sales 321.2MM *EMP* 4,228
Accts Whitley Penn Llp Houston Tex
SIC 8211 Public elementary school; Public junior high school; Public senior high school; Public elementary school; Public junior high school; Public senior high school
Admn Mgr: Gary Manns
IT Man: Juanita Dorsette
Psych: Monica Dabney

D-U-N-S 13-657-9807
MANSFIELD INDUSTRIAL INC
(*Suby of* K2 INDUSTRIAL SERVICES INC) ★
1325 W Detroit Blvd, Pensacola, FL 32534-1817
Tel (850) 477-6437 *Founded/Ownrshp* 2003
Sales 44.7MM^E *EMP* 538^E
Accts Grant Thornton Llp Chicago I
SIC 7349 Cleaning service, industrial or commercial; Cleaning service, industrial or commercial
Pr: Ted Mansfield
CFO: A Allen
**Treas:* Richard Bartell
Treas: M C Vezinat
VP: Dean Mansfield
**VP:* Scott R Van Duinen
Site Mgr: Tony Richardson

D-U-N-S 03-372-3990
MANSFIELD OIL CO OF GAINESVILLE INC
(*Suby of* MANSFIELD ENERGY CORP) ★
1025 Airport Pkwy, Gainesville, GA 30501-6833
Tel (678) 450-2000 *Founded/Ownrshp* 1957
Sales 7.7MMM *EMP* 259^E
SIC 5172

D-U-N-S 01-964-4947 IMP/EXP
MANSFIELD PAPER CO INC
380 Union St Ste 117, West Springfield, MA 01089-4180
Tel (413) 781-2000 *Founded/Ownrshp* 1946
Sales 42.2MM^E *EMP* 80^E
SIC 5113 Bags, paper & disposable plastic; Cups, disposable plastic & paper; Towels, paper; Napkins, paper; Bags, paper & disposable plastic; Cups, disposable plastic & paper; Towels, paper; Napkins, paper
CEO: Michael Shapiro
**Pr:* Scott Parent
**CFO:* Carol Teixeira
**Treas:* Robert Shapiro
**VP:* Davis Paulides
IT Man: Jill Gagnon
Opers Mgr: Shawn Thieboeau
Mktg Dir: Kim Imbriglio

D-U-N-S 19-614-6781 IMP/EXP
MANSFIELD PLUMBING PRODUCTS LLC
(*Suby of* ORGANIZACION CORONA S A)
150 E 1st St, Perrysville, OH 44864-9421
Tel (419) 938-5211 *Founded/Ownrshp* 2004
Sales 156.1MM^E *EMP* 698
SIC 3261 3463 3088 3431 3432 5074 Vitreous plumbing fixtures; Plumbing fixture forgings, nonferrous; Plastics plumbing fixtures; Bathtubs: enameled iron, cast iron or pressed metal; Shower stalls, metal; Plumbing fixture fittings & trim; Plumbing fittings & supplies; Vitreous plumbing fixtures; Plumbing fixture forgings, nonferrous; Plastics plumbing fixtures; Bathtubs: enameled iron, cast iron or pressed metal; Shower stalls, metal; Plumbing fixture fittings & trim; Plumbing fittings & supplies
Pr: Jim Morando
CFO: Phillip Taggart
VP: Paul Stover
Dir IT: Jake Bright
Dir IT: Jeff Lutz
Netwrk Mgr: Brian Fuhrmann
VP Mktg: Richard Oreagan
VP Mktg: Gary Pember
Manager: Bill Halsted
Sales Asso: Heidi Mills

D-U-N-S 96-672-2150
MANSFIELD PUBLIC SCHOOL DISTRICT
4 S Eagleville Rd, Storrs, CT 06268-2574
Tel (860) 429-3350 *Founded/Ownrshp* 1998
Sales 11.8MM^E *EMP* 300
SIC 8211 Public elementary & secondary schools; Public elementary & secondary schools
Schl Brd P: Mark Laplaca

D-U-N-S 07-979-9233
MANSFIELD PUBLIC SCHOOLS
2 Park Row, Mansfield, MA 02048-2433
Tel (508) 261-7500 *Founded/Ownrshp* 2015
Sales 5.5MM^E *EMP* 442^E
SIC 8211 Public elementary & secondary schools
Schl Brd P: Michael Trowbridge

D-U-N-S 07-598-9673
MANSFIELD UNIVERSITY OF PENNSYLVANIA (INC) (PA)
(*Suby of* STATE SYSTEM HIGHER EDUCATN PA) ★
S Academy St, Mansfield, PA 16933
Tel (570) 662-4000 *Founded/Ownrshp* 1857
Sales 34.7MM *EMP* 250
Accts Clifton Larson Allen Llp Harr
SIC 8221 9411 University; Administration of educational programs; ; University; Administration of educational programs;
CEO: Allan J Golden
V Ch: Courtney Hull
**Pr:* Francis L Hendricks
**Pr:* Maravene Loeschke
Ofcr: Robert Davis
Ofcr: Paul Delosa
Ofcr: Spencer Edwards
Ofcr: Alan Zellner
Sr VP: David Stinebeck
VP: Doris Kyle
VP: Linda Stager
VP: Roy Stewart
VP: Adam Tressler

D-U-N-S 00-794-2824 IMP/EXP
MANSON CONSTRUCTION CO (WA)
(*Suby of* MANSON CONSTRUCTION HOLDING CO) ★
5209 E Marginal Way S, Seattle, WA 98134-2409
Tel (206) 762-0850 *Founded/Ownrshp* 1905
Sales 268.6MM^E *EMP* 750
SIC 1629

D-U-N-S 19-409-7960
MANSON CONSTRUCTION HOLDING CO
5209 E Marginal Way S, Seattle, WA 98134-2409
Tel (206) 762-0850 *Founded/Ownrshp* 2012
Sales 268.6MM^E *EMP* 751^E
SIC 1629 Marine construction; Marine construction
Pr: Eric V Haug

MANSON GOLF
See A MANSON-MOWAT JOINT VENTURE

D-U-N-S 01-135-9671
MANSON GULF LLC
(*Suby of* MANSON CONSTRUCTION CO) ★
392 Old Bayou Dularge Rd, Houma, LA 70363-7527
Tel (985) 580-1900 *Founded/Ownrshp* 1997
Sales 38.0MM^E *EMP* 150
Accts Moss-Adams Llp Seattle Washi
SIC 1629 Marine construction; Dock construction; Pier construction; Dredging contractor; Marine construction; Dock construction; Pier construction; Dredging contractor
VP: Robert Leblanc
Sfty Mgr: David Davis
Snr Mgr: Mark Laminack

D-U-N-S 60-543-9228
MANSUETO VENTURES LLC
FAST COMPANY MAGAZINE
7 World Trade Ctr Fl 29, New York, NY 10007-2174
Tel (212) 389-5300 *Founded/Ownrshp* 2005
Sales 79.3MM^E *EMP* 210
SIC 2721 Magazines: publishing only, not printed on site; Magazines: publishing only, not printed on site
CFO: Mark Rosenberg
Creative D: Kristine Kern
**Prin:* Jane Hazel
Ex Dir: Keith Hammonds
Mng Dir: Bob Lapointe
CTO: Reg Ungberg
Dir IT: Soma Mathiy
Dir IT: Soma Naylor
Web Dev: Yongzhi Huang
Software D: John Guaragno
VP Opers: Dennis Martineau

D-U-N-S 13-656-6382
MANTA INDUSTRIAL INC
4527 Columbia Ave, Hammond, IN 46327-1666
Tel (219) 937-8100 *Founded/Ownrshp* 2003
Sales 22.0MM *EMP* 150
SIC 7349

D-U-N-S 00-445-7503
MANTALINE CORP (OH)
4754 E High St, Mantua, OH 44255-9201
Tel (330) 274-2264 *Founded/Ownrshp* 1964
Sales 30.0MM^E *EMP* 135
SIC 3061 2822 3069

D-U-N-S 02-865-1552
MANTECA FORD-MERCURY INC
555 N Main St, Manteca, CA 95336-3926
Tel (209) 239-3561 *Founded/Ownrshp* 1997
Sales 20.7MM^E *EMP* 45
SIC 5511 Automobiles, new & used; Automobiles, new & used
Pr: Phil Waterford
Sec: Maria Cleghorn

D-U-N-S 05-322-7435
MANTECA TRAILER AND MOTOR HOME LLC (CA)
R V'S SACRAMENTO
204 S Vasconcellos Ave, Manteca, CA 95336-8682
Tel (209) 239-1267 *Founded/Ownrshp* 1970
Sales 32.1MM^E *EMP* 71
SIC 5561 7538

D-U-N-S 06-012-4047
MANTECA UNIFIED SCHOOL DISTRICT
2271 W Louise Ave, Manteca, CA 95337-8381
Tel (209) 825-3200 *Founded/Ownrshp* 1966
Sales 88.7MM^E *EMP* 1,400
Accts Vavrinek Trine Day & Co Ll
SIC 8211 Public combined elementary & secondary school; Public combined elementary & secondary school
Exec: Bryan Ehrenholm
**Prin:* Frank Gonzales
Pr Dir: Victoria Brunn
HC Dir: Bhatti Rupinder

D-U-N-S 13-962-7525
■ **MANTECH ADVANCED SYSTEMS INTERNATIONAL INC**
(*Suby of* MANTECH INTERNATIONAL CORP) ★
12015 Lee Jackson Mem Hwy, Fairfax, VA 22033-3300
Tel (703) 218-6000 *Founded/Ownrshp* 1985
Sales 45.2MM^E *EMP* 462
SIC 8711 Engineering services
Pr: Kevin Phillips
Pr: Peter Lamontagne
**Treas:* John A Moore Jr
**VP:* Matthew P Galaski

MANTECH ADVANCED SYSTEMS INTL
See MANTECH MISSION CYBER AND TECHNOLOGY SOLUTIONS INC

D-U-N-S 84-996-3566
■ **MANTECH ELECTRONICS INTEROPERABILITY SERVICES INC**
(*Suby of* MANTECH INTERNATIONAL CORP) ★
12015 Lee Jackson Mem Hwy, Fairfax, VA 22033-3300
Tel (703) 218-6396 *Founded/Ownrshp* 2008
Sales 19.0MM^E *EMP* 550
SIC 7373 7371 Computer integrated systems design; Custom computer programming services
Pr: Dan Keefe

D-U-N-S 83-891-8183
■ **MANTECH GRAY HAWK SYSTEMS INC**
(*Suby of* MANTECH INTERNATIONAL CORP) ★
7799 Leesburg Pike 700s, Falls Church, VA 22043-2408
Tel (703) 610-9232 *Founded/Ownrshp* 2005
Sales 60.9MM^E *EMP* 5,600
SIC 7373 7378 Systems integration services; Computer maintenance & repair; Systems integration services; Computer maintenance & repair
CEO: Harry Howton
**Pr:* Marshall Godwin
**Sr VP:* Michael Weixel
Board of Directors: Jeffrey S Brown, Geroge J Pederson, Kevin M Phillips

D-U-N-S 78-951-7976
■ **MANTECH INFORMATION SYSTEMS & TECHNOLOGY CORP**
(*Suby of* MANTECH INTERNATIONAL CORP) ★
12015 Lee Jackson Mem Hwy, Fairfax, VA 22033-3300
Tel (703) 218-6000 *Founded/Ownrshp* 2003
Sales 43.7MM^E *EMP* 300
SIC 7373 7371 Computer integrated systems design; Custom computer programming services
Pr: L William Varner
**Ch:* George J Pedersen
**Sr VP:* Margo Mentus
**VP:* Daniel J Keefe
**VP:* Kevin M Phillips
Snr Ntwrk: Mark Rigopoulos
IT Man: Catherine Stanton
Sftwr Eng: Jonathan Holmes
Opers Mgr: Patricia Buchanan
Sls Mgr: Scott Anderson
Board of Directors: Robert Butler, Diane Farah, Hui Markva, Paul Thorson

D-U-N-S 05-351-8312
▲ **MANTECH INTERNATIONAL CORP**
12015 Lee Jackson Hwy, Fairfax, VA 22033-3300
Tel (703) 218-6000 *Founded/Ownrshp* 1968
Sales 1.7MMM *EMP* 7,100^E
Tkr Sym MANT *Exch* NGS
SIC 7373 8711 7379 Systems software development services; Systems engineering, computer related; Engineering services; Computer related consulting services; Systems software development services; Systems engineering, computer related; Engineering services; Computer related consulting services
Ch Bd: George J Pedersen
Mng Pt: Jerry Donahoe
Pr: Louis M Addeo
Pr: Terry M Ryan
Pr: Terry Ryan
Pr: L William Varner
CFO: Judith L Bjornaas
CFO: John Moore
CFO: Kevin M Phillips
CFO: Ronald Spoehel
Bd of Dir: Joe Garcia
Chf Mktg O: Carl Buising
Ex VP: Jeffrey S Brown
Ex VP: Magdalena Conde-Jimenez
Ex VP: Bonnie J Cook
Ex VP: Carlos S Echalar
Ex VP: Ed Glabus
Ex VP: Daniel J Keefe
Ex VP: Sally Sullivan
Ex VP: Stan Surrette
Sr VP: Christopher Bishop
Board of Directors: Richard L Armitage, Mary K Bush, Barry G Campbell, Walter R Fatzinger Jr, Richard J Kerr, Kenneth A Minihan, Stephen W Porter

D-U-N-S 19-814-8751
■ MANTECH MISSION CYBER AND TECHNOLOGY SOLUTIONS INC
MANTECH ADVANCED SYSTEMS INTL
(*Suby of* MANTECH INTERNATIONAL CORP) ★
12015 Lee Jackson Mem Hwy, Fairfax, VA 22033-3300
Tel (703) 218-6000 *Founded/Ownrshp* 2002
Sales 31.3MM[E] *EMP* 469
SIC 8742 Management consulting services; Industry specialist consultants; Management consulting services; Industry specialist consultants
Pr: L William Varner
**Pr:* Daniel J Keefe
**CEO:* George J Pedersen
**Ex VP:* Kevin M Phillips
VP: Calvin III
Ex Dir: Steven Mantech
Prgrm Mgr: Kevin Brunner

D-U-N-S 12-318-2763
■ MANTECH SECURITY TECHNOLOGIES CORP
(*Suby of* MANTECH INTERNATIONAL CORP) ★
12015 Lee Jackson Mem Hwy, Fairfax, VA 22033-3300
Tel (703) 218-6000 *Founded/Ownrshp* 2000
Sales 28.0MM[E] *EMP* 576
SIC 8711 Engineering services
Pr: Louis M Addeo
COO: Bob Cole
**Ch:* George Pedersen
VP: Charles L Curran
VP: John P Ireland
VP: Nick Paone
Dir IT: Dan Webley
IT Man: Heather Anderson
IT Man: David Gower
IT Man: Kukrit Pantoomano

D-U-N-S 06-618-3039
■ MANTECH SRS TECHNOLOGIES INC
(*Suby of* MANTECH INTERNATIONAL CORP) ★
12015 Lee Jackson Mem Hwy, Fairfax, VA 22033-3300
Tel (703) 351-7300 *Founded/Ownrshp* 2000
Sales 43.0MM[E] *EMP* 904
Accts Kpmg Llp Costa Mesa Ca
SIC 8748 7371 Test development & evaluation service; Computer software development; Test development & evaluation service; Computer software development
Pr: Terry M Ryan
**Pr:* Kevin M Phillips
VP: Robert Boyd
Dir Bus: Anthony Quattromani
Secur Mgr: Mark McGovern

D-U-N-S 17-424-5993
■ MANTECH SYSTEMS ENGINEERING CORP
MANTECH-MESC
(*Suby of* MANTECH INTERNATIONAL CORP) ★
2250 Corp Park Dr Ste 500, Herndon, VA 20171-4842
Tel (703) 814-4200 *Founded/Ownrshp* 1985
Sales 111.4MM[E] *EMP* 2,501
SIC 7373 8711 Systems engineering, computer related; Engineering services; Systems engineering, computer related; Engineering services
CEO: George J Pedersen
**Pr:* Kenneth J Farquhar
**Treas:* John A Moore Jr
**Ex VP:* Jeffrey S Brown
**Ex VP:* M Stuart Davis
**Ex VP:* Sally Sullivan
**Sr VP:* Matthew P Galaski
**VP:* Louis M Addeo
**VP:* Kent A Bridges
**VP:* Kevin M Phillips
QC Dir: Liz Burnett

D-U-N-S 80-100-8228
■ MANTECH TELECOMMUNICATIONS AND INFORMATION SYSTEMS CORP
(*Suby of* MANTECH INTERNATIONAL CORP) ★
12015 Lee Jackson Mem Hwy, Fairfax, VA 22033-3300
Tel (703) 218-6000 *Founded/Ownrshp* 1982
Sales 84.2MM[E] *EMP* 1,113
SIC 7373 Computer systems analysis & design
Pr: Dan Keefe
Pr: Tom Baker
**Prin:* Ronald R Spoehl
Ex Dir: Hunter Trice
Snr Sftwr: Ben Newman
Software D: Nathaniel Hall

MANTECH-MESC
See MANTECH SYSTEMS ENGINEERING CORP

D-U-N-S 04-684-8081
MANTENO COMMUNITY UNIT SCHOOL DISTRICT 5
MANTENO CUSD 5
84 N Oak St, Manteno, IL 60950-1522
Tel (815) 468-1459 *Founded/Ownrshp* 1955
Sales 20.3MM[E] *EMP* 320
SIC 8211 Public combined elementary & secondary school; School board; Public combined elementary & secondary school; School board
Bd of Dir: Mark Stauffenberg
VP: Gary Preston
Exec: Deb Fortin
Psych: Chuck Parsons

MANTENO CUSD 5
See MANTENO COMMUNITY UNIT SCHOOL DISTRICT 5

D-U-N-S 00-223-5166
MANTH-BROWNELL INC (NY)
1120 Fyler Rd, Kirkville, NY 13082-9445
Tel (315) 687-7263 *Founded/Ownrshp* 1951, 1950
Sales 67.4MM[E] *EMP* 180
SIC 3451 Screw machine products; Screw machine products
Ch Bd: Wesley R Skinner Jr
**CFO:* Glenn Spaarling
**CFO:* Glenn Sparling
**VP:* Rob Pike
Opers Mgr: James Wilsey

D-U-N-S 00-602-0549 IMP
MANTHEI INC (MI)
3996 Charlevoix Ave, Petoskey, MI 49770-8426
Tel (231) 347-4672 *Founded/Ownrshp* 1945, 1967
Sales 27.4MM[E] *EMP* 150
SIC 2435 Veneer stock, hardwood
Pr: Tom Manthei
**Treas:* Daniel Manthei
**VP:* James Manthei
Sls Mgr: Jason Miller

MANTIS CRANES
See TADANO MANTIS CORP

MANTIS MANUFACTURING DIVISION
See SCHILLER GROUNDS CARE INC

MANTUA BED FRAMES
See MANTUA MANUFACTURING CO

D-U-N-S 00-415-7210 IMP
MANTUA MANUFACTURING CO (OH)
MANTUA BED FRAMES
7900 Northfield Rd, Cleveland, OH 44146-5525
Tel (440) 232-8865 *Founded/Ownrshp* 1952, 1988
Sales 37.9MM[E] *EMP* 120
SIC 2514 Frames for box springs or bedsprings: metal; Frames for box springs or bedsprings: metal
Pr: David Jaffe
VP: Dirk Smith
IT Man: Jim Williams
Plnt Mgr: Mike Bosler
VP Mktg: Neil Dwyer

D-U-N-S 82-910-4129
MANU KAI LLC
157 Bldg Pacific Missile, Kekaha, HI 96752
Tel (808) 335-4842 *Founded/Ownrshp* 2006
Sales 7.4MM[E] *EMP* 456
SIC 8071 8748 7372 Biological laboratory; Telecommunications consultant; Prepackaged software; Biological laboratory; Telecommunications consultant; Prepackaged software

D-U-N-S 06-631-6522 IMP
MANUAL WOODWORKERS & WEAVERS INC
3737 Howard Gap Rd, Hendersonville, NC 28792-3174
Tel (828) 692-7333 *Founded/Ownrshp* 1974
Sales 92.7MM[E] *EMP* 506[E]
SIC 2392 Household furnishings
Pr: Travis L Oates
**CFO:* James Clarke
**Co-Pr:* Molly Oates Sherrill
Exec: Gregory Horn
Genl Mgr: Keith Lyerly
VP Opers: Randy Gilliland
Plnt Mgr: Scott Sargent
Prd Mgr: Nathan Byrd
Sls Mgr: Susan Sullivan

MANUEL AUTO LEASING
See MANUEL AUTO SALES LTD

D-U-N-S 09-409-6203
MANUEL AUTO SALES LTD
MANUEL AUTO LEASING
8075 Boulevard 26, North Richland Hills, TX 76180-7157
Tel (817) 788-2994 *Founded/Ownrshp* 1990
Sales 23.1MM[E] *EMP* 89
SIC 5511 Automobiles, new & used; Vans, new & used; Pickups, new & used; Automobiles, new & used; Vans, new & used; Pickups, new & used
Pr: Tommy Manuel
**VP:* Rosalie Manuel

D-U-N-S 09-013-6763
MANUEL FREIJE ARCE INC
Km 3 2 Brrio Plmas Rr 165, Catano, PR 00962
Tel (787) 769-2933 *Founded/Ownrshp* 1952
Sales 39.7MM[E] *EMP* 75
SIC 5063 5074 Wiring devices; Plumbing fittings & supplies
Pr: Ariel Freije Betances
**Treas:* Carlos Betances
**Sec:* Manuel Freije Betances Jr
**VP:* Rafael Echeverria

D-U-N-S 18-116-6323
MANUEL HUERTA TRUCKING INC
21 Kipper St, Rio Rico, AZ 85648-6236
Tel (520) 281-4876 *Founded/Ownrshp* 1977
Sales 27.7MM[E] *EMP* 150
SIC 4213 Trucking, except local; Trucking, except local
Pr: Manuel Huerta
**VP:* Cecilia Huerta
CTO: Adrian Ramos
Dir IT: Norma Carasco
IT Man: Rafael Espericueta

D-U-N-S 61-079-8654
MANUEL LUIS CONSTRUCTION CO INC
M LUIS CONSTRUCTION CO
12200 Plum Orchard Dr, Silver Spring, MD 20904-7842
Tel (410) 545-0641 *Founded/Ownrshp* 1985
Sales 41.4MM[E] *EMP* 100[E]
SIC 1611 1771 7353 Highway & street paving contractor; Concrete work; Heavy construction equipment rental; Highway & street paving contractor; Concrete work; Heavy construction equipment rental
CEO: Cidalia Luis-Akbar
**VP:* Natalia Luis

MANUEL LUJAN AGENCIES
See MANUEL LUJAN INSURANCE INC

D-U-N-S 07-834-0247
MANUEL LUJAN INSURANCE INC
MANUEL LUJAN AGENCIES
7770 Jefferson St Ne # 100, Albuquerque, NM 87109-4359
Tel (505) 266-7771 *Founded/Ownrshp* 1997
Sales NA *EMP* 105
SIC 6411 Insurance agents, brokers & service
Ch Bd: Edward L Lujan
**Pr:* Larry E Lujan
COO: Steve Riddle
CFO: Bredt Clay
Sr VP: Cricket Musch
**VP:* Joe Lujan
**VP:* Tom Padilla

D-U-N-S 62-193-8448
MANUEL VILLA ENTERPRISES INC
LA PERLA TAPATIA
710 Lander Ave, Turlock, CA 95380-5641
Tel (209) 669-2500 *Founded/Ownrshp* 1980
Sales 55.4MM[E] *EMP* 230
SIC 2099 Tortillas, fresh or refrigerated; Tortillas, fresh or refrigerated
Pr: Manuel Villa

D-U-N-S 61-207-3361
MANUEL W LLOYD INC
GEEKS IN A FLASH
1900 Eastwood Rd Ste 27, Wilmington, NC 28403-7205
Tel (910) 210-0485 *Founded/Ownrshp* 1989
Sales 13.8MM[E] *EMP* 300
SIC 5734 8748 Computer & software stores; Communications consulting; Computer & software stores; Communications consulting
CEO: Manuel W Lloyd

D-U-N-S 08-384-0520 IMP
MANUFACTURED ASSEMBLIES CORP
MAC
1625 Fieldstone Way, Vandalia, OH 45377-9317
Tel (937) 454-0722 *Founded/Ownrshp* 1991
Sales 30.0MM[E] *EMP* 200
SIC 3699

D-U-N-S 83-567-6024
MANUFACTURED DUCT & SUPPLY CO
M D S
6945 Business Ct, Doraville, GA 30340-1446
Tel (770) 263-8688 *Founded/Ownrshp* 1995
Sales 20.4MM[E] *EMP* 30
SIC 5075 3444 Warm air heating & air conditioning; Ducts, sheet metal
CEO: Roger Torri
**CFO:* Patrick Dixon
VP: Jim Boykin
**VP:* Kenny Simpson
Genl Mgr: Joey Britt
Sls Mgr: Jeff Fix

D-U-N-S 00-697-6724 IMP/EXP
■ MANUFACTURERS AND TRADERS TRUST CO
M&T
(*Suby of* WILMINGTON TRUST CORP) ★
1 M And T Plz, Buffalo, NY 14203-2309
Tel (716) 842-4200 *Founded/Ownrshp* 1856, 2011
Sales NA *EMP* 14,243
SIC 6022 State trust companies accepting deposits, commercial; State trust companies accepting deposits, commercial
CEO: Robert G Wilmers
**V Ch:* Carl L Campbell
**CFO:* Michael P Pinto
**Ofcr:* Richard S Gold
**Ex VP:* Emerson L Brumback
**Ex VP:* Atwood Collins III
**Ex VP:* John F Cook
VP: Robert S Graber
Brnch Mgr: Wendy Pia
Sales Exec: Mark Fuller

D-U-N-S 00-958-6256
MANUFACTURERS BANK
(*Suby of* SUMITOMO MITSUI BANKING CORPORATION)
515 S Figueroa St Ste 400, Los Angeles, CA 90071-3323
Tel (213) 489-6200 *Founded/Ownrshp* 1990
Sales NA *EMP* 269
SIC 6022 State trust companies accepting deposits, commercial; State trust companies accepting deposits, commercial
CEO: Mitsugu Serizawa
Pr: Koichi Miyata
**Pr:* Naresh Sheth
**Ex VP:* Adrian Danescu
Ex VP: Yoshihiro Takamura
Ex VP: Vicente Timiraos
Sr VP: Thomas Cowan
**Sr VP:* Ted Mergenthaler
Sr VP: Alan Naiman
Sr VP: Carol Nieman
Sr VP: David Orr
Sr VP: Richard Salmon
Sr VP: Kazuya Tojo
Sr VP: Sean Walker
Sr VP: Donn Yamada
VP: Manny Ahsan
VP: Blanca Alfaro
VP: Chris Butcher
VP: Ron Cerros
VP: William Chan
VP: Suyi Chen

D-U-N-S 96-826-0323 IMP/EXP
■ MANUFACTURERS CHEMICALS LLC
(*Suby of* SYNALLOY CORP) ★
4325 Old Tasso Rd Ne, Cleveland, TN 37312-5836
Tel (423) 476-6666 *Founded/Ownrshp* 1919
Sales 120.8MM[E] *EMP* 406
SIC 2899 Chemical preparations; Chemical preparations
Pr: Larry Sloan
**Ex VP:* J Greg Gibson
**Ex VP:* Kevin Hrebenar
VP: Mike Junkins
**VP:* Ron Smesny

D-U-N-S 00-601-0599 IMP/EXP
MANUFACTURERS EQUIPMENT & SUPPLY CO
MESCO
2401 Lapeer Rd, Flint, MI 48503-4350
Tel (810) 239-2173 *Founded/Ownrshp* 1945
Sales 32.9MM[E] *EMP* 65[E]
SIC 5085 4225 4731 Industrial supplies; General warehousing & storage; Freight transportation arrangement
Ch: R Mark Timyan
**Pr:* Gregg M Gruizenga
**Treas:* Steve J Timyan
Prgrm Mgr: Tom Tereau
Prgrm Mgr: Rich Tuck
IT Man: Andrew Tichelaar
VP Sls: Christine Jones
Sls Mgr: George Heiman

D-U-N-S 01-073-0120 IMP
MANUFACTURERS INDUSTRIAL GROUP LLC (TN)
M I G
659 Natchez Trace Dr, Lexington, TN 38351-4125
Tel (731) 968-3601 *Founded/Ownrshp* 1997
Sales 119.2MM[E] *EMP* 407
SIC 3499 2531 Automobile seat frames, metal; Public building & related furniture; Automobile seat frames, metal; Public building & related furniture
CEO: Andre Gist
Mtls Mgr: Jeff Woods

D-U-N-S 01-133-6740 IMP
MANUFACTURERS RESERVE SUPPLY INC
MRS LUMBER
40 Woolsey St, Irvington, NJ 07111-4012
Tel (973) 373-1881 *Founded/Ownrshp* 1931
Sales 31.8MM *EMP* 30
SIC 5031

D-U-N-S 86-938-0840
MANUFACTURERS SERVICES LIMITED
(*Suby of* CELESTICA INC)
300 Baker Ave Ste 106, Concord, MA 01742-2131
Tel (978) 287-5630 *Founded/Ownrshp* 2004
Sales 171.9MM[E] *EMP* 2,280
SIC 3571 3577 3572 3661 3663 Electronic computers; Computer peripheral equipment; Computer storage devices; Telephone sets, all types except cellular radio; Cellular radio telephone; Electronic computers; Computer peripheral equipment; Computer storage devices; Telephone sets, all types except cellular radio; Cellular radio telephone
VP Opers: John Boucher
Treas: Sean T Lannan
Sr Cor Off: Robert Donahue
Sr Cor Off: Albert Motini
Chf Cred: Tom Pugh
Bd of Dir: Robert Bradshaw
Bd of Dir: George Chamillard
Bd of Dir: Thompson Dean
Bd of Dir: Jeffrey Fishman
Bd of Dir: John Fort
Bd of Dir: Dermott O'Flanagan
Bd of Dir: John J Walsh
Bd of Dir: William Weyand
Bd of Dir: Curtis Wozniak
Bd of Dir: Karl Wyss
Ofcr: Rodolfo Archbold
Ex VP: Bruce Leasure
Ex VP: Bert Notini
Ex VP: James N Poor
VP: Richard Buckingham
VP: Frank Coyle

D-U-N-S 62-708-8719 IMP
MANUFACTURERS SUPPLY CO
MANSCO
4235 Corporate Exch Dr, Hudsonville, MI 49426-1950
Tel (616) 669-4190 *Founded/Ownrshp* 1991
Sales 26.3MM[E] *EMP* 50[E]
SIC 5072 5085 Hardware; Fasteners & fastening equipment
Pr: James H Mol
Off Mgr: Michelle Schippers
IT Man: Garrett Lampson
S&M/VP: Mark Hendrickson

D-U-N-S 10-730-9502
MANUFACTURERS TRANSPORTATION INC
1411 Millwood Rd, McKinney, TX 75069-7159
Tel (972) 562-8686 *Founded/Ownrshp* 1997
Sales 24.0MM[E] *EMP* 9
SIC 4731 Truck transportation brokers; Truck transportation brokers
Pr: Curtis Robinson
**Sec:* Penny Robinson
**VP:* Matthew Robinson

D-U-N-S 07-841-5672
MANUFACTURING CONSULTING SERVICES LLC (TX)
SUMMIT ENERGY EQUIPMENT
41 Pioneer Pkwy, Sulphur Springs, TX 75482-6637
Tel (903) 951-1217 *Founded/Ownrshp* 2006
Sales 36.4MM[E] *EMP* 96
SIC 5211 Insulation & energy conservation products
CEO: Bryan Hurley
**CFO:* Mark Ashton

MANUFACTURING FACILITY
See WOODCASE FINE CABINETRY INC

D-U-N-S 17-527-8746
MANUFACTURING GROUP OF AMERICA INC
2841 Pierce St, Dallas, TX 75233-1535
Tel (214) 467-4444 *Founded/Ownrshp* 1984
Sales 35.8MM[E] *EMP* 700
SIC 2434 5031 Wood kitchen cabinets; Vanities, bathroom: wood; Structural assemblies, prefabricated: wood; Kitchen cabinets; Wood kitchen cabinets; Vanities, bathroom: wood; Structural assemblies, prefabricated: wood; Kitchen cabinets
CEO: James Bradley West
Sr VP: Mike Ferguson

D-U-N-S 18-498-5328 IMP
MANUFACTURING RESOURCES INTERNATIONAL INC
MRI
6415 Shiloh Rd E, Alpharetta, GA 30005-8345
Tel (770) 295-1201 *Founded/Ownrshp* 2004
Sales 36.1MM[E] *EMP* 97[E]
SIC 3823 Digital displays of process variables

Pr: Peter Kaszycki
VP: Michael Lecave
VP: David Williams
**Prin:* William R Dunn
Sftwr Eng: Michael Dunn

D-U-N-S 80-695-1570
MANUFACTURING TECHNIQUES INC
MTEQ
140 Technology Park Dr, Kilmarnock, VA 22482-3837
Tel (804) 436-9000 *Founded/Ownrshp* 2005
Sales 57.4MM^E *EMP* 150^E
SIC 3679 8733 Harness assemblies for electronic use: wire or cable; Physical research, noncommercial; Harness assemblies for electronic use: wire or cable; Physical research, noncommercial
Pr: Mary Williams
**Sec:* Gregory A Williams
Ofcr: Andrew Davis
Ofcr: Angela Moulton
**VP:* Clara Schuster
Prgrm Mgr: Kurt Mortensen
Genl Mgr: Greg Demeo
IT Man: Danny Sullivan
Software D: Jacob Bowman

D-U-N-S 03-341-1950 IMP/EXP
MANUFACTURING TECHNOLOGY INC
1702 W Washington St, South Bend, IN 46628-2061
Tel (574) 233-9490 *Founded/Ownrshp* 2001
Sales 47.6MM *EMP* 170
SIC 3548 7692 Welding apparatus; Welding repair; Welding apparatus; Welding repair
Pr: Robert C Adams II
Pr: Michael Skinner
**CFO:* Guy Harper
**VP:* Daniel C Adams
**Genl Mgr:* Doug Wait
Genl Mgr: William Wilczynski
Sftwr Eng: John Kingsbury
Sftwr Eng: David Zitnik
Mtls Mgr: Solloway Gary
Sfty Mgr: Dan Maglish
Plnt Mgr: Frank Lanko

D-U-N-S 60-245-6402
MANUGISTICS GROUP INC
(*Suby of* JDA SOFTWARE GROUP INC) ★
14400 N 87th St, Scottsdale, AZ 85260-3649
Tel (480) 308-3000 *Founded/Ownrshp* 2006
Sales 35.2MM^E *EMP* 916
SIC 7372 Prepackaged software; Prepackaged software
CEO: Joe Cowan
COO: Chris Kozio
Chf Mktg O: Larry Ferrere

D-U-N-S 06-927-8166
MANUGISTICS INC
(*Suby of* MANUGISTICS GROUP INC) ★
14400 N 87th St, Scottsdale, AZ 85260-3649
Tel (480) 308-3000 *Founded/Ownrshp* 1986
Sales 28.9MM^E *EMP* 679^E
SIC 7371 5045 7379 7376 7372 Computer software development; Computer software; Computer related consulting services; Computer facilities management; Prepackaged software
CEO: Joseph Cowan

D-U-N-S 07-118-7686 IMP
MANUGRAPH AMERICAS INC
(*Suby of* MANUGRAPH INDIA LIMITED)
158 Damhill Rd, Millersburg, PA 17061
Tel (717) 362-3243 *Founded/Ownrshp* 2006
Sales 26.0MM^E *EMP* 110
SIC 3555 Printing presses; Printing presses
Pr: Brian La Bine
CFO: Bill Hummer
**CFO:* Clarence Smith
VP: Jack Little
**VP:* Kyle R Monroe
Genl Mgr: Suresh Shah
S&M/VP: Ron Ehrhardt
Sls Dir: Ed Heim

D-U-N-S 60-459-7773 EXP
MANUTECH ASSEMBLY INC
8181 Nw 91st Ter Ste 10, Medley, FL 33166-2121
Tel (305) 888-2800 *Founded/Ownrshp* 2010
Sales 58.0MM^E *EMP* 500
SIC 3612 3677 Power transformers, electric; Inductors, electronic; Power transformers, electric; Inductors, electronic
Ch: Nadia Durban
**Pr:* Lance P Durban
**VP:* Sam Seyfi
Sls Mgr: Valerie Gauthier

D-U-N-S 01-003-0695
MANWEB SERVICES INC
FREIJE ENGINEERED SOLUTIONS CO
11800 Exit 5 Pkwy Ste 106, Fishers, IN 46037-7989
Tel (317) 863-0007 *Founded/Ownrshp* 2003
Sales 56.2MM^E *EMP* 200^E
SIC 1711 1731 Refrigeration contractor; Electrical work; Refrigeration contractor; Electrical work
CEO: Michael P Webster
COO: Mike Farrell
**CFO:* Brian Fillenwarth
Ex VP: Jeff Nicholas
VP: John Fisher
IT Man: Brent Frantz
Sls Mgr: Robert Ritz
Snr Mgr: David McCormick

D-U-N-S 07-968-6665
MAO FOODS LLC
100 G T Thames Dr Ste D, Starkville, MS 39759-8836
Tel (662) 648-8352 *Founded/Ownrshp* 2014
Sales 6.8MM^E *EMP* 500
SIC 5812 Hamburger stand

MAOF
See MEXICAN AMERICAN OPPORTUNITY FOUNDATION

D-U-N-S 00-318-5758
MAOLA MILK AND ICE CREAM CO LLC
MARYLAND & VIRGINIA MILK PROD
(*Suby of* MARVA MAID DAIRY DIVISION) ★
305 Avenue C, New Bern, NC 28560-3113
Tel (252) 638-1131 *Founded/Ownrshp* 1935, 2003
Sales 78.2MM^E *EMP* 335^E
SIC 2026 2024 Fluid milk; Ice cream, bulk; Fluid milk; Ice cream, bulk
**Genl Mgr:* Steve Nicoll
IT Man: Amy Horrell
Sfty Mgr: Sue Shivar
Plnt Mgr: Darrell Duvall
Snr Mgr: Lisa Dixon

MAP AUTOMOTIVE OF MILWAUKEE
See MAP AUTOMOTIVE WAREHOUSE INC

D-U-N-S 09-078-8696
MAP AUTOMOTIVE WAREHOUSE INC
MAP AUTOMOTIVE OF MILWAUKEE
1000 Camera Ave Ste D, Saint Louis, MO 63126-1037
Tel (314) 752-7477 *Founded/Ownrshp* 1986
Sales 20.8MM^E *EMP* 50
SIC 5013 Automotive batteries
Pr: Jeff Lowe
Dist Mgr: Bradley Miller

D-U-N-S 61-170-3414
MAP CARGO GLOBAL LOGISTICS
2501 Santa Fe Ave, Redondo Beach, CA 90278-1117
Tel (310) 297-8300 *Founded/Ownrshp* 1990
Sales 35.5MM^E *EMP* 85
SIC 4731 2448 Domestic freight forwarding; Cargo containers, wood & wood with metal; Domestic freight forwarding; Cargo containers, wood & wood with metal
Pr: Marek Adam Panasewicz
VP: Quinn Marsh
Genl Mgr: Jarry Sessions

D-U-N-S 61-919-1042
MAP COMMUNICATIONS INC
840 Greenbrier Cir, Chesapeake, VA 23320-3097
Tel (757) 424-1191 *Founded/Ownrshp* 1990
Sales 75.3MM^E *EMP* 495
SIC 7389 Telephone services; Telephone services
Pr: Garry J Morrison
VP: Jennifer Lane
**VP:* Don Thaler
Exec: Karen Oluwabusola
Snr Sftwr: Larry Clifton
Sales Exec: Debbie Rice
Sls Mgr: Willie Cintron

MAP CRUDE PETRO & NATURAL GAS
See MARATHON OIL CO

D-U-N-S 95-749-1335 IMP
MAP INDUSTRIES INC
OEM TUBE ASSEMBLIES
191 Stone Container Dr, Clarksville, TN 37040-5026
Tel (931) 206-9256 *Founded/Ownrshp* 1995
Sales 27.7MM^E *EMP* 130
SIC 3443 Fabricated plate work (boiler shop); Fabricated plate work (boiler shop)
Ch Bd: Earl O Bradley III
**Pr:* Barry Rollins
**CFO:* Chris Patton
Mtls Mgr: Jan Seay

D-U-N-S 06-858-8789
MAP INTERNATIONAL (INC) (IL)
MEDICAL ASSISTANCE PROGRAMS
4700 Glynco Pkwy, Brunswick, GA 31525-6901
Tel (912) 265-6010 *Founded/Ownrshp* 1954
Sales 320.0MM *EMP* 200
Accts Capin Crouse Llp Atlanta Geo
SIC 8399 Health & welfare council; Health & welfare council
Pr: Steve Stirling
**CEO:* Chok-Pin Foo
**CFO:* Daniel C Reed
**Ch:* Immanuel Phangaraj
VP: Edwin Corr
Assoc Dir: Jacqueline Cameron
IT Man: Dennis Rice

MAP OF EASTON
See MOLDED ACOUSTICAL PRODUCTS OF EASTON INC

D-U-N-S 16-735-3437 IMP/EXP
■ **MAP PHARMACEUTICALS INC**
(A DEVELOPMENT STAGE ENTERPRISE)
(*Suby of* ALLERGAN INC) ★
2400 Byshore Pkwy Ste 200, Mountain View, CA 94043
Tel (650) 625-8790 *Founded/Ownrshp* 2003
Sales 23.0MM *EMP* 116^E
SIC 2834 Pharmaceutical preparations; Pharmaceutical preparations
Pr: Timothy S Nelson
**CEO:* David Ei Pyott
**CFO:* Christopher Y Chai
**Ofcr:* Thomas A Armer PHD
**Sr VP:* Charlene A Friedman
**Sr VP:* Anastasios E Gianakakos
Sr VP: Tassos Gianakakos
Sr VP: Donald J Kellerman
VP: Alan H Cohen
VP: Frederick H Graff
VP: Thomas P McCracken
VP: Alan Petro
Board of Directors: Gerri A Henwood, Bernard J Kelley, Matthew V McPherron, W James O'shea, Scott R Ward, H Ward Wolff

D-U-N-S 62-326-0700
MAP ROYALTY INC
3000 El Camino Real 5-70, Palo Alto, CA 94306-2100
Tel (650) 324-9095 *Founded/Ownrshp* 1989
Sales 24.1MM^E *EMP* 92
SIC 6792 Oil royalty traders; Oil royalty traders
CEO: Jane Woodward
CFO: Steve Hall
**Sr VP:* Keith Davidge
MIS Dir: Guy Hensler
MIS Dir: Guy Mills
Dir IT: Jim Dueltgen

MAP SERVICE
See MICHIGAN AIR PRODUCTS CO

MAP SYSTEMS AND SOLUTIONS
See MAPSYS INC

MAP YOUR SHOW
See GARDNER BUSINESS MEDIA INC

D-U-N-S 02-494-1077
■ **MAPCO EXPRESS INC**
(*Suby of* DELEK US HOLDINGS INC) ★
7102 Commerce Way, Brentwood, TN 37027-2896
Tel (615) 771-6701 *Founded/Ownrshp* 2001
Sales 133.8MM^E *EMP* 1,800
SIC 5541 5411 Gasoline service stations; Convenience stores, chain; Gasoline service stations; Convenience stores, chain
Pr: Uzi Yemin
**COO:* Lyn Gregory
**CFO:* Ed Morgan
Dist Mgr: Jason Durrance
Store Mgr: Robin Box
**VP Mktg:* Paul Pierce
Board of Directors: Carlos E Jord, Ezra U Yemin

D-U-N-S 80-747-4044
MAPCO INC
423 W Cevallos, San Antonio, TX 78204-1610
Tel (210) 277-6450 *Founded/Ownrshp* 1990
Sales 76.1MM^E *EMP* 150
Accts Ridout Barrett & Co Pc
SIC 1542 Commercial & office building, new construction; Commercial & office buildings, renovation & repair; Custom builders, non-residential; Commercial & office building, new construction; Commercial & office buildings, renovation & repair; Custom builders, non-residential
Pr: Michael Padron
**Sec:* Maria Padron
Dir IT: Gary Stewart

D-U-N-S 14-834-5382 IMP/EXP
MAPEI CORP
(*Suby of* MAPEI SPA)
1144 E Newport Center Dr, Deerfield Beach, FL 33442-7725
Tel (954) 246-8888 *Founded/Ownrshp* 1983
Sales 265.0MM^E *EMP* 875
SIC 2891 Adhesives; Adhesives
Pr: Luigi Di Geso
VP: Matthew Nordloh
Dir Bus: Laith Haboubi
**Prin:* Rainer Blair
Genl Mgr: Luigi Digeso
Dir IT: Oscar Garcia
IT Man: Mikhail Bunich
IT Man: Latasha Butler
IT Man: Walt Reister
Plnt Mgr: Claude Brouin
Plnt Mgr: Tom Monteagu
Board of Directors: Dr Giorgio Squinzi

D-U-N-S 00-338-3452 IMP
MAPES PIANO STRING CO
1 Wire Mill Rd, Elizabethton, TN 37643-2757
Tel (423) 543-3195 *Founded/Ownrshp* 1955
Sales 61.7MM^E *EMP* 200
SIC 3495 3931 Instrument springs, precision; Strings, musical instrument; Instrument springs, precision; Strings, musical instrument
Ch Bd: William L Schaff
**Ex VP:* Robert L Schaff
Ex VP: Robert Schaff
**VP:* Frank L Schaff
IT Man: Frank Schaff
Sls Mgr: Andy Wilson

D-U-N-S 05-525-4867
MAPFRE INSURANCE CO
901 Franklin Ave, Garden City, NY 11530-2933
Tel (516) 564-8000 *Founded/Ownrshp* 2011
Sales NA *EMP* 2
SIC 6411 Insurance agents, brokers & service; Insurance agents, brokers & service
Pr: Gerral Felson

D-U-N-S 17-725-4497
MAPFRE INSURANCE CO
MAPFRE RE INSURANCE
(*Suby of* MAPFRE RE INSURANCE) ★
100 Campus Dr, Florham Park, NJ 07932-1020
Tel (973) 443-0443 *Founded/Ownrshp* 2000
Sales NA *EMP* 14
SIC 6311 Life insurance carriers; Life reinsurance; Life insurance carriers; Life reinsurance
Pr: Javier Fernandez-Cid
**CFO:* John J Lynch
**Ofcr:* Carlos Sanzo
**Sr VP:* Javier San Basilio
**VP:* Mariam George

D-U-N-S 16-757-9080
MAPFRE PRAICO CORP
(*Suby of* MAPFRE AMERICA SA)
297 Ave Chardon Urb Tres, San Juan, PR 00918
Tel (787) 250-6500 *Founded/Ownrshp* 2004
Sales NA *EMP* 600^E
SIC 6411 Insurance agents & brokers; Insurance agents & brokers
CEO: Raul Costilla
**Ch Bd:* Antonio Huertas
VP: Antonio Esposito

MAPFRE RE INSURANCE
See MAPFRE INSURANCE CO

MAPFRE RE INSURANCE
See R E MAPFRE HOLDINGS INC

D-U-N-S 01-283-5133
MAPFRE USA CORP (FL)
(*Suby of* MAPFRE USA CORP) ★
3401 Nw 82nd Ave Ste 100, Doral, FL 33122-1052
Tel (305) 477-5552 *Founded/Ownrshp* 1988
Sales 53.7MM^E *EMP* 1,495
SIC 8742 Management consulting services; Management consulting services
Pr: Jorge Fernandez Silva

D-U-N-S 10-583-1531
MAPFRE USA CORP
(*Suby of* MAPFRE, SA)
211 Main St, Webster, MA 01570-2249
Tel (508) 943-9000 *Founded/Ownrshp* 2008
Sales NA *EMP* 2,373
SIC 6331 Fire, marine & casualty insurance; Automobile insurance; Fire, marine & casualty insurance; Automobile insurance
Pr: Jaime Tamayo
**CFO:* Randall V Becker
CFO: Jose Martinez
**Treas:* Robert E McKenna
Ex VP: David Cochrane
Area Mgr: Andres Lorenzana
Genl Mgr: Esteban Tejera
IT Man: Jayne Koziol
IT Man: Ines J Torres
Info Man: Ray Perez
Doctor: Ana Wandurraga

MAPLE ALLEY INN
See OPPORTUNITY COUNCIL

D-U-N-S 01-824-4608
MAPLE CITY ICE CO (INC) (OH)
371 Cleveland Rd, Norwalk, OH 44857-9027
Tel (419) 668-2531 *Founded/Ownrshp* 1917
Sales 25.2MM^E *EMP* 85
SIC 5181 Beer & other fermented malt liquors; Beer & other fermented malt liquors
Pr: Patricia Hipp
**Treas:* Jeff Hipp
**VP:* John Hipp

D-U-N-S 15-700-9580
MAPLE CREEK BAPTIST CHURCH
609 S Main St, Greer, SC 29650-2348
Tel (864) 877-1791 *Founded/Ownrshp* 1887
Sales 11.7MM^E *EMP* 350
SIC 8661 Baptist Church; Baptist Church
Trst: Melvin Smith

D-U-N-S 88-392-2510
MAPLE CREEK MINING INC
56854 Pleasant Ridge Rd, Alledonia, OH 43902-9716
Tel (740) 926-9205 *Founded/Ownrshp* 1994
Sales 25.0MM^E *EMP* 400
SIC 1222 Bituminous coal-underground mining; Bituminous coal-underground mining
Pr: Robert E Murray
**Treas:* Michael Loiacono
**VP:* John Ferelli

D-U-N-S 00-302-3272
MAPLE DONUTS INC (PA)
3455 E Market St, York, PA 17402-2696
Tel (717) 757-7826 *Founded/Ownrshp* 1946, 1975
Sales 80.9MM^E *EMP* 250
SIC 2051 5461 Doughnuts, except frozen; Bakeries; Doughnuts, except frozen; Bakeries
Pr: Charles F Burnside
**Treas:* Susan M Burnside
**VP:* Ralph E Wooten
VP Sls: Damian Burnside

D-U-N-S 03-270-5838
MAPLE GROVE HOSPITAL CORP
9875 Hospital Dr, Maple Grove, MN 55369-4648
Tel (763) 581-1000 *Founded/Ownrshp* 2006
Sales 151.1MM *EMP* 34^E
Accts Deloitte & Touche Llp Minneap
SIC 8062 General medical & surgical hospitals; General medical & surgical hospitals
Pr: Andrew S Cochrane
Dir Lab: Stephanie Baumann
Dir Rx: Megan Matack
Nurse Mgr: Rebecca Farmer
CIO: Pat Taffe
Mktg Dir: Jennifer Krippner
Pathlgst: Sue Schlafmann
Doctor: Leigh Rowan-Kelly MD
Pharmcst: Kirsten Bosch
Pharmcst: Kelly Hadsall
Pharmcst: Amanda Walker

MAPLE HEIGHTS BOARD EDUCATION
See MAPLE HEIGHTS CITY SCHOOL DISTRICT

D-U-N-S 09-393-0071
MAPLE HEIGHTS CITY SCHOOL DISTRICT (OH)
MAPLE HEIGHTS BOARD EDUCATION
5740 Lawn Ave, Maple Heights, OH 44137-3870
Tel (216) 587-6100 *Founded/Ownrshp* 1915
Sales 25.4MM^E *EMP* 500
SIC 8211 Public senior high school; Public junior high school; Public elementary school; Public senior high school; Public junior high school; Public elementary school
**Pr:* Michael White
**Treas:* Chris Krouse
VP: Michelle Holmes
Dir Sec: Richard Ritchie
Dir IT: Jim Filitic
Schl Brd P: Pam Crews

MAPLE HILL CHRYSLER PLYMOUTH
See TRANSIT L L C

D-U-N-S 00-644-7627
MAPLE ISLAND INC
2497 7th Ave E Ste 105, Saint Paul, MN 55109-4485
Tel (651) 773-1000 *Founded/Ownrshp* 1935
Sales 24.5MM^E *EMP* 90
SIC 2023 Dry, condensed, evaporated dairy products; Dry, condensed, evaporated dairy products
CEO: Greg Johnson
**Pr:* Daniel O'Brien
Dir IT: Harry Drager
Opers Mgr: Randy Biebl

MAPLE KNOLL VILLAGE
See KNOLL MAPLE COMMUNITIES INC

MAPLE LEAF FARMS
See MAPLE LEAF INC

D-U-N-S 01-652-2823
MAPLE LEAF FARMS INC
SERENADE FOODS
(*Suby of* MAPLE LEAF FARMS) ★
9166 N 200 E, Milford, IN 46542-9722
Tel (574) 453-4500 *Founded/Ownrshp* 1967
Sales 7.2MM^E *EMP* 1,100
SIC 0259 2015 Duck farm; Duck slaughtering & processing; Duck farm; Duck slaughtering & processing
Ch Bd: Terry L Tucker
**Pr:* Scott M Tucker
**CFO:* Scott Reinholt
**CFO:* John Tucker
VP: Tony Flesch
Dir Lab: Annette Doster
Comm Dir: David Lee
CIO: Bruce Baum
CTO: Joel Harstine
Netwrk Eng: James Chesley
Plnt Mgr: Lee Allen

MAPLE LEAF FOODS
See BUFFALO BASIC INGREDIENTS INC

D-U-N-S 02-381-5108
MAPLE LEAF FOODS USA INC
(*Suby of* MAPLE LEAF FOODS INC)
195 Spy Glass Way, Hendersonville, TN 37075-8587
Tel (615) 826-7467 *Founded/Ownrshp* 2001
Sales 7.3MM^E *EMP* 450
SIC 5461 Bakeries; Bakeries
Pr: Richard Lan
VP: Michelle Fehr

D-U-N-S 15-342-7885 IMP/EXP
MAPLE LEAF INC
MAPLE LEAF FARMS
101 E Church St, Leesburg, IN 46538-7701
Tel (574) 453-4455 *Founded/Ownrshp* 1958
Sales 7.2MM^E *EMP* 1,100
SIC 0259 2015 5159 Duck farm; Ducks, processed; Chicken, processed; Feathers; Duck farm; Ducks, processed; Chicken, processed; Feathers
Ch Bd: Terry L Tucker
CFO: Scott Reinholt
Co-Pr: John Tucker
VP: Mike Turk
Dir Lab: Rhonda Murdoch
Genl Mgr: Wes Rader

D-U-N-S 96-806-6188
MAPLE LTC GROUP LLC
1435 Highway 258n, Kinston, NC 28504-7208
Tel (252) 523-9094 *Founded/Ownrshp* 2010
Sales 23.9MM^E *EMP* 342
SIC 5047 Medical equipment & supplies; Medical equipment & supplies

MAPLE MOUNTAIN
See EVERCLEAR VALLEY INC

D-U-N-S 16-182-0212 IMP
MAPLE MOUNTAIN GROUP INC
NEWAYS INTERNATIONAL
(*Suby of* Z CAPITAL HF ADVISER LLC) ★
588 S 2000 W, Springville, UT 84663-3047
Tel (801) 418-2000 *Founded/Ownrshp* 2013
Sales 94.4MM^E *EMP* 70^E
SIC 2833 5122 Drugs & herbs: grading, grinding & milling; Cosmetics; Drugs & herbs: grading, grinding & milling; Cosmetics
CEO: Robert Conlee
**CFO:* James Sloan
CFO: Scott St Clair
CFO: Debbie Stiner
**VP:* Will Burgess
Dir Soc: Callie Rose
Mng Dir: Tomomi Kosugi
Mng Dir: Paul Vanwynsberghe
QA Dir: Caprice Nutley
QA Dir: Bill Roth
Software D: Sjon Von Bose

MAPLE MOUNTAIN HOMES
See MAPLE MOUNTAIN INDUSTRIES INC

D-U-N-S 86-932-8385 IMP
MAPLE MOUNTAIN INDUSTRIES INC
MAPLE MOUNTAIN HOMES
1820 Mulligan Hill Rd, New Florence, PA 15944-9549
Tel (724) 676-4703 *Founded/Ownrshp* 1994
Sales 47.5MM^E *EMP* 300
SIC 2512 2511 5999 7699 1521 1542 Upholstered household furniture; Wood household furniture; Farm machinery; Farm machinery repair; New construction, single-family houses; Nonresidential construction; Upholstered household furniture; Wood household furniture; Farm machinery; Farm machinery repair; New construction, single-family houses; Nonresidential construction
Pr: Cheryl Woods
**Treas:* Amy M McDowell
**VP:* William R Woods
IT Man: Dave Daucher

D-U-N-S 00-301-6409 IMP
MAPLE PRESS CO (PA)
MAPLE-VAIL
480 Willow Springs Ln, York, PA 17406-6047
Tel (717) 764-5911 *Founded/Ownrshp* 1903
Sales 249.6MM^E *EMP* 900
SIC 2732 2791 2789 2752 Books: printing & binding; Photocomposition, for the printing trade; Bookbinding & related work; Commercial printing, lithographic; Books: printing & binding; Photocomposition, for the printing trade; Bookbinding & related work; Commercial printing, lithographic
CEO: James S Wisotzkey
**Pr:* John U Wisotzkey
**Sec:* Richard Polan Jr
**Sec:* Patricia K Zwergel
VP: Bill Long
**VP:* G Scott Simons
Plnt Mgr: Curt Dolinger

D-U-N-S 03-181-3538
MAPLE RIVER GRAIN & AGRONOMY LLC
1630 1st Ave S, Casselton, ND 58012-3910
Tel (701) 347-4465 *Founded/Ownrshp* 1904
Sales 137.9MM *EMP* 14
Accts Erickson And Associates Ltd
SIC 5153 5191 Grain elevators; Farm supplies; Grain elevators; Farm supplies
Genl Mgr: Sid Mauch

MAPLE SHADE MAZDA
See SHADE MAPLE MOTOR CORP

D-U-N-S 10-005-2737
MAPLE SHADE TOWNSHIP SCHOOL DISTRICT
170 Frederick Ave, Maple Shade, NJ 08052-3224
Tel (856) 779-1750 *Founded/Ownrshp* 1950
Sales 17.7MM^E *EMP* 300
SIC 8211 9111 Public elementary & secondary schools; Mayors' offices; Public elementary & secondary schools; Mayors' offices
Prin: Joseph Meloche

MAPLE VALLEY ANTHON OTO SCHL
See MAPLE VALLEY COMMUNITY SCHOOL DISTRICT

D-U-N-S 09-734-8882
MAPLE VALLEY COMMUNITY SCHOOL DISTRICT
MAPLE VALLEY ANTHON OTO SCHL
410 S 6th St, Mapleton, IA 51034-1108
Tel (712) 881-1315 *Founded/Ownrshp* 1888
Sales 11.1MM^E *EMP* 345
SIC 8211 Public combined elementary & secondary school; Public elementary & secondary school; Public combined elementary & secondary school; Public elementary & secondary school
**Prin:* Mahlon Carothers
**Prin:* Dan Doherty
Instr Medi: Ellen Boyle
Board of Directors: Loren Blackley, Dr Jack Janzhorn, Gaylon Nevins, Fred Paulsrud, Kendall Sexton

MAPLE-VAIL
See MAPLE PRESS CO

D-U-N-S 01-142-3076
MAPLECREST LINCOLN-MERCURY INC
2800 Springfield Ave, Vauxhall, NJ 07088-1099
Tel (908) 964-0544 *Founded/Ownrshp* 1963
Sales 26.3MM^E *EMP* 55^E
SIC 5511 7538 Automobiles, new & used; General automotive repair shops; Automobiles, new & used; General automotive repair shops
Pr: Stephen Giordano
CFO: Tim Rhoades
VP: Irene Giordano
Genl Mgr: Dave Vorsheimer
Off Mgr: Lori Smith
Sls Mgr: Gary Rossi
Sls Mgr: David Vorcheimer

MAPLEHURST BAKERIES
See WESTON FOODS US INC

D-U-N-S 04-113-3034 EXP
MAPLEHURST BAKERIES LLC
(*Suby of* MAPLEHURST BAKERIES) ★
50 Maplehurst Dr, Brownsburg, IN 46112-9085
Tel (317) 858-9000 *Founded/Ownrshp* 2009
Sales 257.6MM^E *EMP* 1,031
SIC 2051 Cakes, pies & pastries; Cakes, pies & pastries
VP: Kevin Whitlock
VP: Jonathan Feigen
VP: Donald Niemeyer
VP: Carl Singer
Plnt Mgr: Brandon Bell
Plnt Mgr: Curt Ramsey
Sls Mgr: Troy Pavlitsa
Sls Mgr: Peter Schirmbeck

D-U-N-S 06-800-5743
MAPLEHURST FARMS INC
936 S Moore Rd, Rochelle, IL 61068-9789
Tel (815) 562-8723 *Founded/Ownrshp* 1997
Sales 220.0MM^E *EMP* 75
SIC 5153 2879 4212 Grain & field beans; Agricultural chemicals; Local trucking, without storage; Grain & field beans; Agricultural chemicals; Local trucking, without storage
CEO: Carol Hayenga
**Pr:* Lyn Carmichael
**CFO:* Barbara Koehnke
Opers Mgr: Steve Delhotal

D-U-N-S 05-515-9693
MAPLES GAS CO INC
101 65th Ave, Meridian, MS 39307-7017
Tel (601) 485-6080 *Founded/Ownrshp* 1960
Sales 46.5MM^E *EMP* 33
SIC 5171 Petroleum bulk stations
Pr: Dudley M Maples
**VP:* Phillip Maples

D-U-N-S 05-579-7609 IMP
MAPLES INDUSTRIES INC
2210 Moody Ridge Rd, Scottsboro, AL 35768-4114
Tel (256) 259-1327 *Founded/Ownrshp* 1984
Sales 424.8MM^E *EMP* 1,900
SIC 2273 Rugs, tufted; Rugs, tufted
Pr: John Maples
CFO: William Martin
**VP:* John Wade Maples III
CIO: Jackie Ba
Dir IT: Jacki Bass
Dir IT: Jamie Sharper
VP Opers: Larry Bailey
S&M/VP: Linda Bass
Sls Mgr: Leanne Cook

D-U-N-S 04-721-5384
MAPLETON COMMUNICATIONS LLC
RADIO MIDFORD
10900 Wilshire Blvd # 150, Los Angeles, CA 90024-6501
Tel (310) 209-7221 *Founded/Ownrshp* 2001
Sales 52.0MM *EMP* 150
SIC 4832 Radio broadcasting stations; Radio broadcasting stations
CEO: Adam Nathnson
VP: Mercia Darton

D-U-N-S 03-044-2248
MAPLETON PUBLIC SCHOOLS
MAPLETON SCHOOL DISTRICT
591 E 80th Ave, Denver, CO 80229-5806
Tel (303) 288-2066 *Founded/Ownrshp* 1956
Sales 46.7MM^E *EMP* 700
Accts Bondi & Co Llc
SIC 8211 Public elementary school; Public junior high school; Public senior high school; Public elementary school; Public junior high school; Public senior high school
Sales Asso: Charlotte Ciancio
CFO: Don Herman
Treas: Martha Geonetta
Teacher Pr: Sue-Lynn Toussaint

MAPLETON SCHOOL DISTRICT
See MAPLETON PUBLIC SCHOOLS

D-U-N-S 00-211-9386
MAPLEVALE FARMS INC (NY)
2063 Allen Street Ext, Falconer, NY 14733-1710
Tel (716) 355-4114 *Founded/Ownrshp* 1969, 1975
Sales 108.2MM^E *EMP* 110
SIC 5141 Food brokers; Food brokers
Ch Bd: Douglas Neckers
**VP:* Bruce Neckers
Opers Mgr: Gary Neckers
Mktg Mgr: Ken Deubell
Sls Mgr: David Panek

MAPLEWOOD, THE
See BLOOMER MEDICAL CENTER

D-U-N-S 02-090-6454 EXP
MAPLEWOOD BEVERAGE PACKERS LLC
ARIZONA ICED TEA
45 Camptown Rd, Maplewood, NJ 07040-3034
Tel (973) 416-4582 *Founded/Ownrshp* 2001
Sales 40.3MM^E *EMP* 165
SIC 2086 Carbonated beverages, nonalcoholic: bottled & canned; Carbonated beverages, nonalcoholic: bottled & canned

D-U-N-S 04-143-1949
MAPLEWOOD ENTERPRISES LLC
219 Beach 100th St Fl 2, Rockaway Park, NY 11694-2824
Tel (718) 634-3800 *Founded/Ownrshp* 2013
Sales 22.0MM *EMP* 8
SIC 5731 Consumer electronic equipment; Consumer electronic equipment
CEO: Sam Kuszer
VP: David Shaab

D-U-N-S 13-260-5353
MAPLEWOOD TOYOTA
2873 Maplewood Dr, Saint Paul, MN 55109-1875
Tel (651) 482-1322 *Founded/Ownrshp* 1982
Sales 39.2MM^E *EMP* 100
SIC 5511 7538 5531 Automobiles, new & used; Engine repair, except diesel: automotive; Automotive parts; Automobiles, new & used; Engine repair, except diesel: automotive; Automotive parts
Pr: Stephen Mc Daniels
**CFO:* Tom Lahr
**Genl Mgr:* Tom Beedy
Mktg Dir: Andy Hulcher
Sls Mgr: Jeff Stearns
Sales Asso: Keith Vincent

D-U-N-S 06-056-2287
MAPLEWOOD-RICHMOND HEIGHTS SCHOOL DISTRICT
7539 Manchester Rd, Saint Louis, MO 63143-2913
Tel (314) 644-4400 *Founded/Ownrshp* 1840
Sales 20.9MM *EMP* 180
SIC 8211 Public elementary school; Public junior high school; Public senior high school; Public elementary school; Public junior high school; Public senior high school
**CFO:* Carlton Brookes
**CFO:* Cynthia Z Fields
Dir IT: Chris Hoelzer
IT Man: Todd Allan
IT Man: James Gardner
Pr Dir: Brian Adkisson
Pr Dir: Tom Wickersham
Schl Brd P: Francis Chemlir
Psych: Mary Darst
Psych: Allegra Grawer
Psych: Justin Harcharic

D-U-N-S 78-267-1804
MAPP CONSTRUCTION LLC
344 3rd St, Baton Rouge, LA 70801-1307
Tel (225) 757-0111 *Founded/Ownrshp* 2003
Sales 116.4MM^E *EMP* 150
Accts Hannis T Bourgeois Llp Bato
SIC 1542 Commercial & office building, new construction; Commercial & office buildings, renovation & repair; Commercial & office building, new construction; Commercial & office buildings, renovation & repair
Pr: Michael Polito
**CFO:* John McKowen
VP: Dana Emberton
**VP:* Mark Lahaye
VP: Richard Setliff
Exec: Eileen Long
IT Man: Clayton Samson
Sfty Mgr: George Stevens
Opers Mgr: Jim Tyler
Snr PM: AME Duan
Snr PM: Brad Reese

D-U-N-S 11-946-2229
MAPPING ALLIANCE PARTNERSHIP
URS
10550 Richmond Ave # 155, Houston, TX 77042-5022
Tel (713) 914-6699 *Founded/Ownrshp* 2002
Sales 25.7MM^E *EMP* 250
SIC 8711 8748 Engineering services; Business consulting; Engineering services; Business consulting
Mng Pt: Ed Matuszak
Mng Pt: Oha Alba
Ex VP: Dhamo Dhamotharan
Sr VP: John Barrett
VP: Robert Cate
Snr PM: Annette Brewster
Snr Mgr: Kevin Lynch

D-U-N-S 96-139-1021
MAPR TECHNOLOGIES INC
MAPR TECHNOLOGY
350 Holger Way, San Jose, CA 95134-1362
Tel (408) 428-9472 *Founded/Ownrshp* 2009
Sales 69.9MM^E *EMP* 150^E
SIC 7371 Computer software development & applications
CEO: John Schroeder
Pr: Dave Jespersen
Pr: Matt Mills
CFO: Dan Atler
Sr VP: Steve Fitz
Sr VP: Anil Gadre
Sr VP: Pinaki Mukerji
VP: Roba Anderson
VP: John Bertero
VP: Dave Feldman
VP: Xavier Guerin
VP: Steve Jenkins
VP: Michele Nemschoff
VP: Suresh Ollala
VP: Patrik Svanstorm
VP: Kim Williams
Dir Surg: Alan Geary
Dir Bus: Tom White
Board of Directors: Michael Lehman

MAPR TECHNOLOGY
See MAPR TECHNOLOGIES INC

MAPS
See NEW CO-OPERATIVE INC

D-U-N-S 16-108-2615
MAPSYS INC
MAP SYSTEMS AND SOLUTIONS
920 Michigan Ave, Columbus, OH 43215-1165
Tel (614) 255-7258 *Founded/Ownrshp* 1985
Sales 20.1MM *EMP* 40
SIC 7372 7371 5045 Business oriented computer software; Custom computer programming services; Computers, peripherals & software; Business oriented computer software; Custom computer programming services; Computers, peripherals & software
Pr: Steve Bernard
**Sec:* Paul Neal
**VP:* Jim Heiberger
**VP:* Terry Payne
Software D: Mahmoud Jallaq
Software D: Greg Mallory
Sftwr Eng: Michael Payne
Snr PM: Mike Shonk

MAQUET
See DATASCOPE CORP

D-U-N-S 02-234-8156
MAQUET CARDIOVASCULAR LLC
45 Barbour Pond Dr, Wayne, NJ 07470-2094
Tel (973) 709-7000 *Founded/Ownrshp* 2009
Sales 38.7MM^E *EMP* 170^E
SIC 8011 Cardiologist & cardio-vascular specialist
CEO: Raoul Quintero
**CFO:* Maximo Nougues
**Sr VP:* Philip Freed
**VP:* Jeff Harris
**VP:* Joseph Knight
VP: Christoph Lenze
Dir Soc: Johanna Etzler
Dir Soc: Bridget Tomlinson
Area Mgr: Amit Agarwal
Mktg Mgr: Tom Shannon

D-U-N-S 83-089-5319 IMP
MAQUET CARDIOVASCULAR US SALES LLC
MAQUET MEDICAL SYSTEMS USA
(*Suby of* MAQUET GMBH)
45 Barbour Pond Dr, Wayne, NJ 07470-2094
Tel (201) 995-8700 *Founded/Ownrshp* 2009
Sales 131.3MM^E *EMP* 483^E
SIC 5047 Medical equipment & supplies; Medical equipment & supplies
Pr: Raoul Quintero
CFO: Maximo Nougues
Sr VP: Philip Freed

D-U-N-S 16-802-1850 IMP
MAQUET INC
MAQUET MEDICAL SYSTEM USA
(*Suby of* GETINGE AB)
45 Barbour Pond Dr, Wayne, NJ 07470-2094
Tel (973) 709-7000 *Founded/Ownrshp* 2006
Sales 340.9MM^E *EMP* 842^E
SIC 5047 Medical & hospital equipment; Medical equipment & supplies; Medical & hospital equipment; Medical equipment & supplies
CEO: Raoul Quintero
CFO: Reinhard Mayer
Ex VP: Scott Corbeil
Rgnl Mgr: Goran Steiner
Area Mgr: Rafa Szymkowski
Dir IT: Tyrone Marnotes
IT Man: Christine Prater
IT Man: Pamela Wong
IT Man: Amanda Zayas
VP Sls: Christoph Lenze
Sls Mgr: Anthony Christopher

MAQUET MEDICAL SYSTEM USA
See MAQUET INC

MAQUET MEDICAL SYSTEMS USA
See MAQUET CARDIOVASCULAR US SALES LLC

D-U-N-S 82-531-2304
MAQUET MEDICAL SYSTEMS USA LLC
(*Suby of* MAQUET GMBH)
120 Baytech Dr, San Jose, CA 95134-2302
Tel (408) 635-3900 *Founded/Ownrshp* 2007
Sales 79.0MME *EMP* 525
SIC 3845 Ultrasonic scanning devices, medical; Ultrasonic scanning devices, medical
CEO: Heribert Ballhaus
Ex VP: Heinz Jacqui
VP: Reinhard Mayer
VP: Tina Morales
VP: Hilde Van Der Westhuizen
Web Dev: Alex Millican
Software D: Colleen Pestana

MAQUOKETA VALLEY ELECTRIC COOP
See MAQUOKETA VALLEY RURAL ELECTRIC COOPERATIVE

D-U-N-S 00-694-0332
MAQUOKETA VALLEY RURAL ELECTRIC COOPERATIVE
MAQUOKETA VALLEY ELECTRIC COOP
109 N Huber St, Anamosa, IA 52205-1453
Tel (319) 462-3542 *Founded/Ownrshp* 1936
Sales 32.5MM *EMP* 60
SIC 4911 1711 Electric services; Plumbing, heating, air-conditioning contractors; Electric services; Plumbing, heating, air-conditioning contractors
CEO: James M Lauzon
Pr: Larry Swanson
Treas: Judy Gotto
Bd of Dir: Bruce Reade
Bd of Dir: Gary Weber
Genl Mgr: Brent Vandorn
IT Man: Brent Wegmann
Sfty Mgr: Cory Kieler
Sales Exec: Patty Manuel

D-U-N-S 06-202-1639
MAR (MD) LLC
(*Suby of* OASIS SYSTEMS LLC) ★
1803 Res Blvd Ste 204, Rockville, MD 20850
Tel (301) 231-0100 *Founded/Ownrshp* 2015
Sales 25.8MM *EMP* 150
Accts Bdo Usa Llp Mclean Virginia
SIC 7373 Marine engineering; Sanitary engineers; Architectural services; Labor resource services; Computer systems analysis & design; Systems engineering, computer related; Computer software development; Systems software development services
CEO: Michael P Norcio
VP: Laura Evans
VP: Daniel Hackenberg
VP: Samuel J Sunukjian
Ex Dir: Bob Koch
Prgrm Mgr: Matthew Grant
Prgrm Mgr: Andy Killion
Tech Mgr: James Lane
Software D: Sachin Bansal
Software D: Shahzad Khan
Ql Cn Mgr: Deborah Pollack

D-U-N-S 06-902-8728 IMP
■ **MAR COR PURIFICATION INC (PA)**
(*Suby of* CANTEL MEDICAL CORP) ★
4450 Township Line Rd, Skippack, PA 19474
Tel (800) 633-3080 *Founded/Ownrshp* 1970
Sales 123.0MME *EMP* 600
SIC 3569 Filters; Filters
Pr: Curt Weitnauer
**VP:* Andrew G Stitzinger
Mtls Mgr: Kate M Getty

D-U-N-S 00-631-9586
MAR GRAPHICS
523 S Meyer Ave, Valmeyer, IL 62295-3120
Tel (618) 935-2111 *Founded/Ownrshp* 1961
Sales 29.9MME *EMP* 90
SIC 2752 Commercial printing, offset
Pr: Richard D Roever
**Sec:* Audrey A Roever
**VP:* Bobbie Klinkhardt
**VP:* Scott Roever
Plnt Mgr: Al Linnemann

D-U-N-S 14-675-3694
MAR LAM INDUSTRIES INC
834 E Hammond Ln, Phoenix, AZ 85034-6507
Tel (602) 253-0003 *Founded/Ownrshp* 1985
Sales 20.4MME *EMP* 200
SIC 1799 1743 3281 Counter top installation; Marble installation, interior; Cut stone & stone products; Counter top installation; Marble installation, interior; Cut stone & stone products
Pr: Lon S Armel
**VP:* Jon A Armel

D-U-N-S 86-898-1858
MAR PIZZA INC
DOMINO'S PIZZA
15198 Downey Ave, Paramount, CA 90723-4594
Tel (562) 630-0005 *Founded/Ownrshp* 1997
Sales 26.6MME *EMP* 500
SIC 5812 Pizzeria, chain; Pizzeria, chain
Pr: Tony Manos
Mktg Mgr: Robin Christie

D-U-N-S 17-410-8423
MAR-B PARTNERSHIP
MCDONALD'S
816 N Elm Pl, Broken Arrow, OK 74012-2545
Tel (918) 251-6150 *Founded/Ownrshp* 1984
Sales 8.9MME *EMP* 286
SIC 5812 Fast-food restaurant, chain; Fast-food restaurant, chain
Pt: Bob Wagner

D-U-N-S 05-293-4759 IMP
MAR-BAL INC
10095 Queens Way, Chagrin Falls, OH 44023-5406
Tel (440) 543-7526 *Founded/Ownrshp* 1970
Sales 35.3MME *EMP* 375
SIC 3089 2821 3081 Molding primary plastic; Polyesters; Unsupported plastics film & sheet; Molding primary plastic; Polyesters; Unsupported plastics film & sheet
CEO: Scott Balogh
**VP:* Carolyn E Balogh
**VP:* Steven Balogh
**VP:* Kevin Casey

D-U-N-S 82-891-5475 IMP
MAR-BAL INC
10095 Queens Way, Chagrin Falls, OH 44023-5406
Tel (440) 543-7526 *Founded/Ownrshp* 1970
Sales 107.7MME *EMP* 480
SIC 3089 2821 3081 Molding primary plastic; Polyesters; Unsupported plastics film & sheet; Molding primary plastic; Polyesters; Unsupported plastics film & sheet
Pr: Scott Balogh
**VP:* Steven Balogh
Exec: Bruce Acord
Prgrm Mgr: Robert Tapolcsanyi
Dir IT: Ted Rye
Plnt Mgr: Marvin Benjamin
Ql Cn Mgr: Russ Farrell
Ql Cn Mgr: Maggie Osler

D-U-N-S 03-106-5410 EXP
MAR-CONE APPLIANCE PARTS CO
MARCONE SUPPLY
1 Cityplace Dr Ste 400, Saint Louis, MO 63141-7065
Tel (877) 993-9196 *Founded/Ownrshp* 1932
Sales 265.3MME *EMP* 650
SIC 5064 Appliance parts, household; Appliance parts, household
Ch Bd: Mitchell Markow
**Pr:* Jim Souers
VP: John Carroll
Brnch Mgr: Jackson Ballard
Brnch Mgr: Gregory Brown
Brnch Mgr: Terry Fluri
Brnch Mgr: Luisa Goncalves
Brnch Mgr: George Kacsur
Brnch Mgr: Rebecca Kinsey
Brnch Mgr: Mike Kuzujian
Brnch Mgr: Maurice Leyva

D-U-N-S 06-387-2071
MAR-ECO INC
KEYSTONE FORD
301 Walker Rd, Chambersburg, PA 17201-3507
Tel (717) 264-5104 *Founded/Ownrshp* 1981
Sales 28.4MME *EMP* 66
SIC 5511 5531 7538 5561 Automobiles, new & used; Automobile & truck equipment & parts; General automotive repair shops; Recreational vehicle dealers; Automobiles, new & used; Automobile & truck equipment & parts; General automotive repair shops; Recreational vehicle dealers
Pr: Aldine Martin
Treas: Martin Kamer
VP: Kurt I Schweitzer
Exec: Don Hill
Sls Mgr: Sam Cook
Sls Mgr: Chad Sites

MAR-HYDE
See 3M BONDO CORP

D-U-N-S 60-123-1657 EXP
MAR-JAC POULTRY INC
PROCESSING DIVISION
(*Suby of* MARJAC HOLDINGS LLC) ★
1020 Aviation Blvd, Gainesville, GA 30501-6839
Tel (770) 531-5000 *Founded/Ownrshp* 1984
Sales 314.2MME *EMP* 1,200E
Accts Frost Pllc Little Rock Arka
SIC 0254 Poultry hatcheries; Poultry hatcheries
CEO: Al B Jamal
**CEO:* J Pete Martin
CFO: Tanveer Papa
**CFO:* Mulham Shbeib
**CFO:* Mirza M Yaqub
VP: Don H Bull
**VP:* Doug Carnes
Rgnl Mgr: Greg Kinsey
Rgnl Mgr: Michael Melenick
Brnch Mgr: Taylor Sipsy
QA Dir: Mickey Carr

D-U-N-S 07-932-5490
MAR-JAC POULTRY MS LLC
261 Marshall Durbin Dr, Waynesboro, MS 39367
Tel (601) 735-3132 *Founded/Ownrshp* 2014
Sales 94.4MME *EMP* 1,000
SIC 2048 Prepared feeds
Genl Mgr: Dwayne Rawson

MAR-KELL SEAL
See QUADION LLC

D-U-N-S 06-578-6873 IMP
MAR-LEE COMPANIES INC
(*Suby of* PSB INDUSTRIES)
180 Authority Dr, Fitchburg, MA 01420-6045
Tel (978) 343-9600 *Founded/Ownrshp* 2008
Sales 24.9MME *EMP* 167
SIC 3544

D-U-N-S 17-724-1309 IMP/EXP
MAR-LEES SEAFOOD LLC
10 N Front St, New Bedford, MA 02740-7327
Tel (508) 991-6026 *Founded/Ownrshp* 2010
Sales 46.2MME *EMP* 200
SIC 2091 Seafood products: packaged in cans, jars, etc.; Seafood products: packaged in cans, jars, etc.
**CFO:* Kimberly Lannigan
**VP:* George Tarabaih
Exec: William Hall

MAR-MAC CONSTRUCTION PRODUCTS
See MAR-MAC MANUFACTURING CO INC

D-U-N-S 00-335-7837 IMP
MAR-MAC MANUFACTURING CO INC (SC)
MAR-MAC CONSTRUCTION PRODUCTS
334 N Seventh St, Mc Bee, SC 29101-8871
Tel (843) 335-5814 *Founded/Ownrshp* 1953
Sales 26.3MME *EMP* 185
SIC 2389 Disposable garments & accessories; Disposable garments & accessories
Pr: John S Mc Leod Jr
**Treas:* Yvonne Howle

D-U-N-S 61-280-7016 IMP
MAR-MAC WIRE INC
229 Mar Mac Wire Rd, Mc Bee, SC 29101-8537
Tel (843) 335-5000 *Founded/Ownrshp* 1953
Sales 20.9MME *EMP* 95E
SIC 3315 Wire, ferrous/iron; Wire, ferrous/iron
Pr: John W Martin III
COO: Max A Johnson
IT Man: Ricky Sullivan
Sfty Mgr: Gene Player
Opers Mgr: Brandy Melton

D-U-N-S 02-839-3643
MAR-VAL FOOD STORE NO 1 INC
MAR-VAL FOOD STORE STE 6
856 N Sacramento St Ste C, Lodi, CA 95240-1251
Tel (209) 369-3611 *Founded/Ownrshp* 1953
Sales 45.0MME *EMP* 200
SIC 5411

MAR-VAL FOOD STORE STE 6
See MAR-VAL FOOD STORE NO 1 INC

D-U-N-S 01-763-7968
MARAMONT CORP
5600 1st Ave, Brooklyn, NY 11220-2550
Tel (718) 238-0974 *Founded/Ownrshp* 1981
Sales 103.3MME *EMP* 450
SIC 2099 8322 Ready-to-eat meals, salads & sandwiches; Salads, fresh or refrigerated; Sandwiches, assembled & packaged: for wholesale market; Individual & family services; Ready-to-eat meals, salads & sandwiches; Individual & family services
Pr: George Chivari
**CFO:* Linda Jannzzkowski
MIS Dir: Barry Mittelmann

D-U-N-S 14-462-8161 IMP/EXP
MARAN INC
SQUEEZE
1400 Brdwy Rm 2800, New York, NY 10018
Tel (212) 382-3310 *Founded/Ownrshp* 1977
Sales 75.0MME *EMP* 59E
Accts Weitzman & Rubin Pc Jerich
SIC 5137 Women's & children's clothing
Ch Bd: David Greenberg
**CFO:* Richard Huang
VP: Jenny Gruber
VP Sls: Janey Pilzer

D-U-N-S 06-887-0880
MARANA AEROSPACE SOLUTIONS INC
(*Suby of* RELATIVITY CAPITAL LLC) ★
24641 E Pinal Air Park Rd, Marana, AZ 85653-9504
Tel (520) 682-4181 *Founded/Ownrshp* 1990
Sales 130.0MME *EMP* 673
SIC 4581 Aircraft maintenance & repair services; Aircraft servicing & repairing; Aircraft maintenance & repair services; Aircraft servicing & repairing
CEO: James F Martin
Pr: Mike Michaels
**Sec:* Gayla Bella
Sr VP: Steve Maceyko
Sr VP: Greg Mitchell
**VP:* Colin Buxton
VP: Michael Melvin
**VP:* Lou Moore
**VP:* Carl Shultz
**Prin:* Greg Emerson
Admn Mgr: Ruthann Poole

D-U-N-S 07-898-5702
MARANA HEALTH CENTER INC
MHC HEALTHCARE
13395 N Marana Main St, Marana, AZ 85653-7008
Tel (520) 682-4111 *Founded/Ownrshp* 1957
Sales 34.2MM *EMP* 350E
Accts Bitner & Collings Pllc Tucson
SIC 8021 8011 8093 5912 Offices & clinics of dentists; Offices & clinics of medical doctors; Mental health clinic, outpatient; Drug stores; Offices & clinics of dentists; Offices & clinics of medical doctors; Mental health clinic, outpatient; Drug stores
CEO: Clinton Kuntz
**Pr:* Marvin N Swink
**CFO:* Jania Arnoldi
CFO: Carol Field
**Treas:* Susan Edwards
**VP:* Albert Delgado
Dir Rx: Greg Redding
Prac Mgr: James Workman
CIO: Adam De Osa
CIO: Adam De La Osa
IT Man: Christina Ritter

D-U-N-S 07-983-6348
MARANA UNIFIED SCHOOL DISTRICT
11279 W Grier Rd, Marana, AZ 85653-9609
Tel (520) 682-4749 *Founded/Ownrshp* 2015
Sales 39.5MME *EMP* 1,170E
SIC 8211 Public elementary & secondary schools
CFO: Dan Contorno
CTO: Ross Demma
Pr Dir: Tamara Crawley
HC Dir: Irisan Manalo

D-U-N-S 10-000-1668
MARANA UNIFIED SCHOOL DISTRICT PARENT/CITIZEN ORGANIZATION
11279 W Grier Rd, Marana, AZ 85653-9609
Tel (520) 682-3243 *Founded/Ownrshp* 1941
Sales 76.0MME *EMP* 1,600
SIC 8211 Public elementary & secondary schools; Public elementary & secondary schools
**Pr:* Dan Post
Exec: Brian Lundenbach
DP Exec: Barbara Vondersaar
Dir IT: Mitch Eichenseer
Dir IT: Dan Hunt
IT Man: Judith Braeutigam
IT Man: Jan Truitt
IT Man: Laurie Wright
Psych: John Berkman
Psych: Kimberly Bernazanni
Psych: Leatanya Koppa

MARANATHA CHRISTIAN ACADEMY
See CALVARY CHAPEL OF COSTA MESA

D-U-N-S 14-557-8394
MARAND BUILDERS INC
4534 Old Pnville Rd Ste A, Charlotte, NC 28217
Tel (704) 525-1824 *Founded/Ownrshp* 1999
Sales 62.0MME *EMP* 107
Accts Greer & Walker Llp Charlotte
SIC 1542 Commercial & office building contractors; Commercial & office building contractors
Pr: Francisco Alvarado
VP: Hayes Nathan
Snr Mgr: Ricky Hancock

D-U-N-S 03-560-5307 IMP
MARANGONI TREAD NORTH AMERICA INC
708 Myatt Dr, Madison, TN 37115-2168
Tel (615) 868-4050 *Founded/Ownrshp* 1998
Sales 30.4MME *EMP* 75
SIC 3559 5169 3011 Tire retreading machinery & equipment; Chemicals & allied products; Tread rubber, camelback for tire retreading; Tire retreading machinery & equipment; Chemicals & allied products; Tread rubber, camelback for tire retreading
Pr: William Sweatman
IT Man: Vicki Bentrum
Sls Mgr: Giuseppe Marangoni

D-U-N-S 11-207-4179
MARATHON ASSET MANAGEMENT LP
1 Bryant Park Fl 38, New York, NY 10036-6737
Tel (212) 500-3000 *Founded/Ownrshp* 1998
Sales 93.5MME *EMP* 190E
SIC 6282 Manager of mutual funds, contract or fee basis; Manager of mutual funds, contract or fee basis
CEO: Bruce Richards
COO: Andrew Rabinowitz
Sr VP: Matthew Breckenridge
Sr VP: Nishi Kapoor
VP: Nitin Chexal
VP: Richard Horn
VP: Anupam Ladha
VP: Natalie Louie
VP: Michael Lynch
VP: Jared Z Mintz
VP: Michael Passantino
VP: Arthur Rosenberg

MARATHON BATTERY
See MARATHONNORCO AEROSPACE INC

D-U-N-S 02-333-5987
MARATHON CHEESE CORP
304 East St, Marathon, WI 54448-9643
Tel (715) 443-2211 *Founded/Ownrshp* 2007
Sales 250.6MME *EMP* 2,000
SIC 2022 5143

D-U-N-S 00-120-7638 IMP
MARATHON CO
90 Oneil Blvd, Attleboro, MA 02703-4218
Tel (508) 222-5544 *Founded/Ownrshp* 1953
Sales 21.8MME *EMP* 125
SIC 5541 Gasoline service stations; Gasoline service stations
Pr: Roy Forman
**Treas:* Audrey Robbins
Board of Directors: Guy Forman, Roger Forman, Charles Miller

D-U-N-S 17-299-8684 EXP
MARATHON COACH INC
91333 N Coburg Indus Way, Coburg, OR 97408-9432
Tel (541) 343-9991 *Founded/Ownrshp* 1993
Sales 43.3MME *EMP* 359
SIC 3716 Recreational van conversion (self-propelled), factory basis; Recreational van conversion (self-propelled), factory basis
Pr: Steven R Schoellhorn
**CEO:* Robert Schoellhorn
**CFO:* Stan Pickett
VP: Rob Piubeni
IT Man: Michelle Bale
Opers Mgr: Carroll White
Mktg Mgr: Beth Stegall
Sls Mgr: Went Slobbe
Sls Mgr: Pam Spinarskimcnitt

D-U-N-S 17-427-6329
MARATHON ELECTRICAL CONTRACTORS INC
614 38th St S, Birmingham, AL 35222-2452
Tel (205) 323-8500 *Founded/Ownrshp* 1987
Sales 67.0MM *EMP* 390
SIC 1731 General electrical contractor; General electrical contractor
Pr: Larry D Argo
**COO:* Bruce Taylor
**Sec:* Robert Bratton
**Sec:* Mark Harry
**VP:* Chris McGregor
**VP:* William H Proctor
IT Man: David Weldon
Sfty Dirs: J R Dove

D-U-N-S 94-661-4872
MARATHON ENERGY CORP
OLYMPIC FLAME FUEL OIL
868 39th St, Brooklyn, NY 11232-3230
Tel (718) 435-2200 *Founded/Ownrshp* 1996
Sales 28.3MME *EMP* 65
SIC 5983 5074 Fuel oil dealers; Oil burners; Fuel oil dealers; Oil burners
Pr: Jerry Drenis
**CFO:* Jeff Grygier
**VP:* Bobby Beys
VP: Gus Sfakianos

D-U-N-S 05-628-8970 IMP
MARATHON ENTERPRISES INC
SABETT HOT DOG
9 Smith St, Englewood, NJ 07631-4607
Tel (201) 935-3330 *Founded/Ownrshp* 1964
Sales 25.8MME *EMP* 100

SIC 2013 Sausages & other prepared meats; Frankfurters from purchased meat; Ham, boneless: from purchased meat; Bologna from purchased meat; Sausages & other prepared meats; Frankfurters from purchased meat; Ham, boneless: from purchased meat; Bologna from purchased meat
Pr: Boyd G Adelman
**VP:* Mark Rosen
VP: Nikki Rosen
**VP:* Philip Venturini
IT Man: Jerry Melissaratis

D-U-N-S 62-487-3139 IMP/EXP
■ **MARATHON EQUIPMENT CO (DELAWARE)**
(*Suby of* DOVER ENGINEERED SYSTEMS INC) ★
Highway 9 S, Vernon, AL 35592
Tel (205) 695-9105 *Founded/Ownrshp* 1990
Sales 100.6MM^{E} *EMP* 540
SIC 3589 Commercial cooking & foodwarming equipment; Commercial cooking & foodwarming equipment
Pr: Pat Carroll
**CFO:* Darren Bird
VP: Kent Spiers
**VP:* Tom Vatter
VP: Bill Wilkerson
Dir Risk M: Ronnie Cargile
Dir IT: Christina Harris
IT Man: Shawn Gottwald
VP Opers: Dave Young
Natl Sales: Jim Squier
Manager: Tom Bailey

D-U-N-S 01-704-3266
MARATHON FLINT OIL CO INC (MI)
GENESEE PETRO
1919 S Dort Hwy, Flint, MI 48503-4395
Tel (810) 234-6678 *Founded/Ownrshp* 1949, 1978
Sales 24.6MM *EMP* 26
SIC 5171 5541 5983 Petroleum bulk stations; Filling stations, gasoline; Fuel oil dealers; Petroleum bulk stations; Filling stations, gasoline; Fuel oil dealers
Pr: David Roeser
**VP:* Christopher Roeser
VP Sls: Andrewv Roeser

MARATHON GROUP , THE
See CENTER STATE MANAGEMENT CORP

D-U-N-S 60-437-0135
MARATHON HEALTH INC
20 Winooski Falls Way # 400, Winooski, VT 05404-2228
Tel (802) 857-0400 *Founded/Ownrshp* 2006
Sales 50.0MM *EMP* 360^{E}
SIC 8741 Nurses & other medical assistants; Primary care medical clinic; Nursing & personal care facility management; Nursing & personal care facility management
CEO: Jerry Ford
**CFO:* Scott Laplant
**Ch:* Richard Tarrant
VP: Eric Schrumpf
Chf Nrs Of: Barb Bergmann
Chf Nrs Of: Barbara Swan
Dir IT: William Campbell
IT Man: Drew O'Connor
IT Man: Andrew Oconnor
IT Man: Maureen Whitney
VP Sls: Greg Hiss
Board of Directors: Ronald Roberts

D-U-N-S 80-814-7490
MARATHON INDUSTRIES INC
MARATHON TRUCK BODIES
25597 Springbrook Ave, Santa Clarita, CA 91350-2427
Tel (661) 286-1118 *Founded/Ownrshp* 1993
Sales 25.0MM *EMP* 175
SIC 3713 5012 Truck & bus bodies; Automobiles & other motor vehicles; Truck & bus bodies; Automobiles & other motor vehicles
CEO: Roger K Hess
**Pr:* Chad Hess
**COO:* Jeff Berg
**Sr VP:* Bob Berro
Sfty Mgr: Ramon Perez
**VP Sls:* Tom Garcia
Manager: Dennis Laurin

D-U-N-S 02-026-1079
■ **MARATHON INTERNATIONAL OIL CO**
(*Suby of* MAP CRUDE PETRO & NATURAL GAS) ★
5555 San Felipe St # 2796, Houston, TX 77056-2796
Tel (713) 629-6600 *Founded/Ownrshp* 1961
Sales 120.7MM^{E} *EMP* 2,000
SIC 1311 1382 6519 Crude petroleum production; Natural gas production; Oil & gas exploration services; Real property lessors; Crude petroleum production; Natural gas production; Oil & gas exploration services; Real property lessors
Pr: V G Beghini
**VP:* D C Gerard
**VP:* K M Henning

D-U-N-S 01-326-0497
MARATHON MEDIA GROUP LLC
737 N Michigan Ave # 2060, Chicago, IL 60611-5660
Tel (312) 640-9700 *Founded/Ownrshp* 1996
Sales 91.0MM^{E} *EMP* 546
SIC 4832 Radio broadcasting stations; Radio broadcasting stations
CFO: Dan Odonnell
Sr Cor Off: Jared Golden
Ex VP: Bruce Buzil
VP: Jeffrey Mulder

MARATHON OIL
See SMART OIL LLC

MARATHON OIL
See BELL STORES INC

D-U-N-S 05-512-2568 IMP/EXP
■ **MARATHON OIL CO**
MAP CRUDE PETRO & NATURAL GAS
(*Suby of* MARATHON OIL CORP) ★
5555 San Felipe St # 2796, Houston, TX 77056-2799
Tel (713) 629-6600 *Founded/Ownrshp* 1981
Sales 856.9MM^{E} *EMP* 3,000
SIC 2911 5171 5541 1311 4612 4613 Petroleum refining; Gasoline blending plants; Intermediate distillates; Heavy distillates; Petroleum bulk stations; Petroleum terminals; Filling stations, gasoline; Crude petroleum production; Natural gas production; Crude petroleum pipelines; Refined petroleum pipelines; Petroleum refining; Gasoline blending plants; Intermediate distillates; Heavy distillates; Petroleum bulk stations; Petroleum terminals; Filling stations, gasoline; Crude petroleum production; Natural gas production; Crude petroleum pipelines; Refined petroleum pipelines
Pr: Clarence P Cazalot Jr
CFO: J T Mills
Sr VP: Philip E Behrman
Sr VP: G D Golder
Sr VP: Steven B Hinchman
Sr VP: Steve J Lowden
Sr VP: Mary E Peters
Dir IT: Anne Hunt
Opers Mgr: William Browne

D-U-N-S 00-202-8801 IMP/EXP
▲ **MARATHON OIL CORP** (DE)
5555 San Felipe St # 2796, Houston, TX 77056-2796
Tel (713) 629-6600 *Founded/Ownrshp* 1887
Sales 11.2MMM *EMP* 3,330
Accts Pricewaterhousecoopers Llp Ho
Tkr Sym MRO *Exch* NYS
SIC 1311 2911 5171 5541 Crude petroleum production; Natural gas production; Petroleum refining; Petroleum bulk stations & terminals; Gasoline service stations; Crude petroleum & natural gas; Crude petroleum production; Natural gas production; Petroleum refining; Petroleum bulk stations & terminals; Gasoline service stations
Pr: Lee M Tillman
CFO: John R Sult
Ex VP: Sylvia J Kerrigan
Ex VP: Russell Poese
Ex VP: David E Roberts Jr
Sr VP: Philip E Behrman
Sr VP: G David Golder
Sr VP: Steven J Lowden
Sr VP: Mary Ellen Peters
VP: Paul Baillargeon
VP: T Mitch Little
VP: T Little
VP: Garry Peiffer
VP: Lance W Robertson
VP: Michael Steewart
VP: Patrick Wagner
VP: Gary E Wilson
VP Bus Dev: George Salama
VP Bus: Steven Guidry
Board of Directors: Gregory H Boyce, Pierre Brondeau, Chadwick C Deaton, Philip Lader, Michael E J Phelps, Dennis H Reilley

D-U-N-S 06-706-2200
▲ **MARATHON PATENT GROUP INC**
2331 Mill Rd Ste 100, Alexandria, VA 22314-4687
Tel (703) 232-1701 *Founded/Ownrshp* 2012
Sales 21.4MM *EMP* 6^{E}
Accts Singerlewak Llp Los Angeles
Tkr Sym MARA *Exch* NAS
SIC 6794 Patent buying, licensing, leasing
Ch Bd: Doug Croxall
COO: James Crawford
CFO: Frank Knuettel II
CFO: Frank Marsico
Chf Mktg O: Daniel Gelbtuch
**Ex VP:* John Stetson
VP: Rick Sanchez
CTO: Umesh Jani

D-U-N-S 96-299-3101 IMP
■ **MARATHON PETROLEUM CO LP**
(*Suby of* MARATHON PETROLEUM CORP) ★
539 S Main St, Findlay, OH 45840-3229
Tel (419) 422-2121 *Founded/Ownrshp* 1998
Sales 25.3MMM^{E} *EMP* 24,210
SIC 5172 2951 2865 Gasoline; Asphalt paving mixtures & blocks; Cyclic crudes & intermediates; Gasoline; Asphalt paving mixtures & blocks; Cyclic crudes & intermediates
Pr: Gary Heminger
Pr: Ronald G Becker
CFO: Donald Templin
VP: Pamela Beall
VP: Pamela Km Beall
VP: Anthony R Kenney
VP: C Michael Palmer
VP: Craig Pierson
VP: Donald Wehrly
Area Mgr: Randy Thompson
Brnch Mgr: Joseph Baker

D-U-N-S 96-839-3996 IMP/EXP
▲ **MARATHON PETROLEUM CORP**
539 S Main St, Findlay, OH 45840-3229
Tel (419) 422-2121 *Founded/Ownrshp* 2009
Sales 98.1MMM *EMP* 29,865^{E}
Accts Pricewaterhousecoopers Llp T
Tkr Sym MPC *Exch* NYS
SIC 2911 5172 Petroleum refining; Gasoline; Petroleum refining; Gasoline
Pr: Gary R Heminger
CFO: Timothy T Griffith
Ex VP: Donald C Templin
Sr VP: Richard D Bedell
Sr VP: C Michael Palmer
Sr VP: George P Shaffner
VP: Sarah Fowler
VP: Danna Garrett-Winn
VP: Sophie Jennequin
VP: Anthony R Kenney
VP: Andrea Kuenzl
VP: Sasa Kung
VP: Agnes Nikolaus
VP: John J Quaid
VP: Michelle Tang
VP: Donald W Wehrly
VP: J Michael Wilder
VP: Gillian Wu
Comm Man: Sid Barth
Board of Directors: John P Surma, Evan Bayh, Thomas J Usher, David A Daberko, Steven A Davis, William L Davis, Donna A James, Charles R Lee, James E Rohr, Seth E Schofield, John W Snow

D-U-N-S 00-790-2836
■ **MARATHON PIPE LINE LLC**
(*Suby of* MARATHON PETROLEUM CORP) ★
539 S Main St Ste 7614, Findlay, OH 45840-3229
Tel (419) 422-2121 *Founded/Ownrshp* 2011
Sales 103.0MM^{E} *EMP* 487
SIC 4612 4613 Crude petroleum pipelines; Refined petroleum pipelines; Crude petroleum pipelines; Refined petroleum pipelines
CEO: Gary R Heminger
VP: Pamela K Beall
VP: Clifford C Cook
VP: R K McCord
VP: Rodney P Nichols
VP: John Parziale
VP: Michael A Peak
VP: G L Peiffer
VP: Mary E Peters
VP: J D Sparkman
VP: Jerry C Welch
Exec: Steve Cummins

MARATHON TRUCK BODIES
See MARATHON INDUSTRIES INC

D-U-N-S 84-865-3234
MARATHON VENTURES INC
HERMANS-PEAR'S COFFEE
901 Fort Crook Rd N, Bellevue, NE 68005-4335
Tel (402) 934-8210 *Founded/Ownrshp* 2004
Sales 24.6MM^{E} *EMP* 50
SIC 5149 5046 Coffee, green or roasted; Tea; Coffee brewing equipment & supplies
Pr: John S Larsen
**CFO:* Duane McCreedy
VP: Adam Gaines
**VP Sls:* Todd Parr

D-U-N-S 83-510-7574
■ **MARATHONNORCO AEROSPACE INC**
MARATHON BATTERY
(*Suby of* AEROCONTROLEX) ★
8301 Imperial Dr, Waco, TX 76712-6524
Tel (254) 776-0650 *Founded/Ownrshp* 1968
Sales 78.0MM *EMP* 140
SIC 3812 Acceleration indicators & systems components, aerospace; Acceleration indicators & systems components, aerospace
Pr: Sergio Rodriguez
**CEO:* Raymond F Laubenthal
CFO: James Gentry
CFO: Kenton Van Harten
**Treas:* Gregory Rufus
VP: Larry Howell
IT Man: Mark Philipes
Mtls Mgr: Ken Pratt
Opers Mgr: Dennis Jolley
Ql Cn Mgr: Dann Marks
Mktg Dir: Terry Hancock

MARATHONVACATION.COM
See REMAX MARATHON VACATION REAL ESTATE

D-U-N-S 96-753-1752 IMP
■ **MARAZZI DISTRIBUTION INC**
MARAZZI TILE & STONE
(*Suby of* AMERICAN MARAZZI TILE INC) ★
359 Clay Rd, Mesquite, TX 75182-9710
Tel (702) 248-3040 *Founded/Ownrshp* 2011
Sales 29.6MM^{E} *EMP* 79
SIC 5032 Brick, stone & related material; Granite building stone; Marble building stone
Pr: Gianni Mattioli
**Sec:* David Carlile
VP Mfg: Claudio Caselli
Sls Mgr: Jerry Joyce

MARAZZI TILE & STONE
See MARAZZI DISTRIBUTION INC

D-U-N-S 06-122-3780
MARBEV LLC
BUDWEISER
825 Stone Ave, Monroe, LA 71201-8719
Tel (318) 323-8112 *Founded/Ownrshp* 1992
Sales 30.6MM^{E} *EMP* 74
SIC 5181 Beer & other fermented malt liquors; Beer & other fermented malt liquors
Prin: Charles V Marsala Jr
Exec: Charles Marsala
Area Mgr: Cody Swillie
Dir IT: Mike Brown
Sales Exec: Mike Lee
VP Mktg: Tyler Flemister
Sls Dir: Trey Green
Sls Mgr: Russell Kicey
Sls Mgr: Ken Phillips

D-U-N-S 19-861-2640 IMP
MARBLE CRAFTERS INC
MARBLE CRAFTERS USA
11 Nealy Blvd, Marcus Hook, PA 19061-5312
Tel (610) 497-6000 *Founded/Ownrshp* 1988
Sales 20.3MM^{E} *EMP* 100
SIC 1411 5211 Granite, dimension-quarrying; Paving stones
Pr: Robert Capoferri
VP: Joe Loftis
**Prin:* Annemarie Alexander
Snr PM: Russell Dunlap
Snr Mgr: Jim Castelli

MARBLE CRAFTERS USA
See MARBLE CRAFTERS INC

D-U-N-S 05-788-2714
MARBLE FALLS INDEPENDENT SCHOOL DISTRICT
1800 Colt Cir, Marble Falls, TX 78654-4200
Tel (830) 693-4357 *Founded/Ownrshp* 1900
Sales 40.1MM *EMP* 627
Accts West Davis & Company Llp Au
SIC 8211 Public elementary school; Public junior high school; Public senior high school; Public elementary school; Public junior high school; Public senior high school
Bd of Dir: Rick Edwards
Bd of Dir: Kelly Fox
Bd of Dir: Kevin Naumann
Ex Dir: Dottie De La Hoya

D-U-N-S 14-722-8456 IMP
MARBLE SYSTEMS INC
2737 Dorr Ave, Fairfax, VA 22031-4901
Tel (703) 204-1818 *Founded/Ownrshp* 2010
Sales 52.6MM^{E} *EMP* 101
SIC 5032 Marble building stone; Tile & clay products; Marble building stone; Tile & clay products
Pr: Munir Turunc
**VP:* Artemiz Turunc Akyatan
Genl Mgr: Ihsan Sadak

MARBLE WORKS
See WIENMAR INC

D-U-N-S 07-228-0027
MARBORG INDUSTRIES (CA)
728 E Yanonali St, Santa Barbara, CA 93103-3233
Tel (805) 963-1852 *Founded/Ownrshp* 1974
Sales 140.2MM^{E} *EMP* 254
Accts Bartlett Pringle & Wolf Llp
SIC 4953 7359 7699 4212 Rubbish collection & disposal; Portable toilet rental; Septic tank cleaning service; Local trucking, without storage; Rubbish collection & disposal; Portable toilet rental; Septic tank cleaning service; Local trucking, without storage
Pr: Mario Borgatello Jr
**VP:* David Borgatello
Off Mgr: Roberto Medina
Dir IT: Greg Carlson
IT Man: Dennis Taylor

D-U-N-S 12-277-3211
MARBUCCO CORP
GRANITE STATE GLASS
4 Aviation Way, Gilford, NH 03249-6600
Tel (603) 528-4748 *Founded/Ownrshp* 1983
Sales 28.9MM^{E} *EMP* 150
SIC 5231 1793

D-U-N-S 62-489-0752 IMP
MARBURG TECHNOLOGY INC
GLIDE-WRITE
304 Turquoise St, Milpitas, CA 95035-5431
Tel (408) 262-8400 *Founded/Ownrshp* 1988
Sales 37.9MM^{E} *EMP* 245
SIC 3577 Disk & diskette equipment, except drives; Disk & diskette equipment, except drives
CEO: Francis Burga
**CFO:* Mohammad Ebrahimi
**VP:* Francis Guevara

MARBURGER FOODS
See MPI HOLDINGS INC

MARBURN CURTAINS
See MARBURN STORES INC

D-U-N-S 01-185-1334
MARBURN STORES INC
MARBURN CURTAINS
13a Division St, Fairview, NJ 07022-1564
Tel (201) 943-0222 *Founded/Ownrshp* 1956
Sales 27.7MM^{E} *EMP* 155
SIC 5714 5719

D-U-N-S 05-734-8047
MARC ANDREWS INC
512 Fashion Ave Rm 32rear, New York, NY 10018-4682
Tel (212) 840-1800 *Founded/Ownrshp* 1984
Sales 35.7MM^{E} *EMP* 180
SIC 5136 5137 Men's & boys' outerwear; Women's & children's outerwear; Men's & boys' outerwear; Women's & children's outerwear
Ex VP: Suzanne Schwartz

MARC CENTER
See MARC COMMUNITY RESOURCES INC

D-U-N-S 10-155-8851
MARC CENTER OF MESA
MARC PRODUCTION SERVICES
924 N Country Club Dr, Mesa, AZ 85201-4108
Tel (480) 969-3800 *Founded/Ownrshp* 2003
Sales 25.9MM *EMP* 179^{E}
Accts Sechler Cpa Pc Phoenix Az
SIC 8322 Rehabilitation services; Rehabilitation services
CEO: Randall Gray

D-U-N-S 08-649-2089
MARC COMMUNITY RESOURCES INC
MARC CENTER
924 N Country Club Dr, Mesa, AZ 85201-4108
Tel (480) 969-3800 *Founded/Ownrshp* 1957
Sales 28.3MM *EMP* 575
Accts Eide Bailly Llp Phoenix Ariz
SIC 8361 Home for the mentally retarded; Home for the mentally retarded
Ch: Jim Middleton
**Pr:* Randall Gray
**CFO:* John Moore
**Treas:* Theresa Carmichael
**Ex VP:* Holly Collins
Ex VP: Norm Duve
**Ex VP:* Diane Logan
**VP:* Janey Durham
**VP:* Diane Hough
**VP:* Donald Jackson
**VP:* Brian Kotsur
**VP:* Chris Schneck
**VP:* Tom Verploegen

MARC ECKO COLLECTION
See MEE APPAREL LLC

D-U-N-S 17-189-6272 IMP
MARC FISHER LLC
MARK FISHER FOOTWEAR
777 W Putnam Ave, Greenwich, CT 06830-5091
Tel (203) 302-2800 *Founded/Ownrshp* 1997
Sales 34.6MM^{E} *EMP* 48
SIC 5139 Footwear
COO: Richard Danderline
CFO: Matthew Burris

Ex VP: Geralyn Lyman
Ex VP: Mark Parsley
VP: Thomas Gibb
VP Sls: Terry Solis
Snr Mgr: Marc Fisher

D-U-N-S 09-448-7477 IMP
MARC GLASSMAN INC
MARC'S XPECT DRUGS
5841 W 130th St, Cleveland, OH 44130-9308
Tel (216) 265-7700 *Founded/Ownrshp* 1978
Sales 1.3MMM^E *EMP* 7,000
SIC 5331 Variety stores; Variety stores
Ch Bd: Marc Glassman
**Pr:* Kevin Yaugher
**CFO:* Beth Weiner
VP: Bob Guddy
VP: Jim Hocking
VP: Melanie Petropoulos
VP: Mike Tomko
**Prin:* Harold E Leidner
Off Mgr: Michelle McFadden
IT Man: Stephanie Seney
Opers Mgr: Jim Howe

D-U-N-S 06-228-2249
MARC HEITZ CHEVROLET INC
1221 Ed Noble Pkwy, Norman, OK 73072-4801
Tel (405) 321-7021 *Founded/Ownrshp* 2004
Sales 29.3MM^E *EMP* 99
SIC 5511 5531 7538 7532 Automobiles, new & used; Pickups, new & used; Vans, new & used; Automotive parts; General automotive repair shops; Body shop, automotive; Automobiles, new & used; Pickups, new & used; Vans, new & used; Automotive parts; General automotive repair shops; Body shop, automotive
Pr: Marc Heitz
**VP:* Chad Baker
**VP:* Larry W Houchins
Sales Asso: Marcus Aviles
Sales Asso: Tiffany Bateman
Sales Asso: Bobby Blansett
Sales Asso: Isreal Sheppard
Sales Asso: Derek Stratton

D-U-N-S 00-448-7059 IMP
MARC JACOBS INC
(*Suby of* LVMH MOET HENNESSY LOUIS VUITTON INC) ★
72 Spring St Fl 9, New York, NY 10012-4046
Tel (212) 965-4000 *Founded/Ownrshp* 1985
Sales 22.5MM^E *EMP* 80
SIC 5139 Shoes
Pr: Carolyn Rossoli
**VP:* Sallie Scripter

MARC LIFE
See MUNICH AMERICAN REASSURANCE CO PAC INC

D-U-N-S 04-512-1241
MARC MILLER BUICK-GMC INC
ERNIE MILLER G M C
4700 S Memorial Dr, Tulsa, OK 74145-6905
Tel (918) 663-4700 *Founded/Ownrshp* 1965
Sales 47.6MM^E *EMP* 124
SIC 5511 5521 Automobiles, new & used; Pickups, new & used; Vans, new & used; Used car dealers; Automobiles, new & used; Pickups, new & used; Vans, new & used; Used car dealers
Pr: William M Miller
VP: Jody Miller

MARC PRODUCTION SERVICES
See MARC CENTER OF MESA

D-U-N-S 09-845-6470
MARC REALTY LLC
M R
55 E Jackson Blvd Ste 500, Chicago, IL 60604-4396
Tel (312) 554-0100 *Founded/Ownrshp* 1976
Sales 50.4MM^E *EMP* 300
SIC 6531 Real estate brokers & agents; Real estate brokers & agents
VP: John Lajka
VP: Ariane Sank
Exec: Sylvia Ziman
Mng Dir: Brad Black
IT Man: Sergey Seleznev

D-U-N-S 00-450-5319
MARC USA INC
225 W Station Square Dr # 500, Pittsburgh, PA 15219-1174
Tel (412) 562-2000 *Founded/Ownrshp* 1955
Sales 53.4MM^E *EMP* 270
SIC 7311 8743 8732 7331 Advertising agencies; Promotion service; Public relations & publicity; Market analysis or research; Direct mail advertising services; Advertising agencies; Promotion service; Public relations & publicity; Market analysis or research; Direct mail advertising services
Ch Bd: Tony Bucci
**Pr:* Michele Fabrizi
**CFO:* Stuart Zolot
**Ofcr:* Jean McLaren
**Ex VP:* Sharon Aulicino
**Ex VP:* Chris Heitmann
Ex VP: Norb Sieber
Ex VP: Jerry Thompson
**Ex VP:* Tricia Warrick
Sr VP: Susan Bertocchi
Sr VP: Paul Magnani

D-U-N-S 82-707-4753 IMP/EXP
MARCAL MANUFACTURING LLC
SOUNDVIEW PAPER COMPANY
(*Suby of* SOUNDVIEW PAPER MILLS LLC) ★
1 Market St, Elmwood Park, NJ 07407-1401
Tel (201) 703-6225 *Founded/Ownrshp* 2008
Sales 264.4MM^E *EMP* 800^E
SIC 2676 Sanitary paper products; Towels, paper: made from purchased paper; Napkins, paper: made from purchased paper; Toilet paper: made from purchased paper; Sanitary paper products; Towels, paper: made from purchased paper; Napkins, paper: made from purchased paper; Toilet paper: made from purchased paper
COO: Karl Meyers
CFO: Mike Roth
Ofcr: Ed Oliveira
VP: Don Bryant
VP: Tim Crawford
Genl Mgr: Michael Bonin
Dir IT: Gerald Zavecz
VP Mktg: Greg Kane
VP Sls: Jim Rochford
Mktg Dir: Steve Ott
Sls Dir: Mike Conciatori

D-U-N-S 07-846-3743
MARCAL PAPER MILLS LLC
(*Suby of* SOUNDVIEW PAPER MILLS LLC) ★
1 Market St, Elmwood Park, NJ 07407-1493
Tel (201) 796-4000 *Founded/Ownrshp* 2012
Sales 223.1MM^E *EMP* 800
SIC 2676 Sanitary paper products; Sanitary paper products
Pr: Mark Vertucci
CFO: Robert Jackson
VP: Debi Mims
Snr Ntwrk: Jason Rice
Mill Mgr: Robert Washington
Sfty Mgr: Donna McGauley
Plnt Mgr: Gary Bielous
Mktg Mgr: Ilyne Germaise
Snr Mgr: John Rebisz

D-U-N-S 80-123-6142 IMP/EXP
MARCEGAGLIA USA INC
(*Suby of* MARCEGAGLIA SRL)
1001 E Waterfront Dr, Munhall, PA 15120-1098
Tel (412) 462-2185 *Founded/Ownrshp* 1992
Sales 140.3MM^E *EMP* 135
SIC 3317 3312 Welded pipe & tubes; Iron & steel: galvanized, pipes, plates, sheets, etc.; Stainless steel; Welded pipe & tubes; Iron & steel: galvanized, pipes, plates, sheets, etc.; Stainless steel
Pr: Francesco Tabarrini
Pr: David A Cornelius
CEO: Antonio Marcegaglia
CFO: David Comelius
CFO: Robert Minster
Plnt Mgr: Ferdinando Saglio
Ql Cn Mgr: Harold Bittner
Sales Asso: Robert Cochenour
Sales Asso: Lisa Quenzler

MARCELL ELECTRONICS INTL
See FABRICATED COMPONENTS CORP

D-U-N-S 01-078-3447
MARCELLUS CENTRAL SCHOOL DISTRICT
2 Reed Pkwy, Marcellus, NY 13108-1140
Tel (315) 673-6000 *Founded/Ownrshp* 1949
Sales 19.2MM^E *EMP* 300
SIC 8211 Public elementary & secondary schools; Public elementary & secondary schools
IT Man: Lorraine Phillips

D-U-N-S 17-522-5721
MARCH ASSOCIATES INC
601 Hamburg Tpke Ste 300, Wayne, NJ 07470-2049
Tel (973) 904-0213 *Founded/Ownrshp* 1986
Sales 21.5MM^E *EMP* 46
SIC 1542 Commercial & office building contractors
Pr: Louis D March
COO: John Driesse
**VP:* Karl Hoermann
Site Mgr: Tim Cloidt
VP Mktg: Peter Leon
VP Mktg: Todd Viegut
VP Sls: Paul Coxon

D-U-N-S 06-593-7021
MARCH ELECTRONICS INC
25 Feldland St, Bohemia, NY 11716-2411
Tel (631) 563-6000 *Founded/Ownrshp* 1972
Sales 24.4MM^E *EMP* 39
Accts Schulman & Glaves Roslyn Heig
SIC 5065 Electronic parts; Electronic parts
Pr: John Vilardi
Genl Mgr: Ron Alonso

MARCH GROUP, THE
See MARCH GROUP DELAWARE LLC

D-U-N-S 00-479-1756
MARCH GROUP DELAWARE LLC
MARCH GROUP, THE
1375 Gateway Blvd, Boynton Beach, FL 33426-8304
Tel (469) 619-5410 *Founded/Ownrshp* 1986
Sales 23.5MM^E *EMP* 180
SIC 6211 8742 Security brokers & dealers; Management consulting services; Security brokers & dealers; Management consulting services
Ch: George Gifford
**CFO:* Mark Meyer
VP: Takashi Fujimoto
**VP:* Perry Sheraw
VP Mktg: Deborah Walker

D-U-N-S 11-271-6279 IMP
■ MARCH NORDSON INC
MARCH PLASMA SYSTEMS, INC.
(*Suby of* NORDSON CORP) ★
2470 Bates Ave Ste A, Concord, CA 94520-1294
Tel (925) 827-1240 *Founded/Ownrshp* 1999
Sales 35.0MM^E *EMP* 99
SIC 2836 Plasmas
CEO: James Getty
**CFO:* Raymond L Cushing

D-U-N-S 06-134-4883
MARCH OF DIMES FOUNDATION
1275 Mamaroneck Ave, White Plains, NY 10605-5298
Tel (914) 428-7100 *Founded/Ownrshp* 1938
Sales 195.8MM *EMP* 1,200
Accts Kpmg Llp New York Ny
SIC 8399 Fund raising organization, non-fee basis; Fund raising organization, non-fee basis
Pr: Jennifer L Howse
**COO:* Jane Massey
**Ch:* Ken May
**Treas:* Childs Al
Treas: Nancy T Lukitsch
Trst: Jos F Cordero
Trst: Billy B Hill
VP: Frank P Lynch
**VP:* Richard Mulligan
Ex Dir: Janice Dumsha
Ex Dir: Kimberly Jewell

MARCH PLASMA SYSTEMS, INC.
See MARCH NORDSON INC

D-U-N-S 14-638-3562
MARCH VISION CARE INC
(*Suby of* MARCH HOLDINGS, INC.)
6701 Center Dr W Ste 790, Los Angeles, CA 90045-1563
Tel (310) 665-0975 *Founded/Ownrshp* 2005
Sales NA *EMP* 42
SIC 6321 Accident & health insurance
Pr: Glen A March Jr
Pr: Shawn Shahzad
CFO: Patricia Boucher
**CFO:* Gavin Galimi
Treas: A M Glenville Jr
**Ex VP:* Cabraini March
CTO: Armando Rosario
Software D: Chockalingam Mahalingam
VP Opers: Johnna Jonasson
Genl Couns: Dan Rogoff

D-U-N-S 12-167-9419
MARCH-WESTIN CO INC
360 Frontier Ave, Morgantown, WV 26505-3008
Tel (304) 599-4880 *Founded/Ownrshp* 1984
Sales 52.6MM *EMP* 268
Accts Brown Edwards & Company Llp
SIC 1542 8711 Commercial & office building contractors; Consulting engineer; Commercial & office building contractors; Consulting engineer
Pr: Phillip L Weser
Pr: Tom Smith
**CFO:* Kevin L Salisbury
**VP:* Jamie Ridgeway
**VP:* Robert Weser
Comm Dir: Kimberly Hayes
Comm Dir: Kim Thaler

D-U-N-S 13-892-3524
MARCH/HODGE/LAMARCH CLEVELAND LLC
WESTSIDE AUTOMOTIVE GROUP
9600 Brookpark Rd, Cleveland, OH 44129-6812
Tel (216) 351-9999 *Founded/Ownrshp* 2002
Sales 26.5MM^E *EMP* 80
SIC 5511 New & used car dealers; New & used car dealers
Off Mgr: Karen Grove
Sales Asso: Michael Thomas

D-U-N-S 02-322-9016 IMP/EXP
MARCHANT-SCHMIDT INC
24 W Larsen Dr, Fond Du Lac, WI 54937-8518
Tel (920) 921-4760 *Founded/Ownrshp* 1979
Sales 37.0MM^E *EMP* 85
SIC 3556 8711 Food products machinery; Engineering services; Food products machinery; Engineering services
CEO: Nyleen Schmidt
**VP:* Lyle M Schmidt
**VP:* Richard Schmidt
Off Mgr: Karen Lane
Sales Asso: Sean Kok
Sales Asso: Manpreet Maa

D-U-N-S 12-814-9932
▲ MARCHEX INC
520 Pike St Ste 2000, Seattle, WA 98101-2319
Tel (206) 331-3300 *Founded/Ownrshp* 2003
Sales 182.6MM *EMP* 367^E
Tkr Sym MCHX *Exch* NGS
SIC 7313 ; On-line data base information retrieval; Marketing consulting services; Electronic media advertising representatives
Ex Dir: Russell C Horowitz
**Ch Bd:* Clark Kokich
CFO: Michael Arends
**V Ch Bd:* Nicolas Hanauer
Bd of Dir: Wayne Wisehart
Ofcr: Ethan Caldwell
Ex VP: Matthew Berk
Sr VP: John Busby
Sr VP: Ziad Ismail
Sr VP: Michael Miller
Sr VP: Matt Muilenburg
VP: Daniel Behrendt
VP: Rod Diefendorf
VP: Travis Fairchild
VP: Peter Greb
VP: Bill Keadle
Dir Risk M: Gary Nafus
Dir Rx: Iain Starr
Dir Bus: Nadia Edwards
Dir Bus: Ken Seligman
Board of Directors: Dennis Cline, Anne Devereux-Mills, Ian Morris, M Wayne Wisehart

D-U-N-S 83-293-4660
■ MARCHI THERMAL SYSTEMS INC
(*Suby of* ULTRA CLEAN HOLDINGS INC) ★
3108 Diablo Ave, Hayward, CA 94545-2702
Tel (510) 300-1500 *Founded/Ownrshp* 2015
Sales 113.2MM^E *EMP* 1,034^E
SIC 3826 Thermal analysis instruments, laboratory type
CEO: James E Hawthorne

D-U-N-S 08-420-0385 EXP
MARCHO FARMS INC (PA)
176 Orchard Ln, Harleysville, PA 19438-1681
Tel (215) 721-7131 *Founded/Ownrshp* 1968
Sales 22.4MM^E *EMP* 140
SIC 2011 Veal from meat slaughtered on site; Veal from meat slaughtered on site
Pr: Wayne A Marcho
**Treas:* Wayne Marcho
**VP:* Martha G Marcho

D-U-N-S 07-727-7648 IMP/EXP
MARCHON EYEWEAR INC
(*Suby of* C V S OPTICAL LAB DIV) ★
201 Old Country Rd Fl 3, Melville, NY 11747-2731
Tel (631) 756-8530 *Founded/Ownrshp* 2008
Sales 212.3MM^E *EMP* 1,055
SIC 5048 Frames, ophthalmic; Optometric equipment & supplies; Frames, ophthalmic; Optometric equipment & supplies
Ch Bd: Claudio Gottardi
**COO:* Marty Fox
**CFO:* Phil Hibbert
VP: Pierre Bessez
VP: Ken Clay
VP: Ron Kitt
VP: Achille Rachello
VP: Donna Rollins
VP: Micha Siebenhandl
VP: Nicola Zotta
Exec: Kelly Belanger
Exec: Krista Kester

D-U-N-S 09-952-0108
MARCKISOTTO MARKETS INC
GIANT EAGLE
1705 S Braddock Ave, Pittsburgh, PA 15218-1865
Tel (412) 371-4614 *Founded/Ownrshp* 1981
Sales 33.5MM *EMP* 185
SIC 5411 Supermarkets; Supermarkets, chain
Pr: Frank P Marckisotto
**Sec:* Darlene Marckisotto

D-U-N-S 06-826-7889
MARCO BOOK CO INC (NY)
EVERBIND MARCO
60 Industrial Rd, Lodi, NJ 07644-2608
Tel (973) 458-0485 *Founded/Ownrshp* 1954
Sales 24.7MM^E *EMP* 50
SIC 5192 2789 Books; Bookbinding & related work
CEO: Stewart Penn
Mktg Mgr: Ed Yamada

MARCO COMPANY, THE
See MARCO DISPLAY SPECIALISTS GP LC

D-U-N-S 17-727-6490
MARCO CONTRACTORS INC
100 Commonwealth Dr, Warrendale, PA 15086-7501
Tel (724) 741-0300 *Founded/Ownrshp* 1987
Sales 37.3MM *EMP* 70^E
Accts Hill Barth & King Llc Wexfor
SIC 1542 Commercial & office building, new construction; Commercial & office buildings, renovation & repair; Commercial & office building, new construction; Commercial & office buildings, renovation & repair
Pr: Martin R Smith
Snr Mgr: Richard Grguras

D-U-N-S 06-839-4527
MARCO CRANE & RIGGING CO
221 S 35th Ave, Phoenix, AZ 85009-4722
Tel (602) 272-2671 *Founded/Ownrshp* 1972
Sales 20.1MM^E *EMP* 124
SIC 7353 Heavy construction equipment rental; Cranes & aerial lift equipment, rental or leasing; Earth moving equipment, rental or leasing; Heavy construction equipment rental; Cranes & aerial lift equipment, rental or leasing; Earth moving equipment, rental or leasing
CEO: Daniel Mardian Jr
**Pr:* James E Nixon
**Treas:* Kevin Bries
**VP:* Samson Meyer
IT Man: Becky Alvis

D-U-N-S 04-581-5755 EXP
MARCO DESTIN INC (FL)
WINGS
10800 Nw 106th St Ste 6, Medley, FL 33178-1250
Tel (305) 471-9394 *Founded/Ownrshp* 1996, 1998
Sales 64.3MM^E *EMP* 450
SIC 5651 Family clothing stores; Family clothing stores
Pr: Eliezer Tabib
**CFO:* Dror Levy
**VP:* Jay Ardan
Creative D: Renata Florio

D-U-N-S 11-876-9884 IMP/EXP
MARCO DISPLAY SPECIALISTS GP LC
MARCO COMPANY, THE
3209 Marquita Dr, Fort Worth, TX 76116-5120
Tel (817) 244-8300 *Founded/Ownrshp* 2001
Sales 71.1MM *EMP* 500
Accts Kellogg And Kellogg Pc For
SIC 2521 2541 3993 3089 3081 Tables, office: wood; Store & office display cases & fixtures; Signs & advertising specialties; Washers, plastic; Unsupported plastics film & sheet; Tables, office: wood; Store & office display cases & fixtures; Signs & advertising specialties; Washers, plastic; Unsupported plastics film & sheet
COO: Charlotte Neal
CFO: Jon W Stewart
Opers Mgr: Danny Towne

D-U-N-S 96-487-6010 IMP
MARCO DISPLAY SPECIALISTS LP
(*Suby of* MARCO CO) ★
3209 Marquita Dr, Fort Worth, TX 76116-5120
Tel (817) 244-8300 *Founded/Ownrshp* 1984
Sales 71.1MM^E *EMP* 500
SIC 2541 3993 Store & office display cases & fixtures; Signs & advertising specialties; Store & office display cases & fixtures; Signs & advertising specialties
Prin: Darrell L Cooper
CFO: Jon Stewart

D-U-N-S 00-527-3735 IMP
MARCO GROUP INTERNATIONAL INC
3425 E Locust St, Davenport, IA 52803-3534
Tel (563) 324-2519 *Founded/Ownrshp* 1944

Sales 82.3MM[E] *EMP* 90[E]
SIC 5084 5032 Industrial machinery & equipment; Sand, construction; Industrial machinery & equipment; Sand, construction
Pr: Michael W Marthens
VP: Cheryl Lester
Dir IT: Bryan Gregory
IT Man: Samantha Hayen
VP Opers: Matt Molumby
VP Sls: James Claassen
Mktg Dir: Andrea Olson
Board of Directors: Michael W Marthens

D-U-N-S 06-285-9558
MARCO INC
4510 Heatherwood Rd, Saint Cloud, MN 56301-9500
Tel (320) 259-3000 *Founded/Ownrshp* 1973
Sales 180.0MM *EMP* 900
SIC 7371 4813 7313 7812

D-U-N-S 96-258-3774 IMP
MARCO INDUSTRIES INC
9410 E 54th St, Tulsa, OK 74145-8102
Tel (918) 622-4535 *Founded/Ownrshp* 1991
Sales 31.2MM[E] *EMP* 150[E]
SIC 3448 Prefabricated metal buildings; Prefabricated metal buildings
Pr: Mark Polumbus
Opers Mgr: Clay Polumbus
Opers Mgr: Gregg Potter
Manager: Zach Buege
Manager: Matt Caissie
Manager: Colin Condon
Manager: Kent Haney
Sls Mgr: Ben Oskarsson
Sales Asso: Craig Barker

D-U-N-S 04-303-9890 IMP
MARCO OPHTHALMIC INC (FL)
11825 Central Pkwy, Jacksonville, FL 32224-2637
Tel (904) 642-9330 *Founded/Ownrshp* 1962
Sales 39.3MM[E] *EMP* 65
SIC 5048 Optometric equipment & supplies
Pr: David A Marco
**Ex VP:* David Gurvis
**VP:* Charon M Dyer
**VP:* David A Gurvis
**VP:* Jack F Shorstein
Exec: Erika Bauer
Area Mgr: Janet Catlin
Area Mgr: Brian Cullather
Area Mgr: Aaron Elder
Area Mgr: Tressa Floyd
Area Mgr: Dave Hale

D-U-N-S 80-465-0984
MARCO PETROLEUM INDUSTRIES INC
38b South Rd, North Hampton, NH 03862-2432
Tel (603) 964-1644 *Founded/Ownrshp* 1993
Sales 40.5MM[E] *EMP* 80
SIC 5172 Petroleum products; Petroleum products
Pr: Paul J Marston
**CFO:* Peter George

D-U-N-S 10-121-3403 IMP/EXP
MARCO POLO INTERNATIONAL INC
532 Broadhollow Rd # 135, Melville, NY 11747-3626
Tel (631) 629-4520 *Founded/Ownrshp* 1983
Sales 87.7MM[E] *EMP* 25
SIC 5162 Plastics materials; Plastics products
CEO: Marco Liuzzo
**Prin:* Rosaria Liuzzo

D-U-N-S 14-494-7553 IMP
MARCO STEEL & ALUMINUM INC
11524 County Rd 128 W, Odessa, TX 79760
Tel (432) 563-5051 *Founded/Ownrshp* 1985
Sales 23.5MM[E] *EMP* 52
SIC 5051 Metals service centers & offices
Pr: Morris Rubenstein
**CFO:* Brenda Blair
Genl Mgr: Rick Hellinghausen
Genl Mgr: Jay Roberts

D-U-N-S 04-696-4367 IMP
MARCO SUPPLY CO INC
18339 Old Statesville Rd G, Cornelius, NC 28031-9044
Tel (540) 344-6211 *Founded/Ownrshp* 1970
Sales 21.3MM[E] *EMP* 123
SIC 5085 Industrial supplies; Electric tools; Fasteners, industrial: nuts, bolts, screws, etc.; Industrial supplies; Electric tools; Fasteners, industrial: nuts, bolts, screws, etc.
Ch Bd: David Jones
**Pr:* Marshall Jones
**VP:* Antoinette Jones
Sls Mgr: Frank Orndorff

D-U-N-S 05-319-3082
MARCO SUPPLY CO INC
STOCKYARDS HARDWARE
999 W 37th St, Chicago, IL 60609-1540
Tel (773) 927-2427 *Founded/Ownrshp* 1970
Sales 23.6MM[E] *EMP* 35
SIC 5085 Industrial fittings; Valves & fittings
Pr: Lance Marco
Brnch Mgr: Rick Melvin
Sls Mgr: Erin Cheek

D-U-N-S 04-558-8811
MARCO SUPPLY INC
4M PARTS WAREHOUSE
402 E Chambers St, Cleburne, TX 76031-5626
Tel (817) 645-9145 *Founded/Ownrshp* 1966
Sales 23.3MM[E] *EMP* 55
SIC 5013 5531 Automotive supplies & parts; Automotive supplies; Automobile & truck equipment & parts; Automotive parts
Pr: Bill Martindale
COO: Shirley Poteet
**VP:* Brian Martindale
**VP:* Mary Jo Martindale

D-U-N-S 06-723-9079
MARCOBAY CONSTRUCTION INC
4025 S Pipkin Rd, Lakeland, FL 33811-1424
Tel (863) 680-2293 *Founded/Ownrshp* 1974
Sales 49.6MM[E] *EMP* 80
SIC 1542 Commercial & office building, new construction
Pr: Howard D Bayless
**Treas:* Mark Phillips
**VP:* Steve Cowperthwaite
VP Opers: Chuck McGee
Snr Mgr: Will Yancey

D-U-N-S 12-535-7900
MARCOISLANDREALESTATE.COM INC
870 Bald Eagle Dr Ste 4a, Marco Island, FL 34145-2550
Tel (239) 394-2500 *Founded/Ownrshp* 2001
Sales 28.0MM *EMP* 8
Accts Pat Ferguson Marco Island Fl
SIC 6531 Real estate agents & managers; Real estate agents & managers
Pr: Kent Hedrick
Opers Mgr: Jeffrey Poteet

D-U-N-S 08-975-1499 IMP/EXP
MARCOLIN USA EYEWEAR CORP
VIVA INTERNATIONAL GROUP
(*Suby of* MARCOLIN SPA)
3140 Rte 22, Branchburg, NJ 08876-3548
Tel (800) 345-8482 *Founded/Ownrshp* 2013
Sales 221.8MM[E] *EMP* 550
SIC 5099 5048 Sunglasses; Ophthalmic goods; Frames, ophthalmic; Lenses, ophthalmic; Sunglasses; Ophthalmic goods; Frames, ophthalmic; Lenses, ophthalmic
CEO: Sabrizio Gamberini
COO: Ellen Navarro
CFO: Frfank Dwyer
**CFO:* Paolo Piazza
**CFO:* Sal Rianna
Ex VP: Sherry Lay
Sr VP: Jan Cory
VP: Alexandra Gil
VP: Cory Jan
VP: Regina Lage
Mfg Dir: John Hecker

D-U-N-S 03-028-9941 IMP/EXP
MARCOLIN USA INC
(*Suby of* MARCOLIN SPA)
3140 Us Highway 22, Branchburg, NJ 08876-3548
Tel (480) 951-7174 *Founded/Ownrshp* 2008
Sales 87.7MM[E] *EMP* 300
SIC 5048 Frames, ophthalmic; Frames, ophthalmic
Ch: Vittorio Levi
**Pr:* Maurizio Marcolin
**CEO:* Giovanni Zoppas
**CFO:* Joseph Ivenz
Sr VP: Ben Wolf
VP: Bob Dunn
VP: Greg Pollock
VP: Tom Seltze

D-U-N-S 19-439-1124
MARCON & BOYER INC
DUGGAN AND MARCON
645 Hamilton St Ste 300, Allentown, PA 18101-2191
Tel (610) 866-5959 *Founded/Ownrshp* 1981
Sales 110.2MM[E] *EMP* 670
SIC 3448 1742 1743 1799 Panels for prefabricated metal buildings; Drywall; Tile installation, ceramic; Fireproofing buildings; Panels for prefabricated metal buildings; Drywall; Tile installation, ceramic; Fireproofing buildings
Pr: L Charles Marcon
**Sec:* Kenneth H Kline Jr
**Sr VP:* Frank B Boyer
**VP:* Robert H Handschue
Exec: Marianne Martinez
Dir IT: Tina Mills
Dir IT: Gail Shively

D-U-N-S 96-248-7893
MARCONE APW LLC
1 Cityplace Dr, Saint Louis, MO 63141-7014
Tel (314) 993-9196 *Founded/Ownrshp* 2010
Sales 22.8MM[E] *EMP* 150
SIC 5064 Appliance parts, household; Appliance parts, household
Brnch Mgr: Michael Hill

MARCONE SUPPLY
See MAR-CONE APPLIANCE PARTS CO

D-U-N-S 79-111-8276
MARCOR ENTERPRISES INC
(*Suby of* PREMIUM TRANSPORTATION STAFFING INC) ★
190 Highland Dr, Medina, OH 44256-3199
Tel (330) 722-7974 *Founded/Ownrshp* 1996
Sales 130.0MM *EMP* 20[E]
SIC 7363 Employee leasing service; Employee leasing service
CEO: William Schoenstein
**Pr:* Nancy Normile

MARCO'S FOODS
See READY FOODS INC

MARCOS MEXICAN RESTAURANT
See MARCOS MEXICAN RESTAURANTS INC

D-U-N-S 11-300-9104
MARCOS MEXICAN RESTAURANTS INC
MARCOS MEXICAN RESTAURANT
11111 Wilcrest Green Dr # 350, Houston, TX 77042-4813
Tel (713) 661-8893 *Founded/Ownrshp* 1983
Sales 11.6MM[E] *EMP* 875
SIC 5812 5813 Mexican restaurant; Bar (drinking places)
Pr: Ghulam M Bombaywala

D-U-N-S 01-619-3331
MARCOS PIZZA INC
5252 Monroe St Fl 1, Toledo, OH 43623-3140
Tel (419) 885-4844 *Founded/Ownrshp* 1978
Sales 13.2MM *EMP* 700
SIC 5812 Pizzeria, chain; Pizzeria, chain
Pr: Bryon Stephens
Pr: Don Vlcek
**Prin:* Pasquale Giammarco
IT Man: Shawn Chowdhary

D-U-N-S 04-149-0764
MARCOTTE FORD SALES INC
FORD RENT-A-CAR SYSTEM
1025 Main St, Holyoke, MA 01040-5395
Tel (413) 536-1900 *Founded/Ownrshp* 1980
Sales 26.9MM[E] *EMP* 52
SIC 5511 Automobiles, new & used; Automobiles, new & used
Pr: Bryan A Marcotte
Dir Rx: Patty McQuade
IT Man: Lisa Reniewicz
VP Sls: Kevin O'Grady
Sls Mgr: Fran Gregory
Sls Mgr: Chris Pariseau
Sales Asso: Jeff Duffy
Sales Asso: Mark Lyon
Sales Asso: Steve Mailloux
Sales Asso: Andrew Tesini

MARCPARC AND MARCPARC VALET
See IMPERIAL PARKING (US) LLC

D-U-N-S 94-112-7623
MARCPARC INC
1233 20th St Nw Ste 104, Washington, DC 20036-2345
Tel (202) 218-0392 *Founded/Ownrshp* 1996
Sales 32.1MM[E] *EMP* 950[E]
SIC 7521 Automobile parking; Automobile parking
Pr: Marc Slavin
COO: Paul Harbolick
Ex VP: Todd Dengel
VP: Lawrence McCray
VP: Eric Webb
VP: Bobby Williams
IT Man: Shekiya Broadus
IT Man: Peter Kaiser

MARCRAFT APPAREL GROUP
See MARCRAFT CLOTHES INC

D-U-N-S 06-430-3308 IMP
MARCRAFT CLOTHES INC
MARCRAFT APPAREL GROUP
301 Island Rd, Mahwah, NJ 07430-2127
Tel (201) 828-2085 *Founded/Ownrshp* 1972
Sales 96.4MM[E] *EMP* 80
SIC 5136 Suits, men's & boys'; Suits, men's & boys'
Ch Bd: Sheldon Brody
**Pr:* Gary Brody
**CFO:* Brad Goldstein

MARC'S XPECT DRUGS
See MARC GLASSMAN INC

D-U-N-S 06-474-9864
MARCUM LLP
750 3rd Ave Fl 11, New York, NY 10017-2716
Tel (212) 485-5500 *Founded/Ownrshp* 1951
Sales 251.3MM *EMP* 1,325
SIC 8721 Certified public accountant; Certified public accountant
Genl Pt: Jeffrey M Weiner
Pt: James T Ashe
Pt: David Bukzin
Pt: Bart H Friedman
Pt: Joseph J Perry
Pt: Lawrence Schienthal
Pt: James Smart
Pt: Daniel Vitulli
Pt: Beth M Wiener
COO: Paul Sherman
CFO: Edward Scicchitano
VP: John Miller
Dir Bus: Gary Slutsky
Dir Bus: Victor Tricarico

D-U-N-S 02-297-6130
▲ **MARCUS & MILLICHAP**
23975 Park Sorrento # 400, Calabasas, CA 91302-4014
Tel (818) 212-2250 *Founded/Ownrshp* 2011
Sales 572.1MM[E] *EMP* 18[E]
Tkr Sym MMI *Exch* NYS
SIC 6531 Buying agent, real estate; Buying agent, real estate
Prin: John Kerin
VP: Cliff David
VP: Farhan Kabani
VP: Bill Rose
Exec: Lisa Young
Assoc Dir: Charles Hilding
Assoc Dir: Seth Richard
Assoc Dir: David Sperling
Dir Bus: Ryan Gomez
Ex Dir: Lori Schneider
Mng Dir: Steven Rock

D-U-N-S 11-329-1710
MARCUS & MILLICHAP CO
777 S California Ave, Palo Alto, CA 94304-1102
Tel (650) 494-1400 *Founded/Ownrshp* 1971
Sales 75.4MM[E] *EMP* 1,308
SIC 6531 Real estate brokers & agents
Ch: George M Marcus
**Pr:* Harvey E Green
CFO: Martin Louie
**CFO:* Alex Yamolinski
Ex VP: Gene A Berman
Sr VP: William E Hughes
Sr VP: Gary Lucas
Sr VP: Richard H Peltz
VP: Brett Hatcher
VP: Rick Peltz
VP: Kent Williams

D-U-N-S 06-912-5151
MARCUS & MILLICHAP REAL ESTATE INVESTMENT SERVICES OF INDIANA INC
(*Suby of* MARCUS & MILLICHAP CO) ★
2626 Hanover St, Palo Alto, CA 94304-1132
Tel (650) 494-1400 *Founded/Ownrshp* 1971
Sales 20.9MM[E] *EMP* 1,300
SIC 6531 Real estate brokers & agents
Pr: Harvey E Green
**Ch Bd:* George M Marcus
**Co-Ch Bd:* William A Millichap
Sr VP: Michael Mele
VP: Kevin McCrann

D-U-N-S 04-005-9123 IMP
MARCUS BROTHERS TEXTILES INC
MARCUS FABRICS
980 Avenue Of The America, New York, NY 10018-7807
Tel (212) 354-8700 *Founded/Ownrshp* 1975
Sales 47.5MM[E] *EMP* 71
SIC 5131 5949 Textile converters; Sewing, needlework & piece goods
CEO: Martin Marcus
**Pr:* Stephanie Dell 'olio
**Treas:* Arthur Marcus
VP: Melody Brown
Opers Mgr: Joe Sullivan
Sls Dir: Michael Watson
Mktg Mgr: Lisa Shepard
Mktg Mgr: Lisa Stewart

D-U-N-S 06-816-3757
MARCUS CONSTRUCTION CO INC (MN)
2580 Highway 12 E, Willmar, MN 56201-5826
Tel (320) 222-6616 *Founded/Ownrshp* 1956
Sales 79.5MM *EMP* 55
Accts Conway Deuth & Schmiesing Pl
SIC 1542 1541 1771 1791 Commercial & office building, new construction; Industrial buildings & warehouses; Warehouse construction; Industrial buildings, new construction; Paper/pulp mill construction; Concrete work; Structural steel erection; Concrete reinforcement, placing of; Agricultural building contractors; Commercial & office building contractors; Industrial buildings & warehouses; Warehouse construction; Industrial buildings, new construction; Paper/pulp mill construction; Concrete work; Structural steel erection; Concrete reinforcement, placing of
Pr: Ross Marcus
VP: Todd Erickson
IT Man: Toni Baumgartner
Sfty Mgr: Steve Dresler
Sls Dir: James Bach

D-U-N-S 05-874-2347
▲ **MARCUS CORP**
100 E Wisconsin Ave # 1, Milwaukee, WI 53202-4107
Tel (414) 905-1000 *Founded/Ownrshp* 1935
Sales 488.0MM *EMP* 7,100[E]
Tkr Sym MCS *Exch* NYS
SIC 7011 7833 Hotels & motels; Resort hotel; Drive-in motion picture theaters; Hotels & motels; Resort hotel; Drive-in motion picture theaters
Pr: Gregory S Marcus
**Ch Bd:* Stephen H Marcus
Pr: Kirk A Rose
CFO: Douglas A Neis
Treas: Bruce Hoffmann
Chf Invest: Brian Stark
Ex VP: Rolando B Rodriguez
Sr VP: Jeff Tomachek
Sr VP: Gary Gentile
Sr VP: Mark Gramz
Sr VP: David J Merritt
Sr VP: Thomas P Riley
VP: Chris Anderson
VP: Ken Day
VP: Katie Falvey
VP: Michael Lindley
VP: Marie McSzkowski
VP: Jeff Peterson
VP: Amy Wangerin
Exec: Thomas F Kissinger
Comm Man: Joan Voelzke
Board of Directors: Brian J Stark, James D Ericson, Katherine M Gehl, Diane M Gershowitz, Bronson J Haase, Timothy E Hoeksema, Daniel F McKeithan Jr, Philip L Milstein, Bruce J Olson, Allan H Selig

D-U-N-S 00-259-1923
MARCUS DAIRY INC (CT)
12 Willow St, Newburgh, NY 12550-5013
Tel (800) 243-2511 *Founded/Ownrshp* 1923
Sales 27.7MM[E] *EMP* 180
SIC 2026 Milk processing (pasteurizing, homogenizing, bottling); Milk processing (pasteurizing, homogenizing, bottling)
Pr: Neil Marcus
**VP:* Jeffrey Marcus
Sls Mgr: Thomas Schiappa

D-U-N-S 07-971-2584
MARCUS DALY MEMORIAL HOSPITAL CORP (MT)
1200 Westwood Dr, Hamilton, MT 59840-2345
Tel (406) 363-2211 *Founded/Ownrshp* 1931
Sales 50.7MM *EMP* 500
Accts Cliftonlarsonallen Llp Minne
SIC 8062 General medical & surgical hospitals; General medical & surgical hospitals
CEO: John Bartos
Chf Rad: Brad Peterson
**CFO:* Donja Erdman
Ofcr: June Bartholome
VP: Matthew Munding
Dir Soc: Andea Londerville
Dir Rad: Scott Mc Cormick
Dir Rad: Scott McCormick
Dir Rx: Gary Curran
Dir Rx: Kellie Jones
Mng Ofcr: Luke Channer

D-U-N-S 62-688-1361
■ **MARCUS DAVID CORP**
TOWN & COUNTRY TOYOTA
(*Suby of* SONIC AUTOMOTIVE INC) ★
9101 South Blvd, Charlotte, NC 28273-6938
Tel (704) 552-7600 *Founded/Ownrshp* 1990
Sales 48.0MM[E] *EMP* 150
SIC 5511 Automobiles, new & used; Pickups, new & used; Vans, new & used; Automobiles, new & used; Pickups, new & used; Vans, new & used
Genl Mgr: Sanjay Prakash
**Prin:* Steve Bell
**Prin:* Sean Williams
Genl Mgr: Steve Okane
**Off Mgr:* Bernie Spears
Mktg Dir: Jose Vasquez
Sls Mgr: Louis O'Pharrow
Sales Asso: Iris Austin

Sales Asso: Jeffrey Dancy
Sales Asso: Nicolas Dardiz
Sales Asso: Edgar Ferrufino

D-U-N-S 83-558-9342
MARCUS EVANS INC
(*Suby of* MARCUS EVANS (UK HOLDINGS) LIMITED)
455 N Cityfront Plaza Dr # 900, Chicago, IL 60611-5597
Tel (312) 329-0609 *Founded/Ownrshp* 1994
Sales 66.8MM^E *EMP* 620
SIC 8742 Business consultant; Business consultant
Pr: Theron Burraway
*Ch Bd: Marcus Evans
COO: Paul Northover
COO: Geoffrey Reid
*CFO: Steve Drago
CFO: Jacques Hauwaert
Dir Soc: Severine Greck
Dir Soc: Katie Williamson
Off Mgr: Samantha Stewart
IT Man: Martin Fierro
VP Opers: John Dees

MARCUS FABRICS
See MARCUS BROTHERS TEXTILES INC

D-U-N-S 09-770-4894 IMP/EXP
MARCUS FOOD CO
240 N Rock Rd Ste 246, Wichita, KS 67206-2245
Tel (316) 686-7649 *Founded/Ownrshp* 1980
Sales 205.1MM *EMP* 23
SIC 5144 5142

D-U-N-S 07-019-7871
MARCUS FOUNDATION INC
1266 W Paces Ferry Rd Nw # 615, Atlanta, GA 30327-2306
Tel (404) 240-7700 *Founded/Ownrshp* 1995
Sales 35.3MM *EMP* 10
SIC 6733 Private estate, personal investment & vacation fund trusts
CEO: Bernard Marcus
*Sec: Frederick Slagle
Pgrm Dir: Daniel Sperling

MARCUS HOTELS AND RESORTS
See MARCUS HOTELS INC

D-U-N-S 80-789-9760
■ **MARCUS HOTELS INC**
MARCUS HOTELS AND RESORTS
(*Suby of* MARCUS CORP) ★
100 E Wisconsin Ave, Milwaukee, WI 53202-4107
Tel (414) 905-1200 *Founded/Ownrshp* 1990
Sales 225.0MM^E *EMP* 3,500
SIC 7011 Hotels; Hotels
Pr: Thomas Kissinger
*COO: Joseph Khairallah
*Sr VP: Chris Anderson
Sr VP: Andrea Foster
Sr VP: Tom Mason
*Sr VP: Thomas P Riley
VP: Bill Eichelberg
*VP: Gary Gentile
VP: Jeff Henschel
VP: Kevin M Hickman
VP: Brett Huske
VP: Ted Lorenzi
*VP: Steve Martin
VP: David Morley
VP: Duane Quintana
VP: Scott Richter
VP: Scott Schoenberger
VP: Pam Seidl
VP: Alan Stegman
VP: Michael Swasey
VP: Chad Waetzig

D-U-N-S 80-097-2044
MARCUS JEWISH COMMUNITY CENTER OF ATLANTA INC
5342 Tilly Mill Rd, Atlanta, GA 30338-4426
Tel (678) 812-4000 *Founded/Ownrshp* 1950
Sales 25.4MM *EMP* 300
Accts Bdo Usa Llp Atlanta Ga
SIC 8322 Community center; Community center
Pr: Garrett Vandegrift
*CEO: Howard Hyman
*CFO: Janice Wolf
*VP: Steven Cadranel
Art Dir: Blake Hall
Board of Directors: Jenise Walls

D-U-N-S 06-689-0880
■ **MARCUS THEATRES CORP**
(*Suby of* MARCUS CORP) ★
100 E Wisconsin Ave, Milwaukee, WI 53202-4107
Tel (414) 905-1500 *Founded/Ownrshp* 1935
Sales 68.0MM^E *EMP* 1,050
SIC 7832 Motion picture theaters, except drive-in; Motion picture theaters, except drive-in
*Pr: Bruce J Olson
Treas: Doug Neis
Chf Mktg O: Ann Stadler
Ofcr: Kim Lueck
Ex VP: Mark Gramz
Sr VP: Samuel Gourley
VP: Gregory Marcus
VP: Jeff Tomachek
Ex Dir: Kathy Bennett
Genl Mgr: Lisa Fryda
Genl Mgr: Brian Shander

D-U-N-S 01-779-5030
MARCUS THOMAS LLC
4781 Richmond Rd, Cleveland, OH 44128-5919
Tel (216) 292-4700 *Founded/Ownrshp* 2000
Sales 21.8MM^E *EMP* 98
SIC 7311 Advertising agencies; Advertising agencies
Pr: Jim Nash
VP: Tim Bennett
VP: Scott Chapin
VP: Kara Gildone
VP: King Hill
VP: Carrie Kandes
VP: Jason Mitton
VP: Raphael Rivilla
VP: James Sollisch
VP: Joanne Teets
VP: Jamie Venorsky
VP: Ian Verschuren
VP: Amber Zent
Creative D: Brian Gillen
Creative D: Eric Holman

MARCUS UNIFORMS
See JACK L MARCUS INC

MARCUS WHITMAN CENTRAL SCHOOLS
See GORHAM MIDDLESEX CENTRAL SCHOOL DISTRICT

D-U-N-S 03-413-3173 IMP
MARDEL INC (OK)
VALUES BY DESIGN
7727 Sw 44th St, Oklahoma City, OK 73179-4815
Tel (405) 745-1300 *Founded/Ownrshp* 1981
Sales 95.6MM *EMP* 714
SIC 5999 5943 Religious goods; Office forms & supplies; Religious goods; Office forms & supplies
CEO: Mart Green
*Ch Bd: David Green
Store Mgr: Matt Varnell
CTO: Joe Warfield
VP Opers: Jason Green
Opers Mgr: Richard Price
VP Mktg: Kelly Black
Merch Mgr: Jennifer Ramirez

D-U-N-S 01-901-1311 IMP
MARDENS INC
MARDEN'S SURPLUS & SALVAGE
184 College Ave, Waterville, ME 04901-6220
Tel (207) 873-6111 *Founded/Ownrshp* 1963
Sales 111.2MM^E *EMP* 850
SIC 5311 Department stores, discount; Department stores, discount
Pr: Harold A Marden
*Treas: John E Marden
*VP: David M Marden
Trfc Mgr: Tim Nason

MARDEN'S SURPLUS & SALVAGE
See MARDENS INC

MARDER BRANDS
See MARDER TRAWLING INC

D-U-N-S 60-760-2257 EXP
MARDER TRAWLING INC
MARDER BRANDS
22 S Water St, New Bedford, MA 02740-7286
Tel (508) 992-1722 *Founded/Ownrshp* 1985
Sales 31.4MM^E *EMP* 60
Accts Sharkansky Llp
SIC 5146 Seafoods
Pr: Brian I Marder
*Treas: Daniel Marder

MARDI GRAS CASINO
See GOLDEN MARDI GRAS INC

MARDI GRAS CASINO AND RESORT
See RACING CORP OF WEST VIRGINIA

D-U-N-S 10-147-8782
MARDONE INC
J & B CLEANING SERVICE
9401 Lee Hwy Ste 102, Fairfax, VA 22031-1803
Tel (703) 273-6464 *Founded/Ownrshp* 1982
Sales 11.3MM^E *EMP* 500
SIC 7349 Janitorial service, contract basis; Janitorial service, contract basis
Pr: William Pidone
Treas: Cheryl Pidone
*VP: Gene Gould

D-U-N-S 13-941-0120
■ **MARE-BEAR INC**
STARDUST RESORT & CASINO
(*Suby of* CALIFORNIA HOTEL AND CASINO) ★
2950 Industrial Rd, Las Vegas, NV 89109-1100
Tel (702) 732-6111 *Founded/Ownrshp* 1985
Sales 34.0MM^E *EMP* 915
SIC 7011 5812 5813 Casino hotel; Family restaurants; Bar (drinking places); Casino hotel; Family restaurants; Bar (drinking places)
Pr: William S Boyd
Ex VP: Keith Smith
*Sr VP: Robert L Boughner
Sr VP: Joseph Fuscaldo
*Sr VP: Donald D Snyder
VP: Jim Carter
VP: Rick Darnold
VP: David Krasn
VP: Tom McPherson
*VP: Tony Taeubel
Mktg Dir: Seth Brown

D-U-N-S 08-006-9792
MARED INDUSTRIES INC
DETROIT INDUSTRIAL TOOL
15222 Keswick St, Van Nuys, CA 91405-1013
Tel (818) 988-6900 *Founded/Ownrshp* 1976
Sales 34.7MM^E *EMP* 150
SIC 5085 Tools; Tools
Ch Bd: Edward Guttenberg
*CFO: Paul Cirino
*VP: Paul Mooney
CTO: Nicolas Young

D-U-N-S 07-893-3157
MARED MECHANICAL CONTRACTORS CORP
4230 W Douglas Ave, Milwaukee, WI 53209-3529
Tel (414) 536-0411 *Founded/Ownrshp* 1998
Sales 21.5MM^E *EMP* 105
Accts Winter Kloman Moter & Repp
SIC 1731 1711 General electrical contractor; Warm air heating & air conditioning contractor; Ventilation & duct work contractor; Process piping contractor
Pr: Hank Brancaccio
*VP: Jay A Dubester

D-U-N-S 18-606-1370 IMP
MAREK BROTHERS SYSTEMS INC
2115 Judiway St, Houston, TX 77018-5834
Tel (713) 681-9213 *Founded/Ownrshp* 1948
Sales 186.4MM^E *EMP* 907
SIC 1742 Drywall; Drywall
CEO: R Stan Marek Jr
*Pr: Paul A Marek
*Pr: R Stan Marek
*CFO: Doyle Crow
CFO: Charles Grogan
Exec: Marcus Bollom
Sls Mgr: Donna Cucurullo

D-U-N-S 04-595-1845
MAREK GROUP INC
W228n821 Westmound Dr, Waukesha, WI 53186-1691
Tel (262) 549-8900 *Founded/Ownrshp* 1973
Sales 38.1MM^E *EMP* 155^E
SIC 2752 Commercial printing, offset; Commercial printing, offset
CEO: Frank S Marek
*Pr: Tamara L Marek
Sr VP: Robert Cothran
Creative D: Mark Sprester
Dir Bus: Hannah Straub
Admn Mgr: Sue Zieche
Genl Mgr: Lance Johnson
Dir IT: Robert Davis
IT Man: Brian Mangan
Opers Mgr: Rich Daniels
Sls Mgr: Brad Flagge

D-U-N-S 96-005-8824 IMP
MAREL INC
(*Suby of* MAREL HF.)
8145 Flint St, Lenexa, KS 66214-3301
Tel (913) 888-9110 *Founded/Ownrshp* 1995
Sales 100.0MM *EMP* 120
SIC 5046 Commercial cooking & food service equipment; Commercial cooking & food service equipment
Pr: Einar Einarsson
*CFO: Deborah Bernas
*VP: Larry Campbell
*VP: Troels Svendsen
*VP: David Whitem
VP: David Wilson
Area Mgr: Larry Couch
Genl Mgr: Arnbjorn Eythorsson
Genl Mgr: Steini Gretarsson
IT Man: Loftur Loftsson
VP Opers: Heidi Andersen

D-U-N-S 19-909-1372 IMP
MAREL SEATTLE INC
(*Suby of* MAREL SALMON A/S)
2001 W Garfield St C106, Seattle, WA 98119-3115
Tel (206) 781-1827 *Founded/Ownrshp* 1989
Sales 41.6MM^E *EMP* 94
SIC 3556 Meat, poultry & seafood processing machinery; Dehydrating equipment, food processing
CEO: Arni Oddur Thordarson
*Pr: Henrik Rasmussen
*COO: Sigsteinn Grtarsson
*CFO: Erik Kaman
*CFO: Kenneth Osen
*CFO: Margaret Raihl
Dir Soc: Helena Bjarnadottir
IT Man: Jeremy Boyungs
Sls Mgr: Denny Smith

D-U-N-S 00-327-7589 IMP
MAREL STORK POULTRY PROCESSING INC
(*Suby of* MAREL HF.)
1024 Airport Pkwy, Gainesville, GA 30501-6814
Tel (770) 532-7041 *Founded/Ownrshp* 1975
Sales 103.2MM^E *EMP* 220
SIC 3556 3535 Poultry processing machinery; Meat processing machinery; Overhead conveyor systems; Poultry processing machinery; Meat processing machinery; Overhead conveyor systems
CEO: Anton De Weerd
*Pr: Einar Einarsson
CFO: Deborah Bernas
VP: Mark Finnimore
*VP: Mike Sales
VP: David White
Exec: Mayke Theloesen
Area Mgr: Larry Couch
Area Mgr: Donn Larue
Area Mgr: Rob Macintyre
Area Mgr: Chuck McKain

D-U-N-S 18-062-6046
■ **MARELICH MECHANICAL CO INC**
(*Suby of* EMCOR GROUP INC) ★
24041 Amador St, Hayward, CA 94544-1201
Tel (510) 785-5500 *Founded/Ownrshp* 1998
Sales 43.9MM^E *EMP* 200
SIC 1711 1623 3822 Plumbing, heating, air-conditioning contractors; Mechanical contractor; Pipeline construction; Auto controls regulating residntl & coml environmt & applncs; Plumbing, heating, air-conditioning contractors; Mechanical contractor; Pipeline construction; Auto controls regulating residntl & coml environmt & applncs
Pr: Keith R Atteberry
Ex VP: Don Dufosee
*VP: Chad Johnston
*VP: Terry J Kvochak
VP: William Mosely
*VP: Andrew Ostrowski
*VP: John Powell
VP: Frank Sisca
VP: Marlin J Whitney
Ex Dir: Donald Dufossee
DP Exec: Joe Harrison

D-U-N-S 78-559-4235 IMP
MAREMONT EXHAUST PRODUCTS INC
(*Suby of* IMCO) ★
2400 Maremont Pkwy, Loudon, TN 37774-1087
Tel (865) 458-4681 *Founded/Ownrshp* 2006
Sales 29.5MM^E *EMP* 250
SIC 3714 5013 Exhaust systems & parts, motor vehicle; Exhaust systems (mufflers, tail pipes, etc.); Exhaust systems & parts, motor vehicle; Exhaust systems (mufflers, tail pipes, etc.)
Pr: Kenneth Banks

D-U-N-S 07-481-9681
MARET SCHOOL INC
3000 Cathedral Ave Nw, Washington, DC 20008-3498
Tel (202) 797-7211 *Founded/Ownrshp* 1937
Sales 24.6MM *EMP* 130
Accts Watkins Meegan Llc Bethesda
SIC 8211 Kindergarten; Private elementary school; Private junior high school; Private senior high school; Kindergarten; Private elementary school; Private junior high school; Private senior high school
Prin: Mary Talbott
Ex Dir: Sarah Dunkelberger

D-U-N-S 09-215-6728
MARFO CO
TRADING CORP OF AMERICA
799 N Hague Ave, Columbus, OH 43204-1424
Tel (614) 276-3352 *Founded/Ownrshp* 1977
Sales 25.7MM^E *EMP* 120
SIC 5094 3911 Jewelry; Jewelry apparel
CEO: Bill Giovanello
*CFO: Peter Wang
VP: Carol Gatzke
*Prin: Alan Johnson
Opers Mgr: Chris Frase
Trfc Mgr: Crystal Kordes
Sls&Mrk Ex: Bonita Wiseman

D-U-N-S 15-970-2422 IMP
MARFOOD USA INC
(*Suby of* MARFRIG GLOBAL FOODS S/A.)
21655 Trolley Indus Dr, Taylor, MI 48180-1811
Tel (313) 292-4100 *Founded/Ownrshp* 1997
Sales 57.9MM^E *EMP* 150^E
SIC 5147 Meats, cured or smoked; Meats, cured or smoked
CEO: Fernando Momeete
*Pr: Alain Martinet
CFO: Pedro Oliveria
*VP: Paolo Rivolo
Opers Mgr: Christiano Oliveira
Plnt Mgr: Peter Castronova
Ql Cn Mgr: Nasir Anaza
Natl Sales: Bill Nakalsky
VP Sls: Bob Molitor
S&M/VP: Ron Mills
Mktg Mgr: Nakia Mills

D-U-N-S 83-099-2111
■ **MARFORK COAL CO INC**
SLIP RIDGE CEDAR GROVE
(*Suby of* ALPHA NATURAL RESOURCES INC) ★
Over 1 Rr 3, Whitesville, WV 25209
Tel (304) 854-1852 *Founded/Ownrshp* 1993
Sales 46.6MM^E *EMP* 500
SIC 1221 1222 1241 Bituminous coal & lignite-surface mining; Bituminous coal-underground mining; Coal mining services; Bituminous coal & lignite-surface mining; Bituminous coal-underground mining; Coal mining services
Pr: Carl D Lucas
*Treas: Philip J Cavatoni

MARGARET A CARGILL PHILANTHROP
See MARGARET A CARGILL PHILANTHROPIC SERVICES LLC

D-U-N-S 01-437-8163
MARGARET A CARGILL PHILANTHROPIC SERVICES LLC
MARGARET A CARGILL PHILANTHROP
6889 Rowland Rd Ste 100, Eden Prairie, MN 55344-3373
Tel (952) 540-4050 *Founded/Ownrshp* 2010
Sales 54.8MM *EMP* 60
SIC 8699 Charitable organization; Charitable organization
CEO: Christine Morse
*COO: Paul Busch
VP: Celia Ellingson

D-U-N-S 01-704-9030
MARGARET BALDWIN
SPECIALTY CREATIONS
6405 Cedar Creek Cir, Sapulpa, OK 74066-9329
Tel (903) 714-1603 *Founded/Ownrshp* 2006
Sales 53.0MM *EMP* 4
SIC 7389
Owner: Margaret Baldwin

MARGARET HOLMES
See MCCALL FARMS INC

D-U-N-S 07-743-4587
MARGARET MARY COMMUNITY HOSPITAL INC
321 Mitchell Ave, Batesville, IN 47006-8909
Tel (812) 934-6624 *Founded/Ownrshp* 1932
Sales 78.4MM *EMP* 499
Accts Blue & Co Llc Indianapolis
SIC 8062 8051 General medical & surgical hospitals; Skilled nursing care facilities; General medical & surgical hospitals; Skilled nursing care facilities
Pr: Timothy Putnam
Chf Rad: James Browne
COO: Bonnie Ploeger
*CFO: Brian R Daeger
VP: Kimberly Inscho
VP: Nancy Marticke
Exec: Sharon Kreuzman
Dir Risk M: Michelle Werner
Dir Lab: Annette Yamaguchi
Dir Rx: Herb Hunter
Dir Sec: Derek Rainbolt

MARGARET R PARDEE MEMORIAL HOS
See HENDERSON COUNTY HOSPITAL CORP

MARGARET SANGER CENTER INTL
See PLANNED PARENTHOOD OF NEW YORK CITY INC

D-U-N-S 00-636-4932
MARGARET TIETZ NURSING
612 Allerton Ave, Bronx, NY 10467-7404
Tel (718) 519-5937 *Founded/Ownrshp* 2010
Sales 29.2MM *EMP* 14^E
Accts Loeb & Troper Llp New York N

SIC 8051 Skilled nursing care facilities
Prin: Zubair Shaikh

D-U-N-S 07-273-5004 IMP
MARGARETTZ NG & RHBN CR
(*Suby of* BETH ABRAHAM HEALTH SERVICES) ★
16411 Chapin Pkwy, Jamaica, NY 11432-1816
Tel (718) 523-6400 *Founded/Ownrshp* 1971
Sales 31.0MM *EMP* 325
Accts Loeb & Troper Llp New York
SIC 8051 Skilled nursing care facilities; Skilled nursing care facilities
Ch: Mark Weinstein
**CFO:* Stephen Mann
**Treas:* Allen Szrolovits
**Ex Dir:* Gerald H Hart
HC Dir: Stephanie Zim

D-U-N-S 07-967-9353 IMP
MARGARET WOODBURY STRONG MUSEUM (INC) (NY)
STRONG NATIONAL MUSEUM OF PLAY
1 Manhattan Square Dr, Rochester, NY 14607-3941
Tel (585) 263-2700 *Founded/Ownrshp* 1968
Sales 11.0MM *EMP* 304
Accts Bonadio & Co Llp Pittsford N
SIC 8412 Museum; Museum
Pr: G Rollie Adams
VP: J P Dyson
VP: Scott Eberle
VP: Lisa Feinstein
Pr Dir: Shane Rhinewald
Assoc Ed: Patricia Hogan

D-U-N-S 07-563-2476
MARGARITAS MANAGEMENT GROUP INC
TIO JANS MRGRITAS MEXICAN REST
200 Griffin Rd Ste 1, Portsmouth, NH 03801-7145
Tel (603) 430-8905 *Founded/Ownrshp* 1993
Sales 59.7MME *EMP* 1,200
SIC 5812 Mexican restaurant; Mexican restaurant
CEO: John Pellitier
CFO: Mario Mancini
**CFO:* Bonnie Monahan
**Sec:* E Stanton Bagley
**VP:* David Pelletier
Dir Soc: Dan Lederer
Genl Mgr: Christopher McVicker
Genl Mgr: Ryan O'Leary
Dir IT: Regina Jerome
VP Opers: Patrick Dowling
Mktg Dir: Paul Timmons

D-U-N-S 80-835-8233
MARGARITAVILLE ENTERPRISES LLC
6900 Turkey Lake Rd # 200, Orlando, FL 32819-4707
Tel (407) 224-3213 *Founded/Ownrshp* 2006
Sales 206.5MME *EMP* 1,000
SIC 5087 Restaurant supplies; Restaurant supplies
CEO: John Cohlan
**CFO:* Eric Forward

MARGATE VOLVO
See LINCOLN MARGATE INC

D-U-N-S 00-952-9009 IMP
MARGE CARSON INC
1260 E Grand Ave, Pomona, CA 91766-3801
Tel (909) 622-3423 *Founded/Ownrshp* 1951
Sales 21.0MME *EMP* 84
SIC 2512 2511 Living room furniture: upholstered on wood frames; Wood household furniture
CEO: James Labarge
**CFO:* Dominic Ching
Dir IT: Jim Barge
IT Man: Kevin Sazi
Plnt Mgr: Braulio Ornelas
Sls&Mrk Ex: Laura La Barge
Sls&Mrk Ex: Laura Lady
VP Sls: Mike Elliott
Mktg Mgr: Igor Jukanovic

MARGLEN INDUSTRIES
See C&M HOLDINGS INC

D-U-N-S 05-620-9141
MARGLEN INDUSTRIES INC
1748 Ward Mountain Rd Ne, Rome, GA 30161-3469
Tel (706) 295-5621 *Founded/Ownrshp* 1998
Sales 22.0MME *EMP* 183
SIC 3085 Plastics bottles; Plastics bottles
CEO: Mieke Hanssens
**Pr:* John William Burnes

D-U-N-S 06-597-2309
MARGOLIN WINER & EVENS LLP
400 Garden City Plz # 500, Garden City, NY 11530-3323
Tel (516) 747-2000 *Founded/Ownrshp* 1966
Sales 30.1MME *EMP* 200
SIC 8721 Certified public accountant; Certified public accountant
Mng Pt: Teddy Selinger
**Pt:* Jeffrey Bass
**Pt:* Robert Brodsky
**Pt:* Fred Bruckner
**Pt:* John Collins
**Pt:* Howard Fielstein
**Pt:* Arthur Goldstein
**Pt:* Gary Herskin
**Pt:* Jeff Levine
**Pt:* Lawrence Lioz
**Pt:* Alan Materazo
**Pt:* Ed O'Hara
**Pt:* Wayne Olson
**Pt:* Jeff Oster
**Pt:* Charles Peluso
**Pt:* Michael Peress
**Pt:* Ron Rich
**Pt:* Marvin Rosen
**Pt:* Menachem Rosenberg
**Pt:* Craig Savel
**Pt:* Terry Strassberg

D-U-N-S 05-250-1061
MARGOLIS & EDELSTEIN
170 S Indepe Mall W Ste W, Philadelphia, PA 19106
Tel (215) 922-1100 *Founded/Ownrshp* 1959
Sales 29.3MME *EMP* 265
SIC 8111 General practice attorney, lawyer; General practice attorney, lawyer
Mng Pt: Michael P McKenna
Sr Pt: James Kahn
Sr Pt: Alan W Margolis
Pt: Bruce E Barrett
Pt: Joseph S Bekelja
Pt: Michael J Cawley
Off Admin: Edith Hunger
IT Exec: Stephen Homesack

MARGRO
See KIRBY AGRI INC

MARIA DELOS SANTO HEALTH CENTE
See DELAWARE VALLEY COMMUNITY HEALTH INC

D-U-N-S 80-566-4203
MARIA HO MANA INSURANCE
PACIFA TRAVEL
346 Southhill Blvd, Daly City, CA 94014-1454
Tel (415) 317-6448 *Founded/Ownrshp* 2006
Sales NA *EMP* 1
SIC 6411 Insurance agents, brokers & service; Insurance agents, brokers & service
Owner: Maria Ho

D-U-N-S 17-788-1752
MARIA JOY MEDICAL GROUP
26w171 Roosevelt Rd, Wheaton, IL 60187-6002
Tel (630) 909-7000 *Founded/Ownrshp* 1983
Sales 11.8MM *EMP* 400
SIC 8093 Rehabilitation center, outpatient treatment; Rehabilitation center, outpatient treatment
Pr: Kathleen Yosko
VP: Peter Harvey

MARIA PARHAM HOSPITAL
See HENDERSON/VANCE HEALTHCARE INC

D-U-N-S 61-091-5469
MARIA REGINA RESIDENCE INC
(*Suby of* SISTERS OF SAINT JOSEPH) ★
1725 Brentwood Rd Bldg 1, Brentwood, NY 11717-5543
Tel (631) 299-3000 *Founded/Ownrshp* 2001
Sales 19.2MM *EMP* 330
SIC 8059 Nursing home, except skilled & intermediate care facility; Nursing home, except skilled & intermediate care facility
**Adm Dir:* Sister Helen Clancey

D-U-N-S 96-052-1839 IMP
MARIAH FOODS CORP
PEER FOODS
(*Suby of* EMGE FOODS) ★
1333 Indiana Ave, Columbus, IN 47201-6986
Tel (812) 378-3366 *Founded/Ownrshp* 1996
Sales 32.3MME *EMP* 150
SIC 2011 Meat packing plants; Meat packing plants
Pr: Larry O Connell
**Treas:* Donna Recupido
Ql Cn Mgr: James Wiltsey

D-U-N-S 11-504-3887 IMP
MARIAK INDUSTRIES INC
MARIAK WINDOW FASHION
575 W Manville St, Rancho Dominguez, CA 90220-5509
Tel (310) 661-4400 *Founded/Ownrshp* 1987
Sales 172.4MME *EMP* 380
SIC 5023 2591 Vertical blinds; Blinds vertical; Vertical blinds; Blinds vertical
CEO: Leo Elinson
**VP:* Patrice Elinson
Off Mgr: Ryan Martinez
Off Mgr: Lorena Silva
VP Opers: Russ Elinson

MARIAK WINDOW FASHION
See MARIAK INDUSTRIES INC

D-U-N-S 05-310-8619
MARIAM INC (MD)
DARCAR
12210 Cherry Hill Rd, Silver Spring, MD 20904-1968
Tel (301) 622-7000 *Founded/Ownrshp* 1982
Sales 480.3MME *EMP* 1,000
SIC 5511 Automobiles, new & used; Automobiles, new & used
Pr: John R Darvish
**VP:* George D Noel
Prgrm Mgr: Dawn Smith
Genl Mgr: Shakil Aziz
Genl Mgr: James Delgado
Genl Mgr: Lalin Gallart
Genl Mgr: James Onderdonk
Genl Mgr: Marvin Rawls
Off Mgr: Darin Willard
Sales Exec: Radhi Uchechi
Sls Mgr: Omar Elsharkawy

D-U-N-S 00-543-9252 IMP
MARIAN CHICAGO INC
(*Suby of* MARIAN WORLDWIDE INC) ★
396 Wegner Dr, West Chicago, IL 60185-2672
Tel (630) 293-7800 *Founded/Ownrshp* 1984
Sales 24.4MME *EMP* 30
SIC 5063 Insulators, electrical
Pr: David C Hurrle
**Treas:* Alan E Leighton
**Prin:* Bill Witchger
Sls Mgr: Michael Hurrle

MARIAN ESTATES
See ERNMAUR INC

D-U-N-S 10-830-2514
MARIAN FARMS INC
MARIAN GARDENS
619 State Road 50, Groveland, FL 34736-9408
Tel (352) 429-4151 *Founded/Ownrshp* 1981
Sales 60.7MME *EMP* 200
SIC 5191 0181 Greenhouse equipment & supplies; Nursery stock, growing of; Greenhouse equipment & supplies; Nursery stock, growing of
Pr: Shaun Hillary
COO: Steve Strasberger
**VP:* Dennis Hillary
Genl Mgr: Melissa McCue
Sfty Dirs: Keith Nyhuis
Sales Asso: Caroline Hillary
Sales Asso: Mark Hillary
Sales Asso: Cathy Plyler

D-U-N-S 05-997-6175
MARIAN FRANCISCAN CENTER INC
(*Suby of* COVENANT HEALTH CARE SYSTEM INC) ★
13950 W Capitol Dr 2, Brookfield, WI 53005-2441
Tel (414) 461-8850 *Founded/Ownrshp* 1989
Sales 33.4MM *EMP* 400
SIC 8051 Skilled nursing care facilities; Skilled nursing care facilities
Pr: James Gresham

MARIAN GARDENS
See MARIAN FARMS INC

D-U-N-S 79-692-2680
MARIAN MANOR CENTER INC
(*Suby of* HEALTHPRIME INC) ★
18591 Quarry St, Riverview, MI 48193-4522
Tel (734) 282-2100 *Founded/Ownrshp* 1985
Sales 5.6MME *EMP* 520
SIC 8051 Skilled nursing care facilities; Skilled nursing care facilities

D-U-N-S 01-868-3062
MARIAN MANOR FOR AGED AND INFIRM INC
MARIAN MANOR NURSING HOME
130 Dorchester St, Boston, MA 02127-2642
Tel (617) 268-3333 *Founded/Ownrshp* 1968
Sales 23.1MME *EMP* 500
SIC 8051 Skilled nursing care facilities; Skilled nursing care facilities
Dir Risk M: Paul Macpherson
**Prin:* Novyl Igo
CTO: Carlos Terron
Nrsg Dir: Rene Brown

MARIAN MANOR NURSING HOME
See MARIAN MANOR FOR AGED AND INFIRM INC

MARIAN MEDICAL CENTER
See DIGNITY HEALTH

D-U-N-S 07-205-4927
MARIAN UNIVERSITY INC
3200 Cold Spring Rd, Indianapolis, IN 46222-1960
Tel (317) 955-6000 *Founded/Ownrshp* 1851
Sales 79.4MM *EMP* 305
Accts Bkd Llp Indianapolis In
SIC 8221 College, except junior; College, except junior
Pr: Daniel J Elsner
Pr: Cyndi Kamp
CFO: Brian Harris
CFO: Mary Reiman
Ofcr: Ryan Boyle
Ofcr: Steve Dickey
Ex VP: Thomas Enneking
VP: Mark Apple
VP: Daniel Conway
**VP:* William Curran
VP: Paul Evans
**VP:* Paul Pj Woolston
VP: Paul Woolston
Assoc Dir: John Shelton
Assoc Dir: Latonya Turner

D-U-N-S 13-019-3097
MARIAN UNIVERSITY INC
45 S National Ave, Fond Du Lac, WI 54935-4621
Tel (920) 923-8787 *Founded/Ownrshp* 1936
Sales 31.5MM *EMP* 450
Accts Schenck Sc Fond Du Lac Wisco
SIC 8221 Colleges universities & professional schools; Colleges universities & professional schools
Pr: Stevens Disaldo
VP: Mark Apple
Genl Mgr: Nikki Kramer
Store Mgr: Mary Mangan-Flood

D-U-N-S 05-520-4333 IMP
MARIAN WORLDWIDE INC
1011 E Saint Clair St, Indianapolis, IN 46202-3569
Tel (317) 638-6525 *Founded/Ownrshp* 1971
Sales 57.5MME *EMP* 180
SIC 3679 3053 2672 2891 3083 Electronic circuits; Gaskets, all materials; Tape, pressure sensitive: made from purchased materials; Adhesives & sealants; Laminated plastics plate & sheet; Electronic circuits; Gaskets, all materials; Tape, pressure sensitive: made from purchased materials; Adhesives & sealants; Laminated plastics plate & sheet
Pr: Bill Witchger
COO: Brad Countryman
**CFO:* Alan Leighton
CFO: Wayne Rinker
VP: Phil Taylor
**VP:* Eugene J Witchger
CIO: Bob Simmons
IT Man: Mike Gill
VP Opers: Kevin Pickett
Mtls Mgr: Becky Vanmeter
Opers Mgr: Raymond Mendez

D-U-N-S 38-359-6065
MARIANE INC
TACO BELL
7870 Knapp Rd, Houghton Lake, MI 48629-9617
Tel (989) 422-3534 *Founded/Ownrshp* 1987
Sales 16.6MME *EMP* 550
SIC 5812 Fast-food restaurant, chain; Fast-food restaurant, chain
Pr: Randolph Stuck

D-U-N-S 09-253-8586 IMP
MARIANI ENTERPRISES INC
MARIANI LANDSCAPE
300 Rockland Rd, Lake Bluff, IL 60044-1813
Tel (847) 810-6820 *Founded/Ownrshp* 1959
Sales 38.3MM *EMP* 90
Accts Edward Jacks & Company Llc
SIC 0781 0782 Landscape planning services; Lawn care services; Landscape planning services; Lawn care services
CEO: Frank Mariani
**Pr:* Fred Wacker
CFO: Andrew Schallmoser
**VP:* John Mariani
Brnch Mgr: Jon Rudey
Off Mgr: Tracey Wold

MARIANI LANDSCAPE
See MARIANI ENTERPRISES INC

D-U-N-S 05-763-8348 IMP/EXP
MARIANI NUT CO INC
709 Dutton St, Winters, CA 95694-1748
Tel (530) 795-3311 *Founded/Ownrshp* 1971
Sales 50.3MME *EMP* 110
SIC 0173 Walnut grove; Almond grove
CEO: Jack Norman Mariani
**Sec:* Martin Mariani
**VP:* Dennis Mariani
VP: Robin Stenson
IT Man: Ruben Martinez
IT Man: Lawrence Saenz
Sls&Mrk Ex: Matt Mariani

D-U-N-S 00-796-3945 IMP/EXP
MARIANI PACKING CO INC (CA)
500 Crocker Dr, Vacaville, CA 95688-8706
Tel (707) 452-2800 *Founded/Ownrshp* 1982
Sales 133.3MME *EMP* 350
SIC 0723 2034 5148 Fruit (farm-dried) packing services; Fruit drying services; Dried & dehydrated fruits; Fresh fruits & vegetables; Fruit (farm-dried) packing services; Fruit drying services; Dried & dehydrated fruits; Fresh fruits & vegetables
CEO: Mark A Mariani
**V Ch:* George Sousa Jr
CFO: Forrest Chandler
**Sec:* Marian Ciabattari
**Ex VP:* Craig Mackley
**Ex VP:* Paul Mariani
VP: Scott Fulihara
**VP:* George Sousa Sr
IT Man: Valarie Armstrong
Opers Mgr: Shaun Campbell
Plnt Mgr: Bob McCabe

D-U-N-S 07-975-6789
MARIANJOY INC (IL)
MARIANJOY REHABILITATION HOSPI
26w171 Roosevelt Rd, Wheaton, IL 60187-6002
Tel (630) 462-4000 *Founded/Ownrshp* 1969
Sales 74.7MM *EMP* 813
SIC 8069 8093 Specialty hospitals, except psychiatric; Rehabilitation center, outpatient treatment; Specialty hospitals, except psychiatric; Rehabilitation center, outpatient treatment
Pr: Kathleen C Yosko
**Ch:* John Mueller
**Treas:* Brett Dale
**VP:* John Brady
VP: Denise Lebloch
VP: Paul Pyrcik
VP: Margaret Rumpsa
Dir Lab: John Lawson
Assoc Dir: Anjum Sayyad
Dir Rad: Carl Dean
**Prin:* John Wallerius

MARIANJOY REHABILITATION HOSPI
See MARIANJOY INC

D-U-N-S 04-557-0736 IMP/EXP
MARIANNA INDUSTRIES INC
11222 I St Ste A, Omaha, NE 68137-1238
Tel (402) 593-0211 *Founded/Ownrshp* 1969
Sales 280.3MME *EMP* 300E
SIC 5122 2844 7231 Drugs, proprietaries & sundries; Hair preparations; Cosmetics; Toilet preparations; Shampoos, rinses, conditioners: hair; Hair preparations, including shampoos; Cosmetic preparations; Beauty shops; Drugs, proprietaries & sundries; Hair preparations; Cosmetics; Toilet preparations; Shampoos, rinses, conditioners: hair; Hair preparations, including shampoos; Cosmetic preparations; Beauty shops
VP: William Cosentino
**CFO:* Robert Campney
**CFO:* Annette Eggert
Treas: Lori C Christensen
Exec: Patty Kousgaard
Exec: Folkers Mitch
**Prin:* Michael Cosentino
Dept Mgr: Mitchell Folkers
QA Dir: Katherine Fox
QA Dir: Sarah Lane
QA Dir: Kelli Malousek

D-U-N-S 94-753-2552
MARIANNA SUNLAND FACILITY
SUNLAND CENTER
3700 Williams Dr, Marianna, FL 32446-7973
Tel (850) 482-9484 *Founded/Ownrshp* 1963
Sales 14.3MME *EMP* 750
SIC 8361 Residential care; Residential care
Sr VP: Carol Mc Mc Millan

MARIANNE'S
See UBI LIQUIDATING CORP

D-U-N-S 15-205-9929
MARIAS HOLDINGS CORP
MARIA'S ITALIAN KITCHEN
16535 Arminta St, Van Nuys, CA 91406-1745
Tel (818) 786-1506 *Founded/Ownrshp* 1984
Sales 14.5MME *EMP* 300
SIC 5812 Italian restaurant; Delicatessen (eating places); Italian restaurant; Delicatessen (eating places)
Pr: Madeline Alfano
CFO: Allan Sargent
CFO: Steve Tatsumi
**VP:* David Fox
Exec: Jose Gonzales
Opers Mgr: Madelyn Reitzen

MARIA'S ITALIAN KITCHEN
See MARIAS HOLDINGS CORP

D-U-N-S 04-623-5800
MARIC MECHANICAL INC
1903 75th St, East Elmhurst, NY 11370-1107
Tel (718) 721-4690 *Founded/Ownrshp* 1982
Sales 26.9MM *EMP* 35
Accts Wheeler Wottitz & Pagan New
SIC 1711 Heating & air conditioning contractors; Ventilation & duct work contractor; Heating & air conditioning contractors; Ventilation & duct work contractor
Ch Bd: Frank Maric
*VP: Gerald Maric
Off Mgr: Linda Zahn

D-U-N-S 11-816-8285 IMP
MARICH CONFECTIONERY CO INC
2101 Bert Dr, Hollister, CA 95023-2562
Tel (831) 634-4700 *Founded/Ownrshp* 1983
Sales 33.6MME *EMP* 150
SIC 2064 2099 2068 Candy & other confectionery products; Food preparations; Salted & roasted nuts & seeds
Pr: Bradley M Van Dam
*Ch: Ronald B Packard
IT Man: Jose Her
Opers Mgr: Kristi Thornton
Mktg Mgr: Doug Lange
Sls Mgr: Ellen Silverman

D-U-N-S 96-127-3620
■ MARICOM SYSTEMS INC
(*Suby of* COMPUTER SCIENCES CORP) ★
7142 Ambassador Rd, Baltimore, MD 21244-2707
Tel (410) 298-2770 *Founded/Ownrshp* 2011
Sales 30.3MME *EMP* 175E
SIC 7379 7371 Computer related consulting services; Custom computer programming services; Computer related consulting services; Custom computer programming services
CEO: Maria Beckett
*CFO: Bill Gibson
VP: Winsome Humphrey
*VP: Marty Nelson
IT Man: Bryan Prince
Pgrm Dir: David Collins

D-U-N-S 14-911-1213
MARICOPA ASSOCIATION OF GOVERNMENTS
302 N 1st Ave Ste 300, Phoenix, AZ 85003-1562
Tel (602) 254-6300 *Founded/Ownrshp* 1967
Sales 24.3MM *EMP* 110
SIC 8748 Urban planning & consulting services; Urban planning & consulting services
Ex Dir: Dennis Smith
IT Man: Chris Johnson
IT Man: Rebecca Kimbrough
Snr Mgr: William Owsley

D-U-N-S 60-940-3634
MARICOPA CITY
39700 W Civic Center Plz, Maricopa, AZ 85138-3501
Tel (520) 568-9098 *Founded/Ownrshp* 2005
Sales NA *EMP* 325E
Accts Heinfeld Meech & Co PcT
SIC 9111 City & town managers' offices; ; City & town managers' offices;
Plng Mgr: Kazi Haque

D-U-N-S 02-257-4493
MARICOPA COMMUNITY COLLEGE
6002 W Sherman St, Phoenix, AZ 85043-3535
Tel (480) 731-8000 *Founded/Ownrshp* 2008
Sales 10.2MME *EMP* 329E
SIC 8222 Community college
Prin: Adolfo Lopez
Exec: Janice Humbarger
Exec: Phillip Randolph
Exec: Amanda Vital
Dir IT: Miguel Corzo
Dir IT: Richard Lang
Dir IT: Carol Myers
Dir IT: Susan Wallen
IT Man: Doug Harper

D-U-N-S 07-449-1515
MARICOPA COUNTY COMMUNITY COLLEGE DISTRICT
2411 W 14th St, Tempe, AZ 85281-6941
Tel (480) 731-8000 *Founded/Ownrshp* 1962
Sales 242.6MME *EMP* 11,000
SIC 8222

D-U-N-S 18-650-7216
MARICOPA COUNTY SPECIAL HEALTH CARE DISTRICT
MARICOPA INTEGRATED HEALTH SYS
2601 E Roosevelt St, Phoenix, AZ 85008-4973
Tel (602) 344-5011 *Founded/Ownrshp* 2005
Sales 338.4MME *EMP* 4,000E
SIC 8062 Hospital, AMA approved residency; Hospital, AMA approved residency
CEO: Steve Purves
Dir Recs: Manny Sapienza
COO: Bill Van Askie
CFO: Michael Ayres
Bd of Dir: Mark Dewane
Bd of Dir: Dolores Gomez
Sr VP: Mike Robertson
Dir OR: Deana Manning
Dir Inf Cn: Rita Neibaur
Dir Risk M: Mary Mc Kelvey
Dir Rx: Joyce Kossick
Dir Rx: Ken Prayzer

MARICOPA INTEGRATED HEALTH SYS
See MARICOPA COUNTY SPECIAL HEALTH CARE DISTRICT

D-U-N-S 80-896-3586
MARICOPA INTEGRATED HEALTH SYSTEM
2601 E Roosevelt St, Phoenix, AZ 85008-4973
Tel (602) 344-5011 *Founded/Ownrshp* 1995
Sales 118.8MME *EMP* 4,000
SIC 8082 Home health care services; Home health care services
*CEO: Steve Purves
Ofcr: John Middleton
Chf Nrs Of: Sherry Stotler
Nurse Mgr: Pam Cox
Nurse Mgr: Irma Dominguez
CIO: David Kempson

MARICOPA PACKERS
See SUN PACIFIC MARICOPA

D-U-N-S 15-129-0546
MARIE CALLENDER PIE SHOPS INC
MARIE CALLENDER'S PIE SHOPS
(*Suby of* PERKINS & MARIE CALLENDERS LLC) ★
6075 Poplar Ave Ste 800, Memphis, TN 38119-4717
Tel (901) 766-6400 *Founded/Ownrshp* 2006
Sales 60.4MME *EMP* 2,000
SIC 5812 Restaurant, family: chain; Restaurant, family: chain
Pr: Phillip Ratner
VP: Nick Saba
VP: Jim Vickers
Rgnl Mgr: John Sweeney
Area Supr: Bill Talley

D-U-N-S 80-784-7355
MARIE CALLENDER WHOLESALERS INC
(*Suby of* CASTLE HARLAN PARTNERS III LP) ★
170 E Rincon St, Corona, CA 92879-1327
Tel (951) 737-6760 *Founded/Ownrshp* 2000
Sales 20.3MME *EMP* 65
SIC 5142 Bakery products, frozen
Pr: Phillip Ratner
*Sr VP: Gerald Tanaka
VP: Nick Saba
*VP: Kurt Schweickhart

MARIE CALLENDER'S PIE SHOPS
See MARIE CALLENDER PIE SHOPS INC

MARIE CALLENDER'S PIE SHOPS
See CASTLE HARLAN PARTNERS III LP

D-U-N-S 07-875-7989
MARIE MINNIE BAKERS INC
AWREY BAKERIES
12301 Farmington Rd, Livonia, MI 48150-1747
Tel (734) 522-1100 *Founded/Ownrshp* 2013
Sales 46.6MME *EMP* 120
SIC 2053 2051 Frozen bakery products, except bread; Bread, cake & related products
Ch Bd: Ronald Beebe
*VP: Diane Lynch

MARIES MAJIC MART
See SIARC INC

D-U-N-S 15-374-9585
MARIETTA AREA HEALTH CARE INC
MARIETTA MEMORIAL HOSPITAL
401 Matthew St, Marietta, OH 45750-1635
Tel (740) 374-1400 *Founded/Ownrshp* 1984
Sales 57.9MM *EMP* 15
SIC 8062 General medical & surgical hospitals; General medical & surgical hospitals
Pr: Larry Unroe

D-U-N-S 03-006-6104
MARIETTA CITY BOARD OF EDUCATION
701 3rd St, Marietta, OH 45750-1801
Tel (740) 374-6500 *Founded/Ownrshp* 1900
Sales 9.2MME *EMP* 350
SIC 8211 Public elementary & secondary schools; Public elementary & secondary schools
Prin: Dr Dora Jean Bumgarner
*Pr: Herman Hambuck II
*Treas: Etty Merey
*VP: Donna Beale

D-U-N-S 79-548-1915
MARIETTA CITY SCHOOL DISTRICT
111 Academy Dr, Marietta, OH 45750-8053
Tel (740) 374-6500 *Founded/Ownrshp* 2007
Sales 26.7MM *EMP* 315E
SIC 8211 Public elementary & secondary schools; Public elementary & secondary schools
Prin: David Bruce Combs
CFO: David Combs
VP: Michelle Secrest
HC Dir: Matthew Dehemlow

D-U-N-S 85-856-7605
MARIETTA CITY SCHOOLS (INC)
250 Howard St Ne, Marietta, GA 30060-1953
Tel (770) 422-3500 *Founded/Ownrshp* 1892
Sales 73.2MME *EMP* 1,400
Accts Bambo Sonaike Cpa Llc Mariett
SIC 8211 Elementary & secondary schools; Elementary & secondary schools
Bd of Dir: Margaret Barfield
Bd of Dir: Jeanie Carter
Bd of Dir: Tom Cheater
*Prin: Harold T Barnett
*Prin: Dayton Hibbs
*Prin: Dr Donna Ryan
MIS Dir: David Digiovanni
MIS Dir: John Pickering
Pr Dir: Sommer Vega
Schl Brd P: Randy Weiner

D-U-N-S 07-496-9924
MARIETTA COLLEGE
215 5th St Dept 32, Marietta, OH 45750-4071
Tel (740) 376-4643 *Founded/Ownrshp* 1835
Sales 67.3MM *EMP* 300
Accts Crowe Horwath Llp Columbus O
SIC 8221 College, except junior; College, except junior
Pr: Jean Scott
*Ch: Tim Cooper
*Treas: William H Donnelly
Ofcr: Rebecca Cutlip
Ofcr: Chris Hall
Ofcr: Tomi Racz
Ofcr: Ralph Wirkner
VP: Adaleine Jackson
*VP: Marcia Koester
VP: Lori Lewis
Dir Lab: Dan Jones
Assoc Dir: Scott McVicar

D-U-N-S 01-076-5394 IMP/EXP
MARIETTA CORP
(*Suby of* MARIETTA HOLDING CORP) ★
37 Huntington St, Cortland, NY 13045-3098
Tel (607) 753-6746 *Founded/Ownrshp* 2004
Sales 276.1MME *EMP* 1,500
SIC 2844 2834 2541 Toilet preparations; Druggists' preparations (pharmaceuticals); Store & office display cases & fixtures; Cosmetic preparations; Toilet preparations; Druggists' preparations (pharmaceuticals); Store & office display cases & fixtures
CEO: Donald W Sturdivant
COO: Eileen Anderson
*CFO: Perry Morgan
*Treas: James Matthews
*Sr VP: Chris Calhoun
*Sr VP: Beth Corl
*Sr VP: Ray Ferretti
*Sr VP: David Hempson
Sr VP: John Watson
VP: Michael Stokoe
Exec: Theresa Murphy
Creative D: Tim Tryon
Dir Bus: Marietta Fletcher

MARIETTA DAILY JOURNAL, THE
See TIMES-JOURNAL INC

D-U-N-S 00-327-7217 EXP
MARIETTA DRAPERY & WINDOW COVERINGS CO INC
22 Trammell St Sw, Marietta, GA 30064-3371
Tel (770) 428-3335 *Founded/Ownrshp* 1975
Sales 102.7MME *EMP* 170
SIC 5023 2391 2591 2392 Window furnishings; Venetian blinds; Vertical blinds; Window shades; Draperies, plastic & textile: from purchased materials; Mini blinds; Blinds vertical; Venetian blinds; Bedspreads & bed sets: made from purchased materials; Window furnishings; Venetian blinds; Vertical blinds; Window shades; Draperies, plastic & textile: from purchased materials; Mini blinds; Blinds vertical; Venetian blinds; Bedspreads & bed sets: made from purchased materials
CEO: Douglas C Bentley
*Pr: Andrew F Bentley
*CFO: Frederick A Bentley
Sls Mgr: Darrell Duffel

D-U-N-S 07-462-7592 IMP/EXP
MARIETTA ERAMET INC
(*Suby of* ERAMET HOLDING MANGANESE)
16705 State Route 7, Marietta, OH 45750-8519
Tel (740) 374-1000 *Founded/Ownrshp* 1999
Sales 112.0MME *EMP* 205
SIC 3313 Ferroalloys; Ferroalloys
CFO: Michel Masci
CFO: Marc Blanquart
CFO: Jean-Didier Dujardin
VP: Philippe Joly
Dir Lab: Robert Habeb
Dept Mgr: Dean Douglass
Telecom Ex: Julie King

D-U-N-S 60-871-4882
MARIETTA HOLDING CORP
(*Suby of* KIK INTERNATIONAL LLC)
37 Huntington St, Cortland, NY 13045-3096
Tel (607) 753-6746 *Founded/Ownrshp* 2015
Sales 261.4MME *EMP* 1,501
SIC 6719 2841 Personal holding companies, except banks; Soap: granulated, liquid, cake, flaked or chip; Personal holding companies, except banks; Soap: granulated, liquid, cake, flaked or chip
CEO: Donald W Sturdivant
*Pr: Brian O'Neil
*CFO: Perry Morgan
*Treas: James Mattews
Treas: James Matthews
*Sr VP: David P Hempson
*Sr VP: Dan Keefe

MARIETTA MEMORIAL HOSPITAL
See MARIETTA AREA HEALTH CARE INC

D-U-N-S 06-871-7859
MARIETTA MEMORIAL HOSPITAL INC
401 Matthew St, Marietta, OH 45750-1699
Tel (740) 374-1400 *Founded/Ownrshp* 1984
Sales 307.2MM *EMP* 1,100
SIC 8062 8069 General medical & surgical hospitals; Alcoholism rehabilitation hospital; General medical & surgical hospitals; Alcoholism rehabilitation hospital
Ch Bd: Tom Tucker
Pr: J Stott Cantley
COO: Scott Cantley
CFO: Eric Young
Treas: Glen Hale
VP: Orive E Fischer
VP: Bobbie Howard
VP: Naresh Nayak
Exec: Tammy Anderson
Exec: Janet Campbell
Exec: Gail Galan
Exec: Cheryl Stachera
Dir Lab: Mike McGowan
Dir Rx: Wes Jones

MARIETTA NDT
See MARIETTA NONDESTRUCTIVE TESTING LLC

D-U-N-S 82-836-5937
MARIETTA NONDESTRUCTIVE TESTING LLC
MARIETTA NDT
530 Commerce Park Dr Se, Marietta, GA 30060-2782
Tel (770) 528-9000 *Founded/Ownrshp* 2008
Sales 31.4MME *EMP* 143
SIC 3081 Photographic & X-ray film & sheet; Photographic & X-ray film & sheet
CFO: Daryle Higginbotham
IT Man: Steve Norred
Prd Mgr: Ronnie Sanders

MARIETTA POWER
See BOARD OF LIGHTS AND WATER

D-U-N-S 13-201-7380 EXP
MARIETTA X-RAY INC
(*Suby of* MARIETTA NDT) ★
530 Commerce Park Dr Se A, Marietta, GA 30060-2708
Tel (770) 528-9000 *Founded/Ownrshp* 2002
Sales 27.3MME *EMP* 75E
SIC 5047 7699 3844 X-ray machines & tubes; X-ray equipment repair; Radiographic X-ray apparatus & tubes
Pr: Rebecca Higginbotham
*CFO: Daryle Higginbotham

D-U-N-S 13-106-4474 IMP
MARIGOLD MINING CO
(*Suby of* SILVER STANDARD RESOURCES INC)
Ih 80 W, Valmy, NV 89438
Tel (775) 635-2317 *Founded/Ownrshp* 2014
Sales 57.6MME *EMP* 355
SIC 1041 Gold ores mining; Gold ores mining
Pr: John Smith
*Treas: Matt Freeman

D-U-N-S 07-868-1812
MARIKA LLC
5553-B Bandini Blvd, Bell, CA 90201
Tel (323) 888-7755 *Founded/Ownrshp* 2011
Sales 150.0MME *EMP* 100
SIC 2339 Athletic clothing: women's, misses' & juniors'; Women's & misses' athletic clothing & sportswear; Athletic clothing: women's, misses' & juniors'; Women's & misses' athletic clothing & sportswear
CEO: Frank M Zarabi
CFO: Patrick Shaowl
Sr VP: Carrie Henley
VP: Rich Lyons

D-U-N-S 02-897-5159
MARIMART INC
WOODLAND HILLS HONDA
6111 Topanga Canyon Blvd, Woodland Hills, CA 91367-3629
Tel (818) 887-7111 *Founded/Ownrshp* 1959
Sales 27.2MME *EMP* 75
SIC 5511 Automobiles, new & used; Automobiles, new & used
Pr: Howard A Keyes
Genl Mgr: Ramin Hakakian

D-U-N-S 09-247-9765
MARIMON BUSINESS SYSTEMS INC
7300 Gessner Rd, Houston, TX 77040-3144
Tel (713) 856-2000 *Founded/Ownrshp* 1979
Sales 50.8MME *EMP* 130
SIC 5112 7629 5044 7389 Stationery & office supplies; Business machine repair, electric; Office equipment; Design services; Stationery & office supplies; Business machine repair, electric; Office equipment; Design services
Pr: Yolanda B Marimon
*Sec: Anthony R Marimon
Ex VP: Todd Bradley
VP: Sam Demerit
CTO: Tim Collins
Dir IT: Solomon Peretz
Dir IT: Eddie Woodward
Info Man: Vicki Strom

D-U-N-S 07-466-8575
MARIN ACADEMY
1600 Mission Ave, San Rafael, CA 94901-1859
Tel (415) 453-4550 *Founded/Ownrshp* 1945
Sales 20.1MM *EMP* 100
Accts Armanino Mckenna Llp San Ramo
SIC 8211 Preparatory school; Preparatory school
Owner: Elleanor Brizendine
*CFO: Mike Joyce
Bd of Dir: Mary Collie
Trst: Patrick Bennett
Comm Dir: David Brin
Psych: Daniel Siegel

D-U-N-S 82-960-2338
MARIN CLEAN ENERGY
1125 Tamalpais Ave, San Rafael, CA 94901
Tel (415) 464-6028 *Founded/Ownrshp* 2008
Sales 100.6MM *EMP* 34
Accts Vavrinek Trine Day & Company
SIC 3264 Energy conservation consultant; Porcelain electrical supplies
CEO: Dawn Weisz

D-U-N-S 62-429-4393
MARIN COMMUNITY CLINIC
MARIN COMMUNITY CLINICS
1177 Francisco Blvd E B, San Rafael, CA 94901-5403
Tel (415) 798-3100 *Founded/Ownrshp* 1974
Sales 31.4MM *EMP* 99
SIC 8011 Primary care medical clinic; Primary care medical clinic
Ex Dir: John Shen
COO: Peggy Dracker
CFO: Arthur Feagles
Exec: Liz Digan
Dir IT: Leah Canvasser

MARIN COMMUNITY CLINICS
See MARIN COMMUNITY CLINIC

D-U-N-S 02-000-5732
MARIN COMMUNITY COLLEGE DISTRICT
COLLEGE OF MARIN
835 College Ave, Kentfield, CA 94904-2590
Tel (415) 457-8811 *Founded/Ownrshp* 1926
Sales 48.2MME *EMP* 1,100
SIC 8222 8221 Community college; Colleges universities & professional schools; Community college; Colleges universities & professional schools
Pr: David Wayne Coon
Ofcr: John Adams
Ofcr: Stephen Anderson
VP: Angelina Duarte
*VP: Albert Harrison
*VP: Gregory Nelson
*VP: Stephanie O'Brien
Mng Dir: Andrea Liguori
Dir IT: Kevin Berger

Psych: Caitlin Escobar
HC Dir: Lucas Drisdell

D-U-N-S 06-886-8660
MARIN COUNTRY DAY SCHOOL
5221 Paradise Dr, Corte Madera, CA 94925-2107
Tel (415) 927-5900 Founded/Ownrshp 1956
Sales 22.5MM EMP 145
Accts Hood And Strong Llp San Franc
SIC 8211 Private elementary school; Private elementary school
Pr: Lucinda Lee Katz
*CFO: Mayer Riff
Exec: Christine Harlan
Off Mgr: Annie Stuart
IT Man: Robert Bardenhagen

D-U-N-S 08-988-3292
MARIN COUNTY OFFICE OF EDUCATION
1111 Las Gallinas Ave, San Rafael, CA 94903-1843
Tel (415) 472-4110 Founded/Ownrshp 1854
Sales 21.7MM^E EMP 385
Accts Gilbert Accountancy Corporatio
SIC 8211 8331 Public elementary & secondary schools; Specialty education; Job training & vocational rehabilitation services; Public elementary & secondary schools; Specialty education; Job training & vocational rehabilitation services
Ex Dir: Jane Lange
Psych: Christina Fass

D-U-N-S 06-885-8851
MARIN GENERAL HOSPITAL
(Suby of MARIN HEALTH CARE DISTRICT) ★
250 Bon Air Rd, Greenbrae, CA 94904-1784
Tel (415) 925-7000 Founded/Ownrshp 2010
Sales 323.2MM EMP 1,100
Accts Moss Adams Llp San Francisco
SIC 8062 8011 General medical & surgical hospitals; Offices & clinics of medical doctors; General medical & surgical hospitals; Offices & clinics of medical doctors
CEO: Lee Domanico
*CEO: David Bradley
CFO: David Cox
*CFO: Theresa Daughton
Treas: Nadder Mirsepassi
Bd of Dir: Cathie Warner
Ofcr: Somayaji Bulusu
VP: Denise Perry
Exec: Linda Lang
Dir Inf Cn: Kathy Mathew
Dir Risk M: Jan Sams
Comm Dir: Jamie Maites
Dir Rx: Ziba Ansari-Jaberi
Board of Directors: Robert Macinnes

D-U-N-S 16-710-4830
MARIN HEALTH CARE DISTRICT
100b Drakes Landing Rd, Greenbrae, CA 94904
Tel (415) 464-2090 Founded/Ownrshp 2000
Sales 320.4MM^E EMP 1,101^E
SIC 8062 General medical & surgical hospitals; General medical & surgical hospitals
Chf Mktg O: Joe Sklar
CIO: Somayaji Bulusu

MARIN INDEPENDENT JOURNAL
See CALIFORNIA NEWSPAPERS INC

D-U-N-S 86-117-2765
MARIN INDIVIDUAL PRACTICE ASSOCIATION
4 Hamilton Landing # 100, Novato, CA 94949-8247
Tel (415) 884-1840 Founded/Ownrshp 1993
Sales 29.5MM EMP 45
SIC 7363 Pilot service, aviation; Pilot service, aviation
CEO: Joel Criste

MARIN INDUSTRIAL DISTRIBUTORS
See JACKSONS HARDWARE INC

D-U-N-S 02-137-5212
MARIN LUXURY CARS LLC
ASTON MARTI JAGUAR LAND
195 Casa Buena Dr, Corte Madera, CA 94925-1709
Tel (415) 460-4600 Founded/Ownrshp 2001
Sales 58.5MM^E EMP 123
SIC 5511 Automobiles, new & used; Automobiles, new & used
DP Exec: Tom King
Sls Mgr: Vincent Betar
Sls Mgr: David Carico
Sls Mgr: Joel Fong
Sls Mgr: Horacio Socarras
Sls Mgr: Dan Stephan
Sales Asso: Tom Kane

D-U-N-S 03-097-5783
MARIN MUNICIPAL WATER DISTRICT
220 Nellen Ave, Corte Madera, CA 94925-1169
Tel (415) 945-1455 Founded/Ownrshp 1912
Sales 67.7MM EMP 235
Accts Badawi & Associates Cpas Oak
SIC 4941 4971 Water supply; Irrigation systems; Water supply; Irrigation systems
Genl Mgr: Krishna Kumar
Dir Vol: Suzanne Whelan
CFO: Terry Stigall
Exec: Libby Pischel
Dir Lab: Grabow Larry
Genl Mgr: Paul Helliker
IT Man: Bob Fairchild
IT Man: Shaun Ferry
IT Man: Helen Ng
Sys Mgr: Jimmy Jimenez

MARIN RESOURCE RECOVERY CENTER
See MARIN SANITARY SERVICE

D-U-N-S 04-653-3493
MARIN SANITARY SERVICE
MARIN RESOURCE RECOVERY CENTER
1050 Andersen Dr, San Rafael, CA 94901-5316
Tel (415) 456-2601 Founded/Ownrshp 1948
Sales 85.5MM^E EMP 145
Accts Chiao Smith & Associates Cpa
SIC 4953 5099 4212 Garbage: collecting, destroying & processing; Recycling, waste materials; Wood chips; Local trucking, without storage; Garbage: collecting, destroying & processing; Recycling, waste materials; Wood chips; Local trucking, without storage
CEO: Patricia Garbarino
VP: Dave Garbarino
VP: John Oranje
VP: Ron Piombo
IT Man: Doug Griffith
Opers Mgr: Paul Cerruti

D-U-N-S 83-287-7877
▲ MARIN SOFTWARE INC
123 Mission St Fl 25, San Francisco, CA 94105-5139
Tel (415) 399-2580 Founded/Ownrshp 2006
Sales 99.3MM EMP 571^E
Accts Pricewaterhousecoopers Llp Sa
Tkr Sym MRIN Exch NYS
SIC 7374 Data processing & preparation; Data processing & preparation
CEO: David A Yovanno
CFO: Paul Auvil
CFO: Catriona Fallon
CFO: John A Kaelle
Ch: Christopher Lien
Ex VP: Avik Dey
Ex VP: Stephen E Kim
VP: Jeremy Evans
VP: Peter Lindberg
VP: David Lutz
VP: Simon Turner
Board of Directors: Paul R Auvil III, James J Barrese, L Gordon Crovitz, Bruce W Dunlevie, Donald P Hutchison, Allan Leinwand

D-U-N-S 09-998-7158
MARINA ASSOCIATES LTD
HARRAHS ATLANTIC CY CASINO HT
777 Harrahs Blvd, Atlantic City, NJ 08401-1911
Tel (609) 441-5000 Founded/Ownrshp 1979
Sales 59.2MM^E EMP 2,949
SIC 7011 5812 Casino hotel; Eating places; Casino hotel; Eating places
CEO: Timothy Wilmott
Pr: Ricky Mazer
VP: Luann Pappas
VP: Carlos Tolosa
Exec: Jim Byrnes
CTO: Arlene Guzan

D-U-N-S 96-243-5975
MARINA CLUB CONDOMINIUM
655 Absecon Blvd Ste B, Atlantic City, NJ 08401-2573
Tel (609) 348-0040 Founded/Ownrshp 2010
Sales 15.1MM^E EMP 1,828
SIC 6513 Apartment building operators; Apartment building operators
Prin: Larry Lipton

MARINA DEL REY HOSPITAL
See CFHS HOLDINGS INC

D-U-N-S 83-201-7235
MARINA DEL REY HOSPITAL
4650 Lincoln Blvd, Marina Del Rey, CA 90292-6306
Tel (310) 823-8911 Founded/Ownrshp 2008
Sales 20.9MM^E EMP 601
SIC 8062 General medical & surgical hospitals; General medical & surgical hospitals
CEO: Sean Fowler
Chf Path: James Keefe
Off Mgr: Jose Gomez

MARINA DEL REY TOYOTA
See WESTSIDE INVESTMENTS INC

D-U-N-S 17-855-8909 IMP
MARINA DISTRICT DEVELOPMENT CO LLC
BORGATA HOTEL CASINO AND SPA
1 Borgata Way, Atlantic City, NJ 08401-1946
Tel (609) 317-1000 Founded/Ownrshp 1995
Sales 738.2MM^E EMP 7,000^E
Accts Deloitte & Touche Llp Las Ve
SIC 7011 Casino hotel; Resort hotel; Casino hotel; Resort hotel
Pr: Tom Ballance
CFO: Ellis Landau
*Sr VP: Auggie Cipollini
Sr VP: Joe Lupo
VP: Ted Herzchel
VP: Nicolas Kurban
VP: Jay B Rosenthal
VP: Drew Schlesinger
VP: Hugh Turner
Dir Soc: Andrew Crater
Off Mgr: Andrea Marcato

D-U-N-S 82-758-1641
MARINA DISTRICT FINANCE CO INC
BORGATA HOTEL CASINO AND SPA,
(Suby of BORGATA HOTEL CASINO AND SPA) ★
1 Borgata Way, Atlantic City, NJ 08401-1946
Tel (609) 317-1000 Founded/Ownrshp 2000
Sales 738.2MM EMP 5,709
SIC 7011 Hotels & motels; Hotels & motels
Pr: Keith E Smith
COO: Robert L Boughner
CFO: Josh Hirsberg
Board of Directors: William S Boyd, Marianne Boyd Johnson

D-U-N-S 01-314-6543
MARINA DODGE INC
943 Ridge Rd, Webster, NY 14580-2553
Tel (585) 671-3000 Founded/Ownrshp 1989
Sales 23.0MM^E EMP 48
SIC 5511 Automobiles, new & used; Pickups, new & used; Vans, new & used; Automobiles, new & used; Pickups, new & used; Vans, new & used
Pr: John Gabriele
*Sec: Sonya Romantini
Genl Mgr: Tom Rosati
Sales Asso: Kylie Mitzel

D-U-N-S 15-385-4989
MARINA LANDSCAPE INC
1900 S Lewis St, Anaheim, CA 92805-6718
Tel (714) 939-6600 Founded/Ownrshp 1982
Sales 57.6MM^E EMP 430
SIC 0782

D-U-N-S 07-908-4227
MARINA PHARMACY CORP
7160 Dallas Pkwy Ste 400, Plano, TX 75024-7111
Tel (855) 254-9279 Founded/Ownrshp 2013
Sales 56.4MM^E EMP 59^E
SIC 7389
Pr: Larry Deans

MARINA SQUARE AUTO CENTER
See KELDANERI CORP

D-U-N-S 17-077-1955
MARINA TRUMP ASSOCIATES LP
(Suby of TRUMP ENTERTAINMENT RESORTS INC) ★
1000 Boardwalk, Atlantic City, NJ 08401-7415
Tel (609) 441-8406 Founded/Ownrshp 2004
Sales 1.9MM^E EMP 417^E
SIC 7011 Casino hotel
Owner: Donald Trump
Ofcr: Robert M Pickus

D-U-N-S 08-648-6677
MARINE ACCESSORIES CORP
1752 Henry G Lane St, Maryville, TN 37801-3702
Tel (865) 981-9898 Founded/Ownrshp 2015
Sales 63.4MM^E EMP 400
SIC 2394 3732 3537 3441 Liners & covers, fabric: made from purchased materials; Canopies, fabric: made from purchased materials; Boat building & repairing; Industrial trucks & tractors; Fabricated structural metal; Liners & covers, fabric: made from purchased materials; Canopies, fabric: made from purchased materials; Boat building & repairing; Industrial trucks & tractors; Fabricated structural metal
CEO: Rick Reyenger
VP: Tom Monroe

D-U-N-S 07-882-8839 IMP
MARINE ACQUISITION (US) INC
SEASTAR SOLUTIONS
(Suby of AMERICAN SECURITIES LLC) ★
640 N Lewis Rd, Limerick, PA 19468-1228
Tel (610) 495-7011 Founded/Ownrshp 2013
Sales 228.8MM^E EMP 2,589^E
SIC 3531 5551 Marine related equipment; Marine supplies & equipment
VP: Kimberly Koennecker
Pdt Mgr: Richard Lawrence

D-U-N-S 07-023-0389 IMP
MARINE ACQUISITION CORP
SEASTAR SOLUTIONS
(Suby of AMERICAN SECURITIES LLC) ★
1 Sierra Pl, Litchfield, IL 62056-3029
Tel (217) 324-9400 Founded/Ownrshp 2014
Sales 138.0MM^E EMP 300^E
SIC 5088 Marine propulsion machinery & equipment; Marine supplies; Marine propulsion machinery & equipment; Marine supplies
Pr: Yvan Cote
Sales Exec: Susie Strauss

D-U-N-S 17-935-8221
MARINE BANCORP INC
3050 Wabash Ave, Springfield, IL 62704-6413
Tel (217) 726-0600 Founded/Ownrshp 1990
Sales NA EMP 360
SIC 6022 State trust companies accepting deposits, commercial; State trust companies accepting deposits, commercial
Pr: Roger Chandler
CFO: Kathy Seadler
Ex VP: David Bramlet
Ex VP: Susan Raaum
VP: Cathy Tintori

MARINE BANK
See CIBM BANK

D-U-N-S 06-086-2224
MARINE BANK
MARINE BANK OF SPRINGFIELD
(Suby of MARINE BANCORP INC) ★
3050 Wabash Ave, Springfield, IL 62704-7426
Tel (217) 726-0600 Founded/Ownrshp 1970, 1993
Sales NA EMP 192
SIC 6022 State trust companies accepting deposits, commercial; State trust companies accepting deposits, commercial
CEO: Chris R Zettek
Pr: Roger W Chandler
Trst Ofcr: Stacy Foli
Trst Ofcr: Cathy Hanlon
Trst Ofcr: Bridget Johnson
Ex VP: Howard Neuger
Ex VP: Kevin Pozzi
Ex VP: Susan Raaum
Ex VP: John Wilson
Sr VP: Joe Stanley
VP: Michael Bogers
VP: Steve Keenan
VP: Cathy Tintori
VP: Ann Walker
VP: Nathan Wisehart

MARINE BANK OF SPRINGFIELD
See MARINE BANK

D-U-N-S 00-193-3779
MARINE BIOLOGICAL LABORATORY
MBL
7 M B L St, Woods Hole, MA 02543-1015
Tel (508) 548-3705 Founded/Ownrshp 1888
Sales 53.4MM EMP 300
SIC 8731 8299 Biological research; Educational service, nondegree granting: continuing educ.; Biological research; Educational service, nondegree granting: continuing educ.
Ex Dir: Sheldon Segal
*CEO: Gary Borisy
COO: Paul Speer
*CFO: Homer Lane
*Ch: John W Rowe
*Treas: Mary Conrad
VP: Gaius Shaver
Dir Lab: Marshall Otter
Adm Dir: Diana Kenney
Prgrm Mgr: Diane Cook
Dir IT: Scott Koerner
Board of Directors: Pamela Clapp, Richard D Cutler, Richard D Cutler, William Reznikoff, Joan V Ruderman

D-U-N-S 06-156-5024
MARINE BUILDERS INC
208 Church St, Jeffersonville, IN 47130-9411
Tel (812) 283-7932 Founded/Ownrshp 1972
Sales 20.3MM^E EMP 92
SIC 3731 3441 Towboats, building & repairing; Commercial passenger ships, building & repairing; Fabricated structural metal
Pr: David W Evanczyk
*Sec: Sarah Evanczyk
*VP: Byron Evanczyk

D-U-N-S 02-464-7018
MARINE CHEVROLET CO
1408 Western Blvd, Jacksonville, NC 28546-6661
Tel (910) 455-2121 Founded/Ownrshp 1975
Sales 43.5MM^E EMP 100
SIC 5511 7538 7532 7515 5012 Automobiles, new & used; Pickups, new & used; General automotive repair shops; Top & body repair & paint shops; Passenger car leasing; Automobiles & other motor vehicles; Automobiles, new & used; Pickups, new & used; General automotive repair shops; Top & body repair & paint shops; Passenger car leasing; Automobiles & other motor vehicles
VP: Alicia Alford
*Pr: Michael K Alford
CFO: Heather Crespoarce
Off Mgr: Crystal Massie
Opers Mgr: Les Petty
Sls Mgr: Paul Henry
Sls Mgr: James Tinsley
Sales Asso: Pale Bacerra
Sales Asso: James Boswell
Sales Asso: Daniel Gallen
Sales Asso: Dale Newman

D-U-N-S 02-267-7270
MARINE CONTRACTING GROUP LLC
308 Saint Michael St, Mobile, AL 36602-2819
Tel (251) 433-1005 Founded/Ownrshp 2005
Sales 24.3MM^E EMP 175
SIC 5082 General construction machinery & equipment; General construction machinery & equipment
IT Man: Chris Williams

MARINE CORPS COMMUNITY SVCS
See MORALE WELFARE RECREATION ACTIVITY

D-U-N-S 83-059-9234
MARINE CREDIT UNION
811 Monitor St Ste 100, La Crosse, WI 54603-3101
Tel (608) 784-7329 Founded/Ownrshp 1949
Sales NA EMP 300
SIC 6062 6163 State credit unions; Loan brokers; State credit unions; Loan brokers
Pr: Shawn Hanson
Pr: Ken Downs
*COO: Brad Noel
*CFO: John Nilles
*Treas: Dianne Mirrison
*VP: Adam Keer
*VP: Deb Lappen
VP: Katie Tolokken

D-U-N-S 08-050-1141
MARINE CREDIT UNION FOUNDATION INC (WI)
811 Monitor St Ste 100, La Crosse, WI 54603-3101
Tel (920) 923-7280 Founded/Ownrshp 2005
Sales 39.8MM^E EMP 215
SIC 6733 Trusts, except educational, religious, charity: management; Trusts, except educational, religious, charity: management
Treas: Charles Schranz
Brnch Mgr: Dean Chady
Sls Dir: Liz Malott

MARINE DIVISION
See KOP-COAT INC

MARINE ELECTRICAL PRODUCTS
See MEP ACQUISITION CORP

D-U-N-S 00-248-5191 IMP
MARINE EQUIPMENT AND SUPPLY CO (PA)
MESCO
1401 Metropolitan Ave, Thorofare, NJ 08086
Tel (856) 853-8320 Founded/Ownrshp 1910
Sales 46.3MM^E EMP 75^E
SIC 5088 5091 Marine propulsion machinery & equipment; Marine supplies; Boats, canoes, watercrafts & equipment; Marine propulsion machinery & equipment; Marine supplies; Boats, canoes, watercrafts & equipment
Pr: Donald H Kirkland Sr
VP: Jim Del Cioppo
*VP: Donald H Kirkland Jr

D-U-N-S 11-924-8789 IMP/EXP
MARINE FASTENERS INC
(Suby of WURTH GROUP OF NORTH AMERICA INC) ★
4150 Church St Ste 1066, Sanford, FL 32771-6991
Tel (407) 321-2994 Founded/Ownrshp 2008
Sales 22.7MM^E EMP 53
SIC 5072 Nuts (hardware); Bolts; Screws; Rivets
CEO: Keith Brantley
*Pr: Carl Brantley
*CFO: Chris Vandoren
Brnch Mgr: Richard Buche
Brnch Mgr: Jeff Cowan
IT Man: Samantha Aston
VP Mktg: Clint Smith
Sales Asso: Hugh Flanders

D-U-N-S 09-313-6232
MARINE FEDERAL CREDIT UNION (INC) (NC)
4180 Western Blvd, Jacksonville, NC 28546-6740
Tel (910) 577-7333 *Founded/Ownrshp* 1957
Sales NA *EMP* 300
SIC 6061 Federal credit unions; Federal credit unions
Pr: Craig L Chamberlin
COO: Robert Dickerson
**Ex VP:* Chuck Collins III
**Sr VP:* Tonda Grimmett
Admn Mgr: Karen Beblo
Brnch Mgr: William Bradford
Brnch Mgr: Donald Graddy
IT Man: Annette Sweet

MARINE FOOD EXPRESS
See MARINE FOODS EXPRESS LTD

D-U-N-S 11-911-9001 IMP/EXP
MARINE FOODS EXPRESS LTD
MARINE FOOD EXPRESS
5757 South Loop E, Houston, TX 77033-1604
Tel (713) 221-8899 *Founded/Ownrshp* 2002
Sales 21.5MM^E *EMP* 35
SIC 5146 Seafoods
Pt: Jason Poon
CFO: Gerald Huang
Sales Asso: Jeff Boies

D-U-N-S 19-177-2938 IMP
MARINE GROUP BOAT WORKS LLC
997 G St, Chula Vista, CA 91910-3414
Tel (619) 427-6767 *Founded/Ownrshp* 2008
Sales 48.5MM^E *EMP* 115
SIC 3731 Shipbuilding & repairing
CFO: Laura Machado
**Ch:* Arthur E Engel
**VP:* Todd Roberts
Comm Dir: Leah Yam
Off Mgr: Jill Salgado

D-U-N-S 10-251-2501 IMP/EXP
MARINE HARVEST USA LLC
(*Suby of* MARINE HARVEST USA HOLDING, LLC)
8550 Nw 17th St Ste 105, Doral, FL 33126-1036
Tel (305) 591-8550 *Founded/Ownrshp* 2011
Sales 72.8MM^E *EMP* 50
SIC 5146 Seafoods

D-U-N-S 82-981-9981
■ **MARINE HOLDING US CORP**
(*Suby of* ZODIAC POOL SOLUTIONS NORTH AMERICA INC) ★
6000 Condor Dr, Moorpark, CA 93021-2601
Tel (805) 529-2000 *Founded/Ownrshp* 2004
Sales 117.0MM^E *EMP* 653
SIC 6799 Investors; Investors
Pr: Francois Mirallie
**CFO:* Joel Silva
**Sec:* Mark Cortell

D-U-N-S 11-907-7303
MARINE HYDRAULICS INTERNATIONAL INC
MHI SHIP REPAIR & SERVICES
(*Suby of* A M H) ★
543 E Indian River Rd, Norfolk, VA 23523-1797
Tel (757) 545-6400 *Founded/Ownrshp* 2015
Sales 80.5MM^E *EMP* 385
SIC 3731 7629 Military ships, building & repairing; Electrical repair shops; Military ships, building & repairing; Electrical repair shops
Pr: Gary R Brandt
COO: Terry P Mulroy
CFO: Andrew Slizewski
Ex VP: Thomas Epley
VP: Kim Lauterbach
VP: Terence Mulroy
VP: Michael Walker
Prgrm Mgr: Charlie Griffin
Genl Mgr: Carl Lemme
IT Man: Patricia Baumann

MARINE LIFT SYSTEMS
See TAMPA FORK LIFT INC

D-U-N-S 83-633-5005
MARINE LUMBER OPERATOR INC
MARVIN DESIGN GALLERY
134 Orange St, Nantucket, MA 02554-4018
Tel (508) 228-0900 *Founded/Ownrshp* 2008
Sales 22.0MM^E *EMP* 100
SIC 5211 5251 5712 5261 5719 Millwork & lumber; Builders' hardware; Furniture stores; Garden supplies & tools; Housewares
Pr: Dennis Gazaille
**VP:* Mark Songer
**Genl Mgr:* Ronald B Foster

D-U-N-S 04-927-7718
MARINE POLLUTION CONTROL CORP
MPC ENVIRONMENTAL
8631 W Jefferson Ave, Detroit, MI 48209-2691
Tel (313) 849-2333 *Founded/Ownrshp* 1967
Sales 42.9MM^E *EMP* 65
SIC 4952 4953 5084

D-U-N-S 62-606-8456
MARINE PRESERVATION ASSOCIATION INC
MPA
20645 N Pima Rd Ste 100, Scottsdale, AZ 85255-5595
Tel (480) 991-5500 *Founded/Ownrshp* 1990
Sales 89.0MM *EMP* 3
SIC 8611 Trade associations; Trade associations
Pr: Robert Aldag
Treas: Stephen E Fortino

D-U-N-S 01-281-2702
▲ **MARINE PRODUCTS CORP**
2801 Buford Hwy Ne # 520, Brookhaven, GA 30329-2143
Tel (404) 321-7910 *Founded/Ownrshp* 2000
Sales 171.0MM *EMP* 605^E
Accts Grant Thornton Llp Atlanta G
Tkr Sym MPX *Exch* NYS
SIC 3732 Boat building & repairing; Boats, fiberglass: building & repairing; Boat building & repairing; Boats, fiberglass: building & repairing
Pr: Richard A Hubbell
**Ch Bd:* R Randall Rollins
COO: Lou Paladeau
CFO: Ben M Palmer
Treas: John Burt
**Ex VP:* James A Lane Jr
**VP:* Linda H Graham
VP: Linda Graham
IT Man: Casey Hempen
IT Man: Jeff Smith
Board of Directors: Bill J Dismuke, Larry L Prince, Gary W Rollins, Henry B Tippie, James B Williams

D-U-N-S 13-695-6096 IMP
MARINE SHELTERS HOLDINGS LLC
LONE STAR MARINE SHELTERS
6800 Harborside Dr, Galveston, TX 77554-2830
Tel (409) 941-1200 *Founded/Ownrshp* 2003
Sales 21.5MM *EMP* 125
SIC 3441 Fabricated structural metal; Fabricated structural metal
Pr: Clayton E Hazzard
CFO: Michael R Kaiser
Sls Mgr: Dennis Freels

D-U-N-S 61-839-8580 EXP
MARINE SPILL RESPONSE CORP
MSRC
220 Spring St Ste 500, Herndon, VA 20170-6207
Tel (703) 326-5600 *Founded/Ownrshp* 1990
Sales 293.5MM^E *EMP* 450
Accts Bdo Usa Llp Bethesda Md
SIC 4959 Oil spill cleanup; Oil spill cleanup
Pr: Steve Ben
**CFO:* Douglas Ferrari
IT Man: Keith Whitney
Opers Supe: Dusty Henry
Sfty Mgr: Chris Muzzy
VP Mktg: Judith Norell
Genl Couns: Gina Pace
Snr Mgr: Kevin Peterson

D-U-N-S 08-209-7528
MARINE SPORTS LLC
HARRISON MARINE CENTER
2330 Twin View Blvd, Redding, CA 96003-1534
Tel (530) 243-0175 *Founded/Ownrshp* 1999
Sales 29.2MM^E *EMP* 150
SIC 5551 7699 Boat dealers; Boat repair; Boat dealers; Boat repair
Pr: Ned Dole
**VP:* Rod Dole

D-U-N-S 04-287-8769 IMP
■ **MARINE SYSTEMS INC** (LA)
(*Suby of* KIRBY CORP) ★
116 Capital Blvd, Houma, LA 70360-7943
Tel (985) 223-7100 *Founded/Ownrshp* 1966, 1982
Sales 29.0MM^E *EMP* 100
SIC 7538 7699 Diesel engine repair: automotive; Marine engine repair
Pr: Dorman L Strahan
**Ex VP:* David W Grzebinski
**Ex VP:* David D Whisenhunt
**Sr VP:* Thomas W Bottoms Sr
**VP:* Lynn Ahlemeyer
**VP:* Lynn A Ahlemeyer
**VP:* Mia C Cradeur
**VP:* John A Manno
**Prin:* P Scott Mangan
**Prin:* Lynn Strahan

D-U-N-S 88-461-0593
MARINE TECHNOLOGIES INC
6604 Fort Smallwood Rd, Baltimore, MD 21226-1708
Tel (410) 355-2000 *Founded/Ownrshp* 1992
Sales 24.6MM^E *EMP* 75
SIC 1629 Dams, waterways, docks & other marine construction
Pr: Terry Clarke
**VP:* Dave Capino
VP: Sean Francis

D-U-N-S 60-349-4071 IMP/EXP
■ **MARINE TERMINALS CORP**
(*Suby of* M T C HOLDINGS) ★
389 Terminal Way, San Pedro, CA 90731-7430
Tel (310) 519-2300 *Founded/Ownrshp* 1931
Sales 32.4MM^E *EMP* 300
SIC 4491

D-U-N-S 02-356-4099 IMP/EXP
MARINE TRAVELIFT INC
EXACTECH HOLDINGS
49 E Yew St, Sturgeon Bay, WI 54235-1976
Tel (920) 743-6202 *Founded/Ownrshp* 2003
Sales 25.5MM^E *EMP* 85
SIC 3531 3536 Marine related equipment; Cranes, industrial plant; Marine related equipment; Cranes, industrial plant
Pr: J Stephen Pfeifer
**CFO:* Peter Kerwin
**Ch:* John Ashton
VP: Paul Lundahl
VP: Christiane Stueckemann
Genl Mgr: Anna Seyfer
Trfc Mgr: Tom Heimbecher
Sls Mgr: Scott Alger

D-U-N-S 02-727-5189
MARINE VIEW BEVERAGE INC
JENNINGS DISTRIBUTING
22200 Dauntless Dr Nw, Poulsbo, WA 98370-9548
Tel (360) 394-9631 *Founded/Ownrshp* 2002
Sales 24.5MM^E *EMP* 60^E
SIC 5181 5182 Beer & other fermented malt liquors; Wine; Beer & other fermented malt liquors; Wine
Pr: Lance Kahn
**VP:* B J Bjerke
**VP:* Michael Bjerke

D-U-N-S 04-564-7915
MARINE WELL CONTAINMENT CO LLC
9807 Katy Fwy Ste 1200, Houston, TX 77024-1201
Tel (281) 820-8800 *Founded/Ownrshp* 2011
Sales 35.8MM^E *EMP* 55^E
SIC 1389 Servicing oil & gas wells
CEO: Don Armijo
**CEO:* Martin Massey
**CFO:* Astley Blair
**CFO:* Don Armijo Astley Blair
Ofcr: Carmine Dulisse
Plng Mgr: Shannon Straube
CTO: Charlie Miller
IT Man: Lauren Kemink
Opers Mgr: Sammy McDaniel

MARINELLO SCHOOL OF BEAUTY
See B & H EDUCATION INC

D-U-N-S 00-292-9946 EXP
▲ **MARINEMAX INC**
2600 Mccormick Dr Ste 200, Clearwater, FL 33759-1029
Tel (727) 531-1700 *Founded/Ownrshp* 1998
Sales 751.3MM *EMP* 1,289
Accts Kpmg Llp Tampa Florida
Tkr Sym HZO *Exch* NYS
SIC 5551 Boat dealers; Motor boat dealers; Canoe & kayak dealers; Sailboats & equipment; Boat dealers; Motor boat dealers; Canoe & kayak dealers; Sailboats & equipment
CEO: William H McGill
**Ch Bd:* William H McGill Jr
**CFO:* Michael H McLamb
VP: Charles A Cashman
VP: Anthony E Cassella Jr
VP: Paulee C Day
VP: James Kelaita
VP: William Brett McGill
VP: Josie Tucci
Assoc Dir: Joe Jackson
Sls Mgr: Brian Mayfield
Board of Directors: Hilliard M Eure III, Evelyn Follit, Clint Moore, Charles R Oglesby, Joseph A Watters, Dean S Woodman

D-U-N-S 06-570-4264 EXP
■ **MARINEMAX MID-ATLANTIC** (PA)
(*Suby of* MARINEMAX INC) ★
1500 Riverside Dr N, Brick, NJ 08724-1805
Tel (732) 840-2100 *Founded/Ownrshp* 1973, 1999
Sales 25.1MM^E *EMP* 210
SIC 5551 4493 Boat dealers; Marine supplies; Boat yards, storage & incidental repair; Boat dealers; Marine supplies; Boat yards, storage & incidental repair
Pr: Mike Aiello

MARINER BOATS
See INTERNATIONAL BOAT RENTALS INC

MARINER FINANCE
See MILESTONE PARTNERS MANAGEMENT CO LP

D-U-N-S 06-725-7501
MARINER HEALTH CARE INC
MARINER HEALTHCARE MANAGEMENT
(*Suby of* NATIONAL SENIOR CARE INC) ★
1 Ravinia Dr Ste 1500, Atlanta, GA 30346-2115
Tel (678) 443-7000 *Founded/Ownrshp* 2004
Sales 4.4MMM^E *EMP* 35,000
SIC 5912 8051 8093 8741 8062 3443 Drug stores & proprietary stores; Extended care facility; Rehabilitation center, outpatient treatment; Nursing & personal care facility management; General medical & surgical hospitals; Chambers & caissons; Drug stores & proprietary stores; Extended care facility; Mental retardation hospital; Rehabilitation center, outpatient treatment; Nursing & personal care facility management; General medical & surgical hospitals; Chambers & caissons
CEO: Harry Grunstein
**CEO:* Tony E Oglesby
CFO: Kevin Seramur
CFO: Bernard Turk
**Treas:* Boyd P Gentry
Ex VP: Michael Boxer
CIO: Sara Goldberg
QA Dir: Angela Jackson
Dir IT: Mike Ellis
Plnt Mgr: Ariel Valladolid
Mktg Dir: Carlos McCulloch

MARINER HEALTHCARE MANAGEMENT
See MARINER HEALTH CARE INC

D-U-N-S 61-552-0939 IMP/EXP
MARINER INTERNATIONAL TRAVEL INC
MOORINGS, THE
(*Suby of* TUI TRAVEL LIMITED)
93 N Park Place Blvd, Clearwater, FL 33759-3917
Tel (727) 530-5424 *Founded/Ownrshp* 2005
Sales 28.2MM^E *EMP* 800
SIC 7999 5551 Pleasure boat rental; Sailboats & equipment; Pleasure boat rental; Sailboats & equipment
CEO: Jonathan Grisdale
Ofcr: Karen Luke
VP: Samantha Stimpson
Genl Mgr: Josie Tucci
CIO: Vinord George
Mktg Mgr: Ian Pedersen
Sls Mgr: Leslie Sides
Board of Directors: Peter Cochran, Jonathan Grisdale

D-U-N-S 11-327-5510
MARINER INVESTMENT GROUP LLC
(*Suby of* MIG HOLDINGS LLC)
500 Mmaroneck Ave Ste 101, Harrison, NY 10528
Tel (914) 670-4300 *Founded/Ownrshp* 1992
Sales 32.9MM^E *EMP* 166^E
SIC 6726 Investment offices; Investment offices
CEO: Bracebridge H Young
**Pr:* Charles Hal
**Treas:* Scott Baso
**Ofcr:* Dmitry Green
Dir Risk M: Catherine Blondell
Mng Dir: Danielle Beyer
Mng Dir: Laura Koller
Mng Dir: Noel Meller
Mng Dir: Christopher Munson
CTO: Tucker Goodrich
Mktg Dir: William Turchyn

D-U-N-S 05-151-4180
MARINERS CHURCH
5001 Newport Coast Dr, Irvine, CA 92603-0164
Tel (949) 769-8100 *Founded/Ownrshp* 1965
Sales 18.4MM^E *EMP* 350^E
Accts Mayer Hoffman Mccann Pc Irvin
SIC 8661 Non-denominational church; Non-denominational church
CEO: Kenton Beshore
**CFO:* Jeremy Moser
Pgrm Dir: Sandy Almquist

D-U-N-S 07-108-6102
MARINERS HOSPITAL INC (FL)
(*Suby of* BAPTIST HEALTH SOUTH FLORIDA INC) ★
91500 Overseas Hwy, Tavernier, FL 33070-2547
Tel (305) 852-4418 *Founded/Ownrshp* 1966
Sales 49.9MM *EMP* 192
Accts Deloitte & Touche Llp
SIC 8062 General medical & surgical hospitals; General medical & surgical hospitals
CEO: Rick Freeburg
V Ch: David Johnson
VP: Cheryl Cottrell
Dir Lab: Cleopatra Puerto
Dir IT: Luis Bellmas
Dir IT: Sheldon Cohen
Dir IT: Gabriel Coneybear
IT Man: Mary De Graaff
IT Man: Candy Fincke
IT Man: Mike Lanier
Netwrk Eng: Devica Samsundar

D-U-N-S 00-613-5388 IMP
MARINETTE MARINE CORP
(*Suby of* BAY SHIPBUILDING) ★
1600 Ely St, Marinette, WI 54143-2434
Tel (715) 735-9341 *Founded/Ownrshp* 2008
Sales 14.9MM^E *EMP* 900
SIC 3731

D-U-N-S 10-008-3336
MARINETTE SCHOOL DISTRICT
2139 Pierce Ave, Marinette, WI 54143-3947
Tel (715) 735-1406 *Founded/Ownrshp* 1887
Sales 23.5MM^E *EMP* 465
Accts Virchow Krause & Co
SIC 8211 Public combined elementary & secondary school; Public combined elementary & secondary school
Prin: James Kranpitz
Prin: Robert J Picard
Schl Brd P: Cindy Bailey

D-U-N-S 13-941-1003 IMP
MARINEX INC
735 Challenger St, Brea, CA 92821-2948
Tel (714) 578-1600 *Founded/Ownrshp* 1984
Sales 42.0MM *EMP* 10^E
SIC 5013 Automotive supplies & parts; Automotive supplies & parts
Pr: Michael S Hyun
Mng Dir: Henry Parks
Mktg Mgr: Steve Choe

D-U-N-S 80-994-5314
MARINO BUILDING SYSTEMS CORP
AMERICAN PANEL TEC
1640 New Market Ave 1a, South Plainfield, NJ 07080-1641
Tel (732) 968-0555 *Founded/Ownrshp* 1994
Sales 25.9MM^E *EMP* 125
SIC 3448 Trusses & framing: prefabricated metal
Ch Bd: John Marino
**Pr:* John Lanzilotta
Exec: Mary Lockhart
Plnt Mgr: Keith Sherman
Snr Mgr: Mark Rudden

MARINO WARE DIVISION
See WARE INDUSTRIES INC

D-U-N-S 05-845-1840 IMP
MARIO CAMACHO FOODS LLC
(*Suby of* ANGEL CAMACHO ALIMENTACION SL)
2502 Walden Woods Dr, Plant City, FL 33566-7167
Tel (813) 305-4534 *Founded/Ownrshp* 1937, 2007
Sales 85.0MM *EMP* 25
SIC 5148 Vegetables, fresh
Pr: Shawn Kaddoura
IT Man: Ken Starling

MARIO CONTRACT LIGHTING
See MARIO INDUSTRIES OF VIRGINIA INC

D-U-N-S 00-130-3726 IMP
MARIO INDUSTRIES OF VIRGINIA INC (VA)
MARIO CONTRACT LIGHTING
2490 Patterson Ave Sw, Roanoke, VA 24016-2528
Tel (540) 342-7800 *Founded/Ownrshp* 1926
Sales 20.2MM^E *EMP* 120
SIC 3645 Residential lighting fixtures; Lamp & light shades; Residential lighting fixtures; Lamp & light shades
Pr: Louis Scutellaro
**VP:* M Dean Martin
**VP:* Joseph Semeniro

D-U-N-S 10-439-6275
MARIO SINACOLA & SONS EXCAVATING INC
10950 Research Rd, Frisco, TX 75033-2042
Tel (214) 387-3900 *Founded/Ownrshp* 1981
Sales 156.9MM^E *EMP* 400
SIC 1794 Excavation work; Excavation work
Pr: James M Sinacola
CFO: Neil Motley
**Sec:* David G Sinacola
**VP:* Neal Mortley
IT Man: Ryan Ecklund
Sfty Dirs: Ben Baldwin
Mtls Mgr: Mike Ferguson
Snr Mgr: Greg Samples

D-U-N-S 60-910-3429
■ MARIO TRICOCIS HAIR SALON & DAY SPA
(*Suby of* ELIZABETH ARDEN SALON-HOLDINGS INC) ★
900 N Michigan Ave # 1850, Chicago, IL 60611-1542
Tel (800) 874-2624 *Founded/Ownrshp* 1989
Sales 8.1MM^E *EMP* 1,600
SIC 7231 Hairdressers; Cosmetology & personal hygiene salons; Hairdressers; Cosmetology & personal hygiene salons
Pr: Mario Tricoci

MARION AREA HEALTH CENTER
See FREDERICK C SMITH CLINIC INC

D-U-N-S 10-000-3441
MARION BOARD OF EDUCATION INC
MARION SCHOOL DISTRICT
200 Manor St, Marion, AR 72364-1936
Tel (870) 739-5100 *Founded/Ownrshp* 1869
Sales 20.7MM^E *EMP* 485
SIC 8211 Public elementary & secondary schools; Public elementary & secondary schools
**Ch Bd:* Jan Thomas

D-U-N-S 05-624-4627
MARION BODY WORKS INC
211 W Ramsdell St, Marion, WI 54950-9683
Tel (715) 754-5261 *Founded/Ownrshp* 1980
Sales 52.1MM *EMP* 200
SIC 3711 3713 Military motor vehicle assembly; Truck bodies & parts; Military motor vehicle assembly; Truck bodies & parts
Pr: Curtis H Ignacio
**VP:* Nancy S Ignacio
IT Man: Amy Prellwitz
IT Man: Vincenzo Speziale
Mfg Dir: Curt Kjendalen
Sfty Mgr: Brian Bradley
Opers Mgr: Rhonda Haber
Prd Mgr: Perry Tom
Prd Mgr: Doug Wendt
VP Sls: Shane Krueger
Manager: Chris Simon
Board of Directors: Dale Feinauer, Phillip Florek, Richard Gallagher, Lynne Simpson

D-U-N-S 03-752-8916
MARION CITY SCHOOLS
LINCOLN CENTRE
420 Presidential Dr B, Marion, OH 43302-5173
Tel (740) 223-4422 *Founded/Ownrshp* 1905
Sales 43.4MM^E *EMP* 650
Accts Kennedy Cottrell & Associates
SIC 8211 Public elementary & secondary schools; Public elementary & secondary schools
CFO: Jeri Wires
VP: Steve Williams
MIS Dir: Monte Detterman
Pr Dir: Becky Gilliam
Schl Brd P: Rocky White
Teacher Pr: Steve Fujii

D-U-N-S 19-301-1368
MARION CO SCHOOL DISTRICT
SUPERINTENDENT'S OFFICE
1010 Highway 13 N Ste 2, Columbia, MS 39429-2047
Tel (601) 736-7193 *Founded/Ownrshp* 2008
Sales 11.6MM^E *EMP* 365
SIC 8211 Public elementary & secondary schools; Public elementary & secondary schools

D-U-N-S 01-082-5271
■ MARION COMMUNITY HOSPITAL INC
OCALA REGIONAL MEDICAL CENTER
(*Suby of* HCA INC) ★
1431 Sw 1st Ave, Ocala, FL 34471-6500
Tel (352) 401-1000 *Founded/Ownrshp* 1994
Sales 195.0MM^E *EMP* 1,100
SIC 8062 General medical & surgical hospitals; General medical & surgical hospitals
Prin: Samuel N Hazen
Chf Rad: John Cain
VP: Lori McGriff
Dir Lab: Jim Certa
Dir Rx: Jerry Cummings
IT Man: Holly McEachern
IT Man: Gloria Nolan
VP Mktg: Allison Johnson
Doctor: Ali Nasser
Doctor: Nagender Reddy
Nrsg Dir: Terri McDonald

D-U-N-S 05-048-1118
MARION COMMUNITY SCHOOLS
750 W 26th St, Marion, IN 46953-2929
Tel (765) 662-2546 *Founded/Ownrshp* 1890
Sales 50.0MM^E *EMP* 1,000
SIC 8211 Public elementary & secondary schools; Public elementary & secondary schools
Treas: Patricia Nauman
Dir IT: Troy Freeman
Dir IT: David Richey
HC Dir: Sue Nicholson

D-U-N-S 09-152-2565
MARION COMMUNITY UNIT 2 SCHOOL DISTRICT
1700 W Cherry St, Marion, IL 62959-1212
Tel (618) 993-2321 *Founded/Ownrshp* 1951
Sales 22.2MM^E *EMP* 423
SIC 8211 9411 Public combined elementary & secondary school; Administration of educational programs; Public combined elementary & secondary school; Administration of educational programs
**CFO:* Patrick Brown

MARION COUNTY AUDITOR OFFICE
See COUNTY OF MARION

D-U-N-S 10-000-0652
MARION COUNTY BOARD EDUCATION
188 Winchester Dr, Hamilton, AL 35570-6626
Tel (205) 921-3191 *Founded/Ownrshp* 1900
Sales 25.3MM^E *EMP* 500
SIC 8211 Public elementary & secondary schools; School board
Pr: L C Fowler
Dir Sec: Chris Cook
HC Dir: Kevin Dulaney

D-U-N-S 07-322-8454
MARION COUNTY BOARD OF COUNTY COMMISSIONERS
601 Se 25th Ave, Ocala, FL 34471-2690
Tel (352) 438-2323 *Founded/Ownrshp* 1944
Sales NA *EMP* 1,500
Accts Purgis Gray And Company Llp
SIC 9111 Executive offices; Executive offices;
Ch Bd: Stan Ncctain
**Ch Bd:* Cherly Stone
Ex Dir: Jeffrey Askew

D-U-N-S 08-966-8917
MARION COUNTY BOARD OF EDUCATION INC
200 Gaston Ave, Fairmont, WV 26554-2739
Tel (304) 367-2100 *Founded/Ownrshp* 1930
Sales 55.5MM^E *EMP* 1,210
SIC 8211 School buses; Public elementary & secondary schools; School board
Pr: Richard Pellegrin
**Treas:* Kim Wade

MARION COUNTY PUBLIC SCHL SYS
See MARION COUNTY PUBLIC SCHOOLS

D-U-N-S 07-832-0868
MARION COUNTY PUBLIC SCHOOLS
MARION COUNTY PUBLIC SCHL SYS
512 Se 3rd St, Ocala, FL 34471-2212
Tel (352) 671-7700 *Founded/Ownrshp* 1844
Sales 357.9MM *EMP* 5,000
Accts Purvis Gray & Company Llp Oc
SIC 8211 Public elementary & secondary schools; Public elementary & secondary schools
Prin: Mike Graff
Prin: Walt Miller
Ex Dir: Carmen Maines
Dir Sec: Brian Marcum
MIS Dir: Scott Hansen
MIS Dir: Vickye Vaughns
Pr Dir: Kevin Christian
Teacher Pr: Lisa Krysalka

D-U-N-S 10-002-7572
MARION COUNTY PUBLIC SCHOOLS
MARION COUNTY SCHOOL DISTRICT
755 E Main St, Lebanon, KY 40033-1701
Tel (270) 692-3721 *Founded/Ownrshp* 1800
Sales 24.3MM^E *EMP* 489
Accts Russell W Hinton State Audit
SIC 8211 9411 Public elementary & secondary schools; Administration of educational programs; Public elementary & secondary schools; Administration of educational programs
Teacher Pr: Jennifer Osbourne
Snr Mgr: Teresa Preston

MARION COUNTY SCHOOL DISTRICT
See MARION COUNTY PUBLIC SCHOOLS

D-U-N-S 07-153-5538
MARION COUNTY SCHOOL DISTRICT
204 Betsy Pack Dr, Jasper, TN 37347-3324
Tel (423) 942-3434 *Founded/Ownrshp* 1900
Sales 21.5MM^E *EMP* 450
SIC 8211 Public elementary school; Public junior high school; Public senior high school; Public elementary school; Public junior high school; Public senior high school

D-U-N-S 07-861-8292
MARION COUNTY SCHOOL DISTRICT
719 N Main St, Marion, SC 29571-2517
Tel (843) 423-1811 *Founded/Ownrshp* 2012
Sales 33.5MM^E *EMP* 800
SIC 8211 School board; School board
MIS Dir: Kevin Owens
Pr Dir: Nancy N Etman
Teacher Pr: Paula Grant

D-U-N-S 00-622-7714
MARION COUNTY SCHOOL DISTRICT 103
965 N Boones Ferry Rd, Woodburn, OR 97071-9674
Tel (503) 981-9555 *Founded/Ownrshp* 1883
Sales 23.8MM^E *EMP* 603
SIC 8211 Public elementary school; Public junior high school; Public senior high school; Public elementary school; Public junior high school; Public senior high school
Board of Directors: Greg Baisch, Robin Deloach, Virginia Heide, Lorin Stanley, Steve William

D-U-N-S 01-099-4809
MARION COUNTY SCHOOL TRANSPORTATION
(*Suby of* MARION COUNTY BOARD OF EDUCATION INC) ★
614 Virginia Ave, Fairmont, WV 26554-5130
Tel (304) 367-2161 *Founded/Ownrshp* 2001
Sales 8.0MM^E *EMP* 1,148^E
SIC 4151 School buses
Prin: Tj James

D-U-N-S 07-979-9663
MARION COUNTY SCHOOLS
188 Winchester Dr, Hamilton, AL 35570-6626
Tel (205) 921-3191 *Founded/Ownrshp* 2015
Sales 4.3MM^E *EMP* 390^E
SIC 8211 Public elementary & secondary schools

D-U-N-S 07-979-9725
MARION COUNTY SCHOOLS
200 Gaston Ave, Fairmont, WV 26554-2739
Tel (304) 367-2100 *Founded/Ownrshp* 2015
Sales 8.5MM^E *EMP* 1,012^E
SIC 8211 Public elementary & secondary schools
Teacher Pr: Andy Neptune
Psych: Shawna Hathaway

D-U-N-S 15-151-4866 IMP
■ MARION COVANTA INC
(*Suby of* COVANTA SYSTEMS, INC.)
4850 Brooklake Rd Ne, Brooks, OR 97305-9252
Tel (503) 393-0890 *Founded/Ownrshp* 1982
Sales 27.0MM^E *EMP* 38
SIC 4911 Distribution, electric power
CEO: Anthony J Orlando
**Treas:* Louis M Walters
**Ex VP:* John M Klett
**Ex VP:* Seth Moynef
VP: Russel Johnston

MARION DISTRICT
See OHIO-AMERICAN WATER CO INC)

D-U-N-S 07-978-0854
MARION FORD INC
LINCOLN
1910 W Coolidge Ave, Marion, IL 62959-1088
Tel (618) 993-6666 *Founded/Ownrshp* 1975
Sales 38.5MM^E *EMP* 90
SIC 5511 Automobiles, new & used; Automobiles, new & used
Pr: Michael Absher
Ofcr: Jon Wofford
Genl Mgr: Brad Poole
Store Mgr: John McKeown
Sales Exec: Gary Sutton
Sls Mgr: Russ Brown
Sales Asso: Pam Braswell

D-U-N-S 07-805-2131
MARION FRANCIS UNIVERSITY
4822 E Palmetto St, Florence, SC 29506-4530
Tel (843) 661-1110 *Founded/Ownrshp* 1970
Sales 31.9MM *EMP* 751
Accts Cline Brandt Kochenower & Co
SIC 8221 Colleges universities & professional schools; University; Colleges universities & professional schools; University
Pr: Luther F Carter
VP: Joseph Heyward
**VP:* John J Kispert
Netwrk Mgr: Mark Lancaster
Mtls Mgr: Tony Falvino
Mtls Mgr: Brandon Heembrock
Pr Dir: Garry Ballard

D-U-N-S 06-906-5449
MARION GENERAL HOSPITAL INC (OH)
(*Suby of* OHIOHEALTH CORP) ★
1000 Mckinley Park Dr, Marion, OH 43302-6397
Tel (740) 383-8400 *Founded/Ownrshp* 1955, 1986
Sales 200.5MM^E *EMP* 1,300^E
SIC 8062 Hospital, AMA approved residency; Hospital, AMA approved residency
Pr: John Sanders
Ofcr: Michael Cruea
VP: Carol Solie
Dir Risk M: Christina Richards
Dir Rx: Justin Hamper
Comm Man: Jane Binau
CTO: David Beard
IT Man: Dave Carmichael
Sls&Mrk Ex: Phyllis Butterworth
Pathlgst: Niranjan Shah
Nrsg Dir: Eric Wallis

D-U-N-S 07-596-3397
MARION GENERAL HOSPITAL INC
441 N Wabash Ave, Marion, IN 46952-2690
Tel (765) 660-6000 *Founded/Ownrshp* 1902
Sales 159.9MM *EMP* 1,212
Accts Blue & Co Llc Indianapolis
SIC 8062 General medical & surgical hospitals; General medical & surgical hospitals
Pr: Paul L Usher
Dir Vol: Sheila Stewart
CFO: Robyn Powell
Bd of Dir: Jeffrey Bragg
Bd of Dir: Salil Rajmaira
Exec: Randy Deffenbaugh
Exec: Susan Robilotto
Dir Inf Cn: Barbara Eppley
Off Admin: Jeremy Bailey
Trfc Dir: Jan Geuy
Obsttrcn: Kabuiya Mugera

MARION HEIGHTS APARTMENTS
See ST JOSEPH RESIDENCE INC

D-U-N-S 04-013-9735
■ MARION HOSPITAL CORP
HEARTLAND REGIONAL MEDICAL CTR
(*Suby of* COMMUNITY HEALTH SYSTEMS INC) ★
3333 W Deyoung St, Marion, IL 62959-5884
Tel (618) 998-7800 *Founded/Ownrshp* 1996
Sales 95.1MM^E *EMP* 577
SIC 8062 8011 General medical & surgical hospitals; Offices & clinics of medical doctors; General medical & surgical hospitals; Offices & clinics of medical doctors
CEO: Steven Lunn
**Pr:* Martin G Schweinhart
**CFO:* Loren Rials
Dir Lab: Kelly Richards
Dir Rad: Lisa Greenwood
Dir Rx: Kristin Brooks-Shrum
Chf Nrs Of: Melissa Adkins
CIO: Larry Koch
QA Dir: Marg Fletcher
Mktg Dir: Andrea Turner
Surgeon: Rachel Trather

D-U-N-S 04-562-9300 IMP
MARION IMPORT CORP
MARION IMPORTS
2965 Alabama Ave, Haleyville, AL 35565-2327
Tel (205) 486-7106 *Founded/Ownrshp* 1964
Sales 29.3MM^E *EMP* 100
SIC 5193 Flowers & florists' supplies
Pr: James G Mays
**Sec:* Ruby Mays
**VP:* Reva Butler

MARION IMPORTS
See MARION IMPORT CORP

D-U-N-S 04-580-4531
MARION INDEPENDENT SCHOOL DISTRICT
MISD
777 S 15th St, Marion, IA 52302-4966
Tel (319) 377-4691 *Founded/Ownrshp* 1898
Sales 19.5MM^E *EMP* 500
SIC 8211 Public elementary & secondary schools; School board; Public elementary & secondary schools; School board
Prin: William C Jacobsen
**Prin:* Mike Murphy
**Prin:* Dr Greg Thomas
Schl Brd P: David Law

D-U-N-S 10-554-2802
MARION INDUSTRIES INC
(*Suby of* E G I) ★
999 Kellogg Pkwy, Marion, OH 43302-1791
Tel (740) 223-0075 *Founded/Ownrshp* 2000
Sales 228.8MM^E *EMP* 753
SIC 3714 Motor vehicle wheels & parts; Motor vehicle wheels & parts
Ch Bd: James R Conway
**Pr:* Jerome Curtis
**CEO:* Rick Charville
Sr Cor Off: Louis Scutellaro
**VP:* Gerald Lehrke
Genl Mgr: Myron Crowell
Mtls Mgr: Jason Leuthold

D-U-N-S 05-057-3450
MARION LEIGH CORP (NJ)
MARION SECURITY AGENCY
52 N Bridge Ave, Red Bank, NJ 07701-1013
Tel (732) 530-7133 *Founded/Ownrshp* 1982
Sales 6.0MM *EMP* 350
SIC 7381 Protective services, guard; Protective services, guard
CEO: Marion L Phillips
**Pr:* Robert B Phillips Jr
VP: Anthony Frusco

MARION MANOR
See LEVERING MANAGEMENT INC

D-U-N-S 00-614-0347
MARION PLYWOOD CORP
222 S Parkview Ave, Marion, WI 54950-9698
Tel (715) 754-5231 *Founded/Ownrshp* 1894
Sales 57.6MM^E *EMP* 450
SIC 2435 2426 Plywood, hardwood or hardwood faced; Veneer stock, hardwood; Hardwood dimension & flooring mills; Plywood, hardwood or hardwood faced; Veneer stock, hardwood; Hardwood dimension & flooring mills
Pr: Peter T Rogers
COO: Dave Williams
Prd Mgr: Doug Wendt
Sls Mgr: Mike Burkart

MARION SCHOOL DISTRICT
See MARION BOARD OF EDUCATION INC

D-U-N-S 96-336-5742
MARION SCHOOL DISTRICT
200 Manor St, Marion, AR 72364-1936
Tel (870) 739-5100 *Founded/Ownrshp* 2010
Sales 15.3MM^E *EMP* 307^E
SIC 8211 Elementary & secondary schools
Prin: Jan Thomas

D-U-N-S 07-799-9654
MARION SCHOOL DISTRICT 2
MULLINS HIGH SCHOOL
719 N Main St, Marion, SC 29571-2517
Tel (843) 423-1811 *Founded/Ownrshp* 1899
Sales 16.2MM^E *EMP* 338
Accts Kenneth Cobb & Company Pc
SIC 8211 Public elementary & secondary schools; Public elementary & secondary schools

MARION SECURITY AGENCY
See MARION LEIGH CORP

D-U-N-S 04-081-5821
MARION TECHNICAL COLLEGE
1467 Mount Vernon Ave, Marion, OH 43302-5694
Tel (740) 389-4636 *Founded/Ownrshp* 1970
Sales 29.0MM^E *EMP* 195
Accts Balestra Harr & Scherer Cpas
SIC 8222 Technical institute; Technical institute
Pr: J Richard Bryson
COO: Tami Galloway
VP: Dennis Budkowski
DP Exec: Vicky Wood
IT Man: Joanna Duvall
Sls&Mrk Ex: Nikki Workman

D-U-N-S 12-915-5144
■ MARION WEST COMMUNITY HOSPITAL
OCALA REGIONAL MEDICAL CENTER
(*Suby of* HCA INC) ★
4600 Sw 46th Ct, Ocala, FL 34474-5783
Tel (352) 291-3000 *Founded/Ownrshp* 2002
Sales 91.9MM^E *EMP* 1,200
SIC 8062 General medical & surgical hospitals; General medical & surgical hospitals
CEO: Garry Karsner
**CEO:* Rex Etheredge
Snr Mgr: Scott Hankinson

D-U-N-S 00-341-6534 IMP
MARIOTTI BUILDING PRODUCTS INC (PA)
1 Louis Industrial Dr, Old Forge, PA 18518-2058
Tel (570) 344-0443 *Founded/Ownrshp* 1931, 1963
Sales 73.0MM^E *EMP* 82
SIC 5031 5932 Building materials, exterior; Building materials, secondhand
Pr: Eugene L Mariotti
**Treas:* Louis C Mariotti IV
**VP:* Robert A Mariotti
IT Man: Chris Mariotti
Opers Mgr: Francis Pupa
Mktg Dir: Leigh Williams
Sls Mgr: Mike Mariotti

D-U-N-S 62-719-6140
MARIPOSA COMMUNITY HEALTH CENTER INC
1852 N Mastick Way, Nogales, AZ 85621-1061
Tel (520) 377-9410 *Founded/Ownrshp* 1980
Sales 20.0MM *EMP* 125
SIC 8011 8322 Medical centers; Individual & family services; Medical centers; Individual & family services
Pr: Judith Claremon
**Treas:* Robert Lieiro
**VP:* Sigrid Maitrejean
Off Mgr: Clare Shannon
Doctor: Michael D Kedansky MD
Doctor: Victor J Weavermd MD
Pharmcst: Carol Knickerson

MARIPOSA HORTICULTURAL ENTPS
See MARIPOSA LANDSCAPES INC

D-U-N-S 07-964-1763
MARIPOSA INTERMEDIATE HOLDINGS LLC
(*Suby of* NEIMAN MARCUS GROUP INC) ★
1618 Main St, Dallas, TX 75201-4720
Tel (214) 743-7600 *Founded/Ownrshp* 2013
Sales 5.1MMM^E *EMP* 16,500^E
SIC 5311 Department stores

D-U-N-S 11-281-2896
MARIPOSA LANDSCAPES INC
MARIPOSA HORTICULTURAL ENTPS
15529 Arrow Hwy, Irwindale, CA 91706-2002
Tel (623) 463-2200 *Founded/Ownrshp* 1986
Sales 43.1MM^E *EMP* 250^E
SIC 0782 Garden maintenance services; Lawn care services; Landscape contractors; Garden maintenance services; Lawn care services; Landscape contractors
Pr: Terry Noriega
VP: Larry Rudd
**VP:* Antonio Valenzuela
**Genl Mgr:* Ren Flugel

D-U-N-S 94-042-6120
MARIS GROVE INC
100 Maris Grove Way, Glen Mills, PA 19342-1282
Tel (610) 459-1090 *Founded/Ownrshp* 2005
Sales 66.5MM *EMP* 350
Accts Mcgladrey Llp Baltimore Md
SIC 8051 6513 Skilled nursing care facilities; Apartment building operators; Skilled nursing care facilities; Apartment building operators
CFO: Randall Cox

D-U-N-S 61-643-2902
MARISA INDUSTRIES INC
1426 Pacific Dr, Auburn Hills, MI 48326-1571
Tel (248) 475-9600 *Founded/Ownrshp* 1989
Sales 36.7MM^E *EMP* 270
SIC 8711 7373 Engineering services; Computer integrated systems design; Engineering services; Computer integrated systems design
Pr: Jesse Lopez
Ex VP: Dutch Jones
**VP:* Stephen Bruck
VP: Mark Doetsch
Sys Mgr: Mary Bonnell

D-U-N-S 87-464-4719 IMP
MARISCOS BAHIA INC
MARISCOS BAHIA SEAFOOD
8300 Rex Rd, Pico Rivera, CA 90660-3719
Tel (323) 771-8412 *Founded/Ownrshp* 1994
Sales 50.0MM *EMP* 37
SIC 5146 Seafoods
CEO: Hector M Canino Jr
**VP:* Rebecca Z Canino
**VP:* Tony Vega

MARISCOS BAHIA SEAFOOD
See MARISCOS BAHIA INC

D-U-N-S 07-049-1568
MARIST BROTHERS OF NEWYORK INC
MARIST HIGH SCHL KUNIOTO JAPAN
26 First Ave, Pelham, NY 10803-1452
Tel (914) 738-1218 *Founded/Ownrshp* 1942
Sales 20.1MM^E *EMP* 330
SIC 8661 Monastery; Monastery
Pr: Donnell Neary

D-U-N-S 02-067-1178
MARIST COLLEGE
3399 North Rd, Poughkeepsie, NY 12601-1387
Tel (845) 575-3000 *Founded/Ownrshp* 1929
Sales 228.9MM *EMP* 1,300
Accts Grant Thornton Llp New York
SIC 8221 College, except junior; College, except junior
Pr: Dennis J Murray
**CFO:* John Pecchia
Ex VP: Jeffrey Brackett
Ex VP: Roy Merolli
VP: Artin Arslanian
**VP:* Geoffrey L Brackett
VP: Deborah Dicaprio
VP: Deborah Raikes-Colbert
VP: Robert L West
Assoc Dir: Chris Doyle
Assoc Dir: Bobbie Tellitocci

MARIST HIGH SCHL KUNIOTO JAPAN
See MARIST BROTHERS OF NEWYORK INC

D-U-N-S 06-620-5642
MARIST HIGH SCHOOL
(*Suby of* MARIST BROTHERS OF NEWYORK INC) ★
4200 W 115th St, Chicago, IL 60655-4397
Tel (773) 881-5300 *Founded/Ownrshp* 1963
Sales 20.1MM^E *EMP* 1^E
SIC 8211 Private elementary & secondary schools
Pr: Brother Rich Kerry
Off Mgr: Eve Gambla
Dir IT: Ronald Varriale

D-U-N-S 07-812-2413
MARIST SCHOOL INC
3790 Ashford Dnwody Rd Ne, Brookhaven, GA 30319-1899
Tel (770) 457-7201 *Founded/Ownrshp* 1897
Sales 24.1MM^E *EMP* 180
Accts Bdo Seidman Llp Atlanta Geo
SIC 8211 Private senior high school; Private senior high school
Pr: John H Harhager
**VP:* Susan Hansen

D-U-N-S 01-298-8175
MARITECH WINDOWS LLC (TX)
1813 Kelly Blvd, Carrollton, TX 75006-5511
Tel (469) 568-5636 *Founded/Ownrshp* 2007
Sales NA *EMP* 320
SIC 3442

D-U-N-S 92-842-1726
■ **MARITIME ADMINISTRATION**
(*Suby of* US DEPARTMENT OF TRANSPORTATION) ★
1200 New Jersey Ave Se, Washington, DC 20590-0001
Tel (202) 366-4141 *Founded/Ownrshp* 1950
Sales NA *EMP* 900
SIC 9621 Regulation, administration of transportation; ; Regulation, administration of transportation;
Ofcr: Gene Simmons
Ofcr: Lorraine Wakeman
**Prin:* David T Matsuda
Ex Dir: Joel Szabat
CIO: Donna K Seymour
IT Man: Tim Cogan
IT Man: Deveeda Midgette
Snr Mgr: Dale Vandagriff

D-U-N-S 15-406-9827
MARITIME ASSOCIATION I L A PENSION
11550 Fuqua St Ste 425, Houston, TX 77034-4306
Tel (281) 484-4343 *Founded/Ownrshp* 1956
Sales NA *EMP* 14
SIC 6411 Insurance agents; Insurance agents

D-U-N-S 92-715-9459 IMP
MARITIME CONTAINER SERVICES INC
10400 Nw 95th Ave, Medley, FL 33178-1300
Tel (305) 885-1288 *Founded/Ownrshp* 1996
Sales 15.9MM^E *EMP* 500
SIC 4789 Pipeline terminal facilities, independently operated
Pr: Doris B Buzaglo

D-U-N-S 09-773-9627
MARITIME ENERGY
MARITIME FARMS AT WALDOBORO
234 Park St, Rockland, ME 04841-2126
Tel (207) 594-4487 *Founded/Ownrshp* 1977
Sales 26.7MM^E *EMP* 110
SIC 5983 5171 5411 Fuel oil dealers; Petroleum bulk stations; Convenience stores, independent; Fuel oil dealers; Petroleum bulk stations; Convenience stores, independent
Pr: John Ware
VP: Susan Page
**VP:* Susan Ware
Sfty Dirs: Jeff Marcotte
Sls Mgr: Rit Roberts

D-U-N-S 02-007-0496
MARITIME EXCHANGE FOR DELAWARE RIVER & BAY (PA)
240 Cherry St, Philadelphia, PA 19106-1906
Tel (215) 925-2615 *Founded/Ownrshp* 1875
Sales 23.0MM *EMP* 15
Accts Bee Bergvall & Co Pc Warringt
SIC 8611 Shipping & steamship company association
Pr: Rochford Dennis
**Ch Bd:* Richard De Gennaro
**Pr:* Dennis Rockford
**Treas:* Dorothy Mather Ix
**VP:* Lisa Himber

MARITIME FARMS AT WALDOBORO
See MARITIME ENERGY

MARITIME GENERAL AGENCY
See GOWRIE GROUP INSURANCE

D-U-N-S 60-099-5364
MARITIME MANAGEMENT SERVICES
MMS
21400 Intl Blvd Ste 302, Seatac, WA 98198-6086
Tel (206) 824-8500 *Founded/Ownrshp* 2005
Sales 34.8MM *EMP* 125
SIC 8741 Management services; Management services
Pr: Trevor Stabbert
VP Opers: Blake Peevey

D-U-N-S 17-420-1277
■ **MARITRANS OPERATING CO LP**
(*Suby of* OVERSEAS SHIPHOLDING GROUP INC) ★
2 Harbour Pl 302, Tampa, FL 33602
Tel (813) 209-0600 *Founded/Ownrshp* 2007
Sales 31.1MM^E *EMP* 453
SIC 4424 Deep sea domestic transportation of freight; Deep sea domestic transportation of freight
CEO: Robert E Johnston
Pt: John J Burns
CFO: Walter T Bromfield
VP: Christopher J Flanagan
VP: Matthew J Yacavone
Rgnl Mgr: Jose Parra

D-U-N-S 00-696-7921
MARITZ HOLDINGS INC (MO)
1375 N Highway Dr, Fenton, MO 63099-0001
Tel (636) 827-4000 *Founded/Ownrshp* 1923
Sales 1.2MMM *EMP* 2,955
Accts Kpmg Llp St Louis Mo
SIC 4725 8748 8732 4899 Arrangement of travel tour packages, wholesale; Employee programs administration; Market analysis or research; Data communication services; Arrangement of travel tour packages, wholesale; Employee programs administration; Market analysis or research; Data communication services
CEO: W Stephen Maritz
**Pr:* John McArthur
Pr: Lisa Weaner
**CFO:* James W Kienker
Bd of Dir: Ron Zika
Sr VP: Gil Hoffman
**Sr VP:* Richard T Ramos
**Sr VP:* John Risberg
VP: Kathleen Bibbins
VP: Carlos Dunlap
VP: Richard Zeller
Creative D: Mike Cheaure
Creative D: Jeff Gasiorowski
Dir Bus: Jennifer Passini

D-U-N-S 82-914-3192
MARITZ LLC
(*Suby of* MARITZ HOLDINGS INC) ★
1375 N Highway Dr, Fenton, MO 63099-0001
Tel (636) 827-4000 *Founded/Ownrshp* 2008
Sales 57.6MM^E *EMP* 2,500
SIC 4725 8748 8732 4899 Arrangement of travel tour packages, wholesale; Employee programs administration; Market analysis or research; Data communication services; Arrangement of travel tour packages, wholesale; Employee programs administration; Market analysis or research; Data communication services

D-U-N-S 05-397-6585
MARITZ TRAVEL CO
(*Suby of* MARITZ HOLDINGS INC) ★
1375 N Highway Dr, Fenton, MO 63099-0001
Tel (636) 827-4000 *Founded/Ownrshp* 1955
Sales 180.9MM^E *EMP* 1,363
SIC 4724 Travel agencies; Travel agencies
CEO: Steve Maritz
**Pr:* Christine Duffy
COO: Dennis Hummel
COO: Rich Phillips
**CFO:* Rich Ramos
VP: Joseph Bradley
VP: Alfredo Legorreta
VP: Rhea Stagner
VP: Pradeep Tewani
**Exec:* John Risberg
Prgrm Mgr: Paula Keeven
Board of Directors: Christie Hicks

D-U-N-S 07-963-7115
MARITZCX HOLDINGS LLC
10235 S Jordan Gtwy Fl 5, South Jordan, UT 84095-4197
Tel (385) 695-2800 *Founded/Ownrshp* 2014
Sales 207.7MM^E *EMP* 2,000
SIC 8742 6719 Management consulting services; Investment holding companies, except banks
CEO: Carine Clark
Sr VP: Chad Latimer
VP: Justin Thompson

D-U-N-S 06-852-5286
MARITZCX RESEARCH LLC
(*Suby of* MARITZ HOLDINGS INC) ★
1355 N Highway Dr, Fenton, MO 63026-1935
Tel (636) 827-4000 *Founded/Ownrshp* 1974
Sales 78.7MM^E *EMP* 700
SIC 8732 Market analysis or research; Market analysis or research
Pr: Michael Brereton
Genl Pt: Anna Schmitt
**COO:* Gary Eversole
Treas: Richard T Ramos
Div VP: Karan Schmiderer
Ex VP: John Risberg
**Ex VP:* Jim Stone
VP: Jeanne Baker
VP: Randal D Brandt
VP: David Estes
VP: John Farley
VP: Dennis Hummel
**VP:* Eric Levy
VP: Mindy McGrath
VP: David Mulkey
VP: Paula Schapp
Creative D: Tom Scheve

D-U-N-S 15-693-9969 EXP
MARJAC HOLDINGS LLC
1020 Aviation Blvd, Gainesville, GA 30501-6839
Tel (770) 531-5000 *Founded/Ownrshp* 1996
Sales 314.2MM^E *EMP* 1,200^E
Accts Moore Stephens Frost Little R
SIC 2015 Chicken slaughtering & processing; Chicken slaughtering & processing

MARJAM SUPPLY COMPANY
See MARJAM SUPPLY CO INC

D-U-N-S 09-577-3107 IMP/EXP
MARJAM SUPPLY CO INC
MARJAM SUPPLY COMPANY
885 Conklin St, Farmingdale, NY 11735-2400
Tel (631) 249-4900 *Founded/Ownrshp* 1979
Sales 386.3MM *EMP* 614
SIC 5211 5031 Lumber & other building materials; Building materials, interior; Lumber & other building materials; Building materials, interior
Pr: Mark Buller
**VP:* James Buller
Mng Dir: Donald Poat
Area Mgr: Joel King
Brnch Mgr: Heather Jenkins
Brnch Mgr: Aaron Mansbach
Brnch Mgr: Edwin Nieves
Brnch Mgr: Mike Sand
Brnch Mgr: Sam Singleton
Genl Mgr: Leo Giovanni
CTO: Lou Ferraro

D-U-N-S 01-290-6699
MARK & SON METAL PRODUCTS INC
333 Railroad Ave, Bedford Hills, NY 10507-1404
Tel (914) 666-6496 *Founded/Ownrshp* 1983
Sales 25.7MM^E *EMP* 50
SIC 5051 Structural shapes, iron or steel
Pr: Jeffrey Herman
**VP:* Henry Marfe

D-U-N-S 93-142-3461
MARK 1 RESTORATION CO
1021 Maryland Ave, Dolton, IL 60419-2225
Tel (708) 849-8246 *Founded/Ownrshp* 1994
Sales 23.6MM *EMP* 30
SIC 1542 Commercial & office buildings, renovation & repair; Commercial & office buildings, renovation & repair
Pr: Mark A Snedden
VP: Lee Maniatis

D-U-N-S 05-125-1379
MARK 1 RESTORATION SERVICE INC
109 Lafayette St, Riverside, NJ 08075-3104
Tel (856) 764-9700 *Founded/Ownrshp* 1980
Sales 46.4MM^E *EMP* 150
SIC 1521 1542 1721 Repairing fire damage, single-family houses; Commercial & office buildings, renovation & repair; Residential painting; Repairing fire damage, single-family houses; Commercial & office buildings, renovation & repair; Residential painting
Pr: Mark J Schultz
**Sec:* Fred Schultz

MARK A FALCON GEN BLDG CONTR
See FALCON CONSTRUCTION CO

D-U-N-S 13-072-9668
MARK ANDERSON AND ASSOCIATES INC
VETERINARY CONCEPTS
303 Mc Kay Ave, Spring Valley, WI 54767
Tel (715) 778-5822 *Founded/Ownrshp* 1980
Sales 35.6MM^E *EMP* 105
SIC 5113 5047 Industrial & personal service paper; Containers, paper & disposable plastic; Veterinarians' equipment & supplies; Industrial & personal service paper; Containers, paper & disposable plastic; Veterinarians' equipment & supplies
Pr: Mark L Anderson Dvm
Pr: Sharon Bendenburg
**VP:* Carol Anderson

MARK ARCHITECTRUAL LIGHTING
See MARK LIGHTING FIXTURE CO INC

D-U-N-S 04-287-0501 IMP
MARK C POPE ASSOCIATES INC (GA)
4910 Martin Ct Se, Smyrna, GA 30082-4938
Tel (770) 435-2471 *Founded/Ownrshp* 1950, 1963
Sales 20.6MM^E *EMP* 56
SIC 5063 5013 5084

D-U-N-S 11-069-0430
MARK CERRONE INC
2368 Maryland Ave, Niagara Falls, NY 14305-1718
Tel (716) 282-5244 *Founded/Ownrshp* 1999
Sales 76.2MM *EMP* 150
Accts Bonadio & Co Llp Amherst N
SIC 1542 Nonresidential construction; Nonresidential construction
CEO: Mark Cerrone
**Pr:* Stephanie Churakos
**VP:* Vincent Cerrone
**VP:* George Churakos

D-U-N-S 04-180-3487
MARK CHEVROLET INC
WAYNE MITSUBISHI
33200 Michigan Ave, Wayne, MI 48184-1876
Tel (734) 722-9100 *Founded/Ownrshp* 1987
Sales 24.5MM^E *EMP* 50
SIC 5511 Automobiles, new & used
Pr: Charles Cabana
**Sec:* Kelly Callop
Store Mgr: Dennis Trygg
Store Mgr: Jeremy Wilds

D-U-N-S 04-433-6741
MARK CHRISTOPHER CHEVROLET INC (DE)
MARK CHRISTOPHER HUMMER
2131 E Convention Ctr Way, Ontario, CA 91764-4495
Tel (909) 390-2900 *Founded/Ownrshp* 1986
Sales 82.6MM^E *EMP* 185^E
SIC 5511 5521 3714 Automobiles, new & used; Pickups, new & used; Used car dealers; Motor vehicle parts & accessories; Automobiles, new & used; Pickups, new & used; Used car dealers; Motor vehicle parts & accessories
CEO: Chris Leggio
COO: Greg Heath
**Sec:* Loretta Holtz
**VP:* Shirley Leggid
Off Mgr: Jeanette Rexford
Sls Mgr: Mike Cagey
Sls Mgr: Vince Catalano
Sls Mgr: Osama Fakhoury
Sls Mgr: Karl Scheiffele

MARK CHRISTOPHER HUMMER
See MARK CHRISTOPHER CHEVROLET INC

MARK COMPANY
See SANTA ANA CREEK DEVELOPMENT CO

D-U-N-S 10-754-4207
MARK DIVERSIFIED INC
650 Howe Ave Ste 1045, Sacramento, CA 95825-4700
Tel (916) 923-6275 *Founded/Ownrshp* 1983
Sales 30.0MM *EMP* 50
SIC 1542 1541 Commercial & office building, new construction; Industrial buildings, new construction; Commercial & office building, new construction; Industrial buildings, new construction
Pr: David Mark
**Ofcr:* Cecil J Mark

D-U-N-S 05-967-7968
MARK DODGE CHRYSLER JEEP LLC
(*Suby of* ROUNDTREE AUTOMOTIVE GROUP LLC) ★
3777 Gerstner Mem Blvd, Lake Charles, LA 70607-3235
Tel (337) 474-2640 *Founded/Ownrshp* 2000
Sales 25.1MM^E *EMP* 60
SIC 5511 Automobiles, new & used; Automobiles, new & used
Pr: Mark E Boniol
Sales Exec: Marsh Buice
Sls Mgr: Aaron Ginsburgh
Sls Mgr: Joseph Weber

D-U-N-S 04-679-8179 IMP
MARK DRI PRODUCTS INC
15 Harbor Park Dr, Port Washington, NY 11050-4604
Tel (516) 484-6200 *Founded/Ownrshp* 1958
Sales 26.8MM^E *EMP* 200
SIC 3951 5112 Markers, soft tip (felt, fabric, plastic, etc.); Pens &/or pencils; Markers, soft tip (felt, fabric, plastic, etc.); Pens &/or pencils
Pr: Andre Reichmann
**CEO:* Charles Reichmann
COO: Lynn Paugh

D-U-N-S 04-682-0197
MARK DUNNING INDUSTRIES
MDI
100 Race Track Rd, Dothan, AL 36303-0911
Tel (334) 983-1506 *Founded/Ownrshp* 1980
Sales 145.7MM^E *EMP* 250
SIC 4953 Garbage: collecting, destroying & processing; Garbage: collecting, destroying & processing
Pr: J Mark Dunning

MARK ECKO ENTERPRISES
See MEE ACCESSORIES LLC

D-U-N-S 12-719-8062
MARK ENTERPRISES CAR CO II LLC
ALLSTATE
6910 E Mcdowell Rd, Scottsdale, AZ 85257-3206
Tel (480) 425-5300 *Founded/Ownrshp* 1999
Sales 39.3MM^E *EMP* 80
SIC 5511 Automobiles, new & used; Automobiles, new & used
Exec: Steve Clark

D-U-N-S 18-756-3648
MARK FACEY & CO
225 N Main St Ste 500, Bristol, CT 06010-4997
Tel (860) 589-0221 *Founded/Ownrshp* 1986
Sales 53.5MM^E *EMP* 2,000
SIC 7389

MARK FISHER FOOTWEAR
See MARC FISHER LLC

D-U-N-S 12-092-7475 IMP/EXP
MARK FOODS INC
20 W 22nd St Ste 901, New York, NY 10010-5878
Tel (212) 255-6048 *Founded/Ownrshp* 2002
Sales 200.0MM *EMP* 10
SIC 5146 Seafoods; Seafoods
Pr: Barry Markman

D-U-N-S 00-767-5713
MARK G ANDERSON CONSULTANTS INC
730 11th St Nw Fl 4, Washington, DC 20001-4510
Tel (202) 942-3900 *Founded/Ownrshp* 1996
Sales 51.3MM *EMP* 111
Accts Cohn & Reznick Llp Tysons Vi
SIC 8741 Construction management; Construction management
Pr: Mark G Anderson
CFO: Matthew P Anderson
VP: James Kennedy
Dir IT: Susan Prahinski

D-U-N-S 05-332-4831
MARK GILBERT INC
MARK GILBERT MOTORS CARS
6520 Deerview Trl, Durham, NC 27712-9230
Tel (919) 309-9555 *Founded/Ownrshp* 1988
Sales 25.0MM *EMP* 3
SIC 5012 Automotive brokers; Automotive brokers
Pr: Mark R Gilbert

MARK GILBERT MOTORS CARS
See MARK GILBERT INC

D-U-N-S 09-577-4279
MARK GOLDEN MAINTENANCE LTD INC
420 Doughty Blvd Ste 4, Inwood, NY 11096-1356
Tel (516) 239-3400 *Founded/Ownrshp* 1979, 1986
Sales 19.1MM^E *EMP* 1,150
SIC 7349 5087 Cleaning service, industrial or commercial; Janitors' supplies; Cleaning service, industrial or commercial; Janitors' supplies
Pr: Robert Golden
**VP:* Mark Ashkinazy

D-U-N-S 00-449-7887 IMP
■ MARK GROUP INC
MARK GROUP OF NEW YORK
(*Suby of* MARK GROUP LIMITED)
2 Logan Sq Ste 1101, Philadelphia, PA 19103-2733
Tel (215) 334-5273 *Founded/Ownrshp* 2009
Sales 23.9MM^E *EMP* 140
SIC 1742 Plastering, drywall & insulation
CEO: Jeff Bartos
**COO:* Dave Hopkins
**CFO:* Linda Hart
Off Mgr: Monica Pires

MARK GROUP OF NEW YORK
See MARK GROUP INC

MARK HANCOCK DEVELOPMENT
See CAMELOT HOMES INC

D-U-N-S 06-069-7034
MARK III CONSTRUCTION INC
MARK III DVLPERS DSGN/BUILDERS
5101 Florin Perkins Rd, Sacramento, CA 95826-4817
Tel (916) 381-8080 *Founded/Ownrshp* 1975
Sales 51.2MM^E *EMP* 75
SIC 1731 1542 1711 General electrical contractor; Electronic controls installation; Commercial & office building, new construction; Plumbing contractors; Fire sprinkler system installation
CEO: Daniel Carlton
Pr: Jennifer O'Brien Cooley
Treas: Michael O'Brien
Mktg Mgr: Angela Tombolini

MARK III DVLPERS DSGN/BUILDERS
See MARK III CONSTRUCTION INC

D-U-N-S 02-662-2621
MARK III PLANT CONSTRUCTION LTD
1000 Highway 90 E, Sealy, TX 77474-9401
Tel (979) 885-4141 *Founded/Ownrshp* 2000
Sales 43.7MM^E *EMP* 150
SIC 1629

D-U-N-S 83-048-6473
MARK IV INVESCO LLC
501 Jhn Jms Adbn Pkwy 400, Amherst, NY 14228-1143
Tel (716) 689-4972 *Founded/Ownrshp* 1969
Sales NA *EMP* 766
SIC 3052

D-U-N-S 11-504-7268
MARK LAND ELECTRIC INC
7876 Deering Ave, Canoga Park, CA 91304-5005
Tel (818) 883-5110 *Founded/Ownrshp* 1981
Sales 28.8MM^E *EMP* 82^E
SIC 1731 Electrical work
CEO: Lloyd Saitman
**CFO:* John Bennet
CFO: John Bennett
**VP:* Stewart Franklin
VP: Rick Peters
Snr PM: James Richardson
Snr Mgr: Claudio Salinas

D-U-N-S 00-187-4825 IMP
■ MARK LIGHTING FIXTURE CO INC (NJ)
MARK ARCHITECTRUAL LIGHTING
(*Suby of* ACUITY BRANDS LIGHTING INC) ★
3 Kilmer Rd Ste 2, Edison, NJ 08817-2400
Tel (732) 985-8441 *Founded/Ownrshp* 1965, 2009
Sales 23.8MM^E *EMP* 100
SIC 3646 Commercial indusl & institutional electric lighting fixtures; Fluorescent lighting fixtures, commercial; Commercial indusl & institutional electric lighting fixtures; Fluorescent lighting fixtures, commercial
Pr: Scott Coppola
**VP:* Joseph Dibernardo
**Genl Mgr:* Christopher McQuillan

MARK LIPMAN DIV
See GUARDSMARK LLC

D-U-N-S 80-490-5644
MARK MELVIN DEVELOPMENT CO
MELVIN MARK
111 Sw Columbia St # 1380, Portland, OR 97201-5814
Tel (503) 223-4777 *Founded/Ownrshp* 1950
Sales 22.7MM^E *EMP* 60
SIC 6552 Land subdividers & developers, commercial
Ch Bd: Melvin Pete Mark
**Pr:* Jim Mark
**Pr:* Dan Petrusich
VP: Tom Becic
VP: Maria Duncan
VP: Tim Parker
**Exec:* Marian Mirsky
Mng Dir: David Schaffer
Mng Dir: Greg Wellington

D-U-N-S 07-879-4556
MARK MILLER HOLDINGS LLC
MARK MILLER TOYOTA DOWNTOWN
84 W 700 S, Salt Lake City, UT 84101-2731
Tel (801) 364-2100 *Founded/Ownrshp* 2005
Sales 23.5MM^E *EMP* 175
SIC 5511 Automobiles, new & used; Automobiles, new & used
Genl Mgr: Bill Niemann

D-U-N-S 61-145-1220
MARK MILLER INC
MILLER, MARK TOYOTA
730 S West Temple, Salt Lake City, UT 84101-2745
Tel (801) 364-2100 *Founded/Ownrshp* 1990
Sales 26.7MM^E *EMP* 72
SIC 5511 Automobiles, new & used; Automobiles, new & used
Pr: Mark Miller
**Sec:* Steve McIntyre
Sales Asso: Andrew Ross

D-U-N-S 17-363-7216
MARK MILLER SUBARU LLC
LARRY H MILLER TOYOTA
10920 S State St, Sandy, UT 84070-4101
Tel (801) 553-5200 *Founded/Ownrshp* 1986
Sales 59.0MM *EMP* 200
SIC 5511 5531 7515 Automobiles, new & used; Automotive accessories; Automotive parts; Passenger car leasing; Automobiles, new & used; Automotive accessories; Automotive parts; Passenger car leasing
Pr: Karen G Miller
**Pr:* Mark Miller
**Treas:* Gregory S Miller
**Sec:* Larry H Miller
Genl Mgr: Jeff Miller
Dir IT: Dave Austin
Netwrk Eng: Mike Harrelson

MARK MILLER TOYOTA DOWNTOWN
See MARK MILLER HOLDINGS LLC

MARK ONE CONSTRUCTION CO
See MARK ONE ELECTRIC CO INC

D-U-N-S 05-585-2982
MARK ONE CORP
517 Alpine Rd, Gaylord, MI 49735-9531
Tel (989) 732-2427 *Founded/Ownrshp* 1990
Sales 26.9MM^E *EMP* 100
SIC 3549 3569 3535 Assembly machines, including robotic; Lubricating equipment; Conveyors & conveying equipment
Pr: Francis J Kestler
**VP:* Keith Crandall
Pdt Mgr: Nick Seccia

D-U-N-S 00-716-8230
MARK ONE ELECTRIC CO INC (MO)
MARK ONE CONSTRUCTION CO
909 Troost Ave, Kansas City, MO 64106-3088
Tel (816) 842-7023 *Founded/Ownrshp* 1947, 1974
Sales 91.6MM^E *EMP* 200
SIC 1731 General electrical contractor; General electrical contractor
Pr: Rosana Privitera Biondo
Pr: April Ramirezwiedner
Ofcr: Chuck Aylward
VP: Vince Migliazzo
**VP:* Anthony L Privitera II
**VP:* Joseph A Privitera
**VP:* Josephine A Privitera
**VP:* Richard Sheldrake
Exec: Racheal Williams
Off Mgr: Stephen Sprouse
Sfty Dirs: Dave Ezell

D-U-N-S 14-784-3478 IMP/EXP
MARK POLLACK & ASSOCIATES INC
POLLACK ASSOCIATES
150 Varick St Fl 10, New York, NY 10013-1218
Tel (212) 627-7766 *Founded/Ownrshp* 1987
Sales 44.2MM^E *EMP* 60
SIC 5131 Textiles, woven
Pr: Richard M Sullivan
**VP:* Susan Doty Sullivan
VP Opers: Susan Whalen
Natl Sales: Gregg Boyd
Manager: Melissa Villa

D-U-N-S 07-542-8318 IMP
MARK RONALD ASSOCIATES INC
R M A
1227 Central Ave, Hillside, NJ 07205-2613
Tel (908) 558-0011 *Founded/Ownrshp* 1974
Sales 33.0MM^E *EMP* 90
SIC 3081 5162 Polyvinyl film & sheet; Plastics materials; Polyvinyl film & sheet; Plastics materials
Pr: Leslie J Satz
**VP:* Charles Riotto
**VP:* Ronald M Satz
Sfty Mgr: Al Leone
Sfty Mgr: Nick Sofer
Mktg Dir: Michael Rochefort

D-U-N-S 78-136-1720
MARK SCOTT CONSTRUCTION INC
M S
2835 Contra Costa Blvd, Pleasant Hill, CA 94523-4221
Tel (925) 944-0502 *Founded/Ownrshp* 1991
Sales 50.0MM^E *EMP* 150
SIC 1542 Commercial & office building, new construction; Commercial & office building, new construction
CEO: Mark A Scott
VP: Larry Clark
Opers Mgr: Tony Gasparini
Opers Mgr: Tony Gastarini

MARK SHALE
See AL BASKIN CO

D-U-N-S 04-283-5132 IMP
MARK STEEL CORP
1230 W 200 S, Salt Lake City, UT 84104-1898
Tel (801) 521-0670 *Founded/Ownrshp* 1968
Sales 44.4MM^E *EMP* 130
SIC 3443 3441 Fabricated plate work (boiler shop); Building components, structural steel; Fabricated plate work (boiler shop); Building components, structural steel
Pr: James R Vemich
**Ch Bd:* Bruce Markosian
**Sec:* Arline Markosian
Off Mgr: Mary Peterson
Dir IT: Jason Vandehei
IT Man: Lewis Housley
QC Dir: Bijit Zsiga
Site Mgr: Jeff Evans
Sfty Mgr: Scott Lehew
Sls Mgr: Jeff Eggleston
Sls Mgr: Les Griffith
Board of Directors: Arline Markosian

D-U-N-S 11-493-1533 IMP
MARK STEEL INTERNATIONAL LLC
21250 Hawthorne Blvd # 350, Torrance, CA 90503-5541
Tel (213) 623-8066 *Founded/Ownrshp* 2002
Sales 108.0MM^E *EMP* 7
SIC 5051 Steel; Steel

D-U-N-S 12-180-0924
MARK THOMAS FORD INC
3098 State Route 5, Cortland, OH 44410-9207
Tel (330) 638-1010 *Founded/Ownrshp* 1997
Sales 22.4MM^E *EMP* 45
SIC 5511 7538 7532 5521 Automobiles, new & used; General automotive repair shops; Top & body repair & paint shops; Used car dealers
Pr: Tom Levak
VP: Curtis Stantial
Off Mgr: Linda Helmuth
Off Mgr: Pat Sieg
Sls Mgr: Robert Mines
Sales Asso: Jason Banic
Sales Asso: Brad Huffman

D-U-N-S 10-828-7939
MARK TRAVEL CORP
FUNJET VACATIONS
8907 N Port Washington Rd, Milwaukee, WI 53217-1634
Tel (414) 228-7472 *Founded/Ownrshp* 1974
Sales 113.9MM^E *EMP* 1,000
SIC 4725 Arrangement of travel tour packages, wholesale; Arrangement of travel tour packages, wholesale
CEO: William E Lamacchia
COO: Kevin Froemming
**COO:* Thomas E Meier
**CFO:* William Lamacchia Jr
Ex VP: Bob Lacroix
Ex VP: Thomas Meier
Ex VP: David Wade
**VP:* Randi Becker
VP: Lynn Clark
VP: Barbie Groves
VP: John Hanratty
**VP:* Ron Jacobs
VP: Lisa Kosiski
**VP:* Sharon Lamacchia
VP: Howard McCalla
VP: Terry Morrison
Dir Bus: Tom Brussow
Dir Bus: Luba Djordjevic

D-U-N-S 78-558-8625
MARK TWAIN MEDICAL CENTER
MARK TWAIN ST JOSEPHS HOSPITAL
(*Suby of* C H W) ★
768 Mountain Ranch Rd, San Andreas, CA 95249-9707
Tel (209) 754-3521 *Founded/Ownrshp* 1991
Sales 56.0MM *EMP* 325
Accts Kpmg Llp San Francisco Ca
SIC 8062 General medical & surgical hospitals; General medical & surgical hospitals
CEO: Craig J Marks
Chf Path: Rick R Baier
Dir Recs: Ruth Huffman
Pr: Greg Jordan
COO: Jacob Lewis
CFO: Jacob Lews
Treas: Linda Lewis
VP: Anita Paque
Dir Lab: Barbara Bennett
Dir Rad: Lincoln D Ruin
Dir Rx: Anna Meehan
Dir Rx: Jill Ortiz

MARK TWAIN ST JOSEPHS HOSPITAL
See MARK TWAIN MEDICAL CENTER

D-U-N-S 01-063-5068 IMP/EXP
MARK VII EQUIPMENT INC
(*Suby of* WASHTEC AG)
5981 Tennyson St, Arvada, CO 80003-6904
Tel (303) 423-4910 *Founded/Ownrshp* 2006
Sales 48.0MM *EMP* 205
SIC 3589

D-U-N-S 15-359-8748
MARK VLLL LLC
4426 Lowman Rd, Smithville, MO 64089-8562
Tel (816) 532-6397 *Founded/Ownrshp* 1996
Sales 22.0MM *EMP* 22
SIC 8742 Hospital & health services consultant; Hospital & health services consultant

D-U-N-S 15-427-2033
MARK WRIGHT CONSTRUCTION INC
MWCI ROOFING
3326 N Winstel Blvd, Tucson, AZ 85716-1433
Tel (520) 323-7071 *Founded/Ownrshp* 1984
Sales 21.2MM^E *EMP* 125
SIC 1542 1521 1761 Commercial & office building contractors; New construction, single-family houses; Roofing contractor; Commercial & office building contractors; New construction, single-family houses; Roofing contractor
Pr: Mark Wright
**Sec:* Mary Lou Wright

D-U-N-S 36-435-6436
MARK YOUNG CONSTRUCTION INC
7200 Miller Pl, Frederick, CO 80504-6609
Tel (303) 776-1449 *Founded/Ownrshp* 1989
Sales 67.3MM *EMP* 127
SIC 1542 Commercial & office building, new construction; Commercial & office buildings, renovation & repair; Commercial & office building, new construction; Commercial & office buildings, renovation & repair
Pr: David Guida
**Prin:* Richard F Greenleaf
Prin: George F Sanderson

MARK-L CONSTRUCTION
See MARK-L INC

D-U-N-S 10-770-0213
MARK-L INC
MARK-L CONSTRUCTION
1180 Claycraft Rd, Gahanna, OH 43230-6640
Tel (614) 863-8832 *Founded/Ownrshp* 1981
Sales 27.6MM^E *EMP* 50
SIC 1542 Commercial & office building, new construction
Pr: Mark A Laivins Sr
**VP:* Tamara Laivins

D-U-N-S 04-639-4698
MARK-LINE INDUSTRIES INC
51687 County Road 133, Bristol, IN 46507-9800
Tel (574) 825-5851 *Founded/Ownrshp* 1968
Sales 24.0MM^E *EMP* 125^E
SIC 2451 Mobile buildings: for commercial use
Pr: L Michael Arnold
**Pr:* Michael L Arnold
**Pr:* John Catalino
COO: Brad Arnsdorf
**CFO:* Trace Cole
Dir IT: Dan Merrick
IT Man: Christine Kline
IT Man: Clay Schiavoni
Prd Mgr: Jay Breden
Sls Mgr: Jay Vanvlerah

D-U-N-S 00-308-6469
MARK/TRECE INC
2001 Stockton Rd, Joppa, MD 21085-1717
Tel (410) 879-0060 *Founded/Ownrshp* 1962
Sales 36.8MM^E *EMP* 200
SIC 3555 Printing plates; Printing plates
Ch Bd: Richard A Godfrey
V Ch: Donald G McCauhey

CFO: Donald G Mc Caughey Jr
**Treas:* Donald G McCaughey

D-U-N-S 06-764-8042 EXP
MARKA VIP INC
5435 E La Palma Ave, Anaheim, CA 92807-2022
Tel (714) 695-9010 *Founded/Ownrshp* 2010
Sales 36.7MM^E *EMP* 825
SIC 5961 7997 Catalog & mail-order houses; Membership sports & recreation clubs; Catalog & mail-order houses; Membership sports & recreation clubs
CEO: Ahmed Khatib
**VP:* Ahmad Naboulsi
Snr Mgr: Amer Abulaila

MARKAL COMPANY
See LA-CO INDUSTRIES INC

MARKANT OFFICE FURNITURE
See MARKANT USA INC

D-U-N-S 01-827-5367 IMP
MARKANT USA INC
MARKANT OFFICE FURNITURE
(*Suby of* MARKANT NEDERLAND B.V.)
3720 West River Dr Ne # 101, Comstock Park, MI 49321-8980
Tel (616) 281-5559 *Founded/Ownrshp* 2001
Sales 45.8MM^E *EMP* 170
SIC 5021 Office furniture; Office furniture
Pr: Remco Bergsma
Manager: Simone Kilgore

MARKAR & PEMKO PRODUCTS
See PEMKO MANUFACTURING CO

D-U-N-S 94-338-6987
■ **MARKEL AMERICAN INSURANCE CO**
(*Suby of* MARKEL CORP) ★
N14w23800 Stone Ridge Dr # 300, Waukesha, WI 53188-1144
Tel (262) 548-9880 *Founded/Ownrshp* 1986
Sales NA *EMP* 100^E
SIC 6411 Insurance agents, brokers & service; Insurance agents, brokers & service
Ch Bd: Alan I Kirshner
**Pr:* Timberlee T Grove
**Pr:* Audrey Hanken
**V Ch Bd:* Steven Markel
**VP:* John Dwyer

D-U-N-S 00-232-7740 IMP
MARKEL CORP (PA)
435 School Ln, Plymouth Meeting, PA 19462-2744
Tel (610) 272-4577 *Founded/Ownrshp* 1922
Sales 38.6MM^E *EMP* 150
SIC 3082 3357 3714 3496 3315 3083 Tubes, unsupported plastic; Nonferrous wiredrawing & insulating; Motor vehicle parts & accessories; Miscellaneous fabricated wire products; Steel wire & related products; Laminated plastics plate & sheet; Tubes, unsupported plastic; Nonferrous wiredrawing & insulating; Motor vehicle parts & accessories; Miscellaneous fabricated wire products; Steel wire & related products; Laminated plastics plate & sheet
Ch Bd: Warren G Mang
**Pr:* Kim Reynolds
**CFO:* James A Hoban
**VP:* Robert Jerman
**VP:* Charles Marino
**VP:* David Panish
Genl Mgr: Dee Hobin
Dir IT: Kevin Kray
IT Man: Carol Benedict
**VP Opers:* Darrell Sams
Plnt Mgr: Matthew Kelly

D-U-N-S 00-313-4582
▲ **MARKEL CORP**
4521 Highwoods Pkwy, Glen Allen, VA 23060-6148
Tel (804) 747-0136 *Founded/Ownrshp* 1930
Sales NA *EMP* 7,200^E
Accts Kpmg Llp Richmond Virginia
Tkr Sym MKL *Exch* NYS
SIC 6331 6211 Fire, marine & casualty insurance & carriers; Property damage insurance; Underwriters, security; Fire, marine & casualty insurance & carriers; Property damage insurance; Underwriters, security
Ch Bd: Alan I Kirshner
**V Ch:* Steven A Markel
Pr: F Michael Crowley
Pr: Thomas S Gayner
Pr: Britt Glisson
Pr: John K Latham
Pr: Matt Parker
Pr: Richard R Whitt III
CFO: Anne G Waleski
**V Ch Bd:* Anthony F Markel
Ofcr: Nick Conca
Assoc VP: Lauren Effron
Assoc VP: Jim Kocha
Assoc VP: Kathleen Olear
Ex VP: Gerard Albanese Jr
Ex VP: Bradley J Kiscaden
Ex VP: Whitt Richard
VP: Scott Delatorre
VP: Betty Goldstein
VP: Mike Kotlowski
Board of Directors: J Alfred Broaddus Jr, K Bruce Connell, Douglas C Eby, Stewart M Kasen, Lemuel E Lewis, Darrell D Martin, Michael O'reilly, Jay M Weinberg, Debora J Wilson

D-U-N-S 07-798-8798
■ **MARKEL CORP**
ASSOCIATED INTL INSUR CO
(*Suby of* MARKEL NORTH AMERICA INC) ★
21600 Oxnard St Ste 400, Woodland Hills, CA 91367-4800
Tel (818) 595-0600 *Founded/Ownrshp* 1999
Sales NA *EMP* 60
SIC 6411 Insurance agents, brokers & service; Insurance agents, brokers & service
Pr: Anthony Markel
**Ch Bd:* Alan Kirshner
**V Ch Bd:* Steven Markel
VP: Mollie Stone
VP: Robert Vlazer

D-U-N-S 80-489-1802
■ **MARKEL INSURANCE CO**
(*Suby of* MARKEL CORP) ★
4600 Cox Rd Ste 100, Glen Allen, VA 23060-6753
Tel (804) 527-2700 *Founded/Ownrshp* 1986
Sales NA *EMP* 251
SIC 6411 Insurance agents, brokers & service; Insurance agents, brokers & service
Pr: Britton L Glisson
VP: George D Faison Jr
VP: Emmett Morgan
VP: Mark Nichols
VP: Robin Russo
VP: Mary Allen Waller
VP: Thomas F Wisneski
Mktg Mgr: Linda Lee

D-U-N-S 62-162-5425
■ **MARKEL MIDWEST**
(*Suby of* MARKEL CORP) ★
10 Parkway N Ste 100, Deerfield, IL 60015-2526
Tel (847) 572-6000 *Founded/Ownrshp* 1978
Sales NA *EMP* 100
SIC 6351 Liability insurance
Ch: Steven A Markel
**Pr:* Anthony F Markel
Dir IT: Neal Davies

D-U-N-S 13-665-5342
■ **MARKEL NORTH AMERICA INC**
(*Suby of* MARKEL CORP) ★
4521 Highwoods Pkwy, Glen Allen, VA 23060-6148
Tel (804) 747-0136 *Founded/Ownrshp* 1999
Sales NA *EMP* 800
SIC 6351 Surety insurance; Surety insurance
Ch Bd: Alan I Kirshner
**Ex VP:* Paul Springman
VP: Britton L Glisson
VP: Brude A Kay

D-U-N-S 10-173-2030
■ **MARKEL SERVICE INC**
(*Suby of* MARKEL CORP) ★
4600 Cox Rd Ste 100, Glen Allen, VA 23060-6753
Tel (804) 747-0136 *Founded/Ownrshp* 1980
Sales NA *EMP* 197^E
SIC 6411 Insurance brokers; Insurance brokers
Pr: Anthony F Markel
**Ch Bd:* Alan I Kirshner
**V Ch Bd:* Steven A Markel
Sr VP: Karen Passey
**VP:* Bruce Kay

D-U-N-S 06-745-3159
■ **MARKEL SHAND INC**
SPECIALTY INSUR ORGANIZATION
(*Suby of* MARKEL MIDWEST) ★
10 Parkway N Ste 100, Deerfield, IL 60015-2526
Tel (847) 572-6000 *Founded/Ownrshp* 1988
Sales NA *EMP* 170
SIC 6351 6321 8742 Liability insurance; Accident & health insurance; Management consulting services; Liability insurance; Accident & health insurance; Management consulting services
Pr: Michael Rosenburg
Ch Bd: Paul Springman
Pr: Michael A Rosenberg
Sr VP: Edgar W Phoebus
VP: Joanne M Cichon
Mktg Dir: Leatha Heaton
Board of Directors: Steven A Markel

D-U-N-S 19-282-7269
■ **MARKEL UNDERWRITING MANAGERS INC**
(*Suby of* MARKEL CORP) ★
310 State Route 35, Red Bank, NJ 07701-5921
Tel (732) 224-0500 *Founded/Ownrshp* 1996
Sales NA *EMP* 130
SIC 6351 Liability insurance; Liability insurance
Pr: Glen E Curley
**VP:* Ray Steer
Mktg Mgr: Barb Lugher

D-U-N-S 83-264-8096
■ **MARKEL VENTURES INC**
(*Suby of* MARKEL CORP) ★
4521 Highwoods Pkwy, Glen Allen, VA 23060-6148
Tel (804) 747-0136 *Founded/Ownrshp* 2005
Sales 347.5MM^E *EMP* 503^E
SIC 8741 Business management; Business management
Pr: Thomas S Gayner
**Treas:* Anne G Waleski

D-U-N-S 00-108-5158 IMP
■ **MARKEM-IMAJE CORP** (NH)
(*Suby of* DOVER ENGINEERED SYSTEMS INC) ★
150 Congress St, Keene, NH 03431-4307
Tel (603) 352-1130 *Founded/Ownrshp* 1928, 2009
Sales 291.1MM^E *EMP* 2,800
SIC 2893

D-U-N-S 07-843-9785
MARKEN LLP
(*Suby of* MARKEN LIMITED)
4307 Emperor Blvd Ste 210, Durham, NC 27703-8328
Tel (919) 472-0403 *Founded/Ownrshp* 2011
Sales 21.5MM^E *EMP* 125
SIC 4731 Freight transportation arrangement; Freight transportation arrangement
CEO: Wes Wheeler
CFO: Allan Dullan
Ch: Robert Ellis
VP: Mark R Hembarsky
VP: Paul J Rice
CTO: Mickail Aclan
Mktg Mgr: Christine Noble
Genl Couns: Doaa Faphallah
Counsel: Ruth Bhakta

D-U-N-S 00-978-3127
MARKET & JOHNSON INC
2350 Galloway St, Eau Claire, WI 54703-3441
Tel (715) 834-1213 *Founded/Ownrshp* 1948
Sales 218.2MM *EMP* 250
Accts Wipfli Llp Eau Claire Wiscon
SIC 1542 1541 Hospital construction; School building construction; Institutional building construction; Industrial buildings, new construction; Hospital construction; School building construction; Institutional building construction; Industrial buildings, new construction
CEO: Dan Market

D-U-N-S 79-741-2236 IMP
MARKET AMERICA INC
(*Suby of* MARKET AMERICA WORLDWIDE INC) ★
1302 Pleasant Ridge Rd, Greensboro, NC 27409-9415
Tel (336) 605-0040 *Founded/Ownrshp* 2002
Sales 340.6MM^E *EMP* 650^E
SIC 5199 General merchandise, non-durable; General merchandise, non-durable
Pr: Ridinger
COO: Marc Ashley
CFO: Kevin Curley
Bd of Dir: Luzby Hernandez
Chf Mktg O: Peter Gold
Ex VP: Dennis Franks
Ex VP: Marty Weismann
Ex VP: Martin Weissman
Sr VP: Loren Ridinger
VP: Steve Ashley
VP: Shannon Kendrick
VP: Chris Peddycord
VP: Samantha Ritchie
Dir Soc: Jennifer Trudgeon
Creative D: William Treadwell

D-U-N-S 11-487-3388
MARKET AMERICA WORLDWIDE INC
1302 Pleasant Ridge Rd, Greensboro, NC 27409-9415
Tel (336) 605-0040 *Founded/Ownrshp* 2002
Sales 340.6MM^E *EMP* 730
Accts Dixon Hughes Goodman Llp High
SIC 5199 General merchandise, non-durable; General merchandise, non-durable
CEO: Ridinger
**Pr:* James H Ridinger
**COO:* Marc Ashley
**Ex VP:* Dennis Franks
**Ex VP:* Martin Weissman
**Sr VP:* Loren Ridinger
**VP:* Kevin Buckman

MARKET BASKET
See DEMOULAS SUPER MARKETS INC

MARKET BASKET
See RETAIL INVESTORS OF TEXAS MANAGEMENT LLC

D-U-N-S 01-188-2859
MARKET BASKET INC
813 Franklin Lakes Rd, Franklin Lakes, NJ 07417-2113
Tel (201) 891-2000 *Founded/Ownrshp* 1960
Sales 32.0MM *EMP* 400
SIC 5421 5431 5411 5812 Meat & fish markets; Fruit & vegetable markets; Delicatessens; Caterers; Meat & fish markets; Fruit & vegetable markets; Delicatessens; Caterers
Pr: Anthony Chernalis

D-U-N-S 07-201-1992
MARKET BASKET PRODUCE INC
(*Suby of* DEMOULAS SUPER MARKETS INC) ★
875 East St, Tewksbury, MA 01876-1495
Tel (978) 851-8000 *Founded/Ownrshp* 1973
Sales 561.1MM^E *EMP* 7,000
SIC 5411 Supermarkets, chain; Supermarkets, chain
Pr: A T Demoulas
**Treas:* Donald Mulligan
**Treas:* D H Sullivan

D-U-N-S 07-842-9180
MARKET BASKET STORES INC
(*Suby of* MARKET BASKET) ★
2420 Nederland Ave, Nederland, TX 77627-6048
Tel (409) 727-3104 *Founded/Ownrshp* 1975
Sales 197.2MM^E *EMP* 2,000
SIC 5411 Supermarkets; Supermarkets
CEO: Bruce C Thompson
**Pr:* Skylar Thompson
CFO: Thomas Cormier
Sr VP: Keith Dauterive
**VP:* Alletta Thompson
CTO: Danny Wallace
Dir IT: Jed Watts

D-U-N-S 09-129-9537
MARKET CONTRACTORS LTD (OR)
SORBELLA PRACTICE BUILDERS
10250 Ne Marx St, Portland, OR 97220-1152
Tel (503) 517-6735 *Founded/Ownrshp* 1977
Sales 55.3MM^E *EMP* 125
Accts Sherman Young & Associates P
SIC 1542 5712 Commercial & office building, new construction; Commercial & office buildings, renovation & repair; Cabinet work, custom; Commercial & office building, new construction; Commercial & office buildings, renovation & repair; Cabinet work, custom
Ch: John Boden
**Pr:* Steve F Sorensen
COO: Steve Sorensen
**CFO:* Michelle Hughes
**VP:* Steve Torrensen
Creative D: Greg Gray
Prgrm Mgr: Jennifer Barker
Prgrm Mgr: Melanie Bloom
Dept Mgr: Judy Hanson

D-U-N-S 10-319-0351 EXP
MARKET DAY LLC
(*Suby of* GORDON FOOD SERVICE INC) ★
1300 Gezon Pkwy Sw, Wyoming, MI 49509-9300
Tel (630) 285-1470 *Founded/Ownrshp* 2013
Sales 338.3MM^E *EMP* 1,300
SIC 5141 Food brokers; Food brokers
Pr: Kristine Holtz
CFO: Mary Larson
Ex VP: William S Sivak
Software D: Bill Raymond
Ql Cn Mgr: Rick Hill
Mktg Dir: Margie Roman

D-U-N-S 09-625-3075
MARKET DECISIONS CORP (OR)
M D C RESEARCH
8959 Sw Barbur Blvd # 204, Portland, OR 97219-4024
Tel (503) 245-4479 *Founded/Ownrshp* 1978
Sales 29.8MM^E *EMP* 250
SIC 8732 Market analysis or research; Market analysis or research
Pr: Michael Oilar
**COO:* Douglas Verigin
CFO: Sue Christensen
IT Man: Todd Richardson
VP Mktg: David Deleon
Mktg Dir: Alice Blackwell

MARKET DISTRIBUTORS
See MARKET MEATS INC

D-U-N-S 01-334-9589
MARKET DYNAMICS GROUP LLC
FOOD DYNAMICS
130 Lizotte Dr, Marlborough, MA 01752-3080
Tel (508) 650-5353 *Founded/Ownrshp* 1999
Sales 20.8MM^E *EMP* 115
SIC 5141 Food brokers; Food brokers

MARKET EXPRESS
See B MART

D-U-N-S 11-588-1328
MARKET FINANCIAL GROUP LTD
240 Commerce Dr Ste F, Crystal Lake, IL 60014-3549
Tel (815) 459-3300 *Founded/Ownrshp* 2008
Sales NA *EMP* 55
SIC 6411 Insurance agents
CEO: Rich Waters
**COO:* Frank Barbella
Ex VP: Ryan Light
Exec: George Boehm
Dir IT: Eric Koskie
Mktg Dir: Molly Donohue
Mktg Dir: Joan Soboleski

D-U-N-S 36-368-0906
MARKET FORCE INFORMATION INC
371 Centennial Pkwy # 210, Louisville, CO 80027-1348
Tel (303) 402-6920 *Founded/Ownrshp* 2005
Sales 73.9MM^E *EMP* 510
SIC 8732 Market analysis or research; Market analysis or research
CEO: Ray Walsh
COO: Mike Dzura
**CFO:* Joe Correia
Bd of Dir: Paul Berberian
**Ofcr:* Cheryl Flink PHD
**Ofcr:* Matt Nydell
VP: Ritter Gaylord
VP: Bernard Lefang
VP: Bret McInnis
Mng Ofcr: Paul Ironside
Mng Dir: Bradley Christian

MARKET FRESH OF LANSING
See P & W FOODS OF LANSING INC

D-U-N-S 00-348-5083
MARKET GROCERY CO (GA)
MODERN GROCERY
16 Forest Pkwy Bldg K1, Forest Park, GA 30297-2099
Tel (404) 361-7340 *Founded/Ownrshp* 1938, 1988
Sales 51.0MM *EMP* 75
SIC 5141 5194 5147 5145 5131 5122 Groceries, general line; Tobacco & tobacco products; Meats, fresh; Candy; Notions; Patent medicines; Groceries, general line; Tobacco & tobacco products; Meats, fresh; Candy; Notions; Patent medicines
CEO: Don A Barnette
Genl Mgr: Bob Barnette
Dir IT: Wayne Amos

MARKET HALL FOODS
See PASTA SHOP

D-U-N-S 05-628-0576
MARKET INDUSTRIES LTD
(*Suby of* UTI (US) HOLDINGS INC) ★
110 N Marine Dr, Portland, OR 97217-8030
Tel (503) 283-2405 *Founded/Ownrshp* 2006
Sales 130.0MM^E *EMP* 183^E
SIC 4731 4213 Brokers, shipping; Contract haulers
Pr: Gary Wilson
**Pr:* Garry Wilson

D-U-N-S 11-390-9159
MARKET LEADER INC
110 110th Ave Ne Ste 700, Bellevue, WA 98004-5867
Tel (425) 952-5464 *Founded/Ownrshp* 2013
Sales 32.4MM^E *EMP* 278^E
SIC 7311 6531 Advertising consultant; Real estate agents & managers

D-U-N-S 80-677-2216
MARKET LINK INC
(*Suby of* ALLIED GLOBAL LLC) ★
3600 Army Post Rd, Des Moines, IA 50321-2906
Tel (515) 285-3420 *Founded/Ownrshp* 2013
Sales 25.7MM^E *EMP* 300
SIC 7389 Telemarketing services; Telemarketing services
CEO: Kourtney Keough
**Pr:* Courtney Keough
Sr VP: Bob Beaman
**VP:* Chuck Berger
IT Man: Josh Brainard

MARKET LOGISTICS
See MARKET TRANSPORT LTD

D-U-N-S 07-991-4198
MARKET MEATS INC
MARKET DISTRIBUTORS
355 Food Center Dr Ste A6, Bronx, NY 10474-7577
Tel (718) 991-5800 *Founded/Ownrshp* 1983
Sales 20.2MM^E *EMP* 50
SIC 5147 5144 5142 Meats, fresh; Poultry & poultry products; Meat, frozen: packaged; Poultry, frozen: packaged
Pr: Howard Saltiel
Off Mgr: Seth Fleisher

D-U-N-S 09-006-7435
MARKET MERCHANDISERS INC (KS)
12302 Johnson Dr, Shawnee, KS 66216-1912
Tel (913) 281-9992 *Founded/Ownrshp* 1997
Sales 31.0MM *EMP* 10
SIC 5141 Food brokers; Food brokers
Pr: Mark W Croft

D-U-N-S 09-625-1343
MARKET OF CHOICE INC (OR)
PRICE CHOPPER
2580 Willakenzie Rd, Eugene, OR 97401-4805
Tel (541) 345-3349 *Founded/Ownrshp* 1978
Sales 119.5MM^E *EMP* 700
SIC 5411 Supermarkets, independent; Supermarkets, independent
Pr: Richard L Wright Jr
**CFO:* Lawrence Brody
Exec: Marcus Whittaker
Genl Mgr: Heinz Beierling

MARKET ON THE MOVE
See 3000 CLUB

MARKET ONE BUILDERS
See MARKETONE BUILDERS INC

D-U-N-S 04-346-5871
MARKET PLACE CHRYSLER PLYMOUTH INC (NY)
MARKET PLACE SUZUKI
3755 W Henrietta Rd, Rochester, NY 14623-3701
Tel (585) 359-4900 *Founded/Ownrshp* 1981
Sales 22.3MM^E *EMP* 50
SIC 5511 Automobiles, new & used; Pickups, new & used; Automobiles, new & used; Pickups, new & used
Pr: Dennis Petrisak
**VP:* Tony Diguardi
Off Mgr: Betty Dhondt
Sales Exec: Anthony Diguardi

MARKET PLACE FOODS
See JOHANNESONS INC

MARKET PLACE SUZUKI
See MARKET PLACE CHRYSLER PLYMOUTH INC

D-U-N-S 04-620-2321
MARKET PROBE INC
2655 N Mayfair Rd, Milwaukee, WI 53226-1310
Tel (414) 778-6000 *Founded/Ownrshp* 1976
Sales 32.2MM^E *EMP* 240
SIC 8732 Market analysis or research; Market analysis or research
Pr: Dr T R RAO
**CFO:* Karen Ethington
Ex VP: Judith Ricker
Sr VP: Will Gordon
Sr VP: Tim McCutcheon
Sr VP: Lalit Sangtani
Sr VP: Kris Smet
VP: Jeff Andreasen
VP: Vasu Balakrishnan
VP: Anu Bhalla
VP: Jill Carnick
VP: Danielle Conem
VP: Andrea Corrado
VP: Martine Degreef
VP: Carol French
VP: Eddie James
**VP:* Bonnie Lockwood
VP: Jack Loo
VP: Margie Reaka
VP: Jill Rogers
Dir Bus: Jaelyn Ren

D-U-N-S 14-158-8652
MARKET RESOURCE PARTNERS LLC
1650 Arch St, Philadelphia, PA 19103-2029
Tel (215) 587-8800 *Founded/Ownrshp* 2002
Sales 31.3MM^E *EMP* 75^E
SIC 7379
CEO: Kevin Cunningham
Pr: James Regan
COO: Jack Butler
VP: Kristin Carey
CIO: Romano Ditoro

D-U-N-S 82-560-4903
MARKET SCAN INFORMATION SYSTEMS INC
811 Camarillo Springs Rd B, Camarillo, CA 93012-9465
Tel (800) 658-7226 *Founded/Ownrshp* 1994
Sales 24.2MM^E *EMP* 150
SIC 7371 Computer software development & applications; Computer software development & applications
CEO: Stephen Smythe
**Pr:* Rusty West
**CEO:* Rustie G West
CTO: Nick Kulyk

D-U-N-S 60-544-6251
MARKET STRATEGIES INC
MARKET STRATEGIES INTL
17430 College Pkwy, Livonia, MI 48152-2363
Tel (734) 542-7600 *Founded/Ownrshp* 1989
Sales 127.3MM^E *EMP* 860
SIC 8742 8732 Marketing consulting services; Market analysis or research; Marketing consulting services; Market analysis or research
Ch Bd: Andrew Morrison PHD
**Pr:* George Wilkerson
**CEO:* Rob Stone PHD
**COO:* Reginald Baker
COO: Kevin Orians
**CFO:* Philip Giroux
Sr VP: Kenneth V Athaide
VP: Janice Anderson
VP: Patricia Clark
VP: Rob Delghiaccio
VP: Lindsey Dickman
VP: Paul Donagher
VP: Alexander Gage
VP: Paul Hartley
VP: Tish Hasting
VP: Katherine Katy
VP: Jay Lash
VP: Silvo Lenart
VP: Marybeth Marino
VP: Shannon McGuire
VP: Susan McIntyre

MARKET STRATEGIES INTL
See MARKET STRATEGIES INC

D-U-N-S 55-593-3654
MARKET STREET BANCSHARES INC
520 S 42nd St, Mount Vernon, IL 62864-6299
Tel (618) 244-5157 *Founded/Ownrshp* 1986
Sales 59.1MM *EMP* 8
Accts Crowe Horwath Llp Louisville
SIC 6719 Public utility holding companies; Public utility holding companies
Pr: Hunt Bonan
COO: Forrest Langenfeld
**Sec:* Frank William Bonan
Sales Exec: Holtkamp Guy

MARKET STREET GRILL
See GASTRONOMY INC

D-U-N-S 14-467-1067
MARKET TRACK LLC
233 S Wacker Dr, Chicago, IL 60606-7147
Tel (312) 529-5102 *Founded/Ownrshp* 2012
Sales 49.1MM^E *EMP* 1,102^E
SIC 8742 Management consulting services
CEO: Wayne Mincey
CFO: Tim Burditt
Ofcr: Paul Salay
VP: Todd Birchenough
Mng Dir: Tim Branigin

D-U-N-S 07-643-7417
MARKET TRANSPORT LTD
MARKET LOGISTICS
(*Suby of* MARKET INDUSTRIES LTD) ★
110 N Marine Dr, Portland, OR 97217-8097
Tel (503) 283-3279 *Founded/Ownrshp* 2008
Sales 130.0MM *EMP* 375
SIC 4213 Contract haulers; Refrigerated products transport; Contract haulers; Refrigerated products transport
Pr: Greg P Galbraith
VP: Mike Olsen
VP: Michael Olson
VP: Don Thornton
CIO: Jay Hemmady
Dir IT: Bob Thorn
Opers Mgr: Guy Cook
Opers Mgr: Patrick Fitzgerald
Opers Mgr: Kathy Korb
Opers Mgr: Tina Luckey
Opers Mgr: Tae No

D-U-N-S 15-586-4528
▲ **MARKETAXESS HOLDINGS INC**
299 Park Ave Fl 10, New York, NY 10171-3804
Tel (212) 813-6000 *Founded/Ownrshp* 2000
Sales 262.7MM *EMP* 303^E
Tkr Sym MKTX *Exch* NGS
SIC 6211 Security brokers & dealers; Bond dealers & brokers; Stock brokers & dealers; Stock option dealers; Security brokers & dealers; Bond dealers & brokers; Stock brokers & dealers; Stock option dealers
Ch Bd: Richard M McVey
CFO: Antonio L Delise
Ofcr: Ron Steinfeld
VP: Bill Barnett
VP: James Carney
VP: Douglas Marzano
Genl Mgr: Mike Sanzillo
CIO: Nicholas Themelis
CTO: Paul Miller
QA Dir: Mark Liao
IT Man: Naresh Kumar
Board of Directors: Steven L Begleiter, Stephen P Casper, Jane Chwick, William F Cruger, David G Gomach, Carlos M Hernandez, Ronald M Hersch, John Steinhardt, James J Sullivan

D-U-N-S 79-646-9500
MARKETBRIDGE CORP
4800 Montgomery Ln # 500, Bethesda, MD 20814-3429
Tel (240) 752-1800 *Founded/Ownrshp* 1991
Sales 31.3MM^E *EMP* 161^E
SIC 8742 Marketing consulting services; Marketing consulting services
CEO: Tim Furey
Pr: Michael I Connolly
**COO:* Bashar Mardam Bey
**Sr VP:* Mike Kelleher
**Sr VP:* Jason Robinson
**Sr VP:* Stephanie Russell
**VP:* Cary Comer
**VP:* Liam O Connor
VP: John Desarbo
**VP:* Steven Lewis
Prgrm Mgr: Rebecca Mervis

D-U-N-S 08-108-9372
MARKETFARE FOODS LLC
(*Suby of* GREENCORE US HOLDINGS INC) ★
222 Rosewood Dr Fl 2, Danvers, MA 01923-4502
Tel (978) 716-2530 *Founded/Ownrshp* 2012
Sales 90.1MM^E *EMP* 400
SIC 5142 Packaged frozen goods; Packaged frozen goods
CEO: Liam McClennon
VP: Bill Stanley

D-U-N-S 15-533-0673
MARKETING & MEDIA SERVICES LLC
MMSI
(*Suby of* R2C GROUP) ★
931 Jefferson Blvd # 1001, Warwick, RI 02886-2247
Tel (401) 737-7730 *Founded/Ownrshp* 2006
Sales 25.0MM *EMP* 22
SIC 8742 7311

D-U-N-S 60-850-3637
MARKETING & RESEARCH RESOURCES
7101 Guilford Dr Ste 100, Frederick, MD 21704-5198
Tel (240) 575-7100 *Founded/Ownrshp* 1989
Sales 24.1MM^E *EMP* 200
Accts Thomas E Allwine Cpa Dunkir
SIC 8732 7336 8743 Market analysis or research; Art design services; Promotion service; Market analysis or research; Art design services; Promotion service
Pr: David Vershel
COO: John Bekier

D-U-N-S 06-840-1285
MARKETING ALLIANCE GROUP INC
2830 N Dug Gap Rd Sw, Dalton, GA 30720-4946
Tel (706) 277-9707 *Founded/Ownrshp* 1998
Sales 175.3MM^E *EMP* 600^E
SIC 2752 Commercial printing, lithographic; Commercial printing, lithographic
Pr: Brian Hair
**CFO:* Frank Grant
IT Man: Donnie Bowers
Natl Sales: John Kile
Natl Sales: Paige Spurlock
Mktg Mgr: Cortney Bowersox
Sls Mgr: Sandy McDowell
Sls Mgr: Mike Oric

D-U-N-S 79-941-0878 IMP
MARKETING AND ENGINEERING SOLUTIONS (MES) INC
625 Bear Run Ln, Lewis Center, OH 43035-7133
Tel (740) 201-8112 *Founded/Ownrshp* 1998
Sales 39.5MM *EMP* 51
SIC 5051 8742 Metals service centers & offices; Marketing consulting services
Pr: Hiten Shah

D-U-N-S 01-984-8407
MARKETING ARCHITECTS INC
110 Cheshire Ln Ste 200, Minneapolis, MN 55441
Tel (952) 449-2500 *Founded/Ownrshp* 1996
Sales 24.3MM^E *EMP* 67^E
SIC 8742 7319 Marketing consulting services; Media buying service
CEO: Charles M Hengel
CFO: J Brent Longval
Ex VP: Christopher Crowhurst
VP: Ryan Kinkaid
VP: Eric Pilhofer
VP: Katie Scheetz
Exec: Meghan Howard
**Prin:* Jeff Clement
**Prin:* Brent Longval
IT Man: Angela Voss
Prd Dir: John Priess

MARKETING ARM, THE
See MARKETING ARM INC

D-U-N-S 96-168-2341
■ **MARKETING ARM INC**
MARKETING ARM, THE
(*Suby of* OMNICOM GROUP INC) ★
1999 Bryan St Fl 18, Dallas, TX 75201-3136
Tel (214) 259-3200 *Founded/Ownrshp* 1999
Sales 86.2MM^E *EMP* 255^E
SIC 8742 Marketing consulting services; Marketing consulting services
CEO: Ray Clark
Pr: Tony Amador
**COO:* Brad Penman
**CFO:* Jennifer Henry
**Chf Mktg O:* Daniel G Belmont
Ex VP: Jordan Schlacter
**Ex VP:* Nowell Upham
Ex VP: Brad Vettese
Sr VP: Eric Holmen
Sr VP: Mike Paley
Sr VP: Jordis Rosenquest
**VP:* Erin Dwyer
**VP:* Jeff Erickson
**VP:* Jason Katz
VP: Dan Keats
VP: Lara Beth Seager
Assoc Dir: Alexandra Tuel
Creative D: Ashleigh Adams
Creative D: Jonathan Chin
Creative D: Amy Erschen
Creative D: Becky Frolker-Beals
Board of Directors: Michael Rodriguez

D-U-N-S 01-416-1553
MARKETING ASSOCIATES LLC
1 Kennedy Sq, Detroit, MI 48226
Tel (313) 965-3000 *Founded/Ownrshp* 2007
Sales 31.8MM^E *EMP* 145^E
SIC 7311 7331 7371 7375 Advertising agencies; Direct mail advertising services; Computer software development & applications; Data base information retrieval
V Ch: Jim Stewart
Ex VP: Sameer Desai
Creative D: Jerry Curtis
CIO: Andy Frey
QA Dir: Melissa Tipton
Web Dev: Daniel Peck
Software D: Carrie Nelson
Prd Mgr: Pat Cubbler
Prd Mgr: Mike Nucci
Snr PM: Mary Buckley
Snr PM: Brad Wilkinson
Board of Directors: James Stewart

D-U-N-S 06-813-8048
MARKETING CARD TECHNOLOGY LLC
8245 Lemont Rd, Darien, IL 60561-1761
Tel (630) 985-7900 *Founded/Ownrshp* 2013
Sales 21.9MM^E *EMP* 90
SIC 7331 2771 Direct mail advertising services; Greeting cards
Pr: Pushparaj Venkitsamy
**VP:* SRI Lala

D-U-N-S 14-764-1380
MARKETING CONNECTIONS GROUP INC
1406 Red Tail Dr, Verona, WI 53593-7966
Tel (608) 497-1192 *Founded/Ownrshp* 2000
Sales 13.6MM^E *EMP* 320
SIC 8742 Marketing consulting services; Marketing consulting services
Pr: Lisa Piemann
VP: Patrick V Denheuel
**VP:* Patrick Van Denheuvel

MARKETING DEPARTMENT
See ST LUKES HEALTH VENTURES INC

D-U-N-S 00-652-5828 IMP
MARKETING DISPLAYS INC
MDI TRAFFIC CONTROL PRODUCTS
38271 W 12 Mile Rd, Farmington Hills, MI 48331-3041
Tel (248) 553-1900 *Founded/Ownrshp* 1965
Sales 30.0MM^E *EMP* 165
Accts Matthew Reich Perna & Rotter
SIC 3993 3354 2396 Signs, not made in custom sign painting shops; Aluminum extruded products; Automotive & apparel trimmings; Signs, not made in custom sign painting shops; Aluminum extruded products; Automotive & apparel trimmings
Pr: Lisa Sarkisian
**Treas:* Christopher Kluesner
Mng Dir: Michel Granger
Snr Mgr: Tom Carol

D-U-N-S 04-214-4001
MARKETING DRIVE LLC
PARENT IS MATCH MARKETING
(*Suby of* MATCH MARKETING GROUP INC)
800 Connecticut Ave 3e01, Norwalk, CT 06854-5601
Tel (203) 857-6100 *Founded/Ownrshp* 2013
Sales 23.3MM^E *EMP* 170
SIC 7311 Advertising agencies; Advertising agencies
Pr: Michael Harris
CFO: Debbie Kass
Sr VP: Dan Bowens
VP: Diana Abshire
VP: Tanya Cavanaugh
VP: Carolyn Manfreda
VP: Ann Muller
Creative D: Eric Juhasz
Genl Mgr: Manuel Angom
Genl Mgr: Enrique Noora
Art Dir: Dan Lang

MARKETING IMPACT
See PRINTCOMM INC

D-U-N-S 01-331-2053
MARKETING INC
200 Carleton Ave, East Islip, NY 11730-1222
Tel (631) 277-7000 *Founded/Ownrshp* 1979
Sales 21.7MM^E *EMP* 500
SIC 8732 Market analysis or research; Market analysis or research
Prin: Steven H Gittelman
**Treas:* Howard Gershowitz
Dir IT: Alison Finfrock
Web Prj Mg: Debbie H Ons

D-U-N-S 07-318-4335 IMP/EXP
MARKETING MANAGEMENT INC
M M I
4717 Fletcher Ave, Fort Worth, TX 76107-6826
Tel (817) 731-4176 *Founded/Ownrshp* 1966
Sales 84.6MM^E *EMP* 215
SIC 5141 Food brokers; Food brokers
CEO: Herbert L Pease
**Pr:* Randy Hurr
CFO: Donna Smith
**Ch:* Mary Pease
**Treas:* Kimberly R Pease
Sr Cor Off: Herbert Poledna
**Sr VP:* Pat Abbey
Sr VP: Woody Lynch
VP: Terrie Engle
VP: Lindsey Hurr
**VP:* Paul Nichols
VP: Corina Ponciano
Comm Dir: Joni Grulke
Dir Bus: Jesse Gaibor

D-U-N-S 96-837-2375
MARKETING ONE FINANCIAL CORP
8196 Sw Hall Blvd Ste 102, Beaverton, OR 97008-4676
Tel (503) 295-0187 *Founded/Ownrshp* 1992
Sales NA *EMP* 395
SIC 6719 Investment holding companies, except banks; Investment holding companies, except banks
Pr: Joel Caplan
**CFO:* Joel S Caplan
**Chf Mktg O:* James M Truax

D-U-N-S 13-766-0663
MARKETING PROFESSIONALS INC
5100 E La Palma Ave # 116, Anaheim, CA 92807-2081
Tel (714) 578-0500 *Founded/Ownrshp* 1985
Sales 18.5MM^E *EMP* 350
SIC 8742 7319 Marketing consulting services; Retail trade consultant; Display advertising service; Marketing consulting services; Retail trade consultant; Display advertising service
Pr: Joseph L Smith
**CFO:* Cynthia A Simms
**Ch:* George M Schnitzer

D-U-N-S 03-311-9665
MARKETING REPRESENTATIVES INC
MRI
74 Northwest Dr, Plainville, CT 06062-1164
Tel (860) 747-0003 *Founded/Ownrshp* 1998
Sales 27.1MM^E *EMP* 30
SIC 5065 Electronic parts & equipment
Pr: Robert H Dean
COO: Mark Barthel
Opers Mgr: Victor Cassarino
Mktg Dir: Jaron Ulrich
Sls Mgr: Tom Hamilton

D-U-N-S 03-095-0935
MARKETING RESEARCH SERVICES INC
M R S I
(*Suby of* OPINION RESEARCH CORP) ★
310 Culvert St Fl 2, Cincinnati, OH 45202-2229
Tel (513) 579-1555 *Founded/Ownrshp* 2012
Sales 15.5MM^E *EMP* 300
SIC 8732 Market analysis or research; Market analysis or research
Pr: Todd Earhart
Sr Pt: William Eder
Sr Pt: Linda Maichl
**Ex VP:* John Barth
Ex VP: Richard Brumfied
**Ex VP:* Richard Brumfield

Ex VP: Richard Catrone
**Ex VP:* Elise Delahanty
Ex VP: Neil Gartner
**Ex VP:* Lori Kelley
**Ex VP:* David Murray
**Ex VP:* Sheilah Wagner
VP: Ryan Brock
VP: Laura Kleckner
Exec: Jason Ebbing

D-U-N-S 14-249-4942 IMP
MARKETING RESULTS LTD
3985 Groves Rd, Columbus, OH 43232-4138
Tel (614) 575-9300 *Founded/Ownrshp* 2002
Sales 21.1MM *EMP* 25
Accts Mellman & Perdue Columbus Oh
SIC 5023 Office & public building furniture; Home furnishings; Hand tools; Home furnishings
VP: Karen Waldmann
Prin: Brady Churches

D-U-N-S 07-933-0311
■ **MARKETING SERVICES GROUP INC**
(*Suby of* BALKAMP INC) ★
2601 S Holt Rd, Indianapolis, IN 46241-5736
Tel (317) 381-2268 *Founded/Ownrshp* 2014
Sales 8.6MM^E *EMP* 342^E
SIC 7336 2759 Commercial art & graphic design; Commercial printing
Dir Surg: Jennifer Rode

MARKETING SFTWR CO A CAL CORP
See MARKETING SOFTWARE CO LLC

D-U-N-S 18-695-5550
MARKETING SOFTWARE CO LLC
MARKETING SFTWR CO A CAL CORP
(*Suby of* AUTOMATED PRESORT SERVICES) ★
6200 Canoga Ave Ste 102, Woodland Hills, CA 91367-2429
Tel (818) 346-1600 *Founded/Ownrshp* 2015
Sales 22.2MM^E *EMP* 47
SIC 7374 Data processing & preparation; Data processing & preparation
Pr: Gary Abrams
Pr: Paul Storch
Treas: Walter Silva
Chf Mktg O: Kevin Blayne
VP: Sandra Mills

MARKETING SPECIALTIES
See MSI PACKAGING INC

D-U-N-S 05-432-7866
MARKETING STORE WORLDWIDE L L C
(*Suby of* HAVI GROUP LIMITED PARTNERSHIP) ★
55 W Monroe St Fl 14, Chicago, IL 60603-5005
Tel (630) 693-1400 *Founded/Ownrshp* 1991
Sales 105.0MM^E *EMP* 1,000
SIC 7311 8742 Advertising agencies; Marketing consulting services; Advertising agencies; Marketing consulting services
Pt: Mark Landolt
**COO:* Howard Katz
**VP:* Robert Bredy
VP: Maria Garcia-Herman
VP: Dave Jaski
VP: Michael Jenneman
VP: Troy Mastin
VP: Rob Pieper
Tech Mgr: Tom Ryan
Art Dir: Robert Lee

D-U-N-S 18-664-9810
MARKETING WERKS INC
(*Suby of* CROSSMARK INC) ★
130 E Randolph St # 2400, Chicago, IL 60601-6322
Tel (312) 228-0800 *Founded/Ownrshp* 2013
Sales 32.5MM^E *EMP* 165
SIC 8742 8743 Marketing consulting services; Sales promotion; Marketing consulting services; Sales promotion
Co-CEO: Scott Moller
**COO:* Rick Miller
**CFO:* John Stanek
**Co-CEO:* Julie Guida
**Chf Mktg O:* Jay Lenstrom

D-U-N-S 84-891-7027
MARKETLAB INC
(*Suby of* WATER STREET HEALTHCARE PARTNERS LLC) ★
6850 Southbelt Dr Se, Caledonia, MI 49316-7680
Tel (616) 656-3322 *Founded/Ownrshp* 2011
Sales 43.8MM^E *EMP* 95
SIC 5047 3841 3821 Medical laboratory equipment; Medical instruments & equipment, blood & bone work; Laboratory apparatus & furniture; Medical laboratory equipment; Medical instruments & equipment, blood & bone work; Laboratory apparatus & furniture
CEO: Mike Bieker
**Pr:* Steve Bosio
**CFO:* Bob Schmidt
Ex VP: Linda Hurley
CIO: Mike Ulanski
CTO: Phil Lloyd
IT Man: Kristie Keyes
Sales Asso: Laura Durga
Sales Asso: Josh Robach
Snr Mgr: Kerri Milarch

D-U-N-S 19-420-5134
MARKETLAB RESEARCH INC
FOCUS POINTE
100 E Penn Sq Ste 1200a, Philadelphia, PA 19107-3308
Tel (215) 561-5500 *Founded/Ownrshp* 1988
Sales 22.7MM^E *EMP* 120
SIC 8732 Market analysis or research; Market analysis or research
CEO: Noel Sitzmann
**Pr:* Laura Livers
**Ex VP:* Ileen Branderbit
**Sr VP:* Shawn Y Gore
**VP:* Kay Savio
Ex Dir: Adele Albert
Ex Dir: Kelly Frake
Mng Dir: Wally Balden

CIO: Robert Stephens
Snr PM: Ryan Blome
Snr PM: Andrea Labe

D-U-N-S 62-356-9311
■ **MARKETLINX INC**
MLS SOLUTIONS
(*Suby of* CORELOGIC INC) ★
1951 Kidwell Dr Ste 300, Vienna, VA 22182-4053
Tel (703) 610-5000 *Founded/Ownrshp* 2010
Sales 13.7MM^E *EMP* 307
SIC 7372 2741 Business oriented computer software; Directories: publishing & printing; Business oriented computer software; Directories: publishing & printing
Pr: Bryan Foreman
**CEO:* Steve Roney
**CFO:* Lisa Sellon
**Ex VP:* Kevin Lagerwey
VP: George Livermore
VP: Matthew McGuire
Opers Supe: Greg Morrison
Sls Dir: Chris Bennett

D-U-N-S 92-959-8886
MARKETLIVE INC
617 2nd St Ste B, Petaluma, CA 94952-5160
Tel (707) 780-1600 *Founded/Ownrshp* 1996
Sales 20.0MM^E *EMP* 110
SIC 7374 Computer graphics service; Computer graphics service
Pr: Ken Burke
Pr: Josh Baumrind
Sr VP: Jeff Kreutz
VP: Angela Bandlow
VP: Suzanne Cushing
VP: Julie Hogin
VP: George Loyer
Dir Bus: Kate Horning
Snr Sftwr: Kelly Davidson
Snr Sftwr: Nikhil Sharma
Snr Sftwr: Kelly Taylor

D-U-N-S 82-830-0637
▲ **MARKETO INC**
901 Mariners Island Blvd, San Mateo, CA 94404-1592
Tel (650) 376-2300 *Founded/Ownrshp* 2006
Sales 149.9MM *EMP* 715^E
Tkr Sym MKTO *Exch* NGS
SIC 7371 7372 Custom computer programming services; Computer software writing services; Prepackaged software; Custom computer programming services; Computer software writing services; Prepackaged software
CEO: Phillip M Fernandez
Pr: Matt Heinz
COO: Ron Barale
CFO: Frederick A Ball
Chf Mktg O: Sanjiv P Dholakia
Ex VP: Steve Winter
Ex VP: Steven M Winter
Sr VP: Margo M Smith
Exec: Rhiana Duenas
Creative D: Davis Lee
Mng Dir: Mark Siciliano
Board of Directors: Lynne Biggar, Susan L Bostrom, Douglas A Pepper, Roger S Siboni, Wesley R Wasson

D-U-N-S 79-212-8345
MARKETON INC
4205 Baldwin Ave, El Monte, CA 91731-1101
Tel (626) 618-1060 *Founded/Ownrshp* 2005
Sales 26.5MM^E *EMP* 146^E
SIC 5411 Grocery stores
CEO: Constanio Miguel
VP: Maria Diaz
**VP:* William Miguel

D-U-N-S 79-943-1861
MARKETONE BUILDERS INC
MARKET ONE BUILDERS
1419 N Market Blvd Ste 1, Sacramento, CA 95834-1937
Tel (916) 928-7474 *Founded/Ownrshp* 1997
Sales 27.8MM^E *EMP* 49
SIC 1542 Nonresidential construction
Pr: Thomas P Ford
CFO: Mark Weiner
**Exec:* James Fitzgerald
Exec: Steve Soderberg
Snr PM: Michael Brown

D-U-N-S 06-853-8490
MARKETONE INTERNATIONAL LLP
610 Lincoln St Ste 125, Waltham, MA 02451-2018
Tel (978) 450-0100 *Founded/Ownrshp* 1998
Sales 23.5MM^E *EMP* 90^E
SIC 8732 Market analysis or research
Pt: Frederick M Ewald
**Pt:* Enrico Brosio
**Pt:* John Strehle
CFO: Elizabeth Turpin
Dir Rx: Dawn Aguiar
Mng Dir: Steven Elliott
Mng Dir: Vijay Nair
Mng Dir: Marc Ramdayal
Prgrm Mgr: Carlos Best
Prgrm Mgr: Michiel Maaskant
Prgrm Mgr: Tom Oreilly

MARKETPLACE
See BI-LO HOLDINGS FOUNDATION INC

MARKETPLACE
See WINN-DIXIE STORES INC

MARKETPLACE CHAPLAINS USA
See MARKETPLACE MINISTRIES INC

D-U-N-S 82-810-6463
MARKETPLACE EVENTS LLC
HOME & FLOWER SHOW
31105 Bainbridge Rd Ste 3, Solon, OH 44139-6400
Tel (440) 349-2374 *Founded/Ownrshp* 2008
Sales 27.7MM^E *EMP* 100
SIC 7389 Promoters of shows & exhibitions
CEO: Tom Baugh
**CFO:* Mark White
**VP:* Mike Webster
Off Admin: Sarah Carr

Opers Mgr: Alison Farrell
Mktg Dir: Shalini Kapur
Sls Dir: Joe Trimble
Mktg Mgr: Sabrina Colella
Sls Mgr: Martin Egli

D-U-N-S 08-411-4396
MARKETPLACE FOODS INC
MARKETPLACE LIQUOR
330 S Main St, Rice Lake, WI 54868-2293
Tel (715) 234-6991 *Founded/Ownrshp* 1977
Sales 64.2MM^E *EMP* 500
SIC 5411 5921 Supermarkets, independent; Liquor stores; Supermarkets, independent; Liquor stores
Pr: Frank Betchkal
**VP:* Doris Betchkal

MARKETPLACE GRILL
See RESTAURANT MANAGEMENT GROUP LLC

MARKETPLACE LIQUOR
See MARKETPLACE FOODS INC

D-U-N-S 78-461-4752
MARKETPLACE MINISTRIES INC
MARKETPLACE CHAPLAINS USA
2001 W Plano Pkwy, Dallas, TX 75201
Tel (972) 941-4400 *Founded/Ownrshp* 1984
Sales 14.9MM *EMP* 1,200
Accts Capin Crouse Llp Dallas Tx
SIC 8661 Religious organizations; Religious organizations
CEO: Gilford A Stricklin
**Pr:* Richard Dewtt
CFO: Larry King
**Sr VP:* C G Maclin
VP: George Cotter
VP: Steve Hefta
**VP:* Chaley Quackenbush
VP: Joel Rayfield
VP: Shane Satterfield
**VP:* Dan Shotts
VP Mktg: Jason Brown

D-U-N-S 11-255-4832
MARKETRESEARCH.COM INC
PACKAGED FACTS
11200 Rockville Pike # 504, Rockville, MD 20852-3154
Tel (240) 747-3000 *Founded/Ownrshp* 1998
Sales 25.7MM^E *EMP* 110
SIC 8748 Publishing consultant
Ch: Robert Granader
Sr VP: Beverly Parker
**VP:* Kelly Carlson
**VP:* Rocco Distefano
Off Mgr: Lee Massey
Snr Sftwr: Youssou Ndao
Dir IT: Sean Courtney
Ql Cn Mgr: Randall Long
Mktg Mgr: Richard Washington

D-U-N-S 05-960-3142
MARKETRON BROADCAST SOLUTIONS LLC
(*Suby of* WICKS GROUP OF COMPANIES LLC (DE CORP)) ★
101 Empty Saddle Trl, Hailey, ID 83333-8437
Tel (208) 788-6272 *Founded/Ownrshp* 2007
Sales 25.7MM^E *EMP* 130
SIC 7372 7371 Prepackaged software; Custom computer programming services; Prepackaged software; Custom computer programming services
Pr: Jeff Haley
**CFO:* Walter Denekas
**Ofcr:* Deborah Esayian
**Sr VP:* Tony Gaughan
**Sr VP:* Jeff London
**VP:* Martin Kristiseter
VP: Renee Roth
VP: Mark Springfield
VP Sls: Todd Kalman
**VP Sls:* Eric Treworgy

D-U-N-S 12-780-8116
■ **MARKETRX INC**
COGNIZANT
(*Suby of* COGNIZANT TECHNOLOGY SOLUTIONS CORP) ★
500 Frank W Burr Blvd, Teaneck, NJ 07666-6804
Tel (201) 801-0233 *Founded/Ownrshp* 2007
Sales 51.2MM^E *EMP* 145^E
SIC 7371 Computer software development & applications; Computer software development & applications
Pr: Jaswinder S Chadha
Pr: Ivan Radojcic
**VP:* Philip Brennan
**VP:* Patrick Brundage
**VP:* Navdeep Chadha
VP: Stephanie D Foye
VP: Steve Kernan
Assoc Dir: Rich Gallagher
Assoc Dir: Ananth Madabushi
Assoc Dir: Manav Malhotra
Assoc Dir: Indrajit Mitra
Assoc Dir: Al Weedman

D-U-N-S 02-731-7551 IMP
MARKETS LLC
COST CUTTERS
4350 Cordata Pkwy, Bellingham, WA 98226-8019
Tel (360) 714-9797 *Founded/Ownrshp* 1909
Sales 161.4MM^E *EMP* 800
SIC 5411 Supermarkets, chain; Supermarkets, chain
CFO: Aaron Tam
VP: Andrew Baum
Dist Mgr: James Estes
Off Mgr: Lindsey Kelley
CIO: Rick N Treese
Netwrk Mgr: Michael Zamora
VP Opers: Clark Jordan
Mktg Dir: Dean Priestman
Pr Dir: Sue Cole
Mktg Mgr: Geri Reichenbach

D-U-N-S 17-189-9326
MARKETSOURCE INC
(*Suby of* ALLEGIS GROUP INC) ★
11700 Great Oaks Way, Alpharetta, GA 30022-2448
Tel (770) 674-5000 *Founded/Ownrshp* 1993
Sales 98.4MM^E *EMP* 8,500
SIC 8742 Marketing consulting services; Marketing consulting services
Pr: Rick Haviland
**Ex VP:* Mike Christensen
**VP:* Bob Hunter
VP: Chris Walter
Dir Bus: Jeff Zdanowski
Ex Dir: Deborah Keeney
Prgrm Mgr: Russell Curtis
Dist Mgr: Stephanie Cole
Dist Mgr: John Garitta
Mktg Dir: Julia Holland
Manager: Charles Lynch

D-U-N-S 11-436-0832
MARKETSPHERE CONSULTING LLC
14301 Fnb Pkwy Ste 111, Omaha, NE 68154-7200
Tel (402) 392-4000 *Founded/Ownrshp* 2002
Sales 24.8MM^E *EMP* 63
SIC 8748 Business consulting; Business consulting
CEO: Lonnie Janecek
Pr: Enzo Santilli
Bd of Dir: Debbie H Di Meo
Snr Mgr: Adriane Counts

D-U-N-S 17-196-0172
■ **MARKETSTAR CORP**
(*Suby of* OMNICOM GROUP INC) ★
2475 Washington Blvd, Ogden, UT 84401-2315
Tel (801) 393-1155 *Founded/Ownrshp* 1999
Sales 98.4MM^E *EMP* 2,500
SIC 8742 Marketing consulting services; Marketing consulting services
CEO: David Treadway
**COO:* Aaron Tracy Hall
CFO: Harris Ej
**CFO:* Elroy J Harris
VP: Vaughn Aust
VP: Aaron T Exec
VP: Mark Jones
VP: Michelle Parker
VP Bus Dev: Dave Forseberg
Exec: Andrew Schow
Exec: Amy Weglarz
Dir Bus: Kara Harrison
Dir Bus: Nathan Messerly

MARKETTE STORES, THE
See WEST OIL INC

D-U-N-S 04-132-1592
■ **MARKETWATCH INC**
C B S MARKETWATCH
(*Suby of* DOW JONES & CO INC) ★
201 California St Fl 13, San Francisco, CA 94111-5015
Tel (415) 439-6400 *Founded/Ownrshp* 2005
Sales 13.2MM^E *EMP* 337
SIC 7383 News ticker service; News ticker service
Ch Bd: Larry S Kramer
**Pr:* Kathleen B Yates
CFO: Jeni Halpern
**CFO:* Paul Mattison
CFO: Joan Platt
CFO: Amanda Reed
CFO: Arthur Wasserspring
**Ex VP:* William Bishop
Ex VP: Jeff Davis
VP: Frank Barnako
VP: Mike Orr
Exec: Margaret Deluna

D-U-N-S 00-924-7461
MARKEY MACHINERY CO INC
7266 8th Ave S, Seattle, WA 98108-3403
Tel (206) 622-4697 *Founded/Ownrshp* 1999
Sales 21.6MM *EMP* 42^E
SIC 3531 Marine related equipment; Ship winches; Capstans, ship
Pr: Blaine Dempke
**VP:* Robert A Lecoque
VP: Robert Lecoque

D-U-N-S 07-204-6360
MARKEYS AUDIO/VISUAL INC
MARKEY'S RENTAL & STAGING
2365 Enterprise Park Pl, Indianapolis, IN 46218-4290
Tel (317) 783-1155 *Founded/Ownrshp* 1979
Sales 21.5MM *EMP* 160
Accts Isenberg & Chivington Pc Indi
SIC 7359 Audio-visual equipment & supply rental; Audio-visual equipment & supply rental
CEO: Charles J Markey Jr
**Pr:* Mark Miller
CFO: Joy Brinduse
**Treas:* Allison Jecker
VP: Kurt Wiegand
CTO: Eric Ebert
IT Man: Lois Thiel-Hyatte
Board of Directors: Scott Hirschman, Allison Jecker, Charles Markey Jr, Mark Miller, Gregory Steeb

MARKEY'S RENTAL & STAGING
See MARKEYS AUDIO/VISUAL INC

D-U-N-S 88-324-1820
MARKFEST INC
FESTIVAL FOODS
(*Suby of* MDSFEST INC) ★
1613 N Central Ave, Marshfield, WI 54449-1550
Tel (715) 384-8866 *Founded/Ownrshp* 2005
Sales 30.3MM^E *EMP* 310
SIC 5411 Grocery stores, independent; Grocery stores, independent
Pr: Mark Skogen
CFO: John Schaefer
**Sec:* Barbara Skogen
**VP:* David Skogen
Exec: Jenny Zahn

D-U-N-S 08-930-5072
MARKHAM CONTRACTING CO INC
22820 N 19th Ave, Phoenix, AZ 85027-1310
Tel (623) 869-9100 *Founded/Ownrshp* 1977
Sales 59.9MM *EMP* 200
Accts Pittman & Murdough Pllc Phoe
SIC 1611 1771 1623 Highway & street paving contractor; Grading; Concrete work; Underground utilities contractor; Highway & street paving contractor; Grading; Concrete work; Underground utilities contractor
Pr: Michael F Markham Jr
**VP:* Hollis R Loper
**VP:* Heather E Markham
VP: Johnnie P Mata

D-U-N-S 00-221-4484
MARKIN TUBING INC
Pearl Creek Rd, Wyoming, NY 14591
Tel (585) 495-6211 *Founded/Ownrshp* 1958
Sales 22.7MM^E *EMP* 150
SIC 3317 3312 Tubes, wrought: welded or lock joint; Structural shapes & pilings, steel; Tubes, wrought: welded or lock joint; Structural shapes & pilings, steel
Pr: Barton P Dambra
**Ch:* Maurice Cunnife
**VP:* Arthur A Smith

D-U-N-S 18-766-1152 IMP
MARKING SERVICES INC
8265 N Faulkner Rd, Milwaukee, WI 53224-2842
Tel (414) 973-1331 *Founded/Ownrshp* 1988
Sales 28.2MM^E *EMP* 122
SIC 2679 8711 Labels, paper: made from purchased material; Mechanical engineering; Labels, paper: made from purchased material; Mechanical engineering
CEO: Jeff Dickinson
**VP:* Jeff Gault
Opers Mgr: John Dykstra
Sales Asso: Kristine Gostomski

D-U-N-S 05-436-8774
MARKING SYSTEMS INC
M S I
2601 Market St, Garland, TX 75041-2423
Tel (972) 475-0770 *Founded/Ownrshp* 1971
Sales 35.4MM^E *EMP* 74
SIC 2679 3479 Labels, paper: made from purchased material; Name plates: engraved, etched, etc.
Pr: Mathew Van Beber
VP: Greg V Beber
**VP:* Greg Van Beber
Off Mgr: Cristina Magherscu
Opers Mgr: Mihai Borcoman
Sls Mgr: Jim Clark

D-U-N-S 82-757-6930
MARKIT GROUP LIMITED
620 8th Ave Fl 35, New York, NY 10018-1693
Tel (212) 931-4900 *Founded/Ownrshp* 2001
Sales 1.0MM *EMP* 3,000
SIC 7374 Management investment, open-end; Data processing service
CEO: Lance Uggla
Ex VP: Shane Akeroyd
Ex VP: Chip Carver
Ex VP: Armins Rusis
VP: Jared Baker
VP: Henry Caballero
VP: Daniel Caperton
VP: J Hallmark
VP: Chaitanya Hanmantgad
VP: Rachel Harling
VP: Jasmine Ho
VP: Jamie Hull
VP: Bryan Katri
VP: Jordan Landrum
VP: Adam Lehman
VP: Jim Levy
VP: Jennifer Milton
VP: Bharat Parameswaran
VP: Elizebeth Phan
VP: Chris Pickering
VP: Brian Pierce

D-U-N-S 06-390-9308
MARKIT INC
250 Mill St Ste 303, Rochester, NY 14614-1026
Tel (585) 777-4018 *Founded/Ownrshp* 1999
Sales 524.0MM *EMP* 70^E
SIC 8742 Sales (including sales management) consultant; Sales (including sales management) consultant
Pr: Dmitri Tereschenko
Mng Dir: Claire Lobo

D-U-N-S 10-172-1798
MARKIT NORTH AMERICA INC
(*Suby of* MARKIT GROUP LIMITED)
620 8th Ave Fl 35, New York, NY 10018-1693
Tel (212) 931-4900 *Founded/Ownrshp* 2004
Sales 132.5MM^E *EMP* 350^E
SIC 6289 Financial reporting; Financial reporting
Pr: Kevin Gould
**CEO:* Lance Uggla

D-U-N-S 04-051-0927 IMP
MARKLAND INDUSTRIES INC
1111 E Mcfadden Ave, Santa Ana, CA 92705-4103
Tel (714) 245-2850 *Founded/Ownrshp* 1978
Sales 32.5MM^E *EMP* 225^E
SIC 3751 Motorcycle accessories; Motorcycle accessories
Pr: Donald R Markland

MARKLE MFG CO
See MARKLE STEEL CO INC

D-U-N-S 08-086-5884
MARKLE STEEL CO INC
MARKLE MFG CO
10619 N Interstate 35, San Antonio, TX 78233-6627
Tel (210) 655-7130 *Founded/Ownrshp* 1987
Sales 31.9MM^E *EMP* 70
SIC 5051 3441 Steel; Fabricated structural metal; Steel; Fabricated structural metal
Pr: John Bauer
**Pr:* Siegfried Friese
**VP:* Roland Friese
VP: Rico Sardelli
CTO: Andrew Alvarado

D-U-N-S 03-206-0675
MARKLEY MOTORS INC
HONDA CARS BY MARKLEY
3401 S College Ave, Fort Collins, CO 80525-2606
Tel (970) 226-2213 *Founded/Ownrshp* 1936
Sales 73.7MM^E *EMP* 180
SIC 5511 Automobiles, new & used; Automobiles, new & used
Ch Bd: Eugene A Markley
**Pr:* Douglas E Markley
Treas: Marlin Walter
Ex VP: Steve Roper
Sales Exec: John Buttermore
Sls Mgr: Tim Northburg

D-U-N-S 08-603-5958
MARKLOGIC CORP
999 Skyway Rd Ste 200, San Carlos, CA 94070-2722
Tel (650) 655-2300 *Founded/Ownrshp* 2004
Sales 146.6MM^E *EMP* 525^E
SIC 7371 Computer software development & applications; Computer software development & applications
Pr: Gary Bloom
Pr: Elisa Smith
CFO: Peter Norman
CFO: Dave Ponzini
Ofcr: Catherine Chan
Ex VP: Keith Carlson
Ex VP: John Shap
Sr VP: John Harrison
Sr VP: Gary Lang
Sr VP: Joe Pasqua
VP: Andrew Grygiel
VP: David Martin
VP: John Pomeroy
VP: Mark Tice
VP: Ted Yarnell
Board of Directors: Tom Banahan, Gary Bloom, Mark Kvamme, Christopher Lindblad, Greg J Santora

D-U-N-S 04-369-3662
MARKMAN PEAT CORP
ROBERTS SOIL COMPANY
900 Eagle Ridge Rd, Le Claire, IA 52753-9535
Tel (563) 289-3478 *Founded/Ownrshp* 1969
Sales 41.9MM^E *EMP* 65
SIC 1499 Peat mining
CEO: Jeffrey T Widdop
Natl Sales: Mike Satkowiak

D-U-N-S 15-814-0546
MARKMONITOR HOLDINGS INC
425 Market St Ste 500, San Francisco, CA 94105-2464
Tel (415) 278-8400 *Founded/Ownrshp* 2000
Sales 22.8MM^E *EMP* 427
SIC 7371 Computer software development & applications; Computer software development & applications
Pr: Irfan Salim
**VP:* Tom Ryden

D-U-N-S 18-740-4798
■ **MARKMONITOR INC**
(*Suby of* THOMSON REUTERS CORP) ★
425 Market St Ste 500, San Francisco, CA 94105-2464
Tel (415) 278-8400 *Founded/Ownrshp* 2012
Sales 35.4MM^E *EMP* 402
SIC 7379 ;
CEO: Mark Frost
**Chf Mktg O:* Frederick Felman
**Sr VP:* Tom Ryden
**Sr VP:* Ariel Zach
**VP:* Charlie Abrahams
VP: Elisa Cooper
**VP:* Matt Serlin
**VP:* David Silver
VP: Te Smith
Snr Sftwr: Sassan Shahriary
Sls Mgr: Marcello Tallarigo
Board of Directors: Warren Jenson, Susan Whiting

MARKO FOAM PRODUCTS
See MARKO PRODUCTS INC

D-U-N-S 00-956-0509 IMP
MARKO PRODUCTS INC (DE)
MARKO FOAM PRODUCTS
2500 White Rd Ste A, Irvine, CA 92614-6276
Tel (800) 862-7561 *Founded/Ownrshp* 1962
Sales 25.5MM^E *EMP* 175
SIC 3086 5999 Plastics foam products; Packaging materials: boxes, padding, etc.; Plastics foam products; Packaging materials: boxes, padding, etc.
Ch Bd: Donald J Peterson
**Pr:* Tyson Peterson
VP: Robert Mallon

D-U-N-S 15-354-4432
MARKON COOPERATIVE INC
1023 S Main St, Salinas, CA 93901-2302
Tel (831) 757-9737 *Founded/Ownrshp* 1985
Sales 34.5MM^E *EMP* 36
SIC 5148 Fresh fruits & vegetables
Pr: Timothy York
**Sec:* Kent Mc Cleland
**VP:* Barb Epperson
**VP:* Mark Shaw
Off Mgr: Carol Alvarez
MIS Dir: John Eldredge
Mktg Mgr: Leslie Phelps
Snr Mgr: John Fay

D-U-N-S 13-812-4214
MARKONE FINANCIAL LLC
6410 Sthpint Pkwy Ste 300, Jacksonville, FL 32216
Tel (904) 899-8300 *Founded/Ownrshp* 2001
Sales NA *EMP* 77
SIC 6141 Automobile loans, including insurance
Mng Dir: Bruce Newmark
Sr VP: Joe Giliberto
IT Man: Nikh Nath
Sls Mgr: Randy Spradlin

D-U-N-S 06-113-5182
MARKOR ENTERPRISES INC
MCDONALD'S
1126 Bradshaw Dr, Florence, AL 35630-1438
Tel (256) 764-3335 *Founded/Ownrshp* 1964
Sales 10.4MM^E *EMP* 375
SIC 5812 Fast-food restaurant, chain; Fast-food restaurant, chain
Pr: Robert Korink
VP: Mike Martin

D-U-N-S 61-982-3362 IMP
MARKOS & WIDLY FOUNDATION
AMERICAN FURNITURE ALLIANCE
785 E Harrison St Ste 100, Corona, CA 92879-1350
Tel (951) 279-0900 *Founded/Ownrshp* 1987
Sales 24.6MM^E *EMP* 130
SIC 2515 5021 Mattresses & bedsprings; Furniture; Mattresses & bedsprings; Furniture
CEO: Mark Markos
**Pr:* John Widly

D-U-N-S 00-432-7417 IMP
MARKOVITZ ENTERPRISES INC (PA)
FLOWLINE DIVISION
1400 New Butler Rd, New Castle, PA 16101
Tel (724) 452-4500 *Founded/Ownrshp* 1930, 1989
Sales 42.9MM^E *EMP* 250
SIC 3498 3462 Pipe fittings, fabricated from purchased pipe; Iron & steel forgings; Pipe fittings, fabricated from purchased pipe; Iron & steel forgings
Pr: James S Markovitz
**Pr:* Brad Hood
**Treas:* Anthony W Bartley
Sr Cor Off: Phil Mavrich
IT Man: Kyle Blake
Info Man: Sally Palkovich
VP Opers: Bob Garvin
Plnt Mgr: Terry Gibbson
Sls Mgr: David Bender
Sls Mgr: Margaret Clark

MARKQUART CHEVROLET
See MARKQUART INC

D-U-N-S 05-449-4539
MARKQUART INC (WI)
MARKQUART CHEVROLET
2191 S Prairie View Rd, Chippewa Falls, WI 54729-6305
Tel (715) 833-0444 *Founded/Ownrshp* 1970, 1981
Sales 70.3MM^E *EMP* 200
SIC 5511 Automobiles, new & used; Automobiles, new & used
Pr: David Markquart
**Prin:* Leroy Marquart

D-U-N-S 00-692-5515
MARKS & MORGAN JEWELERS INC (GA)
(*Suby of* SIGNET HOLDINGS LTD)
375 Ghent Rd, Fairlawn, OH 44333-4601
Tel (330) 668-5000 *Founded/Ownrshp* 1924
Sales 57.3MM^E *EMP* 1,200
SIC 5944 Jewelry, precious stones & precious metals

D-U-N-S 03-252-9364
MARKS BROTHERS INC
9455 Nw 104th St, Medley, FL 33178-1356
Tel (305) 805-6900 *Founded/Ownrshp* 1998
Sales 38.7MM^E *EMP* 115
Accts Berkowitz Pollack Brant Miami
SIC 1611 1629 Airport runway construction; Highway & street paving contractor; Land preparation construction; Airport runway construction; Highway & street paving contractor; Land preparation construction
Pr: Martin Marks
**Treas:* Thomas P Piero
VP: Robby Haas Jr
**VP:* Robert Haas
**VP:* James McQuaide
**VP:* Kurt H Olson

D-U-N-S 05-222-9981 IMP
MARKS BROTHERS INC (OR)
12265 Se 282nd Ave, Boring, OR 97009-7493
Tel (503) 663-0211 *Founded/Ownrshp* 1945, 1997
Sales 21.1MM^E *EMP* 50
SIC 3444 3443 Sheet metalwork; Fabricated plate work (boiler shop)
Pr: Nathan Marks
**Pr:* Nason J Marks
**VP:* Diane Marks

D-U-N-S 02-773-8350
MARKS CARD SHOPS INC
MARK'S HALLMARK SHOP
11805 Ne 99th St Ste 1350, Vancouver, WA 98682-2321
Tel (503) 234-4331 *Founded/Ownrshp* 1990
Sales 40.5MM^E *EMP* 450
SIC 5947 5199 Greeting cards; Gift shop; Gifts & novelties; Greeting cards; Gift shop; Gifts & novelties
Pr: James Cox
**Sec:* Sue Waters

MARK'S HALLMARK SHOP
See MARKS CARD SHOPS INC

MARK'S LEISURE TIME MARINE
See MEYERS RV SUPERSTORE INC

D-U-N-S 61-651-2828
MARKS ONEILL OBRIEN DOHERTY & KELLY PC
1800 John F Kennedy Blvd # 1900, Philadelphia, PA 19103-7421
Tel (215) 564-6688 *Founded/Ownrshp* 1986
Sales 23.5MM^E *EMP* 100
SIC 8111 General practice law office
Pr: Jerome E Marks
**VP:* Joseph M O'Neill
Off Mgr: Tom Leicht
Off Admin: Dottie Huha
DP Exec: John Oleniacz
IT Man: John Oleniacz
Counsel: Sebastian Goldstein
Counsel: Rosemary Kemmerle
Counsel: John J Moran

MARKS PAINT ALAMEDA
See MARKS PAINT MART

D-U-N-S 06-416-6135
MARKS PAINT MART
MARKS PAINT ALAMEDA
4211 Telegraph Ave, Oakland, CA 94609-2407
Tel (510) 653-0986 *Founded/Ownrshp* 1973
Sales 30.5MM^E *EMP* 22^E
SIC 5198 5231 Paints; Paint; Wallpaper
Pr: Anthony J Rago
**VP:* Donna Rago

D-U-N-S 07-105-0330
MARKS PANETH LLP
685 3rd Ave Fl 4, New York, NY 10017-8408
Tel (212) 503-8800 *Founded/Ownrshp* 1966
Sales 114.2MM^E *EMP* 560^E
SIC 8721 Certified public accountant; Certified public accountant
Mng Pt: Mark Levenfus
Pt: Steven L Brass
Mng Pt: Steven Baum
Mng Pt: Harry Moehringer
CFO: Brian L Fox
Exec: Steve Brass
IT Man: Ross Hauptman
Mktg Mgr: Kelly Parkhurst
Snr Mgr: Michael Arichea
Snr Mgr: Peter Blumkin
Snr Mgr: Joshua Hartman

MARK'S PLUMBING PARTS
See JOHN W GASPARINI INC

D-U-N-S 60-887-3097
MARKS TRANSPORT INC
CHAMPION SCION GULF FREEWAY
(*Suby of* AUTO NATION INC)
12111 Gulf Fwy, Houston, TX 77034-4501
Tel (713) 943-9900 *Founded/Ownrshp* 2001
Sales 31.3MM^E *EMP* 95
SIC 5511 5521 New & used car dealers; Automobiles, new & used; Pickups, new & used; Vans, new & used; Used car dealers; New & used car dealers; Automobiles, new & used; Pickups, new & used; Vans, new & used; Used car dealers
Pr: David Casto
**VP:* Maura Berney
Genl Mgr: Marian Palmore
Genl Mgr: Rafael Valdes

D-U-N-S 83-190-1207 IMP
■ **MARKS USA I LLC**
(*Suby of* NAPCO SECURITY TECHNOLOGIES INC) ★
365 Bayview Ave, Amityville, NY 11701-2801
Tel (800) 526-0233 *Founded/Ownrshp* 2008
Sales 26.7MM^E *EMP* 441^E
SIC 5072 Security devices, locks
Prin: Donna Ehman
VP: Scott Schramme

MARK'S VALLEY GRADING & EXCVTG
See MARKS VALLEY GRADING INC

D-U-N-S 80-044-6841
MARKS VALLEY GRADING INC
MARK'S VALLEY GRADING & EXCVTG
2425 N Center St, Mesa, AZ 85201-1002
Tel (480) 892-8025 *Founded/Ownrshp* 1993
Sales 21.8MM^E *EMP* 90
Accts John Tondrowski Fountain Hill
SIC 1794 Excavation work
Pr: Donald M Haight
**VP:* Brandon Haight

D-U-N-S 07-026-7521
MARKSMAN METAL CO INC
12260 42nd St Ne, Saint Michael, MN 55376-9531
Tel (763) 497-4640 *Founded/Ownrshp* 1976
Sales 25.3MM^E *EMP* 80
SIC 3444 3599 3469 3479 Sheet metalwork; Machine shop, jobbing & repair; Metal stampings; Painting of metal products
Pr: Peter Scharber
CFO: Rob Westland
**VP:* Flori Scharber
Genl Mgr: Don Fahey
Plnt Mgr: Mike Scharber
Prd Mgr: Rob Westlund
QI Cn Mgr: Cliff Willman

MARKSTEIN BEVERAGE COMPANY
See MARKSTEIN BEVERAGE CO OF SACRAMENTO

MARKSTEIN BEVERAGE CO
See MARKSTEIN SALES CO

D-U-N-S 11-818-2336 IMP
MARKSTEIN BEVERAGE CO
505 S Pacific St, San Marcos, CA 92078-4049
Tel (760) 744-9100 *Founded/Ownrshp* 1978
Sales 75.5MM^E *EMP* 120
SIC 5181 Beer & other fermented malt liquors; Beer & other fermented malt liquors
CEO: Kenneth W Markstein
**VP:* Steven Markstein
Exec: Susy Eckerle
Dir IT: Herman Huppert
S&M/VP: Tom Sarrette
Sls Mgr: Susan Tulenchik

D-U-N-S 02-880-0589
MARKSTEIN BEVERAGE CO OF SACRAMENTO
MARKSTEIN BEVERAGE COMPANY
60 Main Ave, Sacramento, CA 95838-2034
Tel (916) 920-3911 *Founded/Ownrshp* 1974
Sales 109.6MM^E *EMP* 150
SIC 5181 5149 Beer & ale; Soft drinks; Mineral or spring water bottling; Beer & ale; Soft drinks; Mineral or spring water bottling
CEO: Hayden Markstein
**Ch Bd:* Richard Markstein
**Pr:* Steve Markstein

Ex VP: Markstein Hayden
VP: Butch McElwee
Area Mgr: John Equinoa
Dir IT: Herman Huppert
IT Man: Ryan Strautman
VP Sls: Jim Janus
Sls Mgr: Jason Whitworth

D-U-N-S 78-181-8369 IMP
MARKSTEIN SALES CO
MARKSTEIN BEVERAGE CO
1645 Drive In Way, Antioch, CA 94509-8507
Tel (925) 755-1919 *Founded/Ownrshp* 1955
Sales 24.0MM^E *EMP* 130
SIC 5921 Beer (packaged)
Pr: Laura Lee Markstein
* *CFO:* Robert C Markstein
Genl Mgr: Jennifer Grant
Off Mgr: Lana Imes
Opers Mgr: Dan Berkley
Opers Mgr: Tom Roberts
Sls Mgr: Luis Ferreila
Sls Mgr: Steve Janowski
Snr Mgr: Matt Sage

D-U-N-S 03-449-6146
▲ MARKWEST ENERGY PARTNERS LP
1515 Arapahoe St, Denver, CO 80202-3150
Tel (303) 925-9200 *Founded/Ownrshp* 2002
Sales 2.1MMM *EMP* 1,404^E
Accts Deloitte & Touche Llp Denver
Tkr Sym MWE *Exch* NYS
SIC 1321 4922 1389 Natural gas liquids; Fractionating natural gas liquids; Natural gasoline production; Pipelines, natural gas; Storage, natural gas; Gas compressing (natural gas) at the fields; Processing service, gas; Natural gas liquids; Fractionating natural gas liquids; Natural gasoline production; Pipelines, natural gas; Storage, natural gas; Gas compressing (natural gas) at the fields; Processing service, gas
Ch Bd: Frank M Semple
Genl Pt: Markwest Energy GP
CFO: Nancy K Buese
CFO: Nancy Masten-Buese
CFO: Gerry Twoniuk
Treas: Stephen C Newman
Ofcr: Robert Craft
VP: Bryan Teets
VP Bus Dev: Bert Dillman
Exec: Pam Collins
Dir Bus: Jim Bryant

D-U-N-S 18-835-4799 EXP
■ MARKWEST HYDROCARBON INC
(*Suby of* MARKWEST ENERGY PARTNERS LP) ★
1515 Arapahoe St, Denver, CO 80202-3150
Tel (303) 290-8700 *Founded/Ownrshp* 2008
Sales 298.1MM^E *EMP* 318^E
SIC 1321 4924 Fractionating natural gas liquids; Propane (natural) production; Isobutane (natural) production; Butane (natural) production; Natural gas distribution; Fractionating natural gas liquids; Propane (natural) production; Isobutane (natural) production; Butane (natural) production; Natural gas distribution
Pr: Frank M Semple
Pr: Dan Cory
* *COO:* John C Mollenkopf
* *CFO:* Nancy K Buese
CFO: Nancy K Masten-Buese
* *Treas:* Andrew L Schroeder
* *Sr VP:* C Corwin Bromley
Sr VP: Randy S Nickerson
VP: Richard A Ostberg
VP: Richard Ostberg
Mktg Dir: Russ Moran
Board of Directors: Michael L Beatty, Donald C Heppermann, William A Kellstrom, Anne E Mounsey, Karen Rogers, William F Wallace, Donald D Wolf

D-U-N-S 03-960-8421
■ MARKWEST JAVELINA CO LLC
(*Suby of* MARKWEST ENERGY PARTNERS LP) ★
1515 Arapahoe St 1, Denver, CO 80202-3150
Tel (303) 925-9200 *Founded/Ownrshp* 2008
Sales 21.4MM^E *EMP* 64
SIC 1389 Processing service, gas
Pr: Frank M Semple

D-U-N-S 96-360-8331
■ MARKWEST LIBERTY MIDSTREAM & RESOURCES LLC
(*Suby of* MARKWEST ENERGY PARTNERS LP) ★
1515 Arapahoe St, Denver, CO 80202-3150
Tel (866) 858-0482 *Founded/Ownrshp* 2009
Sales 34.0MM^E *EMP* 123^E
SIC 4922 Storage, natural gas
CEO: Frank Semple
* *CFO:* Nancy Buese
* *Treas:* Andy Schroeder

D-U-N-S 14-326-8097
■ MARKWEST OKLAHOMA GAS CO LLC
(*Suby of* MARKWEST ENERGY PARTNERS LP) ★
1515 Arapahoe St Ste 1600, Denver, CO 80202-2137
Tel (303) 925-9200 *Founded/Ownrshp* 2003
Sales 52.7MM^E *EMP* 98
SIC 1382 Oil & gas exploration services; Oil & gas exploration services
CEO: Frank M Semple
* *VP:* Nancy K Buese

D-U-N-S 13-540-7760 IMP/EXP
MARKWINS BEAUTY PRODUCTS INC
(*Suby of* MARKWINS INTERNATIONAL CORP) ★
22067 Ferrero, City of Industry, CA 91789-5214
Tel (909) 595-8898 *Founded/Ownrshp* 2003
Sales 43.1MM^E *EMP* 66
SIC 5122 Cosmetics
Pr: Eric Chen
* *Sr VP:* Shawn Haynes
* *Sr VP:* James Koeppl

D-U-N-S 11-331-3969 IMP
MARKWINS INTERNATIONAL CORP
22067 Ferrero, Walnut, CA 91789-5214
Tel (909) 595-8898 *Founded/Ownrshp* 1983
Sales 296.4MM *EMP* 302
Accts Mcgladrey Llp Los Angeles Ca
SIC 2844 Cosmetic preparations; Cosmetic preparations
Pr: Sung-Tsei Eric Chen
Pr: Jeff Rogers
CFO: Leslie H Hernandez
VP: Mark Law

MARKYS CAVIAR INTL FD EMPORIUM
See OPTIMUS INC

D-U-N-S 04-974-9075
MARLABS INC
1 Corporate Pl S Fl 3, Piscataway, NJ 08854-6116
Tel (732) 694-1000 *Founded/Ownrshp* 1996
Sales 154.6MM^E *EMP* 900
SIC 7371 Computer software development & applications; Computer software development & applications
Pr: Vadakekkara Siby A
Pt: Sandhya Durai
Pr: Hari Koman
* *Pr:* Balram Srinivasan
* *CFO:* Krishnan Ramachandran
VP: Georgy Jose
* *VP:* Jay Nair
VP: Venu Palyam
Exec: Seema Adhangale
Assoc Dir: Shibu Varghese
Dir Bus: Sam Alexander

MARLAND CLUTCH
See FORMSPRAG LLC

D-U-N-S 78-154-2709
MARLBORO CENTRAL SCHOOL DISTRICT
1510 Route 9w Ste 202, Marlboro, NY 12542-5425
Tel (845) 236-5804 *Founded/Ownrshp* 1950
Sales 11.5MM^E *EMP* 350
SIC 8211 Public elementary & secondary schools; Public elementary & secondary schools
Prin: Raymond Castellani
IT Man: Suzanne Smith
Schl Brd P: Stephen Jennison
Snr Mgr: Robin Hecht

MARLBORO CENTRAL SCHOOL DST
See MARLBORO SCHOOL DISTRICT

D-U-N-S 15-956-8005
MARLBORO COUNTY SCHOOL DISTRICT
122 Broad St, Bennettsville, SC 29512-4002
Tel (843) 479-4016 *Founded/Ownrshp* 1850
Sales 39.6MM^E *EMP* 751
Accts Derrick Stubbs 7 Stith Llp C
SIC 8211 Public elementary & secondary schools; Public elementary & secondary schools
Ex Dir: Herbert Gould
MIS Dir: James Tool
Dir IT: Jimmy Toole
Schl Brd P: Michael Toms
Teacher Pr: Barbara McCall
HC Dir: Deborah McLaurin

D-U-N-S 00-279-7587
MARLBORO ELECTRIC COOPERATIVE INC (SC)
25415-401 Byp E, Bennettsville, SC 29512
Tel (843) 479-3855 *Founded/Ownrshp* 1939
Sales 75.6MM *EMP* 33
Accts Mclemo Iddlebrooks & Co Llc M
SIC 4911 Distribution, electric power; Distribution, electric power
CEO: William Fleming Jr
* *CFO:* Annie Crowley

D-U-N-S 10-005-6175
MARLBORO SCHOOL DISTRICT
MARLBORO CENTRAL SCHOOL DST
1510 Route 9w, Marlboro, NY 12542-5425
Tel (845) 236-5800 *Founded/Ownrshp* 1935
Sales 47.9MM *EMP* 360
SIC 8211 8748 Public elementary school; Public junior high school; Public senior high school; Business consulting; Public elementary school; Public junior high school; Public senior high school; Business consulting

D-U-N-S 04-751-2215
MARLBORO TOWNSHIP (INC)
1979 Township Dr, Marlboro, NJ 07746-2247
Tel (732) 536-0200 *Founded/Ownrshp* 1848
Sales NA *EMP* 450
Accts Wiss & Company Llp Iselin N
SIC 9111 Executive offices; ; Executive offices;
Adm Dir: Sarah Paris
Adm Dir: Donna Pignatelli
Dir IT: Joseph Orlando
Snr Mgr: Matt Baeder

D-U-N-S 07-825-2350
MARLBORO TOWNSHIP BOARD OF EDUCATION
1980 Township Dr, Marlboro, NJ 07746-2247
Tel (732) 972-2000 *Founded/Ownrshp* 1925
Sales 88.7MM *EMP* 700
Accts Walter J Brash Pine Brook N
SIC 8211 Public elementary & secondary schools; High school, junior or senior; Public elementary & secondary schools; High school, junior or senior
Tech Mgr: Lee Quackenbush

D-U-N-S 07-979-9153
MARLBORO TOWNSHIP SCHOOL DISTRICT
1980 Township Dr, Marlboro, NJ 07746-2247
Tel (732) 972-2000 *Founded/Ownrshp* 2015
Sales 7.2MM^E *EMP* 717^E
SIC 8211 Public elementary & secondary schools
Teacher Pr: Jonanthan Hart
HC Dir: Linda Attanasio

D-U-N-S 07-172-3472
MARLBOROUGH HOSPITAL
157 Union St, Marlborough, MA 01752-1297
Tel (508) 481-5000 *Founded/Ownrshp* 1890, 1986
Sales 70.0MM *EMP* 650
SIC 8062 General medical & surgical hospitals; General medical & surgical hospitals
CEO: Steven Roach
Chf Rad: Christopher Fowler
Chf Rad: Ronald H Garrell
* *Ch Bd:* Neil Ferris
* *Pr:* Karen Moore
* *CFO:* Robert Crosby
CFO: Jeffrey Dion
* *CFO:* Steven McCue
Ofcr: Nancy Manchester
* *VP:* Ellen Carlucci
VP: David Duncan
VP: Charles Pagnam
VP: Veronica Rosa
VP: Michele Streeter
VP: Allison Wollen
Dir Lab: Theresa Canale
Dir Rad: Ronald Garrell
Dir Rad: Ducksoo Kim
Dir Rad: Mark Sykes
Dir Bus: Tim Yang

D-U-N-S 01-323-6576
MARLBOROUGH PUBLIC SCHOOLS
17 Washington St, Marlborough, MA 01752-2225
Tel (508) 460-3553 *Founded/Ownrshp* 1890
Sales 1.1M *EMP* 660
SIC 8211 Public elementary & secondary schools; Public elementary & secondary schools
Schl Brd P: Arthur Vigeant

D-U-N-S 03-037-6685
MARLBOROUGH SCHOOL (CA)
250 S Rossmore Ave, Los Angeles, CA 90004-3742
Tel (323) 935-1147 *Founded/Ownrshp* 1889
Sales 34.4MM *EMP* 115
Accts Armanino Llp San Ramon Ca
SIC 8211 Preparatory school; Preparatory school
HC Dir: Jeanette W Chitjian

D-U-N-S 13-310-7164
■ MARLETTE HOMES
(*Suby of* CLAYTON HOMES INC) ★
400 W Elm Ave, Hermiston, OR 97838-1021
Tel (541) 567-5546 *Founded/Ownrshp* 2009
Sales 127.4MM^E *EMP* 1,654^E
SIC 3999 Advertising curtains
Pr: Walter E Wells
Genl Mgr: Michael Wolf
Mtls Mgr: K C Cannell
Sfty Mgr: David Hodges
Plnt Mgr: Richard Schmidt

D-U-N-S 00-531-7763
MARLETTE HOMES INC
221 Us Highway 20, Middlebury, IN 46540-7201
Tel (219) 825-5881 *Founded/Ownrshp* 1989
Sales 35.6MM^E *EMP* 850
SIC 2451 Mobile homes, except recreational; Mobile buildings: for commercial use; Mobile homes, except recreational; Mobile buildings: for commercial use
Pr: William G Edwards
Treas: Douglas Muir
* *VP:* John P Guequierre
VP: Robert A Smith
VP: Myles Standish

D-U-N-S 07-632-3633
MARLETTE REGIONAL HOSPITAL
M R H
2770 Main St, Marlette, MI 48453-1141
Tel (989) 635-4000 *Founded/Ownrshp* 1951
Sales 46.5MM^E *EMP* 480
SIC 8062 General medical & surgical hospitals; General medical & surgical hospitals
CEO: Daniel Babcock
Chf Rad: Peter Clive
* *Ch Bd:* Les Phillips
CFO: Dan Babcock
Dir OR: Trisha Ludescher
Dir Rx: Leonard Ligeski
Site Mgr: Brenda Krause
Nrsg Dir: Hilda Hebberd
Snr Mgr: William Halacoglu

D-U-N-S 04-282-4013 EXP
MARLEY BEVERAGE CO LLC
MARLEY BEVERAGES
27777 Franklin Rd # 1640, Southfield, MI 48034-2337
Tel (248) 746-7044 *Founded/Ownrshp* 2009
Sales 20.4MM^E *EMP* 50
SIC 5149 Beverages, except coffee & tea

MARLEY BEVERAGES
See MARLEY BEVERAGE CO LLC

D-U-N-S 00-713-1816 IMP
■ MARLEY CO LLC
S P X
(*Suby of* SPX CORP) ★
13515 Balntyn Corp Pl, Charlotte, NC 28277-2706
Tel (704) 752-4400 *Founded/Ownrshp* 1922, 2001
Sales 219.1MM^E *EMP* 2,600
SIC 3443 3433 3586 3561 3634 Cooling towers, metal plate; Heat exchangers, plate type; Heating equipment, except electric; Measuring & dispensing pumps; Pumps & pumping equipment; Heating units, electric (radiant heat): baseboard or wall; Cooling towers, metal plate; Heat exchangers, plate type; Heating equipment, except electric; Measuring & dispensing pumps; Pumps & pumping equipment; Heating units, electric (radiant heat): baseboard or wall
CEO: Steve Zeller
* *CFO:* Patrick J O'Leary
VP: Darren Dickson
* *VP:* Robert B Foreman
* *VP:* Christopher J Kearney
VP: Sue Simmonds
Manager: David Lusignolo
Board of Directors: Robert E Drury, G A Eisenberg

D-U-N-S 07-913-8997
■ MARLEY ENGINEERED PRODUCTS LLC
(*Suby of* SPX CORP) ★
470 Beauty Spot Rd E, Bennettsville, SC 29512-2770
Tel (843) 479-4006 *Founded/Ownrshp* 2002
Sales 23.4MM^E *EMP* 91^E
SIC 8711 Heating & ventilation engineering
Rgnl Mgr: Sean Pesce
QA Dir: Jamie Rhodes
Opers Mgr: Larry Caulder
Opers Mgr: Todd Hoover
Sls Dir: Paul Adair

D-U-N-S 92-740-3212
MARLEY PRECISION INC
(*Suby of* MARUEI INDUSTRIES CO.,LTD.)
455 Fritz Keiper Blvd, Battle Creek, MI 49037-7305
Tel (269) 963-7374 *Founded/Ownrshp* 1995
Sales 26.3MM^E *EMP* 250
SIC 3714 Motor vehicle parts & accessories; Motor vehicle parts & accessories
Pr: Shigemitsu Takagi
* *Pr:* Hiro Kitagawa
* *Ex VP:* Kenji Takagi
* *VP:* Todd Greer
Genl Mgr: Ken Reeves

D-U-N-S 02-646-0891 IMP
■ MARLEY-WYLAIN CO
WEIL-MCLAIN
(*Suby of* SPX CORP) ★
999 Mcclintock Dr Ste 200, Burr Ridge, IL 60527-0824
Tel (630) 560-3703 *Founded/Ownrshp* 2009
Sales 84.4MM^E *EMP* 300^E
SIC 3433 Boilers, low-pressure heating: steam or hot water; Boilers, low-pressure heating: steam or hot water
Pr: Tom Blashill
* *CFO:* Dan Watanapongse
* *Sr VP:* Tony Curran
VP: Wayne Barksdale
* *VP:* Greg Brennxcke
* *VP:* Keith McLeod
* *VP:* Paul Michelich
* *VP:* Bob Somers
* *VP:* Gordon Stretch
* *Dir IT:* Jeff Grayam
IT Man: John Kopf

D-U-N-S 82-549-1082
■ MARLIN BUSINESS BANK
(*Suby of* MARLIN BUSINESS SERVICES CORP) ★
2795 E Cottonwood Pkwy # 120, Salt Lake City, UT 84121-7092
Tel (888) 479-9111 *Founded/Ownrshp* 2005
Sales NA *EMP* 25^E
SIC 6111 Federal & federally sponsored credit agencies; Federal & federally sponsored credit agencies
Pr: Raymond Dardano
* *Ofcr:* George F Coburn

D-U-N-S 13-838-8793
▲ MARLIN BUSINESS SERVICES CORP
300 Fellowship Rd, Mount Laurel, NJ 08054-1201
Tel (888) 479-9111 *Founded/Ownrshp* 2003
Sales 88.7MM *EMP* 285^E
Tkr Sym MRLN *Exch* NGS
SIC 7389 7359 6022 Financial services; Equipment rental & leasing; State commercial banks; Financial services; Equipment rental & leasing; State commercial banks
CEO: Edward J Siciliano
CFO: W Taylor Kamp
Assoc VP: Roger Beil
Sr VP: Edward R Dietz
VP: Mark Giallombardo
VP: Mark Scardigli
VP: David Sowell
VP: Greg Sting
VP: Russell L Walraven
Prgrm Mgr: Mark Kelly
Sales Exec: Gary Crawford
Board of Directors: John J Calamari, Lawrence J Deangelo, Scott Heimes, Kevin J McGinty, Matthew J Sullivan, J Christopher Teets, James W Wert

D-U-N-S 62-159-5763
MARLIN COASTAL LLC
(*Suby of* MARLIN ENERGY LLC) ★
3861 Ambssdor Cffery Pkwy, Lafayette, LA 70503-5267
Tel (337) 769-0032 *Founded/Ownrshp* 2004
Sales 80.0MM *EMP* 30
SIC 1311 1382 Crude petroleum & natural gas; Oil & gas exploration services; Crude petroleum & natural gas; Oil & gas exploration services
CFO: Eugene Menzel

D-U-N-S 19-096-3749
MARLIN ENERGY LLC
3861 Ambassador Caffery P, Lafayette, LA 70503-5270
Tel (337) 769-0032 *Founded/Ownrshp* 2003
Sales 88.5MM^E *EMP* 35^E
SIC 1311 1382 Crude petroleum & natural gas production; Oil & gas exploration services
CFO: Beau Minvielle
VP: Clint Credeur

D-U-N-S 61-163-9688
MARLIN EQUITY PARTNERS III LP
338 Pier Ave, Hermosa Beach, CA 90254-3617
Tel (310) 364-0100 *Founded/Ownrshp* 2009
Sales 45.6MM^E *EMP* 230^E
SIC 6799 Investors; Venture capital companies; Investors; Venture capital companies

D-U-N-S 80-044-9055
MARLIN EQUITY PARTNERS LLC
338 Pier Ave, Hermosa Beach, CA 90254-3617
Tel (310) 364-0100 *Founded/Ownrshp* 2005
Sales 2.9MMM^E *EMP* 8,300
SIC 6282 Investment advisory service; Investment advisory service

D-U-N-S 82-615-9175
MARLIN HOLDCO LP
3301 Benson Dr Ste 601, Raleigh, NC 27609-7331
Tel (919) 325-3000 *Founded/Ownrshp* 2007
Sales 688.6MM^E *EMP* 1,601
SIC 4953

MARLIN MAZDA
See MAZDA OF NORTH MIAMI

D-U-N-S 62-362-6954
MARLIN MIDSTREAM LLC
12140 Wickchester Ln # 100, Houston, TX 77079-1219
Tel (832) 200-3702 *Founded/Ownrshp* 2002
Sales 24.8MM[E] *EMP* 15
SIC 5172 Gasoline
Ch: W Keith Maxwell III
**CFO:* Amanda Bush
**Treas:* Dennis Vermette
**Ex VP:* Terry D Jones
**Ex VP:* Nathen Kroeker
**VP:* Terry Guth
**VP:* Jeremy Ham

D-U-N-S 15-218-2168
MARLIN NETWORK INC
I MARLIN
1200 E Woodhurst Dr Ste V, Springfield, MO 65804-4240
Tel (417) 885-4534 *Founded/Ownrshp* 1985
Sales 21.6MM[E] *EMP* 100
SIC 7311 8742 Advertising agencies; Marketing consulting services
CEO: Dennis Marlin
Sr VP: Doug Austin
Prd Mgr: Don Leveque
**Genl Couns:* Joseph Shepard
Art Dir: Matt Rose

D-U-N-S 80-312-9738
MARLIN OFFSHORE SERVICES INC
1330 Post Oak Blvd # 2160, Houston, TX 77056-3038
Tel (281) 565-1191 *Founded/Ownrshp* 2003
Sales 72.9MM *EMP* 8
Accts Pricewaterhousecoopers Llp Ho
SIC 1381 Drilling oil & gas wells; Drilling oil & gas wells
Pr: Robert J Gervais
VP: Tom Alleman

D-U-N-S 06-982-3110
MARLING & ASSOCIATES INC (MI)
20/20 CMP
20882 Harper Ave, Harper Woods, MI 48225-1142
Tel (313) 886-6210 *Founded/Ownrshp* 1966
Sales 42.6MM[E] *EMP* 120
SIC 5084 Materials handling machinery; Materials handling machinery
Pr: Robert F Marling
Off Mgr: Lynn Stultz

D-U-N-S 00-896-0544
MARLING LUMBER CO INC (WI)
1801 E Washington Ave, Madison, WI 53704-5201
Tel (608) 244-4777 *Founded/Ownrshp* 1895
Sales 27.4MM[E] *EMP* 120
SIC 5211 3442 Lumber & other building materials; Cabinets, kitchen; Metal doors
Pr: John E Marling
**CFO:* Scott Bowers
**VP:* Kurt Marling
Sls Mgr: Curt Bostic
Sales Asso: Bryan Buenzli
Sales Asso: Doug Castro
Sales Asso: Doug Morgeson

D-U-N-S 01-439-4985
MARLINGTON LOCAL SCHOOL DISTRICT
10320 Moulin Ave Ne, Alliance, OH 44601-5906
Tel (330) 823-7458 *Founded/Ownrshp* 1956
Sales 24.5MM *EMP* 300
Accts Rea & Associates Inc
SIC 8211 Public elementary school; Public junior high school; Public senior high school; Public elementary school; Public junior high school; Public senior high school
Psych: Jon Young

D-U-N-S 36-231-0112 IMP/EXP
MARLITE INC
(*Suby of* NUDO PRODUCTS INC) ★
1 Marlite Dr, Dover, OH 44622-2361
Tel (330) 343-6621 *Founded/Ownrshp* 2015
Sales 49.9MM[E] *EMP* 200
SIC 2542 Partitions & fixtures, except wood; Partitions & fixtures, except wood
Pr: Daryl Rosser
**CFO:* Kimberly McBride
**VP:* Mark Jutte
**VP:* Greg Leary
**VP:* Greg Triplett
Telecom Ex: Betsy Young
Mktg Dir: Donna Dehart
Manager: Greg Endo
Manager: Michel Maeda-Shimura
Manager: Tim Pinnow

D-U-N-S 02-425-8766 IMP
MARLO FURNITURE CO INC (DC)
3300 Marlo Ln, Forestville, MD 20747-4442
Tel (301) 735-2000 *Founded/Ownrshp* 1955
Sales 41.5MM[E] *EMP* 300
SIC 5712 Furniture stores; Furniture stores
Pr: Neal Glickfield
COO: Greg Zakarian
**CFO:* Daniel Romney
**VP:* Mark Stuart
**VP:* David Weinstein

D-U-N-S 78-043-7844 IMP
MARLOW WATSON INC
WATSON-MARLOW/BREDEL PUMPS
(*Suby of* SPIRAX-SARCO ENGINEERING PLC)
37 Upton Technology Park, Wilmington, MA 01887
Tel (800) 282-8823 *Founded/Ownrshp* 1991
Sales 81.0MM *EMP* 77
SIC 5084 Pumps & pumping equipment
CEO: James Whalen
Pr: Steven Lavargna
Ofcr: Paul Callahan
VP: Bill Mandel
VP: William Mandel
Tech Mgr: Michael Felder
Sls Mgr: Mark Atkinson
Sls Mgr: Kurt Krummrich
Sls Mgr: Peter Lambert

D-U-N-S 36-128-4875
MARLTON REHABILITATION HOSPITAL
(*Suby of* VIBRA HEALTHCARE LLC) ★
92 Brick Rd, Marlton, NJ 08053-2177
Tel (856) 988-8778 *Founded/Ownrshp* 2005
Sales 31.2MM *EMP* 230
SIC 8093 Rehabilitation center, outpatient treatment; Rehabilitation center, outpatient treatment
CEO: Michael Long
Dir Inf Cn: Lisa Keller
QA Dir: Phyllisi Schlichtmann
Nrsg Dir: Christine Kreeley
Occ Thrpy: Susan Lynn
HC Dir: Patti Brown

D-U-N-S 02-122-7376 IMP
MARLYN NUTRACEUTICALS INC
NATURALLY VITAMIN SUPPLEMENTS
4404 E Elwood St, Phoenix, AZ 85040-1909
Tel (480) 991-0200 *Founded/Ownrshp* 1987
Sales 25.2MM[E] *EMP* 80
SIC 2833 8011 Medicinal chemicals; Vitamins, natural or synthetic: bulk, uncompounded; Offices & clinics of medical doctors
CEO: Joachim Lehmann
**Pr:* Meliha Jelinic
Sfty Mgr: Melvina Bricker
Sfty Mgr: Sara Garske
Plnt Mgr: Dean Harbison

MARMALADE CAFE
See MARMALADE LLC

D-U-N-S 18-043-8889
MARMALADE LLC
MARMALADE CAFE
21300 Victory Blvd # 740, Woodland Hills, CA 91367-2525
Tel (310) 829-0093 *Founded/Ownrshp* 1991
Sales 21.9MM[E] *EMP* 575
SIC 5812 Cafe; Caterers; Cafe; Caterers
**CEO:* Richard G Morrow
Opers Mgr: Robert Fogarty

MARMAXX GROUP, THE
See NEWTON BUYING CORP

D-U-N-S 83-289-3460 IMP
■ **MARMAXX OPERATING CORP**
T.J. MAXX
(*Suby of* TJ MAXX) ★
770 Cochituate Rd, Framingham, MA 01701-4666
Tel (508) 390-1000 *Founded/Ownrshp* 1989
Sales 1.6MMM[E] *EMP* 20,000
SIC 5311 5651 Department stores, discount; Family clothing stores; Department stores, discount; Family clothing stores
CEO: Carol Maerowitz
**Pr:* Ernie Herrman
**VP:* Jeffrey Naylor
Dist Mgr: Reggie Coleman
Dist Mgr: Chris Jones
Dist Mgr: Karen Nelson
IT Man: Ann Dalton
Doctor: Regina Bartels

D-U-N-S 07-885-9298
MARMEN ENERGY CO
1820 N Plum Ave, Brandon, SD 57005-3031
Tel (605) 582-4500 *Founded/Ownrshp* 2013
Sales 68.7MM[E] *EMP* 220
SIC 3643 1799 3531 Electric connectors; Service station equipment installation, maintenance & repair; Marine related equipment
Pr: Patrick Pellerin

MARMI
See WOLFF SHOE CO

D-U-N-S 03-125-1820 IMP
MARMIE MOTORS INC
1724 10th St, Great Bend, KS 67530-4505
Tel (620) 792-2571 *Founded/Ownrshp* 1961
Sales 23.4MM[E] *EMP* 56
SIC 5511 New & used car dealers
Pr: Jerry Marmie
**Treas:* Jerry L Marmie

D-U-N-S 96-227-3814
■ **MARMON DISTRIBUTION SERVICES INC**
(*Suby of* MARMON HOLDINGS INC) ★
225 E Cunningham St, Butler, PA 16001-6018
Tel (724) 283-3000 *Founded/Ownrshp* 2009
Sales 162.2MM[E] *EMP* 960
SIC 5051 4213 Metals service centers & offices; Trucking, except local; Metals service centers & offices; Trucking, except local
Pr: Alan Wilkinson
**CFO:* Andrew N Seka
MIS Dir: Jay Powell
Opers Mgr: Greg Paugh
Corp Couns: Bambi Tucker

D-U-N-S 01-021-6679 IMP
■ **MARMON GROUP LLC** (CA)
PAN AMERICAN SCREW DIV
(*Suby of* UNION TANK CAR CO) ★
181 W Madison St Ste 2600, Chicago, IL 60602-4504
Tel (312) 372-9500 *Founded/Ownrshp* 1973
Sales 476.5MM[E] *EMP* 358
SIC 3452 5072 Bolts, nuts, rivets & washers; Bolts, nuts & screws; Bolts, nuts, rivets & washers; Bolts, nuts & screws
CEO: Frank Ptak

D-U-N-S 79-587-1581 IMP/EXP
■ **MARMON GROUP LLC**
(*Suby of* MARMON HOLDINGS INC) ★
181 W Madison St Ste 2600, Chicago, IL 60602-4504
Tel (312) 372-9500 *Founded/Ownrshp* 2012
Sales 1.1MMM[E] *EMP* 1,700
SIC 8748 Business consulting; Business consulting
CEO: Frank Ptak
**Treas:* Robert C Gluth
Sr VP: Mark Carrier
**VP:* James Angus
VP: Steve Bohnenkamp
VP: Leon Drake
**VP:* Kenneth P Fischl
VP: Don Hannon
VP: Paola Palmer
VP: Craig Phelon
**VP:* Randy Rizzo
**VP:* Robert Schaumann
VP: Kristi Thomasson
VP: Loren Veltrop
VP: Dan Veytsman
**VP:* Robert W Webb
**VP:* Henry J West
Dir Risk M: Donna Walker
Comm Dir: David Dees

D-U-N-S 09-141-4706 IMP
■ **MARMON HIGHWAY TECHNOLOGIES LLC**
(*Suby of* MARMON GROUP LLC) ★
5915 Chalkville Rd 300, Birmingham, AL 35235-8609
Tel (205) 508-2000 *Founded/Ownrshp* 1985
Sales 74.8MM[E] *EMP* 300
SIC 3714 Motor vehicle parts & accessories; Motor vehicle parts & accessories

D-U-N-S 05-227-8728 IMP/EXP
■ **MARMON HOLDINGS INC**
(*Suby of* BERKSHIRE HATHAWAY INC) ★
181 W Madison St Ste 2600, Chicago, IL 60602-4504
Tel (312) 372-9500 *Founded/Ownrshp* 1980, 2008
Sales 5.3MMM[E] *EMP* 20,881
Accts Deloitte & Touche Llp Chicago
SIC 5051 3351 3743 4741 3423 3589 Metals service centers & offices; Copper pipe; Tubing, copper & copper alloy; Wire, copper & copper alloy; Railway motor cars; Rental of railroad cars; Caulking tools, hand; Can openers, not electric; Water treatment equipment, industrial; Water purification equipment, household type; Metals service centers & offices; Copper pipe; Tubing, copper & copper alloy; Wire, copper & copper alloy; Railway motor cars; Rental of railroad cars; Caulking tools, hand; Can openers, not electric; Water treatment equipment, industrial; Water purification equipment, household type
Pr: Frank Ptak
**V Ch:* John Nichols
**CFO:* Robert K Lorch
**Ch:* Thomas J Pritzker
**Sr VP:* Robert W Webb
VP: Robert C Gluth

D-U-N-S 04-525-6138 IMP/EXP
■ **MARMON INDUSTRIAL LLC**
(*Suby of* MARMON HOLDINGS INC) ★
181 W Madison St Fl 26, Chicago, IL 60602-4510
Tel (312) 372-9500 *Founded/Ownrshp* 1995
Sales 529.6MM[E] *EMP* 5,188
SIC 3743 4741 3589 6159 3965 3492 Railway motor cars; Rental of railroad cars; Water treatment equipment, industrial; Machinery & equipment finance leasing; Fasteners; Control valves, fluid power: hydraulic & pneumatic; Railway motor cars; Rental of railroad cars; Water treatment equipment, industrial; Machinery & equipment finance leasing; Fasteners; Control valves, fluid power: hydraulic & pneumatic
Pr: John Nichols
CFO: Bob Lorch
Sr VP: Robert W Webb
VP: Lawrence Rist

D-U-N-S 00-147-9690 IMP/EXP
■ **MARMON INDUSTRIES LLC** (DE)
(*Suby of* ROCKWOOD HOLDING COMPANY)
181 W Madison St Ste 2600, Chicago, IL 60602-4504
Tel (312) 372-9500 *Founded/Ownrshp* 1969
Sales 47.6MM[E] *EMP* 650
Accts Ernst & Young Llp Chicago Il
SIC 3465 3621 3714 Hub caps, automobile: stamped metal; Rotors, for motors; Wheels, motor vehicle; Brake drums, motor vehicle; Hub caps, automobile: stamped metal; Rotors, for motors; Wheels, motor vehicle; Brake drums, motor vehicle
Pr: Robert A Pritzker
**VP:* Robert C Gluth
**VP:* Robert W Webb

D-U-N-S 07-919-5591
■ **MARMON RETAIL & END USER TECHNOLOGIES INC**
(*Suby of* MARMON HOLDINGS INC) ★
181 W Madison St Fl 26, Chicago, IL 60602-4510
Tel (312) 372-9500 *Founded/Ownrshp* 2013
Sales 400.0MM[E] *EMP* 125[E]
SIC 2599 Restaurant furniture, wood or metal
Prin: Robert B Davidson

D-U-N-S 07-874-5765 IMP
■ **MARMON RETAIL PRODUCTS INC**
RETAIL HOME IMPROVEMENT PDTS
(*Suby of* MARMON RETAIL & END USER TECHNOLOGIES INC) ★
1002 Industrial Way, Crothersville, IN 47229-9415
Tel (812) 793-2929 *Founded/Ownrshp* 2012
Sales 400.0MM *EMP* 125
SIC 3357 3351 Nonferrous wiredrawing & insulating; Copper rolling & drawing; Nonferrous wiredrawing & insulating; Copper rolling & drawing
Genl Mgr: Jared Argyle
Pr: Darren Salapka
Genl Mgr: Robert Kennedy
CTO: Brian Mill
Plnt Mgr: Rick McDonald
Prd Mgr: Vern Reardon
Sls&Mrk Ex: Alexis Ruddick

D-U-N-S 60-621-1287
■ **MARMON RETAIL SERVICES INC**
(*Suby of* MARMON HOLDINGS INC) ★
181 W Madison St, Chicago, IL 60602-4510
Tel (312) 332-0317 *Founded/Ownrshp* 2002
Sales 356.8MM[E] *EMP* 1,600[E]
SIC 2541 2542 Store fixtures, wood; Fixtures, store: except wood; Store fixtures, wood; Fixtures, store: except wood

D-U-N-S 04-817-5764 EXP
■ **MARMON UTILITY LLC**
(*Suby of* MARMON HOLDINGS INC) ★
53 Old Wilton Rd, Milford, NH 03055-3119
Tel (603) 673-2040 *Founded/Ownrshp* 1996
Sales 113.4MM[E] *EMP* 200
SIC 3357 Communication wire; Communication wire
Opers Mgr: Ann Hunt

D-U-N-S 82-845-7189
■ **MARMON WATER LLC**
(*Suby of* MARMON GROUP LLC) ★
1769a Jamestown Rd, Williamsburg, VA 23185
Tel (757) 258-2451 *Founded/Ownrshp* 2002
Sales 30.1MM[E] *EMP* 170[E]
SIC 5963 Bottled water delivery

D-U-N-S 00-791-0052 IMP/EXP
■ **MARMON/KEYSTONE LLC**
(*Suby of* BERKSHIRE HATHAWAY INC) ★
225 E Cunningham St, Butler, PA 16001-6018
Tel (724) 283-3000 *Founded/Ownrshp* 1907
Sales 314.3MM[E] *EMP* 950
SIC 5051 4213

D-U-N-S 07-340-6332 IMP
■ **MARMOT MOUNTAIN LLC**
(*Suby of* JARDEN CORP) ★
5789 State Farm Dr # 100, Rohnert Park, CA 94928-6308
Tel (707) 544-4590 *Founded/Ownrshp* 2004
Sales 50.2MM[E] *EMP* 200
SIC 2329

D-U-N-S 06-294-5571
MARNELL CORRAO ASSOCIATES INC
222 Via Marnell Way, Las Vegas, NV 89119-3522
Tel (702) 739-2000 *Founded/Ownrshp* 1982
Sales 52.4MM[E] *EMP* 126
SIC 1542 Commercial & office building contractors; Commercial & office building contractors
CEO: Anthony A Marnell II
**Pr:* Ary A Benoualid
CEO: Mike Anzelc
CFO: Jay Barrett
CFO: Rick Colvin
**Treas:* James A Barrett Jr
VP: Michael Woodward
Sfty Dirs: Dave Warnock

D-U-N-S 80-733-2973
MARNELL SHER GAMING LLC
M RESORT
12300 Las Vegas Blvd S, Henderson, NV 89044-9506
Tel (702) 298-4000 *Founded/Ownrshp* 2006
Sales 92.2MM[E] *EMP* 1,350[E]
SIC 7011 Resort hotel; Resort hotel
Pr: Anthony A Marnell III
**CFO:* James Barrett
CFO: Jason Early
**Ex VP:* Kari Dimler
**Ex VP:* Joseph Magliarditi
Sr VP: Bruce Howard
VP: Salinda Conklin
**VP:* Jay Francis
VP: Jania Lambert
VP: Anthony Matthews
**VP:* Cherisse Nicastro
**VP:* Stan Tims
**VP:* Robert Willis
Exec: Michael Demers

D-U-N-S 19-661-2295 IMP/EXP
MARNOY INTERESTS LTD
OFFICE PAVILION-HOUSTON
10030 Bent Oak Dr, Houston, TX 77040-3267
Tel (713) 803-0000 *Founded/Ownrshp* 1992
Sales 85.7MM[E] *EMP* 85
SIC 5021 Office furniture; Office furniture
Mng Pt: Steve Marnoy
**Pt:* Mollie Ellerkamp
**Pt:* Jim Gray
**Pt:* Shelly Liles
**Pt:* Aj Scardino
**Pt:* Maria Stringer

D-U-N-S 09-873-0773 IMP
■ **MAROCO LTD**
MAJESTIC ATHLETIC
(*Suby of* VF IMAGEWEAR INC) ★
2320 Newlins Mill Rd, Easton, PA 18045-7815
Tel (610) 746-6800 *Founded/Ownrshp* 2007
Sales 69.9MM[E] *EMP* 650
SIC 2329 2339 2261 5611 5621 5699 Men's & boys' sportswear & athletic clothing; Athletic (warmup, sweat & jogging) suits: men's & boys'; Athletic clothing: women's, misses' & juniors'; Finishing plants, cotton; Clothing, sportswear, men's & boys'; Ready-to-wear apparel, women's; Uniforms & work clothing; Sports apparel; Men's & boys' sportswear & athletic clothing; Athletic (warmup, sweat & jogging) suits: men's & boys'; Athletic clothing: women's, misses' & juniors'; Finishing plants, cotton; Clothing, sportswear, men's & boys'; Ready-to-wear apparel, women's; Uniforms & work clothing; Sports apparel
CEO: Faust E Capobianco III
**COO:* Jeff Green

D-U-N-S 07-737-3686
MAROEVICH OSHEA & COGHLAN INSURANCE INC
M O C INSURANCE SERVICES
44 Montgomery St Ste 1700, San Francisco, CA 94104-4704
Tel (415) 957-0600 *Founded/Ownrshp* 1969
Sales NA *EMP* 60
SIC 6411 Insurance brokers
CEO: Van Maroevich
**CFO:* Gerald Clifford
**Sr VP:* Peter Brown
**Sr VP:* Steve Elkins
**Sr VP:* Harry Humphrey
Sr VP: Fred Nagle
VP: Bill Grindell
**VP:* Theresa M Maroevich
VP: Paul Perlite
Dir Bus: Tyler Chalk

Dir Bus: Nicholas Dieter
Dir Bus: Brian Randolph

D-U-N-S 00-184-2277
MAROIS BROTHERS INC (MA)
115 Blackstone River Rd, Worcester, MA 01607-1491
Tel (508) 791-8134 *Founded/Ownrshp* 1919
Sales 23.0MM *EMP* 65
Accts Morris & Morris Pc Needham
SIC 1794 Excavation & grading, building construction; Excavation & grading, building construction
Pr: David M Winn
**Treas:* Ralph Marois
**Ex VP:* John R Brown

D-U-N-S 05-542-0558
MARON ELECTRIC CO
(*Suby of* MENLO INC) ★
5401 Fargo Ave, Skokie, IL 60077-3211
Tel (847) 626-6500 *Founded/Ownrshp* 1972
Sales 54.7MM *EMP* 182
Accts Fgmk Llc Bannockburn Illino
SIC 1731 General electrical contractor; General electrical contractor
Pr: Eric Nixon
Sec: Donald Schwartz
VP: Alan Kazemi
Dir IT: Jerry Seiling
Board of Directors: Robert E Neiman

D-U-N-S 07-891-2029
MARON PRODUCTS INC
1301 Industrial Dr, Mishawaka, IN 46544-5799
Tel (574) 259-1971 *Founded/Ownrshp* 1957
Sales 30.6MM^E *EMP* 85
SIC 3444 3469 Sheet metalwork; Stamping metal for the trade
Pr: Paul Mc Mahon
Plnt Mgr: Ken Whitley

MARONDA HOMES
See MARONDA INC

D-U-N-S 05-929-8232
MARONDA HOMES INC
IMPERIAL LUMBER & SUPPLY
(*Suby of* MARONDA HOMES) ★
11 Timberglen Dr, Imperial, PA 15126-9345
Tel (724) 695-1200 *Founded/Ownrshp* 1972
Sales 22.6MM^E *EMP* 75
SIC 1521 New construction, single-family houses
Pr: William Wolf
**Pr:* William J Wolfe
Ex VP: Richard Brown
VP: Greg Cox
VP: Dino Ferrari
VP: George Friedman
VP: Chad Johannesen
VP: Luther Riley
VP: Ray Sigmund
**VP:* Ron Wolfe
Sales Asso: Andrea Conway

D-U-N-S 14-705-5461
MARONDA HOMES INC OF FLORIDA
(*Suby of* MARONDA HOMES) ★
11 Timberglen Dr, Imperial, PA 15126-9345
Tel (724) 695-1200 *Founded/Ownrshp* 1972
Sales 65.3MM^E *EMP* 300
SIC 1521 New construction, single-family houses; New construction, single-family houses
Pr: William J Wolf
VP: Ronald Wolf

D-U-N-S 05-930-1606
MARONDA INC
MARONDA HOMES
11 Timberglen Dr, Imperial, PA 15126-9267
Tel (724) 695-1200 *Founded/Ownrshp* 1972
Sales 169.3MM^E *EMP* 380
SIC 6552 1521 Subdividers & developers; New construction, single-family houses; Subdividers & developers; New construction, single-family houses
Ch Bd: William J Wolf
**Pr:* Ron Wolf
**Sec:* Ronald W Wolf

D-U-N-S 60-952-6371
MARONDA SYSTEMS INC FLORIDA
(*Suby of* MARONDA HOMES) ★
11 Timberglen Dr, Imperial, PA 15126-9267
Tel (724) 695-1200 *Founded/Ownrshp* 1990
Sales 25.5MM^E *EMP* 275
SIC 2439 Trusses, wooden roof; Trusses, wooden roof
Pr: William J Wolf
**VP:* Samuel L Katanich

D-U-N-S 08-322-0848
MAROON GROUP LLC
1390 Jaycox Rd, Avon, OH 44011-1372
Tel (440) 937-1000 *Founded/Ownrshp* 1977
Sales 48.1MM^E *EMP* 56
SIC 5169 Chemicals & allied products
CEO: Mark Reichard
COO: Mike McKenna
CFO: Brian Wilson
Chf Cred: Howard Hubert
CTO: Mark Maroon
Sls Mgr: Rodger Cram
Sls Mgr: Steve Mensen

D-U-N-S 12-891-3345
■ **MAROONE CHEVROLET FT LAUDERDALE INC**
(*Suby of* AUTONATION INC) ★
1300 N Federal Hwy, Fort Lauderdale, FL 33304-1428
Tel (954) 564-5271 *Founded/Ownrshp* 1997
Sales 23.4MM^E *EMP* 80
SIC 5511 Automobiles, new & used; Pickups, new & used; Automobiles, new & used; Pickups, new & used
Pr: Michael Maroone

D-U-N-S 06-693-0256 EXP
■ **MAROONE CHEVROLET LLC**
MAROONE CHVRLET PEMBROKE PINES
(*Suby of* AUTONATION INC) ★
8600 Pines Blvd, Pembroke Pines, FL 33024-6534
Tel (954) 433-3377 *Founded/Ownrshp* 1998
Sales 128.6MM^E *EMP* 572
SIC 5511 Automobiles, new & used; Pickups, new & used; Automobiles, new & used; Pickups, new & used
Sls Mgr: Nikita Ramlogan

MAROONE CHEVROLET OF MIAMI
See ABRAHAM CHEVROLET-MIAMI INC

MAROONE CHEVROLET OF WEST DADE
See BEACON MOTORS INC

MAROONE CHVRLET PEMBROKE PINES
See MAROONE CHEVROLET LLC

MAROONE FORD OF MARGATE
See MULLINAX FORD SOUTH INC

MAROONE FORD OF MIAMI
See BULL MOTORS LLC

MAROONE HONDA
See HOLLYWOOD IMPORTS LIMITED INC

D-U-N-S 00-213-6877 IMP
MAROTTA CONTROLS INC (NJ)
78 Boonton Ave, Montville, NJ 07045
Tel (973) 334-7800 *Founded/Ownrshp* 1943
Sales 31.2MM^E *EMP* 150^E
Accts Jh Cohn Llp Roseland Nj
SIC 3494 3823 Valves & pipe fittings; Industrial instrmnts msrmnt display/control process variable; Valves & pipe fittings; Industrial instrmnts msrmnt display/control process variable
Ch Bd: Thomas S Marotta
**Pr:* Patrick A Marotta
CEO: Lance W Lord
**CFO:* Kevin L Price
Treas: Louis J Vetere
**VP:* Steven A Fox
**VP:* Walter Gilmore
VP: Michael Leahan
**Dir Sec:* Michael J Leahan
Prgrm Mgr: Ed Specht
Prgrm Mgr: Megan Surowiec
Board of Directors: Gary Cademartori, Lance W Lord, Patrick Marotta, Thomas C Marotta, Fred P Moasally, Wayne Positan, Will Trafton, Joseph Zimonis

D-U-N-S 60-317-6090
MAROTTA ENTERPRISES INC
CLEANING TECHNOLOGIES
2106 N Saint Marys St, San Antonio, TX 78212-4139
Tel (210) 737-0709 *Founded/Ownrshp* 1989
Sales 20.8MM^E *EMP* 120
SIC 5087

D-U-N-S 01-918-7603
MAROTTO CORP
ALL AMERICAN MAINTENANCE
9620 Topanga Canyon Pl D, Chatsworth, CA 91311-4139
Tel (818) 775-0320 *Founded/Ownrshp* 1989
Sales 11.2MM^E *EMP* 319
SIC 7349 Building maintenance, except repairs; Building maintenance, except repairs
Pr: Mario Marotto
**VP:* Nancy Stout

D-U-N-S 05-896-8942
MAROUS BROTHERS CONSTRUCTION INC
1702 Joseph Lloyd Pkwy, Willoughby, OH 44094-8028
Tel (440) 951-3904 *Founded/Ownrshp* 1980
Sales 148.1MM^E *EMP* 300
SIC 1521 1751 Single-family housing construction; Carpentry work; Single-family housing construction; Carpentry work
Pr: Adelbert Marous
**Sec:* Kenneth Marous
**VP:* Scott Marous

D-U-N-S 88-419-2584
MARPAC CONSTRUCTION LLC
1225 S Weller St Ste 500, Seattle, WA 98144-1906
Tel (206) 329-4992 *Founded/Ownrshp* 1995
Sales 31.1MM *EMP* 48
SIC 1522 1542 Multi-family dwelling construction; Commercial & office building, new construction
**IT Man:* Donald Mar
Netwrk Mgr: SAI Chaleunphonh
Snr Mgr: Jimmy Sornito

D-U-N-S 07-376-2064
MARPLE NEWTOWN SCHOOL AUTHORITY
40 Media Line Rd, Newtown Square, PA 19073-4647
Tel (610) 359-4200 *Founded/Ownrshp* 1953
Sales 41.1MM^E *EMP* 708
SIC 8211 Public senior high school; Public senior high school
Psych: Maria Toglia

D-U-N-S 05-209-2640 IMP/EXP
MARPOSS CORP
(*Suby of* MARPOSS SPA)
3300 Cross Creek Pkwy, Auburn Hills, MI 48326-2758
Tel (248) 370-0404 *Founded/Ownrshp* 1963
Sales 44.7MM^E *EMP* 130
SIC 5084 Measuring & testing equipment, electrical; Measuring & testing equipment, electrical
Pr: Edward Vella
Treas: Maureen Allen
Mng Dir: Edoardo Possati
Telecom Ex: Tom Korth
IT Man: Tom Sun
Tech Mgr: Luca Trevisani
VP Opers: John Ozimek
Ql Cn Mgr: Antonio Bolognesi
Sales Exec: Rose Nelson
Manager: Phil Kimble
Sls Mgr: John Beaumont

MARQUARDT HEATING
See HOPSON OIL CO INC

D-U-N-S 07-085-0102 IMP
MARQUARDT SWITCHES INC (DE)
(*Suby of* MARQUARDT MECHATRONIK GMBH)
2711 Us Route 20, Cazenovia, NY 13035-9405
Tel (315) 655-8050 *Founded/Ownrshp* 1975, 1981
Sales 219.7MM *EMP* 555
Accts Fust Charles Chambers Llp Sy
SIC 3625 3613 Switches, electric power; Switchgear & switchboard apparatus; Switches, electric power; Switchgear & switchboard apparatus
Pr: Jochen Becker
**Ch Bd:* Harold Marquardt
**CFO:* John Jelfo

D-U-N-S 01-369-4877
MARQUEE CINEMAS INC
552 Ragland Rd, Beckley, WV 25801-9727
Tel (304) 255-4036 *Founded/Ownrshp* 1998
Sales 34.8MM^E *EMP* 650
SIC 7832 Motion picture theaters, except drive-in; Motion picture theaters, except drive-in
Pr: Curtis McCall
Pr: Toni McCall
**Treas:* Cindy Ramsden
**VP:* James Cox
Genl Mgr: Jeremy Rawls
Mktg Dir: Robin Shumate

D-U-N-S 06-953-6225
MARQUES FOOD DISTRIBUTORS INC (LA)
700 Brown Ave, Harvey, LA 70058-4020
Tel (504) 366-3745 *Founded/Ownrshp* 1949
Sales 47.2MM^E *EMP* 65
SIC 5141 5144 Groceries, general line; Eggs; Groceries, general line; Eggs
Pr: Willie Alphonse Marque
**VP:* Steven Marks
**VP:* Karen W Marque
VP Opers: Steven Marque

MARQUETTE
See RETIREMENT LIVING INC

D-U-N-S 10-003-5757
MARQUETTE AREA PUBLIC SCHOOLS
1201 W Fair Ave, Marquette, MI 49855-2668
Tel (906) 225-4295 *Founded/Ownrshp* 1852
Sales 71.2M *EMP* 400
Accts Anderson Tackman & Company P
SIC 8211 Public elementary & secondary schools; Public senior high school; Public junior high school; Public elementary school; Public elementary & secondary schools; Public senior high school; Public junior high school; Public elementary school

MARQUETTE BANK
See MARQUETTE NATIONAL CORP

D-U-N-S 78-785-5548
MARQUETTE BANK
10000 W 151st St, Orland Park, IL 60462-3140
Tel (708) 364-9144 *Founded/Ownrshp* 1946
Sales NA *EMP* 550^E
SIC 6022 State commercial banks; State commercial banks
Pr: George Moncada
**Ch:* Paul McCarthy
Ex VP: Betty Kosky
Sr VP: Thomas Burgin
Sr VP: Lee Zagrakalaf
VP: Jack Baker
VP: Robert Gallardo
VP: Jeff Macdonald
VP: Kathi Rogers
VP: Jann Wilcox
Adm Dir: Dawn Seavey

D-U-N-S 79-560-5323
MARQUETTE BANK
(*Suby of* MARQUETTE COMMUNITY DEVELOPMENT CORP) ★
6316 S Western Ave, Chicago, IL 60636-2443
Tel (708) 226-8026 *Founded/Ownrshp* 2007
Sales NA *EMP* 414^E
SIC 6021 National commercial banks; National commercial banks
COO: Bert Colianni
Ofcr: David McKay
Ex VP: Thomas Grogan
VP: Alan Kwasneski
Opers Mgr: Karen Pytel
VP Mktg: Joyce Callis
Mktg Dir: Summer Luetgert

D-U-N-S 10-527-0925
MARQUETTE BOARD OF LIGHT AND POWER
CITY MARQUETTE BD LIGHT & PWR
2200 Wright St, Marquette, MI 49855-1366
Tel (906) 228-0311 *Founded/Ownrshp* 1964
Sales 29.0MM *EMP* 82
SIC 4911 Distribution, electric power; Distribution, electric power
V Ch: Karen Johnson
Ex Dir: Mary Adamini

D-U-N-S 17-749-6353
MARQUETTE COMMUNITY DEVELOPMENT CORP
(*Suby of* MARQUETTE BANK) ★
6316 S Western Ave, Chicago, IL 60636-2443
Tel (773) 476-5100 *Founded/Ownrshp* 1987
Sales 66.5MM^E *EMP* 85^E
SIC 8741 Management services
Prin: Robert Gallardo
Ofcr: Kimberly Blaxton
Ofcr: Betty Grist

MARQUETTE EQUIP FINANCE
See MARQUETTE FINANCIAL COMPANIES

D-U-N-S 13-925-5319
MARQUETTE FINANCIAL COMPANIES
MARQUETTE EQUIP FINANCE
60 S 6th St Ste 3800, Minneapolis, MN 55402-4438
Tel (612) 661-3880 *Founded/Ownrshp* 1982
Sales NA *EMP* 990

SIC 6712 6022 6141 Bank holding companies; State commercial banks; Personal credit institutions

D-U-N-S 07-477-8614 IMP
MARQUETTE GENERAL HOSPITAL INC
420 W Magnetic St, Marquette, MI 49855-2794
Tel (906) 228-9440 *Founded/Ownrshp* 1973
Sales 328.2MM^E *EMP* 3,100
SIC 8062 General medical & surgical hospitals; General medical & surgical hospitals
CEO: A Gary Muller
COO: Greg Pauly
CFO: Don Grisham
**CFO:* Gary Worden
Sr VP: Allison Rimm
**VP:* Mark Aho
VP: Richard Jones
**VP:* Paulette J Lindberg
Exec: James Gallagher
Dir Rx: Scott Erickson
Dir Rx: Wendy Griffin

MARQUETTE GROUP
See GENERAL YELLOW PAGES CONSULTANTS INC

D-U-N-S 88-458-2305
MARQUETTE MANAGEMENT INC
175 Highpoint Dr, Romeoville, IL 60446-3802
Tel (888) 908-5886 *Founded/Ownrshp* 1991
Sales 17.5MM^E *EMP* 350
SIC 6513 Apartment building operators; Apartment building operators
Pr: Richard Harb
**Treas:* Bruno Bottarelli
VP: Mindy Helms
**VP:* Nicholas M Ryan

D-U-N-S 18-530-0670
MARQUETTE NATIONAL CORP
MARQUETTE BANK
10000 W 151st St, Orland Park, IL 60462-3140
Tel (773) 476-5100 *Founded/Ownrshp* 1981
Sales NA *EMP* 365
SIC 6021 6022 National commercial banks; State commercial banks; National commercial banks; State commercial banks
Ch Bd: Paul M Mc Carthy
**Pr:* George S Moncada
**V Ch Bd:* Barry M Sabloff
Ex VP: Paul Eckroth
**Ex VP:* Jerome R Martin
**VP:* Daniel P McKeown
VP: John O'Brien
MIS Mgr: Cesar Rodriguez
Board of Directors: Mary Acker Klingenberger

MARQUETTE PAPER COMPANY
See MURNANE PAPER CO

D-U-N-S 01-723-0095
MARQUETTE PUBLIC SERVICE GARAGE INC
919 W Baraga Ave, Marquette, MI 49855-4028
Tel (906) 226-3592 *Founded/Ownrshp* 1965
Sales 24.8MM *EMP* 47
SIC 5511 7532 Automobiles, new & used; Body shop, automotive; Automobiles, new & used; Body shop, automotive
Pr: John S Veiht
**Sec:* Phyllis C Maki
**VP:* James D Veiht

D-U-N-S 83-276-1840
MARQUETTE REAL ESTATE HOLDINGS LLC
(*Suby of* POHLAD COMPANIES) ★
3500 Amrcn Blvd W Ste 200, Bloomington, MN 55431
Tel (952) 831-1000 *Founded/Ownrshp* 1998
Sales 69.1MM^E *EMP* 520
SIC 6799 Real estate investors, except property operators

D-U-N-S 06-875-6642
MARQUETTE SAVINGS BANK
920 Peach St, Erie, PA 16501-1404
Tel (814) 455-4481 *Founded/Ownrshp* 1908
Sales NA *EMP* 121
Accts Crowe Horwath Llp Cleveland
SIC 6036 6163 State savings banks, not federally chartered; Loan brokers; State savings banks, not federally chartered; Loan brokers
CEO: Michael B Edwards
Ofcr: Meredith Johnson
**Ex VP:* Louis J Natalie
**VP:* David L Carll
VP: Anita Hans
VP: Lisa Lopez
**VP:* Kelly A Montefiori
VP: Kelly Montefiori
VP: David Slomski
**VP:* Julie M Wilson
Brnch Mgr: Jennifer Bond

D-U-N-S 00-643-9962
MARQUETTE UNIVERSITY (WI)
1250 W Wisconsin Ave, Milwaukee, WI 53233-2225
Tel (414) 288-7223 *Founded/Ownrshp* 1861, 1881
Sales 418.6MM *EMP* 3,000^E
Accts Kpmg Llp Milwaukee Wi
SIC 8221 University; University
Pr: Rev Scott Pilarz
Pr: Jeff Janz
**CFO:* John C Lamb
VP: Cindy Bauer
VP: Tom Ganey
VP: Cole Johnson
VP: Betsy Philipose
VP: Michael Vanderhoef
Assoc Dir: Courtney Hanson
Assoc Dir: Christopher Jeske
CTO: Cindy Gruber

D-U-N-S 82-525-1903 IMP/EXP
MARQUEZ BROTHERS ENTERPRISES INC
15480 Valley Blvd, City of Industry, CA 91746-3325
Tel (626) 330-3310 *Founded/Ownrshp* 1993
Sales 109.0MM^E *EMP* 200
SIC 5141 Groceries, general line; Groceries, general line
Pr: Gustavo Marquez

CFO: Dave Villanueva
**VP:* Jaime Marquez
**VP:* Juan Marquez
VP Opers: Francisco Lara

D-U-N-S 04-523-3020 IMP
MARQUEZ BROTHERS INTERNATIONAL INC
M B
5801 Rue Ferrari, San Jose, CA 95138-1857
Tel (408) 960-2700 *Founded/Ownrshp* 1981
Sales 209.7MM^E^ *EMP* 600
SIC 2022 Natural cheese; Natural cheese
CEO: Gustavo Marquez
CFO: David Villaneuva
CFO: David Villanueva
Ofcr: Sam Butler
Ex VP: Randy Funk
**Ex VP:* Jaime Marquez
VP: Mariaesthe Marquez
Genl Mgr: Juan De La Torre
Genl Mgr: Tim Luce
Dir IT: Sathya Narayanan
IT Man: Ames Gross

D-U-N-S 96-699-5425
MARQUEZ BROTHERS SOUTHWEST INC
7310 W Roosevelt St # 38, Phoenix, AZ 85043-2217
Tel (623) 478-9900 *Founded/Ownrshp* 1996
Sales 25.0MM *EMP* 53
SIC 5149 Specialty food items; Specialty food items
Pr: Gustavo Marquez
**CFO:* Dave Villanueva
**Treas:* Jaime Marquez
**VP:* Juan Marquez
**VP:* Maria Carmen Marquez

D-U-N-S 16-989-1095 IMP
MARQUEZ BROTHERS TEXAS LP
(*Suby of* M B) ★
8207 North Loop E Ste 200, Houston, TX 77029-1261
Tel (713) 672-0900 *Founded/Ownrshp* 2002
Sales 53.3MM^E^ *EMP* 130
SIC 5143 Cheese; Cheese
Pt: Gustavo Marquez Jr
Genl Mgr: Miguel La Torre

D-U-N-S 14-499-1668 IMP
MARQUEZ INC
OREGON TILE & MARBLE
1845 Se 3rd Ave, Portland, OR 97214-4548
Tel (503) 231-0376 *Founded/Ownrshp* 1985
Sales 20.7MM^E^ *EMP* 50
SIC 5032 Tile, clay or other ceramic, excluding refractory
Pr: Hector Marquez
**Sec:* Viviana Marquez

MARQUIP
See WASHINGTON CHAIN & SUPPLY INC

D-U-N-S 00-231-4230 EXP
MARQUIP LLC
(*Suby of* BARRY-WEHMILLER PAPERSYSTEMS INC) ★
1300 N Airport Rd, Phillips, WI 54555-1527
Tel (715) 339-2191 *Founded/Ownrshp* 2000, 2001
Sales 119.4MM^E^ *EMP* 543
Accts Ernst & Young Llp St Louis
SIC 3554 Box making machines, paper; Box making machines, paper
Dir IT: Bill Martin

MARQUIP WARD UNITED
See WARD MACHINERY CO

D-U-N-S 15-713-7394
MARQUIPWARDUNITED INC
8020 Forsyth Blvd, Saint Louis, MO 63105-1707
Tel (314) 862-8000 *Founded/Ownrshp* 2003
Sales 7.1MM^E^ *EMP* 300
SIC 1751 Lightweight steel framing (metal stud) installation; Lightweight steel framing (metal stud) installation
Pr: Robert Chantmas

MARQUIS ALANCE ENRGY GROUP USA
See SECURE ENERGY SERVICES

MARQUIS CENTENNIAL
See MARQUIS COMPANIES I INC

D-U-N-S 79-345-1857
MARQUIS COMPANIES I INC
MARQUIS CENTENNIAL
725 Se 202nd Ave, Portland, OR 97233-6105
Tel (503) 665-3118 *Founded/Ownrshp* 1989
Sales 164.8MM^E^ *EMP* 1,015
SIC 8741 Nursing & personal care facility management; Nursing & personal care facility management
Pr: Phillip G Fogg Jr
CFO: David Lewis
**VP:* Gary A Wart
Exec: April Olsen
Genl Mgr: Jim Santa
Off Mgr: Robyn Henderson
Nurse Mgr: Melissa Cook
IT Man: Lani Bennett
VP Opers: Kathy Levee
Opers Mgr: Daniel Casillas
VP Mktg: Charles Bloom

D-U-N-S 05-383-5369 IMP
MARQUIS CORP
MARQUIS SPAS
(*Suby of* WEXCO INC) ★
596 Hoffman Rd, Independence, OR 97351-9601
Tel (503) 838-0888 *Founded/Ownrshp* 1986
Sales 27.1MM^E^ *EMP* 145^E^
SIC 3999 Hot tubs; Hot tubs
Ch: Jeffrey L Kurth
**Pr:* John M Schrenck
CTO: Phil Olszewski
VP Mktg: James Johnston
Mktg Dir: Kerry Kurth
Manager: Rick Pettit

D-U-N-S 78-337-4692 EXP
MARQUIS ENERGY LLC
11953 Prairie Indus Pkwy, Hennepin, IL 61327-5160
Tel (815) 925-9125 *Founded/Ownrshp* 2005
Sales 41.6MM^E^ *EMP* 49
SIC 2869 Ethylene; Ethylene
Pr: Mark Marquis
CFO: Thomas Marquis
**CFO:* Denny Thorneburg
Plnt Mgr: Jeff Knutson
Prd Mgr: Jason Marquis
Pr Dir: Dana Gustafson

D-U-N-S 02-834-7151
MARQUIS MOTORS INC
ACURA MISSION VIEJO
28802 Marguerite Pkwy, Mission Viejo, CA 92692-3808
Tel (949) 347-0500 *Founded/Ownrshp* 1968
Sales 34.0MM *EMP* 45
SIC 5511 Automobiles, new & used; Automobiles, new & used
Genl Mgr: James Curland
**Sec:* Tracey Olsen
Board of Directors: Melvin M Curland

MARQUIS SPAS
See MARQUIS CORP

D-U-N-S 07-960-4077
MARQUIS YACHTS LLC
CARVER
(*Suby of* J&D ACQUISITIONS LLC) ★
790 Markham Dr, Pulaski, WI 54162
Tel (920) 822-3214 *Founded/Ownrshp* 2010
Sales 38.0MM *EMP* 310^E^
SIC 3732 Yachts, building & repairing; Yachts, building & repairing
CFO: Kathy Drake
VP: Josh Delforge
VP: Paul Liss
Sfty Dirs: Alan Wichlacz
Mfg Mgr: Mick Reid

D-U-N-S 00-176-4646 IMP
MARR SCAFFOLDING CO (MA)
DANIEL MARR & SON COMPANY
1 D St, Boston, MA 02127-2466
Tel (617) 269-7200 *Founded/Ownrshp* 1945
Sales 32.5MM^E^ *EMP* 140
SIC 7353 Heavy construction equipment rental; Heavy construction equipment rental
CEO: Daniel F Marr Lll
**Pr:* Daniel F Marr III
**CFO:* Matt Botto
**Treas:* David B Marr
**VP:* David Hughes
VP: David Marr
**VP:* Thomas J McCafferty
**VP:* Paul S Tilley
**VP:* Paula Wiles
CTO: Dan Young
QA Dir: Fred Spring

D-U-N-S 08-962-6451
MARRAKECH INC
6 Lunar Dr Ste 1, Woodbridge, CT 06525-2318
Tel (203) 389-2970 *Founded/Ownrshp* 1971
Sales 10.0MM *EMP* 450
Accts Guilmartin Dipiro & Sokolowski
SIC 8361 Rehabilitation center, residential: health care incidental; Rehabilitation center, residential: health care incidental
Ex Dir: Francis E Mc Carthy
**Ch:* Steven P Shwartz
Sr VP: Laura Stewart
VP: Marissa Artis
VP: Larry Brown
VP: Jennifer Falzone
VP: Lisa Jardin
VP: Susan McGuigan
Dir Risk M: Diane Millan
Ex Dir: Francis M Carthy
Prgrm Mgr: Sabina Cardoso

D-U-N-S 07-148-0057
MARRANO CORP
2730 Transit Rd, Buffalo, NY 14224-2523
Tel (716) 675-1200 *Founded/Ownrshp* 1963
Sales 85.0MM *EMP* 50
SIC 1521 New construction, single-family houses; Townhouse construction; New construction, single-family houses; Townhouse construction
Pr: Patrick Marrano
Ex VP: Michael Kreamer
Exec: Lawrence Reger
Sales Asso: Linda Van Nortwick

D-U-N-S 08-454-1549
MARRINSON GROUP INC
MANOR PINES CONVALESCENT CTR
1601 Ne 26th St, Wilton Manors, FL 33305-1410
Tel (954) 566-8353 *Founded/Ownrshp* 1966
Sales 24.6MM^E^ *EMP* 293
SIC 8059 Convalescent home; Convalescent home
Pr: Ralph A Marrinson
CFO: Scott Lipman
Mktg Dir: Wendy Chipkin
Nrsg Dir: Eileen Fivey
HC Dir: April McLeod

MARRIOTT
See MIRRIAM MARQUIS WASHINGTON DC

MARRIOTT
See RADSK ASSOCIATES LTD

MARRIOTT
See SUNRISE CONNECTICUT AVENUE ASSISTED LIVING LLC

MARRIOTT
See MCKIBBON HOTEL MANAGEMENT INC

MARRIOTT
See SAGE HOSPITALITY RESOURCES LLC

MARRIOTT
See KANSAS CITY DOWNTOWN HOTEL GROUP LLC

MARRIOTT
See OAKLAND RENAISSANCE ASSOCIATES

MARRIOTT
See RESORT AT SINGER ISLAND PROPERTIES INC

MARRIOTT
See COLUMBIA PROPERTIES HILTON HEAD LLC

MARRIOTT
See CHSP NEWTON LLC

MARRIOTT
See P R MARRIOT MANAGEMENT CORP

D-U-N-S 80-850-9611
MARRIOTT
515 Loudon Rd, Albany, NY 12211-1459
Tel (518) 783-2523 *Founded/Ownrshp* 2007
Sales 139.3MM *EMP* 2^E^
SIC 7011 Hotels & motels; Hotels & motels
Prin: Norman Kvam

MARRIOTT BUFFALO-AMHERST HOTEL
See BUFFALO MARRIOTT NIAGARA

D-U-N-S 80-850-6526
■ **MARRIOTT CORP**
(*Suby of* MARRIOTT INTERNATIONAL INC) ★
4040 Central Florida Pkwy, Orlando, FL 32837-7662
Tel (407) 206-2300 *Founded/Ownrshp* 2007
Sales 37.7MM^E^ *EMP* 1,000
SIC 7011 Hotels & motels; Hotels & motels
CEO: Steve Contos
Dir Soc: Emily Jacobs
Genl Mgr: Vanessa Valle

MARRIOTT EXECUSTAY
See TRANSITIONS GROUP INC

D-U-N-S 12-896-7820
MARRIOTT GRAND RESIDENCE
1001 Heavenly Village Way, South Lake Tahoe, CA 96150-6983
Tel (530) 542-8400 *Founded/Ownrshp* 2003
Sales 7.9MM^E^ *EMP* 320
SIC 7011 Hotels & motels; Hotels & motels
Pr: Steve Weitz
Owner: Marriot International

D-U-N-S 80-835-3580
■ **MARRIOTT HOTEL SERVICES INC**
(*Suby of* MARRIOTT INTERNATIONAL INC) ★
10400 Fernwood Rd, Bethesda, MD 20817-1102
Tel (301) 380-3000 *Founded/Ownrshp* 1976
Sales 45.7MM^E^ *EMP* 353^E^
SIC 7011 Hotels & motels
Prin: James David
Exec: Abdellah Aguenaou
Exec: Abdellah Aguenaous
Exec: Michael Poompan
Exec: Manny Topinio
Exec: Franz Zimmer
Dir Teleco: Tom Wilder
Genl Mgr: Kenny Didier
Genl Mgr: Richard Hulse
Genl Mgr: Thomas Rosepink
Sales Exec: Dendi Basuworo

D-U-N-S 61-760-0572
MARRIOTT HOTELS INTERNATIONAL INC
OGDEN MARRIOTT
247 24th St, Ogden, UT 84401-1425
Tel (801) 627-1190 *Founded/Ownrshp* 2006
Sales 9.1MM^E^ *EMP* 300
SIC 7011 7991 5813 5812 Hotels & motels; Physical fitness facilities; Drinking places; Eating places; Hotels & motels; Physical fitness facilities; Drinking places; Eating places
Prin: Walter Isonbert

D-U-N-S 80-851-3233
MARRIOTT INC
333 Adams St, Brooklyn, NY 11201-3714
Tel (718) 246-7000 *Founded/Ownrshp* 2003
Sales 68.0MM *EMP* 434
SIC 7011 Hotels & motels; Hotels & motels
Pr: Sam Ibrahim

D-U-N-S 78-587-4744
■ **MARRIOTT INTERNATIONAL ADMINISTRATIVE SERVICES INC**
(*Suby of* MARRIOTT INTERNATIONAL INC) ★
1 Marriott Dr, Washington, DC 20058-0001
Tel (301) 380-7503 *Founded/Ownrshp* 1998
Sales 39.6MM^E^ *EMP* 250
SIC 7011 Hotels & motels; Hotels & motels
Pr: William R Tiefel
**CFO:* Kevin Kimball
Ofcr: Cristen Barsi
Ofcr: Suzanne Fawzi
**Ex VP:* A Bradford Bryan Jr
Ex VP: Bradford A Bryn
Ex VP: Jeffrey W Ferguson
Ex VP: John Graves
**Ex VP:* Carolyn B Handlon
Ex VP: Lester Pulse
Ex VP: Arne Sorenson
Sr VP: Michael Beardsley
Sr VP: Ed French
Sr VP: Bruce Himelstein
Sr VP: Joseph E Lavin
Sr VP: David Mann
Sr VP: Howard Melnick
Sr VP: Julie Repetti
Sr VP: Bradley Wood
VP: Dawn Booth
VP: Theresa Coetzee

D-U-N-S 01-300-5702
▲ **MARRIOTT INTERNATIONAL INC**
10400 Fernwood Rd, Bethesda, MD 20817-1102
Tel (301) 380-3000 *Founded/Ownrshp* 1971
Sales 13.8MMM *EMP* 123,500
Accts Ernst & Young Llp Mclean Vir
Tkr Sym MAR *Exch* NGS
SIC 7011 6794 6531 Hotels & motels; Franchises, selling or licensing; Time-sharing real estate sales, leasing & rentals; Hotels & motels; Franchises, selling or licensing; Time-sharing real estate sales, leasing & rentals
Pr: Arne M Sorenson
Owner: James C Fisher
Pr: Ed Fuller
Pr: Robert J McCarthy
Pr: Tim Sheldon
COO: Rajeev Menon
**CFO:* Carl T Berquist
**Chf Mktg O:* Stephanie Linnartz
Ex VP: Anthony G Capuano
Ex VP: Paul Foskey
Ex VP: Carolyn B Handlon
Ex VP: Richard S Hoffman
**Ex VP:* Edward A Ryan
Sr VP: John Geller
Sr VP: David J Grissen
Sr VP: Norman K Jenkins
Sr VP: Tom Papelian
Sr VP: David M Sampson
VP: Toni Stoeckl
Exec: Jim Bangert
Exec: Evelyn Jones
Board of Directors: Mary K Bush, Deborah Marriott Harrison, Frederick A Henderson, Lawrence W Kellner, Debra L Lee, George Munoz, Steven S Reinemund, W Mitt Romney, Susan Schwab

D-U-N-S 18-919-6012
MARRIOTT INTERNATIONAL INC
(*Suby of* RYMAN HOSPITALITY PROPERTIES INC) ★
6000 W Osceola Pkwy, Kissimmee, FL 34746-4414
Tel (407) 586-0000 *Founded/Ownrshp* 2012
Sales 54.9MM^E^ *EMP* 464
SIC 7011 Hotels & motels; Hotels & motels
Ch Bd: Colin V Reed
VP: Amy Atkinson
Exec: Earlest Bell
Dir Soc: Gayle Morris
Dir Soc: Amanda Power
Genl Mgr: Tammy Hensley
Sales Exec: Ann Gillen
Natl Sales: Chris Schappert
Mktg Mgr: Shelly Carter
Sls Mgr: Skye Buckner
Sls Mgr: Brandee Gaar

MARRIOTT LOUISVILLE DOWNTOWN
See RLJ II-MH LOUISVILLE DT LESSEE LLC

D-U-N-S 11-539-4611 IMP/EXP
■ **MARRIOTT OWNERSHIP RESORTS INC**
(*Suby of* MARRIOTT VACATIONS WORLDWIDE CORP) ★
6649 W Wood Blvd Ste 500, Orlando, FL 32821-6066
Tel (863) 688-7700 *Founded/Ownrshp* 2011
Sales NA *EMP* 6,500
SIC 6141 6531 6552 7011 Financing: automobiles, furniture, etc., not a deposit bank; Time-sharing real estate sales, leasing & rentals; Subdividers & developers; Hotels & motels; Financing: automobiles, furniture, etc., not a deposit bank; Time-sharing real estate sales, leasing & rentals; Subdividers & developers; Hotels & motels
Pr: Stephen P Weisz
**CFO:* Victora Dolan
**CFO:* Tamara Glover
**Sec:* W David Mann
**Ofcr:* Michael E Yonker
Ex VP: John Geller
Sr VP: Ronald Wilensky
VP: Benay Burns
VP: Jonathan Canger
**VP:* Sterling D Colton
VP: Reggie Plummer
VP: Lynne Roach
VP: Miguel Ruano
Exec: Bruce Rohman
Board of Directors: Richard E Marriott

D-U-N-S 15-262-6180
■ **MARRIOTT RESORTS HOSPITALITY CORP**
(*Suby of* MARRIOTT OWNERSHIP RESORTS INC) ★
6649 W Wood Blvd Ste 500, Orlando, FL 32821-6066
Tel (407) 206-6000 *Founded/Ownrshp* 1998
Sales 41.6MM^E^ *EMP* 2,000
SIC 7011 Hotels & motels; Hotels & motels
Pr: Stephen P Weisz
**CFO:* Karl Sweeney
**Treas:* Raymond G Murphy
**VP:* William J Love

D-U-N-S 79-847-0639
■ **MARRIOTT RESORTS TITLE CO INC**
(*Suby of* MARRIOTT INTERNATIONAL INC) ★
6649 W Wood Blvd Ste 500, Orlando, FL 32821-6066
Tel (407) 206-6000 *Founded/Ownrshp* 1998
Sales 3.6MM^E^ *EMP* 500
SIC 7011 Hotels & motels; Hotels & motels
Pr: Steve Weisz
VP: Jeff Hansen
**VP:* Karl Sweeney

MARRIOTT TAMPA WESTSHORE
See COLUMBIA PROPERTIES WESTSHORE LLC

D-U-N-S 96-978-3906
▲ **MARRIOTT VACATIONS WORLDWIDE CORP**
6649 Westwood Blvd, Orlando, FL 32821-8029
Tel (407) 206-6000 *Founded/Ownrshp* 2011
Sales 1.5MMM^E^ *EMP* 10,000^E^
Tkr Sym VAC *Exch* NYS
SIC 6531 7011 Real estate agents & managers; Resort hotel; Real estate agents & managers; Resort hotel
Pr: Stephen P Weisz
Pr: Rance Ryan
COO: Lee Cunningham
**COO:* R Lee Cunningham
COO: Robert A Miller
**CFO:* John E Geller Jr
Ofcr: Dwight D Smith
**Ex VP:* Clifford M Delorey
**Ex VP:* James H Hunter IV

Ex VP: Lizabeth Kane-Hanan
Ex VP: Brian E Miller
Ex VP: Wanda Schlett
Ex VP: Michael E Yonker
VP: John Albert
VP: Troy Asche
VP: Jane Berg
VP: Bob Bukovic
VP: Barbara Egolf
VP: Darla Everitt
VP: Mary Finnell
VP: Edgar Gum
Board of Directors: C E Andrews, Raymond L Gellein Jr, Thomas J Hutchinson III, William W McCarten, Dianna F Morgan

MARRIOTT WATERSIDE NORFOLK
See NWM HOTEL MANAGEMENT LLC

D-U-N-S 78-587-4363
■ MARRIOTT WORLDWIDE SALES AND MARKETING INC
(*Suby of* MARRIOTT WORLDWIDE CORPORATION)
10400 Fernwood Rd, Bethesda, MD 20817-1102
Tel (301) 634-5100 *Founded/Ownrshp* 1998
Sales 90.3MM^E *EMP* 3,636
SIC 8741 Hotel or motel management; Hotel or motel management
Pr: J W Marriott Jr
**VP:* Joseph Ryan
**VP:* William Shaw
Genl Mgr: Judith Kalfon
Manager: Valerie Russell
Sls Mgr: Katie Cornwell
Sls Mgr: Jodi Hall
Sls Mgr: Christina Krause
Sls Mgr: Courtney Timmermans

D-U-N-S 03-136-8962
MARRONES INC
800 E 14th St, Pittsburg, KS 66762-3466
Tel (620) 231-6610 *Founded/Ownrshp* 1945
Sales 27.9MM^E *EMP* 49
SIC 5141 Groceries, general line
Pr: Albert J Marrone Jr
**Sec:* Ronald L Marrone
**VP:* Dale Wayne Marrone
Sls&Mrk Ex: Julian Delzell

MARS
See MODERN AMERICAN RECYCLING SERVICE INC

MARS
See MOTORS & ARMATURES INC

D-U-N-S 61-353-2936
MARS & CO CONSULTING LLC
124 Mason St Ste 1, Greenwich, CT 06830-6674
Tel (203) 862-5200 *Founded/Ownrshp* 1992
Sales 22.4MM^E *EMP* 250^E
SIC 8742 Management consulting services; Management consulting services
Ex VP: Michael Turner
Sr VP: Steven Signorelli
VP: Al Carmona
Brnch Mgr: Sylvain Panzani
Genl Mgr: Steve Chiu

D-U-N-S 06-392-1274 IMP
MARS 2000 INC
CLEAR CHOICE
40 Agnes St, Providence, RI 02909-3418
Tel (401) 421-5275 *Founded/Ownrshp* 1996
Sales 109.6MM^E *EMP* 850
SIC 3089 Molding primary plastic; Molding primary plastic
Pr: Karl J Krikorian
**CFO:* Claudette Soucy
Genl Mgr: Bibianna Roggero
Opers Mgr: Wayne Roggero

D-U-N-S 07-422-0302
MARS ADVERTISING INC
TACTICAL PROMOTION ADM
25200 Telegraph Rd Fl 5, Southfield, MI 48033-7496
Tel (248) 936-2200 *Founded/Ownrshp* 1972
Sales 51.5MM^E *EMP* 300
SIC 7311 Advertising agencies; Advertising agencies
CEO: Kenneth Barnett
**Pr:* Marilyn Barnett
COO: Rob Rivenburgh
**CFO:* Carol Butash
CFO: Bill Rozek
Ofcr: Mark Jacobs
Sr VP: Jake Berry
Sr VP: Eric Dermont
Sr VP: Maribeth Fasseel
Sr VP: Janine Flaccavento
Sr VP: Sue Golden
Sr VP: Steve Nottingham
Sr VP: Kerry Shaw
Sr VP: Doug Stone
VP: Mary Casperson
VP: David Colucci
VP: Kathleen Curran
VP: Lisa Feder
VP: Barbara Hagen
VP: Cheryl Hatfield
VP: Arthur Littsey

D-U-N-S 01-410-8260
MARS AREA SCHOOL DISTRICT (PA)
545 Route 228, Mars, PA 16046-3151
Tel (724) 625-1518 *Founded/Ownrshp* 1901
Sales 22.2MM^E *EMP* 280
Accts Hosack Specht Muetzel & Wood
SIC 8211 8661 Public elementary & secondary schools; Religious organizations; Public elementary & secondary schools; Religious organizations
Bd of Dir: David Howes
Prin: Fabian Morris

D-U-N-S 03-681-4572
MARS CHOCOLATE NORTH AMERICA LLC
M & M MARS
(*Suby of* MARS INC) ★
800 High St, Hackettstown, NJ 07840-1552
Tel (908) 852-1000 *Founded/Ownrshp* 1950
Sales 861.8MM^E *EMP* 2,675
SIC 2064 2066 Candy & other confectionery products; Chocolate & cocoa products; Candy & other confectionery products; Chocolate & cocoa products
Pr: Todd R Lachman
CFO: Paul Davies
VP: Mark Mattia
**VP:* Jim Murphy
**VP:* Mike Wittman

D-U-N-S 00-445-4781
MARS ELECTRIC CO
38868 Mentor Ave, Willoughby, OH 44094-7997
Tel (440) 946-2250 *Founded/Ownrshp* 1952
Sales 52.6MM *EMP* 98
SIC 5063 5719 Electrical supplies; Lighting fixtures; Lighting fixtures; Electrical supplies; Lighting fixtures; Lighting fixtures
Pr: Mark Doris
COO: John Kisley
**VP:* Dan Nitowsky
Brnch Mgr: Charles Curtis
Brnch Mgr: Darren Giles
Sales Asso: Dave Bush
Sales Asso: Bill Clingerman
Sales Asso: Mike Demitro
Sales Asso: Eric Freeman
Sales Asso: Ron Ingraham
Snr Mgr: Scott Shepard

D-U-N-S 00-828-5991 EXP
MARS FOOD US LLC
(*Suby of* MARS INC) ★
2001 E Cashdan St Ste 201, Rancho Dominguez, CA 90220-6438
Tel (310) 933-0670 *Founded/Ownrshp* 1968
Sales 117.7MM^E *EMP* 616
SIC 2044 Rice milling; Rice milling
VP: Thomas Bunkley
VP: Vreij Kolandjian
VP: Robert Kozlowicz
Exec: Lorraine Beranello

D-U-N-S 07-452-5809
MARS HILL UNIVERSITY
100 Athletic St, Mars Hill, NC 28754-9134
Tel (866) 642-4968 *Founded/Ownrshp* 1856
Sales 57.0MM *EMP* 275
SIC 8221 College, except junior; College, except junior
Pr: Dan G Lunsford

D-U-N-S 00-325-0685 IMP/EXP
MARS INC
6885 Elm St, Mc Lean, VA 22101-6031
Tel (703) 821-4900 *Founded/Ownrshp* 1952
Sales 4.3MMM^E *EMP* 76,000
SIC 2047 2044 2024 2066 2064 5812 Cat food; Enriched rice (vitamin & mineral fortified); Ice cream, packaged: molded, on sticks, etc.; Chocolate candy, solid; Candy bars, including chocolate covered bars; Chocolate candy, except solid chocolate; Caterers; Cat food; Enriched rice (vitamin & mineral fortified); Ice cream, packaged: molded, on sticks, etc.; Chocolate candy, solid; Candy bars, including chocolate covered bars; Chocolate candy, except solid chocolate; Caterers
Pr: Grant F Reid
**CFO:* Reuben Gamoran
Treas: R E Barns
**Treas:* Rich Czermak
Ofcr: Andrew Clark
Ofcr: Margaret Peterlin
Ex VP: Julie Callaghan
Ex VP: Jacqueline B Mars
**Ex VP:* Aileen Richards
Sr VP: Richard Continelli
VP: Henry Azcarraga
VP: Patrick Breton
VP: Chris Jones
**VP:* David Kamenetzky
VP: Peter Littlewood
VP: Valerie Mars
VP: Phil Moody
VP: Alberto Mora
VP: Paul Ryan
VP: Dan Sherwood
VP: Jacek Szarzynski

D-U-N-S 16-492-8462
MARS INDUSTRIES INC
MARS STELL
2401 Rose St, Franklin Park, IL 60131-3322
Tel (847) 455-6277 *Founded/Ownrshp* 1994
Sales 75.0MM *EMP* 60
SIC 6719 Investment holding companies, except banks; Investment holding companies, except banks
Pr: Robert Perkaus
**VP:* Don Shanon
**VP:* Myron Weiss

D-U-N-S 06-930-3097 IMP
MARS INTERNATIONAL INC
60 Kingsbridge Rd, Piscataway, NJ 08854-3919
Tel (908) 233-0044 *Founded/Ownrshp* 1974
Sales 45.0MM^E *EMP* 60^E
SIC 3824

MARS JAMES HITCHENS & WILLIAMS
See MORRIS JAMES LLP

D-U-N-S 11-043-4847 IMP
MARS MM INC
1301 Wilson Dr, West Chester, PA 19380-5954
Tel (610) 719-4300 *Founded/Ownrshp* 2002
Sales 11.4MM^E *EMP* 300
SIC 1731 Electronic controls installation; Electronic controls installation
Pr: Paul S Michaels
Exec: Calvin Wise
Dir IT: Gaston Baudat
Dir IT: Bruce Beadle
Dir IT: Ron Bernardini
Dir IT: Collin Fletcher
Dir IT: Les Martzall
Dir IT: Doug Myers
Dir IT: Fiona Naughton
Dir IT: James Poole
Dir IT: Cary Sagady

D-U-N-S 00-713-4919 EXP
MARS PETCARE US INC
(*Suby of* MARS INC) ★
315 Cool Springs Blvd, Franklin, TN 37067-1632
Tel (615) 807-4626 *Founded/Ownrshp* 2007
Sales 837.0MM^E *EMP* 2,671
SIC 2047 Dog & cat food; Cat food; Dog food; Dog & cat food; Cat food; Dog food
Pr: Douglas J Cahill
**Pr:* Grant F Reid
**CFO:* Philip K Woodlief
**VP:* Richard A Hannasch
**VP:* David Horton
**VP:* Joseph J Meyers
**Prin:* Luc Mongeau

D-U-N-S 09-944-8060 IMP
MARS RETAIL GROUP INC
(*Suby of* MARS INC) ★
2 Cactus Garden Dr, Henderson, NV 89014
Tel (702) 458-8864 *Founded/Ownrshp* 1984
Sales 62.8MM^E *EMP* 450
SIC 2066 5441 Chocolate & cocoa products; Candy; Chocolate & cocoa products; Candy
Pr: Susan G Saideman
**Treas:* Chantelle Pritchard
**VP:* D H Badger
**VP:* Scott Mogren

D-U-N-S 08-101-9663
MARS STEEL CORP
2401 25th Ave, Franklin Park, IL 60131-3322
Tel (847) 455-6277 *Founded/Ownrshp* 1975
Sales 23.0MM^E *EMP* 52
SIC 5051

MARS STELL
See MARS INDUSTRIES INC

D-U-N-S 02-247-9752
MARS SUPER MARKETS INC
9627 Philadelphia Rd # 100, Baltimore, MD 21237-4155
Tel (410) 590-0500 *Founded/Ownrshp* 1952
Sales 255.9MM^E *EMP* 1,700
SIC 5411 Supermarkets, chain; Supermarkets, chain
Pr: E Philip Hanlon
Ex VP: Ted Anna
**Ex VP:* Christopher D'Anna
**Ex VP:* Theodore D'Anna
**Sr VP:* Philip Hanlon
**VP:* Thomas Veystrk

D-U-N-S 11-536-6387
MARSAU ENTERPRISES INC
1209 N 30th St, Enid, OK 73701-2700
Tel (580) 233-3910 *Founded/Ownrshp* 1980
Sales 100.0MM *EMP* 600
SIC 1389 Construction, repair & dismantling services
Pr: Marlin Esau
VP: Rob Niles

MARSCO GLASS PRODUCTS
See ENGINEERED GLASS PRODUCTS LLC

D-U-N-S 04-410-2010
MARSDEN BLDG MAINTENANCE CO OF OMAHA (INC) (NE)
2801 Bell Ave, Des Moines, IA 50321-1418
Tel (515) 245-4350 *Founded/Ownrshp* 1963
Sales 7.8MM^E *EMP* 400
SIC 7349 Janitorial service, contract basis; Janitorial service, contract basis
Pr: Adrian Marsden Sr
**VP:* Richard Lubbers

D-U-N-S 05-709-4476
MARSDEN HOLDING LLC
2124 University Ave W, Saint Paul, MN 55114-1838
Tel (877) 780-4445 *Founded/Ownrshp* 1952
Sales 753.8MM^E *EMP* 8,000
SIC 1731 Safety & security specialization; Safety & security specialization
Pr: Maureen Hill
CFO: Dan McCarthy
Treas: Daniel G McCarthy
VP: Ray Cole
VP: Matt Johnson
VP: Cory Krug
CIO: Doug Desota
Opers Mgr: Steve Erickson
Opers Mgr: Robin Kemp
Sls&Mrk Ex: Tony Curtis
Sls&Mrk Ex: Kelly Thies
Board of Directors: Carla Smith

MARSH
See THOMAS RUTHERFOORD INC

MARSH
See SEABURY & SMITH INC

MARSH
See SEITLIN & CO

D-U-N-S 83-262-3008
■ MARSH & MCLENNAN AGENCY LLC
(*Suby of* MARSH LLC) ★
360 Hamilton Ave Ste 930, White Plains, NY 10601-1847
Tel (914) 397-1600 *Founded/Ownrshp* 2008
Sales NA *EMP* 3,087^E
SIC 6411 Insurance brokers; Insurance brokers
Pr: Benjamin F Allen
COO: William Corrigan
Ex VP: Kirk Leadbetter
Ex VP: Stewart Martin
Sr VP: Joan Cunnick
Sr VP: Edward Katz
Sr VP: Christy Miller
Sr VP: Ben Newman
Sr VP: Keith Victory
Sr VP: Sharon Werner
VP: Brett Baker
VP: Holly Bozant
VP: Jason Davis
VP: Tonya Lamothe

D-U-N-S 04-156-4378 IMP/EXP
▲ MARSH & MCLENNAN COMPANIES INC
1166 Ave of The Americas, New York, NY 10036
Tel (212) 345-5000 *Founded/Ownrshp* 1871
Sales NA *EMP* 57,000
Accts Deloitte & Touche Llp New Yor
Tkr Sym MMC *Exch* NYS
SIC 6411 6282 8742 Insurance brokers; Insurance agents; Insurance information & consulting services; Policyholders' consulting service; Investment advisory service; Investment research; Compensation & benefits planning consultant; General management consultant; Insurance brokers; Insurance agents; Insurance information & consulting services; Policyholders' consulting service; Investment advisory service; Investment research; Compensation & benefits planning consultant; General management consultant
Pr: Daniel S Glaser
Ch Bd: Peter Zaffino
V Ch: John T Sinnott
Pr: Michael Anderson
Pr: Alexander Moczarski
CEO: Ricardo Brockmann
CEO: Mark Feuer
CEO: Martin South
COO: Georg Braeuchle
COO: Emichael Caulfield
COO: Judy Chang
COO: Joseph J Fico
COO: Charles Fry
COO: David Lessing
COO: Bill Pieron
COO: Bill Pieroni
COO: Jane D Roche
CFO: Matthew B Artley
CFO: Jerome H Bailey
CFO: J Michael Bischoff
CFO: Joseph Levandusk i
Board of Directors: R Divid Yost, H Edward Hanway, Elaine La Roche, Lord Lang, Maria Silvia Bastos Marque, Steven A Mills, Bruce P Nolop, Marc D Oken, Morton Z Schapiro, Lloyd M Yates

D-U-N-S 15-114-5844
■ MARSH AFFINITY GROUP SERVICES
(*Suby of* SEABURY & SMITH (DELAWARE) INC) ★
12421 Meredith Dr, West Des Moines, IA 50398-0002
Tel (515) 243-1900 *Founded/Ownrshp* 1984
Sales NA *EMP* 400
SIC 6411 Insurance brokers; Insurance brokers
Pr: Kirke Dorweiler
Treas: Alan Bieler
**Treas:* Jeffrey Schlingbum
Sr VP: Gail Colatrella
Sr VP: Rebecca Crosby
Sr VP: Steve Ginsburg
Sr VP: John Havey
Sr VP: Kathleen Wiljanen
VP: Terry Boettcher
VP: Hans Dellenbach
VP: Tricia Hamilton
**VP:* Thomas R Hopkins
VP: Tom Kristensen
VP: Khai Lovan
VP: Darrel Nelson

MARSH BELLOFRAM COR
See BELLOFRAM CORP

D-U-N-S 60-541-3012
MARSH BUILDING PRODUCTS INC
2030 Winners Cir, Dayton, OH 45404-1130
Tel (937) 222-3321 *Founded/Ownrshp* 1989
Sales 22.1MM^E *EMP* 60
SIC 5031 7699 5211 Building materials, exterior; Building materials, interior; Door & window repair; Siding
Pr: Ken Middleton
**VP:* Mike Middleton
**Prin:* Mary C Gronefeld
Sls Mgr: Don Swaine

D-U-N-S 06-155-2600
■ MARSH CLEARSIGHT LLC
(*Suby of* MARSH USA INC) ★
540 W Madison St Ste 1200, Chicago, IL 60661-7608
Tel (312) 627-6000 *Founded/Ownrshp* 1967
Sales 67.3MM^E *EMP* 500
SIC 7373 Systems software development services; Systems software development services
Pr: Paul Marushka
Pr: Kelly Flaherty
CFO: Brian Seldess
CFO: Samantha Wood
Ofcr: Richard Watman
Sr VP: Stratford Dick
Sr VP: Eric Espeseth
Sr VP: Bret Kirkland
Sr VP: Jim Kuhr
Sr VP: Anna Lukosus
Sr VP: Dan Pascucci
VP: Dennis Fanneron
VP: Kevin Pyne

D-U-N-S 14-240-1319
MARSH CREEK LLC
(*Suby of* KAKTOVIK INUPIAT CORP) ★
2000 E 88th Ave, Anchorage, AK 99507-3879
Tel (907) 258-0050 *Founded/Ownrshp* 2004
Sales 63.0MM *EMP* 160
Accts Bdo Usa Llp Anchorage Ak
SIC 1731 8748 8744 4959 Energy management controls; Telecommunications consultant; ; Environmental cleanup services; Energy management controls; Telecommunications consultant; ; Environmental cleanup services
CEO: Mick McKay
**COO:* Jonathan Ealy
**CFO:* Douglas P Koprowski
VP: Dave Marinucci
Sales Exec: Brian Wakefield

D-U-N-S 04-722-2682
MARSH DRUGS LLC
(*Suby of* MARSH SUPERMARKETS INC) ★
9800 Crosspoint Blvd, Indianapolis, IN 46256-3300
Tel (317) 594-2100 *Founded/Ownrshp* 1968
Sales 72.1MM *EMP* 300

SIC 5912 Drug stores; Drug stores
CEO: Frank Lazaren
CFO: Robert Riesveck
Ex VP: Lee Nicholson

D-U-N-S 00-643-7784 IMP
MARSH ELECTRONICS INC (WI)
1563 S 101st St, Milwaukee, WI 53214-4032
Tel (414) 475-6000 *Founded/Ownrshp* 1935
Sales 23.9MM^E *EMP* 102
SIC 5065 Electronic parts & equipment; Electronic parts & equipment
Pr: John Casper
**VP:* James S Banovish
Brnch Mgr: John Waringa
VP Mktg: Bill Siok
Sales Asso: Diane Harrison
Sales Asso: Nancy Schwalbe
Sales Asso: Kimberly Wherry

D-U-N-S 00-323-3111 IMP
MARSH FURNITURE CO
MARSH KITCHENS
1001 S Centennial St, High Point, NC 27260-8126
Tel (336) 884-7363 *Founded/Ownrshp* 1906
Sales 87.2MM^E *EMP* 550
SIC 2434 5712 2421

MARSH KITCHENS
See MARSH FURNITURE CO

MARSH LANDING COUNTRY CLUB
See M L PARTNERSHIP

D-U-N-S 07-940-4169
■ **MARSH LLC**
(*Suby of* MARSH & MCLENNAN COMPANIES INC) ★
1166 Avenue Of The Americ, New York, NY 10036-2750
Tel (212) 345-5000 *Founded/Ownrshp* 1999
Sales NA *EMP* 5,073^E
SIC 6411 6282 8742 Insurance brokers; Insurance agents; Insurance information & consulting services; Policyholders' consulting service; Investment advisory service; Investment research; Compensation & benefits planning consultant; General management consultant; Insurance brokers; Insurance agents; Insurance information & consulting services; Policyholders' consulting service; Investment advisory service; Investment research; Compensation & benefits planning consultant; General management consultant
Pr: Peter Zaffino
Ex VP: Rebecca Crosby
Sr VP: Brian Andrews
Sr VP: Elaine Bradshaw
Sr VP: Brian Cameron
Sr VP: John Denton
Sr VP: Thomas Egreany
Sr VP: Edward Haas
Sr VP: Brian Houghlin
Sr VP: Gerard Kelly
Sr VP: Alexander Levine
Sr VP: David Parrott
Sr VP: Stephen Stewart
VP: Michelle Burns
VP: Joseph Depaul
VP: Theresa Laily
VP: Michael Leshaw
VP: Randy Simonson
VP: Sharon Walker

D-U-N-S 11-122-4189
MARSH MCLENNAN
540 W Madison St Ste 1200, Chicago, IL 60661-3600
Tel (312) 627-6000 *Founded/Ownrshp* 2002
Sales NA *EMP* 600^E
SIC 6411
Mng Pt: Leonard Miller
CFO: Sean Shover
Sr VP: Jim Anderson
Sr VP: Laurie Bahr
Sr VP: Denise N Banks
Sr VP: Lisa Bastick
Sr VP: James Biggins
Sr VP: Michael Calhoun
Sr VP: Rebecca Clark
Sr VP: Dawn Colby
Sr VP: Susan Denecke
Sr VP: Gary Eklund
Sr VP: Kimberly Elibee
Sr VP: Christopher Freund
Sr VP: Meredith Frick
Sr VP: Kate Gaynor
Sr VP: Nick Gerbich
Sr VP: Mark Hall
Sr VP: Robert Hong
Sr VP: Jennifer Janovetz
Sr VP: Nicholas Jemas

D-U-N-S 03-926-7450 IMP
MARSH POTTERY LLC
CAROLINA POTTERY
3599 Andrew L Tucker Rd, Fort Mill, SC 29715-8742
Tel (803) 547-0052 *Founded/Ownrshp* 2001
Sales 40.9MM^E *EMP* 220
SIC 5719 Housewares; Wicker, rattan or reed home furnishings; Housewares; Wicker, rattan or reed home furnishings
CFO: Jim Patterson

D-U-N-S 05-843-6098
■ **MARSH RISK & INSURANCE SERVICES INC**
MMC
(*Suby of* MARSH & MCLENNAN COMPANIES INC) ★
777 S Figueroa St # 2200, Los Angeles, CA 90017-5800
Tel (213) 624-5555 *Founded/Ownrshp* 1997
Sales NA *EMP* 687
SIC 6411 Insurance brokers; Insurance brokers
Mng Dir: Paul Gibbs
Sr VP: Thomas Behny
Sr VP: Robert Finkelstein
Sr VP: Robert Rappoport
Sr VP: Melody Schwartz
VP: Charles Colella
Mng Dir: Steve Flynn
Dir IT: Joan Brown
IT Man: Robert Allen
Snr Mgr: Michael Rastigue

MARSH SALDANA
See SALDANA & ASSOCIATES INC

D-U-N-S 62-370-0916
MARSH SUPERMARKETS HOLDING CORP
9800 Crosspoint Blvd, Indianapolis, IN 46256-3300
Tel (317) 594-2100 *Founded/Ownrshp* 2006
Sales 2.1MMM^E *EMP* 14,000
SIC 5411 Supermarkets, chain; Convenience stores, chain; Supermarkets, 55,000-65,000 square feet (superstore); Supermarkets, 66,000-99,000 square feet; Supermarkets, chain; Convenience stores, chain; Supermarkets, 55,000-65,000 square feet (superstore); Supermarkets, 66,000-99,000 square feet
Pr: Thomas R O'Boyle Jr
COO: Bill Holsworth
**CFO:* Terry Huser
Sr Cor Off: Ronald Sims
Ex VP: Mark Varner
VP: Jodi D Marsh
Admn Mgr: Jay Cluck
Admn Mgr: John Nightengale

D-U-N-S 00-694-0282 IMP
MARSH SUPERMARKETS INC
(*Suby of* MARSH SUPERMARKETS HOLDING CORP) ★
9800 Crosspoint Blvd, Indianapolis, IN 46256-3300
Tel (317) 594-2100 *Founded/Ownrshp* 1931
Sales 2.1MMM^E *EMP* 13,300
SIC 5411 Supermarkets, chain; Convenience stores, chain; Supermarkets, 55,000-65,000 square feet (superstore); Supermarkets, 66,000-99,000 square feet; Supermarkets, chain; Convenience stores, chain; Supermarkets, 55,000-65,000 square feet (superstore); Supermarkets, 66,000-99,000 square feet
Ch Bd: Frank Lazaran
**CFO:* Robert J Riesbeck
VP: Andrew Alper
VP: Harlen Brinson
VP: Roy Fossum
VP: Terry Huser
VP: Arthur Marsh
VP: Dave Reed
VP: Michael Savage
VP: Mike Sealand
VP: David Siebert
VP: Ronald Sims
VP: Mark Varner
Mng Ofcr: Danny Omaila
Comm Man: Bryan Zerfas

D-U-N-S 00-174-9258
■ **MARSH USA INC** (DE)
(*Suby of* MARSH & MCLENNAN COMPANIES INC) ★
1166 Ave Of The Americas, New York, NY 10036-2708
Tel (212) 345-6000 *Founded/Ownrshp* 1923, 1969
Sales NA *EMP* 38,000
SIC 6411 6331 6351 6282 Insurance brokers; Insurance agents; Fire, marine & casualty insurance: stock; Property damage insurance; Boiler insurance; Surety insurance bonding; Fidelity or surety bonding; Investment advisory service; Insurance brokers; Insurance agents; Fire, marine & casualty insurance: stock; Property damage insurance; Boiler insurance; Surety insurance bonding; Fidelity or surety bonding; Investment advisory service
Ch Bd: Joseph Mc Sweeny
V Ch: Heidi Miller
V Ch: Steven Schloss
Pr: Henry S Allen
Pr: Marcus Humphrey
Pr: Megan Lee
Pr: Timothy J Mahoney Jr
Pr: Joseph M McSweeny
Pr: Alexander Moczarksi
Pr: Alexander W Vietor
CEO: Peter Zaffino
CFO: Douglas Davis
CFO: Patricia Hagemann
CFO: Courtney Leimkuhler
Ofcr: Scott Gilbert
Sr VP: Ann M Avnet
Sr VP: Harold Dorbin
Sr VP: Fred Heath
Sr VP: Machua Millett
Sr VP: Michael Murphy
Sr VP: Paul Perks

D-U-N-S 96-347-2381
MARSHAL GROUP LLC
304 S Summit Dr, Washington, IL 61571-3228
Tel (309) 444-4641 *Founded/Ownrshp* 2007
Sales 50.0MM *EMP* 9
SIC 5511 New & used car dealers; New & used car dealers
**CFO:* Jack Defatnick

D-U-N-S 03-456-8899
MARSHAL MIZE FORD INC
5348 Highway 153, Hixson, TN 37343-4946
Tel (423) 870-4053 *Founded/Ownrshp* 1977
Sales 48.5MM^E *EMP* 115
SIC 5511 7515 7513 5012 Automobiles, new & used; Passenger car leasing; Truck rental & leasing, no drivers; Automobiles & other motor vehicles; Automobiles, new & used; Passenger car leasing; Truck rental & leasing, no drivers; Automobiles & other motor vehicles
Pr: Lewis Dyer
**Sec:* Steve Henderson
Genl Mgr: Thad Narramore
Sls Mgr: Grady Gant
Sales Asso: Eddie Ackerman
Sales Asso: Carl Causey
Sales Asso: Brian Cruz
Sales Asso: Pascal D Desutter
Sales Asso: Eric E Jenkins
Sales Asso: Gabe Mosley
Sales Asso: Greg Owens

D-U-N-S 80-273-0275
MARSHALL & ILSLEY TRUST CO NATIONAL ASSOCIATION
M & ITRUST
(*Subsi of* BMO FINANCIAL CORP) ★
111 E Kilbourn Ave # 200, Milwaukee, WI 53202-6633
Tel (414) 287-8700 *Founded/Ownrshp* 1973
Sales 88.5MM^E *EMP* 700
SIC 6733 Private estate, personal investment & vacation fund trusts; Private estate, personal investment & vacation fund trusts
CEO: Kenneth Krei
**Pr:* Morry L Birnbaum
**Pr:* David W Schulz
Trst Ofcr: Thomas Tuttle
VP: Forrest Dupre
VP: Christopher Gloe
**VP:* Anthony L Lesczwaski
VP: Todd Perala
VP: Jason Weiner
CIO: Tommy Huis
Netwrk Eng: Ian D Carlson

D-U-N-S 16-184-4105
MARSHALL & STERLING ENTERPRISES INC
THEODORE TUNICK INSURANCE
110 Main St Ste 4, Poughkeepsie, NY 12601-3080
Tel (845) 454-0800 *Founded/Ownrshp* 1864
Sales NA *EMP* 350
SIC 6411 Insurance agents, brokers & service; Insurance agents, brokers & service
Ch Bd: Timothy E Dean
**CFO:* Tim Rychcik
Sr VP: Jon Brodsky
**VP:* Betty Fanelli
**VP:* Frank S Maranto
VP: Matt Marrone
VP: John Morgan
VP: Deke Rothacker
VP: Jeremy Schokman
VP: Mario Vtniello
VP: Jim Wellock

D-U-N-S 00-833-3635
■ **MARSHALL & SWIFT/BOECKH LLC**
(*Suby of* CORELOGIC INC) ★
10001 W Innovation Dr # 102, Milwaukee, WI 53226-4851
Tel (262) 780-2800 *Founded/Ownrshp* 2014
Sales NA *EMP* 350
SIC 6411 Property & casualty insurance agent; Property & casualty insurance agent
Sr VP: Mark Burkhart
VP: Linda Fischer
VP: Jerry Fox
VP: Dhaval Vasavada
Off Admin: Heather Norris
Tech Mgr: Ed Martinez
Sftwr Eng: James Labadie
VP Sls: David Berenson
Sls Mgr: Robert Blythe
Snr PM: Lynn Riperti

D-U-N-S 03-050-6109
MARSHALL AIR SYSTEMS INC (NC)
419 Peachtree Dr S, Charlotte, NC 28217-2098
Tel (704) 525-6230 *Founded/Ownrshp* 1976
Sales 33.7MM^E *EMP* 100
SIC 3589 Commercial cooking & foodwarming equipment; Commercial cooking & foodwarming equipment
CEO: Deborah B Stuck
**Ch:* Robert M Stuck
Sales Asso: Brett Furr

D-U-N-S 06-999-6130
MARSHALL ASSOCIATES INC
1131 W Blackhawk St Fl 2, Chicago, IL 60642-2404
Tel (312) 266-8500 *Founded/Ownrshp* 1973
Sales 20.3MM *EMP* 115
Accts Mcgladrey Llp Schaumburg Ill
SIC 8742 Household furniture; Toys; Lawn & garden machinery & equipment; Sales (including sales management) consultant
Pr: David Stumbras
**Ch Bd:* John Kazmer
VP: Daniel Devito
Sls Dir: Brian Dowling
Sales Asso: Jennifer Berman

MARSHALL AUDIO/VIDEO SYSTEMS
See MARSHALL INDUSTRIES INC

D-U-N-S 18-738-4552
MARSHALL AVERA
AVERA MARSHALL REGIONAL MEDICAL CENTER
(*Suby of* AVERA HEALTH) ★
300 S Bruce St, Marshall, MN 56258-1934
Tel (507) 537-9007 *Founded/Ownrshp* 2004
Sales 68.7MM *EMP* 1^E
Accts Eide Bailly Llp Minneapolis
SIC 8011 Medical centers; Medical centers
Pr: Mary Maertens
VP: Angela Chesley
Off Mgr: Darci Cunningham
Off Mgr: Laura Marquardt
Surgeon: Rochelle Stark
Pharmcst: Greg Delaney
Pharmcst: Angie Hughes

D-U-N-S 10-225-3325
MARSHALL AVERA FOUNDATION
AVERA MARSHAL REGIONAL MEDICAL
300 S Bruce St, Marshall, MN 56258-1934
Tel (507) 537-9145 *Founded/Ownrshp* 1944
Sales 1.8MM *EMP* 500
Accts Eide Bailly Llp Minneapolis
SIC 8051 8062 7991 8082 8322 Skilled nursing care facilities; General medical & surgical hospitals; Physical fitness facilities; Home health care services; Senior citizens' center or association; Skilled nursing care facilities; General medical & surgical hospitals; Physical fitness facilities; Home health care services; Senior citizens' center or association
Pr: Bil Bumgarner
**VP:* Sharon Williams
Occ Thrpy: Allison Naber

D-U-N-S 07-359-6710
MARSHALL B KETCHUM UNIVERSITY
OPTOMETRIC CENTER OF LOS ANGEL
2575 Yorba Linda Blvd, Fullerton, CA 92831-1615
Tel (714) 870-7226 *Founded/Ownrshp* 1911
Sales 22.1MM *EMP* 180
SIC 8221 8042

MARSHALL BRASS
See S H LEGGITT CO

D-U-N-S 00-582-7993
MARSHALL CO LTD (TX)
1001 2nd St, Corpus Christi, TX 78404-2303
Tel (361) 883-4369 *Founded/Ownrshp* 1941, 1992
Sales 20.0MM *EMP* 50
Accts Bonnes & Pullin Pc Corpus
SIC 1542 Commercial & office building, new construction; Commercial & office buildings, renovation & repair; Commercial & office building, new construction; Commercial & office buildings, renovation & repair
Pr: Michael Dodson
**Pt:* Richard Dodson
**Treas:* Karla Kim Wilburn

D-U-N-S 00-382-9140
MARSHALL CONSTRUCTION CO LTD
190 T C Jester Blvd, Houston, TX 77007-3143
Tel (713) 861-8163 *Founded/Ownrshp* 1933
Sales 30.2MM *EMP* 25
Accts Wingard & Associates Pc Ho
SIC 1542 School building construction; Institutional building construction; School building construction; Institutional building construction
Pr: John P Marshall
**VP:* David G Marshall

D-U-N-S 10-208-6931
MARSHALL COUNTY BOARD OF EDUCATION
12380 Us Highway 431, Guntersville, AL 35976-9351
Tel (256) 582-3171 *Founded/Ownrshp* 1930
Sales 38.0MM^E *EMP* 855
SIC 8211 Public combined elementary & secondary school; Public elementary school; Public junior high school; Public senior high school; Public combined elementary & secondary school; Public elementary school; Public junior high school; Public senior high school
IT Man: Gemma Twaddle

D-U-N-S 60-628-7746
MARSHALL COUNTY BOARD OF EDUCATION
700 Jones Cir, Lewisburg, TN 37091-2427
Tel (931) 359-1581 *Founded/Ownrshp* 1995
Sales 30.9MM^E *EMP* 587
SIC 8211 Public elementary & secondary schools; County supervisors' & executives' offices; School board

D-U-N-S 08-890-5989
MARSHALL COUNTY BOARD OF EDUCATION (INC)
214 Middle Grave Creek Rd, Moundsville, WV 26041-6009
Tel (304) 843-4400 *Founded/Ownrshp* 1900
Sales 43.6MM^E *EMP* 682
SIC 8211 Public elementary school; Public junior high school; Public senior high school; County supervisors' & executives' offices; School board
Pr: Beth Phillips
**Treas:* James Tuel

D-U-N-S 07-896-2719
MARSHALL COUNTY HEALTH CARE AUTHORITY
MARSHALL MEDICAL CENTER SOUTH
2505 Us Highway 431, Boaz, AL 35957-5908
Tel (256) 894-6600 *Founded/Ownrshp* 1956
Sales 134.6MM^E *EMP* 1,200
Accts Warren Averett Kimbrough & M
SIC 8062 Hospital, professional nursing school; Hospital, professional nursing school
CEO: Gary R Gore
**CFO:* Kathy Nelson
Dir Soc: Libby McClendon

D-U-N-S 08-626-8596
MARSHALL COUNTY MEDICAL CENTRE (OK)
1 Hospital Dr, Madill, OK 73446
Tel (580) 795-3384 *Founded/Ownrshp* 1964
Sales 23.0MM *EMP* 100
SIC 8062 General medical & surgical hospitals; General medical & surgical hospitals
**CFO:* Thomas Briggs
MIS Dir: Mike Wacker
Surgeon: James W Carlson

D-U-N-S 02-194-5308
MARSHALL COUNTY SCHOOL DISTRICT
122 S Spring St, Holly Springs, MS 38635-3018
Tel (662) 252-3024 *Founded/Ownrshp* 1900
Sales 26.1MM *EMP* 425
Accts J E Vance & Co Pa Cpa Tupel
SIC 8211 Public elementary & secondary schools; Public elementary & secondary schools
Pr Dir: Brenda Bailey
Teacher Pr: Tammy Day
HC Dir: Dianna Edwards
HC Dir: Emily Hurdle

D-U-N-S 19-331-5694
MARSHALL COUNTY SCHOOL DISTRICT
86 High School Rd, Benton, KY 42025-7039
Tel (270) 527-8628 *Founded/Ownrshp* 1880
Sales 13.0MM *EMP* 400
SIC 8211 Public elementary & secondary schools; Public elementary & secondary schools
**Treas:* Gill Morris

D-U-N-S 07-979-9758
MARSHALL COUNTY SCHOOLS
700 Jones Cir, Lewisburg, TN 37091-2427
Tel (931) 359-1581 *Founded/Ownrshp* 2015
Sales 9.5MM^E *EMP* 587^E
SIC 8211 Public elementary & secondary schools
HC Dir: Deborah Wade

D-U-N-S 07-979-9767
MARSHALL COUNTY SCHOOLS
214 Middle Grave Creek Rd, Moundsville, WV 26041-6009
Tel (304) 843-4400 *Founded/Ownrshp* 2015
Sales 6.2MM^E *EMP* 721^E
SIC 8211 Public elementary & secondary schools
Pr Dir: Scott Varner

D-U-N-S 07-059-5921
MARSHALL DENNEHEY WARNER COLEMAN & GOGGIN PC
2000 Market St Fl 23, Philadelphia, PA 19103-7006
Tel (215) 575-2600 *Founded/Ownrshp* 1960
Sales 166.7MM^E *EMP* 1,047
SIC 8111 General practice law office; General practice law office
Ch Bd: Christopher E Dougherty
**Ch Bd:* Peter S Miller
**CEO:* Thomas A Brophy
**CEO:* Robert Coleman
COO: Sean Blake
**Ch:* Philip B Toran
**Sr VP:* Thomas De Lorenzo
**Sr VP:* Scott G Dunlop
**Sr VP:* Niki Ingram
**Sr VP:* Kathleen McGrath
**Sr VP:* Mark Thompson
Exec: Cathy Cosgrove
Board of Directors: Coleen Bannon, Mari Anne Boyne, Liz Brown, Patti Day, Karen Rudderow, Larry Schempp

D-U-N-S 08-495-8131
MARSHALL DESIGN-BUILD LLC
4437 Atlanta Hwy, Montgomery, AL 36109-3115
Tel (334) 277-8820 *Founded/Ownrshp* 1976
Sales 30.6MM *EMP* 20
Accts Barlett Gunter & Yeager Pc O
SIC 1542 Commercial & office building, new construction; Commercial & office building, new construction
CFO: Becky Murchison
Genl Mgr: Chester W Marshall
Site Mgr: Wayne Dickey
Site Mgr: Andy Kelley

MARSHALL DISTRIBUTING
See 4162 DOERR ROAD INC

MARSHALL DURBIN FARMS
See MARSHALL DURBIN FOOD CORP

D-U-N-S 05-864-1457
MARSHALL DURBIN FARMS INC
2830 Commerce Blvd, Irondale, AL 35210-1216
Tel (205) 956-3505 *Founded/Ownrshp* 1963
Sales NA *EMP* 400
SIC 0251 0254 2048

D-U-N-S 00-796-0263
MARSHALL DURBIN FOOD CORP
MARSHALL DURBIN FARMS
(*Suby of* MAR-JAC POULTRY INC) ★
2830 Commerce Blvd, Irondale, AL 35210-1216
Tel (205) 841-7315 *Founded/Ownrshp* 1967, 2014
Sales 160.9MM^E *EMP* 1,200
SIC 0252 0254 2048 0251 2015 5144 Chicken eggs; Chicken hatchery; Poultry feeds; Broiling chickens, raising of; Chicken slaughtering & processing; Poultry: live, dressed or frozen (unpackaged); Chicken eggs; Chicken hatchery; Poultry feeds; Broiling chickens, raising of; Chicken slaughtering & processing; Poultry: live, dressed or frozen (unpackaged)
Pr: Melissa Durbin
**CFO:* Mark Jeter
**Sec:* Elise Durbin
**VP:* Freddie Mitchell
**VP:* David Bart Payne

D-U-N-S 01-732-4823
MARSHALL E CAMPBELL CO
2975 Lapeer Rd, Port Huron, MI 48060-2558
Tel (810) 985-7105 *Founded/Ownrshp* 1932
Sales 64.7MM^E *EMP* 75
SIC 5063 5085 Electrical supplies; Industrial supplies; Fasteners, industrial: nuts, bolts, screws, etc.; Industrial tools; Electrical supplies; Industrial supplies; Fasteners, industrial: nuts, bolts, screws, etc.; Industrial tools
Pr: Jack M Campbell
**CFO:* Bill Bedard
**VP:* Scott D Campbell
Dir IT: Tom Malone
Mktg Mgr: Dan Reinhart
Sales Asso: Randy Atkin
Sales Asso: Tyson Connolly
Sales Asso: Jerry Czostkowski
Sales Asso: Ken Juzysta
Sales Asso: William Lawry
Sales Asso: Barry Purcell

D-U-N-S 07-430-4262 IMP
MARSHALL ELECTRIC CORP
425 N State Road 25, Rochester, IN 46975-9700
Tel (574) 223-4367 *Founded/Ownrshp* 1974
Sales 24.3MM^E *EMP* 150
Accts Bkd Llp
SIC 3677 Electronic coils, transformers & other inductors; Electronic coils, transformers & other inductors
Pr: John C Marrs
**Treas:* Amy S Floor
VP: Ted Denton
Brnch Mgr: Joe Sullivan

D-U-N-S 09-600-3918 IMP
MARSHALL ELECTRONICS INC
MOGAMI
1910 E Maple Ave, El Segundo, CA 90245-3411
Tel (310) 333-0606 *Founded/Ownrshp* 1979
Sales 31.2MM^E *EMP* 145
SIC 5961

D-U-N-S 12-254-8691
MARSHALL ETC INC
MARSHALL WIRELESS
12825 Flushing Meadows Dr # 28, Saint Louis, MO 63131-1837
Tel (636) 938-9000 *Founded/Ownrshp* 1997
Sales 37.9MM^E *EMP* 80^E
SIC 4812 Cellular telephone services
Pr: Dan Marshall
IT Man: Roger Bieri
Sales Asso: Benjamin Watson

D-U-N-S 03-117-1507
MARSHALL FORD SALES INC
1075 W Terra Ln, O Fallon, MO 63366-2317
Tel (636) 978-3673 *Founded/Ownrshp* 1960
Sales 33.5MM^E *EMP* 80
SIC 5511 Automobiles, new & used; Automobiles, new & used
Pr: Leo Marshall

D-U-N-S 07-704-5284
MARSHALL GERSTEIN & BORUN LLP
233 S Wacker Dr Ste 6300, Chicago, IL 60606-6471
Tel (312) 474-6300 *Founded/Ownrshp* 1955
Sales 40.1MM^E *EMP* 190
SIC 8111 General practice law office; General practice law office
Mng Pt: Jeffrey S Sharp
**Pt:* Patrick Ertel
**Pt:* Robert Gerstein
Pt: Donald W Rupert
Pr: Jamie Daly
Pr: Araceli Hernandez
Ex Dir: Steven Wingert
Brnch Mgr: Jennifer Lape
CIO: Debbie Coady
Dir IT: Jose Mendoza
IT Man: Kevin Lach

MARSHALL HEALTH CARE &
See MARSHALL NURSING SERVICES INC

MARSHALL HOSPITAL
See MARSHALL MEDICAL CENTER

D-U-N-S 06-975-1378
MARSHALL INDEPENDENT SCHOOL DISTRICT
MARSHALL PUBLIC SCHOOL
1305 E Pinecrest Dr, Marshall, TX 75670-7349
Tel (903) 927-8700 *Founded/Ownrshp* 1894
Sales 50.4MM *EMP* 917
SIC 8211 Public elementary & secondary schools; Public elementary & secondary schools
Bd of Dir: David Densmore
Ofcr: Casey Broadus
MIS Dir: Eddie Mulanax
MIS Dir: Paul Spaulding
Dir IT: Ron Lehr
Pr Dir: Richard Fluker
Pr Dir: David Weaver
Teacher Pr: Greg Morris
HC Dir: Rhonda Kilgore

D-U-N-S 02-952-6860
MARSHALL INDUSTRIAL SUPPLY INC
5100 Porter Harvey Dr, Guntersville, AL 35976-6749
Tel (256) 582-2401 *Founded/Ownrshp* 1981
Sales 23.0MM^E *EMP* 22
SIC 5999 Cleaning equipment & supplies; Cleaning equipment & supplies
Pr: Gerald Livingston

D-U-N-S 00-248-3345
MARSHALL INDUSTRIAL TECHNOLOGIES INC
529 S Clinton Ave, Trenton, NJ 08611-1893
Tel (609) 394-7153 *Founded/Ownrshp* 1951, 1989
Sales 45.3MM^E *EMP* 175
SIC 1796 1731 1711 3599 Machinery installation; Electrical work; Heating & air conditioning contractors; Machine shop, jobbing & repair; Machinery installation; Electrical work; Heating & air conditioning contractors; Machine shop, jobbing & repair
Pr: John Mako
COO: Linda Napolitan
**VP:* Rocco F Carnevale
**VP:* Richard Osenlund

D-U-N-S 04-611-0409 IMP
MARSHALL INDUSTRIES INC (UT)
MARSHALL AUDIO/VIDEO SYSTEMS
3800 W 2100 S, Salt Lake City, UT 84120-1206
Tel (801) 266-2428 *Founded/Ownrshp* 1963
Sales 27.0MM^E *EMP* 60
SIC 5065 5731 7622 Sound equipment, electronic; Intercommunication equipment, electronic; Radio, television & electronic stores; Intercommunication equipment repair
VP: Dennis J Savage
**Pr:* Brian Rhead Sorensen
CFO: Henry Chin
**Treas:* Shanna Burkinshaw
**VP:* Rodney Marshall
CIO: Randy McCleve
IT Man: Christian Baker
IT Man: Kelli Koji
Opers Mgr: Daren Handy

D-U-N-S 01-422-4943 IMP/EXP
MARSHALL MACHINERY INC (PA)
KUBOTA
348 Bethel School Rd, Honesdale, PA 18431-3031
Tel (570) 729-7117 *Founded/Ownrshp* 1960
Sales 28.0MM *EMP* 48
SIC 5211 5261 7359

D-U-N-S 06-780-5069
MARSHALL MEDICAL CENTER
MARSHALL HOSPITAL
1100 Marshall Way, Placerville, CA 95667-6533
Tel (530) 622-1441 *Founded/Ownrshp* 1959
Sales 222.8MM *EMP* 1,500
Accts Moss Adams Llp Stockton Ca
SIC 8062 8071 8082 General medical & surgical hospitals; Home health care services; Medical laboratories; X-ray laboratory, including dental; General medical & surgical hospitals; Medical laboratories; X-ray laboratory, including dental; Home health care services
Ofcr: James Whipple
Dir Vol: Jennifer Fiterre
**COO:* Shannon Truesdell
**CFO:* Laurie Eldridge
Dir IT: Kimberley Bunch
IT Man: Ronnie Cabusora
IT Man: Marlene Markowich
IT Man: Lynda Vernon
QC Dir: Kassie Waters
Mktg Dir: T Abraham
Pathlgst: Michael Berry

MARSHALL MEDICAL CENTER FAMILY
See UNIVERSITY PHYSICIANS & SURGEONS INC

MARSHALL MEDICAL CENTER SOUTH
See MARSHALL COUNTY HEALTH CARE AUTHORITY

D-U-N-S 07-931-9895
MARSHALL MEDICAL CENTER SOUTH
2505 Us Highway 431, Boaz, AL 35957
Tel (256) 593-8310 *Founded/Ownrshp* 2014
Sales 134.5MM *EMP* 33^E
SIC 8011 Physicians' office, including specialists
Owner: Larry W Greer

D-U-N-S 10-763-6953
■ **MARSHALL MIDDLEBY INC**
MIDDLEBY COOKING SYSTEMS GROUP
(*Suby of* MIDDLEBY CORP) ★
1400 Toastmaster Dr, Elgin, IL 60120-9274
Tel (847) 289-0204 *Founded/Ownrshp* 1983
Sales 250.0MM^E *EMP* 1,200
SIC 3556 3585 3631 Ovens, bakery; Mixers, feed, except agricultural; Refrigeration equipment, complete; Household cooking equipment; Ovens, bakery; Mixers, feed, except agricultural; Refrigeration equipment, complete; Household cooking equipment
Ch Bd: William F Whitman Jr
**Pr:* Selim A Bassoul
**CFO:* David B Baker
**Treas:* Martin Lindsay

D-U-N-S 07-042-4858
MARSHALL MILLER & ASSOCIATES INC
MMA
(*Suby of* CARDNO LIMITED)
534 Industrial Park Rd, Bluefield, VA 24605-9364
Tel (276) 322-5467 *Founded/Ownrshp* 2012
Sales 23.6MM^E *EMP* 181^E
SIC 8748

D-U-N-S 01-719-6718
MARSHALL MUSIC CO
MAESTRO MOTORS
3240 E Saginaw St, Lansing, MI 48912-4734
Tel (517) 337-9700 *Founded/Ownrshp* 1948
Sales 19.1MM *EMP* 300
Accts Plante & Moran Pllc East Lan
SIC 5736 7699 5735 Band instruments; String instruments; Pianos; Musical instrument repair services; Records; Band instruments; String instruments; Pianos; Musical instrument repair services; Records
Pr: Daniel T Marshall
CFO: Ann Meyer
**Ch:* Mary Jane Marshall
**Ch:* Willis W Marshall
**VP:* Bruce Woodhull

D-U-N-S 09-773-9023
MARSHALL NURSING SERVICES INC
MARSHALL HEALTH CARE &
9 Beal St, Machias, ME 04654
Tel (207) 255-3387 *Founded/Ownrshp* 1996
Sales 362.7MM *EMP* 110
Accts Downeast Accounting Bangor M
SIC 8051 Extended care facility; Extended care facility
Dir Recs: Patricia Rocco
Dir Soc: Adrianne Lemos
Dir Env Sv: Patrick Dennison
Off Mgr: Jessica Ackley
Off Mgr: Helen P Dennison
Nrsg Dir: Shannon Todd
Board of Directors: Peter Marshall

D-U-N-S 07-918-7678
■ **MARSHALL PHYSICIAN SERVICES LLC**
MESA MEDICAL GROUP
(*Suby of* TEAM HEALTH HOLDINGS INC) ★
1792 Alysheba Way Ste 150, Lexington, KY 40509-2285
Tel (877) 601-6372 *Founded/Ownrshp* 2013
Sales 28.5MM^E *EMP* 1,184^E
SIC 8011 Freestanding emergency medical center
Pr: James Foster MD
Pr: John Mullins
Chf Mktg O: Christophe R Pund MD
Chf Mktg O: T J Richardson MD

MARSHALL PUBLIC SCHOOL
See MARSHALL INDEPENDENT SCHOOL DISTRICT

D-U-N-S 10-003-8165
MARSHALL PUBLIC SCHOOL
ISD413
401 S Saratoga St, Marshall, MN 56258-3172
Tel (507) 537-6924 *Founded/Ownrshp* 1884
Sales 29.6MM *EMP* 275
Accts Hoffman & Brobst Pllc Marsha
SIC 8211 Public senior high school; Public senior high school
**CFO:* Bruce Lamprecht
Treas: Bill Mulso
IT Man: Becky Palmer
Instr Medi: Nancy Chooft

D-U-N-S 06-366-9212
MARSHALL PUBLIC SCHOOLS
BUEKER MIDDLE SCHOOL
860 W Vest St, Marshall, MO 65340-1666
Tel (660) 886-7414 *Founded/Ownrshp* 1880
Sales 20.7MM^E *EMP* 325
SIC 8211 Public elementary & secondary schools; Public elementary school; Public junior high school; Public senior high school; Public elementary & secondary schools; Public elementary school; Public junior high school; Public senior high school
Psych: Debra Foreman
Psych: Julie Orey

D-U-N-S 09-294-6573
MARSHALL PUBLIC SCHOOLS (INC)
100 E Green St, Marshall, MI 49068-1533
Tel (269) 781-1250 *Founded/Ownrshp* 1868
Sales 23.4MM^E *EMP* 252
Accts Plante & Moran Pllc Portage
SIC 8211 Public elementary school; Public junior high school; Public senior high school; Public elementary school; Public junior high school; Public senior high school
Cmptr Lab: Terry Lambert

MARSHALL REGIONAL MEDICAL CTR
See HARRISON COUNTY HOSPITAL ASSOCIATION

D-U-N-S 03-494-0130 IMP
MARSHALL RETAIL GROUP LLC
MARSHALL ROUSSO
3755 W Sunset Rd Ste A, Las Vegas, NV 89118-3931
Tel (702) 385-5233 *Founded/Ownrshp* 2014
Sales 180.5MM^E *EMP* 850
SIC 5661 5621 5641 5611 Men's shoes; Women's shoes; Women's clothing stores; Women's sportswear; Ready-to-wear apparel, women's; Children's & infants' wear stores; Men's & boys' clothing stores; Men's shoes; Women's shoes; Women's clothing stores; Women's sportswear; Ready-to-wear apparel, women's; Children's & infants' wear stores; Men's & boys' clothing stores
CEO: Todd Marshall
Pr: Margarite Panetta
**Pr:* Michael Wilkins
Sr VP: Roderick McOwan
Sr VP: Mark Rimler
VP: Marguerite Gray
Rgnl Mgr: Geri Bennett
Store Mgr: Gina Ballard
CIO: Rob Warren
Dir IT: Ken Simpson

MARSHALL ROUSSO
See MARSHALL RETAIL GROUP LLC

D-U-N-S 00-958-5951
MARSHALL TOOL & SUPPLY LLC
(*Suby of* PRODUCTION TOOL SUPPLY CO LLC) ★
9000 Lurline Ave, Chatsworth, CA 91311-6105
Tel (818) 775-0008 *Founded/Ownrshp* 1938, 2014
Sales 32.5MM^E *EMP* 58
SIC 5085 Industrial supplies
CEO: James Dewitt
Brnch Mgr: Eric De Leeuw
Sls Mgr: Bob Farrell
Sls Mgr: Darril Stroecker
Sales Asso: Merri Degraff
Sales Asso: Jose Morales
Sales Asso: Steve Taylor
Sales Asso: George Wolfe

D-U-N-S 06-276-7694
MARSHALL TURKEYS INC
715 W Tilden St, Postville, IA 52162-7795
Tel (563) 864-7676 *Founded/Ownrshp* 1971
Sales 20.3MM^E *EMP* 300
SIC 2015 Turkey, processed; Turkey, processed
Treas: Tom Dietrick

MARSHALL UNIV GRADUATE COLLEGE
See MARSHALL UNIVERSITY

D-U-N-S 06-813-0798
MARSHALL UNIVERSITY
MARSHALL UNIV GRADUATE COLLEGE
1 John Marshall Dr, Huntington, WV 25755-0003
Tel (304) 696-2385 *Founded/Ownrshp* 1837
Sales 174.8MM *EMP* 1,632
Accts Cliftonlarsonallen Llp Plymou
SIC 8221 University; University
Pr: Gary White
**Pr:* Dan Angel PHD
Bd of Dir: Jeri Fogel
Ofcr: Karen Beach
Ofcr: Jan Weece
**Sr VP:* Herbert J Karlet
Sr VP: Anita Lockridge
Sr VP: Gayle L Ormiston
**VP:* Dr Betty Cleckley
VP: John Maher
**VP:* Dr Charles McKown
VP: Lance West
Dir Lab: Darwin McCunn
Comm Dir: Luke Lassiter
Comm Dir: Ginny Painter
Comm Dir: Dave Wellman

D-U-N-S 12-374-8097
MARSHALL UNIVERSITY FOUNDATION
519 John Marshall Dr, Huntington, WV 25703-1400
Tel (304) 696-6264 *Founded/Ownrshp* 1947
Sales 29.4MM *EMP* 35
SIC 6732 Trusts: educational, religious, etc.; Trusts: educational, religious, etc.
Pr: Dr Ronald Area
**CFO:* Scott Anderson
**VP:* Lance West

D-U-N-S 03-615-6615
MARSHALL UNIVERSITY RESEARCH CORP
1 John Marshall Dr, Huntington, WV 25755-0003
Tel (304) 696-6598 *Founded/Ownrshp* 1987
Sales 33.2MM *EMP* 350^E
Accts Hayflich Grigoraci Pllc Hunti

SIC 8731 Commercial physical research; Commercial physical research
Pr: Gary White
**Treas:* Karla J Murphy
VP: Shawn Cheeks
VP: Matt Meriweather
VP: Mark Mitchell
VP: Danielle Ocheltree
**VP:* Gayle Ormiston
VP: Keith Spears
VP Admn: Makenzee Ruley
Genl Mgr: Cheryl King
Info Man: Simon Collier

MARSHALL WIRELESS
See MARSHALL ETC INC

D-U-N-S 82-581-0278
MARSHALL WYTHE SCHOOL OF LAW
613 S Henry St, Williamsburg, VA 23185-4110
Tel (757) 221-3800 *Founded/Ownrshp* 1982
Sales 7.0MM *EMP* 600
SIC 8221 Colleges universities & professional schools; Colleges universities & professional schools
Pr: Taylor Reveley

D-U-N-S 07-665-9127
MARSHALLS HOLDING CO
KENWORTH NORTHWEST
20220 International Blvd, Seatac, WA 98198-5703
Tel (206) 433-5911 *Founded/Ownrshp* 1997
Sales 89.9MM *EMP* 180
SIC 5012 5013 Trucks, commercial; Truck parts & accessories; Trucks, commercial; Truck parts & accessories
Pr: Marshall Cymbaluk
**VP:* Kathreen Cymbaluk
Dir IT: John Morgus
Sls Mgr: Shane Petersen

D-U-N-S 04-341-1693 IMP/EXP
■ **MARSHALLS OF MA INC** (MA)
(*Suby of* TJ MAXX) ★
770 Cochituate Rd, Framingham, MA 01701-4666
Tel (508) 390-1000 *Founded/Ownrshp* 1958
Sales 1.4MMME *EMP* 20,000
SIC 5651 Family clothing stores; Family clothing stores
Pr: Richard Sherr
**Treas:* Mary B Reynolds
**VP:* Alfred Appel
MIS Dir: Bob Hernandez
MIS Dir: Carol Hubert
IT Man: Ken Kozikowski
Mfg Mgr: Lyn Costello
Opers Mgr: Jerry Rosei
VP Mktg: Kerry Hamilton

D-U-N-S 00-528-8378 EXP
MARSHALLTOWN CO (IA)
104 S 8th Ave, Marshalltown, IA 50158-3039
Tel (641) 753-5999 *Founded/Ownrshp* 1905
Sales 1.5MM *EMP* 300
SIC 3423 Hand & edge tools; Hand & edge tools
Pr: Joseph T Carter
Sls&Mrk Ex: Scott Phillips
VP Mktg: Dan Kester
Mktg Dir: Tim Brennecke
Manager: Steve Louk

D-U-N-S 02-163-3797
MARSHALLTOWN COMMUNITY SCHOOL DISTRICT
1002 S 3rd Ave, Marshalltown, IA 50158-3329
Tel (641) 754-1000 *Founded/Ownrshp* 1876
Sales 50.0MM *EMP* 950
SIC 8211 Public elementary & secondary schools; Public elementary & secondary schools
Pr Dir: Andrew Potter
Sls Mgr: Derek Whitehill
Psych: Meri Edel
Psych: Carrie Talbott

D-U-N-S 07-584-1296
MARSHALLTOWN MEDICAL & SURGICAL CENTER
3 S 4th Ave, Marshalltown, IA 50158-2924
Tel (641) 754-5151 *Founded/Ownrshp* 1902
Sales 77.4MM *EMP* 690E
Accts Denman & Company Llp West De
SIC 8062 General medical & surgical hospitals; General medical & surgical hospitals
Pr: Tl Briggs
Chf Path: Sal Syed
CFO: Todd Burch
**Treas:* Carol Hibbs
VP: Bob Downey
VP: Gina James
**VP:* Mike Mason
Dir Rx: Jules Burian
Dir Rx: Bill Dahlke
Dir IT: Mike Vanbaale
Pharmcst: Jim Landmark

D-U-N-S 87-844-0411
■ **MARSHALS SERVICE UNITED STATES**
(*Suby of* UNITED STATES DEPT OF JUSTICE) ★
3601 Pennsy Dr, Landover, MD 20785-1612
Tel (202) 307-9001 *Founded/Ownrshp* 1789
Sales NA *EMP* 4,000
SIC 9221 Marshals' offices, police; ; Marshals' offices, police

D-U-N-S 96-864-2087
MARSHFIELD CARE CENTER LLC
RICE HLTH CARE FCLTIES WSCONSI
(*Suby of* RICE HEALTH CARE FACILITIES OF WISCONSIN INC) ★
814 W 14th St, Marshfield, WI 54449-4030
Tel (715) 387-1188 *Founded/Ownrshp* 2004
Sales 12.2MME *EMP* 346E
SIC 8051 Skilled nursing care facilities

D-U-N-S 07-981-7262
MARSHFIELD CLINIC HEALTH SYSTEM INC
1000 N Oak Ave, Marshfield, WI 54449-5702
Tel (715) 387-5511 *Founded/Ownrshp* 2012
Sales 1.0MMME *EMP* 99E
SIC 8011 Clinic, operated by physicians
CEO: Susan Turney
**COO:* Daniel Ramsey
**CFO:* John Cook
**Treas:* Tim Peterson

D-U-N-S 07-477-6030
MARSHFIELD CLINIC INC
(*Suby of* MARSHFIELD CLINIC HEALTH SYSTEM INC) ★
1000 N Oak Ave, Marshfield, WI 54449-5702
Tel (715) 387-5511 *Founded/Ownrshp* 1916
Sales 1.0MMME *EMP* 99E
Accts Kpmg Llp Columbus Oh
SIC 8011 Clinic, operated by physicians; Clinic, operated by physicians
Pr: Brian H Ewert MD
V Ch: Mark J Bradley
COO: James S Coleman
**CFO:* Gary Jankowski
CFO: Brent Miler
**Treas:* Mark A Lepage
Treas: Mark Lepage
Ofcr: Steve Youso
VP: Gary Mayeux
**VP:* Douglas Reding MD
**VP:* C Todd Stewart
Dir Lab: Pamela Carter
Dir Rx: Dick Gritt

D-U-N-S 06-830-5739
MARSHFIELD CLINIC RESEARCH FOUNDATION INC
1000 N Oak Ave, Marshfield, WI 54449-5703
Tel (715) 387-5241 *Founded/Ownrshp* 1959
Sales 21.1MME *EMP* 200
SIC 8733 Medical research; Medical research
Pathlgst: Kathryn A Kolquist

D-U-N-S 00-406-7125 IMP/EXP
■ **MARSHFIELD DOORSYSTEMS INC** (DE)
(*Suby of* MASONITE INTERNATIONAL CORP) ★
1401 E 4th St, Marshfield, WI 54449-4555
Tel (715) 384-2141 *Founded/Ownrshp* 2000, 2011
Sales 85.9MME *EMP* 662
SIC 2431 3442 Doors, wood; Metal doors; Doors, wood; Metal doors
CEO: Donald Bergman
**Pr:* Jerry Mannigel
IT Man: Shirley Geldernick
Sfty Mgr: Justin Lekies
Sfty Mgr: Mark Meurette
Manager: Doug Bachand
Manager: Jim Dawson
Manager: Kyle Killough
Manager: Kirk Soe
Sales Asso: Lisa Steines

D-U-N-S 07-477-8119
MARSHFIELD ELECTRIC & WATER DEPT
MARSHFIRLD UTILITIES
2000 S Central Ave, Marshfield, WI 54449-4921
Tel (715) 384-8515 *Founded/Ownrshp* 1933
Sales 34.8MME *EMP* 43
Accts Hawkins Ash Baptie & Company
SIC 4911 Electric services; Electric services
**VP:* Mike Eberl
Off Mgr: Kent Mueller
Off Mgr: Adam Waldera

D-U-N-S 07-979-9259
MARSHFIELD PUBLIC SCHOOLS
76 S River St, Marshfield, MA 02050-2453
Tel (781) 834-5000 *Founded/Ownrshp* 2015
Sales 9.6MME *EMP* 568E
SIC 8211 Public elementary & secondary schools

D-U-N-S 05-358-1898
MARSHFIELD R-1 SCHOOL DISTRICT
HUBBLE ELEMENTARY
170 State Highway Dd, Marshfield, MO 65706-1513
Tel (417) 859-2120 *Founded/Ownrshp* 1992
Sales 21.9MME *EMP* 350
SIC 8211 Public elementary & secondary schools; Public elementary & secondary schools
Pr: Steve Rasmick
VP: Pat Elinzler
Cmptr Lab: Tamara Pierce
Cmptr Lab: Machelle Shields
HC Dir: Christina Roberts

D-U-N-S 10-008-3369
MARSHFIELD SCHOOL DISTRICT (INC)
1010 E 4th St, Marshfield, WI 54449-4538
Tel (715) 387-1101 *Founded/Ownrshp* 1885
Sales 22.6MME *EMP* 470
SIC 8211 Public elementary school; Public junior high school; Public senior high school; Public elementary school; Public junior high school; Public senior high school
Teacher Pr: Lara Baehr
HC Dir: Judy Akin

MARSHFIRLD UTILITIES
See MARSHFIELD ELECTRIC & WATER DEPT

MARSH'S SUNFRESH SUPERMARKET
See GENERAL STORE 2 INC

D-U-N-S 96-965-7725
MARSICO CAPITAL MANAGEMENT LLC
RBC CAPITOL MARKETS
1200 17th St Ste 1600, Denver, CO 80202-5824
Tel (303) 454-5600 *Founded/Ownrshp* 2007
Sales 21.5MME *EMP* 65
SIC 6282 Investment advice
CFO: Neil Gloude
Ofcr: David Price
Ex VP: Christie Austin
Ex VP: Cornelius Gloude
Ex VP: Kenneth Johnson
Ex VP: Thomas Kerwin
Ex VP: David Lubchenco
VP: Wesley Bradish
VP: Lynnett Fuller
VP: John Hanley
VP: Aaron Krasnow
VP: Cory Ross

D-U-N-S 62-720-6555
MARSONER INC
APPLE DISTRIBUTING
430 W Warner Rd Ste 119, Tempe, AZ 85284-2968
Tel (480) 921-8006 *Founded/Ownrshp* 1992
Sales 29.3MME *EMP* 200E
SIC 8748 Business consulting; Business consulting
CEO: Reinhold Marsoner
Off Mgr: Catherine Cox

D-U-N-S 02-719-4760
MARSTALLER MOTORS INC
LINCOLN MERCURY
1601 S Valley Mills Dr, Waco, TX 76711-2117
Tel (254) 756-5511 *Founded/Ownrshp* 1940
Sales 28.0MME *EMP* 70
SIC 5511 Automobiles, new & used; Automobiles, new & used
Pr: Charles H Marstaller Jr
**VP:* Ronald D Marstaller

MART CART
See ASSEMBLED PRODUCTS CORP

D-U-N-S 03-846-8039
MART INC
1503 Perry St, Irving, TX 75060-3246
Tel (972) 721-1522 *Founded/Ownrshp* 1977
Sales 23.8MME *EMP* 40
Accts Perryman Chaney Russell Llp
SIC 1542 Commercial & office buildings, renovation & repair; Commercial & office building, new construction
Pr: Vernon Proctor
**VP:* Linda Proctor
**VP:* Tim Proctor
IT Man: Cheryl Mowrey

D-U-N-S 02-153-2155
MART PRODUCE CORP
70 N 100 E, Rupert, ID 83350-9440
Tel (208) 436-0611 *Founded/Ownrshp* 1986
Sales 27.8MME *EMP* 75
SIC 5148 Potatoes, fresh
Genl Mgr: Jeff Harper
**VP:* Jack Duncan
Board of Directors: Paul Duncan, Doug Hansen, Gary Hansen, Richard Hansen

D-U-N-S 06-997-5829
MARTAM CONSTRUCTION INC
1200 Gasket Dr, Elgin, IL 60120-7305
Tel (847) 608-6800 *Founded/Ownrshp* 1973
Sales 42.6MME *EMP* 40
Accts Michael R Horst Cpa Hawthor
SIC 1611 1622 1623 General contractor, highway & street construction; Bridge construction; Water main construction; Sewer line construction; Pipeline construction; General contractor, highway & street construction; Bridge construction; Water main construction; Sewer line construction; Pipeline construction
Pr: Robert Kutrovatz
**Treas:* Cynthia Holland
**Prin:* Tamas Kutrovacz
Off Mgr: Kristin Sudol

D-U-N-S 10-402-4708 IMP/EXP
MARTCO LLC
ROYOMARTIN
(*Suby of* MARTIN COMPANIES LLC ROM) ★
2189 Memorial Dr, Alexandria, LA 71301-3610
Tel (318) 448-0405 *Founded/Ownrshp* 1981
Sales 168.1MME *EMP* 850
SIC 2493 2435 Strandboard, oriented; Plywood, hardwood or hardwood faced; Strandboard, oriented; Plywood, hardwood or hardwood faced
Pt: Jonathan E Martin
Pr: Roy O Martin III
Pr: Adrian Schoonover
VP: Mark Dicarlo
VP: Joe Mackay
VP: Scott Poole
VP: Mickey Rachal
VP: Terry Secrest
Software D: John Laponsie
Sls Mgr: Pat Abney
Sls Mgr: Wayne Miller

MARTEC INTERNATIONAL
See CARL F EWIG INC

D-U-N-S 13-660-0111
MARTECH MEDICAL PRODUCTS INC
1500 Delp Dr, Harleysville, PA 19438-2900
Tel (215) 256-8833 *Founded/Ownrshp* 1978
Sales 34.7MME *EMP* 180E
SIC 3069 3842 3083 Medical & laboratory rubber sundries & related products; Surgical appliances & supplies; Laminated plastics plate & sheet; Medical & laboratory rubber sundries & related products; Surgical appliances & supplies; Laminated plastics plate & sheet
Pr: David Markel
Pr: Donna Wolfe
**CFO:* John Stevens
VP: Donna Wolf
Opers Mgr: Mayola Mann
Prd Mgr: Morgan Terry
Ql Cn Mgr: Xuan Liang
Mktg Mgr: Justin Sirna
Mktg Mgr: Ruud Van Kemenade

D-U-N-S 13-148-0451 EXP
MARTEK BIOSCIENCES CORP
(*Suby of* KONINKLIJKE DSM N.V.)
6480 Dobbin Rd Ste J, Columbia, MD 21045-4701
Tel (410) 740-0081 *Founded/Ownrshp* 1985
Sales 72.6MME *EMP* 525E
SIC 2836 Biological products, except diagnostic; Biological products, except diagnostic
CEO: Peter Nitze
Sr VP: Dr David J Kyle
VP: Joe Buron
VP: Feitel David
VP: Thomas Fisher
VP: Joe Speroni
VP: Joseph Weis
CTO: Lee Jensen
CTO: Pat Lowe
Opers Mgr: Leah Gratton
S&M/VP: Philip Fass

D-U-N-S 83-087-5089
MARTEL CONSTRUCTION INC
1203 S Church Ave, Bozeman, MT 59715-5801
Tel (406) 586-8585 *Founded/Ownrshp* 1968
Sales 36.9MME *EMP* 99
SIC 1542 Nonresidential construction; Nonresidential construction
Pr: William Martel
**CFO:* Steven A Irion
Treas: Wayne Crosby
**Ex VP:* Steve Conway
**Ex VP:* Jason L Martel
VP: Brad Pesek
IT Man: Anthony Martel
Sfty Mgr: Frank Harriman

D-U-N-S 00-486-6257
▲ **MARTEN TRANSPORT LTD**
129 Marten St, Mondovi, WI 54755-1700
Tel (715) 926-4216 *Founded/Ownrshp* 1946
Sales 672.9MM *EMP* 3,240E
Accts Grant Thornton Llp Minneapoli
Tkr Sym MRTN *Exch* NGS
SIC 4213 Refrigerated products transport; Contract haulers; Refrigerated products transport; Contract haulers
Ch Bd: Randolph L Marten
Pr: Timothy M Kohl
COO: Bob Smith
CFO: James J Hinnendael
Ex VP: Timothy P Nash
Sr VP: John H Turner
Dir IT: Randy Baier
Sys Admin: Kevin Ingvalson
VP Opers: Doug Petit
Opers Mgr: Dean Gobrecht
Opers Mgr: Angel Rivera
Board of Directors: Jerry M Bauer, Robert L Demorest, Larry B Hagness, G Larry Owens, Thomas J Winkel

MARTEN VOLVO VOLKSWAGON
See MARTENS CARS OF WASHINGTON INC

D-U-N-S 02-428-3632
MARTENS CARS OF WASHINGTON INC
MARTEN VOLVO VOLKSWAGON
(*Suby of* IMPERIAL INVESTMENT CO INC) ★
5206 River Rd, Bethesda, MD 20816-1416
Tel (301) 656-6166 *Founded/Ownrshp* 1944
Sales 23.8MME *EMP* 90
SIC 5511 Automobiles, new & used; Automobiles, new & used
CEO: Harry Martens

THE MARTENS COMPANIES
See IMPERIAL INVESTMENT CO INC

D-U-N-S 82-467-0954 IMP/EXP
MARTEX FARMS
Carr 1 Km 96 2 St Ca, Santa Isabel, PR 00757
Tel (787) 845-4909 *Founded/Ownrshp* 1989
Sales 14.8MM *EMP* 350
Accts Luis B Gonzalez & Co Psc S
SIC 0179 0174 0181 2037 Avocado orchard; Banana grove; Mango grove; Lime grove; Plants, foliage & shrubberies; Fruit juices
Pt: Venancio C Marti
Pt: Veny Mart
Pt: Gustavo A Marti
Off Mgr: Aurea Rodrigez

D-U-N-S 03-009-8313 IMP/EXP
MARTEX FIBER SOUTHERN CORP
3200b Southport Rd, Spartanburg, SC 29302
Tel (864) 583-6412 *Founded/Ownrshp* 1975
Sales 71.5MME *EMP* 185E
SIC 5093

D-U-N-S 09-755-1113
MARTEX WELL SERVICES LLP
805 Cox Rd, Marshall, TX 75671
Tel (903) 938-3574 *Founded/Ownrshp* 1978
Sales 20.7MME *EMP* 90E
SIC 1389 Construction, repair & dismantling services; Oil field services
Pt: Richard Roark
Pt: Kenneth Q Carlile
Opers Mgr: Darell Preston
Sls Dir: Richard Willis

D-U-N-S 07-666-4309
MARTHA AND MARY HEALTH SERVICES
19160 Front St Ne, Poulsbo, WA 98370
Tel (360) 779-7500 *Founded/Ownrshp* 1891
Sales 15.4MM *EMP* 400
SIC 8741 Hospital management; Nursing & personal care facility management; Hospital management; Nursing & personal care facility management
CEO: Chad Solvie
Dir Recs: Janet Muenzenberger
COO: Joanna Carlson
**CFO:* Weigee Seaton
Ex Dir: Karen Carter
Mktg Mgr: Rob Gelder

D-U-N-S 80-181-6570
MARTHA JEFFERSON HEALTH SERVICES CORP
MARTHA JEFFERSON WOMEN'S HEALT
500 Martha Jefferson Dr, Charlottesville, VA 22911-4668
Tel (434) 654-7000 *Founded/Ownrshp* 1903
Sales 25.8M *EMP* 1,600
SIC 8741 Hospital management; Hospital management
Ch: Peter Brooks
**Pr:* James E Haden
**Ch:* William Achenbach
**Treas:* J Michael Burrus

D-U-N-S 04-698-9141
MARTHA JEFFERSON HOSPITAL
(Suby of SENTARA HEALTHCARE) ★
500 Martha Jefferson Dr, Charlottesville, VA 22911-4668
Tel (434) 654-7000 Founded/Ownrshp 2011
Sales 252.1MM EMP 2,272^E
SIC 8062 General medical & surgical hospitals; General medical & surgical hospitals
CEO: James E Haden
*CFO: Joseph Burris
*Treas: J Michael Burris
VP: Ray Mishler
Dir Lab: Nancy Lewis
Chf Nrs Of: Amy Black
QA Dir: Dorothy Somerville
IT Man: Josh Baumann
IT Man: Tami Duggan
Mktg Dir: Michael Cordell
Doctor: Michael Baylor

D-U-N-S 93-399-8817
MARTHA JEFFERSON HOSPITAL
(Suby of MARTHA JEFFERSON HOSPITAL) ★
459 Locust Ave, Charlottesville, VA 22902-4871
Tel (434) 982-7000 Founded/Ownrshp 1986
Sales 6.2MM^E EMP 2,187^E
SIC 8082 Home health care services
Pr: James Haden

MARTHA JEFFERSON WOMEN'S HEALT
See MARTHA JEFFERSON HEALTH SERVICES CORP

D-U-N-S 09-873-1284
MARTHA LLOYD SCHOOL INC
66 Lloyd Ln, Troy, PA 16947-1199
Tel (570) 297-2185 Founded/Ownrshp 1928
Sales 1.8MM EMP 300
Accts Mengel Metzger Barr & Co Llp
SIC 6531 Real estate agents & managers; Real estate agents & managers
Pr: William Miller
*Ch Bd: Henry Dunn

D-U-N-S 08-170-2024 IMP
▲ MARTHA STEWART LIVING OMNIMEDIA INC
601 W 26th St Rm 900, New York, NY 10001-1143
Tel (212) 827-8000 Founded/Ownrshp 2015
Sales 141.9MM EMP 274^E
Tkr Sym MSO Exch NYS
SIC 2721 2731 4813 7812 Magazines: publishing only, not printed on site; Book publishing; ; Motion picture production & distribution, television; Magazines: publishing only, not printed on site; Book publishing; ; Motion picture production & distribution, television
CEO: Daniel W Dienst
*Ch Bd: Martha Stewart
Pr: Holly Brown
Pr: Zaki Kamandy
Pr: Soyoung OH
CFO: Kenneth P West
Ofcr: Joe Lagani
Ex VP: Ann Casey Bukawyn
Ex VP: Shelley S Nandkeolyar
Sr VP: Allison Jacques
VP: Stacey Lager
Exec: Patricia Pollack
Dir Soc: Marc Marrone

D-U-N-S 00-752-8979 IMP
■ MARTHA STEWART LIVING OMNIMEDIA LLC
(Suby of MARTHA STEWART LIVING OMNIMEDIA INC) ★
20 W 43rd St, New York, NY 10036-7400
Tel (212) 827-8000 Founded/Ownrshp 1997
Sales 40.1MM^E EMP 350
SIC 2721 Magazines: publishing only, not printed on site; Magazines: publishing only, not printed on site
CEO: Robin Marino
CFO: Allison Jaques
*Bd of Dir: Jeffrey W Ubben
Assoc VP: Jodi Gruber
Ex VP: Ann C Bukawyn
Ex VP: Dora B Cardinale
Sr VP: Claudio S Goldbarg
Sr VP: Alison A Matz
Sr VP: Sally Preston
VP: Nancy Ashbrooke
VP: Michael Fisher
VP: Kim Hackett
VP: Ann Henry
VP: Alison Jacques
VP: Beth Silver
Assoc Dir: Diondra Humphries
Assoc Dir: Jessica Stonehouse

D-U-N-S 07-379-8373
MARTHAS VINEYARD HOSPITAL INC
(Suby of PARTNERS HEALTHCARE SYSTEM INC) ★
1 Hospital Rd, Oak Bluffs, MA 02557
Tel (508) 693-9012 Founded/Ownrshp 1985
Sales 64.8MM EMP 200
SIC 8062 General medical & surgical hospitals; General medical & surgical hospitals
Pr: Timothy J Walsh
*Treas: Earle R Ray
Ofcr: James Ferriter
Dir OR: Donna Hayes
Surgeon: Denise Fraser
Pharmcst: Jean Cirillo
Pharmcst: Diane Hartmann
Phys Thrpy: Julie Whitehill
Snr Mgr: Carol Bardwell

D-U-N-S 12-672-8356
MARTHAS VINEYARD MORTGAGE CO LLC
107 Beach Rd Ste 101, Vineyard Haven, MA 02568-5524
Tel (508) 696-1801 Founded/Ownrshp 2000
Sales NA EMP 2
SIC 6163 Mortgage brokers arranging for loans, using money of others; Mortgage brokers arranging for loans, using money of others

D-U-N-S 79-608-0075
MARTHAS VINEYARD PUBLIC SCHOOL
SUPERVISORY UNION 19
4 Pine St, Vineyard Haven, MA 02568-6337
Tel (508) 693-2007 Founded/Ownrshp 1957
Sales 24.1MM EMP 425
Accts Sullivan Rogers & Company Ll
SIC 8211 Public senior high school; Public senior high school
*Treas: Marylee Schroeder
Schl Brd P: Susan Mercer

D-U-N-S 06-010-6978
MARTHAS VINEYARD SAVINGS BANK
78 Main St, Edgartown, MA 02539-8238
Tel (508) 627-4266 Founded/Ownrshp 1955
Sales NA EMP 80
SIC 6035 Savings institutions, federally chartered; Savings institutions, federally chartered
Pr: Edward E Mayhew Jr
*Treas: Cathy Bettencourt
*Ex VP: Brad Egan
*Ex VP: Bob Wheeler
*VP: Henry Corey
VP Admn: Charlie Kroll
Brnch Mgr: Robert Rippcondi
CIO: Chris Wells

D-U-N-S 96-998-8950
MARTIFER SOLAR INC
505 Montgomery St Fl 11, San Francisco, CA 94111-2585
Tel (415) 874-3388 Founded/Ownrshp 2010
Sales 71.2MM EMP 1^E
Accts Wu Hoover & Co Llp San Fran
SIC 3674 Photovoltaic devices, solid state; Photovoltaic devices, solid state
CEO: Ricardo Abecassis

MARTIGNETTI COMPANIES
See MARTIGNETTI CORP

D-U-N-S 87-620-3373
MARTIGNETTI CORP
MARTIGNETTI COMPANIES
975 University Ave, Norwood, MA 02062-2643
Tel (781) 255-5703 Founded/Ownrshp 1991
Sales 216.1MM^E EMP 394
SIC 5182 5921 Wine; Liquor; Liquor stores; Wine; Hard liquor; Wine; Liquor; Liquor stores; Wine; Hard liquor
Pr: Carl J Martignetti
*Treas: Carmine A Martignetti
VP: Peter Colettis
VP: Ed Devito
VP: Ronnie Pollara

D-U-N-S 04-102-9208 IMP
MARTIGNETTI GROCERY CO INC
CAROLINA WINE COMPANY
975 University Ave, Norwood, MA 02062-2643
Tel (781) 278-2000 Founded/Ownrshp 1986
Sales 338.7MM^E EMP 700^E
SIC 5182 Liquor; Liquor stores; Liquor
Pr: Carmine Martignetti
*Treas: Carl Martignetti
VP: Neal Fisher
Area Mgr: Tom McGrath
Dist Mgr: Ken Ochs
Netwrk Mgr: Bob Gagne
Mktg Dir: Tim Bruce
Sls Mgr: Jim Fadden
Sls Mgr: Mike Gorman
Sls Mgr: Brian Mundy
Sls Mgr: John Romano

D-U-N-S 02-499-7314
MARTIN & BAYLEY INC
HUCK'S
1311a W Main St, Carmi, IL 62821-1389
Tel (618) 382-2334 Founded/Ownrshp 2001
Sales 292.3MM^E EMP 1,500
Accts Harding Shymanski & Company
SIC 5411 Convenience stores; Convenience stores
CEO: Todd Jenney
*Pr: Mark Bayley
*Ch: Frank Bayley
*V Ch Bd: Charles Martin
VP: Jason Bryson
VP: Audrey L Elwood
VP: Kevin Knapp
VP: Teresa Knasel
VP: John Long
*VP: Jim Whetstone
Brnch Mgr: Judy Heffington

D-U-N-S 08-654-9839
MARTIN ADVERTISING INC
2801 University Blvd # 200, Birmingham, AL 35233-2860
Tel (205) 930-9200 Founded/Ownrshp 1977
Sales 21.8MM^E EMP 116
SIC 7311 Advertising agencies; Advertising agencies
Pr: David C Martin
*CFO: Mary A Martin
*Treas: Nanci Sexton
VP: Jim Bickers

D-U-N-S 04-389-2777
■ MARTIN AGENCY INC
INGENUITY MEDIA GROUP
(Suby of INTERPUBLIC GROUP OF COMPANIES INC) ★
1 Shockoe Plz, Richmond, VA 23219-4132
Tel (804) 649-1496 Founded/Ownrshp 1994
Sales 88.0MM^E EMP 600
SIC 7331 7311 8743 7313 Direct mail advertising services; Advertising agencies; Public relations services; Radio, television, publisher representatives; Direct mail advertising services; Advertising agencies; Public relations services; Radio, television, publisher representatives
Ch Bd: John Adams Jr
Pr: Ren J Ferran
*CEO: Matthew Williams
*COO: Beth Rilee-Kelley
*CFO: Rene J Ferran
CFO: Amanda Martin
CFO: Terry Thompson
*CFO: Janet White
Sr VP: Andie McKinney
VP: Wade Alger
VP: Hugh Callahan
VP: Vanessa Fortier
VP: Jason Komulainen
VP: Kevin Ragland
VP: Rebecca Smith
VP: Cliff Sorah
VP: Tom Sparks
VP: Adam Stockton
VP: Jeanette Tyson
VP: Rich Weinstein
VP: Jacob Wells

D-U-N-S 04-607-8366
MARTIN AND SNYDER PRODUCT SALES CO
8880 Hubbell St, Detroit, MI 48228-2396
Tel (313) 272-4900 Founded/Ownrshp 1966
Sales 146.9MM EMP 27
Accts Plante & Moran Pllc Ann Arbo
SIC 5194 5145 Tobacco & tobacco products; Candy; Chewing gum; Tobacco & tobacco products; Candy; Chewing gum
Pr: Frank Daiza
Treas: Kathleen Spence
*VP: George Daiza

MARTIN APPLIANCE SALES & SVC
See DENMAR ASSOCIATES LLC

MARTIN ASPHALT
See MARTIN PRODUCT SALES LLC

D-U-N-S 02-855-2644
MARTIN ASSOCIATES GROUP INC
MARTIN, JOHN A & ASSOCIATES
950 S Grand Ave Fl 4, Los Angeles, CA 90015-1436
Tel (213) 483-6490 Founded/Ownrshp 1961
Sales 59.0MM^E EMP 350
SIC 8711 Structural engineering; Structural engineering
CEO: John A Martin Jr
*VP: Barry Schindler
Dir Bus: Michael McCoy
Sys Mgr: Marvin Mittelstaedt

D-U-N-S 60-213-6632
MARTIN ATTEA
ATTEA APPLIANCE
1509 Clinton St, Buffalo, NY 14206-3008
Tel (716) 822-0378 Founded/Ownrshp 1988
Sales 206.5MM EMP 2^E
Accts Morgan Beyer & Wayne Cpa P
SIC 5064 5722 Electrical appliances, major; Electric household appliances, major; Electrical appliances, major; Electric household appliances, major
Owner: Martin Attea

D-U-N-S 05-191-6658 EXP
MARTIN AUTOMATIC INC
1661 Northrock Ct, Rockford, IL 61103-1296
Tel (815) 654-4800 Founded/Ownrshp 1968
Sales 60.9MM^E EMP 180
SIC 3565 3625 3823 3555 Packaging machinery; Relays & industrial controls; Industrial instrmnts msrmnt display/control process variable; Presses, gravure; Packaging machinery; Relays & industrial controls; Industrial instrmnts msrmnt display/control process variable; Presses, gravure
Ch: John R Martin
Pr: Roger Cederholm
Pr: James Ward
CFO: John Bauch
Sec: Ronald L Gieseke
Comm Dir: Kelly Hart
Rgnl Mgr: Bob Hoffman
Rgnl Mgr: Gavin Rittmeyer
Rgnl Mgr: Brian Sager
Genl Mgr: David Ho
CIO: Emil Borys
Board of Directors: Richard L Verkler

MARTIN AUTOMOTIVE
See MARTIN CADILLAC CO INC

MARTIN AUTOMOTIVE GROUP
See VISION FORD LINCOLN HYUNDAI INC

D-U-N-S 03-431-0227
MARTIN AUTOMOTIVE GROUP INC
MARTIN TRUCK CENTER
2948 Highway 90 E, Lake Charles, LA 70615-3634
Tel (337) 433-0506 Founded/Ownrshp 1966
Sales 39.2MM^E EMP 77
SIC 5511 7513 Automobiles, new & used; Trucks, tractors & trailers: new & used; Pickups, new & used; Truck rental & leasing, no drivers; Automobiles, new & used; Trucks, tractors & trailers: new & used; Pickups, new & used; Truck rental & leasing, no drivers
Pr: Edward G Martin Jr
*Sec: Hazel B Martin
VP: Tad Martin
Genl Mgr: Roger Watral
VP Opers: K Martin

MARTIN AUTOPARK
See MARTIN CHEVROLET - BUICK INC

D-U-N-S 02-855-2578
MARTIN BROS/MARCOWALL INC
17104 S Figueroa St, Gardena, CA 90248-3097
Tel (310) 532-5335 Founded/Ownrshp 1966
Sales 25.0MM^E EMP 150
SIC 1742 Plastering, drywall & insulation; Plastering, drywall & insulation
CEO: Mohammad Chahine
VP: Dave Aguilera
VP: Damon Hoover

D-U-N-S 02-204-4762
MARTIN BROTHERS DISTRIBUTING CO INC
6623 Chancellor Dr, Cedar Falls, IA 50613-6966
Tel (319) 266-1775 Founded/Ownrshp 2001
Sales 546.7MM^E EMP 400
SIC 5141 5169 5046 5087 Groceries, general line; Chemicals & allied products; Restaurant equipment & supplies; Service establishment equipment; Groceries, general line; Chemicals & allied products; Restaurant equipment & supplies; Service establishment equipment
CEO: Brooks Martin
*Pr: John Martin
CFO: Gerald Johnson
*Treas: Martin Jeff
*Treas: Jeffery Martin
Netwrk Mgr: Lee Winterscheidt
Opers Mgr: Jacob Sego
Sales Exec: Michael Moss
Mktg Mgr: Sara Kies
Manager: Dean Schwartz
Sls Mgr: Brian Hathcock

D-U-N-S 08-614-7907
MARTIN BUICK-OLDSMOBILE-GMC TRUCK INC
RANDY WISE BICK-OLDSMOBILE-GMC
2530 Owen Rd, Fenton, MI 48430-1768
Tel (810) 629-0113 Founded/Ownrshp 1963
Sales 40.0MM^E EMP 89
SIC 5511 Automobiles, new & used; Trucks, tractors & trailers: new & used; Automobiles, new & used; Trucks, tractors & trailers: new & used
Pr: Randolph Wise
Sec: Diane Jaques
Store Mgr: Troy Hummel
Sls Mgr: Donald Nord
Sls Mgr: Mark Zerka
Sales Asso: Dayna Suess

D-U-N-S 00-787-3383
MARTIN CADILLAC CO INC (CA)
MARTIN AUTOMOTIVE
12101 W Olympic Blvd, Los Angeles, CA 90064-1082
Tel (310) 820-3611 Founded/Ownrshp 1950, 1977
Sales 71.8MM^E EMP 250
SIC 5511 Automobiles, new & used; Automobiles, new & used
CEO: Dana R Martin
*Pr: Tom Tait
*VP: Mary Martin

D-U-N-S 05-001-2269
MARTIN CADILLAC INC
MARTIN DODGE-JEEP-CHRYSLER
(Suby of MARTIN MANAGEMENT GROUP INC) ★
2209 Scottsville Rd, Bowling Green, KY 42104-4105
Tel (270) 846-0600 Founded/Ownrshp 1985
Sales 33.6MM^E EMP 84
SIC 5511 Automobiles, new & used; Pickups, new & used; Vans, new & used; Automobiles, new & used; Pickups, new & used; Vans, new & used
Pr: Lee Michaelson
*VP: David Alexander
VP: Jerry Starkey

D-U-N-S 03-372-4097
MARTIN CAR FINANCING INC
MARTIN, MILTON TOYOTA
3150 Mlton Mrtn Tyota Way, Gainesville, GA 30507-8200
Tel (770) 532-4355 Founded/Ownrshp 1957
Sales 78.8MM EMP 76
Accts Ross Lane & Company Atlanta
SIC 5511 Automobiles, new & used; Automobiles, new & used
Pr: Milton M Martin
CFO: Chad Smith
*Sec: Carole Hope
VP: Stephen Bass
Exec: Ricky Martin
Off Admin: Nancy Bellamy
Sales Exec: Evan Martin

D-U-N-S 02-954-0226
MARTIN CHEVROLET
23505 Hawthorne Blvd, Torrance, CA 90505-4739
Tel (323) 772-6494 Founded/Ownrshp 2001
Sales 33.0MM^E EMP 100
SIC 5511 7538 Automobiles, new & used; General automotive repair shops; Automobiles, new & used; General automotive repair shops
Pr: Joe Giacomin
*Sec: Fran Williams
Sls Mgr: Stuart Monterroso

D-U-N-S 02-614-3750
MARTIN CHEVROLET - BUICK INC
MARTIN AUTOPARK
420 W Southline St, Cleveland, TX 77327-5029
Tel (281) 592-2644 Founded/Ownrshp 1941
Sales 28.2MM^E EMP 60
SIC 5511 Automobiles, new & used; Pickups, new & used; Vans, new & used; Automobiles, new & used; Pickups, new & used; Vans, new & used
Pr: Skip Martin
*Sec: Brian L Bounds
*VP: Robert B Furman Jr
Genl Mgr: Mike Herbert
Off Mgr: Tonya Beamon
Sls Mgr: Leslie Galloway

D-U-N-S 07-854-1019
MARTIN CHEVROLET OF CRYSTAL LAKE INC (IL)
5220 Northwest Hwy, Crystal Lake, IL 60014-8010
Tel (815) 459-4000 Founded/Ownrshp 2012
Sales 21.9MM^E EMP 55
SIC 5511 Automobiles, new & used
Pr: Todd J Martin
*Genl Mgr: Dan Hoyland
Off Mgr: Cindy Hillebrand
Sls Mgr: Steve Miehle
Sales Asso: Mike Lakhani

D-U-N-S 01-712-5816
MARTIN CHEVROLET SALES INC (MI)
MARTIN CHRYSLER-JEEP
8800 Gratiot Rd, Saginaw, MI 48609-4898
Tel (989) 681-3900 Founded/Ownrshp 1914
Sales 40.0MM^E EMP 94
SIC 5511 Automobiles, new & used; Automobiles, new & used

Ch Bd: William A Martin
**Sec:* Patricia A Hoewe
Exec: Jill Bauman
IT Man: Ben Forta
Sales Asso: Scott Fuller
Sales Asso: Nick Kerns
Sales Asso: Marty Stoll

MARTIN CHRYSLER-JEEP
See MARTIN CHEVROLET SALES INC

D-U-N-S 19-966-1034 IMP
MARTIN COLOR-FI INC
(*Suby of* DIMELING SCHREIBER & PARK L P) ★
320 Neeley St, Sumter, SC 29150-7452
Tel (803) 436-4276 *Founded/Ownrshp* 1988
Sales 76.3MM^E *EMP* 450
SIC 2824 2273 2281 2865 Organic fibers, noncellulosic; Polyester fibers; Nylon fibers; Carpets & rugs; Manmade & synthetic fiber yarns, spun; Cyclic crudes & intermediates; Organic fibers, noncellulosic; Polyester fibers; Nylon fibers; Carpets & rugs; Manmade & synthetic fiber yarns, spun; Cyclic crudes & intermediates
Pr: Stephen Zagorski

D-U-N-S 00-818-4608
MARTIN COMPANIES LLC ROM
2189 Memorial Dr, Alexandria, LA 71301-3610
Tel (318) 445-1973 *Founded/Ownrshp* 1923
Sales 251.5MM^E *EMP* 1,200
SIC 0811 Timber tracts; Timber tracts, softwood; Timber tracts; Timber tracts, softwood
CEO: Jonathan E Martin
**Pr:* Roy O Martin III
**Sr VP:* E Scott Poole
Snr Mgr: Bobby Burke

D-U-N-S 55-628-3570
MARTIN CONCRETE CONSTRUCTION INC
4040 Royal Dr Nw Ste 800, Kennesaw, GA 30144-6475
Tel (770) 795-0406 *Founded/Ownrshp* 1991
Sales 22.4MM^E *EMP* 80^E
SIC 1771 1542 Concrete work; Commercial & office building, new construction
Pr: Jeffrey A Martin
**Sr VP:* Alan Gilly
**VP:* Rick Galloway
**VP:* Cory Lee

D-U-N-S 01-719-4911
MARTIN CONSTRUCTION INC
2367 W Villard St, Dickinson, ND 58601-2403
Tel (701) 483-3478 *Founded/Ownrshp* 1978
Sales 40.3MM *EMP* 50
Accts Brady Martz & Associates Pc
SIC 1629 Land preparation construction; Earthmoving contractor; Land clearing contractor; Trenching contractor; Land preparation construction; Earthmoving contractor; Land clearing contractor; Trenching contractor
Pr: Kurt Martin
**VP:* Yolanda Crespo
Sfty Mgr: Karen Good
Opers Mgr: B J Martin

D-U-N-S 08-632-4068
MARTIN COUNTY BOARD OF EDUCATION
300 N Watts St, Williamston, NC 27892-2056
Tel (252) 792-1575 *Founded/Ownrshp* 1919
Sales 50.2MM^E *EMP* 1,027
SIC 8211 County commissioner; ; School board
Ch Bd: Van Health

D-U-N-S 05-410-7867
■ **MARTIN COUNTY COAL CORP**
(*Suby of* APPALACHIA HOLDING CO) ★
3201 Ridgetop Rd, Inez, KY 41224
Tel (606) 395-6881 *Founded/Ownrshp* 1971
Sales 27.9MM^E *EMP* 500
SIC 1221 1222 Bituminous coal surface mining; Bituminous coal-underground mining; Bituminous coal surface mining; Bituminous coal-underground mining
VP: Richard H Verheij
**Pr:* Howard Mahon

D-U-N-S 80-091-4319
MARTIN COUNTY SCHOOL DISTRICT
SCHOOL BD MARTIN CNTY SCHL DST
500 Se Ocean Blvd, Stuart, FL 34994-2572
Tel (772) 219-1200 *Founded/Ownrshp* 1945
Sales 135.4MM^E *EMP* 2,831
Accts David W Martin Cpa Tallahas
SIC 8211 Public elementary & secondary schools; Elementary school; Finishing school, secondary; High school, junior or senior; Public elementary & secondary schools; Elementary school; Finishing school, secondary; High school, junior or senior
Dir Sec: Mark Coco
Dir IT: Chris Hall
Netwrk Eng: Shane Williams
Pr Dir: Jamie Adlock
Teacher Pr: Richard Bilay

D-U-N-S 07-979-9687
MARTIN COUNTY SCHOOLS
300 N Watts St, Williamston, NC 27892-2099
Tel (252) 792-1575 *Founded/Ownrshp* 2015
Sales 10.3MM^E *EMP* 743^E
SIC 8211 Public elementary & secondary schools
Teacher Pr: Lisa Bowen
Teacher Pr: Stacy Leggett
HC Dir: Sharon Kinion

D-U-N-S 10-688-9629
MARTIN COUNTY SCHOOLS
INEZ ELEMENTARY SCHOOL
104 E Main St 100, Inez, KY 41224-8928
Tel (606) 298-3572 *Founded/Ownrshp* 1800
Sales 23.1MM^E *EMP* 527
SIC 8211 Public elementary & secondary schools; Public elementary & secondary schools

MARTIN DE PORRES ACADEMY
See MARTIN DE PORRES SCHOOL FOR EXCEPTIONAL CHILDREN INC

D-U-N-S 07-851-1573
MARTIN DE PORRES SCHOOL FOR EXCEPTIONAL CHILDREN INC (NY)
MARTIN DE PORRES ACADEMY
621 Elmont Rd Bldg B, Elmont, NY 11003-4028
Tel (516) 502-2840 *Founded/Ownrshp* 1972
Sales 20.4MM *EMP* 250
Accts Oconnor Davies Llp Harrison
SIC 8211 Private elementary & secondary schools; Secondary school; School for the retarded; Private elementary & secondary schools; Secondary school; School for the retarded
Exec: Harrison Claiborne
**Prin:* David Robinson
**Ex Dir:* Edward Dana

MARTIN DISTRIBUTORS
See LUMBER INVESTORS LLC

MARTIN DODGE-JEEP-CHRYSLER
See MARTIN CADILLAC INC

D-U-N-S 02-633-3799
MARTIN EAGLE OIL CO INC
FAST BREAK FOOD MART
2700 James St, Denton, TX 76205-7699
Tel (940) 383-2351 *Founded/Ownrshp* 1973
Sales 60.2MM^E *EMP* 60
SIC 5172 5541 5411 Petroleum products; Gasoline service stations; Convenience stores, independent; Petroleum products; Gasoline service stations; Convenience stores, independent
Pr: Cecil F Martin
**Sec:* Betty Martin
**VP:* Phillip Childers III
**VP:* Gary Martin
IT Man: Doris Moore
**VP Mktg:* Steve Martin

D-U-N-S 01-041-1015
MARTIN ENERGY SERVICES LLC
(*Suby of* MARTIN RESOURCE MANAGEMENT CORP) ★
3 Riverway Ste 400, Houston, TX 77056-1947
Tel (713) 350-6800 *Founded/Ownrshp* 1999
Sales 1.2MMM *EMP* 250
SIC 5171 4492 5172 5551 Petroleum terminals; Marine towing services; Diesel fuel; Gasoline; Service station supplies, petroleum; Marine supplies; Petroleum terminals; Marine towing services; Diesel fuel; Gasoline; Service station supplies, petroleum; Marine supplies
CEO: Ruben S Martin
**CFO:* Robert D Bondurant
**Ofcr:* Damon King
VP: George Dodgen
VP: Dean Krakosky
Sls Mgr: Gerry Stout

D-U-N-S 02-568-2873 IMP/EXP
MARTIN ENGINEERING CO
1 Martin Pl, Neponset, IL 61345-9766
Tel (309) 852-2384 *Founded/Ownrshp* 1944
Sales 200.8MM^E *EMP* 850
SIC 3829 3532 Measuring & controlling devices; Mining machinery; Flotation machinery (mining machinery); Cleaning machinery, mineral; Measuring & controlling devices; Mining machinery; Flotation machinery (mining machinery); Cleaning machinery, mineral
Pr: Scott E Hutter
**CFO:* Ronald Ron J Vick
**Ch:* Edwin Peterson
**VP:* Robert J Nogaj
Exec: Sue Nolasco
Mng Dir: Michael Hengl
Genl Mgr: Edward Peterson
IT Man: Mark Luciani
VP Opers: Jenny Bohannon
VP Opers: Robert Nogaj
Sfty Mgr: Marty Yepsen

D-U-N-S 07-799-5611
MARTIN ENGINEERING INC
127 Stone Hill Rd, Chapin, SC 29036-8978
Tel (803) 781-1930 *Founded/Ownrshp* 2005
Sales 31.2MM *EMP* 135^E
Accts Dial Hite & Associates Llc
SIC 1542 Commercial & office building, new construction; Commercial & office building, new construction
CEO: Elizabeth T Martin
**Pr:* Whitney M Delbridge
CFO: Ron Vick
**VP:* Tom Morey
**VP:* Jim Royster

D-U-N-S 00-394-3342
MARTIN ENGLE & ASSOCIATES INC
EM
5565 Glenridge Connector # 900, Atlanta, GA 30342-4797
Tel (678) 553-4400 *Founded/Ownrshp* 1997
Sales NA *EMP* 1,514
SIC 6411 Insurance adjusters; Insurance adjusters
Pr: John Quinn
**Ch Bd:* Kevin L Engle
**CFO:* Janice Warford
**Treas:* Christopher McCoy
**Ofcr:* Martha Boggs
Sr VP: John Ketch
Sr VP: Bentley Laytin
**VP:* Jay Campbell
**VP:* W Todd Evans
**VP:* J Robert Gambell

D-U-N-S 05-396-3849 EXP
MARTIN EQUIPMENT OF ILLINOIS INC
JOHN DEERE
400 W Martin Dr, Goodfield, IL 61742-7535
Tel (309) 965-2502 *Founded/Ownrshp* 1980
Sales 50.8MM^E *EMP* 162
SIC 5082 7353 General construction machinery & equipment; Heavy construction equipment rental; General construction machinery & equipment; Heavy construction equipment rental
Pr: Robert S Martin Jr
**Pr:* Robert Martin Jr
**Ch:* Robert Martin Sr
**VP:* Gregory Allan Martin
Store Mgr: Joe Dalton
Sls Mgr: Jeremy Smith
Sales Asso: Pat Green

D-U-N-S 02-289-2947
MARTIN FALK PAPER CO-MINNEAPOLIS
FALK PAPER & PACKAGING
618 N 3rd St, Minneapolis, MN 55401-1232
Tel (612) 332-8626 *Founded/Ownrshp* 1958
Sales 25.2MM^E *EMP* 35
SIC 5113 5162 2679 5046 Industrial & personal service paper; Plastics film; Book covers, paper; Commercial cooking & food service equipment
Pr: John Duffey
**CFO:* Anna Margl
**VP:* Robert Margl
Sales Exec: Jeff Graunke

D-U-N-S 15-698-8032
MARTIN FAMILY FORD INC
1001 Jamestown Rd, Morganton, NC 28655-9277
Tel (828) 584-4600 *Founded/Ownrshp* 1984
Sales 45.0MM *EMP* 59
SIC 5511 Automobiles, new & used; Automobiles, new & used
Pr: C Michael Martin
Sls Mgr: J D Abee

D-U-N-S 03-206-2601
MARTIN FARM REPAIR
20211 State Road 23, Mineral Point, WI 53565-8526
Tel (608) 776-2640 *Founded/Ownrshp* 1981
Sales 3.4MM^E *EMP* 300
SIC 6519 0241 0115 0139 Farm land leasing; Dairy farms; Corn; Hay farm; Farm land leasing; Dairy farms; Corn; Hay farm
Owner: John Martin

D-U-N-S 08-394-1716 IMP/EXP
MARTIN FLUID POWER CO INC
84 Minnesota Dr, Troy, MI 48083-4608
Tel (248) 585-8170 *Founded/Ownrshp* 1977
Sales 32.4MM^E *EMP* 90
SIC 5085 3053 Seals, industrial; Gaskets & sealing devices
Pr: Wayne Michael King
**VP:* Ryan King
Brnch Mgr: Vince Lopez
Plnt Mgr: Jim McLauchlan
Mktg Dir: Keith Hoffman
Sls Mgr: Chuck McAllister

D-U-N-S 62-050-0405
MARTIN FRED MOTOR CO
FRED MARTIN SUPERSTORE
3195 Barber Rd, Norton, OH 44203-1011
Tel (330) 848-6537 *Founded/Ownrshp* 1999
Sales 71.8MM^E *EMP* 185
SIC 5511 Automobiles, new & used; Automobiles, new & used
Pr: Adam Huff
**Treas:* William Huff
**Prin:* Scott Heaton
**Prin:* John K Krajewski
**Prin:* Daylor Neal
**Prin:* Ben Petrone
Sls Dir: Cody Huff
Sls Mgr: Jason Bauer
Sales Asso: Brandon Murgatroyd
Sales Asso: Holly Rhodes

MARTIN FURNITURE
See GILBERT MARTIN WOODWORKING CO INC

MARTIN GENERAL HOSPITAL
See WILLIAMSTON HOSPITAL CORP

MARTIN GENERAL STORES
See MARTIN OIL CO

D-U-N-S 80-632-7263
MARTIN GROUP LIMITED LIABILITY CO
96 Freneau Ave Ste 2, Matawan, NJ 07747-3471
Tel (732) 441-0006 *Founded/Ownrshp* 2006
Sales 45.0MM *EMP* 25
SIC 8741 Construction management
Sls&Mrk Ex: Jerry Martin

MARTIN GUITAR COMPANY, THE
See C F MARTIN & CO INC

MARTIN HONDA
See MARTIN NEWARK DEALERSHIP INC

D-U-N-S 12-623-0213
■ **MARTIN HOSPITAL CORP**
VOLUNTEER COMMUNITY HOSPITAL
(*Suby of* COMMUNITY HEALTH SYSTEMS INC) ★
161 Mount Pelia Rd, Martin, TN 38237-3811
Tel (731) 587-4261 *Founded/Ownrshp* 2003
Sales 28.7MM *EMP* 1^E
SIC 8062 General medical & surgical hospitals; General medical & surgical hospitals
CEO: Darrell Blaylock
**CFO:* Debra Horn
VP: Betty Wilson
**Prin:* Steve Westenhofer
QA Dir: Sandi Wilkinson
Pharmcst: Pete Pittman
HC Dir: Karen Winschel

D-U-N-S 00-403-1076 IMP
MARTIN INC
MARTIN INDUSTRIAL SUPPLY
125 N Court St, Florence, AL 35630-4739
Tel (256) 383-3131 *Founded/Ownrshp* 1934
Sales 203.6MM^E *EMP* 220
SIC 5085 Industrial supplies; Industrial supplies
Ch Bd: Edith Martin Ruggles
**Pr:* Donald F Ruggles
**VP:* D Gordon Ruggles
Genl Mgr: Candy Linam
Sales Asso: Wayne Hardy
Sales Asso: Wally Pickett

MARTIN INDUSTRIAL SUPPLY
See MARTIN INC

MARTIN, JOHN A & ASSOCIATES
See MARTIN ASSOCIATES GROUP INC

D-U-N-S 00-694-4003
MARTIN K EBY CONSTRUCTION CO INC (KS)
EQUIP CO
(*Suby of* EBY CORP) ★
610 N Main St Ste 500, Wichita, KS 67203-3619
Tel (316) 268-3500 *Founded/Ownrshp* 1937
Sales 93.2MM *EMP* 135^E
SIC 1542 Commercial & office building contractors; Commercial & office building contractors
Pr: Michael A Grier
**Ch Bd:* James R Grier III
**CFO:* R Adam Dunn
**Treas:* Linda Walton
Bd of Dir: Starla Criser
Bd of Dir: Gordon Kessler
**Ex VP:* Kurt T Grier
**Sr VP:* Larry Weis
**VP:* Lynn Anderson
**VP:* Karman Diehl
**VP:* Adam Dunn
Board of Directors: Charles K Eby, James R Grier III, Kurt T Grier, Michael A Grier

D-U-N-S 06-727-8838
MARTIN LEO CHEVROLET INC
LEO MARTIN USED CARS
217 Highway 332 W, Lake Jackson, TX 77566-4019
Tel (979) 230-2500 *Founded/Ownrshp* 1970
Sales 26.4MM^E *EMP* 60
SIC 5511 7532 5599 Automobiles, new & used; Pickups, new & used; Vans, new & used; Body shop, automotive; Body shop, trucks; Utility trailers
Ch: Leo G Martin Jr
**Ch Bd:* Leo G Martin Sr
**Pr:* Gary N Martin
**Treas:* Donald R Andrews
**Treas:* Pamela K Lawhon
**VP:* June B Martin
Genl Mgr: Richard Stairs

D-U-N-S 00-790-9880 IMP
MARTIN LIMESTONE INC
LIMEVILLE QUARRY
(*Suby of* BUFFALO CRUSHED STONE) ★
3580 Division Hwy, East Earl, PA 17519-9217
Tel (717) 335-4500 *Founded/Ownrshp* 1933, 1946
Sales 184.0MM^E *EMP* 1,151
SIC 3273 3271 1611 1422 8741 5211 Ready-mixed concrete; Blocks, concrete or cinder: standard; Highway & street paving contractor; Crushed & broken limestone; Business management; Lumber & other building materials; Ready-mixed concrete; Blocks, concrete or cinder: standard; Highway & street paving contractor; Crushed & broken limestone; Business management; Lumber & other building materials
Pr: Howard Winey
**VP:* Donald Detwiler
**VP:* Paul I Detwiler Jr

D-U-N-S 00-895-2939
MARTIN LINEN SUPPLY CO INC
11620 Wilshire Blvd # 870, Los Angeles, CA 90025-1793
Tel (310) 473-4833 *Founded/Ownrshp* 1963
Sales 11.4MM^E *EMP* 380
SIC 7213 Linen supply
Pr: Jill Werner
**Treas:* Bruce Moskowitz

D-U-N-S 05-350-0583
MARTIN LITHOGRAPH INC
MLI INTGRTED GRAPHIC SOLUTIONS
505 N Rome Ave, Tampa, FL 33606-1250
Tel (813) 254-1553 *Founded/Ownrshp* 1970
Sales 20.8MM^E *EMP* 43
SIC 2752 Commercial printing, lithographic
Pr: Martin Saavedra Jr
**CFO:* Ralph Del Rio
**Sec:* Jennifer Saavedra
**VP:* Janice Saavedra

D-U-N-S 11-090-5085
MARTIN LUTHER KING/DREW MEDICAL CENTER
1670 E 120th St, Los Angeles, CA 90059-3026
Tel (310) 773-4926 *Founded/Ownrshp* 2002
Sales 23.4MM^E *EMP* 91^E
SIC 8011 Medical centers
CEO: Hank Wells
COO: Linda McAuley
CFO: Anthony Gray
CFO: Tony Gray
Exec: Peter Meade
Dir Rx: Amy Gutierrez
Off Mgr: Kitty Thomas
IT Man: Antonia Richardson
Pathlgst: Hezla Mohamed
Pathlgst: Lucilene F Tolentino
HC Dir: Jackie Wilson

D-U-N-S 04-096-6475
MARTIN LUTHER MANOR
MEADOW WOODS
1401 E 100th St, Minneapolis, MN 55425-2614
Tel (952) 948-5154 *Founded/Ownrshp* 2005
Sales 13.5MM^E *EMP* 350
SIC 8051 8052 8059 8361 Skilled nursing care facilities; Intermediate care facilities; Personal care home, with health care; Rehabilitation center, residential: health care incidental; Skilled nursing care facilities; Intermediate care facilities; Personal care home, with health care; Rehabilitation center, residential: health care incidental
**Pr:* Howard Paulsen
**VP:* Betty Jenneman Garvey

D-U-N-S 07-423-4220
MARTIN LUTHER MEMORIAL HOME INC
5075 Willoughby Rd, Holt, MI 48842-1054
Tel (517) 694-6570 *Founded/Ownrshp* 2005
Sales 8.4MM^E *EMP* 422
SIC 8361 Home for the aged; Home for the aged

Pr: Robert Zeinstra
Off Mgr: Kista Brayton

D-U-N-S 00-922-6262
MARTIN MANAGEMENT GROUP INC
1048 Ashley St Ste 401, Bowling Green, KY 42103-2453
Tel (270) 783-8080 *Founded/Ownrshp* 1998
Sales 191.7MM^E *EMP* 600
SIC 5561 Travel trailers: automobile, new & used; Travel trailers: automobile, new & used
Pr: Lee Michaelson
CFO: Tommy Dennard
VP: Jerry Starkey
Mktg Dir: Adrienne Seligman

D-U-N-S 19-649-7184 IMP
■ **MARTIN MARIETTA MAGNESIA SPECIALTIES LLC**
(*Suby of* MARTIN MARIETTA MATERIALS INC) ★
755 Lime Rd, Woodville, OH 43469-9727
Tel (419) 849-4223 *Founded/Ownrshp* 1963
Sales 38.3MM^E *EMP* 328
SIC 3295

D-U-N-S 80-975-0912 IMP/EXP
▲ **MARTIN MARIETTA MATERIALS INC**
2710 Wycliff Rd, Raleigh, NC 27607-3033
Tel (919) 781-4550 *Founded/Ownrshp* 1993
Sales 2.9MMM *EMP* 7,193
Tkr Sym MLM *Exch* NYS
SIC 1423 1422 1442 3295 3297 Crushed & broken granite; Crushed & broken limestone; Construction sand & gravel; Magnesite, crude: ground, calcined or dead-burned; Heat resistant mixtures; Crushed & broken granite; Crushed & broken limestone; Construction sand & gravel; Magnesite, crude: ground, calcined or dead-burned; Heat resistant mixtures
Ch Bd: C Howard Nye
Pr: David Hagerman
CFO: Anne H Lloyd
Treas: Kelly Maglio
Sr VP: Roselyn R Bar
Sr VP: Daniel L Grant
Sr VP: Dana F Guzzo
Sr VP: Donald A McCunniff
VP: Carlton Brady
VP: Bob Dillard
VP: John Harmon
VP: Larry Ward
Board of Directors: Sue W Cole, David G Maffucci, William E McDonald, Frank H Menaker Jr, Michael J Quillen, Dennis L Rediker, Richard A Vinroot, Stephen P Zelnak Jr

D-U-N-S 00-793-6560 IMP
■ **MARTIN MARIETTA MATERIALS SOUTHWEST INC** (TX)
(*Suby of* MARTIN MARIETTA MATERIALS INC) ★
5710 W Hausman Rd Ste 121, San Antonio, TX 78249-1646
Tel (210) 208-4400 *Founded/Ownrshp* 1934
Sales 601.7MM^E *EMP* 635
SIC 1422 3273 2951 3274 1442 Crushed & broken limestone; Ready-mixed concrete; Concrete, asphaltic (not from refineries); Hydrated lime; Quicklime; Construction sand & gravel; Crushed & broken limestone; Ready-mixed concrete; Concrete, asphaltic (not from refineries); Hydrated lime; Quicklime; Construction sand & gravel
Pr: Howard C Nye
**CFO:* Anne H Lloyd
**Sr VP:* Roselyn R Bar
**Sr VP:* Daniel L Grant
**Sr VP:* Dana F Guzzo
**VP:* W D Bankston
**VP:* David L Wenzel
Area Mgr: Brian Federico
Brnch Mgr: Larry Robert
IT Man: Chris Clark
Plnt Mgr: Scott Hoard
Board of Directors: G R Phillipson, William S Yearsley

D-U-N-S 80-279-3851
MARTIN MEMORIAL FOUNDATION INC
2135 Se Ocean Blvd, Stuart, FL 34996-3305
Tel (772) 223-5634 *Founded/Ownrshp* 1983
Sales 28.8MM *EMP* 40
Accts Ernst & Young Llp Greenville
SIC 8399 Fund raising organization, non-fee basis
CEO: Richmond Harmon
**CEO:* Richmond M Harman
**VP:* Mark Cocorullo

D-U-N-S 15-465-7449
MARTIN MEMORIAL HEALTH SYSTEMS INC
200 Se Hospital Ave, Stuart, FL 34994-2346
Tel (772) 287-5200 *Founded/Ownrshp* 1983
Sales 913.7MM^E *EMP* 2,972
SIC 8741 8062 Hospital management; Nursing & personal care facility management; General medical & surgical hospitals; Hospital management; Nursing & personal care facility management; General medical & surgical hospitals
Pr: Mark E Robitaille
Chf Rad: Eileen McGlynn
CFO: Chuck Cleaver
Chf Mktg O: Howard Robbins MD
**Chf Mktg O:* Michael Skehan
Ofcr: Susan Hudson
**Sr VP:* L Mark Cocorullo
**Sr VP:* Donna H Griffith
Sr VP: Donna Griffith
**Sr VP:* Robert L Lord Jr
**Sr VP:* Karen Ripper
**VP:* Amy Barry
**VP:* John Tagliareni
Dir Risk M: Sharon Beiser

D-U-N-S 07-846-7651
MARTIN MEMORIAL MEDICAL CENTER INC (FL)
MARTIN MEMORIAL MEDICAL CENTER SOUTH
(*Suby of* MARTIN MEMORIAL HEALTH SYSTEMS INC) ★
200 Se Hospital Ave, Stuart, FL 34994-2346
Tel (772) 287-5200 *Founded/Ownrshp* 1938, 1983
Sales 910.9MM *EMP* 2,972^E
SIC 8062 General medical & surgical hospitals; General medical & surgical hospitals
Pr: Mark Robitaille
**CFO:* Chuck Cleaver
**CFO:* L Mark Cocorullo
**Treas:* John Lowenberg
**Sr VP:* Donna H Griffith
Sr VP: Howard M Robbins
**VP:* Craig Chindemi
VP: Edmund Collins
VP: Miguel Coty
Dir Risk M: Julie Pike
Dir Risk M: Linda Pinkston
Dir Rx: Dave Harlow
Dir Bus: Carol Plato-Nicosia

MARTIN MEMORIAL MEDICAL CENTER SOUTH
See MARTIN MEMORIAL MEDICAL CENTER INC

D-U-N-S 09-967-6020
▲ **MARTIN MIDSTREAM PARTNERS LP**
4200 Stone Rd, Kilgore, TX 75662-6935
Tel (903) 983-6200 *Founded/Ownrshp* 1951
Sales 1.6MMM *EMP* 921^E
Tkr Sym MMLP *Exch* NGS
SIC 4226 1321 4424 2819 2875 Petroleum & chemical bulk stations & terminals for hire; Natural gas liquids production; Coastwide transportation, freight; Sulfur, recovered or refined, incl. from sour natural gas; Fertilizers, mixing only; Petroleum & chemical bulk stations & terminals for hire; Natural gas liquids production; Coastwide transportation, freight; Sulfur, recovered or refined, incl. from sour natural gas; Fertilizers, mixing only
Pr: Ruben S Martin
Genl Pt: Martin Midstream GP LLC
Pr: Wes Martin
CFO: Robert D Bondurant
VP: Jeff Ballew
VP: Al Sumpter
Dir Risk M: Mike Murley
CTO: Linda Dougan
IT Man: Kristen O'Leary
Mktg Mgr: Jeff Posey

MARTIN, MILTON TOYOTA
See MARTIN CAR FINANCING INC

D-U-N-S 94-363-1598
MARTIN MONTGOMERY CONTRACTORS LLC
8245 Tournament Dr # 300, Memphis, TN 38125-8898
Tel (901) 374-9400 *Founded/Ownrshp* 1995
Sales 97.0MM *EMP* 125
SIC 1542 1541 8741 Commercial & office building, new construction; Commercial & office buildings, renovation & repair; Industrial buildings, new construction; Renovation, remodeling & repairs: industrial buildings; Construction management; Commercial & office building, new construction; Commercial & office buildings, renovation & repair; Industrial buildings, new construction; Renovation, remodeling & repairs: industrial buildings; Construction management
CEO: H Montgomery Martin
VP: Scott Barnes
VP: George Bratton
VP: Jeff Emerson
VP: Richard T Meena
VP: Joel Thomas

D-U-N-S 87-851-2664
MARTIN NEWARK DEALERSHIP INC
MARTIN HONDA
298 E Cleveland Ave, Newark, DE 19711-3711
Tel (302) 454-9300 *Founded/Ownrshp* 1994
Sales 71.4MM^E *EMP* 225
SIC 5511 7538 7515 7513 5531 Automobiles, new & used; General automotive repair shops; Passenger car leasing; Truck rental & leasing, no drivers; Automotive & home supply stores; Automobiles, new & used; General automotive repair shops; Passenger car leasing; Truck rental & leasing, no drivers; Automotive & home supply stores
Pr: Scott Lustgarten
**VP:* Linda Lustgarten

D-U-N-S 01-385-9160
MARTIN OIL CO
MARTIN GENERAL STORES
528 N 1st St, Bellwood, PA 16617-1922
Tel (814) 742-8438 *Founded/Ownrshp* 1962
Sales 125.2MM *EMP* 202
SIC 5983 5171 5541 5411

D-U-N-S 82-994-3989 EXP
■ **MARTIN OPERATING PARTNERSHIP LP**
(*Suby of* MARTIN MIDSTREAM PARTNERS LP) ★
4200 Stone Rd, Kilgore, TX 75662-6935
Tel (903) 983-6200 *Founded/Ownrshp* 1956
Sales 515.0MM^E *EMP* 708
SIC 5172 Petroleum products; Petroleum products
Pt: Ruben S Martin III
CFO: Bob Bondurang

D-U-N-S 00-479-7486
MARTIN PETERSEN CO INC
9800 55th St, Kenosha, WI 53144-7812
Tel (262) 658-1326 *Founded/Ownrshp* 1918
Sales 56.5MM *EMP* 280
SIC 1711 1629 3441 Plumbing contractors; Waste water & sewage treatment plant construction; Fabricated structural metal; Plumbing contractors; Waste water & sewage treatment plant construction; Fabricated structural metal
Pr: John Donnell
**CFO:* Rob Jossart
**VP:* Dan Ashburn
VP: Floyd Davis
**VP:* Kevin Louis
IT Man: Kathy Lois
Snr PM: Mike Bahr
Snr PM: Eric Evjen
Snr PM: Mark Ziegler

D-U-N-S 05-303-0870
MARTIN PETROLEUM CORP
TEXACO
1 Florida Tpke Mile Mark Mile Marker, Pompano Beach, FL 33064
Tel (954) 972-0123 *Founded/Ownrshp* 1978
Sales 33.9MM^E *EMP* 157
SIC 5541 5172 Filling stations, gasoline; Petroleum products; Filling stations, gasoline; Petroleum products
Pr: Tom Rushmore

MARTIN PREFERRED LOGISTICS
See PREFERRED FOODS MARTIN L P

D-U-N-S 80-489-3030
MARTIN PRODUCE INC
143 W 154th St, South Holland, IL 60473-1016
Tel (773) 851-7150 *Founded/Ownrshp* 1987
Sales 38.0MM *EMP* 65
SIC 5149 5113 5148 Groceries & related products; Cooking oils & shortenings; Dried or canned foods; Disposable plates, cups, napkins & eating utensils; Cups, disposable plastic & paper; Napkins, paper; Eating utensils, disposable plastic; Fruits; Vegetables
Pr: Martin Maciel

D-U-N-S 13-956-3332 IMP
MARTIN PRODUCT SALES LLC
MARTIN ASPHALT
(*Suby of* MARTIN RESOURCE MANAGEMENT CORP) ★
4200 Stone Rd, Kilgore, TX 75662-6935
Tel (903) 983-6200 *Founded/Ownrshp* 1986
Sales 397.0MM *EMP* 206
SIC 5052 5032 5172 Gases, liquefied petroleum (propane); Sulfur; Liquid storage; Systems software development services; Sulfur; Asphalt mixture; Crude oil
Pr: Ruben S Martin III
COO: Randall L Tauscher
CFO: Bob Bondurant
Ex VP: Robert D Bondurant
VP: Chris Booth
Opers Mgr: Meg Wilson

D-U-N-S 14-711-1751 IMP/EXP
MARTIN RESOURCE MANAGEMENT CORP
4200 Stone Rd, Kilgore, TX 75662-6935
Tel (903) 983-6200 *Founded/Ownrshp* 1963
Sales 1.8MMM^E *EMP* 2,300
Accts Kpmg Llp Shreveport La
SIC 2911 4924 5984 5172 Gases & liquefied petroleum gases; Natural gas distribution; Liquefied petroleum gas, delivered to customers' premises; Fuel oil; Crude oil; Gases, liquefied petroleum (propane); Gases & liquefied petroleum gases; Natural gas distribution; Liquefied petroleum gas, delivered to customers' premises; Fuel oil; Crude oil; Gases, liquefied petroleum (propane)
Pr: Ruben S Martin III
**CFO:* Bob Bondurant
**Treas:* Wesley M Skelton
Sr VP: Ed Grimm
Sr VP: Scot A Shoup
VP: Mike Lawrence
**VP:* Douglas Towns
Dir Risk M: Mike Murley
Genl Mgr: Donnie Fickey
Sls Mgr: Hugh Harbour
Counsel: John B Blackburn

D-U-N-S 96-671-3864
MARTIN RESOURCE MGT CORP AND AFFILIATES EMPLOYEE BENEFIT TRUST
4200 Stone Rd, Kilgore, TX 75662-6935
Tel (903) 983-6200 *Founded/Ownrshp* 2011
Sales NA *EMP* 2^E
SIC 6411 Insurance agents, brokers & service; Insurance agents, brokers & service

D-U-N-S 60-790-1105
MARTIN RESOURCES INC
(*Suby of* MARTIN RESOURCE MANAGEMENT CORP) ★
4200 Stone Rd, Kilgore, TX 75662-6935
Tel (903) 983-6200 *Founded/Ownrshp* 1986
Sales 51.7MM^E *EMP* 88
SIC 5191 5052 Fertilizers & agricultural chemicals; Sulfur; Fertilizers & agricultural chemicals; Sulfur
Pr: Rueben S Martin III

D-U-N-S 00-319-8306
MARTIN S ABATTOIR AND WHOLESALE MEATS INC (NC)
1600 Martin Rd, Godwin, NC 28344-9068
Tel (910) 567-6102 *Founded/Ownrshp* 1954
Sales 29.3MM^E *EMP* 200
SIC 2011 2048 2041 2013 Boxed beef from meat slaughtered on site; Prepared feeds; Flour & other grain mill products; Sausages & other prepared meats; Boxed beef from meat slaughtered on site; Prepared feeds; Flour & other grain mill products; Sausages & other prepared meats
Pr: Carlton Martin
**Sec:* Lynell Martin
**VP:* W C Martin Jr

MARTIN SADDLERY
See EQUIBRAND CORP

D-U-N-S 60-919-1168 IMP
MARTIN SCOTT WINES LTD
31 W 27th St Fl 7, New York, NY 10001-6914
Tel (516) 327-0808 *Founded/Ownrshp* 1989
Sales 77.2MM^E *EMP* 80^E
SIC 5182 Wine; Wine
CEO: Martin Gold
**Sr VP:* Eric Celt
**Sr VP:* Scott Gerber
**Sr VP:* William Hayde

D-U-N-S 04-668-5921
MARTIN SELIG
MARTIN SELIG REAL ESTATE
1000 2nd Ave Ste 1800, Seattle, WA 98104-1043
Tel (206) 467-7600 *Founded/Ownrshp* 1958
Sales 26.0MM^E *EMP* 175^E
SIC 6512 6531 Commercial & industrial building operation; Shopping center, property operation only; Real estate agents & managers
Owner: Martin Selig
CFO: Pete Parker

MARTIN SELIG REAL ESTATE
See MARTIN SELIG

D-U-N-S 96-194-3623
MARTIN SERVICES GROUP INC
1278 E Earl Rd, East Earl, PA 17519-9701
Tel (717) 351-5652 *Founded/Ownrshp* 2009
Sales 38.3MM *EMP* 5
Accts Weinhold Nickel & Company Ll
SIC 5172 Petroleum brokers; Petroleum brokers
Pr: Judith Weaver

D-U-N-S 00-802-9613 IMP
MARTIN SPROCKET & GEAR INC
3100 Sprocket Dr, Arlington, TX 76015-2898
Tel (817) 258-3000 *Founded/Ownrshp* 1951
Sales 284.2MM^E *EMP* 1,700
SIC 3566 3568 3535 3321 3462 3429

D-U-N-S 04-427-4343 IMP/EXP
MARTIN STRAND-TECH INC
(*Suby of* O.R.I. MARTIN - ACCIAIERIA E FERRIERA DI BRESCIA SPA)
258 Deming Way, Summerville, SC 29483-4752
Tel (843) 873-3331 *Founded/Ownrshp* 1998
Sales 29.0MM^E *EMP* 34
Accts Ernst & Young Llp Greenville
SIC 3496 Miscellaneous fabricated wire products; Miscellaneous fabricated wire products
Pr: Francesco Giardina
**Treas:* Faye Hutcherson
**VP:* Terry Johnson
Advt Dir: Jan Holcomb

D-U-N-S 02-548-8891
MARTIN SULLIVAN INC
246 E Main St Ste 201, Galesburg, IL 61401-4739
Tel (309) 343-1423 *Founded/Ownrshp* 1994
Sales 138.1MM^E *EMP* 85
SIC 5083 5261 Agricultural machinery & equipment; Lawn & garden equipment; Agricultural machinery & equipment; Lawn & garden equipment
CEO: Mark Kleine
**Pr:* Jim Haynes
VP: Rusty Spence
Dir IT: Crystal Bohm
Manager: John Winston

D-U-N-S 00-310-3975 IMP
MARTIN SUPPLY CO INC (MD)
2740 Loch Raven Rd, Baltimore, MD 21218-4785
Tel (410) 366-1696 *Founded/Ownrshp* 1942, 1984
Sales 23.9MM^E *EMP* 30
SIC 5084 5085 Printing trades machinery, equipment & supplies; Signmaker equipment & supplies
Pr: Victor Lebow
**Treas:* Sharon Hare
**Ex VP:* Victor Lebow III

D-U-N-S 13-057-3058
MARTIN SWANTY CHRYSLER DODGE INC
MARTIN SWANTY DODGE
2640 E Andy Devine Ave, Kingman, AZ 86401-4822
Tel (928) 718-1000 *Founded/Ownrshp* 1984
Sales 29.7MM^E *EMP* 70
SIC 5511 Automobiles, new & used; Automobiles, new & used
Pr: Martin Swanty

MARTIN SWANTY DODGE
See MARTIN SWANTY CHRYSLER DODGE INC

D-U-N-S 96-511-3624
MARTIN THOMAS ENTERPRISES INC
MEI LABELS
19014 E Admiral Pl, Catoosa, OK 74015-2861
Tel (918) 739-4015 *Founded/Ownrshp* 2012
Sales 22.5MM^E *EMP* 90
SIC 2672 2759 Coated & laminated paper; Commercial printing
CEO: Lynn Higgs
CFO: Louie Crider
VP: Cindy Chasteen
VP Admn: Michael Chamberlain
Opers Mgr: Dennis McCurley
Sls Mgr: Michael Burger
Art Dir: Keri Quinn

D-U-N-S 02-638-0055 IMP
MARTIN TIRE CO
MTC WHOLESALE
1341 N Lee Trevino Dr, El Paso, TX 79936-6445
Tel (915) 592-6496 *Founded/Ownrshp* 1945
Sales 38.7MM^E *EMP* 75
SIC 5531 5014

D-U-N-S 05-966-6834
MARTIN TRANSPORT INC
(*Suby of* MARTIN RESOURCE MANAGEMENT CORP) ★
4200 Stone Rd, Kilgore, TX 75662-6935
Tel (281) 860-4313 *Founded/Ownrshp* 1981
Sales 180.0MM *EMP* 1,000
SIC 4213 Trucking, except local; Trucking, except local
CEO: Ruben S Martin III
**CEO:* Ruben S Martin III
**Treas:* Wesley M Skelton
**Sr VP:* Johnny Murry
VP: Joe McCreery

D-U-N-S 03-861-0200
MARTIN TRANSPORTATION SYSTEMS INC
M T S
7300 Clyde Park Ave Sw, Byron Center, MI 49315-8387
Tel (616) 455-8850 *Founded/Ownrshp* 1997
Sales 221.0MM^E *EMP* 1,000
SIC 4212 4213 Local trucking, without storage; Trucking, except local; Local trucking, without storage; Trucking, except local
Pr: Richard M Dabney
CFO: Don Armbrester
Treas: Altimore Harrison Jr

MARTIN TRAVEL & SEA CRUISE
See MARTIN TRAVEL INC

D-U-N-S 04-706-4225
MARTIN TRAVEL INC
MARTIN TRAVEL & SEA CRUISE
3535 Franklin Rd Sw Ste B, Roanoke, VA 24014-2255
Tel (540) 343-5400 *Founded/Ownrshp* 1989
Sales 21.0MM *EMP* 22
SIC 4724 Travel agencies; Travel agencies
Pr: Mel Ludovici
COO: Linda Lee
**Ch:* Bittle Porterfield
**Treas:* Charlotte Porterfield
VP: Gerald Schertz
Snr Ntwrk: Brian Brindle
Dir IT: Gregory Walton
Obsttrcn: Steven Farber
Doctor: Witold Brozyna
Doctor: Shelby Dickerson

MARTIN TRUCK CENTER
See MARTIN AUTOMOTIVE GROUP INC

D-U-N-S 00-416-1584 IMP
MARTIN WHEEL CO INC
(*Suby of* AMERICANA DEVELOPMENT INC) ★
342 West Ave, Tallmadge, OH 44278-2192
Tel (330) 633-3278 *Founded/Ownrshp* 1999
Sales 24.6MM^E *EMP* 100
SIC 3714 3011 Motor vehicle wheels & parts; Pneumatic tires, all types; Motor vehicle wheels & parts; Pneumatic tires, all types
CEO: Jimmy Yang
**Pr:* Thomas J Hartmann
**Treas:* Dolly Yang
Natl Sales: David Nowlin
Mktg Dir: Darell Ruthruff
Manager: Steve Mueller

MARTIN YALE INDUSTRIES, INC
See WEDCOR HOLDINGS INC

D-U-N-S 05-784-7626 IMP
MARTIN YALE INDUSTRIES LLC
(*Suby of* LV2 EQUITY PARTNERS LLC) ★
251 Wedcor Ave, Wabash, IN 46992-4201
Tel (260) 563-0641 *Founded/Ownrshp* 2014
Sales 39.4MM^E *EMP* 129^E
SIC 3579 Paper cutters, trimmers & punches; Paper cutters, trimmers & punches
Pr: Greg German

MARTIN-BAKER
See TAG MANUFACTURING INC

D-U-N-S 16-945-3243 IMP
MARTIN-BAKER AMERICA INC
(*Suby of* KILLINCHY AEROSPACE HOLDINGS LIMITED)
423 Walters Ave, Johnstown, PA 15904-1134
Tel (814) 262-9325 *Founded/Ownrshp* 2015
Sales 30.0MM *EMP* 115
SIC 3728 Seat ejector devices, aircraft; Military aircraft equipment & armament; Seat ejector devices, aircraft; Military aircraft equipment & armament
Pr: John Martin
VP: Robert Martin
Genl Mgr: Ron Cordone
Mfg Mgr: Jack Rovan
Sls&Mrk Ex: Brian Galiote

D-U-N-S 05-786-1650 IMP/EXP
MARTIN-BROWER CO L L C
(*Suby of* REYES HOLDINGS LLC) ★
6250 N River Rd Ste 9000, Rosemont, IL 60018-4241
Tel (847) 227-6500 *Founded/Ownrshp* 1998
Sales 2.8MMM^E *EMP* 3,900
SIC 5142 5113 5149 5087 Packaged frozen goods; Industrial & personal service paper; Groceries & related products; Restaurant supplies; Packaged frozen goods; Industrial & personal service paper; Groceries & related products; Restaurant supplies
Pr: Gregory Nickele
**COO:* Robert McGonigle
**CFO:* Joseph Tomczak
CFO: Bill Williams
**Ch:* J Christopher Reyes
**Treas:* Kurt Roemer
**Ex VP:* David K Reyes
**Ex VP:* M Jude Reyes
**Sr VP:* Dan Doheny
**Sr VP:* Nicholas L Giampietro
VP: Pearson Claire
Exec: Randy French

D-U-N-S 15-148-8491 IMP/EXP
MARTIN-BROWER PUERTO RICO INC
(*Suby of* REYES HOLDINGS LLC) ★
Km 5 5 Bo Cndlaria Rr 865, TOA Baja, PR 00949
Tel (787) 795-0065 *Founded/Ownrshp* 1998
Sales 24.6MM^E *EMP* 80
SIC 5141

D-U-N-S 61-287-0196
■ **MARTIN-DECKER TOTCO INC**
MD TOTCO
(*Suby of* NATIONAL OILWELL VARCO INC) ★
1200 Cypress Creek Rd, Cedar Park, TX 78613-3614
Tel (512) 340-5000 *Founded/Ownrshp* 2005
Sales 53.5MM^E *EMP* 450
SIC 7353 3533 5082 3823 3677 3596 Oil field equipment, rental or leasing; Oil & gas field machinery; Oil field equipment; Industrial instrmnts msrmnt display/control process variable; Electronic coils, transformers & other inductors; Scales & balances, except laboratory; Oil field equipment, rental or leasing; Oil & gas field machinery; Oil field equipment; Industrial instrmnts msrmnt display/control process variable; Electronic coils, transformers & other inductors; Scales & balances, except laboratory
Pr: Clay Williams
CFO: Wanda Labaume
Genl Mgr: Casey Barho
Genl Mgr: Tinh Nguyen
Snr Sftwr: William Johnson
Dir IT: Mikel Moore
IT Man: Ben Machart
IT Man: Yong Riggins
Sftwr Eng: Ken Meyer
Sftwr Eng: Adam Ulbrich
Mfg Mgr: Michael Hansen

D-U-N-S 08-838-9408 IMP
MARTIN-HARRIS CONSTRUCTION LLC
(*Suby of* BIG-D CAPITAL CORP) ★
3030 S Highland Dr, Las Vegas, NV 89109-1047
Tel (702) 385-5257 *Founded/Ownrshp* 2014
Sales 172.0MM^E *EMP* 140^E
SIC 1541 1542 Warehouse construction; Specialized public building contractors; Warehouse construction; Specialized public building contractors
Pr: Frank E Martin
Sr VP: Guy Martin
VP: Ray Newmiller

D-U-N-S 04-120-2656
■ **MARTIN-WILLIAMS INC**
KARWOSKI & COURAGE DIV
(*Suby of* OMNICOM GROUP INC) ★
150 S 5th St Ste 900, Minneapolis, MN 55402-4428
Tel (612) 342-9898 *Founded/Ownrshp* 1998
Sales 40.2MM^E *EMP* 130
SIC 7311 Advertising agencies; Advertising agencies
CEO: Thomas Modry
**Ch Bd:* Tim Frojd
**Pr:* Mike Gray
Ofcr: Tom Maudry
VP: Tim Burke
VP: Laura Etches-Terry
VP: Wayne Talley
Assoc Dir: Steve Renier
Creative D: Kyle Fiebelkorn
Creative D: Dan Roettger
Dir IT: Marty Enerson

D-U-N-S 00-978-1972
MARTIN/HORN INC
210 Carlton Rd, Charlottesville, VA 22902-5972
Tel (434) 293-6171 *Founded/Ownrshp* 1970
Sales 34.9MM^E *EMP* 75
Accts Shelton & Company Cpas Pc
SIC 1542 Commercial & office building contractors
Pr: John D Horn
**Ch Bd:* Jack M Horn
**Sec:* Julie Brown
**Ex VP:* R Douglass Horn
VP: Doug Horn
**VP:* William E Horn
Board of Directors: William E Horn

D-U-N-S 80-273-1166
MARTIN/MARTIN INC
(*Suby of* MARTIN ASSOCIATES GROUP INC) ★
12499 W Colfax Ave, Lakewood, CO 80215-3720
Tel (303) 431-6100 *Founded/Ownrshp* 1988
Sales 36.5MM^E *EMP* 174^E
SIC 8711 Consulting engineer; Civil engineering; Structural engineering; Consulting engineer; Civil engineering; Structural engineering
Ch: John A Martin Jr
**Pr:* Gary Thomas
**CEO:* Traylor Martin
**VP:* Neil Dunbar
**VP:* Duane Jansen
Dir Bus: David Farnum
Prin: Ben Nelson

MARTINDALE FEED MILL
See ALAN RITCHEY INC

D-U-N-S 06-277-6636
MARTINES PALMEIRO CONSTRUCTION LLC
1630 Welton St Ste 200, Denver, CO 80202-4254
Tel (303) 926-4949 *Founded/Ownrshp* 2011
Sales 23.8MM^E *EMP* 70
SIC 1521 1522 Single-family housing construction; Single-family home remodeling, additions & repairs; Renovation, hotel/motel
Pr: Michael Martines
**VP:* Cory Palmeiro
Genl Mgr: Tom Anderson

MARTINEZ & TUREK
See MARTINEZ AND TUREK INC

D-U-N-S 02-179-1488
MARTINEZ AND TUREK INC (CA)
MARTINEZ & TUREK
300 S Cedar Ave, Rialto, CA 92376-9100
Tel (909) 820-6800 *Founded/Ownrshp* 1980
Sales 33.5MM^E *EMP* 120
SIC 3599 Machine shop, jobbing & repair; Machine shop, jobbing & repair
Pr: Larry Tribe
**CFO:* Donald A Turek
**VP:* Thomas J Martinez
**VP:* John Romero
IT Man: Tammy Solo
**VP Mfg:* Laurence Martinez

D-U-N-S 07-149-6934
MARTINEZ DISTRIBUTORS CORP
MDIST
7379 Nw 31st St, Miami, FL 33122-1240
Tel (305) 882-8282 *Founded/Ownrshp* 1997
Sales 79.0MM *EMP* 76
Accts Vildosola Cadenas And Associat
SIC 5147 Meats & meat products; Meats & meat products
Pr: Fabian J Martinez
**Sec:* Enrique Martinez
**VP:* Marta I Martinez

D-U-N-S 13-277-3789
MARTINEZ FARMS INC
2440 Cactus Rd, San Diego, CA 92154-8007
Tel (619) 661-6571 *Founded/Ownrshp* 1955
Sales 16.2MM^E *EMP* 400
SIC 0181 Nursery stock, growing of; Nursery stock, growing of
Pr: Richard Martinez
**Ch Bd:* Jose Martinez

D-U-N-S 04-479-9158
MARTINEZ MANAGEMENT INC
MCDONALD'S
625 E White Mountain Blvd Ste F, Pinetop, AZ 85935
Tel (928) 367-5902 *Founded/Ownrshp* 1991
Sales 10.7MM *EMP* 300
SIC 5812 Fast-food restaurant, chain; Fast-food restaurant, chain
Pr: Abe Martinez
**Treas:* Sharon Martinez

D-U-N-S 07-394-0702
MARTINEZ UNIFIED SCHOOL DISTRICT
921 Susana St, Martinez, CA 94553-1895
Tel (925) 335-5800 *Founded/Ownrshp* 1967
Sales 39.0MM *EMP* 365
SIC 8211 Public elementary school; Public junior high school; Public senior high school; Public elementary school; Public junior high school; Public senior high school
Trst: Kathi McLaughlin
VP: Deidre Siguenza
Dir IT: Max Eissler

D-U-N-S 12-437-6786 IMP
MARTINREA AUTOMOTIVE-STRUCTURES (USA) INC
TKA FABCO
(*Suby of* MARTINREA INDUSTRIES INC) ★
1 Fabco Dr, Springfield, TN 37172-6843
Tel (615) 212-0586 *Founded/Ownrshp* 2006
Sales 226.9MM^E *EMP* 450
SIC 3714 Motor vehicle parts & accessories; Motor vehicle parts & accessories
Pr: Nick Orlando
Genl Mgr: Richard Haveman
Genl Mgr: Kurt Spencer
Opers Mgr: Tracey Hall
Plnt Mgr: Leo La Bla
Prd Mgr: Jeremy Colby
Ql Cn Mgr: Bill Oglesby

D-U-N-S 80-179-1075 IMP
MARTINREA HOPKINSVILLE LLC
(*Suby of* MARTINREA INTERNATIONAL INC)
1500 Frank Yost Ln, Hopkinsville, KY 42240-6818
Tel (270) 475-2000 *Founded/Ownrshp* 1998
Sales 227.4MM^E *EMP* 340^E
SIC 5013 Automotive engines & engine parts; Automotive engines & engine parts
Pr: Tim Parys
Genl Mgr: Kurt Spencer
Genl Mgr: Tom Troyan
Snr Mgr: Nathan Bryant
Snr Mgr: Phillip Shaw

D-U-N-S 04-927-4830 IMP
MARTINREA HOT STAMPINGS INC
(*Suby of* MARTINREA INDUSTRIES INC) ★
19200 Glendale St, Detroit, MI 48223-3459
Tel (313) 272-8400 *Founded/Ownrshp* 2006
Sales 24.7MM^E *EMP* 200^E
SIC 3465 8734

D-U-N-S 10-307-8213 IMP
MARTINREA INDUSTRIES INC
(*Suby of* MARTINREA INTERNATIONAL INC)
10501 Mi State Road 52, Manchester, MI 48158-9432
Tel (734) 428-2400 *Founded/Ownrshp* 2002
Sales 353.7MM^E *EMP* 1,350
SIC 3714 3317 3089 3544 Motor vehicle parts & accessories; Steel pipe & tubes; Plastic containers, except foam; Special dies, tools, jigs & fixtures; Motor vehicle parts & accessories; Steel pipe & tubes; Plastic containers, except foam; Special dies, tools, jigs & fixtures
CEO: Morris Rowlett
**Ch Bd:* Robert Wildeboer
**Pr:* Fred Jaekel
**CFO:* Robert Eckert
**CFO:* Nick Orlando
Genl Mgr: Tom Troyan
Ql Cn Mgr: Charles Muhammad

D-U-N-S 82-972-1799 IMP
MARTINREA JONESVILLE LLC
(*Suby of* MARTINREA INTERNATIONAL INC)
260 Gaige St, Jonesville, MI 49250-9431
Tel (517) 849-2195 *Founded/Ownrshp* 2009
Sales 151.3MM^E *EMP* 700^E
SIC 3465 Body parts, automobile: stamped metal; Body parts, automobile: stamped metal
CEO: Nick Orlando
Prgrm Mgr: Becky Widmayer
Genl Mgr: Pete Bertolni

D-U-N-S 07-939-1325
MARTINREA RIVERSIDE LLC
(*Suby of* MARTINREA INTERNATIONAL INC)
5233 Nw 41st St, Riverside, MO 64150-7815
Tel (289) 982-3000 *Founded/Ownrshp* 2014
Sales 75.1MM^E *EMP* 300
SIC 3465 Automotive stampings; Automotive stampings
Ch: Robert Wildeboer

D-U-N-S 07-867-1286
MARTINS BULK MILK SERVICE INC (WI)
1101 Water St, Wilton, WI 54670-7739
Tel (608) 435-6561 *Founded/Ownrshp* 1975
Sales 35.7MM^E *EMP* 100^E
SIC 4213

D-U-N-S 13-562-7388
MARTINS COUNTRY MARKETS LLC
1717 W Main St Ste 3, Ephrata, PA 17522-1129
Tel (717) 738-3754 *Founded/Ownrshp* 1983
Sales 43.0MM^E *EMP* 380
Accts Leid Lorah & Company Pc De
SIC 5411 Grocery stores, independent; Grocery stores, independent
Pt: John B Martin Jr
**Pt:* Amos B Martin

MARTIN'S FAMILY CLOTHING
See WAKEFIELDS INC

D-U-N-S 01-394-7551 IMP
MARTINS FAMOUS PASTRY SHOPPE INC
1000 Potato Roll Ln, Chambersburg, PA 17202-8897
Tel (717) 263-9580 *Founded/Ownrshp* 1957
Sales 165.8MM^E *EMP* 464
SIC 2051 Rolls, bread type: fresh or frozen; Buns, bread type: fresh or frozen; Rolls, bread type: fresh or frozen; Buns, bread type: fresh or frozen
Pr: James A Martin
**Treas:* Donna F Martin
**VP:* Ronald G Gipe
**VP:* James Martin
VP: Tony Martin
Sales Asso: Amy Reed
Genl Couns: Jeffrey Van Bastelaar

MARTIN'S FOOD CENTER VT
See MARTINS FOODS OF S BURLINGTON INC

MARTIN'S FOOD MARKET
See GIANT FOOD STORES LLC

D-U-N-S 05-276-5294
MARTINS FOODS OF S BURLINGTON INC
MARTIN'S FOOD CENTER VT
(*Suby of* HANNAFORD BROS CO LLC) ★
145 Pleasant Hill Rd, Scarborough, ME 04074-9309
Tel (207) 883-2911 *Founded/Ownrshp* 1969
Sales 210.1MM^E *EMP* 3,087
SIC 5411 Supermarkets, chain; Supermarkets, chain
Pr: Hugh G Farrington
Ch Bd: James L Moody Jr
Treas: Gary Bowne
Prin: Ronald Hodge
Board of Directors: Judy S Thompson, Richard H Wadhams Jr, Judith A White

D-U-N-S 06-582-2348
MARTINS GOLICK INC
GOLICK-MARTIN
140 Sylvan Ave Ste 102, Englewood Cliffs, NJ 07632-2554
Tel (201) 592-8800 *Founded/Ownrshp* 1968
Sales 22.9MM^E *EMP* 81
SIC 5141 Food brokers; Food brokers
Pr: Manny Martins
**Ex VP:* Joseph Lanzilli
VP: Raul Francisco
VP: J Lanzill
IT Man: Lorraine Leyden

D-U-N-S 02-243-5515
MARTINS INC
MARTIN'S WEST
6821 Dogwood Rd, Baltimore, MD 21244-2608
Tel (410) 265-1300 *Founded/Ownrshp* 1964
Sales 29.3MM *EMP* 600
SIC 5812 Caterers; Caterers
Ch: Martin R Resnick
**Pr:* Wayne Resnick
**CFO:* Joseph K Mburu
VP: John Tores
Genl Mgr: Raimund Hofmeister

D-U-N-S 08-426-5693
MARTINS PETERBILT OF EASTERN KENTUCKY LLC
I-75 Exit 38, London, KY 40744
Tel (606) 878-6410 *Founded/Ownrshp* 1965
Sales 34.7MM^E *EMP* 107
SIC 5012 5013 7538 Truck tractors; Truck parts & accessories; Truck engine repair, except industrial
**CEO:* Terry Martin
**Treas:* Troy W Martin

D-U-N-S 00-235-4637
MARTINS POINT HEALTH CARE INC (ME)
USFHP AT MARTIN'S POINT
331 Veranda St Ste 1, Portland, ME 04103-5544
Tel (207) 774-5801 *Founded/Ownrshp* 1971
Sales 571.8MM *EMP* 729
Accts Baker Newman & Noyes Portland
SIC 8093 Specialty outpatient clinics; Specialty outpatient clinics
Pr: Dr David Howes
**Ch Bd:* Michael Thomas
Pr: Reed Eichner
**COO:* Dale Bradford
**COO:* Larry Henry
CFO: Dennis Reese
Treas: George Campbell
**Bd of Dir:* Katherine Greenleaf
Sr VP: Shannon Banks
VP: Jeffry Bland
VP: Ellen Harrison
VP: Pat Weiser

D-U-N-S 06-168-5384 IMP
MARTINS POTATO CHIPS INC (PA)
5847 Lincoln Hwy W, Thomasville, PA 17364-9796
Tel (717) 792-3065 *Founded/Ownrshp* 1941, 1971
Sales 43.2MM^E *EMP* 200
SIC 2096 5145 2099 Potato chips & other potato-based snacks; Pretzels; Food preparations; Potato chips & other potato-based snacks; Pretzels; Food preparations
Pr: Kenneth A Potter Jr
**Treas:* Steven Fitz
**VP:* David J Potter
Rgnl Mgr: Paul McLanahan
IT Man: Ron Brinton
IT Man: Michael Stringent
VP Opers: Glenn Zearfoss

QC Dir: Doug Branstetter
Plnt Mgr: Butch Potter
S&M/VP: Gary Schuler

MARTIN'S QUALITY EGGS
See E K MARTIN & SONS INC

D-U-N-S 09-684-4063
MARTINS RUN (PA)
MARTINS RUN LIFE CARE CMNTY
11 Martins Run Ofc, Media, PA 19063-1089
Tel (610) 353-7660 *Founded/Ownrshp* 1978, 1980
Sales 14.8MM *EMP* 280
Accts Cliftonlarsonallen Llp Plymou
SIC 8361 Residential care; Residential care
CEO: Linda Sterthous
**CFO:* Mike McGlone
Treas: Marc Shames
**Sr VP:* Lorraine Dellafranco
**VP:* Lynn Plasha

MARTINS RUN LIFE CARE CMNTY
See MARTINS RUN

D-U-N-S 04-640-0701
MARTINS SUPER MARKETS INC
760 Cotter St, South Bend, IN 46613-1824
Tel (574) 234-5848 *Founded/Ownrshp* 1947
Sales 356.9MM[E] *EMP* 3,100
SIC 5411 Supermarkets, independent; Supermarkets, independent
Pr: Robert E Bartels Jr
**Ch Bd:* Robert E Bartels
CFO: Gregory Freehauf
VP: Dan Bailey
Rgnl Mgr: Adam Miller
Genl Mgr: Ken Bruce
CIO: Scott Johnson
Dir IT: John Raab
IT Man: Ed Delaurelle
S&M/VP: Michelle Waldrop
Pharmcst: Sheila Haluda

D-U-N-S 96-499-3997
MARTINS TRAILSIDE EXPRESS INC
168 Toddy Dr, East Earl, PA 17519-9261
Tel (717) 354-9486 *Founded/Ownrshp* 2010
Sales 27.1MM *EMP* 37
Accts Weinhold Nickel & Company Ll
SIC 5411 Convenience stores; Convenience stores
Pr: Judith A Weaver
**Sec:* Janelle Bixler
**VP:* Jamie T Weaver

MARTIN'S WEST
See MARTINS INC

MARTIN'S WINE CELLAR
See DAVIDY MARTIN JR LLC

D-U-N-S 06-541-5614
MARTINSVILLE CITY OF (INC)
55 W Church St, Martinsville, VA 24112-6209
Tel (276) 403-5000 *Founded/Ownrshp* 1791
Sales NA *EMP* 743
Accts Robinsons Farmer Cox Associa
SIC 9111 City & town managers' offices; ; City & town managers' offices;
Ex VP: Clark Lingle
Exec: Scott Coleman
IT Man: Kathryn Washington
Sys/Mgr: Ester Artis
Snr Mgr: Sean Dunn

D-U-N-S 10-067-4241
MARTINSVILLE CITY SCHOOL DISTRICT
746 Indian Trl, Martinsville, VA 24112-4520
Tel (276) 632-6313 *Founded/Ownrshp* 1996
Sales 23.0MM *EMP* 305
SIC 8211 Public elementary & secondary schools; School board; Public elementary & secondary schools; School board
Teacher Pr: Darlene Stroud
HC Dir: Felicia Preston

D-U-N-S 06-599-7157
■ **MARTINSVILLE NEWCO**
MEMORIAL HOSPITAL
(*Suby of* LIFEPOINT HEALTH INC) ★
320 Hospital Dr, Martinsville, VA 24112-1900
Tel (276) 666-7200 *Founded/Ownrshp* 2006
Sales 82.1MM[E] *EMP* 800
SIC 8062 General medical & surgical hospitals; General medical & surgical hospitals
Ex Dir: Joseph Roach
COO: Mike Sharrod
Ofcr: Brad Meeks
Dir Risk M: Sammy Nagar
Doctor: Howard Brown
Doctor: Rebin Titus
Pgrm Dir: Tooba Kazmi

D-U-N-S 10-683-1845
MARTON ROOFING INDUSTRIES LTD
5207 Ashbrook Dr, Houston, TX 77081-2903
Tel (713) 664-7000 *Founded/Ownrshp* 1976
Sales 22.6MM[E] *EMP* 100
Accts Uhy Llp Houston Texas
SIC 1761 1771 Roofing contractor; Concrete work
Pr: Cathleen Marton
Genl Pt: Marton Roofing LP
Genl Pt: Kathlyn Marton
Pt: Patty Glass
VP: Toby Beckwith
VP: Chris Black
Genl Couns: Harry Dollar

MARTORI FARMS
See EAGLE PRODUCE LLC

MARTY CANCILA DODGE WORLD
See FLORISSANT DODGE SALES INC

D-U-N-S 01-376-3776
MARTY FELDMAN CHEVROLET INC
42355 Grand River Ave, Novi, MI 48375-1839
Tel (248) 348-7000 *Founded/Ownrshp* 1980
Sales 31.6MM[E] *EMP* 70
SIC 5511 Automobiles, new & used; Pickups, new & used; Vans, new & used; Automobiles, new & used; Pickups, new & used; Vans, new & used
Pr: Martin G Feldman
Sls Mgr: Shaun Benard
Sls Mgr: Jamin Blitchok
Sls Mgr: Ed Jackson
Sls Mgr: Jim Masterson
Sls Mgr: Andrew Pavlik

D-U-N-S 03-169-5030
MARTY FIRE DEPARTMENT
MARTY INDIAN SCHOOL
100 S Main St Bldg A, Marty, SD 57361
Tel (605) 384-5432 *Founded/Ownrshp* 2010
Sales NA *EMP* 300
SIC 9224 Fire department, not including volunteer; ; Fire department, not including volunteer;
Prin: Michael Elsberry
Prin: Todd Standingcloud

D-U-N-S 02-962-6967
MARTY FRANICH FORD LINCOLN MERCURY INC
550 Auto Center Dr, Watsonville, CA 95076-3728
Tel (831) 722-4181 *Founded/Ownrshp* 1948
Sales 25.6MM[E] *EMP* 50
SIC 5511 7538 Automobiles, new & used; General automotive repair shops; Automobiles, new & used; General automotive repair shops
Pr: Steven Franich
**Treas:* Mark Franich
**VP:* Doug Inman

MARTY INDIAN SCHOOL
See MARTY FIRE DEPARTMENT

MARTY SHOES
See M & J SHOES LLC

MARTY SUSSMAN HONDA
See MARTY SUSSMAN MOTORS INC

D-U-N-S 80-307-5209
MARTY SUSSMAN MOTORS INC
MARTY SUSSMAN HONDA
(*Suby of* MARTY SUSSMAN ORGANIZATION INC) ★
1543 Easton Rd, Abington, PA 19001-2403
Tel (215) 657-7050 *Founded/Ownrshp* 1984
Sales 36.2MM *EMP* 100
SIC 5511 7538 Automobiles, new & used; General automotive repair shops; Automobiles, new & used; General automotive repair shops
CEO: Martin E Sussman
**Pr:* Eric Sussman
**Treas:* Elaine Sussman
**VP:* Mike Goegz
**VP:* Joseph Wilkocz

D-U-N-S 15-397-5586
MARTY SUSSMAN ORGANIZATION INC
1940 Jenkintown Rd, Jenkintown, PA 19046-2254
Tel (215) 887-1800 *Founded/Ownrshp* 1965
Sales 64.3MM[E] *EMP* 200
SIC 5511 Automobiles, new & used; Automobiles, new & used
Ch Bd: Martin E Sussman
**Pr:* Eric Sussman
CFO: Michael Goetz
**Treas:* Elaine Sussman

MARTYS GMC BUICK PONTIAC ISUZU
See MARTYS INC

D-U-N-S 04-276-3599
MARTYS INC
MARTYS GMC BUICK PONTIAC ISUZU
5 Kingston Collection Way, Kingston, MA 02364-3019
Tel (781) 585-7570 *Founded/Ownrshp* 1999
Sales 26.8MM[E] *EMP* 55
SIC 5511 7538 7537 Automobiles, new & used; General truck repair; Automotive transmission repair shops; Automobiles, new & used; General truck repair; Automotive transmission repair shops
Pr: Christine Alicandro
**VP:* Martin Alicandro
Sls Mgr: Ron Almeida
Sales Asso: Jason Conroy

D-U-N-S 00-167-0876 EXP
MARUBENI AMERICA CORP (NY)
(*Suby of* MARUBENI CORPORATION)
375 Lexington Ave, New York, NY 10017-5644
Tel (212) 450-0100 *Founded/Ownrshp* 1951
Sales 7.7MMM[E] *EMP* 4,175
Accts Ernst & Young Llp New York N
SIC 5131 5084 5012 5169 5172 5094 Textiles, woven; Industrial machinery & equipment; Automobiles & other motor vehicles; Industrial chemicals; Petroleum products; Crude oil; Fuel oil; Gasoline; Precious metals; Textiles, woven; Industrial machinery & equipment; Automobiles & other motor vehicles; Industrial chemicals; Petroleum products; Crude oil; Fuel oil; Gasoline; Precious metals
Pr: Naoya Iwashita
Pr: Masato Nakamura
Pr: Koji Yamanaka
**COO:* Takashi Ishigami
COO: Yuichi Ishimaru
COO: Shigemi Naito
CFO: Masanori Mizuno
**Treas:* Hironori Hanada
Treas: Yuka Nakamura
Sr Cor Off: Masao Kato
Sr Cor Off: Tom Mustico
Bd of Dir: Koichi Mochizuki
Bd of Dir: Yoshiya Toyoda
Ofcr: Karen Wong
Ex VP: Toru Nishimi
Ex VP: Joe Van Dorn
Sr VP: Michael Doyle
Sr VP: Shinichiro Kawazoe
**Sr VP:* Howard Tiegel
VP: Mick Amano
**VP:* Jerome E Barnett

D-U-N-S 80-644-0467
MARUBENI AUTO & CONSTRUCTION MACHINERY (AMERICA) INC
(*Suby of* MARUBENI CORPORATION)
450 Lexington Ave, New York, NY 10017-3904
Tel (212) 450-0447 *Founded/Ownrshp* 2002
Sales 167.0MM[E] *EMP* 325
SIC 5082 7353 7699 General construction machinery & equipment; Heavy construction equipment rental; Construction equipment repair; General construction machinery & equipment; Heavy construction equipment rental; Construction equipment repair
Pr: Takuji Harada

D-U-N-S 12-148-2764 IMP
MARUBENI CITIZEN-CINCOM INC
40 Boroline Rd Ste 6, Allendale, NJ 07401-1616
Tel (201) 818-0100 *Founded/Ownrshp* 2003
Sales 27.1MM[E] *EMP* 50
SIC 5084 5047 5013 5088 5065 Machine tools & accessories; Medical & hospital equipment; Automotive servicing equipment; Aeronautical equipment & supplies; Electronic parts & equipment
Pr: Shigeyuki Baba
COO: Toru Nishimi
**Treas:* Matt Hiroshige
CIO: Chris O'Donovan
IT Man: Vincent Antignani
IT Man: Joe Dulinski
Manager: Richard Miller
Sls Mgr: Richard Kuhn

D-U-N-S 14-141-1699 IMP
MARUBENI OIL & GAS (USA) INC
(*Suby of* MARUBENI CORPORATION)
777 N Eldridge Pkwy, Houston, TX 77079-4425
Tel (832) 379-1100 *Founded/Ownrshp* 2003
Sales 63.6MM[E] *EMP* 30[E]
SIC 1311 Natural gas production
Pr: Kazuaki Tanaki
**COO:* Perry Murphree
Genl Mgr: Charlie Hughes
Dir IT: Marty Gosnell

D-U-N-S 82-639-2479 EXP
MARUBENI POWER SERVICES INC
(*Suby of* MARUBENI CORPORATION)
375 Lexington Ave, New York, NY 10017-5644
Tel (212) 450-0640 *Founded/Ownrshp* 2005
Sales 167.6MM[E] *EMP* 1,061[E]
SIC 1629 4911 8711 Power plant construction; Electric services; Engineering services; Power plant construction; Electric services; Engineering services
CEO: Toshi Fukumura
CFO: Eisuke Kamide
**Ex VP:* Richard Straebel
Sr VP: Shinichiro Kawazoe
**Sr VP:* Xavier Tournier
VP: Ryota Kobayashi
VP: Abby Saigal
VP: Hiroshi Tachitachi
**VP:* Daniel Welt
**VP:* Hiroki Yamamoto
Genl Mgr: Carsten Holtermann

D-U-N-S 78-727-6633 IMP/EXP
MARUBENI SPECIALTY CHEMICALS INC
(*Suby of* MARUBENI AMERICA CORP) ★
10 Bank St Ste 740, White Plains, NY 10606-1952
Tel (914) 428-8900 *Founded/Ownrshp* 1991
Sales 241.7MM *EMP* 62
Accts Ernst & Young Llp New York N
SIC 5169 Chemicals, industrial & heavy; Chemicals, industrial & heavy
Pr: Jo Harada
**VP:* Tsuyoshi Honkawa
Genl Mgr: Toshinori Takeyama

MARUBENI STEEL PROCESSING
See MISA METAL PROCESSING INC

D-U-N-S 04-307-1377 IMP
MARUBENI-ITOCHU STEEL AMERICA INC
MISA
(*Suby of* MARUBENI-ITOCHU STEEL INC.)
150 E 42nd St Fl 7, New York, NY 10017-5612
Tel (212) 660-6000 *Founded/Ownrshp* 2001
Sales 717.4MM[E] *EMP* 1,358
Accts Deloitte & Touche Llp New Yor
SIC 5051 Metals service centers & offices; Metals service centers & offices
CEO: Takeshi Mitomi
**Ch Bd:* Katsuya Masai
**CFO:* Shuji Suzuki
VP: Gregory Dephillis
VP: Shohei Tanaka
IT Man: Yoshie Yabu
VP Sls: Bradley Miller
Sls Mgr: Birgit Robbyns
Snr Mgr: Dympna Purtill

D-U-N-S 18-307-9367 IMP/EXP
MARUBENI-ITOCHU TUBULARS AMERICA INC
ITOCHU PIPE & TUBE
(*Suby of* MARUBENI-ITOCHU STEEL INC.)
580 Westlake Park Blvd, Houston, TX 77079-2662
Tel (281) 368-7000 *Founded/Ownrshp* 2001
Sales 49.5MM[E] *EMP* 59
SIC 5051 Pipe & tubing, steel; Pipe & tubing, steel
Pr: Shigeki Furutate
CFO: Mike Lamb
Genl Mgr: Terry Oikawa
Snr Mgr: Motoki Minamiyama

D-U-N-S 06-460-7096 IMP
MARUCHAN INC
(*Suby of* TOYO SUISAN KAISHA, LTD.)
15800 Laguna Canyon Rd, Irvine, CA 92618-3103
Tel (949) 789-2300 *Founded/Ownrshp* 1972
Sales 221.2MM[E] *EMP* 600
SIC 2098 2099 Noodles (e.g. egg, plain & water), dry; Food preparations; Noodles (e.g. egg, plain & water), dry; Food preparations
CEO: Noritaka Sumimoto
Exec: Natlie Plumb
Dir IT: Takashi Ueno
IT Man: Gary Leeper
Prd Mgr: Satoshi Asano
Sls&Mrk Ex: James R Santo
Manager: Gregg Sommer
Sls Mgr: Nico Masuda

D-U-N-S 16-727-8261
MARUHA CAPITAL INVESTMENT INC
(*Suby of* MARUHA NICHIRO CORPORATION)
2101 4th Ave Ste 1700, Seattle, WA 98121-2377
Tel (206) 382-0640 *Founded/Ownrshp* 2001
Sales 376.1MM[E] *EMP* 204[E]
SIC 6799 2091 Investors; Seafood products: packaged in cans, jars, etc.; Investors; Seafood products: packaged in cans, jars, etc.
Pr: Hiroshi Okazaki
**Treas:* Tatsuya Yamamoto
**VP:* Katsuhiko Uota

D-U-N-S 09-900-4004 IMP
MARUICHI AMERICAN CORP
(*Suby of* MARUICHI STEEL TUBE LTD.)
11529 Greenstone Ave, Santa Fe Springs, CA 90670-4622
Tel (562) 903-8600 *Founded/Ownrshp* 1978
Sales 70.0MM[E] *EMP* 85
SIC 3317 Pipes, seamless steel; Tubes, seamless steel; Pipes, seamless steel; Tubes, seamless steel
Pr: Wataru Cho Morita
**Ch Bd:* Teruo Horikawa
**CEO:* Yasunori Yoshimura
**VP:* Makoto Ishikawa
**VP:* Takehiko Katsumata
VP: Shigeru Nakajima
Exec: James Laforteze
Dir IT: Mike Tamaki
Plnt Mgr: Sunny Sanchez
Ql Cn Mgr: Kureha Ando
Manager: David Shaffer

D-U-N-S 78-863-0960 IMP
MARUICHI LEAVITT PIPE & TUBE LLC
(*Suby of* MARUICHI STEEL TUBE LTD.)
1717 W 115th St, Chicago, IL 60643-4398
Tel (773) 239-7700 *Founded/Ownrshp* 2001
Sales 26.1MM[E] *EMP* 125[E]
SIC 3317 Seamless pipes & tubes; Seamless pipes & tubes
Pr: T Konishi
COO: Parry D Katsafanas
**CFO:* David J Klima
**VP:* Joe Fattori
**VP:* S Honda
**IT Man:* Pat Knutson
IT Man: Jim McGuire
Plnt Mgr: Bill Goodrich
Prd Mgr: Mark Forges
Sls Mgr: Mark Goodkind
Sales Asso: Patrick Doyle

D-U-N-S 00-189-2108
MARUKA USA INC (NJ)
(*Suby of* MARUKA MACHINERY CO., LTD.)
45 Route 46 Ste 610, Pine Brook, NJ 07058-9390
Tel (973) 487-3800 *Founded/Ownrshp* 1947, 1990
Sales 47.8MM[E] *EMP* 115
SIC 5084 7699 1796 Machine tools & accessories; Plastic products machinery; Industrial machinery & equipment repair; Machinery installation; Machine tools & accessories; Plastic products machinery; Industrial machinery & equipment repair; Machinery installation
Pr: Gary Lowery
**Ex VP:* Yosuke Yasuda
Mng Dir: Tsuneo Takahashi
Genl Mgr: Yutaka Kitajima
IT Man: Kazuhiko Koike
Sls Mgr: Frank Bell

D-U-N-S 03-319-7294 IMP/EXP
MARUKAI CORP
MARUKAI WHOLESALE MART
(*Suby of* DON QUIJOTE HOLDINGS CO., LTD.)
2310 Kamehameha Hwy, Honolulu, HI 96819-2378
Tel (808) 845-5051 *Founded/Ownrshp* 1970, 2013
Sales 91.5MM[E] *EMP* 590
SIC 5311 Department stores, discount; Department stores, discount
Pr: Hidejiro Matsu
VP: Richard Matsu

MARUKAI WHOLESALE MART
See MARUKAI CORP

D-U-N-S 07-879-7040 IMP/EXP
MARUKAN VINEGAR (U S A) INC
(*Suby of* MARUKAN VINEGAR CO.,LTD.)
16203 Vermont Ave, Paramount, CA 90723-5042
Tel (562) 630-6060 *Founded/Ownrshp* 1649
Sales 21.3MM[E] *EMP* 105
SIC 2099 Vinegar; Vinegar
Ch Bd: Yasuo Sasada
**Pr:* Toshio Takeuchi
**CEO:* Denzaemon Sasada
CFO: Yoshi Tsumura
**Ex VP:* Junichi Oyama
**VP:* Shugi Yamada
IT Man: Mike Wakita
Mktg Mgr: Tom McReynolds

MARUS DENTAL
See DENTAL EQUIPMENT LLC

MARV SMITH SIGNS
See MUSCO SPORTS LIGHTING INC

MARVA MAID DAIRY DIVISION
See MARYLAND AND VIRGINIA MILK PRODUCERS COOPERATIVE ASSOCIATION INC

D-U-N-S 00-200-5650 IMP
MARVAL INDUSTRIES INC
M I I
315 Hoyt Ave, Mamaroneck, NY 10543-1899
Tel (914) 381-2400 *Founded/Ownrshp* 1956
Sales 41.1MM[E] *EMP* 70

SIC 2869 5162 3089 3087 Industrial organic chemicals; Plastics materials; Thermoformed finished plastic products; Custom compound purchased resins; Industrial organic chemicals; Plastics materials; Thermoformed finished plastic products; Custom compound purchased resins
CEO: Alan Zimmerman
**Ch Bd:* Thomas Zimmerman
**VP:* Emil Kocur
Opers Mgr: Logan Osberg

D-U-N-S 18-582-5569 IMP
■ **MARVEL ENTERTAINMENT LLC**
(*Suby of* WALT DISNEY CO) ★
135 W 50th St Fl 7, New York, NY 10020-1201
Tel (212) 576-4000 *Founded/Ownrshp* 2009
Sales 97.1MM^E^ *EMP* 300^E^
SIC 2721 6794 3944 7929 Comic books: publishing only, not printed on site; Magazines: publishing only, not printed on site; Patent buying, licensing, leasing; Electronic games & toys; Entertainment service; Comic books: publishing only, not printed on site; Magazines: publishing only, not printed on site; Patent buying, licensing, leasing; Electronic games & toys; Entertainment service
CEO: Isaac Perlmutter
Pr: Michael Helfant
Pr: Timothy E Rothwell
COO: Michael Halfant
COO: Ralph Lancellotti
CFO: Kenneth P West
Ex VP: David Maisel
Ex VP: John Turitzin
VP: Mitchell Bell
VP: David Bogart
VP: Stephen Broussard
VP: Daniele Campbell
VP: David Grant
VP: Jeff Klein
VP: Cort Lane
VP: Mike Pasciullo
VP: Madison Reinhart
VP: Kristin Vincent
VP: Brad Winderbaum
VP Bus Dev: Benjamin Hung

D-U-N-S 00-512-0050 IMP
MARVEL GROUP INC (DE)
3843 W 43rd St, Chicago, IL 60632-3409
Tel (773) 523-4804 *Founded/Ownrshp* 1946, 2003
Sales 96.0MM^E^ *EMP* 440
SIC 2522 Office furniture, except wood; Office furniture, except wood
Pr: John J Dellamore
VP: Chris Bone
VP: Joe Fortin
VP: Michael Glab
VP: Ken Wolfanger
VP: Maria Zbela-Mudd
Prgrm Mgr: Vasile Moldovan
Admn Mgr: Mary Bleskin
Dir IT: Kenneth Wolfanger
Dir IT: Ken Wolfhanger
IT Man: Alfreda Godlewski

D-U-N-S 09-005-0188 IMP/EXP
MARVEL INTERNATIONAL INC
MARVEL SPECIALTIES
7 Calle Beatriz, Guaynabo, PR 00968-8004
Tel (787) 754-6430 *Founded/Ownrshp* 2005
Sales 21.5MM^E^ *EMP* 73
SIC 2013 5142 Sausages & other prepared meats; Frozen fish, meat & poultry; Meat, frozen: packaged; Poultry pies, frozen
Pr: Marcelo Tortoriello
**Pr:* Alberto Baco
**Treas:* Karen Nolla
**VP:* Magda Segarra

D-U-N-S 18-147-4730 IMP/EXP
MARVEL MANUFACTURING CO INC
3501 Marvel Dr, Oshkosh, WI 54902-7115
Tel (920) 236-7200 *Founded/Ownrshp* 2004
Sales 30.0MM^E^ *EMP* 95
SIC 3541 Machine tools, metal cutting type
Pr: John Petek
Pr: Archie Stam
**VP:* Robert Beach
**VP:* James Jourdan
Dist Mgr: Ross Ploeckelman
IT Man: Noah Luft
Ql Cn Mgr: John Rozenbloom
S&M/VP: Bob Beach
Sls Mgr: Garry Toddish
Sls Mgr: Bill Verbrick

MARVEL SPECIALTIES
See MARVEL INTERNATIONAL INC

D-U-N-S 00-259-8589
MARVEL STANLEY INC (PA)
1221 Ford Rd, Bensalem, PA 19020-4518
Tel (215) 638-7800 *Founded/Ownrshp* 1966
Sales 32.0MM^E^ *EMP* 45
Accts Locke & Associates Pc
SIC 5142 5149 5143 5144 Packaged frozen goods; Canned goods: fruit, vegetables, seafood, meats, etc.; Butter; Cheese; Eggs
Pr: Stanley W Marvel III
**CFO:* William Thorp
**VP:* Maloney Frederick
VP: Fred Maloney

D-U-N-S 95-881-9906 IMP
MARVELL SEMICONDUCTOR INC
(*Suby of* MARVELL TECHNOLOGY GROUP LTD)
5488 Marvell Ln, Santa Clara, CA 95054-3606
Tel (408) 222-2500 *Founded/Ownrshp* 1995
Sales 411.0MM^E^ *EMP* 1,900
SIC 3674 Semiconductors & related devices; Semiconductors & related devices
Ch Bd: Sehat Sutardja
COO: Weili Dai
CFO: George Hervey
CFO: Michael Rashkin
VP: Alan Armstrong
VP: Sukhi Nagesh
VP: Thomas Savage
Prgrm Mgr: Yogesh N Malhan
Rgnl Mgr: Michael Lampe
Genl Mgr: Hoo Kuong
CTO: Pantas Sutardja
Board of Directors: John Gabriel Kassakian

D-U-N-S 86-798-7323 IMP
MARVELL TECHNOLOGY GROUP LTD
(*Suby of* MARVELL TECHNOLOGY GROUP LTD)
5488 Marvell Ln, Santa Clara, CA 95054-3606
Tel (408) 222-2500 *Founded/Ownrshp* 1991
Sales 311.2MM^E^ *EMP* 1,410^E^
SIC 6719 Personal holding companies, except banks; Personal holding companies, except banks
CEO: Sehat Sutardja
**Pr:* Weili Dai
**CFO:* George A De Urioste
Assoc VP: Jacky Chow
VP: Kaushik Banerjee
VP: Chris Chang
VP: Matthew Gloss
VP: James Laufman
VP: Bouchung Lin
VP: AVI Sokol
VP: Moshe Steiner

D-U-N-S 00-260-4114
MARVIC SUPPLY CO INC (PA)
4083 E Swamp Rd, Doylestown, PA 18902-1141
Tel (215) 348-8400 *Founded/Ownrshp* 1967
Sales 33.6MM^E^ *EMP* 65
SIC 5033

MARVIN DESIGN GALLERY
See MARINE LUMBER OPERATOR INC

D-U-N-S 00-956-6167 IMP
MARVIN ENGINEERING CO INC
MARVIN GROUP, THE
261 W Beach Ave, Inglewood, CA 90302-2904
Tel (310) 674-5030 *Founded/Ownrshp* 1963
Sales 232.3MM^E^ *EMP* 700
SIC 3728 Aircraft parts & equipment; Aircraft parts & equipment
CEO: Gerald M Friedman
Pr: Bryan Deblois
**Pr:* Howard Gussman
COO: Jim Fish
COO: Oded Nechustan
**CFO:* Leon Tsimmerman
VP: Geoff Loui
VP: Yadin Shohet
Prgrm Mgr: Ej Chiartano
Prgrm Mgr: Rene Monzon
Prgrm Mgr: Jerry Valdez
Board of Directors: David Gussman, Madeline Gussman

D-U-N-S 07-487-1047
MARVIN F POER AND CO
12700 Hillcrest Rd # 125, Dallas, TX 75230-2009
Tel (972) 770-1100 *Founded/Ownrshp* 1976
Sales 48.5MM^E^ *EMP* 200
SIC 8742 Real estate consultant; Real estate consultant
Ch Bd: Marvin F Poer
**Pr:* Bill Dubois
Sr VP: Miles Friend
Sr VP: Nicholas Muros
Sr VP: Ken Parsons
**Sr VP:* Tom Rawlston
Sr VP: Tom Rawlstons
VP: Kenneth Graeber
**VP:* Kathryn McBride
VP: Kris Miller
VP: Joe Monzon
**VP:* David Poer
VP: Frederick Sewall
Dir Bus: Marc Bragin
Dir Bus: Justin Goertz
Dir Bus: Philip Utterback

MARVIN GROUP, THE
See MARVIN ENGINEERING CO INC

MARVIN GROUP THE
See MARVIN LAND SYSTEMS INC

D-U-N-S 00-691-1283
MARVIN K BROWN AUTO CENTER INC
MARVIN K BROWN GMC
1441 Camino Del Rio S, San Diego, CA 92108-3521
Tel (619) 291-2040 *Founded/Ownrshp* 1965
Sales 62.2MM^E^ *EMP* 150
SIC 5511 5531 7538 Automobiles, new & used; Pickups, new & used; Automotive & home supply stores; General automotive repair shops; Automobiles, new & used; Pickups, new & used; Automotive & home supply stores; General automotive repair shops
CEO: Jennifer K Brown
**Pr:* James E Brown
**Sec:* Sandra Wood
**VP:* Dave Grundstrom
Sls Mgr: Bill Cooper
Sls Mgr: Brett Fletcher
Sales Asso: Tony Maravilla

MARVIN K BROWN GMC
See MARVIN K BROWN AUTO CENTER INC

D-U-N-S 14-431-7047
MARVIN KELLER TRUCKING INC
1500 West Pointe Way, Sullivan, IL 61951-9170
Tel (217) 728-9800 *Founded/Ownrshp* 1965
Sales 32.4MM^E^ *EMP* 90
SIC 4213 Trucking, except local
Pr: Joe Keller
VP: Rick Ellis

D-U-N-S 92-878-0170 IMP
MARVIN LAND SYSTEMS INC
MARVIN GROUP THE
(*Suby of* MARVIN ENGINEERING CO INC) ★
261 W Beach Ave, Inglewood, CA 90302-2904
Tel (310) 674-5030 *Founded/Ownrshp* 1995
Sales 21.0MM^E^ *EMP* 44
SIC 3711 Military motor vehicle assembly; Military motor vehicle assembly
Pr: Gerald M Friedman
**CFO:* Leon Tsimmerman
Prgrm Mgr: Javier Lopez
Pgrm Dir: Yadin Shohet

D-U-N-S 00-616-4511 IMP
MARVIN LUMBER AND CEDAR CO (MN)
MARVIN WINDOWS & DOORS
Hwy 11 & W Lake St, Warroad, MN 56763
Tel (218) 386-1430 *Founded/Ownrshp* 1920
Sales 553.3MM^E^ *EMP* 3,573
SIC 2431

D-U-N-S 62-331-0927
MARVIN TEST SOLUTIONS INC
(*Suby of* MARVIN ENGINEERING CO INC) ★
1770 Kettering, Irvine, CA 92614-5616
Tel (949) 263-2222 *Founded/Ownrshp* 1997
Sales 21.6MM *EMP* 70
SIC 3825 Instruments to measure electricity
Pr: Loofie Gutterman
Pr: David Manor
**CFO:* Leon Tsimmerman
**Treas:* Gerald Friedman
Prgrm Mgr: Eyal Hinkis
Ql Cn Mgr: George Trujillo

D-U-N-S 11-491-6232
MARVIN W MIELKE INC
MW MIELKE
1040 Industrial Pkwy, Medina, OH 44256-2449
Tel (330) 725-8845 *Founded/Ownrshp* 1984
Sales 25.0MM *EMP* 100
SIC 1711 Plumbing contractors; Sprinkler contractors; Warm air heating & air conditioning contractor
Pr: David A Mielke
Treas: Mike Fisher
**Treas:* Mary Anne Mielke
**VP:* Terry Mielke
VP Opers: Scott Givens

MARVIN WINDOWS & DOORS
See MARVIN LUMBER AND CEDAR CO

MARVIN WINDOWS AND DOORS
See MARVINS WINDOWS AND DOORS OF TENNESSEE INC

D-U-N-S 83-254-6308 EXP
MARVIN WINDOWS INC
(*Suby of* MARVIN LUMBER AND CEDAR CO) ★
401 State Ave N, Warroad, MN 56763
Tel (218) 386-1430 *Founded/Ownrshp* 2009
Sales 24.8MM^E^ *EMP* 100^E^
SIC 2431 Millwork
Prin: John W Marvin
Mktg Mgr: Ann Rauch

D-U-N-S 11-527-9168 IMP/EXP
MARVIN WINDOWS OF TENNESSEE INC
101 Marvin Dr, Ripley, TN 38063-7365
Tel (731) 635-5190 *Founded/Ownrshp* 1980
Sales 96.8MM^E^ *EMP* 700
SIC 2431 3231 Doors, wood; Doors, glass: made from purchased glass; Doors, wood; Doors, glass: made from purchased glass
CEO: John W Marvin
**Pr:* Susan Marvin

D-U-N-S 07-864-3509
MARVINS FOOD SERVER
BUY FOR LESS
2415 E Admiral Pl, Tulsa, OK 74110-5343
Tel (918) 835-3555 *Founded/Ownrshp* 1975
Sales 23.1MM^E^ *EMP* 390
SIC 5411 Supermarkets, independent; Supermarkets, independent
Pr: James Marvin
Off Mgr: Clarivil Arnandez

MARVINS FOODS STORES
See CVM INC

MARVIN'S, INC.
See MARVINS LLC

D-U-N-S 08-997-6385 IMP
MARVINS LLC
MARVIN'S, INC.
(*Suby of* CENTRAL NETWORK RETAIL GROUP LLC) ★
7480 Parkway Dr Ste 100, Leeds, AL 35094-4823
Tel (205) 702-7305 *Founded/Ownrshp* 1945, 2015
Sales 169.2MM^E^ *EMP* 550
SIC 5211 5074 5031 5072

D-U-N-S 03-119-8367
MARVINS WINDOWS AND DOORS OF TENNESSEE INC
MARVIN WINDOWS AND DOORS
101 Marvin Dr, Ripley, TN 38063-7365
Tel (731) 635-5190 *Founded/Ownrshp* 1980
Sales 133.5MM^E^ *EMP* 700
SIC 2431 3231 Doors, wood; Doors, glass: made from purchased glass; Doors, wood; Doors, glass: made from purchased glass
CEO: John Marvin
Genl Mgr: Greg York
Site Mgr: Hal Williams
Sls Mgr: Walter Ward

D-U-N-S 01-455-1923
MARWEN INC
SCRANTON DODGE
1146 Wyoming Ave, Scranton, PA 18509-2715
Tel (570) 344-1261 *Founded/Ownrshp* 1983
Sales 36.2MM^E^ *EMP* 93
SIC 5511 7538 6141

D-U-N-S 79-338-7465 IMP
MARWEST LLC
WEST COAST SHIP CHANDLERS
1611 17th St, Oakland, CA 94607-1641
Tel (510) 444-7200 *Founded/Ownrshp* 2000
Sales 40.7MM^E^ *EMP* 77
SIC 5088 Marine supplies; Marine supplies
CEO: Julian Hillery
Pr: Charlie Michelson

MARWIL
See ROL - TECH INC

MARWIN BALL VALVES DIV
See RICHARDS INDUSTRIES INC

D-U-N-S 04-517-3960
MARWIT CAPITAL PARTNERS II LP
100 Bayview Cir Ste 550, Newport Beach, CA 92660-2984
Tel (949) 861-3636 *Founded/Ownrshp* 1962
Sales NA *EMP* 315
SIC 6159 5699 Small business investment companies; Western apparel; Small business investment companies; Western apparel
Pt: Mathew L Witte
Pt: Chris L Britt
Pt: Laurie Sey Mour
Off Mgr: Linda Chason

D-U-N-S 06-335-2488
MARX OKUBO ASSOCIATES INC
455 N Sherman St Ste 200, Denver, CO 80203-4428
Tel (303) 861-0300 *Founded/Ownrshp* 1982
Sales 21.0MM^E^ *EMP* 100
SIC 8748 Environmental consultant
Ch Bd: Leo James Marx
**Pr:* Parrish Boren
Sr VP: Phillip Helms
VP: Edward Bernard
VP: Ronald Burgess
VP: Chris Geier
VP: George Wilson
Off Mgr: Tianna Huffman
Off Mgr: Andrea Ingleton
Off Mgr: Betsy Miller
Off Mgr: Elizabeth Tausz

D-U-N-S 02-144-6299
MARX SHEET METAL & MECHANICAL INC
373 High Blvd, Wilkes Barre, PA 18702-4358
Tel (570) 824-4737 *Founded/Ownrshp* 1972
Sales 25.6MM^E^ *EMP* 97
SIC 1711 1761 5075 Mechanical contractor; Sheet metalwork; Warm air heating & air conditioning; Air conditioning & ventilation equipment & supplies
Pr: Donald Marx
**Sec:* Lorraine Marx
Snr PM: Jim Degrazia
Snr PM: Thomas Rodino

MARXMODA
See FACILITY MATRIX GROUP INC

MARXMODA
See WORK SQUARED INC

D-U-N-S 05-876-1763
MARY ALICE FORTIN FOUNDATION
201 Chilean Ave, Palm Beach, FL 33480-4629
Tel (561) 659-1226 *Founded/Ownrshp* 1987
Sales 42.2MM *EMP* 2
SIC 8699 Charitable organization; Charitable organization
Pr: Danielle Hitcocks
**Pr:* Danielle Hickox

D-U-N-S 86-798-7117
MARY ANNS SPECIALTY FOODS INC
1511 E 2nd St, Webster City, IA 50595-1743
Tel (515) 832-4740 *Founded/Ownrshp* 1994
Sales 77.6MM^E^ *EMP* 150
SIC 5147 5812

D-U-N-S 08-915-7044
MARY B TURNER TRUCKING CO LLC
108 E College Ave, Boiling Springs, NC 28017
Tel (704) 434-5080 *Founded/Ownrshp* 1961
Sales 25.0MM *EMP* 110
SIC 4213 Trucking, except local; Refrigerated products transport; Trucking, except local; Refrigerated products transport

D-U-N-S 06-602-9117
MARY BALDWIN COLLEGE
MBC
109 E Frederick St, Staunton, VA 24401-3669
Tel (540) 887-7000 *Founded/Ownrshp* 1842
Sales 29.7MM *EMP* 355
Accts Brown Edwards & Company Ll
SIC 8221 College, except junior; College, except junior
Ch Bd: Claire L Arnold
**Pr:* Pamela Fox
Ofcr: Nicholas Hall
**Prin:* James Lott
Ex Dir: Steve Grande
Off Mgr: Angela Cline
Store Mgr: Brad Clatterbuck
DP Exec: William Betlej
IT Man: Elizabeth Stelling
Snr Mgr: Claire Kent

D-U-N-S 06-264-9249 IMP
MARY BIRD PERKINS CANCER CENTER (LA)
4950 Essen Ln Ste 300, Baton Rouge, LA 70809-3739
Tel (225) 215-1135 *Founded/Ownrshp* 1968
Sales 33.1MM *EMP* 117
Accts Postlethwaite & Netterville B
SIC 8093 8011 Specialty outpatient clinics; Oncologist
Pr: Todd D Stevens
Ofcr: Charity Gay
**VP:* Paul Nowacki
Snr Mgr: Wayne Newhauser

D-U-N-S 83-764-7585
■ **MARY BLACK HEALTH SYSTEMS INC**
(*Suby of* QUORUM HEALTH RESOURCES LLC) ★
1700 Skylyn Dr, Spartanburg, SC 29307-1041
Tel (864) 573-3000 *Founded/Ownrshp* 1999
Sales 84.8MM^E^ *EMP* 1,100
SIC 8062 General medical & surgical hospitals; General medical & surgical hospitals
CEO: Sean Dardeau
**CFO:* Micheal Mart
Exec: Ronnie Hyatt
Dir Rx: William Galarneau
**Ex Dir:* Glenn A Robinson
Mktg Dir: Connie Legrand
Doctor: David Weir

D-U-N-S 17-808-7615
MARY BRECKENRIDGE HEALTHCARE INC
170 Prosperous Pl, Lexington, KY 40509-1803
Tel (859) 253-3637 *Founded/Ownrshp* 1988
Sales 12.8MM^E^ *EMP* 350
SIC 8741 Management services; Management services
CEO: Bill Hall

D-U-N-S 09-812-4712
MARY CARIOLA CHILDRENS CENTER INC
1000 Elmwood Ave Ste 100, Rochester, NY 14620-3093
Tel (585) 271-2897 *Founded/Ownrshp* 1952
Sales 25.9MM *EMP* 600
Accts Bonadio & Co Llp Pittsford
SIC 8322 8361 Child related social services; Residential care for children; Child related social services; Residential care for children
Pr: Paul C Scott
Ofcr: Cindy Lewis
Dir IT: Bridget Borsa
Pr Dir: Mary Cariola

MARY CHILES HOSPITAL
See GATEWAY REGIONAL HEALTH SYSTEM INC

MARY COLLEGE
See UNIVERSITY OF MARY (INC)

MARY ETHEL CASTELO SCHOOL
See GLOUCESTER CITY SCHOOL DIST

D-U-N-S 11-825-6577
MARY FREE BED GUILD OF GRAND RAPIDS MICHIGAN
235 Wealthy St Se, Grand Rapids, MI 49503-5247
Tel (616) 242-0403 *Founded/Ownrshp* 1913
Sales 71.9MM *EMP* 622
Accts Plante & Moran Pllc Grand Ra
SIC 8069 5999 8741 6512 Specialty hospitals, except psychiatric; Medical apparatus & supplies; Orthopedic & prosthesis applications; Management services; Nonresidential building operators; Specialty hospitals, except psychiatric; Medical apparatus & supplies; Orthopedic & prosthesis applications; Management services; Nonresidential building operators
Pr: William Blessing
VP: Randall L De Neff
**VP:* Randall Deneff
Mktg Dir: Jane Briarly

D-U-N-S 07-929-2645
MARY FREE BED REHABILITATION HOSPITAL
235 Wealthy St Se, Grand Rapids, MI 49503-5247
Tel (616) 242-0300 *Founded/Ownrshp* 1913
Sales 65.0MM^E^ *EMP* 1,100
Accts Plante & Moran Pllc Grand Ra
SIC 8069 8093 Specialty hospitals, except psychiatric; Rehabilitation center, outpatient treatment; Specialty hospitals, except psychiatric; Rehabilitation center, outpatient treatment
CEO: Kent Riddle
**Ch Bd:* David Muir
**Pr:* William Blessing
COO: Dave Holsworth
CFO: Randall Deneff
**Treas:* Chad Bush
VP: Jen Lannon
VP: Patrick Logan
VP: Curt Meyer
VP: Tim Pietryga
VP: Tom Stranz
Dir Risk M: Bruce Brasser

D-U-N-S 82-526-7912
MARY GREELEY MEDICAL CENTER FOUNDATION
(*Suby of* CITY OF AMES) ★
1111 Duff Ave, Ames, IA 50010-5745
Tel (515) 239-2011 *Founded/Ownrshp* 1969
Sales 1.9MM *EMP* 1,400
Accts Rsm Mcgladrey Inc Des Moines
SIC 8062 General medical & surgical hospitals; General medical & surgical hospitals
Pr: Brian Dieter
Chf Path: Trisha Schlick
**CFO:* Michael Tretina
**VP:* Neal Loes
**VP:* Lynn Whisler
Dir Case M: Darla Handsaker
Off Mgr: Tricia Clausen
Board of Directors: Connie Dudding, Selden Spencer

MARY HITCHCOCK MEMORIAL HOSP
See MAXIFACIAL DENTAL SURGERY

D-U-N-S 06-991-0297
MARY HITCHCOCK MEMORIAL HOSPITAL
DARTMOUTH-HITCHCOCK
1 Medical Center Dr, Lebanon, NH 03756-1000
Tel (603) 650-5000 *Founded/Ownrshp* 1889
Sales 987.4MM *EMP* 8,000^E^
SIC 8062

D-U-N-S 03-294-0256
MARY HUMPHREY
C/O NEW YORK ATHLETIC CLUB
180 Central Park S Rm 812, New York, NY 10019-1562
Tel (212) 767-7065 *Founded/Ownrshp* 1972
Sales 55.9MM *EMP* 1
SIC 7338 Secretarial & typing service
Owner: Mary Humphrey
Exec: Andrew Ladd
Comm Dir: James O'Brien
Off Mgr: Oswaldo Ferreira
MIS Dir: John Neary
Dir IT: Walter Schluter
IT Man: Vincent Ventura
Netwrk Mgr: Claudia Hernandez
Sls Mgr: Laura Weisinger

D-U-N-S 96-675-9081
MARY IMMACULATE HOSPITAL AUXILIARY
150 Kingsley Ln, Norfolk, VA 23505-4602
Tel (757) 889-5000 *Founded/Ownrshp* 2011
Sales 189.6MM *EMP* 1
Accts Deloitte Tax Llp Mclean Va
SIC 5947 Gift, novelty & souvenir shop; Gift, novelty & souvenir shop
Prin: Greg Simia

D-U-N-S 06-600-2734
MARY IMMACULATE HOSPITAL INC
BON SECOURS MARY IMMACULATE HO
2 Bernardine Dr, Newport News, VA 23602-4499
Tel (757) 886-6000 *Founded/Ownrshp* 1956
Sales 186.2MM *EMP* 850^E^
SIC 8062 General medical & surgical hospitals; General medical & surgical hospitals
CEO: Richard Hanson
**CEO:* John Barrett
**Ex VP:* Cynthia Farrand
Doctor: Joan Ross
HC Dir: Cynthia Miller

D-U-N-S 02-067-2820
MARY IMOGENE BASSETT HOSPITAL
BASSETT MEDICAL CENTER
1 Atwell Rd, Cooperstown, NY 13326-1394
Tel (607) 547-3456 *Founded/Ownrshp* 1924
Sales 451.1MM *EMP* 3,200
SIC 8062 8011 5999 General medical & surgical hospitals; Offices & clinics of medical doctors; Hearing aids; General medical & surgical hospitals; Offices & clinics of medical doctors; Hearing aids
Pr: Vance M Brown
COO: Bertine McKenna
CFO: Sue Andrews
Chf Cred: Steven Heneghan
VP: Kenneth Deans
VP: Brian Tiffany
Dir Case M: Lorry Stubley
Genl Mgr: Carol Smola
Off Mgr: Suzanne Tompson
Off Mgr: Brian Wright
CIO: Cynthia Bartow
Board of Directors: Scott Barrett, Richard Beebe

D-U-N-S 05-696-5395
MARY INSTITUTE AND SAINT LOUIS COUNTRY DAY SCHOOL
101 N Warson Rd, Saint Louis, MO 63124-1399
Tel (314) 993-5100 *Founded/Ownrshp* 1859
Sales 37.7MM *EMP* 230
SIC 8211 Private combined elementary & secondary school; Private combined elementary & secondary school
Exec: Pat Huber
Prin: Melanie Dugan
Dir IT: Tom Wyman
Snr Mgr: Carrie Marks
Board of Directors: Lisa Coulter

D-U-N-S 13-955-7789 IMP/EXP
MARY KAY HOLDING CORP
16251 Dallas Pkwy, Addison, TX 75001-6820
Tel (972) 687-6300 *Founded/Ownrshp* 1985
Sales NA *EMP* 3,600
SIC 5963 3961 3172 4724 Cosmetic sales, house-to-house; Compacts, except precious metal; Cosmetic bags; Travel agencies; Cosmetic sales, house-to-house; Compacts, except precious metal; Cosmetic bags; Travel agencies
Ch Bd: Richard Rogers
**Pr:* David B Holl
**CFO:* Terry Smith
Sr VP: Kathryn Anastasio
**Sr VP:* Nathan Moore
VP: Sharon Drobeck
VP: Randall Oxford
Dir IT: Robert Bullock

D-U-N-S 04-999-4452
MARY KAY INC
(*Suby of* MARY KAY HOLDING CORP) ★
16251 Dallas Pkwy, Addison, TX 75001-6820
Tel (972) 687-6300 *Founded/Ownrshp* 1988
Sales 807.5MM^E^ *EMP* 3,500^E^
SIC 5963 Cosmetic sales, house-to-house; Cosmetic sales, house-to-house
Pr: David Holl
CFO: Sherry Polonsky
**CFO:* Terry Smith
Ex VP: Kregg Jodie
Ex VP: Russel Mack
Ex VP: Myra O'Barker
**Sr VP:* Nathan Moore
Sr VP: Wilbur Smither
VP: Myra A Barker
VP: Laura Beitler
**VP:* Patrick Cargo
VP: Shelia Galliher
VP: Israel Gonzales
VP: Terry Jacks
VP: Adrie Lee
VP: Eva Liebermann
VP: Laura McKinney
VP: Mike Scott
VP: Shaya Seward
VP: Carlos Troncoso
VP: Crayton W Webb

D-U-N-S 07-697-5077
MARY LANNING MEMORIAL HOSPITAL ASSOCIATION
715 N Saint Joseph Ave, Hastings, NE 68901-4451
Tel (402) 463-4521 *Founded/Ownrshp* 1914
Sales 128.8MM *EMP* 950^E^
SIC 8062 General medical & surgical hospitals; General medical & surgical hospitals
COO: Mark Callahan
**Pr:* Eric Barber
**Pr:* Brad Meet
Bd of Dir: Robert Anderson
Sr VP: Joann Lomax
VP: Bruce Curright
VP: Shawn Riggs
VP: Charlene Sanders
Dir Case M: Patrick Kern
Dir Lab: Chris Page
Dir Rx: Roger Gland

D-U-N-S 05-261-0235 IMP/EXP
MARY LEE PACKAGING CORP (MO)
GILSTER-MARY LEE
615 Old Saint Marys Rd, Perryville, MO 63775-1836
Tel (573) 547-1705 *Founded/Ownrshp* 1969, 1971
Sales 1.0MMM^E^ *EMP* 4,200
SIC 2043 2099 2045 3089 2098 Cereal breakfast foods; Popcorn, packaged: except already popped; Blended flour: from purchased flour; Plastic containers, except foam; Macaroni products (e.g. alphabets, rings & shells), dry; Cereal breakfast foods; Popcorn, packaged: except already popped; Blended flour: from purchased flour; Plastic containers, except foam; Macaroni products (e.g. alphabets, rings & shells), dry
Pr: Donald E Welge
**Treas:* Michael W Welge
Dir IT: Rick Hayden

MARY MANNING WALSH HOME
See MARY MANNING WALSH NURSING HOME CO INC

D-U-N-S 07-682-8821
MARY MANNING WALSH NURSING HOME CO INC
MARY MANNING WALSH HOME
1339 York Ave, New York, NY 10021-4707
Tel (646) 475-4898 *Founded/Ownrshp* 1952
Sales 52.9MM *EMP* 550
Accts O Connor Davies Munns & Dobbin
SIC 8051 Skilled nursing care facilities; Skilled nursing care facilities
**Ch Bd:* Patricia Handel
**VP:* Rev Gerald Walsh
HC Dir: Hilda Tong

D-U-N-S 01-732-7321 IMP
MARY MAXIM INC
2001 Holland Ave, Port Huron, MI 48060-7362
Tel (810) 987-2000 *Founded/Ownrshp* 1956
Sales 39.0MM^E^ *EMP* 128
SIC 5199 5949 5961 Fabrics, yarns & knit goods; Knitting goods & supplies; Needlework goods & supplies; Mail order house; Fabrics, yarns & knit goods; Knitting goods & supplies; Needlework goods & supplies; Mail order house
Pr: Rusty McPhedrain
**Pr:* Larry L Phedrain
**Treas:* Tom Jackson
**VP:* Brian Harris
MIS Mgr: Robert Gabler
Board of Directors: William R Neal

D-U-N-S 13-189-2952
MARY RUTAN HEALTH ASSOCIATION OF LOGAN COUNTY
MARY RUTAN HOSPITAL
205 E Palmer Rd, Bellefontaine, OH 43311-2281
Tel (937) 592-4015 *Founded/Ownrshp* 1974
Sales 4.1MM *EMP* 744
Accts Plante & Moran Pllc Columbus
SIC 8741 Management services; Management services
Pr: Mandy Goble
**CFO:* Ron Carmin
Ex VP: Sonda Burns
VP: Mary Ann Kelly
CIO: Robert Reynolds

MARY RUTAN HOSPITAL
See MARY RUTAN HEALTH ASSOCIATION OF LOGAN COUNTY

D-U-N-S 07-942-3851
MARY RUTAN HOSPITAL
(*Suby of* MARY RUTAN HEALTH ASSOCIATION OF LOGAN COUNTY) ★
205 E Palmer Rd, Bellefontaine, OH 43311-2298
Tel (937) 592-4015 *Founded/Ownrshp* 1984
Sales 89.1MM *EMP* 700
Accts Plante & Moran Pllc Columbus
SIC 8062 General medical & surgical hospitals; General medical & surgical hospitals
Ch Bd: Thomas Simon
**Pr:* Mandy Goble
CFO: Tammy Bowen
**VP:* Ron Carmen
VP: Marcia Davis
Dir Lab: Robert J Bailey
Dir Lab: Andy Burton
Dir Rad: Debbie Boyle
Nurse Mgr: Jim Hamilton
Dir IT: Jerome Hoover
Dir IT: Robert Reynolds

D-U-N-S 96-327-9844
MARY SAINT HOMES INC
2021 Albany Ave, West Hartford, CT 06117-2701
Tel (860) 570-8200 *Founded/Ownrshp* 2010
Sales 29.3MM *EMP* 18
Accts Deloitte Tax Llp Philadelphia
SIC 8051 Skilled nursing care facilities
Prin: Debra J Trevelin
Nrsg Dir: Aysha Kuhlor
HC Dir: Deb Jefferson
HC Dir: Ellen Nirenstein

D-U-N-S 96-484-7565
MARY SHERMAN HOSPITAL FOUNDATION INC
SULLIVAN COUNTY COMMUNITY HOSP
2200 N Section St, Sullivan, IN 47882-7523
Tel (812) 268-4311 *Founded/Ownrshp* 1985
Sales 5.8MM *EMP* 325
SIC 8062 Hospital, AMA approved residency; Hospital, AMA approved residency
CEO: Michelle Smith
**Pr:* Trudie Lee
Dir Lab: Donna Bowman
CTO: David Fuqua

D-U-N-S 18-972-8251
MARY STARKE HARPER GERIATRIC PSYCHIATRIC
200 University Blvd, Tuscaloosa, AL 35401-1250
Tel (205) 759-0900 *Founded/Ownrshp* 2005
Sales 21.3MM^E^ *EMP* 32^E^
SIC 8062 General medical & surgical hospitals; General medical & surgical hospitals

MARY WASHINGTON HEALTHCARE
See WASHINGTON HEALTHCARE PHYSICIANS MARY

D-U-N-S 06-237-4186
MARY WASHINGTON HEALTHCARE SERVICES INC
HOME CARE AMERICA
(*Suby of* WASHINGTON HEALTHCARE MARY) ★
2300 Fall Hill Ave # 234, Fredericksburg, VA 22401-3342
Tel (540) 741-2507 *Founded/Ownrshp* 1989
Sales 31.5MM^E^ *EMP* 325
SIC 8742 5912 8721 Business consultant; Drug stores; Billing & bookkeeping service; Business consultant; Drug stores; Billing & bookkeeping service
CEO: Fred M Rankin III
**Pr:* Marie Fredrick
COO: Robin Thacker
Sr VP: Eric Fletcher
VP: Tina Ervin
VP: Marie Frederick
Snr PM: Tom Theado

D-U-N-S 01-163-7402
MARY-LAWRENCE CORP
PENNINGTON SUPERMARKET
25 Route 31 S Ste X, Pennington, NJ 08534-2511
Tel (609) 737-0058 *Founded/Ownrshp* 1981
Sales 31.3MM^E^ *EMP* 240
SIC 5411 Supermarkets, independent; Supermarkets, independent
Pr: Lawrence Rothwell
**VP:* Mike Rothwell

D-U-N-S 07-784-7374
MARYFIELD INC
PENNYBURN AT MARYFIELD
109 Penny Rd, High Point, NC 27260-2500
Tel (336) 886-2444 *Founded/Ownrshp* 1947
Sales 25.2MM *EMP* 400
Accts Dixon Hughes Pllc Asheville
SIC 8051 6513 Skilled nursing care facilities; Apartment building operators; Skilled nursing care facilities; Apartment building operators
CEO: Sister Lucy Hennessy
COO: Charles Mathis
IT Man: Vonda Hollingsworth

D-U-N-S 07-840-5859
MARYGROVE COLLEGE
INSTITUTE OF MUSIC AND DANCE
8425 W Mcnichols Rd, Detroit, MI 48221-2546
Tel (313) 927-1200 *Founded/Ownrshp* 1910
Sales 30.7MM *EMP* 265
Accts Bkd Llp Fort Wayne In
SIC 8221 Colleges universities & professional schools; Colleges universities & professional schools
Pr: James Birge
**CFO:* David Nelson
Ofcr: Christopher Cieslak
VP: Vince Abatemarco
Dir IT: David Shulty
Sls&Mrk Ex: Karen Cameron
Board of Directors: John Senko

D-U-N-S 12-574-8582
MARYHAVEN CENTER OF HOPE INC
(*Suby of* CATHOLIC HEALTH SYSTEM OF LONG ISLAND INC) ★
51 Terryville Rd, Port Jeff STA, NY 11776-1359
Tel (631) 474-4120 *Founded/Ownrshp* 1934
Sales 58.2MM *EMP* 1,600
SIC 8322 7389 Social services for the handicapped; Fund raising organizations; Social services for the handicapped; Fund raising organizations
CEO: Lewis Grossman
**CFO:* Susan Barrett

D-U-N-S 07-163-9884
MARYHAVEN INC (OH)
1791 Alum Creek Dr, Columbus, OH 43207-1757
Tel (614) 449-1530 *Founded/Ownrshp* 1959
Sales 21.9MM *EMP* 275^E^
SIC 8069 Alcoholism rehabilitation hospital; Drug addiction rehabilitation hospital; Alcoholism rehabilitation hospital; Drug addiction rehabilitation hospital
CEO: Paul Coleman
VP: Sallie Gallegos
VP: Ron Kerr
VP: Tom Lianez
Exec: Joyce Clark
Exec: Marci Miller
CTO: Sofia Mohamed
Dir IT: Sofia Mohammed
Dir IT: Josh Penning
Opers Supe: James Alexander

MARYHOUSE
See AVERA ST MARYS

MARYKNOLL FATHERS & BROTHERS
See CATHOLIC FOREIGN MISSION SOCIETY OF AMERICA INC

D-U-N-S 19-623-0841
MARYL GROUP INC
MARYL PACIFIC CONSTRUCTION
55 Merchant St Ste 2000, Honolulu, HI 96813-4329
Tel (808) 545-6464 *Founded/Ownrshp* 1986
Sales 137.2MM^E^ *EMP* 180
SIC 6552 1542 1521 Subdividers & developers; Shopping center construction; Single-family housing construction
Pr: Mark Richards
**CFO:* Tiffiany Trang
**Ex VP:* Mark Kong
VP: Colleen Miyasato
**VP:* Cheryl Richards

VP: Michael Rose
VP: Lynne Rosevear
Genl Mgr: John Amado
VP Opers: Thomas Chung
VP Opers: Brad Oyama

MARYL PACIFIC CONSTRUCTION
See MARYL GROUP INC

D-U-N-S 04-811-3190
MARYL PACIFIC CONSTRUCTION INC (HI)
(*Suby of* MARYL GROUP INC) ★
55 Merchant St Ste 2000, Honolulu, HI 96813-4329
Tel (808) 545-2920 *Founded/Ownrshp* 1999
Sales 52.3MM *EMP* 112
SIC 1542 Nonresidential construction; Nonresidential construction
Pr: Mark Richards
**VP:* Cheryl Richards

MARYLAND & VIRGINIA MILK PROD
See MAOLA MILK AND ICE CREAM CO LLC

D-U-N-S 00-323-9563
MARYLAND AND VIRGINIA MILK PRODUCERS COOPERATIVE ASSOCIATION INC (VA)
MARVA MAID DAIRY DIVISION
1985 Isaac Newton Sq W # 200, Reston, VA 20190-5033
Tel (703) 742-6800 *Founded/Ownrshp* 1920
Sales 1.3MMM *EMP* 550
Accts Herliem & Company Inc Reading
SIC 5143 2026 5084 Milk; Fluid milk; Food industry machinery; Milk; Fluid milk; Food industry machinery
Pr: Dwayne Myers
**CFO:* Jorge Gonzalez
**Treas:* Jay Bryant
Treas: Robert Shore
VP: Grant Gayman
**VP:* R Steven Graybeal
**VP:* Richard Mosemann
Exec: Mike John
Admn Mgr: Eli Addae
CTO: Kathy Rice
Dir IT: Kathleen Short

D-U-N-S 16-881-2352
MARYLAND AVIATION ADMINISTRATION
BWI
(*Suby of* MARYLAND DEPARTMENT OF TRANSPORTATION) ★
Baltimore Wash Intl Arpt, Baltimore, MD 21240
Tel (410) 859-7111 *Founded/Ownrshp* 1972
Sales 50.6MM^E *EMP* 550
SIC 4111 Airport transportation; Airport transportation
Ex Dir: Paul J Wiedefeld
Bd of Dir: Richard H Pettingill
VP: Thomas L Osborne
VP: Scott L Porter
VP: John Rosaschi
Genl Mgr: Michelle Emley

D-U-N-S 87-917-6188
MARYLAND DEPARTMENT OF AGRICULTURE
MDA
(*Suby of* EXECUTIVE OFFICE OF STATE OF MARYLAND) ★
50 Harry S Truman Pkwy, Annapolis, MD 21401-8960
Tel (410) 841-5700 *Founded/Ownrshp* 1973
Sales NA *EMP* 425
SIC 9641 ;
Exec: Julie Oberg
Comm Man: Vanessa Orlando
IT Man: Charles Cawley
Snr Mgr: Carol Holko
Snr Mgr: Kenneth Ramsburg
Snr Mgr: Robert Tatman

D-U-N-S 87-982-5511
MARYLAND DEPARTMENT OF ASSESSMENTS AND TAXATION
(*Suby of* EXECUTIVE OFFICE OF STATE OF MARYLAND) ★
301 W Preston St Ste 808, Baltimore, MD 21201-2320
Tel (410) 767-1184 *Founded/Ownrshp* 1975
Sales NA *EMP* 372
SIC 9311 Taxation department, government; ;Taxation department, government;

D-U-N-S 87-820-7109
MARYLAND DEPARTMENT OF BUDGET AND MANAGEMENT
(*Suby of* EXECUTIVE OFFICE OF STATE OF MARYLAND) ★
45 Calvert St Rm 170, Annapolis, MD 21401-1994
Tel (410) 260-7059 *Founded/Ownrshp* 1776
Sales NA *EMP* 869^E
SIC 9311 Budget agency, government; ; Budget agency, government;
Prin: Neil Bergsman

D-U-N-S 87-889-4773
MARYLAND DEPARTMENT OF GENERAL SERVICES
DGS
(*Suby of* EXECUTIVE OFFICE OF STATE OF MARYLAND) ★
301 W Preston St Ste 1401, Baltimore, MD 21201-2388
Tel (410) 767-4960 *Founded/Ownrshp* 1776
Sales NA *EMP* 600
SIC 9199 General government administration; ; General government administration;
Ofcr: Ellery Handy

D-U-N-S 87-889-4849 IMP
MARYLAND DEPARTMENT OF HEALTH & MENTAL HYGIENE
(*Suby of* EXECUTIVE OFFICE OF STATE OF MARYLAND) ★
201 W Preston St Fl 5, Baltimore, MD 21201-2301
Tel (410) 767-6500 *Founded/Ownrshp* 1776
Sales NA *EMP* 7,500
SIC 9431 Administration of public health programs; ; Administration of public health programs;
Pr: John Commers
Ofcr: Dionne Grier
Pharmcst: Nevine Abdallah-Helmi
Snr Mgr: Julianne Stoll
Snr Mgr: Robert Sutton

D-U-N-S 09-057-2780
MARYLAND DEPARTMENT OF HUMAN RESOURCES
(*Suby of* EXECUTIVE OFFICE OF STATE OF MARYLAND) ★
311 W Saratoga St, Baltimore, MD 21201-3500
Tel (410) 767-7109 *Founded/Ownrshp* 1999
Sales NA *EMP* 7,020
SIC 9441 Administration of social & human resources; ; Administration of social & human resources;
Ofcr: Dawn Dent
Ofcr: Becky Gray
Ofcr: Aaron Vonmoore
Exec: Andy Devilbiss
Ex Dir: Carnitra White
Mng Dir: Tanya Williams
Prgrm Mgr: Richard Berger
Dist Mgr: Daniel Allotey
Dist Mgr: Ann Mitchell
Off Mgr: Lynn Bowens
Off Mgr: Christine Seipp

D-U-N-S 87-993-1251
MARYLAND DEPARTMENT OF JUVENILE SERVICES
(*Suby of* EXECUTIVE OFFICE OF STATE OF MARYLAND) ★
120 W Fayette St, Baltimore, MD 21201-3741
Tel (410) 230-3333 *Founded/Ownrshp* 1984
Sales NA *EMP* 1,000
SIC 9223 Prison, government; ; Prison, government;
Bd of Dir: Christina McGriff
Ofcr: Grace Sutton
VP: Mathew Fonseca
VP: Linda Kellum
Exec: Eric Solomon
Prgrm Mgr: Sonya White-Norman
CIO: Elizabeth Wright
Telecom Mg: Nancy Seidman
IT Man: Michael Dibattista

D-U-N-S 87-820-7505
MARYLAND DEPARTMENT OF NATURAL RESOURCES
(*Suby of* EXECUTIVE OFFICE OF STATE OF MARYLAND) ★
580 Taylor Ave Bldg E3, Annapolis, MD 21401-2363
Tel (410) 260-8100 *Founded/Ownrshp* 1969
Sales NA *EMP* 1,460
SIC 9512 Land, mineral & wildlife conservation; ; Land, mineral & wildlife conservation;

D-U-N-S 87-813-7462
MARYLAND DEPARTMENT OF TRANSPORTATION
(*Suby of* EXECUTIVE OFFICE OF STATE OF MARYLAND) ★
7201 Corporate Center Dr, Hanover, MD 21076-1415
Tel (410) 865-1037 *Founded/Ownrshp* 1971
Sales 3.8MMM *EMP* 1,000^E
Accts Sb & Company Llc Hunt Valley
SIC 8748 4131 Business consulting; Intercity & rural bus transportation; Business consulting; Intercity & rural bus transportation
Ofcr: Theresa Moulden
Ofcr: Wilma Young-Hill
**Prin:* Robert Ehrlich
**Prin:* Donald A Halligan
Brnch Mgr: Wanda Hostetter
Brnch Mgr: Teledia Jenkins
Brnch Mgr: Debra Seward
Brnch Mgr: Melissa Shifflett
Brnch Mgr: Rebecca Snyder
VP Mktg: Lisa Dickerson
VP Mktg: Trent M Kittleman

D-U-N-S 87-835-8332
MARYLAND DEPT HUMAN RESOURCES
(*Suby of* EXECUTIVE OFFICE OF STATE OF MARYLAND) ★
311 W Saratoga St, Baltimore, MD 21201-3500
Tel (410) 767-7109 *Founded/Ownrshp* 1995
Sales NA *EMP* 800
SIC 9441 Administration of social & human resources; ; Administration of social & human resources;
VP: Alvin C Collins
DP Exec: Denise Christ
QA Dir: Jewel Wilson
Opers Mgr: Valerie Carpenter

D-U-N-S 87-901-6178
MARYLAND DEPT OF PUBLIC SAFETY & CORRECTIONAL SERVICES
DPSCS
(*Suby of* EXECUTIVE OFFICE OF STATE OF MARYLAND) ★
300 E Joppa Rd Ste 1000, Towson, MD 21286-3068
Tel (410) 339-5000 *Founded/Ownrshp* 1956
Sales NA *EMP* 11,626
SIC 9223 Prison, government; ; Prison, government;
VP: Donna Wiltshire
Ex Dir: Rick Binetti
CIO: Ron Brothers
IT Man: Farid Keshavarz
Plnt Mgr: Jim Cluster
Mktg Dir: Lida Poole
Snr Mgr: Kevin Combs

D-U-N-S 95-812-8563
MARYLAND DRIVE-THRU LLC
CHECKERS DRIVE-IN RESTAURANT
15942 Shady Grove Rd, Gaithersburg, MD 20877-1315
Tel (301) 921-8777 *Founded/Ownrshp* 1996
Sales 9.5MM^E *EMP* 350^E
SIC 5812 Drive-in restaurant; Drive-in restaurant
Pr: Jay Smith
**Prin:* Robert Begelman
**Prin:* Adam Schwartz
**Prin:* David Terzian

D-U-N-S 11-803-0845
MARYLAND ECONOMIC DEVELOPMENT CORP
HYATT REGENCY CHESAPEAKE BAY
100 Heron Blvd, Cambridge, MD 21613-3420
Tel (410) 901-1234 *Founded/Ownrshp* 2002
Sales 21.3MM^E *EMP* 400
SIC 7011 Hotels & motels; Hotels & motels
CEO: Robert Brennan
Genl Mgr: Skip Coleman
Dir IT: Victor Kapusta

D-U-N-S 15-120-1696
MARYLAND ECONOMIC DEVELOPMENT CORP
MEDCO
300 E Lombard St Ste 1000, Baltimore, MD 21202-3228
Tel (410) 727-8049 *Founded/Ownrshp* 1984
Sales 129.0MM *EMP* 80
Accts Sc&H Tax & Advisory Services L
SIC 8742 Construction project management consultant; Construction project management consultant
Pr: Martin G Knott Jr
**Ch Bd:* Leonard R Sachs
CFO: Henry A Berliner
**Ex Dir:* Robert Brennan

MARYLAND EDUCATIONAL OPPORTUNI
See DELTA SIGMA THETA SORORITY INC

D-U-N-S 00-585-9590
MARYLAND ELECTRIC CO (MI)
28412 Rosebriar St, Saint Clair Shores, MI 48081-1544
Tel (586) 792-3110 *Founded/Ownrshp* 1925
Sales 23.0MM *EMP* 100^E
Accts Plante & Moran Pllc Clinton
SIC 1731 General electrical contractor; General electrical contractor
Pr: Ellen J Dancey
**Sec:* Robert Weir
**VP:* David Dancey
Board of Directors: Stephen Wellein

D-U-N-S 61-926-8134
MARYLAND EMERGENCY MEDICINE NTWRK INC
110 S Paca St Ste 200, Baltimore, MD 21201-1668
Tel (410) 328-8025 *Founded/Ownrshp* 2003
Sales 53.8MM *EMP* 400
SIC 8742 Hospital & health services consultant
Pr: Brian Browne
**CFO:* Daniel Griffith

D-U-N-S 07-740-6726
MARYLAND ENVIRONMENTAL SERVICE
(*Suby of* EXECUTIVE OFFICE OF STATE OF MARYLAND) ★
259 Najoles Rd, Millersville, MD 21108-2515
Tel (410) 729-8200 *Founded/Ownrshp* 1970
Sales NA *EMP* 700
SIC 9511 Waste management program administration, government; ;Waste management program administration, government;
COO: Susan McCauley
**CFO:* Henry Cook
CFO: Janet Irvin
Ofcr: Erin Murphy
Exec: Ruth Zellers
Comm Dir: Christina Garrigan
Ex Dir: Steven Tomczewski
DP Dir: Tom McCabe
IT Man: Russell Brown
Opers Mgr: Randy Bolt
Opers Mgr: Jeffery Fried

D-U-N-S 96-960-9366
MARYLAND FAMILY CARE INC
301 Saint Paul St, Baltimore, MD 21202-2102
Tel (410) 332-9313 *Founded/Ownrshp* 2011
Sales 31.0MM *EMP* 2
Accts Cohen Rutherford Knight Pc Be
SIC 8351 Child day care services; Child day care services
Prin: Mildred Watts

D-U-N-S 09-656-4919
MARYLAND FOOD BANK INC (MD)
2200 Halethorpe Farms Rd, Baltimore, MD 21227-4551
Tel (410) 737-8282 *Founded/Ownrshp* 1978
Sales 74.2MM *EMP* 75
Accts Gross Mendelsohn & Associates
SIC 8699 Food co-operative; Food co-operative
CEO: Deborah Flateman
CFO: Barbara Jeffries
Sr Cor Off: Paula Minsk
**Ex VP:* Mark Jorritsma
Ex VP: Beth Martino

D-U-N-S 19-064-7404
MARYLAND FOODS INC
CHILI'S
1960 Gallows Rd Ste 200, Vienna, VA 22182-3827
Tel (703) 827-0320 *Founded/Ownrshp* 1988
Sales 35.5MM^E *EMP* 2,500
Accts Watkins Meegan Drury & Compa
SIC 5812 5813 Restaurant, family: chain; American restaurant; Bar (drinking places); Restaurant, family: chain; American restaurant; Bar (drinking places)
Pr: Linda Hardee
**Sec:* Louise Sawyer
**VP:* Edmund Spivack

MARYLAND GENERAL HLTH SYSTEMS
See UNIVERSITY OF MARYLAND MIDTOWN HEALTH INC

D-U-N-S 06-939-8303
MARYLAND GENERAL HOSPITAL INC
(*Suby of* MARYLAND GENERAL HLTH SYSTEMS) ★
827 Linden Ave, Baltimore, MD 21201-4606
Tel (410) 225-8000 *Founded/Ownrshp* 1911
Sales 1.8MM *EMP* 1,100
SIC 8062 General medical & surgical hospitals; General medical & surgical hospitals
Pr: Brian Bailey
**Ch Bd:* Marily Carp
**VP:* Donald E Ray

D-U-N-S 00-466-8831
MARYLAND HOSPITALITY INC (VA)
MHI HOTELS
6411 Ivy Ln Ste 510, Greenbelt, MD 20770-1405
Tel (301) 474-3307 *Founded/Ownrshp* 1957
Sales 27.0MM^E *EMP* 1,500
SIC 7011 8741 8742 Hotels; Management services; Management consulting services; Hotels; Management services; Management consulting services
Pr: Kim Sims
CFO: William Zaiser
**VP:* Christopher Sims
**VP:* Steven Smith
IT Man: Jametta Wagner

D-U-N-S 02-248-0693
MARYLAND HOTEL SUPPLY CO INC
MARYLAND QUALITY MEATS
701 W Hamburg St, Baltimore, MD 21230-2597
Tel (410) 539-7055 *Founded/Ownrshp* 1949
Sales 20.5MM^E *EMP* 90
SIC 5142 5144 5147 2013 2011 5812 Vegetables, frozen; Frozen fish, meat & poultry; Poultry & poultry products; Meats, fresh; Sausages & other prepared meats; Meat packing plants; Seafood shack; Vegetables, frozen; Frozen fish, meat & poultry; Poultry & poultry products; Meats, fresh; Sausages & other prepared meats; Meat packing plants; Seafood shack
VP: Terry McDonnell
Pr: Russell D Niller III
VP Sls: Dennis R Steele

D-U-N-S 09-940-3511
MARYLAND INDUSTRIAL TRUCKS INC
1330 W Nursery Rd, Linthicum Heights, MD 21090-1100
Tel (410) 636-1255 *Founded/Ownrshp* 1979
Sales 25.0MM^E *EMP* 45
SIC 5084 Materials handling machinery
Pr: George Rose

D-U-N-S 06-938-8296
MARYLAND INSTITUTE
ART STORE CENTER
1300 W Mount Royal Ave, Baltimore, MD 21217-4134
Tel (410) 383-2063 *Founded/Ownrshp* 1826
Sales 111.2MM *EMP* 400
Accts Kpmg Llp Baltimore Md
SIC 8221 Colleges universities & professional schools; Colleges universities & professional schools
Pr: Fred Lazarus IV
CFO: Douglas Mann
VP: Lucie Hughes
Adm Dir: Diana Caldwell
Ex Dir: Kathy Cowan
Prgrm Mgr: Devon Burgoyne
Plnt Mgr: Robert Alholm
Sls Mgr: Firmin Debrabander

MARYLAND JOCKEY CLUB
See PIMLICO RACING ASSOCIATION INC

D-U-N-S 05-990-3947
MARYLAND LLC IHG MANAGEMENT
CROWN PLAZA LOS ANGELES
5985 W Century Blvd, Los Angeles, CA 90045-5477
Tel (310) 642-7500 *Founded/Ownrshp* 2004
Sales 30.0MM *EMP* 250
SIC 7011 Hotels & motels

D-U-N-S 07-740-4507
MARYLAND MANAGEMENT CO
2613 Cabover Dr Ste 100, Hanover, MD 21076-1597
Tel (410) 553-0078 *Founded/Ownrshp* 1967
Sales 16.5MM^E *EMP* 350
SIC 6531 Real estate managers; Real estate managers
CEO: Philip E Ratcliffe
**Pr:* James A Clauson
**VP:* Mary K Ashburn
**VP:* Eric R Huston
VP: Mark Knott
**VP:* William F Krone
Manager: Dawn Depasquale

D-U-N-S 04-399-1041 IMP
MARYLAND MEGGITT INC
MEGGITT SENSING SYSTEMS
(*Suby of* MEGGITT PLC)
20511 Seneca Meadows Pkwy, Germantown, MD 20876-7003
Tel (301) 556-2990 *Founded/Ownrshp* 1975
Sales 21.3MM^E *EMP* 85
SIC 3829 Measuring & controlling devices; Vibration meters, analyzers & calibrators; Measuring & controlling devices; Vibration meters, analyzers & calibrators
Pr: Derek Carbin
Ofcr: John Churchill
Ql Cn Mgr: Martin Luplow

D-U-N-S 60-449-7834 IMP
MARYLAND PAPER CO LIMITED PARTNERSHIP
16144 Elliott Pkwy, Williamsport, MD 21795-4080
Tel (301) 223-6550 *Founded/Ownrshp* 1989
Sales 49.1MM^E *EMP* 198
SIC 2621 Paper mills; Paper mills
Pt: Mathew D Chakola
Opers Mgr: David Chakola
Opers Mgr: George Delaplaine
Plnt Mgr: Leo Martin

D-U-N-S 08-261-7820 IMP/EXP
MARYLAND PLASTICS INC
(*Suby of* BIO MEDIC CORP) ★
251 E Central Ave, Federalsburg, MD 21632-1313
Tel (410) 754-5566 *Founded/Ownrshp* 1976
Sales 24.0MM *EMP* 75
SIC 3089 Kitchenware, plastic; Injection molding of plastics; Injection molded finished plastic products; Laboratory sundries: cases, covers, funnels, cups, etc.; Cutlery; Kitchenware, plastic; Injection molding of plastics; Injection molded finished plastic products
Pr: John Soper

VP: George Nicoletos
MIS Mgr: Pat Townsend
Opers Mgr: Gail Townsend
Ql Cn Mgr: Paul Bestys
Natl Sales: Dick White

D-U-N-S 36-430-0004
MARYLAND PRIMARY CARE PHYSICIANS LLC
1111 Bnfield Blvd Ste 200, Millersville, MD 21108
Tel (410) 729-5100 *Founded/Ownrshp* 1996
Sales 29.4MM[E] *EMP* 300
SIC 8011 General & family practice, physician/surgeon; General & family practice, physician/surgeon
CEO: Donald Buntz
Pr: Michael Riebman
CFO: Lisa Weber
Exec: Carol Fletcher
CIO: Thomas J Forsyth
Dir IT: Louise Cooke
Opers Mgr: Pat Ledda
Mktg Dir: Fred Rost
Doctor: Angela Calle
Doctor: Jonathan Forman
Doctor: Jamie Harms

MARYLAND QUALITY MEATS
See MARYLAND HOTEL SUPPLY CO INC

D-U-N-S 02-146-7675
MARYLAND RURAL DEVELOPMENT CORP
428 Fourth St Ste 8, Annapolis, MD 21403-2560
Tel (410) 990-0052 *Founded/Ownrshp* 1979
Sales 5.1MM *EMP* 300
Accts Clark & Anderson Pa Glen Bur
SIC 8748 Urban planning & consulting services; Urban planning & consulting services
Ex Dir: R Kevin Brooks

D-U-N-S 07-741-2070
MARYLAND SCHOOL FOR BLIND
MSB
3501 Taylor Ave, Baltimore, MD 21236-4406
Tel (410) 444-5000 *Founded/Ownrshp* 1853
Sales 46.5MM *EMP* 360
Accts Sc&H Tax & Advisory Services L
SIC 8211 School for physically handicapped; School for physically handicapped
Pr: Michael J Bina
**Ch Bd:* Edward J Veilleux
**CFO:* Robin Churchill
VP: Phyllis Simmons
Doctor: Lorraine Rocissano
Nrsg Dir: Lucille Beveridge

D-U-N-S 00-695-0976 IMP
MARYLAND SOUTHERN ELECTRIC COOPERATIVE INC (MD)
SMECO
15035 Burnt Store Rd, Hughesville, MD 20637-2699
Tel (301) 274-3111 *Founded/Ownrshp* 1937
Sales 490.5M *EMP* 375
SIC 4911 Transmission, electric power; Distribution, electric power; Transmission, electric power; Distribution, electric power
Pr: A Joseph Slater
**COO:* Kenneth M Capps
**CFO:* Sonja M Cox
CFO: Thomas E Kandel
**Ch:* Joseph V Stone
**Treas:* Kenneth L Dyson
**Sec:* Fern Brown
Sr VP: Sonja Cox
Sr VP: Mark Macdougall
**Sr VP:* Joseph Trentacosta
VP: Ken Capps
VP: Andrew Yeskie
Comm Dir: Terry Ressler
Board of Directors: Daniel W Dyer, Richard A Winkler

D-U-N-S 08-105-5154
MARYLAND SOUTHERN HOSPITAL INC
SOUTHERN MARYLAND HOSPITAL CTR
44 Canal Center Plz # 325, Alexandria, VA 22314-1548
Tel (301) 868-8000 *Founded/Ownrshp* 1971
Sales 168.4MM[E] *EMP* 1,300
SIC 8062 8011 General medical & surgical hospitals; Offices & clinics of medical doctors; General medical & surgical hospitals; Offices & clinics of medical doctors
CEO: Michael J Chiaramonte
**Pr:* Francis P Chiaramonte
COO: Alan Vahabvadeh
**VP:* Dorothy Chiaramonte
Dir Rx: Jack M Namara
Obsttrcn: Salem I Al-Naber
Obsttrcn: Raj B Samtani
Doctor: Maheteme Bayeh
Doctor: David J Haidak MD
Doctor: Jaque Zefrin
Pharmcst: Caterina Barbaro

D-U-N-S 12-134-5425
MARYLAND SOUTHERN OIL INC
S M O
(*Suby of* WILLS GROUP INC) ★
109 N Maple Ave, La Plata, MD 20646-3701
Tel (301) 932-3600 *Founded/Ownrshp* 1986
Sales 27.6MM[E] *EMP* 146
Accts Mcgladrey & Pullen Llp Baltim
SIC 1711 5983 Plumbing, heating, air-conditioning contractors; Fuel oil dealers; Plumbing, heating, air-conditioning contractors; Fuel oil dealers
CEO: J Blacklock Wills Jr
IT Man: Carl Fuller
Sls Mgr: Albert Dellapenna

D-U-N-S 19-752-7146
MARYLAND SOUTHERN VOCATIONAL INDUSTRIES
EPIC SMVI
8000 Parston Dr, Forestville, MD 20747-4428
Tel (301) 516-7300 *Founded/Ownrshp* 1985
Sales 8.1MM *EMP* 300
Accts Murphy & Murphy Cpa Llc La Pl
SIC 8331 Job training & vocational rehabilitation services; Job training & vocational rehabilitation services

Ex Dir: Kathryn St Clair
QA Dir: Lena Ford

D-U-N-S 87-804-5038
MARYLAND STATE DEPARTMENT OF EDUCATION
(*Suby of* EXECUTIVE OFFICE OF STATE OF MARYLAND) ★
200 W Baltimore St, Baltimore, MD 21201-2549
Tel (410) 767-0462 *Founded/Ownrshp* 1991
Sales NA *EMP* 1,478
SIC 9411 Administration of educational programs; ; Administration of educational programs;
Adm Dir: Vincent Tyler
Ex Dir: Ned F Sparks
Off Mgr: Jasmine Brown
MIS Dir: Peter Cevenini
Pr Dir: Kimberlee Schultz
Snr PM: Leonard Smith

MARYLAND STEEL SPARROWS POINT
See E2 ACQUISITION CORP

D-U-N-S 06-488-8639
MARYLAND THERMOFORM CORP (MD)
2717 Wilmarco Ave, Baltimore, MD 21223-3339
Tel (410) 947-5063 *Founded/Ownrshp* 1973, 1994
Sales 29.9MM[E] *EMP* 72
SIC 3089 Thermoformed finished plastic products
Pr: James M Hall
**CFO:* Scott W Macdonald
VP: Dennis Chyba
Genl Mgr: Terry Robinson
Plnt Mgr: Scott Donald

D-U-N-S 01-664-1664
■ **MARYLAND TIERCO INC**
SIX FLAGS AMERICA
(*Suby of* SIX FLAGS ENTERTAINMENT CORP) ★
13710 Central Ave, Mitchellville, MD 20721
Tel (301) 249-1500 *Founded/Ownrshp* 1992
Sales 11.8MM[E] *EMP* 650
SIC 7996 Theme park, amusement; Theme park, amusement
Ch Bd: Kieran E Burke
Treas: Russeell Kutenan

D-U-N-S 96-376-4019
MARYLAND TRASPORTATION AUTHORITY
2400 Ste 115, Baltimore, MD 21224
Tel (410) 537-5710 *Founded/Ownrshp* 2010
Sales 22.5MM[E] *EMP* 1,000
SIC 4785 Toll operations; Toll operations
Prin: Allen Garman

D-U-N-S 06-940-4150
MARYLAND TREATMENT CENTERS INC
MOUNTAIN MANOR BALTIMORE
3800 Frederick Ave, Baltimore, MD 21229-3618
Tel (410) 233-1400 *Founded/Ownrshp* 1985
Sales 18.4MM[E] *EMP* 300
SIC 8052 8322 8361 8093 Intermediate care facilities; Substance abuse counseling; Residential care; Specialty outpatient clinics; Intermediate care facilities; Substance abuse counseling; Residential care; Specialty outpatient clinics
Pr: Marc Fishman
CFO: Sue Leidlich
**CFO:* Susan Liedlich
**Ex VP:* Barbara Groves
**Ex VP:* William Roby

D-U-N-S 11-350-4869
MARYLAND TRUCK TIRE SERVICES INC
6601 Pulaski Hwy, Baltimore, MD 21237-1216
Tel (410) 483-1600 *Founded/Ownrshp* 2002
Sales 27.5MM[E] *EMP* 50
SIC 5012 5014 Commercial vehicles; Tires & tubes
Pr: Robert M Ignozzi
**Treas:* Ron Rhodes

D-U-N-S 04-549-4457 IMP/EXP
MARYLAND-NATIONAL CAPITAL PARK AND PLANNING COMMISSION
6611 Kenilworth Ave # 103, Riverdale, MD 20737-1332
Tel (301) 454-1540 *Founded/Ownrshp* 1927
Sales 178.5MM[E] *EMP* 5,000
SIC 7999 Recreation services; Recreation services
Ex Dir: Patricia C Barney
**Sec:* Joseph C Zimmerman
Snr Mgr: Renee Kenney

D-U-N-S 11-207-4948
MARYLANE HOSPITAL
BAY STATE MEDICAL CENTER
759 Chestnut St, Springfield, MA 01199-1001
Tel (413) 794-5436 *Founded/Ownrshp* 2002
Sales 25.4MM *EMP* 10[E]
SIC 8082 Home health care services; Home health care services
Prin: Joanne Ohare

D-U-N-S 03-080-0890
MARYLHURST UNIVERSITY
17600 Pacific Hwy 43, Marylhurst, OR 97036-8002
Tel (503) 636-8141 *Founded/Ownrshp* 1976
Sales 20.0MM *EMP* 115
SIC 8221 College, except junior; College, except junior
Pr: Nancy A Wilgenbusch
VP: David Dickson
**VP:* Michael Lammers
VP: Lynn Mawe
VP: David Nelson
**VP:* David Plopkin
VP: Nicola Sysyn
Prgrm Mgr: Susan Marcus
CTO: Deb Odell
IT Man: Michael Phou
Mktg Dir: Simona Boucek

D-U-N-S 07-529-3118
MARYMOUNT CALIFORNIA UNIVERSITY
MARYMOUNT COLLEGE
30800 Palos Verdes Dr E, Rancho Palos Verdes, CA 90275-6273
Tel (310) 377-5501 *Founded/Ownrshp* 1948
Sales 35.3MM *EMP* 250[E]

Accts Singerlewak Llp Los Angeles
SIC 8222 Junior college; Junior college
Pr: Michael S Brophy
VP: Jim Reeves
Sys Mgr: Pat Kelley
Doctor: Sharon Valente

MARYMOUNT COLLEGE
See MARYMOUNT CALIFORNIA UNIVERSITY

D-U-N-S 07-675-8887 IMP
MARYMOUNT HOSPITAL INC
(*Suby of* CLEVELAND CLINIC FOUNDATION) ★
9500 Euclid Ave, Cleveland, OH 44195-0001
Tel (216) 581-0500 *Founded/Ownrshp* 2000
Sales NA *EMP* 500
SIC 8062 8063 8051 8082 General medical & surgical hospitals; Psychiatric hospitals; Skilled nursing care facilities; Home health care services; General medical & surgical hospitals; Psychiatric hospitals; Skilled nursing care facilities; Home health care services
CEO: David Kilarski
Off Mgr: Bi Welch

D-U-N-S 07-524-4947
MARYMOUNT MANHATTAN COLLEGE
221 E 71st St, New York, NY 10021-4532
Tel (212) 517-0400 *Founded/Ownrshp* 1960
Sales 59.3MM *EMP* 630
Accts Kpmg Llp New York Ny
SIC 8221 College, except junior; College, except junior
Pr: Judson R Shaver
**Ch Bd:* James Buckman
Sr VP: Misty Beasley
**VP:* Paul Ciraulo
**VP:* Carol L Jackson
**VP:* David Podell
VP: Jim Rogers
**VP:* Marilyn Wilkie
Mng Dir: Theresa Lang
CIO: Dale Hochstein
CTO: Sabatino Verlezza

MARYMOUNT MANOR
See MID AMERICA HEALTH CARE LIMITED PARTNERSHIP

D-U-N-S 05-033-5496
MARYMOUNT SCHOOL OF NEW YORK (INC)
1026 5th Ave, New York, NY 10028-0106
Tel (212) 744-4486 *Founded/Ownrshp* 1969
Sales 20.5MM[E] *EMP* 180
SIC 8211 Kindergarten; Elementary school; Secondary school
Ex Dir: Rita Pietropinto
IT Man: Negash Abdurahman

D-U-N-S 04-055-4214
MARYMOUNT UNIVERSITY
2807 N Glebe Rd, Arlington, VA 22207-4299
Tel (703) 284-1500 *Founded/Ownrshp* 1950
Sales 100.1MM *EMP* 625
Accts Brown Edwards & Company Llp R
SIC 8221 University; University
Pr: James E Bundschuh
**Pr:* Matthew D Shank
COO: Ronald Hester
CFO: George Lasnier
Treas: Al Diaz
Ofcr: P Murphy
Ex VP: Upendra Malani
VP: Joseph Foster
VP: Sherri Hughes
**VP:* Ralph Kidder
VP: Emily Mahony
VP: Linda McMahon
VP: Dick Miller
VP: Michelle Murphy
Exec: Jon Watson
Dir Risk M: Margaret Axelrod
Assoc Dir: Johnnie Johnson
Assoc Dir: Kristin McMahon

D-U-N-S 19-463-6759
MARYS CENTER FOR MATERNAL AND CHILD CARE INC
2333 Ontario Rd Nw, Washington, DC 20009-2627
Tel (202) 420-7093 *Founded/Ownrshp* 1988
Sales 34.5MM *EMP* 190[E]
SIC 8099 8011 8093 Childbirth preparation clinic; Pediatrician; Specialty outpatient clinics; Childbirth preparation clinic; Pediatrician; Specialty outpatient clinics
Pr: Maria S Gomez
**COO:* David Tatro
**CFO:* Josephine Morris-Young
VP: Rebecca Diamond
**VP:* Joan Yengo
Chf Nrs Of: Dara Koppelman
Chf Nrs Of: Gina Pistulka
Dir IT: Ramesh Herath
Sys Admin: M D Huda
IT Man: Lynne Zaris
Nutrtnst: Paige Zaitlin

D-U-N-S 07-840-2051
MARYS HARVEST FRESH FOODS INC
2705 Ne Argyle St, Portland, OR 97211-1952
Tel (503) 281-8400 *Founded/Ownrshp* 2012
Sales 30.1MM[E] *EMP* 99
SIC 5148 Fresh fruits & vegetables; Fresh fruits & vegetables
Pr: Charisse Spada
**Treas:* Ernest Spada Jr

D-U-N-S 06-876-3473 IMP/EXP
MARYS RIVER LUMBER CO
4515 Ne Elliott Cir, Corvallis, OR 97330-9449
Tel (541) 752-0122 *Founded/Ownrshp* 1974
Sales 50.9MM[E] *EMP* 230
SIC 2421 Siding (dressed lumber); Lumber: rough, sawed or planed; Siding (dressed lumber); Lumber: rough, sawed or planed
Pr: Brad Kirkbride
Sales Exec: Don Dye

D-U-N-S 00-270-1753
MARYS WOODS AT MARYLHURST CONDOMINIUMS OWNERS ASSOCIATION (OR)
MARY'S WOODS RETIREMENT CENTER
17400 Holy Names Dr # 70, Lake Oswego, OR 97034-5187
Tel (503) 635-7381 *Founded/Ownrshp* 1997
Sales 21.5MM *EMP* 175
SIC 8361 Residential care; Residential care
Pr: David Galt
Exec: Ricardo Ysasaga
Mktg Dir: Cheri Mussotto
HC Dir: Josann Stedmann

MARY'S WOODS RETIREMENT CENTER
See MARYS WOODS AT MARYLHURST CONDOMINIUMS OWNERS ASSOCIATION

MARYSVILLE AUTO PLANT
See HONDA OF AMERICA MFG INC

MARYSVILLE BOARD OF EDUCATION
See MARYSVILLE EXEMPTED VILLAGE SCHOOL DISTRICT

D-U-N-S 01-945-0295
MARYSVILLE EXEMPTED VILLAGE SCHOOL DISTRICT
MARYSVILLE BOARD OF EDUCATION
1000 Edgewood Dr, Marysville, OH 43040-2105
Tel (937) 644-8105 *Founded/Ownrshp* 1800
Sales 34.9MM[E] *EMP* 600
Accts Wilson Shannon & Snow Inc Ne
SIC 8211 Public elementary & secondary schools; Public elementary & secondary schools
MIS Dir: Christopher Deis

D-U-N-S 10-000-7186
MARYSVILLE JOINT UNIFIED SCHOOL DISTRICT
1919 B St, Marysville, CA 95901-3731
Tel (530) 741-6000 *Founded/Ownrshp* 1966
Sales 82.9MM[E] *EMP* 1,553
SIC 8211 Public elementary & secondary schools; Public elementary & secondary schools
Ofcr: Jami Marros
Ex Dir: Lennie Tate

D-U-N-S 18-173-1766
MARYSVILLE OHIO SURGICAL CENTER LLC
122 Professional Pkwy, Marysville, OH 43040-8053
Tel (937) 642-6622 *Founded/Ownrshp* 2002
Sales 34.7MM[E] *EMP* 707[E]
SIC 8062 General medical & surgical hospitals

D-U-N-S 08-090-0533
MARYSVILLE SCHOOL DISTRICT
4220 80th St Ne, Marysville, WA 98270-3423
Tel (360) 653-7058 *Founded/Ownrshp* 2004
Sales 35.1MM[E] *EMP* 786
SIC 8211 Public elementary & secondary schools; Public elementary & secondary schools
**Pr:* Chris Nation
Ofcr: Doyle Phillip
VP: Theresa Hart
VP: Mike Sweet
Dir IT: Ken Ainsworth
Netwrk Mgr: Andrew Struiksma
Sls&Mrk Ex: Peggy King
Schl Brd P: Tom Albright

MARYVALE HOSPITAL
See MARYVALE SAMARITAN MEDICAL CENTER

D-U-N-S 04-320-8391
MARYVALE SAMARITAN MEDICAL CENTER
MARYVALE HOSPITAL
5102 W Campbell Ave, Phoenix, AZ 85031-1703
Tel (623) 848-5000 *Founded/Ownrshp* 1960
Sales 51.4MM *EMP* 48[E]
SIC 8062 8011 General medical & surgical hospitals; Offices & clinics of medical doctors; General medical & surgical hospitals; Offices & clinics of medical doctors
Prin: Debra Heinz
Chf Mktg O: Gina Conflitti
Dir Rad: Michael Miller
Telecom Ex: Deanna Wise
Dir QC: Diane Goodwyn
Sfty Dirs: Darin Young

MARYVALE SCHOOL SYSTEM
See CHEEKTOWAGA-MARYVALE UNION FREE SCHOOL DISTRICT

D-U-N-S 80-949-1558
MARYVIEW HOSPITAL
MARYVIEW MEDICAL CENTER
3636 High St, Portsmouth, VA 23707-3270
Tel (757) 398-2200 *Founded/Ownrshp* 1984
Sales 96.2MM[E] *EMP* 1,397
SIC 8062 General medical & surgical hospitals; General medical & surgical hospitals
Ch: Dick Hansen
**Ch:* Dominick Calgi
**Ch:* Bray J Robert
**Sec:* Michael Kerner
Dir Risk M: Linda Rodriguez
Off Mgr: Sharon M Teller

MARYVIEW MEDICAL CENTER
See MARYVIEW HOSPITAL

D-U-N-S 18-675-3281
MARYVILLE CITY SCHOOLS
833 Lawrence Ave, Maryville, TN 37803-4857
Tel (865) 982-7121 *Founded/Ownrshp* 2010
Sales 28.5MM[E] *EMP* 594[E]
SIC 8211 Public elementary & secondary schools
Ch Bd: Christi Sayles
Ch Bd: Denny Garner
MIS Dir: Sharon Angiam
Pr Dir: Sharon Anglim
HC Dir: Heather Ledbetter

D-U-N-S 07-490-8815
MARYVILLE COLLEGE
502 E Lmar Alexander Pkwy, Maryville, TN 37804-5919
Tel (865) 981-8000 Founded/Ownrshp 1819
Sales 52.3MM EMP 261
SIC 8221 8661 Colleges & universities; Religious organizations; Colleges & universities; Religious organizations
Pr: William T Bogart
*Ch Bd: Richard Ragsdale
*Pr: Gerald Gibson
Ofcr: Gail Anderson
Ofcr: Mike Boudreau
VP: Dolphus Henry
VP: Vandy Kemp
VP: Dana Smith
Dir IT: John Berry
Dir IT: Mark Fugate
Web Dev: Russ Porter

D-U-N-S 86-871-1532
MARYVILLE DATA SYSTEMS INC
MARYVILLE TECHNOLOGIES
540 Maryville Centre Dr # 300, Saint Louis, MO 63141-5826
Tel (636) 519-4100 Founded/Ownrshp 1994
Sales 31.0MM EMP 136
Accts Rubinbrown Llp Saint Louis M
SIC 7373 Systems integration services; Systems integration services
Pr: Joseph M Blomker
Pr: Jim Bunch
*CFO: William T Jerry
Dir IT: Bryan Ard
IT Man: Stuart Huels
Manager: Chris Wood

MARYVILLE SAINTS
See MARYVILLE UNIVERSITY OF ST LOUIS

MARYVILLE TECHNOLOGIES
See MARYVILLE DATA SYSTEMS INC

D-U-N-S 07-196-2146
MARYVILLE UNIVERSITY OF ST LOUIS
MARYVILLE SAINTS
650 Maryville Univ Dr, Saint Louis, MO 63141-7299
Tel (314) 529-9300 Founded/Ownrshp 1872
Sales 74.9MM EMP 650
Accts Bkd Llp St Louis Missouri
SIC 8221 University; University
Pr: Mark Lombardi
Assoc VP: Jim Harf
Assoc VP: Martin Parkes
Ex VP: Eric Pustmueller
VP: Peter Green
Assoc Dir: Stephanie Treadway
Board of Directors: Deborah Davis

MARYWOOD RETREAT CENTER
See DIOCESE OF ST AUGUSTINE INC

D-U-N-S 07-918-6920
MARYWOOD UNIVERSITY
2300 Adams Ave, Scranton, PA 18509-1598
Tel (570) 348-6211 Founded/Ownrshp 1917
Sales 70.4MM EMP 700^E
SIC 8221 College, except junior; College, except junior
Pr: Anne Munley
*VP: Joseph X Garvey
VP: Amanda Greenwood
VP: Susan Hansen
VP: Clayton Pheasant
Comm Dir: Juneann Greco
Mng Dir: Paul Sevensky
Brnch Mgr: Joan Diehl
Genl Couns: Deborah Brouillette
Snr Mgr: Rick Hoffenberg

D-U-N-S 00-529-7510
■ MARZETTI FROZEN PASTA INC
(Suby of INN MAID PRODUCTS) ★
803 8th St Sw, Altoona, IA 50009-2306
Tel (515) 967-4254 Founded/Ownrshp 2004
Sales 53.9MM^E EMP 270
SIC 2038 2098 Frozen specialties; Macaroni & spaghetti; Frozen specialties; Macaroni & spaghetti
Pr: Rosa L Bruce
*Treas: John L Boylan
Chf Mktg O: David Hammerberg
Genl Mgr: Micheal Warren
Sfty Mgr: Ryan Ellis
Plnt Mgr: Bud Chiles
Ql Cn Mgr: Tim Berryhill
Ql Cn Mgr: Debbie Harkness

D-U-N-S 11-325-4481
MAS BUILDING & BRIDGE INC
18 Sharon Ave, Norfolk, MA 02056-1530
Tel (508) 520-2277 Founded/Ownrshp 2002
Sales 24.1MM^E EMP 96
SIC 1622 1541 Bridge construction; Industrial buildings & warehouses
Pr: Michael A Socci

D-U-N-S 07-692-1139 IMP/EXP
MAS INC
2718 Brecksville Rd, Richfield, OH 44286-9735
Tel (330) 659-3333 Founded/Ownrshp 1971
Sales 32.6MM^E EMP 43
SIC 5064 5092 Electrical appliances, television & radio; Electrical entertainment equipment; Electrical appliances, major; Video games
Pr: Brian T Parsell
*Ch Bd: C Edwin Howard
*Ex VP: Ken E Weegar

D-U-N-S 83-631-3015
MAS MARKETING NETWORK
MID ATLANTIC SPECIALITIES
368 E Main St, Somerville, NJ 08876-3110
Tel (908) 725-9944 Founded/Ownrshp 1991
Sales 29.0MM EMP 9
SIC 8742 Marketing consulting services; Sales (including sales management) consultant; Marketing consulting services; Sales (including sales management) consultant
Pr: Matthew A Sack

D-U-N-S 96-945-1327 EXP
MAS MELONS & GRAPES LLC
41 Kipper St, Rio Rico, AZ 85648-6236
Tel (520) 377-2372 Founded/Ownrshp 1997
Sales 21.5MM EMP 20
SIC 5148 Fruits

D-U-N-S 92-610-4035
MAS MUTUAL LIFE INSURANCE CO INC
FLANAGAN FINICIAL GROUP
333 E City Ave Ste 901, Bala Cynwyd, PA 19004-1517
Tel (610) 660-9922 Founded/Ownrshp 1985
Sales NA EMP 60
SIC 6311 6282 Life insurance; Investment advice
Pr: Harris Fishman
VP: Chuck Paff
VP: Anthony Spatichia

D-U-N-S 00-317-5213 IMP
MASA CORP (VA)
5445 Henneman Dr Ste 200, Norfolk, VA 23513-2415
Tel (757) 855-3013 Founded/Ownrshp 1961, 1982
Sales 25.0MM^E EMP 140
SIC 2621 2672 5113 5199 3953 2899 Poster & art papers; Coated & laminated paper; Labels (unprinted), gummed: made from purchased materials; Tape, pressure sensitive: made from purchased materials; Shipping supplies; Packaging materials; Marking devices; Chemical preparations; Poster & art papers; Coated & laminated paper; Labels (unprinted), gummed: made from purchased materials; Tape, pressure sensitive: made from purchased materials; Shipping supplies; Packaging materials; Marking devices; Chemical preparations
Pr: Thomas E Fraim
COO: Wayne Prince
Sr VP: Samuel Adsit
Off Mgr: Pam Farraher
CTO: Randy Haines
Sls Mgr: Ted Brackman

D-U-N-S 60-773-1853
MASABA INC
MASABA MINING EQUIPMENT
1617 317th St, Vermillion, SD 57069-3703
Tel (605) 624-9555 Founded/Ownrshp 2005
Sales 41.4MM^E EMP 130
SIC 3532 8711 Amalgamators (metallurgical or mining machinery); Engineering services; Amalgamators (metallurgical or mining machinery); Engineering services
Pr: Jerad Higman
VP: Heath Johnson
VP: Jim Peterson

MASABA MINING EQUIPMENT
See MASABA INC

D-U-N-S 07-962-6281
MASADA BAKERY LLC (GA)
(Suby of T B C) ★
1500 Oakbrook Dr, Norcross, GA 30093-2245
Tel (404) 377-4555 Founded/Ownrshp 2014
Sales 20.1MM^E EMP 163
SIC 2051 Bread, cake & related products
CEO: Cordia W Harrington
*Pr: Joseph J Waters
*CFO: C Thomas Harrington
Genl Mgr: Koby Stein

D-U-N-S 02-766-5553
MASAMI FOODS INC
(Suby of MARUSHOHOTTA CO.,LTD.)
5222 Tingley Ln, Klamath Falls, OR 97603-9317
Tel (541) 884-1735 Founded/Ownrshp 1992
Sales 29.3MM^E EMP 160
SIC 2011 2013 Beef products from beef slaughtered on site; Pork products from pork slaughtered on site; Sausages & other prepared meats; Beef products from beef slaughtered on site; Pork products from pork slaughtered on site; Sausages & other prepared meats
Pr: Masami Ishida
*VP: Mitsunori Funakushi

D-U-N-S 08-816-5972
MASCARO CONSTRUCTION CO LP
1720 Metropolitan St, Pittsburgh, PA 15233-2260
Tel (412) 321-4901 Founded/Ownrshp 1997
Sales 212.0MM EMP 220
Accts Henry Rossi & Co Llp Monroe
SIC 1542 Commercial & office building, new construction; Commercial & office buildings, renovation & repair; Commercial & office building, new construction; Commercial & office buildings, renovation & repair
Genl Pt: John C Mascaro Jr
Pt: Jeffrey Mascaro
Pt: John C Mascaro Sr
Pt: Michael Mascaro
Pt: Charles Solkovy
Sr VP: Mark Belmar
VP: Bob Breisinger
VP: Ron Cortes
VP: Robert Czerniewski
VP: Steve Pittman
VP: Steve Powell
VP: Christy Uffelman
Dir Bus: Michael Ellis

D-U-N-S 19-600-5990
MASCHHOFFS LLC
7475 State Route 127, Carlyle, IL 62231-3103
Tel (618) 594-0203 Founded/Ownrshp 2005
Sales 646.6MM^E EMP 1,859
SIC 0213 Hogs; Hogs
Pr: Mark Greenwood
*Ch Bd: Kenneth Maschhoff
CFO: Jason Logsdon
VP: Aaron M Gaines
VP: Tim Laatsch

D-U-N-S 07-954-5098
MASCHIOPACK NORTH AMERICA LLC (GA)
(Suby of COLONIAL GROUP INC) ★
3710 Atlanta Industrial, Atlanta, GA 30331-1053
Tel (844) 888-4227 Founded/Ownrshp 2014
Sales 24.0MM EMP 8
SIC 3089 Plastic containers, except foam
Pr: Robert H Demere Jr
*VP: Peter Brunn

D-U-N-S 15-121-6769 IMP
MASCHMEYER CONCRETE CO OF FLORIDA
1142 Watertower Rd, Lake Park, FL 33403-2397
Tel (561) 848-9112 Founded/Ownrshp 1986
Sales 54.1MM^E EMP 190
SIC 3273 3312 Ready-mixed concrete; Wire products, steel or iron
Pr: Troy W Maschmeyer Jr
*COO: Jeffrey A Bishop
*CFO: J Randy Hough
CFO: Randy Hough
Genl Mgr: Steve Bishop
IT Man: Diana Rosas
Tech Mgr: Richard Lorenz
Opers Mgr: Brian Curtis
Sales Asso: Gary Demyer
Sales Asso: Kim Hardin

D-U-N-S 10-210-3665
MASCI CORP
5752 S Ridgewood Ave, Port Orange, FL 32127-6442
Tel (386) 322-4500 Founded/Ownrshp 1996
Sales 25.0MM^E EMP 90
SIC 1623 0711 1611 1771 1794 Underground utilities contractor; Soil preparation services; General contractor, highway & street construction; Concrete work; Excavation work
Pr: Leonel Masci
*VP: Ivanna Masci
*VP: Leticia Wright
Off Mgr: Letitia Masci

MASCO
See MEDICAL ACADEMIC AND SCIENTIFIC COMMUNITY ORGANIZATION INC

D-U-N-S 04-831-8133 IMP/EXP
MASCO BATH CORP (TN)
MASCO BATH SOUTH
8445 Keystone Xing # 100, Indianapolis, IN 46240-2454
Tel (317) 254-5959 Founded/Ownrshp 1984
Sales NA EMP 1,450
SIC 3088 3842

MASCO BATH SOUTH
See MASCO BATH CORP

D-U-N-S 00-503-4749 IMP
■ MASCO BUILDER CABINET GROUP
(Suby of MASCO CORP) ★
5353 W Us Highway 223, Adrian, MI 49221-8901
Tel (517) 264-9153 Founded/Ownrshp 1946
Sales 305.7MM^E EMP 4,000
SIC 2434 Wood kitchen cabinets; Vanities, bathroom: wood; Wood kitchen cabinets; Vanities, bathroom: wood
Pr: Karen L Strauss
*CFO: Mike McCullough
VP: John Czerwonka
VP: Chuck Loudermilk
*VP: W Jay Potter
*VP: Michael Thompson
VP Mktg: Mark Ayers
Board of Directors: Raymond Kennedy, Richard G Mosteller

D-U-N-S 14-438-7198
■ MASCO BUILDING PRODUCTS CORP
(Suby of MASCO CORP) ★
21001 Van Born Rd, Taylor, MI 48180-1340
Tel (313) 274-7400 Founded/Ownrshp 1985
Sales 1.1MMM^E EMP 30,000
SIC 3429 3639 3644 Door locks, bolts & checks; Major kitchen appliances, except refrigerators & stoves; Outlet boxes (electric wiring devices); Door locks, bolts & checks; Major kitchen appliances, except refrigerators & stoves; Outlet boxes (electric wiring devices)
Pr: Allan Barry
*VP: Lebo Larry

D-U-N-S 09-997-0035 IMP/EXP
■ MASCO CABINETRY LLC
(Suby of MASCO CORP) ★
4600 Arrowhead Dr, Ann Arbor, MI 48105-2773
Tel (313) 274-7400 Founded/Ownrshp 2007
Sales 916.8MM^E EMP 4,000
SIC 2434 Wood kitchen cabinets; Wood kitchen cabinets
CFO: Karen Strauss
COO: Donald Demarie Jr
*Prin: Richard A Manoogian
*Prin: Rick Roetken
Mng Dir: Chad Miller
Area Mgr: Brian Covey
Brnch Mgr: Keith Allen
Brnch Mgr: Ken Spangler
Brnch Mgr: Terry Stoltenberg
Trfc Mgr: Flavio Derosa

D-U-N-S 07-574-2361 IMP
■ MASCO CABINETRY MIDDLEFIELD LLC
(Suby of MASCO CABINETRY LLC) ★
15535 Old State Rd, Middlefield, OH 44062-8208
Tel (440) 632-5333 Founded/Ownrshp 2011
Sales 407.3MM^E EMP 3,022
SIC 2434 Wood kitchen cabinets; Vanities, bathroom: wood; Wood kitchen cabinets; Vanities, bathroom: wood
Pr: Keith Scherzer
CFO: John Pederson
VP: Eugene A Gargaro
*VP: Andrew Rattray
QA Dir: Brian Gorby
VP Sls: Roland Minogue

D-U-N-S 95-911-7078
■ MASCO CABINETRY TRANSPORT CO
MERILLAT
(Suby of MASCO CORP) ★
4600 Arrowhead Dr, Ann Arbor, MI 48105-2773
Tel (734) 205-4600 Founded/Ownrshp 1990
Sales 29.4MM^E EMP 250
SIC 2434 Wood kitchen cabinets; Wood kitchen cabinets
Pr: Karen Strauss

D-U-N-S 01-275-5930
■ MASCO CONTRACTOR SERVICES EAST INC
(Suby of MASCO CORP) ★
612 River Rd, Fair Haven, NJ 07704-3273
Tel (732) 933-4433 Founded/Ownrshp 1999
Sales 121.5MM^E EMP 5,000
SIC 1742 Insulation, buildings; Insulation, buildings
Pr: Steven Raia
*CFO: Tom Jarvis
*VP: Dennis Raia

D-U-N-S 00-532-0924 IMP/EXP
▲ MASCO CORP
21001 Van Born Rd, Taylor, MI 48180-1300
Tel (313) 274-7400 Founded/Ownrshp 1929
Sales 8.5MMM EMP 32,000
Accts Pricewaterhousecoopers Llp D
Tkr Sym MAS Exch NYS
SIC 2434 3432 3088 3429 1742 Wood kitchen cabinets; Vanities, bathroom: wood; Faucets & spigots, metal & plastic; Plumbers' brass goods: drain cocks, faucets, spigots, etc.; Plastic plumbing fixture fittings, assembly; Plastics plumbing fixtures; Tubs (bath, shower & laundry), plastic; Bathroom fixtures, plastic; Hot tubs, plastic or fiberglass; Builders' hardware; Locks or lock sets; Acoustical & insulation work; Wood kitchen cabinets; Vanities, bathroom: wood; Faucets & spigots, metal & plastic; Plumbers' brass goods: drain cocks, faucets, spigots, etc.; Plastic plumbing fixture fittings, assembly; Plastics plumbing fixtures; Tubs (bath, shower & laundry), plastic; Bathroom fixtures, plastic; Hot tubs, plastic or fiberglass; Builders' hardware; Locks or lock sets; Acoustical & insulation work
Pr: Keith J Allman
*Ch Bd: Verne G Istock
Pr: Melonie Colaianne
Pr: W Timothy Yahhi
CFO: John G Sznewajs
Treas: James Tompkins
VP: Phil Cabibi
VP: Kenneth G Cole
VP: John P Lindow
Off Mgr: Shannon Anschuetz
VP Mktg: Michael O'Brien
Board of Directors: Mark R Alexander, Dennis W Archer, J Michael Losh, Richard A Manoogian, Christopher A O'herlihy, Donald R Parfet, Lisa A Payne, John C Plant, Mary Ann Van Lokeren

D-U-N-S 09-201-2210 IMP/EXP
■ MASCO CORP OF INDIANA
(Suby of MASCO CORP) ★
55 E 111th St, Indianapolis, IN 46280-1071
Tel (317) 848-1812 Founded/Ownrshp 1973
Sales 240.0MM^E EMP 1,204
SIC 3432 Plumbing fixture fittings & trim; Faucets & spigots, metal & plastic; Plastic plumbing fixture fittings, assembly; Plumbing fixture fittings & trim; Faucets & spigots, metal & plastic; Plastic plumbing fixture fittings, assembly
Pr: John G Sznewajs
*Treas: Rick Burkman
Ofcr: Pam Cunningham
VP: Jay Burnett
*VP: Tom Chapman
*VP: Richard G Hosteller
VP: John Kabbes
*VP: Kevin A Kennedy
VP: Craig Selover
*VP: Dana Severs
VP: Renee Straber

MASCO HOME SERVICES, INC.
See TOPBUILD HOME SERVICES INC

D-U-N-S 11-648-9399
MASCO PETROLEUM INC
110 Commerce St, Aberdeen, WA 98520-4521
Tel (360) 537-9744 Founded/Ownrshp 1999
Sales 34.3MM^E EMP 52^E
SIC 5172 Fuel oil; Fuel oil
Pr: James C Mason
*VP: Sean Mason

MASCO SERVICES GROUP CORP.
See TOPBUILD SERVICES GROUP CORP

D-U-N-S 60-739-1281
MASCO SERVICES INC
(Suby of MASCO) ★
375 Longwood Ave Ste 5, Boston, MA 02215-5329
Tel (617) 730-3013 Founded/Ownrshp 1992
Sales 25.5MM EMP 50
Accts Deloitte & Touche Llp Boston
SIC 8748 Telecommunications consultant; Telecommunications consultant
Pr: Richard M Sheay
*Treas: Holli Roth
Ex Dir: Margaret Dumas

D-U-N-S 13-761-1695
MASCOMA SAVINGS BANK
67 N Park St, Lebanon, NH 03766-1350
Tel (603) 448-3650 Founded/Ownrshp 1899
Sales NA EMP 250
SIC 6022 State commercial banks; State commercial banks
Pr: Stephen F Christy
COO: Barry McCabe
*CFO: Donald N Thompson
Bd of Dir: Edward Kerrigan
Ofcr: Teresa Fazio
Ofcr: Sheryl McDevitt
Ofcr: Gayle McFarland

Sr VP: Debbie Carter
Sr VP: John Ziegler
VP: Peter Begin
VP: Carol Cone
VP: Shirley Mower-Fenoff
Exec: Anne D'Aveni

D-U-N-S 60-509-1115

■ MASCOT PETROLEUM CO INC
(*Suby of* SUNOCO INC) ★
1801 Market St Fl 10, Philadelphia, PA 19103-1610
Tel (215) 977-3000 *Founded/Ownrshp* 1976
Sales 1.0MMMᴱ *EMP* 6,000
SIC 4932 5411 Gas & other services combined; Convenience stores, independent; Gas & other services combined; Convenience stores, independent
VP: Robert Owens
**Treas:* Paul A Mulholland
**VP:* Bruce G Fischer
**VP:* John A Ruddy Jr

D-U-N-S 02-773-8624

MASCOTT EQUIPMENT CO INC
435 Ne Hancock St, Portland, OR 97212-3997
Tel (503) 282-2587 *Founded/Ownrshp* 1960
Sales 28.9MMᴱ *EMP* 60
SIC 5013 5172 Automobile service station equipment; Petroleum products
Pr: Bill Mascott
**Pr:* W J Mascott I
Exec: Teri Flitcraft

D-U-N-S 15-628-5009

MASCOUTAH COMMUNITY UNIT SCHOOL DISTRICT 19
622 S Jefferson St, Mascoutah, IL 62258-2615
Tel (618) 566-2927 *Founded/Ownrshp* 1969
Sales 27.3MMᴱ *EMP* 500ᴱ
Accts Rice Sullivan & Co Ltd Be
SIC 8211 Public elementary & secondary schools; Public elementary & secondary schools
Pr Dir: Gene Isbell

D-U-N-S 13-110-7625

MASER CONSULTING PA
331 Newman Springs Rd # 203, Red Bank, NJ 07701-5691
Tel (732) 383-1950 *Founded/Ownrshp* 1984
Sales 74.0MM *EMP* 450
Accts Raymond Perri & De Seno Llc
SIC 8711 8742 8713 Engineering services; Management consulting services; Surveying services; Engineering services; Management consulting services; Surveying services
CEO: Richard M Maser
COO: Kevin Haney
**Treas:* Raymond Walker
Dept Mgr: Daniel W Busch
Dept Mgr: Edwin Caballero
Dept Mgr: David Ferraro
Dept Mgr: Dave Roberts
Dept Mgr: Ralph Tango
Dept Mgr: Chris Theodos
Dir IT: Roger McLarnon
Sls&Mrk Ex: Robert Dibartolo

MASERATI FINANCIAL SERVICES
See CNH INDUSTRIAL CAPITAL AMERICA LLC

D-U-N-S 60-218-6285 IMP/EXP

MASERATI NORTH AMERICA INC
(*Suby of* MASERATI SPA)
250 Sylvan Ave, Englewood Cliffs, NJ 07632-2527
Tel (201) 816-2600 *Founded/Ownrshp* 2001
Sales 24.1MMᴱ *EMP* 35
SIC 5511 Automobiles, new & used
CEO: Bob Graczyk
Pr: David Cordero
CFO: Joseph Marsella
CFO: Joseph Mercello
VP: Bradley Bickle
VP: Dan Cantrell
VP: Rick Fuller
VP: Michael Libbey
VP: Peter Salzer
Area Mgr: Ryan Gilmore
Area Mgr: Sean Seltzer

MASERATI OF BALTIMORE
See TOWSON AUTOMOTIVE INC

D-U-N-S 13-051-3414

MASERGY COMMUNICATIONS INC
2740 Dallas Pkwy Ste 260, Plano, TX 75093-4834
Tel (214) 442-5700 *Founded/Ownrshp* 2011
Sales 129.7MMᴱ *EMP* 250
SIC 4813 ;
CEO: Chris Macfarland
CFO: Rob Bodnar
CFO: Steve Vannattan
Sr VP: CAM Anderson
Sr VP: John Dumbleton
Sr VP: Tim Naramore
Sr VP: Greg Nelson
VP: Michael Bacich
VP: John Badillo
VP: Jeanne Baniewicz
VP: Keith Hatley
VP: Tony Hertado
VP: Dean Manzoori
VP: Nick Rattey
VP: Terry Traina
VP: Chris Werpy
VP: Joe Wright
VP: Marilyn Zemba
Dir Bus: Shannon Wilshire

D-U-N-S 04-259-6685

MASH CO SERVICES LLC
INTEGRITY HEALTH PLUS
14812 Venture Dr, Farmers Branch, TX 75234-2426
Tel (214) 377-9845 *Founded/Ownrshp* 2013
Sales 24.0MM *EMP* 120
SIC 8071 Medical laboratories
Pr: Wade Rosenburg
**COO:* Kyle Pletcher
**CFO:* Doug Benson

D-U-N-S 79-179-3318

MASHANTUCKET PEQUOT TRIBAL NATION
FOXWOODS RESORT CASINO
2 Matts Path, Mashantucket, CT 06338-3804
Tel (860) 396-6500 *Founded/Ownrshp* 1983
Sales NA *EMP* 6,000ᴱ
SIC 9131 Indian reservation; ; Indian reservation;
Pr: Felix D Rappaport
V Ch: Fatima Dames
**V Ch:* Kenneth Reels
**COO:* Todd Greenberg
**COO:* Felix Rappaport
Treas: Cinque Dames
**Chf Mktg O:* Rebecca G Carr
Ofcr: Hector Gonzalez
Sr VP: Franco Pilli
VP: Jessica A Baran
VP: Anthony Mason
VP: Nelson N Parker
VP: Scott Rider
**Int Pr:* William Sherlock

D-U-N-S 07-036-6489

MASHBURN CONSTRUCTION CO INC
1820 Sumter St, Columbia, SC 29201-2502
Tel (803) 400-1000 *Founded/Ownrshp* 1976
Sales 84.2MMᴱ *EMP* 110ᴱ
SIC 1542 Commercial & office building, new construction; Shopping center construction; Institutional building construction; Commercial & office building, new construction; Shopping center construction; Institutional building construction
CEO: Harry Mashburn
**Pr:* Paul Mashburn
**Pr:* Lynn M Shealy
**CFO:* Robert Parsons
**Ex VP:* H Lee Mashburn Jr
**VP:* Jane C Andrews
Sfty Mgr: Janeann Amick
Mktg Dir: Mary Beard
Snr Mgr: Dennis Childs

D-U-N-S 18-621-8525 EXP

MASHBURN EQUIPMENT LLC
425 Frontage Rd, Ringgold, GA 30736-3090
Tel (706) 935-3485 *Founded/Ownrshp* 2002
Sales 33.6MMᴱ *EMP* 38
SIC 5082 7359 General construction machinery & equipment; Equipment rental & leasing

D-U-N-S 18-408-9878

MASHPEE PUBLIC SCHOOLS
150a Old Barnstable Rd, Mashpee, MA 02649-3232
Tel (508) 539-1500 *Founded/Ownrshp* 1996
Sales NA *EMP* 348
SIC 9411 8211 State education department; Public elementary & secondary schools; State education department; Public elementary & secondary schools

D-U-N-S 05-529-6867

MASHUDA CONTRACTORS INC
N6504 State Road 73, Princeton, WI 54968-8463
Tel (920) 295-3329 *Founded/Ownrshp* 1920
Sales 20.7MMᴱ *EMP* 100
Accts Smith & Gesteland Llp
SIC 1611 General contractor, highway & street construction; General contractor, highway & street construction
Pr: Clifford Mashuda Jr

D-U-N-S 78-042-1038 IMP

▲ MASIMO CORP
52 Discovery, Irvine, CA 92618-3105
Tel (949) 297-7000 *Founded/Ownrshp* 1989
Sales 586.6MM *EMP* 1,200
Accts Grant Thornton Llp Irvine Ca
Tkr Sym MASI *Exch* NGS
SIC 3845 Patient monitoring apparatus; Phonocardiographs; Patient monitoring apparatus; Phonocardiographs
Ch Bd: Joe Kiani
COO: Tara Clark
COO: Anand Sampath
CFO: Mark P De Raad
CFO: Jenny Wilson
Bd of Dir: Julie Bradley
Ofcr: Liz Carlisle
Ex VP: Paul Jansen
Ex VP: Yongsam Lee
Ex VP: Tom McClenahan
VP: Brad Snow
Board of Directors: Steven J Barker, Robert Coleman, Sanford Fitch, Tom Harkin, Jack Lasersohn, Craig Reynolds

MASLAND CONTRACT
See DIXIE GROUP INC

MASLAND CONTRACT
See TDG OPERATIONS LLC

D-U-N-S 01-312-1389 IMP

MASLINE ELECTRONICS INC (NY)
511 Clinton Ave S, Rochester, NY 14620-1104
Tel (585) 546-5373 *Founded/Ownrshp* 1932, 1964
Sales 27.8MMᴱ *EMP* 37
Accts Kaperski Owen & Dinan Cpas Ll
SIC 5065 Electronic parts; Connectors, electronic; Capacitors, electronic; Resistors, electronic
Pr: Glenn Masline
**Pr:* Winona S Masline
Sr VP: Patricia Rathbun
**VP:* Sheila Gerling
Manager: John Rodriguez
Sls Mgr: Phillip Nelson
Sales Asso: Brooks Watts

D-U-N-S 09-372-9168 EXP

MASLO CO INC
11 Lee Blvd, Malvern, PA 19355-1234
Tel (610) 540-9000 *Founded/Ownrshp* 1980
Sales 25.0MMᴱ *EMP* 25
SIC 5093 Waste paper
Pr: Robert S Loose Jr
**Pr:* Stephen M Loose

D-U-N-S 13-089-4632

MASON & HANGER CORP
(*Suby of* DAY & ZIMMERMANN GROUP INC) ★
1500 Spring Garden St # 500, Philadelphia, PA 19130-4067
Tel (215) 299-8275 *Founded/Ownrshp* 2006
Sales 1.3MMᴱ *EMP* 314ᴱ
SIC 3483 Ammunition, except for small arms
Pr: William Holmes
**Treas:* Richard Salazar
VP: James E Jones Jr
Brnch Mgr: Ron Henton

D-U-N-S 14-430-8004

MASON & HANGER GROUP INC
(*Suby of* DAY & ZIMMERMANN GROUP INC) ★
300 W Vine St Ste 1300, Lexington, KY 40507-1814
Tel (859) 252-9980 *Founded/Ownrshp* 2006
Sales 23.7MMᴱ *EMP* 100ᴱ
SIC 8711 8712 Engineering services; Architectural engineering; Engineering services; Architectural engineering
Pr: Michael Mc Areavy
**Pr:* Theodore Daniels
COO: Jack Stemm
**Sr VP:* Rick Troop
VP: D Daniel
VP: Jim Jones
VP: Michael McAreazy
VP: Ronald D Smith
Dir IT: Toy Mays
IT Man: Will Speilberg
Ql Cn Mgr: James Cordova

D-U-N-S 08-366-4933

MASON & WRIGHT ENTERPRISES
MCDONALD'S
844 Chesnee Hwy, Gaffney, SC 29341-3410
Tel (864) 489-3900 *Founded/Ownrshp* 2000
Sales 5.1MMᴱ *EMP* 280
SIC 5812 Fast-food restaurant, chain; Fast-food restaurant, chain
Owner: Bill Mason

D-U-N-S 02-309-8239

MASON BROTHERS CO
222 4th St Ne, Wadena, MN 56482-1200
Tel (218) 631-2222 *Founded/Ownrshp* 1962
Sales 33.7MMᴱ *EMP* 250
SIC 5147 5143 5141 5142

D-U-N-S 78-291-7199

MASON BUILDING GROUP INC
35 Albe Dr, Newark, DE 19702-1321
Tel (302) 292-0600 *Founded/Ownrshp* 1991
Sales 25.2MMᴱ *EMP* 150
SIC 1751 1542 Carpentry work; Framing contractor; Nonresidential construction; Carpentry work; Framing contractor; Nonresidential construction
Pr: Christopher Mason
**Sec:* Rita Thomas

D-U-N-S 09-872-6896

MASON CITY CLINIC PC
250 S Crescent Dr, Mason City, IA 50401-2926
Tel (641) 494-5200 *Founded/Ownrshp* 1973
Sales 32.4MMᴱ *EMP* 225
SIC 8011 Clinic, operated by physicians; Clinic, operated by physicians; Psychiatric clinic
Pr: Dale Armstrong
Off Mgr: Kristie Whitehill
CIO: Dana Young
IT Man: Bruce Forshay
IT Man: Kimberly Hagedorn
Sfty Mgr: Joan Butterfield
Surgeon: Steven Allgood
Surgeon: Timothy Gibbons
Surgeon: Harsha Jayawardena
Surgeon: Darron Jones
Surgeon: Eric Potthoff

D-U-N-S 03-107-1327

MASON CITY COMMUNITY SCHOOL DISTRICT (INC)
1515 S Pennsylvania Ave, Mason City, IA 50401-6041
Tel (641) 421-4400 *Founded/Ownrshp* 1885
Sales 43.9MM *EMP* 650
Accts Hogan-Hansen Mason City Iowa
SIC 8211 Public elementary & secondary schools; Public elementary & secondary schools
Pr: Samuel Hunt
**Prin:* Gary D Hoffman
CIO: Dave Hickey
Schl Brd P: Robert Thoms
Teacher Pr: Jodie Anderson

D-U-N-S 09-519-4874

MASON CITY SCHOOL DISTRICT
211 N East St, Mason, OH 45040-1760
Tel (513) 398-0474 *Founded/Ownrshp* 1815
Sales 49.0MMᴱ *EMP* 680
SIC 8211 Public elementary school; Public senior high school; School board; Public elementary school; Public senior high school; School board
**Treas:* Richard Gardner
Exec: Tracey Carson
IT Man: Melanie Jordan
Schl Brd P: Kevin Wisz
Teacher Pr: Marla Niebiling
Snr Mgr: Karen Ansberry

D-U-N-S 00-616-1962 IMP

MASON COMPANIES INC (WI)
1251 1st Ave, Chippewa Falls, WI 54729-1691
Tel (715) 720-4200 *Founded/Ownrshp* 1904, 1976
Sales 111.0MMᴱ *EMP* 415
SIC 5961 5661 Catalog sales; Shoe stores; Catalog sales; Shoe stores
CEO: Dan Hunt
Ex VP: Tim Mason
**VP:* Joe Fesenmaier
IT Man: Jade Spangenberg
IT Man: George Wood
Web Dev: Courtney Christian
Web Dev: Carolyn Kranz
Web Dev: Chelsea Otte
Ql Cn Mgr: Debra Lange

Mktg Dir: Darin Schemenauer
Mktg Mgr: Aaron Zwiefelhofer

D-U-N-S 09-480-0414

MASON CONSOLIDATED SCHOOLS
2400 Mason Eagle Dr, Erie, MI 48133-9373
Tel (734) 848-9348 *Founded/Ownrshp* 1956
Sales 19.1MMᴱ *EMP* 340
Accts Cooley Hehl Wohlgamuth & Carlt
SIC 8211 Public combined elementary & secondary school; School board; Public combined elementary & secondary school; School board
**CFO:* Michelle Strick

D-U-N-S 04-890-1623

MASON CONSTRUCTION LTD
6285 Walden Rd, Beaumont, TX 77707-5599
Tel (409) 842-4455 *Founded/Ownrshp* 1970
Sales 67.7MMᴱ *EMP* 250
SIC 1794 Excavation & grading, building construction; Excavation & grading, building construction
Pt: Charles E Mason Jr
Pt: Becky Mason
Pt: Brad Mason
Pt: Mary Bess Townsend
VP: Gilbert Andrus
Exec: Robert Chapman
Exec: Ralph Shillings
Site Mgr: Phillip Verrett
Sfty Mgr: Cody Alford
Sfty Mgr: Dustin Rowe

D-U-N-S 00-400-3471 EXP

MASON CORP (AL)
123 W Oxmoor Rd, Birmingham, AL 35209-6357
Tel (205) 942-4100 *Founded/Ownrshp* 1948
Sales 31.0MMᴱ *EMP* 162
SIC 3441 Building components, structural steel; Building components, structural steel
Ch Bd: Frank L Mason
**Pr:* Russell W Chambliss
CFO: Jules Mason
**VP:* Wallace E Lessley
Dist Mgr: Danny Williamson
Genl Mgr: Beau Chambliss
Dir IT: Mike Rose
IT Man: Frank Chambliss
Mktg Dir: Josh Hoffman
Sales Asso: Bill Champion

D-U-N-S 00-546-0209

MASON CORP
1049 Us Highway 41, Schererville, IN 46375-1303
Tel (219) 865-8040 *Founded/Ownrshp* 1950
Sales 36.5MMᴱ *EMP* 100
SIC 2819 Tin (stannic/stannous) compounds or salts, inorganic; Tin (stannic/stannous) compounds or salts, inorganic
Pr: Todd Hofer
**Ch Bd:* Ralph Mason
**Pr:* Don Mason
**Pr:* Von Mason
COO: Mike Mason
Plnt Mgr: Rod Memmoring

D-U-N-S 05-803-1188

MASON COUNTY BOARD OF EDUCATION
MASON COUNTY SCHOOL DISTRICT
1200 Main St, Point Pleasant, WV 25550-1317
Tel (304) 675-4540 *Founded/Ownrshp* 1933
Sales 35.7MMᴱ *EMP* 600
SIC 8211 Public elementary & secondary schools; Public elementary & secondary schools
**CFO:* Chris Campbell
**Prin:* William Capehart
IT Man: Gary Hendricks

D-U-N-S 14-161-4912

MASON COUNTY PUBLIC UTILITY DISTRICT 1
21971 N Us Highway 101, Shelton, WA 98584-7446
Tel (360) 877-5249 *Founded/Ownrshp* 2003
Sales 47.8MM *EMP* 23
Accts Brian Sonntag Cgfm Olympia
SIC 1623 Water, sewer & utility lines; Water, sewer & utility lines
CTO: John Bennett

D-U-N-S 05-730-7225

MASON COUNTY PUBLIC UTILITY DISTRICT NO 3
P U D
2621 E Johns Prairie Rd, Shelton, WA 98584-8231
Tel (360) 426-8255 *Founded/Ownrshp* 1934
Sales 81.8MMᴱ *EMP* 119ᴱ
Accts Brian Sonntag Cgfm Olympia
SIC 4911 Generation, electric power; Generation, electric power
Off Mgr: Nancy Bolender
Telecom Mg: Ladonna Schuh
MIS Mgr: John Bennet

MASON COUNTY SCHOOL DISTRICT
See MASON COUNTY BOARD OF EDUCATION

D-U-N-S 08-603-2927

MASON DISTRICT HOSPITAL
HAVANA MEDICAL ASSOCIATES
615 N Promenade St Ste 1, Havana, IL 62644-1274
Tel (309) 543-4431 *Founded/Ownrshp* 1955
Sales 22.3MM *EMP* 210ᴱ
SIC 8062 General medical & surgical hospitals; General medical & surgical hospitals
CEO: Harry Wolin
Chf Rad: Muhammad Zaheer
CFO: Robert Stolba
Dir OR: Darcy Bull
Dir Rx: Penny Roch
Dir Pat Ac: Vanessa Durham
QA Dir: Doug Kosier
Dir IT: Aron Coots
Dir IT: Arron Cots
Software D: Katie Sarnes
Nrsg Dir: Katherine Tarvin

D-U-N-S 00-932-9660
■ MASON DIXON INTERMODAL INC
UNIVERSAL INTERMODAL SVCS INC
(*Suby of* UNIVERSAL TRUCKLOAD SERVICES INC) ★
4400 Wyoming St, Dearborn, MI 48126
Tel (313) 836-0460 *Founded/Ownrshp* 2006
Sales 34.6MM^E *EMP* 250
SIC 4213 Trucking, except local; Trucking, except local
Pr: Tim Phillips
**VP:* Jeff Hinkle
Genl Mgr: Ron Zingaro

D-U-N-S 04-500-6343
■ MASON ELECTRIC CO
(*Suby of* ESTERLINE TECHNOLOGIES CORP) ★
13955 Balboa Blvd, Sylmar, CA 91342-1084
Tel (818) 361-3366 *Founded/Ownrshp* 1996
Sales 68.9MM^E *EMP* 350
SIC 3728 Aircraft parts & equipment; Aircraft parts & equipment
VP: Steven Brune
VP: Mike Balbuena
Telecom Ex: William Schroll
Sls&Mrk Ex: Leticia Moore

D-U-N-S 61-927-3282
MASON FAMILY RESORTS LLC
GREAT WOLF LODGE
(*Suby of* GREAT WOLF LODGE) ★
2501 Great Wolf Dr, Mason, OH 45040-8085
Tel (513) 339-0141 *Founded/Ownrshp* 2005
Sales 19.7MM^E *EMP* 450
SIC 5812 7011 7299 Family restaurants; Hotels & motels; Banquet hall facilities; Family restaurants; Hotels & motels; Banquet hall facilities
Genl Mgr: Ericka Vaughn
Sls Mgr: J Hesse

MASON GENERAL HOSPITAL
See PUBLIC HOSPITAL DISTRICT 1 OF MASON COUNTY WA

D-U-N-S 00-122-5853 IMP
MASON INDUSTRIES INC (NY)
M I
350 Rabro Dr, Hauppauge, NY 11788-4237
Tel (631) 348-0282 *Founded/Ownrshp* 1958
Sales 45.4MM^E *EMP* 350
SIC 3625 3829 3052 3069 3441 3678 Measuring & controlling devices; Noise control equipment; Hard rubber & molded rubber products; Rubber hose; Fabricated structural metal; Electronic connectors; Noise control equipment; Measuring & controlling devices; Rubber hose; Hard rubber & molded rubber products; Fabricated structural metal; Electronic connectors
Ch Bd: Norm Mason
**VP:* Patrick Lama
Sfty Mgr: Armando Gamble
Plnt Mgr: Henry Smith
Natl Sales: Jim Sadler
Manager: Dave Bloom
Manager: Mike Schurott
Sls Mgr: Steve Fey
Sls Mgr: Mark Laboe

D-U-N-S 78-583-4516
MASON ROAD SHEET METAL INC
M R SHEET METAL
6450 Clara Rd Ste 190, Houston, TX 77041-5365
Tel (713) 466-5054 *Founded/Ownrshp* 2001
Sales 23.3MM^E *EMP* 100
SIC 3444 Sheet metalwork
Pr: Christopher Jinks

MASON STEEL
See MASON STRUCTURAL STEEL INC

D-U-N-S 00-445-1720
MASON STRUCTURAL STEEL INC (OH)
MASON STEEL
7500 Northfield Rd, Walton Hills, OH 44146-6187
Tel (440) 439-1040 *Founded/Ownrshp* 1958
Sales 33.9MM^E *EMP* 100
SIC 3441 5031 5074 Fabricated structural metal; Doors & windows; Window frames, all materials; Fireplaces, prefabricated
CEO: Leonard N Polster
**Pr:* Keith Polster
VP: Bob Deszcz
**Prin:* J Moldaver
**Prin:* Joseph Patchan
**Prin:* Sol W Wyman

D-U-N-S 07-662-3136
MASON TENDER DISTRICT COUNCIL TRUST FUND
MTDC WELFARE FUND
520 8th Ave Rm 600, New York, NY 10018-4196
Tel (212) 452-9700 *Founded/Ownrshp* 1947
Sales NA *EMP* 26
Accts Schultheis & Panettieri Llp H
SIC 6371 Union trust funds; Union trust funds

D-U-N-S 07-523-7552
MASON TENDERS DISTRICT COUNCIL GREATER NEW YORK
520 8th Ave Rm 650, New York, NY 10018-6539
Tel (212) 452-9400 *Founded/Ownrshp* 1923
Sales 165.7MM *EMP* 3
Accts Schultheis & Panettieri Llp
SIC 8631 Labor unions & similar labor organizations; Labor unions & similar labor organizations
Pr: Pat Piscitelli
Counsel: Tamir Rosenblum

D-U-N-S 13-146-1659
MASON TIRE & AUTO SERVICE INC
GOODYEAR
750 Highway 17 N, Surfside Beach, SC 29575-6023
Tel (843) 238-3339 *Founded/Ownrshp* 1985
Sales 21.6MM^E *EMP* 60
SIC 5531 7538 Automotive tires; General automotive repair shops
Pr: Joseph E Mason Jr
**Sec:* Catherine St Blanchard
**VP:* Ozzy St Blanchard
Genl Mgr: Frankie Fisher

D-U-N-S 03-926-2092 EXP
MASON VITAMINS INC (FL)
15750 Nw 59th Ave, Miami Lakes, FL 33014-6716
Tel (305) 428-6800 *Founded/Ownrshp* 1967, 2006
Sales 21.8MM^E *EMP* 100
SIC 2834 Vitamin, nutrient & hematinic preparations for human use; Vitamin preparations; Vitamin, nutrient & hematinic preparations for human use; Vitamin preparations
CEO: Yosuke Honjo
**Pr:* Ofelia Perez
CFO: Jaunita Rodriguez
VP: Vijay Gokarn
Web Dev: Danny Lim
**VP Sls:* Gary Pigott

D-U-N-S 78-077-6188
MASON WELLS BUYOUT FUND II LIMITED PARTNERSHIP
411 E Wisconsin Ave, Milwaukee, WI 53202-4461
Tel (414) 727-6400 *Founded/Ownrshp* 1992
Sales 232.8MM^E *EMP* 500
SIC 3594 3492 3593 6211 Fluid power pumps; Control valves, fluid power: hydraulic & pneumatic; Fluid power cylinders, hydraulic or pneumatic; Investment firm, general brokerage; Fluid power pumps; Control valves, fluid power: hydraulic & pneumatic; Fluid power cylinders, hydraulic or pneumatic; Investment firm, general brokerage
Pr: John Byrnes
CFO: Jim Domach
VP: Christopher Pummill
Mng Dir: Greg Myers

D-U-N-S 80-273-0218 EXP
MASON WELLS INC
411 E Wisconsin Ave # 1280, Milwaukee, WI 53202-4435
Tel (414) 727-6400 *Founded/Ownrshp* 1982
Sales 555.9MM^E *EMP* 990
SIC 6799 Investors; Investors
Pr: John T Byrnes
**CFO:* Jim Domach
**VP:* William Krugler
**VP:* Christopher Pummill
**VP:* Thomas Smith

D-U-N-S 17-485-5668
MASON-MCDUFFIE REAL ESTATE INC
BETTER HOMES AND GARDENS
1555 Riviera Ave Ste E, Walnut Creek, CA 94596-7321
Tel (925) 924-4600 *Founded/Ownrshp* 1927
Sales 33.7MM^E *EMP* 360
SIC 6531 Real estate agent, residential; Real estate agent, residential
Ch Bd: David Cobo
**Pr:* Edmond Krafchow
**CFO:* Michael Levedhl
**VP:* John Auka
VP: Linda Howard
Sales Asso: Shelbie Butler
Sales Asso: Ava Chavez
Sales Asso: Stacey Davis
Sales Asso: Eileen Erickson
Sales Asso: Ross Gibbons
Sales Asso: Steve Kim

D-U-N-S 87-681-1709
MASONIC CARE COMMUNITY
2150 Bleecker St, Utica, NY 13501-1738
Tel (315) 798-4800 *Founded/Ownrshp* 2007
Sales 34.7MM *EMP* 72^E
SIC 8641 Civic associations
Prin: William Luley
Ex Dir: Rob Raffle
Off Mgr: Stephanie Freeman
Dir IT: Kevin Conroy
IT Man: Dan Anthony
QC Dir: Linda Vebrowski
Prd Mgr: Shannon McNamara
Sls&Mrk Ex: Kathy Contino-Turner
HC Dir: Maria Centolella

MASONIC CENTER
See GRAND LODGE OF FREE & ACCEPTED MASONS OF STATE OF MICHIGAN

D-U-N-S 07-373-8775
MASONIC CHARITY FOUNDATION OF NEW JERSEY
MASONIC HOME OF NJ
902 Jacksonville Rd, Burlington, NJ 08016-3814
Tel (609) 239-3900 *Founded/Ownrshp* 1898
Sales 41.4MM *EMP* 661
Accts Jh Cohn Llp Roseland Nj
SIC 8051 Skilled nursing care facilities; Skilled nursing care facilities
**Treas:* Ian P Korman
Ex Dir: William Marshall
Off Mgr: Rick Manall
QC Dir: Cheryl Rahilly
HC Dir: Linda Andress

D-U-N-S 00-379-6831
MASONIC HEALTHCARE INC (OH)
3 Masonic Dr, Springfield, OH 45504-3658
Tel (937) 525-3001 *Founded/Ownrshp* 1995
Sales 8.2MM^E *EMP* 500
SIC 8051 Skilled nursing care facilities; Skilled nursing care facilities
Pr: Marion Leeman
**COO:* Greg Holm
**CFO:* David Stacy
**VP:* Jerry Guess
Exec: David Stacey
**Prin:* Nancy Archabold

MASONIC HOME BLOOMINGTON
See MINNESOTA MASONIC HOME CARE CENTER

MASONIC HOME JOURNAL
See MASONIC HOMES OF KENTUCKY

MASONIC HOME OF NJ
See MASONIC CHARITY FOUNDATION OF NEW JERSEY

D-U-N-S 07-547-9659
MASONIC HOME OF PENNSYLVANIA INC
(*Suby of* MASONIC HOMES OF THE GRAND LOD) ★
801 Ridge Pike Ofc, Lafayette Hill, PA 19444-1799
Tel (610) 825-6100 *Founded/Ownrshp* 1871
Sales 16.5MM^E *EMP* 392^E
SIC 8361 8051 Home for the aged; Skilled nursing care facilities
CEO: Joseph Murphy
Dir Recs: Debra Horne
COO: William C Davis Jr
Mktg Mgr: Marybeth Meehan
Nrsg Dir: Victoria Ridge

D-U-N-S 07-186-9382
MASONIC HOMES OF CALIFORNIA INC
1111 California St, San Francisco, CA 94108-2252
Tel (415) 776-7000 *Founded/Ownrshp* 1898
Sales 20.5MM^E *EMP* 425
Accts Moss Adams Llp Stockton Ca
SIC 8361 Children's home; Children's home
Pr: David R Doan
**CFO:* Timothy A Wood
Ofcr: Dick Kellogg
**VP:* Andrew Uehling
Dir IT: James Henretty

D-U-N-S 04-294-2839
MASONIC HOMES OF KENTUCKY
MASONIC HOME JOURNAL
240 Masonic Home Dr, Masonic Home, KY 40041-9000
Tel (502) 897-4910 *Founded/Ownrshp* 1867
Sales 33.7MM *EMP* 250
Accts Mountjoy Chilton Medley Llp L
SIC 8361 8051 Residential care; Orphanage; Skilled nursing care facilities; Residential care; Orphanage; Skilled nursing care facilities
Snr Mgr: Dana Gerdon

MASONIC HOMES OF THE GRAND LOD
See MASONIC VILLAGES OF GRAND LODGE OF PENNSYLVANIA

D-U-N-S 02-587-9649
MASONIC HOMES PROPERTIES INC
3761 Johnson Hall Dr, Masonic Home, KY 40041-9002
Tel (502) 897-4907 *Founded/Ownrshp* 1867
Sales 29.6MM^E *EMP* 575
SIC 8641 8051 8049 Civic associations; Skilled nursing care facilities; Nurses & other medical assistants; Civic associations; Skilled nursing care facilities; Nurses & other medical assistants
Ch: Martin Walters
**Pr:* Gary Marsh
**Treas:* Virgil T Larimore
**VP:* Ronnie G Bell
Exec: Jarrod Guthrie
CTO: Debra Sinnsinneran
Mktg Dir: Emily Staples

D-U-N-S 05-652-3884
MASONIC MANAGEMENT SERVICES CORP (CT)
(*Suby of* MASONICARE CORP) ★
22 Masonic Ave, Wallingford, CT 06492-3048
Tel (203) 679-5900 *Founded/Ownrshp* 1995
Sales 64.6MM *EMP* 1
Accts Pricewaterhousecoopers Llp Ha
SIC 8641 Civic associations; Civic associations
CEO: Stephen McPherson

MASONIC PATHWAYS
See MICHIGAN MASONIC HOME

MASONIC TEMPLE
See YORK RITE CORP

D-U-N-S 80-433-3771
MASONIC VILLAGES OF GRAND LODGE OF PENNSYLVANIA
MASONIC HOMES OF THE GRAND LOD
1 Masonic Dr, Elizabethtown, PA 17022-2199
Tel (717) 367-1121 *Founded/Ownrshp* 1910
Sales 149.4MM *EMP* 2,000
SIC 8361 Home for the aged; Children's home; Home for the aged; Children's home
CEO: Joseph E Murphy
Treas: Richard Dugdale
VP: Jeanie Hummer
VP: Douglas Policastro
Exec: Claudia Stephens
Dir Risk M: Connie Kopp
Dir Lab: Stacy Piper
CIO: Donald Johnston
Netwrk Mgr: Anne Dunkelberger
Sfty Mgr: Robin Pepperman
Sls&Mrk Ex: Marybeth Meehan

D-U-N-S 11-617-5225
MASONICARE AT ASHLAR VILLAGE INC
(*Suby of* MASONICARE CORP) ★
Cheshire Rd, Wallingford, CT 06492
Tel (203) 679-6425 *Founded/Ownrshp* 1983
Sales 27.6MM *EMP* 90
SIC 6513 Apartment building operators; Apartment building operators
Pr: Jon Paul Venoit

D-U-N-S 04-404-5826
MASONICARE CORP
22 Masonic Ave, Wallingford, CT 06492-3048
Tel (203) 679-5900 *Founded/Ownrshp* 1995
Sales 203.0MM^E *EMP* 2,500
SIC 8069 8082 8322 Geriatric hospital; Home health care services; Adult day care center; Geriatric hospital; Home health care services; Adult day care center
CFO: Darin M Spero
**CEO:* Steven McPherson
VP: James Albert
VP: Tracy Lamee
Doctor: Gail Labadia

D-U-N-S 96-450-1832
MASONICARE HEALTH CENTER
22 Masonic Ave, Wallingford, CT 06492-3048
Tel (203) 679-5900 *Founded/Ownrshp* 2012
Sales 58.5MM *EMP* 65^E
SIC 8399 Health & welfare council; Health & welfare council
CEO: Barry Spero

D-U-N-S 96-675-8554
MASONICARE HOME HEALTH AND HOSPICE INC
(*Suby of* MASONICARE CORP) ★
104 S Turnpike Rd, Wallingford, CT 06492-4320
Tel (203) 678-7857 *Founded/Ownrshp* 2011
Sales 36.8MM *EMP* 1^E
SIC 8052 Personal care facility; Personal care facility
Prin: Marion Donahue
**VP:* Susan Adams

D-U-N-S 00-538-8708
MASONICARE PARTNERS HOME HEALTH AND HOSPICE INC (CT)
111 Founders Plz Ste 200, East Hartford, CT 06108-8306
Tel (860) 528-2273 *Founded/Ownrshp* 2009
Sales 24.1MM *EMP* 18^E
SIC 8052 Personal care facility; Personal care facility
VP: Carolyn Reid

D-U-N-S 00-507-0578 IMP
■ MASONITE CORP
(*Suby of* MASONITE INTERNATIONAL CORPORATION)
1 Tampa City Center 20, Tampa, FL 33602
Tel (813) 877-2726 *Founded/Ownrshp* 1973
Sales 1.0MMM^E *EMP* 4,928
SIC 2431 3469 Doors, wood; Doors & door parts & trim, wood; Stamping metal for the trade; Doors, wood; Doors & door parts & trim, wood; Stamping metal for the trade
Pr: Frederick J Lynch
COO: Lawrence Repar
**Treas:* Joanne Freiberger
Bd of Dir: Jonathan Foster
VP: Jim Kingry
VP: James Rabe
VP: Mike Stoddard
Genl Mgr: Mike Hildebrandt
CIO: John Przedpelski
Web Dev: Jack Brown
Web Dev: Ed Shea

D-U-N-S 04-909-7880 IMP
MASONITE CORP
LOUISIANA MILLWORK
1001 S 4th Ave, Laurel, MS 39440-5110
Tel (601) 649-6000 *Founded/Ownrshp* 1925
Sales 21.4MM^E *EMP* 450
SIC 2493 Hardboard & fiberboard products
Prin: Dennis Markwood
Comm Man: Jennifer Smith
Plnt Mgr: John Dembowski
Plnt Mgr: Peter Hayes

D-U-N-S 85-849-9569 IMP/EXP
■ MASONITE HOLDINGS INC
(*Suby of* MASONITE INTERNATIONAL CORPORATION)
201 N Franklin St Ste 300, Tampa, FL 33602-5105
Tel (813) 877-2726 *Founded/Ownrshp* 1991
Sales 228.8MM^E *EMP* 5,000
SIC 2431 3442 Doors & door parts & trim, wood; Metal doors; Doors & door parts & trim, wood; Metal doors
Pr: Fred Lynch
Treas: Joanne Freiberger

D-U-N-S 05-278-1353 IMP
■ MASONITE INTERNATIONAL CORP
(*Suby of* MASONITE INTERNATIONAL CORPORATION)
201 N Franklin St, Tampa, FL 33602-5182
Tel (813) 877-2726 *Founded/Ownrshp* 1925
Sales 1.8MMM *EMP* 9,650
Tkr Sym DOOR *Exch* NYS
SIC 2431 3442 Doors, wood; Metal doors; Doors, wood; Metal doors
Pr: Frederick J Lynch
COO: Lawrence P Repar
CFO: Mark J Erceg
Sr VP: Gail N Auerbach
Sr VP: Robert E Lewis
VP: John Kufner
Exec: Rick Hunt
Creative D: Lorena Morales
Dept Mgr: Jamie Fenske
Plnt Mgr: Rob Morris
Plnt Mgr: Mark Ponzi
Board of Directors: Jody L Bilney, Robert J Byrne, Peter R Dachowski, Jonathan F Foster, George A Lorch, Rick J Mills, Francis M Scricco, John C Wills

D-U-N-S 61-300-4035
MASONOMICS INC
1501 Willis Rd, North Chesterfield, VA 23237-2914
Tel (804) 714-0095 *Founded/Ownrshp* 1996
Sales 36.8MM^E *EMP* 300
Accts Gregory And Associates
SIC 1741 Masonry & other stonework; Masonry & other stonework
Pr: Bradley Talley

D-U-N-S 03-389-8636 IMP
MASONRY ARTS INC
2105 3rd Ave N, Bessemer, AL 35020-4915
Tel (205) 428-0780 *Founded/Ownrshp* 1979
Sales 20.0MM^E *EMP* 150
SIC 1741 Masonry & other stonework; Masonry & other stonework
Pr: Roy V Swindal
**CFO:* Theresa N Williams
**VP:* John E Swindal
Sfty Dirs: Christie Rosser

D-U-N-S 09-467-3936 IMP
MASONRY CENTER INC
1424 N Orchard St, Boise, ID 83706-2276
Tel (208) 327-1625 *Founded/Ownrshp* 1979
Sales 23.7MM^E *EMP* 71^E

SIC 5032 5031 Brick, stone & related material; Brick, except refractory; Ceramic wall & floor tile; Doors & windows
Pr: Scott Chandler
Sales Exec: Monica Munroe

D-U-N-S 03-049-4785 IMP
MASONRY REINFORCING CORP OF AMERICA
WIRE-BOND
400 Rountree Rd, Charlotte, NC 28217-2131
Tel (704) 525-5554 *Founded/Ownrshp* 1975
Sales 41.3MM^E^ *EMP* 250
SIC 3496 Concrete reinforcing mesh & wire; Concrete reinforcing mesh & wire
Ch Bd: Ralph O Johnson Jr
**Pr:* Ralph O Johnson III
CFO: Mark Clure
**CFO:* Mark McClure
Genl Mgr: Greg Burton
Opers Mgr: Ian Walsh
Plnt Mgr: Ted Erickson

D-U-N-S 94-789-2782
MASONS MILL & LUMBER CO INC
9885 Tanner Rd, Houston, TX 77041-7622
Tel (713) 462-6975 *Founded/Ownrshp* 1993
Sales 21.1MM^E^ *EMP* 57
SIC 5031 2431 2435 Hardboard; Plywood; Millwork; Hardwood veneer & plywood
Pr: Michael Spellings
**Sec:* Anne Spellings
**VP:* Eric Boer
Ql Cn Mgr: Barbara Rogers
Sls Mgr: Sam Damiani
Sales Asso: Joel Alexander
Sales Asso: Mike Garza

D-U-N-S 04-490-2393 IMP
MASONS SUPPLY CO
2637 Se12th Ave, Portland, OR 97202
Tel (503) 234-4321 *Founded/Ownrshp* 1965
Sales 38.1MM^E^ *EMP* 115
SIC 5032 5085

D-U-N-S 07-275-4054
MASPETH FEDERAL SAVINGS & LOAN ASSOCIATION INC (NY)
5618 69th St, Maspeth, NY 11378-1897
Tel (718) 335-1300 *Founded/Ownrshp* 1947
Sales NA *EMP* 200
SIC 6035 6163 Federal savings & loan associations; Loan brokers; Federal savings & loan associations; Loan brokers
CEO: Kenneth Rudzewick
Ofcr: Ada Morales
Ex VP: Eugene Kapica
Sr VP: Catherine Oelkers
Sr VP: Phyllis Pampalone
Sr VP: George Ries
VP: Rita Garofalo
VP: Margaret Kass
VP: Margaret Kowaliski
VP: Richard Maher
VP: Michael Palermo

MASS AUDUBON
See MASSACHUSETTS AUDUBON SOCIETY INC

D-U-N-S 17-359-3567 IMP
MASS BAY BREWING CO INC
HARPOON BREWERY
306 Northern Ave, Boston, MA 02210-2330
Tel (617) 542-6137 *Founded/Ownrshp* 1986
Sales 42.4MM^E^ *EMP* 169
SIC 2082 5921 Malt beverages; Malt beverages; Beer (packaged)
CEO: Richard A Doyle
**Pr:* Daniel C Kenary
**CFO:* Warren Dibble
Sr VP: Charlie Story
VP: Al Marzi
Creative D: Adam Bailey
Comm Man: Merrill Allen
Genl Mgr: Cecile Llorens
Opers Mgr: Chris Sweatman
Opers Mgr: Edward Valenta
VP Mktg: Charlie Storey

D-U-N-S 01-476-1105
MASS BAY TRANSIT AUTHORITY INSPECTORS ASSOCIATES
147 W 4th St, Boston, MA 02127-1815
Tel (617) 268-4401 *Founded/Ownrshp* 1981
Sales 197.2M *EMP* 400
SIC 4785 Transportation inspection services; Transportation inspection services
Pr: John Horan

MASS COMMUNICATION
See ALCORN STATE UNIVERSITY

D-U-N-S 17-723-9597
MASS CRANE & HOIST SERVICES INC
72 Progress Ave, Tyngsboro, MA 01879-1436
Tel (978) 244-0477 *Founded/Ownrshp* 1987
Sales 34.0MM^E^ *EMP* 45^E^
SIC 5084 Industrial machinery & equipment; Cranes, industrial
Pr: Scott A Frost
**Pr:* George A Frost
**VP:* Jonathan J Frost

D-U-N-S 00-799-7463 IMP
MASS ELECTRIC CONSTRUCTION CO
(*Suby of* KIEWIT INFRASTRUCTURE CO) ★
400 Totten Pond Rd # 400, Waltham, MA 02451-2051
Tel (781) 290-1000 *Founded/Ownrshp* 2005
Sales 292.4MM^E^ *EMP* 1,137^E^
Accts Kpmg Llp Omaha Ne
SIC 1731 1623 General electrical contractor; Cable laying construction; Cable television line construction; Telephone & communication line construction; Transmitting tower (telecommunication) construction; General electrical contractor; Cable laying construction; Cable television line construction; Telephone & communication line construction; Transmitting tower (telecommunication) construction
Treas: Stephen S Thomas
Ex VP: Joseph A Forsythe
Ex VP: H Bryan Greene
Ex VP: Neal Parece
Ex VP: Alfredo E Sori
Ex VP: Frederick A Zambon
Sr VP: Tony Forsythe
Sr VP: Frederick A Hammel Jr
Sr VP: Shawn G Kelly
Sr VP: Bill Nordberg
Sr VP: Jack E Oram Jr
Sr VP: Philip F Shepley
Sr VP: John Testa
VP: Howard L Barton Jr
VP: Bill Breen
VP: Rick Caramante
VP: Scott A Churill
VP: Dick Frederico
VP: Greg Gzehoviak
VP: Michael J Piechoski
VP: Mark Steffen

D-U-N-S 96-196-4272
MASS ELECTRIC CONSTRUCTION CO
(*Suby of* PETER KIEWIT SONS INC) ★
4790 Regent Blvd Ste 100, Irving, TX 75063-2403
Tel (972) 505-4700 *Founded/Ownrshp* 2002
Sales 70.3MM^E^ *EMP* 220
SIC 1623 7382 Communication line & transmission tower construction; Security systems services
Pr: Alfredo E Sori
**Pr:* Nigel Gallaher
**Ex VP:* Tony Forsythe
**Sr VP:* Philip Shepley
VP: William Breen
**VP:* John Fisher
**VP:* Gregory A Hill
**VP:* Lee Lucas
Sfty Mgr: Benjamin Washington
Snr PM: Felix Senkovsky
Snr Mgr: Rob Rothey

D-U-N-S 93-111-9705
■ MASS GRAVEL INC
(*Suby of* WASTE MANAGEMENT OF MASSACHUSETTS INC) ★
1001 Fannin St Ste 4000, Houston, TX 77002-6711
Tel (713) 512-6200 *Founded/Ownrshp* 1999
Sales 22.3MM^E^ *EMP* 225
SIC 4953 Dumps, operation of; Sanitary landfill operation; Dumps, operation of; Sanitary landfill operation
Pr: Dave Lohnes

D-U-N-S 07-060-9870
MASS INSURERS INSOLVENCY FUND
1 Bowdoin Sq Ste 200, Boston, MA 02114-2919
Tel (617) 227-7020 *Founded/Ownrshp* 1972
Sales NA *EMP* 1
SIC 6411 Insurance agents; Insurance agents
Pr: Paul Gulko
**CFO:* Cathleen Laven

D-U-N-S 06-641-0564 IMP
MASS MARKETING INC
SUPER S FOODS
401 Isom Rd Ste 210, San Antonio, TX 78216-5134
Tel (210) 314-7005 *Founded/Ownrshp* 1973
Sales 115.0MM^E^ *EMP* 1,400
SIC 5411 Grocery stores, chain
Pr: John Dieterle
**CEO:* David S McBurnett
COO: James Amen
Store Mgr: Lupe Contreras
CTO: James Hanson
Sales Exec: David Ekmans
Sales Exec: George Haranda

MASS MARKETS
See TMONE LLC

D-U-N-S 00-420-0973
MASS MOVEMENT INC (MA)
65 Green St Ste 1, Foxboro, MA 02035-2865
Tel (508) 543-2073 *Founded/Ownrshp* 1996
Sales 21.0MM^E^ *EMP* 90
SIC 4213 Household goods transport
Pr: Dominic Simonetti
COO: Chuck Fedorka
CFO: Justin Perreault
**Sec:* James R Sullivan

D-U-N-S 13-234-7456
MASS MUTUAL DBS FINANCIAL GROUP
1000 Corporate Dr Ste 700, Fort Lauderdale, FL 33334-3638
Tel (954) 938-8800 *Founded/Ownrshp* 1980
Sales NA *EMP* 100
SIC 6311 6331 6211 Life insurance; Fire, marine & casualty insurance; Security brokers & dealers
Owner: David B Schulman
Ofcr: Janet Gonzalez

MASS MUTUAL LIFE INSURANCE CO
See CAPITOL FINANCIAL PARTNERS

D-U-N-S 05-346-0796
MASS POLYMERS CORP (MA)
69 Adams St, Newton, MA 02458-1126
Tel (617) 964-9400 *Founded/Ownrshp* 1971, 1985
Sales 48.2MM^E^ *EMP* 22
SIC 5162 Plastics materials
Pr: Albert Dazzo
**VP:* Stephan Dazzo

D-U-N-S 12-138-3061
MASS PRECISION INC
MACHINING AND FRAME DIVISION
2110 Oakland Rd, San Jose, CA 95131-1565
Tel (408) 786-0350 *Founded/Ownrshp* 1984
Sales 51.8MM *EMP* 420
SIC 3444 3599 Sheet metalwork; Machine shop, jobbing & repair; Sheet metalwork; Machine shop, jobbing & repair
Pr: Al Stucky Jr
**CFO:* W Ray Allen
VP: Jim Shelton
Prgrm Mgr: Jason Bortoli
Prgrm Mgr: Michael Draper
DP Exec: Donita Lovett
QA Dir: Don Heimann
IT Man: Cliff Drumeller
IT Man: Kevin Pham
Sls Mgr: Terry Grove

D-U-N-S 02-300-8167
MASS SERVICE & SUPPLY LLC
920 W 10th St, Pueblo, CO 81003-2028
Tel (719) 583-4140 *Founded/Ownrshp* 1996
Sales 22.0MM *EMP* 17
SIC 1521 Single-family housing construction; Single-family housing construction
Off Mgr: Sandra Harvey
Ql Cn Mgr: Aaron Shorter
Snr PM: Rick Fleming

D-U-N-S 02-083-9320
MASS TRANSPORTATION AUTHORITY INC
M T A
1401 S Dort Hwy, Flint, MI 48503-2878
Tel (810) 767-0100 *Founded/Ownrshp* 1971
Sales 39.0MM^E^ *EMP* 500
SIC 4111 Bus line operations; Bus line operations
Genl Mgr: Robert J Foy
Exec: Terry Lange
Genl Mgr: Edgar H Benning

D-U-N-S 07-196-1122
MASSAC MEMORIAL HOSPITAL FOUNDATION
28 Chick St, Metropolis, IL 62960-2467
Tel (618) 524-2176 *Founded/Ownrshp* 1956
Sales 22.3MM *EMP* 200
SIC 8062 General medical & surgical hospitals; General medical & surgical hospitals
CEO: Bill Hartley
**Ch Bd:* Doyle Louis
**CFO:* Chelle Ketlinger
Chf Nrs Of: Janet Barrett
CIO: Nick Senado
Opers Mgr: Cessinee Thornton
Mktg Dir: Mark Edwards
Cert Phar: Kathy Dowd

MASSACHSTTS SPREME JDICIAL CRT
See MASSACHUSETTS SUPREME JUDICIAL COURT

MASSACHUSETS EYE EAR INFERMERY
See LEILA A MANKARIOUS

D-U-N-S 07-381-2745
MASSACHUSETTS AUDUBON SOCIETY INC
MASS AUDUBON
208 S Great Rd, Lincoln, MA 01773-4816
Tel (781) 259-9500 *Founded/Ownrshp* 1999
Sales 29.5MM *EMP* 700
Accts Alexander Aronson Finning & Co
SIC 8641 Environmental protection organization; Environmental protection organization
Pr: Laura Johnson
**Treas:* Jeffrey Peters
VP: Nicole McKoon
**VP:* Bancroft Poor
Ex Dir: Jaci Barton
Ex Dir: Christine Turnbull
MIS Dir: Louise Grindrod
Sls&Mrk Ex: Kristi Kienholz
VP Mktg: Lindsey Counsell

D-U-N-S 87-889-3502
MASSACHUSETTS BAY COMMUNITY COLLEGE FOUNDATION INC
A MASS BAY
50 Oakland St, Wellesley, MA 02481-5307
Tel (781) 239-3000 *Founded/Ownrshp* 1964
Sales 24.9MM *EMP* 375
Accts O Connor & Drew Pc Braintre
SIC 8221 College, except junior; College, except junior
Pr: John Odonnell
Pr: Mark Nason
Ofcr: Stephen Digiovanni
**VP:* Richard Haskell
Exec: Robin Nelson-Bailey
**Prin:* Carole M B Joseph
Ex Dir: David W Faulkner
CIO: Michael J Lyons
Dir IT: Sanon Danier
IT Man: Laura Brown
IT Man: John Inferrera

D-U-N-S 10-224-7488
MASSACHUSETTS BAY COMMUTER RAILROAD CO LLC
MBCR
89 South St, Boston, MA 02111-2651
Tel (617) 222-8080 *Founded/Ownrshp* 2002
Sales 91.1MM^E^ *EMP* 1,700
SIC 4011 4111 Railroads, line-haul operating; Commuter bus operation; Commuter rail passenger operation; Railroads, line-haul operating; Commuter bus operation; Commuter rail passenger operation
CFO: Jim Citro
Sr Cor Off: David Schevis
Genl Mgr: James F O Leary
Genl Mgr: Kevin Lydon

D-U-N-S 00-176-6260
MASSACHUSETTS BAY TRANSPORTATION AUTHORITY
(*Suby of* MASSACHUSETTS DEPARTMENT OF TRANSPORTATION) ★
Mbta 10 Park Plz Ste 3910, Boston, MA 02116
Tel (617) 222-3106 *Founded/Ownrshp* 1918, 2004
Sales NA *EMP* 6,100
Accts Kpmg Llp Boston Ma
SIC 9621 Transit system or authority: government, non-operating; ; Transit system or authority: government, non-operating;
Ch: John R Jenkins
**Treas:* Wesley G Wallace Jr
Ofcr: Conary Beckford
Ofcr: Tony Dang
Ofcr: Gerald Dorsainvil
Ofcr: Brian Howley
Ofcr: Vinney Moy
Ofcr: Lucas Sayers
Ofcr: David Silen
Ofcr: Binh Tran
Ofcr: Danny Vieira
Ofcr: Michael Weeks
Exec: Lauren Armstrong
Exec: Nancy Wallace
Dir Risk M: Lee Ross

D-U-N-S 19-013-3392
MASSACHUSETTS BEHAVIORAL HEALTH PARTNERSHIP
(*Suby of* BEACON HEALTH OPTIONS) ★
1000 Washington St # 310, Boston, MA 02118-2798
Tel (617) 790-4000 *Founded/Ownrshp* 2000
Sales 12.7MM^E^ *EMP* 300
SIC 8741 Nursing & personal care facility management; Nursing & personal care facility management
CEO: Nancy Lane
Genl Mgr: Avanele Cole

D-U-N-S 05-524-9515
MASSACHUSETTS BOARD OF HIGHER EDUCATION SYSTEM
(*Suby of* EXECUTIVE OFFICE OF COMMONWEALTH OF MASSACHUSETTS) ★
1 Ashburton Pl Rm 1401, Boston, MA 02108-1518
Tel (617) 727-7785 *Founded/Ownrshp* 1981
Sales NA *EMP* 6,400
SIC 9411 ;
IT Man: Clantha McCurdy
IT Man: Ron Wong

MASSACHUSETTS BRD OF HGHR
See WORCESTER STATE UNIVERSITY

D-U-N-S 96-485-4876
MASSACHUSETTS BRICKLAYERS & MASONS HEALTH AND WELFARE FUND
645 Wlliam T Mrrssey Blvd, Dorchester, MA 02122-3563
Tel (617) 436-5500 *Founded/Ownrshp* 2010
Sales 27.3MM *EMP* 35^E^
Accts Manzi & Associates Llc North
SIC 8631 Trade union; Trade union

D-U-N-S 09-587-6983
MASSACHUSETTS CHEMISTRY & TECHNOLOGY ALLIANCE INC
621 Huntington Ave, Boston, MA 02115-5801
Tel (617) 879-7000 *Founded/Ownrshp* 1873
Sales NA *EMP* 300
SIC 8299 8221 7911 Art school, except commercial; Colleges universities & professional schools; Dance studios, schools & halls

MASSACHUSETTS COLLEGE OF
See MCPHS UNIVERSITY

D-U-N-S 87-804-3553
MASSACHUSETTS COLLEGE OF LIBERAL ARTS
MCLA
375 Church St, North Adams, MA 01247-4124
Tel (413) 662-5000 *Founded/Ownrshp* 1977
Sales 25.5MM *EMP* 305
Accts O Connor & Drew Pc Braintr
SIC 8221 College, except junior; College, except junior
Pr: Mary K Grant
**CFO:* James Stakenas
**Treas:* Gerald Desmarais
**VP:* Cynthia Brown
VP: Edward Damon
VP: Benjamin Lamb
Store Mgr: Gina Degrenier
Off Admin: Annette Allen
Dir IT: Matt Mervis
IT Man: Laura Brown
Mfg Mgr: Richard Naduea

D-U-N-S 83-768-0198
MASSACHUSETTS COMMUNITY COLLEGES
(*Suby of* MASSACHUSETTS BOARD OF HIGHER EDUCATION SYSTEM) ★
85 Devonshire St Fl 7, Boston, MA 02109-3575
Tel (617) 542-2911 *Founded/Ownrshp* 1995
Sales 36.5MM^E^ *EMP* 6,000
SIC 8222 9199 Community college; ; Community college;

D-U-N-S 00-145-5971
MASSACHUSETTS CONTAINER CORP (MA)
(*Suby of* CONNECTICUT CONTAINER CORP) ★
300 Cedar Hill St, Marlborough, MA 01752-3036
Tel (508) 481-1100 *Founded/Ownrshp* 1963
Sales 24.3MM^E^ *EMP* 114
SIC 2653 Corrugated & solid fiber boxes; Corrugated & solid fiber boxes
Pr: Lawrence Perkins
**VP:* Louis Cerruzi
**VP:* Harry Perkins

D-U-N-S 06-778-7366
MASSACHUSETTS CONVENTION CENTER AUTHORITY
HYNES CONVENTION CENTER
(*Suby of* EXECUTIVE OFFICE OF COMMONWEALTH OF MASSACHUSETTS) ★
415 Summer St, Boston, MA 02210-1719
Tel (617) 954-2000 *Founded/Ownrshp* 1983
Sales NA *EMP* 300
Accts Cliftonlarsonallen Llp Boston
SIC 9111 Executive offices; ; Executive offices;
CEO: Travis McReedy
COO: Frederick Peterson
CFO: Travis A McCready
CFO: Lisa Signori
**CFO:* Johanna Storella
Bd of Dir: Jay Gonzalez
Bd of Dir: Gregg P Lisciotti
Ofcr: Scott Lunn
Ofcr: Frank Murray
Sr VP: Carol Fulp
Assoc Dir: Soozin Park
Dir Soc: Arthur Fritch
Dir Soc: Evan Harwood

D-U-N-S 87-850-9116
MASSACHUSETTS DEPARTMENT OF CHILDREN AND FAMILIES
(*Suby of* EOHHS) ★
600 Washington St, Boston, MA 02111-1704
Tel (617) 748-2000 *Founded/Ownrshp* 1980
Sales NA *EMP* 2,867
SIC 9111 Executive offices; Executive offices
Ofcr: Amy Cason
Off Mgr: Connie Fidalgo
Off Admin: Kelley Teele
Opers Supe: Peter Silva

D-U-N-S 87-813-8775
MASSACHUSETTS DEPARTMENT OF CONSERVATION AND RECREATION
(*Suby of* MASSACHUSETTS EXECUTIVE OFFICE OF ENERGY & ENVIRONMENTAL AFFAIRS) ★
251 Causeway St Ste 600, Boston, MA 02114-2119
Tel (617) 626-1250 *Founded/Ownrshp* 1898
Sales NA *EMP* 400
SIC 9511 Environmental agencies; ; Environmental agencies;
CFO: Lauren Johnson

D-U-N-S 79-953-8178
MASSACHUSETTS DEPARTMENT OF ELEMENTARY AND SECONDARY EDUCATION
(*Suby of* EXECUTIVE OFFICE OF COMMONWEALTH OF MASSACHUSETTS) ★
75 Pleasant St, Malden, MA 02148-4906
Tel (781) 338-3000 *Founded/Ownrshp* 1993
Sales NA *EMP* 500^E
SIC 9411 8211 State education department; ; Elementary & secondary schools; State education department; ; Elementary & secondary schools
Pr: David E Leblanc
Ofcr: Joanne Laubach
MIS Dir: Emily Chew
Nutrtnst: Ahmed Bilimoria
Nutrtnst: Alan Dechter
Nutrtnst: Richard Finnigan
Nutrtnst: Robin Haunton
Nutrtnst: Arthur Krochmal
Nutrtnst: Chiniqua Milligan
Nutrtnst: Belinda Wilson
HC Dir: John Bynoe

D-U-N-S 09-096-2085
MASSACHUSETTS DEPARTMENT OF ENVIRONMENTAL PROTECTION
(*Suby of* MASSACHUSETTS EXECUTIVE OFFICE OF ENERGY & ENVIRONMENTAL AFFAIRS) ★
1 Winter St, Boston, MA 02108-4747
Tel (617) 292-5500 *Founded/Ownrshp* 1980
Sales NA *EMP* 1,200
SIC 9511 Environmental agencies; ; Environmental agencies;
Off Mgr: Barbara Wyche
Netwrk Mgr: Rick Hawkins
Counsel: Samuel Bennett
Snr Mgr: John Miano

D-U-N-S 82-484-8642
MASSACHUSETTS DEPARTMENT OF PUBLIC SAFETY
(*Suby of* EXECUTIVE OFFICE OF COMMONWEALTH OF MASSACHUSETTS) ★
1 Ashburton Pl Rm 2133, Boston, MA 02108-1518
Tel (617) 727-7775 *Founded/Ownrshp* 1969
Sales NA *EMP* 22,200
SIC 9221 9229 9223 State police; ; Public order & safety statistics centers; ; Correctional institutions; ; State police; ; Public order & safety statistics centers; ; Correctional institutions;
IT Man: Paul Garrity

D-U-N-S 00-472-6456
MASSACHUSETTS DEPARTMENT OF REVENUE
(*Suby of* ADMINISTRATION AND FINANCE MASSACHUSETTS EXECUTIVE OFFICE FOR) ★
100 Cambridge St, Boston, MA 02114-2509
Tel (617) 626-2201 *Founded/Ownrshp* 1966
Sales NA *EMP* 2,200
SIC 9311 Finance, taxation & monetary policy; ; Finance, taxation & monetary policy;
Ofcr: Daniel Oconnell
Ofcr: Karen Rix
Creative D: Peter Olejnik

D-U-N-S 87-870-0798
MASSACHUSETTS DEPARTMENT OF STATE POLICE
(*Suby of* MASSACHUSETTS DEPARTMENT OF PUBLIC SAFETY) ★
470 Worcester Rd, Framingham, MA 01702-5309
Tel (508) 820-2350 *Founded/Ownrshp* 1865
Sales NA *EMP* 2,400^E
SIC 9221 State police; ; State police;
IT Man: Deborah Broderick
IT Man: Awilda Morgan

D-U-N-S 82-484-8659
MASSACHUSETTS DEPARTMENT OF TRANSPORTATION
(*Suby of* EXECUTIVE OFFICE OF COMMONWEALTH OF MASSACHUSETTS) ★
10 Park Plz Ste 4160, Boston, MA 02116-3979
Tel (857) 368-4636 *Founded/Ownrshp* 1969
Sales NA *EMP* 6,100^E
SIC 9621 Regulation, administration of transportation; ; Regulation, administration of transportation;
CEO: Stephanie Pollack
Admn Mgr: Frank Depaola
Dir IT: Diane Nawrocki
Dir IT: Frank Spada
IT Man: Paul Jay
IT Man: Carol Sugerman
Genl Couns: Maryellen Lyons
Snr Mgr: Shoukry Elnahal

D-U-N-S 87-813-9013
MASSACHUSETTS DEPT OF FISH AND GAME
(*Suby of* MASSACHUSETTS EXECUTIVE OFFICE OF ENERGY & ENVIRONMENTAL AFFAIRS) ★
251 Causeway St Ste 400, Boston, MA 02114-2119
Tel (617) 626-1500 *Founded/Ownrshp* 1974
Sales NA *EMP* 300
SIC 9512 Wildlife conservation agencies; ; Wildlife conservation agencies;
COO: Rachel N Calabro
Genl Couns: Douglas Rice
Counsel: Laura Dietz
Counsel: Ariana Johnson
Snr Mgr: Thomas La Rosa
Snr Mgr: Walter Mulligan

D-U-N-S 82-484-8162
MASSACHUSETTS DEPT OF HOUSING AND COMMUNITY DEVELOPMENT
(*Suby of* MASSACHUSETTS DEPARTMENT OF ECONOMIC DEVELOPMENT)
100 Cambridge St Fl 3, Boston, MA 02114-2509
Tel (617) 573-1114 *Founded/Ownrshp* 1969
Sales NA *EMP* 463^E
SIC 9531

D-U-N-S 87-836-9362
MASSACHUSETTS DEPT OF MENTAL HEALTH
(*Suby of* EOHHS) ★
25 Staniford St, Boston, MA 02114-2503
Tel (617) 626-8000 *Founded/Ownrshp* 1900
Sales NA *EMP* 4,000
SIC 9431

D-U-N-S 87-865-1041
MASSACHUSETTS DEPT OF MENTAL RETARDATION
DMR METRO REGION
(*Suby of* EOHHS) ★
500 Harrison Ave Ste 1r, Boston, MA 02118-2439
Tel (617) 727-5608 *Founded/Ownrshp* 1987
Sales NA *EMP* 7,555
SIC 9431 Mental health agency administration, government; ; Mental health agency administration, government;
**CFO:* Jeanette Maillet
CIO: Jack Coyne

D-U-N-S 87-829-8900
MASSACHUSETTS DEPT OF PUBLIC HEALTH
(*Suby of* EOHHS) ★
250 Washington St, Boston, MA 02108-4603
Tel (617) 624-6000 *Founded/Ownrshp* 1975
Sales NA *EMP* 3,000
SIC 9431 Public health agency administration, government; ; Public health agency administration, government;
Ofcr: John Bernardo
Ofcr: Robert Locke
Prgrm Mgr: Scott Calisti
Prgrm Mgr: Shirin Karanfiloglu
Plng Mgr: Paul Holloway
Nurse Mgr: Eugenia Goldsby
IT Man: Lourdes Ordinola
IT Man: Sally Rizzo
Psych: Robert McMackin
Genl Couns: Katherine Borden
Genl Couns: Joel Buenaventura

D-U-N-S 87-850-8167
MASSACHUSETTS DEPT OF TRANSITIONAL ASSISTANCE
(*Suby of* EOHHS) ★
600 Washington St Fl 5, Boston, MA 02111-1704
Tel (617) 348-8500 *Founded/Ownrshp* 1960
Sales NA *EMP* 3,250
SIC 9441 Administration of social & manpower programs; ; Administration of social & manpower programs;
IT Man: Mary Sheehan

D-U-N-S 94-757-9306
MASSACHUSETTS DEPT OF WORKFORCE DEVELOPMENT
(*Suby of* EXECUTIVE OFFICE OF COMMONWEALTH OF MASSACHUSETTS) ★
1 Ashburton Pl Rm 2112, Boston, MA 02108-1518
Tel (617) 626-7122 *Founded/Ownrshp* 1997
Sales NA *EMP* 2,239^E
SIC 9651 Labor regulatory agency; Labor regulatory agency
Prin: Jane C Edmonds

D-U-N-S 08-065-8078
MASSACHUSETTS DEPT OF YOUTH SERVICES
(*Suby of* EOHHS) ★
600 Washington St Fl 4, Boston, MA 02111-1704
Tel (617) 727-7575 *Founded/Ownrshp* 1990
Sales NA *EMP* 418
SIC 9223 ;
Prgrm Mgr: William Gellis
Dir IT: Carol Macfarland

D-U-N-S 87-858-7658
MASSACHUSETTS EDUCATIONAL FINANCING AUTHORITY
M E F A
160 Federal St Fl 4, Boston, MA 02110-1721
Tel (617) 224-4800 *Founded/Ownrshp* 1981
Sales NA *EMP* 53
Accts Price Waterhouse Coopers
SIC 6111 Student Loan Marketing Association; Student Loan Marketing Association
Ex Dir: Thomas M Graf
Mng Pt: Neil Markson
**Ch Bd:* Joe Hunt
VP: Micheal Hogan
**Ex Dir:* Thomas Graf
IT Man: James Leighton
Mktg Dir: Penny Hauck

D-U-N-S 00-695-2626 IMP
MASSACHUSETTS ELECTRIC CO
NATIONAL GRID
(*Suby of* NATIONAL GRID USA) ★
40 Sylvan Rd, Waltham, MA 02451-1120
Tel (781) 907-1000 *Founded/Ownrshp* 1887
Sales 1.1MMM^E *EMP* 1,396
SIC 4911 Distribution, electric power; Generation, electric power; Transmission, electric power; Distribution, electric power; Generation, electric power; Transmission, electric power
Pr: Marcy L Reed
**Treas:* Malcolm Charles Cooper
**Ex VP:* Ellen Smith
**Sr VP:* Pat Hogan
**Sr VP:* Colin Owyang
VP: David Pretyman
**VP:* Ross Turrini
**VP:* Martin Wheatcroft
**VP:* Edward White
Prgrm Mgr: Patricia Harper
Prgrm Mgr: Harry McDonough
Board of Directors: Colin Owyang, Linda Claire Ryan, Ellen Smith

D-U-N-S 82-484-8428
MASSACHUSETTS EXECUTIVE OFFICE OF EDUCATION
EDUCATION, EXECUTIVE OFFICE OF
1 Ashburton Pl Rm 1403, Boston, MA 02108-1518
Tel (617) 979-8340 *Founded/Ownrshp* 2015
Sales NA *EMP* 450
SIC 9411 Administration of educational programs
Prin: Piedad Robertson
**CFO:* David Bunker
Board of Directors: David Bunker

D-U-N-S 82-484-8451
MASSACHUSETTS EXECUTIVE OFFICE OF ENERGY & ENVIRONMENTAL AFFAIRS
OFFICE COASTAL ZONE MANAGEMENT
(*Suby of* EXECUTIVE OFFICE OF COMMONWEALTH OF MASSACHUSETTS) ★
100 Cambridge St Ste 900, Boston, MA 02114-2534
Tel (617) 626-1000 *Founded/Ownrshp* 1974
Sales NA *EMP* 2,657
SIC 9511 9512 9641 Air, water & solid waste management; ; Land, mineral & wildlife conservation; ; Regulation of agricultural marketing; ; Air, water & solid waste management; ; Land, mineral & wildlife conservation; ; Regulation of agricultural marketing;

D-U-N-S 82-484-8477
MASSACHUSETTS EXECUTIVE OFFICE OF HEALTH AND HUMAN SERVICES
EOHHS
(*Suby of* EXECUTIVE OFFICE OF COMMONWEALTH OF MASSACHUSETTS) ★
1 Ashburton Pl Rm 1111, Boston, MA 02108-1518
Tel (617) 573-1600 *Founded/Ownrshp* 1975
Sales NA *EMP* 23,000
SIC 9431 9441 Administration of public health programs; ; Administration of social & manpower programs; Administration of public health programs; ; Administration of social & manpower programs
**CFO:* Matthew Klitus
Off Mgr: Susan Saia

D-U-N-S 60-342-0563
MASSACHUSETTS EYE AND EAR ASSOCIATES INC
243 Charles St, Boston, MA 02114-3002
Tel (617) 523-7900 *Founded/Ownrshp* 1986
Sales 106.0MM *EMP* 32^E
SIC 8011 Eyes, ears, nose & throat specialist: physician/surgeon; Eyes, ears, nose & throat specialist: physician/surgeon
Pr: F Cortis Smith
CTO: Jesse Spivack
Doctor: Ilya Malikin

D-U-N-S 04-057-0892
MASSACHUSETTS EYE AND EAR INFIRMARY
243 Charles St, Boston, MA 02114-3002
Tel (617) 573-3499 *Founded/Ownrshp* 1827
Sales 152.0MM *EMP* 1,550
SIC 8069 Eye, ear, nose & throat hospital; Eye, ear, nose & throat hospital
CEO: John Fernandez
Chf Rad: Hugh Curtin
**Pr:* Ephraim Friedman
**COO:* Jeff Pike M P H
**CFO:* Carrol Ann Williams
**Treas:* J Frank Gerrity
**VP:* Javier Balloffet
VP: Robert Biggio
VP: Bruce Jordan
VP: Jennifer Street
Dir Lab: Lisa Bove
Dir Lab: Wenyi Cai

D-U-N-S 07-382-5945
MASSACHUSETTS EYE AND EAR INFIRMARY & PHYSICIAN STAFF INC
243 Charles St, Boston, MA 02114-3002
Tel (617) 573-3499 *Founded/Ownrshp* 1988
Sales 221.6MM *EMP* 1,050
SIC 8069 8011 Eye, ear, nose & throat hospital; Plastic surgeon; Eye, ear, nose & throat hospital; Plastic surgeon
Pr: John Fernandez
**CFO:* Peter Chinetti
**Treas:* William Darling
Prin: Anthony P Adamis
Prin: Saumil N Merchant
Doctor: Ramon A Franco Jr
Doctor: Janay L Wiggs MD
Board of Directors: Sheldon Buckler Phd

D-U-N-S 04-943-5415
MASSACHUSETTS FINANCIAL SERVICES CO
M F S
(*Suby of* SUN LIFE ASSURANCE COMPANY OF CANADA)
111 Huntington Ave, Boston, MA 02199-7610
Tel (617) 954-5000 *Founded/Ownrshp* 1969
Sales 724.9MM^E *EMP* 1,700
SIC 6282 6211 6289 Investment advisory service; Mutual funds, selling by independent salesperson; Stock transfer agents; Investment advisory service; Mutual funds, selling by independent salesperson; Stock transfer agents
CEO: Robert J Manning
V Ch: David A Antonelli
Pr: Jean Anderson
Pr: Fenn Duncan
Pr: Catherine Manganese
Pr: Mike W Roberge
COO: Robin Stelmach
CFO: Amrit Kawal
CFO: Amrit Konwal
Treas: W London
Chf Mktg O: Andrew Washburn
Ofcr: Michael Pandolfi
VP: Elizabeth Pratt
VP: Marcus Smith
Exec: Michele Perrotti
Dir Lab: Gina Aldis
Assoc Dir: Paul Brito
Assoc Dir: Benjamin Dick
Assoc Dir: Brendan Mannix

D-U-N-S 07-313-0411 IMP
MASSACHUSETTS GENERAL HOSPITAL
GENERAL HOSPITAL, THE
(*Suby of* PARTNERS HEALTHCARE SYSTEM INC) ★
55 Fruit St, Boston, MA 02114-2696
Tel (617) 724-6454 *Founded/Ownrshp* 1811
Sales 2.2MMM *EMP* 10,156
SIC 8062 8011 General medical & surgical hospitals; Hospital, affiliated with AMA residency; Hospital, professional nursing school; Offices & clinics of medical doctors; General medical & surgical hospitals; Hospital, affiliated with AMA residency; Hospital, professional nursing school; Offices & clinics of medical doctors
CEO: David Torchiana
Chf Path: Robert B Colvin
Chf Path: David N Louis
Chf Rad: James H Thrall
**Pr:* Peter L Slavin
**CFO:* Laura Wysk
**Ch:* Cathy E Minehan
**Treas:* Peter K Markell
Bd of Dir: Frank Pedlow
Bd of Dir: Cathleen Poliquin
Bd of Dir: Daniel Rosenthal
Bd of Dir: David Ryan
Bd of Dir: Antonia Stephen
Bd of Dir: Andrea Stidsen
Bd of Dir: Cameron Wright
Trst: Charles C Ames
Trst: John W Henry
Trst: Edward P Lawrence
Trst: Phillip A Sharp
Ofcr: Emily Parker
Sr VP: Jeff Davis

D-U-N-S 13-924-1389
MASSACHUSETTS GENERAL PHYSICIANS ORGANIZATION INC
(*Suby of* GENERAL HOSPITAL) ★
55 Fruit St 208, Boston, MA 02114-2621
Tel (617) 724-0578 *Founded/Ownrshp* 1983
Sales 44.8MM^E *EMP* 1,000^E
SIC 8011 Offices & clinics of medical doctors; Offices & clinics of medical doctors
Pr: Daniel A Ginsburg
**Pr:* Peter Slavin
Assoc Dir: Eric Isselbacher
Adm Dir: Carol Milbury
Adm Dir: Dianne Moschella
Doctor: Cheryl Bunker MD
Doctor: Stephen Goldfinger MD
Snr Mgr: Jane Ritzenthaler
Snr Mgr: Ann Snow

D-U-N-S 09-218-4407 IMP
MASSACHUSETTS HEALTH CARE SERVICES INC
HOME STAFF
40 Millbrook St Ste 1, Worcester, MA 01606-2836
Tel (508) 755-4600 *Founded/Ownrshp* 1977
Sales 8.9MM *EMP* 450
SIC 8082 Home health care services; Home health care services
Pr: Nancy Stassi
**VP:* John Stassi
Opers Mgr: Theresa Eckstrom
Pr Mgr: Judith Mansur

D-U-N-S 03-081-1111
MASSACHUSETTS HIGHER EDUCATION ASSISTANCE CORP
AMERICAN STUDENT ASSISTANCE
100 Cambridge St Ste 1600, Boston, MA 02114-2518
Tel (617) 728-4507 *Founded/Ownrshp* 1956
Sales NA *EMP* 580
Accts Cbiz Tofias Boston Ma
SIC 6111 Student Loan Marketing Association; Student Loan Marketing Association
Pr: Paul C Combe
**Ch Bd:* Richard A Wiley
Pr: John Zurick
**CFO:* Michael F Finn
CFO: Barbara Matez
**V Ch Bd:* Patricia A McWade
**VP:* Susan Nathan
**VP:* Arnold Sammis
**VP:* Shelley Saunders
**VP:* Alexander Shapiro
VP: Mae St Julien
Exec: Donna Shelby
Assoc Dir: Ann Brieck

D-U-N-S 07-382-1704
MASSACHUSETTS HOUSING FINANCE AGENCY PROPERTY ACQUISITION AND DISPOSITION CORP
MASSHOUSING
1 Beacon St, Boston, MA 02108-3107
Tel (617) 854-1000 *Founded/Ownrshp* 1968
Sales NA *EMP* 325
SIC 6162 9531 Mortgage bankers & correspondents; Housing agency, government; ; Mortgage bankers & correspondents; Housing agency, government;
Ch Bd: Michael J Dirrane
**CFO:* Michael Fitzmaurice
**Ch:* Ronald A Homer
**Treas:* Andris J Silins
Ofcr: Tim Lanzillo
Ofcr: Deborah Morse
Ofcr: Tyrone Reed
Ofcr: Paul Silverstone
Ofcr: Antonio Torres
Sr VP: Sergio Ferreira
Sr VP: Paul Scola

D-U-N-S 00-142-5594
MASSACHUSETTS INSTITUTE OF TECHNOLOGY
MIT
77 Massachusetts Ave, Cambridge, MA 02139-4307
Tel (617) 253-1000 *Founded/Ownrshp* 1861
Sales 2.1MMM^E *EMP* 12,000
SIC 8221 University; University
Pr: L Rafael Reif
**Ch:* Dana Mead
**Treas:* Israel Ruiz
VP: Kirk D Kolenbrander
**VP:* Kirk Kolendrander
VP: Julie Lucas
VP: R G Morgan
VP: Kathryn Willmore
Exec: Edward Fields
Dir Pat Ca: Christine Ruzycki
Assoc Dir: Michael Myers
Comm Man: Alyssa May

D-U-N-S 11-293-8055
MASSACHUSETTS LABORERS HEALTH AND WELFARE FUND
14 New England Exec Park, Burlington, MA 01803-5219
Tel (781) 238-0700 *Founded/Ownrshp* 1954
Sales NA *EMP* 30
SIC 6371 Union welfare, benefit & health funds; Union welfare, benefit & health funds

D-U-N-S 83-712-6572
MASSACHUSETTS LEGAL ASSISTANCE CORP
7 Winthrop Sq Fl 2, Boston, MA 02110-1245
Tel (617) 367-8544 *Founded/Ownrshp* 1983
Sales 20.0MM *EMP* 13
Accts Alexander Aronson Finning &
SIC 8111 General practice attorney, lawyer; General practice attorney, lawyer
Ex Dir: Lonnie Powers
Comm Dir: Donna Southwell
Comm Man: Catherine Rizos
IT Man: Karen Telfer
Opers Mgr: Danielle Hines-Graham

D-U-N-S 87-939-9764
MASSACHUSETTS MARITIME ACADEMY INC
101 Academy Dr, Buzzards Bay, MA 02532-3405
Tel (508) 830-5000 *Founded/Ownrshp* 1891
Sales 32.2MM *EMP* 210
Accts O Connor & Drew Pc Braintree
SIC 8221 Colleges universities & professional schools; Colleges universities & professional schools
Pr: Francis McDonald
CFO: Rose M Cass
Ofcr: Michael Campbell
Ofcr: Fran Tishkevich
Ofcr: Melissa Turner
VP: Anne Fallon
**VP:* Richard Gurnon
**VP:* Michael Joyce
Exec: James Wirzburger
Mtls Mgr: Kevin Conrad
Doctor: Raguraman Krishnasamy

D-U-N-S 07-535-7079
MASSACHUSETTS MEDICAL SOCIETY INC
NEW ENGLAND JOURNAL OF MEDICIN
860 Winter St, Waltham, MA 02451-1411
Tel (781) 893-4610 *Founded/Ownrshp* 1781
Sales 122.6MM *EMP* 700
Accts Cbiz Tofias Boston Ma
SIC 2721 8621 Trade journals: publishing & printing; Medical field-related associations; Trade journals: publishing & printing; Medical field-related associations
Pr: Dale Magee
VP: Charles Alagero
**VP:* Corinne Broderick
Comm Dir: Frank Fortin
Ex Dir: Bill Paige
Mng Dir: Rob Stuart
CIO: Sara Fleming
DP Exec: Brian Stoughton
Dir IT: Leon Barzin
Dir IT: Julie Mock
IT Man: Jean Costello

D-U-N-S 07-172-4900
MASSACHUSETTS MUNICIPAL WHOLESALE ELECTRIC CO
M M W E C
327 Moody St, Ludlow, MA 01056-1246
Tel (413) 589-0141 *Founded/Ownrshp* 1969
Sales 40.4MM^E *EMP* 70^E
Accts Vitale Caturano & Company Pc
SIC 4911 Generation, electric power; Generation, electric power
CEO: Ronald Decurzio
Treas: Matthew Ide
CIO: Daniel Suppin
Plnt Mgr: Karl Winkler
Secur Mgr: Kim Boas

MASSACHUSETTS MUTUAL LF INSUR
See CBIZ INSURANCE SERVICES INC

D-U-N-S 00-695-6049 IMP/EXP
MASSACHUSETTS MUTUAL LIFE INSURANCE CO
MASSMUTUAL
1295 State St, Springfield, MA 01111-0001
Tel (413) 788-8411 *Founded/Ownrshp* 1851
Sales NA *EMP* 27,091
SIC 6321 6324 6411 6282 Disability health insurance; Health insurance carriers; Group hospitalization plans; Pension & retirement plan consultants; Investment advice; Disability health insurance; Health insurance carriers; Group hospitalization plans; Pension & retirement plan consultants; Investment advice
Ch Bd: Roger W Crandall
Ch Bd: James Birle
Pr: Rich Cartier
CEO: Mark T Bertolini
CFO: Michael Rollings
Treas: Todd Picken
Ex VP: Eddie Ahmed
Ex VP: William Glavin
Ex VP: Mark D Roellig
Ex VP: Elizabeth A Ward
Sr VP: Bob Casale
Sr VP: Rodney J Dillman
Sr VP: Stephen L Kuhn
Sr VP: Dennis Stempel
VP: Stefano Martini

D-U-N-S 62-533-3000
MASSACHUSETTS MUTUAL LIFE INSURANCE CO
HILTON PHOENIX AIRPORT
2435 S 47th St, Phoenix, AZ 85034-6410
Tel (480) 894-1600 *Founded/Ownrshp* 1988
Sales NA *EMP* 99
SIC 6311 Life insurance
Pr: John Masaryk

D-U-N-S 94-243-0513
MASSACHUSETTS MUTUAL LIFE INSURANCE CO
HILTON WOODCLIFF LAKE
200 Tice Blvd, Woodcliff Lake, NJ 07677-8410
Tel (201) 391-3600 *Founded/Ownrshp* 1980
Sales NA *EMP* 220
SIC 6311 Life insurance; Life insurance
Pr: Gary Tucker
CFO: Barbara Foley
Sls Dir: Debbie Ignelzi

D-U-N-S 87-824-9424
MASSACHUSETTS NATIONAL GUARD
(*Suby of* MASSACHUSETTS DEPARTMENT OF PUBLIC SAFETY) ★
50 Maple St, Milford, MA 01757-3680
Tel (508) 473-3350 *Founded/Ownrshp* 1996
Sales NA *EMP* 6,000
SIC 9711 National Guard; ; National Guard;
Prin: L Scott Rice

D-U-N-S 94-758-1120
MASSACHUSETTS OFFICE OF CONSUMER AFFAIRS AND BUSINESS REGULATION
(*Suby of* EXECUTIVE OFFICE OF COMMONWEALTH OF MASSACHUSETTS) ★
10 Park Plz Ste 5170, Boston, MA 02116-3980
Tel (617) 727-7755 *Founded/Ownrshp* 1996
Sales NA *EMP* 525
SIC 9651 Regulation, miscellaneous commercial sectors; Regulation, miscellaneous commercial sectors
Prin: Daniel Crane
CFO: Grahm Holmes

D-U-N-S 00-176-6328
MASSACHUSETTS PORT AUTHORITY
MASSPORT
1 Harborside Dr Ste 200s, Boston, MA 02128-2905
Tel (617) 561-1600 *Founded/Ownrshp* 1956
Sales 123.6MM^E *EMP* 1,102
Accts Pricewaterhousecoopers Llp Bo
SIC 4581 4491 6799 6512 4785 Airport terminal services; Waterfront terminal operation; Piers, incl. buildings & facilities: operation & maintenance; Investors; Commercial & industrial building operation; Toll bridge operation; Airport terminal services; Waterfront terminal operation; Piers, incl. buildings & facilities: operation & maintenance; Investors; Commercial & industrial building operation; Toll bridge operation
CEO: Thomas P Glynn
**Ch Bd:* Mark Robinson
**CFO:* John Pranckevicius
Exec: Meg Shannon
Prgrm Mgr: Richard Bessom
Prgrm Mgr: James Donegan
Genl Mgr: Mike Caro
CIO: Francis X Anglin
MIS Dir: Lou Hinkley
QA Dir: Glenn Adams
IT Man: Stephanie Furfaro

D-U-N-S 87-722-2257
MASSACHUSETTS REGISTRY OF MOTOR VEHICLES
(*Suby of* EXECUTIVE OFFICE OF COMMONWEALTH OF MASSACHUSETTS) ★
25 Newport Avenue Ext # 4, Quincy, MA 02171-1748
Tel (617) 351-3500 *Founded/Ownrshp* 2006
Sales NA *EMP* 750
SIC 9621 Motor vehicle licensing & inspection office, government;

D-U-N-S 07-382-3833
MASSACHUSETTS SOCIETY FOR PREVENTION CRUELTY ANIMALS
MSPCA/ANGELL MEM ANIMAL HOSP
350 S Huntington Ave, Boston, MA 02130-4803
Tel (617) 522-7282 *Founded/Ownrshp* 1868
Sales 52.3MM^E *EMP* 540^E
SIC 8699 0742 2721 Animal humane society; Animal hospital services, pets & other animal specialties; Magazines: publishing only, not printed on site; Animal humane society; Animal hospital services, pets & other animal specialties; Magazines: publishing only, not printed on site
Pr: Gus W Thornton Dvm
Pr: John Bowen
CFO: Kim Gazzola
**Treas:* Robert S Cummings
Ofcr: Naomi Ostrow
IT Man: Maureen Milano
Mktg Dir: Bonnie Jarm
Mktg Mgr: Elli Plihcik
Ansthlgy: Ashley Barton
Doctor: Rebecca Stlaske

D-U-N-S 08-231-1556 IMP
MASSACHUSETTS SPORTSERVICE INC
DELAWARE NORTH COMPANIES
(*Suby of* DELAWARE NORTH COMPANIES SPORTSERVICE INC) ★
100 Legends Way, Boston, MA 02114-1300
Tel (617) 624-1600 *Founded/Ownrshp* 1970
Sales 16.8MM^E *EMP* 475
SIC 5812 5813 5947 Concessionaire; Beer garden (drinking places); Novelties; Concessionaire; Beer garden (drinking places); Novelties
CEO: Gary Elsmore
**Pr:* Nancy Parker
Sr VP: Amy Latimer
VP: Hugh Lombardi

D-U-N-S 36-070-5065
MASSACHUSETTS SUPREME JUDICIAL COURT
MASSACHSTTS SPREME JDICIAL CRT
(*Suby of* COMMONWEALTH OF MASSACHUSETTS) ★
1 Pemberton Sq Ste 2500, Boston, MA 02108-1717
Tel (617) 557-1020 *Founded/Ownrshp* 1628
Sales NA *EMP* 6,700
SIC 9211 State courts; ; State courts;

D-U-N-S 07-380-5871
MASSACHUSETTS TEACHERS ASSOCIATION STAFF ORGANIZATION INC
M T A
2 Heritage Dr 8, Quincy, MA 02171-2119
Tel (617) 878-8000 *Founded/Ownrshp* 1913
Sales 45.7MM *EMP* 155
Accts Kirkland Albrecht & Fredrickso
SIC 8621 Education & teacher association; Education & teacher association
Pr: Catherine Boudreau
Treas: Laurie Larson
Bd of Dir: Stephen Gencarella
**VP:* Timothy Sullivan
**Ex Dir:* Ann Clarke
**Ex Dir:* Edward Sullivan
MIS Dir: Vicki Bethea
Dir IT: Glenn Coolong
Counsel: Americo Salini Jr

D-U-N-S 00-176-6278
MASSACHUSETTS TURNPIKE AUTHORITY
(*Suby of* MASSACHUSETTS DEPARTMENT OF TRANSPORTATION) ★
10 Park Plz Ste 5170, Boston, MA 02116-3980
Tel (617) 248-2800 *Founded/Ownrshp* 1952
Sales 45.7MM^E *EMP* 1,200
SIC 4785 9199 Toll road operation; Tunnel operation, vehicular; ; Toll road operation; Tunnel operation, vehicular;
Ch Bd: John Cogliano
V Ch: Jordan Levy
CFO: Ann Journeay
CFO: Joe McCann
**CFO:* Joseph McCann
Bd of Dir: Matthew Amorello
Ofcr: Jennifer Flagg
Dir Bus: Steve Jacques
Ex Dir: Allan Lebobidge
CIO: William Catina
DP Dir: Silvio Petratlia

D-U-N-S 07-916-1389
MASSACHUSETTS WATER RESOURCES AUTHORITY
MWRA
Charl Navy Yard 100 First, Boston, MA 02129
Tel (617) 788-4917 *Founded/Ownrshp* 1985
Sales 80.0MM^E *EMP* 1,200
SIC 1623 Water, sewer & utility lines; Water, sewer & utility lines
Ex Dir: Frederick Leskey

D-U-N-S 15-725-5522
MASSACHUSETTS WATER RESOURCES AUTHORITY
MWRA
(*Suby of* EXECUTIVE OFFICE OF COMMONWEALTH OF MASSACHUSETTS) ★
100 1st Ave, Boston, MA 02129-2043
Tel (617) 242-6000 *Founded/Ownrshp* 1972
Sales NA *EMP* 1,200
Accts Kpmg Llp Boston Ma
SIC 9511 Waste management program administration, government; Water control & quality agency, government; Waste management program administration, government; Water control & quality agency, government
Ch: Richard K Sullivan Jr
**COO:* Michael Hornbrook
**CFO:* Rachel Madden
Treas: Thomas Durkin
VP: Kristin Macdougall
Dir: Stephen Estes-Smargiasi
**Ex Dir:* Fred Laskey
Ex Dir: Frederick A Lskey
Prgrm Mgr: Daniel Nvule
Dir IT: Pamela Soukamneuth
Sys Mgr: Richard Cane

D-U-N-S 12-545-0168
MASSANA CONSTRUCTION INC
MASSMANN STUDIOS
115 Howell Rd, Tyrone, GA 30290-2036
Tel (770) 632-2081 *Founded/Ownrshp* 2001
Sales 37.7MM^E *EMP* 150
SIC 1622 1629 Bridge, tunnel & elevated highway; Dams, waterways, docks & other marine construction
Pr: Mark Massmann
Area Mgr: Mike Keyser
Div Mgr: Rob Starr

MASSAPEQUA HIGH SCHOOL
See MASSAPEQUA UNION FREE SCHOOL DISTRICT

D-U-N-S 60-504-4767
MASSAPEQUA IMPORTS 1 LTD
LEXUS OF MASSAPEQUA
4950 Sunrise Hwy, Massapequa Park, NY 11762-2904
Tel (516) 795-7600 *Founded/Ownrshp* 1989
Sales 28.4MM^E *EMP* 100^E
SIC 5511 7532 Automobiles, new & used; Body shop, automotive; Automobiles, new & used; Body shop, automotive
Pr: John Staluppi
Sales Asso: Chris Bahamonde
Sales Asso: Fred Sachmechi

D-U-N-S 04-919-5720
MASSAPEQUA UNION FREE SCHOOL DISTRICT
MASSAPEQUA HIGH SCHOOL
4925 Merrick Rd, Massapequa, NY 11758-6201
Tel (516) 308-5900 *Founded/Ownrshp* 1800
Sales 52.4MM^E *EMP* 1,000
Accts Rs Abrams & Co Llp Ronkonk
SIC 8211 Public elementary & secondary schools; Public elementary & secondary schools
Dir Sec: Robert Schilling
IT Man: Adrienne Gomez
Teacher Pr: Dina Maggiacomo
HC Dir: John Piropato

D-U-N-S 60-939-6197 EXP
MASSARO CORP
120 Delta Dr, Pittsburgh, PA 15238-2806
Tel (412) 963-2800 *Founded/Ownrshp* 1989
Sales 55.5MM^E *EMP* 72^E
SIC 1542 1541 Commercial & office building, new construction; Commercial & office buildings, renovation & repair; Industrial buildings & warehouses
CEO: Joseph A Massaro Jr
**Pr:* Joseph A Massaro III
COO: Demeshia Seals
**CFO:* Michael Katz
VP: Randy Hartsock
**VP:* Steven M Massaro
VP: Anthony Moses
VP: Joseph Tavella
**Prin:* David E Massaro
**Prin:* Linda M Massaro
Off Mgr: Vivian Anderson

D-U-N-S 94-867-7075
MASSASOIT COMMUNITY COLLEGE
1 Massasoit Blvd, Brockton, MA 02302-3996
Tel (508) 588-9100 *Founded/Ownrshp* 1965
Sales 40.3MM^E *EMP* 1,203
Accts O Connor & Drew Pc Cpas Brai
SIC 8222 Community college; Community college
Pr: Charles Wall
COO: Bonnie Paglia
CFO: John Caffelle
CFO: Betty Learned
**CFO:* William A Mitchell
CFO: Phillip Pergola
Sr VP: Ralph Kidder
**VP:* Barbara Finklestein
**VP:* David Tracey
Ex Dir: Linda Bean
CIO: Colin Moran

D-U-N-S 07-571-9864
MASSASOIT GREYHOUND ASSOCIATION INC
RAYNHAM DOG TRACK
1958 Broadway, Raynham, MA 02767-1900
Tel (508) 824-4071 *Founded/Ownrshp* 1934
Sales 18.5MM^E *EMP* 800
SIC 7948 Dog racing; Dog racing
Ch Bd: George L Carney Jr
**Pr:* Jarvis Hunt
**VP:* Joseph F Carney

D-U-N-S 03-805-1228
MASSBIOLOGICS
460 Walk Hill St, Boston, MA 02126-3120
Tel (617) 474-3000 *Founded/Ownrshp* 2001
Sales 55.3MM^E *EMP* 200
SIC 2836 8071 Vaccines; Medical laboratories; Vaccines; Medical laboratories
IT Man: John Fitzmaurice

MASSCO
See MAINTENANCE SUPPLY CO INC

D-U-N-S 94-576-1351
MASSE CONTRACTING INC
5644 N Highway 1, Lockport, LA 70374-2100
Tel (985) 532-2380 *Founded/Ownrshp* 1994
Sales 17.8MM^E *EMP* 800^E
SIC 7363 Manpower pools; Manpower pools
Pr: Craig P Masse

D-U-N-S 01-077-9924
MASSENA CENTRAL SCHOOL DISTRICT
84 Nightengale Ave, Massena, NY 13662-2594
Tel (315) 764-3700 *Founded/Ownrshp* 1956
Sales 47.7MM *EMP* 450
Accts Seyarth & Seyfarth Cpas Pc
SIC 8211 Public elementary & secondary schools; Public elementary & secondary schools
IT Man: Nickolas Brouillette

D-U-N-S 96-787-0648
MASSENA MEMORIAL HOSPITAL
POWN OF MASSENA
1 Hospital Dr, Massena, NY 13662-1097
Tel (315) 764-1711 *Founded/Ownrshp* 1952
Sales 45.5MM *EMP* 400
SIC 8062 General medical & surgical hospitals; General medical & surgical hospitals
CEO: Charles F Fahd
Pr: Kejian Tang
Ofcr: Sue Beaulieu
Dir Lab: Kevin Ward
Dir Rx: Eric Miller
QA Dir: Betty Macdonald
Dir IT: Gina Bain
Mtls Dir: Carey Latreille
Obsttrcn: Tae Choi

MASSEY COAL EXPORT COMPANY
See APPALACHIA HOLDING CO

D-U-N-S 00-338-9749
MASSEY CONSTRUCTION INC (TN)
MASSEY ELECTRIC CO
3204 Regal Dr, Alcoa, TN 37701-3233
Tel (865) 573-4200 *Founded/Ownrshp* 1957
Sales 35.9MM^E *EMP* 138
SIC 1731 General electrical contractor; General electrical contractor
CEO: C Randy Massey
**Pr:* Lynn C Singleton
**Sec:* Angela R Massey
Bd of Dir: Dennie Massey
Ex VP: Gordon Massey
**VP:* Timothy M Blair
Off Mgr: Jan Seals
Dir IT: Josh Stabile

MASSEY ELECTRIC CO
See MASSEY CONSTRUCTION INC

MASSEY HYUNDAI
See MASSEY INC

D-U-N-S 82-523-3679
MASSEY INC
MASSEY HYUNDAI
1706 Massey Blvd, Hagerstown, MD 21740-6962
Tel (301) 739-6756 *Founded/Ownrshp* 1974
Sales 22.4MM^E *EMP* 46
SIC 5511 Automobiles, new & used
Pr: Jerry E Massey
Genl Mgr: Faith Massey
Sales Exec: James Carter
Sales Exec: Danny Fritz
Sls Mgr: Chris Gaston
Sls Mgr: Todd Kaiser
Sales Asso: David Claycomb
Sales Asso: Eric Hopkins
Sales Asso: John Kindall
Sales Asso: Doug Potter
Sales Asso: Scott Sword

D-U-N-S 02-466-1340
MASSEY MOTOR CO
MASSEY TOYOTA
4760 Us Highway 70 W, Kinston, NC 28504-9123
Tel (252) 523-6111 *Founded/Ownrshp* 1938
Sales 32.9MM *EMP* 40
SIC 5511 7538 5945 New & used car dealers; General automotive repair shops; Automobiles, new & used; General automotive repair shops; Models, toy & hobby
Pr: Gordon R Kelley
VP: Faye Potter
Sls Mgr: Dean Cox
Sls Mgr: Gary Malpass
Sls Mgr: Earl Morgan
Sls Mgr: Daniel New
Sls Mgr: David Phillips
Sls Mgr: Ray Wooten

MASSEY SAAB OF ORLANDO
See SONIC - NORTH CADILLAC INC

D-U-N-S 03-262-7127
MASSEY SERVICES INC
GREENUP LAWN CARE
315 Groveland St, Orlando, FL 32804-4052
Tel (407) 645-2500 *Founded/Ownrshp* 1985
Sales 172.9MM^E *EMP* 1,318
SIC 7342 Exterminating & fumigating; Pest control in structures; Termite control; Exterminating & fumigating; Pest control in structures; Termite control
Ch Bd: Harvey L Massey
**Pr:* Anthony L Massey
**CFO:* Gwyn Elias
Ofcr: Michael Haynes
**VP:* Barbara A Corino
**VP:* Edward Dougherty
**VP:* Lynne Frederick
**VP:* Paul Giordano
**VP:* Adam Jones
**VP:* Jean Nowry
**VP:* Ian Robinson

MASSEY TOYOTA
See MASSEY MOTOR CO

D-U-N-S 00-895-6609
MASSEY WOOD & WEST INC
MWW
1713 Westwood Ave, Richmond, VA 23227-4336
Tel (804) 355-1721 *Founded/Ownrshp* 1975
Sales 30.8MM^E *EMP* 179
Accts Dixon Hughes Goodman Llp Rich
SIC 5983 5541 7353 1711 3442 5172 Fuel oil dealers; Gasoline service stations; Heavy construction equipment rental; Mechanical contractor; Storm doors or windows, metal; Petroleum products; Fuel oil dealers; Gasoline service stations; Heavy construction equipment rental; Mechanical contractor; Storm doors or windows, metal; Petroleum products
Pr: Gerard W Bradley
**Sec:* Patricia Nelson
**VP:* Kirk M Clausen
**VP:* Pamela B Clausen
**VP:* Jeff Shanaberger

MASSEY-YARDLEY DODGE CHRYSLR
See YARDLEY CAR CO

D-U-N-S 06-484-6074 IMP
MASSEYS PLATE GLASS AND ALUMINUM INC
734 E Main St, Branford, CT 06405-2918
Tel (203) 488-2377 *Founded/Ownrshp* 1991
Sales 39.4MM *EMP* 135
Accts Marcum Llp New Haven Ct
SIC 1793 Glass & glazing work; Glass & glazing work
CEO: Robert J Massey Jr
**Pr:* Laura Massey
**Treas:* Jean Massey

MASSHOUSING
See MASSACHUSETTS HOUSING FINANCE AGENCY PROPERTY ACQUISITION AND DISPOSITION CORP

D-U-N-S 04-346-5046
MASSILLON CABLE TV INC (OH)
814 Cable Ct Nw, Massillon, OH 44647-4284
Tel (330) 833-4134 *Founded/Ownrshp* 1965
Sales 33.1MM^E *EMP* 110
SIC 4841 8748 4813 Cable television services; Telecommunications consultant; ; Cable television services; Telecommunications consultant;
Treas: Richard W Gessner
**Pr:* Robert B Gessner
**VP:* Richard Gessner Jr
**VP:* Elizabeth McAllister
**Prin:* H Chas Hess
**Prin:* Jacob F Hess
**Prin:* M P L Kirchhofer
Dir IT: Dave Hoffer
IT Man: David Wagner
Netwrk Eng: Chris Altland
Board of Directors: Dwight Netzley, Richard Reichel, Walter T Sorg Jr

D-U-N-S 08-523-8582
MASSILLON CITY SCHOOLS
930 17th St Ne, Massillon, OH 44646-4853
Tel (330) 830-3900 *Founded/Ownrshp* 1904
Sales 35.2MM^E *EMP* 518
Accts Ciuni & Panichi Inc Clevela
SIC 8211 Public elementary & secondary schools; High school, junior or senior; Public elementary & secondary schools; High school, junior or senior
Treas: Theresa Emmereling
Cmptr Lab: Tom Mottice
Cmptr Lab: Linda Murphy
Dir IT: Rebecca Toomey
IT Man: Rolland Gerstenmaier
Schl Brd P: Marshall Weinberg
HC Dir: Elaine Karp

MASSILLON CMNTY HLTH SYSTEMS
See MASSILLON COMMUNITY HOSPITAL

D-U-N-S 62-260-7260
MASSILLON COMMUNITY HEALTH SYSTEMS LLC
875 8th St Ne, Massillon, OH 44646-8503
Tel (330) 832-8761 *Founded/Ownrshp* 2006
Sales 28.0MM^E *EMP* 1,450
SIC 8062 General medical & surgical hospitals; General medical & surgical hospitals
CEO: Michael Reichfield
VP: Elizabeth Pruitt
Dir Lab: Janelle Gill

D-U-N-S 01-085-4255
MASSILLON COMMUNITY HOSPITAL
MASSILLON CMNTY HLTH SYSTEMS
(*Suby of* MASSILLON COMMUNITY HEALTH SYSTEMS LLC) ★
875 8th St Ne, Massillon, OH 44646-8503
Tel (330) 832-8761 *Founded/Ownrshp* 1905, 2006
Sales 28.0MM^E *EMP* 850
SIC 8062 General medical & surgical hospitals; General medical & surgical hospitals
Pr: Michael Reichfield

D-U-N-S 17-493-3325
MASSILLON COMMUNITY HOSPITAL HEALTH PLAN
HOMETOWN HEALTH NETWORK
100 Lillian Gish Blvd Sw, Massillon, OH 44647-6587
Tel (330) 837-6880 *Founded/Ownrshp* 1985
Sales NA *EMP* 160
SIC 6324 Health maintenance organization (HMO), insurance only; Health maintenance organization (HMO), insurance only
Pr: William Epling
MIS Dir: David March

D-U-N-S 62-012-5638 IMP
MASSIMO ZANETTI BEVERAGE USA INC
KAUAI COFFEE CO
(*Suby of* MASSIMO ZANETTI BEVERAGE GROUP SPA)
1370 Progress Rd, Suffolk, VA 23434-2148
Tel (757) 215-7300 *Founded/Ownrshp* 2005
Sales 600.0MM^E *EMP* 375
SIC 0179 Coffee farm; Coffee farm
CEO: John Boyle
Pr: Michael Rakowski
CEO: Massimo Zanetti
COO: Larry Quier
COO: Rajaram Venkatasamy
VP: Cindy Allen
VP: John Fitzgerald
VP: Chuck Gasstrom
VP: Ali Itani
VP: Brian Kubicki
Area Mgr: Marcie Waranch

D-U-N-S 61-096-9370 IMP
MASSIVE PRINTS
2035 E Vista Bella Way, Compton, CA 90220-6108
Tel (310) 667-8991 *Founded/Ownrshp* 1989
Sales 63.3MM^E *EMP* 500
SIC 5699 T-shirts, custom printed; T-shirts, custom printed
CEO: Courtney Dubar
**Pr:* Thomas C Dubar
VP Opers: Cole Warren

D-U-N-S 00-696-5982 IMP
MASSMAN CONSTRUCTION CO
4400 W 109th St Ste 300, Leawood, KS 66211-1319
Tel (913) 291-2600 *Founded/Ownrshp* 1908
Sales 153.9MM^E *EMP* 250
SIC 1629 1622 Dam construction; Bridge construction; Dam construction; Bridge construction
Pr: H J Massman IV
VP: Patrick Byrne
**VP:* Joseph T Kopp
**VP:* William G Praderio
**VP:* Paul D Scharmer
**VP:* Mark H Schnoebelen
**Prin:* Henry Massman IV
Off Admin: Brenda Isaac
CIO: Irvin McCoy
Software D: Robert Maersch
Sfty Dirs: Danny Bishop

MASSMANN STUDIOS
See MASSANA CONSTRUCTION INC

MASSMUTUAL
See MASSACHUSETTS MUTUAL LIFE INSURANCE CO

D-U-N-S 13-462-6667
MASSMUTUAL INTERNATIONAL LLC
(*Suby of* MASSACHUSETTS MUTUAL LIFE INSURANCE CO) ★
1295 State St, Springfield, MA 01111-0001
Tel (413) 788-8411 *Founded/Ownrshp* 1983
Sales NA *EMP* 2,600^E
SIC 6311 Life insurance carriers; Life insurance carriers
**Pr:* Rodney J Dillman
VP: Michael Doshier

D-U-N-S 13-765-9280
MASSMUTUAL MORTGAGE FINANCE LLC
(*Suby of* MASSACHUSETTS MUTUAL LIFE INSURANCE CO) ★
1295 State St, Springfield, MA 01111-0001
Tel (413) 788-8411 *Founded/Ownrshp* 1984
Sales 837.5MM^E *EMP* 2,387
SIC 6531 Real estate managers; Real estate managers
Pr: Gary E Wendlandt
**Treas:* Anne Isley

D-U-N-S 80-798-6612
MASSMUTUAL RETIREMENT SERVICES LLC
HARTFORD RETIREMENT SVCS LLC
(*Suby of* MASSACHUSETTS MUTUAL LIFE INSURANCE CO) ★
500 Boylston St, Boston, MA 02116-3740
Tel (800) 854-0647 *Founded/Ownrshp* 2013
Sales NA *EMP* 400
SIC 6411 Pension & retirement plan consultants; Pension & retirement plan consultants

MASSPORT
See MASSACHUSETTS PORT AUTHORITY

MASSRY REALTY PARTNERS
See TRI CITY RENTALS MANAGEMENT CORP

MAST
See CITY OF KANSAS CITY MO FIRE DEPARTMENT

D-U-N-S 05-536-1778
MAST DRUG CO INC
DRUGS AMERICA
1910 Ross Mill Rd, Henderson, NC 27537-8789
Tel (252) 492-6344 *Founded/Ownrshp* 1969
Sales 22.6MM^E *EMP* 120
SIC 5912 Drug stores
Pr: Bill Mast
**COO:* Chad Duke
**CFO:* Polly Beal
**VP:* Richard Flye
Brnch Mgr: June Smith
Mktg Mgr: Starr Ellington

D-U-N-S 09-876-1919
MAST GENERAL STORE INC
OLD BOONE MERCANTILE
Hwy 194 W, Valle Crucis, NC 28691
Tel (828) 963-6511 *Founded/Ownrshp* 1883
Sales 43.7MM *EMP* 500
Accts Elliot Davis Pllc Columbia
SIC 5311 Department stores, non-discount; Department stores, non-discount
Pr: John E Cooper Jr
CFO: Mark Gould
**CFO:* Claire McGuire
**Treas:* Faye Cooper
**VP:* Fred Martin
VP Sls: Brenda Binning
Mktg Dir: Angela Warren

MAST GLOBAL FASHIONS
See MAST INDUSTRIES INC

MAST GLOBAL FASHIONS
See MGF SOURCING US LLC

MAST GLOBAL LOGISTICS
See LIMITED BRANDS LOGISTICS SERVICES INC

D-U-N-S 05-345-8006 IMP
■ **MAST INDUSTRIES INC**
MAST GLOBAL FASHIONS
(*Suby of* INTIMATE BRANDS HOLDING LLC) ★
3 Limited Pkwy, Columbus, OH 43230-1467
Tel (614) 415-7000 *Founded/Ownrshp* 2015
Sales 349.2MM^E *EMP* 200
SIC 5137 5136 Women's & children's clothing; Men's & boys' clothing; Women's & children's clothing; Men's & boys' clothing
CEO: Leslie H Wexner
**Pr:* James M Schwartz
Ex VP: Rick Jackson
**VP:* Stuart Burgdoerfer
VP: Anny Hung
Dir IT: Peter Szabo

D-U-N-S 02-845-8300
■ **MAST LOGISTICS SERVICES INC**
(*Suby of* L BRANDS INC) ★
2 Limited Pkwy, Columbus, OH 43230-1445
Tel (614) 856-6000 *Founded/Ownrshp* 1991
Sales 35.7MM^E *EMP* 144^E
SIC 8742 Distribution channels consultant
Pr: Richard J Jackson
Off Mgr: Debra Ausiello
Opers Mgr: David Sewall

D-U-N-S 62-128-6939
MAST TECHNOLOGY INC
Lcaap Bldg 139 State Hwy, Independence, MO 64051
Tel (816) 796-0480 *Founded/Ownrshp* 1965
Sales 36.1MM^E *EMP* 115
SIC 5084

D-U-N-S 08-665-7442
MAST TRUCKING INC
6471 County Road 625, Millersburg, OH 44654-8833
Tel (330) 674-8913 *Founded/Ownrshp* 1969
Sales 31.4MM^E *EMP* 100
SIC 4213 Trucking, except local; Refrigerated products transport
Pr: Willis Mast
**VP:* Elsie Mast
**VP:* Kevin Mast
Sfty Mgr: Keith Rolko
Opers Mgr: Nikolas Marty
Opers Mgr: Robert Rausch

D-U-N-S 00-692-4385 IMP
▲ **MASTEC INC**
800 S Douglas Rd Ste 1200, Coral Gables, FL 33134-3165
Tel (305) 599-1800 *Founded/Ownrshp* 1929
Sales 4.6MMM *EMP* 15,550
Tkr Sym MTZ *Exch* NYS
SIC 1623 8741 Water, sewer & utility lines; Cable television line construction; Transmitting tower (telecommunication) construction; Manhole construction; Construction management; Water, sewer & utility lines; Cable television line construction; Transmitting tower (telecommunication) construction; Manhole construction; Construction management
CEO: Jose R Mas
**Ch Bd:* Jorge Mas
Pr: Jason Kaufman
COO: Robert Apple
CFO: George Pita
Ex VP: Alberto De Cardenas
VP: Chris Bracken
VP: Charles Campbell
Area Mgr: Glen Hannibal
Software D: Jaswinder Singh
Site Mgr: James Costello
Board of Directors: Ernst N Csiszar, Robert J Dwyer, Frank E Jaumot, Julia L Johnson, Javier Palomarez, Jose S Sorzano, John Van Heuvelen

D-U-N-S 00-952-5802
■ **MASTEC NETWORK SOLUTIONS LLC**
(*Suby of* MASTEC INC) ★
806 S Douglas Rd Ste 1100, Coral Gables, FL 33134-3157
Tel (866) 545-1782 *Founded/Ownrshp* 2008
Sales 24.4MM^E *EMP* 100^E
SIC 1731 1799 Voice, data & video wiring contractor; Antenna installation
Pr: Austin Shanselcer
Genl Mgr: Richard Newman

D-U-N-S 96-226-4532
■ **MASTEC NETWORK SOLUTIONS LLC**
(*Suby of* MASTEC INC) ★
2859 Paces Ferry Rd Se # 600, Atlanta, GA 30339-5701
Tel (404) 541-1300 *Founded/Ownrshp* 2008
Sales 191.5MM^E *EMP* 595^E
SIC 4812 7373 Radio telephone communication; Turnkey vendors, computer systems; Radio telephone communication; Turnkey vendors, computer systems
Pr: Rick Suarez
**VP:* Gene Carson Sr
**VP:* Moses Hardie
**VP:* Ramon Mas Sr

D-U-N-S 04-223-6278
■ **MASTEC NORTH AMERICA INC** (FL)
(*Suby of* MASTEC INC) ★
800 S Douglas Rd Ste 1200, Coral Gables, FL 33134-3165
Tel (305) 599-1800 *Founded/Ownrshp* 1998, 1999
Sales 1.9MMM^E *EMP* 7,250
SIC 1623 Water, sewer & utility lines; Cable television line construction; Transmitting tower (telecommunication) construction; Manhole construction; Water, sewer & utility lines; Cable television line construction; Transmitting tower (telecommunication) construction; Manhole construction
CEO: Jose Ramon Mas
**Pr:* Ray E Harris
**COO:* Robert Apple
**CFO:* C Robert Campbell
**VP:* Charles R Campbell
Board of Directors: Ernst N Csiszar, Robert J Dwyer, Frank E Jaumot, Julia L Johnson, Jorge Mas, Jose S Sorzano, John Van Heuvelen

D-U-N-S 60-460-7080
■ **MASTECH APPLICATIONS SERVICES INC**
(*Suby of* IGATE CORP) ★
1000 Commerce Dr Ste 500, Pittsburgh, PA 15275-1039
Tel (412) 787-2100 *Founded/Ownrshp* 2000
Sales 19.9MM^E *EMP* 450
SIC 7373 Systems integration services; Systems integration services
Co-Ch Bd: Sunil Wadhwani
Sr VP: Paul Thomson

D-U-N-S 82-487-6853
▲ MASTECH HOLDINGS INC
1305 Cherrington Pkwy # 400, Coraopolis, PA 15108-4355
Tel (412) 787-2100 *Founded/Ownrshp* 1986
Sales 113.5MM *EMP* 850E
Tkr Sym MHH *Exch* ASE
SIC 7373 Systems integration services; Systems integration services
Pr: D Kevin Horner
**Ch Bd:* Ashok Trivedi
**Ch Bd:* Sunil Wadhwani
Pr: Tim L Bosse
CFO: John J Cronin Jr
Sr VP: Murali Balasubramanyam
VP: Scott Aicher
VP: Denis D Deet
VP: Kevin Kutzavitch
Board of Directors: John Ausura, Brenda Galilee, Gerhard Watzinger

D-U-N-S 15-300-7948
■ MASTECH INC
(*Suby of* MASTECH HOLDINGS INC) ★
1305 Cherrington Pkwy, Coraopolis, PA 15108-4355
Tel (412) 787-2100 *Founded/Ownrshp* 1986
Sales 96.4MME *EMP* 660
SIC 7371 Software programming applications; Custom computer programming services; Software programming applications; Custom computer programming services
Ch Bd: Sunil Wadhwani
**Ch Bd:* Ashok Trivedi
**CEO:* D Kevin Horner
**CFO:* Jack Cronin
VP: Risher Dumpit
Exec: Srividhya Seshadri
Dir Bus: Madhup Malhotra
Mng Dir: Jeremy Pigott
Div Mgr: Suchitra Sharma
Snr Sftwr: Deepak Babu
Snr Sftwr: Haresh Bahadur

D-U-N-S 09-383-1068
MASTEN ENTERPRISES LLC
420 Bernas Rd, Cochecton, NY 12726-5423
Tel (845) 932-8206 *Founded/Ownrshp* 2000
Sales 22.1MME *EMP* 150
SIC 1429 Grits mining (crushed stone); Grits mining (crushed stone)
**Prin:* John Bernas

D-U-N-S 00-536-9418
MASTER AUTOMATIC MACHINE CO INC (MI)
40485 Schoolcraft Rd, Plymouth, MI 48170-2706
Tel (734) 414-0500 *Founded/Ownrshp* 1942, 1959
Sales 35.0MME *EMP* 170E
SIC 3451 Screw machine products; Screw machine products
Ch Bd: John D Evasic Jr
**Pr:* Mark Evasic
CFO: Steve Sierakowski
**Ex VP:* William Evasic
VP: Bill Evasic
Exec: Jennifer Steele
Genl Mgr: Mike Mroue
CTO: Steve Binning
CTO: Dave Stoffregen
Ql Cn Mgr: Peter Beningo
Ql Cn Mgr: Brett Lenhausen

D-U-N-S 09-775-0863 IMP
MASTER BOAT BUILDERS INC
14979a Alba Ave, Coden, AL 36523-3111
Tel (251) 824-2388 *Founded/Ownrshp* 1979
Sales 30.1MME *EMP* 150
SIC 3731 Shipbuilding & repairing; Shipbuilding & repairing
Pr: James Michael Rice
**Sec:* Richard A Rice
**VP:* Mike Weatherly
**Prin:* J W Rice
Off Mgr: Cindy Rowell

D-U-N-S 00-505-3616 IMP/EXP
MASTER CHEMICAL CORP (OH)
501 W Boundary St, Perrysburg, OH 43551-1200
Tel (419) 874-7902 *Founded/Ownrshp* 1951
Sales 97.7MME *EMP* 338
SIC 2992 3559 Cutting oils, blending: made from purchased materials; Oils & greases, blending & compounding; Recycling machinery; Cutting oils, blending: made from purchased materials; Oils & greases, blending & compounding; Recycling machinery
Ch Bd: Joe H Wright
CFO: Cary Glay
CFO: Dan Witt
VP: Xinfang Lu
VP: Michael Weismiller
Ex Dir: Patrick Gouhin
Ex Dir: John Greene
Dist Mgr: Allen Jones
Genl Mgr: Garret Garcia
Genl Mgr: Steven Sigmon
CTO: Steven Florio

D-U-N-S 10-218-1380
MASTER CONCESSIONAIR LLC
WORLD WIDE CONCESSIONS
5727 Nw 7th St Ste 97, Miami, FL 33126-3105
Tel (305) 871-0559 *Founded/Ownrshp* 2003
Sales 34.0MM *EMP* 225
Accts Morrison Brown Argiz & Farra
SIC 5812 Concessionaire; Concessionaire
CEO: Pedro Amaro
COO: William Alberni
CFO: Guillermo Cardona
Prin: Belkys Steigerwald
Genl Mgr: Guillermo Delcalvo

MASTER CONCESSIONS
See MASTER RESTAURANT DEVELOPERS LLC

D-U-N-S 09-012-1567 EXP
MASTER CONCRETE CORP
Km Hm 6 Candelaria W Rr 2, TOA Baja, PR 00949
Tel (787) 740-5252 *Founded/Ownrshp* 1969
Sales 28.1MME *EMP* 290
SIC 3273 Ready-mixed concrete; Ready-mixed concrete
Ch Bd: Victor S Maldonado
**Sec:* Ana Maria Maldonado
**VP:* Carmin Betincourt

D-U-N-S 06-814-9962
MASTER CONSTRUCTION CO INC (ND)
1572 45th St N, Fargo, ND 58102-2847
Tel (701) 237-4950 *Founded/Ownrshp* 1973
Sales 22.0MME *EMP* 110
SIC 1794 7359 1611 Excavation work; Equipment rental & leasing; Concrete construction: roads, highways, sidewalks, etc.; Excavation work; Equipment rental & leasing; Concrete construction: roads, highways, sidewalks, etc.
Pr: Fred Schlanser Jr
CFO: Jacob Anthony
**CFO:* Vickie Hendrickson
Telecom Mg: Dan Tehle

D-U-N-S 06-883-6113
MASTER CRAFT CARPET SERVICE INC (MI)
15001 Fogg St, Plymouth, MI 48170-6029
Tel (313) 387-7000 *Founded/Ownrshp* 1974
Sales 29.5MME *EMP* 52
SIC 5023 5713 Carpets; Carpets
Pr: Dan Ulfig
Off Mgr: Lynn Zeragot
IT Man: Traci Middendorf

D-U-N-S 02-415-4890
MASTER CRAFT SLEEP PRODUCTS INC (AL)
(*Suby of* EASTERN SLEEP PRODUCTS CO) ★
100 29th St E, Jasper, AL 35501-6360
Tel (205) 221-6523 *Founded/Ownrshp* 1982
Sales 36.4MME *EMP* 450
SIC 2515 5021 2511 Mattresses, innerspring or box spring; Furniture; Wood household furniture; Mattresses, innerspring or box spring; Furniture; Wood household furniture
Pr: Charles H Neal
**VP:* David A Williams
VP Admn: Denise Hathaway
Off Mgr: Carolyn Williams

D-U-N-S 84-716-3883 IMP/EXP
MASTER CUTLERY LLC
700 Penhorn Ave Ste 1, Secaucus, NJ 07094-2158
Tel (201) 583-8997 *Founded/Ownrshp* 2015
Sales 21.1MME *EMP* 100
SIC 3421 Cutlery
Pr: Victor Lee
Treas: Cathy Lee
VP Opers: Jackie Lee

MASTER DISTRIBUTORS
See MASTER INTERNATIONAL CORP

D-U-N-S 01-033-7574
MASTER ELECTRIC CO INC (MN)
8555 W 123rd St, Savage, MN 55378-1150
Tel (952) 890-3555 *Founded/Ownrshp* 1973
Sales 20.8MM *EMP* 75
Accts Harrington & Langer St Paul
SIC 1731 Communications specialization; Telephone & telephone equipment installation; Fiber optic cable installation; Communications specialization; Telephone & telephone equipment installation; Fiber optic cable installation
CEO: Jeff Loftsgaarden
**VP:* Kim Loftsgaarden
IT Man: Kurt Rechtzigel
IT Man: Larry Stier

D-U-N-S 11-813-3495
MASTER EXCAVATORS INC
MEI ENGINEERING CONTRACTORS
9950 Sw 168th Ter, Miami, FL 33157-4329
Tel (305) 238-0119 *Founded/Ownrshp* 1984
Sales 35.7MME *EMP* 150
SIC 1794 Excavation work; Excavation work
Pr: Bernard Feely
**Sec:* Linda Feely
Off Mgr: Diana Kansman
Off Mgr: Dianna Kensman

D-U-N-S 02-637-2250
MASTER FIBERS INC
(*Suby of* CYREISA, S.A.)
1710 E Paisano Dr, El Paso, TX 79901-3157
Tel (915) 544-2299 *Founded/Ownrshp* 1959
Sales 29.4MME *EMP* 80
SIC 5093 5113 4953 2611 Waste paper; Cardboard & products; Refuse systems; Pulp mills; Waste paper; Cardboard & products; Refuse systems; Pulp mills
Pr: Alonso Gonzalez
**Pr:* Ricardo Ordaz

D-U-N-S 11-261-9742
MASTER FLEET LLC
3360 Spirit Way, Green Bay, WI 54304-5663
Tel (920) 494-4711 *Founded/Ownrshp* 2002
Sales 32.3MME *EMP* 70E
SIC 5511 Trucks, tractors & trailers: new & used
Pr: Larry Chaplin
**VP:* Tom Anderson
Dir Bus: David Haessly
**Genl Mgr:* Kimm Dewitt
IT Man: Steven Wolfe
Opers Mgr: James Dole

MASTER GARDNER CO
See PRECISION CONVERTERS INC

D-U-N-S 87-456-5393
MASTER GRAPHICS LLC
1100 S Main St, Rochelle, IL 61068-3509
Tel (815) 562-5800 *Founded/Ownrshp* 1994
Sales 38.3MME *EMP* 99
SIC 2752 Commercial printing, offset; Commercial printing, offset
Genl Mgr: Jeff Duga
IT Man: Dan Ceniceros
IT Man: Carol Smith
Plnt Mgr: Frank Folkens
VP Sls: Philip Desiere

MASTER HALCO
See MASTER-HALCO INC

MASTER IMPORTS
See GENERAL BEVERAGE SALES CO-MILWAUKEE

D-U-N-S 05-146-9039 IMP
MASTER INTERNATIONAL CORP
MASTER DISTRIBUTORS
1301 Olympic Blvd, Santa Monica, CA 90404-3725
Tel (310) 452-1229 *Founded/Ownrshp* 1966
Sales 177.1MME *EMP* 150
SIC 5065 Electronic parts; Electronic parts
CEO: Ihsan Nizam
**Pr:* Jamill Nizam
Genl Mgr: Jeff Pluhar
Manager: Syed Shah
Sales Asso: Riad Nizam

D-U-N-S 09-415-0661
MASTER KLEAN JANITORIAL INC
2149 S Clermont St Denver, Denver, CO 80222
Tel (303) 753-6084 *Founded/Ownrshp* 1976
Sales 27.8MME *EMP* 750E
SIC 7349 Janitorial service, contract basis; Janitorial service, contract basis
Pr: Steven T Jetter
CFO: Bill Borger
**VP:* William L Borger
Exec: Barb Laney
Brnch Mgr: Mura Golden
MIS Dir: Charles White
Dir IT: Charlie White
Opers Mgr: Larry Atherton
Opers Mgr: Clifford Faust
Sls Mgr: Amanda Timmons

D-U-N-S 05-410-5218 IMP
■ MASTER LOCK CO LLC
(*Suby of* FORTUNE BRANDS HOME & SECURITY INC) ★
137 W Forest Hill Ave, Oak Creek, WI 53154-2901
Tel (414) 444-2800 *Founded/Ownrshp* 2011
Sales 210.1MME *EMP* 700
SIC 3429 3462 Padlocks; Locks or lock sets; Door locks, bolts & checks; Iron & steel forgings; Padlocks; Locks or lock sets; Door locks, bolts & checks; Iron & steel forgings
VP: Paul S Buskey
VP: Robert Rice Sr
QC Dir: Dave Chovan
Ql Cn Mgr: Joe Downs
Trfc Mgr: Kari Roberts
Natl Sales: Rafael Delgado
Sls Mgr: Robert Nash
Pgrm Dir: Don Gardner

MASTER MACHINE PRODUCTS
See METRIC MACHINING

D-U-N-S 00-819-1074
MASTER MARINE INC
(*Suby of* U S MARINE INC) ★
14284 Shell Belt Rd Ste A, Bayou La Batre, AL 36509-2357
Tel (251) 824-4151 *Founded/Ownrshp* 1961
Sales 26.7MME *EMP* 85
SIC 3731 Barges, building & repairing; Cargo vessels, building & repairing; Fishing vessels, large: building & repairing
Pr: Randy Orr
**VP:* Steven Roppoli
**VP:* Doug Thorn
Genl Mgr: Caren Saman
Plnt Mgr: Bruce Goff

D-U-N-S 15-751-3516 IMP
MASTER MECHANICAL INC
1027 Gemini Rd Ste B, Eagan, MN 55121-2453
Tel (651) 905-1600 *Founded/Ownrshp* 1986
Sales 45.2MM *EMP* 110
SIC 1711 Mechanical contractor; Mechanical contractor
Pr: Gordon Peters
**CEO:* David Schultz
**CFO:* Robert Johnson
**VP:* Thomas Palermo

D-U-N-S 05-106-6272 IMP/EXP
MASTER METER INC
101 Regency Pkwy, Mansfield, TX 76063-5093
Tel (817) 842-8000 *Founded/Ownrshp* 1985
Sales 36.5MME *EMP* 146
SIC 3824 Water meters; Water meters
Pr: Jerald A Potter
CFO: Kobi Brenner
VP: Jamie Allan
**VP:* Ronald D Veach
Dir Bus: Ron Koch
Prd Mgr: Anthony Bentley
Ql Cn Mgr: Scott Bruneau
Mktg Dir: Ian Macleod
Manager: Brian Eaton
Sls Mgr: Scott Allison

D-U-N-S 00-519-8510 IMP
MASTER MOLDED PRODUCTS LLC (IL)
1000 Davis Rd, Elgin, IL 60123-1314
Tel (847) 695-9700 *Founded/Ownrshp* 1945
Sales 39.1MME *EMP* 120
SIC 3089 Injection molding of plastics; Injection molding of plastics
CEO: Arthur Schueneman
Pr: Morris Rowlett
CFO: Lisa Fiorenza
Ex VP: John Weinhart

D-U-N-S 00-511-9961
MASTER PAPER BOX CO INC
3641 S Iron St, Chicago, IL 60609-1322
Tel (773) 927-0252 *Founded/Ownrshp* 1927
Sales 22.2MME *EMP* 103
SIC 2657 2652 Folding paperboard boxes; Setup paperboard boxes; Folding paperboard boxes; Setup paperboard boxes
Pr: Bill Farago Sr
Plnt Mgr: John Buber
Plnt Mgr: Samuel Yozze

MASTER POOLS
See BEAUTY POOLS INC

MASTER PRINT
See VOMELA SPECIALTY CO

D-U-N-S 05-442-4767
MASTER PRINT INC
(*Suby of* MASTER PRINT) ★
8401 Terminal Rd, Newington, VA 22122
Tel (703) 550-9555 *Founded/Ownrshp* 2014
Sales 24.8MME *EMP* 115
SIC 2752 2789 2761 Commercial printing, offset; Lithographing on metal; Bookbinding & related work; Manifold business forms
Pr: David Dickens

D-U-N-S 17-404-7464 IMP/EXP
MASTER PRODUCTS CORP
Km 20 6 Barrio C Rr 2, TOA Baja, PR 00951
Tel (787) 740-5254 *Founded/Ownrshp* 1984
Sales 21.7MME *EMP* 100
Accts Jesus M Mora Nieves Cpa Gua
SIC 2891 5031 Cement, except linoleum & tile; Building materials, interior
Pr: Ricardo Cardona
**Sec:* Ana Maria Maldonado
**VP:* Luis Aranguren
MIS Mgr: Pablo Reyes

D-U-N-S 62-776-6645
MASTER PROTECTION HOLDINGS INC
(*Suby of* SIMPLEXTIME RECORDER LLC) ★
13050 Metro Pkwy Ste 1, Fort Myers, FL 33966-4800
Tel (239) 896-1680 *Founded/Ownrshp* 1990
Sales 29.1MME *EMP* 1,000
Accts Deloitte & Touche Llp New Yor
SIC 7389 1711 5999 Fire extinguisher servicing; Fire sprinkler system installation; Safety supplies & equipment; Fire extinguisher servicing; Fire sprinkler system installation; Safety supplies & equipment
Pr: Dean De Buhr
**Ch Bd:* Wiliam R Berkley
VP: Gaylon R Claiborn
VP: Nickolas K Fisher
VP: Thomas L Kennedy
VP: John H Simon

D-U-N-S 05-801-9985
MASTER PROTECTION LP
FIREMASTER
(*Suby of* MASTER PROTECTION HOLDINGS INC) ★
13050 Metro Pkwy Ste 1, Fort Myers, FL 33966-4800
Tel (239) 896-1680 *Founded/Ownrshp* 1990
Sales 29.1MM *EMP* 40
SIC 7389 1731 5999 Fire protection service other than forestry or public; Fire detection & burglar alarm systems specialization; Alarm & safety equipment stores; Fire protection service other than forestry or public; Fire detection & burglar alarm systems specialization; Alarm & safety equipment stores
Pr: Robert F Chauvin
**CFO:* Mark Meisner
IT Man: Robert Rice
Opers Mgr: Rick Korecki

D-U-N-S 04-609-8034 IMP
MASTER PUMPS & EQUIPMENT CORP (TX)
MASTER PUMPS & POWER
805 Port America Pl # 100, Grapevine, TX 76051-7670
Tel (817) 251-6745 *Founded/Ownrshp* 1993
Sales 77.0MME *EMP* 90
SIC 5084 7699 Pumps & pumping equipment; Compressors, except air conditioning; Pumps & pumping equipment repair; Compressor repair; Pumps & pumping equipment; Compressors, except air conditioning; Pumps & pumping equipment repair; Compressor repair
Ch Bd: Donald W Moilan
**Ex VP:* James O'Donnell
VP: James Odonnell
Store Mgr: Allen Poovey
Sales Asso: Terry Kyle

MASTER PUMPS & POWER
See MASTER PUMPS & EQUIPMENT CORP

D-U-N-S 01-213-8632
MASTER PURVEYORS INC (NY)
OLD BOHEMIAN
355 Food Center Dr B14, Bronx, NY 10474-7577
Tel (718) 542-1000 *Founded/Ownrshp* 1957
Sales 28.2MME *EMP* 40
SIC 5147 Meats, fresh
Pr: Sam Solasz
**Treas:* Mark Solasz
**VP:* Scott Solasz

D-U-N-S 80-958-7103
MASTER RESTAURANT DEVELOPERS LLC
MASTER CONCESSIONS
1395 Brickell Ave Fl 14, Miami, FL 33131-3371
Tel (305) 871-0559 *Founded/Ownrshp* 2005
Sales 29.2MME *EMP* 500
SIC 1542 Restaurant construction; Restaurant construction

D-U-N-S 06-487-2906
MASTER SECURITY CO LLC
10946 Beaver Dam Rd, Cockeysville, MD 21030-2223
Tel (410) 584-8789 *Founded/Ownrshp* 2006
Sales 37.5MM *EMP* 210E
Accts Coyne & Mc Clean
SIC 7381 Security guard service; Security guard service
VP: Mark Carmen

MASTER SHEET METAL CONTRACTORS
See MILLER ENGINEERING CO

MASTER SHEET METAL CONTRS DIV
See NELSON PIPING CO

D-U-N-S 94-197-3638 IMP/EXP
MASTER SPAS INC
6927 Lincoln Pkwy, Fort Wayne, IN 46804-5623
Tel (260) 436-9100 Founded/Ownrshp 1996
Sales 40.2MM^E EMP 225
SIC 3999 5999 Hot tubs; Spas & hot tubs; Hot tubs; Spas & hot tubs
CEO: Robert Lauter
*Pr: Terry Valmassoi
Natl Sales: Kevin Richards

MASTER TAG
See INTERNATIONAL MASTER PRODUCTS CORP

D-U-N-S 82-716-8886
MASTER TECHNOLOGY GROUP INC
8555 W 123rd St, Savage, MN 55378-1150
Tel (952) 960-1212 Founded/Ownrshp 2005
Sales 26.3MM EMP 120
Accts Harrington Langer & Associates
SIC 1731 Voice, data & video wiring contractor; Voice, data & video wiring contractor
CEO: Jeff Loftsgaarden
*Pr: Ryan Blundell
*Prin: Kim Loftsgaarden
Div Mgr: Tim Junkert
Dir IT: Erik Schindeldecker

MASTER TILE & STONE
See MASTER TILE INC

D-U-N-S 12-098-1225
MASTER TILE INC
MASTER TILE & STONE
7350 Denny St Ste 100, Houston, TX 77040-4857
Tel (832) 467-8850 Founded/Ownrshp 2006
Sales 21.2MM^E EMP 59
SIC 5032 Ceramic wall & floor tile
Pr: Nafeh Sebai
Sec: William D Anthony

D-U-N-S 87-630-6163 IMP
MASTER WOODCRAFT CABINETRY LLC
232 N Marshall Indus Ave, Marshall, TX 75670-2442
Tel (903) 935-0500 Founded/Ownrshp 2007
Sales 50.0MM^E EMP 200
SIC 2434 2541 Wood kitchen cabinets; Counter & sink tops; Wood kitchen cabinets; Counter & sink tops
CEO: Gene Ponder
*CFO: Patsy Ponder
Trst: James Walls
VP: Rozenna Lewane
VP: Alan Ponder
Manager: Kelly Adams

D-U-N-S 09-931-2423 IMP/EXP
MASTER-CRAFT INDUSTRIAL EQUIPMENT CORP
333 Southwell Blvd, Tifton, GA 31794-8828
Tel (229) 386-0610 Founded/Ownrshp 1977
Sales 22.7MM^E EMP 76
SIC 3537 3531 Forklift trucks; Construction machinery; Backhoe mounted, hydraulically powered attachments
Pr: Jack Haswell
*Treas: Jason Haswell
*VP: Jackie Haswell

D-U-N-S 00-826-1620 IMP
MASTER-HALCO INC
MASTER HALCO
(Suby of ITOCHU INTERNATIONAL INC) ★
3010 Lbj Fwy Ste 800, Dallas, TX 75234-7770
Tel (972) 714-7300 Founded/Ownrshp 1977
Sales 394.6MM^E EMP 1,615
SIC 3315 5039 3496 3446 5031 1799 Chain link fencing; Fence gates posts & fittings: steel; Wire fence, gates & accessories; Miscellaneous fabricated wire products; Architectural metalwork; Lumber, plywood & millwork; Building materials, exterior; Fence construction; Chain link fencing; Fence gates posts & fittings: steel; Wire fence, gates & accessories; Miscellaneous fabricated wire products; Architectural metalwork; Lumber, plywood & millwork; Building materials, exterior; Fence construction
CEO: Ken Fishbein
CFO: Scott Suh
VP: Jerry Short
Brnch Mgr: Mark Buchanan
Brnch Mgr: Kendall Wiley
Genl Mgr: Curt Cook
Netwrk Eng: Martin Straigis
Mfg Dir: Bart Moon
Plnt Mgr: Mike Earhart
Plnt Mgr: Jeffrey Novak
Plnt Mgr: Randy Rryker

D-U-N-S 17-503-9569
MASTER-LEE ENERGY SERVICES CORP
5631 State Route 981, Latrobe, PA 15650-5303
Tel (724) 532-4459 Founded/Ownrshp 1987
Sales 31.3MM^E EMP 200
SIC 1799 Nuclear power refueling; Nuclear power refueling
Pr: Richard Douds
CFO: Louis Acito

D-U-N-S 14-478-6626
MASTER-TEC FLOORS INC
SIGN POST PROS
3109 N T St, Pensacola, FL 32505-5013
Tel (850) 454-0008 Founded/Ownrshp 2003
Sales 978.0MM EMP 3
SIC 1752 5713 Floor laying & floor work; Floor covering stores; Floor laying & floor work; Floor covering stores
CEO: Matthew S Kovach
*COO: Martin D Cudlin
*CFO: Brandy L Kovach
*VP: Martin Cudlin

D-U-N-S 80-009-3135 IMP/EXP
■ MASTERACK INC
LEGGETT PLATT
(Suby of LEGGETT & PLATT INC) ★
905 Memorial Dr Se, Atlanta, GA 30316-1499
Tel (404) 525-5501 Founded/Ownrshp 2013
Sales 47.4MM^E EMP 250
SIC 3465 5012 Body parts, automobile: stamped metal; Commercial vehicles; Body parts, automobile: stamped metal; Commercial vehicles
Pr: Ross L Haith Jr
COO: Mark Adamczyk
CFO: Michael A Glauber
VP: Tony Greene
VP: Mark Hickman
Dir IT: Wayne Partain
Sfty Dirs: Tiffany Martin
Sales Asso: Sonny George

D-U-N-S 02-254-4501 IMP
■ MASTERBRAND CABINETS INC
HOMECREST
(Suby of FORTUNE BRANDS HOME & SECURITY INC) ★
1 Masterbrand Cabinets Dr, Jasper, IN 47546-2248
Tel (812) 482-2527 Founded/Ownrshp 1998
Sales 1.9MMM^E EMP 11,000
SIC 2434 Wood kitchen cabinets; Wood kitchen cabinets
Pr: David M Randich
COO: Dennis Thimling
Ex VP: Brian Eckman
Ex VP: Sean Fisher
Ex VP: Robert Foote
Ex VP: Gary Lautzehiser
Ex VP: Gary G Lautzenhiser
Ex VP: Rob Mullally
Ex VP: Brenda Neuhoff
Ex VP: Mark Warnsman
VP: Bob Donnelly
VP: John Fogg
VP: Kenny Gibson
VP: Robert Jacobs
VP: David Krawec
VP: Gordon McCance
VP: Roland Minogue
VP: Billie Timm
Exec: Adria Henke
Exec: Lee Huther
Dir Risk M: Emily Bromm

D-U-N-S 08-376-4811 IMP
MASTERBUILT MANUFACTURING INC (GA)
1 Masterbuilt Ct, Columbus, GA 31907-1313
Tel (706) 327-5622 Founded/Ownrshp 1985
Sales 99.2MM EMP 62
Accts Robinson Grimes & Company Pc
SIC 3631 3714 Household cooking equipment; Trailer hitches, motor vehicle; Household cooking equipment; Trailer hitches, motor vehicle
CEO: John McLemore
COO: Lynne Jacobs
*CFO: Glenn Scarborough
*Treas: Lynne McLemore
*VP: Don McLemore
VP: Lin Qiu
CTO: Tommy Zittrauer
Sys Mgr: Cristina Robinson
Plnt Mgr: Dan Baker
Ql Cn Mgr: Stephen Smith
Natl Sales: Ron Lamberg

D-U-N-S 11-856-9339
▲ MASTERCARD INC
2000 Purchase St, Purchase, NY 10577-2405
Tel (914) 249-2000 Founded/Ownrshp 1966
Sales 9.4MMM EMP 10,300^E
Accts Pricewaterhousecoopers Llp Ne
Tkr Sym MA Exch NYS
SIC 7389 Credit card service; Credit card service
Pr: Ajay S Banga
V Ch: Walt W Macnee
Pr: Gary J Flood
Pr: Steve Grigg
Pr: Timothy H Murphy
Pr: Robert Reeg
Pr: Richelle Weisbrod
CEO: Ram Chari
COO: Reeg Robert
CFO: Martina Hund-Mejean
Bd of Dir: Nancy Karch
Ofcr: Melissa Ballenger
Ofcr: Ronald E Garrow
Ofcr: Timothy Murphy
Assoc VP: Kara-Mae Lim
Ex VP: John De De Lavis
Ex VP: Michael Galvin
Ex VP: Felix Marx
Ex VP: Donna Terman
VP: Armando Alemany
VP: Jeff Allen
Board of Directors: Rima Qureshi, Silvio Barzi, Jackson Tai, David R Carlucci, Steven J Freiberg, Julius Genachowski, Richard Haythornthwaite, Merit E Janow, Nancy J Karch, Jose Octavio Reyes Lagunes, Marc Olivie

D-U-N-S 05-048-3783
■ MASTERCARD INTERNATIONAL INC
MASTERCARD WORLDWIDE
(Suby of MASTERCARD INC) ★
2000 Purchase St, Purchase, NY 10577-2509
Tel (914) 249-2000 Founded/Ownrshp 1966
Sales 398.0MM^E EMP 3,000
SIC 7389 6099 Credit card service; Travelers' checks issuance; Automated teller machine (ATM) network; Credit card service; Travelers' checks issuance; Automated teller machine (ATM) network
Pr: Ajay Banga
Pr: Ajay Bhalla
Pr: Javier Perez
Pr: Rob Reeg
*CEO: Robert W Selander
*COO: Alan Heuer
CFO: Frank Cotroneo
*CFO: Chris McWilton
*Ch: Stephanie Voquer
*Treas: Sachin Mehra
Treas: Stephen Piccininni
*Chf Mktg O: Alfredo Gangotena
Assoc VP: Souheil Yammine
Ex VP: Gary Flood
Ex VP: Australasia Grobler
Ex VP: Arthur Kranzley
Ex VP: Maria Polumbo
Sr VP: Aroon Maben
Sr VP: Steven Sklar
VP: Rob Barrale
VP: Geraldine Cooper

MASTERCARD WORLDWIDE
See MASTERCARD INTERNATIONAL INC

D-U-N-S 80-952-8300
MASTERCONTROL INC
6330 S 3000 E Ste 200, Salt Lake City, UT 84121-6236
Tel (801) 742-9722 Founded/Ownrshp 2002
Sales 56.0MM^E EMP 140
Accts Jeff Peck Cfo
SIC 7372 Prepackaged software; Prepackaged software
Ch Bd: Richard Beckstrand
*Pr: Jonathan Beckstrand
*CFO: Jeff Peck
*Sr VP: Randall Autry
*VP: Kevin Ash
*VP: Greg Beeber
VP: James King
*VP: Jim Murrin
VP: Marc Vandenbulcke
Dir Soc: Jill Bumgardner
QA Dir: Leandro Fracasso

D-U-N-S 13-026-7685
MASTERCORP INC
3505 N Main St, Crossville, TN 38555-5417
Tel (931) 484-1752 Founded/Ownrshp 1973
Sales 146.0MM^E EMP 3,400
SIC 7349 7217 Building cleaning service; Cleaning service, industrial or commercial; Janitorial service, contract basis; Carpet & furniture cleaning on location; Building cleaning service; Cleaning service, industrial or commercial; Janitorial service, contract basis; Carpet & furniture cleaning on location
Pr: Alan Grindstaff
*COO: David Goff
*CFO: Kevin Swafford
*Sec: Charlotte Grindstaff
*Sr VP: Steve Hicks
*VP: David Maier
Genl Mgr: Toby Sweat
Dir IT: Jonathan Loveday
IT Man: Obie Williams
VP Opers: Michael Quagrello

D-U-N-S 05-266-2467 IMP/EXP
■ MASTERCRAFT BOAT CO LLC (TN)
(Suby of MCBC HOLDINGS INC) ★
100 Cherokee Cove Dr, Vonore, TN 37885-2129
Tel (423) 884-2221 Founded/Ownrshp 1968, 2000
Sales 228.5MM^E EMP 500
SIC 3799 Jet skis; Motorboats, inboard or outboard: building & repairing; Boat trailers; Boat trailers
CEO: Terry McNew
COO: Terry Bell
COO: Shane Chittum
CFO: Tim Oxley
Bd of Dir: Mike Moberley
Sr VP: Carl Craig
VP: Jay S Povlin
VP: Greg Stanley
Prgrm Mgr: Jim Brown
MIS Dir: David Kirkland
Dir IT: Travis Moye

D-U-N-S 94-367-8672
MASTERCRAFT CABINETS INC
(Suby of ELKAY MANUFACTURING CO INC) ★
23655 E 19th Ave Ste 300, Aurora, CO 80019-3702
Tel (303) 375-8220 Founded/Ownrshp 1996
Sales 34.4MM^E EMP 450
SIC 2434 Wood kitchen cabinets; Wood kitchen cabinets
Ch Bd: Ron Katz
*Pr: Thomas Cook
VP: Joseph Kearns
Genl Mgr: Kenneth Pfarr
Plnt Mgr: Jim Hernandez

D-U-N-S 05-464-3978
MASTERCRAFT INC
711 S Poplar St, Lagrange, IN 46761-2407
Tel (260) 463-8702 Founded/Ownrshp 1971, 1990
Sales 66.5MM^E EMP 270
SIC 2512 2514 2515 Upholstered household furniture; Metal household furniture; Mattresses, innerspring or box spring; Box springs, assembled; Upholstered household furniture; Metal household furniture; Mattresses, innerspring or box spring; Box springs, assembled
Pr: Clifton D Reynolds
*VP: Doug Cline
VP Sls: Dave Toney

D-U-N-S 00-615-6400
MASTERCRAFT INDUSTRIES INC (WI)
HOLIDAY KITCHEN DIV
120 W Allen St, Rice Lake, WI 54868-2227
Tel (715) 736-9228 Founded/Ownrshp 1946, 2011
Sales 52.3MM^E EMP 200
SIC 2434 Wood kitchen cabinets; Wood kitchen cabinets
Pr: David West
*VP: Dennis Winkler
IT Man: Todd Keup
Plnt Mgr: Mark Lauerman

D-U-N-S 61-832-2213
MASTERCRAFT WOOD PRODUCTS LP
232 N Marshall Indus Ave, Marshall, TX 75670-2442
Tel (903) 935-0500 Founded/Ownrshp 2006
Sales 39.2MM^E EMP 350
SIC 2434 Wood & wood by-products; Wood kitchen cabinets
Genl Pt: Gene Ponder
VP: Rozenna Lewane
VP: Lisa Perssler
VP: Anita Windham
VP Opers: Randy Owens

D-U-N-S 83-160-8455
MASTERFLIGHT FOUNDATION
6000 Il Route 173, Richmond, IL 60071-9486
Tel (949) 547-1479 Founded/Ownrshp 2009
Sales 23.3MM EMP 74
SIC 8641 Civic social & fraternal associations; Civic social & fraternal associations

D-U-N-S 80-898-1034
MASTERFOODS USA INC
(Suby of MARS INC) ★
800 High St, Hackettstown, NJ 07840-1552
Tel (908) 852-1000 Founded/Ownrshp 2007
Sales 32.9MM^E EMP 62^E
SIC 5141 Groceries, general line
Pr: Michael Murphy
Mktg Dir: Craig Stansky
Sls Mgr: Merri Scott

D-U-N-S 02-332-2704
MASTERGRAPHICS INC
2979 Triverton Pike Dr # 200, Fitchburg, WI 53711-7510
Tel (608) 256-4884 Founded/Ownrshp 2004
Sales 22.2MM^E EMP 118
SIC 7334 5045 5084 5049 2759 2672 Blueprinting service; Computers; Computer software; Printing trades machinery, equipment & supplies; Drafting supplies; Commercial printing; Coated & laminated paper
Pr: Michael Wilkes
Sales Exec: William Schurr
Mktg Mgr: Jenifer Barnum

D-U-N-S 01-942-8168 IMP
MASTERMANS LLP
11 C St, Auburn, MA 01501-2159
Tel (508) 755-7861 Founded/Ownrshp 1961
Sales 78.8MM^E EMP 100
SIC 5085 Industrial supplies; Industrial supplies
Genl Pt: Linda Masterman
*Pt: Tod Masterman
Prin: Chris Cutting
IT Man: Anthony Larson
Sls Mgr: Rick Rearick
Sales Asso: Emily Eisenmenger
Sales Asso: Tara Volesky
Board of Directors: Richard Taylor

MASTERMARK PLASTIC PRODUCTS
See AVON PLASTICS INC

D-U-N-S 83-171-5953
MASTERMOLD LLC
111 Grell Ln, Johnson Creek, WI 53038-9796
Tel (608) 847-1185 Founded/Ownrshp 1996
Sales 31.6MM^E EMP 350^E
SIC 7389 Personal service agents, brokers & bureaus; Personal service agents, brokers & bureaus
Pr: John Butt

D-U-N-S 60-387-7267 IMP/EXP
MASTERPIECE INTERNATIONAL LIMITED
39 Broadway Rm 1410, New York, NY 10006-3085
Tel (212) 825-4800 Founded/Ownrshp 1989
Sales 59.4MM^E EMP 170
SIC 4731 Customhouse brokers; Freight forwarding; Customhouse brokers; Freight forwarding
Pr: Dave Epstein
*VP: David C Cohen
Brnch Mgr: Tina Sullivan
IT Man: Timothy Mahon

D-U-N-S 80-827-7276 EXP
MASTERPIECE MACHINE AND MANUFACTURING CO
10245 W Airport Blvd, Stafford, TX 77477-3300
Tel (713) 952-4102 Founded/Ownrshp 2006
Sales 34.4MM^E EMP 87
SIC 3531 Construction machinery
Co-Ownr: Abbas Arian
*Co-Ownr: Trevor Goodchild
*Co-Ownr: Georgios Varsamis
*Co-Ownr: Laurence Wisniewski
Genl Mgr: Michael Cheatwood
Mfg Mgr: Randy Ford

D-U-N-S 80-097-5310 IMP
MASTERPIECE STUDIOS INC
(Suby of OCCASIONS GROUP INC) ★
1750 Tower Blvd, North Mankato, MN 56003-1706
Tel (507) 388-8788 Founded/Ownrshp 2006
Sales 32.3MM^E EMP 215^E
SIC 5112 Stationery; Stationery
Pr: Dave Humbert
Ex VP: Doug Faust
Prd Mgr: Paul Meyer
Sales Exec: Frank Sundboom

MASTERPLAN
See COHR INC

D-U-N-S 04-967-8097
MASTERPLAN INC
308 7th Ave, Pittsburgh, PA 15222-3909
Tel (412) 434-0990 Founded/Ownrshp 1969
Sales 29.7MM^E EMP 125
SIC 6282 6211 Investment advisory service; Investment firm, general brokerage; Investment advisory service; Investment firm, general brokerage
Pr: Kim T Fleming
Ch Bd: Willard J Tillotson Jr
Pr: Kimberly Fleming
Treas: Joseph Niesslein
VP: James Beck

D-U-N-S 07-623-3162
MASTERS COLLEGE AND SEMINARY
21726 Placerita Canyon Rd, Santa Clarita, CA 91321-1200
Tel (661) 259-3540 Founded/Ownrshp 1927
Sales 47.3MM EMP 600
Accts Capincrouse Llp Cpas Tarzan
SIC 8221 College, except junior; Theological seminary; College, except junior; Theological seminary
CEO: John F Macarthur
CFO: Jason Hartung
Ofcr: Samuel Dawson
Ofcr: Boyd Johnson
Ofcr: Bryan Kortcamp
VP: Robert Hotton
VP: John Hughes
Exec: Jerry Ehlen
Off Mgr: Jocelyn Devaney

Snr Sftwr: Stephanie Wilson
CIO: Nate Prince

D-U-N-S 07-384-6115 EXP
MASTERS GALLERY FOODS INC
328 Count Hwy Pp Pp, Plymouth, WI 53073-4143
Tel (920) 893-8431 *Founded/Ownrshp* 1991
Sales 800.0MM *EMP* 445
SIC 5143

D-U-N-S 13-489-2806
MASTERS INC
(*Suby of* DIRECT ENERGY US HOME SERVICES INC) ★
7891 Beechcraft Ave, Gaithersburg, MD 20879-1580
Tel (301) 948-8950 *Founded/Ownrshp* 2003
Sales 42.7MM^E *EMP* 500
SIC 1711 Plumbing, heating, air-conditioning contractors; Plumbing, heating, air-conditioning contractors
Pr: Ronald Bryant
Ex VP: Bill Duval
VP: Tom Bodmer
**VP:* Richard Colton
**VP:* Jamie Flewellyn
**VP:* Jeff Kohan
**VP:* Don Oesterbald
Board of Directors: Josh Cascade, Carl Stanton

D-U-N-S 84-492-0269
MASTERS INSURANCE AGENCY INC
ANICO
9785 Maroon Cir Ste 340, Englewood, CO 80112-5922
Tel (303) 814-1596 *Founded/Ownrshp* 1994
Sales NA *EMP* 200
SIC 6411 6331 6311 Insurance agents, brokers & service; Automobile insurance; Life insurance
Pr: Jeff Johnson

D-U-N-S 00-109-9324 IMP
MASTERS MACHINE CO INC (ME)
500 Lower Round Pond Rd, Round Pond, ME 04564
Tel (207) 529-5191 *Founded/Ownrshp* 1957
Sales 35.9MM^E *EMP* 114
SIC 3545 Precision tools, machinists'
Pr: Richard Masters
**VP:* George Master Jr
Plnt Mgr: Steve Masters
Board of Directors: Virginia Manning

D-U-N-S 82-554-5874
MASTERS MATES AND PILOTS HEALTH & BENEFIT PLANS
M M & P HEALTH & BENEFIT PLANS
700 Maritime Blvd Ste A, Linthicum Heights, MD 21090-1916
Tel (410) 850-8500 *Founded/Ownrshp* 1990
Sales NA *EMP* 40
SIC 6371 Pension, health & welfare funds; Pension, health & welfare funds

D-U-N-S 96-757-1741
MASTERS MATES AND PILOTS VACATION FUND
700 Maritime Blvd, Linthicum Heights, MD 21090-1916
Tel (410) 850-8500 *Founded/Ownrshp* 2011
Sales 30.0MM *EMP* 2^E
Accts Gorfine Schiller & Gardyn Pa
SIC 6733 Vacation funds for employees; Vacation funds for employees
Prin: Donald Marcus

MASTERS MILLWORK COMPANY, THE
See ARCHITECTURAL COMPONENTS GROUP INC

THE MASTERS OF DISASTERS
See J P M PRODUCTIONS INC

D-U-N-S 61-895-8677
MASTERS PARTNERS LLC
AVALAR REALTY NORTH TEXAS
6211 Colleyville Blvd # 100, Colleyville, TX 76034-6299
Tel (469) 635-7600 *Founded/Ownrshp* 2005
Sales 22.0MM *EMP* 20
SIC 6531 Real estate brokers & agents

D-U-N-S 04-635-5827
MASTERS PHARMACEUTICAL INC
11930 Kemper Springs Dr, Cincinnati, OH 45240-1642
Tel (513) 354-2690 *Founded/Ownrshp* 2000
Sales 45.0MM^E *EMP* 180^E
SIC 7389 Brokers' services; Brokers' services
Pr: Dennis Smith
**Pr:* Wayne A Corona
Pr: Christine Madden
**CFO:* Kevin Moore
VP: Mel Cameron
VP: John Edmiston
VP: Rick Lauer
VP: Jennifer Seiple
VP: Darren Stepinski
Snr Sftwr: Josh Vega
IT Man: Lore Breetz

D-U-N-S 09-529-3320
MASTERS RESTAURANT ASSOCIATES INC
219 N 2nd St Ste 100, Minneapolis, MN 55401-1452
Tel (612) 339-2404 *Founded/Ownrshp* 1979
Sales 5.0MM *EMP* 300
SIC 5812 8742 Eating places; Restaurant & food services consultants; Eating places; Restaurant & food services consultants
Pr: John Rimarcik
VP: Jo Nystrom

D-U-N-S 07-870-5324
MASTERS SCHOOL
49 Clinton Ave, Dobbs Ferry, NY 10522-2200
Tel (914) 479-6400 *Founded/Ownrshp* 1877
Sales 31.9MM *EMP* 125
Accts Marks Paneth Llp New York Ny
SIC 8211 Secondary school; Secondary school
Dir Teleco: Jim Heuer
Assoc Dir: Tim Custer
Dir IT: Dan Pereire
Mktg Dir: Bob Horne

D-U-N-S 02-407-2514
MASTERS SUPPLY INC (KY)
CREATIVE KITCHENS AND BATH
4505 Bishop Ln, Louisville, KY 40218-4507
Tel (502) 657-0248 *Founded/Ownrshp* 1958
Sales 62.0MM^E *EMP* 114
SIC 5085 5074 Industrial supplies; Valves & fittings; Plumbing & hydronic heating supplies; Industrial supplies; Valves & fittings; Plumbing & hydronic heating supplies
Pr: David W Wachtel
**CFO:* John L Burke
**VP:* Jack Bell
**VP:* John A Bowling
Brnch Mgr: Ken Rue
Brnch Mgr: Mark Stucker
Sales Asso: Melani Fosson

MASTERS WHOLESALE & DISTRG
See MASTERS WHOLESALE DISTRIBUTING AND MANUFACTURING INC

D-U-N-S 07-612-9444
MASTERS WHOLESALE DISTRIBUTING AND MANUFACTURING INC
MASTERS WHOLESALE & DISTRG
2504 Mercantile Dr Ste A, Rancho Cordova, CA 95742-8201
Tel (916) 635-2504 *Founded/Ownrshp* 1974
Sales 35.5MM^E *EMP* 34
Accts Brown Fink Boyce & Astle Ll
SIC 5063 5023 5064 Lighting fixtures; Floor coverings; Draperies; Electrical appliances, major
CEO: Thomas Borge
**Pr:* Maurice Habra

D-U-N-S 05-229-8072 EXP
MASTERSON CO INC
4023 W National Ave, Milwaukee, WI 53215-1000
Tel (414) 902-2210 *Founded/Ownrshp* 1987
Sales 62.9MM^E *EMP* 200
SIC 2087 4783 Syrups, flavoring (except drink); Containerization of goods for shipping; Syrups, flavoring (except drink); Containerization of goods for shipping
CEO: Joe Masterson
**Treas:* Michael B Masterson
**Treas:* Martin Zoberman
**Ex VP:* Nancy Masterson
VP: Susan Hough
QA Dir: Ellie Schroeder
VP Sls: David Erickson

D-U-N-S 14-750-7776
MASTERSTOUCH BRAND LLC
8409 Kerns St Ste 102, San Diego, CA 92154-6289
Tel (619) 600-4354 *Founded/Ownrshp* 2010
Sales 80.0MM *EMP* 16
Accts Arana & Cordova Pc Nogales
SIC 5148 Fresh fruits & vegetables

D-U-N-S 14-229-2866 IMP/EXP
MASTERTASTE INC
KERRY INGREDIENTS AND FLAVOURS
(*Suby of* KERRY INC) ★
160 Terminal Ave, Clark, NJ 07066-1319
Tel (732) 882-0202 *Founded/Ownrshp* 2002
Sales 51.8MM^E *EMP* 249
SIC 2087 Flavoring extracts & syrups; Flavoring extracts & syrups
Pr: Gerry Behan
**CFO:* Mike Gransee

D-U-N-S 93-337-8242
MASTERWORD SERVICES INC
303 Stafford St, Houston, TX 77079-2345
Tel (281) 589-0810 *Founded/Ownrshp* 1993
Sales 20.6MM *EMP* 65
SIC 7389 Translation services
Pr: Ludmila A Golovine
Software D: Lu Wang

D-U-N-S 87-287-1215 IMP
MASTERWORK ELECTRONICS INC
630 Martin Ave, Rohnert Park, CA 94928-2049
Tel (707) 588-9906 *Founded/Ownrshp* 1994
Sales 29.6MM^E *EMP* 340
SIC 3672 Printed circuit boards
CEO: Robert E Weed
CFO: Carl Mack
Genl Mgr: Greg Felton
Mtls Mgr: Brooke Ross

MASTERWORK PAINT & DCTG CTRS
See MASTERWORK PAINT CO

D-U-N-S 00-431-9398
■ **MASTERWORK PAINT CO**
MASTERWORK PAINT & DCTG CTRS
(*Suby of* HOMAX PRODUCTS) ★
5739 Centre Ave, Pittsburgh, PA 15206-3707
Tel (412) 361-8770 *Founded/Ownrshp* 2014
Sales 26.4MM^E *EMP* 72
SIC 5198 5231 Paints; Paint
Pr: Marion Samakow
Sec: Thomas G Samakow
VP: Michael K Samakow

D-U-N-S 80-996-0941 IMP
MASTERWORKS INTERNATIONAL INC
7100 Business Park Dr B, Houston, TX 77041-4021
Tel (713) 896-0101 *Founded/Ownrshp* 1993
Sales 21.0MM^E *EMP* 40
SIC 5045 Computers
Ch Bd: Robert J Munn
**Pr:* Bruce Cutler
**VP:* Edward J Higgins
Genl Mgr: Melissa Montero
Sls Dir: Alan Wheatley

MASTHEAD HOSE & SUPPLY
See BRIDGESTONE HOSEPOWER LLC

MASTIC HM EXTERIORS BY PLY GEM
See MASTIC HOME EXTERIORS INC

D-U-N-S 00-423-9000 IMP
■ **MASTIC HOME EXTERIORS INC**
MASTIC HM EXTERIORS BY PLY GEM
(*Suby of* PLY GEM INDUSTRIES INC) ★
2600 Grand Blvd Ste 900, Kansas City, MO 64108-4626
Tel (816) 426-8200 *Founded/Ownrshp* 2006
Sales 268.7MM^E *EMP* 1,559
SIC 3081 3089 Plastic film & sheet; Siding, plastic; Plastic film & sheet; Siding, plastic
Pr: John Wayne
VP Mktg: Fred Vapenik
VP Sls: Frank G Riess
Manager: Jeff Reynolds

D-U-N-S 08-902-7924
MASTIN KIRKLAND BOLLING INC
MKB REALTORS
3801 Electric Rd, Roanoke, VA 24018-4510
Tel (540) 989-4555 *Founded/Ownrshp* 1972
Sales 100.0MM *EMP* 100
SIC 6531 Real estate brokers & agents; Real estate brokers & agents
Pr: Betty Kirkland
COO: Elisha Walker
CFO: Lara Bingeman
**Sec:* R Lee Mastin
**VP:* Ann Boldridge
VP: Chan Bolling
**VP:* W Chan Bolling
**VP:* Stephen Hoover
Manager: John Walker
Sales Asso: Bonnie Cecil
Sales Asso: Karin Colozza

D-U-N-S 12-162-2849 IMP
MASTORAN RESTAURANTS INC
BURGER KING
822 Lexington St Fl 2, Waltham, MA 02452-4848
Tel (781) 893-3002 *Founded/Ownrshp* 1985
Sales 27.7MM^E *EMP* 900
SIC 5812 Fast-food restaurant, chain; Fast-food restaurant, chain
Pr: Larry W Kohler
**Treas:* Paige Kohler

MASTRIA AUTO GROUP
See MASTRIA BUICK PONTIAC GMC-TRUCK CADILLAC CO INC

D-U-N-S 08-480-2388
MASTRIA BUICK PONTIAC GMC-TRUCK CADILLAC CO INC
MASTRIA AUTO GROUP
1525 New State Hwy, Raynham, MA 02767-5442
Tel (508) 880-7000 *Founded/Ownrshp* 1977
Sales 30.1MM^E *EMP* 65
SIC 5511 7532 5531 5013 Automobiles, new & used; Body shop, automotive; Automotive parts; Automotive supplies & parts; Automobiles, new & used; Body shop, automotive; Automotive parts; Automotive supplies & parts
Pr: Richard Mastria Jr
COO: Ede Ferriera
Off Mgr: Kristin Moore
IT Man: Rod Taylor
Opers Mgr: Stephen Ferreria
Pr Dir: Mark Almeida
Sls Mgr: Greg Connor
Sls Mgr: Chris Dunn
Sls Mgr: Bruce Garcia
Sls Mgr: Eddie Jreij
Sales Asso: Derek Damon

D-U-N-S 36-277-3207 EXP
MASTRIA SUBARU OF RAYNHAM INC
1255 New State Hwy, Raynham, MA 02767-5438
Tel (508) 880-9799 *Founded/Ownrshp* 2005
Sales 59.4MM^E *EMP* 200
SIC 5511 5531 New & used car dealers; Automotive parts; Automobiles, new & used; Automotive parts
Pr: Eddie Ferriera
**CFO:* Robert A Mastria Sr
Genl Mgr: Chris Dunn
Sales Asso: Jerome Cahoon
Sales Asso: Wayne Groves
Sales Asso: Alex Lozano

D-U-N-S 03-168-4942
MASTRO GROUP LLC
16441 N 49th St, Scottsdale, AZ 85254
Tel (480) 889-1188 *Founded/Ownrshp* 1998
Sales 6.6MM^E *EMP* 449^E
SIC 5813 Tavern (drinking places)

D-U-N-S 01-068-0106
MASTROIANNI FAMILY ENTERPRISES LTD
JAYS CATERING
10581 Garden Grove Blvd, Garden Grove, CA 92843-1128
Tel (714) 636-6045 *Founded/Ownrshp* 1975
Sales 31.7MM^E *EMP* 400
SIC 7389 5812 Decoration service for special events; Caterers; Decoration service for special events; Caterers
Pr: Eleanor Mastroianni
VP: Jay Mastroianni
Creative D: Joel Stanton

D-U-N-S 13-960-9759 IMP
MASTRONARDI PRODUCE-USA INC
28700 Plymouth Rd, Livonia, MI 48150-2336
Tel (734) 727-0900 *Founded/Ownrshp* 2005
Sales 28.3MM *EMP* 505^E
SIC 5148 Vegetables; Vegetables
Pr: Paul Mastronardi
**COO:* Kevin Safrance
**CFO:* Steve Attridge
**VP:* Frank Mastronardi
Board of Directors: Don Mastronardi, Paul Mastronardi

D-U-N-S 80-827-6203
MASTROS RESTAURANTS LLC
(*Suby of* LANDRYS INC) ★
6300 Canoga Ave Ste 1100, Woodland Hills, CA 91367-8042
Tel (818) 598-5656 *Founded/Ownrshp* 2013

Sales 25.9MM^E *EMP* 900^E
SIC 5812 Steak restaurant; Steak restaurant

MASUNE FIRST AID AND SAFETY CO
See MASUNE FIRST AID INC

D-U-N-S 07-147-4688
MASUNE FIRST AID INC
MASUNE FIRST AID AND SAFETY CO
(*Suby of* CHEMSEARCH DIVISION) ★
500 Fillmore Ave, Tonawanda, NY 14150-2509
Tel (716) 695-4999 *Founded/Ownrshp* 1986
Sales 22.8MM^E *EMP* 180
SIC 5084 5099 5199 Materials handling machinery; Signs, except electric; First aid supplies; Materials handling machinery; Signs, except electric; First aid supplies
CEO: John Greenberger
**Pr:* Irvin L Levy
VP: Joseph Cleveland
S&M/VP: Mark Ladouceur
Board of Directors: Milton P Levy Jr

D-U-N-S 06-238-0318
MAT CONCESSIONAIRE LLC
860 Macarthur Cswy, Miami, FL 33132-1600
Tel (305) 929-0560 *Founded/Ownrshp* 2009
Sales 100.0MM *EMP* 9
SIC 5812 Concessionaire; Concessionaire
CFO: Christophe Couallier

MAT EXPRESS
See MAT PARCEL EXPRESS INC

D-U-N-S 82-585-8470 IMP/EXP
MAT HOLDINGS INC
MAT-AUTOMOTIVE
6700 Wildlife Way, Long Grove, IL 60047
Tel (847) 821-9630 *Founded/Ownrshp* 2006
Sales 1.2MMM^E *EMP* 11,000
Accts Bdo Seidman Llp
SIC 2842 3714 3563 Specialty cleaning, polishes & sanitation goods; Motor vehicle parts & accessories; Air & gas compressors including vacuum pumps; Specialty cleaning, polishes & sanitation goods; Motor vehicle parts & accessories; Air & gas compressors including vacuum pumps
CEO: Steve Wang
**Pr:* George Ruhl
CFO: Martin Beck
**CFO:* Greg Purse
**Sr VP:* Heather Korsvik
VP: Grace Chang
VP: Duncan Greathead
VP: Jay King
VP: Manny Klein
Genl Mgr: Patrick Naumann
CTO: Jeff Livermore

D-U-N-S 80-949-3856 IMP
MAT INDUSTRIES LLC
(*Suby of* MAT HOLDINGS INC) ★
6700 Wildlife Way, Long Grove, IL 60047
Tel (847) 821-9630 *Founded/Ownrshp* 2004
Sales 118.4MM^E *EMP* 173
Accts Bdo Seidman Llp
SIC 3563 Air & gas compressors; Air & gas compressors
Mtls Mgr: Rand Cooper

D-U-N-S 19-073-1422
MAT PARCEL EXPRESS INC
MAT EXPRESS
2719 Kurtz St Ste C, San Diego, CA 92110-3117
Tel (619) 849-9600 *Founded/Ownrshp* 1985
Sales 29.5MM^E *EMP* 100
SIC 4212 Local trucking, without storage
Pr: Thomas A Eggert
Treas: Jessica Perez
**VP:* Diane Eggert
**VP:* Matthew Eggert
Genl Mgr: Alan Eggert

MAT-AUTOMOTIVE
See MAT HOLDINGS INC

MATA
See MEMPHIS AREA TRANSIT AUTHORITY

MATADOR RESOURCES COMPANY
See MRC ENERGY CO

D-U-N-S 07-838-4474
▲ **MATADOR RESOURCES CO**
5400 Lbj Fwy Ste 1500, Dallas, TX 75240-1017
Tel (972) 371-5200 *Founded/Ownrshp* 1983
Sales 431.0MM *EMP* 99^E
Accts Kpmg Llp Dallas Texas
Tkr Sym MTDR *Exch* NYS
SIC 1311 Crude petroleum & natural gas; Natural gas production; Oil shale mining; Crude petroleum & natural gas; Natural gas production; Oil shale mining
Ch Bd: Joseph Wm Foran
Pr: Matthew V Hairford
COO: David E Lancaster
COO: Ava Monroe
Treas: Kathryn L Wayne
Ex VP: Craig Adams
Ex VP: Van H Singleton
VP: Sandra K Fendley
VP: Billy Goodwin
VP: Robert T Macalik
VP Prd: Trent Green

D-U-N-S 07-853-9640
MATAGORDA COUNTY HOSPITAL DISTRICT
MATAGORDA GENERAL HOSPITAL
104 7th St, Bay City, TX 77414-4853
Tel (979) 245-6383 *Founded/Ownrshp* 1939
Sales 59.7MM *EMP* 375^E
SIC 8062 General medical & surgical hospitals; General medical & surgical hospitals
CEO: Steven Smith
CFO: Bryan Pochnow
**CFO:* Bryan Prochnow
Dir Risk M: Terri Cox
Dir Lab: Laura Massey
Ex Dir: Judy Sablatura

Off Mgr: Amanda Smith
MIS Dir: Maryanne Cervantes
Dir IT: Maryann Servantes
Opers Mgr: Paula Wallace
Nrsg Dir: Laura Noster

MATAGORDA GENERAL HOSPITAL
See MATAGORDA COUNTY HOSPITAL DISTRICT

D-U-N-S 05-960-7275 IMP
MATAGRANO INC
440 Forbes Blvd, South San Francisco, CA 94080-2015
Tel (650) 829-4829 *Founded/Ownrshp* 1972
Sales 112.6MM[E] *EMP* 175
SIC 5181 5149 Beer & other fermented malt liquors; Mineral or spring water bottling; Juices; Beer & other fermented malt liquors; Mineral or spring water bottling; Juices
Pr: Louis Matagrano
CFO: Bill Hill
* *CFO:* William Hill
* *VP:* Tom Haas
* *VP:* Frank Matagrano Jr
Opers Mgr: Bruce Davidson
Mktg Mgr: Dick Unsinn
Sls Mgr: Robert Henley

D-U-N-S 60-471-2554
MATAMOROS ENTERPRISES INC
4818 Irvington Blvd, Houston, TX 77009-2727
Tel (713) 692-1923 *Founded/Ownrshp* 1983
Sales 21.5MM[E] *EMP* 103
SIC 5147 5144 5421 Meats, fresh; Poultry: live, dressed or frozen (unpackaged); Meat & fish markets; Meats, fresh; Poultry: live, dressed or frozen (unpackaged); Meat & fish markets
Pr: Raul De Hoyos

D-U-N-S 96-705-5349
MATAN B SETER FOUNDATION INC
65 Livingston Ave, Roseland, NJ 07068-1725
Tel (973) 597-2510 *Founded/Ownrshp* 2011
Sales 88.9MM *EMP* 2
Accts Kpmg Llp New York Ny
SIC 8699 Charitable organization; Charitable organization

D-U-N-S 07-782-6196
MATANDY STEEL & METAL PRODUCTS LLC
MATANDY STEEL SALES
1200 Central Ave, Hamilton, OH 45011-3825
Tel (513) 887-5274 *Founded/Ownrshp* 1987
Sales 143.7MM[E] *EMP* 100
SIC 5051 3312 3444 3399 Metals service centers & offices; Sheet or strip, steel, cold-rolled: own hot-rolled; Studs & joists, sheet metal; Nails: aluminum, brass or other nonferrous metal or wire; Metals service centers & offices; Sheet or strip, steel, cold-rolled: own hot-rolled; Studs & joists, sheet metal; Nails: aluminum, brass or other nonferrous metal or wire
Pr: Andrew Schuster
Genl Mgr: Aaron Higdon

MATANDY STEEL SALES
See MATANDY STEEL & METAL PRODUCTS LLC

D-U-N-S 04-133-8013
MATANUSKA ELECTRIC ASSOCIATION INC
M E A
163 E Industrial Way, Palmer, AK 99645-6703
Tel (907) 745-3231 *Founded/Ownrshp* 1941
Sales 120.9MM *EMP* 186
SIC 4911 Transmission, electric power; Distribution, electric power; Transmission, electric power; Distribution, electric power
Genl Mgr: Joe Griffith
* *CFO:* Matt Reisterer
Treas: Peter Burchell
Bd of Dir: James Hermon
Genl Mgr: D Carmony
Mtls Mgr: Debra Affinito
Plnt Mgr: Robert C Drake

D-U-N-S 10-091-0306
MATANUSKA SUSITNA BOROUGH SCHOOL DISTRICT
MSBSD
501 N Gulkana St, Palmer, AK 99645-6147
Tel (907) 746-9255 *Founded/Ownrshp* 1964
Sales 69.5MM[E] *EMP* 1,300
SIC 8211 Public elementary & secondary schools; Public elementary & secondary schools
Pr: Susan Pougher
VP: Marie Burton
* *VP:* Erick Cordero
* *VP:* Ole Larson
IT Man: Rebecca Wright

D-U-N-S 05-017-5843
MATANUSKA TELEPHONE ASSOCIATION INC
M T A
480 Commercial Dr, Palmer, AK 99645-6714
Tel (907) 745-3211 *Founded/Ownrshp* 1953
Sales 57.1MM *EMP* 300
SIC 4813 Local telephone communications; Local telephone communications
CEO: Greg Berberich
CFO: Wanda Phillips
* *CFO:* Wanda Tankersley
Ofcr: Jennifer Lesh
Exec: Sue Moore
IT Man: Emelia Bartholomew

D-U-N-S 01-923-1406
MATARAZZO BROS CO INC
MATARAZZO TOMATO
290 4th St, Chelsea, MA 02150-1524
Tel (617) 889-0516 *Founded/Ownrshp* 1948
Sales 20.8MM[E] *EMP* 58
SIC 5148 Vegetables, fresh
Pr: Anthony Aresco
* *Treas:* Sebastian Aresco

MATARAZZO TOMATO
See MATARAZZO BROS CO INC

D-U-N-S 00-411-8907
MATAWAN-ABERDEEN REGIONAL SCHOOL DISTRICT (NJ)
1 Crest Way, Matawan, NJ 07747-2247
Tel (732) 290-2705 *Founded/Ownrshp* 1927
Sales 68.1MM *EMP* 575
SIC 8211 Public elementary & secondary schools; Public elementary & secondary schools

MATC
See MADISON AREA TECHNICAL COLLEGE DISTRICT

D-U-N-S 08-003-2474
■ MATCH GROUP INC
(*Suby of* IAC/INTERACTIVECORP) ★
8300 Douglas Ave, Dallas, TX 75225-5603
Tel (214) 576-9352 *Founded/Ownrshp* 2009
Sales 3.9MM[E] *EMP* 4,800
Tkr Sym MTCH *Exch* NGS
SIC 7299 7374 Dating service; Data processing & preparation
CEO: Sam Yagan
* *Ch Bd:* Gregory R Blatt
CFO: Gary Swidler
Dir Sec: Amarnath Thombre
Board of Directors: Joseph Levin, Thomas J McInerney, Pamela S Seymon, Alan G Spoon, Mark Stein, Gregg Winiarski

D-U-N-S 03-909-0894
■ MATCH.COM LLC
(*Suby of* IAC/INTERACTIVECORP) ★
8300 Douglas Ave Ste 800, Dallas, TX 75225-5826
Tel (214) 576-9352 *Founded/Ownrshp* 2008
Sales 38.9MM[E] *EMP* 425
SIC 7299 Dating service; Dating service
CEO: Greg Blatt
Sr VP: Presz Mike
* *VP:* Curtis Anderson
VP: Andy Chen
* *VP:* Phil Eigenmann
VP: Monika Flood
VP: Ayesha Gilarde
* *VP:* Thomas McInerney
VP: Lisa Nelson
* *VP:* Michael Schwerdtman
Creative D: Rob Daffin

D-U-N-S 08-302-4687 IMP
MATCHMASTER DYEING & FINISHING INC
ANTEX KNITTING MILLS
3750 S Broadway, Los Angeles, CA 90007-4436
Tel (323) 232-2061 *Founded/Ownrshp* 1977
Sales 48.9MM *EMP* 364
SIC 2269 Finishing plants; Dyeing: raw stock yarn & narrow fabrics; Printing of narrow fabrics; Finishing plants; Dyeing: raw stock yarn & narrow fabrics; Printing of narrow fabrics
Pr: William Tenenblatt

D-U-N-S 00-225-9083
MATCO ELECTRIC CORP
3913 Gates Rd, Vestal, NY 13850-2323
Tel (607) 729-4921 *Founded/Ownrshp* 1965, 2010
Sales 58.9MM *EMP* 248
SIC 1731 General electrical contractor; General electrical contractor
Pr: Mark Freije
* *CFO:* Ken Elliott
* *Treas:* Kathleen Towery
Exec: Everett Jones
Sls&Mrk Ex: James Keough
Snr PM: Devin Ashman

MATCO PRODUCTS
See MATCO-NORCA INC

MATCO TOOLS
See NMTC INC

D-U-N-S 05-462-9977 IMP
MATCO-NORCA INC (NY)
MATCO PRODUCTS
1944 Route 22, Brewster, NY 10509-3604
Tel (845) 278-7570 *Founded/Ownrshp* 1955, 1970
Sales 24.9MM[E] *EMP* 65
SIC 5074 Plumbing & hydronic heating supplies
Ch Bd: Russell Stern
* *Pr:* Dov Matz
CFO: Terry Fleck
Bd of Dir: Debbie Krivak
* *VP:* Emanuel Matz
* *VP:* Michael Matz
VP: Michael Stapleton
VP Opers: John Grasso
Opers Mgr: Raul Lozano
VP Sls: Bardreau Scott
Mktg Mgr: Melissa Hunt

MATCON
See MATERIAL CONTROL SYSTEMS INC

D-U-N-S 96-542-2942
MATCON TRADING CORP
2020 Ponce De Leon Blvd # 1204, Coral Gables, FL 33134-4476
Tel (305) 442-6333 *Founded/Ownrshp* 1994
Sales 119.0MM *EMP* 5
SIC 6792 2951 Oil royalty traders; Asphalt paving mixtures & blocks
Pr: Jesus Iglesias
Treas: Ena Iglesias

D-U-N-S 96-172-9592
MATCOR AUTOMOTIVE (MICHIGAN) INC
(*Suby of* MATCOR AUTOMOTIVE INC)
401 S Steele St, Ionia, MI 48846-9401
Tel (616) 527-4050 *Founded/Ownrshp* 2009
Sales 24.0MM[E] *EMP* 120
SIC 3465 5013 Body parts, automobile: stamped metal; Automotive stampings; Body parts, automobile: stamped metal; Automotive stampings
Pr: Art Artuso
* *CFO:* Dave Cosgrove
* *VP:* Gilliano Tiberini
Mtls Mgr: Dave Singh

D-U-N-S 02-763-8938 IMP
MATCOR METAL FABRICATION WELCME INC
835 Salem Rd, Lexington, NC 27295-1086
Tel (336) 731-5700 *Founded/Ownrshp* 2009
Sales 27.2MM[E] *EMP* 140
SIC 3541 Machine tools, metal cutting type; Machine tools, metal cutting type
Pr: Arthur Artuso
* *Pr:* Frank Lucus
* *Treas:* Rod Harrison
* *Treas:* Galliano Tiberini
* *VP:* Manfred Kretschmer

D-U-N-S 16-987-1667
MATCOR-MATSU PARTNERSHIP
9650 Kellner Rd Sw, Huntsville, AL 35824-1713
Tel (256) 772-5888 *Founded/Ownrshp* 2004
Sales 39.8MM[E] *EMP* 350
SIC 6719 Investment holding companies, except banks; Investment holding companies, except banks
Prin: Arthur Artuso

D-U-N-S 05-708-7678 IMP
MATE PRECISION TOOLING INC
1295 Lund Blvd, Anoka, MN 55303-1092
Tel (763) 421-0230 *Founded/Ownrshp* 1964
Sales 60.0MM[E] *EMP* 340
SIC 3542 5084 3545 3544 1761 Punching & shearing machines; Industrial machinery & equipment; Machine tool accessories; Special dies, tools, jigs & fixtures; Sheet metalwork; Punching & shearing machines; Industrial machinery & equipment; Machine tool accessories; Special dies, tools, jigs & fixtures; Sheet metalwork
CEO: Dean A Sundquist
* *Pr:* Kevin Nicholson
CFO: Duane Vandenburg
* *CFO:* Duane Vandenburge
VP: Frank Baeumler
VP: Michael Brown
VP: Kevin Jordan
VP: Jim Thomas
IT Man: Greg Gerlach
VP Mfg: Tom Treuenfels
Mfg Mgr: Bill King

MATECH
See MACHINING TECHNOLOGIES INC

D-U-N-S 06-173-4349
MATENAER CORP
810 Schoenhaar Dr, West Bend, WI 53090-2632
Tel (262) 338-0700 *Founded/Ownrshp* 1992
Sales 106.9MM[E] *EMP* 115
SIC 5051 3452 Metals service centers & offices; Washers, metal; Metals service centers & offices; Washers, metal
Pr: Chip Stringer
Off Mgr: Joan Williams

D-U-N-S 07-103-7761
■ MATEP LLC
(*Suby of* NSTAR LLC) ★
474 Brookline Ave, Boston, MA 02215-5415
Tel (617) 598-2700 *Founded/Ownrshp* 2010
Sales 56.9MM[E] *EMP* 90
SIC 4911 Generation, electric power
Pr: William Dicroce
VP: Kelly McCarthy
Genl Mgr: Scott McBurney
Netwrk Mgr: Darrin Rescigno
Mktg Dir: Paul Terrio

MATER DEI PROVINCIAL ATE
See DAUGHTERS OF CHARITY OF ST VINCENT DE PAUL OF INDIANA INC

D-U-N-S 07-186-7774
MATER MISERICORDIAE HOSPITAL
MERCY MEDICAL CENTER MERCED
333 Mercy Ave, Merced, CA 95340-8319
Tel (209) 564-5000 *Founded/Ownrshp* 2006
Sales 78.6MM[E] *EMP* 1,200
SIC 8062 General medical & surgical hospitals; General medical & surgical hospitals
CEO: David Dunham
COO: Chuck Kassis
CFO: Terry Bohllke
CFO: Doreen Hartmann
CFO: Michael Strasser
Dir Risk M: Mika Grisham
Dir Lab: Glen Bruss
Dir Rad: Anthony Cordeiro
Info Man: Cheryl Baijnauth
Mktg Dir: Paul Feltz
Ansthlgy: Davin Soehnen

D-U-N-S 02-700-4043
MATERA PAPER CO INC
835 N Ww White Rd, San Antonio, TX 78219-2714
Tel (210) 892-5101 *Founded/Ownrshp* 1984
Sales 102.8MM[E] *EMP* 182
SIC 5087 Janitors' supplies; Janitors' supplies
Ch Bd: John Strieber
* *Pr:* John Richardson
Treas: Steve Marshal
VP: Chris Goeschel
* *VP:* B J Moore
* *VP:* Barry Stevens
Sls Mgr: Tammy Lovelady
Sales Asso: Jason Norris
Sales Asso: Jeff Wimpy

D-U-N-S 01-930-8779 IMP
MATERIA INC
60 N San Gabriel Blvd, Pasadena, CA 91107-3748
Tel (626) 243-5660 *Founded/Ownrshp* 1998
Sales 30.1MM[E] *EMP* 140
SIC 2819 Catalysts, chemical; Catalysts, chemical
CEO: Michael Giardello
COO: Steve Wright
VP: Jennifer Beerman
VP: Christopher Cruce
VP: Todd Najera
* *VP:* Mark S Trimmer

D-U-N-S 04-830-6997 EXP
MATERIAL CONTROL INC
CONVEYOR COMPONENTS CO DIV
130 Seltzer Rd, Croswell, MI 48422-9180
Tel (630) 892-4274 *Founded/Ownrshp* 1968
Sales 72.9MM[E] *EMP* 250
SIC 3535 Bucket type conveyor systems; Bucket type conveyor systems
Pr: Clinton F Stimpson III
Ex Dir: Robert Hutchins
Trfc Mgr: Danette Rosenberg

MATERIAL CONTROL SYSTEMS
See CONTROL SYSTEMS INTERNATIONAL INC

D-U-N-S 17-480-2231 IMP
MATERIAL CONTROL SYSTEMS INC
MATCON
201 N Main St, Port Byron, IL 61275-9790
Tel (309) 523-3774 *Founded/Ownrshp* 1938
Sales 26.1MM[E] *EMP* 52
SIC 5099 2542 Containers: glass, metal or plastic; Racks, merchandise display or storage: except wood
Pr: Donn R Larson
* *CFO:* Judy Scott
CIO: Dave McClanihan
Sfty Mgr: Kim Johnson

D-U-N-S 61-214-7736
MATERIAL DELIVERY INC
MDI ROCK
2815 E Rose Garden Ln, Phoenix, AZ 85050-4705
Tel (602) 569-8722 *Founded/Ownrshp* 1988
Sales 32.8MM[E] *EMP* 170
SIC 5211 5032 Sand & gravel; Stone, crushed or broken; Sand & gravel; Stone, crushed or broken
Pr: Michael Denny
IT Man: Teresa Mittleiter

D-U-N-S 01-798-4655
MATERIAL DIFFERENCE TECHNOLOGIES LLC
3665 Markwood Ct, Oxford, MI 48370-2917
Tel (248) 310-9722 *Founded/Ownrshp* 2009
Sales 40.0MM *EMP* 8
SIC 5162 7389 Plastics materials & basic shapes; ; Plastics materials & basic shapes;
Owner: Guy Jensen
* *Mng Pt:* Terry Ingham

D-U-N-S 00-232-1875
MATERIAL DISTRIBUTORS INC (PA)
8 Cynwyd Rd Frnt B, Bala Cynwyd, PA 19004-3345
Tel (610) 667-4800 *Founded/Ownrshp* 1958
Sales 25.1MM[E] *EMP* 25
SIC 5031 Building materials, interior
Pr: Richard S Grossman
* *Treas:* Andrew Grossman
VP: David Beccaria
* *VP:* Alan Grossman

D-U-N-S 00-645-4268
MATERIAL DISTRIBUTORS INC
M D I
211 N 11th St, Marshall, MN 56258-2750
Tel (507) 532-4463 *Founded/Ownrshp* 2001
Sales 29.4MM[E] *EMP* 30
SIC 5031 Plywood; Lumber: rough, dressed & finished; Building materials, exterior; Building materials, interior
Pr: Steve Sanders
* *VP:* Juli Sanders

D-U-N-S 61-780-4224
MATERIAL HANDLING EXCHANGE INC
1800 Churchman Ave # 100, Indianapolis, IN 46203-2920
Tel (317) 788-7225 *Founded/Ownrshp* 1989
Sales 29.4MM[E] *EMP* 30
SIC 5084 5251 Materials handling machinery; Tools
Pr: Kevin Lawrence
COO: Carrie Lawrence
IT Man: Debbie Williams
Mktg Mgr: Michael Kruggel
Sales Asso: Chris Summers

D-U-N-S 08-094-6155 IMP
MATERIAL HANDLING INC
631 N Glenwood Ave, Dalton, GA 30721-2816
Tel (706) 278-1104 *Founded/Ownrshp* 1975
Sales 35.9MM[E] *EMP* 100
Accts Joseph Decosimo And Company Ll
SIC 5084 7353 7699 Lift trucks & parts; Cranes & aerial lift equipment, rental or leasing; Industrial machinery & equipment repair; Lift trucks & parts; Cranes & aerial lift equipment, rental or leasing; Industrial machinery & equipment repair
Ch Bd: Amar V Sain
* *Pr:* Pat Sain
* *Sec:* Michael Sain
Exec: Bill Gleaton
Sales Exec: John Patterson
Sls Mgr: Corrie Axe

D-U-N-S 96-698-6267
MATERIAL HANDLING RESOURCES LLC
(*Suby of* OHL) ★
7355 Cockrill Bend Blvd, Nashville, TN 37209-1025
Tel (615) 350-5827 *Founded/Ownrshp* 1996
Sales 32.4MM[E] *EMP* 45
SIC 5084 7699 Conveyor systems; Industrial truck repair
Sls Mgr: Joe Tracey

D-U-N-S 05-142-2053
MATERIAL HANDLING SUPPLY INC
MHS LIFT
1 Old Salem Rd, Gloucester City, NJ 08030
Tel (856) 541-1290 *Founded/Ownrshp* 1970
Sales 70.6MM[E] *EMP* 135
Accts Amper Politziner & Mattia Llp
SIC 5084 7359 Materials handling machinery; Equipment rental & leasing; Materials handling machinery; Equipment rental & leasing
Pr: Andrew Levin
* *CFO:* David Brown
* *Treas:* Brett Levin

D-U-N-S 05-479-8004
MATERIAL HANDLING SUPPLY INC (CA)
(Suby of ENVICOR) ★
12900 Firestone Blvd, Santa Fe Springs, CA 90670-5405
Tel (562) 921-7715 Founded/Ownrshp 1962, 1971
Sales 30.8MM^E EMP 98
SIC 5084 7629 5046 Food industry machinery; Engines & transportation equipment; Materials handling machinery; Electrical repair shops; Commercial equipment; Food industry machinery; Engines & transportation equipment; Materials handling machinery; Electrical repair shops; Commercial equipment
CEO: Alexander Stephen Lynn
*Ch Bd: Donn C Lynn Jr
COO: Carl Lopez
*Sec: John Hanson
VP Sls: Brett Levin

D-U-N-S 12-631-6764
MATERIAL HANDLING SYSTEMS INC
3955 E Blue Lick Rd, Louisville, KY 40229-6047
Tel (502) 636-0690 Founded/Ownrshp 2004
Sales 79.9MM^E EMP 60
SIC 5084 Packaging machinery & equipment; Packaging machinery & equipment
CEO: Tony Mouser
Pr: Patrick Cowgill
*Pr: Gregory Judge
*COO: Scott McReynolds
COO: Mark Springstube
*CFO: Brian Johnson
Genl Mgr: Paul McGowan
*VP Mktg: Rush Fullerton
Mktg Dir: Anthony Holland

D-U-N-S 78-706-1977
MATERIAL HANDLING TECHNOLOGIES INC
113 International Dr, Morrisville, NC 27560-8792
Tel (919) 388-0050 Founded/Ownrshp 1992
Sales 36.9MM^E EMP 75
SIC 5084 3535

D-U-N-S 10-153-4209 IMP/EXP
MATERIAL IN MOTION INC
726 Palomar Ave, Sunnyvale, CA 94085-2914
Tel (650) 967-3300 Founded/Ownrshp 2001
Sales 70.2MM^E EMP 200
SIC 3571 5999 Electronic computers; Electronic computers; Electronic parts & equipment
CEO: Ted Salah
IT Man: Rohit Kumar

D-U-N-S 01-975-3419
MATERIAL LOGISTICS & SERVICES LLC
(Suby of WAREHOUSE SPECIALISTS INC) ★
1160 N Mayflower Dr, Appleton, WI 54913-9656
Tel (920) 830-5000 Founded/Ownrshp 2010
Sales 39.5MM^E EMP 1,200
SIC 4225 General warehousing
Pr: Robert Schroeder
CFO: Daniel Vandenheuvel
VP: Bill Lindeke
VP: Kevin Nixon
VP: Dan Sellers
Counsel: Ben Haupt

D-U-N-S 88-314-7639
MATERIAL MANAGEMENT RESOURCES INC
MMR
1304 Langham Creek Dr # 200, Houston, TX 77084-5042
Tel (281) 944-4212 Founded/Ownrshp 1994
Sales 22.0MM EMP 17
SIC 8742 Materials mgmt. (purchasing, handling, inventory) consultant; Materials mgmt. (purchasing, handling, inventory) consultant
Pr: Wayne L Caldwell
*VP: Kevin D Graham

D-U-N-S 79-614-0556
MATERIAL PACKAGING CORP
ASH GROVE PACKAGING
(Suby of ASH GROVE CEMENT CO) ★
23018 S State Route 291, Harrisonville, MO 64701-4394
Tel (816) 380-4473 Founded/Ownrshp 1987
Sales 257.9MM^E EMP 2,500^E
SIC 3241 Cement, hydraulic; Cement, hydraulic
Pr: Jeff Sutton

D-U-N-S 06-457-2563 IMP
MATERIAL SCIENCES CORP
(Suby of ZINK ACQUISITION HOLDINGS INC) ★
2250 Pratt Blvd, Elk Grove Village, IL 60007-5917
Tel (847) 439-2210 Founded/Ownrshp 2014
Sales 117.5MM^E EMP 267
SIC 3479 3471 Painting of metal products; Coating of metals & formed products; Coating, rust preventive; Electroplating of metals or formed products; Painting of metal products; Coating of metals & formed products; Coating, rust preventive; Electroplating of metals or formed products
CEO: Pat Murley
*Pr: Clifford D Nastas
*CFO: James D Pawlak
*CFO: Jim Todd
Bd of Dir: Frank Hohmann
*Sr VP: Steve Tatalovich
*VP: Matthew M Murphy
VP: Robert Rocowski
VP: Anton Vitzthum
*VP: Michael R Wilson
CIO: Sue Brody

D-U-N-S 96-413-4683
MATERIAL SCIENCES CORP
2250 Pratt Blvd, Elk Grove Village, IL 60007-5917
Tel (888) 603-1553 Founded/Ownrshp 1982
Sales 136.9MM^E EMP 567
SIC 3312 5051 Sheet or strip, steel, cold-rolled: own hot-rolled; Steel; Sheet or strip, steel, cold-rolled: own hot-rolled; Steel
CEO: Patrick Murley
*COO: Michael Noble
*CFO: James L Todd
*Sr VP: Steve Tatalovich
*VP: Michael E Noble

D-U-N-S 04-617-0577
MATERIAL SERVICE CORP
HANSON MATERIAL SERVICE
(Suby of HANSON AGGREGATES LLC) ★
2235 Entp Dr Ste 3504, Westchester, IL 60154
Tel (708) 731-2600 Founded/Ownrshp 2006
Sales 113.5MM^E EMP 600
SIC 1422 1442 Crushed & broken limestone; Construction sand mining; Gravel mining; Crushed & broken limestone; Construction sand mining; Gravel mining
Pr: Gerald Nagel
Pr: Dennis Dolan
Pr: Michael Stanczak
CFO: Walter Serwa
VP: Gerry Nagel
Sls Mgr: Darren Melvin
Counsel: David Ruben

D-U-N-S 79-100-2264
■ **MATERIAL SERVICE RESOURCES CORP**
(Suby of GENERAL DYNAMICS CORP) ★
222 N La Salle St # 1200, Chicago, IL 60601-1003
Tel (630) 325-7736 Founded/Ownrshp 1992
Sales 90.3MM^E EMP 2,188
SIC 1442 1221 Construction sand mining; Gravel mining; Bituminous coal & lignite-surface mining
Ch Bd: Lester Crown
Pr: Michael Stanczak

D-U-N-S 18-690-1377
MATERIAL SUPPLY INC
MSI HVAC
11700 Industry Ave, Fontana, CA 92337-6934
Tel (951) 727-2200 Founded/Ownrshp 1986
Sales 85.8MM^E EMP 250
SIC 3444 5075 7623 1711 Metal ventilating equipment; Warm air heating & air conditioning; Air filters; Ventilating equipment & supplies; Air conditioning repair; Heating & air conditioning contractors; Metal ventilating equipment; Warm air heating & air conditioning; Air filters; Ventilating equipment & supplies; Air conditioning repair; Heating & air conditioning contractors
CEO: Dion Quinn
*VP: Bob Billiu
*VP: Jon Dautrich
*VP: Robert Hascall

D-U-N-S 79-119-1216
MATERIAL WORKS LTD
101 S Main St, Red Bud, IL 62278-1104
Tel (618) 282-4200 Founded/Ownrshp 1992
Sales 27.3MM^E EMP 118
SIC 7389 Metal slitting & shearing
Pr: Kevin Voges
VP: Eric Fritshe
VP: Alan Mueth
IT Man: Kevin Zeiger
Snr Mgr: Barry Albert
Snr Mgr: Kenneth Booker
Snr Mgr: Robert Rahlfs
Snr Mgr: Scott Voss

D-U-N-S 10-220-6112 IMP
MATERIALS GROUP LLC
TMG
575 Byrne Industrial Dr, Rockford, MI 49341-1085
Tel (616) 863-6046 Founded/Ownrshp 2001
Sales 24.0MM^E EMP 16
SIC 5131 Plastic piece goods, woven

MATERIALS INNOVATION
See JSR MICRO INC

D-U-N-S 07-731-7758
MATERIALS INNOVATION AND RECYCLING AUTHORITY
MIRA
100 Constitution Plz Fl 6, Hartford, CT 06103-1703
Tel (860) 757-7700 Founded/Ownrshp 1973
Sales 38.1MM^E EMP 45
SIC 4953 Sanitary landfill operation
Pr: Thomas D Kirk
*CFO: James P Bolduc
CTO: William Stotts
Dir IT: Gary Bonafilia
Pr Dir: Paul Nonnenmacher

MATERIALS MANAGEMENT CO
See GARLANDS INC

D-U-N-S 04-200-3038 IMP/EXP
MATERIALS MARKETING LTD (TX)
120 W Josephine St, San Antonio, TX 78212-4107
Tel (210) 731-8453 Founded/Ownrshp 1965
Sales 21.0MM^E EMP 75
SIC 5032 Tile, clay or other ceramic, excluding refractory; Stone, crushed or broken
Pr: Donald B Rymer Jr
*Ch Bd: James T Rymer
Pr: Roger Ramirez
CFO: Ryan Engel
*CFO: Mario Garcia
*Treas: William O Hampson
*VP: Richard Harowitz
VP: Annie Kearney
VP: John Valentine
Brnch Mgr: John Flores
Brnch Mgr: Scott Meredith

D-U-N-S 10-670-9587 IMP
MATERIALS PROCESSING CORP
MPC SURPLUS
2300 Pilot Knob Rd, Mendota Heights, MN 55120-1116
Tel (651) 681-8099 Founded/Ownrshp 2006
Sales 25.7MM^E EMP 250
SIC 3339 3829

D-U-N-S 04-027-6248 IMP/EXP
MATERIALS PROCESSING INC
SMALL PARTS
3500 Depauw Blvd, Indianapolis, IN 46268-1170
Tel (317) 803-3010 Founded/Ownrshp 1975
Sales 138.2MM^E EMP 800
SIC 3443 3083 5051 Metal parts; Plastic finished products, laminated; Metals service centers & offices; Metal parts; Plastic finished products, laminated; Metals service centers & offices
CEO: John E Barnes
*Treas: James P Bauer
*V Ch Bd: Clay T Barnes
*VP: Michael H Winings
Dir IT: Mark McDonald

D-U-N-S 00-561-8264
MATERIALS SOFTWARE SYSTEM INC
9327 Midlothian Tpke 2e, North Chesterfield, VA 23235-4944
Tel (804) 272-0081 Founded/Ownrshp 1998
Sales 26.5MM^E EMP 700^E
SIC 7371 Computer software systems analysis & design, custom; Computer software systems analysis & design, custom
Pr: Venu M Pasumarthi
Ofcr: Praveen Kumar
VP: M S Sastry
Off Mgr: Lalitha Mandalika

D-U-N-S 03-071-8738
MATERIALS TRANSPORT CO
(Suby of ASH GROVE MATERIALS CORP) ★
11011 Cody St, Shawnee Mission, KS 66210-1313
Tel (913) 345-2030 Founded/Ownrshp 1973
Sales 16.0MM^E EMP 300
SIC 4212 3273 Local trucking, without storage; Ready-mixed concrete; Local trucking, without storage; Ready-mixed concrete
Pr: Chuck Wietenhoft
*Treas: Joe Rieger

D-U-N-S 00-731-8280 IMP/EXP
MATERIALS TRANSPORTATION CO
1408 Commerce Dr, Temple, TX 76504-5134
Tel (254) 298-2900 Founded/Ownrshp 2011
Sales 30.0MM EMP 150
SIC 3559 3556 Automotive related machinery; Food products machinery; Automotive related machinery; Food products machinery
Pr: Jim Granfor
*CFO: Russell Wilson
VP: Bob Neil
VP: Terry Orf
IT Man: Heather Robinette
IT Man: David Von Rosenberg
Software D: Kelsey Golden
Plnt Mgr: Peter Denharder
VP Mktg: Jim Linella
VP Sls: Stephen Hicks
Sls Dir: Carl Cort

D-U-N-S 00-210-4875 IMP
MATERION ADVANCED MATERIALS TECHNOLOGIES AND SERVICES INC (NY)
MATERION MICROELECTRONICS
(Suby of MATERION BRUSH INC) ★
2978 Main St, Buffalo, NY 14214-1004
Tel (716) 837-1000 Founded/Ownrshp 1912
Sales 110.6MM^E EMP 370
SIC 3339 Primary nonferrous metals; Primary nonferrous metals
Pr: Donald Klinkowicz
Treas: Derrick Brown
VP: Scott Haluska
Genl Mgr: Matthew Willson
Dir IT: George Wityak
IT Man: Jeff Hazlett
IT Man: Richard Sager
VP Opers: Mark Devillier
Sfty Dirs: Robert Hanley
Sfty Mgr: Roger Balcerak
Mfg Mgr: William Barry

D-U-N-S 12-082-8280 IMP
MATERION BREWSTER LLC
(Suby of MATERION ADVANCED MATERIALS TECHNOLOGIES AND SERVICES INC) ★
42 Mount Ebo Rd S, Brewster, NY 10509-4005
Tel (845) 279-0900 Founded/Ownrshp 1998
Sales 26.0MM^E EMP 75
SIC 3499 3674 Friction material, made from powdered metal; Semiconductors & related devices

D-U-N-S 00-421-2999 IMP
MATERION BRUSH INC (OH)
(Suby of MATERION CORP) ★
6070 Parkland Blvd Ste 1, Mayfield Heights, OH 44124-4191
Tel (216) 486-4200 Founded/Ownrshp 1931
Sales 194.8MM^E EMP 1,200
SIC 3351 3356 3264 3339 3341 3674 Copper & copper alloy sheet, strip, plate & products; Strip, copper & copper alloy; Plates, copper & copper alloy; Tubing, copper & copper alloy; Nickel & nickel alloy pipe, plates, sheets, etc.; Porcelain parts for electrical devices, molded; Beryllium metal; Secondary precious metals; Semiconductors & related devices; Copper & copper alloy sheet, strip, plate & products; Strip, copper & copper alloy; Plates, copper & copper alloy; Tubing, copper & copper alloy; Nickel & nickel alloy pipe, plates, sheets, etc.; Porcelain parts for electrical devices, molded; Beryllium metal; Secondary precious metals; Semiconductors & related devices
CFO: John D Grampa
*Sec: Michael C Hasychak
VP: Mark Asany
VP: Gregory Chemnitz
VP: David Deubner
VP: John Grampa
VP: Heiner Lichtenberger
VP: John Scheatzle
Prin: B R Harman
Prin: E A Levine
Mng Dir: Tony Ong
Board of Directors: Charles Brush

D-U-N-S 01-567-0768
MATERION BRUSH INTERNATIONAL INC
(Suby of MATERION CORP) ★
6070 Parkland Blvd Ste 3, Mayfield Heights, OH 44124-4191
Tel (216) 486-4200 Founded/Ownrshp 2000
Sales 28.5MM^E EMP 100
SIC 5051 Metals service centers & offices; Metals service centers & offices
Pr: Richard Trate
COO: Lyle Macaulay
Sr VP: Daniel Skoch
VP: Patrick Carpenter
VP: Gregory Chemnitz
VP: David Deubner
VP: John Grampa
VP: Fritz Grensing
VP: Mark Jasany
VP: Joseph Kaiser
VP: James Marrotte
VP: Tom Piazza

D-U-N-S 01-560-3793
MATERION CERAMICS INC
(Suby of MATERION BRUSH INC) ★
6100 S Tucson Blvd, Tucson, AZ 85706-4520
Tel (520) 741-3411 Founded/Ownrshp 1930
Sales 71.1MM^E EMP 1,200
SIC 3351 3264 Copper & copper alloy sheet, strip, plate & products; Strip, copper & copper alloy; Plates, copper & copper alloy; Tubing, copper & copper alloy; Porcelain electrical supplies; Copper & copper alloy sheet, strip, plate & products; Strip, copper & copper alloy; Plates, copper & copper alloy; Tubing, copper & copper alloy; Porcelain electrical supplies
Pr: John Scheatzle
Sfty Mgr: Richard Manes
Plnt Mgr: Ken Harrison
Sales Exec: Lee Vandermark

• D-U-N-S 62-291-3080 IMP/EXP
MATERION CORP
6070 Parkland Blvd Ste 1, Mayfield Heights, OH 44124-4191
Tel (216) 486-4200 Founded/Ownrshp 1931
Sales 1.1MMM EMP 2,671
SIC 3339 3351 3356 3341 3674 Beryllium metal; Copper & copper alloy sheet, strip, plate & products; Nickel & nickel alloy pipe, plates, sheets, etc.; Secondary precious metals; Semiconductors & related devices; Beryllium metal; Copper & copper alloy sheet, strip, plate & products; Nickel & nickel alloy pipe, plates, sheets, etc.; Secondary precious metals; Semiconductors & related devices
Ch Bd: Richard J Hipple
Pr: Donald G Klimkowicz
CFO: Joseph P Kelley
Treas: Michael C Hasychak
Bd of Dir: Craig Shular
VP: Gregory R Chemnitz
VP: Christopher Eberhardt
VP: James Marrotte
VP: Tom Maschke
VP: Walter G Maxwell
VP: John Scheatzle
VP: Ian Tribick
VP Bus Dev: Matthew Willson
Board of Directors: Edward G Crawford, Joseph P Keithley, Vinod M Khilnani, William B Lawrence, M Mohan Reddy, Craig S Shular, Darlene J S Solomon, Robert B Toth, Geoffrey Wild

MATERION MICROELECTRONICS
See MATERION ADVANCED MATERIALS TECHNOLOGIES AND SERVICES INC

D-U-N-S 01-560-1664 IMP
MATERION NATURAL RESOURCES INC (UT)
(Suby of MATERION CORP) ★
10 Miles North Hwy 6, Delta, UT 84624
Tel (435) 864-2701 Founded/Ownrshp 2001
Sales 57.6MM^E EMP 1,862
SIC 1099 3339 Beryllium ore mining; Primary nonferrous metals; Beryllium ore mining; Primary nonferrous metals
Pr: Alex Boulton
Ex Dir: Darla Callister
Opers Mgr: Dough Murpock

D-U-N-S 06-933-7764 EXP
MATERION PRECISION OPTICS AND THIN FILM COATINGS INC
(Suby of MATERION ADVANCED MATERIALS TECHNOLOGIES AND SERVICES INC) ★
2 Lyberty Way, Westford, MA 01886-3616
Tel (978) 692-7513 Founded/Ownrshp 2009
Sales 44.2MM^E EMP 293
SIC 3827 Optical instruments & lenses; Optical instruments & lenses
VP: Robert Naranjo
*Sec: Thomas F Mauser
Genl Mgr: Kevin Downing
Dir IT: Chow Francis
Mfg Mgr: Steve Congon
Mfg Mgr: Dale E Lhussier
Mktg Dir: Sharon Palermo
Sls Mgr: Evelyn Downey

D-U-N-S 04-536-5541 IMP
MATERION TECHNICAL MATERIALS INC
(Suby of MATERION CORP) ★
5 Wellington Rd, Lincoln, RI 02865-4411
Tel (401) 333-1700 Founded/Ownrshp 1982
Sales 87.8MM^E EMP 200
SIC 3331 3339 3423 Primary copper smelter products; Nickel refining (primary); Hand & edge tools; Primary copper smelter products; Nickel refining (primary); Hand & edge tools
Pr: Al Lubrano
*Treas: M C Hasychak
VP: Ulrich Greschner
VP: Joseph Kaiser
VP: Larry Meathe
*VP: Robert Tavares
Plng Mgr: John Walsh
VP Mktg: Edward Strother

D-U-N-S 01-560-2274
MATERION TECHNOLOGIES INC (AZ)
(*Suby of* MATERION CORP) ★
6100 S Tucson Blvd, Tucson, AZ 85706-4520
Tel (520) 746-0699 *Founded/Ownrshp* 2001
Sales 24.5MM^E *EMP* 100
SIC 3331 Primary copper; Primary copper
Pr: Jordon Frazier
Treas: Gary W Schiavoni
VP: Michael C Hasychak
VP: James P Marrotte
VP: John J Pallam
Dir IT: David E Jech
IT Man: Debbie Handley
Mktg Mgr: Joe Occhipinti
Sls Mgr: Lee Vandermark

D-U-N-S 01-848-6316 IMP
MATESICH DISTRIBUTING CO
1190 E Main St, Newark, OH 43055-8803
Tel (740) 349-8686 *Founded/Ownrshp* 1993
Sales 29.1MM^E *EMP* 91
SIC 5181 Beer & other fermented malt liquors; Beer & other fermented malt liquors
CEO: John C Matesich III
Sec: James M Matesich
VP: Stephen Pintz
Genl Mgr: Pam Ferick

D-U-N-S 15-709-6772
MATH FOR AMERICA INC
915 Broadway Fl 16, New York, NY 10010-7116
Tel (646) 437-0904 *Founded/Ownrshp* 2004
Sales 26.8MM *EMP* 20^E
Accts Grant Thornton Llp New York
SIC 8621 7361 Education & teacher association; Executive placement; Education & teacher association; Executive placement
Pr: John Ewing

D-U-N-S 15-412-5140
MATHEMATICA INC
600 Alexander Park # 100, Princeton, NJ 08540-6346
Tel (609) 945-3372 *Founded/Ownrshp* 1986
Sales 220.0MM *EMP* 1,000
Accts Parentebeard Llc Philadelphia
SIC 8732 Economic research; Economic research
Pr: Paul Decker
CFO: Jay B Style
Sr VP: Barbara Devaney
Sr VP: Amy Johnson
Sr VP: Patrick Mooney
Sr VP: Mary T Moore
Sr VP: Craig Thornton
Sr VP: Judith Wooldridge
VP: Laura Eckly
VP: Murray Gillham
VP: Henrik Madsen
VP: Geraldine Mooney
VP: Buck Rodgers
VP: Jonathan Smith
VP: Pamela Tapscott
Assoc Dir: Daniel Shapiro

D-U-N-S 15-430-8522
MATHEMATICA POLICY RESEARCH INC
(*Suby of* MATHEMATICA INC) ★
600 Alexander Park, Princeton, NJ 08540-6346
Tel (609) 799-3535 *Founded/Ownrshp* 1986
Sales 132.6MM^E *EMP* 929
SIC 8732 Economic research; Economic research
Pr: Paul Decker
Ofcr: Natalya Savitz
Ex VP: George Carcagno
Sr VP: Neil Clover
Sr VP: Barbara Devaney
Sr VP: Thomas Fraker
Sr VP: Amy Johnson
Sr VP: Patrick Mooney
Sr VP: Mary Moore
Sr VP: Craig Thornton
Sr VP: Judith Wooldridge
VP: Alison Barger
VP: Rob Glazier
VP: Marsha Gold
VP: Harrison N Greene Jr
VP: Daniel Kasprzyk
VP: Chris Mayer
VP: Sheena McConnell
VP: Schochet Peter
VP: Margo Rosenbach
VP: Chris Trenholm

D-U-N-S 61-136-7715
MATHENA INC
(*Suby of* WEIR GROUP PLC(THE))
3900 S Hwy 81 Service Rd, El Reno, OK 73036-6808
Tel (405) 422-3600 *Founded/Ownrshp* 2012
Sales 89.0MM *EMP* 90
SIC 3699 3822 Oil field equipment, rental or leasing; Security control equipment & systems; Surface burner controls, temperature
Pr: John Mathena
VP: Greg Cantrell
VP: David Mathena
VP: Harold Mathena
VP: Trebor Nall

D-U-N-S 05-977-7433
MATHENY IMPORTS INC
JAGUAR JACKSONVILLE
11211 Atlantic Blvd, Jacksonville, FL 32225-2905
Tel (904) 642-1500 *Founded/Ownrshp* 1969
Sales 30.3MM *EMP* 38
SIC 5511

D-U-N-S 06-072-2568
MATHENY MEDICAL AND EDUCATIONAL CENTER
MATHENY MEDICAL AND EDUCTL CTR
65 Highland Ave, Peapack, NJ 07977
Tel (908) 234-0011 *Founded/Ownrshp* 1946
Sales 47.2MM^E *EMP* 600^E
Accts Parentebeard Llc Philadelphia
SIC 8069 8211 Children's hospital; Specialty education; Children's hospital; Specialty education
Ch Bd: Anne Brady
Pr: Steven Proctor
Ofcr: Kevin Ralph

MATHENY MEDICAL AND EDUCTL CTR
See MATHENY MEDICAL AND EDUCATIONAL CENTER

D-U-N-S 01-612-4836
MATHENY MOTOR TRUCK CO INC (WV)
315 Ann St, Parkersburg, WV 26101-5321
Tel (304) 485-4418 *Founded/Ownrshp* 1922, 1980
Sales 54.9MM^E *EMP* 150^E
SIC 5012 5013 5511

D-U-N-S 06-999-3871
MATHER LIFEWAYS
MATHER PLACE OF WILMETTE
1603 Orrington Ave # 1800, Evanston, IL 60201-5019
Tel (847) 492-7500 *Founded/Ownrshp* 1941
Sales 23.6MM *EMP* 450
SIC 8322 Adult day care center; Adult day care center
Ch: Roger Lumpp
Pr: Mary Leary
CFO: Carol Sussenbach
VP: Linda Hollinger-Smith
VP: David Kane
VP: Christopher Manella
VP: Gale Morganv

MATHER PLACE OF WILMETTE
See MATHER LIFEWAYS

D-U-N-S 00-721-0040
MATHERLY MECHANICAL CONTRACTORS LLC
1520 Ocama Blvd, Midwest City, OK 73110-7947
Tel (405) 737-3488 *Founded/Ownrshp* 2010
Sales 27.3MM *EMP* 150
SIC 1711 3444 Mechanical contractor; Sheet metalwork; Mechanical contractor; Sheet metalwork
Treas: Philip Walker
VP: Mike Clark
VP: David Munson
Snr PM: Roger Carson

D-U-N-S 00-541-8871
MATHERNE INSTRUMENTATION SPECIALISTS INC (LA)
131 Capital Blvd, Houma, LA 70360-7948
Tel (985) 876-9808 *Founded/Ownrshp* 1999
Sales 32.1MM^E *EMP* 75
SIC 1389 Oil field services
Pr: Chad Matherne

D-U-N-S 06-245-4301
MATHES ELECTRIC SUPPLY CO INC
6 41st Ln, Pensacola, FL 32505-4304
Tel (850) 432-4161 *Founded/Ownrshp* 1973
Sales 48.0MM^E *EMP* 36
SIC 5063 Electrical supplies
Pr: Jerry W Mathes
Pr: Kimberly Ann Mathes Cheney
Pr: Chris Cunningham
Pr: Christopher N Cunningham
Sales Exec: Steve Colony
Sales Asso: Jimmy Boyett

D-U-N-S 10-296-3121
MATHESON FAST FREIGHT INC
(*Suby of* MATHESON TRUCKING INC) ★
9780 Dino Dr, Elk Grove, CA 95624-9477
Tel (916) 686-4600 *Founded/Ownrshp* 1984
Sales 21.5MM^E *EMP* 400
SIC 4213 Less-than-truckload (LTL) transport; Less-than-truckload (LTL) transport
Ch Bd: Robert B Matheson
Pr: Mark B Matheson
Sec: Laurie Johnson
Ex VP: Carole L Matheson
VP: Donald G Brocca
VP: Louise Lehman
VP: Jose Miranda
VP: James Powell

D-U-N-S 07-504-4388
MATHESON POSTAL SERVICES INC (CA)
(*Suby of* MATHESON TRUCKING INC) ★
9785 Goethe Rd, Sacramento, CA 95827-3559
Tel (916) 685-2330 *Founded/Ownrshp* 1968
Sales 77.0MM^E *EMP* 750
SIC 4212 Mail carriers, contract; Mail carriers, contract
Pr: Mark Matheson
CEO: Robert B Matheson
Sec: Laurie Johnson
Ex VP: Carole L Matheson
Genl Mgr: Tim Noel

D-U-N-S 17-909-2028 IMP/EXP
MATHESON TRI-GAS INC
(*Suby of* TAIYO NIPPON SANSO CORPORATION)
150 Allen Rd Ste 302, Basking Ridge, NJ 07920-2977
Tel (908) 991-9200 *Founded/Ownrshp* 1992
Sales 1.4MMM *EMP* 3,322
SIC 2813 5084 Industrial gases; Nitrogen; Oxygen, compressed or liquefied; Argon; Welding machinery & equipment; Safety equipment; Industrial gases; Nitrogen; Oxygen, compressed or liquefied; Argon; Welding machinery & equipment; Safety equipment
Ch Bd: William J Kroll
Pr: Scott Kallman
VP: Daniel Guerra
VP: Scott Kalman
Dir Bus: Lori McDowell
IT Man: C Guerra
Tech Mgr: Kavita Murthi
Prd Mgr: Michael Jenkins
Mktg Mgr: Beth Sullivan
Sls Mgr: Chris Hopwood
Snr PM: Steven Malsky

D-U-N-S 00-945-9660
MATHESON TRUCKING INC
9785 Goethe Rd, Sacramento, CA 95827-3559
Tel (916) 685-2330 *Founded/Ownrshp* 1964
Sales 350.5MM^E *EMP* 1,650
SIC 4213 4731 Trucking, except local; Less-than-truckload (LTL) transport; Freight transportation arrangement; Trucking, except local; Less-than-truckload (LTL) transport; Freight transportation arrangement
Pr: Mark Matheson
CEO: Patricia Kepner
Ofcr: Charles J Mellor
Ex VP: Carole L Matheson
VP: Laurie Johnson
VP Bus Dev: Don Brocca
Rgnl Mgr: Dewey Adair
Area Mgr: Don Osness
Snr Ntwrk: Peter Evison
Opers Supe: Calvin Spellman
Opers Mgr: Nicole King

D-U-N-S 00-948-1672 EXP
MATHEUS LUMBER CO INC
15800 Woodinville Redmond, Woodinville, WA 98072-9059
Tel (206) 284-7500 *Founded/Ownrshp* 1985
Sales 280.0MM *EMP* 82
Accts Berntson Porter
SIC 5031 Lumber: rough, dressed & finished; Plywood; Lumber: rough, dressed & finished; Plywood
CEO: Gary Powell
Pr: Ben Powell
CFO: Dave Colley
VP: Dan Powell
VP: James Reynolds
VP: Larry Tommerup
Off Mgr: Dawn Rychlik
Opers Mgr: Jim Thompson

D-U-N-S 79-100-1923 IMP
MATHEW ENTERPRISE INC
STEVENS CREEK CHRYSLER
4100 Stevens Creek Blvd, San Jose, CA 95129-1335
Tel (408) 248-1800 *Founded/Ownrshp* 2007
Sales 25.9MM^E *EMP* 60
SIC 5511 Automobiles, new & used; Automobiles, new & used
CEO: Mathew Zaheri
CFO: Calvin Pham
Exec: Shay Moshen
Prin: Chris Hall
Opers Mgr: Amir Farsio

MATHEW EQUIPMENT COMPANY
See MATHEWS CO

D-U-N-S 02-301-6058
MATHEW HALL LUMBER CO
127 6th Ave N, Saint Cloud, MN 56303-4749
Tel (320) 252-1920 *Founded/Ownrshp* 1968
Sales 20.5MM^E *EMP* 110
SIC 5211 2439 5713 Millwork & lumber; Trusses, wooden roof; Carpets; Millwork & lumber; Trusses, wooden roof; Carpets
Pr: Loran T Hall
Treas: Daniel J Hall
VP: John E Hall
VP: Brian Koopman
Exec: Linda Stern
Sales Asso: Damon Rudnitski

D-U-N-S 01-801-6683
MATHEW ZECHMAN CO INC
152 Reaser Ct, Elyria, OH 44035-6285
Tel (440) 366-2442 *Founded/Ownrshp* 1980
Sales 23.1MM *EMP* 13
Accts Majkut & Pooley Ltd Elyria
SIC 5194 5145 Tobacco & tobacco products; Confectionery; Tobacco & tobacco products; Confectionery
CEO: Mike Sedivec
Pr: Victor Sedivec

D-U-N-S 03-956-5791 IMP
MATHEWS ASSOCIATES INC
BATTERY ASSEMBLERS
220 Power Ct, Sanford, FL 32771-9530
Tel (407) 323-3390 *Founded/Ownrshp* 1993
Sales 54.4MM^E *EMP* 160
SIC 3691 3629 3812 3672 Batteries, rechargeable; Electronic generation equipment; Search & navigation equipment; Printed circuit boards; Batteries, rechargeable; Electronic generation equipment; Search & navigation equipment; Printed circuit boards
CEO: Daniel Perreault
Pr: Philip Perreault
Treas: Judy J Perreault

D-U-N-S 00-110-2656 IMP
MATHEWS BROTHERS CO (ME)
22 Perkins Rd, Belfast, ME 04915-6034
Tel (207) 338-3360 *Founded/Ownrshp* 1854, 1978
Sales 30.6MM^E *EMP* 130
SIC 2431 3089 Window frames, wood; Window sashes, wood; Windows, plastic; Window frames, wood; Window sashes, wood; Windows, plastic
CEO: John Hawthorne
Pr: Scott Hawthorne
Treas: Alex Hawthorne
Treas: Brent West
IT Man: Mark Bishop
IT Man: Tim Robinson
VP Opers: Kyle Hawthorne
Mktg Dir: Bob Maynes
Sls Dir: John Magri
Sls Mgr: Judy Hart
Sales Asso: Cheryl Leblanc

D-U-N-S 04-790-6912
MATHEWS CO
MATHEW EQUIPMENT COMPANY
500 Industrial Rd, Crystal Lake, IL 60012-3684
Tel (815) 459-2210 *Founded/Ownrshp* 1965
Sales 30.4MM^E *EMP* 85
SIC 3523 Haying machines: mowers, rakes, stackers, etc.; Cutters & blowers, ensilage; Driers (farm): grain, hay & seed; Grounds mowing equipment
Pr: Joseph Shulfer
Ch Bd: David L Mathews
Treas: Judith Sedlack
VP: Jeff Sedlack
Creative D: Julie Austin
Genl Mgr: Lynn Hummer
MIS Mgr: Linda Pulk
Manager: Kevin Ryan

D-U-N-S 00-411-1811
MATHEWS CONSTRUCTION OF TAMPA INC
448 Lucerne Ave, Tampa, FL 33606-3839
Tel (813) 621-6390 *Founded/Ownrshp* 1962
Sales 40.0MM *EMP* 70
SIC 1542 1541 Commercial & office building, new construction; Shopping center construction; Hospital construction; Industrial buildings, new construction; Warehouse construction; Commercial & office building, new construction; Shopping center construction; Hospital construction; Industrial buildings, new construction; Warehouse construction
Pr: David E Oellerich
CFO: Michele Pilger
Ex VP: Michael Mahoney
VP: George Goodspeed
Board of Directors: Julian T Erwin, David E Oellerich, Herman J Oellerich

D-U-N-S 01-830-2653
MATHEWS FORD LINCOLN MERCURY SANDUSKY INC
610 E Perkins Ave, Sandusky, OH 44870-4912
Tel (419) 626-4721 *Founded/Ownrshp* 1979
Sales 20.3MM^E *EMP* 60
SIC 5511 Automobiles, new & used; Automobiles, new & used
Pr: Thurman Mathews Jr
Sec: Bob Mathews
VP: Tim Mathews
Genl Mgr: Tom Ripleya
Off Mgr: Beth Mathews
Off Mgr: Beth Matthews
Sales Asso: John Byington
Sales Asso: Kevin Killingsworth

MATHEWS FORD-OREGON
See OREGON FORD INC

D-U-N-S 80-307-5860 IMP
MATHEWS INC
MISSION ARCHERY
919 River Rd, Sparta, WI 54656-2469
Tel (608) 269-2728 *Founded/Ownrshp* 1992
Sales 26.8MM^E *EMP* 130
SIC 3949 Bows, archery; Bows, archery
CEO: Matt McPherson
Pr: Steve McPherson
Creative D: Mark Griffin
Sfty Dirs: Marc Brueggen
Mktg Mgr: Brad Treu
Snr Mgr: Joel Maxfield

D-U-N-S 01-815-9939
MATHEWS KENNEDY FORD L-M INC
MATHEWS MITSUBISHI
1155 Delaware Ave, Marion, OH 43302-6417
Tel (740) 387-3673 *Founded/Ownrshp* 1961
Sales 34.2MM^E *EMP* 100
SIC 5511 7538 7532 7515 Automobiles, new & used; General automotive repair shops; Top & body repair & paint shops; Passenger car leasing; Automobiles, new & used; General automotive repair shops; Top & body repair & paint shops; Passenger car leasing
Pr: Thurman R Mathews
Sec: Jean Mitchell
VP: Thomas Mathews

D-U-N-S 10-419-5040
MATHEWS KENNEDY FORD LINCOLN MERCURY INC
MATTHEWS AUTO GROUP
1155 Delaware Ave, Marion, OH 43302-6417
Tel (740) 375-0333 *Founded/Ownrshp* 1961
Sales 31.1MM^E *EMP* 130
SIC 5511 Automobiles, new & used; Automobiles, new & used
Pr: Thurman Mathews
Sec: Jean Mitchell
VP: Thomas Mathews

MATHEWS MITSUBISHI
See MATHEWS KENNEDY FORD L-M INC

D-U-N-S 00-887-0250
MATHILE FAMILY FOUNDATION
6450 Sand Lake Rd Ste 100, Dayton, OH 45414-2679
Tel (937) 264-4600 *Founded/Ownrshp* 1989
Sales 31.2MM *EMP* 7
Accts Ernst & Young Us Llp Indianap
SIC 6732 Trusts: educational, religious, etc.; Trusts: educational, religious, etc.
Ex Dir: Greg Edwards
Treas: Maryann Mathile
Sec: Donna Beeson
Ofcr: Nina Vasiliu

D-U-N-S 04-119-9100
MATHIOWETZ CONSTRUCTION CO
30676 County Road 24, Sleepy Eye, MN 56085-4359
Tel (507) 794-5730 *Founded/Ownrshp* 1924
Sales 40.0MM^E *EMP* 180
SIC 1611 Highway & street construction; Highway & street construction
CEO: Brian J Mathiowetz
CFO: Jackie Farasyn
Sec: Ronda Mathiowetz
VP: Julie A Anderson
VP: David Domm
Dir Bus: Brad Ommodt
Sfty Dirs: Scott Surprenant
Mtls Mgr: Jim Warwick

D-U-N-S 03-303-7193 IMP/EXP
MATHIS BROS OKLAHOMA CITY LLC
MATHIS BROTHERS
3434 W Reno Ave, Oklahoma City, OK 73107-6134
Tel (405) 943-3434 *Founded/Ownrshp* 1959
Sales 404.2MM^E *EMP* 1,500
Accts Grant Thornton
SIC 5712 Furniture stores; Furniture stores
CEO: Larry Mathis
Pr: Bill Mathis
CFO: Sissy Holloway

**VP:* Calvin F Worth
VP: Calvin Worth
Exec: Christina Meza
Genl Mgr: Robin Hood
Off Mgr: Jean Riggs
Dir IT: Rich Mitton
IT Man: Octavio Rabago
Software D: Ruston Huckabee

MATHIS BROTHERS
See MATHIS BROS OKLAHOMA CITY LLC

D-U-N-S 04-537-2539
MATHIS INDEPENDENT SCHOOL DISTRICT
602 E San Patricio Ave, Mathis, TX 78368-2429
Tel (361) 547-3378 *Founded/Ownrshp* 1912
Sales 22.4MM *EMP* 250
Accts Lovvorn & Kieschnick Llp Cor
SIC 8211 Public elementary school; Public junior high school; Public senior high school; School board; Public elementary school; Public junior high school; Public senior high school; School board
Site Mgr: Peter Fernandez

D-U-N-S 04-261-1442
MATHISEN OIL CO INC
10911 Jasmine St, Fontana, CA 92337-6966
Tel (909) 355-7515 *Founded/Ownrshp* 1965
Sales 23.7MM^E *EMP* 27^E
SIC 5171 Petroleum bulk stations
Pr: James Mathisen
**VP:* Audrey J Mathisen
**VP:* Gene C Mathisen
Opers Mgr: Larry Stillwell

D-U-N-S 13-114-2747 IMP
MATHWORKS INC
3 Apple Hill Dr, Natick, MA 01760-2098
Tel (508) 647-7000 *Founded/Ownrshp* 1997
Sales 875.9MM^E *EMP* 1,800
SIC 7371 Motor vehicle supplies & new parts; Computer software development & applications
Pr: Jack Little
Pt: Sari Germanos
**Treas:* Jeanne O'Keefe
Chf Mktg O: Jim Tung
VP: Shirley Jeffreys
Prgrm Mgr: Thomas Lowell
Snr Sftwr: Abhishek Angne
Snr Sftwr: Meera Atreyam
Snr Sftwr: Sherif Azary
Snr Sftwr: Peter Muellers
Snr Sftwr: Jianming Ye
Board of Directors: Cleve Moler

D-U-N-S 00-794-6221
MATHY CONSTRUCTION CO (WI)
DUNN BLACKTOP DIVISION
920 10th Ave N, Onalaska, WI 54650-2166
Tel (608) 783-6411 *Founded/Ownrshp* 1945, 1959
Sales 327.2MM^E *EMP* 476
SIC 1611 1771 1442 5171 General contractor, highway & street construction; Highway & street paving contractor; Resurfacing contractor; Blacktop (asphalt) work; Construction sand mining; Gravel mining; Petroleum bulk stations; General contractor, highway & street construction; Highway & street paving contractor; Resurfacing contractor; Blacktop (asphalt) work; Construction sand mining; Gravel mining; Petroleum bulk stations
Pr: Charles F Mathy
VP: Tim Jones
**VP:* Steven C Mathy
Genl Mgr: Tony Tomashek
IT Man: Debra Knutson
IT Man: Kristi Whitehead
Sfty Mgr: Mark Clark
Sfty Mgr: Willy Hardin
Snr Mgr: Greg Malone

D-U-N-S 00-486-2702
MATICH CORP (CA)
1596 E Harry Shepard Blvd, San Bernardino, CA 92408-0197
Tel (909) 382-7400 *Founded/Ownrshp* 1954
Sales 64.7MM^E *EMP* 150
SIC 1611 2951 General contractor, highway & street construction; Asphalt paving mixtures & blocks; General contractor, highway & street construction; Asphalt paving mixtures & blocks
CEO: Stephen A Matich
**Ch:* Martin A Matich
**Treas:* Randall Valadez
**Ex VP:* Patrick A Matich
VP: Wayne Hendrix

MATISIA CONSULTANT
See MATISIA INC

D-U-N-S 96-179-6971
MATISIA INC
MATISIA CONSULTANT
1518 1st Ave S Ste 201, Seattle, WA 98134-1456
Tel (206) 395-2600 *Founded/Ownrshp* 2006
Sales 23.0MM *EMP* 50
SIC 8742 7389 General management consultant; ; General management consultant;
Pr: Kristina Roth
**Pr:* Darren Alger

MATIX CLOTHING COMPANY
See DVS SHOE CO INC

D-U-N-S 09-616-0411 IMP
MATLAB INC
1112 Nc Highway 49 S, Asheboro, NC 27205-9584
Tel (336) 629-4161 *Founded/Ownrshp* 1979
Sales 21.3MM^E *EMP* 120
SIC 2851 Paints & allied products; Paints & allied products
Pr: Gayle F Peddycord Kurdian
CFO: Don Reynolds
Ofcr: Hasan Mahmud
**VP:* Bill Kurdian
VP: Wm Kurdian
**Prin:* William Kurdian
CIO: Gayle Peddycord
Sales Exec: Terry Jennings
Sls&Mrk Ex: Lew Jones

D-U-N-S 02-393-3430
MATLET GROUP LLC
60 Delta Dr, Pawtucket, RI 02860-4556
Tel (401) 834-3007 *Founded/Ownrshp* 2005
Sales 145.8MM^E *EMP* 430
SIC 2759 Commercial printing; Commercial printing
CFO: Gary Stiffler
**COO:* John Gaffney
Ex VP: Ed Wiegand
VP: Louis Simon
VP Opers: Zeynel Zerek
Sls Mgr: Ed Quinn

D-U-N-S 04-515-2535
MATLICK ENTERPRISES INC
UNITED FIRE EQUIPMENT COMPANY
335 N 4th Ave, Tucson, AZ 85705-8442
Tel (520) 622-3639 *Founded/Ownrshp* 1978
Sales 22.4MM^E *EMP* 72
SIC 5999 7389 Alarm & safety equipment stores; Fire extinguisher servicing
CEO: Stanley Matlick
**Pr:* Daniel Matlick
**Sec:* Shirley Matlick
**VP:* Deborah Matlick
Genl Mgr: Deborah Livingston
IT Man: Tom Futrell

D-U-N-S 80-562-0437
MATLINPATTERSON ATA HOLDINGS LLC
520 Madison Ave Fl 35, New York, NY 10022-4350
Tel (212) 651-9500 *Founded/Ownrshp* 2005
Sales 57.3MM^E *EMP* 3,000
SIC 4581 Aircraft servicing & repairing; Aircraft servicing & repairing
CFO: Lorence Titlebaum

D-U-N-S 10-152-6460
MATLINPATTERSON GLOBAL ADVISERS LLC
520 Madison Ave Fl 35, New York, NY 10022-4350
Tel (212) 651-9500 *Founded/Ownrshp* 2002
Sales 696.3M *EMP* 7,164
Accts Hymes & Associates Cpa Pc Bro
SIC 6733 Private estate, personal investment & vacation fund trusts; Private estate, personal investment & vacation fund trusts
Mng Pt: Peter Schoels
CFO: Larry Teiteldaum
Sr VP: Graham Albert
VP: Catie Abrams
VP: Diane Chien
VP: Jay Garrett
VP: Brian Norris
VP: Adam Sherman
Mng Dir: Lawrence Lavine
Dir IT: Anthony Vestuto

D-U-N-S 05-451-9507
MATOMY USA INC
(*Suby of* MATOMY MEDIA GROUP LTD)
77 Water St Fl 12, New York, NY 10005-4408
Tel (212) 771-1578 *Founded/Ownrshp* 2011
Sales 32.7MM^E *EMP* 350
SIC 7313 7311 Radio, television, publisher representatives; Electronic media advertising representatives; Advertising agencies; Radio, television, publisher representatives; Electronic media advertising representatives; Advertising agencies
CEO: Ofer Druker
**CFO:* Sagi Niri
**Ex VP:* Assaf Suprasky
**Sr VP:* Erez Gross
**Sr VP:* David Zerah

D-U-N-S 09-003-4471 IMP/EXP
MATOSANTOS COMMERCIAL CORP
Parque Industrial Ca, Vega Baja, PR 00693
Tel (787) 793-6900 *Founded/Ownrshp* 1940, 1983
Sales 133.7MM^E *EMP* 115
Accts Rsm Roc & Company San Juan P
SIC 5141 5113 5087 Groceries, general line; Industrial & personal service paper; Janitors' supplies; Groceries, general line; Industrial & personal service paper; Janitors' supplies
Pr: Manuel Matosantos Jr
**VP:* Geronimo Matosantos

D-U-N-S 16-179-9556
MATRANAS PRODUCE INC
201 Louisiana St, Westwego, LA 70094-4113
Tel (504) 341-0940 *Founded/Ownrshp* 1984
Sales 44.0MM^E *EMP* 65
SIC 5148 Fresh fruits & vegetables
Pr: Camile J Matrana Sr
**VP:* Camile J Matrana Jr

D-U-N-S 83-061-7630 IMP/EXP
MATRIC GROUP LLC
2099 Hill City Rd, Seneca, PA 16346-3711
Tel (814) 677-0716 *Founded/Ownrshp* 2005
Sales 52.0MM *EMP* 370
SIC 3672 3511 3663 3679 3571 3569 Printed circuit boards; Turbines & turbine generator sets; Radio & TV communications equipment; Electronic switches; Electronic computers; Assembly machines, non-metalworking; Printed circuit boards; Turbines & turbine generator sets; Radio & TV communications equipment; Electronic switches; Electronic computers; Assembly machines, non-metalworking
CFO: Tod George
Sec: Terry Havens-Turner

D-U-N-S 05-908-5357 IMP/EXP
MATRIC LIMITED
(*Suby of* MATRIC GROUP LLC) ★
2099 Hill City Rd, Seneca, PA 16346-3711
Tel (814) 677-0716 *Founded/Ownrshp* 1993
Sales 36.0MM^E *EMP* 280
SIC 3672 3679 3571 3569 3663 3511

D-U-N-S 79-169-8749
MATRIX ABSENCE MANAGEMENT INC
(*Suby of* DELPHI FINANCIAL GROUP INC) ★
2421 W Peoria Ave Ste 200, Phoenix, AZ 85029-4940
Tel (800) 980-1006 *Founded/Ownrshp* 1998
Sales NA *EMP* 416
SIC 6411 Insurance claim processing, except medical; Insurance claim processing, except medical
CEO: Ivars Zvirbulis
**Pr:* Kenneth F Cope
**COO:* William Schutz
**CFO:* Michael Fredrickson
VP: Marti Cardi
VP: Charles Denaro
VP: Paul Dube
VP: Glenn Pierce
VP: Bert Stone
**VP:* Suzanne Wilson
Brnch Mgr: Michelle Woodson

MATRIX BUSINESS TECHNOLOGIES
See MATRIX TELECOM INC

D-U-N-S 79-429-4848
MATRIX CONSTRUCTION GROUP INC
13420 Sw 128th St, Miami, FL 33186-5800
Tel (305) 597-9400 *Founded/Ownrshp* 2003
Sales 22.7MM^E *EMP* 250
SIC 1542 Custom builders, non-residential; Custom builders, non-residential
Pr: Angel Acosta
**VP:* Ricardo Ardawin

D-U-N-S 19-287-4746
MATRIX DESIGN GROUP LLC
ALLIACNCE DESIGN GROUP
3299 Tower Rd, Newburgh, IN 47630-8301
Tel (812) 490-1525 *Founded/Ownrshp* 2004
Sales 22.2MM^E *EMP* 55^E
SIC 8711 Electrical or electronic engineering
Pr: Aric Pryor
**Sr VP:* David Clardy
VP: Dave Burch
**VP:* David Burch
**VP:* Allen Harding
VP: Robert Krehbiel

D-U-N-S 11-151-9513
MATRIX HEALTHCARE SERVICES INC
MYMATRIXX
3111 W Dr Martin, Tampa, FL 33607
Tel (813) 247-2077 *Founded/Ownrshp* 2001
Sales NA *EMP* 150
Accts Warren Averett Llc Tampa Fl
SIC 6411 Insurance claim processing, except medical; Insurance claim processing, except medical
CEO: Steven A Macdonald
**Pr:* Artemis Emslie
**CFO:* Thomas W Cardy
**Sr VP:* Mike Bunkley
**Sr VP:* Lindsay Rios
**Sr VP:* Alan P Walls
**CTO:* John S Kime
Board of Directors: Jason Beans

D-U-N-S 11-880-4561
MATRIX HG INC
115 Mason Cir Ste B, Concord, CA 94520-8530
Tel (925) 459-9200 *Founded/Ownrshp* 2002
Sales 27.1MM^E *EMP* 80
SIC 1711

D-U-N-S 02-083-0303
MATRIX HUMAN SERVICES (MI)
OFF THE STREET
120 Parsons St, Detroit, MI 48201-2002
Tel (313) 831-1000 *Founded/Ownrshp* 1906
Sales 19.7MM *EMP* 320
Accts Godfrey Hammel Danneels & Co P
SIC 8322 8331 5932 Individual & family services; Job training services; Shoes, secondhand; Clothing, secondhand; Individual & family services; Job training services; Shoes, secondhand; Clothing, secondhand
CEO: Marcella Wilson PHD
VP: Carla Chambers
**VP:* Audrey Gulley
**VP:* Kayleen Lemont
**VP:* Teresa A Rodges
**VP:* Paul Sonnecken

D-U-N-S 00-146-0435
MATRIX I LLC
PEP MICROPEP
(*Suby of* PEP) ★
1 Catamore Blvd Ste 3, East Providence, RI 02914-1233
Tel (401) 434-3040 *Founded/Ownrshp* 1963, 2003
Sales 23.1MM^E *EMP* 74
SIC 3089 3544 Injection molding of plastics; Special dies, tools, jigs & fixtures
Pr: John S Harker
**CEO:* Alan M Huffenus
VP: Deb Bocian
Mktg Mgr: Steve Chung
Mktg Mgr: Daniel Rocker
Mktg Mgr: Stephanie Virchaux
Sales Asso: Don Norris

MATRIX INTEGRATED FACILITY MGT
See NILAND BUILDING SERVICES INC

MATRIX INTEGRATED FACILITY MGT
See MATRIX LLC

D-U-N-S 13-040-5475
MATRIX INTEGRATION LLC
417 Main St, Jasper, IN 47546-3131
Tel (812) 634-1550 *Founded/Ownrshp* 1997
Sales 22.6MM^E *EMP* 92
SIC 5734 5999 Computer & software stores; Telephone & communication equipment
Pr: Brenda Stallings
Chf Mktg O: Amy Williams
**Ex VP:* Daniel V Fritch
**VP:* Doug Libbert
**VP:* Nathan Stallings
**VP:* Chad Williams
Exec: Tom Presley
Rgnl Mgr: Joe Mendoza
Dir IT: Juan Mack
Netwrk Eng: Matt Duncan
Netwrk Eng: Steven Hawkins

MATRIX INTERIORS
See MICI CORP

D-U-N-S 07-730-6918
MATRIX LLC
MATRIX INTEGRATED FACILITY MGT
780 5th Ave Ste 115, King of Prussia, PA 19406-4065
Tel (607) 766-0700 *Founded/Ownrshp* 1996
Sales 45.1MM^E *EMP* 2,000
SIC 7349 Janitorial service, contract basis; Janitorial service, contract basis
CEO: James R Peduto
**Pr:* Peter R Criville
**Ex VP:* Thomas Niland

D-U-N-S 96-997-9769
MATRIX MEDICAL NETWORK OF GEORGIA LLC
9201 E Mountain View Rd # 220, Scottsdale, AZ 85258-5172
Tel (480) 862-1700 *Founded/Ownrshp* 2000
Sales 65.9MM^E *EMP* 413^E
SIC 8741 Nursing & personal care facility management
CEO: Walter W Cooper
Pr: Ron Head
COO: Roger De Lusignan
CFO: Joseph Maturo
Chf Mktg O: Donna Moore
Chf Mktg O: Marcia Naveh
Ex VP: Tom Brodmerkel
Sr VP: Chris Conte
Sr VP: Brian Esterly
Sr VP: John Hopkins
Sr VP: Charles Kanach
Sr VP: Stephen Tatarian
Sr VP: Joseph Villa
VP: Heidi Cannon
VP: Sally Dimond
VP: Joel Franklin
VP: Dianne Robinson
VP: Mary Sajdak
VP: Matthew Wazny
Dir Rx: Olivier Wamain
Board of Directors: Timothy Nolan

D-U-N-S 96-972-0957 IMP
MATRIX METALS HOLDINGS INC
NEPCO
(*Suby of* SANMAR GROUP)
126 Collins Rd, Richmond, TX 77469-3021
Tel (281) 633-4263 *Founded/Ownrshp* 2008
Sales 140.0MM^E *EMP* 691
SIC 3325 Alloy steel castings, except investment; Alloy steel castings, except investment
CFO: Anthony Quinto

D-U-N-S 18-069-6247 IMP
MATRIX METALS LLC
KEOKUK STEEL CASTINGS CO
(*Suby of* MATRIX METALS HOLDINGS INC) ★
126 Collins Rd, Richmond, TX 77469-3021
Tel (281) 342-5511 *Founded/Ownrshp* 2001
Sales 140.0MM *EMP* 550
SIC 3325 Alloy steel castings, except investment; Alloy steel castings, except investment
CEO: Robert Kukowski
**CFO:* Tony Quinto
**VP:* Al Kinnard
**Dir Bus:* Ken West
**CTO:* Shrirang Kulkarni

D-U-N-S 07-854-4784
■ **MATRIX PDM ENGINEERING INC**
(*Suby of* MATRIX SERVICE CO) ★
5100 E Skelly Dr Ste 800, Tulsa, OK 74135-6565
Tel (918) 624-6300 *Founded/Ownrshp* 2011
Sales 9.6MM^E *EMP* 2,000
SIC 1542 1623 8711 Nonresidential construction; Water, sewer & utility lines; Engineering services
VP: Kenneth L Erdmann

D-U-N-S 07-716-3350
MATRIX RESOURCES INC
1000 Abernathy Rd Ste 500, Atlanta, GA 30328-5605
Tel (770) 677-2400 *Founded/Ownrshp* 1982
Sales 186.5MM *EMP* 1,500
SIC 8742

D-U-N-S 11-510-5827 IMP/EXP
▲ **MATRIX SERVICE CO**
5100 E Skelly Dr Ste 700, Tulsa, OK 74135-6577
Tel (918) 838-8822 *Founded/Ownrshp* 1984
Sales 1.3MMM *EMP* 4,826
Accts Deloitte & Touche Llp Tulsa
Tkr Sym MTRX *Exch* NGS
SIC 1542 1623 7349 Nonresidential construction; Water, sewer & utility lines; Oil & gas line & compressor station construction; Oil & gas pipeline construction; Telephone & communication line construction; Building maintenance services; Nonresidential construction; Water, sewer & utility lines; Oil & gas line & compressor station construction; Oil & gas pipeline construction; Telephone & communication line construction; Building maintenance services
Pr: John R Hewitt
COO: Joseph F Montalbano
CFO: Kevin S Cavanah
VP: Jack Frost
VP Bus Dev: Douglas Montalbano
Sfty Mgr: Rod Bouwman
Sfty Mgr: Steve Vail
Snr PM: Jonathan Hoekstra
Board of Directors: Michael J Hall, I Edgar Hendrix, Paul K Lackey, Tom E Maxwell, James H Miller, Jim W Mogg

D-U-N-S 78-012-8570 IMP
■ **MATRIX SERVICE INC**
(*Suby of* MATRIX SERVICE CO) ★
5100 E Skelly Dr Ste 700, Tulsa, OK 74135-6577
Tel (918) 838-8822 *Founded/Ownrshp* 1984
Sales 531.8MM^E *EMP* 1,738
SIC 1623 1629 1799 7699 Oil & gas pipeline construction; Oil & gas pipeline construction; Chemical plant & refinery construction; Petroleum storage tanks, pumping & draining; Tank repair & cleaning services
Pr: James P Ryan
**CFO:* Kevin Cavanah

*VP: Kevin A Durkin
*VP: Bradley J Rinehart
*VP: William R Sullivan
*VP: Alan Updyke
Exec: Karen Spradlin

D-U-N-S 78-678-2508
■ MATRIX SME INC
(Suby of MATRIX SERVICE CO) ★
5100 E Skelly Dr Ste 700, Tulsa, OK 74135-6577
Tel (918) 838-8822 Founded/Ownrshp 1985
Sales 124.1MM^E EMP 756
SIC 1731 1623 1629 Electrical work; Water, sewer & utility lines; Oil & gas pipeline construction; Oil & gas line & compressor station construction; Oil refinery construction; Electrical work; Water, sewer & utility lines; Oil & gas pipeline construction; Oil & gas line & compressor station construction; Oil refinery construction
Pr: Matthew I Pettrizo
*Treas: Jason W Turner
*VP: James J Collins Jr
Dir IT: William Moore
IT Man: Darrel Lutton
Sls Mgr: Michael Meadows

D-U-N-S 15-417-7885
MATRIX SYSTEM AUTOMOTIVE FINISHES LLC
(Suby of QUEST SPECIALTY CHEMICALS INC) ★
850 Ladd Rd Bldg E, Walled Lake, MI 48390-3020
Tel (248) 668-8135 Founded/Ownrshp 1983
Sales 37.4MM^E EMP 100
SIC 5198 2851 Paints; Paints & allied products; Paints; Paints & allied products
Pr: W Kent Gardner
Genl Mgr: Dave Brunori
Sys Mgr: Kevin Ells
Sls&Mrk Ex: Kelly Mack
Manager: Robert Perez

D-U-N-S 08-476-0131
MATRIX SYSTEMS INC
1041 Byers Rd, Miamisburg, OH 45342-5487
Tel (937) 438-9033 Founded/Ownrshp 1977, 2002
Sales 33.4MM^E EMP 92
SIC 8711 7373 3873 Engineering services; Computer integrated systems design; Watches, clocks, watchcases & parts
CEO: Holly Tsourides
*Pr: James Young
CFO: Kelly Cain
*CFO: John Schomburg
Bd of Dir: John Kennedy
VP: Steven J Koranda
*VP: Jeffrey S Young
IT Man: Steve King
MIS Mgr: A J Root
Sftwr Eng: Roger Becker
Sftwr Eng: Steve Hass

D-U-N-S 09-997-0691
MATRIX TECHNOLOGIES INC
1760 Indian Wood Cir, Maumee, OH 43537-4070
Tel (419) 897-7200 Founded/Ownrshp 1980
Sales 66.0MM^E EMP 130
SIC 7373 Systems integration services; Systems integration services
Pr: David L Bishop
V Ch: Deborah Zimmerman
CFO: John Stowell
CFO: Benjamin Swift
*Treas: Donald J Krompak
*VP: David J Blaida
Creative D: Ken Gerke
Rgnl Mgr: Joe Dietz
Dept Mgr: Robert Hall
CIO: Mike Geremski
Sfty Mgr: Bassam Hammoud

D-U-N-S 10-518-7376 IMP
■ MATRIX TECHNOLOGIES LLC
THERMO FISHER SCIENTIFIC
(Suby of APOGENT HOLDING COMPANY)
2 Radcliff Rd, Tewksbury, MA 01876-1182
Tel (603) 595-0505 Founded/Ownrshp 1985
Sales 35.2MM^E EMP 151^E
SIC 3821 Laboratory equipment: fume hoods, distillation racks, etc.; Laboratory equipment: fume hoods, distillation racks, etc.
Manager: Peter Mottla

D-U-N-S 78-437-6659
MATRIX TELECOM INC
MATRIX BUSINESS TECHNOLOGIES
433 Las Colinas Blvd E # 500, Irving, TX 75039-5654
Tel (888) 411-0111 Founded/Ownrshp 2013
Sales 164.8MM^E EMP 329
SIC 4813 Long distance telephone communications; Telephone communication, except radio
CEO: Charles G Taylor Jr
Sr VP: Brian Gustas
*VP: Brian D Gustas
Netwrk Eng: Mitch Todd

MATRIXCARE
See MDI ACHIEVE (TEXAS) INC

D-U-N-S 13-152-1809 IMP/EXP
■ MATRIXX GROUP INC
CITADEL PLASTICS
(Suby of CITADEL PLASTICS HOLDINGS INC) ★
15000 Highway 41 N, Evansville, IN 47725-9360
Tel (812) 421-3600 Founded/Ownrshp 2007
Sales 279.0MM^E EMP 153
SIC 5162 Plastics resins; Plastics resins
CEO: Mike Huff
*Pr: Kevin Andrews
Pr: Robert Brinkmann
*Pr: Raymond Wright
*VP: Kymberly Peters
*VP: Michael E Wright
VP Sls: J Seymour
Sls Mgr: Mike McLellan

D-U-N-S 19-283-9731
■ MATSON ALASKA INC
(Suby of MATSON NAVIGATION CO INC) ★
2550 W Tyvola Rd, Charlotte, NC 28217-4574
Tel (704) 973-7000 Founded/Ownrshp 2015
Sales 967.6MM^E EMP 1,621^E
Tkr Sym HRZL Exch OTO
SIC 4424 4731 4412 Deep sea domestic transportation of freight; Water transportation to noncontiguous territories, freight; Freight transportation arrangement; Deep sea foreign transportation of freight; Deep sea domestic transportation of freight; Water transportation to noncontiguous territories, freight; Freight transportation arrangement; Deep sea foreign transportation of freight
CEO: Steven L Rubin
COO: William A Hamlin
CFO: Michael T Avara
Ex VP: Michael F Zendan II
Sr VP: Marion Davis
Sr VP: Ali Behruz Nikkhoo
Sr VP: Geoffrey Thurston
Sr VP: Robert S Zuckerman
Exec: Gary Degard
VP Sls: Karen Richards
Board of Directors: Jeffrey A Brodsky, Kurt M Cellar, James Lachance, Martin Tuchman, David N Weinstein

D-U-N-S 07-843-2469
▲ MATSON INC
1411 Sand Island Pkwy, Honolulu, HI 96819-4322
Tel (808) 848-1211 Founded/Ownrshp 2012
Sales 1.7MMM EMP 3,721^E
Accts Deloitte & Touche Llp Honolul
Tkr Sym MATX Exch NYS
SIC 4499 Water transportation cleaning services; Water transportation cleaning services
Pr: Matthew J Cox
CFO: Joel M Wine
VP: Vic Angoco
*VP: John E Dennen
VP: Ronald J Forest
VP: Kenny Gill
VP: Peter Heilmann
VP: Peter F Weis
Snr Mgr: Timothy Bowling

D-U-N-S 12-265-4718
MATSON INDUSTRIES INC
132 Main St, Brookville, PA 15825-1213
Tel (814) 849-5334 Founded/Ownrshp 1984
Sales 38.0MM EMP 155^E
SIC 2421 Sawmills & planing mills, general; Sawmills & planing mills, general
Pr: Paul D Sorek
*Sec: Len Domenick
*Ex VP: Becky Matson
*VP: Barbara Conti
*VP: Richard G Conti

D-U-N-S 18-944-1561
■ MATSON LOGISTICS INC
(Suby of MATSON NAVIGATION CO INC) ★
1815 S Meyers Rd Ste 700, Oakbrook Terrace, IL 60181-5263
Tel (630) 203-3500 Founded/Ownrshp 1999
Sales 87.1MM^E EMP 159
SIC 4731 Agents, shipping; Agents, shipping
*Pr: R K Rolfe
*Sec: Paul Ito
VP: Grace Cerocke
Exec: Lynne Murrell

D-U-N-S 00-691-2620
■ MATSON NAVIGATION CO INC (HI)
(Suby of MATSON INC) ★
555 12th St, Oakland, CA 94607-4046
Tel (510) 628-4000 Founded/Ownrshp 1882, 1980
Sales 1.0MMM^E EMP 2,751
SIC 4424 4491 4492 Deep sea domestic transportation of freight; Marine cargo handling; Stevedoring; Marine terminals; Tugboat service; Deep sea domestic transportation of freight; Marine cargo handling; Stevedoring; Marine terminals; Tugboat service
Pr: Matthew J Cox
*CFO: Joel M Wine
*Treas: Benedict J Bowler
Sr VP: P Burns
*Sr VP: Peter T Heilman
*Sr VP: David L Hoppes
Sr VP: Kevin O'Rourke
*Sr VP: Kevin C O Rourke
VP: Vic Angoco
VP: John Dennen
VP: Gary Eyring
*VP: Paul Londynsky
VP: Doug Matthew
VP: Ku'uhaku Park
*VP: Peter F Weis
Dir Risk M: Mary Tanios
Dir Bus: Tracy Matthews

D-U-N-S 13-658-4203 IMP
MATSU ALABAMA INC
(Suby of MATCOR AUTOMOTIVE INC)
9650 Kellner Rd Sw, Huntsville, AL 35824-1713
Tel (256) 772-5888 Founded/Ownrshp 2003
Sales 51.5MM^E EMP 260
SIC 3711 Automobile bodies, passenger car, not including engine, etc.; Automobile bodies, passenger car, not including engine, etc.
CEO: Arthur G Artuso
CFO: Manfred Kretschmer
Board of Directors: John Carney

D-U-N-S 96-172-8040 IMP
MATSU OHIO INC
(Suby of MATCOR AUTOMOTIVE INC)
228 E Morrison St, Edgerton, OH 43517-9389
Tel (419) 298-2394 Founded/Ownrshp 2009
Sales 38.3MM^E EMP 122
SIC 3465 Body parts, automobile: stamped metal; Body parts, automobile: stamped metal
Pr: Dave Rutila
*Pr: Art Artuso
*VP: Galliano Tiberini
Brnch Mgr: Richard Ponpey
DP Dir: Steve Welters

D-U-N-S 79-787-3440
MATSU USA INC
9650 Kellner Rd Sw, Huntsville, AL 35824-1713
Tel (256) 772-5888 Founded/Ownrshp 2003
Sales NA EMP 350
SIC 3711

D-U-N-S 13-153-0438
MATSUDA LLC
2605 Tunbridge Ln, Saint Augustine, FL 32092-5006
Tel (502) 645-7189 Founded/Ownrshp 1983
Sales 21.0MM EMP 75^E
SIC 1622 1611 Bridge construction; General contractor, highway & street construction
Pr: G W Chandler
Sec: Michael Wilbert
VP: Allan Buckles

D-U-N-S 17-511-9411 IMP/EXP
MATSUI INTERNATIONAL CO INC
UNIMARK
(Suby of MATSUI SHIKISO CHEMICAL CO.,LTD.)
1501 W 178th St, Gardena, CA 90248-3203
Tel (310) 767-7812 Founded/Ownrshp 1990
Sales 39.5MM^E EMP 180
SIC 2899 Ink or writing fluids; Ink or writing fluids
Pr: Masa Matsui
CFO: Yachun WEI
Mng Dir: Chuck Boyce
Genl Mgr: Akiko Matsui
Ql Cn Mgr: Johnny Chavez

D-U-N-S 87-938-1606 IMP
MATSUO INDUSTRIES USA INC
(Suby of MATSUO INDUSTRIES,INC.)
408 Municipal Dr, Jefferson City, TN 37760-5033
Tel (865) 475-9085 Founded/Ownrshp 1995
Sales 42.2MM^E EMP 180
SIC 3694 3465 3643 3714 3493 Automotive electrical equipment; Current-carrying wiring devices; Automobile springs; Motor vehicle parts & accessories; Body parts, automobile: stamped metal; Automotive electrical equipment; Body parts, automobile: stamped metal; Current-carrying wiring devices; Motor vehicle parts & accessories; Automobile springs
Owner: Teruo Matsuo
*Pr: Mamoru Yakeda
Ex VP: Akihisa Kurya
Sls&Mrk Ex: Nakio Iosbe

D-U-N-S 78-840-2097
MATSUSHITA INTERNATIONAL CORP
1141 Via Callejon, San Clemente, CA 92673-6230
Tel (949) 498-1000 Founded/Ownrshp 1990
Sales 23.6MM^E EMP 161
SIC 6799 3711 3714 Real estate investors, except property operators; Automobile assembly, including specialty automobiles; Motor vehicle parts & accessories; Real estate investors, except property operators; Automobile assembly, including specialty automobiles; Motor vehicle parts & accessories
Pr: Hiroyuki Matsushita

D-U-N-S 07-879-0833 IMP
MATSUURA MACHINERY USA INC (MN)
325 Randolph Ave, Saint Paul, MN 55102-3759
Tel (651) 289-9700 Founded/Ownrshp 2012
Sales 66.8MM^E EMP 280
SIC 5084 Industrial machinery & equipment; Industrial machinery & equipment
CEO: John Scwartz
Pr: John Shafer
Rgnl Mgr: Dave Hudson

D-U-N-S 80-760-6694
MATT BLATT INC
BLATT, MATT AUTO SALES
501 Delsea Dr N, Glassboro, NJ 08028-1452
Tel (856) 881-0444 Founded/Ownrshp 1989
Sales 33.2MM^E EMP 80
SIC 5511 5521 New & used car dealers; Used car dealers; New & used car dealers; Used car dealers
Pr: Roy Greenblatt
Sls Dir: Joe Gallotti

D-U-N-S 00-222-7593 IMP/EXP
MATT BREWING CO INC (NY)
F X MATT BREWING CO
830 Varick St, Utica, NY 13502-4030
Tel (315) 624-2400 Founded/Ownrshp 1888
Sales 21.5MM^E EMP 150
SIC 2082

MATT BURNE HONDA
See BURNE AUTOMOBILE DEALERSHIP INC

D-U-N-S 03-414-7066
MATT CANESTRALE CONTRACTING INC
106 E Fredericktown Rd, La Belle, PA 15450
Tel (724) 785-6550 Founded/Ownrshp 1986
Sales 51.0MM EMP 42
SIC 4491 4212 Unloading vessels; Local trucking, without storage; Unloading vessels; Local trucking, without storage
Pr: Matt Canestrale
*Sec: Lorraine Canestrale

D-U-N-S 11-623-2463
MATT CASTRUCCI INC III
MATT CASTRUCCI NISSAN
3013 Mall Park Dr, Dayton, OH 45459-3672
Tel (937) 434-4723 Founded/Ownrshp 1997
Sales 56.7MM^E EMP 140
SIC 5511 Automobiles, new & used
Pr: Matt Castrucci
*VP: Al Castrucci
Sls Mgr: Rob Long

MATT CASTRUCCI NISSAN
See MATT CASTRUCCI INC III

D-U-N-S 55-621-0136
MATT CONSTRUCTION CORP
9814 Norwalk Blvd Ste 100, Santa Fe Springs, CA 90670-2997
Tel (562) 903-2277 Founded/Ownrshp 1991
Sales 36.2MM^E EMP 131^E
SIC 8742 Construction project management consultant; Construction project management consultant
CEO: Paul J Matt
*Pr: Steve F Matt
COO: Ron Defazio
CFO: Tom Andrew
*Sec: Alan B Matt
Sr VP: Trent Anderson
VP: Michael Fedorchek
VP: Roger Fricke
VP: Abe Massoudi
VP: Bart Shively
VP: Daniel Stafford
VP: Robert Welch
Exec: Jim Muenzer
Dir Bus: Steve Luchetta

D-U-N-S 10-774-1050
MATT INDUSTRIES INC
GRPHICS GRAFEK
Dupli Pk Dr, Syracuse, NY 13218
Tel (315) 472-1316 Founded/Ownrshp 1980
Sales 31.0MM^E EMP 150
SIC 2759 5112 Envelopes: printing; Envelopes; Envelopes: printing; Envelopes
Pr: J Kemper Matt
*CFO: Peter Hujar
Ex VP: Todd Luchsinger
*VP: Thomas Booth
*VP: John Mather
*VP: J Kemper Matt Jr
Div Mgr: David Martin
Prd Mgr: Sheri Sexton

D-U-N-S 00-176-5296 IMP/EXP
MATTAPAN SUPPLY CO (MA)
PORTLAND GROUP BOSTON
1464 Blue Hill Ave, Boston, MA 02126-2256
Tel (617) 296-6900 Founded/Ownrshp 1931
Sales 24.2MM^E EMP 230
SIC 5074 Heating equipment (hydronic); Plumbing fittings & supplies; Heating equipment (hydronic); Plumbing fittings & supplies
Pr: Howard Rose
*Treas: Richard Fox

D-U-N-S 17-407-3098
MATTCO MANUFACTURING INC
12000 Eastex Fwy, Houston, TX 77039-6126
Tel (281) 449-0361 Founded/Ownrshp 1987
Sales 32.0MM^E EMP 49
SIC 3533

D-U-N-S 79-617-0355
MATTEI INSURANCE SERVICES INC
6400 Se Lake Rd Ste 190, Portland, OR 97222-2189
Tel (503) 298-7247 Founded/Ownrshp 1992
Sales NA EMP 715
SIC 6411 Loss prevention services, insurance
Pr: Richard F Mattei
Sls Mgr: Arlene Thompson

D-U-N-S 00-828-6643 IMP/EXP
▲ MATTEL INC
333 Continental Blvd, El Segundo, CA 90245-5032
Tel (310) 252-2000 Founded/Ownrshp 1945
Sales 6.0MMM EMP 31,000
Accts Pricewaterhousecoopers Llp Lo
Tkr Sym MAT Exch NGS
SIC 3944 3942 Games, toys & children's vehicles; Dolls & stuffed toys; Dolls, except stuffed toy animals; Stuffed toys, including animals; Games, toys & children's vehicles; Dolls & stuffed toys; Dolls, except stuffed toy animals; Stuffed toys, including animals
Ch Bd: Christopher A Sinclair
Pr: Richard Dickson
Pr: Timothy J Kilpin
CFO: Kevin M Farr
Treas: Mandana Sadigh
Chf Cred: Catherine Balsam-Schwaber
Ex VP: Tim Kilpin
Ex VP: Robert Normile
Sr VP: H Scott Topham
Exec: Christine Warman
Area Mgr: Sujit Pandey
Board of Directors: Michael J Dolan, Trevor A Edwards, Frances D Fergusson, Ann Lewnes, Kathy White Loyd, Dominic Ng, Dean A Scarborough, Dirk Van De Put

D-U-N-S 03-978-3514 EXP
■ MATTEL TOY CO
(Suby of MATTEL INC) ★
333 Continental Blvd, El Segundo, CA 90245-5032
Tel (310) 252-2357 Founded/Ownrshp 1945
Sales 221.8MM^E EMP 1,900
SIC 5092 Toys & games; Toys & games
CEO: Robert Eckert
COO: Bruce L Stein

MATTERNS HATCHERY
See EMPIRE KOSHER POULTRY INC

D-U-N-S 09-705-7157
▲ MATTERSIGHT CORP
200 W Madison St Ste 1300, Chicago, IL 60606-3454
Tel (877) 235-6925 Founded/Ownrshp 2011
Sales 30.3MM EMP 197^E
Tkr Sym MATR Exch NGM
SIC 8742 7373 Management consulting services; Computer systems analysis & design; Management consulting services; Computer systems analysis & design
Pr: Kelly D Conway
*Ch Bd: Tench Coxe
COO: David R Gustafson
CFO: Christopher Min
CFO: Sheau-Ming Ross
CFO: Sheau-Ming K Ross
Ex VP: Christopher J Danson
Ex VP: Richard M Dresden
VP: Mark Sauer
VP: Tina Valdez
Snr Ntwrk: Damon Henslee
Board of Directors: Philip R Dur, Henry J Feinberg, John T Kohler, David B Mullen, Michael J Murray, John C Staley

D-U-N-S 06-250-3842
MATTESON AUTO SALES INC
PLANET SCION
5540 Auto Ct, Matteson, IL 60443-1486
Tel (708) 720-8600 *Founded/Ownrshp* 1972
Sales 32.4MM^E *EMP* 80^E
SIC 5511 Automobiles, new & used; Automobiles, new & used
Pr: Ronald Postma

D-U-N-S 83-133-5096
MATTHEW 25 MINISTRIES INC
11060 Kenwood Rd, Blue Ash, OH 45242-1816
Tel (513) 793-6256 *Founded/Ownrshp* 1991
Sales 154.7MM *EMP* 16
SIC 8399 Community development groups; Community development groups
Pr: Wendell Metty
**Pr:* Wendell Mettey
**Treas:* Don Olson

D-U-N-S 02-035-5178 IMP
MATTHEW MEDICAL & SCIENTIFIC BOOK INC
MATTHEWS BOOK
(*Suby of* MATTHEWS BOOK CO) ★
11559 Rock Island Ct, Maryland Heights, MO 63043-3522
Tel (314) 432-1400 *Founded/Ownrshp* 1962
Sales 20.1MM^E *EMP* 150
SIC 5942 Book stores
CEO: Linda Nash
**COO:* Jim Klund
COO: JAS Klund
CFO: Mike Smegner
Chf Mktg O: Deborah King
Dir IT: James Haick

D-U-N-S 07-949-3324
MATTHEW WARREN INC
MW INDUSTRIES
500 E Ottawa St, Logansport, IN 46947-2610
Tel (773) 649-0321 *Founded/Ownrshp* 1995
Sales 23.4MM^E *EMP* 51^E
SIC 3493 Coiled flat springs
Pr: William Marcum
**CFO:* Chet Kwasniak
**VP:* Robert Rutledge
S&M/VP: Scott Keihle

D-U-N-S 14-153-4284
MATTHEW WARREN INC
MW INDUSTRIES
(*Suby of* GENSTAR CAPITAL LLC) ★
9501 Tech Blvd Ste 401, Rosemont, IL 60018
Tel (847) 349-5760 *Founded/Ownrshp* 2011
Sales 263.3MM^E *EMP* 1,055
SIC 3493 Coiled flat springs; Cold formed springs; Helical springs, hot wound: railroad equipment etc.; Hot wound springs, except wire; Coiled flat springs; Cold formed springs; Helical springs, hot wound: railroad equipment etc.; Hot wound springs, except wire
CEO: William Marcum
Pr: Chris Thomas
**CFO:* Chester Kwasniak
VP: Donald Lyons
Mktg Mgr: Sarah Kosar

MATTHEWS AURORA FNRL SOLUTIONS
See AURORA CASKET CO LLC

MATTHEWS AUTO GROUP
See MATHEWS KENNEDY FORD LINCOLN MERCURY INC

MATTHEWS BOOK
See MATTHEW MEDICAL & SCIENTIFIC BOOK INC

D-U-N-S 00-253-9195
MATTHEWS BOOK CO (MO)
11559 Rock Island Ct, Maryland Heights, MO 63043-3522
Tel (314) 432-1400 *Founded/Ownrshp* 1889, 1972
Sales 47.0MM^E *EMP* 185
SIC 5192 5942 Books; Book stores; Books; Book stores
CEO: Linda Nash
COO: Jim Klund
**CFO:* Mike Smegner
VP: Gedas Dunas
Dir IT: Deborah King
Web Dev: John Kemp
Manager: Leann Carey
Manager: Pam Hamer
Manager: Kim Schroeder
Snr Mgr: Dave Roundtree

MATTHEWS BUSES
See MATTHEWS GROUP INC

D-U-N-S 05-794-3979
MATTHEWS BUSES INC
(*Suby of* MATTHEWS BUSES) ★
2900 State Route 9, Ballston Spa, NY 12020-3904
Tel (518) 584-2400 *Founded/Ownrshp* 1985
Sales 40.6MM^E *EMP* 100
SIC 5012 Buses; Buses
Ch Bd: Glenn J Matthews
**CFO:* Kathy Drapeau
**VP:* Bradley Matthews
Sls Mgr: Doug Gifford

D-U-N-S 02-450-9507
MATTHEWS CONSTRUCTION CO INC (NC)
210 1st Ave S Ste C, Conover, NC 28613-2161
Tel (828) 464-7325 *Founded/Ownrshp* 1965
Sales 43.7MM *EMP* 60
Accts Whisnant & Company Llp Hickor
SIC 1541 1542 Industrial buildings, new construction; Commercial & office building, new construction; Industrial buildings, new construction; Commercial & office building, new construction
CEO: Bobby E Matthews
**Pr:* Gary Matthews
**CFO:* Kevin Tolbert
Ex VP: Andy Matthews
**Ex VP:* N Andy Matthews
VP: David Reitzel

Sales Exec: David N Bratton
Snr PM: Scott Johnson

D-U-N-S 05-519-1613 EXP
MATTHEWS CURRIE FORD CO
130 Tamiami Trl N, Nokomis, FL 34275-2199
Tel (941) 488-6787 *Founded/Ownrshp* 1963
Sales 48.2MM^E *EMP* 98
SIC 5511 7538 7515 7513 5521 7532 Automobiles, new & used; Pickups, new & used; General automotive repair shops; Passenger car leasing; Truck rental & leasing, no drivers; Used car dealers; Top & body repair & paint shops; Automobiles, new & used; Pickups, new & used; General automotive repair shops; Passenger car leasing; Truck rental & leasing, no drivers; Used car dealers; Top & body repair & paint shops
Pr: Ed Bielen
**Prin:* Wilmer Currie III
Off Mgr: Peggy Mallaber
IT Man: Ed Gleason
Sls Mgr: Brad Bielen
Sls Mgr: Travis Morales
Sls Mgr: Danny Peckham
Sales Asso: Ken McMahon
Sales Asso: Mark Peters
Sales Asso: Kenny Rogers
Sales Asso: David White

D-U-N-S 02-052-6294
MATTHEWS GROUP INC (VA)
TMG CONSTRUCTION
18919 Lincoln Rd, Purcellville, VA 20132-4145
Tel (540) 338-0411 *Founded/Ownrshp* 1992
Sales 40.0MM^E *EMP* 64
Accts Lanigan Ryan Malcolm & Doyle
SIC 1542 Nonresidential construction
Pr: Tatiana C Matthews
Bd of Dir: Gwen Krahl
Ofcr: Megan Maday
**VP:* Joseph N Matthews
Exec: Alan Weiss
Snr PM: Donald Feather
Snr PM: Jason Lynch
Snr PM: Ben Montgomery

D-U-N-S 18-360-8025
MATTHEWS GROUP INC
MATTHEWS BUSES
2900 Route 9, Ballston Spa, NY 12020
Tel (518) 584-2400 *Founded/Ownrshp* 1985
Sales 43.2MM^E *EMP* 153
SIC 5012

D-U-N-S 00-400-4602
MATTHEWS INDUSTRIES INC (AL)
23 2nd St Sw, Decatur, AL 35601-2861
Tel (256) 353-0271 *Founded/Ownrshp* 1949
Sales 20.5MM^E *EMP* 65
SIC 3585 Parts for heating, cooling & refrigerating equipment
Ch Bd: Ralph E Matthews
VP: Pamela Patterson
VP Sls: Jeff Hale

D-U-N-S 83-613-4346 EXP
■ **MATTHEWS INTERNATIONAL (ARKANSAS) CORP**
(*Suby of* MATTHEWS INTERNATIONAL CORP) ★
501 E Lincoln Ave, Searcy, AR 72143-7409
Tel (501) 268-3504 *Founded/Ownrshp* 1959
Sales 22.2MM^E *EMP* 145
SIC 3366 3281 Bronze foundry; Castings (except die): bronze; Cut stone & stone products; Bronze foundry; Castings (except die): bronze; Cut stone & stone products
Pr: David J Decarlo

D-U-N-S 00-434-1533 IMP
▲ **MATTHEWS INTERNATIONAL CORP** (PA)
2 N Shore Ctr Ste 200, Pittsburgh, PA 15212-5851
Tel (412) 442-8200 *Founded/Ownrshp* 1850
Sales 1.4MMM *EMP* 10,300
Accts Pricewaterhousecoopers Llp P
Tkr Sym MATW *Exch* NGS
SIC 3366 1542 3569 3995 3953 2796 Bronze foundry; Mausoleum construction; Cremating ovens; Burial caskets; Marking devices; Platemaking services; Bronze foundry; Mausoleum construction; Cremating ovens; Burial caskets; Marking devices; Platemaking services
Pr: Joseph C Bartolacci
**Ch Bd:* John D Turner
CFO: Steven F Nicola
VP: David F Beck
VP: Pat Cox
VP: Cindy Mills
VP: Brian D Walters
VP Sls: Steve Duffy
Board of Directors: Gregory S Babe, Katherine E Dietze, Terry L Dunlap, Morgan K O'brien, John P O'leary Jr, Don W Quigley Jr, David A Schawk, Alvaro Garcia-Tunon, Jerry R Whitaker

D-U-N-S 62-090-8780
■ **MATTHEWS MEDIA GROUP INC**
(*Suby of* OMNICOM GROUP INC) ★
700 King Farm Blvd Fl 5, Rockville, MD 20850-6164
Tel (301) 984-7191 *Founded/Ownrshp* 2000
Sales 22.9MM^E *EMP* 170
SIC 8743 Public relations services; Public relations services
Pr: John Benbrook
VP: Gaynor Anders
VP: Anders Gaynor
VP: Jeff Goldfarb
VP: Mary Schwarz
VP: Helen West
Creative D: Kahrin Deines
Creative D: Michael Digioia
Creative D: Jeanne Wagner
Dir IT: Tai Osurman

D-U-N-S 86-725-6570
MATTHEWS MOTORS 2 INC
70 W, Clayton, NC 27520
Tel (919) 550-2333 *Founded/Ownrshp* 1994
Sales 22.6MM *EMP* 32^E

Accts Travis J Hill Cpa Clayton N
SIC 5521 Used car dealers; Used car dealers
Pr: Steven H Matthews
CFO: David Beebe

MATTHEWS PAOLI FORD
See PHILADELPHIA MOTORS LLC

D-U-N-S 01-367-1011
MATTHEWS PONTIAC-CADILLAC INC (NY)
SATURN
3721 Vestal Rd, Vestal, NY 13850-2228
Tel (607) 798-8000 *Founded/Ownrshp* 1964, 1986
Sales 28.6MM^E *EMP* 77
SIC 5511 Automobiles, new & used; Automobiles, new & used
Pr: James F Matthews
**Treas:* Lawrence E Davis
Genl Mgr: Bob Gaeta
Sls Mgr: Phil Hudak

D-U-N-S 00-890-2967
MATTHEWS-HARGREAVES CHEVROLET CO
2000 E 12 Mile Rd, Royal Oak, MI 48067-1503
Tel (248) 398-8800 *Founded/Ownrshp* 1977
Sales 52.5MM^E *EMP* 80
SIC 5511 Automobiles, new & used; Pickups, new & used; Trucks, tractors & trailers: new & used; Automobiles, new & used; Pickups, new & used; Trucks, tractors & trailers: new & used
Pr: W Robert Allen
CFO: Yvonne Golnick
Top Exec: Mark Pawelski
**VP:* Lawrence J Burr
Store Mgr: Andrea Jurkowski
VP Mktg: Walter Tutak
Sales Asso: Heather Bessant
Sales Asso: Rick Denrty

D-U-N-S 12-534-8883 IMP/EXP
MATTHEY JOHNSON HOLDINGS INC
(*Suby of* JOHNSON MATTHEY PLC)
435 Devon Park Dr Ste 600, Wayne, PA 19087-1944
Tel (610) 971-3000 *Founded/Ownrshp* 1998
Sales 416.2MM^E *EMP* 1,775^E
SIC 3341 3339 3356 2834 3399 3714 Platinum group metals, smelting & refining (secondary); Gold smelting & refining (secondary); Silver smelting & refining (secondary); Platinum group metal refining (primary); Gold refining (primary); Silver refining (primary); Precious metals; Platinum group metals: rolling, drawing or extruding; Gold & gold alloy: rolling, drawing or extruding; Powders, pharmaceutical; Metal powders, pastes & flakes; Paste, metal; Exhaust systems & parts, motor vehicle; Platinum group metals, smelting & refining (secondary); Gold smelting & refining (secondary); Silver smelting & refining (secondary); Platinum group metal refining (primary); Gold refining (primary); Silver refining (primary); Precious metals; Platinum group metals: rolling, drawing or extruding; Gold & gold alloy: rolling, drawing or extruding; Powders, pharmaceutical; Metal powders, pastes & flakes; Paste, metal; Exhaust systems & parts, motor vehicle
Pr: Robert Talley
**Treas:* Karil J Black
**VP:* Edward Ravert
**VP:* Edward H Ravert Jr
VP: A J Trifiletti

D-U-N-S 00-232-6734 IMP/EXP
MATTHEY JOHNSON INC
JOHNSON MATTHEY CHEMICAL
(*Suby of* MATTHEY JOHNSON HOLDINGS INC) ★
435 Devon Park Dr Ste 600, Wayne, PA 19087-1944
Tel (610) 971-3000 *Founded/Ownrshp* 1909
Sales 368.2MM^E *EMP* 1,650
SIC 3341 3339 3356 2834 3399 3714 Platinum group metals, smelting & refining (secondary); Gold smelting & refining (secondary); Silver smelting & refining (secondary); Platinum group metal refining (primary); Gold refining (primary); Silver refining (primary); Precious metals; Platinum group metals: rolling, drawing or extruding; Gold & gold alloy: rolling, drawing or extruding; Silver & silver alloy: rolling, drawing or extruding; Powders, pharmaceutical; Metal powders, pastes & flakes; Paste, metal; Exhaust systems & parts, motor vehicle; Platinum group metals, smelting & refining (secondary); Gold smelting & refining (secondary); Silver smelting & refining (secondary); Platinum group metal refining (primary); Gold refining (primary); Silver refining (primary); Precious metals; Platinum group metals: rolling, drawing or extruding; Gold & gold alloy: rolling, drawing or extruding; Silver & silver alloy: rolling, drawing or extruding; Powders, pharmaceutical; Metal powders, pastes & flakes; Paste, metal; Exhaust systems & parts, motor vehicle
CEO: Robert Macleod
**Pr:* R M Talley
**CEO:* Neil Carson
COO: Richard Trout
CFO: Jim Wilcox
**Ch:* Tim Stevenson
**Treas:* K J Black
Sr VP: Dan Ramsey
VP: Bill Castleberry
VP: Paul Evans
VP: Charles McKinney
**VP:* E H Ravert Jr
VP: Edward H Ravert Jr
Board of Directors: P N Hawker, Roger M Kilburn, L C Pentz, F K Shefffy

D-U-N-S 05-577-4186 IMP
MATTHEY JOHNSON PHARMACEUTICAL MATERIALS INC
PHARM ECO LABORATORIES
(*Suby of* MATTHEY JOHNSON HOLDINGS INC) ★
25 Patton Rd, Devens, MA 01434-3803
Tel (978) 784-5000 *Founded/Ownrshp* 2007
Sales 25.6MM^E *EMP* 150
SIC 2834 8731 Pharmaceutical preparations; Commercial physical research; Pharmaceutical preparations; Commercial physical research
Pr: John B Fowler
CFO: Richard Gabriel

**Treas:* Karil J Black
**VP:* Edward H Ravert Jr
**Prin:* John Sheldrick
Genl Mgr: Jay Reddy
IT Man: Gil Lapointe
IT Man: Nancy Valenti
Sfty Mgr: Gary Hastings
Plnt Mgr: Dean Defrancesco
Sls&Mrk Ex: Paula J Lorence

D-U-N-S 00-250-4264 IMP
MATTHIAS PAPER CORP (PA)
301 Arlington Blvd, Swedesboro, NJ 08085-1370
Tel (856) 467-6970 *Founded/Ownrshp* 1915, 1986
Sales 25.2MM^E *EMP* 30
Accts Elko & Associates Ltd
SIC 5113 2679 Paper & products, wrapping or coarse; Paper products, converted
CEO: John R Matthias
**VP:* Warren E Storck
Site Mgr: Bob Phelan
Opers Mgr: Michael D'Alessandro
Sales Exec: Massey Ray

MATTING PRODUCTS DIV
See RJF INTERNATIONAL CORP

D-U-N-S 01-848-6324
MATTINGLY FOODS INC
302 State St, Zanesville, OH 43701-3200
Tel (740) 454-0136 *Founded/Ownrshp* 1946
Sales 87.2MM^E *EMP* 240
SIC 5149 5142 5141 Canned goods: fruit, vegetables, seafood, meats, etc.; Milk, canned or dried; Fruit juices, frozen; Vegetables, frozen; Fish, frozen: packaged; Meat, frozen: packaged; Groceries, general line; Canned goods: fruit, vegetables, seafood, meats, etc.; Milk, canned or dried; Fruit juices, frozen; Vegetables, frozen; Fish, frozen: packaged; Meat, frozen: packaged; Groceries, general line
CEO: Rick Barnes
**Ch Bd:* Robert K Mattingly
**Pr:* Barbara Callahan
**CFO:* Rusty Deaton
**VP:* Andrew Hess
**VP:* Brandon Hess
Dir IT: Venu Singireddy
Mktg Dir: Katie Coe

D-U-N-S 10-005-6191
MATTITUCK-CUTCHOGUE UNION FREE SCHOOL DISTRICT
15125 Main Rd, Mattituck, NY 11952-2375
Tel (631) 298-8460 *Founded/Ownrshp* 1934
Sales 16.0MM *EMP* 324
SIC 8211 Public elementary & secondary schools; Public elementary & secondary schools
Pr: Beverly Wowak

D-U-N-S 04-644-9112
MATTOON COMMUNITY UNIT SCHOOL DISTRICT 2
1701 Charleston Ave, Mattoon, IL 61938-3936
Tel (217) 238-8885 *Founded/Ownrshp* 1948
Sales 24.5MM^E *EMP* 499
Accts West & Company Llc
SIC 8211 9411 Public elementary & secondary schools; Administration of educational programs; Public elementary & secondary schools; Administration of educational programs
Sls Mgr: Mark Jackley

D-U-N-S 61-273-6512 IMP
MATTOON PRECISION MANUFACTURING INC
(*Suby of* NUKABE CORPORATION)
2408 S 14th St, Mattoon, IL 61938-5748
Tel (217) 235-6000 *Founded/Ownrshp* 1989
Sales 44.3MM *EMP* 160
SIC 3714 3363 Axles, motor vehicle; Motor vehicle brake systems & parts; Aluminum die-castings; Axles, motor vehicle; Motor vehicle brake systems & parts; Aluminum die-castings
Ch: Noriyoshi Nishida
**Pr:* Robert Shamdin
Treas: Michelle Diebel
**Sec:* Takesi Nakani
Genl Mgr: Glen Pruett
Ql Cn Mgr: Corde Ayers
Ql Cn Mgr: Ayers Corde
Ql Cn Mgr: Joey Mellendorf

D-U-N-S 02-562-2416 IMP
MATTOON RURAL KING SUPPLY INC (IL)
4216 Dewitt Ave, Mattoon, IL 61938-6643
Tel (217) 254-6678 *Founded/Ownrshp* 1962
Sales 76.9MM^E *EMP* 160^E
SIC 5399

MATTRESS 1-JACKSONVILLE
See SOS FURNITURE CO INC

D-U-N-S 07-200-0685
MATTRESS DISCOUNTERS CORP
9822 Fallard Ct, Upper Marlboro, MD 20772-6707
Tel (301) 856-6755 *Founded/Ownrshp* 1978
Sales NA *EMP* 600
SIC 5712 2515

D-U-N-S 07-913-7049
MATTRESS DISCOUNTERS OPERATIONS LLC
(*Suby of* SLEEPYS LLC) ★
1000 S Oyster Bay Rd, Hicksville, NY 11801-3527
Tel (301) 604-0703 *Founded/Ownrshp* 2012
Sales 61.4MM^E *EMP* 600^E
SIC 5712 2515 Bedding & bedsprings; Mattresses & bedsprings; Bedding & bedsprings; Mattresses & bedsprings

MATTRESS FIRM, THE
See MATTRESS FIRM INC

MATTRESS FIRM
See MATTRESS HOLDING CORP

MATTRESS FIRM, THE
See ELITE MANAGEMENT TEAM INC

D-U-N-S 96-726-0931
▲ MATTRESS FIRM HOLDING CORP
5815 Gulf Fwy, Houston, TX 77023-5341
Tel (713) 923-1090 Founded/Ownrshp 1986
Sales 1.8MMM EMP 6,900E
Accts Deloitte & Touche Llp Housto
Tkr Sym MFRM Exch NGS
SIC 5712 Mattresses; Mattresses
CEO: R Stephen Stagner
*Ch Bd: William E Watts
*Pr: Dale R Carlsen
COO: Rob Kilgore
COO: Kenneth E Murphy III
CFO: Alexander S Weiss
Ex VP: Kindel L Elam
Ex VP: Karrie D Forbes
Ex VP: Bruce Levy
Sr VP: Brian Baxter
Sr VP: Cathy Hauslein
Exec: James Bays
Board of Directors: John W Childs, Robert E Creager, Charles R Eitel, David A Fiorentino, Joseph M Fortunato, Ronald J Mittelstaedt, Adam L Suttin, Frederick C Tinsey III

D-U-N-S 08-108-8358 EXP
■ MATTRESS FIRM INC
MATTRESS FIRM, THE
(Suby of MATTRESS FIRM) ★
5815 Gulf Fwy, Houston, TX 77023-5341
Tel (713) 923-1090 Founded/Ownrshp 2002
Sales 210.3MME EMP 550
SIC 5712 Furniture stores; Furniture stores
Ch: Gary Fazio
*CEO: Steve Stagner
*CFO: James R Black
Bd of Dir: Adam Suttin
Ex VP: Alexander Weiss
Dir Bus: Nathan Bruno
Area Mgr: Charlie Baker
Area Mgr: Fred Bethel
Area Mgr: Wes Bridges
Area Mgr: Meagan Carroll
Area Mgr: Michael Corner

D-U-N-S 78-832-9589 IMP/EXP
■ MATTRESS GIANT CORP
(Suby of MATTRESS FIRM HOLDING CORP) ★
5815 Gulf Fwy, Houston, TX 77023-5341
Tel (713) 923-1090 Founded/Ownrshp 2012
Sales 156.8MME EMP 1,005
SIC 5712 Bedding & bedsprings; Mattresses; Bedding & bedsprings; Mattresses
Pr: Barrie Brown
CFO: Elaine D Crowley
CFO: Bob Pulciani
CFO: Steve Williams
*Sec: Steven List
Sr Cor Off: Michael Glazer
VP: Luis Rechoni
VP: Terri Stevens
Brnch Mgr: Hava Zejnllahu
Dist Mgr: Steve Poertner
MIS Dir: Don Barker

D-U-N-S 16-233-9985 IMP
■ MATTRESS HOLDING CORP
MATTRESS FIRM
(Suby of MATTRESS FIRM HOLDING CORP) ★
5815 Gulf Fwy, Houston, TX 77023-5341
Tel (713) 923-1090 Founded/Ownrshp 2008
Sales 239.6MME EMP 960
SIC 5712 Furniture stores; Bedding & bedsprings; Mattresses; Furniture stores; Bedding & bedsprings; Mattresses
Ch Bd: Gary Fazio
CEO: R Stephen Stagner
CFO: James R Black
Ex VP: Daniel McGuire
Area Mgr: Kris Nuno
VP Opers: Michael P Cannizzaro
Mktg Mgr: Bruce Kirby

MATTRESS KING
See MATTRESS LIQUIDATORS INC

D-U-N-S 00-971-8540
MATTRESS LIQUIDATORS INC
MATTRESS KING
5333 Bannock St Ste 100, Denver, CO 80216-1618
Tel (303) 574-9030 Founded/Ownrshp 1997
Sales 61.4MME EMP 300
SIC 5712 Mattresses; Mattresses
Pr: Sarah Thomas
*VP: David Dolan
Opers Mgr: Gary Svec

MATTRESS WHSE SLEEP OUTFITTERS
See INNOVATIVE MATTRESS SOLUTIONS LLC

D-U-N-S 60-495-4610 IMP
MATTRESS WORLD INC
700 Hilltop Dr, Itasca, IL 60143-1326
Tel (708) 728-9487 Founded/Ownrshp 1988
Sales 36.8MME EMP 248
SIC 5712 Mattresses; Mattresses
Pr: Tommie L Saylors
*VP: Catherine M Saylors

D-U-N-S 06-643-3418
MATTS BUILDING MATERIALS INC
MATT'S CASH & CARRY BUILDING M
404 E Interstate 2, Pharr, TX 78577-6544
Tel (956) 787-5513 Founded/Ownrshp 2002
Sales 37.4MME EMP 135
SIC 5211 5411 Lumber & other building materials; Grocery stores; Lumber & other building materials; Grocery stores
Pr: Danny C Smith
*Treas: Diana Smith
*Treas: Martha L Smith
*Sec: Oscar Sandoval

MATT'S CASH & CARRY BUILDING M
See MATTS BUILDING MATERIALS INC

D-U-N-S 07-866-5924 IMP/EXP
MATTSCO SUPPLY CO
1111 N 161st East Ave, Tulsa, OK 74116-4035
Tel (918) 836-0451 Founded/Ownrshp 1975
Sales 47.3MME EMP 35
SIC 5051 5085 Pipe & tubing, steel; Valves & fittings
Pr: Carlyn Mattox
*VP: Robert Mattox

D-U-N-S 60-605-4476 IMP
▲ MATTSON TECHNOLOGY INC
47131 Bayside Pkwy, Fremont, CA 94538-6517
Tel (510) 657-5900 Founded/Ownrshp 1988
Sales 178.4MM EMP 297E
Tkr Sym MTSN Exch NGS
SIC 3559 Semiconductor manufacturing machinery; Semiconductor manufacturing machinery
Pr: Fusen E Chen
*Ch Bd: Kenneth Kannappan
COO: J Michael Dodson
*V Ch Bd: Kenneth Smith
Sr VP: Tyler W Purvis
CTO: Shawming MA
Dir IT: Paul Timans
Board of Directors: Richard Dyck, Scott Kramer, Scott Peterson, Thomas St Dennis

D-U-N-S 02-064-2625
MATURE SERVICES INC (OH)
415 S Portage Path, Akron, OH 44320-2327
Tel (330) 253-4597 Founded/Ownrshp 1975, 1978
Sales 12.0MM EMP 1,329
Accts Bober Markey Fedorovich & Co
SIC 8322 Geriatric social service; Geriatric social service
Pr: Linda Valentine
*Ch Bd: Lee Walko
*V Ch Bd: James Loveless
CTO: Dena Gilbert
IT Man: Dena Haswell
Board of Directors: David Barnhardt, Cynthia Bayer, Michael Demagall, Thomas Fuller, Pamela Hawkins, Richard Horak, Stephen Shamrock, Harvey Sterns, Barbara Venesy

D-U-N-S 05-671-9784
MATUS ENTERPRISES INC
HERITAGE SHOPS
152 N Penna Ave Ste 1, Wilkes Barre, PA 18701-3604
Tel (570) 822-8990 Founded/Ownrshp 1971
Sales 23.0MME EMP 200
SIC 5947 Greeting cards; Gift shop; Greeting cards; Gift shop
Pr: Christopher D Matus
*Sec: Arlene Matus

MAU WORKFORCE SOLUTIONS
See MANAGEMENT ANALYSIS & UTILIZATION INC

D-U-N-S 00-892-8285
MAU-SHERWOOD SUPPLY CO (OH)
M S
8400 Darrow Rd Ste 1, Twinsburg, OH 44087-2375
Tel (330) 405-1200 Founded/Ownrshp 1908, 1981
Sales 21.4MME EMP 25
SIC 5085 5169 5072 Industrial supplies; Chemicals & allied products; Hardware
Pr: JC Rexroth
Prin: Mg McAleenan
Prin: WD Turner

D-U-N-S 09-935-1983
MAUDLIN INTERNATIONAL TRUCKS INC
IDEALEASE OF OCALA
2300 S Division Ave, Orlando, FL 32805-6233
Tel (407) 849-6440 Founded/Ownrshp 1997
Sales 72.2MME EMP 160
SIC 5511 5531 7538 7532 Trucks, tractors & trailers: new & used; Truck equipment & parts; Truck engine repair, except industrial; Top & body repair & paint shops; Trucks, tractors & trailers: new & used; Truck equipment & parts; Truck engine repair, except industrial; Top & body repair & paint shops
CEO: John A Maudlin
*CFO: William T Wilson
IT Man: Pam Morse
Sls Mgr: Dennis Nagle

D-U-N-S 18-632-0180
MAUGER AND CO INC
ABBOTS HEATING OIL
1157 Phoenixville Pike, West Chester, PA 19380-4254
Tel (610) 429-8200 Founded/Ownrshp 1964
Sales 21.8MM EMP 38
SIC 5172 5983 Petroleum products; Fuel oil dealers; Petroleum products; Fuel oil dealers
CEO: Clyde A Mauger IV
*VP: Zachary A Mauger
*Prin: Phil Robinson

D-U-N-S 07-860-2866
MAUI ACQUISITION CORP
13386 International Pkwy, Jacksonville, FL 32218-2383
Tel (904) 741-5400 Founded/Ownrshp 1998
Sales 546.6MME EMP 2,252E
SIC 3069 2389 Life jackets, inflatable: rubberized fabric; Men's miscellaneous accessories; Life jackets, inflatable: rubberized fabric; Men's miscellaneous accessories
CEO: Warren B Kanders
*Pr: Scott Obrien
*VP: Gray Hudkins

D-U-N-S 04-865-2614
MAUI CHEMICAL AND PAPER PRODUCTS INC
875 Alua St Ste 101, Wailuku, HI 96793-1455
Tel (808) 244-7311 Founded/Ownrshp 1969
Sales 46.9MME EMP 55E
SIC 5113 5169 Industrial & personal service paper; Specialty cleaning & sanitation preparations
Pr: Miles Kawasaki
*VP: Todd Kawasaki
*VP: Podd Kewasaki
*VP: Harry Nakagawa
*VP: Warren Ohta

Sls Mgr: Sam Tabieros
Sales Asso: Brent Fukagawa

D-U-N-S 10-308-1329
MAUI CLOTHING CO INC
MAUI CLOTHING OUTLET
362 Huku Lii Pl Ste 106, Kihei, HI 96753-8995
Tel (808) 891-6311 Founded/Ownrshp 1982
Sales 24.2MME EMP 200
SIC 5699 5621 5611 5641

MAUI CLOTHING OUTLET
See MAUI CLOTHING CO INC

MAUI DIVERS JEWELRY
See MAUI DIVERS OF HAWAII LIMITED

D-U-N-S 09-464-8862 IMP/EXP
MAUI DIVERS OF HAWAII LIMITED
MAUI DIVERS JEWELRY
1520 Liona St, Honolulu, HI 96814-2493
Tel (808) 946-7979 Founded/Ownrshp 1979
Sales 84.7MME EMP 517E
SIC 3911 5944 5094

D-U-N-S 00-692-7164 IMP
■ MAUI ELECTRIC CO LIMITED (HI)
(Suby of HAWAIIAN ELECTRIC CO INC) ★
210 W Kamehameha Ave, Kahului, HI 96732-2253
Tel (808) 871-8461 Founded/Ownrshp 1921
Sales 285.4MME EMP 312
SIC 4911 ;
Prin: Edward Reinhardt
*Prin: Edward Hirata
*Prin: T Michael May
*Prin: Paul A Oyer
*Prin: Richard A Von Gnechten
Admn Mgr: Eileen Wachi
Sfty Dirs: Joseph Kentz
Sfty Dirs: Robert Motooka
Sales Exec: David Tester
Sls&Mrk Ex: Eilene Wachi

D-U-N-S 78-422-3625
MAUI FRESH INTERNATIONAL LLC
(Suby of SAN RAFAEL DISTRIBUTING INC) ★
1601 E Olympic Blvd # 509, Los Angeles, CA 90021-1944
Tel (213) 688-0880 Founded/Ownrshp 2012
Sales 33.2MME EMP 65
SIC 5148 Fresh fruits & vegetables
Off Mgr: Suzi Arentz

MAUI JIM SUNGLASSES
See MAUI JIM USA INC

D-U-N-S 18-783-1508 IMP/EXP
MAUI JIM USA INC
MAUI JIM SUNGLASSES
1 Aloha Ln, Peoria, IL 61615-1871
Tel (309) 589-6158 Founded/Ownrshp 1980
Sales 180.0MME EMP 500
SIC 5099 3851

D-U-N-S 00-913-2184
▲ MAUI LAND & PINEAPPLE CO INC
200 Village Rd, Lahaina, HI 96761-8723
Tel (808) 877-3351 Founded/Ownrshp 1909
Sales 33.0MM EMP 1,066
Accts Accuity Llp Honolulu Hawaii
Tkr Sym MLP Exch NYS
SIC 6531 7011 Real estate agents & managers; Resort hotel; Real estate agents & managers; Resort hotel
Ch Bd: Warren H Haruki
Pr: Ryan L Churchill
Pr: Robert McNatt
CFO: Tim T Esaki
VP: Thomas Selby
Board of Directors: Stephen M Case, David A Heenan, Duncan Macnaughton, Arthur C Tokin

D-U-N-S 07-767-7102
MAUI MEDICAL GROUP INC
2180 Main St Ste 102, Wailuku, HI 96793-1625
Tel (808) 242-6464 Founded/Ownrshp 1961
Sales 34.4MM EMP 250
Accts Cw Associates Cpas Honolulu
SIC 8011 Clinic, operated by physicians; Clinic, operated by physicians
Pr: William H Mitchell MD
CFO: Jennifer Akiona
*Treas: William Fagan DC
*Sec: William DC Fagan
VP: Bert Akitake
VP: Nan Amaral
*VP: Ann E Biedel
VP: George Powell
Obsttrcn: Ashley Byno
Obsttrcn: Tamarin McCartin
Podiatrist: Steven King

D-U-N-S 19-754-0198
MAUI NIX INC
MAUI NIX SURF SHOP
717 N Atlantic Ave, Daytona Beach, FL 32118-3804
Tel (386) 253-1222 Founded/Ownrshp 1988
Sales 20.1MME EMP 150
SIC 5699 5941 Sports apparel; Bathing suits; T-shirts, custom printed; Water sport equipment; Surfing equipment & supplies
Pr: Nicholas Karamitos
*Sec: Peter Karamitos
*Ex VP: George Karamitos
Genl Mgr: Brian Smith

MAUI NIX SURF SHOP
See MAUI NIX INC

D-U-N-S 17-365-1191
■ MAUI OPERATING LLC
WESTIN MAUI RESORT & SPA, THE
(Suby of STARWOOD HOTELS & RESORTS WORLDWIDE INC) ★
2365 Kaanapali Pkwy, Lahaina, HI 96761-1900
Tel (808) 661-2588 Founded/Ownrshp 1998
Sales 84.0MM EMP 750
SIC 7011 7389 Hotels & motels; Restaurant reservation service; Hotels & motels; Restaurant reservation service
Genl Mgr: Greg Lundberg
Sales Exec: Tyler Coons

D-U-N-S 03-321-7241 IMP/EXP
■ MAUI PINEAPPLE CO LTD
(Suby of MAUI LAND & PINEAPPLE CO INC) ★
870 Haliimaile Rd, Makawao, HI 96768-9768
Tel (808) 877-1624 Founded/Ownrshp 1969
Sales NA EMP 1,000
SIC 2033 Fruits: packaged in cans, jars, etc.; Fruits: packaged in cans, jars, etc.
CEO: David Cole
Ch Bd: Richard Cameron
Ch Bd: Daniel Kest
CEO: Douglas R Schenk
Ex VP: James McCann
Ex VP: Paul Meyer
VP: Eduardo Chenchin
VP: L Douglas Maccluer
VP: Brian B Orlopp

MAUI PRINCE HOTEL & RESORT
See MAKENA HOTEL LLC

D-U-N-S 83-501-0190
MAUI SCHOOL DISTRICT
(Suby of EDUCATION BOARD) ★
54 S High St Fl 4, Wailuku, HI 96793-2102
Tel (808) 984-8000 Founded/Ownrshp 1880
Sales 85.0MME EMP 2,400
SIC 8211 9411 Public elementary & secondary schools; ; Public elementary & secondary schools;

D-U-N-S 00-916-0391
MAUI SODA & ICE WORKS LTD
918 Lower Main St, Wailuku, HI 96793-2007
Tel (808) 244-7951 Founded/Ownrshp 1947
Sales 21.4MME EMP 69
Accts Gary K Wasano
SIC 2086 2024 2097 Carbonated beverages, nonalcoholic: bottled & canned; Ice cream, bulk; Ice cream, packaged: molded, on sticks, etc.; Block ice; Ice cubes
Pr: Michael A Nobriga
*Ch: David Nobriga
*VP: Catherine Nogriga Kim

MAUI TOYOTA
See M 75 INC

D-U-N-S 05-678-2188 IMP/EXP
MAUI VARIETIES LTD
2810 Paa St Ste A, Honolulu, HI 96819-4429
Tel (808) 838-7773 Founded/Ownrshp 1955
Sales 52.6MME EMP 300E
SIC 5251 Hardware; Hardware
Pr: Tadami Kamitaki
*VP: Wayne Kamitaki
Store Mgr: Bret Grandstrom
Dir IT: Cory Chagami

MAUI WASTE SERVICES
See OAHU WASTE SERVICES INC

D-U-N-S 07-585-6542
MAULDIN & JENKINS LLC (GA)
200 Galleria Pkwy Se, Atlanta, GA 30339-5918
Tel (770) 955-8600 Founded/Ownrshp 1941, 1959
Sales 46.3MME EMP 257
Accts Mauldin & Jenkins Llc Atlant
SIC 8721 Certified public accountant; Certified public accountant
Mng Pt: Elton Wolf Jr
Exec: Peggy Rowan

MAULDIN ROAD WRRF
See RENEWABLE WATER RESOURCES

D-U-N-S 08-121-8026
MAUMEE CITY SCHOOL DISTRICT
MAUMEE CITY SCHOOLS
716 Askin St, Maumee, OH 43537-3602
Tel (419) 893-3200 Founded/Ownrshp 1870
Sales 20.4MME EMP 350
Accts Julian & Grube Inc Westervi
SIC 8211 Public elementary school; Public junior high school; Public senior high school; Public elementary school; Public junior high school; Public senior high school
CFO: Carol Grimm
*Treas: Paul Brotzki
Ofcr: Loren Burkey
VP: Stephanie Piechowiak
*VP: Janet Wolff
Off Admin: Kristin Kolacki
Sls&Mrk Ex: Paul Buttafuoco
Teacher Pr: Lisa Posadny
Psych: Krista Foley

MAUMEE CITY SCHOOLS
See MAUMEE CITY SCHOOL DISTRICT

MAUNA LANI BAY HT & BUNGALOWS
See MAUNA LANI RESORT (OPERATION) INC

MAUNA LANI BAY HT & BUNGALOWS
See MAUNA LANI RESORT (OPERATION) INC

D-U-N-S 00-716-7687
MAUNA LANI RESORT (OPERATION) INC
MAUNA LANI BAY HT & BUNGALOWS
(Suby of TOKYU CORPORATION)
68-1400 Mauna Lani Dr # 102, Kamuela, HI 96743-9726
Tel (808) 885-6677 Founded/Ownrshp 1977
Sales 36.7MME EMP 500
SIC 7011 5812 Resort hotel; American restaurant; Resort hotel; American restaurant
Pr: Hisashi Konno
Exec: Clayton Arakawa
*Prin: Akito Toba
Opers Mgr: Gina Kapeliela
Sls Mgr: Adam Harms

D-U-N-S 79-964-1303
MAUNA LANI RESORT (OPERATION) INC
MAUNA LANI BAY HT & BUNGALOWS
68-1400 Mauna Lani Dr, Kamuela, HI 96743-9726
Tel (808) 885-6622 *Founded/Ownrshp* 1983
Sales 14.6MM^E *EMP* 750
SIC 7011 Hotels; Hotels

D-U-N-S 06-628-9703 IMP
MAUNA LOA MACADAMIA NUT CORP
(*Suby of* HAWAIIAN HOST INC) ★
500 Alakawa St Rm 111, Honolulu, HI 96817-4576
Tel (808) 848-0500 *Founded/Ownrshp* 2015
Sales 36.7MM^E *EMP* 350
SIC 2068 5149 8742 2066 2064 Salted & roasted nuts & seeds; Coffee, green or roasted; Management consulting services; Chocolate & cocoa products; Candy & other confectionery products
Pr: Keith Sakamoto
**Treas:* Norman Kukino
VP: Ramona Cappello
Off Mgr: Mary Goss
VP Mktg: Scott Wallace

D-U-N-S 00-886-8234
MAUND AUTOMOTIVE GROUP LP (TX)
CHARLES MAUND IMPORTS
6900 Burnet Rd, Austin, TX 78757-2432
Tel (512) 458-1111 *Founded/Ownrshp* 1956, 1957
Sales 43.4MM^E *EMP* 130
SIC 5511

D-U-N-S 00-550-0830 IMP
MAURELL PRODUCTS INC
CREST BOATS
2710 S M 52, Owosso, MI 48867-9203
Tel (989) 725-5188 *Founded/Ownrshp* 1999
Sales 28.1MM^E *EMP* 180
SIC 3732 Houseboats, building & repairing; Houseboats, building & repairing
Pr: Linda Tomczak
**COO:* Patrick May

D-U-N-S 03-456-0494
MAURER & SCOTT INC
MAURER & SCOTT SALES
122 Thomas St, Coopersburg, PA 18036-2100
Tel (610) 282-8900 *Founded/Ownrshp* 1954
Sales 20.4MM^E *EMP* 99
SIC 5169 Industrial chemicals; Industrial chemicals
Prin: Scott Maurer
**Pr:* Jerome Kostantewicz

MAURER & SCOTT SALES
See MAURER & SCOTT INC

D-U-N-S 01-427-0128
MAURER & SCOTT SALES INC
122 Thomas St, Coopersburg, PA 18036-2100
Tel (610) 262-1800 *Founded/Ownrshp* 1984
Sales 38.4MM^E *EMP* 90^E
SIC 5169 Explosives; Explosives
Pr: Amy Beans
**Sec:* Larry Beans
**VP:* John Melick

MAURER MANUFACTURING
See LAKES ENTERPRISES INC

D-U-N-S 04-359-5743 IMP
MAURICE A AUERBACH INC
AUERPAK BRAND
117 Seaview Dr Fl 1, Secaucus, NJ 07094-1831
Tel (201) 807-9292 *Founded/Ownrshp* 1952
Sales 26.5MM^E *EMP* 45
SIC 5148 Fruits; Vegetables
Pr: Paul J Auerbach
**VP:* Jeffrey B Schwartz
Opers Mgr: Ian Zimmerman

MAURICE ELECTRICAL SUPPLY CO.
See ELECTRICAL WHOLESALERS METRO DC INC

D-U-N-S 00-796-4448
MAURICE J SOPP & SON
SOPP CHEVROLET
6400 Atlantic Ave, Bell, CA 90201-2520
Tel (323) 562-8600 *Founded/Ownrshp* 1946
Sales 32.5MM^E *EMP* 145
SIC 5511 5531

D-U-N-S 00-895-0032
MAURICE PINCOFFS CO INC
4221 Way Out West Dr # 100, Houston, TX 77092-1455
Tel (713) 681-5461 *Founded/Ownrshp* 1978
Sales 24.1MM^E *EMP* 67
SIC 5051 5091 Iron & steel (ferrous) products; Steel; Nails; Pipe & tubing, steel; Fitness equipment & supplies; Iron & steel (ferrous) products; Steel; Nails; Pipe & tubing, steel; Fitness equipment & supplies
Pr: John I Griffin
**VP:* John Michael Evans
**VP:* Scott A Wilkinshaw
Board of Directors: John Donnelly

D-U-N-S 00-198-8567 IMP/EXP
MAURICE SPORTING GOODS INC
1910 Techny Rd, Northbrook, IL 60062-5356
Tel (847) 715-1500 *Founded/Ownrshp* 1923
Sales 430.6MM^E *EMP* 800
SIC 5091 Fishing equipment & supplies; Hunting equipment & supplies; Fishing equipment & supplies; Hunting equipment & supplies
Pr: Jory Katlin
CFO: Jason Sterling
VP: Doug Jenner
VP: Jan Jordan
Exec: Scott Makway
Netwrk Mgr: Michael Wozney
MIS Mgr: Joe Peters
VP Opers: Bill Mellin
VP Opers: William Mellin
Sls Mgr: David Nielsen
Snr PM: Robert Rasmussen

MAURICE VILLENCY CLASSICS
See MAURICE VILLENCY INC

D-U-N-S 04-258-9036 IMP
MAURICE VILLENCY INC
MAURICE VILLENCY CLASSICS
200 Robbins Ln Unit D, Jericho, NY 11753-2341
Tel (212) 725-4840 *Founded/Ownrshp* 1940
Sales 20.1MM^E *EMP* 150
SIC 5712 Furniture stores; Furniture stores
Ch Bd: Robert Villency
**Sec:* Ruth Villency
**VP:* John Lombardi

D-U-N-S 02-325-0950
■ **MAURICES INC**
(*Suby of* DRESS BARN INC) ★
1651 Nathaniel Poole Trl B, Brockport, NY 14420-3012
Tel (585) 637-4370 *Founded/Ownrshp* 2008
Sales 16.5MM^E *EMP* 1,077^E
SIC 5621 Women's clothing stores

D-U-N-S 05-343-0419 IMP
■ **MAURICES INC**
(*Suby of* ASCENA RETAIL GROUP INC) ★
105 W Superior St, Duluth, MN 55802-2095
Tel (218) 727-8431 *Founded/Ownrshp* 1977
Sales 300.1MM^E *EMP* 3,000
SIC 5621 Ready-to-wear apparel, women's; Ready-to-wear apparel, women's
CEO: David Gaffe
Pr: Traci Warren
**CFO:* George Goldfarb
**CFO:* Brian Thun
Chf Mktg O: Arianne Martinovich
**Chf Mktg O:* Ali Wing
Ofcr: Brad Hartmann
Ex VP: Sue Ross
Ex VP: Erin Stern
Sr VP: Mike Herrick
Sr VP: Neil McPhail
VP: Eric Bibelnieks
VP: Gerard Darby
VP: Mike Machones
VP: Michael Rosa
VP: Angela Sawyer
Exec: Craig Dykstra
Exec: Lynne Mihalik

D-U-N-S 80-011-8556
■ **MAURICES INC (MICHIGAN)**
(*Suby of* MAURICES INC) ★
105 W Superior St, Duluth, MN 55802-2095
Tel (218) 727-8431 *Founded/Ownrshp* 1931
Sales 9.5MM^E *EMP* 324^E
SIC 5621 5611 Ready-to-wear apparel, women's; Clothing, sportswear, men's & boys'
Ch: Andre Brenninkmeyer
**CFO:* Paul Schlarman
Brnch Mgr: Jennifer Espinosa
Brnch Mgr: Carl Marluse

D-U-N-S 07-916-7968
MAURICIO ESPINOSA
BURGEONING
3523 Division St, Los Angeles, CA 90065-3301
Tel (909) 253-9108 *Founded/Ownrshp* 2010
Sales 125.2MM *EMP* 5
SIC 7389 Personal service agents, brokers & bureaus; Personal service agents, brokers & bureaus
Prin: Mauricio Espinosa

D-U-N-S 03-022-8394
MAURO MOTORS INC
MERCEDES BENZ OF NORTH HAVEN
620 Washington Ave, North Haven, CT 06473-1121
Tel (203) 239-1313 *Founded/Ownrshp* 1992
Sales 62.4MM^E *EMP* 180
SIC 5511 Automobiles, new & used; Automobiles, new & used
Pr: Michael Mauro
Genl Mgr: Tom Neville
CIO: Ken Forsythe
Mktg Mgr: Mike Piccolino

D-U-N-S 07-979-8822
MAURY COUNTY PUBLIC SCHOOLS
501 W 8th St, Columbia, TN 38401-3182
Tel (931) 388-8403 *Founded/Ownrshp* 2015
Sales 87.8MM *EMP* 1,640^E
SIC 8211 Public elementary & secondary schools
Ofcr: Krashawn Dawson Sr

D-U-N-S 00-955-6036 IMP
MAURY MICROWAVE INC
2900 Inland Empire Blvd, Ontario, CA 91764-4804
Tel (909) 987-4715 *Founded/Ownrshp* 1995
Sales 32.2MM^E *EMP* 115
SIC 3679 Microwave components
CEO: Gregory M Maury
**Pr:* Marc A Maury
CFO: Michael Howo
CTO: Gary Simpson
Dir IT: Gary Moy
MIS Mgr: Don Kaiser
Sftwr Eng: Joshua Fair
VP Sls: Ted Lewis
Sls Mgr: Jim Adamson
Snr Mgr: Roman Meierer

D-U-N-S 06-909-2286
MAURY REGIONAL HOSPITAL
MAURY REGIONAL MEDICAL CENTER
1224 Trotwood Ave, Columbia, TN 38401-4802
Tel (931) 381-1111 *Founded/Ownrshp* 1953
Sales 289.0MM^E *EMP* 2,100
Accts Pershing Yoakley & Associates
SIC 8062 General medical & surgical hospitals; General medical & surgical hospitals
CEO: Alan Watson
Chf Rad: Wes Brewer
Pr: Mark Hinson
**COO:* Paul Betz
CFO: Nick Swift
Bd of Dir: Barbara Bishop
Exec: Mary Patton
Dir OR: Tony Benton
Dir Risk M: Beth Fleming
Dir Rad: Franklin Cole
Dir Rad: Pam Wilson
Dir Rx: Jeff Binkley
Dir Bus: Patrick Harlan
Comm Man: David Thomas

MAURY REGIONAL MEDICAL CENTER
See MAURY REGIONAL HOSPITAL

D-U-N-S 61-317-8701 IMP/EXP
MAUSER USA LLC
(*Suby of* MAUSER HOLDING INTERNATIONAL GMBH)
35 Cotters Ln, East Brunswick, NJ 08816-2032
Tel (732) 353-7100 *Founded/Ownrshp* 2006
Sales 480.3MM^E *EMP* 1,000
SIC 3412 2655 Barrels, shipping: metal; Fiber cans, drums & containers; Barrels, shipping: metal; Fiber cans, drums & containers
CFO: Winfried Klar
**Treas:* Elizabeth G Miller
VP: Michael Steubing
**VP:* Siegfried Weber
Genl Mgr: William Benitez
IT Man: Brian Farraye
Opers Mgr: George Guerrero
Plnt Mgr: Graeme Jones
Plnt Mgr: Dennis Mullin
Sales Exec: Anthony Piersanti
Sls Mgr: Frank Angio

D-U-N-S 01-344-4773
MAUSNER EQUIPMENT CO INC
8 Heritage Ln, Setauket, NY 11733-3018
Tel (631) 689-7358 *Founded/Ownrshp* 1933
Sales 27.5MM *EMP* 137
SIC 3545 5084 3823 Precision measuring tools; Measuring & testing equipment, electrical; Industrial instrmnts msrmnt display/control process variable; Precision measuring tools; Measuring & testing equipment, electrical; Industrial instrmnts msrmnt display/control process variable
Pr: Seymour Mausner
**Sec:* Dorothy Mausner
**VP:* Leonard Mausner

D-U-N-S 17-735-1228 IMP
■ **MAVAL INDUSTRIES LLC**
MAVAL MANUFACTURING INC.
(*Suby of* REMY INTERNATIONAL INC) ★
1555 Enterprise Pkwy, Twinsburg, OH 44087-2239
Tel (330) 405-1600 *Founded/Ownrshp* 2015
Sales 56.3MM^E *EMP* 135
SIC 3714 8711 Power steering equipment, motor vehicle; Consulting engineer; Power steering equipment, motor vehicle; Consulting engineer
Pr: John Dougherty
**VP:* Dale Lumby
**VP:* John Statler
QA Dir: Joe Azar

MAVAL MANUFACTURING INC.
See MAVAL INDUSTRIES LLC

D-U-N-S 60-971-7462 IMP
MAVEN ENGINEERING CORP
15946 Derwood Rd, Rockville, MD 20855-2123
Tel (301) 519-3402 *Founded/Ownrshp* 2005
Sales 28.7MM *EMP* 34
SIC 3724 3511 Research & development on aircraft engines & parts; Steam engines; Research & development on aircraft engines & parts; Steam engines
Pr: Kavita Dawson
COO: Ferruico Kochinski
**VP:* Behnam Farzam
**VP:* Ajay Wadhwani
Mng Dir: Vinod Kakar
Genl Mgr: Georges Chaveca
Opers Mgr: Jim Skolaski
VP Sls: Jose Velazquez
Sls Mgr: Chris Paulston
Sls Mgr: Frank Ruggiere

MAVENIR SYSTEMS, INC.
See MITEL MOBILITY INC

D-U-N-S 93-165-5831 IMP
MAVERICK ARMS INC
(*Suby of* MOSSBERG CORP) ★
1001 Industrial Blvd, Eagle Pass, TX 78852-5242
Tel (830) 773-9007 *Founded/Ownrshp* 1988
Sales 95.2MM^E *EMP* 550
SIC 3484 Shotguns or shotgun parts, 30 mm. & below; Shotguns or shotgun parts, 30 mm. & below
Pr: Alan I Mossberg
IT Man: Bavesh Patel
Sfty Mgr: Roger Montalvo
Sales Exec: Gavier Conteras

MAVERICK AUTO PARTS
See FULL SERVICE AUTO PARTS LLC

D-U-N-S 15-195-2033
MAVERICK BOAT CO INC
M B C
3207 Industrial 29th St, Fort Pierce, FL 34946-8642
Tel (772) 465-0631 *Founded/Ownrshp* 1984
Sales 26.5MM^E *EMP* 120
SIC 3732 Fishing boats: lobster, crab, oyster, etc.: small; Skiffs, building & repairing; Fishing boats: lobster, crab, oyster, etc.: small; Skiffs, building & repairing
Pr: Douglas Deal
VP: Stephen Farinacci
Sls Dir: Skip Lyshon

D-U-N-S 93-008-5498 IMP
MAVERICK BRANDS LLC
COCO LIBRE
2400 Wyandotte St B103, Mountain View, CA 94043-2373
Tel (650) 739-0555 *Founded/Ownrshp* 2006
Sales 21.6MM^E *EMP* 30
SIC 5149 5145 Beverages, except coffee & tea; Snack foods; Beverages, except coffee & tea; Snack foods
CFO: Craig Moore
**CFO:* Mitch Wortzman
Sr VP: Peter Wilson
VP Sls: Kurt Kaifes
Mktg Dir: Alicia Davis
Manager: Leanne Middleton

D-U-N-S 15-647-5147
MAVERICK BUILDING SERVICES INC
22 Chestnut St, Rutherford, NJ 07070-1215
Tel (201) 355-2238 *Founded/Ownrshp* 1986
Sales 21.1MM^E *EMP* 600
SIC 7349 Janitorial service, contract basis; Janitorial service, contract basis
Pr: Jose P Garcia
**CFO:* Oscar Castro

D-U-N-S 82-530-4520
MAVERICK CAPITAL LTD
300 Crescent Ct Ste 1850, Dallas, TX 75201-1877
Tel (214) 880-4068 *Founded/Ownrshp* 1993
Sales 32.4MM^E *EMP* 65
SIC 6282 Investment advisory service
Mng Pt: Lee S Ainslie III
Mng Pt: Andrew Warford
COO: Logan Hemphill
CFO: Jake Friedman
Mng Dir: Alex Slack
Off Mgr: Catherine Meyer
Info Man: Richard Irwin
Counsel: Ginessa Avila
Snr Mgr: John McCafferty

D-U-N-S 00-813-7882
MAVERICK CONSTRUCTION CORP
1 Westinghouse Plz Bldg D, Hyde Park, MA 02136-2075
Tel (617) 361-6700 *Founded/Ownrshp* 1997
Sales 20.3MM^E *EMP* 80
SIC 1623 Communication line & transmission tower construction
Pr: Michael D McNally
**Pr:* Christopher F Sage
VP: Ralph Canina

MAVERICK ELECTRONICS
See HEILIND ELECTRONICS INC

D-U-N-S 86-706-9742
MAVERICK ENGINEERING INC
120 S Main St Ste 350, Victoria, TX 77901-8150
Tel (361) 576-0180 *Founded/Ownrshp* 1993
Sales 24.3MM^E *EMP* 270
SIC 8711 Professional engineer; Professional engineer
CEO: Al Rahmani
**CFO:* Darrell O'Neal
**VP:* James Field
**VP:* William F Fordtran

D-U-N-S 86-754-8760 IMP
MAVERICK ENTERPRISES INC
(*Suby of* PCM COMPANIES LLC) ★
751 E Gobbi St, Ukiah, CA 95482-6205
Tel (707) 463-5591 *Founded/Ownrshp* 1992
Sales 29.3MM^E *EMP* 105
SIC 3353 Foil, aluminum; Foil, aluminum
Pr: Steve Otterbeck
Treas: Jay Frysinger
**Ex VP:* Jon Henderson
**VP:* Fred Koeppel
VP: Kerry Manahan-Ehlow
Exec: Donna Baxter
Exec: Janice Brown

D-U-N-S 00-440-4262
MAVERICK FUNDING CORP
1160 Parsippany Blvd # 200, Parsippany, NJ 07054-1811
Tel (973) 585-6099 *Founded/Ownrshp* 2007
Sales NA *EMP* 98
SIC 6162 Mortgage bankers & correspondents

MAVERICK HOME HEALTH AGENCY
See RIO BRAVO HEALTH SYSTEMS LLC

D-U-N-S 07-996-2470
MAVERICK HOTEL PARTNERS LLC
FILAMENT HOSPITALITY
466 Green St Ste 302, San Francisco, CA 94133-4067
Tel (415) 655-9526 *Founded/Ownrshp* 2014
Sales 75.0MM *EMP* 300
SIC 8741 Hotel or motel management

D-U-N-S 02-517-0307
MAVERICK PUMP SERVICES LLC
9791 Titan Park Cir, Littleton, CO 80125-9345
Tel (303) 981-8349 *Founded/Ownrshp* 2008
Sales 500.0MM *EMP* 12
SIC 7389 ;

MAVERICK QUICK SHOPS
See COX OIL CO INC

D-U-N-S 14-740-3930
MAVERICK TECHNOLOGIES HOLDINGS LLC
MAVERICK TECNOLOGIES
265 Admiral Trost Dr, Columbia, IL 62236-2173
Tel (618) 281-9100 *Founded/Ownrshp* 1999
Sales 127.4MM^E *EMP* 400
SIC 8711 8748 1731 Consulting engineer; Business consulting; Electrical work; Consulting engineer; Business consulting; Electrical work
CEO: Paul J Galeski
**Sr VP:* Rob Gellings
**Sr VP:* Kirk Norris
**Sr VP:* Larry Ray
**VP:* Paul Dunn
Dir IT: Michael Roe

D-U-N-S 13-376-4030
MAVERICK TECHNOLOGIES LLC
(*Suby of* MAVERICK TECHNOLOGIES HOLDINGS LLC) ★
265 Admiral Trost Dr, Columbia, IL 62236-2173
Tel (618) 281-9100 *Founded/Ownrshp* 1999
Sales 125.8MM^E *EMP* 400
SIC 8711 8748 1731 Consulting engineer; Business consulting; Electrical work; Consulting engineer; Business consulting; Electrical work
CEO: Paul J Galeski
CFO: Matt Johnson
VP: Peter Esparrago
VP: Mark Hall
VP: Charles Judy
VP: Stephanie Maclean

VP: Larry Ray
VP: Bill Stew
Rgnl Mgr: Alan Denlow
Genl Mgr: Lisa Luecthefeld
Software D: Bryan Cook

MAVERICK TECNOLOGIES
See MAVERICK TECHNOLOGIES HOLDINGS LLC

D-U-N-S 09-992-3310
MAVERICK TRANSPORTATION LLC
(*Suby of* MAVERICK USA INC) ★
13301 Valentine Rd, North Little Rock, AR 72117-9311
Tel (501) 955-1222 *Founded/Ownrshp* 1980
Sales 243.4MM^E *EMP* 1,771
Accts Hudson & Cisne
SIC 4213 Building materials transport; Building materials transport
Ch: Steven Williams
**COO:* Stephen Selig
**Ex VP:* Doug Richey
**VP:* Letha Haymes
Exec: Jim Paladino
IT Man: Shawn Bynum
Trfc Dir: Daniel Cameron
Sls Dir: Justin Brown
Manager: Drew Allbritton

D-U-N-S 08-691-8398 IMP/EXP
MAVERICK TUBE CORP
TENARIS
(*Suby of* TENARIS SA)
2200 West Loop S Ste 800, Houston, TX 77027-3532
Tel (713) 767-4400 *Founded/Ownrshp* 1977
Sales 315.5MM^E *EMP* 1,577
SIC 3317 Steel pipe & tubes; Welded pipe & tubes; Well casing, wrought: welded, lock joint or heavy riveted; Steel pipe & tubes; Welded pipe & tubes; Well casing, wrought: welded, lock joint or heavy riveted
Pr: German Cura
**CFO:* Chris North
Sales Exec: Joe Maxwell
Sls Dir: Federico Gianinetto
Board of Directors: Brad Lowe

D-U-N-S 83-297-6703
MAVERICK USA INC
13301 Valentine Rd, North Little Rock, AR 72117-9311
Tel (501) 945-6130 *Founded/Ownrshp* 1980
Sales 243.4MM^E *EMP* 1,771^E
SIC 4213 Building materials transport; Building materials transport
Pr: Stephen Selig
**CEO:* Steve Williams
VP: Wayne Brown
**VP:* John A Culp
VP: Kim Gary
VP: Debbie Mitchell
VP: Dean Newell
Telecom Ex: Shawn Bynum
VP Opers: John Coppens
Pr Mgr: Spring Dixon

D-U-N-S 00-794-7997
MAVERIK INC
(*Suby of* FJ MANAGEMENT INC) ★
880 W Center St, North Salt Lake, UT 84054-2913
Tel (307) 885-3861 *Founded/Ownrshp* 1959, 2012
Sales 996.2MM^E *EMP* 2,900
SIC 5541 5411 Filling stations, gasoline; Convenience stores, chain; Filling stations, gasoline; Convenience stores, chain
Pr: Mike Call
VP: David Hancock
VP: Kirk Hansen
VP: John Hillam
VP: Kim Lazerus
Store Dir: Paula Lewis
CIO: Hubert Williams
CTO: Bob York
Dir IT: Darren Sitter
Opers Mgr: Michael Heiner
Mktg Dir: Brad Call

D-U-N-S 80-055-4896 IMP
MAVERIK LACROSSE LLC
(*Suby of* KOHLBERG SPORTS GROUP INC) ★
535 W 24th St Fl 5, New York, NY 10011-1140
Tel (516) 213-3050 *Founded/Ownrshp* 2010
Sales 191.6M^E *EMP* 5,019^E
SIC 3949 Lacrosse equipment & supplies, general

MAVIS DISCOUNT TIRE
See MAVIS TIRE SUPPLY LLC

D-U-N-S 01-291-5732 IMP
MAVIS TIRE SUPPLY LLC
MAVIS DISCOUNT TIRE
358 Saw Mill River Rd # 17, Millwood, NY 10546-1054
Tel (914) 666-6750 *Founded/Ownrshp* 1964, 1983
Sales 772.5MM^E *EMP* 1,431
SIC 5014 5531 Automobile tires & tubes; Truck tires & tubes; Automotive tires; Automobile tires & tubes; Truck tires & tubes; Automotive tires
Pr: Steven S Sorbaro
VP: David Sorbaro
Brnch Mgr: Alberto Olaya
Mktg Mgr: Jeff Braun
Snr Mgr: Edward Schwartz

D-U-N-S 07-271-2342
MAVO SYSTEMS INC
MAVO SYSTEMS WISCONSIN
4330 Centerville Rd, Saint Paul, MN 55127-3676
Tel (763) 788-7713 *Founded/Ownrshp* 1982
Sales 44.0MM *EMP* 217
Accts Cliftonlarsonallen Llp Minnea
SIC 1799 1742 7349 Asbestos removal & encapsulation; Asbestos removal & encapsulation; Insulation, buildings; Air duct cleaning
CEO: Dana Sawrey
**COO:* Jay Robertson
**CFO:* Larry Reese
IT Man: Shanda Lovering

MAVO SYSTEMS WISCONSIN
See MAVO SYSTEMS INC

MAW
See MID-AMERICA FOOD DISTRIBUTOR LLC

D-U-N-S 00-248-9441
MAWSON & MAWSON INC (PA)
1800 E Old Lincoln Hwy, Langhorne, PA 19047-3013
Tel (215) 750-1100 *Founded/Ownrshp* 1895, 1947
Sales 49.0MM *EMP* 75
Accts Cahan Somerman Spewak & Lips
SIC 4213 4212 Heavy hauling; Local trucking, without storage; Heavy hauling; Local trucking, without storage
Pr: Michael Fonzi
**Sec:* James Shetzley
**VP:* Michael Hatkins
Dir IT: Gene Nowosielski
Sfty Dirs: Charlie Ketterer
Opers Mgr: Joe Maguire
Sales Exec: Gregory Mann

MAX 10
See BERMO ENTERPRISES INC

D-U-N-S 96-764-8762
MAX AND MARIAN FARASH CHARITABLE FOUNDATION
255 East Ave, Rochester, NY 14604-2625
Tel (585) 218-9855 *Founded/Ownrshp* 2011
Sales 63.1MM *EMP* 1
SIC 6732 Trusts: educational, religious, etc.; Trusts: educational, religious, etc.
Ch Bd: Nathan J Robfogel

D-U-N-S 04-259-3343
MAX ARNOLD & SONS LLC
MAXFUEL C-STORES
702 N Main St, Hopkinsville, KY 42240-2790
Tel (270) 885-8488 *Founded/Ownrshp* 1961
Sales 191.0MM^E *EMP* 230
SIC 5171 5541 5411 5812 Petroleum bulk stations; Gasoline service stations; Convenience stores, chain; Delicatessen (eating places); Petroleum bulk stations; Gasoline service stations; Convenience stores, chain; Delicatessen (eating places)
Pr: Bob Arnold
CFO: Gary Logan
**Treas:* Doris Imogene Arnold
Dist Mgr: Cathy Fuqua
Off Mgr: Eddie Prevette
Plnt Mgr: Russell Jones
Mktg Mgr: Justin Frizzell

D-U-N-S 12-168-7701
MAX BLUE TRUCKING INC
1015 E Westinghouse Blvd, Charlotte, NC 28273-5805
Tel (704) 588-8780 *Founded/Ownrshp* 1984
Sales 34.3MM^E *EMP* 120^E
SIC 4212 Dump truck haulage
Pr: Denton Williams Jr
VP: Jeremiah Williams

D-U-N-S 19-919-8610
MAX CARGO INC
19825 Hamilton Ave, Torrance, CA 90502-1341
Tel (310) 323-8100 *Founded/Ownrshp* 1997
Sales 30.0MM *EMP* 18^E
SIC 4731 Freight transportation arrangement
Pr: Choong R Chung
Genl Mgr: Brian Kim

D-U-N-S 11-815-9136 IMP
MAX CHEMICAL INC
6 Calle La Brisa, San Juan, PR 00924-3834
Tel (787) 765-6100 *Founded/Ownrshp* 1985
Sales 32.2MM^E *EMP* 148
Accts Nigaglioni & Rivera Carreras
SIC 2952 Roof cement: asphalt, fibrous or plastic; Roof cement: asphalt, fibrous or plastic
VP: July Penton
**Pr:* Enrique Blanco
**VP:* Sergio Blanco
**VP:* Julio Penton
Genl Mgr: Julio Pentean

MAX CONSTRUCTION COMPANY
See DJM BUILDERS INC

D-U-N-S 07-912-0465
MAX CREDIT UNION
400 Eastdale Cir, Montgomery, AL 36117-2114
Tel (334) 260-2600 *Founded/Ownrshp* 1955
Sales NA *EMP* 351
SIC 6061 Federal credit unions; Federal credit unions
Pr: H Greg McClellan Jr
V Ch: Ron Thompson
CIO: Scott Lindley

D-U-N-S 00-483-5146
MAX ENVIRONMENTAL TECHNOLOGIES INC (PA)
1815 Washington Rd Ste 1, Pittsburgh, PA 15241-1423
Tel (412) 595-7638 *Founded/Ownrshp* 1955, 1995
Sales 74.2MM^E *EMP* 95
SIC 4953 Hazardous waste collection & disposal; Refuse collection & disposal services; Hazardous waste collection & disposal; Refuse collection & disposal services
Pr: Lawrence W Spencer
Treas: Merle Light
**VP:* Karl Churman
VP: Michael Nadzum
**VP:* Henry Springer
Off Mgr: Lynn Frohnapfel
Sfty Mgr: Carl Spadaro
Plnt Mgr: Roy Ulery
Sls Mgr: Ralph McGillvary
Snr PM: Ken Interval

D-U-N-S 01-235-8461 IMP
MAX FINKELSTEIN INC
2840 31st St, Astoria, NY 11102-2131
Tel (718) 274-8900 *Founded/Ownrshp* 1919
Sales 242.7MM^E *EMP* 150
SIC 5014 5531 Automobile tires & tubes; Truck tires & tubes; Automotive tires; Automobile & truck equipment & parts; Automobile tires & tubes; Truck tires & tubes; Automotive tires; Automobile & truck equipment & parts
Pr: Harold Finkelstein
VP: Jerome Finkelstein
VP: Scott Pattcoff

VP: Howard Rosenthal
VP: Ira Silver
IT Man: Michael Sedlock
Sls Dir: Ian Campbell

D-U-N-S 08-165-1150
MAX FOOTE CONSTRUCTION CO LLC (LA)
225 Antibes St W Ste 3, Mandeville, LA 70448-4793
Tel (985) 624-8569 *Founded/Ownrshp* 1979
Sales 81.2MM^E *EMP* 140
SIC 1629 Waste water & sewage treatment plant construction; Waste water & sewage treatment plant construction
CEO: Max F Foote Jr
**Pr:* Roy Thompson
**CEO:* Max E Foote Jr
**VP:* David Brown
**VP:* Dana B Bullard
**VP:* Thomas Deville
**VP:* Kenneth Emrick
Off Mgr: Chris Sharp
IT Man: Michael Middleton
Mtls Mgr: Ralph Holloway

D-U-N-S 00-978-0875
MAX GRAY CONSTRUCTION INC
2501 5th Ave W, Hibbing, MN 55746-2040
Tel (218) 262-6622 *Founded/Ownrshp* 1983
Sales 24.5MM^E *EMP* 150
SIC 1542 1541 Commercial & office building contractors; Industrial buildings, new construction
Pr: James M Erickson

D-U-N-S 14-717-6218
MAX GROUP CORP
17011 Green Dr, City of Industry, CA 91745-1800
Tel (626) 935-0050 *Founded/Ownrshp* 1985
Sales 80.6MM^E *EMP* 75^E
SIC 5045 Computer peripheral equipment; Disk drives; Keying equipment; Printers, computer; Computer peripheral equipment; Disk drives; Keying equipment; Printers, computer
CEO: Su-Tzu Tsai
**Pr:* Chung-Jen Tsai

D-U-N-S 13-429-8095 IMP
MAX HOME LLC
101 Max Pl, Fulton, MS 38843-6611
Tel (662) 862-9966 *Founded/Ownrshp* 2003
Sales 89.3MM^E *EMP* 400
SIC 2512 Upholstered household furniture; Upholstered household furniture
Ex VP: Aaron Larry
Plnt Mgr: Vince Crocker

D-U-N-S 00-382-3762
MAX J KUNEY CO (WA)
120 N Ralph St, Spokane, WA 99202-4744
Tel (509) 535-0651 *Founded/Ownrshp* 1930
Sales 57.2MM^E *EMP* 140
SIC 1622 1611 Highway & street paving contractor; Bridge construction; Bridge construction; Highway & street paving contractor
Pr: Max J Kuney IV
**Sec:* Robert Haney
**VP:* Daniel Kuney
**VP:* Greg Waugh
Sfty Dirs: Tom Landwehr

D-U-N-S 16-776-6153
MAX JANTZ EXCAVATING LLC
26503 11 Rd, Montezuma, KS 67867-9065
Tel (620) 846-2634 *Founded/Ownrshp* 1976
Sales 40.0MM *EMP* 160
SIC 1794 Excavation work; Excavation work
**Prin:* Dean Chesnut
**Prin:* John Minick

MAX LEATHER
See GBG USA INC

D-U-N-S 09-945-7616 IMP
MAX LEON INC
MAX STUDIO.COM
3100 New York Dr, Pasadena, CA 91107-1524
Tel (626) 797-6886 *Founded/Ownrshp* 1979
Sales 125.3MM^E *EMP* 500
SIC 2339 5632 Sportswear, women's; Apparel accessories; Sportswear, women's; Apparel accessories
Pr: Leon Max
Pr: Carrie Specker
CTO: Matt Rich
Dir IT: Justin Harris
Opers Mgr: Balmore Ruano

D-U-N-S 03-758-5957
MAX MADSEN IMPORTS INC
MAX MADSEN MITSUBISHI
2424 Ogden Ave, Downers Grove, IL 60515-1709
Tel (630) 960-5040 *Founded/Ownrshp* 1987
Sales 38.6MM^E *EMP* 107
SIC 5511 Automobiles, new & used; Automobiles, new & used
Pr: Max Madsen
**VP:* Scott Grove
Exec: Jeff Kenner
Genl Mgr: Adam Grove
Sls Mgr: Ken Byram

MAX MADSEN MITSUBISHI
See MAX MADSEN IMPORTS INC

MAX PACKAGING
See GADSDEN COFFEE CO INC

D-U-N-S 62-163-7474 IMP
MAX RAVE LLC
(*Suby of* BCBG MAX AZRIA GROUP INC) ★
2761 Fruitland Ave, Vernon, CA 90058-3607
Tel (201) 861-1416 *Founded/Ownrshp* 2006
Sales 240.2MM^E *EMP* 2,900
SIC 5621 Ready-to-wear apparel, women's; Ready-to-wear apparel, women's
CEO: Max Azria

D-U-N-S 94-336-4083
MAX RESTAURANT GROUP LLC
249 Pearl St Fl 2, Hartford, CT 06103-2110
Tel (860) 522-9806 *Founded/Ownrshp* 1996

Sales 27.4MM^E *EMP* 200
SIC 8741

MAX STUDIO.COM
See MAX LEON INC

MAX TOOL
See IMPERIAL INDUSTRIAL SUPPLY CO

D-U-N-S 12-088-6544
MAX TOOL INC
119b Citation Ct, Birmingham, AL 35209-6306
Tel (205) 942-2466 *Founded/Ownrshp* 1985
Sales 22.9MM *EMP* 46
SIC 5085 Abrasives; Abrasives
Pr: Dudley Barton
**VP:* Dave Browning
CIO: Chandler Poston
Sales Asso: Jeremy Beard

D-U-N-S 14-219-5028
MAX TRANS LLC
MAXTRANS
219 Us Highway 45 W Ste D, Humboldt, TN 38343-5872
Tel (800) 650-9085 *Founded/Ownrshp* 2003
Sales 37.3MM^E *EMP* 90
SIC 4213 Trucking, except local
VP: Gary Beasley
Sfty Dirs: Chris Beasley
VP Sls: Jeff Mansfield

MAX TRANSIT
See BIRMINGHAM-JEFFERSON COUNTY TRANSIT AUTHORITY

MAX-R
See PRESTWICK GROUP INC

D-U-N-S 19-059-0208
MAXAIR INC
MAXAIR MECHANICAL
814 Livingston Ct Se, Marietta, GA 30067-2208
Tel (770) 956-1200 *Founded/Ownrshp* 2009
Sales 51.2MM^E *EMP* 90
SIC 1542 8711 Commercial & office building, new construction; Mechanical engineering
Pr: Jonathan Sterling
VP: Joy L Dean

MAXAIR MECHANICAL
See MAXAIR INC

D-U-N-S 11-115-2273
MAXAM NORTH AMERICA INC
(*Suby of* MAXAM EUROPE SA)
6975 S Union Park Ctr # 525, Midvale, UT 84047-5575
Tel (801) 233-6000 *Founded/Ownrshp* 2000
Sales 47.5MM^E *EMP* 230
SIC 2892 5169 Explosives; Explosives; Explosives; Explosives
CEO: German Morales
**Pr:* Stanton Johnso
**CFO:* Rocio Summers
**VP:* Fernando Beitia
VP: Stanton Johnson
**VP:* Carl Lubbe
VP: Len McBeth
**VP:* John Watson
Sfty Mgr: Darrel Bostwick
Sls Mgr: Gary Kimber
Sls Mgr: Mike Pruss

D-U-N-S 07-859-9096
MAXAM US LLC
(*Suby of* MAXAM NORTH AMERICA INC) ★
225 Six Mile Hollow Rd, Midvale, UT 84047
Tel (801) 233-6000 *Founded/Ownrshp* 2011
Sales 34.6MM *EMP* 50^E
SIC 2892 Dynamite
Genl Mgr: Ander Arrate
Genl Mgr: Dan Francelj

D-U-N-S 60-245-4944 IMP/EXP
MAXCESS INTERNATIONAL CORP
(*Suby of* MAXCESS INTERNATIONAL HOLDING CORP) ★
222 W Memorial Rd, Oklahoma City, OK 73114-2300
Tel (405) 755-1600 *Founded/Ownrshp* 1989
Sales 137.2MM^E *EMP* 690
SIC 3554 3565 6719 Paper industries machinery; Packaging machinery; Investment holding companies, except banks; Paper industries machinery; Packaging machinery; Investment holding companies, except banks
CFO: Merlyn D Devries
VP: Dan Crofford
**VP:* Tom Herold
VP: Ron Schmidt
Exec: Lee Harwell
Mng Dir: David Calhoun
Dist Mgr: Jan Gronewold
Dist Mgr: Thomas Varner
CTO: Robby Ross
Dir IT: Mike Schlosser
Mtls Mgr: Karen Delong

D-U-N-S 07-925-8855
MAXCESS INTERNATIONAL HOLDING CORP
(*Suby of* WH ACQUISITIONS INC) ★
222 W Memorial Rd, Oklahoma City, OK 73114-2300
Tel (405) 755-1600 *Founded/Ownrshp* 2014
Sales 137.2MM^E *EMP* 690^E
SIC 3554 3565 6719 Paper industries machinery; Packaging machinery; Investment holding companies, except banks; Paper industries machinery; Packaging machinery; Investment holding companies, except banks
CEO: Greg Jehlik
COO: Doug Knudtson
CFO: Dave Hawkins

D-U-N-S 06-884-9108 IMP
MAXCO SUPPLY INC
605 S Zediker Ave, Parlier, CA 93648-2033
Tel (559) 646-8449 *Founded/Ownrshp* 1972
Sales 134.2MM^E *EMP* 200

SIC 5113 2436 3554 Shipping supplies; Softwood veneer & plywood; Box making machines, paper; Shipping supplies; Softwood veneer & plywood; Box making machines, paper
Pr: Max Flaming
**COO:* David Bryant
VP: Kevin Martin
Genl Mgr: Kevin Brower
Genl Mgr: Joe Sepe
**VP Mfg:* Robert Grote

D-U-N-S 06-430-5212 IMP
MAXELL CORP OF AMERICA
(*Suby of* HITACHI MAXELL,LTD.)
3 Garret Mountain Plz # 300, Woodland Park, NJ 07424-3352
Tel (973) 653-2400 *Founded/Ownrshp* 1969
Sales 27.0MM^E^ *EMP* 125
SIC 3691 3652 Storage batteries; Pre-recorded records & tapes; Storage batteries; Pre-recorded records & tapes
Pr: Hideaki Numoto
VP: Len Haine
VP: Barbara Sommer
VP: Koichi Yanagawa
Dir IT: Dianne Naughton
Opers Mgr: Sandra Smith
Mktg Mgr: Peter Brinkman
Mktg Mgr: Rich Hall
Mktg Mgr: Lynn Lang

D-U-N-S 01-766-9995
MAXEY ENERGY CO
EXXON PRODUCTS/MAXEY ENERGY CO
447 W Main St, Uvalde, TX 78801-5509
Tel (830) 278-3711 *Founded/Ownrshp* 1978
Sales 37.2MM *EMP* 16
Accts Egly Holcombe & Peebles Pllc
SIC 5171 Petroleum bulk stations; Petroleum bulk stations
Pr: Merlin Maxey
**Pr:* W Merlin Maxey
**VP:* Ellen Maxey
VP: Greg Maxey

MAXFLI GOLF DIVISION
See FOCUS GOLF SYSTEMS

MAXFUEL C-STORES
See MAX ARNOLD & SONS LLC

D-U-N-S 15-400-2117 IMP
MAXI AIDS INC
HEAR MORE
42 Executive Blvd, Farmingdale, NY 11735-4710
Tel (631) 752-0521 *Founded/Ownrshp* 1986
Sales 40.9MM^E^ *EMP* 77
SIC 5047 3841 Medical equipment & supplies; Surgical & medical instruments
Ch Bd: Elliot Zaretsky
**Treas:* Pamela Stein
Bd of Dir: Harold Zaretsky
Ex Dir: Larry Di Blasi
Genl Mgr: Barry Greenblatt
Dir IT: Harris Boshak
Dir IT: Carlo Vasques

D-U-N-S 08-934-7736
■ **MAXI DRUG INC**
RITE AID
(*Suby of* RITE AID CORP) ★
30 Hunter Ln, Camp Hill, PA 17011-2400
Tel (717) 761-2633 *Founded/Ownrshp* 2007
Sales 71.8MM^E^ *EMP* 5,000
SIC 5912 Drug stores & proprietary stores; Drug stores & proprietary stores
Ch Bd: John T Standley

D-U-N-S 01-931-6889
MAXI FOODS LLC (CA)
8616 California Ave, Riverside, CA 92504-2860
Tel (951) 688-0538 *Founded/Ownrshp* 1997
Sales 20.0MM^E^ *EMP* 100
SIC 5411 Grocery stores

D-U-N-S 92-992-6327
MAXI-SEAL HARNESS SYSTEMS INC
(*Suby of* PETERSON MANUFACTURING CO) ★
13312 5th St Ste B, Grandview, MO 64030-3005
Tel (816) 841-6700 *Founded/Ownrshp* 1995
Sales 41.4MM^E^ *EMP* 120
SIC 3496 Miscellaneous fabricated wire products; Miscellaneous fabricated wire products
CEO: Don Armacost Jr
Genl Mgr: Tim Barnett
Ql Cn Mgr: Robin Simpson
Sls Mgr: Tricia Soulon

D-U-N-S 14-507-9708
MAXIFACIAL DENTAL SURGERY
MARY HITCHCOCK MEMORIAL HOSP
1 Medical Center Dr, Lebanon, NH 03756-1000
Tel (603) 650-5000 *Founded/Ownrshp* 1983
Sales 5.0MM *EMP* 7,500
Accts Ernst & Young Us Llp Indian
SIC 8011 Cardiologist & cardio-vascular specialist; Cardiologist & cardio-vascular specialist
Pr: Nancy Formella
**COO:* Daniel Jantzen
Ofcr: Thomas Corindia
Ofcr: Arthur Nichols
Dir Rad: Jocelyn D Chertoff
Dir Rad: Marc Seltzer
Off Mgr: Catherine I Garfield-Legare
Off Mgr: Donna Pourby
Mktg Mgr: Kathleen Barrell
Mktg Mgr: Rolf Olsen
Pathlgst: Nora R Atcliffe

D-U-N-S 36-218-2185
MAXIM CRANE WORKS HOLDINGS INC
(*Suby of* PLATINUM EQUITY LLC) ★
1225 Wash Pike Ste 100, Bridgeville, PA 15017-2844
Tel (412) 504-0200 *Founded/Ownrshp* 2008
Sales 227.2MM^E^ *EMP* 2,900^E^
SIC 7353 7359 Heavy construction equipment rental; Equipment rental & leasing; Heavy construction equipment rental; Equipment rental & leasing
VP: Don Goebel
**CFO:* Jay Vanhorn
VP: John Werner
Dir Bus: Jess Macmillan
VP Admn: Richard Swartz
Trfc Dir: Richie Beck
Sfty Mgr: Raymond Bingham
Opers Mgr: Donald Powell
Sls Mgr: Dick Stuart

D-U-N-S 36-218-5451
MAXIM CRANE WORKS LP
(*Suby of* MAXIM CRANE WORKS HOLDINGS INC) ★
1225 Wash Pike Ste 100, Bridgeville, PA 15017-2844
Tel (412) 504-0200 *Founded/Ownrshp* 1994
Sales 227.2MM^E^ *EMP* 2,000
SIC 7353 Heavy construction equipment rental; Heavy construction equipment rental
CEO: Bryan Carlisle
CFO: Joe Vaccaerello
Sr VP: Larry T Rettinger
Sr VP: John Werner
VP: Don Goebel
VP: Joe Keefe
VP: Larry Rettinger
Area Mgr: Chris Jones
Genl Mgr: Barry Assad
Dir IT: Gary Perez
Dir IT: Sal Pirozzi

MAXIM EGG FARMS
See MAXIM FARM EGG CO INC

MAXIM EGG FARMS
See MAXIM PRODUCTION CO INC

D-U-N-S 05-030-8311
MAXIM FARM EGG CO INC (TX)
MAXIM EGG FARMS
580 Maxim Dr, Boling, TX 77420-0020
Tel (979) 657-2891 *Founded/Ownrshp* 1962
Sales 107.0MM *EMP* 45
SIC 5144 Eggs; Eggs
CEO: Vincent J Reina
**Pr:* Vincent Reina Jr
CFO: Michael Castleberry
**VP:* Christofer Reina

D-U-N-S 13-184-2531
MAXIM GROUP LLC
405 Lexington Ave Fl 2, New York, NY 10174-0003
Tel (212) 895-3500 *Founded/Ownrshp* 2002
Sales 108.1MM^E^ *EMP* 350
SIC 6211 Brokers, security; Brokers, security
CEO: Michael Rabinowitz
**COO:* John Sergio
**CFO:* Timothy G Murphy
Chf Mktg O: John Garrity
Ofcr: Gerard McCarthy
Sr VP: Stephen Anderson
Sr VP: Daniel Balestra
Sr VP: Robert Burchman
Sr VP: John-Paul Cirigliano
Sr VP: John Conover
Sr VP: Tommaso Denardo
Sr VP: Shaw Elashmawy
Sr VP: Kenneth Epstein
Sr VP: Rob Ford
Sr VP: Jack Gager
Sr VP: Keith Goodman
Sr VP: Andrew Grossman
Sr VP: Rodney Ibrahim
Sr VP: Paul Katz
Sr VP: Peter Kaufman
Sr VP: Brian Kinstlinger

MAXIM HEALTH CARE
See MAXIM HEALTH SYSTEMS LLC

D-U-N-S 80-931-3299
MAXIM HEALTH CARE SERVICES
MAXIM HEALTHCARE SERVICES
(*Suby of* MAXIM HEALTHCARE SERVICES INC) ★
622 Georges Rd Ste 201, North Brunswick, NJ 08902-3377
Tel (732) 246-0600 *Founded/Ownrshp* 1994
Sales 10.2MM^E^ *EMP* 600
SIC 8082 7361 Home health care services; Employment agencies; Home health care services; Employment agencies
Pr: Laurie Hamilton
**Ch Bd:* James Kelly

D-U-N-S 15-288-6479
MAXIM HEALTH SYSTEMS LLC
MAXIM HEALTH CARE
(*Suby of* MAXIM HEALTHCARE SERVICES INC) ★
7227 Lee Deforest Dr, Columbia, MD 21046-3236
Tel (410) 910-1500 *Founded/Ownrshp* 1996
Sales 191.5MM^E^ *EMP* 4,150
SIC 8011 8099 Medical centers; Health screening service; Medical centers; Health screening service
CFO: Dave Franchak
Opers Supe: Christina Lapinska

MAXIM HEALTHCARE SERVICES
See MAXIM HEALTH CARE SERVICES

D-U-N-S 60-629-0401
MAXIM HEALTHCARE SERVICES INC
7227 Lee Deforest Dr, Columbia, MD 21046-3236
Tel (410) 910-1500 *Founded/Ownrshp* 1988
Sales 1.2MMM *EMP* 35,000
Accts Pricewaterhousecoopers Llp Ba
SIC 8082 Home health care services; Home health care services
CEO: W Bradley Bennett
COO: Christopher Powell
**COO:* Paula Sotir
**CFO:* William Butz
CFO: Raymond Carbone
**Ofcr:* Julie Judge
**VP:* Jacqueline Baratian
VP: Andrew Friedell
VP: Bart Kelly
**VP:* W John Langley
**VP:* Toni Jean Lisa
VP: Jimmy Nichols
VP: Jake Reed
VP: Michael Rose
VP: Nancy Roy
Dir Risk M: Eric Stieritz
Dir Bus: Jeff Harper

D-U-N-S 07-958-2033
MAXIM INC
MAXIM MAGAZINE
415 Madison Ave Fl 3, New York, NY 10017-7927
Tel (212) 372-3829 *Founded/Ownrshp* 2014
Sales 34.9MM^E^ *EMP* 75^E^
SIC 5192 Magazines
Prin: Brownridge Kent
Sr VP: Bill Shaw
VP: Jill Tully
Assoc Dir: Samantha Shelly
Dir Rx: Kelsey Knight
CTO: Dan Greenwald
IT Man: Daniel Brundige
Prd Dir: Gustavo Gonzalez
Mktg Mgr: Laura Carlucci
Mktg Mgr: Rhudy Correa
Sales Asso: Jake Lauer

D-U-N-S 10-211-2489 IMP
▲ **MAXIM INTEGRATED PRODUCTS INC**
160 Rio Robles, San Jose, CA 95134-1813
Tel (408) 601-1000 *Founded/Ownrshp* 1983
Sales 2.3MMM *EMP* 8,250
Accts Deloitte & Touche Llp San Jos
Tkr Sym MXIM *Exch* NGS
SIC 3674 Microcircuits, integrated (semiconductor); Microcircuits, integrated (semiconductor)
Pr: Tunc Doluca
**Ch Bd:* B Kipling Hagopian
CFO: Bruce E Kiddoo
Sr VP: Edwin B Medlin
VP: David A Caron
VP: Dan Christman
Mng Dir: David Nam
Mng Dir: Arkadii Samoilov
Sls Dir: Jon Imperato
Corp Couns: Jennifer Law
Counsel: Chuck Crider
Board of Directors: James R Bergman, Joseph R Bronson, Robert E Grady, William P Sullivan, William D Watkins, A R Frank Wazzan

MAXIM MAGAZINE
See MAXIM INC

D-U-N-S 96-674-3783
MAXIM MANAGEMENT SERVICES LLC
3085 Harlem Rd Ste 350, Buffalo, NY 14225-2591
Tel (716) 844-5600 *Founded/Ownrshp* 1996
Sales 21.6MM^E^ *EMP* 226
SIC 8741 Administrative management; Administrative management

D-U-N-S 08-597-0606
MAXIM PRODUCTION CO INC
MAXIM EGG FARMS
580 Maxim Dr, Boling, TX 77420-0020
Tel (979) 657-2891 *Founded/Ownrshp* 1962
Sales 27.8MM^E^ *EMP* 320^E^
SIC 0252 Chicken eggs; Chicken eggs
CEO: Vincent J Reina Sr
Pr: Vince Reina
CFO: Michael Castleberry
VP: A J Rath
VP: Christopher Reina
Board of Directors: Vincent J Reina

D-U-N-S 07-304-5184
MAXIMA SUPPLY LLC
3909 Holt Rd, Holt, MI 48842-9701
Tel (877) 662-9462 *Founded/Ownrshp* 1999
Sales 24.1MM^E^ *EMP* 26
SIC 5141 Food brokers

D-U-N-S 06-320-5186
■ **MAXIMA TECHNOLOGIES & SYSTEMS INC**
STEWART WARNER
(*Suby of* MAXIMA TECHNOLOGIES & SYSTEMS LLC) ★
1811 Rohrerstown Rd, Lancaster, PA 17601-2321
Tel (717) 569-5713 *Founded/Ownrshp* 1902, 1992
Sales 31.5MM^E^ *EMP* 300
SIC 3089 Automotive parts, plastic
Pr: Oddie V Leopando
**CFO:* Avee Poston
Netwrk Mgr: Susan Navarro

D-U-N-S 05-291-7721 IMP
■ **MAXIMA TECHNOLOGIES & SYSTEMS LLC**
(*Suby of* ACTUANT CORP) ★
1811 Rohrerstown Rd, Lancaster, PA 17601-2321
Tel (717) 581-1000 *Founded/Ownrshp* 2006
Sales 70.2MM^E^ *EMP* 500
SIC 3823 3824 3825 3812 3613 Industrial instrmnts msrmnt display/control process variable; Tachometer, centrifugal; Speedometers; Elapsed time meters, electronic; Search & navigation equipment; Switchgear & switchboard apparatus; Industrial instrmnts msrmnt display/control process variable; Tachometer, centrifugal; Speedometers; Elapsed time meters, electronic; Search & navigation equipment; Switchgear & switchboard apparatus
Pr: John Buck
Pr: Dennis Roberts
Prgrm Mgr: Francisco Lopez
Dir IT: John Rubis
Dir IT: Daniel Whalen
VP Opers: Terry Bell
Plnt Mgr: Brady Umberger
Ql Cn Mgr: Ignacio Alcocer
Ql Cn Mgr: Henri McVey
Ql Cn Mgr: Terry Zimmerman
VP Sls: Matt Sturdy

D-U-N-S 12-545-5613 IMP/EXP
MAXIMO SUPERMERCADOS INC
SUPERMAX
Centro De Distribucion De, Catano, PR 00962
Tel (787) 783-1555 *Founded/Ownrshp* 2002
Sales 71.8MM^E^ *EMP* 650
SIC 5411 Supermarkets, chain
Pr: Jose Revuelta
**Pr:* Francisco J Uriarte Otheguy
**Sec:* Nelson Gonzalez
**VP:* Steven C Lausel

D-U-N-S 11-750-7657
MAXIMS NUTRICARE INC
PAPA PITA BAKERY
6208 W Dannon Way, West Jordan, UT 84081-5694
Tel (801) 282-3100 *Founded/Ownrshp* 1983
Sales 38.0MM *EMP* 80
SIC 5149

D-U-N-S 02-636-4484
MAXIMUM INDEPENDENT BROKERAGE LLC
222 S Riverside Plz # 2340, Chicago, IL 60606-6116
Tel (312) 559-9348 *Founded/Ownrshp* 2002
Sales NA *EMP* 46
SIC 6411 Insurance agents, brokers & service
CEO: Joe Messina
**CFO:* Tom Hagan
**Ex VP:* Anthony Verrecchia
Sr VP: Adrian Smith
VP: Mark Jatczak
VP: Ed Perdomo
VP: Kandy Pinkstaff
VP: Darren Racine

MAXIMUM QUALITY FD PPR & PLTY
See MAXIMUM QUALITY FOODS INC

D-U-N-S 07-817-5023
MAXIMUM QUALITY FOODS INC
MAXIMUM QUALITY FD PPR & PLTY
3351 Tremley Point Rd # 2, Linden, NJ 07036-3575
Tel (908) 474-0003 *Founded/Ownrshp* 1975
Sales 121.7MM^E^ *EMP* 100
SIC 5141 Groceries, general line; Groceries, general line
Prin: Gary

D-U-N-S 79-999-3428
MAXIMUM RESEARCH INC
1860 Greentree Rd, Cherry Hill, NJ 08003-2031
Tel (856) 874-9000 *Founded/Ownrshp* 2000
Sales 21.7MM^E^ *EMP* 200
Accts Bagell Josephs Levine & Comp
SIC 8732 Market analysis, business & economic research; Market analysis, business & economic research
Pr: Robert Malmud
VP: Jen Dambach

D-U-N-S 36-422-1593
■ **MAXIMUS FEDERAL SERVICES INC**
(*Suby of* MAXIMUS INC) ★
1891 Metro Center Dr, Reston, VA 20190-5287
Tel (703) 251-8500 *Founded/Ownrshp* 2005
Sales 227.1MM^E^ *EMP* 1,350
SIC 8742 Hospital & health services consultant; Hospital & health services consultant
Pr: Thomas Romeo
VP: Peter Rogers

D-U-N-S 83-241-1727
MAXIMUS HOLDINGS INC
(*Suby of* SYMPHONY TECHNOLOGY GROUP LLC) ★
2475 Hanover St, Palo Alto, CA 94304-1114
Tel (650) 935-9500 *Founded/Ownrshp* 2009
Sales 177.3MM^E^ *EMP* 1,006^E^
SIC 7372 Prepackaged software; Prepackaged software
CEO: Dominic Gallello
**CFO:* Jim Johnson

D-U-N-S 08-234-7477
▲ **MAXIMUS INC**
1891 Metro Center Dr, Reston, VA 20190-5287
Tel (703) 251-8500 *Founded/Ownrshp* 1975
Sales 2.1MMM *EMP* 13,000
Tkr Sym MMS *Exch* NYS
SIC 8742 8741 Management consulting services; Management services; Management consulting services; Management services
CEO: Richard A Montoni
**Ch Bd:* Peter B Pond
Pr: Bruce L Caswell
CFO: Richard J Nadeau
CFO: David N Walker
Ex VP: Gary Garofalo
Sr VP: Bruce Cowans
Sr VP: Harold Horton
Sr VP: Nora Paape
Sr VP: Steven Whitney
Sr VP: Chris Zitzow
VP: Nelson Clugston
VP: Phyllis Fish
VP: Daniel Goodwin
VP: Nancy Heiser
VP: Lisa Miles
VP: Anna Sever
Dir Bus: Barbara Foley
Board of Directors: Russell A Beliveau, John J Haley, Paul R Lederer, Raymond B Ruddy, Marilyn R Seymann, James R Thompson Jr, Wellington E Webb

D-U-N-S 00-830-0162
MAXINE SWIM GROUP INC
6600 Katella Ave, Cypress, CA 90630-5104
Tel (714) 358-8922 *Founded/Ownrshp* 1960
Sales 49.3MM *EMP* 150
Accts White Nelson & Co Llp Anahe
SIC 2339 Bathing suits: women's, misses' & juniors'
Pr: Vincent Rojas
**Pr:* Allan Colvin

D-U-N-S 00-535-7355 IMP
MAXION WHEELS
HAYES LEMMERZ INTERNATIONAL
(*Suby of* IOCHPE HOLDINGS LLC) ★
39500 Orchard Hill Pl # 500, Novi, MI 48375-5370
Tel (734) 737-5000 *Founded/Ownrshp* 2012
Sales 2.0MMM *EMP* 8,000
SIC 3714 Wheels, motor vehicle; Wheels, motor vehicle
CEO: Pieter Klinkers
Pr: Don Polk
COO: Michael Wood

CFO: Oscar Becker
Treas: Eric Moraw
VP: Nancy Casadevall
VP: Steven Esau
VP: Matt Griffith
VP: Kelly Knepley
VP: John A Salvette
VP: Brian Walls
Dir Risk M: Michael Coffman
Dir Bus: Toshihiko Harada

D-U-N-S 03-076-5429
MAXION WHEELS USA LLC
(*Suby of* HAYES LEMMERZ INTERNATIONAL) ★
39500 Orchard Hill Pl # 500, Novi, MI 48375-5370
Tel (734) 737-5000 *Founded/Ownrshp* 2012
Sales 465.0MM^E *EMP* 6,500
SIC 3714 Wheels, motor vehicle; Wheels, motor vehicle
CEO: Pieter Klinkers
Treas: Eric Moraw
VP: Steve Esau
VP: John Salvette

D-U-N-S 08-851-3739
MAXIS HEALTH SYSTEM
(*Suby of* CATHOLIC HEALTH EAST) ★
3805 West Chester Pike # 100, Newtown Square, PA 19073-2329
Tel (570) 281-1000 *Founded/Ownrshp* 1998
Sales 19.5MM^E *EMP* 1,200
Accts Deloitte Tax Llp Philadelphia
SIC 8062 General medical & surgical hospitals; General medical & surgical hospitals
Pr: Mary Theresa Vautrinop
**Pr:* Sister Jean Coughlin
**CFO:* Richard Hager
VP: Ron Boldt
CTO: Joseph Casarella

D-U-N-S 15-888-9563
MAXIT HEALTHCARE LLC
LEIDOS HEALTH
705 E Main St, Westfield, IN 46074-9440
Tel (317) 867-2682 *Founded/Ownrshp* 2006
Sales 15.8MM^E *EMP* 300^E
SIC 8082 Home health care services; Home health care services
Pr: Don Bosse
Pr: Jessica Campbell
Pr: Gord Curl
Pr: Kevin Hill
Pr: Wes Knox
Pr: Andrea Merrin
Pr: David Moody
Pr: Ray Murray
Pr: Tina Nash
**Pr:* Mike Sweeney
Pr: Eric Utzinger
CFO: Keith Weppler
Ofcr: Jennifer Arthur
Ofcr: John Poggetto
Ex VP: Reese Gomez
Ex VP: Kim Parrish
Ex VP: Robin Shine
Sr VP: Leanne Hester
VP: Bob Betts
VP: Lou Bon
VP: Melissa Hinshaw

D-U-N-S 00-532-0809 IMP
MAXITROL CO (MI)
23555 Telegraph Rd, Southfield, MI 48033-4176
Tel (248) 356-1400 *Founded/Ownrshp* 1946
Sales 48.7MM^E *EMP* 280
SIC 3625 3822 3823 3612 3494 Relays & industrial controls; Valves & pipe fittings; Temperature controls, automatic; Appliance regulators; Gas burner, automatic controls; Transformers, except electric; Temperature instruments: industrial process type; Pressure measurement instruments, industrial; Controllers for process variables, all types; Relays & industrial controls; Temperature controls, automatic; Appliance regulators; Gas burner, automatic controls; Temperature instruments: industrial process type; Pressure measurement instruments, industrial; Controllers for process variables, all types; Transformers, except electric; Valves & pipe fittings
Ch Bd: Bonnie Kern-Koskela
**COO:* Larry Koskela
**CFO:* Christopher Kelly
VP: David Holcomb
**VP:* Brian O'Sullivan
**VP:* John Schlachter
Mng Dir: Mary K Hauswirth
Off Mgr: Phyllis Gentz
**VP Mfg:* Ivin Riddle
Ql Cn Mgr: Tony Abeauvais
Ql Cn Mgr: Anthony Beauvais

D-U-N-S 17-876-5702 IMP
▲ **MAXLINEAR INC**
5966 La Place Ct Ste 100, Carlsbad, CA 92008-8830
Tel (760) 692-0711 *Founded/Ownrshp* 2003
Sales 133.1MM *EMP* 336
Tkr Sym MXL *Exch* NYS
SIC 3674 Semiconductors & related devices; Semiconductors & related devices
Ch Bd: Kishore Seendripu
CFO: Adam C Spice
VP: Tim Gallagher
VP: Michael J Lachance
VP: Brian J Sprague
VP: William G Torgerson
**CTO:* Curtis Ling
Board of Directors: Steven C Craddock, Albert J Moyer, Thomas E Pardun, Donald E Schrock, Theodore Tewksbury

D-U-N-S 80-917-5367 IMP
MAXLITE INC
12 York Ave, West Caldwell, NJ 07006-6411
Tel (800) 555-5629 *Founded/Ownrshp* 1993
Sales 26.9MM^E *EMP* 70
SIC 3648 Arc lighting fixtures
Pr: Yon W Sung
**Ex VP:* Thomas Rhee
Sr VP: Jim Hunter
**VP:* Bill Masi
VP: Richard Matthews
VP: Chris Primous
VP: Paul Shaskan
**VP:* David Wyatt
Genl Mgr: Todd Kim
Genl Mgr: Jay Lee
Software D: Vin Han

D-U-N-S 94-877-4393
MAXM CORP
SOLARCOMM WIRELESS
2143 E 5th St, Tempe, AZ 85281-3034
Tel (480) 945-3505 *Founded/Ownrshp* 1996
Sales 22.0MM *EMP* 13
SIC 5999 Communication equipment; Communication equipment
Pr: Erik Molden
**VP:* Lynda Molden

D-U-N-S 14-785-5340 IMP
MAXMARA USA INC
(*Suby of* MAX MARA FASHION GROUP SRL)
530 Fashion Ave Fl 21, New York, NY 10018-4813
Tel (212) 536-6200 *Founded/Ownrshp* 1987
Sales 119.0MM^E *EMP* 300
SIC 5621 Women's clothing stores; Women's clothing stores
Ch Bd: Luigi Maramotti
**Pr:* Luigi Caroggio
CFO: Luca Arrigoni
**Treas:* Gabriele D Agostino
**VP:* Kristine Westerby
Genl Mgr: Alan Fong
Dir IT: Kevin Ludvinsky
VP Sls: Jennifer Jerome
Pr Mgr: Erica Hoeft
Pr Mgr: Emma Tully

MAXON, A HONEYWELL COMPANY
See MAXON CORP

D-U-N-S 06-824-8657
MAXON CO INC (NY)
76 N Broadway, Irvington, NY 10533-1207
Tel (914) 591-7111 *Founded/Ownrshp* 1955
Sales NA *EMP* 80
SIC 6411 Insurance brokers
Pr: Stanley Rubenzahl
COO: Hana Rubin
Mktg Dir: Ernie Mele
Board of Directors: Doris Garrett, Ernie Mele, Hana Rubin

D-U-N-S 00-641-9774 IMP/EXP
■ **MAXON CORP**
MAXON, A HONEYWELL COMPANY
(*Suby of* HONEYWELL INC) ★
201 E 18th St, Muncie, IN 47302-4199
Tel (765) 284-3304 *Founded/Ownrshp* 1916, 2007
Sales 50.4MM^E *EMP* 450
SIC 3433 3494

D-U-N-S 06-769-4315 EXP
■ **MAXON FURNITURE INC**
(*Suby of* HNI CORP) ★
2210 2nd Ave, Muscatine, IA 52761-5257
Tel (800) 876-4274 *Founded/Ownrshp* 2002
Sales 55.4MM^E *EMP* 450
SIC 2522 Panel systems & partitions, office: except wood; Panel systems & partitions, office: except wood
Pr: Woody Brooks

D-U-N-S 87-620-5774 IMP
MAXON LIFT CORP
11921 Slauson Ave, Santa Fe Springs, CA 90670-2221
Tel (562) 464-0099 *Founded/Ownrshp* 1957
Sales 221.8MM^E *EMP* 110
SIC 5084 3537 3534 Lift trucks & parts; Industrial trucks & tractors; Elevators & moving stairways; Lift trucks & parts; Industrial trucks & tractors; Elevators & moving stairways
Pr: Casey Lugash
Ex VP: Lawerence Lugash
VP: Larry Jones
**VP:* Brenda Leung
VP: Bill Moore
VP: John Teng
Exec: Lee Garrett
Exec: Anton Griessner
DP Dir: Arnold Kowal
QA Dir: Woody Woodrum
IT Man: Lorena Baltazar

D-U-N-S 78-118-1524
MAXONS RESTORATIONS INC
280 Madison Ave, New York, NY 10016-0801
Tel (212) 447-6767 *Founded/Ownrshp* 1990
Sales 36.0MM^E *EMP* 47
SIC 4959 Sanitary services
Pr: Damon Gersh
Ex VP: Kris Cuozzo
Ex VP: C R Gross
**Ex VP:* Howard White
VP: Wendy Lehman
Rgnl Mgr: Richard Bailin
Rgnl Mgr: Ed Christenson
Opers Mgr: Kelly Dolan
Opers Mgr: Bob Held
Mktg Mgr: Ruta Sinusas

D-U-N-S 92-674-1893
MAXOR NATIONAL PHARMACY SERVICES CORP
MAXOR PHARMACIES
320 S Polk St Ste 100, Amarillo, TX 79101-1436
Tel (806) 324-5400 *Founded/Ownrshp* 1990
Sales 96.1MM^E *EMP* 481
Accts Brown Graham & Company Amaril
SIC 5912 Drug stores; Drug stores
CEO: John Ward
**Pr:* Carl Birdsong
CFO: Gilbert D'Andria
**CFO:* Jerry Havard
**Ch:* Jerry Hodge
Treas: Cynthia Garner
**Sec:* Cynthia Carner
Sr VP: Steve Smith
VP: Lori Brown
VP: Heath Hodge
VP: Hanna Rubenzohl
VP: Allen D Sapp Jr
VP: Karyn Swindull
Exec: Margaret Hodge
Comm Dir: Rachael Kagan
Dir Rx: Deleca Reynolds-Barnes

MAXOR PHARMACIES
See MAXOR NATIONAL PHARMACY SERVICES CORP

D-U-N-S 79-202-9642
▲ **MAXPOINT INTERACTIVE INC**
3020 Carrington Mill Blvd, Morrisville, NC 27560-5432
Tel (800) 916-9960 *Founded/Ownrshp* 2006
Sales 63.4MM^E *EMP* 378^E
Tkr Sym MXPT *Exch* NYS
SIC 7311 Advertising agencies
CEO: Joseph Epperson
**COO:* Gretchen Joyce
VP: Michelle Engle
**VP:* Kip Gordon
VP: Eddie Jennings
VP: Chris Kozloski
VP: Susan Lee
VP: Sean Murphy
VP: Lynn Vitello
Genl Mgr: Amy Gittelman
Off Mgr: Cara Wehner
Board of Directors: Len Jordan

MAX'S WINE DIVE TASTING ROOM
See LASCO ENTERPRISES LLC

MAXSENT
See CDA INC

D-U-N-S 84-705-0630 IMP
■ **MAXTEK COMPONENTS CORP**
(*Suby of* TEKTRONIX INC) ★
2905 Sw Hocken Ave, Beaverton, OR 97005-2411
Tel (503) 627-4133 *Founded/Ownrshp* 1994
Sales 47.7MM^E *EMP* 300^E
SIC 3674 8731 3679 8711 Integrated circuits, semiconductor networks, etc.; Hybrid integrated circuits; Electronic research; Electronic circuits; Engineering services; Integrated circuits, semiconductor networks, etc.; Hybrid integrated circuits; Electronic research; Electronic circuits; Engineering services
Pr: Tom Buzak
Treas: Frank T McFaden
VP: Jan Erik Barkenaes
VP: Robert S Lutz
VP: H Paul Montgomery
VP: James F O'Reilly
Board of Directors: James A Lico

D-U-N-S 17-766-7219 IMP
MAXTOR CORP
(*Suby of* SEAGATE TECHNOLOGY (US) HOLDINGS INC) ★
4575 Scotts Valley Dr, Scotts Valley, CA 95066-4517
Tel (831) 438-6550 *Founded/Ownrshp* 2007
Sales 418.7MM^E *EMP* 15,085
SIC 3572 Disk drives, computer

MAXTRANS
See MAXTRANS LLC

D-U-N-S 07-981-1123
MAXUM ENTERPRISES LLC
PILOT THOMAS LOGISTICS
777 Main St Ste 2000, Fort Worth, TX 76102-5332
Tel (405) 848-3500 *Founded/Ownrshp* 2012
Sales 1.0MMM^E *EMP* 110^E
SIC 5171 5172 Petroleum terminals; Lubricating oils & greases; Engine fuels & oils; Gases, liquefied petroleum (propane)
CEO: Scott Prince
CFO: Jeff Roberts

D-U-N-S 78-516-3291
MAXUM PETROLEUM INC
(*Suby of* PILOT FLYING J) ★
5508 Lonas Dr, Knoxville, TN 37909-3221
Tel (865) 588-7488 *Founded/Ownrshp* 2012
Sales 221.8MM^E *EMP* 399
SIC 5172 Crude oil; Engine fuels & oils; Diesel fuel; Gasoline; Crude oil; Engine fuels & oils; Diesel fuel; Gasoline
CEO: James A Haslan III
**Pr:* Michael Hughes
**COO:* George Ristevski
**Treas:* Paul H Runko
Sr VP: Michael A Brown
Sr VP: Steve Cross
Sr VP: Jeffrey Dill
VP: Mike McDonald
VP: Malcolm Miller
VP: Ryan A Secrist
Software D: Scott Chaney

D-U-N-S 03-871-9212
MAXUM SERVICES INC
941 S Lewis St Ste A, New Iberia, LA 70560-6313
Tel (337) 364-9526 *Founded/Ownrshp* 2000
Sales 9.2MM^E *EMP* 300
SIC 1389 Oil field services; Oil field services
Pr: Broc Segura

D-U-N-S 19-927-6960
MAXUS COMMUNICATIONS LLC
(*Suby of* WPP 2012 LIMITED)
498 Fashion Ave, New York, NY 10018-6798
Tel (212) 297-8300 *Founded/Ownrshp* 2005
Sales 110.0MM^E *EMP* 1,000
SIC 8999 Communication services; Communication services
Pr: Louis Jones
Sr Pt: Jane Barasch
Sr Pt: Brian Gearhart
Sr Pt: Laura Lefever
Sr Pt: Tobias Wolf
CEO: Donna Triolo
COO: Carla Loffredo
CFO: Neil Sternberg
Ofcr: Jonathan Adams
Exec: Sasha Giesberg
Assoc Dir: Amanda Leighton
Dir Rx: Jolene Solanki
Dir Bus: Karen Kaufman
Dir Bus: Andreas Rapp

D-U-N-S 12-464-4712
MAXVILLE LLC
GILMAN BUILDING PRODUCTS
(*Suby of* GILMAN BUILDING PRODUCTS LLC) ★
6640 County Road 218, Jacksonville, FL 32234-3047
Tel (904) 289-7261 *Founded/Ownrshp* 1973
Sales 20.0MM^E *EMP* 140
SIC 2421 Building & structural materials, wood; Wood chips, produced at mill; Building & structural materials, wood; Wood chips, produced at mill
Pr: William H Davis
**Ch:* Bernard D Bergreen
**Sr VP:* Dominick Sorrentino
**VP:* Victor Garrett
**VP:* Natalie P Moody
**VP:* Joseph Robilotto
**VP:* Philip Skoropat
**VP:* Ben Wood
Off Mgr: Kristina Austin

D-U-N-S 93-865-7389
MAXWELL BUILDERS INC
333 W Hampden Ave Ste 325, Englewood, CO 80110-2333
Tel (303) 762-1812 *Founded/Ownrshp* 2001
Sales 23.6MM *EMP* 32
Accts Bauerle & Company Pc Denver
SIC 1542 Commercial & office building contractors; Commercial & office building contractors
CEO: David Maxwell
**Pr:* Lonia Maxwell
**VP:* Mike Willingham
Dir Bus: Chris Strom

MAXWELL, DON CHEVROLET
See KRUEGER SERVICES INC

D-U-N-S 82-636-9720
MAXWELL FOODS LLC
938 Millers Chapel Rd, Goldsboro, NC 27534-7772
Tel (919) 778-3130 *Founded/Ownrshp* 1989
Sales 46.9MM^E *EMP* 1,000
SIC 0213 Hogs; Hogs
Pr: J L Maxwell III
CFO: Tom Howell
VP: Jere Walter Pelletier III
Genl Mgr: Robert Ivey

MAXWELL HARDWOOD FLOORING
See MAXWELL HARDWOOD INC

D-U-N-S 78-749-3550 IMP
MAXWELL HARDWOOD INC
MAXWELL HARDWOOD FLOORING
190 Wilson Mill Rd, Monticello, AR 71655-9791
Tel (870) 367-2436 *Founded/Ownrshp* 1992
Sales 28.3MM^E *EMP* 200
SIC 2426 Flooring, hardwood; Flooring, hardwood
Pr: Thomas Maxwell
**VP:* Sarah B Maxwell
**VP:* Kristi Prince
Sales Exec: Darrell Orrell

MAXWELL ROUND ROCK NISSAN
See MAXWELL-NII INC

D-U-N-S 07-242-4682 IMP
MAXWELL SUPPLY OF TULSA INC
1719 N Sheridan Rd, Tulsa, OK 74115-4623
Tel (918) 836-8606 *Founded/Ownrshp* 1974
Sales 24.7MM^E *EMP* 30
SIC 5082 General construction machinery & equipment
Ch Bd: Jerry Thomason
**VP:* Kim Oliver
**VP:* Charlie Thomason

D-U-N-S 10-884-3624 IMP/EXP
MAXWELL SYSTEMS INC
VIEWPOINT
(*Suby of* VIEWPOINT CONSTRUCTION SFTWR) ★
600 W Germantown Pike # 300, Plymouth Meeting, PA 19462-2217
Tel (610) 277-3515 *Founded/Ownrshp* 2014
Sales 50.3MM^E *EMP* 210
SIC 5045 Computers; Computer software; Computers; Computer software
Ch: Manolis Kotzabasakis
**Pr:* James Flynn
**CFO:* Ben Ertischek
**CFO:* Bill Tobia
VP: Eric Foster
**VP:* Matt Harris
VP: Bob Hodges
VP: Dan Lehman
VP: Mike Zarzeka
Dir Soc: Matt Asherman
Snr Ntwrk: Daniel Kobrin

D-U-N-S 00-956-7942 IMP
▲ **MAXWELL TECHNOLOGIES INC**
3888 Calle Fortunada, San Diego, CA 92123-1825
Tel (858) 503-3300 *Founded/Ownrshp* 1965
Sales 186.5MM *EMP* 448^E
Accts Bdo Usa Llp San Diego Califo
Tkr Sym MXWL *Exch* NGS
SIC 3629 Capacitors & condensers; Capacitors, a.c., for motors or fluorescent lamp ballasts; Capacitors, fixed or variable; Power conversion units, a.c. to d.c.: static-electric; Capacitors & condensers; Capacitors, a.c., for motors or fluorescent lamp ballasts; Capacitors, fixed or variable; Power conversion units, a.c. to d.c.: static-electric
Pr: Franz Fink
**Ch Bd:* Mark Rossi
Pr: Curt Alexander
CFO: David Lyle
CFO: Kevin S Royal
Sr VP: Michael Finger
VP: Van M Andrews
VP: Jeremy Cowperthwaite
VP: Tesfaye Hailemichael
VP: Chris Humphrey
VP: Sacha Jenny
VP: Michael J Liedtke

VP: Larry Longden
VP: William Zhu
Board of Directors: Rick Bergman, Jos L Cortes, Robert Guyett, Roger Howsmon, Yon Yoon Jorden, David Schlotterbeck

D-U-N-S 11-884-7222
■ MAXWELL-NII INC
MAXWELL ROUND ROCK NISSAN
(*Suby of* GROUP 1 AUTOMOTIVE INC) ★
3050 N Interstate 35, Round Rock, TX 78681-2406
Tel (512) 244-8500 *Founded/Ownrshp* 1999
Sales 21.9MM^E *EMP* 60
SIC 5511 Automobiles, new & used
Genl Mgr: Gui McRee
Sls Mgr: Mike Handwerger

MAXX PROPERTIES
See JRD MANAGEMENT CORP

MAXXAM
See SAM HOUSTON RACE PARK LTD

D-U-N-S 00-690-8156
▲ MAXXAM INC
1330 Post Oak Blvd # 2000, Houston, TX 77056-3058
Tel (832) 251-5960 *Founded/Ownrshp* 1955, 2011
Sales 78.0MM^E *EMP* 1,080^E
Tkr Sym MAXX *Exch* OTO
SIC 6531 7948 Real estate agent, residential; Real estate agent, commercial; Jockey, horse racing; Real estate agent, residential; Real estate agent, commercial; Jockey, horse racing
Ch Bd: Charles E Hurwitz
**Pr:* Shawn M Hurwitz
CFO: Emily Madison
VP: Robert E Cole
VP: Diane M Dudley
VP: John T Laduc
VP: Joshua A Reiss
VP: Ronald L Reman
IT Man: Dave Clark

D-U-N-S 62-606-4513
■ MAXXAM PROPERTY CO
(*Suby of* MAXXAM INC) ★
1330 Post Oak Blvd # 2000, Houston, TX 77056-3058
Tel (713) 975-7600 *Founded/Ownrshp* 1987
Sales 22.4MM^E *EMP* 200^E
SIC 6719 Investment holding companies, except banks; Investment holding companies, except banks
Pr: Shawn Hurwitz
**Pr:* James D Noteware
**Pr:* Paul Swartz
**VP:* John T Laduc
**VP:* Anthoney Pierno
**Genl Mgr:* Kay Hines

D-U-N-S 05-652-5152 IMP
■ MAXXIM REBUILD CO LLC
(*Suby of* ALPHA NATURAL RESOURCES LLC) ★
5703 Crutchfield Dr, Norton, VA 24273-3902
Tel (276) 679-7020 *Founded/Ownrshp* 1988
Sales 190.5MM^E *EMP* 2,000
SIC 1241 Coal mining services; Coal mining services

MAXXIS INTERNATIONAL-USA
See CHENG SHIN RUBBER USA INC

D-U-N-S 00-527-9864
MAXYIELD COOPERATIVE
CENEX
313 3rd Ave Nw, West Bend, IA 50597-8572
Tel (515) 887-7211 *Founded/Ownrshp* 1915
Sales 324.0MM *EMP* 157
Accts Meriwether Wilson And Company
SIC 5153 5191 2999 0723 Grain elevators; Farm supplies; Coke (not from refineries), petroleum; Bean cleaning services; Grain elevators; Farm supplies; Coke (not from refineries), petroleum; Bean cleaning services
CEO: Keith Hime
**Pr:* Howard Haas
CFO: Susan Post
**Sec:* Eric Marchand
**VP:* David Garrelts
Genl Mgr: Keith Hein
Netwrk Mgr: Jeff Wittkopf
Sfty Dirs: Tom Winkel
Snr Mgr: Jennifer Allen
Snr Mgr: Chad Besch
Snr Mgr: Harry Bormann

MAY ELECTRIC
See AMERICAN ELECTRIC INC

MAY GROUP INTERNATIONAL
See TECHNOGRAPHIX LLC

D-U-N-S 08-158-2637
MAY INSTITUTE INC
41 Pacella Park Dr, Randolph, MA 02368-1755
Tel (781) 440-0400 *Founded/Ownrshp* 1975
Sales 99.6MM *EMP* 2,000
Accts Cbiz Tofias Boston Ma
SIC 8361 Rehabilitation center, residential: health care incidental; Rehabilitation center, residential: health care incidental
Ch Bd: Jory Berkwits
**Pr:* Walter P Christian PHD
**CEO:* Lauren C Solotar
**COO:* Ralph B Sperry
CFO: Debra Blair
**Treas:* Michael Milczarek
**Ex VP:* Aubrey Macfarlane
VP: Terese Brennan
VP: Jocelyn Lemaire
VP: Stephen D Merrill
Ex Dir: Jaimie Hoover

D-U-N-S 06-538-4612
MAY SUPPLY CO
1775 Erickson Ave, Harrisonburg, VA 22801-8555
Tel (540) 433-2611 *Founded/Ownrshp* 1997
Sales 20.9MM^E *EMP* 50
SIC 5074 5999 Plumbing fittings & supplies; Heating equipment (hydronic); Plumbing & heating supplies
Pr: Larry G Fanella
**COO:* William H Schulz
Sales Asso: Harry Wine

MAY TECHNOLOGY & MFG CO
See MAY TOOL AND MOLD CO INC

D-U-N-S 00-716-8685
MAY TOOL AND MOLD CO INC
MAY TECHNOLOGY & MFG CO
2922 Wheeling Ave, Kansas City, MO 64129-1100
Tel (816) 923-6262 *Founded/Ownrshp* 1986
Sales 24.6MM^E *EMP* 110
SIC 3544 3545 Special dies, tools, jigs & fixtures; Special dies & tools; Precision tools, machinists'; Special dies, tools, jigs & fixtures; Special dies & tools; Precision tools, machinists'
CEO: Ernest May
**Pr:* Steve May
**Sec:* Theresa May
**VP:* Reno May
Dir Bus: Jim Connelly
Dir IT: Darrell Myers
IT Man: Christian Irwin

D-U-N-S 00-985-9430
MAY TRUCKING CO
4185 Brooklake Rd Ne, Salem, OR 97303-9729
Tel (503) 393-7030 *Founded/Ownrshp* 1966
Sales 210.0MM *EMP* 900
SIC 4213 Contract haulers; Refrigerated products transport; Contract haulers; Refrigerated products transport
CEO: C Marvin May
**Pr:* David M Daniels
CFO: Andrew Mantey
**CFO:* Dave Temple
VP: Brad Weatherman
Dir Risk M: Rob Cahill
Comm Dir: Lisa Davis
Opers Mgr: Kory Knox
Sls Mgr: McNeal Mike
Snr Mgr: Boyd Puckett

D-U-N-S 11-132-7057
MAYA ANGELOU PUBLIC CHARTER SCHOOL
600 Pennsylvania Ave Se # 210, Washington, DC 20003-4344
Tel (202) 761-4385 *Founded/Ownrshp* 1998
Sales 22.0MM *EMP* 43^E
SIC 8211 Elementary & secondary schools
**Prin:* Heather D Wathington

D-U-N-S 19-753-6100
MAYA FOODS INC
EL RIO GRANDE SUPER MARKET
2515 W Jefferson Blvd, Dallas, TX 75211-2629
Tel (214) 884-4444 *Founded/Ownrshp* 2005
Sales 24.3MM^E *EMP* 150^E
SIC 5411 Supermarkets, chain
Pr: Hamdy Shalabi
Exec: Zack Mustafa

D-U-N-S 83-248-3924
MAYA MANAGEMENT GROUP LLC
11411 Hillguard Rd, Dallas, TX 75243-5501
Tel (214) 751-2290 *Founded/Ownrshp* 2008
Sales 100.0MM *EMP* 60
SIC 8742 Management consulting services; Management consulting services
VP: Aman Shalabi

D-U-N-S 02-531-6365
MAYA STEELS FABRICATION INC (CA)
301 E Compton Blvd, Gardena, CA 90248-2015
Tel (310) 532-8830 *Founded/Ownrshp* 1982
Sales 26.2MM^E *EMP* 64
SIC 3441 Fabricated structural metal
CEO: Meir Amsalam
**CEO:* Yechiel Yogev
COO: Sean Dempsey
Treas: Yogev Yechiel
**VP:* Sara Haddad
Genl Mgr: Gerald Sanders
Sfty Dirs: Matt Kripal

D-U-N-S 02-190-9120
MAYAGEZ MEDICAL CENTER
CENTRO PEDIATRICO MAYAGUEZ
410 Ave Hostos, Mayaguez, PR 00682-1560
Tel (787) 652-9200 *Founded/Ownrshp* 2009
Sales 67.2MM^E *EMP* 780
SIC 8741 8011 Hospital management; Medical centers; Hospital management; Medical centers
Pr: Sr Jos Quirs

MAYBORN GROUP
See MAYBORN USA INC

D-U-N-S 03-127-4363 IMP
MAYBORN USA INC
MAYBORN GROUP
(*Suby of* MAYBORN GROUP LIMITED)
1 Edgewater Dr Ste 100, Norwood, MA 02062-4669
Tel (781) 269-7490 *Founded/Ownrshp* 1946
Sales 36.1MM *EMP* 13
SIC 3069 3085 3634 3821 Baby pacifiers, rubber; Nipples, rubber; Teething rings, rubber; Plastics bottles; Bottle warmers, electric: household; Sterilizers; Baby pacifiers, rubber; Nipples, rubber; Teething rings, rubber; Plastics bottles; Bottle warmers, electric: household; Sterilizers
CEO: Steve Parkin
Pr: Brenda O'Grady Liistro
Sec: George Idicula
Genl Mgr: Vinnie D'Alleva

D-U-N-S 06-697-4114
MAYBURY ASSOCIATES INC
MAYBURY MATERIAL HANDLING
90 Denslow Rd, East Longmeadow, MA 01028-3160
Tel (413) 525-4216 *Founded/Ownrshp* 1976
Sales 30.6MM^E *EMP* 66
SIC 5084 3537

MAYBURY MATERIAL HANDLING
See MAYBURY ASSOCIATES INC

D-U-N-S 78-706-8209 IMP
MAYCO INTERNATIONAL LLC
NJT ENTERPRISES LLC
(*Suby of* VENTURE HOLDINGS B.V.)
42400 Merrill Rd, Sterling Heights, MI 48314-3238
Tel (586) 803-6000 *Founded/Ownrshp* 2006
Sales 198.4MM^E *EMP* 735
SIC 3089 Injection molding of plastics; Injection molding of plastics
CFO: Al Grajek
Prgrm Mgr: Scott Grajek
Prgrm Mgr: Don Henschel
Prgrm Mgr: Ken Rushing
Mtls Mgr: Mike Zartman
Sfty Mgr: Laura Phelps
Ql Cn Mgr: Jim Burns

MAYCO PLASTICS
See STONEBRIDGE INDUSTRIES INC

D-U-N-S 00-295-3776 IMP
MAYDAY MANUFACTURING CO (TX)
(*Suby of* TAILWIND TECHNOLOGIES INC) ★
3100 Jim Christal Rd, Denton, TX 76207-2600
Tel (940) 898-8301 *Founded/Ownrshp* 1966
Sales 36.8MM^E *EMP* 150
SIC 3728 3769 3568 3452 3366 3365 Aircraft parts & equipment; Guided missile & space vehicle parts & auxiliary equipment; Power transmission equipment; Bolts, nuts, rivets & washers; Copper foundries; Aluminum foundries; Aircraft parts & equipment; Guided missile & space vehicle parts & auxiliary equipment; Power transmission equipment; Bolts, nuts, rivets & washers; Copper foundries; Aluminum foundries
Ch: Matthew Jesch
**CFO:* Cheryl Whiteman
**Ex VP:* J Spence Nelson
**VP:* James W Brown III
**VP:* Joseph W Brown
VP: David Whiteman
Dir IT: Brian Nelson
Sls&Mrk Ex: Gus Whiteman
S&M/VP: Tom Shaw

D-U-N-S 18-360-0881 IMP
MAYEKAWA USA INC
(*Suby of* MAYEKAWA MFG. CO., LTD.)
1850 Jarvis Ave, Elk Grove Village, IL 60007-2440
Tel (773) 516-5070 *Founded/Ownrshp* 1987
Sales 29.7MM^E *EMP* 125
SIC 3585 5078 3563 Refrigeration equipment, complete; Refrigeration equipment & supplies; Air & gas compressors; Refrigeration equipment, complete; Refrigeration equipment & supplies; Air & gas compressors
Pr: Tadashi Maekawa
**COO:* Takeo Kanazawa

D-U-N-S 00-212-1333 IMP
MAYER BROS APPLE PRODUCTS INC (NY)
3300 Transit Rd, West Seneca, NY 14224-2525
Tel (716) 668-1787 *Founded/Ownrshp* 1852
Sales 27.8MM^E *EMP* 150
SIC 2033 2086 5499 5963 Fruit juices: fresh; Pasteurized & mineral waters, bottled & canned; Juices, fruit or vegetable; Bottled water delivery; Fruit juices: fresh; Pasteurized & mineral waters, bottled & canned; Juices, fruit or vegetable; Bottled water delivery
Ch Bd: John A Mayer
Exec: Carolyn Tothill
Exec: Linda Tryka
Opers Mgr: Eric Mayer
Ql Cn Mgr: Theresa Place
Sls Mgr: James Kalec

D-U-N-S 01-029-1136
MAYER BROWN LLP
71 S Wacker Dr Ste 1000, Chicago, IL 60606-4716
Tel (312) 782-0600 *Founded/Ownrshp* 1881, 1940
Sales 594.3MM^E *EMP* 5,334
SIC 8111 General practice law office; General practice law office
Pt: Tyrone C Fahner
Pt: Scott A Anenberg
Pt: Joel Bertocchi
Pt: Edward S Best
Pt: Bruce Bettigole
Pt: Timothy S Bishop
Pt: Robert E Bloch
Pt: Cynthia Burch
**Pt:* Alan S Cohen
Pt: Barbara E Cohen
Pt: Marc R Cohen
Pt: Joseph P Collins
Pt: Pat Conti
**Pt:* Debora De Hoyos
Pt: Thomas J Delaney
Pt: Douglas A Doetsch
Pt: Robert M Dow Jr
Pt: John Ferrell
Pt: Eric John Finseth
Pt: Robert V Fitzsimmons
Pt: Joseph Goldstein
Board of Directors: David Staiano

D-U-N-S 00-690-0419
MAYER ELECTRIC SUPPLY CO INC
3405 4th Ave S, Birmingham, AL 35222-2300
Tel (205) 583-3500 *Founded/Ownrshp* 1979
Sales 737.3MM *EMP* 900
SIC 5063 5719 Electrical apparatus & equipment; Lighting fixtures; Electrical apparatus & equipment; Lighting fixtures, commercial & industrial; Lighting fixtures; Lighting, lamps & accessories
Ch Bd: Nancy Collat Goedecke
**Pr:* Glenn Goedecke
**Pr:* Wes Smith
**COO:* Charles A Collat Jr
VP: Sheila Dale
VP: Michael Likis
VP: Karen Rogers
Brnch Mgr: Mark Gorfuch
Brnch Mgr: Ken Swank
Opers Mgr: Jason Cates
Opers Mgr: Ron Reitzel

MAYER FABRICS
See MAYER-PAETZ INC

MAYER LAMINATES MA
See MEYER DECORATIVE SURFACES USA INC

D-U-N-S 00-182-7161
MAYER MALBIN CO INC (NY)
4101 36th Ave, Long Island City, NY 11101-1593
Tel (718) 937-5100 *Founded/Ownrshp* 1908, 1959
Sales 43.8MM^E *EMP* 45
SIC 5074 5084 Plumbing fittings & supplies; Heating equipment (hydronic); Industrial machinery & equipment; Plumbing fittings & supplies; Heating equipment (hydronic); Industrial machinery & equipment
Ch: Robert Gordon
**Pr:* Dan Gordon
**Treas:* Jonathan Gordon
Sales Exec: Marc Selden

MAYER POLLOCK STEEL
See POLLOCK CORP

D-U-N-S 00-235-8448
MAYER POLLOCK STEEL CORP
POLLOCK READING
(*Suby of* MAYER POLLOCK STEEL) ★
850 Industrial Hwy, Pottstown, PA 19464
Tel (610) 323-5500 *Founded/Ownrshp* 1959
Sales 38.6MM *EMP* 75
Accts Mcgladrey Llp Philadelphia P
SIC 5093 1795 Metal scrap & waste materials; Demolition, buildings & other structures; Metal scrap & waste materials; Demolition, buildings & other structures
Pr: Mayer Pollock II
**Sec:* Dennis J Owens
**VP:* Scott Orr

D-U-N-S 01-118-4090 IMP
MAYER TEXTILE MACHINE CORP
KARL MAYER NORTH AMERICA
310 N Chimney Rock Rd, Greensboro, NC 27409-1808
Tel (336) 294-1572 *Founded/Ownrshp* 1956
Sales 28.6MM^E *EMP* 30
SIC 5084 Textile machinery & equipment; Textile machinery & equipment
Pr: Gerd Rohmert
**Pr:* Anthony Hooimeije
**Treas:* Eileen Dombrowsky
**VP:* Mike Burke
**VP:* Gerhard Meuter
Board of Directors: Fritz Mayer, Ingo Mayer, Ulrich Mayer, Elke Mumtaz

D-U-N-S 18-774-6396
MAYER-JOHNSON LLC
2100 Wharton St Ste 400, Pittsburgh, PA 15203-1942
Tel (800) 588-4548 *Founded/Ownrshp* 2004
Sales 15.9MM^E *EMP* 300
SIC 5045 Computer software; Computer software

D-U-N-S 01-643-4201 IMP
MAYER-PAETZ INC
MAYER FABRICS
500 S Kitley Ave, Indianapolis, IN 46219-8233
Tel (317) 267-2626 *Founded/Ownrshp* 1961
Sales 25.9MM^E *EMP* 42
SIC 5131 Upholstery fabrics, woven; Upholstery fabrics, woven
Pr: Richard F Mayer Sr
**CFO:* Stephen T Mayer
**VP:* Richard F Mayer Jr
Exec: Nathan Fritz
Exec: Julie Maldonado
Mktg Mgr: Charles Krupp

D-U-N-S 07-926-2349
MAYERLING GROUP INC
12065 Creekview Rd, Granada Hills, CA 91344-2021
Tel (323) 707-4748 *Founded/Ownrshp* 2014
Sales 100.0MM *EMP* 37
SIC 8742 Hospital & health services consultant; Hospital & health services consultant
Pr: Abraham Abramian

MAYERS
See SOUTHERN TIER NEWS CO INC

D-U-N-S 00-184-9991 IMP
MAYERS ELECTRIC CO INC
4004 Erie Ct Ste B, Cincinnati, OH 45227-2167
Tel (513) 272-2900 *Founded/Ownrshp* 1948
Sales 22.1MM *EMP* 150
SIC 1731 General electrical contractor; General electrical contractor
Pr: Howard Mayers
**VP:* Jim Hopper

D-U-N-S 83-103-1658
MAYES EDUCATION INC
WALDORF COLLEGE
(*Suby of* COLUMBIA SOUTHERN EDUCATION GROUP INC) ★
106 S 6th St, Forest City, IA 50436-1713
Tel (641) 585-2450 *Founded/Ownrshp* 2008
Sales 20.2MM^E *EMP* 215
SIC 8221 Colleges & universities; Colleges & universities
CEO: Robert Mayes
Pr: Cindy Carter
**Treas:* Thomas Cooley
VP: Mason Harms
VP: Jessica McBride
Comm Dir: Heather Jordon
Off Admin: Tora Buffington
CIO: Ken Styron
Dir IT: Bruce Morgan
IT Man: Matt Hernes
Mktg Dir: Barbara Barrows

D-U-N-S 02-855-4327 IMP
MAYESH WHOLESALE FLORIST INC
5401 W 104th St, Los Angeles, CA 90045-6011
Tel (310) 342-0980 *Founded/Ownrshp* 1978
Sales 68.0MM^E *EMP* 150
SIC 5193 5992 Flowers, fresh; Florists; Flowers, fresh; Florists
CEO: Patrick Dahlson
**COO:* Cindie Boer
Brnch Mgr: Todd Smith

Genl Mgr: Isabelle Buckley
Genl Mgr: Tom Metzger
Off Admin: Theresa Gondek

MAYFAIR INFANTSWEAR
See TAWIL ASSOCIATES INC

D-U-N-S 05-015-9078 IMP
MAYFAIR INVESTMENT CO INC
PACKAGING MATERIALS COMPANY
222 Celtic Dr, Madison, AL 35758-1841
Tel (256) 772-2470 *Founded/Ownrshp* 1979
Sales 22.1MM^E *EMP* 115
SIC 2653 Boxes, corrugated: made from purchased materials; Boxes, corrugated: made from purchased materials
Pr: J Benny Nelson
**Sec:* William H Johnson Jr

D-U-N-S 00-534-5020 IMP
MAYFAIR PLASTICS INC
845 Dickerson Rd, Gaylord, MI 49735-9204
Tel (989) 732-2441 *Founded/Ownrshp* 1952
Sales 29.2MM^E *EMP* 85
SIC 3089 Injection molding of plastics
CEO: Carl R Janssens
**Pr:* Scott Weir
**VP:* Michelle Schwarz
VP: Mary Thrasher
Ql Cn Mgr: Jace Fredin
Ql Cn Mgr: Philip Kuusisto

D-U-N-S 07-775-2780
MAYFIELD CITY SCHOOL DISTRICT
1101 Som Center Rd, Cleveland, OH 44124-2006
Tel (440) 995-6800 *Founded/Ownrshp* 1903
Sales 83.0MM *EMP* 729
Accts Mary Taylor Cpa/Robert R Hin
SIC 8211 Public elementary school; Public junior high school; Public senior high school; Public elementary school; Public junior high school; Public senior high school
Treas: Scott Snyder
VP: George Hughes
IT Man: Darcy Klimkowski
HC Dir: Denise Cirino

D-U-N-S 00-333-7268 IMP
■ **MAYFIELD DAIRY FARMS LLC** (TN)
(*Suby of* DEAN HOLDING CO) ★
806 E Madison Ave, Athens, TN 37303-3858
Tel (423) 745-2151 *Founded/Ownrshp* 1930, 1990
Sales 253.8MM^E *EMP* 1,700
SIC 2026 2024 Milk processing (pasteurizing, homogenizing, bottling); Ice cream, packaged: molded, on sticks, etc.; Milk processing (pasteurizing, homogenizing, bottling); Ice cream, packaged: molded, on sticks, etc.
Off Mgr: Pat Purdy
Dir IT: Brett Miller
Plnt Mgr: Mark Howard

D-U-N-S 05-036-2490 IMP
MAYFIELD EQUIPMENT CO
RAINBOW AGRICULTURAL SERVICES
235 E Perkins St, Ukiah, CA 95482-4401
Tel (707) 462-2404 *Founded/Ownrshp* 1983
Sales 26.3MM^E *EMP* 88
SIC 5083 5191 5211 Irrigation equipment; Farm implements; Agricultural machinery; Farm equipment parts & supplies; Farm supplies; Animal feeds; Lumber & other building materials; Irrigation equipment; Farm implements; Agricultural machinery; Farm equipment parts & supplies; Farm supplies; Animal feeds; Lumber & other building materials
Pr: James Mayfield
**Ch:* John Mayfield Jr
**VP:* Ted Mayfield
Brnch Mgr: Keith Shields
Sales Asso: Todd Yandell
Snr Mgr: Mark Wedegaertner

D-U-N-S 17-448-2844
MAYFIELD GRAIN CO INC
313 N 9th St, Mayfield, KY 42066-1834
Tel (270) 247-1661 *Founded/Ownrshp* 1986
Sales 35.0MM *EMP* 15
SIC 5191 5153 5261 Fertilizer & fertilizer materials; Chemicals, agricultural; Grain elevators; Fertilizer; Fertilizer & fertilizer materials; Chemicals, agricultural; Grain elevators; Fertilizer
Pr: Donald Wray
**Sec:* William H Latimer
**VP:* Bobby Whitford

D-U-N-S 02-699-9250
MAYFIELD PAPER CO INC
1115 S Hill St, San Angelo, TX 76903-7395
Tel (325) 653-1444 *Founded/Ownrshp* 1971
Sales 68.0MM^E *EMP* 160
SIC 5113

MAYFIELD VILLAGE
See SKODA MINOTTI HOLDINGS LLC

D-U-N-S 05-616-8958 IMP/EXP
MAYFLOWER DISTRIBUTING CO INC
1155 Medallion Dr, Saint Paul, MN 55120-1220
Tel (651) 452-4892 *Founded/Ownrshp* 1981
Sales 53.4MM^E *EMP* 95
SIC 5199 5087 5169 Party favors, balloons, hats, etc.; Restaurant supplies; Gases, compressed & liquefied; Party favors, balloons, hats, etc.; Restaurant supplies; Gases, compressed & liquefied
CEO: Joe Abelovitz
**Pr:* Martin Abelovitz
**Sec:* Karole Abelovitz
VP: Steve Huston
Exec: Bruce Kane

MAYFLOWER HEALTH CENTER
See MAYFLOWER RETIREMENT CENTER INC

D-U-N-S 15-281-4794
MAYFLOWER RETIREMENT CENTER INC
MAYFLOWER HEALTH CENTER
1620 Mayflower Ct Ofc, Winter Park, FL 32792-2585
Tel (407) 672-1620 *Founded/Ownrshp* 1973
Sales 23.4MM *EMP* 205
Accts Moore Stephens Lovelace Pa
SIC 8051 6513 Skilled nursing care facilities; Retirement hotel operation; Skilled nursing care facilities; Retirement hotel operation
Pr: David McGuffin
CFO: Cheryl Lane
Dir Soc: Chris Rothenberger
Off Mgr: Agnes Predergast
Mktg Mgr: Glenda Bradham

D-U-N-S 60-610-4149
MAYFLOWER TEXTILE SERVICES CO
2601 W Lexington St, Baltimore, MD 21223-1441
Tel (410) 566-4460 *Founded/Ownrshp* 1985
Sales 27.3MM^E *EMP* 90
SIC 5023 7213 Linens & towels; Linen supply; Linens & towels; Linen supply
Pr: Mukul Mehta
**VP:* Niamat Kalra

D-U-N-S 09-719-0094
MAYFLOWER TOURS INC
FAITHFUL HOLIDAYS
1225 Warren Ave, Downers Grove, IL 60515-3597
Tel (630) 435-8500 *Founded/Ownrshp* 1979
Sales 23.8MM^E *EMP* 150
SIC 4725 Tour operators; Tour operators
Pr: John P Stachnik
**COO:* Nishendu Patel
**VP:* Ronald Smith
CIO: Nish Patel

D-U-N-S 00-693-7650
MAYFLOWER TRANSIT LLC
AERO MAYFLOWER TRANSIT COMPANY
(*Suby of* UNIGROUP INC) ★
1 Mayflower Dr, Fenton, MO 63026-2934
Tel (636) 305-4000 *Founded/Ownrshp* 1927
Sales 55.6MM^E *EMP* 500
SIC 4213 4731 4225 4226 Trucking, except local; Contract haulers; Domestic freight forwarding; Foreign freight forwarding; General warehousing & storage; Household goods, warehousing; Trucking, except local; Contract haulers; Domestic freight forwarding; Foreign freight forwarding; General warehousing & storage; Household goods, warehousing
CEO: James G Powers
**Ch Bd:* Gerald P Stadler
**Pr:* Pat Larch
**CFO:* Ralph Pregler

D-U-N-S 01-368-8727
■ **MAYFLOWER VEHICLE SYSTEMS LLC**
(*Suby of* COMMERCIAL VEHICLE GROUP INC) ★
629 Suth Battleground Ave, Kings Mountain, NC 28086
Tel (704) 937-4400 *Founded/Ownrshp* 2008
Sales 5.8MM^E *EMP* 336^E
SIC 3714 Motor vehicle parts & accessories
Prin: Darryl Rowlins
Exec: Bob Osburn
Dir IT: Randall Toney

MAYFLWER NRSING RHBLTATION CTR
See OAKWOOD LIVING CENTERS OF MASSACHUSETTS INC

D-U-N-S 14-905-0127
MAYFRAN HOLDINGS INC
6650 Beta Dr, Cleveland, OH 44143-2352
Tel (440) 461-4100 *Founded/Ownrshp* 2004
Sales 59.8MM^E *EMP* 290^E
SIC 5084 3535 3568 2296 Industrial machinery & equipment; Belt conveyor systems, general industrial use; Power transmission equipment; Tire cord & fabrics; Industrial machinery & equipment; Belt conveyor systems, general industrial use; Power transmission equipment; Tire cord & fabrics
Ch Bd: J D Sullivan
Dir IT: Kevin Hatridge
IT Man: Linda Avery

D-U-N-S 10-786-2724 IMP
MAYFRAN INTERNATIONAL INC
(*Suby of* TSUBAKIMOTO CHAIN CO.)
6650 Beta Dr, Cleveland, OH 44143-2352
Tel (440) 461-4100 *Founded/Ownrshp* 2012
Sales 62.6MM *EMP* 250^E
Accts Deloitte & Touche Llp Clevela
SIC 3535 Belt conveyor systems, general industrial use; Belt conveyor systems, general industrial use
Pr: Naoshige Sakai
Dir IT: Tom Neibecker
Dir IT: Mike Pfaff
IT Man: Dave Wiley
Netwrk Mgr: Erik Silders
Mtls Mgr: Robert Clinton
Manager: Teresa Spadaro
Opers Mgr: Larry Sorrels
VP Mktg: Richard Westfall
VP Sls: Mac Dalton
Manager: William Bowen

D-U-N-S 16-854-8662 IMP
MAYLINE CO LLC
(*Suby of* MAYLINE INVESTMENTS INC) ★
619 N Commerce St, Sheboygan, WI 53081-3901
Tel (920) 457-5537 *Founded/Ownrshp* 1999
Sales 69.0MM *EMP* 250
SIC 2521 Wood office furniture; Wood office furniture
Pr: Allan Klotsche
**CFO:* Daniel Kotynski
VP Opers: Mark Troyer
Mktg Mgr: Lori Lockwood

D-U-N-S 00-607-0775 IMP/EXP
MAYLINE INVESTMENTS INC
555 Skokie Blvd, Northbrook, IL 60062-2812
Tel (847) 948-9340 *Founded/Ownrshp* 2007
Sales 97.0MM^E *EMP* 401
SIC 2522 2521 Office furniture, except wood; Office cabinets & filing drawers: except wood; Panel systems & partitions, office: except wood; Wood office furniture; Office furniture, except wood; Office cabinets & filing drawers: except wood; Panel systems & partitions, office: except wood; Wood office furniture
Ch Bd: Charles Barancik
**Pr:* Paul Simons
**Treas:* Michael E Gronli
**Ex VP:* Chris Mc Namee
**Ex VP:* Eric Volcheff
**VP:* Don Clements
S&M/VP: Rod Ganiard

D-U-N-S 00-193-6533
MAYMEAD FARMS INC
1995 Roan Creek Rd, Mountain City, TN 37683-7022
Tel (423) 727-2000 *Founded/Ownrshp* 1976
Sales 100.0MM^E *EMP* 6^E
SIC 0212 Beef cattle except feedlots
Pr: Wally B Roark
**Sec:* Mae Mount Roark
**VP:* Thomas G Purpur

D-U-N-S 00-337-8320
MAYMEAD INC (TN)
(*Suby of* MAYMEAD FARMS INC) ★
1995 Roan Creek Rd, Mountain City, TN 37683-7022
Tel (423) 727-2000 *Founded/Ownrshp* 1930
Sales 100.0MM *EMP* 91^E
SIC 1611 2951 Highway & street paving contractor; Asphalt paving mixtures & blocks
Pr: Wiley B Roark
**Pr:* Barton K Mount
**Sec:* Mae Mount Roark
Brnch Mgr: David Worley
Genl Mgr: Tom Reece
IT Man: John Harbin

D-U-N-S 93-850-1830
MAYMEAD MATERIALS INC
1995 Roan Creek Rd, Mountain City, TN 37683-7022
Tel (423) 727-2000 *Founded/Ownrshp* 1994
Sales 58.2MM^E *EMP* 195^E
SIC 5032 Stone, crushed or broken; Stone, crushed or broken
Pr: Barton K Mount
**Sec:* May M Roark
**VP:* Wiley B Roark

D-U-N-S 12-089-9422
MAYNARD COOPER & GALE PC
1901 6th Ave N Ste 2400, Birmingham, AL 35203-4604
Tel (205) 254-1000 *Founded/Ownrshp* 1984
Sales 59.1MM^E *EMP* 340
SIC 8111 Specialized law offices, attorneys; General practice attorney, lawyer; Specialized law offices, attorneys; General practice attorney, lawyer
Pr: Mark L Drew
**Treas:* Fournier J Gale III
Ofcr: Sarah Stewart
**VP:* N Lee Cooper
Exec: Walt Graham
Dir IT: Vitale Buford
Dir IT: Jason Dover
IT Man: Leanne Bains
IT Man: Lee Cooper
Counsel: W Bailey
Counsel: Rebekah Graham

D-U-N-S 12-025-8579 EXP
MAYNARD INC
7175 S Mcguire St, Fayetteville, AR 72704-5237
Tel (479) 443-6677 *Founded/Ownrshp* 1982
Sales 27.0MM^E *EMP* 125
SIC 3469 Machine parts, stamped or pressed metal
Pr: Joe Maynard
Ql Cn Mgr: Fred Maples

D-U-N-S 80-562-6020
MAYNARD SELECT LLC
617 Norris Ave, Nashville, TN 37204-3707
Tel (615) 255-0603 *Founded/Ownrshp* 2006
Sales 26.0MM^E *EMP* 100
SIC 1711 Plumbing, heating, air-conditioning contractors
CEO: Pete Zabaski
Sales Asso: Doug Amsterdam

D-U-N-S 00-608-5914 IMP/EXP
MAYNARD STEEL CASTING CO INC
2856 S 27th St, Milwaukee, WI 53215-3603
Tel (414) 645-0440 *Founded/Ownrshp* 1912
Sales 36.6MM^E *EMP* 205^E
SIC 3325 Alloy steel castings, except investment; Alloy steel castings, except investment
Pr: Michael Wabiszewski
Ch: Edmund D Wabiszewski
VP: Mike Barber
VP: Greg Graf
VP: Bruce Jorgensen
VP: Eugene O'Kelly
Telecom Ex: Bob Thill
Snr Mgr: Hathibelagal Roshan

D-U-N-S 05-964-4930
MAYNARDS ELECTRIC SUPPLY INC
3445 Winton Pl Ste 107, Rochester, NY 14623-2982
Tel (585) 272-0860 *Founded/Ownrshp* 1956
Sales 67.5MM^E *EMP* 106
SIC 5063 5719 Electrical construction materials; Lighting fixtures; Electrical construction materials; Lighting fixtures
Pr: Bruce Hellman
**VP:* Glenn Hellman

D-U-N-S 10-226-7291
MAYNARDS FOOD CENTER OF WESTBROOK INC
127 N Elk St, Elkton, SD 57026-2147
Tel (605) 542-8771 *Founded/Ownrshp* 1982
Sales 25.9MM^E *EMP* 259
SIC 5411 Grocery stores, independent; Grocery stores, independent
Pr: Maynard Kramer
**Treas:* Gary Thompson
VP: Brian Kramer
Genl Mgr: Gary Carleson
Off Mgr: Elaine Van Dyke

D-U-N-S 15-272-6857
MAYNE & MERTZ INC
505 N Big Spring St # 300, Midland, TX 79701-4301
Tel (432) 683-1600 *Founded/Ownrshp* 1982
Sales 33.1MM *EMP* 14
SIC 1382 Oil & gas exploration services; Oil & gas exploration services
Pr: W Taylor Mayne
**VP:* Len P Mertz

D-U-N-S 86-722-0261
MAYNE PHARMA INC
METRICS, INC.
(*Suby of* MAYNE PHARMA GROUP LIMITED)
1240 Sugg Pkwy, Greenville, NC 27834-9006
Tel (252) 752-3800 *Founded/Ownrshp* 2012
Sales 85.0MM *EMP* 350^E
SIC 5122 2834 Commercial physical research; Pharmaceuticals; Pharmaceutical preparations
Pr: Stefan Cross
**CFO:* Wes Edwards
Ex VP: John Ross
VP: Jeffrey Basham
VP: Jerry Sakowski
Cmptr Lab: Anthony Pipho
Cmptr Lab: Nicole Wilkerson
Sfty Mgr: Wesley Thigpen
Sls Dir: Tom Salus

D-U-N-S 09-573-8209
MAYO AVIATION INC
7735 S Peoria St, Englewood, CO 80112-4102
Tel (303) 792-4000 *Founded/Ownrshp* 1978
Sales 22.2MM^E *EMP* 85
SIC 4522 4581 7363 4512 Air transportation, nonscheduled; Ambulance services, air; Aircraft servicing & repairing; Temporary help service; Air transportation, scheduled
CEO: Bill Mayo
**Ch:* Gwendolyn Mayo
Exec: William Jmayo
Sfty Dirs: Mark Wulber
Snr Mgr: Scott Anderson
Snr Mgr: Wade Tefft

MAYO CLINIC
See MAYO FOUNDATION FOR MEDICAL EDUCATION AND RESEARCH

D-U-N-S 16-714-1923 IMP
MAYO CLINIC
MAYO CLINIC ROCHESTER
200 1st St Sw, Rochester, MN 55905-0002
Tel (507) 284-2511 *Founded/Ownrshp* 1819
Sales 9.4MMM *EMP* 67,000
SIC 8062 8733 8071 8011 General medical & surgical hospitals; Noncommercial research organizations; Medical laboratories; Offices & clinics of medical doctors; General medical & surgical hospitals; Noncommercial research organizations; Medical laboratories; Offices & clinics of medical doctors
Pr: John H Noseworthy
**CFO:* Kedrick D Adkins Jr
CFO: Jeff Bolton
CFO: Bradley Schmidt
**VP:* Jeffrey W Bolton
**VP:* Wyatt W Decker
**VP:* William C Rupp
**Prin:* Denis A Cortese
**Prin:* Paul Haines
QA Dir: Stephen Swenson
IT Man: Shashi Dewan

D-U-N-S 15-366-5211 IMP
MAYO CLINIC ARIZONA
MAYO CLINIC HOSPITAL
(*Suby of* MAYO CLINIC) ★
13400 E Shea Blvd, Scottsdale, AZ 85259-5499
Tel (480) 301-8000 *Founded/Ownrshp* 1986
Sales 258.2MM^E *EMP* 2,800
SIC 8011 Primary care medical clinic; Physicians' office, including specialists; Primary care medical clinic; Physicians' office, including specialists
Ch Bd: Wyatt W Decker MD
V Ch: Amy Vrable
CFO: Mike Vuhl
CFO: Boris Zavalkovskiy
Dir IT: Maureen Rector
IT Man: John Custer
Surgeon: Alyssa D Baliad Chapital
Ansthlgy: Froukje M Beynen
Ansthlgy: Andrew D Gorlin
Ansthlgy: Frances L Hu
Plas Surg: Deborah S Bash

D-U-N-S 07-149-5303
MAYO CLINIC HEALTH SYSTEM - RED WING
FAIRVIEW REDWING HEALTH SVCS
(*Suby of* MAYO CLINIC) ★
701 Hewitt Blvd, Red Wing, MN 55066-2848
Tel (651) 267-5000 *Founded/Ownrshp* 2012
Sales 99.0MM *EMP* 760
SIC 8062 General medical & surgical hospitals; General medical & surgical hospitals
CEO: Tom Witt
CFO: Michael Larson
Chf Mktg O: Jack Alexander MD
VP: Jan Graner
VP: Judy Treharne
Sales Asso: Jessica Hinckley
Sales Asso: Brenda Stephens
Surgeon: Joshua Bodie
Surgeon: Matthew Eich
Obsttrcn: Seth Heckman
Obsttrcn: Seanna Thompson

D-U-N-S 17-019-1662
MAYO CLINIC HEALTH SYSTEM -ST JAMES
(*Suby of* MAYO CLINIC HOSPITAL-ROCHESTER) ★
1025 Marsh St, Mankato, MN 56001-4752
Tel (507) 625-4031 *Founded/Ownrshp* 1984
Sales 158.9M^E *EMP* 1,300
SIC 8082 Home health care services; Home health care services
Pr: Greg Kutcher
Ofcr: Jerome Crest
VP: Richard Grace
Dir Sec: Ken Combs
MIS Dir: Tom Borowski
Info Man: Sarah Daniels
Pathlgst: Dennis Gremel
Doctor: Glenn S Harman
Doctor: Ron S Mith

Doctor: David T Owens
Doctor: Gregory Taylor
Board of Directors: Bob Weiss

D-U-N-S 09-858-1689
MAYO CLINIC HEALTH SYSTEM IN WAYCROSS INC
(*Suby of* MAYO CLINIC JACKSONVILLE (A NON-PROFIT CORP)) ★
1900 Tebeau St, Waycross, GA 31501-6357
Tel (912) 283-3030 *Founded/Ownrshp* 2012
Sales 141.4MM *EMP* 1,300
SIC 8062 8051 General medical & surgical hospitals; Skilled nursing care facilities; General medical & surgical hospitals; Skilled nursing care facilities
CEO: Kenneth T Calamia
Ofcr: Robert Trimm
Off Mgr: Kelli Delk
Off Mgr: Cheryl Tatum
IT Man: Amanda Baldwin
IT Man: Cheryl Dubose
Surgeon: Thomas Wehmann
Ansthlgy: Victor Aranda
Diag Rad: Brian Singleton
Pgrm Dir: Angela Jenkins-Jacobs

D-U-N-S 07-649-9565
MAYO CLINIC HEALTH SYSTEM—OWATONNA
(*Suby of* MAYO CLINIC) ★
2200 Nw 26th St, Owatonna, MN 55060-5503
Tel (507) 451-1120 *Founded/Ownrshp* 2009
Sales 85.1MM *EMP* 350
SIC 8011 Clinic, operated by physicians; Clinic, operated by physicians
Pr: Brian Bunkers
Surgeon: K Dean Olsen
Doctor: Kari E Bunkers MD
Doctor: Anthony F Chou MD
Doctor: Greg Jones
Doctor: Henry Krahn
Doctor: Kiernan J Minehan MD
Doctor: Vikas S Mittal MD
Doctor: Gerard Ohalloran
Doctor: Steven J Thompson MD
Doctor: Linda Wallner MD

D-U-N-S 15-758-5043
MAYO CLINIC HEALTH SYSTEM-ALBERT LEA AND AUSTIN
(*Suby of* MAYO CLINIC HOSPITAL-ROCHESTER) ★
404 W Fountain St, Albert Lea, MN 56007-2437
Tel (507) 373-2384 *Founded/Ownrshp* 2005
Sales 146.7M^E *EMP* 1,200^E
SIC 8062 8069 8051 8063 8011 General medical & surgical hospitals; Substance abuse hospitals; Skilled nursing care facilities; Psychiatric hospitals; Clinic, operated by physicians; General medical & surgical hospitals; Substance abuse hospitals; Skilled nursing care facilities; Psychiatric hospitals; Clinic, operated by physicians
CEO: Mark Ciota
CFO: Scott Rafferty
VP: Ronald Harmon
**VP:* Bruce Mairose

D-U-N-S 07-652-0667
MAYO CLINIC HEALTH SYSTEM-AUSTIN
(*Suby of* MAYO CLINIC HOSPITAL-ROCHESTER) ★
1000 1st Dr Nw, Austin, MN 55912-2941
Tel (507) 433-7351 *Founded/Ownrshp* 2005
Sales 120.4MM *EMP* 778
SIC 8399 Health systems agency; Health systems agency
Pr: David Agerter
CFO: Dick Graber
CFO: Kristen Johnson
CFO: Paula A Nelson
VP: Sarah Daniels
Netwrk Mgr: Shawn Riley
VP Opers: Laura Lowe
Nutrtnst: Tianna Bechly
Doctor: James Burke MD
Doctor: Waclaw Wedzina
Phys Thrpy: Debra Berg

D-U-N-S 09-280-0689
MAYO CLINIC HEALTH SYSTEM-CANNON FALLS
(*Suby of* MAYO CLINIC HOSPITAL-ROCHESTER) ★
32021 County 24 Blvd, Cannon Falls, MN 55009-5003
Tel (507) 263-3951 *Founded/Ownrshp* 1958
Sales 26.6MM *EMP* 183
SIC 8062 General medical & surgical hospitals; General medical & surgical hospitals
Pr: Thomas Witt MD
VP: Carol Weis
Dir Lab: Gloria Nepreud

D-U-N-S 02-329-6390
MAYO CLINIC HEALTH SYSTEM-EAU CLAIRE CLINIC INC (WI)
(*Suby of* MAYO CLINIC HOSPITAL-ROCHESTER) ★
1400 Bellinger St, Eau Claire, WI 54703-5222
Tel (715) 838-5222 *Founded/Ownrshp* 1992
Sales 489.0M^E *EMP* 4,000
Accts Wipfli Llp Eau Claire Wiscon
SIC 8062 General medical & surgical hospitals; General medical & surgical hospitals
CEO: Dr Randall Linton
Off Mgr: Janet Goodwin
Surgeon: Aundrea Rainville
Obsttrcn: Jennifer Bantz
Obsttrcn: Blenda Yun
Doctor: Robert C Peck

D-U-N-S 06-815-7601
MAYO CLINIC HEALTH SYSTEM-EAU CLAIRE HOSPITAL INC
(*Suby of* MAYO CLINIC HOSPITAL-ROCHESTER) ★
1221 Whipple St, Eau Claire, WI 54703-5200
Tel (715) 838-3311 *Founded/Ownrshp* 2002
Sales 11.2MM^E *EMP* 1,290^E
SIC 8062 8011 General medical & surgical hospitals; Offices & clinics of medical doctors; General medical & surgical hospitals; Offices & clinics of medical doctors

Pr: Dr Randall Linton
Dir Vol: Victoria Zehms
VP: Dennis Olson
Dir Rad: Gregory C Brickner
Dir Rad: Scott Cole
Dir Rad: Suzan Degan
VP Admn: Edward Wittrock
Ex Dir: Patricia Pope
IT Man: Josh Anderson
Mktg Mgr: Deborah Campbell
Doctor: Christine Blink

D-U-N-S 11-427-6769
MAYO CLINIC HEALTH SYSTEM-FRANCISCAN HEALTHCARE INC
(*Suby of* MAYO CLINIC HOSPITAL-ROCHESTER) ★
700 West Ave S Fl 1, La Crosse, WI 54601-4783
Tel (608) 785-0940 *Founded/Ownrshp* 1871
Sales 72.0M *EMP* 3,445
SIC 8062 8051 General medical & surgical hospitals; Convalescent home with continuous nursing care; General medical & surgical hospitals; Convalescent home with continuous nursing care
CEO: Timothy Johnson MD
Dir Vol: Elaine George
**CEO:* Robert Nesse MD
**CFO:* Tom Tiggelaar
CFO: Tom Tiggelar
VP: Diane Holmay
**VP:* Ron Paczkowski
Dir Lab: Gordon Triebs
Dir Rad: Lawrence Furlong
Dir Rad: Joseph Hooyman
Dir Rad: Martin Nelson
Dir Rad: Jonathan Uy

D-U-N-S 07-971-3459
MAYO CLINIC HEALTH SYSTEM-FRANCISCAN MEDICAL CENTER INC
700 West Ave S, La Crosse, WI 54601-4783
Tel (608) 785-0940 *Founded/Ownrshp* 1883
Sales 187.5MM^E *EMP* 3,300
SIC 8062 General medical & surgical hospitals; General medical & surgical hospitals
Pr: Robert Nesse
CFO: Mike Buhl
**CFO:* Thomas Tiggelaar
Snr Mgr: Dennis Costakos

D-U-N-S 09-230-3767
MAYO CLINIC HEALTH SYSTEM-LAKE CITY (MN)
MAYO CLINIC-SAINT MARYS HOSPIT
(*Suby of* MAYO CLINIC HOSPITAL-ROCHESTER) ★
500 W Grant St, Lake City, MN 55041-1143
Tel (651) 345-1100 *Founded/Ownrshp* 1918, 2005
Sales 44.4MM *EMP* 1^E
SIC 8011 Offices & clinics of medical doctors
CEO: Tom Witt
Dir Recs: Jill Deboef
Dir Rx: Kelly Kennedy
Dir Rx: Ryan Kennedy
Psych: Gary Feigal
Phys Thrpy: Marcia Walker

D-U-N-S 06-479-1809
MAYO CLINIC HEALTH SYSTEM-MANKATO
(*Suby of* MAYO CLINIC HOSPITAL-ROCHESTER) ★
1025 Marsh St, Mankato, MN 56001-4752
Tel (507) 625-4031 *Founded/Ownrshp* 1968
Sales 319.4MM *EMP* 2,830^E
SIC 8062 General medical & surgical hospitals; General medical & surgical hospitals
Pr: Gregory R Kutcher
CFO: Ryan Ashlando
VP: Jerome Crest
VP: Richard Grace
Pathlgst: Tina Carns
Pathlgst: Jose Crespo
Pathlgst: Eric Evans
Doctor: Kingsley Iheasirim
Doctor: Susan Pearson
Doctor: Andrew Reeves

D-U-N-S 06-819-7813
MAYO CLINIC HEALTH SYSTEM-OAKRIDGE INC
MAYO CLINIC-SAINT MARYS HOSPIT
(*Suby of* MAYO CLINIC HOSPITAL-ROCHESTER) ★
13025 8th St, Osseo, WI 54758-7634
Tel (715) 597-3121 *Founded/Ownrshp* 1963
Sales 21.3MM *EMP* 190
SIC 8051 Skilled nursing care facilities; Skilled nursing care facilities
Dir Rad: Kathy Sieg
Dir Sec: Steve Roach
HC Dir: Lisa Iverson

D-U-N-S 09-789-7045
MAYO CLINIC HEALTH SYSTEM-RED CEDAR INC
MAYO CLINIC-SAINT MARYS HOSPIT
(*Suby of* MAYO CLINIC HOSPITAL-ROCHESTER) ★
2321 Stout Rd, Menomonie, WI 54751-7003
Tel (715) 233-7500 *Founded/Ownrshp* 1976
Sales 95.4MM *EMP* 300
SIC 8062 General medical & surgical hospitals; General medical & surgical hospitals
CEO: Hank Simpson
Chf Rad: Janel Glantz
**CFO:* Jeanie Lubinsky
Dir Lab: Barbara Fischer
Dir Rx: John Miller
Genl Mgr: Paul Mitchell
Dir IT: Frank Wrogg
Psych: Steven Siegle
Obsttrcn: Cara Syth
Obsttrcn: John Witgert
Podiatrist: Jeffery Giesking

D-U-N-S 08-345-4108
MAYO CLINIC HEALTH SYSTEMS (MN)
301 2nd St Ne, New Prague, MN 56071-1709
Tel (952) 758-4431 *Founded/Ownrshp* 1992
Sales 36.9MM^E *EMP* 280
SIC 8062 General medical & surgical hospitals; General medical & surgical hospitals
CEO: Marry Climp

**CEO:* Rob Nesse
Ofcr: Anna Herrmann
DP Exec: Chris Tietz
Surgeon: Bret Cardwell

D-U-N-S 12-035-4782
MAYO CLINIC HEALTH SYTEM-WASECA
WASECA MEDICAL CENTER
(*Suby of* MAYO CLINIC HEALTH SYSTEM-MANKATO) ★
501 State St N, Waseca, MN 56093-2811
Tel (507) 835-1210 *Founded/Ownrshp* 1998
Sales 21.7MM *EMP* 200
SIC 8062 General medical & surgical hospitals; General medical & surgical hospitals
Ex VP: Michael Milbrath
Phys Thrpy: Ryan Buchele
Board of Directors: Virgil Christenson, Deb Coo K, Jerry Crest, James Day MD, Neil Fruechte, James Rundquist Dvm, Tom West

MAYO CLINIC HOSPITAL
See MAYO CLINIC ARIZONA

D-U-N-S 00-647-1700
MAYO CLINIC HOSPITAL-ROCHESTER (MN)
MAYO CLINIC-SAINT MARYS HOSP
(*Suby of* MAYO CLINIC) ★
200 1st St Sw, Rochester, MN 55905-0002
Tel (507) 284-2511 *Founded/Ownrshp* 1919
Sales 988.0MM *EMP* 32,271
SIC 8011 8062 8071 8733 8221

D-U-N-S 15-322-3151 IMP
MAYO CLINIC JACKSONVILLE (A NONPROFIT CORP)
SCOTT LYNCH MD
(*Suby of* MAYO CLINIC) ★
4500 San Pablo Rd S, Jacksonville, FL 32224-1865
Tel (904) 953-2000 *Founded/Ownrshp* 1986
Sales 657.5MM *EMP* 5,500
SIC 8062 General medical & surgical hospitals; General medical & surgical hospitals
Ch Bd: Marilyn Carlson Nelson
**CEO:* William C Rupp
**CFO:* Mary J Hoffman
Dir IT: Paul Lanko
IT Man: Goutam Behera
IT Man: Carla Jerdee
Sys Mgr: Kevin Hoot
Doctor: Gerardo Colon-Otero MD

MAYO CLINIC ROCHESTER
See MAYO CLINIC

MAYO CLINIC-SAINT MARYS HOSP
See MAYO CLINIC HOSPITAL-ROCHESTER

MAYO CLINIC-SAINT MARYS HOSPIT
See MAYO CLINIC HEALTH SYSTEM-OAKRIDGE INC

MAYO CLINIC-SAINT MARYS HOSPIT
See MAYO CLINIC HEALTH SYSTEM-RED CEDAR INC

MAYO CLINIC-SAINT MARYS HOSPIT
See MAYO CLINIC HEALTH SYSTEM-LAKE CITY

MAYO CLINIC-SAINT MARYS HOSPIT
See CHARTERHOUSE INC

D-U-N-S 10-849-9682
MAYO COLLABORATIVE SERVICES LLC
MAYO MEDICAL LABORATORIES
(*Suby of* MAYO CLINIC) ★
3050 Superior Dr Nw, Rochester, MN 55905-1770
Tel (507) 284-4293 *Founded/Ownrshp* 1978
Sales 31.0MM^E *EMP* 759^E
SIC 8071 Medical laboratories; Medical laboratories
Ch: Linda G Alvarado
**CEO:* John H Noseworthy MD
**COO:* Brian Meade
CFO: Jeffery Bolton
**Treas:* Jeff Froisland
Ofcr: Alan Schilmoeller
**VP:* Marie E Brown
Dir Lab: Barb Fischer
Dir Sec: David Steen
IT Man: Terry Johnson
IT Man: Gary Walker
Board of Directors: Brian Meade, Rebecca S Bahn MD, James Rogers, Marie Brown, Daniel Roline, Franklin Cockerill, Nan B Sawyer, Richard Ehman MD, Andre Terzic MD, Jeff Froisland, John Wald MD, Richard Helmers MD, Mary Jo Williamson, David Herbert, Walter R Wilson MD, Andras Khoors MD, Hilary Matthews

D-U-N-S 09-231-6967
MAYO CONSTRUCTION CO INC
13960 Highway 5, Cavalier, ND 58220-9502
Tel (701) 265-8438 *Founded/Ownrshp* 1978
Sales 80.0MM *EMP* 125
SIC 1611 General contractor, highway & street construction; General contractor, highway & street construction
Pr: Gregory Mayo
**Sec:* Trevor Christianson
Sfty Dirs: John Korpes
Mtls Mgr: Brian Mickelson

D-U-N-S 79-001-5101 IMP
MAYO FOUNDATION FOR MEDICAL EDUCATION AND RESEARCH
MAYO CLINIC
(*Suby of* MAYO CLINIC) ★
200 1st St Sw, Rochester, MN 55905-0001
Tel (507) 284-2511 *Founded/Ownrshp* 1984
Sales 1.0MMM *EMP* 52,700
SIC 8741 Hospital management; Hospital management
Pr: William Litchy
COO: Gaile Hansen
Ofcr: Nikiki J Hager
Ofcr: Beth Knowles
Exec: Katina Bjorkstrand
Dir Lab: Nancy Moody
Dir Rad: Gerald Tabaka
Dir Rx: John Kranze

Dir Rx: Eric Nelson
Dir Rx: Kim Rux
Chf Nrs Of: Jan M Hofer

D-U-N-S 11-123-3602
MAYO GROUP DEVELOPMENT LLC
28 Damrell St Ste 200, Boston, MA 02127-3076
Tel (617) 983-5120 *Founded/Ownrshp* 2003
Sales 28.4MM^E *EMP* 100^E
SIC 6552 6531 Subdividers & developers; Rental agent, real estate
Pr: John A McGrail
**Genl Couns:* Taran Grigsby
Genl Couns: Lauren Gustafson

D-U-N-S 00-318-8018 IMP
MAYO KNITTING MILL INC (NC)
2204 W Austin St, Tarboro, NC 27886-2467
Tel (252) 823-3101 *Founded/Ownrshp* 1931
Sales 57.0MM^E *EMP* 571
SIC 2252 5949 2251 Socks; Sewing, needlework & piece goods; Women's hosiery, except socks; Socks; Sewing, needlework & piece goods; Women's hosiery, except socks
Pr: Ben C Mayo II
**VP:* Bryan T Mayo
**VP:* C W Mayo IV

MAYO MEDICAL LABORATORIES
See MAYO COLLABORATIVE SERVICES LLC

D-U-N-S 00-805-9867 IMP
MAYO MFG CORP
4101 Terry St, Texarkana, TX 75501-6759
Tel (903) 838-0518 *Founded/Ownrshp* 1965
Sales 24.9MM^E *EMP* 130
SIC 2512 Upholstered household furniture; Living room furniture: upholstered on wood frames
Pr: Michael L Mayo
**VP:* Patrick J Mayo
**VP:* Don G McCoy
Dir IT: Ken Cheatham

MAYO REGIONAL HOSPITAL
See HOSPITAL ADMINISTRATION DISTRICT 4

D-U-N-S 00-233-1044
MAYO RESOURCES INC (KY)
Fl 2 Rr 292, Lovely, KY 41231
Tel (606) 395-6841 *Founded/Ownrshp* 1987
Sales 50.0MM *EMP* 90
SIC 1222 Bituminous coal-underground mining; Bituminous coal-underground mining
Pr: Jim Both
**Sec:* Ted McGinnis
Off Mgr: Gladyes Parsons

D-U-N-S 02-907-7430
MAYOCLINIC ASSOC
1353 9th Ave Se, Rochester, MN 55904-5374
Tel (507) 281-4711 *Founded/Ownrshp* 2001
Sales 43.1MM^E *EMP* 577^E
SIC 8731 Biological research
Owner: Daniel Mayoclinic
Acupntre: Frank Lan
Doctor: Karen Cowan
Doctor: Margaret Grenisen
Doctor: Johanna Iturrino
Doctor: Dayna Schwarz
Doctor: Joseph Skemp
Assoc Ed: Jeffrey Hosenpud

MAYOR
See TOWN OF STRATFORD

MAYOR AND CITY COUNCIL OF CUMB
See CITY OF CUMBERLAND

D-U-N-S 05-391-9510
MAYOR AND CITY COUNCIL OF OCEAN CITY
TOWN OF OCEAN CITY
301 N Baltimore Ave, Ocean City, MD 21842-3922
Tel (410) 289-8221 *Founded/Ownrshp* 1860
Sales NA *EMP* 1,385
Accts Sb & Company Llc Hunt Valley
SIC 9121 City council; ; City council;
Dir Risk M: Eric Lagstrom
Dir: Matthew Margotta
IT Man: James Deptula
Pr Dir: Donna Abbott

MAYOR OFFICE
See CITY OF DANBURY

MAYORGA COFFEE
See MAYORGA ORGANICS LLC

D-U-N-S 82-603-9815 IMP
MAYORGA ORGANICS LLC
MAYORGA COFFEE
1029 E Gude Dr 110, Rockville, MD 20850-1333
Tel (301) 315-8093 *Founded/Ownrshp* 2007
Sales 51.2MM^E *EMP* 50
SIC 5149 5812 7389 2095 Coffee & tea; Coffee, green or roasted; Contract food services; Brokers' services; Roasted coffee; Coffee & tea; Coffee, green or roasted; Contract food services; Brokers' services; Roasted coffee
CEO: Kerry Mayorga
**Pr:* Martin Mayorga
VP: Matthew Brown
Dir Bus: Andy Rein
VP Opers: Roger Fransen
VP Opers: Eric Rosenthal

D-U-N-S 96-723-4043
MAYORS AGAINST ILLEGAL GUNS ACTION FUND
3rd Ave Fl 16, New York, NY 10022
Tel (212) 583-6001 *Founded/Ownrshp* 2011
Sales 36.0MM *EMP* 2^E
SIC 5941 Firearms
**Prin:* Diane Gubelli

D-U-N-S 60-688-8431
MAYORS FUND TO ADVANCE NEW YORK CITY
253 Broadway Fl 8, New York, NY 10007-2327
Tel (212) 788-7794 *Founded/Ownrshp* 2005

Sales 26.6MM *EMP* 2
Accts Mcgladrey Llp New York Ny
SIC 8621 Professional membership organizations; Professional membership organizations
Pr: Meagan Sheekey
Ex Dir: Darren Blockh

D-U-N-S 11-861-1607 IMP/EXP
MAYORS JEWELERS INC
BIRKS & MAYORS
(*Suby of* GROUPE BIRKS INC)
5870 Hiatus Rd, Tamarac, FL 33321-6424
Tel (954) 590-9000 *Founded/Ownrshp* 2003
Sales 63.5MM^E *EMP* 384
SIC 5944 Jewelry stores; Clocks; Jewelry stores; Clocks
Ch Bd: Lorenzo Rossi Di Montelera
**CEO:* Jean Christophe Bedos
**COO:* Joseph A Keifer III
**CFO:* Michael Rabinovitch
**Ch:* Thomas A Andruskevich
Ex VP: Joseph Keifer
**Ex VP:* Deborah Nicodemus
Sr VP: Aida Alvarez
VP: Frank Cimilluca
VP: Karen Formica
VP: Eva Hartling
VP: Albert Rahm

MAYOR'S OFFICE
See CITY OF CHICAGO

MAYOR'S OFFICE
See COUNTY OF WILLIAMSON

MAYOR'S OFFICE
See CITY OF DETROIT

MAYOR'S OFFICE
See CARTER COUNTY TENNESSEE

MAYOR'S OFFICE
See CITY OF COLUMBUS

MAYOR'S OFFICE
See CITY OF BALTIMORE

MAYOR'S OFFICE
See CITY OF TORRINGTON

MAYOR'S OFFICE
See CITY OF ALLENTOWN

MAYOR'S OFFICE
See CITY OF PROVIDENCE

MAYOR'S OFFICE
See CITY OF MIAMI

MAYOR'S OFFICE
See CITY OF NEW ROCHELLE

MAYOR'S OFFICE
See COUNTY OF SALT LAKE

MAYOR'S OFFICE
See COUNTY OF HAMILTON

MAYOR'S OFFICE
See CITY OF MIDDLETOWN

MAYOR'S OFFICE
See CITY OF TALLMADGE

MAYOR'S OFFICE
See COUNTY OF COCKE

MAYOR'S OFFICE
See CITY OF NEW IBERIA

MAYOR'S OFFICE
See CITY OF NIAGARA FALLS

MAYORS OFFICE
See CITY OF LOGANSPORT

MAYOR'S OFFICE
See CITY OF NILES

MAYOR'S OFFICE
See MUNICIPIO DE TOA ALTA

MAYOR'S OFFICE
See TOWN OF MADISON

D-U-N-S 83-020-7507
MAYPRO GROUP LLC
2975 Westchester Ave, Purchase, NY 10577-2518
Tel (914) 251-0701 *Founded/Ownrshp* 2006
Sales 61.3MM^E *EMP* 50
SIC 5169 5149 Chemicals & allied products; Health foods
CEO: Steve Yamada

D-U-N-S 08-972-2144 IMP/EXP
MAYPRO INDUSTRIES LLC
(*Suby of* MAYPRO GROUP LLC) ★
2975 Westchester Ave G1, Purchase, NY 10577-2533
Tel (914) 251-0701 *Founded/Ownrshp* 2006
Sales 61.0MM *EMP* 50
SIC 5149 5169

D-U-N-S 09-814-9339 IMP/EXP
MAYS CHEMICAL CO INC
MAYS LIFE SCIENCES
5611 E 71st St, Indianapolis, IN 46220-3920
Tel (317) 842-8722 *Founded/Ownrshp* 1980
Sales 426.2MM^E *EMP* 433
SIC 5169 8741 Industrial chemicals; Industrial management; Industrial chemicals; Industrial management
Pr: William Mays
**Pr:* Kristin Mays-Corbitt
**COO:* Bill West
VP: Essie Fagen-Johnson
**VP:* Eric Gillispie
VP: Jeanette Jones
VP: John Thompson
VP: Wilmer A West
Rgnl Mgr: Lane Coleman
Genl Mgr: Sarah Viruet
Dir IT: Tony Davitto

D-U-N-S 78-736-3464 IMP
MAYS CHEMICAL CO OF PUERTO RICO INC
MAYS OCHOA
W Gate Industrial Park, Catano, PR 00962
Tel (787) 788-8000 *Founded/Ownrshp* 2008
Sales 39.8MM^E *EMP* 63
SIC 5169 5141 Industrial chemicals; Food brokers
CEO: Rafael Marti
Genl Mgr: Sarah Viruet
IT Man: Luis Dominguez

D-U-N-S 84-943-7942
MAYS HOUSECALL HOME HEALTH
805 Sw C St, Antlers, OK 74523-3838
Tel (580) 298-3947 *Founded/Ownrshp* 1993
Sales 15.2MM^E *EMP* 600
SIC 8082 Home health care services; Home health care services
CEO: Erik Drennen

MAYS LIFE SCIENCES
See MAYS CHEMICAL CO INC

D-U-N-S 07-450-8177
MAYS MEATS INC
541 E Main Ave, Taylorsville, NC 28681-2728
Tel (828) 632-2034 *Founded/Ownrshp* 1987
Sales 24.0MM *EMP* 62
SIC 5149 5421 Sausage casings; Meat & fish markets
Pr: Jimmy Wayne Mays
**VP:* Michael Lee Mays

MAYS OCHOA
See MAYS CHEMICAL CO OF PUERTO RICO INC

MAYS SPORTING GDS & AWARD CTR
See LARRY D MAYS

D-U-N-S 03-114-0098
MAYSE AUTOMOTIVE GROUP INC
2032 S Elliott Ave, Aurora, MO 65605-9618
Tel (417) 678-2118 *Founded/Ownrshp* 1989
Sales 32.1MM^E *EMP* 85
SIC 5511 5012 Automobiles, new & used; Pickups, new & used; Vans, new & used; Automotive brokers; Trucks, noncommercial; Vans, noncommercial; Automobiles, new & used; Pickups, new & used; Vans, new & used; Automotive brokers; Trucks, noncommercial; Vans, noncommercial
CEO: Rick Mayse
**Treas:* Sheila Mayse
**VP:* Matt Mayse

D-U-N-S 02-268-7246
MAYSER POLYMER USA INC
4812 Dewitt Rd, Canton, MI 48188-2442
Tel (734) 858-1290 *Founded/Ownrshp* 2008
Sales 23.5MM *EMP* 70
Accts Brickley Delong Pc Muskego
SIC 3714 5013 Motor vehicle parts & accessories; Motor vehicle supplies & new parts
Pr: William Fournier
Ql Cn Mgr: Allison Patti

D-U-N-S 00-643-6034 IMP
MAYSTEEL INDUSTRIES LLC
6199 Highway W, Allenton, WI 53002-9545
Tel (262) 251-1632 *Founded/Ownrshp* 2013
Sales 60.0MM *EMP* 300
SIC 3444

D-U-N-S 03-474-3583
MAYSVILLE LOCAL SCHOOL DISTRICT
TREASURES OFFICE
3715 Panther Dr, Zanesville, OH 43701-7086
Tel (740) 453-0877 *Founded/Ownrshp* 1957
Sales 22.2MM *EMP* 300
Accts Dave Yost-Audito Of State Ath
SIC 8211 Public elementary school; Public junior high school; Public senior high school; Public elementary school; Public junior high school; Public senior high school
**Treas:* Lewis Sidwell

D-U-N-S 78-020-9453
MAYSVILLE LOCAL SCHOOL DISTRICT
3715 Panther Dr, Zanesville, OH 43701-7086
Tel (740) 453-0754 *Founded/Ownrshp* 1957
Sales 25.0MM *EMP* 270^E
SIC 8211 Public elementary & secondary schools; Public elementary & secondary schools
**Pr:* Mike Fulkerson
**VP:* Sandra Barnes

D-U-N-S 00-796-9819
MAYTAG AIRCRAFT CORP
(*Suby of* MERCURY AIR GROUP INC) ★
6145 Lehman Dr Ste 300, Colorado Springs, CO 80918-3440
Tel (719) 593-1600 *Founded/Ownrshp* 1951, 1984
Sales 26.8MM^E *EMP* 500
SIC 7349 4581 7699 8999 7538 4111 Building maintenance services; Aircraft servicing & repairing; Airport terminal services; Aircraft & heavy equipment repair services; Weather related services; General automotive repair shops; Airport transportation services, regular route; Building maintenance services; Aircraft servicing & repairing; Airport terminal services; Aircraft & heavy equipment repair services; Weather related services; General automotive repair shops; Airport transportation services, regular route
CEO: Joseph Czyzyk
Pr: David D Nelson
COO: Larry Mynatt
CFO: Robert Schlax
Sec: Kathryn A Pleshek

MAYTAG APPLIANCES
See MAYTAG CORP

D-U-N-S 00-528-5689 IMP
■ **MAYTAG CORP**
MAYTAG APPLIANCES
(*Suby of* WHIRLPOOL CORP) ★
2000 N M 63, Benton Harbor, MI 49022-2632
Tel (269) 923-5000 *Founded/Ownrshp* 1893, 2006
Sales 5.0MMM^E *EMP* 60,000
SIC 3633 3631 3632 3639 3635 3581 Household laundry equipment; Laundry dryers, household or coin-operated; Gas ranges, domestic; Electric ranges, domestic; Household refrigerators & freezers; Dishwashing machines, household; Garbage disposal units, household; Household vacuum cleaners; Automatic vending machines; Household laundry equipment; Laundry dryers, household or coin-operated; Gas ranges, domestic; Electric ranges, domestic; Household refrigerators & freezers; Dishwashing machines, household; Garbage disposal units, household; Household vacuum cleaners; Automatic vending machines
Ch Bd: Jeff M Fettig
Pr: William L Beer
Pr: Thomas A Briatico
Pr: Arthur B Learmonth
Pr: David R McConnaughey
Pr: Keith G Minton
Ex VP: David Binkley
Sr VP: Paul J Bognar
Sr VP: Mark W Krivoruchka
VP: Stefan H Grunwald
VP: Thomas J Piersa
VP: Vitas A Stukas
Exec: Jeri Harris

MAYVIEW CONVALESCENT CENTER
See MAYVIEW CONVALESCENT HOME INC

D-U-N-S 07-557-6405
MAYVIEW CONVALESCENT HOME INC
MAYVIEW CONVALESCENT CENTER
513 E Whitaker Mill Rd, Raleigh, NC 27608-2699
Tel (919) 828-2348 *Founded/Ownrshp* 1957
Sales 858.3MM *EMP* 165
SIC 8051 Skilled nursing care facilities; Skilled nursing care facilities
Pr: Travis H Tomlinson Jr
**Treas:* Travis H Tomlinson Sr
**VP:* W Parker Tomlinson

D-U-N-S 00-610-0630 IMP
MAYVILLE ENGINEERING CO INC
715 South St, Mayville, WI 53050-1823
Tel (920) 387-4500 *Founded/Ownrshp* 1946
Sales 467.7MM^E *EMP* 1,925
SIC 3469 Stamping metal for the trade; Stamping metal for the trade
CEO: Robert D Kamphuis
**CFO:* Todd Butz
Ex VP: Ed Paradowski
VP: Bob Kamphuis
VP: Jeff Pharris
**VP:* Rick Torn
VP: Ron Weber
**VP:* Bob Wiedenhaft
Exec: Scott Bachhuber
Genl Mgr: Mike Janzer
CIO: Randall Hagedorn

MAYWD-MELROSE PK-BRDVIEW SD 89
See BROADVIEW BOARD OF EDUCATION-SCHOOL DISTRICT 89

D-U-N-S 07-909-4125
MAYWEI INC
708 La Vlla Marina Unit H, Marina Del Rey, CA 90292
Tel (917) 370-6659 *Founded/Ownrshp* 2013
Sales 25.0MM *EMP* 2
SIC 5093 Wire & cable scrap; Wire & cable scrap
Pr: Lisa Ni

D-U-N-S 07-127-9798 IMP/EXP
MAZAK CORP
(*Suby of* YAMAZAKI MAZAK TRADING CORPORATION)
8025 Production Dr, Florence, KY 41042-3092
Tel (859) 342-1700 *Founded/Ownrshp* 1974
Sales 250.3MM^E *EMP* 750
SIC 3541 5084 Numerically controlled metal cutting machine tools; Metalworking machinery; Numerically controlled metal cutting machine tools; Metalworking machinery
Pr: Brian J Papke
**Ch Bd:* Teruyuki Yamazaki
CFO: Tetsuo Niwa
**Treas:* Kazunari Matsunami
**Treas:* Daniel Sweeney
Ex VP: Kelly Matsunmai
VP: Keith Henderson
Genl Mgr: Bruce Hill
MIS Dir: Bob Fuersich
Sfty Mgr: John Feldmann
Mfg Mgr: Rocky Rowland
Board of Directors: Yoshihiko Yamazaki

D-U-N-S 60-552-7923 IMP
MAZAK OPTONICS CORP
(*Suby of* YAMAZAKI MAZAK TRADING CORPORATION)
2725 Galvin Ct, Elgin, IL 60124-7956
Tel (847) 252-4500 *Founded/Ownrshp* 2005
Sales 75.0MM^E *EMP* 100
SIC 5084 Industrial machinery & equipment; Industrial machine parts; Industrial machinery & equipment; Industrial machine parts
VP: Al Bohlen
**Pr:* William Citron
Treas: Hironori Yahata
Ex VP: Ken Nakashima
Genl Mgr: Aaron Queen
Genl Mgr: Kyle Uehara
IT Man: Dan Creekmur
Manager: Brody Fanning
Manager: Geoff Laughlin

MAZDA
See ANDERSON MOTOR CO OF CRYSTAL LAKE INC

MAZDA
See O SHELTON GARLYN INC

MAZDA 112
See CARS UNLIMITED OF SUFFOLK LLC

MAZDA CITY OF ORANGE PARK
See TOM BUSH MOTORS INC

MAZDA CONTINENTAL MOTORS
See CONTINENTAL MOTOR CO INC

MAZDA GALLERY
See AUTOMOTIVE GALLERIES INC

D-U-N-S 60-128-4128 IMP/EXP
MAZDA MOTOR OF AMERICA INC
MAZDA NORTH AMERCN OPERATIONS
(*Suby of* MAZDA MOTOR CORPORATION)
7755 Irvine Center Dr, Irvine, CA 92618-2906
Tel (949) 727-1990 *Founded/Ownrshp* 1970
Sales 526.4MM^E *EMP* 948
SIC 5511 5531

MAZDA NORTH AMERCN OPERATIONS
See MAZDA MOTOR OF AMERICA INC

D-U-N-S 80-012-9595 EXP
MAZDA OF NORTH MIAMI
MARLIN MAZDA
20700 Nw 2nd Ave, Miami, FL 33169-2102
Tel (305) 654-3825 *Founded/Ownrshp* 1992
Sales 50.6MM^E *EMP* 200
SIC 5511 5531 7538 5012 7515 5521 Automotive parts; General automotive repair shops; Automobiles; Automobiles, new & used; Passenger car leasing; Used car dealers; New & used car dealers; Automotive parts; General automotive repair shops; Automobiles; Passenger car leasing; Used car dealers
Pr: Allen Ray
CFO: Ron Duval
Sls Mgr: Manny Funcia
Sales Asso: Yaimara Batista
Sales Asso: Yeyca Quintero

MAZDA PARTS
See COOK MOTORCARS LIMITED

MAZDA SAAB OF BEDFORD
See PARTNERS AUTOMOTIVE GROUP OF BEDFORD INC

MAZDA SOUTH
See ROGER BEASLEY IMPORTS INC

MAZE NAILS DIV
See W H MAZE CO

MAZEL COMPANY, THE
See AURORA WHOLESALERS LLC

MAZELLA COMPANIES
See MAZZELLA HOLDING CO INC

D-U-N-S 79-622-5332
MAZZA & SONS INC
3230 Shafto Rd, Tinton Falls, NJ 07753-7598
Tel (732) 922-9292 *Founded/Ownrshp* 1981
Sales 22.7MM^E *EMP* 80
SIC 4953 Recycling, waste materials
Pr: Dominick J Mazza Jr
**VP:* James F Mazza

D-U-N-S 96-894-0754
MAZZELLA HOLDING CO INC
MAZELLA COMPANIES
21000 Aerospace Pkwy, Cleveland, OH 44142-1072
Tel (513) 772-4466 *Founded/Ownrshp* 2011
Sales 90.8MM^E *EMP* 300^E
SIC 5051 5085 5088 5072 Rope, wire (not insulated); Industrial supplies; Marine supplies; Builders' hardware; Rope, wire (not insulated); Industrial supplies; Marine supplies; Builders' hardware
CEO: Tony Mazzella
**VP:* James J Mazzella
Genl Mgr: Margaret Owen

D-U-N-S 00-317-9256
MAZZELLA JHH CO INC (VA)
J HENRY HOLLAND
(*Suby of* MAZZELLA LIFTING TECHNOLOGIES INC) ★
5931 Thurston Ave, Virginia Beach, VA 23455-3308
Tel (757) 460-3300 *Founded/Ownrshp* 1947, 2011
Sales 30.1MM^E *EMP* 47
SIC 5085 5072 2298 Industrial supplies; Builders' hardware; Wire rope centers
CEO: Anthony J Mazzella
**Pr:* Craig Hayward
**Treas:* Stephanie Miller
**VP:* Larry Lusk

D-U-N-S 00-418-7357 IMP
MAZZELLA LIFTING TECHNOLOGIES INC (OH)
(*Suby of* MAZELLA COMPANIES) ★
21000 Aerospace Pkwy, Cleveland, OH 44142-1072
Tel (440) 239-7000 *Founded/Ownrshp* 1959, 2013
Sales 41.4MM^E *EMP* 105
SIC 3496 Miscellaneous fabricated wire products; Miscellaneous fabricated wire products
CEO: Anthony Mazzella
VP: Mark Erny
VP: James J Mazzella
Brnch Mgr: Kevin Gallagher
Genl Mgr: Tony Polito
Plnt Mgr: Terry Pipik
Sales Asso: Al Abel

D-U-N-S 17-341-1687 IMP/EXP
MAZZETTA CO LLC
1990 Saint Johns Ave # 100, Highland Park, IL 60035-3133
Tel (847) 433-1150 *Founded/Ownrshp* 1987
Sales 86.0MM^E *EMP* 50^E
SIC 5146 Seafoods
QA Dir: Dave Fitzgerald
Sales Asso: Jeffrey Kaplan

D-U-N-S 02-294-3559
MAZZETTI INC
220 Montgomery St Ste 650, San Francisco, CA 94104-3491
Tel (415) 362-3266 *Founded/Ownrshp* 1962
Sales 24.9MM^E *EMP* 130

SIC 8711 Electrical or electronic engineering; Mechanical engineering; Consulting engineer; Electrical or electronic engineering; Mechanical engineering; Consulting engineer
CEO: Walt Vernon
**CFO:* Darryl Wandry
Chf Mktg O: Brigette Thomas
Dir IT: Mike Rinken
Pr Dir: Emily Toliver
Mktg Mgr: John Mazzetti
Snr Mgr: Melinda Epler
Snr Mgr: Arash Guity
Snr Mgr: Mel Malyemezian

D-U-N-S 04-632-9058
MAZZIOS LLC
MAZZIO'S PIZZA
4441 S 72nd East Ave, Tulsa, OK 74145-4610
Tel (918) 663-8880 *Founded/Ownrshp* 1961
Sales 151.3MM[E] *EMP* 3,780
SIC 5812 6794 Pizzeria, chain; Franchises, selling or licensing; Pizzeria, chain; Franchises, selling or licensing
**Pr:* Craig Bothwell
CFO: Sonya Wilson
**Sr VP:* Michael E Bartlett
**Sr VP:* Brad Williams
Sr VP: Bradford J Williams
VP: Gregory Lippert
VP: Patrick Patterson
IT Man: Tom Elliott
IT Man: Dale Southerland
Opers Mgr: Leo Voss
VP Sls: Karen Lesiker

MAZZIO'S PIZZA
See MAZZIOS LLC

MB
See MCBEE ASSOCIATES INC

D-U-N-S 07-884-2583
MB AEROSPACE ACP HOLDINGS III CORP
2711 Centerville Rd # 400, Wilmington, DE 19808-1660
Tel (586) 772-2500 *Founded/Ownrshp* 2013
Sales 59.8MM[E] *EMP* 175[E]
SIC 3724 Aircraft engines & engine parts; Aircraft engines & engine parts
CEO: Craig Gallagher
**CFO:* Gregor Goodwin

D-U-N-S 05-990-9523 IMP
MB AEROSPACE STERLING HEIGHTS INC
38111 Comm Dr, Sterling Heights, MI 48312
Tel (586) 977-9200 *Founded/Ownrshp* 1999
Sales 22.8MM[E] *EMP* 75
SIC 3599 Machine shop, jobbing & repair
CEO: Craig Gallagher
**Pr:* Kevin Johnston
Pr: Alidor Lefere
COO: Luke Jones
Exec: John Perfetti
Off Mgr: Robbi Swanson

D-U-N-S 07-845-2523
MB AEROSPACE US HOLDINGS INC (MI)
(*Suby of* MB AEROSPACE ACP HOLDINGS III CORP) ★
25250 Easy St, Warren, MI 48089-4130
Tel (586) 772-2500 *Founded/Ownrshp* 2011
Sales 56.8MM[E] *EMP* 216[E]
SIC 8711 Aviation &/or aeronautical engineering
CEO: Craig Gallagher
**CFO:* Gregor Goodwin
**Ex VP:* Mike Smith
**VP:* Kevan Johnston

D-U-N-S 07-870-3218
MB AEROSPACE WARREN LLC
GENTZ AERO
(*Suby of* MB AEROSPACE US HOLDINGS INC) ★
25250 Easy St, Warren, MI 48089-4130
Tel (586) 772-2500 *Founded/Ownrshp* 2006
Sales 56.8MM[E] *EMP* 210
SIC 3769 3443 3444 3724 3398 Guided missile & space vehicle parts & auxiliary equipment; Fabricated plate work (boiler shop); Sheet metalwork; Aircraft engines & engine parts; Metal heat treating; Guided missile & space vehicle parts & auxiliary equipment; Fabricated plate work (boiler shop); Sheet metalwork; Aircraft engines & engine parts; Metal heat treating
Sr VP: Bill Evans II
CFO: James Stevens
Ex VP: Wayne Gibson
Genl Mgr: Don Bierstine
Prd Dir: Roger Bartolomei
Plnt Mgr: Terrace Reese

D-U-N-S 00-979-7366
MB CONTRACTORS INC
3825 Blue Ridge Dr Sw, Roanoke, VA 24018-1553
Tel (540) 342-6758 *Founded/Ownrshp* 1983
Sales 30.3MM[E] *EMP* 75
SIC 1541 1542 Industrial buildings, new construction; Commercial & office building, new construction
Pr: Todd Morgan
**CEO:* John E Hammer III
**Treas:* Kay Hammer
**Ex VP:* Mike Cagle
Off Mgr: Christina Bradley

D-U-N-S 06-036-4791
■ **MB FINANCIAL BANK**
(*Suby of* MB FINANCIAL BANK NA) ★
936 N Western Ave, Chicago, IL 60622-4616
Tel (773) 772-4500 *Founded/Ownrshp* 2004
Sales NA *EMP* 95
SIC 6035 Federal savings banks; Federal savings banks
Pr: Julian Kulas
Ch Bd: Paul Nadzikewycz
Pr: Paul Bandriwsky
COO: Harry Kucewicz
Ofcr: Suzon Lanz
Sr VP: Stewart Kapnick
VP: Mary Korb
VP: Irene Subota
Mng Dir: Michael Musselman
CTO: Jo Boylan

D-U-N-S 00-693-1463
■ **MB FINANCIAL BANK NA** (IL)
(*Suby of* MB FINANCIAL INC) ★
6111 N River Rd Ste 800, Rosemont, IL 60018-5111
Tel (847) 653-4800 *Founded/Ownrshp* 1933, 2001
Sales NA *EMP* 1,340
SIC 6021 National commercial banks; National commercial banks
Ch: Ron Santo
**Pr:* Mitchell Feiger
Ofcr: Brian Bye
Ofcr: Jeremy Epstein
Ofcr: George Freeman
Ofcr: Thomas P Fitz Gibbon
Ofcr: Richard Huttel
Ofcr: Mary Lapierre
Ofcr: Ryan Novack
Ofcr: Drew Osika
Ofcr: Allison Winchester
Trst Ofcr: Katherine Kong
**Ex VP:* Mark A Heckler
**Ex VP:* Michael J Morton
Sr VP: Scott Baranski
Sr VP: Elizabeth A Di Cola
Sr VP: Sueann Griffin
Sr VP: Karen Perlman
Sr VP: Randy Perryman
Sr VP: John Sassaris
Sr VP: Sarah Willett
Board of Directors: Stanley R Banas, Samuel M Budwig Jr, Charles F Clarke Jr, Allan J Dixon, Patrick Henry, Marshall S Leaf, Eugene Saywer, Richard M Wolff

D-U-N-S 92-887-5145 IMP
▲ **MB FINANCIAL INC**
800 W Madison St, Chicago, IL 60607-2630
Tel (888) 422-6562 *Founded/Ownrshp* 2001
Sales NA *EMP* 1,775[E]
Tkr Sym MBFI *Exch* NGS
SIC 6035 Savings institutions, federally chartered; Savings institutions, federally chartered
Pr: Mitchell Feiger
**Ch Bd:* Thomas H Harvey
Pr: Charles Jackson
Pr: Brian Nagorsky
COO: Randall T Conte
CFO: Jill E York
Bd of Dir: Christina Aguinaga
Chf Mktg O: Rob Gilland
Ofcr: Agata Dolinski
Ofcr: Kirsten Friedl
Ofcr: Jeffery Husserl
Ofcr: Veronica McGowan
Ofcr: Michael J Morton
Trst Ofcr: Abimbola Okubanjo
Ex VP: Rosemarie Bouman
Ex VP: Susan G Peterson
Ex VP: Brian J Wildman
Sr VP: Mitch Morgenstern
Sr VP: Juanita Myrick
Sr VP: Joseph Sheils
Sr VP: Richard West
Board of Directors: David P Bolger, C Bryan Daniels, Charles J Gries, Richard J Holmstrom, Karen J May, Ronald D Santo, Jennifer W Steans, Renee Togher

D-U-N-S 09-194-1133
MB FOOD PROCESSING INC
(*Suby of* M.B. CONSULTING GROUP, LTD.)
5190 S Fallsburg Main St, South Fallsburg, NY 12779
Tel (845) 436-5001 *Founded/Ownrshp* 2000
Sales 1.5MM[E] *EMP* 350
SIC 2015 Poultry slaughtering & processing
Pr: Dean Koplik

D-U-N-S 00-344-7836
MB HAYNES CORP (NC)
H & M CONSTRUCTORS
187 Deaverview Rd, Asheville, NC 28806-1707
Tel (828) 254-6141 *Founded/Ownrshp* 1921, 1966
Sales 272.6MM[E] *EMP* 440
SIC 1542 1623 1711 7382 Commercial & office building, new construction; Electric power line construction; Plumbing, heating, air-conditioning contractors; Security systems services; Commercial & office building, new construction; Electric power line construction; Plumbing, heating, air-conditioning contractors; Security systems services
Pr: N Ellis Cannady III
CFO: Hester Faison
**CFO:* R Faison Hester
**Ch:* N Ellis Cannady Jr
Treas: Chris Mace
Ex VP: Jeff Ball
**Ex VP:* Brett P Cannady
**Sr VP:* Fred Lewis
VP: Tony Clinton
VP: Michael Dixon
VP: Nat Harrison
VP: Steve Warner

MB INDUSTRIAL
See MCFADDEN-DALE INDUSTRIAL HARDWARE LLC

D-U-N-S 07-909-6120 IMP
MB INDUSTRIES INC (PA)
130 Spruce St Apt 28b, Philadelphia, PA 19106-4340
Tel (267) 318-7534 *Founded/Ownrshp* 2013
Sales 180.0MM *EMP* 23
SIC 5051 Steel
CEO: Nathan MA
**VP:* Barry Bernsten

D-U-N-S 03-392-9456
MB JONES OIL CO INC (GA)
611 S Main St, Wrens, GA 30833-4534
Tel (706) 547-7275 *Founded/Ownrshp* 1954, 1969
Sales 22.7MM[E] *EMP* 20
SIC 5172 Petroleum products
CEO: Anderson B Jones
**CFO:* Tracy S Carter
**Treas:* John J Jones
**VP:* Jeff Gay
VP Opers: Henry Colley
Sfty Mgr: Billy Usry

D-U-N-S 07-992-0367
MB OKC LLC
OKC DODGERS
2 S Mickey Mantle Dr, Oklahoma City, OK 73104-2433
Tel (405) 218-1000 *Founded/Ownrshp* 2014
Sales 24.1MM[E] *EMP* 300
SIC 5091 Sharpeners, sporting goods
Pr: Michael Byrnes
Sr VP: Jenna Byrnes

D-U-N-S 06-708-9227
MB REAL ESTATE SERVICES INC
181 W Madison St Ste 4700, Chicago, IL 60602-4584
Tel (312) 726-1700 *Founded/Ownrshp* 1981
Sales 66.7MM[E] *EMP* 400
SIC 6512 6552 6531 1542 Commercial & industrial building operation; Land subdividers & developers, commercial; Real estate leasing & rentals; Commercial & office building, new construction; Commercial & industrial building operation; Land subdividers & developers, commercial; Real estate leasing & rentals; Commercial & office building, new construction
CEO: Peter E Ricker
**Pr:* John T Murphy
CFO: Kevin Buckley
Ofcr: Patricia Aluisi
**Ex VP:* Mark A Buth
**Ex VP:* Gary A Denenberg
Ex VP: Nicholas Perzioso
Sr VP: Michael Hull
Sr VP: Daniel Nikitas
VP: Chris Dilley
VP: David Graff
VP: Walter Hennig
VP: Timothy Shields
VP: Ann Tomlinson
VP: Marc Westmeyer

D-U-N-S 05-477-0532
MB REIT (FLORIDA) INC (FL)
2901 Butterfield Rd, Oak Brook, IL 60523-1106
Tel (630) 218-8000 *Founded/Ownrshp* 1977, 2006
Sales 13.3MM[E] *EMP* 300
SIC 1521 1522 1542 Single-family housing construction; Multi-family dwellings, new construction; Nonresidential construction; Single-family housing construction; Multi-family dwellings, new construction; Nonresidential construction
Pr: Brenda G Gujral
**Treas:* Jack H Potts

MB TRACTOR AND EQUIPMENT
See SUMMA HUMMA ENTERPRISES LLC

D-U-N-S 82-958-3769
MB TRADING HOLDINGS LLC
(*Suby of* TRADEKING LLC) ★
1926 E Maple Ave, El Segundo, CA 90245-3493
Tel (480) 212-1112 *Founded/Ownrshp* 2015
Sales 30.1MM[E] *EMP* 173[E]
SIC 6211 Security brokers & dealers; Security brokers & dealers
CEO: Ross Ditlove
Pr: Steve Demarest

D-U-N-S 00-111-9825
MB WESTFIELD INC (MA)
MIDSTATE BERKSHIRE
109 Apremont Way, Westfield, MA 01085-1303
Tel (413) 568-8676 *Founded/Ownrshp* 1956
Sales 35.3MM[E] *EMP* 133
SIC 3724 3661 3674 Aircraft engines & engine parts; Telephone & telegraph apparatus; Semiconductor circuit networks; Aircraft engines & engine parts; Telephone & telegraph apparatus; Semiconductor circuit networks
Pr: Duane Pekar
VP: Mike Meczywor
VP Opers: Paul Texiera
S&M/VP: Bob Zagaja

MBA CONSTRUCTION
See MBA GENERAL CONTRACTING LLC

D-U-N-S 00-282-5493
MBA GENERAL CONTRACTING LLC
MBA CONSTRUCTION
33126 Magnolia Cir, Magnolia, TX 77354-1629
Tel (855) 785-7171 *Founded/Ownrshp* 2007
Sales 33.8MM[E] *EMP* 42[E]
SIC 1542 Commercial & office building contractors
Owner: Cory G Martin
Treas: John Groth
**Prin:* Daniel Acevedo
**Prin:* Mark Brown
Sfty Mgr: Dusty Hawker
Snr PM: Mark Ferguson
Snr PM: Jonathan Hay
Snr PM: James Hogan
Snr PM: Steve Kauer

D-U-N-S 88-386-0462 IMP
MBA POLYMERS INC
500 W Ohio Ave, Richmond, CA 94804-2040
Tel (510) 231-9031 *Founded/Ownrshp* 1994
Sales 42.1MM[E] *EMP* 90[E]
SIC 4953

MBA POULTRY
See TECUMSEH POULTRY LLC

D-U-N-S 16-109-3984
MBA PROPERTIES INC
MCCORMACK BARON SALAZAR
720 Olive St Ste 2500, Saint Louis, MO 63101-2313
Tel (314) 621-3400 *Founded/Ownrshp* 1985
Sales 25.7MM *EMP* 376
Accts Rubinbrown Llp Saint Louis M
SIC 6531 6552 Real estate managers; Land subdividers & developers, residential; Real estate managers; Land subdividers & developers, residential
CEO: Richard D Baron
**Pr:* Al Ragan
**Pr:* Tony Salazar
**Pr:* Tim Zaleski
**CFO:* Linda Heiney
VP: Tom Cella
**VP:* Kevin McCormack

D-U-N-S 80-702-8621
■ **MBANK**
MACKINAC FINANCIAL
(*Suby of* MACKINAC FINANCIAL CORP) ★
130 S Cedar St, Manistique, MI 49854-1438
Tel (906) 341-8401 *Founded/Ownrshp* 2007
Sales NA *EMP* 28[E]
SIC 6022 State commercial banks; State commercial banks
Pr: Kelly George
**CFO:* Ernie Krueger
Sr VP: Paul Hinkson
Sr VP: Boris Martysz
VP: Jesse Deering
VP: Jake Martin
Brnch Mgr: Barbara Miller

MBARI
See MONTEREY BAY AQUARIUM RESEARCH INSTITUTE

D-U-N-S 07-433-8427
MBB AUTO LLC
MERCEDEZ BENZ OF BROOKLYN
1800 Shore Pkwy, Brooklyn, NY 11214-6607
Tel (718) 258-5100 *Founded/Ownrshp* 2012
Sales 71.8MM[E] *EMP* 82[E]
SIC 5511 Automobiles, new & used
Pr: Douglas Wells
COO: Roger Pittman
VP: Edward Feldman
**VP:* Michael Sclafani Sr
Store Mgr: Domenic Gramuglia
Dir IT: Robert Ramellini
Sls Mgr: Leo Kava
Sls Mgr: Barry Martin
Sls Mgr: Pat Noce
Sls Mgr: Jonathan Strahl
Sales Asso: Johnny Chan

MBC
See MARY BALDWIN COLLEGE

D-U-N-S 92-641-2453
MBC HOLDINGS INC
1613 S Defiance St, Archbold, OH 43502-9488
Tel (419) 445-1015 *Founded/Ownrshp* 1994
Sales 150.0MM[E] *EMP* 721
Accts Plante & Moran Pllc Toledo
SIC 1622 1611 Bridge construction; Highway & street paving contractor; Bridge construction; Highway & street paving contractor
Pr: Dean E Miller
**Sec:* Steven A Everhart
VP: Keith Fletcher
**VP:* Robert Miller
VP: Larry Winkleman
Mtls Mgr: Sean Galliger
Snr Mgr: Ben Polafek

MBCR
See MASSACHUSETTS BAY COMMUTER RAILROAD CO LLC

D-U-N-S 80-306-4633
MBD CONSTRUCTION CO INC
8305 Tom Dr, Baton Rouge, LA 70815-8051
Tel (225) 928-5569 *Founded/Ownrshp* 1989
Sales 21.4MM[E] *EMP* 100
SIC 1542 1541 Commercial & office building, new construction; Commercial & office buildings, renovation & repair; Industrial buildings, new construction; Renovation, remodeling & repairs: industrial buildings; Commercial & office building, new construction; Commercial & office buildings, renovation & repair; Industrial buildings, new construction; Renovation, remodeling & repairs: industrial buildings
Pr: Andrew McLindon
Genl Mgr: Jeff Perryman
Off Mgr: Amy Armstrong

MBE
See TTG ENGINEERS

D-U-N-S 82-474-1631
MBF INSPECTION SERVICES INC
805 N Richardson Ave, Roswell, NM 88201-4920
Tel (575) 625-0599 *Founded/Ownrshp* 2005
Sales 111.3MM *EMP* 30
Accts Bobby D Carroll Cpa
SIC 7389 Pipeline & power line inspection service; Pipeline & power line inspection service
Pr: Frank L Sturges
VP: Mark Daniels

MBG MARKETING
See MICHIGAN BLUEBERRY GROWERS ASSOCIATION

D-U-N-S 79-186-1123
MBH ARCHITECTS INC
DH ARCHITECTS
2470 Mariner Square Loop, Alameda, CA 94501-1010
Tel (510) 865-8663 *Founded/Ownrshp* 1989
Sales 39.8MM[E] *EMP* 210
SIC 8712 Architectural services; Architectural services
Pr: Dennis Heath
**Treas:* Clay Fry
Bd of Dir: Dave Marquardt
Sr VP: Marcela Coopersmith
Sr VP: Brooke Hauch
**VP:* Joseph Smart
Dir Bus: Gordon Crespo
**Prin:* Rebecca Ross
Admn Mgr: Teresa Doroliat
MIS Dir: Gerald McDaniel
Dir IT: Georganne Benesch

D-U-N-S 61-691-4768
MBI DIRECT MAIL INC
M B I
710 W New Hampshire Ave, Deland, FL 32720-7231
Tel (386) 736-9998 *Founded/Ownrshp* 1989
Sales 30.3MM *EMP* 85

SIC 7331 Direct mail advertising services; Direct mail advertising services
Pr: James Grogan
Bd of Dir: Michael Grogan
VP: Karen Pietrobono
VP Admn: Shannon Yannone
Natl Sales: Odessa Smith

D-U-N-S 07-846-2094
MBI ENERGY LOGISTICS LLC
M B I
(Suby of MBI ENERGY SERVICES) ★
12980 35th St Sw, Belfield, ND 58622-9703
Tel (701) 575-8242 Founded/Ownrshp 2011
Sales 91.1MM^E EMP 1,450^E
SIC 4731 Freight transportation arrangement
CEO: Jim Arthaud
Pr: Jeff Kistelecky
*VP: Jason Homiston
Sfty Mgr: Brian Bosch

MBI ENERGY SERVICES
See MISSOURI BASIN WELL SERVICE INC

D-U-N-S 07-539-5921 IMP
MBI INC
DANBURY MINT
47 Richards Ave, Norwalk, CT 06857-0001
Tel (203) 853-2000 Founded/Ownrshp 1969
Sales 104.6MM^E EMP 600^E
SIC 5961 Toys & games (including dolls & models), mail order; Book club, mail order; Jewelry, mail order; Stamps, mail order; Toys & games (including dolls & models), mail order; Book club, mail order; Jewelry, mail order; Stamps, mail order
Ch: Theodore R Stanley
*Pr: Peter Maglathlin
*CFO: Michael Wilbur
*VP: Russell Friedman
VP: Dave Macoy
VP: Michael McClammy
VP: Jenny Plath
VP: Michael Rogers
VP: Jay Zibelman
Creative D: Bob Gabler
CTO: Tim Crispyn

D-U-N-S 15-481-8223
▲ MBIA INC
1 Manhattanville Rd # 301, Purchase, NY 10577-2100
Tel (914) 273-4545 Founded/Ownrshp 1974
Sales NA EMP 180^E
Tkr Sym MBI Exch NYS
SIC 6351 Surety insurance; Financial management for business; Surety insurance
CEO: Joseph W Brown
*Ch Bd: Charles R Rinehart
Pr: William C Fallon
Ofcr: C Edward Chaplin
VP: Steve Sutcliffe
Mng Dir: Alex Jackson
Board of Directors: Maryann Bruce, Sean D Carney, David A Coulter, Keith D Curry, Steven J Gilbert, Lois A Scott, Theodore Shasta, Richard C Vaughan

D-U-N-S 82-648-3872
■ MBIA INSURANCE CORP
(Suby of MBIA INC) ★
1 Manhattanville Rd # 301, Purchase, NY 10577-2100
Tel (914) 273-4545 Founded/Ownrshp 1978
Sales NA EMP 169^E
SIC 6351 Surety insurance
Pr: Neil G Budnick
*CFO: Marc Morris
VP: Max Blackler
*VP: Michael Jacobson
VP: Sherman Sham
Ex Dir: John Jordan
Mng Dir: Gerhard Oberholzer
Mng Dir: Andrea Randolph
Mng Dir: Roger E Shields

D-U-N-S 07-915-0310
MBK-WI INC (WI)
FREEDOM GRAPHIC SYSTEMS
1101 S Janesville St, Milton, WI 53563-1838
Tel (608) 373-6500 Founded/Ownrshp 1987
Sales 121.0MM EMP 550
SIC 2752 Commercial printing, lithographic; Commercial printing, lithographic
Pr: Martin Liebert
CFO: Terrance Brady

MBL
See MARINE BIOLOGICAL LABORATORY

D-U-N-S 88-490-0531
MBLOX INC
ZOOVE
1901 S Bascom Ave Ste 400, Campbell, CA 95008-2238
Tel (408) 617-3700 Founded/Ownrshp 1999
Sales 31.4MM^E EMP 80
SIC 7371 Computer software development & applications
Ch Bd: Simon Duffy
Pr: David Bernstein
*CEO: Thomas M Cotney Jr
*CFO: Steve Love
*CFO: John Stone
*Co-Ch Bd: Andrew Bud
*Co-Ch Bd: Gary Cuccio
Bd of Dir: Howard Oringer
*Chf Mktg O: Michele Turner
Ex VP: Katherine Stoltz
*Sr VP: Ed Santulli
VP: Bruce Bales
VP: Mike Caffey
VP: Mike Gauthier
VP: Brandon Trollip
VP: Wanda Truxillo
Exec: David Coelho
Exec: Margaret Mackenzie
Exec: Pam Rissmann
Exec: Erik Young
Board of Directors: Rory O'driscoll, Susan Swenson

MBM
See MEADOWBROOK MEAT CO INC

D-U-N-S 00-537-6322
MBM FABRICATORS CO INC (MI)
36333 Northline Rd, Romulus, MI 48174-3645
Tel (734) 941-0100 Founded/Ownrshp 1962
Sales 40.0MM^E EMP 215
SIC 1791 3441 Structural steel erection; Fabricated structural metal; Structural steel erection; Fabricated structural metal
Pr: Donald A Makins
VP: Al Green
Genl Mgr: Joe Leslie
Genl Mgr: Piper Myers

D-U-N-S 96-595-6860
MBMJ CAPITAL LLC
FAST A/R FUNDING
15503 Ventura Blvd, Encino, CA 91436-3114
Tel (888) 833-2286 Founded/Ownrshp 2009
Sales NA EMP 115^E
SIC 6153

D-U-N-S 79-332-3007
■ MBNA MARKETING SYSTEMS INC
(Suby of FIA CARD SERVICES NATIONAL ASSOCIATION) ★
1100 N King St, Wilmington, DE 19884-0011
Tel (302) 456-8588 Founded/Ownrshp 1990
Sales 84.2MM^E EMP 1,484
SIC 7389 Telemarketing services; Telemarketing services
CEO: Bruce Hammonds
*Treas: Vernon Wright

D-U-N-S 07-313-4553
■ MBNA TECHNOLOGY INC
(Suby of FIA CARD SERVICES NATIONAL ASSOCIATION) ★
16001 Dallas Pkwy, Addison, TX 75001-3311
Tel (972) 233-7101 Founded/Ownrshp 1990
Sales 98.4MM^E EMP 1,720
SIC 7374 6282 Data processing service; Investment advice; Data processing service; Investment advice
Ch Bd: Ronald W Davies
Pr: Douglas R Denton
Exec: John M Gala
Pr Mgr: Victoria Henrion

D-U-N-S 10-391-7399 IMP
MBO BINDER & CO OF AMERICA
MBO OF AMERICA
(Suby of MASCHINENBAU OPPENWEILER BINDER GMBH & CO. KG)
4 E Stow Rd Ste 12, Marlton, NJ 08053-3150
Tel (856) 396-0002 Founded/Ownrshp 1983
Sales 31.9MM^E EMP 50
SIC 5084 Printing trades machinery, equipment & supplies
Pr: Manfred Minich
*Treas: Reinhard Heinisch
Treas: Kenneth Keyte
Area Mgr: Christof Aurich
Area Mgr: Judith Taraborrelli
IT Man: Dave Dillard
Natl Sales: Werner King
Mktg Dir: Ryan Manieri
Sls Dir: Lance Martin
Manager: Peter Brousseau
Manager: Paul Bruno

D-U-N-S 01-703-8600
MBO CORP (OK)
(Suby of MBO HOLDINGS INC) ★
1 Main St, Earlsboro, OK 74840
Tel (405) 997-5201 Founded/Ownrshp 1993
Sales 32.7MM EMP 70
SIC 4813 4841 Telephone communication, except radio; Cable television services; Telephone communication, except radio; Cable television services
Pr: V David Miller II
*Treas: Dan Overland

D-U-N-S 01-697-2916
MBO HOLDINGS INC
1 W Main St, Earlsboro, OK 74840
Tel (405) 997-5201 Founded/Ownrshp 1993
Sales 32.4MM EMP 70
SIC 4813 Telephone communication, except radio; Telephone communication, except radio
Pr: V David Miller II
Treas: Susan Baldwin
*Treas: Dan Overland

MBO OF AMERICA
See MBO BINDER & CO OF AMERICA

D-U-N-S 11-295-1889
MBO PARTNERS INC
13454 Sun Vley Dr Ste 300, Herndon, VA 20171
Tel (703) 793-6000 Founded/Ownrshp 1996
Sales 33.0MM^E EMP 100
SIC 8742 Business planning & organizing services
CEO: Gene Zaino
Chf Mktg O: Melissa Mayer
*Ofcr: Aassia Haq
VP: Jay Lash
VP: Monica Lucero
VP: Kimball Norup
VP: Amy Odonnell
*VP: Dave Putt
VP: Julian Richards
VP: Tom Rumberg
Exec: Dave Walsh

D-U-N-S 18-184-9329
MBP INVESTORS LLC
11311 Mccormick Rd, Hunt Valley, MD 21031-1004
Tel (410) 321-1900 Founded/Ownrshp 2012
Sales 43.1MM^E EMP 134^E
SIC 8731 8711 Energy research; Engineering services; Electrical or electronic engineering
Pr: David Townsend
COO: Richard R Cundiff III
CFO: Daniel Emswiler
VP: Josh Ferguson

D-U-N-S 00-977-7921 IMP/EXP
MBR CONSTRUCTION SERVICES INC
307 June Ave, Blandon, PA 19510-9550
Tel (610) 926-1490 Founded/Ownrshp 2004
Sales 61.6MM^E EMP 300^E
SIC 1731 1711 General electrical contractor; Plumbing, heating, air-conditioning contractors; General electrical contractor; Plumbing, heating, air-conditioning contractors
CEO: Kenneth R Field
*Pr: Brendon Field
Treas: George Firrantello
Mktg Mgr: John Healy

D-U-N-S 02-978-6477
MBR OPERATING CO INC
ST REGIS RESORT MONARCH BEACH
(Suby of WASHINGTON HOLDINGS) ★
1 Monarch Beach Resort, Dana Point, CA 92629-4085
Tel (949) 234-3200 Founded/Ownrshp 2014
Sales 69.3MM^E EMP 1,100
SIC 7011 Resort hotel; Resort hotel
Pr: Paul Makarechian
Exec: Richard Brown
Exec: Joe Trevino
Sls Dir: Sandra Tye
Sls Mgr: Denise McConnell
Sls Mgr: Tiffany McGovern
Sls Mgr: Samantha Spiro
Sls Mgr: Danielle Staffieri
Sls Mgr: Betty Tindall
Snr Mgr: Patricia St Regis
Board of Directors: Mark Rob

MBS
See MILLER-BOWIE SUPPLY CO

D-U-N-S 61-430-7374
MBS EQUIPMENT CO
TM MOTION PICTURE EQP RENTALS
4060 Ince Blvd, Culver City, CA 90232-2602
Tel (310) 558-3100 Founded/Ownrshp 2005
Sales 20.9MM^E EMP 216^E
SIC 7819 Services allied to motion pictures
Pr: Tom May
Ex Dir: Bob Socha

MBS INCOPORATED
See MAINTENANCE BUILDERS SUPPLY LTD

D-U-N-S 12-624-3612
■ MBS INSIGHT INC
M B S
(Suby of E-DIALOG INC) ★
265 Broadhollow Rd # 400, Melville, NY 11747-4833
Tel (631) 851-5000 Founded/Ownrshp 2010
Sales 23.4MM^E EMP 250
SIC 7331 Direct mail advertising services; Direct mail advertising services
Ch Bd: John Healy
*Pr: Lissa Napolillo
*COO: Philip T Carroll
*Chf Cred: Andrea Miskovsky
Sr VP: Randall James
*Sr VP: Sari Tamilio
VP: David Braunstein
VP: Glenn Onos
VP: Helene Pacifico
VP: Bruce Richards
VP Mktg: Lauren Carroll

D-U-N-S 79-117-9328
MBS MANAGEMENT SERVICES INC
1 Galleria Blvd Ste 1950, Metairie, LA 70001-7580
Tel (504) 849-0866 Founded/Ownrshp 1987
Sales 10.0MM^E EMP 300
SIC 6531 Real estate managers; Real estate managers
Pr: Michael B Smuck
*Sec: Carol A Smuck

D-U-N-S 00-687-0711 IMP
MBS TEXTBOOK EXCHANGE INC
2711 W Ash St, Columbia, MO 65203-4613
Tel (573) 445-2243 Founded/Ownrshp 1909
Sales 1.8MMM^E EMP 1,125
SIC 5192 Books; Books
CEO: Robert K Pugh
*Ch Bd: Leonard Riggio
*Pr: Dan M Schuppan
*CFO: Andrew R Gingrich
VP: Juan Daniel
VP: Nelson Durk
VP: Dave Easton
VP: David Henderson
Exec: Amy Longenecker
Area Mgr: David Lewis
Genl Mgr: Susan Thompson

MBSC DIV
See BUILDING MAINTENANCE SERVICE LLC

D-U-N-S 19-838-5809
MBT BANCSHARES INC
MISSOURI BANK
1044 Main St Ste 100, Kansas City, MO 64105-2135
Tel (816) 881-8200 Founded/Ownrshp 1984
Sales NA EMP 30
SIC 6022 State commercial banks
Pr: Grant Burcham
*V Ch: Kenneth Lawrence
*Ch: J Thomas Burcham
Sr VP: Jim Goetz
VP: Linda Marcum
VP: Suzie Muse
VP: Jeff Phillips

D-U-N-S 13-333-7563
▲ MBT FINANCIAL CORP
102 E Front St, Monroe, MI 48161-2162
Tel (734) 241-3431 Founded/Ownrshp 2000
Sales NA EMP 381
Tkr Sym MBTF Exch NGS
SIC 6021 National commercial banks; National commercial banks
Pr: H Douglas Chaffin
Pr: Adam Tuttle
COO: John Kerry
*CFO: John L Skibski
Bd of Dir: Michael Lash
Ex VP: Donald M Lieto
Ex VP: Audrey Mistor
Ex VP: Thomas G Myers
Sr VP: Herbert Lock
VP: Thomas Assenmacher
VP: John Betrus
VP: Jeff Schillag
Exec: Amanda Phebus

D-U-N-S 07-947-4195
MBT INFRA INTERNATIONAL LLC
19 W 34th St Rm 1021, New York, NY 10001-3006
Tel (347) 604-6155 Founded/Ownrshp 2009
Sales 30.0MM EMP 5
SIC 6221 Commodity traders, contracts; Commodity traders, contracts
Pt: Venkata Maddala
Pt: Sab Sharma

MBUSD
See MANHATTAN BEACH CITY SCHOOL DISTRICT

D-U-N-S 93-291-5960 IMP
MBW INC
184 Gov Dukakis Dr, Orange, MA 01364-2033
Tel (978) 544-6462 Founded/Ownrshp 1993
Sales 25.1MM^E EMP 140
SIC 2679 Paper products, converted; Paper products, converted
Pr: James B Jones
*Treas: George D Jones III
*VP: Mary Elisabeth L Jones
*VP: Wendy Jones
Exec: Joe Sorborski
Plnt Mgr: David Keeney
Prd Mgr: Roy Howard

MBX SYSTEMS
See MOTHERBOARD EXPRESS CO

MC
See MINNOTTE CONTRACTING CORP

MC
See CERTECH INC

D-U-N-S 00-698-7408
MC ALLISTER TOWING & TRANS INC
(Suby of MCALLISTER TOWING & TRANSPORTATION CO INC) ★
17 Battery Pl Ste 1200, New York, NY 10004-1105
Tel (212) 269-3200 Founded/Ownrshp 1864, 1969
Sales 140.0MM EMP 350
SIC 4424 Coastwide transportation, freight; Coastwide transportation, freight
Pr: Brian McAllister
VP: Lawrence Lore
VP: Virginia Norfolk
Opers Mgr: Allen Aden

MC ALLISTER'S
See MAC RESTAURANT CORP

D-U-N-S 82-830-9570
MC ASSEMBLY HOLDINGS INC
425 North Dr, Melbourne, FL 32934-9209
Tel (321) 253-0541 Founded/Ownrshp 1984
Sales 243.1MM^E EMP 1,600
SIC 8734 3672 Testing laboratories; Printed circuit boards; Testing laboratories; Printed circuit boards
Pr: George W Moore
*COO: Luis Ramirez
*CFO: Mark McReynolds
*VP: Tim Jameson
*VP: Jake Kulp
*VP: Carol McCauslin
*VP: Jim Roche
*VP: Tom Rossi

D-U-N-S 79-116-8367
MC ASSEMBLY INTERNATIONAL LLC
(Suby of M C ASSEMBLY) ★
425 North Dr, Melbourne, FL 32934-9209
Tel (321) 253-0541 Founded/Ownrshp 2004
Sales 94.9MM^E EMP 310
SIC 3825 1389 Test equipment for electronic & electrical circuits; Testing, measuring, surveying & analysis services; Test equipment for electronic & electrical circuits; Testing, measuring, surveying & analysis services
CEO: George Moore

MC AULIFFE'S INDUSTRIAL
See MCAULIFFE BROS INC

D-U-N-S 18-533-9330
MC BRIDE & SON HOMES INC
(Suby of MCBRIDE & SON ENTERPRISES INC) ★
16091 Swingley Ridge Rd, Chesterfield, MO 63017-2056
Tel (636) 537-2000 Founded/Ownrshp 2000
Sales 179.7MM^E EMP 1,600
SIC 1521 New construction, single-family houses; New construction, single-family houses
Pr: John F Eilermann Jr
*Treas: Michael D Arri
Prd Mgr: Ruth McCormick
Sls Mgr: Amy Ameling
Sls Mgr: Holli Colbert
Sls Mgr: Tom Davidson
Sls Mgr: Carole Gerretsen
Sls Mgr: Kelli Knopf
Sls Mgr: Judy Kocinski
Sls Mgr: Kimberly Lamartina
Sls Mgr: Matt Love

MC CAFFREY'S MARKET
See PRINCETON MARKET INC

MC CANDLESS ISUZU TRUCKS
See MCCANDLESS INTERNATIONAL TRUCKS INC

MC CANN'S ENGINEERING & MFG CO
See MEMC LIQUIDATING CORP

D-U-N-S 00-285-7860
■ **MC CARLS INC**
MCCARL'S
(*Suby of* TALEN ENERGY SERVICES HOLDINGS LLC) ★
1413 9th Ave, Beaver Falls, PA 15010-4106
Tel (724) 843-5660 *Founded/Ownrshp* 1946, 1999
Sales 195.2MM^E *EMP* 1,000
SIC 1711 Mechanical contractor; Process piping contractor; Ventilation & duct work contractor; Warm air heating & air conditioning contractor; Mechanical contractor; Process piping contractor; Ventilation & duct work contractor; Warm air heating & air conditioning contractor
Pr: Robert W Santillo
**VP:* William Cornell
VP: Paul Morrison
Mktg Dir: Dan Rains
Board of Directors: Gary L Banzhoff

D-U-N-S 18-685-2091
MC CARROLL ENTERPRISES INC
SOUTH TACOMA HONDA
7802 South Tacoma Way, Tacoma, WA 98409-3837
Tel (253) 472-2300 *Founded/Ownrshp* 1988
Sales 65.0MM *EMP* 70
SIC 5511 7538 Automobiles, new & used; General automotive repair shops; Automobiles, new & used; General automotive repair shops
Pr: Ed Mc Carroll
Genl Mgr: Dan Kiekenapp
Sales Asso: Jon Buckner
Sales Asso: Jerry Fortner
Sales Asso: Stan Lassley
Sales Asso: Cheryl Martin
Sales Asso: Joey Spitzer
Sales Asso: James Townsend

D-U-N-S 17-566-9639
MC CARTY CORP
13494 Pond Springs Rd, Austin, TX 78729-4410
Tel (512) 331-1344 *Founded/Ownrshp* 1986
Sales 79.5MM^E *EMP* 250
SIC 1541 6411 Industrial buildings, new construction; Insurance agents, brokers & service; Industrial buildings, new construction; Insurance agents, brokers & service
Pr: Mike Mc Carty
**VP:* James N McIntyre

MC CARTY-HULL
See MCCARTY-HULL CIGAR CO INC

MC CAULOU'S DEPARTMENT STORE
See MC-CAULOUS INC

MC CLANCY SEASONING CO
See REMAC CORP

MC CLASKEY ENTERPRISES
See TOD E MC CLASKEY SR

D-U-N-S 01-612-4950
MC CLINTON CHEVROLET CO
1325 7th St, Parkersburg, WV 26101-4913
Tel (304) 422-6501 *Founded/Ownrshp* 1915
Sales 30.3MM^E *EMP* 85
SIC 5511 7538 Automobiles, new & used; Pickups, new & used; Vans, new & used; General automotive repair shops; Automobiles, new & used; Pickups, new & used; Vans, new & used; General automotive repair shops
Pr: James S Mc Clinton Jr
**VP:* James S Mc Clinton III

D-U-N-S 08-486-1954
■ **MC CLURE CO INC**
MC CLURE MECHANICAL SERVICES
(*Suby of* TALEN ENERGY SERVICES HOLDINGS LLC) ★
4101 N 6th St, Harrisburg, PA 17110-1617
Tel (717) 233-6431 *Founded/Ownrshp* 1998
Sales 94.3MM^E *EMP* 350
SIC 1711 Plumbing contractors; Warm air heating & air conditioning contractor; Process piping contractor; Ventilation & duct work contractor; Plumbing contractors; Warm air heating & air conditioning contractor; Process piping contractor; Ventilation & duct work contractor
Pr: Thomas F Brown Jr
**CFO:* Kevin T Bobb
**Ex VP:* Todd C Ray
**VP:* Jerry S Wills
QI Cn Mgr: Mike Vickery
Snr Mgr: Steve Geyer

D-U-N-S 07-559-2378
MC CLURE ENGINEERING ASSOCIATES INC
ROCKFORD DIV
4700 Kennedy Dr, East Moline, IL 61244-4299
Tel (309) 792-9350 *Founded/Ownrshp* 1969
Sales 20.7MM^E *EMP* 176
Accts Carpentier Mitchell Goddard
SIC 8711 8713 Consulting engineer; Surveying services; Consulting engineer; Surveying services
Ch: Larry M Johnson-Collins
**Pr:* Larry Johnson
**CFO:* Timothy J Ziegler
**Ch:* Edward M Collins
**Sr VP:* Paul De Bruyne
**VP:* Harlan Doland
**VP:* J R Novotney
**VP:* David Wright
Div Mgr: Mark Rice
Advt Dir: Susan Hurley

MC CLURE MECHANICAL SERVICES
See MC CLURE CO INC

D-U-N-S 83-201-5395
MC COMPANIES
15170 N Hayden Rd Ste 1, Scottsdale, AZ 85260-2571
Tel (480) 998-5400 *Founded/Ownrshp* 2009
Sales 37.9MM^E *EMP* 350^E
SIC 8742 Real estate consultant; Real estate consultant
Prin: Ross McCallister
Prin: Ken McElroy
VP Mktg: Eric Brown

D-U-N-S 09-892-4681
MC CONNAUGHHAY DUFFY COONRAD POPE & WEAVER PA
1709 Hermitage Blvd # 200, Tallahassee, FL 32308-2705
Tel (850) 385-1246 *Founded/Ownrshp* 1974
Sales 21.6MM^E *EMP* 230
SIC 8111 General practice law office; General practice law office
Pr: James N Mc Connaughhay
Mng Pt: Jana McConnaughhay
Treas: Robert Pope
**Sec:* Mary Wakeman
VP: M Kemmerly
**VP:* Kimmerly Thomas

MC CONNELL CO-OP
See PEARL CITY ELEVATOR INC

D-U-N-S 02-258-1441
MC COOK LTD
MCDONALD'S
923 Cabernet Dr, Chesterfield, MO 63017-8304
Tel (314) 843-7112 *Founded/Ownrshp* 1980
Sales 7.8MM^E *EMP* 300
SIC 5812 Fast-food restaurant, chain; Fast-food restaurant, chain
Pr: Dave Kirkhuff
**Prin:* Janth Kirkhuff

D-U-N-S 82-466-5343
MC COOK PUBLIC SCHOOLS
MCCOOK PUBLIC SCHOOLS
700 W 7th St, Mc Cook, NE 69001-3079
Tel (308) 345-2510 *Founded/Ownrshp* 1888
Sales 14.0MM^E *EMP* 355
SIC 8211 Public combined elementary & secondary school; Public combined elementary & secondary school
Prin: Ron Karr

MC CORMICK CONSTRUCTION CO
See JH MCCORMICK INC

D-U-N-S 06-575-1091
■ **MC COY CO INC**
MC COY SALES
(*Suby of* ORION ENTERPRISES INC) ★
3130 Brinkerhoff Rd, Kansas City, KS 66115-1202
Tel (913) 342-1653 *Founded/Ownrshp* 1969
Sales 30.5MM^E *EMP* 120
SIC 5074 3084 3432 Plumbing & hydronic heating supplies; Plastics pipe; Plumbing fixture fittings & trim; Plumbing & hydronic heating supplies; Plastics pipe; Plumbing fixture fittings & trim
Pr: Joseph Mc Coy
**Treas:* Clay Reeder
**VP:* Bill Mc Coy
**VP:* James B Mc Coy
**VP:* John Mc Coy
Sales Asso: Jeff McCoy
Sales Asso: Alan Merriman

MC COY GROUP
See MC COY INSURANCE INC

D-U-N-S 10-672-4032
MC COY INSURANCE INC
MC COY GROUP
2099 Southpark Ct, Dubuque, IA 52003-8095
Tel (563) 556-3773 *Founded/Ownrshp* 1999
Sales 207.9MM^E *EMP* 1,596^E
SIC 5012 7538 4213 Trucks, commercial; Trailers for trucks, new & used; General truck repair; Contract haulers
Pr: Michael L Mc Coy
VP: John Mc Coy
**VP:* John R McCoy

MC COY SALES
See MC COY CO INC

D-U-N-S 09-809-8221
MC CREARY COUNTY SCHOOL DISTRICT
120 Raider Way, Stearns, KY 42647-6110
Tel (606) 376-2591 *Founded/Ownrshp* 1912
Sales 27.4MM^E *EMP* 717
Accts Marr Miller & Myers Psc Cpa
SIC 8211 8741 Public elementary & secondary schools; Management services; Public elementary & secondary schools; Management services
Pr: Arhur D Wright

MC CREE GEN CONTR & ARCHITECTS
See MCCREE INC

D-U-N-S 00-699-3984
MC CURDY & CO INC
1465 Jefferson Rd, Rochester, NY 14623-3149
Tel (585) 473-6030 *Founded/Ownrshp* 1946
Sales 5.2MM^E *EMP* 310
SIC 6512 Shopping center, property operation only; Commercial & industrial building operation; Shopping center, property operation only; Commercial & industrial building operation
CEO: Gilbert K Mc Curdy
**CFO:* Sidney Rosenbloom
**Ch:* Gilbert G Mc Curdy
Treas: Donald J Krupa
**VP:* Angelo Chiarella

MC CURLEY IMPORTS
See BILL MCCURLEY CHEVROLET INC

D-U-N-S 11-258-9270
MC DANIEL CHEVROLET CADILLAC BUICK INC
MC DANIEL OLDSMOBILE
1065 Mount Vernon Ave, Marion, OH 43302-5536
Tel (740) 389-6335 *Founded/Ownrshp* 1983
Sales 36.2MM^E *EMP* 150
SIC 5511 Automobiles, new & used; Automobiles, new & used
Pr: Michael J Mc Daniel
Exec: Becky Franco
**Genl Mgr:* Jeff Cerny
**Genl Mgr:* James P Waddell
Sales Exec: Rob Knight

MC DANIEL OLDSMOBILE
See MC DANIEL CHEVROLET CADILLAC BUICK INC

D-U-N-S 10-584-4955
■ **MC DAVID DAVID NISSAN INC**
DAVID MC DAVID NISSAN
(*Suby of* ASBURY AUTOMOTIVE GROUP INC) ★
11911 Gulf Fwy, Houston, TX 77034-3599
Tel (713) 941-0600 *Founded/Ownrshp* 1988
Sales 39.6MM^E *EMP* 125
SIC 5511 Automobiles, new & used; Automobiles, new & used
Genl Mgr: Jim Masters
VP: Randy Foust
Exec: Mark Marlin

MC DAVID HONDA
See MCDAVID HOUSTON-HON LP

D-U-N-S 93-141-6622
MC DAVID PLANO ACRA LP
DAVID MC, DAVID ACURA
4051 W Plano Pkwy, Plano, TX 75093-5624
Tel (972) 964-6000 *Founded/Ownrshp* 1986
Sales 41.7MM^E *EMP* 140
SIC 5511 Automobiles, new & used; Automobiles, new & used
Genl Mgr: Renee Huff
Sales Asso: Muffadal Haider

D-U-N-S 04-320-3249 IMP
MC DEAN INC
22980 Indian Creek Dr, Sterling, VA 20166-6732
Tel (571) 262-8234 *Founded/Ownrshp* 1966
Sales 1.2MMM^E *EMP* 3,000
SIC 1731 General electrical contractor; General electrical contractor
Pr: William H Dean
COO: Ron Williams
**Treas:* Norman Douglas Cumins
**VP:* Daniel August
**VP:* James Brabham
VP: Richard Van Dyke
**VP:* Rhett Wade
Comm Man: Paul Kaspar
Div Mgr: Glen McDean
Genl Mgr: James Pattee
DP Exec: Vernon Hall

D-U-N-S 85-845-1578
MC DERMOTT AUTO GROUP
MCDERMOTT CHEVROLET
655 Main St Ste 1, East Haven, CT 06512-2031
Tel (203) 466-1000 *Founded/Ownrshp* 1980
Sales 24.9MM^E *EMP* 85^E
SIC 5511 Automobiles, new & used; Automobiles, new & used
Pr: David McDermott
**Pt:* Sally Mc Dermott
Off Mgr: Maria Desrosier
Sls Mgr: Kaitlin McDermott
Sales Asso: Liam Collins

MC DONALD CADILLAC
See MC DONALD PONTIAC-CADILLAC-GMC INC

D-U-N-S 18-420-6910
MC DONALD COUNTY R1 SCHOOL DISTRICT
10 Stampede Dr, Anderson, MO 64831-7801
Tel (417) 845-8410 *Founded/Ownrshp* 1966
Sales 33.1MM^E *EMP* 595
SIC 8211 Public elementary & secondary schools; Public elementary & secondary schools
Teacher Pr: Staci Williams

D-U-N-S 01-259-6722
MC DONALD METAL & ROOFING SUPPLY CORP (NY)
MCDONALD METAL & ROOFING SUP
1 Avenue M, Brooklyn, NY 11230-4617
Tel (718) 339-0555 *Founded/Ownrshp* 1957
Sales 20.3MM^E *EMP* 20
SIC 5033 Roofing & siding materials
Ch Bd: Richard Rosenthal

D-U-N-S 03-877-7215
MC DONALD PONTIAC-CADILLAC-GMC INC
MC DONALD CADILLAC
5155 State St, Saginaw, MI 48603-3787
Tel (989) 790-5155 *Founded/Ownrshp* 1980
Sales 55.2MM^E *EMP* 143
SIC 5511 Automobiles, new & used; Pickups, new & used; Vans, new & used; Automobiles, new & used; Pickups, new & used; Vans, new & used
Pr: T William Mc Donald Jr
**Pr:* T William Mc Donald
IT Man: Becca Beeckman
Sls Mgr: Dan Seitz
Sls Mgr: Leon Washington
Sales Asso: Bill Urbanski
Sales Asso: Al Wilke

MC DONALD WHOLESALE COMPANY
See MAJOR EAGLE INC

D-U-N-S 07-251-5000
MC DONALDS
CORMAC, INC
(*Suby of* ALLMAC LEASING) ★
150 Hidden Valley Pkwy, Norco, CA 92860-3815
Tel (951) 735-6832 *Founded/Ownrshp* 1971
Sales 7.0MM^E *EMP* 310
SIC 5812 Fast-food restaurant, chain; Fast-food restaurant, chain
Owner: Karen Linton

D-U-N-S 62-348-0100
MC DONALDS OF CALHOUN INC
MCDONALD'S
806 Columbia Ave W, Battle Creek, MI 49015-3030
Tel (269) 965-1402 *Founded/Ownrshp* 1993
Sales 25.8MM^E *EMP* 1,543
SIC 5812 8742 6794 Fast-food restaurant, chain; Management consulting services; Patent owners & lessors; Fast-food restaurant, chain; Management consulting services; Patent owners & lessors
Pr: H Jim Brasseur

D-U-N-S 15-531-6813
MC DONALDS OF ENDICOTT INC
MCDONALD'S
521 E Main St, Endicott, NY 13760-5099
Tel (607) 785-1999 *Founded/Ownrshp* 1980
Sales 8.8MM^E *EMP* 400
SIC 5812 Fast-food restaurant, chain; Fast-food restaurant, chain
Pr: Elizabeth Dibbil
**Pr:* Elizabeth Dibble
**VP:* Beth Dibble

MC DONOUGH CNTY REHABILITATION
See COUNTY OF MC DONOUGH

D-U-N-S 07-268-2271
MC DOWELL COUNTY BOARD OF EDUCATION
MC DOWELL PUBLIC SCHOOLS
30 Central Ave, Welch, WV 24801-2008
Tel (304) 436-8441 *Founded/Ownrshp* 1935
Sales 40.8MM *EMP* 675
Accts Independent
SIC 8211 Public elementary & secondary schools; High school, junior or senior; School board; Public elementary & secondary schools; High school, junior or senior; School board
Prin: Suzette Cook

D-U-N-S 09-333-6857
MC DOWELL COUNTY BOARD OF EDUCATION (INC)
MC DOWELL COUNTY SCHOOLS
334 S Main St, Marion, NC 28752-4527
Tel (828) 652-4535 *Founded/Ownrshp* 1890
Sales 49.9MM^E *EMP* 1,000
Accts Johnson Price & Sprinkle Pa
SIC 8211 Public elementary & secondary schools; Public elementary & secondary schools
**CTO:* Slutsky Aaron
Dir IT: Aaron Slutsky
IT Man: Kelly Combes
Pr Dir: Glenda Dean

MC DOWELL COUNTY SCHOOLS
See MC DOWELL COUNTY BOARD OF EDUCATION (INC)

MC DOWELL PUBLIC SCHOOLS
See MC DOWELL COUNTY BOARD OF EDUCATION

D-U-N-S 02-407-4205
MC ELECTRONICS LLC
1891 Airway Dr, Hollister, CA 95023-9099
Tel (831) 637-1651 *Founded/Ownrshp* 2012
Sales 77.8MM^E *EMP* 399
SIC 3679 Harness assemblies for electronic use: wire or cable; Harness assemblies for electronic use: wire or cable
CEO: Shawn Thompson
Pr: Alan Clark
CIO: Joel Peterson

D-U-N-S 02-207-2755
MC ELENEY MOTORS INC
MCELENEY CHEV-BUICK-GMC-TOYOTA
2421 Lincoln Way, Clinton, IA 52732-7207
Tel (563) 243-7000 *Founded/Ownrshp* 1914
Sales 34.1MM^E *EMP* 130
SIC 5511 7538 5521 Automobiles, new & used; Pickups, new & used; General automotive repair shops; Used car dealers; Automobiles, new & used; Pickups, new & used; General automotive repair shops; Used car dealers
Pr: John McEleney
COO: Mark Chasey
VP Mktg: Robert Eads
VP Mktg: Steve Luskey
VP Mktg: Marv Thompson
Mktg Dir: Jenn Clydesdale
Mktg Dir: John Connolly
Sls Mgr: Matt Rittmer

D-U-N-S 11-534-2859
MC ELROY DEUTSCH MULVANEY & CARPERNTER LLP
MDM&C
1300 Mount Kemble Ave, Morristown, NJ 07960-8009
Tel (973) 993-8100 *Founded/Ownrshp* 1983
Sales 120.0MM *EMP* 550
SIC 8111 General practice law office; General practice law office
Mng Pt: Edward B Deutsch
Pt: Joseph P Lasala
Pt: James M Mulvaney
Mng Pt: Glen Laird
CFO: John A Dunlea
IT Man: Jamie Howlett
Counsel: Robert Berta
Counsel: Joseph Campbell
Counsel: Robert Clifford
Counsel: Daniel Esposito
Counsel: Everett Gale

MC ELWAIN OLDSMOBILE
See MCELWAIN MOTORS LTD

MC FARLAND CASCADE
See MCFARLAND CASCADE HOLDINGS INC

D-U-N-S 03-584-1410
MC FARLAND STATE BANK
(*Suby of* NORTHERN BANKSHARES, INC)
5990 Us Highway 51, Mc Farland, WI 53558-9422
Tel (608) 838-3141 *Founded/Ownrshp* 1905
Sales NA *EMP* 31
SIC 6022 State commercial banks; State commercial banks
Pr: E David Locke
**Pr:* Steve Swanson
Ofcr: Diana Collins
Ofcr: Debbie Hodge
**Ex VP:* James E Walker

Sr VP: Mark Schubring
VP: Matt Golden
Brnch Mgr: Jeff Boudreau

D-U-N-S 19-693-0572
MC FARLAND UNIFIED SCHOOL DISTRICT
601 2nd St, Mc Farland, CA 93250-1121
Tel (661) 792-3081 *Founded/Ownrshp* 1980
Sales 18.8MM^E *EMP* 300
SIC 8211 Public elementary & secondary schools; Public elementary & secondary schools

MC FARLANE IMPLEMENT
See MC FARLANE MANUFACTURING CO INC

D-U-N-S 00-642-6381 IMP/EXP
MC FARLANE MANUFACTURING CO INC (WI)
MC FARLANE IMPLEMENT
780 Carolina St, Sauk City, WI 53583-1369
Tel (608) 643-3321 *Founded/Ownrshp* 1919
Sales 63.0MM *EMP* 180
SIC 3441 5083 5191 3523

MC GHEE TYSON AIRPORT
See METROPOLITAN KNOXVILLE AIRPORT AUTHORITY

MC GINNIS COLLISION CENTER
See MCGINNIS CADILLAC INC

D-U-N-S 13-755-8532
MC GINNIS LOCHRIDGE KILGORE LLP
600 Congress Ave, Austin, TX 78701-3238
Tel (512) 495-6021 *Founded/Ownrshp* 1946
Sales 24.1MM^E *EMP* 152
SIC 8111 General practice law office; General practice law office
Pt: Tom Barton
Pt: Travis Barton
Pt: Kevin M Beiter
Pt: Bill Bingham
Pt: John Breihan
Pt: Brook Brown
Mng Pt: Cristina Urbieta
Pr: Angie Espinoza
Pr: Mary Leonard
Pr: Tammy Matthes
Pr: Jennifer Regalado

MC GINNIS SISTERS
See MCGINNIS SISTERS FOOD CENTER INC

D-U-N-S 03-842-6743
MC GOWAN BUILDERS INC
160 E Union Ave, East Rutherford, NJ 07073-2124
Tel (201) 865-4666 *Founded/Ownrshp* 2001
Sales 30.0MM^E *EMP* 57
SIC 1542 Commercial & office building, new construction
Ch Bd: Patrick J Mc Gowan
**Pr:* Martin C Mc Gowan
**CFO:* A Forte Maldonado
**CFO:* Forte Maldonado
VP: Sean McSharry

MC GRATH NISSAN
See NISSAN MC GRATH INC

D-U-N-S 18-757-0577
MC GRAW COMMERCIAL INSURANCE SERVICE INC
3601 Haven Ave, Menlo Park, CA 94025-1064
Tel (650) 780-4800 *Founded/Ownrshp* 1984
Sales NA *EMP* 141
SIC 6411 Insurance agents & brokers
Pr: Michael J Mc Graw
Treas: Brian McSweeney
**Sec:* Joan D Mc Graw
**VP:* John M Mc Graw
Manager: Jason Alexander

D-U-N-S 09-701-2074
MC GRAW INSURANCE SERVICES CO
3601 Haven Ave, Menlo Park, CA 94025-1033
Tel (650) 780-4800 *Founded/Ownrshp* 1976
Sales NA *EMP* 100
Accts Larson & Rosenberger Llp Glen
SIC 6411 Insurance agents, brokers & service
Ch Bd: John V Mc Graw
**CFO:* Richard Fowler
**Ex VP:* Timothy Summers
Web Dev: Vidya Gedela

D-U-N-S 00-798-9015 IMP
MC GREGOR CO (IA)
MCGREGOR'S FURNITURE
111 W Main St, Marshalltown, IA 50158-5843
Tel (641) 753-6627 *Founded/Ownrshp* 1896
Sales 33.7MM^E *EMP* 140
SIC 5712 5713 Furniture stores; Carpets; Furniture stores; Carpets
Pr: James R Mc Gregor III
**VP:* Robert S Mc Gregor

D-U-N-S 03-389-3603
MC GUFFEY SCHOOL DISTRICT
90 Mcguffey Dr, Claysville, PA 15323-2304
Tel (724) 948-3731 *Founded/Ownrshp* 1942
Sales 18.9MM^E *EMP* 276
SIC 8211 Public elementary & secondary schools; Public elementary & secondary schools

D-U-N-S 01-155-6677
MC GUIRE AUTO SALES
MCGUIRE CHVCADILLAC OLDS ISUZU
41 Main St 47, Newton, NJ 07860-2023
Tel (973) 383-1300 *Founded/Ownrshp* 1900
Sales 25.0MM *EMP* 45
SIC 5511 Automobiles, new & used; Automobiles, new & used
Pr: Michael Mc Guire
**VP:* Camille Mc Guire
Sls Mgr: Frank Philhower

D-U-N-S 09-332-8599
MC GUIRE MEMORIAL (INC)
2119 Mercer Rd, New Brighton, PA 15066-3421
Tel (724) 843-3400 *Founded/Ownrshp* 1963
Sales 21.2MM^E *EMP* 400^E
SIC 8052 Intermediate care facilities; Intermediate care facilities
CFO: Jack Roth
VP: Karen Scanlon
VP: Chris Shay
Ex Dir: John Dobi
Ex Dir: Mary Thaddeus

MC GUIRES CATERING
See MC GUIRES IRISH PUB INC

D-U-N-S 10-695-5594
MC GUIRES IRISH PUB INC
MC GUIRES CATERING
600 E Gregory St, Pensacola, FL 32502-4153
Tel (850) 433-2849 *Founded/Ownrshp* 1977
Sales 22.7MM^E *EMP* 600
SIC 5812 5813 Caterers; Tavern (drinking places); Caterers; Tavern (drinking places)
Pr: Molly Martin
**Sec:* William M Martin

D-U-N-S 03-961-5745
MC HENRY COMMUNITY HIGH SCHOOL DISTRICT 156
4716 W Crystal Lake Rd, McHenry, IL 60050-5427
Tel (815) 385-7900 *Founded/Ownrshp* 1850
Sales 17.0MM^E *EMP* 281
SIC 8211 Public elementary & secondary schools; Public elementary & secondary schools
**CFO:* Jeff Ehardt
IT Man: Bill Hobson
Schl Brd P: Steve Bellmore

D-U-N-S 08-205-2341
MC HENRY ELEMENTARY DISTRICT 15
1011 N Green St, McHenry, IL 60050-5720
Tel (815) 578-0862 *Founded/Ownrshp* 1894
Sales 3.4MM^E *EMP* 315
SIC 8211 Elementary school; School board; Elementary school; School board
Pr: Lucy I Fick
Off Mgr: Mary Pautz
Board of Directors: Christopher Cardamone, Paula Ekstrom, Michael Guy, Michael Morris, Michael Rakestraw

D-U-N-S 19-804-3841
MC INDUSTRIAL INC
(*Suby of* MCCARTHY HOLDINGS INC) ★
3117 S Big Bend Blvd, Saint Louis, MO 63143-3901
Tel (314) 646-4100 *Founded/Ownrshp* 2005
Sales 53.8MM *EMP* 261
Accts Rubinbrown Llp Saint Louis M
SIC 1541 Industrial buildings, new construction; Industrial buildings, new construction
Pr: Tom Felton
**CFO:* J Douglas Audiffred
**Treas:* Danel J Dillon
**Sr VP:* Robert Kohlburn
VP: Mike Mooney
Sfty Mgr: Jon Sigafoos

D-U-N-S 10-351-3768
MC INERNEY INC
HOOT MCINERNEY CADILLAC-TOYOTA
37777 S Gratiot Ave, Clinton Township, MI 48036-2706
Tel (586) 463-9000 *Founded/Ownrshp* 1982
Sales 38.8MM^E *EMP* 140
SIC 5511 Automobiles, new & used; Automobiles, new & used
Pr: Martin J Mc Inerney
**Genl Mgr:* Robert Mc Inerney
Sls Mgr: Craig Muran

MC IRONWORKS
See MICHELMAN-CANCELLIERE IRONWORKS INC

MC KAIG CHEVROLET GEO
See LMK AUTO GROUP LIMITED

D-U-N-S 93-933-7333
MC KAREN INDUSTRIES INC
MCDONALD'S
4131 N Central Expy # 640, Dallas, TX 75204-2102
Tel (214) 520-2596 *Founded/Ownrshp* 1990
Sales 15.0MM *EMP* 300
SIC 5812 8741 Fast-food restaurant, chain; Restaurant management; Fast-food restaurant, chain; Restaurant management
Pr: Karen Skinner
**VP:* Craig York

MC KAY'S FOOD & DRUG
See FAIRLAND MARKET INC

D-U-N-S 09-372-6594
MC KEE GROUP
FOXFIELD AT NAAMAN'S CREEK
940 W Sproul Rd Ste 301, Springfield, PA 19064-1255
Tel (610) 604-9800 *Founded/Ownrshp* 1969
Sales 20.9MM^E *EMP* 160
SIC 6512 7513 Nonresidential building operators; Truck rental & leasing, no drivers
Pr: Frank J McKee
VP: Kathryn Black

MC KENNA VW PORSCHE AUDI BMW
See MCKENNA MOTOR CO INC

MC KENNY-SLNAS HNDA MITSUBISHI
See M & S AUTOMOBILE SALES INC

MC KENZIE TAXIDERMY SUPPLY
See MCKENZIE SPORTS PRODUCTS LLC

D-U-N-S 04-349-6975
MC KIM FOODS INC
MC KIM'S IGA FOODLINER
13th & State St, Lawrenceville, IL 62439
Tel (618) 943-2767 *Founded/Ownrshp* 1968
Sales 25.1MM^E *EMP* 300
SIC 5411 Grocery stores; Grocery stores
Pr: John R Mc Kim
**Treas:* Barbara Mc Kim
**VP:* Brett Mc Kim

MC KIM'S IGA FOODLINER
See MC KIM FOODS INC

D-U-N-S 00-483-8074
MC KNIGHT CONSTRUCTION CO INC (GA)
635 Nw Frontage Rd, Augusta, GA 30907-2451
Tel (706) 863-7784 *Founded/Ownrshp* 1946
Sales 65.9MM *EMP* 100
Accts Cherry Bekaert Llp Augusta G
SIC 1542 1541 Shopping center construction; Hospital construction; Institutional building construction; Industrial buildings, new construction; Shopping center construction; Hospital construction; Institutional building construction; Industrial buildings, new construction
Pr: William D Mc Knight
Sls Mgr: Connie Kindberg

D-U-N-S 01-034-7144
MC KNIGHT FOUNDATION
710 S 2nd St Ste 400, Minneapolis, MN 55401-2290
Tel (612) 333-4220 *Founded/Ownrshp* 1953
Sales 113.1MM *EMP* 40
SIC 6732 Educational trust management; Educational trust management
Pr: Kate Wolford
Treas: Ted Staryk
Ofcr: Erin Gavin
Ofcr: Ron Kroese
Ofcr: Arleta Little
Ofcr: Sarah Lovan
Ofcr: Becky Monnens
Ofcr: Eric Muschler
Prgrm Mgr: Karyn Johnson
Prgrm Mgr: Eileen Maler
Prgrm Mgr: Kristen Marx

MC LARTY AUTOMALL
See FORD MC LARTY INC

D-U-N-S 03-627-4306
MC LAUGHLIN MOTORS INC
MCLAUGHLIN FORD
950 N Main St, Sumter, SC 29150-2831
Tel (803) 773-1481 *Founded/Ownrshp* 1957
Sales 21.2MM^E *EMP* 50
SIC 5511

D-U-N-S 11-747-6077
MC LAUGHLIN OLDSMOBILE CADILLAC INC
MCLAUGHLIN MOTORS
4101 41st St, Moline, IL 61265-6780
Tel (309) 797-5654 *Founded/Ownrshp* 1984
Sales 22.3MM^E *EMP* 62
SIC 5511 7532 Automobiles, new & used; Top & body repair & paint shops; Automobiles, new & used; Top & body repair & paint shops
Pr: Pete McLaughlin
**VP:* Greg Swanson

D-U-N-S 06-086-3032
MC LEAN COUNTY UNIT SCHOOL DISTRICT 5
1809 Hovey Ave, Normal, IL 61761-4315
Tel (309) 452-4476 *Founded/Ownrshp* 1948
Sales 69.7MM^E *EMP* 1,117
SIC 8211 Public elementary school; Public junior high school; Public senior high school; Public elementary school; Public junior high school; Public senior high school
Treas: Dawn Watson
IT Man: Elizabeth Sparrow

D-U-N-S 05-145-2047
MC LEAN HOME
75 Great Pond Rd, Simsbury, CT 06070-1999
Tel (860) 658-3700 *Founded/Ownrshp* 2010
Sales 27.6MM *EMP* 44^E
SIC 8059 Nursing & personal care; Nursing & personal care
Prin: Terry Dell
VP: Lisa Clark
Exec: Cathy Taft

D-U-N-S 80-680-4837
MC LEANS CP INSTALLATION
4520 State Highway 136, Amarillo, TX 79108-7617
Tel (806) 383-5047 *Founded/Ownrshp* 1963
Sales 20.5MM^E *EMP* 16^E
SIC 1799 Corrosion control installation; Corrosion control installation
Pr: Dennis Mc Lean
**VP:* Calvin McLean
**VP:* Judy McLeans
**VP:* Scott Young

MC LEAS TIRE & AUTOMOTIVE SVC
See MC LEAS TIRE SERVICE INC

D-U-N-S 15-276-0831
MC LEAS TIRE SERVICE INC
MC LEAS TIRE & AUTOMOTIVE SVC
800 Piner Rd, Santa Rosa, CA 95403-2021
Tel (707) 542-0363 *Founded/Ownrshp* 1986
Sales 32.4MM^E *EMP* 77
SIC 5531 5014 7539 Automotive tires; Automobile tires & tubes; Truck tires & tubes; Brake repair, automotive; Tune-up service, automotive; Front end repair, automotive; Wheel alignment, automotive
CEO: Larry L McLea
**Pr:* Lester V McLea
**VP:* Richard W McLea

MC LENNAN COMMUNITY COLLEGE
See MC LENNAN COUNTY JUNIOR COLLEGE DISTRICT

D-U-N-S 06-897-5598
MC LENNAN COUNTY JUNIOR COLLEGE DISTRICT (TX)
MC LENNAN COMMUNITY COLLEGE
1400 College Dr, Waco, TX 76708-1402
Tel (254) 299-8000 *Founded/Ownrshp* 1966
Sales 18.4MM *EMP* 700
SIC 8222 Junior college; Junior college
Pr: Johnette Mc Kown
Dir Vol: Rita Tejada
Pr: Patricia Chavet
CFO: Joan Williams
Trst: Randy Cox
Ofcr: Thomas Frost
VP: Drew Canham
VP: Alvin Pollard
Assoc Dir: Becky Parker
Assoc Dir: Joshua Rieff
Assoc Dir: April Robinson
Board of Directors: Pauline Chavez, Randy Cox, Don Hay, Linda Hilliard, James Lewis Bob Sheehy

D-U-N-S 14-701-0904
MC LEOD ADDICTIVE DISEASE CENTER INC
MCLEOD ADDICTIVE DISEASE CENTE
515 Clanton Rd, Charlotte, NC 28217-1309
Tel (704) 332-9001 *Founded/Ownrshp* 1978
Sales 20.7MM *EMP* 115
SIC 8069 8093 Alcoholism rehabilitation hospital; Drug addiction rehabilitation hospital; Alcohol clinic, outpatient; Drug clinic, outpatient; Alcoholism rehabilitation hospital; Drug addiction rehabilitation hospital; Alcohol clinic, outpatient; Drug clinic, outpatient
Pr: Eugene Hall
Trst: Rick Brown
Prgrm Mgr: Michael Current
Prgrm Mgr: Shannon Stewart
Off Admin: Jessica Jones
Off Admin: Jessie Smith
Off Admin: Lynette Thompson
Dir IT: Trina Fullard
Dir IT: Helen Romano
IT Man: Tonda Wilde
Opers Supe: Danny Graves

D-U-N-S 19-379-3101
MC LLC
JIFFY LUBE
1422 Edinger Ave Ste 150, Tustin, CA 92780-6299
Tel (714) 444-4940 *Founded/Ownrshp* 2004
Sales 14.3MM^E *EMP* 888
SIC 7549 Lubrication service, automotive

D-U-N-S 00-543-5904
MC LUCKIE OIL CO INC
120 S 1st Ave, Coal City, IL 60416-1313
Tel (815) 634-8374 *Founded/Ownrshp* 1946
Sales 20.9MM *EMP* 4
Accts Mccarthy & Mchugh Ltd Joliet
SIC 5171 Petroleum bulk stations & terminals; Petroleum bulk stations & terminals
Pr: David L McLuckie

D-U-N-S 78-152-3352 IMP
MC MACHINERY SYSTEMS INC
MITSUBISHI EDM/LASER
(*Suby of* MITSUBISHI CORP (AMERICAS)) ★
1500 N Michael Dr Ofc, Wood Dale, IL 60191-1067
Tel (630) 860-4217 *Founded/Ownrshp* 1991
Sales 57.2MM^E *EMP* 160
SIC 5065 5084

MC MAHAN CONSTRUCTION CO
See MCMAHAN CO INC

D-U-N-S 01-345-8054
MC MAHONS OF CENTRAL SQUARE INC
240 Oneida St, Syracuse, NY 13202-3317
Tel (315) 475-2111 *Founded/Ownrshp* 1954
Sales 60.0MM *EMP* 7
SIC 5143 5451 Dairy products, except dried or canned; Dairy products stores; Dairy products, except dried or canned; Dairy products stores
Pr: William Byrne
**Pr:* William M Byrne Jr

D-U-N-S 80-517-0164
MC MANAGEMENT INC
301 State Route 10, Whippany, NJ 07981-2104
Tel (973) 884-9555 *Founded/Ownrshp* 1990
Sales 55.4MM^E *EMP* 700
SIC 8742 Management consulting services; Management consulting services
Pr: Paul Gunther
CTO: Jay Jainauch

D-U-N-S 07-490-7270
MC MINN COUNTY
MC MINN COUNTY BOARD EDUCATION
6 E Madison Ave, Athens, TN 37303-3697
Tel (423) 745-2743 *Founded/Ownrshp* 1819
Sales NA *EMP* 800
Accts Henderson Hutcherson & Mccullo
SIC 9111 Executive offices; ; Executive offices;

MC MINN COUNTY BOARD EDUCATION
See MC MINN COUNTY

MC MINN MEMORIAL NURSING HOME
See DHMC LLC

D-U-N-S 00-792-1596
MC MINNVILLE ELECTRIC SYSTEM
200 W Morford St, McMinnville, TN 37110-2528
Tel (931) 473-3144 *Founded/Ownrshp* 1939
Sales 21.3MM *EMP* 33
SIC 4911 Electric services; Electric services
Ex Dir: Rodney Boyd

D-U-N-S 79-884-8537 IMP/EXP
MC NAIRN PACKAGING INC
6 Elise St, Westfield, MA 01085-1414
Tel (413) 568-1989 *Founded/Ownrshp* 1991
Sales 36.0MM^E *EMP* 110
SIC 2621 Packaging paper; Packaging paper
Pr: Ken W A Miller
**COO:* Bart Gogarty
**CFO:* Dennis Czosnek
MIS Mgr: Larry Coe
Prd Mgr: Alan Kitch

D-U-N-S 13-816-3258
MC NAIRY COUNTY BOARD OF EDUCATION
BOARD OF EDUCATION OFFICE
170 W Court Ave Ste 107, Selmer, TN 38375-2134
Tel (731) 645-3267 *Founded/Ownrshp* 2000
Sales 18.8MM^E *EMP* 690
SIC 8211 Public combined elementary & secondary school; School board; Public combined elementary & secondary school; School board

MC NEESE STATE UNIV BKSTR
See MC NEESE STATE UNIVERSITY

D-U-N-S 07-843-0295
MC NEESE STATE UNIVERSITY
MC NEESE STATE UNIV BKSTR
(*Suby of* UNIVERSITIES OF LOUISIANA SYSTEM) ★
4205 Ryan St, Lake Charles, LA 70605-4500
Tel (337) 475-5000 *Founded/Ownrshp* 1970
Sales 52.5MM *EMP* 894
SIC 8221 9411 University; Administration of educational programs; ; University; Administration of educational programs;
Pr: Philip Williams
Pr: Dennis Stutes
**VP:* Jeanne Daboval
VP: Kalil P Ieyoub
**VP:* Eddie Meche
VP: Eddie P Meche
**VP:* Richard Reid
VP: Richard H Reid
Assoc Dir: Shannon Guillory
Mng Ofcr: Michael Snowden
Ex Dir: Braylon Harris

MC PHERSON OIL PRODUCTS
See MCPHERSON COMPANIES INC

MC QUADE'S MARKET PLACE
See E & A MARKETS INC

D-U-N-S 02-765-1249
MC ROBERT MOTOR CO INC
GRESHAM FORD
1999 E Powell Blvd, Gresham, OR 97080-8047
Tel (503) 665-0101 *Founded/Ownrshp* 2003
Sales 32.5MM^E *EMP* 75
SIC 5511 Automobiles, new & used; Automobiles, new & used
Pr: Silvestre Gonzales
**Sec:* Bess Wills
Sales Asso: Sam Rich

D-U-N-S 02-041-3720
MC ROBERTS CORP
87 Nassau St, New York, NY 10038-3710
Tel (212) 425-2500 *Founded/Ownrshp* 1993
Sales 93.9MM^E *EMP* 3,800
SIC 7381 Detective & armored car services; Detective & armored car services
Pr: Meredith Mc Roberts
**CFO:* Jeff Chludzinski
VP: Paul Bristow
IT Man: Michael Martone

D-U-N-S 00-421-7626
MC SIGN CO (OH)
8959 Tyler Blvd, Mentor, OH 44060-2184
Tel (440) 209-6200 *Founded/Ownrshp* 1995, 2015
Sales 41.6MM^E *EMP* 160
SIC 3993 2752 7336 Neon signs; Commercial art & graphic design; Commercial printing, lithographic; Signs & advertising specialties; Commercial printing, lithographic; Commercial art & graphic design
Pr: Tim Eippert
COO: Tim Ruff
VP: Ryan Goldberg
VP: Jeff Mottice
Exec: Ralph Sassi
Prgrm Mgr: Dan Powell
CTO: Jim Mueller
Natl Sales: Robbye Chasteen
Natl Sales: Tanya Plescia
Natl Sales: Paul Southard

D-U-N-S 03-210-4291
MC SOUTHWEST INC
R E MONKS CONSTRUCTION CO
8355 Vollmer Rd, Colorado Springs, CO 80908-4721
Tel (719) 495-3621 *Founded/Ownrshp* 1983
Sales 62.6MM^E *EMP* 150
SIC 1629 Earthmoving contractor; Land clearing contractor; Dam construction; Earthmoving contractor; Land clearing contractor; Dam construction
Pr: Richard Monks
**Owner:* Daniel Monks
**Sec:* Cheri Bergst
**VP:* George Wehner
Opers Mgr: Greigg Newlon

MC SPORTS
See MICHIGAN SPORTING GOODS DISTRIBUTORS INC

MC SQUARE
See CREATIVE MANAGEMENT SERVICES LLC

D-U-N-S 07-994-2077
MC TIRES
538 Olive Ave Ste 304, Vista, CA 92083-3481
Tel (760) 846-5613 *Founded/Ownrshp* 2014
Sales 250.0MM *EMP* 2
SIC 5014 5531 Tires, used; Automotive tires
Owner: Rosa Calderon

D-U-N-S 61-136-5115 IMP/EXP
MC TUBULAR PRODUCTS INC
(*Suby of* METAL ONE HOLDINGS AMERICA INC) ★
757 N Eldridge Pkwy # 650, Houston, TX 77079-4528
Tel (281) 870-1212 *Founded/Ownrshp* 2003
Sales 31.1MM^E *EMP* 26^E
SIC 5051 Pipe & tubing, steel
CEO: Mikihiko Matsushita
**Pr:* Hiroyuki Morita
**Ex VP:* Nobuhiko Hayashi
**Ex VP:* Jun Utagawa
Snr Mgr: William Barnes

MC WHORTER'S TIRE CO
See MCWHORTHER TIRE CO LTD

D-U-N-S 95-711-7120
MC WIL GROUP LTD
WILMAC
209 N Beaver St, York, PA 17401-5321
Tel (717) 854-7857 *Founded/Ownrshp* 1995
Sales 93.1MM^E *EMP* 1,500
SIC 8059 8051 8069 6513 8742 6552 Convalescent home; Skilled nursing care facilities; Substance abuse hospitals; Apartment building operators; Hospital & health services consultant; Land subdividers & developers, commercial; Convalescent home; Skilled nursing care facilities; Substance abuse hospitals; Apartment building operators; Hospital & health services consultant; Land subdividers & developers, commercial
Pr: Karen Mc Cormack
Treas: Vincent Reigle
**VP:* Richard W Bricker
**VP:* D James Mc Cormack
**VP:* Ray A Wilson

D-U-N-S 10-389-8771
MC&A INC
615 Piikoi St Ste 1000, Honolulu, HI 96814-3141
Tel (808) 589-5568 *Founded/Ownrshp* 1983
Sales 46.9MM *EMP* 220
Accts G Ushijima Cpa Llc Honolulu
SIC 4725 Arrangement of travel tour packages, wholesale; Tours, conducted; Arrangement of travel tour packages, wholesale; Tours, conducted
Ch Bd: Chris Resich
**CFO:* Clayton Tsuchiyama
**Sr VP:* Michael Fukumoto
**Sr VP:* Mary Beth Kahn
VP: Paul Johnson
Dir Soc: Sue Orsini
Ex Dir: Sharon Baylay
Ex Dir: Leslie Brewster
Mng Dir: Mario Cucinella

D-U-N-S 02-834-4372
MC-CAULOUS INC
MC CAULOU'S DEPARTMENT STORE
3512 Mt Diablo Blvd, Lafayette, CA 94549-3895
Tel (925) 283-3380 *Founded/Ownrshp* 1963
Sales 54.9MM^E *EMP* 500
SIC 5651 5999 5947 Family clothing stores; Cosmetics; Gift shop; Family clothing stores; Cosmetics; Gift shop
Pr: David R Mc Caulou
CFO: Ken Stoddard

D-U-N-S 02-811-6184
MC-NEECE BROSOIL CO INC
691 E Heil Ave, El Centro, CA 92243-4603
Tel (760) 352-4721 *Founded/Ownrshp* 1959
Sales 65.4MM^E *EMP* 85
SIC 5172 5984 Service station supplies, petroleum; Gasoline; Liquefied petroleum gas dealers; Service station supplies, petroleum; Gasoline; Liquefied petroleum gas dealers
Pr: Robert Mc Neece II
**Treas:* Michael Mc Neece

MCA
See NIKKEI MC ALUMINUM AMERICA INC

D-U-N-S 11-436-1033
MCA COMMUNICATIONS INC
525 Northville St, Houston, TX 77037-1230
Tel (281) 591-2434 *Founded/Ownrshp* 1983
Sales 26.3MM *EMP* 115
SIC 1731 7382 Telephone & telephone equipment installation; Security systems services; Telephone & telephone equipment installation; Security systems services
Pr: Richard Cortez
**Ofcr:* Ray G Hernandez
**VP:* Ricky C Cortez

MCAAA
See MICHIGAN COMMUNITY ACTION AGENCY ASSOCIATION

D-U-N-S 00-401-3579
MCABEE CONSTRUCTION INC (AL)
5724 21st St, Tuscaloosa, AL 35401-2555
Tel (205) 349-2212 *Founded/Ownrshp* 1962
Sales 150.6MM *EMP* 800
Accts Jamison Money Farmer Pc Tusca
SIC 1711 1796 3443 1531 Plumbing, heating, air-conditioning contractors; Installing building equipment; Fabricated plate work (boiler shop); Operative builders; Plumbing, heating, air-conditioning contractors; Installing building equipment; Fabricated plate work (boiler shop); Operative builders
CEO: Leroy McAbee
**Pr:* Gary Nichols
**Treas:* Ruth B McAbee
**VP:* Wendell McAbee
**VP:* Leah A Sexton
IT Man: Kevin Shipp
Sfty Mgr: Michael Shirk

D-U-N-S 92-685-0702
MCADA DRILLING FLUIDS INC
720 Avenue F N, Bay City, TX 77414-9573
Tel (979) 244-3444 *Founded/Ownrshp* 1989
Sales 52.8MM^E *EMP* 145
SIC 5169 Drilling mud; Drilling mud
Pr: James S McAda
**VP:* Sherri S Mills
Off Mgr: Patti Rodriquez
Board of Directors: Helen R McAda

D-U-N-S 11-411-1412
MCADAMS GRAPHICS INC
7200 S 1st St, Oak Creek, WI 53154-2004
Tel (414) 768-8080 *Founded/Ownrshp* 1982
Sales 33.7MM^E *EMP* 115
SIC 2752 2759 Commercial printing, offset; Commercial printing; Commercial printing, offset; Commercial printing
Pr: Gerald E McAdams
**VP:* Dan McAdams
**VP:* Peter McAdams
Genl Mgr: Alan McAdams

D-U-N-S 04-781-3886
MCAF LLC
MCSWAIN CARPETS & FLOORS
2430 E Kemper Rd, Cincinnati, OH 45241-5805
Tel (513) 771-1400 *Founded/Ownrshp* 1968
Sales 31.1MM^E *EMP* 115
SIC 5713

D-U-N-S 07-426-3708
MCAFEE & TAFT A PROFESSIONAL CORP
211 N Robinson Ave Fl 10, Oklahoma City, OK 73102-7176
Tel (405) 235-9621 *Founded/Ownrshp* 1952
Sales 41.5MM^E *EMP* 300
SIC 8111 General practice attorney, lawyer; General practice attorney, lawyer
COO: Matt Bown
COO: Tony Puckett
CFO: Michael Mewbourn
**Ch:* John Hermes
Bd of Dir: Michael E Joseph
Bd of Dir: Michael F Lauderdale
Bd of Dir: Dianna McCaulla
Bd of Dir: Elizabeth Tyrrell
VP: Cynthia David
VP: Michael Duncan
VP: Richard Miller
VP: Thomas Mullen
Exec: Stephanie Chapman
Exec: Martha West

D-U-N-S 60-620-5433
■ **MCAFEE INC**
(*Suby of* INTEL CORP) ★
2821 Mission College Blvd, Santa Clara, CA 95054-1838
Tel (408) 346-3832 *Founded/Ownrshp* 2011
Sales 1.6MMM^E *EMP* 7,852
SIC 7372 Prepackaged software; Application computer software; Business oriented computer software; Prepackaged software; Application computer software; Business oriented computer software
Pr: Michael Decesare
Pr: Jean-Claude Broido
Pr: Tom Miglis
COO: Peter Watkins
CFO: Jonathan Chadwick
Bd of Dir: Kevin Jacobs
Chf Mktg O: Penny Baldwin
Chf Mktg O: David Milam
Ofcr: Mark Cochran
Ex VP: Bryan Reed Barney
Ex VP: Michael Decesare
Ex VP: Michael Fey
Ex VP: Joseph Gabbert
Ex VP: Todd Gebhart
Ex VP: Roger King
Ex VP: George Kurtz
Ex VP: Barry McPherson
Ex VP: Gerhard Watzinger
Sr VP: John Giamatteo
Sr VP: Rees Johnson
Sr VP: Stuart McClure

D-U-N-S 07-956-5058
■ **MCAFEE SECURITY LLC**
(*Suby of* MCAFEE INC) ★
2821 Mission College Blvd, Santa Clara, CA 95054-1838
Tel (888) 847-8760 *Founded/Ownrshp* 2006
Sales 90.2MM^E *EMP* 6,210
SIC 7372 Prepackaged software; Application computer software; Business oriented computer software; Prepackaged software; Application computer software; Business oriented computer software
Pr: Michael Decesare
CFO: Bob Kelly
Sr VP: Edward Hayden
Sr VP: Louis Riley

D-U-N-S 80-136-6191 IMP
MCAIRLAIDS INC
(*Suby of* MCAIRLAID'S VLIESSTOFFE GMBH)
180 Corporate Dr, Rocky Mount, VA 24151-3899
Tel (540) 352-5050 *Founded/Ownrshp* 2006
Sales 53.3MM^E *EMP* 165
SIC 2621 Absorbent paper; Absorbent paper
Ch Bd: Alexander Maksimow
**Pr:* Peter J Gawley
**VP:* Andreas Schmidt
Exec: Peter Gonzales
Sls Dir: David Stevenson

D-U-N-S 09-476-9726
MCALESTER REGIONAL HEALTH CENTER AUTHORITY
MRHC
1 E Clark Bass Blvd, McAlester, OK 74501-4209
Tel (918) 421-6767 *Founded/Ownrshp* 1978
Sales 108.5MM^E *EMP* 630
SIC 8062 Hospital, affiliated with AMA residency; Hospital, affiliated with AMA residency
CEO: David Keith
**CFO:* Melissa Walker
**Sr VP:* Danny Hardman
**CIO:* Frank Hilbert
Doctor: Derek Norman
Doctor: Paul Thomas
HC Dir: Terry Keith

D-U-N-S 05-566-3348
MCALESTER SCHOOL DISTRICT I 80
200 E Adams Ave, McAlester, OK 74501-4728
Tel (918) 423-4771 *Founded/Ownrshp* 1907
Sales 18.0MM^E *EMP* 370
SIC 8211 Public elementary & secondary schools; Public elementary & secondary schools
IT Man: Ramona Bucker
Psych: Diane Erwin

D-U-N-S 18-844-8864
MCALISTERS CORP
MCALISTER'S DELI
(*Suby of* ROARK CAPITAL GROUP INC) ★
4501 N Point Pkwy Ste 100, Alpharetta, GA 30022-2412
Tel (601) 956-0030 *Founded/Ownrshp* 2005
Sales 15.8MM^E *EMP* 297
SIC 5812 Delicatessen (eating places); Delicatessen (eating places)
CEO: Steve Desutter
Pr: Frank G Paci
Pr: Carin Stutz
CFO: Carl Jakaitis
CFO: Hans Weger
Ofcr: Jeff Sturgis
VP: Peter Wright
VP Mktg: Donna Josephson
Mktg Dir: Robin Blanton

MCALISTER'S DELI
See MCALISTERS CORP

MCALISTERS DELI
See SOUTHERN DELI LLC

MCALISTER'S DELI
See SAXTON GROUP INC

MCALISTERS GOURMET DELI
See JME INC

D-U-N-S 08-313-7620 IMP
MCALLEN INDEPENDENT SCHOOL DISTRICT
MCALLEN ISD
2000 N 23rd St, McAllen, TX 78501-6126
Tel (956) 618-6000 *Founded/Ownrshp* 1915
Sales 257.3MM *EMP* 3,500
Accts Long Chilton Llp Mcallen Te
SIC 8211 Public elementary school; Public junior high school; Public senior high school; Public special education school; Public elementary school; Public junior high school; Public senior high school; Public special education school
Bd of Dir: Richard Moore
Brnch Mgr: Eileen Davis
Cmptr Lab: Carmon Suentes
Psych: Edna Trevino

MCALLEN ISD
See MCALLEN INDEPENDENT SCHOOL DISTRICT

D-U-N-S 06-946-3438
■ **MCALLEN MEDICAL CENTER INC**
(*Suby of* UNIVERSAL HEALTH SERVICES INC) ★
1102 W Trenton Rd, Edinburg, TX 78539-9105
Tel (956) 388-6600 *Founded/Ownrshp* 1994
Sales 23.8M *EMP* 650
SIC 8062 Hospital, medical school affiliated with residency; Hospital, medical school affiliated with residency
CEO: Chris Smolik
CFO: Dennis Rusch
Pr Mgr: Linda Moreno

D-U-N-S 15-009-6840 IMP
■ **MCALLEN MEDICAL CENTER LP**
SOUTH TEXAS HEALTH SYSTEM
(*Suby of* UNIVERSAL HEALTH SERVICES INC) ★
301 W Expressway 83, McAllen, TX 78503-3098
Tel (956) 632-4000 *Founded/Ownrshp* 1982
Sales 267.3MM^E *EMP* 2,500
SIC 8062 General medical & surgical hospitals; General medical & surgical hospitals
Pt: Doug Matney
Exec: Roxanna Godinez
Dir Lab: Grace Garza
Dir Rx: Lisa Ramirez
Mng Dir: Louis Garcia
IT Man: Juan Juarez
Pr Dir: Lisa Killion
Pathlgst: Antonio Alvarez-Mendoza
Doctor: Ana Gutierrez
Pharmcst: Biju Abraham
HC Dir: Nilda Mejia

MCALLEN P&RS SERVICE CENTER
See GE ENGINE SERVICES - MCALLEN L P

D-U-N-S 00-787-0082 EXP
MCALLISTER EQUIPMENT CO (IL)
12500 S Cicero Ave, Alsip, IL 60803-2994
Tel (708) 389-7700 *Founded/Ownrshp* 1955
Sales 22.1MM^E *EMP* 95
SIC 7353 5082 Cranes & aerial lift equipment, rental or leasing; Cranes, construction; Cranes & aerial lift equipment, rental or leasing; Cranes, construction
Pr: Jack Moser
VP: Don Adamitis
VP: Dave Hildebrand
**VP:* Trish Maher
VP: Mike Phillips
VP: Greg Quirk
Area Mgr: Mike Bond
Area Mgr: Bob Kosche
Area Mgr: Scott Mortensen
Area Mgr: Ken Peloquin
IT Man: Earnest Acree

D-U-N-S 04-583-5399
MCALLISTER FEEDER LINES INC
17 Battery Pl Ste 1200, New York, NY 10004-1105
Tel (212) 269-3200 *Founded/Ownrshp* 1864
Sales 47.3MM^E *EMP* 600
SIC 4449 Transportation (freight) on bays & sounds of the ocean; Transportation (freight) on bays & sounds of the ocean
Pr: Brian A McAllister
Pr: Joseph Buckheister
Pr: Virginia Norfolk
**VP:* Eric McAllister
Mng Dir: Andrew McAllister
Opers Mgr: Fabian Dean

D-U-N-S 07-860-9088
MCALLISTER TOWING & TRANSPORTATION CO INC
17 Battery Pl Ste 1200, New York, NY 10004-1105
Tel (212) 269-3200 *Founded/Ownrshp* 1969

Sales 162.3MM^E *EMP* 700
SIC 4492

D-U-N-S 00-246-7355 IMP
MCALPIN INDUSTRIES INC
255 Hollenbeck St, Rochester, NY 14621-3294
Tel (585) 266-3060 *Founded/Ownrshp* 1964
Sales 26.8MM^E *EMP* 150^E
SIC 3444 Sheet metalwork; Sheet metalwork
CEO: Kenneth McAlpin
**Ex VP:* Mike McAlpin
VP: Richard Wlos
Exec: Paul Switzer
CIO: Pearl Ecker
CTO: Oula Nahas
IT Man: Denise Hess
Mfg Mgr: Patti Closson
Opers Mgr: Lisa Kendrick
Plnt Mgr: Dave Krieger

MCALVAIN CONSTRUCTION
See MCALVAIN GROUP OF COMPANIES INC

D-U-N-S 84-202-3095
MCALVAIN CONSTRUCTION INC
5559 W Gowen Rd, Boise, ID 83709-5626
Tel (208) 362-2125 *Founded/Ownrshp* 1995
Sales 51.9MM *EMP* 35^E
Accts Cooper Norman Boise Idaho
SIC 1542 Nonresidential construction; Nonresidential construction
Pr: Torry McAlvain
Exec: Ron Hatch
Exec: Torrance McAlvain
**Prin:* William McAlvain

D-U-N-S 96-156-7179
MCALVAIN GROUP OF COMPANIES INC
MCALVAIN CONSTRUCTION
5559 W Gowen Rd, Boise, ID 83709-5626
Tel (208) 362-2125 *Founded/Ownrshp* 1995
Sales 23.4MM^E *EMP* 125
SIC 1542 Commercial & office building contractors; Commercial & office building contractors
Pr: Torry McAlvain
COO: Steve Kaufman
Off Mgr: Candice Catrell
Dir IT: Gay L Anderson

D-U-N-S 02-967-4108
MCANALLY ENTERPRISES INC
HENNY PENNY EGGS
28 Under The Mountain Rd, North Franklin, CT 06254-1421
Tel (951) 928-1935 *Founded/Ownrshp* 1939
Sales 26.5MM^E *EMP* 400
SIC 0252 Chicken eggs; Chicken eggs
Pr: Carlton R Lofgren
**Co-Trst:* Larry A McAnally
**Trst:* Raye M Lofgren
**VP:* Donald E Brown
**VP:* Nyle A McAnally

D-U-N-S 00-718-3965
MCANANY CONSTRUCTION INC (KS)
15320 Midland Dr, Shawnee Mission, KS 66217-9605
Tel (913) 631-5440 *Founded/Ownrshp* 1954
Sales 34.2MM *EMP* 60
Accts Tpp Certified Public Accountan
SIC 1611 Surfacing & paving; Grading
Pr: Pat McAnany
**Treas:* Phil J McAnany
**VP:* Roger Vossman

D-U-N-S 04-146-4090
MCANDERSON INC
MCDONALD'S
101 N Kerr Ave, Wilmington, NC 28405-3405
Tel (910) 799-7548 *Founded/Ownrshp* 1974
Sales 16.1MM^E *EMP* 375
SIC 5812 Fast-food restaurant, chain; Fast-food restaurant, chain
Pr: Dennis W Anderson

MCANDREWS, HELD & MALLOY
See MCANDREWS HELD AND MALLOY LTD

D-U-N-S 36-463-4097
MCANDREWS HELD AND MALLOY LTD
MCANDREWS, HELD & MALLOY
500 W Madison St Fl 34, Chicago, IL 60661-4584
Tel (312) 775-8000 *Founded/Ownrshp* 1988
Sales 27.0MM^E *EMP* 192
SIC 8111 Legal services; Legal services
Pr: Robert A Surrette
Pr: Connie Cain
Pr: Renee Dedeaux
Pr: Claudette Doss
Pr: Janet Lindsey
Pr: Phyllis Witt
Bd of Dir: Priscilla Gallagher
Bd of Dir: Tom Wimbiscus
Prin: John Held
Opers Mgr: Scott McBride
Board of Directors: James M Hafertepe, Leland G Hansen, Peter J McAndrews, Dean A Pelletier, Eligio C Pimentel, Jonathan R Sick

D-U-N-S 01-425-8495
MCANENY BROTHERS INC
470 Industrial Park Rd, Ebensburg, PA 15931-4114
Tel (814) 472-9800 *Founded/Ownrshp* 1979
Sales 114.3MM^E *EMP* 285
SIC 5141 5147 5148 5194 5113 5142

D-U-N-S 94-535-5931
MCANGUS GOUDELOCK & COURIE LLC
MGC LAW
1320 Main St Fl 10, Columbia, SC 29201-3258
Tel (803) 779-2300 *Founded/Ownrshp* 1998
Sales 29.4MM^E *EMP* 135
Accts Bauknight Pietras & Stormer P
SIC 8111 Legal services; Legal services
**Pt:* Lauren Citrano
**Pt:* Sterling G Davies
**Pt:* Scott B Garrett
**Pt:* John Jeffries
**Pt:* H George Kurani
**Pt:* Lou Waple

COO: Mike Lefever
Comm Dir: Powers Strickland
Dir IT: Roland Hundley
IT Man: Samantha Woods
Netwrk Eng: Samantha Sandridge

D-U-N-S 00-530-5412
MCANINCH CORP (IA)
4001 Delaware Ave, Des Moines, IA 50313-2543
Tel (515) 267-2500 *Founded/Ownrshp* 1959
Sales 140.6MM^E *EMP* 500
SIC 1623 1794 Sewer line construction; Water main construction; Excavation & grading, building construction; Sewer line construction; Water main construction; Excavation & grading, building construction
Ch Bd: Dwayne Mc Aninch
**Ch Bd:* Dwayne McAninch
**Pr:* Douglas McAninch
**CFO:* Chad Pohlmeier
**Ex VP:* Emery L Sanford
Ex VP: Roy Sanford
**VP:* David Manning
**VP:* Dave Stitz
**VP:* Mark Watkins
Dir Bus: Patrick Ruelle

D-U-N-S 02-142-6929
MCARDLE LTD
1600 E Main St Ste B, Saint Charles, IL 60174-4726
Tel (630) 584-6580 *Founded/Ownrshp* 1977
Sales 53.2MM^E *EMP* 818
SIC 7011 5812 5813 7997 1531 Hotels & motels; Eating places; Cocktail lounge; Country club, membership; Condominium developers; Hotels & motels; Eating places; Cocktail lounge; Country club, membership; Condominium developers
Pr: David A McArdle
**VP:* Edward J McArdle

D-U-N-S 00-324-4332
MCARDLE PRINTING CO INC
(*Suby of* BLOOMBERG BNA) ★
800 Comm Dr, Upper Marlboro, MD 20774
Tel (301) 390-8500 *Founded/Ownrshp* 1947, 1985
Sales 38.7MM^E *EMP* 162
SIC 2752 Commercial printing, lithographic; Commercial printing, offset; Commercial printing, lithographic; Commercial printing, offset
Ch Bd: Paul Wajcik
**Pr:* Lisa Arsenault
**CFO:* Charles Feeney
**CFO:* Mark Samphilipo
VP: Frank Heneghan
Ex Dir: Bob Velte

MCARTHUR DAIRY
See DEAN DAIRY HOLDINGS LLC

D-U-N-S 12-271-8489
MCARTHUR FARMS INC
1550 Ne 208th St, Okeechobee, FL 34972-7295
Tel (863) 763-4673 *Founded/Ownrshp* 1927
Sales 25.9MM^E *EMP* 165
SIC 0241 0174 Milk production; Dairy heifer replacement farm; Citrus fruits; Milk production; Dairy heifer replacement farm; Citrus fruits
Ch: Nancy Jean Davis
**Pr:* Bob Rydzewski

MCARTHUR'S BAKERY
See MCARTHURS PARTY CAKE BAKERY INC

D-U-N-S 08-937-6677
MCARTHURS PARTY CAKE BAKERY INC
MCARTHUR'S BAKERY
3055 Lemay Ferry Rd, Saint Louis, MO 63125-3923
Tel (314) 894-0900 *Founded/Ownrshp* 1983
Sales 29.9MM^E *EMP* 88^E
Accts David A Shildmyer Cpa Saint
SIC 5149 5461 2051 Bakery products; Cakes; Cookies; Bread; Bread, cake & related products
Pr: Randall McArthur
Treas: Brian McArthur

MCAULEY CENTER
See MERCY MEMORIAL HOSPITAL OF URBANA OHIO

MCAULEY SETON HOME CARE
See SISTERS LONG TERM

D-U-N-S 00-286-2407
MCAULIFFE BROS INC (OH)
MC AULIFFE'S INDUSTRIAL
1297 W 5th St, Marysville, OH 43040-9291
Tel (937) 642-2911 *Founded/Ownrshp* 1920, 1957
Sales 21.1MM^E *EMP* 90
SIC 5251 Hardware
Pr: J Daniel Fitzgerald
**Sec:* Jim Fitzgerald

D-U-N-S 13-357-9446
▲ **MCBC HOLDINGS INC**
100 Cherokee Cove Dr, Vonore, TN 37885-2129
Tel (423) 884-2221 *Founded/Ownrshp* 2000
Sales 228.5MM^E *EMP* 1,079
Tkr Sym MCFT *Exch* NGM
SIC 3732 3799 Jet skis; Motorboats, inboard or outboard: building & repairing; Boat trailers; Jet skis; Motorboats, inboard or outboard: building & repairing; Boat trailers
Ch Bd: John Pouschine
**Pr:* John Dorton
**VP:* Scott Crutchfield
VP: Timothy Williams
Sls Mgr: David Russell

D-U-N-S 93-379-9942
MCBEE ASSOCIATES INC
MB
997 Old Eagle School Rd # 205, Wayne, PA 19087-1706
Tel (610) 964-9680 *Founded/Ownrshp* 1977
Sales 26.0MM^E *EMP* 150
SIC 8742 Hospital & health services consultant; Hospital & health services consultant
Pr: Carl M Bushner
**CFO:* Art Kulikowski
**Treas:* Carl Bushner
Ofcr: Sandy Piersol
**VP:* Martin A Brutscher
**VP:* Mike Dordick
**VP:* Kathy Emanuel
**VP:* Jeff Silvershein
**VP:* Frank X Smith
Dir IT: Meg Adams
IT Man: Rob Nordeman

D-U-N-S 06-890-0786 IMP
MCBEE SUPPLY CORP (OH)
INTERSTATE MCBEE
4901 Lakeside Ave E, Cleveland, OH 44114-3931
Tel (216) 881-0015 *Founded/Ownrshp* 1958
Sales 33.4MM^E *EMP* 100
SIC 5013 Motor vehicle supplies & new parts; Motor vehicle supplies & new parts
Pr: Ann Buescher
CFO: Lawrence Graham
**Prin:* Brad Buescher

D-U-N-S 85-885-0795
MCBLT VENTURES INC
MCDONALD'S
12155 Metro Pkwy Ste 25, Fort Myers, FL 33966-8346
Tel (239) 561-1090 *Founded/Ownrshp* 1991
Sales 14.9MM^E *EMP* 400
SIC 5812 Fast-food restaurant, chain; Fast-food restaurant, chain
Pr: Tom G Fewster Sr
**VP:* Barbara A Fewster
**VP:* Thomas Fewster

D-U-N-S 04-551-8784
MCBRIDE & SON CONTRACTING CO INC
16091 Swingley Ridge Rd # 300, Chesterfield, MO 63017-2056
Tel (314) 336-0252 *Founded/Ownrshp* 1947
Sales 40.0MM^E *EMP* 400
SIC 1751 1771 1761 1721 1742 1711 Carpentry work; Foundation & footing contractor; Roofing contractor; Commercial painting; Residential painting; Drywall; Plumbing, heating, air-conditioning contractors; Carpentry work; Foundation & footing contractor; Roofing contractor; Commercial painting; Residential painting; Drywall; Plumbing, heating, air-conditioning contractors
Ch Bd: Richard T Sullivan Jr
**Pr:* W Doyle Paul
**VP:* Dave Marxkors

D-U-N-S 17-921-6239
MCBRIDE & SON ENTERPRISES INC
16091 Swingley Ridge Rd # 300, Chesterfield, MO 63017-2056
Tel (636) 537-2000 *Founded/Ownrshp* 1985
Sales 180.6MM^E *EMP* 1,700
SIC 1522 1542 Apartment building construction; Commercial & office building contractors; Apartment building construction; Commercial & office building contractors
CEO: John F Eilermann Jr
**CFO:* Michael Arri

D-U-N-S 07-733-4126
MCBRIDE CLINIC INC
1110 N Lee Ave, Oklahoma City, OK 73103-2699
Tel (405) 230-9000 *Founded/Ownrshp* 1923
Sales 27.8MM^E *EMP* 260
SIC 8011 Clinic, operated by physicians; Orthopedic physician; Rheumatology specialist, physician/surgeon; Clinic, operated by physicians; Orthopedic physician; Rheumatology specialist, physician/surgeon
Off Mgr: Rhonda West
Surgeon: Bentley Edmonds
Surgeon: Robert German
Surgeon: Bradley Margo
Surgeon: James Mitchell
Surgeon: Mark Pascale
Doctor: Eugene Arthur
Doctor: Charles Funderburk
Doctor: David Holden
Doctor: Robert Hynd MD
Doctor: Warren Low

D-U-N-S 60-671-8679
MCBRIDE CLINIC ORTHOPEDIC HOSPITAL LLC
MCBRIDE ORTHOPEDIC HOSPITAL
9600 Broadway Ext, Oklahoma City, OK 73114-7408
Tel (405) 486-2515 *Founded/Ownrshp* 2002
Sales 124.0MM *EMP* 711^E
Accts Somerset Cpas Pc Indianapo
SIC 8069 Specialty hospitals, except psychiatric; Specialty hospitals, except psychiatric
Ch Bd: Mark S Pascale
CEO: Mark Galliart
COO: Jim Berry
CFO: Greg Gisler
VP: Toni Young
Dir OR: Cathy Ramsay
Dir Rx: Tim Anderson
Mtls Mgr: Matthew Fay
Mktg Dir: Julie Muller
Surgeon: Connie Newport
Doctor: M Khan

D-U-N-S 11-517-4963
MCBRIDE CONSTRUCTION RESOURCES INC
224 Nickerson St, Seattle, WA 98109-1644
Tel (206) 283-7121 *Founded/Ownrshp* 2009
Sales 29.9MM *EMP* 95
Accts Cliftonlarsonallen Llp Bellev
SIC 1521 1542 General remodeling, single-family houses; Commercial & office buildings, renovation & repair; General remodeling, single-family houses; Commercial & office buildings, renovation & repair
CEO: Rick Witte
**Pr:* Dennis Edward
**Treas:* Della Burkland
VP: Todd Bride
**VP:* Troy Brogdon
**VP:* Connor McBride

MCBRIDE ORTHOPEDIC HOSPITAL
See MCBRIDE CLINIC ORTHOPEDIC HOSPITAL LLC

D-U-N-S 78-791-5446
MCBRIDE QUALITY CARE SERVICES INC
209 E Chippewa St, Mount Pleasant, MI 48858-1609
Tel (989) 772-1261 *Founded/Ownrshp* 1984
Sales 9.7MM *EMP* 500^E
SIC 8361 Residential care; Residential care
Pr: Alberta McBride

D-U-N-S 78-370-1287 IMP
MCBRIDE RESEARCH LABORATORIES INC
DESIGN ESSENTIALS
2272 Park Central Blvd, Decatur, GA 30035-3824
Tel (770) 593-7200 *Founded/Ownrshp* 1990
Sales 27.0MM^E *EMP* 30
SIC 5122 Hair preparations
CEO: Cornell McBride Sr
**CFO:* Harriet J McBride
**Treas:* Cornell McBride Jr
Rgnl Mgr: Raina Jackson
Sls Dir: Terry Armstrong
Manager: Rosalind Brumant

D-U-N-S 00-328-6556
MCBURNEY CORP (GA)
1650 Intl Ct Ste 100, Norcross, GA 30093
Tel (770) 925-7100 *Founded/Ownrshp* 1911
Sales 29.7MM^E *EMP* 150
SIC 7349

MCBURNIE OIL & COUNTRY GAS
See ENERGYUSA PROPANE INC

MCC
See MOBILE CLIMATE CONTROL CORP

MCC
See MALOOF CONTRACTING CO INC

MCC
See MEMPHIS COMMUNICATIONS CORP

MCC
See MILLENNIUM CHALLENGE CORP

MCC
See MIDCONTINENTAL CHEMICAL CO INC

MCC CAPITAL PARTNERS
See PROPEL EQUITY PARTNERS LLC

D-U-N-S 15-020-2596
MCC CONSTRUCTION CORP
1527 Cole Blvd Ste 100, Lakewood, CO 80401-3421
Tel (303) 741-0404 *Founded/Ownrshp* 2005
Sales 22.2MM^E *EMP* 100
SIC 1542 Commercial & office buildings, renovation & repair; Commercial & office buildings, renovation & repair
Pr: Norman F Kaus
**Ch:* Geoffrey G Wormer
**Treas:* Walter Crummy
**VP:* Thomas J Harper Jr
VP: Eric Lamb
VP: Peter Salvati
IT Man: Mitch O'Dell
Snr Mgr: Mike Oakes

D-U-N-S 83-803-0492
MCC DEVELOPMENT CORP
(*Suby of* MITSUBISHI MATERIALS CORPORATION)
151 Cassia Way, Henderson, NV 89014-6616
Tel (702) 932-3944 *Founded/Ownrshp* 1988
Sales 35.9MM^E *EMP* 718
SIC 3273 Ready-mixed concrete; Ready-mixed concrete
Prin: Y Ota
**Pr:* Ken McCloud
Exec: Jennifer Deitrich
**Prin:* T Matsuoaka
**Prin:* T Uchiyama
Off Admin: Marti Mondello

MCC ELDERLY HOUSING CNSTR
See T MORRISSEY CORP

MCC GROUP, THE
See MECHANICAL CONSTRUCTION CO LLC

D-U-N-S 11-897-2512
MCC GROUP L L C
3001 17th St, Metairie, LA 70002-3805
Tel (504) 833-8291 *Founded/Ownrshp* 1958
Sales 98.7MM^E *EMP* 700
SIC 1711 1542 1731 Mechanical contractor; Commercial & office building contractors; Electrical work; Mechanical contractor; Commercial & office building contractors; Electrical work
CEO: Joseph A Jaeger Jr
**Ex VP:* Philip Catanzaro
**Ex VP:* Philip Garcia Jr
**Ex VP:* Carol Lagasse
**Sr VP:* Edward O'Connor
VP: Tom Boudreaux
VP: Glenn Perilloux
Off Mgr: Vicki Sortino
Opers Mgr: Dave Dallimore
Opers Mgr: Cindy Mauterer
Genl Couns: Andre Maillho
Board of Directors: Fred Esstopinal, D Waesche

D-U-N-S 19-758-2369 IMP
■ **MCC HOLDINGS INC**
CRANE CHEMPHARMA
(*Suby of* CRANE INTERNATIONAL HOLDINGS INC) ★
4526 Res Frest Dr Ste 400, The Woodlands, TX 77381
Tel (936) 271-6500 *Founded/Ownrshp* 1999
Sales 352.7MM^E *EMP* 2,300^E
SIC 3491 7699 Industrial valves; Valve repair, industrial
Pr: Alex Alcala
**Pr:* Louis V Pinkham
**COO:* Kevin Olsen
**CFO:* Kevin Burke
Genl Mgr: Augustus I Dupont
VP Sls: Wolfgang Maar
Mktg Mgr: Siddhartha Burra
Sls Mgr: Mary Barrett
Sls Mgr: Richard Ford

D-U-N-S 00-578-0432
MCC INC (WI)
MURPHY CONSTRUCTION COMPANY
2600 N Roemer Rd, Appleton, WI 54911-8626
Tel (715) 758-6751 *Founded/Ownrshp* 1932
Sales 97.9MM^E *EMP* 335
SIC 3273 1442 1611 Ready-mixed concrete; Construction sand & gravel; Highway & street construction; Ready-mixed concrete; Construction sand & gravel; Highway & street construction
Pr: Joe Murphy
* *Treas:* Rick Kranzusch
* *VP:* Brian Murphy
IT Man: Michelle Sasman
Ql Cn Mgr: Scott Paque

D-U-N-S 84-719-5153
MCC INC
MCCORMICK CONSTRUCTION COMPANY
7900 69th Ave, Rockford, MN 55373-4554
Tel (763) 477-4774 *Founded/Ownrshp* 1992
Sales 74.0MM *EMP* 175
SIC 1541 Industrial buildings & warehouses; Industrial buildings & warehouses
Pr: Jon Walters
* *CFO:* Mark Schmind
* *VP:* Dan Shefland
IT Man: Lisa Weber
Sales Exec: Mark Hillebrand

D-U-N-S 12-269-5232
MCC MECHANICAL LLC
3001 17th St, Metairie, LA 70002-3805
Tel (504) 833-8291 *Founded/Ownrshp* 1983
Sales 23.6MM^E *EMP* 100
SIC 1711 1542 1731 3444 8711

D-U-N-S 00-843-5666
MCC MECHANICAL OF CAROLINAS LLC
3001 17th St, Metairie, LA 70002-3805
Tel (504) 833-8291 *Founded/Ownrshp* 1999
Sales 23.1MM^E *EMP* 130
SIC 1711 Mechanical contractor; Mechanical contractor
CEO: Joseph A Jaeger
* *CFO:* Edward O'Connor
* *Ex VP:* Philip Catanzaro
* *Ex VP:* Philip Garcia Jr
* *Sr VP:* Ed Nenon
VP: Glenn Perilloux
Opers Mgr: Carol Lagass

MCC U.S
See MENNONITE CENTRAL COMMITTEE US

D-U-N-S 82-811-2990
MCC/CATAMOUNT LLC
1527 Cole Blvd Ste 100, Lakewood, CO 80401-3421
Tel (303) 741-0404 *Founded/Ownrshp* 2008
Sales 40.5MM *EMP* 90
SIC 1542 Nonresidential construction; Nonresidential construction
IT Man: Shelly Abeyta
IT Man: Walter Crummy

MCCABE DO IT CENTER
See ROBERT MCCABE CO INC

D-U-N-S 06-626-0126
MCCABE HAMILTON & RENNY CO LIMITED
(*Suby of* J B G CORP) ★
521 Ala Moana Blvd # 311, Honolulu, HI 96813-4928
Tel (808) 524-3255 *Founded/Ownrshp* 1972
Sales 20.0MM^E *EMP* 340
SIC 4491 Stevedoring; Stevedoring
Ch: Robert Guard
* *Pr:* John Fahling
* *CEO:* Tim Guard
CFO: Kim Chock
* *CFO:* Kim Hudson-Chock
Genl Mgr: Van Suzuki
IT Man: Romeo Manibog

D-U-N-S 18-506-4003
MCCABE WEISBERG AND CONWAY PC
123 S Broad St Ste 1400, Philadelphia, PA 19109-1060
Tel (215) 790-1010 *Founded/Ownrshp* 1990
Sales 35.8MM^E *EMP* 225
SIC 8111 General practice law office; General practice law office
Pr: Terrence J McCabe
* *CFO:* Nurash Sabnani
* *Treas:* Margaret Gairo
Treas: Gairo Margaret
Chf Mktg O: Terry M Cabe
* *VP:* Marc S Weisberg
VP: Marc Weisberg
* *Prin:* Lisa L Wallace
Dir IT: Joel Bryan
Dir IT: Joel Dillon
Counsel: Lisa Wallace

D-U-N-S 03-190-3891
MCCADDON CADILLAC BUICK GMC INC
2460 48th Ct, Boulder, CO 80301-2405
Tel (303) 442-3160 *Founded/Ownrshp* 1958
Sales 23.4MM^E *EMP* 55
SIC 5511 5521 Automobiles, new & used; Used car dealers; Automobiles, new & used; Used car dealers
Pr: George M Mc Caddon
* *VP:* Mark J Mc Caddon
Sls Mgr: Sean Krammer

MCCAFFERTY AUTO GROUP
See FORD MCCAFFERTY SALES INC

D-U-N-S 00-864-1768
MCCAFFERTY FORD OF MECHANICSBURG INC
6320 Carlisle Pike, Mechanicsburg, PA 17050-2308
Tel (717) 766-4733 *Founded/Ownrshp* 2000
Sales 31.7MM^E *EMP* 75
SIC 5511 Automobiles, new & used; Automobiles, new & used
Pr: Fred Beans
* *Treas:* J Todd Buch
* *VP:* John Haines

D-U-N-S 62-382-2343
MCCAFFERY INTERESTS INC
875 N Michigan Ave # 1800, Chicago, IL 60611-1803
Tel (312) 944-3777 *Founded/Ownrshp* 1990
Sales 21.6MM^E *EMP* 25^E
SIC 6552 6531 Land subdividers & developers, commercial; Real estate managers
Ch: Daniel McCaffery
* *Pr:* Edmond Woodbury
* *CFO:* Angela Woolfolk
VP: Carlton Diehl
Mng Dir: Susan Ahlert
Mng Dir: Clayton McCaffery
Mng Dir: John Ziegenhein
Rgnl Mgr: Amy Boduch
Mktg Dir: Heather Skomba

MCCAFFREY'S
See EDGEWOOD VILLAGE MARKET INC

D-U-N-S 19-522-2252
MCCAIN ELLIOS FOODS INC
(*Suby of* MCCAIN USA INC) ★
11 Gregg St, Lodi, NJ 07644-2704
Tel (201) 368-0600 *Founded/Ownrshp* 1963
Sales 29.2MM^E *EMP* 160
SIC 2038 Pizza, frozen; Pizza, frozen
Pr: Tim Driscoll
* *Pr:* Van S Chaayk
* *Treas:* Randy Myles
* *VP:* Mark Bohen
* *VP:* H McCain
* *VP:* Peter Reijula

D-U-N-S 00-110-4736 IMP/EXP
MCCAIN FOODS USA INC (ME)
(*Suby of* MCCAIN USA INC) ★
2275 Cabot Dr, Lisle, IL 60532-3653
Tel (630) 955-0400 *Founded/Ownrshp* 1952
Sales 818.2MM^E *EMP* 4,000
SIC 2037 Potato products, quick frozen & cold pack; Vegetables, quick frozen & cold pack, excl. potato products; Potato products, quick frozen & cold pack; Vegetables, quick frozen & cold pack, excl. potato products
Pr: Frank Finn
COO: Dirk Van De Put
* *VP:* Michael Campbell
VP: Richard Efting
VP: Doug Fraser
VP: Kurt Kinsey
VP: Keith Orchard
VP: Ronald Pullsbury
VP: Robert H Thomas
Assoc Dir: Amanda Colgan
Rgnl Mgr: Michael Graves

D-U-N-S 18-312-5970 IMP
MCCAIN INC
2365 Oak Ridge Way, Vista, CA 92081-8348
Tel (760) 727-8100 *Founded/Ownrshp* 1987
Sales 89.0MM *EMP* 600
SIC 3669 5084 3444 Traffic signals, electric; Industrial machinery & equipment; Sheet metalwork; Traffic signals, electric; Industrial machinery & equipment; Sheet metalwork
CEO: Jeffrey L McCain
* *COO:* Christine Jersey
Dir Bus: Donald Maas
Mng Dir: Felix Cuellar
IT Man: Kevin Drummond
IT Man: Travis Harrell
VP Opers: Deetlefs Kleinjan
Plnt Mgr: Tom Moran
Ql Cn Mgr: Hilda Maldonado
Natl Sales: Nathan Welch
Mktg Mgr: Trisha Tunilla

D-U-N-S 80-728-3650 EXP
MCCAIN USA INC
(*Suby of* MCCAIN FOODS LIMITED)
2275 Cabot Dr, Lisle, IL 60532-3653
Tel (800) 938-7799 *Founded/Ownrshp* 1985
Sales 847.4MM^E *EMP* 4,100
SIC 2037 2038 5411 Potato products, quick frozen & cold pack; Fruit juices; Pizza, frozen; Grocery stores; Potato products, quick frozen & cold pack; Fruit juices; Pizza, frozen; Grocery stores
Pr: Gilles Lessard
* *Sec:* Randy A Myles
VP: Joe Culligan
Mktg Mgr: Lauren Madsen
Sls Mgr: Paul Allen
Sls Mgr: Bill Stayskal

MCCALL D T SONS FURN APPL TV
See D T MC CALL & SONS

D-U-N-S 00-334-4710 IMP/EXP
MCCALL FARMS INC (SC)
MARGARET HOLMES
6615 S Irby St, Effingham, SC 29541-3577
Tel (843) 662-2223 *Founded/Ownrshp* 1952, 1967
Sales 221.6MM^E *EMP* 700
SIC 2033 Vegetables: packaged in cans, jars, etc.; Vegetables: packaged in cans, jars, etc.
Pr: Marion Swink
* *Pr:* Henry Swink
* *VP:* Henry Mc Call Swink
* *VP:* Mark Tarkenton
Genl Mgr: Frank Branton
Off Mgr: Leah Kern
IT Man: Matt Chmielecki
IT Man: Jean Chopchinski
Plnt Mgr: Calvin Tiemann

D-U-N-S 00-254-4492 IMP
MCCALL HANDLING CO
8801 Wise Ave Ste 200, Baltimore, MD 21222-5004
Tel (410) 388-2600 *Founded/Ownrshp* 1989
Sales 45.7MM^E *EMP* 110
SIC 5084 Materials handling machinery; Lift trucks & parts; Cleaning equipment, high pressure, sand or steam; Materials handling machinery; Lift trucks & parts; Cleaning equipment, high pressure, sand or steam
Pr: James B Kenny
CFO: Bill Mullin
* *VP:* Dave Hoehn
Dir IT: Skip Clayton

D-U-N-S 00-967-3559
MCCALL OIL AND CHEMICAL CORP
5480 Nw Front Ave, Portland, OR 97210-1198
Tel (503) 221-6400 *Founded/Ownrshp* 1983
Sales 180.0MM *EMP* 29^E
SIC 5172 Petroleum products; Petroleum products
Ch Bd: Robert H McCall
* *Pr:* Jim Charriere
* *CFO:* Mike Walsh

D-U-N-S 11-298-1303 IMP
MCCALL PATTERN CO
BUTTERCK MCCALL VOGUE PATTERN
(*Suby of* MP HOLDINGS INC)
120 Broadway Fl 34, New York, NY 10271-3499
Tel (212) 465-6800 *Founded/Ownrshp* 1990
Sales 35.7MM^E *EMP* 288
Accts Bkd Llp Kansas City Mo
SIC 2741 2731 2721 Patterns, paper: publishing only, not printed on site; Catalogs: publishing only, not printed on site; Pamphlets: publishing only, not printed on site; Textbooks: publishing only, not printed on site; Magazines: publishing only, not printed on site; Patterns, paper: publishing only, not printed on site; Catalogs: publishing only, not printed on site; Pamphlets: publishing only, not printed on site; Textbooks: publishing only, not printed on site; Magazines: publishing only, not printed on site
Ch Bd: Frank J Rizzo
* *Pr:* Robin Davies
* *CFO:* John W Kobiskie
* *Sr VP:* Kathleen Klausner
Sr VP: Stacey Long
* *VP:* Nancy Dicocco
* *VP:* Gail Hamilton
MIS Dir: Bruce Bidwell
IT Man: Roman Roncal
Mktg Dir: Joseph Anselmo
Mktg Dir: Janet Wolf

D-U-N-S 04-322-4757
MCCALL TOYOTA INC
MCCOMBS TOYOTA
8333 W Interstate 10, San Antonio, TX 78230-3860
Tel (210) 349-4949 *Founded/Ownrshp* 1954, 1988
Sales 71.8MM^E *EMP* 300
SIC 5511 5521 Automobiles, new & used; Used car dealers; Automobiles, new & used; Used car dealers
Pr: B J McCombs
Sls Mgr: Mario Addari
Sls Mgr: Richard Galvan
Sls Mgr: Alex Lind
Sls Mgr: Jose Noriega
Board of Directors: John Chervinskis

D-U-N-S 10-237-9885 EXP
■ **MCCALL-TII INC**
FORT BEND TOYOTA
(*Suby of* GROUP 1 AUTOMOTIVE INC) ★
20465 Southwest Fwy, Richmond, TX 77469-7174
Tel (281) 341-5900 *Founded/Ownrshp* 2007
Sales 31.8MM^E *EMP* 100
SIC 5511 Automobiles, new & used; Automobiles, new & used
Pr: Frank Grese Jr
* *VP:* Darryl M Burman
* *VP:* John C Rickel
Exec: Richard Yarbrough
Sls Mgr: Trae Tracy
Sales Asso: Gary Taylor
Sales Asso: Huy Tran

D-U-N-S 06-111-8428
MCCALLA RAYMER LLC
FORECLOUSRE & BANKRUPTCY SVCS
1544 Old Alabama Rd, Roswell, GA 30076-2102
Tel (770) 643-7200 *Founded/Ownrshp* 1982
Sales 48.9MM^E *EMP* 225
SIC 8111

D-U-N-S 11-316-6136
MCCALLIE ASSOCIATES INC
3906 Raynor Pkwy Ste 200, Bellevue, NE 68123-6053
Tel (402) 291-2203 *Founded/Ownrshp* 1982
Sales 26.8MM^E *EMP* 140
SIC 7373 Systems engineering, computer related; Systems engineering, computer related
Pr: Jennifer S Maassen
* *CFO:* Brian Bald
Dir IT: Jay McMaster
Sftwr Eng: Martin Barche
Netwrk Eng: Rob Grant
VP Opers: Franklin Fish
Sales Exec: Jean Templeton

D-U-N-S 07-488-9148
MCCALLIE SCHOOL
500 Dodds Ave, Chattanooga, TN 37404-3932
Tel (423) 493-5526 *Founded/Ownrshp* 1905
Sales 68.3MM *EMP* 220
Accts The Blevins Group Chattanooga
SIC 8211 Private elementary & secondary schools; Private elementary & secondary schools
Pgrm Dir: Stan Corcoran

D-U-N-S 03-600-3184
MCCALLION TEMPS INC (PA)
601 N Bthlhem Pike Bldg A, Montgomeryville, PA 18936
Tel (215) 855-8000 *Founded/Ownrshp* 1979, 1999
Sales 16.7MM^E *EMP* 1,000
SIC 7363 7361 Temporary help service; Employment agencies; Temporary help service; Employment agencies
CEO: James Mc Callion III
* *Pr:* James McCallion
* *VP:* Lisa McCallion

D-U-N-S 00-350-3646
MCCALLS INC OF JOHNSONVILLE S C (SC)
MCCALL'S SUPPLY
394 Lake City Hwy, Johnsonville, SC 29555-5043
Tel (843) 386-3323 *Founded/Ownrshp* 1960
Sales 55.0MM *EMP* 150
SIC 5075 Warm air heating & air conditioning; Warm air heating & air conditioning
Pr: Dairen Jacobs
* *CFO:* Carla Mc Call
* *VP:* Constance McCall Baxley

MCCALL'S SUPPLY
See MCCALLS INC OF JOHNSONVILLE S C

D-U-N-S 16-433-7313
MCCAMM MANAGEMENT CO
MCDONALD'S
8514 Jacomo Ridge Ct, Lees Summit, MO 64064-2792
Tel (816) 229-5554 *Founded/Ownrshp* 1984
Sales 9.8MM^E *EMP* 375
SIC 5812 Fast-food restaurant, chain; Fast-food restaurant, chain
Pr: Art Phillips

D-U-N-S 04-848-0164
MCCANDLESS INTERNATIONAL TRUCKS INC
MC CANDLESS ISUZU TRUCKS
3780 Losee Rd, North Las Vegas, NV 89030-3300
Tel (702) 642-8789 *Founded/Ownrshp* 1969
Sales 45.2MM^E *EMP* 90
SIC 5511 7538 7532 5531 Automobiles, new & used; Automobile & truck equipment & parts; General truck repair; Top & body repair & paint shops; Automobiles, new & used; General truck repair; Top & body repair & paint shops; Automobile & truck equipment & parts
Pr: John McCandless
* *Sec:* Stephen R Feuerhelm
* *VP:* Chris J McCandless
* *VP:* E Scott McCandless
* *VP:* J Michael McCandless

MCCANDLESS INTL TRCKS COLO
See MCCANDLESS TRUCK CENTER LLC

D-U-N-S 06-335-0854 EXP
■ **MCCANDLESS TRUCK CENTER LLC**
MCCANDLESS INTL TRCKS COLO
(*Suby of* NAVISTAR INC) ★
16704 E 32nd Ave, Aurora, CO 80011-1521
Tel (331) 332-5000 *Founded/Ownrshp* 1999
Sales 104.8MM^E *EMP* 182
SIC 5013 7538 5012 Truck parts & accessories; Truck engine repair, except industrial; Trucks, commercial; Truck parts & accessories; Truck engine repair, except industrial; Trucks, commercial
Pr: Scott McCandless
* *Sec:* John Balnis

D-U-N-S 07-936-9466
MCCANN AEROSPACE MACHINING LLC
(*Suby of* ACCURUS AEROSPACE CORP) ★
180 Trans Tech Dr, Athens, GA 30601-1600
Tel (706) 548-5009 *Founded/Ownrshp* 2014
Sales 67.5MM *EMP* 150^E
SIC 3599 3769 Machine shop, jobbing & repair; Guided missile & space vehicle parts & auxiliary equipment; Machine shop, jobbing & repair; Guided missile & space vehicle parts & auxiliary equipment
Pr: Steve Pulliam
Pr: Jeff Hughes

D-U-N-S 02-589-1276
MCCANN INDUSTRIES INC
DO IT BEST
543 S Rohlwing Rd, Addison, IL 60101-4211
Tel (630) 627-8700 *Founded/Ownrshp* 1967
Sales 37.7MM^E *EMP* 160
SIC 7353 5082 Heavy construction equipment rental; General construction machinery & equipment; Heavy construction equipment rental; General construction machinery & equipment
CEO: Jim McCann
* *Ch Bd:* Richard J Mc Cann
* *Pr:* James McCann
CFO: John R Schneide
* *CFO:* John R Schneider
Sls Mgr: Dennis Tovar

D-U-N-S 60-635-0130
MCCANN PLASTICS INC
5600 Mayfair Rd, Canton, OH 44720-1539
Tel (330) 499-1515 *Founded/Ownrshp* 1989
Sales 35.1MM^E *EMP* 85
SIC 3087 Custom compound purchased resins
Pr: Michael A McCann
* *Treas:* John Craig
Exec: John Colangelo
Dir IT: Doug Amburgey
IT Man: Joe Duke
IT Man: Mark Irwin
VP Mktg: Michael Cann

D-U-N-S 78-442-4871
■ **MCCANN WORLDGROUP LLC**
(*Suby of* INTERPUBLIC GROUP OF COMPANIES INC) ★
622 3rd Ave Ste 3, New York, NY 10017-6707
Tel (646) 865-5000 *Founded/Ownrshp* 1997
Sales 838.8MM^E *EMP* 20,000
SIC 7311 7319 Advertising agencies; Media buying service; Advertising agencies; Media buying service
CEO: Nick Brien
Mng Pt: Paul Gardner
Ch Bd: Joyce King Thomas
Pr: Devika Bulchandani
Pr: Rob Doubal
Pr: Yasuyuki Katagi
Pr: Luca Lindner
Pr: Chris Macdonald
Pr: Gustavo Martinez
Pr: Hank Summy
Pr: Laurence Thomson
CEO: Bill Kolb
CEO: Mark Lund
CEO: Michael McLaren
CEO: Ed Powers
CEO: Fred Schuster
COO: Murray Dudgeon
COO: Patrick Lafferty
CFO: Tara Comonte

CFO: Ramesh Rajan
Ch: Prasoon Joshi
Board of Directors: Susan Irwin

D-U-N-S 00-698-7416
■ **MCCANN-ERICKSON USA INC** (DE)
(*Suby of* INTERPUBLIC GROUP OF COMPANIES INC) ★
622 3rd Ave Fl 16, New York, NY 10017-6743
Tel (646) 865-2000 *Founded/Ownrshp* 1902, 1964
Sales 270.1MM^E *EMP* 1,700
SIC 8732 7311 Market analysis or research; Advertising agencies; Market analysis or research; Advertising agencies
Pr: Chris Macdonald
**Ch Bd:* Jonh Dooner
**Pr:* Luca Lindner
COO: Patrick Smith
**Ch:* Harris Diamond
**Ofcr:* Suzanne Power
Ex VP: Stewart Alter
Ex VP: Martha Brooks
Ex VP: Devika Bulchandani
Ex VP: Brian Dilorenzo
Ex VP: Peggy Kelly
Ex VP: Dana Mansfield
Ex VP: Robert Montagnese
Ex VP: Richard O'Leary
Sr VP: Loukia Brattain
Sr VP: Jesse Johanson
Sr VP: Mike Medeiros
Sr VP: Kevin Scher
Sr VP: Jonathan Swallen
VP: Kimberly Almonroeder
VP: Jan Franks

D-U-N-S 60-654-4336
MCCAR REALTY INC
MDC HOMES
4125 Old Milton Pkwy, Alpharetta, GA 30005-4443
Tel (770) 886-4996 *Founded/Ownrshp* 1985
Sales 49.7MM^E *EMP* 370
SIC 1521 1522 New construction, single-family houses; Residential construction; New construction, single-family houses; Residential construction
CEO: Steve Roberts
**Ch Bd:* Dan McSwain
Pr: Bob Kosnik
**Pr:* Keith McSwain
Sales Exec: Randy Branan
Mktg Dir: Amy Singstock
Sls Mgr: Tim Hultgren

MCCARL'S
See MC CARLS INC

D-U-N-S 04-073-1382
MCCARTER & ENGLISH LLP
2 Tower Center Blvd Fl 11, East Brunswick, NJ 08816-1100
Tel (732) 393-1900 *Founded/Ownrshp* 1844
Sales 206.4MM^E *EMP* 900
SIC 8111 General practice attorney, lawyer; General practice attorney, lawyer
Mng Pt: Steven Vajaty Jr
Pt: F Traynor Beck
Pt: Erik Belt
Pt: Richard A Beran
Pt: Howard M Berkower
Pt: Sarah B Biser
Pt: Lisa W S Bonsall
Pt: John B Brescher Jr
Pt: Gerard G Brew
Pt: William H Bright
Pt: Lee Bromberg
Pt: Joseph J Cherico
Pt: Patrick M Collins
Pt: Richard C Cooper
Pt: Joseph R Disalvo
Pt: Gary L Duescher
Pt: Alfred L Ferguson
Pt: Stephen M Fields
Pt: John E Flaherty
Pt: James J Freebery
Pt: Frederic J Giordano

D-U-N-S 02-466-6711 IMP
MCCARTER ELECTRICAL CO (NC)
516 Hillside Ave, Laurinburg, NC 28352-3023
Tel (910) 276-2055 *Founded/Ownrshp* 1957, 1963
Sales 45.7MM^E *EMP* 200
SIC 1796 1731 Machine moving & rigging; General electrical contractor; Machine moving & rigging; General electrical contractor
CEO: Tom Jackson
**Pr:* Susan McCarter
VP: Jeff Church
VP: Buddy McCarter
**VP:* Rodney McCarter
Div Mgr: Mark Cole

D-U-N-S 09-285-1484 IMP
MCCARTHY AUTO OF BLUE SPRINGS NISSAN INC
3030 Nw South Outer Rd, Blue Springs, MO 64015-1765
Tel (816) 224-7500 *Founded/Ownrshp* 1997
Sales 25.0MM^E *EMP* 50
SIC 5511 Automobiles, new & used; Pickups, new & used; Vans, new & used; Automobiles, new & used; Pickups, new & used; Vans, new & used
Pr: Steve Tobert
Sales Asso: Robert Cole
Sales Asso: Matt Smith

D-U-N-S 00-195-1375 IMP
MCCARTHY BUILDING COMPANIES INC
(*Suby of* MCCARTHY HOLDINGS INC) ★
1341 N Rock Hill Rd, Saint Louis, MO 63124-1441
Tel (314) 968-3300 *Founded/Ownrshp* 1864, 1977
Sales 2.6MMM *EMP* 1,041
Accts Rubinbrown Llp Saint Louis M
SIC 1542 1541 Institutional building construction; Commercial & office building, new construction; Industrial buildings, new construction; Institutional building construction; Commercial & office building, new construction; Industrial buildings, new construction
CEO: Michael D Bolen
**Pr:* Robert H Calbert
**Pr:* Rich A Henry
**Pr:* Randy M Highland
**Pr:* Michael J McWay
Pr: Jim Stevenson
**Pr:* Scott Wittkop
CFO: Doug Audiffred
**CFO:* J Douglas Audiffred
Ex VP: Robert Betz
**Sr VP:* Matthew Lawson
VP: Ben Johanneman
VP: Josh Lawrence
VP: Mike Oster
VP: Jaime Perera
Dir Bus: Jerry Schreiber

D-U-N-S 03-895-5787
MCCARTHY BURGESS & WOLFF INC
26000 Cannon Rd, Bedford, OH 44146-1807
Tel (440) 735-5100 *Founded/Ownrshp* 1980
Sales 38.3MM^E *EMP* 159
SIC 7389 Telemarketing services
Pr: Freida M Wolff
Dir Bus: Paul Joseph
**Prin:* Stephen Wolff
Dept Mgr: James Tournas
DP Exec: Kerry Kershaw
Dir IT: Steve Hurt
IT Man: Renita McMillen
IT Man: Steve Wolgemuth
Sls Dir: Lucas Eyring
Sls Dir: Scott Shuller
Sls Dir: Todd Siegel

D-U-N-S 04-109-2645
MCCARTHY CAPITAL FUND V LP
1601 Dodge St, Omaha, NE 68102-1637
Tel (402) 932-8600 *Founded/Ownrshp* 2011
Sales 82.2MM^E *EMP* 450^E
SIC 6799 Investors; Investors
Pt: Patrick Duffy
Genl Pt: Dana Bradford
Pt: C Tyler Barger
Pt: Robert Y Emmert
Pt: Michael R McCarthy
Prin: Michael J McGovern

D-U-N-S 07-064-9673
MCCARTHY CHEVEROLET INC
675 N Rawhide Dr, Olathe, KS 66061-3688
Tel (913) 324-7200 *Founded/Ownrshp* 1999
Sales 64.4MM^E *EMP* 200
SIC 5511 Automobiles, new & used; Automobiles, new & used
Pr: John McCarthy
Genl Mgr: Alan Hinderer

D-U-N-S 08-871-1643
MCCARTHY HOLDINGS INC
1341 N Rock Hill Rd, Saint Louis, MO 63124-1441
Tel (314) 968-3300 *Founded/Ownrshp* 1977
Sales 2.7MMM *EMP* 2,157^E
Accts Rubinbrown Llp Cpas Saint Lo
SIC 1542 1541 Institutional building construction; Commercial & office building, new construction; Industrial buildings, new construction; Institutional building construction; Commercial & office building, new construction; Industrial buildings, new construction
Ch Bd: Michael D Bolen
**Pr:* Scott Wittkop
**CFO:* J Douglas Audiffred
**Treas:* Danel Dillon
**Sr VP:* Matthew Lawson
Off Mgr: Luanne Santiago
Sfty Dirs: Oscar Paniagua
Sfty Mgr: Scotty Dupriest
Sfty Mgr: Manuel Tonche
Ql Cn Mgr: Paul Tonner
Snr PM: Jeff Troop

D-U-N-S 00-694-0829
MCCARTHY IMPROVEMENT CO (IA)
(*Suby of* MCCARTHY-BUSH CORP) ★
5401 Victoria Ave Ste 300, Davenport, IA 52807-3942
Tel (563) 359-0321 *Founded/Ownrshp* 1897
Sales 127.5M^E *EMP* 375
SIC 1611 General contractor, highway & street construction; General contractor, highway & street construction
Pr: Joseph D Bush
**Ch Bd:* John L Bush
**Treas:* Lawrence P Bush
**VP:* Travis K Booth
**VP:* Steve Gray
**VP:* Andrew M Wolf
Snr PM: David Boyer
Snr PM: Nick Wolf

D-U-N-S 07-867-7014
MCCARTHY STRAUB JV I
1341 N Rock Hill Rd, Saint Louis, MO 63124-1441
Tel (314) 646-4189 *Founded/Ownrshp* 2012
Sales 59.9MM^E *EMP* 2,874
SIC 1542 Nonresidential construction; Nonresidential construction
VP: Scott Wittkop

D-U-N-S 01-511-5355 IMP
MCCARTHY TIRE SERVICE CO INC
340 Kidder St, Wilkes Barre, PA 18702-5688
Tel (570) 822-3151 *Founded/Ownrshp* 1926
Sales 232.0MM *EMP* 700
SIC 5014 5531

D-U-N-S 94-757-0891
MCCARTHY-BUSH CORP
5401 Victoria Ave Ste 700, Davenport, IA 52807-2991
Tel (563) 359-0500 *Founded/Ownrshp* 1993
Sales 153.0M *EMP* 450^E
Accts Deloitte Tax Llp Davenport I
SIC 1611 1422 3274 2819 3441 4213 General contractor, highway & street construction; Limestones, ground; Quicklime; Calcium carbide; Fabricated structural metal; Contract haulers; General contractor, highway & street construction; Limestones, ground; Quicklime; Calcium carbide; Fabricated structural metal; Contract haulers
CEO: Greg Bush
CFO: Lawrence Bush
**Ch:* John L Bush

D-U-N-S 00-481-7045
MCCARTNEY CONSTRUCTION CO
331 Albert Rains Blvd, Gadsden, AL 35901-2552
Tel (256) 547-6386 *Founded/Ownrshp* 1946
Sales 61.1MM^E *EMP* 175
SIC 1611 Highway & street paving contractor; Highway & street paving contractor
Pr: Michael B Mc Cartney
**Sec:* John Mc Cartney

D-U-N-S 03-486-4579
MCCARTNEY PRODUCE LLC
211 S Fentress St, Paris, TN 38242-4032
Tel (731) 642-2362 *Founded/Ownrshp* 2012
Sales 49.1MM^E *EMP* 114^E
SIC 5148 Fruits, fresh; Vegetables, fresh; Fruits, fresh; Vegetables, fresh
Pr: Joe Porter
**CFO:* Debbie Woodard
**Treas:* Jeff Perkins
**VP:* Don Bush
CIO: Debbie Woodward
**VP Sls:* Raymon Randolph

D-U-N-S 01-381-6277
MCCARTNEYS INC
819 Howard Ave, Altoona, PA 16601-4727
Tel (814) 944-8139 *Founded/Ownrshp* 1957
Sales 26.6MM^E *EMP* 50
SIC 5021 5112 5044 5943 Office furniture; Stationery & office supplies; Office equipment; Office forms & supplies
Pr: John T Baker
**Treas:* Jeanne Baker
Genl Mgr: Dennis Horton

D-U-N-S 08-108-1218 IMP/EXP
MCCARTY EQUIPMENT CO LTD
(*Suby of* GHX INDUSTRIAL LLC) ★
1802 S Treadaway Blvd, Abilene, TX 79602-4948
Tel (325) 691-5558 *Founded/Ownrshp* 2012
Sales 52.7MM^E *EMP* 116
SIC 5084 5085 Oil well machinery, equipment & supplies; Industrial supplies; Rubber goods, mechanical; Oil well machinery, equipment & supplies; Industrial supplies; Rubber goods, mechanical
Pr: Kelly McCarty
Area Mgr: Chris Carter
Sales Asso: Randy Chamness

D-U-N-S 00-738-5578
■ **MCCARTY-HULL CIGAR CO INC**
MC CARTY-HULL
(*Suby of* MCLANE CO INC) ★
4714 Ne 24th Ave, Amarillo, TX 79107-5802
Tel (806) 383-1313 *Founded/Ownrshp* 1924
Sales 138.3MM *EMP* 79
SIC 5194 5145 Cigarettes; Chewing tobacco; Cigars; Candy; Fruits, fountain; Cigarettes; Chewing tobacco; Cigars; Candy; Fruits, fountain
Pr: Gordon Atkins
**Sr VP:* James L Kent
VP: Chuck Cota

MCCAULEY CONSTRUCTION CO
See CREATIVE BUILDERS INC

D-U-N-S 03-088-5354
MCCAULEY MECHANICAL CONSTRUCTION INC
8787 S 78th Ave, Bridgeview, IL 60455-1862
Tel (708) 233-0606 *Founded/Ownrshp* 2004
Sales 41.1MM^E *EMP* 110
SIC 1711 1623 Warm air heating & air conditioning contractor; Pipeline construction; Warm air heating & air conditioning contractor; Pipeline construction
Pr: Kathleen McCauley
**VP:* James McCauley Jr

MCCC
See MONTGOMERY COUNTY COMMUNITY COLLEGE FOUNDATION

D-U-N-S 93-339-7767
MCCI HOLDINGS LLC
MCCI MEDICAL GROUP
4960 Sw 72nd Ave Ste 406, Miami, FL 33155-5506
Tel (305) 461-6060 *Founded/Ownrshp* 2006
Sales 48.2MM^E *EMP* 658^E
SIC 8011 Offices & clinics of medical doctors
Doctor: Sharon Acevedo

MCCI MEDICAL GROUP
See MCCI HOLDINGS LLC

D-U-N-S 83-680-8253
MCCLAIN & ASSOCIATES LTD
2458 Old Dorsett Rd, Maryland Heights, MO 63043-2423
Tel (636) 896-0085 *Founded/Ownrshp* 1995
Sales 35.0MM *EMP* 37
SIC 4213 Trucking, except local; Trucking, except local
Pr: Michael McClain
**VP:* Kelly McClain
Sales Asso: Jill Cross

D-U-N-S 96-260-3739
MCCLAIN FOREST PRODUCTS LLC
1050 Girdley St, West Plains, MO 65775-5247
Tel (417) 257-7795 *Founded/Ownrshp* 2004
Sales 51.1MM^E *EMP* 200
SIC 5031 Lumber, plywood & millwork; Lumber, plywood & millwork
CFO: Larry Rainwater
Prd Mgr: Capri Keasler

D-U-N-S 03-050-8928
MCCLAIN SONICS INC
SONIC DRIVE-IN
425 Christine Dr, Ridgeland, MS 39157-3437
Tel (601) 914-3401 *Founded/Ownrshp* 2000
Sales 37.8MM^E *EMP* 1,000
SIC 5812 Drive-in restaurant; Drive-in restaurant
Pr: Ronald G McClain
Treas: R Clark Spencer
VP: Cary L Harvey
Exec: Debbie Porter

MCCLAIN'S RV SUPERSTORES
See R V MCCLAINS INC

D-U-N-S 00-300-6855 IMP/EXP
MCCLARIN PLASTICS LLC (PA)
15 Industrial Dr, Hanover, PA 17331-9530
Tel (717) 637-2241 *Founded/Ownrshp* 1952, 2015
Sales 49.6MM^E *EMP* 170
SIC 3083 Plastic finished products, laminated; Thermoplastic laminates: rods, tubes, plates & sheet; Plastic finished products, laminated; Thermoplastic laminates: rods, tubes, plates & sheet
Pr: Jerry Armstrong
**Treas:* John W Kennedy
**VP:* Michael J Clifford
VP: Wade Wolcott
**Prin:* Robin Rebert

D-U-N-S 18-682-4751 IMP
MCCLARIN PLASTICS LLC
AMTECH
180 E Jones Rd, Wapato, WA 98951-1508
Tel (509) 877-5950 *Founded/Ownrshp* 2015
Sales 24.2MM^E *EMP* 330
SIC 3089 3088 3229 Molding primary plastic; Plastic processing; Hot tubs, plastic or fiberglass; Molding primary plastic; Plastic processing; Hot tubs, plastic or fiberglass; Glass fiber products
CEO: Doug Christie
**CFO:* Kim Brazell
Sls Mgr: Charles Vannoy

D-U-N-S 01-655-3971
▲ **MCCLATCHY CO**
2100 Q St, Sacramento, CA 95816-6816
Tel (916) 321-1844 *Founded/Ownrshp* 1857
Sales 1.1MMM *EMP* 6,200^E
Accts Deloitte & Touche Llp Sacrame
Tkr Sym MNI *Exch* NYS
SIC 2711 Newspapers: publishing only, not printed on site; Newspapers: publishing only, not printed on site
Pr: Patrick J Talamantes
COO: Helga Comisky
CFO: Elaine Lintecum
Ex VP: James Calloway
Ex VP: Fraser Van Asch
Sr VP: Mark Vasch
VP: Anders Gyllenhaal
VP: Christian A Hendricks
VP: Jose Mendoza
VP: Karole Morgan
VP: Karole Morgan-Prager
VP: Robert J Weil
VP: Mark Zieman
Board of Directors: Elizabeth Ballantine, Leroy Barnes Jr, Molly Maloney Evangelisti, Kathleen Foley Feldstein, Craig I Forman, Kevin S McClatchy, William McClatchy, Clyde W Ostler, Frederick R Ruiz

D-U-N-S 07-932-4326
MCCLATCHY CO
2100 Q St, Sacramento, CA 95816-6816
Tel (916) 321-1941 *Founded/Ownrshp* 1998
Sales 72.8M^E *EMP* 10,000
SIC 8999

D-U-N-S 94-179-7990
MCCLATCHY MEDICAL CENTER
(*Suby of* METHODIST HEALTHCARE) ★
7235 Hacks Cross Rd, Olive Branch, MS 38654-4213
Tel (662) 893-7878 *Founded/Ownrshp* 2011
Sales 25.5MM^E *EMP* 1,696^E
SIC 8011 Medical centers
Prin: William Hardee McClatchy

D-U-N-S 00-918-2114 IMP
■ **MCCLATCHY NEWSPAPERS INC**
SACRAMENTO BEE
(*Suby of* MCCLATCHY CO) ★
2100 Q St, Sacramento, CA 95816-6899
Tel (916) 321-1000 *Founded/Ownrshp* 1998
Sales 951.0MM^E *EMP* 5,143
SIC 2711 2759 7375 Newspapers, publishing & printing; Commercial printing; On-line data base information retrieval; Newspapers, publishing & printing; Commercial printing; On-line data base information retrieval
Ch Bd: Erwin Potts
**Treas:* James P Smith
VP: Dan Schaub
CTO: John Stark
Dir IT: Carol Vila
IT Man: Scott Vanarts
Web Dev: Tom Markart
Sftwr Eng: Saul Moses
VP Opers: Robert Weil
VP Opers: Frank Whittaker
Sales Exec: Jim Paquette

D-U-N-S 00-607-3266
MCCLEARY INC
TRANS-ASTRO
239 Oak Grove Ave, South Beloit, IL 61080-1936
Tel (815) 389-3053 *Founded/Ownrshp* 1960
Sales 33.6MM^E *EMP* 145^E
SIC 2096 2064 Tortilla chips; Popcorn balls or other treated popcorn products; Tortilla chips; Popcorn balls or other treated popcorn products
Ch Bd: Pat McCleary
Pr: Nancy Schilsky
**Pr:* Jerry Stokely
Prd Mgr: Leon Schwitters

D-U-N-S 07-876-5856
MCCLELLAND AND HINE INC (TX)
2200 Thousnd Oaks Dr 100, San Antonio, TX 78232
Tel (210) 366-2500 *Founded/Ownrshp* 1982
Sales NA *EMP* 60
SIC 6411 Insurance brokers
Pr: Gilbert C Hine Jr
CFO: Ron Lloyd
VP: Lisa Barnes
VP: Shannon Dahlke
**VP:* Shelly Hine

CIO: Robert McCallum
CTO: McCallum Robert
IT Man: Pershing Berthelot

MCCLEOD MED CENTER-DARLINGTON
See MCLEOD REGIONAL MEDICAL CENTER OF PEE DEE INC

D-U-N-S 62-306-2379 IMP
MCCLESKEY CONSTRUCTION CO INC
MCCLESKEY MAUSOLEUM ASSOCIATES
723 Church St, Buford, GA 30518-3224
Tel (770) 447-9370 *Founded/Ownrshp* 1983
Sales 34.5MM[E] *EMP* 150
SIC 1542 Mausoleum construction; Mausoleum construction
Pr: Samuel W McCleskey
**Pr:* Robert E De Beltrand
**CFO:* Larry S Yarbrough
Exec: Barbara Moon

MCCLESKEY MAUSOLEUM ASSOCIATES
See MCCLESKEY CONSTRUCTION CO INC

D-U-N-S 19-412-1901
■ **MCCLIER CORP**
(*Suby of* AECOM) ★
303 E Wacker Dr Ste 900, Chicago, IL 60601-5222
Tel (312) 938-0300 *Founded/Ownrshp* 1996
Sales 13.0MM[E] *EMP* 506
SIC 8712 8711 1542 1541 Architectural services; Engineering services; Commercial & office building, new construction; Commercial & office buildings, renovation & repair; Industrial buildings, new construction; Renovation, remodeling & repairs: industrial buildings; Architectural services; Engineering services; Commercial & office building, new construction; Commercial & office buildings, renovation & repair; Industrial buildings, new construction; Renovation, remodeling & repairs: industrial buildings
Pr: Ken Terpin
Treas: Ron E Osborne
Sales Exec: Mark Berezin
Sales Exec: Joseph Mulvey
Mktg Dir: Susan L Bonn

D-U-N-S 07-834-1862
MCCLINTON ENERGY GROUP L L C (TX)
11200 W Interstate 20 E, Odessa, TX 79765-2501
Tel (432) 563-5500 *Founded/Ownrshp* 2011, 2014
Sales 73.9MM[E] *EMP* 150[E]
SIC 1381 3351 Drilling oil & gas wells; Tubing, copper & copper alloy; Drilling oil & gas wells; Tubing, copper & copper alloy
VP: Joyce Whatley

D-U-N-S 06-044-5350
MCCLONE AGENCY INC
MCCLONE INSURANCE GROUP
150 Main St Ste 102, Menasha, WI 54952-3385
Tel (920) 725-3232 *Founded/Ownrshp* 1988
Sales NA *EMP* 111
SIC 6411 Insurance agents
Pr: Mike Mc Clone
VP: Sue Kosmer
**VP:* Brian McClone
**VP:* Pam McClone
VP: Patrick McClone
VP: Robert McClone
Opers Mgr: Rich Schiller

D-U-N-S 83-098-7731
MCCLONE CONSTRUCTION CO
5170 Hillsdale Cir Ste B, El Dorado Hills, CA 95762-5774
Tel (916) 358-5495 *Founded/Ownrshp* 1993
Sales 149.8MM *EMP* 500
Accts Gallina Llp Roseville Califo
SIC 1771 1751 Concrete work; Carpentry work; Concrete work; Carpentry work
CEO: Brett Steed
**Pr:* Tim Eble
**COO:* Grant Orr
**CFO:* Ted Hoffman
**VP:* Roy Cloud
**VP:* Mark McClone
**VP:* Kevin Miller
VP: Ken Ridens
**VP:* John Salluce
IT Man: Elizabeth Armatys

MCCLONE INSURANCE GROUP
See MCCLONE AGENCY INC

D-U-N-S 62-075-3129 IMP
MCCLOSKEY MOTORS INC
MCCLOSKEY SUZUKI ISUZU
6710 N Academy Blvd, Colorado Springs, CO 80918-1207
Tel (719) 268-6966 *Founded/Ownrshp* 1985
Sales 20.2MM[E] *EMP* 60
SIC 5511 5521 New & used car dealers; Used car dealers; New & used car dealers; Used car dealers
Pr: Joseph McCloskey
Mktg Mgr: Christine Garcia

MCCLOSKEY SUZUKI ISUZU
See MCCLOSKEY MOTORS INC

MCCLOUD SERVICES
See WB MCCLOUD & CO INC

D-U-N-S 00-799-6127 IMP
MCCLUNG-LOGAN EQUIPMENT CO INC (NC)
(*Suby of* M-L HOLDINGS CO) ★
4601 Washington Blvd A, Baltimore, MD 21227-4495
Tel (410) 242-6500 *Founded/Ownrshp* 1939, 1983
Sales 56.4MM[E] *EMP* 146
Accts Hertzbach & Company Pa Balt
SIC 5082 General construction machinery & equipment; General construction machinery & equipment
Ch Bd: Robert Matz
**Pr:* Darrin Brown
CFO: Kathleen Pepperman
**Ch:* Thomas Logan
VP: Austin Frederick
VP: Janice Kunkel
VP: Mike Mayhugh
Mng Dir: Mark Ciulla
Mktg Mgr: Evan Himelfarb
Sls Mgr: John Chartier
Sls Mgr: Bob Kaase

MCCLURE AND ZIMMERMAN
See J W JUNG SEED CO

D-U-N-S 01-650-9580
MCCLURE OIL CORP
ASCO OIL PRODUCTS
Junction Of Hwy 35 & 37, Marion, IN 46953
Tel (765) 674-9771 *Founded/Ownrshp* 1975
Sales 69.6MM[E] *EMP* 400
SIC 5411 5172 Convenience stores, independent; Engine fuels & oils; Convenience stores, independent; Engine fuels & oils
Pr: Edward Mc Clure
Pr: Randy Myers
Sec: G Richard Mc Clure
VP: Kelly Mc Clure
VP: Thomas Smith

D-U-N-S 19-857-8155
MCCLURE PROPERTIES LTD
WEST COST TOMATO
502 6th Ave W, Palmetto, FL 34221-5110
Tel (941) 722-4545 *Founded/Ownrshp* 1995
Sales 336.6MM[E] *EMP* 12,000
SIC 0161 Rooted vegetable farms; Rooted vegetable farms
**Pt:* Corrine A McClure
**Pt:* Daniel C McClure

D-U-N-S 00-450-2746
■ **MCCLURE-JOHNSTON CO**
(*Suby of* BEACON ROOFING SUPPLY INC) ★
201 Corey Ave, Braddock, PA 15104-1397
Tel (412) 351-4300 *Founded/Ownrshp* 1914, 2012
Sales 31.8MM[E] *EMP* 135
SIC 5033 5031 Roofing, asphalt & sheet metal; Siding, except wood; Windows; Roofing, asphalt & sheet metal; Siding, except wood; Windows
Ch Bd: Brian P Hogan
CFO: Wm F Oxenreiter III
**Treas:* William F Oxenreiter III
**VP:* John D Oxenreiter
Sales Exec: Mike Kearney
**VP Sls:* Michael T Hogan
Sales Asso: Brent Barr
Sales Asso: Andy Yoder

D-U-N-S 05-911-2011
MCCLUSKEY CHEVROLET INC
8525 Reading Rd, Cincinnati, OH 45215-5598
Tel (513) 761-1111 *Founded/Ownrshp* 1975
Sales 51.9MM[E] *EMP* 146
SIC 5511 7515 7513 5521 5012 Automobiles, new & used; Pickups, new & used; Vans, new & used; Passenger car leasing; Truck rental & leasing, no drivers; Used car dealers; Automobiles & other motor vehicles; Automobiles, new & used; Pickups, new & used; Vans, new & used; Passenger car leasing; Truck rental & leasing, no drivers; Used car dealers; Automobiles & other motor vehicles
CEO: Daniel McCluskey
**Pr:* Keith P McCluskey
**Sec:* Gina Owens
Off Mgr: Gina Quatkemeyer
Sls Dir: Paul Cluxton
Sls Mgr: Walt Kelsey
Sls Mgr: Fred Porciello
Sales Asso: Craig Knisley

D-U-N-S 19-405-3104
MCCLYMONDS SUPPLY & TRANSIT CO INC
296 Currie Rd Rr 422, Portersville, PA 16051
Tel (724) 368-8040 *Founded/Ownrshp* 1977
Sales 49.3MM[E] *EMP* 305
SIC 4212 5032 4213 Local trucking, without storage; Sand, construction; Gravel; Limestone; Trucking, except local; Local trucking, without storage; Sand, construction; Gravel; Limestone; Trucking, except local
Pr: Mark McClymonds
**CFO:* Patrick G McGinnis
Dir IT: Dan Sullivan

MCCO
See MEDICAL CENTER CO INC

D-U-N-S 02-532-0693 IMP
MCCOLLISTERS TRANSPORTATION GROUP INC
MCCOLLSTERS TRNSPRTION SYSTEMS
1800 Re 130 N, Burlington, NJ 08016
Tel (609) 386-0600 *Founded/Ownrshp* 1998
Sales 164.3MM[E] *EMP* 647
SIC 4213 4212 Contract haulers; Household goods transport; Local trucking, without storage; Contract haulers; Household goods transport; Local trucking, without storage
Pr: Dan McCollister
Pr: Mike Cunniff
COO: Ray Conlin
**CFO:* Gary Morgan
Sr VP: Dennis Mazar
VP: Marc Gumm
VP: D J Warden
Dir Bus: Jack Ring
Opers Mgr: Danny Barlow
Opers Mgr: Michael Maturi
Opers Mgr: Darryl Neely

D-U-N-S 00-249-5406
MCCOLLISTERS TRANSPORTATION SYSTEMS INC
(*Suby of* MCCOLLISTERS TRANSPORTATION GROUP INC) ★
1800 N Route 130, Burlington, NJ 08016-3017
Tel (215) 750-1097 *Founded/Ownrshp* 1945
Sales 34.5MM[E] *EMP* 200
SIC 4213 Contract haulers; Household goods transport; Contract haulers; Household goods transport
Pr: H Daniel Mc Collister
Genl Mgr: Tom Weight

D-U-N-S 00-877-4788
MCCOLLISTERS TRANSPORTATION SYSTEMS OF NEW JERSEY
1344 N West Blvd, Vineland, NJ 08360-2270
Tel (800) 257-9595 *Founded/Ownrshp* 2007
Sales 100.0MM *EMP* 59
SIC 4213 4225 4214 Household goods transport; General warehousing; Local trucking with storage; Household goods transport; General warehousing; Local trucking with storage
Prin: H Daniel McCollister
**Prin:* Dale Traver McCollister

MCCOLLSTERS TRNSPRTION SYSTEMS
See MCCOLLISTERS TRANSPORTATION GROUP INC

MCCOLLY REAL ESTATE
See MCCOLLY REALTORS INC

D-U-N-S 11-492-0036
MCCOLLY REALTORS INC
MCCOLLY REAL ESTATE
850 Deer Creek Dr, Schererville, IN 46375-1352
Tel (219) 322-5508 *Founded/Ownrshp* 1974
Sales 750.0MM *EMP* 53
SIC 6531 Real estate brokers & agents; Real estate brokers & agents
Pr: Ronald F McColly
**Pr:* Ronald F Mc Colly
**VP:* Martha Jane McColly
Off Mgr: Howard Marshall

D-U-N-S 08-712-8484
MCCOMAS-LACINA CONST CO
1310 Highland Ct, Iowa City, IA 52240-4538
Tel (319) 338-8760 *Founded/Ownrshp* 1977
Sales 37.4MM[E] *EMP* 120
SIC 1542 Commercial & office buildings, renovation & repair; Commercial & office building, new construction; Commercial & office buildings, renovation & repair; Commercial & office building, new construction
Pr: Chuck McComas
**VP:* Dave Lacina

D-U-N-S 12-583-8904
MCCOMB SCHOOL DISTRICT
695 Minnesota Ave, McComb, MS 39648-4044
Tel (601) 684-4661 *Founded/Ownrshp* 1976
Sales 24.7MM[E] *EMP* 450
Accts Patrick E Lowery And Associat
SIC 8211 Public elementary & secondary schools; Public elementary & secondary schools
MIS Dir: Sue Jarvis

D-U-N-S 08-597-0036
MCCOMBS ENERGY LTD
5599 Saint Felipe St 12 # 1200, Houston, TX 77056
Tel (713) 621-0033 *Founded/Ownrshp* 1998
Sales 90.2MM *EMP* 12
SIC 1311 Crude petroleum production; Natural gas production; Crude petroleum production; Natural gas production
Pr: Bill Forney Jr
VP: Charles Forney
VP: Johnny Forney
VP: Phillip Forney
VP: Ricky Haikin
VP: Larry Wyont

MCCOMBS TOYOTA
See MCCALL TOYOTA INC

D-U-N-S 86-761-4356
MCCOMIC CONSOLIDATED INC
10721 Treena St Ste 200, San Diego, CA 92131-1016
Tel (858) 653-3003 *Founded/Ownrshp* 1994
Sales 33.8MM *EMP* 2
SIC 6552 Subdividers & developers; Subdividers & developers
Pr: R Barry McComic
**VP:* R Geoffrey McComic

D-U-N-S 07-078-8766
MCCONNELL & JONES LLP
4828 Loop Central Dr # 1000, Houston, TX 77081-2222
Tel (713) 968-1600 *Founded/Ownrshp* 1996
Sales 21.5MM[E] *EMP* 250
SIC 8721 Accounting, auditing & bookkeeping
Mng Pt: Wayne McConnell
**Pt:* Thomas Jones
**Pt:* Ira Wayne McConnell

D-U-N-S 03-404-2200
MCCONNELL AUTOMOTIVE CORP (AL)
3150 Dauphin St, Mobile, AL 36606-4079
Tel (251) 476-4141 *Founded/Ownrshp* 1955, 1961
Sales 49.6MM[E] *EMP* 130[E]
SIC 5511 Automobiles, new & used; Automobiles, new & used
Ch Bd: James V McConnell Jr
**Pr:* Edwin W McConnell
**CFO:* Julia Hatton
Brnch Mgr: Remonica Gamble

D-U-N-S 05-643-4442 IMP
MCCONNELL CABINETS INC
COASTAL WOOD PRODUCTS
13110 Louden Ln, City of Industry, CA 91746-1507
Tel (626) 937-2200 *Founded/Ownrshp* 1944
Sales NA *EMP* 740
SIC 2434

D-U-N-S 00-899-5003
MCCONNELL GROUP INC
1901 Res Blvd Ste 502, Rockville, MD 20850
Tel (301) 309-8310 *Founded/Ownrshp* 1996
Sales 35.4MM[E] *EMP* 230
SIC 8733 Medical research; Medical research
Pr: Irving W McConnell
**Ex VP:* Helene Rodriguez

D-U-N-S 78-490-7206
MCCONNELL JONES LANIER & MURPHY LLP
MJLM ENGRG & TECHNICAL SVCS
4828 Loop Central Dr, Houston, TX 77081-2212
Tel (713) 968-1600 *Founded/Ownrshp* 1987
Sales 32.2MM[E] *EMP* 229
SIC 8721 8711 Accounting, auditing & bookkeeping; Engineering services; Accounting, auditing & bookkeeping; Engineering services
Pt: Wayne McConnell
Pt: Thomas Jones
Pt: Odysseus Lanier
Pt: Sharon Murphy
Dir IT: Evelyn Hatter

D-U-N-S 09-035-9217
MCCONNELL VALDES LLC
270 Ave Munoz Rivera, San Juan, PR 00918-1901
Tel (787) 767-2500 *Founded/Ownrshp* 1946
Sales 34.0MM *EMP* 300[E]
SIC 8111 General practice law office
V Ch: Ivan Marrero
Corp Couns: Carlos Fern
Counsel: Sandra Negron-Monge

MCCOOK PUBLIC SCHOOLS
See MC COOK PUBLIC SCHOOLS

D-U-N-S 02-734-6501
MCCORD BROS INC
MCCORDS DDGE CHRYSLER JEEP RAM
990 Tennant Way, Longview, WA 98632-2408
Tel (360) 425-3900 *Founded/Ownrshp* 1978
Sales 21.0MM[E] *EMP* 50
SIC 5511 5561 Automobiles, new & used; Pickups, new & used; Recreational vehicle dealers; Automobiles, new & used; Pickups, new & used; Recreational vehicle dealers
Pr: Marion McCord
**VP:* Rob Bardonski
VP: Rob Brodonski
Off Mgr: Marie Morey
Off Mgr: Tera Trekas
Sls Mgr: Ken Kirby

MCCORDS DDGE CHRYSLER JEEP RAM
See MCCORD BROS INC

D-U-N-S 06-318-7264
MCCORDS VANCOUVER AUTO CENTER INC (WA)
VANCOUVER TOYOTA & RV CENTER
10455 Ne 53rd St, Vancouver, WA 98662-6179
Tel (360) 253-4440 *Founded/Ownrshp* 1982
Sales 78.3MM *EMP* 140
SIC 5511 5561 Automobiles, new & used; Recreational vehicle dealers; Automobiles, new & used; Recreational vehicle dealers
Pr: Marvin C Mc Cord
**Treas:* Shirley Mc Cord
Genl Mgr: Greg Leonard
Sls Mgr: Nathan Needham

D-U-N-S 03-358-1430
MCCORKLE NURSERIES INC
4904 Luckys Bridge Rd, Dearing, GA 30808-2106
Tel (706) 595-9702 *Founded/Ownrshp* 1963
Sales 22.8MM[E] *EMP* 200[E]
SIC 0181 Nursery stock, growing of; Nursery stock, growing of
Pr: Donald E McCorkle Jr
**CFO:* William Janci
**VP:* Jack McCorkle
Opers Mgr: Chris McCorkle
Board of Directors: Chris S Mc Corkle, Donald Mc Corkle Sr, Jack H Mc Corkle and Bever

MCCORMACK BARON RAGAN
See BARON MCCORMACK MANAGEMENT INC

MCCORMACK BARON SALAZAR
See MBA PROPERTIES INC

D-U-N-S 04-361-4130 IMP/EXP
▲ **MCCORMICK & CO INC**
18 Loveton Cir, Sparks, MD 21152-9271
Tel (410) 771-7301 *Founded/Ownrshp* 1889
Sales 4.2MMM *EMP* 10,007
Accts Ernst & Young Llp Baltimore
Tkr Sym MKC *Exch* NYS
SIC 2099 2087 2038 2037 Spices, including grinding; Seasonings: dry mixes; Gravy mixes, dry; Sauces: dry mixes; Extracts, flavoring; Frozen specialties; French toast, frozen; Vegetables, quick frozen & cold pack, excl. potato products; Spices, including grinding; Seasonings: dry mixes; Gravy mixes, dry; Sauces: dry mixes; Extracts, flavoring; Frozen specialties; French toast, frozen; Vegetables, quick frozen & cold pack, excl. potato products
CEO: Alan D Wilson
Pr: Randy Carper
Pr: Brendan Foley
Pr: Lawrence E Kurzius
Pr: Lawrence Kurzuiz
Pr: Charles T Langmead
Pr: Chuck Langmead
Pr: Mark T Timbie
CFO: Mike Smith
CFO: Gordon M Stetz Jr
Ofcr: Peter Villiger
Sr VP: Lisa Manzone
VP: Brandon Clairmont
VP: Jeffery D Schwartz
Exec: Shannon Bell
Exec: James Downing
Exec: James Hepner
Exec: Len King
Dir Rx: Bjoern Leyser
Dir Bus: Suzanne Roy
Board of Directors: John P Bilbrey, Michael Conway, J Michael Fitzpatrick, Freeman A Hrabowski III, Patricia Little, Michael D Mangan, Margaret M V Preston, Jacques Tapiero

D-U-N-S 16-014-1230
MCCORMICK & SCHMICK HOLDING CORP
(*Suby of* MCCORMICK & SCHMICKS SEAFOOD RESTAURANTS INC) ★
720 Sw Washington St # 550, Portland, OR 97205-3507
Tel (800) 552-6379 *Founded/Ownrshp* 1997
Sales 76.0MM^E *EMP* 4,300
SIC 5812 Seafood restaurants; Seafood restaurants
Pr: William P Mc Cormick
**CFO:* Emanuel N Hilario
CFO: Michelle Lantow
Genl Mgr: Brian Cooper
Genl Mgr: Mia Harriman
Genl Mgr: Scott Kennedy
Genl Mgr: Jim Rooney
Sls&Mrk Ex: Gregg Le Le Blanc

D-U-N-S 12-238-2773
MCCORMICK & SCHMICK MANAGEMENT GROUP
(*Suby of* MCCORMICK & SCHMICKS SEAFOOD RESTAURANTS INC) ★
1510 West Loop S, Houston, TX 77027-9505
Tel (512) 836-0500 *Founded/Ownrshp* 1970
Sales 25.4MM^E *EMP* 1,000
SIC 5812 Restaurant, family: independent; Restaurant, family: independent
Pr: William P McCormick
Genl Mgr: Melody Casbarian
Genl Mgr: Oaul Pierce

D-U-N-S 14-754-4642 IMP
MCCORMICK & SCHMICKS SEAFOOD RESTAURANTS INC
(*Suby of* LANDRYS INC) ★
1510 West Loop S, Houston, TX 77027-9505
Tel (800) 552-6379 *Founded/Ownrshp* 2012
Sales 138.1MM^E *EMP* 6,582^E
SIC 5812 Seafood restaurants; Seafood restaurants
CEO: William T Freeman
CFO: Michelle M Lantow
Ex VP: Michael B Liedberg
VP: Kelly A B Gordon
VP: Christopher C Westcott
Exec: Humphrey Lansiquot
Rgnl Mgr: Kathryn Henderson
Genl Mgr: Mehrez Ayari
Genl Mgr: John Bremer
Genl Mgr: Greg Kerr
Genl Mgr: Daniel Shinaut
Board of Directors: Eric P Bauer, J Rice Edmonds, Elliott H Jurgensen Jr, James R Parish, Douglas L Schmick, Christine F Deputy Ott

D-U-N-S 02-597-5970
MCCORMICK ADVERTISING CO (TX)
MCCORMICK COMPANY
701 S Taylor St Ste 400, Amarillo, TX 79101-2424
Tel (806) 374-5333 *Founded/Ownrshp* 1926, 1954
Sales 29.3MM *EMP* 93
Accts Hudgins Crosier Sumpter Pc A
SIC 7311 Advertising agencies; Advertising agencies
Ch: Kathryn Cornett
**Pr:* Laura Mayfield
**VP:* Evan Davies
**VP:* Suzanne Sutton-Vermeulen
**VP:* Zach Tassell
Prd Mgr: Megan Ferchen
Prd Mgr: Karla Schuning
Art Dir: Steve Nottingham
Art Dir: Mike Peterson
Art Dir: Susan Porter

MCCORMICK BARSTOW
See MCCORMICK BARSTOW SHEPPARD WAYTE & CARRUTH LLP

D-U-N-S 09-564-8846
MCCORMICK BARSTOW SHEPPARD WAYTE & CARRUTH LLP
MCCORMICK BARSTOW
7647 N Fresno St, Fresno, CA 93720-2578
Tel (559) 433-1300 *Founded/Ownrshp* 1995
Sales 34.3MM^E *EMP* 246^E
SIC 8111 Antitrust & trade regulation law; Corporate, partnership & business law; Bankruptcy law; Antitrust & trade regulation law; Corporate, partnership & business law; Bankruptcy law
Mng Pt: Jeffrey M Reid
Pt: Kenneth A Baldwin
Pt: Michael F Ball
Pt: Todd W Baxter
Pt: Mario L Beltramo Jr
Pt: Todd Daxter
Pt: Christopher S Hall
Pt: Matthew Hawkins
Pt: Gregory Mason
Pt: David McNamara
Pr: Sherrea Lee
VP: Mike Graves

MCCORMICK COMPANY
See MCCORMICK ADVERTISING CO

MCCORMICK CONSTRUCTION COMPANY
See MCC INC

D-U-N-S 00-713-8191 IMP/EXP
MCCORMICK DISTILLING CO INC
TEQUILA ROSE DISTILLING CO
1 Mc Cormick Ln, Weston, MO 64098-9558
Tel (816) 640-2276 *Founded/Ownrshp* 1992
Sales 25.9MM^E *EMP* 152
SIC 2085 Distilled & blended liquors; Distilled & blended liquors
Pr: James A Zargo
CFO: Chris Fernandez
Ch: Ed Pechar
V Ch Bd: Mick Harris
VP: Bob Otto
Rgnl Mgr: Greg Dent
Area Mgr: Molly Lachance
Info Man: Phil Colclough
Netwrk Eng: Travis Moeck
Prd Mgr: Lisa Williams
Ql Cn Mgr: Jessi Coock

D-U-N-S 04-457-4945
MCCORMICK EQUIPMENT CO INC
112 Northeast Dr, Loveland, OH 45140-7144
Tel (513) 677-8888 *Founded/Ownrshp* 1986
Sales 38.5MM^E *EMP* 77
SIC 5084 Industrial machinery & equipment; Industrial machinery & equipment
Pr: R Peter Kimener
**CFO:* Bruce A Buckley
Brnch Mgr: Fred Nasrallah
VP Opers: Mark Hurd

D-U-N-S 05-180-3237
MCCORMICK INC
4000 12th Ave N, Fargo, ND 58102-2910
Tel (701) 277-1225 *Founded/Ownrshp* 1981
Sales 228.5MM *EMP* 500
Accts Eide Bailly Llp Fargo North
SIC 1611 1629 1623 General contractor, highway & street construction; Power plant construction; Land preparation construction; Water & sewer line construction; General contractor, highway & street construction; Power plant construction; Land preparation construction; Water & sewer line construction
Pr: Stephen D McCormick
Pr: Steve McCormick
Treas: Bradley Ballweber
VP: John McCormick III
VP: Tom McCormick

D-U-N-S 09-929-9716 IMP
MCCORMICK INTERNATIONAL USA INC
(*Suby of* ARGO TRACTORS SPA)
2590 Breckinridge Blvd, Duluth, GA 30096-4968
Tel (678) 924-9885 *Founded/Ownrshp* 2000
Sales 45.2MM^E *EMP* 55
SIC 5083 Farm & garden machinery
Pr: Simeone Morra
**CEO:* Tiago Bonomo
**CFO:* Alberto Crema
**CFO:* Rhett Crook
**Prin:* Rodney Miller
Opers Mgr: Crystal Davis
Sls Mgr: Kyle Watts

D-U-N-S 00-324-8275 IMP
MCCORMICK PAINT WORKS CO (MD)
MCCORMICK PAINT'S
2355 Lewis Ave, Rockville, MD 20851-2391
Tel (301) 770-3235 *Founded/Ownrshp* 1960
Sales 40.0MM *EMP* 200
Accts Rubino & Mcgeehin Bethesda M
SIC 2851 5231 Paints & paint additives; Paint; Paints & paint additives; Paint
Ch Bd: Thomas P McCormick
**Pr:* J Casey McCormick
**CFO:* Yamna M Stanger
**Sr VP:* Malcolm Allison
Sr VP: Justin Jones
**VP:* Michael McCormick
MIS Dir: Mario Yuri
Dir IT: Mark Bauer
IT Man: Eric Cheeks
VP Sls: Jim Hennessy
Manager: Keith Carpenter

MCCORMICK PAINT'S
See MCCORMICK PAINT WORKS CO

D-U-N-S 13-431-9578
MCCORMICK PLACE CONVENTION CENTER
METROPOLITAN PEER & EXPO AUTH
2301 S Lake Shore Dr # 1, Chicago, IL 60616-1497
Tel (312) 791-7900 *Founded/Ownrshp* 1960
Sales 51.7MM^E *EMP* 600
SIC 7389 6512 Convention & show services; Tourist information bureau; Nonresidential building operators; Convention & show services; Tourist information bureau; Nonresidential building operators
CEO: Juan Ochoa
**CEO:* Jim Rielly

D-U-N-S 11-871-1852
MCCORMICK TRUCKING INC
625 S Church St Ste 100, Murfreesboro, TN 37130-4271
Tel (615) 867-7618 *Founded/Ownrshp* 1986
Sales 36.4MM^E *EMP* 450
SIC 4213 4212 Contract haulers; Mail carriers, contract
Pr: Robert A McCormick
Sec: Betty McCormick
VP: Brandy Markum

D-U-N-S 00-807-9972
MCCORVEY SHEET METAL WORKS LP
DUCT DIRECT
8610 Wallisville Rd, Houston, TX 77029-1314
Tel (713) 672-7545 *Founded/Ownrshp* 1948
Sales 104.0MM^E *EMP* 500^E
SIC 3444 Sheet metalwork; Sheet metalwork
Pr: Tony McCorvey
Ofcr: Courtney Petty
VP: Larry McNease
VP: Billy Ware
Prin: Kristal Crites
Div Mgr: Michael Baxter
Sfty Mgr: Robert Gaitan

D-U-N-S 82-843-0913
MCCOURT CONSTRUCTION CO INC
60 K St, Boston, MA 02127-1617
Tel (617) 269-2330 *Founded/Ownrshp* 1976
Sales 122.3MM^E *EMP* 300^E
SIC 1611 1622 Highway & street construction; Bridge, tunnel & elevated highway; Highway & street construction; Bridge, tunnel & elevated highway
Pr: Richard McCourt
**COO:* Steven A Frick
**Treas:* Virginia R McCourt
**VP:* Jack Murphy

D-U-N-S 00-986-8175
MCCOY & MILLS INC
MCCOY MILLS FORD
700 W Commonwealth Ave, Fullerton, CA 92832-1613
Tel (714) 526-5500 *Founded/Ownrshp* 1967
Sales 30.6MM^E *EMP* 70
SIC 5511 Automobiles, new & used; Automobiles, new & used
Pr: James W Miller
**VP:* Jana Bogart
Sls Mgr: Jase Kaefer

D-U-N-S 06-117-4769
MCCOY CORP (TX)
MCCOY'S BUILDING SUPPLY
1350 N Ih 35, San Marcos, TX 78666-7130
Tel (512) 353-5400 *Founded/Ownrshp* 1966
Sales 549.2MM^E *EMP* 2,200
SIC 5211 5251 5231

D-U-N-S 14-563-4572 IMP
MCCOY ELKHORN COAL CORP
(*Suby of* JAMES RIVER COAL CO) ★
1148 Long Fork Rd, Kimper, KY 41539-5936
Tel (606) 835-2233 *Founded/Ownrshp* 1987
Sales 46.7MM^E *EMP* 270^E
SIC 1222 Bituminous coal-underground mining; Bituminous coal-underground mining
Pr: Randall K Taylor
**VP:* Patricia R Ward

MCCOY ENTERPRISES
See MCCOY-ROCKFORD INC

MCCOY FREIGHTLINER
See JMR GROUP LLC

D-U-N-S 10-719-4383 IMP/EXP
MCCOY GLOBAL USA INC
(*Suby of* MCCOY CORPORATION)
4225 Highway 90 E, Broussard, LA 70518-3407
Tel (337) 837-8847 *Founded/Ownrshp* 1983
Sales 37.5MM^E *EMP* 75
SIC 3561 7699 Industrial pumps & parts; Industrial machinery & equipment repair
Pr: Jim Nowotny
**Pr:* James Rakievich
**Treas:* Tom Watts
VP: Dave Brown
Genl Mgr: Dan Bangert
Telecom Ex: Jamie Hanley
Mfg Mgr: Chris Roland
Plnt Mgr: Armando Cruz
Mktg Mgr: Bonnie White
Sales Asso: Guy Hebert

D-U-N-S 78-206-0693 IMP
MCCOY INVESTMENTS INC
INDIANAPOLIS DRY STRIPPING
2719 Tobey Dr, Indianapolis, IN 46219-1417
Tel (317) 545-0665 *Founded/Ownrshp* 1987
Sales 25.4MM^E *EMP* 30
SIC 5082 1799 General construction machinery & equipment; Paint & wallpaper stripping
Pr: Brian McCoy
**VP:* Steve L McCoy
Sls Mgr: John Heinzelman
Sales Asso: Jeff Blackwell

MCCOY MILLS FORD
See MCCOY & MILLS INC

D-U-N-S 02-783-2948
MCCOY MOTOR CO
MILLS FORD
1600 W Lincoln Ave, Anaheim, CA 92801-5501
Tel (714) 776-1330 *Founded/Ownrshp* 1930
Sales 23.4MM^E *EMP* 80
SIC 5511 Automobiles, new & used; Automobiles, new & used
Pr: Scott Mills
**Sec:* Ronald J Mills
**VP:* John Demmin
**VP:* Robert F Mills

D-U-N-S 03-200-1406
MCCOY SALES CORP
MOTION AND FLOW CONTROL PDTS
7941 Shaffer Pkwy, Littleton, CO 80127-3734
Tel (303) 762-8012 *Founded/Ownrshp* 1980
Sales 38.7MM^E *EMP* 80
SIC 5074

D-U-N-S 03-300-0837
MCCOY TREE SURGERY CO
3201 Broce Dr, Norman, OK 73072-2453
Tel (405) 579-6000 *Founded/Ownrshp* 1963
Sales 85.7MM^E *EMP* 500
SIC 0783 Tree trimming services for public utility lines; Tree trimming services for public utility lines
Pr: Bruce McCoy
**Sec:* Sam Batty
**VP:* Mark Kline

D-U-N-S 13-111-5669 IMP/EXP
MCCOY-ROCKFORD INC
MCCOY ENTERPRISES
6869 Old Katy Rd, Houston, TX 77024-2105
Tel (713) 862-4600 *Founded/Ownrshp* 1983
Sales 179.3MM^E *EMP* 275
Accts Pricewaterhousecoopers Llp Ho
SIC 5021 1799 Office furniture; Office furniture installation; Office furniture; Office furniture installation
Pr: Stan Bunting
**Treas:* David Barnett
**VP:* Wayne Cotton Carlson
VP: Randy Eilts
VP: Amy Lopez
VP: Kansas Sartin
Trfc Mgr: Frank Minni
Snr PM: Joe Vega
Snr Mgr: Felecia Bradley

MCCOY'S BUILDING SUPPLY
See MCCOY CORP

MCCRACKEN COUNTY BOARD EDUCATN
See MCCRACKEN COUNTY PUBLIC SCHOOLS

D-U-N-S 15-935-2442
MCCRACKEN COUNTY PUBLIC SCHOOLS
MCCRACKEN COUNTY BOARD EDUCATN
5347 Benton Rd, Paducah, KY 42003-0912
Tel (270) 538-4000 *Founded/Ownrshp* 1901
Sales 44.1MM^E *EMP* 1,000
SIC 8211 Public elementary & secondary schools; Public elementary & secondary schools
Treas: Taylor Holley
IT Man: Tony Burking

D-U-N-S 84-727-3575
MCCRAE MANAGEMENT & INVESTMENTS LTD
NEWSOUND HEARING AID CENTERS
26222 Rr 12, Dripping Springs, TX 78620-4903
Tel (512) 858-0300 *Founded/Ownrshp* 2011
Sales 66.1MM^E *EMP* 305^E
SIC 5047 Hearing aids
Prin: Randy L Schoenborn
Pt: Laureen Hurlburt
Pt: Randy Schoenborn
Snr Mgr: Derek Peterson

D-U-N-S 05-372-1981 IMP
MCCRAITH BEVERAGES INC
20 Burrstone Rd, New York Mills, NY 13417-1596
Tel (315) 768-2337 *Founded/Ownrshp* 1971
Sales 27.6MM^E *EMP* 65
SIC 5181 5182 Beer & other fermented malt liquors; Ale; Wine coolers, alcoholic
Pr: Thomas O Mc Craith
**VP:* Susan Mc Craith-Szuba
Genl Mgr: Joe Bonanza
Off Mgr: Judy White

D-U-N-S 06-885-2839
MCCRARY CONSTRUCTION CO
200 Industrial Rd Ste 130, San Carlos, CA 94070-6297
Tel (650) 594-0228 *Founded/Ownrshp* 1973
Sales 25.5MM *EMP* 10
SIC 1542 School building construction; Specialized public building contractors; School building construction; Specialized public building contractors
Pr: Murray M McCrary
**Sec:* Arlene McCrary

D-U-N-S 06-637-4299
MCCRAW OIL CO INC
2207 N Center St, Bonham, TX 75418-2112
Tel (903) 583-7481 *Founded/Ownrshp* 1978
Sales 34.3MM^E *EMP* 45^E
SIC 5171 Petroleum bulk stations & terminals
Pr: Wm Doyce Taylor
VP: Rodney Brent
Genl Mgr: Becky Moore
IT Man: Kristopher Davis
Opers Mgr: Dwayne Havens

D-U-N-S 00-696-5552
MCCRAY LUMBER CO
RIVER VALLEY RELOAD SALES
10741 El Monte St, Shawnee Mission, KS 66211-1406
Tel (913) 341-6900 *Founded/Ownrshp* 1947
Sales 66.4MM^E *EMP* 299
SIC 5211

D-U-N-S 00-347-5233
MCCREA EQUIPMENT CO INC (DC)
MCCREA HEATING AND AC SVCS
4463 Beech Rd, Temple Hills, MD 20748-6794
Tel (301) 423-6623 *Founded/Ownrshp* 1936
Sales 43.1MM^E *EMP* 210
SIC 1711 Warm air heating & air conditioning contractor; Warm air heating & air conditioning contractor
Pr: Wayne Lanhardt
**Ex VP:* Robert E Everett
Genl Mgr: Michael Gibson
IT Man: Rich Weiss

MCCREA HEATING AND AC SVCS
See MCCREA EQUIPMENT CO INC

D-U-N-S 07-493-1494
MCCREADY FOUNDATION INC
MCCREADY MEMORIAL HOSPITAL
201 Hall Hwy, Crisfield, MD 21817-1237
Tel (410) 968-1200 *Founded/Ownrshp* 1922
Sales 23.0MM^E *EMP* 300
Accts Pks & Company Pa Salisbury M
SIC 8062 8051 General medical & surgical hospitals; Skilled nursing care facilities; General medical & surgical hospitals; Skilled nursing care facilities
CEO: Charles Pinkerman
**Pr:* McCready Pediatrics
CFO: Gary Broadwater
Dir Lab: Kristen Scott
**Prin:* Bob Jones
CIO: Ken Sterling
**Sys/Dir:* Novella Bozman
Cert Phar: Amanda Hill
HC Dir: Hope Fontaine
HC Dir: Lisa Lord

MCCREADY MEMORIAL HOSPITAL
See MCCREADY FOUNDATION INC

D-U-N-S 15-071-3766 IMP
MCCREARY MODERN INC
2564 S Us 321 Hwy, Newton, NC 28658-9349
Tel (828) 464-6465 *Founded/Ownrshp* 1985
Sales 121.7MM^E *EMP* 600
Accts Whisnant & Company Llp Hickor
SIC 2512 Upholstered household furniture; Upholstered household furniture
Pr: Bill Quirk
**Treas:* Jonell Harrison
**Ex VP:* Rick Coffee
Genl Mgr: Terry Crafton
Dir IT: Dennis Baker
Plnt Mgr: Mark Harris

D-U-N-S 00-784-4137
MCCREE INC (FL)
MC CREE GEN CONTR & ARCHITECTS
500 E Princeton St, Orlando, FL 32803-1448
Tel (407) 898-4821 *Founded/Ownrshp* 1926, 1953
Sales 76.9MM^E *EMP* 170
SIC 1542 1541 Commercial & office building, new construction; Industrial buildings, new construction; Commercial & office building, new construction; Industrial buildings, new construction
Pr: Richard T McCree Jr
**CFO:* Evan Landis

VP: Rich Gaines
**VP:* Thomas Griffin
**VP:* Joe Robertson
**VP:* Michael Waldrop

D-U-N-S 60-375-8223 IMP/EXP
■ MCCROMETER INC
(*Suby of* DANAHER CORP) ★
3255 W Stetson Ave, Hemet, CA 92545-7763
Tel (951) 652-6811 *Founded/Ownrshp* 1996
Sales 28.8MM^E *EMP* 230
SIC 3824 Water meters; Water meters
Pr: Melissa Aquino
**VP:* Ian Rule
Manager: William Strong
Sales Asso: Howard Crum

D-U-N-S 00-678-8350
MCCRORY CONSTRUCTION CO LLC
522 Lady St, Columbia, SC 29201-3016
Tel (803) 799-8100 *Founded/Ownrshp* 2002
Sales 73.5MM *EMP* 80
Accts Elliott Davis Llc Columbia
SIC 1542 1541 Commercial & office building, new construction; Hospital construction; Religious building construction; School building construction; Industrial buildings, new construction
CEO: Allen Amsler
VP: Allen Bridgers
VP: Randy Morrison
**Exec:* Gail Chapman
Ex Dir: Elizabeth Tharp
Mktg Dir: Dennis Shealy
Snr PM: John Caruk
Snr PM: Adam Whitley

MCCS
See MAINE COMMUNITY COLLEGE SYSTEM

MCCSC
See MONROE COUNTY COMMUNITY SCHOOL CORP

D-U-N-S 00-720-5255 IMP
MCCUBBIN HOSIERY LLC
5310 Nw 5th St Ste 100, Oklahoma City, OK 73127-5828
Tel (405) 236-8351 *Founded/Ownrshp* 2013
Sales 41.7MM^E *EMP* 97
Accts Dana Everett
SIC 5137 Hosiery: women's, children's & infants'
**CFO:* Dana Everett

D-U-N-S 60-760-2455 IMP/EXP
MCCUE CORP
13 Centennial Dr, Peabody, MA 01960-7901
Tel (978) 741-8500 *Founded/Ownrshp* 1988
Sales 45.0MM^E *EMP* 110
SIC 5046 Store fixtures & display equipment; Store fixtures & display equipment
Pr: David S McCue
COO: William Sullivan
CFO: Joseph Falcao
VP: David Diantonio
VP: Paul Ryan
IT Man: Peter Whittemore
Mfg Mgr: Jeff Hutchinson
Mfg Mgr: Scott Tierney
Opers Mgr: Richard Mariano
VP Sls: Bill Rothwell
Manager: Dave Ambrosino

D-U-N-S 04-896-3649
MCCULLERS INVESTMENTS INC (NC)
715 Iredell St, Durham, NC 27705-4804
Tel (919) 286-4449 *Founded/Ownrshp* 1960, 1966
Sales 6.2MM^E *EMP* 320
SIC 7349 Building maintenance services; Building maintenance services
Pr: C Kenneth McCullers
**VP:* Morgan Osborne
Sls Mgr: Sam McFalls

D-U-N-S 07-468-2147
MCCULLOUGH-HYDE MEMORIAL HOSPITAL INC
110 N Poplar St, Oxford, OH 45056-1204
Tel (513) 523-2111 *Founded/Ownrshp* 1957
Sales 54.9MM *EMP* 500^E
Accts Blue & Co Llc Columbus Oh
SIC 8062 General medical & surgical hospitals; General medical & surgical hospitals
Ch: Richard Norman
Chf Path: John Svirbely
Chf Rad: Mary Moebius
**Pr:* Bryan D Hehemann
CFO: John Clements
**CFO:* Chris Lauer
**Sec:* Alan D Oak
Exec: Annette Skinner
Dir Risk M: Ann Kamphaus
Dir Sec: Amy Lockwood
Dir IT: Kathy Dickman

MCCUN-BROOKS HOSP HM HLTH SVCS
See MERCY MCCUNE-BROOKS HOSPITAL

D-U-N-S 02-873-3749
MCCUNE MOTORS
736 Rosecrans St, San Diego, CA 92106-9800
Tel (619) 477-1101 *Founded/Ownrshp* 1971
Sales 43.0MM^E *EMP* 180
SIC 5511 Automobiles, new & used; Automobiles, new & used
Pr: Richard Mc Cune Jr

D-U-N-S 13-413-4436
MCCURDY & CANDLER LLC
MCCURDY AND CANDLER
160 Clairemont Ave # 550, Decatur, GA 30030-2568
Tel (678) 916-4650 *Founded/Ownrshp* 1950
Sales 28.3MM^E *EMP* 315
SIC 8111 General practice law office; General practice law office
Ex VP: Alvan Raab
Exec: John Jakovenko
Dir IT: Michael Causey

MCCURDY AND CANDLER
See MCCURDY & CANDLER LLC

D-U-N-S 07-857-7352
MCCURLEY INTEGRITY DEALERSHIPS LLC
1325 N Autoplex Way, Pasco, WA 99301-3853
Tel (509) 547-5555 *Founded/Ownrshp* 2010
Sales 130.8MM *EMP* 166
SIC 5511 New & used car dealers; New & used car dealers
Sls Mgr: Beau Mohondro

D-U-N-S 07-138-9969
MCCURTAIN MEMORIAL MEDICAL MANAGEMENT INC (OK)
1301 E Lincoln Rd, Idabel, OK 74745-7300
Tel (580) 286-7623 *Founded/Ownrshp* 1954, 1974
Sales 21.9MM *EMP* 245
Accts Eide Bailly Llp Oklahoma City
SIC 8062 General medical & surgical hospitals; General medical & surgical hospitals
CEO: Bristol Messer
Chf Rad: Raymond Smith
**CFO:* Ray Whitmore
Ofcr: Jhani Tapley
Sr VP: Dana Stowell
**VP:* Billie Tomlinson
**Prin:* John Derryberry Jr
**Prin:* Jim McClendon
**Prin:* Neal Stuart
Mktg Dir: Brenda Porton
Obsttrcn: John Migliaccio

D-U-N-S 62-281-8326
MCCUSKER-GILL INC
60 Research Rd Ofc C, Hingham, MA 02043-4393
Tel (781) 740-5800 *Founded/Ownrshp* 1991
Sales 22.2MM^E *EMP* 165
SIC 1761 1711 Sheet metalwork; Heating & air conditioning contractors; Ventilation & duct work contractor; Sheet metalwork; Heating & air conditioning contractors; Ventilation & duct work contractor
Pr: Kevin Gill
Exec: Dale Hatfield
S&M/VP: Joseph Thompson

D-U-N-S 01-382-6847
MCCUTCHEON ENTERPRISES INC
WASTEWATER SERVICE CO DIV
250 Park Rd, Apollo, PA 15613-8730
Tel (724) 568-3623 *Founded/Ownrshp* 1989
Sales 73.7MM^E *EMP* 85
SIC 4953 4212 1629 4959 Refuse systems; Refuse collection & disposal services; Hazardous waste transport; Waste water & sewage treatment plant construction; Environmental cleanup services
Pr: Calvin S McCutcheon
COO: Tim Dobrosky
CFO: Bob Schwab
CTO: Kevin Beer
DP Exec: Dee Sacherich

D-U-N-S 02-123-1295
MCDADE-WOODCOCK INC (NM)
2404 Claremont Ave Ne, Albuquerque, NM 87107-1832
Tel (505) 275-7759 *Founded/Ownrshp* 1979
Sales 48.6MM *EMP* 120
Accts Ricc Porch & Company Llc Al
SIC 1731 General electrical contractor; General electrical contractor
Pr: Robin W Rives
**Ch:* Bobby C Mc Dade
**Treas:* Sharon Pedroncelli
DP Exec: Ben Murray
Dir IT: James Stone
Snr PM: Dennis Simmons

D-U-N-S 00-431-3334 IMP
MCDANEL ADVANCED CERAMIC TECHNOLOGY LLC (PA)
510 9th Ave, Beaver Falls, PA 15010-4700
Tel (724) 843-8300 *Founded/Ownrshp* 1919, 2005
Sales 24.6MM^E *EMP* 119
SIC 3299 Sand lime products; Sand lime products
CEO: Kim Rheingrover
**VP:* John Dodsworth
VP: John Godsworth
VP Mfg: W Lori Hoskisson
Snr PM: Charles Dooner

D-U-N-S 07-493-5248
MCDANIEL COLLEGE INC
2 College Hl, Westminster, MD 21157-4303
Tel (410) 848-7000 *Founded/Ownrshp* 1867
Sales 64.0MM *EMP* 500^E
Accts Baker Tilly Virchow Krause
SIC 8221 7011 College, except junior; Hotels; College, except junior; Hotels
Pr: Roger N Casey
**Treas:* Arthur Wisner
Ex VP: Kenny Daugherty
Sr VP: David Gring
VP: Florence W Hines
VP: Lori A Lewis
**VP:* Phillip Sayre
**VP:* Ethan Seidel
Assoc Dir: Cathy Nosel
Opers Supe: Erica Immler

D-U-N-S 83-221-3057
MCDANIEL FIRE SYSTEMS LLC
1325 Remington Rd Ste H, Schaumburg, IL 60173-4815
Tel (219) 462-0571 *Founded/Ownrshp* 2009
Sales 34.3MM^E *EMP* 425
SIC 1711 Sprinkler contractors; Fire sprinkler system installation; Sprinkler contractors; Fire sprinkler system installation
**CFO:* James L Drake Jr

D-U-N-S 17-562-0467
MCDANIEL FOOD MANAGEMENT INC
MAC'S IGA FOODS
1106 Stubbs Ave Ste B, Monroe, LA 71201-5641
Tel (318) 649-5964 *Founded/Ownrshp* 1984
Sales 24.6MM^E *EMP* 160
SIC 5411 Grocery stores, independent; Grocery stores, independent
Pr: Cleavon McDaniel

D-U-N-S 06-648-2266
MCDANIEL SUPPLY CO INC
1275 E Cherry St, Jesup, GA 31546-3237
Tel (912) 427-9022 *Founded/Ownrshp* 1972
Sales 26.7MM^E *EMP* 55
SIC 5145 5122 5136 Snack foods; Drugs, proprietaries & sundries; Men's & boys' clothing; Handkerchiefs, men's & boys'; Sportswear, men's & boys'
Pr: Jerry Dallas McDaniel

D-U-N-S 16-984-8640
MCDANIEL TECHNICAL SERVICES INC
MTSI
2009 N Willow Ave, Broken Arrow, OK 74012-9109
Tel (918) 294-1628 *Founded/Ownrshp* 2000
Sales 44.6MM *EMP* 300
SIC 8711 Engineering services; Engineering services
Pr: Dustin T McDaniel
CFO: Roger Hanes
CFO: Earle Rice
**Sec:* Marcia A McDaniel
Sr VP: Jeff Trost
VP: Randy Miller

D-U-N-S 00-279-9617
■ MCDANIEL TELEPHONE CO (WA)
TDS
(*Suby of* TDS TELECOMMUNICATIONS CORP) ★
160 Stowell Rd, Salkum, WA 98582
Tel (608) 831-1000 *Founded/Ownrshp* 1929
Sales 853.0MM *EMP* 99
SIC 4813 Telephone communication, except radio; Telephone communication, except radio
Prin: David Wittwer
**Ch Bd:* Larry Boehmn
**Pr:* Mike Leavesseur

D-U-N-S 10-252-9930 IMP
■ MCDATA CORP
(*Suby of* BROCADE COMMUNICATIONS SYSTEMS INC) ★
4 Brocade Pkwy, Broomfield, CO 80021-8900
Tel (720) 558-8000 *Founded/Ownrshp* 1995
Sales 70.4MM^E *EMP* 1,297
SIC 3679 5045 3825 3577

MCDAVID, DAVID HONDA
See IRVING MCDAVID HONDA LP

D-U-N-S 02-662-4528
MCDAVID HOUSTON-HON LP
MC DAVID HONDA
11911 Gulf Fwy, Houston, TX 77034-3537
Tel (713) 948-1900 *Founded/Ownrshp* 1998
Sales 25.8MM^E *EMP* 125
SIC 5511 Automobiles, new & used; Automobiles, new & used
Pt: Dawn Q Mc David
Sls Mgr: Andrew Alvarez

D-U-N-S 01-815-3155 IMP/EXP
MCDAVID INC (IL)
MCDAVID SPORTS MEDICAL PRODUCT
10305 Argonne Dr, Woodridge, IL 60517-4909
Tel (630) 783-0600 *Founded/Ownrshp* 1980
Sales 25.3MM^E *EMP* 105^E
SIC 3842 5091 3949 Braces, orthopedic; Braces, elastic; Sporting & recreation goods; Sporting & athletic goods; Braces, orthopedic; Braces, elastic; Sporting & recreation goods; Sporting & athletic goods
Pr: Robert F Mc David
**VP:* Terry Fee
VP: Mary Horwath
Dir IT: Bryan Banner
Dir IT: Chris Connelly
Sales Exec: Robert McDavid
Mktg Mgr: Carland Lindsey

D-U-N-S 05-014-6851
■ MCDAVID IRVING-HON LP
DAVID MCDAVID AUTO GROUP
(*Suby of* ASBURY AUTOMOTIVE SOUTHERN CALIFORNIA LLC) ★
3700 W Airport Fwy, Irving, TX 75062-5903
Tel (972) 790-6100 *Founded/Ownrshp* 1969
Sales 168.7MM^E *EMP* 694
SIC 5511 Automobiles, new & used; Automobiles, new & used
Genl Pt: B David McDavid Sr
Pt: Jimmy McDavid
VP: Allen Levenson
IT Man: Jose Fores
Sls Dir: Travis Quadlander
Sls Mgr: Jason Burton
Sls Mgr: Paul Caudillo
Sls Mgr: David Henry
Sls Mgr: Ronnie Myers
Sls Mgr: Matt Volpi

MCDAVID SPORTS MEDICAL PRODUCT
See MCDAVID INC

MCDERMOTT CHEVROLET
See MC DERMOTT AUTO GROUP

D-U-N-S 12-269-1694 IMP/EXP
■ MCDERMOTT INC
(*Suby of* MCDERMOTT INTERNATIONAL INC) ★
757 N Eldridge Pkwy # 101, Houston, TX 77079-4526
Tel (281) 870-5000 *Founded/Ownrshp* 1995
Sales 1.2MMM^E *EMP* 5,000
SIC 1629 Marine construction; Marine construction
CEO: David D Ickson
Sr VP: Gary L Carlson
Sr VP: Scott V Cummins
Sr VP: Perry L Elders
Sr VP: Liane K Hinrichs
Sr VP: John McCormack
Sr VP: William R Robinson
VP: Timothy Chetwynd
VP: Claire Hunter
VP: Steven W Roll
VP: Steven Roll
VP: William L Soester

D-U-N-S 04-775-8503 IMP
▲ MCDERMOTT INTERNATIONAL INC
757 N Eldridge Pkwy, Houston, TX 77079-4527
Tel (281) 870-5000 *Founded/Ownrshp* 1959
Sales 2.3MMM *EMP* 13,800^E
Accts Deloitte & Touche Llp Housto
Tkr Sym MDR *Exch* NYS
SIC 1389 1623 Construction, repair & dismantling services; Oil field services; Roustabout service; Servicing oil & gas wells; Pipeline construction; Construction, repair & dismantling services; Oil field services; Roustabout service; Servicing oil & gas wells; Pipeline construction
Pr: David Dickson
CFO: Stuart A Spence
Bd of Dir: Mary Shafer-Malicki
Sr VP: Scott V Cummins
Sr VP: Tony Duncan
Sr VP: Liane K Hinrichs
Sr VP: Stewart A Mitchell
Dir Risk M: Talal Soghaier
Comm Dir: Rick Goins
Dir Bus: Ian Marquis
Dir Bus: Charlie Oldenburg
Board of Directors: John F Bookout III, Roger A Brown, Stephen G Hanks, Gary P Luquette, Mary L Shafer-Malicki, William H Schumann III, David A Trice

D-U-N-S 00-819-8731 IMP
■ MCDERMOTT INVESTMENTS LLC
(*Suby of* MCDERMOTT INTERNATIONAL INC) ★
757 N Eldridge Pkwy # 101, Houston, TX 77079-4526
Tel (281) 870-5000 *Founded/Ownrshp* 1946
Sales 485.3MM^E *EMP* 11,400
SIC 1629 Industrial plant construction; Industrial plant construction
Ch Bd: Roger E Tetrault
CFO: Daniel R Gaubert
Ex VP: E Allen Womack Jr
Ex VP: James F Wood
Board of Directors: Richard E Woolbert

D-U-N-S 07-688-9054
MCDERMOTT WILL & EMERY LLP INC
M W E
227 W Monroe St Ste 4400, Chicago, IL 60606-5058
Tel (312) 372-2000 *Founded/Ownrshp* 1934
Sales 1.5MMM^E *EMP* 25,000
SIC 8111

D-U-N-S 06-675-3336 EXP
MCDEVITT TRUCKS INC
1 Mack Ave, Manchester, NH 03103-5916
Tel (603) 668-1700 *Founded/Ownrshp* 1973
Sales 100.0MM *EMP* 150
SIC 5012 5013 7538 Trucks, commercial; Truck parts & accessories; General truck repair; Trucks, commercial; Truck parts & accessories; General truck repair
Pr: John J McDevitt Jr
CFO: David Citarelli
**Treas:* Kevin McDevitt
**Treas:* Joel Moran
**Prin:* Jim Busby
**Prin:* Jim Conner
Genl Mgr: Jim Lagana
Mktg Dir: Bill McDevitt

D-U-N-S 12-164-4736
MCDONALD & WETLE INC
2020 Ne 194th Ave, Portland, OR 97230-7442
Tel (503) 667-0175 *Founded/Ownrshp* 1970
Sales 24.0MM^E *EMP* 110
SIC 1761 Roofing contractor; Sheet metalwork; Roofing contractor; Sheet metalwork
Pr: Robert E Bolt
Off Mgr: Dan Corcoran

D-U-N-S 06-732-0804
MCDONALD AUTOMOTIVE GROUP LLC
MCDONALD VOLVO
6060 S Broadway, Littleton, CO 80121-8013
Tel (303) 795-1100 *Founded/Ownrshp* 2002
Sales 105.8MM^E *EMP* 310
SIC 5511 Automobiles, new & used; Automobiles, new & used
Pr: Douglas McDonald
Prin: Tom Poole
Prin: Greg Shellabarger
Sales Asso: Tony Rozell

D-U-N-S 00-411-6737
MCDONALD CONSTRUCTION CORP (FL)
5610 S Florida Ave, Lakeland, FL 33813-2526
Tel (863) 646-5763 *Founded/Ownrshp* 1962
Sales 60.1MM^E *EMP* 425
SIC 1629 Earthmoving contractor; Earthmoving contractor
Ch Bd: Paul D Mc Donald
**CFO:* Bill Albritton
**VP:* James R Johnson
**Prin:* Paula McDonald Runo

D-U-N-S 06-962-0743
MCDONALD ELECTRICAL CORP
72 Sharp St Ste C8, Hingham, MA 02043-4364
Tel (781) 340-0008 *Founded/Ownrshp* 1999
Sales 22.1MM^E *EMP* 95
SIC 1731 Electrical work; General electrical contractor
Pr: Michael P McDonald
**VP:* Thomas A Cooney

MCDONALD FINANACIAL GROUP
See KEYBANC CAPITAL MARKETS INC

MCDONALD GARDEN CENTER
See MCDONALD NURSERIES INC

D-U-N-S 07-776-0056
MCDONALD HOPKINS LLC (OH)
600 Superior Ave E # 2100, Cleveland, OH 44114-2690
Tel (216) 348-5400 *Founded/Ownrshp* 1933, 1999
Sales 60.8MM^E *EMP* 250
SIC 8111 General practice law office; General practice law office
Ch Bd: Edward G Quinlisk
Pr: Bernadette Barnes
Pr: Jamie Bochenek

Pr: Jenny Brown
Pr: Lisa Gooch
Pr: Sharon Hach
Pr: Carrie Harris
Pr: Carrie Jesse
Pr: Roberta Krueger
Pr: Junette Powell
VP: Dale Vlasek
Board of Directors: Jane Pine Wood

MCDONALD METAL & ROOFING SUP
See MC DONALD METAL & ROOFING SUPPLY CORP

D-U-N-S 06-538-1584 IMP
MCDONALD NURSERIES INC (VA)
MCDONALD GARDEN CENTER
1139 W Pembroke Ave, Hampton, VA 23661-1119
Tel (757) 722-3125 *Founded/Ownrshp* 1973
Sales 63.5MM^E *EMP* 200
SIC 5191 5261 Garden supplies; Garden supplies & tools; Garden supplies; Garden supplies & tools
Pr: Eddie M Anderson
**Pr:* Anderson Edward Mark
**VP:* Sara G Anderson
IT Man: Geoff Hardy
IT Man: Ruth King
Opers Mgr: Tom Vandyke

MCDONALD OFFICE
See M & A SCOTT CORP

D-U-N-S 06-142-4917
MCDONALD OIL CO INC
MONEY BACK
1700 Lukken Indus Dr W, Lagrange, GA 30240-4004
Tel (706) 884-6191 *Founded/Ownrshp* 1972
Sales 82.3MM^E *EMP* 200
SIC 5541 5921 6519 Filling stations, gasoline; Liquor stores; Real property lessors; Filling stations, gasoline; Liquor stores; Real property lessors
Pr: John A McDonald
VP: Scott Gordy

D-U-N-S 04-775-5376 IMP
MCDONALD STEEL CORP
100 Ohio Ave, Mc Donald, OH 44437-1954
Tel (330) 530-9118 *Founded/Ownrshp* 1981
Sales 21.1MM *EMP* 105
SIC 3312 Bars & bar shapes, steel, hot-rolled; Bars & bar shapes, steel, hot-rolled
Pr: Tim Egnot
**CFO:* Michael J Havalo
CFO: Daniel Wargo
**Ch:* Daniel B Roth
**VP Opers:* William K Clark

D-U-N-S 18-339-8247 IMP
MCDONALD TECHNOLOGIES INTERNATIONAL INC
2310 Mcdaniel Dr, Carrollton, TX 75006-6843
Tel (972) 421-4100 *Founded/Ownrshp* 2007
Sales 41.2MM^E *EMP* 150
SIC 3672 3679 8711 Printed circuit boards; Harness assemblies for electronic use: wire or cable; Consulting engineer; Printed circuit boards; Harness assemblies for electronic use: wire or cable; Consulting engineer
Ch Bd: PIP Sivakumar
Pr: Gary Sadler
**CFO:* Rob Peck
**Genl Mgr:* Carcy Clinton
Sftwr Eng: Doug Staudt
Opers Mgr: Ken Fout
Ql Cn Mgr: Sarah Fraze
Ql Cn Mgr: Varghese Thoma
Sls&Mrk Ex: Ron Roades
Manager: Harsha Deivanayagam

D-U-N-S 07-316-2695
MCDONALD TRANSIT ASSOCIATES INC
(*Suby of* RATP DEV USA LLC) ★
3800 Sandshell Dr Ste 185, Fort Worth, TX 76137-2441
Tel (817) 232-9551 *Founded/Ownrshp* 1978
Sales 94.7MM *EMP* 3,600
Accts Weaver And Tidwell Llp Fort
SIC 8742 Business consultant; Business consultant
Pr: Robert T Babbitt
Pr: Daniel Swanson
CFO: Fred E Crosley
Sr VP: Kenneth R Fischer
Sr VP: Stephen A Keiper
Sr VP: Tim Lett
Sr VP: Patrick May
Sr VP: John L Wilson
VP: John P Bartosiewicz
VP: Kevin Kane
Genl Mgr: Ronald Biggs

D-U-N-S 07-316-1408
MCDONALD TRANSIT CO
T, THE
(*Suby of* MCDONALD TRANSIT ASSOCIATES INC) ★
1600 E Lancaster Ave, Fort Worth, TX 76102-6720
Tel (817) 215-8600 *Founded/Ownrshp* 1983
Sales 10.4MM^E *EMP* 475^E
SIC 8741 Management services; Management services
Pr: Paul Ballard
**CFO:* Rob Harmon
CFO: Wendy Raffaeli
**Ch:* Scott Mahaffey
Ofcr: Yvonne Oliver
Sr VP: Nancy Amos
VP: Bo Cung
VP: Ken Frost
Dir Risk M: Inmon Wiley
Dir: Curvie Hawkins
Ex Dir: Richard Ruddell

MCDONALD VOLVO
See MCDONALD AUTOMOTIVE GROUP LLC

D-U-N-S 02-021-0361
MCDONALD WHOLESALE CO
2350 W Broadway, Eugene, OR 97402-2790
Tel (541) 345-8421 *Founded/Ownrshp* 2007
Sales 84.9MM *EMP* 118
Accts Isler Cpa Eugene Or
SIC 5141 Groceries, general line; Groceries, general line
Pr: Gary Thomsen
**Ch Bd:* Charles R Huey
**VP:* Jake Vanderveen
Board of Directors: Greg Betts, Greg Garn, Brian Huey, Charles R Huey, Kent Huey, Gary Thomsen, Jake Vanderveen

MCDONALD'S
See JDD INVESTMENT CO

MCDONALD'S
See WOLFE ENTERPRISE

MCDONALD'S
See GREGORY B LURING

MCDONALD'S
See DUKART MANAGEMENT CORP

MCDONALD'S
See SANDOVAL ENTERPRISES INC

MCDONALD'S
See G & R FOODS INC

MCDONALD'S
See VINEYARD INDUSTRIES INC

MCDONALD'S
See PHILLIPS BROTHERS RESTAURANTS INC

MCDONALD'S
See LYNN MANAGEMENT CO INC

MCDONALD'S
See AARMY CORP

MCDONALD'S
See TRAA CORP

MCDONALD'S
See LAURIER ENTERPRISES INC

MCDONALD'S
See MCINTYRE MANAGEMENT CORP

MCDONALD'S
See CHRISTINAS FOODS LLC

MCDONALD'S
See BEST OPERATIONS INC

MCDONALD'S
See HEISNER ENTERPRISES PARTNERSHIP

MCDONALD'S
See HEIDMAN INC

MCDONALD'S
See MAC-CLARK RESTAURANTS INC

MCDONALD'S
See D & P ASSOCIATES

MCDONALD'S
See NORTH STAR RESTAURANTS INC

MCDONALD'S
See MICALE MGT CORP

MCDONALD'S
See DOB SAB INC

MCDONALD'S
See PROSPERITY FOODS INC

MCDONALD'S
See GRIGGS ENTERPRISES INC

MCDONALD'S
See JAAR INC

MCDONALD'S
See ANDI INC

MCDONALD'S
See MC COOK LTD

MCDONALD'S
See RICE ENTERPRISES LLC

MCDONALD'S
See MURKEL ENTERPRISES LLC

MCDONALD'S
See HALJOHN INC

MCDONALD'S
See LARSON ENTERPRISES INC

MCDONALD'S
See LILLY ENTERPRISES INC

MCDONALD'S
See MACATAC INC

MCDONALD'S
See MCSPI INC

MCDONALD'S
See G W D MANAGEMENT CORP

MCDONALD'S
See MADERA CORP

MCDONALD'S
See STAGG RESTAURANTS PARTNERSHIP

MCDONALD'S
See MELTON MANAGEMENT INC

MCDONALD'S
See BROS MANAGEMENT INC

MCDONALD'S
See PEZOLD MANAGEMENT ASSOCIATES INC

MCDONALD'S
See S S M INC

MCDONALD'S
See MCANDERSON INC

MCDONALD'S
See L/B CORP

MCDONALD'S
See BEAR-MAR INC

MCDONALD'S
See MARTINEZ MANAGEMENT INC

MCDONALD'S
See HARPER MANAGEMENT INC

MCDONALD'S
See CICCHINI ENTERPRISES

MCDONALD'S
See SPEEDY ARCHES LTD

MCDONALD'S
See BENTON ENTERPRISES INC

MCDONALD'S
See E E R INC

MCDONALD'S
See JIMS MANAGEMENT CO

MCDONALD'S
See JAMES E BARNES ENTERPRISES INC

MCDONALD'S
See CONQUISTADORES INC

MCDONALD'S
See BAIM ENTERPRISES INC

MCDONALD'S
See TERHUNES INC

MCDONALD'S
See JTS ENTERPRISES OF TAMPA LIMITED

MCDONALD'S
See WARMEL CORP

MCDONALD'S
See LETTUCE FEED YOU INC

MCDONALD'S
See M & S FOODS OF IOWA INC

MCDONALD'S
See TANDEM INC

MCDONALD'S
See OERTHER FOODS INC

MCDONALD'S
See NERANGIS ENTERPRISES INC

MCDONALD'S
See MARKOR ENTERPRISES INC

MCDONALD'S
See QSC ENTERPRISES INC

MCDONALD'S
See RAHE INC

MCDONALD'S
See MAC-LAFF INC

MCDONALD'S
See YASNY INC

MCDONALD'S
See GOAL FOODS INC

MCDONALD'S
See TEXAMAC INC

MCDONALD'S
See BHT INC

MCDONALD'S
See HUNT ENTERPRISES INC

MCDONALD'S
See JOHNSTONE FOODS INC

MCDONALD'S
See RONALD H FEWSTER

MCDONALD'S
See GIANNOLAS INC

MCDONALD'S
See TREFZ CORP

MCDONALD'S
See WIL MAY ENTERPRISES INC

MCDONALD'S
See RETZER RESOURCES INC

MCDONALD'S
See KLEIN/KAUFMAN CORP

MCDONALD'S
See GOLDEN STOCK ENTERPRISES INC

MCDONALD'S
See COLLEY GROUP LLC

MCDONALD'S
See C & R MANAGEMENT INC

MCDONALD'S
See P P V INC

MCDONALD'S
See UPCHURCH MARINAS INC

MCDONALD'S
See GOLDEN ARCH ENTERPRISES LLC

MCDONALD'S
See GIA ENTERPRISES

MCDONALD'S
See PAUL M ROSS

MCDONALD'S
See C L P CORP

MCDONALD'S
See R D & J PARTNERSHIP

MCDONALD'S
See RON-RIC INC

MCDONALD'S
See REAAL INC

MCDONALD'S
See CHARTLAND CORP

MCDONALD'S
See WRIGHT MANAGEMENT INC

MCDONALD'S
See REDARHCS INC

MCDONALD'S
See MASON & WRIGHT ENTERPRISES

MCDONALD'S
See S T C INC

MCDONALD'S
See M & J MANAGEMENT CORP

MCDONALD'S
See DJ CLARK INC

MCDONALD'S
See MCMANGA FOODS

MCDONALD'S
See CEDAR CORP

MCDONALD'S
See CLARA CORP

MCDONALD'S
See KING CHRIS CO INC

MCDONALD'S
See VALLEY MANAGEMENT INC

MCDONALD'S
See MAN-CAL INC

MCDONALD'S
See BOSELLI INVESTMENTS LLC

MCDONALD'S
See HUDSON MANAGEMENT CORP

MCDONALD'S
See CONRAD J FREEMAN INC

MCDONALD'S
See A J F INC

MCDONALD'S
See DELAMOR ENTERPRISES LP

MCDONALD'S
See M SHANNON INC

MCDONALD'S
See PASCHEN MANAGEMENT CORP

MCDONALD'S
See MCFADKE INC

MCDONALD'S
See LPG ENTERPRISES INC

MCDONALD'S
See RACCOON VALLEY PARTNERSHIP

MCDONALD'S
See HALJOHN - SAN ANTONIO INC

MCDONALD'S
See BRENDS INC

MCDONALD'S
See BILL BARNES

MCDONALD'S
See NEWLAND MANAGEMENT LLC

MCDONALD'S
See C P H SERVICE LLC

MCDONALD'S
See MCESSY INVESTMENT CO

MCDONALD'S
See CIRILOS INC

MCDONALD'S
See AGK RESTAURANTS INC

MCDONALD'S
See GOODRUM ENTERPRISES INC

MCDONALD'S
See KDE INC

MCDONALD'S
See BRICKMAN MANAGEMENT CO INC

MCDONALD'S
See RIPPON ASSOCIATES LLC

MCDONALD'S
See WILLIAM ROY INC

MCDONALD'S
See MAC ATTACK INC

MCDONALD'S
See ASPEN FOOD SERVICE INC

MCDONALD'S
See MC DONALDS OF ENDICOTT INC

MCDONALD'S
See PICKARD ENTERPRISES INC

MCDONALD'S
See ALLEN ALLIANCE CO

MCDONALD'S
See LUKA INC

MCDONALD'S
See SUNWAY RESTAURANT CORP

MCDONALD'S
See MCCAMM MANAGEMENT CO

MCDONALD'S
See ADAMS & OREILLY INC

MCDONALD'S
See HAFEZ CORP

MCDONALD'S
See MAR-B PARTNERSHIP

MCDONALD'S
See ROMAD CO

MCDONALD'S
See MADRI INC

MCDONALD'S
See GENE M FORBES ENTERPRISES INC

MCDONALD'S
See RIO VISTA MANAGEMENT GROUP INC

MCDONALD'S
See DEJON ENTERPRISES INC

MCDONALD'S
See B MC R CO

MCDONALD'S
See MOTMANCO INC

MCDONALD'S
See M K G ENTERPRISES INC

MCDONALD'S
SeeYIN MC DONALDS MANAGEMENT

MCDONALD'S
SeeWHEELDON FOODS IA LLC

MCDONALD'S
See ALLMAC LEASING

MCDONALD'S
See R L M K INC

MCDONALD'S
See JOVAN INC

MCDONALD'S
See FINDLAY MANAGEMENT INC

MCDONALD'S
See D BAILEY MANAGEMENT COMP

MCDONALD'S
See ERNIE SANDOVAL ENTERPRISES INC

MCDONALD'S
See CANCHOLA GROUP INC

MCDONALD'S
See BRE MID AMERICA INC

MCDONALD'S
See MC DONALDS OF CALHOUN INC

MCDONALD'S
See J W EBERT CORP

MCDONALD'S
See GCGC FAIR CORP

MCDONALD'S
See MJPT II & ASSOCIATES LTD

MCDONALD'S
See F & D HUEBNER LLC

MCDONALD'S
See KILIAN MANAGEMENT SERVICES INC

MCDONALD'S
See BENNETT LK ENTERPRISES LLC

MCDONALD'S
See GUESTS INC

MCDONALD'S
See DBR INC

MCDONALD'S
SeeTANNER MANAGEMENT CO LLC

MCDONALD'S
See P HENDEL PRODUCTS PARTNERSHIP

MCDONALD'S
See MICHAEL T KLAK

MCDONALD'S
See ALNACA LLC

MCDONALD'S
See LLOYD STOKES

MCDONALD'S
See MCBLT VENTURES INC

MCDONALD'S
See HAVI GLOBAL SOLUTIONS LLC

MCDONALD'S
See RAY MASKER JR

MCDONALD'S
See ERROL SERVICE

MCDONALD'S
See D & L MANAGEMENT

MCDONALD'S
SeeYHD FOODS INC

MCDONALD'S
See DDS & PARTNERSHIP INC

MCDONALD'S
See R & W INC

MCDONALD'S
See MC KAREN INDUSTRIES INC

MCDONALD'S
See ACE PARTERNERSHIP OF CHARLESTON

MCDONALD'S
See KADES CORP

MCDONALD'S
See DAVID COSTA ENTERPRISES INC

MCDONALD'S
See HARRIS JOINT VENTURE

MCDONALD'S
SeeTEN D ENTERPRISES INC

MCDONALD'S
See JIM LAR CORP

MCDONALD'S
See BRANSCUM INVESTMENTS LLC

D-U-N-S 02-607-8402
MCDONALDS
429 7th Ave, New York, NY 10001-2001
Tel (212) 736-7890 *Founded/Ownrshp* 1975
Sales 10.9MM^E *EMP* 455
SIC 5812 Fast-food restaurant, chain; Fast-food restaurant, chain
Pr: Irwin Kruger
**VP:* Dave Andresen

D-U-N-S 04-153-4264 IMP/EXP
▲ MCDONALDS CORP
1 Mcdonalds Dr, Oak Brook, IL 60523-1911
Tel (630) 623-3000 *Founded/Ownrshp* 1955
Sales 27.4MMM *EMP* 420,000
Accts Ernst & Young Llp Chicago Il
Tkr Sym MCD *Exch* NYS
SIC 5812 6794 Fast-food restaurant, chain; Franchises, selling or licensing; Fast-food restaurant, chain; Franchises, selling or licensing
Pr: Stephen J Easterbrook
Pr: Russell P Smyth
COO: Steeves Glen
CFO: Kevin M Ozan
Treas: Carlos Teran
Chf Mktg O: Bill Lamar
Ofcr: Peter J Bensen
Ofcr: David Fairhurst
Ex VP: Jose Armario
Ex VP: Richard R Floersch
Ex VP: Robert Gibbs
Ex VP: Douglas M Goare
Ex VP: Silvia Lagnado
Ex VP: Gloria Santona
Ex VP: Jim Sappington
Ex VP: Jeff Stratton
Sr VP: Brian Mullens
VP: Darren Hall
VP: Michele Porter
VP: David Simmons
VP: Joel Yashinsky
Board of Directors: Sheila Penrose, Susan E Arnold, John W Rogers Jr, Robert A Eckert, Roger W Stone, Margaret H Georgiadis, Miles D White, Enrique Hernandez Jr, Jeanne P Jackson, Richard H Lenny, Walter E Massey, Andrew J McKenna, Cary D McMillan

D-U-N-S 88-490-4723
MCDONALDS E L S GROUP
2413 Robeson St Ste 4, Fayetteville, NC 28305-5500
Tel (910) 486-9000 *Founded/Ownrshp* 1982
Sales 7.6MM^E *EMP* 350
SIC 5812 Fast-food restaurant, chain; Fast-food restaurant, chain
Owner: Eli Leonard Saleeby
Off Mgr: Elaine Saleeby

D-U-N-S 06-901-4868
MCDONALDS OF CLIFTON HEIGHTS
18 Clover Ln, Newtown Square, PA 19073-4103
Tel (610) 356-8775 *Founded/Ownrshp* 1973
Sales 700.0M *EMP* 300
SIC 5812 Fast-food restaurant, chain; Fast-food restaurant, chain
Owner: John P Niggeman

D-U-N-S 05-501-9277
■ MCDONALDS RESTAURANT OPERATIONS INC
(*Suby of* MCDONALDS CORP) ★
2111 Mcdonalds Dr, Oak Brook, IL 60523-5500
Tel (630) 623-3000 *Founded/Ownrshp* 1980
Sales 5.3MMM^E *EMP* 380,000
SIC 5812 8741 Fast-food restaurant, chain; Financial management for business; Fast-food restaurant, chain; Financial management for business
Pr: James Collins
Sr VP: Frank Muschetto
VP: Kim Correll
VP: Steve Levigne
VP: Julia Ploeg
VP: Robert Switzer
Exec: Denise Horne
Comm Man: Niki Campbell
Genl Mgr: Lee Renz
Mktg Dir: Brian Durkin
Mktg Dir: Chmiel Wayne

D-U-N-S 61-529-9281
■ MCDONALDS RESTAURANTS OF ALASKA INC
(*Suby of* MCDONALDS USA LLC) ★
2111 Mcdonalds Dr, Oak Brook, IL 60523-5500
Tel (630) 623-3000 *Founded/Ownrshp* 2006
Sales 26.9MM^E *EMP* 2,000^E
SIC 5812 Fast-food restaurant, chain; Fast-food restaurant, chain
CEO: James A Skinner
CIO: David Weick

D-U-N-S 88-426-3468
■ MCDONALDS RESTAURANTS OF CALIFORNIA INC
(*Suby of* MCDONALDS USA LLC) ★
1 Mcdonalds Dr, Oak Brook, IL 60523-1911
Tel (630) 623-3000 *Founded/Ownrshp* 2006
Sales 131.7MM^E *EMP* 10,750
SIC 5812 Fast-food restaurant, chain; Fast-food restaurant, chain
Ch Bd: James A Skinner
Treas: Windy Cavin
Treas: Nancy Custis
VP: Carl Dill

D-U-N-S 61-529-8168
■ MCDONALDS RESTAURANTS OF COLORADO INC
(*Suby of* MCDONALDS USA LLC) ★
1 Mcdonalds Dr, Oak Brook, IL 60523-1911
Tel (630) 623-3000 *Founded/Ownrshp* 2006
Sales 20.4MM^E *EMP* 2,000
SIC 5812 Fast-food restaurant, chain; Fast-food restaurant, chain
CEO: James A Skinner

D-U-N-S 88-426-3807
■ MCDONALDS RESTAURANTS OF CONNECTICUT INC
(*Suby of* MCDONALDS USA LLC) ★
1 Mcdonalds Dr, Oak Brook, IL 60523-1911
Tel (630) 623-3000 *Founded/Ownrshp* 2006
Sales 28.5MM^E *EMP* 2,050
SIC 5812 Fast-food restaurant, chain; Fast-food restaurant, chain
CEO: James A Skinner
**Pr:* Mike Roberts

D-U-N-S 78-068-0745
■ MCDONALDS RESTAURANTS OF DISTRICT OF COLUMBIA INC
(*Suby of* MCDONALDS USA LLC) ★
1 Mcdonalds Dr, Oak Brook, IL 60523-1911
Tel (630) 623-3000 *Founded/Ownrshp* 2006
Sales 18.4MM^E *EMP* 2,000
SIC 5812 Fast-food restaurant, chain; Fast-food restaurant, chain
CEO: James A Skinner

D-U-N-S 88-426-3880
■ MCDONALDS RESTAURANTS OF FLORIDA INC
(*Suby of* MCDONALDS USA LLC) ★
1 Mcdonalds Dr, Hinsdale, IL 60523-1911
Tel (630) 623-3000 *Founded/Ownrshp* 1974
Sales 113.0MM^E *EMP* 6,650
SIC 5812 Fast-food restaurant, chain; Fast-food restaurant, chain
CEO: James A Skinner
**Pr:* Edward Rensi
**VP:* Jack M Greenberg

D-U-N-S 14-835-1588
■ MCDONALDS RESTAURANTS OF GEORGIA INC
(*Suby of* MCDONALDS USA LLC) ★
1 Mcdonalds Dr, Oak Brook, IL 60523-1911
Tel (630) 623-3000 *Founded/Ownrshp* 1979
Sales 35.0MM^E *EMP* 2,500
SIC 5812 Fast-food restaurant, chain; Fast-food restaurant, chain
CEO: James A Skinner
Pr: Edward H Rensi
VP: Robert J Doran
**VP:* George T Rummell
VP: W Robert Sanders
VP: Delbert H Wilson
**VP:* Shelby Yastrow

D-U-N-S 01-187-9665 IMP
■ MCDONALDS RESTAURANTS OF ILLINOIS INC
(*Suby of* MCDONALDS USA LLC) ★
21 Mcdonalds Dr, Oak Brook, IL 60523
Tel (630) 623-3000 *Founded/Ownrshp* 1980
Sales 42.3MM^E *EMP* 1,550
SIC 5812 Fast-food restaurant, chain; Fast-food restaurant, chain
CEO: James A Skinner

D-U-N-S 09-718-2562
■ MCDONALDS RESTAURANTS OF INDIANA INC
(*Suby of* MCDONALDS USA LLC) ★
2111 Mcdonalds Dr, Oak Brook, IL 60523-5500
Tel (630) 623-3000 *Founded/Ownrshp* 1973
Sales 62.6MM^E *EMP* 3,000
SIC 5812 Fast-food restaurant, chain; Fast-food restaurant, chain
CEO: James A Skinner
**Pr:* Mike Roberts
**VP:* Jack Greenberg
**VP:* Donald P Horowitz
**VP:* Gerald Newman
CIO: David Weick

D-U-N-S 88-426-3997
■ MCDONALDS RESTAURANTS OF IOWA INC
(*Suby of* MCDONALDS USA LLC) ★
1 Mcdonalds Dr, Hinsdale, IL 60523-1911
Tel (630) 623-3000 *Founded/Ownrshp* 2006
Sales 12.9MM^E *EMP* 900
SIC 5812 Fast-food restaurant, chain; Fast-food restaurant, chain
CEO: James A Skinner

D-U-N-S 88-445-3234
■ MCDONALDS RESTAURANTS OF KANSAS INC
(*Suby of* MCDONALDS USA LLC) ★
1 Mcdonalds Dr, Oak Brook, IL 60523-1911
Tel (630) 623-3000 *Founded/Ownrshp* 2006
Sales 8.2MM^E *EMP* 600
SIC 5812 Fast-food restaurant, chain; Fast-food restaurant, chain
CEO: James A Skinner

D-U-N-S 88-445-3242
■ MCDONALDS RESTAURANTS OF KENTUCKY INC
(*Suby of* MCDONALDS USA LLC) ★
1 Mcdonalds Dr, Oak Brook, IL 60523-1911
Tel (630) 623-3000 *Founded/Ownrshp* 1999
Sales 12.4MM^E *EMP* 800
SIC 5812 Fast-food restaurant, chain; Fast-food restaurant, chain
CEO: James A Skinner

D-U-N-S 12-654-3347
■ MCDONALDS RESTAURANTS OF MARYLAND INC
(*Suby of* MCDONALDS USA LLC) ★
1 Mcdonalds Dr, Oak Brook, IL 60523-1911
Tel (630) 623-3000 *Founded/Ownrshp* 1975
Sales 72.7MM^E *EMP* 4,700
SIC 5812 Fast-food restaurant, chain; Fast-food restaurant, chain
CEO: James A Skinner
VP: Ken Barun
VP: Phyllis Fields
VP: Eric Leininger
CIO: David Grooms
CIO: Chris Millington

D-U-N-S 78-081-6059 IMP
■ MCDONALDS RESTAURANTS OF MASSACHUSETTS INC
(*Suby of* MCDONALDS USA LLC) ★
1 Mcdonalds Dr, Oak Brook, IL 60523-1911
Tel (630) 623-3000 *Founded/Ownrshp* 2006
Sales 30.3MM^E *EMP* 2,000
SIC 5812 Fast-food restaurant, chain; Fast-food restaurant, chain
CEO: James A Skinner

D-U-N-S 88-445-3390 IMP
■ MCDONALDS RESTAURANTS OF MICHIGAN INC
(*Suby of* MCDONALDS USA LLC) ★
1 Mcdonalds Dr, Oak Brook, IL 60523-1911
Tel (630) 623-3000 *Founded/Ownrshp* 1972
Sales 115.8MM^E *EMP* 7,300
SIC 5812 Fast-food restaurant, chain; Fast-food restaurant, chain
Ch Bd: James A Skinner
**Pr:* Allan Feldman
**Treas:* Carletond Pearl
**VP:* Matthew H Paull
**VP:* Edward H Rensi

D-U-N-S 09-525-9974
■ MCDONALDS RESTAURANTS OF MINNESOTA INC
(*Suby of* MCDONALDS USA LLC) ★
1 Mcdonalds Dr, Oak Brook, IL 60523-1911
Tel (630) 623-3000 *Founded/Ownrshp* 1980
Sales 51.5MM^E *EMP* 2,500
SIC 5812 Fast-food restaurant, chain; Fast-food restaurant, chain
Genl Mgr: W Maney
**CEO:* James A Skinner

D-U-N-S 06-248-1288
■ MCDONALDS RESTAURANTS OF MISSOURI INC
(*Suby of* MCDONALDS USA LLC) ★
1 Mcdonalds Dr, Oak Brook, IL 60523-1911
Tel (630) 623-3000 *Founded/Ownrshp* 1980
Sales 29.0MM^E *EMP* 2,000
SIC 5812 Fast-food restaurant, chain; Fast-food restaurant, chain
CEO: James A Skinner
**Pr:* Michael Quinlan
**Treas:* Robert Ryan
**VP:* Jack Greenberg
**VP:* Donald P Horowitz

D-U-N-S 88-445-5080
■ MCDONALDS RESTAURANTS OF NEBRASKA INC
(*Suby of* MCDONALDS USA LLC) ★
1 Mcdonalds Dr, Oak Brook, IL 60523-1911
Tel (630) 623-3000 *Founded/Ownrshp* 1975
Sales 11.5MM^E *EMP* 700
SIC 5812 Fast-food restaurant, chain; Fast-food restaurant, chain
CEO: James A Skinner

D-U-N-S 88-445-5098 IMP
■ MCDONALDS RESTAURANTS OF NEVADA INC
(*Suby of* MCDONALDS USA LLC) ★
1 Mcdonalds Dr, Oak Brook, IL 60523-1911
Tel (630) 623-3000 *Founded/Ownrshp* 1980
Sales 19.3MM^E *EMP* 1,150
SIC 5812 Fast-food restaurant, chain; Fast-food restaurant, chain
CEO: James A Skinner
**Pr:* Alan Feldman
**Treas:* Carleton Pearl

D-U-N-S 11-819-5346
■ MCDONALDS RESTAURANTS OF NEW JERSEY INC
(*Suby of* MCDONALDS USA LLC) ★
1 Mcdonalds Dr, Oak Brook, IL 60523-1911
Tel (630) 623-3000 *Founded/Ownrshp* 1971
Sales 13.1MM^E *EMP* 1,000
SIC 5812 Fast-food restaurant, chain; Fast-food restaurant, chain
CEO: James A Skinner

D-U-N-S 09-525-9917
■ MCDONALDS RESTAURANTS OF NEW YORK INC
(*Suby of* MCDONALDS USA LLC) ★
1 Mcdonalds Dr, Oak Brook, IL 60523-1911
Tel (630) 623-3000 *Founded/Ownrshp* 1980
Sales 23.3MM^E *EMP* 1,250
SIC 5812 Fast-food restaurant, chain; Fast-food restaurant, chain
CEO: James A Skinner
**Pr:* Edward H Rensi
**Treas:* Carleton D Pearl
VP: Michael L Conley
VP: G Lowell Dixon
**VP:* Jack M Greenberg
**VP:* Jerry R Lane
**VP:* Matthew Paull
**VP:* Shelby Yastrow
Board of Directors: G Lowell Dixon, George T Rummel, Gloria Santona

D-U-N-S 88-445-4216
■ MCDONALDS RESTAURANTS OF NORTH CAROLINA INC
(*Suby of* MCDONALDS USA LLC) ★
1 Mcdonalds Dr, Oak Brook, IL 60523-1911
Tel (630) 623-3000 *Founded/Ownrshp* 1995
Sales 33.1MM^E *EMP* 3,000
SIC 5812 Fast-food restaurant, chain; Fast-food restaurant, chain
CEO: James A Skinner

D-U-N-S 07-235-7734
■ MCDONALDS RESTAURANTS OF OHIO INC
(*Suby of* MCDONALDS USA LLC) ★
1 Mcdonalds Dr, Oak Brook, IL 60523-1911
Tel (630) 623-3000 *Founded/Ownrshp* 1980
Sales 122.5MM^E *EMP* 7,604
SIC 5812 Fast-food restaurant, chain; Fast-food restaurant, chain
CEO: James A Skinner
COO: Glen Steeves

D-U-N-S 88-445-5106
■ MCDONALDS RESTAURANTS OF OKLAHOMA INC
(*Suby of* MCDONALDS USA LLC) ★
1 Mcdonalds Dr, Oak Brook, IL 60523-1911
Tel (630) 623-3000 *Founded/Ownrshp* 1983
Sales 25.6MM^E *EMP* 2,300
SIC 5812 Fast-food restaurant, chain; Fast-food restaurant, chain
CEO: James A Skinner

D-U-N-S 88-445-5353
■ MCDONALDS RESTAURANTS OF OREGON INC
(*Suby of* MCDONALDS USA LLC) ★
1 Mcdonalds Dr, Oak Brook, IL 60523-1911
Tel (630) 623-3000 *Founded/Ownrshp* 1979
Sales 4.9MM^E *EMP* 300^E
SIC 5812 Fast-food restaurant, chain; Fast-food restaurant, chain
CEO: James A Skinner

D-U-N-S 02-927-8967 IMP
■ MCDONALDS RESTAURANTS OF PENNSYLVANIA INC
(*Suby of* MCDONALDS USA LLC) ★
1 Mcdonalds Dr, Oak Brook, IL 60523-1911
Tel (630) 623-3000 *Founded/Ownrshp* 1979
Sales 20.4MMM *EMP* 4,250
SIC 5812 Fast-food restaurant, chain; Fast-food restaurant, chain
Ch Bd: James A Skinner

D-U-N-S 78-081-5937
■ MCDONALDS RESTAURANTS OF SOUTH CAROLINA INC
(*Suby of* MCDONALDS USA LLC) ★
1 Mcdonalds Dr, Oak Brook, IL 60523-1911
Tel (630) 623-3000 *Founded/Ownrshp* 2006
Sales 19.5MM^E *EMP* 2,000
SIC 5812 Fast-food restaurant, chain; Fast-food restaurant, chain
CEO: James A Skinner

D-U-N-S 88-445-5403
■ MCDONALDS RESTAURANTS OF TENNESSEE INC
(*Suby of* MCDONALDS USA LLC) ★
1 Mcdonalds Dr, Oak Brook, IL 60523-1911
Tel (630) 623-3000 *Founded/Ownrshp* 1976
Sales 19.9MM^E *EMP* 1,700^E
SIC 5812 Fast-food restaurant, chain; Fast-food restaurant, chain
CEO: James A Skinner
**Pr:* Mike Roberts

D-U-N-S 61-530-3554
■ MCDONALDS RESTAURANTS OF TEXAS INC
(*Suby of* MCDONALDS USA LLC) ★
1 Mcdonalds Dr, Oak Brook, IL 60523-1911
Tel (630) 623-3000 *Founded/Ownrshp* 2006
Sales 40.9MM^E *EMP* 2,000
SIC 5812 Fast-food restaurant, chain; Fast-food restaurant, chain
CEO: James A Skinner

D-U-N-S 10-318-4222
■ MCDONALDS RESTAURANTS OF VIRGINIA INC
(*Suby of* MCDONALDS USA LLC) ★
1 Mcdonalds Dr, Oak Brook, IL 60523-1911
Tel (630) 623-3000 *Founded/Ownrshp* 2000
Sales 2.1MM *EMP* 5,500
SIC 5812 Fast-food restaurant, chain; Fast-food restaurant, chain
CEO: James A Skinner
**CEO:* James Askinner

D-U-N-S 88-445-5684
■ MCDONALDS RESTAURANTS OF WASHINGTON INC
(*Suby of* MCDONALDS USA LLC) ★
1 Mcdonalds Dr, Oak Brook, IL 60523-1911
Tel (630) 623-3000 *Founded/Ownrshp* 2006
Sales 36.2MM^E *EMP* 2,700
SIC 5812 8741 Fast-food restaurant, chain; Financial management for business; Fast-food restaurant, chain; Financial management for business
CEO: James A Skinner

D-U-N-S 88-445-5734
■ MCDONALDS RESTAURANTS OF WEST VIRGINIA INC
(*Suby of* MCDONALDS USA LLC) ★
1 Mcdonalds Dr, Oak Brook, IL 60523-1911
Tel (630) 623-3000 *Founded/Ownrshp* 2006
Sales 7.7MM^E *EMP* 600
SIC 5812 Fast-food restaurant, chain; Fast-food restaurant, chain
CEO: James A Skinner
Treas: Michael Richard

D-U-N-S 11-819-5056
■ MCDONALDS RESTAURANTS OF WISCONSIN INC
(*Suby of* MCDONALDS USA LLC) ★
1 Mcdonalds Dr, Oak Brook, IL 60523-1911
Tel (630) 623-3000 *Founded/Ownrshp* 1972
Sales 35.0MM^E *EMP* 2,200
SIC 5812 Fast-food restaurant, chain; Fast-food restaurant, chain
CEO: James A Skinner
**Pr:* Alan Feedman
**CEO:* Jack Greenberg
**Sr VP:* Mike Conley

D-U-N-S 78-059-2130 IMP/EXP
■ MCDONALDS USA LLC
(*Suby of* MCDONALDS CORP) ★
2111 Mcdonalds Dr, Oak Brook, IL 60523-5500
Tel (630) 623-3000 *Founded/Ownrshp* 2004
Sales 21.8MMM^E *EMP* 390,000
SIC 5812 Fast-food restaurant, chain; Fast-food restaurant, chain
Pr: James Johannesen
VP: William Whitman
Off Mgr: Wendy Orange

D-U-N-S 84-130-2669
MCDONNEL GROUP L L C
3350 Ridgelake Dr Ste 170, Metairie, LA 70002-3890
Tel (504) 219-0032 *Founded/Ownrshp* 1999
Sales 28.6MM^E *EMP* 63
SIC 1542 1541 Nonresidential construction; Commercial & office building contractors; Industrial buildings & warehouses
Pr: Ben Allan McDonnel
VP: David McDonnel
Sfty Mgr: Tony Montalbano
Mktg Dir: Stacey Schexnayder

D-U-N-S 95-954-9122
MCDONNELL BOEHNEN HULBERT & BERGHOFF LTD
300 S Wacker Dr Ste 3200, Chicago, IL 60606-6709
Tel (312) 291-8996 *Founded/Ownrshp* 1996
Sales 22.3MM^E *EMP* 144
SIC 8111 General practice law office; General practice law office
Mng Pt: Marcus Thymian
Pt: Paul Berghoff
Pt: Dan Boehnen
Pt: Brad Hulbert
Pt: Matthew Sampson
CFO: Richard Szymanski
Advt Mgr: Megan McKon
Counsel: Richard Martin

D-U-N-S 96-782-0841
MCDONNELL DOUGLAS CORP RETIREE HEALTH CARE TR
1 Chase Manhattan Plz # 13, New York, NY 10005-1401
Tel (212) 552-2992 *Founded/Ownrshp* 2011
Sales 35.5MM *EMP* 2^E
Accts Rsm Mcgladrey Inc New York N
SIC 8099 Health & allied services; Health & allied services

D-U-N-S 07-745-7877
MCDONOGH SCHOOL INC
OWINGS MILLS CORPORATE CAMPUS
8600 Mcdonogh Rd, Owings Mills, MD 21117-1009
Tel (410) 363-0600 *Founded/Ownrshp* 1873
Sales 60.6MM *EMP* 330
SIC 8211 Private combined elementary & secondary school; Private combined elementary & secondary school
Pr: Arthur H Adler
**CEO:* Charles W Britton
**Treas:* Wayne L Rogers
Top Exec: Oletha Devane
**VP:* Larry Johnston
**VP:* Howard S Klein
Comm Dir: David J Decoteau Toia
Sales Asso: John Stedding
Board of Directors: Linda Brand, Carol Carroll, Cathy Davis, Olivia D Grant, Marcia Levy, Virginia Olcerst, Carol Schmelz, Susan Waskey, Pat White

D-U-N-S 61-686-4088
MCDONOUGH BOLYARD PECK INC
3040 Williams Dr Ste 300, Fairfax, VA 22031-4654
Tel (703) 641-9088 *Founded/Ownrshp* 1989
Sales 57.7MM^E *EMP* 280
SIC 8711 Consulting engineer; Consulting engineer
Ch Bd: Charles E Bolyard Jr
**Pr:* Blake V Peck
VP: George B Fink Jr
Opers Mgr: Gerald Timothy
Snr PM: Alan Terpolilli
Board of Directors: Chris Payne

D-U-N-S 07-197-5775
MCDONOUGH COUNTY HOSPITAL DISTRICT
MCDONOUGH DISTRICT HOSPITAL
525 E Grant St, Macomb, IL 61455-3313
Tel (309) 833-4101 *Founded/Ownrshp* 1958
Sales 50.3MM^E *EMP* 600
Accts Bkd Llp St Louis Mo
SIC 8051 8062 Skilled nursing care facilities; General medical & surgical hospitals; Skilled nursing care facilities; General medical & surgical hospitals
CEO: Kenny Boyd
Bd of Dir: Allan Reusch
**VP:* Linda Dace
**VP:* Wanda Foster
VP: Kay Lee
Dir Rad: Mary Schutte
Dir Rx: Kristi Green
Off Mgr: Gwen McGuire
CIO: Harlan Baker
MIS Dir: Jeannie Hamilton
Dir IT: Don Baker
Board of Directors: Kenneth Wright, Jack Baily, Crystal A Bedwell, Chuck Butterfield, Rick Iverson, Rita Moore, Pam Murphy, Noel Oliver, Matt Reynolds, Kent Slater

MCDONOUGH DISTRICT HOSPITAL
See MCDONOUGH COUNTY HOSPITAL DISTRICT

D-U-N-S 02-784-2363 IMP
MCDONOUGH HOLDINGS INC (FN)
MCDONOUGH MARINE SERVICE
21050 N Pima Rd Ste 100, Scottsdale, AZ 85255-6700
Tel (602) 544-5900 *Founded/Ownrshp* 2006
Sales 163.3MM^E *EMP* 1,043
SIC 2431 4449 2426 2421 Millwork; Staircases, stairs & railings; Moldings, wood: unfinished & prefinished; River transportation, except on the St. Lawrence Seaway; Hardwood dimension & flooring mills; Sawmills & planing mills, general; Millwork; Staircases, stairs & railings; Moldings, wood: unfinished & prefinished; River transportation, except on the St. Lawrence Seaway; Hardwood dimension & flooring mills; Sawmills & planing mills, general
Pr: Brendan Riccobene
**CEO:* Dale Knight
**CFO:* Stan Hrnci
CFO: Stan Hrncir
**Treas:* Larry Hillwig
**VP:* Matt Urrea

D-U-N-S 01-004-9823
MCDONOUGH INC
MCDONOUGH TOYOTA
918 Richmond Ave, Staunton, VA 24401-4903
Tel (540) 886-6201 *Founded/Ownrshp* 1975
Sales 26.9MM *EMP* 48
SIC 5511 Automobiles, new & used; Automobiles, new & used
Pr: Steven F McDonough
Sec: Elizabeth B McDonough
Sales Asso: Roy Eavey
Sales Asso: Brad White

MCDONOUGH MARINE SERVICE
See MCDONOUGH HOLDINGS INC (FN)

MCDONOUGH TOYOTA
See MCDONOUGH INC

D-U-N-S 79-662-4526
MCDOUGAL FAMILY PARTNERSHIP LTD
5001 W Loop 289, Lubbock, TX 79414-1614
Tel (806) 797-3162 *Founded/Ownrshp* 1992
Sales 43.1MM^E *EMP* 226
SIC 6798 Real estate investment trusts; Real estate investment trusts
Pt: Mike Mc Dougal
CFO: Mike McDougal
Mktg Dir: Max Webb

D-U-N-S 09-288-0541
MCDOUGALL & SONS INC
305 Olds Station Rd, Wenatchee, WA 98801-5938
Tel (509) 662-2136 *Founded/Ownrshp* 1964
Sales 55.9MM *EMP* 400
SIC 0723 Fruit (fresh) packing services; Fruit (fresh) packing services
Pr: Stuart McDougall
**Treas:* Irene Birdsall
**VP:* Bryon McDougall
IT Man: Trevor League
Board of Directors: Tony Purdum

D-U-N-S 00-881-8189
MCDOWALL CO
MCDOWELL COMFORT MANAGEMENT
1431 Prosper Dr, Waite Park, MN 56387-1891
Tel (320) 251-8640 *Founded/Ownrshp* 1952
Sales 35.8MM *EMP* 100
Accts Schlenner Wenner & Co Cpas
SIC 1711 7623 1761 Heating & air conditioning contractors; Ventilation & duct work contractor; Air conditioning repair; Roofing contractor; Architectural sheet metal work; Heating & air conditioning contractors; Ventilation & duct work contractor; Air conditioning repair; Roofing contractor; Architectural sheet metal work
Pr: John W Mc Dowall
**Treas:* Lawrence Mc Dowall
**VP:* Cheryl Mc Dowall
Genl Mgr: Karen Athmann
VP Mktg: Mark Dingmann

D-U-N-S 05-619-3568
MCDOWELL & CO
1201 Commerce Dr, Richardson, TX 75081-2406
Tel (972) 612-1100 *Founded/Ownrshp* 1971
Sales 26.1MM^E *EMP* 39
SIC 5085 5065 Rubber goods, mechanical; Packing, industrial; Seals, industrial; Semiconductor devices
Pr: Rusty McDowell
**VP:* Nancy McDowell
**VP:* Herbert Reese

MCDOWELL COMFORT MANAGEMENT
See MCDOWALL CO

D-U-N-S 07-979-8907
MCDOWELL COUNTY SCHOOLS
334 S Main St, Marion, NC 28752-4527
Tel (828) 652-4535 *Founded/Ownrshp* 2015
Sales 30.8MM^E *EMP* 850^E
SIC 8211 Public elementary & secondary schools
Teacher Pr: Bryan Oliver

D-U-N-S 07-979-8974
MCDOWELL COUNTY SCHOOLS
30 Central Ave, Welch, WV 24801-2008
Tel (304) 436-8441 *Founded/Ownrshp* 2015
Sales 5.3MM^E *EMP* 313^E
SIC 8211 Public elementary & secondary schools

D-U-N-S 07-907-0017
MCDOWELL HOSPITAL INC (NC)
430 Rankin Dr, Marion, NC 28752-6568
Tel (828) 659-5000 *Founded/Ownrshp* 1927
Sales 55.1MM *EMP* 323
SIC 8062 General medical & surgical hospitals; General medical & surgical hospitals
Pr: Lynn Boggs
VP: Clint Stewart
Obsttrcn: Andrea Moore
Pharmcst: Nick Green
Pharmcst: Lynn Sprinkle

D-U-N-S 09-378-4106
MCDOWELL LUMBER CO INC
2473 Falling Oak Rd, Asheboro, NC 27205-2055
Tel (336) 241-2544 *Founded/Ownrshp* 1970
Sales 20.8MM^E *EMP* 70
SIC 5031 Lumber: rough, dressed & finished
Pr: Tony McDowell
COO: Ashley McDowell
Treas: Tony Dowell
**VP:* Mark McDowell

D-U-N-S 79-431-2413 IMP
■ MCDOWELL RESEARCH CO INC
(*Suby of* ULTRALIFE CORP) ★
2000 Technology Pkwy, Newark, NY 14513-2175
Tel (315) 332-7100 *Founded/Ownrshp* 2006
Sales 88.8MM^E *EMP* 800
SIC 3669 Intercommunication systems, electric; Intercommunication systems, electric
Pr: John D Kavazanjian
Chf Mktg O: Jeff Luke
**VP:* Julius Cirin
VP: Philip Fain
VP: Andrew Naukam
VP: Michael Ward
Prgrm Mgr: Kathleen Watts
Off Mgr: Teodor Tarsici
Opers Mgr: Don Emanuele
Opers Mgr: Jackie Rusnak
Sls Mgr: Jeffrey Cason

D-U-N-S 07-979-8985
MCDUFFIE COUNTY
716 Lee St, Thomson, GA 30824-1831
Tel (706) 986-4000 *Founded/Ownrshp* 2015
Sales 8.9MM^E *EMP* 511^E
SIC 8211 Public elementary & secondary schools
Pr Dir: Lynn Cato
Teacher Pr: Letasha Johnson
HC Dir: Lisa Hill

D-U-N-S 09-263-6729
MCDUFFIE COUNTY BOARD OF EDUCATION (GA)
716 Lee St, Thomson, GA 30824-1831
Tel (706) 986-4048 *Founded/Ownrshp* 1872, 1983
Sales 24.2MM^E *EMP* 500
Accts Russell W Hinton Cpa Cgfm-D
SIC 8211 Public elementary & secondary schools; Public elementary & secondary schools
Schl Brd P: Greg Derry

D-U-N-S 14-049-0769
MCE AUTOMOTIVE INC
TOYOTA OF GREER
13770 E Wade Hampton Blvd, Greer, SC 29651-2775
Tel (864) 989-0779 *Founded/Ownrshp* 2003
Sales 33.4MM^E *EMP* 70^E
SIC 5511 Automobiles, new & used; Automobiles, new & used
Pr: Mark Escude
**CFO:* Jimmy Hutchinson
IT Man: Michele Duckett
Mktg Dir: Terry Childers
Sls Mgr: Mark Higdon
Sales Asso: Jeff Cassidy
Sales Asso: Nathan Stewart

D-U-N-S 00-164-3712 IMP
MCE COMPUTER TECHNOLOGY INC
(*Suby of* MCE-COMPUTER-PERIPHERIE-GMBH)
4040 Moorpark Ave Ste 112, San Jose, CA 95117-1852
Tel (925) 960-2000 *Founded/Ownrshp* 2000
Sales 26.0MM *EMP* 17
SIC 5045 Computer peripheral equipment; Computer peripheral equipment

D-U-N-S 10-295-0870
MCE CORP
6515 Trinity Ct Frnt, Dublin, CA 94568-2665
Tel (925) 803-4111 *Founded/Ownrshp* 1983
Sales 42.4MM^E *EMP* 100
Accts Johnston Gremaux & Rossi Llp
SIC 1611 0782 Highway & street construction; Lawn & garden services; Highway & street construction; Lawn & garden services
CEO: Maynard A Crowther
**Pr:* Jeff Core
Ex VP: Stan Smalley
**Sr VP:* Greg Haney
**VP:* Dan Furtado
**VP:* Steve Loweree
VP: Dean McDonald
Sfty Dirs: Karen Briones

MCELENEY CHEV-BUICK-GMC-TOYOTA
See MC ELENEY MOTORS INC

D-U-N-S 62-097-7470
MCELROY COAL CO
(*Suby of* MURRAY ENERGY CORP) ★
1000 Consol Energy Dr, Canonsburg, PA 15317-6506
Tel (724) 485-4000 *Founded/Ownrshp* 2013
Sales 51.3MM^E *EMP* 335^E
SIC 1221 Bituminous coal surface mining; Bituminous coal surface mining
Pr: P B Lilly
VP: Larry Hull
**VP:* J N Magro
VP: George Rosato
CTO: Rex Cooper
Corp Couns: Lori Mason

D-U-N-S 00-721-7482 IMP/EXP
MCELROY MANUFACTURING INC
833 N Fulton Ave, Tulsa, OK 74115-6408
Tel (918) 836-8611 *Founded/Ownrshp* 1962
Sales 59.8MM^E *EMP* 280^E
SIC 3559 Foundry machinery & equipment; Foundry machinery & equipment
Pr: Arthur H McElroy II
**CFO:* Donna M Dutton
**Ex VP:* Peggy M Tanner
**Prin:* William A Goffe
**Prin:* Jack H Santee
Software D: Mark Mileur
Software D: Edward Mostrom
Plnt Mgr: Bart Bartlett
Sales Exec: Dave Hughes
Manager: Kenny Nunley

D-U-N-S 00-805-6475 IMP/EXP
MCELROY METAL MILL INC
1500 Hamilton Rd, Bossier City, LA 71111-3890
Tel (318) 747-8000 *Founded/Ownrshp* 1963
Sales 335.4MM^E *EMP* 750

SIC 3448 Prefabricated metal buildings; Prefabricated metal buildings
Pr: Ian McElroy
**CFO:* John N Turley
Rgnl Mgr: Gary Lockart
Store Mgr: Keith Deville
Store Mgr: Alex Miller
MIS Dir: Gloria Stahl
IT Man: Barbara Campbell
Tech Mgr: Jonathon Caraway
Sfty Mgr: Kathy Beeson
Opers Mgr: Gene Clark
Opers Mgr: John Hinthorne

D-U-N-S 15-317-9916
MCELROY TRUCK LINES INC
111 Highway 80 Spur, Cuba, AL 36907-8701
Tel (205) 392-5579 *Founded/Ownrshp* 1963
Sales 86.5MM^E *EMP* 650
SIC 4213 8741 Trucking, except local; Administrative management; Business management; Trucking, except local; Administrative management; Business management
Ch Bd: Jay McElroy
CFO: Roger Booker
**CFO:* Billy Rawson
**VP:* Sean McElroy
Exec: Craig Vonineag
Sfty Dirs: Tyler Green
Sfty Dirs: Tom Spivey
Sfty Mgr: Lisa James
Sfty Mgr: Mary Summerville
Opers Mgr: Tommy Gullahorn

D-U-N-S 00-883-6983
MCELROYS INC
3209 Sw Topeka Blvd, Topeka, KS 66611-2292
Tel (785) 266-4870 *Founded/Ownrshp* 1956
Sales 23.7MM^E *EMP* 96
SIC 1711 Mechanical contractor
Ch Bd: Homer I Mc Elroy
**Pr:* Jerry D Mc Elroy
VP: Dan Beal
VP: Brad Hutton
VP: Wade Jueneman
Exec: Justin Pippitt

D-U-N-S 07-575-2352
MCELVAIN ENERGY INC
1050 17th St Ste 2500, Denver, CO 80265-2080
Tel (303) 893-0933 *Founded/Ownrshp* 1946
Sales 21.8MM^E *EMP* 47
SIC 1311 6552 Natural gas production; Crude petroleum production; Land subdividers & developers, commercial; Land subdividers & developers, residential
Pr: Guy W McElvain
Pr: Joe Kelloff
**COO:* Steve Shefte
**CFO:* David Sykes
**VP:* Catherine M Harvey
IT Man: Steve Kurutz
Opers Supe: Mark Wolfe
Genl Couns: Kip Joda

D-U-N-S 01-406-6708
MCELWAIN MOTORS LTD
MC ELWAIN OLDSMOBILE
812 Beaver Ave, Ellwood City, PA 16117-1939
Tel (724) 758-4588 *Founded/Ownrshp* 1956
Sales 21.7MM^E *EMP* 50
SIC 5511 Automobiles, new & used
Pr: Floyd McElwain Jr
**Pr:* Frank Mc Elwain
**Sec:* Kevin Mc Elwain
**VP:* Floyd D Mc Elwain
VP: H F McElwain
**Prin:* Harold Mc Elwain
Sls Mgr: Justin McKim

D-U-N-S 03-730-6557
MCENDAFFER CATTLE CO
MCENDAFFER FEED YARD
412 Highland Dr, Sterling, CO 80751-8608
Tel (970) 522-5330 *Founded/Ownrshp* 1977
Sales 30.0MM *EMP* 16
SIC 0751 0211 Livestock services, except veterinary; Beef cattle feedlots
Owner: Bret McEndaffer

MCENDAFFER FEED YARD
See MCENDAFFER CATTLE CO

D-U-N-S 05-650-8237
MCENROE VOICE & DATA CORP
LANIER BUSINESS PRODUCTS
10955 Golden West Dr A, Hunt Valley, MD 21031-8216
Tel (410) 785-1600 *Founded/Ownrshp* 1972
Sales 23.8MM^E *EMP* 83
SIC 5045 5044 5065 7378 7629 Computer peripheral equipment; Office equipment; Telephone & telegraphic equipment; Computer & data processing equipment repair/maintenance; Business machine repair, electric
Pr: Kathleen M Del Monte
**VP:* John L Del Monte
VP: John Monte
MIS Dir: Mike Ferro

D-U-N-S 03-611-7349
MCENTIRE PRODUCE INC
2040 American Italian Way, Columbia, SC 29209-5084
Tel (803) 799-3388 *Founded/Ownrshp* 1973
Sales 4.7MM^E *EMP* 400
SIC 2037

D-U-N-S 11-555-5542
MCESSY INVESTMENT CO
MCDONALD'S
1025 W Everett Rd Ste 3, Lake Forest, IL 60045-2668
Tel (847) 234-3427 *Founded/Ownrshp* 1981
Sales 183.9M *EMP* 700
SIC 5812 Fast-food restaurant, chain; Fast-food restaurant, chain
Pr: William H McEssy

D-U-N-S 07-879-1002
MCEVOY GROUP LLC
680 2nd St, San Francisco, CA 94107-2015
Tel (415) 537-4200 *Founded/Ownrshp* 2007
Sales 28.3MM^E *EMP* 225^E
SIC 8748 Publishing consultant

D-U-N-S 94-591-4265 IMP
MCEVOY OF MARIN LLC
MCEVOY RANCH
5935 Red Hill Rd, Petaluma, CA 94952-9437
Tel (707) 778-2307 *Founded/Ownrshp* 1998
Sales 23.6MM^E *EMP* 100
SIC 5199 Oils, animal or vegetable
Prd Mgr: Becky Rusake
Sales Asso: Stacy Stranzl

D-U-N-S 02-726-7913
MCEVOY OIL CO
4040 Irongate Rd, Bellingham, WA 98226-8028
Tel (360) 734-5650 *Founded/Ownrshp* 1964
Sales 22.2MM^E *EMP* 20
SIC 5171 Petroleum bulk stations
Pr: Patrick McEvoy
**CFO:* Christine Wright
**VP:* Marcia McEvoy

MCEVOY RANCH
See MCEVOY OF MARIN LLC

MCEWEN LUMBER CO
See HOOD INDUSTRIES INC

D-U-N-S 79-457-6223 EXP
MCF OPERATING LLC
MRS. CLARK'S FOODS
(*Suby of* AGRI INDUSTRIES INC) ★
740 Se Dalbey Dr, Ankeny, IA 50021-3908
Tel (515) 299-6400 *Founded/Ownrshp* 2012
Sales 38.4MM^E *EMP* 85
SIC 7389

MCFA
See MITSUBISHI CATERPILLAR FORKLIFT AMERICA INC

D-U-N-S 00-577-9269
MCFADDEN & MILLER LTD (TX)
11350 Luna Rd, Dallas, TX 75229-3114
Tel (972) 401-2356 *Founded/Ownrshp* 1946, 1986
Sales 20.0MM^E *EMP* 80
SIC 1541 1542 Warehouse construction; Commercial & office building, new construction
Pr: Mark Jacobson
**VP:* Jon Jacobson
Off Mgr: Doni Messer

D-U-N-S 00-703-6973
MCFADDEN COMMUNICATIONS LLC (TN)
TOOF COMMERCIAL PRINTING
670 S Cooper St, Memphis, TN 38104-5353
Tel (901) 274-3632 *Founded/Ownrshp* 1864, 2002
Sales 45.5MM^E *EMP* 209
SIC 2752 Commercial printing, lithographic; Commercial printing, lithographic
**COO:* Rick Smith
Treas: Deborah Martin
VP: C W Brown
VP: Jeff McLain
VP: Bill Todd
Exec: Jeanette Kirkpatrick
Plnt Mgr: Ronnie Kiihnl

D-U-N-S 62-525-5914
MCFADDEN-DALE INDUSTRIAL HARDWARE LLC
MB INDUSTRIAL
129 N Maple St, Corona, CA 92880-1735
Tel (951) 734-3620 *Founded/Ownrshp* 1990
Sales 22.9MM^E *EMP* 67
SIC 5072 5251 Hardware; Hardware
Pr: James R Marshall
Store Mgr: Avlie Villalobos

D-U-N-S 08-831-0131
MCFADKE INC
MCDONALD'S
502 W Alto Dr, Hobbs, NM 88240-3844
Tel (575) 393-0331 *Founded/Ownrshp* 1977
Sales 12.3MM^E *EMP* 400
SIC 5812 Fast-food restaurant, chain; Fast-food restaurant, chain
Pr: Kenneth J Fadke

MCFARLAND CASCADE
See LD MCFARLAND CO LIMITED

D-U-N-S 15-535-7791
MCFARLAND CASCADE HOLDINGS INC
MC FARLAND CASCADE
1640 Marc Ave, Tacoma, WA 98421-2939
Tel (253) 572-3033 *Founded/Ownrshp* 1984
Sales 139.7MM^E *EMP* 352
SIC 2491 6552 6531 Poles & pole crossarms, treated wood; Wood products, creosoted; Land subdividers & developers, commercial; Real estate managers; Poles & pole crossarms, treated wood; Wood products, creosoted; Land subdividers & developers, commercial; Real estate managers
Pr: Brian McManus
**Pr:* Wayne Wilkeson
**VP:* Greg D Mc Farland

D-U-N-S 06-961-5482
MCFARLAND CLINIC PC
1215 Duff Ave, Ames, IA 50010-5469
Tel (515) 239-4400 *Founded/Ownrshp* 1946
Sales 147.8MM^E *EMP* 1,400
SIC 8011 Clinic, operated by physicians; Clinic, operated by physicians
CEO: Steve Koger
**Ch Bd:* Dr Michael Kitchell
CTO: David Meier
Dir IT: Stan Davis
Counsel: Jane Mathison

MCFARLAND JOHNSON
See MCFARLAND-JOHNSON INC

D-U-N-S 05-233-1881
MCFARLAND-JOHNSON INC
MCFARLAND JOHNSON
49 Court St Ste 240, Binghamton, NY 13901-4647
Tel (570) 879-3004 *Founded/Ownrshp* 1992
Sales 28.0MM^E *EMP* 110
SIC 8711 Consulting engineer; Consulting engineer
CEO: Richard J Brauer
**CFO:* Frank J Greco
**VP:* James M Festa
**VP:* Fredrick D Mock
**VP:* Chad Nixon
Info Man: John Burk
Snr PM: Chad Phillips
Snr PM: Carl Tortolano

D-U-N-S 07-007-7271
MCFARLIN GROUP INC (FL)
1800 N Orange Blossom Trl, Orlando, FL 32804-5605
Tel (407) 425-3170 *Founded/Ownrshp* 1995
Sales 21.6MM^E *EMP* 135
Accts Harman & Peaslee Cpa S Plant
SIC 6719 Investment holding companies, except banks; Investment holding companies, except banks
Pr: Robert E Sutton Jr
Treas: George Dewey

D-U-N-S 01-642-7858
MCFARLING FOODS INC
333 W 14th St, Indianapolis, IN 46202-2204
Tel (317) 687-6827 *Founded/Ownrshp* 1948
Sales 150.0MM^E *EMP* 195
SIC 5147 5149 5144 5146 Meats & meat products; Groceries & related products; Poultry products; Eggs; Fish & seafoods; Meats & meat products; Groceries & related products; Poultry products; Eggs; Fish & seafoods
Ch Bd: Donald P Mc Farling
**VP:* Mike Atwood
**VP:* Greg Clay
**VP:* Leonard I McFarling
**VP:* Robert E Mc Farling Jr
**VP:* Patrick J McCune
**VP:* Charles D McFarling
VP: Bob Rider
VP: Jerry Ward
IT Man: Anthony Descenzo
Sfty Mgr: David Brown

MCFETRIDGE SPORT CENTER
See SMG

D-U-N-S 80-817-2428
■ **MCFSA LTD**
ARGYLE SECURITY GROUP
(*Suby of* ARGYLE SECURITY INC) ★
12903 Delivery, San Antonio, TX 78247-3476
Tel (210) 495-5245 *Founded/Ownrshp* 2013
Sales 33.2MM^E *EMP* 150
SIC 1731 Safety & security specialization; Safety & security specialization
CEO: Budea Johns
CFO: Richard Watts
Genl Mgr: Jessica Rosen
Genl Couns: Matthew Kepke

D-U-N-S 02-397-9979
MCG CAPITAL CORP
1001 19th St N Fl 10, Arlington, VA 22209-1734
Tel (703) 247-7500 *Founded/Ownrshp* 1990
Sales 26.8MM *EMP* 224
SIC 6282 6159 Investment advisory service; Small business investment companies

D-U-N-S 13-590-3867
MCG HEALTH INC
1120 15th St, Augusta, GA 30912-0006
Tel (706) 721-6569 *Founded/Ownrshp* 1994
Sales 404.7MM^E *EMP* 3,095^E
SIC 8062 Hospital, medical school affiliation; Hospital, medical school affiliation
Pr: Donald Snell
**COO:* Patricia Sodomka
**CFO:* Dennis R Roemer
**VP:* Dudley Harrington
VP: Sheila Oneal
VP: R Swift
Off Mgr: Don Wicklund
MIS Dir: Kathleen Herald
Ansthlgy: Eugene K Betts
Doctor: Emily M Cribb
Doctor: Sharad A Ghamande MD

MCGANN ASSOCIATES
See AMANO MCGANN INC

D-U-N-S 00-213-4864 IMP/EXP
MCGARD LLC
3875 California Rd, Orchard Park, NY 14127-4198
Tel (716) 662-1151 *Founded/Ownrshp* 1964
Sales 125.5MM^E *EMP* 400^E
SIC 5072 Security devices, locks; Security devices, locks
**CFO:* David Powers
**Ex VP:* Peter McCauley
VP: Jeff Sullivan
Comm Dir: Bill Turnage
CIO: Craig Alf
QA Dir: David Roy
Opers Supe: Gary McLouth
Plnt Mgr: Bob Wagner
Sls&Mrk Ex: John Mondo
VP Mktg: Christophe Smith
Manager: Marshall Brown

D-U-N-S 96-231-5503
MCGARRAH/JESSEE LP
121 W 6th St, Austin, TX 78701-2913
Tel (512) 225-2000 *Founded/Ownrshp* 1996
Sales 28.6MM^E *EMP* 90
SIC 7311 Advertising agencies; Advertising agencies
Pt: Bryan Jessee
**Pt:* Mark McGarrah
**CFO:* Anne Bergen
**Genl Mgr:* Britton Upham

D-U-N-S 14-439-3154 EXP
MCGARVEY CONSTRUCTION CO INC
MCGARVEY DEVELOPMENT CO
9260 Ester Park Cmns 10 Ste, Estero, FL 33928
Tel (239) 738-7800 *Founded/Ownrshp* 1984
Sales 23.6MM^E *EMP* 54
SIC 1542 Nonresidential construction
Pr: Joanne H Mc Garvey
COO: Bill Price
Ex VP: William Price Jr
Sr VP: Joseph Gomez
VP: Keith Veir
Snr Mgr: Jeff McGarvey

MCGARVEY DEVELOPMENT CO
See MCGARVEY CONSTRUCTION CO INC

D-U-N-S 00-624-3992
MCGARVIN-MOBERLY CONSTRUCTION CO
1001 Us Highway 20 N, Worland, WY 82401-9700
Tel (307) 347-4268 *Founded/Ownrshp* 1963
Sales 26.2MM *EMP* 35
Accts Stine Buss Wolff Wilson & Asso
SIC 1611 General contractor, highway & street construction; Airport runway construction; General contractor, highway & street construction; Airport runway construction
Pr: Philip Cines
**VP:* Ernest Skretteberg
**VP:* Gordon Sticka

D-U-N-S 83-876-3451
MCGAW MEDICAL CENTER OF NORTHWESTERN UNIVERSITY
NORTHWESTERN MCGAW CTR FOR GRA
240 E Huron St Ste 1-2, Chicago, IL 60611-2909
Tel (312) 503-7975 *Founded/Ownrshp* 1960
Sales 76.8MM *EMP* 40
SIC 8062 Hospital, medical school affiliation

D-U-N-S 09-898-4487
MCGAW YMCA
1000 Grove St, Evanston, IL 60201-4294
Tel (847) 475-7400 *Founded/Ownrshp* 1885
Sales 13.8MM *EMP* 300
SIC 8351 7991 8322 7032 8641 Child day care services; Youth organizations; Physical fitness facilities; Youth camps; Individual & family services; Child day care services; Physical fitness facilities; Individual & family services; Youth camps; Youth organizations
Ex Dir: Mark A Dennis Jr
**COO:* Monique Parsons
**CFO:* Nancy Petrillo

D-U-N-S 07-111-2593 IMP/EXP
MCGEAN-ROHCO INC
2910 Harvard Ave, Newburgh Heights, OH 44105-3010
Tel (216) 441-4900 *Founded/Ownrshp* 1974
Sales 62.8MM *EMP* 140
SIC 2899 2819 3471

D-U-N-S 00-302-8727
MCGEARY GRAIN INC
MCGEARY ORGANICS
941 Wheatland Ave Ste 401, Lancaster, PA 17603-3180
Tel (717) 394-6843 *Founded/Ownrshp* 1996
Sales 22.2MM *EMP* 19
SIC 5153 2873

MCGEARY ORGANICS
See MCGEARY GRAIN INC

D-U-N-S 07-904-6207
MCGEE BROTHERS CO INC (NC)
4608 Carriker Rd, Monroe, NC 28110-7490
Tel (704) 753-4582 *Founded/Ownrshp* 1971
Sales 92.1MM^E *EMP* 500^E
SIC 1741 1521 Masonry & other stonework; Single-family housing construction; Masonry & other stonework; Single-family housing construction
Pr: Sam McGee
**Treas:* Mike R McGee
**VP:* Cletus Huntley
VP: John McGee
Off Mgr: Jackie Tyree

D-U-N-S 00-708-9550 IMP
MCGEE CO
1140 S Jason St, Denver, CO 80223-3113
Tel (505) 883-9613 *Founded/Ownrshp* 1951
Sales 32.3MM^E *EMP* 86
SIC 5013 5084 Automotive servicing equipment; Industrial machinery & equipment; Recapping machinery, for tires; Automotive servicing equipment; Industrial machinery & equipment; Recapping machinery, for tires
Pr: Charles J Mc Gee
**VP:* Joanne E Mc Gee
Brnch Mgr: Paul Stanley
Genl Mgr: John Lebresch
Mktg Dir: Ian McGee
Sls Mgr: Dwanye Ballengee
Sls Mgr: Frank Ryan

D-U-N-S 00-315-6635 EXP
MCGEE CORP (NC)
12701 E Independence Blvd, Matthews, NC 28105-4103
Tel (704) 882-1500 *Founded/Ownrshp* 1948
Sales 25.2MM^E *EMP* 80
SIC 3448 3441 3444 Prefabricated metal buildings; Fabricated structural metal; Sheet metalwork
Pr: Richard M Mc Gee
**Treas:* Tommy L Broome
**VP:* John C Oakes
Prd Mgr: Jeff Cress

D-U-N-S 84-702-9543 IMP
MCGEE GROUP INC
(*Suby of* A TO Z SHEET METAL) ★
510 Comm Pk Dr Se, Marietta, GA 30060
Tel (770) 422-0010 *Founded/Ownrshp* 1976
Sales 30.2MM^E *EMP* 93^E
SIC 5048 Ophthalmic goods; Ophthalmic goods; Optometric equipment & supplies
CEO: A Wayne McGee
**CFO:* Pam Elder
Exec: Wayne McGee

Exec: Paula Meason
Creative D: Bart Tierney
Sls Mgr: Holly Autorina

D-U-N-S 07-381-5938
MCGEE MOTORCARS INC
860 Washington St, Hanover, MA 02339-1609
Tel (781) 826-8333 *Founded/Ownrshp* 1974
Sales 25.6MM^E *EMP* 75
SIC 5511 Automobiles, new & used; Automobiles, new & used
Pr: Robert M McGee
Sls Dir: Chris White
Sls Mgr: Jamie McKay

D-U-N-S 03-242-1349 EXP
MCGEE TIRE STORES INC
3939 Us Highway 98 S # 101, Lakeland, FL 33812-4248
Tel (863) 667-3347 *Founded/Ownrshp* 1974
Sales 120.9MM^E *EMP* 290
SIC 5531 7538 Automotive tires; General automotive repair shops; Automotive tires; General automotive repair shops
Pr: Michael J Mc Gee
**CFO:* Terry Borglund
**Sec:* Cynthia L McGee
**VP:* Terrance J McGee

D-U-N-S 02-391-4559 IMP
MCGEORGE CAR CO INC DAVID R
MCGEORGE TOYOTA
8225 W Broad St, Richmond, VA 23294-4126
Tel (804) 755-9200 *Founded/Ownrshp* 1970
Sales 59.6MM^E *EMP* 110
SIC 5511 Automobiles, new & used; Pickups, new & used; Trucks, tractors & trailers: new & used; Automobiles, new & used; Pickups, new & used; Trucks, tractors & trailers: new & used
CEO: Robert L McGeorge
**Pr:* David R McGeorge
Pr: Richarda Tiffin
**VP:* Virginia R McGeorge
Genl Mgr: Bob Farlow
Genl Mgr: Oj Schneider
Off Mgr: Rhonda Bishop
Mktg Dir: Nick Scola
Sls Mgr: Kenneth Puryear
Sales Asso: Tom Baskin
Sales Asso: Chris Brown
Board of Directors: D W Conner

D-U-N-S 00-690-3645
MCGEORGE CONTRACTING CO INC (AR)
GRANITE MOUNTAIN QUAR NUMBER 1
1501 Heartwood St, White Hall, AR 71602-4705
Tel (870) 534-7120 *Founded/Ownrshp* 1933
Sales 96.2MM^E *EMP* 252
SIC 1611 1423 General contractor, highway & street construction; Crushed & broken granite; General contractor, highway & street construction; Crushed & broken granite
Pr: Haskel L Dickinson II
**Ch Bd:* W Scott Mc George
**Sec:* Drew Atkinson
**VP:* Gerald Majors
**VP:* Wallace P Mc George III
Genl Mgr: Thomas Dickinson

MCGEORGE SCHOOL OF LAW
See UNIVERSITY OF PACIFIC

MCGEORGE TOYOTA
See MCGEORGE CAR CO INC DAVID R

D-U-N-S 00-681-5018 IMP
MCGILL AIRCLEAN LLC
(*Suby of* UNITED MCGILL CORP) ★
1777 Refugee Rd, Columbus, OH 43207-2119
Tel (614) 829-1200 *Founded/Ownrshp* 2004
Sales 23.0MM^E *EMP* 70
SIC 3564 1796 Precipitators, electrostatic; Pollution control equipment installation
Pr: James D McGill
IT Man: Norman Boyer
Natl Sales: Jerry Childress
Sls Mgr: T J Shay

D-U-N-S 00-681-5117 EXP
MCGILL AIRFLOW LLC
(*Suby of* UNITED MCGILL CORP) ★
1 Mission Park, Groveport, OH 43125-1149
Tel (614) 829-1200 *Founded/Ownrshp* 2004
Sales 22.5MM^E *EMP* 200
SIC 3444 Ducts, sheet metal; Ducts, sheet metal
Pr: James D McGill
VP: John Montell
Dir Surg: Mike Galeano
Opers Mgr: Joe Schelble
Sls Mgr: Rick Boyer
Sls Mgr: Tony McGill
Sales Asso: Shiela Shallcross

D-U-N-S 16-124-9297 IMP/EXP
MCGILL CORP
1 Mission Park, Groveport, OH 43125-1149
Tel (614) 829-1200 *Founded/Ownrshp* 1986
Sales 62.8MM^E *EMP* 400
SIC 3564 3444 5169 Precipitators, electrostatic; Air purification equipment; Ducts, sheet metal; Sealants; Precipitators, electrostatic; Air purification equipment; Ducts, sheet metal; Sealants
Ch Bd: James D McGill

D-U-N-S 00-510-4138
■ **MCGILL MANUFACTURING CO INC**
(*Suby of* REGAL BELOIT AMERICA INC) ★
2300 Evans Ave, Valparaiso, IN 46383-4054
Tel (219) 465-2200 *Founded/Ownrshp* 1905, 2015
Sales 150.0MM^E *EMP* 510
SIC 3562 Ball & roller bearings; Roller bearings & parts; Ball & roller bearings; Roller bearings & parts
Pr: Tony Pajk
Sr Cor Off: Chuck Hibbett
Prgrm Mgr: Brian Esham
Genl Mgr: John Hickel
IT Man: Larry Pembelson

D-U-N-S 07-789-7858
MCGILL-TOOLEN CATHOLIC HIGH SCHOOL
1501 Old Shell Rd, Mobile, AL 36604-2226
Tel (251) 445-2900 *Founded/Ownrshp* 1886
Sales 21.1MM^E *EMP* 115
Accts Sw Chiepalich Mobile Alaba
SIC 8211 Catholic senior high school
Pr: Bry Shields
Bd of Dir: John Lockette
VP: Nancy Fontenot
**Prin:* Michelle Haas
Ex Dir: Kathy M Killion

D-U-N-S 02-660-3092
MCGINNIS CADILLAC INC
MC GINNIS COLLISION CENTER
12221 Katy Fwy, Houston, TX 77079-1597
Tel (281) 496-8700 *Founded/Ownrshp* 1967
Sales 25.4MM^E *EMP* 105
Accts Svadlenak See & Company Pc
SIC 5511 Automobiles, new & used; Automobiles, new & used
Ch Bd: Rolland S Mc Ginnis
**Pr:* Kevin Mc Ginnis
**Treas:* Lois Allison
Sls&Mrk Ex: Kevin Ginnis

D-U-N-S 07-502-8969
MCGINNIS INC (OH)
(*Suby of* MCNATIONAL INC) ★
502 2nd St E, South Point, OH 45680-9446
Tel (740) 377-4391 *Founded/Ownrshp* 1971
Sales 45.6MM^E *EMP* 205
SIC 4491 3731 Marine cargo handling; Barges, building & repairing; Marine cargo handling; Barges, building & repairing
Pr: Rickey Lee Griffith
**CEO:* Bruce D McGinnis
**Sec:* Bill Jessie
Ex VP: Michael Monahan
VP: David Manning
**VP:* D Dwaine Stephens
Dir IT: Arron Canfield
Dir IT: Rebekah Waugh
IT Man: Wade Flannery
Sfty Dirs: Bo Lauder
Trfc Dir: Kathy Truesdell

D-U-N-S 01-498-6491
MCGINNIS SISTERS FOOD CENTER INC
MC GINNIS SISTERS
3825 Saw Mill Run Blvd # 1, Pittsburgh, PA 15227-2698
Tel (412) 882-6400 *Founded/Ownrshp* 1946
Sales 21.3MM^E *EMP* 100
SIC 5411 5812 Grocery stores, independent; Delicatessens; Caterers
Pr: Bonnie Mc Ginnis
**VP:* Sharon Mc Ginnis Young
VP: Sharon M Young

D-U-N-S 80-661-5985
MCGIVNEY & KLUGER PC
23 Vreeland Rd Ste 220, Florham Park, NJ 07932-1510
Tel (973) 822-1110 *Founded/Ownrshp* 1994
Sales 25.0MM^E *EMP* 150
SIC 8111 General practice attorney, lawyer; General practice attorney, lawyer
CFO: Kevin Cavanagh
**Chf Mktg O:* Charles McGivney
**VP:* Jeffrey Kluger
Counsel: James McGovern
Counsel: Yanet Noble

D-U-N-S 09-209-3616
MCGLINCHEY STAFFORD PLLC
12th Flr 601 Poydras St Flr 12, New Orleans, LA 70130
Tel (504) 586-1200 *Founded/Ownrshp* 1974
Sales 70.9MM^E *EMP* 387
SIC 8111 General practice law office; General practice law office
CFO: Brian Baudot
Bd of Dir: Bennet Koren
Chf Mktg O: Eric R Fletche
VP: James Wertheim
Dir IT: Thad Hymel
Telecom Mg: Debbie Appiah
IT Man: Yvette Johnston
Web Dev: Dennis Cullen
Mktg Mgr: Kristen Harwell
Counsel: Barbara F Yaksic

MCGLORY MAINTENANCE
See SHERWOOD SERVICES INC

MCGOHAN BRABENDER
See MCGOHAN/BRABENDER AGENCY INC

D-U-N-S 12-900-9551
MCGOHAN/BRABENDER AGENCY INC
MCGOHAN BRABENDER
3931 S Dixie Dr, Moraine, OH 45439-2313
Tel (937) 293-1600 *Founded/Ownrshp* 1972
Sales NA *EMP* 73^E
SIC 6411 Insurance agents, brokers & service
CEO: Scott McGohan
**Pr:* Tim Brabender
**CEO:* Patrick L McGohan
CFO: Beth Ferrin
**CFO:* Rodney L Miller
Creative D: Phil Meilinger
IT Man: Kevin Grabeman
IT Man: Jay Hawkins
VP Opers: Bud Hauser

D-U-N-S 00-679-1313
MCGOUGH CONSTRUCTION CO INC
2737 Fairview Ave N, Saint Paul, MN 55113-1372
Tel (651) 633-5050 *Founded/Ownrshp* 1956
Sales 443.3MM^E *EMP* 809
SIC 1541 1542 Industrial buildings, new construction; Nonresidential construction; Industrial buildings, new construction; Nonresidential construction
CEO: Thomas McGough Jr
**Ch Bd:* Lawrence J McGough
**Pr:* Thomas J McGough
**COO:* Michael Hangge
**Sec:* Richard Opitz
Ofcr: Paul Boefpslug
Ofcr: Paul Boespflug
Ex VP: Tim McGough
Sr VP: Bob Eno
VP: Dan Malecha
VP: Jeff Roundtree
**VP:* Keith Schuler
Dir Risk M: Amy Thompson

D-U-N-S 09-430-2788
MCGOUGH OLDSMOBILE G M C ISUZU
CAPITAL MOTOR COMPANY
11845 Rifle Range Rd, Tallassee, AL 36078-4589
Tel (334) 567-2222 *Founded/Ownrshp* 1989
Sales 30.0MM *EMP* 60
SIC 7538 7515 7513 5521 5511 General automotive repair shops; Passenger car leasing; Truck rental & leasing, no drivers; Used car dealers; New & used car dealers; General automotive repair shops; Passenger car leasing; Truck rental & leasing, no drivers; Used car dealers; New & used car dealers
Owner: Harris McGough

D-U-N-S 02-064-4944
MCGOWAN & CO INC (OH)
20595 Lorain Rd Ste 300, Cleveland, OH 44126-2062
Tel (440) 333-6300 *Founded/Ownrshp* 1954
Sales NA *EMP* 95^E
SIC 6411 Property & casualty insurance agent
Pr: Thomas B Mc Gowan IV
VP: Tim Lee
VP: Thomas McGowan
VP: Terrence Phelan
Mng Dir: Colin Dean
Off Mgr: Christina Kowalski
Dir IT: Dane Holman
Sales Exec: Kevin Milligan
Mktg Dir: Suzanne Young

D-U-N-S 78-409-7065
MCGOWAN WORKING PARTNERS INC
1837 Crane Ridge Dr, Jackson, MS 39216-4902
Tel (601) 982-3444 *Founded/Ownrshp* 1991
Sales 78.0MM^E *EMP* 112
SIC 1311 Crude petroleum production; Crude petroleum production
Pr: David B Russell
**Treas:* Debbie Chapman
**VP:* James A Phyfer Jr

D-U-N-S 13-423-2433
MCGRAFT HONDA
1411 E Main St, Saint Charles, IL 60174-2342
Tel (630) 443-6400 *Founded/Ownrshp* 2003
Sales 50.0MM *EMP* 150
SIC 5511 Automobiles, new & used; Automobiles, new & used
Owner: Gary McGraft

MCGRANN DIGITAL IMAGING
See MCGRANN PAPER CORP

D-U-N-S 08-516-6726 IMP
MCGRANN PAPER CORP
MCGRANN DIGITAL IMAGING
3800 Arco Corprt Dr # 350, Charlotte, NC 28273-4284
Tel (704) 583-2101 *Founded/Ownrshp* 1974
Sales 144.9MM^E *EMP* 65
SIC 5111 2752 Fine paper; Printing paper; Advertising posters, lithographed; Fine paper; Printing paper; Advertising posters, lithographed
Pr: Adam McGrann
CFO: Michael Antonishak
CFO: Barbara Cook
S&M/VP: Keith Castle

D-U-N-S 10-320-5167
MCGRATH AND ASSOCIATES INC
1920 S Kingshighway Blvd, Saint Louis, MO 63110-3214
Tel (314) 772-7600 *Founded/Ownrshp* 1983
Sales 25.4MM^E *EMP* 60
SIC 1541 8742 Industrial buildings, new construction; Construction project management consultant
Pr: Ken Knobbe Jr
**Sec:* Thomas Rich
Sfty Mgr: Steve Laney
Opers Mgr: Carol Barrett
Snr Mgr: Tony Vansaghi

D-U-N-S 02-205-2617
MCGRATH AUTOMOTIVE GROUP INC
MIKE MCGRATH AUTO CENTER
4610 Center Point Rd Ne, Cedar Rapids, IA 52402-2412
Tel (319) 688-2937 *Founded/Ownrshp* 1956
Sales 89.1MM^E *EMP* 225
SIC 5511 Automobiles, new & used; Automobiles, new & used
Pr: Patrick C McGrath
**Treas:* Rick Sayre
**VP:* Stan Cairy
**VP:* Michael P Mc Grath
**VP:* Patrick Mc Grath
Sls Mgr: Gavin McGrath
Sales Asso: Jeff Webster

MCGRATH CITY HONDA
See MKM AUTOMOTIVE INC

D-U-N-S 06-079-0529
MCGRATH CONTRACTORS LLC
(*Suby of* SENTINEL INDUSTRIES INC) ★
1000 Omalley Rd Ste 107, Anchorage, AK 99515-3083
Tel (907) 569-6868 *Founded/Ownrshp* 2001
Sales 35.0MM *EMP* 45
SIC 1542 Nonresidential construction; Nonresidential construction

MCGRATH LEXUS
See MCGRATH-COLOSIMO LTD

D-U-N-S 08-862-2139
MCGRATH NORTH MULLIN & KRATZ PC LLO
1601 Dodge St Ste 3700, Omaha, NE 68102-1650
Tel (402) 341-3070 *Founded/Ownrshp* 1970
Sales 26.9MM^E *EMP* 198
SIC 8111 General practice law office; General practice law office
Ch Bd: David L Hefflinger
Pr: Patti Bacon
Pr: Stephanie Debauche
Pr: Julie Howard
Pr: Louise Sledge
**Treas:* James P Fitzgerald
**VP:* Lee Hamann
Snr Sftwr: Guy Lawson
Dir IT: Jeremy Carson
Opers Mgr: Kristopher Covi
Snr Mgr: Roger Wells

D-U-N-S 09-622-6253
▲ **MCGRATH RENTCORP** (CA)
5700 Las Positas Rd, Livermore, CA 94551-7806
Tel (925) 606-9200 *Founded/Ownrshp* 1979
Sales 408.1MM *EMP* 995^E
Tkr Sym MGRC *Exch* NGS
SIC 7359 5084 Equipment rental & leasing; Electronic equipment rental, except computers; Rental store, general; Measuring & testing equipment, electrical; Equipment rental & leasing; Electronic equipment rental, except computers; Rental store, general; Measuring & testing equipment, electrical
Pr: Dennis C Kakures
COO: Joseph F Hanna
CFO: Keith E Pratt
Ofcr: Randle F Rose
**VP:* Scott Alexander
VP: Richard Brown
VP: Kristina Trease-Whitney
VP: David M Whitney
Dir Bus: Kristina Van Trease
Mktg Mgr: Stacey Ubelhoer
Board of Directors: William J Dawson, Elizabeth A Fetter, Robert C Hood, M Richard Smith, Dennis P Stradford, Ronald H Zech

D-U-N-S 55-619-0544
MCGRATH-COLOSIMO LTD
MCGRATH LEXUS
500 E Ogden Ave, Westmont, IL 60559-1228
Tel (630) 323-5600 *Founded/Ownrshp* 1991
Sales 50.0MM^E *EMP* 119
SIC 5511 7538 Automobiles, new & used; General automotive repair shops; Automobiles, new & used; General automotive repair shops
Pr: Michael J Mc Grath
CFO: Dan Hunt
Genl Mgr: Tracy Isselhardt
Sls Dir: Mike McGrath
Sls Mgr: Eric Hoffman
Sales Asso: Greg Luzinski
Sales Asso: Dave Nelson

D-U-N-S 03-708-5792
MCGRATHS PUBLICK FISH HOUSE LLC
1935 Davcor St Se, Salem, OR 97302-1146
Tel (503) 399-8456 *Founded/Ownrshp* 1980
Sales 37.1MM^E *EMP* 1,000
SIC 5812

MCGRAW AMARSH & MCLENNAN AGCY
See MCGRAW WENTWORTH INC

D-U-N-S 18-170-5898
MCGRAW DAVISSON STEWART INC
MCGRAW DVSSON STEWART REALTORS
4105 S Rockford Ave, Tulsa, OK 74105-4205
Tel (918) 592-6000 *Founded/Ownrshp* 1965
Sales 800.0MM *EMP* 550
SIC 6531 Real estate brokers & agents; Real estate brokers & agents
Pr: Joseph R McGraw
**Pr:* John Woolman
Sales Asso: Mickie Bingham
Sales Asso: Suzann Crockett
Sales Asso: Jan Jackson
Sales Asso: John Judd
Sales Asso: Jenna Majors
Sales Asso: Julia Morley
Sales Asso: Mimi Sandberg
Sales Asso: Mark Wojciehowski

MCGRAW DVSSON STEWART REALTORS
See MCGRAW DAVISSON STEWART INC

D-U-N-S 00-121-3206
▲ **MCGRAW HILL FINANCIAL INC**
55 Water St Ste Conc2, New York, NY 10041-0016
Tel (212) 512-2000 *Founded/Ownrshp* 1888
Sales 5.0MMM *EMP* 17,000
Accts Ernst & Young Llp New York N
Tkr Sym MHFI *Exch* NYS
SIC 7323 6282 Credit reporting services; Commercial (mercantile) credit reporting bureau; Investment advice; Investment advisory service; Credit reporting services; Commercial (mercantile) credit reporting bureau; Investment advice; Investment advisory service
Pr: Douglas L Peterson
COO: Michael Roberts
CFO: Jack F Callahan Jr
Ex VP: Lucy Fato
Ex VP: D Edward Smyth
Ex VP: Charles Teschner
Sr VP: Emmanuel N Korakis
Sr VP: Barbara A Munder
VP: Charlotte Frank
VP: Ken Michaels
VP: Peter Palma
VP: Lawrence Zingale
Exec: Peter Scheschuk
Creative D: Paula Darmofal
Board of Directors: Kurt L Schmoke, Winfried F W Bischoff, Sidney Taurel, Hilda Ochoa-Brillembourg, Richard E Thornburgh, William D Green, Charles E Haldeman Jr, Rebecca J Jacoby, Robert P McGraw, Harold W McGraw III, Michael Rake, Edward B Rust Jr

D-U-N-S 96-562-0743
■ **MCGRAW WENTWORTH INC**
MCGRAW AMARSH & MCLENNAN AGCY
(*Suby of* MARSH & MCLENNAN AGENCY LLC) ★
3331 W Big Beaver Rd # 200, Troy, MI 48084-2814
Tel (248) 822-8000 *Founded/Ownrshp* 2012
Sales NA *EMP* 72
SIC 6411 Insurance information & consulting services

Pr: Thomas P McGraw
**VP:* William D Wentworth
Mng Dir: Rebecca McLaughlan
Dir IT: Christi Soussan

D-U-N-S 00-130-7248
MCGRAW-EDISON CO (DE)
(*Suby of* EATON ELECTRIC HOLDINGS LLC) ★
600 Travis St Ste 5400, Houston, TX 77002-3013
Tel (713) 209-8400 *Founded/Ownrshp* 1985, 2007
Sales 519.0MM[E] *EMP* 13,144
SIC 3613 3641 3645 3646 Fuses & fuse equipment; Fuses, electric; Lamps, fluorescent, electric; Residential lighting fixtures; Fluorescent lighting fixtures, residential; Garden, patio, walkway & yard lighting fixtures: electric; Commercial indusl & institutional electric lighting fixtures; Fluorescent lighting fixtures, commercial; Fuses & fuse equipment; Fuses, electric; Lamps, fluorescent, electric; Residential lighting fixtures; Fluorescent lighting fixtures, residential; Garden, patio, walkway & yard lighting fixtures: electric; Commercial indusl & institutional electric lighting fixtures; Fluorescent lighting fixtures, commercial
Pr: Terry A Klebe
**Treas:* Alan J Hill
**VP:* Diane K Schumacher

D-U-N-S 05-829-6054
MCGRAW-HILL BROADCASTING CO INC
2 Penn Plz Fl 12, New York, NY 10121-2298
Tel (212) 904-2000 *Founded/Ownrshp* 2014
Sales NA *EMP* 575
SIC 4833 Television broadcasting stations

D-U-N-S 07-880-2466
MCGRAW-HILL GLOBAL EDUCATION HOLDINGS LLC
2 Penn Plz Fl 20, New York, NY 10121-2100
Tel (646) 766-2000 *Founded/Ownrshp* 2013
Sales 1.7MMM[E] *EMP* 3,500[E]
SIC 2731 Textbooks: publishing & printing; Textbooks: publishing & printing
Pr: David Levin
Pr: Sally Shankland
**CFO:* Patrick Milano
**Ofcr:* Stephen J Laster
**Sr VP:* Teresa Martin-Retortillo
Sr VP: Heath Morrison
**Sr VP:* Maryellen Valaitis
**CIO:* David Wright

D-U-N-S 06-827-7348
MCGRAW-HILL GLOBAL EDUCATION LLC
MCGRAW-HILL HIGHER EDUCATION
(*Suby of* MCGRAW-HILL GLOBAL EDUCATION HOLDINGS LLC) ★
2 Penn Plz Fl 20, New York, NY 10121-2100
Tel (646) 766-2000 *Founded/Ownrshp* 2013
Sales 158.6MM[E] *EMP* 3,500
SIC 8299 Educational services
Pr: David Levin
COO: Stephen Robbins
CFO: Patrick Milano
Treas: David Kraut
Ofcr: Stephen Laster
Sr VP: Teresa Martin-Retortillo
Sr VP: David Stafford
Sr VP: Maryellen Valaitis
Exec: Harper Christopher
Mng Dir: Gina Boedeker
Mng Dir: Douglas Reiner
Board of Directors: Nancy Lublin

MCGRAW-HILL HIGHER EDUCATION
See MCGRAW-HILL GLOBAL EDUCATION LLC

MCGRAW-HILL SCHL EDCATN HLDNGS
See CTB/MCGRAW-HILL LLC

D-U-N-S 07-909-2445
MCGRAW-HILL SCHOOL EDUCATION HOLDINGS LLC
2 Penn Plz Fl 5, New York, NY 10121-0600
Tel (646) 766-2000 *Founded/Ownrshp* 2013
Sales 750.0MM *EMP* 2,000
SIC 2731 Books: publishing only; Books: publishing only
Pr: David Levin
**CFO:* Patrick Milano
**Sr VP:* Teresa Martin-Retortillo
**Sr VP:* David B Stafford
**Sr VP:* Maryellen Valaitis
**CIO:* David Wright

D-U-N-S 07-880-2474
MCGRAW-HILL SCHOOL EDUCATION LLC
(*Suby of* MCGRAW-HILL SCHOOL EDUCATION HOLDINGS LLC) ★
2 Penn Plz Fl 20, New York, NY 10121-2100
Tel (646) 766-2060 *Founded/Ownrshp* 2013
Sales 129.8MM[E] *EMP* 1[E]
SIC 2731 Book publishing; Books: publishing & printing
Pr: David Levin
CFO: Patrick Milano
Ofcr: Stephen J Laster
Sr VP: Teresa Martin-Retortillo
Sr VP: Maryellen Valaitis
CIO: David Wright

D-U-N-S 80-159-3823
MCGRAW/KOKOSING INC
(*Suby of* KOKOSING INC) ★
6235 Wstrville Rd Ste 200, Westerville, OH 43081
Tel (614) 212-5700 *Founded/Ownrshp* 1992
Sales 97.9MM[E] *EMP* 500
Accts Crowe Horwath Llp
SIC 1541 1542 Renovation, remodeling & repairs: industrial buildings; Industrial buildings, new construction; Nonresidential construction; Renovation, remodeling & repairs: industrial buildings; Industrial buildings, new construction; Nonresidential construction
Pr: Daniel B Walker
**Treas:* Timothy J Freed
Exec: Spencer Beeching
**Genl Mgr:* Chris A Bergs

MCGREEVER AND DANLEE VERY
See MORRIS NATIONAL INC

D-U-N-S 00-794-2303
MCGREGOR CO (WA)
TOMCO SEED
401 Colfax Airport Rd, Colfax, WA 99111-6002
Tel (509) 397-4355 *Founded/Ownrshp* 1882
Sales 137.0MM[E] *EMP* 325
SIC 5191 3523 2874

MCGREGOR METALWORKING
See MORGAL MACHINE TOOL CO

D-U-N-S 12-129-6719
MCGREGOR-SURMOUNT CORP
365 Carr Dr, Brookville, OH 45309-1921
Tel (937) 833-6768 *Founded/Ownrshp* 1983
Sales 48.4MM[E] *EMP* 190
SIC 3629 3672 Electronic generation equipment; Printed circuit boards; Electronic generation equipment; Printed circuit boards
CEO: Larry Mc Gregor
Ql Cn Mgr: Wade Bashline

MCGREGOR'S FURNITURE
See MC GREGOR CO

D-U-N-S 16-610-7610
MCGRENHO L L C
INDY TRUCK SALES
1325 W Thompson Rd, Indianapolis, IN 46217-9267
Tel (317) 787-0200 *Founded/Ownrshp* 2002
Sales 41.9MM[E] *EMP* 170
SIC 5511 New & used car dealers; New & used car dealers
CFO: David Lockwell

D-U-N-S 04-563-1934 IMP
MCGRIFF INDUSTRIES INC
MCGRIFF TIRE CO.
86 Walnut St Ne, Cullman, AL 35055
Tel (256) 739-0780 *Founded/Ownrshp* 1955
Sales 134.0MM[E] *EMP* 280
SIC 5531 7534 Rebuilding & retreading tires; Automotive tires; Trucking, except local; Automotive tires; Rebuilding & retreading tires
Ch Bd: Bertis McGriff
**Pr:* Barry McGriff
Sec: Jeff M Griff
**Sec:* Jeff McGriff
MIS Mgr: Vicky Carden
Plnt Mgr: Jim Osborne

MCGRIFF SEIBELS & WILLIAMS
See MCGRIFF SEIBELS & WILLIAMS OF GEORGIA INC

D-U-N-S 07-210-2213
■ **MCGRIFF SEIBELS & WILLIAMS INC**
(*Suby of* BB&T INSURANCE HOLDINGS INC) ★
2211 7th Ave S, Birmingham, AL 35233-2340
Tel (205) 252-9871 *Founded/Ownrshp* 2004
Sales NA *EMP* 745
SIC 6411

D-U-N-S 79-824-2681
■ **MCGRIFF SEIBELS & WILLIAMS OF GEORGIA INC**
MCGRIFF SEIBELS & WILLIAMS
(*Suby of* MCGRIFF SEIBELS & WILLIAMS INC) ★
5605 Glenridge Dr Ste 300, Atlanta, GA 30342-1374
Tel (404) 497-7500 *Founded/Ownrshp* 1989
Sales NA *EMP* 60
SIC 6411 Insurance brokers
Pr: Pat Hopkins
Ex VP: Vincent Hau
Ex VP: Brad Newman
**Sr VP:* Jim Clark
**Sr VP:* Reed Davis
Sr VP: Greg McCollister
**Sr VP:* Paul Sparks
VP: Trey Phillips
VP: Robert Taylor
Exec: Tom Coker
Off Mgr: Phyllis Barnett

D-U-N-S 02-410-9493
■ **MCGRIFF SEIBELS & WILLIAMS OF TEXAS INC**
(*Suby of* MCGRIFF SEIBELS & WILLIAMS INC) ★
818 Town And Country Blvd, Houston, TX 77024-4550
Tel (713) 877-8975 *Founded/Ownrshp* 1991
Sales NA *EMP* 170
SIC 6411 Insurance agents, brokers & service
Pr: Thomas A Ebner
V Ch: Bert Swails
Pr: Bob Dunmire
**Ch:* Peter A Barbara
**Sec:* Patrick Dessauer
Ofcr: Lisa Moberly
**Sr Ex VP:* Douglas Hodo Jr
Ex VP: Weldon Corbett
Sr VP: Cynthia Bryan-Williams
Sr VP: Jeffrey Buchanan
Sr VP: Gail Chilton
Sr VP: Terri Cook
Sr VP: George Dobbin
Sr VP: Dave Lewis
Sr VP: Scott McClure
Sr VP: Steve McKinnon
Sr VP: Olivier Parchois
Sr VP: Sandy Pierce
Sr VP: Jed Skeete
VP: Joe Aulbert
VP: Cynthia Bryan

MCGRIFF TIRE CO.
See MCGRIFF INDUSTRIES INC

D-U-N-S 11-806-6729 IMP
MCGRORY GLASS INC
1400 Grandview Ave, Paulsboro, NJ 08066-1801
Tel (856) 579-3200 *Founded/Ownrshp* 1984
Sales 23.3MM[E] *EMP* 60
SIC 3211 5039 3231 3229 3083 Construction glass; Glass construction materials; Products of purchased glass; Pressed & blown glass; Laminated plastics plate & sheet

Pr: Christopher McGrory
Sec: Gary McGrory
VP: Charles McGrory

MCGUCKIN HARDWARE
See HIGHT ENTERPRISES LTD

D-U-N-S 09-641-3786 IMP
MCGUFF CO INC (CA)
3524 W Lake Center Dr, Santa Ana, CA 92704-6987
Tel (714) 545-2491 *Founded/Ownrshp* 1972
Sales 30.9MM[E] *EMP* 85[E]
SIC 5047 Medical equipment & supplies
Pr: Ronald M McGuff
VP Opers: Alicia Johnston
Mktg Mgr: William Blair
Mktg Mgr: Ronald Guff

D-U-N-S 79-522-9645 EXP
MCGUFFY ENERGY SERVICES LP
18635 Telge Rd, Cypress, TX 77429-1781
Tel (281) 255-6955 *Founded/Ownrshp* 2005
Sales 26.2MM[E] *EMP* 85
SIC 2813 Industrial gases
Mng Pt: Steven Wormald
CFO: Darrell Gordon

D-U-N-S 00-691-0038
MCGUIRE AND HESTER
9009 Railroad Ave, Oakland, CA 94603-1245
Tel (510) 562-1262 *Founded/Ownrshp* 1926
Sales 137.2MM[E] *EMP* 300[E]
SIC 1623 7353 Underground utilities contractor; Heavy construction equipment rental; Underground utilities contractor; Heavy construction equipment rental
CEO: Michael R Hester
**Treas:* Louis Roessler
**Ex VP:* Robert Doud
Div Mgr: Andrew Vasconi
Genl Mgr: Mabel Cater
Trfc Dir: Victor Camarillo
Trfc Dir: Ramon Gomez
Snr Mgr: Matt Daley
Snr Mgr: Bruce Daseking

D-U-N-S 02-773-9283 IMP
MCGUIRE BEARING CO
TRIPLE PHASE
947 Se Market St, Portland, OR 97214-3574
Tel (503) 238-1570 *Founded/Ownrshp* 1977
Sales 58.7MM[E] *EMP* 158
SIC 5085

D-U-N-S 01-165-0926
MCGUIRE CADILLAC INC
910 Us Highway 1 N, Woodbridge, NJ 07095-1403
Tel (732) 326-0300 *Founded/Ownrshp* 1914
Sales 22.8MM[E] *EMP* 75
SIC 5511 Automobiles, new & used; Automobiles, new & used
Pr: Regan McGuire
Sls Mgr: Emil Califano

MCGUIRE CHVCADILLAC OLDS ISUZU
See MC GUIRE AUTO SALES

MCGUIRE FURNITURE
See KOHLER INTERIORS FURNITURE CO

D-U-N-S 09-106-2328
MCGUIRES FORD LINCOLN MERCURY
MCGUIRES FORD OF HERSHEY
100 N Thistledown Dr, Palmyra, PA 17078-9002
Tel (717) 838-8300 *Founded/Ownrshp* 1999
Sales 22.3MM[E] *EMP* 75
SIC 5511 Automobiles, new & used; Automobiles, new & used
Pr: Rob Rohrer
Pr: Keith Rohrer
VP: K Robert Rohrer

MCGUIRES FORD OF HERSHEY
See MCGUIRES FORD LINCOLN MERCURY

D-U-N-S 05-890-2008
MCGUIREWOODS LLP
800 E Canal St, Richmond, VA 23219-3916
Tel (804) 775-1000 *Founded/Ownrshp* 1952
Sales 327.5MM[E] *EMP* 1,710
SIC 8111 General practice law office; General practice law office
Pt: David P Pusateri
Pt: John D Adams
Pt: Terrence M Bagley
Pt: Robert Couture
Pt: Robert H Patterson Jr
Pt: Ellen Ruff
Pt: William J Strickland
Mng Pt: Thomas E Cabaniss
Mng Pt: Brian K Parker
COO: Eva Tashjian-Brown
CFO: Elizabeth Burke
Chf Mktg O: Tim Mullane
Sr VP: Christopher R Nolen

D-U-N-S 83-105-0091
MCGUYER HOMEBUILDERS INC
PIONEER HOMES
7676 Woodway Dr Ste 104, Houston, TX 77063-1521
Tel (713) 952-6767 *Founded/Ownrshp* 1988
Sales 109.3MM[E] *EMP* 375
SIC 1531 1521 Operative builders; Single-family housing construction; Operative builders; Single-family housing construction
Ch Bd: Frank McGuyer
**Pr:* Mike Love
**Pr:* Gary R Tesch
CFO: Anna Moore
Ex Dir: Charles H Phillips
Dir IT: Ravi Machiraju
Dir IT: Paul Piro
Prd Mgr: Jason Bradley
Prd Mgr: Billy Easterwood
Mktg Dir: Jamie Patterson
Sls Dir: Greg Carr

MCH
See MADERA COMMUNITY HOSPITAL

MCH & HEALTH SYSTEM
See MEMORIAL COMMUNITY HOSPITAL CORP

D-U-N-S 00-682-6528
MCH ELECTRIC INC
7693 Longard Rd, Livermore, CA 94551-8208
Tel (209) 835-9755 *Founded/Ownrshp* 2001
Sales 22.2MM[E] *EMP* 140[E]
SIC 1731 Electrical work; Electrical work
Pr: James Humphrey
**CFO:* Christine Morris

D-U-N-S 96-217-9631
MCH PEDIATRIC CARDIOLOGY LLC
(*Suby of* NICKLAUS CHILDRENS HOSPITAL) ★
3100 Sw 62nd Ave, Miami, FL 33155-3009
Tel (305) 666-6511 *Founded/Ownrshp* 2000
Sales 11.8MM[E] *EMP* 335[E]
SIC 8069 Children's hospital

D-U-N-S 12-748-8026
MCH TRANSPORTATION CO
3180 Utica Ave, Jackson, MS 39209-7339
Tel (601) 353-9382 *Founded/Ownrshp* 1986
Sales 20.0MM[E] *EMP* 145[E]
SIC 4213 Trucking, except local; Trucking, except local
CEO: James A Harrell
**Pr:* Jim Caskey
**CFO:* Ben Watkins
Treas: Olivia W Harrell
VP: Bertha E Dossett
VP Opers: Jim Stewart

D-U-N-S 11-439-3515
MCHALE & MCHALE LANDSCAPE DESIGN INC
6212 Leapley Rd, Upper Marlboro, MD 20772-3713
Tel (301) 599-8300 *Founded/Ownrshp* 1981
Sales 30.4MM[E] *EMP* 160
SIC 0781 0782 Landscape architects; Landscape contractors; Landscape architects; Landscape contractors
Pr: Kevin McHale
**Treas:* Julie McHale
**VP:* Stephen McHale

MCHC
See MOUNTAIN COMPREHENSIVE HEALTH CORP

MCHC
See MENDOCINO COMMUNITY HEALTH CLINIC INC

D-U-N-S 07-016-2144
MCHENRY COUNTY COLLEGE
COMMUNITY COLLEGE DST 528
(*Suby of* ILLINOIS COMMUNITY COLLEGE BD) ★
8900 Us Highway 14, Crystal Lake, IL 60012-2761
Tel (815) 455-3700 *Founded/Ownrshp* 1967
Sales 15.5MM *EMP* 1,000
Accts Sikich Naperville Illinois
SIC 8222 8221 9411 Community college; Colleges universities & professional schools; Administration of educational programs; Community college; Colleges universities & professional schools; Administration of educational programs
Pr: Dr Vicky Smith
**CFO:* Robert Tenuta
Treas: Ronald Ally
**Treas:* Larry West
**VP:* Laura Brown
VP: Kate Midday
**VP:* Anthony Miksa
Mktg Dir: Christine Haggerty
Psych: Luisa Lauf
Psych: Amy Taylor

MCHENRY MANAGEMENT GROUP, THE
See MCHENRY MANAGEMENT GROUP INC

D-U-N-S 80-942-5163
MCHENRY MANAGEMENT GROUP INC
MCHENRY MANAGEMENT GROUP, THE
600 Independence Pkwy # 105, Chesapeake, VA 23320-5188
Tel (757) 410-0233 *Founded/Ownrshp* 2008
Sales 23.6MM[E] *EMP* 170
Accts Cherry Bekaert & Holland Ll
SIC 8711 Engineering services; Engineering services
CEO: Shane Dowling
VP: John Callan
**VP:* Bill Mercier
**VP:* Christopher Wenz
Prgrm Mgr: Tom Murphy
Dir IT: Scott Cobb

D-U-N-S 12-687-5004
MCHENRY SCHOOL DISTRICT 15
1011 N Green St, McHenry, IL 60050-5720
Tel (815) 385-7210 *Founded/Ownrshp* 1993
Sales 71.3MM *EMP* 500
Accts Eder Casella & Co Mchenry
SIC 8211 Public elementary & secondary schools; Public elementary & secondary schools
Bd of Dir: Kim Huemann
Bd of Dir: Kathie Robinson
Dir IT: Daniel Deroche
IT Man: Andrew Dreher
Psych: Clarence Arnold
Psych: Laurel Graham
Psych: Julia Thomas
HC Dir: Amelia Wuerger

D-U-N-S 96-357-7502
MCHS - WEBSTER
750 W Texas Ave, Webster, TX 77598-3259
Tel (281) 332-3496 *Founded/Ownrshp* 2010
Sales 105.4MM *EMP* 10[E]
SIC 8051 Skilled nursing care facilities; Skilled nursing care facilities

D-U-N-S 01-748-6225
MCHS DALLAS 308
3326 Burgoyne St, Dallas, TX 75233-1304
Tel (214) 330-9291 *Founded/Ownrshp* 2010
Sales 772.0MM *EMP* 1[E]
SIC 7699 Industrial machinery & equipment repair; Industrial machinery & equipment repair

D-U-N-S 96-329-8026
MCHS SOUTH HOLLAND
2145 E 170th St, South Holland, IL 60473-3788
Tel (708) 895-3255 Founded/Ownrshp 2010
Sales 22.3MM EMP 13E
SIC 8051 Skilled nursing care facilities; Skilled nursing care facilities

D-U-N-S 96-338-9130
MCHS WALNUT CREEK
1226 Rossmoor Pkwy, Walnut Creek, CA 94595-2538
Tel (925) 975-5000 Founded/Ownrshp 2010
Sales 22.8MM EMP 16E
SIC 8051 Skilled nursing care facilities; Skilled nursing care facilities
Prin: Van Dang

D-U-N-S 13-087-2773
MCHUGH ENTERPRISES INC
1737 S Michigan Ave, Chicago, IL 60616-1211
Tel (312) 986-8000 Founded/Ownrshp 1985
Sales 391.0MME EMP 1,000E
SIC 1542 1522 1622 1771 1742 6552 Nonresidential construction; Multi-family dwelling construction; Bridge construction; Tunnel construction; Highway construction, elevated; Concrete work; Drywall; Subdividers & developers; Nonresidential construction; Multi-family dwelling construction; Bridge construction; Tunnel construction; Highway construction, elevated; Concrete work; Drywall; Subdividers & developers
Pr: James P McHugh
*Treas: Patrick Seery

MCI CARPET ONE FLOOR & HOME
See MCI INC

D-U-N-S 04-476-0643
■ **MCI COMMUNICATIONS CORP**
VERIZON BUSINESS
(Suby of VERIZON BUSINESS GLOBAL LLC) ★
22001 Loudoun County Pkwy, Ashburn, VA 20147-6105
Tel (703) 886-5600 Founded/Ownrshp 1968, 2006
Sales 5.0MMME EMP 39,000
SIC 4813 4812 4822 7372 Local & long distance telephone communications; Long distance telephone communications; Local telephone communications; Voice telephone communications; Cellular telephone services; Paging services; Cable, telegram & telex services; Facsimile transmission services; Telegram services; Telex services; Prepackaged software; Business oriented computer software; Local & long distance telephone communications; Long distance telephone communications; Local telephone communications; Voice telephone communications; Cellular telephone services; Paging services; Cable, telegram & telex services; Facsimile transmission services; Telegram services; Telex services; Prepackaged software; Business oriented computer software
CEO: Gerald H Taylor
Pr: Timothy F Price
Tech Mgr: Pete Laverde
Counsel: Pat Escobedo
Board of Directors: Clifford L Alexander Jr, Judith Areen, Michael H Bader, Robert P Brace, Richard M Jones, Gordon S Macklin, Richard B Sayford, Judith Whittaker, John R Worthington

D-U-N-S 08-312-2643
■ **MCI COMMUNICATIONS SERVICES INC**
VERIZON BUSINESS
(Suby of VERIZON BUSINESS GLOBAL LLC) ★
22001 Loudoun County Pkwy, Ashburn, VA 20147-6105
Tel (703) 886-5600 Founded/Ownrshp 1992, 2006
Sales 433.9MME EMP 1,100E
SIC 4813 Telephone communication, except radio; Telephone communication, except radio
CEO: Michael Capellas

D-U-N-S 07-073-7424
MCI INC
MCI CARPET ONE FLOOR & HOME
26 1st Ave N, Waite Park, MN 56387-1213
Tel (320) 253-5078 Founded/Ownrshp 1995
Sales 23.4MM EMP 65
Accts Cliftonlarsonallen Llp St Cl
SIC 5713 5712 5231 5719 Floor covering stores; Carpets; Vinyl floor covering; Floor tile; Furniture stores; Office furniture; Wallcoverings; Window furnishings; Floor covering stores; Carpets; Vinyl floor covering; Floor tile; Furniture stores; Office furniture; Wallcoverings; Window furnishings
CEO: Ryan Corrigan
*Sr VP: Harold Loch
*Sr VP: Brian Poepping
VP: Pat Lemke

D-U-N-S 82-974-8420
MCI INTERMEDIA INC
(Suby of MCIMETRO ACCESS TRANSMISSION SERVICES LLC)
22001 Loudoun County Pkwy, Ashburn, VA 20147-6105
Tel (703) 886-5600 Founded/Ownrshp 2010
Sales 5.2MME EMP 495E
SIC 4813 Telephone communication, except radio

D-U-N-S 82-943-0458
■ **MCI INTERNATIONAL INC**
VERIZON BUSINESS
(Suby of MCI COMMUNICATIONS CORP) ★
22001 Loudoun County Pkwy, Ashburn, VA 20147-6105
Tel (703) 886-5600 Founded/Ownrshp 1976
Sales 136.4MME EMP 955
SIC 4813 4812 4822 7372 Local & long distance telephone communications; Long distance telephone communications; Local telephone communications; Voice telephone communications; Cellular telephone services; Paging services; Cable, telegram & telex services; Facsimile transmission services; Telegram services; Telex services; Prepackaged software; Business oriented computer software; Local & long distance telephone communications; Long distance telephone communications; Local telephone communications; Voice telephone communications; Cellular telephone services; Paging services; Cable, telegram & telex services; Facsimile transmission services; Telegram services; Telex services; Prepackaged software; Business oriented computer software
Pr: Robert A Toohey
*Chf Mktg O: Anthony Recine
*Sr VP: Martin Burvill
*Sr VP: Christopher Formant

D-U-N-S 02-062-2762
■ **MCI INTERNATIONAL SERVICES INC**
VERIZON BUSINESS
(Suby of MCI INTERNATIONAL INC) ★
22001 Loudoun County Pkwy, Ashburn, VA 20147-6105
Tel (703) 723-4401 Founded/Ownrshp 1974
Sales 136.4MME EMP 650
SIC 4813 Telephone communication, except radio; Telephone communication, except radio
CEO: Michael D Cappellas
Ofcr: Grace Wong
VP: Troy Yenser
Mng Dir: Jesper Pedersen
Mng Dir: Simon Phoon
Admn Mgr: Cheryl U Ginyard-Jones
Snr Ntwrk: In Cho
Manager: Philip Mello
Snr Mgr: Erik Sherk

D-U-N-S 19-737-9071
MCI LIQUIDATION INC
(Suby of INDEPENDENT PUBLICATIONS, INC.)
50 Dow St, Manchester, NH 03101-1211
Tel (603) 624-1442 Founded/Ownrshp 1998
Sales 14.2MME EMP 455E
SIC 2711 Newspapers
Pr: Terry Williams
VP: Shana Hoch
IT Man: Guido Cafasso
IT Man: Kathleen Johnson
VP Opers: Irene Ngai
Sales Exec: Steve Pare

D-U-N-S 60-698-0225
MCI SALES AND SERVICE INC
(Suby of MCII) ★
200 E Oakton St, Des Plaines, IL 60018-1948
Tel (847) 285-2000 Founded/Ownrshp 1994
Sales 53.8MME EMP 200
SIC 5012 Buses; Buses
Pr: Richard Heller
*COO: Tom Sorrells
VP: Michael R Denny
VP: J M McIlwain
VP: J M McLlwain
*VP: Patrick Scully
VP: Guenter Tiffert
VP: Peter M Tully

D-U-N-S 02-002-9971 IMP
MCI SERVICE PARTS INC
(Suby of MCII) ★
1700 E Golf Rd Fl 3, Schaumburg, IL 60173-5862
Tel (847) 285-2000 Founded/Ownrshp 1993
Sales 138.2MME EMP 325
SIC 5013 Automotive supplies & parts; Automotive supplies & parts
Pr: Richard A Heller
COO: Janice Karijolic
*VP: Pete Cotter

MCII
See MOTOR COACH INDUSTRIES INTERNATIONAL INC

D-U-N-S 14-780-9672
MCII HOLDINGS INC
(Suby of KPS CAPITAL PARTNERS LP) ★
1700 E Golf Rd, Schaumburg, IL 60173-5804
Tel (866) 624-2622 Founded/Ownrshp 2010
Sales 423.5MME EMP 1,500E
SIC 6512 Nonresidential building operators; Nonresidential building operators
Pr: Thomas C Sorrells

D-U-N-S 00-815-8396 IMP/EXP
MCILHENNY CO
(Suby of E MC ILHENNYS SON CORP) ★
Hwy 329, Avery Island, LA 70513
Tel (337) 365-8173 Founded/Ownrshp 1907
Sales 58.9MME EMP 205
SIC 2035 2099 Seasonings & sauces, except tomato & dry; Seasonings: dry mixes; Sauces: dry mixes; Seasonings & sauces, except tomato & dry; Seasonings: dry mixes; Sauces: dry mixes
Pr: Anthony A Simmons
Chf Mktg O: Jason West
Ex VP: Harold Osborn
VP: Lisa Bell
VP: Jan Carrol
VP: Stephen Romero
VP: Angie Schaubert
VP: Michael J Terrell
VP: Yiannis Tziamtzis
IT Man: Marybeth Farris
IT Man: Tony Simmons

MCIM
See MICHIGAN COMMERCIAL INSURANCE MUTUAL CORP

D-U-N-S 01-728-9000
MCINERNEY INC
NORTHLAND CHRYSLER-PLYMOUTH
14100 W 8 Mile Rd, Oak Park, MI 48237-3045
Tel (248) 398-8200 Founded/Ownrshp 1962
Sales 56.4MME EMP 200
SIC 5511 Automobiles, new & used; Automobiles, new & used
Pr: Martin J Mc Inerney
*Pr: Martin McInerney
*VP: James Mc Inerney
*VP: John J Mc Inerney
*VP: Robert Mc Inerney
VP: John McInerney
Off Mgr: Phillip Mitchell
Sls Mgr: Jack Mc Inerney
Sls Mgr: Jack McInerney

D-U-N-S 08-747-8137
MCINERNEYS WOODHAVEN CHRYSLER JEEP DODGE INC
23940 Allen Rd, Woodhaven, MI 48183-3374
Tel (734) 692-3700 Founded/Ownrshp 1977
Sales 21.2MME EMP 50
SIC 5511 Automobiles, new & used
Pr: Thomas M Mc Inerney Sr
Top Exec: Dan M Inerney
Sales Asso: Mike Queen
Board of Directors: James Mc Inerney

D-U-N-S 03-433-7683
MCINNIS BROTHERS CONSTRUCTION INC
119 Pearl St, Minden, LA 71055-3335
Tel (318) 377-6134 Founded/Ownrshp 1966
Sales 54.6MM EMP 130
SIC 1541 1542 Industrial buildings, new construction; Commercial & office building, new construction
Ch: George E McInnis
*Pr: Harry E McInnis Jr
Treas: Philip M Cinnis
Treas: Philip McInnis
*VP: Ben Baldwin
*VP: Richard Harris
*VP: M Philip McInnis
Genl Mgr: Howard Hines

MCINNIS HEALTH GROUP
See BOSTON HEALTH CARE FOR HOMELESS PROGRAM INC

D-U-N-S 00-223-3542
MCINTOSH BOX & PALLET CO INC (NY)
5864 Pyle Dr, East Syracuse, NY 13057-9459
Tel (315) 446-9350 Founded/Ownrshp 1961, 2001
Sales 24.8MM EMP 160
SIC 2441 2448

D-U-N-S 19-858-3056
MCINTOSH CORP
MCINTOSH MECHANICAL
8141 E 48th St, Tulsa, OK 74145-6906
Tel (918) 270-1414 Founded/Ownrshp 1957
Sales 36.1MME EMP 200
SIC 7623 1711 Air conditioning repair; Heating systems repair & maintenance
Ch Bd: Tom Owens
Pr: Daniel D Owens
Treas: John W Owens
Board of Directors: Daniel Owens, John Owens, Kathryn Owens, Tom Owens

D-U-N-S 10-001-4109
MCINTOSH COUNTY BOARD OF EDUCATION
200 Pine St Se, Darien, GA 31305-9756
Tel (912) 437-6645 Founded/Ownrshp 1930
Sales 19.7MME EMP 350
SIC 8211 Public elementary & secondary schools; School board; Public elementary & secondary schools; School board
*Ch Bd: Bonita Caldwell
*V Ch Bd: Dwight Jordan
*Prin: Holly Boone
*Prin: Joseph Mauldan

D-U-N-S 07-979-9084
MCINTOSH COUNTY SCHOOLS
200 Pine St Se, Darien, GA 31305-9756
Tel (912) 437-6645
Sales 4.8MME EMP 367E
SIC 8211 Public elementary & secondary schools
MIS Dir: Merwan Massa
Teacher Pr: Diane Richardson

D-U-N-S 05-739-0825
MCINTOSH ENERGY CO INC
MAC FOOD MART
1923 Bremer Rd, Fort Wayne, IN 46803-3002
Tel (260) 748-0346 Founded/Ownrshp 1953
Sales 25.0MME EMP 40
SIC 5171 5541 Petroleum bulk stations; Filling stations, gasoline; Petroleum bulk stations; Filling stations, gasoline
CEO: Russel McIntosh
*Pr: Ray McIntosh

D-U-N-S 00-222-6744 IMP
MCINTOSH LABORATORY INC
2 Chambers St, Binghamton, NY 13903-2699
Tel (607) 723-3512 Founded/Ownrshp 1947, 2012
Sales 20.4MME EMP 150E
SIC 3651

MCINTOSH MECHANICAL
See MCINTOSH CORP

D-U-N-S 17-584-5718
MCINTYRE ELWELL & STRAMMER GENERAL CONTRACTORS INC
1645 Barber Rd Ste E, Sarasota, FL 34240-7920
Tel (941) 377-6800 Founded/Ownrshp 1987
Sales 42.3MME EMP 87
SIC 1542 Commercial & office buildings, renovation & repair; Commercial & office buildings, renovation & repair
Pr: John A McIntyre
*Treas: Tina Earnest
*VP: Ryan McIntyre
*VP: Fred Strammer

MCINTYRE GROUP
See KENZIE AND CO LLC

D-U-N-S 01-614-0626
MCINTYRE MANAGEMENT CORP (PA)
MCDONALD'S
654 Front St, Hellertown, PA 18055-1770
Tel (610) 838-4995 Founded/Ownrshp 1979
Sales 12.9MME EMP 400
SIC 5812 Fast-food restaurant, chain; Fast-food restaurant, chain
Pr: Charles McIntyre

D-U-N-S 06-869-0406
MCIS INC
(Suby of MARSHFIELD CLINIC INC) ★
1701 N Fig Ave, Marshfield, WI 54449-1484
Tel (715) 221-8211 Founded/Ownrshp 2013
Sales 65.0MM EMP 45
SIC 7372 Application computer software; Application computer software

MCIT
See MINNESOTA COUNTIES INTERGOVERNMENTAL TRUST

MCIU
See MONTGOMERY COUNTY INTERMEDIATE UNIT

MCJUNKIN RED MAN CORPORATION
See MRC GLOBAL (US) INC

D-U-N-S 11-816-7956
MCK ENTERPRISES INC
COMPUTER MEDIA TECHNOLOGY
(Suby of CMT HOLDINGS INC) ★
590 Laurelwood Rd, Santa Clara, CA 95054-2420
Tel (408) 734-3339 Founded/Ownrshp 1992
Sales 43.3MME EMP 35
SIC 5045 Computers, peripherals & software
Pr: Kurt M Klein
CFO: Patrick Chris
VP: Chris Kloes
VP: Victor Villegas
VP Mktg: Angela Restani
Sales Asso: Michelle Baumann
Sales Asso: Kyle Schafer

D-U-N-S 07-498-2273
MCKAMISH INC
50 55th St, Pittsburgh, PA 15201-2311
Tel (412) 781-6262 Founded/Ownrshp 1975
Sales 122.0MME EMP 260
SIC 1711 Mechanical contractor; Mechanical contractor
Pr: David H McKamish
*Sec: Dennis R McKamish
VP: David Casciani
*VP: Jamie A Clemente
Mtls Mgr: Ed Idzakovich

D-U-N-S 02-559-7071
MCKAY AUTO PARTS INC
MCKAY NAPA
414 N Old Route 66, Litchfield, IL 62056-1053
Tel (217) 324-3969 Founded/Ownrshp 1965
Sales 50.9MME EMP 160
SIC 5531 8741 Automobile & truck equipment & parts; Management services; Automobile & truck equipment & parts; Automotive parts; Management services
Pr: James V McKay
*Pr: James Mc Kay
*Treas: Ed Hammann
*VP: Alan Haenel
Off Mgr: Peggy Snell

MCKAY NAPA
See MCKAY AUTO PARTS INC

D-U-N-S 01-972-8000
■ **MCKAY PRESS INC** (MI)
(Suby of CONSOLIDATED GRAPHICS INC) ★
7600 W Wackerly St, Midland, MI 48642-7405
Tel (989) 631-2360 Founded/Ownrshp 1994
Sales 30.4MME EMP 135
SIC 2759 Commercial printing; Commercial printing
Pr: Greg Ward
*Pr: Kevin Strand
*VP: Jim Nigro
Sfty Dirs: Mark Melvin
Snr Mgr: Scott McDonald

D-U-N-S 03-652-6827
MCKAY-DEE HOSPITAL CENTER
4401 Harrison Blvd, Ogden, UT 84403-3195
Tel (801) 387-2800 Founded/Ownrshp 2012
Sales 427.2MM EMP 117E
SIC 8011 Internal medicine practitioners
CFO: Doug Smith
Ofcr: Tom Horne
Exec: Tyler Ehlert
Dir Rx: Carol Hunter
QA Dir: Annette Poulsen
Sfty Mgr: Dave Lucas
Psych: Dennis Ahern
Psych: Bryan Bushman
Surgeon: Bob Moesinger
Ansthlgy: Robert Blocker
Doctor: Sergio Collado

D-U-N-S 60-715-6809
MCKEAN DEFENSE GROUP LLC
1 Crescent Dr Ste 400, Philadelphia, PA 19112-1015
Tel (215) 271-6108 Founded/Ownrshp 2006
Sales 135.8MME EMP 450E
SIC 8711 Engineering services; Engineering services
CEO: Joseph L Carlini
*Pr: Larry D Burrill
CFO: David Walls
Ofcr: Joseph Whipp
Sr VP: Don Lehner
VP: Jane Jennings
*Prin: Leonard F Destefano Jr
Prgrm Mgr: Bernie Disantis
Off Mgr: Kenneth Hawley
Snr Sftwr: Scott EBY
Snr Ntwrk: Zachary Andrus

D-U-N-S 36-062-5743
MCKECHNIE VEHICLE COMPONENTS USA INC
MVC
(*Suby of* MVC HOLDINGS LLC) ★
27087 Gratiot Ave Fl 2, Roseville, MI 48066-2947
Tel (586) 491-2600 *Founded/Ownrshp* 2009
Sales 47.4MM *EMP* 350
Accts Cenko Vendittelli Haynes Troy
SIC 3714 3498 3465 3471 3089 Motor vehicle wheels & parts; Fabricated pipe & fittings; Automotive stampings; Plating & polishing; Automotive parts, plastic; Motor vehicle wheels & parts; Fabricated pipe & fittings; Automotive stampings; Plating & polishing; Automotive parts, plastic
CEO: Mike Torakis
**Pr:* Linda Torakis
**CFO:* Steve Aretakis
CFO: Ron Schneider
**VP:* Mike Auten
**VP:* Tim Coots
Ql Cn Mgr: Kirby Dennis

D-U-N-S 14-469-4742
MCKEE AUTO CENTER INC
400 1st Ave, Perry, IA 50220-1921
Tel (515) 465-3564 *Founded/Ownrshp* 1995
Sales 22.0MM *EMP* 24
SIC 5511 Automobiles, new & used
Pr: Anthony McKee
VP: Debbie McKee

MCKEE ELECTRIC
See SURGENER ELECTRIC INC

D-U-N-S 00-333-2723 EXP
MCKEE FOODS CORP
10260 Mckee Rd, Collegedale, TN 37315
Tel (423) 238-7111 *Founded/Ownrshp* 1934
Sales 1.7MMME *EMP* 6,000
SIC 2051 2052 2099 2043 Cakes, bakery: except frozen; Cookies; Food preparations; Cereal breakfast foods; Cakes, bakery: except frozen; Cookies; Food preparations; Cereal breakfast foods
Pr: Mike Kee
**CFO:* Barry Patterson
VP: Tim Broughton
**VP:* Joe Davis
Dir Risk M: Micheline Parkey
Creative D: John Petticord
Genl Mgr: Eva Disbro
Dir IT: Danny McDowell
Dir IT: Chris McKee
IT Man: Charles Leeds
IT Man: Brian Nelson

D-U-N-S 13-666-2512
MCKEE OIL CO
2235 E Fort Union Blvd, Salt Lake City, UT 84121-3140
Tel (801) 943-9717 *Founded/Ownrshp* 2003
Sales 30.6MME *EMP* 183E
SIC 5541 Gasoline service stations
Pr: Robert H McKee

D-U-N-S 03-652-6122
MCKEE SHEPARD & GRIASKA MEDICAL ASSOCIATES
51 N 39th St Ste 1, Philadelphia, PA 19104-2640
Tel (215) 662-8978 *Founded/Ownrshp* 2001
Sales 429.9MM *EMP* 17
SIC 8011 General & family practice, physician/surgeon; General & family practice, physician/surgeon
Pr: Karen J Nichols MD

MCKEES ROCK FORGINGS DIVISION
See STANDARD FORGED PRODUCTS LLC

D-U-N-S 05-762-2227
MCKEESPORT AREA SCHOOL DISTRICT
3590 Oneil Blvd, McKeesport, PA 15132-1641
Tel (412) 664-3610 *Founded/Ownrshp* 1966
Sales 58.2MME *EMP* 1,257
SIC 8211 Public elementary school; Public junior high school; Public senior high school; Public elementary school; Public junior high school; Public senior high school
Pr: Wayne Washowich
VP: Angie Kilbert
VP: Kim Potts
IT Man: Don Williams
Pr Dir: Kristen Davis
Pr Dir: Kristen Giran
Teacher Pr: James Humanic
Psych: Beth Pierce
Psych: Jennifer Pursh
Psych: Laurel Soffa
Psych: David Stash

D-U-N-S 15-044-4966
MCKEEVER ENTERPRISES INC
PRICE CHOPPER
4216 S Hocker Dr, Independence, MO 64055-4754
Tel (816) 478-3095 *Founded/Ownrshp* 1985
Sales 121.2MME *EMP* 1,000
SIC 5411

MCKELL EXCAVATION
See R A MCKELL EXCAVATING INC

D-U-N-S 08-710-3354
MCKELLA 2-8-0 INC
MCKELLA 280
7025 Central Hwy, Pennsauken, NJ 08109-4312
Tel (856) 813-1153 *Founded/Ownrshp* 2008
Sales 30.0MME *EMP* 85
SIC 2752 2791 7336 Commercial printing, lithographic; Typesetting; Commercial art & graphic design
Pr: Joseph Lagrossa
CFO: Rose Balcabage
**VP:* Rose M Balcavage
IT Man: Ron Edder
IT Man: Adam Kirchhoff
IT Man: Kelli McGee
VP Prd: Jerry Jack
Plnt Mgr: Bill Coll

MCKELLA 280
See MCKELLA 2-8-0 INC

D-U-N-S 04-012-7102
MCKENDREE UNIVERSITY
701 College Rd, Lebanon, IL 62254-1291
Tel (618) 537-4481 *Founded/Ownrshp* 1828
Sales 46.6MM *EMP* 600
Accts Bkd Llp St Louis Mo
SIC 8221 College, except junior; College, except junior
Pr: James M Dennis
Pr: George Manning
Sr VP: Victoria Dowling
VP: Joni Bastain
VP: Joni Bastian
Ex Dir: Pamela Chambers
Off Admin: Julie Boucher
Dir IT: George Kriss
Pr Dir: Lisa Brandon
Mktg Mgr: Pamela Osley
Psych: Michelle Koester

D-U-N-S 07-208-8602
MCKENDREE VILLAGE INC
4343 Lebanon Pike Ofc, Hermitage, TN 37076-1256
Tel (615) 889-6990 *Founded/Ownrshp* 1986
Sales 638.0M *EMP* 395
Accts Lattimore Black Morgan & Cain
SIC 8361 Rest home, with health care incidental; Rest home, with health care incidental
**Ch Bd:* Bob Sullins
CFO: Nellie Cole
Genl Mgr: Franklin Pasos
Off Mgr: Alice Channing
Off Mgr: Kelly Human
Mktg Dir: Mary Wilson
Nrsg Dir: Susan Dulaney

D-U-N-S 36-143-8356
MCKENNA HEALTH CARE FOUND
600 N Union Ave, New Braunfels, TX 78130-4194
Tel (830) 606-2180 *Founded/Ownrshp* 2005
Sales 9.5MME *EMP* 900
SIC 8062 General medical & surgical hospitals; General medical & surgical hospitals
Owner: Tim Brierty
Mtls Dir: Ed Root

D-U-N-S 11-334-2740
MCKENNA LONG & ALDRIDGE LLP
1900 K St Nw Ste Ll100, Washington, DC 20006-1102
Tel (202) 496-7145 *Founded/Ownrshp* 1995
Sales NA *EMP* 1,100
SIC 8111 Administrative & government law; Environmental law; Labor & employment law; Criminal law

MCKENNA MEMORIAL HOSPITAL
See CHRISTUS SANTA ROSA HOSPITAL NEW BRAUNFELS

MCKENNA MIKE WNDWARD VLKSWAGEN
See FORD WINDWARD

D-U-N-S 02-106-3193
MCKENNA MOTOR CO INC
MC KENNA VW PORSCHE AUDI BMW
10900 Firestone Blvd, Norwalk, CA 90650-2241
Tel (562) 868-3233 *Founded/Ownrshp* 1990
Sales 51.4MME *EMP* 100E
SIC 5511 Automobiles, new & used; Automobiles, new & used
Pr: Daniel J McKenna III
Genl Mgr: Steve Keefe
Genl Mgr: Shawn Lawler

D-U-N-S 10-311-1043
MCKENNA MOTORS HUNTINGTON BEACH INC
VOLKSWAGEN/ISUZU
18711 Beach Blvd, Huntington Beach, CA 92648-2005
Tel (714) 842-2000 *Founded/Ownrshp* 1983
Sales 25.9MME *EMP* 64
SIC 5511 Automobiles, new & used; Automobiles, new & used
CEO: Daniel McKenna
**VP:* Neil Okun
**Genl Mgr:* Greg Conner
**Genl Mgr:* Joe Cram
Genl Mgr: Tam Nguyen
Sls Mgr: Romy Bhardwaj
Sls Mgr: Primo Garcia
Sls Mgr: Dean Kidder

MCKENNEY CHEVROLET CATALOG BUI
See MCKENNEY CHEVROLET INC

D-U-N-S 02-443-1926
MCKENNEY CHEVROLET INC (NC)
MCKENNEY CHEVROLET CATALOG BUI
831 S Main St, Lowell, NC 28098-1954
Tel (704) 823-1040 *Founded/Ownrshp* 1981
Sales 50.6MM *EMP* 62
SIC 5511 Automobiles, new & used; Automobiles, new & used
Pr: H Ray Mc Kenney
Sls Mgr: David Polk
Sales Asso: Jim Scoggins
Sales Asso: Bill Starke

D-U-N-S 00-389-5687
MCKENNEYS INC (GA)
(*Suby of* MCKENNEY'S MANAGEMENT CORPORATION)
1056 Moreland Indus Blvd, Atlanta, GA 30316-3296
Tel (404) 622-5000 *Founded/Ownrshp* 1943
Sales 154.4MME *EMP* 700
SIC 1711 8711

D-U-N-S 00-386-9062
MCKENZIE ELECTRIC COOPERATIVE INC (ND)
MEC
908 4th Ave Ne, Watford City, ND 58854-7608
Tel (701) 842-2311 *Founded/Ownrshp* 1947
Sales 90.6MM *EMP* 42
SIC 4911 Distribution, electric power; Distribution, electric power
CEO: John Skurupey
Opers Mgr: Jim Hansen
Board of Directors: Glen Aamodt, Dennis Johnson, Earl Pelton, Ray Tescher, Travis Thompson

MCKENZIE MARKET
See MCKENZIE OIL CO INC

D-U-N-S 06-366-4296 IMP
MCKENZIE OIL CO INC
MCKENZIE MARKET
222 N Eufaula Ave, Eufaula, AL 36027-1516
Tel (334) 687-3531 *Founded/Ownrshp* 1973
Sales 53.9MME *EMP* 100
SIC 5172 6512 Gasoline; Nonresidential building operators; Gasoline; Nonresidential building operators
Pr: Dan B McKenzie
**VP:* Martha McKenzie

MCKENZIE ORTHOPEDIC GROUP
See SLOCUM ORTHOPEDIC

MCKENZIE PETROLEUM
See JOHN R MCKENZIE JOBBER INC

D-U-N-S 08-685-9741 IMP/EXP
MCKENZIE SPORTS PRODUCTS LLC
MC KENZIE TAXIDERMY SUPPLY
1910 Saint Luke Church Rd, Salisbury, NC 28146-7956
Tel (704) 279-7985 *Founded/Ownrshp* 2012
Sales 84.9MME *EMP* 540
SIC 3949 3423 Targets, archery & rifle shooting; Taxidermist tools & equipment; Targets, archery & rifle shooting; Taxidermist tools & equipment
IT Man: Brad Corl
S&M/VP: Tom Powell

D-U-N-S 00-408-2145
MCKENZIE TANK LINES INC (FL)
1966 Commonwealth Ln, Tallahassee, FL 32303-3196
Tel (850) 576-1221 *Founded/Ownrshp* 1949
Sales 181.0MME *EMP* 819
SIC 4213 3715 3443 Liquid petroleum transport, non-local; Truck trailers; Fabricated plate work (boiler shop); Liquid petroleum transport, non-local; Truck trailers; Fabricated plate work (boiler shop)
Pr: James C Shaeffer
Ch Bd: Joseph Audie
CFO: Robert Landrum
Sec: Robert G Landrum Jr
VP: Dana F Dudley
VP: Dana J Dudley
VP: Jack Faulkner
VP: John D Jackson
Dir Risk M: Josh Shelton
Board of Directors: S M Dyson, G M Landrum

D-U-N-S 62-798-7407
■ **MCKENZIE-WILLAMETTE MEDICAL SERVICES**
(*Suby of* COMMUNITY HEALTH SYSTEMS INC) ★
1460 G St, Springfield, OR 97477-4112
Tel (541) 726-4400 *Founded/Ownrshp* 1984
Sales 151.7MME *EMP* 2,100
SIC 8062 General medical & surgical hospitals; General medical & surgical hospitals
CEO: Chad Campbell
**Pr:* Roy Orr
**CFO:* Steve Dougherty
**CFO:* Jason McClosan
Dir Lab: Robert Weaver
Off Mgr: Terry Higgley
Nurse Mgr: Mary Sorenson
CTO: Amy Lathrop
Ansthlgy: Barbara Coda
Anesthlgy: Daniel Hagengruber
Snr Mgr: Cynthia Harlowe

MCKERNAN PACKG CLEARING HSE
See E J MCKERNAN CO

D-U-N-S 00-833-0057
MCKESS HOLDINGS INC
5005 3rd Ave S, Seattle, WA 98134-2423
Tel (206) 832-8043 *Founded/Ownrshp* 2000
Sales 30.6MME *EMP* 440E
SIC 8744 Facilities support services; Facilities support services
CEO: Dean Allen
**Pr:* Ash Awad
COO: Karen Little
**Sec:* J Teplicky
VP: Mark Deweirdt
VP: Bob Frey
VP: Mike Grizzle
Prgrm Mgr: Michael Dean
Prgrm Mgr: Spencer Huppert
Prgrm Mgr: Jesse Sycuro
Admn Mgr: Leslie Miller
Board of Directors: Doug Moore

MCKESSON AUTOMATION HEALTHCARE
See AESYNT INC

D-U-N-S 17-766-7227 IMP/EXP
▲ **MCKESSON CORP**
1 Post St Fl 18, San Francisco, CA 94104-5284
Tel (415) 983-8300 *Founded/Ownrshp* 1833
Sales 179.0MMM *EMP* 70,400
Accts Deloitte & Touche Llp San Fra
Tkr Sym MCK *Exch* NYS
SIC 5122 5047 5199 7372 Drugs, proprietaries & sundries; Pharmaceuticals; Proprietary (patent) medicines; Druggists' sundries; Medical equipment & supplies; First aid supplies; General merchandise, non-durable; Prepackaged software; Drugs, proprietaries & sundries; Pharmaceuticals; Proprietary (patent) medicines; Druggists' sundries; Medical equipment & supplies; First aid supplies; General merchandise, non-durable; Prepackaged software
Ch Bd: John H Hammergren
Pr: Patrick Blake
Pr: John Figueroa
CFO: James A Beer
Ofcr: Kenneth Tarkoff
Ex VP: Jorge L Figueredo
Ex VP: Bansi Nagji
Ex VP: Lori A Schechter
VP: Ross Biddle
VP: James Carino
VP: Mark Cox
VP: Larry Kurtz
VP: Nigel A Rees
Assoc Dir: Michelle Rush
Comm Man: Maxine Milazzo
Board of Directors: Andy D Bryant, Wayne A Budd, N Anthony Coles, Alton F Irby III, M Christine Jacobs, Donald R Knauss, Marie L Knowles, David M Lawrence, Edward A Mueller

D-U-N-S 13-389-0736 IMP
■ **MCKESSON INFORMATION SOLUTIONS LLC**
MCKESSON TECH SOLUTIONS GROUP
(*Suby of* MCKESSON CORP) ★
5995 Windward Pkwy, Alpharetta, GA 30005-4184
Tel (404) 338-6000 *Founded/Ownrshp* 2003
Sales 158.1MME *EMP* 3,000
SIC 7373 Systems software development services; Systems software development services

D-U-N-S 82-460-5141
■ **MCKESSON MEDICAL-SURGICAL HOLDINGS INC**
(*Suby of* MCKESSON MEDICAL-SURGICAL INC) ★
9954 Mayland Dr Ste 4000, Henrico, VA 23233-1484
Tel (804) 264-7500 *Founded/Ownrshp* 1997
Sales 219.5MME *EMP* 3,000
SIC 5047 Medical & hospital equipment; Medical equipment & supplies; Medical laboratory equipment; Surgical equipment & supplies; Medical & hospital equipment; Medical equipment & supplies; Medical laboratory equipment; Surgical equipment & supplies
Pr: Emad Rizk
**Pr:* Paul Julian
**CFO:* Rene Gobeille
**Sr VP:* Carolyn J Wukitch
**VP:* Elaine Lemke
**VP:* John Leonard

D-U-N-S 02-390-4428 EXP
■ **MCKESSON MEDICAL-SURGICAL INC** (VA)
(*Suby of* MCKESSON CORP) ★
9954 Mayland Dr Ste 4000, Richmond, VA 23233-1484
Tel (804) 264-7500 *Founded/Ownrshp* 1980, 2010
Sales 1.9MMME *EMP* 3,000
SIC 5047 Medical & hospital equipment; Medical equipment & supplies; Medical laboratory equipment; Surgical equipment & supplies; Medical & hospital equipment; Medical equipment & supplies; Medical laboratory equipment; Surgical equipment & supplies
Pr: McComb Stanton
**Pr:* Brian S Tyler
**CFO:* James Beer
CFO: Jeffery Davis
Treas: Larry Burk
**Treas:* Nicholas A Loiacono
**Ex VP:* Patrick J Blake
**Ex VP:* John H Hammergren
Ex VP: Paul Julian
**Sr VP:* Jerry E Neal
**VP:* Willie C Bogan
VP: Joan Eliasek
VP: Pat McClenaghan
VP: Pat McClennagen
VP: Doug Shaver

D-U-N-S 02-047-7410
■ **MCKESSON MEDICAL-SURGICAL MEDIMART INC** (MN)
(*Suby of* MCKESSON CORP) ★
8121 10th Ave N, Minneapolis, MN 55427-4401
Tel (763) 595-6000 *Founded/Ownrshp* 1959, 1998
Sales 101.2MME *EMP* 750
SIC 5047 5999

D-U-N-S 10-227-2143
■ **MCKESSON MEDICAL-SURGICAL MINNESOTA SUPPLY INC**
(*Suby of* MCKESSON CORP) ★
8121 10th Ave N, Minneapolis, MN 55427-4401
Tel (763) 595-6000 *Founded/Ownrshp* 1975
Sales 46.2MME *EMP* 300
SIC 5047 Medical equipment & supplies; Medical equipment & supplies
Pr: Gary Keeler
Sr VP: John McDonough
VP: Joan Eliasek
VP: John H Hammergren
VP: Paul C Julian

MCKESSON MEDMANAGEMENT
See CPS MEDMANAGEMENT LLC

D-U-N-S 83-050-0737
■ **MCKESSON PHARMACY SYSTEMS LLC**
(*Suby of* MCKESSON CORP) ★
30881 Schoolcraft Rd, Livonia, MI 48150-2010
Tel (734) 421-0260 *Founded/Ownrshp* 2008
Sales 96.7MME *EMP* 650
SIC 7372 5122 Prepackaged software; Pharmaceuticals; Prepackaged software; Pharmaceuticals
Pr: Nathan Mott
Pr: Brian Grobbel

D-U-N-S 83-073-2793
■ **MCKESSON PLASMA AND BIOLOGICS LLC**
(*Suby of* MCKESSON CORP) ★
401 Mason Rd, La Vergne, TN 37086-3243
Tel (615) 287-5257 *Founded/Ownrshp* 2008
Sales 27.1MME *EMP* 25
SIC 5122 Drugs, proprietaries & sundries
VP: Travis Poe
Dir Bus: Adam Hart

D-U-N-S 87-757-7775
■ **MCKESSON SPECIALTY ARIZONA INC**
(*Suby of* MCKESSON CORP) ★
4343 N Scottsdale Rd # 370, Scottsdale, AZ 85251-3343
Tel (480) 663-4000 *Founded/Ownrshp* 1994
Sales 115.7MME *EMP* 700E
SIC 5122 Druggists' sundries; Druggists' sundries
Pr: Brian Tyler
**CFO:* Bill O Neill

VP: Jason Williams
**VP:* Peggy Yelinek
Off Mgr: Jacki Baldwin
Mktg Dir: Greg Zych
Snr PM: Vinayak Bhat

D-U-N-S 60-319-3363
■ MCKESSON SPECIALTY DISTRIBUTION LLC
(*Suby of* MCKESSON CORP) ★
4100 Quest Way, Memphis, TN 38115-5022
Tel (415) 983-8300 *Founded/Ownrshp* 2004
Sales 22.0MM^E *EMP* 50
SIC 5122 5047 7372 Drugs, proprietaries & sundries; Medical & hospital equipment; Prepackaged software
Pr: Mark Walchirk
CFO: Jennifer Smith Webster
VP: Ben Vanmannen
VP: Stephanie Waddington
Assoc Dir: Carrie Potter

D-U-N-S 07-916-6586
■ MCKESSON SPECIALTY HEALTH INNOVATIVE PRACTICE SERVICES LLC
(*Suby of* MCKESSON CORP) ★
10101 Woodloch Forest Dr, The Woodlands, TX 77380-1975
Tel (281) 863-1000 *Founded/Ownrshp* 2001
Sales 13.7MM^E *EMP* 650
SIC 8082 Home health care services
VP: Gerardo Castaneda
Dir Bus: David Adler
Off Mgr: Rhonda Henschel
Snr Sftwr: Lucy Hu
IT Man: Bronwen Lanning
Info Man: John Wolfe
Mktg Dir: Sandra Simpson
Mktg Mgr: Amy Robertson
Sls Mgr: John Archie
Counsel: Joshua Derienzis

MCKESSON TECH SOLUTIONS GROUP
See MCKESSON INFORMATION SOLUTIONS LLC

D-U-N-S 15-290-5089
■ MCKESSON TECHNOLOGIES INC
MEDAPHIS PHYSICIAN
(*Suby of* MCKESSON CORP) ★
11475 Great Oaks Way # 400, Alpharetta, GA 30022-2440
Tel (770) 237-4300 *Founded/Ownrshp* 2007
Sales 257.3MM^E *EMP* 5,100
SIC 7374 8741 8721 7322 7373 Computer processing services; Business management; Billing & bookkeeping service; Collection agency, except real estate; Systems integration services; Systems software development services; Computer processing services; Business management; Billing & bookkeeping service; Collection agency, except real estate; Systems integration services; Systems software development services
COO: Chris E Perkins
CFO: Stephen Scheppmann
Ex VP: Asif Ahmad
**Sr VP:* Paul J Quiner
VP: Rick Flynt
VP: Anne Law
CIO: Randall Spratt
CIO: Michael Wood
Genl Couns: Mike Missailidis

D-U-N-S 04-583-2920
MCKIBBON BROTHERS INC (GA)
HOLIDAY INN
402 Washington St Se, Gainesville, GA 30501-3619
Tel (770) 534-3381 *Founded/Ownrshp* 1950
Sales 40.7MM^E *EMP* 700
SIC 7011 8741 5812 Hotels & motels; Hotel or motel management; Restaurant, family: independent; Hotels & motels; Hotel or motel management; Restaurant, family: independent
CEO: John B Mc Kibbon Jr
**Ch Bd:* Steve P Mc Kibbon Sr
**Pr:* Van Herring
CFO: David Hughs
Treas: Dennis Jackson

D-U-N-S 14-195-1256
MCKIBBON HOTEL MANAGEMENT INC
MARRIOTT
(*Suby of* HOLIDAY INN) ★
402 Washington St Se, Gainesville, GA 30501-3619
Tel (770) 534-3381 *Founded/Ownrshp* 1996
Sales 21.7MM^E *EMP* 374
SIC 7011 Hotels & motels; Hotels & motels
CEO: John B McKibbon III
**CFO:* David J Hughs
**VP:* Bruce Baerwalde
**VP:* Randy Hassen

D-U-N-S 02-436-1313
MCKIE FORD LINCOLN INC (SD)
ABRA AUTOBODY & GLASS
7 E Omaha St, Rapid City, SD 57701-2933
Tel (605) 348-1400 *Founded/Ownrshp* 1952
Sales 54.8MM^E *EMP* 134
SIC 5511 Automobiles, new & used; Automobiles, new & used
CEO: Steve Kalkman
**VP:* Mark McKie
Brnch Mgr: Ken Shoun
Sales Exec: Troy Claymore
Sls Mgr: Adam Ray
Sales Asso: Thomas Anderson
Sales Asso: Chris Erickson
Sales Asso: Tim Fischer
Sales Asso: John Fox
Sales Asso: Chris Jones
Sales Asso: Mark Kampfe

D-U-N-S 09-573-1329 IMP
MCKILLICAN AMERICAN INC
(*Suby of* 120947 WASHINGTON INC)
3808 N Sullivan Rd 33a, Spokane Valley, WA 99216-1608
Tel (780) 453-3841 *Founded/Ownrshp* 1979
Sales 33.8MM^E *EMP* 95
SIC 5072 5198 5031 Hardware; Hand tools; Power tools & accessories; Builders' hardware; Paint brushes, rollers, sprayers; Building materials, exterior; Hardware; Hand tools; Power tools & accessories; Builders' hardware; Paint brushes, rollers, sprayers; Building materials, exterior
CEO: Gary E McKillican
**Pr:* Jamie Barnes
**VP:* Kevin Slabaugh
**Prin:* Chris McKillican
**Prin:* Shauna Murphy
Brnch Mgr: Bryan Lawley
IT Man: Rick Worlton
Sales Asso: Daniel Sexton

D-U-N-S 04-693-9948
MCKIM & CREED PA
1730 Varsity Dr Ste 500, Raleigh, NC 27606-2689
Tel (919) 233-8091 *Founded/Ownrshp* 1978
Sales 84.7MM^E *EMP* 284
SIC 8711 8713

D-U-N-S 96-370-1573
MCKING CONSULTING CORP
2810 Old Lee Hwy Ste 300, Fairfax, VA 22031-4376
Tel (703) 204-2385 *Founded/Ownrshp* 2000
Sales 19.9MM^E *EMP* 350^E
SIC 8748 Business consulting; Business consulting
Pr: Duane McCliggott
**CFO:* Robert B Bennett
**VP:* John McCliggott
VP: Mark Scally

MCKINGHT CARE CENTER
See PRESBYTERIAN HOMES OF ARDEN HILLS INC

D-U-N-S 07-276-1570
MCKINLEY ASSOCIATES INC (MI)
320 N Main St Ste 200, Ann Arbor, MI 48104-1100
Tel (734) 769-8520 *Founded/Ownrshp* 1968, 1972
Sales 51.0MM^E *EMP* 600
SIC 6531 Real estate managers; Cooperative apartment manager; Real estate brokers & agents; Real estate managers; Cooperative apartment manager; Real estate brokers & agents
Pr: Albert Berriz
**Ch Bd:* Paul Diamond
**COO:* Royal E Caswell III
**Treas:* D Keith Hayward
**Sr VP:* Matt Mason
**VP:* Cheryl Rabbitt

D-U-N-S 07-192-1340
MCKINLEY CHILDRENS CENTER INC
762 Cypress St, San Dimas, CA 91773-3505
Tel (909) 599-1227 *Founded/Ownrshp* 1890
Sales 13.6MM^E *EMP* 300
Accts Harrington Group Cpas Llp P
SIC 8361 8211 Boys' Towns; Private elementary & secondary schools; Boys' Towns; Private elementary & secondary schools
CEO: Anil Vadatary
CFO: Mike Fraser
**CFO:* Michael Frazer
Dir: Rhonda Beltran
Dir IT: Mike Sturdivan
IT Man: Neil Barton

D-U-N-S 00-982-5480 IMP
MCKINLEY EQUIPMENT CORP
17611 Armstrong Ave, Irvine, CA 92614-5760
Tel (949) 271-2460 *Founded/Ownrshp* 1948
Sales 37.4MM^E *EMP* 67
SIC 5084 Materials handling machinery; Materials handling machinery
Pr: W Michael Mc Kinley
**VP:* William White Mc Kinley
VP: William W Mc Kinley
Genl Mgr: Mark McKinley
IT Man: Lennette Hollister
VP Sls: Dave Harlan

D-U-N-S 11-747-9204
MCKINLEY INC
(*Suby of* MCKINLEY ASSOCIATES INC) ★
320 N Main St Ste 200, Ann Arbor, MI 48104-1127
Tel (734) 769-8520 *Founded/Ownrshp* 1968
Sales 32.5MM^E *EMP* 200
SIC 6531 Rental agent, real estate; Rental agent, real estate
CEO: Albert M Berriz
Pr: Gregory Rose
CFO: Robert J Gluck
Treas: Jeff Clinchman
Treas: Jim Willet
Ofcr: Royal E Caswell III
Ofcr: D Keith Hayward
VP: Cheryl Rabbitt

D-U-N-S 60-714-7105
MCKINLEY INC
MCKINLEY PROPERTIES
320 N Main St Ste 200, Ann Arbor, MI 48104-1127
Tel (734) 769-8520 *Founded/Ownrshp* 1970
Sales 58.4MM^E *EMP* 1,600^E
SIC 6513 Apartment building operators
CEO: Albert Berriz
**COO:* Royal E Caswell III
COO: Royal Caswell
**Treas:* Jim Willet
VP: Garrett Hain
**VP:* Cheryl Rabbitt
VP: Mary Williams
VP Admn: Thelma Betterly
Dist Mgr: Barbara Kirk
Genl Mgr: T J Jenkins
IT Man: Chris Daigneault

MCKINLEY PROPERTIES
See MCKINLEY INC

MCKINLEY RECYCLING
See BIO PAPPEL INTERNATIONAL INC

MCKINNEY
See BLACKWELL STREET PARTNERS LLC

D-U-N-S 17-413-0906
MCKINNEY AUTOMOTIVE CO LIMITED PARTNERSHIP
HONDA CARS OF MC KINNEY
601 S Cent Expy, Mc Kinney, TX 75070
Tel (972) 529-9600 *Founded/Ownrshp* 1993
Sales 40.5MM^E *EMP* 115
SIC 5511 Automobiles, new & used; Vans, new & used; Trucks, tractors & trailers: new & used; Automobiles, new & used; Trucks, tractors & trailers: new & used; Vans, new & used
Pt: Hag Automotive Investment
Pr: J R Hendrick III
Genl Mgr: Keith Abney

D-U-N-S 02-611-3600
MCKINNEY DODGE INC
CHRYSLER JEEP DDGE CY MCKINNEY
700 S Central Expy, McKinney, TX 75070-3834
Tel (972) 569-9650 *Founded/Ownrshp* 2013
Sales 88.9MM *EMP* 99
SIC 5511 Automobiles, new & used; Automobiles, new & used
Pr: Gus Rodriguez
Sec: Johnann McCain
Trfc Dir: Rick Hodges

D-U-N-S 00-793-5125 IMP
MCKINNEY DRILLING CO LLC
(*Suby of* KELLER FOUNDATION) ★
7550 Teague Rd Ste 300, Hanover, MD 21076-1807
Tel (410) 874-1235 *Founded/Ownrshp* 2003
Sales 81.3MM^E *EMP* 450
SIC 1794 5082 Excavation & grading, building construction; Excavating machinery & equipment; Excavation & grading, building construction; Excavating machinery & equipment
Pr: Bill Maher
**CFO:* James Eikenberg
CFO: Philip Tannery
VP: Neal Howard
VP: Richard Rogers
Exec: Nicole Baldwin
Dist Mgr: Austin Pruitt

MCKINNEY HEALTHCARE ASSOC
See NORTH TEXAS DIVISION INC

D-U-N-S 07-137-7600
MCKINNEY INDEPENDENT SCHOOL DISTRICT
MCKINNEY ISD
1 Duvall St, McKinney, TX 75069-3210
Tel (469) 302-4000 *Founded/Ownrshp* 1840
Sales 280.4MM *EMP* 1,130
Accts Evans Pingleton And Howard P
SIC 8211 Public elementary & secondary schools; Public elementary & secondary schools
Ofcr: Joseph Ayers
VP: Lynn Sperry
Ex Dir: Richard Ferman
CIO: David Spann
Pr Dir: Bobbi Hanna
Pr Dir: David Span
Schl Brd P: Aimee Dangel
Psych: Janet Nelson

MCKINNEY ISD
See MCKINNEY INDEPENDENT SCHOOL DISTRICT

D-U-N-S 10-909-8095 IMP
MCKINNIS ROOFING AND SHEET METAL INC
164 S 1st St, Blair, NE 68008-2540
Tel (402) 426-2644 *Founded/Ownrshp* 1992
Sales 27.9MM *EMP* 64
SIC 1761 Roofing contractor; Sheet metalwork
Pr: David C McKinnis
**VP:* Dave Scott
Genl Mgr: Jamie Smith

MCKINNON BROADCASTING
See SAN DIEGOS FIFTY ONE INC

D-U-N-S 03-204-4794
MCKINNON BROADCASTING CO
KUSI TV CHANNEL 51
(*Suby of* MCKINNON BROADCASTING) ★
4575 Viewridge Ave, San Diego, CA 92123-1623
Tel (858) 571-5151 *Founded/Ownrshp* 1990
Sales 43.7MM^E *EMP* 150
SIC 4833 Television broadcasting stations; Television broadcasting stations
CEO: Michael D McKinnon
CFO: Steve Sadler
IT Man: Joejay Santos
Opers Mgr: Vince Douglas
Art Dir: Jared Klein

D-U-N-S 83-737-4941
MCKINNON PUBLISHING CO
(*Suby of* KUSI TV CHANNEL 51) ★
4575 Viewridge Ave, San Diego, CA 92123-1623
Tel (858) 571-5151 *Founded/Ownrshp* 1993
Sales 14.0MM^E *EMP* 600
SIC 4833 Television broadcasting stations; Television broadcasting stations
Pr: Michael McKinnon

D-U-N-S 00-167-3920 IMP
MCKINSEY & CO INC (NY)
55 E 52nd St Fl 21, New York, NY 10055-0028
Tel (212) 446-7000 *Founded/Ownrshp* 1926
Sales 3.2MMM^E *EMP* 17,054
SIC 8742

D-U-N-S 05-549-6004 IMP
MCKINSTRY CO LLC
5005 3rd Ave S, Seattle, WA 98134-2423
Tel (206) 762-3311 *Founded/Ownrshp* 1960
Sales 603.7MM^E *EMP* 1,300
SIC 1711 1623 3446 3444 Plumbing contractors; Ventilation & duct work contractor; Heating & air conditioning contractors; Pipeline construction; Architectural metalwork; Sheet metalwork; Plumbing contractors; Ventilation & duct work contractor; Heating & air conditioning contractors; Pipeline construction; Architectural metalwork; Sheet metalwork
CEO: Dean Allen
COO: Mike Moriarty
CFO: Jim Chamberlin
Ex VP: Paul Thibodaux
Prgrm Mgr: Glenn Bolt
Prgrm Mgr: Sean Currie
Prgrm Mgr: James Miller
CTO: Chris Purcell
Dir IT: Darren Borden
IT Man: Terry Ashley
IT Man: Chrisa Merwina

D-U-N-S 07-874-6529
MCKINSTRY ESSENTION LLC
5005 3rd Ave S, Seattle, WA 98134-2423
Tel (206) 762-3311 *Founded/Ownrshp* 2012
Sales 35.0MM^E *EMP* 530^E
SIC 8744 Facilities support services

D-U-N-S 79-323-8668
MCKISSACK & MCKISSACK OF WASHINGTON INC
901 K St Nw Fl 6th, Washington, DC 20001-6444
Tel (202) 347-1446 *Founded/Ownrshp* 1990
Sales 23.0MM *EMP* 138
Accts Aronson Llc Rockville Maryl
SIC 8741 8712 Management services; Architectural services; Management services; Architectural services
Ch Bd: Deryl McKissack
COO: Cheryl McKissack
**COO:* Chuck Roberts
Sr VP: Derek Lynch
VP: Sam Condit
VP: Ronald Kessler
VP: Kathleen Langan
VP Admn: Joseph V Bowen Jr
Opers Mgr: Mark Babbitt
Mktg Dir: Jean Gerrity
Mktg Dir: Beth Ring

D-U-N-S 05-349-3156
MCKISSACK GROUP INC
1001 Ave Of The Rm 2000, New York, NY 10018
Tel (212) 349-6500 *Founded/Ownrshp* 1991
Sales 28.9MM^E *EMP* 110
SIC 8741 Construction management
Ch Bd: Cheryl Mc Kissack
Pr: Dennis Roberts
CFO: Michael Tolliver
VP: Joseph Devito
VP: Stan Petrow
Exec: John McKenney
Snr Mgr: Aissatou Bey-Grecia

D-U-N-S 01-498-6731
MCKNIGHT DEVELOPMENT CORP
NORTH LANES
310 Grant St Ste 2500, Pittsburgh, PA 15219-2303
Tel (412) 623-8200 *Founded/Ownrshp* 1959
Sales 19.5MM^E *EMP* 400
SIC 7933 5812 Ten pin center; Fast-food restaurant, chain; Ten pin center; Fast-food restaurant, chain
Pr: Jim Rudoff
**Pr:* Bill Rudolff
Sls Dir: Bill Rudolph

MCL CONSTRUCTION
See MEYERS-CARLISLE-LEAPLEY CONSTRUCTION CO INC

D-U-N-S 01-642-5522
MCL INC
M C L CAFETERIAS
2730 E 62nd St, Indianapolis, IN 46220-2958
Tel (317) 257-5425 *Founded/Ownrshp* 1985
Sales 53.6MM^E *EMP* 1,200
SIC 5812 Cafeteria; Cafeteria
Pr: Craig Mc Gaughey
**COO:* Jesse Feil
**Treas:* Tony Hamlin
Mktg Mgr: Jennifer Atteberry

MCLA
See MASSACHUSETTS COLLEGE OF LIBERAL ARTS

D-U-N-S 06-113-7303
MCLAIN PLUMBING & ELECTRICAL SERVICE INC
107 Magnolia St, Philadelphia, MS 39350-3319
Tel (601) 656-6333 *Founded/Ownrshp* 1956
Sales 27.3MM^E *EMP* 140
SIC 1711 Plumbing contractors; Warm air heating & air conditioning contractor; Plumbing contractors; Warm air heating & air conditioning contractor
CEO: John F McLain
**Pr:* Kent McLain
**VP:* Scott McLain
**Genl Mgr:* Philip McLain

D-U-N-S 00-433-0692 IMP/EXP
MCLANAHAN CORP
200 Wall St, Hollidaysburg, PA 16648-1637
Tel (814) 695-9807 *Founded/Ownrshp* 1835
Sales 119.5MM^E *EMP* 326
SIC 3532 3321 3599 3523 Crushers, stationary; Washers, aggregate & sand; Feeders, ore & aggregate; Screeners, stationary; Gray iron castings; Machine shop, jobbing & repair; Farm machinery & equipment; Crushers, stationary; Washers, aggregate & sand; Feeders, ore & aggregate; Screeners, stationary; Gray iron castings; Machine shop, jobbing & repair; Farm machinery & equipment
CEO: Sean McLanahan
**Pr:* George Sidney
CFO: Jay Nartatez
**Ch:* Michael McLanahan
**Treas:* Astride S Mc Lanahan
VP: James Carrieri
Div Mgr: Kirk Sawall
Genl Mgr: John Best
Genl Mgr: Dan Ferguson
Off Mgr: Timothy Knepp
Off Mgr: Lexie McGaughy

D-U-N-S 00-983-0555 IMP/EXP
■ MCLANE CO INC
(*Suby of* BERKSHIRE HATHAWAY INC) ★
4747 Mclane Pkwy, Temple, TX 76504-4854
Tel (254) 771-7500 *Founded/Ownrshp* 2003
Sales 45.8MMM *EMP* 20,128
SIC 5141 5149 5311 5113 Groceries, general line; Specialty food items; Health foods; Department stores, discount; Towels, paper; Groceries, general line; Specialty food items; Health foods; Department stores, discount; Towels, paper
Pr: William G Rosier
**Pr:* Penny Echelberger
**Pr:* Mike Youngblood
**Pr:* Tom Zatina
**Sr VP:* Stuart Clark
**Sr VP:* James L Kent
Sr VP: Tom Sicola
VP: Ruel Athey
VP: Julie Burns
VP: Hampton Inn
**VP:* Kevin J Koch
**VP:* Len Mewhinney
**VP:* Janann Williams
Dir Bus: Mike McMahan

D-U-N-S 12-034-8714
■ MCLANE CO INC
(*Suby of* MCLANE CO INC) ★
1111 5th St W, Northfield, MN 55057-1602
Tel (507) 664-3000 *Founded/Ownrshp* 2002
Sales 185.8MM^E^ *EMP* 435
SIC 5141 Groceries, general line; Groceries, general line
CEO: William G Rosier
**Pr:* Mike Youngblood
**Treas:* Kevin Koch
**Sr VP:* Jim Kent
VP: Jerry Kropman
Snr Mgr: Joleen Thompson

D-U-N-S 19-002-4567
MCLANE FOOD SERVICES INC
1906 Grandview Pkwy, Sturtevant, WI 53177-1272
Tel (262) 504-1600 *Founded/Ownrshp* 2000
Sales 21.4MM^E^ *EMP* 44^E^
SIC 5141 Food brokers
Snr Mgr: Robert May

D-U-N-S 19-868-1582
■ MCLANE FOODSERVICE INC
(*Suby of* MCLANE CO INC) ★
2085 Midway Rd, Carrollton, TX 75006-5063
Tel (972) 364-2000 *Founded/Ownrshp* 2000
Sales 6.4MMM *EMP* 3,618
SIC 8742 5141 5311 5113 Restaurant & food services consultants; Groceries, general line; Department stores; Industrial & personal service paper; Restaurant & food services consultants; Groceries, general line; Department stores; Industrial & personal service paper
CEO: Tom Zatina
Pr: Max Wheeler
**Pr:* Mike Youngblood
**CFO:* Kevin Koch
**Ex VP:* Jim Kent
VP: Gary Bittner
VP: William Larkin
VP: Mike Shirey
VP: Syndee Stiles
Prgrm Mgr: Brandon Hindman
Prgrm Mgr: Resae Robinett
Board of Directors: Russ Craddock, Charlie Gallagher, Lyn Harris, Jeff Hayes, Caroline Mann, Scott Mischnick, Celeste Walls

D-U-N-S 08-340-2081
MCLANE GRAF RAULERSON & MIDDLETON PROFESSIONAL ASSOCIATION
900 Elm St Ste 100, Manchester, NH 03101-2029
Tel (603) 625-6464 *Founded/Ownrshp* 1920
Sales 29.3MM^E^ *EMP* 200
SIC 8111 General practice law office; General practice law office
Pr: Jack Middleton
**Treas:* Charles Degrandpre
CIO: David Moynihan
Board of Directors: Bruce Felmly, Barry Needleman, Mark Wright, Peter Anderson, Joseph Foster, Jeanmarie Papelian, William Zorn, Ellen Arnold, Wilbur Glahn, Michael Quinn, Steven Burke, Rolf Goodwin, John Rich, Steven Camerino, Thomas Hildreth, Peter Rotch, Linda Connell, Ralph Holmes, Mark Rouvalis, Charles De Grandpre, John Hughes, Richard Samuels, R David De Puy, Robert Jauron, Gregory Smith, Thomas Donovan

D-U-N-S 80-570-0325
MCLANE GROUP LP
4001 Central Pointe Pkwy, Temple, TX 76504-2608
Tel (254) 770-6100 *Founded/Ownrshp* 1992
Sales 24.9MM^E^ *EMP* 40
SIC 5141 Groceries, general line
Pt: Robert D McLane Jr
Chf Inves: James Llee
VP: Webster F Stickney Jr

D-U-N-S 10-920-0436
■ MCLANE HIGH PLAINS INC
(*Suby of* MCLANE CO INC) ★
1717 E Loop 289, Lubbock, TX 79403-6501
Tel (806) 766-2900 *Founded/Ownrshp* 1982
Sales 164.7MM^E^ *EMP* 335
SIC 5141 5142 5113 Groceries, general line; Packaged frozen goods; Industrial & personal service paper; Groceries, general line; Packaged frozen goods; Industrial & personal service paper
CEO: William G Rosier
**Pr:* Mike Youngblood
**CFO:* Kevin Koch
**Ex VP:* Jim Kent
VP: Tim Paradoski
VP: Michael William
Area Mgr: Lowell Conley
Sales Exec: Jay Warnick

D-U-N-S 61-055-5695
■ MCLANE NEW JERSEY
(*Suby of* MCLANE CO INC) ★
742 Courses Landing Rd, Penns Grove, NJ 08069-2956
Tel (856) 351-6200 *Founded/Ownrshp* 2002
Sales 116.6MM^E^ *EMP* 401
SIC 5141 5149 Groceries, general line; Groceries & related products; Groceries, general line; Groceries & related products
Pr: Jim Tidmore

D-U-N-S 86-726-4368 IMP
■ MCLANE/BUCKEYE INC
(*Suby of* MCLANE CO INC) ★
401 S Wilcox St Ste 100, Castle Rock, CO 80104-1960
Tel (254) 771-7500 *Founded/Ownrshp* 2004
Sales 50.2MM^E^ *EMP* 200^E^
SIC 5122 Druggists' sundries; Druggists' sundries
Pr: Mark Eisele

D-U-N-S 96-683-4541
■ MCLANE/CAROLINA INC
(*Suby of* MCLANE CO INC) ★
7253 Nc 48, Battleboro, NC 27809-9183
Tel (252) 972-2500 *Founded/Ownrshp* 1996
Sales 221.8MM^E^ *EMP* 558
SIC 5141 5142 5149 Groceries, general line; Packaged frozen goods; Health foods; Specialty food items; Groceries, general line; Packaged frozen goods; Health foods; Specialty food items
Pr: William G Rosier
**Pr:* Mike Youngblood
**CFO:* Kevin Koch
**Sr VP:* Jim Kent
VP: Jim Carpenter
Trfc Dir: Felicia Thorpe
S&M/VP: Martie Mortgart

D-U-N-S 10-893-3946
■ MCLANE/EASTERN INC
(*Suby of* MCLANE CO INC) ★
2828 Mclane Rd, Baldwinsville, NY 13027-1390
Tel (315) 638-7500 *Founded/Ownrshp* 1984
Sales 888.6MM^E^ *EMP* 750
SIC 5141 Food brokers; Food brokers
Pr: Lee Cobb
**Pr:* Michael Youngblood
**Treas:* Kevin Koch
**Sr VP:* Jim Kent
VP: Ernie Hurlbut
Area Mgr: Tom Purcell
Dir IT: Tracy Krivan
Dir IT: Bob Smith

D-U-N-S 82-636-8060 IMP
■ MCLANE/MID-ATLANTIC INC
(*Suby of* MCLANE CO INC) ★
56 Mclane Dr, Fredericksburg, VA 22406-1147
Tel (540) 374-2000 *Founded/Ownrshp* 1992
Sales 221.8MM^E^ *EMP* 659
SIC 5141 Groceries, general line; Groceries, general line
Pr: William G Rosier
Exec: Sam Bass
Exec: Maria Ramos

D-U-N-S 60-395-2367 IMP
■ MCLANE/MIDWEST INC
(*Suby of* MCLANE CO INC) ★
3400 E Main St, Danville, IL 61834-9468
Tel (217) 477-7500 *Founded/Ownrshp* 1989
Sales 353.9MM^E^ *EMP* 691
SIC 5141 Groceries, general line; Groceries, general line
Pr: William G Rosier
Pr: William Rosier
Pr: Michael Youngblood
CFO: Kevin Koch
Ex VP: Jim Kent
Sr VP: Tim Donahoe
VP: Lee Cobb
Area Mgr: Stewart William
VP Mktg: Jerry Rose
VP Sls: Lynn Swanson

D-U-N-S 13-957-0956 IMP
■ MCLANE/PACIFIC INC
(*Suby of* MCLANE CO INC) ★
3876 E Childs Ave, Merced, CA 95341-9520
Tel (209) 725-2500 *Founded/Ownrshp* 1983
Sales 204.7MM^E^ *EMP* 498
SIC 5141 Groceries, general line; Groceries, general line
CEO: William G Rosier
**Pr:* Mike Youngblood
**Treas:* Kevin Koch
**Ex VP:* Jim Kent
VP: Stanley Garndener
VP: Steve Nix

D-U-N-S 14-456-4965
■ MCLANE/SOUTHEAST
(*Suby of* MCLANE CO INC) ★
300 Highway 29 N, Athens, GA 30601-5556
Tel (706) 549-4520 *Founded/Ownrshp* 1980
Sales 161.9MM^E^ *EMP* 462
SIC 5141 Groceries, general line; Groceries, general line
Pr: William G Rosier
Area Mgr: Steve Bell
Area Mgr: Teresa Wolfe

D-U-N-S 80-516-9315 IMP/EXP
■ MCLANE/SOUTHERN CALIFORNIA INC
(*Suby of* MCLANE CO INC) ★
4472 Georgia Blvd, San Bernardino, CA 92407-1854
Tel (909) 887-7500 *Founded/Ownrshp* 1992
Sales 189.3MM^E^ *EMP* 398
SIC 5141 Groceries, general line; Groceries, general line
Pr: David Leach
**Pr:* Grady Rosier
**CEO:* William G Rosier
**CFO:* Kevin Koch
**Ex VP:* Jim Kent
Exec: Marcela Tropea
VP Sls: Terry McLean

D-U-N-S 03-325-8518
■ MCLANE/SOUTHERN INC
(*Suby of* MCLANE CO INC) ★
2104 Mfrs Blvd Ne, Brookhaven, MS 39601
Tel (601) 833-6761 *Founded/Ownrshp* 1986
Sales 221.8MM^E^ *EMP* 521
SIC 5141 Groceries, general line; Groceries, general line
CEO: William G Rosier
**Pr:* Mike Youngblood
**CFO:* Kevin Koch
Bd of Dir: Jim Trent
**Ex VP:* Jim Kent
IT Man: David Sexton

D-U-N-S 14-770-9802
■ MCLANE/SUNEAST INC
(*Suby of* MCLANE CO INC) ★
4747 Mclane Pkwy, Temple, TX 76504-4854
Tel (254) 771-7500 *Founded/Ownrshp* 1985
Sales 476.8MM^E^ *EMP* 1,017
SIC 5141 Groceries, general line; Groceries, general line
CEO: William G Rosier
**Pr:* Mike Youngblood
**CFO:* Kevin J Koch
**Ex VP:* Jim Kent
**Sr VP:* James L Kent
VP: R D Harger
Area Mgr: Sergio Aponte
Area Mgr: Walter Sajna
Opers Mgr: Paul Barnum
VP Sls: Bennie Hancock

D-U-N-S 12-221-2863
■ MCLANE/SUNWEST INC
(*Suby of* MCLANE CO INC) ★
14149 W Mcdowell Rd, Goodyear, AZ 85395-2500
Tel (623) 935-7500 *Founded/Ownrshp* 1985
Sales 221.8MM^E^ *EMP* 518
SIC 5141 Groceries, general line; Groceries, general line
Pr: Ken Mason
**Pr:* Mike Youngblood
**CFO:* Kevin Koch
**Sr VP:* Jim Kent
VP: Tim Campbell

D-U-N-S 06-274-3646
■ MCLANE/WESTERN INC
(*Suby of* MCLANE CO INC) ★
2100 E Ken Pratt Blvd, Longmont, CO 80504-5280
Tel (303) 682-7500 *Founded/Ownrshp* 1972, 1976
Sales 200.6MM^E^ *EMP* 523
SIC 5141 Groceries, general line; Groceries, general line
Pr: William G Rosier
**Treas:* Kevin Koch
**Ex VP:* Jim Kent
VP: Darryl Lyon
Exec: Karen Webb
Area Mgr: Sergey Shatalov
Trfc Dir: Rich Siminas
Opers Mgr: Richard Davidson

MCLAREN FLINT
See MCLAREN REGIONAL MEDICAL CENTER

MCLAREN GREATER LANSING
See INGHAM REGIONAL MEDICAL CENTER

D-U-N-S 04-414-2527
MCLAREN GREATER LANSING
CLAREN GTR LANSING CARDIOTHORA
405 W Greenlawn Ave # 305, Lansing, MI 48910-2898
Tel (517) 483-4780 *Founded/Ownrshp* 2012
Sales 44.8MM^E^ *EMP* 200^E^
SIC 8011 Surgeon
Prin: Kevin Lanciotti
HC Dir: Cheryl Fitzpatrick

D-U-N-S 79-145-6056
MCLAREN HEALTH CARE CORP
G3235 Beecher Rd Ste B, Flint, MI 48532-3650
Tel (810) 342-1100 *Founded/Ownrshp* 1981
Sales NA *EMP* 10,003
SIC 8062 General medical & surgical hospitals; General medical & surgical hospitals
Pr: Philip A Incarnati
Chf Path: Nader Bassily
Dir Recs: Sue Engelbrink
Dir Recs: Laurie Keller
**COO:* Mark O'Halla
COO: Mark S O'Halla
**CFO:* Dennis Kirzemkrski
CFO: Dave Mazurkiewicz
Ex VP: Michael McKenna
VP: Beth Caughlin
VP: Floyd Chasey
VP: Cheryl Legood
**VP:* David Mazurkiewicz
VP: Teresa Mikan
VP: Greg Purtell
VP: Kelly Raimondo
Int Pr: Justin F Klamerus

D-U-N-S 96-636-2761
MCLAREN LAPEER REGION
LAPEER REGION MEDICAL CENTER
1375 N Main St, Lapeer, MI 48446-1350
Tel (810) 667-5580 *Founded/Ownrshp* 2011
Sales 103.9MM *EMP* 31^E^
SIC 8069 Chronic disease hospital
CEO: Barton Buxton
CFO: Mary Callahan

D-U-N-S 03-998-5366
MCLAREN MEDICAL MANAGEMENT INC
(*Suby of* MCLAREN HEALTH CARE CORP) ★
G1080 N Ballenger Hwy A, Flint, MI 48504-4427
Tel (810) 342-1040 *Founded/Ownrshp* 1994
Sales 20.2MM *EMP* 15
SIC 8741 Hospital management; Nursing & personal care facility management; Hospital management; Nursing & personal care facility management
Pr: Margaret Dimond
**CFO:* Dennis Kizeminski
Off Mgr: Stacy Neil

D-U-N-S 07-930-1511
MCLAREN NORTHERN MICHIGAN
NORTHERN MICHIGAN REGIONAL HOSPITAL
(*Suby of* MCLAREN HEALTH CARE CORP) ★
416 Connable Ave, Petoskey, MI 49770-2212
Tel (231) 487-4000 *Founded/Ownrshp* 2012
Sales 191.0MM *EMP* 1,003
SIC 8062 General medical & surgical hospitals; General medical & surgical hospitals
Pr: Tom Mroczkowski
Pr: Reezie Devet
COO: Mary-Anne D Ponti
CFO: Timothy Joway
VP: Kirk Lufkin MD
Off Mgr: Cindy Holman
Nurse Mgr: Tammy Hightower
Nutrtnst: Janet Havens
Doctor: Tara Conti
Doctor: Erine Erickson MD
Doctor: Patrick Maloney

D-U-N-S 01-087-0863
MCLAREN OAKLAND (MI)
POH MEDICAL CENTER
50 N Perry St, Pontiac, MI 48342-2217
Tel (248) 338-5000 *Founded/Ownrshp* 1952
Sales 143.1MM *EMP* 1,200
Accts Plante & Moran Pllc Portage
SIC 8062 Hospital, medical school affiliated with residency; Hospital, medical school affiliated with residency
CEO: Patrick Lamberti
Ch Bd: Leo Bowman
CFO: Thomas Schilling
Bd of Dir: Pat Lamberty
Genl Mgr: Fred Hamilton
Doctor: K Buitkus
Board of Directors: Kenneth Lim Do, Clemon Pardelas Do, Joan Riley

D-U-N-S 06-883-6915
MCLAREN PORT HURON
1221 Pine Grove Ave, Port Huron, MI 48060-3511
Tel (810) 987-5000 *Founded/Ownrshp* 1880
Sales 182.8MM *EMP* 2,000
Accts Plante & Moran Pllc Portage
SIC 8062 Hospital, medical school affiliated with nursing & residency; Hospital, medical school affiliated with nursing & residency
Ch: Patrick Moran
**CEO:* Thomas Defaw
COO: Jerome Hess
COO: Randall Wagner
**CFO:* John Liston
**Sec:* David Whipple
Chf Mktg O: Michael Basha
Ofcr: Jim Lotts
Ofcr: George Stracenrider
Ofcr: Marcia Trenn
Sr VP: Randy Wendland
VP: Dennis Hoover
VP: Michael Tawney
Dir Risk M: Margaret Boddy
Dir Lab: Richard Anderson
Dir Lab: Kathy Dupes
Dir Lab: V I Golat
Dir Rad: Kanu B Dalal
Dir Rx: Michael Laeder
Dir Rx: Brian Shinavier

D-U-N-S 07-544-4281
MCLAREN REGIONAL MEDICAL CENTER
MCLAREN FLINT
(*Suby of* MCLAREN HEALTH CARE CORP) ★
401 S Ballenger Hwy, Flint, MI 48532-3638
Tel (810) 342-2000 *Founded/Ownrshp* 1984
Sales 403.2MM *EMP* 2,250
SIC 8062 Hospital, medical school affiliated with nursing & residency; Hospital, medical school affiliated with nursing & residency
CEO: Donald Kooy
VP: Lisa Salmons
Dir Lab: James M Nielsen
Dir Rad: Mark Camens
Dir Rad: Charlene Thrall
Dir Rx: Ann Lavoie
Mktg Mgr: Hudson Giles
Pathlgst: Julio Badin
Pathlgst: Nader B Hanna
Pathlgst: Ernesto Quiachon
Surgeon: Paul Charpentier

D-U-N-S 18-276-0900
MCLARNEY CONSTRUCTION INC
355 S Daniel Way, San Jose, CA 95128-5120
Tel (408) 246-8600 *Founded/Ownrshp* 1987
Sales 66.7MM *EMP* 46
Accts Robert Lee & Associates Llp
SIC 1542 Commercial & office building, new construction; Commercial & office building, new construction
Pr: Kevin M McLarney
**CFO:* Nicole Merriam
**VP:* Brett McLarney
Sales Exec: Lauren Doherty

D-U-N-S 15-818-4346
MCLARTY AUTO MALL INC
MCLARTY FORD
3232 Summerhill Rd, Texarkana, TX 75503-3968
Tel (903) 794-7121 *Founded/Ownrshp* 1998
Sales 28.1MM^E^ *EMP* 100
SIC 5511 Automobiles, new & used; Automobiles, new & used
Pr: Todd Shores
VP: Donna McLarty
**Genl Mgr:* Paul Lambert

MCLARTY FORD
See MCLARTY AUTO MALL INC

D-U-N-S 01-850-6733 IMP
■ MCLAUGHLIN & MORAN INC
40 Slater Rd, Cranston, RI 02920-4459
Tel (401) 463-5454 *Founded/Ownrshp* 1936
Sales 56.6MM^E^ *EMP* 100

SIC 5181 Beer & other fermented malt liquors; Beer & other fermented malt liquors
Ch Bd: Paul P Moran
**Pr:* Terrence P Moran
**VP:* Charles M Borkoski

D-U-N-S 00-526-5509 IMP
MCLAUGHLIN BODY CO
2430 River Dr, Moline, IL 61265-1500
Tel (309) 762-7755 *Founded/Ownrshp* 1902
Sales 505.8M *EMP* 350
Accts H Mcgladrey Llp Moline Il
SIC 3713 3441 3559 3523 Truck & bus bodies; Fabricated structural metal; Frame straighteners, automobile (garage equipment); Farm machinery & equipment; Truck & bus bodies; Fabricated structural metal; Frame straighteners, automobile (garage equipment); Farm machinery & equipment
Ch Bd: Raymond L Mc Laughlin
**Pr:* John Mann
VP: Peter Britt
VP: L Ehlers
VP: Dan McLaughlin
VP: Tom Ronk
**VP:* William Storm
VP: Jerry Vonderhaar
Exec: Sara Watson
Dir Bus: Mark Fennell
Genl Mgr: Randy Frederick

D-U-N-S 04-055-2176
MCLAUGHLIN CO
9210 Corporate Blvd # 250, Rockville, MD 20850-6515
Tel (202) 293-5566 *Founded/Ownrshp* 1929
Sales NA *EMP* 19
SIC 6411 Insurance agents, brokers & service; Insurance agents, brokers & service
Pr: Theodore M Pappas
**Ch:* John T Pappas
**Ex VP:* Cheri Brewer
**Ex VP:* Brenda Mantz

MCLAUGHLIN FORD
See MC LAUGHLIN MOTORS INC

D-U-N-S 00-625-0583 IMP
MCLAUGHLIN GORMLEY KING CO (MN)
M G K
(*Suby of* SUMITOMO CHEMICAL COMPANY, LIMITED)
8810 10th Ave N, Minneapolis, MN 55427-4372
Tel (763) 593-3405 *Founded/Ownrshp* 1902, 2012
Sales 20.6MM^E *EMP* 100
SIC 2879 Pesticides, agricultural or household; Pyrethrin concentrates & preparations; Pesticides, agricultural or household; Pyrethrin concentrates & preparations
CEO: Steven M Gullickson
Pr: Kurt Maroushek
COO: Donald Sundquist
**Ch:* William D Gullickson Jr
**Treas:* Randy Nelson
VP: Dennis Foster
Exec: Monika Morris
Exec: Steve Zoubek
Dir Lab: Steve Kleysmat
Off Mgr: Karen Schroeder
Dir IT: Doug Cook

D-U-N-S 00-511-3592 IMP
MCLAUGHLIN GROUP INC (SC)
2006 Perimeter Rd, Greenville, SC 29605-5299
Tel (864) 277-5870 *Founded/Ownrshp* 1920, 1962
Sales 30.0MM^E *EMP* 149
SIC 3545 3546 3541 3532 3531 3441 Drills (machine tool accessories); Drill bits, metalworking; Power-driven handtools; Machine tools, metal cutting type; Mining machinery; Construction machinery; Fabricated structural metal
Pr: Dave Gasmovic
VP: Mike Moore
Ex Dir: Bruce Hubbard

MCLAUGHLIN MOTORS
See MC LAUGHLIN OLDSMOBILE CADILLAC INC

D-U-N-S 04-469-7373
MCLAUGHLIN RESEARCH CORP
MRC
130 Eugene Oneill Dr, New London, CT 06320-6402
Tel (860) 447-2298 *Founded/Ownrshp* 1947
Sales 31.2MM^E *EMP* 200
SIC 8711 7371 Engineering services; Custom computer programming services; Engineering services; Custom computer programming services
CEO: Conn L Kelly
Pr: James Bouthillier
Ch: Andra C Kelly
VP: Domenic Gargano
VP: Vincent Pinto

D-U-N-S 96-489-3650
MCLEAN AFFILIATES INC
75 Great Pond Rd, Simsbury, CT 06070-1980
Tel (860) 658-3700 *Founded/Ownrshp* 2010
Sales 28.5MM *EMP* 1
SIC 7699 Cleaning services; Cleaning services
Prin: Pat Pannone

D-U-N-S 00-695-0232
MCLEAN CONTRACTING CO
6700 Mclean Way, Glen Burnie, MD 21060-6480
Tel (410) 553-6700 *Founded/Ownrshp* 1933, 1903
Sales 135.9MM^E *EMP* 300
Accts Mcgladrey & Pullen Llp Timon
SIC 1622 1629 1623 3449 Bridge construction; Sewer line construction; Pier construction; Miscellaneous metalwork; Bridge construction; Pier construction; Sewer line construction; Miscellaneous metalwork
Pr: George Bosmajian III
CFO: Cindy Wray
**Treas:* Cynthia Wray
**Ex VP:* Frederick W Rich
**VP:* Tyrus Fisher
**VP:* Cory Heisey
Exec: Pamela Herda
IT Man: Gregory Seidl

D-U-N-S 00-363-3729
MCLEAN EQUIPMENT LTD
4101 Trimmier Rd, Killeen, TX 76542-3606
Tel (254) 634-4514 *Founded/Ownrshp* 1993
Sales 35.3MM^E *EMP* 150
SIC 1623 Telephone & communication line construction; Gas main construction; Telephone & communication line construction; Gas main construction
Pt: James D McLean Jr
Pt: Gary L McLean
Genl Mgr: Steve Shepherd

D-U-N-S 06-552-2807
MCLEAN FUND
MCLEAN VILLAGE
75 Great Pond Rd, Simsbury, CT 06070-1980
Tel (860) 658-3700 *Founded/Ownrshp* 1969
Sales 1.6MM *EMP* 500
SIC 6732 8059 8051 8052 8361 0971 Charitable trust management; Convalescent home; Rest home, with health care; Skilled nursing care facilities; Intermediate care facilities; Home for the aged; Residential care for the handicapped; Game preserve; Charitable trust management; Convalescent home; Rest home, with health care; Skilled nursing care facilities; Intermediate care facilities; Home for the aged; Residential care for the handicapped; Game preserve
Pr: David Bordonaro
Dir Recs: Kathy Kane
Pt: Daniel P Brown
**COO:* Nancy Wright
**VP:* Augusto Gautier
VP: Bonnie Ku
Off Mgr: Susan Keith
Dir IT: Arthur George
IT Man: Heather Baxter
Nrsg Dir: Diane Bristol
HC Dir: Kelly Koretz

D-U-N-S 04-651-4535
MCLEAN HOSPITAL CORP
(*Suby of* GENERAL HOSPITAL) ★
115 Mill St, Belmont, MA 02478-1048
Tel (617) 855-2000 *Founded/Ownrshp* 1993
Sales 102.7MM *EMP* 1,213
SIC 8063 Psychiatric hospitals; Psychiatric hospitals
Ch: David Barlow
**Pr:* Scott Rauch
**CFO:* David A Lagasse
CFO: Cathy O'Connell
Ofcr: Sue Demarco
Ex VP: Allison Berger
**Ex VP:* Michele L Gougeon
**Sr VP:* Catharine Cook
**Sr VP:* Philip G Levendusky
Sr VP: Philip Levendusky
VP: Catharyn Gildesgame
Dir Rx: Rosen Stanley

D-U-N-S 02-490-7388
MCLEAN IMPLEMENT INC (IL)
JOHN DEERE
793 Illinois Route 130, Albion, IL 62806-5209
Tel (618) 445-3676 *Founded/Ownrshp* 1964
Sales 126.8MM *EMP* 75
SIC 5083 Farm implements; Farm implements
Pr: Marilyn K Mason
Genl Mgr: Bob Mason
IT Man: Jackie Fewkes
**Sls Mgr:* Melinda Clark
Sls Mgr: Chad Nalley

D-U-N-S 00-227-3076 IMP
MCLEAN PACKAGING CORP
1504 Glen Ave, Moorestown, NJ 08057-1104
Tel (856) 359-2600 *Founded/Ownrshp* 1961
Sales 57.1MM^E *EMP* 325
SIC 2652 2653 3089 2657 Setup paperboard boxes; Boxes, corrugated: made from purchased materials; Boxes, plastic; Folding paperboard boxes; Setup paperboard boxes; Boxes, corrugated: made from purchased materials; Boxes, plastic; Folding paperboard boxes
CEO: Joseph Fenkel
**Pr:* Stuart Fenkel
**VP:* Jeffrey Besnick
**VP:* David Seidenberg
Off Mgr: Denise Tyas
IT Man: Dave Howley
Plnt Mgr: R J Howarth
Prd Mgr: Shawn Hintosh
Natl Sales: Michael Jacobs
Natl Sales: Mike Piergalline
VP Sls: Bob Eliason

D-U-N-S 00-433-7721
MCLEAN PUBLISHING CO (PA)
COURIER EXPRESS
(*Suby of* INDEPENDENT PUBLICATIONS, INC.)
500 Jeffers St, Du Bois, PA 15801-2430
Tel (814) 371-4200 *Founded/Ownrshp* 1899
Sales 32.5MM^E *EMP* 600
SIC 2711 2752 Newspapers, publishing & printing; Commercial printing, lithographic; Newspapers, publishing & printing; Commercial printing, lithographic
Ch Bd: William L Mc Lean III
**Treas:* Charles Catherwood
**Genl Mgr:* Joseph Grecco
Prd Mgr: Charlie Butler
Sls Mgr: Linda Smith

MCLEAN THERMAL
See PENTAIR TECHNICAL PRODUCTS

MCLEAN VILLAGE
See MCLEAN FUND

MCLELLAN EQUIPMENT
See MCLELLAN INDUSTRIES INC

D-U-N-S 01-254-9494 IMP/EXP
MCLELLAN INDUSTRIES INC
MCLELLAN EQUIPMENT
251 Shaw Rd, South San Francisco, CA 94080-6605
Tel (650) 873-8100 *Founded/Ownrshp* 1968
Sales 23.5MM^E *EMP* 189
SIC 3713 Truck bodies (motor vehicles); Truck bodies (motor vehicles)
CEO: Molly Mausser
**Pr:* Dale McLellan
VP: Scott McLellan
**VP:* Scott McLellen

D-U-N-S 07-941-7382
MCLEMORE BUILDING MAINTENANCE INC
110 Fargo St, Houston, TX 77006-2097
Tel (713) 528-7775 *Founded/Ownrshp* 1970
Sales 32.0MM^E *EMP* 700
SIC 7349 Janitorial service, contract basis; Janitorial service, contract basis
Pr: Donald McLemore
**CEO:* Curtis McLemore
**CFO:* Stephanie McLemore
**VP:* Keith McLemore
VP: Keith A McLemore
VP: Keith McLemore
**VP:* Torah Lea McLemore
Brnch Mgr: John Denson

D-U-N-S 06-757-3915
MCLENDON ENTERPRISES INC (GA)
2365 Aimwell Rd, Vidalia, GA 30474-9064
Tel (912) 537-7887 *Founded/Ownrshp* 1979
Sales 55.8MM^E *EMP* 120^E
Accts Draffin & Tucker Llp Albany
SIC 1629 Earthmoving contractor; Land clearing contractor; Earthmoving contractor; Land clearing contractor
Pr: Benny D McLendon
VP: Sheryl McLendon
Sfty Dirs: Allen Hollis

D-U-N-S 02-739-8627 IMP
MCLENDON HARDWARE INC
MCLENDON HOME SERVICES
440 Rainier Ave S, Renton, WA 98057-2401
Tel (425) 264-1541 *Founded/Ownrshp* 1926
Sales 214.2MM^E *EMP* 460
SIC 5031 5251 Lumber, plywood & millwork; Hardware; Lumber, plywood & millwork; Hardware
Pr: Gail McLendon
**Treas:* Debra Judd
Sr VP: Gail McLendonbaer
**VP:* Michael McLendon
Store Mgr: Shelly Hoyt

MCLENDON HOME SERVICES
See MCLENDON HARDWARE INC

D-U-N-S 06-898-1463
MCLENNAN COUNTY MEDICAL EDUCATION AND RESEARCH FOUNDATION
FAMILY PRACTICE CENTER
1600 Providence Dr, Waco, TX 76707-2261
Tel (254) 750-8259 *Founded/Ownrshp* 1969
Sales 3.4MM *EMP* 300
Accts Jaynes Reitmeier Boyd & Ther
SIC 8621 Medical field-related associations; Medical field-related associations
Pr: Roland Goertz
**Sec:* Allen E Patterson

MCLEOD ADDICTIVE DISEASE CENTE
See MC LEOD ADDICTIVE DISEASE CENTER INC

D-U-N-S 00-696-1361
MCLEOD COOPERATIVE POWER ASSOCIATION
1231 Ford Ave N, Glencoe, MN 55336-2127
Tel (320) 864-3148 *Founded/Ownrshp* 1935
Sales 22.5MM *EMP* 35
SIC 4911 Distribution, electric power; Distribution, electric power
Pr: Keith Peterson
**Treas:* Gerald Roepke
**Sec:* Doug Kirtz
**VP:* Roger Karstens
Genl Mgr: Carrie Buckley

MCLEOD COUNTY
See COUNTY OF MCLEOD

D-U-N-S 11-335-3341
MCLEOD EXPRESS LLC
5002 Cundiff Ct, Decatur, IL 62526-9627
Tel (217) 706-5045 *Founded/Ownrshp* 2001
Sales 82.8MM^E *EMP* 425
SIC 4213 Trucking, except local; Trucking, except local
Pr: Mark McLeod
Dir IT: Derek Agar

D-U-N-S 14-267-5631 IMP
MCLEOD FARMS INC
5002 Cundiff Rd, Decatur, IL 62526
Tel (217) 709-3936 *Founded/Ownrshp* 1988
Sales 21.0MM^E *EMP* 350
SIC 0191 4213 General farms, primarily crop; Trucking, except local; General farms, primarily crop; Trucking, except local
Pr: Mark R McLeod

D-U-N-S 96-631-9712
MCLEOD HEALTH
555 E Cheves St, Florence, SC 29506-2617
Tel (843) 777-2256 *Founded/Ownrshp* 2011
Sales 123.2MM *EMP* 2
Accts Deloitte Tax Llp Atlanta Ga
SIC 8099 Health & allied services; Health & allied services
Prin: Suzanne Salhab
Chf Rad: Greg Cleveland
COO: John Sherman
Chf Mktg O: Coy Irvin
Ofcr: Debbie Locklair
Ofcr: Dale Lusk
VP: Edward Tinsley
VP: Carmen Winfield
Exec: Carl Chelen
Exec: Samuel Dozier
Exec: Mary Emerson
Dir OR: Carolyn York
Dir Inf Cn: Michelle Dore
Dir Lab: Sandra Bridgers
Dir Rad: Reggie Cooks

D-U-N-S 78-142-2852 IMP/EXP
MCLEOD HEALTH SERVICES INC
(*Suby of* MCCLEOD MED CENTER-DARLINGTON) ★
555 E Cheves St, Florence, SC 29506-2617
Tel (843) 777-5146 *Founded/Ownrshp* 1990
Sales 119.1MM^E *EMP* 5,000
SIC 8062 General medical & surgical hospitals; General medical & surgical hospitals
Pr: Robert L Colones
COO: Teresa Dullaghan
VP: Cathy Frederick
VP: Robert Hinshelwood
Exec: Maureen Byrd
Exec: Heather Grier
Exec: Peter Hyman
Exec: Sylvenia McCutcheon
Exec: Davis Sawyer
Dir Risk M: Tiffini Shealy
CIO: Jenean Blackmon

D-U-N-S 07-886-0096
MCLEOD MEDICAL CENTER-DILLON
301 E Jackson St, Dillon, SC 29536-2509
Tel (843) 774-4111 *Founded/Ownrshp* 2003
Sales 40.5MM *EMP* 46^E
SIC 8011 Offices & clinics of medical doctors; Offices & clinics of medical doctors
Pr: Robert L Colones
COO: Debbie Locklair
Nrsg Dir: Nancy Barnes

D-U-N-S 07-042-5793
MCLEOD PHYSICIAN ASSOCIATES INC (SC)
(*Suby of* MCLEOD HEALTH SERVICES INC) ★
555 E Cheves St, Florence, SC 29506-2617
Tel (843) 777-7000 *Founded/Ownrshp* 1997
Sales 99.1MM^E *EMP* 30
SIC 8011 General & family practice, physician/surgeon; General & family practice, physician/surgeon
**Sr VP:* Dr Charles Jordan
VP: Dane Ficco
**VP:* Mike Payne

MCLEOD REGIONAL MED CNTR OF
See SAINT EUGENE MEDICAL CENTER

D-U-N-S 07-370-9784
MCLEOD REGIONAL MEDICAL CENTER OF PEE DEE INC
MCCLEOD MED CENTER-DARLINGTON
555 E Cheves St, Florence, SC 29506-2617
Tel (843) 777-7753 *Founded/Ownrshp* 1930
Sales 594.1MM *EMP* 5,000
Accts Deloitte Tax Lp Atlanta Ga
SIC 8062 Hospital, medical school affiliated with residency; Hospital, medical school affiliated with residency
Ch Bd: Ronnie Ward
Chf Rad: Cheney Meiere
**CEO:* Robert L Colones
CFO: Michael P Browning
CFO: H McCutcheon
VP: Mark Cameron
Dir Lab: Louis Wright
Off Mgr: Robin Hewitt
CIO: Janice Fraley
IT Man: Rick Bass
Mktg Dir: Vicki Bazen

D-U-N-S 14-823-0746
■ **MCLEODUSA HOLDINGS INC**
(*Suby of* MCLEODUSA INC) ★
1770 Boyson Rd, Hiawatha, IA 52233-2342
Tel (319) 364-0000 *Founded/Ownrshp* 1991
Sales 110.1MM^E *EMP* 1,547^E
SIC 4813 4812 Telephone communication, except radio; Radio telephone communication; Telephone communication, except radio; Radio telephone communication
Ch Bd: Royce Holland
Mng Dir: Mary Greiner

D-U-N-S 80-886-2957
■ **MCLEODUSA INC**
(*Suby of* PAETEC HOLDING CORP) ★
6400 C St Sw, Cedar Rapids, IA 52404-7463
Tel (319) 364-0000 *Founded/Ownrshp* 2008
Sales 248.5MM^E *EMP* 1,600
SIC 4813 4812 Telephone communication, except radio; Local telephone communications; Long distance telephone communications; Radio telephone communication; Telephone communication, except radio; Local telephone communications; Long distance telephone communications; Radio telephone communication
CEO: Royce Holland
**Pr:* Michael McDaniel
**CFO:* Joseph H Ceryanec
Bd of Dir: Jeffrey D Benjamin
**Ex VP:* Richard J Buyens
**VP:* Kurt O Langel
**VP:* Chris McFarland
VP: Cheri Roach
VP: Christopher Ryan

D-U-N-S 82-584-1596
■ **MCLEODUSA NETWORK SERVICES INC**
(*Suby of* MCLEOD USA TELECOMMUNICATIONS SERVICES, INC.)
1770 Boyson Rd, Hiawatha, IA 52233-2342
Tel (319) 364-0000 *Founded/Ownrshp* 1998
Sales 22.6MM^E *EMP* 300
SIC 4813 Telephone communication, except radio; Telephone communication, except radio
Ch Bd: Royce Holland

D-U-N-S 02-980-1750
MCLEROY OIL CO OF INDEPENDENCE INC
9425 Huhn Blvd, Kansas City, MO 64133-1197
Tel (816) 356-5625 *Founded/Ownrshp* 1959
Sales 30.0MM *EMP* 96^E
SIC 5541 5921 6512 Filling stations, gasoline; Liquor stores; Bank building operation; Filling stations, gasoline; Liquor stores; Bank building operation
Treas: Ronald L McLeroy
VP: Ronald Leroy
**Genl Mgr:* Warren Fosket

D-U-N-S 05-690-3339
MCLINTOCKS
IZZY ORTEGA'S
750 Mattie Rd, Pismo Beach, CA 93449-2098
Tel (805) 773-1892 *Founded/Ownrshp* 1973
Sales 9.5MM^E *EMP* 300
SIC 5812 5813 Steak restaurant; Saloon; Steak restaurant; Saloon
Pr: Bruce Breault
**Pr:* Tuny Ortali
CFO: Richard Nott

D-U-N-S 80-939-2749 IMP
MCLOONE METAL GRAPHICS INC
(*Suby of* JSJ CORP) ★
75 Sumner St, La Crosse, WI 54603-3132
Tel (608) 784-1260 *Founded/Ownrshp* 1980
Sales 27.8MM^E *EMP* 130
SIC 2759 3999 Screen printing; Screen printing; Identification tags, except paper
Pr: Nelson Jacobson
**VP:* Keith Rosenthal
Exec: Darren Keady
Genl Mgr: Ashley Anderson
Genl Mgr: William Backes
Genl Mgr: Claudia Castillo
Genl Mgr: Karida Celestine
Genl Mgr: Gerard Enzmann
IT Man: Sheila Wagner
Info Man: Dave Love

D-U-N-S 83-889-2842
MCM CAPITAL PARTNERS
25201 Chagrin Blvd # 360, Beachwood, OH 44122-5633
Tel (216) 514-1840 *Founded/Ownrshp* 1992
Sales 103.1MM^E *EMP* 343^E
SIC 6211 Security brokers & dealers; Security brokers & dealers
Mng Pt: Mark Mansour
Mng Pt: Fred Disanto
Bd of Dir: William M Weber
Ofcr: Lynette Biskis
VP: Robert Kingsbury
VP: Gregory Meredith
**Ex Dir:* James Poffenberger
**Ex Dir:* Steve Ross
**Ex Dir:* Gerry Weimann
Mktg Mgr: Kevin F Hayes

D-U-N-S 13-751-6469
MCM COMMERCIAL CONCRETE INC
9518 Grant Rd Ste B, Houston, TX 77070-4275
Tel (713) 466-7670 *Founded/Ownrshp* 2002
Sales 39.8MM^E *EMP* 275
SIC 1542 Commercial & office building, new construction; Commercial & office building, new construction
Pr: Matt C Mabry
**VP:* Jeremy King
IT Man: Kelly Oliver

D-U-N-S 06-294-2453
MCM CONSTRUCTION INC
6413 32nd St, North Highlands, CA 95660-3001
Tel (916) 334-1221 *Founded/Ownrshp* 1973
Sales 150.0MM *EMP* 370
SIC 1622 Bridge construction; Bridge construction
Pr: James A Carter
VP: H McGovern
**VP:* Harry D McGovern
VP: Kevin Wood
Exec: Dan Shaw
Sfty Mgr: Ed Orsi

D-U-N-S 09-157-0762
MCM CORP (NC)
702 Oberlin Rd Ste 300, Raleigh, NC 27605-1357
Tel (919) 833-1600 *Founded/Ownrshp* 1977, 2000
Sales NA *EMP* 175^E
SIC 6331 Property damage insurance; Fire, marine & casualty insurance: stock; Property damage insurance; Fire, marine & casualty insurance: stock
Ch Bd: George E King
**CEO:* Stephen L Stephano
**CFO:* Kevin Ham
Sr VP: Deborah Wrinkle
**VP:* Brenda Lewis
Netwrk Eng: Ryan Smith

D-U-N-S 02-776-9869 EXP
MCM CUSTOM VEHICLES LLC
SOUTHERN COMFORT
7769 Gadsden Hwy, Trussville, AL 35173-2641
Tel (205) 655-1063 *Founded/Ownrshp* 2009
Sales 23.6MM *EMP* 100
Accts Lovoy Summerville & Shelton
SIC 7549 Automotive customizing services, non-factory basis
Pr: Mathew C McSweeney
**CFO:* Michael McSweeney

D-U-N-S 78-910-8958 IMP
MCM ELECTRONICS INC
(*Suby of* NEWARK ELECTRONICS CORP) ★
650 Congress Park Dr, Centerville, OH 45459-4072
Tel (888) 235-4692 *Founded/Ownrshp* 1996
Sales 51.9MM *EMP* 130
SIC 5961 Computer equipment & electronics, mail order; Computer equipment & electronics, mail order
Pr: Chris Haworth
CFO: Steve Campbell
Treas: Paul M Barlak
Sr VP: Brian Vervynck
VP: Stephen Campbell
**VP:* Joseph R Daprile
VP: Tom Marine
**VP:* Steven Webb
VP: Mark Whiteling
Exec: Amy Turner
MIS Dir: Pamela Bockov
Board of Directors: Thomas H Hudak

D-U-N-S 05-517-8263
MCM FABRICATORS INC
GLOBAL FABRICATORS
720 Commerce Way, Shafter, CA 93263-9530
Tel (661) 589-2774 *Founded/Ownrshp* 1990
Sales 55.1MM^E *EMP* 140
SIC 3441 Fabricated structural metal; Fabricated structural metal
Pr: Jim L Moses
**VP:* Bill Chaney
**VP:* Gary E Moses
Off Mgr: Michelle Garretson
Sales Exec: Chris Flint
Snr PM: Matt Neufeld
Snr Mgr: Jose Acosta

D-U-N-S 05-503-6466
MCM INC
14854 82nd St Ne, SaintThomas, ND 58276-9547
Tel (701) 257-6750 *Founded/Ownrshp* 1995
Sales 51.8MM^E *EMP* 150
SIC 0133 0111 0119 Sugar beet farm; Wheat; Bean (dry field & seed) farm
Pr: Ronald G McMartin Jr

D-U-N-S 01-301-3136
MCM MANAGEMENT CORP
35980 Woodward Ave # 210, Bloomfield Hills, MI 48304-0903
Tel (248) 932-9600 *Founded/Ownrshp* 1993
Sales 62.1MM^E *EMP* 250^E
SIC 1795 Demolition, buildings & other structures; Demolition, buildings & other structures
CEO: David Mardigian
**Pr:* Robert Mardigian
CFO: Craig Sickmiller
IT Man: Emilie Mardigian
Sls&Mrk Ex: Randy Ector

D-U-N-S 00-594-0965 IMP
MCM OIL TOOLS INC (TX)
10422 W Gulf Bank Rd, Houston, TX 77040-3128
Tel (713) 541-1212 *Founded/Ownrshp* 2002
Sales 35.1MM^E *EMP* 70
SIC 5082 Oil field equipment
Pr: Shiraz Saleh

D-U-N-S 13-163-0233
MCM SERVICES GROUP LLC
1300 Corp Ctr Curv Ste 101, Saint Paul, MN 55121
Tel (651) 888-7301 *Founded/Ownrshp* 2012
Sales 30.0MM *EMP* 15
SIC 7311 8742 Advertising agencies; Marketing consulting services; Advertising agencies; Marketing consulting services
CEO: Randy Juen
**VP:* Jennifer Juen

D-U-N-S 00-584-2695
MCMAHAN CO INC (KY)
MC MAHAN CONSTRUCTION CO
6402 Railroad Ave, Crestwood, KY 40014-8721
Tel (502) 241-8811 *Founded/Ownrshp* 1940
Sales 15.9MM^E *EMP* 300
SIC 6531 1521 Real estate agent, residential; New construction, single-family houses; Real estate agent, residential; New construction, single-family houses
Pr: Arvel E Mc Mahan
**Sec:* Jerry Mc Mahan
Chf Mktg O: Molly McMahan
Off Admin: Brianna Munn
Sls Mgr: Kevin Farris
Sales Asso: April Prather
Sales Asso: John Smither
Sales Asso: Karlyn Thomas

D-U-N-S 18-205-0922
MCMAHON ASSOCIATES INC
425 Commerce Dr Ste 200, Fort Washington, PA 19034-2717
Tel (215) 283-9444 *Founded/Ownrshp* 1976
Sales 28.3MM^E *EMP* 120
SIC 8711 Civil engineering; Consulting engineer; Civil engineering; Consulting engineer
Ch Bd: Joseph W McMahon
**Pr:* Joseph J Desantis
CFO: Lou Possanza
**VP:* John S Depalma
**VP:* Gary R McNaughton
**VP:* Casey A Moore
VP: Casey Moore
VP: Bill Steffens
**VP:* William T Steffens
VP: William Steffens
Genl Mgr: Thomas Hall

D-U-N-S 80-265-4012
MCMAHON CONTRACTING LP
3019 Roy Orr Blvd, Grand Prairie, TX 75050-7108
Tel (972) 263-6907 *Founded/Ownrshp* 1993
Sales 26.0MM *EMP* 106
Accts Psk Llp Arlington Texas
SIC 1611 1623 1794 Highway & street paving contractor; Underground utilities contractor; Excavation work; Highway & street paving contractor; Underground utilities contractor; Excavation work
Pt: Jayce McMahon
Pr: Shawn McMahon

D-U-N-S 05-823-5698
MCMAHON STEEL CO INC
1880 Nirvana Ave, Chula Vista, CA 91911-6118
Tel (619) 671-9700 *Founded/Ownrshp* 1970
Sales 32.9MM^E *EMP* 120
SIC 3429 1791 3441 Structural steel erection; Manufactured hardware (general); Fabricated structural metal; Manufactured hardware (general); Structural steel erection; Fabricated structural metal
Pr: Derek J McMahon
**VP:* Kevin McMahon

D-U-N-S 04-640-0537
MCMAHON TIRE SERVICE INC
2828 W Coliseum Blvd, Fort Wayne, IN 46808-3634
Tel (260) 483-8473 *Founded/Ownrshp* 1969
Sales 30.0MM^E *EMP* 63
SIC 5531 5014 Automotive tires; Automobile tires & tubes
Pr: Patrick McMahon
**VP:* Paul W Zurcher
Store Mgr: Jason Byerly

MCMAHON'S RV SERVICE
See MEGA RV CORP

D-U-N-S 10-310-9252
MCMANGA FOODS
MCDONALD'S
8605 Indiana Ave, Riverside, CA 92504-4046
Tel (951) 689-8400 *Founded/Ownrshp* 1999
Sales 17.2MM^E *EMP* 400
SIC 5812 Fast-food restaurant, chain; Fast-food restaurant, chain
Pr: Thomas Mangione

D-U-N-S 00-693-1349 EXP
MCMASTER-CARR SUPPLY CO (IL)
600 N County Line Rd, Elmhurst, IL 60126-2081
Tel (630) 834-9600 *Founded/Ownrshp* 1901
Sales 350.1MM^E *EMP* 200^E
Accts Pricewaterhousecoopers Llp
SIC 5085 Industrial supplies; Industrial supplies
Pr: Robert Delaney
Pr: Dick Adams
Ofcr: John Francis
Brnch Mgr: Andy Walters
MIS Dir: Tracy Rourke
Dir IT: Ben Callanta
Dir IT: John Kurtz
Dir IT: Jeff Pugielli
Dir IT: Jeff Puglielli
IT Man: Mike Delaney
IT Man: Pete Fitzpatrick

D-U-N-S 96-651-3561
MCMASTER-CARR SUPPLY CO EMPLOYEES WELFARE TRUST
600 N County Line Rd, Elmhurst, IL 60126-2081
Tel (630) 834-9600 *Founded/Ownrshp* 2011
Sales 85.0MM *EMP* 896^E
Accts Pricewaterhousecoopers Chicag
SIC 5099 Durable goods; Durable goods
Prin: Carr McMaster
CIO: Edwin Whitlow
DP Dir: Jack Dowd
IT Man: Terry Haubenriser
Netwrk Mgr: Rich Camerza
Mktg Dir: Andy Flores
Sls Mgr: John Downey
Sales Asso: Trisha Harmon

MCMC
See MID-COLUMBIA MEDICAL CENTER

D-U-N-S 87-757-2388
MCMC LLC
COLUMBIA MEDICAL CONSULTANTS
300 Crown Colony Dr # 203, Quincy, MA 02169-0929
Tel (617) 375-7700 *Founded/Ownrshp* 2002
Sales 92.2MM^E *EMP* 506^E
SIC 8742 Hospital & health services consultant; Hospital & health services consultant
CEO: Michael Lindberg
Pr: Ron Williams
**CFO:* Pamela Ochs-Piasecki
Ex VP: Lisa Oskoui
**Sr VP:* Brenda Calia
Sr VP: Joe Lawless
VP: Colleen Horiates
VP: Lawrence Reynolds
Off Mgr: Imants Mohseni
CTO: Chris Nattania
QA Dir: Trisha Hardee

D-U-N-S 02-957-4472
MCMENAMINS INC
ROCK CREEK RESTAURANT & TAVERN
430 N Killingsworth St, Portland, OR 97217-2441
Tel (503) 223-0109 *Founded/Ownrshp* 1983
Sales 215.6MM^E *EMP* 1,400^E
SIC 5813 5812 Drinking places; Eating places; Drinking places; Eating places
Pr: Michael R McMenamin
**Pr:* Brian C McMenamin
Genl Mgr: Amie Budelmann
Software D: D J Simcoe
Mktg Dir: Mike Walker

D-U-N-S 80-884-1605 IMP/EXP
MCMICHAEL MILLS INC
130 Shakey Rd, Mayodan, NC 27027-8587
Tel (336) 548-4242 *Founded/Ownrshp* 1993
Sales 47.7MM^E *EMP* 280
SIC 2241 Rubber & elastic yarns & fabrics; Rubber & elastic yarns & fabrics
Pr: Dalton L McMichael Jr
**CFO:* Martha Ford
**VP:* Billy Corns
IT Man: Jannet Mayab

D-U-N-S 02-921-8484 IMP
MCMILLAN BROS ELECTRIC INC (CA)
1950 Cesar Chavez, San Francisco, CA 94124-1132
Tel (415) 826-5100 *Founded/Ownrshp* 1965
Sales 79.5MM^E *EMP* 190
SIC 1731 8711 Electrical work; Engineering services; Electrical work; Engineering services
Pr: Patrick J McMillan
**Pr:* William J Musgrave
**CFO:* Russell Schmittou
Ofcr: Sue Majeski
**VP:* David Auch
VP: Willian J Musgrave
VP: Musgrave William
Div Mgr: Rod Clark
Div Mgr: Jim Murray
IT Man: Mark Mahoney
VP Opers: Michael Barbagelata

D-U-N-S 04-096-1922 IMP
MCMILLAN ELECTRIC CO
400 Best Rd, Woodville, WI 54028-9535
Tel (715) 698-2488 *Founded/Ownrshp* 1976
Sales 70.6MM^E *EMP* 300^E
SIC 3621 Motors, electric; Motors, electric
CEO: Douglas McMillan
Pr: David Dahlen
**Pr:* Ron Wolfgram
**CFO:* Rick Naylor
VP: Greg Luecke
QA Dir: Dave Gaunky
Dir IT: Mark Ramenski
Sys Mgr: Luke Golden
VP Mfg: Evan Anderson
QI Cn Mgr: Thomas Smith
S&M/VP: Tom Rundle

D-U-N-S 07-115-2786
MCMILLAN PAZDAN SMITH LLC (SC)
400 Augusta St Ste 200, Greenville, SC 29601-3552
Tel (864) 242-2033 *Founded/Ownrshp* 2009
Sales 22.0MM *EMP* 140
SIC 8712 Architectural engineering; Architectural engineering
COO: Chad Cousins
Admn Mgr: Joseph Pazdan

D-U-N-S 60-539-5206
MCMILLIAN PROPERTY PROTECTION
12530 Tambourine Dr Apt A, Stafford, TX 77477-1276
Tel (281) 534-4304 *Founded/Ownrshp* 2005
Sales 500.0M *EMP* 500
SIC 1799 Special trade contractors; Special trade contractors
Prin: Glen McMillian

D-U-N-S 18-371-8212
MCMILLIN COMMUNITIES INC
MCMILLIN REALTY
2750 Womble Rd Ste 200, San Diego, CA 92106-6114
Tel (619) 561-5275 *Founded/Ownrshp* 1985
Sales 125.0MM^E *EMP* 1,000^E
SIC 6799 Investors; Investors
Pr: Mark McMillin
**Pr:* Kenneth Baumgartner
**CFO:* Gary Beason
**VP:* Bryce Jones
VP: Frank Zaidle
**Genl Mgr:* Joe W Shielly

D-U-N-S 01-599-5397
MCMILLIN COMPANIES LLC
MCMILLIN HOMES
2750 Womble Rd Ste 200, San Diego, CA 92106-6114
Tel (619) 477-4117 *Founded/Ownrshp* 1998
Sales 50.0MM *EMP* 120
SIC 6799 Real estate investors, except property operators; Real estate investors, except property operators
CEO: Scott McMillin
**Pr:* Mark D McMillin
Sr VP: Jeff Brazel
Sr VP: Donald Faye
Sr VP: Robin Lewis
VP: Greg Araujo
VP: Nicholas Lee
VP: Don Mitchelle
VP: Carrie Williams
VP Opers: Mark Doyle

MCMILLIN HOMES
See MCMILLIN COMPANIES LLC

MCMILLIN HOMES
See MCMILLIN MANAGEMENT SERVICES LP

D-U-N-S 02-936-4838
MCMILLIN MANAGEMENT SERVICES LP
MCMILLIN HOMES
(*Suby of* MCMILLIN COMPANIES LLC) ★
2750 Womble Rd Ste 200, San Diego, CA 92106-6114
Tel (619) 477-4117 *Founded/Ownrshp* 1998
Sales 42.1MM^E *EMP* 300
SIC 6722 8611 Management investment, open-end; Business associations; Management investment, open-end; Business associations
Genl Pt: Scott McMillin
Pt: Mark McMillin

MCMILLIN REALTY
See MCMILLIN COMMUNITIES INC

D-U-N-S 07-979-9746
MCMINN COUNTY SCHOOLS
3 S Hill St, Athens, TN 37303-4289
Tel (423) 745-1612 *Founded/Ownrshp* 2015
Sales 20.6MM^E *EMP* 531^E
SIC 8211 Public elementary & secondary schools

D-U-N-S 02-877-6714
MCMINNVILLE SCHOOL DISTRICT 40
1500 Ne Baker St, McMinnville, OR 97128-3004
Tel (503) 565-4000 *Founded/Ownrshp* 1916
Sales 112.1M *EMP* 750
SIC 8211 Public elementary school; Public junior high school; Public senior high school; Public elementary school; Public junior high school; Public senior high school
Schl Brd P: Tim Roberts

MCMM
See M C HOLDINGS INC

D-U-N-S 04-623-9898
■ **MCMORAN EXPLORATION CO** (DE)
MMR
(*Suby of* FM) ★
1615 Poydras St, New Orleans, LA 70112-1254
Tel (504) 582-4000 *Founded/Ownrshp* 1994, 2013
Sales 50.8MM^E *EMP* 121^E
SIC 1311 1382 Crude petroleum & natural gas; Oil & gas exploration services; Crude petroleum & natural gas; Oil & gas exploration services
CEO: Richard C Adkerson
**Pr:* James R Moffett
**CFO:* Kathleen L Quirk

D-U-N-S 19-699-8074
■ **MCMORAN OIL & GAS LLC**
(*Suby of* MCMORAN EXPLORATION CO) ★
1615 Poydras St Ste 600, New Orleans, LA 70112-1238
Tel (504) 582-4000 *Founded/Ownrshp* 1998
Sales 20.6MM^E *EMP* 16^E
SIC 1382 1311 Oil & gas exploration services; Crude petroleum & natural gas
Pr: Glenn A Kleinert
**Ch Bd:* Robert Allison Jr
**CEO:* James C Flores
VP: John H Althans

VP: Todd R Cantrall
VP: Wm D Davas
VP: W S Davis
VP: Kathleen L Quirk
VP Opers: William R Richey

MCMUA
See MORRIS COUNTY MUNICIPAL UTILITIES AUTHORITY

D-U-N-S 07-116-9130 IMP
MCMURRAY FABRICS INC
105 Vann Pl, Aberdeen, NC 28315-8612
Tel (910) 944-2128 *Founded/Ownrshp* 1968
Sales 138.6MM^E *EMP* 514
SIC 2257 Weft knit fabric mills; Weft knit fabric mills
Pr: Brian L McMurray
**VP:* Connie McMurray
Dir IT: Paul Whitely
Plnt Mgr: Carlton Modlin
Sls&Mrk Ex: Erica Holsclaw

D-U-N-S 16-131-3465
MCMURRAY STERN INC
15511 Carmenita Rd, Santa Fe Springs, CA 90670-5609
Tel (562) 623-3000 *Founded/Ownrshp* 1980
Sales 41.6MM^E *EMP* 50
SIC 5021 4226 Filing units; Document & office records storage
CEO: Linda Stern
**CFO:* Mark Feldstein
Genl Mgr: Jen Heimbach
Dir IT: Juan Vicario
Sls Dir: Collin Straus

D-U-N-S 09-607-0032 IMP/EXP
MCMURRY CONSTRUCTION CO INC
5335 Distriplex Farms Dr, Memphis, TN 38141-8231
Tel (901) 362-0967 *Founded/Ownrshp* 1978
Sales 30.2MM^E *EMP* 100
SIC 1522 Hotel/motel, new construction
Pr: Thomas A McMurry
**Sec:* Bobbie Langston
**VP:* Larry McMurray
**VP:* Greg McMurry

D-U-N-S 10-990-9262
MCMURRY READY-MIX CO
5684 Old Yellowstone Hwy, Casper, WY 82604
Tel (307) 473-9581 *Founded/Ownrshp* 2001
Sales 60.2MM *EMP* 140
SIC 1611 Highway & street construction; Highway & street construction
Pr: W N McMurry
**VP:* Ron McMurry
Dir IT: Michelle Harris
Sls Mgr: Jeff Hochendoner

D-U-N-S 07-314-1699
MCMURRY UNIVERSITY
Mcm Sta, Abilene, TX 79697-0001
Tel (325) 793-3800 *Founded/Ownrshp* 1923
Sales 24.0MM *EMP* 270^E
Accts Davis Kinard & Co Pc Abilen
SIC 8221 College, except junior; College, except junior
Pr: Sandra Harper
Pr: Debra Hulse
**VP:* Steve Crisman
**VP:* Dr Paul Fabrizio
**VP:* Brad Poorman
**VP:* David Voskuill
**VP:* Lisa Love Williams
Store Mgr: Patricia Tatum
Info Man: Michael Stephens
Sls Mgr: Christopher Andrews

MCN
See MICHCON PIPELINE CO

D-U-N-S 80-774-4995 IMP/EXP
MCN BUILD LLC
1214 28th St Nw, Washington, DC 20007-3315
Tel (202) 333-3424 *Founded/Ownrshp* 2007
Sales 120.0MM *EMP* 45
SIC 1541 1542 Industrial buildings & warehouses; School building construction; Commercial & office building, new construction; Institutional building construction; Religious building construction
CEO: Rudy Seikaly
Off Mgr: Anna Florence

D-U-N-S 10-120-2539
MCN DISTRIBUTORS INC
300 N Connecting Rd, Central Islip, NY 11749-4839
Tel (631) 254-2000 *Founded/Ownrshp* 1983
Sales 26.9MM^E *EMP* 60
SIC 5075 1711 Air conditioning equipment, except room units; Electrical heating equipment; Heating & air conditioning contractors
Ch: James J Fox
**Ch Bd:* James J Fox

MCNA DENTAL
See MANAGED CARE OF NORTH AMERICA INC

MCNABB CARPET WAREHOUSE OUTLET
See DONALD E MCNABB CO

D-U-N-S 07-372-2886
MCNAIR LAW FIRM PA
1221 Main St Ste 1800, Columbia, SC 29201-3279
Tel (803) 799-9800 *Founded/Ownrshp* 1971
Sales 26.3MM^E *EMP* 225
SIC 8111 General practice attorney, lawyer; General practice attorney, lawyer
Exec: Charles S Porter
**Prin:* William Youngblood
Genl Mgr: Rita McKinney
Off Mgr: Kathy Ham
Genl Couns: Robert W Dibble Jr
Snr Mgr: Bill Youngblood

D-U-N-S 07-979-8748
MCNAIRY COUNTY SCHOOLS
170 W Court Ave, Selmer, TN 38375-2134
Tel (731) 645-3267 *Founded/Ownrshp* 2015
Sales 6.1MM^E *EMP* 548^E
SIC 8211 Public elementary & secondary schools
HC Dir: Carol A Wood

D-U-N-S 05-967-7856
MCNALLY INDUSTRIES LLC
SUN COUNTRY INDUSTRIES
340 W Benson Ave, Grantsburg, WI 54840-7004
Tel (715) 463-8300 *Founded/Ownrshp* 2002
Sales 65.5MM^E *EMP* 240
SIC 3594 3568 3469 Fluid power pumps; Bearings, plain; Machine parts, stamped or pressed metal; Fluid power pumps; Bearings, plain; Machine parts, stamped or pressed metal
**CFO:* Martin Maxfield
**Sr VP:* Jim Segelstrom
Sr VP: Printjim Segelstrom
**VP:* Lori Lien
**VP:* Jeff Linke
IT Man: John Josephson
IT Man: Trent Mulcrone

MCNAMARA AT SANDPOINT
See FARRIS FLORAL INC

D-U-N-S 01-897-1895
MCNAMARA MOTORS INC
MILLER NISSAN, JEEP, VOLVO
145 State Route 120, Lebanon, NH 03766-1491
Tel (603) 448-7002 *Founded/Ownrshp* 1991
Sales 20.1MM^E *EMP* 80
SIC 5511 Automobiles, new & used; Automobiles, new & used
VP: Heidi Eldred
CFO: James Barnicle
Sales Asso: Shane Clawson

D-U-N-S 60-200-3725
MCNATIONAL INC
502 2nd St E, South Point, OH 45680-9446
Tel (740) 377-4391 *Founded/Ownrshp* 1988
Sales 123.3MM^E *EMP* 800^E
SIC 3731 7699 4491 Barges, building & repairing; Cargo vessels, building & repairing; Aircraft & heavy equipment repair services; Marine cargo handling; Barges, building & repairing; Cargo vessels, building & repairing; Aircraft & heavy equipment repair services; Marine cargo handling
Pr: Rick Griffith
**CEO:* Bruce D McGinnis
**Prin:* C Barry Gipson

D-U-N-S 01-964-9586
MCNATT HOLDINGS INC
6210 N Florida Ave, Tampa, FL 33604-6626
Tel (813) 237-8861 *Founded/Ownrshp* 1988
Sales 7.5MM^E *EMP* 300
SIC 7219 7216 Laundry, except power & coin-operated; Drycleaning plants, except rugs; Laundry, except power & coin-operated; Drycleaning plants, except rugs
Pr: Henry McNatt Jr

D-U-N-S 01-086-8578
MCNAUGHTON & GUNN INC
960 Woodland Dr, Saline, MI 48176-1280
Tel (734) 429-5411 *Founded/Ownrshp* 1975
Sales 22.7MM^E *EMP* 156^E
SIC 2732 2789 Books: printing & binding; Bookbinding & related work; Books: printing & binding; Bookbinding & related work
Pr: Julie McFarland
**Pr:* Julie Mc Farland
**Pr:* Robert L Mc Naughton
VP: Jim Clark
Manager: Frank Gaynor
Manager: Marc Moore
Manager: Davis Scott
Manager: Chris Shore
Board of Directors: Jack Dempsey, Julie Mc Farland, Robert L Mc Naughton, Larry McPherson

MCNAUGHTON BOOK SERVICE
See BRODART CO

MCNAUGHTON-MCKAY ELECTRIC CO
See MCNAUGHTON-MCKAY SOUTHEAST INC

D-U-N-S 00-695-8474
MCNAUGHTON-MCKAY ELECTRIC CO
1357 E Lincoln Ave, Madison Heights, MI 48071-4126
Tel (248) 541-2805 *Founded/Ownrshp* 1930
Sales 689.2MM *EMP* 740
Accts Kpmg Llp
SIC 5065 5063 Electronic parts & equipment; Electrical apparatus & equipment; Electronic parts & equipment; Electrical apparatus & equipment
Pr: Donald D Slominski Jr
COO: John R McNaughton
**CFO:* John D Kuczmanski
**VP:* Greg Chun
**VP:* Kathleen M Gollin
VP: John Kuczmanski
VP: Richard S Miller
**VP Opers:* Scott Sellers
**VP Sls:* Richard Dahlstrom

D-U-N-S 00-196-1317 IMP
MCNAUGHTON-MCKAY ELECTRIC CO OF OHIO INC (MI)
MCNAUGHTON-MCKAY ELECTRIC OHIO
(*Suby of* MCNAUGHTON-MCKAY ELECTRIC CO) ★
2255 Citygate Dr, Columbus, OH 43219-3567
Tel (614) 476-2800 *Founded/Ownrshp* 1996
Sales 93.7MM^E *EMP* 200
SIC 5063 Electrical apparatus & equipment; Motors, electric; Transformers, electric; Electrical supplies; Electrical apparatus & equipment; Motors, electric; Transformers, electric; Electrical supplies
CEO: Donald D Slominski Jr
**Sec:* Michael G Mimnaugh
**Ex VP:* Richard M Dahlstrom
**Ex VP:* John R McNaughton III
**VP:* Kathleen M Gollin
**VP:* John D Kuczmanski
**Genl Mgr:* William Parsons

MCNAUGHTON-MCKAY ELECTRIC OHIO
See MCNAUGHTON-MCKAY ELECTRIC CO OF OHIO INC

D-U-N-S 00-332-1320
MCNAUGHTON-MCKAY SOUTHEAST INC (NC)
MCNAUGHTON-MCKAY ELECTRIC CO
(*Suby of* MCNAUGHTON-MCKAY ELECTRIC CO) ★
6685 Best Friend Rd, Norcross, GA 30071-2918
Tel (770) 825-8600 *Founded/Ownrshp* 1932
Sales 128.5MM^E *EMP* 285
SIC 5063 Electrical supplies; Electrical supplies
Pr: Donald D Slominski Jr
Ex VP: Richard M Dahlstrom
Ex VP: John R McNaughton III
VP: David Beattie
VP: Kathleen M Gollin
VP: John D Kuczmanski

MCNAY TRUCKLINE
See RICHARD MCNAY INC

D-U-N-S 01-894-6590
MCNC
NCREN
3021 Cornwallis Rd, Rtp, NC 27709-0126
Tel (919) 248-1900 *Founded/Ownrshp* 1980
Sales 75.5MM *EMP* 74
Accts Batchelor Tillery & Roberts Ll
SIC 8731 7374 Electronic research; Commercial physical research; Computer (hardware) development; Data processing & preparation; Electronic research; Commercial physical research; Computer (hardware) development; Data processing & preparation
Ch Bd: Tom Rabon
**Pr:* Joe Freddoso
**COO:* Tommy Jacobson
**CFO:* Patricia Moody
Comm Man: John Moore
Snr Ntwrk: Shane Rockriver
Sfty Mgr: Gary Coronado
Genl Couns: Terri McGaughey

D-U-N-S 11-872-8505
MCNC RESEARCH AND DEVELOPMENT INSTITUTE
3021 Cornwallis Rd, Durham, NC 27709-0126
Tel (919) 248-1900 *Founded/Ownrshp* 1980
Sales 36.8MM *EMP* 75
Accts Batchelor Tillery & Roberts Ll
SIC 8733 Research institute; Research institute
Pr: David P Rizzo
CFO: Patricia Moody
**CFO:* Rex D Williams
Exec: Besty Hine
Snr Ntwrk: Will Parker
Snr Ntwrk: Ray Suitte
IT Man: Peter Janca
Netwrk Mgr: Gonzalo Gonzal
Netwrk Mgr: Shane ROC

MCNEARY HEALTHCARE SERVICES
See MCNEARY INC

D-U-N-S 60-783-5345
MCNEARY INC
MCNEARY HEALTHCARE SERVICES
6525 Morrison Blvd # 200, Charlotte, NC 28211-3532
Tel (704) 365-4150 *Founded/Ownrshp* 1968
Sales NA *EMP* 98
SIC 6411 Insurance information & consulting services
Pr: William Yaeger
**CEO:* Samuel L Booke III
Ex VP: Fife Brad
**Ex VP:* Mark Francis
**Ex VP:* Randy Giddens
Ex VP: Eric Threatt
Sr VP: Robert Bosshardt
Sr VP: Dan Brandon
Sr VP: Angela Nicholas
Sr VP: Lynne Skelton
VP: Karen Asplund
VP: Glenn Curtis
VP: Candyce Eller
VP: Sherri Hartsell
VP: Keith Sharpe
VP: Jack Turner
VP: Barbara Valentine

MCNEEL CAPITAL
See MCNEEL INTERNATIONAL CORP

D-U-N-S 00-194-7118 IMP/EXP
MCNEEL INTERNATIONAL CORP (FL)
MCNEEL CAPITAL
(*Suby of* COVERIS HOLDING CORP) ★
5401 W Kennedy Blvd # 751, Tampa, FL 33609-2447
Tel (813) 286-8680 *Founded/Ownrshp* 1989, 2015
Sales 110.5MM^E *EMP* 500
SIC 3089 Plastic containers, except foam; Plastic containers, except foam
Pr: Clayton W McNeel
CFO: Rene Wood
**VP:* Ian E McNeel
**VP:* David Ramos

D-U-N-S 14-827-8609 EXP
MCNEELY PLASTIC PRODUCTS INC
1111 Industrial Park Dr, Clinton, MS 39056-3208
Tel (601) 924-1712 *Founded/Ownrshp* 1979
Sales 45.7MM *EMP* 41
Accts Grantham Poole Randall Reit
SIC 5699 5087 2821 3999 Work clothing; Janitors' supplies; Thermosetting materials; Barber & beauty shop equipment
Pr: Greg McNeely
**VP:* Dave Clarke
**VP:* Edgar Davis
VP: Wayne Davis
**VP:* Shannon Watts
Natl Sales: Bill Adams

MCNEES WALLACE & NURICK
See WALLACE MCNEES & LLC NURICK

D-U-N-S 09-762-1197 IMP/EXP
MCNEIL & NRM INC
(*Suby of* MCNEIL & NRM INTL INC) ★
96 E Crosier St, Akron, OH 44311-2342
Tel (330) 761-1855 *Founded/Ownrshp* 1979
Sales 20.0MM^E *EMP* 100
SIC 3559 3599 3542 Rubber working machinery, including tires; Custom machinery; Machine tools, metal forming type; Rubber working machinery, including tires; Custom machinery; Machine tools, metal forming type
CEO: Paul Yared
**Ch Bd:* F H Yared
CFO: Robert Nelson
Treas: Joel Siegfried
**Ex VP:* A Melek
**Ex VP:* A P Singh
VP: Lynden Gamble
VP: John McCormick
CTO: Gerald Doble
Plnt Mgr: R Decrow
Trfc Mgr: Jerry Pickens

D-U-N-S 10-786-1999
MCNEIL & NRM INTL INC
96 E Crosier St, Akron, OH 44311-2342
Tel (330) 253-2525 *Founded/Ownrshp* 1985
Sales 28.0MM^E *EMP* 180
SIC 3559 3599 Rubber working machinery, including tires; Custom machinery; Rubber working machinery, including tires; Custom machinery
Ch Bd: F H Yared
**CFO:* R A Nelson
**Treas:* Joel Siegfried
**Ex VP:* Al M Melek

D-U-N-S 16-015-9638
■ **MCNEIL CONSUMER PHARMACEUTICALS CO**
(*Suby of* JOHNSON & JOHNSON CONSUMER INC) ★
7050 Camp Hill Rd, Fort Washington, PA 19034-2210
Tel (215) 273-7700 *Founded/Ownrshp* 2011
Sales 37.7MM^E *EMP* 305^E
SIC 2834 Druggists' preparations (pharmaceuticals)
Pr: James T Lenehan
VP: Robert Miller
VP: Karen Ulmer
VP Bus Dev: Christine Knoblauch
Admn Mgr: Oray Boston
QA Dir: Laureen Longhitano
IT Man: Brenda Grob
IT Man: Cathy Kenlin
Mtls Mgr: Juan Lugo
Ql Cn Mgr: Tessa Mooney
Ql Cn Mgr: Dolly Ngo

D-U-N-S 83-650-4860
MCNEIL INDUSTRIAL INC
8425 Madison St, Omaha, NE 68127-4122
Tel (402) 339-5544 *Founded/Ownrshp* 1995
Sales 34.3MM^E *EMP* 50
SIC 5078 Commercial refrigeration equipment
Pr: Bernard J McNeil
Sls Mgr: Daryle Wilken

MCNEIL-PPC, INC.
See JOHNSON & JOHNSON CONSUMER INC

D-U-N-S 60-800-2416
■ **MCNEILUS COMPANIES INC**
(*Suby of* TOTAL MIXER TECHNOLOGIES LLC) ★
524 E Highway St, Dodge Center, MN 55927-9181
Tel (507) 374-6321 *Founded/Ownrshp* 1970
Sales 353.2MM^E *EMP* 1,600
SIC 3713 Cement mixer bodies; Garbage, refuse truck bodies; Cement mixer bodies; Garbage, refuse truck bodies
Pr: Michael J Wuest
**CEO:* Charles Szews
VP: Gary Burgess
VP: Jim Diehl
VP: Thomas Quigley
VP: Tracy Timmerman
Admn Mgr: Matt Schindle
Brnch Mgr: Bill Smith
Dir IT: Heather Lee
IT Man: Kevin Bell
Tech Mgr: Mike Brown

D-U-N-S 02-276-0326 IMP
MCNEILUS STEEL INC
702 2nd Ave Se, Dodge Center, MN 55927-8903
Tel (507) 374-6336 *Founded/Ownrshp* 1948
Sales 441.3MM *EMP* 475
Accts Mcgladrey Llp Rochester Min
SIC 5051 Structural shapes, iron or steel; Concrete reinforcing bars; Reinforcement mesh, wire; Structural shapes, iron or steel; Concrete reinforcing bars; Reinforcement mesh, wire
Pr: Leland P McNeilus
**CFO:* Daniel Blaisdell
IT Man: Darren Boeck
IT Man: Kory Kliner
Sls Mgr: Ben Hansen
Sls Mgr: Tom Lilledahl
Sls Mgr: Cory Mergen
Sls Mgr: Adam Watterson
Sales Asso: Josie Kliner
Board of Directors: Leland Patrick McNeilus

D-U-N-S 05-448-7756 IMP/EXP
■ **MCNEILUS TRUCK AND MANUFACTURING INC** (MN)
(*Suby of* MCNEILUS COMPANIES INC) ★
524 County Rd 34 E, Dodge Center, MN 55927
Tel (614) 868-0760 *Founded/Ownrshp* 1970
Sales 220.7MM^E *EMP* 720
SIC 3713 3531 3537 3272 Cement mixer bodies; Garbage, refuse truck bodies; Concrete plants; Mixers, concrete; Industrial trucks & tractors; Concrete products; Cement mixer bodies; Garbage, refuse truck bodies; Concrete plants; Mixers, concrete; Industrial trucks & tractors; Concrete products
CEO: Charles Szews
Pr: Brad Nelson
CFO: Sonny Tara
Ofcr: Todd Golberg
IT Man: Charity Hunt
Plnt Mgr: Robert Parrish
Plnt Mgr: Henry Pedigo
Trfc Mgr: Mike Freerkson

D-U-N-S 00-294-7703 IMP/EXP
MCNICHOLS CO (OH)
2502 N Rocky Point Dr # 750, Tampa, FL 33607-1421
Tel (813) 282-3828 Founded/Ownrshp 1952
Sales 157.0MM^E EMP 325
SIC 5051 Metals service centers & offices; Metals service centers & offices
Ch: Eugene Mc Nichols
*Pr: Scott McNichols
*CEO: Gene McNichols
*CFO: Craig A Stein
*Treas: Larry F Jones
*Ex VP: David Brenneman
*VP: Jennifer McNichols
*VP: Steven McNichols
Ex Dir: Katherine Woodrow
Brnch Mgr: Brad Hulse
Brnch Mgr: John Spain

D-U-N-S 08-128-5066 EXP
MCNISH CORP
AMWELL DIV
840 N Russell Ave, Aurora, IL 60506-2856
Tel (630) 892-7921 Founded/Ownrshp 1946
Sales 32.7MM^E EMP 135
SIC 3589 Water treatment equipment, industrial; Water treatment equipment, industrial
Pr: James A Mc Nish
*CFO: Mark Delaney
*VP: Jim Barbel
*VP: Lloyd Cates
*VP: Dan Harker
VP: A Schlicht
*Prin: Ronald E Heinlen
Mtls Mgr: Lane Sheldon
Mfg Mgr: Bernard Pupino
Manager: Randy Stevenson
Manager: Jeffrey C Thomas

D-U-N-S 03-860-9954
MCNISH GROUP INC
26622 Woodward Ave # 200, Royal Oak, MI 48067-0956
Tel (248) 544-4800 Founded/Ownrshp 1968
Sales NA EMP 40
SIC 6411 Insurance agents
Pr: William J Mc Nish
VP: John McNish

MCNT
See MEDICAL CLINIC OF NORTH TEXAS P A

D-U-N-S 03-473-9250
MCNUTT OIL CO INC
1817 W Lmar Alxander Pkwy, Maryville, TN 37801-3765
Tel (865) 983-4280 Founded/Ownrshp 1965
Sales 20.3MM^E EMP 13
SIC 5171 Petroleum bulk stations
Ch Bd: Charles F Mc Nutt
*Pr: Clara B Mc Nutt
*Sec: Susan E Mc Nutt
*VP: Karen Mc Nutt Gale
VP: Pete Gale

MCNY
See METROPOLITAN COLLEGE OF NEW YORK

MCOE
See MONTEREY COUNTY OFFICE OF EDUCATION

D-U-N-S 02-256-7908
MCP COMPUTER PRODUCTS INC
MILLENNIUM COMPUTER PRODUCTS
1565 Creek St Ste 103, San Marcos, CA 92078-2426
Tel (760) 744-8524 Founded/Ownrshp 1999
Sales 25.0MM EMP 15
SIC 5045 Computer peripheral equipment
CEO: Rikki Ghai
*Pr: Raj Ghai
IT Man: Pete Brownell
S&M/VP: Sergi Ghai

MCP HAHNEMANN UNIVERSITY
See PHILADELPHIA HEALTH AND EDUCATION CORP

D-U-N-S 12-087-4599 IMP
MCP INDUSTRIES INC
MISSION RUBBER CO
708 S Temescal St Ste 101, Corona, CA 92879-2096
Tel (951) 736-1881 Founded/Ownrshp 1950
Sales 126.4MM^E EMP 350
SIC 3069 3259 3089 Molded rubber products; Sewer pipe or fittings, clay; Injection molding of plastics; Molded rubber products; Sewer pipe or fittings, clay; Injection molding of plastics
CEO: Walter N Garrett
*Sec: Charlotte Garrett
*VP: Owen Garrett
VP: Chris Vansell
QA Dir: Sergio Hernandez
Sls&Mrk Ex: Kathy Kerecman
Manager: Gene Mauhili
Manager: Vince Velez

D-U-N-S 10-108-3173
MCPC INC
MCPC TECH PDTS & SOLUTIONS
1801 Superior Ave E # 300, Cleveland, OH 44114-2107
Tel (440) 238-0102 Founded/Ownrshp 2002
Sales 559.3MM^E EMP 450
SIC 5045 Computers, peripherals & software; Computers, peripherals & software
CEO: Michael Trebilcock
*Pr: Lance Frew
*Pr: Andy Jones
*CFO: Rob Young
Ex VP: Peter Dimarco
*Ex VP: Jason Taylor
VP: Mitch Breneman
VP: Ira Grossman
VP: Brian Kinne
Prgrm Mgr: Jean Cotugno
Admn Mgr: Kimberly Sauer

MCPC TECH PDTS & SOLUTIONS
See MCPC INC

D-U-N-S 04-876-3387
MCPEEKS DODGE OF ANAHEIM
1221 S Auto Center Dr, Anaheim, CA 92806-5634
Tel (714) 635-2340 Founded/Ownrshp 1982
Sales 23.4MM^E EMP 48
SIC 5511 7539 Automobiles, new & used; Automotive repair shops; Automobiles, new & used; Automotive repair shops
Pr: Frank A Busalacchi Sr
*Pr: Frank Busalacchi Jr
*VP: Grethe Busalacchi
IT Man: Kevin Buzzard
Sls Mgr: Ronnie Bostek

D-U-N-S 06-926-5536
MCPHEE ELECTRIC LTD (CT)
(Suby of PHALCON LTD) ★
505 Main St, Farmington, CT 06032-2912
Tel (860) 677-9797 Founded/Ownrshp 1974, 2006
Sales 109.2MM EMP 500
Accts Blum Shapiro & Company Pc
SIC 1731 General electrical contractor; General electrical contractor
CEO: Michael Mc Phee
*Pr: Marcus McPhee
*CEO: Michael McPhee
*CFO: John Conroy
Dir Bus: Michael Balinskas
Mng Dir: Bradley Pritchett
Sfty Dirs: Steve Dauphinais

D-U-N-S 03-061-6759
MCPHERSON BOARD OF PUBLIC UTILITIES INC
401 W Kansas Ave, McPherson, KS 67460-4740
Tel (620) 245-2515 Founded/Ownrshp 1880
Sales 58.9MM EMP 73
Accts Swindoll Janzen Hawk & Lloyd
SIC 4911 Distribution, electric power; Distribution, electric power
Genl Mgr: Rick N Anderson

D-U-N-S 04-395-1466
MCPHERSON COLLEGE
1600 E Euclid St, McPherson, KS 67460-3847
Tel (620) 241-0731 Founded/Ownrshp 1887
Sales 22.4MM EMP 145
Accts Swindoll Janzen Hawk & Loyd L
SIC 8221 College, except junior; College, except junior
Pr: Michael Schneider
Ex VP: Dodson James
VP: Kent Eaton
Ex Dir: Marlene Beeson
VP Mktg: Christi Hpokins

D-U-N-S 05-721-2979 IMP
MCPHERSON COMPANIES INC
MC PHERSON OIL PRODUCTS
5051 Cardinal St, Trussville, AL 35173-1871
Tel (205) 661-2799 Founded/Ownrshp 1971
Sales 242.0MM^E EMP 270
SIC 5171 5411 5541 Petroleum bulk stations; Convenience stores; Gasoline service stations; Petroleum bulk stations; Convenience stores; Gasoline service stations
Ch Bd: Charles K Mc Pherson
Pr: Ken Mc Pherson
Snr Mgr: Charles McPherson

D-U-N-S 06-574-7735
MCPHERSON CONTRACTORS INC
3501 Sw Fairlawn Rd # 100, Topeka, KS 66614-3976
Tel (785) 273-3880 Founded/Ownrshp 1972
Sales 46.3MM^E EMP 75
Accts Mayer Hoffman Mccann Pc Top
SIC 1542 Commercial & office building, new construction; Commercial & office building, new construction
CEO: Michael McPherson
*Pr: Bruce McPherson
*Sec: Jane Gunn
*VP: Bill Sims

MCPHERSON EMS
See MCPHERSON HOSPITAL INC

D-U-N-S 07-331-4726
MCPHERSON HOSPITAL INC
MCPHERSON EMS
1000 Hospital Dr, McPherson, KS 67460-2326
Tel (620) 241-0917 Founded/Ownrshp 1920
Sales 22.8MM EMP 270
Accts Wendling Noe Nelson & Johnson
SIC 8062 General medical & surgical hospitals; General medical & surgical hospitals
CEO: Rob Monical
Pr: David Buller
*CFO: George Halama
CFO: Richard Imbimbo
Bd of Dir: Daniel Avant
Bd of Dir: Bill Burke
Bd of Dir: Joseph L Faison
Bd of Dir: Chad F Harrington
Bd of Dir: Guy T Selander
Bd of Dir: Doug Skura
Ofcr: Cindy Brown
*VP: Terri Goering
VP: Sue Unruh

D-U-N-S 04-500-2458
MCPHERSON UNIFIED SCHOOL DISTRICT 418
514 N Main St, McPherson, KS 67460-3406
Tel (620) 241-9400 Founded/Ownrshp 1965
Sales 26.0MM^E EMP 500
SIC 8211 Public combined elementary & secondary school; Public combined elementary & secondary school
VP: Chris Wiens
Prin: Becky Greer
Prin: Pam Klenda
Schl Brd P: Brad Burt
Psych: Mary Jostaab

D-U-N-S 78-006-1722
MCPHERSONS (US) INC
(Suby of OCCASIONS GROUP INC) ★
957 N Meridian St, Sunman, IN 47041-7771
Tel (812) 623-2225 Founded/Ownrshp 2006
Sales 21.8MM^E EMP 200
SIC 2771 Greeting cards; Greeting cards
Genl Mgr: Darryl Mills
*Prin: Kyle Brock
*Prin: Penny Hartman
*Prin: Waverly Jutzi
*Prin: Kenny Schuman
Genl Mgr: Lisa Mosmeier

D-U-N-S 07-658-0695
MCPHS UNIVERSITY
MASSACHUSETTS COLLEGE OF
179 Longwood Ave, Boston, MA 02115-5804
Tel (617) 732-2132 Founded/Ownrshp 1852
Sales 262.9MM EMP 300
Accts Cbiz Tofias Boston Ma
SIC 8221 Service academy; Service academy
Pr: Charles Monahan Jr
*CFO: Richard J Lessard
VP: George Humphrey
VP: Marguerite Johnson
Assoc Dir: Julie Soper
CIO: Tom Scanlon
CTO: Anthonia Chigbo
DP Dir: Carrie Glass
IT Man: Daniel Barbas
Pharmcst: Donna Bartlett
Counsel: Deborah O'Malley

MCPS
See MONTGOMERY COUNTY PUBLIC SCHOOLS

MCPS FOR CAMPGROUNDS
See MCPS OF CENTRAL PA

D-U-N-S 02-027-4764
MCPS OF CENTRAL PA
MCPS FOR CAMPGROUNDS
418 Hazel St, New Berlin, PA 17855-8064
Tel (570) 966-5700 Founded/Ownrshp 2009
Sales 48.2MM EMP 1
SIC 7389 Financial services; Financial services
Pr: Art Lieberman
VP: Deanne Bower

D-U-N-S 00-225-6360
MCQUADE AND BANNIGAN INC (NY)
M Q B
1300 Stark St, Utica, NY 13502-4495
Tel (315) 788-2612 Founded/Ownrshp 1917
Sales 34.6MM^E EMP 52
SIC 5082 7359 General construction machinery & equipment; Scaffolding; Ladders; Contractors' materials; Equipment rental & leasing
Ch: Thomas F Sebastian
*Treas: Michael Bannigan
Treas: Steve Zocco
*VP: Robert Bannigan
Opers Mgr: Lynn Jacks
Sales Exec: Keith Hartmann
Sls Mgr: Chuck Schweitzer
Sls Mgr: Ken Wolff

D-U-N-S 04-113-2995 IMP/EXP
MCQUAY INTL EDI
13600 Industrial Pk Blvd, Minneapolis, MN 55441-3743
Tel (763) 553-5340 Founded/Ownrshp 2013
Sales 45.0MM^E EMP 192^E
SIC 5075

MCR
See MEDICAL CENTER OF ROCKIES

D-U-N-S 80-827-7128
MCR DEVELOPMENT LLC
152 W 57th St Fl 46, New York, NY 10019-3310
Tel (212) 277-5601 Founded/Ownrshp 2002
Sales 42.7MM^E EMP 400^E
SIC 6531

D-U-N-S 02-850-9656
MCR FEDERAL LLC
M C R
(Suby of MCR LLC) ★
2010 Corp Rdg Ste 350, Mclean, VA 22102
Tel (703) 506-4600 Founded/Ownrshp 2004
Sales 53.3MM^E EMP 610
SIC 8742 8748 8711 7371 7379 3721 Management consulting services; Business consulting; Engineering services; Custom computer programming services; Computer related consulting services; Aircraft; Management consulting services; Business consulting; Engineering services; Custom computer programming services; Computer related consulting services; Aircraft
Pr: Vincent J Kiernan
COO: Roderick Duke
CFO: Marcia O'Brien
Treas: Robert K Zillian
Sr VP: Kevin Boyle
Sr VP: John Cochran
Sr VP: Jason Dechoretz
Prgrm Mgr: Chris Becker
Prgrm Mgr: Samuel Carbaugh
Prgrm Mgr: Garrison Harris
Genl Mgr: Alberto Neoil

D-U-N-S 09-635-6670
MCR LLC
2010 Corp Rdg Ste 350, Mclean, VA 22102
Tel (703) 506-4600 Founded/Ownrshp 2004
Sales 61.7MM^E EMP 650
SIC 8742 8748 8711 7371 7379 3721 Management consulting services; Business consulting; Engineering services; Custom computer programming services; Computer related consulting services; Aircraft; Management consulting services; Business consulting; Engineering services; Custom computer programming services; Computer related consulting services; Aircraft
Pr: Vincent J Kiernan
CFO: Marcia Obrien
Ofcr: Chante McDonald
Sr VP: John Cochran
Sr VP: Jason Dechoretz
Sr VP: Chris Neubauer
Tech Mgr: Donald Trapp

D-U-N-S 14-733-6390
MCR PRINTING AND PACKAGING CORP
15630 Timberidge Ln, Chino Hills, CA 91709-8706
Tel (619) 488-3169 Founded/Ownrshp 2005
Sales 31.4MM^E EMP 175
SIC 2671 Paper coated or laminated for packaging
CEO: Mario Ramirez
Pr: Camilo Ramirez
CFO: Gus Ramirez

MCR SAFETY
See SHELBY GROUP INTERNATIONAL INC

D-U-N-S 00-316-5941 IMP
▲ **MCRAE INDUSTRIES INC**
400 N Main St, Mount Gilead, NC 27306-9038
Tel (910) 439-6147 Founded/Ownrshp 1959
Sales 42.1MM^E EMP 205
Tkr Sym MCRAA Exch OTO
SIC 3577 3143 3144 Optical scanning devices; Boots, dress or casual: men's; Work shoes, men's; Women's footwear, except athletic; Optical scanning devices; Boots, dress or casual: men's; Work shoes, men's; Women's footwear, except athletic
Ch Bd: D Gary Mc Rae
*Pr: Victor A Karam
Bd of Dir: James McRae
VP: Robert Bracewell
*VP: James W Mc Rae
*VP: Harold W Smith
Exec: Betty Coble

D-U-N-S 07-628-7226
MCREL INTERNATIONAL
4601 Dtc Blvd Ste 500, Denver, CO 80237-2596
Tel (303) 337-0990 Founded/Ownrshp 1966
Sales 22.9MM EMP 118
SIC 8733 Educational research agency; Educational research agency
Pr: Tim Waters
Pr: Jean Williams
COO: Ceri Dean
*CFO: Sue Desch
Treas: Judith Richards
*Treas: C Patrick Woods
Bd of Dir: Ken Anderson
Bd of Dir: Beverly G Ausfahl
Bd of Dir: Tom Hawley
Bd of Dir: Dwight Jones
Bd of Dir: D K King
Bd of Dir: Cheryl Kulas
Bd of Dir: Donna Mathern
Bd of Dir: Jim McBride
Bd of Dir: Wayne Sanstead
Ex VP: Lou Cicchinelli
VP: Louis Cicchinelli
VP: Brian McNulty
Exec: Melissa Gray
Dir Surg: Juanita Lyons
Dir Surg: Adrienne Schure

D-U-N-S 01-413-0075
MCROB AUTOMOTIVE INC
INVER GROVE HONDA
4605 S Robert Trl, Inver Grove Heights, MN 55077-1104
Tel (651) 306-8600 Founded/Ownrshp 2005
Sales 27.4MM^E EMP 70
SIC 5511 Automobiles, new & used
CEO: Stephen McDaniels
Sales Asso: Tom Cerise
Sales Asso: John McCorkel
Sales Asso: Evelyn Wood
Sales Asso: Jeremy Young

D-U-N-S 05-456-1154
MCROBERTS PROTECTIVE AGENCY INC (NY)
(Suby of MC ROBERTS CORP) ★
87 Nassau St, New York, NY 10038-3710
Tel (732) 886-0990 Founded/Ownrshp 1938, 1974
Sales 76.5MM^E EMP 2,500
Accts Lawson Rescinio Schibell & A
SIC 7381 1731 Detective services; Protective services, guard; Security guard service; Fire detection & burglar alarm systems specialization; Detective services; Protective services, guard; Security guard service; Fire detection & burglar alarm systems specialization
Ch Bd: Meredith McRoberts
*CFO: Michael Lutz

D-U-N-S 60-573-0659
MCS & METROPLEX CONTROL SYSTEM
12903 Delivery, San Antonio, TX 78247-3476
Tel (210) 495-5245 Founded/Ownrshp 2005
Sales 108.1MM EMP 2^E
SIC 1731 Access control systems specialization; Access control systems specialization
Owner: Don Carr

MCS DESIGN
See MCS INDUSTRIES INC

D-U-N-S 36-159-5267
MCS ENGRAVERS INC
6625 Auburn Rd, Utica, MI 48317-5209
Tel (586) 731-9570 Founded/Ownrshp 1986
Sales 73.0MM EMP 7
SIC 3479 Name plates: engraved, etched, etc.
Pr: William Rowan
*Treas: Georgean Rowan

D-U-N-S 09-683-5673
MCS GROUP INC
1601 Market St Ste 800, Philadelphia, PA 19103-2311
Tel (215) 496-9698 Founded/Ownrshp 1980
Sales 40.2MM EMP 500
SIC 7389 8744 7334 Legal & tax services; Paralegal service; Process serving service; Facilities support services; Photocopying & duplicating services; Legal & tax services; Paralegal service; Process serving service; Facilities support services; Photocopying & duplicating services

CEO: Rosemary Gould Esposito
**Pr:* David J Bean
**CFO:* Russell T Pickus
VP: Loren Laquintano
Off Mgr: Latonia Stewart

D-U-N-S 09-787-8516 IMP/EXP
MCS INDUSTRIES INC
MCS DESIGN
2280 Newlins Mill Rd, Easton, PA 18045-7813
Tel (610) 253-6268 *Founded/Ownrshp* 1980
Sales 264.4MM^E *EMP* 950
SIC 2499 3089 3499 3993 3231 Picture & mirror frames, wood; Injection molding of plastics; Picture frames, metal; Signs & advertising specialties; Products of purchased glass; Picture & mirror frames, wood; Injection molding of plastics; Picture frames, metal; Signs & advertising specialties; Products of purchased glass
CEO: Richard Master
**Pr:* Josh Macneel
**CEO:* Greg Yocco
CFO: Greg Yacco
VP: John Alvator
**VP:* Bob Goldfarb
VP: Anne M Plla
VP: Sandy Reiter
**VP:* Jim Scheyer
Ex Dir: Dianne Hockman
MIS Dir: Mike Kelley

MCS LIFE INSURANCE
See MEDICAL CARD SYSTEM INC

D-U-N-S 80-020-3580
MCS OF TAMPA INC
MISSION CRITICAL SOLUTION
8510 Sunstate St, Tampa, FL 33634-1312
Tel (813) 872-0217 *Founded/Ownrshp* 1988
Sales 90.8MM^E *EMP* 280
SIC 1731 7373 4813 7378 Communications specialization; Computer integrated systems design; Telephone communication, except radio; Computer maintenance & repair; Communications specialization; Computer integrated systems design; Telephone communication, except radio; Computer maintenance & repair
Pr: Gilbert T Gonzales
**CFO:* Brian Calka
CFO: Duane Kezele
CFO: Becky Walther
**Treas:* Kim Gonzales
**Ex VP:* David Dallmann
**Ex VP:* James V Slagle Jr
VP: James Slagle
Brnch Mgr: Chris Ruefer
Dir IT: Dave Dollman
Sales Exec: Arnold Solomon

D-U-N-S 07-855-9010
MCS/TEXAS DIRECT INC
5600 Stratum Dr, Fort Worth, TX 76137-2710
Tel (817) 234-9000 *Founded/Ownrshp* 1970
Sales 21.0MM *EMP* 219
SIC 7331 Direct mail advertising services
Pr: John W Windle Jr
**COO:* Alon Stephens
DP Dir: Les Underwood

D-U-N-S 06-974-9679
MCSA LLC (AR)
MEDICAL CENTER SOUTH ARKANSAS
700 W Grove St, El Dorado, AR 71730-4416
Tel (870) 863-2000 *Founded/Ownrshp* 1921, 1996
Sales 79.5MM^E *EMP* 730
SIC 8062 General medical & surgical hospitals; General medical & surgical hospitals
COO: Kevin Decker
CFO: Frank Canova
CFO: Frank Cavona
Ofcr: Chuck Long
Exec: Martha Crow
Dir Lab: Glenda Johnson
Dir Rad: Johnny Brewer
**Chf Nrs Of:* Keitha Griffith
Dir Sec: Terry Martin
QA Dir: Whitney Tolbert
Mktg Dir: Candy Calloway

D-U-N-S 02-019-1269
MCSC
11 W Carlisle St, Mooresville, IN 46158-1558
Tel (317) 840-3650 *Founded/Ownrshp* 2009
Sales 9.7MM^E *EMP* 490^E
SIC 7832 Motion picture theaters, except drive-in
Prin: Becky McKinney

MCSH
See FORT WORTH SURGICARE PARTNERS LTD

D-U-N-S 19-895-4190
MCSHANE CONSTRUCTION CO LLC
9550 W Higgins Rd Ste 200, Rosemont, IL 60018-4906
Tel (847) 292-4300 *Founded/Ownrshp* 1988
Sales 81.2MM^E *EMP* 100^E
Accts Warady & Davis
SIC 1542 1541 Commercial & office building, new construction; Industrial buildings, new construction; Commercial & office building, new construction; Industrial buildings, new construction
CEO: James McShane
**CEO:* James A McShane
COO: Mark Saturno
Ofcr: Jonathan Bagnall
**Ex VP:* Mark T Tritschler
VP: Bill Brady
**VP:* Keith G Dafcik
VP: Keith Dafcik
**VP:* Mathew R Dougherty
VP: Ellen Hilgendorf
VP: Craig Morris
VP: Vicki Mutchler
**VP:* Jeffrey A Raday
**VP:* Sheri Tantari
VP: Greg Terwilliger

D-U-N-S 12-232-5277
MCSHANE DEVELOPMENT CO LLC
MCSHANE WILLIAMS WAY MOB 1
9550 W Higgins Rd Ste 200, Rosemont, IL 60018-4906
Tel (847) 292-4300 *Founded/Ownrshp* 1984
Sales 124.8MM^E *EMP* 300
SIC 6552 Land subdividers & developers, commercial; Land subdividers & developers, commercial
CEO: James McShane
**Pr:* Hunter Barrier
CFO: Melvin Meyer
**Ex VP:* Mat Dougherty P E
VP: William Lu
VP: Anthony Pricco
VP: Jeff Stringer
Prin: Molly McShane

MCSHANE WILLIAMS WAY MOB 1
See MCSHANE DEVELOPMENT CO LLC

D-U-N-S 03-872-6634
MCSI INC
2975 Northwoods Pkwy, Peachtree Corners, GA 30071-1537
Tel (770) 441-5263 *Founded/Ownrshp* 1981
Sales 91.0MM^E *EMP* 2,036
SIC 1731 5065 7359 Communications specialization; Communication equipment; Audio-visual equipment & supply rental; Communications specialization; Communication equipment; Audio-visual equipment & supply rental
Pr: D Gordon Strickland
**Ch Bd:* Timothy R Chrisman
CFO: James R Vonier
Ofcr: Larry K Knipple
CTO: Chris Johnson
VP Opers: Mary A Stewart
VP Mktg: Joe Robinson
Mktg Mgr: Deborah Wilson
Board of Directors: Robert G Hecht, William D King, Henry Radcliffe

D-U-N-S 02-900-0965
MCSPI INC
MCDONALD'S
3353 Durahart St, Riverside, CA 92507-3460
Tel (951) 784-2336 *Founded/Ownrshp* 1966
Sales 10.0MM^E *EMP* 300
SIC 5812 Fast-food restaurant, chain; Fast-food restaurant, chain
Pr: Thomas R Spiel
**VP:* Candace Spiel

MCSS
See MADISON COUNTY BOARD OF EDUCATION

MCSWAIN CARPETS & FLOORS
See MCAF LLC

D-U-N-S 11-288-9308 IMP/EXP
■ **MCSWAIN MANUFACTURING CORP**
(*Suby of* PCC) ★
382 Circle Freeway Dr, West Chester, OH 45246-1208
Tel (513) 619-1222 *Founded/Ownrshp* 2012
Sales 33.5MM^E *EMP* 148
SIC 3599 Machine shop, jobbing & repair; Machine shop, jobbing & repair
Pr: Michael Meshay
**VP:* Bill Michalski
**Prin:* Michael A Hirschfeld

D-U-N-S 07-657-4474
MCSWEENEY & RICCI INSURANCE AGENCY INC
420 Washington St Ste 200, Braintree, MA 02184-4774
Tel (781) 848-8600 *Founded/Ownrshp* 1964
Sales NA *EMP* 70
SIC 6411 Insurance agents
CEO: Louis G Ricci Sr
**Pr:* Mary Lou Leary
**Pr:* Mary Lou Ricci
**COO:* Timothy Kane
**CFO:* John E Curry
**Treas:* Mary Ellen Sullivan
Ex VP: Timothy Hall
Dir Risk M: Martin Kinsman
Mng Dir: Paul Marks
Brnch Mgr: Andrew Boyle
Brnch Mgr: Paula Himmelman

D-U-N-S 18-759-3041 IMP
MCT DAIRIES INC
TRUGMAN-NASH
(*Suby of* ALLIED DAIRY PRODUCTS INC) ★
15 Bleeker St, Millburn, NJ 07041-1468
Tel (973) 258-9600 *Founded/Ownrshp* 1998
Sales 23.8MM^E *EMP* 24
SIC 5143 Dairy products, except dried or canned
Pr: Ken Meyers
**CFO:* Vincent McCann
**Ex VP:* David Raff
VP: Denis Neville

MCT WHOLESALE
See MACON CIGAR & TOBACCO CO

D-U-N-S 07-651-4418
MCTECH CORP
8100 Grand Ave Ste 100, Cleveland, OH 44104-3164
Tel (216) 391-7700 *Founded/Ownrshp* 1997
Sales 32.7MM *EMP* 40^E
SIC 1541 Highway & street construction; General contractor, highway & street construction; Custom builders, non-residential; Renovation, remodeling & repairs: industrial buildings; Wrecking & demolition work; Industrial buildings & warehouses
Pr: Mark F Perkins
CFO: John George
**Sec:* Lisa Cifani
Plnt Mgr: David Zupanic

D-U-N-S 12-699-6230
MCV ASSOCIATED PHYSICIANS
MCV PHYSICIANS
830 E Main St Ste 1900, Richmond, VA 23219-2701
Tel (804) 358-6100 *Founded/Ownrshp* 1991
Sales 292.6MM *EMP* 1,337
Accts Kpmg Llp Mclean Va
SIC 8741 8721 Business management; Accounting, auditing & bookkeeping; Business management; Accounting, auditing & bookkeeping
Pr: John Ward
IT Man: Keith Purcell

MCV PHYSICIANS
See MCV ASSOCIATED PHYSICIANS

D-U-N-S 02-958-8480
MCW FUELS INC
10100 Santa Monica Blvd # 300, Los Angeles, CA 90067-4107
Tel (818) 484-5208 *Founded/Ownrshp* 2006
Sales 61.4MM^E *EMP* 20
SIC 5171 5172 Petroleum bulk stations; Lubricating oils & greases
CEO: David Sutton
**CEO:* Aleksander Blyumkin
**COO:* Sammy Dabbas
VP: Gabriel Quintana

D-U-N-S 12-816-4139
MCW SOLUTIONS LLC
M C W
20098 Ashbrook Pl Ste 150, Ashburn, VA 20147-3394
Tel (703) 726-1292 *Founded/Ownrshp* 2003
Sales 24.8MM^E *EMP* 75
SIC 7373 3699 3651 Local area network (LAN) systems integrator; Security control equipment & systems; Audio electronic systems
CFO: Eric Kunz
Prin: Ghattas Hajjo
Off Mgr: Leigh Miller
Dir IT: Michael Darling
Software D: Jeff Nido
Opers Mgr: Chris Reeley
Mktg Mgr: Melissa Dunlap
Snr PM: Aaron Johanson
Snr PM: Ben Whitford

MCWANE CAST IRON PIPE COMPANY
See MCWANE INC

D-U-N-S 00-400-1715 IMP/EXP
MCWANE INC
MCWANE CAST IRON PIPE COMPANY
2900 Highway 280 S # 300, Birmingham, AL 35223-2469
Tel (205) 871-9774 *Founded/Ownrshp* 1921, 1975
Sales 1.2MMM^E *EMP* 4,883
SIC 3491 1221 3321 3312 3494 Fire hydrant valves; Bituminous coal surface mining; Ductile iron castings; Coke oven products (chemical recovery); Valves & pipe fittings; Fire hydrant valves; Bituminous coal surface mining; Ductile iron castings; Coke oven products (chemical recovery); Valves & pipe fittings
Ch: C Philip McWane
**Pr:* G Ruffner Page Jr
Pr: Melanie Williamson
**CFO:* Charles F Nowlin
Treas: Glenda Burson
**Ex VP:* Dennis R Charko
Ex VP: Leon G McCullough
**Sr VP:* Michael Keel
Sr VP: Jeff Otterstedt
**VP:* Arne C Feyling
VP: Key Foster
VP: Kevin McCarthy
VP: Chris Nichols
VP: Ruffner Page
VP: Jeet Radia
Exec: Benida Slippo
Exec: Alvin Tucker
Comm Dir: Mickie Coggin

D-U-N-S 00-914-0070
MCWANE INC
AB & I FOUNDRY
7825 San Leandro St, Oakland, CA 94621-2515
Tel (510) 632-3467 *Founded/Ownrshp* 1906
Sales 31.5MM^E *EMP* 215
SIC 3321 3494 Soil pipe & fittings: cast iron; Gray iron castings; Valves & pipe fittings; Soil pipe & fittings: cast iron; Gray iron castings; Valves & pipe fittings
Pr: Allan Boscacci
**Ch Bd:* Clifford Wixson
**CFO:* John Callagy
VP: Kevin McCullough
Rgnl Mgr: Ray Butcher
Sfty Mgr: John Deseck
Manager: Shannon Hooper
Manager: Ethan Shull
Sls Mgr: Brian Lee

D-U-N-S 94-342-9027
MCWHINNEY HOLDING CO LLLP
2725 Rocky Mountain Ave # 200, Loveland, CO 80538-8716
Tel (970) 962-9990 *Founded/Ownrshp* 1994
Sales 25.8MM^E *EMP* 72^E
SIC 6552 Subdividers & developers
Mng Pt: Chad McWhinney
Prin: Robert Scott
Opers Mgr: Sylvester Mabry

D-U-N-S 05-223-3780
MCWHORTHER TIRE CO LTD
MC WHORTER'S TIRE CO
1008 Texas Ave, Lubbock, TX 79401-3318
Tel (806) 762-0231 *Founded/Ownrshp* 1979
Sales 41.9MM^E *EMP* 80
SIC 5531 7539 7534 Automotive tires; Batteries, automotive & truck; Automotive accessories; Automotive repair shops; Tire repair shop; Tire recapping
Pr: Rock Rickel
**VP:* Jim Riebel

D-U-N-S 00-218-3630 IMP
■ **MCWILLIAMS FORGE CO** (NJ)
(*Suby of* PCC) ★
387 Franklin Ave, Rockaway, NJ 07866-4014
Tel (973) 627-0200 *Founded/Ownrshp* 1945, 2007
Sales 60.0MM *EMP* 80^E
SIC 3462 3769 3463 Nuclear power plant forgings, ferrous; Machinery forgings, ferrous; Pump & compressor forgings, ferrous; Aircraft forgings, ferrous; Guided missile & space vehicle parts & auxiliary equipment; Nonferrous forgings; Nuclear power plant forgings, ferrous; Machinery forgings, ferrous; Pump & compressor forgings, ferrous; Aircraft forgings, ferrous; Guided missile & space vehicle parts & auxiliary equipment; Nonferrous forgings
Pr: Alexander M Mc Williams
**Ex VP:* Timothy C McWilliams
Dir IT: Gordon Hayes
IT Man: David Goldstein
Sfty Dirs: Jose Rivera
QI Cn Mgr: Joseph Pascoe

D-U-N-S 08-711-7891
MD ADVANTAGE INSURANCE CO OF NEW JERSEY
100 Franklin Corner Rd, Trenton, NJ 08648-2104
Tel (888) 355-5551 *Founded/Ownrshp* 2002
Sales NA *EMP* 40
SIC 6331 Fire, marine & casualty insurance; Fire, marine & casualty insurance
CEO: Patricia A Costante
Pr: James Constantine
**CFO:* Stephen B Cohen
Ex VP: Joseph Hudson
VP: Barry Burdick
VP: Nina Gowaty
VP: Tom McGinn
VP: Rose Patricelli
VP: Janet Puro
Counsel: Thomas Leyhane

MD ANDERSON CANCER CENTER
See M D ANDERSON SERVICES CORP

MD ANDERSON CANCER CENTER
See UNIVERSITY OF TEXAS M D ANDERSON CANCER CENTER

D-U-N-S 88-428-0389
MD ANDERSON PHYSICIANS NETWORK
1515 Holcombe Blvd, Houston, TX 77030-4000
Tel (713) 745-9720 *Founded/Ownrshp* 1994
Sales 65.1MM *EMP* 62
Accts Deloitte Tax Llp Houston Tx
SIC 8621 Professional membership organizations; Professional membership organizations
COO: William Hyslop
**Ch Bd:* William Murphy
**Pr:* Hugh Wilfong MD
**CEO:* Robert N Shaw
**CFO:* Kim Burgen
**V Ch Bd:* Robert L Jones
VP: Pamela Redden
VP: Nancy Richardson
Off Mgr: Judy Reichelderfer

D-U-N-S 04-889-1157
MD AUTO GROUP LLC
I-90 NISSAN
5013 Detroit Rd, Sheffield Village, OH 44054-2810
Tel (440) 934-6001 *Founded/Ownrshp* 2014
Sales 240.0MM *EMP* 35
SIC 5511 Automobiles, new & used

MD CARE HEALTHPLAN
See MD CARE INC

D-U-N-S 02-030-3729
■ **MD CARE INC**
MD CARE HEALTHPLAN
(*Suby of* HUMANA INC) ★
1640 E Hill St, Signal Hill, CA 90755-3612
Tel (562) 344-3400 *Founded/Ownrshp* 2004, 2012
Sales NA *EMP* 75
SIC 6321 Health insurance carriers
Pr: Long Dang

D-U-N-S 02-849-2598
MD DEPT OF HOUSING & COMMUNITY DEVELOPMENT
(*Suby of* EXECUTIVE OFFICE OF STATE OF MARYLAND) ★
7800 Harkins Rd, Lanham, MD 20706-1333
Tel (410) 514-7000 *Founded/Ownrshp* 1987
Sales NA *EMP* 889
Accts Reznick Group Pc Baltimore
SIC 9531 Housing programs; ; Housing programs;
CFO: Steven Silver
**CFO:* Susan Traylor
Sr Cor Off: Raymond Skinner
Ofcr: Jennifer Bruce
Ofcr: Anne Bruder
Ofcr: Collin Ingraham
Sr VP: David Cotton

MD EXPRESS
See M D LOGISTICS INC

D-U-N-S 05-431-3767 IMP
MD HELICOPTERS INC (AZ)
(*Suby of* PATRIARCH PARTNERS LLC) ★
4555 E Mcdowell Rd, Mesa, AZ 85215-9734
Tel (480) 346-6474 *Founded/Ownrshp* 1999, 2006
Sales 59.8MM^E *EMP* 275^E
SIC 3721 Helicopters; Helicopters
CEO: Lynn Tilton
Pr: John Surmay
**COO:* Carl Schopfer
**CFO:* Mike Kelley
VP: Dorothy Coia
VP: Gary Dolski
VP: Greg Gauer
VP: Brian Reid
VP: Don Runyon
VP: Sergio Villarreal
Exec: Kim Ruddick
Exec: Eric Tossavainen

D-U-N-S 83-235-4042
MD INVESTORS CORP
METALDYNE
(*Suby of* ASP MD HOLDINGS INC) ★
47659 Halyard Dr, Plymouth, MI 48170-2429
Tel (734) 207-6200 *Founded/Ownrshp* 2012
Sales 896.5MM^E *EMP* 6,500

SIC 6799 Investors; Investors
CEO: Thomas A Amato
CFO: Terry Iwasaki
Treas: Buddy Martin
VP: James Hug
VP: Richard Lefebvre
Dir IT: Dick Lefabvre

MD IT TRANSCRIPTION SERVICES
See HEALTH CARECHAIN INC

MD SKINCARE
See DR DENNIS GROSS SKINCARE

MD TOTCO
See MARTIN-DECKER TOTCO INC

MD&A
See TURBO PARTS LLC

MDA
See MUSCULAR DYSTROPHY ASSOCIATION INC

MDA
See MARYLAND DEPARTMENT OF AGRICULTURE

D-U-N-S 07-971-8473
MDA COMMUNICATIONS HOLDINGS LLC
3825 Fabian Way, Palo Alto, CA 94303-4604
Tel (650) 852-4000 *Founded/Ownrshp* 2015
Sales 129.8MM[E] *EMP* 2,800
SIC 3663 Satellites, communications

D-U-N-S 05-518-9781
MDA INFORMATION SYSTEMS INC
(*Suby of* MACDONALD, DETTWILER AND ASSOCIATES LTD)
820 W Diamond Ave Ste 300, Gaithersburg, MD 20878-1469
Tel (240) 833-8200 *Founded/Ownrshp* 2002
Sales 65.6MM *EMP* 180[E]
SIC 8711 8748 Engineering services; Business consulting; Engineering services; Business consulting
Pr: Gregory T Koeln
**CEO:* Herbert Satterlee III
**Treas:* Chris Caporaletti
**Sr VP:* Larry Heitkemper
**VP:* David Cunningham
**VP:* Roger Mitchell
**VP:* Dawn Sienicki
Dir Sec: Jim Bradley
Snr Ntwrk: Aidan Carvajal
IT Man: Joan Duvall
IT Man: April Hagmeyer

D-U-N-S 07-858-7090
MDA INFORMATION SYSTEMS LLC
(*Suby of* MACDONALD, DETTWILER AND ASSOCIATES LTD)
820 W Diamond Ave Ste 300, Gaithersburg, MD 20878-1469
Tel (240) 833-8200 *Founded/Ownrshp* 2012
Sales 83.7MM *EMP* 99[E]
Accts Kpmg Llp Mclean Va
SIC 7371 Custom computer programming services; Custom computer programming services
CEO: Herbert Satterlee III

D-U-N-S 80-832-2200
MDA MANUFACTURING INC
(*Suby of* DAIKIN AMERICA INC) ★
State Dock Rd W, Decatur, AL 35601
Tel (256) 306-5000 *Founded/Ownrshp* 2013
Sales 100.0MM *EMP* 9
SIC 2819 Industrial inorganic chemicals
Pr: David Hendrixson
**Sec:* Mike Warner

D-U-N-S 07-843-0740
MDA US SYSTEMS LLC
1250 Lincoln Ave Ste 100, Pasadena, CA 91103-2466
Tel (626) 296-1373 *Founded/Ownrshp* 2012
Sales 29.4MM[E] *EMP* 350[E]
SIC 8711 8731 Engineering services; Commercial physical research
Pr: Eric Kucher
Dir Bus: Tom McCarthy
**Prin:* Mohammad Manki
Genl Mgr: Ted Cheng
QA Dir: Scott Vanderzyl
IT Man: Frank Bleisch
Opers Mgr: Joe Cocks
Mktg Dir: Christopher Hyde

D-U-N-S 80-284-9211
MDADVANTAGE HOLDINGS INC
2 Princess Rd Ste 2, Lawrenceville, NJ 08648-2320
Tel (609) 896-2404 *Founded/Ownrshp* 2002
Sales NA *EMP* 78
SIC 6331 Fire, marine & casualty insurance
Ch Bd: Patricia A Costante
**CFO:* Stephen B Cohen

MDC
See MIAMI DADE COLLEGE

MDC DRYWALL
See MIDWEST DRYWALL CO INC

D-U-N-S 06-970-2181
▲ MDC HOLDINGS INC
4350 S Monaco St Ste 500, Denver, CO 80237-3400
Tel (303) 773-2727 *Founded/Ownrshp* 1972
Sales 1.6MMM *EMP* 1,140
Accts Ernst & Young Llp Irvine Cal
Tkr Sym MDC *Exch* NYS
SIC 1521 6162 7389 New construction, single-family houses; Mortgage bankers; New construction, single-family houses; Mortgage bankers; Financial services
CEO: Larry A Mizel
**Pr:* David D Mandarich
COO: Ludivell Jones
**CFO:* Robert N Martin
Sr VP: Christopher M Anderson
**Sr VP:* Michael Touff
VP: Shelley Casagrande
VP: Paul Forsythe
VP: Kendall Fults
VP: Tammy Gonzales
VP: Frann Gray
VP: Christine Laplaca
VP: Ryan Linder
VP: Carrie Luyster
VP: Phil Nowick
VP: Kenneth J Ryerson
VP: Mary Schaub
VP: Lynn Starrett
VP: Kelly Taga
VP: Robert Wagner
Board of Directors: Raymond T Baker, Michael A Berman, David E Blackford, Herbert T Buchwald, Paris G Reece III, David Siegel

MDC HOMES
See MCCAR REALTY INC

D-U-N-S 62-397-3968
▲ MDC PARTNERS INC
745 5th Ave Fl 19, New York, NY 10151-2003
Tel (646) 429-1800 *Founded/Ownrshp* 1986
Sales 1.2MMM *EMP* 5,250
Tkr Sym MDCA *Exch* NGS
SIC 7311 8748 Advertising agencies; Business consulting; Advertising agencies; Business consulting
Ch Bd: Scott L Kauffman
Pr: Michael Bassik
CFO: David B Doft
Sr Cor Off: Michael Sabatino
Chf Mktg O: Terence Donnelly
Ex VP: Barbara Creagh
Ex VP: David Norton
Sr VP: Glenn Gibson
Sr VP: David C Ross
VP: Tricia Benn
VP: Matt Chesler
VP: Alexandra Delanghe
VP: Christine Laplaca
VP: Frann Vettor-Gray
Board of Directors: Clare Copeland, Michal Kirby, Irwin Simon

D-U-N-S 00-916-5895 IMP
MDC VACUUM PRODUCTS LLC
INSULATED SEAL
23842 Cabot Blvd, Hayward, CA 94545-1600
Tel (510) 265-3500 *Founded/Ownrshp* 1976, 2005
Sales 46.5MM[E] *EMP* 180
SIC 3491 3674 Industrial valves; Pressure valves & regulators, industrial; Industrial valves; Pressure valves & regulators, industrial; Wafers (semiconductor devices)
CEO: Bill Lebaron
**COO:* MO Boukelif
**CFO:* Rick Kent
VP: Tina Lavars
Prgrm Mgr: Mark Spencer
Genl Mgr: Dan Childers
Genl Mgr: Vernon Olson
S&M/VP: Maarten Kramer
Sls Dir: Marie Wise
Manager: Shawn Jones
Sls Mgr: Erick Forbes

MDC WALLCOVERINGS
See EPKO INDUSTRIES INC

MDCC
See MISSISSIPPI DELTA COMMUNITY COLLEGE (INC)

MDD
See DRISCOLL MATSON & LLP DAMICO

MDDATACOR, INC.
See MDDATACOR LLC

D-U-N-S 03-269-7356
MDDATACOR LLC
MDDATACOR, INC.
(*Suby of* SYMPHONY PERFORMANCE HEALTH INC) ★
11545 Wills Rd Ste 100, Alpharetta, GA 30009-2098
Tel (678) 319-0039 *Founded/Ownrshp* 2014
Sales 7.8MM[E] *EMP* 400
SIC 8082 Home health care services
CEO: Al Vega
**CFO:* George Dunaway
VP: Terri Davis
VP: Russell Olsen
Netwrk Eng: Brian Manis
VP Sls: David Wellons

MDEQ
See MICHIGAN DEPARTMENT OF ENVIRONMENTAL QUALITY

MDHHS
See MICHIGAN DEPARTMENT OF HEALTH & HUMAN SERVICES

MDHS FAMILY AND CHILDRENS SVCS
See MISSISSIPPI DEPARTMENT OF HUMAN SERVICES

MDI
See MARK DUNNING INDUSTRIES

D-U-N-S 10-656-0832
MDI ACHIEVE (TEXAS) INC
MATRIXCARE
(*Suby of* LOGIBEC INC)
10900 Hampshire Ave S # 100, Bloomington, MN 55438-2699
Tel (314) 439-6400 *Founded/Ownrshp* 1982
Sales 39.8MM[E] *EMP* 215[E]
SIC 8748 Systems engineering consultant, ex. computer or professional; Systems engineering consultant, ex. computer or professional
CEO: Marc Brunet
**Ch Bd:* Todd A Spence
**Pr:* John Damgaard
**CFO:* Thomas K Andrew
**CFO:* Brian Cosgrove
**Chf Mktg O:* Phil Christianson
**Ofcr:* Denise Wassenaar
**Ex VP:* Di Anne Carrigan
**Sr VP:* Dennis Jakubowicz
**Sr VP:* Kevin Whitehurst
**VP:* Donna Boschert
VP: Bob Eisenhower

D-U-N-S 16-878-5876
MDI HOLDINGS LLC
C/O COURT SQ CAPITL PARTNERS
399 Park Ave Fl 14, New York, NY 10022-4772
Tel (212) 559-1127 *Founded/Ownrshp* 2006
Sales 228.8MM[E] *EMP* 2,900
SIC 2899 2842 2874 2992 2752 3577 Chemical preparations; Cleaning or polishing preparations; Phosphates; Lubricating oils; Offset & photolithographic printing; Printers & plotters; Chemical preparations; Plating compounds; Rust resisting compounds; Stencil correction compounds; Cleaning or polishing preparations; Phosphates; Lubricating oils; Offset & photolithographic printing; Printers & plotters
Pr: Joseph M Silvestri
Mng Pt: John Weber

MDI ROCK
See MATERIAL DELIVERY INC

MDI TRAFFIC CONTROL PRODUCTS
See MARKETING DISPLAYS INC

MDIST
See MARTINEZ DISTRIBUTORS CORP

D-U-N-S 02-907-9316
MDJ INC
HOME LUMBER COMPANY
15451 San Fernando Msn, Mission Hills, CA 91345-1368
Tel (909) 381-1771 *Founded/Ownrshp* 1949
Sales 85.0MM *EMP* 90
SIC 5031 5211 Lumber, plywood & millwork; Lumber & other building materials; Lumber, plywood & millwork; Lumber & other building materials
Pr: Milton Johnson
**Sec:* Kelle Vollkommer
**VP:* Brent Johnson

MDL
See MEDICAL DIAGNOSTIC LABORATORIES LLC

D-U-N-S 83-763-0248
MDLIVE INC
13630 Nw 8th St Ste 205, Sunrise, FL 33325-6238
Tel (800) 400-6354 *Founded/Ownrshp* 2012
Sales 24.6MM[E] *EMP* 250[E]
SIC 8082 Home health care services
Pr: Randy Parker
Pr: Dr Steve Gurland
COO: Greg Swayne
CFO: Kuldeep Hajela
Chf Mktg O: Malinda McFarlane
Ofcr: Chuck Hector
Ofcr: Deborah Mulligan
Ofcr: David Sculley
Ex VP: Susan Mihojevich
Ex VP: Arlene Rodriguez
Ex VP: Gregory Strauss
VP: Drew Ben-Aharon
VP: Brendan Keaney
Creative D: Ron Noel
Dir Bus: Robert Dafnis
Dir Bus: Christina Mohil

D-U-N-S 01-071-2748
MDM BRICKELL HOTEL GROUP LTD
J W MARRIOTT
1109 Brickell Ave, Miami, FL 33131-3101
Tel (305) 374-1224 *Founded/Ownrshp* 1997
Sales 24.6MM[E] *EMP* 220
SIC 8741 Hotel or motel management; Hotel or motel management
Exec: Eduardo Roca
Genl Mgr: Slorencia Tabeni

D-U-N-S 78-508-7255
MDM COMMERCIAL ENTERPRISES INC
LG FULFILLMENT
1102 A1a N Ste 205, Ponte Vedra, FL 32082-4098
Tel (904) 241-2340 *Founded/Ownrshp* 1990
Sales 40.0MM *EMP* 28[E]
Accts Swindell Bohn Durden & Phill
SIC 5064 Television sets; Air conditioning room units, self-contained; Television sets; Air conditioning room units, self-contained
CEO: Steve Austin
**Pr:* Steve E Austin
**Pr:* Lee Whittaker
Pr: Travis Whittaker
CFO: Debbie Hitchcock
**CFO:* Susan Slappey
**Sec:* Laurie Austin
VP: Loris Cabrera
VP: Dave Lingor
VP: Chris Luley
Brnch Mgr: David Stroly

D-U-N-S 00-323-3301
MDM ENTERPRISES INC
SUNBELT SPAS
3924 Dunvale Rd, Houston, TX 77063-5818
Tel (281) 575-9814 *Founded/Ownrshp* 1979
Sales 27.4MM[E] *EMP* 102
SIC 3088 Hot tubs, plastic or fiberglass; Hot tubs, plastic or fiberglass
Pr: Robert Markiton

D-U-N-S 15-295-4525
MDM HOTEL GROUP LTD
MIAMI DADELAND MARRIOTT
9090 S Dadeland Blvd, Miami, FL 33156-7820
Tel (305) 670-1035 *Founded/Ownrshp* 1990
Sales 27.1MM[E] *EMP* 250[E]
SIC 7011 5812 5813 Hotels & motels; Eating places; Drinking places; Hotels & motels; Eating places; Drinking places
Genl Pt: Luis A Pulenta
Exec: Brian Barton
Genl Mgr: Bob Fabiano
Genl Mgr: Mildred Riscigno
Sls&Mrk Ex: Eddie McBorolin
Sls Dir: Mechi Etcheberry

D-U-N-S 61-380-1307
MDM SUPPLY INC
2609 Bozeman Ave, Helena, MT 59601-2923
Tel (406) 443-4012 *Founded/Ownrshp* 1990
Sales 34.1MM[E] *EMP* 72
SIC 5074 Plumbing fittings & supplies; Plumbing fittings & supplies
Pr: Thomas Rosendahl
**Pr:* Lou Dumas
**VP:* Craig Skinn
IT Man: Bill Bradford
Sls Mgr: Dennis Bennett

MDM&C
See MC ELROY DEUTSCH MULVANEY & CARPERNTER LLP

MDMC
See MISSOURI DELTA MEDICAL CENTER

MDOC
See DEPARTMENT OF CORRECTIONS MICHIGAN

D-U-N-S 07-987-1280
MDR INC
ACCU-BORE DIRECTIONAL DRILLING
100 Oak Rd, Benicia, CA 94510
Tel (707) 750-5376 *Founded/Ownrshp* 2010
Sales 26.0MM *EMP* 90
SIC 8711 Construction & civil engineering
Prin: Michael Robirds

D-U-N-S 17-210-9142
MDR LLC
14101 Nw 4th St, Sunrise, FL 33325-6209
Tel (954) 845-9500 *Founded/Ownrshp* 1984
Sales 20.2MM[E] *EMP* 150
SIC 2834 Vitamin preparations; Vitamin preparations

D-U-N-S 79-043-0032 IMP
MDR METALS LLC
600 W 83rd St, Hialeah, FL 33014-3612
Tel (305) 444-1198 *Founded/Ownrshp* 2007
Sales 30.0MM *EMP* 6
SIC 5051 5046 Aluminum bars, rods, ingots, sheets, pipes, plates, etc.; Cooking equipment, commercial; Aluminum bars, rods, ingots, sheets, pipes, plates, etc.; Cooking equipment, commercial
VP: Juan Pelaez
VP Sls: Mario Calltjas

D-U-N-S 07-525-8780
MDRC
16 E 34th St Fl 19, New York, NY 10016-4326
Tel (212) 532-3200 *Founded/Ownrshp* 1974
Sales 75.1MM *EMP* 225
Accts Grant Thornton Llp New York
SIC 8641 8733 Civic social & fraternal associations; Noncommercial social research organization; Civic social & fraternal associations; Noncommercial social research organization
Pr: Gordon Berlin
Ofcr: Angelica Manigbas
**Sr VP:* Jesus M Amadeo
**Sr VP:* Robert Ivry
**VP:* Fred Doolittle
**VP:* Barbara Goldman
**VP:* Sharon Rowser
VP: John Wallace
Telecom Ex: Paul Feliu
Snr Ntwrk: Joel Alleger
CTO: Inna Kruglaya

D-U-N-S 79-010-4814
MDS COMMUNICATIONS CORP
MOUNT DEVELOPMENT SERVICES
545 W Juanita Ave, Mesa, AZ 85210-6033
Tel (480) 752-8140 *Founded/Ownrshp* 1992
Sales 21.0MM[E] *EMP* 200
SIC 7389 Fund raising organizations; Fund raising organizations
Pr: Jonathan D Mount Jr
COO: Patrick Hodgkins
CFO: Brenda Gelder
**VP:* Julia Macdonald
Dir Soc: Justin Burleigh
Sls&Mrk Ex: Shelley Nelson

D-U-N-S 12-997-0773
MDS FOODS INC
4676 Erie Ave Sw Ste A, Navarre, OH 44662-9658
Tel (330) 879-9780 *Founded/Ownrshp* 2003
Sales 21.7MM[E] *EMP* 50
SIC 5143 Cheese
Pr: James Straughn
**Ex VP:* Pete Effinger
**VP:* Lisa Straughn

D-U-N-S 04-153-9784
MDS PHARMA SERVICES (US) INC
(*Suby of* NORDION INC)
2200 Rnpance Blvd Ste 400, King of Prussia, PA 19406
Tel (610) 239-7900 *Founded/Ownrshp* 1996
Sales 59.2MM[E] *EMP* 3,042
SIC 8734 Testing laboratories; Testing laboratories
Pr: David Spaight
**CFO:* Rudy Howard
Ex VP: Alan Torrie
Sr VP: Robert Bland
Sr VP: Robert Breckon
**Sr VP:* Cameron T Hicks
**Sr VP:* James Mc Clurg
Sr VP: Teresa F Winslow
VP: James D Hulse
VP: Lori McDonald
VP: James Miskel
VP: Cinda Orr
VP: Vijay Vashi
**VP:* Peter D Winkley
Dir Bus: Judy Rubin
Dir Bus: Lorraine Rusch

D-U-N-S 78-065-6372
MDSA LLC
MIGHTY DISTRIBUTING SYS AMER
(*Suby of* GONHER, S.A. DE C.V.)
650 Engineering Dr, Norcross, GA 30092-2821
Tel (770) 448-3900 *Founded/Ownrshp* 2009

Sales 232.0MM^E *EMP* 180
SIC 5013 6794 Franchises, selling or licensing; Automotive supplies & parts; Automotive supplies & parts; Franchises, selling or licensing
Pr: Kenneth S Voelker
**Ch Bd:* Thomas R Barry
Pr: Ron Ferguson
COO: Kenneth Volker
**Sr VP:* Gary Vann
**VP:* Brad Bradshaw
VP: Jesse Bradshaw
VP: Scott Dees
VP: Barry Teagle
VP: Pelham Wilder
Comm Man: Rachel Overby

D-U-N-S 79-669-0993
MDSFEST INC
237 2nnd Ave S, Onalaska, WI 54650
Tel (608) 779-2720 *Founded/Ownrshp* 2005
Sales 67.3MM^E *EMP* 1,078^E
SIC 5411 Grocery stores, chain
CFO: Kirk Stoa

MDSI
See MANAGEMENT DATA SYSTEMS INTERNATIONAL INC

D-U-N-S 12-551-1639
MDT ARMOR CORP
308 Alabama St, Auburn, AL 36832-4343
Tel (334) 321-0762 *Founded/Ownrshp* 2003
Sales 24.5MM^E *EMP* 76^E
SIC 3312 Armor plate
CEO: Steven Esses
Ofcr: David Murphy
Ex VP: Shlomo Ashkena
**Ex VP:* Jonathan Whartman
**VP:* Michael Kitchen
**VP:* Leeland Nall
Genl Mgr: Shlomi Ashknavi

D-U-N-S 96-947-4027
MDT LABOR LLC
MDT TECHNICAL
2325 Paxton Church Rd B, Harrisburg, PA 17110-9688
Tel (717) 585-6322 *Founded/Ownrshp* 2011
Sales 21.0MM *EMP* 150
SIC 7361 Employment agencies; Employment agencies
Pr: Jodi Hon
COO: Mike Boyle
VP: Tammy Simonetti
Mng Dir: John Pigman

MDT TECHNICAL
See MDT LABOR LLC

D-U-N-S 01-577-0014
▲ MDU COMMUNICATIONS INTERNATIONAL INC
60d Commerce Way, Totowa, NJ 07512-3109
Tel (973) 237-9499 *Founded/Ownrshp* 1998
Sales 27.3MM *EMP* 105^E
Tkr Sym MDTV *Exch* OTO
SIC 4841 4813 8999 Cable television services; ; Communication services; Cable television services; ; Communication services
CEO: John Edward Boyle
Pr: Chris Nassau
VP: Daren Benzi
VP: Moh Elbaz
VP: Carmen Ragusa Jr
VP: Michael Stanway
VP: Marisol Summers
VP Sls: Patrick Cunningham
Board of Directors: Carolyn C Howard, Richard Newman, Gregory L Osborn

D-U-N-S 09-029-0441
■ MDU CONSTRUCTION SERVICES GROUP INC
(*Suby of* MDU RESOURCES GROUP INC) ★
1150 W Century Ave, Bismarck, ND 58503-0942
Tel (701) 530-1000 *Founded/Ownrshp* 2003
Sales 1.1MMM^E *EMP* 4,030
SIC 4911 Generation, electric power; Transmission, electric power; Distribution, electric power; Generation, electric power; Transmission, electric power; Distribution, electric power
Pr: Jeff Thiede
**COO:* Craig Keller

D-U-N-S 16-942-5324
MDU ENTERPRISES INC
BULK TV & INTERNET
8537 Six Forks Rd Ste 100, Raleigh, NC 27615-6545
Tel (919) 850-3208 *Founded/Ownrshp* 2004
Sales 50.6MM^E *EMP* 100
SIC 5063 Antennas, receiving, satellite dishes; Antennas, receiving, satellite dishes
Pr: Dave O Connell
**CFO:* Malcolm Clarke
**VP:* Thomas Conley
VP: Craig Snelgrove
Genl Mgr: Tara Morgan
VP Sls: James H Jessel
Sls Mgr: Jay Carothers

D-U-N-S 00-696-2286 IMP/EXP
▲ MDU RESOURCES GROUP INC
1200 W Century Ave, Bismarck, ND 58503-0911
Tel (701) 530-1000 *Founded/Ownrshp* 1924
Sales 4.6MMM *EMP* 9,133
Accts Deloitte & Touche Llp Minneap
Tkr Sym MDU *Exch* NYS
SIC 4911 4924 4922 1221 1442 1311 Generation, electric power; Transmission, electric power; Distribution, electric power; Natural gas distribution; Pipelines, natural gas; Surface mining, lignite; Construction sand & gravel; Crude petroleum production; Natural gas production; Generation, electric power; Transmission, electric power; Distribution, electric power; Natural gas distribution; Pipelines, natural gas; Surface mining, lignite; Construction sand & gravel; Crude petroleum production; Natural gas production
Pr: David L Goodin
Genl Pt: Deborah Bergan
CFO: Doran N Schwartz
Bd of Dir: Jon Hunke
Bd of Dir: Patricia Moss
Chf Mktg O: Dawn Sackman
Ex VP: John Castleberry
Ex VP: Dennis Haider
Ex VP: Craig Keller
Ex VP: Robert Lunder
Ex VP: William E Schneider
VP: William R Connors
VP: Anne Jones
VP: Nathan W Ring
Board of Directors: Thomas Everist, Karen B Fagg, Mark A Hellerstein, A Bart Holaday, Dennis W Johnson, William E McCracken, Patricia L Moss, Harry J Pearce, John K Wilson

D-U-N-S 96-777-7371
MDU RESOURCES GROUP INC EMPLOYEE BENEFIT TRUST
1200 W Century Ave, Bismarck, ND 58503-0911
Tel (701) 530-1751 *Founded/Ownrshp* 2011
Sales NA *EMP* 3^E
SIC 6411 Insurance agents, brokers & service; Insurance agents, brokers & service
Ch: Dennis W Johnson

D-U-N-S 07-959-1382
MDV SPARTANNASH CO
850 76th St, Grand Rapids, MI 49518
Tel (616) 878-2000 *Founded/Ownrshp* 2014
Sales 28.9MM^E *EMP* 99
SIC 5141 Groceries, general line
Treas: William Jacobs
**Treas:* Rene Hunter

D-U-N-S 02-312-3180
■ MDVIP INC
(*Suby of* PROCTER & GAMBLE CO) ★
1875 Nw Corp Blvd Ste 300, Boca Raton, FL 33431-8561
Tel (888) 936-3847 *Founded/Ownrshp* 2001
Sales 65.2MM^E *EMP* 250
SIC 8062 General medical & surgical hospitals; General medical & surgical hospitals
CEO: Brett Jorgensen
**Pr:* Mark Murrison
**CEO:* Bret Jorgensen
**CFO:* Matthew Hashem
Bd of Dir: Andrew Schlein
Chf Mktg O: Chris Lillich
Ex VP: Dan Behroozi
Ex VP: Steven Cohen
VP: Michael Prindle
Exec: Diane Neveloff
Assoc Dir: Jennifer Coleman
Assoc Dir: Roger Necochea
Assoc Dir: Emily Olexy
Assoc Dir: Vidette Pires
Assoc Dir: Mauricio Rodriguez
Assoc Dir: Tony Siebel
Dir Soc: Jennifer Granger
Dir Soc: Elizabeth Young

D-U-N-S 03-683-3952
MDWISE INC
1200 Madison Ave Ste 400, Indianapolis, IN 46225-1616
Tel (317) 630-2828 *Founded/Ownrshp* 1994
Sales NA *EMP* 43
Accts Crowe Horwath Llp Indianapoli
SIC 6324 Health maintenance organization (HMO), insurance only; Health maintenance organization (HMO), insurance only
Pr: Charlotte Macbeth
CFO: Terry Bright
**Sr VP:* Susan Overton
**VP:* Katherine Wentworth
Dir IT: John Goerges
Pharmcst: Barbara Wilder

D-U-N-S 00-722-7496
MDX MEDICAL INC
VITALS
160 Chubb Ave Ste 301, Lyndhurst, NJ 07071-3526
Tel (201) 842-0760 *Founded/Ownrshp* 2009
Sales 31.7MM^E *EMP* 102^E
SIC 7371 Custom computer programming services
**Pr:* Tony Bellomo
**Pr:* Jeff Cutler
Pr: Andrew Holz
Pr: Josh Kramon
**CEO:* Heyward Donigan
**CFO:* Bryan Perler
Chf Mktg O: Orlena Yeung
Sr VP: Dennis Charland
VP: David Blumenthal
VP: Erika Boyer
VP: Laura Fitzgerald
**VP:* John Jordan
**Exec:* Jeanne Wisniewski
Creative D: Michael Ramos

D-U-N-S 80-904-5859
ME DEPT OF BEHAVIORAL AND DEVELOPMENTAL SERVICES
(*Suby of* MAINE DEPARTMENT OF HEALTH AND HUMAN SERVICES) ★
40 State House Sta, Augusta, ME 04333-0040
Tel (207) 287-4200 *Founded/Ownrshp* 1981
Sales NA *EMP* 1,800
SIC 9431 Mental health agency administration, government; ; Mental health agency administration, government;

ME ELECMETAL
See ME GLOBAL INC

ME ENGINEERS
See M-E ENGINEERS INC

D-U-N-S 62-527-0889
ME FIELDS INC
FIELDS INFINITI
2100 Srontag Rd, Glencoe, IL 60022
Tel (847) 998-5200 *Founded/Ownrshp* 1971
Sales 74.0MM^E *EMP* 122
SIC 5511 Automobiles, new & used; Automobiles, new & used
CEO: John R Fjelds
**Treas:* Earl Klein
Off Mgr: Gina Walter
Sales Asso: Sam Badro
Sales Asso: George Fan

D-U-N-S 02-938-8576 IMP
ME FOX & CO INC
128 Component Dr, San Jose, CA 95131-1180
Tel (408) 435-8510 *Founded/Ownrshp* 1965
Sales 75.4MM *EMP* 100
Accts Good & Fowler Llp South San
SIC 5181 5149 Beer & other fermented malt liquors; Soft drinks; Mineral or spring water bottling; Juices; Beer & other fermented malt liquors; Soft drinks; Mineral or spring water bottling, Juices
Ch Bd: Michael E Fox Sr
**Pr:* Terence Fox
**CFO:* Doug Webenbauer
**Treas:* Catherine Fox
**Ex VP:* Mary Ellen Fox
**VP:* Dennis P Fox
**VP:* Ken Robinson
**VP:* Mark Spoden
IT Man: Dennis Jones

D-U-N-S 07-748-2193 IMP/EXP
ME GLOBAL INC
ME ELECMETAL
(*Suby of* INVERSIONES ELECMETAL S.A.)
3901 University Ave Ne, Minneapolis, MN 55421-3764
Tel (763) 788-1651 *Founded/Ownrshp* 2001
Sales 43.9MM^E *EMP* 236
SIC 3325 3321 Steel foundries; Gray & ductile iron foundries; Steel foundries; Gray & ductile iron foundries
Pr: Mike Fulton
**VP:* Jim Bregi
**VP:* Alfred M Fulton
**VP:* Mark Garton
**VP:* John Sellars
VP: Zen Xu

ME-JANE
See LOUISE PARIS LTD

ME-N-ED'S PIZZERIA
See MILANO RESTAURANTS INTERNATIONAL CORP

D-U-N-S 07-841-4380
MEA FINANCIAL SERVICES INC (MI)
MEA GROUP TRAVEL
(*Suby of* M E A) ★
1480 Kendale Blvd, East Lansing, MI 48823-2012
Tel (517) 351-2122 *Founded/Ownrshp* 1973
Sales NA *EMP* 91
Accts Maner Costerisan & Ellis Pc
SIC 6411 7389 Insurance agents, brokers & service; Financial services
Ex Dir: Paul H Gonzalez
IT Man: Rene' E Carpenter

MEA GROUP TRAVEL
See MEA FINANCIAL SERVICES INC

D-U-N-S 06-686-2558
MEAD AND HUNT INC
2440 Deming Way, Middleton, WI 53562-1562
Tel (608) 273-6380 *Founded/Ownrshp* 1987
Sales 83.0MM *EMP* 530
SIC 8712 8711 Architectural engineering; Consulting engineer; Architectural engineering; Consulting engineer
CEO: Rajan I Sheth
CFO: Don Gotrik
VP: John Barefoot
VP: Jon Faucher
VP: Andrew Platz
VP: Amy Squitieri
IT Man: Robert Halpop
Snr PM: Mikel Boone
Snr Mgr: Rose Agnew

D-U-N-S 00-891-0051
MEAD BUILDING CENTERS OF COLUMBUS LLC
MEAD LUMBER
(*Suby of* DO IT BEST) ★
1740 Bill Babka Dr, Columbus, NE 68601-1989
Tel (402) 564-5225 *Founded/Ownrshp* 1998
Sales 34.7MM^E *EMP* 33
SIC 5211 5251 Lumber & other building materials; Hardware
CEO: Robert W Mead
**Pr:* Craig Bradshaw
Genl Mgr: Curtis Loosvelt
CIO: Tim Koll

D-U-N-S 02-943-2432
MEAD CLARK LUMBER CO
2667 Dowd Dr, Santa Rosa, CA 95407-7860
Tel (707) 576-3333 *Founded/Ownrshp* 1979
Sales 27.5MM^E *EMP* 98
SIC 5211 5251 Lumber & other building materials; Builders' hardware; Lumber & other building materials; Builders' hardware
CEO: Randal J Destruel
**Pr:* Kevin Destruel
Pr: Patty Mitchell
**VP:* Matt Petersen
Mktg Dir: Jeff Scott

D-U-N-S 00-423-1445 IMP
MEAD CORP
4751 Hempstead Station Dr, Dayton, OH 45429-5165
Tel (937) 495-6323 *Founded/Ownrshp* 1930
Sales 44.0MM^E *EMP* 500
SIC 2621 2631 2653 2656 2611 2421 Printing paper; Writing paper; Copy paper; Book, bond & printing papers; Corrugating medium; Boxes, corrugated: made from purchased materials; Sanitary food containers; Pulp mills; Lumber: rough, sawed or planed

D-U-N-S 36-271-7808
MEAD HOLDING CO INC
DO IT BEST
2218 11th St, Columbus, NE 68601-5777
Tel (402) 564-5225 *Founded/Ownrshp* 2003
Sales 248.4MM *EMP* 260
Accts Ketel Thorstenson Llp Rapid
SIC 6719 5211 Personal holding companies, except banks; Lumber & other building materials; Personal holding companies, except banks; Lumber & other building materials
CEO: Robert W Mead
**Pr:* Craig Bradshaw
**Sec:* Perry Mead

D-U-N-S 00-637-0092 EXP
■ MEAD JOHNSON & CO LLC
MEAD JOHNSON NUTRITION
(*Suby of* MEAD JOHNSON NUTRITION CO) ★
2400 W Lloyd Expy, Evansville, IN 47712-5095
Tel (812) 429-5000 *Founded/Ownrshp* 2009
Sales 311.4MM^E *EMP* 650^E
SIC 2099 2834 2032 Food preparations; Pharmaceutical preparations; Canned specialties; Food preparations; Pharmaceutical preparations; Canned specialties
CEO: Peter Kasper Jakobsen
Sr VP: Sandy Mac Pherson
VP: Rick Baumgart
VP: William Cross
**VP:* Tom De Weerdt
VP: Leroy McBrien
VP: Roberto Moran
VP: Nicky Tesh
Dir Risk M: David Zaslavsky
Assoc Dir: Jeff Anderson
Assoc Dir: Wilfred Castillo
Assoc Dir: Jeannine Delwiche
Assoc Dir: Sonja Garth
Assoc Dir: Juan Gonzalez
Assoc Dir: F M Hutcheson
Assoc Dir: Christopher McKinney
Assoc Dir: Bradley Taylor
Assoc Dir: Kelly Walsh

MEAD JOHNSON NUTRITION
See MEAD JOHNSON & CO LLC

D-U-N-S 82-805-0877
▲ MEAD JOHNSON NUTRITION CO
2701 Patriot Blvd, Glenview, IL 60026-8039
Tel (847) 832-2420 *Founded/Ownrshp* 1905
Sales 4.4MMM *EMP* 7,700^E
Tkr Sym MJN *Exch* NYS
SIC 2023 2834 Baby formulas; Vitamin preparations; Baby formulas; Vitamin preparations
Pr: Peter K Jakobsen
COO: Charles M Urbain
CFO: Michel M Cup
Treas: H M Bains Jr
Treas: Kevin Wilson
Ofcr: Jose Feito
Ofcr: Dirk Hondmann
Sr VP: Timothy Brown
Sr VP: Lynn H Clark
Sr VP: Graciela I Monteagudo
Sr VP: James Jeffrey Jobe
Sr VP: William C P'Pool
Sr VP: Blair Sailes
Sr VP: Patrick M Sheller
Sr VP: Sandra Yu
VP: Sandra Bereti
VP: Matthew Chapple
VP: Audrae Erickson
VP: Joaquin Franco
VP: Mariana Livore
VP: Edouard Nab
Board of Directors: Michael A Sherman, Steven M Altschuler, Elliott Sigal, Howard B Bernick, Robert S Singer, Kimberly A Casiano, Anna C Catalano, Celeste A Clark, James M Cornelius, Stephen W Golsby, Michael Grobstein, Peter G Ratcliffe

MEAD LUMBER
See MEAD BUILDING CENTERS OF COLUMBUS LLC

D-U-N-S 00-619-6158
MEAD METALS INC
555 Cardigan Rd, Saint Paul, MN 55126-3999
Tel (651) 484-1400 *Founded/Ownrshp* 1961
Sales 25.8MM^E *EMP* 33
SIC 5051 Iron or steel flat products; Pipe & tubing, steel; Copper; Sheets, metal
Pr: Sandra Crawford
**Ch Bd:* Jon Holt
**Sec:* Jim Bast

D-U-N-S 00-785-7444 IMP
MEAD OBRIEN INC
1429 Atlantic Ave, North Kansas City, MO 64116-4018
Tel (816) 471-3993 *Founded/Ownrshp* 1961
Sales 30.7MM^E *EMP* 55
SIC 5085 Valves & fittings
CEO: Michael B Mead
**Pr:* Ron Morrison
COO: Nicholas Erickson
**Sec:* Jeanette A Mead
Brnch Mgr: Dave Kuelker
Sls Mgr: Vicki Hobson

D-U-N-S 06-141-1880
■ MEAD PACKAGING INTERNATIONAL INC (OH)
(*Suby of* WESTROCK MWV LLC) ★
1801 Piedmont Ave Ne, Atlanta, GA 30324-5214
Tel (404) 875-2711 *Founded/Ownrshp* 1965, 2002
Sales 130.0MM *EMP* 125^E
SIC 6719 Personal holding companies, except banks; Personal holding companies, except banks

D-U-N-S 09-368-0502
MEAD SCHOOL DISTRICT #354
2323 E Farwell Rd, Mead, WA 99021-6011
Tel (509) 465-7480 *Founded/Ownrshp* 1890
Sales 81.6MM^E *EMP* 1,020
Accts Troy Kelley

SIC 8211 Public combined elementary & secondary school; Public combined elementary & secondary school
Bd of Dir: Tom Hunt
VP: Maureen Oconnor
IT Man: Carol Hatcher
Teacher Pr: Keri Hutchins
Pgrm Dir: Bob Olson

D-U-N-S 02-044-3263
MEADE COUNTY BOARD OF EDUCATION
1155 Old Ekron Rd, Brandenburg, KY 40108-1701
Tel (270) 422-7500 *Founded/Ownrshp* 1950
Sales 29.6MM^E *EMP* 700
SIC 8211 Public combined elementary & secondary school; Public combined elementary & secondary school
**CFO:* Susan Fackler

D-U-N-S 00-694-4599
MEADE COUNTY RURAL ELECTRIC COOPERATIVE CORP
1351 Highway 79, Brandenburg, KY 40108-7004
Tel (270) 422-2162 *Founded/Ownrshp* 1937
Sales 47.8MM *EMP* 65
SIC 4911 Electric services; Electric services
Pr: Burns Mercer
**Treas:* Tim Gossett
VP: Linda Barr
**VP:* David Poe

MEADE DISTRICT HOSPITAL
See MEADE HOSPITAL DISTRICT

MEADE DODGE
See MEADE GROUP INC

MEADE ELECTRIC CO
See L & H CO INC

D-U-N-S 00-693-1364
MEADE ELECTRIC CO INC
(*Suby of* L & H CO INC) ★
9550 W 55th St Ste A, Countryside, IL 60525-3641
Tel (773) 626-0796 *Founded/Ownrshp* 1980
Sales 188.5MM^E *EMP* 600
SIC 1731 General electrical contractor; General electrical contractor
Pr: Frank J Lizzadro
**Ch Bd:* Joseph F Lizzadro
**VP:* Mike Kenutson
VP: Michael Knutson
VP: Perry Manago
VP: Bob Schacht
Div Mgr: Dan Plefka
Off Mgr: Jan Labuhn
IT Man: Jay Anzalone
IT Man: Mike Lizzadro
Pgrm Dir: Joe Holland

D-U-N-S 07-981-0992
MEADE EQUIPMENT LLC
(*Suby of* MEADE HOLDINGS LLC)
840 State St Ste 200, Bristol, TN 37620-2280
Tel (276) 628-5126 *Founded/Ownrshp* 2015
Sales 50.0MM *EMP* 105^E
SIC 5082 7699 Excavating machinery & equipment; Construction equipment repair

D-U-N-S 02-844-8835
MEADE GROUP INC
MEADE DODGE
6951 19 Mile Rd, Sterling Heights, MI 48314-3209
Tel (586) 803-6250 *Founded/Ownrshp* 1982
Sales 88.0MM^E *EMP* 288
SIC 5511 Automobiles, new & used; Automobiles, new & used
Ch Bd: Kenneth G Meade
**Pr:* Barron Meade
**CFO:* Terry Tadlock
**Treas:* Stacy Weiler
Exec: Shane Taranto
IT Man: Troy Dieter

D-U-N-S 07-332-8569
MEADE HOSPITAL DISTRICT
MEADE DISTRICT HOSPITAL
510 E Carthage St, Meade, KS 67864-6401
Tel (620) 873-2141 *Founded/Ownrshp* 1951
Sales 35.4MM^E *EMP* 210
SIC 8062

D-U-N-S 10-007-2404
MEADE SCHOOL DISTRICT 46-1
1230 Douglas St, Sturgis, SD 57785-1869
Tel (605) 347-2649 *Founded/Ownrshp* 1969
Sales 16.7MM^E *EMP* 300^E
Accts Gary L Larson Cpa Sioux Falls
SIC 8211 School board; School board
Pr: Terry Koontz

D-U-N-S 07-980-0371
MEADEN & MOORE LLP
1100 Superior Ave E # 1100, Cleveland, OH 44114-2523
Tel (216) 241-3272 *Founded/Ownrshp* 1980
Sales 35.7MM^E *EMP* 200
SIC 8721 Certified public accountant; Certified public accountant
Pr: James P Carulas
Pr: Larry J Holland
COO: Bill Smith
VP: Michelle Buckley
VP: Michael Castillo
VP: Karen Cooney
VP: David E Daywalt
VP: Peter Demarco
VP: David Disalvo
VP: Theodore C Hocevar
VP: Theodore Hocevar
VP: Joe Mentrek
VP: John Norton
VP: Cindy Shadler
VP: Viv Shanefelt
VP: Alfred Tobin

D-U-N-S 00-509-1087 IMP
MEADEN PRECISION MACHINED PRODUCTS CO (IL)
MEADEN SCREW PRODUCTS COMPANY
16w210 83rd St, Burr Ridge, IL 60527-5827
Tel (630) 655-0888 *Founded/Ownrshp* 1939
Sales 20.8MM^E *EMP* 75
SIC 3451 Screw machine products
Ch Bd: John A Meaden Jr
Pr: Thomas F Meaden
Genl Mgr: Jerry Paskovich

MEADEN SCREW PRODUCTS COMPANY
See MEADEN PRECISION MACHINED PRODUCTS CO

MEADOR CHRYSLER JEEP DODGE RAM
See HLK AUTO GROUP INC

D-U-N-S 08-085-5042
MEADOR STAFFING SERVICES INC
TEMPORARY STAFFING SERVICES
722a Fairmont Pkwy, Pasadena, TX 77504-2804
Tel (713) 941-0616 *Founded/Ownrshp* 1968
Sales 162.6MM^E *EMP* 10,000
SIC 7361 7363 Placement agencies; Temporary help service; Industrial help service; Engineering help service; Placement agencies; Temporary help service; Industrial help service; Engineering help service
Pr: Ben F Meador Jr
Pr: Brian Critelli
VP: Linda Fields
**VP:* Darla Haygood
**VP:* Janice Meador
**VP:* Faye Smith
**VP:* Melinda Torrison
Dir Risk M: Kathleen Matranga
Sls&Mrk Ex: Gale Templeton

D-U-N-S 12-206-5550
MEADOW LARK AGENCY INC
935 Lake Elmo Dr, Billings, MT 59105-3123
Tel (406) 256-0063 *Founded/Ownrshp* 1983
Sales 75.3MM *EMP* 120^E
SIC 4731 Truck transportation brokers; Truck transportation brokers
CEO: Amanda Roth
**Pr:* Mike Kandas
**CFO:* Michelle Borsum
**Sec:* Donna Jones
Genl Mgr: Donald Patenaude
Dir IT: Lynnette Baisch
Opers Mgr: Steph Brazill
Opers Mgr: Scott Hagfeldt
Opers Mgr: Mandy Roth
Mktg Dir: Russell Van Lieshout

MEADOW VALLEY CONTRACTORS
See MEADOW VALLEY CORP

D-U-N-S 10-685-7154
MEADOW VALLEY CONTRACTORS INC
(*Suby of* MEADOW VALLEY CONTRACTORS) ★
3333 E Camelback Rd # 240, Phoenix, AZ 85018-2345
Tel (702) 643-9472 *Founded/Ownrshp* 1980
Sales 30.5MM^E *EMP* 83
SIC 1611 1622 1629 1771 Highway & street construction; Bridge, tunnel & elevated highway; Earthmoving contractor; Concrete work
CEO: David Matthews
**Pr:* Bradley E Larson
**Pr:* Victor L Vescovo
COO: Robert Terril
**Ch:* Ted Beneski
**VP:* Kenneth D Nelson
**VP:* Robert Alan Terril

D-U-N-S 87-840-3500
MEADOW VALLEY CORP
MEADOW VALLEY CONTRACTORS
(*Suby of* MEADOW VALLEY HOLDINGS LLC) ★
3333 E Camelback Rd # 240, Phoenix, AZ 85018-2345
Tel (602) 437-5400 *Founded/Ownrshp* 1980
Sales 93.7MM^E *EMP* 510^E
SIC 1611 5032 General contractor, highway & street construction; Airport runway construction; Concrete mixtures; General contractor, highway & street construction; Airport runway construction; Concrete mixtures
Ch: Ted W Beneski
Pr: Robert W Bottcher
Pr: Grant Larson
Pr: L David Mathews
Pr: Robert A Terril
Treas: David D Doty
VP: Gary Burnell
VP: Kenneth D Nelson
Off Mgr: Nancy McCafferty

D-U-N-S 83-121-9311
MEADOW VALLEY HOLDINGS LLC
(*Suby of* INSIGHT EQUITY ACQUISITION CO LLC) ★
4602 E Thomas Rd, Phoenix, AZ 85018-7710
Tel (602) 437-5400 *Founded/Ownrshp* 2008
Sales 93.8MM^E *EMP* 510^E
SIC 1611 5032 General contractor, highway & street construction; Airport runway construction; Concrete mixtures; General contractor, highway & street construction; Airport runway construction; Concrete mixtures
Pr: Ted W Beneski
**CEO:* Bradley E Larson
**CFO:* David D Doty

MEADOW WOODS
See MARTIN LUTHER MANOR

D-U-N-S 94-517-4696
MEADOWBROOK CARE CENTER INC
320 W Merrick Rd, Freeport, NY 11520-3248
Tel (516) 377-8200 *Founded/Ownrshp* 1996
Sales 16.7MM^E *EMP* 300
SIC 8051 Skilled nursing care facilities; Skilled nursing care facilities
Ch Bd: Jack Friedman
**Pr:* Simon Pelman
**VP:* ARI Friedman

MEADOWBROOK CLAIMS SERVICE
See MEADOWBROOK INC

D-U-N-S 00-196-8999
MEADOWBROOK DISTRIBUTING CORP
(*Suby of* PEPSI BOTTLING VENTURES LLC) ★
550 New Horizons Blvd, Amityville, NY 11701-1139
Tel (631) 226-9000 *Founded/Ownrshp* 1950, 1980
Sales 39.0MM^E *EMP* 220
SIC 5149 2086 5141 4225 Soft drinks; Soft drinks: packaged in cans, bottles, etc.; Groceries, general line; General warehousing & storage; Soft drinks; Soft drinks: packaged in cans, bottles, etc.; Groceries, general line; General warehousing & storage
VP: Mike Pensa

D-U-N-S 94-853-6370
MEADOWBROOK GOLF GROUP INC
5385 Gateway Blvd Ste 12, Lakeland, FL 33811-1785
Tel (407) 589-7200 *Founded/Ownrshp* 1995
Sales 155.1MM^E *EMP* 2,700
SIC 8742 8741 7992 5941 Management consulting services; Management services; Public golf courses; Sporting goods & bicycle shops; Management consulting services; Management services; Public golf courses; Sporting goods & bicycle shops
Pr: Ron E Jackson
**CFO:* Eric Burk
**CFO:* K Eric Burk
CFO: Calvin Sellers
**Ex VP:* Greg Plotner
**VP:* Scott Beasley

D-U-N-S 07-424-8923
■ **MEADOWBROOK INC**
MEADOWBROOK CLAIMS SERVICE
(*Suby of* MEADOWBROOK INSURANCE GROUP INC) ★
26255 American Dr, Southfield, MI 48034-6112
Tel (248) 358-1100 *Founded/Ownrshp* 1995
Sales NA *EMP* 929
SIC 6411 Insurance agents & brokers; Insurance information & consulting services; Loss prevention services, insurance; Insurance agents & brokers; Insurance information & consulting services; Loss prevention services, insurance
Ch Bd: Robert Naftaly
**Pr:* Robert S Cubbin
**CFO:* Caryn Spun
**Treas:* Josephine Duco
Sr VP: Mickey Fay
Sr VP: Heidi Langella

D-U-N-S 79-885-1069
■ **MEADOWBROOK INSURANCE GROUP INC**
(*Suby of* FOSUN INTERNATIONAL LIMITED)
26255 American Dr, Southfield, MI 48034-6112
Tel (248) 358-1100 *Founded/Ownrshp* 2015
Sales NA *EMP* 954^E
Tkr Sym MIG *Exch* NYS
SIC 6411 6211 Insurance agents, brokers & service; Property & casualty insurance agent; Fire, marine & casualty insurance; Property & casualty insurance agent; Underwriters, security
Pr: Robert S Cubbin
CFO: Karen M Spaun
Ex VP: Christopher J Timm
Sr VP: Kent R Allen
Sr VP: James M Mahoney
Sr VP: Archie S McIntyre
Sr VP: R Christopher Spring
Sr VP: Roger S Walleck
VP: Stephen A Belden
VP: Michael G Costello
VP: Tom Gyscek
VP: Gregg Haver
VP: Todd Lanski
VP: John Leonard
VP: Stuart Presson
VP: Jodi Roth
VP: Stephen Smith

MEADOWBROOK MANOR BOLINGBROOK
See BUTTERFIELD HEALTH CARE INC

MEADOWBROOK MANOR NAPERVILLE
See BUTTERFIELD HEALTH CARE II INC

D-U-N-S 02-477-8391
■ **MEADOWBROOK MEAT CO INC** (NC)
MBM
(*Suby of* MCLANE CO INC) ★
2641 Meadowbrook Rd, Rocky Mount, NC 27801-9498
Tel (252) 985-7200 *Founded/Ownrshp* 1977, 2012
Sales 1.0MMM^E *EMP* 3,000
SIC 5147 5113 5149 5142

MEADOWBROOK NURSING HOME
See CGSR INC

D-U-N-S 14-419-0345 IMP
MEADOWCRAFT INC
PLANTATION PATTERNS
151 Narrows Pkwy Ste D, Birmingham, AL 35242-8638
Tel (205) 853-2220 *Founded/Ownrshp* 1985
Sales NA *EMP* 772
SIC 2514 3999 2393

D-U-N-S 14-927-5609
MEADOWGATE TECHNOLOGIES LLC
171 Jersey St Ste 1, Trenton, NJ 08611-2400
Tel (609) 393-3618 *Founded/Ownrshp* 2002
Sales 60.7MM *EMP* 14
SIC 5045 8711 Computers; Engineering services; Computers; Engineering services
Genl Mgr: Leslie Siskovic

D-U-N-S 02-284-2579
MEADOWLAND FARMERS COOP
25861 Us Highway 14, Lamberton, MN 56152-1146
Tel (507) 752-7335 *Founded/Ownrshp* 1905
Sales 169.3MM^E *EMP* 84
SIC 5153 5191 0723 Grain elevators; Chemicals, agricultural; Fertilizer & fertilizer materials; Feed; Seeds: field, garden & flower; Crop preparation services for market; Grain elevators; Chemicals, agricultural; Crop preparation services for market
CEO: John D Valentin
**Sec:* Terry Quiring
**VP:* Steve Nelson

D-U-N-S 05-630-7853
MEADOWLAND OF CARMEL INC
1952 Route 6, Carmel, NY 10512-2311
Tel (845) 225-8468 *Founded/Ownrshp* 1966
Sales 22.5MM^E *EMP* 50
SIC 5511

MEADOWLANDS HOSPITAL MED CTR
See MHA LLC

MEADOWLANDS NISSAN
See ELMWOOD MOTORS INC

MEADOWLARK HILLS
See MANHATTAN RETIREMENT FOUNDATION INC

D-U-N-S 09-832-2779
MEADOWOOD ASSOCIATES A LIMITED PARTNERSHIP
MEADOWOOD RESORT AND CNTRY CLB
900 Meadowood Ln, Saint Helena, CA 94574-9620
Tel (707) 963-3646 *Founded/Ownrshp* 1979
Sales 20.6MM^E *EMP* 300
SIC 5812 7011 7997 Eating places; Resort hotel; Country club, membership; Eating places; Resort hotel; Country club, membership
Pt: Bob Ringstab
Pt: H William Harland
COO: Barbara Wallace
Genl Mgr: Brook Herrema
Genl Mgr: Alex Kim
Genl Mgr: Hayley Russell
MIS Dir: James Reichstadt
Dir IT: Todd Gallagher
Dir IT: James Syring
IT Man: Robert Cantrell
IT Man: Bryan Hutter

D-U-N-S 10-884-9126
MEADOWOOD CORP
MEADOWOOD RETIREMENT COMMUNITY
3205 Skittack Pike, Worcester, PA 19490
Tel (610) 584-1000 *Founded/Ownrshp* 1988
Sales 25.5MM *EMP* 300
SIC 8361 8051 Home for the aged; Skilled nursing care facilities; Home for the aged; Skilled nursing care facilities
Ch Bd: Bill Black
CFO: Lois Rothenberger
**Treas:* James Stratton
**VP:* H Drake Williams J
**VP:* Drake H Williams
**Ex Dir:* Paul Nordeman
Ex Dir: Sherry S Outten

MEADOWOOD RESORT AND CNTRY CLB
See MEADOWOOD ASSOCIATES A LIMITED PARTNERSHIP

MEADOWOOD RETIREMENT COMMUNITY
See MEADOWOOD CORP

MEADOWS, THE
See MEADOWS HOLDINGS LP

D-U-N-S 82-513-4088
MEADOWS BANK
8912 Spanish Ridge Ave # 100, Las Vegas, NV 89148-1311
Tel (702) 227-6360 *Founded/Ownrshp* 2008
Sales NA *EMP* 46
SIC 6022 State commercial banks; State commercial banks
Pr: Arvind Menon
**CFO:* Chris R Swndseid
Chf Cred: Clay Wanta
Sr VP: Susan Hescher
Sr VP: Linda Kuhn
VP: David Boser
VP: Lisa Coats
VP: Eric Colvin
VP: Jeff Cromar
VP: Helen Lewis
VP: Gonzalez Louis
VP: Branden Martin
VP: Mike Rogers
VP: Dede Samson
VP: Brian Schumacher

D-U-N-S 13-747-2093
MEADOWS CONSTRUCTION SERVICES INC
4401 Etiwanda Ave Ste C, Mira Loma, CA 91752-3722
Tel (951) 681-6900 *Founded/Ownrshp* 2002
Sales 30.0MM *EMP* 20
SIC 1542 Commercial & office building contractors; Commercial & office building contractors
CEO: Rebecca Brown
**COO:* Ian Wicklow

D-U-N-S 05-491-8883
MEADOWS FARMS INC
MEADOWS FARMS NURSERIES
43054 John Mosby Hwy, Chantilly, VA 20152-4260
Tel (703) 327-3940 *Founded/Ownrshp* 1972
Sales 46.1MM^E *EMP* 200
SIC 5261

MEADOWS FARMS NURSERIES
See MEADOWS FARMS INC

MEADOWS GOLF CLUB , THE
See GRAND VALLEY STATE UNIVERSITY

D-U-N-S 96-915-8224
MEADOWS HEALTHCARE ALLIANCE INC
MEADOWS REGIONAL MEDICAL CENTE
1 Meadows Pkwy, Vidalia, GA 30474-8759
Tel (912) 538-5866 *Founded/Ownrshp* 1992
Sales 2.0MM *EMP* 1,000
Accts Draffin & Tucker Llp Albany

SIC 8099 8062 Blood related health services; General medical & surgical hospitals
CEO: Alan Kent
**CFO:* John Cornell
Sls Mgr: Ashley Collins

D-U-N-S 18-257-3345
MEADOWS HOLDINGS LP
MEADOWS, THE
1655 N Tegner St, Wickenburg, AZ 85390-1461
Tel (928) 684-4026 *Founded/Ownrshp* 1994
Sales 20.5MM^E *EMP* 180
SIC 8062 General medical & surgical hospitals; General medical & surgical hospitals
Pt: Brian Lamb
Off Mgr: Betty Hanson
S&M/Mgr: Nancy Koplow

MEADOWS MECHANICAL
See MEADOWS SHEET METAL AND AIR CONDITIONING INC

D-U-N-S 80-538-5564
MEADOWS MUSEUM ART AT CENT COLLEGE
MEADOWS MUSEUM OF ART
2911 Centenary Blvd, Shreveport, LA 71104-3335
Tel (318) 869-5169 *Founded/Ownrshp* 1975
Sales 31.1MM *EMP* 5
SIC 8412 Museum; Museum

MEADOWS MUSEUM OF ART
See MEADOWS MUSEUM ART AT CENT COLLEGE

MEADOWS OFFICE FURNITURE
See MEADOWS OFFICE SUPPLY CO INC

D-U-N-S 04-155-5723 IMP
MEADOWS OFFICE SUPPLY CO INC
MEADOWS OFFICE FURNITURE
885 3rd Ave Fl 29, New York, NY 10022-4834
Tel (212) 741-0333 *Founded/Ownrshp* 1967
Sales 76.0MM^E *EMP* 106
SIC 5021 Office furniture; Office furniture
Pr: Rosalie Edson
**CEO:* Sheri David
**CFO:* Stanley Fessler
**Mng Dir:* Pat Escobedo
Genl Mgr: Clint Barlow
Dir IT: Gerry Gatch
IT Man: Marissa Allen
Snr PM: Anastasia Pastena
Snr PM: Michael Sorbera

MEADOWS REGIONAL MEDICAL CENTE
See MEADOWS HEALTHCARE ALLIANCE INC

D-U-N-S 01-012-2257
MEADOWS REGIONAL MEDICAL CENTER INC
1703 Meadows Ln, Vidalia, GA 30474-8915
Tel (912) 537-8921 *Founded/Ownrshp* 1994
Sales 95.9MM^E *EMP* 670^E
SIC 8062 8051 General medical & surgical hospitals; Skilled nursing care facilities; General medical & surgical hospitals; Skilled nursing care facilities
CEO: Alan Kent
**CFO:* John Cornell
VP: Karen McColl
Dir Risk M: Melony Jacobs
Dir Rx: Michelle Cox
Sls&Mrk Ex: Tim Walker
Sls Mgr: Diana Coursey
HC Dir: Joette Gay

D-U-N-S 15-185-6598
MEADOWS SCHOOL
8601 Scholar Ln, Las Vegas, NV 89128-7302
Tel (702) 254-1610 *Founded/Ownrshp* 1984
Sales 20.4MM *EMP* 117
Accts Piercy Bowler Taylor & Kern L
SIC 8211 Private combined elementary & secondary school; Private combined elementary & secondary school
Pr: Carolyn Goodman
**Pr:* Roland V Sturm
**Treas:* Pamela Levin
**Treas:* Richard W Truesdell
Ex Dir: Pierce June
CTO: Madeline Neu

D-U-N-S 00-953-0775
MEADOWS SHEET METAL AND AIR CONDITIONING INC (CA)
MEADOWS MECHANICAL
333 Crown Vista Dr, Gardena, CA 90248-1705
Tel (310) 695-6105 *Founded/Ownrshp* 1949, 1979
Sales 24.4MM^E *EMP* 50
SIC 3444 1711 Sheet metalwork; Heating & air conditioning contractors
CEO: Madonna Rose
**CFO:* Dennis Johnson
**Ex VP:* Thomas Nolan
VP: Bill Thompson
IT Man: Kathy Viodes

MEADOWVIEW NURSING CENTER
See HUDSON COUNTY MEADOWVIEW HOSPITAL

MEADOWVIEW REGIONAL MED CTR
See MEADOWVIEW REGIONAL MEDICAL CENTER LLC

D-U-N-S 12-132-6792
■ **MEADOWVIEW REGIONAL MEDICAL CENTER LLC**
MEADOWVIEW REGIONAL MED CTR
(*Suby of* HISTORIC LIFEPOINT HOSPITALS INC) ★
989 Medical Park Dr, Maysville, KY 41056-8750
Tel (606) 759-3160 *Founded/Ownrshp* 2002
Sales 53.8MM *EMP* 300
SIC 8062 General medical & surgical hospitals; General medical & surgical hospitals
CEO: Robert Parker
Dir OR: Sherrie Goodwin
Dir Rad: John Rigsby
Dir IT: Theresa Fite
IT Man: Shawn Drake
IT Man: Steve Meese
QC Dir: Amy K Midkiff
Phys Thrpy: Don Becker
Diag Rad: John Clarke

MEADOWVIEW SCHOOL
See EATON REGIONAL EDUCATION SERVICE AGENCY

MEADOWWOOD BEHAVIORAL HEALTH
See FOCUS HEALTH CARE OF DELAWARE LLC

D-U-N-S 06-683-9515 IMP
MEADVILLE FORGING CO LP
MFC
(*Suby of* KELLER GROUP INC) ★
15309 Baldwin Street Ext, Meadville, PA 16335-9401
Tel (814) 332-8200 *Founded/Ownrshp* 1999
Sales 63.0MM^E *EMP* 400
SIC 3462 Iron & steel forgings; Iron & steel forgings
Pt: John Keller
Pt: William P Glavin
Pt: James Martin
Off Mgr: Luann Way
MIS Mgr: Dennis Gregory
Board of Directors: Rachelle Derlek

D-U-N-S 06-874-8409
MEADVILLE MEDICAL CENTER (PA)
751 Liberty St, Meadville, PA 16335-2591
Tel (814) 333-5000 *Founded/Ownrshp* 1880
Sales 155.5MM^E *EMP* 995
Accts Bkd Llp Springfield/Joplin/B
SIC 8062 8011 General medical & surgical hospitals; Offices & clinics of medical doctors; General medical & surgical hospitals; Offices & clinics of medical doctors
Pr: Anthony J De Fail
**Pr:* Tilit Pllgt
**CFO:* David A Poland
Ofcr: Sallie Frisina
Sr VP: Daniel Caplan
VP: Robert Concilus
VP: Valerie Waid
Off Admin: Dessie Rosipko
Surgeon: Sean Debuysere
Obsttrcn: Jodi Maxfield
Ansthlgy: Amy Paczkoskie

D-U-N-S 60-936-3408
MEADVILLE MEDICAL CENTER
MMC
1034 Grove St, Meadville, PA 16335-2945
Tel (814) 333-5000 *Founded/Ownrshp* 1985
Sales 167.3MM *EMP* 1,800^E
Accts Bkd Llp Springfield Mo
SIC 8062 General medical & surgical hospitals; General medical & surgical hospitals
CFO: David Poland
**CEO:* Anthony Defail
CFO: Renato Suntay
Treas: John McMahon
VP: John McCandless
QA Dir: Linda Zadrozny
Netwrk Mgr: Dave Gaddess
Mktg Dir: Duane Koller
Doctor: Anthony Colantonio
Doctor: Robert Concilus
Doctor: Roderick Fernandez

MEADWESTVACO CONSUMER
See WESTROCK CONSUMER PACKAGING GROUP LLC

MEAG POWER
See MUNICIPAL ELECTRIC AUTHORITY OF GEORGIA

D-U-N-S 06-478-0661
MEAGHER & GEER PLLP
33 S 6th St Ste 4400, Minneapolis, MN 55402-3710
Tel (612) 338-0661 *Founded/Ownrshp* 1929
Sales 22.0MM^E *EMP* 145^E
SIC 8111 General practice law office; General practice law office
Pt: James F Roegge
**Pt:* Charles H Becker
**Pt:* Stacy A Broman
Pt: Robert Graff
**Pt:* Becker Charles H
**Pt:* Rodger A Hagen
**Pt:* Laura J Hanson
**Pt:* William M Hart
**Pt:* Michael D Hutchens
**Pt:* Bradley M Jones
**Pt:* John J McDonald Jr
**Pt:* Mary M L O'Brien
**Pt:* Christian J Preus
Pt: Thomas Propson
**Pt:* Timothy W Ridley
**Pt:* James M Riley
**Pt:* Robert E Salmon
**Pt:* Greg Stephen
**Pt:* R Gregory Stephens
Pt: Jeffrey Thompson
**Pt:* Leatha Grein Wolter

MEALEY'S FURNITURE WARMINSTER
See K&D FUTURE INC

D-U-N-S 61-007-2878
MEANS ENGINEERING INC
5927 Geiger Ct, Carlsbad, CA 92008-7305
Tel (760) 931-9452 *Founded/Ownrshp* 1996
Sales 23.3MM^E *EMP* 70
SIC 3826 3699 3559 Analytical instruments; Electrical equipment & supplies; Semiconductor manufacturing machinery
CEO: David William Means
**Ex VP:* Lisa Means
Mfg Mgr: Chuck Roles
Sls Mgr: John Craft

D-U-N-S 05-769-3145 IMP/EXP
MEANS INDUSTRIES INC
3715 E Washington Rd, Saginaw, MI 48601-9623
Tel (989) 754-1433 *Founded/Ownrshp* 1989
Sales 122.9MM^E *EMP* 400
SIC 3714 3465 Transmission housings or parts, motor vehicle; Automotive stampings; Transmission housings or parts, motor vehicle; Automotive stampings
Pr: D William Shaw
Pr: Steve Ruth
**Pr:* Bill Shaw
COO: Kim McGregor
Chf Mktg O: Mark Willett
**VP:* Ed Shemanski
QA Dir: Terry Dora
QA Dir: Troy Golombisky
IT Man: Karen Esckelfon
Info Man: Karen Eckelson
Opers Mgr: Rob Shortland

D-U-N-S 04-105-8652
MEANY INC (IL)
17401 Laflin Ave, East Hazel Crest, IL 60429-1845
Tel (708) 957-0400 *Founded/Ownrshp* 1955
Sales 21.1MM^E *EMP* 100
SIC 1731 General electrical contractor
Pr: Daniel R Dominy
**VP:* Jack D Dominy

D-U-N-S 19-939-9346
MEARS DESTINATION SERVICES INC
MEARS TRANSPORTATION GROUP
324 W Gore St, Orlando, FL 32806-1037
Tel (407) 422-4561 *Founded/Ownrshp* 1983
Sales 55.1MM^E *EMP* 750
SIC 4111 4141 4119 8999 Intra-airport, regular route; Local bus charter service; Limousine rental, with driver; Personal services; Intra-airport, regular route; Local bus charter service; Limousine rental, with driver; Personal services
CEO: Charles E Carns Jr
**Pr:* Paul S Mears III
**CFO:* Timothy L Baker
Ex VP: Dan Ford
**Ex VP:* James B Mears
VP: Shannon Gravitte
**VP:* Joseph Lenart
VP: Joseph Leonart
VP: Christine Mathews
**VP:* John Wolfe
Exec: John Wolf

D-U-N-S 03-122-7978
MEARS FERTILIZER INC
629 N Industrial Rd, El Dorado, KS 67042-9144
Tel (316) 321-3674 *Founded/Ownrshp* 1964
Sales 28.3MM *EMP* 43
SIC 2873 2875 5172 5191

D-U-N-S 08-556-2010
■ **MEARS GROUP INC**
(*Suby of* QUANTA SERVICES INC) ★
4500 N Mission Rd, Rosebush, MI 48878-8721
Tel (989) 433-2929 *Founded/Ownrshp* 2000
Sales 143.5MM^E *EMP* 450
Accts Pricewaterhousecoopers Llp Ho
SIC 1623 8711 Oil & gas line & compressor station construction; Communication line & transmission tower construction; Engineering services; Oil & gas line & compressor station construction; Communication line & transmission tower construction; Engineering services
Pr: Scot Fluharty
**Treas:* Nicholas M Grindstaff
VP: David D Brittain
**VP:* William C Burdine
**VP:* John W Fluharty II
VP: William Garrow
VP: James H Haddox
VP: Derrick A Jensen
VP: William Marshall
VP: Peter Obrien
VP: Doug Waslen
**VP:* Steven J Wilhelm

MEARS TRANSPORTATION GROUP
See PROPERTY GENERAL INC

MEARS TRANSPORTATION GROUP
See MEARS DESTINATION SERVICES INC

MEASE HEALTH CARE
See TRUSTEES OF MEASE HOSPITAL INC

D-U-N-S 02-081-9236
MEASE HOSPITALS
(*Suby of* BAYCARE EDUCATION SERVICES) ★
601 Main St, Dunedin, FL 34698-5848
Tel (727) 734-6354 *Founded/Ownrshp* 1994
Sales 87.5MM *EMP* 30
SIC 8071 Medical laboratories; Medical laboratories
VP: John Couris
VP: Lisa Johnson
Ex Dir: Holly Duncan
Mktg Mgr: Susan Boydell

D-U-N-S 07-920-4517
MEASE MANOR CONTINUING CARE INC
700 Mease Plz, Dunedin, FL 34698-6680
Tel (727) 733-1161 *Founded/Ownrshp* 1961
Sales 18.6MM^E *EMP* 300
Accts Moore Stephens Lovelace Pa Orl
SIC 6513 8052 8051 Retirement hotel operation; Intermediate care facilities; Skilled nursing care facilities; Retirement hotel operation; Intermediate care facilities; Skilled nursing care facilities
Ex Dir: John M Norton
MIS Mgr: Dennis Tribble

D-U-N-S 10-818-3682
MEASURED PROGRESS INC
100 Education Way, Dover, NH 03820-5816
Tel (603) 749-9102 *Founded/Ownrshp* 1983
Sales 93.7MM *EMP* 340
Accts William Steele & Associates Pc
SIC 8732 Educational research; Educational research
Pr: Martin Borg
COO: George Herrmann
CFO: Shelly Craig
CFO: Bob Kmetz
Sec: Patti Ayer
Founder: Stuart Kahl
Sr VP: Timothy Crockett
VP: James Bowen
VP: Richard Dobbs
VP: Mike Russell
Prgrm Mgr: Pamela Berube
Board of Directors: Dan Caton, Karen Cowe, Mark Elgart, Alice Irby

D-U-N-S 03-715-9514
MEASUREMENT INC
M I
423 Morris St, Durham, NC 27701-2128
Tel (919) 683-2413 *Founded/Ownrshp* 1980
Sales 83.0MM *EMP* 407^E
Accts Thomas Knight Trent King An
SIC 2752 8748 2791 2789 2759 Commercial printing, offset; Testing service, educational or personnel; Typesetting; Bookbinding & related work; Commercial printing; Commercial printing, offset; Testing service, educational or personnel; Typesetting; Bookbinding & related work; Commercial printing
Pr: Henry H Scherich
**VP:* Holly Baker
**VP:* Michael Bunch
VP: James Henning
VP: Thomas Kelsh
**VP:* Kirk Ridge
Mng Dir: Jaison Morgan
Prgrm Mgr: Suzanne Johnson
Prgrm Mgr: Corey Palermo
Admn Mgr: Susan Kaney
Snr Sftwr: David Vaughn

D-U-N-S 02-935-1079 IMP
MEASUREMENT SPECIALTIES INC
TE CONNECTIVITY
(*Suby of* TE CONNECTIVITY LTD.)
1000 Lucas Way, Hampton, VA 23666-1573
Tel (757) 766-1500 *Founded/Ownrshp* 2014
Sales 412.6MM *EMP* 3,721
SIC 3829 Measuring & controlling devices; Photopitometers; Pressure transducers; Vibration meters, analyzers & calibrators; Measuring & controlling devices; Photopitometers; Pressure transducers; Vibration meters, analyzers & calibrators
Pr: Frank D Guidone
**COO:* Joe Gleeson
**CFO:* Mark Thompson
Ex VP: Jean-Francois Allier
**Ex VP:* Glen Macgibbon
Exec: Brenda Lawrence
Dir Bus: Randall Akers
Prgrm Mgr: Lee Fairchild
Genl Mgr: Jolly MA
**CTO:* Mitch Thompson
Dir IT: Dan Dylla

D-U-N-S 00-117-9050
MEASUREMENT SYSTEMS INC
ULTRA ELEC MEASUREMENT SYSTEMS
(*Suby of* ULTRA ELECTRONICS HOLDINGS PLC)
50 Barnes Park Rd N # 102, Wallingford, CT 06492-5940
Tel (203) 949-3500 *Founded/Ownrshp* 1996
Sales 21.9MM^E *EMP* 80
SIC 3625 3577 Electric controls & control accessories, industrial; Computer peripheral equipment
Pr: Ken L Tasch
CFO: William Nossal
VP: Robert Esposipo
VP: David Olchowski
Prd Mgr: David Corneau

D-U-N-S 80-032-0868 EXP
MEASUREMENT TECHNOLOGY GROUP INC
RED SEAL MEASUREMENT
1310 Emerald Rd, Greenwood, SC 29646-9558
Tel (864) 223-1212 *Founded/Ownrshp* 2007
Sales 41.7MM^E *EMP* 108
SIC 3824 Fluid meters & counting devices; Fluid meters & counting devices
Prin: Bertha Huber

D-U-N-S 96-347-2787
MEAT AND SEAFOOD SOLUTIONS LLC
SOUTHERN FOODS
(*Suby of* P D C) ★
3500 Old Battleground Rd, Greensboro, NC 27410-2420
Tel (336) 545-3827 *Founded/Ownrshp* 2010
Sales 88.8MM^E *EMP* 200
SIC 5146 5147 Fish & seafoods; Meats & meat products; Fish & seafoods; Meats & meat products
CEO: Malcolm R Sullivan Jr
**Pr:* Bill Mutton
**COO:* Jim Cremins
VP: Sue James
Sls Mgr: Paul Amburn

MEAT CUTTERS UNION LOCAL 546
See UF C W LOCAL 546

D-U-N-S 07-018-8305
MEAT MARKET INC
NORTH FRESNO FOODS
454 W Alluvial Ave, Pinedale, CA 93650-1160
Tel (559) 436-6741 *Founded/Ownrshp* 1976
Sales 26.5MM^E *EMP* 55^E
SIC 5147 5144 5146 5421 Meats, fresh; Meats, cured or smoked; Poultry: live, dressed or frozen (unpackaged); Fish, fresh; Fish, cured; Meat & fish markets
CEO: Jeffrey Aivazian
**VP:* Deborah Aivazian
Exec: Ty Kinney

D-U-N-S 02-324-5855
MEAT PROCESSORS INC
MEAT PROCESSORS OF GREEN BAY
2210 Hutson Rd, Green Bay, WI 54303-4796
Tel (920) 499-4841 *Founded/Ownrshp* 1987
Sales 20.9MM^E *EMP* 48
SIC 5147 5144 5146 5142 Meats, fresh; Poultry products; Fish & seafoods; Packaged frozen goods
Pr: Douglas Farah
**VP:* Jim Farah
Genl Mgr: Wayne Hultman
Opers Mgr: Chris Scholz

MEAT PROCESSORS OF GREEN BAY
See MEAT PROCESSORS INC

D-U-N-S 01-304-3096
MEATH-PATRICK INC
BUCK SUPPLY & DISTRIBUTION
22 Veterans Ln, Plattsburgh, NY 12901-1257
Tel (518) 561-4300 *Founded/Ownrshp* 1978
Sales 22.2MM^E^ *EMP* 31
SIC 5113 5087 5046 Industrial & personal service paper; Bags, paper & disposable plastic; Boxes, paperboard & disposable plastic; Shipping supplies; Janitors' supplies; Restaurant equipment & supplies
Ch Bd: David F Meath
**VP:* Terry Blake
Exec: Patricia Bryar

D-U-N-S 02-498-5889 EXP
MEATS BY LINZ INC
414 State St, Calumet City, IL 60409-2618
Tel (708) 862-0830 *Founded/Ownrshp* 1961
Sales 22.7MM^E^ *EMP* 44^E^
SIC 5147 5812 2013 2011 Meats, cured or smoked; Meats, fresh; Eating places; Sausages & other prepared meats; Meat packing plants
Pr: Robert Linz
**VP:* Frederick Linz
VP: Becky Robbins
Sls Mgr: Camille Ballay
Sls Mgr: Frank Luna

MEAU
See MITSUBISHI ELECTRIC AUTOMATION INC

D-U-N-S 07-448-9378
MEB GENERAL CONTRACTORS INC
4016 Holland Blvd, Chesapeake, VA 23323-1522
Tel (757) 487-5858 *Founded/Ownrshp* 1982
Sales 179.7MM^E^ *EMP* 224^E^
SIC 1542 1629 1541 Commercial & office building contractors; Waste water & sewage treatment plant construction; Warehouse construction; Commercial & office building contractors; Waste water & sewage treatment plant construction; Warehouse construction
Pr: George B Clarke IV
**Sec:* William A Paulette
**Sr VP:* Mark F Olmstead
**VP:* Thomas Atherton
**VP:* William R Blowe
**VP:* David M Ervin
VP: David Ervin
**VP:* Eric Keplinger
VP: Fred Wagner
CIO: Matt Weaver
Snr Mgr: Wesley Bynum

MEB MANAGEMENT SERVICES
See MORRISON EKRE & BART MANAGEMENT SERVICES INC

D-U-N-S 18-873-4867
MEBILODDE OF PLYMOUTH
WESTTRAIL NURSING HOME
395 W Ann Arbor Trl, Plymouth, MI 48170-1641
Tel (734) 453-3983 *Founded/Ownrshp* 1983
Sales 352.1MM *EMP* 55
SIC 8051 Skilled nursing care facilities; Skilled nursing care facilities
Pr: Daniel M Abramson
**VP:* Louise Ann Padmos

MEC
See MCKENZIE ELECTRIC COOPERATIVE INC

MEC
See CENTER MANUFACTURING INC

D-U-N-S 04-285-0834
MEC CONSTRUCTION LLC
ARMEC
(*Suby of* NORTH AMERICAN DRILLERS LLC) ★
130 Meadow Ridge Rd # 28, Mount Morris, PA 15349-9351
Tel (304) 592-5175 *Founded/Ownrshp* 2009
Sales 30.5MM^E^ *EMP* 300
SIC 1623 1241 1542 1622

MEC INTERACTION
See MEDIAEDGE CIA LLC

D-U-N-S 83-191-2592
MEC INTERNATIONAL CORP
5855 N Glen Park Rd, Milwaukee, WI 53209-4435
Tel (414) 228-5000 *Founded/Ownrshp* 2006
Sales 36.7MM^E^ *EMP* 275
SIC 3625 3674 3825 Electric controls & control accessories, industrial; Industrial electrical relays & switches; Microprocessors; Test equipment for electronic & electrical circuits; Electric controls & control accessories, industrial; Industrial electrical relays & switches; Microprocessors; Test equipment for electronic & electrical circuits
Pr: P Michael Stoehr
IT Man: Tim Benning
IT Man: Mark Slezak
Ql Cn Mgr: Robert Schultz
Snr Mgr: Terry Martin

MEC NORTHWEST
See MILEGON LLC

D-U-N-S 61-692-0708
MEC PENNSYLVANIA RACING
210 Race Track Rd, Meadow Lands, PA 15347
Tel (724) 225-9300 *Founded/Ownrshp* 1999
Sales 10.2MM^E^ *EMP* 872
SIC 7948 5812 Harness horse racing; Eating places; Harness horse racing; Eating places
Genl Mgr: John Marshal

MEC WELDING
See EUTECTIC CORP

MEC2
See MECHANICAL ENGINEERING AND CONSTRUCTION CORP

MECA
See METROPOLITAN ENTERTAINMENT & CONVENTION AUTHORITY

D-U-N-S 04-802-7429
MECA INC
401 N Carroll St, Madison, WI 53703-1803
Tel (608) 257-0681 *Founded/Ownrshp* 1958
Sales 37.5MM^E^ *EMP* 200
SIC 5021 Household furniture; Office furniture; Household furniture; Office furniture
Prin: Bradley C Mullins
Sec: Carol M Mullins

D-U-N-S 11-479-1192 IMP
MECANEX USA INC
(*Suby of* RUAG SCHWEIZ AG)
119 White Oak Dr, Berlin, CT 06037-1638
Tel (860) 828-6531 *Founded/Ownrshp* 1998
Sales 32.3MM^E^ *EMP* 30
SIC 5088 Aircraft equipment & supplies
CEO: Thomas Schilliger
**VP:* Patricia Saglimbeni
Opers Mgr: Dennis Ubillus
Ql Cn Mgr: Patricia Reed
Mktg Dir: Bernhard Eichinger
Mktg Dir: Hans Fritz
Mktg Mgr: Torbjirn Andersson
Mktg Mgr: Stefan Eriksson
Sls Mgr: Aldo Quiroz

MECC
See MIDWEST EMPLOYERS CASUALTY CO

D-U-N-S 00-787-4811
MECCA & SONS TRUCKING CORP
580 Luis Munoz Marin Blvd, Jersey City, NJ 07310-1416
Tel (201) 792-5866 *Founded/Ownrshp* 1950
Sales 22.7MM^E^ *EMP* 100
SIC 4213 Trucking, except local
Pr: Helen Mecca
**CFO:* Sandy Anest
VP: Peggy Mecca
Sfty Mgr: Mayra Camargo

D-U-N-S 07-684-3895
MECCA ELECTRONICS INDUSTRIES INC
1016 44th Dr, Long Island City, NY 11101-7014
Tel (718) 361-9001 *Founded/Ownrshp* 1974
Sales 153.8MM^E^ *EMP* 25
Accts Billet Feit And Preis Pc
SIC 5092 Video games; Video games
Ch Bd: Raymond Aboody
**Sec:* Danny Mashal

D-U-N-S 62-738-4303 IMP/EXP
MECCA ENTERPRISES INC
JSA INTERNATIONAL
1541 N Powerline Rd, Pompano Beach, FL 33069-1620
Tel (954) 969-8440 *Founded/Ownrshp* 1989
Sales 26.0MM *EMP* 18
SIC 5194 5141 Tobacco & tobacco products; Groceries, general line; Tobacco & tobacco products; Groceries, general line
Pr: Abdallah Nada
VP: Abdl Lah Nada
Off Mgr: Amy Ali

D-U-N-S 82-866-9007
MECCANICA HOLDINGS USA INC
(*Suby of* FINMECCANICA SPA)
1625 I St Nw Fl 12, Washington, DC 20006-4073
Tel (202) 292-2620 *Founded/Ownrshp* 2008
Sales NA *EMP* 10,265
SIC 6719 Investment holding companies, except banks; Investment holding companies, except banks
CEO: Simone Bemporad

D-U-N-S 09-646-7170
MECCON INDUSTRIES INC
(*Suby of* MONICO INC) ★
2703 Bernice Rd, Lansing, IL 60438-1011
Tel (708) 474-8300 *Founded/Ownrshp* 1979
Sales 72.5MM^E^ *EMP* 150
SIC 1711 Mechanical contractor; Mechanical contractor
Pr: John Curran
**Treas:* Stephan Curran
**VP:* Paul Beugel
VP: Paul R Cuan
**VP:* Paul Curran
VP: Gary Kebert
**VP:* Charles Stafford
Dir IT: Brandon Wilson

D-U-N-S 10-321-7287
MECHANICAL BREAKDOWN PROTECTION INC
250 Ne Mulberry St, Lees Summit, MO 64086-4533
Tel (816) 347-0900 *Founded/Ownrshp* 1982
Sales NA *EMP* 35
Accts Larson Allen
SIC 6399 Warranty insurance, automobile
Pr: Kevin Orr
**CFO:* George Meiners
CFO: George H Meiners
**Ch:* James W Orr Jr
Natl Sales: Barry Kindler

D-U-N-S 04-122-3363
MECHANICAL CONSTRUCTION CO LLC
MCC GROUP, THE
3001 17th St, Metairie, LA 70002-3899
Tel (504) 833-8291 *Founded/Ownrshp* 2002
Sales 52.0MM^E^ *EMP* 200^E^
SIC 1711 Mechanical contractor; Mechanical contractor
CFO: Charles Cassreino
**Treas:* Carol Lagasse
**VP:* Thomas W Boudreaux
**VP:* Glenn M Perilloux
Off Mgr: Sierra Cook
Snr PM: Bob Thornton

D-U-N-S 00-386-1168
MECHANICAL CONSTRUCTION MANAGERS LLC (OH)
RIECK SERVICES
5245 Wadsworth Rd, Dayton, OH 45414-3507
Tel (937) 424-5395 *Founded/Ownrshp* 1949
Sales 32.7MM *EMP* 200^E^
Accts Thorn Lewis + Duncan Inc D
SIC 1711 1761 Heating & air conditioning contractors; Sheet metalwork; Roofing contractor; Heating & air conditioning contractors; Sheet metalwork; Roofing contractor
Pr: Larry Cottle
COO: Rieck Peter
CFO: Michael Stemen
Sr VP: Randall Swanson
VP: Steven B Mayers
VP: Douglas Wallker
Info Man: Tom Graham

MECHANICAL CONTRACTORS
See LUCKINBILL INC

D-U-N-S 00-316-9232
MECHANICAL CONTRACTORS INC (NC)
1733 University Coml Pl, Charlotte, NC 28213-6444
Tel (704) 597-3720 *Founded/Ownrshp* 1948
Sales 27.6MM^E^ *EMP* 150
SIC 1711

MECHANICAL DRIVES AND BELTING
See LOS ANGELES RUBBER CO

D-U-N-S 02-831-1421
MECHANICAL DRIVES CO
L A RUBBER CO
2915 E Washington Blvd, Los Angeles, CA 90023-4218
Tel (323) 263-4131 *Founded/Ownrshp* 1957
Sales 50.9MM^E^ *EMP* 54
SIC 5085 Bearings; Gears; Power transmission equipment & apparatus
CEO: Michael Durst
**CEO:* T Wayne Gehan
**VP:* David Durst

D-U-N-S 11-922-6660
MECHANICAL DYNAMICS & ANALYSIS LTD
RENEWAL PARTS MAINTENANCE
(*Suby of* MITSUBISHI HITACHI POWER SYSTEMS AMERICAS INC) ★
19 British American Blvd, Latham, NY 12110
Tel (518) 399-3616 *Founded/Ownrshp* 2006
Sales 92.3MM^E^ *EMP* 391
SIC 8711 7699

D-U-N-S 14-315-8025
MECHANICAL ENGINEERING AND CONSTRUCTION CORP
MEC2
6159 Edmondson Ave Ste A, Catonsville, MD 21228-1826
Tel (443) 200-1000 *Founded/Ownrshp* 2003
Sales 31.6MM^E^ *EMP* 125
SIC 1711 8711 Plumbing, heating, air-conditioning contractors; Mechanical engineering; Plumbing, heating, air-conditioning contractors; Mechanical engineering
Pr: Richard E Beattie
**VP:* Frederick B Kawa III
**VP:* Michelle Lee Wittig

D-U-N-S 04-227-0835 IMP
MECHANICAL EQUIPMENT CO (NC)
1301 Industrial Dr, Matthews, NC 28105-5310
Tel (704) 847-2100 *Founded/Ownrshp* 1938, 1955
Sales 20.8MM^E^ *EMP* 30
SIC 5084 Pumps & pumping equipment; Heat exchange equipment, industrial
CFO: Michael J Godsey
**Pr:* Scott Fletcher
**Sr VP:* Bennie V Crider
**Sr VP:* Walter H Lee
IT Man: Angela Tice

D-U-N-S 00-818-5043 IMP/EXP
MECHANICAL EQUIPMENT CO INC
MECO
68375 Compass Way E, Mandeville, LA 70471-8713
Tel (985) 249-5500 *Founded/Ownrshp* 1949
Sales 37.9MM^E^ *EMP* 196
Accts Postlethwaite & Netterville M
SIC 3589 Water treatment equipment, industrial; Water treatment equipment, industrial
Pr: George V Gsell
**CFO:* Reano Siragusa
**VP:* Sharif A Disi
**VP:* Kim Klein
Rgnl Mgr: Jim Clemens
Plng Mgr: Wayne Desselles
IT Man: Scott Smith
Mtls Mgr: Wayne Switzer

D-U-N-S 60-977-9459
MECHANICAL INC
HELM GROUP, THE
(*Suby of* HELM GROUP INC) ★
2279 E Yellow Creek Rd, Freeport, IL 61032-9693
Tel (815) 235-1955 *Founded/Ownrshp* 1990
Sales 50.4MM^E^ *EMP* 200
SIC 1711 3441

D-U-N-S 04-873-6540
MECHANICAL SALES INC
7222 S 142nd St Ste 5, Omaha, NE 68138-6512
Tel (402) 339-0306 *Founded/Ownrshp* 1997
Sales 32.4MM *EMP* 70
SIC 5075 Warm air heating equipment & supplies; Air conditioning equipment, except room units
CEO: William Wieseler
**Pr:* Mark Morris
**VP:* Jeff Backemeyer
**VP:* Robert Harper

D-U-N-S 00-553-0951 IMP
MECHANICAL SERVANTS LLC
CONVENIENCE VALET
(*Suby of* WEINBERG CAPITAL GROUP INC) ★
2755 Thomas St, Melrose Park, IL 60160-2959
Tel (708) 486-1500 *Founded/Ownrshp* 2015
Sales 100.2MM^E^ *EMP* 96
SIC 5122 Druggists' sundries; Druggists' sundries
Pr: David A Baum
**COO:* Edward Edick
**CFO:* Barry Margolin
**Ex VP:* Jim Blosser
VP: Rich Stern
Dir IT: Eugene Amante
Ql Cn Mgr: Towana Elmore
Mktg Dir: Tom Lamanna
Manager: Judy Esteppe

D-U-N-S 12-121-6972
MECHANICAL SERVICE & SYSTEMS INC
MSS
6906 S 300 W, Midvale, UT 84047-1049
Tel (801) 255-9333 *Founded/Ownrshp* 1984
Sales 29.8MM^E^ *EMP* 90
SIC 1711

D-U-N-S 01-905-2588
MECHANICAL SERVICES INC
MAINE CONTROLS
400 Presumpscot St, Portland, ME 04103-5292
Tel (207) 774-0220 *Founded/Ownrshp* 2000
Sales 21.7MM^E^ *EMP* 100
SIC 1711 Heating systems repair & maintenance; Warm air heating & air conditioning contractor; Heating systems repair & maintenance; Warm air heating & air conditioning contractor
Pr: Christopher Green
Exec: Hope Shaw
Sls&Mrk Ex: James Poitras

D-U-N-S 12-898-1466
■ **MECHANICAL SERVICES OF CENTRAL FLORIDA INC**
(*Suby of* EMCOR GROUP INC) ★
9820 Satellite Blvd, Orlando, FL 32837-8447
Tel (407) 857-3510 *Founded/Ownrshp* 2003
Sales 42.3MM^E^ *EMP* 220^E^
SIC 1711 7623 1761 Heating & air conditioning contractors; Refrigeration repair service; Sheet metalwork; Heating & air conditioning contractors; Refrigeration repair service; Sheet metalwork
CEO: William M Dillard
**Pr:* Bernie Horne
**CFO:* Debbie Alazraki
**VP:* Michael Billard
**VP:* Tim Miles
Dir IT: Eric Clark
Sfty Dirs: John Beaudry
Sls Dir: Bill Speer

D-U-N-S 10-580-3076
MECHANICAL SUPPLY CO
1001 Crews Rd, Matthews, NC 28105-9401
Tel (704) 847-9641 *Founded/Ownrshp* 1983
Sales 56.4MM^E^ *EMP* 40
SIC 5074 Plumbing & heating valves; Plumbing fittings & supplies
Pr: Scott B Reid
CFO: Dennis Mullins
**VP:* Dennis M Mullen
IT Man: Ken Young
Sales Exec: Sue Honeycutt
Sls Mgr: Joe Lee

D-U-N-S 94-397-7660
MECHANICAL SYSTEMS & SERVICES INC
1001 Tuckaseegee Rd, Charlotte, NC 28208-4438
Tel (704) 372-4344 *Founded/Ownrshp* 1996
Sales 63.7MM *EMP* 315
SIC 8742 1711 Construction project management consultant; Heating & air conditioning contractors; Ventilation & duct work contractor; Construction project management consultant; Heating & air conditioning contractors; Ventilation & duct work contractor
CEO: D Hunter Edwards Jr
**CFO:* Jennifer Tindal
Sr VP: Michael Carter
**VP:* Eric Bolin
VP: Charles Gallagher
**VP:* Matt Howard
**VP:* Rick Lambeth
Dist Mgr: Chad Davis
Dir IT: John White
Sys Mgr: Thomas Coles
Sftwr Eng: Richard Gonzales

D-U-N-S 02-692-2108
MECHANICAL SYSTEMS CO LLC
4067 New Getwell Rd, Memphis, TN 38118-6016
Tel (901) 369-9822 *Founded/Ownrshp* 2009
Sales 22.1MM *EMP* 76
SIC 1711 Mechanical contractor; Mechanical contractor
Pr: Lee Walker IV
**Ex VP:* Chris Claude
**VP:* Bill Wren
Off Mgr: Sherry Jenne

D-U-N-S 01-691-8419
MECHANICAL SYSTEMS OF DAYTON INC (OH)
MSD
4401 Springfield St, Dayton, OH 45431-1040
Tel (937) 254-3235 *Founded/Ownrshp* 1984
Sales 40.7MM^E^ *EMP* 100
SIC 1711 Plumbing, heating, air-conditioning contractors; Mechanical contractor
CEO: Beverly Stewart
**CFO:* Mark Turvene
**VP:* John Stewart
Mtls Mgr: Kevin Vivier

MECHANICAL TECHNOLOGY
See BAY MECHANICAL INC

D-U-N-S 00-521-6940 IMP
MECHANICAL TOOL & ENGINEERING CO INC (IL)
MTE HYDRAULICS
4701 Kishwaukee St, Rockford, IL 61109-2926
Tel (815) 397-4701 *Founded/Ownrshp* 1946
Sales 65.0MM^E^ *EMP* 260
SIC 3594 3542 Pumps, hydraulic power transfer; Presses: forming, stamping, punching, sizing (machine tools); Pumps, hydraulic power transfer; Presses: forming, stamping, punching, sizing (machine tools)

Pr: Richard D Nordlof
**Pr:* Gregory S Nordlof
**Sec:* Gerald Lang
**Prin:* John Fulton
Ex Dir: Donna Hampton
Genl Mgr: Randy Welch
Dir IT: Kathy Ross
VP Mktg: Gary Marshall
Manager: Mike Stewart
Sls Mgr: Paul Rupprecht
Sls Mgr: Richard Thurman
Board of Directors: John Fulton

D-U-N-S 00-691-0780
MECHANICS BANK (CA)
(*Suby of* EB ACQUISITION CO LLC) ★
3170 Hilltop Mall Rd, Richmond, CA 94806-5231
Tel (800) 797-6324 *Founded/Ownrshp* 1905
Sales NA *EMP* 650
SIC 6022 State commercial banks; State commercial banks
CEO: Kristen Weisser
Ch Bd: Dianne Daiss Felton
V Ch: Diane Felton
Pr: Blake Brydon
Pr: Tracy Calkins
Pr: Tammy Espland
Pr: Diane Marieiro
Pr: Nicholas Mellon
Pr: Maxine Mendoza
Pr: Arlene Mulchaey
Pr: Alfredo Pedroza
Pr: Cary Schroeder
Pr: Phyllis Scipi
Pr: Christa Steele
COO: Steven I Barlow
CFO: Clint Chew
CFO: CJ Johnson
Treas: Garrett Lambert
V Ch Bd: Micheal Banner
Ofcr: Larry Cretan
Ofcr: Nathan Duda

D-U-N-S 06-984-7861
MECHANICS COOPERATIVE BANK
308 Bay St, Taunton, MA 02780-1834
Tel (508) 823-7744 *Founded/Ownrshp* 1877
Sales NA *EMP* 30
SIC 6022 6141 State commercial banks; Personal credit institutions; State commercial banks; Personal credit institutions
Pr: Joseph T Baptista Jr
**Ch Bd:* Edmund J Brennan
Pr: Tom Steele
CFO: Andrew Hewitt
**V Ch Bd:* Richard Bentley
Ex VP: Joseph Baptista
Sr VP: Deborah Grimes
**Sr VP:* Karen E Heywood
**Sr VP:* Phillip E Poore
VP: Jessica Coulombe
VP: Matt Ledin
VP: John McMahon
VP: Anthony Medeiros
VP: Matt Shaw

D-U-N-S 09-536-3768
MECHANICSBURG AREA SCHOOL DISTRICT (INC)
100 E Elmwood Ave, Mechanicsburg, PA 17055-4243
Tel (717) 691-4500 *Founded/Ownrshp* 1963
Sales 59.7MM *EMP* 553
Accts Greenawalt & Company Pc Me
SIC 8211 Public senior high school; Public junior high school; Public elementary school; Public senior high school; Public junior high school; Public elementary school
Pr: Joseph L Hood
CFO: Alan Vandrew
HC Dir: Suzanne Walker

MECHANICSVILLE TOYOTA
See PAGE III INC

D-U-N-S 11-881-1827 IMP
MECHANIX WEAR INC
28525 Witherspoon Pkwy, Valencia, CA 91355-5417
Tel (661) 257-0474 *Founded/Ownrshp* 1984
Sales 36.2MM^E *EMP* 80
SIC 2381 3021 7218 Fabric dress & work gloves; Rubber & plastics footwear; Safety glove supply
CEO: James M Hale
**Pr:* Bari Waalk
**CFO:* Kevin Reynolds
CFO: Patricia Riggs
Sr VP: Jessica Diligiro
**VP:* Sherrie Hale

D-U-N-S 13-940-2333 IMP
MECHATRONICS INC
8152 304th Ave Se, Preston, WA 98050
Tel (425) 222-5900 *Founded/Ownrshp* 1979
Sales 51.2MM^E *EMP* 130
SIC 5085 5063 3564 Bearings; Electronic wire & cable; Blowers & fans; Bearings; Electronic wire & cable; Blowers & fans
Pr: Kent G Ross
**Sr VP:* Julie Cushman
Rgnl Mgr: Bill Harr
MIS Dir: Randy Sneesby
Mktg Mgr: David Hazlett
Sales Asso: Christina Valdez

D-U-N-S 96-897-4766
MECHDYNE CORP
11 E Church St Ste 400, Marshalltown, IA 50158-5011
Tel (641) 754-4649 *Founded/Ownrshp* 1996
Sales 33.1MM^E *EMP* 100
SIC 3577 7812 Computer peripheral equipment; Cartoon production, television; Computer peripheral equipment; Cartoon production, television
Pr: Christopher L Clover
**CFO:* Scott Porter
CFO: Scott Torter
**VP:* John Bethel
**VP:* James Gruening
**VP:* Mike Hancock
**VP:* Kurt Hoffmeister
**VP:* Cathy Laspara
IT Man: Ruzan Morrison

Opers Mgr: Clint Collins
Mktg Mgr: Susan Fleming

D-U-N-S 02-255-8068 IMP/EXP
MECHOSHADE SYSTEMS INC
(*Suby of* J B HOLDINGS GROUP INC) ★
4203 35th St, Long Island City, NY 11101-2301
Tel (718) 729-2020 *Founded/Ownrshp* 1968
Sales 106.7MM^E *EMP* 500
SIC 2591 Window shades; Window shades
Ch Bd: Joel Berman
**Pr:* Jan Berman
**CFO:* Norman Rathfelder
VP: Mel Byars
VP: John Wilk
Mng Dir: Stephen Hebeisen
Dir IT: Carolyn Gary
Dir IT: Kate Julisf
IT Man: Tawanda Cooper
IT Man: Radu Negoescu
Sys Mgr: Zoya Davelman

D-U-N-S 83-203-5732 IMP
MECHOSHADE WEST INC
(*Suby of* MECHOSHADE SYSTEMS INC) ★
2851 W Indian School Rd, Phoenix, AZ 85017-4253
Tel (602) 285-0667 *Founded/Ownrshp* 2000
Sales 26.4MM^E *EMP* 120
SIC 2591 Drapery hardware & blinds & shades; Drapery hardware & blinds & shades
Pr: Jan Berman
Off Mgr: Ada Real
VP Opers: John Wilk
Plnt Mgr: Eric Quan

D-U-N-S 00-154-0079 IMP
MECHTRONICS CORP (NY)
511 Fishkill Ave, Beacon, NY 12508-1253
Tel (845) 231-1400 *Founded/Ownrshp* 1944
Sales 29.8MM^E *EMP* 190
SIC 3993 Displays, paint process; Displays, paint process
Ch Bd: Richard J Fellinger
Pr: Anthony Squitieri
CFO: Tim Helmig
VP: Keith Arndt
Dir Bus: Michael Mele
Off Admin: Marylouise Warren
DP Exec: Theo White
Art Dir: Amy Lasagna

D-U-N-S 17-597-2611
MECHWORKS MECHANICAL CONTRACTORS INC
102 Professional Park Dr A, Beaufort, NC 28516-2474
Tel (252) 504-3201 *Founded/Ownrshp* 1997
Sales 24.0MM *EMP* 90
SIC 1711 Mechanical contractor; Mechanical contractor
Pr: Ronald E Lovings
**Sr VP:* Trapàs Pratt
**VP:* David Sims
**VP:* Andy Swofford
Off Mgr: Loretta Bailey

D-U-N-S 15-768-8573
MECKLENBERG COUNTY PUBLIC SCHOOL DISTRICT
175 Mayfield Dr, Boydton, VA 23917-2817
Tel (434) 738-6111 *Founded/Ownrshp* 1870
Sales 36.1MM^E *EMP* 900
SIC 8211 School board; School board
VP: James Jennings
CIO: Linda Hodges
IT Man: Chad Wollenberg
Teacher Pr: Laura Pittard

D-U-N-S 83-667-0216
MECKLENBURG HEALTH CARE CENTER INC
2415 Sandy Porter Rd, Charlotte, NC 28273-3695
Tel (704) 583-0430 *Founded/Ownrshp* 1995
Sales 817.0MM *EMP* 100
SIC 8051 Skilled nursing care facilities; Skilled nursing care facilities
Pr: W Heywood Fralin
**Treas:* Melissa K Snuggs
**VP:* N Ronald Covington Jr
**VP:* Karen H Waldron
HC Dir: Caroline Jones

D-U-N-S 03-050-5648
MECKLENBURG RADIOLOGY ASSOCIATES PA
3623 Latrobe Dr Ste 216, Charlotte, NC 28211-2117
Tel (704) 384-4177 *Founded/Ownrshp* 1970
Sales 22.4MM^E *EMP* 60
SIC 8011 Radiologist
Pr: Donald E Toothman MD
**VP:* Dr Henry T Adkins
**VP:* Dr James A Fagan
Mktg Dir: Charlene Eichinger
Doctor: Robert Barr
Doctor: Richard Dunlop
Doctor: Bennett Hollenberg
Doctor: Erik Insko
Doctor: Michael Lenker
Doctor: John Nixon
Doctor: Robert Quarles

D-U-N-S 82-534-1035
MECKLER BULGER & TILSON LLP
123 N Wacker Dr Fl 16, Chicago, IL 60606-1768
Tel (312) 474-7900 *Founded/Ownrshp* 1994
Sales 20.0MM^E *EMP* 115^E
SIC 8111 Specialized law offices, attorneys; Administrative & government law; Product liability law
Pt: Bruce Meckler
Pt: Alex V Barbour
Pt: Joseph O Brien Jr
Pt: Brian W Bulger
Pt: Jack Carriglio
Pt: Janet Davis
Pt: Hallie Miller Fahey
Pt: J Stuart Garbutt
Pt: Paul R Garry
Pt: Brent Graber
Pt: Frank Grossi
Pt: Brett Heinrich

Pt: James Kallianis
Pt: Chris Kentra
Pt: Phillip King
Pt: Mari Henry Leigh
Pt: Michael Leonard
Pt: Michael Loeffler
Pt: Michael Marick
Pt: Robert Paul Norman
Pt: Joseph D O'Brien Jr

D-U-N-S 14-853-5755
MECKLEY SERVICES INC
5701 Gen Wshngtn Dr Ste O, Alexandria, VA 22312-2408
Tel (703) 333-2040 *Founded/Ownrshp* 1994
Sales 28.2MM^E *EMP* 40^E
SIC 1542 Commercial & office buildings, renovation & repair
Pr: Kenneth Meckley
**COO:* John Navolio
**COO:* Donald Walker
**Prin:* Wendi Rosato

MECO
See MECHANICAL EQUIPMENT CO INC

D-U-N-S 06-901-3340
MECO CONSTRUCTORS INC
684 Dunksferry Rd, Bensalem, PA 19020-6513
Tel (215) 671-9535 *Founded/Ownrshp* 1972
Sales 31.4MM^E *EMP* 100
SIC 1794 Excavation work
Pr: Andrew R Ebert III
**CFO:* Frank Gallo

D-U-N-S 00-339-1661 IMP
MECO CORP (TN)
AUSSIE GRILL AND INNOBELLA
(*Suby of* UNAKA CO INC) ★
1500 Industrial Rd, Greeneville, TN 37745-3541
Tel (423) 639-1171 *Founded/Ownrshp* 1958, 1996
Sales 37.2MM^E *EMP* 110
SIC 3631 2514 5023 Barbecues, grills & braziers (outdoor cooking); Chairs, household: metal; Tables, household: metal; Grills, barbecue; Barbecues, grills & braziers (outdoor cooking); Chairs, household: metal; Tables, household: metal; Grills, barbecue
Pr: Mark Profitt
**Ch Bd:* Robert Austin Jr
VP: Michael Duncan
VP: Bob Hebner
**Genl Mgr:* Buddy Yonz
DP Exec: Raymond Spear
MIS Dir: Jay Martin
Dir IT: Martin Hund
QC Dir: Nolan Olivier
Snr Mgr: Eric Feyen

D-U-N-S 14-814-8810
MECO OF ATLANTA INC
4471 Amwiler Rd, Atlanta, GA 30360-2816
Tel (770) 448-6933 *Founded/Ownrshp* 1984
Sales 25.4MM^E *EMP* 67
SIC 1796 7699 5084 1799 Machinery installation; Industrial machinery & equipment repair; Engines, gasoline; Industrial machine parts; Service station equipment installation, maintenance & repair
CEO: Frank R Scudder
**CFO:* Michael R Scudder
**Sec:* Pamela Scudder
**VP:* Mark A Scudder

D-U-N-S 05-205-0262
MECO OF NORTH FLORIDA INC
(*Suby of* MECO OF ATLANTA INC) ★
3626 Phoenix Ave, Jacksonville, FL 32206-2357
Tel (904) 354-6789 *Founded/Ownrshp* 1999
Sales 21.5MM^E *EMP* 67
SIC 5084 Petroleum industry machinery
Pr: Mark Scudder
**Treas:* Pamela Scudder
**VP:* Michael R Scudder
Mktg Mgr: Tony Richardson

MECO OMAHA
See MODERN EQUIPMENT CO INC

D-U-N-S 96-952-0142
MECOSTA COUNTY MEDICAL CENTER
605 Oak St, Big Rapids, MI 49307-2048
Tel (231) 796-8691 *Founded/Ownrshp* 1988
Sales 59.1MM *EMP* 60^E
Accts Plante & Moran Pllc Grand Ra
SIC 8062 General medical & surgical hospitals; General medical & surgical hospitals
CEO: Sam Daugherty
**Ch:* Dave Borth
Dir Rx: Emily Leyder
QA Dir: Carol Wilson
IT Man: Nancy Hansen
Obsttrcn: Gail Desnoyers
Doctor: Dennis Besley
Doctor: Robert Davidson
Doctor: Michael Dickinson
Phys Thrpy: Christi Norman
HC Dir: Kim Easler

D-U-N-S 06-018-7077
MECOSTA COUNTY MEDICAL CENTER FOUNDATION (MI)
605 Oak St, Big Rapids, MI 49307-2048
Tel (231) 796-8691 *Founded/Ownrshp* 1925
Sales 359.2M *EMP* 310
SIC 8062 General medical & surgical hospitals; General medical & surgical hospitals
CEO: Sam Daugherty
Dir Bus: Emily Leyder
Dir Pat Ac: Nancy Hansen
MIS Dir: Fran Gacon

MECOSTA-OSCEOLA CAREER CENTER
See MECOSTA-OSCEOLA INTERMEDIATE SCHOOL DISTRICT

D-U-N-S 02-089-7047
MECOSTA-OSCEOLA INTERMEDIATE SCHOOL DISTRICT
MECOSTA-OSCEOLA CAREER CENTER
15760 190th Ave, Big Rapids, MI 49307-9096
Tel (231) 796-3543 *Founded/Ownrshp* 1958
Sales 22.1MM *EMP* 298
SIC 8211 Public elementary & secondary schools; Public elementary & secondary schools
Psych: Ormand Hook

D-U-N-S 05-191-3226
■ **MECS INC**
(*Suby of* E I DU PONT DE NEMOURS AND CO) ★
14522 South Outer 40 Rd # 1, Chesterfield, MO 63017-5737
Tel (314) 275-5700 *Founded/Ownrshp* 1992
Sales 56.7MM^E *EMP* 200
SIC 8711 Sanitary engineers; Sanitary engineers
CEO: Nick Bhambri
Treas: Ken Kershaw
VP: Mehmet Altin
VP: Theodore Cocos
VP: Linda Colby
VP: A G Corey
**VP:* Sharon A Facchin
VP: Robert Hams
VP: James Harris
**VP:* Wim Kint
VP: Cap Kovarik
VP: J M Rhoades
**VP:* Patrick Ritschel
**VP:* Paul Rossetti
VP: Kirk Schall
VP: Gary Smith
Exec: Larry Paschke

MECU
See MUNICIPAL EMPLOYEES CREDIT UNION OF BALTIMORE INC

MECU-WEST
See TRUWEST CREDIT UNION

MED, THE
See SHELBY COUNTY HEALTH CARE CORP

D-U-N-S 04-436-8413
MED AMERICA HEALTH SYSTEMS CORP
1 Wyoming St, Dayton, OH 45409-2722
Tel (937) 223-6192 *Founded/Ownrshp* 1982
Sales 968.3MM *EMP* 4,700
SIC 8062 8741 8082 General medical & surgical hospitals; Management services; Home health care services; General medical & surgical hospitals; Management services; Home health care services
Pr: T G Breitenbach
**CFO:* Timothy Jackson

D-U-N-S 60-793-6531
MED AMERICA INSURANCE CO OF NEW YORK
(*Suby of* EXCELLUS HEALTH PLAN INC) ★
165 Court St, Rochester, NY 14647-0001
Tel (585) 238-4209 *Founded/Ownrshp* 1987
Sales NA *EMP* 115
Accts Deloitte & Touche Llp Rochest
SIC 6321 Disability health insurance; Disability health insurance
Pr: Bill Jones
**CFO:* Emil Duda
**Sec:* Ralph Cox

D-U-N-S 02-546-9426
MED ASSETS INC
5543 Legacy Dr, Plano, TX 75024-3502
Tel (800) 390-7459 *Founded/Ownrshp* 2010
Sales 95.7MM^E *EMP* 586^E
SIC 5099 Durable goods
QA Dir: Alex Matuson
Software D: Benny Asnake
Ql Cn Mgr: Akber Ali
Corp Couns: Justin Thompson
Snr PM: Alan Dickerson

D-U-N-S 61-616-9389
MED CALL HEALTHCARE INC
430 W Erie St Ste 205, Chicago, IL 60654-7692
Tel (312) 795-0765 *Founded/Ownrshp* 1989
Sales 13.4MM^E *EMP* 300
SIC 7363 7361 Medical help service; Employment agencies; Medical help service; Employment agencies
Pr: James Hoke
**VP:* David Hoke
**VP:* Michael Oppman

MED CENTER ONE
See ROBINSON HEALTH SYSTEM INC

D-U-N-S 61-467-0099
MED CENTRIX INC
(*Suby of* INGALLS HEALTH SYSTEM) ★
71 W 156th St Ste 500, Harvey, IL 60426-4265
Tel (708) 915-6454 *Founded/Ownrshp* 1985
Sales 17.1MM^E *EMP* 346
SIC 8011 Surgeon; Physicians' office, including specialists; Surgeon; Physicians' office, including specialists
Pr: John Czech
Board of Directors: Alan Bruggeman, Donald Curtis, Harold Gouwens, Robert Harris, Raymond Romanus M D, Mark Salvino, Charles Waterman

MED EXPRESS URGENT CARE
See URGENT CARE HOLDINGS INC

D-U-N-S 14-801-7312
MED FLIGHT AIR AMBULANCE INC
2301 Yale Blvd Se Ste D3, Albuquerque, NM 87106-4355
Tel (505) 842-4433 *Founded/Ownrshp* 1987
Sales 32.4MM^E *EMP* 315
SIC 4522 Ambulance services, air; Ambulance services, air
Pr: Larry D Levy
**VP:* Kevin P Levy
Snr Mgr: Johannes Mostert

D-U-N-S 96-162-2615
MED FUSION LLC
2501 S State Hwy 121, Lewisville, TX 75067
Tel (972) 966-7000 *Founded/Ownrshp* 2008
Sales 50.0MM *EMP* 489
SIC 8071 Medical laboratories
CEO: Jon L Hart
COO: Thomas J Gooding
CFO: Patty Pryor
VP: Jessica Landestrait
Snr Ntwrk: Shane Chastain

D-U-N-S 03-064-6491
MED JAMES INC (KS)
8595 College Blvd Ste 200, Overland Park, KS 66210-2617
Tel (913) 663-5500 *Founded/Ownrshp* 1976
Sales NA *EMP* 130
SIC 6411 Insurance agents
Pr: Med James
Sr VP: Pam Donahue
**VP:* Bill Murray
**VP:* Dave Schuhler
Sftwr Eng: Burke Peltier
Sls Dir: Jim Slaughter

MED ONE CAPITAL FUNDING
See MED ONE CAPITAL INC

D-U-N-S 62-580-3135
MED ONE CAPITAL INC
MED ONE CAPITAL FUNDING
10712 S 1300 E, Sandy, UT 84094-5094
Tel (801) 566-6433 *Founded/Ownrshp* 1993
Sales NA *EMP* 50
SIC 6159 7352 Machinery & equipment finance leasing; Medical equipment rental
Ch Bd: Larry R Stevens
Chf Cred: Bryce Ray
**Ex VP:* Brent Allen
Ex VP: Tom Lindsey
**Sr VP:* Troy Tait
**VP:* Jeffrey B Easton
VP: Brian Gates
VP: Doug Green
VP: John McManigal
**VP:* Mark Stevens
Dir Bus: Bill Varley

D-U-N-S 11-938-7186
MED SERVICES INC
100 Knickerbocker Ave C, Bohemia, NY 11716-3127
Tel (631) 218-6450 *Founded/Ownrshp* 2005
Sales 155.0MM *EMP* 55
SIC 3845 7699 Electromedical equipment; Medical equipment repair, non-electric; Electromedical equipment; Medical equipment repair, non-electric
Pr: Steven Cortese
Sr VP: Stefani Katz

D-U-N-S 78-125-5393
MED STAR SURGICAL & BREATHING EQUIPMENT INC
LANDAUER MEDSTAR
(*Suby of* MONTGOMERY MEDICAL EQUIPMENT) ★
270 Community Dr, Great Neck, NY 11021-5504
Tel (718) 460-2900 *Founded/Ownrshp* 1989
Sales 76.9MM^E^ *EMP* 150^E^
SIC 5047 Medical equipment & supplies; Medical equipment & supplies
Pr: Quaiser Pirzada
Ch Bd: Aurangzeb Prizada
Sls Mgr: Bill Martinetti

MED TEC MEDICAL SERVICES
See MERCY MEDICAL SERVICES INC

MED VET ASSOCIATES
See MEDVET ASSOCIATES INC

D-U-N-S 18-225-1553
MED-ACOUSTICS INC
(*Suby of* WILLIAM DEMANTS OG HUSTRU IDA EMILIES (MILLAS) FOND - KALDET OTICON-FONDEN)
1685 E Park Place Blvd, Stone Mountain, GA 30087-3447
Tel (770) 498-1631 *Founded/Ownrshp* 1987
Sales 441.7MM^E^ *EMP* 7,392
Accts Paul A Thomas Cpa
SIC 5047 1742 Medical & hospital equipment; Acoustical & insulation work; Medical & hospital equipment; Acoustical & insulation work
Pr: Greg Ollick

D-U-N-S 18-670-8256
MED-CARE DIABETIC & MEDICAL SUPPLIES INC
933 Clint Moore Rd, Boca Raton, FL 33487-2802
Tel (800) 407-0109 *Founded/Ownrshp* 2002
Sales 131.9MM^E^ *EMP* 300
Accts Glenn R Luisi Accountant Pa
SIC 5047 Medical equipment & supplies; Medical equipment & supplies
Pr: Steven Silverman
COO: Jon Porush
**VP:* Lorri Silverman
Off Mgr: Allen Wyle
Opers Mgr: Ellen Weill
Mktg Dir: Cortney Silverman

D-U-N-S 07-161-8128
MED-CRAFT INC
2450 Nw 110th Ave, Miami, FL 33172-1915
Tel (305) 594-7444 *Founded/Ownrshp* 1982
Sales 25.7MM^E^ *EMP* 45
SIC 5088 7699 Transportation equipment & supplies; Aircraft & heavy equipment repair services
Pr: Mario Duenas
CFO: Carol Duenas
**Sec:* Lucelly Duenas
VP: Nelson Duenas
VP Sls: Juan Castilla
Snr Mgr: Atanas Irinchev

D-U-N-S 87-841-7567 IMP
MED-FIT SYSTEMS INC
3553 Rosa Way, Fallbrook, CA 92028-2663
Tel (760) 723-3618 *Founded/Ownrshp* 1993
Sales 20.7MM^E^ *EMP* 128
SIC 3949 5047 Exercise equipment; Therapy equipment; Exercise equipment; Therapy equipment
Pr: Dean Sbragia
**VP:* Juergen Kopf

D-U-N-S 02-739-7301
MED-LANTIC MANAGEMENT SERVICES INC
(*Suby of* MEDICAL MUTUAL LIABILITY INSURANCE SOCIETY OF MARYLAND) ★
225 International Cir, Hunt Valley, MD 21030-1390
Tel (410) 785-0050 *Founded/Ownrshp* 1985
Sales NA *EMP* 103
SIC 6411 Insurance agents, brokers & service
Pr: David Murray
Netwrk Eng: Richard Muse

D-U-N-S 12-149-5378
MED-LOZ LEASE SERVICE INC
MED-LOZ OIL FIELD SUPPLY
3050 Us Highway 83, Zapata, TX 78076-4238
Tel (956) 765-6029 *Founded/Ownrshp* 1984
Sales 27.4MM^E^ *EMP* 160
SIC 1389 1382 Excavating slush pits & cellars; Removal of condensate gasoline from field (gathering) lines; Gas field services; Oil & gas exploration services; Excavating slush pits & cellars; Removal of condensate gasoline from field (gathering) lines; Gas field services; Oil & gas exploration services
Pr: Juan A Medina
**Treas:* Minerva Lozano
**Sec:* Dolores Medina
**Ex VP:* Delfino Lozano III

MED-LOZ OIL FIELD SUPPLY
See MED-LOZ LEASE SERVICE INC

D-U-N-S 04-065-4576
■ **MED-SOUTH INC**
(*Suby of* COMMUNITY HEALTH MANAGEMENT INC) ★
406 Medical Center Dr, Jasper, AL 35501-3400
Tel (205) 221-8200 *Founded/Ownrshp* 1984
Sales 37.5MM^E^ *EMP* 118
SIC 5999 5699 7352 Medical apparatus & supplies; Uniforms; Medical equipment rental
Pr: Patrick Willingham
VP: William Merrick
Dir IT: Charles Stewart

D-U-N-S 04-935-8224
MED-STAFF OKLAHOMA LLC
(*Suby of* ACCOUNTABLE HEALTHCARE HOLDINGS CORP) ★
11205 S 139th East Ave, Broken Arrow, OK 74011-1714
Tel (918) 317-0270 *Founded/Ownrshp* 2012
Sales 24.8MM^E^ *EMP* 760
SIC 7361 7363 Employment agencies; Help supply services; Employment agencies; Help supply services

D-U-N-S 15-022-0465
MED-TRANS INC
714 W Columbia St, Springfield, OH 45504-2734
Tel (937) 325-4926 *Founded/Ownrshp* 1988
Sales 20.7MM^E^ *EMP* 124
Accts Clark Schaefer Hackett & Co
SIC 4119 Ambulance service
Pr: Luanne George
**Ch Bd:* William George
**VP:* Edward G Bailey

D-U-N-S 04-150-1917 IMP
■ **MED-X CORP** (OK)
MED-X DRUG
(*Suby of* STEPHEN L LAFRANCE PHARMACY INC) ★
1714 Utica Sq, Tulsa, OK 74114-1400
Tel (918) 743-9968 *Founded/Ownrshp* 1967, 2004
Sales 30.9MM^E^ *EMP* 415
SIC 5912 Drug stores; Drug stores
Pr: Milt Wolff
**VP:* Diana Wolff

MED-X DRUG
See MED-X CORP

D-U-N-S 88-376-0159
■ **MED3000 GROUP INC**
(*Suby of* MCKESSON CORP) ★
680 Andersen Dr, Pittsburgh, PA 15220-2759
Tel (412) 937-8887 *Founded/Ownrshp* 2013
Sales 48.3MM^E^ *EMP* 1,100
Accts Schneider Downs & Co Incpi
SIC 8742 8721 Management consulting services; Billing & bookkeeping service; Management consulting services; Billing & bookkeeping service
Ch Bd: Patrick V Hampson
Treas: Drew Hurt
Ex VP: Daniel Wiens
VP: Kevin Amos
VP: Ron Parker
VP: Scott Sanner
VP: David Sassano
VP: Pat Stroh
Exec: Angela Hoffman
**Exec:* Paul McLeod MD
Ex Dir: Susanne Bowyer

MED3000 HEATLH SOLUTIONS
See MED3000 INVESTMENTS INC

D-U-N-S 16-506-5264
■ **MED3000 INVESTMENTS INC**
MED3000 HEATLH SOLUTIONS
(*Suby of* MED3000 GROUP INC) ★
680 Andersen Dr Ste 10, Pittsburgh, PA 15220-2759
Tel (412) 937-8887 *Founded/Ownrshp* 1987
Sales 13.4MM^E^ *EMP* 1,000
SIC 8071 Medical laboratories; Medical laboratories
CEO: Patrick Hampson
**CFO:* David Dillon
Ex VP: Richard Schickler
**Sr VP:* Stephen Ura
VP: Ricci Beverly
VP: Jeff Hoffman
Snr Mgr: Hillary Harlan
Board of Directors: Paul A McLeod

D-U-N-S 05-122-9602 IMP
MEDA PHARMACEUTICALS INC
(*Suby of* MEDA AB)
265 Davidson Ave, Somerset, NJ 08873-4120
Tel (732) 564-2200 *Founded/Ownrshp* 2007
Sales 198.6MM^E^ *EMP* 747
SIC 2834 Pharmaceutical preparations; Pharmaceutical preparations
CEO: Maria Carell
COO: Barbara Klein
**CFO:* Jeffrey Hostler
CFO: Mary Smith
**Treas:* David Vernieri
Sr VP: Mark Spiers
VP: Susie Lecker
VP: Mark Wertlieb
Dir IT: Thomas Battoglia
IT Man: John Rupinski
Mfg Mgr: Andrew Wallace

D-U-N-S 79-692-6624
MEDAC INC
804 Scott Nixon Mem Dr, Augusta, GA 30907-2464
Tel (706) 650-1034 *Founded/Ownrshp* 1992
Sales 39.7MM^E^ *EMP* 396^E^
SIC 8721 Billing & bookkeeping service
CEO: Bellinger P Moody
**Pr:* Bijon Memar
**CEO:* Gregory Zinser
CFO: Ronald Reed
Treas: Christine Wilkie
Ex VP: Gary Keeling
Sr VP: Nicholas Mareletto
Sr VP: Edward Townsend
Sr VP: Mark Weinstein
Sr VP: Diane Wray
VP: Matthew Harrison
VP: Melanie Lafferty
VP: Krista Schultz

D-U-N-S 07-994-3577
MEDAILLE COLLEGE
18 Agassiz Cir, Buffalo, NY 14214-2695
Tel (716) 880-2000 *Founded/Ownrshp* 1875
Sales 38.3MM *EMP* 693
Accts Lumsden Mccormick Llp Buffal
SIC 8221 College, except junior; College, except junior
Pr: Richard T Jurasek
V Ch: Chuck Moran Jr
COO: Timothy Dzierba
CFO: Charles Gradowski
**Treas:* Michael K Walsh
Bd of Dir: Amanda Sahhar
Bd of Dir: Nicholas Wagner
Trst: Elizabeth Altmaier
Trst: Dominick Antonelli
Trst: Juanita Hunter
Trst: Joseph Mattina
Trst: Kathleen Owens
Trst: Lawrence Quinn
Trst: Samuel Savarino
VP: Carol B Wittmeyer
Assoc Dir: Katie Lengel

D-U-N-S 18-261-9627
MEDAIRE INC
MEDLINK
1250 W Washington St # 442, Tempe, AZ 85281-1796
Tel (480) 333-3700 *Founded/Ownrshp* 2006
Sales 25.1MM^E^ *EMP* 173
SIC 3842 8331 8748 8011 5047 First aid, snake bite & burn kits; Job training & vocational rehabilitation services; Safety training service; Offices & clinics of medical doctors; Medical & hospital equipment; First aid, snake bite & burn kits; Job training & vocational rehabilitation services; Safety training service; Offices & clinics of medical doctors; Medical & hospital equipment
Pr: Grant Jeffery
**Ch Bd:* Joan Sullivan Garrett
**CEO:* James Allen Williams
**CFO:* Roger D Sandeen
**Treas:* Neil Warren Hickson
Ofcr: Bill Dolny
VP: Gary Delvecchio
VP: Heidi Macfarlane
Mng Dir: Peter Tuggey
Dir IT: Carl Erickson
Dir IT: Raymond Lane
Board of Directors: Gregory J Bell, Joan Sullivan Garrett, Terry Giles, Roy Herberger, John Jessup, John Gilbert McCormack, Sandra Wilkenfeld Wadswort

D-U-N-S 00-613-0371 IMP
MEDALCRAFT MINT INC
2660 W Mason St, Green Bay, WI 54303-4963
Tel (920) 499-4249 *Founded/Ownrshp* 1947
Sales 21.6MM^E^ *EMP* 105
SIC 3469 3993 Metal stampings; Signs & advertising specialties
Pr: Ron Chimenti
**CFO:* Joe Anderson
Mfg Dir: Tim Oshefsky
Sls&Mrk Ex: Joe Estrada
Sales Asso: Melissa Marin

D-U-N-S 85-887-7108
MEDALIST CORP
2236 Rutherford Rd # 107, Carlsbad, CA 92008-8836
Tel (760) 214-2149 *Founded/Ownrshp* 2014
Sales 30.0MM *EMP* 4
SIC 3339 Antimony refining (primary)
CEO: Jim Stutts
**COO:* Michael Cagle

D-U-N-S 00-609-1334
■ **MEDALIST INDUSTRIES INC**
C-TECH SYSTEMS DIVISION
(*Suby of* ILLINOIS TOOL WORKS INC) ★
2700 Elmhurst Rd, Elk Grove Village, IL 60007-6315
Tel (847) 766-9000 *Founded/Ownrshp* 1954, 1996
Sales 126.0MM *EMP* 9
SIC 3452 Screws, metal; Bolts, metal; Nuts, metal; Washers, metal; Screws, metal; Bolts, metal; Nuts, metal; Washers, metal
Pr: James S Dahlke
Treas: James A Lathrop
VP: Michael Gregg
VP: James G Gumm
VP: William C O'Loughlin

MEDALIST LASERFAB
See DEFIANCE METAL PRODUCTS OF WI INC

MEDALLA
See CERVECERIA INDIA INC

D-U-N-S 08-671-3372
MEDALLIA INC
395 Page Mill Rd Ste 100, Palo Alto, CA 94306-2066
Tel (650) 321-3000 *Founded/Ownrshp* 2000
Sales 97.5MM^E^ *EMP* 150
SIC 7372 8732 Business oriented computer software; Market analysis, business & economic research; Business oriented computer software; Market analysis, business & economic research
CEO: Borge Hald
Pr: Amy Pressman-Hald
CFO: Chris Watts
Ofcr: Ken Fine
VP: Alan Grebene
VP: Russell Haswell
VP: Nelson Pascua
VP: David Rice
VP: Dorian Stone
Dir Bus: Carlton Osborne
Off Mgr: Tracey Dinneen
Board of Directors: Frank Slootman

D-U-N-S 13-299-9603
■ **MEDALLION BANK**
(*Suby of* MEDALLION FINANCIAL CORP) ★
1100 E 6600 S Ste 510, Salt Lake City, UT 84121-7422
Tel (801) 284-7065 *Founded/Ownrshp* 2002
Sales NA *EMP* 10^E^
SIC 6029 Commercial banks; Commercial banks
Pr: John M Taggart
Pr: Justin Haley
VP: Mike De Carlo
Natl Sales: George Demare
Sls&Mrk Ex: John Haymond

D-U-N-S 04-671-2626 EXP
MEDALLION CABINETRY INC
(*Suby of* ELKAY MANUFACTURING CO INC) ★
1 Medallion Way Ste 10501, Waconia, MN 55387-7000
Tel (952) 442-5171 *Founded/Ownrshp* 1993
Sales 144.6MM^E^ *EMP* 600
SIC 2434 Wood kitchen cabinets; Wood kitchen cabinets
CEO: Timothy J Jahnke
VP: Rudy Detweiler
Ql Cn Mgr: Nancy Patterson
Natl Sales: Jim Haubenschild

MEDALLION CNSTR CLEAN-UP
See SERVICE BY MEDALLION

D-U-N-S 95-934-8293
▲ **MEDALLION FINANCIAL CORP**
437 Madison Ave Fl 38, New York, NY 10022-7015
Tel (212) 328-2100 *Founded/Ownrshp* 1995
Sales NA *EMP* 159^E^
Tkr Sym TAXI *Exch* NGS
SIC 6159 6153 Automobile finance leasing; Short-term business credit; Automobile finance leasing; Short-term business credit
Ch Bd: Alvin Murstein
**Pr:* Andrew M Murstein
COO: Marc Adelson
CFO: Larry D Hall
Ofcr: Marisa T Silverman
Ex VP: Michael J Kowalsky
Sr VP: Marie Russo
Board of Directors: Henry L Aaron, Henry D Jackson, Stanley Kreitman, Frederick A Menowitz, David L Rudnick, Lowell P Weicker Jr

D-U-N-S 14-739-4241 IMP
■ **MEDALLION FOODS INC**
(*Suby of* RALCORP HOLDINGS INC) ★
3636 Medallion Ave, Newport, AR 72112-9096
Tel (870) 523-3500 *Founded/Ownrshp* 2005
Sales 68.9MM^E^ *EMP* 250
SIC 2096 Corn chips & other corn-based snacks; Tortilla chips; Corn chips & other corn-based snacks; Tortilla chips

MEDALLION HOMES
See RITZ-CRAFT CORP OF PENNSYLVANIA INC

D-U-N-S 13-805-8644 IMP
MEDALLION INSTRUMENTATION SYSTEMS LLC
17150 Hickory St, Spring Lake, MI 49456-9712
Tel (616) 847-3700 *Founded/Ownrshp* 2003
Sales 60.0MM^E^ *EMP* 135
SIC 3714 3824 Motor vehicle parts & accessories; Fluid meters & counting devices; Motor vehicle parts & accessories; Fluid meters & counting devices
Mng Dir: Nick Hoiles
Prin: Martin Payne
Prgrm Mgr: John Bishop
IT Man: Cheryl Crane
IT Man: Carin Langlois
Sftwr Eng: Jacob Vanderwall
Mtls Mgr: Craig Vanhekken
Natl Sales: Lance Norris
Pgrm Dir: Philip Vanderwall

D-U-N-S 88-487-2284
MEDALLION LANDSCAPE MANAGEMENT INC
10 San Bruno Ave, Morgan Hill, CA 95037-9214
Tel (408) 782-7500 *Founded/Ownrshp* 1995
Sales 28.0MM^E^ *EMP* 165
SIC 0781 Landscape counseling services; Landscape planning services
CEO: John Gates
**Pr:* Joyce Dawson
Pr: Roger Green
**COO:* Ildefonso Fonsie Bettencourt
CFO: Robert Rosenberg
Sr VP: Juan Armenta
Brnch Mgr: John Bettencourt

VP Opers: Fonsie Bettencourt
Sales Asso: Adan Magana

D-U-N-S 94-997-2553
MEDALLION MIDSTREAM LLC
222 Las Colinas Blvd W, Irving, TX 75039-5421
Tel (972) 746-4401 *Founded/Ownrshp* 2011
Sales 34.1MME *EMP* 37E
SIC 5094 Medallions
Pr: Randy N Lentz
**CFO:* Paul Doll
**VP:* Dana B Amaya
**VP:* Ralph C Lewis
Opers Mgr: Clayton Hewett
**Opers Mgr:* Blaine Meyer

D-U-N-S 08-369-1667
MEDALLION PARTNERS LIMITED DIVIDEND HOUSING ASSOCIATION LIMITEDPARTNERSHIP
834 King Hwy Ste 100, Kalamazoo, MI 49001-2579
Tel (269) 381-0350 *Founded/Ownrshp* 1973
Sales 10.2MME *EMP* 280
SIC 6531 Cooperative apartment manager; Cooperative apartment manager
CEO: Marvin Veltkamp
**Genl Pt:* William S Antisdale
**Genl Pt:* C and W Development
**Genl Pt:* Joseph H Hollander
**Pr:* Mark Wester
**CFO:* Thomas P Penland
VP: Scott Beltz
Sls Mgr: Marvin Dveltkamp

MEDALLION, THE
See SEVEN ACRES JEWISH SENIOR CARE SERVICES INC

MEDALLLIC ART COMPANY
See NORTHWEST TERRITORIAL MINT LLC

D-U-N-S 80-672-6527
MEDAMERICA BILLING SERVICES INC
CALIFORNIA EMERGENCY PHYSICIAN
(*Suby of* CALIFORNIA EMERGENCY PHYSICIANS FOUNDATION) ★
1601 Cummins Dr Ste D, Modesto, CA 95358-6411
Tel (209) 491-7710 *Founded/Ownrshp* 1993
Sales 31.6MME *EMP* 400E
SIC 8721 Billing & bookkeeping service; Billing & bookkeeping service
CEO: Michael F Harrington
Sr Pt: Charles Ayers
Sr Pt: Alice Hunter
Sr Pt: Robert Kollen
Sr Pt: John Naftel
Sr Pt: Martin Oretsky
Pt: Erik Davenport
Pt: Jaime Rivas
Ofcr: James V Proffitt
Assoc Dir: Keith Loring
Div Mgr: Melissa Foreman

D-U-N-S 03-099-8215
MEDAMERICA INC
(*Suby of* CALIFORNIA EMERGENCY PHYSICIANS FOUNDATION) ★
2100 Powell St Ste 900, Emeryville, CA 94608-1844
Tel (510) 350-2600 *Founded/Ownrshp* 1983
Sales 26.7MME *EMP* 150
SIC 8742

D-U-N-S 04-957-7047
MEDAMERICA INC
(*Suby of* EXCELLUS HEALTH PLAN INC) ★
165 Court St, Rochester, NY 14647-0001
Tel (585) 238-4456 *Founded/Ownrshp* 1997
Sales NA *EMP* 69
SIC 6321 Disability health insurance
Pr: Bill Jones
**Ch Bd:* William L Naylon
**COO:* Ralph Cox
**CFO:* Emil Duda
IT Man: Kathy Szymanski
VP Sls: William E Jones

MEDAPHIS PHYSICIAN
See MCKESSON TECHNOLOGIES INC

D-U-N-S 19-045-2631
■ **MEDAREX INC**
(*Suby of* BRISTOL-MYERS SQUIBB CO) ★
707 State Rd Bldg A, Princeton, NJ 08540-1438
Tel (609) 430-2880 *Founded/Ownrshp* 2009
Sales 24.3MME *EMP* 500
SIC 8731 Commercial physical research; Commercial physical research
Pr: Howard H Pien
CFO: Christian S Schade
Ex VP: M A Ppelbum
Sr VP: Dr Nils Lonberg
Sr VP: W Bradford Middlekauff
Sr VP: Dr Ronald A Pepin
Assoc Dir: Amelia Black
Assoc Dir: Alfred Mottram
IT Man: James Mielke
Counsel: Jonathan Kaplan

D-U-N-S 00-890-8758 IMP
MEDART INC (MO)
124 Manufacturers Dr, Arnold, MO 63010-4727
Tel (636) 282-2300 *Founded/Ownrshp* 1912
Sales 125.0MME *EMP* 158
SIC 5084 5088 Engines, gasoline; Marine supplies; Engines, gasoline; Marine supplies
Pr: J Michael Medart
**CFO:* Dave Strubberg
**VP:* J Scott Price
Genl Mgr: Steve White
IT Man: Mike Boyer
Sls Mgr: Ken Erickson
Sls Mgr: John Untereiner
Board of Directors: John Sulack

D-U-N-S 09-395-2070
▲ **MEDASSETS INC**
100 N Point Ctr E Ste 200, Alpharetta, GA 30022-8261
Tel (678) 323-2500 *Founded/Ownrshp* 1999
Sales 720.2MM *EMP* 3,350E
Tkr Sym MDAS *Exch* NGS
SIC 7372 Prepackaged software; Prepackaged software
Ch Bd: R Halsey Wise
Pr: Amy Dellamora Amick
Pr: Bryan Hardman
Pr: Christal Herbst
**Pr:* Michael P Nolte
Pr: Keith L Thurgood
Pr: Bill Tomoschuk
CFO: Anthony Colaluca
**V Ch Bd:* Terrence J Mulligan
**V Ch Bd:* Bruce F Wesson
Ex VP: Charles O Garner
Sr VP: Kate Banks
Sr VP: Robert P Borchert
Sr VP: Deborah Deinstadt
Sr VP: Michael Gaddy
Sr VP: Joe Sfara
VP: Terry Stein
VP: Ryan Wheeler
**Exec:* Rand A Ballard
Comm Man: Karen Bryant
Board of Directors: John A Bardis, Frederick A Hessler, Harris Hyman IV, Vernon R Loucks Jr, C A Lance Piccolo, Kevin M Twomey, Carol J Zierhoffer

D-U-N-S 78-375-2298
■ **MEDASSETS NET REVENUE SYSTEMS LLC**
(*Suby of* MEDASSETS INC) ★
200 N Point Ctr E Ste 400, Alpharetta, GA 30022-8274
Tel (678) 248-8200 *Founded/Ownrshp* 1999
Sales 85.7MME *EMP* 1,100
SIC 8742 7371 Hospital & health services consultant; Computer software development; Hospital & health services consultant; Computer software development
VP: Rand A Ballard
Pr: Richard Lambert
Prgrm Mgr: Laura Rackley
Software D: Mike Morgensen
Sftwr Eng: Ramone Hamilton
Snr PM: Scott Broka

D-U-N-S 07-710-9262
■ **MEDASSETS SUPPLY CHAIN SYSTEMS LLC**
(*Suby of* MEDASSETS INC) ★
200 N Point Ctr E Ste 400, Alpharetta, GA 30022-8274
Tel (770) 667-7200 *Founded/Ownrshp* 2001
Sales 35.7MME *EMP* 800
SIC 7389 Purchasing service; Purchasing service
Sr VP: David Evans

D-U-N-S 03-856-9252
MEDASSIST OF MECKLENBURG
NC MEDASSIST
601 E 5th St Ste 350, Charlotte, NC 28202-3060
Tel (704) 536-1790 *Founded/Ownrshp* 1998
Sales 22.9MM *EMP* 4
Accts C Dewitt Foard & Co Pa Cpas C
SIC 8322 Individual & family services; Individual & family services
Ex Dir: Lori Giang
Assoc Dir: Susan Royster
Dir Rx: Dustin Allen
Ex Dir: Susan Besina
Ex Dir: Giang Lori
Mktg Mgr: Kate Thakkar
Pharmcst: Cindy Delap
Pharmcst: Pat Lowman
Pharmcst: Andrea Rogers
Cert Phar: Jackie Goncavles
Cert Phar: Larry Wntrezak

D-U-N-S 60-753-7946
MEDAVANTE INC
100 American Blvd Ste 106, Hamilton, NJ 08619
Tel (609) 528-9400 *Founded/Ownrshp* 2006
Sales 61.7MME *EMP* 115
SIC 5122 Pharmaceuticals; Pharmaceuticals
CEO: Paul M Gilbert
**CFO:* Steven Downing
**Sr VP:* Peter Sorantin
Sr VP: Thomas Weir
**VP:* Jeanne M Davie
VP: Christopher Randolph
VP: Angela Wilmer
Dir Bus: William Fischer
**Prin:* Janet B W Williams
VP Opers: Joseph Schmidt
Mktg Dir: Elisabeth Prochnik

MEDCARE
See GWINNETT HOSPITAL SYSTEM INC

MEDCARE AMBULANCE
See COMMUNITY EMRGCY MEDICAL SVCS OF OHIO

D-U-N-S 07-937-5537
MEDCARE EMERGENCY HEALTH INC
338 High St, Greenfield, MA 01301-2611
Tel (413) 773-4500 *Founded/Ownrshp* 2013
Sales 28.1MME *EMP* 100E
SIC 5012 Ambulances
CEO: George Gilpin
**CFO:* Douglas Sabean

D-U-N-S 02-111-5162
MEDCATH CORP
10800 Sikes Pl Ste 200, Charlotte, NC 28277-8139
Tel (704) 815-7700 *Founded/Ownrshp* 2001
Sales 304.2MME *EMP* 414E
Accts Deloitte & Touche Llp Raleig
SIC 8099 8062 Medical services organization; General medical & surgical hospitals; Medical services organization; General medical & surgical hospitals
Pr: Lora Ramsey
Pr: David Bussone
COO: Michael G Servais
CFO: Douglas Davenport
CFO: Kay Harrold
CFO: Jeffrey L Hinton
**Sr VP:* Joan McCanless
**Sr VP:* Paul Daniel Perritt
VP: Bill Greenfield
VP: Larissa Spraker
VP: Brent White
Board of Directors: Pamela G Bailey, John T Casey, James A Deal, Robert S McCoy Jr, Jacque J Sokolov MD

D-U-N-S 60-816-1295
MEDCATH INC
(*Suby of* MEDCATH CORP) ★
10720 Sikes Pl Ste 300, Charlotte, NC 28277-8143
Tel (704) 815-7700 *Founded/Ownrshp* 1998
Sales 120.3MME *EMP* 2,937E
SIC 8069 8093 8742 Specialty hospitals, except psychiatric; Specialty outpatient clinics; Hospital & health services consultant
Ch Bd: Stephen R Puckett
**Pr:* Ed French
**CFO:* Jeff Hinton
CFO: David Laird
CFO: James Parker
**Treas:* Art Parker
VP: Gary Bryant
VP: Judy Littrell
VP: Deanna Rutherford
VP: David Salix
VP: Jeff Sandene
VP: Jerry Scienski
VP: Doug Walkins

MEDCENTER ONE CARE CENTER
See MEDCENTER ONE MANDAN

MEDCENTER ONE HEALTH SYSTEMS
See SANFORD BISMARCK

D-U-N-S 18-103-7417
MEDCENTER ONE MANDAN
MEDCENTER ONE CARE CENTER
(*Suby of* MEDCENTER ONE HEALTH SYSTEMS) ★
201 14th St Nw, Mandan, ND 58554-2063
Tel (701) 663-4274 *Founded/Ownrshp* 1990
Sales 15.4MM *EMP* 300
SIC 8051 Skilled nursing care facilities; Skilled nursing care facilities
Pr: Terry Brosseau

D-U-N-S 07-690-4705
MEDCENTRAL HEALTH SYSTEM
335 Glessner Ave, Mansfield, OH 44903-2269
Tel (419) 526-8000 *Founded/Ownrshp* 1963
Sales 247.9MM *EMP* 2,700E
SIC 8062 General medical & surgical hospitals; General medical & surgical hospitals
VP: Beth Hildreth
COO: Ron Distl
Bd of Dir: Ronald Kerst
Bd of Dir: John Siegenthaler
VP: Pam Crawford
VP: Ana Mistretta
VP: Michael Patterson
VP: Brad Peffley
VP: Cindy Sheets
Exec: Carl Bartels
Prac Mgr: Megan Blum

D-U-N-S 83-288-4709
MEDCENTRIX INC
INGALLS PROFESSIONAL PHRM IV
(*Suby of* INGALLS HEALTH SYSTEM) ★
31 W 155th St, Harvey, IL 60426-3556
Tel (708) 589-2019 *Founded/Ownrshp* 2009
Sales 28.1MME *EMP* 24E
SIC 5912 Drug stores & proprietary stores
Prin: Ron Rutkowski

MEDCITYSUPPLY
See BUYONLINENOW INC

MEDCLEAN
See MICKEYS LINEN & TOWEL SUPPLY INC

MEDCO
See LIBERTY BELL EQUIPMENT CORP

MEDCO
See MERIT ELECTRONIC DESIGN CO INC

MEDCO
See MARYLAND ECONOMIC DEVELOPMENT CORP

D-U-N-S 80-425-3446
MEDCO CONSTRUCTION LLC
4005 Crutcher St Ste 200, Dallas, TX 75246-1781
Tel (214) 820-2492 *Founded/Ownrshp* 2006
Sales 22.7MME *EMP* 60
SIC 1521 Single-family housing construction
Pr: Denward Freeman
VP: GP Howard
VP: Rod Luedtke
VP: Chris Robinson
VP: Louis Schindler
VP: L Shindler

D-U-N-S 78-397-7218
■ **MEDCO HEALTH SOLUTIONS**
MERCK
(*Suby of* EXPRESS SCRIPTS HOLDING CO) ★
5701 E Hillsborough Ave # 1300, Tampa, FL 33610-5429
Tel (813) 317-2000 *Founded/Ownrshp* 2004
Sales 57.4MME *EMP* 864
SIC 5961 Pharmaceuticals, mail order; Pharmaceuticals, mail order

D-U-N-S 11-291-1839 EXP
■ **MEDCO HEALTH SOLUTIONS INC**
EXPRESS SCRIPTS HOLDING CO
(*Suby of* EXPRESS SCRIPTS HOLDING CO) ★
100 Parsons Pond Dr, Franklin Lakes, NJ 07417-2604
Tel (201) 269-3400 *Founded/Ownrshp* 2012
Sales 2.0MMME *EMP* 21,712E
SIC 5961 Pharmaceuticals, mail order
Pr: George Paz
**Ch Bd:* David B Snow Jr
Pr: Steven Fitzpatrick
**Pr:* Kenneth O Klepper
Pr: Timothy Wentworth
COO: Daniel Soper
**CFO:* Richard J Rubino
Treas: Gary Tully
**Chf Mktg O:* Jack A Smith
Chf Mktg O: Jack Smith
**Sr VP:* Gabriel R Cappucci
Sr VP: Thomas M Moriarty
Sr VP: Frank Sheehy
VP: Stephen Bell
VP: Bob Benson
VP: Felix Frueh
VP: Frank Gentilella
VP: Thomas Kissinger
VP: William Lagos
VP: John J Long
VP: Alan Lotvin
Board of Directors: Howard W Barker Jr, John L Cassis, Michael Goldstein, Charles M Lillis Phd, Myrtle S Potter, William L Roper MD, David D Stevens, Blenda J Wilson Phd

D-U-N-S 78-397-8307
■ **MEDCO HEALTH SOLUTIONS OF COLUMBUS NORTH LTD**
(*Suby of* EXPRESS SCRIPTS HOLDING CO) ★
5151 Blazer Pkwy Ste B, Dublin, OH 43017-9307
Tel (614) 299-5539 *Founded/Ownrshp* 1991
Sales 31.4MME *EMP* 600
SIC 5961 Pharmaceuticals, mail order; Pharmaceuticals, mail order
VP: William C Kelley III

D-U-N-S 62-111-2895
■ **MEDCO HEALTH SOLUTIONS OF SPOKANE INC**
NATIONAL SERVICES
(*Suby of* EXPRESS SCRIPTS HOLDING CO) ★
23102 E Appleway Ave, Liberty Lake, WA 99019-9585
Tel (509) 928-8738 *Founded/Ownrshp* 1986
Sales 32.8MME *EMP* 350
SIC 5961 Pharmaceuticals, mail order; Pharmaceuticals, mail order
VP: Richard Jones
VP: Epstein Robert
Genl Mgr: Merck Care
Info Man: Stacy Niles
Opers Mgr: Kristi Sterner

MEDCO MEDICAL SUPPLY
See MEDCO RESPIRATORY INSTRUMENTS INC

D-U-N-S 05-626-4823
MEDCO RESPIRATORY INSTRUMENTS INC
MEDCO MEDICAL SUPPLY
10305 Round Up Ln Ste 100, Houston, TX 77064-5560
Tel (713) 956-5288 *Founded/Ownrshp* 1971
Sales 26.8MM *EMP* 132
Accts Kolkhorst And Kolkhorst Houst
SIC 5999 7359 Hospital equipment & supplies; Equipment rental & leasing; Hospital equipment & supplies; Equipment rental & leasing
Pr: John C Calhoun IV
Sec: Ann Clark
Rgnl Mgr: Andrew Wallick

D-U-N-S 04-241-3104
■ **MEDCO TOOL OF NEW JERSEY INC**
(*Suby of* LIBERTY BELL EQUIPMENT CORP) ★
3201 S 76th St, Philadelphia, PA 19153-3279
Tel (215) 492-6700 *Founded/Ownrshp* 1994
Sales 54.1MME *EMP* 165
SIC 5013 5072 Tools & equipment, automotive; Hardware
Pr: Richard Bell
Sr VP: Holger Baeuerle

MEDCOMP
See MEDICAL COMPONENTS INC

MEDCONNECTION
See MOBILE MEDICAL RESPONSE INC

D-U-N-S 11-605-6490
MEDCOR INC
4805 Prime Pkwy, McHenry, IL 60050-7002
Tel (815) 363-9500 *Founded/Ownrshp* 1984
Sales 72.3MME *EMP* 1,000
SIC 8099 Medical services organization; Medical services organization
Pr: Philip C Seeger
**CEO:* Kais Salhut
**COO:* Bennet W Petersen
**CFO:* Cheryl Smith
Ofcr: Paula Franklin
**Ex VP:* Curtis Smith
**VP:* Robert Dooley
**VP:* Thomas Glimp
**VP:* Peter Kleeburg
VP: Eric Robinson
VP: Tim Sahori
**VP:* Tim Sahouri

MEDCORP
See AMERICAN AMBULETTE & AMBULANCE SERVICE INC

D-U-N-S 79-515-9995
MEDCORP INC
745 Medcorp Dr, Toledo, OH 43608-1376
Tel (419) 727-7000 *Founded/Ownrshp* 1988
Sales 10.9MME *EMP* 290E
SIC 8082 4119 Home health care services; Ambulance service; Home health care services; Ambulance service
Pr: Fred Isch
CFO: Randy Simon
Exec: Elizabeth Bergman

D-U-N-S 04-173-5783
MEDCOST LLC
165 Kimel Park Dr, Winston Salem, NC 27103-6945
Tel (336) 760-3090 *Founded/Ownrshp* 1997
Sales 30.7MM *EMP* 250
Accts Dixon Hughes Goodman Llp Char
SIC 8011 Health maintenance organization; Health maintenance organization
Ex VP: Melinda Rains
Software D: Robert Agresti
VP Mktg: Mary Kahler
Mktg Mgr: Cindy Bistany

D-U-N-S 60-149-0456
MEDE AMERICA OF OHIO LLC
(*Suby of* EMDEON BUSINESS SERVICES LLC) ★
2045 Midway Dr, Twinsburg, OH 44087-1933
Tel (330) 425-3241 *Founded/Ownrshp* 2015
Sales 101.7M^E *EMP* 506^E
SIC 7371 Computer software development
VP: John Long

D-U-N-S 82-497-8407
MEDEANALYTICS INC
5858 Horton St Ste 170, Emeryville, CA 94608-2007
Tel (510) 647-1300 *Founded/Ownrshp* 2015
Sales 50.1MM^E *EMP* 165^E
SIC 8741 Financial management for business
CEO: Andrew Hurd
Ch Bd: James Quist
CEO: Anthony McKeever
Ofcr: Salvatore Detrane
Ofcr: Terry Fouts
Ofcr: Barbara Piascik
Sr VP: Sandy Cugliotta
Sr VP: Amy Ferretti
Sr VP: Ralph Keiser
Sr VP: Stephen Lerch
Sr VP: Steve Lerch
Sr VP: Scott Paddock
Sr VP: Ken Perez
Sr VP: Robert Raddeman
Sr VP: Elizabeth Rushforth
Sr VP: Marc Taxay
Sr VP: Doug Thompson
Sr VP: Ping Zhang
VP: Pat Merell
VP: Dawn Snyder-Ramsey
VP: Doug Williams

D-U-N-S 80-151-1999
MEDECINS SANS FRONTIERES USA INC
DOCTORS WITHOUT BORDERS USA
(*Suby of* MEDECINS SANS FRONTIERES (HK) LIMITED)
333 7th Ave Fl 2, New York, NY 10001-5089
Tel (212) 679-6800 *Founded/Ownrshp* 1987
Sales 221.1MM *EMP* 100^E
Accts Tait Weller & Baker Llp Phila
SIC 8399 7363 Advocacy group; Fund raising organization, non-fee basis; Medical help service
Pr: Deane Marchbein
**CFO:* Maureen Burnley
Treas: John E Plum
Ofcr: Stephen Figge
Ofcr: Michael Goldfarb
**VP:* Aditya Nadimpalli
VP: Christine Nadori
Exec: Lydia Elhassan
**Ex Dir:* Sophie Delaunay
Ex Dir: Joelle Tanguy
Mktg Dir: Charlie Kunzer

D-U-N-S 60-281-3511
MEDECISION INC
(*Suby of* BLUE CROSS AND BLUE SHIELD) ★
550 E Swedesford Rd # 220, Wayne, PA 19087-1620
Tel (484) 588-0102 *Founded/Ownrshp* 2008
Sales NA *EMP* 325^E
SIC 6324 7371 Hospital & medical service plans; Computer software development & applications; Hospital & medical service plans; Computer software development & applications
CEO: Deborah Gabe
Owner: Augusta Kairys
Pt: Donna Fendley
Ch Bd: Colleen Reitan
COO: Carole A Hodsdon
CFO: Kenneth Young
Ch: Terri Kline
Ofcr: John P McGahey
Ofcr: Susan L Newton
Ofcr: Jennifer Ponski
Ex VP: Ellen Donahue-Dalton
Ex VP: Andrew P Schuyler
Sr VP: Kathleen D'Amariio
Sr VP: Kathleen D'Amario
Sr VP: Mary Sirois
VP: Matt Adamson
VP: Jerry Baker
VP: Kathy D'Amario
VP: John Delaney
VP: Terri Gregorio
VP: Dick Haviland

D-U-N-S 04-473-1685 IMP
MEDECO SECURITY LOCKS INC
(*Suby of* ASSA ABLOY INC) ★
3625 Alleghany Dr, Salem, VA 24153-2041
Tel (540) 380-5000 *Founded/Ownrshp* 1998
Sales 29.1MM^E *EMP* 280
SIC 3499 Locks, safe & vault: metal; Locks, safe & vault: metal
Pr: Thomas Kaika
Pr: Allan Ritchey
**Treas:* Joseph P Hurley
VP: Paul Taylor
VP: Bobby Woolwine
Genl Mgr: Rick Mason
Info Man: Norma Saferight
Sftwr Eng: Donald Johnston
Mktg Dir: Mark Imhof
Sls Dir: Daniel Gills
Manager: Michael Kennedy

D-U-N-S 01-644-8669
MEDEFIL INC
250 Windy Point Dr, Glendale Heights, IL 60139-3805
Tel (630) 682-4600 *Founded/Ownrshp* 1998
Sales 46.9MM^E *EMP* 65
SIC 5047 Medical equipment & supplies
Pr: Pradeep Aggarwal
**VP:* Sandeep Aggarwal
Opers Mgr: Erick Palacios
Sls Dir: Randy Blackwell

D-U-N-S 87-781-8091 IMP
■ **MEDEGEN LLC**
(*Suby of* CAREFUSION CORP) ★
4501 E Wall St, Ontario, CA 91761-8143
Tel (909) 390-9080 *Founded/Ownrshp* 2010
Sales 184.5MM^E *EMP* 1,282
SIC 3089 Injection molded finished plastic products; Injection molded finished plastic products
CEO: Charles Stroupe
Mfg Mgr: John Turner

D-U-N-S 05-552-7753
■ **MEDEGEN MEDICAL PRODUCTS LLC**
(*Suby of* MEDEGEN LLC) ★
209 Medegen Dr, Gallaway, TN 38036
Tel (901) 867-2951 *Founded/Ownrshp* 1999
Sales 184.5MM^E *EMP* 440
SIC 3089 Injection molded finished plastic products; Injection molded finished plastic products
Treas: Paul Jazwin
VP: Jim Jenkins
Sys/Mgr: Gib Worth

D-U-N-S 05-200-2029 IMP/EXP
MEDELA INC
(*Suby of* MEDELA AG)
1101 Corporate Dr, McHenry, IL 60050-7006
Tel (800) 435-8316 *Founded/Ownrshp* 1980
Sales 137.4MM^E *EMP* 300^E
SIC 5047 3596 Medical & hospital equipment; Medical & hospital equipment; Scales & balances, except laboratory; Baby scales
Pr: Carolin Archibald
Pr: Karen Csech
Pr: Sam Levey
CFO: Jack Cox
CFO: Ruedi Temprpli
VP: Donald Alexander
VP: Frank Bauer
VP: Patrik Bosshard
VP: Stephen Flint
VP: Melissa Gonzales
VP: Mitch Odahowski
VP: Brian Silver
VP: Ruedi Temperli
VP: Tom Wolff
Board of Directors: Michael Larsson, Kurt Rudolph, Urs Tanner

D-U-N-S 07-601-8845 IMP
■ **MEDERI INC**
(*Suby of* ALMOST FAMILY INC) ★
9510 Ormsby Station Rd # 300, Louisville, KY 40223-4081
Tel (502) 891-1000 *Founded/Ownrshp* 2006
Sales 13.0MM^E *EMP* 600
SIC 8082 Home health care services; Home health care services
Pr: Sandra Dufay
**Sec:* David Nesslein
MIS Dir: Jamie Cowan

MEDEX AMBULANCE
See MEDICAL EXPRESS AMBULANCE SERVICE INC

D-U-N-S 04-709-8152
MEDFIELD PUBLIC SCHOOLS
459 Main St Fl 3, Medfield, MA 02052-2009
Tel (508) 359-2302 *Founded/Ownrshp* 1920
Sales 13.2MM^E *EMP* 280
SIC 8211 Public elementary & secondary schools; Public elementary & secondary schools
Dir IT: Eoin Ocorcora
Schl Brd P: Susan Russo

D-U-N-S 96-765-4745
MEDFIRST CONSULTING HEALTHCARE STAFFING LIMITED LIABILITY CO
2141 Chelsea Ridge Dr, Columbiana, AL 35051-3855
Tel (205) 565-5170 *Founded/Ownrshp* 2010
Sales 11.0MM *EMP* 279
SIC 7379 7361 Computer related consulting services; Employment agencies; Computer related consulting services; Employment agencies

MEDFLIGHT OF OHIO
See OHIO MEDICAL TRANSPORTATION INC

D-U-N-S 03-916-4678
MEDFONE NATIONWIDE INC
1136 W Diversey Pkwy, Chicago, IL 60614-2676
Tel (312) 324-4505 *Founded/Ownrshp* 2011
Sales 6.0MM^E *EMP* 278^E
SIC 7363 Medical help service; Medical help service
CEO: Justin Reitz

D-U-N-S 02-560-8191
MEDFORD AREA PUBLIC SCHOOL DISTRICT
124 W State St, Medford, WI 54451-1760
Tel (715) 748-4620 *Founded/Ownrshp* 1994
Sales 15.2MM^E *EMP* 300^E
SIC 8211 Public elementary & secondary schools; School board; Public elementary & secondary schools; School board
Bd of Dir: Barbara Knight
VP: Paul Dixon

D-U-N-S 02-334-5846
MEDFORD COOPERATIVE INC
COUNTY MARKET
160 Medford Plz, Medford, WI 54451-2200
Tel (715) 748-9212 *Founded/Ownrshp* 1911
Sales 41.6MM^E *EMP* 180
SIC 5251 5172 5191 5171 5411 Hardware; Gases, liquefied petroleum (propane); Feed; Seeds: field, garden & flower; Fertilizer & fertilizer materials; Petroleum bulk stations; Grocery stores, independent; Hardware; Gases, liquefied petroleum (propane); Feed; Seeds: field, garden & flower; Fertilizer & fertilizer materials; Petroleum bulk stations; Grocery stores, independent
Pr: Renne M Zenner
**Pr:* Brad Dahlvig
**VP:* Donald S Purvis
Exec: Michelle Gubser
Genl Mgr: Graham Courtney Jr
Genl Mgr: Leon Weber
Sls&Mrk Ex: Pat Hempel

D-U-N-S 07-696-0764
MEDFORD LEAS FOUNDATION
1 Medford Leas Ste A, Medford, NJ 08055-2254
Tel (609) 654-3000 *Founded/Ownrshp* 1914
Sales 34.8MM *EMP* 400
Accts Grant Thornton Llp Philadelph
SIC 8051 Extended care facility; Extended care facility
Pr: Richard A Cleaver
Pr: C Miller Diddle
CEO: Jeremy Vickers
CFO: Susan Kensill
Treas: John Cope
VP: Thomas Zemaitis
Exec: Brad Mauger
Dir Soc: Kathy Martin

D-U-N-S 07-640-1066
MEDFORD SCHOOL DISTRICT 549C
815 S Oakdale Ave, Medford, OR 97501-3531
Tel (541) 842-3621 *Founded/Ownrshp* 1885
Sales 57.1MM^E *EMP* 1,024
SIC 8211 Public elementary & secondary schools; Elementary school; High school, junior or senior; Public elementary & secondary schools; Elementary school; High school, junior or senior
**CFO:* Brad Earl
CFO: Cheryl Foote
Netwrk Mgr: Jeff Bales

D-U-N-S 60-589-6575
MEDFORD TOWNSHIP PUBLIC SCHOOL
3 Mill Run Ct, Medford, NJ 08055-2437
Tel (609) 654-6416 *Founded/Ownrshp* 2005
Sales 6.8MM^E *EMP* 321^E
SIC 8211 Public elementary & secondary schools
Pr: Michael Etter

D-U-N-S 05-167-8530
MEDFORD TOWNSHIP SCHOOL DISTRICT
137 Hartford Rd, Medford, NJ 08055-9516
Tel (609) 654-6416 *Founded/Ownrshp* 1850
Sales 93.6M *EMP* 350
Accts Holman & Frenia Pc Medford
SIC 8211 Public elementary & secondary schools; Public elementary & secondary schools
Treas: Elissa Armbruster
Board of Directors: Chad Fires

D-U-N-S 11-437-4007
MEDFUSION INC
5501 Dillard Dr, Cary, NC 27518-9233
Tel (919) 882-2800 *Founded/Ownrshp* 2013
Sales 20.8MM^E *EMP* 150
SIC 4813 ;
CEO: Steve Malik
Pr: Vern Davenport
CFO: Dan Edelson
VP: Michael Boch
VP: Vickie Laughridge
VP: Michael Raymer
Dir Bus: David Pedersen
CTO: Vikram Natarajan
Mktg Mgr: Chelsea Junget
Mktg Mgr: Jolene Lofrese
Snr PM: Sandra Harris
Board of Directors: John Crumpler, David Jones

D-U-N-S 10-391-3430 IMP
MEDGYN PRODUCTS INC
100 W Industrial Rd, Addison, IL 60101-4508
Tel (630) 627-4105 *Founded/Ownrshp* 1975
Sales 21.5MM^E *EMP* 55
SIC 5047 3842 Medical equipment & supplies; Gynecological supplies & appliances
Pr: Lakshman M Agadi
COO: Aarathi Singh
Natl Sales: Dale Dambek
S&M/Dir: Rieni Muphuswamy
Sls Mgr: Michael Escudier
Sls Mgr: Mohammad Farahmand
Sls Mgr: Brenda Goussed
Sls Mgr: Michael Gray
Sls Mgr: J E Lee
Sls Mgr: Rick Lee
Sls Mgr: Rafael Luna

D-U-N-S 05-360-5908
MEDHOST INC
(*Suby of* HEALTHTECH HOLDINGS INC) ★
6100 W Plano Pkwy # 3100, Plano, TX 75093-8342
Tel (972) 560-3100 *Founded/Ownrshp* 2010
Sales 23.3MM^E *EMP* 160
SIC 7372 Prepackaged software; Prepackaged software
Pr: Craig Herrod
**CFO:* Doug Stewart
VP: Barbara Bryan
VP: Eric Rock
Snr Mgr: Kristin Kilpatrick

D-U-N-S 15-200-7423
MEDHOST OF TENNESSEE INC
MEDHOST SERVICES
(*Suby of* HEALTHTECH HOLDINGS INC) ★
6550 Carothers Pkwy # 100, Franklin, TN 37067-6693
Tel (615) 761-1000 *Founded/Ownrshp* 2000
Sales 93.5MM^E *EMP* 400
SIC 7371 Computer software development & applications; Computer software development & applications
CEO: Bill Anderson
**Pr:* Craig Herrod
**CFO:* Kenneth Misch
VP: Steve Massey
VP: Chuck Steinmetz
VP: Kenneth Williamson
Exec: Mike Bible
Exec: Cindy Meagher
Exec: Pat Murphy
Exec: Melodie Thigpen
Software D: Taroh Hinata
Board of Directors: Thomas E Givens, Phillip C Molner, Scott W Seelbach, Debbie Sudduth, Lisa Sullivan

MEDHOST SERVICES
See MEDHOST OF TENNESSEE INC

D-U-N-S 55-585-5209 IMP
MEDI USA LP
6481 Franz Warner Pkwy, Whitsett, NC 27377-9214
Tel (336) 446-0163 *Founded/Ownrshp* 1985
Sales 27.1MM^E *EMP* 130
SIC 5632 5047 Hosiery; Medical equipment & supplies
Pt: Michael Weihermuller
Pt: Steafon Weihermuller
Rgnl Mgr: Troy McKeown
IT Man: Markus Frischholz
IT Man: Michael Potter
Plnt Mgr: Astrid Hudson
Natl Sales: Ed Wilbourne
Sls Dir: Keith Friedman
Mktg Mgr: Sanaz Alagha
Manager: Tyrone Byrd
Manager: Jon Edwards

MEDI-PARK PHARMACY
See OSF SAINT FRANCIS INC

D-U-N-S 05-947-0927
■ **MEDI-PHYSICS INC**
GE HEALTHCARE
(*Suby of* GE HEALTHCARE LIMITED)
350 Campus Dr Fl 5, Marlborough, MA 01752-3082
Tel (508) 480-9235 *Founded/Ownrshp* 2000
Sales 158.6MM^E *EMP* 25
SIC 5122 Medicinals & botanicals; Medicinals & botanicals
CEO: Jeff Immelt
Pr: Pascale Witz
Treas: Vito Pulito
VP: Donald Quinn

MEDIA ARTIST MANAGEMENT
See MEDIA HOLDING GROUP INC

D-U-N-S 80-258-6318
MEDIA BANK LLC
600 W Chicago Ave Ste 350, Chicago, IL 60654-2816
Tel (312) 676-4646 *Founded/Ownrshp* 2006
Sales 20.2MM^E *EMP* 197
SIC 7371 Computer software development & applications; Computer software development & applications
CEO: Bill Wise
**Pr:* Nic Galassi
COO: John Bauschard
CFO: Nick Galassi
Ofcr: Greg Koerner

MEDIA COMMUNICATIONS
See INSPIRATIONAL NETWORKS

MEDIA DISTRIBUTORS
See DISCOUNT MEDIA PRODUCTS LLC

D-U-N-S 07-968-0912
▲ **MEDIA GENERAL INC**
333 E Franklin St, Richmond, VA 23219-2213
Tel (804) 887-5000 *Founded/Ownrshp* 1969
Sales 674.9MM *EMP* 5,300^E
SIC 4833 Television broadcasting stations
Pr: Vincent L Sadusky
COO: Deborah A McDermott
CFO: James F Woodward
VP: Andrew C Carington
VP: John O Lewis
Board of Directors: J Stewart Bryan III, Diana F Cantor, Dennis J Fitzsimons, Douglas W McCormick, John R Muse, Wyndham Robertson, Thomas J Sullivan, Royal W Carson III H C Cha

D-U-N-S 17-037-8066 IMP
■ **MEDIA GENERAL OPERATIONS INC**
VIRGINIA BUSINESS MAGAZINE
(*Suby of* MGOC INC) ★
333 E Franklin St, Richmond, VA 23219-2213
Tel (804) 649-6000 *Founded/Ownrshp* 2000
Sales 238.5MM^E *EMP* 1,580
SIC 2711 4833 Newspapers; Television broadcasting stations; Newspapers; Television broadcasting stations
Pr: George L Mahoney
COO: Reid O Ashe
CFO: John Butler
Treas: John A Butler
**Treas:* James F Woodward
Ex VP: Aaron Lorson
VP: Darby Greenhill

D-U-N-S 07-982-9521
MEDIA HOLDING GROUP INC
MEDIA ARTIST MANAGEMENT
99 Hudson St Fl 5, New York, NY 10013-2993
Tel (212) 574-7978 *Founded/Ownrshp* 2015
Sales 40.0MM *EMP* 67
SIC 7922 Agent or manager for entertainers; Booking agency, theatrical
**Pr:* Danny Fukuda
**Treas:* Michael Adam

D-U-N-S 87-978-6655
■ **MEDIA LAUNCH INC**
TOURDATES.COM
(*Suby of* YAHOO INC) ★
25 Taylor St, San Francisco, CA 94102-3916
Tel (310) 593-6152 *Founded/Ownrshp* 2001
Sales 25.2MM^E *EMP* 129
SIC 4813
Ch Bd: David Goldberg
Pr: Robert Roback
CFO: Jeff Mickeal
Ex VP: Briggs Ferguson
VP: Heather Crosby
VP: Jamey Kirkes
Board of Directors: Thomas C Hoegh, Sergio S Zyman, Richard D Snyder Warren Li

D-U-N-S 04-562-9549
MEDIA LINK LLC
1901 Ave Of Ste 177, Los Angeles, CA 90067
Tel (646) 722-3632 *Founded/Ownrshp* 2003
Sales 40.0MM *EMP* 102
SIC 8748 Business consulting

MEDIA MANAGEMENT GROUP
See ADVISORY CREDIT SERVICES INC

D-U-N-S 05-524-4347
MEDIA PLANNING GROUP USA LLC
M P G
(*Suby of* MEDIA PLANNING GROUP SA)
200 Hudson St, New York, NY 10013-1807
Tel (646) 587-5000 *Founded/Ownrshp* 2006
Sales 75.3MM^E *EMP* 382
SIC 7319 Media buying service; Media buying service
CEO: Shaun Holliday
Mng Pt: Marie Oldham
COO: John McLoughlin
**CFO:* Gary McCorry
Ex VP: David Handelman
Ex VP: Jason Kanefsky
Sr VP: Gregory Aston
Sr VP: Deva Bronson
Sr VP: Jacquelyn Gerhardt
Sr VP: Danny Huynh
Sr VP: Linda Narbey
Sr VP: Christopher O'Connor
VP: Caroline Crowell
VP: Jennifer Ford
VP: Meghan Koopman
VP: Jon Krasnoff
VP: Elaine Levine
VP: Lynn Martin
VP: Jill Montagna
VP: Peter Moylan
VP: George Sargent

D-U-N-S 05-855-5970 IMP
■ **MEDIA PRINTING CORP**
(*Suby of* EARTH COLOR NEW YORK INC) ★
4300 N Powerline Rd, Pompano Beach, FL 33073-3071
Tel (954) 984-7300 *Founded/Ownrshp* 1999
Sales 38.0MM^E *EMP* 140
SIC 2752 Commercial printing, offset; Commercial printing, offset
CEO: Robert Kashan
**Pr:* James Grubman
**VP:* Clay Grubman
Genl Mgr: Tim Miranda
Sfty Mgr: John Checchia

D-U-N-S 07-671-7503
■ **MEDIA RECOVERY INC**
(*Suby of* CAPITAL SOUTHWEST CORPORATION)
5501 L B Johnson Fwy 350, Dallas, TX 75240
Tel (214) 630-9625 *Founded/Ownrshp* 1997
Sales 152.0MM^E *EMP* 214^E
SIC 7373 Computer system selling services
Pr: Gerry Smith
**CFO:* David Chisum
Mfg Dir: Angela Kerr

MEDIA SERVICES
See OBERMAN TIVOLI MILLER & PICKERT INC

MEDIA SOLUTIONS
See MSOLUTIONS LLC

D-U-N-S 85-945-4097
MEDIA SOLUTIONS LLC
(*Suby of* ANDERSON MEDIA CORP) ★
9632 Madison Blvd, Madison, AL 35758-9157
Tel (256) 772-8131 *Founded/Ownrshp* 2007
Sales 22.6MM^E *EMP* 78^E
SIC 2721 Magazines: publishing & printing
Pr: John Franznick
Prin: Deborah Vullo

D-U-N-S 15-142-9453
MEDIA SOURCE INC
7858 Industrial Pkwy, Plain City, OH 43064-9468
Tel (614) 373-7635 *Founded/Ownrshp* 2014
Sales 35.5MM^E *EMP* 89
SIC 5192 Books
Pr: Randall J Asmo
CFO: Dave Myers
VP: Andrew Thorne
Off Mgr: Ronda Lehman

D-U-N-S 12-115-2008
MEDIA STORM LLC
WATER COOLER GROUP
99 Washington St Ste 3, Norwalk, CT 06854-3080
Tel (203) 852-8001 *Founded/Ownrshp* 2001
Sales 32.8MM^E *EMP* 170
SIC 7311 Advertising agencies; Advertising agencies
**Mng Pt:* Craig C Woerz
**CFO:* Frank Connolly
Mng Dir: Charles Fiordalis
Mng Dir: Margaret Lewis
**Mng Dir:* Jamie Melecio
Plng Mgr: Stacey Bekas
Plng Mgr: Sarah Kinsley
Snr Mgr: Michelle Guglielmelli

D-U-N-S 03-285-5699
MEDIA TEMPLE INC
(*Suby of* GODADDY.COM LLC) ★
8520 National Blvd Bldg A, Culver City, CA 90232-2418
Tel (877) 578-4000 *Founded/Ownrshp* 2013
Sales 52.9MM^E *EMP* 203
SIC 4813 7371 ; Computer software development & applications; ; Computer software development & applications
CEO: Russell P Reeder
**Ch Bd:* Marc Dumont
**Pr:* Rod Stoddard
**CFO:* John Carey
Chf Mktg O: Kim Brubeck
**CTO:* Albert Lopez
Software D: Nick Molina
VP Mktg: Jacob Shin
Art Dir: Maggie Tielker
Snr PM: Matthew Pennaz

D-U-N-S 06-305-6832
MEDIA TENNEY GROUP
OMP PRINTING & GRAPHICS
28 Robinson Rd, Clinton, NY 13323-1419
Tel (315) 853-5569 *Founded/Ownrshp* 1965
Sales 29.1MM^E *EMP* 70
SIC 2741 2711 Shopping news: publishing & printing; Newspapers
Ch Bd: Claudia Cleary

D-U-N-S 08-005-5924
■ **MEDIABRANDS WORLDWIDE INC**
INITIATIVE MEDIA
(*Suby of* INTERPUBLIC GROUP OF COMPANIES INC) ★
100 W 33rd St, New York, NY 10001-2900
Tel (212) 605-7000 *Founded/Ownrshp* 1994
Sales 167.6MM^E *EMP* 1,300
SIC 7319 7311 Media buying service; Advertising consultant; Media buying service; Advertising consultant
CEO: Jim Elms
Pr: Peter Mears
COO: Caroline Bivens
COO: Ed Powers
CFO: Jeff Lupinacci
CFO: Mark Sanders
CFO: Greg Walsch
CFO: Greg Walsh
Ex VP: Alain Damond
Ex VP: Dennis Donlin
Ex VP: Janice Finkel-Greene
Ex VP: Sarah Ivey
Ex VP: Sarah Power
Sr VP: Teriann Link
VP: Marc Ducnuigeen
VP: Andrew Herreria
VP: Dab Nanus
VP: Greg Stimson
Exec: Lorie Furay
Exec: Alec Jones
Assoc Dir: Michael Davis

D-U-N-S 03-240-9059
MEDIACOM
(*Suby of* GREY ADVERTISING) ★
498 7th Ave, New York, NY 10018-6798
Tel (212) 912-4200 *Founded/Ownrshp* 2001
Sales 21.9MM^E *EMP* 100
SIC 7319 Media buying service
CEO: Stephen Allan
Sr Pt: Kyong Coleman
Sr Pt: Neal Lucey
Sr Pt: Joanna Sammartino
Mng Pt: Luke Bozeat
Mng Pt: Michael Neale
Mng Pt: Andrew Pappalardo
Mng Pt: Chuck Shaw
**COO:* Harvey Goldhersz
CFO: Joe Locrotondo
Chf Inves: Nicole Turley
Ex VP: Evp Sheridan
VP: Mark Crane
**VP:* Nick Pahade
VP: Audrey Sudran
Exec: Kate Pierce
Assoc Dir: Liam Dawson
Assoc Dir: Caroline McWhirter
Assoc Dir: Natalia Rocha
Assoc Dir: Helen Wallace
Assoc Dir: Matt Zambelli

D-U-N-S 78-598-2690
MEDIACOM BROADBAND LLC
(*Suby of* MEDIACOM COMMUNICATIONS CORP) ★
1 Mediacom Way, Chester, NY 10918-4810
Tel (845) 443-2600 *Founded/Ownrshp* 2001
Sales 948.4MM *EMP* 2,472^E
SIC 4841 Cable & other pay television services; Subscription television services; Cable & other pay television services; Subscription television services
CEO: Rocco B Commisso
**CFO:* Mark E Stephan
**Ex VP:* John G Pascarelli
**Ex VP:* Italia Commisso Weinand
**Sr VP:* Brian M Walsh
**Sr VP:* Joseph E Young

D-U-N-S 10-679-1739
MEDIACOM COMMUNICATIONS CORP
1 Mediacom Way, Chester, NY 10918-4850
Tel (845) 443-2600 *Founded/Ownrshp* 2011
Sales 2.4MMM^E *EMP* 4,520^E
SIC 4841 4813 Cable & other pay television services; Cable television services; Closed circuit television services; Subscription television services; ; Cable & other pay television services; Cable television services; Closed circuit television services; Subscription television services;
CEO: Rocco B Commisso
CFO: Mark E Stephan
Ofcr: Weinand Italia
Ex VP: John G Pascarelli
Ex VP: Italia Commisso Weinand
Sr VP: David McNaughton
Sr VP: Edward S Pardini
Sr VP: Brian M Walsh
Sr VP: Joseph E Young
VP: Joseph Commisso
VP: Phyllis Degroat
VP: Greg Euker
VP: Marjorie Kakeh
VP: Ken Katzenberger
VP: Paul Lalanne
VP: Peter Lyon
VP: Dave McKee
VP: Joe Selvage
VP: Dan Templin
VP: Bill Wegener
VP: John Woods

D-U-N-S 94-776-9360
MEDIACOM LLC
(*Suby of* MEDIACOM COMMUNICATIONS CORP) ★
1 Mediacom Way, Chester, NY 10918-4810
Tel (845) 443-2600 *Founded/Ownrshp* 1995
Sales 711.6MM *EMP* 1,890^E
SIC 4841 Cable & other pay television services; Cable & other pay television services
CEO: Rocco B Commisso
CFO: Mark E Stephan
Ex VP: John G Pascarelli
Sr VP: Brian M Walsh
Sr VP: Italia Commisso Weinand
Sr VP: Joseph E Young

D-U-N-S 00-830-3807
MEDIACOM SOUTHEAST LLC
1104 N Westover Blvd, Albany, GA 31707-6625
Tel (229) 888-0242 *Founded/Ownrshp* 1997
Sales 220.5MM^E *EMP* 4,591
SIC 4841 4813 Cable & other pay television services; Telephone communication, except radio; Cable & other pay television services; Telephone communication, except radio
Prin: Rocco Commisso
**Pt:* Rocco B Commisso
**Pt:* Mediacom LLC
Off Mgr: Jennifer Weeks

D-U-N-S 02-307-7659
MEDIACOM WORLDWIDE LLC
(*Suby of* GREY ADVERTISING) ★
498 Fashion Ave, New York, NY 10018-6798
Tel (212) 912-4200 *Founded/Ownrshp* 1997
Sales 95.5MM^E *EMP* 425
SIC 7311 Advertising consultant; Advertising consultant
CEO: Harvey Goldhersz
Mng Pt: Nick Cohen
COO: Euan Jarvie
**CFO:* Mark Piazza
Chf Mktg O: Stephanie Fiermanglobal
Ofcr: Helen Brownworldwide
Ofcr: Julian Neuburgerglobal
Ex VP: Peter Olsen
Exec: Mike Sporleder
Exec: Brenda Wrolson
Dir Bus: Fraser Riddellglobal
Dir Bus: Leslie Santiago

D-U-N-S 07-135-7425
MEDIAEDGE CIA LLC
MEC INTERACTION
(*Suby of* GROUP M WORLDWIDE LLC) ★
825 7th Ave, New York, NY 10019-6014
Tel (212) 474-0000 *Founded/Ownrshp* 2004
Sales 47.2MM^E *EMP* 20^E
SIC 7311 7319 Advertising agencies; Media buying service; Advertising agencies; Media buying service
Sr Pt: Chris Copeland
Sr Pt: Archana Deshmukh
Sr Pt: Elizabeth Obrien
Pt: Verna Payne
Pt: Carrie Soriano
Mng Pt: Axel Dumont
Mng Pt: Julia Jones
Mng Pt: Peggy Kelly
CEO: Lee Doyle
CFO: Mark Sanders
VP: Jeanne Burkle
VP: Gary Quinn
Exec: Josephine Ng
Exec: Christina Tan
Comm Man: Matthew Cirri
Comm Man: Alison Gerson
Comm Man: Amarillis Lozano
Comm Man: Ivelisse Marrero
Comm Man: Marci Sovitsky
Comm Man: Priyanka Sud
Comm Man: Megan Warfield

D-U-N-S 80-774-7220
MEDIAMATH INC
4 World Trade Ctr, New York, NY 10007-2366
Tel (646) 840-4200 *Founded/Ownrshp* 2007
Sales 218.7MM^E *EMP* 564^E
SIC 7379 ;
CEO: Joseph Zawadzki
Pr: ARI Buchalter
Pr: Michael Lamb
CFO: Jeannie Mun
Bd of Dir: Mark Mitchell
Chf Mktg O: Joanna O'Connell
Ex VP: Steven Kaufman
Sr VP: Rachel Meranus
Sr VP: Dave Reed
Sr VP: Dan Rosenberg
VP: Jeremy Crandall
VP: Jake Engwerd
VP: Neil Fried
VP: Joey Hyche
VP: Kym Insana
VP: Michael Mullaney
VP: Gareth Ouellette
VP: Jesse Parker
VP: Eric Picard
VP: Ajit Thupil
VP: Chris Victory
Board of Directors: Michael Barrett

D-U-N-S 78-782-4291
■ **MEDIANEWS GROUP INC**
(*Suby of* DIGITAL FIRST MEDIA LLC) ★
101 W Colfax Ave Ste 1100, Denver, CO 80202-5315
Tel (303) 954-6360 *Founded/Ownrshp* 2013
Sales 3.2MMM^E *EMP* 12,947
Tkr Sym MNWG *Exch* OTO
SIC 2711 Newspapers, publishing & printing; Newspapers, publishing & printing
Pr: Steve Rossi
V Ch: Joel Robinson
Pr: Nolan Epple
**Pr:* Joseph Euteneurer
Pr: Sandra Neely
**Pr:* Mark J Winkler
**COO:* Anthony Tierno
**CFO:* Michael Koren
**CFO:* Ronald A Mayo
**Treas:* James L McDougald
Sr VP: Steve Hesse
Sr VP: Robert Jendusa
VP: Steven M Barkmeier
VP: Brock Berry
VP: David M Bessen
VP: Michael Fluker
**VP:* Guy Gilmore
VP: Sara Glines
VP: Doug Graham
VP: Dutch Greve
VP: Stephen M Hesse
Board of Directors: Heath Freeman, Eric Krauss, Bruce Schnelwar

D-U-N-S 15-639-8286
MEDIANT COMMUNICATIONS INC
3 Columbus Cir Ste 2110, New York, NY 10019-8712
Tel (212) 785-0077 *Founded/Ownrshp* 2002
Sales 49.3MM^E *EMP* 177
SIC 7371 Computer software development & applications; Computer software development & applications
CEO: Arthur Rosenzweig
Ch Bd: John Purcell
Pr: Robert M Lemmond
COO: Sherry Moreland
CFO: Antal Foldi
VP: Charles Jelicks
Genl Mgr: Chris Miller
Prd Mgr: Vincent Misiano
S&M/VP: Lisa Warren

D-U-N-S 01-868-2198
MEDIAOCEAN LLC
45 W 18th St, New York, NY 10011-4609
Tel (212) 633-8100 *Founded/Ownrshp* 1999
Sales 69.2MM^E *EMP* 400
SIC 7311 Advertising agencies; Advertising agencies
Ch: Michael Donovan
**CEO:* Bill Wise
Sr VP: Mike Palmer
Sr VP: Manu Warikoo
VP: Christian Arts
VP: David Bigler
VP: Gordon Cohen
VP: Stephanie Dorman
VP: Steve Geller
VP: Maria Pousa
VP: Leo Wang

D-U-N-S 88-366-6190
MEDIAPOWER INC
DR NEWTON'S AND NATURALS
(*Suby of* MP DIRECT INC) ★
26 Thomas Dr, Westbrook, ME 04092-3824
Tel (207) 775-4363 *Founded/Ownrshp* 1995
Sales 18.7MM^E *EMP* 470
SIC 7313 Electronic media advertising representatives; Electronic media advertising representatives
CEO: Kenneth Byers
**Pr:* Christopher Homer
**Treas:* Carole Byers
Dir IT: Bryon Newcomb
Sls Mgr: Rob Warmer

D-U-N-S 18-130-2050
■ **MEDIATECH INC**
CORNING
(*Suby of* CORNING INC) ★
9345 Discovery Blvd, Manassas, VA 20109-3992
Tel (703) 471-5955 *Founded/Ownrshp* 2011
Sales 37.4MM^E *EMP* 120
SIC 2836 Biological products, except diagnostic; Biological products, except diagnostic
Pr: Lydia A Kenton Walsh
**CFO:* Peter Stangeby
**Treas:* Robert P Vanni
**Ex VP:* John Elliott Jr
**VP:* Jason Walsh
**CTO:* Louis Gallo
Plnt Mgr: George Turner

D-U-N-S 04-017-7253 IMP
MEDIATEK USA INC
2840 Junction Ave, San Jose, CA 95134-1922
Tel (408) 526-1899 *Founded/Ownrshp* 1997
Sales 85.2MM^E *EMP* 245^E
SIC 3571 3674 Electronic computers; Semiconductors & related devices
Ch Bd: Ming-Kai Tsai
**V Ch:* Jyh-Jer Cho
**Pr:* Ching-Jiang Hsieh
**CFO:* David Ku
**Sr VP:* Cheng-Te Chuang
**Sr VP:* Jeffrey Ju
VP: Joe Chen
VP: Kou-Hung Loh
Snr Mgr: Ape Chien

D-U-N-S 87-642-1413
MEDIAVEST WORLDWIDE INC
(*Suby of* MMS USA HOLDINGS INC) ★
1675 Broadway, New York, NY 10019-5820
Tel (212) 468-4000 *Founded/Ownrshp* 2002
Sales 30.0MM^E *EMP* 85
SIC 7319 Media buying service
Ch Bd: Laura Desmond
**CEO:* Bill Tucker
**CFO:* Daniel Mattei
Ex VP: Brian Elwarner
Ex VP: Jim Helberg
Ex VP: Sarah Kramer
Ex VP: Nancy Tortorella
Sr VP: Kelly Andrews
Sr VP: Karen Balik
Sr VP: Andrew Blotner
Sr VP: Jonathan Bokor
Sr VP: Danielle Bottari
Sr VP: Gina Broderick
Sr VP: Norm Chait
Sr VP: Dan Donnelly
Sr VP: Anne Elkins
Sr VP: Amy Garfinkel
Sr VP: Jill Griffin
Sr VP: Lauren Hanrahan
Sr VP: Triolo Jack
Sr VP: Jennifer Karayeanes

MEDICA ASSOCIATES
See MEDICAL ASSOCIATES OF CLINTON IOWA PLC

D-U-N-S 78-933-8191
MEDICA HEALTH PLANS
401 Carlson Pkwy, Minnetonka, MN 55305-5359
Tel (952) 992-3056 *Founded/Ownrshp* 2001
Sales 131.0MM^E *EMP* 1,386
SIC 8011 Health maintenance organization; Health maintenance organization
Pr: David Tilford
Pt: Eli Hazum
**Chf Mktg O:* Charles Fazio
**Ex VP:* Aaron Reynolds
**Sr VP:* Glenn E Andis

Sr VP: Deb Knutson
VP: Geoff Bartsh
**VP:* Pennina Safer
Dir Teleco: David Eckhardt
Dir IT: Cirsten Paine
IT Man: Alicia Beauclaire

D-U-N-S 07-846-8562
MEDICA HEALTH PLANS OF WISCONSIN
401 Carlson Pkwy, Hopkins, MN 55305-5359
Tel (952) 992-2900 *Founded/Ownrshp* 2012
Sales NA *EMP* 3
Accts Mcgladrey Llp Minneapolis Mn
SIC 6324 Health maintenance organization (HMO), insurance only
Pr: Kim Bachmeier
Dir IT: Christopher Grillo
IT Man: Paymon Vasseghi

D-U-N-S 96-189-8751 IMP
MEDICAGO USA INC
7 Triangle Dr, Durham, NC 27709
Tel (919) 313-9670 *Founded/Ownrshp* 2010
Sales 30.7MM^E *EMP* 79
SIC 2836 Vaccines & other immunizing products
**Ch Bd:* Dr Randal Chase
**Pr:* Andy Sheldon
**CFO:* Pierre Labb

MEDICAID SPECIALISTS
See L & S ASSOCIATES INC

D-U-N-S 09-198-0482
MEDICAL & SURGICAL CLINIC OF IRVING P A
MSCITX.COM
2021 N Macarthur Blvd # 150, Irving, TX 75061-2210
Tel (972) 253-4200 *Founded/Ownrshp* 2000
Sales 24.8MM^E *EMP* 200
SIC 8011 Medical centers
Pr: Roy Bernard Rochon
**Treas:* Chris Shelton
**VP:* Jack Ireland
**Prin:* Karen Perry Holland
**Prin:* Jack E Ireland
**Prin:* James Saalfield
**Prin:* Christopher Shelton
**Prin:* Roy Whitaker
**Ex Dir:* Jeffry M Duke
Psych: Allan Furman
Doctor: Susan Heller

D-U-N-S 07-380-3645
MEDICAL ACADEMIC AND SCIENTIFIC COMMUNITY ORGANIZATION INC
MASCO
375 Longwood Ave Fl 5, Boston, MA 02215-5395
Tel (617) 632-2310 *Founded/Ownrshp* 1972
Sales 26.3MM *EMP* 80
Accts Cbiz Tofias Boston Ma
SIC 6552 7521 4111 4812 7389 6512 Subdividers & developers; Automobile parking; Bus transportation; Paging services; Telephone answering service; Purchasing service; Commercial & industrial building operation; Subdividers & developers; Automobile parking; Bus transportation; Paging services; Telephone answering service; Purchasing service; Commercial & industrial building operation
Pr: Marilyn Swartz Lloyd
Pr: George Hrabovsky
**Pr:* Marilyn Swartz-Lloyd
**CFO:* Holly Roth
**VP:* P J Cappadona
**VP:* Sarah Hamilton
Plng Mgr: Janice Henderson

D-U-N-S 09-236-4462 IMP/EXP
■ **MEDICAL ACTION INDUSTRIES INC**
(*Suby of* OWENS & MINOR INC) ★
25 Heywood Rd, Arden, NC 28704-9302
Tel (631) 231-4600 *Founded/Ownrshp* 2014
Sales 287.8MM *EMP* 815^E
SIC 3842 Applicators, cotton tipped; Bandages: plastic, muslin, plaster of paris, etc.; Adhesive tape & plasters, medicated or non-medicated; Bandages & dressings; Applicators, cotton tipped; Bandages: plastic, muslin, plaster of paris, etc.; Adhesive tape & plasters, medicated or non-medicated; Bandages & dressings
CEO: Paul D Meringolo
**Pr:* Paul Chapman
Board of Directors: Henry A Berling, William W Burke, Kenneth W Davidson, Pamela R Levy, Kenneth R Newsome

D-U-N-S 96-860-5485
MEDICAL ADVANCED PAIN SPECIALISTS PA
7400 France Ave S Ste 100, Edina, MN 55435-4738
Tel (763) 537-6000 *Founded/Ownrshp* 1995
Sales 21.0MM^E *EMP* 80
SIC 8011 8049 Specialized medical practitioners, except internal; Physical therapist
Pr: David M Schultz
**Prin:* James V Anderson
**Prin:* Thomas G Cohn
**Prin:* David D Nerothin
**Prin:* Brian D Vacca
Psych: Paul Heideman
Doctor: Lee M Espeland
Doctor: Robert Long
Snr Mgr: Todd Johnson

D-U-N-S 06-994-3934
MEDICAL ARTS ASSOCIATES LTD PC
600 John Deere Rd Ste 200, Moline, IL 61265-6897
Tel (309) 779-4245 *Founded/Ownrshp* 1959
Sales 23.1MM *EMP* 160
Accts Kent G Klauer Cpa Pc Molin
SIC 8011 Clinic, operated by physicians; Clinic, operated by physicians
Pr: Alex Pareigis MD
**Treas:* Edward Ebert

MEDICAL ARTS PHARMACY
See SOUTH BEND CLINIC L L P

D-U-N-S 00-625-6267
■ **MEDICAL ARTS PRESS INC** (MN)
(*Suby of* STAPLES INC) ★
8500 Wyoming Ave N, Minneapolis, MN 55445-1831
Tel (763) 493-7300 *Founded/Ownrshp* 1961
Sales 71.8MM^E *EMP* 658
SIC 5961 Mail order house; Mail order house
CEO: Ronald L Sargent
**CEO:* Steve Wexler
Off Mgr: Susan Allend
Off Mgr: Sharon Peterson
Sls&Mrk Ex: Steven Tang

D-U-N-S 87-836-9578
MEDICAL ASSISTANCE MASSACHUSETTS
(*Suby of* EOHHS) ★
600 Washington St Fl 5, Boston, MA 02111-1704
Tel (617) 210-5000 *Founded/Ownrshp* 1996
Sales NA *EMP* 900
SIC 9441 Medical assistance program administration, government; ; Medical assistance program administration, government;

MEDICAL ASSISTANCE PROGRAMS
See MAP INTERNATIONAL (INC)

D-U-N-S 08-537-9303
MEDICAL ASSOCIATES CLINIC PC
MULTISPECIALTY MEDICAL CLINIC
1500 Associates Dr, Dubuque, IA 52002-2201
Tel (563) 584-4400 *Founded/Ownrshp* 1924
Sales 83.4MM^E *EMP* 900
SIC 8011 Physicians' office, including specialists; Clinic, operated by physicians; Physicians' office, including specialists; Clinic, operated by physicians
CEO: John Tallent
CEO: Larry Cremer
COO: Nancy Ertl
**COO:* Brian Schatz
Dir IT: Sharon Adkins
Sls Mgr: Jeff Gonner
Surgeon: Scott Schemmel
Obsttrcn: Joseph Berger
Obsttrcn: Peter Tinsman

MEDICAL ASSOCIATES HEALTH CTRS
See PROHEALTH CARE MEDICAL ASSOCIATES INC

D-U-N-S 12-886-4451
MEDICAL ASSOCIATES HEALTH PLAN INC
MEDICAL ASSOCIATES HMO
(*Suby of* MEDICAL ASSOCIATES CLINIC PC) ★
1605 Associates Dr # 101, Dubuque, IA 52002-2270
Tel (563) 556-8070 *Founded/Ownrshp* 1987
Sales NA *EMP* 60
Accts Mcgladrey & Pullen Llp
SIC 6324 Health maintenance organization (HMO), insurance only
Pr: Tom O'Brien
**Pr:* Tom O Brien

MEDICAL ASSOCIATES HMO
See MEDICAL ASSOCIATES HEALTH PLAN INC

D-U-N-S 05-423-5478
MEDICAL ASSOCIATES OF CLINTON IOWA PLC
MEDICA ASSOCIATES
915 13th Ave N, Clinton, IA 52732-5067
Tel (563) 243-2511 *Founded/Ownrshp* 1963
Sales 56.3MM^E *EMP* 281
SIC 3842 Hearing aids; Hearing aids
COO: Thomas Moser
CFO: James Dobbyn
Exec: Michelle Waltz
Dir IT: A J Boonstra
Dir IT: Donna Oliver
IT Man: Kevin Hansen
Pathlgst: Salwa S Albaghdadi
Surgeon: Akinlolu A Beckley
Surgeon: Rajiv Khanna
Plas Surg: Melanie Giesler
Doctor: Saadi Albaghdadi
Board of Directors: Xerxes Colah MD, John M O'shea MD, James R Olney MD, Luke Spellman

D-U-N-S 79-731-8649
MEDICAL ASSOCIATES OF LEHIGH VALLEY PC
1605 N Cedar Crest Blvd # 110, Allentown, PA 18104-2351
Tel (610) 973-1400 *Founded/Ownrshp* 1995
Sales 19.4MM^E *EMP* 300
SIC 8011 8721 Internal medicine practitioners; Internal medicine, physician/surgeon; Accounting, auditing & bookkeeping; Internal medicine practitioners; Internal medicine, physician/surgeon; Accounting, auditing & bookkeeping
Pr: Ronald R Julia MD
Treas: Thomas Brandecher MD
VP: John D Farrell MD
Doctor: David Caccese

D-U-N-S 06-104-4822
MEDICAL ASSOCIATES REALTY L P (IA)
(*Suby of* MEDICAL ASSOCIATES CLINIC PC) ★
1500 Associates Dr, Dubuque, IA 52002-2201
Tel (563) 584-4435 *Founded/Ownrshp* 1924, 1995
Sales 36.1MM^E *EMP* 662
SIC 8011 6512 Primary care medical clinic; Commercial & industrial building operation; Primary care medical clinic; Commercial & industrial building operation
VP: Dr George Kraemer
**CFO:* Jeff Gonner
Dir Lab: Marilyn Roth
Off Mgr: Paula Dessle
Psych: Stephen Frommelt
Psych: Martha Gould
Psych: Marion Huettner
Surgeon: Benjamin Roling
Doctor: Kenneth Steffen

D-U-N-S 07-865-9439
MEDICAL BILLING & MANAGEMENT SERVICES LLC
111 Continental Dr # 315, Newark, DE 19713-4317
Tel (610) 564-5314 *Founded/Ownrshp* 1968
Sales 22.9MM^E *EMP* 200
SIC 8741 Management services; Management services
Pr: Thomas Schovee
VP: Greg Wertz

D-U-N-S 07-845-0392
MEDICAL BUSINESS SERVICE INC
(*Suby of* ZOTEC PARTNERS LLC) ★
2525 Ponce De Leon Blvd # 300, Coral Gables, FL 33134-6044
Tel (305) 446-2378 *Founded/Ownrshp* 2011
Sales 13.1MM^E *EMP* 300
SIC 8721 Billing & bookkeeping service; Billing & bookkeeping service
CEO: Thomas J Herald
**Pr:* Bing Herald
**COO:* Peggy McCloskey
**CFO:* John F Kelleher
Ex VP: Anthony H Martinez
**Ex VP:* H Anthony Martinez Jr
Netwrk Mgr: Mukul Lalchandani

D-U-N-S 10-574-1268
MEDICAL CARD SYSTEM INC
MCS LIFE INSURANCE
Mcs Plaza 255 Ponce St Mcs Pla, San Juan, PR 00917
Tel (787) 758-2500 *Founded/Ownrshp* 1999
Sales NA *EMP* 135^E
SIC 6411 Medical insurance claim processing, contract or fee basis
VP: David Concepcion
**VP:* Jose D Ferrer
**VP:* Guillermo Melendez
VP: Jose Rodrigues
**VP:* Domingo Rodriguez
CIO: Ivars Blums

D-U-N-S 07-173-3638
MEDICAL CARE DEVELOPMENT INC
11 Parkwood Dr, Augusta, ME 04330-6299
Tel (207) 622-7566 *Founded/Ownrshp* 1966
Sales 44.0MM *EMP* 619
Accts Berry Dunn Mcneil & Pa Ker Po
SIC 6513 8059 Retirement hotel operation; Home for the mentally retarded, exc. skilled or intermediate; Retirement hotel operation; Home for the mentally retarded, exc. skilled or intermediate
Pr: Mark Battista
Ofcr: Pablo Aguilar
Ofcr: Luis Benavente
Ofcr: Moussa Dambo
Ofcr: Lisa Miller
Exec: Steven Gove
Ex Dir: Joseph Carter
Genl Mgr: Sandy Cole
CTO: Maureen Conley
DP Dir: Robert Brosius
IT Man: Heather Metten

D-U-N-S 16-230-2488
MEDICAL CARE OF BOSTON MANAGEMENT CORP
APG
1135 Tremont St Fl 5, Boston, MA 02120-2140
Tel (617) 754-8500 *Founded/Ownrshp* 1983
Sales 54.8MM *EMP* 150
SIC 8011 8741 Primary care medical clinic; Management services; Primary care medical clinic; Management services
CEO: Rick Markello

D-U-N-S 80-967-6047
MEDICAL CEN
691 Cherry St Fl 5, Macon, GA 31201-7392
Tel (478) 633-6831 *Founded/Ownrshp* 2008
Sales 646.1MM *EMP* 2
SIC 8099 Health & allied services; Health & allied services
Prin: A Don Faulk Jr

MEDICAL CENTER, THE
See BOWLING GREEN-WARREN COUNTY COMMUNITY HOSPITAL CORP

D-U-N-S 08-969-9508
MEDICAL CENTER
MEDICAL CENTER HOSPITAL
(*Suby of* COLUMBUS REGIONAL HEALTHCARE SYSTEM INC) ★
710 Center St, Columbus, GA 31901-1547
Tel (706) 660-6255 *Founded/Ownrshp* 1987
Sales 366.3MM *EMP* 1,500
Accts Pershing Yoakley & Associates
SIC 8062 General medical & surgical hospitals; General medical & surgical hospitals
Owner: James R Wheeler
Chf Path: Alan Clepper
Chf Mktg O: Michael Gorum
Ofcr: Darlene Mitchell
Sr VP: Allen Butcher
Sr VP: Laura Drew
**VP:* Wayne Joyner
Chf Nrs Of: Regina Blount
Chf Nrs Of: Michelle Breitfelder
Dir Sec: Jeff Williams
Admn Mgr: Rachel Lewis
Board of Directors: Lance Duke, Freda Stewart, Jeff Williams

D-U-N-S 11-058-9376
MEDICAL CENTER AT BOWLING GREEN
(*Suby of* C H C) ★
250 Park St, Bowling Green, KY 42101-1795
Tel (270) 745-1000 *Founded/Ownrshp* 1978
Sales 213.5MM^E *EMP* 1,900^E
SIC 8062 General medical & surgical hospitals; General medical & surgical hospitals
CEO: Connie D Smith
**VP:* Fred Genter
VP: Mark Robison
Mktg Dir: Sandy Feria

D-U-N-S 07-375-8773
MEDICAL CENTER AT PRINCETON NEW JERSEY
UNIVERSITY MED CTR AT PRNCETON
1 Plainsboro Rd, Plainsboro, NJ 08536-1913
Tel (609) 497-4000 *Founded/Ownrshp* 1929
Sales 266.3MM^E *EMP* 2,343
SIC 8062 General medical & surgical hospitals; General medical & surgical hospitals
Pr: Barry A Rabner
**Ex VP:* Joseph Bonnano
**VP:* Elizabeth Buff
**VP:* Carol Norris
**VP:* Joe Stampe
**VP:* Bruce Traub
Dir Rad: Gerard A Compito
Off Mgr: Marie Porter
CIO: Charles Schwenz
Dir IT: Ed Henry
Surgeon: Lawrence Jordan

D-U-N-S 00-481-9044
MEDICAL CENTER BARBOUR
820 W Washington St, Eufaula, AL 36027-1899
Tel (334) 688-7000 *Founded/Ownrshp* 2007
Sales 41.6MM^E *EMP* 234
SIC 8011 Medical centers; Medical centers
CEO: Ralph Clark
Chf Rad: Barbara Shelley
**CEO:* Steve Honeycutt
COO: Brenda Mitchell
CFO: Debbie Norton
Dir Lab: Anthony Hurst
Dir Rx: Allan Finlayson
Dir QC: Suzie Register
Mktg Dir: Chasity Barnes
Mktg Dir: Jenny Strickland
Pathlgst: Krishna Reddy

D-U-N-S 04-841-6713
MEDICAL CENTER CO INC
MCCO
2250 Circle Dr, Cleveland, OH 44106-2664
Tel (216) 368-4256 *Founded/Ownrshp* 1932
Sales 39.1MM *EMP* 31
Accts Kpmg Llp Columbus Oh
SIC 4961 4931 4941 Steam & air-conditioning supply; Electric & other services combined; Water supply; Steam & air-conditioning supply; Electric & other services combined; Water supply
Pr: Michael B Heise
Doctor: Reggie Campbell

D-U-N-S 79-805-4052
MEDICAL CENTER EMRGENCY SERVICES PC
EMERGENCY DEPT
4201 Saint Antoine St 3r, Detroit, MI 48201-2153
Tel (313) 745-3330 *Founded/Ownrshp* 1984
Sales 41.1MM *EMP* 90
SIC 8011 Offices & clinics of medical doctors; Offices & clinics of medical doctors
Pr: Brooks Bock
**VP:* Dr Padraic Sweeney
Exec: Cheryl Smith
VP Mktg: Steve Martin
Doctor: Gloria Kuhn

D-U-N-S 05-825-5951
MEDICAL CENTER FUND OF CINCINNATI
2830 Victory Pkwy Ste 160, Cincinnati, OH 45206-2073
Tel (513) 475-8150 *Founded/Ownrshp* 1977
Sales 25.7MM *EMP* 7
Accts Barnes Dennig & Co Ltd Cin
SIC 8621 Medical field-related associations; Medical field-related associations
Ex Dir: John R Gillespie
**Pr:* Gregory Rouan

MEDICAL CENTER HEALTH SYSTEM
See ECTOR COUNTY HOSPITAL DISTRICT

MEDICAL CENTER HOSPITAL
See MEDICAL CENTER

D-U-N-S 96-168-7097
MEDICAL CENTER HOSPITAL AUTHORITY
707 Center St, Columbus, GA 31901-1575
Tel (706) 660-6142 *Founded/Ownrshp* 2010
Sales 33.2MM *EMP* 14^E
Accts Robinson Grimes & Company Pc
SIC 8062 General medical & surgical hospitals
Prin: David McMicken

D-U-N-S 84-066-2092
■ **MEDICAL CENTER OF BATON ROUGE INC**
LAKESIDE HOSPITAL
(*Suby of* HCA INC) ★
4700 S I 10 Service Rd W, Metairie, LA 70001-1269
Tel (504) 780-8282 *Founded/Ownrshp* 1995
Sales 20.2MM^E *EMP* 350
SIC 8069 Specialty hospitals, except psychiatric; Specialty hospitals, except psychiatric
Pr: Sherald Steward
CFO: Tim Breslen
**CFO:* Annette Strait
Off Mgr: Sharon Black
Obsttrcn: Maga Martinez-Vazque

D-U-N-S 02-607-6112
MEDICAL CENTER OF LOUISIANA AT NEW ORLEANS
CHARITY HOSPITAL
1532 Tulane Ave, New Orleans, LA 70112-2860
Tel (504) 903-3000 *Founded/Ownrshp* 1800
Sales 122.0M^E *EMP* 4,000
SIC 8062 General medical & surgical hospitals; General medical & surgical hospitals
CFO: Bernie Hebert

MEDICAL CENTER OF MANCHESTER
See COFFEE COUNTY HOSPITAL GROUP INC

D-U-N-S 88-393-1222
■ MEDICAL CENTER OF MCKINNEY
COLUMBIA REHAB
(*Suby of* HCA INC) ★
4500 Medical Center Dr, McKinney, TX 75069-1652
Tel (972) 547-8000 *Founded/Ownrshp* 1991
Sales 55.3MM^E *EMP* 800
SIC 8093 8062 Rehabilitation center, outpatient treatment; General medical & surgical hospitals; Rehabilitation center, outpatient treatment; General medical & surgical hospitals
CEO: Ernest Lynch
Chf Path: Steven J Herbert
Chf OB: Renee L Chan
COO: Brent Hubbard
**CFO:* Dwayne Ray
Dir Rx: Fung Chang
Psych: Eduardo Acosta
Psych: Steven Morgan
Psych: Kent Turner
Phys Thrpy: Tori Owen

D-U-N-S 79-056-5928
MEDICAL CENTER OF ROCKIES
MCR
(*Suby of* UNIVERSITY OF COLORADO HEALTH) ★
2500 Rocky Mountain Ave, Loveland, CO 80538-9004
Tel (970) 624-2500 *Founded/Ownrshp* 2002
Sales NA *EMP* 4,000
SIC 8062 General medical & surgical hospitals; General medical & surgical hospitals
CEO: George Hayes
**Ex Dir:* Laurie Tuka

D-U-N-S 11-850-3395
MEDICAL CENTER OF SOUTHEAST TEXAS L P
IASIS HEALTHCARE
(*Suby of* IASIS HEALTHCARE LLC) ★
2555 Jimmy Johnson Blvd, Port Arthur, TX 77640-2007
Tel (409) 724-7389 *Founded/Ownrshp* 2003
Sales 170.2MM *EMP* 765^E
SIC 8062 General medical & surgical hospitals; General medical & surgical hospitals
CEO: Matt Roberts
Exec: Carol Hebert
Dir Lab: Laurie George
Sales Exec: Tabby Deguia
Pgrm Dir: Becky Ledford

MEDICAL CENTER OF TRINITY
See NEWPORT RICHEY HOSPITAL INC

D-U-N-S 82-739-0340
■ MEDICAL CENTER PHARMACY
(*Suby of* DANVILLE REGIONAL MEDICAL CENTER AUXILIARY) ★
142 S Main St, Danville, VA 24541-2922
Tel (434) 799-2131 *Founded/Ownrshp* 2008
Sales 51.3MM^E *EMP* 1^E
SIC 5122 Pharmaceuticals
CEO: Eric Deaton
Pharmcst: Sheri Slattery

MEDICAL CENTER PLANO
See COLUMBIA MEDICAL CENTER OF PLANO SUBSIDIARY LP

D-U-N-S 15-199-0678
MEDICAL CENTER SHOALS INC
MEDICAL CENTER-SHOALS
201 Avalon Ave, Muscle Shoals, AL 35661-2805
Tel (256) 386-1600 *Founded/Ownrshp* 1993
Sales 11.4MM^E *EMP* 400
SIC 8062 General medical & surgical hospitals; General medical & surgical hospitals
CEO: Sandy Barnes
**CEO:* Connie Hawthorn

MEDICAL CENTER SOUTH ARKANSAS
See MCSA LLC

MEDICAL CENTER-SHOALS
See MEDICAL CENTER SHOALS INC

MEDICAL CITY DALLAS HOSPITAL
See MEDICAL CITY DALLAS IMAGING CENTER LLP

MEDICAL CITY DALLAS HOSPITAL
See COLUMBIA HOSPITAL AT MEDICAL CITY DALLAS SUBSIDIARY LP

D-U-N-S 61-038-7297
MEDICAL CITY DALLAS IMAGING CENTER LLP
MEDICAL CITY DALLAS HOSPITAL
7777 Forest Ln Ste C840, Dallas, TX 75230-2594
Tel (972) 566-7000 *Founded/Ownrshp* 2005
Sales 15.4MM^E *EMP* 2,700
SIC 8099 Medical services organization
CEO: Troy Villareal

MEDICAL CLAIMS PROCESSING
See CARELIFE INC

D-U-N-S 07-418-9770
MEDICAL CLINIC OF HOUSTON LLP
1701 Sunset Blvd, Houston, TX 77005-1798
Tel (713) 526-5511 *Founded/Ownrshp* 1967
Sales 30.4MM^E *EMP* 200
SIC 8011 Clinic, operated by physicians; Internal medicine, physician/surgeon; Clinic, operated by physicians; Internal medicine, physician/surgeon
Doctor: Mildred Bennett
Doctor: Patrick Cook
Doctor: Sandeep Lahoti MD
Doctor: William McKee
Doctor: Russell Radoff

MEDICAL CLINIC OF NORTH TEXAS
See IMPEL MANAGEMENT SERVICES LLC

D-U-N-S 02-033-7796
MEDICAL CLINIC OF NORTH TEXAS P A
MCNT
9003 Airport Fwy Ste 300, Fort Worth, TX 76180-9628
Tel (817) 514-5200 *Founded/Ownrshp* 1994
Sales 20.6MM^E *EMP* 380
SIC 8011 Clinic, operated by physicians; Internal medicine, physician/surgeon; Clinic, operated by physicians; Internal medicine, physician/surgeon
CEO: Karen Kennedy
**Pr:* David Russell
**COO:* Patrick Adams
Dir IT: Mike Wester
Psych: Dipali Kapoor
Obsttrcn: Kristina Carnevale
Obsttrcn: Martin W Fielder
Obsttrcn: Byron Kallam
Doctor: Carlos Kier

MEDICAL COLLEGE OF VIRGINIA
See VCU HEALTH SYSTEM AUTHORITY

D-U-N-S 62-437-6596
MEDICAL COLLEGE OF VIRGINIA FOUNDATION INC
1228 E Broad St, Richmond, VA 23298
Tel (804) 828-9734 *Founded/Ownrshp* 1949
Sales 74.2MM *EMP* 8
SIC 8399 Fund raising organization, non-fee basis; Fund raising organization, non-fee basis
Pr: Michael Dowdy
CFO: Jennings D Dawson III
Counsel: Pamela Boston

D-U-N-S 93-763-9060
MEDICAL COLLEGE OF WISCONSIN INC
8701 W Watertown Plank Rd, Milwaukee, WI 53226-3548
Tel (414) 456-8296 *Founded/Ownrshp* 1918
Sales 990.8MM *EMP* 4,700
Accts Pricewaterhousecoopers Llp Bo
SIC 8221 Colleges universities & professional schools; Colleges universities & professional schools
Pr: John R Raymond Sr
**CFO:* Marjorie Spencer
**Ex VP:* Joseph E Kerschner
VP: Daniel Wickeham
Dir Lab: Dani Didier
Assoc Dir: James Thomas
**Prin:* T Michael Bolger
Off Mgr: Brad Schiereck
CIO: Terry Pouquette
Dir IT: Huoy-Jii Khoo
Dir IT: Kathy Lang

D-U-N-S 03-800-0253 IMP
MEDICAL COMPONENTS INC
MEDCOMP
1499 Delp Dr, Harleysville, PA 19438-2936
Tel (215) 256-4201 *Founded/Ownrshp* 1979
Sales 26.2MM^E *EMP* 54^E
SIC 5047 Instruments, surgical & medical
Pr: Timothy M Schweikert
**Pr:* David Markel

D-U-N-S 18-825-3942
MEDICAL CONSULTANTS INC
EMERGNCY PHYSCIANS BILLING SVC
(*Suby of* INTERMEDIX CORP) ★
3303 S Meridian Ave, Oklahoma City, OK 73119-1026
Tel (405) 682-3303 *Founded/Ownrshp* 1999
Sales 30.1MM^E *EMP* 425
SIC 8748 Business consulting; Business consulting
Pr: Ken Goodin
Pr: Keith Tucker
**CFO:* Gary Plunkett
CIO: Morris Slocum
DP Exec: Jeff Alexander
Dir IT: Mike Hendrix
IT Man: Michael Kalcich

MEDICAL COURIERS
See HOSPITAL COURIERS CORP

MEDICAL CTR SOUTHEASTERN OKLA
See DURANT HMA INC

MEDICAL DATA EXCHANGE
See CYBER-PRO SYSTEMS INC

D-U-N-S 79-283-4137
MEDICAL DATA SYSTEMS INC
2001 9th Ave Ste 312, Vero Beach, FL 32960-6413
Tel (772) 770-2255 *Founded/Ownrshp* 1985
Sales 43.7MM^E *EMP* 600
SIC 7389 5734 Personal service agents, brokers & bureaus; Software, business & non-game; Personal service agents, brokers & bureaus; Software, business & non-game
Pr: Giles Miller
**CFO:* Gary Ball
CFO: Tammy Ortiz
Sr VP: Estelle Welte
**VP:* Amy Miller
Off Mgr: Jason Beeken
CIO: Rick Masterson
Dir IT: Linda Harvard
Dir IT: Tim McDonald
IT Man: Leigh Webster
Software D: Steve Gradolph

D-U-N-S 86-767-3159 IMP/EXP
MEDICAL DEPOT INC
DRIVE MEDICAL DESIGN & MFG
99 Seaview Blvd Ste 210, Port Washington, NY 11050-4632
Tel (516) 998-4600 *Founded/Ownrshp* 2000
Sales 55.0MM *EMP* 500
Accts Rosen Seymour Shapss Martin &
SIC 3841 Surgical & medical instruments; Surgical & medical instruments
CEO: Harvey P Diamond
Pr: Barry Fink
**Pr:* Richard S Kolodny
Pr: Thomas Reynolds
Pr: Randy Rosen
CFO: Thomas San Antonio
Chf Mktg O: Judy Levin
Ex VP: Allen Clem
**Ex VP:* Douglas Francis
**Ex VP:* Jeffrey Schwartz
**Ex VP:* Michael Serhan
Ex VP: Mitchell Yoel
VP: Michael Kelly
VP: Derek Lampert
VP: Mark Lavacca
VP: Lance Lerch
VP: Edward J Link
VP: Ryan Mahoney
VP: Sabine Margolis
VP: Jim McGuiness
VP: David Meily

D-U-N-S 96-764-8713
MEDICAL DEVELOPERS LLC
(*Suby of* 21ST CENTURY ONCOLOGY HOLDINGS INC) ★
2270 Colonial Blvd, Fort Myers, FL 33907-1412
Tel (239) 461-8589 *Founded/Ownrshp* 2011
Sales NA *EMP* 800
SIC 6719 Investment holding companies, except banks
Prin: Daniel E Dosoretz
**Treas:* Frank English

D-U-N-S 00-234-7529
MEDICAL DIAGNOSTIC LABORATORIES LLC (NJ)
MDL
2439 Kuser Rd, Hamilton, NJ 08690-3303
Tel (609) 570-1000 *Founded/Ownrshp* 1997
Sales 54.8MM^E *EMP* 325^E
SIC 8731 8734 Commercial research laboratory; Testing laboratories; Commercial research laboratory; Testing laboratories
CEO: Eli Mordechia
**VP:* Martin E Adelson
VP: Eli Mordechai
Dir Lab: Peter Winchester
Genl Mgr: Melissa Starkey
QA Dir: Kimberly Cabets
Dir IT: Janet Cohen
Software D: Gary Volochinsky
Sales Exec: Casey Brown
Sales Exec: Melissa Daniele
Sales Exec: Chris Defalco

MEDICAL DIMENSIONS
See LAFAYETTE HEALTH VENTURES INC

D-U-N-S 82-867-1482
■ MEDICAL DOCTOR ASSOCIATES LLC
(*Suby of* CROSS COUNTRY HEALTHCARE INC) ★
4775 Peachtree Industrial, Berkeley Lake, GA 30092-3011
Tel (770) 246-9191 *Founded/Ownrshp* 1987
Sales 20.8MM^E *EMP* 200^E
SIC 8741 7361 Hospital management; Nursing & personal care facility management; Placement agencies; Hospital management; Nursing & personal care facility management; Placement agencies
Pr: B Franklin Phillips
CFO: Deborah Campbell
VP: Anne Anderson
VP: Dave Wittrock
Exec: Curtis Shumard
Creative D: Melissa Walter
Comm Man: Wanda Collins
DP Exec: Don Chapman
Dir IT: Peng Chai
IT Man: Elias Lee
IT Man: Dan Thompson

D-U-N-S 07-279-5391
MEDICAL EDGE HEALTHCARE GROUP PA
ADVANCED CANCER RESOURCE
9229 Lbj Fwy Ste 250, Dallas, TX 75243-4403
Tel (972) 739-3001 *Founded/Ownrshp* 1994
Sales NA *EMP* 650
SIC 8741

D-U-N-S 05-092-7300
MEDICAL EDUCATION ASSISTANCE CORP
UNIVERSITY PHYSICIAN PRACTICE
222 E Main St, Johnson City, TN 37604-5708
Tel (423) 433-6050 *Founded/Ownrshp* 1978
Sales 34.9MM *EMP* 400
Accts Rodefer Moss & Co Pllc King
SIC 8071 8011 Medical laboratories; Offices & clinics of medical doctors; Medical laboratories; Offices & clinics of medical doctors
Pr: Philip C Bagnell
**Treas:* David Collins
**VP:* William Browder
**Ex Dir:* Russell Lewis

D-U-N-S 01-245-5505
MEDICAL EDUCATION RESOURCES LLC
43 Golden Dr, Bedford, NH 03110-4415
Tel (603) 472-9001 *Founded/Ownrshp* 2007
Sales 22.0MM *EMP* 15
SIC 7313 Electronic media advertising representatives; Printed media advertising representatives; Electronic media advertising representatives; Printed media advertising representatives

D-U-N-S 09-859-3320
MEDICAL ENTERPRISES LTD (INC)
PROFESSIONAL BUILDING SERVICES
3925 W Northside Dr, Jackson, MS 39209-2502
Tel (601) 922-2528 *Founded/Ownrshp* 1976
Sales 54.4MM *EMP* 105
Accts Ernst & Young Jackson Ms
SIC 5047 5999 7352 1542 7349 Medical equipment & supplies; Convalescent equipment & supplies; Hospital equipment & supplies; Medical equipment rental; Nonresidential construction; Building maintenance, except repairs; Medical equipment & supplies; Convalescent equipment & supplies; Hospital equipment & supplies; Medical equipment rental; Nonresidential construction; Building maintenance, except repairs
CEO: John M Bower
**Pr:* Dr John Bower

D-U-N-S 01-300-9878
MEDICAL EXPRESS AMBULANCE SERVICE INC (IL)
MEDEX AMBULANCE
5650 Howard St, Skokie, IL 60077-2623
Tel (847) 673-6333 *Founded/Ownrshp* 1997
Sales 14.3MM^E *EMP* 300
SIC 4119 Ambulance service; Ambulance service
CEO: Lauren Rubinson
Opers Mgr: Jim Wittemann

MEDICAL EYE BANK OF MARYLAND
See TISSUE BANKS INTERNATIONAL INC

D-U-N-S 85-857-3967
MEDICAL EYE SERVICES INC
(*Suby of* EYE CARE NETWORK OF CALIFORNIA INC) ★
345 Baker St E, Costa Mesa, CA 92626-4518
Tel (714) 619-4660 *Founded/Ownrshp* 1976
Sales NA *EMP* 100
SIC 6411 Insurance claim processing, except medical
Pr: Aspasia Shappet
Rgnl Mgr: Kerry Carpio
Sls Mgr: Rodney Mattos
Snr Mgr: Alma Gomez

D-U-N-S 61-325-9746
MEDICAL FACILITIES OF AMERICA INC
2917 Penn Forest Blvd # 200, Roanoke, VA 24018-4374
Tel (540) 989-3618 *Founded/Ownrshp* 1984
Sales 26.5MM^E *EMP* 200
SIC 8051 Skilled nursing care facilities; Skilled nursing care facilities
Ch: W Heywood Fralin
**Pr:* William H Fralin Jr
**COO:* Keith Helmer
**CFO:* Novel Martin
**Ex VP:* Brenda Moore
**Sr VP:* Karen H Waldron
VP: Sharon Gawronski
Exec: Suzanne Handlin
Exec: Gina Jones
Dir IT: Scott Epperly
VP Opers: David Hassenpflug

D-U-N-S 80-789-4555
MEDICAL FACILITIES OF AMERICA LXXII (72) LP
ASHEVILLE HEALTH CARE CENTER
1984 Us 70 Hwy, Swannanoa, NC 28778-8212
Tel (828) 298-2214 *Founded/Ownrshp* 1989
Sales 725.2MM *EMP* 125
SIC 8051 8052 8059 Skilled nursing care facilities; Intermediate care facilities; Rest home, with health care; Skilled nursing care facilities; Intermediate care facilities; Rest home, with health care
Pt: W Heywood Fralin
**Genl Pt:* Kay F Bechtel Trust
**Pt:* N Ronald Covington Jr
**Pt:* Medical Fac of NC
**Pt:* Melissa K Snuggs
**Pt:* G Wayne Fralin Trust
**Pt:* Estate of Elbert Wal
**Pt:* Karen H Waldron
Dir Soc: Holly Self
HC Dir: Susan Lippold

D-U-N-S 07-474-5803
MEDICAL FACILITIES OF AMERICA VI AND XIII (LIMITED PARTNERSHIP)
VIRGINIA BEACH HEATHCARE & REH
2917 Penn Forest Blvd # 200, Roanoke, VA 24018-4374
Tel (540) 989-3618 *Founded/Ownrshp* 1977
Sales 22.4MM^E *EMP* 1,083
SIC 8051 Skilled nursing care facilities; Skilled nursing care facilities
Pt: W Heywood Fralin

D-U-N-S 84-169-4974
MEDICAL FACULTY ASSOCIATES INC
GWU MEDICAL FACULTY ASSOCIATES
2150 Pennsylvania Ave Nw, Washington, DC 20037-3201
Tel (202) 741-3000 *Founded/Ownrshp* 2000
Sales 339.1MM *EMP* 1,600^E
SIC 8011 Offices & clinics of medical doctors; Offices & clinics of medical doctors
CEO: Stephen L Badger
**Pr:* Alan Waserman MD
**CFO:* Kenneth W Marter
Bd of Dir: Anil Dubey
Pathlgst: Robert V Jones
Pathlgst: Donald S Karcher
Pathlgst: John F Keiser
Pathlgst: Sana O Tabbara
Obsttrcn: Anna Maria Gray
Obsttrcn: Jennifer Keller
Obsttrcn: AMR Madkour

D-U-N-S 82-917-1698
MEDICAL FOUNDATION OF CENTRAL MISSISSIPPI INC
BAPTIST MEDICAL CLINICS
1225 N State St Ste 504, Jackson, MS 39202-2064
Tel (601) 292-4261 *Founded/Ownrshp* 2002
Sales 27.6MM *EMP* 99^E
Accts Bkd Llp Jackson Ms
SIC 8011 Offices & clinics of medical doctors; Offices & clinics of medical doctors
Pr: Elizabeth Mullins
Ex VP: Jerry Cotton

D-U-N-S 07-202-8277
MEDICAL FOUNDATION OF NC INC
880 Mlk Jr Blvd, Chapel Hill, NC 27514
Tel (919) 966-1201 *Founded/Ownrshp* 1949
Sales 30.2MM *EMP* 17
Accts Blackman & Sloop Cpas Pa Chap
SIC 8621 Medical field-related associations; Medical field-related associations
Pr: David Anderson
**VP:* Jane McNeer

D-U-N-S 03-988-7435
MEDICAL GROUP INSURANCE SERVICE INC
MGIS SERVICES,
1849 W North Temple Ste D, Salt Lake City, UT 84116-3067
Tel (801) 990-2400 *Founded/Ownrshp* 1968
Sales NA *EMP* 75
SIC 6411 Insurance agents, brokers & service; Insurance agents & brokers
Pr: Dale W Brunken

Pr: Keith Oser
**CFO:* Matt Frost
**CFO:* Blaine Moon
CFO: Todd Orullian
Sr VP: Stephen Brunken
VP: Mark Chai
VP: Molly Farrell
VP: Michael G Green
VP: Steven J Lempp
VP: Keith Mangrum
VP: Kurt Meyer
VP: Paul Mfischerkell
VP: Forrest Pritchett
VP: Matthew B Ririe

D-U-N-S 00-488-8439
MEDICAL GROUP MANAGEMENT ASSOCIATION
4288 Ashington Dr, Birmingham, AL 35242-7807
Tel (205) 981-0011 *Founded/Ownrshp* 1979
Sales 462.0M *EMP* 650
SIC 8062 Hospital, medical school affiliation; Hospital, medical school affiliation
Ex Dir: Lisa Beard

D-U-N-S 04-776-0012
MEDICAL HEALTH MART PHARMACY INC
MEDICAL PHARMACY WEST
6400 Main St, Zachary, LA 70791-4039
Tel (225) 654-6883 *Founded/Ownrshp* 1968
Sales 23.7MM *EMP* 18
SIC 5912 Drug stores; Drug stores
Pr: John O Letard
**VP:* Audrey Letard

MEDICAL IMAGING EQUIPMENT
See PHILIPS MEDICAL SYSTEMS (CLEVELAND) INC

D-U-N-S 83-221-0533
MEDICAL IMAGING HOLDINGS INC
(*Suby of* GALEN PARTNERS LLC) ★
615 Industrial Dr Ste B, Cary, IL 60013-3342
Tel (847) 737-9066 *Founded/Ownrshp* 2009
Sales 22.6MM^E *EMP* 186^E
SIC 6719 8071 Investment holding companies, except banks; Ultrasound laboratory; Investment holding companies, except banks; Ultrasound laboratory
Pr: Jim Spearman
Treas: Irina Kettler

D-U-N-S 78-175-2563
MEDICAL IMAGING OF COLORADO LLC
INVISION
10700 E Geddes Ave # 200, Englewood, CO 80112-3861
Tel (303) 761-9190 *Founded/Ownrshp* 1999
Sales 27.7MM^E *EMP* 125
SIC 8011 Radiologist
Off Mgr: Janet Guizzetti
Doctor: Laurence Gaynor

D-U-N-S 00-386-1163 IMP
MEDICAL IMAGING SOLUTIONS GROUP INC
MIS
229 Arnold Mill Rd, Woodstock, GA 30188-4145
Tel (770) 592-9191 *Founded/Ownrshp* 1998
Sales 22.0MM^E *EMP* 49
SIC 5047 7699 7352 Medical & hospital equipment; Hospital equipment repair services; Medical equipment rental
CEO: Arnold L Bates
Pr: Scott Bunting
**CFO:* Vivian Bates
VP: Bobby Hagan
Genl Mgr: Jim Bates
Opers Mgr: Bill Stickney
Manager: John Cooper
Manager: Don McCauley

D-U-N-S 06-515-2530
MEDICAL INFORMATION TECHNOLOGY INC
Meditech Cir, Westwood, MA 02090
Tel (781) 821-3000 *Founded/Ownrshp* 1969
Sales 517.0MM *EMP* 4,000^E
SIC 7372 Prepackaged software; Prepackaged software
Pr: Howard Messing
**Ch Bd:* A Neil Pappalardo
CFO: Jennifer Holland
CFO: Barbara A Manzolillo
**V Ch Bd:* Lawrence A Polimeno
Bd of Dir: Deborah Cooley
Bd of Dir: Kathy Perregaux
Bd of Dir: Bernard Winston
Ex VP: Michelle O'Connor
Ex VP: Hoda Sayed-Friel
Sr VP: Stuart N Lefthes
VP: David Anderson
VP: Don Branca
VP: Rosalyn Elton
VP: Tom Newman
Board of Directors: Roland L Driscoll, Edward B Roberts, L P Dan Valente

MEDICAL INSURANCE EXCHANGE
See MEDICAL UNDERWRITERS OF CALIFORNIA

D-U-N-S 07-886-4402
MEDICAL LIABILITY MUTUAL INSURANCE CO
2 Park Ave Fl 25, New York, NY 10016-9394
Tel (212) 576-9800 *Founded/Ownrshp* 1975
Sales NA *EMP* 85
SIC 6351 Liability insurance
Pr: Robert A Menotti MD
**Treas:* Charles N Aswad MD
Treas: Matthew Liebman
**VP:* Donald J Fager
VP: Fredrica Jarcho
**VP:* K Wayne Kahle
VP: Nancy Libke
VP: Louis Neuburger
VP: Edgar Robinson
VP: Kenneth Skelly
VP: Waxman Stephanie
Exec: James Rhatigan

MEDICAL MAL PRACTICE
See TEXAS MEDICAL LIABILITY TRUST (INC)

D-U-N-S 19-674-8321
MEDICAL MANAGEMENT CONSULTANTS INC
MMC
8150 Beverly Blvd, Los Angeles, CA 90048-4513
Tel (310) 659-3835 *Founded/Ownrshp* 1982
Sales 74.7MM^E *EMP* 5,000
SIC 7363 8742 8748 8721 Help supply services; Hospital & health services consultant; Employee programs administration; Payroll accounting service; Help supply services; Hospital & health services consultant; Employee programs administration; Payroll accounting service
Pr: Mashi Rahmani
Dir Risk M: Julie Leonor
CTO: Crystal Obrien
IT Man: Paul Rahmani

D-U-N-S 82-722-9493
MEDICAL MANAGEMENT INTERNATIONAL INC
BANFIELD PET HOSPITAL
(*Suby of* MARS INC) ★
8000 Ne Tillamook St, Portland, OR 97213-6655
Tel (503) 922-5000 *Founded/Ownrshp* 1994
Sales 1.8MMM^E *EMP* 7,000
SIC 0742 5047 Veterinary services, specialties; Animal hospital services, pets & other animal specialties; Veterinarians' equipment & supplies; Veterinary services, specialties; Animal hospital services, pets & other animal specialties; Veterinarians' equipment & supplies
CEO: Tony Ueber
CFO: Phil Freeman
CFO: Margie Mendoza
Ofcr: Thomas Rabus
Sr VP: Daniel Aja
Sr VP: Susan Harwood
Sr VP: Debbie Kujovich
**Sr VP:* Hugh B Lewis
Sr VP: Jeannine Taaffe
VP: John Bork
VP: Jeffrey Brant
VP: Kimball Carr
VP: Jeffery Ellison
**VP:* John May
VP: Marta Monetti

D-U-N-S 86-863-7869
MEDICAL MANAGEMENT OPTIONS LLC
M M O
728 North Blvd, Baton Rouge, LA 70802-5724
Tel (225) 293-6774 *Founded/Ownrshp* 1993
Sales 23.0MM^E *EMP* 600
SIC 8361 8322 Halfway group home, persons with social or personal problems; Substance abuse counseling; Halfway group home, persons with social or personal problems; Substance abuse counseling
**COO:* Jamie Simpson

D-U-N-S 05-974-6458
MEDICAL MANAGEMENT PROFESSIONALS LLC
(*Suby of* ZOTEC PARTNERS LLC) ★
5959 Shallowford Rd # 575, Chattanooga, TN 37421-2240
Tel (423) 894-6570 *Founded/Ownrshp* 2001
Sales 20.0MM^E *EMP* 495^E
SIC 8099 Medical services organization; Medical services organization
Ex VP: Darrell Hulsey
**Treas:* Kelly J Marek
VP: George Ehrhardt
**VP:* Jerome P Grisko Jr
**VP:* Bruce J Kowalski
VP: W Stone
IT Man: Jeff Bennett
VP Opers: Mark Hammond
Opers Mgr: Carol Mitchell

D-U-N-S 07-917-7136
MEDICAL MANAGEMENT RESOURCES GROUP LLC (AZ)
4800 N 22nd St, Phoenix, AZ 85016-4701
Tel (602) 955-1000 *Founded/Ownrshp* 2002
Sales 20.8MM^E *EMP* 406
SIC 8741 Management services; Management services
CEO: Mark Rosenberg
CFO: Donald Snyder

MEDICAL MANAGER
See EMDEON CORP

MEDICAL MATERIAL OFFICE
See DAVID GRANT MEDICAL CENTER

MEDICAL MISSION SISTER'S
See SOCIETY OF CATHOLIC MEDICAL MISSIONARIES INC

MEDICAL MOBILITY
See HOME HEALTH DEPOT INC

MEDICAL MURRAY
See MURRAY INC

D-U-N-S 03-771-6735
MEDICAL MUTUAL INSURANCE CO OF MAINE
1 City Ctr Stop 9, Portland, ME 04101-4009
Tel (207) 775-2791 *Founded/Ownrshp* 2002
Sales NA *EMP* 54
SIC 6321 Mutual accident & health associations
CEO: Terrance J Sheehan
**CFO:* Domenic Restuccia
**Ch:* William L Medd MD
Sr VP: Michael McCall
VP: Mary Knox
Exec: Cheryl Peaslee
CIO: Steve Hodgkin
IT Man: Ray Croteau
IT Man: Gott Kevin
Web Dev: Mark McGhie
Netwrk Eng: Alan De Gouveia

D-U-N-S 08-416-4995
MEDICAL MUTUAL INSURANCE CO OF NORTH CAROLINA
MEDICAL SECURITY INSURANCE CO
700 Spring Forest Rd # 400, Raleigh, NC 27609-9124
Tel (919) 872-7117 *Founded/Ownrshp* 1975
Sales NA *EMP* 100
SIC 6351 Liability insurance; Liability insurance
CEO: Allen Dale Jenkins
Chf Mktg O: Jim Kay
VP: Gary Bossert
VP: Jason Sandner
Dir Risk M: Jason Lee
Sales Exec: Darlene Steinhart

D-U-N-S 08-055-2359
MEDICAL MUTUAL LIABILITY INSURANCE SOCIETY OF MARYLAND
225 International Cir # 300, Hunt Valley, MD 21030-4358
Tel (410) 785-0050 *Founded/Ownrshp* 1975
Sales NA *EMP* 105
SIC 6351 Liability insurance; Liability insurance
Ch Bd: George S Malouf Jr
Pt: John McCullough
V Ch: Mary Ellen
**Pr:* Jeffrey M Poole
**CEO:* Robert R Neall
Assoc VP: Elizabeth Svoysky
**Sr VP:* Wesley M Foster Jr
VP: William Ober
VP: Foster Wesley
Doctor: Malouf George
Doctor: Charles Mess

D-U-N-S 07-112-6262
MEDICAL MUTUAL OF OHIO
CONSUMERS LIFE INSURANCE CO
2060 E 9th St Frnt Ste, Cleveland, OH 44115-1355
Tel (216) 687-7000 *Founded/Ownrshp* 1945
Sales NA *EMP* 2,500
SIC 6324 Hospital & medical service plans; Dental insurance; Group hospitalization plans; Hospital & medical service plans; Dental insurance; Group hospitalization plans
CEO: Rick A Chiricosta
Ex VP: Jared Chaney
**Ex VP:* Kathy Golovan
**Ex VP:* Steffany Larkins
**Ex VP:* Ray Mueller
Ex VP: Kevin Sidon
Ex VP: Susan Tyler
VP: Asuncion Barton
VP: Sonny Barton
VP: Mary Edwards
VP: Tom Laub
VP: Victoria Nadzam
VP: Dan Polk
VP: Janice Santoll
VP: Heather Thiltgen
VP: John Uhlir

D-U-N-S 08-877-8332
MEDICAL MUTUAL SERVICES LLC
ANTARES MANAGEMENT SOLUTIONS
(*Suby of* CONSUMERS LIFE INSURANCE CO) ★
17800 Royalton Rd, Strongsville, OH 44136-5149
Tel (440) 878-4800 *Founded/Ownrshp* 1997
Sales 31.4MM^E *EMP* 600
SIC 7374 7375 Data processing & preparation; Information retrieval services; Data processing & preparation; Information retrieval services
Ex VP: Jeff Perry
VP: Tom Stepec
Web Dev: Joseph Gabella
Software D: John Mikolich
Netwrk Eng: Brian Berman
Natl Sales: Kevin Gill
Mktg Mgr: Gayle Harmon

D-U-N-S 07-413-3398
MEDICAL PACKAGING CORP
HYGENIA
941 Avenida Acaso, Camarillo, CA 93012-8755
Tel (805) 388-2383 *Founded/Ownrshp* 1974
Sales 21.5MM^E *EMP* 100
SIC 3842 2835 Surgical appliances & supplies; In vitro & in vivo diagnostic substances; Surgical appliances & supplies; In vitro & in vivo diagnostic substances
Pr: Frederic L Nason
**Sec:* Susan J Nason
QA Dir: Vince Huerta

MEDICAL PARK PHARMACY
See MEMORIAL PHARMACY INC

MEDICAL PHARMACY WEST
See MEDICAL HEALTH MART PHARMACY INC

D-U-N-S 00-733-5474
MEDICAL PLASTICS LABORATORY INC
(*Suby of* LAERDAL MEDICAL CORP) ★
226 Fm 116, Gatesville, TX 76528-1061
Tel (254) 865-7221 *Founded/Ownrshp* 1951
Sales 17.3MM^E *EMP* 310
SIC 3083 5046 Laminated plastics plate & sheet; Mannequins; Laminated plastics plate & sheet; Mannequins
Pr: David Broussard

D-U-N-S 02-165-1086
MEDICAL PLUS SUPPLIES INC
M P S
4025 W Fuqua St, Houston, TX 77045-6303
Tel (713) 440-6700 *Founded/Ownrshp* 1991
Sales 40.8MM^E *EMP* 120^E
SIC 5047 Medical equipment & supplies; Medical equipment & supplies
Pr: Esteban Rodriguez

D-U-N-S 00-229-0302 IMP
MEDICAL PRODUCTS LABORATORIES INC (PA)
9990 Global Rd, Philadelphia, PA 19115-1006
Tel (215) 677-2700 *Founded/Ownrshp* 1928, 1965
Sales 46.9MM^E *EMP* 185
SIC 2834 Pharmaceutical preparations; Pharmaceutical preparations
Pr: Elliot Stone
CFO: Mark Sherr
VP: Arun Patel
VP: Steven Stone
**VP:* Dave Waxler
Dir Bus: Howard Wolf
Ex Dir: Joanne Pierce
CIO: Arlene Stone
QA Dir: Osama Allam
QA Dir: Lee Zagar
QI Cn Mgr: Bharat Patel

D-U-N-S 11-885-2599
MEDICAL PROFESSIONAL MUTUAL INSURANCE CO
PRO MUTUAL
(*Suby of* COVERYS) ★
1 Financial Ctr Fl 13, Boston, MA 02111-2688
Tel (800) 225-6168 *Founded/Ownrshp* 1975
Sales NA *EMP* 385
SIC 6331 Fire, marine & casualty insurance; Fire, marine & casualty insurance
Pr: Gregg Hanson
Ch Bd: Dr Brandal Richardson
V Ch Bd: Brenda E Richardson
Prin: Kenneth A Heisler
Sys/Mgr: John Donehue
Sys/Mgr: Robert Gilmore

MEDICAL PROFILES & ENGINEERING
See MP&E INC

D-U-N-S 14-191-8958
MEDICAL PROPERTIES TRUST INC
1000 Urban Center Dr # 501, Vestavia, AL 35242-2225
Tel (205) 969-3755 *Founded/Ownrshp* 2004
Sales 312.5MM *EMP* 6,000^E
SIC 6798 Real estate investment trusts; Real estate investment trusts
Ch Bd: Edward K Aldag Jr
COO: Emmett E McLean
**CFO:* R Steven Hamner
Board of Directors: G Steven Dawson, Robert E Holmes, Sherry A Kellett, William G McKenzie, L Glenn Orr Jr, Paul Sparks Jr

MEDICAL PROTECTIVE
See PRINCETON INSURANCE CO

D-U-N-S 00-693-7171
■ **MEDICAL PROTECTIVE CO**
(*Suby of* MEDPRO GROUP INC) ★
5814 Reed Rd, Fort Wayne, IN 46835-3500
Tel (260) 485-9622 *Founded/Ownrshp* 1909
Sales NA *EMP* 275
SIC 6351 6411 Surety insurance; Insurance agents, brokers & service; Insurance agents; Property & casualty insurance agent; Surety insurance; Insurance agents, brokers & service; Insurance agents; Property & casualty insurance agent
Pr: Timothy Kenesey
**Ch Bd:* Kaj Ahlmann
**Pr:* David E Rosendahl
Pr: Sue Shumaker
**Treas:* Dan Landrigan
**Sr VP:* Timothy Beck
Sr VP: Robert Ignasiak
VP: Gregory Chronis
**VP:* Robert L Ignasiak
**VP:* James D Kunce
VP: Gene Ostermann
VP: Timothy Ryall
VP: Timothy M Smith
VP: Anthony Villanueva
**VP:* Mark Walthour
VP: Joel Whitcraft
VP: Mark Wittel

MEDICAL PRSNNEL POOL OF DAYTON
See INTERIM HEALTHCARE OF DAYTON INC

D-U-N-S 86-797-9619
MEDICAL REHABILITATION CENTERS LLC
EXCEPTIONAL LIVING CENTERS
1050 Chinoe Rd Ste 300, Lexington, KY 40502-6571
Tel (859) 255-0075 *Founded/Ownrshp* 1992
Sales 133.2MM^E *EMP* 2,000
Accts Crowe Horwath Llp South Bend
SIC 8742 Management consulting services; Management consulting services
**Pr:* C Lynn Redmond
**Treas:* Jim Johnson
Treas: Steven Wood
Sr VP: John Nabours
VP: Tracy Life
VP: Stacie Turner
**VP:* Wayne Tush
Mng Ofcr: Tom Watts
Off Mgr: Janet Gillespie
CTO: Donna Williams

D-U-N-S 01-649-0000
MEDICAL REIMBURSEMENTS OF AMERICA LLC
7105 Moores Ln, Brentwood, TN 37027-2840
Tel (877) 324-2722 *Founded/Ownrshp* 1999
Sales 26.1MM^E *EMP* 325^E
SIC 7363 Help supply services; Help supply services
CEO: Bob Rolfe
**Pr:* Lyle Beasley
**Ch:* Stuart McWhorter
**Founder:* Michael Ford
**Ex VP:* Lawrence Rosenberg
Sr VP: Patrick O'Connell
VP: Leanne Erwin
VP: Chad Powers
IT Man: Steve McDowell

MEDICAL RESEARCH CONSULTANTS
See DWMRC HOLDINGS INC

MEDICAL RESEARCH FOUNDATION OF
See OREGON HEALTH & SCIENCE UNIVERSITY FOUNDATION INC

D-U-N-S 05-742-6678 IMP
MEDICAL RESOURCES INC
1455 Broad St Ste 4, Bloomfield, NJ 07003-3039
Tel (973) 707-1100 *Founded/Ownrshp* 1992
Sales 27.8MM^E *EMP* 850
SIC 8071 Medical laboratories; Medical laboratories
CEO: D Gordon Strickland
**Pr:* John Valla
CFO: David Ccabe
**VP:* David M McCabe

D-U-N-S 09-149-3908
MEDICAL RESOURCES INC
SHOPPING RESOURCES
320 Nevada St Ste 201, Newton, MA 02460-1449
Tel (617) 219-5900 *Founded/Ownrshp* 1971
Sales 15.1MM^E *EMP* 400
SIC 8099 8082 Medical services organization; Home health care services; Medical services organization; Home health care services
Pr: Walter Talancy
**Treas:* Gail C Talancy
Off Mgr: Nancy Parker
Dir IT: Fred Moynihan

D-U-N-S 87-769-2665
MEDICAL SECURITY CARD CO LLC
SCRIPTSAVE
4911 E Broadway Blvd # 200, Tucson, AZ 85711-3630
Tel (520) 888-8070 *Founded/Ownrshp* 1994
Sales 21.7MM^E *EMP* 125
SIC 8621 Health association
Pr: Lori Bryant
**CFO:* Jennifer Lebrecht
**CFO:* Gerald T Miron
CFO: Jerry Miron
**Ch:* Charles Horn
Ex VP: John R Grace
VP: Jim Ayers
**VP:* Mark Chamness
VP: Rph Mark Chamness
**VP:* Paula Dunn
VP: Mike Flory
**VP:* John Friend
VP: Jerry Parker
**VP:* Marcus Sredzinski

MEDICAL SECURITY INSURANCE CO
See MEDICAL MUTUAL INSURANCE CO OF NORTH CAROLINA

D-U-N-S 01-779-8802
MEDICAL SERVICE CO
24000 Broadway Ave, Bedford, OH 44146-6329
Tel (440) 232-3000 *Founded/Ownrshp* 1949
Sales 43.5MM^E *EMP* 65^E
SIC 5912 7352 Drug stores; Medical equipment rental; Drug stores; Medical equipment rental
Pr: Joel D Marx
**Pr:* Darrel Lowery
**VP:* John Geller
**VP:* Dana McLaughlin
Brnch Mgr: Ann Hufford

MEDICAL SERVICES COMPANY
See ASSOCIATED MEDICAL PRODUCTS INC

D-U-N-S 18-901-6587
MEDICAL SERVICES INC
HAYWARD AREA MEMORIAL HOSPITAL
11040 N State Road 77, Hayward, WI 54843-6391
Tel (715) 634-8911 *Founded/Ownrshp* 1986
Sales 39.5MM *EMP* 207
Accts Rsm Mcgladrey Inc Duluth Mn
SIC 8062 8051 General medical & surgical hospitals; Skilled nursing care facilities; General medical & surgical hospitals; Skilled nursing care facilities
CEO: Barbara A Peickert
**Pr:* Tim Gullingsrud
Ofcr: Pat Miller
VP: Jeff Laskey
**VP:* Brad Zeller
Dir Rad: Gregory Lehman
IT Man: Ann Gleichert

D-U-N-S 03-008-9726
MEDICAL SERVICES OF AMERICA INC
171 Monroe Ln, Lexington, SC 29072-3904
Tel (803) 957-0500 *Founded/Ownrshp* 1973
Sales 160.6MM^E *EMP* 3,000
Accts Scott And Company Llp Columbi
SIC 8082 8741 8011 8071 7352 5999 Home health care services; Hospital management; Cardiologist & cardio-vascular specialist; Medical laboratories; Medical equipment rental; Medical apparatus & supplies; Home health care services; Hospital management; Cardiologist & cardio-vascular specialist; Medical laboratories; Medical equipment rental; Medical apparatus & supplies
Pr: Ronnie L Young
**VP:* James F Hardman
**VP:* John D Keim
Exec: Cheryl Brown
Exec: Ruth Keene
Dir Rx: Joni Sane
Rgnl Mgr: Anna Willis
CIO: Kenny Boggs
Dir IT: Diana Peck
Dir IT: Brooks Sligh
IT Man: Karen Boozer

D-U-N-S 03-080-8492
MEDICAL SOLUTIONS INC
1729 Norton St, Rochester, NY 14609-2219
Tel (585) 259-0984 *Founded/Ownrshp* 1996
Sales 4.3MM^E *EMP* 300
SIC 8082 7361 Home health care services; Employment agencies; Home health care services; Employment agencies
Pr: Greg Zimmer

D-U-N-S 79-524-9759
MEDICAL SOLUTIONS LLC
1010 N 102nd St Ste 300, Omaha, NE 68114-2122
Tel (402) 758-2800 *Founded/Ownrshp* 2012
Sales 37.8MM^E *EMP* 300
SIC 7361 Nurses' registry
Pr: Scott A Anderson
VP: Melanie Monroe
Dir IT: Shannon Willison
Sales Exec: Jeff Casper

D-U-N-S 93-888-5027
MEDICAL SPECIALISTS OF PALM BEACHES INC
5700 Lake Worth Rd # 204, Greenacres, FL 33463-4727
Tel (561) 968-7968 *Founded/Ownrshp* 1995
Sales 37.8MM^E *EMP* 290
SIC 8011 8721 8741 Offices & clinics of medical doctors; Accounting, auditing & bookkeeping; Management services; Offices & clinics of medical doctors; Accounting, auditing & bookkeeping; Management services
CEO: John Brown
**Pr:* Phillip Ludwig
**COO:* Shawn Franklin
**Ch:* Stephen M Krasner
**Treas:* Thomas Rosenfield MD
**Treas:* Robert M Tome
**VP:* Robert M Levin
CTO: Denice Carr

D-U-N-S 15-360-8369 IMP
MEDICAL SPECIALTIES DISTRIBUTORS LLC
(*Suby of* NEW MOUNTAIN CAPITAL I LLC) ★
800 Technology Center Dr # 3, Stoughton, MA 02072-4721
Tel (781) 344-6000 *Founded/Ownrshp* 2013
Sales 414.6MM^E *EMP* 373
SIC 5047 7352 Medical equipment & supplies; Medical equipment rental; Medical equipment & supplies; Medical equipment rental
Pr: James Beck
Ex VP: Peter Huie
Ex VP: Richard Worthen
Dist Mgr: Frank Pujol
Sls Mgr: Robert Bellaci
Sls Mgr: Jeff Sweitzer

D-U-N-S 11-408-3509
MEDICAL STAFFING ASSOCIATES INC
HEART 2 HEART HOME CARE
659 3rd St Uppr, Beaver, PA 15009-2115
Tel (724) 775-1118 *Founded/Ownrshp* 2001
Sales 11.8MM^E *EMP* 350
SIC 7363 Medical help service; Medical help service
CFO: Elizabeth Butera

D-U-N-S 03-644-7865
MEDICAL STAFFING NETWORK HOLDINGS INC
901 Nw 51st St Ste 110, Boca Raton, FL 33431-4415
Tel (561) 322-1300 *Founded/Ownrshp* 1998
Sales 77.5MM^E *EMP* 950
SIC 7363 7361 Medical help service; Employment agencies; Medical help service; Employment agencies
CEO: Brian R Poplin
**Ch Bd:* Robert J Adamson
**Pr:* Kevin S Little
**CFO:* Ruth Wallace
**Ofcr:* Mohsin Y Meghji
**Ex VP:* Peggy Donelan
**Ex VP:* Hank Drummond
**Sr VP:* Kathy Degiovanni
Snr PM: Margie Schneider
Board of Directors: Anne Boykin Phd, C Daryl Hollis, Philip A Incarnati, Edward J Robinson, David Wester

MEDICAL STAFFING SERVICES
See HICKEY AND EASTON LTD

MEDICAL SUPPLY DEPOT, THE
See LIFELINE PHARMACEUTICALS LLC

D-U-N-S 09-777-9912
MEDICAL TEAM INC
HOME CARE TEAM, THE
1902 Campus Commons Dr # 650, Reston, VA 20191-1589
Tel (703) 390-2300 *Founded/Ownrshp* 1978
Sales 43.0MM^E *EMP* 1,000
SIC 8082 Home health care services; Home health care services
Pr: Leslie Pembrook
**VP:* Nicolas Tzirimis

D-U-N-S 15-647-5279 EXP
MEDICAL TEAMS INTERNATIONAL
14150 Sw Milton Ct, Tigard, OR 97224-8024
Tel (503) 624-1000 *Founded/Ownrshp* 1984
Sales 165.0MM *EMP* 91
Accts Jones & Roth Pc Hillsboro
SIC 8099 8399 Blood related health services; Community development groups
CEO: Jeff Pinneo
Pr: Marlene Minor
**Ch:* Mark Dodson
**Treas:* Jeff Rideout
**VP:* Pamela Blikstad
**VP:* Bill Essig
**VP:* Linda Ranz
**VP:* Steve Vickers
VP: Rachel Wolverton
VP: Bill Zook
Exec: Dave Farquhar

D-U-N-S 96-573-8060
MEDICAL TECHNOLOGIES INNOVATORS INC
10800 Nw 106th St Ste 20, Medley, FL 33178-1250
Tel (305) 260-0753 *Founded/Ownrshp* 2009
Sales 21.3MM *EMP* 9
Accts Ocariz Garrastacho Hevia & M
SIC 5047 Medical & hospital equipment; Medical & hospital equipment
Sec: Nathan Wannemacher

D-U-N-S 05-681-0260 IMP
MEDICAL TECHNOLOGY INC
BLEDSOE BRACE SYSTEMS
2601 Pinewood Dr, Grand Prairie, TX 75051-3516
Tel (972) 647-0884 *Founded/Ownrshp* 2007
Sales 68.5MM^E *EMP* 250
SIC 3842 8011 Orthopedic appliances; Braces, orthopedic; Offices & clinics of medical doctors; Orthopedic appliances; Braces, orthopedic; Offices & clinics of medical doctors
Pr: Gary Henley
**Ch Bd:* Greg Nelson
**Pr:* Gary Bledsoe
COO: Ray Hazelton
CFO: Drue Pounds
**Treas:* Sergio Monioya
VP: Sergio Montoya
**VP:* Gregory R Nelson
CIO: James Clent
Dir IT: Kim Meier
Dir IT: Chris Simpson

D-U-N-S 01-291-8350
▲ **MEDICAL TRANSCRIPTION BILLING CORP**
7 Clyde Rd, Somerset, NJ 08873-5049
Tel (732) 873-5133 *Founded/Ownrshp* 1999
Sales 18.3MM *EMP* 2,200
Tkr Sym MTBC *Exch* NAS
SIC 7372 Prepackaged software; Prepackaged software
Ch Bd: Mahmud Haq
Pr: Howard Resnick
**Pr:* Stephen A Snyder
CFO: Bill Korn
Act CFO: Abdul Rauf
VP: Muhammad Chebli
VP: John Cox
VP: Christine Salimbene
CIO: Ul Hadi

D-U-N-S 83-105-1110
MEDICAL TRANSPORT LLC
5792 Arrowhead Dr, Virginia Beach, VA 23462-3219
Tel (757) 671-8911 *Founded/Ownrshp* 2006
Sales 28.5MM^E *EMP* 405^E
SIC 4119 Ambulance service; Ambulance service
Pr: Russell Blow
IT Man: Kim Messenger
Opers Mgr: Darren Clark
Opers Mgr: Anthony Wilson

D-U-N-S 94-497-2322
MEDICAL TRANSPORTATION MANAGEMENT INC
M T M
16 Hawk Ridge Cir Ste 120, Lake Saint Louis, MO 63367-1861
Tel (636) 561-5686 *Founded/Ownrshp* 1995
Sales 102.3MM^E *EMP* 700
SIC 4119 Local passenger transportation; Local passenger transportation
Ch Bd: Peg Griswold
**Pr:* Alaina Macia
**CFO:* Gary Richardson
**CFO:* Donald Tiemeyer
Ofcr: Leonard Lawson
Ex VP: Brenda Battle
**Ex VP:* Lynn Griswold
VP: Aaron Crowell
**VP:* Alison Whitelaw
Dir Bus: Rhonda Hollingsworth
Prgrm Mgr: Michelle Moses

D-U-N-S 00-947-7402
MEDICAL TRANSPORTATION SERVICES LLC
PHYSICIANS TRANSPORT SERVICE
360 Herndon Pkwy Ste 700, Herndon, VA 20170-4867
Tel (703) 941-7025 *Founded/Ownrshp* 1997
Sales 21.7MM^E *EMP* 100^E
SIC 4119 Ambulance service
COO: Randolph Breton
Med Dir: Dr Lewis Eljaiek
Snr Mgr: Jonathan Whitbey

D-U-N-S 08-386-2391
MEDICAL UNDERWRITERS OF CALIFORNIA
MEDICAL INSURANCE EXCHANGE
6250 Claremont Ave, Oakland, CA 94618-1324
Tel (510) 428-9411 *Founded/Ownrshp* 1975
Sales NA *EMP* 80^E
SIC 6411 Insurance claim adjusters, not employed by insurance company
Pr: William K Scheuber
CFO: Jim King
**Treas:* L Richard Mello
**VP:* Ron Neupauer
**VP:* Stephen Stimel
Dir IT: Fransciol Browne
Dir IT: Don Decosta
Dir IT: Reynolds Glover

D-U-N-S 16-845-3525
MEDICAL UNIVERSITY HOSPITAL AUTHORITY
(*Suby of* MEDICAL UNIVERSITY OF SOUTH CAROLINA) ★
169 Ashley Ave, Charleston, SC 29425-8905
Tel (843) 792-2300 *Founded/Ownrshp* 2000
Sales 463.2MM^E *EMP* 4,000^E
Accts Kpmg Llp Atlanta Ga
SIC 8062 General medical & surgical hospitals; General medical & surgical hospitals
Ex Dir: W Stuart Smith
Surg Cl Rc: Patty Burn

D-U-N-S 07-756-1637
MEDICAL UNIVERSITY OF OHIO
3000 Arlington Ave, Toledo, OH 43614-2595
Tel (419) 383-4000 *Founded/Ownrshp* 2004
Sales 146.4MM^E *EMP* 3,200
SIC 8062 8221 Hospital, affiliated with AMA residency; College, except junior; Hospital, affiliated with AMA residency; College, except junior
Pr: Lloyd Jacobs
**VP:* Mark Chaftang
CIO: Melodie Rufener-Weedley
QA Dir: Margaret McFadden
Pathlgst: Kara Gatto-Weis
Pathlgst: Nurjehan A Quraisky
Surgeon: Jihad T Abbas
Surgeon: David C Allison
Surgeon: Douglas R Bowman
Surgeon: Krishma Malik
Surgeon: Abdul A Mustapha

D-U-N-S 14-483-3928
MEDICAL UNIVERSITY OF SC FOUNDATION
18 Bee St, Charleston, SC 29425-8910
Tel (843) 792-2677 *Founded/Ownrshp* 2001
Sales 50.1MM *EMP* 8
Accts Elliott Davis Llcpllc Charles
SIC 6732 Educational trust management; Educational trust management
CEO: Tom Anderson
**CFO:* Robyn Frampton

D-U-N-S 06-931-6271
MEDICAL UNIVERSITY OF SOUTH CAROLINA (SC)
(*Subsy of* BUDGET & CTRL BD EXEC DIRS OFF) ★
169 Ashley Ave, Charleston, SC 29425-8905
Tel (843) 792-2300 *Founded/Ownrshp* 1824
Sales 781.7MM *EMP* 5,500
Accts Kpmg Llp Greensboro Nc
SIC 8062 8221 8069 Hospital, medical school affiliated with nursing & residency; University; Specialty hospitals, except psychiatric; Hospital, medical school affiliated with nursing & residency; University; Specialty hospitals, except psychiatric
Pr: Raymond Greenburg
CFO: Janet Scarborough
**CFO:* Patrick Wamsley
CFO: Flora Zorn
Trst: Margret M Addison
Trst: Stanley C Baker
Trst: William H Bingham
Trst: Phillip D Fasser
Trst: Cotesworth P Fishburne
Trst: Donald R Johnson II
Trst: Robert C Lake Jr
Trst: Ed Conyers O' Briyan
Trst: Paula E Orr
Trst: Claudia W Peeples
Trst: Thomas C Rowland
Trst: Mark Sanford
Trst: Charles W Schulze
Trst: Allen E Stalvey
Trst: Robin M Tallon Jr
Trst: Charles B Thomas Jr
Trst: James E Wiseman

D-U-N-S 07-364-7849
MEDICAL WEST COMMUNITY HEALTH
BROOKS, CAROLYN E
444 Montgomery St, Chicopee, MA 01020-1969
Tel (413) 598-7440 *Founded/Ownrshp* 1999
Sales NA *EMP* 160
SIC 6324 Health maintenance organization (HMO), insurance only; Health maintenance organization (HMO), insurance only
CEO: Richard Shuman
Obsttrcn: Natasha Reid
Surg Cl Rc: James Delsie
Doctor: Emilio M Elchionna MD
Doctor: Michael R Soell MD
Doctor: Brian H Toole MD

D-U-N-S 14-190-3562
MEDICAL WEST RESPIRATORY SVCS LLC
9301 Dielman Indus Dr, Saint Louis, MO 63132-2204
Tel (314) 993-8100 *Founded/Ownrshp* 2003
Sales 107.8MM^E *EMP* 180
SIC 5047 8082 Medical & hospital equipment; Home health care services; Medical & hospital equipment; Home health care services

D-U-N-S 02-154-5292
MEDICALISTICS LLC
14677 Midway Rd Ste 130, Addison, TX 75001-4976
Tel (469) 206-1230 *Founded/Ownrshp* 2009
Sales 24.0MM *EMP* 36
SIC 7371 Custom computer programming services; Custom computer programming services

D-U-N-S 05-071-4963
MEDICALODGES INC
201 W 8th St, Coffeyville, KS 67337-5807
Tel (620) 251-6700 *Founded/Ownrshp* 1998
Sales 104.6MM *EMP* 2,500
Accts Meara Welch Browne Pc Leaw
SIC 8051 Skilled nursing care facilities; Skilled nursing care facilities
Ch: Richard Butler
**Pr:* Garen Cox
Pr: Travis McBride
**COO:* Fred Benjamin
COO: Fred B Fache
**COO:* Clifford Fischer
**CFO:* Scott L Hines
Bd of Dir: Diane Voss
**VP:* Cathy Fisher
**VP:* Marilyn Peak
**VP:* J D Seller
Exec: Terry Brown

MEDICAP
See CLARKS RX LLC

D-U-N-S 09-652-1620
MEDICAP PHARMACIES INC
MEDICINE SHOP INTERNATIONAL
2850 Elm Point Indus Dr, Saint Charles, MO 63301-4350
Tel (314) 993-6000 *Founded/Ownrshp* 1971
Sales 41.1MM^E *EMP* 200
SIC 5912 6794 Drug stores; Franchises, selling or licensing; Drug stores; Franchises, selling or licensing
Pr: Greg Johansen
Treas: Darrell Gilbert
VP: Bill Stonebraker
VP: Rick Swalwell
CIO: Travas Powell

MEDICARE
See THEDACARE INC

D-U-N-S 78-367-0081
MEDICARE MUCHO MAS HOLDINGS INC
(*Suby of* INNOVACARE SERVICES CO LLC) ★
Torrechardon 350 Av Chard 350th Avenue, San Juan, PR 00918
Tel (787) 622-3000 *Founded/Ownrshp* 2004
Sales NA *EMP* 300
SIC 6324 Hospital & medical service plans
CEO: Val Dean
**Pr:* Timothy O'Donnell

D-U-N-S 62-260-5640
■ **MEDICARE PAYMENT ADVISORY COMMISSION**
MEDPAC
(*Suby of* CONGRESS UNITED STATES) ★
425 I St Nw Ste 701, Washington, DC 20001-2542
Tel (202) 220-3700 *Founded/Ownrshp* 1997
Sales 4.0MM^E *EMP* 280
SIC 8231 Libraries
CEO: Ann Johnson
Assoc Dir: Jennifer Stolbach
IT Man: Paula Crowell

MEDICINE HEALTH CENTER
See METHODIST RICHARDSON MEDICAL CENTER FOUNDATION INC

MEDICINE LODGE HOLDINGS
See IMDS HOLDINGS CORP

MEDICINE SHOP INTERNATIONAL
See MEDICAP PHARMACIES INC

D-U-N-S 04-086-1601
▲ **MEDICINES CO**
8 Sylvan Way, Parsippany, NJ 07054-3801
Tel (973) 290-6000 *Founded/Ownrshp* 1996
Sales 724.4MM *EMP* 571^E
Accts Ernst & Young Llp Metropark
Tkr Sym MDCO *Exch* NGS
SIC 2834 Pharmaceutical preparations; Intravenous solutions; Pharmaceutical preparations; Intravenous solutions
Ch Bd: Clive A Meanwell
**Pr:* Glenn P Sblendorio
Ch: Fred Eshelman
Ex VP: Jeffrey Frazier
Sr VP: William B O'Connor
Sr VP: Stephen M Rodin
VP: Jason Campagna
VP: Brian Carothers
VP: Daniel Char
VP: Barbara Dawson
VP: Makis Deliargyris
VP: Ping Gao
VP: Cees Heiman
VP: David Kallend
VP: Jeffrey Key
VP: William Knopf
VP: Alan Levy
VP: Jill Massey
VP: Mike McGuire
VP: Elaine Morten
VP: Marco Navetta
Board of Directors: William W Crouse, Robert J Hugin, John C Kelly, Armin M Kessler, Robert G Savage, Melvin K Spigelman, Elizabeth H S Wyatt

D-U-N-S 82-848-7418
MEDICIS GLOBAL SERVICES CORP
7720 N Dobson Rd, Scottsdale, AZ 85256-2740
Tel (602) 808-8800 *Founded/Ownrshp* 2002
Sales 25.9MM^E *EMP* 88^E
SIC 2834 Pharmaceutical preparations
Pr: Jonah Shacknai
**Pr:* Mark A Prygocki Sr
**CFO:* Richard D Peterson
CFO: Richard Peterson
**Ex VP:* Vincent Ippolito
VP: Doug Bakin
VP: Manuel Estrada
VP: John Schohl
VP: Karen Smith
**Exec:* Jason D Hanson
Assoc Dir: Ronald Staugaard

D-U-N-S 18-283-7492 IMP/EXP
■ **MEDICIS PHARMACEUTICAL CORP**
(*Suby of* VALEANT PHARMACEUTICALS INTERNATIONAL, INC)
700 Us Highway 202/206, Bridgewater, NJ 08807-1704
Tel (866) 246-8245 *Founded/Ownrshp* 2012
Sales 91.3MM^E *EMP* 646^E
SIC 2834 Pharmaceutical preparations; Dermatologicals; Pharmaceutical preparations; Dermatologicals
CEO: Jonah Shacknai
**COO:* Jason D Hanson
**CFO:* Richard D Peterson
**Ex VP:* Seth Rodner
**Ex VP:* Mitchell Wortzman PHD
VP: Manuel Estrada
VP: Xiaoming Lin
VP: Tim Miller
Ex Dir: Robert Curwin
Admn Mgr: Janice Kopulos
Admn Mgr: Jamie Muhlenfeld

D-U-N-S 12-770-8837
■ **MEDICITY INC**
(*Suby of* AETNA INC) ★
56 E Broadway Ste 600, Salt Lake City, UT 84111-2211
Tel (801) 322-4444 *Founded/Ownrshp* 2011
Sales 28.3MM^E *EMP* 250
SIC 7372 Business oriented computer software; Business oriented computer software
CEO: Nancy Ham
**Pr:* Brent Dover
Pr: Jeffrey Laidlaw
Pr: Jaime Pickle
**CFO:* David Urry
**Treas:* Elaine R Cofrancesco
Ofcr: Gifford B Smith MD
Ex VP: David Coyle
Sr VP: Joe Alea
Sr VP: Greg Fuller
Sr VP: Mark Hanna
Sr VP: Ashish V Shah
VP: Janice Hale
VP: William Mintz
VP: David Palkoner
VP: Andy Piccolo
Comm Man: Michelle Dinsdale

D-U-N-S 00-341-5650 IMP
MEDICO INDUSTRIES INC (PA)
1500 Highway 315 Blvd, Wilkes Barre, PA 18702-7090
Tel (570) 825-7711 *Founded/Ownrshp* 1938, 1972
Sales 72.9MM *EMP* 350
Accts Kronick Kalada Berdy & Co Cpas
SIC 3489 5211 3795 3483 3462 Artillery or artillery parts, over 30 mm.; Electrical construction materials; Tanks & tank components; Ammunition, except for small arms; Iron & steel forgings; Artillery or artillery parts, over 30 mm.; Electrical construction materials; Tanks & tank components; Ammunition, except for small arms; Iron & steel forgings
Pr: Thomas A Medico
**Treas:* Lawrence Medico

D-U-N-S 07-292-2883
MEDICO INSURANCE CO
1515 S 75th St, Omaha, NE 68124-1618
Tel (402) 391-6900 *Founded/Ownrshp* 1930
Sales NA *EMP* 120^E
SIC 6321 Accident insurance carriers; Health insurance carriers; Accident insurance carriers; Health insurance carriers
Pr: Tim Hall
**CFO:* Patricia Keairnes

D-U-N-S 07-803-8437
MEDICO LIFE INSURANCE CO
(*Suby of* MEDICO INSURANCE CO) ★
1515 S 75th St, Omaha, NE 68124-1618
Tel (402) 391-6900 *Founded/Ownrshp* 1968
Sales NA *EMP* 117
SIC 6321 6311 Accident insurance carriers; Health insurance carriers; Life insurance carriers; Accident insurance carriers; Health insurance carriers; Life insurance carriers
CEO: G W Egermayer
Treas: Evert Peacock
Sr VP: Bob Hacker
VP: Nancy Clausen
VP: Bill Jetter
Sls Dir: Amy Begley
Sls Dir: Dave Peters

D-U-N-S 05-772-9253
MEDICOMP INC
600 Atlantis Rd, Melbourne, FL 32904-2315
Tel (321) 676-0010 *Founded/Ownrshp* 2011
Sales 20.5MM^E *EMP* 78^E
SIC 3845 Cardiographs
Pr: Dan Balda
**CFO:* Kimberly Collins
Rgnl Mgr: Robert Robinson
MIS Dir: Eddie Pope
Manager: Christopher Dimare
Manager: Jules Junion
Manager: Corey Throckmorton

MEDICONE MEDICAL RESPONSE
See JCSD EMERGENCY MEDICAL GROUP INC

D-U-N-S 94-300-1271
■ **MEDICONNECT GLOBAL INC**
PASSPORTMD
(*Suby of* INSURANCE SERVICES OFFICE INC) ★
10897 S River Front Pkwy P, South Jordan, UT 84095-5624
Tel (801) 545-3700 *Founded/Ownrshp* 2012
Sales 45.5MM^E *EMP* 300
SIC 7372 Prepackaged software; Prepackaged software
Pr: Joel Portice
Ofcr: Alan Hall
Ofcr: James Sorenson
Sr VP: Bryan Christiansen
VP: Deb Behunin
VP: Adam Harrison
VP: Kevin Lentsch
VP: Scott Maratea
VP: Allred Miller
Exec: Rebecca Colley
Exec: John Pyhtila
Board of Directors: Martin Frey, Charles E Johnson, Michael Miracle, Scott S Parker

D-U-N-S 60-854-0865
MEDICOR LTD
5575 Simmons St Ste 1, North Las Vegas, NV 89031-9008
Tel (702) 932-4560 *Founded/Ownrshp* 1999
Sales 31.3MM *EMP* 410
Accts Greenberg & Company Llc Sprin
SIC 3842 Prosthetic appliances; Prosthetic appliances
Dir Risk M: Dennis Stogsdill
**COO:* Jim J McGhan
CFO: Paul R Kimmel
Ex VP: Mark Sperberg
Board of Directors: Mark E Brown, Eugene I Davis, Robert L Forbuss, Thomas Y Hartley, Samuel Clay Rogers

D-U-N-S 78-954-0478
MEDICS AMBULANCE SERVICE INC
2500 Nw 29th Mnr, Pompano Beach, FL 33069-1031
Tel (305) 687-4040 *Founded/Ownrshp* 1978
Sales 10.1MM^E *EMP* 400
SIC 4119 Ambulance service; Ambulance service
CEO: Malcolm Cohen
**Pr:* Mitchell Cohen
VP: Matt Johnson

D-U-N-S 84-037-1087
▲ **MEDIDATA SOLUTIONS INC**
350 Hudson St Fl 9, New York, NY 10014-4535
Tel (212) 918-1800 *Founded/Ownrshp* 1999
Sales 335.0MM *EMP* 1,077
Tkr Sym MDSO *Exch* NGS
SIC 7372 Prepackaged software; Application computer software; Business oriented computer software; Prepackaged software; Application computer software; Business oriented computer software
Ch Bd: Tarek A Sherif
**Pr:* Glen M De Vries
COO: Michael L Capone
CFO: Rouven Bergmann
Chf Cred: Steven I Hirschfeld
Ex VP: Michael I Otner
Ex VP: Eileen Schloss
Sr VP: Joseph Grispo
Mng Dir: Takeru Yamamoto
Genl Mgr: Marc Berger
Off Mgr: Glenda Wilder
Board of Directors: Carlos Dominguez, Neil M Kurtz, George W McCulloch, Lee A Shapiro, Robert B Taylor

D-U-N-S 36-288-6256
MEDIEVAL TIMES ENTERTAINMENT INC
(*Suby of* MEDIEVAL TIMES ENTERTAINMENT INC) ★
7662 Beach Blvd, Buena Park, CA 90620-1838
Tel (714) 523-1100 *Founded/Ownrshp* 2007
Sales 43.7MM^E *EMP* 1,864^E
SIC 7041 7996 Membership-basis organization hotels; Theme park, amusement
Pr: Kenneth H Kim

D-U-N-S 93-214-0481
MEDIEVAL TIMES ENTERTAINMENT INC
6363 N State Highway 161 # 400, Irving, TX 75038-2269
Tel (214) 596-7600 *Founded/Ownrshp* 2001
Sales 150.6MM^E *EMP* 2,000^E
SIC 8741 Restaurant management; Restaurant management
CEO: Perico Montaner
VP: Andrew Roberts
CTO: Chris Robertson
Dir IT: Larry Branch
Mktg Dir: Synthia Johnson
Sls Mgr: Tiffany Blacklock
Sls Mgr: Michael Bryant
Sls Mgr: Mayra Hurtado
Sls Mgr: Shane Rowan
Sls Mgr: Alexandra Zagorski

D-U-N-S 36-288-6009
MEDIEVAL TIMES USA INC
MEDIEVAL TMES DNNER TOURNAMENT
7662 Beach Blvd, Buena Park, CA 90620-1838
Tel (714) 521-4740 *Founded/Ownrshp* 2002
Sales 24.5MM^E *EMP* 622^E
SIC 5812 Dinner theater
CEO: Kenneth H Kim
CFO: Eric Chiusolo
**Sec:* Daniel Kim
**VP:* Kevin Ralph
Genl Mgr: Michael Martin
Genl Mgr: Lynda Washkau
S&M/VP: Celeste Lanuza
Mktg Mgr: Monica Lingle
Sls Mgr: Rachel Daniels

MEDIEVAL TIMES DNNER TOURNAMENT
See MEDIEVAL TIMES USA INC

D-U-N-S 00-228-8975 IMP
▲ **MEDIFAST INC**
3600 Crondall Ln, Owings Mills, MD 21117-2233
Tel (410) 581-8042 *Founded/Ownrshp* 1980
Sales 285.2MM *EMP* 579^E
Accts Mcgladrey Llp Baltimore Mary
Tkr Sym MED *Exch* NYS
SIC 2099 2023 8093 Food preparations; Dietary supplements, dairy & non-dairy based; Weight loss clinic, with medical staff; Food preparations; Dietary supplements, dairy & non-dairy based; Weight loss clinic, with medical staff
Ch Bd: Michael C Macdonald
Pr: Mona Ameli
Pr: Paul Intlekofer
**Pr:* Margaret Sheetz
CFO: Timothy G Robinson
Ex VP: Donald Gould
**Ex VP:* Jason L Groves
Ex VP: Brian Lloyd
Ex VP: Dominick Vietri
Ex VP: Leo Williams
VP: Linda Arterburn
VP: Herman Dunst
VP: Kenneth Kopp
VP: Alexandra Landow
VP: Richard Law
Board of Directors: Harvey C Barnum Jr, Barry B Bondroff, Kevin G Byrnes, Charles P Connolly, Catherine T Maguire, John P McDaniel, Jerry D Reece, Donald F Reilly, Carl E Sassano

D-U-N-S 02-183-0230
MEDIFAX-EDI LLC
(*Suby of* CHANGE HEALTHCARE HOLDINGS, INC.)
26 Century Blvd, Nashville, TN 37214-3685
Tel (615) 932-3226 *Founded/Ownrshp* 2010
Sales 618.9MM^E *EMP* 3,419^E
SIC 7374 7389 Data processing & preparation; Financial services

MEDIFECTA HEALTHCARE TRAINING
See INSTITUTE FOR PROFESSIONAL CARE EDUCATION LLC

D-U-N-S 06-171-9658
MEDIGAIN LLC
2800 Dallas Pkwy Ste 200, Plano, TX 75093-5994
Tel (972) 675-7350 *Founded/Ownrshp* 2011
Sales 43.6MM^E *EMP* 313^E
SIC 8741 Business management; Business management
Pr: Greg Hackney
Pr: Robert Romero
Genl Mgr: Kelly Webb
Software D: David Pierce
VP Mktg: Clint Hughes

D-U-N-S 18-592-2820
MEDIKMARK INC
(*Suby of* STRADIS HEALTHCARE) ★
3600 Bur Wood Dr, Waukegan, IL 60085-8399
Tel (847) 887-8400 *Founded/Ownrshp* 2014
Sales 21.0MM^E *EMP* 50
SIC 5047 Medical equipment & supplies; Medical equipment & supplies
Ch: David Sanders
**Pr:* James Ronk
VP Opers: Steve Aperavich
VP Sls: April Kraak

D-U-N-S 36-165-1706
MEDILODGE GROUP INC
MISSION GROUP, THE
64500 Van Dyke Rd, Washington, MI 48095-2583
Tel (586) 752-5008 *Founded/Ownrshp* 1987
Sales 55.8MM^E *EMP* 906
SIC 8399 Advocacy group; Advocacy group
Pr: Frank Wronski

D-U-N-S 07-888-0639 IMP
MEDIMA LLC
5727 Strickler Rd, Clarence, NY 14031-1372
Tel (716) 741-0400 *Founded/Ownrshp* 2008
Sales 100.0MM^E *EMP* 6
SIC 3339 3313 Silicon & chromium; Ferroalloys; Silicon & chromium; Ferroalloys

D-U-N-S 11-888-0632
MEDIMEDIA LLC
PHOENIX MARKETING GROUP
(*Suby of* MM USA HOLDINGS INC) ★
350 Starke Rd Ste 100, Carlstadt, NJ 07072-2113
Tel (973) 633-8111 *Founded/Ownrshp* 2010
Sales 17.5MM^E *EMP* 332
SIC 8732 Market analysis or research; Market analysis or research
Pr: Tom Langan
Genl Mgr: Carmen Mazzatta
QA Dir: Jessica Reese
Site Mgr: William Gecawich

D-U-N-S 96-738-4921
MEDIMMUNE BIOLOGICS INC
1 Medimmune Way, Gaithersburg, MD 20878-2204
Tel (301) 398-0000 *Founded/Ownrshp* 2011
Sales 1.4MM *EMP* 3,000
SIC 8731 Biological research; Biological research
Assoc Dir: Joyce Bovello

D-U-N-S 19-063-9906 IMP
MEDIMMUNE LLC
(*Suby of* ASTRAZENECA PLC)
1 Medimmune Way, Gaithersburg, MD 20878-2204
Tel (301) 398-1200 *Founded/Ownrshp* 2007
Sales 1.1MMM^E *EMP* 6,030
SIC 2834 Pharmaceutical preparations; Pharmaceutical preparations
Pr: Tony Zook
Owner: Jonathan Klein-Evans
Pr: Barbara White
COO: Matthew Bell
CFO: Tim Gray
CFO: Gregory S Patrick
CFO: Timothey Pearson
Ex VP: William C Bertrand Jr
Ex VP: Scott P Carmer
Ex VP: Max Donley
Ex VP: Bahija Jallal
Ex VP: Peter Kiener
Ex VP: Peter A Kiener
Ex VP: Bernardus Machielse
Ex VP: Edward T Mathers
Ex VP: Andrew D Skibo
Ex VP: Alexander Zukiwski
Sr VP: David Berman
Sr VP: Edward Bradley
Sr VP: Peter Greenleaf
Sr VP: Pamela J Lupien

D-U-N-S 80-705-3012
MEDIMMUNE LLC
(*Suby of* MEDIMMUNE LLC) ★
319 Bernardo Ave, Mountain View, CA 94043-5225
Tel (650) 919-6500 *Founded/Ownrshp* 1992
Sales 40.3MM^E *EMP* 340
SIC 2836 2834 Vaccines; Pharmaceutical preparations; Vaccines; Pharmaceutical preparations
Pr: Melvin D Booth
Assoc Dir: David Pritchett
Dir IT: Shirley Bittlingmeier

D-U-N-S 78-838-8288
MEDIMPACT HEALTHCARE SYSTEMS INC
(*Suby of* MEDIMPACT HOLDINGS INC) ★
10181 Scripps Gateway Ct, San Diego, CA 92131-5152
Tel (858) 566-2727 *Founded/Ownrshp* 1989
Sales 114.6MM^E *EMP* 650^E
SIC 8621 Medical field-related associations; Medical field-related associations
Ch Bd: Frederick Howe
CFO: David G Wheeler Jr
Sr VP: Jerry Parker
VP: Ginny Carpenter
VP: Richard Lieblich
VP: Mike Lyon
VP: Jeanine Mc Bride
VP: Louis C Tripoli
Exec: Elena Pamilar
Prac Mgr: Harvey Katzman
CIO: Greg Gehrich

D-U-N-S 96-871-5586
MEDIMPACT HOLDINGS INC
10181 Scripps Gateway Ct, San Diego, CA 92131-5152
Tel (858) 790-6646 *Founded/Ownrshp* 2010
Sales 114.6MM^E *EMP* 183^E
SIC 6799 Investors
Sr VP: Michelle Jahn
Sftwr Eng: Dianne Marchand

D-U-N-S 04-177-1528 IMP
MEDIN CORP
11 Jackson Rd, Totowa, NJ 07512-1001
Tel (973) 779-2400 *Founded/Ownrshp* 1960
Sales 23.6MM^E *EMP* 75

SIC 3841 3914 3411 Surgical & medical instruments; Surgical instruments & apparatus; Silverware & plated ware; Metal cans
Pr: Jay Schainholz
VP: Dan Wrocklage
Ql Cn Mgr: Forrest Rudnick

D-U-N-S 02-464-0567
MEDINA CENTRAL SCHOOL DISTRICT
1 Mustang Dr, Medina, NY 14103-1856
Tel (585) 798-2700 *Founded/Ownrshp* 1953
Sales 19.4MM^E *EMP* 360
Accts Raymond F Wager Cpa
SIC 8211 Public elementary & secondary schools; Public elementary & secondary schools
Pr: Nancy Snyder
Cmptr Lab: Jody Sargent
IT Man: Christine Griffin
HC Dir: Eunice Arendt

D-U-N-S 08-014-5238
MEDINA CITY SCHOOL DISTRICT
739 Weymouth Rd, Medina, OH 44256-2037
Tel (330) 725-8831 *Founded/Ownrshp* 1824
Sales 86.6MM *EMP* 755
Accts Mary Taylor Cpa-Auditor Of Sta
SIC 8211 Public elementary school; Public junior high school; Public senior high school; Public elementary school; Public junior high school; Public senior high school
**Treas:* David Chambers
Pr Dir: Amy Busby
Schl Brd P: Tom Cahalan
Teacher Pr: Jim Shields

MEDINA CONSTRUCTION
See BENS ASPHALT & MAINTENANCE CO INC

D-U-N-S 08-039-0404
MEDINA COUNTY SHELTERED INDUSTRIES INC
WINDFALL INDUSTRIES
150 Quadral Dr Ste D, Wadsworth, OH 44281-8352
Tel (330) 334-4491 *Founded/Ownrshp* 1963
Sales 2.4MM *EMP* 315
Accts Laura J Macdonald Cpa Inc
SIC 8331 Sheltered workshop; Sheltered workshop
Ex Dir: Jim Brown

D-U-N-S 07-763-8567
MEDINA ELECTRIC INC
22510 Highway 55, Hamel, MN 55340-9357
Tel (763) 478-6828 *Founded/Ownrshp* 2009
Sales 33.1MM *EMP* 186
Accts Copeland Buhl & Company Llp
SIC 1731 General electrical contractor; General electrical contractor
Pr: Wally Cisewski
CFO: Julie Fuentes

D-U-N-S 06-041-9181
MEDINA HOSPITAL
1000 E Washington St, Medina, OH 44256-2167
Tel (330) 725-1000 *Founded/Ownrshp* 1942
Sales 101.8MM *EMP* 900
SIC 8062

D-U-N-S 00-420-8583
MEDINA SUPPLY CO (OH)
(*Suby of* SCHWAB INDUSTRIES INC) ★
230 E Smith Rd, Medina, OH 44256-3616
Tel (330) 723-3681 *Founded/Ownrshp* 1974
Sales 35.6MM^E *EMP* 300
SIC 1442 3273 3281 5211 Construction sand & gravel; Ready-mixed concrete; Cut stone & stone products; Brick; Concrete & cinder block; Construction sand & gravel; Ready-mixed concrete; Cut stone & stone products; Brick; Concrete & cinder block
Pr: Jerry A Schwab
**Treas:* Mary Lynn Schwab
**VP:* David Schwab
Opers Mgr: Don Last
Plnt Mgr: David Scheck
Sls Mgr: Rich Brady

D-U-N-S 01-054-0144
MEDINA VALLEY INDEPENDENT SCHOOL DISTRICT
8449 Fm 471 S, Castroville, TX 78009-5313
Tel (830) 931-2243 *Founded/Ownrshp* 1960
Sales 28.3MM^E *EMP* 510
SIC 8211 Public elementary & secondary schools; Public elementary & secondary schools
Exec: Edward Balderas

MEDIPEDS FOOTCARE PRODUCTS
See PEDS LEGWEAR (USA) INC

D-U-N-S 18-985-1215
MEDIPLEX OF NEW JERSEY
800 River Rd, New Milford, NJ 07646-3127
Tel (201) 967-1700 *Founded/Ownrshp* 2004
Sales 20.4MM *EMP* 319
SIC 8051 Skilled nursing care facilities; Skilled nursing care facilities

MEDIQ NAT SUPPORT LOCAL SVC
See MEDIQ/PRN LIFE SUPPORT SERVICES LLC

MEDIQ USA HOLDINGS
See BYRAM HEALTHCARE CENTERS INC

D-U-N-S 13-921-3029
■ **MEDIQ/PRN LIFE SUPPORT SERVICES LLC**
MEDIQ NAT SUPPORT LOCAL SVC
(*Suby of* HILL-ROM CO INC) ★
1700 Suckle Hwy, Pennsauken, NJ 08110-1427
Tel (856) 662-3200 *Founded/Ownrshp* 2008
Sales 13.8MM^E *EMP* 900
SIC 7352 7699 Medical equipment rental; Life saving & survival equipment, non-medical: repair; Medical equipment rental; Life saving & survival equipment, non-medical: repair
CEO: Regis Farrell
**Pr:* Ernest Waaser
VP: Lynne Shapiro

D-U-N-S 08-691-1794 IMP
■ **MEDIQUE PRODUCTS**
(*Suby of* UNIFIRST CORP) ★
17080 Alico Commerce Ct # 1, Fort Myers, FL 33967-8509
Tel (239) 790-1962 *Founded/Ownrshp* 1999
Sales 24.8MM^E *EMP* 100
SIC 5122 Pharmaceuticals
Prin: John Aspinwall
**Prin:* Todd Lewis

D-U-N-S 79-430-1960 IMP
MEDISCA INC
(*Suby of* MEDISCA PHARMACEUTIQUE INC)
661 State Route 3 Unit C, Plattsburgh, NY 12901-6531
Tel (514) 333-7811 *Founded/Ownrshp* 1992
Sales 60.0MM^E *EMP* 52
SIC 5122 Pharmaceuticals
Ch Bd: Antonio Dos Santos

MEDISENSE
See ABBOTT DIABETES CARE INC

D-U-N-S 96-317-8157
MEDISYNC MIDWEST LIMITED LIABILITY CO
25 Merchant St Ste 220, Cincinnati, OH 45246-3740
Tel (513) 533-1199 *Founded/Ownrshp* 1996
Sales NA *EMP* 85
SIC 6331 8742 Fire, marine & casualty insurance; Hospital & health services consultant
Pr: Ray Kaiser
**CEO:* Robert E Matthews
**CFO:* Robert E Roettker
Sr VP: Sharon Earle
Comm Man: Terri Wellman
CIO: Ronald Rysanek
Dir IT: Roger Cass
IT Man: Mark Blackham
IT Man: Charlie Hardtke
Snr Mgr: William Ealy

MEDISYS FAMILY CARE
See MEDISYS JAMAICA HOSPITAL & MEDICAL CENTER

D-U-N-S 13-267-1970
MEDISYS HEALTH NETWORK INC
JAMAICA HOSPITAL
8900 Van Wyck Expy, Jamaica, NY 11418-2832
Tel (718) 206-6000 *Founded/Ownrshp* 1995
Sales 6.4MM *EMP* 3,000
SIC 8741 Hospital management; Hospital management
CEO: David P Rosen
**COO:* Bruce J Flanz
**CFO:* Mounir F Doss
CIO: Sami Boshut
IT Man: Patrick Rudden

D-U-N-S 10-525-4580 IMP
MEDISYS JAMAICA HOSPITAL & MEDICAL CENTER
MEDISYS FAMILY CARE
8900 Van Wyck Expy, Jamaica, NY 11418-2832
Tel (718) 206-6000 *Founded/Ownrshp* 1891
Sales 44.7MM^E *EMP* 3,000
SIC 8062 General medical & surgical hospitals; General medical & surgical hospitals
CEO: Bruce J Flanz
**Pr:* David Rosen
**COO:* William Lynch
**CFO:* Mounir F Doss

D-U-N-S 18-444-7550
MEDITAB SOFTWARE INC
333 Hegenberger Rd # 800, Oakland, CA 94621-1416
Tel (510) 632-2021 *Founded/Ownrshp* 2007
Sales 31.1MM^E *EMP* 250
SIC 7372 Prepackaged software; Prepackaged software
Pr: Mike Patel
**COO:* Kal Patel
IT Man: Feros Khan
IT Man: Bhavesh Shah
Software D: Prakash Rajput
Mktg Dir: Christine Alfano
Sls Dir: Kareem Marmosh
Manager: Ronak Kotecha

D-U-N-S 79-912-5679 IMP
MEDITCO INC
PHOENICIA SPECIALTY FOODS
12141 Westheimer Rd, Houston, TX 77077-6607
Tel (281) 558-8225 *Founded/Ownrshp* 1992
Sales 40.0MM^E *EMP* 35^E
SIC 5149 Specialty food items; Specialty food items
Pr: Zohrab Tcholakian
**VP:* Raffi Tcholakian
Exec: Robert Garcia
Genl Mgr: Moses Abayan
Genl Mgr: Ann-Marie Tcholakian

D-U-N-S 79-223-0856
MEDITECH HEALTH SERVICES INC
1650 Palma Dr Ste 101, Ventura, CA 93003-5749
Tel (800) 538-0900 *Founded/Ownrshp* 1986
Sales 9.7MM^E *EMP* 400^E
SIC 8099 7361 8082 Medical services organization; Nurses' registry; Home health care services; Medical services organization; Nurses' registry; Home health care services
Pr: Sharon J Bick
Sales Exec: Debra Dianopoli

D-U-N-S 05-667-5853
MEDITERRANEAN SHIPPING CO (USA) INC
420 5th Ave Fl 8, New York, NY 10018-2709
Tel (212) 764-8280 *Founded/Ownrshp* 1989
Sales 353.5MM^E *EMP* 1,000
SIC 4731 Agents, shipping; Agents, shipping
Ch Bd: Nicola Arena
**Sr VP:* John J Mullaney
VP: Gerald Baldwin
Rgnl Mgr: Alastair Law
Area Mgr: Graham Dalzell
Genl Mgr: Tony Manning

D-U-N-S 19-076-8908
MEDITERRANEAN SPECIALTIES LLC
(*Suby of* INTERNATIONAL MARKETING SYSTEMS LTD) ★
2 Corporate Dr, Shelton, CT 06484-6238
Tel (203) 929-2254 *Founded/Ownrshp* 2005
Sales 24.5MM *EMP* 1^E
Accts Seperack & Company Llc Norwa
SIC 5141 Food brokers; Food brokers
Pr: Thomas O'Hara
VP: Kirsten Vincent

MEDITRACT
See TRACT MANAGER INC

D-U-N-S 19-326-9789
▲ **MEDIVATION INC**
525 Market St Fl 36, San Francisco, CA 94105-2747
Tel (415) 543-3470 *Founded/Ownrshp* 2004
Sales 710.4MM *EMP* 370^E
Tkr Sym MDVN *Exch* NGM
SIC 2834 8731 Pharmaceutical preparations; Adrenal pharmaceutical preparations; Drugs acting on the gastrointestinal or genitourinary system; Biotechnical research, commercial; Pharmaceutical preparations; Adrenal pharmaceutical preparations; Drugs acting on the gastrointestinal or genitourinary system; Biotechnical research, commercial
Pr: David T Hung
CFO: Rick Bierly
Chf Mktg O: Lynn Seely
Ofcr: Joseph M Lobacki
VP: Michele D Bronson
VP: Michele Bronson
VP: Stewart Hallett
VP: Hank Mansbach
VP: Teresa Perney
VP: Andrew A Protter
VP: Dave Santos
Assoc Dir: Kyung Sin
Assoc Dir: Rob Tatum
Board of Directors: Kim D Blickenstaff, Kathryn E Falberg, C Patrick Machado, Dawn Svoronos, W Anthony Vernon, Wendy L Yarno

D-U-N-S 06-819-9363 IMP/EXP
■ **MEDIVATORS INC** (MN)
(*Suby of* CANTEL MEDICAL CORP) ★
14605 28th Ave N, Minneapolis, MN 55447-4822
Tel (763) 553-3300 *Founded/Ownrshp* 1974, 2001
Sales 114.8MM^E *EMP* 650
SIC 3841 3842 3845 3589 Surgical & medical instruments; Hemodialysis apparatus; Sterilizers, hospital & surgical; Surgical appliances & supplies; Electromedical equipment; Patient monitoring apparatus; Sewage & water treatment equipment; Surgical & medical instruments; Hemodialysis apparatus; Sterilizers, hospital & surgical; Surgical appliances & supplies; Electromedical equipment; Patient monitoring apparatus; Sewage & water treatment equipment
Pr: Jorgen Hansen
**Ex VP:* Don Byrne
**Ex VP:* Paul E Helms
Ex VP: Paul Helms
**Ex VP:* Javier Henao
Sr VP: Denise Bauer
**Sr VP:* Dennise A Baur
**Sr VP:* Kevin Finkle
Sr VP: Robert Mosher
**Sr VP:* Craig Smith
VP: Matt Conlon
VP: Joe Dawson
VP: Michael Herring
VP: Craig B Smith
**VP:* Mike Spicer
VP: Bruce Stoltzfus
Dir Lab: Howard Nelson

D-U-N-S 06-158-0341
MEDIVIEW INC
AUSTIN REGIONAL CLINIC
6937 N Interstate 35, Austin, TX 78752-3295
Tel (512) 421-4418 *Founded/Ownrshp* 1996
Sales 57.6MM *EMP* 65
Accts Ernst & Young Llp Austin Tex
SIC 8742 Hospital & health services consultant; Hospital & health services consultant
Pr: Norman Chenven MD
CIO: Dick Scroggins
IT Man: Chris Webber

D-U-N-S 17-724-0249
MEDIWARE INFORMATION SYSTEMS INC
11711 W 79th St, Lenexa, KS 66214-1497
Tel (913) 307-1000 *Founded/Ownrshp* 2012
Sales 130.6MM^E *EMP* 318^E
SIC 7372 Prepackaged software; Prepackaged software
CEO: Thomas Kelly Mann
Pr: Robert Tysall-Blay
CFO: Robert Watkins
Ex VP: Mike Crabtree
Ex VP: Robert C Weber
Sr VP: Alan Wittmer
VP: Neil Moore
VP: Paul O'Toole
VP: Ken Periera
Snr Sftwr: Attila Majoros
CIO: Phil Wang

D-U-N-S 01-522-9599 EXP
MEDIX SPECIALTY VEHICLES INC
3008 Mobile Dr, Elkhart, IN 46514-5524
Tel (574) 266-0911 *Founded/Ownrshp* 2001
Sales 37.1MM *EMP* 64
SIC 3711 Ambulances (motor vehicles), assembly of; Ambulances (motor vehicles), assembly of
Pr: Thomas Moleski
CFO: Kevin Dillard
VP: Alan McFerren
Sls Mgr: David Wood

D-U-N-S 12-248-4574
MEDIX STAFFING SOLUTIONS INC
477 E Bttrfeld Rd Ste 400, Lombard, IL 60148
Tel (866) 446-3349 *Founded/Ownrshp* 2001
Sales 36.9MM^E *EMP* 175
SIC 7361 Employment agencies
Ch: Louis Apostolou
**Pr:* Andrew Limouris
CFO: Brian Anstiss
**Ofcr:* Phil Apostolou
Dir Rx: Casey Dillon
Off Admin: Courtney Barber
Off Admin: Jessica Gordon
IT Man: Adam Wenig
Sls Mgr: Steve Barrie
Sls Mgr: Derek Chapman
Snr Mgr: Luke McGinn
Board of Directors: Eric Born

MEDLEH GROUP
See MEDRANO & LEHANE HOLDINGS INC

D-U-N-S 00-652-7196
MEDLER ELECTRIC CO (MI)
2155 Redman Dr, Alma, MI 48801-9313
Tel (989) 463-1108 *Founded/Ownrshp* 1918
Sales 44.3MM *EMP* 111
SIC 5063 Electrical apparatus & equipment; Electrical apparatus & equipment
Pr: Ronald Hiene
**VP:* Robert Mead
**VP:* David Simon
Brnch Mgr: Scott Smith
Netwrk Eng: Bill Hallman
Sales Exec: Bill Michael
VP Sls: Kelly Vliet
Sls Mgr: Dan Throop

D-U-N-S 96-327-7400
MEDLEY CAPITAL CORP
375 Park Ave Ste 3304, New York, NY 10152-3307
Tel (212) 759-0777 *Founded/Ownrshp* 2011
Sales 149.2MM *EMP* 3
Accts Ernst & Young Llp New York
Tkr Sym MCC *Exch* NYS
SIC 6726 Investment advice; Investment offices; Management investment funds, closed-end
Ch Bd: Brook Taube
CFO: Richard T Allorto Jr
Chf Cred: John D Fredericks

D-U-N-S 79-510-3340
MEDLEY COMMUNICATIONS INC
41531 Date St, Murrieta, CA 92562-7086
Tel (951) 245-5200 *Founded/Ownrshp* 1985
Sales 29.1MM^E *EMP* 180
SIC 1731 8748 Cable television installation; Communications consulting; Cable television installation; Communications consulting
Pr: Darrin Medley

D-U-N-S 07-952-3375
MEDLEY MANAGEMENT INC
375 Park Ave Fl 33, New York, NY 10152-0002
Tel (212) 759-0777 *Founded/Ownrshp* 2014
Sales 72.1MM *EMP* 70^E
Accts Mcgladrey Llp New York New Y
Tkr Sym MDLY *Exch* NYS
SIC 6726 Management investment funds, closed-end
Ch Bd: Brook T Co
**Ch Bd:* Brook Taube
**Ch Bd:* Seth Taube
**Pr:* Jeffrey Tonkel
CFO: Richard Allorto
Sr VP: Peter Burton
Sr VP: Mark Giuliani
Sr VP: Frank Wang
VP: Victor Dessis
VP: Ruwan Gunatilake
VP: Steven Henke
VP: Dale Hersey
VP: Theodore Knoop
VP: Burke Loeffler
VP: Andrew Pacini
Board of Directors: Jeffrey T Leeds, Guy Rounsaville Jr, Philip K Ryan

D-U-N-S 92-930-2388 IMP
MEDLEY MATERIAL HANDLING CO
4201 Will Rogers Pkwy, Oklahoma City, OK 73108-2083
Tel (806) 374-5345 *Founded/Ownrshp* 2012
Sales 62.1MM *EMP* 140
Accts Thom-Dobson-Womack Inc Okla
SIC 5084 7699 7353 Industrial machinery & equipment; Industrial machinery & equipment repair; Heavy construction equipment rental; Industrial machinery & equipment; Industrial machinery & equipment repair; Heavy construction equipment rental
Pr: Mark Medley
CFO: Don Keller
Exec: Mitzi Jones
Brnch Mgr: Robert McClain
Genl Mgr: Scott Davis
Genl Mgr: Cliff Peterson
IT Man: Ryan Medley
Sls Mgr: Mark Snider

D-U-N-S 02-546-0908 EXP
MEDLINE INDUSTRIES INC (IL)
1 Medline Pl, Mundelein, IL 60060-4486
Tel (847) 949-5500 *Founded/Ownrshp* 1977, 1966
Sales 7.2MMM *EMP* 12,000
SIC 3841 5047 5999 Surgical & medical instruments; Instruments, surgical & medical; Medical apparatus & supplies; Surgical & medical instruments; Instruments, surgical & medical; Medical apparatus & supplies
CEO: Charles N Mills
Pr: Dennis Devlin
Pr: Julia Downey
Pr: Pete Herbrand
**Pr:* Andrew Mills
Pr: Jeff Rubel
**COO:* Jim Abrams
CFO: Bill Abington
CFO: Michael Fineberg
**CFO:* Kristofer Howard
**Ch:* James S Mills
**Ch:* Jon M Mills
Ex VP: Zach Pocklington
Sr VP: Michael Calogero
Sr VP: Dan Johnson
Sr VP: Richard H Lee
VP: Michael Carroll
VP: Debashish Chakravarthy

VP: Larry Corrigan
VP: Paul Dudzik
VP: Ann Fahey-Widman

MEDLINE RENEWAL
See SURGICAL INSTRUMENT SERVICES AND SAVINGS INC

MEDLINK
See MEDAIRE INC

MEDLINK OF NEWYORK
See HEALTH SERVICES OF NORTHERN NEWYORK INC

D-U-N-S 19-130-4732
■ MEDLINK OF OHIO INC
(*Suby of* ALMOST FAMILY INC) ★
20600 Chagrin Blvd # 290, Cleveland, OH 44122-5327
Tel (216) 751-5900 *Founded/Ownrshp* 2002
Sales 9.6MM^{E} *EMP* 700
SIC 8049 8082 Nurses, registered & practical; Home health care services; Nurses, registered & practical; Home health care services
Pr: Stuart R Russell

D-U-N-S 06-016-1742
MEDLOCK SOUTHWEST MANAGEMENT CORP
MEDLOCK SOUTHWEST MANGEMENT
519 Main St, Lubbock, TX 79401-3524
Tel (806) 763-5323 *Founded/Ownrshp* 1986
Sales 5.3MM^{E} *EMP* 320
Accts Kenneth C Boothe & Company Pc
SIC 6513 Apartment building operators; Apartment building operators
Pr: Winfred E Medlock Jr
Treas: Juanita Lundberg
**VP:* Kay Medlock

MEDLOCK SOUTHWEST MANGEMENT
See MEDLOCK SOUTHWEST MANAGEMENT CORP

D-U-N-S 00-511-5782
MEDMARK SERVICES INC
401 E Corp Dr Ste 220, Lewisville, TX 75057
Tel (214) 379-3300 *Founded/Ownrshp* 2008
Sales 49.3MM^{E} *EMP* 339
SIC 8741 Hospital management; Hospital management
CEO: David K White
**CFO:* Daniel Gutschenritter
**CFO:* Ronald Rubin
**VP:* Frank Baumann
**VP:* Raymond Dattoli
**VP:* Robin Johnson
**VP:* Joanne Prada
Dir IT: Vin Crispino
Sls Dir: Michelle Manning
Genl Couns: Susan Meyercord

D-U-N-S 79-149-7431 EXP
▲ MEDNAX INC
1301 Concord Ter, Sunrise, FL 33323-2843
Tel (954) 384-0175 *Founded/Ownrshp* 1979
Sales 2.4MMM *EMP* 4,629^{E}
Accts Pricewaterhousecoopers Llp Ft
Tkr Sym MD *Exch* NYS
SIC 8011 Specialized medical practitioners, except internal; Pediatrician; Physical medicine, physician/surgeon; Specialized medical practitioners, except internal; Pediatrician; Physical medicine, physician/surgeon
CEO: Roger J Medel
Pr: Joseph M Calabro
CFO: Vivian Lopez-Blanco
Bd of Dir: Dany Garcia
Sr VP: Dominic J Andreano
VP: Jennifer Arriza
Exec: Karen Smith
Exec: Jonathan Woodcock
Dir Bus: Michael Ames
Dir Bus: Rosemarie Ugalde
Genl Mgr: Janet Graff
Board of Directors: Cesar L Alvarez, Waldemar A Carlo, Michael B Fernandez, Roger K Freeman, Paul G Gabos, Pascal J Goldschmidt, Manuel Kadre, Donna E Shalala, Enrique J Sosa

MEDONE RENTALS
See FREEDOM MEDICAL INC

D-U-N-S 07-941-4993
MEDORA SNACKS LLC
(*Suby of* BFY HOLDINGS I LLC)
79 Industrial Pl, Middletown, NY 10940-3608
Tel (516) 566-2300 *Founded/Ownrshp* 2015
Sales 35.0MM^{E} *EMP* 13
SIC 5145 Snack foods; Snack foods
Pr: Barry Renow

D-U-N-S 18-192-3301
MEDOSWEET FARMS INC
915 1st Ave S, Kent, WA 98032-6138
Tel (253) 852-4110 *Founded/Ownrshp* 1982
Sales 36.0MM^{E} *EMP* 60
SIC 5143 Dairy products, except dried or canned; Dairy products, except dried or canned
Pr: Cliff Flintoff
**Ch:* Clifford Flintoff
**Treas:* Carolyn Flintoff
VP: Brian Flintoff
**VP:* Craig Flintoff

MEDPAC
See MEDICARE PAYMENT ADVISORY COMMISSION

D-U-N-S 80-642-9424
MEDPACE INC
(*Suby of* CINVEN PARTNERS LLP)
5375 Medpace Way, Cincinnati, OH 45227-1543
Tel (513) 579-9911 *Founded/Ownrshp* 2014
Sales 302.1MM^{E} *EMP* 996
SIC 8731 5122 5047 Biotechnical research, commercial; Pharmaceuticals; Medical equipment & supplies; Biotechnical research, commercial; Pharmaceuticals; Medical equipment & supplies
Pr: August Troendle
COO: Kurt Brykman
COO: Kurt A Brykman
Bd of Dir: Fred Davenport
VP: Richard D Scheyer
VP: Franklin O Smith
VP: Dan Weng
Assoc Dir: Ben Bohache
Assoc Dir: Candace Bonta
Assoc Dir: Dennis Breen
Assoc Dir: Matthew Kelso
Assoc Dir: Tian-Sheng Lu
Assoc Dir: Mark Metzner
Assoc Dir: Gary Rickels
Assoc Dir: Kristin Schaefers
Dir Bus: Eric Hauser
Dir Bus: Stacie Wickliffe

D-U-N-S 83-307-0019
MEDPAK HOLDINGS INC
(*Suby of* EXCELLERE CAPITAL MANAGEMENT LLC) ★
100 Fillmore St Ste 300, Denver, CO 80206-4921
Tel (303) 765-2400 *Founded/Ownrshp* 2009
Sales 20.7MM^{E} *EMP* 280
SIC 3565 3089 Packaging machinery; Blister or bubble formed packaging, plastic; Packaging machinery; Blister or bubble formed packaging, plastic
Prin: Robert A Martin
**Prin:* Matthew C Hicks

MEDPLAS
See UNITED PLASTICS GROUP INC

D-U-N-S 82-633-9926
MEDPLAST ENGINEERED PRODUCTS INC
(*Suby of* MEDPLAST INC) ★
405 W Geneva Dr, Tempe, AZ 85282-2003
Tel (480) 968-6653 *Founded/Ownrshp* 2007
Sales 34.9MM^{E} *EMP* 85
SIC 3069 3089 Molded rubber products; Injection molded finished plastic products
Pr: Harold Faig
**CFO:* James Doerr
Dir IT: Dan Streufert

D-U-N-S 07-963-6553
MEDPLAST HOLDINGS INC
405 W Geneva Dr, Tempe, AZ 85282-2003
Tel (480) 553-6400 *Founded/Ownrshp* 2007
Sales NA *EMP* 700
SIC 6719 Investment holding companies, except banks; Investment holding companies, except banks
CEO: Harol Faig

D-U-N-S 83-312-0814
MEDPLAST INC
405 W Geneva Dr, Tempe, AZ 85282-2003
Tel (480) 553-6400 *Founded/Ownrshp* 2007
Sales 77.6MM^{E} *EMP* 86^{E}
SIC 6719 Personal holding companies, except banks
CEO: Harol Faig
CFO: James Doerr
Ex VP: Mike Farrell
Ex VP: Langton Matthew
VP: Kevin Hosmer
VP: Phil Owens
VP: Keith Starks
Prgrm Mgr: Michele Kaminski
Genl Mgr: Matt Hallead
Genl Mgr: Buddie Lusterio
Dir IT: Dan Streufert

D-U-N-S 62-221-5176
■ MEDPLUS INC
(*Suby of* QUEST DIAGNOSTICS INC) ★
4690 Parkway Dr, Mason, OH 45040-8172
Tel (513) 229-5500 *Founded/Ownrshp* 1991
Sales 35.1MM^{E} *EMP* 370
SIC 8011 Offices & clinics of medical doctors; Offices & clinics of medical doctors
Pr: Richard Mahoney
COO: Philip Present
VP: Edward Bayliss
Snr Sftwr: Subrata Chattopadhya
Snr Sftwr: Phil Jones
Snr Sftwr: Thomas Koenig
Snr Sftwr: Shiwan Li
Snr Sftwr: Brian McDonald
Snr Sftwr: Marcus Pearson
Snr Sftwr: Sunil Ramineni
Snr Sftwr: Nate Sweet

D-U-N-S 62-143-1444
MEDPOINT COMMUNICATIONS INC
MEETINGPOINT
909 Davis St Ste 500, Evanston, IL 60201-3645
Tel (847) 869-4700 *Founded/Ownrshp* 1990
Sales 21.8MM^{E} *EMP* 75
SIC 7311 Advertising agencies
CEO: William Cooney
**COO:* John Losch
**Ex VP:* Margaret Q Cooney

D-U-N-S 80-789-3441
■ MEDPRO GROUP INC
(*Suby of* COLUMBIA INSURANCE CO) ★
5814 Reed Rd, Fort Wayne, IN 46835-3568
Tel (260) 485-9622 *Founded/Ownrshp* 2005
Sales NA *EMP* 380
SIC 6351 Surety insurance; Surety insurance
CEO: Tim Kenesey
**CFO:* Joe Svitek
Treas: Anthony Bowser
**Ex VP:* Dan Landrigan
**Sr VP:* Trent Heinemeyer
Sr VP: Mark Walthour
VP: Tony Ball
VP: Jim Kunce
VP: Tim Wiggins
Exec: Jennifer Cheatham
Dir Risk M: Crystal Haarer
Dir Risk M: Crystal Schmeltz

MEDPRO STAFFING
See MANAGEMENT HEALTH SYSTEMS INC

D-U-N-S 80-435-0564
MEDPRO TECHNOLOGIES LLC
111 W 16th Ave Ste 400, Anchorage, AK 99501-6206
Tel (210) 477-2418 *Founded/Ownrshp* 2008
Sales 23.6MM *EMP* 154
SIC 8742 Hospital & health services consultant; Hospital & health services consultant
Genl Mgr: Craig Martin

D-U-N-S 01-538-5425
MEDQUEST INC
(*Suby of* MQ ASSOCIATES INC) ★
3480 Preston Ridge Rd # 600, Alpharetta, GA 30005-5462
Tel (678) 992-7200 *Founded/Ownrshp* 2002
Sales 54.2MM^{E} *EMP* 1,460
SIC 8071 X-ray laboratory, including dental; Ultrasound laboratory; X-ray laboratory, including dental; Ultrasound laboratory
CEO: Chris Winkle
COO: Dan Schaffer
COO: Michael Villa
CFO: Tod Andrews
CFO: Thomas Gentry
**Ch:* Gene Venesky
Software D: Jason Kelly
VP Opers: Alan Muir
Mktg Mgr: Therese Hendrix
Snr Mgr: Bruce Elder

D-U-N-S 12-928-1494
MEDRANO & LEHANE HOLDINGS INC
MEDLEH GROUP
4809 Westway Park Blvd # 100, Houston, TX 77041-2003
Tel (713) 986-4800 *Founded/Ownrshp* 1998
Sales 21.0MM *EMP* 300
SIC 7334 Photocopying & duplicating services; Photocopying & duplicating services
CEO: Dan Lehane
**Pr:* Michael Medrano
Snr Ntwrk: George Michalinos
Dir IT: Kyle Laughbaum
Sls Mgr: Matt Simmons

MEDRELIEF STAFFING
See ADVANCED HEALTH EDUCATION CENTER LTD

MEDRIC
See ACUMEN LLC

D-U-N-S 83-676-3375
MEDRISK INC
2701 Renaissance Blvd, King of Prussia, PA 19406-2781
Tel (610) 768-5812 *Founded/Ownrshp* 1994
Sales NA *EMP* 230^{E}
SIC 6411 Insurance agents, brokers & service; Insurance agents, brokers & service
CEO: Shelley L Boyce
**Pr:* Michael Ryan
COO: Terry Beidelman
COO: Jerry Poole
CFO: Thomas Bruno
**CFO:* Thomas Weir
Ex VP: Jamie Davis
Ex VP: Joseph McCullough
Ex VP: Roger Nelson
VP: Nancy Brennan
VP: Michael Erickson
**VP:* Ruth Estrich
VP: Patricia Lairson
**VP:* Ed McBurnie
VP: Victor Pytleski
VP: Jennifer Tronc

MEDS
See MIDWEST EMERGENCY DEPARTMENT SERVICES INC

MEDSAFE
See W JOE SHAW LTD

D-U-N-S 36-077-9040
■ MEDSERVE INC
(*Suby of* STERICYCLE INC) ★
28161 N Keith Dr, Lake Forest, IL 60045-4528
Tel (847) 367-5910 *Founded/Ownrshp* 2009
Sales 39.6MM^{E} *EMP* 200
SIC 4953 Medical waste disposal; Medical waste disposal
CEO: Roger Ramsey
**Pr:* Michael M Fields
**CFO:* Michael Mamaux
VP: Steven Fields
VP: John Warren
VP: Dan W Wesson

D-U-N-S 12-319-2507
MEDSHARE INTERNATIONAL INC
3240 Clifton Springs Rd, Decatur, GA 30034-4608
Tel (770) 323-5858 *Founded/Ownrshp* 1998
Sales 28.7MM *EMP* 32^{E}
Accts Michael Labounty & Associates
SIC 8699 Charitable organization
CEO: Meridith L Rentz
COO: Charles Redding
CFO: Edward Ryan
**Prin:* Brenda Ball
Opers Mgr: Simon Dibley
VP Mktg: Ken Rogers

D-U-N-S 80-774-0902
MEDSHORE AMBULANCE SERVICE INC
1011 Ella St, Anderson, SC 29621-4807
Tel (864) 224-4444 *Founded/Ownrshp* 1999
Sales 16.5MM^{E} *EMP* 300^{E}
SIC 4119 Ambulance service; Ambulance service
Pr: Greg L Shore
Ofcr: Scott Lefiak
**Prin:* Don McCown
**Prin:* Steve Shore

D-U-N-S 01-671-3716
MEDSOLUTIONS INC
EVICORE HEALTHCARE
730 Cool Springs Blvd # 80, Franklin, TN 37067-7289
Tel (615) 468-0600 *Founded/Ownrshp* 2014
Sales NA *EMP* 800
SIC 6324 8322 Dental insurance; Health maintenance organization (HMO), insurance only; Community center; Dental insurance; Health maintenance organization (HMO), insurance only; Community center
Pr: Curt Thorne
Pr: Joe Steele
CFO: David S Bassin
CFO: David Bassin
Chf Mktg O: Gregg Allen
Ex VP: Gregg P Allen
Ex VP: Roger Cheek
Sr VP: Tj Fjelseth
VP: David Baird
VP: Mitch Barnes
VP: Ken Cara
VP: Adam Corona
VP: Ed Ernest
VP: Norman Scarborough
Exec: Gregg P Allen

D-U-N-S 82-677-2030
MEDSORB DOMINICANA SA
CARWILD
3 State Pier Rd, New London, CT 06320-5817
Tel (860) 442-4914 *Founded/Ownrshp* 1993
Sales 62.9MM^{E} *EMP* 400
SIC 3842 Cotton & cotton applicators; Gauze, surgical; Sponges, surgical; Cotton & cotton applicators; Gauze, surgical; Sponges, surgical
Pr: Joel Wildstein
CFO: Rebecca Wildstein

MEDSOURCE
See GRIFFIN HOSPITAL INC

D-U-N-S 05-888-9606
■ MEDSOURCE TECHNOLOGIES HOLDINGS LLC
(*Suby of* ACCELLENT LLC) ★
100 Fordham Rd Bldg C, Wilmington, MA 01887-2168
Tel (978) 570-6900 *Founded/Ownrshp* 2004
Sales 54.6MM^{E} *EMP* 1,300
SIC 3841 8711 Surgical & medical instruments; Engineering services; Surgical & medical instruments; Engineering services
Ch Bd: Richard Effress
**CFO:* Joseph Caffarelli
**CFO:* William J Kullback
**VP:* Daniel Croteau
**VP:* Jim Drill
VP: Douglas Woodruff

D-U-N-S 07-170-1192
■ MEDSOURCE TECHNOLOGIES LLC
(*Suby of* MEDSOURCE TECHNOLOGIES HOLDINGS LLC) ★
100 Fordham Rd Ste 1, Wilmington, MA 01887-2154
Tel (978) 570-6900 *Founded/Ownrshp* 1970
Sales 25.8MM^{E} *EMP* 445
SIC 3841 3842 Surgical & medical instruments; Surgical appliances & supplies; Surgical & medical instruments; Surgical appliances & supplies

D-U-N-S 12-817-4427
MEDSPEED LLC
655 W Grand Ave Ste 320, Elmhurst, IL 60126-1065
Tel (630) 617-5050 *Founded/Ownrshp* 1999
Sales 78.1MM^{E} *EMP* 300
Accts Bnham Ichen & Knox Llp
SIC 4731 Transportation agents & brokers; Transportation agents & brokers
CEO: Jake Crampton
COO: Tim O'Day
CFO: Don Parker
VP: Wes Crampton
Opers Supe: Eric Butterbach
Opers Supe: Tiffany Decarlo
Opers Supe: Robert Heller

MEDSTAFF HEALTHCARE SOLUTIONS
See LOCAL STAFF LLC

D-U-N-S 10-320-5746
MEDSTAR AMBULANCE INC
705 Bradbury Ln, Sparta, IL 62286-2102
Tel (618) 443-3088 *Founded/Ownrshp* 1981
Sales 24.0MM^{E} *EMP* 200
SIC 4119 8099 Ambulance service; Medical rescue squad; Ambulance service; Medical rescue squad
Pr: Deborah Kelley
**CFO:* Charles R Kelley

D-U-N-S 19-428-5474
MEDSTAR AREA METROPOLITAN AMBULANCE AUTHORITY
AREA METRO AMBULANCE AUTH
2900 Alta Mere Dr, Fort Worth, TX 76116-4115
Tel (817) 923-3700 *Founded/Ownrshp* 1992
Sales 67.8MM^{E} *EMP* 458
SIC 8741 4119 Administrative management; Ambulance service; Administrative management; Ambulance service
Ch: Zim Zimmerman
Comm Man: Tammy Moore
IT Man: Frank Acosta
Opers Mgr: David Lamb
Board of Directors: Douglas Hooten, Joan Jordan

MEDSTAR FRANKLIN SQ MED CTR
See FRANKLIN SQUARE HOSPITAL CENTER INC

D-U-N-S 36-151-6370
MEDSTAR HEALTH INC
MEDSTAR HEALTH VNA
5565 Sterrett Pl Ste 500, Columbia, MD 21044-2679
Tel (410) 772-6500 *Founded/Ownrshp* 1987
Sales 3.2MMM^{E} *EMP* 24,100

SIC 8741 8062 8082 8051 8011 Management services; Business management; General medical & surgical hospitals; Home health care services; Skilled nursing care facilities; Offices & clinics of medical doctors; Physical medicine, physician/surgeon; Physicians' office, including specialists; Management services; Business management; General medical & surgical hospitals; Home health care services; Skilled nursing care facilities; Offices & clinics of medical doctors; Physical medicine, physician/surgeon; Physicians' office, including specialists
Pr: Kenneth A Samet
Pt: Paul B Fowler
Ch Bd: William R Roberts
Pr: Nancy Dibenedetto
Pr: Gieselle Estes
CFO: Michael J Curran
Treas: Bob Hall
V Ch Bd: William J Oetgen Jr
Bd of Dir: James G Kane
Ex VP: M Joy Drass
Ex VP: Stephen RT Evans
Ex VP: Oliver M Johnson II
Ex VP: Carl J Schindelar
Ex VP: William L Thomas
VP: Stuart Bell
VP: Barbara Bfrink
VP: Allan Birenberg
VP: Geannine Darby
VP: Steve Harner
VP: Cheryl Lunnen
VP: Kevin Mell

D-U-N-S 15-768-7161
MEDSTAR HEALTH INFUSION INC
(*Suby of* MEDSTAR HEALTH INC) ★
7379 Wa Blvd Ste 103, Elkridge, MD 21075-6358
Tel (410) 796-0305 *Founded/Ownrshp* 1996
Sales 41.1MM *EMP* 32
SIC 5047 Medical equipment & supplies; Medical equipment & supplies
Pr: Traci Anderson
**Ch:* Eric Wagner
**Treas:* Mark Meginnis
VP: Steve Harner

D-U-N-S 96-959-3842
MEDSTAR HEALTH RESEARCH INSTITUTE
108 Irving St Nw, Washington, DC 20010-3017
Tel (202) 877-3756 *Founded/Ownrshp* 2011
Sales 26.0MM *EMP* 3
Accts Kpmg Llp Washington Dc
SIC 8733 Research institute; Research institute
Pr: Neil Weissman

D-U-N-S 18-903-0067
MEDSTAR HEALTH RESEARCH INSTITUTE INC
MEDSTAR RESEARCH INSTITUTE
(*Suby of* MEDSTAR HEALTH INC) ★
6525 Belcrest Rd Ste 700, Hyattsville, MD 20782-2031
Tel (301) 560-7300 *Founded/Ownrshp* 1963
Sales 18.3MM^E^ *EMP* 408
SIC 8733 8731 8071 Medical research; Commercial physical research; Medical laboratories; Medical research; Commercial physical research; Medical laboratories
Pr: Neil J Weissman MD
VP: Robert Ratner MD
IT Man: Christina Stanger

MEDSTAR HEALTH VNA
See GOOD SAMARITAN HOSPITAL OF MD INC

MEDSTAR HEALTH VNA
See MONTGOMERY GENERAL HOSPITAL INC

MEDSTAR HEALTH VNA
See UNION MEMORIAL HOSPITAL

MEDSTAR HEALTH VNA
See MEDSTAR HEALTH INC

D-U-N-S 61-505-0291
MEDSTAR INC
(*Suby of* HENRY FORD MACOMB HOSPITAL CORP) ★
380 N Gratiot Ave, Clinton Township, MI 48036-3123
Tel (586) 468-0577 *Founded/Ownrshp* 1985
Sales 21.0MM *EMP* 200
Accts Plante & Moran Pllc Southfiel
SIC 8011 Freestanding emergency medical center; Freestanding emergency medical center
CEO: Kolby Miller

MEDSTAR RESEARCH INSTITUTE
See MEDSTAR HEALTH RESEARCH INSTITUTE INC

D-U-N-S 07-913-2662
MEDSTAR SOUTHERN MARYLAND HOSPITAL CENTER INC (MD)
44 Canal Center Plz # 325, Alexandria, VA 22314-1592
Tel (301) 868-8000 *Founded/Ownrshp* 2012
Sales 20.9MM^E^ *EMP* 115^E^
SIC 8741 Management services

MEDSTAR ST. MARY'S HOSPITAL
See ST MARYS HOSPITAL OF SAINT MARYS COUNTY INC

MEDSTAR WASHINGTON HOSP CTR
See WASHINGTON HOSPITAL CENTER CORP

D-U-N-S 01-502-6664
MEDSTAR-GEORGETOWN MEDICAL CENTER INC
GEORGETOWN UNIVERSITY HOSPITAL
(*Suby of* MEDSTAR HEALTH INC) ★
3800 Reservoir Rd Nw, Washington, DC 20007-2113
Tel (202) 444-2000 *Founded/Ownrshp* 1898
Sales 459.5MM^E^ *EMP* 4,000
SIC 8062 8221 8069 General medical & surgical hospitals; Hospital, medical school affiliated with nursing & residency; Colleges universities & professional schools; Specialty hospitals, except psychiatric; General medical & surgical hospitals; Hospital, medical school affiliated with nursing & residency; Colleges universities & professional schools; Specialty hospitals, except psychiatric
Ex Dir: Joy Drass
**CFO:* Pipper Williams
Ex VP: Michael J Curran
VP: Richard Goldberg
VP: Carol Mason
Assoc Dir: Christopher Peabody
Dir Rx: Jeffrey Cox
Adm Dir: Anthony Camel
Ex Dir: Sylvia Lesic
Nurse Mgr: Lisa Cusaac
Nurse Mgr: Debra Williams

D-U-N-S 07-931-8867
MEDSTRATUM LLC
MEDSTRATUM MEDICAL SUPPLIES
3353 Peachtree Rd Ne # 312, Atlanta, GA 30326-1063
Tel (404) 988-0058 *Founded/Ownrshp* 2014
Sales 25.0MM *EMP* 25
SIC 5047 Medical equipment & supplies; Medical equipment & supplies

MEDSTRATUM MEDICAL SUPPLIES
See MEDSTRATUM LLC

D-U-N-S 96-206-9365
MEDSYNERGIES INC
909 Hidden Rdg Ste 300, Irving, TX 75038-3801
Tel (972) 791-1224 *Founded/Ownrshp* 1996
Sales 143.3MM^E^ *EMP* 700^E^
SIC 8741 8742 8721 Management services; Hospital & health services consultant; Billing & bookkeeping service; Management services; Hospital & health services consultant; Billing & bookkeeping service
Ch Bd: Joseph Boyd
**Pr:* Frank Marshall
**CEO:* John Robert Thomas
**COO:* Ellen Mahony
**CFO:* Doug Hansen
Ofcr: Nick Bohra
Sr VP: James Dye
Sr VP: Clayton Harbeck
VP: Jules Ellis
VP: Celine Fynes
VP: David Gregorio
VP: Tracy McLellan
VP: Chris Walker
Board of Directors: Britt Berrett

D-U-N-S 14-317-8577
MEDSYNERGIES NORTH TEXAS INC
PHYSERVE PHYSICIAN SERVICES
130 Vintage Dr, Dallas, TX 75243
Tel (972) 739-3001 *Founded/Ownrshp* 2010
Sales 74.6MM^E^ *EMP* 3,300
SIC 8741 Hospital management; Hospital management
CEO: Carl Soderstrom
Pr: Clay Heighten
Pr: Frank Marshall
CEO: John Thomas
COO: Ellen Mahony
CFO: Michael A Austin
CFO: Douglas Hansen
VP: Harold Simmons
Prin: Greg Benson
Prin: Bob Gay
Prin: Dave Halbert

D-U-N-S 07-831-9981
MEDTECH GROUP INC
(*Suby of* VENTION MEDICAL INC) ★
6 Century Ln, South Plainfield, NJ 07080-1396
Tel (908) 561-0717 *Founded/Ownrshp* 1979
Sales 28.0MM^E^ *EMP* 250^E^
SIC 3841 Diagnostic apparatus, medical; Diagnostic apparatus, medical
CEO: George Blank
**VP:* Heriberto Diaz

D-U-N-S 06-027-2465 IMP
■ **MEDTECH PRODUCTS INC**
NEW SKIN
(*Suby of* PRESTIGE BRANDS HOLDINGS INC) ★
660 White Plains Rd, Tarrytown, NY 10591-5139
Tel (914) 524-6810 *Founded/Ownrshp* 2004
Sales 25.3MM^E^ *EMP* 95
SIC 2841 2834 Soap & other detergents; Pharmaceutical preparations; Soap & other detergents; Pharmaceutical preparations
Pr: Matthew Mannelly
**CFO:* Ronald M Lombardi
**Ex VP:* Timothy J Connors
**Sr VP:* Jean A Boyko PHD
**Sr VP:* John Parkinson
**VP:* Samuel C Cowley

MEDTERA
See STRUCTURAL GRAPHICS LLC

D-U-N-S 12-120-5355
■ **MEDTOX LABORATORIES INC**
(*Suby of* MEDTOX SCIENTIFIC INC) ★
402 County Road D W # 402, Saint Paul, MN 55112-3597
Tel (651) 636-2044 *Founded/Ownrshp* 1978
Sales 18.2MM^E^ *EMP* 283
Accts Deloitte & Touche Llp Minneap
SIC 8071 Testing laboratories; Urinalysis laboratory; Biological laboratory; Bacteriological laboratory; Testing laboratories; Urinalysis laboratory; Biological laboratory; Bacteriological laboratory
CEO: Floyd S Eberts III
VP: Melissa Devries
VP: Kelly Rand
VP: James A Schoonover
**Prin:* Richard Braun
Prgrm Mgr: Deanna Hanzely
QA Dir: Rich Huerta
Sales Asso: Peter Lewis

D-U-N-S 11-505-8828
■ **MEDTOX SCIENTIFIC INC**
(*Suby of* LABORATORY CORP OF AMERICA HOLDINGS) ★
402 County Road D W, Saint Paul, MN 55112-3522
Tel (651) 628-6118 *Founded/Ownrshp* 2012
Sales 25.9MM^E^ *EMP* 633^E^
SIC 8071 8734 2835 Medical laboratories; Testing laboratories; Forensic laboratory; In vitro & in vivo diagnostic substances; Microbiology & virology diagnostic products; Medical laboratories; Testing laboratories; Forensic laboratory; In vitro & in vivo diagnostic substances; Microbiology & virology diagnostic products
Pr: Richard J Braun
**Chf Mktg O:* James A Schoonover
Ofcr: Doug Swedzinski
VP: Jennifer Collins
VP: Bob Fogerson
VP: Mitchell Owens
**VP:* Susan E Puskas
Dir Lab: Cindy Myhre
Dir Lab: Nicole Osterhaus
Software D: Gregory Henderson
Opers Mgr: Barb Mayer

MEDTRNIC PWRED SRGCAL SLUTIONS
See MEDTRONIC POWERED SURGICAL SOLUTIONS

MEDTRONIC
See OSTEOTECH INC

D-U-N-S 17-759-5899
■ **MEDTRONIC ATS MEDICAL INC**
(*Suby of* MEDTRONIC INC) ★
3800 Annapolis Ln N # 175, Minneapolis, MN 55447-5444
Tel (763) 553-7736 *Founded/Ownrshp* 2010
Sales 28.3MM^E^ *EMP* 321^E^
SIC 3841 Surgical & medical instruments; Surgical & medical instruments
Pr: Michael J Coyle
**CFO:* Gary L Ellis
**VP:* Philip J Albert
VP: David R Elizondo
**VP:* Cameron Findlay
**VP:* Doug A Hoekstra
VP: W Allen Putnam

D-U-N-S 78-933-8969 IMP
■ **MEDTRONIC CARDIOVASCULAR**
(*Suby of* MEDTRONIC INC) ★
3576 Unocal Pl, Santa Rosa, CA 95403-1774
Tel (707) 545-1156 *Founded/Ownrshp* 1999
Sales 394.1MM^E^ *EMP* 5,038
SIC 3841 Surgical instruments & apparatus; Catheters; Surgical instruments & apparatus; Catheters
CEO: Omar Ishrak
Pr: Scott Ward
Ex VP: Michael J Coyle
Ex VP: Gary Ellis
Ex VP: Christopher J Oconnell
Ex VP: Katie Szyman
VP: Ross Alen
VP: David Whitescarver
Prgrm Mgr: Mislael Concepcion
Rgnl Mgr: Dianne Medina
Info Man: Elisabeth Byers

D-U-N-S 06-107-9989 IMP
■ **MEDTRONIC CARE MANAGEMENT SERVICES LLC**
CARDIOCOM, LLC
(*Suby of* MEDTRONIC INC) ★
7980 Century Blvd, Chanhassen, MN 55317-8000
Tel (888) 243-8881 *Founded/Ownrshp* 2013
Sales 47.4MM^E^ *EMP* 210
SIC 3841 Surgical & medical instruments; Surgical & medical instruments
CEO: Gary Ellis
**COO:* Mike Genau
**Treas:* Linda Harty
**Genl Mgr:* Sheri Dodd

D-U-N-S 00-626-1481 IMP
■ **MEDTRONIC INC**
(*Suby of* MEDTRONIC PUBLIC LIMITED COMPANY)
710 Medtronic Pkwy, Minneapolis, MN 55432-5604
Tel (763) 514-4000 *Founded/Ownrshp* 2015
Sales 16.1MMM^E^ *EMP* 49,000
Tkr Sym MDT *Exch* NYS
SIC 3845 3842 3841 Electromedical equipment; Pacemaker, cardiac; Surgical appliances & supplies; Implants, surgical; Surgical & medical instruments; Blood transfusion equipment; Catheters; Medical instruments & equipment, blood & bone work; Electromedical equipment; Pacemaker, cardiac; Surgical appliances & supplies; Implants, surgical; Surgical & medical instruments; Blood transfusion equipment; Catheters; Medical instruments & equipment, blood & bone work
Ch Bd: Omar Ishrak
Pr: Bob Blankemeyer
Pr: Jean-Luc Butel
Pr: Michael J Coyle
Pr: Steve La Neve
Pr: Steve Laneve
Pr: Katie Szyman
Pr: Tom Tefft
**CFO:* Gary L Ellis
Ofcr: McDonnell Suzanne
Ex VP: Chris O'Connell
Ex VP: Christopher J O'Connell
Sr VP: Steven B Kelmar
Sr VP: Richard Kuntz
Sr VP: Rick Kuntz
Sr VP: Bradley E Lerman
Sr VP: Scott Solano
Sr VP: Keith Williams
VP: Penny Hunt
VP: William V Murray
VP: Kenneth M Riff
Board of Directors: Victor J Dzau

D-U-N-S 82-862-9431
■ **MEDTRONIC INC**
(*Suby of* MEDTRONIC INC) ★
4340 Swinnea Rd, Memphis, TN 38118-6603
Tel (901) 396-3133 *Founded/Ownrshp* 2008
Sales 91.1MM^E^ *EMP* 427^E^
SIC 3845 Electromedical equipment
Pr: Micheal De Mane
Exec: David Sheldon

D-U-N-S 06-775-9258 IMP
■ **MEDTRONIC INTERVENTIONAL VASCULAR INC**
(*Suby of* MEDTRONIC INC) ★
37a Cherry Hill Dr, Danvers, MA 01923-2565
Tel (978) 777-0042 *Founded/Ownrshp* 1989
Sales 99.6MM^E^ *EMP* 750
SIC 3841 Catheters; Catheters
Prin: Mark Chartier
VP: John Mazzola
Mfg Mgr: Paula Brooks

D-U-N-S 02-252-5963
■ **MEDTRONIC LATIN AMERICA INC**
(*Suby of* MEDTRONIC INC) ★
710 Medtronic Pkwy, Minneapolis, MN 55432-5603
Tel (763) 574-4000 *Founded/Ownrshp* 1987
Sales 62.4MM^E^ *EMP* 375^E^
SIC 3845 Electromedical equipment
CEO: Omar Ishrak
V Ch: Kelly Matthew
**CEO:* Arthur D Collins Jr
COO: Ryan Ferrasci
Dir Bus: Jay Henderson
Area Mgr: Branden Florence
Area Mgr: Brady Stewart
QA Dir: Daniela Petrescu
IT Man: Diane Dixon
Ansthlgy: Christine Gahler
Pgrm Dir: Jaclyn Peterson

D-U-N-S 84-962-6338 IMP
■ **MEDTRONIC MINIMED INC**
(*Suby of* MEDTRONIC INC) ★
18000 Devonshire St, Northridge, CA 91325-1219
Tel (800) 646-4633 *Founded/Ownrshp* 2001
Sales 668.1MM^E^ *EMP* 3,500
SIC 3845 Electromedical equipment; Electromedical equipment
Pr: Catherine Szyman
CFO: Kevin Sayer
Sr VP: Kevin Wells
**VP:* Eric P Geismar
**VP:* Ron Lund
**VP:* George J Montague
VP: Nancy Synch
Exec: Kim Eberhardt
Sales Exec: Stephanie Meli
Counsel: Tae Lee
Snr Mgr: Pablo Vazquez

D-U-N-S 09-830-8849 IMP
■ **MEDTRONIC POWERED SURGICAL SOLUTIONS**
MEDTRNIC PWRED SRGCAL SLUTIONS
(*Suby of* MEDTRONIC INC) ★
4620 N Beach St, Haltom City, TX 76137-3219
Tel (817) 788-6400 *Founded/Ownrshp* 2001
Sales 47.7MM^E^ *EMP* 250
SIC 3841 Surgical & medical instruments; Surgical & medical instruments
CEO: Omar S Ishrak
**Pr:* Mark Fletcher
**Treas:* Linda S Harty
**VP:* Gary L Ellis
**VP:* Roy Galbin
**VP:* Tommy Johns
Sales Exec: Roy Galvin

D-U-N-S 00-479-5036 IMP
MEDTRONIC PUERTO RICO INC
Parque Industrial Carr Ca Que Industrial, Juncos, PR 00777
Tel (787) 561-2200 *Founded/Ownrshp* 2001
Sales 228.8MM^E^ *EMP* 2,400
SIC 3841 Surgical & medical instruments; Surgical & medical instruments
Pr: Bill Hawkins
**VP:* Manuel Santiogo

D-U-N-S 09-045-2434
■ **MEDTRONIC PUERTO RICO INC**
(*Suby of* MEDTRONIC INC) ★
3 Carr 149 Km, Villalba, PR 00766-3401
Tel (787) 847-3500 *Founded/Ownrshp* 2001
Sales 128.0MM^E^ *EMP* 1,200
Accts Price Waterhouse Llp
SIC 3841 Surgical & medical instruments; Ultrasonic medical cleaning equipment; Inhalation therapy equipment; Medical instruments & equipment, blood & bone work; Surgical & medical instruments; Ultrasonic medical cleaning equipment; Inhalation therapy equipment; Medical instruments & equipment, blood & bone work
Prin: Olga Otero

D-U-N-S 83-035-0380
■ **MEDTRONIC SOFAMOR DANEK INC**
(*Suby of* MEDTRONIC INC) ★
1800 Pyramid Pl, Memphis, TN 38132-1703
Tel (901) 396-3133 *Founded/Ownrshp* 2009
Sales 77.4MM^E^ *EMP* 262^E^
SIC 3842 Surgical appliances & supplies
Prin: Michael Demane
COO: David Miller
Exec: Cathy Martin
Prgrm Mgr: Jeffrey Dinardo
Rgnl Mgr: Wade Haskell
Area Mgr: Brent Daugherty
Area Mgr: Gregory Lande
Area Mgr: Brett Schoenfeld
Area Mgr: Jody Strauss
Mktg Dir: Bradley Thomas
Sls Mgr: Jim Courville

D-U-N-S 10-629-3954 IMP/EXP
■ **MEDTRONIC SOFAMOR DANEK USA INC**
(*Suby of* MEDTRONIC INC) ★
1800 Pyramid Pl Bldg A, Memphis, TN 38132-1703
Tel (901) 396-2695 *Founded/Ownrshp* 1999
Sales 137.8MM^E^ *EMP* 1,000
SIC 3842 Implants, surgical; Implants, surgical
Ch: Omar Ishrak
**CFO:* Gary Ellis
**Ex VP:* Michael J Coyle
**Ex VP:* Christopher J Oconnell
**Sr VP:* Katie Szyman

VP: CPA Michael Burrage
VP: Stephen Oesterle
VP: Caroline Stockdale
Off Mgr: Cathy Martin
Snr Sftwr: Andrew Bzostek

D-U-N-S 09-082-0309
■ MEDTRONIC SPINE LLC (DE)
(*Suby of* MEDTRONIC INC) ★
1221 Crossman Ave, Sunnyvale, CA 94089-1103
Tel (408) 548-6500 *Founded/Ownrshp* 2008
Sales 56.4MM^E *EMP* 1,090
SIC 3841 Surgical & medical instruments; Surgical & medical instruments
Pr: Bill Hawkins
CFO: Robert Jordheim
VP: Karen D Talmadge
Dir IT: Jon Redick
Prd Mgr: Carrie Wolf

D-U-N-S 17-001-5171 IMP
■ MEDTRONIC USA INC
(*Suby of* MEDTRONIC PUBLIC LIMITED COMPANY)
710 Medtronic Pkwy, Minneapolis, MN 55432-5604
Tel (763) 514-4000 *Founded/Ownrshp* 2015
Sales 2.5MMM^E *EMP* 40,000
SIC 3841 5047 Surgical & medical instruments; Medical & hospital equipment; Surgical & medical instruments; Medical & hospital equipment
Pr: Omar Ishrak
**CFO:* Gary Ellis
**Treas:* Linda A Harty
Sr VP: Jean L Butel
Sr VP: Janet S Fiola
Sr VP: Stephen H Mahle
Sr VP: Stephen N Oesterle
Sr VP: Scott R Ward
Sr VP: Barry W Wilson
**VP:* Keyna Skeffington
Ex Dir: Mary Maida

D-U-N-S 79-618-9157
■ MEDTRONIC VIDAMED INC
(*Suby of* MEDTRONIC INC) ★
710 Medtronic Pkwy, Minneapolis, MN 55432-5603
Tel (763) 514-4000 *Founded/Ownrshp* 2002
Sales 23.6MM^E *EMP* 300
SIC 3841 Surgical & medical instruments; Diagnostic apparatus, medical; Surgical & medical instruments; Diagnostic apparatus, medical
Pr: Thomas Teft

D-U-N-S 18-809-2456
■ MEDTRONIC WORLD HEADQUARTERS
(*Suby of* MEDTRONIC INC) ★
710 Medtronic Pkwy, Minneapolis, MN 55432-5603
Tel (763) 574-4000 *Founded/Ownrshp* 2001
Sales 221.8MM^E *EMP* 2,500
SIC 5047 Medical & hospital equipment; Medical & hospital equipment
CEO: Art Collins
VP: Penny Hunt
Prin: Michael Hegland
Software D: T Ryan

D-U-N-S 83-546-5063
■ MEDTRONIC XOMED INC
(*Suby of* MEDTRONIC INC) ★
6743 Southpoint Dr N, Jacksonville, FL 32216-6218
Tel (904) 296-9600 *Founded/Ownrshp* 1999
Sales 103.1MM^E *EMP* 1,000
SIC 3842 3841 Implants, surgical; Instruments, microsurgical: except electromedical; Implants, surgical; Instruments, microsurgical: except electromedical
Pr: Mark J Fletcher
VP: Jerry Bussell
VP: Mike Darragh
**VP:* Gary L Ellis
**VP:* Cameron Findlay
**VP:* Jaime A Frias
**VP:* Doug A Hoekstra
**VP:* Jacob M Paul
**Prin:* Bob Blankemeyer

D-U-N-S 02-160-5592
MEDTRUST LLC (TX)
6655 First Park Ten Blvd, San Antonio, TX 78213-4308
Tel (210) 496-2323 *Founded/Ownrshp* 2001
Sales 30.4MM^E *EMP* 450
Accts Kreischer Miller
SIC 7361 Employment agencies; Employment agencies
VP: Craig Hershovitz
Ex Dir: Lisa Martinez
Pr Mgr: Tammy Hester

D-U-N-S 11-414-9008 IMP
MEDURI FARMS INC
12375 Smithfield Rd, Dallas, OR 97338-9587
Tel (503) 623-0308 *Founded/Ownrshp* 1984
Sales 188.3MM^E *EMP* 500
SIC 2035 Fruits, brined; Fruits, brined
Pr: Joseph J Meduri
Genl Mgr: Dominic Meduri
Dir IT: Darryl Greth
Dir IT: Darryl Hawes
Opers Mgr: Dennis Bell
Plnt Mgr: Brad Gagner

D-U-N-S 18-583-3311
MEDUSIND SOLUTIONS INC
(*Suby of* MEDUSIND SOLUTIONS INDIA PRIVATE LIMITED)
31103 Rancho Viejo Rd, San Juan Capistrano, CA 92675-1759
Tel (949) 240-8895 *Founded/Ownrshp* 2002
Sales 43.2MM^E *EMP* 900
SIC 7389 Personal service agents, brokers & bureaus; Personal service agents, brokers & bureaus
Ch: Rajiv Sahney
**Pr:* Robert Beck
**CEO:* Vipul Bansal
**CFO:* Dhiren Kapadia
Sr VP: Jacques Kapadia
**Sr VP:* Kranti Munje

MEDVED CADILLAC
See MEDVED CHEVROLET INC

D-U-N-S 03-188-7383
MEDVED CHEVROLET INC
MEDVED CADILLAC
11001 W I 70 Frontage Rd, Wheat Ridge, CO 80033-2186
Tel (303) 421-0100 *Founded/Ownrshp* 1988
Sales 136.3MM^E *EMP* 450
SIC 5511

MEDVED-BRUTYN
See CASTLE ROCK FORD-MERCURY INC

MEDVENTURE TECHNOLOGY
See FREUDENBERG MEDICAL MIS INC

D-U-N-S 84-804-3790
MEDVET ASSOCIATES INC
MED VET ASSOCIATES
300 E Wilson Bridge Rd # 100, Worthington, OH 43085-2300
Tel (614) 846-5800 *Founded/Ownrshp* 2009
Sales 39.9MM^E *EMP* 348
SIC 0742 Veterinary services, specialties; Veterinary services, specialties
CEO: O John Kralovec
**Pr:* Eric Schertel
CFO: Denise Badgley
Treas: John Gordon
Surgeon: Karl Maritato

D-U-N-S 07-527-9638 IMP/EXP
MEDWAY PLASTICS CORP
2250 E Cherry Indus Cir, Long Beach, CA 90805-4414
Tel (562) 630-1175 *Founded/Ownrshp* 1974
Sales 45.7MM^E *EMP* 110
SIC 3089 Injection molded finished plastic products
Pr: Thomas Hutchinson Jr
**CEO:* Thomas A Hutchinson Jr
**CFO:* Mary Hutchinson
VP: Gerald Hutchinson
**VP:* Gerry Hutchinson
**VP:* Rick Hutchinson
MIS Dir: Frank Frieshman
Plnt Mgr: Jerry Hutchinson

D-U-N-S 05-972-7623
■ MEDYTOX SOLUTIONS INC
(*Suby of* RENNOVA HEALTH, INC.)
400 S Australian Ave # 855, West Palm Beach, FL 33401-5045
Tel (561) 855-1626 *Founded/Ownrshp* 2015
Sales 57.9MM *EMP* 187^E
Tkr Sym ASYI *Exch* OTO
SIC 8071 Testing laboratories; Blood analysis laboratory; Urinalysis laboratory; Testing laboratories; Blood analysis laboratory; Urinalysis laboratory
CEO: Seamus Lagan
COO: Samuel R Mitchell Jr
CFO: Jason P Adams
CFO: Jeffrey L Wadman
Chf Cred: Steven Burdelski
VP: Sharon L Hollis

D-U-N-S 82-490-0633 IMP
MEE ACCESSORIES LLC
MARK ECKO ENTERPRISES
475 10th Ave Fl 9, New York, NY 10018-9718
Tel (917) 262-1000 *Founded/Ownrshp* 1996
Sales 46.7MM^E *EMP* 350
SIC 2329 5136 5621 5611 Men's & boys' sportswear & athletic clothing; Sportswear, men's & boys'; Women's clothing stores; Men's & boys' clothing stores; Men's & boys' sportswear & athletic clothing; Sportswear, men's & boys'; Women's clothing stores; Men's & boys' clothing stores
CEO: Mark Ecko
**Pr:* Seth Gerszberg
Chf Mktg O: Jill Kronenberg
Ex VP: Kent Chapman
Ex VP: Terri Dickins
Ex VP: Gregg Donnenfeld
VP: Sarah Casalan
**VP:* Greg Lucci
Genl Mgr: Lee Bissonnette
Mktg Dir: Ruth Wood
Mktg Mgr: Ashish Mittal

D-U-N-S 16-942-9086 IMP
MEE APPAREL LLC
MARC ECKO COLLECTION
501 10th Ave Fl 7, New York, NY 10018-1117
Tel (917) 262-1000 *Founded/Ownrshp* 2000
Sales NA *EMP* 1,000
SIC 2329 Men's & boys' sportswear & athletic clothing

D-U-N-S 04-848-9140 IMP
MEE INDUSTRIES INC (CA)
16021 Adelante St, Irwindale, CA 91702-3255
Tel (626) 359-4550 *Founded/Ownrshp* 1969
Sales 21.8MM^E *EMP* 80
SIC 3585 0711 Humidifying equipment, except portable; Soil preparation services; Humidifying equipment, except portable; Soil preparation services
Pr: Darcy Sloane
**CEO:* Thomas Rupert Mee III
VP Opers: Sean Lee

D-U-N-S 00-629-2486
MEECO LLC
1600 S Kingshighway Blvd 2s, Saint Louis, MO 63110-2246
Tel (314) 773-1122 *Founded/Ownrshp* 2008
Sales 25.0MM *EMP* 17
Accts Sharamitaro & Associates Pc
SIC 3547 Finishing equipment, rolling mill
Treas: Judith Lamm

D-U-N-S 07-982-6901
MEECO SULLIVAN LLC
3 Chancellor Ln, Warwick, NY 10990-3411
Tel (800) 232-3625 *Founded/Ownrshp* 2013
Sales 22.0MM *EMP* 225
SIC 2499 4493 Floating docks, wood; Marinas
CEO: Steve Sullivan
**VP:* Dan Adams
**VP:* Bob Sullivan

D-U-N-S 02-781-8582 IMP
MEEDER EQUIPMENT CO
RANSOME MANUFACTURING
3495 S Maple Ave, Fresno, CA 93725-2494
Tel (303) 289-3101 *Founded/Ownrshp* 1986
Sales 24.0MM *EMP* 92
SIC 8711 3559 5084 3714 Engineering services; Building construction consultant; Refinery, chemical processing & similar machinery; Industrial machinery & equipment; Propane conversion equipment; Propane conversion equipment, motor vehicle; Engineering services; Building construction consultant; Refinery, chemical processing & similar machinery; Industrial machinery & equipment; Propane conversion equipment; Propane conversion equipment, motor vehicle
Pr: Jeffrey D Vertz
**Sec:* James Moe
**VP:* Wane Morgan
Brnch Mgr: Jimmy McMullen
Sales Asso: Andy Avila
Sales Asso: Joe Ezermack
Sales Asso: Dave Miller

D-U-N-S 08-561-2208
MEEHAN AUTOMOBILES INC
IMPERIAL CHEVROLET
18 Uxbridge Rd, Mendon, MA 01756-1002
Tel (508) 473-3100 *Founded/Ownrshp* 1992
Sales 33.7MM^E *EMP* 85
SIC 5511 Automobiles, new & used; Automobiles, new & used
Pr: Kevin P Meehan
Genl Mgr: Dave Fleier
Sls Mgr: Kevin Coady
Sls Mgr: Lou Frasca
Sls Mgr: Hank Landry
Sls Mgr: Jamie Waitt
Sls Mgr: Mike Walsh

D-U-N-S 94-109-3080
MEEHAN CONTRACTORS LTD
NATIONWIDE CONSTRUCTION
2151 N Holland Rd, Mansfield, TX 76063-5505
Tel (817) 473-0484 *Founded/Ownrshp* 1996
Sales 30.0MM *EMP* 30
SIC 1542 Commercial & office buildings, renovation & repair
Snr PM: Reggie Parsons

MEEK LUMBER
See WHOLESALE LUMBER AND MATERIALS CO

MEEK LUMBER & HARDWARE
See C C M CORP

D-U-N-S 10-250-2994
MEEK LUMBERYARD INC
MEEKS
1311 E Woodhurst Dr, Springfield, MO 65804-4282
Tel (417) 521-2801 *Founded/Ownrshp* 1930
Sales 84.9MM^E *EMP* 384
SIC 5211 Lumber & other building materials; Lumber & other building materials
Pr: Terry O Meek
Netwrk Eng: Art Garcia
Sales Asso: Randy Gish
Sales Asso: Greg Hicks
Sales Asso: Bryan Leonard
Sales Asso: Chuck Sommer

D-U-N-S 07-178-3971
MEEKER MEMORIAL HOSPITAL
(*Suby of* COUNTY OF MEEKER)
612 S Sibley Ave, Litchfield, MN 55355-3340
Tel (320) 693-3242 *Founded/Ownrshp* 1951
Sales 32.6MM^E *EMP* 250^E
SIC 8062 General medical & surgical hospitals; General medical & surgical hospitals
Ch Bd: Mike Hugerty
**CEO:* Kayle Rasmussen
**CFO:* Steve Plaisance
Dir Rad: Melissa Freeman
DP Dir: Deb Wilson
QA Dir: Vickie Haverkamp
Sls&Mrk Ex: Lori Rice

MEEK'S
See CHA-DOR REALTY

MEEKS
See MEEK LUMBERYARD INC

D-U-N-S 03-114-0361
MEEKS BUILDING CENTER
1311 E Woodhurst Dr, Springfield, MO 65804-4282
Tel (417) 521-2801 *Founded/Ownrshp* 1975
Sales 39.1MM^E *EMP* 201
SIC 5211 Lumber & other building materials; Lumber & other building materials
Genl Pt: Terry O Meek
**Pt:* William C Meek

MEEK'S LUMBER & HARDWARE
See WESTERN BUYERS

D-U-N-S 04-290-6110
MEEMIC INSURANCE CO
(*Suby of* ACIA) ★
1685 N Opdyke Rd, Auburn Hills, MI 48326-2656
Tel (248) 373-5700 *Founded/Ownrshp* 1998, 2009
Sales NA *EMP* 130
SIC 6331 Fire, marine & casualty insurance; Property damage insurance; Fire, marine & casualty insurance: stock; Automobile insurance
Pr: Steven D Monahan
Pr: Pat Rollman
CFO: Christine C Schmitt
VP: Michael Dreger
VP: Harold Eppley
VP: Robert Ross
VP: Judith Walczak
Brnch Mgr: Lynn Hillicoss
CIO: William P Sabados
Opers Mgr: Tammy Cischke
Mktg Dir: Stephanie Custer

D-U-N-S 79-169-9085
■ MEENAN OIL CO LP
(*Suby of* STAR GAS PARTNERS LP) ★
475 Commerce St, Hawthorne, NY 10532-1345
Tel (914) 941-8800 *Founded/Ownrshp* 2004
Sales 66.2MM^E *EMP* 600
SIC 5983 5171 7382 Fuel oil dealers; Petroleum bulk stations; Security systems services; Fuel oil dealers; Petroleum bulk stations; Security systems services
Genl Pt: Irik Sevin
Genl Mgr: Barry Radcliffe

D-U-N-S 00-638-3079 EXP
MEESE INC
MODROTO
(*Suby of* TINGUE BROWN & CO) ★
535 N Midland Ave, Saddle Brook, NJ 07663-5505
Tel (201) 796-4490 *Founded/Ownrshp* 1931, 1978
Sales 22.7MM^E *EMP* 35
SIC 3089 2394 3443 Plastic containers, except foam; Canvas & related products; Containers, shipping (bombs, etc.): metal plate; Plastic containers, except foam; Canvas & related products; Containers, shipping (bombs, etc.): metal plate
Pr: Ryan
**Ch Bd:* William J Tingue
**CFO:* John H Hurst
CFO: John Hurst
Ex VP: Patricia McIntosh
**VP:* Michael Dorsey

MEETINGPOINT
See MEDPOINT COMMUNICATIONS INC

D-U-N-S 06-174-1880
MEETINGS & INCENTIVES WORLDWIDE INC
10520 7 Mile Rd, Caledonia, WI 53108-9652
Tel (262) 835-6710 *Founded/Ownrshp* 1967
Sales 75.8MM *EMP* 170
Accts Scribnercohen & Company Milwa
SIC 4724 8742 Television film production; Magazines: publishing only, not printed on site; Travel agencies; Travel agencies; Business planning & organizing services
Pr: Jean Johnson
**CFO:* Tina Madden
**Ex VP:* Daniel W Neider
Prgrm Mgr: Anna Tiemann

D-U-N-S 00-484-8516
▲ MEETME INC
100 Union Square Dr, New Hope, PA 18938-1365
Tel (215) 862-1162 *Founded/Ownrshp* 1997
Sales 44.8MM *EMP* 121^E
Accts Mcgladrey Llp Blue Bell Pen
Tkr Sym MEET *Exch* NGS
SIC 4813 7375 ; ; Information retrieval services
CEO: Geoffrey Cook
CFO: David D Clark
Ex VP: Fred Beckley
Ex VP: Frederic Beckley
Sr VP: Sandeep Chand
VP: Brian Harvey
Dir Risk M: William Alena
Creative D: Laura Reilly
CTO: Richard Friedman
CTO: Jonah Harris
Board of Directors: John A Abbott, Jean Clifton, Ernesto Cruz, Spencer Rhodes, Jason Whitt

D-U-N-S 17-540-3075
MEGA APPRAISERS INC
14724 Ventura Blvd # 800, Sherman Oaks, CA 91403-3508
Tel (818) 246-7370 *Founded/Ownrshp* 2005
Sales 1.2MM *EMP* 600
SIC 7389 Appraisers, except real estate; Appraisers, except real estate
Pr: Levon Hairapetian

D-U-N-S 06-204-7550 EXP
■ MEGA BRANDS AMERICA INC
ROSE ART INDUSTRIES
(*Suby of* MEGA BRANDS INC)
3 Ada Ste 200, Irvine, CA 92618-2322
Tel (949) 727-9009 *Founded/Ownrshp* 2005
Sales 150.7MM^E *EMP* 1,600
SIC 3944 Blocks, toy; Blocks, toy
CEO: Marc Bertrand
**CFO:* Vic Bertrand
Off Mgr: Tina Stromstad
Netwrk Mgr: Colin Schmitt
Plnt Mgr: Steven Ferris

D-U-N-S 05-815-6100 EXP
MEGA CORP
700 Osuna Rd Ne, Albuquerque, NM 87113-1037
Tel (505) 345-2661 *Founded/Ownrshp* 1980
Sales 27.2MM^E *EMP* 102
SIC 4212

MEGA OFFICE FURNITURE
See TSRC INC*

MEGA PICK N SAVE
See DITTO II LLC

D-U-N-S 09-640-0333
MEGA RV CORP (CA)
MCMAHON'S RV SERVICE
6441 Burt Rd, Irvine, CA 92618
Tel (949) 653-6711 *Founded/Ownrshp* 2000
Sales 21.8MM^E *EMP* 75
SIC 5561 Recreational vehicle dealers
CEO: Brent McMahon
Exec: Judy Becker

D-U-N-S 17-121-8220
MEGA TECHWAY INC
46 Alpha Park, Cleveland, OH 44143-2208
Tel (440) 605-0700 *Founded/Ownrshp* 2004
Sales 74.0MM^E *EMP* 125
SIC 5065 Electronic parts & equipment; Electronic parts & equipment
Pr: Richard Sadler
**CFO:* Karl Weinfurtner

VP: Ted Fragoso
Prgrm Mgr: Jeffrey Marn
Board of Directors: Edward Weinfurtner

MEGA TOYS
See PC WOO INC

MEGA WESTERN SALES
See GREAT WESTERN SALES INC

D-U-N-S 83-044-6089
MEGACORP LOGISTICS LLC
7040 Wrightsville Ave, Wilmington, NC 28403-3683
Tel (910) 332-0820 *Founded/Ownrshp* 2009
Sales 100.0MM *EMP* 100
SIC 4731 Freight transportation arrangement
Rgnl Mgr: Brian Simpkins
Sfty Dirs: Diane Hack
Trfc Dir: Josh Gentry
Trfc Dir: April Rosenacker
Opers Mgr: Renae Meek
Opers Mgr: Jill New
Natl Sales: Brad Colvin
Natl Sales: Elissa Pinter

D-U-N-S 01-488-1445 IMP/EXP
MEGADOOR USA INC
(*Suby of* ASSA ABLOY ENTRANCE SYSTEMS IDDS AB)
611 Highway 74 S Ste 100, Peachtree City, GA 30269-3082
Tel (770) 631-2600 *Founded/Ownrshp* 1984
Sales 35.9MM^E *EMP* 38
Accts Edward Blosser
SIC 5039 Doors, sliding
Pr: Ulf Peterson
**COO:* Edward Blosser
Mng Dir: Ulf Petersson
IT Man: Michael Gheorghe
Mktg Mgr: Mary Posey

D-U-N-S 18-544-4825 IMP
MEGADYNE MEDICAL PRODUCTS INC
11506 S State St, Draper, UT 84020-9453
Tel (801) 576-9669 *Founded/Ownrshp* 1985
Sales 53.9MM *EMP* 140
SIC 3841 Surgical instruments & apparatus; Surgical instruments & apparatus
CEO: Robert Farnsworth
Pr: Paul Borgmeier
**Pr:* Matt Sansom
**CFO:* Michael Facer
VP: Tom Aramayo
VP: Dave Shimkus
Dir IT: Jeff Roberts
VP Mktg: Mike Hintze
VP Mktg: Jill Trasamar
VP Sls: Wayne Chavel
Mktg Mgr: Cameron Creek

MEGAFOODS
See CONSUMERS COOPERATIVE ASSOCIATION OF EAU CLAIRE

D-U-N-S 83-310-3208
MEGAMEX FOODS LLC
333 S Anita Dr Ste 1000, Orange, CA 92868-3318
Tel (714) 385-4500 *Founded/Ownrshp* 2009
Sales 775.7MM^E *EMP* 670^E
SIC 5141 Food brokers; Food brokers
Mng Dir: Luis Marconi
Sls Dir: Cindy Wong

D-U-N-S 07-986-0071
MEGAPATH CLOUD CO LLC
6800 Koll Center Pkwy, Pleasanton, CA 94566-7045
Tel (925) 201-2500 *Founded/Ownrshp* 2015
Sales 266.2MM^E *EMP* 300^E
SIC 4813 Data telephone communications
CEO: Donald Craig Young
CFO: Paul Milley
VP: Derek Heins

D-U-N-S 08-099-6932
■ **MEGAPATH CORP**
(*Suby of* GLOBAL TELECOM & TECHNOLOGY AMERICAS INC) ★
6800 Koll Center Pkwy # 200, Pleasanton, CA 94566-7053
Tel (925) 201-2500 *Founded/Ownrshp* 2015
Sales 170.6MM^E *EMP* 250
SIC 4813 7375 ; Information retrieval services; ; Information retrieval services
CEO: Richard Calder
COO: James Cragg
**CFO:* Paul Milley
**Co-Pr:* Kurt Hoffman
**Co-Pr:* Mark Senda
Ex VP: David McMorrow
Sr VP: Tony Capers
Sr VP: Arnaud Gautier
Sr VP: Tom Valaski
**Sr VP:* David Williams
VP: Derek Heins
VP: Matthew Hutchinson
VP: Devi Jaspal
VP: Robert McCarthy
VP: Brenda Viloria

D-U-N-S 03-054-2161
MEGAPATH GROUP INC (DE)
(*Suby of* MEGAPATH CLOUD CO LLC) ★
2510 Zanker Rd, San Jose, CA 95131-1127
Tel (408) 952-6400 *Founded/Ownrshp* 1996
Sales 235.5MM^E *EMP* 2,110^E
SIC 4813 Voice telephone communications; Data telephone communications; ; Voice telephone communications; Data telephone communications;
CEO: D Craig Young
**COO:* Brett Flinchum
COO: Catherine Hemmer
**CFO:* Jeffrey Bailey
CFO: Justin Spencer
Ofcr: Eric Weiss
Ex VP: Joseph Devich
Ex VP: John McDevitt
Ex VP: Frank C Thomas Jr
**Sr VP:* Douglas A Carlen
VP: Stephan Derodeff
VP: Jake Heinz

VP: SAE Song
VP: Ken Zerkel

D-U-N-S 13-776-0372
MEGAPATH INC
6800 Koll Center Pkwy # 200, Pleasanton, CA 94566-7053
Tel (877) 611-6342 *Founded/Ownrshp* 2000
Sales NA *EMP* 1,772
SIC 4813

MEGAPLAST NORTH AMERICA
See MOLLER GROUP NORTH AMERICA INC

D-U-N-S 04-743-5131
MEGASTAR FINANCIAL CORP
1080 Cherokee St, Denver, CO 80204-4039
Tel (303) 321-8800 *Founded/Ownrshp* 1999
Sales NA *EMP* 181
Accts Spiegel Accountancy Corp Cpa
SIC 6162 Mortgage bankers; Mortgage bankers
Pr: Anita P Fitzgerald
**CFO:* David Dell
CFO: Cheryl Lyons
**CFO:* Scott Pieper
**Sr VP:* Barbara Funke
VP: Carlene Graham
**VP:* Tracy Schneible
Brnch Mgr: Maryfrances Ahlquist

D-U-N-S 78-693-8352 IMP
MEGATOYS INC
6443 E Slauson Ave, Commerce, CA 90040-3107
Tel (323) 887-8138 *Founded/Ownrshp* 1999
Sales 28.6MM *EMP* 2
SIC 5945 Toys & games; Toys & games
Pr: Tak Kwan Woo
**Pr:* Peter Woo
Sls Mgr: Luis Cuevas

D-U-N-S 08-419-9736
MEGATRAN INDUSTRIES INC
NWL TRANSFORMERS
312 Rising Sun Rd, Bordentown, NJ 08505-9626
Tel (609) 227-4300 *Founded/Ownrshp* 1968
Sales 66.9MM^E *EMP* 300
SIC 3675 3612 3822 3625 Electronic capacitors; Power transformers, electric; Reactor transformers; Auto controls regulating residntl & coml environmt & applncs; Relays & industrial controls; Electronic capacitors; Power transformers, electric; Reactor transformers; Auto controls regulating residntl & coml environmt & applncs; Relays & industrial controls
Pr: James P Seitz
**Treas:* Edna Seitz
**Ex VP:* David Seitz
VP: Robert Guenther
**VP:* Lottie Randow
Genl Mgr: John Scannella
IT Man: Bob Kropiewnicki
IT Man: Diane Micewicz
Sfty Mgr: Gary Richardson
Plnt Mgr: Vince Scannella
Ql Cn Mgr: Philip Atherton

D-U-N-S 62-778-9803 IMP
MEGATRON INC
KTB USA
11241 Richmond Ave, Houston, TX 77082-6657
Tel (281) 558-0034 *Founded/Ownrshp* 1988
Sales 33.8MM^E *EMP* 28
SIC 5063 7694 Motor controls, starters & relays: electric; Electric motor repair
Pr: Adrian J Guzman
**VP:* Maria T Guzman

D-U-N-S 13-310-1332 IMP
MEGAWINE INC
16129 Cohasset St, Van Nuys, CA 91406-2908
Tel (818) 781-9686 *Founded/Ownrshp* 2006
Sales 33.8MM^E *EMP* 42
SIC 5182 Wine
Pr: Boris Shats

D-U-N-S 87-981-3327
MEGEN CONSTRUCTION CO INC
11130 Ashburn Rd, Cincinnati, OH 45240-3813
Tel (513) 742-9191 *Founded/Ownrshp* 1993
Sales 36.8MM *EMP* 40^E
SIC 8741 Construction management; Construction management
Pr: Evans N Nwankwo
**Treas:* Catherine Nwankwo
**VP:* Fleet P Fangman
**VP:* Frank A Regueyra
Off Mgr: Lachelle Hill
VP Opers: Benjamin Nwankwo
Sfty Mgr: Charles Wilder
Opers Mgr: Chukwuma Ekwueme
Mktg Mgr: Kate Walls
Snr PM: John Fitzgerald

MEGGER
See AVO MULTI-AMP CORP

D-U-N-S 86-864-1705 IMP
MEGGITT (NORTH HOLLYWOOD) INC
MEGGITT CONTROL SYSTEM
(*Suby of* MEGGITT PLC)
12838 Saticoy St, North Hollywood, CA 91605-3505
Tel (818) 765-8160 *Founded/Ownrshp* 2006
Sales 81.8MM^E *EMP* 300
SIC 3491 Industrial valves; Industrial valves
CEO: James Simpkins
CFO: Jim Simpkins
Prgrm Mgr: Kim Cockbill
Genl Mgr: Amy Merkley
Dir IT: Derek Aitken
IT Man: Mary Rustia
Mfg Dir: Tom Houghtalin
Sfty Dirs: Eduardo Armendariz
Ql Cn Mgr: Son Le
Ql Cn Mgr: Clyde Ransom
Mktg Mgr: Jen Larsen

D-U-N-S 78-778-6912 IMP
MEGGITT (ORANGE COUNTY) INC
MEGGITT SENSING SYSTEMS
(*Suby of* MEGGITT PLC)
14600 Myford Rd, Irvine, CA 92606-1005
Tel (949) 493-8181 *Founded/Ownrshp* 2006
Sales 59.0MM^E *EMP* 260^E
SIC 3829 Vibration meters, analyzers & calibrators; Vibration meters, analyzers & calibrators
Pr: Mel Hilderbrand
CEO: Stuart Parker
Treas: Veronica Reyes
Snr Sftwr: Zachary Tan
QA Dir: Rose Smith
IT Man: Leticia Johnson
QC Dir: Gil Gonzalez
Manager: Wendy Becker
Manager: Brooke Bunzmann
Manager: Maryann Villanueva
Snr PM: Todd Hilken

D-U-N-S 60-102-0951 IMP
MEGGITT (ROCKMART) INC
MEGGITT POLYMERS & COMPOSITES
(*Suby of* MEGGITT PLC)
669 Goodyear Ave, Rockmart, GA 30153-2554
Tel (770) 684-7855 *Founded/Ownrshp* 2013
Sales 150.0MM *EMP* 975
SIC 3728 Fuel tanks, aircraft; Fuel tanks, aircraft
Pr: David Horner
**Sr VP:* Tom Litttle
VP: Velma Brooks
VP: John Mlinchek
VP: Arsenault Richard
**VP:* Ann Theis
VP: Greg Williams
VP Mktg: Terry Lindsey
Sls Dir: Marie Getker

D-U-N-S 36-194-1875 IMP
MEGGITT AIRCRAFT BRAKING SYSTEMS CORP
MABSC
(*Suby of* MEGGITT PLC)
1204 Massillon Rd, Akron, OH 44306-4188
Tel (330) 796-4400 *Founded/Ownrshp* 2013
Sales 500.0MM^E *EMP* 1,100
SIC 3728 Brakes, aircraft; Wheels, aircraft; Brakes, aircraft; Wheels, aircraft
Pr: Luke Duardogan
CFO: Mark Taylor
Treas: Edward Clear
VP: Gary Rimburger
Genl Mgr: Joseph McCutcheon
QA Dir: Todd Figard
QA Dir: Kurt Kuenzig
Dir IT: Ron Angelo
IT Man: Dave Allison
IT Man: Paul Brown
IT Man: Jeremy Gallagher

MEGGITT ARCFT BRAKING SYSTEMS
See NASCO AIRCRAFT BRAKE INC

MEGGITT CONTROL SYSTEM
See MEGGITT (NORTH HOLLYWOOD) INC

MEGGITT CONTROL SYSTEMS
See MEGGITT SAFETY SYSTEMS INC

D-U-N-S 00-735-4751
MEGGITT DEFENSE SYSTEMS INC
(*Suby of* MEGGITT PLC)
9801 Muirlands Blvd, Irvine, CA 92618-2521
Tel (949) 465-7700 *Founded/Ownrshp* 1998
Sales 68.3MM^E *EMP* 220
SIC 3728 Military aircraft equipment & armament; Military aircraft equipment & armament
Pr: Roger Brum
**CFO:* Greg Brostek
CFO: Jeff Murphy
Ofcr: Ryan Yamazaki
Dir Bus: Rob Couture
Prgrm Mgr: Wes Fenton
Snr Sftwr: Warren Emens
IT Man: Christine Gunning
VP Opers: Eric Jensen
Mktg Mgr: Gerald Zerfas

MEGGITT POLYMERS & COMPOSITES
See MEGGITT (ROCKMART) INC

D-U-N-S 10-832-8621 IMP
MEGGITT SAFETY SYSTEMS INC
MEGGITT CONTROL SYSTEMS
(*Suby of* MEGGITT PLC)
1785 Voyager Ave Ste 100, Simi Valley, CA 93063-3365
Tel (805) 584-4100 *Founded/Ownrshp* 2006
Sales 119.0MM^E *EMP* 500
SIC 3699 3724 3728 Betatrons; Exhaust systems, aircraft; Engine heaters, aircraft; Aircraft parts & equipment; Betatrons; Exhaust systems, aircraft; Engine heaters, aircraft; Aircraft parts & equipment
Pr: Dennis Hutton
Pr: Diane Bird
Treas: Jim Tarter
Ofcr: Cherril Glazer
Sr VP: Brian Bondarenko
Sr VP: Ken Thrasher
VP: Alistair Burns
VP: Douglas Calder
VP: Lisa Lawhorn
**VP:* Dolores Watai
VP: Dave Wilson
Exec: Roselle Rios

MEGGITT SENSING SYSTEMS
See MARYLAND MEGGITT INC

MEGGITT SENSING SYSTEMS
See MEGGITT (ORANGE COUNTY) INC

D-U-N-S 00-765-5863 IMP
MEGGITT TRAINING SYSTEMS INC
(*Suby of* MEGGITT-USA INC) ★
296 Brogdon Rd, Suwanee, GA 30024-8615
Tel (612) 379-2000 *Founded/Ownrshp* 1996
Sales 97.9MM^E *EMP* 354
SIC 3699 Electronic training devices; Electronic training devices
CEO: Ronald Vadas
**CFO:* Jeff Murphy
Ofcr: Darren Shavers
VP: Richard Lewis
VP Bus Dev: Kevin Dietrick
Prgrm Mgr: Sousan Bakhtari
Prgrm Mgr: Dave Bell
Prgrm Mgr: Mike Demario
Prgrm Mgr: Monica England
Prgrm Mgr: John Madigan
Prgrm Mgr: Andrew Puleo

D-U-N-S 17-814-6171 IMP
MEGGITT-USA INC
(*Suby of* MEGGITT PLC)
1955 Surveyor Ave, Simi Valley, CA 93063-3369
Tel (805) 526-5700 *Founded/Ownrshp* 2005
Sales 313.8MM^E *EMP* 700^E
SIC 3728 3829 3679 Aircraft parts & equipment; Vibration meters, analyzers & calibrators; Electronic switches; Aircraft parts & equipment; Vibration meters, analyzers & calibrators; Electronic switches
Pr: Eric Lardiere
Pr: Peter Stammers
CFO: Andy Crowe
**Treas:* Robert W Soukup
Sr VP: Richard Hayden
Sr VP: Phyllis Pearce
VP: Robert Graham
Mng Dir: Stephen Salt
Prgrm Mgr: Chris Fitzsimmons
QA Dir: Art Quintana
Dir IT: Craig Feldman
Board of Directors: Michael A Stacey, Terry Twigger

D-U-N-S 14-846-6365 IMP/EXP
MEGLOBAL AMERICAS INC
(*Suby of* MEGLOBAL B.V.)
3320 Ridgecrest Dr # 100, Midland, MI 48642-5864
Tel (989) 636-5393 *Founded/Ownrshp* 2004
Sales 595.0MM *EMP* 16
SIC 5169 Industrial chemicals

D-U-N-S 17-683-8084 IMP
■ **MEGTEC SYSTEMS INC**
(*Suby of* B&W BABCOCK & WILCOX) ★
830 Prosper St, De Pere, WI 54115-3104
Tel (920) 336-5715 *Founded/Ownrshp* 2014
Sales 217.8MM^E *EMP* 800
SIC 3822 3555 3567 3823 Auto controls regulating residntl & coml environmt & applncs; Printing trades machinery; Driers & redriers, industrial process; Thermal conductivity instruments, industrial process type; Auto controls regulating residntl & coml environmt & applncs; Printing trades machinery; Driers & redriers, industrial process; Thermal conductivity instruments, industrial process type
Pr: Mohit Uberoi
**CFO:* Greg Linn
**Treas:* James P Langelotti
Sr VP: Ken Zak
VP: Harald Bauer
VP: Eytan Benhamou
VP: Doug Carey
VP: Pat Collins
VP: Gerald Norz
VP: Jeff Quass
VP: Rodney Schwartz
VP: William Smith

D-U-N-S 00-851-4036 IMP
■ **MEGUIARS INC**
BRILLIANT SOLUTIONS
(*Suby of* 3M CO) ★
17991 Mitchell S, Irvine, CA 92614-6015
Tel (949) 752-8000 *Founded/Ownrshp* 2008
Sales 58.5MM^E *EMP* 225
SIC 2842 Cleaning or polishing preparations; Automobile polish; Furniture polish or wax; Cleaning or polishing preparations; Automobile polish; Furniture polish or wax
Pr: Barry J Meguiar
**Ch Bd:* Michael W Meguiar
VP: Darrell F Askey
VP: Michael Crawford
VP: John Dillon
VP: Richard Koeth
Area Mgr: Stephanie Deanda
Area Mgr: Carmen Jones
Software D: Jack Sokol
Ql Cn Mgr: Jeff Hagen
Ql Cn Mgr: Tom Macdonald

D-U-N-S 00-152-6854 IMP
MEHADRIN DAIRY CORP (NY)
MEHADRIN ICE CREAM
100 Trumbull St, Elizabethport, NJ 07206-2105
Tel (718) 456-9494 *Founded/Ownrshp* 1952
Sales 29.7MM^E *EMP* 50
SIC 5143 Dairy products, except dried or canned; Ice cream & ices
Ch Bd: Samuel Farkas
**Pr:* Sam Leifer
**Treas:* Daniel W Einberger

MEHADRIN ICE CREAM
See MEHADRIN DAIRY CORP

D-U-N-S 04-143-8185
MEHARRY MEDICAL COLLEGE
1005 Dr Db Todd Jr Blvd, Nashville, TN 37208-3501
Tel (615) 327-6111 *Founded/Ownrshp* 1876
Sales 149.0MM *EMP* 1,100
Accts Crosslin & Associates Pc Nas
SIC 8221 Colleges universities & professional schools; Colleges universities & professional schools
CEO: A Cherrie Epps
**Pr:* Wayne J Riley
Assoc VP: Jacqueline Gardner
**Ex VP:* Frank S Royal Jr
**Sr VP:* Lamel Bandy-Neal
Sr VP: Saletta Holloway
Sr VP: Barbara Johnson
Sr VP: Charles Mouton
VP: Karen Berson
Prgrm Mgr: Angela Brown
Off Mgr: Keadra Babb

D-U-N-S 00-319-7340 IMP/EXP
MEHERRIN AGRICULTURAL & CHEMICAL CO (NC)
HAMPTON FARMS
413 Main St, Severn, NC 27877
Tel (252) 585-1744 *Founded/Ownrshp* 1958
Sales 377.6MM^E *EMP* 1,000
Accts Dixon Hughes Pllc Greensboro
SIC 5159 5191 5145 Peanuts (bulk), unroasted; Chemicals, agricultural; Nuts, salted or roasted; Peanuts (bulk), unroasted; Chemicals, agricultural; Nuts, salted or roasted
Pr: G Dallas Barnes Jr
**CFO:* Jeff Vinson
**Treas:* George M Davis III
**VP:* William E McKeown
Sfty Dirs: Don Rosie
Board of Directors: G Barnes, Guy Fisher, Elbert Long

D-U-N-S 05-445-6574
MEHERRIN LEASING INC
(*Suby of* MITCHELL INC GRAYSON) ★
2462 Sussex Dr, Emporia, VA 23847-6312
Tel (434) 634-3212 *Founded/Ownrshp* 1988
Sales 37.2MM *EMP* 4
SIC 6719 Investment holding companies, except banks; Investment holding companies, except banks
Pr: Grayson H Mitchell Jr
**Sec:* Loretta H Mitchell
**VP:* Raymond Bricker

D-U-N-S 01-302-4963
MEHL ELECTRIC CO INC
74 S Main St, Pearl River, NY 10965-2492
Tel (845) 735-4004 *Founded/Ownrshp* 1983
Sales 60.7MM^E *EMP* 400
SIC 1731 Electrical work; Electrical work
Ch Bd: Robert Bocchino
**Pr:* Robert Williamson
VP: Carmin Goldsack
**VP:* Ernie Pierguidi

D-U-N-S 78-357-5749
MEHLING & ASSOCIATES INC
AT HOME HEALTH CARE
9846 Hwy 31 E, Tyler, TX 75705-2329
Tel (903) 592-8001 *Founded/Ownrshp* 1986
Sales 21.8MM^E *EMP* 450
SIC 8082 Home health care services; Home health care services
Pr: Douglas R Mehling
VP: Beverly Bowman
VP: Julie McCown
VP: Lindsay Sneed
Dir IT: Joseph Goucher
IT Man: James Conlee
Mktg Dir: Lynn Ruben
Sls Dir: Michelle Maiorka

D-U-N-S 07-990-9925
MEHLVILLE R-IX SCHOOL DISTRICT
3120 Lemay Ferry Rd, Saint Louis, MO 63125-4416
Tel (314) 892-5000 *Founded/Ownrshp* 1951
Sales 102.7MM *EMP* 1,100
Accts Daniel Jones & Associates Pc
SIC 8211 Public elementary & secondary schools; School board; Public elementary & secondary schools; School board
Schl Brd P: Ron Fedorchak

MEI
See MINNESOTA ELEVATOR INC

MEI
See MIDWEST ELASTOMERS INC

D-U-N-S 03-373-7107 IMP
MEI CORP
1132 Dividend Ct, Peachtree City, GA 30269-1926
Tel (770) 631-9394 *Founded/Ownrshp* 1967
Sales 20.4MM^E *EMP* 22
SIC 5013 Truck parts & accessories
Pr: David W Pitts
**VP:* Charles H Pitts III
Dir Bus: Tod Ellison
Sls Dir: Jerry McKown
Manager: Rick May
Sls Mgr: Tim Tolin
Sales Asso: Mike Murdock

D-U-N-S 19-051-7974
MEI ELECTRICAL INC
(*Suby of* YATES COMPANIES INC) ★
11725 Industriplex Blvd # 5, Baton Rouge, LA 70809-5190
Tel (225) 751-3730 *Founded/Ownrshp* 2000
Sales 30.7MM *EMP* 300
SIC 1731 Electrical work; Electrical work
Pr: James Parker
CFO: Brandon Dunn
**Sec:* Alinda Goss
**VP:* Ed Dodd

MEI ENGINEERING CONTRACTORS
See MASTER EXCAVATORS INC

MEI GROUP
See MOORE EXCAVATION INC

D-U-N-S 06-878-2700
MEI HOTELS INC
1375 E 9th St Ste 2800, Cleveland, OH 44114-1795
Tel (216) 589-0441 *Founded/Ownrshp* 1998
Sales 22.5MM^E *EMP* 250
SIC 8741 6512 Hotel or motel management; Commercial & industrial building operation; Hotel or motel management; Commercial & industrial building operation
CEO: David Moyar
CFO: Dale Pelletier
**Ch:* Bert Moyar

MEI LABELS
See MARTIN THOMAS ENTERPRISES INC

D-U-N-S 00-281-1607 IMP/EXP
MEI LLC (OR)
MEI RIGGING & CRATING
3838 Western Way Ne, Albany, OR 97321-7421
Tel (541) 917-3626 *Founded/Ownrshp* 1990, 1998
Sales 36.6MM *EMP* 185
Accts Perkins & Company Pc Portland
SIC 3559 3599 Semiconductor manufacturing machinery; Machine & other job shop work; Semiconductor manufacturing machinery; Machine & other job shop work
CFO: Seth Christensen
Genl Mgr: Jack Lumus
Sftwr Eng: Roger Smith
VP Opers: Jim Mueller
Manager: Jay Rice
Sls Mgr: Jim Simer
Snr PM: Randy Brooks

MEI RIGGING & CRATING
See MEI LLC

D-U-N-S 85-914-5658
MEI TECHNOLOGIES INC
18050 Saturn Ln Ste 300, Houston, TX 77058-4502
Tel (281) 283-6200 *Founded/Ownrshp* 1992
Sales 97.4MM *EMP* 721^E
Accts Whitley Penn Llp Houston Tex
SIC 8711 8733 Engineering services; Physical research, noncommercial; Engineering services; Physical research, noncommercial
CEO: Ed Muniz
**CEO:* David Cazes
**COO:* Alfred Sam Boyd
**CFO:* Karen Todd
VP: Kamran Mortezavi
VP: Mir Mortezavi
**VP:* Alicia Muniz
**VP:* Stephanie Murphy
VP: Michael Vanchau
Exec: Sherry Stewart
Dir Lab: Nathan Jarmon
Dir Lab: Nolandd Talley
Dir Bus: Bob Swanson

D-U-N-S 96-831-0412
MEI-GSR HOLDINGS LLC
GRAND SIERRA RESORT AND CASINO
2500 2nd St, Reno, NV 89595-1200
Tel (775) 789-2000 *Founded/Ownrshp* 2010
Sales 59.6MM^E *EMP* 1,500
SIC 7011 Casino hotel; Casino hotel
Pr: Bryan Edwards
VP: Allan Su
Genl Mgr: Tracy Mimno
VP Sls: Jessica Baran

D-U-N-S 10-658-6514 IMP
MEIER BROS TIRE SUPPLY INC
2649 N 900 E Rd, Ashkum, IL 60911
Tel (815) 698-2122 *Founded/Ownrshp* 1983
Sales 20.1MM *EMP* 34
SIC 5014 Tires & tubes; Automobile tires & tubes; Truck tires & tubes; Tires & tubes; Automobile tires & tubes; Truck tires & tubes
Pr: Darwin Meier
**Treas:* Dennis Meier
**VP:* Wayne Meier

D-U-N-S 02-492-7196
MEIER OIL SERVICE INC
405 N Second St, Ashkum, IL 60911-6033
Tel (815) 698-2343 *Founded/Ownrshp* 1947
Sales 139.7MM *EMP* 30
SIC 5171 5172 Petroleum bulk stations; Petroleum products; Petroleum bulk stations; Petroleum products
Pr: Michael Meier
**Sec:* Troy Meier
Genl Mgr: Dan Tonton
Off Mgr: Larry Bretvelt

D-U-N-S 00-225-1478
MEIER SUPPLY CO INC
JOHNSON CONTROLS
275 Broome Corporate Pkwy, Conklin, NY 13748-1511
Tel (607) 797-7700 *Founded/Ownrshp* 1957
Sales 89.1MM^E *EMP* 135
SIC 5075 5078 Air conditioning & ventilation equipment & supplies; Refrigeration equipment & supplies; Air conditioning & ventilation equipment & supplies; Refrigeration equipment & supplies
CEO: Frank A Meier Jr
**VP:* Micheal Meier
Brnch Mgr: Dennis Boback
Brnch Mgr: Lee Varrenti
Sales Asso: Ed Wisniewski

MEIGS COUNTY COURTHOUSE
See COUNTY OF MEIGS

D-U-N-S 07-503-6491
MEIGS LOCAL SCHOOL DISTRICT
41765 Pomeroy Pike, Pomeroy, OH 45769-9411
Tel (740) 992-5650 *Founded/Ownrshp* 1966
Sales 17.8MM^E *EMP* 300
Accts Caudill & Associates Cpa Por
SIC 8211 Public combined elementary & secondary school; School board; Public combined elementary & secondary school; School board
Ex Dir: Paul McElroy
Schl Brd P: Larry Tucker

D-U-N-S 15-192-8884 IMP
MEIJER COMPANIES LTD
2929 Walker Ave Nw, Grand Rapids, MI 49544-9428
Tel (616) 453-6711 *Founded/Ownrshp* 1987
Sales 14.3MMM^E *EMP* 65,000
Accts Ernst & Young Llp
SIC 5311 5411 5912 Department stores, discount; Supermarkets, chain; Drug stores; Department stores, discount; Supermarkets, chain; Drug stores
V Ch Bd: Mark A Murray
Ch Bd: Douglas Meijer
Ch Bd: Hank Meijer
Pr: J K Symancyk
CFO: Dan Webb
Sr VP: Janet Kelley
CTO: Daniel Johnson

D-U-N-S 11-831-0700 IMP
MEIJER DISTRIBUTION INC
(*Suby of* MEIJER INC) ★
2929 Walker Ave Nw, Grand Rapids, MI 49544-9428
Tel (616) 453-6711 *Founded/Ownrshp* 1999
Sales NA *EMP* 500
SIC 5141 Groceries, general line; Groceries, general line
CEO: Hank Meijer
**Pr:* Mark A Murray
**Co-Ch Bd:* Douglas Meijer
**Treas:* Daniel E Webb
Sr VP: Jim Postma
**VP:* Janet Emerson
**VP:* Rick Keyes
VP: Tim Lesneski
VP: Nat Love
VP: Michael Major
VP: Tom McCall
VP: Karen Mellema
VP: Tom Nakfoor

D-U-N-S 00-695-9555 IMP
MEIJER INC (MI)
(*Suby of* MEIJER COMPANIES LTD) ★
2929 Walker Ave Nw, Grand Rapids, MI 49544-9428
Tel (616) 453-6711 *Founded/Ownrshp* 1934
Sales 14.3MMM *EMP* 65,000
Accts Ernst & Young Llp
SIC 5311 5411 Department stores, discount; Supermarkets, chain; Department stores, discount; Supermarkets, chain
Co-Ch Bd: Hank Meijer
**Pr:* Rick Keyes
Pr: Dave Perron
COO: Fred Silva
COO: Rose Zornes
CFO: James V Walsh
**CFO:* Dan Webb
**Co-Ch Bd:* Douglas Meijer
Bd of Dir: Pamela Carter
Bd of Dir: Barrie Loeks
Ex VP: William S Noakes
Ex VP: Robert Riley
Sr VP: Bob Jager
**Sr VP:* Janet Kelley
Sr VP: Bill Stewart
VP: Jay Bayley
VP: Dave Clark
VP: Richard Dubnick
VP: Tim Lesneski
VP: Tom Nakfoor
VP: Joann Ogee

D-U-N-S 60-617-0116 IMP
MEIJI CORP
(*Suby of* MEIJI ELECTRIC INDUSTRIES CO.,LTD.)
150 E Pierce Rd Ste 550, Itasca, IL 60143-1232
Tel (847) 364-9333 *Founded/Ownrshp* 1987
Sales 50.0MM *EMP* 61
SIC 5063 Electrical apparatus & equipment
Pr: Hiroki Sugiwaki
**Ch:* Masahiro Hayashi
Sales Asso: Emanuel Escalante
Sales Asso: Oscar Gabino
Sales Asso: Tammi Gansert
Sales Asso: Jennifer Uchisawa

D-U-N-S 07-190-1805
MEIKO AMERICA INC
MEIKO INTERNATIONAL AIR SVC
(*Suby of* MEIKO TRANS CO., LTD.)
19600 Magellan Dr, Torrance, CA 90502-1103
Tel (310) 483-7400 *Founded/Ownrshp* 1973
Sales 44.7MM *EMP* 155
Accts Nagano Morita Llp Los Angeles
SIC 4731 4225 4212 Shipping documents preparation; Customhouse brokers; General warehousing; Local trucking, without storage; Shipping documents preparation; Customhouse brokers; General warehousing; Local trucking, without storage
Pr: Hisashi Kanamori
**Pr:* Kazuyoshi Ito
Ofcr: Junco Clark
Ex VP: Ken Fukusumi
**VP:* Yotaro Hirai
Brnch Mgr: Ryohei Kageyama
Brnch Mgr: Yusuke Kokubo
Brnch Mgr: Tom Miura
Brnch Mgr: Toshiyasu Miwa
Genl Mgr: Mary Novak
IT Man: Ken Leung

MEIKO INTERNATIONAL AIR SVC
See MEIKO AMERICA INC

MEILLAND STAR ROSES
See CP MEILLAND LLC

MEINEKE DISCOUNT MUFFLERS
See DRIVEN BRANDS INC

MEISNER DATACOM
See MEISNER ELECTRIC INC OF FLORIDA

D-U-N-S 14-778-2668
MEISNER ELECTRIC INC OF FLORIDA
MEISNER DATACOM
220 Ne 1st St, Delray Beach, FL 33444-3710
Tel (561) 278-8362 *Founded/Ownrshp* 1983
Sales 92.1MM^E *EMP* 345
SIC 1731 General electrical contractor; General electrical contractor
Pr: Tim Onnen
**COO:* Todd Gurne
**CFO:* Douglas Hutchison
**Ex VP:* Kirsten Stanley
**VP:* William Kale

D-U-N-S 13-826-1347
MEISTER SUPPLY CO
M S C
5714 Rittiman Plz, San Antonio, TX 78218-5229
Tel (210) 930-6700 *Founded/Ownrshp* 2003
Sales 20.3MM^E *EMP* 11^E
SIC 5063 Electrical apparatus & equipment
**VP:* Judy Meister
Sales Asso: Jose Hernandez
Sales Asso: Susie Schatz

D-U-N-S 93-353-1725
MEITEC INC
2800 Vetrns Meml Blvd # 260, Metairie, LA 70002-6178
Tel (504) 455-2600 *Founded/Ownrshp* 1995
Sales 29.5MM^E *EMP* 150
SIC 1731 Electrical work; Electrical work
Pr: Ross V Bubrig
VP: Mary Gaudet
**VP:* Thomas E Isbell III
**VP:* Ben Seale
**VP:* Gary Williams
Snr Mgr: Robert Buse

D-U-N-S 00-322-0378
MEIYU AUTOMATION CORP (PA)
(*Suby of* MEIYU-GIKEN CO.,LTD.)
4940 Ritter Rd Ste 107, Mechanicsburg, PA 17055-6920
Tel (717) 791-1220 *Founded/Ownrshp* 1999
Sales 22.1MM^E *EMP* 300
SIC 3549 Assembly machines, including robotic; Assembly machines, including robotic
Pr: Mark Downing
Sls Mgr: Ned Montgomery

D-U-N-S 82-557-7794
MEJICO EXPRESS INC
GRUPOEX
14849 Firestone Blvd Fl 1, La Mirada, CA 90638-6017
Tel (714) 690-8300 *Founded/Ownrshp* 1988
Sales 23.7MM^E *EMP* 650
SIC 4513 Letter delivery, private air; Letter delivery, private air
Pr: Jose Leon
Opers Mgr: Raul Cancinos

D-U-N-S 04-847-6683 IMP
MEL BERNIE AND CO INC
1928 JEWELRY COMPANY
3000 W Empire Ave, Burbank, CA 91504-3109
Tel (818) 841-1928 *Founded/Ownrshp* 1968
Sales 61.2MM^E *EMP* 325
SIC 3961 Costume jewelry; Costume jewelry
CEO: Melvyn Bernie
CFO: Paul Edmeier

D-U-N-S 04-202-5924 IMP
MEL CHEMICALS INC
M E I
(*Suby of* LUXFER GROUP LIMITED)
500 Brbrtown Pt Breeze Rd, Flemington, NJ 08822-4702
Tel (908) 782-5800 *Founded/Ownrshp* 1951, 1964
Sales 75.3MM^E *EMP* 110
SIC 5169 3295 2819 3339 2899 Chemicals & allied products; Minerals, ground or otherwise treated; Industrial inorganic chemicals; Primary nonferrous metals; Chemical preparations; Chemicals & allied products; Minerals, ground or otherwise treated; Industrial inorganic chemicals; Primary nonferrous metals; Chemical preparations
Ch Bd: Alan Foster
Treas: Vinny Davis
**Treas:* Janet Raphagen
**Treas:* Kathleen Snook
Dir IT: Robert Colon
Natl Sales: Bill Fee
Board of Directors: Dick R Hirons, Brian Purves

MEL CLAYTON FORD
See MLC AUTOMOTIVE INC

D-U-N-S 01-456-8554
MEL GRATA CHEVROLET-TOYOTA-SCION INC (PA)
MEL GRATA TOYOTA
2757 E State St, Hermitage, PA 16148-2717
Tel (724) 347-7702 *Founded/Ownrshp* 1985
Sales 33.4MM^E *EMP* 65
SIC 5511 7515 7513 5521 7538 Automobiles, new & used; Passenger car leasing; Truck rental & leasing, no drivers; Used car dealers; General automotive repair shops; Automobiles, new & used; Passenger car leasing; Truck rental & leasing, no drivers; Used car dealers; General automotive repair shops
Pr: Melvin Grata
VP Mktg: Bill Lewis
Sls Mgr: Chris Shander

MEL GRATA TOYOTA
See MEL GRATA CHEVROLET-TOYOTA-SCION INC

D-U-N-S 05-308-4448
MEL HAMBELTON FORD INC (KS)
11771 W Kellogg St, Wichita, KS 67209-1240
Tel (316) 462-1550 *Founded/Ownrshp* 1969, 1984
Sales 45.7MM^E *EMP* 148
SIC 5511 7538 7515 5531 5521 Automobiles, new & used; General automotive repair shops; Passenger car leasing; Automotive & home supply stores; Used car dealers; Automobiles, new & used; General automotive repair shops; Passenger car leasing; Automotive & home supply stores; Used car dealers
Pr: Mel Hambelton
Genl Mgr: Phil Nightingale
Off Mgr: Annie Wake
Sls Mgr: Brian Geddeis
Sls Mgr: James Shock
Sls Mgr: Jason Wolff
Sales Asso: Reggie Harlmon
Sales Asso: Ryan Trilli

D-U-N-S 94-406-6849
MEL HAMBELTON FORD INC
11771 W Kellogg St, Wichita, KS 67209-1240
Tel (316) 462-3673 *Founded/Ownrshp* 1984
Sales 41.4MM^E *EMP* 120
SIC 5511 Automobiles, new & used; Automobiles, new & used
Pr: Mel Hambelton
**VP:* Lisa Hambelton
Sls Mgr: John Dotts
Sls Mgr: Sam Jawad
Sls Mgr: Robert Kinney
Sls Mgr: John Santellan
Sales Asso: Osiel Ayala

Sales Asso: George Nebrat
Sales Asso: Travis Whisler

MEL RAPTON HONDA
See MEL RAPTON INC

D-U-N-S 05-236-4866
MEL RAPTON INC
MEL RAPTON HONDA
3630 Fulton Ave, Sacramento, CA 95821-1852
Tel (916) 436-8364 *Founded/Ownrshp* 1970
Sales 50.5MM^E^ *EMP* 150
SIC 5511 5531 7538 7532 Automobiles, new & used; Automotive parts; General automotive repair shops; Body shop, automotive; Automobiles, new & used; Automotive parts; General automotive repair shops; Body shop, automotive
Pr: Katina Rapton
**VP:* Curtis Rapton
Store Mgr: Doug Townsend
Sls Mgr: Chris Cottongim
Sls Mgr: Brian Hood
Sls Mgr: Chris Rice
Sls Mgr: Pat Silva

D-U-N-S 14-453-2025 EXP
MEL STEVENSON & ASSOCIATES INC
SPEC ROOFING CONTRACTORS SUP
2840 Roe Ln, Kansas City, KS 66103-1543
Tel (913) 262-0505 *Founded/Ownrshp* 1985
Sales 219.0MM^E^ *EMP* 190
SIC 5033 5082 5023 Roofing & siding materials; Siding, except wood; General construction machinery & equipment; Window covering parts & accessories; Roofing & siding materials; Siding, except wood; General construction machinery & equipment; Window covering parts & accessories
Pr: Mel Stevenson
Pr: Dan Hollabaugh
**CFO:* John Ruhlman
**Sr VP:* Steve Wright
**VP:* Brook Benge
**VP:* Shawn Gastner

D-U-N-S 02-585-3649
MEL-O-CREAM DONUTS INTERNATIONAL INC (IL)
5456 International Pkwy, Springfield, IL 62711-7086
Tel (217) 483-1825 *Founded/Ownrshp* 1932
Sales 23.7MM^E^ *EMP* 80
Accts Kerber Eck & Braeckel Llp
SIC 2053 Doughnuts, frozen
Pr: David W Waltrip
**CFO:* Andy Williams
Prd Mgr: Dan Alewelt
Ql Cn Mgr: Larry Lester
Snr Mgr: John Armstrong

D-U-N-S 13-976-0102 IMP
MELALEUCA INC
MELALEUCA WELLNESS COMPANY
4609 W 65th S, Idaho Falls, ID 83402-6003
Tel (208) 522-0700 *Founded/Ownrshp* 1985
Sales 535.7MM^E^ *EMP* 2,000
SIC 2833 5122 2844 2841 2834 Vitamins, natural or synthetic: bulk, uncompounded; Drugs, proprietaries & sundries; Toilet preparations; Soap & other detergents; Pharmaceutical preparations; Vitamins, natural or synthetic: bulk, uncompounded; Drugs, proprietaries & sundries; Toilet preparations; Soap & other detergents; Pharmaceutical preparations
Pr: Frank L Vandersloot
COO: McKay Christensen
CFO: Thomas Knutson
Treas: John Burden
VP: Brian Carmack
VP: Paul Conley
VP: Jerry Felton
VP: Nasser Fredj
VP: Paul Haacke
VP: Fernando Pargas
VP: Michael Sackley
VP: Sheba Sofi

MELALEUCA WELLNESS COMPANY
See MELALEUCA INC

D-U-N-S 00-881-9039
MELANSON CO INC (NH)
353 West St, Keene, NH 03431-2442
Tel (603) 352-4232 *Founded/Ownrshp* 1946, 1954
Sales 44.9MM^E^ *EMP* 250
SIC 3444 1761 Sheet metalwork; Roofing contractor; Sheet metalwork; Roofing contractor
Pr: Robert W Therrien
CFO: Robert Mucha
**CFO:* Beverly G Therrien
**Ex VP:* Alex Kossakoski
**VP:* Robert O Lefebvre Jr
**VP:* Peter F Mangan
VP: Dave Nallett
VP: George Pichette
**VP:* David P Therrien
VP: Todd Watkins
Prd Mgr: David Drouin

MELART JEWELERS
See REEDS JEWELERS INC

D-U-N-S 55-641-1791
MELBOURNE INTERNAL MEDICINE ASSOCIATES PA
1223 Gateway Dr, Melbourne, FL 32901-2607
Tel (321) 725-4500 *Founded/Ownrshp* 1968
Sales 53.4MM^E^ *EMP* 900
SIC 8011 Internal medicine, physician/surgeon; Internal medicine, physician/surgeon
Ch: A Thomas Hollingsworth
**Pr:* Robert Seelman
CFO: Richard Nescio
**Treas:* Brian J Bussen
Ofcr: Debra Johansen
Ofcr: Al O'Connell
Exec: Lisa Yarnell-Haire
**Prin:* Nelson Sang M D
Off Mgr: Donna Bradley
Off Mgr: Cathy Metzinger
CIO: Gary Wright

D-U-N-S 78-218-0103
MELCO ELECTRIC II INC
(*Suby of* US BUILDER SERVICES LLC) ★
12530 Wiles Rd, Coral Springs, FL 33076-2202
Tel (954) 346-7780 *Founded/Ownrshp* 2006
Sales 13.4MM^E^ *EMP* 350
SIC 1731 Electrical work; Electrical work
Pr: Michael Miebach

D-U-N-S 93-834-2524 IMP
MELCO INC
(*Suby of* MBC HOLDINGS INC) ★
1613 S Defiance St, Archbold, OH 43502-9488
Tel (419) 446-9106 *Founded/Ownrshp* 1994
Sales 29.2MM *EMP* 20
Accts Plante & Moran Pllc Toledo
SIC 1794 8748 Excavation work; Environmental consultant; Excavation work; Environmental consultant
Pr: Mark Murray
**Sec:* Steven Everhart
**VP:* Dean Miller
**Genl Mgr:* Robert Miller

D-U-N-S 03-725-7664
MELCO STEEL INC
109 E 3rd St, Kenner, LA 70062-7003
Tel (504) 468-3330 *Founded/Ownrshp* 1979
Sales 21.5MM^E^ *EMP* 20
SIC 5051 Steel
Pr: Frank Melito
**VP:* Alvin Schultz

D-U-N-S 00-232-7963 IMP/EXP
MELCOR CORP (NJ)
(*Suby of* LAIRD TECHNOLOGIES INC) ★
4707 Detroit Ave, Cleveland, OH 44102-2216
Tel (609) 393-4178 *Founded/Ownrshp* 1996
Sales 17.1MM^E^ *EMP* 333
SIC 3674 Thermoelectric devices, solid state; Thermoelectric devices, solid state
Pr: Charles Weber
VP: Aim Karas
VP: James Karas
VP: Robert Smythe
Comm Man: Kathy Salvatore
IT Man: Carol Rooney
QC Dir: Mike Hollander

D-U-N-S 80-760-1281
MELE ASSOCIATES INC
11 Taft Ct Ste 101, Rockville, MD 20850-5355
Tel (240) 453-6990 *Founded/Ownrshp* 1993
Sales 24.5MM^E^ *EMP* 140
SIC 8748 8741 Business consulting; Business management
Pr: Mel Chiogioji
**COO:* Alan Chiogioji
Ex VP: James Amerault
Ex VP: Paul R Ilg
Sr VP: David Nash
VP: Alexander Causey
VP: Fukunaga Frank
VP: Richard Irwin
**VP:* Brian McCarron Sr
VP: John McConnel
**VP:* John McConnell Sr
VP: Jack Melito
VP: Dennis Plockmeyer
VP: Judy Talcott
**VP:* Ed Thal Sr

D-U-N-S 00-222-7882 IMP
MELE COMPANIES INC (NY)
FARRINGTON PACKAGING
2007 Beechgrove Pl, Utica, NY 13501-1703
Tel (315) 733-1412 *Founded/Ownrshp* 1912, 2002
Sales 28.7MM^E^ *EMP* 100
SIC 5199 3089 5112 Jewelry boxes; Packaging materials; Plastic hardware & building products; Stationery & office supplies
Ch Bd: Raymond R Mele
**CEO:* Michael J Valentine
**VP:* Brendan Wjenkins
Dir IT: Bill Richardson
Sales Exec: Michael Volza

MELETIO ELECTRICAL SUPPLY CO
See JMJ SUPPLY CO

D-U-N-S 00-418-2283
MELIN TOOL CO INC
5565 Venture Dr Ste C, Cleveland, OH 44130-9302
Tel (216) 362-4200 *Founded/Ownrshp* 1968
Sales 20.8MM^E^ *EMP* 70
SIC 3545 3541 Machine tool accessories; Machine tools, metal cutting type
Pr: Mike Wochna
**Ch Bd:* Mildred Rathberger
Mtls Mgr: Catherine Bindel
Sales Asso: Nicole Heckard

D-U-N-S 19-264-4011
MELINK CORP
5140 River Valley Rd, Milford, OH 45150-9108
Tel (513) 965-7300 *Founded/Ownrshp* 1997
Sales 22.2MM^E^ *EMP* 68
SIC 8711 8748 3822 Heating & ventilation engineering; Energy conservation consultant; Appliance controls except air-conditioning & refrigeration
Pr: Stephen K Melink
Ofcr: Amanda Ford
VP: Donna Jones
VP Opers: Darren Witter

D-U-N-S 60-943-8015
MELISSA & DOUG INC
141 Danbury Rd, Wilton, CT 06897-4411
Tel (203) 762-4500 *Founded/Ownrshp* 2007
Sales 74.7MM^E^ *EMP* 200^E^
SIC 5092 Toys & hobby goods & supplies; Toys & hobby goods & supplies
COO: Ron Osher
VP: Chris Myers

D-U-N-S 07-924-3274 IMP/EXP
MELISSA & DOUG LLC
141 Danbury Rd, Wilton, CT 06897-4411
Tel (203) 762-4500 *Founded/Ownrshp* 2007
Sales 153.4MM^E^ *EMP* 200^E^
SIC 5092 Toys & hobby goods & supplies; Toys & hobby goods & supplies
Dir IT: Philip Robinson
Sls Mgr: Lonny Weinstein
Sales Asso: Matt Shrum
Sales Asso: Michael Walker

D-U-N-S 08-833-4334
MELISSA BRADLEY REAL ESTATE INC
55 Broadway Blvd, Fairfax, CA 94930-1653
Tel (415) 455-1140 *Founded/Ownrshp* 1997
Sales 8.2MM^E^ *EMP* 300
SIC 6531 Real estate agents & managers; Real estate agents & managers
CEO: Melissa Bradley
**Pr:* Robert Bradley
VP: Jason Lytz

D-U-N-S 15-426-3248
MELISSA DATA CORP
MAILERS SOFTWARE
22382 Avenida Empresa, Rcho STA Marg, CA 92688-2112
Tel (949) 589-5200 *Founded/Ownrshp* 1985
Sales 30.1MM^E^ *EMP* 110
SIC 7371

MELISSA'S PRODUCE
See WORLD VARIETY PRODUCE INC

D-U-N-S 78-205-5289
MELITA CORP
828 E 144th St, Bronx, NY 10454-1702
Tel (718) 392-7280 *Founded/Ownrshp* 1991
Sales 48.6MM^E^ *EMP* 201
SIC 2051 5411 Bread, cake & related products; Grocery stores; Bread, cake & related products; Grocery stores
Ch Bd: Emanuel Darmanin
**COO:* Joann Atek
**CFO:* Michael Cassar
VP Prd: Jack Darmanin

D-U-N-S 62-799-4759 IMP
MELITTA NORTH AMERICA INC
MELITTA USA
(*Suby of* MELITTA BENTZ GMBH & CO. KG)
13925 58th St N, Clearwater, FL 33760-3721
Tel (727) 535-2111 *Founded/Ownrshp* 1996
Sales 36.3MM^E^ *EMP* 150
SIC 2095 3634 5499 Roasted coffee; Coffee makers, electric: household; Coffee; Roasted coffee; Coffee makers, electric: household; Coffee
Pr: Martin T Miller
**VP:* Fred Lueck

MELITTA USA
See MELITTA NORTH AMERICA INC

D-U-N-S 00-199-0522 IMP
MELITTA USA INC (FL)
(*Suby of* MELITTA NORTH AMERICA INC) ★
13925 58th St N, Clearwater, FL 33760-3721
Tel (727) 535-2111 *Founded/Ownrshp* 1963
Sales 30.2MM^E^ *EMP* 100^E^
SIC 2095 3634 Roasted coffee; Coffee makers, electric: household; Roasted coffee; Coffee makers, electric: household
Pr: Martin Miller
**CFO:* Fred Lueck
Mng Dir: Arthur Ciancio
IT Man: Ronald Harry
Opers Mgr: Mark Cardenas
Plnt Mgr: Ken Donovan
Plnt Mgr: Tim Taglang
Sales Exec: Jeff Cooke

D-U-N-S 02-855-6058
MELLANO & CO
MELLANO ENTERPRISES
766 Wall St, Los Angeles, CA 90014-2316
Tel (213) 622-0796 *Founded/Ownrshp* 1975
Sales 103.1MM^E^ *EMP* 275
SIC 5193 Flowers & florists' supplies; Flowers & florists' supplies
Pr: John Mellano
**Pr:* Michael Matthew Mellano
**Sec:* Battista Castellano
VP: Bruce Brady
**VP:* Michelle Castellano
**VP:* Bob Mellano
**VP:* H Mike Mellano Sr
Exec: Jason Valenzuela
Genl Mgr: Bob Showalter
Sls Mgr: Glynn Brock
Sales Asso: Amy Ha

MELLANO ENTERPRISES
See MELLANO & CO

D-U-N-S 14-632-3238
MELLANOX TECHNOLOGIES INC
(*Suby of* MELLANOX TECHNOLOGIES, LTD.)
350 Oakmead Pkwy, Sunnyvale, CA 94085-5400
Tel (408) 970-3400 *Founded/Ownrshp* 1999
Sales 463.6MM *EMP* 876^E^
Accts Pricewaterhousecoopers Llp Sa
SIC 3674 Semiconductors & related devices; Semiconductors & related devices
Ch Bd: Eyal Waldman
COO: Shai Cohen
CFO: Michael Gray
CFO: Merle McClendon
VP: Mehdi Asghari
VP: Eyal Babish
VP: Aviram Gutman
VP: Yaron Haviv
VP: Michael Kagan
VP: Deirling Kevin
VP: Evelyn Landman
VP: Yuval Leader
VP: Ronnen Lovinger
VP: Henning Lysdal
VP: Ayelet Margalit-Ilovich
VP: Yiftah Shahar
VP: Marc Sultzbaugh
VP: Alon Webman
Board of Directors: Dov Baharav, Glenda Dorchak, Irwin Federman, Thomas Weatherford

D-U-N-S 11-350-5424
MELLES GRIOT INC
2051 Palomar Airport Rd # 200, Carlsbad, CA 92011-1462
Tel (760) 438-2254 *Founded/Ownrshp* 2007
Sales 35.9MM^E^ *EMP* 93^E^
SIC 3827 3699 Optical instruments & lenses; Laser systems & equipment
Pr: Peter J Blackbeard
**Sec:* William Polito
VP: Zora Ljolije
VP: Lynn Sticklandf
CTO: Michael Dorich
VP Sls: Lynn Strickland

MELLING AUTOMOTIVE PRODUCTS
See MELLING TOOL CO

D-U-N-S 03-590-8680
MELLING PRODUCTS NORTH LLC
(*Suby of* MELLING AUTOMOTIVE PRODUCTS) ★
333 Grace St, Farwell, MI 48622-9772
Tel (989) 588-6147 *Founded/Ownrshp* 1981
Sales 26.7MM^E^ *EMP* 75
SIC 3498 3465 3714 Tube fabricating (contract bending & shaping); Body parts, automobile: stamped metal; Motor vehicle parts & accessories
Owner: Mark Melling
**Sec:* Thomas C Evanson
**VP:* David Dent
Exec: Donna Macdonald
Off Mgr: Jennifer Gibbs
Off Mgr: Jennifer Struble

D-U-N-S 00-537-5217 IMP
MELLING TOOL CO (MI)
MELLING AUTOMOTIVE PRODUCTS
2620 Saradan Dr, Jackson, MI 49202-1258
Tel (517) 787-8172 *Founded/Ownrshp* 1956
Sales 315.3MM^E^ *EMP* 700
SIC 3451 3714 3625 3568 3561 3494 Screw machine products; Oil pump, motor vehicle; Relays & industrial controls; Power transmission equipment; Pumps & pumping equipment; Valves & pipe fittings; Screw machine products; Oil pump, motor vehicle; Relays & industrial controls; Power transmission equipment; Pumps & pumping equipment; Valves & pipe fittings
Pr: Mark Melling
Pr: Ayres Filho
CFO: Todd Vanmarter
VP: Dave Corravo
VP: Pat Richardson
Prgrm Mgr: Scott Holton
Genl Mgr: Scot Gazlay
Dir IT: David Corrabo
Dir IT: Mike Morse
QC Dir: Andrew Collins
Plnt Mgr: Bob Adair

D-U-N-S 00-509-7216
MELLMO INC
120 S Sierra Ave, Solana Beach, CA 92075-1811
Tel (858) 847-3272 *Founded/Ownrshp* 2008
Sales 31.8MM^E^ *EMP* 140^E^
SIC 7371 Custom computer programming services
Ch Bd: Santiago Becerra
**Pr:* Jaime Zuluaga
**CEO:* Quinton Alsbury
**CFO:* Claire Remillard
Chf Mktg O: Freddy Mangum
**Ex VP:* Steve Neat
**Sr VP:* Dan Blake
VP: David Becerra
VP: Justin Cox
VP: Becerra David
VP: Langston David
VP: Thibaut De Lataillade
VP: Brad Freitag
VP: Al Guddemi
VP: Wendy Hynes
VP: Joel Katz
VP: Ali Shirnia

MELLON ARENA PITTSBURGH
See SMG PITTSBURGH LP

D-U-N-S 18-310-6046
MELLON CAPITAL MANAGEMENT CORP
(*Suby of* MBC INVESTMENTS CORPORATION)
50 Fremont St Ste 3900, San Francisco, CA 94105-2240
Tel (415) 905-5448 *Founded/Ownrshp* 2007
Sales 81.5MM^E^ *EMP* 250^E^
SIC 6282 Investment advice; Investment advice
CEO: Gabriela Parcella
**Pr:* Charles J Jacklin
Pr: Nadia Kindschi
Pr: Marylynn Siri-Outhay
CFO: David Manuel
Treas: Joanne S Huber
Chf Cred: Chris Appler
Ofcr: Robert McGrath
Ofcr: Jeffrey Vaughn
Ex VP: Brenda J Akley
Ex VP: Oliver Buckley
Ex VP: David Jiang
Ex VP: Richard Watson
VP: Paul Benson
VP: Robert Chen
VP: Jill Gill
VP: Peter Goslin
VP: Diane Hallett
VP: John-Peter Heinrich
VP: Mary Leibig
VP: John Manley

MELLON CERTIFIED RESTORATION
See JIM MELLON GENERAL CONTRACTING INC

D-U-N-S 79-100-7516
■ **MELLON TRUST OF NEW ENGLAND NA**
(*Suby of* BANK OF NEW YORK MELLON CORP) ★
1 Boston Pl Fl 8, Boston, MA 02108-4407
Tel (617) 722-7000 *Founded/Ownrshp* 2006
Sales 868.3MM *EMP* 1,960
SIC 6733 Trusts; Trusts
Prin: Margerett Harrison

D-U-N-S 96-736-0947 IMP/EXP
MELLOTT CO
100 Mellott Dr Ste 100, Warfordsburg, PA 17267-8555
Tel (301) 678-2000 *Founded/Ownrshp* 1952
Sales 120.1MM^E *EMP* 110^E
SIC 5084 Crushing machinery & equipment; Crushing machinery & equipment
Pr: Richard Blake
**Treas:* Herman L Mellott
**VP:* Brian Mellott
IT Man: Gene Hockenberry
Opers Mgr: Stanley Lawrence

D-U-N-S 10-278-6019
MELLOY BROTHERS ENTERPRISES INC
MELLOY PARTS
7707 Lomas Blvd Ne, Albuquerque, NM 87110-7413
Tel (505) 265-8721 *Founded/Ownrshp* 1975
Sales 102.3MM^E *EMP* 332^E
SIC 5511 Automobiles, new & used; Pickups, new & used; Automobiles, new & used; Pickups, new & used
Pr: Robert E Melloy
**VP:* Patrick C Melloy

D-U-N-S 03-569-4504 IMP/EXP
MELLOY BROTHERS INC
MELLOY JAGUAR
(*Suby of* MELLOY BROTHERS ENTERPRISES INC) ★
7707 Lomas Blvd Ne, Albuquerque, NM 87110-7413
Tel (505) 265-7701 *Founded/Ownrshp* 1958
Sales 36.9MM^E *EMP* 92
SIC 5511 Automobiles, new & used; Pickups, new & used; Automobiles, new & used; Pickups, new & used
Pr: Robert Melloy
**Sec:* Patrick Melloy
Store Mgr: Charles Mashburn
VP Mktg: Guy Melloy
Mktg Dir: Gus Carrillo
Sls Mgr: Roy Benson

MELLOY DODGE
See ALBUQUERQUE MOTOR CO INC

MELLOY JAGUAR
See MELLOY BROTHERS INC

MELLOY PARTS
See MELLOY BROTHERS ENTERPRISES INC

D-U-N-S 17-713-1562 IMP
MELMARC PRODUCTS INC
4040 W Carriage Dr, Santa Ana, CA 92704-6303
Tel (714) 549-2170 *Founded/Ownrshp* 1987
Sales 25.0MM *EMP* 330
SIC 2396 2339 2395 Men's & boys' sportswear & athletic clothing; Women's & misses' athletic clothing & sportswear; Automotive & apparel trimmings; Pleating & stitching; Automotive & apparel trimmings; Screen printing on fabric articles; Women's & misses' athletic clothing & sportswear; Pleating & stitching
Pr: Brian Hirth
**COO:* Leila Drager
**CFO:* Harish Naran
CTO: Rod Pick
IT Man: David Turnbull
Opers Mgr: Sue Pereira
Sls&Mrk Ex: Tom Inashita

MELMARK HOME
See MELMARK INC

D-U-N-S 07-948-1842
MELMARK INC
MELMARK HOME
2600 Wayland Rd, Berwyn, PA 19312-2307
Tel (610) 353-1726 *Founded/Ownrshp* 1966
Sales 70.1MM *EMP* 1,000^E
Accts Fesnak Llp Blue Bell Pa
SIC 8211 8361 School for the retarded; School for physically handicapped; Self-help group home; School for the retarded; School for physically handicapped; Self-help group home
Pr: Joanne Gillis-Donovan
**COO:* George P Linke Jr
**CFO:* Delyn Byerly
**Ch:* Robert Marcus
**Treas:* Michael Bradley
Ex VP: Peter Troy
VP: Stephen Luce
**VP:* Peter J Troy
**VP:* Joseph Zakrzewski
Mktg Dir: Michelle Bradsher

D-U-N-S 19-675-1358
MELMEDICA CHILDRENS HEALTHCARE INC
CHILDREN'S HEALTHCARE SERVICES
(*Suby of* PARAMEDICAL SERVICE OF AMERICA INC) ★
17600 Crawford Ave, Country Club Hills, IL 60478-4889
Tel (708) 335-9142 *Founded/Ownrshp* 2006
Sales 4.4MM^E *EMP* 300
Accts Ernest & Young Llp Cpa S
SIC 8082 Home health care services; Home health care services
Pr: Karen Gunter
**Treas:* Julius Hill
**VP:* Sandra Matteson

D-U-N-S 61-874-5640
MELO INTERNATIONAL INC
3700 Kelley Ave, Cleveland, OH 44114-4533
Tel (440) 519-0526 *Founded/Ownrshp* 1982
Sales 10.1MM^E *EMP* 350
SIC 8742 Retail trade consultant; Retail trade consultant
CEO: Rondee Kamins

D-U-N-S 80-917-8833 IMP
MELODY FOODS INC
30777 Northwestern Hwy # 300, Farmington Hills, MI 48334-2549
Tel (248) 851-6990 *Founded/Ownrshp* 1993
Sales 130.0MM^E *EMP* 509
Accts Follmer Rudzewicz Plc Southfi
SIC 5143 2026 5149 5145 Milk & cream, fluid; Ice cream & ices; Yogurt; Milk processing (pasteurizing, homogenizing, bottling); Juices; Snack foods; Milk & cream, fluid; Ice cream & ices; Yogurt; Milk processing (pasteurizing, homogenizing, bottling); Juices; Snack foods
Prin: Michael J George
**Treas:* Thomas A George
**VP:* Robert T George

MELODY TOYOTA
See FAA SAN BRUNO INC

D-U-N-S 05-766-5721
MELOTTE DISTRIBUTING INC
1442 Main St, Green Bay, WI 54302-1700
Tel (920) 435-1986 *Founded/Ownrshp* 1979
Sales 24.9MM^E *EMP* 65
SIC 5147 5149 5142 Meats, fresh; Groceries & related products; Packaged frozen goods
CEO: Harry Melotte
CFO: Steve Haase
**Treas:* Nancy Melotte
Prd Mgr: Keith Wilson

D-U-N-S 62-197-9723 IMP
MELR INC
(*Suby of* JONES NEW YORK) ★
250 Rittenhouse Cir, Bristol, PA 19007-1616
Tel (215) 785-4000 *Founded/Ownrshp* 2014
Sales 34.4MM^E *EMP* 1,500
SIC 5621 Ready-to-wear apparel, women's; Ready-to-wear apparel, women's
Ch Bd: Sidney Kimmel
**Pr:* Howard Buerkle
**Treas:* Wesley Card
VP: Patrick M Farrell
**VP:* Herbert J Goodfriend

MELROSE BAKERY
See NAPOLEON BAKERY INC

D-U-N-S 08-653-0508
MELROSE CITY OF (INC)
562 Main St, Melrose, MA 02176-3142
Tel (781) 979-4160 *Founded/Ownrshp* 1649
Sales NA *EMP* 740
Accts Powers & Sullivan Llc Cpas
SIC 9111 Mayors' offices; ; Mayors' offices;
V Ch: Monica Medeiros
V Ch: John Tramontozzi
COO: George Doyle
**CFO:* Patrick Dellorusso
**Treas:* Arthur Flavin
Ex Dir: Michael Pasquariello
Opers Mgr: Kathy Brodeur
HC Dir: Ruth Clay
Snr Mgr: Michael Kent

D-U-N-S 00-567-3012
MELROSE DAIRY PROTEINS LLC (DE)
1000 Kraft Dr Se, Melrose, MN 56352-1456
Tel (320) 256-7461 *Founded/Ownrshp* 1968
Sales 68.1MM^E *EMP* 150
SIC 2022 Cheese, natural & processed; Cheese, natural & processed

D-U-N-S 06-213-6598
MELROSE PARK HAR INC (PA)
HAN AH REUM SUPERMARKET
7320 Old York Rd Ste 200, Elkins Park, PA 19027-3007
Tel (215) 782-1801 *Founded/Ownrshp* 1998
Sales 23.0MM *EMP* 25
SIC 5411 Supermarkets; Supermarkets
Pr: IL Yeon Kwon

D-U-N-S 07-979-9218
MELROSE PUBLIC SCHOOLS
360 Lynn Fells Pkwy, Melrose, MA 02176-2244
Tel (781) 662-2000 *Founded/Ownrshp* 2015
Sales 5.3MM^E *EMP* 285^E
SIC 8211 Public elementary & secondary schools
Teacher Pr: Donna Keohane
HC Dir: Pat Ruggiero

D-U-N-S 79-130-3592
MELROSE US 3 LLC
(*Suby of* MELROSE OVERSEAS HOLDINGS LIMITED)
2600 S Custer Ave, Wichita, KS 67217-1324
Tel (859) 887-6390 *Founded/Ownrshp* 2005
Sales 57.7MM^E *EMP* 1,193
SIC 3089 Injection molding of plastics; Injection molding of plastics
Pr: Bruce Graben

D-U-N-S 83-156-2025
MELTECH CORP INC
3321 75th Ave Ste G, Landover, MD 20785-1519
Tel (301) 773-3450 *Founded/Ownrshp* 1999
Sales 23.2MM^E *EMP* 56
Accts William Batdorf & Company Pc
SIC 1541 8741 1542 1742 7349 1522 Renovation, remodeling & repairs: industrial buildings; Management services; Nonresidential construction; Plastering, drywall & insulation; Building maintenance services; Residential construction; Renovation, remodeling & repairs: industrial buildings; Management services; Nonresidential construction; Plastering, drywall & insulation; Building maintenance services; Residential construction
Ch Bd: Joanne Pettit-Krishack
Sfty Mgr: John Frecker
Snr Mgr: Rick Duke

D-U-N-S 07-171-6651
MELTER USA LLC
16850 Saturn Ln Ste 100, Houston, TX 77058-2143
Tel (281) 218-6080 *Founded/Ownrshp* 2011
Sales 20.9MM^E *EMP* 1
SIC 1382 Oil & gas exploration services; Oil & gas exploration services
Pr: Antoio Uribe Quintanilla
VP: Felipe Dejesus Villareal Casti

MELTON ELECTRIC CO OF HOUSTON
See MELTON ELECTRIC INC

D-U-N-S 04-630-7898
MELTON ELECTRIC INC
MELTON ELECTRIC CO OF HOUSTON
2309 Karbach St, Houston, TX 77092-8003
Tel (713) 680-0011 *Founded/Ownrshp* 1969
Sales 64.3MM^E *EMP* 200
SIC 1731 General electrical contractor; General electrical contractor
Ch Bd: Charles W Melton

MELTON EXPRESS PARTS & SERVICE
See MELTON SALES INC

D-U-N-S 03-448-7751
MELTON MANAGEMENT INC
MCDONALD'S
6342 Lantana Rd, Lake Worth, FL 33463-6606
Tel (561) 641-6717 *Founded/Ownrshp* 1986
Sales 28.2MM^E *EMP* 1,400
SIC 5812 Fast-food restaurant, chain; Fast-food restaurant, chain
Pr: Keith Melton

D-U-N-S 01-745-6682
MELTON MOTORS INC
15100 Eureka Rd, Southgate, MI 48195-2614
Tel (734) 283-2600 *Founded/Ownrshp* 1961
Sales 24.0MM *EMP* 50
SIC 5511 Automobiles, new & used; Automobiles, new & used
Pr: George Melton
**VP:* Dennis R Melton

D-U-N-S 19-522-2414
MELTON SALES & SERVICE INC
600 Main Rd, Milford, ME 04461-3250
Tel (207) 827-0910 *Founded/Ownrshp* 1949
Sales 23.5MM^E *EMP* 500
SIC 3795 Specialized tank components, military; Specialized tank components, military
Ch Bd: John F Melton
**Pr:* Richard W Melton

D-U-N-S 03-290-5929
MELTON SALES INC
MELTON EXPRESS PARTS & SERVICE
200 N Lynn Riggs Blvd, Claremore, OK 74017-6816
Tel (918) 341-1512 *Founded/Ownrshp* 1950
Sales 29.5MM^E *EMP* 100
SIC 5511 5521 Automobiles, new & used; Pickups, new & used; Vans, new & used; Used car dealers; Automobiles, new & used; Pickups, new & used; Vans, new & used; Used car dealers
Pr: Robert Melton
**Sec:* Sandy Melton
**VP:* Larry Melton

D-U-N-S 01-221-6768
MELTON STATES ROSEN LLC
Hunts Pt Coop Bldg C16, Bronx, NY 10474
Tel (718) 842-4447 *Founded/Ownrshp* 1950
Sales 20.5MM^E *EMP* 120
SIC 5147 Meats, fresh; Meats, fresh
Pr: Dennis Huey
**VP:* David Gage

D-U-N-S 00-686-3419
MELTON TRUCK LINES INC (OK)
808 N 161st East Ave, Tulsa, OK 74116-4115
Tel (918) 234-1000 *Founded/Ownrshp* 1954
Sales 91.1MM^E *EMP* 700
SIC 4213 Trucking, except local; Trucking, except local
Pr: Bob Peterson
CFO: Robert Peterson
**CFO:* Robert Ragan
**Sr VP:* Russ Elliott
**Sr VP:* Randy Rhines
**Sr VP:* Jeff Robinson
**Sr VP:* Dan Taylor
**VP:* Angie Buchanan
VP: Lawrence Daniels
**VP:* Mike Dargel
**VP:* Brice Peters
VP: Mike Williams
Board of Directors: Kyle Burchart, Lisa Mason, Elizabeth G Peterson, Jan Stone

MELTWATER GROUP, THE
See MELTWATER NEWS US INC

D-U-N-S 78-516-1154
MELTWATER NEWS US INC
MELTWATER GROUP, THE
(*Suby of* MELTWATER US HOLDINGS INC) ★
225 Bush St Ste 1000, San Francisco, CA 94104-4218
Tel (415) 829-5900 *Founded/Ownrshp* 2007
Sales 40.7MM^E *EMP* 80
SIC 7383 News syndicates
CEO: Jorn Lyseggen
**CFO:* Rik Thorbecke
Chf Mktg O: Valerie Fawzi
Dir Bus: Keighley-Ann Bell
Dir Bus: Marion Hardy
Dir Bus: Marion Wallace
**Ex Dir:* Niklas De Besche
**Ex Dir:* Paal Larsen
Ex Dir: Kevin Lorenz
Ex Dir: Jonas Oppedal
Mng Dir: Christopher Bergsager

D-U-N-S 79-908-5266
MELTWATER US HOLDINGS INC
(*Suby of* MELTWATER HOLDING B.V.)
225 Bush St Ste 1000, San Francisco, CA 94104-4218
Tel (415) 236-3144 *Founded/Ownrshp* 2007
Sales 41.0MM^E *EMP* 100
SIC 7383 6719 News syndicates; Investment holding companies, except banks
CEO: Jorn Lyseggen

D-U-N-S 06-805-1283
MELTZER LIPPE & GOLDSTEIN LLP
190 Willis Ave Ste Gl, Mineola, NY 11501-2639
Tel (516) 747-0300 *Founded/Ownrshp* 1970
Sales 24.6MM^E *EMP* 130
SIC 8111 General practice law office; General practice law office
Pt: Lewis S Meltzer
Pt: Neil H Ackerman
Pt: Thomas J Bianco
Pt: Howard M Esterces
Pt: Jonathan D Farrell
Pt: Loretta M Gastwirth
**Pt:* Sheldon Goldstein
Pt: Carmelo Grimaldi
Pt: Ira Halperin
Pt: Richard M Howard
Pt: AVI Z Kestenbaum
**Pt:* Richard Lippe
Pt: Michael H Masri
Pt: Gary M Meltzer
Pt: John P Proszak
Pt: Michael J Schaffer
Pt: Peter A Schneider
CFO: Barbara Meltzer
Ex VP: Annette Callahan
VP: Arlene Malek

D-U-N-S 94-310-1071
MELVIN L DAVIS OIL CO INC
11042 Blue Star Hwy, Stony Creek, VA 23882-3207
Tel (434) 246-2353 *Founded/Ownrshp* 1997
Sales 45.5MM *EMP* 100
SIC 5411 Grocery stores, independent; Grocery stores, independent
**Pr:* Rex Davis
**VP:* J Rex Davis

MELVIN MARK
See MARK MELVIN DEVELOPMENT CO

D-U-N-S 08-161-2590
MELVINDALE-NORTHERN ALLEN PARK PUBLIC SCHOOLS
18530 Prospect St, Melvindale, MI 48122-1508
Tel (313) 389-3300 *Founded/Ownrshp* 1927
Sales 27.8MM *EMP* 266
Accts Plante & Moran Llp
SIC 8211 Public elementary & secondary schools; High school, junior or senior; Public elementary & secondary schools; High school, junior or senior
CEO: Cora Kelly

D-U-N-S 07-779-4758
MELWOOD HORTICULTURAL TRAINING CENTER INC
5606 Dower House Rd, Upper Marlboro, MD 20772-3604
Tel (301) 599-8000 *Founded/Ownrshp* 1963
Sales 80.6MM *EMP* 1,800
SIC 8331 8322 Vocational training agency; Work experience center; Individual & family services; Vocational training agency; Work experience center; Social services for the handicapped
Pr: Earl Copus Jr
**COO:* Mary Buszuwski
Treas: George Watkins
VP: Richard Gallaher
VP: Scott Gibson
VP: Deborah Goins
VP: Robert Grom
VP: Jermaine Hunter
Prin: Douglas H Lemmonds
Dir IT: Jarvis Grigsby
Dir IT: Chad Hebner

D-U-N-S 07-839-1850
MELWOOD-WERNER HOUSING INC
6188 Oxon Hill Rd, Oxon Hill, MD 20745-3113
Tel (301) 982-6207 *Founded/Ownrshp* 2012
Sales 194.6M *EMP* 1,200
Accts Mcgladrey Llp Gaithersburg M
SIC 7021 Lodging house, except organization; Lodging house, except organization
CEO: Dana Stebbins
**Treas:* Ronald Stubblefield
**VP:* Jonathon Rondeau
**Prin:* Donna Hurley

MEMBER DRIVEN TECHNOLOGIES
See IT GROUP LLC

D-U-N-S 08-288-2481
MEMBER ONE FEDERAL CREDIT UNION
202 4th St Ne, Roanoke, VA 24016-2038
Tel (540) 982-8811 *Founded/Ownrshp* 1940
Sales NA *EMP* 140
SIC 6061 Federal credit unions; Federal credit unions
Ex Dir: Frank G Carter
**CFO:* Alan Wade
**Ex VP:* Jean Hopstetter
**Sr VP:* Karen Lynch
**Sr VP:* Tim Rowe
VP: Carman Boone
VP: Scott Crawford
VP: Jason Specht
VP Mktg: Daniel Bliley
Snr Mgr: Jonie Arrington

MEMBER WORKS
See VERTRUE LLC

D-U-N-S 09-788-1064
MEMBERS 1ST FEDERAL CREDIT UNION (PA)
5000 Louise Dr, Mechanicsburg, PA 17055-4899
Tel (717) 697-1161 *Founded/Ownrshp* 1950
Sales NA *EMP* 900
SIC 6061 Federal credit unions; Federal credit unions
CEO: Bob Marquette
**Ch Bd:* Jackie Eakin
**Pr:* Robert Marquette
CFO: Eric Bush
**V Ch Bd:* Michael Whiteman
Ofcr: Melany Radel
Ofcr: Kristi Raykos
**Ex VP:* Craig Golfieri
**Ex VP:* Kevin Lee
**Ex VP:* Stephen Murray
Ex VP: Jay Parrish
Sr VP: Frank Fischer
Sr VP: Jason Hicks
VP: Robert Keith
VP: Dave Kimmel
VP: Karl Krug
VP: Judi McGee
VP: Glenn Rambler
VP: Frank Serina

VP: Omar Shute
Comm Man: Tammy Mislyan

D-U-N-S 00-954-9713
MEMBERS AMERICA CREDIT UNION
YELLOW FINANCIAL CREDIT UNION
9777 Ridge Dr, Lenexa, KS 66219-9746
Tel (913) 345-4545 *Founded/Ownrshp* 1957
Sales NA *EMP* 340
SIC 6159 5932 Small business investment companies; Used merchandise stores
CEO: Dennis Pierce
**Pr:* Michael A Patrick
**Sr VP:* Guy Russo
Snr Mgr: Sharon Roeske

D-U-N-S 07-277-0209
MEMBERS BUILDING MAINTENANCE LLC
11363 Denton Dr Ste 127, Dallas, TX 75229-3434
Tel (972) 241-8131 *Founded/Ownrshp* 1979
Sales 15.0MM^E *EMP* 380
SIC 7349 Janitorial service, contract basis; Janitorial service, contract basis
Prin: Odes H Kim
**Prin:* Ann Kim
VP Mktg: Sonny Song

MEMBERS GROUP, THE
See MEMBERS GROUP LLC

D-U-N-S 07-350-4607
MEMBERS GROUP LLC
MEMBERS GROUP, THE
(*Suby of* AFFILIATES MANAGEMENT CO) ★
1500 Nw 118th St, Des Moines, IA 50325-8242
Tel (515) 457-2000 *Founded/Ownrshp* 1994
Sales 29.5MM^E *EMP* 200
SIC 8611 7374 8721 Business associations; Data processing service; Accounting services, except auditing; Business associations; Data processing service; Accounting services, except auditing
CEO: Shazia Manus
Pr: Ben Rempe
**CFO:* Michael Powers
VP: Ryan Anderson
Software D: Venkat Dandu
VP Opers: Paula Stevens
Opers Mgr: Aimee Dunn
VP Mktg: April Schmaltz
VP Mktg: Georgann Smith
Mktg Dir: Jason Medick

MEMBERS UNITED CORPORATE
See BALANCE SHEET SOLUTIONS LLC

MEMBRANA - CHARLOTTE
See CELGARD LLC

MEMBRANE SEPARATION GROUP
See GE HEALTHCARE

D-U-N-S 11-271-6311
MEMBRANE TECHNOLOGY AND RESEARCH INC
MTR
39630 Eureka Dr, Newark, CA 94560-4805
Tel (650) 328-2228 *Founded/Ownrshp* 1982
Sales 34.3MM^E *EMP* 70
Accts Perisho Tombor Ramirez Filler
SIC 8731 3823 Commercial research laboratory; On-stream gas/liquid analysis instruments, industrial
Ch: Colin Bailey
**CEO:* Hans Wijmans
**COO:* Nicolas Wynn
**CFO:* Meryl Rains
**VP:* Janet Farrant
Exec: Eg Weiss
Snr Sftwr: Xiaotong WEI
IT Man: Doug Gottschlich
Mfg Dir: Craig Wildemuth
Opers Supe: Andrew Farley
Manager: Ray Richey

D-U-N-S 00-848-2242 IMP
■ **MEMC LIQUIDATING CORP**
MC CANN'S ENGINEERING & MFG CO
(*Suby of* MANITOWOC FSG OPERATIONS INC) ★
4570 Colorado Blvd, La Mirada, CA 90638
Tel (818) 637-7200 *Founded/Ownrshp* 1969
Sales 38.5MM^E *EMP* 250
SIC 3556 3586 3585 3581 Beverage machinery; Measuring & dispensing pumps; Refrigeration & heating equipment; Automatic vending machines; Beverage machinery; Measuring & dispensing pumps; Refrigeration & heating equipment; Automatic vending machines
CEO: Gerald McCann
CTO: Susan Martinez

D-U-N-S 93-848-8913 IMP/EXP
■ **MEMC PASADENA INC**
(*Suby of* SUNEDISON INC) ★
3000 N S St, Pasadena, TX 77503
Tel (713) 740-1420 *Founded/Ownrshp* 1995
Sales 36.5MM^E *EMP* 150
SIC 2869 3674 2822 2821 Industrial organic chemicals; Semiconductors & related devices; Synthetic rubber; Plastics materials & resins; Industrial organic chemicals; Semiconductors & related devices; Synthetic rubber; Plastics materials & resins
Pr: Samuel Tennison
**COO:* Robin Prokop
**CFO:* Brian Wuebbels
**VP:* Jeremy Avenier
CTO: Jameel Ibrahim

D-U-N-S 92-677-5180
■ **MEMC SOUTHWEST INC**
(*Suby of* SUNEDISON INC) ★
6416 S Us Highway 75, Sherman, TX 75090-9493
Tel (903) 891-5000 *Founded/Ownrshp* 1995
Sales 105.4MM^E *EMP* 1,400
SIC 3674 Silicon wafers, chemically doped; Silicon wafers, chemically doped
Pr: Jim Lang

MEMCO
See PAMARCO GLOBAL GRAPHICS INC

MEMCO
See COMMERCIAL DRYWALL INC

D-U-N-S 09-582-2342 IMP
MEMCO INC
MEMCO SAFETY SUPPLY
296 Carlton Rd, Hollister, MO 65672-5156
Tel (417) 334-6681 *Founded/Ownrshp* 1976
Sales 24.2MM^E *EMP* 55
SIC 5085 Industrial supplies; Crates, except paper; Signmaker equipment & supplies; Industrial supplies; Crates, except paper; Signmaker equipment & supplies
Pr: Julie Middleton
**Sec:* Robert Middleton
**Ex VP:* Rob L Middleton
**VP:* Kimberly Crosby
Sls Dir: Stephanie Compton
Board of Directors: Julie Middleton Robert Mid

MEMCO SAFETY SUPPLY
See MEMCO INC

D-U-N-S 07-018-0022
MEMEGED TEVUOT SHEMESH
TITAN SOLAR
6711 Valjean Ave, Van Nuys, CA 91406-5819
Tel (866) 575-1211 *Founded/Ownrshp* 2011
Sales 40.0MM *EMP* 172
SIC 1711 5074 Solar energy contractor; Heating equipment & panels, solar; Solar energy contractor; Heating equipment & panels, solar
Owner: Ofir Haimoff
Genl Mgr: Mori Ben

MEMIC
See MAINE EMPLOYERS MUTUAL INSURANCE CO

D-U-N-S 80-979-0231 IMP
■ **MEMOREX PRODUCTS INC**
(*Suby of* IMATION CORP) ★
17777 Center Court Dr N S, Cerritos, CA 90703-9320
Tel (562) 653-2800 *Founded/Ownrshp* 2005
Sales 33.0MM^E *EMP* 159
SIC 5064 5065 5045 3652 3651 Electrical entertainment equipment; Radio & television equipment & parts; Computer peripheral equipment; Pre-recorded records & tapes; Household audio & video equipment; Electrical entertainment equipment; Radio & television equipment & parts; Computer peripheral equipment; Pre-recorded records & tapes; Household audio & video equipment
Pr: Michael Golacinski
**Ch Bd:* Allan Yap
**CFO:* Kevin McDonnell
VP: Randy Finchum
VP: Allen H Gharapetian
VP: Allen Gharatetian
Pdt Mgr: Mark Becknauld
Pdt Mgr: Melanie Lukesh

MEMORIAL BLOOD CENTERS
See INNOVATIVE BLOOD RESOURCES

MEMORIAL CAMPUS
See COLUMBIA UNITED PROVIDERS INC

MEMORIAL CARE MEDICAL CENTERS
See MEMORIAL HEALTH SERVICES

D-U-N-S 02-547-2216
MEMORIAL COMMUNITY HEALTH INC
MEMORIAL HOSPITAL
1423 7th St, Aurora, NE 68818-1141
Tel (402) 694-3171 *Founded/Ownrshp* 1960
Sales 20.8MM *EMP* 280^E
Accts Dohman Akerlund & Eddy Llc
SIC 8062 General medical & surgical hospitals; General medical & surgical hospitals
CEO: Diane Keller
**Pr:* Dennis Ferguson
**Pr:* Norm Luthy
**Treas:* John Ferguson
Dir Lab: Joe Sandmeier
Dir Rx: Jim Tollefsen
Off Mgr: Sabrina Dickey
Sls&Mrk Ex: Reann Regier
Podiatrist: Kristen Anderson
Doctor: Tim Arthur
Nrsg Dir: Cheryl Erickson

D-U-N-S 08-021-2566
MEMORIAL COMMUNITY HOSPITAL CORP
MCH & HEALTH SYSTEM
810 N 22nd St, Blair, NE 68008-1128
Tel (402) 426-2182 *Founded/Ownrshp* 1956
Sales 33.2MM *EMP* 305
Accts Kpmg Llp Omaha Ne
SIC 8062 General medical & surgical hospitals; General medical & surgical hospitals
CEO: Sally Harvey
**Pr:* Robert Copple
CFO: Dan Schonlau
**Ch:* Terry Dutton
**Treas:* Dan Hunt
Exec: Inglish Camero
Dir Rx: Patti Smith
Mktg Dir: Molly Dahlgren
Obsttrcn: Andrea Vermaas
Doctor: Lynda Arnold
Doctor: Matthew Garris

D-U-N-S 96-792-5350
MEMORIAL GROUP INC
4500 Memorial Dr, Belleville, IL 62226-5360
Tel (618) 257-5607 *Founded/Ownrshp* 2011
Sales 40.5MM *EMP* 3
Accts Bkd Llp Saint Louis Mo
SIC 8399 Social services
Prin: Ken Kubicek

MEMORIAL HEALTH
See MEMORIAL HOSPITAL JACKSONVILLE INC

MEMORIAL HEALTH
See CENTER FOR BREAST CARE

D-U-N-S 06-983-3697
MEMORIAL HEALTH CARE INC
GIFT SHOP
826 W King St, Owosso, MI 48867-2120
Tel (989) 725-8101 *Founded/Ownrshp* 1919
Sales 88.0MM *EMP* 71^E
SIC 8641 5947 Civic social & fraternal associations; Gift shop; Civic social & fraternal associations; Gift shop
CEO: Brian L Long
Exec: Janet Johnston
Exec: Iyla Waters
Dir Inf Cn: Megan Smith
Nurse Mgr: Cara Renfrow
Telecom Mg: Todd Wyzynajtys
Opers Supe: Lisa Hasyn
Doctor: Michael Schmidt
Nrsg Dir: Diana Kilgore
Nrsg Dir: Dean Schultz
Pharmcst: Alicia Cicinelli

D-U-N-S 11-916-5301
MEMORIAL HEALTH CARE SYSTEM FOUNDATION INC
MEMORIAL HOSPITAL
(*Suby of* CHI) ★
2525 De Sales Ave, Chattanooga, TN 37404
Tel (423) 495-2525 *Founded/Ownrshp* 1985
Sales 2.7MM *EMP* 5,000
Accts Catholic Health Initiatives E
SIC 8062 General medical & surgical hospitals; General medical & surgical hospitals
CEO: Ruth Brinkley
**Pr:* Debra L Moore
**COO:* Deborah Moore
**VP:* Michael Sutton
Surgeon: Scott Hurlbert

D-U-N-S 00-744-3109
MEMORIAL HEALTH CARE SYSTEM INC
CHI
(*Suby of* CATHOLIC HEALTH INITIATIVES) ★
2525 Desales Ave, Chattanooga, TN 37404-1161
Tel (423) 495-2525 *Founded/Ownrshp* 1985
Sales 557.3MM *EMP* 8,800
Accts Catholic Health Initiatives E
SIC 8082 Home health care services; Home health care services
Pr: James M Hobson
**Pr:* Shawn Morrow
**CFO:* Cheryl A Sadro
**Sr VP:* Debra L Moore
**VP:* Leigh Bertholf
**VP:* Diona Brown
Off Mgr: Liz Browning
Off Mgr: Bob Scherger

D-U-N-S 07-698-4533
MEMORIAL HEALTH CARE SYSTEMS SEWARD NEBRASKA
SEWARD MEMORIAL HOSPITAL
300 N Columbia Ave, Seward, NE 68434-2228
Tel (402) 643-2971 *Founded/Ownrshp* 1949
Sales 27.2MM *EMP* 350
SIC 8062 8059 8011 General medical & surgical hospitals; Nursing home, except skilled & intermediate care facility; Offices & clinics of medical doctors; General medical & surgical hospitals; Nursing home, except skilled & intermediate care facility; Offices & clinics of medical doctors
CEO: Roger Reamer
**CFO:* Greg Jerger
CIO: Sam Smetter
Cmptr Lab: Theresa Schroeber
Sls&Mrk Ex: Carol Carlson
Dir Health: Pam Jacobson
HC Dir: Kim Haney
HC Dir: Lori Williams

D-U-N-S 07-478-3994
MEMORIAL HEALTH CENTER INC
ASPIRUS MEDFORD CLINIC
135 S Gibson St, Medford, WI 54451-1622
Tel (715) 748-8100 *Founded/Ownrshp* 1962
Sales 65.2MM *EMP* 525
SIC 8062 8051

D-U-N-S 96-670-6280
MEMORIAL HEALTH INC
4700 Waters Ave, Savannah, GA 31404-6220
Tel (912) 350-8000 *Founded/Ownrshp* 2011
Sales 24.9MM *EMP* 94^E
SIC 8099 Health & allied services
Prin: James Depew
CFO: Suzanne Heck
Chf Cred: Ken Resmini
VP: Darcy Davis

D-U-N-S 06-234-8485
MEMORIAL HEALTH PARTNERS FOUNDATION INC
5600 Brainerd Rd Ste 500, Chattanooga, TN 37411-5371
Tel (423) 495-6870 *Founded/Ownrshp* 2013
Sales 61.9MM *EMP* 3
SIC 8641 Civic social & fraternal associations; Civic social & fraternal associations
Prin: Sheila Manley

D-U-N-S 96-957-8207
MEMORIAL HEALTH PARTNERS FOUNDATION INC
6028 Shallowford Rd Ste D, Chattanooga, TN 37421-7237
Tel (423) 495-8491 *Founded/Ownrshp* 2011
Sales 53.4MM *EMP* 3
Accts Catholic Health Initiatives E
SIC 8641 Civic social & fraternal associations; Civic social & fraternal associations
Prin: Paula Register

D-U-N-S 06-296-0708
MEMORIAL HEALTH PARTNERS INC
(*Suby of* MEMORIAL HEALTH CARE SYSTEM FOUNDATION INC) ★
6028 Shallowford Rd Ste D, Chattanooga, TN 37421-7237
Tel (423) 495-4848 *Founded/Ownrshp* 1998
Sales 63.4MM *EMP* 2
SIC 8011 6324 Offices & clinics of medical doctors; Hospital & medical service plans; Offices & clinics of medical doctors; Hospital & medical service plans
CEO: Glyn Hughes
COO: Jacki Jackson
VP: Joy S Kirby
**Prin:* Jean Overmyer
Ex Dir: Vance Freeman
CIO: Kevin Burbules

D-U-N-S 60-208-4118
MEMORIAL HEALTH SERVICES
MEMORIAL CARE MEDICAL CENTERS
17360 Brookhurst St # 160, Fountain Valley, CA 92708-8003
Tel (714) 377-6748 *Founded/Ownrshp* 1937
Sales 2.0MMM *EMP* 6,000^E
Accts Pricewaterhousecoopers Llp L
SIC 8062 Health systems agency; General medical & surgical hospitals
Pr: Barry Arbuckle
CFO: Karen Testman
Treas: Rick Graniere
Bd of Dir: Sandy Longobardy
Bd of Dir: Jaci Songstad
Sr VP: Judy Fix
VP: Regina Berman
VP: Devon Dougherty
VP: Deborah Eagle
VP: John Metcalf
VP: Gerald Russell
VP: Cheryl Sadro
VP: Khalid Sheikh

D-U-N-S 07-619-4356
MEMORIAL HEALTH SERVICES - UNIVERSITY OF CALIFORNIA AT IRVINE CENTER FOR HEALTH EDUCATION
2801 Atlantic Ave, Long Beach, CA 90806-1701
Tel (562) 933-2000 *Founded/Ownrshp* 1907
Sales 360.1MM^E *EMP* 10,000^E
SIC 8062 8011 8741 General medical & surgical hospitals; Offices & clinics of medical doctors; Hospital management; General medical & surgical hospitals; Offices & clinics of medical doctors; Hospital management
Pr: Diana Hendel
**Treas:* Darrel Brownell
Sr VP: Wendy Dorchester
MIS Dir: Howard Frechen
Dir IT: Ron Morte
HC Dir: Irene Rosales
Snr Mgr: Robin Watson

MEMORIAL HEALTH SYSTEM
See MEMORIAL HOSPITAL CORP

D-U-N-S 14-840-1813
MEMORIAL HEALTH SYSTEM
701 N 1st St, Springfield, IL 62781-0001
Tel (217) 788-3000 *Founded/Ownrshp* 1981
Sales 67.4MM *EMP* 2,400^E
SIC 8741 8062 Hospital management; General medical & surgical hospitals; Hospital management; General medical & surgical hospitals
Pr: Robert T Clarke
CEO: Edgar J Curtis
CFO: Andrew Costic
CFO: Robert Kay
Chf Mktg O: Robert Vautrain
Ex VP: Doug Rahn
VP: Rajesh G Govindaiah
VP: Marsha A Prater
Adm Dir: Rebecca Anderson
CIO: Wayne Fischer
CIO: Kerra Guffey

D-U-N-S 05-109-8184
MEMORIAL HEALTH SYSTEM OF EAST TEXAS
CHI ST. LUKE'S HEALTH MEMORIAL
1201 W Frank Ave, Lufkin, TX 75904-3357
Tel (936) 634-8111 *Founded/Ownrshp* 1944
Sales 121.8MM *EMP* 940
Accts Axley & Rode Llp Lufkin Tx
SIC 8062 General medical & surgical hospitals; General medical & surgical hospitals
Pr: Bryant H Krenek Jr
**Pr:* Gary Looper
COO: Shawn Barnett
**COO:* Peggy Mortensen
**CFO:* Ken Miller
Treas: Floyd Dickens
Ofcr: Mary Kay Degroot
Ex VP: Don Morris
VP: John Angstadt
VP: Tyane Dietz
**VP:* Rick Hefner
VP: Mike Taylor
Exec: Melinda New
Dir Rx: Eric Ip

D-U-N-S 14-740-8694
MEMORIAL HEALTH SYSTEMS CORP
325 S Belmont St, York, PA 17403-2608
Tel (717) 843-8623 *Founded/Ownrshp* 2012
Sales 293.5M *EMP* 950
Accts Parentebeard Llc York Pa
SIC 8741 8399 Hospital management; Nursing & personal care facility management; Fund raising organization, non-fee basis; Hospital management; Nursing & personal care facility management; Fund raising organization, non-fee basis
Pr: Sally J Dixon
CFO: Richard Imbimbo
Ofcr: Joe Barron
VP: Susan Gordon
Prin: John Dehaas
Prin: Michael Hady
CIO: Jim Mahoney

IT Man: Joyce Allen
Netwrk Eng: John Sebastian
Pharmcst: Jason Kirby
HC Dir: Jackie Eisenhour

D-U-N-S 02-171-6881
MEMORIAL HEALTH SYSTEMS INC
FLORIDA HOSP OCEANSIDE-ORMOND
301 Memorial Medical Pkwy, Daytona Beach, FL 32117-5167
Tel (386) 231-3081 *Founded/Ownrshp* 1961
Sales 49.1MM *EMP* 1,500
SIC 8062 General medical & surgical hospitals; General medical & surgical hospitals
Pr: Daryl Tol
**COO:* Darwinda Copeland
**CFO:* Debbie Thomas
**Chf Mktg O:* Michelle Goeb-Burkett
Ofcr: Magie Epting
Surgeon: Christian Birkedal

D-U-N-S 13-271-1263
MEMORIAL HEALTH SYSTEMS INC
MEMORIAL HEALTHCARE SYSTEM
3501 Johnson St, Hollywood, FL 33021-5421
Tel (954) 265-5846 *Founded/Ownrshp* 1961
Sales 73.9MM^E *EMP* 600
SIC 8062 General medical & surgical hospitals; General medical & surgical hospitals
Ch: Michael Schultz
**Pr:* Daryl Tol
Ex VP: Aurelio Fache
**VP:* Sandra K Johnson
Exec: Ray Kendrick
Chf Nrs Of: Bella Cabrera
Sfty Dirs: Rick Henninger
Surgeon: Thomas Bass
Doctor: Steven Bibevski
Genl Couns: Sarah Griffith
Genl Couns: Harry Raleigh

D-U-N-S 11-075-2359
MEMORIAL HEALTH UNIVERSITY MEDICAL CENTER INC
4700 Waters Ave, Savannah, GA 31404-6283
Tel (912) 350-8000 *Founded/Ownrshp* 1984
Sales 469.3MM *EMP* 5,000
Accts Dixon Hughes Goodman Llp Ashe
SIC 8062 8011 General medical & surgical hospitals; Offices & clinics of medical doctors; General medical & surgical hospitals; Offices & clinics of medical doctors
Pr: Margaret Gill
Dir Recs: Margie Canady
**COO:* Mary Chatman
**Ch:* J Curtis Lewis
**Treas:* J Harry Haslam Jr
Treas: Karen B Pannell
Sr VP: David Byck
**Sr VP:* Ramon V Meguiar
Sr VP: Don E Tomberlin
**VP:* Ira P Berman
VP: Patty Lavely
**VP:* Phoenicia Miracle
VP: Angela Mixon
**VP:* Robert M Tynan
Dir Rad: Barbara Brown

D-U-N-S 13-735-8821
MEMORIAL HEALTHCARE IPA A MEDICAL CORP
(*Suby of* MONARCH HEALTHCARE A MEDICAL GROUP INC) ★
11 Technology Dr, Irvine, CA 92618-2302
Tel (562) 981-9500 *Founded/Ownrshp* 1998
Sales 41.5MM *EMP* 35
Accts Kellog & Andelson
SIC 8011 Offices & clinics of medical doctors; Offices & clinics of medical doctors
Pr: John Turner MD
**CEO:* Patricia Page-Lapenn
COO: Cathy Gates
**VP:* Abelardo Pita MD

MEMORIAL HEALTHCARE SYSTEM
See MEMORIAL HEALTH SYSTEMS INC

D-U-N-S 92-848-5044
MEMORIAL HEALTHTEC LABRATORIES INC
(*Suby of* LONG BEACH MEMORIAL MEDICAL CENTER) ★
2865 Atlantic Ave Ste 203, Long Beach, CA 90806-7426
Tel (562) 933-0777 *Founded/Ownrshp* 1995
Sales 6.2MM^E *EMP* 896^E
SIC 5047 Medical laboratory equipment
Pr: Sandra Reese

MEMORIAL HERMANN
See NORTHEAST HOSPITAL FOUNDATION

MEMORIAL HERMANN BAPTIST BEAUM
See BAPTIST HOSPITALS OF SOUTHEAST TEXAS

D-U-N-S 03-499-7192
MEMORIAL HERMANN BAPTIST BELMONT
MEMORIAL HERMANN BPTIST ORNGE
608 Strickland Dr, Orange, TX 77630-4717
Tel (409) 883-9361 *Founded/Ownrshp* 2001
Sales 53.4MM^E *EMP* 1,600
SIC 8062 General medical & surgical hospitals; General medical & surgical hospitals
CEO: David Pirmer
IT Man: Roland Anderson
HC Dir: Sheila Schoolfield

D-U-N-S 01-079-1515
MEMORIAL HERMANN BAPTIST HOSPITAL
BAPTISTAL HOSPITAL OF SE TEXAS
3080 College St, Beaumont, TX 77701-4606
Tel (409) 212-5000 *Founded/Ownrshp* 1990
Sales 129.7MM^E *EMP* 1,700
SIC 8062 General medical & surgical hospitals; General medical & surgical hospitals
CEO: David Parmer
CFO: Carol Moreen
CFO: Gary Troutman
Dir Lab: Robert Jessen
QA Dir: Julia Hyett

Telecom Mg: Jerry Frye
Software D: Kelly Demerie
Software D: Shawna Lambert-Pitt
Sls&Mrk Ex: Mary Poole
HC Dir: Betty Bullard

MEMORIAL HERMANN BPTIST ORNGE
See MEMORIAL HERMANN BAPTIST BELMONT

D-U-N-S 17-194-7042
MEMORIAL HERMANN CONTINUING CARE CORP
MEMORIAL HRMANN CNTINUING CARE
(*Suby of* MEMORIAL HERMANN HEALTH SYSTEM) ★
929 Gessner Rd Ste 2600, Houston, TX 77024-2593
Tel (713) 461-8372 *Founded/Ownrshp* 1982
Sales 17.3MM^E *EMP* 520
SIC 8361 Rehabilitation center, residential: health care incidental; Rehabilitation center, residential: health care incidental
CEO: James A Faucett
VP: Jim Faucett
Doctor: Emma Curry

D-U-N-S 78-914-2965
MEMORIAL HERMANN FOUNDATION
909 Frostwood Dr, Houston, TX 77024-2301
Tel (713) 827-7012 *Founded/Ownrshp* 1969
Sales 22.1MM *EMP* 35
SIC 8399 Fund raising organization, non-fee basis; Fund raising organization, non-fee basis
CEO: Ileana Trevino
Genl Mgr: Esther Eke-Huber
Genl Mgr: Jennifer Guiton
Genl Mgr: Cheryl Jackson
Off Admin: Sheila Jordan
Off Admin: Melissa Pena
Opers Mgr: Tina Spears
Psych: Sloan Gordon
Doctor: Ajay Jain
Doctor: George Peterkin
Pharmcst: Beatrice John

D-U-N-S 07-418-7949
MEMORIAL HERMANN HEALTH SYSTEM
MEMORIAL HERMANN MEMORIAL CITY HOSPITAL
(*Suby of* MEMORIAL HERMANN HEALTHCARE SYSTEM) ★
909 Frostwood Dr Ste 2100, Houston, TX 77024-2301
Tel (713) 242-3000 *Founded/Ownrshp* 1982
Sales 3.7MMM *EMP* 14,000
SIC 8062 8093 General medical & surgical hospitals; Specialty outpatient clinics; General medical & surgical hospitals; Specialty outpatient clinics
Pr: Dan Wolterman
Chf Rad: Khanh Huynh
CEO: Susan Distefano
**COO:* Chuck Stokes
CFO: Nancy Bennett
**CFO:* Dennis Laraway
Dir Rad: Alla Vargo
IT Man: Joe Dickson
Mtls Mgr: Karen Cooper
Sfty Mgr: Nasima Rahimtoola
Mktg Dir: Corrina Abrego

D-U-N-S 10-267-4629 IMP
MEMORIAL HERMANN HEALTHCARE SYSTEM
929 Gessner Rd Ste 2600, Houston, TX 77024-2593
Tel (713) 338-5555 *Founded/Ownrshp* 1982
Sales 14.6MMM *EMP* 22,000
SIC 8059 8062 Hospital, affiliated with AMA residency; Convalescent home; Rest home, with health care; Convalescent home; General medical & surgical hospitals
CEO: Daniel J Wolterman
Chf Rad: Terrance Oconner
Pr: Emily Handwerk
Pr: Vicki Pellerz
**COO:* Dale St Arnold
CFO: Carroll Aulbaugh
**CFO:* Stacey Bevil
CFO: John Gay
CFO: Kevin Lovinggood
CFO: Larry Smith
**Treas:* Carrol E Aubaugh
Bd of Dir: Bette Smyth
Chf Mktg O: Maurice Liebman
Ofcr: Charles Bumpass
Assoc VP: Perry Flowers
Assoc VP: James Polfreman
**VP:* David Bradshaw
VP: Frank Brown
VP: Ramona Cahn
Exec: Robert Blake
Dir Risk M: Rebecca Harper

D-U-N-S 79-134-1832
MEMORIAL HERMANN KATY HOSPITAL
(*Suby of* MEMORIAL HERMANN HEALTH SYSTEM) ★
23900 Katy Fwy, Katy, TX 77494-1323
Tel (281) 644-7000 *Founded/Ownrshp* 1981
Sales 198.5MM *EMP* 326^E
SIC 8062 General medical & surgical hospitals; General medical & surgical hospitals
Pr: Dan Wolterman
CFO: Kevin Lovingood
Dir Lab: Tianay Brown
Off Admin: Leilani Bell
CIO: Emma Curry
DP Dir: Tina Harbert
Sfty Dirs: Tom Burnett

D-U-N-S 96-961-0976
MEMORIAL HERMANN MEDICAL GROUP
909 Frostwood Dr Fl 2, Houston, TX 77024-2307
Tel (713) 448-5555 *Founded/Ownrshp* 2012
Sales 89.6MM *EMP* 56^E
SIC 8099 Health screening service; Health screening service
Prin: James A Faucett
CFO: Janet Smith

MEMORIAL HERMANN MEMORIAL CITY
See INSTITUTE FOR REHABILITATION & RESEARCH

MEMORIAL HERMANN MEMORIAL CITY HOSPITAL
See MEMORIAL HERMANN HEALTH SYSTEM

D-U-N-S 61-904-6951
MEMORIAL HERMANN ORTHOPEDIC & SPINE HOSPITAL
FOUNDATION SURGICAL HOSPITAL
5410 West Loop S, Bellaire, TX 77401-2103
Tel (713) 314-4444 *Founded/Ownrshp* 2007
Sales 26.5MM^E *EMP* 110^E
SIC 8069 8011 Orthopedic hospital; Neurosurgeon
CEO: Andrew Knizley
Chf Rad: Scott Staewen
COO: George Walker
CFO: Jennie Campbell
VP: Jerome Mee
Dir Lab: Tham Hoang
Dir Rad: Augustine Magana
Dir Rx: Penny Carroll
IT Man: Kevin Varner

D-U-N-S 12-473-5577
MEMORIAL HERMANN SUGAR LAND SURGICAL HOSPITAL LLP
SUGARLAND SURGICAL HOSPITAL
(*Suby of* UNITED SURGICAL PARTNERS INTERNATIONAL INC) ★
16906 Southwest Fwy, Sugar Land, TX 77479-2350
Tel (281) 243-1000 *Founded/Ownrshp* 2001
Sales 23.9MM *EMP* 90
SIC 8062 General medical & surgical hospitals; General medical & surgical hospitals

MEMORIAL HOME HEALTH CARE
See BEACON HEALTH VENTURES INC

MEMORIAL HOSP & HLTH CARE CTR
See LITTLE CO OF MARY HOSPITAL OF INDIANA INC

MEMORIAL HOSPITAL
See MEMORIAL COMMUNITY HEALTH INC

MEMORIAL HOSPITAL
See MARTINSVILLE NEWCO

MEMORIAL HOSPITAL
See MOORE COUNTY HOSPITAL DISTRICT

MEMORIAL HOSPITAL
See YORK PENNSYLVANIA HOSPITAL CO LLC

MEMORIAL HOSPITAL
See PROTESTANT MEMORIAL MEDICAL CENTER INC

MEMORIAL HOSPITAL
See GONZALES HEALTHCARE SYSTEMS

MEMORIAL HOSPITAL
See ADAIR COUNTY HEALTH CENTER INC

MEMORIAL HOSPITAL
See PROTESTANT MEMORIAL MEDICAL CENTER INC

MEMORIAL HOSPITAL
See MEMORIAL HEALTH CARE SYSTEM FOUNDATION INC

D-U-N-S 05-416-1351
MEMORIAL HOSPITAL
MEMORIAL HOSPITAL HEALTHLINK
715 S Taft Ave, Fremont, OH 43420-3296
Tel (419) 334-6657 *Founded/Ownrshp* 1915
Sales 69.7MM *EMP* 550
SIC 8062 General medical & surgical hospitals; General medical & surgical hospitals
CEO: Pamella Jensen
Dir Case M: Sharon Chudzinski
Dir Lab: Ron Billow
**Prin:* John Al Gorman
Mktg Dir: Lisa Murphy
Mktg Dir: Andy Smith
Ansthlgy: James Stierwalt
Doctor: Fateh Ahmed
Doctor: Kelly Randall
Pharmcst: Patricia Beaschler

D-U-N-S 06-052-2653
MEMORIAL HOSPITAL
ALBANY MEMORIAL HOSPITAL
600 Northern Blvd, Albany, NY 12204-1083
Tel (518) 471-3221 *Founded/Ownrshp* 1868
Sales 90.0MM *EMP* 1,110
Accts Pricewaterhousecooper Llp
SIC 8062 General medical & surgical hospitals; General medical & surgical hospitals
CEO: Norman Dascher
Chf Rad: Michael Gabor
COO: Karen Tossey
Exec: Norm Dasher
Dir OR: Patricia Lefebvere
Dir Lab: Juan Patz
Chf Nrs Of: Margaret Sorenson
CIO: John Collins
CIO: Robert Duthe
CIO: Lou Spychalski
Doctor: Hasan Atalay

D-U-N-S 06-983-3523
MEMORIAL HOSPITAL
826 W King St, Owosso, MI 48867-2120
Tel (989) 723-5211 *Founded/Ownrshp* 1919
Sales 115.2MM *EMP* 1,000
Accts Plante & Moran Pllc East Lans
SIC 8062 General medical & surgical hospitals; General medical & surgical hospitals
Pr: James Full
**CFO:* Brian Long
VP: Jim Barb
VP: Tom Ogg
VP: Shirley Tate-Gibson
Dir Lab: Margaret Noth
Ex Dir: Lynda Beaton
Surgeon: Daniel Williams

D-U-N-S 06-985-2580
MEMORIAL HOSPITAL
MEMORIAL HOSPITAL OF RHODE ISLAND
(*Suby of* CARE NEW ENGLAND HEALTH SYSTEM INC) ★
111 Brewster St, Pawtucket, RI 02860-4474
Tel (401) 729-2000 *Founded/Ownrshp* 2013
Sales 148.7MM *EMP* 1,400
SIC 8062 6513 General medical & surgical hospitals; Apartment building operators; General medical & surgical hospitals; Apartment building operators
Pr: James Sanale MD
CFO: Susan Albin
CFO: Paul Beaudoin
Trst: Karl Sherry
Trst Ofcr: William Kapos
VP: Robert Ackermann
VP: Thomas J Gough
VP: Marie K Kessel
VP: Judy Van Tilburg
Dir Case M: Julie Scallon
Chf Nrs Of: Elizabeth Jordan

D-U-N-S 07-341-0854
MEMORIAL HOSPITAL
T M H MEMORIAL HOSPITAL
750 Hospital Loop, Craig, CO 81625-8750
Tel (970) 824-9411 *Founded/Ownrshp* 1950
Sales 29.7MM^E *EMP* 200
SIC 8062 General medical & surgical hospitals; General medical & surgical hospitals
CEO: John Rossfeld
**CFO:* Bryan Chalmers
CFO: Jeff Chilson
Dir Lab: Kristine Cooper
Dir Rad: Christine Winn
Off Mgr: Sandra Chamberlain
Dir IT: Mary Davis
IT Man: Bryan Adams
Ansthlgy: Tamara K Rice

D-U-N-S 13-329-0783
MEMORIAL HOSPITAL
3073 White Mountain Hwy, North Conway, NH 03860-7101
Tel (603) 356-5461 *Founded/Ownrshp* 1971
Sales 63.3MM *EMP* 3
SIC 8011 Orthopedic physician; Orthopedic physician
Owner: Scott McKinnon
**Owner:* Gary Poquette
VP: Curtis Kerbs
Dir Inf Cn: Andrea Murphy
Dir Rad: Sherry Cormier
Dir Rx: Jim Keohane
Dir Rx: Joseph Larue
Prac Mgr: Aline Lacasse
Doctor: Mary Vigeant

D-U-N-S 15-450-6505
MEMORIAL HOSPITAL
LOGANSPORT MEMORIAL HOSPITAL
1101 Michigan Ave, Logansport, IN 46947-1596
Tel (574) 753-7541 *Founded/Ownrshp* 1925
Sales 61.2MM *EMP* 507
SIC 8062 General medical & surgical hospitals; General medical & surgical hospitals
Pr: David Ameen
CFO: Chad Higgins
Trst: Brian Morrill
Ofcr: Sandra Elliot
VP: James Schrader
Dir Inf Cn: Anna McClane
Dir Lab: Hershell Hamilton
Dir Rx: Jeff Lee
Dir Pat Ac: Richard Stoving
Off Mgr: Carol Earnest
CIO: Beth Jump

D-U-N-S 86-859-9317
MEMORIAL HOSPITAL - WEST VOLUSIA INC
ADVENTIST HEALTH SYSTEM SUNBEL
(*Suby of* ADVENTIST HEALTH SYSTEM/SUNBELT INC) ★
701 W Plymouth Ave, Deland, FL 32720-3291
Tel (386) 943-4522 *Founded/Ownrshp* 1957
Sales 141.4MM *EMP* 1,000^E
SIC 8062 General medical & surgical hospitals; General medical & surgical hospitals
CEO: Tim Cook
Pr: Nancy Clark
**Pr:* Ed Noseworthy
**COO:* Hector De Jesus
**CFO:* Nigel Hinds
VP: Rick Robinson
Dir Teleco: Roy M Laughlin
Dir Rad: Wesley Harden
Adm Dir: Ellen Hillyer
MIS Dir: Velma Songy
Dir IT: David Piper

D-U-N-S 06-921-6992
MEMORIAL HOSPITAL AND MANOR AUXILIARY INC (GA)
1500 E Shotwell St, Bainbridge, GA 39819-4256
Tel (229) 246-3500 *Founded/Ownrshp* 1960
Sales 79.4MM^E *EMP* 490
Accts Draffin & Tucker Llp Albany
SIC 8062 8051 General medical & surgical hospitals; Skilled nursing care facilities; General medical & surgical hospitals; Skilled nursing care facilities
CEO: Ruthie Giles
Chf Rad: Jerjis Alajaji
Pr: Maeve Whitworth
**CEO:* Mamie Howard
**CEO:* Carol Lewis
COO: Lee Harris
**CFO:* Danna Sue Hadsock
CFO: Faye N Herrig
Dir OR: Martha Odum
Dir Inf Cn: Anita J Chesser
Dir Risk M: Jan J Bennett
Dir Rad: Eduardo Stincer
Dir Rx: Ellen King

MEMORIAL HOSPITAL AND MED CTR
See MIDLAND COUNTY HOSPITAL DISTRICT

D-U-N-S 05-423-4877
MEMORIAL HOSPITAL ASSOCIATION INC
1454 N County Road 2050, Carthage, IL 62321-3551
Tel (217) 357-8574 Founded/Ownrshp 1950
Sales 22.0MM EMP 138E
Accts Eide Bailly Llp Dubuque Iowa
SIC 8062 5912 7352 5999 General medical & surgical hospitals; Drug stores; Medical equipment rental; Medical apparatus & supplies; General medical & surgical hospitals; Drug stores; Medical equipment rental; Medical apparatus & supplies
CEO: Ada Bair
CFO: Teresa Smith
Exec: Dan Asbury
Exec: Shelly Fox
Dir OR: Dina Schaller
Dir Risk M: Nancy Huls
Dir Lab: Royce Kesselirng
Dir Lab: Cyndy Wollbrink
Dir Rx: Ed Phelan
Admn Mgr: Suzad Goetz
Dir IT: Cyndi Froh

D-U-N-S 01-035-7325
MEMORIAL HOSPITAL ASSOCIATION INC OF CAMBRIDGE MINNESOTA
CAMBRIDGE MEDICAL CENTER
701 Dellwood St S, Cambridge, MN 55008-1920
Tel (763) 689-7700 Founded/Ownrshp 1954
Sales 83.6MM EMP 770
SIC 8062 General medical & surgical hospitals; General medical & surgical hospitals
Pr: Dennis Doran
Genl Mgr: Nicole Klanderud
Surgeon: Richard Birdwell
Surgeon: Patricia Schuster
Doctor: Dale Berry

D-U-N-S 07-397-3752
MEMORIAL HOSPITAL AT NORTH CONWAY N H
3073 White Mountain Hwy, North Conway, NH 03860-7101
Tel (603) 356-4949 Founded/Ownrshp 1910
Sales 63.1MM EMP 460E
Accts Ernst & Young Llp Manchester
SIC 8052 8062 Intermediate care facilities; General medical & surgical hospitals; Intermediate care facilities; General medical & surgical hospitals
Pr: Scott McKinnon
*Ex Dir: Becky Adams
*Ex Dir: Gary Poquette
Doctor: Douglas Taylor

D-U-N-S 07-947-5109
MEMORIAL HOSPITAL AUXILIARY INC
4500 13th St, Gulfport, MS 39501-2515
Tel (228) 867-4000 Founded/Ownrshp 1946
Sales 366.7MME EMP 2,500
Accts Scott Niolet Pass Christian
SIC 8062 General medical & surgical hospitals; General medical & surgical hospitals
CEO: Gary Marchand
Pr: John Baxter
COO: Kent Nicaud
*Ch: Myrtis Franke
*Sec: Edward O Reid
VP: John Doulis
VP: Nancy Downs
VP: Jennifer Dumal
Exec: Christy Smith
Dir Rx: Charles Eisenberg
Div Mgr: Mike West

D-U-N-S 07-576-1783
MEMORIAL HOSPITAL CORP
MEMORIAL HEALTH SYSTEM
1400 E Boulder St, Colorado Springs, CO 80909-5599
Tel (719) 365-5000 Founded/Ownrshp 1998
Sales 397.1MME EMP 2,438
SIC 8062 General medical & surgical hospitals; General medical & surgical hospitals
CEO: Mike Scialdone
COO: Bob Brazil
COO: Colette Martin
*COO: Bill Mohon
CFO: Gary Flansburg
CFO: Elgin Glanzer
CFO: Tracy Narvet
Treas: Margaret Carmack
Ofcr: Frank Zautcke
VP: Mark Duster
VP: David Graham
VP: Oda Roozeboom
VP: Mary Yantis
VP: Mary Jo Yantis
Dir Rx: Jim Lewis
Dir Rx: Kyle Miller

D-U-N-S 61-007-3702
MEMORIAL HOSPITAL FLAGLER INC
FLORIDA HOSPITAL FLAGLER
60 Memorial Medical Pkwy, Palm Coast, FL 32164-5980
Tel (386) 586-2000 Founded/Ownrshp 1989
Sales 173.2MM EMP 218
SIC 8062 General medical & surgical hospitals; General medical & surgical hospitals
Pr: David Ottati
Chf Rad: George Byers
*COO: Joanne King
CFO: France Crunk
*CFO: Valerie Ziesmer
Ofcr: Ken Mattison
Dir Risk M: Kathy Hopkins
Dir Lab: Shirley Pearson
Dir Rad: Peter Roe
Dir Rx: John Lee
Chf Nrs Of: Patricia Dolan

D-U-N-S 07-682-8409
MEMORIAL HOSPITAL FOR CANCER AND ALLIED DISEASES
1275 York Ave, New York, NY 10065-6094
Tel (212) 639-2000 Founded/Ownrshp 1884
Sales 2.6MMM EMP 9,269
SIC 8069 Specialty hospitals, except psychiatric; Cancer hospital; Cancer hospital
CEO: Craig B Thompson MD
Pathlgst: Alice Ho

MEMORIAL HOSPITAL HEALTHLINK
See MEMORIAL HOSPITAL

D-U-N-S 07-478-3408
MEMORIAL HOSPITAL INC
MEMORIAL MEDICAL CENTER
216 Sunset Pl, Neillsville, WI 54456-1799
Tel (715) 743-3101 Founded/Ownrshp 1954
Sales 31.3MME EMP 250E
SIC 8062 8051 8011 General medical & surgical hospitals; Skilled nursing care facilities; Offices & clinics of medical doctors; General medical & surgical hospitals; Skilled nursing care facilities; Offices & clinics of medical doctors
CEO: David Baltzer
Chf Path: Keith Henry
*Pr: Bob Barth
*CEO: Glen Grady
CFO: Roger Sneath
*VP: Rick Szymanski
Dir OR: Karen King
Dir Rad: Paul Harmer
CIO: Val King
IT Man: Shelley Janke
Surgeon: Maureen Kidd

D-U-N-S 12-032-2375
MEMORIAL HOSPITAL INC
MANCHESTER MEMORIAL HOSPITAL
210 Marie Langdon Dr, Manchester, KY 40962-6388
Tel (606) 598-5104 Founded/Ownrshp 1955
Sales 51.5MM EMP 500
SIC 8062 General medical & surgical hospitals; General medical & surgical hospitals
CEO: Erika Skula
*Pr: Dennis Myers
*COO: Helen Wilson
CFO: Richard Bogge
CFO: Erica Skula
*Bd of Dir: Eric Lunde
Ofcr: Dennis Meyers
VP: Robert Arais
VP: David H Deutsch
VP: Thomas Gardner
VP: John Hanks
VP: Sarah Lewis
*VP: Benny Nolen
VP: Mark Strachota
VP: Mike Turber
*VP: Daniel T Walker
Dir Inf Cn: Rita Collett
Dir Rx: Michael Ledford

D-U-N-S 06-960-4072
MEMORIAL HOSPITAL INC OF TOWANDA PENNSYLVANIA (PA)
91 Hospital Dr, Towanda, PA 18848-9702
Tel (570) 268-4713 Founded/Ownrshp 1946
Sales 38.7MM EMP 500
Accts Parentebeard Llc Philadelphia
SIC 8062 General medical & surgical hospitals; General medical & surgical hospitals
Pr: Gary A Baker
*CFO: William Rohrbach
VP: Lynn Dibble
VP: Tonya Garges
Dir OR: Rebecca Bellows
Dir Risk M: Kathy McDonald
Dir Lab: Steve Grazaitis
Admn Mgr: Cindy Carroll
Off Mgr: Desiree Pratt
Off Admin: Anne Staats
CIO: Karen Brown

D-U-N-S 06-588-8422
■ **MEMORIAL HOSPITAL JACKSONVILLE INC**
MEMORIAL HEALTH
(Suby of HCA INC) ★
3625 University Blvd S, Jacksonville, FL 32216-4207
Tel (904) 399-6111 Founded/Ownrshp 1995
Sales 295.2MME EMP 1,380
SIC 8062 General medical & surgical hospitals; General medical & surgical hospitals
CEO: James O'Loughlin
Chf Rad: Nina Kazerooni
CFO: Ashley Johnson
Exec: Barbara Courson
Dir Risk M: Kelly Mullee
Dir Rad: Mary Alderman
Dir Rad: Shannon Beardsley
Dir Rad: Michael J Borbely
Dir Rad: Richard Buxton
Dir Rad: James Caraway
Dir Rad: Timothy B Daniel
Dir Rx: Adrianne Schmidt

D-U-N-S 07-465-0961
MEMORIAL HOSPITAL LOS BANOS
(Suby of SUTTER C H S) ★
520 W I St, Los Banos, CA 93635-3419
Tel (209) 826-0591 Founded/Ownrshp 1982
Sales 38.2MM EMP 160
SIC 8062

D-U-N-S 07-893-3447
MEMORIAL HOSPITAL OF BURLINGTON COMMUNITY FOUNDATION INC (WI)
AURORA MEM HOSP BURLINGTON
(Suby of AURORA HEALTH CARE INC) ★
252 Mchenry St, Burlington, WI 53105-1828
Tel (262) 767-6000 Founded/Ownrshp 1922
Sales 30.4MME EMP 635
SIC 8062

D-U-N-S 07-834-0387
MEMORIAL HOSPITAL OF CARBON COUNTY
MACC ENERGY BASIN CLINIC
2221 Elm St, Rawlins, WY 82301-5108
Tel (307) 324-2221 Founded/Ownrshp 1919
Sales 38.2MME EMP 186
SIC 8062 General medical & surgical hospitals; General medical & surgical hospitals
CEO: Dana Barnett
*Ch Bd: Mark Kostovny
CFO: Chelle Keplinger
*CFO: Michelle Keplinger
*CFO: David Pike
*VP: Karran Bedwell
*VP: Mel Muldrow
Dir Sec: Joseph Heinlein
Dir IT: Toby Schaef
Dir IT: Justin Schwick
Doctor: Karen Pate

D-U-N-S 07-995-8476
MEMORIAL HOSPITAL OF CONVERSE COUNTY
111 S 5th St, Douglas, WY 82633-2434
Tel (307) 358-2122 Founded/Ownrshp 1942, 1951
Sales 44.7MM EMP 380
Accts Lovelett Skogen & Associates
SIC 8062 General medical & surgical hospitals; General medical & surgical hospitals
Pr: Brian Smith
*CEO: Ryan Smith
*CFO: Curtis R Dugger
*VP: James F Morgan
Doctor: Kara Underwood
Nrsg Dir: Lori Koby

D-U-N-S 07-491-9259
MEMORIAL HOSPITAL OF EASTON MD INC
219 S Washington St, Easton, MD 21601-2996
Tel (410) 822-1000 Founded/Ownrshp 1982
Sales 114.5MME EMP 1,241
SIC 8062 General medical & surgical hospitals; General medical & surgical hospitals
Pr: Joseph Ross
V Ch: Charles Lea Jr
Ofcr: Ken Kozel
Dir Soc: Lee Lewis
Nurse Mgr: Kim Billingslea
Dir QC: Donna Prahal
IT Man: Ted Book
IT Man: Judy Smith
Ansthlgy: Kevin Nebab
Doctor: Alan Greene
Pharmcst: Tom Sisca

D-U-N-S 06-664-6183
MEMORIAL HOSPITAL OF GARDENA
(Suby of AVANTI HEALTH SYSTEM LLC) ★
4060 Woody Blvd, Los Angeles, CA 90023
Tel (323) 268-5514 Founded/Ownrshp 2009
Sales 110.1MME EMP 400
SIC 8062 General medical & surgical hospitals; General medical & surgical hospitals
CEO: Araceli Lonergan
*CFO: Daniel Heckathorne
VP: Hector Hernandez
Dir OR: Martin Perez
Pharmcst: Gary Fong
Pharmcst: Linh Nguyen
Cert Phar: Joseph Neri
HC Dir: Tessie Meza

D-U-N-S 04-072-6275
MEMORIAL HOSPITAL OF LARAMIE COUNTY
CHEYENNE REGIONAL MEDICAL CTR
214 E 23rd St, Cheyenne, WY 82001-3748
Tel (307) 633-7667 Founded/Ownrshp 1919
Sales 290.0MM EMP 1,270
Accts Eide Bailly Llp Fargo North
SIC 8062 Hospital, AMA approved residency; Hospital, AMA approved residency
CEO: John Lucas MD
Chf Rad: Daniel Possehn
*CFO: Kerry Warburton
Chf Mktg O: David Lind
Ofcr: Aimee Dendrinos
*VP: Ashutosh Goel
VP: Kevin Stansbury
Dir Rad: Bill Cummins
Dir Rx: Sarah A Blkely
Dir Rx: Cheyenne Cent
Chf Nrs Of: Mary Calkins

MEMORIAL HOSPITAL OF RHODE ISLAND
See MEMORIAL HOSPITAL

D-U-N-S 07-548-2133
■ **MEMORIAL HOSPITAL OF SALEM COUNTY**
SOUTH JERSEY PHYSICAL THERAPY
(Suby of COMMUNITY HEALTH SYSTEMS INC) ★
310 Woodstown Rd, Salem, NJ 08079
Tel (856) 935-1000 Founded/Ownrshp 1919
Sales 70.5MME EMP 720
SIC 8062 General medical & surgical hospitals; General medical & surgical hospitals
CEO: Richard Grogan
*CFO: Robert Ehinger
*Ch: Thomas Pankot
*VP: Brenda Hamilton
S&M/VP: Stewart Moss
Board of Directors: Richard Grogan

D-U-N-S 01-037-5376
MEMORIAL HOSPITAL OF SHERIDAN COUNTY
1401 W 5th St, Sheridan, WY 82801-2705
Tel (307) 672-1000 Founded/Ownrshp 1921
Sales 78.4MME EMP 422
SIC 8062 General medical & surgical hospitals; General medical & surgical hospitals
Ch: Ron Mischke
Pr: Debrah Anderson
Pr: Joseph Garcia
*CEO: Mike McCafferty
COO: Andi Bell
*CFO: Ed Joeman
Trst: Sara Smith
*Sr VP: Gary Miller
Dir Lab: Gary Sellenrick
Dir Rad: John Miller
Chf Nrs Of: Peggy Callantine

MEMORIAL HOSPITAL OF SOUTH BEN
See ELKHART GENERAL HOSPITAL INC

MEMORIAL HOSPITAL OF SOUTH BEN
See BEACON HEALTH SYSTEM INC

MEMORIAL HOSPITAL OF SOUTH BEN
See BEACON MEDICAL GROUP INC

D-U-N-S 06-470-1261 IMP
MEMORIAL HOSPITAL OF SOUTH BEND INC
(Suby of BEACON HEALTH SYSTEM INC) ★
615 N Michigan St, South Bend, IN 46601-1087
Tel (574) 647-7751 Founded/Ownrshp 2013
Sales 374.2MM EMP 23E
SIC 8062 General medical & surgical hospitals; Hospital, medical school affiliated with nursing & residency; General medical & surgical hospitals; Hospital, medical school affiliated with nursing & residency
Pr: Kreg Gruber
Dir Rx: Mark Herriman

D-U-N-S 07-296-4521
MEMORIAL HOSPITAL OF SWEETWATER COUNTY
1200 College Dr, Rock Springs, WY 82901-5868
Tel (307) 362-3711 Founded/Ownrshp 1948
Sales 64.4MM EMP 435
Accts Clifton Larson Allen Llp Minn
SIC 8062 General medical & surgical hospitals
Ex Dir: Gerard Klein
CFO: Robert Scott
Ex Dir: M Ferry
Dir IT: Rich Tyler
Sls Mgr: Erasmus Potter
Pathlgst: Jim Martinsky
Surgeon: John Iliya
Obsttrcn: Casey Cadina
Anesthlgy: Mike Holland
Anesthlgy: Ronald McKee
Pharmcst: Sarah Bartek

D-U-N-S 78-777-1054
■ **MEMORIAL HOSPITAL OF TAMPA LP**
COLUMBIA HCA
(Suby of HCA INC) ★
2901 W Swann Ave, Tampa, FL 33609-4057
Tel (813) 873-6400 Founded/Ownrshp 2013
Sales 68.9MME EMP 500E
SIC 8062 General medical & surgical hospitals; General medical & surgical hospitals
CEO: John Mainieri
Dir Soc: Susan Kadechka
Pharmcst: Nancy Kazarian
Pharmcst: Alberto Mosquera
Diag Rad: Richard Knight
Snr Mgr: Ashit Vijapura

D-U-N-S 07-733-0587
MEMORIAL HOSPITAL OF TEXAS COUNTY
520 Medical Dr, Guymon, OK 73942-4499
Tel (580) 338-6515 Founded/Ownrshp 1949
Sales 35.9MME EMP 180
SIC 8062 General medical & surgical hospitals
CEO: Julie West
CFO: Bomer Starsky
Dir Rx: Chet Oblander
*Prin: Jim Grocholski
CIO: Sheldon Spence
Doctor: Emmanuel Barias
Doctor: Tom Griffen
Doctor: Kelly R McMuy
Doctor: Paul M Reed
Doctor: Chris Slater

D-U-N-S 07-503-8703
MEMORIAL HOSPITAL OF UNION COUNTY
500 London Ave, Marysville, OH 43040-1594
Tel (937) 644-6115 Founded/Ownrshp 1952
Sales 81.5MM EMP 800
SIC 8062 Hospital, affiliated with AMA residency; Hospital, affiliated with AMA residency
CEO: Olas A Hubbs
COO: Laurie Whittington
*CFO: Jeff Ehlers
*Ch: Dennis Stone
VP: Victor Trianfo
Exec: Julie Hamilton
Dir Lab: Eric Keifer
Dir Rad: Mareva Page
Dir Rx: Britt Cummins
Genl Mgr: Debbie Pucci
MIS Dir: Carl Zani

D-U-N-S 06-919-0452
MEMORIAL HOSPITAL OF WASHINGTON COUNTY INC
WASHINGTON CNTY RGONAL MED CTR
610 Sparta Rd, Sandersville, GA 31082-1860
Tel (478) 240-2000 Founded/Ownrshp 1961
Sales 42.0MME EMP 330
SIC 8062 8051 General medical & surgical hospitals; Skilled nursing care facilities; General medical & surgical hospitals; Skilled nursing care facilities
Ch Bd: Jimmy Childre
Chf Rad: Lawrence Steinfeld
COO: Tim Richardson
*Ofcr: Cynthia Parker
Dir Lab: Lynn Miller
Dir Soc: Ashley Gheeling
Dir Rad: Sherri Black
Dir Rx: Josh Branan
Dir Rx: Josh Brannen
Dir Env Sv: Sammy Knight
Dir Sec: Chris Callaway

D-U-N-S 03-023-1377
MEMORIAL HOSPITAL OF WILLIAM F AND GERTRUDE F JONES INC
JONES MEMORIAL HOSPITAL
191 N Main St, Wellsville, NY 14895-1150
Tel (585) 593-1100 Founded/Ownrshp 1921
Sales 36.1MM EMP 373
SIC 8062 General medical & surgical hospitals; General medical & surgical hospitals
CEO: Eva Benedict
CFO: Tracy Gates
Ofcr: Call Andrew
VP: Donna Bliven
VP: Susan Nicol
VP: Brenda Torrey
Dir Lab: Elaine Austin

Dir Rad: Carrie Walker
Dir Rx: Jody Bellows
Off Mgr: Sue Kay
S&M/VP: Robert Bruckner

D-U-N-S 06-988-8634
MEMORIAL HOSPITAL ROXBORO
(*Suby of* SOLIS HEALTHCARE LP) ★
5800 Ridge Ave, Philadelphia, PA 19128-1737
Tel (215) 483-9900 *Founded/Ownrshp* 2007
Sales 8.7MM[E] *EMP* 604
SIC 8062 Hospital, medical school affiliated with nursing & residency; Hospital, medical school affiliated with nursing & residency
CEO: John J Donnelly Jr
CFO: Michael Metts
VP: Add Anderson

D-U-N-S 84-847-7378
MEMORIAL HOSPITAL SALEM COUNTY
310 Route 45, Salem, NJ 08079-2064
Tel (856) 935-1000 *Founded/Ownrshp* 1985
Sales 73.9MM[E] *EMP* 775
SIC 8062 General medical & surgical hospitals; General medical & surgical hospitals
CEO: Ryan Jensen
**CEO:* Jim Angle
**CFO:* Peter Verrecchia
Dir Lab: Rita Nunez
**Prin:* Susan Cusack
CIO: Brian McCarthy
Ansthlgy: Carl Fehder
Nrsg Dir: Tracie Chambers
Pharmcst: David Marini

D-U-N-S 07-315-1573
MEMORIAL HOSPITAL SEMINOLE HOSPITAL DISTRICT
209 Nw 8th St, Seminole, TX 79360-3447
Tel (432) 758-5811 *Founded/Ownrshp* 1971
Sales 20.0MM *EMP* 230[E]
SIC 8062 8051 General medical & surgical hospitals; Skilled nursing care facilities; General medical & surgical hospitals; Skilled nursing care facilities
Pr: Jeff Gray
CFO: Traci Anderson

MEMORIAL HRMANN CNTINUING CARE
See MEMORIAL HERMANN CONTINUING CARE CORP

MEMORIAL MEDICAL CENTER
See CONEMAUGH VALLEY MEMORIAL HOSPITAL

MEMORIAL MEDICAL CENTER
See SUTTER CENTRAL VALLEY HOSPITALS

MEMORIAL MEDICAL CENTER
See MEMORIAL HOSPITAL INC

MEMORIAL MEDICAL CENTER
See BON SECOURS-MEMORIAL REGIONAL MEDICAL CENTER INC

MEMORIAL MEDICAL CENTER
See PHC-LAS CRUCES INC

D-U-N-S 07-562-0179
MEMORIAL MEDICAL CENTER
701 N 1st St, Springfield, IL 62781-0001
Tel (217) 788-3000 *Founded/Ownrshp* 1981
Sales 1.8MMM *EMP* 2,849
SIC 8062 General medical & surgical hospitals; General medical & surgical hospitals
Pr: Edgar J Curtis
**COO:* Douglas Rahn
CFO: Tim Schmidt
Sr VP: Rajesh G Govindaiah
VP: David Chapman
VP: Callahan Chuck
VP: Kevin England
VP: Scott Kiriakos
VP: Marsha A Prater
Dir Risk M: Barb Kline
Dir Rx: Les Ono

D-U-N-S 03-001-8725
MEMORIAL MEDICAL CENTER INC (WI)
MMC BEHAVIORAL HEALTH SERVICES
1615 Maple Ln, Ashland, WI 54806-3689
Tel (715) 682-5500 *Founded/Ownrshp* 1968
Sales 59.3MM *EMP* 425
Accts Mcgladrey Llp Duluth Minneso
SIC 8062 Hospital, affiliated with AMA residency; Hospital, affiliated with AMA residency
CEO: Jason T Douglas
Chf Rad: Michael Semotuk
COO: Dan Nursin
**CFO:* Kent Umonseau
CFO: Brad Veller
**VP:* Les Whitaker
CIO: Patrick Anderson
QA Dir: Nancy Dufek
Dir IT: Adam Besio
Dir IT: Wendi Kreinbring
Psych: Hazel McClaire

D-U-N-S 07-508-6520
MEMORIAL MEDICAL CENTER INC
2450 S Telshor Blvd, Las Cruces, NM 88011-5076
Tel (575) 522-8641 *Founded/Ownrshp* 1996
Sales 241.8MM *EMP* 1,450
SIC 8062

D-U-N-S 07-258-2190
MEMORIAL MEDICAL CENTER OF WEST MICHIGAN
SPECTRUM HEALTH LUDINGTON HOSP
(*Suby of* SPECTRUM HEALTH SYSTEM) ★
1 N Atkinson Dr, Ludington, MI 49431-1906
Tel (231) 843-2591 *Founded/Ownrshp* 2013
Sales 55.6MM *EMP* 446
SIC 8062 General medical & surgical hospitals; General medical & surgical hospitals
Pr: Mark Vipperman
**CFO:* Bruno Bettin
**Treas:* Mark Lenz
VP: Tim Heinrich
VP: Bob Johnson
VP: David Klinger

Dir Lab: Mark Zingery
Dir Rad: Marylou Earnshaw
QA Dir: Kathleen Saxton
Dir IT: Dave Crowley
VP Opers: Drew Dostal

D-U-N-S 82-893-0391
MEMORIAL MEDICAL CENTER-LIVINGSTON
1717 Highway 59 Loop N, Livingston, TX 77351-5703
Tel (936) 327-4381 *Founded/Ownrshp* 2008
Sales 20.0MM *EMP* 403
SIC 8062 General medical & surgical hospitals; General medical & surgical hospitals
Pr: Bryant Krenek
**COO:* Barbara Willis
Dir Sec: Mike Morrow

D-U-N-S 07-456-4469
MEMORIAL MEDICAL CENTER-WOODSTOCK
3701 Doty Rd, Woodstock, IL 60098-7509
Tel (815) 334-3880 *Founded/Ownrshp* 1991
Sales 99.3MM[E] *EMP* 3,000
SIC 8062 8051 General medical & surgical hospitals; Skilled nursing care facilities; General medical & surgical hospitals; Skilled nursing care facilities
CEO: Mike Eesley
Sr VP: Barbara Johnson
Dir OR: Diana Franzen
Dir Inf Cn: Karen Vanburen
Dir Lab: Nabil Ali
Dir Lab: Judy Bjurstrom
Dir Lab: Laura Thomas
Dir Rad: John Heinrich
Dir IT: Judy Andronowitc
Mtls Mgr: John Cashmore
Obsttrcn: Richard Cook

MEMORIAL MEDICAL CTR E TEXAS
See MEMORIAL SPECIALTY HOSPITAL

D-U-N-S 11-017-4034
MEMORIAL MEDICAL GROUP A PROFESSIONAL CORP
19191 S Vermont Ave Fl 3, Torrance, CA 90502-1018
Tel (310) 354-4351 *Founded/Ownrshp* 1969
Sales 21.5MM *EMP* 2
SIC 8011 Physicians' office, including specialists; Physicians' office, including specialists
Pr: Robert Margolis MD

D-U-N-S 80-882-9555
MEMORIAL MISSION HOSPITAL
(*Suby of* MISSION HEALTH SYSTEM INC) ★
400 Ridgefield Ct, Asheville, NC 28806-2213
Tel (828) 257-7120 *Founded/Ownrshp* 2007
Sales 58.1MM[E] *EMP* 1[E]
SIC 5961 5912 Pharmaceuticals, mail order; Drug stores & proprietary stores
Pr: Ronald A Paulus MD
**CFO:* Charles F Ayscue
**Sr VP:* Dale Fell MD

D-U-N-S 60-343-9600
MEMORIAL MOTORCARS LTD INC
JAGUAR CENTRAL HOUSTON
7025 Old Katy Rd, Houston, TX 77024-2128
Tel (713) 293-6000 *Founded/Ownrshp* 1999
Sales 38.5MM[E] *EMP* 205
SIC 5511 Automobiles, new & used; Automobiles, new & used
Pr: Pete Delongchamps

D-U-N-S 06-468-3121
MEMORIAL MOTORS INC
LAKELAND TOYOTA
2925 Mall Hill Dr, Lakeland, FL 33810-6716
Tel (863) 688-5451 *Founded/Ownrshp* 1975
Sales 71.8MM[E] *EMP* 120
SIC 5511 Automobiles, new & used; Automobiles, new & used
Pr: Christopher Doherty
COO: Laurie Wilkins
**VP:* Jamie Wagner
Exec: Rob Siefke
Sls Mgr: Darrin Allison
Sls Mgr: Ernie Alvarez
Sls Mgr: Chris Avila
Sls Mgr: Daniele Blavio
Sls Mgr: Beth Curington
Sls Mgr: Shawn Dubose
Sls Mgr: Joe Herrington

D-U-N-S 78-618-6135
MEMORIAL NORTH PARK HOSPITAL
2151 Hamill Rd, Hixson, TN 37343-4028
Tel (423) 495-7100 *Founded/Ownrshp* 2006
Sales 76.6MM[E] *EMP* 1,275[E]
SIC 8062 General medical & surgical hospitals
Prin: Jim Hobson
COO: Jackie Jackson
VP: Lisa McCluskey
Pr Dir: Lisa M Culsky
Nrsg Dir: Diona Brown

D-U-N-S 07-424-5338
MEMORIAL PHARMACY INC
MEDICAL PARK PHARMACY
(*Suby of* BON SECOURS HEALTH SYSTEM INC) ★
8260 Atlee Rd, Mechanicsville, VA 23116-1844
Tel (804) 764-7300 *Founded/Ownrshp* 2005
Sales 51.7MM[E] *EMP* 900
SIC 5912 Drug stores; Drug stores

D-U-N-S 96-630-9218
MEMORIAL PHYSICIAN SERVICES
701 N 1st St, Springfield, IL 62781-0001
Tel (217) 528-0307 *Founded/Ownrshp* 2011
Sales 32.5MM[E] *EMP* 4
Accts Rsm Mcgladrey Inc Chicago Il
SIC 8011 General & family practice, physician/surgeon; General & family practice, physician/surgeon
Pr: Edgar J Curtis

D-U-N-S 96-213-5757
MEMORIAL PHYSICIANS PLLC
(*Suby of* YAKIMA VALLEY MEMORIAL HOSPITAL ASSOCIATION INC) ★
3800 Summitview Ave, Yakima, WA 98902-2715
Tel (509) 248-7849 *Founded/Ownrshp* 2009
Sales 23.9MM[E] *EMP* 375
SIC 8011 Offices & clinics of medical doctors; Offices & clinics of medical doctors

D-U-N-S 96-889-7681
■ **MEMORIAL PRODUCTION OPERATING LLC**
(*Suby of* MEMORIAL PRODUCTION PARTNERS LP) ★
500 Dallas St Ste 1800, Houston, TX 77002-2067
Tel (713) 588-8300 *Founded/Ownrshp* 2011
Sales 56.4MM[E] *EMP* 466[E]
SIC 8741 Business management; Administrative management; Construction management
CEO: John A Weinzierl

D-U-N-S 07-850-6228
■ **MEMORIAL PRODUCTION PARTNERS GP LLC**
(*Suby of* MEMORIAL RESOURCE DEVELOPMENT CORP) ★
1401 Mckinney St Ste 1025, Houston, TX 77010-2052
Tel (713) 579-5700 *Founded/Ownrshp* 2012
Sales 9.9MM[E] *EMP* 453[E]
SIC 1311 Crude petroleum & natural gas
Prin: Robert A Innamorati

D-U-N-S 96-912-9605
▲ **MEMORIAL PRODUCTION PARTNERS LP**
500 Dallas St Ste 1800, Houston, TX 77002-2067
Tel (713) 588-8300 *Founded/Ownrshp* 2011
Sales 494.1MM *EMP* 483[E]
Tkr Sym MEMP *Exch* NGS
SIC 1311 Crude petroleum & natural gas production; Crude petroleum & natural gas production
Ch Bd: John A Weinzierl
Genl Pt: Memorial P LLC
Genl Pt: William J Scarff
COO: Larry R Forney
CFO: Andrew Cozby
Ofcr: Chris Cooper
VP: Gregory M Robbins
VP: Robert L Stillwell
Counsel: Brad Coffey
Snr Mgr: John Deck

MEMORIAL REGIONAL HOSPITAL
See SOUTH BROWARD HOSPITAL DISTRICT

D-U-N-S 07-943-4733
▲ **MEMORIAL RESOURCE DEVELOPMENT CORP**
500 Dallas St Ste 1800, Houston, TX 77002-2067
Tel (713) 588-8300 *Founded/Ownrshp* 2014
Sales 899.3MM *EMP* 505[E]
Tkr Sym MRD *Exch* NGS
SIC 1311 Crude petroleum & natural gas; Crude petroleum & natural gas
CEO: John A Weinzierl
**Ch Bd:* Tony R Weber
Pr: William J Scarff
COO: Larry R Forney
CFO: Andrew J Cozby
Treas: Gregory Robbins
Treas: Bobby Stillwell
Sr VP: Kyle N Roane
VP: Dennis G Venghaus
Dir Risk M: Ginny Penzell
Off Admin: Candy Evans
Board of Directors: Scott A Gieselman, Kenneth A Hersh, Robert A Innamorati, Carol L O'neill, Pat Wood III

D-U-N-S 07-526-5157 IMP
MEMORIAL SLOAN-KETTERING CANCER CENTER
1275 York Ave, New York, NY 10065-6007
Tel (212) 639-2000 *Founded/Ownrshp* 1884
Sales 582.6MM *EMP* 9,325[E]
SIC 8069 Cancer hospital; Cancer hospital
CEO: Craig B Thompson
Ch Bd: Douglas A Warner III
V Ch: Richard R Barakat
V Ch: Yuman Fong
V Ch: William R Jarnagin
V Ch: David M Panicek
Pr: Harold Varmus MD
COO: John R Gunn
Treas: Clifton S Robbins
Bd of Dir: Marie-Jos E Kravis
Sr VP: Thomas J Fahey Jr
Sr VP: Michael P Gutnick
Sr VP: Kathryn Martin
Sr VP: James S Quirk
VP: Kerry Bessey
VP: Murray F Brennan
VP: Eric Cottington
VP: Jason Klein
VP: Kathy Lewis
VP: Patricia C Skarulis
Assoc Dir: Anne-Marie Lesny

D-U-N-S 04-595-4695
MEMORIAL SPECIALTY HOSPITAL
MEMORIAL MEDICAL CTR E TEXAS
1201 W Frank Ave, Lufkin, TX 75904-3357
Tel (936) 639-7975 *Founded/Ownrshp* 1993
Sales 13.8MM *EMP* 770
Accts Catholic Health Initiatives E
SIC 8062 General medical & surgical hospitals; General medical & surgical hospitals
Sr VP: Jadie Barrie
Dir Lab: Lisa Lanier
Dir Rad: Chris Beasley
Nurse Mgr: Yvette Compean
Sfty Mgr: Jeff Hyde
Doctor: Troy Coleman

D-U-N-S 05-538-6465 IMP
MEMORY CO LLC
25 Downing Dr, Phenix City, AL 36869-3342
Tel (334) 448-0708 *Founded/Ownrshp* 2001
Sales 97.3MM[E] *EMP* 300

SIC 5199 Gifts & novelties; Gifts & novelties
CEO: Charles D Sizemore
**Pr:* G Randy Brown
Ex VP: Don Trandem
**VP:* Jennifer Freeman
Sls Mgr: Bruce Garber
Sls Mgr: Sarah Mixon

D-U-N-S 94-918-7991 IMP
MEMORY EXPERTS INTERNATIONAL (USA) INC
(*Suby of* EXPERTS EN MEMOIRE INTERNATIONALE INC, LES)
1651 E Saint Andrew Pl, Santa Ana, CA 92705-4932
Tel (714) 258-3000 *Founded/Ownrshp* 1996
Sales 21.1MM[E] *EMP* 74[E]
SIC 3572 3577 Computer storage devices; Computer peripheral equipment; Computer storage devices; Computer peripheral equipment
Ch Bd: Guadulupe Reusing
**CEO:* Gerard Reusing
**VP:* Rino Lampasona
**VP:* Julian Reusing
**VP:* Lawrence Reusing

D-U-N-S 15-199-9422
MEMPHIS AREA TRANSIT AUTHORITY
MATA
1370 Levee Rd, Memphis, TN 38108-1011
Tel (901) 722-7100 *Founded/Ownrshp* 1974
Sales 55.0MM *EMP* 450
SIC 4131 Intercity bus line; Intercity bus line
Pr: William Hudson
Off Admin: Jerri Daniels
CTO: Dorothy Harris
MIS Dir: Tommy Wallace
IT Man: Maury Miles
Sls&Mrk Ex: Lawson Albritton

MEMPHIS COMMERCIAL APPEAL THE
See MEMPHIS PUBLISHING CO

D-U-N-S 07-354-4157 IMP
MEMPHIS COMMUNICATIONS CORP
MCC
4771 Summer Ave, Memphis, TN 38122-4724
Tel (901) 725-9271 *Founded/Ownrshp* 1972
Sales 32.2MM[E] *EMP* 95
SIC 5999 5065 5044 Communication equipment; Alarm & safety equipment stores; Audio-visual equipment & supplies; Security control equipment & systems; Sound equipment, electronic; Video equipment, electronic; Office equipment; Copying equipment
CEO: Scot Berry
Dir IT: Chris Day
VP Sls: Scot A Berry
Sls Mgr: Tim Barlow
Sales Asso: Doug Corbitt
Sales Asso: Embry Viner

D-U-N-S 18-539-0010 IMP
MEMPHIS CONTRACT PACKAGING INC
SOFTEE PRODUCTS
95 Ball Park St, Somerville, TN 38068-1711
Tel (901) 465-5502 *Founded/Ownrshp* 1988
Sales 28.4MM[E] *EMP* 50
SIC 2844 Toilet preparations; Cosmetic preparations; Toilet preparations
CEO: Billy Hoard
CFO: Shannon Williams
**Treas:* Shannon H Williams
VP: Carlos Brando
**VP:* Charles Bridges
**VP:* John Brown
**VP:* Linda Hoard
**VP:* Clayton Maxey
**VP:* Ed Myers
Tech Mgr: Greg Chapman

D-U-N-S 08-133-9491
MEMPHIS DEVELOPMENT FOUNDATION
ORPHEUM THEATRE
203 S Main St, Memphis, TN 38103-3905
Tel (901) 525-3000 *Founded/Ownrshp* 1976
Sales 10.2MM *EMP* 320
SIC 7922 6512 Theatrical producers & services; Theater building, ownership & operation; Theatrical producers & services; Theater building, ownership & operation
CEO: Pat Halloran
COO: Paulette Luker
Ofcr: Donna Darwin
Ex VP: Paulette Smithers
VP: Alice Roberts
VP: Kanette Rodgers
VP: Teresa Ward
Prin: William Tustin
Store Mgr: Glenda Young

D-U-N-S 83-258-0174
MEMPHIS GOODWILL INC
1213 Walnut Rd, Sardis, MS 38666-9104
Tel (901) 323-6221 *Founded/Ownrshp* 2008
Sales 25.1MM *EMP* 256
SIC 5722 Household appliance stores; Household appliance stores
Pr: Michael A Martini

MEMPHIS INTERNATIONAL AIRPORT
See MEMPHIS-SHELBY COUNTY AIRPORT AUTHORITY

D-U-N-S 05-983-2352 IMP
MEMPHIS LAMP INC
NEW ORLEANS LAMP
250 Broad Ave Memphis 381 38112 Memphis, Memphis, TN 38112
Tel (941) 552-2440 *Founded/Ownrshp* 1970
Sales 41.9MM[E] *EMP* 200
SIC 5063 Lighting fixtures; Light bulbs & related supplies; Lighting fixtures; Light bulbs & related supplies
Pr: David Marrs

D-U-N-S 15-723-1366
MEMPHIS MEDICAL CENTER AIR AMBULANCE SERVICE INC
HOSPITAL WING
1080 Eastmoreland Ave, Memphis, TN 38104-3327
Tel (901) 522-4400 *Founded/Ownrshp* 1986
Sales 23.0MM *EMP* 62
Accts Thompson Dunavant Plc Memphis
SIC 4522 Ambulance services, air
Pr: Robert Gordon
**VP:* Gary Shorb
Sfty Dirs: Miles Dunagan
Sfty Mgr: Al Williams
Snr Mgr: David Childress
Snr Mgr: Phil Scruggs

MEMPHIS MEDICAL SERVICES
See SCOTLAND COUNTY MEMORIAL HOSPITAL

D-U-N-S 10-245-0736
MEMPHIS PATHOLOGY LABORATORY
(*Suby of* AMERICAN ESOTERIC LABORATORIES) ★
1701 Century Center Cv, Memphis, TN 38134-8975
Tel (901) 405-8200 *Founded/Ownrshp* 2004
Sales 11.2MM^E *EMP* 350^E
SIC 8071 Pathological laboratory; Pathological laboratory
Genl Pt: John Mazzei
Pt: Gary L Larue
Pt: David Smalley PHD
VP: Pam O'Brien

D-U-N-S 00-702-8723 IMP
■ **MEMPHIS PUBLISHING CO**
MEMPHIS COMMERCIAL APPEAL THE
(*Suby of* JOURNAL MEDIA GROUP INC) ★
495 Union Ave, Memphis, TN 38103-3221
Tel (901) 529-2345 *Founded/Ownrshp* 2015
Sales 47.6MM^E *EMP* 500
SIC 2711 Newspapers, publishing & printing; Newspapers, publishing & printing
Pr: Joseph Pepe
COO: Tom Travis
CFO: Jerry McMichael
CFO: Daniel Moehle
Exec: Joan Allison
IT Man: David Gish
Netwrk Eng: Bill Stafford
Mktg Dir: Paul Jewell

D-U-N-S 03-478-1542
MEMPHIS SCALE WORKS INC
OHIO SCALE SYSTEMS
3418 Cazassa Rd, Memphis, TN 38116-3628
Tel (330) 759-1000 *Founded/Ownrshp* 1976
Sales 25.6MM^E *EMP* 80
SIC 5046 7699 Scales, except laboratory; Scale repair service; Scales, except laboratory; Scale repair service
Pr: Jerry Michie
Sls Mgr: Tom Pease
Sls Mgr: Patrick White
Sls Mgr: James Williams

D-U-N-S 00-792-2024
MEMPHIS STONE & GRAVEL CO (TN)
1111 Wilson St, Memphis, TN 38106-2329
Tel (901) 774-4000 *Founded/Ownrshp* 1909, 1988
Sales 64.4MM^E *EMP* 250
SIC 1442 Gravel mining; Gravel mining
CEO: Richard Moore Jr
**Pr:* James Madison
**Treas:* Gilbert Wilson
**VP:* William Kelly III
**VP:* Johnny Priest

D-U-N-S 08-602-2209
MEMPHIS ZOO INC
ELEPHANT'S TRUNK
2000 Prentiss Pl, Memphis, TN 38112-5033
Tel (901) 333-6517 *Founded/Ownrshp* 1951
Sales 22.1MM *EMP* 206
Accts Dixon Hughes Goodman Llp Memp
SIC 8399 8641 Fund raising organization, non-fee basis; Civic social & fraternal associations; Fund raising organization, non-fee basis; Civic social & fraternal associations
Pr: Chuck Brady
**Ofcr:* James Jalenak
VP: Elizabeth Boggan
VP: Nancy Kelso

D-U-N-S 05-256-3020
MEMPHIS-SHELBY COUNTY AIRPORT AUTHORITY
MEMPHIS INTERNATIONAL AIRPORT
2491 Winchester Rd # 113, Memphis, TN 38116-3851
Tel (901) 922-8000 *Founded/Ownrshp* 1969
Sales 113.4MM *EMP* 305
Accts Dixon Hughes Goodman Llp Memp
SIC 4581 Airport terminal services; Airport hangar rental; Airport terminal services; Airport hangar rental
Pr: Larry D Cox
**Ch:* Arnold E Pearl
Ofcr: Jerry Brandon
Ofcr: Fred Hawkins
Ofcr: Sammie Terry
**Ex VP:* Scott Brockman
VP: Jim Covington
**VP:* Bob A Martin
VP: Richard White
Dir: James Hay
Comm Man: Clifford J Robinson

D-U-N-S 05-711-4506
MEMRY CORP
SAES MEMRY
(*Suby of* SAES GETTERS SPA)
3 Berkshire Blvd, Bethel, CT 06801-1037
Tel (203) 739-1100 *Founded/Ownrshp* 2008
Sales 45.4MM^E *EMP* 363^E
SIC 3841 Surgical & medical instruments; Surgical & medical instruments
CEO: Dean Tulumaris
V Ch: P Belcher
**Pr:* Nicola Dibartolomeo
CFO: Robert P Belcher
**CFO:* John Schosser
**CFO:* Richard F Sowerby
VP: Libby Albanese
VP: William Morton
VP: Joseph Pasqualucci
VP: Robert J Thatcher
VP: Dean J Tulumaris
VP: Tim Wheeler
VP: Ming H Wu

MEMSI
See SIEMENS HEARING INC

D-U-N-S 13-519-3816
MEMTEKS-USA INC
355 Mallard Ln Ste 200, Earlysville, VA 22936-9790
Tel (434) 973-9800 *Founded/Ownrshp* 2003
Sales 17.4MM^E *EMP* 353
SIC 2254 2342 2339 5137 Underwear, knit; Brassieres; Sportswear, women's; Sportswear, women's & children's; Women's & children's sportswear & swimsuits; Underwear: women's, children's & infants'; Underwear, knit; Brassieres; Sportswear, women's; Sportswear, women's & children's; Women's & children's sportswear & swimsuits; Underwear: women's, children's & infants'
CEO: Yalcin Ozbey
**VP:* Nina Lyn Ozbey

D-U-N-S 09-856-6318
MENA HOSPITAL COMMISSION
MENA REGIONAL HEALTH SYSTEM
311 Morrow St N, Mena, AR 71953-2516
Tel (479) 394-6100 *Founded/Ownrshp* 1950
Sales 48.6MM^E *EMP* 300
SIC 8062 General medical & surgical hospitals; General medical & surgical hospitals
Ch: Leon Philpott
**Pr:* Ewanta Turner
**CEO:* Jay Quebedeaux
**CFO:* Laura Allen
CFO: Matt Briskell
**CFO:* Paul Rodgers
**VP:* Carol Woods
**VP:* Mary Ann Zachery
Dir Lab: Scott Eakins
Dir Rad: Todd Laing
Dir Rx: Angie Aynes
Board of Directors: Michael Mercer, Mary Ellen Winters, Mina Anderle, Pam Posey, Teresa Wise, Darlene Burk, Sue Powell, Cindy Cloud, John Roberts, Scott Eakins, Steve Schulte, Shawn Free, Kay Sibley, Connie Hernandez, Beth Smith, Pam Laexander, Humberto Sosa, Russell Lockhart, West Wilson, Karen Medford, Mary Winters

MENA PUBLIC SCHOOL
See MENA SCHOOL DISTRICT

MENA REGIONAL HEALTH SYSTEM
See MENA HOSPITAL COMMISSION

D-U-N-S 01-032-0471
MENA SCHOOL DISTRICT
MENA PUBLIC SCHOOL
501 Hickory Ave, Mena, AR 71953-3044
Tel (479) 394-1710 *Founded/Ownrshp* 1930
Sales 20.7MM^E *EMP* 467
SIC 8211 9411 Public elementary & secondary schools; Administration of educational programs; Public elementary & secondary schools; Administration of educational programs

D-U-N-S 09-761-5566
MENADE INC
1525 Lakeville Dr Ste 115, Kingwood, TX 77339-2068
Tel (281) 348-0853 *Founded/Ownrshp* 2000
Sales 51.1MM^E *EMP* 200
SIC 1622 Bridge, tunnel & elevated highway; Bridge, tunnel & elevated highway
Pr: Jerry Wade
**VP:* James Savage

D-U-N-S 00-582-5385
MENARD ELECTRIC COOPERATIVE (IL)
14300 Hwy 97, Petersburg, IL 62675
Tel (217) 632-7746 *Founded/Ownrshp* 1936
Sales 26.4MM *EMP* 52
SIC 4911 Distribution, electric power; Distribution, electric power
Pr: Lynn Frasco
**VP:* Gary Martin
Off Mgr: Wayne Jones

D-U-N-S 00-620-3210 IMP
MENARD INC (WI)
MIDWEST MANUFACTURING
5101 Menard Dr, Eau Claire, WI 54703-9604
Tel (715) 876-5911 *Founded/Ownrshp* 1962
Sales 16.2MMM^E *EMP* 40,000
SIC 2431 5211 Millwork; Lumber & other building materials; Millwork; Lumber & other building materials
Pr: John Menard Jr
Recvr: Benjamin Postelwaite
Recvr: Darius Shade
Pr: Frederic Masse
COO: Scott Collette
COO: Charlie Menard
**CFO:* Pete Liupakka
VP: Uriah Krause
Dir Bus: Marty Taube
Dept Mgr: Jose Burgos
Dept Mgr: Amber Hallquist

D-U-N-S 07-942-6899
MENARDI MIKROPUL LLC
(*Suby of* ENVIRONMENTAL FILTRATION TECHNOLOGIES LLC) ★
1 Maxwell Dr, Trenton, SC 29847-2227
Tel (803) 663-6551 *Founded/Ownrshp* 1913
Sales 46.0MM *EMP* 100
SIC 3569 Filtration devices, electronic; Filters
Pr: Per Lind
VP: Mike Gelinas
VP: Michael Warriek

D-U-N-S 12-599-1286 EXP
MENARDI MIKROPUL LLC
A NEDERMAN COMPANY
(*Suby of* ENVIRONMENTAL FILTRATION TECHNOLOGIES LLC) ★
4433 Chesapeake Dr, Charlotte, NC 28216-3412
Tel (704) 998-2600 *Founded/Ownrshp* 1999
Sales 25.9MM^E *EMP* 150
SIC 3564 2393 Blowers & fans; Bags & containers, except sleeping bags: textile; Blowers & fans; Textile bags
CEO: Tom Gilboy
**Owner:* Richard Bearse
**Pr:* Per Lind

D-U-N-S 00-607-3126 IMP/EXP
MENASHA CORP
1645 Bergstrom Rd, Neenah, WI 54956-9766
Tel (920) 751-1000 *Founded/Ownrshp* 1849
Sales 1.8MMM^E *EMP* 4,000
Accts Pricewaterhousecoopers Llp Mi
SIC 2631 2653 2679 3086 0811 Paperboard mills; Corrugated & solid fiber boxes; Paper products, converted; Packaging & shipping materials, foamed plastic; Timber tracts; Paperboard mills; Corrugated & solid fiber boxes; Paper products, converted; Packaging & shipping materials, foamed plastic; Timber tracts
Pr: James M Kotek
**Ch Bd:* Donald C Shepard
**CFO:* Thomas M Rettler
**Treas:* Lee Ann Hammen
Ex VP: Jerry Hessel
VP: Jackie Barry
VP: Don Riviere
Area Mgr: Andrew Malecha
Genl Mgr: Jeff Corke
Dir IT: Dan Barfknecht
Dir IT: Brian Henze

D-U-N-S 05-606-5352
MENASHA ELECTRIC & WATER UTILITIES
MENASHA UTILITIES
321 Milwaukee St, Menasha, WI 54952-2704
Tel (920) 967-3400 *Founded/Ownrshp* 1905
Sales 52.3MM *EMP* 60
Accts Schenck Green Bay Wisconsin
SIC 5064 5074 8748 Water heaters, electric; Boilers, steam; Telecommunications consultant; Water heaters, electric; Boilers, steam; Telecommunications consultant
Pr: Phil Hansen
Pr: Jake Oelke
Treas: Cinda Johnson
VP: Pat Connors
VP: Beverly Lindquist
Genl Mgr: Tim Herlitzka
Genl Mgr: Randy Jaeckels
Netwrk Mgr: Rich Loga

D-U-N-S 10-008-3419
MENASHA JOINT SCHOOL DISTRICT
328 6th St, Menasha, WI 54952-2768
Tel (920) 967-1400 *Founded/Ownrshp* 1882
Sales 21.3MM^E *EMP* 376
Accts Schenck Sc Cpas Green Bay W
SIC 8211 Public elementary & secondary schools; Public elementary & secondary schools
Prin: Mark Vanderzee
Treas: Eric Thiede
MIS Dir: Peter Pfundtner

D-U-N-S 10-797-5224 IMP
MENASHA PACKAGING CO LLC
(*Suby of* MENASHA CORP) ★
1645 Bergstrom Rd, Neenah, WI 54956-9701
Tel (920) 751-1000 *Founded/Ownrshp* 2001
Sales 624.2MM^E *EMP* 2,200
SIC 2653 Sheets, corrugated: made from purchased materials; Sheets, corrugated: made from purchased materials
Pr: Michael K Waite
**CEO:* James M Kotek
**Sr VP:* Thomas M Rettler
VP: Gail A Constncio
**VP:* Rick J Fantini
**VP:* Evan S Pritz
Opers Mgr: Pat Driessen
Opers Mgr: Dennis Graf
Sls Dir: Brian Sullivan

MENASHA UTILITIES
See MENASHA ELECTRIC & WATER UTILITIES

D-U-N-S 84-906-8205 IMP
MENCHIES GROUP INC
17555 Ventura Blvd # 200, Encino, CA 91316-3890
Tel (818) 708-0316 *Founded/Ownrshp* 2008
Sales 38.6MM^E *EMP* 78
SIC 5143 Yogurt
CEO: Amit Kleinberger
VP: Yotom Regev
Snr Mgr: Jarod Bekebrede
Snr Mgr: Jennifer Brookley
Snr Mgr: Adam Caldwell
Snr Mgr: Annie Charlton
Snr Mgr: Kalli Salo
Snr Mgr: Pedro Vazquez

D-U-N-S 82-772-0850
MENCO PACIFIC INC
43180 Bus Pk Dr Ste 101, Temecula, CA 92590-3608
Tel (760) 747-4405 *Founded/Ownrshp* 2007
Sales 22.1MM^E *EMP* 89
SIC 1542 1522 Nonresidential construction; Residential construction
Pr: Oscar Mendoza

D-U-N-S 60-737-6647
MENDELSON HOLDING CO LTD INC
8300 Pennsylvania Ave, Upper Marlboro, MD 20772-2610
Tel (301) 420-6400 *Founded/Ownrshp* 1989
Sales 88.5MM^E *EMP* 1,503
SIC 5421 Food & freezer plans, meat; Food & freezer plans, meat
Prin: Ira Mendelsonchb
**Ch:* Ira Mendelson
**Treas:* Matthew Young

D-U-N-S 07-525-9911
MENDES & MOUNT LLP
750 7th Ave Fl 24, New York, NY 10019-9399
Tel (212) 261-8000 *Founded/Ownrshp* 2005
Sales 30.3MM^E *EMP* 350
SIC 8111 General practice law office; General practice law office
Mng Pt: Thomas J Quinn
Pt: Daniel M Bianca
Pt: Mark F Bruckman
Pt: Maryann D'Amato
Pt: Garrett J Fitzpatrick
Pt: Ronald R Houdlett
Pt: John F Larkin III
Pt: George C Lock
Pt: John G McAndrews
Pt: James A McGuire
Pt: Edward J McMurrer
Pr: Jennifer Hussain
Treas: Xavier Gonin

D-U-N-S 09-001-5694 IMP
MENDEZ & CO INC
2 Carr 20 St Ca, San Juan, PR 00936
Tel (787) 793-8888 *Founded/Ownrshp* 1912, 1940
Sales 229.7MM *EMP* 525
Accts Llm&D Psc San Juan Puerto
SIC 5182 5141 Liquor; Groceries, general line; Liquor; Groceries, general line
Ch Bd: Salustiano Alvarez
**Pr:* Jose A Alvarez Gallardo
**Treas:* Pablo Jose Alvarez
**VP:* Carlos Alvarez Jr
**VP:* Carlos Alvarez Mendez
Genl Mgr: Rafael Lopez Jr
IT Man: Sandra Rodriguez
Mktg Dir: Brenda Pizarro
Mktg Mgr: Enrique Anduze

D-U-N-S 03-253-1477
MENDEZ ENTERPRISES INC
4280 Sw 73rd Ave, Miami, FL 33155-4548
Tel (305) 264-7203 *Founded/Ownrshp* 1964
Sales 25.0MM^E *EMP* 10
SIC 5194 Cigars; Cigarettes; Cigars; Cigarettes
Pr: Domingo Mendez
**Treas:* Jesus Mendez Jr
**VP:* Hilda V Mendez
Off Mgr: Veronica Mendez

D-U-N-S 95-902-0061
MENDIX INC
(*Suby of* MENDIX TECHNOLOGY B.V.)
268 Summer St Fl 4, Boston, MA 02210-1188
Tel (857) 263-8200 *Founded/Ownrshp* 2008
Sales 22.6MM^E *EMP* 120
SIC 5045 Computer software
CEO: Derek Roos
CFO: Marcel Karssen
Ofcr: Kirby Wadsworth
VP: Olivier Maes
VP: Mark Rogers
VP: Warren Utt
VP: Paul Zymba
CTO: Roald Kruit
Sls Dir: Todd Hogan
Mktg Mgr: Eric Peters
Sales Asso: Jim Speredelozzi

D-U-N-S 02-956-4937
MENDO MILL AND LUMBER CO (CA)
ACE HARDWARE
1870 N State St, Ukiah, CA 95482-3191
Tel (707) 462-8806 *Founded/Ownrshp* 1946
Sales 35.0MM *EMP* 230
Accts Dillwood Burkel & Sully Llp
SIC 5251 Hardware; Hardware
Ch Bd: David Ziegler
**Ch Bd:* Joe Mayfield
**Pr:* Mike Mayfield
**Pr:* John Venhvizen
**CFO:* Bob Hildebrand
VP: Jeff Ward
Merch Mgr: Ken Smith

D-U-N-S 10-293-9048 IMP
■ **MENDOCINO BREWING CO INC**
(*Suby of* UNITED BREWERIES (HOLDINGS) LIMITED)
1601 Airport Rd, Ukiah, CA 95482-6456
Tel (707) 463-2087 *Founded/Ownrshp* 1983
Sales 34.0MM *EMP* 91^E
Tkr Sym MENB *Exch* OTO
SIC 2082 Malt beverages; Brewers' grain; Beer (alcoholic beverage); Gift, novelty & souvenir shop; Malt beverages; Brewers' grain; Beer (alcoholic beverage)
Pr: Yashpal Singh
**Ch Bd:* Vijay Mallya
CFO: Mahadevan Narayanan
Board of Directors: Scott R Heldfond, Michael Laybourn, Jerome G Merchant, Kent D Price

D-U-N-S 03-885-6241 IMP
MENDOCINO COAST DISTRICT HOSPITAL
700 River Dr, Fort Bragg, CA 95437-5403
Tel (707) 961-1234 *Founded/Ownrshp* 1971
Sales 59.6MM^E *EMP* 320
SIC 8062 General medical & surgical hospitals; General medical & surgical hospitals
CEO: Jonathan Baker
CFO: Wayne Allen
CFO: Jacob Lewis
**CFO:* Mark Smith
**Ch:* Patricia Jauregui Darland
**Treas:* Tom Birdsell
**Treas:* Camille Ranker
Ofcr: Amber Curtis
VP: Amy McColley
Dir Lab: Emmet Oconnell
**Prin:* John Kermen
Board of Directors: Jim Hay, John Kermer, Charlene McAllister, Don Tucker

MENDOCINO COLLEGE
See MENDOCINO-LAKE COMMUNITY COLLEGE DISTRICT

D-U-N-S 08-387-0196
MENDOCINO COMMUNITY HEALTH CLINIC INC
MCHC
333 Laws Ave, Ukiah, CA 95482-6540
Tel (707) 468-1010 *Founded/Ownrshp* 1992
Sales 27.6MM *EMP* 235
Accts Bkd Llp Springfield Mo
SIC 8011 Primary care medical clinic; Primary care medical clinic
CEO: John Pavoni
Off Mgr: Alicia Gordon
IT Man: Lisa Schat
Plnt Mgr: Tim Johnson
Obsttrcn: Karen Crabtree
Pharmcst: Gary Wakeman

D-U-N-S 01-936-7486
MENDOCINO FOREST PRODUCTS CO LLC
1360 19th Hole Dr Ste 200, Calpella, CA 95418
Tel (707) 620-2961 *Founded/Ownrshp* 1998
Sales 143.2MM^E *EMP* 400
SIC 5031 2421 Lumber, plywood & millwork; Sawmills & planing mills, general; Lumber, plywood & millwork; Sawmills & planing mills, general
CEO: Sandy Dean
Pr: John Russell
CEO: Bob Mertz
COO: Nathan Fairall
CFO: Jim Pelkey
Dir IT: Jon L Roi
Mktg Mgr: Erica Savage

D-U-N-S 01-936-7254
MENDOCINO REDWOOD CO LLC
850 Kunzler Ranch Rd, Ukiah, CA 95482-7294
Tel (707) 463-5110 *Founded/Ownrshp* 1998
Sales 71.1MM^E *EMP* 400
SIC 0811 Timber tracts, hardwood; Timber tracts, softwood; Timber tracts, hardwood; Timber tracts, softwood
IT Man: Patrick Orourke
VP Opers: Henry Long

D-U-N-S 07-466-6082
MENDOCINO-LAKE COMMUNITY COLLEGE DISTRICT
MENDOCINO COLLEGE
1000 Hensley Creek Rd, Ukiah, CA 95482-7821
Tel (707) 468-3000 *Founded/Ownrshp* 1973
Sales 4.7MM *EMP* 325
Accts Matson & Isom Redding Califo
SIC 8221 8222 Colleges universities & professional schools; Community college; Colleges universities & professional schools; Community college
Pr: Arturo Reyes
**Pr:* Marilyn Brock
Pr: Roe Darnell
Ofcr: Kurt Combs
**Ex VP:* Don Basconcellos
**VP:* Carl Ehmann
**VP:* Tom Kesey
**VP:* Kathy Lehner
DP Exec: Karen Christopherson
Psych: Susan Anderson
Psych: Steve Crossman

D-U-N-S 10-003-2267
MENDON-UPTON SCHOOL DISTRICT
150 North Ave, Mendon, MA 01756-1011
Tel (508) 634-1585 *Founded/Ownrshp* 1960
Sales 21.9MM^E *EMP* 400
SIC 8211 Public elementary & secondary schools; School board; Public elementary & secondary schools; School board
**Treas:* Joseph Leacu
**Prin:* Joseph Maruszczak

D-U-N-S 03-055-3689
MENDOTA COMMUNITY HOSPITAL INC
SUBLETTE CLINIC, THE
1401 E 12th St, Mendota, IL 61342-9216
Tel (815) 539-7461 *Founded/Ownrshp* 1950
Sales 34.6MM *EMP* 350
SIC 8062

MENDOTA HEARTH
See JOHNSON GAS APPLIANCE CO

D-U-N-S 14-149-1139
MENDOTA HOLDINGS INC
2700 Blue Waters Rd # 400, Saint Paul, MN 55121-1468
Tel (651) 905-8981 *Founded/Ownrshp* 2003
Sales 26.9MM^E *EMP* 150^E
SIC 1771 Flooring contractor
Pr: David G Moeller
**CFO:* William Marketon
**VP:* David A Johnson

D-U-N-S 61-000-5738
MENDOTA INSURANCE CO
(*Suby of* MIC HOLDINGS INC)
2805 Dodd Rd Ste 300, Eagan, MN 55121-2161
Tel (800) 422-0792 *Founded/Ownrshp* 2007
Sales NA *EMP* 230^E
SIC 6331 Property damage insurance; Property damage insurance
Pr: Robert Zieper
VP: Richard Slater
Board of Directors: Norman Asplund Berg, Austin Chapman, Clarence George Frame, Robert England Grant, Edward Hersey Hamm

D-U-N-S 14-454-4152 IMP/EXP
MENEHUNE WATER CO INC
HAWAII WATER
(*Suby of* MENEHUNE WATER JAPAN, INC.)
99-1205 Halawa Valley St # 301, Aiea, HI 96701-3291
Tel (808) 487-7777 *Founded/Ownrshp* 1985
Sales 26.1MM^E *EMP* 135
SIC 5499 5149 Water: distilled mineral or spring; Mineral or spring water bottling
Pr: Ken Simon
**VP:* Randal Iijima

MENEMSHA CNSTR SOLUTIONS
See MENEMSHA DEVELOPMENT GROUP INC

D-U-N-S 78-962-9656
MENEMSHA DEVELOPMENT GROUP INC
MENEMSHA CNSTR SOLUTIONS
20521 Earl St, Torrance, CA 90503-3006
Tel (310) 676-6591 *Founded/Ownrshp* 1992
Sales 64.5MM^E *EMP* 130
SIC 1542 8741 8712 7373 Nonresidential construction; Construction management; Architectural services; Computer-aided design (CAD) systems service; Nonresidential construction; Construction management; Architectural services; Computer-aided design (CAD) systems service
CEO: John V Daigle
**COO:* Laurie Collins
**Treas:* Tom Speroni
VP: Jason Tropp
Prgrm Mgr: Tisha Helgoe
Ql Cn Mgr: Yuri Osipov
Snr PM: Ryan Garcia
Snr Mgr: Jon Bayha

MENHOLT DENNY FRONTR CHEVROLET
See DENNY MENHOLT CHEVROLET

D-U-N-S 09-899-0885
MENIFEE COUNTY SCHOOLS
202 Backstreet, Frenchburg, KY 40322
Tel (606) 768-8002 *Founded/Ownrshp* 1920
Sales NA *EMP* 353
SIC 9411 ;

MENIL COLLECTION
See MENIL FOUNDATION INC

D-U-N-S 07-218-7222 IMP
MENIL FOUNDATION INC
MENIL COLLECTION
1533 Sul Ross St, Houston, TX 77006-4729
Tel (713) 525-9400 *Founded/Ownrshp* 1954
Sales 52.8MM *EMP* 70
Accts Blazek & Vetterling Houston
SIC 8412 Art gallery, noncommercial; Art gallery, noncommercial
Pr: Janet Hobby
**Treas:* Harry C Pinson
**VP:* Mark Wawro
Off Mgr: Susan Kmetz
Snr Mgr: Jean Ellis
Snr Mgr: Bradford Epley

D-U-N-S 00-101-4559
MENLO COLLEGE (CA)
BOWMAN LIBRARY
1000 El Camino Real, Atherton, CA 94027-4300
Tel (650) 543-3753 *Founded/Ownrshp* 1994, 2011
Sales 21.6MM *EMP* 125
Accts Armanino Llp San Ramon Calif
SIC 8221 Colleges universities & professional schools; Colleges universities & professional schools
Pr: Richard Moran
COO: Derek Stimel
**Ex VP:* Steven Weiner
VP: David Placey
VP: Catherine E Reeves
Comm Dir: Darcy Blake
CIO: Allan Chen
IT Man: Calvin Choi
IT Man: Mark Fowler
HC Dir: Bob Wilms
Snr Mgr: Venkat Naidu

D-U-N-S 92-880-3352
MENLO HEALTH ALLIANCE
MENLO HEALTH CLINIC
1300 Crane St, Menlo Park, CA 94025-4260
Tel (650) 498-6640 *Founded/Ownrshp* 1988
Sales 164.6MM *EMP* 2
SIC 8011 Surgeon; Surgeon
Prin: Martin Bronk MD

MENLO HEALTH CLINIC
See MENLO HEALTH ALLIANCE

D-U-N-S 07-701-6954
MENLO INC
5401 Fargo Ave, Skokie, IL 60077-3211
Tel (773) 274-7600 *Founded/Ownrshp* 1972
Sales 54.7MM^E *EMP* 185
SIC 1731 General electrical contractor; General electrical contractor
Pr: Eric Nixon
**Sec:* Donald Schwartz

D-U-N-S 78-438-0016 IMP
■ **MENLO LOGISTICS INC**
MENLO WORLDWIDE LOGISTICS
(*Suby of* XPO LOGISTICS WORLDWIDE LLC) ★
560 Mission St Ste 2950, San Francisco, CA 94105-3193
Tel (415) 486-2660 *Founded/Ownrshp* 1990
Sales 463.9MM^E *EMP* 2,200
SIC 4731 4225 4213 8741

D-U-N-S 06-887-7026
MENLO MEDICAL CLINIC A MEDICAL CORP
1300 Crane St, Menlo Park, CA 94025-4260
Tel (650) 498-6500 *Founded/Ownrshp* 1946
Sales 26.5MM^E *EMP* 150
SIC 8011 Clinic, operated by physicians; Clinic, operated by physicians
Pt: Nancy Adelman MD
Pt: Gayle S Hunt-Cahan Anp-C
Pt: Katherine A Blenko MD
Pt: Martin Bronk MD
Pt: Edmond D Butler MD
Pt: Suzanne C Christie MD
Pt: James A Cisco MD
Pt: Nancy P Cummings MD
Pt: Ramona M Desai MD
Pt: Manjul S Dixit MD
Pt: Thomas J Fiene MD
Pt: Susan Garay MD
Pt: David L Gregg MD
Pt: Julia A Hallee MD
Pt: Kathryn J Hallsten
Pt: David M Hansen MD
Pt: Jerome Hester MD
Pt: Jeannette A Hovsepian MD
Pt: Donna J Lee MD
Pt: F B McDowell MD
Pt: Frank McNee MD

D-U-N-S 07-738-5508
MENLO SCHOOL
50 Valparaiso Ave, Atherton, CA 94027-4401
Tel (650) 330-2000 *Founded/Ownrshp* 1915
Sales 42.5MM *EMP* 170
Accts Lautze & Lautze San Francisco
SIC 8299 Educational services; Educational services
CEO: Norman Colb
**CFO:* William Silver
Trst: John Zeisler
Exec: Geanne Honig
**Prin:* Nathaniel Healy
Dir IT: Eric Spross
Netwrk Mgr: Eric Destefano
Mktg Dir: Shayne Olson

MENLO WORLDWIDE EXPEDITE
See MENLO WORLDWIDE FORWARDING INC

D-U-N-S 00-691-8577
■ **MENLO WORLDWIDE FORWARDING INC**
MENLO WORLDWIDE EXPEDITE
(*Suby of* UNITED PARCEL SERVICE INC) ★
1 Lagoon Dr Ste 400, Redwood City, CA 94065-1564
Tel (650) 596-9600 *Founded/Ownrshp* 2002, 2004
Sales 148.5MM^E *EMP* 6,500^E
SIC 4513 4215 4522 4731 6159 6351 Letter delivery, private air; Package delivery, private air; Parcel delivery, private air; Courier services, except by air; Package delivery, vehicular; Parcel delivery, vehicular; Flying charter service; Customhouse brokers; Freight forwarding; Equipment & vehicle finance leasing companies; Liability insurance; Letter delivery, private air; Package delivery, private air; Parcel delivery, private air; Courier services, except by air; Package delivery, vehicular; Parcel delivery, vehicular; Flying charter service; Customhouse brokers; Freight forwarding; Equipment & vehicle finance leasing companies; Liability insurance
CEO: John H Williford

D-U-N-S 78-438-0581
■ **MENLO WORLDWIDE GOVERNMENT SERVICES LLC**
(*Suby of* MENLO LOGISTICS INC) ★
560 Mission St Ste 2950, San Francisco, CA 94105-3193
Tel (650) 378-5200 *Founded/Ownrshp* 2003
Sales 71.7MM^E *EMP* 2,200
SIC 4731 4225 4213 8741 Freight transportation arrangement; General warehousing & storage; Less-than-truckload (LTL) transport; Management services; Freight transportation arrangement; General warehousing & storage; Less-than-truckload (LTL) transport; Management services
Pr: Robert L Biano Jr
COO: Gary D Kowalski
Treas: Stephen K Krull
VP: John C Beckett
VP: Joseph M Dagnese
VP: K Andrew Dyer

MENLO WORLDWIDE LOGISTICS
See MENLO LOGISTICS INC

MENLOVE DODGE-TOYOTA
See MENLOVE-JOHNSON INC

D-U-N-S 03-530-2108
MENLOVE-JOHNSON INC
MENLOVE DODGE-TOYOTA
420 N Redwood Rd Unit F, North Salt Lake, UT 84054-2810
Tel (801) 295-3481 *Founded/Ownrshp* 1965
Sales 48.0MM^E *EMP* 170
SIC 5511 Automobiles, new & used; Automobiles, new & used
Pr: Wesley Johnson
**Sec:* Carol Johnson
Genl Mgr: Sean Kealey
Sls Mgr: Troy Bennett

D-U-N-S 00-416-4885 IMP
MENNEL MILLING CO
320 Findlay St, Fostoria, OH 44830-1854
Tel (419) 435-8151 *Founded/Ownrshp* 1886
Sales 50.5MM^E *EMP* 200
SIC 2041 2048 4221

D-U-N-S 06-470-1212
MENNEL MILLING CO OF MICHIGAN INC
(*Suby of* MENNEL MILLING CO)
301 S Mill St, Dowagiac, MI 49047-1473
Tel (269) 782-5175 *Founded/Ownrshp* 1973
Sales 21.1MM^E *EMP* 200
SIC 2041 Wheat flour; Wheat flour
Genl Mgr: Frank Herbes
**Pr:* Don Mennel
MIS Dir: Tom Torrey
Prd Mgr: Ron Boucher

D-U-N-S 01-162-3295
MENNELLAS POULTRY CO INC
100 George St, Paterson, NJ 07503-2319
Tel (973) 345-1300 *Founded/Ownrshp* 1944
Sales 25.9MM^E *EMP* 55
SIC 5144 5142 Poultry & poultry products; Poultry products; Packaged frozen goods
Pr: Keith Mennella
**Pr:* John Mennella
**Treas:* Thomas Mennella
**VP:* Vincent S Mennella
Off Mgr: Frank Coch

D-U-N-S 00-214-6660 IMP
■ **MENNEN CO**
(*Suby of* COLGATE-PALMOLIVE CO) ★
191 E Hanover Ave, Morristown, NJ 07960-3100
Tel (973) 630-1500 *Founded/Ownrshp* 1878, 1992
Sales 18.7MM^E *EMP* 420
SIC 2844 2842 Toilet preparations; Shampoos, rinses, conditioners: hair; Lotions, shaving; Deodorants, personal; Deodorants, nonpersonal; Toilet preparations; Shampoos, rinses, conditioners: hair; Lotions, shaving; Deodorants, personal; Deodorants, nonpersonal
Pr: William S Shanahan
**Treas:* Brian J Heidtke
**VP:* Andrew Hendry
VP: M Marcus

D-U-N-S 05-994-7952 IMP
MENNIES MACHINE CO
MMC ARMORY
Mennie Dr Rr 71, Mark, IL 61340
Tel (815) 339-2226 *Founded/Ownrshp* 1970
Sales 90.8MM^E *EMP* 260^E
SIC 3544 8742 Special dies, tools, jigs & fixtures; Materials mgmt. (purchasing, handling, inventory) consultant; Special dies, tools, jigs & fixtures; Materials mgmt. (purchasing, handling, inventory) consultant
Pr: Cheryl Mennie
**Pr:* William Mennie
**CFO:* Gary Hegland
**Treas:* Jennifer Smoode
Chf Mktg O: John Ploplis
Genl Mgr: Richard Cavaletto
CIO: Gary Antony
Dir IT: Hubert Mennie
VP Opers: Bill Mennie
Manager: Mark Mancini
Ql Cn Mgr: Mike Bartoluzzi

MENNINGER CLINIC
See MENNINGER FOUNDATION

D-U-N-S 18-240-6694
MENNINGER CLINIC
12301 Main St, Houston, TX 77035-6207
Tel (713) 275-5000 *Founded/Ownrshp* 2002
Sales 57.7MM *EMP* 425
SIC 8093 Mental health clinic, outpatient; Mental health clinic, outpatient
CEO: Ed Coffey
CFO: Kenneth Klein
Ofcr: Jewel Stevens
Exec: Nicolas Valadez
Comm Dir: Nancy Trowbridge
Dir Rx: Juanice Colwell
Dir Bus: Stephanie Cunningham
Nurse Mgr: Philippa Ashford
Nurse Mgr: Linda Green
Nurse Mgr: Daniel Johnson
Nurse Mgr: Christi Peters

D-U-N-S 07-988-1579
MENNINGER FOUNDATION
MENNINGER CLINIC
12301 Main St, Houston, TX 77035-6207
Tel (713) 275-5000 *Founded/Ownrshp* 1919
Sales 4.4MM *EMP* 350^E
SIC 8063 8011 8733 Psychiatric hospitals; Psychiatrist; Research institute; Psychiatric hospitals; Psychiatrist; Research institute
CEO: Ian Aitken
CFO: Kenny J Klein
**Exec:* Efrain Bleiberg
Exec: Tina Holmes
QA Dir: Gayle Garland
Sls&Mrk Ex: George Hopwood
Psych: Jon G Allen

D-U-N-S 60-486-3803
MENNO HAVEN PENN HALL INC
PENN HALL RETIREMENT COMMUNITY
1425 Philadelphia Ave, Chambersburg, PA 17201-1386
Tel (717) 261-0220 *Founded/Ownrshp* 1991
Sales 40.2MM *EMP* 500
SIC 8361 8052 8051 Rest home, with health care incidental; Intermediate care facilities; Skilled nursing care facilities; Rest home, with health care incidental; Intermediate care facilities; Skilled nursing care facilities
CEO: Rodney Mason
Bd of Dir: Martha Walker
VP: Lorraine EBY
Exec: Bryan Lucas
Dir IT: John Baker
Dir IT: Jim Hinkle
Nrsg Dir: Denise Shatzer

D-U-N-S 04-215-4542
MENNO TRAVEL SERVICE INC
104 Lake St, Ephrata, PA 17522-2415
Tel (717) 733-4131 *Founded/Ownrshp* 1947
Sales 24.6MM^E *EMP* 156
Accts Dotzel & Company Inc York
SIC 4724 Travel agencies; Travel agencies
CEO: Michael Bedient
**COO:* Gail Smith
**CFO:* Ron Parent
**CFO:* Vickie Unruh

D-U-N-S 07-120-6171
MENNO-HAVEN INC (PA)
2011 Scotland Ave, Chambersburg, PA 17201-1451
Tel (717) 262-1000 *Founded/Ownrshp* 1962
Sales 45.1MM *EMP* 360
SIC 8051 Skilled nursing care facilities; Skilled nursing care facilities
CEO: Rod Mason
**CFO:* Ana Crider

D-U-N-S 06-988-0458 IMP/EXP
MENNONITE CENTRAL COMMITTEE US
MCC U.S
21 S 12th St, Akron, PA 17501-1605
Tel (717) 859-1151 *Founded/Ownrshp* 1937
Sales 28.1MM^E *EMP* 700
SIC 8322

D-U-N-S 09-018-0266 IMP/EXP
MENNONITE GENERAL HOSPITAL INC
Carr 14 Km 131 Sctor Lmas St Ca, Cayey, PR 00736
Tel (787) 535-1001 *Founded/Ownrshp* 1943
Sales 48.0MM^E *EMP* 1,172
Accts Parissi Psc San Juan Pr

SIC 8062 General medical & surgical hospitals; General medical & surgical hospitals
Pr: Victor Ortiz
**Pr:* Ruben Santos
**VP:* Jos E Rivera
**Ex Dir:* Domingo Torres

D-U-N-S 09-422-7253
MENNONITE HOME
WOOD CREST VILLA
1520 Harrisburg Pike, Lancaster, PA 17601-2697
Tel (717) 393-1301 *Founded/Ownrshp* 1903
Sales 40.5MM *EMP* 551
Accts Parentebeard Llc Philadelphia
SIC 8361 Home for the aged; Home for the aged
Pr: J Nelson Kling
V Ch: Phil Leaman
**CFO:* John Miller
Off Mgr: Janet Myers
CTO: Keith Hamilton
Dir IT: Robert Martin
IT Man: Dennis Bowden
Nrsg Dir: Sheri Workman

D-U-N-S 18-114-8495
MENNONITE HOME OF ALBANY INC
MENNONITE VILLAGE
5353 Columbus St Se, Albany, OR 97322-7199
Tel (541) 928-7232 *Founded/Ownrshp* 1947
Sales 25.7MM *EMP* 300
Accts Hansen Hunter & Co Pc Beave
SIC 8059 8052 8051 Nursing home, except skilled & intermediate care facility; Intermediate care facilities; Skilled nursing care facilities; Nursing home, except skilled & intermediate care facility; Intermediate care facilities; Skilled nursing care facilities
Pr: Ron Litwiller
V Ch: Weldon Burkholder
**CFO:* Chester Patterson
**VP:* Bob Johnson
Off Mgr: Jeannie Reed
VP Opers: Donna Bremiller
Mktg Dir: Whitney Olsen
Nrsg Dir: Judith Gott
Nrsg Dir: Angela Trahan
HC Dir: Shauna Hansell
HC Dir: Sonia Ortiz

D-U-N-S 07-433-0754
MENNONITE MUTUAL AID INC
1110 N Main St, Goshen, IN 46528-2600
Tel (574) 533-9511 *Founded/Ownrshp* 1945
Sales 14.8MM^E *EMP* 285
Accts Bkd Llp Fort Wayne In
SIC 8741 6411 Management services; Administrative management; Insurance agents; Management services; Administrative management; Insurance agents
Pr: Howard Brenneman
**Treas:* John L Liechty
**VP:* Steven L Garboden
Tech Mgr: John Swartzendruber

MENNONITE VILLAGE
See MENNONITE HOME OF ALBANY INC

D-U-N-S 02-534-2234 EXP
MENOMINEE ACQUISITION CORP
CLEARWATER PAPER - MENOMINEE
(*Suby of* DUNN PAPER INC) ★
144 1st St, Menominee, MI 49858-3302
Tel (906) 863-5595 *Founded/Ownrshp* 2014
Sales 29.2MM^E *EMP* 125
SIC 2671 Waxed paper: made from purchased material; Waxed paper: made from purchased material
Pr: Russell Taylor
**CFO:* Dianne Scheu
**VP:* Tom Moore
Netwrk Mgr: Roger Behnke
Plnt Mgr: Kevin French
**VP Sls:* Hugo Vivero

MENOMINEE CASINO BINGO AND HT
See MENOMINEE TRIBAL GAMING CORP

MENOMINEE CASINO RESORT
See MENOMINEE INDIAN GAMING AUTHORITY

D-U-N-S 80-151-3433
MENOMINEE INDIAN GAMING AUTHORITY
MENOMINEE CASINO RESORT
(*Suby of* MENOMINEE INDIAN TRIBE OF WISCONSIN) ★
Hwy 47 & 55 At Duquin Rd, Keshena, WI 54135
Tel (715) 799-3600 *Founded/Ownrshp* 1992
Sales 48.0MM *EMP* 540
SIC 7999 Bingo hall; Gambling establishment; Lottery operation; Bingo hall; Gambling establishment; Lottery operation
Genl Mgr: James Riter
CFO: Beth Gilsoul
Dir Sec: Wayne Higgins
IT Man: Rod Connahvichnah
Netwrk Mgr: Diana Schuls
Mktg Mgr: Mae Tourtillott

D-U-N-S 03-017-5194
MENOMINEE INDIAN TRIBE OF WISCONSIN
W2908 Tribal Off Loop Rd, Keshena, WI 54135
Tel (715) 799-5100 *Founded/Ownrshp* 1908
Sales NA *EMP* 741
SIC 9131 Indian reservation; ; Indian reservation;
V Ch: Gary Besay
**Ch:* Craig Corn

D-U-N-S 01-022-3873
MENOMINEE TRIBAL ENTERPRISES
Hwy 47 N, Neopit, WI 54150
Tel (715) 756-2311 *Founded/Ownrshp* 1975
Sales 24.0MM^E *EMP* 150
Accts Baker Tilly Virchow Krause Ll
SIC 2421 Sawmills & planing mills, general
Pr: Adrian Miller
Bd of Dir: Alex Peters
Top Exec: Marshall Pecore
IT Man: Rebecca Onesti
Plnt Mgr: Pershing Frechette
Mktg Dir: Josh Besaw

D-U-N-S 95-923-2851
MENOMINEE TRIBAL GAMING CORP
MENOMINEE CASINO BINGO AND HT
Hwy 4755 Duqueine Rd, Keshena, WI 54135
Tel (715) 799-3600 *Founded/Ownrshp* 1987
Sales 14.2MM^E *EMP* 550
SIC 7999 7011 5812 Gambling & lottery services; Hotels; Eating places; Gambling & lottery services; Hotels; Eating places
Ch Bd: Stephanie Awonohopay
**CFO:* Robert Goslin
**V Ch Bd:* Delores S Yaiser
Exec: Joann Eisfelder
Dir Sec: Jeff Wilber
Genl Mgr: Harley Lyons
Genl Mgr: James Reiter

D-U-N-S 78-555-1631
MENOMINEE-DELTA-SCHOOLCRAFT COMMUNITY ACTION AGENCY
HUMAN RESOURCE AUTHORITY
507 1st Ave N, Escanaba, MI 49829-3931
Tel (906) 786-7080 *Founded/Ownrshp* 1965
Sales 3.2MM *EMP* 290
SIC 8322 Individual & family services; Individual & family services
Ex Dir: William Dubord

D-U-N-S 03-023-0502
MENORAH CAMPUS INC
2700 N Forest Rd, Getzville, NY 14068-1527
Tel (716) 639-3311 *Founded/Ownrshp* 1924
Sales 14.8MM *EMP* 650
SIC 8051 Extended care facility; Extended care facility
Ex Dir: David M Dunkelman
COO: Randi Dressel

D-U-N-S 07-280-7423
MENORAH HOME & HOSPITAL FOR AGED & INFIRM INC
1516 Oriental Blvd, Brooklyn, NY 11235-2328
Tel (718) 646-4441 *Founded/Ownrshp* 1912
Sales 42.3MM *EMP* 400^E
SIC 8051 Skilled nursing care facilities; Skilled nursing care facilities
Ex Dir: Jane Rosenthal
**CFO:* Neil Schlissel

D-U-N-S 15-190-0651
MENORAH MANOR INC
BERNARD SAMSUN NURSING CENTER
255 59th St N, Saint Petersburg, FL 33710-8589
Tel (727) 735-6200 *Founded/Ownrshp* 1981
Sales 21.3MM *EMP* 260
Accts Moore Stephens Lovelace Pa Cl
SIC 8051 8322 Convalescent home with continuous nursing care; Old age assistance; Convalescent home with continuous nursing care; Old age assistance
CEO: Seth D Levy
**COO:* Robert Goldstein
**CFO:* Donna Perryman
Chf Nrs Of: Anabelle Cunanan-Locsin
HC Dir: Kelly Heron

D-U-N-S 80-337-2069
MENORAH MEDICAL CENTER INC
5721 W 119th St, Overland Park, KS 66209-3753
Tel (913) 498-6000 *Founded/Ownrshp* 1989
Sales 118.8MM^E *EMP* 800
SIC 8011 8062 Clinic, operated by physicians; General medical & surgical hospitals; Clinic, operated by physicians; General medical & surgical hospitals
Pr: Steve Wilkinson
Pr: Ron Crabbs
CFO: Debra Gasford
Dir Lab: Sue Johnson
Dir Rx: Zack Mc Mahon
Dir QC: Annie Wehagezickwolf
Plas Surg: Jeffrey Colyer
Doctor: Cindy C Chang MD
Doctor: Sam Weems
Pharmcst: Robert Province

D-U-N-S 07-691-5800
MENORAH PARK CENTER FOR SENIOR LIVING BET MOSHAV ZEKENIM HADATI
27100 Cedar Rd, Cleveland, OH 44122-1156
Tel (216) 831-6500 *Founded/Ownrshp* 1906
Sales 71.1MM *EMP* 1,096
Accts Mcgladrey Llp Cleveland Ohio
SIC 8051 6513 8322 Skilled nursing care facilities; Apartment building operators; Outreach program; Skilled nursing care facilities; Apartment building operators; Outreach program
Pr: Ira Kaplan
**Pr:* Enid Roseinberg
CFO: Robert S Matitia
CFO: Bob Schaefer
Treas: Michael Peterman
**Ex Dir:* Steven Raichilson
Off Mgr: Kris Christian
CIO: Richard Schwalberg
VP Mktg: Lisa Cullen
Nrsg Dir: Barbara Marcelletti
HC Dir: Lisa Cohen

D-U-N-S 06-510-1974 IMP
▲ MENS WEARHOUSE INC
6380 Rogerdale Rd, Houston, TX 77072-1649
Tel (281) 776-7000 *Founded/Ownrshp* 1973
Sales 3.2MMM *EMP* 26,100
Accts Deloitte & Touche Llp Housto
Tkr Sym MW *Exch* NYS
SIC 5611 5621 5632 5661 5699 Men's & boys' clothing stores; Suits, men's; Clothing accessories: men's & boys'; Tie shops; Women's clothing stores; Apparel accessories; Women's shoes; Uniforms & work clothing; Men's & boys' clothing stores; Suits, men's; Clothing accessories: men's & boys'; Tie shops; Women's clothing stores; Apparel accessories; Women's shoes; Uniforms & work clothing
CEO: Douglas S Ewert
**Ch Bd:* William B Sechrest
Pr: Paul Fitzpatrick
COO: Bruce K Thorn
CFO: Jon W Kimmins
Chf Cred: Gary G Ckodre
Chf Mktg O: Mary Beth Blake
Chf Mktg O: Diane Ridgwaycross
Ofcr: Ben Baum
Ex VP: Charlie Bresler
Ex VP: Eric J Lane
Ex VP: Susan G Neal
Ex VP: Mark Neutze
Ex VP: Hyon Park
Ex VP: William C Silveira
Ex VP: Matt Stringer
Ex VP: Jim Thorne
Sr VP: Theodore T Biele
Sr VP: Jeffrey Marshall
Sr VP: Brian T Vaclavik
VP: Lorne Cytrynbaum
Board of Directors: B Michael Becker, Irene Chang Britt, Rinaldo S Brutoco, David H Edwab, Grace Nichols, Allen I Questrom, Sheldon I Stein

MENSCO DIV
See FLOW SOLUTIONS INC

D-U-N-S 95-690-2274 IMP
MENSHEN PACKAGING USA INC
(*Suby of* GEORG MENSHEN GMBH & CO. KG)
21 Industrial Park, Waldwick, NJ 07463-1512
Tel (201) 444-1383 *Founded/Ownrshp* 1996
Sales 39.5MM^E *EMP* 98
SIC 2842 Industrial plant disinfectants or deodorants; Industrial plant disinfectants or deodorants
Prin: Susan Kobernick
VP: Rogelio Ayala
VP Opers: Jeff Dugal
VP Opers: Daniel Lyons
Sfty Mgr: Darrin Taynor
VP Sls: Jeffrey Stern

D-U-N-S 04-907-7910
MENSOR LP
(*Suby of* WIKA HOLDING L P) ★
201 Barnes Dr, San Marcos, TX 78666-5994
Tel (512) 396-4200 *Founded/Ownrshp* 1969
Sales 21.8MM^E *EMP* 70
SIC 3823 Pressure measurement instruments, industrial; Controllers for process variables, all types
CEO: Alexander Wiegand
Pr: Lee Graham
CTO: Jason Otto
IT Man: Henry Zamora
Sftwr Eng: Chris Cox
Ql Cn Mgr: Tom Turner
Sales Exec: Todd Hadbavny
Sales Exec: Jon Plattner
Natl Sales: Paul Giffen
Sls Mgr: Katja Hinz
Sls Mgr: Steve Keithley

D-U-N-S 19-816-4931
MENTA GROUP INC
195 Poplar Pl, North Aurora, IL 60542-1404
Tel (630) 907-2400 *Founded/Ownrshp* 1988
Sales 9.8MM^E *EMP* 350
SIC 8299 8322 Educational services; Individual & family services; Educational services; Individual & family services
Pr: Ken Carwell
**CFO:* Brian McGowan
**VP:* Beth Conran
**VP:* Laura Mann
Genl Mgr: Linda Prewett
IT Man: Scott Marquardt
Sls Mgr: Jim Lundstrom

D-U-N-S 02-080-0595
MENTAL HEALTH AND MENTAL RETARDATION AUTHORITY OF HARRIS COUNTY (TX)
M H M R AUTHORIY HARRIS COUNTY
9401 Southwest Fwy, Houston, TX 77074-1407
Tel (713) 970-7000 *Founded/Ownrshp* 1965
Sales 213.5MM *EMP* 1,500
Accts Whitley Penn Llp Houston Tex
SIC 8063 Psychiatric hospitals; Psychiatric hospitals
Ex Dir: Dr Steven B Schnee
CFO: Alex Lim
Prgrm Mgr: Ally Frankovich
Nurse Mgr: Yen Phan
Doctor: Linda Wittig MD
Pgrm Dir: Sarita Wesley
Snr Mgr: Ramos Mata
Snr Mgr: Monica Waters

D-U-N-S 11-258-8322
MENTAL HEALTH AND RECOVERY SERVICES BOARD INC
1205 Newark Rd, Zanesville, OH 43701-2620
Tel (740) 454-8557 *Founded/Ownrshp* 1968
Sales 20.0MM *EMP* 9
SIC 8093 Specialty outpatient clinics; Mental health clinic, outpatient; Drug clinic, outpatient; Alcohol clinic, outpatient; Specialty outpatient clinics; Mental health clinic, outpatient; Drug clinic, outpatient; Alcohol clinic, outpatient

MENTAL HEALTH AND VOCATIONAL C
See OCCUPATIONAL CENTER OF UNION COUNTY

D-U-N-S 03-993-2926
MENTAL HEALTH ASSOCIATION OF SOUTH CENTRAL KANSAS
555 N Woodlawn St # 3105, Wichita, KS 67208-3673
Tel (316) 685-1821 *Founded/Ownrshp* 1967
Sales 8.5MM *EMP* 325^E
SIC 8322 Social service center; Social service center
Pr: Carol Manning

D-U-N-S 15-397-5412
MENTAL HEALTH ASSOCIATION OF SOUTHEASTERN PENNSYLVANIA
1211 Chestnut St Fl 11, Philadelphia, PA 19107-4122
Tel (215) 751-1800 *Founded/Ownrshp* 1951
Sales 17.8MM *EMP* 350
Accts Tait Weller & Baker Llp Phila
SIC 8093 8399 Mental health clinic, outpatient; Advocacy group; Mental health clinic, outpatient; Advocacy group
CEO: Michael Brody
**CFO:* Rita C Dame
**Ch:* Steven Weinstein
Prgrm Mgr: Erme Maula

D-U-N-S 04-020-3564
MENTAL HEALTH CARE INC
GRACEPOINT
5707 N 22nd St, Tampa, FL 33610-4350
Tel (813) 239-8083 *Founded/Ownrshp* 1962
Sales 29.2MM *EMP* 650
Accts Rnero Gordimer & Company Pa T
SIC 8322 Rehabilitation services; Rehabilitation services
CFO: Steven Welch
CFO: Ravji Bhatty
**CFO:* Steve Welch
Treas: Sally Parsons
Sr VP: David Kendrick
VP: Roaya Tyson
Exec: Vito Navatta
Exec: Nancy Pape
Ex Dir: Lorna Miller
Ex Dir: Sandra Tabor
Prgrm Mgr: Vimbai Mudimu
Board of Directors: Joseph Rutherford

MENTAL HEALTH CENTER
See COUNTY OF CALAVERAS

D-U-N-S 09-574-8943
MENTAL HEALTH CENTER OF BOULDER COUNTY INC
1333 Iris Ave, Boulder, CO 80304-2226
Tel (303) 443-8500 *Founded/Ownrshp* 1962
Sales 35.1MM *EMP* 310
Accts Bkd Llp Coloroda Springs Co
SIC 8093 Mental health clinic, outpatient; Mental health clinic, outpatient
Ex Dir: Barbara Ryan
Off Mgr: Andrea Hantscheruk
IT Man: Ivy Danzl
Psych: Amy Deweese
Psych: Andrea Foote
Psych: Phyllis Klaif
Psych: Angela Pike
Psych: Jean Rosmarin
Psych: Carol Spar
Psych: Sarah Wu
Snr Mgr: Jane Bryant

D-U-N-S 18-222-9567
MENTAL HEALTH CENTER OF DENVER
4141 E Dickenson Pl, Denver, CO 80222-6012
Tel (303) 504-6501 *Founded/Ownrshp* 1987
Sales 66.9MM^E *EMP* 570
Accts Cliftonlarsonallen Llp Greenw
SIC 8093 Mental health clinic, outpatient; Mental health clinic, outpatient
CEO: Carl Clark
Pr: Barbara Shaw
**CFO:* Forrest Cason
Assoc Dir: Dawn Davenport
Prgrm Mgr: Lyndsay Barrett
Prgrm Mgr: Angie Elzi
Prgrm Mgr: Lynn Garst
Prgrm Mgr: Terri Hamblen
Prgrm Mgr: Davis Schiele
Off Mgr: Michelle Flores
CTO: Christina Loetscher

D-U-N-S 07-397-8280
MENTAL HEALTH CENTER OF GREATER MANCHESTER INC
GREATER MANCH MENTAL HEALTH
401 Cypress St, Manchester, NH 03103-3699
Tel (603) 668-4111 *Founded/Ownrshp* 1960
Sales 23.4MM *EMP* 300
Accts Kittell Branagan & Sargent Cpa
SIC 8093 Mental health clinic, outpatient; Mental health clinic, outpatient
CEO: Peter Janelle
**CFO:* Paul Michaud
**CFO:* Arlene Robbins
Bd of Dir: Leslie Clukay
**Ofcr:* Jane Guilmette
**Ex VP:* William Ryder
VP: Mary Lavalley
**VP:* Kendall Snow
**VP:* Quentin Turnbull
Off Mgr: Deborah Compo
Dir IT: Daniel Fortier

D-U-N-S 02-074-3563
MENTAL HEALTH CONVELESCENT SERVICES INC
LAKEWOOD PARK HEALTH CENTER
12023 Lakewood Blvd, Downey, CA 90242-2635
Tel (562) 869-0978 *Founded/Ownrshp* 1975
Sales 11.4MM *EMP* 300
SIC 8051 Skilled nursing care facilities; Skilled nursing care facilities
Pr: Daniel C Zilafro

D-U-N-S 80-429-6291
MENTAL HEALTH COOPERATIVE INC
275 Cumberland Bnd # 237, Nashville, TN 37228-1805
Tel (615) 726-3340 *Founded/Ownrshp* 1992
Sales 34.6MM^E *EMP* 454
Accts Frasier Dean & Howard Pllc Na
SIC 8093 Mental health clinic, outpatient; Mental health clinic, outpatient
CEO: Pam Womack
**COO:* Allen Tepper
CFO: Kim Smith
CIO: Mark Wisniewski
Pr Dir: Jennifer Felts
Snr Mgr: Amanda Myatt

D-U-N-S 02-033-3597
MENTAL HEALTH MENTAL RETARDATION OF TARRANT COUNTY
MHMR OF TARRANT COUNTY
3840 Hulen St, Fort Worth, TX 76107-7277
Tel (817) 569-4300 *Founded/Ownrshp* 1969
Sales 122.5MM *EMP* 1,500
Accts Weaver And Tidwell Llp Fort W

SIC 8093 8322 8361 Mental health clinic, outpatient; General counseling services; Home for the mentally retarded; Mental health clinic, outpatient; General counseling services; Home for the mentally retarded
CEO: Susan Garnett
**CEO:* James F Mc Dermott
Comm Dir: Catherine Carlton

D-U-N-S 02-111-8286
MENTAL HEALTH RESOURCE CENTER INC
(*Suby of* RENAISSANCE BEHAVIORAL HEALTH SYSTEMS INC) ★
10550 Deerwood Park Blvd # 600, Jacksonville, FL 32256-2811
Tel (904) 642-9100 *Founded/Ownrshp* 1977
Sales 34.5MM *EMP* 272
Accts Ralston & Company Pa Cpa Jack
SIC 8063 8093 Psychiatric hospitals; Specialty outpatient clinics; Psychiatric hospitals; Specialty outpatient clinics
Pr: Robert A Sommers
IT Man: Frankie Len

D-U-N-S 08-411-0717
MENTAL HEALTH RESOURCES INC
762 Transfer Rd Ste 21, Saint Paul, MN 55114-1489
Tel (651) 659-2900 *Founded/Ownrshp* 1976
Sales 22.2MM *EMP* 155
Accts Harrington Langer & Associates
SIC 8399 Health systems agency; Health systems agency
Pr: Michael Trangle
VP: Ann Henderson

MENTAL HEALTH SERVICES
See ARKANSAS HEALTH CENTER

MENTAL HEALTH STATE OF MO DEPT
See MISSOURI DEPARTMENT OF MENTAL HEALTH

D-U-N-S 01-348-1833
MENTAL HEALTH SYSTEMS INC
JOSHUA TREE CENTER FOR CHANGE
9465 Farnham St, San Diego, CA 92123-1308
Tel (858) 573-2600 *Founded/Ownrshp* 1978
Sales 74.9MM *EMP* 835
Accts David Frank Cpa Temecula Cal
SIC 8093 Specialty outpatient clinics; Specialty outpatient clinics
Ch: James Callaghan
**CEO:* Kimberly Bond
**COO:* Wendy Broughton
**Sr VP:* Michael Hawkey
**VP:* David Calandra
**VP:* David Conn
VP: Delrena Swaggerty
**VP:* Laura L Whitehouse
Prgrm Mgr: Kay Masaryk
Prgrm Mgr: Chuck Williams
Psych: Laura Otis-Miles
Board of Directors: Ernest Wright

D-U-N-S 18-798-0693
MENTAL RETARDATION SERVICES INC
CVI JANITORIAL SERVICE
9 Industrial Blvd, Plattsburgh, NY 12901-1910
Tel (518) 563-0930 *Founded/Ownrshp* 1978
Sales 1.4MM *EMP* 350
SIC 8322 Social services for the handicapped; Social services for the handicapped
Ex Dir: Richard Minogue

D-U-N-S 00-210-5757 IMP/EXP
MENTHOLATUM CO
(*Suby of* ROHTO USA INC) ★
707 Sterling Dr, Orchard Park, NY 14127-1587
Tel (716) 677-2500 *Founded/Ownrshp* 1889
Sales 48.5MM[E] *EMP* 200
SIC 2834 2844 Pharmaceutical preparations; Analgesics; Lip balms; Toilet preparations; Pharmaceutical preparations; Analgesics; Lip balms; Toilet preparations
CEO: Akiyoshi Yoshida PHD
**Pr:* Kunio Yamada
Sr Cor Off: David Moore
**VP:* Francis Chan
Rgnl Mgr: Barbara Regan
Tech Mgr: Kathi Winterstein
Ql Cn Mgr: David Greco
VP Mktg: Jim Nass
Mktg Mgr: Kevin Bosiacki
Mktg Mgr: D'Anna Farrar
Sls Mgr: Laura Curry

MENTOR BOARD OF EDUCATION
See MENTOR EXEMPTED VILLAGE SCHOOL DISTRICT

D-U-N-S 09-533-0635
MENTOR CITY OF (INC)
8500 Civic Center Blvd, Mentor, OH 44060-2418
Tel (440) 255-1100 *Founded/Ownrshp* 1885
Sales NA *EMP* 480
Accts James G Zupka Cpa Inc Gar
SIC 9199 Civil rights commission, government; Civil rights commission, government
Pr: Robert M Shiner
**Pr:* Ray Kirchner
Pr: Suzanne Walker
Ofcr: Jim Collier
Ofcr: Michael Danzey
Prin: Elizabeth Limestahl

D-U-N-S 01-084-9602
MENTOR EXEMPTED VILLAGE SCHOOL DISTRICT
MENTOR BOARD OF EDUCATION
6451 Center St, Mentor, OH 44060-4109
Tel (440) 255-4444 *Founded/Ownrshp* 1953
Sales 103.9MM *EMP* 1,000
Accts Mary Taylor Cpa Cleveland O
SIC 8211 Public elementary school; Public junior high school; Public senior high school; Public elementary school; Public junior high school; Public senior high school
**Treas:* Daniel L Wilson
Off Admin: Carrie Kornmiller
Dir IT: Jeremy Shorr
Dir IT: Mark Wardeiner
Trfc Dir: Joyel Ansorge
Pr Dir: Kristen Kirby
Psych: Faith Kover
HC Dir: Margaret Watson

D-U-N-S 03-137-4879
▲ MENTOR GRAPHICS CORP
8005 Sw Boeckman Rd, Wilsonville, OR 97070-7777
Tel (503) 685-7000 *Founded/Ownrshp* 1981
Sales 1.2MMM *EMP* 5,558[E]
Accts Kpmg Llp Portland Oregon
Tkr Sym MENT *Exch* NGS
SIC 7373 Computer-aided system services; Computer-aided system services
Ch Bd: Walden C Rhines
Pr: Greg Helton
**Pr:* Gregory K Hinckley
CFO: Mike Mitchem
Ofcr: Michael Vishny
VP: Douglas Altschuler
VP: Simon Bloch
VP: Dean Freed
VP: Aj Incorvaia
VP: Henry Potts
VP: Joseph D Sawicki
VP: Eric Selosse
VP: Ananthan Thandri
Dir Bus: Andrew Patterson
Dir Bus: Julian Sun
Board of Directors: Keith L Barnes, Peter L Bonfield, Paul A Mascarenas, J Daniel McCranie, Patrick B McManus, Jeffrey M Stafeil

D-U-N-S 01-818-0679
MENTOR LUMBER AND SUPPLY CO
MENTOR WHOLESALE LUMBER
7180 Center St, Mentor, OH 44060-4979
Tel (440) 255-8814 *Founded/Ownrshp* 1963
Sales 37.1MM[E] *EMP* 150
SIC 5031 5211 Lumber: rough, dressed & finished; Lumber & other building materials; Lumber: rough, dressed & finished; Lumber & other building materials
Pr: Reed H Martin
**Ch Bd:* Jerome T Osborne
**CFO:* Barbie Rita
Sr VP: Robert Sanderson
VP: Ray Sanderson
**VP:* Mack Stewart
VP Mktg: Rick Hanson

D-U-N-S 80-261-3138
MENTOR REM
(*Suby of* NMH INVESTMENT LLC) ★
9775 Rockside Rd Ste 200, Cleveland, OH 44125-6266
Tel (216) 642-5339 *Founded/Ownrshp* 2007
Sales 28.7MM[E] *EMP* 4,746[E]
SIC 8211 Specialty education
Prin: Mary Kay Ziccardi

D-U-N-S 10-539-8163
MENTOR TECHNICAL GROUP CORP
Alhambra Granada Blvd Ga, Caguas, PR 00725
Tel (787) 743-0897 *Founded/Ownrshp* 2000
Sales 27.4MM *EMP* 440
Accts Rsm Roc & Company San Juan P
SIC 8734 Calibration & certification; Calibration & certification
Pr: Luis David Soto
**Pt:* Julin Rodrguez
VP: Julian Rodriguez
Genl Mgr: Felix Bernard
Genl Mgr: Cesar Mirabal

D-U-N-S 16-745-0993 IMP
■ MENTOR TEXAS LP
(*Suby of* MENTOR WORLDWIDE LLC) ★
3041 Skyway Cir N, Irving, TX 75038-3540
Tel (972) 252-6060 *Founded/Ownrshp* 2002
Sales 71.4MM[E] *EMP* 350
SIC 3842 Implants, surgical; Implants, surgical
Pr: Andy Tymkiw
COO: Michael Magura
Exec: Malcolm Gilmore
CTO: Peter Chaump
Opers Mgr: Mike Rossman
Ql Cn Mgr: Lisa Starr
Sls&Mrk Ex: Jose Echavarria
Sls&Mrk Ex: Alex Jarvis
Sls&Mrk Ex: Angelo Maria

MENTOR WHOLESALE LUMBER
See MENTOR LUMBER AND SUPPLY CO

D-U-N-S 04-671-2931 IMP
■ MENTOR WORLDWIDE LLC
(*Suby of* ETHICON INC) ★
5425 Hollister Ave, Santa Barbara, CA 93111-3341
Tel (805) 879-6000 *Founded/Ownrshp* 2009
Sales 226.4MM[E] *EMP* 1,200
SIC 3842 3845 3841 Surgical appliances & supplies; Prosthetic appliances; Implants, surgical; Cosmetic restorations; Ultrasonic medical equipment, except cleaning; Medical instruments & equipment, blood & bone work; Surgical appliances & supplies; Prosthetic appliances; Implants, surgical; Cosmetic restorations; Ultrasonic medical equipment, except cleaning; Medical instruments & equipment, blood & bone work
Pr: David Shepherd
Pr: Dean Freed
Pr: Noam Krantz
COO: Edward Northup
Sr VP: Eugene G Lover
VP: David J Adornetto
VP: David Amerson
VP: Kathleen Beauchamp
VP: Don Cantow
VP: Tom Floodeen
VP: Udo Graf
VP: Lynn Hunt
VP: Loren McFarlnd
VP: Henry Potts
Exec: Wendy Malkin
Exec: Vincent Monsaignon
Exec: Jessica Scott
Exec: Bryan Theobald

D-U-N-S 17-694-4531
MENTORING MINDS L P
4908 Hightech Dr, Tyler, TX 75703-2625
Tel (903) 509-4002 *Founded/Ownrshp* 2003
Sales 24.5MM[E] *EMP* 45
SIC 5049 School supplies
CEO: Robert L Bush
**Pt:* Lisa Lujan
**Pt:* Michael Lujan
**COO:* Theresa Avirett
**CFO:* Shad A Madsen
Genl Mgr: Andrew Muollo

D-U-N-S 07-953-4750
MENTORMATE INC
(*Suby of* TAYLOR CORP) ★
3036 Hennepin Ave, Minneapolis, MN 55408-2614
Tel (612) 823-4000 *Founded/Ownrshp* 2014
Sales 23.1MM[E] *EMP* 240
SIC 7371 Computer software development & applications; Computer software development & applications
CEO: Bjorn Stansvik
Pr: James Williams
COO: Jamie Bolseth
VP: Roger Ferguson
Creative D: Mike Hagan
CTO: Dimitar Dobrev
Web Dev: Petar Kadakevliev
Software D: Adam Malone
Opers Mgr: Stefanie Trimble
Snr PM: Ian Good
Snr Mgr: Stephen Fluin

D-U-N-S 05-125-9547
MENTZER OIL CO
AMOCO SOUTH
311 E 7th St, North Platte, NE 69101-3104
Tel (308) 532-4059 *Founded/Ownrshp* 1984
Sales 50.0MM *EMP* 35[E]
SIC 5541 5171 Filling stations, gasoline; Petroleum bulk stations; Filling stations, gasoline; Petroleum bulk stations
Pr: Donald Mentzer
**Sec:* Donna Mentzer
**Genl Mgr:* Cindy Halligan
**Genl Mgr:* Doug Mentzer

D-U-N-S 62-699-8835 IMP
MENU FOODS INC
(*Suby of* SIMMONS PET FOOD INC) ★
9130 Griffith Morgan Ln, Pennsauken, NJ 08110-3211
Tel (856) 662-7412 *Founded/Ownrshp* 2010
Sales 59.0MM[E] *EMP* 285
SIC 2047 Dog food; Cat food; Dog food; Cat food
Pr: Robert W Bras
**Pr:* David Jackson

D-U-N-S 01-389-7041 IMP
MENU FOODS MIDWEST CORP
(*Suby of* SIMMONS PET FOOD INC) ★
1400 E Logan Ave, Emporia, KS 66801-6822
Tel (620) 342-1323 *Founded/Ownrshp* 1997, 2011
Sales 119.7MM[E] *EMP* 321
SIC 2047 Dog & cat food; Dog & cat food
CEO: Mark Simmons
**Pr:* David Jackson
VP: Steve Lindsay
Exec: Janice Schade

D-U-N-S 04-350-4588
MENU MAKER FOODS INC (MO)
GRAVES MENU MAKER FOODS
913 Big Horn Dr, Jefferson City, MO 65109-0336
Tel (573) 893-3000 *Founded/Ownrshp* 1968
Sales 89.5MM[E] *EMP* 130
SIC 5141 5087 2011 5149 Groceries, general line; Cleaning & maintenance equipment & supplies; Meat packing plants; Groceries & related products; Groceries, general line; Cleaning & maintenance equipment & supplies; Meat packing plants; Groceries & related products
Pr: Dick Graves
**CEO:* Tracy Graves
Genl Mgr: Lance Gorney
IT Man: Calenvieoo Graves
IT Man: John Timbers
Plnt Mgr: Russ Steen
Sls&Mrk Ex: Tom Stickler
Manager: Roy McConnell
Sls Mgr: Kent Carl

D-U-N-S 14-001-4627
MENZIES AVIATION (TEXAS) INC
AMI
(*Suby of* JOHN MENZIES (108) LIMITED)
2520 W Airfield Dr, Dallas, TX 75261-4028
Tel (972) 929-1020 *Founded/Ownrshp* 1953
Sales 110.5MM[E] *EMP* 1,600
SIC 4512 Air passenger carrier, scheduled; Air passenger carrier, scheduled
Pr: Larry Synder
**Treas:* Tristan Turnbull
**VP:* Todd Kilgore
VP: Clive Macmillan
**VP:* Mike Pattinson
Dir Risk M: Rocky Woods

MENZNER HARDWOODS
See MENZNER LUMBER AND SUPPLY CO

D-U-N-S 02-333-6043 IMP
MENZNER LUMBER AND SUPPLY CO
MENZNER HARDWOODS
105 Main St, Marathon, WI 54448-9646
Tel (715) 443-1326 *Founded/Ownrshp* 1969
Sales 69.1MM[E] *EMP* 300
SIC 2431 2435 Moldings, wood: unfinished & prefinished; Hardwood veneer & plywood; Moldings, wood: unfinished & prefinished; Hardwood veneer & plywood
Pr: Phil Menzner
**VP:* Lori Menzner
Dir IT: Jeff Swim

D-U-N-S 00-590-4198 IMP
MEOPTA USA INC (NY)
TYROLIT COMPANY
(*Suby of* MEOPTA - OPTIKA, S.R.O.)
50 Davids Dr, Hauppauge, NY 11788-2040
Tel (631) 436-5900 *Founded/Ownrshp* 1957
Sales 42.9MM[E] *EMP* 140
SIC 3827 Lenses, optical: all types except ophthalmic; Lenses, optical: all types except ophthalmic
Pr: Gerald J Rausnitz
**Treas:* Egon Rausnitz
Genl Mgr: Reinhard Seipp
Ql Cn Mgr: Danny Simmons
Sls Mgr: Jon Giles

D-U-N-S 96-396-0182 IMP
MEOW INC
REBECCA TAYLOR SHOWROOM
(*Suby of* KELLWOOD CO LLC) ★
307 W 36th St Fl 16, New York, NY 10018-6470
Tel (212) 704-0607 *Founded/Ownrshp* 1996
Sales 29.6MM[E] *EMP* 57[E]
SIC 5137 Dresses; Sportswear, women's & children's
Ch Bd: Lynn Shanahan
**CEO:* Elizabeth Bugdaycay
**COO:* Bruce Miglinccio

D-U-N-S 10-925-3435 IMP/EXP
MEP ACQUISITION CORP
MARINE ELECTRICAL PRODUCTS
1401 Tower Rd, Lebanon, MO 65536-9280
Tel (417) 588-3128 *Founded/Ownrshp* 2005
Sales 56.0MM[E] *EMP* 300
SIC 3679 Harness assemblies for electronic use: wire or cable; Harness assemblies for electronic use: wire or cable
Pr: Brian Barbo
**CFO:* Rich Williams
Mtls Mgr: Jim Mooney

D-U-N-S 79-206-0845
MEP HOLDING CO INC
2350 N Shadeland Ave, Indianapolis, IN 46219-1736
Tel (317) 543-3460 *Founded/Ownrshp* 2006
Sales 67.7MM[E] *EMP* 335
SIC 1711 8748 Ventilation & duct work contractor; Warm air heating & air conditioning contractor; Refrigeration contractor; Heating systems repair & maintenance; Business consulting; Ventilation & duct work contractor; Warm air heating & air conditioning contractor; Refrigeration contractor; Heating systems repair & maintenance; Business consulting
Pr: Paul Morey
**COO:* Michael Schmoll

D-U-N-S 00-917-5191
MEPCO LABEL SYSTEMS
1313 S Stockton St, Lodi, CA 95240-5942
Tel (209) 946-0201 *Founded/Ownrshp* 1963
Sales 22.3MM[E] *EMP* 96
SIC 2759 Publication printing
CEO: Jennifer Tracy
**Pr:* Tom Gassner
**CEO:* Alfred M Gassner
**CEO:* Carol Gassner
Ex VP: Jeniffer Tracy
Genl Mgr: Frank Griffen
DP Exec: Braulio Gomez
VP Opers: Philip Tracy
Manager: Lari Hill
Manager: Curtis Jackson
Manager: Joshua Walker

MEPPI
See MITSUBISHI ELECTRIC POWER PRODUCTS INC

D-U-N-S 07-385-0919
MEQUON-THIENSVILLE SCHOOL DISTRICT
5000 W Mequon Rd, Mequon, WI 53092-2044
Tel (262) 238-5900 *Founded/Ownrshp* 1945
Sales 26.8MM[E] *EMP* 415
SIC 8211 Public elementary & secondary schools; Public elementary & secondary schools
Bd of Dir: Wendy Francour
Psych: Todd Reineking

D-U-N-S 05-752-3423
MERA SOFTWARE SERVICES INC
2350 Mission College Blvd # 340, Santa Clara, CA 95054-1532
Tel (650) 703-7226 *Founded/Ownrshp* 2012
Sales 6.5MM[E] *EMP* 1,300
SIC 7371 Computer software writing services
CEO: James Hymel

D-U-N-S 78-075-8426 IMP
■ MERAKI LLC
(*Suby of* CISCO SYSTEMS INC) ★
500 T A Francois Blvd 4 Ste 400, San Francisco, CA 94158
Tel (415) 632-5800 *Founded/Ownrshp* 2012
Sales 67.3MM[E] *EMP* 305
SIC 5734 Computer software & accessories; Computer software & accessories
Ex VP: Teri Fournier
VP: Ben Calderon
IT Man: Chris Hilsenbeck
Sftwr Eng: Jonathan Scoles
Opers Mgr: Steph Bruce
Mktg Mgr: Olivia Pei
Manager: Ladd Austere
Manager: T J Michie
Sls Mgr: David Gervon
Sls Mgr: Clint Nelson

D-U-N-S 06-957-7286 IMP
MERAMEC GROUP INC
338 Ramsey Dr, Sullivan, MO 63080-1456
Tel (573) 468-3101 *Founded/Ownrshp* 1963
Sales 57.3MM[E] *EMP* 200
SIC 3021 3069 3499 Rubber & plastics footwear; Heels, boot or shoe: rubber, composition or fiber; Furniture parts, metal; Rubber & plastics footwear; Heels, boot or shoe: rubber, composition or fiber; Furniture parts, metal
Ch Bd: Robert Dieckhaus

*Pr: Thomas H Dieckhaus
Plnt Mgr: Jason Blankenship

D-U-N-S 04-771-5750
MERAMEC INSTRUMENT TRANSFORMER CO
1 Andrews Way, Cuba, MO 65453-1800
Tel (573) 885-2521 Founded/Ownrshp 1969
Sales 42.9MM^E EMP 125
SIC 3612 Transformers, except electric; Transformers, except electric
Pr: Nichols Sanazaro Jr
*Pr: Nichols Sanazaro
*Treas: Carolyn Sanazaro
*VP: Andrew J Sanazaro Jr
*VP: Daniel Sanazaro
Sfty Mgr: Joe Moreland
Sls Mgr: Terry Fieser
Board of Directors: Carolyn Ising, Christy Moreland

D-U-N-S 07-033-3877
MERAMEC VALLEY R-III SCHOOL DISTRICT
126 N Payne St, Pacific, MO 63069-1260
Tel (636) 271-1400 Founded/Ownrshp 1866
Sales 30.6MM^E EMP 600
SIC 8211 Public elementary & secondary schools; Public elementary & secondary schools
HC Dir: Barbara Hager

D-U-N-S 00-445-8204 IMP
MERC ACQUISITIONS INC (OH)
ELECTRIC SWEEPER SERVICE CO
1933 Highland Rd, Twinsburg, OH 44087-2224
Tel (216) 925-5918 Founded/Ownrshp 1924, 1989
Sales 23.6MM^E EMP 28
SIC 5064 Appliance parts, household; Vacuum cleaners, household
Pr: Robert Merckle
*VP: Gale Merckle

D-U-N-S 84-346-3787 IMP/EXP
MERCADAGRO INTERNATIONAL CORP
MIC FOOD DIVISION
8701 Sw 137th Ave Ste 308, Miami, FL 33183-4498
Tel (786) 507-0540 Founded/Ownrshp 1987
Sales 48.1MM^E EMP 215
SIC 5142 Packaged frozen goods; Packaged frozen goods
Pr: Cira I Lardizabal
VP: Maria Krogh
VP: Maria Lardizabal
*VP: Maria Lardizibal
*VP: Isabel Roldan
*Prin: Alfredo Lardizibal
Sls Dir: Derek Krogh

MERCADO JUAREZ
See DOS GRINGOS INC

D-U-N-S 05-574-5996 IMP
MERCADO LATINO INC (CA)
245 Baldwin Park Blvd, City of Industry, CA 91746-1404
Tel (626) 333-6862 Founded/Ownrshp 1963
Sales 255.5MM^E EMP 350
SIC 5141 5148 Groceries, general line; Fresh fruits & vegetables; Groceries, general line; Fresh fruits & vegetables
Pr: Graciliano Rodriguez
*CFO: George Rodriguez
*Sr VP: Richard Rodriguez
IT Man: Mohammad Siddiqui

D-U-N-S 19-129-0725
MERCADO MEXICO CAFE
POSADOS MEXICAN CAFE
2214 W Southwest Loop 323, Tyler, TX 75701-8433
Tel (903) 534-1754 Founded/Ownrshp 1989
Sales 5.8MM EMP 500
SIC 5812 Mexican restaurant; Mexican restaurant
Pr: Andrew Gugar
*CFO: William H Parks
*VP: Paul Bambrey
*VP: Carla Parks
*VP: Larry Routh

D-U-N-S 09-720-6999
MERCANTIL COMMERCEBANK FLORIDA BANCORP INC
(Suby of MERCANTIL COMMERCEBANK HOLDING CORP) ★
220 Alhambra Cir Fl 11, Coral Gables, FL 33134-5146
Tel (305) 460-4000 Founded/Ownrshp 1987
Sales NA EMP 187
SIC 6021 National commercial banks; National commercial banks
Ch Bd: Guillermo Villar
Pr: Millar Wilson
Ofcr: Elsa Garrote
Ofcr: Brian Hanley
Ex VP: Augusto Sigarreta
VP: Alexis Nahon
VP: W Brant Wallace
Board of Directors: Frederick C Copeland Jr, Pamella J Dana, Brian D Oneill

D-U-N-S 19-217-1791
MERCANTIL COMMERCEBANK HOLDING CORP
(Suby of MERCANTIL SERVICIOS FINANCIEROS, C.A.)
220 Alhambra Cir, Coral Gables, FL 33134-5174
Tel (305) 441-5555 Founded/Ownrshp 1987
Sales NA EMP 239
Accts Pricewatershousecoopers Llp
SIC 6021 7389 8721 National commercial banks; Financial services; Accounting, auditing & bookkeeping; National commercial banks; Financial services; Accounting, auditing & bookkeeping
Ch: Gustavo Vollmer A
Pr: Alberto Peraza
CEO: Millar Wilson
CFO: Alfonso Figueredo
CFO: Philip Henriquez
Ofcr: T Branco
Ofcr: Gonzalo Delgado
Ofcr: Isabel Fernandez
Ofcr: Antonio Lehrmann
Ofcr: Jaclyn Luis
Ofcr: Lolita Peroza
Ofcr: Cary Polanco
Ofcr: Lourdes Rodriguez
Ofcr: Evan Sicle
Ofcr: Peter H Smith
Ofcr: John Triana
Top Exec: Rosa Costantino
Ex VP: Melanie Garman
Ex VP: Andres Sala
Sr VP: Theresa Bello
Sr VP: Frank Gambin

D-U-N-S 80-308-8913
MERCANTILE ADJUSTMENT BUREAU LLC
165 Lawrence Bell Dr # 100, Buffalo, NY 14221-7900
Tel (716) 929-8200 Founded/Ownrshp 2004
Sales 34.6MM^E EMP 325
SIC 7322 Collection agency, except real estate; Collection agency, except real estate
CEO: Jeffrey Miller
COO: Lance Dellamea
CFO: Pamela Brewer
Ex VP: William Burns
Sr VP: Don Schwake
VP: Dan Frisicaro
Dept Mgr: John Lodico
QA Dir: Laurie Manganaro
Dir IT: Bob Price

D-U-N-S 10-924-5746
▲ MERCANTILE BANCORP INC
200 N 33rd St, Quincy, IL 62301-3714
Tel (217) 223-7300 Founded/Ownrshp 1983
Sales NA EMP 252^E
Tkr Sym MBCRQ Exch OTO
SIC 6021 National commercial banks; National commercial banks
Pr: Lee R Keith
CFO: Michael P McGrath
Ofcr: Holly Cole
Ofcr: Ferd E Niemann
Sr Tst Off: Robin Fitzgibbons
Sr Tst Off: Jo Ann Wilmott
Trst Ofcr: Teresa Kuchling
Trst Ofcr: Richard Milgrim
Ex VP: Daniel J Cook
Ex VP: Daniel Cook
Ex VP: Michael McGrath
VP: Ron Ansari
VP: Ramona Schoonover
VP: Janet Spory
VP: Cheri Stanton
VP: Elizabeth Willer
VP: Sheri Wood

D-U-N-S 94-314-0426
MERCANTILE BANK
1560 Orange Ave Ste 300, Winter Park, FL 32789-5558
Tel (407) 622-3528 Founded/Ownrshp 2010
Sales NA EMP 1,015
SIC 6022 State commercial banks; State commercial banks
Pr: Ernie Diaz
*CFO: Ken Brewer
*Ex VP: Charles B Lowe Jr
*Ex VP: Theresa Spellings
Sr VP: Nadine Genet
VP: Grace Cook
VP: Terence Coyle
VP: Todd Labuzienski

D-U-N-S 09-680-9590
▲ MERCANTILE BANK CORP (MI)
310 Leonard St Nw, Grand Rapids, MI 49504-4224
Tel (616) 406-3000 Founded/Ownrshp 1997
Sales NA EMP 731^E
Tkr Sym MBWM Exch NGS
SIC 6022 State commercial banks; State commercial banks
Ch Bd: Michael H Price
Pr: Greg Hansen
Pr: Glenda Stursma
COO: Robert B Kaminski Jr
CFO: Charles E Christmas
CFO: Don Winkleman
Chf Mktg O: Monica Kreiger
Ofcr: Amy Ervin
Ofcr: Jeffrey Kaiser
Ofcr: Misti Stanton
Ofcr: Mark Wait
Ex VP: Samuel G Stone
Sr VP: Teresa Stephens
Sr VP: Matt Zimmerman
VP: Joe Allen
VP: Benjamin Bakken
VP: David Deboer
VP: Deborah Drake
VP: Jeff Hicks
VP: Sarah Hodgkins
VP: Sandy Jager
Board of Directors: David M Cassard, Edward J Clark, Jeff A Gardner, Edward B Grant, Thomas R Sullivan

D-U-N-S 36-429-3415
■ MERCANTILE BANK OF MICHIGAN
(Suby of MERCANTILE BANK CORP) ★
310 Leonard St Nw, Grand Rapids, MI 49504-4224
Tel (616) 406-3000 Founded/Ownrshp 1997
Sales NA EMP 250
SIC 6022 State commercial banks; State commercial banks
CEO: Robert Kaminski Jr
*Pr: Robert B Kaminski
*CFO: Charles E Christmas
*Ch: Michael H Price
Ofcr: Nick Hamadanchi
Ofcr: Dan Quist
Sr VP: Tom Hoban
Sr VP: Wayne Smith
VP: Keane Blaszczynski
VP: Mark Conn
Brnch Mgr: Robert Staley

D-U-N-S 96-227-8391
MERCANTILE CREDIT INC
50 W 34th St Apt 9a10, New York, NY 10001-3061
Tel (212) 643-3254 Founded/Ownrshp 1993
Sales NA EMP 10
SIC 6153 Mercantile financing; Mercantile financing
Pr: Johnny Sajnani
*VP: Sohail Farooqi

D-U-N-S 00-691-8684
■ MERCANTILE PENINSULA BANK
(Suby of PNC FINANCIAL SERVICES GROUP INC) ★
1 W Church St, Selbyville, DE 19975-2003
Tel (302) 436-8236 Founded/Ownrshp 2007
Sales NA EMP 374
SIC 6022 State commercial banks; State commercial banks
Pr: Robert E Dickerson
Sr VP: D Brent Hurley
VP: James D Barr
VP: Russell D Brittingham
VP: Kenneth R Graham
VP: B Philip Lynch Jr
VP: Janet Mc Cabe
VP: Wayne C Morton
VP: Gerald Warren
Board of Directors: P Coleman Townsend Jr, Thurman Adams Jr, Eugene Bunting, R Carol Campbell, Robert E Dickerson, David C Doane, D Brent Hurley, Richard I Lewis, J C Murray, William O Murray

D-U-N-S 06-678-4158
■ MERCANTILE POTOMAC VALLEY BANK
(Suby of PNC FINANCIAL SERVICES GROUP INC) ★
702 Russell Ave Ste 200, Gaithersburg, MD 20877-2635
Tel (301) 977-3000 Founded/Ownrshp 2007
Sales NA EMP 98
SIC 6022 State commercial banks
Ch: R Dennis Homberg

D-U-N-S 13-100-6983
■ MERCATOR SOFTWARE INC
(Suby of ASCENTIAL SOFTWARE CORPORATION)
50 Washington St, Westborough, MA 01581-1013
Tel (508) 366-3888 Founded/Ownrshp 2003
Sales 20.5MM^E EMP 441
SIC 7373 7372 Systems software development services; Prepackaged software; Systems software development services; Prepackaged software
Pr: Roy C King
Pr: Eric A Amster
*CFO: Kenneth J Hall
*Chf Mktg O: Michael J Collins
*Ex VP: David S Linthicum
*Sr VP: David L Goret
VP: Jonathqn Cohen
VP: Albert Denz
VP: Cindy Drankoski
VP: Dave Power
VP: David Raye

D-U-N-S 00-574-6628
MERCATUS CENTER INC (VA)
3301 Fairfax Dr Ste 450, Arlington, VA 22201-4426
Tel (703) 993-4930 Founded/Ownrshp 1987
Sales 20.6MM EMP 37
Accts Rogers & Company Pllc Vienna
SIC 8732 Educational research
Pr: Tyler Cowen
*Treas: Gary Leff
VP: Richard Williams
Prgrm Mgr: Christopher Koopman
Off Mgr: Sherry Burroughs
Mktg Dir: Jim Johnston

D-U-N-S 01-303-5779
MERCED CITY SCHOOL DISTRICT
444 W 23rd St, Merced, CA 95340-3723
Tel (209) 385-6600 Founded/Ownrshp 1905
Sales 71.0MM^E EMP 1,500
SIC 8211 Public elementary school; Kindergarten; Public elementary school; Kindergarten
Exec: Sherry Munday
Teacher Pr: Doug Collins
Snr Mgr: Ken Testa

MERCED COLLEGE
See MERCED COMMUNITY COLLEGE DISTRICT

D-U-N-S 07-466-7072
MERCED COMMUNITY COLLEGE DISTRICT
MERCED COLLEGE
3600 M St, Merced, CA 95348-2806
Tel (209) 384-6000 Founded/Ownrshp 1963
Sales 32.1MM^E EMP 750
SIC 8222 8221 Community college; Colleges universities & professional schools; Community college; Colleges universities & professional schools
Pr: Ronald Taylor
*Pr: Dennis Jordan
*VP: Robert Haden
*VP: Cindy Lashbrook
VP: Toni McCall
VP: Joanne Schultz
VP: John Spevak
VP: Christopher Vitelli
*Prin: Joe Gutierrez
*Prin: Jean Upton
Pgrm Dir: Janice Stearns

D-U-N-S 04-846-3178
MERCED COUNTY OFFICE OF EDUCATION
632 W 13th St, Merced, CA 95341-5908
Tel (209) 381-6600 Founded/Ownrshp 1952
Sales 112.3MM EMP 900
Accts Vavrinek Trine Day & Co Ll
SIC 8211 Public elementary & secondary schools; Public elementary & secondary schools
Off Admin: Susan Butterman
Snr Ntwrk: Brian Yost
Netwrk Eng: Mark Mahacek
Pr Dir: Cindy Heaton
Schl Brd P: Rudy Albritton

D-U-N-S 00-598-2442
MERCED IRRIGATION DISTRICT
744 W 20th St, Merced, CA 95340-3601
Tel (209) 722-5761 Founded/Ownrshp 1919
Sales 103.3MM^E EMP 164
Accts Burr Pilger Nayer Inc San Jos
SIC 4911 4971 Electric services; Water distribution or supply systems for irrigation; Electric services; Water distribution or supply systems for irrigation
Pr: Tim Pellissier
*Treas: Andre Urquidez
*VP: Dave Long
Genl Mgr: Sweigard John
Genl Mgr: Ted Selb
Genl Mgr: John Sweigard
Dir IT: Kyle Ford

D-U-N-S 12-984-0687
MERCED SYSTEMS INC
(Suby of NICE-SYSTEMS LTD)
333 Twin Dolphin Dr # 500, Redwood City, CA 94065-1445
Tel (650) 486-4000 Founded/Ownrshp 2012
Sales 20.9MM^E EMP 175
SIC 7372 Prepackaged software; Prepackaged software
Pr: Zeevi Bregman
Pr: Barak Eilam
Pr: Amir Orad
Pr: Yochai Rozenblat
Pr: Raghav Sahgal
Pr: Yaron Tchwella
CFO: Dafna Gruber
Chf Mktg O: Benny Einhorn
Chf Mktg O: Harold Goldberg
Ex VP: Barry Cooper
Ex VP: Brian Day
Ex VP: Sigal Gill-More Feferman
Ex VP: Eran Liron

D-U-N-S 01-423-3373
MERCED UNION HIGH SCHOOL DISTRICT CAPITAL FACILITIES CORP
3430 A St, Atwater, CA 95301-5100
Tel (209) 385-6400 Founded/Ownrshp 1919
Sales 59.5MM^E EMP 1,050
SIC 8211 Public senior high school; Public adult education school; Public senior high school; Public adult education school
CEO: Sam Spangler
*VP: Ida Johnson
Dir Sec: Kelly Bentz
MIS Dir: Jorge Arteaga
Netwrk Eng: Jonathan Watry
Psych: Kurt Smoot

MERCEDES BENZ FORT WASHINGTON
See PARK AVENUE MOTOR CARS FORT WASHINGTON LP

MERCEDES BENZ HOUSTON GREENWAY
See HOUSTON AUTO M IMPORTS GREENWAY LTD

MERCEDES BENZ OF ANN ARBOR
See SONIC ANN ARBOR IMPORTS INC

MERCEDES BENZ OF AUSTIN
See CONTINENTAL IMPORTS INC

MERCEDES BENZ OF BAKERSFIELD
See SANGERA BUICK INC

D-U-N-S 61-812-8722
MERCEDES BENZ OF BELLEVUE
BARRIER MOTORS
11850 Bel Red Rd, Bellevue, WA 98005-2484
Tel (425) 455-8535 Founded/Ownrshp 1990
Sales 36.0MM^E EMP 100
SIC 5511 Automobiles, new & used; Automobiles, new & used
Pr: Jimmy Barrier
Exec: Tim Clanin
Genl Mgr: Kjell Schei
Genl Mgr: Michael Vena
IT Man: Jorge Gonzales
Sls Mgr: Eric Lee
Sls Mgr: Tim McDonnell
Sales Asso: Bob Badolato
Sales Asso: Gary Lu

MERCEDES BENZ OF BEVERLY HILLS
See GROUP 1 MILLER AUTOMOTIVE

MERCEDES BENZ OF BIRMINGHAM
See BIJ MOTORS AL LLC

MERCEDES BENZ OF BOERNE
See HELLER MOTORS LLP

MERCEDES BENZ OF BUCKHEAD
See BARAN CO LLC

D-U-N-S 18-711-7494 IMP
MERCEDES BENZ OF CINCINNATI
8727 Montgomery Rd, Cincinnati, OH 45236-2125
Tel (513) 984-9000 Founded/Ownrshp 1988
Sales 34.2MM^E EMP 100
SIC 5511 Automobiles, new & used; Automobiles, new & used
Pr: Dana Hackney
*Sec: Bill Combs
*VP: Tommy Hall
Genl Mgr: Brian Hackney
Genl Mgr: Jack Hoffman
Sls Dir: Mike Campo
Sls Mgr: Chris Dow
Sls Mgr: Ted Reidy
Sales Asso: Jasen Price

MERCEDES BENZ OF ENCINO
See FIRST MOTOR GROUP OF ENCINO LLC

MERCEDES BENZ OF ESCONDIDO
See ESCONDIDO MOTORS LTD

MERCEDES BENZ OF FORT MITCHELL
See M5 MOTORS INC

MERCEDES BENZ OF HENDERSON
See JONES HENDERSON ACQUISITION LLC

D-U-N-S 03-469-9751
MERCEDES BENZ OF KNOXVILLE
10131 Parkside Dr, Knoxville, TN 37922-1945
Tel (865) 777-2222 Founded/Ownrshp 1917
Sales 47.0MM EMP 81
SIC 5511 7539 5531 Automobiles, new & used; Automotive repair shops; Automotive parts; Automobiles, new & used; Automotive repair shops; Automotive parts
Owner: Samuel J Furrow
Sls Mgr: Buck Arnwine

D-U-N-S 07-846-5994
MERCEDES BENZ OF MAPLES (FL)
501 Airport Rd S, Naples, FL 34104-3598
Tel (239) 643-5007 *Founded/Ownrshp* 1975, 1985
Sales 37.8MM *EMP* 60
SIC 5511 Automobiles, new & used; Automobiles, new & used
Pr: Wolfgang Liebig
**VP:* Thomas Liebig
Genl Mgr: Tom Neglio
Genl Mgr: David Wachs
Genl Mgr: David Wasch
**Genl Mgr:* Ed Williams
Sales Asso: Dennis Stout
Board of Directors: Gerhard Liebig

MERCEDES BENZ OF MIAMI
See LP EVANS MOTORS WPB INC

D-U-N-S 01-123-3400
MERCEDES BENZ OF MORRISTOWN
CRESTMONT MM
34 Ridgedale Ave, Morristown, NJ 07960-4241
Tel (973) 267-5000 *Founded/Ownrshp* 1986
Sales 35.7MM^E *EMP* 100
SIC 5511 7538 7532 5521 Automobiles, new & used; General automotive repair shops; Top & body repair & paint shops; Used car dealers; Automobiles, new & used; General automotive repair shops; Top & body repair & paint shops; Used car dealers
Pr: Daniel M Peyton
Sls Mgr: Juan Hernandez
Sls Mgr: Scott Kaufman

D-U-N-S 01-419-4794
MERCEDES BENZ OF NAPLES
REGENCY AUTOHAUS
501 Airport Rd S, Naples, FL 34104-3598
Tel (239) 643-5007 *Founded/Ownrshp* 1981
Sales 31.8MM^E *EMP* 85
SIC 5511 7538 5531 Automobiles, new & used; General automotive repair shops; Automotive & home supply stores; Automobiles, new & used; General automotive repair shops; Automotive & home supply stores
Pr: Terry Taylor
Sls Mgr: Frank Carrasquillo
Sales Asso: Lori Damato

MERCEDES BENZ OF NORTH HAVEN
See MAURO MOTORS INC

MERCEDES BENZ OF OAKLAND
See EUROMOTORS OAKLAND INC

MERCEDES BENZ OF ORLAND PARK
See ORLAND PARK MOTOR CARS INC

MERCEDES BENZ OF PALM BEACH
See GULFSTREAM MOTORS INC

D-U-N-S 17-839-8947
MERCEDES BENZ OF PLEASANTON
5885 Owens Dr, Pleasanton, CA 94588-3939
Tel (925) 463-2525 *Founded/Ownrshp* 1987
Sales 23.0MM^E *EMP* 50
SIC 5511 Automobiles, new & used; Automobiles, new & used
VP: Sibylle Waizenegger
**Pr:* Uwe Waizenegger
Sls Mgr: Mike Venegas
Sls Mgr: Raymond Yeung
Sales Asso: Virgil Canseco
Sales Asso: Ismael Dastagirzada
Sales Asso: Adam Farani
Sales Asso: Michael Feldman
Sales Asso: Jenny Lam
Sales Asso: Matthew Lore
Sales Asso: Mike Malott

MERCEDES BENZ OF SACRAMENTO
See VON HOUSEN SACRAMENTO INC

MERCEDES BENZ OF SAN DIEGO
See EUROPA AUTO IMPORTS INC

MERCEDES BENZ OF SAN JUAN
See HELLER-BIRD MOTORS LTD

D-U-N-S 14-418-8153 IMP
MERCEDES BENZ OF SUGAR LAND
15625 Southwest Fwy, Sugar Land, TX 77478-3882
Tel (281) 207-1500 *Founded/Ownrshp* 2004
Sales 48.5MM^E *EMP* 125
SIC 5511 Automobiles, new & used; Automobiles, new & used
Prin: Ken Enders
CFO: James Sparks
VP: David Cole
VP: Howard Rich
Exec: Lars Jones
Dir Bus: Derek Brown
VP Sls: Mike Baches

MERCEDES BENZ OF VALENCIA
See VALENCIA HOLDING CO LLC

D-U-N-S 05-047-2984
MERCEDES BENZ OF WESTMINSTER
GLAUSER MERCEDES-BENZ
10391 Westminster Blvd, Westminster, CO 80020-4180
Tel (303) 410-7800 *Founded/Ownrshp* 1960
Sales 30.2MM^E *EMP* 83
SIC 5511 5521 Automobiles, new & used; Used car dealers; Automobiles, new & used; Used car dealers
VP: Kingsley Stoken
Sls Mgr: Bart Byers
Sales Asso: Win Lewis
Sales Asso: Jason Surges

MERCEDES BENZ USA
See ISRINGHAUSEN IMPORTS INC

D-U-N-S 09-907-1136 EXP
MERCEDES ELECTRIC SUPPLY INC
8550 Nw South River Dr, Medley, FL 33166-7427
Tel (305) 887-5550 *Founded/Ownrshp* 1979
Sales 30.6MM^E *EMP* 43
SIC 5063 Electrical supplies
Pr: Mercedes C Laporta
**VP:* Victor J Laporta
Sales Asso: Jim Perrott

D-U-N-S 08-959-4337
MERCEDES INDEPENDENT SCHOOL DISTRICT
206 W 6th St, Mercedes, TX 78570-3504
Tel (956) 514-2000 *Founded/Ownrshp* 1900
Sales 65.0MM *EMP* 925
SIC 8211 Public senior high school; Public junior high school; Public elementary school; Public senior high school; Public junior high school; Public elementary school
CFO: Nancy Samsung
Exec: Olga Badillo
IT Man: Dave Avila

D-U-N-S 83-447-2680 IMP
MERCEDES MEDICAL LLC
7590 Commerce Ct, Sarasota, FL 34243-3217
Tel (941) 355-3333 *Founded/Ownrshp* 1993
Sales 34.0MM^E *EMP* 45
SIC 5047 Medical equipment & supplies
CEO: Alex Miller
**Pr:* Noelle Haft
**COO:* Andy Wright
**CFO:* Troy Barnett
**Ex VP:* Robert S Haft
VP: Ken Combs
**VP:* Dave Johnson
CTO: Darleen Richter
IT Man: Mike Chadwick
VP Sls: David Johnson
Mktg Dir: Whitney Prewitt

D-U-N-S 04-110-4852
MERCEDES RESTAURANTS INC
FAMOUS DAVE'S
2402 W Nebraska Ave, Peoria, IL 61604-3112
Tel (309) 676-6443 *Founded/Ownrshp* 1982
Sales 15.0MM^E *EMP* 380
SIC 5812 5813 Steak restaurant; Cocktail lounge; Steak restaurant; Cocktail lounge
Pr: Laurel E Rainwater
**Pr:* Steve Shaw

MERCEDES- BENZ
See CONTEMPORARY MOTORCARS INC

MERCEDES-BENZ
See R & H MOTOR CARS LTD

MERCEDES-BENZ
See CHARLES BARKER LUXURY IMPORTS INC

MERCEDES-BENZ
See ATLANTA CLASSIC CARS INC

MERCEDES-BENZ
See CALIBER MOTORS INC

D-U-N-S 07-574-2999 IMP
MERCEDES-BENZ CREDIT CORP (DE)
36455 Corporate Dr, Farmington Hills, MI 48331-3552
Tel (248) 991-6700 *Founded/Ownrshp* 2000
Sales NA *EMP* 400
SIC 5511 7519 Automobiles, new & used; Utility trailer rental

D-U-N-S 80-561-8399
MERCEDES-BENZ FINANCIAL SERVICES USA LLC
DAIMLER TRUCK FINANCIAL
(*Suby of* DAIMLER FINANCIAL SERVICES AG)
36455 Corporate Dr, Farmington Hills, MI 48331-3552
Tel (248) 991-6700 *Founded/Ownrshp* 2007
Sales NA *EMP* 400
SIC 6159 Pari-mutuel totalizator equipment finance leasing & maint.; Pari-mutuel totalizator equipment finance leasing & maint.
Pr: Klaus Entenmann
Pr: Dietmar Exler
**Pr:* Peter Zieringer
VP: Maurice Commins
VP: Steven Goodale
VP: Geoff Robinson
**VP:* Bryan Stevens
Dir Risk M: Michael Eastridge
Pr Mgr: Jennifer Korman
Mktg Mgr: Kimberly Marks
Snr Mgr: Robert Chesters

MERCEDES-BENZ FORT LAUDERDALE
See STAR MOTORS LLC

D-U-N-S 03-474-8897
MERCEDES-BENZ MANHATTAN INC
(*Suby of* MERCEDES-BENZ USA LLC) ★
536 W 41st St, New York, NY 10036-6201
Tel (212) 760-0600 *Founded/Ownrshp* 1981
Sales 80.0MM^E *EMP* 250
SIC 5511 Automobiles, new & used; Automobiles, new & used
Pr: Claus Laugan

MERCEDES-BENZ OF BEDFORD
See MOTORCARS ACQUISITION IV LLC

MERCEDES-BENZ OF BELMONT
See AUTOBAHN INC

MERCEDES-BENZ OF CHERRY HILL
See HSF ENTERPRISES INC

MERCEDES-BENZ OF CORAL GABLES
See BILL USSERY MOTORS BODY SHOP INC

MERCEDES-BENZ OF FORT MYERS
See SONIC F M AUTOMOTIVE LLC

MERCEDES-BENZ OF GREENWICH
See WATSON ENTERPRISES INC

MERCEDES-BENZ OF HOUSTON NORTH
See HOUSTON AUTO M IMPORTS NORTH LTD

D-U-N-S 06-765-3931
MERCEDES-BENZ OF LAGUNA NIGUEL
MISSION IMPORTS A CALIFORNIA
1 Star Dr, Laguna Niguel, CA 92677-4589
Tel (949) 347-3700 *Founded/Ownrshp* 1973
Sales 62.6MM^E *EMP* 115
SIC 5511 Automobiles, new & used; Automobiles, new & used
Pr: Lorelei Pingree
CFO: Jodie Robison
**VP:* Penny Spellens
Genl Mgr: Pat Bolter
Telecom Ex: Dave Bailey
IT Man: Ciro Damian
Mktg Dir: Brian Taber
Sls Mgr: Erwin Artacho
Sls Mgr: Russ Ellis
Sls Mgr: Gerhard Jurinek

MERCEDES-BENZ OF LITTLETON
See EUROPEAN MOTOR CARS OF LITTLETON

D-U-N-S 55-555-6823
MERCEDES-BENZ OF LONG BEACH
2300 E Spring St, Signal Hill, CA 90755-2118
Tel (562) 988-8300 *Founded/Ownrshp* 2005
Sales 25.1MM^E *EMP* 100
SIC 5511 Automobiles, new & used; Automobiles, new & used
Owner: Damoy Shelly
Genl Mgr: Bob Milner
Sls Mgr: Brian Goodermont
Sls Mgr: Mohamed Kharboush
Sls Mgr: Brett Ogan
Sls Mgr: Brian Walker

MERCEDES-BENZ OF MEMPHIS
See AUTORAMA INC

MERCEDES-BENZ OF NASHVILLE
See MIDDLE TENNESSEE MOTOR CARS INC

MERCEDES-BENZ OF POMPANO
See RKR MOTORS INC

MERCEDES-BENZ OF PRINCETON
See PRINCETON MOTORSPORT INC

MERCEDES-BENZ OF SAN FRANCISCO
See EUROMOTORS INC

MERCEDES-BENZ OF SMITHTOWN
See COMPETITION IMPORTS INC

MERCEDES-BENZ OF SOUTH ATLANTA
See ATLANTA EUROCARS LLC

MERCEDES-BENZ OF TAMPA
See PRECISION MOTORCARS INC

MERCEDES-BENZ OF TEMECULA
See JONES/BLUMENTHAL TEMECULA LLC

MERCEDES-BENZ OF TYSONS CORNER
See HBL LLC

MERCEDES-BENZ OF WILSONVILLE
See DON RASMUSSEN CO

D-U-N-S 88-373-8494
MERCEDES-BENZ RESEARCH & DEVELOPMENT NORTH AMERICA INC
(*Suby of* DAIMLER NORTH AMERICA CORP) ★
309 N Pastoria Ave, Sunnyvale, CA 94085-4109
Tel (650) 845-2500 *Founded/Ownrshp* 2013
Sales 21.7MM^E *EMP* 89
SIC 8731 Commercial physical research
Pr: Akhtar Jameel
**VP:* Wilson Chris
**VP:* Reckels Dieter
**VP:* Holfelder Wieland
IT Man: Michael Molino

MERCEDES-BENZ ROCKVILLE CENTRE
See LAKEVIEW AUTO SALES AND SERVICE INC

D-U-N-S 04-089-7604 IMP
MERCEDES-BENZ US INTERNATIONAL INC
6482 Basswood Dr, Troy, MI 48098-2084
Tel (248) 576-1303 *Founded/Ownrshp* 2010
Sales 52.2MM^E *EMP* 118^E
SIC 5511 Automobiles, new & used
Prin: Joseph Bland

D-U-N-S 82-483-9872 IMP/EXP
MERCEDES-BENZ US INTERNATIONAL INC
MERCEDES-BENZ USA
(*Suby of* DAIMLER AG)
1 Mercedes Dr, Vance, AL 35490-2900
Tel (205) 507-2252 *Founded/Ownrshp* 1994
Sales 1.1MMM^E *EMP* 3,000^E
SIC 3711 3714 Motor vehicles & car bodies; Motor vehicle parts & accessories; Motor vehicles & car bodies; Motor vehicle parts & accessories
CEO: Markus Schaefer
Pr: Rolf Wrona
**CEO:* Markus Schaefer
**CEO:* Herbert Werner
COO: Ruediger Schrage
VP: Jason Hoff
VP: Christian Treiber
Exec: Gavin Chan
Mng Dir: Joerg Lamparter
Mng Dir: Ian Prophet
Prgrm Mgr: Tim Cobben
Board of Directors: Markus Schaefer

MERCEDES-BENZ USA
See MERCEDES-BENZ US INTERNATIONAL INC

D-U-N-S 00-180-2511 IMP/EXP
MERCEDES-BENZ USA LLC (DE)
(*Suby of* MERCEDES-BENZ US INTERNATIONAL INC) ★
303 Perimeter Ctr N, Atlanta, GA 30346-3402
Tel (201) 573-0600 *Founded/Ownrshp* 2000
Sales 1.1MMM^E *EMP* 1,400
SIC 5012 5013 7538 5511 Automobiles; Automotive supplies & parts; General automotive repair shops; Automobiles, new & used; Automobiles; Automotive supplies & parts; General automotive repair shops; Automobiles, new & used
Pr: Stephen Cannon
**CFO:* Harald Henn
**CFO:* John Ieronimo
Ch: Michael Bassermann
Ex Ofcr: Tommy Shi
**Ex VP:* Sonja Bower
**VP:* Andrew McLaren
VP: Mark McNabb
**VP:* Drew Slaven
Area Mgr: Dawn Ringo
Dept Mgr: Robert Angner

MERCEDEZ BENZ OF BROOKLYN
See MBB AUTO LLC

MERCEDEZ BENZ OF FAYETTEVILLE
See VALLEY MOTORS INC

MERCEDEZ BENZ OF ORLANDO
See CONTEMPORARY CARS INC

D-U-N-S 08-845-9540
■ **MERCER (US) INC**
(*Suby of* MERCER INC) ★
1166 Ave Of The Americ, New York, NY 10036-2708
Tel (212) 345-7000 *Founded/Ownrshp* 1975
Sales 749.7MM^E *EMP* 15,643
SIC 8742 Compensation & benefits planning consultant; Personnel management consultant; Compensation & benefits planning consultant; Personnel management consultant
CEO: Julio Portalatin
Pr: E Michael Caulfield
Pr: Patricia A Milligan
COO: Robert C Fox
CFO: Steve Mele
CFO: Terry Thompson
CFO: Tim Weininger
Treas: Daniel Percella
Ofcr: Mark Gilbert
VP: Lake Charles
VP: Kathy Mather
VP: Karen Pauley
VP: Shari Souza

D-U-N-S 11-638-9958
MERCER ADVISORS INC
1801 E Cabrillo Blvd, Santa Barbara, CA 93108-2897
Tel (805) 565-1681 *Founded/Ownrshp* 2015
Sales 39.9MM^E *EMP* 175
SIC 6282 8742 Investment advisory service; Investment advisory service; Financial consultant
Pr: David H Barton
COO: Christopher Weill
CFO: Deb Atwater
Chf Cred: Scott Kvancz
Ofcr: Kristy Resch
Ex VP: Will Mannon
VP: Terri Spath
CIO: Donald Calcagni
CTO: Jerry Baltes

D-U-N-S 10-006-9772
MERCER AREA SCHOOL DISTRICT
545 W Butler St, Mercer, PA 16137-1061
Tel (724) 662-5100 *Founded/Ownrshp* 1964
Sales 17.3MM^E *EMP* 320
Accts Mc Gill Power Bell & Associa
SIC 8211 Public elementary & secondary schools; Public elementary & secondary schools

D-U-N-S 06-814-0383
MERCER COUNTY BOARD OF EDUCATION (WV)
1403 Honaker Ave, Princeton, WV 24740-3065
Tel (304) 487-1551 *Founded/Ownrshp* 1934
Sales 101.8MM^E *EMP* 1,398
SIC 8211 Public elementary school; Public junior high school; Public senior high school; Vocational high school; School board
Pr: Gilbert Bailey
**Treas:* Joy Hubbard

D-U-N-S 15-647-2516
MERCER COUNTY BOARD OF SOCIAL SERVICES (INC)
200 Woolverton St, Trenton, NJ 08650
Tel (609) 989-4320 *Founded/Ownrshp* 1986
Sales 17.1MM^E *EMP* 550
SIC 8322 Social service center; Social service center

D-U-N-S 07-695-0807
MERCER COUNTY COMMUNITY COLLEGE
WEST WINDSOR CAMPUS
1200 Old Trenton Rd, Trenton, NJ 08690
Tel (609) 586-4800 *Founded/Ownrshp* 1966
Sales 51.0MM^E *EMP* 1,500
SIC 8222 Junior college; Junior college
Pr: Thomas Sepe
**Pr:* Dr Patricia C Donohue
Ofcr: Karl Blackwell
Ofcr: Edward Mooney
**VP:* Jacob Eapen
**VP:* Donald Generals
VP: Ed Gwazda
**VP:* Dr Mellissia Zanjani
Exec: Toni Racioppio
Assoc Dir: Jason Taylor
**Prin:* Lionel Frank
Board of Directors: Lionel Frank

D-U-N-S 09-997-5856
MERCER COUNTY COMMUNITY HOSPITAL
AUXILIARY GIFT SHOP
800 W Main St, Coldwater, OH 45828-1698
Tel (419) 375-4678 *Founded/Ownrshp* 1952
Sales 58.4MM^E *EMP* 450
SIC 8062 General medical & surgical hospitals; General medical & surgical hospitals
CEO: Lisa Klenke
Exec: Terese Burnette
Dir Rad: Sara Bruening
Dir Rad: Chris Kramer
Mtls Mgr: Laurie Summers
Pathlgst: Donn Fishbein
Pathlgst: Paul Thorpe
Podiatrist: Tom Liette

D-U-N-S 06-370-0231
MERCER COUNTY JOINT TOWNSHIP COMMUNITY HOSPITAL
800 W Main St, Coldwater, OH 45828-1613
Tel (419) 678-2341 *Founded/Ownrshp* 1972
Sales 46.9MM^E *EMP* 450
SIC 8062 General medical & surgical hospitals; General medical & surgical hospitals

Pr: Lisa Klenke
**Prin:* Paula Detterman
QA Dir: Penny Cooper
Pr Dir: Renee Kinney
Snr Mgr: John Cox

D-U-N-S 07-979-8743
MERCER COUNTY PUBLIC SCHOOLS
1403 Honaker Ave, Princeton, WV 24740-3065
Tel (304) 487-1551 *Founded/Ownrshp* 2015
Sales 8.5MM^E *EMP* 1,342^E
SIC 8211 Public elementary & secondary schools

D-U-N-S 07-864-3070
MERCER COUNTY SCHOOL DISTRICT
1002 Sw 6th St, Aledo, IL 61231-2100
Tel (309) 582-2441 *Founded/Ownrshp* 2012
Sales 29.7MM *EMP* 234^E
SIC 8211 Public combined elementary & secondary school
Prin: Connie Hilligoss
Psych: Donna Boswell

D-U-N-S 96-822-3391
MERCER COUNTY SCHOOL DISTRICT
371 E Lexington St, Harrodsburg, KY 40330-1226
Tel (859) 733-7000 *Founded/Ownrshp* 2011
Sales 15.9MM^E *EMP* 366^E
Accts White And Company Psc Cpas
SIC 8211 Public elementary & secondary schools
Prin: Davette Baker
Pr Dir: Becky Holt
Teacher Pr: Nancy Simmons
Teacher Pr: Jessica Simms

D-U-N-S 07-846-7533
MERCER COUNTY SPECIAL SERVICES SCHOOL DISTRICT
1020 Old Trenton Rd, Trenton, NJ 08690-1206
Tel (609) 631-2103 *Founded/Ownrshp* 2012
Sales 5.7MM^E *EMP* 371^E
SIC 8211 Elementary & secondary schools
Prin: Annmarie Ricci
Bd of Dir: Rosemarie Bonomo
IT Man: Nancy Swirsky
Schl Brd P: Camille Rainiero
Teacher Pr: Christine Macdonald

D-U-N-S 02-982-4893 IMP
MERCER FOODS LLC
1836 Lapham Dr, Modesto, CA 95354-3900
Tel (209) 529-0150 *Founded/Ownrshp* 1980
Sales 23.9MM^E *EMP* 75
SIC 2034 Dehydrated fruits, vegetables, soups
Pr: David A Noland
VP: Clark Driftmier
VP: Jeffrey Hulme
Ql Cn Mgr: Cynthia Apodaca
S&M/VP: Mike Alaga

D-U-N-S 55-545-1012
■ **MERCER FORGE CORP**
FIA
(*Suby of* NEENAH FOUNDRY CO) ★
200 Brown St, Mercer, PA 16137-4140
Tel (724) 662-2750 *Founded/Ownrshp* 1998
Sales 31.7MM^E *EMP* 200
SIC 3462 Iron & steel forgings; Iron & steel forgings
Pr: James Ackerman
VP: Jeff Tomhave
VP Sls: Jeff Patrisso
Sales Asso: Paul Ackerman

D-U-N-S 61-621-3125
■ **MERCER HEALTH & BENEFITS LLC**
(*Suby of* MERCER (US) INC) ★
1166 Ave Of The Americas, New York, NY 10036-2708
Tel (212) 345-7000 *Founded/Ownrshp* 2004
Sales 71.2MM^E *EMP* 2,500
SIC 8742 Hospital & health services consultant; Hospital & health services consultant
Pr: Bernard Morency
COO: Roy Gonella
Sales Asso: David Matey

D-U-N-S 18-292-2612
■ **MERCER HUMAN RESOURCE CONSULTING OF MASSACHUSETTS INC**
(*Suby of* MARSH & MCLENNAN COMPANIES INC) ★
99 High St, Boston, MA 02110-2320
Tel (617) 450-6000 *Founded/Ownrshp* 2005
Sales 113.6MM^E *EMP* 500
SIC 8742 Human resource consulting services; Human resource consulting services
Prin: Gerald Fazio
Treas: P R Mohan
VP: Suzanne Nolan
Mng Dir: Neal Drawas
Off Mgr: Ann M Camera
Ql Cn Mgr: Barbara Fiorillo
Snr Mgr: Patricia Daniels

D-U-N-S 94-882-5971
■ **MERCER INC**
(*Suby of* MARSH & MCLENNAN COMPANIES INC) ★
1166 Avenue Of The Americ, New York, NY 10036-2726
Tel (212) 345-7000 *Founded/Ownrshp* 1991
Sales NA *EMP* 15,723
SIC 8748 Economic consultant; Economic consultant
Ch Bd: Peter Coster
**COO:* Ken Haderer
**CFO:* Helen Shan
**Chf Mktg O:* Michelle Bottomley
Ex VP: Yves Roy
Prin: James Horrell
Prin: Dan Priga
Prin: Lisa Weber
Admn Mgr: Douglas Vander Linde
CIO: Paul Corkery
CIO: Darren J Lee

D-U-N-S 14-131-0958
■ **MERCER INSURANCE GROUP INC**
(*Suby of* UFG) ★
10 N Hwy 31, Pennington, NJ 08534
Tel (609) 737-0426 *Founded/Ownrshp* 2011
Sales NA *EMP* 202^E
SIC 6411 Insurance agents, brokers & service; Insurance agents, brokers & service
Pr: Andrew R Speaker
V Ch: Roland Boehm
**CFO:* David B Merclean
Sr VP: Paul Cockery
**Sr VP:* Paul R Corkery
Sr VP: Paul Corkery
**Sr VP:* Paul D Erhardt
VP: James Curtin
VP: John G Danka
Exec: Nancy Yusko
VP Admn: John Danka

D-U-N-S 60-544-5980
■ **MERCER INVESTMENT CONSULTING INC**
(*Suby of* MERCER (US) INC) ★
1166 Ave Of The Americas, New York, NY 10036-2708
Tel (212) 345-7000 *Founded/Ownrshp* 1975
Sales 91.5MM^E *EMP* 620
SIC 6282 Investment advice; Investment advice
Pr: Michelle Burns
COO: Roy Gonella
CFO: David Mahew
**CFO:* David L Mayhew
CFO: Bob V Pelt
CFO: Joe Rotberg
CFO: Terri Thompson
Sr Cor Off: Larry Woemer
Ofcr: Andrew Beagley
Ofcr: Clare Collins-Newton
Ofcr: Steve Mele
Ofcr: Michael Sternklar
VP: Jackie Kleiner
VP: Neal Pomroy

D-U-N-S 07-184-6729
MERCER ISLAND SCHOOL DISTRICT
4160 86th Ave Se, Mercer Island, WA 98040-4196
Tel (206) 236-3330 *Founded/Ownrshp* 1950
Sales 27.1MM^E *EMP* 450
SIC 8211 Public elementary & secondary schools; Public elementary & secondary schools
Ofcr: Randy Bolerjack
Dir IT: Andreeves Ronser
IT Man: Jacquie Fauver
Netwrk Eng: Ghassan Mamar
Schl Brd P: Janet Frohnmeyer

D-U-N-S 01-759-3112 EXP
MERCER LANDMARK INC (OH)
CW SERVICE
426 W Market St, Celina, OH 45822-2127
Tel (419) 628-3093 *Founded/Ownrshp* 1934
Sales 207.7MM^E *EMP* 160
SIC 5153 5999 Grains; Feed & farm supply; Grains; Feed & farm supply
Pr: Daren Deffenbaugh
**CFO:* Tim Weininger
Brnch Mgr: Ken Puthoff
CIO: Bob Barrett
IT Man: Tom Knapke
IT Man: Teresa Meyer
Sfty Dirs: Ben Snyder

D-U-N-S 07-857-3170
■ **MERCER LLC**
(*Suby of* MARSH & MCLENNAN COMPANIES INC) ★
1166 Avenue Of The Americ, New York, NY 10036-2720
Tel (212) 345-5000 *Founded/Ownrshp* 1997
Sales 27.7MM^E *EMP* 122^E
SIC 8748 Employee programs administration
CEO: M Burns
Mng Dir: Neal Pomroy
IT Man: Bill Bowman
IT Man: Neil Millar
IT Man: Sahar Rostami
Snr Mgr: Kerry King

D-U-N-S 78-764-7734 IMP/EXP
MERCER LMT GROUP INC
690 Puritan Ave, Lawrenceville, NJ 08648-4600
Tel (609) 989-0399 *Founded/Ownrshp* 1989
Sales 22.7MM^E *EMP* 45
SIC 3446 Fences, gates, posts & flagpoles
Pr: Anthony Lesenskyj
Pr: Jim Fattori
COO: Pete Fischel
**CFO:* Pat Lang
**VP:* George Lesenskyj
VP Mfg: Bernie Henry
Plnt Mgr: Joe Dublas
Sls Mgr: Roby Grenier
Sls Mgr: Scott Hendrix
Sls Mgr: Valerie Kokosz

D-U-N-S 08-711-2066
MERCER STREET FRIENDS CENTER INC
7 Dunmore Ave, Ewing, NJ 08618-1937
Tel (609) 802-2613 *Founded/Ownrshp* 1966
Sales 14.3MM^E *EMP* 350
Accts Eisneramper Llp Bridgewater
SIC 8322 Senior citizens' center or association; Homemakers' service; Child guidance agency; Senior citizens' center or association; Homemakers' service; Child guidance agency
Ex Dir: Barry H Cole
**Ch Bd:* Daniel T Rodgers
Sales Exec: Jennifer Kovac

D-U-N-S 08-675-9743
MERCER TRANSPORTATION CO INC
1128 W Main St, Louisville, KY 40203-1432
Tel (502) 584-2301 *Founded/Ownrshp* 1977
Sales 431.6MM *EMP* 325
SIC 4213

D-U-N-S 15-688-4868 EXP
MERCER VALVE CO INC
9609 Nw 4th St, Oklahoma City, OK 73127-2962
Tel (405) 470-5213 *Founded/Ownrshp* 1984
Sales 53.9MM^E *EMP* 260
SIC 3491 3494 Industrial valves; Valves & pipe fittings; Industrial valves; Valves & pipe fittings
Pr: Richard Taylor
CFO: Scott Thompson
Sfty Mgr: Harmony Cook
Ql Cn Mgr: Ken Walton
Sls Mgr: Erik Belakjon
Sls Mgr: Guy Unger

MERCER WELL SERVICE
See BSI HOLDINGS MANAGEMENT LLC

MERCER-FRASER COMPANY
See FRASER MERCER CO

D-U-N-S 06-978-5640
MERCERSBURG ACADEMY
300 E Seminary St, Mercersburg, PA 17236-1551
Tel (717) 328-6173 *Founded/Ownrshp* 1893
Sales 28.9MM^E *EMP* 170
SIC 8211 Preparatory school
Pr: Douglas Hale
CFO: Maria Kimsey
Top Exec: Heather Prescott
Assoc Dir: Katherine Larue
Assoc Dir: Jo Wrzesinsky
Snr Mgr: Skip Sydnor

D-U-N-S 01-765-8725
MERCHANDISE INC
MI
5929 State Rte 128, Miamitown, OH 45041
Tel (513) 353-2200 *Founded/Ownrshp* 1963
Sales 53.2MM^E *EMP* 70
SIC 5122 5199 5099 5085 Drugs, proprietaries & sundries; Cosmetics; Medicine cabinet sundries; General merchandise, non-durable; Video & audio equipment; Compact discs; Tapes & cassettes, prerecorded; Video cassettes, accessories & supplies; Industrial supplies; Drugs, proprietaries & sundries; Cosmetics; Medicine cabinet sundries; General merchandise, non-durable; Video & audio equipment; Compact discs; Tapes & cassettes, prerecorded; Video cassettes, accessories & supplies; Industrial supplies
Pr: Donald W Karches
**VP:* Elizabeth Ann Karches

D-U-N-S 15-453-6817
MERCHANDISE MART PROPERTIES INC
(*Suby of* VORNADO REALTY TRUST) ★
222 Merchandise Mart Plz # 470, Chicago, IL 60654-1072
Tel (312) 527-4141 *Founded/Ownrshp* 1998
Sales 104.1MM^E *EMP* 550
SIC 6531 Rental agent, real estate; Rental agent, real estate
CEO: Mark Falanga
CFO: Steve Lau
Sr VP: John H Brennen
Sr VP: Randall Clark
Sr VP: Paul Heinen
Sr VP: Myron Maurer
Sr VP: Susan McCullough
VP: Julie Amato-Kohl
VP: Troy Durst
VP: Kate Flaherty
VP: Andrew Glasow
VP: Susan Glick
VP: Steve Johnson
VP: Cheryl Longstreet
VP: Laurette Lutiger
VP: Tim McGee
VP: Toni McIntosh
VP: Bill Noonan
VP: Dick Norfolk
VP: Brian Quirk
VP: Melvin Schlitt

D-U-N-S 17-190-9278
MERCHANDISING CORP OF AMERICA INC
M C A
11121 Carmel Commons Blvd # 200, Charlotte, NC 28226-2958
Tel (704) 944-4600 *Founded/Ownrshp* 1996
Sales 98.4MM^E *EMP* 4,560
SIC 8748 Business consulting; Business consulting
Pr: Tom Palombo
VP: Donna Brockway
VP: Gentlesk Philip

D-U-N-S 16-631-7698
MERCHANDISING SOLUTIONS GROUP INC
MSG
260 Peachtree St Nw, Atlanta, GA 30303-1202
Tel (800) 417-1320 *Founded/Ownrshp* 2003
Sales 217.8MM^E *EMP* 3,500
SIC 5199 1542 Personal service agents, brokers & bureaus; General merchandise, non-durable; Custom builders, non-residential
CEO: Rick Clark
Pr: Karen Reeves
CFO: Tanya Valera
Dir Sec: Shane Walker

D-U-N-S 94-720-4715
MERCHANT & GOULD PC
3200 Idaho Ave S, Minneapolis, MN 55426-3414
Tel (612) 332-5300 *Founded/Ownrshp* 1900
Sales 24.3MM^E *EMP* 254
SIC 8111 Patent, trademark & copyright law; Patent, trademark & copyright law
**Pt:* Randall King
**Pt:* Daniel W McDonald
**CFO:* Tracey Skjeveland

D-U-N-S 36-063-9814
MERCHANT CASH AND CAPITAL LLC
460 Park Ave S Fl 10, New York, NY 10016-7315
Tel (212) 545-3180 *Founded/Ownrshp* 2005
Sales 107.6MM^E *EMP* 150
SIC 6799 Investors; Financial services
Founder: Stephen Sheinbaum
CEO: Jeff Beckwith
COO: Tomo Matsuo
CFO: Michael Kennedy
CFO: Zalman Skoblo
Web Dev: Sushma Korrapati
Software D: Kaif Memon
Sftwr Eng: Chuan He
Opers Mgr: Monica Scotti
Sales Exec: Jarett Zackman

D-U-N-S 12-926-3070
MERCHANT ESOLUTIONS INC
(*Suby of* CIELO S/A.)
3600 Bridge Pkwy Ste 102, Redwood City, CA 94065-6139
Tel (866) 663-6132 *Founded/Ownrshp* 2012
Sales 35.9MM^E *EMP* 186
SIC 7389 6153 Computer software development; Credit card services, central agency collection; Financial services; Credit card services, central agency collection
CEO: Tom Bell
Pr: Mark Graham
Pr: Charles Jadallah
Pr: Dwight Point
**COO:* James M Aviles
**CFO:* James J Kelly Jr
CFO: Jim Kelly
**CFO:* Marcelo Perez
VP: Brandon Allard
VP: Mark Bergner
VP: Ed Brachocki
VP: James Cantlen
VP: Michael Fields
VP: Brian Higgins
VP: Jason Key
VP: Kim Schommer
Dir Risk M: Randy Warren

D-U-N-S 94-332-0296
MERCHANT INDUSTRY LLC
3636 33rd St Ste 306, Long Island City, NY 11106-2329
Tel (718) 249-2000 *Founded/Ownrshp* 2007
Sales 20.7MM *EMP* 190
SIC 7389 Credit card service; Credit card service
CFO: Jennifer Vartanov
CTO: Frank Kotlar
VP Mktg: Lev Shuster
Sls Mgr: Allen Dukat

D-U-N-S 82-675-8534
■ **MERCHANT LINK INC**
(*Suby of* CHASE PAYMENTECH SOLUTIONS) ★
8401 Colesville Rd # 900, Silver Spring, MD 20910-3382
Tel (301) 562-5000 *Founded/Ownrshp* 1993
Sales 24.4MM^E *EMP* 75^E
SIC 7374 Data processing service
Pr: Dan Lane
CFO: Christina Smith
Ex VP: Laura Kirby-Meck
Ex VP: Laura Meck
VP: Geoffrey Krieg
Dir Bus: Jorge Bertran
Snr Sftwr: Alexander Zemerov
QA Dir: Elias Yirga
Software D: Sameer Jadhav
Software D: Vijayalakshmi Sivaraman
Software D: Omid Tajalli

D-U-N-S 09-784-6828 IMP
MERCHANT OF TENNIS INC
US MERCHANT
8737 Wilshire Blvd, Beverly Hills, CA 90211-2701
Tel (310) 228-4000 *Founded/Ownrshp* 1984
Sales 130.8MM^E *EMP* 1,400
SIC 5941 5621 5661 5961 5999 Sporting goods & bicycle shops; Dress shops; Shoe stores; Television, home shopping; Candle shops; Sporting goods & bicycle shops; Dress shops; Shoe stores; Television, home shopping; Candle shops
CEO: Jeff Green
**Sec:* Marie Green
Sr VP: Bruce Carter

MERCHANT SERVICES
See UNIVERSAL CARD INC

D-U-N-S 02-999-1395
MERCHANT SERVICES INC
1 S Van Ness Ave Fl 5, San Francisco, CA 94103-5416
Tel (415) 241-3797 *Founded/Ownrshp* 2014
Sales 32.5MM^E *EMP* 1,000
SIC 7374 Data processing service; Data processing service
CEO: Lorraine Stimmell
**Sr VP:* Le Tran-Tl

D-U-N-S 00-820-5103
MERCHANT SERVICES INTL INC
HERB DENMARK
79 Skoures Ln, Newtown, PA 18940-3603
Tel (215) 598-1165 *Founded/Ownrshp* 1998
Sales 50.0MM *EMP* 50
SIC 7389 ;
Pr: Herb Denmark

MERCHANTS & FARMERS BANK
See M & F FINANCIAL SERVICES INC

D-U-N-S 96-342-0299
▲ **MERCHANTS & MARINE BANCORP INC**
3118 Pascagoula St, Pascagoula, MS 39567-4215
Tel (228) 762-3311 *Founded/Ownrshp* 1932
Sales NA *EMP* 114^E
Tkr Sym MMPM *Exch* OTO
SIC 6022 State commercial banks; State commercial banks
Ch Bd: Royce Cumbest
COO: C Henry Fox Jr
CFO: Elise Bourgeois
Sec: Barbara B Bass
Sr VP: Martin J Regan
Sr VP: G Todd Trenchard

D-U-N-S 03-634-3705
■ **MERCHANTS & MARINE BANK** (MS)
(*Suby of* MERCHANTS & MARINE BANCORP INC) ★
3118 Pascagoula St, Pascagoula, MS 39567-4215
Tel (228) 762-3311 *Founded/Ownrshp* 1931
Sales NA *EMP* 114^E
SIC 6022 State commercial banks; State commercial banks
Pr: Royce Cumbest
Sr VP: Clarence H Fox Jr
VP: Gregory Trenchard
VP: James Wheat
Brnch Mgr: Brenda Tingle
Opers Mgr: Shelly Brockway

D-U-N-S 00-696-4548
■ MERCHANTS AND FARMERS BANK
(*Suby of* RENASANT CORP) ★
134 W Washington St, Kosciusko, MS 39090-3633
Tel (662) 289-5121 *Founded/Ownrshp* 2013
Sales NA *EMP* 560
SIC 6022 6141 State commercial banks; Consumer finance companies; State commercial banks; Consumer finance companies
CEO: Hugh S Potts Jr
Pr: Scott Wiggers

D-U-N-S 96-648-4532
MERCHANTS AND FARMERS BANK
221 E Washington St, Kosciusko, MS 39090-3745
Tel (662) 289-5121 *Founded/Ownrshp* 2011
Sales NA *EMP* 46^{E}
SIC 6022 State commercial banks; State commercial banks
Ex Ofcr: Fred Bell
Ex Ofcr: James Tims

D-U-N-S 10-723-6317
■ MERCHANTS AND FARMERS TELEPHONE CO
TDS
(*Suby of* TDS TELECOMMUNICATIONS CORP) ★
125 W Main St, Hillsboro, IN 47949
Tel (765) 798-2145 *Founded/Ownrshp* 1999
Sales 853.0MM *EMP* 2,700
SIC 4813 Local & long distance telephone communications; Local & long distance telephone communications
Pr: David Wittwer
**Sec:* Debbie Meier
**Ofcr:* Noel Hutton

D-U-N-S 04-631-8887
MERCHANTS AUTOMOTIVE GROUP INC
MERCHANTS LEASING
1278 Hooksett Rd, Hooksett, NH 03106-1839
Tel (603) 669-4100 *Founded/Ownrshp* 1962
Sales 137.0MM^{E} *EMP* 250^{E}
Accts Baker Newman & Noyes Llp Manc
SIC 5521 7515 Automobiles, used cars only; Passenger car leasing; Automobiles, used cars only; Passenger car leasing
CEO: Phil Ryan
**Pr:* Stephen Singer
**CEO:* Glen Villano
**CFO:* Paul Barkworth
**Ofcr:* Jack Firriolo
**VP:* Alan Singer
VP: Michael Sydney
VP Sls: Tom Coffey
Manager: Roger Lofstrand
Sales Asso: Rich Interrante
Sales Asso: Lisa Petrucelli

D-U-N-S 12-673-6466
MERCHANTS BANCORP INC
MERCHANTS NATIONAL BANK
100 N High St, Hillsboro, OH 45133-1152
Tel (937) 393-1993 *Founded/Ownrshp* 1996
Sales NA *EMP* 125
SIC 6021 National commercial banks; National commercial banks
Pr: Paul W Pence Jr
Ex VP: James D Evans
Mktg Dir: Wilma Coulter

D-U-N-S 14-451-1839
▲ MERCHANTS BANCSHARES INC
275 Kennedy Dr, South Burlington, VT 05403-6785
Tel (802) 658-3400 *Founded/Ownrshp* 1983
Sales NA *EMP* 329^{E}
Tkr Sym MBVT *Exch* NGS
SIC 6022 State commercial banks; State commercial banks
Pr: Michael R Tuttle
**Ch Bd:* Jeffrey L Davis
CFO: Thomas J Meshako
Ofcr: Zoe P Erdman
Ex VP: Thomas S Leavitt

D-U-N-S 00-793-9556
■ MERCHANTS BANK (VT)
(*Suby of* MERCHANTS BANCSHARES INC) ★
275 Kennedy Dr Ste 100, South Burlington, VT 05403-6700
Tel (802) 865-1995 *Founded/Ownrshp* 1849, 1984
Sales NA *EMP* 317
SIC 6022 State commercial banks; State commercial banks
Pr: Michael R Tuttle
Pr: Stacie Griffiths
CFO: Janet Spitler
Treas: Joshua Southwell
Ofcr: Stacey Belville
Ofcr: James Fraser
Ofcr: Benjamin Hodges
Ofcr: Mike McCormick
Ofcr: Edgar Roy
Sr VP: Michael Cataldo
Sr VP: Molly Dillon
Sr VP: Thomas R Havers
Sr VP: Thomas Leavitt
Sr VP: Jim Reid
VP: Doug Babbitt
VP: Chris Halnon
VP: Cheryl Houchens
Board of Directors: Peter A Bouyea, Jeffrey L Davis, Michael G Furlong, Raymond C Pecor III, Patrick S Robins, Robert A Skiff

D-U-N-S 08-449-3972
MERCHANTS BANK NATIONAL ASSOCIATION
MERCHANTS NATIONAL BANK
(*Suby of* MERCHANTS FINANCIAL GROUP INC) ★
102 E 3rd St, Winona, MN 55987-3416
Tel (507) 457-1100 *Founded/Ownrshp* 1984
Sales NA *EMP* 122
SIC 6021 National commercial banks; National commercial banks
Pr: Greg Evans
CFO: Susan Sabat
CFO: Michael Speltz
Ts Inv Off: Sara Brandon
Trst Ofcr: Gerald E Neal
Ex VP: R L Mahoney
Sr VP: Nate Birkholz
Sr VP: Brian Brakke
VP: Kip Bolstad
VP: Randy Domeyer
VP: Bob Dougherty
VP: Martha Grimes
VP: Dustin Hundt
VP: Alberta Masyga
VP: Trudy Papenfuss
VP: Susan Savat
VP: Arlene Schwerzler
VP: Jerry Trocinski
Exec: Matt Schuldt

D-U-N-S 84-985-9165
MERCHANTS BANK OF INDIANA
11555 N Meridian St # 400, Carmel, IN 46032-6945
Tel (317) 805-4330 *Founded/Ownrshp* 2001
Sales NA *EMP* 80
SIC 6029 Commercial banks
Pr: Mike Dunlap

D-U-N-S 00-530-4845
MERCHANTS BONDING CO (MUTUAL)
2100 Fleur Dr, Des Moines, IA 50321-1158
Tel (515) 243-8171 *Founded/Ownrshp* 1933
Sales NA *EMP* 130
SIC 6351 Fidelity or surety bonding
Pr: Larry Taylor
Pr: Audrey Williams
**CFO:* Don Blum
Ofcr: Connie Israel
**Ex VP:* Mike Foster
VP: Jason Dettbarn
VP: Steve Dorenkamp
VP: Josh Penwell
**Exec:* Stanley McCormick
Dept Mgr: Jacki Kragel
Genl Mgr: Barbara Carlos

D-U-N-S 06-519-4920
MERCHANTS BUILDING MAINTENANCE CO
1190 Monterey Pass Rd, Monterey Park, CA 91754-3615
Tel (323) 881-6701 *Founded/Ownrshp* 1961
Sales 115.2MM^{E} *EMP* 3,000^{E}
SIC 7349 Building maintenance services; Building maintenance services
CEO: Theodore Haas
**Pr:* David Haas
**Treas:* Karen T Haas
VP: Wayne Eames
**VP:* Krista M Haas
Genl Mgr: Marco Ferrel
VP Opers: Adam Navaretta
Opers Mgr: Eliseo Gutierrez
Opers Mgr: Margarita Pantcratz
Sales Exec: Susan Penna
Sls Dir: Ilza Waterman

D-U-N-S 00-818-4749
MERCHANTS CO
MERCHANTS FOODSERVICE
(*Suby of* TATUM DEVELOPMENT CORP) ★
1100 Edwards St, Hattiesburg, MS 39401-5511
Tel (601) 353-2461 *Founded/Ownrshp* 1983
Sales 658.1MM^{E} *EMP* 500
Accts Mcarthur Thames Slay And Dew
SIC 5141 Groceries, general line; Groceries, general line
Pr: Andrew B Mercier
**Ch Bd:* Robert O Tatum
CFO: Allan Daglio
**CFO:* Jarrod Gray
IT Man: Lee Walker
VP Sls: Ken Moore

D-U-N-S 00-782-1960
MERCHANTS DELIVERY MOVING AND STORAGE CO
1215 State St, Racine, WI 53404-3351
Tel (262) 631-5680 *Founded/Ownrshp* 1985
Sales 24.2MM^{E} *EMP* 100
SIC 4213 4214 Household goods transport; Local trucking with storage
Pr: James Eastman
Pr: William Werth
COO: Scott Blasi
**Sec:* Jennifer Eastman
Dir IT: Michelle Whitefoot
Sfty Mgr: Tom Mundy
Opers Mgr: Joseph Trinidad
S&M/VP: Bill Werth

D-U-N-S 00-699-6888 EXP
MERCHANTS DISTRIBUTORS LLC (NC)
M D I
(*Suby of* ALEX LEE INC) ★
5005 Alex Lee Blvd, Hickory, NC 28601-3395
Tel (828) 725-4424 *Founded/Ownrshp* 1931
Sales 221.8MM^{E} *EMP* 3,000
SIC 5141 5142 5147 5148 5194 5122 Groceries, general line; Packaged frozen goods; Meats & meat products; Fresh fruits & vegetables; Tobacco & tobacco products; Cosmetics, perfumes & hair products; Toiletries; Groceries, general line; Packaged frozen goods; Meats & meat products; Fresh fruits & vegetables; Tobacco & tobacco products; Cosmetics, perfumes & hair products; Toiletries
Pr: Steven Hall
COO: John King
**Treas:* Ronald W Knedlik
**VP:* Ray Allen Bolick
**VP:* Donald Garvey
**VP:* Mark Gossett
VP: Michael Greene
**VP:* Dennis McCoy
**VP:* Bob McTeir
VP: Jay Schwartz
Mfg Dir: Jim Messer

D-U-N-S 04-097-4362 IMP
MERCHANTS EXPORT LLC
PORT OF PALM BEACH COLD
200 Dr Mrtn L Kng Jr Blvd Martin, Riviera Beach, FL 33404
Tel (561) 863-7171 *Founded/Ownrshp* 1975
Sales 81.9MM *EMP* 75^{E}
SIC 5142 5148 5141 5143 Frozen fish, meat & poultry; Frozen vegetables & fruit products; Bakery products, frozen; Fresh fruits & vegetables; Groceries, general line; Dairy products, except dried or canned; Frozen fish, meat & poultry; Frozen vegetables & fruit products; Bakery products, frozen; Fresh fruits & vegetables; Groceries, general line; Dairy products, except dried or canned
**Sec:* Maria M Collier
**VP:* Caroline Collier
**VP:* Natalia Collier
**VP:* Jeffrey Ullian
CIO: Juan Marcos
Sls Dir: Steve Shoupp

D-U-N-S 19-895-0933
MERCHANTS FINANCIAL GROUP INC
MERCHANTS NATIONAL BANK
102 E 3rd St, Winona, MN 55987-3416
Tel (507) 457-1100 *Founded/Ownrshp* 1984
Sales NA *EMP* 122
SIC 6021 6022 National commercial banks; State commercial banks; National commercial banks; State commercial banks
CEO: Dick Mahoney
**Pr:* Rod Nelson
**Sec:* Sue Savat
VP: Cindy Adolph
VP: R Mahoney
Software D: Raymond Lacasse
Mktg Mgr: Mark Metzler

MERCHANTS FOODSERVICE
See MERCHANTS CO

D-U-N-S 00-342-5949
MERCHANTS GROCERY CO INC (VA)
800 Maddox Dr, Culpeper, VA 22701-4156
Tel (540) 825-0786 *Founded/Ownrshp* 1917
Sales 135.6MM *EMP* 135
Accts Nicholas Jones & Co Plc Cu
SIC 5194 5141 5145 Tobacco & tobacco products; Groceries, general line; Confectionery; Tobacco & tobacco products; Groceries, general line; Confectionery
Pr: Elvin V Smythers
CFO: Neal Deane
**Sec:* Michael G Hicks
**VP:* David G Cooper
VP Opers: Scott Hansen
Sales Exec: Bruce Davis
Mktg Dir: Kim Phillips
Mktg Mgr: Chris Smythers
Sales Asso: Bubby Hitt
Sales Asso: Tammy Zitz

D-U-N-S 02-379-6105
MERCHANTS INC
MERCHANT'S TIRE & AUTO CENTER
9073 Euclid Ave, Manassas, VA 20110-5306
Tel (703) 368-3171 *Founded/Ownrshp* 1999
Sales 178.2MM *EMP* 1,500
SIC 5014 7539 5531 Automobile tires & tubes; Automotive repair shops; Automotive tires; Automobile tires & tubes; Automotive repair shops; Automotive tires
Pr: J Michael Riggan
Ch Bd: Carol K Bell
CFO: James R Cato
CFO: Jim Matthews
VP: James B Bull
VP: Carl Dunn Jr
VP: Carl Finamore
VP: Lee Fishkin
VP: George Lnoey
VP: John Seal
VP Admn: Bill Craig
Board of Directors: Linda Merchant Bell, Carol Merchant Kirby, Mae S Merchant, Wilson C Merchant III

D-U-N-S 13-168-7519
MERCHANTS INSURANCE GROUP
(*Suby of* AMERICAN EUROPEAN GROUP INC) ★
250 Main St, Buffalo, NY 14202-4104
Tel (716) 849-3333 *Founded/Ownrshp* 2007
Sales NA *EMP* 313
SIC 6331 Fire, marine & casualty insurance: stock; Property damage insurance; Fire, marine & casualty insurance & carriers; Fire, marine & casualty insurance: stock; Property damage insurance; Fire, marine & casualty insurance & carriers
Pr: Brent D Baird
**Ch Bd:* Thomas E Kahn
**COO:* Robert M Zak
**CFO:* Kenneth J Wilson
Bd of Dir: Bob Perno
VP: Robert Fagerburg
VP: Marge Kafka
VP: Shad McKnight
**VP:* Edward M Murphy
VP: Ellen Willard
CTO: Peter Balisteri

MERCHANTS LEASING
See MERCHANTS AUTOMOTIVE GROUP INC

D-U-N-S 04-890-8180 IMP
MERCHANTS METALS INC
ANCHOR DIE CAST
(*Suby of* ATLAS HOLDINGS LLC) ★
900 Ashwood Pkwy Ste 600, Atlanta, GA 30338-7501
Tel (678) 731-8077 *Founded/Ownrshp* 2015
Sales 415.6MM^{E} *EMP* 1,593
SIC 3496 3446 5031 Fencing, made from purchased wire; Mesh, made from purchased wire; Concrete reinforcing mesh & wire; Fences, gates, posts & flagpoles; Fences or posts, ornamental iron or steel; Building materials, exterior; Fencing, wood; Fencing, made from purchased wire; Mesh, made from purchased wire; Concrete reinforcing mesh & wire; Fences, gates, posts & flagpoles; Fences or posts, ornamental iron or steel; Building materials, exterior; Fencing, wood
Pr: David Clarke
CFO: Gary Brandon
CFO: Terry Schillaci
CFO: Mike Singleton
Treas: Tammy R Hinkle
VP: Lyle D Bumgarner
VP: Robert L Burdette
VP: Tim Kelly
VP: Bill Ramsey
VP: William Stewart
**VP:* Robert N Tenczar
VP: Carl Wilkes

D-U-N-S 00-697-6757
MERCHANTS MUTUAL INSURANCE CO (NY)
240 Main St, Buffalo, NY 14202-4104
Tel (716) 849-3333 *Founded/Ownrshp* 1917
Sales NA *EMP* 250
SIC 6331 Property damage insurance; Fire, marine & casualty insurance: mutual; Property damage insurance; Fire, marine & casualty insurance: mutual
Pr: Robert Zak
**Treas:* Kenneth J Wilson
**Sr VP:* Fred Hildebrand
**VP:* Margaret Kafka

MERCHANTS NATIONAL BANK
See MERCHANTS BANK NATIONAL ASSOCIATION

MERCHANTS NATIONAL BANK
See MERCHANTS BANCORP INC

MERCHANTS NATIONAL BANK
See MERCHANTS FINANCIAL GROUP INC

D-U-N-S 15-068-0684
MERCHANTS NATIONAL BANK
(*Suby of* MERCHANTS BANCORP INC) ★
100 N High St, Hillsboro, OH 45133-1152
Tel (937) 393-1134 *Founded/Ownrshp* 1879
Sales NA *EMP* 90
SIC 6021 National commercial banks; National commercial banks
Pr: Paul Pence Jr
**Ch Bd:* Don Fender
Ofcr: Cindy Gold
VP: Mark Schiavone
VP: John Storrs
Mktg Dir: Chrystal Schardt

D-U-N-S 00-698-7549
■ MERCHANTS NEW YORK COMMERCIAL CORP
(*Suby of* VALLEY NATIONAL BANK) ★
555 5th Ave Rm 301, New York, NY 10017-9274
Tel (212) 949-8740 *Founded/Ownrshp* 1881, 2007
Sales NA *EMP* 242
SIC 6022 State commercial banks; State commercial banks
Ch Bd: Irwin Schwartz
**Ch Bd:* Spencer B Witty
**Pr:* Steve A Barrow
**Pr:* James G Lawrence
**COO:* William J Cardew
**Treas:* Eric W Gould
**V Ch Bd:* Rudolf H Hertz
**V Ch Bd:* Charles Silberman

D-U-N-S 06-171-1735
MERCHANTS SECURITY SERVICE OF DAYTON OHIO INC
2015 Wayne Ave, Dayton, OH 45410-2134
Tel (937) 256-9373 *Founded/Ownrshp* 1901
Sales 8.9MM^{E} *EMP* 300
SIC 7381 Security guard service; Security guard service
Pr: James Houpt
Ofcr: Shannon Simuel
Opers Mgr: Dennis McClerren

MERCHANT'S TIRE & AUTO CENTER
See MERCHANTS INC

D-U-N-S 07-021-5434
MERCHANTWAREHOUSE.COM INC (MA)
CAPITAL BANKCARD
1 Federal St Fl 2, Boston, MA 02110-2003
Tel (800) 478-4830 *Founded/Ownrshp* 1998
Sales 39.1MM^{E} *EMP* 205
SIC 5044 Bank automatic teller machines; Bank automatic teller machines
CEO: Scott Zdanis
**Pr:* Henry Helgeson
Ex VP: Brian Graham
VP: Bob Cellucci
VP: Jay Chauhdry
VP: David McSweeney
Snr Sftwr: Marc Castrechini
Mktg Mgr: Stephanie Sperry

D-U-N-S 12-182-0737 IMP/EXP
MERCHSOURCE LLC
15 Cushing, Irvine, CA 92618-4220
Tel (949) 900-0900 *Founded/Ownrshp* 2001
Sales 172.0MM^{E} *EMP* 46
SIC 5112 Stationery & office supplies; Stationery & office supplies
Mng Pt: Johann Clapp

MERCK
See MEDCO HEALTH SOLUTIONS

D-U-N-S 05-455-4290 IMP
▲ MERCK & CO INC (NJ)
2000 Galloping Hill Rd, Kenilworth, NJ 07033-1310
Tel (908) 740-4000 *Founded/Ownrshp* 1928
Sales 42.2MMM *EMP* 70,000^{E}
Tkr Sym MRK *Exch* NYS

SIC 2834 2836 2844 5122 Pharmaceutical preparations; Druggists' preparations (pharmaceuticals); Drugs acting on the respiratory system; Drugs affecting parasitic & infective diseases; Vaccines; Veterinary biological products; Suntan lotions & oils; Animal medicines; Pharmaceutical preparations; Druggists' preparations (pharmaceuticals); Drugs acting on the respiratory system; Drugs affecting parasitic & infective diseases; Vaccines; Veterinary biological products; Suntan lotions & oils; Animal medicines
Ch Bd: Kenneth C Frazier
Pr: Willie A Deese
Pr: Richard R Deluca Jr
Pr: Roger M Perlmutter
Pr: Adam H Schechter
CFO: Robert M Davis
Chf Mktg O: Michael Rosenblatt
Ex VP: Julie Gerberding
Ex VP: Clark Golestani
Ex VP: Mirian M Graddick-Weir
Ex VP: Michael J Holston
Ex VP: Bruce N Kuhlik
Sr VP: Adele D Ambrose
Sr VP: Rita A Karachun
Assoc Dir: Christine Borsellino
Assoc Dir: Claudia Choi
Assoc Dir: Jeanette Demito
Assoc Dir: Jonetta Depp
Assoc Dir: Eric Dobkin
Assoc Dir: Jennifer Drake
Assoc Dir: Adam Duckworth
Board of Directors: Patricia F Russo, Leslie A Brun, Craig B Thompson, Thomas R Cech, Wendell P Weeks, Pamela J Craig, Peter C Wendell, Thomas H Glocer, William B Harrison Jr, C Robert Kidder, Rochelle B Lazarus, Carlos E Represas, Paul B Rothman

D-U-N-S 96-642-5733
MERCK AND CO INC EMPLOYEE BENEFITS TRUST
1 Merck Dr, Whitehouse Station, NJ 08889-3497
Tel (908) 423-1000 *Founded/Ownrshp* 2011
Sales NA *EMP* 2ᴱ
Accts Buckconsultants Secaucus Nj
SIC 6411 Insurance agents, brokers & service; Insurance agents, brokers & service

D-U-N-S 96-940-7324
MERCK AND CO INC GROUP LIFE TRUST
556 Morris Ave, Summit, NJ 07901-1330
Tel (908) 423-1000 *Founded/Ownrshp* 2011
Sales 22.9MM *EMP* 7ᴱ
Accts Buckconsultants Secaucus Nj
SIC 8082 Home health care services; Home health care services

D-U-N-S 96-790-1740
MERCK AND CO INC UNION VEBA TRUST
Ws 3f 65, Whitehouse Station, NJ 08889
Tel (908) 423-1000 *Founded/Ownrshp* 2011
Sales 73.8MM *EMP* 2ᴱ
Accts Mercer Princeton Nj
SIC 6733 Trusts; Trusts

D-U-N-S 05-489-2393
MERCK EMPLOYEES FEDERAL CREDIT UNION INC
HARLAND FINANCIAL SOLUTIONS
126 E Lincoln Ave, Rahway, NJ 07065-4607
Tel (732) 594-4046 *Founded/Ownrshp* 1927
Sales NA *EMP* 25
SIC 6061 Federal credit unions; Federal credit unions
Ex Dir: Nancy Kalvin

D-U-N-S 07-913-1810
■ **MERCK GLOBAL HEALTH INNOVATION FUND LLC**
(*Suby of* MERCK & CO INC) ★
2000 Galloping Hill Rd, Kenilworth, NJ 07033-1310
Tel (908) 423-1000 *Founded/Ownrshp* 2011
Sales 48.3MMᴱ *EMP* 195ᴱ
SIC 6726 Management investment funds, closed-end; Management investment funds, closed-end

D-U-N-S 78-319-2800
■ **MERCK HOLDINGS LLC**
(*Suby of* MERCK SHARP & DOHME CORP) ★
1 Merck Dr, Whitehouse Station, NJ 08889-3497
Tel (908) 423-1000 *Founded/Ownrshp* 1884
Sales 147.3MMᴱ *EMP* 2,700
SIC 2834 6712 Proprietary drug products; Bank holding companies; Proprietary drug products; Bank holding companies
Pr: Richard Henriques
**Pr:* Richard T Clark
**Treas:* Caroline Dorsa
**Sr VP:* Judy Lewent

D-U-N-S 96-688-6728
MERCK PATIENT ASSISTANCE PROGRAM INC
2 Clerico Ln Apt 201, Hillsborough, NJ 08844-1620
Tel (908) 423-1000 *Founded/Ownrshp* 2011
Sales 198.9MM *EMP* 2ᴱ
SIC 8699 Charitable organization; Charitable organization

D-U-N-S 07-865-5871
MERCK RESEARCH LABORATORIES
126 E Lincoln Ave, Rahway, NJ 07065-4607
Tel (732) 594-4000 *Founded/Ownrshp* 2012
Sales 31.4MMᴱ *EMP* 148ᴱ
SIC 8742 Hospital & health services consultant
CEO: Leslie A Brun
Pr: Kenneth C Frazier
Ex Dir: Elliot Chartash
Mktg Mgr: Jessica Joedecke
Counsel: Eric Thies

D-U-N-S 03-716-7426 IMP
■ **MERCK SHARP & DOHME (IA) CORP**
(*Suby of* MERCK HOLDINGS LLC) ★
1 Merck Dr, Whitehouse Station, NJ 08889-3497
Tel (908) 423-1000 *Founded/Ownrshp* 1949
Sales 104.9MMᴱ *EMP* 100
SIC 5122 Pharmaceuticals; Pharmaceuticals
Pr: Grey F Warner
Pr: Merri Baillargeon
**Sr VP:* Francis H Spiegel
VP: Rick Brasher
**VP:* Judy C Luwent

D-U-N-S 00-131-7601 IMP
■ **MERCK SHARP & DOHME CORP**
(*Suby of* MERCK & CO INC) ★
2000 Galloping Hill Rd, Kenilworth, NJ 07033-1310
Tel (908) 740-4000 *Founded/Ownrshp* 1991
Sales 5.2MMMᴱ *EMP* 18,400
SIC 2834 8741 Pharmaceutical preparations; Druggists' preparations (pharmaceuticals); Drugs acting on the respiratory system; Drugs affecting parasitic & infective diseases; Management services; Pharmaceutical preparations; Druggists' preparations (pharmaceuticals); Drugs acting on the respiratory system; Drugs affecting parasitic & infective diseases; Management services
Ch Bd: Kenneth C Frazier
**Pr:* Fred Hassen
**Treas:* E Kevin Moore
Ex VP: Joseph Connors
VP: Richard Kinney
VP: Kanwal Varma
Assoc Dir: Lillian Chavez
Assoc Dir: Yuen Kwan
Genl Mgr: Bin Chen
Genl Mgr: Ian Pawson
QA Dir: Damaris Arroyo

D-U-N-S 60-987-8343
MERCO GROUP INC
7711 N 81st St, Milwaukee, WI 53223-3847
Tel (414) 365-2600 *Founded/Ownrshp* 1989
Sales 101.4MMᴱ *EMP* 225
SIC 5199 5047

D-U-N-S 85-971-6677 EXP
MERCOM CORP
313 Commerce Dr, Pawleys Island, SC 29585-6052
Tel (843) 979-9957 *Founded/Ownrshp* 2000
Sales 105.8MM *EMP* 63
Accts Webster Rogers Llp Myrtle Bea
SIC 5999 Communication equipment; Communication equipment
Pr: Stella Mercado
**CFO:* Jeff Miller
**VP:* Larry Mercado

MERCURY
See FORD CANBY INC

MERCURY
See TOM FORD BOLAND INC

MERCURY
See ELK RIVER FORD INC

D-U-N-S 19-537-0234
MERCURY AIR CARGO INC
APOLLO FREIGHT
(*Suby of* MERCURY AIR GROUP INC) ★
6040 Avion Dr Ste 200, Los Angeles, CA 90045-5654
Tel (310) 258-6100 *Founded/Ownrshp* 1988
Sales 44.9MMᴱ *EMP* 350
SIC 4581 4512 4522 Airports, flying fields & services; Air cargo carrier, scheduled; Air cargo carriers, nonscheduled; Airports, flying fields & services; Air cargo carrier, scheduled; Air cargo carriers, nonscheduled
CEO: Joseph A Czyzyk
**Treas:* Dan K Barnard
**Ex VP:* Clive Langeveldt
**VP:* John Peery
Trfc Dir: Lisa Carroll

D-U-N-S 04-319-0776 IMP
MERCURY AIR GROUP INC (NY)
MERCURY SERVICE
2780 Skypark Dr Ste 300, Torrance, CA 90505-7518
Tel (310) 602-3770 *Founded/Ownrshp* 1956, 2013
Sales 770.7MMᴱ *EMP* 1,200
SIC 5172 7389 4581 Aircraft fueling services; Brokers' services; Hangar operation; Airfreight loading & unloading services; Aircraft fueling services; Brokers' services; Hangar operation; Airfreight loading & unloading services
Pr: Joseph A Czyzyk
CFO: Kent Rosenthal
CFO: Lawrence R Samuels
Ex VP: David Herbst Rejoins
VP: Daniel K Barnard
VP: Carolina Gutierrez
IT Man: George Vaughn
Genl Couns: Kathryn M Schwertfeger
Snr Mgr: Scott Purvis

D-U-N-S 00-220-6639 IMP
MERCURY AIRCRAFT INC (NY)
17 Wheeler Ave, Hammondsport, NY 14840-9566
Tel (607) 569-4200 *Founded/Ownrshp* 1920
Sales 98.2MMᴱ *EMP* 600
SIC 3469 3444

D-U-N-S 07-530-6340
■ **MERCURY CASUALTY CO** (CA)
M C C
(*Suby of* MERCURY GENERAL CORP) ★
555 W Imperial Hwy, Brea, CA 92821-4802
Tel (323) 937-1060 *Founded/Ownrshp* 1962, 1979
Sales NA *EMP* 4,500
SIC 6331 6351 Automobile insurance; Warranty insurance, home; Automobile insurance; Warranty insurance, home
CEO: Gabriel Tirador
**CEO:* George Joseph
Ex VP: Gus Tepper

D-U-N-S 17-796-6694
■ **MERCURY COMPUTER SYSTEMS INC**
MERCURY I/O CENTER EXCELLENCE
(*Suby of* MERCURY SYSTEMS INC) ★
12120 Plum Orchard Dr A, Silver Spring, MD 20904-7820
Tel (301) 588-1900 *Founded/Ownrshp* 1987
Sales 48.8MMᴱ *EMP* 576
Accts Rubino & Mcgeehin Chartered
SIC 3571 8711 Computers, digital, analog or hybrid; Designing: ship, boat, machine & product; Computers, digital, analog or hybrid; Designing: ship, boat, machine & product
Pr: Richard O'Connell
VP: Allen Bowersox
**VP:* Eugene Callaghan
**VP Opers:* Kerry Rye
**VP Mktg:* Louis De Benedetto
Board of Directors: Henry Stuben, Brian Thoreson

D-U-N-S 17-325-5688
■ **MERCURY DEFENSE SYSTEMS INC**
MERCURY SYSTEMS
(*Suby of* MERCURY SYSTEMS INC) ★
10855 Bus Ctr Dr Bldg A, Cypress, CA 90630
Tel (714) 898-8200 *Founded/Ownrshp* 2011
Sales 23.0MMᴱ *EMP* 85
SIC 8711 7374 Engineering services; Data processing service
CEO: Mark Aslett
**Pr:* Brian Perry
**CFO:* Kevin M Bisson
**Sr VP:* Gerald M Haines II
VP: Rich Beeber
**VP:* Charles A Speicher
Prgrm Mgr: Fernando Salazar
Sftwr Eng: Andrew Davis
Sftwr Eng: Ian Steed
Sftwr Eng: Dennis Ternet
Ql Cn Mgr: Edward Pagliochini
Board of Directors: Robert J Kohler, Peter Marino Nancy Lazar

MERCURY ELECTRONICS DIVISION
See DIVERSIFIED TRAFFIC PRODUCTS INC

D-U-N-S 03-270-5659 IMP
MERCURY ENTERPRISES INC
MERCURY MEDICAL
11300 49th St N, Clearwater, FL 33762-4807
Tel (727) 573-7689 *Founded/Ownrshp* 1980
Sales 58.0MMᴱ *EMP* 170
SIC 5047 3841 7699 3842 Medical equipment & supplies; Surgical & medical instruments; Professional instrument repair services; Surgical appliances & supplies; Medical equipment & supplies; Surgical & medical instruments; Professional instrument repair services; Surgical appliances & supplies
CEO: Stanley G Tangalakis
COO: Garry Blount
Dir IT: Gary Repetti
VP Sls: David Tyson
Sls Mgr: Emory Burleson
Sls Mgr: Jose Garcia
Sls Mgr: Debbie Sizemore
Sls Mgr: Don St Germain
Sls Mgr: Ford Staton
Sls Mgr: Nicholas Tides

D-U-N-S 01-885-6757
MERCURY FUEL SERVICE INC
43 Lafayette St, Waterbury, CT 06708-3897
Tel (203) 756-7284 *Founded/Ownrshp* 1946
Sales 106.2MMᴱ *EMP* 110
SIC 5172 5541 5411 5983 1711 2911 Gasoline; Fuel oil; Filling stations, gasoline; Convenience stores, chain; Fuel oil dealers; Warm air heating & air conditioning contractor; Petroleum refining; Gasoline; Fuel oil; Filling stations, gasoline; Convenience stores, chain; Fuel oil dealers; Warm air heating & air conditioning contractor; Petroleum refining
Pr: Michael Devino Jr
**Treas:* Martin F Devino
**VP:* David F Devino
Opers Mgr: George Strileckis
Mktg Mgr: Barbara Koren
Sls Mgr: Jim Barone

D-U-N-S 04-507-8909
MERCURY FULFILLMENT SYSTEMS INC
MERCURY PROMOTIONS & FULFILLME
35610 Mound Rd, Sterling Heights, MI 48310-4725
Tel (248) 825-9340 *Founded/Ownrshp* 2005
Sales 26.5MM *EMP* 68
SIC 8743 5199 Promotion service; Advertising specialties; Promotion service; Advertising specialties
CEO: Jon Sloan
Mng Pt: Tina Harmon
**CFO:* Deanna Lockey
VP: Amy Lamar
VP: Gretchen Thomas
**VP:* Michael Wilson
Prgrm Mgr: April Kula
Prgrm Mgr: Kim McQuade
Mktg Dir: Jill Rocker
Sls Mgr: Laura Blumenau

D-U-N-S 07-530-0004
▲ **MERCURY GENERAL CORP**
4484 Wilshire Blvd, Los Angeles, CA 90010-3710
Tel (323) 937-1060 *Founded/Ownrshp* 1961
Sales NA *EMP* 4,600ᴱ
Tkr Sym MCY *Exch* NYS
SIC 6331 6411 Automobile insurance; Property damage insurance; Fire, marine & casualty insurance & carriers; Insurance agents, brokers & service; Automobile insurance; Property damage insurance; Fire, marine & casualty insurance & carriers; Insurance agents, brokers & service
Pr: Gabriel Tirador
**Ch Bd:* George Joseph
CFO: Theodore R Stalick
Ofcr: Kenneth G Kitzmiller
Sr VP: Allan Lubitz
VP: Abby Hossein
VP: Robert Houlihan
VP: Jason Owens
VP: John E Sutton
VP: Charles Toney
VP: Kenneth Van Wagner
VP: Judy A Walters
Board of Directors: Bruce A Bunner, Michael D Curtius, James G Ellis, Christopher Graves, Richard E Grayson, Martha E Marcon, Donald P Newell, Donald R Spuehler

MERCURY I/O CENTER EXCELLENCE
See MERCURY COMPUTER SYSTEMS INC

D-U-N-S 09-600-7877
■ **MERCURY INSURANCE CO**
(*Suby of* MERCURY GENERAL CORP) ★
4484 Wilshire Blvd, Los Angeles, CA 90010-3710
Tel (323) 937-1060 *Founded/Ownrshp* 1972
Sales NA *EMP* 4,600
SIC 6331 Fire, marine & casualty insurance; Fire, marine & casualty insurance
CEO: Gabe Tirador
**CFO:* Ted Stalick
**Ch:* George Joseph
VP: Randy Petro
**VP:* Judith Walters

D-U-N-S 61-037-0210
■ **MERCURY INSURANCE CO OF FLORIDA**
(*Suby of* MERCURY GENERAL CORP) ★
1901 Ulmerton Rd Fl 6, Clearwater, FL 33762-2307
Tel (727) 561-4000 *Founded/Ownrshp* 2001
Sales NA *EMP* 300
SIC 6331 Automobile insurance; Automobile insurance

D-U-N-S 80-748-6758
■ **MERCURY INSURANCE CO OF ILLINOIS**
(*Suby of* MERCURY GENERAL CORP) ★
400 Lakeview Pkwy Ste 125, Vernon Hills, IL 60061-1850
Tel (847) 816-4300 *Founded/Ownrshp* 1992
Sales NA *EMP* 50
SIC 6331 6411 Automobile insurance; Insurance agents, brokers & service
**Treas:* Keith Parker

D-U-N-S 78-656-3010
■ **MERCURY INSURANCE SERVICES LLC**
(*Suby of* M C C) ★
4484 Wilshire Blvd, Los Angeles, CA 90010-3710
Tel (323) 937-1060 *Founded/Ownrshp* 2000
Sales NA *EMP* 4,000
SIC 6331 Automobile insurance; Property damage insurance; Automobile insurance
CEO: Gabriel Tirador

D-U-N-S 55-659-0040 IMP
■ **MERCURY INTERACTIVE LLC**
(*Suby of* HP INC) ★
3000 Hanover St, Palo Alto, CA 94304-1112
Tel (650) 857-1501 *Founded/Ownrshp* 2015
Sales 73.1MMᴱ *EMP* 2,659
SIC 7372 Prepackaged software; Prepackaged software
Pr: Anthony Zingale
Pr: Moshe Egert
Treas: Jon E Flaxman
VP: Scott Bradley

D-U-N-S 00-215-8855
MERCURY LIGHTING PRODUCTS CO INC (NJ)
20 Audrey Pl, Fairfield, NJ 07004-3416
Tel (973) 244-9444 *Founded/Ownrshp* 1946
Sales 31.4MMᴱ *EMP* 110
SIC 3646 Commercial indusl & institutional electric lighting fixtures; Commercial indusl & institutional electric lighting fixtures
Pr: John Fedinec
**Ex VP:* Scott Fleischer
Sales Exec: Irma Perez
VP Sls: Brian Cunningham
Sls Mgr: Lou Dina
Sales Asso: Rose Priori

D-U-N-S 00-405-9705 IMP
MERCURY LUGGAGE MANUFACTURING CO
MERCURY LUGGAGE/SEWARD TRUNK
4843 Victor St, Jacksonville, FL 32207-7978
Tel (904) 733-9595 *Founded/Ownrshp* 1947
Sales 21.4MMᴱ *EMP* 200
SIC 3161 5099 2542 Luggage; Suitcases; Traveling bags; Sample cases; Luggage; Partitions & fixtures, except wood; Luggage; Suitcases; Traveling bags; Sample cases; Luggage; Partitions & fixtures, except wood
Pr: Andrew Pradella
**CFO:* Randy L Schilson
**Sec:* Joan Pradella
**VP:* Gerard Kenny
**VP:* Michael Laska
Div Mgr: William Henderson
Sls Dir: Bob Pradella
Mktg Mgr: Sam Finch

MERCURY LUGGAGE/SEWARD TRUNK
See MERCURY LUGGAGE MANUFACTURING CO

D-U-N-S 79-881-4765 IMP/EXP
■ **MERCURY MARINE GROUP**
MERCURY MARINE INTERNATIONAL
(*Suby of* BRUNSWICK CORP) ★
W6250 W Pioneer Rd, Fond Du Lac, WI 54935-5636
Tel (920) 929-5000 *Founded/Ownrshp* 1939
Sales 1.1MMMᴱ *EMP* 4,100ᴱ
SIC 3089 3535 Marine engines; Trolley conveyors; Plastic boats & other marine equipment; Trolley conveyors
Pr: John Pfeiffer
**Prin:* Mark Schwabero
Dir Sec: Daniel Bord
Prgrm Mgr: Harry Classen
Genl Mgr: John Temple
Dir IT: Mike Schulz
IT Man: Peter Brill
IT Man: Jim Drossel
Mktg Mgr: Rick Mackie
Genl Couns: Todd Lemke

MERCURY MARINE INTERNATIONAL
See MERCURY MARINE GROUP

MERCURY MEDIA
See DIVERSIFIED MERCURY COMMUNICATIONS LLC

MERCURY MEDICAL
See MERCURY ENTERPRISES INC

D-U-N-S 09-860-0984 EXP
MERCURY OVERSEAS INC
(*Suby of* HANNAN CHIKUSAN CO.,LTD.)
830 Mission St, South Pasadena, CA 91030-3192
Tel (626) 799-9141 *Founded/Ownrshp* 1979
Sales 400.0MM *EMP* 9
SIC 5147 5146 Meats & meat products; Seafoods
Pr: Yutaka Nihira

D-U-N-S 00-123-6876
MERCURY PAINT CORP (NY)
4808 Farragut Rd, Brooklyn, NY 11203-6612
Tel (718) 469-8787 *Founded/Ownrshp* 1961
Sales 23.1MM^E *EMP* 100
SIC 2851 5231 Paints & paint additives; Paint; Paints & paint additives; Paint
Pr: Jeff Berman
VP: Freddy Tichner
Sls Mgr: Ronald Alli

D-U-N-S 83-236-6780 IMP/EXP
MERCURY PAPER INC
(*Suby of* GOLD HONGYE PAPER GROUP CO., LTD.)
495 Radio Station Rd, Strasburg, VA 22657-3706
Tel (540) 465-6900 *Founded/Ownrshp* 2005
Sales 44.1MM^E *EMP* 100
SIC 2621 Tissue paper; Tissue paper
Pr: Duncan Chen
Plnt Mgr: Bill Moore
Ql Cn Mgr: Jason Atkins

D-U-N-S 02-506-3579
MERCURY PARTNERS 90 BI INC (IL)
BRUCKER COMPANY
1200 Greenleaf Ave, Elk Grove Village, IL 60007-5519
Tel (847) 437-9690 *Founded/Ownrshp* 1951, 1997
Sales 39.7MM^E *EMP* 40
SIC 5074 5075 Heating equipment (hydronic); Ventilating equipment & supplies
Pr: Brian J Flanagan
**Pr:* David Sobut
Ofcr: Larry Kasza
Rgnl Mgr: Bill Udziela
Sales Asso: Jesse Escamilla

D-U-N-S 12-129-9429
■ **MERCURY PAYMENT SYSTEMS LLC**
(*Suby of* NATIONAL PROCESSING CO) ★
150 Mercury Village Dr, Durango, CO 81301-8955
Tel (970) 247-5557 *Founded/Ownrshp* 2014
Sales 45.7MM^E *EMP* 208^E
SIC 7389 7372 Financial services; Application computer software
CEO: Matt Taylor
**CFO:* Karsten Voermann
Sr VP: John Berkley
Sr VP: Randy Clark
Sr VP: Pattie Money
Sr VP: Brett Narlinger
**CTO:* Andrew Patterson
Sls Mgr: Brian Pagano

D-U-N-S 00-453-9813 IMP
MERCURY PLASTICS INC (OH)
15760 Madison Rd, Middlefield, OH 44062-8408
Tel (440) 632-5281 *Founded/Ownrshp* 1964, 1998
Sales 60.2MM^E *EMP* 225
SIC 3089 Extruded finished plastic products; Extruded finished plastic products
Pr: William Rowley Jr
**Ch Bd:* William Rowley Sr
CFO: Kurt Hoffmeyer
**Sec:* Mark Baker
MIS Dir: Paul Sharron
MIS Dir: Paul Willrich
Plnt Mgr: Chuck Hayes
Prd Mgr: Dave Tersigni
Ql Cn Mgr: Ed Maresh
Sls Mgr: Scott Gardner

D-U-N-S 16-130-7111 IMP
MERCURY PLASTICS INC
14825 Salt Lake Ave, City of Industry, CA 91746-3131
Tel (626) 369-8457 *Founded/Ownrshp* 1987
Sales 103.4MM^E *EMP* 550
SIC 2673 2759 3089 Plastic bags: made from purchased materials; Bags, plastic: printing; Plastic containers, except foam; Plastic bags: made from purchased materials; Bags, plastic: printing; Plastic containers, except foam
CEO: Benjamin Deutsch
**CEO:* Mark Teo
**CFO:* Anna Rabchev
**Ex VP:* Andrew Deutsch
**VP:* Zachary Deutsch
**VP:* Kamyar Mirdamadi

D-U-N-S 93-288-1493
MERCURY PRINT & MAIL CO INC
NEW ENGLAND PRTG & GRAPHICS
1110 Central Ave, Pawtucket, RI 02861-2262
Tel (401) 724-7600 *Founded/Ownrshp* 1995
Sales 20.0MM^E *EMP* 100
SIC 2752 2741 2791 Commercial printing, lithographic; Miscellaneous publishing; Typesetting
Ch Bd: Peter Ottmar
Pr: Dennis Carroll
**Pr:* Stephen Cronin
Creative D: Nick Decesare
CIO: Keith Authelet
IT Man: David Barriere
Snr PM: Tom McDonald

D-U-N-S 08-076-1760 IMP
MERCURY PRINT PRODUCTIONS INC
2332 Innovation Way 4, Rochester, NY 14624-6225
Tel (585) 458-7900 *Founded/Ownrshp* 1969
Sales 65.1MM^E *EMP* 200^E
SIC 2752 7334 2791 2789 Commercial printing, offset; Photocopying & duplicating services; Typesetting; Bookbinding & related work; Commercial printing, offset; Photocopying & duplicating services; Typesetting; Bookbinding & related work
CEO: Valerie D Mannix
**Pr:* John Place
CFO: Scott Mulcahy
**CFO:* Trudy Starr
VP: Christian Schaumburger
IT Man: Michael Helmerci
IT Man: Brian Shipe
Plnt Mgr: Jeff Quartley
Plnt Mgr: Chris Young
Prd Mgr: Matt Brennan
Sales Exec: Darrin Pancoast

D-U-N-S 00-703-3319 IMP
■ **MERCURY PRINTING CO INC** (TN)
WIMMER COOK BOOKS
(*Suby of* CONSOLIDATED GRAPHICS INC) ★
4650 Shelby Air Dr, Memphis, TN 38118-7405
Tel (901) 345-8480 *Founded/Ownrshp* 1961
Sales 38.1MM^E *EMP* 110
SIC 2759 2789 2791 2752 Commercial printing; Bookbinding & related work; Typesetting; Commercial printing, lithographic; Commercial printing; Bookbinding & related work; Typesetting; Commercial printing, lithographic
Pr: Chris Tooney
VP: Doug McNeill
VP Opers: Randy Simmons
Plnt Mgr: Ralph Smith
VP Sls: Mark McKinney
Mktg Dir: Cathy Armstrong
Sales Asso: Hyden Gloria

D-U-N-S 00-525-8959 IMP
MERCURY PRODUCTS CORP (IL)
1201 Mercury Dr, Schaumburg, IL 60193-3513
Tel (847) 524-4400 *Founded/Ownrshp* 1946, 1995
Sales 97.7MM^E *EMP* 255
SIC 3465 3469 3714 Automotive stampings; Machine parts, stamped or pressed metal; Motor vehicle engines & parts; Exhaust systems & parts, motor vehicle; Automotive stampings; Machine parts, stamped or pressed metal; Motor vehicle engines & parts; Exhaust systems & parts, motor vehicle
Pr: Bruce C Hael
**Pr:* Bruce Havel
CFO: Jack Albright
Exec: Marcy Torres
CTO: Philip Haag
Plnt Mgr: Jack Ehlinger
Prd Mgr: Juan Cortez
Ql Cn Mgr: Ron Anderson

MERCURY PROMOTIONS & FULFILLME
See MERCURY FULFILLMENT SYSTEMS INC

D-U-N-S 01-368-6794
MERCURY RADIO ARTS INC
1270 Ave Of The Americas, New York, NY 10020-1700
Tel (212) 301-1500 *Founded/Ownrshp* 2002
Sales 24.2MM^E *EMP* 200
SIC 4832 Radio broadcasting stations; Radio broadcasting stations
Ch Bd: Glenn Beck
**Pr:* Chris Balfe

MERCURY SERVICE
See MERCURY AIR GROUP INC

MERCURY SYSTEMS
See MERCURY DEFENSE SYSTEMS INC

D-U-N-S 10-676-0549 EXP
▲ **MERCURY SYSTEMS INC**
201 Riverneck Rd, Chelmsford, MA 01824-2820
Tel (978) 256-1300 *Founded/Ownrshp* 1981
Sales 234.8MM *EMP* 629
Accts Kpmg Llp Boston Massachuset
Tkr Sym MRCY *Exch* NGS
SIC 3672 7372 Printed circuit boards; Prepackaged software; Printed circuit boards; Prepackaged software
Pr: Mark Aslett
**Ch Bd:* Vincent Vitto
Pr: Didier M C Thibaud
CFO: Gerald M Haines II
VP: Charles A Speicher
Exec: Linda Silva
Dir Bus: Martin Vazquez
Opers Mgr: Doug Greenlie
Genl Couns: John Storm
Board of Directors: James K Bass, Michael A Daniels, George K Muellner, Mark S Newman, William K O'brien

D-U-N-S 00-595-7212 EXP
MERCURY WIRE PRODUCTS INC
1 Mercury Dr, Spencer, MA 01562-1999
Tel (508) 885-6363 *Founded/Ownrshp* 1966
Sales 58.7MM^E *EMP* 135
SIC 3357 Communication wire; Appliance fixture wire, nonferrous; Coaxial cable, nonferrous; Communication wire; Appliance fixture wire, nonferrous; Coaxial cable, nonferrous
Pr: Robert K Yard
**CFO:* Perry Harrison
**VP:* Christopher Yard
IT Man: Joe Ward

D-U-N-S 02-714-2442
MERCURYGATE INTERNATIONAL INC
200 Regency Forest Dr # 400, Cary, NC 27518-8695
Tel (919) 469-8057 *Founded/Ownrshp* 2000
Sales 30.9MM *EMP* 140
SIC 7371 Software programming applications; Software programming applications
CEO: Monica B Wooden
**Pr:* Steven A Blough
**CFO:* Lynn Casey
Ex VP: Dan Vertachnik
**VP:* Brian Armieri
VP: Kevin Holmes
VP: Kevin Loguidice
VP: Dan Sellers
VP: Doug Surrett
Dir Bus: John Martin
Dir Bus: Peter Yost

MERCY ALLIANCE
See MERCY HEALTH SYSTEM CORP

MERCY BEHAVIORAL HEALTH
See MERCY LIFE CENTER CORP

MERCY CARE COMMUNITY PHYSICIAN
See MERCY PHYSICIAN SERVICES INC

D-U-N-S 10-231-9621
MERCY CARE MANAGEMENT INC
MERCY CARE NORTH
(*Suby of* MERCYCARE SERVICE CORP) ★
701 10th St Se, Cedar Rapids, IA 52403-1251
Tel (319) 398-6011 *Founded/Ownrshp* 1983
Sales 40.7MM *EMP* 2,200
SIC 8011 8741 8322 Freestanding emergency medical center; Management services; Individual & family services; Freestanding emergency medical center; Management services; Individual & family services
Ch Bd: Lee Lui
**Treas:* Emmett Scherrman
VP: Phil Lasson

MERCY CARE NORTH
See MERCY CARE MANAGEMENT INC

MERCY CARE PLAN
See SOUTHWEST CATHOLIC HEALTH NETWORK CORP

D-U-N-S 07-306-7480
MERCY CHILDRENS HOSPITAL
2401 Gillham Rd, Kansas City, MO 64108-4619
Tel (816) 234-3000 *Founded/Ownrshp* 1897
Sales 9.0MM^E *EMP* 3,000
Accts Kpmg Llp Omaha Ne
SIC 8069 Children's hospital; Children's hospital
Pr: Randall L O'Donnell PHD
Chf Rad: James C Brown
**CFO:* Dwight Hyde
Ch: Ed Connolly
**Co-COO:* Karen Cox
**Ex VP:* Sandra Aj Lawrence
**Ex VP:* Charles C Roberts
**Ex VP:* Jo Stueve
VP: Kimberly Brown
VP: Warren Dudley
VP: Brad Leech
VP: Michelle Overstreet
VP: Davoren Tempel
Dir Soc: Anoma Mullegama

D-U-N-S 96-238-9461
MERCY CLINIC OKLAHOMA COMMUNITIES INC
4300 W Memorial Rd, Oklahoma City, OK 73120-8304
Tel (405) 936-5213 *Founded/Ownrshp* 2009
Sales 147.6MM *EMP* 1
Accts Pleus And Company Llc Cheste
SIC 8011 Offices & clinics of medical doctors; Offices & clinics of medical doctors
Ex Dir: Diana Smalley
**Ex Dir:* Christopher Hahne

D-U-N-S 18-610-0939
MERCY CLINICS INC
MERCY MEDICAL CENTER
(*Suby of* CHI-IOWA CORP) ★
207 Crocker St Ste 200, Des Moines, IA 50309-1318
Tel (515) 643-7150 *Founded/Ownrshp* 1995
Sales 20.8MM^E *EMP* 160
Accts Mcgladrey & Pullen Llp Daven
SIC 8011 Physicians' office, including specialists
CEO: Stephen Eckstat
**Pr:* Dave Vellinga
**COO:* Sharon Phillips
Genl Mgr: Cynthia Utley

D-U-N-S 04-482-7764
MERCY COLLEGE
555 Broadway Frnt, Dobbs Ferry, NY 10522-1189
Tel (914) 455-2650 *Founded/Ownrshp* 1963
Sales 153.8MM *EMP* 500
Accts Marks Paneth Llp New York N
SIC 8221 College, except junior; College, except junior
Pr: Kimberly Cline
CFO: Dana Marrone
VP: Jeanne Plecenik
VP: Concetta M Stewart
VP: Deirdre Whitman
Assoc Dir: Jarrett Foster
Assoc Dir: Jennifer Huron
Assoc Dir: Jo Skousen
Dir Sec: Daniel Braccia
Plng Mgr: Marguerite Armas-Busetti
CIO: Mike Salem

D-U-N-S 17-679-0467
MERCY COLLEGE OF HEALTH SCIENCES
(*Suby of* CHI-IOWA CORP) ★
928 6th Ave, Des Moines, IA 50309-1225
Tel (515) 643-3180 *Founded/Ownrshp* 1997
Sales 43.0MM^E *EMP* 2,222^E
Accts Deloitte Tax Llp Houston Tx
SIC 8221 Colleges universities & professional schools
Pr: Barb Decker
VP: Karen Anderson
VP: Brian Tingleff
Nrsg Dir: Mildred Agena
Nrsg Dir: Dale Brown

D-U-N-S 03-800-7899
MERCY COMMUNITY HEALTH INC
CATHOLIC HEALTH EAST
(*Suby of* CATHOLIC HEALTH EAST) ★
2021 Albany Ave, West Hartford, CT 06117-2789
Tel (860) 570-8400 *Founded/Ownrshp* 1996
Sales 3.8MM *EMP* 600
Accts Tax Llp Philadelphia Pa
SIC 8011 8051 Medical centers; Skilled nursing care facilities; Medical centers; Skilled nursing care facilities
Pr: Rich Kisner
CFO: Steve Bolio
CFO: George Thomas
**VP:* Fred Dalicandro
VP: Robert Lipira
Genl Mgr: Carl Saraceni II
QA Dir: Patricia Moran

MERCY CONTINUING CARE
See TRINITY SENIOR LIVING COMMUNITIES

D-U-N-S 13-417-0547 IMP/EXP
MERCY CORPS
45 Sw Ankeny St, Portland, OR 97204-3500
Tel (503) 796-6800 *Founded/Ownrshp* 1979
Sales 275.4MM *EMP* 450
SIC 8322 Refugee service; Refugee service
Pr: Neal L Keny-Guyer
CFO: Beth Dehamel
**Chf Mktg O:* Dara Royer
Ofcr: Matthew Allen
Ofcr: Prakash Basyal
Ofcr: Grace Becton
Ofcr: Christy Delafield
Ofcr: Karissa Dunbar
Ofcr: Allison Dworschak
Ofcr: Lily Frey
Ofcr: Sarah Halfman
Ofcr: Lynn Hector
Ofcr: Rebecca Inman
Ofcr: Megan Kelly
Ofcr: Alexandra Klass
Ofcr: Denise Ledgerwood
Ofcr: Ben Melix
Ofcr: Margaret Munroe
Ofcr: Nathan Oetting
Ofcr: Angela Owen
Ofcr: Manasi Patwardhan

D-U-N-S 80-466-9539
MERCY FITZGERALD HOSPITAL
MERCY HEALTH SYSTEM
(*Suby of* MERCY HEALTH FOUNDATION OF SOUTHEASTERN PENNSYLVANIA) ★
1500 Lansdowne Ave Ste 1, Darby, PA 19023-1200
Tel (610) 237-4000 *Founded/Ownrshp* 1915
Sales 161.7MM^E *EMP* 2,000
SIC 8062 General medical & surgical hospitals; General medical & surgical hospitals
CEO: Susan Croushore
**CFO:* Don Shenk
VP: Christina Fitz-Patrick
Dir Risk M: Susan Brown
Comm Dir: Michael Bannon
Dir Rad: Michael L Brooks
Chf Nrs Of: Linda Kaufman
Ex Dir: Cathy Franklin
Dir Pat Ac: Mike Glitz
Dir IT: Jim Holmes
Dir IT: Rob Russell

D-U-N-S 06-276-5425
MERCY FLOWERS & GIFTS (IA)
701 10th St Se, Cedar Rapids, IA 52403-1251
Tel (319) 398-6124 *Founded/Ownrshp* 1952
Sales 290.6MM *EMP* 7
SIC 5992 5947 Florists; Gift shop; Florists; Gift shop
**Prin:* Margaret Dunshee

D-U-N-S 83-877-2390
MERCY FRANCISCAN HOSPITAL MT AIRY
2446 Kipling Ave, Cincinnati, OH 45239-6650
Tel (513) 853-5101 *Founded/Ownrshp* 2004
Sales 121.0MM^E *EMP* 2,620
SIC 8741 8062 Hospital management; Nursing & personal care facility management; General medical & surgical hospitals; Hospital management; Nursing & personal care facility management; General medical & surgical hospitals
Pr: Rodney Reider
**VP:* Ruby Hemphil Crowford
**VP:* Judy Daleiden
Doctor: Mark Zoellner
Pharmcst: Mark Johnson

D-U-N-S 06-090-5569
MERCY FRANCISCAN HOSPITAL WESTERN HILLS
3131 Queen City Ave, Cincinnati, OH 45238-2316
Tel (513) 389-5000 *Founded/Ownrshp* 1981
Sales 81.0MM *EMP* 886
SIC 8062 General medical & surgical hospitals; General medical & surgical hospitals
Pr: Michael Stephen
VP: Joyce Keegan
Dir Lab: Susan Bonelli
Dir Rad: Stephanie Spencer
Ex Dir: Jeannie Brewer
CTO: Garry Faja
Advt Dir: Aaron A Biley

D-U-N-S 96-784-0393
MERCY FRANCISCAN SENIOR HEALTH AND HOUSING SERVICES INC
7010 Rowan Hill Dr, Cincinnati, OH 45227-3380
Tel (513) 981-5056 *Founded/Ownrshp* 2011
Sales 31.0MM *EMP* 1
SIC 8099 Services; Health & allied services
Prin: Deborah L Welker

D-U-N-S 07-928-4725
MERCY GENERAL HEALTH PARTNERS
MERCY HEALTH
(*Suby of* CATHOLIC HEALTH EAST) ★
1500 E Sherman Blvd, Muskegon, MI 49444-1849
Tel (231) 728-4032 *Founded/Ownrshp* 1998
Sales 187.5MM^E *EMP* 2,000^E
SIC 8062 General medical & surgical hospitals; General medical & surgical hospitals
Pr: Roger Spoelman
**CFO:* Mary Boyd
Surgeon: Robert Schneeberger

D-U-N-S 15-276-1391
MERCY GWYNEDD UNIVERSITY
1325 Sumneytown Pike, Gwynedd Valley, PA 19437
Tel (215) 542-5782 *Founded/Ownrshp* 1948
Sales 65.3MM *EMP* 300
SIC 8221 College, except junior; College, except junior
Pr: Dr Kathleen Owens
VP: Cheryl Horsey
VP: Dennis Murphy
**VP:* Kevin O'Flaherty
Assoc Dir: Kaylin Bassett
Assoc Dir: Anthonia Pressley
Assoc Dir: Kate Shellaway
Ex Dir: Lee A Douglass

D-U-N-S 13-380-6620
MERCY HAMILTON HOSPITAL
3000 Mack Rd, Fairfield, OH 45014-5335
Tel (513) 603-8600 *Founded/Ownrshp* 1800
Sales 244.6MM *EMP* 50
SIC 8062 General medical & surgical hospitals; General medical & surgical hospitals
Pr: Dave Ferrell
VP: Matt Eversole
VP: Mike Hibbard
Dir Inf Cn: Pamela Justice
Pathlgst: Joseph H Brandabur

MERCY HARVARD HOSPITAL
See HARVARD MEMORIAL HOSPITAL INC

MERCY HEALTH
See LAKESHORE COMMUNITY HOSPITAL INC

MERCY HEALTH
See MERCY GENERAL HEALTH PARTNERS

D-U-N-S 04-766-8467
MERCY HEALTH
615 Elsinore Pl Ste 800, Cincinnati, OH 45202-1459
Tel (513) 639-2800 *Founded/Ownrshp* 1986
Sales 4.5MMM *EMP* 35,000
Accts Ernst & Young Llp Cincinnati
SIC 8062 General medical & surgical hospitals; General medical & surgical hospitals
Pr: Michael D Connelly
Dir Recs: Lisa Carroll
Pr: Bob Shroder
CFO: Deborah Bloomfield
CFO: Gary Raju
Ofcr: Brent R Asplin
Ex VP: David A Catalano
Ex VP: Jane D Crowley
Ex VP: Brian Smith
Ex VP: John M Starcher Jr
Sr VP: Yousuf Ahmad
Sr VP: Donald E Casey
Sr VP: Rebecca Sykes
VP: Jeff Copeland
VP: Stephen Grossbart
VP: Michael Hibbard
VP: Cheryl Norman
VP: Kristen H Wevers

D-U-N-S 07-711-8982
MERCY HEALTH
SISTERS OF MERCY HEALTH SYSTEM
14528 South Outer 40 Rd # 100, Chesterfield, MO 63017-5785
Tel (405) 755-1515 *Founded/Ownrshp* 1986
Sales 1.4MMM^E *EMP* 2,500
Accts Ernst & Young Us Llp Clayton
SIC 8741 Hospital management; Hospital management
CEO: Lynn Britton
**Pr:* Ronald Ashworth
**Pr:* Jim R Gebhart
COO: Andy Runge
**CFO:* James Jaacs
CFO: Cheryl Matejka
CFO: Shannon Sock
**Ch:* Sister Rock Rocklage
Bd of Dir: Paul Bergant
Trst: Anita Desalvo
Ex VP: Jon Vitiello
Sr VP: Judy Akins
VP: James Britton
VP: Donna Chandler
VP: Mike M Creary
VP: Gil Hoffman
VP: Jennifer Laperre
VP: Mike Mc Creary
VP: Barb Meyer
VP: Robert E Schimmel
VP: Ron Trulove

D-U-N-S 01-077-0352
MERCY HEALTH & REHABILITATION CENTER NURSING HOME CO INC
3 Saint Anthony St, Auburn, NY 13021-4500
Tel (315) 253-0351 *Founded/Ownrshp* 1970
Sales 22.6MM *EMP* 210
SIC 8051 Skilled nursing care facilities; Skilled nursing care facilities
Nrsg Dir: Karen Dec

D-U-N-S 07-757-4580
MERCY HEALTH - ST CHARLES HOSPITAL LLC
2600 Navarre Ave, Oregon, OH 43616-3207
Tel (419) 696-7200 *Founded/Ownrshp* 1953
Sales 143.0MM^E *EMP* 1,200^E
SIC 8062 General medical & surgical hospitals; General medical & surgical hospitals
CEO: Jeffrey Dempseyn
**Pr:* Jacalyn Liebowitz
**Prin:* F J Gallagher
**Prin:* Joseph W Rossler
**Prin:* Rolf H Scheidel
Ex Dir: Bobbie Kehlmeier

D-U-N-S 07-677-7275
MERCY HEALTH ANDERSON HOSPITAL
MERCY HOSPITAL ANDERSON
7500 State Rd, Cincinnati, OH 45255-2439
Tel (513) 624-4500 *Founded/Ownrshp* 1942
Sales 204.6MM *EMP* 823
SIC 8062 General medical & surgical hospitals; General medical & surgical hospitals
Pr: Patrica Shroer
VP: Julie Holt
Dir Risk M: Kristen Boggs
IT Man: Carol Dalrymple
Snr Mgr: Michael Fesenmeier

D-U-N-S 06-543-0712 IMP
MERCY HEALTH CENTER INC (OK)
(*Suby of* MERCY HEALTH) ★
14528 South Outer 40 Rd # 1, Chesterfield, MO 63017-5785
Tel (405) 755-1515 *Founded/Ownrshp* 1947, 1974
Sales 217.9MM^E *EMP* 2,300
Accts Pleus And Company Llc Chester
SIC 8062 General medical & surgical hospitals; General medical & surgical hospitals
Pr: Jim R Gebhart
Doctor: Ann Parrington MD

D-U-N-S 07-123-4637
MERCY HEALTH FOUNDATION ARDMORE (OK)
1011 14th Ave Nw, Ardmore, OK 73401-1828
Tel (580) 223-5400 *Founded/Ownrshp* 1955, 1990
Sales 1.1MM *EMP* 800
Accts Pleus And Company Llc Chester
SIC 8062 General medical & surgical hospitals; General medical & surgical hospitals
Ex Dir: Andre Moore
**Pr:* Bobby G Thompson
**Pr:* Daryle Voss
**VP:* Patricia R Arnold
**VP:* Marilyn Geiger Regional Vp
Mktg Mgr: Lou Bickerstass

D-U-N-S 07-146-3590
MERCY HEALTH FOUNDATION OF SOUTHEASTERN PENNSYLVANIA
MERCY HEALTH SYSTEM
(*Suby of* CATHOLIC HEALTH EAST) ★
1 W Elm St Ste 100, Conshohocken, PA 19428-4108
Tel (610) 567-6000 *Founded/Ownrshp* 2014
Sales 466.2MM^E *EMP* 8,000
SIC 8062 General medical & surgical hospitals; General medical & surgical hospitals
CEO: David Clark
Dir Vol: Terri Yarabinee
Pr: Janet Borger
Sr VP: Elizabeth Wasserman
VP: Nancy Cherone
VP: Anthony Fanelli
VP: Brian Hannah
VP: Marciag James
VP: Deborah Leonard
VP: Ruth Martynowicz
VP: Michael McCreary
**VP:* Julie Topkis Scanlon
VP: Katrina Shuptar

D-U-N-S 09-835-6335
MERCY HEALTH NETWORK INC
CHI
(*Suby of* CATHOLIC HEALTH INITIATIVES) ★
1755 59th Pl, West Des Moines, IA 50266-7737
Tel (515) 247-3121 *Founded/Ownrshp* 1998
Sales 14.4MM *EMP* 7,500
SIC 8741 Hospital management; Hospital management
Pr: David Vellinga
COO: Sharon Phillips
Sr VP: Joe Levalley
VP: Cristina Thomas
VP: Julie Younger
Exec: Tracy Muhlenburg
Dir OR: Tim Huffman
Dir Lab: Nancy Mathahs
Dir Lab: Nancy Mathias
Dir: Sandy Swanson
Dir Rad: William Young
Dir Rx: John Walker

MERCY HEALTH PARTNERS
See HACKLEY HOSPITAL

D-U-N-S 01-579-6923
■ **MERCY HEALTH PARTNERS** (PA)
(*Suby of* COMMUNITY HEALTH SYSTEMS INC) ★
746 Jefferson Ave, Scranton, PA 18510-1624
Tel (570) 348-7100 *Founded/Ownrshp* 1997, 2011
Sales 75.8MM^E *EMP* 2,295
SIC 8062 General medical & surgical hospitals; General medical & surgical hospitals
CEO: Kevin Cook
VP: Linda Horton
IT Man: Frank Klassner
Genl Couns: Christine M Gubbiotti

D-U-N-S 05-830-0604
MERCY HEALTH PARTNERS
(*Suby of* MERCY HEALTH) ★
4600 Mcauley Pl Ste A, Blue Ash, OH 45242-4765
Tel (513) 981-6000 *Founded/Ownrshp* 1982
Sales 337.0MM^E *EMP* 2,886
Accts Bkd Llp Cincinnati Oh
SIC 8062 General medical & surgical hospitals; General medical & surgical hospitals
CEO: Tom Urban
Chf Rad: Scott T Welton
Ofcr: Richard Schuster
Sr VP: Loretta L Lee
**Sr VP:* Kenneth C Page
Sr VP: Kenneth Page
VP: John Finley
VP: Hui Saldana
Off Mgr: Valerie Charles

D-U-N-S 07-409-7791
MERCY HEALTH PARTNERS - LOURDES INC
LOURDES HOSPITAL
(*Suby of* MERCY HEALTH) ★
1530 Lone Oak Rd Int24, Paducah, KY 42003-7901
Tel (270) 444-2444 *Founded/Ownrshp* 1962
Sales 215.1MM^E *EMP* 1,600
Accts Bkd Llp Cincinnati Oh
SIC 8062 General medical & surgical hospitals; General medical & surgical hospitals
CEO: Steven Grinnell
CFO: Edward W Miller
**CFO:* Mark Thomson
VP Bus Dev: Susan Schaefer
Nurse Mgr: Kurt Ruga
CIO: Carolyn Hansman
Software D: Steve Grinell
Pathlgst: Robert Haugh

D-U-N-S 15-397-9588
MERCY HEALTH PLAN INC
KEYSTONE MERCY HEALTH PLAN
200 Stevens Dr Ste 350, Philadelphia, PA 19113-1520
Tel (215) 937-8000 *Founded/Ownrshp* 1983
Sales NA *EMP* 470
SIC 6324 6321 Hospital & medical service plans; Accident & health insurance; Hospital & medical service plans; Accident & health insurance
Pr: Daniel J Hilferty
CFO: Alan Krigstein
Assoc VP: Heidi Chan
Ex VP: Michael A Rashid
Sr VP: Christopher Drumm
Sr VP: Robert Gilman
VP: Joanne McFall
VP: Karen Michael
VP: Tonya Moody
Comm Dir: Tracy Pou
Snr Ntwrk: Jeffrey Menta

D-U-N-S 88-372-1177
■ **MERCY HEALTH PLANS INC**
PREMIER HEALTH PLANS
(*Suby of* MHP INC) ★
14528 South Outer 40 Rd # 300, Chesterfield, MO 63017-5785
Tel (314) 214-2384 *Founded/Ownrshp* 2010
Sales NA *EMP* 390
SIC 6324 Hospital & medical service plans; Hospital & medical service plans
CEO: Michael Murphy
**CFO:* George Schneider
Ex Dir: Barb Grayson
Ex Dir: Teresa Halloran
Dir IT: James Freeman
Dir IT: Shannon Williams
Telecom Mg: Melvin Turner

D-U-N-S 14-598-1945
MERCY HEALTH SERVICES-IOWA CORP
CATHOLIC HEALTH EAST
(*Suby of* CATHOLIC HEALTH EAST) ★
20555 Victor Pkwy, Livonia, MI 48152-7031
Tel (734) 343-1000 *Founded/Ownrshp* 1993
Sales 665.5MM *EMP* 2,471
SIC 8011 Medical centers
CEO: Jack Weiner
Dir Vol: Mary Rosser
**Pr:* Joseph Swevish
**Pr:* Daniel Varnum
**CFO:* James Peppiatt-Combes
Ofcr: Mark Trimmer
**Prin:* Scott Leighty
**Genl Couns:* Daniel G Hale

D-U-N-S 84-187-5040
MERCY HEALTH SPRINGFIELD COMMUNITIES
SAINT JOHN'S BEHAVIORAL HEALTH
1235 E Cherokee St, Springfield, MO 65804-2203
Tel (417) 885-2000 *Founded/Ownrshp* 1999
Sales 475.0MM *EMP* 6,300
Accts Ernst & Young Us Llp Saint Lo
SIC 8062 General medical & surgical hospitals; General medical & surgical hospitals
CEO: Jon D Swope
**Pr:* Fred McQuery
VP: Kathryn Kiefer
Dir Rx: Keith David
Dir Rx: C W Poell
Dir Rx: Mike Sieg

MERCY HEALTH SYSTEM
See ST AGNES CONTINUING CARE CENTER

MERCY HEALTH SYSTEM
See NAZARETH HOSPITAL

MERCY HEALTH SYSTEM
See MERCY HEALTH FOUNDATION OF SOUTHEASTERN PENNSYLVANIA

MERCY HEALTH SYSTEM
See MERCY FITZGERALD HOSPITAL

D-U-N-S 95-914-3785
MERCY HEALTH SYSTEM - NORTHERN REGION
(*Suby of* MERCY HEALTH) ★
2200 Jefferson Ave, Toledo, OH 43604-7101
Tel (419) 251-1359 *Founded/Ownrshp* 1981
Sales 358.3MM^E *EMP* 7,200
Accts Bkd Llp Cincinnati Oh
SIC 8062 General medical & surgical hospitals; General medical & surgical hospitals
Pr: Steven Mickus
Pr: Christine Browning
Pr: Dee Geer
Pr: Kathleen A Osborne
**CFO:* Samantha Platzke
CFO: Liz Snodgrass
VP: Joseph Sober
Doctor: Dick Evens

D-U-N-S 02-046-0788
MERCY HEALTH SYSTEM CORP
MERCY ALLIANCE
1000 Mineral Point Ave, Janesville, WI 53548-2940
Tel (608) 756-6890 *Founded/Ownrshp* 1989
Sales 523.4MM *EMP* 2,200
Accts Wipfli Llp Milwaukee Wiscon
SIC 8062 General medical & surgical hospitals; General medical & surgical hospitals
CEO: Javon R Bea
Chf Rad: Allan Muraki
**Ch Bd:* Rowland J Mc Clellan
Pr: Mike Bier
**CFO:* Joseph Nemeth
Dir Lab: Ruth Bythe
Dir Lab: Sheila Hillison
Dir Lab: Don Ouimet
Dir Rad: Carol Barletta
Dir Rx: Don R Janczak
Off Mgr: Lizette Amaro

D-U-N-S 09-292-2137
MERCY HEALTH SYSTEM OF NORTHWEST ARKANSAS INC
SAINT MARY'S HOSPITAL
(*Suby of* MERCY HOSPITAL ST LOUIS) ★
2710 S Rife Medical Ln, Rogers, AR 72758-1452
Tel (479) 338-8000 *Founded/Ownrshp* 1977
Sales 66.2MM *EMP* 1,650^E
Accts Ernst & Young Us Llp Clayton
SIC 8062 General medical & surgical hospitals; General medical & surgical hospitals
Pr: Eric Pianalto
VP: Cindy Carmichael
**Prin:* Steven Gus
Doctor: Robert Donnell
Doctor: Vernon O'Neil Tucker
Board of Directors: Dr Minh-Tah Dang, Dr Orlando Augliar-Guzman, Dr Richard Miles

D-U-N-S 78-530-0075
MERCY HEALTH SYSTEM OF SOUTHEASTERN PENNSYLVANIA
(*Suby of* CATHOLIC HEALTH INITIATIVES) ★
1 W Elm St Ste 100, Conshohocken, PA 19428-4108
Tel (610) 567-6000 *Founded/Ownrshp* 1982
Sales 47.8MM *EMP* 1^E
Accts Deloitte Tax Llp Philadelphia
SIC 8062 General medical & surgical hospitals; General medical & surgical hospitals
Ch Bd: Christine McCann
**CEO:* H Ray Welch
**CFO:* Joseph Bradley
Dir Risk M: Joyce H Taft

D-U-N-S 93-887-6661
MERCY HEALTH YOUNGSTOWN LLC
ST ELIZABETH HEALTH CENTER
(*Suby of* MERCY HEALTH) ★
1044 Belmont Ave, Youngstown, OH 44504-1006
Tel (330) 746-7211 *Founded/Ownrshp* 1996
Sales 369.8MM^E *EMP* 4,000
SIC 8062 8071 General medical & surgical hospitals; Hospital, affiliated with AMA residency; Ultrasound laboratory
Pr: Robert Shroder
**Pr:* Genie Aubel
COO: James Davis
Ex VP: Don Koenig
Sr VP: John Finicio
Sr VP: Thomas Kohl
Dir OR: Elaine Jones
Dir Risk M: Gordon Sanders
Dir Rx: Stephanie Gensler
Dir Rx: Linda Lachman
**Prin:* Sarah Quinn

D-U-N-S 17-450-2682
MERCY HEALTHCARE SACRAMENTO
MERCY SAN JUAN HOSPITAL
(*Suby of* C H W) ★
3400 Data Dr, Rancho Cordova, CA 95670-7956
Tel (916) 851-2000 *Founded/Ownrshp* 1981
Sales 402.0MM^E *EMP* 6,131
SIC 8062 General medical & surgical hospitals; General medical & surgical hospitals
Pr: Michael Erne
**COO:* William Hunt
**CFO:* Richard Rothberger
**Chf Mktg O:* Dan Ferguson
**Sr VP:* John Chambers
**Sr VP:* Scott Ideson

MERCY HOME CARE
See MERCY MEDICAL CENTER-CLINTON INC

D-U-N-S 16-113-4028
MERCY HOME FOR CHILDREN INC
273 Willoughby Ave, Brooklyn, NY 11205-1418
Tel (718) 832-1075 *Founded/Ownrshp* 1865
Sales 16.8MM *EMP* 325
Accts Loeb & Troper Llp New York N
SIC 8059 Home for the mentally retarded, exc. skilled or intermediate; Home for the mentally retarded, exc. skilled or intermediate
CEO: Catherine Crumlish
CFO: Karen Shaffer
Ofcr: Doreth Ed
Ofcr: Dorothy Fuller
IT Man: Maria Polito
Pgrm Dir: Michael Degrottole

D-U-N-S 07-610-1906
MERCY HOME SERVICES A CALIFORNIA LIMITED PARTNERSHIP
MERCY MEDICAL CENTER - REDDING
(*Suby of* C H W) ★
2175 Rosaline Ave Ste A, Redding, CA 96001-2549
Tel (530) 225-6000 *Founded/Ownrshp* 1987
Sales 172.7MM^E *EMP* 1,200
SIC 8062 General medical & surgical hospitals; General medical & surgical hospitals
CEO: George A Govier
CFO: Jill Belk
Dir Lab: Robert Folden
Comm Dir: Angela Gaffney
Dir Rad: Steve Buhler
Dir Rx: William Przybyla
IT Man: Wendy Scott
Sfty Mgr: George Knight
Ansthlgy: Shawn Echols
Ansthlgy: Gordon Heminway
Ansthlgy: Carl Koutnik

D-U-N-S 07-173-2499
MERCY HOSPITAL
PORTLAND THORACIC SURGERY
(*Suby of* EASTERN MAINE HEALTHCARE SYSTEMS) ★
144 State St, Portland, ME 04101-3795
Tel (207) 879-3000 *Founded/Ownrshp* 2013
Sales 167.5MM *EMP* 1,200
SIC 8062 Hospital, affiliated with AMA residency; Hospital, affiliated with AMA residency
Pr: Eileen F Skinner
COO: Robert Nutter
CFO: Michael Hachey
**CFO:* Anthony Marple
Ofcr: Alley Pierre
VP: Judi Hawkes
VP: Bette L Neville
VP: Melissa Skahan
Exec: William Clifford
Dir Lab: Cielette Karn
VP Admn: Scott Rusk

D-U-N-S 02-004-7254
MERCY HOSPITAL AND MEDICAL CENTER
2525 S Michigan Ave, Chicago, IL 60616-2332
Tel (312) 567-2201 *Founded/Ownrshp* 1852
Sales 273.3MM *EMP* 1,550
SIC 8062 General medical & surgical hospitals; General medical & surgical hospitals
Pr: John McCarthy
Chf Rad: Amir Sepahdari
Pr: Barbara Townsend
COO: Rick Cerceo
CFO: Bob Diantonio
CFO: Tom Garvey
**CFO:* Eric Krueger
CFO: Gary Zmrhal
**Ex VP:* Richard Cerceo
VP: Ronald Arnone
VP: Mary Caponigro
VP: Thomas Dohm
**VP:* Susan Gallagher
VP: Martin Hebda
VP: Nancy Hill-Davis
VP: Constance Murphy
VP: Maurice Raab
VP: Nicolas P Vogel MD
Exec: Margo Harward
Comm Man: Eileen Knightly

MERCY HOSPITAL ANDERSON
See MERCY HEALTH ANDERSON HOSPITAL

D-U-N-S 96-961-8235
MERCY HOSPITAL ARDMORE INC
1011 14th Ave Nw, Ardmore, OK 73401-1828
Tel (580) 223-5400 *Founded/Ownrshp* 2011
Sales 139.0MM *EMP* 47
Accts Pleus And Company Llc Chester
SIC 8062 General medical & surgical hospitals
Prin: Paul A Foster

D-U-N-S 09-169-0727
MERCY HOSPITAL BERRYVILLE
214 Carter St, Berryville, AR 72616-4303
Tel (870) 423-3355 *Founded/Ownrshp* 1969
Sales 20.6MM *EMP* 220
SIC 8062 8082 8011 General medical & surgical hospitals; Home health care services; Offices & clinics of medical doctors; Medical centers; General medical & surgical hospitals; Home health care services; Offices & clinics of medical doctors; Medical centers
Prin: Gary Pulsifer
Ch Bd: William Dettwiller
CFO: John Hubble
V Ch Bd: Jack Jackson
Sr VP: Kristi Noble
Dir Lab: Beverly Taylor
Off Mgr: Mitzi Worley
Sfty Dirs: Curtis Myers
Sfty Mgr: Curtis Shaw

D-U-N-S 06-962-0524
MERCY HOSPITAL CEDAR RAPIDS IOWA
MERCY MEDICAL CENTER
701 10th St Se, Cedar Rapids, IA 52403-1251
Tel (319) 398-6011 *Founded/Ownrshp* 1900
Sales 269.8MM *EMP* 2,375
Accts Mcgladrey Llp Davenport Iow
SIC 8062 General medical & surgical hospitals; General medical & surgical hospitals
Pr: Timothy L Charles
COO: Bob Hurst
CFO: Phil Peterson
VP: Ingrid Bishop
VP: Diane Stefani
Exec: Mary Hatfield
Exec: Lois Robson
Chf Nrs Of: James V Guliano
Chf Nrs Of: Beth Houlahan
Chf Nrs Of: Nancy Hoyt
Dir Sec: Rod McCool

D-U-N-S 07-868-5005
MERCY HOSPITAL HEALTH CARE CENTER
4572 County Road 61, Moose Lake, MN 55767-9401
Tel (218) 485-4481 *Founded/Ownrshp* 1983
Sales 30.1MM^E *EMP* 350^E
SIC 8051 8062 Skilled nursing care facilities; General medical & surgical hospitals; Skilled nursing care facilities; General medical & surgical hospitals
CEO: Mike Delfs
**CFO:* Gregg Chartrand
CFO: Gregg Shartrand
**Ch:* Bev Peterson
**Treas:* Ms Kristin Labounty
**Treas:* John Wesely
Bd of Dir: Josey Nielsen
Dir OR: Stephanie Kosloski
Dir Inf Cn: Debbie Wolf
Dir Rx: Janet Larson
**Prin:* Jason Douglas

D-U-N-S 06-699-1902
MERCY HOSPITAL INC
(*Suby of* SISTERS PROVIDENCE HEALTH SYS) ★
271 Carew St, Springfield, MA 01104-2398
Tel (413) 748-9000 *Founded/Ownrshp* 1898
Sales 221.8MM^E *EMP* 1,635
SIC 8062 8071 8011 7219 8748 General medical & surgical hospitals; Medical laboratories; Offices & clinics of medical doctors; Laundry, except power & coin-operated; Employee programs administration; General medical & surgical hospitals; Medical laboratories; Offices & clinics of medical doctors; Laundry, except power & coin-operated; Employee programs administration
Pr: Vincent J McCorkle
**Pr:* Daniel P Moen
**Treas:* Arun R Adya
**Treas:* Thomas Robert
VP: Bette Neville
VP: Leonard Pansa
Dir Lab: Ken Geromini
Dir Rad: Parshant Puri
Dir Sec: Ann Carroll
IT Man: Claudine Schiro
Opers Mgr: Paul Malouin

D-U-N-S 07-387-2178
■ **MERCY HOSPITAL INC**
(*Suby of* PLANTATION GENERAL HOSPITAL LP) ★
3663 S Miami Ave, Miami, FL 33133-4237
Tel (305) 854-4400 *Founded/Ownrshp* 2012
Sales 167.4MM^E *EMP* 2,400
SIC 8062 General medical & surgical hospitals; General medical & surgical hospitals
CEO: Barbara J Simmons R N
Chf Rad: Eduardo Franca
Chf Rad: Mark Kravetz
**Pr:* Howard Watts
CFO: Michael Heinrich
**CFO:* Jerry Mashburn
**Ch:* Joel M Jancko
**Treas:* Linda V Wilford
Ofcr: Joseph Pino
VP: Francis Richardson
Exec: Claudia Distrito
Exec: Maria Macias
Dir OR: Roger Grimshaw
Dir Lab: Marie Danois
Dir Lab: Alfonso Ribero
Dir Lab: George Turell
Dir Rad: Ron Barak
Dir Rx: Isabel Vazquez

D-U-N-S 07-350-0266
MERCY HOSPITAL IOWA CITY IOWA INC
500 E Market St, Iowa City, IA 52245-2689
Tel (319) 339-0300 *Founded/Ownrshp* 1873
Sales 175.3MM *EMP* 1,100
SIC 8062 8011 6512 8399

D-U-N-S 07-588-9337
MERCY HOSPITAL JEFFERSON (MO)
JEFFERSON REGIONAL MEDICAL CTR
(*Suby of* MERCY HEALTH) ★
1400 Hwy 61 S, Crystal City, MO 63019
Tel (636) 933-1000 *Founded/Ownrshp* 1957, 2013
Sales 112.3MM *EMP* 1,200^E
Accts Pleus And Company Llc Chest
SIC 8062 General medical & surgical hospitals; General medical & surgical hospitals
CEO: Llyod Ford
**Pr:* Bill McKenna
**CFO:* Jim Meuhlhauser
CFO: James Muehlhaus
Treas: Ron Ravenscraft
VP: Beverly Johnson
Dir Teleco: Ron James
**Prin:* Amy McCally
Dir Sec: Andy Presti
Dir Pat Ac: Sherry Ridings
Nurse Mgr: Theresa Thomas

D-U-N-S 07-626-2500 IMP/EXP
MERCY HOSPITAL JOPLIN
SISTERS OF MERCY HEALTH SYSTEM
(*Suby of* MERCY HEALTH) ★
2817 Saint Johns Blvd, Joplin, MO 64804-1563
Tel (417) 781-2727 *Founded/Ownrshp* 2009
Sales 165.2MM *EMP* 1,500
Accts Ernst & Young Us Llp Saint Lo
SIC 8062 General medical & surgical hospitals; General medical & surgical hospitals
CEO: Gary Pulsipher
Chf Path: Susan Pintado
**CFO:* Shelly Hunter
Ofcr: Florence Lamberg
Ofcr: Michele Stewart
Ofcr: Marilyn Wylie
VP: Dave Goode
Dir Rad: Curtis S Hammerman
**Ex Dir:* Robert Honeywell
IT Man: Debbie Francisco
Anasthlgy: Bradford Ramsey

D-U-N-S 04-012-7953
MERCY HOSPITAL LEBANON
100 Hospital Dr, Lebanon, MO 65536-9210
Tel (417) 533-6100 *Founded/Ownrshp* 1934
Sales 102.6MM *EMP* 400
Accts Ernst & Young Us Llp Clayton
SIC 8062 General medical & surgical hospitals; General medical & surgical hospitals
VP: Doug Hoban

D-U-N-S 07-198-4447
MERCY HOSPITAL LINCOLN
(*Suby of* MERCY HEALTH) ★
1000 E Cherry St, Troy, MO 63379-1513
Tel (636) 528-8551 *Founded/Ownrshp* 2015
Sales 34.4MM^E *EMP* 330
SIC 8062 General medical & surgical hospitals; General medical & surgical hospitals
Pr: Lynn Britton
**COO:* Michael McCurry
**CFO:* Shannon Sock
Pathlgst: Anantha Manpalli
Pathlgst: Scott Martin
Pathlgst: Prabha Partap
Pathlgst: Matthew Poeschl
Doctor: Gregory Gabliani

D-U-N-S 07-877-6949
MERCY HOSPITAL LOGAN COUNTY
200 S Academy Rd, Guthrie, OK 73044-8727
Tel (405) 282-6700 *Founded/Ownrshp* 2013
Sales 21.4MM *EMP* 37^E
Accts Pleus And Company Llc Chester
SIC 8062 General medical & surgical hospitals; General medical & surgical hospitals
COO: Dennis Hunger
CFO: Jane Bissel
Ofcr: Maryjo Messelt
Nurse Mgr: Susan Booth
Doctor: Casey Peters
HC Dir: Glenda Olson
Snr Mgr: Stephen Travis

D-U-N-S 03-022-0727
MERCY HOSPITAL OF BUFFALO
(*Suby of* CATHOLIC HEALTH SYSTEM INC) ★
565 Abbott Rd, Buffalo, NY 14220-2095
Tel (716) 826-7000 *Founded/Ownrshp* 1928
Sales 27.7MM^E *EMP* 2,000
SIC 8062 General medical & surgical hospitals; General medical & surgical hospitals
CEO: Charles J Urlaub
Pr: Karen Burger
**Pr:* Nancy Sheehan
COO: Susan Kingston-Shack
**COO:* Mark A Sullivan
**Treas:* William K Buscaglia Jr
Ofcr: Michael Ebert
**Sr VP:* Richard J Ruh
**Sr VP:* John Stavros
Dir Rad: Gerald Joyce
**Prin:* James R Boldt

D-U-N-S 18-173-5353
MERCY HOSPITAL OF DEFIANCE
1400 E 2nd St, Defiance, OH 43512-2440
Tel (419) 782-8444 *Founded/Ownrshp* 2005
Sales 23.7MM *EMP* 156
SIC 8062 General medical & surgical hospitals; General medical & surgical hospitals
CEO: Chad L Peter
Pharmcst: Marcy Gregory

D-U-N-S 80-836-8893
MERCY HOSPITAL OF DEVILS LAKE
DEVILS LAKE HOSPITAL
1031 7th St Ne, Devils Lake, ND 58301-2798
Tel (701) 662-2131 *Founded/Ownrshp* 1894
Sales 25.3MM *EMP* 230
Accts Catholic Health Initiatives E
SIC 8062 General medical & surgical hospitals; General medical & surgical hospitals
Chf Rad: Richard Johnson
QA Dir: Tonja Seggerman

D-U-N-S 06-875-9463
MERCY HOSPITAL OF PITTSBURGH
(*Suby of* UNIVERSITY OF PITTSBURGH MEDICAL CENTER) ★
1400 Locust St, Pittsburgh, PA 15219-5166
Tel (412) 232-8111 *Founded/Ownrshp* 2007
Sales 108.3MM^E *EMP* 2,010
SIC 8062 Hospital, medical school affiliated with nursing & residency; Hospital, medical school affiliated with nursing & residency
Pr: Will Cook
CFO: Eileen Simmons
Treas: Mark Scott
Trst: Canice Dolan
Ofcr: Kathleen Broskin
VP: Joanne M Andiorio
VP: Carolyn Schallenberger
Dir Lab: Jim Kuzyck
Opthamlgy: Darren Hoover
Doctor: Hossein Noorbakhsh
Genl Couns: Sandra Renwand

D-U-N-S 08-015-6599
MERCY HOSPITAL OF TIFFIN OHIO
45 St Lawrence Dr, Tiffin, OH 44883-8310
Tel (419) 455-7000 *Founded/Ownrshp* 1970
Sales 60.0MM *EMP* 430^E
SIC 8062 General medical & surgical hospitals; General medical & surgical hospitals
Pr: Lynn Detterman
Doctor: Renu Soni

MERCY HOSPITAL OF WILLARD
See SISTERS OF MERCY OF WILLARD OHIO

D-U-N-S 07-566-8418
MERCY HOSPITAL ROGERS
SAINT MARY'S HOSPITAL
2710 S Rife Medical Ln, Rogers, AR 72758-1452
Tel (479) 338-8000 *Founded/Ownrshp* 1995
Sales 193.6MM *EMP* 760
Accts Ernst & Young Us Llp Clayton
SIC 8062 General medical & surgical hospitals; General medical & surgical hospitals
Pr: Eric Pianalto
Doctor: Ankur Gupta
Doctor: Douglas Marciniak
Doctor: Larry Weathers

D-U-N-S 07-918-6011
MERCY HOSPITAL SCRANTON PENNSYLVANIA
REGIONAL HOSPITAL OF SCRANTON
(*Suby of* MERCY HEALTH) ★
746 Jefferson Ave, Scranton, PA 18510-1697
Tel (570) 348-7100 *Founded/Ownrshp* 1917
Sales 110.8MM^E *EMP* 1,485
SIC 8062 8051 Hospital, professional nursing school; Skilled nursing care facilities; Hospital, professional nursing school; Skilled nursing care facilities
CEO: James May
Chf Rad: Jamie Stallman
**Pr:* Theodore J Tomaszewski
**Pr:* M Brooks Turkel
**Sec:* Patrick D Conaboy
**VP:* W David Fitzpatrick
Dir Rx: Tom Mecca
Sfty Dirs: Steve Jarbola
Surgeon: Charles Bannon
Doctor: Dwael Hassanein
Doctor: Olindo Preli MD

D-U-N-S 07-625-6809
MERCY HOSPITAL SPRINGFIELD
1235 E Cherokee St, Springfield, MO 65804-2203
Tel (417) 820-8620 *Founded/Ownrshp* 1999
Sales 964.3MM *EMP* 4,400
Accts Ernst & Young Us Llp Saint Lo
SIC 8062 8011 General medical & surgical hospitals; Offices & clinics of medical doctors; General medical & surgical hospitals; Offices & clinics of medical doctors
CEO: Lynn Britton
Pr: John Swope
COO: Kim Day
COO: Michael McCurry
CFO: Randy Combs
Ex VP: Shannon Sock
Off Mgr: Ten McMurry
CTO: Beverly Brown
Psych: Michael Whetstone
Anasthlgy: Brandon Sloop
Doctor: Creig Lobdell

MERCY HOSPITAL ST. LOUIS
See MERCY HOSPITALS EAST COMMUNITIES

D-U-N-S 07-197-0222
MERCY HOSPITAL WASHINGTON
901 E 5th St Ste 222, Washington, MO 63090-3127
Tel (636) 239-8000 *Founded/Ownrshp* 1975
Sales 68.0MM^E *EMP* 576^E
SIC 8062 General medical & surgical hospitals; General medical & surgical hospitals
Pr: Terri L McLain
Chf Rad: Karl Lenzenhuber
**COO:* Joan Frost
Dir Rad: Vicki Kriete
Dir Rx: Mark Pollock

D-U-N-S 07-195-8003
MERCY HOSPITALS EAST COMMUNITIES
MERCY HOSPITAL ST. LOUIS
615 S New Ballas Rd, Saint Louis, MO 63141-8221
Tel (314) 251-6000 *Founded/Ownrshp* 1891
Sales 1.1MMM *EMP* 10,000
SIC 8062 General medical & surgical hospitals; General medical & surgical hospitals
Pr: Jeffrey Johnston
Chf Path: Damion Kistler
CFO: Shelly Hunter
Ofcr: Anne Krebs
**VP:* Paul Hintze
VP: Robert Ruello
Comm Man: Chris Berra
Ex Dir: Russell Branzell
Dept Mgr: Joe Pecoraro
CIO: Eugene Roth
IT Man: Dave Conover

D-U-N-S 07-377-5504
MERCY HOUSING CALIFORNIA
1999 Broadway Ste 100, Denver, CO 80202-5701
Tel (303) 830-3412 *Founded/Ownrshp* 1967
Sales 40.4MM *EMP* 64
Accts Reznick Group Pc Charlotte N
SIC 8399 Council for social agency; Council for social agency
Reg Dir: Greg Sparks
VP: Jennifer Dolin
**VP:* Stanley Keasling

D-U-N-S 10-906-7298
MERCY HOUSING INC
1999 Broadway Ste 1000, Denver, CO 80202-5704
Tel (303) 830-3300 *Founded/Ownrshp* 1981
Sales 8.0MM *EMP* 1,200
Accts Cohnreznick Llp Charlotte Nc
SIC 1522 6531 Apartment building construction; Real estate managers; Apartment building construction; Real estate managers
Pr: Jane Graf
CFO: Mark Kleinkopf
**Sr VP:* Carol Breslau
Sr VP: Melissa Clayton
**Sr VP:* Cindy Holler
Sr VP: Tina Lowe
**Sr VP:* L Steven Spears
**VP:* Vince Dodds
VP: Donna Jared
**VP:* Michele Mamet
VP: John Marcolina
VP: Dave Mevis
VP: Jennifer Sakin
VP: Kevin Weishaar

D-U-N-S 05-575-2646
■ **MERCY INC** (NV)
AMERICAN MEDICAL RESPONSE
(*Suby of* AMERICAN MEDICAL RESPONSE INC) ★
7201 W Post Rd, Las Vegas, NV 89113-6610
Tel (702) 386-9985 *Founded/Ownrshp* 1968, 1993
Sales 5.9MM^E *EMP* 460
SIC 4119 Ambulance service; Ambulance service
CEO: Michael Williams
**CEO:* Trace Skeen

D-U-N-S 84-597-3861
MERCY INFO SERVICE DIV
14528 South Outer 40 Rd, Chesterfield, MO 63017-5785
Tel (314) 214-8196 *Founded/Ownrshp* 2008
Sales 594.4MM *EMP* 1
SIC 8999 Services; Services
Prin: Mike Kendall

D-U-N-S 08-547-8241
MERCY INPATIENT MEDICAL ASSOCIATES INC
MERCY MEDICAL CENTER
271 Carew St Ste 106, Springfield, MA 01104-2377
Tel (413) 748-9000 *Founded/Ownrshp* 1988
Sales 23.7MM^E *EMP* 45
SIC 8011 8322 Internal medicine practitioners; Individual & family services
Pr: Daniel P Moen
Chf Rad: David B Mernoff
Dir Vol: Nancy Reilly
CFO: Thomas W Robert
**Treas:* Thomas Robert
Ofcr: Paul H Oppenheimer
Sr VP: Mark M Fulco
VP: Sharon A Adams
VP: Diane Dukette
VP: Leonard F Pansa
VP: Stan Ragalski
Dir Teleco: Sean Seslar
Dir Inf Cn: Kevin Sullivan
Dir Risk M: Janell Forget
Dir Rx: Melissa Zaslow

D-U-N-S 03-065-4669
MERCY KANSAS COMMUNITIES INC
SISTERS OF MERCY HEALTH SYSTEM
(*Suby of* MERCY HEALTH) ★
401 Woodland Hills Blvd, Fort Scott, KS 66701-8797
Tel (620) 223-7075 *Founded/Ownrshp* 1919
Sales 73.9MM *EMP* 850
Accts Ernst & Young Us Llp Clayton

SIC 8062 8069 General medical & surgical hospitals; Specialty hospitals, except psychiatric; General medical & surgical hospitals; Specialty hospitals, except psychiatric
Pr: John Woodrich
*Pr: Rita Baker
COO: Rickenia Lee
*CFO: Terri Del Chiaro
CFO: Terry Deltiero
CFO: Terry Tiero
Ex VP: Shannon Sock
VP: Terry Bader
VP: Al Genna
VP: David Martin
Dir Lab: Michael P Chitty
Dir Lab: Jean Sluder

D-U-N-S 00-210-1470
MERCY LIFE CENTER CORP (PA)
1200 Reedsdale St Ste 1, Pittsburgh, PA 15233-2109
Tel (412) 578-6675 Founded/Ownrshp 1983, 1988
Sales 87.3MM EMP 1,600
Accts Deloitte Tax Llp Philadelphia
SIC 8322 Social service center; Social service center
Pr: Susan Welsh
*CFO: Shelly Sullivan
VP: Ray Wolfe
Comm Dir: Jane Miller
Genl Mgr: Carol Seaseth
IT Man: Stephanie Murtaugh
IT Man: Janis Palivick

D-U-N-S 79-718-9719
MERCY LIFE CENTER CORP
MERCY BEHAVIORAL HEALTH
(Suby of MERCY LIFE CENTER CORP) ★
1200 Reedsdale St Ste 1, Pittsburgh, PA 15233-2109
Tel (412) 323-8026 Founded/Ownrshp 1988
Sales 41.8MM EMP 1,592
SIC 8093 Mental health clinic, outpatient; Mental health clinic, outpatient
Pr: Raymond Wolfe

D-U-N-S 07-967-9154
MERCY MARICOPA INTEGRATED CARE
4350 E Cotton Center Blvd D, Phoenix, AZ 85040-8852
Tel (602) 453-8308 Founded/Ownrshp 2015
Sales NA EMP 99
SIC 6324 Hospital & medical service plans
*CEO: Broadway Eddy
*COO: Edge Angelo
*CFO: Dominguez Ramon

D-U-N-S 07-625-0729
MERCY MCCUNE-BROOKS HOSPITAL
MCCUN-BROOKS HOSP HM HLTH SVCS
3125 Dr Russell Smith Way, Carthage, MO 64836-7402
Tel (417) 358-8121 Founded/Ownrshp 1893
Sales 37.9MM^E EMP 431
SIC 8062 8051 General medical & surgical hospitals; Skilled nursing care facilities; General medical & surgical hospitals; Skilled nursing care facilities
Pr: Robert Copeland Jr
CFO: Doug Culver
Mktg Dir: Pam Bartlet
Doctor: Frank Edwards

MERCY MEDICAL CENTER
See MERCY HOSPITAL CEDAR RAPIDS IOWA

MERCY MEDICAL CENTER
See MERCY INPATIENT MEDICAL ASSOCIATES INC

MERCY MEDICAL CENTER
See MERCY CLINICS INC

D-U-N-S 06-592-6099
MERCY MEDICAL CENTER
CATHOLIC HEALTH SERVICES OF LO
(Suby of CATHOLIC HEALTH SYSTEM OF LONG ISLAND INC) ★
1000 N Village Ave, Rockville Centre, NY 11570-1000
Tel (516) 562-6907 Founded/Ownrshp 1913
Sales 185.9MM EMP 1,610
Accts Pricewaterhousecoopers Llp Ne
SIC 8062 General medical & surgical hospitals; General medical & surgical hospitals
CEO: Dr Alan Guerci
*CFO: William Armstrong
*Ex VP: Nancy Simmons
Dir Lab: Bernadette Gladstone
Dir Lab: Louann Regensburg
Ex Dir: Annette Esposito
CIO: Jeff Cash
CIO: Joseph Perron
IT Man: Ayana Bembry
Secur Mgr: Michael Couchon
Surgeon: Brian Donaldson

D-U-N-S 07-763-0069
MERCY MEDICAL CENTER
CHI
(Suby of CATHOLIC HEALTH INITIATIVES) ★
1301 15th Ave W, Williston, ND 58801-3821
Tel (701) 774-7435 Founded/Ownrshp 1996
Sales 76.5MM EMP 500
Accts Catholic Health Initiatives E
SIC 8062 General medical & surgical hospitals; General medical & surgical hospitals
CEO: Dennis L Goebel
Dir Rx: Mark Ceglowski
CIO: Kim Miller
Pathlgst: John Andelin
Diag Rad: Madhusudhan Reddy

MERCY MEDICAL CENTER - REDDING
See MERCY HOME SERVICES A CALIFORNIA LIMITED PARTNERSHIP

D-U-N-S 80-815-6913
MERCY MEDICAL CENTER FOUNDATION - NORTH IOWA
(Suby of CATHOLIC HEALTH EAST) ★
1000 4th St Sw, Mason City, IA 50401-2800
Tel (641) 428-7000 Founded/Ownrshp 1993
Sales 2.1MM EMP 2,660
SIC 8062 General medical & surgical hospitals; General medical & surgical hospitals

Prin: Robert Lembke
*COO: Diane Fischels
*CFO: Rod Schlader
*Treas: Hal Johnson
*Sr VP: Teresa Mock
*VP: Jim Borgstrom
Dir Rad: Bill Lineberger
Dir Rx: Debra Dees
Adm Dir: Barbara Frustaci
Ex Dir: Doreen Fadus
Off Mgr: Liz Decker

D-U-N-S 03-078-5042
MERCY MEDICAL CENTER INC
2700 Nw Stewart Pkwy, Roseburg, OR 97471-1214
Tel (541) 673-0611 Founded/Ownrshp 2006
Sales 190.7MM EMP 1,100
Accts Catholic Health Initiatives E
SIC 8062 General medical & surgical hospitals; General medical & surgical hospitals
Pr: Kelly C Morgan
*COO: Debbie Boswell
CFO: John Kasberger
*CFO: John Kasperger
*VP: Rhul Agarwal
VP: Steve Kehrberg
Dir OR: Tammy Hodson
Dir Rx: Jerry Smead
Off Mgr: Richard Redfield
MIS Dir: Nancy Laney
Telecom Mg: Debbie Bertolino

D-U-N-S 07-494-3556
MERCY MEDICAL CENTER INC
345 Saint Paul St, Baltimore, MD 21202-2123
Tel (410) 332-9000 Founded/Ownrshp 1870
Sales 370.9MM^E EMP 2,139
Accts Cohen Rutherford Knight Pc Be
SIC 8062 8011 General medical & surgical hospitals; Offices & clinics of medical doctors; General medical & surgical hospitals; Offices & clinics of medical doctors
Ch Bd: Sister Helen Amos
*CEO: Thomas R Mullen
*CFO: John E Topper
*Ex VP: Amy Freeman
Sr VP: Nicholas Koas
*Sr VP: Dr Scott Spier
VP: Patrick Vizzard
Dir Teleco: Warren Fox
Telecom Mg: Gloria McKoy
Mtls Mgr: Gordon Christmyer
Mktg Dir: Sam Moskowitz

D-U-N-S 09-155-0256
MERCY MEDICAL CENTER INC
(Suby of SISTERS OF CHARITY OF ST AUGUSTINE HEALTH SYSTEMS INC) ★
1320 Mercy Dr Nw, Canton, OH 44708-2641
Tel (330) 489-1000 Founded/Ownrshp 1908
Sales 301.1MM EMP 80
Accts Plante & Moran Pllc Columbus
SIC 8062 General medical & surgical hospitals; General medical & surgical hospitals
Pr: Thomas E Cecconi
Chf Rad: William Murphy
Dir Recs: Lynne Shaffer
Pr: Matthew Heinle
*COO: David D Cemate
*CFO: David K Stewart
Ofcr: Barbara Yingling
VP: Carolyn Capuano
*VP: Sister Carolyn Capuano
*VP: David L Gormsen
*VP: Matthew A Heinle
VP: Connie Smith
VP: Thomas Turner
VP: James Williams
Dir Lab: Michael Doyle
Dir Lab: Anne Lovejoy
Dir Rx: John Feucht
Board of Directors: Suresh Patel

MERCY MEDICAL CENTER MERCED
See MATER MISERICORDIAE HOSPITAL

D-U-N-S 04-803-0985
MERCY MEDICAL CENTER OF OSHKOSH INC
AFFFINITY HEALTH SYSTEM
2700 W 9th Ave Ste 100, Oshkosh, WI 54904-7863
Tel (920) 223-2000 Founded/Ownrshp 1891
Sales 106.5MM EMP 1,400
SIC 8062 General medical & surgical hospitals; General medical & surgical hospitals
Pr: William Calhoun
*COO: Cliff Lehman
*CFO: Jeff Badger
CFO: Jeffrey Francis
Obsttrcn: Ginger Selle
Doctor: Michael Binder
Pgrm Dir: Jim Werner

D-U-N-S 05-534-8684
MERCY MEDICAL CENTER OF SPRINGFIELD OHIO (INC)
1343 N Fountain Blvd, Springfield, OH 45504-1499
Tel (937) 390-5000 Founded/Ownrshp 1949
Sales 44.1MM^E EMP 868
SIC 8062 General medical & surgical hospitals; General medical & surgical hospitals
Pr: Andrew McCulloch
Chf Rad: Freddy Katai
COO: Marion Purdue
Dir Rad: George Miller
Ansthlgy: Bachar Hachwa
Doctor: Cheryl P Williams

D-U-N-S 10-738-8605
MERCY MEDICAL CENTER-CLINTON INC
MERCY HOME CARE
1410 N 4th St, Clinton, IA 52732-2940
Tel (563) 244-5555 Founded/Ownrshp 1982
Sales 123.0MM^E EMP 900
SIC 8062 8051 5122 Hospital, AMA approved residency; Extended care facility; Drugs, proprietaries & sundries; Hospital, AMA approved residency; Extended care facility; Drugs, proprietaries & sundries
CEO: Donna Oliver

Treas: Dave Meade
VP: Amy Berentes
*VP: Paul Mangin
Dir Rad: Laurel Brandeburg
*Prin: Sean Williams
MIS Dir: Jannell Howard
Dir QC: Linda Hoppe
Phys Thrpy: Bridget Sweenie

D-U-N-S 79-886-0946
■ **MERCY MEDICAL DEVELOPMENT INC**
MERCY OUTPATIENT CENTER
(Suby of MERCY HOSPITAL INC) ★
3659 S Miami Ave Ste 4004, Miami, FL 33133-4231
Tel (305) 860-4660 Founded/Ownrshp 1985
Sales 8.4MM^E EMP 365
SIC 8093 8071 Specialty outpatient clinics; Rehabilitation center, outpatient treatment; Medical laboratories; Specialty outpatient clinics; Rehabilitation center, outpatient treatment; Medical laboratories
Pr: Melvin L Fuenzalida
Pr: Laura Dominguez
*Pr: Melvin Lozano-Fuenzalida

D-U-N-S 15-312-6029
MERCY MEDICAL GROUP
12800 Corporate Hill Dr, Saint Louis, MO 63131-1845
Tel (888) 700-7171 Founded/Ownrshp 2004
Sales 229.5MM EMP 4^E
SIC 8011 Physicians' office, including specialists; Physicians' office, including specialists
Prin: Brenda Ryan
CIO: Dewey Freeman

D-U-N-S 78-780-0002
MERCY MEDICAL SERVICE INC
CAROLINA MEDICAL CENTER MERCY
(Suby of CAROLINAS HEALTHCARE SYSTEM) ★
2001 Vail Ave, Charlotte, NC 28207-1248
Tel (704) 379-5000 Founded/Ownrshp 1991
Sales 57.7MM^E EMP 1,000^E
SIC 8011 Clinic, operated by physicians; Clinic, operated by physicians
Pr: Curtis Copenhaver
*VP: Janet Handy
Dir Teleco: Mason Blandford

D-U-N-S 13-973-9270
MERCY MEDICAL SERVICES INC
MED TEC MEDICAL SERVICES
(Suby of MERCY ST EDWARDS MEDICAL CENTER) ★
5401 Ellsworth Rd, Fort Smith, AR 72903-3219
Tel (479) 314-6060 Founded/Ownrshp 1983
Sales 580.4MM EMP 268
SIC 7363 Medical help service; Medical help service
Pr: John Hoffman

MERCY MEMORIAL HOSP SYSTEMS
See MERCY MEMORIAL HOSPITAL CORP

D-U-N-S 06-371-6542
MERCY MEMORIAL HOSPITAL CORP
MERCY MEMORIAL HOSP SYSTEMS
(Suby of PROMEDICA HEALTH SYSTEMS INC) ★
718 N Macomb St, Monroe, MI 48162-7815
Tel (734) 240-8400 Founded/Ownrshp 2015
Sales 170.8MM^E EMP 1,300
Accts Plante & Moran Pllc Southfiel
SIC 8062 General medical & surgical hospitals; General medical & surgical hospitals
Pr: Annette S Phillips
CFO: Thomas Schilling
Trst: Mark Worrell

D-U-N-S 08-128-1552
MERCY MEMORIAL HOSPITAL OF URBANA OHIO
MCAULEY CENTER
904 Scioto St, Urbana, OH 43078-2226
Tel (937) 653-5231 Founded/Ownrshp 1971
Sales 27.0MM EMP 300
SIC 8062 General medical & surgical hospitals
Pr: Paul Hiltz
*COO: Gary A Hagens
*VP: Sherry Nelson
*VP: Marianne Potina

D-U-N-S 01-928-4160
MERCY METHODIST HOSPITAL
7500 Hospital Dr, Sacramento, CA 95823-5403
Tel (916) 423-6063 Founded/Ownrshp 1998
Sales 51.1MM^E EMP 1,032^E
Accts Deloitte & Touche Llp
SIC 8062 General medical & surgical hospitals
Genl Mgr: Robert Morrison

MERCY OF NORTHERN NEWYORK
See HCA GENESIS INC

MERCY OUTPATIENT CENTER
See MERCY MEDICAL DEVELOPMENT INC

D-U-N-S 06-954-1139
MERCY PHYSICIAN SERVICES INC
MERCY CARE COMMUNITY PHYSICIAN
3011 3rd Ave Se, Cedar Rapids, IA 52401
Tel (319) 369-4500 Founded/Ownrshp 1996
Sales 28.9MM^E EMP 475
SIC 8741 Administrative management; Administrative management
CEO: Timothy Quinn

D-U-N-S 17-920-0126
MERCY PROFESSIONAL PRACTICE ASSOCIATE INC
1111 6th Ave, Des Moines, IA 50314-2613
Tel (515) 247-4445 Founded/Ownrshp 1998
Sales 29.8MM EMP 25
Accts Catholic Health Initiatives E
SIC 8011 General & family practice, physician/surgeon; General & family practice, physician/surgeon
Off Mgr: Barb Burnight
Treas: Steven Kukla

D-U-N-S 06-795-2259
MERCY REGIONAL HEALTH CENTER INC (KS)
1823 College Ave, Manhattan, KS 66502-3381
Tel (785) 776-3322 Founded/Ownrshp 1954, 1996
Sales 115.1M EMP 750
SIC 8062

D-U-N-S 17-416-0978
MERCY REGIONAL HEALTH CENTRE AUXILLIARY
ST MARY'S GIFT SHOP
1823 College Ave, Manhattan, KS 66502-3381
Tel (785) 776-2802 Founded/Ownrshp 1986
Sales 32.4MM^E EMP 1,000
SIC 5947 Gift shop; Gift shop
Treas: Chris Shank
VP: Debbi Elmore
VP: Lori Grubs
VP: Shelley Koltnow
VP: Sherrie String

MERCY REGIONAL MEDICAL CENTER
See CATHOLIC HEALTH INITIATIVES COLORADO FOUNDATION

D-U-N-S 01-702-8654
MERCY REGIONAL MEDICAL CENTER
800 E Main St, Ville Platte, LA 70586-4618
Tel (615) 920-7000 Founded/Ownrshp 2010
Sales 60.7MM EMP 8
SIC 8062 General medical & surgical hospitals
Pr: James S Kaigler
Dir Lab: Stacy Sittig

D-U-N-S 02-073-7358
MERCY REHABILITATION HOSPITAL
14561 North Outer 40 Rd, Chesterfield, MO 63017-5703
Tel (314) 881-4006 Founded/Ownrshp 2008
Sales 30.7MM EMP 38^E
SIC 8049 Offices of health practitioner; Offices of health practitioner
Prin: Donna Flannery

D-U-N-S 13-524-4981
MERCY RESTORATIVE CARE HOSPITAL INC
CAROLINAS SPECIALITY HOSPITAL
2001 Vail Ave Fl 7, Charlotte, NC 28207-1248
Tel (704) 379-6429 Founded/Ownrshp 2002
Sales 22.1MM EMP 135
Accts Cliftonlarsonallen Llp Charlo
SIC 8069 Specialty hospitals, except psychiatric; Specialty hospitals, except psychiatric
CEO: Dan Dunmeyer
*CEO: Dun Dunmeyer
Nrsg Dir: Teisha Davis

D-U-N-S 09-623-4760
MERCY RETIREMENT AND CARE CENTER (CA)
3431 Foothill Blvd, Oakland, CA 94601-3199
Tel (510) 534-8540 Founded/Ownrshp 1872
Sales 23.9MM EMP 160
SIC 8361 8051 Home for the aged; Skilled nursing care facilities; Home for the aged; Skilled nursing care facilities
CEO: Jesse Jantzen
HC Dir: Asha Kooliyadan

MERCY RIVERSIDE
See BAPTIST HOSPITAL OF EAST TENNESSEE INC

MERCY SAN JUAN HOSPITAL
See MERCY HEALTHCARE SACRAMENTO

D-U-N-S 15-479-8891
MERCY SCRIPPS HOSPITAL
4077 5th Ave Mer35, San Diego, CA 92103-2105
Tel (619) 294-8111 Founded/Ownrshp 2004
Sales 623.0MM EMP 4^E
SIC 8011 Physicians' office, including specialists
Prin: Andrew C Ping
VP: David Shaw
Dir Risk M: Kathy Maroni
Dir Risk M: Gayle Sandhu
Dir Rad: George Ochoa
IT Man: Steve Cornelius
Mktg Dir: Tye Kennon
Surgeon: Leo Murphy
Surgeon: Mary Murphy
Surgeon: Steven Shackford
Obsttrcn: Lisa Lipschitz

D-U-N-S 19-419-1953
MERCY SERVICES IOWA CITY INC
(Suby of MERCY HOSPITAL IOWA CITY IOWA INC) ★
500 E Market St, Iowa City, IA 52245-2633
Tel (319) 339-3541 Founded/Ownrshp 1984
Sales 47.0MM^E EMP 1,100
SIC 8011 8082 Offices & clinics of medical doctors; Home health care services; Offices & clinics of medical doctors; Home health care services
Pr: Ronald Reed
*CFO: Michael G Heinrich
*VP: William A Watts

D-U-N-S 13-405-3966
MERCY SHIPS
15862 State Highway 110 N, Lindale, TX 75771-5932
Tel (903) 939-7000 Founded/Ownrshp 1978
Sales 35.4MM^E EMP 650
SIC 8661 Religious organizations; Religious organizations
Pr: Donald Stephens
*CEO: Myron E Ullman III
*Treas: Vanda Davey
Ofcr: Mark Wright
VP: Rob Caircross
VP: Jeff Kramer
VP: David Overton
*VP: Samuel Smith
Mng Dir: Ken Berry
Mng Dir: Peter Schulze
CIO: Chris Gregg
Board of Directors: Francoise Andr, Wolfgang Gross

D-U-N-S 07-566-1504
MERCY ST EDWARDS MEDICAL CENTER
(*Suby of* MERCY HEALTH) ★
7301 Rogers Ave, Fort Smith, AR 72903-4100
Tel (479) 314-6000 *Founded/Ownrshp* 1905
Sales 580.4MM^E *EMP* 1,553
SIC 8062 General medical & surgical hospitals; General medical & surgical hospitals
Pr: Ryan Gehrig
Chf Rad: David Diment
Chf Rad: Rick Nelson
**Sec:* Greta Wilcher
Doctor: Norma Basinger
Doctor: Tamara Johnson
Doctor: Kurt Mehl MD

D-U-N-S 06-904-4386
MERCY SUBURBAN HOSPITAL
(*Suby of* MERCY HEALTH FOUNDATION OF SOUTH-EASTERN PENNSYLVANIA) ★
2701 Dekalb Pike, East Norriton, PA 19401-1820
Tel (215) 748-9000 *Founded/Ownrshp* 1944
Sales 110.6MM *EMP* 1,080
SIC 8062 General medical & surgical hospitals; General medical & surgical hospitals
CEO: Javon R Bea
Pr: Joy Hepkins
**CFO:* Peter Kenniff
Sr VP: Elizabeth Riley-Wasserman
Dir Inf Cn: Jim Hunter
**Prin:* Lifa Nallon
CIO: Christine Brutschea
IT Man: Chris Brutshea
Surgeon: Justin Brower
Surgeon: Eric Kim
Surgeon: Michael Mahoney

D-U-N-S 15-374-4909
MERCY UPMC HOSPITAL
(*Suby of* UNIVERSITY OF PITTSBURGH MEDICAL CENTER) ★
1400 Locust St, Pittsburgh, PA 15219-5114
Tel (412) 232-8111 *Founded/Ownrshp* 2008
Sales 5.1MM *EMP* 2,010
SIC 8062 General medical & surgical hospitals; General medical & surgical hospitals
Pr: Elizabeth Concordia
CFO: Jack Gaenzle
Trst: John R McGinley
VP: Linda Hogan
**Prin:* Michael Grace

D-U-N-S 60-849-0645
MERCY-USA FOR AID AND DEVELOPMENT INC
44450 Pinetree Dr Ste 201, Plymouth, MI 48170-3869
Tel (734) 454-0011 *Founded/Ownrshp* 1988
Sales 10.7MM *EMP* 400
Accts Alan C Young & Associates P
SIC 8699 Charitable organization; Charitable organization
Pr: Umar Al-Qadi
**CFO:* Anas Alhaidar
**Ch:* Iman Elkadi
Treas: Syed Salman
**Treas:* Naushad Virji

D-U-N-S 10-734-6843
MERCYCARE SERVICE CORP
701 10th St Se, Cedar Rapids, IA 52403-1251
Tel (319) 398-6011 *Founded/Ownrshp* 1983
Sales 1.6MM *EMP* 2,500^E
SIC 8011 Medical centers; Medical centers
CEO: A J Tinker
**Pr:* Tim Charles
**Treas:* Emmett Scherman
CIO: Phil Wasson

D-U-N-S 02-113-1909
MERCYFIRST
ST. MARYS OF THE ANGELS HOME I
525 Convent Rd, Syosset, NY 11791-3868
Tel (516) 921-0808 *Founded/Ownrshp* 1900
Sales 42.1MM *EMP* 385
Accts Bdo Usa Llp New York Ny
SIC 8361 Children's home; Residential care for children; Orphanage; Children's home; Residential care for children; Orphanage
CEO: Gerard McCaffery
**Pr:* Bernard Mc Caffrey
**Treas:* Joseph Meares
**Sr VP:* Achim Kretschmer
**VP:* Sr M Seton Agovino
VP: Sharon Dillon
VP: Rebecca Marcone
**VP:* Kerri Sneden
**VP:* Arthur Stockbury
CTO: Severio Ford
Psych: Paul Best

D-U-N-S 06-828-7465
MERCYFIRST
6301 12th Ave, Brooklyn, NY 11219-5213
Tel (718) 232-1500 *Founded/Ownrshp* 2003
Sales 12.5MM^E *EMP* 750^E
Accts O Keefe & Moret Pc New York N
SIC 8361 8322 Group foster home; Adoption services; Group foster home; Adoption services
CEO: Gerard McCassery
VP: Karen Peterson
Ex Dir: Jaquline McKelvey

D-U-N-S 09-951-9340
MERCYHURST UNIVERSITY
501 E 38th St, Erie, PA 16546-0002
Tel (814) 824-2000 *Founded/Ownrshp* 1926
Sales 85.5MM *EMP* 615
Accts Bkd Llp Cincinnati Oh
SIC 8221 8243 8742 8299 College, except junior; Repair training, computer; Administrative services consultant; Educational service, nondegree granting: continuing educ.; College, except junior; Repair training, computer; Administrative services consultant; Educational service, nondegree granting: continuing educ.
Pr: Thomas Gamble
Pr: Betsy Frank
**Treas:* Jane Kelsey
Ofcr: Shawn Wroblewski
**VP:* Gary M Brown
VP: Kelsey Jane
VP: Gerry Tobin
Exec: Marcy Fickes
Off Mgr: Denise Roth
Off Admin: Sheila Tsuro
Trfc Dir: Eric Campbell

D-U-N-S 04-009-4062
MEREDITH AND CLARKE BANK OF NEWPORT INSURANCE SERVICES INC
OCEAN POINT
73 Valley Rd 1, Middletown, RI 02842-5234
Tel (401) 423-1111 *Founded/Ownrshp* 1946
Sales NA *EMP* 2
SIC 6411 Property & casualty insurance agent; Property & casualty insurance agent
Pr: Sydney Smith
**Ex Dir:* Mathew Clark

D-U-N-S 00-346-0326
MEREDITH COLLEGE (NC)
3800 Hillsborough St, Raleigh, NC 27607-5298
Tel (919) 760-8600 *Founded/Ownrshp* 1891
Sales 56.5MM *EMP* 650
Accts Cherry Bekaert Llp Raleigh N
SIC 8221 College, except junior; College, except junior
Pr: Jo Allen
Bd of Dir: Cathie Ostrowski
Assoc VP: Cynthia Edwards
**VP:* Craig Barfield
VP: Charles Barton
**VP:* Lennie Barton
**VP:* Jean Jackson
**VP:* Matthew Poslusny
VP: William F Wade
**Prin:* Jeff Howlett
**Prin:* Diane Strangis

D-U-N-S 00-527-9138 IMP
▲ MEREDITH CORP (IA)
1716 Locust St, Des Moines, IA 50309-3023
Tel (515) 284-3000 *Founded/Ownrshp* 1902
Sales 1.5MMM *EMP* 3,825
Accts Kpmg Llp Des Moines Iowa
Tkr Sym MDP *Exch* NYS
SIC 2721 2731 4833 Magazines: publishing & printing; Book publishing; Books: publishing only; Television broadcasting stations; Magazines: publishing & printing; Book publishing; Books: publishing only; Television broadcasting stations
Ch Bd: Stephen M Lacy
Pr: Martin F Reidy
Pr: Pete Snyder
CFO: Joseph H Ceryanec
**V Ch Bd:* D Mell Meredith Frazier
Ex VP: Doug Lowe
Sr VP: Stan Pavlovsky
Sr VP: Lauren Wiener
VP: Kirk Black
VP: Al Blinke
VP: Alysia Borsa
VP: Debra Corson
VP: Mike Cukyne
VP: Klarn Depalma
VP: Guy Hempel
VP: Patrick McCreery
VP: Darrin McDonald
VP: Larry Oaks
VP: Julie Pinkwater
VP: Laura Rowley
VP: Chris Susil
Board of Directors: Donald A Baer, Donald C Berg, Mary Sue Coleman, Frederick B Henry, Joel W Johnson, Philip A Marineau, Elizabeth E Tallett

D-U-N-S 01-976-5973
MEREDITH VILLAGE SAVINGS BANK
MVSB
24 Nh Route 25, Meredith, NH 03253-6344
Tel (603) 279-7986 *Founded/Ownrshp* 1869
Sales NA *EMP* 120
SIC 6035 Savings institutions, federally chartered; Savings institutions, federally chartered
CEO: Samuel L Laverack
Mng Pt: Kenneth Malone
**Pr:* Sam Laverack
COO: Diane Johnson
**CFO:* Rick Wiman
Ofcr: Renee Birmingham
Ofcr: Michael Bourgault
Ofcr: Judy Horne
**Ex VP:* Richard E Wyman
**Sr VP:* Carol Bickford
**Sr VP:* David Cronin
**Sr VP:* Christine Harris
Sr VP: Jason Hicks
Sr VP: Robert Sargeant
Sr VP: Steven Tucker
**VP:* Mike Barney
**VP:* Brian Chalmers
**VP:* Gracie Cilley
VP: Don Girard
VP: Cynthia Hemeon-Plessner
**VP:* Lynn Hurd

D-U-N-S 05-762-8091 IMP
MEREX AIRCRAFT CO INC
(*Suby of* MEREX HOLDING CORPORATION)
1283 Flynn Rd, Camarillo, CA 93012-8013
Tel (561) 222-7455 *Founded/Ownrshp* 2011
Sales 32.6MM *EMP* 30^E
SIC 5088 3728 3724 Aircraft equipment & supplies; Aircraft parts & equipment; Airframe assemblies, except for guided missiles; Aircraft engines & engine parts; Aircraft equipment & supplies; Aircraft parts & equipment; Airframe assemblies, except for guided missiles; Aircraft engines & engine parts
Pr: Christopher R Celtruda
Pr: David Faulkner
Pr: Leon Stewart
CFO: Jikun Kin
Ex VP: Nathan A Skop
VP Opers: Carl Vickers
Site Mgr: Majic Khabbaz
Board of Directors: Tom Caracciolo, Michael Hompesch, Frank Pados

D-U-N-S 82-777-2443
MEREX TECHNOLOGY LEASING CORP
570 Lake Cook Rd Ste 300, Deerfield, IL 60015-5274
Tel (847) 940-1200 *Founded/Ownrshp* 1994
Sales NA *EMP* 516
SIC 6159 5045 Machinery & equipment finance leasing; Computers, peripherals & software; Machinery & equipment finance leasing; Computers, peripherals & software
CEO: Ian J Pye
**Pr:* Brad V Ihlenfeld
**Treas:* Michael D Brannan
**Sr VP:* Rochelle Slater
Dir IT: Harvey Chebo
IT Man: Mike Kalis

D-U-N-S 00-842-4889 IMP/EXP
MERFISH PIPE & SUPPLY LP
MERFISH PIPE AND SUPPLY CO
(*Suby of* OEP CAPITAL ADVISORS LP) ★
1211 Kress St, Houston, TX 77020-7418
Tel (713) 869-5731 *Founded/Ownrshp* 2012
Sales 31.5MM^E *EMP* 48^E
SIC 5051 5085 Pipe & tubing, steel; Valves & fittings
CEO: Gerald Merfish
Pt: Rochelle M Jacobson
Pt: Robert Setzekorn
Genl Mgr: Bob Rau
Opers Mgr: Norman Kothmann

MERFISH PIPE AND SUPPLY CO
See MERFISH PIPE & SUPPLY LP

D-U-N-S 03-792-3786
MERGE AREA VI COMMUNITY COLLEGE DISTRICT
IOWA VALLEY CMNTY COLLEGE DST
3702 S Center St, Marshalltown, IA 50158-4760
Tel (641) 752-4643 *Founded/Ownrshp* 1986
Sales 18.0MM^E *EMP* 382
SIC 8222 8249 Junior college; Vocational schools; Junior college; Vocational schools
**CFO:* Dan Goillen
Mktg Dir: Robin Anctil

D-U-N-S 18-111-6013
▲ MERGE HEALTHCARE INC
350 N Orleans St Fl 1, Chicago, IL 60654-1975
Tel (312) 565-6868 *Founded/Ownrshp* 1987
Sales 212.3MM *EMP* 1,005^E
Tkr Sym MRGE *Exch* NGS
SIC 7373 7372 Computer integrated systems design; Prepackaged software; Application computer software; Computer integrated systems design; Diagnostic apparatus, medical
Pr: George Kotlarz
Pr: Gary D Bowers
Pr: Jacques Cornet
Pr: Loris Sartor
Pr: Antonio Wells
Sr VP: Gary Bowers
VP: Chrysti Bowers
VP: Mark Bronkalla
VP: Lisa Janssen
VP: Marwan Sati
VP: Jeff Schmidt
VP: Tim Tuttle
VP: Mark Woodward
VP Bus Dev: Jeff Appel

D-U-N-S 11-149-6121
■ MERGE HEALTHCARE SOLUTIONS INC
(*Suby of* MERGE HEALTHCARE INC) ★
900 Walnut Ridge Dr, Hartland, WI 53029-8347
Tel (262) 367-0700 *Founded/Ownrshp* 2010
Sales 52.3MM^E *EMP* 230^E
SIC 7372 Application computer software; Application computer software
Pr: Stephen N Kahane
**CFO:* Kevin Burns
CFO: Michael A Mnto
CFO: John Reichendach
Sr VP: Keith Stahlhut
**Sr VP:* Frank E Stearns Jr
Sr VP: Kang Wang PHD
VP: John Esposito
**VP:* Craig Newfield
Software D: Tom Zhang
Mktg Mgr: Christina Trondsen

D-U-N-S 02-781-5781
MERGENT INC
(*Suby of* CAROUSEL CAPITAL CO LLC) ★
580 Kingsley Park Dr, Fort Mill, SC 29715-6403
Tel (704) 527-2700 *Founded/Ownrshp* 1920, 2008
Sales 34.2MM^E *EMP* 329
SIC 7389 Financial services; Financial services
CEO: Jonathan Worrall
**CFO:* Charles E Miller
VP: Bob Breslin
Assoc Dir: Becky Good
IT Man: Anthony Harp
Opers Mgr: Akira Darroux

D-U-N-S 17-946-1843
MERGENT INC
444 Madison Ave Ste 502, New York, NY 10022-6976
Tel (212) 413-7700 *Founded/Ownrshp* 1997
Sales 17.2MM^E *EMP* 300
SIC 2721 Magazines: publishing only, not printed on site; Magazines: publishing only, not printed on site
CEO: Jonathan Worral
**CFO:* Charles E Miller Jr
VP: Michael Strauss
Mng Dir: Mike Winn
Natl Sales: Jeff Darcy

D-U-N-S 06-154-2239
MERGENTHALER TRANSFER & STORAGE CO INC
AGENT FOR UNITED VAN LINES
1414 N Montana Ave, Helena, MT 59601-2998
Tel (406) 442-9470 *Founded/Ownrshp* 1974
Sales 87.0MM^E *EMP* 388
SIC 4213 4214 7538 Trucking, except local; Household goods transport; Local trucking with storage; Household goods moving & storage, local; General truck repair; Trucking, except local; Household goods transport; Local trucking with storage; Household goods moving & storage, local; General truck repair
Owner: Jerry Mergenthaler
**Pr:* Steve Mergenthaler
**VP:* Dave Gardner
**VP:* Mark Radwanski
Genl Mgr: Marie Lewis
Genl Mgr: Alan Stacey
IT Man: Steven Davidson
IT Man: Mark Dowdy
IT Man: Ronda Pekovitch
Opers Supe: Michael Arellano
Opers Supe: Jill Peterson

D-U-N-S 36-351-6639
MERGENTHALER TRANSFER & STORAGE CO INC
MTS
1414 Carter Dr, Helena, MT 59601
Tel (406) 442-9470 *Founded/Ownrshp* 1930
Sales 25.2MM^E *EMP* 500
SIC 4731 4226 4214 4213 Freight transportation arrangement; Special warehousing & storage; Local trucking with storage; Trucking, except local; Freight transportation arrangement; Special warehousing & storage; Local trucking with storage; Trucking, except local
CEO: Danny Mergenthaler

D-U-N-S 14-753-8263
MERGERMARKET (US) LTD
(*Suby of* MERGERMARKET LIMITED)
330 Hudson St Fl 4, New York, NY 10013-1046
Tel (212) 686-5606 *Founded/Ownrshp* 2003
Sales 30.3MM^E *EMP* 450
SIC 7313 Printed media advertising representatives; Printed media advertising representatives
Ch Bd: Marc Katz
**Pr:* Caspar Hobbs
**CEO:* Hamilton Matthews
COO: Kahn Ellis
Mng Dir: Angus McIntosh
CTO: Ross Heritage
Sls Dir: Jared Wulfow
Mktg Mgr: Joy Barone

MERGIS GROUP, THE
See SFN GROUP INC

D-U-N-S 01-241-1083 IMP/EXP
MERGON CORP
5350 Old Pearman Dairy Rd, Anderson, SC 29625-5348
Tel (864) 222-0422 *Founded/Ownrshp* 1998
Sales 51.3MM^E *EMP* 140
SIC 3089 Plastic containers, except foam; Plastic containers, except foam
Pr: Pat Beirne
**Treas:* Paul Fahy
Genl Mgr: Allan Hinchliffe
IT Man: Brian O'Donovan
Mfg Dir: Shelby Evans
Ql Cn Mgr: Mike Long
VP Sls: Chris Wilson
Sls Mgr: Craig Foster

D-U-N-S 79-964-1006 EXP
MERIAL INC
(*Suby of* AVENTIS INC) ★
3239 Satellite Blvd, Duluth, GA 30096-4640
Tel (678) 638-3000 *Founded/Ownrshp* 2001
Sales 433.1MM^E *EMP* 1,358
SIC 5122 Pharmaceuticals
CEO: Carsten Hellman
Pr: Anthony Maunus
**CFO:* Christophe Hirtz
CFO: Jean Mauldin
Bd of Dir: Marc Cibert
Ofcr: Marshall Barton
Exec: Fulcran Perier
Exec: John Rivera
Assoc Dir: Richard Jenkins
Comm Dir: Natasha Joseph
Dir Bus: Marcus Remmers

D-U-N-S 03-439-3582 EXP
MERIAL LIMITED
(*Suby of* MERIAL UK LLC) ★
1730 Olympic Dr, Athens, GA 30601
Tel (706) 548-9292 *Founded/Ownrshp* 2002
Sales 160.6MM^E *EMP* 230
SIC 2836 Vaccines; Vaccines
Bd of Dir: Cindy Apgar
Exec: Genne Covert
Exec: Melissa Gehry
Ex Dir: Sheryl Dollarhide
Ex Dir: Kim Ward
Brnch Mgr: John M Preston
Dist Mgr: Debby Myers
Dir IT: Mitch Cofman
Dir IT: Mike Hagerty
Dir IT: Craig Hudson
IT Man: Cynthia Blackwell

D-U-N-S 05-421-9928 IMP/EXP
MERIAL SELECT INC
(*Suby of* MERIAL UK LLC) ★
1168 Airport Pkwy, Gainesville, GA 30501-6816
Tel (770) 532-5804 *Founded/Ownrshp* 1987
Sales 190.7MM^E *EMP* 300
SIC 5122 2836 Animal medicines; Vaccines; Animal medicines; Vaccines
Pr: Keith Pritchard
**CFO:* Darrick Zink
Dir IT: Kathy Jones
Snr Mgr: Charles Garriott

D-U-N-S 06-150-6796 IMP
MERIAL UK LLC
(*Suby of* MERIAL LIMITED)
3239 Satellite Blvd, Duluth, GA 30096-4640
Tel (678) 638-3000 *Founded/Ownrshp* 2001
Sales 706.2MM^E *EMP* 4,425

SIC 2836 2834 3841 Vaccines; Veterinary pharmaceutical preparations; Diagnostic apparatus, medical; Vaccines; Veterinary pharmaceutical preparations; Diagnostic apparatus, medical
Treas: Joachim Hinzen
QA Dir: Karen Hulsey

D-U-N-S 12-252-4221
MERIBEL ENTERPRISES LLC
ATLAS MANUFACTURING
2950 Weeks Ave Se, Minneapolis, MN 55414-2832
Tel (612) 331-2566 Founded/Ownrshp 2002
Sales 26.0MM^E EMP 70
SIC 3444 Sheet metalwork

D-U-N-S 02-964-4978
MERICAL INC
2995 E Miraloma Ave, Anaheim, CA 92806-1805
Tel (714) 238-7225 Founded/Ownrshp 1989
Sales 53.1MM^E EMP 275^E
SIC 7389 Packaging & labeling services; Packaging & labeling services
Pr: Jeffrey Stallings
*CEO: Michael Schlinger
*CFO: D Dean Baltzell
VP: Tom Bovich
VP: Deborah Lingenfelter
Off Mgr: Susan Eovacious
Sfty Mgr: Bill Dargan
Sfty Mgr: Neal Fournier

D-U-N-S 00-810-6999
MERICHEM CO
5455 Old Spanish Trl, Houston, TX 77023-5013
Tel (713) 428-5000 Founded/Ownrshp 1965
Sales 120.0MM^E EMP 300
Accts Grant Thornton Llp Cpas Hous
SIC 2911 Petroleum refining; Petroleum refining
Ch Bd: Kenneth F Currie
Ch Bd: Kendra Lee
CEO: Patrick J Hickey
CFO: Bruce D Upshaw
Ex VP: Johnny Walbrick
VP: Dennis Bellville
VP: Ronnie Buras
Exec: Kathy Culbertson
Dir Bus: Terry Mackey
Dir IT: Mike Ryan
Dir IT: Dennis Tsybulski

D-U-N-S 05-538-1917
MERICLES INC
WAFFLE HOUSE
3410 E Sunshine St, Springfield, MO 65804-2188
Tel (417) 882-7366 Founded/Ownrshp 1981
Sales 7.4MM^E EMP 300
SIC 5812 Restaurant, family: chain; Restaurant, family: chain
Pr: Robert Mericle

D-U-N-S 19-309-0925
MERIDEN PUBLIC SCHOOLS
22 Liberty St, Meriden, CT 06450-5609
Tel (203) 630-4171 Founded/Ownrshp 1970
Sales 55.4MM^E EMP 1,200
SIC 8211 9411 Public elementary & secondary schools; Administration of educational programs; Public elementary & secondary schools; Administration of educational programs
Psych: Samantha Boutin
Psych: Samantha Meller

MERIDIAN
See ALL HEALTH CARE SERVICES INC

MERIDIAN
See NY MCG INC

D-U-N-S 80-952-3579
▲ MERIDIAN BANCORP INC
67 Prospect St, Peabody, MA 01960-1604
Tel (617) 567-1500 Founded/Ownrshp 2014
Sales NA EMP 455^E
Tkr Sym EBSB Exch NGS
SIC 6035 Savings institutions, federally chartered; Federal savings & loan associations
Ch Bd: Richard J Gavegnano
COO: John A Carroll
CFO: Mark L Abbate
Bd of Dir: Richard Fernandez
Sr VP: Mary Hagen
Sr VP: James Morgan
Sr VP: Joseph Nash

D-U-N-S 55-682-0210
MERIDIAN BANK
9 Old Lincoln Hwy Ste 101, Malvern, PA 19355-2551
Tel (484) 568-5000 Founded/Ownrshp 2005
Sales NA EMP 117^E
SIC 6029 Commercial banks; Commercial banks
Sr VP: Ed Carpoletti
Sr VP: Benjamin Marsho
Sr VP: Sara Shute
*VP: Erika Burns
VP: Bill Defalco
VP: Karen Divincenzo
VP: Clarence Martindell
VP: Erwin Wenner
VP: Sally Wolgin
Brnch Mgr: James Rossiter
Dir IT: Charlie Hoopes

D-U-N-S 00-292-8257
■ MERIDIAN BANK NATIONAL ASSOCIATION (AZ)
UMB BANK
(Suby of UMB BANK) ★
16435 N Scottsdale Rd, Scottsdale, AZ 85254-1533
Tel (480) 998-8995 Founded/Ownrshp 1978
Sales NA EMP 145
SIC 6021 National commercial banks; National commercial banks
Pr: Gerald Ernst
Ofcr: Michael Garcia
Sr VP: Bert Oster
*Sr VP: B Scott Rubie
Sr VP: Marla Yorston
VP: Marcella Espinoza
*VP: Christopher Gladney

D-U-N-S 09-783-0582
MERIDIAN BEHAVIORAL HEALTHCARE INC
4300 Sw 13th St, Gainesville, FL 32608-4006
Tel (352) 374-5600 Founded/Ownrshp 2000
Sales 30.4MM EMP 550
Accts Purvis Gray & Company Llp G
SIC 8093 Mental health clinic, outpatient; Mental health clinic, outpatient
Pr: Margaritta Labarta
*COO: Jim Winters
CFO: Leo Doucette
CFO: Kim Golden
CFO: Margarita La Barta
*Sr VP: Richard V Anderson
*VP: Joan Batcha
*VP: Myriah Brady
*VP: Heather Edwards
VP: Carrie Glebe
VP: David Murphy
Dir Bus: Sherry Houston
Dir Bus: Karen Rice

D-U-N-S 09-281-5364
▲ MERIDIAN BIOSCIENCE INC (OH)
3471 River Hills Dr, Cincinnati, OH 45244-3023
Tel (513) 271-3700 Founded/Ownrshp 1976
Sales 194.8MM EMP 350^E
Accts Grant Thornton Llp Cincinnati
Tkr Sym VIVO Exch NGS
SIC 2835 2834 In vitro & in vivo diagnostic substances; Pharmaceutical preparations; In vitro & in vivo diagnostic substances; Pharmaceutical preparations
Ch Bd: John A Kraeutler
CFO: Melissa A Lueke
Ofcr: Jared Schwartz
Ex VP: Lawrence J Baldini
Ex VP: Richard L Eberly
Ex VP: Vecheslav A Elagin
VP: James R Leroy
VP: John Lewis
VP: Frank Seurkamp
Sales Asso: Laura Reid
Board of Directors: James M Anderson, Dwight E Ellingwood, John C Mcllwraith, David C Phillips, Catherine A Sazdanoff

D-U-N-S 02-048-6429
MERIDIAN CITIZENS MUTUAL INSURANCE CO
2955 N Meridian St, Indianapolis, IN 46208-4714
Tel (317) 931-7000 Founded/Ownrshp 1914
Sales NA EMP 2,000
SIC 6331 Assessment associations: fire, marine & casualty insurance; Assessment associations: fire, marine & casualty insurance
Pr: Robert Restrepo
Genl Couns: Susan Bowron-White
Snr Mgr: Jo Joswick

D-U-N-S 00-400-4784
MERIDIAN COCA-COLA BOTTLING CO (MS)
2016 Highway 45 N, Meridian, MS 39301-2705
Tel (601) 483-5272 Founded/Ownrshp 1902
Sales 36.5MM^E EMP 170
SIC 2086 Soft drinks: packaged in cans, bottles, etc.; Soft drinks: packaged in cans, bottles, etc.
Ch Bd: Hardy P Graham
*Sec: Richard D James
Exec: Jeff Gibbs
Exec: Alisa McCool
IT Man: Richard Neergaard

D-U-N-S 06-713-5699
MERIDIAN COMMUNITY COLLEGE
910 Highway 19 N, Meridian, MS 39307-5890
Tel (601) 483-8241 Founded/Ownrshp 1937
Sales 1.2MM EMP 920
SIC 8222 Community college; Community college
Pr: Dr Scott Elliott
Pr: Michael Ellmo
Treas: Ann Mullins
Bd of Dir: Gloria Brassfield
Bd of Dir: Doris Harper
Bd of Dir: Tom Maynor
Bd of Dir: George Meyers
VP: Shirley Goodman
VP: Hardy Graham
*VP: Pam Harrison
Ex Dir: Cathy Brookshire

D-U-N-S 06-499-1821
MERIDIAN COMP OF NEW YORK INC
CHD MERIDIAN HEALTHCARE
(Suby of TAKE CARE EMPLOYER SOLUTIONS LLC) ★
20 Burton Hills Blvd # 200, Nashville, TN 37215-6197
Tel (615) 665-9500 Founded/Ownrshp 1996
Sales 15.2MM^E EMP 559
SIC 8011 Offices & clinics of medical doctors; Offices & clinics of medical doctors
CEO: Haywood Cochrane
*CFO: Shannon Wolcott
Sr VP: Lisa Russo
VP: Vincent Bradley
*CIO: Mark Farrington

D-U-N-S 61-479-4436
MERIDIAN CONSTRUCTION CO INC
1375 Piccard Dr Ste 280, Rockville, MD 20850-4395
Tel (301) 670-1677 Founded/Ownrshp 1990
Sales 27.8MM^E EMP 16
Accts Lanigan Ryan Malcolm & Doyle P
SIC 1542 Commercial & office buildings, renovation & repair; Commercial & office building, new construction; Commercial & office buildings, renovation & repair; Commercial & office building, new construction
Pr: Gerry S Nowak

D-U-N-S 11-978-0885
MERIDIAN CONTRACTING INC
MERIDIAN ENGINEERING COMPANY
3223 Los Arboles Ave Ne, Albuquerque, NM 87107-1916
Tel (505) 872-2841 Founded/Ownrshp 2003
Sales 26.1MM EMP 80
Accts Regier Carr & Monroe Llp Tuc
SIC 8711 Civil engineering; Civil engineering
Pr: Mark Sutton

D-U-N-S 05-961-8694
MERIDIAN DRILLING CO LLC
11500 S Meridian Ave, Oklahoma City, OK 73173-8228
Tel (405) 691-1202 Founded/Ownrshp 2012
Sales 323.5MM^E EMP 140
SIC 1381 1799 5084

MERIDIAN ENGINEERING COMPANY
See MERIDIAN CONTRACTING INC

D-U-N-S 09-299-4672
MERIDIAN ENTERPRISES CORP
951 Hornet Dr, Hazelwood, MO 63042-2309
Tel (314) 592-3000 Founded/Ownrshp 1978
Sales 29.6MM^E EMP 100
SIC 8742 Sales (including sales management) consultant; Incentive or award program consultant
Ch: Samuel Toumayan
CFO: Kevin Higgins
Ex VP: Costello Jim
Ex VP: Steven Litzau
Sr VP: Jack Hodge
Sr VP: Steve Puchalsky
VP: Jim Clayman
VP: Mark James
VP: Cheryl Jett
VP: Mike Kalish
VP: Patrick McGinnis
VP: Gary Mollerus
VP: Stephen Schulte
VP: David Scofield
VP: Dave Terrell
Comm Man: Jeannie Chase
Comm Man: Jeannie Murray

D-U-N-S 78-743-1618
MERIDIAN FINACIAL SERVICES INC
10 Meridian St, Boston, MA 02128-1963
Tel (617) 567-1500 Founded/Ownrshp 1991
Sales NA EMP 410
SIC 6712 Bank holding companies; Bank holding companies
Pr: Robert F Verdonck
*Treas: Len V Siuda
*Ex VP: Philip F Freehan

MERIDIAN FORD SALES, INC
See KENDALL FORD OF MERIDIAN LLC

D-U-N-S 95-975-7030
MERIDIAN GOLD INC
(Suby of YAMANA GOLD INC)
4635 Longley Ln Ste 110, Reno, NV 89502-5976
Tel (775) 850-3777 Founded/Ownrshp 1996
Sales 52.9MM^E EMP 511
SIC 1041 1044 Gold ores; Silver ores; Gold ores; Silver ores
Ch Bd: David S Robertson
Pr: Brian J Kennedy
CFO: Peter C Dougherty
Ex VP: Edward H Colt
VP: Richard C Lorson

D-U-N-S 09-757-1954
MERIDIAN GRAPHICS INC
2652 Dow Ave, Tustin, CA 92780-7208
Tel (949) 833-3500 Founded/Ownrshp 2000
Sales 24.3MM^E EMP 65
SIC 2752 2759 Commercial printing, offset; Letterpress printing
Pr: Paul Valencia
*Pr: David Melin
*Sec: Craig Miller
Plnt Mgr: David Jernigan
Prd Mgr: Gerry Dave
Prd Mgr: Dave Martinez
Sales Exec: Michael Dipasquale

MERIDIAN GROUP
See MERIDIAN LEASING CORP

MERIDIAN GROUP
See MERIDIAN IT INC

D-U-N-S 07-385-9035
MERIDIAN GROUP INC
2249 Pinehurst Dr, Middleton, WI 53562-2582
Tel (608) 836-1152 Founded/Ownrshp 1988
Sales 6.6MM^E EMP 300
SIC 6531 Real estate managers; Real estate managers
Pr: Doug Strub
*Ch Bd: Douglas Madsen
*Treas: Kurt Wolff
*Sr VP: Rodney Tapp
VP: Kevin Hill
VP: John Wilkinson

D-U-N-S 96-254-1053
MERIDIAN GROUP INTERNATIONAL INC
(Suby of MEREX TECHNOLOGY LEASING CORP) ★
9 Parkway N Ste 500, Deerfield, IL 60015-2545
Tel (847) 940-1200 Founded/Ownrshp 1979
Sales 273.4MM^E EMP 499
SIC 8742 6159 Financial consultant; Machinery & equipment finance leasing; Financial consultant; Machinery & equipment finance leasing
Pr: Brad Ihlenfeld
*Pr: Mike Brannan
Ex VP: Steve Bickford
*Sr VP: Rochelle Slater
Sr VP: Steve Zogg
VP: Diane Eubanks
VP: William Faherty
*VP: Bill Flaherty
*VP: John O'Connor
Dir IT: Mike Calwas
Sls Mgr: Ben Baenen

D-U-N-S 80-959-7487 IMP
MERIDIAN HEALTH INC
GENESIS HLTHCARE CTRS HOLDINGS
(Suby of GENESIS HEALTHCARE CENTERS HOLDINGS, INC.)
101 E State St, Kennett Square, PA 19348-3109
Tel (610) 444-6350 Founded/Ownrshp 1993
Sales 23.7MM^E EMP 600
SIC 8051 Extended care facility; Extended care facility
Pr: George L Chapman
*Treas: Scott A Estes
Ofcr: Michelle Casserly

D-U-N-S 61-206-6217
MERIDIAN HEALTH PLAN OF MICHIGAN INC
(Suby of CAIDAN MANAGEMENT CO LLC) ★
1 Campus Martius Ste 700, Detroit, MI 48226-5012
Tel (313) 324-3700 Founded/Ownrshp 2011
Sales NA EMP 50
Accts Plante & Moran Llp
SIC 6324 Health maintenance organization (HMO), insurance only
CEO: David B Cotton
*Pr: Jon Cotton
Pr: Sean Cotton
COO: Michael Cotton
CFO: Lowell Sprague
Dir QC: Diane Lecerf
Dir IT: Matthew Voight
IT Man: Matthew Payne
IT Man: Michael Stines
Web Dev: Brian Burge
Cert Phar: Christina Hammack

D-U-N-S 08-153-3853
MERIDIAN HEALTH SERVICES CORP
SUZANNE GRESHAM CENTER
240 N Tillotson Ave, Muncie, IN 47304-3988
Tel (765) 288-1928 Founded/Ownrshp 1971
Sales 50.6MM EMP 225
SIC 8093 8063 8011 Mental health clinic, outpatient; Alcohol clinic, outpatient; Drug clinic, outpatient; Family planning clinic; Psychiatric hospitals; Offices & clinics of medical doctors; Internal medicine practitioners; Physical medicine, physician/surgeon; Mental health clinic, outpatient; Alcohol clinic, outpatient; Drug clinic, outpatient; Family planning clinic; Psychiatric hospitals; Offices & clinics of medical doctors; Internal medicine practitioners; Physical medicine, physician/surgeon
CEO: Hank Milius
*VP: Kirk Shafer
VP: Scott Smalstig
Genl Mgr: Gary Garofolo
Off Mgr: Marcia Freeman
Psych: Melinda Wallpe
Doctor: Irene Hoover
Pgrm Dir: Deceil Moore

D-U-N-S 19-536-2165
MERIDIAN HEALTH SYSTEM INC
(Suby of MERIDIAN HEALTH SYSTEM INC) ★
1340 Campus Pkwy Ste A3, Wall Township, NJ 07753-6830
Tel (732) 206-8100 Founded/Ownrshp 1984
Sales 11.5MM^E EMP 280
SIC 8082 Home health care services; Home health care services

D-U-N-S 61-208-4871
MERIDIAN HEALTH SYSTEM INC
MERIDIAN HOSPITAL
1350 Campus Pkwy, Wall Township, NJ 07753-6821
Tel (732) 751-7500 Founded/Ownrshp 1996
Sales 1.6MMM EMP 8,900
SIC 8062

D-U-N-S 11-417-1155
MERIDIAN HEALTHCARE GROUP INC
3500 Financial Plz # 200, Tallahassee, FL 32312-5900
Tel (850) 325-7777 Founded/Ownrshp 2000
Sales 12.9MM^E EMP 500^E
SIC 7363 Help supply services; Help supply services
CEO: Tom Futch
*CFO: Thomas Abbruscato
*VP: Virginia A Futch

D-U-N-S 07-208-7372
■ MERIDIAN HMA LLC
RALEY HOSPITAL
(Suby of HEALTH MANAGEMENT ASSOCIATES INC) ★
1102 Constitution Ave, Meridian, MS 39301-4001
Tel (601) 693-2511 Founded/Ownrshp 1997
Sales 26.1MM^E EMP 550
SIC 8062 8051 General medical & surgical hospitals; Skilled nursing care facilities; General medical & surgical hospitals; Skilled nursing care facilities
CEO: Pam Tvarkunas
Dir Lab: Joel Gordy
Doctor: Robert Berg
Doctor: Hashim Khan
Diag Rad: John A Oliver
Diag Rad: Sumanth Reddy

MERIDIAN HOSPITAL
See MERIDIAN HEALTH SYSTEM INC

D-U-N-S 96-540-8230
MERIDIAN HOSPITALS CORP
RIVERVIEW MEDICAL CENTER
(Suby of MERIDIAN HEALTH SYSTEM INC) ★
1945 Route 33, Neptune, NJ 07753-4859
Tel (732) 751-7500 Founded/Ownrshp 1996
Sales 530.3MM^E EMP 5,200^E
Accts Pricewaterhousecoopers Llp F
SIC 8062 General medical & surgical hospitals; General medical & surgical hospitals
Pr: Mark Lory
V Ch: Brian Erler
*Pr: Timothy J Hogan
*Pr: Marc Lory
*COO: Jeff Brickman
*COO: Joseph Miller
*CFO: Bill Philips
Treas: James Bollerman
Ofcr: Alexander Lehrer
VP: Wayne Boatwright
VP: Anthony Cava
*VP: Lori Colineri
VP: Frank Goldstein
VP: Marilyn Koczan
VP: Kathleen Murray
*VP: Kelli O'Brien

*VP: Joseph Reichman
VP: David Siegel
VP: Alvis Swinney
Dir Rx: Patrick Murphy

D-U-N-S 07-885-1736
MERIDIAN IMAGING GROUP LLC
224 7th St Fl 3, Garden City, NY 11530-5781
Tel (516) 616-5000 Founded/Ownrshp 2015
Sales 35.0MM EMP 8E
SIC 8011 Radiologist
CFO: Robert Simone

D-U-N-S 94-917-9162
MERIDIAN IMAGING SOLUTIONS INC
FAX PROS, THE
5775 General Wash Dr, Alexandria, VA 22312-2418
Tel (703) 256-2195 Founded/Ownrshp 1995
Sales 29.2MM EMP 100
SIC 7629 5044 5112 5999 3579 7378 Electronic equipment repair; Copying equipment; Stationery & office supplies; Facsimile equipment; Typing & word processing machines; Computer maintenance & repair; Electronic equipment repair; Copying equipment; Stationery & office supplies; Facsimile equipment; Typing & word processing machines; Computer maintenance & repair
CEO: Teresa Sullivan
Pr: Trent Edwards
*Pr: Juliana McKee
*CFO: Laura Smith
*VP: Matt Williams
Mktg Dir: Brandon Phillips
Sls Dir: Patty Graves
Sls Mgr: Scott Westfall

D-U-N-S 94-867-4445 IMP/EXP
MERIDIAN INC
2 Mockingbird Cir, Houston, TX 77074-4122
Tel (713) 272-9707 Founded/Ownrshp 1988
Sales 5.0MME EMP 300
SIC 8082 8093 Visiting nurse service; Rehabilitation center, outpatient treatment; Mental health clinic, outpatient; Visiting nurse service; Rehabilitation center, outpatient treatment; Mental health clinic, outpatient
Pr: Bernadra Ugwu
*VP: Liner Ngiker

D-U-N-S 93-762-1217
MERIDIAN INDUSTRIAL TRUST INC
455 Market St Ste 1700, San Francisco, CA 94105-2456
Tel (415) 281-3900 Founded/Ownrshp 1995
Sales 66.1MM EMP 60
SIC 6798 Real estate investment trusts; Real estate investment trusts
CEO: Allen J Anderson
Pr: Milton K Reeder
Treas: Milton Reeder
Treas: Jaime Suarez
Sr VP: Dennis D Higgs
VP: Peter B Harmon
VP: Celeste K Woo
Board of Directors: C E Doc Cornutt, T Patrick Duncan, Peter O Hanson, John S Moody, Robert E Morgan, James M Pollak, Kenneth N Stensby, Lee W Wilson

D-U-N-S 00-610-6959 IMP/EXP
MERIDIAN INDUSTRIES INC (WI)
MERIDIAN SPECIALTY YARN GROUP
735 N Water St Ste 630, Milwaukee, WI 53202-4104
Tel (414) 224-0610 Founded/Ownrshp 1943
Sales 372.9MME EMP 2,000
SIC 3069 2843 2269 7389 Medical & laboratory rubber sundries & related products; Processing assistants; Dyeing: raw stock yarn & narrow fabrics; Packaging & labeling services; Medical & laboratory rubber sundries & related products; Processing assistants; Dyeing: raw stock yarn & narrow fabrics; Packaging & labeling services
CEO: Bruce E Pindyck
CFO: Douglas C Miller
Exec: Scott Jacobson
Plnt Mgr: Dan Laturno
Plnt Mgr: Keith Wengerd
Plnt Mgr: Ken Zylka
Snr Mgr: Greg Lucas

D-U-N-S 15-451-3527
■ **MERIDIAN INSURANCE GROUP INC**
(Suby of STATE AUTO INSURANCE CO) ★
2955 N Meridian St, Indianapolis, IN 46208-4714
Tel (317) 931-7000 Founded/Ownrshp 2001
Sales NA EMP 400
Accts Pricewater House Coopers Llp
SIC 6331 6411 Fire, marine & casualty insurance; Insurance agents, brokers & service; Fire, marine & casualty insurance; Insurance agents, brokers & service
Pr: Ben Blackmon
Pr: Bob Moone
COO: Steven R Hazelbaker
CFO: Steven E English
Sr VP: Timothy J Hanrahan
Dir IT: Chris Reinhardt
Sales Exec: Scott Sell

D-U-N-S 07-482-4632 IMP
MERIDIAN INTERNATIONAL CENTER
TRAINING & VISITORS SERVICES D
1630 Crescent Pl Nw, Washington, DC 20009-4004
Tel (202) 939-5592 Founded/Ownrshp 1960
Sales 32.7MM EMP 100E
Accts Grant Thornton Llp Mc Lean V
SIC 8399 Social service information exchange; Social service information exchange
Pr: Stuart Holliday
*CFO: Kurt Sodee
Ofcr: Morcos Amal
Ofcr: Bogdan Banu
Ofcr: Sandra Barkan
Ofcr: Elizabeth Barry
Ofcr: Sherry Bell
Ofcr: Sean Callaghan
Ofcr: Joanne Clark
Ofcr: Nancy Fearheiley
Ofcr: Eynon Jill
Ofcr: Erin Koepke
Ofcr: Frank Lennox
Ofcr: Carolyn Nomura
Ofcr: David Paulson
Ofcr: Mark Rebstock
Ofcr: Renee Worthington
Ofcr: Arthur Zegelbone
*Sr VP: Salvatore Pappalardo
VP: Myra Best
VP: Henry Collins

D-U-N-S 03-696-8949
MERIDIAN IT INC
MERIDIAN GROUP
(Suby of MERIDIAN GROUP) ★
9 Parkway N Ste 500, Deerfield, IL 60015-2545
Tel (847) 964-2664 Founded/Ownrshp 2003
Sales 213.3MME EMP 113
SIC 5045 Computers, peripherals & software; Computers, peripherals & software
CEO: Brad Ihlenfeld
*Pr: Lisa Pettay
*CFO: Mike Brannan
*Ex VP: Steve Bickford
Sr VP: Robert Dickert
*Sr VP: Rochelle Slater
VP: Sue Atwood
VP: Al Consena
VP: Chris Ellerman
*VP: Bill Flaherty
VP: Dennis O'Connell
VP: Tim Patronik
VP: Bill Slaherty

D-U-N-S 01-027-4405
MERIDIAN LEASING CORP (IL)
MERIDIAN GROUP
(Suby of MERIDIAN GROUP INTERNATIONAL INC) ★
9 Parkway N Ste 500, Deerfield, IL 60015-2545
Tel (847) 964-2700 Founded/Ownrshp 1979, 1994
Sales NA EMP 250
Accts Deloitte & Touche Llp Chicago
SIC 6159 Machinery & equipment finance leasing; Machinery & equipment finance leasing
CEO: Ian J Pye
*Pr: Brad V Ihlenfeld
*CFO: Michael D Brannan
CFO: William Flaherty
Ex VP: Steve Bickford
Sr VP: John Adams
Sr VP: Robert Dickert
Sr VP: Thomas Horan
Sr VP: Mike Sell
*Sr VP: Rochelle Slater
*VP: Bill Flaherty
VP: Steve Leverton
VP: Dennis O'Connell
VP: John O'Connor
VP: Kam Sweitzer
VP: John Trifone

MERIDIAN LIGHTWEIGHT TECH
See MAGNESIUM PRODUCTS OF AMERICA INC

D-U-N-S 06-590-7065
MERIDIAN MANAGEMENT CORP
(Suby of AMERICORP INC) ★
818 A1a N Ste 300, Ponte Vedra Beach, FL 32082-3298
Tel (904) 285-3400 Founded/Ownrshp 1973
Sales 28.9MME EMP 550
SIC 6531 Real estate managers; Real estate managers
Pr: Elliott S Horne
*Treas: Karol D Horne
*Sec: Tom Brownfield
Sr Cor Off: Elliot Home
Off Mgr: Pegi Beecroft

D-U-N-S 19-806-6706
MERIDIAN MANUFACTURING INC
MERIDIAN MFG GROUP INC
(Suby of TREVLUC HOLDINGS LTD)
2902 Expansion Blvd, Storm Lake, IA 50588-7317
Tel (712) 732-1780 Founded/Ownrshp 1988
Sales 31.7MME EMP 95
SIC 3443 Tanks, lined: metal plate
Pr: Paul Cunningham
*Ch: Russ Edwards
*Sr VP: Glenn Frieson
*Sr VP: Bernie Thiessen
Exec: Lorna Currie
QA Dir: Brian Darden
Plnt Mgr: Terry Pearson
Ql Cn Mgr: Denis Flemming
Mktg Mgr: Sid Lockhart
Manager: Eric Boughey
Manager: Peter Dunn
Board of Directors: Gary Edwards, Kevin Edwards

D-U-N-S 04-950-4624
■ **MERIDIAN MEDICAL TECHNOLOGIES INC**
(Suby of PFIZER INC) ★
6350 Stevens Forest Rd, Columbia, MD 21046-3231
Tel (443) 259-7800 Founded/Ownrshp 2010
Sales 90.3MME EMP 452
SIC 3841 Hypodermic needles & syringes; Hypodermic needles & syringes
Pr: Dennis P O'Brien
*CEO: James H Miller
CFO: Troy Brasfell
*Sr VP: Gerald L Wannarka
VP: Tom Handel
Genl Mgr: Cristina D'Erasmo
DP Exec: Stan Hammond
IT Man: Paul Muma
IT Man: John Wittier
Ql Cn Mgr: Clint Lawson
Snr PM: Kyal Hackett

MERIDIAN MFG GROUP INC
See MERIDIAN MANUFACTURING INC

D-U-N-S 00-976-4379 IMP/EXP
MERIDIAN NUT GROWERS LLC
1625 Shaw Ave, Clovis, CA 93611-4089
Tel (559) 458-7272 Founded/Ownrshp 1998
Sales 47.0MM EMP 17
SIC 5159 Nuts & nut by-products; Nuts & nut by-products
*COO: Mark Dutra
Opers Mgr: Roni Johnson

MERIDIAN PRODUCTS
See SINGLETON FISHERIES INC

D-U-N-S 83-732-6875
■ **MERIDIAN PROJECT SYSTEMS INC**
MERIDIAN SYSTEMS
(Suby of TRIMBLE NAVIGATION LIMITED INC) ★
1720 Pririe Cy Rd Ste 120, Folsom, CA 95630
Tel (916) 294-2000 Founded/Ownrshp 2006
Sales 25.4MME EMP 120
SIC 7372 Business oriented computer software; Application computer software; Business oriented computer software; Application computer software
CEO: Steven W Berglund
Sr VP: Thomas Burke
VP: John Brown
VP: Sallie Sutter
Prgrm Mgr: Toni Smith
IT Man: Eva Ware
Tech Mgr: Michael Shelnutt
Opers Mgr: Louis Binaley
VP Sls: Al Marshall

D-U-N-S 08-160-4282
MERIDIAN PUBLIC SCHOOL DISTRICT
3361 N Meridian Rd, Sanford, MI 48657-9161
Tel (989) 687-2662 Founded/Ownrshp 1920
Sales 11.2MME EMP 280
Accts Lewis & Knopf Cpas Pc Fli
SIC 8211 Public elementary school; Public junior high school; Public senior high school; Public elementary school; Public junior high school; Public senior high school
Pr: John Shaffer

D-U-N-S 10-004-0013
MERIDIAN PUBLIC SCHOOL DISTRICT
1019 25th Ave, Meridian, MS 39301-4999
Tel (601) 483-6271 Founded/Ownrshp 1885
Sales 58.5MME EMP 1,500
Accts Rea Shaw Giffin & Stuart Ll
SIC 8211 Public elementary school; Public junior high school; Public senior high school; Public elementary school; Public junior high school; Public senior high school
Ofcr: Rebecca Stevens

D-U-N-S 61-911-8359 IMP
MERIDIAN RACK & PINION INC
6740 Cobra Way Ste 200, San Diego, CA 92121-4102
Tel (858) 587-8777 Founded/Ownrshp 1989
Sales 78.3MME EMP 130
SIC 5013 5961 Automotive supplies & parts; Mail order house, order taking office only; Automotive supplies & parts; Mail order house, order taking office only
CEO: Dara Greaney
*Pr: Matt Glauber
*CFO: Chris Struempler

D-U-N-S 14-982-5403
■ **MERIDIAN RAIL ACQUISITION CORP**
GREENBRIER RAIL SERVICES
(Suby of GREENBRIER COMPANIES INC) ★
1 Centerpointe Dr Ste 400, Lake Oswego, OR 97035-8614
Tel (503) 684-7000 Founded/Ownrshp 2006
Sales 20.0MME EMP 254E
SIC 3312 Wheels; Wheels
CEO: James Cowan
*Pr: Alejandro Centurion
*VP: Susan Baacke
Plnt Mgr: Robert Dewey

D-U-N-S 13-034-1543
MERIDIAN RESIDENTIAL CAPITAL LLC
FIRST MERIDIAN MORTGAGE
2329 Nostrand Ave Ste 300, Brooklyn, NY 11210-3948
Tel (718) 377-7900 Founded/Ownrshp 2002
Sales NA EMP 122
SIC 6162 Mortgage brokers, using own money; Mortgage brokers, using own money
CEO: Yeoh Oon
Pr: David Mizrahi
CFO: Joe Septimus
Ofcr: Elaine Shaw
Ofcr: Moshe Sitorsky
Ofcr: Rifki Steinmetz
VP: Peter Chiasera
VP: Alyse Mitnick
VP: Moshe Nafisi
VP: Harry Sipper
Brnch Mgr: Jason Berg
Board of Directors: Edward F Smith III

D-U-N-S 78-806-3808
■ **MERIDIAN SECURITY INSURANCE CO**
(Suby of MERIDIAN INSURANCE GROUP INC) ★
2955 N Meridian St, Indianapolis, IN 46208-4714
Tel (317) 931-7542 Founded/Ownrshp 1986
Sales NA EMP 400
SIC 6331 Fire, marine & casualty insurance; Property damage insurance; Fire, marine & casualty insurance; Property damage insurance
Pr: Norma J Oman
CFO: Steve Hazelbaker
VP: James Duemey
VP: Timothy Hanrahan
VP: John Melvin
VP: Thomas Ober
VP: Joyce Wright
Mktg Dir: Scott Jones

MERIDIAN SPECIALTY YARN GROUP
See MERIDIAN INDUSTRIES INC

MERIDIAN SYSTEMS
See MERIDIAN PROJECT SYSTEMS INC

D-U-N-S 08-838-3414
MERIDIAN TECHNOLOGIES INC (FL)
5210 Belfort Rd Ste 400, Jacksonville, FL 32256-6050
Tel (904) 332-0700 Founded/Ownrshp 1998
Sales 27.0MME EMP 86
SIC 5045 7373 Mainframe computers; Local area network (LAN) systems integrator; Turnkey vendors, computer systems; Mainframe computers; Local area network (LAN) systems integrator; Turnkey vendors, computer systems
Pr: Christopher B Pillay
*CFO: Joseph Devaney
*VP: Monteen Pillay
Brnch Mgr: Davis Lane

D-U-N-S 06-430-4223 IMP
MERIDIAN TEXTILES INC
6415 Canning St, Commerce, CA 90040-3121
Tel (323) 869-5700 Founded/Ownrshp 1981
Sales 37.6MME EMP 75
SIC 5131 Textile converters
Pr: Howard Deutchman

D-U-N-S 08-458-2428
MERIDIAN TITLE CORP
202 S Michigan St Ste 300, South Bend, IN 46601-2006
Tel (574) 232-5845 Founded/Ownrshp 1946
Sales NA EMP 242
SIC 6361 Real estate title insurance; Real estate title insurance
Pr: Mark Myers
*CFO: Renee Preniczny
Ofcr: Steve Hargrove
*Ex VP: Frank Antonovitz
IT Man: Josh Coddens
Sftwr Eng: Krista Myers
Sales Exec: Amy Kintz
Sls Dir: Debbie Collins
Counsel: Beau Dunfee

D-U-N-S 13-328-8980
MERIDIAS CAPITAL INC
375 N Stephanie St, Henderson, NV 89014-8771
Tel (702) 938-6800 Founded/Ownrshp 1999
Sales NA EMP 420
SIC 6162 Mortgage bankers & correspondents; Mortgage bankers & correspondents
Pr: Nick Florez
*Ex VP: Brent Demoray

D-U-N-S 88-480-0574
MERIDIUM INC
207 Bullitt Ave Se, Roanoke, VA 24013-1738
Tel (540) 344-9205 Founded/Ownrshp 1993
Sales 60.9MME EMP 289
SIC 7371 Computer software development; Computer software development
Pr: Bonz Hart
*CFO: Carl Miller
*Chf Mktg O: Patricia Foye
Sr VP: Jeff Finochiaro
*Sr VP: Mike Matlock
*Sr VP: Joe Nichols
*Sr VP: Roy E Whitt
VP: Mike Bittner
*VP: Bradley Broughton
VP: Paul Casto
VP: Brian Clark
VP: Christina Goodman
VP: Eric Grogg
VP: Scott Jones
*VP: Kenny Morgan
VP: Vinay Nihalani
VP: Hari Pulijal
VP: Andrew Soignier
VP: Roy Whitt
Exec: Marney Young

D-U-N-S 04-503-4709
MERILIZ INC (CA)
DOME PRINTING AND LITHOGRAPH
340 Commerce Cir, Sacramento, CA 95815-4213
Tel (916) 923-3663 Founded/Ownrshp 1947, 1969
Sales 57.0MME EMP 120
Accts Perry-Smith Llp Sacramento C
SIC 2752 Commercial printing, offset; Commercial printing, offset
Pr: Timothy M Poole
*COO: Andrew Poole
*Chf Mktg O: Robert Poole
*VP: Dave Baker
*VP: Eric Carle
Ql Cn Mgr: Aroliya Wells

MERILLAT
See MASCO CABINETRY TRANSPORT CO

D-U-N-S 79-690-7181
■ **MERILLAT INDUSTRIES INC**
(Suby of MERILLAT LP) ★
865 Pilot Rd, Las Vegas, NV 89119-3726
Tel (702) 897-9800 Founded/Ownrshp 2007
Sales 84.0MME EMP 2,326E
SIC 3999 Manufacturing industries
Plnt Mgr: Steve Johnson

D-U-N-S 96-364-2491 IMP
■ **MERILLAT LP**
(Suby of MASCO CABINETRY LLC) ★
5353 W Us Highway 223, Adrian, MI 49221-8901
Tel (517) 263-0771 Founded/Ownrshp 2011
Sales 179.9MME EMP 3,210
SIC 2434 Wood kitchen cabinets; Wood kitchen cabinets
Genl Pt: Clay Kiefaber
Pt: Eugene A Gargaro Jr
Pt: Warren J Potter
COO: Keith Almond
Treas: Doug Austin
Treas: John Thurman
VP: Jerry Mollien
VP: Michael Thompson
Mng Dir: Jeff Park
Brnch Mgr: Mike Stickles
Div Mgr: John Jackson

D-U-N-S 07-552-9586
MERION LOWER SCHOOL DISTRICT INC (PA)
301 E Montgomery Ave, Ardmore, PA 19003-3338
Tel (610) 645-1983 Founded/Ownrshp 1936
Sales 92.0MME EMP 1,600
Accts Rainer & Company Newtown Squa

SIC 8211 Public junior high school; Public senior high school; Public elementary school; Public junior high school; Public senior high school; Public elementary school
Dir Sec: Dennis Witt
CTO: Mary Zoshak
MIS Dir: George Frazier
Telecom Mg: Mike Perbix
IT Man: Scott Eveslage
Pr Dir: Douglas Young
Schl Brd P: Melissa Gilbert
Teacher Pr: Mia Kim
Psych: Kimberly Contegiacomo
Psych: Joseph Havlick
Psych: Barbara Serratore

D-U-N-S 15-398-4992
MERION PUBLICATIONS INC
ADVANCE NEWSPAPERS
2900 Horizon Dr, King of Prussia, PA 19406-2651
Tel (610) 278-1400 *Founded/Ownrshp* 1985
Sales 48.1MM^E *EMP* 350
SIC 2721 Trade journals: publishing only, not printed on site; Trade journals: publishing only, not printed on site
Pr: Ann Wiest Kielinski
Treas: Kyle Kielinski
**VP:* W M Kielinski
Dir Lab: Jim Cook
Creative D: Susan Basile
CIO: Edmund Collins
Dir IT: Craig Kielinski
IT Man: Jeff Myers
Software D: Sung Joung
Sftwr Eng: Doug Bohl
Sftwr Eng: Andy Park

D-U-N-S 09-761-7067
MERIPLEX COMMUNICATIONS LTD
10111 Richmond Ave # 500, Houston, TX 77042-4216
Tel (713) 977-0756 *Founded/Ownrshp* 2001
Sales 20.5MM^E *EMP* 26^E
SIC 7379 Computer related consulting services
CEO: Arthur Henley
Sr VP: John Tollefsen
VP: David Henley
VP: Elmer Mosbey
VP: Benjamin Swan
Tech Mgr: Mark Gerhauser
Software D: Brian Jones
Netwrk Eng: Jose Alejandro
Netwrk Eng: Adam Richardson
VP Opers: Bruce Rohde
Mktg Mgr: Tom Frangione

D-U-N-S 80-120-5894 IMP/EXP
MERISANT CO
(*Suby of* FLAVORS HOLDINGS INC) ★
125 S Wacker Dr Ste 3150, Chicago, IL 60606-4424
Tel (312) 840-6000 *Founded/Ownrshp* 2009
Sales 152.4MM^E *EMP* 437^E
SIC 2869 Industrial organic chemicals; Industrial organic chemicals
Pr: Paul Block
CFO: Ross Campbell
CFO: Julie Wool
Treas: George Manor
VP: Brian Alsvig
VP: Jonathan W Cole
VP: Vivian Cosey-Glover
VP: Angelo Di Benedetto
VP: Yann Kervoern
VP: Carrie Murphy
VP: Hugues Pitre

D-U-N-S 13-167-8406 IMP
MERISANT US INC
(*Suby of* MERISANT CO) ★
150 S Wacker Dr Ste 3150, Chicago, IL 60606-4207
Tel (312) 840-6000 *Founded/Ownrshp* 2000
Sales 126.6MM^E *EMP* 436
SIC 2869 Sweeteners, synthetic; Sweeteners, synthetic
VP: Brian Alsvig
**CEO:* Paul Murphy
**CFO:* Trisha Rosado
VP: Jane Boyce
IT Man: Keith Halborsen

D-U-N-S 00-294-5814 IMP
MERIT BRASS CO (OH)
1 Merit Dr, Cleveland, OH 44143-1457
Tel (216) 261-9800 *Founded/Ownrshp* 1961
Sales 34.1MM^E *EMP* 253
SIC 3432 5051 5074

D-U-N-S 05-874-0742
MERIT CAPITAL PARTNERS
303 W Madison St Ste 210, Chicago, IL 60606-3300
Tel (312) 592-6111 *Founded/Ownrshp* 1993
Sales 28.1MM^E *EMP* 182
SIC 6722 Management investment, open-end
Mng Pt: Marc J Walfish
Mng Pt: Thomas F Campion
Mng Pt: David M Jones
Mng Pt: Timothy J Mc Kenzie
Mng Pt: Terrance M Shipp
VP: Lauren Hamlin
VP: Joe Polaneczky
VP: Jeremy Stump
Exec: Abby Del Carlo

D-U-N-S 02-304-5677
MERIT CHEVROLET CO
2695 Brookview Dr E, Saint Paul, MN 55119-4794
Tel (651) 739-4400 *Founded/Ownrshp* 1949
Sales 43.9MM^E *EMP* 105
SIC 5511 Automobiles, new & used; Automobiles, new & used
Pr: Bruce Rinkel
Genl Mgr: Tom Krebsbach
Off Mgr: Terry Sanford
Sls Mgr: Robert Notch
Sales Asso: Mike Salmon
Sales Asso: Adam Tarras

MERIT COMPANIES THE
See MERIT PROPERTY MANAGEMENT INC

D-U-N-S 78-398-7423
MERIT CONSTRUCTION CO
2400 Pleasantdale Rd, Atlanta, GA 30340-1560
Tel (770) 448-4200 *Founded/Ownrshp* 1991
Sales 28.0MM^E *EMP* 65
SIC 1542 Commercial & office building, new construction; Commercial & office buildings, renovation & repair
CEO: William L Kizer
**CFO:* Mark B Schilling
VP: Steve Heatherly
CTO: Alan Shoenig

D-U-N-S 18-795-9341
MERIT CONTRACTING INC
ELKHORN EXCAVATING-DIV
1428 Delberts Dr, Monongahela, PA 15063-9752
Tel (724) 258-9009 *Founded/Ownrshp* 1988
Sales 51.5MM^E *EMP* 150
SIC 1542 1541 Commercial & office building, new construction; Industrial buildings, new construction; Factory construction; Industrial plant construction; Water & sewer line construction; Bridge construction; Highway & street construction; Commercial & office building, new construction; Industrial buildings, new construction; Factory construction
Pr: Barbara Gigliotti
**Pr:* Ronald Mc Cracke
**Treas:* Susan J Yackovich
**VP:* Pino Cianflone
**Prin:* Clement Gigliotti Sr
Sfty Mgr: Aaron Laughlin

D-U-N-S 02-193-1047 IMP/EXP
MERIT DISTRIBUTION GROUP LLC
LANCASTER
1310 Union St, Spartanburg, SC 29302-3342
Tel (864) 583-3011 *Founded/Ownrshp* 1953
Sales 659.4MM^E *EMP* 295^E
SIC 5198 Paints; Varnishes; Paint brushes, rollers, sprayers; Paints; Varnishes; Paint brushes, rollers, sprayers
Pr: Mike Smith
**CFO:* Jon Heard
Exec: Ruth Shelton
Rgnl Mgr: John Keeney
Manager: Steve Harrington
Sls Mgr: Pete Ahlstrom
Sls Mgr: Darren Ball
Sls Mgr: Roy Daiell
Sls Mgr: Sally Hanson
Sls Mgr: John Hardy
Sls Mgr: John Shrum

D-U-N-S 10-352-4450 IMP
MERIT ELECTRIC CO
5626 Mitchelldale St, Houston, TX 77092-7028
Tel (713) 681-2808 *Founded/Ownrshp* 1983
Sales 37.7MM^E *EMP* 150
SIC 1731 General electrical contractor; General electrical contractor
Pr: Larry B Wiggins
**Pr:* John Frazier
Bd of Dir: James Wooten
**VP:* Pat Sansaricq
Off Mgr: Dana Keller
Sfty Mgr: Rodrigo Jimenez

D-U-N-S 01-051-7696
MERIT ELECTRIC CO INC (FL)
6520 125th Ave, Largo, FL 33773-3603
Tel (727) 536-5945 *Founded/Ownrshp* 1975, 1990
Sales 23.9MM^E *EMP* 100
SIC 1731 Electrical work
Pr: Gregory H Wooten
**Treas:* James N Wooten
**VP:* Timothy L Wooten
IT Man: Valerie Tice

D-U-N-S 14-976-5369
MERIT ELECTRICAL INC
(*Suby of* YTG LLC) ★
17723 Airline Hwy, Prairieville, LA 70769-3701
Tel (225) 673-8850 *Founded/Ownrshp* 2000
Sales 43.2MM *EMP* 300
Accts Rea Shaw Giffin & Stuart Ll
SIC 1731 Electrical work; Electrical work
Pr: Reggie Williams
CFO: Brandon Dunn
**VP:* Pat Mason
**VP:* Mark Wamsley

D-U-N-S 09-879-6329 IMP
MERIT ELECTRONIC DESIGN CO INC
MEDCO
190 Rodeo Dr, Edgewood, NY 11717-8317
Tel (631) 667-9699 *Founded/Ownrshp* 1976
Sales 43.2MM^E *EMP* 115
Accts Goldstein & Co Llp
SIC 3679 Electronic circuits; Electronic circuits
Pr: Guy Intoci
**CFO:* Cheryl Sickles

D-U-N-S 60-547-0475 IMP
MERIT ENERGY CO LLC
13737 Noel Rd Ste 1200, Dallas, TX 75240-1335
Tel (972) 770-3507 *Founded/Ownrshp* 1989
Sales 692.5MM^E *EMP* 640
SIC 1311 Crude petroleum production; Natural gas production; Crude petroleum production; Natural gas production
Ch Bd: William Gayden
**Pr:* Robert R Matejek
Treas: Jacques Bares
**Ex VP:* Thomas Porter Trimble
VP: Mike Markus
VP: Todd Mundorff
VP Bus Dev: Brad Shawhan
Exec: Melanie Lane
IT Man: John Stroud
IT Man: Dale Walters
Sfty Mgr: Vicki Kniss

D-U-N-S 79-739-3626 IMP
MERIT GEAR LLC
810 Hudson St, Antigo, WI 54409-2247
Tel (715) 623-2307 *Founded/Ownrshp* 2008
Sales 40.5MM^E *EMP* 125
SIC 3566 Gears, power transmission, except automotive; Gears, power transmission, except automotive
Pr: Thomas Rouse
**VP:* Friedrich Neuhoff
**VP:* Larry Steffenf

MERIT HEALTH CENTRAL
See JACKSON HMA LLC

D-U-N-S 16-676-5599
■ **MERIT HEALTH NACHEZ COMMUNITY CAMPUS**
HMA
(*Suby of* HEALTH MANAGEMENT ASSOCIATES INC) ★
129 Jefferson Davis Blvd, Natchez, MS 39120-5103
Tel (601) 445-6200 *Founded/Ownrshp* 1993
Sales 44.2MM *EMP* 300
SIC 8062 General medical & surgical hospitals; General medical & surgical hospitals
Pr: J Allen Tyra
VP: James Armour
Dir OR: Carrie Coleman
Dir Lab: Marc Dillon
Nurse Mgr: Luridean Jackson
QA Dir: Lana Stamper
Dir QC: Mistic Smith
Sfty Dirs: Jason Lynch

MERIT HEALTH RIVER REGION
See VICKSBURG HEALTHCARE LLC

D-U-N-S 14-591-8434
MERIT HEALTH SYSTEMS LLC
1033 Skokie Blvd Ste 360, Northbrook, IL 60062-4137
Tel (502) 753-0890 *Founded/Ownrshp* 2004
Sales 86.7MM^E *EMP* 2,600
SIC 8741 Hospital management; Hospital management
CEO: Michael P Curran
Off Mgr: Erin Schaefer

D-U-N-S 05-138-4657
MERIT INTEGRATED LOGISTICS LLC
29122 Rancho Viejo Rd # 211, San Juan Capistrano, CA 92675-1039
Tel (949) 481-0685 *Founded/Ownrshp* 2013
Sales 55.0MM^E *EMP* 600
SIC 4731 Freight transportation arrangement
CEO: Mike Bletko

D-U-N-S 05-868-9951
■ **MERIT LIFE INSURANCE CO**
(*Suby of* SPRINGLEAF FINANCE CORP) ★
601 Nw 2nd St Unit 1, Evansville, IN 47708-1061
Tel (812) 424-8031 *Founded/Ownrshp* 1974
Sales NA *EMP* 107
Accts Ernst & Young Llp Indianapoli
SIC 6311 Life insurance; Life insurance
CEO: Daniel Leitch III
**Ch Bd:* James Turerff
**Pr:* Robert Womack
CFO: Donald R Breivogel Jr
**CFO:* Philip M Hanley
**Sr VP:* Wayne D Baker
**Sr VP:* Bennie D Hendrix
**Sr VP:* James R Jerwers
**VP:* Larry R Klaholz
**VP:* Gary Smith
**VP:* Peter V Tuters

D-U-N-S 11-301-8956
■ **MERIT MECHANICAL INC**
(*Suby of* COMFORT SYSTEMS USA INC) ★
9630 153rd Ave Ne, Redmond, WA 98052-2546
Tel (425) 883-9224 *Founded/Ownrshp* 2008
Sales 22.0MM^E *EMP* 85
SIC 1711 Mechanical contractor
Pr: Roderick V Kirkwood
**Pr:* Dave Patterson
COO: Kingston Jabin
**Treas:* Brian J Engstrom
**VP:* William Michael Frickberg
**VP:* William George
**VP:* Trent McKenna

D-U-N-S 18-476-3290 IMP
▲ **MERIT MEDICAL SYSTEMS INC**
1600 W Merit Pkwy, South Jordan, UT 84095-2416
Tel (801) 253-1600 *Founded/Ownrshp* 1987
Sales 509.6MM *EMP* 3,105^E
Tkr Sym MMSI *Exch* NGS
SIC 3841 Surgical & medical instruments; Surgical & medical instruments
Ch Bd: Fred P Lampropoulos
Pr: Brent Bowen
Pr: Charlotte Thomsen
COO: Ronald A Frost
CFO: Bernard Birkett
**CFO:* Kent W Stanger
Ofcr: Greg Barnett
Ex VP: Justin Lampropoulos
VP: Michael Blackham
VP: Tony Keaveney
VP: Glenn Norton
VP: Mazhar Shah
Board of Directors: A Scott Anderson, Richard W Edelman, Nolan E Karras, Franklin J Miller, F Ann Millner, Michael E Stillabower

D-U-N-S 61-512-1324
MERIT NETWORK INC
1000 Oakbrook Dr Ste 200, Ann Arbor, MI 48104-6815
Tel (734) 527-5700 *Founded/Ownrshp* 1966
Sales 22.6MM *EMP* 90
Accts Plante & Moran Pllc Chicago
SIC 7375 Information retrieval services; Information retrieval services
CEO: Don Welch
VP: Joe Adams
**VP:* Elwood Downing
VP: Rob Golden
VP: Gavin Leach
**VP:* Karen Smith
**VP:* Bob Stovall
Exec: Jamie Nielsen
Snr Sftwr: Todd White

CTO: Bill Piper
Netwrk Mgr: Carlos Ramos

MERIT OIL
See NUCKLES OIL CO INC

D-U-N-S 03-874-5667
MERIT PROPERTY MANAGEMENT INC
MERIT COMPANIES THE
(*Suby of* FIRSTSERVICE CORPORATION)
15241 Laguna Canyon Rd, Irvine, CA 92618-3146
Tel (949) 448-6000 *Founded/Ownrshp* 2007
Sales 41.0MM^E *EMP* 514
SIC 6531 Real estate managers; Real estate managers
CEO: Melinda Masson
VP: Kelly Lee

D-U-N-S 78-756-0051
MERIT RESOURCES INC
(*Suby of* IOWA NETWORK SERVICES INC) ★
7760 Office Plaza Dr S, West Des Moines, IA 50266-2336
Tel (800) 336-1931 *Founded/Ownrshp* 2013
Sales 21.3MM^E *EMP* 200
SIC 8721 8742 Payroll accounting service; Human resource consulting services
Pr: Joel Duncan
**Pr:* Lisa Welshhons
VP: Charlie Duncan
VP: Joe Lane
VP: Melissa Ness
VP: Brenda Smith
VP: Andy Tebockhorst
VP: Sean Yolish
Dir Bus: Charles Brubaker
Dir Bus: Janette Fiedler
Dir Bus: Christie Newsom

D-U-N-S 03-211-0756
MERIT SERVICE SOLUTIONS LLC
52 E Swedesford Rd # 100, Malvern, PA 19355-1488
Tel (800) 644-6035 *Founded/Ownrshp* 1985
Sales 30.5MM^E *EMP* 85^E
SIC 8741 Management services
Pr: Matt Klein
V Ch: Michael McDevitt
Pr: Rob Haly
VP: Joe Hoey
Exec: Peter Haran
Area Mgr: James Murphy
Area Mgr: Joy Squires
Area Supr: Dave Dunn
Area Supr: Pat Ruppert
Opers Mgr: Samuel Evans
Opers Mgr: Mike Taylor

D-U-N-S 82-693-1946
MERITAGE GROUP LP
The Embarcad Pier 5 St Pier, San Francisco, CA 94111
Tel (415) 399-5330 *Founded/Ownrshp* 2007
Sales 94.1MM^E *EMP* 1,500
SIC 8741 Management services; Management services
Prin: Mark Mindich

D-U-N-S 19-690-5657
▲ **MERITAGE HOMES CORP**
8800 E Raintree Dr # 300, Scottsdale, AZ 85260-3966
Tel (480) 515-8100 *Founded/Ownrshp* 1996
Sales 2.1MMM *EMP* 1,300
Accts Deloitte & Touche Llp Phoenix
Tkr Sym MTH *Exch* NYS
SIC 1521 New construction, single-family houses; New construction, single-family houses
Ch Bd: Steven J Hilton
Pr: John Coleman
Pr: Phillippe Lord
Pr: Clint Szubinski
Pr: James Thrower
COO: Steven M Davis
CFO: Larry W Seay
Ex VP: Davis Steve
Ex VP: C Timothy White
Ex VP: Timothy White
Sr VP: Hilla Sferruzza
VP: Robert Bodnar
VP: Jim Capprita
VP: Peter Hebert
VP: Michael Ilescremieux
VP: Lance Johnson
VP: Kevin Kimball
VP: Mark Reynolds
VP: Austin Woffinden
Div/Sub He: Kirk Perrin
Board of Directors: Peter L Ax, Dana C Bradford, Richard T Burke Sr, Gerald W Haddock, Michael R Odell, Raymond Oppel, Robert G Sarver

D-U-N-S 60-583-1895
■ **MERITAGE HOMES OF FLORIDA INC**
MONTEREY HOMES
(*Suby of* MERITAGE HOMES CORP) ★
8800 E Raintree Dr # 300, Scottsdale, AZ 85260-3966
Tel (480) 515-8500 *Founded/Ownrshp* 2004
Sales 93.1MM^E *EMP* 1,200^E
SIC 1521 Single-family housing construction; Single-family housing construction
Ch Bd: Steven J Hilton
CFO: Larry Seay
Ex VP: Steve Davis
Ex VP: Sandi Karrmann
Ex VP: Tim White

D-U-N-S 15-136-7539
▲ **MERITAGE HOSPITALITY GROUP INC**
3310 Eagle Park Dr Ne # 205, Grand Rapids, MI 49525-4574
Tel (616) 776-2600 *Founded/Ownrshp* 1986
Sales 91.9MM *EMP* 1,700
Tkr Sym MHGU *Exch* OTO
SIC 5812 6794 Fast-food restaurant, chain; Franchises, selling or licensing; Fast-food restaurant, chain; Franchises, selling or licensing
Ch Bd: Robert E Schermer Jr
COO: Alan Pruitt
COO: Jeff Weber
**COO:* Roger L Zingle
**CFO:* Gary A Rose

VP: Robert Potts
**VP:* James R Saalfeld
VP: James Saalfeld
Dir IT: Josiah Becker
Dir IT: Brad Van Horn
Mktg Mgr: Lindsay Stone

MERITAGE II
See MERITAGE MIDSTREAM SERVICES II LLC

D-U-N-S 07-857-1828
MERITAGE MIDSTREAM SERVICES II LLC
MERITAGE II
1331 17th St Ste 1100, Denver, CO 80202-5819
Tel (303) 551-8150 *Founded/Ownrshp* 2012
Sales 200.0MM *EMP* 70
SIC 1389 Gas field services; Oil field services
Treas: William Champion
Off Mgr: Brook Kimber

D-U-N-S 08-009-6111
MERITAGE MIDSTREAM SERVICES IV LLC
(*Suby of* RIVERSTONE HOLDINGS LLC) ★
1331 17th St Ste 1100, Denver, CO 80202-5819
Tel (303) 551-8150 *Founded/Ownrshp* 2015
Sales 28.0MM *EMP* 1
SIC 1321 Natural gas liquids
CEO: Steven Hubkaby

D-U-N-S 78-710-3618
MERITAGE RESORT AND SPA
875 Bordeaux Way, NAPA, CA 94558-7524
Tel (707) 259-0633 *Founded/Ownrshp* 2006
Sales 15.8MM^E *EMP* 350
SIC 7991 Spas; Spas
Prin: Timothy R Busch
Off Mgr: Evan Harrelson
Off Admin: Pat Springer
IT Man: Pamela Dunn
Natl Sales: Craig Tonks

D-U-N-S 15-738-2664
■ **MERITAIN HEALTH INC**
(*Suby of* PRODIGY HEALTH GROUP, INC.)
300 Corporate Pkwy 100s, Amherst, NY 14226-1207
Tel (716) 319-5500 *Founded/Ownrshp* 1986
Sales 83.9MM^E *EMP* 1,300
SIC 8741 Hospital management; Nursing & personal care facility management; Hospital management; Nursing & personal care facility management
Pr: Elliot Cooperstone
**CFO:* Vincent Dimura
Sr VP: Margie Degrace
**Sr VP:* David C Parker
VP: Tom Applehans
VP: Jeffrey Diekema
VP: Kari Niblack
VP: Mark Ruddick
VP: Kevin Wise
Dir IT: Joseph Dickson
Dir IT: James Malvey

D-U-N-S 09-379-9058
MERITAN INC
4700 Poplar Ave Ste 400, Memphis, TN 38117-4411
Tel (901) 766-0600 *Founded/Ownrshp* 1961
Sales 15.6MM *EMP* 650
Accts Zoccola Kaplan Pllc Germanto
SIC 8322 8351 Individual & family services; Senior citizens' center or association; Child day care services; Individual & family services; Senior citizens' center or association; Child day care services
Ch: Allen Brown
**Pr:* Debra Cotney
**CFO:* George Rutherford
Ofcr: Duane Mathis
Ofcr: Jeff Weesner
**Ex VP:* David Poteat
**VP:* James Bryant
Exec: Tammy Pierce
Pgrm Dir: Casondra Amos
Board of Directors: Mickey Johnson, Candace Tookes

MERITCARE
See CULWELL HEALTH INC

D-U-N-S 08-989-3184
MERITECH INC (OH)
4577 Hinckley Indus Pkwy, Cleveland, OH 44109-6009
Tel (216) 459-8333 *Founded/Ownrshp* 1983
Sales 61.9MM^E *EMP* 98
Accts Hausser & Taylor Llc Clevelan
SIC 5044 Office equipment; Office equipment
Pr: Dennis Bednar
CFO: James Glenn
Treas: Keith Stump
**VP:* Mary Ann Bednar
Genl Mgr: Paul Barnhill
Off Mgr: Paul Doerger
Tech Mgr: Mark McKay
Netwrk Eng: Colman Lalka
Sales Exec: Tom Mako
Sls Mgr: Patty Pagliaro

D-U-N-S 80-597-1959 IMP
MERITEK ELECTRONICS CORP
5160 Rivergrade Rd, Baldwin Park, CA 91706-1406
Tel (626) 373-1728 *Founded/Ownrshp* 1993
Sales 45.0MM^E *EMP* 60^E
SIC 5065 Electronic parts
CEO: Pa-Shih Oliver Su
Genl Mgr: Su Oliver
Sales Exec: Kenneth Keim

D-U-N-S 15-731-3115
MERITER HEALTH SERVICES INC
202 S Park St, Madison, WI 53715-1507
Tel (608) 417-5800 *Founded/Ownrshp* 1982
Sales 720.5MM *EMP* 3,330
Accts Kpmg Ll Milwaukee Wi
SIC 8741 Hospital management; Hospital management
CEO: James L Woodward
Pr: Denise Gomez
**Pr:* Terri L Potter
**CFO:* Beth Erdman
**VP:* Sue Erickson
VP: Peter Stromborn
Chf Nrs Of: Pat Grunwald
Genl Mgr: Barbara Bryant
Dir IT: Thomas Blankenheim
Opers Mgr: Lamm Dan
Doctor: Ashvin Patel

D-U-N-S 05-529-6529
MERITER HOSPITAL INC
202 S Park St, Madison, WI 53715-1596
Tel (608) 417-6000 *Founded/Ownrshp* 1983
Sales 454.2MM *EMP* 2,548
Accts Kpmg Llp Milwaukee Wi
SIC 8062 General medical & surgical hospitals; General medical & surgical hospitals
CEO: James L Woodward
Chf Path: Frank Zeller
Pr: Kerra Guffey
**Pr:* Robert Turngren
**COO:* Lynne Myers
**CFO:* Kevin Boren
CFO: Beth Erdman
Chf Mktg O: Geoff Priest
VP: Mark Bundner
**VP:* Sue Erickson
Exec: Jenny Alexander
Exec: Mary Grell
Exec: Bob Harrison
Exec: Terry Hoffstetter
Exec: Mimi Killpack
Exec: Nancy Luedke
Exec: Susan Marks
Exec: Yvonne Pola
Exec: Mandy Porter
Exec: Mary Reudinger
Exec: Marilyn Rhodes

MERITER LABORATORIES
See MERITER MANAGEMENT SERVICES INC

D-U-N-S 11-402-9416
MERITER MANAGEMENT SERVICES INC
MERITER LABORATORIES
(*Suby of* MERITER HEALTH SERVICES INC) ★
202 S Park St, Madison, WI 53715-1507
Tel (608) 417-6000 *Founded/Ownrshp* 1973
Sales 45.8MM^E *EMP* 350
SIC 8071 8741 Testing laboratories; Hospital management; Testing laboratories; Hospital management
Pr: Jim Woodward
Chf Path: Dan Peterson
VP: Chris Ludwig
**VP:* Geoffrey Priest
CIO: Kerra Guffrey
IT Man: Elise Blanchard
IT Man: Ken Moss
Nutrtnst: Susie Brueggemann
Board of Directors: William D Harvey

D-U-N-S 07-880-8793
MERITOR BRAZIL HOLDINGS LLC
2135 W Maple Rd, Troy, MI 48084-7121
Tel (248) 435-1000 *Founded/Ownrshp* 2009
Sales 40.2MM^E *EMP* 434^E
SIC 6719 Investment holding companies, except banks
Ch: Ivor J Ike Evans
**CEO:* Jeffrey Jay A Craig
**CFO:* Kevin Nowlan
**Sr VP:* Sandra Quick

D-U-N-S 17-661-5730
■ **MERITOR HEAVY VEHICLE SYSTEMS LLC**
(*Suby of* MERITOR INC) ★
2135 W Maple Rd, Troy, MI 48084-7121
Tel (248) 435-0786 *Founded/Ownrshp* 1997
Sales 46.8MM^E *EMP* 195^E
SIC 3711 Military motor vehicle assembly
CEO: Jeffrey A Craig
**CFO:* Kevin Nowlan
**VP:* Carl Anderson
Dist Mgr: Devon Delcourt
Dist Mgr: John Quiroz
Sls Mgr: Scott Osborn
Board of Directors: R K Beck, James D Donlon, D W Greenfield, J R Hardy, Mark Schaitkin, Bonnie Wilkinson

D-U-N-S 78-808-2092 IMP/EXP
▲ **MERITOR INC**
2135 W Maple Rd, Troy, MI 48084-7121
Tel (248) 435-1000 *Founded/Ownrshp* 1909
Sales 3.5MMM *EMP* 9,300
Accts Deloitte & Touche Llp Detroit
Tkr Sym MTOR *Exch* NYS
SIC 3714 3493 3625 3465 Motor vehicle parts & accessories; Drive shafts, motor vehicle; Axles, motor vehicle; Exhaust systems & parts, motor vehicle; Automobile springs; Actuators, industrial; Automotive stampings; Motor vehicle parts & accessories; Drive shafts, motor vehicle; Axles, motor vehicle; Exhaust systems & parts, motor vehicle; Automobile springs; Actuators, industrial; Automotive stampings
Pr: Jeffrey A Craig
Ch Bd: Ivor J Evans
Pr: Tim Bowes
Pr: Pedro Ferro
Pr: Juan De La Riva
Pr: Joe Mejaly
Pr: Joe Plomin
Pr: Rakesh Sachdev
Pr: Rob Speed
CFO: James D Donlon
CFO: Kevin Nowlan
Treas: Frank A Voltolina
Sr VP: Vernon G Baker
Sr VP: Sandra Quick
VP: Kent Barth
VP: Jeanne Booth
VP: Diane S Bullock
VP: Sergio Caravalho
VP: Sergio Carvalho
VP: John Grace
VP: Alice McGuire
Board of Directors: Joseph B Anderson Jr, Victoria B Jackson Bridges, Rhonda L Brooks, William J Lyons, William R Newlin, Thomas L Pajonas, Lloyd G Trotter

MERITOR SUSPENSION SYSTEMS COM
See MSSC US INC

D-U-N-S 61-348-7834 IMP
MERITOR WABCO VEHICLE CONTROL SYSTEMS
2135 W Maple Rd, Troy, MI 48084-7121
Tel (248) 273-4698 *Founded/Ownrshp* 1990
Sales 75.6MM^E *EMP* 150
SIC 5013 Automotive brakes; Truck parts & accessories; Automotive brakes; Truck parts & accessories
Pr: Jon Morrison
Snr Sftwr: Susan Nickels
Sftwr Eng: Basil Asmar
Ql Cn Mgr: Thomas Barber
Ql Cn Mgr: Nicholas Hite
Sls&Mrk Ex: Bonnie Gibson

D-U-N-S 07-332-6506
MERITRUST CREDIT UNION
8710 E 32nd St N, Wichita, KS 67226-4008
Tel (316) 683-1199 *Founded/Ownrshp* 1935
Sales NA *EMP* 190
SIC 6062 6163 State credit unions, not federally chartered; Loan brokers; State credit unions, not federally chartered; Loan brokers
Ch: Rick Dodds
V Ch: Marci Johnson
**CEO:* Wade Bruendl
Ofcr: Cassandra Branin
Ofcr: Darlene Hicks
Ofcr: Amy Hollan
Ofcr: Jenni Johnson
Sr VP: Brian Davidson
VP: Ed Foster
VP: Evan Wilson
**Prin:* Duane Van Camp

D-U-N-S 07-802-1344
MERITUM ENERGY HOLDINGS LP
1826 N Loop 1604 W, San Antonio, TX 78248-4517
Tel (210) 876-3560 *Founded/Ownrshp* 2015
Sales 46.1MM^E *EMP* 80^E
SIC 6722 Management investment, open-end
Pr: Chris Hill
Ex VP: Rob Chalmers

D-U-N-S 13-936-9540
MERITUS ENTERPRISES INC
RETAIL PHARMACY/HOME CARE PHRM
(*Suby of* MERITUS HEALTH INC) ★
11116 Medical Campus Rd, Hagerstown, MD 21742-6710
Tel (301) 790-8880 *Founded/Ownrshp* 1985
Sales 29.9MM^E *EMP* 843
Accts Grant Thornton Llp Baltimore
SIC 8011 Physicians' office, including specialists; Occupational & industrial specialist, physician/surgeon; Ambulatory surgical center; Freestanding emergency medical center; Physicians' office, including specialists; Occupational & industrial specialist, physician/surgeon; Ambulatory surgical center; Freestanding emergency medical center
Pr: Joesph P Ross
**CFO:* Raymond Grahe
**CFO:* Deborah Addo Samuels
**VP:* Kelly Corbi
**VP:* Heather Lorenzo
**VP:* Carolyn Simonsen
Dir Rx: Denise Ellis
Off Mgr: Beth Hout
Dir IT: Tim Thorpe

D-U-N-S 78-055-7138
MERITUS HEALTH INC
WASHINGTON COUNTY HOSPITAL
11116 Medical Campus Rd, Hagerstown, MD 21742-6710
Tel (301) 790-8000 *Founded/Ownrshp* 1989
Sales 374.5MM *EMP* 3,105
Accts Grant Thornton Llp Baltimore
SIC 8741 Hospital management; Hospital management
Pr: Joseph Ross
COO: Deborah A Samuels
Ofcr: Kelly Corbi
Ofcr: Lauren Klemm
Ofcr: Tina Weaver
**Sr VP:* Raymond A Grahe
VP: Dale Bushey
VP: Jake Dorst
VP: Sidney Gale
VP: Eileen Jaskuta
VP: Brooks McBurney
VP: Lee Shaver
VP: Carolyn Simonsen
Exec: Tracy Hoover
Dir Lab: Michelle Green

D-U-N-S 07-829-7314
MERITUS MEDICAL CENTER INC
WASHINGTON COUNTY HOSPITAL
(*Suby of* MERITUS HEALTH INC) ★
11116 Medical Campus Rd, Hagerstown, MD 21742-6710
Tel (301) 797-2000 *Founded/Ownrshp* 1991
Sales 346.2MM *EMP* 2,400
SIC 8062 General medical & surgical hospitals; General medical & surgical hospitals
Pr: Joseph Ross
Chf Rad: Paul Marinelli
**Sr VP:* Raymond Grahe
**Sr VP:* Deborah Addo Samuels
VP: Eileen Jaskuta
**VP:* Heather Lorenzo
**VP:* Carolyn Simonsen
Orthpdst: Michael Winslow
Surgeon: Marc Kross
Obsttrcn: William Hamilton
Nrsg Dir: Jesus Cepero

D-U-N-S 06-912-5334
MERIWEST CREDIT UNION
5615 Chesbro Ave Ste 100, San Jose, CA 95123-3057
Tel (408) 363-3200 *Founded/Ownrshp* 1961
Sales NA *EMP* 230
SIC 6061 Federal credit unions; Federal credit unions
CEO: Julie A Kirsch
**CEO:* Steven G Johnson
**CEO:* Christopher Owen
**CFO:* Brian Hennessey
**CFO:* Hudson Lee
CFO: Darci Sosebee
Ofcr: Arnette Grossweiler
**Sr VP:* Mark Antonioli
**Sr VP:* Tony Cortez
**VP:* Lisa Pesta
VP: Gwen Wong
Board of Directors: Richard Alves, Stan Chapman, Barbara Haddock, Arthur Jue, Robert Nadeau, Karl Nigg, Melvin Olsen

D-U-N-S 07-938-8336
MERIWETHER COUNTY BOARD OF EDUCATION
MERIWETHER COUNTY SCHOOL DST
2100 Gaston St, Greenville, GA 30222-2847
Tel (706) 672-4297 *Founded/Ownrshp* 1880
Sales 44.1MM *EMP* 800
Accts Department Of Audits And Accou
SIC 8211 Public elementary & secondary schools; Public elementary & secondary schools
Pr Dir: Lori Garrett

MERIWETHER COUNTY SCHOOL DST
See MERIWETHER COUNTY BOARD OF EDUCATION

D-U-N-S 07-979-8726
MERIWETHER COUNTY SCHOOLS
2100 Gaston St, Greenville, GA 30222-2847
Tel (706) 672-4297 *Founded/Ownrshp* 2015
Sales 18.4MM^E *EMP* 458^E
SIC 8211 Public elementary & secondary schools
Ex Dir: Lori Garett

D-U-N-S 60-408-8794
MERIWETHER HEALTHCARE LLC
WARM SPRINGS MEDICAL CENTER
5995 Spring St, Warm Springs, GA 31830-2149
Tel (706) 655-3331 *Founded/Ownrshp* 2005
Sales 39.1MM^E *EMP* 180
SIC 8062 General medical & surgical hospitals
CEO: Karen Daniel
Dir Inf Cn: Anna Roberson
Dir Rad: Sally Cartwright
Dir Rad: Jennifer Worsley
Dir Rx: Richard Buchanan
CIO: Milo Varnadoe
HC Dir: Tina Underwood

D-U-N-S 78-814-5592
MERIWETHER LOUISIANA LAND & TIMBER LLC
1037 Sam Hston Jones Pkwy, Lake Charles, LA 70611-5502
Tel (617) 832-2929 *Founded/Ownrshp* 2006
Sales 37.0MM *EMP* 1
SIC 5099 Durable goods; Durable goods

D-U-N-S 19-466-0882
MERIWETHER-GODSEY INC
4944 Old Boonsboro Rd, Lynchburg, VA 24503-1828
Tel (434) 384-3663 *Founded/Ownrshp* 1984
Sales 21.1MM^E *EMP* 600
SIC 5812 Caterers; Caterers
Pr: Marie Godsey
**CFO:* Donald C Beck
**VP:* R Edward Godsey
Exec: Steve Canard
Exec: Jay Keller
Dist Mgr: Long Nghiem
Off Admin: Enna Fowler

D-U-N-S 02-313-6690
■ **MERIZON GROUP INC**
MODERN BUSINESS MACHINES
(*Suby of* GLOBAL IMAGING SYSTEMS INC) ★
620 N Lynnd Dr 12200 W, Appleton, WI 54914
Tel (920) 499-9600 *Founded/Ownrshp* 2011
Sales 43.1MM^E *EMP* 144^E
SIC 7379 Computer related consulting services; Computer related consulting services
Pr: Fredrick Merizon
CFO: Steve Veldhorft
**CFO:* Steve Veldhorst
VP: David Spencer
**VP Sls:* Rick Flon
Sls Mgr: Jason Gillette

MERKLE COMPUTER SYSTEMS
See MERKLE GROUP INC

D-U-N-S 06-486-4507
MERKLE GROUP INC (MD)
MERKLE COMPUTER SYSTEMS
7001 Columbia Gateway Dr, Columbia, MD 21046-2289
Tel (443) 542-4000 *Founded/Ownrshp* 1971, 1977
Sales 312.5MM^E *EMP* 897
SIC 7331 Mailing list compilers; Mailing list compilers
Ch Bd: David S Williams
Pr: Zhengda Z Shen
COO: Zhengda Shen
CFO: Rick Gross
CFO: Jean Holder
Co-Pr: Tim Berry
Co-Pr: Patrick Hennessy
Chf Mktg O: Craig Dempster
Ofcr: Libby Barden
Ex VP: Gil Anderson
Ex VP: Tony Giordano
Ex VP: John Lee
Ex VP: Michael McCoy
Ex VP: Matt Mobley
Ex VP: Mike Mojica
Ex VP: Dave Paulus
Ex VP: Tony Steel
Sr VP: Dale Hogg
Sr VP: Angie C Moore
Sr VP: Jason Reis
VP: Cyndie Beckwith

D-U-N-S 13-461-0331
MERKLE INC
(*Suby of* MERKLE COMPUTER SYSTEMS) ★
7001 Columbia Gateway Dr, Columbia, MD 21046-2289
Tel (443) 542-4000 *Founded/Ownrshp* 1999

Sales 238.1MM^E EMP 400^E
SIC 8742 Marketing consulting services; Marketing consulting services
CEO: David S Williams
Pt: Shep Parke
Pt: Dan Schmerzler
Pt: Mathew Ward
Mng Pt: Peter Faber
*Pr: Tim Berry
Pr: Tom Miller
*CFO: Jean Holder
*Ch: Robert N Frerichs
*Chf Mktg O: Craig Dempster
*Ofcr: Elizabeth Barden
*Ofcr: Andy Fisher
*Ofcr: Patrick Hounsell
*Ofcr: Adam Lavelle
Ofcr: Angie Moore
Ex VP: Tony Steel
Sr VP: Andrew Hoeberichts
Sr VP: Glenn Lapidus
Sr VP: Paul Schottmiller
Sr VP: Colin Stewart
Sr VP: Ted Stites
Board of Directors: Robert N Frerichs

D-U-N-S 14-467-6731
MERKLE RESPONSE SERVICES INC
(Suby of MERKLE COMPUTER SYSTEMS) ★
100 Jamison Ct, Hagerstown, MD 21740-5185
Tel (301) 790-3100 Founded/Ownrshp 1997
Sales 54.5MM^E EMP 450
SIC 7331 7374 Direct mail advertising services; Computer processing services; Direct mail advertising services; Computer processing services
Pr: Willaim Sayre
Sales Exec: Kent Grove

D-U-N-S 00-509-3323 IMP
MERKLE-KORFF INDUSTRIES INC (IL)
(Suby of KINETEK INDUSTRIES INC) ★
25 Northwest Point Blvd # 900, Elk Grove Village, IL 60007-1044
Tel (847) 439-3760 Founded/Ownrshp 1911, 2006
Sales 76.8MM^E EMP 375
SIC 3621 Motors, electric; Motors, electric
Pr: Norman Dates
*CFO: Andrew Dawson
VP: Kevin Machalek
VP: Jack Vickerman
VP: Steve Wucki
Off Mgr: Ana Pliego
Netwrk Mgr: John Coakley
Plnt Mgr: Mark Cashman
Plnt Mgr: Rinehard Hofgesang
Sls Mgr: Bernie Santerre

D-U-N-S 80-442-5767
■ **MERKLEY + PARTNERS INC**
(Suby of OMNICOM GROUP INC) ★
200 Varick St Fl 12, New York, NY 10014-7429
Tel (212) 805-7500 Founded/Ownrshp 1993
Sales 35.0MM^E EMP 355
SIC 7311 Advertising agencies; Advertising agencies
Ch Bd: Alex Gellert
Mng Pt: Joe Chanin
CFO: Michael Byrne
*Chf Mktg O: Rob Moorman
*VP: Parry Merkley
Dir: Lee Bjarnason
Dir: Whitney Bryan
Creative D: Chuck Borghese
Art Dir: Jenna Lowy
Art Dir: Alison McElroy
Art Dir: Kirk Mosel

D-U-N-S 06-019-0618
MERLE BOES INC
11372 E Lakewood Blvd, Holland, MI 49424-9605
Tel (616) 392-7036 Founded/Ownrshp 1990
Sales 91.3MM^E EMP 110
SIC 5172 Petroleum brokers; Petroleum brokers
Pr: Michael Boes
Genl Mgr: Jim Kohsel
IT Man: John Beach

D-U-N-S 00-847-9388 IMP
MERLE NORMAN COSMETICS INC
9130 Bellanca Ave, Los Angeles, CA 90045-4772
Tel (310) 641-3000 Founded/Ownrshp 1974
Sales 74.1MM EMP 529
Accts Holthouse Carlin & Van Trigt
SIC 5999 2844 Cosmetics; Cosmetic preparations; Cosmetics; Cosmetic preparations
Ch Bd: Jack B Nethercutt
*CEO: Arthur O Armstrong
*COO: Rosanna McCollough
*VP: Jorge Carzola
VP: Joseph Disomma
VP: Sandra Haeberle
VP: Catherine Jacobus
VP: Gail Melikian
VP: Darlene Moan
*VP: Carol Porta
VP: Thomas F Smith
*VP: Pat Stransky
Board of Directors: Helen Nethercutt, Jack B Nethercutt, Travis J Richards

D-U-N-S 04-306-8944
MERLE WEST MEDICAL CENTER
DIABETES CARE LINK
2865 Daggett Ave, Klamath Falls, OR 97601-1106
Tel (541) 882-6311 Founded/Ownrshp 1998
Sales 447.9MM EMP 5
SIC 5912 Drug stores & proprietary stores
Off Mgr: Lenora Mueller
CTO: Dan Chancellor
CTO: Tom Drew
CTO: Kelly Thomas

D-U-N-S 62-163-2306
MERLES AUTOMOTIVE SUPPLY INC
4015 S Dodge Blvd, Tucson, AZ 85714-2191
Tel (520) 620-9511 Founded/Ownrshp 2012
Sales 44.9MM EMP 160
Accts Bleach Fleischman Pc Tucson
SIC 5013 5531 5082 Automotive supplies & parts; Automotive parts; Mining machinery & equipment, except petroleum; Automotive supplies & parts; Automotive parts; Mining machinery & equipment, except petroleum
Pr: Stephen Sattinger
*CFO: Gerald J Bishop
Store Mgr: Keith Almich
IT Man: Thomas Wacker
Opers Mgr: Bruce Bagenstos

D-U-N-S 07-827-9060 IMP
MERLETTO INC
COSMOPOLITAN MARKETPLACE
2372 W Indian Trl, Aurora, IL 60506-1570
Tel (630) 907-6666 Founded/Ownrshp 2009
Sales 39.2MM^E EMP 200
SIC 2064 Candy & other confectionery products; Candy & other confectionery products
Pr: Arsen M Manasyan
Genl Mgr: Olena Arson
Genl Mgr: Olena Kutsan

MERLI CONCRETE PUMPING
See STEFAN MERLI PLASTERING CO INC

D-U-N-S 07-853-5863
MERLIN ENTERTAINMENTS GROUP US LLC
MADAME TUSSAUDS NEW YORK
(Suby of MERLIN ENTERTAINMENTS GROUP LIMITED)
234 W 42nd St, New York, NY 10036-7215
Tel (212) 512-9604 Founded/Ownrshp 2007
Sales 385.0MM^E EMP 24,000
SIC 7996 Amusement parks; Amusement parks
VP: Colin Armstrong
*VP: Janine Di Gioacchino
*VP: Donald Glen Erlham
*VP: Sarah Reed
Dir Soc: Pamela Haylock
Genl Mgr: Bret Pidgeon

D-U-N-S 18-890-4619 IMP
MERLIN INDUSTRIES INC
2904 E State Street Ext, Hamilton, NJ 08619-4504
Tel (609) 807-1000 Founded/Ownrshp 1988
Sales 30.9MM^E EMP 140^E
SIC 3999 5999 7389 Hot tub & spa covers; Swimming pool chemicals, equipment & supplies; Swimming pool & hot tub service & maintenance; Hot tub & spa covers; Swimming pool chemicals, equipment & supplies; Swimming pool & hot tub service & maintenance
Pr: Andrew Maggion
Genl Mgr: Dale Schrack

D-U-N-S 07-352-1101
MERLIN INTERNATIONAL INC
MERLIN TECHNICAL SOLUTIONS
4b Inverness Ct E Ste 100, Englewood, CO 80112-5324
Tel (303) 221-0797 Founded/Ownrshp 1997
Sales 51.4MM^E EMP 170
SIC 7371 Computer software systems analysis & design, custom; Computer software systems analysis & design, custom
CEO: David Phelps
Pr: Barbara Bridges
Pr: Monty Deel
COO: Jim Regele
CFO: Shawna Meyer
CFO: Jones Tallent
Ofcr: David Regele
Ex VP: Jack Helmly
Sr VP: Craig A Janus
VP: Kevin Gordon
VP: John Trauth
VP: Mark Zalubas

MERLIN TECHNICAL SOLUTIONS
See MERLIN INTERNATIONAL INC

MERLINO FINE FOODS
See ATTILIO A MERLINO & ASSOCIATES INC

D-U-N-S 06-850-9447
MERLO AUTOMOTIVE GROUP INC
GLENDALE CHRYSLER, DODGE & RAM
10070 Manchester Rd, Saint Louis, MO 63122-1827
Tel (314) 965-5100 Founded/Ownrshp 1973
Sales 23.6MM^E EMP 52
SIC 5511

D-U-N-S 79-542-7538 IMP
MERMAID FOODS INC
9301 Solar Dr, Tampa, FL 33619-4403
Tel (813) 999-8945 Founded/Ownrshp 2012
Sales 24.9MM^E EMP 38
SIC 5141 Food brokers
Pr: Jorge Annexy
*VP: Nick Lalios

D-U-N-S 18-796-7039 IMP
MEROLA SALES CO INC
MEROLA TILE
20 Reed Pl, Amityville, NY 11701-2633
Tel (631) 464-4444 Founded/Ownrshp 1989
Sales 27.4MM^E EMP 55
SIC 5032 Ceramic wall & floor tile
CEO: Kevin E Merola
*Pr: John Merola
Sales Exec: Troy Wren

MEROLA TILE
See MEROLA SALES CO INC

D-U-N-S 04-808-9726
MEROLLIS CHEVROLET SALES & SERVICE INC
21800 Gratiot Ave, Eastpointe, MI 48021-2224
Tel (586) 775-8300 Founded/Ownrshp 1928
Sales 32.6MM^E EMP 93
SIC 5511 Automobiles, new & used; Automobiles, new & used
Pr: William Perkins
*Prin: Jim Monfette

D-U-N-S 62-798-8207
MERRELL BROS INC
8811 W 500 N, Kokomo, IN 46901-8776
Tel (574) 699-7782 Founded/Ownrshp 1986
Sales 30.0MM EMP 97
SIC 4959 Sanitary services; Sanitary services
CEO: Ted Merrell
*Pr: Nieta K Merrell
*COO: Ryan Zeck
*CFO: Terry Merrell
Snr Mgr: Blake Merrell
Snr Mgr: Dustin Smith

D-U-N-S 04-322-0623
MERRICK & CO
5970 Greenwood Plaza Blvd # 100, Greenwood Village, CO 80111-4735
Tel (303) 751-0741 Founded/Ownrshp 1955
Sales 77.5MM EMP 495
Accts Eks&H Lllp Denver Colorado
SIC 8711 Consulting engineer; Consulting engineer
Ch Bd: Ralph W Christie Jr
*Pr: David G Huelskamp
*COO: Christopher C Sherry
*CFO: Mark W Henline
*Sr VP: Robert A Berglund
VP: Pete Brace
CTO: Shawn Holton
Sys Admin: Judy Jones
Board of Directors: Douglas E Carnahan Jr, Ralph W Christie Jr, Donald E Evans Jr, David G Huelskamp, Lee James, Tamara Johnson, Matthew J Knudsen Outside, Christopher C Sherry, Jill S Tietjen

D-U-N-S 96-982-8701
MERRICK ANIMAL NUTRITION INC
2415 Parview Rd, Middleton, WI 53562-2571
Tel (608) 831-3440 Founded/Ownrshp 1959
Sales 121.5MM^E EMP 137^E
SIC 2011 Variety meats, fresh edible organs
Pr: William J Merrick

D-U-N-S 11-083-0072
MERRICK BANK CORP
(Suby of CARDWORKS INC) ★
10705 S Jordan Gtwy # 200, South Jordan, UT 84095-3977
Tel (801) 545-6600 Founded/Ownrshp 1996
Sales NA EMP 135
SIC 6021 National commercial banks; National commercial banks
Ch: Robert Perro
*Pr: Rickard Lake
COO: David Oyler
*CFO: David S Young
Sr VP: Charles Crawford
Sr VP: Rob Duffin
Sr VP: Tiffaney Johnston
Sr VP: Peter Ngai
VP: Lane Delano
VP: Elise Ebert
VP: Lenina Fitzjarrell
VP: Lisa Kenney
VP: Rondo Poole
VP: Scott Rose
VP: Mike Thomas
Dir Risk M: James Alberici

D-U-N-S 01-754-3497
MERRICK CHEVROLET CO
15303 Royalton Rd, Strongsville, OH 44136-5440
Tel (440) 878-6700 Founded/Ownrshp 1952
Sales 20.3MM^E EMP 80
SIC 5511 7515 Automobiles, new & used; Pickups, new & used; Trucks, tractors & trailers: new & used; Passenger car leasing; Automobiles, new & used; Pickups, new & used; Trucks, tractors & trailers: new & used; Passenger car leasing
Pr: Robert Serpentini Jr
*Sec: Paul Serpentini
Genl Mgr: Jeanine Hine

MERRICK COUNTY
See LITZENBERG MEMORIAL COUNTY HOSPITAL

D-U-N-S 04-052-5263 IMP/EXP
MERRICK ENGINEERING INC
1275 Quarry St, Corona, CA 92879-1707
Tel (951) 737-6040 Founded/Ownrshp 1975
Sales 88.8MM EMP 600
Accts Moss Adams Llp Irvine Califo
SIC 3089 Injection molding of plastics; Injection molding of plastics
Pr: Abraham M Abdi
*CFO: Katina Brown
Ex VP: Muna Vienna
VP: Francisco Castaneda
Exec: Brown Patina
Brnch Mgr: Shannon Daugherty
Genl Mgr: Sadi Vahidy
MIS Dir: Sivakumar Sethuraman
MIS Dir: Kumar Siva
IT Man: Ali Jawady
IT Man: Sethuraman Kumar

D-U-N-S 04-043-9465
MERRICK INDUSTRIES INC
MERRICK PRINTING
808 E Liberty St, Louisville, KY 40204-1025
Tel (502) 584-6258 Founded/Ownrshp 1971
Sales 30.4MM^E EMP 175^E
SIC 2752 1761 1711 Commercial printing, offset; Sheet metalwork; Roofing contractor; Mechanical contractor; Commercial printing, offset; Sheet metalwork; Roofing contractor; Mechanical contractor
Pr: Fred J Merrick Sr
*Treas: Charles A Van Stockum
VP: Richard Barnett
VP: Kevin Lush
*VP: William P Merrick
*VP: Martha M Van Stockum
VP: Martie Van Stockum
*Prin: M David Merrick
Dir IT: Jennifer Merrick

D-U-N-S 55-671-3329 IMP
MERRICK INDUSTRIES INC
(Suby of TANNEHILL INTERNATIONAL INDUSTRIES INC) ★
10 Arthur Dr, Lynn Haven, FL 32444-1685
Tel (850) 265-3611 Founded/Ownrshp 1991
Sales 51.5MM^E EMP 115
SIC 3596 Weighing machines & apparatus; Weighing machines & apparatus
CEO: Joseph K Tannehill Jr
Pr: Kathy Gower
CFO: Grady Mc Daniel
VP: Ed Boardway
*VP: Grady W McDaniel
Off Mgr: Monroe Wilson
Sfty Mgr: Kathy Gauer
Plnt Mgr: Scott Perry
Manager: Mark Vickery
Sls Mgr: Julie Healy
Board of Directors: Robert Epperson

D-U-N-S 04-427-5683 IMP
MERRICK NATURAL PETWORKS INC (TX)
101 Se 11th Ave Ste 200, Amarillo, TX 79101-3417
Tel (806) 322-2800 Founded/Ownrshp 1968
Sales 76.3MM^E EMP 500
SIC 2047

D-U-N-S 60-089-6158
MERRICK PET CARE INC
(Suby of NESTLE PURINA FACTORY) ★
101 Se 11th Ave Ste 200, Amarillo, TX 79101-3417
Tel (800) 664-7387 Founded/Ownrshp 2015
Sales 76.4MM^E EMP 300
SIC 2047 Dog & cat food; Dog & cat food
CEO: Greg Shearson
Pr: Dan Calkins
CFO: Sam Spradlin
VP: Matt Chisholm
S&M/VP: Todd Martin

D-U-N-S 18-891-7249 IMP
MERRICK PETFOODS INC
BLUE SKY PET FOODS
Fm 2943 E Hwy 60, Hereford, TX 79045
Tel (806) 322-2800 Founded/Ownrshp 1986
Sales 66.5MM^E EMP 400
SIC 5999 0752 5199

MERRICK PRINTING
See MERRICK INDUSTRIES INC

D-U-N-S 05-627-9615
MERRIFIELD GARDEN CENTER CORP
8132 Lee Hwy, Falls Church, VA 22042-1112
Tel (703) 560-9371 Founded/Ownrshp 1971
Sales 60.7MM EMP 350
SIC 5261 5193 0781

MERRILL & ASSOCIATES
See L MERRILL MICHAEL & ASSOCIATES INC

D-U-N-S 07-997-0778
MERRILL AREA PUBLIC SCHOOLS INC
MERRILL SCHOOL DISTRICT
1111 N Sales St, Merrill, WI 54452-3169
Tel (715) 536-4581 Founded/Ownrshp 1900
Sales 26.7MM^E EMP 400
Accts Schenck Sc Steven Point Wisc
SIC 8211 Public elementary school; Public junior high school; Public senior high school; School board; Public elementary school; Public junior high school; Public senior high school; School board
Dir IT: Michael Giese

D-U-N-S 00-486-9319
MERRILL CO INC (DE)
ARNOLD GROUP OF COMPANIES, THE
601 1st Ave Sw, Spencer, IA 51301-5302
Tel (712) 262-1141 Founded/Ownrshp 1965
Sales NA EMP 500
SIC 5013 Automotive supplies & parts; Automotive supplies & parts
Pr: Denis Spooner
*CFO: Steve Lensing
Netwrk Eng: Eric Johnson
Sales Exec: Larry Wegner
Mktg Mgr: Dave Kimbell

MERRILL COMMUNICATIONS
See MERRILL NEW YORK CO INC

D-U-N-S 10-049-7952
MERRILL COMMUNICATIONS LLC
(Suby of MERRILL CORP) ★
1 Merrill Cir, Saint Paul, MN 55108-5267
Tel (651) 646-4501 Founded/Ownrshp 1999
Sales 412.0MM EMP 5,210
SIC 7374 7389 Commercial printing; Data processing & preparation; Mailing & messenger services; Translation services
CEO: Rusty Wiley
*COO: Rick R Atterbury
*COO: Roy Gross
*COO: Rodney D Johnson
*CFO: Robert H Nazarian
Ex VP: Craig Levinsohn
*Ex VP: Brenda J Vale
*Sr VP: Katherine L Miller
VP: Cynthia Warner
IT Man: Jennifer Duffy
IT Man: Andrew Hopkins
Board of Directors: Joseph Bondi, John W Castro, James Continenza, Peter C J Harrison, Alfred Hurley, David Tanner, James R Wiley

D-U-N-S 07-867-9370 IMP/EXP
MERRILL CORP (MN)
1 Merrill Cir, Saint Paul, MN 55108-5264
Tel (651) 646-4501 Founded/Ownrshp 1968
Sales 691.4MM EMP 5,418
Accts Pricewaterhousecoopers Llp Mi
SIC 7389 8111 8999 Personal service agents, brokers & bureaus; Specialized legal services; Communication services; Personal service agents, brokers & bureaus; Specialized legal services; Communication services
CEO: James R Wiley

Pr: Julie Colgan
**COO:* Rick R Atterbury
**COO:* Roy Gross
**COO:* Rodney D Johnson
**CFO:* Tom Donnelly
Treas: Carolyn Strandberg
Chf Mktg O: Rhonda Sneed
**Ofcr:* Todd R Albright
**Ofcr:* Thomas Fredell
Ofcr: Boyd Johnson
**Ofcr:* Katherine L Miller
**Ofcr:* Brenda J Vale
Ex VP: Scott Bernecker
Ex VP: William Guckien
Ex VP: Craig P Levinsohn
Sr VP: Raymond J Goodwin
Sr VP: Ken Lambert
Sr VP: Amy Reichenbach
Sr VP: Jenny Simon
VP: Sue Bornstein
Board of Directors: Joseph Bondi, John W Castro, James Continenza, Peter C J Harrison, Alfred Hurley, David Tanner, James R Wiley

D-U-N-S 00-613-6030
MERRILL DISTRIBUTING INC
1301 N Memorial Dr, Merrill, WI 54452-3188
Tel (715) 536-6322 *Founded/Ownrshp* 1912
Sales 33.8MM^E *EMP* 50
SIC 5194 5145 5142 5812 Tobacco & tobacco products; Confectionery; Packaged frozen goods; Eating places; Tobacco & tobacco products; Confectionery; Packaged frozen goods; Eating places
Ch Bd: Ralph A Schewe
**Pr:* John Schewe
Sls Mgr: Manny Carreiro

D-U-N-S 80-814-7909
MERRILL FABRICATORS INC
(*Suby of* MERRILL TECHNOLOGIES GROUP) ★
520 Republic Ave, Alma, MI 48801-2049
Tel (989) 463-2863 *Founded/Ownrshp* 1996
Sales 73.5MM^E *EMP* 170
SIC 3443 3446 3429 Fabricated plate work (boiler shop); Architectural metalwork; Manufactured hardware (general); Nozzles, fire fighting; Fabricated plate work (boiler shop); Architectural metalwork; Manufactured hardware (general); Nozzles, fire fighting
CEO: Robert A Yackel
**Prin:* Bob Yackel

D-U-N-S 00-796-7474
MERRILL FARMS LLC (CA)
18900 Portola Dr Ste 100, Salinas, CA 93908-1267
Tel (831) 424-7365 *Founded/Ownrshp* 1933
Sales 22.3MM^E *EMP* 75^E
SIC 0161 2097 Vegetables & melons; Manufactured ice
Genl Mgr: Alan Clark
Sfty Mgr: Mike McCord

D-U-N-S 80-605-8012
MERRILL GARDENS LLC
1938 Frview Ave E Ste 300, Seattle, WA 98102
Tel (206) 676-5300 *Founded/Ownrshp* 1890
Sales 64.2MM^E *EMP* 2,000
Accts Ernst & Young Seattle Washin
SIC 6531 Real estate agents & managers; Real estate agents & managers
Pr: Bill Pettit
**Pr:* William D Pettit
**Ch:* Charles Wright
**Ex VP:* Steve Delmore
**Sr VP:* Jason Childers
**Sr VP:* Morei Lingle
**Sr VP:* Doug Spear
VP: Robin Buban
VP: Craig Wheeler
Genl Mgr: Jerrod Ayers
Genl Mgr: Marilyn Jarmusch

D-U-N-S 00-613-5958
MERRILL IRON & STEEL INC (WI)
900 Alderson St, Schofield, WI 54476-1488
Tel (715) 393-4100 *Founded/Ownrshp* 1962
Sales 45.8MM^E *EMP* 340
SIC 3441

D-U-N-S 94-436-3795
■ **MERRILL LYNCH COMMODITIES INC**
(*Suby of* BANK OF AMERICA CORP) ★
20 Greenway Plz Ste 950, Houston, TX 77046-2008
Tel (832) 681-5904 *Founded/Ownrshp* 2015
Sales 224.4MM^E *EMP* 575
SIC 6211 6091 Brokers, security; Underwriters, security; Nondeposit trust facilities; Brokers, security; Underwriters, security; Nondeposit trust facilities
CEO: Brian T Moynihan
Pr: Kuljinder Chase

D-U-N-S 60-650-0635
■ **MERRILL LYNCH GROUP INC**
(*Suby of* BANK OF AMERICA CORP) ★
4 World Financial Ctr # 4, New York, NY 10080-0002
Tel (646) 855-5000 *Founded/Ownrshp* 1987
Sales 1.0MMM^E *EMP* 4,167
SIC 6282 6162 Investment advisory service; Mortgage bankers
Pr: Theresa Lang
Sr VP: Jose Otero
VP: Ken Brady
VP: Ed Darmiento
VP: Vincent Gamba
VP: Jeffrey Kressen
VP: Mark Nisbet
VP: James Parlapiano
VP: Jim Pell
VP: John Scully
VP: Michael Wiener

D-U-N-S 14-464-6452
MERRILL LYNCH INSURANCE GROUP INC
(*Suby of* AEGON USA INC) ★
1700 Merrill Lynch Dr, Pennington, NJ 08534-4128
Tel (609) 274-5351 *Founded/Ownrshp* 2007
Sales NA *EMP* 302
SIC 6311 Life insurance; Life insurance
Mng Dir: Deborah Adlar

**CFO:* Joseph Justice
**Sr VP:* Barry Skolnick
VP: Wendeline Dill
VP: Nancy Hasson
VP: Prasad Konaka
VP: Scott Logan
VP: John Oleary
VP: Mike Omalley
VP: Matthew Pusak
VP: Paul St Amour

D-U-N-S 82-957-2242
■ **MERRILL LYNCH INTERNATIONAL INC**
(*Suby of* BANK OF AMERICA CORP) ★
4 Wrld Fncl Ctr Fl 12, New York, NY 10281-1406
Tel (646) 855-5000 *Founded/Ownrshp* 2015
Sales 78.7MM^E *EMP* 186^E
SIC 6211 Security brokers & dealers
CEO: James B Quigley
Sr VP: G M Broucek
Sr VP: Richard Jones
Sr VP: Tim Krueger
Sr VP: Marcus Malonson
Sr VP: Dave Sorensen
VP: Anthony Aufiero
VP: Lynette Blakeway
VP: Bill Bowman
VP: Gautam Chatterjee
VP: Charles Clark
VP: Micheal Cook
VP: Daphne CHI
VP: Christopher Donaghy
VP: Philippe Hartl
VP: Christopher Hayes
VP: George Huertas
VP: David Incorvaia
VP: Samuel Kaplowitz
VP: Joann Kress
VP: Joal Leopando

D-U-N-S 14-464-6197
■ **MERRILL LYNCH INVESTMENT MANAGEMENT INC**
(*Suby of* BANK OF AMERICA CORP) ★
225 Liberty St Fl C1056, New York, NY 10281-1201
Tel (212) 449-1000 *Founded/Ownrshp* 1976
Sales 2.2MMM^E *EMP* 7,000
SIC 6211 6282 Dealers, security; Investment advisory service; Dealers, security; Investment advisory service
Ch Bd: Stan O'Neal
**CFO:* Ahmass Fakahany
Sr VP: Pieter Der Heide
**VP:* Kerem Karantay
Prin: John Fosina
IT Man: John Woolf
**Genl Couns:* Rosemary Berkery

D-U-N-S 00-892-0951
■ **MERRILL LYNCH PIERCE FENNER & SMITH INC**
(*Suby of* BANK OF AMERICA CORP) ★
111 8th Ave, New York, NY 10011-5201
Tel (800) 637-7455 *Founded/Ownrshp* 2015
Sales 8.0MMM^E *EMP* 46,000
SIC 6211 6411 Brokers, security; Dealers, security; Investment bankers; Insurance brokers; Brokers, security; Dealers, security; Investment bankers; Insurance brokers
Pr: David H Komansky
**Ch Bd:* Thomas Keil Montag
**V Ch:* Stephen L Hammerman
**Treas:* Theresa Lang
Chf Inves: Ronald Albahary
Ofcr: Janine Rusch
**Ex VP:* Barry S Friedberg
**Ex VP:* Edward L Goldberg
**Ex VP:* Jerome P Kenney
**Ex VP:* Winthrop H Smith Jr
Sr VP: Alan S Mann
Sr VP: Henry Pupke
Sr VP: Mandy Rofe
Sr VP: Marvin Waltuch
VP: Emily Arens
VP: Karen Bebee
VP: Joseph Corcoran
VP: Fred Graney
VP: Joseph Kasell
VP: Maury Leone
VP: Ken Mazzio

D-U-N-S 13-136-5116
■ **MERRILL LYNCH PROFESSIONAL CLEARING CORP**
(*Suby of* BANK OF AMERICA CORP) ★
101 Hudson St Fl 7, Jersey City, NJ 07302-3915
Tel (201) 557-0803 *Founded/Ownrshp* 2015
Sales 20.5MM^E *EMP* 115
SIC 6211 Brokers, security; Dealers, security
Ch Bd: Gary Yetman
VP: Jeannine McAteer

D-U-N-S 62-214-2842
MERRILL NEWYORK CO INC
MERRILL COMMUNICATIONS
(*Suby of* MERRILL CORP) ★
246 W 54th St, New York, NY 10019-5502
Tel (212) 229-6500 *Founded/Ownrshp* 1984
Sales 25.5MM^E *EMP* 200
SIC 2759 2752 Financial note & certificate printing & engraving; Commercial printing, lithographic; Financial note & certificate printing & engraving; Commercial printing, lithographic
Pr: B Michael James

MERRILL SCHOOL DISTRICT
See MERRILL AREA PUBLIC SCHOOLS INC

MERRILL TECHNOLOGIES GROUP
See MERRILL TOOL HOLDING CO

D-U-N-S 15-527-3758
MERRILL TOOL & MACHINE INC
(*Suby of* MERRILL TECHNOLOGIES GROUP) ★
21659 Gratiot Rd, Merrill, MI 48637-8717
Tel (989) 643-7981 *Founded/Ownrshp* 1996
Sales 29.0MM^E *EMP* 160^E
SIC 3544 Special dies, tools, jigs & fixtures; Special dies, tools, jigs & fixtures

CEO: Bob Yackel
QI Cn Mgr: Ken Lamb

D-U-N-S 04-717-5245 IMP
MERRILL TOOL HOLDING CO
MERRILL TECHNOLOGIES GROUP
400 Florence St, Saginaw, MI 48602-1203
Tel (989) 791-6676 *Founded/Ownrshp* 1969
Sales 142.1MM^E *EMP* 400
SIC 3443 3599 8734 8711 3724 Fabricated plate work (boiler shop); Machine & other job shop work; Testing laboratories; Engineering services; Aircraft engines & engine parts; Fabricated plate work (boiler shop); Machine & other job shop work; Testing laboratories; Engineering services; Aircraft engines & engine parts
CEO: Robert Yackel
**CFO:* Michael E Beyer
**Ch:* Gary Yackel
**Sec:* Mary K Yackel
Ofcr: Shelley Anderson
Ofcr: Michael Sauer
**VP:* Jeffery J Yackel
Prgrm Mgr: Gary Manthei
Prgrm Mgr: John Shelton
Dir IT: Jason Vardon
Mfg Mgr: Justin Hardy

D-U-N-S 96-795-8419
MERRILL/GLOBAL INC
(*Suby of* MERRILL COMMUNICATIONS LLC) ★
1 Merrill Cir Ste 1433, Saint Paul, MN 55108-5267
Tel (651) 646-4501 *Founded/Ownrshp* 1997
Sales 18.7MM^E *EMP* 564^E
SIC 2759 2752 2791 Commercial printing; Commercial printing, lithographic; Typesetting

D-U-N-S 82-492-9087
MERRILL/MAY INC
(*Suby of* MERRILL CORP) ★
1 Merrill Cir, Saint Paul, MN 55108-5264
Tel (651) 646-4501 *Founded/Ownrshp* 1993
Sales 78.3MM^E *EMP* 550
SIC 2759 Commercial printing; Commercial printing
Pr: Joseph Pettirossi
**VP:* Charlie Hipp
Opers Mgr: Eric Diliberto

D-U-N-S 02-921-9284 IMP
MERRILLS PACKAGING INC
MERRILL'S PACKAGING SUPPLY
1529 Rollins Rd, Burlingame, CA 94010-2305
Tel (650) 259-5959 *Founded/Ownrshp* 1961
Sales 26.9MM^E *EMP* 80
SIC 3081 Packing materials, plastic sheet; Packing materials, plastic sheet
CEO: Kenneth V Merrill
Chf Mktg O: Amy Hauser
Mktg Dir: Brian Meltzner

MERRILL'S PACKAGING SUPPLY
See MERRILLS PACKAGING INC

D-U-N-S 08-294-7466
MERRILLVILLE COMMUNITY SCHOOL DISTRICT
6701 Delaware St, Merrillville, IN 46410-3579
Tel (219) 650-5300 *Founded/Ownrshp* 1965
Sales 44.8MM^E *EMP* 700
SIC 8211 Public elementary school; Public junior high school; Public senior high school; Public elementary school; Public junior high school; Public senior high school
**Pr:* Thomas Bainbridge
**Treas:* Kimberly Fox
Bd of Dir: Mark Gregoline
**VP:* Mark Lucas

D-U-N-S 00-215-3914
■ **MERRIMAC INDUSTRIES INC**
(*Suby of* CRANE CO) ★
41 Fairfield Pl, West Caldwell, NJ 07006-6287
Tel (973) 575-1300 *Founded/Ownrshp* 1954, 2010
Sales 26.9MM^E *EMP* 100^E
SIC 3679 3663 3264 Microwave components; Microwave communication equipment; Amplifiers, RF power & IF; Space satellite communications equipment; Ferrite & ferrite parts
Pr: Bob Tavares
**COO:* Reynold K Green
**VP:* Jayson E Hahn
VP: Lnorman Holden
**VP:* James J Logothetis
**VP:* Lawrence S Ross
**Prin:* Brendan Curran
Genl Mgr: Reynold Green
IT Man: Daphne Rollerson

D-U-N-S 05-922-3946
MERRIMAC MOTORS INC
POMOCO C D J R NEWPORT NWS
12629 Jefferson Ave, Newport News, VA 23602-4315
Tel (757) 369-3565 *Founded/Ownrshp* 1947
Sales 28.0MM^E *EMP* 93
SIC 5511 Automobiles, new & used; Automobiles, new & used
Pr: Rick Gallaer
**Pr:* Stanley R Gallaer Jr
**Sec:* Steve Adams
Board of Directors: Monique McWhite

D-U-N-S 14-426-4892
MERRIMACK BUILDING SUPPLY INC
260 Daniel Webster Hwy, Merrimack, NH 03054-4832
Tel (603) 424-7001 *Founded/Ownrshp* 1985
Sales 25.5MM^E *EMP* 43
SIC 5033 5032 Insulation materials; Drywall materials
Pr: William F Donegan
CEO: Chris Barstow
COO: Dave Myers
Opers Mgr: Chad Napierkoski

D-U-N-S 06-659-8673
MERRIMACK COLLEGE
315 Turnpike St, North Andover, MA 01845-5800
Tel (978) 837-5000 *Founded/Ownrshp* 1947
Sales 98.9MM *EMP* 600

Accts Grant Thornton Lp Boston Ma
SIC 8221 College, except junior; College, except junior
Pr: Christopher E Hopey
**Pr:* Joseph D Calderone
Ofcr: Pat Doherty
Ofcr: Maria Watkins
Assoc VP: Joanne Mermelstein
Sr VP: Carol Glod
VP: Alexa Abowitz
Dir Lab: Gregory Kuzma
Assoc Dir: Lori Dzumeron
Assoc Dir: Kathryn Nielsen
Assoc Dir: Kristen Sullivan
Assoc Dir: Gianna Voccola
Board of Directors: Robert Coppola

D-U-N-S 00-697-1071
MERRIMACK COUNTY SAVINGS BANK
89 N Main St, Concord, NH 03301-4907
Tel (603) 225-2793 *Founded/Ownrshp* 1867
Sales NA *EMP* 135
SIC 6036 State savings banks, not federally chartered; State savings banks, not federally chartered
Pr: Paul Rizzi
Ex VP: Fred Burgess
**Ex VP:* Philip Emma
**Sr VP:* Donna Benson
**Sr VP:* Edward Caron
**Sr VP:* Terry Clarkson
**Sr VP:* Linda Lorden
**Sr VP:* Paul Provost
VP: Thomas Dustin
VP: Jeffrey Hubbard
VP: Arthur Letendre

MERRIMACK MUTUAL FIRE INSUR CO
See CAMBRIDGE MUTUAL FIRE INSURANCE CO INC

D-U-N-S 00-695-1354
MERRIMACK MUTUAL FIRE INSURANCE CO
STATE FIRE INSURANCE COMPANY
95 River Rd, Andover, MA 01810-1078
Tel (978) 475-3300 *Founded/Ownrshp* 1958
Sales NA *EMP* 240^E
SIC 6331 Fire, marine & casualty insurance; Property damage insurance; Fire, marine & casualty insurance; Property damage insurance
Pr: William E Nichols
**CEO:* Malcolm W Brawn
**VP:* Donald Vose
**VP:* Janet Wallace

D-U-N-S 00-122-1410
MERRIMACK PHARMACEUTICALS INC
1 Kendall Sq Ste B7201, Cambridge, MA 02139-1670
Tel (617) 441-1000 *Founded/Ownrshp* 1993
Sales 102.7MM *EMP* 254^E
Accts Pricewaterhousecoopers Llp B
Tkr Sym MACK *Exch* NGM
SIC 2834 8731 Pharmaceutical preparations; Commercial physical research; Pharmaceutical preparations
Pr: Robert J Mulroy
**Ch Bd:* Gary L Crocker
**CFO:* Yasir Al-Wakeel
Sr VP: Fazal R Khan
**Sr VP:* William M McClements
**Sr VP:* Edward J Stewart
VP: Robert Corcoran
VP: Daryl Drummond
VP: Scott Lauder
VP: Istvan Molnar
Assoc Dir: Charlotte McDonagh
Board of Directors: John M Dineen, Vivian S Lee, John Mendelsohn, Michael E Porter, James H Quigley, Russell T Ray

D-U-N-S 09-551-9971
MERRIMACK SCHOOL DISTRICT
SCHOOL ADMINISTRATIVE UNIT 26
36 Mcelwain St, Merrimack, NH 03054-3663
Tel (603) 424-6200 *Founded/Ownrshp* 1971
Sales 39.7MM^E *EMP* 750
SIC 8211 Public junior high school; Public junior high school
IT Man: Mark Merrifeld
Schl Brd P: Chris Ortega

D-U-N-S 00-695-4804 IMP
MERRIMACK VALLEY DISTRIBUTING CO INC (MA)
50 Prince St, Danvers, MA 01923-1438
Tel (978) 777-2213 *Founded/Ownrshp* 1935
Sales 49.4MM^E *EMP* 100
SIC 5181 5182 5149 Beer & ale; Liquor; Wine; Soft drinks; Beer & ale; Liquor; Wine; Soft drinks
Pr: Richard Tatelman
**Ex VP:* Jack Tatelman
VP: Mark Tatelman
Area Mgr: Paul Galante
Area Mgr: Kelly Larosa
Sls Mgr: John Scully

D-U-N-S 08-561-0244
MERRIMACK VALLEY FEDERAL CREDIT UNION INC
1475 Osgood St, North Andover, MA 01845-1012
Tel (978) 975-4095 *Founded/Ownrshp* 1955
Sales NA *EMP* 110
SIC 6141 Personal credit institutions; Personal credit institutions
Ch Bd: Michael Sayler
V Ch: Leon Pratt
**V Ch:* Frank Serio
**CEO:* Peter Matthews Jr
**Treas:* Augustine Longo
VP: William Betton
VP: Alan Jenne
VP: John McSweeney

MERRIMACK VALLEY HOSPITAL
See ESSENT HEALTHCARE OF MASSACHUSETTS INC

D-U-N-S 04-288-0492
MERRIMACK VALLEY SCHOOL DISTRICT (NH)
105 Community Dr, Penacook, NH 03303-1617
Tel (603) 753-6561 *Founded/Ownrshp* 1967
Sales 14.8MM^E *EMP* 400
Accts Grzelak And Company Pc Laconi
SIC 8211 Public elementary & secondary schools; Public elementary & secondary schools

D-U-N-S 01-208-6773
MERRIMACK VALLEY YOUNG MENS CHRISTIAN ASSOCIATION INC
YMCA
101 Amesbury St Ste 400, Lawrence, MA 01840-1322
Tel (978) 975-1330 *Founded/Ownrshp* 1870
Sales 14.2MM *EMP* 400
Accts Shaheen Pallone & Associates P
SIC 8641 7991 8351 7032 8322 Youth organizations; Physical fitness facilities; Child day care services; Youth camps; Individual & family services; Youth organizations; Physical fitness facilities; Child day care services; Youth camps; Individual & family services
Pr: Stephen Ives
CFO: Cathy Landry
CFO: George Peters
**Ch:* Marko B Duffy
VP: Kathleen Boshar
Ex Dir: Maria De Martinez
Ex Dir: Francis J Kenneally III
IT Man: Kathleen Desbois

MERRITT CONSTRUCTION
See MERRITT PROPERTIES LLC

D-U-N-S 00-902-4522 IMP/EXP
MERRITT EQUIPMENT CO (OR)
MERRITT TRAILER
9339 Brighton Rd, Henderson, CO 80640-8229
Tel (303) 286-7787 *Founded/Ownrshp* 1951
Sales 55.0MM^E *EMP* 250
SIC 3715 5012 7539 3714 3537 3469 Semitrailers for truck tractors; Trailers for trucks, new & used; Trailer repair; Motor vehicle parts & accessories; Industrial trucks & tractors; Metal stampings; Semitrailers for truck tractors; Trailers for trucks, new & used; Trailer repair; Motor vehicle parts & accessories; Industrial trucks & tractors; Metal stampings
Pr: Everett T Merritt
**Sec:* Taylor Merritt
**VP:* Dennis Sands

D-U-N-S 60-280-4676
■ **MERRITT HAWKINS & ASSOCIATES LLC**
(*Suby of* AMN HEALTHCARE SERVICES INC) ★
12400 High Bluff Dr, San Diego, CA 92130-3077
Tel (858) 792-0711 *Founded/Ownrshp* 2005
Sales 13.5MM^E *EMP* 300
SIC 7363 Medical help service; Medical help service
CEO: Susan Salka Fka Nowakowski
**CFO:* Brian Scott
**Treas:* John Dillon
VP: Mike Belkin
**VP:* Denise Jackson

D-U-N-S 13-333-8462
MERRITT HOSPITALITY LLC
(*Suby of* HEI HOSPITALITY LLC) ★
101 Merritt 7 Ste 14, Norwalk, CT 06851-1060
Tel (203) 849-8844 *Founded/Ownrshp* 2003
Sales 91.7MM^E *EMP* 1,915^E
SIC 8741 Hotel or motel management; Hotel or motel management
Pr: Ted Darnall
**Ex VP:* Roger Aufieri
Sr VP: William J Scanlon
**Sr VP:* Glenn Tuckman
S&M/VP: Jacqueline Villamil

D-U-N-S 13-812-7506
MERRITT ISLAND AIR & HEAT INC
MIAC
625 Cypress Dr, Merritt Island, FL 32952-3719
Tel (321) 729-1441 *Founded/Ownrshp* 1971
Sales 24.8MM^E *EMP* 75
SIC 1711 7623 Warm air heating & air conditioning contractor; Air conditioning repair
Pr: Roger W Drabyk Jr
**CFO:* Bruce Rubin
**VP:* Brenda Drabyk
IT Man: Brigitte Coovert
IT Man: Robin Yawn
Sls&Mrk Ex: Ron Dawson
Sls Dir: Craig Drabyk

D-U-N-S 87-664-6860
MERRITT PROPERTIES LLC
MERRITT CONSTRUCTION
2066 Lord Baltimore Dr, Baltimore, MD 21244-2501
Tel (410) 298-2600 *Founded/Ownrshp* 1967
Sales 42.0MM^E *EMP* 150
SIC 6531 1531 1522 Real estate agent, commercial; Operative builders; Residential construction
VP: Gary Swatko

MERRITT TRAILER
See MERRITT EQUIPMENT CO

D-U-N-S 03-627-4389 EXP
MERRITT VETERINARY SUPPLIES INC
MVS
1520 Pineview Dr, Columbia, SC 29209-5053
Tel (803) 695-1698 *Founded/Ownrshp* 1938
Sales 37.9MM^E *EMP* 100
SIC 5047 Veterinarians' equipment & supplies; Veterinarians' equipment & supplies
Pr: Lloyd Merritt Jr
**Prin:* Robert Mims

MERRITT WOODWORK
See PROFAC INC

D-U-N-S 08-094-4747
MERRY LAND PROPERTIES LLC
209 7th St Ste 300, Augusta, GA 30901-1486
Tel (706) 722-6756 *Founded/Ownrshp* 1981
Sales 217.9MM *EMP* 785
SIC 6798 Realty investment trusts
Pr: W Tennent Houston
**COO:* Michael N Thompson
Sr VP: John W Gibson
VP: Joseph P Bailey III
VP: Ronald J Benton
VP: J Russ Davis Jr
VP: Dorrie Green
VP: Jay Simons
Board of Directors: Ben O Howell Sr, Boone A Knox Is Chairman O, Robert P Kirby, Hugh Long, Pierce Merry Jr, Paul S Simon

D-U-N-S 04-423-2932
MERRY MAIDS LIMITED PARTNERSHIP
(*Suby of* SERVICEMASTER CONSUMER SERVICES LIMITED PARTNERSHIP) ★
3839 Forest Hill Irene Rd, Memphis, TN 38125-2502
Tel (901) 597-8100 *Founded/Ownrshp* 1988
Sales 117.0MM^E *EMP* 5,000
SIC 7349 Maid services, contract or fee basis; Maid services, contract or fee basis
Pr: Mike Isakson
Pr: Wes Jenkins
**COO:* Brent Armstrong
COO: Sandy McCarrey
IT Man: John Browne
S&M/VP: Sherry Rose

D-U-N-S 07-944-9694
MERRY TECHNOLOGY INC
315 N Rverview St Apt 615, Wichita, KS 67203
Tel (316) 371-9533 *Founded/Ownrshp* 1998
Sales 110.0MM *EMP* 5
SIC 1521 1542

D-U-N-S 00-823-3355
MERRY X-RAY CHEMICAL CORP (CA)
M X R
4444 Viewridge Ave A, San Diego, CA 92123-1670
Tel (858) 565-4472 *Founded/Ownrshp* 1962
Sales 232.7MM^E *EMP* 390^E
SIC 5047 X-ray machines & tubes; X-ray film & supplies; X-ray machines & tubes; X-ray film & supplies
Ch Bd: Leo Zuckerman
**Pr:* Ted Sloan

D-U-N-S 05-413-1656
MERRY X-RAY CORP
4444 Viewridge Ave, San Diego, CA 92123-1670
Tel (858) 565-4472 *Founded/Ownrshp* 1958
Sales 104.1MM^E *EMP* 500
SIC 5047 Hospital equipment & furniture; Hospital equipment & furniture
Pr: Ted Sloan
CFO: Sandie Christensen
Ex VP: Johnny Lopez
**VP:* Al Lewein

D-U-N-S 17-673-4804
MERRYMAN CO EXCAVATION
MERRYMAN EXCAVATION
1501 Lamb Rd, Woodstock, IL 60098-9677
Tel (815) 337-1700 *Founded/Ownrshp* 1995
Sales 25.9MM^E *EMP* 50
SIC 1623 1794 Underground utilities contractor; Excavation work
Pr: Patrick Merryman

MERRYMAN EXCAVATION
See MERRYMAN CO EXCAVATION

D-U-N-S 01-005-3718
MERRYMAN INC SONNY (VA)
JOHN DEERE
5120 Wards Rd, Evington, VA 24550-2224
Tel (434) 821-1000 *Founded/Ownrshp* 1967
Sales 76.5MM^E *EMP* 125
SIC 5012 5599 Buses; Trailers for trucks, new & used; Utility trailers; Buses; Trailers for trucks, new & used; Utility trailers
Ch Bd: Floyd W Merryman Jr
**Pr:* Floyd W Merryman III
**Sec:* Deborah Matney
**VP:* A Patricia Merryman
**VP Sls:* Mark Roberts
Mktg Dir: Dean Farmer
Sales Asso: Jordan Wray

D-U-N-S 03-860-8142
MERRYMAN-FARR LLC
305 Hill Ave, Nashville, TN 37210-4711
Tel (615) 254-8050 *Founded/Ownrshp* 2001
Sales 33.6MM^E *EMP* 125
SIC 1711 Mechanical contractor; Mechanical contractor
Sls&Mrk Ex: Jeff Garrett

D-U-N-S 07-196-5446
MERS INC
ECONOMY BOAT STR CO-WOOD RIVER
200 S Amoco Cutoff, Wood River, IL 62095
Tel (618) 254-4333 *Founded/Ownrshp* 1953
Sales 107.1MM^E *EMP* 110
SIC 5172 Diesel fuel; Service station supplies, petroleum; Diesel fuel; Service station supplies, petroleum
Ch Bd: James F Barton Jr
Pr: Fred Barton
CFO: Walter Sheffield
Genl Mgr: Tom Zupan

D-U-N-S 05-694-5692
MERS/MISSOURI GOODWILL INDUSTRIES
1727 Locust St, Saint Louis, MO 63103-1703
Tel (314) 241-3464 *Founded/Ownrshp* 1917
Sales 151.5MM *EMP* 1,300
Accts Schowalter & Jabouri Pc St
SIC 8331 Job training & vocational rehabilitation services; Job training & vocational rehabilitation services
Pr: David Kutchback
Mng Pt: Jeffrey Haller
**CFO:* Dawayne Barnett
**VP:* Mark Arens
VP: Kristy Lance
**Ex Dir:* Lewis C Chartock
Ex Dir: Brittany Keno
MIS Dir: Jeff Lawson
IT Man: Nate Sides
Snr Mgr: Cindy Higgins

D-U-N-S 02-237-8657
MERSCHMAN SEEDS INC
103 Avenue D, West Point, IA 52656-9446
Tel (319) 837-6111 *Founded/Ownrshp* 1999
Sales 48.9MM^E *EMP* 38^E
SIC 5191 Seeds: field, garden & flower; Fertilizer & fertilizer materials
Ch Bd: William F Merschman
**Pr:* Joseph H Merschman
**Treas:* John Mc Kilip
**Sr VP:* Henry Merschman
Area Mgr: Joe Birky
Area Mgr: Max Curtis
Area Mgr: Scott Ensminger
Area Mgr: Brad Freesmeier
Area Mgr: Dwight Hoffman
Area Mgr: Shawn Macha
Area Mgr: Mike Meier

D-U-N-S 01-720-6801
MERSCORP HOLDINGS INC
1818 Library St Ste 300, Reston, VA 20190-6280
Tel (703) 761-1270 *Founded/Ownrshp* 1997
Sales NA *EMP* 41
SIC 6159 Small business investment companies
Pr: Bill Beckmann
**CFO:* Juanita Russell
**Ex VP:* Dan McLaughlin
**Ex VP:* Carson Mullen
**Sr VP:* Sharon Horstkamp
**Sr VP:* William Hultman
**Sr VP:* Bryan Kanefield
VP: Ed Albrigo
**VP:* Doug Danko
VP: Freddy Feliz
**VP:* Gary Vandeventer

D-U-N-S 07-988-1174
MERSEN USA BAY CITY-MI LLC
(*Suby of* MERSEN USA BN CORP) ★
900 Harrison St, Bay City, MI 48708-8244
Tel (989) 894-2911 *Founded/Ownrshp* 2014
Sales 25.0MM^E *EMP* 120
SIC 3295 Graphite, natural: ground, pulverized, refined or blended
CEO: Christophe Bonmier
Treas: Larry Pegher

D-U-N-S 04-285-9876 IMP
MERSEN USA BN CORP
(*Suby of* MERSEN)
400 Myrtle Ave, Boonton, NJ 07005-1839
Tel (973) 334-0700 *Founded/Ownrshp* 1940
Sales 228.2MM^E *EMP* 1,061
SIC 3624 Brushes & brush stock contacts, electric; Brushes & brush stock contacts, electric
Pr: Bernie Monsalvatge
Pr: Jay Spadaro
CFO: Massimo Neri
Genl Mgr: Cedrick Fontes
Dir IT: Susan Forst
IT Man: Sean Crowe
Sfty Mgr: Colin McMurray
Opers Mgr: Claudio Clemente
Plnt Mgr: Wesley Emmanuel

D-U-N-S 06-020-2140 IMP
MERSEN USA GREENVILLE-MI CORP
(*Suby of* MERSEN USA BN CORP) ★
712 Industrial Park Dr, Greenville, MI 48838-9792
Tel (616) 754-5671 *Founded/Ownrshp* 2007
Sales 32.5MM^E *EMP* 115
SIC 3624 Carbon & graphite products; Carbon & graphite products
Pr: Todd N Taylor
IT Man: Rick Roy

D-U-N-S 11-638-6793 IMP
MERSEN USA NEWBURYPORT-MA LLC
(*Suby of* MERSEN)
374 Merrimac St, Newburyport, MA 01950-1930
Tel (978) 462-6662 *Founded/Ownrshp* 1999
Sales 50.1MM^E *EMP* 90^E
SIC 5063 3613 Fuses & accessories; Switchgear & switchboard apparatus; Fuses & accessories; Switchgear & switchboard apparatus
CEO: Daniel Beaudron
VP: Doyle Anderson
VP: Dean Cousins
VP: Debra Huttenburg
VP: Mark Michaelson
VP: Fred Rampone
VP: Kent Walker
Rgnl Mgr: James Thompson
Genl Mgr: Mitch Taylor
IT Man: Thierry Fresse
IT Man: Wallace Paige

D-U-N-S 14-721-1804 IMP/EXP
MERSEN USA ST MARYS-PA CORP
(*Suby of* MERSEN)
215 Stackpole St, Saint Marys, PA 15857-1401
Tel (814) 781-1234 *Founded/Ownrshp* 1997
Sales 26.5MM^E *EMP* 165^E
SIC 3624 Carbon & graphite products; Carbon & graphite products
Pr: Christophe Boomier
Brnch Mgr: Edward Stumpff
IT Man: Steve Fritz
Mktg Dir: Ronald Braund

D-U-N-S 17-557-9101
MERSINO DEWATERING INC
10162 E Coldwater Rd, Davison, MI 48423-8598
Tel (810) 658-3472 *Founded/Ownrshp* 1995
Sales 59.5MM^E *EMP* 125^E
SIC 5084 1799 Industrial machinery & equipment; Dewatering; Industrial machinery & equipment; Dewatering
Pr: Rodney Mersino
COO: Andrew Ferreri
CFO: Nick Darin
**VP:* Gino Mersino
VP: Marco Mersino
Brnch Mgr: Paul Huber
Brnch Mgr: Rickey Montgomery
IT Man: Andrew Root
IT Man: Jeremy White

D-U-N-S 60-626-4489
MERSINO ENTERPRISES INC
10162 E Coldwater Rd, Davison, MI 48423-8598
Tel (866) 637-7466 *Founded/Ownrshp* 1989
Sales 20.9MM^E *EMP* 100
SIC 7353 Heavy construction equipment rental; Heavy construction equipment rental
Pr: Karen Mersino

D-U-N-S 04-233-1785
MERTES CONTRACTING CORP
2665 S 25th Ave, Broadview, IL 60155-4535
Tel (708) 343-4600 *Founded/Ownrshp* 1964
Sales 39.2MM^E *EMP* 135
SIC 1541 1542 1611 Renovation, remodeling & repairs: industrial buildings; Commercial & office buildings, renovation & repair; General contractor, highway & street construction; Highway & street maintenance; Renovation, remodeling & repairs: industrial buildings; Commercial & office buildings, renovation & repair; General contractor, highway & street construction; Highway & street maintanance
Pr: Edward J Mertes
Pr: Erin Mertes
VP: James Mertes
Off Admin: Sue Mertes

D-U-N-S 00-723-9775 IMP
MERTZ MANUFACTURING INC
MERTZ MANUFACTURING LLC
(*Suby of* MFG HOLDINGS INC) ★
1701 N Waverly St, Ponca City, OK 74601-2141
Tel (580) 762-5646 *Founded/Ownrshp* 2010
Sales 60.0MM *EMP* 301
SIC 3441 Fabricated structural metal; Fabricated structural metal
Pr: Steve Ballinger
CFO: John Soderstrom
**CFO:* John Soderstron
Ex Dir: Stephen Parr
Dir IT: Lowell Le Sebvre
IT Man: Russell Cummings

MERTZ MANUFACTURING LLC
See MERTZ MANUFACTURING INC

D-U-N-S 10-557-2155 IMP
■ **MERU NETWORKS INC**
(*Suby of* FORTINET INC) ★
894 Ross Dr, Sunnyvale, CA 94089-1403
Tel (408) 215-5300 *Founded/Ownrshp* 2015
Sales 90.8MM^E *EMP* 419^E
Tkr Sym MERU *Exch* NGM
SIC 3669 Intercommunication systems, electric; Intercommunication systems, electric
CEO: Ken Xie
**Pr:* Michael Xie
**CFO:* Andrew Del Matto
Sr VP: Ajay Malik
VP: Peter Brant
VP: Ashok Chandran
VP: John Maddison
VP: Amanda Mallow
VP: Tom Palomaki
VP: Patrick Perche
VP: Kishore Reddy
VP: Michelle Spolver
VP: John Whittle

D-U-N-S 08-548-9271
MERUELO ENTERPRISES INC
9550 Firestone Blvd # 105, Downey, CA 90241-5560
Tel (562) 745-2300 *Founded/Ownrshp* 1986
Sales 260.4MM^E *EMP* 501
SIC 1623 Pipeline construction; Pipeline construction
CEO: Alex Meruelo
**CFO:* Al Stoller
Chf Inves: Xavier Gutierrez
Sr VP: Jose Padilla
VP: Mark Ernst
**VP:* Joe Marchica
Area Supr: Miguel Yero
Sfty Mgr: Eli Mendoza
Opers Mgr: Joaquin Medrano
Genl Couns: Jacob Kim
Genl Couns: Matthew Weitz

D-U-N-S 61-247-3470 IMP
MERVIN MANUFACTURING INC
(*Suby of* ALTAMONT CAPITAL PARTNERS LLC) ★
701 N 34th St Ste 100, Seattle, WA 98103-3414
Tel (206) 204-7800 *Founded/Ownrshp* 2013
Sales 23.8MM^E *EMP* 170
SIC 3949 2329

D-U-N-S 02-538-4637
MERVIS INDUSTRIES INC
MERVIS IRON & METAL DIV
3295 E Main St Ste C, Danville, IL 61834-9302
Tel (217) 442-5300 *Founded/Ownrshp* 1935
Sales 152.2MM^E *EMP* 320
Accts Watermark Group Llc Indianap
SIC 5093 Metal scrap & waste materials; Plastics scrap; Waste paper; Metal scrap & waste materials; Plastics scrap; Waste paper
Ch Bd: Louis L Mervis
**Pr:* Adam Mervis
Treas: Richard George
**Treas:* Jennifer Kline
VP: Sybil Mervis
**VP:* Michael A Smith
Mng Dir: Dave Cocagne
Genl Mgr: Travis Foster
Genl Mgr: David Hicks
Genl Mgr: Mike Menges
Off Mgr: Misti Kaag

MERVIS IRON & METAL DIV
See MERVIS INDUSTRIES INC

D-U-N-S 08-071-9545
MERVIS MOTORS INC
RICHMOND DODGE & HONDA
(*Suby of* RICHMOND DODGE HONDA INC) ★
3505 Chester Blvd, Richmond, IN 47374-1020
Tel (765) 966-0909 *Founded/Ownrshp* 1998

Sales 20.0MM^E *EMP* 55
SIC 5511 Automobiles, new & used; Automobiles, new & used
Pr: M Lynn Wetzel
**Sec:* Kelly Wetzel
**VP:* Jera Schwer
**VP:* Nicholas Wetlez
Off Mgr: Valerie Fox
IT Man: Rocco Rossi

MERY MANUFACTURING
See ROGERS MANUFACTURING CO

D-U-N-S 80-527-4727 IMP
MERYL DIAMOND LTD
M D L
1375 Broadway Fl 24, New York, NY 10018-7012
Tel (212) 730-0333 *Founded/Ownrshp* 1993
Sales 95.1MM *EMP* 60
SIC 2339 Sportswear, women's
Pr: Meryl Diamond

D-U-N-S 94-437-4974 IMP
MERZ INC
(*Suby of* MERZ PHARMA GMBH & CO. KGAA)
6501 Six Forks Rd, Raleigh, NC 27615-6515
Tel (336) 856-2003 *Founded/Ownrshp* 1986
Sales 54.2MM^E *EMP* 135
SIC 2834 Pharmaceutical preparations; Pharmaceutical preparations
CEO: Bill Humphries
**Ch Bd:* Dr J Huckmann
**CFO:* Robert W Burgess
**Treas:* Dr Peter Mauritz
**V Ch Bd:* R G Boulton
**V Ch Bd:* Friedhelm Klingenburg
**Co-Pr:* John Delaney
Ofcr: Katrina Church
VP: Greg Besase
VP: Glenn Block
VP: Hyunna Coelho
VP: Dave Fleming
VP: James Hartman
VP: Salisa Hauptmann
VP: Mark Lemko
VP: Brian Pilcher
VP: Stefan Schacht
VP: Cynthia Schwalm
**VP:* Dave Shoup
VP: Mikael Svensson
Dir Bus: Steve Kreider

D-U-N-S 13-711-3929
MERZ NORTH AMERICA INC
(*Suby of* MERZ PHARMA GMBH & CO. KGAA)
6501 Six Forks Rd, Raleigh, NC 27615-6515
Tel (919) 582-8000 *Founded/Ownrshp* 2003
Sales 93.7MM^E *EMP* 310
SIC 3841 Diagnostic apparatus, medical; Diagnostic apparatus, medical
Pr: William Humphries
**CFO:* John Donofrio
**Treas:* Rob Burgess
Sr VP: Adam Gridley
VP: Philippe Adams
VP: Matt Anderson
VP: Gregory B Bass
VP: David Dobrowski
VP Mfg: Oliver Vogt
VP Opers: Matthew Anderson
Ql Cn Mgr: Ashley Goldberg

D-U-N-S 12-620-9282 IMP
MERZ PHARMACEUTICALS LLC
(*Suby of* MERZ PHARMACEUTICALS GMBH)
6501 Six Forks Rd, Raleigh, NC 27615-6515
Tel (919) 582-8000 *Founded/Ownrshp* 1998
Sales 27.2MM^E *EMP* 90
SIC 2834 Pharmaceutical preparations
CEO: Bill Humphries
Ofcr: Prachi Unadkat
VP: Greg Bass
**VP:* Greg Besase
VP: Katrina Church
VP: Dave Fleming
**VP:* Jim Hartman
VP: Mark Lemko
VP: Brian Pilcher
**VP:* Cynthia Schwalm
VP: Dave Shoup
Assoc Dir: Michelle Barrineau
Assoc Dir: Jennifer Merkel

D-U-N-S 13-182-1183 IMP
MESA
4445 S 74th East Ave, Tulsa, OK 74145-4710
Tel (918) 627-3188 *Founded/Ownrshp* 1984
Sales 58.0MM^E *EMP* 210
SIC 1799 5084

D-U-N-S 36-445-2110
MESA & ALMA INC
DANNY'S FAMILY CARWASH
15880 N Grnway Hyden Loop, Scottsdale, AZ 85260-1648
Tel (480) 348-2223 *Founded/Ownrshp* 1988
Sales 17.9MM^E *EMP* 400
SIC 7542 Carwashes; Carwashes
Pr: Daniel L Hendon
CFO: Tim Stocker
Genl Mgr: Edward Downing
Dir IT: Andrew Beckius
VP Opers: Heather Hendon

D-U-N-S 05-815-3370
MESA AIR GROUP INC
410 N 44th St Ste 700, Phoenix, AZ 85008-7690
Tel (602) 685-4000 *Founded/Ownrshp* 1983
Sales 645.1MM^E *EMP* 4,113
SIC 4512 4522 Air passenger carrier, scheduled; Air cargo carrier, scheduled; Flying charter service; Air passenger carrier, scheduled; Air cargo carrier, scheduled; Flying charter service
Ch Bd: Jonathan G Ornstein
Pr: Michael J Lotz
Pr: Christopher J Pappaioanou
COO: Paul Foley
Ofcr: Matthew Cole
Ex VP: Brian S Gillman
Sr VP: David K Butler
Sr VP: David K Butler
Sr VP: Ed Wegel
VP: Kristen Sk Brookshire
VP: David Butler
VP: Sharon L Goddin
VP: Chris Pappaioanou
Board of Directors: Daniel J Altobello, Robert Beleson, Carlos E Bonilla, Joseph L Manson, Peter F Nostrand, Maurice A Parker, Richard R Thayer

D-U-N-S 12-610-7619
MESA AIRLINES INC
(*Suby of* MESA AIR GROUP INC) ★
410 N 44th St Ste 700, Phoenix, AZ 85008-7690
Tel (602) 685-4000 *Founded/Ownrshp* 1996
Sales 282.4MM^E *EMP* 2,700
SIC 4512 4522 4581 Air passenger carrier, scheduled; Air cargo carrier, scheduled; Flying charter service; Aircraft servicing & repairing; Air passenger carrier, scheduled; Air cargo carrier, scheduled; Flying charter service; Aircraft servicing & repairing
Ch: Jonathan Ornstein
**Pr:* Michael Lotz
**COO:* Jorn Bates
**CFO:* George Murmame III
Treas: Henri Vilaire
**Treas:* Darren Zapfe
Sr VP: Michael Ferverda
VP: Jeffrey Domrese
**VP:* Brian Gillman

D-U-N-S 60-585-6103
MESA ASSOCIATES INC
9238 Madison Blvd Ste 116, Madison, AL 35758-9112
Tel (256) 258-2100 *Founded/Ownrshp* 1988
Sales 62.2MM^E *EMP* 427
Accts Hill Fogg & Associates Pc H
SIC 8712 8711 Architectural services; Engineering services; Architectural services; Engineering services
Pr: Ranjana C Savant
**Sr VP:* Reggie Headrick
**VP:* Timothy Cutshaw
**VP:* Mark Wilson
Prgrm Mgr: Aaron Campbell
Prgrm Mgr: Tommy McEntyre
Prgrm Mgr: Richard Roy
Prgrm Mgr: Kazem Shomali
Prgrm Mgr: John Sparr
Dept Mgr: Lisa Lance
Dir IT: Greg Solomon

D-U-N-S 13-118-5183 IMP
MESA BEVERAGE CO INC
(*Suby of* LIQUID INVESTMENTS INC) ★
205 Concourse Blvd, Santa Rosa, CA 95403-8238
Tel (707) 544-0639 *Founded/Ownrshp* 1985
Sales 43.6MM^E *EMP* 200
SIC 5181 5149 5182 Beer & other fermented malt liquors; Mineral or spring water bottling; Wine
Pr: Ronald Fowler
Dist Mgr: Mesa Martinez
Opers Mgr: Shane Hilkey
Sls Mgr: Tony Amaral

D-U-N-S 07-990-7370
MESA COMPRESSION LLC
921 Nw 63rd St Bldg 300, Oklahoma City, OK 73116-7605
Tel (405) 607-9001 *Founded/Ownrshp* 2015
Sales 25.0MM *EMP* 40
SIC 7353 Oil field equipment, rental or leasing
CFO: Sumin Lim

D-U-N-S 06-075-0890
MESA CONSOLIDATED WATER DISTRICT IMPROVEMENT CORP
MESA WATER DISTRICT
1965 Placentia Ave, Costa Mesa, CA 92627-3420
Tel (949) 631-1200 *Founded/Ownrshp* 1960
Sales 34.5MM^E *EMP* 67^E
SIC 4941 Water supply
**Pr:* James R Fisler
**VP:* Shawn Dewane

D-U-N-S 05-582-7059
MESA COUNTY VALLEY SCHOOL DISTRICT 51 (INC)
2115 Grand Ave, Grand Junction, CO 81501-8007
Tel (970) 254-5100 *Founded/Ownrshp* 1951
Sales 172.9MM *EMP* 3,200^E
Accts Chadwick Steinkirchner Davis
SIC 8211 Public elementary & secondary schools; Public elementary & secondary schools
Bd of Dir: Tom Parrish
Dir Sec: Tim Leon
Dist Mgr: Diana Tarasiewicz
Dir IT: Randy Dalton
Pr Dir: Emily Shockley
HC Dir: Tanya Skalecki

D-U-N-S 02-027-3959
MESA DEVELOPMENTAL SERVICES
DD HOUSING
950 Grand Ave, Grand Junction, CO 81501-3451
Tel (970) 243-3702 *Founded/Ownrshp* 1966
Sales 16.7MM *EMP* 395
Accts Eide Bailly Llp Greenwood Vil
SIC 8361 8331 8093 Home for the mentally handicapped; Vocational training agency; Specialty outpatient clinics; Home for the mentally handicapped; Vocational training agency; Specialty outpatient clinics
Pr: Jeff Parker
CFO: Ed Wieland
VP: Marilee Langfitt
IT Man: Christopher Bergquist

D-U-N-S 08-854-6411
MESA DISTRIBUTING COINC
(*Suby of* LIQUID INVESTMENTS INC) ★
3840 Via De La Valle # 300, Del Mar, CA 92014-4268
Tel (858) 452-2300 *Founded/Ownrshp* 1981
Sales 25.1MM^E *EMP* 250
SIC 5181 0182 5182 Beer & other fermented malt liquors; Vegetable crops grown under cover; Wine & distilled beverages; Beer & other fermented malt liquors; Vegetable crops grown under cover; Wine & distilled beverages
Ch Bd: Ronald Fowler

D-U-N-S 11-838-6309
■ **MESA ENERGY SYSTEMS INC**
EMCOR SERVICES
(*Suby of* EMCOR GROUP INC) ★
2 Cromwell, Irvine, CA 92618-1816
Tel (949) 460-0460 *Founded/Ownrshp* 1999
Sales 140.5MM^E *EMP* 450
SIC 1711 7623 Warm air heating & air conditioning contractor; Refrigeration service & repair; Warm air heating & air conditioning contractor; Refrigeration service & repair
Pr: Robert A Lake
**CFO:* Steve Hunt
**VP:* Kip Bagley
**VP:* Michael Ecshner
**VP:* Charles G Fletcher Jr
Opers Mgr: Ted Stutz

MESA FOOD PRODUCTS
See MESA FOODS INC

D-U-N-S 14-431-1255
MESA FOODS INC
MESA FOOD PRODUCTS
3701 W Magnolia Ave, Louisville, KY 40211-1635
Tel (502) 772-2500 *Founded/Ownrshp* 2008
Sales 78.8MM^E *EMP* 275
SIC 2099 Tortillas, fresh or refrigerated; Tortillas, fresh or refrigerated
Pr: Ted Longacre
VP: Steve Bright
VP: Charles Kraut
VP: Chuck Sinon
Plnt Mgr: Jeremy Meyers
Ql Cn Mgr: Tim Herndon

D-U-N-S 05-145-5756 IMP
MESA FULLY FORMED LLC
1111 S Sirrine, Mesa, AZ 85210-8718
Tel (480) 834-9331 *Founded/Ownrshp* 1969
Sales 23.2MM^E *EMP* 170
SIC 3083 3281 1799 Plastic finished products, laminated; Bathroom fixtures, cut stone; Counter top installation; Kitchen & bathroom remodeling; Plastic finished products, laminated; Bathroom fixtures, cut stone; Counter top installation; Kitchen & bathroom remodeling
Pr: Larry Cassaday
**Sec:* Emily Cassaday
Genl Mgr: Stephen M King
IT Man: Carol Grass

D-U-N-S 88-473-9384
MESA GOLFLAND LTD AN ARIZONA LIMITED PARTNERSHIP
GOLFLAND/SUNSPLASH
155 W Hampton Ave, Mesa, AZ 85210-5258
Tel (480) 834-8318 *Founded/Ownrshp* 1995
Sales 10.7MM^E *EMP* 400
SIC 7999 Miniature golf course operation; Miniature golf course operation

D-U-N-S 02-068-9774
MESA IMPORTS INC
HONDA CAR COMPANY
7800 S Autoplex Loop, Tempe, AZ 85284-1054
Tel (877) 297-1484 *Founded/Ownrshp* 1975
Sales 62.7MM^E *EMP* 165
SIC 5511 Automobiles, new & used; Automobiles, new & used
Pr: Robert A Thurston
**VP:* Paul Sparrow

D-U-N-S 10-253-0326
▲ **MESA LABORATORIES INC**
12100 W 6th Ave, Lakewood, CO 80228-1252
Tel (303) 987-8000 *Founded/Ownrshp* 1982
Sales 71.3MM *EMP* 273^E
Accts Eks&H Lllp Denver Colorado
Tkr Sym MLAB *Exch* NGM
SIC 3823 3841 Industrial instrmnts msrmnt display/control process variable; Flow instruments, industrial process type; Analyzers, industrial process type; Data loggers, industrial process type; Hemodialysis apparatus; Industrial instrmnts msrmnt display/control process variable; Flow instruments, industrial process type; Analyzers, industrial process type; Data loggers, industrial process type; Hemodialysis apparatus
Pr: John J Sullivan
Pr: Ed Morrell
**CFO:* John V Sakys
**Ofcr:* Glenn E Adriance
Sr VP: Garrett Krushefski
Sr VP: Bryan T Leo
VP: Scott Calvert
Dir Lab: Robert Bradley
Dir IT: Khoi Nguen
Dir IT: Wendy Royalty
Manager: Owen Israelson
Board of Directors: Michael T Brooks, Robert V Dwyer, Evan C Guillemin, David M Kelly, John B Schmieder

MESA MANOR CARE AND REHABILITATION CENTER
See PEAK MEDICAL COLORADO NO 2 INC

MESA MEDICAL GROUP
See MARSHALL PHYSICIAN SERVICES LLC

MESA MOVING AND STORAGE
See MESA SYSTEMS INC

D-U-N-S 05-302-1572
MESA PACKING LLC
510 Broadway St, King City, CA 93930-3201
Tel (831) 385-9173 *Founded/Ownrshp* 1978
Sales 29.6MM^E *EMP* 125
SIC 0723 Vegetable packing services

MESA PUBLIC SCHOOLS
See MESA UNIFIED SCHOOL DISTRICT 4

D-U-N-S 96-997-4893
MESA REAL ESTATE PARTNERS LP
1900 Saint James Pl # 110, Houston, TX 77056-4125
Tel (713) 580-2726 *Founded/Ownrshp* 2011
Sales 23.0MM *EMP* 2
SIC 6798 Real estate investment trusts; Real estate investment trusts

D-U-N-S 06-111-5955
MESA SOUTHERN CWS ACQUISITION LP
MESA SOUTHERN WELL SERVICING
1437 E St, Jourdanton, TX 78026-1625
Tel (830) 767-2132 *Founded/Ownrshp* 2011
Sales 27.1MM *EMP* 185
Accts Whitley Penn Llp Fort Worth
SIC 4213 Trucking, except local; Trucking, except local
Pt: Mike Hines
**Pt:* Jim Finley
**CFO:* Allan Claiborne
Sls Mgr: Kiech Jung

MESA SOUTHERN WELL SERVICING
See MESA SOUTHERN CWS ACQUISITION LP

D-U-N-S 92-702-7367
MESA SYSTEMS INC
MESA MOVING AND STORAGE
681 Railroad Blvd, Grand Junction, CO 81505-9433
Tel (970) 623-2733 *Founded/Ownrshp* 2005
Sales 37.7MM^E *EMP* 200
SIC 4213 4214 Household goods transport; Household goods moving & storage, local; Household goods transport; Household goods moving & storage, local
CEO: Kevin Head
**COO:* Kevin Haggerty
**CFO:* Steve Elliott
Opers Mgr: Grace Rowe

D-U-N-S 11-040-4477 IMP
MESA TECHNICAL ASSOCIATES INC
478 W Main St, Cobleskill, NY 12043-4644
Tel (518) 234-2000 *Founded/Ownrshp* 2002
Sales 26.2MM *EMP* 15
SIC 8748 Telecommunications consultant; Telecommunications consultant
CEO: Howard B Gartland
**VP:* Carry Odonnell
Mktg Dir: Adam Alalouf

D-U-N-S 18-477-5625
MESA UNDERWRITERS SPECIALTY INSURANCE CO
(*Suby of* MONTPELIER RE US HOLDINGS LTD) ★
6263 N Scottsdale Rd, Scottsdale, AZ 85250-5406
Tel (480) 306-8300 *Founded/Ownrshp* 2010
Sales NA *EMP* 122
SIC 6331 Fire, marine & casualty insurance; Property damage insurance
Pr: Richard R Nenaber
**Treas:* Jennifer W Diberardino
**Sr VP:* Dick Denaber
VP: Dale Houmes
**VP:* Michael H Lanza

D-U-N-S 07-899-0504
MESA UNIFIED SCHOOL DISTRICT 4 (AZ)
MESA PUBLIC SCHOOLS
63 E Main St Ste 101, Mesa, AZ 85201-7422
Tel (480) 472-0000 *Founded/Ownrshp* 1890
Sales 520.3MM *EMP* 9,621
Accts Heinfeld Meech & Co Pc P
SIC 8211 Elementary & secondary schools; Elementary & secondary schools
COO: Julie Landers
CFO: George Zeigler
Ofcr: Jacob Garcia
Mng Dir: Melissa Palmer
Dir Sec: Al Moore
Off Admin: Lisa Thompson
IT Man: Mary Love
Mtls Mgr: Ken Polamalu
Doctor: Rachel Kruppa
Genl Couns: Tom Pickrell

D-U-N-S 03-567-0371
MESA VERDE ENTERPRISES INC
396 La Luz Gate Rd, Alamogordo, NM 88310-9206
Tel (575) 437-2995 *Founded/Ownrshp* 1993
Sales 28.2MM^E *EMP* 80
SIC 1623 1611 Underground utilities contractor; Highway & street paving contractor
Pr: Randal Rabon
**Sec:* Jeffery Rabon
**VP:* Timothy Rabon
Off Mgr: Cheryl Matherly
Snr Mgr: Jeff Crain

MESA VIEW REGIONAL HOSPITAL
See MMC OF NEVADA LLC

MESA WATER DISTRICT
See MESA CONSOLIDATED WATER DISTRICT IMPROVEMENT CORP

D-U-N-S 62-083-6460
■ **MESABA AVIATION INC**
DELTA CONNECTION
(*Suby of* ENDEAVOR AIR INC) ★
1000 Blue Gentian Rd # 200, Eagan, MN 55121-1789
Tel (651) 367-5000 *Founded/Ownrshp* 2010
Sales NA *EMP* 3,700
SIC 4512 Helicopter carrier, scheduled; Helicopter carrier, scheduled
Pr: John G Spanjers
CFO: John Stanjers
**VP:* Bill Donohue
**VP:* Bill Pal Freeman
**VP:* Tom Schmidt
Genl Couns: Max Shemesh

MESABI DAILY NEWS
See MESABI PUBLISHING CO

D-U-N-S 01-392-4965 IMP
■ **MESABI NUGGET DELAWARE LLC**
(*Suby of* STEEL DYNAMICS INC) ★
6500 Hwy 135 N, Aurora, MN 55705
Tel (218) 225-6000 *Founded/Ownrshp* 2001

Sales 40.3MME *EMP* 80
SIC 3312 Blast furnaces & steel mills; Blast furnaces & steel mills
Plnt Mgr: Jeff Hensen
Sfty Dirs: Kimberly Heise

D-U-N-S 00-614-9280
MESABI PUBLISHING CO (MN)
MESABI DAILY NEWS
704 S 7th Ave, Virginia, MN 55792-3086
Tel (218) 741-5544 *Founded/Ownrshp* 1893
Sales 22.4MME *EMP* 600
SIC 2711 2752 Commercial printing & newspaper publishing combined; Commercial printing, lithographic; Commercial printing & newspaper publishing combined; Commercial printing, lithographic
Pr: John B Murphy
**VP:* Elizabeth Burns
Genl Mgr: Scott Asbach
MIS Dir: Roger Johnston
Prd Mgr: Jeff Asbach
Snr Mgr: Mark Sauer

D-U-N-S 04-277-4075
MESABI TRUST INC
60 Wall St Fl 27, New York, NY 10005-2837
Tel (615) 835-2749 *Founded/Ownrshp* 1961
Sales 26.0MM *EMP* 2
SIC 6726 Unit investment trusts; Unit investment trusts
Trst: Norman Sprague Jr
**Trst:* David J Hoffman
**Trst:* Richard G Lareau
**Trst:* Ira A Marshall
Trst: Norman F Sprague
**VP:* Matthew W Seeley

D-U-N-S 79-387-2180
MESCALERO APACHE HOUSING AUTHORITY
(*Suby of* CASINO APACHE TRAVEL CENTER) ★
101 Central Ave, Mescalero, NM 88340
Tel (575) 464-9245 *Founded/Ownrshp* 1852
Sales NA *EMP* 1,000
SIC 9531 Housing programs; Housing programs
Ex Dir: Alvin Benally
**CFO:* Thomas Odell

D-U-N-S 07-761-8650
MESCALERO APACHE TRIBE
108 Old Mescalero Blvd, Mescalero, NM 88340
Tel (575) 464-4494 *Founded/Ownrshp* 1852
Sales NA *EMP* 2,000
SIC 9131 Indian reservation; Indian reservation;
Pr: Carleton Palmer
COO: Brian Parrish
CFO: Lance Kintz
CFO: Bill Ramey
Ex Dir: Timothy Horan
IT Man: Adam Pepers

MESCO
See MARINE EQUIPMENT AND SUPPLY CO

MESCO
See MANUFACTURERS EQUIPMENT & SUPPLY CO

D-U-N-S 00-305-8757
MESHOPPEN STONE INC (PA)
131 Frantz Rd, Meshoppen, PA 18630
Tel (570) 833-2767 *Founded/Ownrshp* 1976, 1992
Sales 22.2MME *EMP* 115
SIC 3281 Flagstones; Flagstones
Pr: William Ruark
**VP:* Steven Ciprich
Sls Mgr: Wallie Dunlap

D-U-N-S 10-003-5849
MESICK CONSOLIDATED SCHOOL DISTRICT
210 E Mesick Ave, Mesick, MI 49668-9252
Tel (231) 885-2727 *Founded/Ownrshp* 1930
Sales 8.3MM *EMP* 342
SIC 8211 Public elementary & secondary schools; Public elementary & secondary schools
Prin: Linda Salling
Prin: Fred Boss
Prin: Deann Jenkins
Schl Brd P: Craig Gabier

D-U-N-S 17-364-3040
MESILLA VALLEY HOSPITAL INC
BHC MESILLA VALLEY HOSPITAL
3751 Del Rey Blvd, Las Cruces, NM 88012-8526
Tel (575) 382-3500 *Founded/Ownrshp* 1987
Sales 24.4MME *EMP* 250
SIC 8063 Hospital for the mentally ill; Hospital for the mentally ill
Pr: Margaret McCowen
**CFO:* Douglas Smith
Dir QC: Kathie Lamkin

MESILLA VALLEY TRANSPORTATION
See MVT SERVICES LLC

D-U-N-S 15-453-7732
MESIROW FINANCIAL HOLDINGS INC
353 N Clark St Lowr Level, Chicago, IL 60654-5439
Tel (312) 595-6000 *Founded/Ownrshp* 1987
Sales 518.5MME *EMP* 1,150
SIC 6211 6282 6531 6552 6411 Stock brokers & dealers; Bond dealers & brokers; Investment bankers; Investment advisory service; Real estate brokers & agents; Subdividers & developers; Insurance brokers; Stock brokers & dealers; Bond dealers & brokers; Investment bankers; Investment advisory service; Real estate brokers & agents; Subdividers & developers; Insurance brokers
CEO: Richard S Price
Pr: Paul Meier
CFO: Kristie P Askvan
CFO: Kristie Paskvan
CFO: Eve Tyree
Ch: Howard M Rossman
Bd of Dir: Richard H Korengold
Bd of Dir: William A Maniscalco
Bd of Dir: Steven N Mesirow
Bd of Dir: Brian J Shevitz
Ofcr: Chris Helmetag
Ex VP: Thomas J Allison
Ex VP: Stephen C Jones
Ex VP: Peter Klingler
Ex VP: Larry H Lattig
Sr VP: Rux Currin
Sr VP: Thomas D Walsh
Sr VP: Mary Kay Wik
VP: Pedro Arellano
VP: Juan C Avila
VP: Jeffrey Bleiweis
Board of Directors: Ralph S Tuliano, Thomas E Galuhn, Julie E Vander Weele, Jeffrey A Golman, Stephen C Vogt, Ruth C Hannenberg, Bruce J Young, Martin B Kaplan, Gerald J Levin, Richard S Price, Paul E Rice, Howard M Rossman, Marc E Sacks

D-U-N-S 61-497-4475
MESIROW FINANCIAL INC
(*Suby of* MESIROW FINANCIAL HOLDINGS INC) ★
353 N Clark St Lowr Level, Chicago, IL 60654-5439
Tel (312) 595-6000 *Founded/Ownrshp* 1982
Sales 301.7MME *EMP* 800
SIC 6211 Security brokers & dealers; Stock brokers & dealers; Bond dealers & brokers; Investment bankers; Security brokers & dealers; Stock brokers & dealers; Bond dealers & brokers; Investment bankers
CEO: Richard S Price
**Pr:* Bruce Young
**CFO:* Kristie Paskvan
Sr VP: Sharon Kexel
Sr VP: Gain O Stein
VP: Jonathan Brandon
VP: Natalie Firestone
VP: Robert A Goshen
VP: Pat Henry
VP: Ruth Jurkschat
VP: Joseph Scheurich
VP: Jeff Sobczynski
Assoc Dir: David King

D-U-N-S 11-416-4528
MESIROW FINANCIAL SERVICES INC
(*Suby of* MESIROW FINANCIAL HOLDINGS INC) ★
353 N Clark St Lowr Level, Chicago, IL 60654-5439
Tel (312) 595-6000 *Founded/Ownrshp* 1987
Sales 73.7MME *EMP* 195
SIC 6282 6531 6552 6411 Investment advisory service; Real estate brokers & agents; Real estate managers; Subdividers & developers; Insurance brokers; Investment advisory service; Real estate brokers & agents; Real estate managers; Subdividers & developers; Insurance brokers
CEO: Richard S Price
**CFO:* Kristie Paskvan
**VP:* Ruth Hannenberg

D-U-N-S 60-818-0949
MESIROW INSURANCE SERVICES INC
(*Suby of* MESIROW FINANCIAL SERVICES INC) ★
353 N Clark St Ste 400, Chicago, IL 60654-3452
Tel (312) 595-6200 *Founded/Ownrshp* 1987
Sales NA *EMP* 150
SIC 6411 Insurance brokers
CEO: Richard S Price
**CFO:* Kristie P Paskvan
Sr VP: Howard Adler
Sr VP: Ludka Soren
VP: Rhonda Labno
VP: Kevin Riordan
VP: Karen Shable
VP: Emily Toy
VP: Irene Weiss

MESKAN FOUNDRY
See LOUIS MESKAN BRASS FOUNDRY INC

D-U-N-S 15-204-9284 EXP
MESKER DOOR LLC
3440 Stanwood Blvd Ne, Huntsville, AL 35811-9021
Tel (256) 852-5846 *Founded/Ownrshp* 2010
Sales 38.1MME *EMP* 150
SIC 3442 5211 Metal doors; Window & door frames; Door & window products; Metal doors; Window & door frames; Door & window products
Pt: Dave Johnson
VP: Mike Dowling
VP: Kevin Gold
VP: Leroy Jackson
Rgnl Mgr: Cameron Layman
Plnt Mgr: Chris Johnson
Sls Mgr: David Jackson

D-U-N-S 00-341-8241
MESKO GLASS AND MIRROR CO INC
801 Wyoming Ave, Scranton, PA 18509-3019
Tel (570) 346-0777 *Founded/Ownrshp* 1930
Sales 26.9MME *EMP* 135
SIC 1793 7536 5231 5719 Glass & glazing work; Automotive glass replacement shops; Glass; Mirrors; Glass & glazing work; Automotive glass replacement shops; Glass; Mirrors
Pr: Joseph N Mesko
**Treas:* John P Mesko
**VP:* Gary C Mesko

D-U-N-S 11-303-3224
MESO SCALE DISCOVERY LLC
1601 Research Blvd, Rockville, MD 20850-3126
Tel (240) 314-2600 *Founded/Ownrshp* 2001
Sales 123.1MME *EMP* 400E
SIC 3826 Analytical instruments; Analytical instruments
CEO: Jacob Wohlstadter
Pr: Jonathan Klein-Evans
COO: Hans Biebuyck
VP: Belinda Patrick
VP: Michael Vock
Exec: Mile Cikara
Genl Mgr: James Wilbur
Snr Sftwr: Mark Roush
QA Dir: Dung Le
QA Dir: Richard Mann
Dir IT: John Kenten

MESQUITE COMMUNITY HOSPITAL
See LONE STAR HMA LP

D-U-N-S 11-978-5033
MESQUITE DEALERSHIP ACQUISITION INC
SATURN
15900 Lyndon B Jhnson Fwy, Mesquite, TX 75150-7209
Tel (972) 686-6200 *Founded/Ownrshp* 1993
Sales 50.0MM *EMP* 55
SIC 5511 Automobiles, new & used; Automobiles, new & used
Pr: Randy Hiley
**VP:* Jason Hiley

D-U-N-S 07-673-6305
■ **MESQUITE HMA GENERAL LLC**
DALLAS REGIONAL MEDICAL CENTER
(*Suby of* HEALTH MANAGEMENT ASSOCIATES INC) ★
1011 N Galloway Ave, Mesquite, TX 75149-2433
Tel (214) 320-7000 *Founded/Ownrshp* 2002
Sales 34.6MME *EMP* 600
SIC 8062 General medical & surgical hospitals; General medical & surgical hospitals
**CFO:* Nick Geer
**CFO:* Shane Wells
Ofcr: Bill Clark
CTO: Noah Downs
Board of Directors: Bing Ceniza, Patrick G Daus, Ricki Graham, Richard Hodgekins, Gaylon Maddox, Kim Salmon, Kim Tayamen, Linda White

D-U-N-S 07-137-9846
MESQUITE INDEPENDENT SCHOOL DISTRICT
405 E Davis St, Mesquite, TX 75149-4701
Tel (972) 288-6411 *Founded/Ownrshp* 1901
Sales 396.4MM *EMP* 4,200
Accts Weaver And Tidwell Llp Da
SIC 8211 Public elementary & secondary schools; Public elementary & secondary schools
Pr: Robert Seward
Ofcr: Larry Brown
Ofcr: Debbie Gilbert
Ofcr: Judyann Robinson
**VP:* Phil Appenzeller
VP: Cheryl Gregory
VP: Joel Palmer
Comm Dir: Elizabeth Fernandez
Adm Dir: Laura Jobe
Ex Dir: Randy Lewallyn
Dir Sec: Christina Ford

D-U-N-S 16-802-4748
■ **MESQUITE POWER LLC**
(*Suby of* SEMPRA ENERGY) ★
37625 W Elliot Rd, Arlington, AZ 85322-8135
Tel (623) 327-0545 *Founded/Ownrshp* 2000
Sales 23.7MME *EMP* 32
SIC 4911 Generation, electric power; Transmission, electric power; Distribution, electric power

D-U-N-S 09-091-6081
MESQUITE SERVICES INC
2313 E Greene St, Carlsbad, NM 88220-9712
Tel (575) 887-4847 *Founded/Ownrshp* 1989
Sales 31.9MME *EMP* 75
SIC 1389 Oil field services
Pr: Clay Wilson

D-U-N-S 78-624-6624
MESQUITE SPECIALTY HOSPITAL
(*Suby of* ERNEST HEALTH INC) ★
1024 N Galloway Ave, Mesquite, TX 75149-2434
Tel (972) 216-2300 *Founded/Ownrshp* 2005
Sales 57.3MME *EMP* 775E
SIC 8742 Hospital & health services consultant
CEO: Michael Exline
Ofcr: Louis Bradley
Nrsg Dir: Beth Wilkinson
HC Dir: Betsy Triplett

D-U-N-S 80-942-5197
MESSAGE SYSTEMS INC
9130 Guilford Rd, Columbia, MD 21046-1803
Tel (410) 872-4910 *Founded/Ownrshp* 2007
Sales 45.0MME *EMP* 150E
SIC 7379 Computer related maintenance services
CEO: Phillip Merrick
Pr: Rowley David
Pr: Chris McFadden
Pr: Ray Newmark
**Pr:* George W Schlossnagle
COO: Sherry Schlossnagle
CFO: Mark Salloom
**Chf Mktg O:* Steve Dille
Sr VP: Dain McCracken
Sr VP: Dille Steve
VP: David Harvey
VP: Matt Ryanczak
VP: David Thalman
Dir Bus: Karen Tracy

D-U-N-S 83-150-3763 IMP
MESSENGER LLC
(*Suby of* PRAIRIE CAPITAL LP) ★
318 E 7th St, Auburn, IN 46706-1804
Tel (260) 925-1700 *Founded/Ownrshp* 2010
Sales 39.5MME *EMP* 183E
SIC 2752 Commercial printing, lithographic; Commercial printing, lithographic
Pr: Kevin Keane
Chf Mktg O: Barrie Fleetwood
VP: Robert Hoaglund
Plnt Mgr: Dave Selig

D-U-N-S 00-429-2942
MESSENGER PUBLISHING CO (OH)
ATHENS MESSENGER, THE
(*Suby of* ADAMS PUBLISHING GROUP LLC) ★
9300 Johnson Hollow Rd, Athens, OH 45701-9028
Tel (740) 592-6612 *Founded/Ownrshp* 1825, 2010
Sales 39.7MME *EMP* 125
SIC 2711 2752 Newspapers, publishing & printing; Commercial printing, offset; Newspapers, publishing & printing; Commercial printing, offset
Pr: Mark Policinski
**Ch Bd:* Clarence Brown Jr
**Treas:* John Aston
VP: Glenn Christensen
Advt Mgr: Chuck Douglas

D-U-N-S 04-160-3499
MESSER CONSTRUCTION CO
5158 Fishwick Dr, Cincinnati, OH 45216-2216
Tel (513) 242-1541 *Founded/Ownrshp* 1975
Sales 1.1MMM *EMP* 900
Accts Deloitte & Touche Llp Cincinn
SIC 1542 1522 1541 Hospital construction; Commercial & office building, new construction; Commercial & office buildings, renovation & repair; School building construction; Hotel/motel, new construction; Multi-family dwellings, new construction; Industrial buildings & warehouses; Renovation, remodeling & repairs: industrial buildings; Warehouse construction; Hospital construction; Commercial & office building, new construction; Commercial & office buildings, renovation & repair; School building construction; Hotel/motel, new construction; Multi-family dwellings, new construction; Industrial buildings & warehouses; Renovation, remodeling & repairs: industrial buildings; Warehouse construction
Ch Bd: Thomas M Keckeis
CFO: Chad Gagnon
**CFO:* E Paul Hitter Jr
**Sr VP:* C Allen Begley
**Sr VP:* Mark R Gillming
**Sr VP:* Mark S Luegering
**Sr VP:* Timothy J Steigerwald
**Sr VP:* Bernard P Suer
VP: Nick Apanius
VP: Steven M Bestard
VP: Daniel C France
VP: Stephen L Keckeis
VP: Thomas M Lampe
VP: Andrew R Lorenz
VP: David E Miller
VP: William E Rutz
VP: Robert E Verst Jr
VP: Thomas Wall
VP: Robert L Williams
Exec: John Blum
Exec: David Doss
Board of Directors: Edward D Diller, Charles S Mechem Jr, Nelson Schwab III, Peter S Strange, Robert L Wehling

D-U-N-S 17-640-2345 IMP
MESSER CUTTING SYSTEMS INC
(*Suby of* MEC HOLDING GMBH)
W141 N 9427 Fountain Blvd W 141 N, Menomonee Falls, WI 53051
Tel (262) 255-5520 *Founded/Ownrshp* 2000
Sales 23.4MME *EMP* 168
SIC 3545 3541 Machine tool accessories; Machine tools, metal cutting type; Machine tool accessories; Machine tools, metal cutting type
Pr: Gary Norville
Prgrm Mgr: Mark Politowski
Rgnl Mgr: Richard Parrott
Genl Mgr: Carlos Esteves
Genl Mgr: Julie Wolf
IT Man: Dave Binger
Plnt Mgr: Gary Werpinski
Sales Exec: Veronica Goodson
Sls Mgr: Scott Kassler

D-U-N-S 07-119-7792
MESSIAH COLLEGE (PA)
1 College Ave Ste 3000, Mechanicsburg, PA 17055-6805
Tel (717) 766-2511 *Founded/Ownrshp* 1909
Sales 126.0MM *EMP* 800
Accts Parentebeard Llc York Pennsy
SIC 8221 College, except junior; College, except junior
Pr: Kim S Phipps
**CFO:* David Walker
**VP:* Randall Basinger
**VP:* John Chopka
**VP:* Barry G Goodling
**Prin:* Eunice F Steinbrecher
Off Mgr: Gloria Lutz
**MIS Mgr:* William Strausbaugh
VP Opers: Kathrynne Shafer

D-U-N-S 96-487-9204
MESSIAH HOME
100 Mount Allen Dr, Mechanicsburg, PA 17055-6171
Tel (717) 697-4666 *Founded/Ownrshp* 2010
Sales 41.5MM *EMP* 15E
Accts Parentebeard Llc Philadelphia
SIC 8082 Home health care services; Home health care services
Prin: Julia A Stout

D-U-N-S 07-121-8242
MESSIAH LIFEWAYS COMMUNITY
MESSIAH VILLAGE
100 Mount Allen Dr, Mechanicsburg, PA 17055-6171
Tel (717) 790-8209 *Founded/Ownrshp* 1896
Sales 40.7MM *EMP* 473
Accts Parente Beard Llc Philadelphi
SIC 8361 8661 Residential care; Religious organizations; Residential care; Religious organizations
Pr: Emerson Lesher
CFO: Carolyn Burke
**CFO:* Julia Stout
VP: Mary Begley
VP: Sharon Engle
VP: Jody Harman
VP: Kristen Heisey
VP: Nicole Sarver
Exec: Lindsey Clinton
Exec: Lindsey Pletcher
Dir Soc: Jamie Seilhamer

MESSIAH VILLAGE
See MESSIAH LIFEWAYS COMMUNITY

D-U-N-S 01-100-0809
MESSICK & GRAY CONSTRUCTION INC (DE)
BRIDGEVILLE MACHINING
9003 Fawn Rd, Bridgeville, DE 19933-2941
Tel (302) 337-8777 *Founded/Ownrshp* 1963
Sales 27.0MME *EMP* 50E

SIC 5084 5083 7699 3441 Industrial machinery & equipment; Agricultural machinery; Industrial machinery & equipment repair; Agricultural equipment repair services; Fabricated structural metal
Pr: Alan Messick
**Sec:* Shirley Messick

D-U-N-S 01-406-2350 EXP
MESSICK FARM EQUIPMENT INC (PA)
187 Merts Dr, Elizabethtown, PA 17022-8803
Tel (800) 222-3373 *Founded/Ownrshp* 1953
Sales 78.5MM^E *EMP* 381
SIC 5083 5082 Farm equipment parts & supplies; Landscaping equipment; General construction machinery & equipment; Farm equipment parts & supplies; Landscaping equipment; General construction machinery & equipment
Pr: Robert Messick
**VP:* Kenneth Messick

D-U-N-S 08-081-8359 IMP/EXP
MESSIER-BUGATTI USA LLC
(*Suby of* MESSIER BUGATTI DOWTY)
1 Carbon Way, Walton, KY 41094-9370
Tel (859) 525-8583 *Founded/Ownrshp* 1998
Sales 95.4MM^E *EMP* 200
SIC 3728 Brakes, aircraft; Brakes, aircraft
VP: Philippe Garnier
VP: Andy Short
Ql Cn Mgr: Kevin Clouse
Ql Cn Mgr: Andrew Rink
Snr Mgr: David Bird

D-U-N-S 18-688-9812
MESSINA FLOOR COVERING LLC
4300 Brookpark Rd Ste 1, Cleveland, OH 44134-1138
Tel (216) 595-0100 *Founded/Ownrshp* 1975
Sales 21.0MM *EMP* 75
SIC 5023 1752

D-U-N-S 06-846-4874
MESSINA GROUP INC
BECO GROUP, THE
200 S Prospect Ave, Park Ridge, IL 60068-4037
Tel (847) 825-8000 *Founded/Ownrshp* 1956
Sales 90.9MM^E *EMP* 2,662
SIC 7363 7361 Temporary help service; Employment agencies; Temporary help service; Employment agencies
VP: Suzanne Meagher

MESSINGER BEARINGS
See KINGSBURY INC

D-U-N-S 00-432-8225 IMP
MESTEK INC
DADANCO - MESTEK
260 N Elm St, Westfield, MA 01085-1614
Tel (413) 568-9571 *Founded/Ownrshp* 1898
Sales 299.3MM^E *EMP* 2,584
Accts Mcgladrey Llp Boston Massach
SIC 3585 3634 3549 3542 3354 Heating equipment, complete; Air conditioning equipment, complete; Air conditioning units, complete: domestic or industrial; Heating units, electric (radiant heat): baseboard or wall; Metalworking machinery; Wiredrawing & fabricating machinery & equipment, ex. die; Coilers (metalworking machines); Cutting-up lines; Punching, shearing & bending machines; Shapes, extruded aluminum; Heating equipment, complete; Air conditioning equipment, complete; Air conditioning units, complete: domestic or industrial; Heating units, electric (radiant heat): baseboard or wall; Metalworking machinery; Wiredrawing & fabricating machinery & equipment, ex. die; Coilers (metalworking machines); Cutting-up lines; Punching, shearing & bending machines; Shapes, extruded aluminum
CEO: Stuart B Reed
Treas: Stephen M Shea
Ofcr: Richard Allorto
Sr VP: Mark Albino
Sr VP: Robert G Dewey
VP: Greg Crosby
VP: Diana Jay
VP: Richard Kessler
Exec: Joanne Berwald
Prin: Bill Rafferty
Ex Dir: Ed Howell

D-U-N-S 04-500-7144 IMP/EXP
MESTEK MACHINERY INC
IOWA PRECISION INDUSTRIES
(*Suby of* DADANCO - MESTEK) ★
5480 6th St Sw, Cedar Rapids, IA 52404-4814
Tel (319) 362-2218 *Founded/Ownrshp* 1996
Sales 50.4MM^E *EMP* 100
SIC 5046 Commercial equipment
Pr: R Bruce Dewey
**Treas:* Stephen M Shea
VP: Mike Bailey
CTO: Ipiserv Santacroce
VP Sls: Richard Burkart
Manager: Bill Dennis
Manager: Scott Husbands

D-U-N-S 93-347-2235 IMP
MESTEX LTD
(*Suby of* DADANCO - MESTEK) ★
4830 Transport Dr, Dallas, TX 75247-6310
Tel (214) 638-6010 *Founded/Ownrshp* 1995
Sales 68.0MM^E *EMP* 240
SIC 3585 1711 3433 Heating & air conditioning combination units; Plumbing, heating, air-conditioning contractors; Heating equipment, except electric; Heating & air conditioning combination units; Plumbing, heating, air-conditioning contractors; Heating equipment, except electric
Trfc Mgr: Aubrey Berhow
Sales Exec: Sean Baugh
Sls Dir: Jim Spehar

MET INTERNATIONAL
See MAJESTIC INTERNATIONAL ELECTRONIC TECHNOLOGIES INC

D-U-N-S 79-477-3713
MET LABORATORIES INC
METLABS
914 W Patapsco Ave, Baltimore, MD 21230-3415
Tel (410) 354-3300 *Founded/Ownrshp* 1992
Sales 34.2MM^E *EMP* 105
SIC 8734 7389 8711 8748

D-U-N-S 60-358-1349
MET ONE INSTRUMENTS INC
1600 Nw Washington Blvd, Grants Pass, OR 97526-1052
Tel (541) 471-7111 *Founded/Ownrshp* 1989
Sales 26.9MM^E *EMP* 127
SIC 3829 Meteorological instruments; Meteorological instruments
Pr: Thomas L Pottberg
**CFO:* James Riley Loftin
CFO: Riley Loftin
**Sec:* Joann C Pottberg
VP: David Gilmore
VP: Herbert Schloesser
Dir IT: Toone Rich
IT Man: Richard Toone
Prd Mgr: Rick Taylor
Mktg Mgr: Peter Pomponi
Sls Mgr: Sky Patton

D-U-N-S 80-043-3133
MET WELD INTERNATIONAL LLC
(*Suby of* GAVIAL ENGINEERING & MFG) ★
5727 Ostrander Rd, Altamont, NY 12009-4209
Tel (518) 765-2318 *Founded/Ownrshp* 2006
Sales 21.4MM^E *EMP* 70
SIC 3498 Fabricated pipe & fittings
Plnt Mgr: William M Mc Grath

MET-CON COMPANIES
See MET-CON CONSTRUCTION INC

D-U-N-S 08-767-9304
MET-CON CONSTRUCTION INC
MET-CON COMPANIES
15760 Acorn Trl, Faribault, MN 55021-7610
Tel (507) 332-2266 *Founded/Ownrshp* 1978
Sales 107.1MM^E *EMP* 250^E
SIC 1541 1542 Industrial buildings & warehouses; Commercial & office building contractors; Industrial buildings & warehouses; Commercial & office building contractors
CEO: Thomas Mc Donough
**Sec:* Sandra Mc Donough
**VP:* Scott Brown
**VP:* Randy McDonough
**VP:* Jim Roush
**VP:* Julie Teske
Dir IT: Travis Beaupre
Sls Mgr: Joel Schafer

D-U-N-S 09-970-6418 EXP
MET-CON INC
465 Canaveral Groves Blvd, Cocoa, FL 32926-4663
Tel (321) 632-4880 *Founded/Ownrshp* 1979
Sales 34.3MM^E *EMP* 100
Accts James Moore & Co Pl Dayto
SIC 3441 1791 1541 Building components, structural steel; Structural steel erection; Industrial buildings, new construction; Building components, structural steel; Structural steel erection; Industrial buildings, new construction
Pr: Billy E Sheffield
**VP:* Dennis Dammann
**VP:* Jeffrey Gibson
**VP:* Robert Reijm

D-U-N-S 00-234-9280 EXP
■ **MET-PRO TECHNOLOGIES LLC**
(*Suby of* CECO ENVIRONMENTAL CORP) ★
460 E Swedesford Rd # 2030, Wayne, PA 19087-1821
Tel (215) 717-7909 *Founded/Ownrshp* 1966
Sales 76.8MM^E *EMP* 337^E
SIC 3564 Air cleaning systems; Air purification equipment; Filters, air: furnaces, air conditioning equipment, etc.; Air cleaning systems; Air purification equipment; Filters, air: furnaces, air conditioning equipment, etc.
Ofcr: Bill Kelley
VP: Mark A Betchaver
VP: Karl Dean
VP: Thomas Edwards
VP: Sonja M Haggert
VP: Gregory Kimmer
VP: William Moffitt
VP: Bob Replogle
VP: James Shive
Creative D: Kevin Bittle
Genl Mgr: Thomas Walker
Board of Directors: Michael J Morris, Stanley W Silverman, Judith A Spires, Robin L Wiessmann

D-U-N-S 82-735-0943
▲ **META FINANCIAL GROUP INC**
5501 S Broadband Ln, Sioux Falls, SD 57108-2253
Tel (605) 782-1767 *Founded/Ownrshp* 1993
Sales NA *EMP* 638^E
Tkr Sym CASH *Exch* NGM
SIC 6035 Federal savings banks; Federal savings banks
Ch Bd: J Tyler Haahr
Pr: Brad Hanson
COO: Ira D Frericks
CFO: John Gaiser
CFO: Glen Herrick
Ex VP: Ronald W Butterfield
Ex VP: Scott Galit
Ex VP: Cindy Smith
VP: Scott Jucht
Dir Risk M: John Hagy
IT Man: Troy Larson

D-U-N-S 07-290-3990
■ **METABANK**
(*Suby of* META FINANCIAL GROUP INC) ★
121 E 5th St, Storm Lake, IA 50588-2339
Tel (712) 732-4117 *Founded/Ownrshp* 1954, 1955
Sales NA *EMP* 250
SIC 6035 Federal savings & loan associations; Federal savings & loan associations
CEO: J Tyler Haar
**Pr:* Fred Hanson
**Ex VP:* Troy Moore
Sr VP: Michael Conlin
Sr VP: Ian Stromberg
Sr VP: Sonja Theisen
VP: Greg Baker
VP: Lisa Binder
VP: Tracee Dierenfield
VP: Kara Gerken
VP: Lisa Gould
VP: Tracy Landsem
VP: Keith Portner
VP: Karen Waller
Exec: Bradley Hanson
Exec: Kathy Thorson
Dir Risk M: Merid Eshete

D-U-N-S 01-237-1829 IMP
METABO CORP
(*Suby of* METABOWERKE GMBH)
1231 Wilson Dr, West Chester, PA 19380-4243
Tel (610) 436-5900 *Founded/Ownrshp* 1971
Sales 28.7MM^E *EMP* 60
SIC 5072 Power handtools
CEO: Martin Cross
**Pr:* John Ham
**Treas:* Dennis Sutton
**Ex VP:* David Smith
Mktg Mgr: Jere Geib

D-U-N-S 13-709-7981
METABOLON INC
617 Davis Dr Ste 400, Durham, NC 27713
Tel (919) 572-1711 *Founded/Ownrshp* 2000
Sales 35.8MM^E *EMP* 100^E
SIC 8731 Commercial research laboratory; Commercial research laboratory
Pr: John Ryals
Pr: Shaun Lonergan
CFO: S Todd Lynch
Ofcr: Darin Leigh
Sr VP: Eric Button
Sr VP: Joseph E Zack
VP: Bruce McCreedy
VP: Reid Trip
Sls Dir: Ryan Welch
Board of Directors: Christopher W Kersey

METACARTA
See QBASE LLC

D-U-N-S 04-089-3786 IMP/EXP
METAFOODS LLC
2970 Clairmont Rd Ne, Brookhaven, GA 30329-1638
Tel (404) 843-2400 *Founded/Ownrshp* 1997
Sales 24.2MM^E *EMP* 28
SIC 5142 Packaged frozen goods

D-U-N-S 10-305-6594 IMP/EXP
METAGENICS INC
(*Suby of* ALTICOR INC) ★
25 Enterprise Ste 200, Aliso Viejo, CA 92656-2709
Tel (949) 366-0818 *Founded/Ownrshp* 2006
Sales 267.3MM^E *EMP* 386
Accts Grant Thornton Irvine Ca
SIC 5122 Vitamins & minerals; Medicinals & botanicals; Vitamins & minerals; Medicinals & botanicals
Pr: Brent Eck
Pr: Jean M Bellin
CFO: Dave Tuit
Ofcr: John Troup
Ex VP: John Babish
VP: J Kuhlman
VP: Michael Kuhlman
VP: Mike Kuhlman
VP: Deanna Minich
VP: Allison Musetich
VP: Willy Pardinas
VP: Matthew L Tripp

D-U-N-S 04-217-7881
METAIRIE CAPITAL LLC
VETERANS FORD
3724 Veterans Mem Blvd, Metairie, LA 70002-5837
Tel (504) 887-8410 *Founded/Ownrshp* 2003
Sales 52.5MM^E *EMP* 150
SIC 5511 Automobiles, new & used; Automobiles, new & used
Sls Mgr: Charles Antrum
Sls Mgr: Wayne Maiorana
Sls Mgr: Roberto Rocha

METAL ACESORIES
See DAYTON SUPERIOR CORP

METAL AIRE
See METAL INDUSTRIES INC

D-U-N-S 79-052-2528 IMP
METAL BOX INTERNATIONAL INC
11600 King St, Franklin Park, IL 60131-1311
Tel (847) 455-8500 *Founded/Ownrshp* 1995
Sales 36.7MM^E *EMP* 200
SIC 2514 3993 3444 2542 2522 Metal bookcases & stereo cabinets; Signs & advertising specialties; Sheet metalwork; Partitions & fixtures, except wood; Office furniture, except wood; Metal bookcases & stereo cabinets; Signs & advertising specialties; Sheet metalwork; Partitions & fixtures, except wood; Office furniture, except wood
Pr: Bruce Saltzberg
Sfty Dirs: Gary Green
Plnt Mgr: Jack Frigo

D-U-N-S 78-298-0718
METAL BUILDING SUPPLY INC
19601 N Mount Olive Rd, Gravette, AR 72736-9130
Tel (479) 787-6264 *Founded/Ownrshp* 1999
Sales 24.1MM^E *EMP* 52
SIC 5039 Structural assemblies, prefabricated: non-wood
Pr: James R Britton
**VP:* Warren D Alexander
Genl Mgr: Jose Mendoza

METAL CASTINGS CO
See ELECTRO-MECHANICAL CORP

D-U-N-S 06-691-0464 IMP/EXP
METAL CONTAINER CORP
(*Suby of* ANHEUSER-BUSCH COMPANIES LLC) ★
3636 S Geyer Rd Ste 400, Saint Louis, MO 63127-1218
Tel (314) 577-2000 *Founded/Ownrshp* 1973
Sales 275.1MM^E *EMP* 1,437
SIC 3411 Aluminum cans; Aluminum cans
Ch: Barry H Beracha
**Pr:* Joseph L Goltzman
VP: Todd A Brown
VP: James E Engelhuber
VP: William C Wilkenloh

D-U-N-S 96-735-1438
METAL CONVERSIONS LTD
175 Longview Ave E, Mansfield, OH 44903-4208
Tel (419) 525-0011 *Founded/Ownrshp* 1997
Sales 29.6MM^E *EMP* 25^E
SIC 5051 Aluminum bars, rods, ingots, sheets, pipes, plates, etc.
CEO: Steve Senser
Pr: Rob Carey
VP: Jay Levant
VP: Carl Roark
VP: Andy Senser
Opers Mgr: Brad Roark

D-U-N-S 07-135-1829
METAL CRAFT MACHINE & ENGINEERING INC
13760 Business Ctr Dr Nw, Elk River, MN 55330-4811
Tel (763) 441-1855 *Founded/Ownrshp* 1978
Sales 30.3MM^E *EMP* 115
SIC 3841 3599 Surgical & medical instruments; Machine & other job shop work; Surgical & medical instruments; Machine & other job shop work
CEO: Trisha L Mowry
**Pr:* Sean Mowry
VP: Trisha Mowery

D-U-N-S 05-493-9509
METAL CULVERTS INC
711 Heisinger Rd, Jefferson City, MO 65109-4711
Tel (573) 636-7312 *Founded/Ownrshp* 1979
Sales 42.3MM^E *EMP* 130
SIC 3444 3498 3312 Culverts, sheet metal; Pipe, sheet metal; Fabricated pipe & fittings; Blast furnaces & steel mills; Culverts, sheet metal; Pipe, sheet metal; Fabricated pipe & fittings; Blast furnaces & steel mills
CEO: Mozelle D Bielski
COO: Ben Bielski
Bd of Dir: Gary Wisch
Plnt Mgr: Steve Clark
Plnt Mgr: Brian Overton
Sls Mgr: Mike Rackers

D-U-N-S 00-507-1311 IMP
METAL CUTTING TOOLS CORP
METCUT
(*Suby of* HARBOUR GROUP LTD) ★
21 Airport Dr, Rockford, IL 61109-2994
Tel (815) 226-0650 *Founded/Ownrshp* 1988
Sales 24.0MM^E *EMP* 130
SIC 3541 Machine tools, metal cutting type

METAL DEK GROUP
See CONSOLIDATED SYSTEMS INC

D-U-N-S 01-829-8138
METAL DESIGN SYSTEMS INC
4150 C St Sw, Cedar Rapids, IA 52404-7451
Tel (319) 362-7454 *Founded/Ownrshp* 1998
Sales 22.4MM^E *EMP* 75
SIC 3441 Fabricated structural metal
Pr: Kreg Tjelmeland
Manager: Matt Rechkemmer

D-U-N-S 82-473-9122
METAL DYNAMICS DETROIT LLC
SIMS METAL MANAGEMENT
(*Suby of* METAL MANAGEMENT INC) ★
3100 Lonyo St, Detroit, MI 48209-1089
Tel (313) 841-1800 *Founded/Ownrshp* 2007
Sales 26.9MM^E *EMP* 84
SIC 5093 8742 Metal scrap & waste materials; Management consulting services; Metal scrap & waste materials; Management consulting services

D-U-N-S 07-198-6160 IMP
METAL EXCHANGE CORP
PENNEX ALUMINUM COMPANY
111 West Port Plz Ste 350, Saint Louis, MO 63146-3013
Tel (314) 434-3500 *Founded/Ownrshp* 1974
Sales 241.0MM^E *EMP* 500
SIC 3369 5093 Nonferrous foundries; Metals service centers & offices; Nonferrous foundries; Metal scrap & waste materials
Ch Bd: Mike Lefton
**Pr:* William J Aronson
**Pr:* Rick Merluzzi
**CFO:* Edward O Merz
**Ex VP:* Tom Akers
**VP:* Daryl Coleman
VP: E A Craver
VP: Michael Kelley
VP: Adrian Storey
IT Man: Dennis Allen
Software D: Jaron Davis

D-U-N-S 09-653-0886
METAL FINISHING CO INC
1423 S Mclean Blvd, Wichita, KS 67213-4302
Tel (316) 267-7289 *Founded/Ownrshp* 1961
Sales 29.0MM^E *EMP* 160
SIC 1721 Aircraft painting; Commercial painting; Aircraft painting; Commercial painting
Pr: Robert H Babst
**Treas:* Edward Dunn Jr
Plnt Mgr: Rene Espinosa

D-U-N-S 09-295-4296 IMP
METAL FLOW CORP
11694 James St, Holland, MI 49424-8963
Tel (616) 392-7976 *Founded/Ownrshp* 1978
Sales 70.0MM *EMP* 230
SIC 3469 Metal stampings; Metal stampings
Ch Bd: Leslie Brown

*Pr: Robert K Knittel
*CFO: Kelly Springer
*Ex VP: Chuck Caesar
Snr Mgr: Kyle Lopshire

D-U-N-S 00-503-4780
METAL FORMING & COINING CORP (OH)
MFC
1007 Illinois Ave, Maumee, OH 43537-1752
Tel (419) 897-9530 Founded/Ownrshp 1953, 1983
Sales 28.3MME EMP 150
SIC 3462 Iron & steel forgings; Iron & steel forgings
Pr: Thomas Wienrich
*CFO: Kurt Geisheimer
*Ex VP: Paul Kessler
Exec: Betsy Way
Genl Mgr: Tim Cripsey
Off Admin: Kim Malak
Mfg Dir: Jim Zare
Sfty Mgr: John Net
Ql Cn Mgr: Stephan Fisher
Sls Mgr: Terry Harris

D-U-N-S 96-201-1271
METAL IMPACT LLC
1501 Oakton St, Elk Grove Village, IL 60007-2101
Tel (847) 718-0192 Founded/Ownrshp 2010
Sales 31.5MME EMP 100
SIC 3544 Extrusion dies; Extrusion dies
Ql Cn Mgr: Divyang Patel

D-U-N-S 04-841-0070 IMP
■ **METAL IMPROVEMENT CO LLC**
(Suby of CURTISS-WRIGHT CORP) ★
80 E State Rt 4 Ste 310, Paramus, NJ 07652-2662
Tel (201) 843-7800 Founded/Ownrshp 1969
Sales 307.6MME EMP 1,800
SIC 3398 Metal heat treating; Shot peening (treating steel to reduce fatigue); Metal heat treating; Shot peening (treating steel to reduce fatigue)
Pr: Gerald Nachman
CFO: James Ruscin
Treas: Gary Benschip
VP: Peter Ohara
VP: J Ruscin
VP: Rob Specht
Exec: Bob Kleppe
Div Mgr: James Groark
Div Mgr: Brent Taylor
Genl Mgr: Dennis Taylor
Dir IT: Dominic Cimino

D-U-N-S 00-408-7953 IMP/EXP
METAL INDUSTRIES INC (FL)
METAL AIRE
(Suby of J T WALKER INDUSTRIES INC) ★
1985 Carroll St, Clearwater, FL 33765-1909
Tel (727) 441-2651 Founded/Ownrshp 1949
Sales 351.7MME EMP 3,500
SIC 3585 Parts for heating, cooling & refrigerating equipment; Parts for heating, cooling & refrigerating equipment
CEO: Jay K Poppleton
*Pr: Damian Macaluso
*CEO: Peter Desoto
CFO: Dan Frankiewicz
*VP: Janet L Fasenmyer
VP: David Hawkins
Mktg Mgr: Barbara Shaloo
Manager: Vic Hoffman

D-U-N-S 10-296-2370 IMP
METAL MANAGEMENT INC
SIMS METAL MANAGEMENT
(Suby of SIMS METAL MANAGEMENT LIMITED)
1600 Harvester Rd, West Chicago, IL 60185-1618
Tel (312) 645-0700 Founded/Ownrshp 2008
Sales 1.0MMME EMP 6,600
SIC 5093 1795 Metal scrap & waste materials; Demolition, buildings & other structures; Metal scrap & waste materials; Demolition, buildings & other structures
CEO: Galvino Claro
*Ch Bd: Daniel W Dienst
*Pr: Robert A Kelman
Ex VP: David Borg
Ex VP: Jimmie Buckland
*Ex VP: Robert C Larry
Ex VP: Larry Snyder
VP: Brian Souza
Ex Dir: Geoffrey Brunsdon
Genl Mgr: Peter Farmer
Genl Mgr: Peter Ricketts

D-U-N-S 04-758-1335 IMP/EXP
METAL MANAGEMENT MIDWEST INC
SIMS METAL MANAGEMENT
(Suby of METAL MANAGEMENT INC) ★
2500 S Paulina St, Chicago, IL 60608-5307
Tel (773) 254-1200 Founded/Ownrshp 1965
Sales 163.6MME EMP 500E
SIC 5093 Ferrous metal scrap & waste; Nonferrous metals scrap; Ferrous metal scrap & waste; Nonferrous metals scrap
Pr: Cristopher Dandror
*Pr: Lewis H Ross
Snr Mgr: Dennis Schalliol

D-U-N-S 11-004-2020
METAL MANAGEMENT MISSISSIPPI LLC
(Suby of METAL MANAGEMENT INC) ★
121 Apache Dr, Jackson, MS 39272-9782
Tel (601) 372-4320 Founded/Ownrshp 2000
Sales 36.6MME EMP 1,054E
SIC 5093 Metal scrap & waste materials
VP: David A Carpenter

D-U-N-S 01-405-9844 EXP
METAL MANAGEMENT PITTSBURGH INC
SIMS METAL MANAGEMENT
(Suby of METAL MANAGEMENT INC) ★
1 Linden Ave E, Jersey City, NJ 07305-4726
Tel (201) 333-2902 Founded/Ownrshp 1958, 1989
Sales 45.3MME EMP 43
SIC 5093 3341 Nonferrous metals scrap; Secondary nonferrous metals
CEO: Galdino Claro
*Pr: Bob Kelman
*Pr: Dennis O'Loughlin
*CFO: Robert C Larry
Exec: Norma Perez
Div Mgr: Bret Heinrichs
Genl Mgr: James Banigan

METAL MANAGEMENT SOUTHWEST
See PROLER SOUTHWEST INC

D-U-N-S 09-181-1232
METAL MASTERS FOODSERVICE EQUIPMENT CO INC
EAGLE FOODSERVICE
(Suby of EAGLE GROUP INC) ★
100 Industrial Blvd, Clayton, DE 19938-8900
Tel (302) 653-3000 Founded/Ownrshp 1978
Sales 105.2MME EMP 460
SIC 3589 3556 Commercial cooking & foodwarming equipment; Food products machinery; Commercial cooking & foodwarming equipment; Food products machinery
Pr: Larry N McAllister
*VP: Betty McAllister
Dir IT: Jim Joyce
Netwrk Mgr: Debbie Wright
Manager: Lynda Donavon

D-U-N-S 18-065-5771
METAL MOULDING CORP
1225 Northgte Bus Pkwy, Madison, TN 37115-2475
Tel (615) 865-9867 Founded/Ownrshp 1987
Sales 22.0MME EMP 75
SIC 3448 3444 Prefabricated metal buildings; Sheet metalwork
Pr: Jimmy Parrish
*Sec: Daryl Hammers
*Genl Mgr: Phil Friedli
Prd Mgr: Jackie Hester

D-U-N-S 87-688-7506 IMP
METAL ONE AMERICA INC
(Suby of METAL ONE HOLDINGS AMERICA INC) ★
6250 N River Rd Ste 2055, Rosemont, IL 60018-4270
Tel (847) 685-5400 Founded/Ownrshp 2003
Sales 54.2MME EMP 70
SIC 5051 Steel; Steel
Pr: Mikihiko Matsushita
Sls Mgr: Thomas Danyluk
Sls Mgr: Lela Stieber
Sls Mgr: Jun Tanaka
Sls Mgr: Lisa Uselton
Sls Mgr: Keng Yeh
Sales Asso: Denise Drube
Sales Asso: Paola Tumy

D-U-N-S 15-822-9232
METAL ONE HOLDINGS AMERICA INC
(Suby of METAL ONE CORP.)
6250 N River Rd Ste 6055, Rosemont, IL 60018-4210
Tel (847) 318-0019 Founded/Ownrshp 2003
Sales 371.5MME EMP 419
SIC 5085 5051 Fasteners, industrial: nuts, bolts, screws, etc.; Wire; Fasteners, industrial: nuts, bolts, screws, etc.; Wire
Pr: Ichiro Furuno
Pr: Tomohiro Kadokura
Treas: Nancy P Bryers

D-U-N-S 05-285-9246 IMP
METAL POWDER PRODUCTS LLC
16855 Suthpark Dr Ste 100, Westfield, IN 46074
Tel (317) 580-2420 Founded/Ownrshp 1946, 1998
Sales 51.4MME EMP 350
SIC 3399

METAL PROCESSING
See ARCELORMITTAL VINTON LLC

D-U-N-S 00-403-5960
METAL PRODUCTS CO (TN)
300 Garfield St, McMinnville, TN 37110-1999
Tel (931) 473-5513 Founded/Ownrshp 1947
Sales 21.0MME EMP 100
SIC 3444 3469 3993 3446 3443 Sheet metalwork; Metal stampings; Signs & advertising specialties; Architectural metalwork; Fabricated plate work (boiler shop)
Pr: Arthur J Dyer

D-U-N-S 01-598-9200
■ **METAL RECYCLING SERVICES LLC**
(Suby of DAVID J JOSEPH CO) ★
334 Beechwood Rd Ste 401, Fort Mitchell, KY 41017-2086
Tel (859) 292-8400 Founded/Ownrshp 2008
Sales 44.7MME EMP 150
SIC 5093 Metal scrap & waste materials; Metal scrap & waste materials
Pr: Bob Eviston

D-U-N-S 08-843-4527 IMP/EXP
METAL SALES MANUFACTURING CORP (KY)
(Suby of INTERLOCK INDUSTRIES INC) ★
545 S 3rd St Ste 200, Louisville, KY 40202-1936
Tel (502) 855-4300 Founded/Ownrshp 1963
Sales 61.9MME EMP 450
SIC 3444

D-U-N-S 07-829-4776 EXP
METAL SEAL PRECISION LTD
7333 Corporate Blvd, Mentor, OH 44060-4857
Tel (440) 205-0016 Founded/Ownrshp 2011
Sales 48.0MME EMP 200E
SIC 3448 Screw machine products; Prefabricated metal components
Pr: John L Habe IV
VP: Allan B Pirnat
Ql Cn Mgr: Michael Bobbitt

D-U-N-S 61-866-2597
METAL SERVICES INC
(Suby of SMITHCO ENGINEERING INC) ★
640 W 41st St, Tulsa, OK 74107-7019
Tel (918) 445-1104 Founded/Ownrshp 1990
Sales 27.3MME EMP 75
SIC 3312 3443 Structural shapes & pilings, steel; Fabricated plate work (boiler shop)
Ch Bd: Judith A Smith
*Pr: Jon Polcha
*Sec: Susan Lawrence
Exec: Barbara Knowles
Plnt Mgr: Lloyd Hursh
Plnt Mgr: Tim McMurrian

METAL SHARK
See GRAVOIS ALUMINUM BOATS LLC

D-U-N-S 05-464-8365
METAL SPINNERS INC
800 Growth Pkwy, Angola, IN 46703-9328
Tel (260) 665-2192 Founded/Ownrshp 1941, 2005
Sales 49.0MME EMP 210
SIC 3469 3449 3341 Spinning metal for the trade; Miscellaneous metalwork; Secondary nonferrous metals; Spinning metal for the trade; Miscellaneous metalwork; Secondary nonferrous metals
Pr: Olin M Wiland
Pr: Craig Wehr
Ofcr: Dan Samsa
VP: Crystal Howald
Plnt Mgr: Carlos Rivas
Ql Cn Mgr: Max Armes
Sales Asso: Richard McCorkle

D-U-N-S 84-207-8578 IMP
METAL STOCK INC
4901 Cottman Ave, Philadelphia, PA 19135-1401
Tel (215) 335-2003 Founded/Ownrshp 1994
Sales 34.2MME EMP 33
Accts Dr Gefen & Company Bala Cynw
SIC 5051 Metals service centers & offices
Pr: Kenneth Bell
*VP: Curtis Engarde
Sfty Mgr: Steve Boehm

D-U-N-S 00-835-8145
METAL SURFACES INC (CA)
6060 Shull St, Bell Gardens, CA 90201-6297
Tel (562) 927-1331 Founded/Ownrshp 1954
Sales 25.3MME EMP 150
SIC 3471 Finishing, metals or formed products
CEO: Charles K Bell
*COO: Sam Bell
CFO: Allan Erlandson
CFO: Craig Snyder
Mng Dir: Armando Celis
CIO: Robert Ledterman
Dir IT: Gerald Margolin

METAL TCHNLGIES-NORTHERN FNDRY
See NORTHERN FOUNDRY LLC

METAL TECH - JACKSON DIE CAST
See JACKSON DIE CASTING LLC

METAL TECH - MNNPOLIS DIE CAST
See MINNEAPOLIS DIE CASTING LLC

METAL TECH OF MURFREESBORO
See METAL TECHNOLOGIES OF MURFREESBORO INC

D-U-N-S 60-395-3253 EXP
METAL TECHNOLOGIES AUBURN LLC
(Suby of METAL TECHNOLOGIES OF INDIANA INC) ★
1537 W Auburn Dr, Auburn, IN 46706-3329
Tel (260) 925-4717 Founded/Ownrshp 2012
Sales 20.5MME EMP 99
SIC 3315 Steel wire & related products; Steel wire & related products
CFO: Greg Riker
Ql Cn Mgr: Cathy Hunter
Ql Cn Mgr: Vincent Markowski
Mktg Dir: Tom McIntosh
Sls Mgr: Craig Barkey

D-U-N-S 80-649-0660 IMP
METAL TECHNOLOGIES INC
909 E State Road 54, Bloomfield, IN 47424-4706
Tel (812) 384-9800 Founded/Ownrshp 1997
Sales 18.9MM EMP 302
Accts Blue & Co Llc Seymour In
SIC 3441 3559 Fabricated structural metal; Automotive related machinery; Fabricated structural metal; Automotive related machinery
Pr: Doug Conrad
CFO: Rick Mumma
*Sec: Larry Parsons
Brnch Mgr: Craig Duncan
Plnt Mgr: Cary Doub

D-U-N-S 16-007-4555
METAL TECHNOLOGIES INC OF ALABAMA
1401 S Grandstaff Dr, Auburn, IN 46706-2664
Tel (260) 925-4717 Founded/Ownrshp 1997
Sales 34.5MME EMP 705
SIC 8711 3321 Acoustical engineering; Gray iron castings; Acoustical engineering; Gray iron castings
Pr: Matthew J Fetter
*CEO: Rick James
VP: John Neiger

D-U-N-S 07-864-4784 IMP/EXP
METAL TECHNOLOGIES OF INDIANA INC
1401 S Grandstaff Dr, Auburn, IN 46706-2664
Tel (260) 925-4717 Founded/Ownrshp 1999
Sales 295.6MME EMP 700
SIC 3321 3443 Gray & ductile iron foundries; Gray & ductile iron foundries; Metal parts
CEO: Rick James
Pr: Pat Frederick
CFO: Greg Riker
*Sr VP: Jeffrey L Turner
VP: John Neiger
VP: Jeffrey Turner
Exec: Sara Brown
QA Dir: Mark Jagger
IT Man: Kyle Nicol
IT Man: Doug Spieth
Opers Mgr: Chad Jerrell

D-U-N-S 05-536-1992 IMP
METAL TECHNOLOGIES OF MURFREESBORO INC
METAL TECH OF MURFREESBORO
314 W Broad St, Murfreesboro, NC 27855-1442
Tel (252) 398-4041 Founded/Ownrshp 1971
Sales 27.4MME EMP 95
SIC 3599 Machine shop, jobbing & repair
Pr: Ray Felton
*Sec: Judy H Felton
*VP: Edward Drock
*VP: Brock Felton
Off Mgr: Melinda Carver

METAL TEK DEVELOPMENT
See MTD AMERICA LTD

D-U-N-S 96-731-9356
METAL TRADES BRANCH LOCAL 638 WELFARE FUND
5 Penn Plz, New York, NY 10001-1810
Tel (212) 465-8888 Founded/Ownrshp 2011
Sales 38.7MM EMP 10E
SIC 8631 Labor unions & similar labor organizations; Labor unions & similar labor organizations

D-U-N-S 00-336-1805 EXP
METAL TRADES INC (SC)
4194 Highway 165, Hollywood, SC 29449-6041
Tel (843) 889-6441 Founded/Ownrshp 1962
Sales 21.9MM EMP 150
Accts Hoffman & Hoffman Cpa Pa Ch
SIC 3441 3443 3497 3731 Sheet metalwork; Awnings & canopies; Combat vessels, building & repairing; Fabricated structural metal; Tank towers, metal plate; Metal foil & leaf; Shipbuilding & repairing
Pr: Shaun Flynn
*CFO: Christine Pedersen
*Ch: Russell B Corbin
*VP: William D Corbin
Mfg Dir: Roger Beaudoin
Opers Mgr: Tim Bass

D-U-N-S 79-697-1794
METAL TRANSPORTATION SYSTEMS INC
6701 Manlius Center Rd # 111, East Syracuse, NY 13057-2999
Tel (800) 298-6878 Founded/Ownrshp 1992
Sales 25.4MME EMP 575
SIC 4213 8741 Trucking, except local; Management services; Trucking, except local; Management services
Pr: Mark R Longshore
*VP: Timothy J Graber
MIS Dir: Don Knapp

D-U-N-S 00-607-2060 IMP/EXP
METAL WARE CORP
NESCO
1700 Monroe St, Two Rivers, WI 54241-2928
Tel (920) 793-1368 Founded/Ownrshp 1920
Sales 63.7MME EMP 105
SIC 3634 3631

D-U-N-S 04-361-7323
METAL-ERA INC
1600 Airport Rd, Waukesha, WI 53188-2460
Tel (262) 549-6900 Founded/Ownrshp 1988
Sales 51.0MME EMP 100
SIC 3444 Roof deck, sheet metal
Pr: Tony Mallinger
*COO: Anthony Mallinger
VP: Judy Colbert
*VP: Scott Kittilstad
*VP: Nick Mallinger
*Prin: Gene Mallinger
CTO: Michael Cebulski
Dir IT: Joe Mallinger
Prd Mgr: Tom Spaight
Ql Cn Mgr: Anthony Loften
Natl Sales: Matt O'Hanlon

D-U-N-S 00-724-8453
METAL-FAB INC
MICRO AIR - DIVISION METAL-FAB
3025 W May St, Wichita, KS 67213-1536
Tel (316) 943-2351 Founded/Ownrshp 1958
Sales 68.7MME EMP 300
SIC 3444 3564 Flues & pipes, stove or furnace: sheet metal; Air cleaning systems; Flues & pipes, stove or furnace: sheet metal; Air cleaning systems
Ch: Kenneth Shannon
*Pr: Steve Hughbanks
VP: Mark OHM
Mfg Dir: Anthony Gormlex
Ql Cn Mgr: Ed Boyles
Sls Mgr: George Harpool
Sls Mgr: Charla Kremer
Sls Mgr: Tyler Marr

D-U-N-S 00-624-9668 IMP
METAL-MATIC INC (MN)
629 2nd St Se, Minneapolis, MN 55414-2109
Tel (612) 928-2856 Founded/Ownrshp 1951
Sales 101.4MME EMP 600
SIC 3317 Tubes, wrought: welded or lock joint; Tubes, wrought: welded or lock joint
CEO: Gerald J Bliss
*Pr: Thomas J Bliss
CFO: Thomas A Jackson
*VP: Gerald Bliss Jr
*VP: James D Bliss
*VP: Robert J Van Krevelen
VP: Robert Van Krevelen
VP: Robert Vankrevelen
Off Mgr: John Pak
Software D: Ben Brandt
Opers Mgr: Robert Baldauff

METALCOTE
See CHEMTOOL INC

D-U-N-S 05-290-7995 IMP
METALCRAFT OF MAYVILLE INC (WI)
SCAG POWER EQUIPMENT DIV
1000 Metalcraft Dr, Mayville, WI 53050-2354
Tel (920) 387-3150 Founded/Ownrshp 1970
Sales 202.0MME EMP 750
SIC 3523 3444 Grounds mowing equipment; Sheet metalwork; Grounds mowing equipment; Sheet metalwork
Pr: Jerry Bailey
*Ch: Edwin A Gallun Jr
*VP: Connie Quinn

VP: Tom Schraufnagel
VP: Dave Sugden
IT Man: Bob Struck
Tech Mgr: Pat Rohloff
VP Opers: Randy Gloede
Sfty Dirs: Tyler Bortz
Sfty Dirs: Jeff Stieve
Natl Sales: Dennis Opalacz

D-U-N-S 60-581-7543 IMP
METALCRAFT TECHNOLOGIES INC
526 Aviation Way, Cedar City, UT 84721-8601
Tel (435) 586-3871 *Founded/Ownrshp* 2003
Sales 25.0MM^E *EMP* 120
SIC 3444 Sheet metalwork; Metal housings, enclosures, casings & other containers
Pr: David J Grant
* *VP:* J Spencer Grant
* *VP:* Charles Taylor
Exec: Nancy Anderson

METALDYNE
See OLDCO M CO LLC

METALDYNE
See MD INVESTORS CORP

D-U-N-S 00-517-4933 IMP
■ **METALDYNE BSM LLC**
METALDYNE FREMONT
(*Suby of* METALDYNE GLOBAL) ★
307 S Tillotson St, Fremont, IN 46737-2157
Tel (260) 495-4315 *Founded/Ownrshp* 2009
Sales 48.9MM^E *EMP* 172
SIC 3714 3462 3369 3365 3325 Motor vehicle parts & accessories; Iron & steel forgings; Nonferrous foundries; Aluminum foundries; Steel foundries; Motor vehicle parts & accessories; Iron & steel forgings; Nonferrous foundries; Aluminum foundries; Steel foundries
CEO: Thomas A Amato
* *CFO:* Mark Blaufuss
* *Treas:* Jan Wan Dijk
* *VP:* Robert Defauw
* *VP:* Juergen Depp
* *VP:* Cristoph Guhe
* *VP:* Ben Schmidt
Admn Mgr: Jean Biroth
Sfty Dirs: Tan Meyer
Plnt Mgr: Chuck Whemhoff

D-U-N-S 11-926-9827 IMP
METALDYNE CORP
(*Suby of* MD INVESTORS CORP) ★
47659 Halyard Dr, Plymouth, MI 48170-2429
Tel (814) 834-1222 *Founded/Ownrshp* 2009
Sales 896.5MM^E *EMP* 6,500
SIC 3714 3711 Motor vehicle parts & accessories; Motor vehicle transmissions, drive assemblies & parts; Transmission housings or parts, motor vehicle; Chassis, motor vehicle; Motor vehicle parts & accessories; Motor vehicle transmissions, drive assemblies & parts; Transmission housings or parts, motor vehicle; Chassis, motor vehicle
Ch Bd: Thomas A Amato
* *Pr:* Thomas V Chambers
Pr: George Thomas
COO: Witkow Edward
COO: Tina Kozak
COO: Beverly Mathews
* *CFO:* Takao Yoshida
Treas: Sandra Galac
* *Ex VP:* Logan Robinson
Ex VP: Jeff Stafeil
VP: Denis Bardou
VP: Dennis Cutright
VP: Robert Defauw
VP: Robert J Defauw
VP: Juergen Depp
VP: James Hudak
VP: Jim Hudak
VP: George Lanni
VP: Myra Moreland
VP: James Munro
VP: Joanne Ryan

METALDYNE FREMONT
See METALDYNE BSM LLC

METALDYNE GLOBAL
See METALDYNE LLC

D-U-N-S 83-245-7977
■ **METALDYNE LLC**
METALDYNE GLOBAL
(*Suby of* METALDYNE PERFORMANCE GROUP INC) ★
47659 Halyard Dr, Plymouth, MI 48170-2429
Tel (734) 207-6200 *Founded/Ownrshp* 2009
Sales 1.1MMM *EMP* 6,500
SIC 3714 Machine tools & accessories; Special dies & tools; Motor vehicle parts & accessories
CEO: Thomas A Amato
COO: Jeff Barringer
COO: Thomas V Chambers
* *CFO:* Mark Blaufuss
CFO: Bill Lowe
VP: Jeff Burris
* *VP:* Robert Defauw
VP: Doug Grimm
* *VP:* Christoph Guhe
VP: Michael Keflar
VP: Dave Manns
VP: Myra Moreland
VP: John Musat
* *VP:* Ben Schmidt
VP: James Strahley
VP: George Thanopoulos
Exec: Thomas Crews

D-U-N-S 09-204-1409 IMP/EXP
METALDYNE M&A BLUFFTON LLC
(*Suby of* METALDYNE) ★
131 W Harvest Rd, Bluffton, IN 46714-9007
Tel (260) 824-2360 *Founded/Ownrshp* 2009
Sales 47.6MM^E *EMP* 236
SIC 3714 7537 Motor vehicle parts & accessories; Motor vehicle parts & accessories; Motor vehicle engines & parts; Automotive transmission repair shops
Pr: Thomas A Amato
* *CFO:* Mark Blaufuss
Sr VP: Scott Butler
* *VP:* Robert Defauw
* *VP:* Bill Dickey
* *VP:* Christoph Guhe
* *VP:* Ben Schmidt
Sfty Mgr: Glen Maclehoney
Plnt Mgr: Robert Flynn
Ql Cn Mgr: Michelle Evans
Ql Cn Mgr: Don Williamson

D-U-N-S 07-954-1112
▲ **METALDYNE PERFORMANCE GROUP INC**
47659 Halyard Dr, Plymouth, MI 48170-2429
Tel (734) 207-6200 *Founded/Ownrshp* 2005
Sales 2.7MMM *EMP* 12,000^E
Tkr Sym MPG *Exch* NYS
SIC 3714 Motor vehicle parts & accessories; Motor vehicle transmissions, drive assemblies & parts; Steering mechanisms, motor vehicle; Sanders, motor vehicle safety
CEO: George Thanopoulos
* *Ch Bd:* Kevin Penn
Pr: Thomas Amato
Pr: Douglas Grimm
CFO: Mark Blaufuss
CFO: Mark P Blaufuss
VP: Robert J Defauw
VP: Bill Dickey
VP: Christoph Guhe
VP: Ben Schmidt

D-U-N-S 08-326-5975
■ **METALDYNE POWERTRAIN COMPONENTS INC**
(*Suby of* METALDYNE GLOBAL) ★
917 Anderson Rd, Litchfield, MI 49252-9776
Tel (517) 542-5555 *Founded/Ownrshp* 2009
Sales 33.8MM^E *EMP* 212
SIC 3519 Parts & accessories, internal combustion engines; Parts & accessories, internal combustion engines
CEO: Thomas A Amato
Prd Mgr: Brandon Donais

D-U-N-S 06-365-4768 IMP/EXP
■ **METALDYNE SINTERED RIDGWAY LLC**
(*Suby of* METALDYNE GLOBAL) ★
1149 Rocky Rd, Ridgway, PA 15853-6427
Tel (814) 776-1141 *Founded/Ownrshp* 2009
Sales 91.6MM^E *EMP* 460
SIC 3399 3441 3462 Powder, metal; Fabricated structural metal; Powder, metal; Fabricated structural metal; Automotive & internal combustion engine forgings
VP: Mark Farrell
IT Man: Janet Sauter
Plnt Mgr: Michael Sloff
Prd Mgr: Jeff Lechien
Ql Cn Mgr: James Sanker
Ql Cn Mgr: George Tahanopoulus
Snr Mgr: Edmond Ilia

D-U-N-S 07-830-9522 IMP
■ **METALEX CORP**
(*Suby of* JASON INC) ★
1530 Artaius Pkwy, Libertyville, IL 60048-3789
Tel (847) 362-8300 *Founded/Ownrshp* 2001
Sales 41.9MM^E *EMP* 105^E
SIC 3449 3469 Lath, expanded metal; Perforated metal, stamped; Lath, expanded metal; Perforated metal, stamped
VP: Bob Birk
Opers Mgr: Steven Targos
Sls Mgr: Ted Dohse
Sls Mgr: John Hughes

D-U-N-S 05-909-9820
METALEX MANUFACTURING INC
5750 Cornell Rd, Blue Ash, OH 45242-2083
Tel (513) 489-0507 *Founded/Ownrshp* 1972
Sales 40.3MM *EMP* 110^E
SIC 3599 3511 3544 3769 3545 Custom machinery; Turbines & turbine generator sets; Special dies, tools, jigs & fixtures; Guided missile & space vehicle parts & auxiliary equipment; Machine tool accessories; Custom machinery; Turbines & turbine generator sets; Special dies, tools, jigs & fixtures; Guided missile & space vehicle parts & auxiliary equipment; Machine tool accessories
Pr: Werner Kummerle
Exec: Kelley Stewart
QA Dir: Katrina Black
Mktg Dir: Scott Dufresne
Snr Mgr: Scott Adkinss

D-U-N-S 01-166-2694 IMP
METALFORMING INC
100 International Dr, Peachtree City, GA 30269-1909
Tel (770) 631-0002 *Founded/Ownrshp* 1997
Sales 25.2MM^E *EMP* 38
SIC 5084 Industrial machinery & equipment
CEO: Geoffrey L Stone
* *CFO:* Allen Chapman
* *Ex VP:* Bill Wilkins

D-U-N-S 04-374-9977 IMP
METALFORMS MANUFACTURING INC
(*Suby of* CERES LABS) ★
7304 Garth St, Beaumont, TX 77705-6886
Tel (409) 842-1626 *Founded/Ownrshp* 1968
Sales 37.8MM^E *EMP* 150
SIC 3443 7699 Industrial vessels, tanks & containers; Heat exchangers, condensers & components; Industrial equipment services; Industrial vessels, tanks & containers; Heat exchangers, condensers & components; Industrial equipment services
Pr: David W Hearn Jr
CFO: Robert Long
Ofcr: Terry Morgan
* *VP:* Glenn Mabry
Dir IT: Randy Cox
Sfty Dirs: Anthony Dallison

METALFX
See ADVANCED MANUFACTURING AND DEVELOPMENT MENLO PARK INC

D-U-N-S 09-033-1737 IMP/EXP
▲ **METALICO INC**
186 North Ave E, Cranford, NJ 07016-2439
Tel (908) 497-9610 *Founded/Ownrshp* 2015
Sales 476.0MM *EMP* 549
Tkr Sym MEA *Exch* ASE
SIC 3341 Secondary nonferrous metals; Lead smelting & refining (secondary); Aluminum smelting & refining (secondary); Secondary nonferrous metals; Lead smelting & refining (secondary); Aluminum smelting & refining (secondary)
Ch Bd: Carlos E Aguero
COO: Michael J Drury
CFO: Kevin Whalen
Treas: Eric W Finlayson
Ex VP: Arnold S Graber
VP: Steven M Alberico
VP: Joseph McGough

METALLGESELLSCHAFT
See GEA NORTH AMERICA INC

D-U-N-S 00-616-8900
METALLICS INC (WI)
W7274 County Road Z, Onalaska, WI 54650-9630
Tel (608) 781-5200 *Founded/Ownrshp* 1946, 1989
Sales 46.2MM^E *EMP* 200
SIC 3479 2759 Etching & engraving; Name plates: engraved, etched, etc.; Decals: printing; Etching & engraving; Name plates: engraved, etched, etc.; Decals: printing
Pr: Doug Dale
Treas: William Nuelle
* *VP:* Todd Dale
Dir IT: Scott Williams
Plnt Mgr: Joe Mathison

D-U-N-S 05-509-0815 IMP
METALLIX REFINING INC
59 Avenue At The Cmn # 201, Shrewsbury, NJ 07702-4806
Tel (732) 936-0050 *Founded/Ownrshp* 2006
Sales 100.0MM^E *EMP* 64
SIC 3339 5093 Precious metals; Precious metals; Gold refining (primary); Platinum group metal refining (primary)
Pr: Eric Leiner
* *Pr:* Pamela Rollins
* *CFO:* Lynn Falk

D-U-N-S 00-200-1923
METALLIZED CARBON CORP
METCAR PRODUCTS
19 S Water St, Ossining, NY 10562-4633
Tel (914) 941-3738 *Founded/Ownrshp* 1945
Sales 20.3MM^E *EMP* 140^E
SIC 3624 3568 Electric carbons; Carbon specialties for electrical use; Fibers, carbon & graphite; Power transmission equipment; Electric carbons; Carbon specialties for electrical use; Fibers, carbon & graphite; Power transmission equipment
Ch Bd: Matt Brennan
CFO: Michael Moles
Exec: Cesar Cruz
Dir IT: Corey Graner
IT Man: Bruce Hard
Prd Mgr: Manuel Debarros

D-U-N-S 10-593-9966
METALLURG HOLDINGS INC
(*Suby of* AMG ADVANCED METALLURGICAL GROUP N.V.)
435 Devon Park Dr Ste 200, Wayne, PA 19087-1937
Tel (610) 293-0838 *Founded/Ownrshp* 1997
Sales 226.8MM^E *EMP* 3,000^E
SIC 3313 1081 Alloys, additive, except copper: not made in blast furnaces; Metal mining services; Alloys, additive, except copper: not made in blast furnaces; Metal mining services
Pr: Heinz C Schimmelbusch
* *Treas:* Arthur R Spector

D-U-N-S 00-137-4669
METALLURG INC
AMG ADVNCED MTLLRGCAL GROUP NV
(*Suby of* METALLURG HOLDINGS INC) ★
435 Devon Park Dr Ste 200, Wayne, PA 19087-1937
Tel (610) 293-2501 *Founded/Ownrshp* 1947
Sales 226.8MM^E *EMP* 3,000
SIC 3313 1081 Alloys, additive, except copper: not made in blast furnaces; Ferrochromium; Ferromolybdenum; Ferrotitanium; Metal mining services; Alloys, additive, except copper: not made in blast furnaces; Metal mining services
Ch: Heinz Schimmelbusch
* *Pr:* Eric E Jackson
* *CFO:* Amy E Ard
* *V Ch Bd:* Arthur R Spector
VP: Dennis Shea

D-U-N-S 79-649-0634
■ **METALMARK CAPITAL LLC**
(*Suby of* CITIGROUP INC) ★
1177 Ave Of The Americas, New York, NY 10036-2714
Tel (212) 823-1900 *Founded/Ownrshp* 2004
Sales 332.7MM^E *EMP* 3,370
SIC 6726 Investment offices; Investment offices
CEO: Howard Hoffen
VP: Martin McNulty
VP: Jeremy Xia
Mng Dir: Mian Husain
Mng Dir: Jefferson Siegal
IT Man: Assaf Rutenberg

D-U-N-S 07-912-8543
■ **METALMARK CAPITAL PARTNERS DESIGNATED PARTNERS FUND LP**
(*Suby of* METALMARK CAPITAL LLC) ★
1177 Ave Of The Americas, New York, NY 10036-2714
Tel (212) 823-1930 *Founded/Ownrshp* 2013
Sales 78.6MM^E *EMP* 3,366^E
SIC 6726 Investment offices

METALMASTER ROOFMASTER
See METALMASTER SHEET METAL INC

D-U-N-S 02-144-1191
METALMASTER SHEET METAL INC
METALMASTER ROOFMASTER
4800 Metalmaster Dr, McHenry, IL 60050-7017
Tel (815) 459-6415 *Founded/Ownrshp* 2013
Sales 39.7MM^E *EMP* 120
SIC 1761 Roofing, siding & sheet metal work; Roofing & gutter work; Sheet metalwork; Roofing, siding & sheet metal work; Roofing & gutter work; Sheet metalwork
Pr: Michael Smeja
* *Prin:* Daniel Smeja
* *VP Opers:* Richard Biosca

D-U-N-S 02-507-1477
METALMAX LLC
900 Cpt Joe Fulghum Dr, Murfreesboro, TN 37129-5554
Tel (615) 494-1693 *Founded/Ownrshp* 2010
Sales 24.0MM *EMP* 45^E
SIC 3446 Architectural metalwork; Architectural metalwork
Owner: Brian Berryman
* *Pr:* Gary Henderson
Off Mgr: Ben Davidoff

D-U-N-S 96-207-7512
METALOGIX SOFTWARE US INC
(*Suby of* INSIGHT CAPITAL PARTNERS) ★
5335 Wisconsin Ave Nw # 510, Washington, DC 20015-2143
Tel (202) 609-9100 *Founded/Ownrshp* 2008
Sales 39.8MM^E *EMP* 82^E
SIC 5045 Computer software
CEO: Steven Murphy
CFO: Nick Margarites
CFO: Frederick Rolandi
CFO: Rick Rolandi
Sr VP: Paul Bjarnason
Sr VP: David Seaman
VP: Anthony Daubenmerkl
VP: Andy Groelinger
VP: Derek Lessard
VP: Tod Tompkins
VP: Chris Wagner

D-U-N-S 36-131-3943 IMP
METALOR TECHNOLOGIES USA CORP
(*Suby of* METALOR TECHNOLOGIES INTERNATIONAL SA)
255 John L Dietsch Blvd, North Attleboro, MA 02763-1069
Tel (508) 699-8800 *Founded/Ownrshp* 1998
Sales 34.6MM^E *EMP* 200^E
Accts Kieliszak Eggert & Company L
SIC 3399 3699 3339 Silver powder; Electrical equipment & supplies; Silver refining (primary); Silver powder; Electrical equipment & supplies; Silver refining (primary)
Pr: Scott Mrrison
* *CFO:* Hubert Angleys
* *CFO:* Antoine Demontmolline
CFO: Antoine D Montmollin
Bd of Dir: Daniel Schlatter
Ex VP: Cheryl Mello
* *VP:* Larry Drummond
Dir Lab: Arnold Savolainen
Opers Mgr: Marc Marcoccio
Opers Mgr: Don Ostrander
Ql Cn Mgr: Linda Meade

D-U-N-S 00-339-8575
METALPLATE GALVANIZING LP
1120 39th St N, Birmingham, AL 35234-2456
Tel (205) 595-4700 *Founded/Ownrshp* 1946, 1974
Sales 65.0MM^E *EMP* 400
SIC 3479

METALS
See LYDALL THERMAL/ACOUSTICAL INC

METALS 2 GO
See M J LATHERN CO INC

D-U-N-S 08-690-4455
METALS AND SERVICES INC
MS
145 N Swift Rd, Addison, IL 60101-1447
Tel (630) 627-2900 *Founded/Ownrshp* 1977
Sales 51.3MM^E *EMP* 67
SIC 5051 3444 Steel; Sheet metalwork; Steel; Sheet metalwork
CEO: Harvey J Baessler
* *Pr:* Ann L Baessler
* *Treas:* Carol Gross
* *VP:* John E Baessler
* *VP:* Mark Baessler

METALS INC
See AAP METALS LLC

D-U-N-S 05-514-1709 IMP
■ **METALS SUPPLY CO LTD**
M S C
(*Suby of* RELIANCE STEEL & ALUMINUM CO) ★
5311 Clinton Dr, Houston, TX 77020-7911
Tel (713) 330-8080 *Founded/Ownrshp* 1968, 2008
Sales 45.7MM^E *EMP* 82
SIC 5051 Steel; Steel
Pr: John Hess
VP: Craig Johnson
VP: Chris Jones
VP Opers: Dale Shultz
Sls Mgr: Brian Kalinec

D-U-N-S 00-513-5306
METALS TECHNOLOGY CORP
120 N Schmale Rd, Carol Stream, IL 60188-2145
Tel (630) 221-2500 *Founded/Ownrshp* 1963
Sales 33.8MM^E *EMP* 115
SIC 3398 Metal heat treating; Metal heat treating
Pr: John B Bell
* *Pr:* Thomas J Bell
* *VP:* Jerome Bell Jr
QC Dir: Ed Vandyck
Sls Mgr: Barbara Gamboa

D-U-N-S 83-498-2746 IMP
METALS USA BUILDING PRODUCTS L P
GERARD ROOFING TECHNOLOGIES
1100 Chase Rd Ste 100, Mesquite, TX 75149-2766
Tel (972) 216-5380 *Founded/Ownrshp* 2001
Sales 38.4MM^E *EMP* 260
SIC 3441 Fabricated structural metal; Fabricated structural metal
Ch Bd: Gerald E Morris

D-U-N-S 03-244-1149 IMP
■ **METALS USA BUILDING PRODUCTS LP**
(*Suby of* METALS USA INC) ★
2440 Albright Dr, Houston, TX 77017-7311
Tel (713) 946-9000 *Founded/Ownrshp* 2001
Sales 272.0MM^E *EMP* 1,600
SIC 3355 5031 1542 Structural shapes, rolled, aluminum; Building materials, exterior; Commercial & office buildings, renovation & repair; Structural shapes, rolled, aluminum; Building materials, exterior; Commercial & office buildings, renovation & repair
Pt: Charles Canning
**Pt:* Robert McPherson
Mktg Mgr: Ronald Brown

D-U-N-S 01-845-1963 IMP
■ **METALS USA CARBON FLAT ROLLED INC**
(*Suby of* METALS USA INC) ★
1070 W Liberty St, Wooster, OH 44691-3308
Tel (330) 264-8416 *Founded/Ownrshp* 1997
Sales 58.1MM^E *EMP* 275
SIC 3312 5051 Blast furnaces & steel mills; Steel; Blast furnaces & steel mills; Steel
Pr: Don Gingery
**CFO:* James Zimmermann
**Treas:* Brian Schmidt
Sls&Mrk Ex: Jeffrey Aultz

METALS USA FLAT
See METALS USA SPECIALTY METALS NORTHCENTRAL INC

D-U-N-S 62-669-9677
■ **METALS USA HOLDINGS CORP**
(*Suby of* RELIANCE STEEL & ALUMINUM CO) ★
2400 E Coml Blvd Ste 905, Fort Lauderdale, FL 33308
Tel (954) 202-4000 *Founded/Ownrshp* 2013
Sales 2.0MMM^E *EMP* 2,200^E
Accts Deloitte & Touche Llp Boca Ra
SIC 5051 3272 3354 Metals service centers & offices; Iron & steel (ferrous) products; Aluminum bars, rods, ingots, sheets, pipes, plates, etc.; Building materials, except block or brick: concrete; Aluminum extruded products; Metals service centers & offices; Iron & steel (ferrous) products; Aluminum bars, rods, ingots, sheets, pipes, plates, etc.; Building materials, except block or brick: concrete; Aluminum extruded products
CEO: Robert C McPherson
**Sr VP:* Roger Krohn
**Sr VP:* William A Smith II
**VP:* Daniel L Henneke
Brnch Mgr: Tracy Bolton
Plnt Mgr: James Pietruszka
Prd Mgr: Jesus Villicana
Ql Cn Mgr: Brian Kirkpatrick

D-U-N-S 15-780-8379 IMP/EXP
■ **METALS USA INC**
(*Suby of* FLAG INTERMEDIATE HOLDINGS CORP) ★
2400 E Coml Blvd Ste 905, Fort Lauderdale, FL 33308
Tel (954) 202-4000 *Founded/Ownrshp* 2005
Sales 1.2MMM^E *EMP* 2,200
SIC 3441 Fabricated structural metal; Fabricated structural metal
CEO: Robert C McPherson III
**Ch Bd:* C Lourenco Goncalves
**Pr:* Roger Krohn
**CFO:* Keith Koci
CFO: McPherson Robert
VP: Randy Sartain
VP: Samuel R Sciple
**VP:* Joe Stewart
Dir IT: Debbie Cardoso
Dir IT: Charlton Williams
Info Man: Glenn Cortopassi

D-U-N-S 01-758-8401
■ **METALS USA PLATES AND SHAPES NORTHCENTRAL INC**
(*Suby of* METALS USA INC) ★
6991 Freedom Ave Nw, Canton, OH 44720-7307
Tel (330) 966-3401 *Founded/Ownrshp* 1939
Sales 30.4MM^E *EMP* 76
SIC 5051 Plates, metal; Plates, metal
Genl Mgr: Chuck Stipanovich

D-U-N-S 03-409-8736
■ **METALS USA PLATES AND SHAPES NORTHEAST LP**
(*Suby of* METALS USA INC) ★
50 Cabot Blvd E, Langhorne, PA 19047-1802
Tel (267) 580-2100 *Founded/Ownrshp* 2000
Sales 199.5MM^E *EMP* 350
SIC 5051 Plates, metal; Plates, metal
CEO: Robert C McPherson
Pt: Lorenco Boncalces
COO: Roger Krohn
Plnt Mgr: Keith Burgeron
Manager: Jack Parton
Manager: John Quint
Sales Asso: Kregg Gibson
Sales Asso: Cheryl Hodgson
Sales Asso: Tyrone Lawson
Sales Asso: Jose Mondragon

D-U-N-S 18-570-5860 IMP/EXP
■ **METALS USA PLATES AND SHAPES SOUTHCENTRAL INC**
(*Suby of* METALS USA INC) ★
101 E Illinois Ave, Enid, OK 73701-7483
Tel (580) 233-0411 *Founded/Ownrshp* 1925
Sales 129.4MM^E *EMP* 130
SIC 5051 Steel; Steel
Pr: David Martens
**Sr VP:* Robert McPherson III

D-U-N-S 04-288-2076 IMP
■ **METALS USA PLATES AND SHAPES SOUTHEAST INC** (AL)
(*Suby of* METALS USA INC) ★
1251 Woodland Ave, Mobile, AL 36610-2559
Tel (251) 456-4531 *Founded/Ownrshp* 1966, 1997
Sales 174.3MM^E *EMP* 300
SIC 5051 Steel; Steel
Pr: Mickey Marshall
**VP:* Kim Calametti
**VP:* Tim Calametti

D-U-N-S 00-693-0200 IMP
■ **METALS USA SPECIALTY METALS NORTHCENTRAL INC**
METALS USA FLAT
(*Suby of* METALS USA INC) ★
3000 Shermer Rd, Northbrook, IL 60062-7713
Tel (847) 291-2400 *Founded/Ownrshp* 1998
Sales 134.9MM^E *EMP* 112
SIC 5051 Metals service centers & offices; Steel; Copper; Metals service centers & offices; Steel; Copper
COO: Russ Russell

D-U-N-S 96-610-0740 IMP
METALSA STRUCTURAL PRODUCTS INC
(*Suby of* METALSA, S.A. DE C.V.)
29545 Hudson Dr, Novi, MI 48377-1733
Tel (248) 669-3704 *Founded/Ownrshp* 2010
Sales 470.4MM^E *EMP* 2,700
SIC 3714 Motor vehicle parts & accessories; Motor vehicle parts & accessories
CEO: Polo Cedillo
**Pr:* Jose Jaime Salazar Reyes
**Treas:* Laura Johnson
**Sec:* Fernando Perez Valdes
**VP:* David Altemar Sanchez Hernande
Plnt Mgr: Luis Darroeta

D-U-N-S 13-248-6551 IMP
METALSA TUSCALOOSA INC
(*Suby of* METALSA AUTOMOTIVE GMBH)
1150 Industrial Park Dr, Tuscaloosa, AL 35401-0403
Tel (205) 330-5500 *Founded/Ownrshp* 2002
Sales 43.5MM^E *EMP* 100
SIC 3714 Motor vehicle body components & frame; Motor vehicle body components & frame
Ch: Dana Vails
Ofcr: Jennifer Cooper
Plnt Mgr: Andreas Hackstedt
Ql Cn Mgr: Jimmie Casey
Ql Cn Mgr: Kevin Chambers

D-U-N-S 02-173-8328 IMP
METALSA-ROANOKE INC
(*Suby of* GRUPO PROEZA, S.A.P.I. DE C.V.)
184 Vista Dr, Roanoke, VA 24019-8514
Tel (540) 966-5300 *Founded/Ownrshp* 1956
Sales 116.5MM^E *EMP* 200
SIC 3713 Truck & bus bodies; Truck & bus bodies
Pr: Steven Helgeson
**CFO:* Emmanuel Lopez Cazarez
**VP:* Angel Loredo
**VP:* Nicolas Villarreal
Sftwr Eng: Anthony Kellett
Mfg Mgr: Darrin Snay
Plnt Mgr: Jarrod Rickard
Ql Cn Mgr: Phil Mnich
Snr Mgr: Joe Handerhan
Snr Mgr: Matt Sanders
Snr Mgr: David Spath

D-U-N-S 60-180-1090 IMP
METALTECH-USA LLC
611 Highway 74 S Ste 900, Peachtree City, GA 30269-3083
Tel (770) 486-8825 *Founded/Ownrshp* 2005
Sales 100.0MM^E *EMP* 20
SIC 5039 Structural assemblies, prefabricated: non-wood; Architectural metalwork
Pr: Nils Simonsen
**VP:* Blaine Gardner
**VP:* Eric Simonsen
Opers Mgr: Jay Wallace
Mktg Mgr: Nichole Martin

D-U-N-S 61-616-2756 IMP
METALTEK INTERNATIONAL INC
SOUTHERN CENTRIFUGAL DIV
905 E Saint Paul Ave, Waukesha, WI 53188-3804
Tel (262) 544-7700 *Founded/Ownrshp* 1985
Sales 320.7MM^E *EMP* 1,000
SIC 3366 3443 3364 Gray & ductile iron foundries; Brass & bronze die-castings; Copper foundries; Nuclear shielding, metal plate; Brass & bronze die-castings
CEO: Robert Smickley
**Pr:* E J Kubick
**CFO:* Richard Danning
**Treas:* Richard Eshleman
Sr Cor Off: Andrew Cope
VP: Jack Lilley
VP: Todd Sternaman
VP Bus Dev: Bob Marshall
Genl Mgr: Dennis Bergeron
Snr Sftwr: Richard Emmerich
Cmptr Lab: Jessica Porter

D-U-N-S 78-222-3569 IMP/EXP
METALTEK INTERNATIONAL INC
8600 Commercial Blvd, Pevely, MO 63070-1525
Tel (636) 479-4499 *Founded/Ownrshp* 1997
Sales 36.7MM^E *EMP* 150
SIC 3325 3369 Alloy steel castings, except investment; Nonferrous foundries; Alloy steel castings, except investment; Nonferrous foundries
Ch Bd: Andrew Cope
**Pr:* Robert Smickley
**VP:* Dean Berger
Sfty Mgr: Tom Durrer
Plnt Mgr: Barry Craig

METALWORKING GROUP, THE
See METALWORKING GROUP HOLDINGS INC

D-U-N-S 00-343-8806 IMP
METALWORKING GROUP HOLDINGS INC (OH)
METALWORKING GROUP, THE
9070 Pippin Rd, Cincinnati, OH 45251-3174
Tel (513) 521-4119 *Founded/Ownrshp* 2000
Sales 63.0MM^E *EMP* 140
SIC 3444 Sheet metalwork; Sheet metalwork
Pr: Mike Schmitt
**CFO:* Doug Watts
**VP:* Brad Brune
Sfty Mgr: Gary Ensell
Plnt Mgr: Jesse Webber

D-U-N-S 08-547-4690 IMP
METALWORKING LUBRICANTS CO
25 W Silverdome Indus Par, Pontiac, MI 48342-2994
Tel (248) 332-3500 *Founded/Ownrshp* 1952
Sales 155.3MM^E *EMP* 243
SIC 5172 2869 2843 2992 Lubricating oils & greases; Phosphoric acid esters; Emulsifiers, except food & pharmaceutical; Cutting oils, blending: made from purchased materials; Rust arresting compounds, animal or vegetable oil base; Lubricating oils & greases; Phosphoric acid esters; Emulsifiers, except food & pharmaceutical; Cutting oils, blending: made from purchased materials; Rust arresting compounds, animal or vegetable oil base
Ch Bd: Robert F Tomlinson
**Treas:* James P Tomlinson Jr
**VP:* Adam Bujoll
**VP:* Dr Nilda Grenier
VP: Kim Onnie
Plnt Mgr: Bob Gumtow

D-U-N-S 00-495-0549
METALWORKS INC
GREAT OPENINGS
902 4th St, Ludington, MI 49431-2693
Tel (231) 845-5136 *Founded/Ownrshp* 1969
Sales 40.5MM^E *EMP* 243^E
SIC 3499 3444 Furniture parts, metal; Sheet metalwork; Furniture parts, metal; Sheet metalwork
Ch Bd: G William Paine
**Pr:* Thomas W Paine
Adm/Dir: Michele King
Sales Exec: Shane Pung
Sls Mgr: Chuck Francis
Board of Directors: Harry C Calcutt III, Ted Knott, George Petritz, Jack Rasmussen

D-U-N-S 04-836-0213 IMP
METALWORKS INC
301 P St Bldg C, Lincoln, NE 68508-6212
Tel (402) 476-1211 *Founded/Ownrshp* 1997
Sales 32.2MM^E *EMP* 52
SIC 5084 Metalworking machinery
Pr: Robert M Ernesti
**VP:* Douglas L Swanson
CIO: Tracy Ernesti
Sales Exec: Ryan Othling

D-U-N-S 01-229-5478
METALWORX INC
340 Deming Way, Summerville, SC 29483-4735
Tel (843) 402-0999 *Founded/Ownrshp* 1997
Sales 22.9MM^E *EMP* 70
SIC 3599 Machine shop, jobbing & repair
Pr: Michael Sawer
**CFO:* Leah Sawer
**VP:* Rod Travis
IT Man: Paul Gleim

D-U-N-S 05-692-5722
METALX LLC
295 S Commerce Dr, Waterloo, IN 46793-9437
Tel (260) 232-3000 *Founded/Ownrshp* 2012
Sales 150.0MM *EMP* 10
SIC 5093 Metal scrap & waste materials; Metal scrap & waste materials
Pr: Danny Rifkin
**Ex VP:* Paul Everett
**Ex VP:* Jim Ustian
**VP:* Steve King
**VP:* Jeff Rynearson
Opers Mgr: Dave Stage

D-U-N-S 00-492-4783 EXP
■ **METAMORA PRODUCTS CORP OF ELKLAND**
(*Suby of* HEADWATERS INC) ★
4057 S Oak St, Metamora, MI 48455-9396
Tel (810) 678-2295 *Founded/Ownrshp* 1966
Sales 127.0MM^E *EMP* 378
SIC 3089

D-U-N-S 06-960-6671
■ **METAMORA PRODUCTS CORP OF ELKLAND**
(*Suby of* METAMORA PRODUCTS CORP OF ELKLAND) ★
112 Industrial Pkwy, Elkland, PA 16920-1457
Tel (814) 258-7122 *Founded/Ownrshp* 1974
Sales 27.0MM^E *EMP* 200
SIC 3089 Injection molded finished plastic products; Injection molded finished plastic products
Pr: Jack Lawless
**VP:* Richard Mac Leod
**VP:* Charles Schiedegger
**VP:* Leonard M Visosky
**VP:* Thomas A Ward
QC Dir: Vince Calvario

D-U-N-S 01-105-5835
METAMORPHOSIS NEW YORK INC (NY)
1865 New Hwy Ste 1, Farmingdale, NY 11735-1501
Tel (631) 396-7480 *Founded/Ownrshp* 2013
Sales 1.0MM *EMP* 280
SIC 5122 7231 Cosmetics; Cosmetology school; Cosmetics; Cosmetology school
Pr: Deyna G Pappalardo
**VP:* Danielle Nafte

D-U-N-S 79-637-5756 IMP
METAPATH SOFTWARE INTERNATIONAL
MOBILE SYSTEMS INTERNATIONAL
(*Suby of* TELENT LIMITED)
1755 N Collins Blvd # 400, Richardson, TX 75080-3562
Tel (972) 907-3600 *Founded/Ownrshp* 2001
Sales 18.6MM^E *EMP* 378^E
SIC 8748 7372 4812 Systems analysis & engineering consulting services; Prepackaged software; Cellular telephone services; Systems analysis & engineering consulting services; Prepackaged software; Cellular telephone services
Ex VP: Clifford P Wagner
Prgrm Mgr: Kevin Godsave

D-U-N-S 36-402-3929
METAPOINT PARTNERS A LIMITED PARTNERSHIP
3 Centennial Dr Ste 110, Peabody, MA 01960-7931
Tel (978) 531-4444 *Founded/Ownrshp* 1988
Sales 29.2MM^E *EMP* 75
SIC 6211 Investment firm, general brokerage
Pt: Keith C Shaughnessy
Pt: Stuart Mathews

D-U-N-S 93-357-9443
METASOURCE LLC
1900 Frost Rd Ste 100, Bristol, PA 19007-1519
Tel (215) 788-8679 *Founded/Ownrshp* 2007
Sales 79.9MM^E *EMP* 280
SIC 5045 Computers, peripherals & software; Computers, peripherals & software
Pr: Adam C Osthed
**CFO:* Randy Powell
**Ch:* Jon Shaw
**Ex VP:* Edward W Mackin Sr
VP: Jim Gerken
VP: Grant Glasscock
VP: Maria Tassiello
Brnch Mgr: Carolyn McFadden
Software D: Jesus Rivera
Mktg Dir: Colin Graf

METASWITCH FAIRFAX CO
See METASWITCH NETWORKS CORP

D-U-N-S 12-230-2557
METASWITCH NETWORKS CORP
METASWITCH FAIRFAX CO
(*Suby of* METASWITCH NETWORKS LTD)
11600 Sunrise Valley Dr, Reston, VA 20191-1412
Tel (703) 480-0500 *Founded/Ownrshp* 1984
Sales 38.5MM^E *EMP* 210
Accts Patterson Weeks & Graves Pll
SIC 7373 Systems engineering, computer related; Systems engineering, computer related
CEO: John Lazar
Pr: Ian Ferguson
VP: Martin Firth
Dir Soc: Andrea Lemos
Comm Dir: Phil Harvey
Prgrm Mgr: Johnny Hawkins
Sftwr Eng: Andy Finney
Sftwr Eng: Jon Harrison
Sftwr Eng: Alex Illingworth
Sftwr Eng: Julia Medlin
Sftwr Eng: Paul Tiplady

D-U-N-S 02-755-1493
METASYS TECHNOLOGIES INC
3460 Summit Ridge Pkwy, Duluth, GA 30096-1622
Tel (678) 218-1600 *Founded/Ownrshp* 2000
Sales 30.4MM *EMP* 189
Accts Forrestall Galeano & Li Cpa
SIC 7371 Computer software development & applications; Computer software development & applications
Pr: Sandeep Gauba
Ofcr: Roy Anderson
**VP:* Steve Alter
VP: Kevin Gibson
**VP:* Nagesh Murthy
VP: Raj Verma
Sls Mgr: Amy Mueller

D-U-N-S 80-037-6779
■ **METAVANTE CORP**
FIDELITY NATIONAL INFO SVCS
(*Suby of* METAVANTE HOLDINGS LLC) ★
4900 W Brown Deer Rd, Milwaukee, WI 53223-2422
Tel (904) 438-6000 *Founded/Ownrshp* 2007
Sales 630.1MM^E *EMP* 5,500
SIC 7374 8742 6153 Data processing & preparation; Management consulting services; Short-term business credit; Data processing & preparation; Management consulting services; Short-term business credit
Pr: Frank Matire
Pr: Steve Taylor
Ofcr: Milagros Cerrud
Ex VP: Debra Bronder
Ex VP: Randy Chetko
Ex VP: Norrie Daroga
Ex VP: Mark Davey
Ex VP: Pat Foy
Ex VP: Jamie Geschke
Ex VP: Don Layden
Ex VP: Frank Martire
Ex VP: Gary Nelson
Ex VP: Steve Rathgaber
Ex VP: Gary Refinski
Ex VP: James Susoreny
Ex VP: Jon Young
Sr VP: Marcia Danzeisen
Sr VP: Daniel Rosien
VP: Jim Andracchi
VP: Neil Roider
VP: Janet Schaal

D-U-N-S 80-844-6632 EXP
■ **METAVANTE HOLDINGS LLC**
(*Suby of* FIDELITY NATIONAL INFORMATION SERVICES INC) ★
601 Riverside Ave, Jacksonville, FL 32204-2946
Tel (904) 438-6000 *Founded/Ownrshp* 2009
Sales 572.8MM^E *EMP* 5,900

SIC 3578 5049 7374 Banking machines; Bank equipment & supplies; Data processing & preparation; Banking machines; Bank equipment & supplies; Data processing & preparation
Pr: Gary Norcross
**VP:* Michael Gravelle

D-U-N-S 78-703-2916 IMP/EXP
METAVATION LLC
(*Suby of* REVSTONE INDUSTRIES LLC) ★
21177 Hilltop St, Southfield, MI 48033-4912
Tel (248) 351-1000 *Founded/Ownrshp* 2009
Sales 116.0MM^E *EMP* 965
SIC 3714 Motor vehicle parts & accessories; Motor vehicle parts & accessories

D-U-N-S 07-912-4138
METAVISION MEDIA LLC
498 7th Ave, New York, NY 10018-6798
Tel (646) 746-6084 *Founded/Ownrshp* 2013
Sales 135.0MM^E *EMP* 90
SIC 7311 Advertising agencies
CEO: Neil Sternberg

METAVIZE SOFTWARE
See UNTANGLE INC

METC
See MICHIGAN ELECTRICTRANSMISSION CO LLC

D-U-N-S 06-659-7147
■ **METCALF & EDDY INC**
(*Suby of* AECOM) ★
701 Edgewater Dr Ste 200, Wakefield, MA 01880-6243
Tel (781) 246-5200 *Founded/Ownrshp* 2000
Sales 37.1MM^E *EMP* 800
SIC 8711 Professional engineer; Professional engineer
CEO: Robert Costello
**Pr:* Steven Guttenplan
**CFO:* Dennis Morrison
VP: Chandra Mysore
Genl Mgr: Paul Catanzano
IT Man: Ho Mandel
**Genl Couns:* Michael Kolloway

D-U-N-S 10-251-1037
METCALF BANK
609 Ne State Route 291, Lees Summit, MO 64086-2507
Tel (816) 525-5300 *Founded/Ownrshp* 2007
Sales NA *EMP* 125^E
SIC 6022 State commercial banks; State commercial banks
Ch Bd: Ben Craig
**Pr:* Jon Stewart
Ex VP: Roberts Paul
Sr VP: Mike Corless
Sr VP: Vicki Fisher
Sr VP: Terry Lindhorst
Sr VP: Cris Smith
VP: Sonci Bleckinger
VP: Catherine Casey
VP: Lauren Clement
VP: David Ross
VP: Paige Scott
VP: John Simmons
VP: Patricia Walker
Adv Bd Mbr: Ruth Navarro

D-U-N-S 10-065-0308
METCALFE COUNTY SCHOOL DISTRICT
109 Sartin Dr, Edmonton, KY 42129-8170
Tel (270) 432-3171 *Founded/Ownrshp* 1985
Sales 9.0MM *EMP* 304
SIC 8211 Public elementary school; Public senior high school; School board; Public elementary school; Public senior high school; School board

D-U-N-S 02-316-9287
METCALFE INC
SENTRY FOODS
726 N Midvale Blvd, Madison, WI 53705-3243
Tel (608) 236-2022 *Founded/Ownrshp* 1955
Sales 33.0MM^E *EMP* 211
SIC 5411 6512 5421 Grocery stores, independent; Commercial & industrial building operation; Fish & seafood markets; Grocery stores, independent; Commercial & industrial building operation; Fish & seafood markets
Pr: Tim Metcalfe
Sr Cor Off: Norman Richter
**VP:* Kevin Metcalfe

D-U-N-S 60-472-3478 IMP
METCAM INC
305 Tidwell Cir, Alpharetta, GA 30004-5638
Tel (770) 475-9633 *Founded/Ownrshp* 1989
Sales 57.0MM^E *EMP* 135
SIC 3444 2542 Sheet metalwork; Telephone booths: except wood; Sheet metalwork; Telephone booths: except wood
CEO: Bruce A Hagenau
**CFO:* Steve Honnold
**VP:* Jerry B Ward
Off Mgr: Stacey Howard
Dir IT: Babashkin Igor

METCAR PRODUCTS
See METALLIZED CARBON CORP

METCARE
See METROPOLITAN HEALTH NETWORKS INC

D-U-N-S 96-849-7110
METCAST SERVICETECH RESOURCES INC
BLAST CLEANING TECHNOLOGIES
16211 W Lincoln Ave, New Berlin, WI 53151-2834
Tel (262) 785-7577 *Founded/Ownrshp* 2008
Sales 21.7MM^E *EMP* 70
SIC 3569 Blast cleaning equipment, dustless
Pr: Carl Panzenhagen
**CFO:* Christopher Bauman
**VP:* Paul Good
Genl Mgr: David Devalkenaere
Board of Directors: Paul Good, Carl Panzenhagen

METCO ENVIRONMENTAL
See TESTAMERICA AIR EMISSION CORP

D-U-N-S 05-474-4305 IMP
METCO INDUSTRIES INC (PA)
1241 Brusselles St, Saint Marys, PA 15857-1999
Tel (814) 781-3630 *Founded/Ownrshp* 1981
Sales 25.4MM^E *EMP* 97
SIC 3399 Powder, metal; Powder, metal
Pr: Richard A Buchheit
**CFO:* Rodney Brennen
Ex VP: Tom Fleming
VP: Richard A Buccheit
VP: Walter Spencer
Dir IT: John Lougee
QC Dir: Jim Wimer
Prd Mgr: Roger Young

D-U-N-S 09-387-9844
METCO LANDSCAPE INC
2200 Rifle St, Aurora, CO 80011-3514
Tel (303) 421-3100 *Founded/Ownrshp* 1998
Sales 27.7MM *EMP* 250^E
Accts Bauerle And Company Pc Den
SIC 0781 Landscape services; Landscape services
CEO: Mark Tomko
**Pr:* Hans West
**CFO:* Melanie Hurt
**VP:* Justin Adams

D-U-N-S 12-402-2760
METCON CONSTRUCTION INC
74 Mountainview Rd, Warren, NJ 07059-6758
Tel (908) 647-3750 *Founded/Ownrshp* 1999
Sales 50.0MM *EMP* 75
SIC 1541 1542 Industrial buildings & warehouses; Nonresidential construction; Commercial & office building contractors
Pr: Alex Enanian

D-U-N-S 02-965-7421
METCON INC
763 Comteen Dr, Pembroke, NC 28372-8902
Tel (910) 521-8013 *Founded/Ownrshp* 2000
Sales 47.8MM^E *EMP* 75^E
SIC 1542 Nonresidential construction
Pr: Aaron Thomas
**VP:* James H Maner

METCUT
See METAL CUTTING TOOLS CORP

D-U-N-S 96-465-5513
METDALSPI LLC
METHODIST HOSPITAL FOR SURGERY
17101 Dallas Pkwy, Addison, TX 75001-7103
Tel (469) 248-3900 *Founded/Ownrshp* 2010
Sales 31.0MM^E *EMP* 156^E
SIC 8069 Specialty hospitals, except psychiatric
Ch: Robert Viere
**Ch Bd:* Michael Schaefer
CFO: Kelly Hayes
**Treas:* Scott Siemer
Dir OR: Deborah Pearcy
Dir OR: Sherry Turner
Dir Lab: Tammy Dux
Dir Rad: Bobby Himel
Dir Rx: Vivian Cheung
IT Man: Antwoine White
Mtls Mgr: Brent Benge

D-U-N-S 10-130-1158
METECH RECYCLING INC
GUARANTEED RECYCLING XPERTS
(*Suby of* METECH INTERNATIONAL LIMITED)
111 Adams Rd Ste 3, Clinton, MA 01510-1550
Tel (508) 795-1950 *Founded/Ownrshp* 2005
Sales 61.5MM^E *EMP* 120
SIC 5093 7376 Scrap & waste materials; Recycling, waste materials; Scrap & waste materials; Computer facilities management
CEO: Andrew Eng
Pr: Chris Ryan
VP: Richard Chenoweth
VP: John Miller

METED
See METROPOLITAN EDISON CO

D-U-N-S 00-213-9244 IMP
METEM CORP
700 Parsippany Rd, Parsippany, NJ 07054-3767
Tel (973) 887-6635 *Founded/Ownrshp* 1962
Sales 57.9MM^E *EMP* 155
SIC 3599 3541 Machine shop, jobbing & repair; Milling machines; Machine shop, jobbing & repair; Milling machines
Pr: Steven H Goldthwaite
Sr VP: Martin Saunders
Exec: Ved Mulraj
Mng Dir: Laszlo Bolovics
Genl Mgr: Laura Fowler
Board of Directors: Steven Goldthwaite

METEOR AUTOMOTIVE
See METEOR SEALING SYSTEMS LLC

D-U-N-S 13-537-6734
METEOR EXPRESS INC
875 Harbour Dr, Scottsboro, AL 35769-7803
Tel (256) 218-3000 *Founded/Ownrshp* 2000
Sales 25.9MM^E *EMP* 115
SIC 4213 Trucking, except local; Heavy hauling
Pr: George H Jones
**VP:* Lynn Buckley
Trfc Dir: Glen Bardon
Opers Mgr: Roxanne Dave

D-U-N-S 09-247-5503 IMP
METEOR SEALING SYSTEMS LLC
METEOR AUTOMOTIVE
(*Suby of* METEOR GUMMIWERKE K.H. BADJE GMBH & CO. KG)
400 S Tuscarawas Ave, Dover, OH 44622-2342
Tel (330) 343-9595 *Founded/Ownrshp* 1998
Sales 52.3MM^E *EMP* 155
SIC 3069 Tubing, rubber; Tubing, rubber
**VP:* Joerg Busse
Ql Cn Mgr: Mark Laughlin
Ql Cn Mgr: Kenneth Ringler
Ql Cn Mgr: Jim Williamson
Sls Mgr: Touston Conrad

D-U-N-S 79-016-1780 IMP
METER DEVICES CO INC
(*Suby of* EJ BROOKS CO) ★
23847 Industrial Park Dr, Farmington Hills, MI 48335-2860
Tel (330) 455-0301 *Founded/Ownrshp* 1981
Sales 45.6MM^E *EMP* 612
SIC 3625 3644 3643 3444 Switches, electric power; Noncurrent-carrying wiring services; Current-carrying wiring devices; Sheet metalwork; Switches, electric power; Noncurrent-carrying wiring services; Current-carrying wiring devices; Sheet metalwork
Pr: Jack Roessner
**VP:* John T Hanft

D-U-N-S 80-705-9840
METER OFFICE OF FORT SMITH
3900 Kelley Hwy, Fort Smith, AR 72904-5610
Tel (479) 784-2282 *Founded/Ownrshp* 2007
Sales 11.5MM^E *EMP* 900
SIC 4971 Water distribution or supply systems for irrigation; Water distribution or supply systems for irrigation

D-U-N-S 07-935-3790
METER READINGS HOLDING LLC
5200 Town Center Cir, Boca Raton, FL 33486-1015
Tel (561) 394-0550 *Founded/Ownrshp* 2014
Sales 3.9MMM^E *EMP* 75,765^E
SIC 3824 3825 3829 7371 7373 Investment holding companies, except banks; Mechanical & electromechanical counters & devices; Instruments to measure electricity; Measuring & controlling devices; Custom computer programming services; Computer integrated systems design
CEO: Marc Leder

D-U-N-S 15-178-6399 IMP
METFORM LLC
(*Suby of* MACLEAN FASTENERS) ★
1000 Allanson Rd, Mundelein, IL 60060-3804
Tel (847) 566-0010 *Founded/Ownrshp* 1979
Sales 74.1MM^E *EMP* 355
SIC 3462 Iron & steel forgings; Iron & steel forgings
**Treas:* Thomas M Pruden
**VP:* Dennis Keesey
**VP:* Gary Sullo
**VP:* Robert Whitney

D-U-N-S 13-972-7395 IMP/EXP
METGLAS INC
(*Suby of* HITACHI METALS AMERICA LLC) ★
440 Allied Dr, Conway, SC 29526-8202
Tel (843) 349-6800 *Founded/Ownrshp* 2003
Sales 69.0MM^E *EMP* 200
SIC 3497 Metal foil & leaf; Metal foil & leaf
CEO: Kazuyuki Konishi
**Pr:* Dodd Smith
**CFO:* Mary P Murray
**Sr VP:* Dave Millure
**VP:* Ryusuke Hasegawa
**VP:* Ryuichi Kamoshita
CTO: Barry Johnson
Dir IT: Robbie Lucas
Plnt Mgr: Taiji Yamada

D-U-N-S 07-548-7660
METHACTON SCHOOL DISTRICT
1001 Kriebel Mill Rd, Norristown, PA 19403-1096
Tel (610) 489-5000 *Founded/Ownrshp* 1950
Sales 55.5MM^E *EMP* 825
Accts Major & Mastro Llc Montgomer
SIC 8211 Public elementary & secondary schools; Public elementary & secondary schools
Pr: Joyce Petrauskas
Bd of Dir: Mark Constable
Ofcr: Mark Stead
VP: Herbert Rothe
Teacher Pr: Robert Harney

D-U-N-S 36-409-2783 IMP
METHANEX METHANOL CO LLC
METHANEX USA SERVICES
(*Suby of* METHANEX CORPORATION)
5850 Granite Pkwy Ste 400, Plano, TX 75024-6748
Tel (972) 308-0419 *Founded/Ownrshp* 1989
Sales 183.9MM^E *EMP* 44
SIC 5169 Alcohols
**Sr VP:* John Floren

METHANEX USA SERVICES
See METHANEX METHANOL CO LLC

D-U-N-S 17-339-3752
METHENY CONCRETE PRODUCTS INC
1617 S Lowery St, Oklahoma City, OK 73129-8343
Tel (405) 947-5566 *Founded/Ownrshp* 1987
Sales 29.3MM^E *EMP* 135^E
SIC 3273 Ready-mixed concrete; Ready-mixed concrete
Pr: Richard Metheny
**VP:* Connie Metheny
Mng Dir: Randy Dunn

METHOD PRODUCTS, INC.
See METHOD PRODUCTS PBC

D-U-N-S 03-651-4797 IMP
METHOD PRODUCTS PBC
METHOD PRODUCTS, INC.
(*Suby of* ECOVER COORDINATION CENTER NV)
637 Commercial St Ste 300, San Francisco, CA 94111-6514
Tel (415) 931-3947 *Founded/Ownrshp* 2012
Sales 22.2MM^E *EMP* 115
SIC 2841

D-U-N-S 00-509-2135 IMP
▲ **METHODE ELECTRONICS INC**
7401 W Wilson Ave, Harwood Heights, IL 60706-4548
Tel (708) 867-6777 *Founded/Ownrshp* 1946
Sales 881.1MM *EMP* 3,960
Tkr Sym MEI *Exch* NYS
SIC 3678 3674 3676 3672 3825 3643 Electronic connectors; Semiconductor circuit networks; Microcircuits, integrated (semiconductor); Resistor networks; Printed circuit boards; Wiring boards; Test equipment for electronic & electrical circuits; Current-carrying wiring devices; Bus bars (electrical conductors); Connectors & terminals for electrical devices; Electronic connectors; Semiconductor circuit networks; Microcircuits, integrated (semiconductor); Resistor networks; Printed circuit boards; Wiring boards; Test equipment for electronic & electrical circuits; Current-carrying wiring devices; Bus bars (electrical conductors); Connectors & terminals for electrical devices
Pr: Donald W Duda
**Ch Bd:* Walter J Aspatore
COO: Thomas D Reynolds
CFO: Douglas A Koman
Treas: Ronald L G Tsoumas
**V Ch Bd:* Christopher J Hornung
VP: Timothy R Glandon
Genl Mgr: Dan Poplawski
IT Man: Joe Pikul
IT Man: Harish Upadhya
Software D: Rex Park
Board of Directors: Warren L Batts, Darren M Dawson, Stephen F Gates, Isabelle C Goosse, Paul G Shelton, Lawrence B Skatoff

D-U-N-S 13-891-5942
■ **METHODIST AMBULATORY SURGERY CENTER**
(*Suby of* HCA INC) ★
19010 Stone Oak Pkwy, San Antonio, TX 78258-3225
Tel (210) 575-5200 *Founded/Ownrshp* 2002
Sales 26.6MM^E *EMP* 1^E
SIC 8011 Ambulatory surgical center
CEO: Elaine Morris
CFO: Tim Carr

METHODIST BEHAVIORAL HLTH SYS
See METHODIST FAMILY HEALTH INC

METHODIST CAMPUS
See METHODIST CHILDRENS HOME

D-U-N-S 07-509-0837
METHODIST CHILDRENS HOME
METHODIST CAMPUS
1111 Herring Ave, Waco, TX 76708-3642
Tel (254) 753-0181 *Founded/Ownrshp* 1890
Sales 77.2MM *EMP* 330
SIC 8322 Crisis center; Crisis center
Pr: Tim Brown
Treas: James Dubois
VP: Cindy Vanover
**Exec:* Judy Broadway
Mktg Dir: Bryan Mize
HC Dir: Kay Abbe
Pgrm Dir: Nichole Ehler

METHODIST CHILDRENS HOSPITAL
See METHODIST HEALTH GROUP INC

D-U-N-S 79-028-2003
METHODIST COLLEGE DEVELOPMENT CORP
5400 Ramsey St, Fayetteville, NC 28311-1498
Tel (910) 630-7000 *Founded/Ownrshp* 2007
Sales 13.4MM^E *EMP* 626
SIC 8221 Colleges universities & professional schools; Colleges universities & professional schools
Prin: Elton Hendricks
Pr: Robin Davenport
VP: George Blanc
VP: Jane Gardiner

METHODIST DALLAS MED CENTRE
See METHODIST HOSPITALS OF DALLAS INC

METHODIST DIAGNOSTIC HOSPITAL
See DCH HEALTH SERVICES INC

D-U-N-S 60-725-8105
METHODIST FAMILY HEALTH INC
METHODIST BEHAVIORAL HLTH SYS
1600 Aldersgate Rd # 300, Little Rock, AR 72205-6676
Tel (501) 661-0720 *Founded/Ownrshp* 2003
Sales 32.8MM *EMP* 585
SIC 8063 Psychiatric hospitals; Psychiatric hospitals
Pr: Andy Alton
**CFO:* L Don Cole
**Treas:* Becky Jones
**VP:* David Beall
Comm Dir: Jane Dennis
Dir Bus: Katie Staggs
Off Mgr: Tiziana Bowers
Off Mgr: Veronica Thompson
Nurse Mgr: Suzy Smith

D-U-N-S 10-545-9080 IMP
METHODIST HEALTH CARE SYSTEM
METHODIST HOSPITAL SYSTEM, THE
(*Suby of* METHODIST HOSPITAL) ★
6565 Fannin St D200, Houston, TX 77030-2703
Tel (713) 793-1602 *Founded/Ownrshp* 1984
Sales 1.2MMM *EMP* 30
Accts Grant Thornton Llp Dallas Tx
SIC 8011 Offices & clinics of medical doctors
Pr: Larry L Mathis
Chf Path: Abida Haque
Dir Vol: Margy Lohoff
V Ch: Ernest Cockrell
**Pr:* Mauro Ferrari
COO: Edward Jones
COO: Jack Julius
CFO: Lowell E Stanton
CFO: Robert Zimmerli
Bd of Dir: Kelly Lange
Bd of Dir: Vidal Martinez
Bd of Dir: Stephen Wende
Sr VP: Lauren Rykert
**VP:* S Jeffrey Atcherman
VP: Steve Burns
VP: Sharon Johnson
VP: Carol Spang
VP: Stephen Spielman
VP: Janette Zercher
Board of Directors: Tobias Samo

METHODIST HEALTH CENTER
See CAPITOL LAKES RETIREMENT COMMUNITY

D-U-N-S 11-733-1041
METHODIST HEALTH FOUNDATION INC
1800 N Capitol Ave Fl 6, Indianapolis, IN 46202-1218
Tel (317) 962-1777 Founded/Ownrshp 1961
Sales 23.2MM EMP 12
Accts Crowe Horwath Llp Indianapol
SIC 8399 5947 Fund raising organization, non-fee basis; Gift shop; Fund raising organization, non-fee basis; Gift shop
Pr: Elizabeth A Stilwell
*CFO: Joe Trager
Ofcr: Dana Shank
*VP: Katy Canter
VP: Joseph Traeger
CTO: Karen Ball
Mktg Dir: Jama Pryor

D-U-N-S 05-295-2090
METHODIST HEALTH GROUP INC
METHODIST CHILDRENS HOSPITAL
(Suby of INDIANA UNIVERSITY HEALTH INC) ★
1701 Senate Blvd, Indianapolis, IN 46202-1239
Tel (317) 962-2000 Founded/Ownrshp 1899, 1997
Sales 185.1MM^E EMP 5,967
SIC 8062 6321 General medical & surgical hospitals; Accident & health insurance; General medical & surgical hospitals; Accident & health insurance
Pr: Dan Evans
Sr VP: Ron Stiver
Snr Mgr: Sue Thompson

D-U-N-S 84-845-7578
METHODIST HEALTH SERVICES CORP
(Suby of IOWA HEALTH SYSTEM) ★
221 Ne Glen Oak Ave, Peoria, IL 61636-0001
Tel (309) 672-5522 Founded/Ownrshp 1985
Sales 47.9M EMP 3,000
SIC 8062 General medical & surgical hospitals; General medical & surgical hospitals
CEO: Deborah Simon
CFO: Calvin Mackay

D-U-N-S 07-853-2725
METHODIST HEALTH SYSTEM IRB
1441 N Beckley Ave, Dallas, TX 75203-1201
Tel (214) 947-8181 Founded/Ownrshp 2012
Sales 20.8MM^E EMP 71^E
SIC 8399 Health & welfare council
VP: Jason Bray
VP: Jim O'Reilly
VP: Robert Simpson
Dir Rx: Jon Albrecht
IT Man: Gloria Garza
Psych: Barry Bass
Psych: Howard Chase
Psych: William Lowry
Snr Mgr: Barry Meyer

METHODIST HEALTHCARE
See METHODIST LE BONHEUR HEALTHCARE

D-U-N-S 01-979-0237
METHODIST HEALTHCARE MEMPHIS HOSPITALS
848 Adams Ave, Memphis, TN 38103-2816
Tel (901) 287-5437 Founded/Ownrshp 1902
Sales 100.5MM^E EMP 1,830
Accts Thompson Dunavant Plc Memphis
SIC 8069 8011 Children's hospital; Offices & clinics of medical doctors; Children's hospital; Offices & clinics of medical doctors
Pr: CAM Welton
Pr: Phyllis Gatlin
VP: Wyatt Howell
Dir Case M: Kenneth Robertson
Dir Lab: Earl Chambers
Dir Rx: Brandon Edgerson
Dir Sec: Michael Berry
Dir Sec: John Lee
Dir QC: Donna Vickery
Phys Thrpy: Caryline Adkins

D-U-N-S 04-313-3859 IMP
METHODIST HEALTHCARE MEMPHIS HOSPITALS
1265 Union Ave, Memphis, TN 38104-3415
Tel (901) 516-7000 Founded/Ownrshp 1918
Sales 1.6MMM EMP 7,000
Accts Dixon Hughes Goodman Llp Ashe
SIC 8062 Hospital, AMA approved residency; Hospital, AMA approved residency
CEO: David Baytos
*Pr: Meri Armour
CFO: Rita Neely
Ex VP: Donna Abney
VP: Michelle Collis
VP: John Pehler
IT Man: Tim McGinnis
Opers Mgr: Alicia Smith
Plnt Mgr: William Troxel
Diag Rad: Hollis Halford

D-U-N-S 01-986-8892
METHODIST HEALTHCARE MINISTRIES OF SOUTH TEXAS INC
M H M
4507 Medical Dr, San Antonio, TX 78229-4401
Tel (210) 692-0234 Founded/Ownrshp 1955
Sales 160.6MM EMP 250
Accts Ernst & Young Us Llp Fort Wor
SIC 8011 7363 Primary care medical clinic; Medical help service; Primary care medical clinic; Medical help service
CEO: Kevin C Moriarty
*COO: George Thomas
*CFO: Tony Lobasso
Sr VP: Peggy Cary
VP: Rebecca Brune
VP: Mark Holiday
Exec: Linda Lopez
Dir: Edward Codina
IT Man: Vanessa Adame
Board of Directors: Alice H Gannon, Joe E Johnston, George N Ricks, Darrell Frank Smith, Shirley S Watkins, V Chm, V Chm

D-U-N-S 06-306-7326 IMP
■ **METHODIST HEALTHCARE SYSTEM OF SAN ANTONIO LTD LLP**
METHODIST HOSPITAL
(Suby of HCA INC) ★
8109 Fredericksburg Rd, San Antonio, TX 78229-3311
Tel (210) 575-8110 Founded/Ownrshp 1995
Sales 728.7M^E EMP 5,400
SIC 8062 8011 General medical & surgical hospitals; Offices & clinics of medical doctors; General medical & surgical hospitals; Offices & clinics of medical doctors
CEO: John E Hornbeak
*CFO: Ed Vasquez
VP: Nicole Bryson
VP: V A Hamilton
VP: Gretchen Schuleman
Dir Case M: Genevieve Hernandez
Dir Lab: Mike Cifelli
Chf Nrs Of: Annie Garcia
Off Mgr: Newton Courtney
Snr Ntwrk: Talley Fritsch
CIO: Ron Hunsucker

METHODIST HOME CARE
See ALLIANCE HEALTH SERVICES INC

D-U-N-S 07-545-2060
METHODIST HOME FOR AGING CORP
FAIRHAVEN
1520 Cooper Hill Rd, Irondale, AL 35210-2303
Tel (205) 951-2442 Founded/Ownrshp 1956, 1978
Sales 38.8MM^E EMP 800
SIC 8051 Skilled nursing care facilities; Skilled nursing care facilities
CEO: Christopher W Tomlin
*Sr VP: Michael D Giles
*VP: Vicki H Jackson
*VP: Regina T Lawler

METHODIST HOME FOR CHILDREN AN
See METHODIST HOME OF SOUTH GEORGIA CONFERENCE INC

D-U-N-S 07-593-5866
METHODIST HOME OF SOUTH GEORGIA CONFERENCE INC (GA)
METHODIST HOME FOR CHILDREN AN
304 Pierce Ave, Macon, GA 31204-2422
Tel (478) 738-2230 Founded/Ownrshp 1872
Sales 12.1MM EMP 300
Accts Howard Moore & Mcduffie Pc Ma
SIC 8361 Children's home; Children's home
Pr: Steve Rumford
V Ch: Robert G Lewis Jr
*VP: Bruce Stanfield

D-U-N-S 80-786-3915
METHODIST HOMES FOR AGING
FAIRHAVEN
(Suby of FAIRHAVEN) ★
1520 Cooper Hill Rd, Irondale, AL 35210-2303
Tel (205) 951-2442 Founded/Ownrshp 1986
Sales 35.3MM EMP 15
SIC 8741 Management services; Management services
Pr: Christopher Tomlin
*VP: Regina T Lawler

METHODIST HOSP PAIN MGT CLINIC
See NEBRASKA METHODIST HOSPITAL INC

METHODIST HOSPITAL
See METHODIST HEALTHCARE SYSTEM OF SAN ANTONIO LTD LLP

D-U-N-S 07-417-2719 IMP
METHODIST HOSPITAL
METHODIST HOSPITAL SYSTEM, THE
6565 Fannin St, Houston, TX 77030-2707
Tel (713) 790-3311 Founded/Ownrshp 2010
Sales 3.0MMM EMP 15,000
SIC 8062 Hospital, affiliated with AMA residency; Hospital, affiliated with AMA residency
Pr: Marc L D
Chf Rad: King Ll
*Ch Bd: John F Bookout
*Ch Bd: David M Underwood
V Ch: Connie M Dyer
*Pr: Ewing Werlein Jr
*CFO: Kevin Burns
CFO: Mick Cantu
CFO: John E Hagal
*Treas: Carlton Baucum
Bd of Dir: Kenneth R Levingston
Ex VP: Marc L Boom
Ex VP: Richard Gonzales
*Ex VP: Roberta Schwartz
Sr VP: Edward Etyrrell
*Sr VP: Edward L Tyrrell
Exec: Anne Eastman
Dir Teleco: Bill Zipprer
Dir Case M: Linda Collins
Dir Env Sv: David Barnard

D-U-N-S 83-880-0068
METHODIST HOSPITAL
BUILDING SERVICE DEPARTMENT
1900 N Capitol Ave Fl 3, Indianapolis, IN 46202
Tel (317) 962-2000 Founded/Ownrshp 1995
Sales 79.5MM^E EMP 6,000
SIC 8062 General medical & surgical hospitals; General medical & surgical hospitals
Pr: Dan Evans
VP: Doug Morris

METHODIST HOSPITAL FOR SURGERY
See METDALSPI LLC

D-U-N-S 15-429-2403
METHODIST HOSPITAL FOUNDATION
(Suby of METHODIST HOSPITAL) ★
6565 Fannin St, Houston, TX 77030-2707
Tel (713) 793-1664 Founded/Ownrshp 1983
Sales 69.1MM EMP 24
Accts Deloitte Tax Llp Houston Tx
SIC 6512 8733 5912 5812 7218 Commercial & industrial building operation; Medical research; Drug stores; Eating places; Industrial launderers
CEO: Peter W Butler
*Pr: Nicole Rubin

METHODIST HOSPITAL NORTHLAKE C
See METHODIST HOSPITALS INC

D-U-N-S 06-669-4803
METHODIST HOSPITAL OF SOUTHERN CALIFORNIA
300 W Huntington Dr, Arcadia, CA 91007-3402
Tel (626) 898-8000 Founded/Ownrshp 1903
Sales 279.4MM EMP 2,200
Accts Kpmg Llp Los Angeles Ca
SIC 8062 General medical & surgical hospitals; General medical & surgical hospitals
CEO: Dan F Ausman
Dir Recs: Bridgitte Didier
CFO: Donald Deshotels
CFO: Bill Grigg
*CFO: William E Grigg
*Sr VP: Clifford R Daniels
*Sr VP: Steven A Sisto
VP: Barry Burns
Exec: Michele Benoit
Dir Inf Cn: Sharon Keehne
Dir Lab: Sonja Malgian
Dir Lab: Sonia Malijian
Dir Lab: Sonia Naljian
Dir Rad: Francis J Moorhead

METHODIST HOSPITAL SYSTEM, THE
See METHODIST HEALTH CARE SYSTEM

METHODIST HOSPITAL SYSTEM
See METHODIST WEST HOUSTON HOSPITAL

METHODIST HOSPITAL SYSTEM, THE
See METHODIST HOSPITAL

D-U-N-S 06-949-0670
METHODIST HOSPITALS INC
METHODIST HOSPITAL NORTHLAKE C
600 Grant St, Gary, IN 46402-6001
Tel (219) 886-4000 Founded/Ownrshp 1941
Sales 324.6MM EMP 3,260
SIC 8062 General medical & surgical hospitals; Hospital, AMA approved residency; General medical & surgical hospitals; Hospital, AMA approved residency
Pr: Michael Davenport
Chf Path: Teresa Vazquez
Dir Recs: Patrick Lester
*Pr: James Burg
*Pr: Ian E McFadden
*CFO: John C Diehl
*CFO: Matthew Doyle
*Ch: Benjamin Luna
*Treas: Bruce Dahltorp
Ofcr: Shelly M Major
*VP: Wright Alcorn
VP: John Diehl
Dir Rad: John A Scott
Dir Rad: Brian D White

D-U-N-S 07-485-3979
METHODIST HOSPITALS OF DALLAS INC
METHODIST DALLAS MED CENTRE
1441 N Beckley Ave, Dallas, TX 75203-1201
Tel (214) 947-8181 Founded/Ownrshp 1921
Sales 1.0MMM EMP 4,804
SIC 8062 Hospital, medical school affiliation; Hospital, medical school affiliation
Ch Bd: John Ford
Pr: Dwight Williams
*CEO: Stephen L Mansfield
*CFO: Michael J Schaefer
Ofcr: Barbara Odom
Ofcr: Nancy E Simon
Ex VP: Kim N Hollo
*Ex VP: Laura Irvine
*Ex VP: Michael O Price
*Ex VP: Pamela Stoyanoff
Sr VP: Adam L Myers
VP: Sam Bagchi
VP: Kathleen Beathard
VP: Deanna Kenard
VP: Harold Kolni
VP: Leslie Pierce

D-U-N-S 07-012-8012
METHODIST JENNIE EDMUNDSON HOSPITAL
(Suby of NEBRASKA METHODIST HEALTH SYSTEM INC) ★
933 E Pierce St, Council Bluffs, IA 51503-4626
Tel (712) 396-6000 Founded/Ownrshp 1887
Sales 94.8MM EMP 750^E
SIC 8062 General medical & surgical hospitals; General medical & surgical hospitals
Pr: Steven Baumart
CFO: Linda Burt
Treas: Allan G Lozier
*Sec: Kathy Tisher
Dir Env Sv: Dave Paul
Dir Sec: Charlie Kelly
Sls&Mrk Ex: Ed Rider
Dir Health: Jane Flury

D-U-N-S 87-732-9107
METHODIST JENNIE EDMUNDSON HOSPITAL
933 E Pierce St, Council Bluffs, IA 51503-4626
Tel (712) 396-6000 Founded/Ownrshp 1800
Sales 9.7MM^E EMP 700
SIC 8062 General medical & surgical hospitals; General medical & surgical hospitals
Pr: Steve Baumert
*VP: Michael Romano
Sls&Mrk Ex: Ed Rider

D-U-N-S 10-629-7500
METHODIST LE BONHEUR HEALTHCARE
METHODIST HEALTHCARE
1211 Union Ave Ste 700, Memphis, TN 38104-6600
Tel (901) 516-7000 Founded/Ownrshp 1981
Sales 124.7MM EMP 11,459
Accts Dixon Hughes Goodman Llp Ash
SIC 8062 General medical & surgical hospitals; General medical & surgical hospitals
Pr: Gary S Shorb
CFO: Hilder Peake
CFO: Kevin Todd
Ex VP: Dona Abbe
*Ex VP: Donna Abney
Ex VP: Chris McLean
*Sr VP: Bill Breen
Sr VP: Steven T Miller
Sr VP: Carol Ross-Spang
Sr VP: Gail Thurmond
*VP: Lynn M Field
*VP: Cato Johnson
VP: Alexander Macgrregor
VP: Carol Spang
*VP: W Steven West
Dir Case M: Emily Durbin
Dir Rx: Alison Apple

D-U-N-S 01-271-4593
METHODIST MEDICAL CENTER FOUNDATION
(Suby of METHODIST HEALTH SERVICES CORP) ★
221 Ne Glen Oak Ave, Peoria, IL 61636-0001
Tel (309) 672-4895 Founded/Ownrshp 1899
Sales 2.7MM EMP 2,150
SIC 8082 Home health care services; Home health care services
CEO: Debbie Simon
*COO: Keith Knepp
*CFO: Robert Quin
Pathlgst: Andrew Armstrong
Pathlgst: Elizabeth Bauer-Marsh
Pathlgst: Juan Gonzalez
Pathlgst: WEI Liu
Pharmcst: Scott Metzger
Board of Directors: Keith Knepp, Robert Quin, Deborah Simon

D-U-N-S 07-560-7689
METHODIST MEDICAL CENTER OF ILLINOIS
UNITYPOINT HEALTH - METHODIST
(Suby of METHODIST HEALTH SERVICES CORP) ★
221 Ne Glen Oak Ave, Peoria, IL 61636-0002
Tel (309) 672-5522 Founded/Ownrshp 1898
Sales 388.4MM EMP 2,400
SIC 8062 Hospital, medical school affiliated with nursing & residency; Hospital, medical school affiliated with nursing & residency
Pr: Debbie Simon
*COO: Steve Brewer
CFO: Calvin M Kay
*CFO: Rob Quin
Treas: R Younggren
*VP: Rebekah Bourland
*VP: Tammy Duvendack
VP: Gene Hoerr
*VP: Keith Knepp
*VP: Joy Ledbetter
*VP: John Miller
*VP: Roberta Parks
*VP: Tony Schierbeck
*VP: Jeanine Spain
*VP: Terry Waters
VP: Steve Weaver

D-U-N-S 07-902-6738
METHODIST MEDICAL CENTER OF OAK RIDGE (TN)
(Suby of COVENANT HEALTH) ★
990 Oak Ridge Tpke, Oak Ridge, TN 37830-6942
Tel (865) 835-1000 Founded/Ownrshp 1959
Sales 147.0MM EMP 1,500^E
SIC 8062 General medical & surgical hospitals; General medical & surgical hospitals
Pr: Mike Belbeck
Chf Rad: Steven Knight
CFO: Julie Utterback
VP: Jeremy Biggs
VP: Rebekah Bourland
VP: Chad Clabough
VP: Jennifer Hanson
VP: Sue Harris
VP: Connie Martin
Dir Lab: Nora Lowe
Dir Lab: Jackie Murray
Board of Directors: David Seay, H W Arrowsmith, Anne Travis, Ralph Aurin, Clement Block, David Compton MD, Gary Coxon, Greg Grimm, Sherry Hoppe, Francis Reid MD, Rev Gordon L Ridenour

D-U-N-S 84-972-6273
METHODIST MEDICAL CENTER OF OAK RIDGE
1420 Centerpoint Blvd C, Knoxville, TN 37932-1960
Tel (865) 374-6864 Founded/Ownrshp 2009
Sales 189.3MM EMP 9^E
SIC 8011 Medical centers
Prin: Nancy Beck
CFO: Julie Utterback

D-U-N-S 17-708-8130
METHODIST MEDICAL GROUP PHYSICIANS INC
(Suby of INDIANA UNIVERSITY HEALTH INC) ★
950 N Meridian St Ste 500, Indianapolis, IN 46204-3908
Tel (317) 962-4023 Founded/Ownrshp 2002
Sales 6.9MM^E EMP 350
Accts Ernst & Young Us Llp Indianap
SIC 8011 Clinic, operated by physicians; Clinic, operated by physicians
Pr: Stephen Pollom MD
*COO: Kyle Allen

D-U-N-S 06-933-4241
METHODIST OAKS (SC)
1000 Methodist Oaks Dr, Orangeburg, SC 29115-1815
Tel (803) 534-1212 Founded/Ownrshp 1954
Sales 22.8MM EMP 400
Accts Derrick Stubbs & Stith Llp C
SIC 8059 Rest home, with health care; Rest home, with health care
CEO: James McGee
Dir Recs: Libby Salisbury
COO: Scott Ewing
CFO: Theresa Caft
CFO: Teresa Craft
*CFO: Jacque Curtin
Off Mgr: Debbie Robinson

IT Man: Andy Thompson
Nrsg Dir: Jona Patrick

METHODIST REHABILITAION CENTER
See MMRC GIFT SHOP

METHODIST REHABILITATION CTR
See MISSISSIPPI METHODIST HOSPITAL AND REHABILITATION CENTER INC

D-U-N-S 05-247-8559
METHODIST RETIREMENT COMMUNITIES
EDGEWATER MTHDST RTRMNT COMM
2505 E Villa Maria Rd, Bryan, TX 77802-2069
Tel (866) 224-9044 *Founded/Ownrshp* 1965
Sales 2.0MM *EMP* 650
Accts Cliftonlarsonallenllp Dallas
SIC 8051 6513 Skilled nursing care facilities; Retirement hotel operation; Skilled nursing care facilities; Retirement hotel operation
CEO: Rev Edward Kester
CFO: Richard M Berman
CFO: Frank Nance
CFO: Brad Stewart
VP: Chuck Childress
VP: Anne Davis
Ex Dir: Matthew Currie
Ex Dir: Marvin Kayse
Mktg Dir: Natasha Crabbe

D-U-N-S 06-897-0367
METHODIST RICHARDSON MEDICAL CENTER FOUNDATION INC
MEDICINE HEALTH CENTER
2831 E President George B, Richardson, TX 75082-3561
Tel (972) 498-4000 *Founded/Ownrshp* 1966
Sales 835.8M *EMP* 624
Accts Bkd Llp Houston Tx
SIC 8062 General medical & surgical hospitals; General medical & surgical hospitals
Pr: Robert Simpson
**Ch:* Joseph Snayd
Dir OR: Cheryl Koch
Psych: Carla Berdeaux
Pathlgst: Sheryl Willis
Obsttrcn: Marcia Gillespie
Diag Rad: Warren Maupin

D-U-N-S 07-201-4418
METHODIST UNIVERSITY INC
5400 Ramsey St, Fayetteville, NC 28311-1420
Tel (910) 630-7000 *Founded/Ownrshp* 1956
Sales 55.3MM^E *EMP* 525^E
Accts Haigh Byrd & Lambert Llp Fa
SIC 8221 College, except junior; College, except junior
Pr: Ben E Hancock Jr
Treas: Rick Rode
VP: Delmas Crisp
**Prin:* M Elton Hendricks
Genl Mgr: Gina Thornton
Off Admin: Hussain Al-Radhi
CIO: Tom Marthers
CTO: Bryan Madej
Dir IT: Samuel Clark
Dir IT: Rick Lepire
IT Man: Keith Duffy

D-U-N-S 95-991-4677
METHODIST WEST HOUSTON HOSPITAL
METHODIST HOSPITAL SYSTEM
18500 Katy Fwy, Houston, TX 77094-1110
Tel (832) 522-1000 *Founded/Ownrshp* 2011
Sales 201.7MM *EMP* 46^E
SIC 8661 8062 Methodist Church; General medical & surgical hospitals
Pr: Sherene Thompson
QC Dir: Sherry Nelson

D-U-N-S 01-965-9044 IMP/EXP
METHODS MACHINE TOOLS INC
65 Union Ave, Sudbury, MA 01776-2277
Tel (978) 443-5388 *Founded/Ownrshp* 1958
Sales 106.2MM^E *EMP* 275
SIC 5084

D-U-N-S 00-177-2342 IMP
METHUEN CONSTRUCTION CO INC (MA)
40 Lowell Rd Ste 2, Salem, NH 03079-4030
Tel (603) 328-2222 *Founded/Ownrshp* 1960
Sales 55.8MM *EMP* 100
Accts Cullen Murphy & Co Pc No
SIC 1611 1771 1623 Highway & street construction; Concrete work; Pipe laying construction; Highway & street construction; Concrete work; Pipe laying construction
CEO: Joseph A Barbone Jr
**Pr:* Leon C Asadoorian
**CFO:* Joseph Gates
**CFO:* Kevin Peck
Dir Bus: Scott Coulombe

D-U-N-S 15-745-6166
METHUEN PUBLIC SCHOOLS
10 Ditson Pl, Methuen, MA 01844-3802
Tel (978) 722-6000 *Founded/Ownrshp* 1978
Sales 50.0MM^E *EMP* 900
SIC 8211 Elementary & secondary schools; Public elementary school; Elementary & secondary schools; Public elementary school
IT Man: Walter Pare
Teacher Pr: Colleen McCarthy
Psych: Martha Tatro
Pathlgst: Douglas Babbitt

METI
See MANAGEMENT AND ENGINEERING TECHNOLOGIES INTERNATIONAL INC

METLABS
See MET LABORATORIES INC

METLIFE
See AMERICAN LIFE INSURANCE CO

METLIFE
See METROPOLITAN LIFE INSURANCE CO (INC)

METLIFE
See METROPOLITAN PROPERTY AND CASUALTY INSURANCE CO

METLIFE
See METROPOLITAN INSURANCE & ANNUITY CO

METLIFE
See METROPOLITAN TOWER LIFE INSURANCE CO

D-U-N-S 00-693-4053
■ **METLIFE AUTO & HOME INSURANCE AGENCY INC** (RI)
(*Suby of* METLIFE INC) ★
9797 Springboro Pike, Dayton, OH 45448-0001
Tel (815) 266-5301 *Founded/Ownrshp* 1915, 2002
Sales NA *EMP* 900
SIC 6411 Insurance agents & brokers; Insurance agents & brokers
Ch Bd: Stephen Kiingel
COO: Darla Fitchum
CFO: Patrick Thiele
Treas: Donald Swanson
Sr VP: Howard Dalton
Sr VP: Andrew Douglass
VP: Kevin Brandenburg
VP: Ruby Schroeder
Brnch Mgr: Tiffani Jackson
Brnch Mgr: Matthew Luedeke
Brnch Mgr: Shawn McAtee

D-U-N-S 18-799-8943
■ **METLIFE BROKERAGE**
(*Suby of* METLIFE) ★
214 Carnegie Ctr Ste 301, Princeton, NJ 08540-6237
Tel (908) 725-1301 *Founded/Ownrshp* 1992
Sales NA *EMP* 100
SIC 6411 Insurance agents & brokers
Pr: Robert Pal
Ex VP: Maria Morris
VP: Fernando Jaime
VP: Michael Monestero
IT Man: Srinu Kavi
IT Man: Juliane Kowalski

D-U-N-S 00-223-7442
METLIFE FOUNDATION
1095 Av Of The Amer Fl B, New York, NY 10036-6726
Tel (908) 253-1644 *Founded/Ownrshp* 2010
Sales 53.5MM *EMP* 37^E
SIC 8641 Civic social & fraternal associations; Civic social & fraternal associations
Pr: Steven Kandarian
Pr: William McCallion
VP: Hilary Kotter
CTO: Nancy Kunkel
IT Man: Michel Awad
IT Man: Tamer Eissa
IT Man: James Ellis
IT Man: Srinu Kavi
VP Mktg: Neil Boudreaux
VP Mktg: Mary Reardon
Mktg Dir: Kristen Esposito

D-U-N-S 03-118-9345
■ **METLIFE GROUP INC**
(*Suby of* METLIFE INC) ★
1095 Ave Of The Americas, New York, NY 10036-6797
Tel (800) 638-5433 *Founded/Ownrshp* 2002
Sales NA *EMP* 348^E
SIC 6411 Insurance agents & brokers
Prin: Richard Barquist
Pr: Doug Ramsey

D-U-N-S 15-481-0295
■ **METLIFE HEALTHCARE NETWORK OF NEW YORK INC**
(*Suby of* METLIFE) ★
2929 Express Dr N Ste 100, Hauppauge, NY 11749-5302
Tel (631) 851-5700 *Founded/Ownrshp* 1986
Sales NA *EMP* 75
SIC 6411 Insurance agents & brokers
Pr: Michael Jaeger
**VP:* John Poland
VP: Zaida Rodriguez
Off Mgr: Michael Tuccillo
Sales Asso: Margaret Ehrhart
Sales Asso: Mark Raffa
Sales Asso: Irene Ruotolo

D-U-N-S 01-290-2141
■ **METLIFE HOME LOANS LLC**
(*Suby of* METLIFE) ★
7880 Bent Branch Dr # 100, Irving, TX 75063-6046
Tel (214) 441-4000 *Founded/Ownrshp* 2008
Sales NA *EMP* 500
SIC 6162 Mortgage bankers & correspondents
Pr: Rodney Gayle
Pr: James Rose

D-U-N-S 11-215-8568
▲ **METLIFE INC**
200 Park Ave Fl 1200, New York, NY 10166-0188
Tel (212) 578-2211 *Founded/Ownrshp* 1999
Sales NA *EMP* 68,000
Tkr Sym MET *Exch* NYS
SIC 6311 6321 6331 Life insurance carriers; Accident & health insurance carriers; Disability health insurance; Fire, marine & casualty insurance: mutual; Property damage insurance; Life insurance carriers; Accident & health insurance carriers; Disability health insurance; Fire, marine & casualty insurance: mutual; Property damage insurance
Ch Bd: Steven A Kandarian
Pr: Jeffrey Archer
Pr: Amy Berg
Pr: Brian Bruneau
Pr: Brian Kiel
Pr: Francesca Pulis
COO: Robert C Henrikson
CFO: John C R Hele
CFO: Trevor Holland
Ofcr: Frans Hijkoop
Ex VP: Ricardo A Anzaldua
Ex VP: Daniel Cavanagh
Ex VP: Steven J Goulart
Ex VP: Beth Hirschhorn
Ex VP: Maria R Morris
Ex VP: Steven L Sheinheit
Sr VP: Sibyl Jacobson

D-U-N-S 00-691-7413
■ **METLIFE INSURANCE CO USA**
(*Suby of* METLIFE INC) ★
11225 N Community Hse Rd, Charlotte, NC 28277-4435
Tel (980) 949-3626 *Founded/Ownrshp* 1863, 2005
Sales NA *EMP* 65,000
SIC 6411 6321 6331 6324 Insurance agents & brokers; Medical insurance claim processing, contract or fee basis; Accident & health insurance; Accident insurance carriers; Health insurance carriers; Fire, marine & casualty insurance; Workers' compensation insurance; Hospital & medical service plans; Group hospitalization plans; Insurance agents & brokers; Medical insurance claim processing, contract or fee basis; Accident & health insurance; Accident insurance carriers; Health insurance carriers; Fire, marine & casualty insurance; Workers' compensation insurance; Hospital & medical service plans; Group hospitalization plans
Ch Bd: Eric T Steigerwalt
CFO: Stanley J Talbi
Ex VP: Peter M Carlson
Sr VP: Stuart L Baritz
Sr VP: Jay S Fishman
Sr VP: Elizabeth C Georgakopoulos
Sr VP: Russell H Johnson
Sr VP: Warren H May
Sys/Dir: Ronald Waid
Board of Directors: Elizabeth M Forget, Gene L Lunman

D-U-N-S 93-280-1343
■ **METLIFE INVESTORS DISTRIBUTION CO**
(*Suby of* METLIFE) ★
1 Met Life Plz, Long Island City, NY 11101-4018
Tel (212) 578-2211 *Founded/Ownrshp* 1987
Sales NA *EMP* 1^E
SIC 6411 Insurance agents & brokers
Pr: Thomas P Lydon Jr
Sr VP: Robin Lenna
VP: Douglas Barone
VP: Linda Bloniarz
VP: Charles Miller
VP: Sean Myles
VP: Laura Sokolski
VP: Robert Tarnok
Exec: Joshua Scribner
IT Man: Bizz Anirudh
IT Man: Johnathan Soberano

D-U-N-S 04-878-8426 IMP
METOKOTE CORP
(*Suby of* PLATINUM EQUITY LLC) ★
1340 Neubrecht Rd, Lima, OH 45801-3120
Tel (419) 996-7800 *Founded/Ownrshp* 2013
Sales 649.6MM^E *EMP* 2,000
SIC 3479 Coating of metals & formed products; Coating of metals & formed products
Pr: Jeffrey J Oravitz
**Ch Bd:* Robert E Lee
**COO:* Jon Barrett
**CFO:* Patrick Osler
VP: Brent Schwartz
**Prin:* William B Balyeat
**Prin:* James C Blankemeyer
**Prin:* Ruth E Moser
CIO: Mark Miller
Plnt Mgr: Bob Sanborn
Board of Directors: James C Blankemeyer

D-U-N-S 00-204-1945 IMP
METPAR CORP (NY)
95 State St, Westbury, NY 11590-5006
Tel (516) 333-2600 *Founded/Ownrshp* 1952
Sales 25.3MM^E *EMP* 80
SIC 3431 3088 Metal sanitary ware; Toilet fixtures, plastic
Pr: Ronald S Mondolino
VP Opers: Vincent Salierno
Mfg Mgr: Jimmy Fallarino
S&M/VP: Jim Storey

METPRO FYBROC DIVISION
See STROBIC AIR CORP

METRA COLUMBUS TRANSIT SYS
See CONSOLIDATED GOVERMENT OF GA INC

D-U-N-S 00-132-3807 IMP
METRA ELECTRONICS CORP
460 Walker St, Holly Hill, FL 32117-2653
Tel (386) 257-1186 *Founded/Ownrshp* 1949
Sales 117.1MM^E *EMP* 501
SIC 3651 Audio electronic systems; Audio electronic systems
Pr: William H Jones Jr
**CFO:* Anthony Guidice
CFO: Tony Guidice
**VP:* Bill Fornino
**VP:* Jan Jones
Dir IT: Mark Schaeffer
IT Man: Gary Lewis
Plnt Mgr: John Lelasher

D-U-N-S 14-863-7366
METRA INDUSTRIES INC
50 Muller Pl, Little Falls, NJ 07424-1133
Tel (973) 812-0333 *Founded/Ownrshp* 1980
Sales 47.6MM^E *EMP* 100
SIC 1623 Water main construction; Sewer line construction
Pr: Gary Stivaly
COO: Carol Quarto
Div Mgr: Richard Goff
IT Man: Robert Deponte

METRA METROPOLITAN RAIL
See NORTHEAST ILLINOIS REGIONAL COMMUTER RAILROAD CORP

D-U-N-S 83-911-3438
■ **METRAHEALTH CARE MANAGEMENT CORP**
(*Suby of* UNITED HEALTHCARE INSURANCE CO) ★
9900 Bren Rd E, Minnetonka, MN 55343-9664
Tel (952) 936-1300 *Founded/Ownrshp* 1994
Sales NA *EMP* 10
SIC 6321 6311 Accident & health insurance; Life insurance; Accident & health insurance; Life insurance
Pr: R Colby
**Sec:* Brigid Spicola

D-U-N-S 01-890-5922
METRATECH CORP
200 West St Ste 12, Waltham, MA 02451-1125
Tel (781) 839-8300 *Founded/Ownrshp* 1998
Sales 25.8MM^E *EMP* 144
SIC 7371 Computer software development; Computer software development
CEO: Scott Swartz
**CFO:* Theodore Les
Bd of Dir: Robert Goodman
Ofcr: James Swartz
VP: Michael Cassani
VP: Mark Hounslow
Netwrk Eng: John Moon
Board of Directors: Rober Crowley, Zenas Hutcheson, Les Strauss, James Swartz

D-U-N-S 10-256-7567 IMP
■ **METREX RESEARCH LLC**
(*Suby of* ANALYTIC ENDODONTICS) ★
1717 W Collins Ave, Orange, CA 92867-5422
Tel (714) 516-7788 *Founded/Ownrshp* 1999
Sales 26.6MM^E *EMP* 82
SIC 2819 3845 8731 Chemicals, high purity: refined from technical grade; Laser systems & equipment, medical; Medical research, commercial; Chemicals, high purity: refined from technical grade; Laser systems & equipment, medical; Medical research, commercial
CFO: Jay Suel
Rgnl Mgr: Thomas Restuccia
Dist Mgr: Ivan Benitez
Dist Mgr: Ryan Bergan
Mktg Dir: Rob Starcher
Mktg Mgr: Jay Denktas
Sls Mgr: Matthew Bobonski
Sales Asso: Jonathan Townsen

D-U-N-S 10-116-1297
METRIC CONSTRUCTION CORP
55 Henshaw St, Boston, MA 02135-2928
Tel (617) 787-1158 *Founded/Ownrshp* 1981
Sales 24.4MM^E *EMP* 40
SIC 1542 Commercial & office building, new construction; Commercial & office buildings, renovation & repair
Pr: Geoffrey Caraboolad
Pr: Gerry-Lynn Darcy
Exec: Larry Sturdivant
Sfty Mgr: Bob Puracchio
Sales Exec: Dave Kilian
Snr PM: Bob Grzyb

D-U-N-S 08-310-4604
METRIC ENGINEERING INC (FL)
13940 Sw 136th St Ste 200, Miami, FL 33186-5541
Tel (305) 235-5098 *Founded/Ownrshp* 1976
Sales 72.2MM^E *EMP* 265
SIC 8711 Civil engineering; Civil engineering; Consulting engineer; Professional engineer
CEO: Victor M Benitez
Pr: Manuel A Benitez
COO: Mariley Perez
Ex VP: Douglas K Cauley
Sr VP: Dale Cody
Sr VP: Robert A Linares
Sr VP: William Wages
VP: Carmen Lovings
VP: Robert Pe
VP: Felix Rodriguez
VP: Charles Stratton

D-U-N-S 79-825-3068
METRIC EQUIPMENT SALES INC
MICROLEASE
(*Suby of* MICROLEASE INC) ★
25841 Industrial Blvd # 200, Hayward, CA 94545-2991
Tel (510) 264-0887 *Founded/Ownrshp* 2013
Sales 88.8MM^E *EMP* 70
SIC 5065 5084 7359 3825 Electronic parts & equipment; Measuring & testing equipment, electrical; Electronic equipment rental, except computers; Instruments to measure electricity; Electronic parts & equipment; Measuring & testing equipment, electrical; Electronic equipment rental, except computers; Instruments to measure electricity
CEO: Nigel Brown
**CEO:* Mike Clark
**CFO:* Nathan Hurst
**Sr VP:* David Sherve
**VP:* Gordon Curwen
VP: Dan Starkey
Dir Lab: Pat Ivie
CTO: Sharon Fischer
Dir IT: Teresa Oconnor
Sls Mgr: Mike Stephenson
Sls Mgr: Richard Yanes

D-U-N-S 06-381-1541 IMP
METRIC MACHINING
MASTER MACHINE PRODUCTS
3263 Trade Center Dr, Riverside, CA 92507-3432
Tel (909) 947-9222 *Founded/Ownrshp* 1973
Sales 7.0MM *EMP* 286
SIC 3541 Machine tools, metal cutting type
Pr: David Parker
Exec: Laura Figueroa
DP Exec: Regie Nola
Ql Cn Mgr: Drake Archer
Sls Mgr: Jeremy Subriar

D-U-N-S 01-843-9773
METRIC ROOFING INC (AZ)
4050 E Presidio St, Mesa, AZ 85215-1113
Tel (602) 533-9900 *Founded/Ownrshp* 1993
Sales 33.9MM^E *EMP* 350

SIC 1761 Roofing contractor; Roofing contractor
Pr: Dennis Curtis
VP: Steve Carroll

METRICS, INC.
See MAYNE PHARMA INC

D-U-N-S 84-714-9247
METRICSTREAM INC
COMPLIANCEONLINE
2600 E Bayshore Rd, Palo Alto, CA 94303-3241
Tel (650) 620-2900 *Founded/Ownrshp* 1999
Sales 330.0MM^E *EMP* 1,600
SIC 7372 Application computer software; Application computer software
CEO: Shellye Archambeau
**COO:* Gaurave Kapoor
**CFO:* Jeffrey Zellmer
**Ch:* Gunjan Sinha
Assoc VP: Jerry Woznicki
**Ex VP:* Venky Yerrapotu
VP: Keri Dawson
VP: Kristin Gruaz
VP: Tim Schmutzler
VP: Susan Smith
IT Man: Preethi Simha
Board of Directors: Ned Gilhuly

D-U-N-S 00-565-5360 IMP
METRIE INC
(*Suby of* METRIE CANADA LTD)
2200 140th Ave E Ste 600, Sumner, WA 98390-9672
Tel (253) 470-5050 *Founded/Ownrshp* 1926, 1999
Sales 213.4MM^E *EMP* 500
SIC 5031 Building materials, exterior; Building materials, interior; Lumber: rough, dressed & finished; Building materials, exterior; Building materials, interior; Lumber: rough, dressed & finished
Pr: E Lawrence Sauder
**Pr:* Claire Eeles
**VP:* Pamela Campbell
**VP:* William Sauder
Genl Mgr: Alan Dobie

D-U-N-S 09-490-1899 IMP
METRIE INC
MOULDING & MILLWORK
9325 Snowden River Pkwy, Columbia, MD 21046-1951
Tel (410) 423-2440 *Founded/Ownrshp* 2000
Sales 33.0MM^E *EMP* 151^E
SIC 5031 Molding, all materials; Millwork
Pr: Greg Stoner
**Pr:* Lawrence Sauder
**CEO:* El Sauder
VP: Ben Lavallee
**VP:* Brent Pay
VP: M J Sauder
Exec: Staci Ranieri
Brnch Mgr: Rich Fahrner
Off Mgr: Stacey Winery

D-U-N-S 10-064-7887 IMP
METRIE INDUSTRIES INC
COMMCO
(*Suby of* SAUDER MOULDINGS LIMITED)
31 Design Dr, North Kansas City, MO 64116-3096
Tel (816) 241-4840 *Founded/Ownrshp* 1998
Sales 21.3MM^E *EMP* 110
SIC 2499 Applicators, wood
Pr: Franklin S Christopher

D-U-N-S 03-080-0130
METRO
600 Ne Grand Ave, Portland, OR 97232-2799
Tel (503) 797-1700 *Founded/Ownrshp* 1969
Sales NA *EMP* 700
SIC 9199

METRO APPLIANCES AND MORE
See METRO BUILDERS SUPPLY INC

METRO AREA TRANSIT
See TRANSIT AUTHORITY OF OMAHA

METRO ATLANTA YMCA
See YOUNG MENS CHRISTIAN ASSOCIATION OF METROPOLITAN ATLANTA INC

D-U-N-S 19-779-4600
METRO AUTO AUCTION INC
2475 S 59th Ave, Phoenix, AZ 85043-7900
Tel (602) 279-9500 *Founded/Ownrshp* 2005
Sales 60.0MM^E *EMP* 212
SIC 5012 Automobile auction; Automobile auction
Pr: Ralph Thomas
Creative D: Ryan McDermott
Off Mgr: Veronica Gracia
IT Man: Ray Ernst

D-U-N-S 10-892-5801
METRO AVIATION INC
1214 Hawn Ave, Shreveport, LA 71107-6612
Tel (318) 222-5529 *Founded/Ownrshp* 1982
Sales 35.6MM^E *EMP* 120^E
SIC 4522 3728

D-U-N-S 09-535-0802
▲ METRO BANCORP INC
3801 Paxton St, Harrisburg, PA 17111-1418
Tel (888) 937-0004 *Founded/Ownrshp* 1999
Sales NA *EMP* 978^E
Tkr Sym METR *Exch* NGS
SIC 6022 State commercial banks; State commercial banks
Ch Bd: Gary L Nalbandian
V Ch: Harry D Madonna
COO: Percival B Moser III
CFO: Mark A Zody
Chf Mktg O: John Cunningham
Ofcr: Steven W Cribbs
Ofcr: Bobbie Ford
Ex VP: Greg Jenkins
Sr VP: Victoria G Chieppa
Sr VP: Elisa M Cintron
Sr VP: Adam L Metz
Sr VP: James R Ridd
VP: Brad Garfinkel
Board of Directors: Samir J Srouji, James R Adair, Douglas R Berry, John J Cardello, Douglas S Gelder, Alan R Hassman, J Rodney Messick, Jessica E Meyers, Michael A Serluco, Thomas F Smida

D-U-N-S 14-427-4701
■ METRO BANK
(*Suby of* METRO BANCORP INC) ★
1249 Market St, Lemoyne, PA 17043-1419
Tel (717) 972-2875 *Founded/Ownrshp* 1999
Sales NA *EMP* 238
SIC 6022 State commercial banks; State commercial banks
Ch Bd: Gary L Nalbandian
Pr: Rory G Ritrievi
Ofcr: Tammy Clark-Mcfadden
Ofcr: Craig Hummer
Ofcr: Adam Metz
Ofcr: David B Skerpon
Ofcr: Brandon Turner
Sr VP: Mike Shaddix
Sr VP: Steve Solk
VP: Tim Bradley
VP: Joseph N Butto
VP: Linda Cook
VP: Troy Erdman
VP: Alan Kilfoyle
VP: John Robert Kubinec
VP: Greg Liegey II
VP: Kristen Mekulsia
VP: Tim Reid
VP: Stephen Staman
VP: Harry M Zimmerman
Exec: Eric Warfel

D-U-N-S 60-544-7531
METRO BANK
800 Martin St S, Pell City, AL 35128-2133
Tel (205) 338-2265 *Founded/Ownrshp* 1989
Sales NA *EMP* 63
SIC 6022 6021 State commercial banks; National commercial banks; State commercial banks; National commercial banks
CEO: Charles Robert Spivey
VP: Kathy Bowman
VP: Teresa Carden
VP: Joni Hawkins
VP: Sandra C Lee
**VP:* Don Perry

D-U-N-S 80-305-9542
METRO BANK
123 N Main St, Chadwick, IL 61014-9429
Tel (815) 684-5141 *Founded/Ownrshp* 1974
Sales NA *EMP* 255
SIC 6022 State commercial banks; State commercial banks
Prin: Sangita Patel
Brnch Mgr: Branden Alexander

D-U-N-S 03-580-8567
METRO BANK NA
(*Suby of* METRO BANK) ★
309 N Clay St, Mount Carroll, IL 61053-1105
Tel (815) 684-5141 *Founded/Ownrshp* 1909
Sales NA *EMP* 245
SIC 6022 6021 State commercial banks; National commercial banks; State commercial banks; National commercial banks
Pr: Richard Erdman
Ch: Emmert Zundahl
Ex VP: Lori Elam
**VP:* Bart Ottens
**VP:* Pam Queckboerner
Dir IT: Pam Partington

METRO BLDRS & ENGINEERS GROUP
See HOUALLA ENTERPRISES LTD

D-U-N-S 60-123-3125
METRO BOBCAT INC
METRO BOBCAT SALES
33 W Old Liberty Rd, Eldersburg, MD 21784-8631
Tel (410) 489-7621 *Founded/Ownrshp* 1992
Sales 28.0MM^E *EMP* 61
SIC 7353 Heavy construction equipment rental; Heavy construction equipment rental
Pr: William Phebus
Brnch Mgr: Irvin Thomas
Off Mgr: Michelle Sullivan
Sales Exec: Dale Bennett
Sls Mgr: Steve Polczynski
Sls Mgr: Joyce Sacks

METRO BOBCAT SALES
See METRO BOBCAT INC

D-U-N-S 07-864-2410
METRO BUILDERS SUPPLY INC (OK)
METRO APPLIANCES AND MORE
5313 S Mingo Rd, Tulsa, OK 74146-5736
Tel (918) 622-7692 *Founded/Ownrshp* 1974
Sales 93.7MM^E *EMP* 300
SIC 5064 Electric household appliances; Electric household appliances
CEO: Nick Stavros
**Pr:* Guy Minix
**Sec:* Jane E Stavros
**VP:* Todd Krauser
VP: Scott Tucker
**VP:* John West
Genl Mgr: Jon Anderson
Genl Mgr: Brian Casey
Genl Mgr: Ann Howell
Genl Mgr: Christy Williams
Sls Mgr: Jay Baird

METRO BUILDING MAINTENANCE
See US METRO GROUP INC

D-U-N-S 15-531-6177 IMP
METRO BUSINESS SYSTEMS INC
11 Largo Dr S, Stamford, CT 06907-2337
Tel (203) 967-3435 *Founded/Ownrshp* 1986
Sales 111.0MM *EMP* 45
SIC 5045 Computers, peripherals & software; Computers, peripherals & software
Pr: Frank Pelli
**COO:* Stellino Savarino
**Treas:* Ralph Boccuzzi
**VP:* Jeff Lorusso
Dir Bus: Marc Goldstein
Sales Exec: Nora Ballaro

D-U-N-S 05-703-1981
METRO CARE CORP
RURAL-METRO
(*Suby of* RURAL/METRO CORP) ★
8465 N Pima Rd, Scottsdale, AZ 85258-4489
Tel (800) 352-2309 *Founded/Ownrshp* 1990
Sales 82.0MM^E *EMP* 2,000
SIC 4119 Ambulance service; Ambulance service
Pr: Michael P Dimino
**Pr:* Michael Dimino
Ofcr: Rex Harmon
**Sr VP:* Mark A Lashley
**Sr VP:* Christopher R Yearout
Exec: Colin Williams
Comm Man: Shondra Young
Off Mgr: Jill Amburgey

METRO CARS
See GREAT LAKES TRANSPORTATION HOLDING LLC

D-U-N-S 80-043-3117
METRO CITY BANK
5441 Buford Hwy Ne # 109, Doraville, GA 30340-1165
Tel (770) 455-4989 *Founded/Ownrshp* 2005
Sales NA *EMP* 48^E
SIC 6022 State commercial banks; State commercial banks
Pr: Farid Tan
Ofcr: Justin Cho
Ofcr: Abdul Mohdnor
Ofcr: Linda Shen
**Ex VP:* Hwa Saeng Kim
Sr VP: Benton Gunter
VP: Alison Kim
VP: Johnny Lee
VP: Sue Yun

METRO COMMUNICATION SERVICES
See L & L SERVICES INC

D-U-N-S 03-264-6387
METRO COMMUNITY PROVIDER NETWORK INC
3701 S Broadway, Englewood, CO 80113-3611
Tel (303) 761-1977 *Founded/Ownrshp* 1987
Sales 34.7MM *EMP* 150^E
SIC 8011 Clinic, operated by physicians; Clinic, operated by physicians
Pr: David Meyers
**COO:* John Kuenning
**CFO:* Sherryl Brandes
**Chf Mktg O:* Barry Martin
Dir IT: Eric Pettit
IT Man: Alicyn Kaiser
IT Man: Olga Martinez
IT Man: Kris Thach

D-U-N-S 94-378-6871
METRO CORRAL PARTNERS INC
GOLDEN CORRAL
203 Lookout Pl Ste B, Maitland, FL 32751-8407
Tel (407) 629-9311 *Founded/Ownrshp* 1994
Sales 4.1MM^E *EMP* 357^E
SIC 5812 Restaurant, family: chain
Prin: Doug Dannen

D-U-N-S 07-656-8468
METRO CREDIT UNION
200 Revere Beach Pkwy, Chelsea, MA 02150-1608
Tel (617) 884-7200 *Founded/Ownrshp* 1923
Sales NA *EMP* 258
SIC 6062 State credit unions, not federally chartered; State credit unions, not federally chartered
Pr: Robert M Cashman
**Ch Bd:* Marvin L Cashman
COO: Paul Swart
Sr VP: Charlene Bauer
Sr VP: Keith Pequeno
VP: Dawn Dawson
VP: Bion Foster
VP: Mary Helming
VP: Maria Justiniano
VP: Greg Spencer
VP: Thomas Wahl

D-U-N-S 03-705-5779 EXP
■ METRO DOOR A CINTAS CORP CO
APTON DOOR
(*Suby of* CINTAS CORP NO 2) ★
3500 Sunrise Hwy, Great River, NY 11739-1001
Tel (631) 277-6490 *Founded/Ownrshp* 2013
Sales 22.8MM^E *EMP* 120
SIC 3446 1799 1522 Fences, gates, posts & flagpoles; Fence construction; Residential construction; Fences, gates, posts & flagpoles; Fence construction; Residential construction
Pr: Scott McDermott
COO: Mark Jackman
**CFO:* Christine M Vetrano
Sr VP: Jeff Chevalier
**Co-Founder:* Jim Karcher
IT Man: Vincent Olson
Opers Mgr: Ellen Kraus
Snr PM: Brian Niemeyer

D-U-N-S 05-694-7849
METRO EAST INDUSTRIES INC
3126 Missouri Ave, East Saint Louis, IL 62205-1127
Tel (618) 271-7210 *Founded/Ownrshp* 1975
Sales 58.2MM^E *EMP* 230^E
SIC 4789 7699

METRO ELECTRIC
See ST LOUIS ELECTRIC SUPPLY INC

D-U-N-S 06-642-0779
METRO ELECTRIC INC
5255 Commercial Dr, Brownsville, TX 78521-5260
Tel (956) 686-2323 *Founded/Ownrshp* 1973
Sales 25.6MM^E *EMP* 126
SIC 1731 General electrical contractor; General electrical contractor
Pr: Jack Gerdes
**VP:* Michael Gerdes
Exec: Irene Sanchez
Genl Mgr: Terry Stephens
Dir IT: Bill Walter
IT Man: James Bantz

D-U-N-S 14-908-4428
METRO FIRE EQUIPMENT INC
63 S Hamilton Pl, Gilbert, AZ 85233-5515
Tel (480) 464-0509 *Founded/Ownrshp* 1972
Sales 39.4MM^E *EMP* 85
SIC 5099 Safety equipment & supplies; Safety equipment & supplies
Pr: Gary Moody
**VP:* Blake Moody
**VP:* Chris Moody
Off Mgr: Laurie Pulzato

METRO FOOD OUTLET
See DIAMOND FOOD MARKETS INC

D-U-N-S 80-865-0738
METRO FOODS INC
(*Suby of* ESMARK CORP) ★
10635 Marina Dr, Olive Branch, MS 38654-3711
Tel (662) 895-9191 *Founded/Ownrshp* 2003
Sales 27.8MM^E *EMP* 55
SIC 5144 5147 5143 4214 Poultry: live, dressed or frozen (unpackaged); Meats & meat products; Meats, fresh; Dairy products, except dried or canned; Butter; Cheese; Local trucking with storage
Pr: Thomas M Mattingly
VP: Donna Gaines
**VP:* David F Mattingly
Exec: Scott Cain
Sls&Mrk Ex: Shaun McCormack
Mktg Dir: Keenan Dodson

METRO FORD
See M GRIECO ENTERPRISES INC

D-U-N-S 02-987-3205 EXP
METRO FORD INC
2860 S Noland Rd, Independence, MO 64055-1343
Tel (816) 254-9800 *Founded/Ownrshp* 1978
Sales 37.2MM^E *EMP* 105
SIC 5511 7514 Automobiles, new & used; Passenger car rental; Automobiles, new & used; Passenger car rental
Pr: Robert Hewlett
Treas: Allen E Wigrs
**Sec:* Allen E Wiegers
Sales Exec: Cory Thompson

D-U-N-S 03-246-9140 IMP/EXP
METRO FORD INC
9000 Nw 7th Ave, Miami, FL 33150-2396
Tel (305) 751-9711 *Founded/Ownrshp* 1983
Sales 39.1MM^E *EMP* 98
SIC 5511 Automobiles, new & used; Pickups, new & used; Vans, new & used; Automobiles, new & used; Pickups, new & used; Vans, new & used
Pr: Lombardo Perez
VP: Luiz Andrade
**VP:* Lombardo Perez Jr
Exec: Adys Garcia
Genl Mgr: Danny Marks
Mktg Mgr: Oneil Hernadez
Sls Mgr: Jesus Alvarez
Sls Mgr: Paul Collins

METRO FORD OF OKC
See M&N DEALERSHIPS XII LLC

D-U-N-S 11-417-3578
METRO FORD SALES & SERVICE INC
6455 S Western Ave, Chicago, IL 60636-2487
Tel (773) 776-7600 *Founded/Ownrshp* 1986
Sales 27.3MM^E *EMP* 65
SIC 5511 7515 5521 Automobiles, new & used; Pickups, new & used; Passenger car leasing; Used car dealers; Automobiles, new & used; Pickups, new & used; Passenger car leasing; Used car dealers
Pr: Patrick Milligan
Off Mgr: Marvin Pinkney

D-U-N-S 01-319-1861 EXP
METRO FORD SALES INC
3601 State St, Schenectady, NY 12304-4296
Tel (518) 382-1010 *Founded/Ownrshp* 1980
Sales 48.1MM^E *EMP* 115
SIC 5511 5012 7532 5531 5521 7538 Automobiles, new & used; Pickups, new & used; Automobiles & other motor vehicles; Automobiles; Trucks, noncommercial; Top & body repair & paint shops; Automotive & home supply stores; Used car dealers; General automotive repair shops; Automobiles, new & used; Pickups, new & used; Automobiles & other motor vehicles; Automobiles; Trucks, noncommercial; Top & body repair & paint shops; Automotive & home supply stores; Used car dealers; General automotive repair shops
Pr: David Dariano
**CEO:* Leonard J Dariano
**VP:* James S De Nooyer

D-U-N-S 08-932-0196
METRO GROUP INC
METRO STEEL
3150 W 900 S, Salt Lake City, UT 84104-4535
Tel (801) 328-2051 *Founded/Ownrshp* 1976
Sales 30.2MM^E *EMP* 95^E
SIC 4731 5051 5093 3341 3312

METRO HARDWOODS
See MIDWEST HARDWOOD CORP

D-U-N-S 08-233-8716
METRO HEALTH CENTER INC
METRO HEALTH CTR SKILLED NRSNG
4310 Richmond Rd, Highland Hills, OH 44122
Tel (216) 464-9500 *Founded/Ownrshp* 1938
Sales 6.7MM^E *EMP* 400
SIC 8051 Skilled nursing care facilities; Skilled nursing care facilities
Exec: Christine Begovic
Exec: Donald Milliron

METRO HEALTH CTR SKILLED NRSNG
See METRO HEALTH CENTER INC

D-U-N-S 00-214-5675
METRO HEALTH FOUNDATION OF MASSACHUSETTS INC (GA)
389 Alden Rd, Fairhaven, MA 02719-4451
Tel (508) 991-8600 *Founded/Ownrshp* 1997
Sales 26.6MM *EMP* 420
Accts Larsonallen Llp Quincy Ma
SIC 8051 Skilled nursing care facilities; Skilled nursing care facilities
Pr: A Jason Geisinger
**Sec:* Jonathan Neagle
Ex VP: Brian Jepson

METRO HEALTH HOSPITAL
See METROPOLITAN HOSPITAL

D-U-N-S 09-225-4106
METRO HEATING AND AIR CONDITIONING INC
SERVICEMASTER CONSMR SERVCS
(*Suby of* SERVICEMASTER CONSUMER SERVICES LIMITED PARTNERSHIP) ★
517 Pylon Dr, Raleigh, NC 27606-1414
Tel (919) 828-5147 *Founded/Ownrshp* 1999
Sales 26.7MM^E *EMP* 359
SIC 1711 Warm air heating & air conditioning contractor; Ventilation & duct work contractor; Warm air heating & air conditioning contractor; Ventilation & duct work contractor
Pr: Brett Chappell
CFO: Dave Dombrowski

METRO HONDA
See METRO MOTORS INC

METRO HONDA
See METRO MOTORS INC

METRO I L A FRINGE BENEFIT FUN
See METROPOLITAN MARINE MAINTENANCE CONTRACTORS ASSOCIATION INC

D-U-N-S 04-841-7992
METRO IMPORTS INC
METRO TOYOTA
13775 Brookpark Rd, Cleveland, OH 44142-1826
Tel (440) 933-7915 *Founded/Ownrshp* 1969
Sales 36.8MM^E *EMP* 90
SIC 5511 Automobiles, new & used; Automobiles, new & used
Pr: Jerald B Schneider
**Sec:* Richard Greenfield
**VP:* Martin Schneider

D-U-N-S 87-621-4834
METRO INFECTIOUS DISEASE CONSULTANTS LLC
MIDC
901 Mcclintock Dr Ste 202, Burr Ridge, IL 60527-0872
Tel (888) 220-6432 *Founded/Ownrshp* 1994
Sales 25.2MM^E *EMP* 180
SIC 8011 Offices & clinics of medical doctors
Pr: Russell Petrak
Treas: Pat Fooliard
**VP:* Nancy Stanton
Genl Mgr: Erin Kelly
Doctor: James Allen MD
Doctor: Elisabeth Cormier

D-U-N-S 80-303-5443
METRO INFINITI INC
821 E Central Ave, Monrovia, CA 91016-4277
Tel (626) 599-7510 *Founded/Ownrshp* 1993
Sales 61.4MM *EMP* 50
SIC 5511 Automobiles, new & used; Automobiles, new & used
CEO: John Hales Hawkins

D-U-N-S 11-740-2594
METRO IRRIGATION SUPPLY CO LTD
1622 Rogers Rd, Fort Worth, TX 76107-6514
Tel (817) 654-2061 *Founded/Ownrshp* 1983
Sales 37.8MM^E *EMP* 46
SIC 5083 Irrigation equipment
Pt: Kelly McColm

METRO LEASING COMPANY
See AMERICAN NATIONAL BANK

METRO LEXUS
See KW 1 ACQUISITION CO LLC

D-U-N-S 05-791-7536 IMP
■ **METRO MACHINE CORP**
GENERAL DYNMICS NASSCO-NORFOLK
(*Suby of* GENERAL DYNAMICS CORP) ★
200 Ligon St, Norfolk, VA 23523-1000
Tel (757) 543-6801 *Founded/Ownrshp* 2011
Sales 195.7MM^E *EMP* 1,049
SIC 3731 Shipbuilding & repairing; Military ships, building & repairing; Shipbuilding & repairing; Military ships, building & repairing
Pr: Frederick J Harris
**Treas:* David H Fogg
VP: Henry Bose
VP: Dave Carver
VP: Bill Pope
Genl Mgr: Dave Baker
Genl Mgr: Carleton Bryant
Genl Mgr: Rod Douglas
**Genl Mgr:* John Strem
QA Dir: Bryan Solomon
IT Man: Nate Fowler

D-U-N-S 15-738-0437
METRO MANAGEMENT & DEVELOPMENT INC
4225 21st St, Long Island City, NY 11101-4906
Tel (718) 706-7755 *Founded/Ownrshp* 1985
Sales 20.6MM^E *EMP* 70^E
SIC 6552 6531 Subdividers & developers; Real estate managers
Pr: Jeffrey Glatzer
**Ch:* Davd Baron
VP: Victor Fuerst
Genl Mgr: Branka Lezaja

D-U-N-S 01-200-1231
METRO MASONRY INC
9499 Cordova Park Rd, Cordova, TN 38018-6569
Tel (901) 737-7001 *Founded/Ownrshp* 2003
Sales 3.0MMM *EMP* 32
SIC 1741 Masonry & other stonework
Pr: Andy Vanderwerf
VP: Lisa Vanderwerf

METRO MATERIALS
See DESERT CONCRETE CO

D-U-N-S 16-252-1090 IMP/EXP
METRO MATTRESS CORP
3545 John Glenn Blvd, Syracuse, NY 13209-1828
Tel (315) 218-1200 *Founded/Ownrshp* 1976
Sales 38.1MM^E *EMP* 175
SIC 5712 Beds & accessories; Beds & accessories
CEO: Dave Shiroff
Pr: Valerie Stewart
**COO:* Albert Meilutis
**CFO:* Jason Mehl
VP Mktg: Robin Moore

D-U-N-S 93-320-0339
METRO MECHANICAL INC
1385 Industrial Dr, Bolton, MS 39041-3229
Tel (601) 866-9050 *Founded/Ownrshp* 1994
Sales 22.0MM^E *EMP* 100^E
SIC 1711 3312 Warm air heating & air conditioning contractor; Ventilation & duct work contractor; Plate, sheet & strip, except coated products; Warm air heating & air conditioning contractor; Ventilation & duct work contractor; Plate, sheet & strip, except coated products
Pr: Frank White
**CFO:* Richard White
VP: Jason Jeringan
**VP:* Bryan Phillips
Dept Mgr: Scott Shiflett
Off Mgr: Lynda Bonner

D-U-N-S 13-942-2950
METRO MEDICAL EQUIPMENT & SUPPLY INC
1600 N Warson Rd, Saint Louis, MO 63132-1028
Tel (314) 383-2879 *Founded/Ownrshp* 1985
Sales 51.3MM *EMP* 10
SIC 5047 Medical equipment & supplies; Medical equipment & supplies
Pr: Karen Moore
VP: Joshua Stevenson

METRO MEDICAL SUPPLY
See ASHLEY MEDICAL SUPPLY INC

METRO METAL SALES
See TRIAMERICA STEEL RESOURCES LLC

D-U-N-S 55-711-7702 IMP/EXP
METRO METALS NORTHWEST INC
5611 Ne Columbia Blvd, Portland, OR 97218-1237
Tel (503) 287-8861 *Founded/Ownrshp* 1991
Sales 131.0MM^E *EMP* 250
SIC 5093 Metal scrap & waste materials; Metal scrap & waste materials
Pr: Victor Winkler
VP: Neil Fitzpatrick
Dir IT: Mike Wyant
Mktg Dir: Dave Grill

D-U-N-S 06-285-1068 IMP
METRO MOLD & DESIGN INC
20600 County Road 81, Rogers, MN 55374-9567
Tel (763) 428-8310 *Founded/Ownrshp* 1973
Sales 78.2MM^E *EMP* 230^E
SIC 3544 Forms (molds), for foundry & plastics working machinery; Forms (molds), for foundry & plastics working machinery
CEO: Timothy S Holland
COO: Tony Nuss
**CFO:* Greg Heinemann
Treas: Carol Holland
VP: Michael Glynn
**VP:* Tom Holland
Dir IT: Ken Peluf
Opers Mgr: John Proulx
Ql Cn Mgr: Dan Ciatti
Ql Cn Mgr: Donna Luehring
S&M/VP: John Gilles

D-U-N-S 79-271-0147
METRO MOTORS INC
METRO HONDA
9399 Autoplex St, Montclair, CA 91763-2300
Tel (909) 542-9646 *Founded/Ownrshp* 1989
Sales 52.5MM^E *EMP* 145
SIC 5511 Automobiles, new & used; Automobiles, new & used
CEO: John H Hawkins
**CEO:* John H Hales
Genl Mgr: Jeff J Proctor
Sls Mgr: David Buckingham
Sls Mgr: John Laine
Sls Mgr: Kevin Wange

D-U-N-S 92-717-0985
METRO MOTORS INC
METRO HONDA
1880 Hartford Ave, Johnston, RI 02919-3243
Tel (401) 553-6000 *Founded/Ownrshp* 1995
Sales 24.5MM^E *EMP* 55^E
SIC 5511 Automobiles, new & used; Automobiles, new & used
Pr: Michael Grieco Jr
Genl Mgr: Sergio Cuellar
Sls Mgr: Ritchie Allman

D-U-N-S 07-919-8877
METRO NASHVILLE DAVIDSON COUNTY SCHOOL DISTRICT
2601 Bransford Ave, Nashville, TN 37204-2811
Tel (615) 259-4636 *Founded/Ownrshp* 2013
Sales 68.5MM^E *EMP* 7,187^E
SIC 8221 Colleges universities & professional schools

D-U-N-S 08-268-9258
METRO NATIONAL CORP
METRONATIONAL COMMERCIAL LAND
945 Bunker Hill Rd # 400, Houston, TX 77024-1358
Tel (713) 973-6400 *Founded/Ownrshp* 1955
Sales 115.7MM^E *EMP* 600
SIC 6512 6531 6722 Nonresidential building operators; Real estate managers; Management investment, open-end; Nonresidential building operators; Real estate managers; Management investment, open-end
CEO: Roy F Johnson
**Pr:* David Kelley
**CFO:* Charles Delacey
**Ex VP:* Perry Hicks
**Sr VP:* William M Mosley Jr
**Sr VP:* Randy Nerren
VP: Clarence Mendel
Dir Sec: Bob Ruiz
Opers Mgr: Jeff Johnson
Snr Mgr: Johnny Spencer

D-U-N-S 17-652-6275
■ **METRO NETWORKS INC**
(*Suby of* WESTWOOD ONE INC) ★
20880 Stone Oak Pkwy, San Antonio, TX 78258-7460
Tel (713) 407-6000 *Founded/Ownrshp* 1999
Sales 22.6MM^E *EMP* 515
SIC 8748 7383 Business consulting; News syndicates; Business consulting; News syndicates
Pr: Chuck Bortnick
Admn Mgr: Joan Ravier
Natl Sales: Courtney Washbrook
Board of Directors: Dana Hall

D-U-N-S 03-795-8899
METRO NEWS SERVICE INC
918 N Dallas Ave, Lancaster, TX 75146-1616
Tel (972) 227-6170 *Founded/Ownrshp* 1975
Sales 15.3MM^E *EMP* 281
SIC 7389 Telemarketing services; Telemarketing services
Pr: Horace W Southward
**VP:* Eric Southward
VP: Kathryn Southward
IT Man: Bryan Jarvis

METRO NISSAN
See ONTARIO NISSAN INC

METRO NISSAN OF MONTCLAIR
See NEW AGE INVESTMENTS INC

METRO NISSAN OF REDLANDS
See NISSAN OF FONTANA INC

D-U-N-S 11-964-5567
METRO ONE LOSS PREVENTION SERVICES GROUP (GUARD DIVISION NY) INC
900 South Ave, Staten Island, NY 10314-3418
Tel (718) 370-3232 *Founded/Ownrshp* 2001
Sales 21.6MM^E *EMP* 850^E
SIC 7381 Guard services; Guard services
Pr: Vincent Carrabba
**VP:* Brandon Carrabba
VP: John Fevelo
Dir Bus: Mark Warfield

D-U-N-S 60-511-4867
▲ **METRO ONE TELECOMMUNICATIONS INC**
1331 Nw Lovejoy St # 900, Portland, OR 97209-2799
Tel (503) 643-9500 *Founded/Ownrshp* 1989
Sales 37.1MM^E *EMP* 632^E
Tkr Sym INFO *Exch* OTC
SIC 7389 7311 Telephone services; Advertising agencies; Telephone services; Advertising agencies
Pr: James F Hensel
**Ch Bd:* Kenneth D Peterson Jr
CFO: William K Hergenhan
Ex VP: Alexander Stevenson
Sr VP: L Lynne Michaelson
Sr VP: John S Miller
VP: Janice Aday
VP: Jack Blesener
VP: R Tod Hutchinson
VP: Michael McCourt
VP: Steven McGavran
VP: Beverley Messenger
Board of Directors: Jonathan A Ater, Richard B Keller II, Mary H Oldshue

D-U-N-S 08-892-0314
METRO OPTICAL SOLUTIONS INC
1129 E Quarry View Way, Sandy, UT 84094-7710
Tel (917) 940-3468 *Founded/Ownrshp* 2001
Sales 50.0MM *EMP* 5^E
SIC 8748 Telecommunications consultant; Telecommunications consultant
Pr: Andrew Hornig

D-U-N-S 00-162-6266
METRO PACKAGING & IMAGING INC
5 Haul Rd, Wayne, NJ 07470-6624
Tel (973) 709-9100 *Founded/Ownrshp* 1964, 1987
Sales 37.3MM^E *EMP* 120
Accts Sax Macy Fromm & Co Pc
SIC 2752 2657 2796 Commercial printing, lithographic; Folding paperboard boxes; Color separations for printing; Commercial printing, lithographic; Folding paperboard boxes; Color separations for printing
Pr: Armand De Torres
**CFO:* Manuel De Torres
**CFO:* Alan Shandler
**VP:* Alicia De Torres
Sfty Mgr: Leo McLaughlin
Opers Mgr: Jon Giovanniello

D-U-N-S 00-580-4690 IMP
METRO PAPER INDUSTRIES OF NY INC
695 W End Ave, Carthage, NY 13619-1055
Tel (315) 493-3010 *Founded/Ownrshp* 2000
Sales 56.1MM^E *EMP* 65
SIC 5113 Industrial & personal service paper; Industrial & personal service paper
Pr: Karim Jadavji
Off Mgr: Paul Brown

D-U-N-S 05-290-2855
METRO PARK WAREHOUSES INC (MO)
METROPARK WAREHOUSES
6920 Executive Dr, Kansas City, MO 64120-2111
Tel (816) 231-0777 *Founded/Ownrshp* 1964
Sales 48.1MM^E *EMP* 250
Accts Bkd Llp Kansas City Mo
SIC 4225 General warehousing; General warehousing
Ch: Donald R Patterson
**Pr:* Robert Banach
Bd of Dir: Jim Sageser
**VP:* Dolores Wedlan
IT Man: Roger Turner
Opers Mgr: Roger Mushinski
VP Mktg: Steve Wedlan

D-U-N-S 96-327-4951
METRO PARKING CORP
PARKSAFE SYSTEMS
8300 Nw 7th Ave, North Miami Beach, FL 33160
Tel (305) 579-5300 *Founded/Ownrshp* 2010
Sales 200.0MM *EMP* 10
SIC 7521 4119 Automobile parking; Local passenger transportation; Automobile parking; Local passenger transportation
Pr: Elliot Alexander
**Pr:* Sao Mya Nwe
**VP:* Myat Maung
**VP:* Mario Nyat
Genl Mgr: Mario Maung

METRO PARKS
See COLUMBUS & FRANKLIN COUNTY METROPOLITAN PARK DISTRICT

METRO PARKS TACOMA
See METROPOLITAN PARK DISTRICT OF TACOMA

D-U-N-S 00-209-0046
METRO PAVING CORP (DC)
5470 Lafayette Pl, Hyattsville, MD 20781-2347
Tel (301) 454-8111 *Founded/Ownrshp* 1994
Sales 24.1MM^E *EMP* 105
SIC 1611 1542 Highway & street paving contractor; Commercial & office buildings, renovation & repair; Highway & street paving contractor; Commercial & office buildings, renovation & repair
Pr: Mitchell Otero
VP: Stephen Fye
VP: Manny Rodriguez

D-U-N-S 07-957-2202 IMP
METRO PLASTICS TECHNOLOGIES INC
9175 E 146th St, Noblesville, IN 46060-4310
Tel (317) 776-0860 *Founded/Ownrshp* 1975
Sales 28.4MM^E *EMP* 80
SIC 3089 Injection molding of plastics
Pr: Lindsey R Hahn
**VP:* Alice L Hahn
Ql Cn Mgr: Chuck Forrestal

D-U-N-S 96-583-2004
METRO PONCE INC
HOSPITAL METROPOLITA
2435 Blvd Luis A Ferre, Ponce, PR 00717-2112
Tel (787) 848-5600 *Founded/Ownrshp* 2008
Sales 9.7MM^E *EMP* 450
SIC 8082 8062 Home health care services; General medical & surgical hospitals; Home health care services; General medical & surgical hospitals
CEO: Eduardo Artau
**Sr VP:* Jamie Rivera

D-U-N-S 15-206-0398
METRO PRODUCE DISTRIBUTORS INC
2700 E 28th St Ste B, Minneapolis, MN 55406-1575
Tel (612) 722-5575 *Founded/Ownrshp* 1986
Sales 48.9MM^E *EMP* 100
SIC 5148 Fresh fruits & vegetables; Fresh fruits & vegetables
Pr: Robert A Spizman
**Sec:* Raleigh Spizman
**VP:* Brad Anderson

D-U-N-S 06-437-7864
METRO READY MIX CONCRETE LLC (TN)
(*Suby of* HARPER INDUSTRIES INC) ★
1136 2nd Ave N, Nashville, TN 37208-1702
Tel (615) 255-1900 *Founded/Ownrshp* 1987
Sales 26.1MM^E *EMP* 190
SIC 3273 5032 Ready-mixed concrete; Sand, construction; Ready-mixed concrete; Sand, construction
Sales Exec: Tom Zoeller

D-U-N-S 79-393-2430
METRO READY MIX LLC
343 W 400 S, Salt Lake City, UT 84101-1707
Tel (801) 456-6833 *Founded/Ownrshp* 2004
Sales 29.1MM^E *EMP* 80
SIC 3273 Ready-mixed concrete; Ready-mixed concrete
**CFO:* Carl Crosser

D-U-N-S 07-777-9239
METRO REGIONAL TRANSIT AUTHORITY
416 Kenmore Blvd, Akron, OH 44301-1099
Tel (330) 762-0341 *Founded/Ownrshp* 1969
Sales 28.5MM^E *EMP* 365^E
SIC 4111 Local & suburban transit; Local & suburban transit
Ex Dir: Robert K Pfaff
**Pr:* Bernard Bear
**Pr:* Saundra Foster
**CFO:* Dean J Harris
Ofcr: Lori Stokes
**VP:* Scott C Meyer
Ex Dir: K Pfaff
Plng Mgr: Roger Bacon
Snr Mgr: Dehavilland Parrish

D-U-N-S 62-677-6038
METRO RESTAURANTS INC
4644 E Fort Lowell Rd, Tucson, AZ 85712-1111
Tel (520) 325-2797 *Founded/Ownrshp* 2000
Sales 17.1MM^E *EMP* 650
SIC 5812 Eating places; Eating places

Pr: Robert B McMahon
**CFO:* Gary Rasmussen

METRO RF
See R F METRO SERVICES INC

D-U-N-S 03-811-7222
METRO ROOFING & METAL SUPPLY CO INC
MRMSCO
805 16th Ave N, Nashville, TN 37203-4384
Tel (615) 327-3935 *Founded/Ownrshp* 1980
Sales 24.2MM[E] *EMP* 40[E]
SIC 5033 Roofing, asphalt & sheet metal
Prin: Robert Link
**Prin:* Karen Dickerson
**Prin:* Joyce Link
**Prin:* Kevin Link
**Prin:* Kim Schwind
Sls Mgr: Virgil Nelson

D-U-N-S 78-680-1571 IMP
METRO ROOFING SUPPLIES INC
69 Jefferson St, Stamford, CT 06902-5916
Tel (203) 359-2745 *Founded/Ownrshp* 1996
Sales 32.6MM[E] *EMP* 35
SIC 5033 Roofing & siding materials
Pr: Anthony Gerosa
**Treas:* Louis Nordt
**Sec:* Carl J Gerosa Jr
**VP:* Richard Broccoli
**VP:* Richard Santarsiero

D-U-N-S 06-478-4051
METRO SALES INC
1640 E 78th St, Minneapolis, MN 55423-4636
Tel (612) 861-4000 *Founded/Ownrshp* 1969
Sales 140.5MM[E] *EMP* 275
SIC 5044 5112 5065 7359 Office equipment; Duplicating machines; Typewriters; Stationery & office supplies; Computer & photocopying supplies; Facsimile equipment; Office machine rental, except computers; Office equipment; Duplicating machines; Typewriters; Stationery & office supplies; Computer & photocopying supplies; Facsimile equipment; Office machine rental, except computers
CEO: Jerry Mathwig
**VP:* Karen A Mathwig
MIS Dir: Wayne Ketter
Dir IT: Dan Macinnes
Dir IT: Vincent Queau
Sls Mgr: Tim Hannagan

D-U-N-S 04-402-0167
METRO SANITATION LLC
EXPRESS SERVICE
11400 Toepfer Rd, Warren, MI 48089-4031
Tel (586) 756-1006 *Founded/Ownrshp* 1998
Sales 53.2MM[E] *EMP* 80
SIC 4953 Refuse collection & disposal services

D-U-N-S 36-111-4549
METRO SEALANT WATERPROOFING SUP INC
7623 Fullerton Rd Ste B, Springfield, VA 22153-2815
Tel (703) 912-4915 *Founded/Ownrshp* 1989
Sales 21.6MM *EMP* 23
SIC 5169 Sealants; Sealants
Pr: David G Viar Jr
**Sec:* Karen Viar
**VP:* David G Viar III
Off Mgr: Kim Petitt

METRO SELF STORAGE
See METRO STORAGE LLC

D-U-N-S 80-072-6747
METRO SERVICE GROUP INC
9641 Old Gentilly Rd, New Orleans, LA 70127-4324
Tel (504) 520-8331 *Founded/Ownrshp* 1982
Sales 57.3MM[E] *EMP* 90
SIC 4953 Refuse collection & disposal services
Pr: Jimmy M Woods
**VP:* Glenn H Woods
Off Mgr: Wanda Bergeron
Sfty Dirs: Trudy Borne

METRO STEEL
See METRO GROUP INC

D-U-N-S 01-806-0942
METRO STORAGE LLC
METRO SELF STORAGE
13528 W Boulton Blvd, Mettawa, IL 60045-4501
Tel (847) 235-8900 *Founded/Ownrshp* 1997
Sales 62.9MM[E] *EMP* 155
SIC 4225 Warehousing, self-storage; Warehousing, self-storage
Pr: R K Kliebenstein
COO: Marty Gallagher
VP: Brian Blankenship
VP: Dennis Nixon
Mng Dir: Jay Harron
Off Mgr: Donna Strentz
IT Man: Scott Nemes

D-U-N-S 61-207-0367
METRO TECH SERVICE CORP
(*Suby of* REEDY INDUSTRIES INC) ★
1827 Walden Office Sq # 304, Schaumburg, IL 60173-4276
Tel (800) 886-7667 *Founded/Ownrshp* 1988
Sales 28.0MM[E] *EMP* 75
SIC 1711 Plumbing, heating, air-conditioning contractors
Pr: William P Reedy
**VP:* Thomas Bonnel
**Prin:* Edmond V Stack

D-U-N-S 17-777-5657
METRO TECHNOLOGY CENTERS
1900 Springlake Dr, Oklahoma City, OK 73111-5238
Tel (405) 424-8324 *Founded/Ownrshp* 1979
Sales 27.5MM[E] *EMP* 280[E]
SIC 8211 Public vocational/technical school; Public vocational/technical school
CEO: Elaine Stith
CFO: Bob Parish
VP: Patricia Means
Dir IT: Kevin Kitchen
Dir IT: Barbara Loudermilk
IT Man: Matt Gindhart

METRO TELE SALES
See CORFACTS INC

METRO TOOL & ABRASIVES
See MID-IOWA TOOLS INC

METRO TOYOTA
See METRO IMPORTS INC

D-U-N-S 11-602-9166
METRO TRANSPORT LLC
METROPOLITAN TRNSP SVCS
1300 Lydia Ave, Kansas City, MO 64106-3410
Tel (816) 471-6050 *Founded/Ownrshp* 1984
Sales 6.7MM[E] *EMP* 300
SIC 4141 4119 4121 Local bus charter service; Local passenger transportation; Limousine rental, with driver; Taxicabs; Local bus charter service; Local passenger transportation; Limousine rental, with driver; Taxicabs
Pr: Frank Genovese
**VP:* Patricia Miller
Exec: Mike Sinatra

D-U-N-S 08-238-5659
METRO UNITED WAY INC
334 E Broadway Ste 100, Louisville, KY 40202-1751
Tel (502) 583-2821 *Founded/Ownrshp* 1917
Sales 27.9MM *EMP* 63
SIC 8399 Fund raising organization, non-fee basis
Pr: Joe Tolan
**COO:* Gilbert Betz
**CFO:* Phillip Bond
**Ex VP:* Jennifer Adrio
**VP:* Mary Gwinne Daughtry
VP: Maggie Elder
**VP:* Randy Mc Queen
VP: Betsy Paulley
VP: Joe Phelps
Rgnl Mgr: Erica Price
MIS Dir: Dennis Renschler

D-U-N-S 61-214-2422
METRO VALLEY PAINTING CORP
659 E Main St, Mesa, AZ 85203-8767
Tel (480) 461-8181 *Founded/Ownrshp* 1990
Sales 8.9MM *EMP* 375
SIC 1721 Painting & paper hanging; Painting & paper hanging
Pr: Michael Dudley
CFO: Nancy Diepstraten
**Sec:* Ted Diepstraten
Plnt Mgr: Kevin Cavanaugh

D-U-N-S 09-755-6534
METRO VOLKSWAGEN INC
2035 W Airport Fwy, Irving, TX 75062-6006
Tel (972) 659-9999 *Founded/Ownrshp* 1979
Sales 27.2MM[E] *EMP* 70
SIC 5511 Automobiles, new & used; Automobiles, new & used
Pr: Robert E Hagestad
**VP:* Brad Hagestad
Sls Mgr: Weston King
Sls Mgr: Myles Kykta
Sls Mgr: Leanna Mohundro
Sls Mgr: Jesse Mulrein
Sls Mgr: Oscar Ramirez

D-U-N-S 06-520-1196
METRO WASTE AUTHORITY
300 E Locust St Ste 100, Des Moines, IA 50309-1864
Tel (515) 323-6519 *Founded/Ownrshp* 1969
Sales 23.2MM *EMP* 52
SIC 4953 Sanitary landfill operation; Sanitary landfill operation
Ex Dir: Tom Hadden
CFO: Grant Johnson
**CFO:* Ron Lacey
Prgrm Mgr: Rhonda Oconnor
Opers Mgr: Mike Fairchild
Pr Dir: REO Menning

D-U-N-S 07-995-6686
METRO WASTEWATER RECLAMATION DISTRICT
6450 York St, Denver, CO 80229-7407
Tel (303) 286-3000 *Founded/Ownrshp* 1966
Sales 218.6MM[E] *EMP* 350
Accts Cliftonlarsonallen Llp Denve
SIC 4952 Sewerage systems; Sewerage systems
Dist Mgr: Cathy Gerali
Ofcr: Scott AST
Ofcr: Mark Barela
Ofcr: Leo Gengler
Ofcr: Lisa Hollander
Ofcr: Barbara Wilson
Div Mgr: Orren West
CTO: Brenda Hungerford
Cmptr Lab: Glen Jones
Cmptr Lab: Rich Macaltine
Snr Mgr: Mike Daniels

D-U-N-S 06-142-1426
METRO WATER-PROOFING INC
2935 Alcove Dr, Scottdale, GA 30079-1136
Tel (404) 292-3460 *Founded/Ownrshp* 1972
Sales 61.7MM[E] *EMP* 350
SIC 1799 Waterproofing; Waterproofing
CEO: Clyde Strickland
**Pr:* Kenneth W Strickland
**Treas:* Sandra J Strickland
**VP:* Myron Bullock
**VP:* Leon D Strickland
**VP:* S Michael Strickland
**VP:* Timothy D Strickland
Snr PM: Jim Stasul

D-U-N-S 01-075-3960
METRO WEST AMBULANCE SERVICE INC (OR)
5475 Ne Dawson Creek Dr, Hillsboro, OR 97124-5797
Tel (503) 648-6658 *Founded/Ownrshp* 1953
Sales 20.3MM[E] *EMP* 300
SIC 4119 Ambulance service; Ambulance service
Pr: James D Fuiten
**VP:* Larry Boxman
**VP:* Erin Miller

D-U-N-S 02-169-0131
METRO WEST REHAB CORP
WHITTIER REHABILITATION HOSPIT
150 Flanders Rd, Westborough, MA 01581-1017
Tel (508) 871-2000 *Founded/Ownrshp* 1992
Sales 3.1MM *EMP* 300
SIC 8322 8069 Rehabilitation services; Specialty hospitals, except psychiatric; Rehabilitation services; Specialty hospitals, except psychiatric
Pr: Alfred L Arcidi
**VP:* Philip M Arcidi
Dir Rx: Leslie Garber

D-U-N-S 06-097-7840
METRO WIRE & CABLE CO
6636 Metropolitan Pkwy, Sterling Heights, MI 48312-1030
Tel (586) 264-3050 *Founded/Ownrshp* 1976
Sales 56.7MM[E] *EMP* 73
SIC 5063 Wire & cable; Electronic wire & cable; Power wire & cable; Wire & cable; Electronic wire & cable; Power wire & cable
Pr: Donald D Ezop
Sales Asso: Steven Hatala

D-U-N-S 10-113-3903
METRO-ATLANTA AMBULANCE SERVICE INC
595 Armstrong St Se, Marietta, GA 30060-2305
Tel (770) 693-8460 *Founded/Ownrshp* 1997
Sales 23.7MM[E] *EMP* 383
SIC 4119 Ambulance service; Ambulance service
CEO: Peter E Quinones
VP Opers: Lee Oliver
Opers Mgr: Danny Henderson
Snr Mgr: Marty Billings

METRO-BUICK OLDS
See REX MOTORS INC

D-U-N-S 02-341-4113
METRO-CLEAN CORP
936 W Greenfield Ave, Milwaukee, WI 53204-2899
Tel (414) 671-6660 *Founded/Ownrshp* 1925, 1965
Sales 4.1MM *EMP* 420
Accts Feld & Schumacher Company Llp
SIC 7349 Janitorial service, contract basis; Window cleaning; Janitorial service, contract basis; Window cleaning
Pr: Phillip J Shelby
**VP:* Jerry Willms
Area Mgr: Bobbie Gaines
Sales Exec: Kim Brown
VP Sls: Erin N Webber

D-U-N-S 96-828-6153
METRO-GOLDWYN-MAYER INC
MGM
(*Suby of* MGM HOLDINGS II INC) ★
245 N Beverly Dr, Beverly Hills, CA 90210-5319
Tel (310) 449-3000 *Founded/Ownrshp* 2005
Sales 68.8MM[E] *EMP* 1,440
SIC 7812 Motion picture production & distribution; Motion picture production & distribution, television; Television film production; Video production; Motion picture production & distribution; Motion picture production & distribution, television; Television film production; Video production
CEO: Gary Barber
COO: Ken Schapiro
CFO: Kenneth J Kay
Treas: Doug Finberg
Ex VP: Matt Davidson
Ex VP: Cheryl Rodman
Ex VP: Rebekah Rudd
Sr VP: Paul Bischoff
Sr VP: Gilberte Deturenne
Sr VP: Simon Graty
Sr VP: Shelley Reid
Sr VP: Megan Yeargin
VP: Matt Dines
VP: Erik Ellner
VP: Alan Feldman
VP: Andrew Landenberger
VP: Gayle Moore
VP: Mike Murashko
VP: Michael Naud
VP: Lamya Shelley
VP: Nan Staddon

D-U-N-S 00-699-1624
METRO-GOLDWYN-MAYER STUDIOS INC (DE)
MGM
(*Suby of* METRO-GOLDWYN-MAYER INC) ★
10250 Constellation Blvd, Los Angeles, CA 90067-6200
Tel (310) 449-3590 *Founded/Ownrshp* 1994
Sales 39.8MM[E] *EMP* 1,000
SIC 7812

D-U-N-S 10-112-6142
METRO-NORTH COMMUTER RAILROAD CO INC
METRO-NORTH RAILROAD
(*Suby of* M T A) ★
420 Lexington Ave, New York, NY 10170-0002
Tel (212) 878-7000 *Founded/Ownrshp* 1983
Sales 338.6MM[E] *EMP* 5,564
SIC 4013 4111 Switching & terminal services; Commuter rail passenger operation; Switching & terminal services; Commuter rail passenger operation
Pr: Howard Permut
Pr: Marjorie Anders
**Treas:* Robert Maclagger
**Sr VP:* George Walker
VP: Seth J Cummins
**VP:* Kim Porcelain
Counsel: Christine Loo
Snr Mgr: Mike Yaeger

METRO-NORTH RAILROAD
See METRO-NORTH COMMUTER RAILROAD CO INC

D-U-N-S 19-596-1388
METRO-TEX FABRICATORS INC
5107 Brooklglen Dr, Houston, TX 77017-5927
Tel (713) 473-3900 *Founded/Ownrshp* 1988
Sales 22.6MM[E] *EMP* 23
SIC 5085 5084 3498 5051 Valves & fittings; Industrial machinery & equipment; Fabricated pipe & fittings; Pipe & tubing, steel
Pr: Terry Delacerda
**VP:* Steve G Lowe

D-U-N-S 17-371-9022
METROBANK N A
9600 Bellaire Blvd # 101, Houston, TX 77036-4533
Tel (713) 776-3876 *Founded/Ownrshp* 2012
Sales NA *EMP* 284
SIC 6021

D-U-N-S 62-788-0453
METROCARE HOME SERVICES INC
120 W John St, Hicksville, NY 11801-1020
Tel (212) 689-7000 *Founded/Ownrshp* 1991
Sales 4.3MM[E] *EMP* 650
SIC 8082 Visiting nurse service; Visiting nurse service
Pr: William Schnell

METROCLEAN
See SOJI SERVICES INC

D-U-N-S 01-197-4057 IMP
METROCORP BANCSHARES INC
9600 Bellaire Blvd # 252, Houston, TX 77036-4500
Tel (713) 776-3876 *Founded/Ownrshp* 1998
Sales NA *EMP* 286
SIC 6022

METROFLEX FACILITY SERVICES
See METROPLEX FACILITY SERVICES INC

D-U-N-S 14-594-8860
METROGROUP CORP
(*Suby of* METROGROUP HOLDING LLC) ★
1805 E Washington St, Mount Pleasant, IA 52641-3206
Tel (319) 385-2284 *Founded/Ownrshp* 2008
Sales 98.4MM[E] *EMP* 1,260
SIC 7331 7389 Direct mail advertising services; Printers' services: folding, collating; Direct mail advertising services; Printers' services: folding, collating
Pr: Glen Marder
**Pr:* James Russel
CFO: Albert Strausser
VP: Brian D Bomberger
**VP:* Don McKevitt
VP: Chad Spannaus
CIO: Thomas J McAlister
IT Man: George Johnson

D-U-N-S 80-716-8849
METROGROUP HOLDING LLC
1805 E Washington St, Mount Pleasant, IA 52641-3206
Tel (319) 385-5135 *Founded/Ownrshp* 2005
Sales 117.5MM[E] *EMP* 1,260[E]
SIC 6719 Personal holding companies, except banks; Personal holding companies, except banks
Pr: Albert Strausser

D-U-N-S 09-034-9523
METROHEALTH INC
HOSPITAL METROPOLITANO
Carr 21 Km 4 3 Las Lomas St Ca, San Juan, PR 00922
Tel (787) 782-9999 *Founded/Ownrshp* 1998
Sales 44.8MM *EMP* 396
SIC 8062 General medical & surgical hospitals; General medical & surgical hospitals
Pr: Eduardo Artau Gomez

D-U-N-S 84-283-8161
METROHEALTH MEDICAL CENTER
METROHEALTH SYSTEM THE
2500 Metrohealth Dr, Cleveland, OH 44109-1900
Tel (216) 778-7800 *Founded/Ownrshp* 1837
Sales 782.2MM *EMP* 6,000[E]
SIC 8062 General medical & surgical hospitals; General medical & surgical hospitals
CEO: Ekran Boutros
**Pr:* Akram Boutros
**CFO:* Nancy Fisher
**CFO:* Craig Richmond
Dir Rad: Sampath Alapati
**Prin:* Sharon Sobol Jordan
**Prin:* J B Silvers PHD
Dir Sec: Tom Miller
Doctor: James C Finley
Diag Rad: Howard Potash

D-U-N-S 07-112-4291
METROHEALTH SYSTEM
2500 Metrohealth Dr, Cleveland, OH 44109-1900
Tel (216) 398-6000 *Founded/Ownrshp* 1953
Sales 859.8MM *EMP* 6,000
Accts Mcgladrey Llp Cleveland Oh
SIC 8062 General medical & surgical hospitals; General medical & surgical hospitals
CEO: Akram Boutros
COO: Ed Hills
COO: Daniel K Lewis
**CFO:* Sharon Dougherty
CFO: Craig Richmond
**VP:* John Carroll
**VP:* Fusilero Jane Rn
**VP:* Vince Miller
Assoc Dir: Melanie Stoltz
Dir Bus: Kathryn Milligan
Chf Nrs Of: Mavis Bechtle

METROHEALTH SYSTEM THE
See METROHEALTH MEDICAL CENTER

METROHM USA
See BRINKMANN INSTRUMENTS INC

D-U-N-S 07-105-8929 IMP
METROLINA GREENHOUSES INC (NC)
16400 Hntrsvle Concrd Rd, Huntersville, NC 28078-6650
Tel (704) 659-9400 *Founded/Ownrshp* 1972
Sales 77.3MM^E *EMP* 650^E
SIC 0181 Flowers: grown under cover (e.g. greenhouse production); Flowers: grown under cover (e.g. greenhouse production)
Pr: Art Van Wingerden
Pr: Tom Vanwingrden
**CFO:* Michael Colitti
Exec: Richard Oliver
Dir IT: Thomas Baird
Dir IT: Thomas Bard
Telecom Mg: Matthew Easley
IT Man: Thomas Brad
Sfty Mgr: Kerry Krivanek
Opers Mgr: Johnny Howie
S&M/VP: Sim McMurry

D-U-N-S 05-495-1061
METROLINA RESTAURANT GROUP LLC
WENDY'S
8040 Arrowridge Blvd # 200, Charlotte, NC 28273-5604
Tel (704) 525-3434 *Founded/Ownrshp* 1998
Sales 6.4MM^E *EMP* 500
SIC 5812 Fast-food restaurant, chain; Fast-food restaurant, chain

D-U-N-S 08-143-2726
METROLINA STEEL INC
11330 Vanstory Dr, Huntersville, NC 28078-8143
Tel (704) 598-7007 *Founded/Ownrshp* 1977
Sales 41.6MM^E *EMP* 53
SIC 5051 Structural shapes, iron or steel; Plates, metal; Tubing, metal; Sheets, metal
Pr: Thomas G Hurt
CFO: Mike Taylor
**VP:* Harry L Belk
**VP:* David B Hurt
Off Mgr: Mandy Hill

D-U-N-S 19-387-9962 EXP
METROLINE INC
2250 Meijer Dr, Troy, MI 48084-7111
Tel (248) 288-7000 *Founded/Ownrshp* 1986
Sales 28.2MM^E *EMP* 50
SIC 5065 5999 Telephone equipment; Telephone equipment & systems
Pr: Barry T Werthmann
**VP:* Anthony Mac

METROLINK
See SOUTHERN CALIFORNIA REGIONAL RAIL AUTHORITY

D-U-N-S 04-862-0462 IMP
■ **METROLOGIC INSTRUMENTS INC**
HONEYWELL
(*Suby of* HONEYWELL INTERNATIONAL INC) ★
90 Coles Rd, Mount Laurel, NJ 08054
Tel (856) 228-8100 *Founded/Ownrshp* 2008
Sales 127.4MM^E *EMP* 1,400
SIC 3577 3699 Magnetic ink & optical scanning devices; Optical scanning devices; Laser systems & equipment; Magnetic ink & optical scanning devices; Optical scanning devices; Laser systems & equipment
CEO: Darius Adamczyk
Pr: Dipanjan Deb
CFO: Kevin J Bratton
CFO: Michael Coluzzi
Ex VP: Joseph Sawitsky
Ex VP: Mark Schmidt
Sr VP: Mark C Shmidt
Sr VP: Jeffrey Yorsz
VP: Ed R Brown
VP: Leroy Dickinson
VP: Gregory Dinoia
VP: Bruce L Harrison
VP: Henri Juvanon
VP: Mark Ryan

METROLUBE
See NEW YORK COMMERCIAL LUBRICANTS INC

D-U-N-S 00-698-7630
METROMEDIA CO
BENNIGAN'S
810 Seventh Ave Fl 29, New York, NY 10019-5871
Tel (212) 606-4437 *Founded/Ownrshp* 1955
Sales 328.6MM^E *EMP* 29,500
SIC 5812 6794 4813 4911

D-U-N-S 17-439-9899 IMP
METROMEDIA TECHNOLOGIES INC
10 E 34th St Fl 9, New York, NY 10016-4327
Tel (212) 273-2100 *Founded/Ownrshp* 1990
Sales 47.9MM^E *EMP* 225
SIC 3577

D-U-N-S 07-887-0281
METROMILE INC
690 Folsom St Ste 200, San Francisco, CA 94107-1397
Tel (888) 244-1702 *Founded/Ownrshp* 2013
Sales NA *EMP* 70
SIC 6331 Automobile insurance
Ch Bd: David Friedberg
**CFO:* Joe Selsavage
**CFO:* Jose Mercado
CTO: Dan Preston

D-U-N-S 17-766-1394
METROMONT CORP
2802 White Horse Rd, Greenville, SC 29611-6119
Tel (804) 222-6770 *Founded/Ownrshp* 2003
Sales 125.0MM^E *EMP* 530
SIC 3272 Concrete stuctural support & building material; Concrete stuctural support & building material
Ch Bd: Richard Pennell
**Pr:* Richard H Pennell Jr
**CFO:* James H Medders
**VP:* Harry A Gleich
**VP:* James H Knight
VP: John Winkle
VP: Jeff Winters
Genl Mgr: Shawn Clark
IT Man: Betsy Geil
Opers Mgr: Chuck Gantt
Plnt Mgr: Mike Stiles

D-U-N-S 11-846-3475
METRON AVIATION INC
(*Suby of* AINA HOLDINGS) ★
45300 Catalina Ct Ste 101, Dulles, VA 20166-2335
Tel (703) 456-0123 *Founded/Ownrshp* 2005
Sales 37.4MM^E *EMP* 167^E
SIC 8748 7371 Systems analysis & engineering consulting services; Computer software development & applications; Systems analysis & engineering consulting services; Computer software development & applications
CEO: Dave Ellison
**Ch Bd:* Don Antonucci
**CFO:* John Young
**Sr VP:* Dave Basil
**Sr VP:* Alan Bloodgood
**Sr VP:* Norm Fujisaki
**Sr VP:* Mike Gundling
**Sr VP:* Carol Huegel
**Sr VP:* Terry Thompson
**VP:* Michael Antonucci
VP: Buzz Campo
VP: John De Wit
**VP:* Rick Ducharme
VP: Greg Feldman
**VP:* Michael Gundling
**VP:* Chip Hathaway
VP: William Sears
VP: Richard Sjogren

D-U-N-S 00-705-9298 IMP
METRON INC
1505 W 3rd Ave, Denver, CO 80223-1440
Tel (303) 592-1903 *Founded/Ownrshp* 2008
Sales 31.6MM^E *EMP* 85
SIC 3699 3613 Fire control or bombing equipment, electronic; Control panels, electric; Switchgear & switchgear accessories; Fire control or bombing equipment, electronic; Control panels, electric; Switchgear & switchgear accessories
CEO: Steven Ferrie
**VP:* Mike Hedges
VP Opers: Mark Shamley
Opers Mgr: Gary Walker

D-U-N-S 10-793-9233
METRON INC
1818 Library St Ste 600, Reston, VA 20190-6281
Tel (703) 467-5641 *Founded/Ownrshp* 1984
Sales 39.9MM^E *EMP* 141
SIC 8742 8733 8731 8711 Management consulting services; Scientific research agency; Commercial physical research; Engineering services; Management consulting services; Scientific research agency; Commercial physical research; Engineering services
CEO: Thomas L Mifflin
Pr: Huegel Carol
**Pr:* Thomas L Corwin
CFO: Duane Baker
**CFO:* Eric W George
CFO: Darryl Martin
CFO: Joseph McDermott
VP: Doug Danko
VP: Smith Janis
**Prin:* Tom A Stefanick
Prgrm Mgr: Andrew Morrison

METRONATIONAL COMMERCIAL LAND
See METRO NATIONAL CORP

METRONET
See CMN-RUS INC

D-U-N-S 96-275-8574
METROPADIA HEALTH SYSTEM INC
HOSPITAL METROPOLITANO
2445 Las America Ave, Ponce, PR 00731
Tel (787) 848-5600 *Founded/Ownrshp* 2010
Sales 20.3MM^E *EMP* 2,050
SIC 8062 General medical & surgical hospitals; General medical & surgical hospitals
Pr: Eduardo Arteau

D-U-N-S 14-501-7203 IMP/EXP
METROPARK USA INC
5750 Grace Pl, Los Angeles, CA 90022-4121
Tel (323) 622-3600 *Founded/Ownrshp* 2003
Sales NA *EMP* 1,200
SIC 5632 5699

METROPARK WAREHOUSES
See METRO PARK WAREHOUSES INC

D-U-N-S 83-508-8261 IMP
METROPCS WIRELESS INC
2250 Lakeside Blvd, Richardson, TX 75082-4304
Tel (214) 570-5800 *Founded/Ownrshp* 1994
Sales NA *EMP* 859
SIC 4812 4813 5999 Cellular telephone services; Local & long distance telephone communications; Telephone & communication equipment

D-U-N-S 19-131-2321
METROPLEX ADVENTIST HOSPITAL INC
METROPLEX HOSPITAL
2201 S Clear Creek Rd, Killeen, TX 76549-4110
Tel (254) 526-7523 *Founded/Ownrshp* 1978
Sales 89.1MM *EMP* 779
SIC 8062 General medical & surgical hospitals; General medical & surgical hospitals
Prin: Carlyle Walton
**Pr:* Kenneth A Finch
**CFO:* Robert Brock
Dir Rx: Steven McClure
Dir Rx: Scott Wood
Opers Mgr: George Efener
Mktg Dir: Robin Bodkin
Obsttrcn: Arturo Romero
Doctor: Hemalkumar Ramani
Doctor: George Rebecca MD
Nrsg Dir: Virginia Henderson

D-U-N-S 80-556-8644
METROPLEX DISTRIBUTION CORP
10739 W Little York Rd # 100, Houston, TX 77041-4074
Tel (713) 856-6170 *Founded/Ownrshp* 2007
Sales 28.2MM^E *EMP* 120
SIC 4731 Freight transportation arrangement; Freight transportation arrangement
Pr: David Pegany

D-U-N-S 09-544-6183 IMP
METROPLEX FACILITY SERVICES INC
METROFLEX FACILITY SERVICES
1184 Quaker St 88, Dallas, TX 75207-5604
Tel (214) 720-0345 *Founded/Ownrshp* 1978
Sales 28.0MM^E *EMP* 40
SIC 5021 Office furniture; Office furniture
Pr: John Courson
**Pr:* Christopher Jason Smith
**VP:* Elaine Stamford
IT Man: Beth Simmons
Sales Asso: Joan Coker

D-U-N-S 79-034-5656
METROPLEX HOLDINGS INC
15 Commerce Dr S, Harriman, NY 10926-3100
Tel (845) 781-5000 *Founded/Ownrshp* 1988
Sales 172.6MM^E *EMP* 230
SIC 6512 5149 5087 Nonresidential building operators; Groceries & related products; Restaurant supplies; Nonresidential building operators; Groceries & related products; Restaurant supplies
CEO: Peter R Grimm
**Ch Bd:* John Paterakis
**Pr:* Philip Praine

METROPLEX HOSPITAL
See METROPLEX ADVENTIST HOSPITAL INC

D-U-N-S 08-588-5176
METROPLEX INC
2 N La Salle St Ste 2300, Chicago, IL 60602-3975
Tel (312) 726-0083 *Founded/Ownrshp* 1977
Sales 4.0MM *EMP* 350
SIC 6531 Condominium manager; Cooperative apartment manager; Real estate agent, residential; Condominium manager; Cooperative apartment manager; Real estate agent, residential
Pr: Jane F Huynh
**VP:* Kathy Maggio
Off Mgr: Patricia Carey
VP Opers: John Kennedy

D-U-N-S 82-850-3230
METROPLEX MULTIFOODS INC
101 E Cherokee St, Jacksonville, TX 75766-4807
Tel (903) 586-1524 *Founded/Ownrshp* 2008
Sales 7.9MM^E *EMP* 377^E
SIC 5812 Eating places
Prin: Drew B Durrett

D-U-N-S 05-451-0149
METROPLEX THEATRES LLC (CA)
2275 W 190th St Ste 201, Torrance, CA 90504-6007
Tel (310) 856-1270 *Founded/Ownrshp* 1999
Sales 10.6MM^E *EMP* 600
SIC 7832 Motion picture theaters, except drive-in; Motion picture theaters, except drive-in

METROPLEX TOYOTA
See REDBIRD MOTOR VEHICLES INC

METROPLTAN CBINETS COUNTERTOPS
See METROPOLITAN CABINET DISTRIBUTORS CORP

METROPLTAN COUNCIL ENVMTL SVCS
See METROPOLITAN COUNCIL MINNESOTA

METROPLTAN MLROOM SVCS FAIRFAX
See METROPOLITAN HEALTHCARE SERVICES INC

METROPLTAN MLWAUKEE AUTO AUCTN
See WISCONSIN SERVICES CORP

D-U-N-S 83-551-5057
METROPLUS HEALTH PLAN INC
NEW YORK CITY HEALTH AND HOSPI
(*Suby of* NEW YORK CITY HEALTH AND HOSPITALS CORP) ★
160 Water St Fl 3, New York, NY 10038-5009
Tel (212) 788-3648 *Founded/Ownrshp* 1994
Sales NA *EMP* 540
SIC 6324 Health maintenance organization (HMO), insurance only; Health maintenance organization (HMO), insurance only
COO: Phillip Passantino
Sr VP: Estelita Mastelero
Assoc Dir: Stephen Catullo
Assoc Dir: Miriam Kelly
Dir Rx: Robert Walker
MIS Dir: Michael Mattola
Dir IT: James Genesi
Mktg Mgr: Vincent Adams
Mktg Mgr: Eddie Padilla

D-U-N-S 06-478-4267
METROPOLITAN AIRPORTS COMMISSION
MAC
6040 28th Ave S, Minneapolis, MN 55450-2701
Tel (612) 726-8100 *Founded/Ownrshp* 1943
Sales 298.3MM *EMP* 575
Accts Bkd Llp Indianapolis Indiana
SIC 4581 Airport; Airport
CEO: Jeffrey W Hamiel
**Ch:* Daniel Boivin
Ofcr: Bob Buth
Ofcr: Kevin Eldridge
Ofcr: Jennifer Micek
Ofcr: Brad Wingate
VP: Don Tritch
Ex Dir: Jeff Hamiel
Ex Dir: Janet Hielsen
QA Dir: Robert Hunter
IT Man: Shane Vandervoort

METROPOLITAN ALLOYS OF DETROIT
See MAC GROUP INTERNATIONAL INC

D-U-N-S 02-022-4135
METROPOLITAN AREA ADVISORY COMMITTEE ON ANTI-POVERTY OF SAN DIEGO COUNTY INC
M A A C PROJECT
1355 3rd Ave, Chula Vista, CA 91911-4302
Tel (619) 426-3595 *Founded/Ownrshp* 1965
Sales 20.6MM^E *EMP* 430
SIC 8331 8351 8748 Job training services; Head start center, except in conjunction with school; Energy conservation consultant; Job training services; Head start center, except in conjunction with school; Energy conservation consultant
CEO: Arnulfo Manriquez
**Pr:* Antonio Pizano
**CFO:* Austin Foye
Dir IT: Richard Gonzalez

METROPOLITAN ASSN FOR RETARDED
See ARC THRIFT STORES

D-U-N-S 06-450-0903 IMP/EXP
METROPOLITAN ATLANTA RAPID TRANSIT AUTHORITY
2424 Piedmont Rd Ne, Atlanta, GA 30324-3311
Tel (404) 848-5000 *Founded/Ownrshp* 1965
Sales 152.6MM *EMP* 4,700
SIC 4111

D-U-N-S 00-959-6214 EXP
METROPOLITAN AUTOMOTIVE WAREHOUSE
AUTO VALUE
535 Tennis Court Ln, San Bernardino, CA 92408-1615
Tel (909) 885-2886 *Founded/Ownrshp* 1953
Sales 412.6MM^E *EMP* 700
SIC 5013 Automotive supplies & parts; Automotive supplies & parts
CEO: John Spencer
COO: Richard Guyett
CFO: Chuck Siemer
VP: Pat Martin

D-U-N-S 00-939-2310
METROPOLITAN BANCGROUP INC
1661 Aaron Brenner Dr, Memphis, TN 38120-1468
Tel (901) 969-8000 *Founded/Ownrshp* 2007
Sales NA *EMP* 91^E
SIC 6022 State commercial banks
Pr: Curt Gebardi
CFO: Greg Barron
Ofcr: Brian Jordan
Mktg Dir: Josh Huff
Snr Mgr: William Madden

D-U-N-S 96-370-4916
METROPOLITAN BANK
(*Suby of* METROPOLITAN BANCGROUP INC) ★
201 S Jackson St, Crystal Springs, MS 39059-2863
Tel (601) 892-3232 *Founded/Ownrshp* 2010
Sales NA *EMP* 28^E
SIC 6021 National commercial banks
CEO: Daniel E McDill

D-U-N-S 94-652-5763
METROPOLITAN BUILDING SERVICES INC
1225 I St Nw, Washington, DC 20005-3914
Tel (202) 289-1300 *Founded/Ownrshp* 1986
Sales 9.5MM^E *EMP* 450
SIC 7349 7381 Janitorial service, contract basis; Security guard service; Janitorial service, contract basis; Security guard service
Pr: Teresa Febres

D-U-N-S 11-885-4322 IMP
METROPOLITAN CABINET DISTRIBUTORS CORP
METROPLTAN CBINETS COUNTERTOPS
505 University Ave, Norwood, MA 02062-2636
Tel (781) 949-8900 *Founded/Ownrshp* 1984
Sales 20.8MM^E *EMP* 120
SIC 2434 2541 Wood kitchen cabinets; Counter & sink tops
Pr: Stuart Elfland
Mfg Dir: Michael Imperatore

METROPOLITAN CERAMICS DIV
See IRONROCK CAPITAL INC

D-U-N-S 07-525-3872
METROPOLITAN COLLEGE OF NEW YORK
MCNY
431 Canal St, New York, NY 10013-1915
Tel (212) 343-1234 *Founded/Ownrshp* 1965
Sales 30.6MM *EMP* 310
Accts Nawrocki Smith Llp Melville
SIC 8221 College, except junior; College, except junior
Pr: Stephen Greenwald
**Sr VP:* Vincent Massaro
VP: Collette Garrity
**VP:* Lincoln Roney
**VP:* John Straumanis
Dir Soc: Anna Suarez
Adm Dir: Ronnie Johnson
Snr Sftwr: Herve Eichwald
CTO: Vadim Kern
Sftwr Eng: Kevin Gao
VP Mfg: Lisa Goren

D-U-N-S 07-478-7867
METROPOLITAN COMMERCIAL BANK
99 Park Ave Frnt 4, New York, NY 10016-1501
Tel (212) 659-0600 *Founded/Ownrshp* 2004
Sales NA *EMP* 93^E
SIC 6022 State commercial banks; State commercial banks
Pr: Mark R Defazio
Ex VP: Frank Skuthan
Sr VP: Laura Capra
Sr VP: Karen Rojeski
Sr VP: Kevin Smith
VP: David Caceres
VP: David Campos
VP: Mark Colyer
VP: Jake Danielski
VP: Dennis Graham
VP: Schneur Grossberger

VP: John Henry
VP: Edward Stoiber
Board of Directors: Maria F Ramirez, William P Reinhardt

METROPOLITAN COMMUNITY COLLEGE
See JUNIOR COLLEGE DISTRICT OF METROPOLITAN KANSAS CITY MISSOURI

D-U-N-S 12-053-2163
METROPOLITAN COMMUNITY COLLEGE
5300 N 30th St, Omaha, NE 68111-1610
Tel (402) 457-2400 *Founded/Ownrshp* 1977
Sales 22.0MM *EMP* 2,200
Accts Cliftonlarsonallen Llp Tucson
SIC 8222 Community college; Community college
Pr: Jo Ann C McDowell
Ex Dir: Todd Hansen
Prac Mgr: Eastwood Boardman
Admn Mgr: Julie Langholp
Genl Couns: James Thibodeau

D-U-N-S 05-471-4704
METROPOLITAN CONTRACT CARPETS INC (PA)
625 Chapel Ave E, Cherry Hill, NJ 08034-1407
Tel (856) 795-1177 *Founded/Ownrshp* 1956
Sales 26.4MM *EMP* 100
SIC 1752 Carpet laying
Pr: Frank Pelosi Jr
**Treas:* Joseph Pelosi
**VP:* Alice Pelosi
Div Mgr: Don Yoos
Opers Mgr: Joe Law

D-U-N-S 60-406-8700
METROPOLITAN CONTRACTING CO LLC
990 Isom Rd, San Antonio, TX 78216-4135
Tel (210) 829-5542 *Founded/Ownrshp* 1989
Sales 52.0MM *EMP* 50
SIC 1611 General contractor, highway & street construction
CEO: Timothy L Swan
**Pr:* Stephen Schuetze
**COO:* Jane Feigenbaum
Snr PM: Fernando Diego
Snr PM: Tom Lindell
Snr Mgr: Greg Curtis

D-U-N-S 08-978-1629
METROPOLITAN CORP
SUBURBAN CHEVROLET DIVISION
4350 Baker Rd Ste 230, Hopkins, MN 55343-8666
Tel (952) 947-5440 *Founded/Ownrshp* 1977
Sales 371.2M *EMP* 480
SIC 5511 Automobiles, new & used; Automobiles, new & used
Ch Bd: Thomas Grossman
**CFO:* Dave Norton

D-U-N-S 14-851-6651
METROPOLITAN CORP
BROOKDALE FORD
4350 Baker Rd Ste 230, Hopkins, MN 55343-8666
Tel (952) 893-1277 *Founded/Ownrshp* 1987
Sales 22.0MM^E^ *EMP* 105
SIC 5511 Automobiles, new & used; Automobiles, new & used
Ch: Thomas Grossman
VP: Dave Norton

D-U-N-S 03-001-8576
METROPOLITAN COUNCIL MINNESOTA
METROPLTAN COUNCIL ENVMTL SVCS
(*Suby of* EXECUTIVE OFFICE OF STATE OF MINNESOTA) ★
390 Robert St N, Saint Paul, MN 55101-1634
Tel (651) 602-1629 *Founded/Ownrshp* 1967
Sales NA *EMP* 1,234
Accts Rebecca Otto State Auditor S
SIC 9532 Urban planning & development commission, government; Rural planning & development agency, government; ; Urban planning & development commission, government; Rural planning & development agency, government;
Ch: Adam Duininck
V Ch: Steven Chavez
**CEO:* Tom Weaver
Ofcr: Richard Plato
Prin: Melba Hensel
Off Mgr: Tamara Rein
Plng Mgr: Jonathan Ehrlich
Sftwr Eng: Pete Owens
Genl Couns: Ann Bloodhart
Genl Couns: Sydnee Woods

METROPOLITAN COUNCIL ON JEWISH
See METROPOLITAN NEW YORK COORDINATING COUNCIL ON JEWISH POVERTY

D-U-N-S 07-208-6507
METROPOLITAN DEVELOPMENT & HOUSING AGENCY
M D H A
701 S 6th St, Nashville, TN 37206-3809
Tel (615) 252-8400 *Founded/Ownrshp* 1938
Sales NA *EMP* 315
SIC 9531 Housing agency, government; ; Housing agency, government;
Ch Bd: Chase Cole
**Ch Bd:* Ralph Mosley
**Treas:* James Harbison
**Treas:* Phil Ryan
Exec: Terri Woodmore
Ex Dir: Loretta Owens

METROPOLITAN DISTRIBUTORS
See CHARLES RIVER DISTRIBUTING CORP

D-U-N-S 04-918-2751
METROPOLITAN DISTRICT
WATER PLLUTION CTRL FACILITIES
555 Main St, Hartford, CT 06103-2915
Tel (860) 247-6487 *Founded/Ownrshp* 1929
Sales 107.5MM *EMP* 684
Accts Blum Shapiro & Company Pc
SIC 4941 4952 Water supply; Sewerage systems; Water supply; Sewerage systems
CEO: M Steven Rhodes
**CEO:* Steven Rhodes
**COO:* Dominic Digangi
COO: Scott Jellison
**Treas:* Stephanie Russo
Exec: James Randazzo
IT Man: Nelson Shick
Sftwr Eng: Allan Pelletier
Snr Mgr: Carl Bard
Snr Mgr: Chuck Gulioso

D-U-N-S 11-981-2162
METROPOLITAN DISTRICT COMMISSION MASSACHUSETTS
(*Suby of* MASSACHUSETTS EXECUTIVE OFFICE OF ENERGY & ENVIRONMENTAL AFFAIRS) ★
20 Somerset St, Boston, MA 02108-5302
Tel (617) 727-5114 *Founded/Ownrshp* 1985
Sales NA *EMP* 820
SIC 9511 9512 Air, water & solid waste management; ; Land, mineral & wildlife conservation; Recreational program administration, government; Air, water & solid waste management; ; Land, mineral & wildlife conservation; Recreational program administration, government

D-U-N-S 00-791-6836
■ **METROPOLITAN EDISON CO** (PA)
METED
(*Suby of* FIRSTENERGY CORP) ★
76 S Main St, Akron, OH 44308-1812
Tel (800) 736-3402 *Founded/Ownrshp* 1922
Sales 367.3MM^E^ *EMP* 678^E^
Accts Pricewaterhousecoopers Llp Cl
SIC 4911 Electric services; Generation, electric power; Distribution, electric power; Transmission, electric power; Electric services; Generation, electric power; Distribution, electric power; Transmission, electric power
Pr: Charles E Jones
CFO: Mark T Clark
Treas: James F Pearson
Ex VP: Leila L Vespoli
VP: Harvey L Wagner

D-U-N-S 17-548-2918
METROPOLITAN EDUCATION DISTRICT
760 Hillsdale Ave Bldg 6, San Jose, CA 95136-1106
Tel (408) 723-6464 *Founded/Ownrshp* 1982
Sales 14.2MM^E^ *EMP* 700^E^
SIC 8249 8331 Vocational schools; Job training & vocational rehabilitation services; Vocational schools; Job training & vocational rehabilitation services
VP: Ksmit Nelson
Exec: Althea Polanski

D-U-N-S 01-154-1364
METROPOLITAN ELECTRICAL CONSTRUCTION INC (CA)
2400 3rd St, San Francisco, CA 94107-3111
Tel (415) 550-6615 *Founded/Ownrshp* 1981
Sales 51.7MM *EMP* 210
Accts Jones Henle & Schunk Danvill
SIC 1731 General electrical contractor; General electrical contractor
CEO: Nick Dutto
**CFO:* Mark Friedeberg
CFO: Doug Snodgrass
Genl Mgr: Jack Minkel
Telecom Mg: Rebecca Ranes
Snr Mgr: Roy Cordero

D-U-N-S 07-991-0874
METROPOLITAN ENTERTAINMENT & CONVENTION AUTHORITY
MECA
455 N 10th St, Omaha, NE 68102-1151
Tel (402) 341-1500 *Founded/Ownrshp* 2015
Sales 41.8MM *EMP* 1^E^
SIC 7929 Entertainment service
Ex Dir: Roger Dixon

D-U-N-S 07-974-5246
METROPOLITAN FAMILY SERVICES (IL)
UNITED CHARITY OF CHICAGO
1 N Dearborn St Fl 10, Chicago, IL 60602-4322
Tel (312) 986-4000 *Founded/Ownrshp* 1857
Sales 55.5MM *EMP* 450
Accts Mcgladrey Llp Chicago Illino
SIC 8699 Charitable organization; Charitable organization
CEO: Ricardo Estrada
CFO: Dennis Hurley
**Ex VP:* Karina Ayala Bermejo
**Ex VP:* Colleen M Jones
**Sr VP:* G Dennis Conroy
VP: Thomas Remakel
Ex Dir: Audrena Spence
Prgrm Mgr: Jennifer Alexander
Opers Mgr: Don Pyznarski

METROPOLITAN FIBER
See PAPERTIGERS INC

D-U-N-S 61-208-6392
METROPOLITAN FOODS INC
DRISCOLL FOODS
174 Delawanna Ave, Clifton, NJ 07014-1550
Tel (973) 672-9400 *Founded/Ownrshp* 1971
Sales 460.6MM^E^ *EMP* 400^E^
SIC 5142 5149 2099 5141 Packaged frozen goods; Dried or canned foods; Food preparations; Food brokers; Packaged frozen goods; Dried or canned foods; Food preparations; Food brokers
Pr: Tim Driscoll
**Pt:* Martin Rapport
Exec: Nancy Cook
Sales Exec: Marty Eskow
Sales Exec: Gabe Raad
Sales Exec: Lisa Smith
Mktg Dir: Jim Liakas
Mktg Dir: Brian McCarron
Manager: Philip Margiotta
Sls Mgr: Edward Carey
Sls Mgr: John Humphrey

METROPOLITAN FREIGHT MGT
See METROPOLITAN TRUCKING INC

D-U-N-S 03-200-2644
METROPOLITAN GLASS INC
6400 Franklin St, Denver, CO 80229-7230
Tel (303) 853-4527 *Founded/Ownrshp* 1964
Sales 21.4MM^E^ *EMP* 85
SIC 1793 5039 Glass & glazing work; Glass construction materials
Pr: Mike Smith
**VP:* Gary Smith
Sfty Dirs: Rick Taylor

D-U-N-S 07-821-7668
METROPOLITAN GOVERNMENT OF NASHVILLE & DAVIDSON COUNTY
NASHVILLE, CITY OF
100 Metro Courthouse, Nashville, TN 37201
Tel (615) 862-5000 *Founded/Ownrshp* 1784
Sales NA *EMP* 18,000
Accts Crosslin & Associates Nashvil
SIC 9111 Executive offices; ; Executive offices;
COO: May Bennett
COO: Marilyn Monk
CFO: Randy Pirtle
Bd of Dir: Peter Westerholm
Ofcr: Theresa Palmer
Assoc Dir: Jim Charles
Assoc Dir: Tom Cross
Dir Sec: Norman Robinson
Sfty Mgr: Thomas Mitchell

D-U-N-S 00-553-6792
METROPOLITAN GRAPHIC ARTS INC
M G A
3818 Grandville Ave, Gurnee, IL 60031-2332
Tel (847) 566-9502 *Founded/Ownrshp* 1963
Sales 21.5MM^E^ *EMP* 45
SIC 2752 7331 2791 Commercial printing, offset; Mailing service; Typesetting
Pr: Joseph Szymanski
**Pr:* Gregory Szymanski
**Ex VP:* Karen Szymanski
**VP:* Brian Szymanski
VP: Gregg Wallace
Exec: Sandy Ekern
Opers Mgr: Ravi Dutt

D-U-N-S 03-937-0598
■ **METROPOLITAN GROUP PROPERTIES & CASUALTY**
(*Suby of* METLIFE) ★
700 Quaker Ln, Warwick, RI 02886-6681
Tel (401) 827-2400 *Founded/Ownrshp* 1991
Sales NA *EMP* 1,350
SIC 6331 6351 Property damage insurance; Liability insurance; Property damage insurance; Liability insurance
Pr: Catherine Rein
**Sr VP:* John S Lombardo

D-U-N-S 79-106-2271 IMP
METROPOLITAN HEALTH COMMUNITY SERVICES CORP
METROPOLITAN HOSPITAL OF MIAMI
5959 Nw 7th St, Miami, FL 33126-3129
Tel (305) 264-1000 *Founded/Ownrshp* 2006
Sales 51.6MM^E^ *EMP* 557^E^
SIC 8062 General medical & surgical hospitals; Hospital, medical school affiliated with nursing & residency
CEO: Eugenio Marini
**Pr:* Eduardo Artau
CFO: Vivian Acevedo
**Treas:* Eduardo Artau Feliciano
**VP:* Karen Artau Feliciano
VP: Miriam Sotolongo
Dir OR: Rick Gorgal
Dir Lab: Raul Bila
Dir Pat Ac: Norma Decardenas
CTO: Edgar Diaz
IT Man: Lystra John

D-U-N-S 94-132-6076 IMP
■ **METROPOLITAN HEALTH NETWORKS INC**
METCARE
(*Suby of* HUMANA INC) ★
2900 N Military Trl, Boca Raton, FL 33431-6365
Tel (561) 805-8500 *Founded/Ownrshp* 2012
Sales 68.3MM^E^ *EMP* 1,140
SIC 8011 Health maintenance organization; Health maintenance organization
CEO: John E Barger III
**Pr:* Bruce D Perkins
**CFO:* Robert J Sabo
**Chf Mktg O:* Luis H Izquierdo
**VP:* Joan O Lenahan III
Int Pr: Dan McCarthy
Off Mgr: Kathleen Bruscell

D-U-N-S 01-965-5446
METROPOLITAN HEALTHCARE SERVICES INC
METROPLTAN MLROOM SVCS FAIRFAX
555 Herndon Pkwy Ste 125, Herndon, VA 20170-5250
Tel (703) 481-0029 *Founded/Ownrshp* 1997
Sales 24.1MM^E^ *EMP* 500
SIC 8099 Health screening service; Health screening service
CEO: David Lentine
**COO:* Daniel Duchesne
**VP:* Kristen Lentine
**Prin:* Gerry Lillis

D-U-N-S 18-350-2152 IMP
METROPOLITAN HOME HEALTH PRODUCTS INC
METROSTAR
5353 Kings Hwy, Brooklyn, NY 11203-6704
Tel (718) 241-5102 *Founded/Ownrshp* 1998
Sales 21.5MM^E^ *EMP* 60
SIC 5047 7352 Medical & hospital equipment; Medical equipment rental
**Pr:* Steven Zakheim
**Ex VP:* Alexander S Balko
IT Man: Marcel Frankel
IT Man: Eli Potash
IT Man: David Winzelberg

D-U-N-S 07-928-8601
METROPOLITAN HOSPITAL
METRO HEALTH HOSPITAL
5900 Byron Center Ave Sw, Wyoming, MI 49519-9606
Tel (616) 252-7200 *Founded/Ownrshp* 1941
Sales 295.7MM *EMP* 2,100
SIC 8062 8069

D-U-N-S 10-553-1164
METROPOLITAN HOSPITAL CENTER ASSOCIATION INC
(*Suby of* NEW YORK CITY HEALTH AND HOSPITALS CORP) ★
1901 1st Ave, New York, NY 10029-7404
Tel (212) 423-6898 *Founded/Ownrshp* 1984
Sales 257.5MM^E^ *EMP* 3,000^E^
SIC 8062 General medical & surgical hospitals; General medical & surgical hospitals
Ex Dir: Meryl Weinberg
Chf Rad: Hussein Matari
**COO:* Elizabeth Guzman
Top Exec: Emmanuel Akinfeleye
Sr VP: Stanford A Roman Jr
Dir Rad: Matthew Taylor
**Ex Dir:* Dennis A Gowie
**Ex Dir:* Anthony Rajkunar
MIS Dir: Tamal Roy
QA Dir: Patricia Jones
Sfty Dirs: John Costello

METROPOLITAN HOSPITAL OF MIAMI
See METROPOLITAN HEALTH COMMUNITY SERVICES CORP

D-U-N-S 09-034-2874
METROPOLITAN INDUSTRIAL FOOD SERVICES INC
464 Ing Jose A Canals St, San Juan, PR 00918
Tel (787) 764-4111 *Founded/Ownrshp* 1970
Sales 10.4MM *EMP* 360
SIC 8741 Restaurant management; Restaurant management
Pr: Gerald Novarro

D-U-N-S 06-248-5149 IMP
METROPOLITAN INDUSTRIES INC
METROPOLITAN PUMP COMPANY
37 Forestwood Dr, Romeoville, IL 60446-1343
Tel (815) 886-9200 *Founded/Ownrshp* 1967
Sales 75.6MM^E^ *EMP* 130
SIC 3561 5064 7699 Pump jacks & other pumping equipment; Industrial machinery & equipment; Pump jacks & other pumping equipment; Water heaters, electric; Pumps & pumping equipment repair
Pr: John R Kochan Jr
VP: Diane Ahrendt
Off Mgr: Cindy Beckett
IT Man: Liz Miller
Sftwr Eng: Wayne Barkley
Mktg Dir: Joe Sanchez
Sls Mgr: Mike Ponx
Sales Asso: Dan Dore
Sales Asso: John Stanzi
Sales Asso: Neil Vogel

D-U-N-S 18-755-5966
■ **METROPOLITAN INSURANCE & ANNUITY CO**
METLIFE
(*Suby of* METLIFE) ★
1 Madison Ave Lbby, New York, NY 10010-3687
Tel (212) 578-2211 *Founded/Ownrshp* 1976
Sales NA *EMP* 3,001
Accts Deloitte & Touche Llp
SIC 6411 Insurance agents & brokers; Insurance agents & brokers
CEO: Robert Benmosche
Sr Cor Off: Allen Wheat
Chf Mktg O: Jeff Wilk
Ofcr: Mark A Schuman
Ex VP: John Dabek
Ex VP: William J Wheeler
Sr VP: William T Friedewald
Sr VP: Ira Friedman
Sr VP: Gene Lunman
Sr VP: David Monfried
VP: Jim Azzinaro
VP: Linda Bloniarz
**VP:* Susan Mary Ende
VP: Gary Fabian
VP: Daniel Flynn
VP: Liz Langone
VP: Theresa Maire
VP: Daniel M Mule
VP: Joseph Reali
VP: Tim Schmidt
VP: Carol Stewart

D-U-N-S 06-828-9149
METROPOLITAN JEWISH HEALTH SYSTEM FOUNDATION (NY)
440 9th Ave Fl 14, New York, NY 10001-1629
Tel (212) 356-5300 *Founded/Ownrshp* 1907
Sales 4.9MM *EMP* 544
SIC 8399 8082 8051 8062 Fund raising organization, non-fee basis; Home health care services; Skilled nursing care facilities; General medical & surgical hospitals; Fund raising organization, non-fee basis; Home health care services; Skilled nursing care facilities; General medical & surgical hospitals
CEO: Eli S Feldman
**Treas:* Isaac Assael
**VP:* Martin Simon

D-U-N-S 00-418-4896
METROPOLITAN JEWISH HEALTH SYSTEM INC (NY)
ALTIERI CAROL
6323 7th Ave Ste 2, Brooklyn, NY 11220-4742
Tel (718) 621-3600 *Founded/Ownrshp* 1995
Sales 71.9MM *EMP* 1,400
Accts Loeb & Troper Llp New York N
SIC 8322 Adult day care center; Adult day care center
CEO: Eli S Feldman
CFO: Michael Epstein
Ofcr: Anne Dawson
Ofcr: Derek Murray

Ex VP: Tom Early
Sr VP: Elliot Brooks
VP: Saiful Khan
VP: Lenard Parisi
VP: Esther Spiegeo
VP: David Wagner
VP: Mary Wagner
Dir Bus: Susan Lage

D-U-N-S 96-782-4306
METROPOLITAN JEWISH HOME CARE INC
MJHS HOSPICE AND PALLIATIVE CA
6323 7th Ave Ste 2, Brooklyn, NY 11220-4742
Tel (718) 921-7742 *Founded/Ownrshp* 2003
Sales 136.1MM *EMP* 103
Accts Loeb & Troper Llp New York N
SIC 8082 Home health care services
CFO: Alexander Balko

METROPOLITAN JEWISH HOSPICE
See MJG NURSING HOME CO INC

D-U-N-S 12-375-8393
METROPOLITAN JOINT BOARD UNITED
ILGWU LOCAL 23 25
275 7th Ave Rm 700, New York, NY 10001-6861
Tel (212) 929-2600 *Founded/Ownrshp* 1964
Sales 2.0MM *EMP* 500
SIC 8631 Labor unions & similar labor organizations; Labor unions & similar labor organizations
Pr: Bruce Reynor
**Pr:* Edgar Romney
Ex Dir: Joseph Fisher
Ex Dir: Jay Mazur

D-U-N-S 05-307-2831
METROPOLITAN KNOXVILLE AIRPORT AUTHORITY (TN)
MC GHEE TYSON AIRPORT
2055 Alcoa Hwy Ste I, Alcoa, TN 37701-3326
Tel (865) 342-3000 *Founded/Ownrshp* 1978
Sales 27.4MM *EMP* 140
Accts Coulter & Justus Pc Knoxvi
SIC 4581 Airport; Airport
Pr: William Marrison
VP Mktg: Jim Evans

D-U-N-S 09-477-5525
METROPOLITAN LIBRARY SYSTEM
DOWNTOWN LIBRARY
300 Park Ave, Oklahoma City, OK 73102-6499
Tel (405) 231-8650 *Founded/Ownrshp* 1965
Sales 37.5MM *EMP* 190
Accts Finley & Cook Pllc Shawnee
SIC 8231 7021 Libraries; Libraries; Rooming & boarding houses
Ex Dir: Tim Rogers
Dir Vol: Heidi Port
IT Man: Anne Fischer

D-U-N-S 00-698-7648
■ **METROPOLITAN LIFE INSURANCE CO (INC)** (NY)
METLIFE
(*Suby of* METLIFE INC) ★
2701 Queens Plz N Ste 1, Long Island City, NY 11101-4021
Tel (212) 578-2211 *Founded/Ownrshp* 2000
Sales NA *EMP* 46,000
SIC 6411 6324 6331 6321 6531 Insurance agents & brokers; Dental insurance; Fire, marine & casualty insurance: mutual; Property damage insurance; Health insurance carriers; Disability health insurance; Real estate brokers & agents; Insurance agents & brokers; Dental insurance; Fire, marine & casualty insurance: mutual; Property damage insurance; Health insurance carriers; Disability health insurance; Real estate brokers & agents
Ch Bd: C Robert Henrikson
**CFO:* William Wheeler
Ex VP: Steven Meyers
Sr VP: Daniel J Cavanagh
Sr VP: David Findley
Sr VP: Anne E Hayden
VP: Ed Barrett
VP: William Bigelow
VP: Alessandra Cox
VP: Diane Lund
VP: Salim Manzar
VP: Joe Massimo
**VP:* Catherine A Rein
VP: Harold Salmon
VP: Christina Teufel
VP: Edward Veazey
Assoc Dir: Eric Horan
Board of Directors: Hugh B Price, Curtis H Barnette, David Satcher, Burton A Dole Jr, William C Steere Jr, Cheryl W Grise, James R Houghton, R Glenn Hubbard, Harry P Kamen, Helene L Kaplan, John M Keane, Charles M Leighton

METROPOLITAN LUMBER & HARDWARE
See METROPOLITAN LUMBER HARDWARE & BUILDING SUPPLIES INC

D-U-N-S 07-882-8624 IMP/EXP
METROPOLITAN LUMBER & HARDWARE INC
246 Urb Country Clb, Carolina, PR 00982
Tel (787) 641-8200 *Founded/Ownrshp* 2009
Sales 71.8MM^E *EMP* 721
SIC 5251 Hardware; Hardware
Pr: Israel Kopel
**VP:* Steven Kopel

D-U-N-S 00-191-1460
METROPOLITAN LUMBER CO (IL)
4200 Cantera Dr Ste 205, Warrenville, IL 60555-3040
Tel (630) 393-2100 *Founded/Ownrshp* 1907, 1995
Sales 23.7MM *EMP* 7
Accts Voorhees & Associates Lombard
SIC 7389 5031 Log & lumber broker; Lumber: rough, dressed & finished; Log & lumber broker; Lumber: rough, dressed & finished
Pr: David F Engelhard
**Sec:* James Brown
**VP:* William E Brown

D-U-N-S 03-459-9779
METROPOLITAN LUMBER HARDWARE & BUILDING SUPPLIES INC
METROPOLITAN LUMBER & HARDWARE
617 11th Ave, New York, NY 10036-2015
Tel (212) 246-9090 *Founded/Ownrshp* 1979
Sales 95.2MM^E *EMP* 200
SIC 5031 5211 5251 Lumber: rough, dressed & finished; Lumber products; Hardware; Lumber: rough, dressed & finished; Lumber products; Hardware
Ch Bd: Robert Gans
**VP:* Spencer Simon

D-U-N-S 04-857-3646
METROPOLITAN MAINTENANCE CO INC
100 E Penn Ave Ste 200, Baltimore, MD 21286-0704
Tel (410) 837-2999 *Founded/Ownrshp* 1969
Sales 10.1MM^E *EMP* 380
SIC 7349 Janitorial service, contract basis; Janitorial service, contract basis
Pr: Wayne Winterstein
**Ch Bd:* Phillip E Ratcliffe
VP: Maribel Hofmann

D-U-N-S 07-105-1122
METROPOLITAN MARINE MAINTENANCE CONTRACTORS ASSOCIATION INC (NY)
METRO I L A FRINGE BENEFIT FUN
301 State Rt 17 Fl 7, Rutherford, NJ 07070-2599
Tel (201) 842-0202 *Founded/Ownrshp* 1947
Sales 41.5MM *EMP* 15
Accts Buchbinder Tunick & Company Ll
SIC 8631 Collective bargaining unit; Collective bargaining unit
Pr: J Randolph Brown
**Ex VP:* John Anastasio

D-U-N-S 13-721-4859
METROPOLITAN MARKET LLC
4025 Delridge Way Sw # 100, Seattle, WA 98106-1249
Tel (206) 284-2530 *Founded/Ownrshp* 1979
Sales 145.9MM^E *EMP* 850
SIC 5411 Grocery stores; Grocery stores
CEO: Terry Robert Halverson
CFO: Brett Miller
Sr VP: Helen Neville
**VP:* Gordon E Halverson
Exec: Angela Rihacek
Store Mgr: Terrie Corrie
VP Opers: Mike Barnhart
S&M/VP: Darrell Vannoy

D-U-N-S 04-177-9240
METROPOLITAN MECHANICAL CONTRACTORS INC
(*Suby of* API GROUP INC) ★
7450 Flying Cloud Dr, Eden Prairie, MN 55344-3582
Tel (952) 941-7010 *Founded/Ownrshp* 2011
Sales 161.1MM *EMP* 350
Accts Kpmg Llp Minneapolis Mn
SIC 1711 8711 Mechanical contractor; Warm air heating & air conditioning contractor; Plumbing contractors; Engineering services; Mechanical contractor; Warm air heating & air conditioning contractor; Plumbing contractors; Engineering services
Pr: Mark Anderson
VP: Tim Daly
VP: Robert Kaczke
Opers Mgr: Kevin Larson
Sales Exec: Mark Hill

D-U-N-S 07-349-4676
METROPOLITAN MEDICAL LABORATORY PLC
1828 E Locust St, Davenport, IA 52803-2038
Tel (563) 324-0471 *Founded/Ownrshp* 1914
Sales 29.1MM^E *EMP* 511
SIC 8071 Pathological laboratory; Pathological laboratory
Pt: Kimball Thompson
Pt: J K Billman Jr
Pt: J F Consamus
Pt: Karen Fitzsimmons
Pt: Ronald Frus
Pt: Christopher Hardy
Pt: Kathern Hart-Dittmer
Pt: Caroline Miller
Pathlgst: Sameena Ahmed

D-U-N-S 15-889-0319
METROPOLITAN MINISTRIES INC
2301 N Tampa St, Tampa, FL 33602-2144
Tel (813) 209-1000 *Founded/Ownrshp* 1972
Sales 21.2MM *EMP* 110
Accts Rivero Gordimer & Company Pa
SIC 8661 8322 Religious organizations; Individual & family services; Religious organizations; Individual & family services
Ex Dir: Rev Morris Hintzman
Pr: Tim Marks
CEO: Morris E Hintzman
COO: Andrea Harding
CFO: Ken Marinik
CFO: Phil Signore
Ofcr: Christine Long
VP: Karleen Koss
Exec: Brenda Keefe
Dir Case M: Karrie Roller
Prgrm Mgr: Dwayne Kinloch

D-U-N-S 08-017-0504
METROPOLITAN MORTGAGE LLC
10803 Se Kent Kangley Rd # 103, Kent, WA 98030-7194
Tel (253) 859-2300 *Founded/Ownrshp* 1999
Sales NA *EMP* 15
SIC 6162 Mortgage bankers & correspondents; Mortgage bankers & correspondents

METROPOLITAN MT PLTY & SEAFOOD
See METROPOLITAN POULTRY CO

D-U-N-S 07-526-2949 IMP
METROPOLITAN MUSEUM OF ART
1000 5th Ave Frnt, New York, NY 10028-0198
Tel (212) 879-5500 *Founded/Ownrshp* 1870
Sales 361.2MM *EMP* 2,372
Accts Pricewaterhousecoopers Llp Ne
SIC 8412 5999 Museum; Art, picture frames & decorations; Museum; Art, picture frames & decorations
Ch Bd: James R Houghton
V Ch: Parker S Gilbert
CFO: Olena Paslawsky
Ofcr: Kimberly Chey
Ofcr: Nancy Chilton
**Sr VP:* Emily Kernan Rafferty
**VP:* J Nicholas Cameron
**VP:* Sharon H Cott
**VP:* Harold Holzer
VP: Brady Myers
**VP:* Philip T Venturino
VP: Lisa Weber
Assoc Dir: Jennifer Russell

D-U-N-S 05-214-4318
METROPOLITAN NASHVILLE AIRPORT AUTHORITY
NASHVILLE INTERNATIONAL AIRPOR
1 Terminal Dr Ste 501, Nashville, TN 37214-4110
Tel (615) 275-1600 *Founded/Ownrshp* 1970
Sales 119.0MM *EMP* 275
Accts Crosslin & Associates Nashvil
SIC 4581 Airport; Airport
CEO: Raul L Regalado
**COO:* M O Burges
Sr VP: Doug Kreulen
VP: Frank Kirkbride
VP: Robert Ramsey
CIO: Vanessa Hiltz
CTO: Vanessa Hickman
IT Man: Lori Morse
IT Man: Audrey Neumann
Snr Mgr: Douglas Reece

D-U-N-S 10-007-3253
METROPOLITAN NASHVILLE PUBLIC SCHOOLS
HUMAN CAPITAL
2601 Bransford Ave, Nashville, TN 37204-2811
Tel (615) 259-4636 *Founded/Ownrshp* 1800
Sales 428.3MM^E *EMP* 10,500
SIC 8211 Public elementary & secondary schools; Public elementary & secondary schools
Bd of Dir: Will Pinkston
Dir Sec: James Wheeler
Pr Dir: Janel Lacy
Pr Dir: Woody McMillin
Instr Medi: Kelly McKinney
HC Dir: Nicole Proffitt

D-U-N-S 09-612-0456
METROPOLITAN NEW YORK COORDINATING COUNCIL ON JEWISH POVERTY
METROPOLITAN COUNCIL ON JEWISH
120 Broadway Fl 7, New York, NY 10271-0021
Tel (212) 453-9500 *Founded/Ownrshp* 1972
Sales 121.0MM^E *EMP* 262
Accts Raich Ende Malter & Co Llp Ne
SIC 8322 Individual & family services; Individual & family services
CEO: Alan Schoor
**Pr:* Steven Price
**COO:* Debra Cohn
CFO: Mel Zachter
Ofcr: Thomas Schellhammer
**VP:* Israel Englander
Exec: Brendan Canning
**Prin:* Rebecca Missel
Prgrm Mgr: Sarah Lloyd
CTO: Steven Alter
Psych: Channah Ginsburg

D-U-N-S 96-956-3381
METROPOLITAN NY COORDINATING COUNCIL ON JEWISH POVERTY
80 Maiden Ln, New York, NY 10038-4811
Tel (212) 453-9500 *Founded/Ownrshp* 2011
Sales 34.0MM *EMP* 2
Accts Buchbinder Tunick & Co Llp Ne
SIC 8699 Charitable organization

D-U-N-S 07-523-8840 IMP
METROPOLITAN OPERA ASSOCIATION INC
Lincoln Ctr, New York, NY 10023
Tel (212) 799-3100 *Founded/Ownrshp* 1936
Sales 288.1MM *EMP* 1,500^E
SIC 7922 Opera company; Opera company
Pr: William Morris
CFO: Stewart Pearce
**Sec:* Kevin Kennedy
**VP:* Frayda Lindemann
**VP:* Mrs Ezra K Zilkha
Comm Dir: Lee Abrahamian
Genl Mgr: Peter Gelbas
Dir IT: Richard Bates
IT Man: Scott Trapani
Mktg Dir: Joe Hayes

D-U-N-S 11-436-1053
METROPOLITAN PAPER RECYCLING INC
847 Shepherd Ave, Brooklyn, NY 11208-5227
Tel (718) 257-0261 *Founded/Ownrshp* 2000
Sales 35.2MM^E *EMP* 108
SIC 4953 Recycling, waste materials
Ch Bd: Gregory Bianco
**COO:* Kevin Walton
**CFO:* Tom Ferro
**Prin:* Salvetore Zizza
Genl Mgr: Glen Murray
Natl Sales: John Siclare

D-U-N-S 07-924-5767
METROPOLITAN PARK DISTRICT OF TACOMA
METRO PARKS TACOMA
4702 S 19th St, Tacoma, WA 98405-1175
Tel (360) 832-7151 *Founded/Ownrshp* 1907
Sales NA *EMP* 400
Accts Troy Kelley Olympia Washingt
SIC 9512 Recreational program administration, government; ; Recreational program administration, government;
Ex Dir: Jack C Wilson
**CFO:* Brett Freshwaters
Exec: Michael Thompson
IT Man: Tara Dunford
Snr Mgr: Lee Fellenberg

METROPOLITAN PEER & EXPO AUTH
See MCCORMICK PLACE CONVENTION CENTER

D-U-N-S 05-434-3017
METROPOLITAN PIER AND EXPOSITION AUTHORITY
HYATT REGENCY MCCORMICK PLACE
301 Ecermak Rd Fl 5, Chicago, IL 60616
Tel (312) 791-7000 *Founded/Ownrshp* 1955
Sales 356.3MM^E *EMP* 2,500^E
SIC 7389 7999 7011 Convention & show services; Exposition operation; Hotels & motels; Convention & show services; Exposition operation; Hotels & motels
Pr: Julie Chavez
**Ch Bd:* Kelly Welsh
**CEO:* Leticia Davis
CFO: Martha Farrell
CFO: James Fricke
Treas: John Brumgart
Dir Soc: Livia Massuda
Dir Soc: Daryl Taylor
**Prin:* Dan Hynes
**Prin:* Roger J Kiley Jr
**Prin:* Carmen Lonstein
Board of Directors: John Ruel, William P Tuggle

D-U-N-S 09-848-8794 IMP
METROPOLITAN PLANT AND FLOWER EXCHANGE INC
2125 Fletcher Ave, Fort Lee, NJ 07024-5061
Tel (212) 366-5417 *Founded/Ownrshp* 1979
Sales 25.1MM^E *EMP* 135
SIC 5992 5193 Flowers, fresh; Plants, potted; Flowers, fresh; Plants, potted
Pr: Frank Vastano
**VP:* William Ludwig

D-U-N-S 02-426-1323 IMP
METROPOLITAN POULTRY CO
METROPOLITAN MT PLTY & SEAFOOD
1920 Stanford Ct, Landover, MD 20785-3219
Tel (301) 773-2175 *Founded/Ownrshp* 1944
Sales 96.0MM *EMP* 175
SIC 5143 5144 5146 5147 Butter; Poultry: live, dressed or frozen (unpackaged); Seafoods; Meats & meat products; Butter; Poultry: live, dressed or frozen (unpackaged); Seafoods; Meats & meat products
CEO: Brian Willard
**Pr:* Scott Willard
Treas: Michael Gahan
**Treas:* Charles B Willard
**Ex VP:* Melvin Willard
Sls&Mrk Ex: Steve Kohan
Sls Mgr: Mike Vancamp

METROPOLITAN PROPERTIES AMER
See METROPOLITAN PROPERTIES OF AMERICA INC

D-U-N-S 05-282-2269
METROPOLITAN PROPERTIES OF AMERICA INC
METROPOLITAN PROPERTIES AMER
101 Federal St, Boston, MA 02110-1817
Tel (617) 603-7000 *Founded/Ownrshp* 1980
Sales 21.5MM^E *EMP* 165
SIC 6512 6513 Commercial & industrial building operation; Apartment building operators
CEO: Jeffrey J Cohen
COO: Susan Fuller
**CFO:* Mark P Consoli
**Treas:* Gary M Romano
VP: Rob Kavanagh
Adm Dir: Michael Rosen
VP Opers: Ann Cavanaugh
Mktg Dir: Victoria Melvin

D-U-N-S 07-569-9959
■ **METROPOLITAN PROPERTY AND CASUALTY INSURANCE CO**
METLIFE
(*Suby of* METLIFE INC) ★
700 Quaker Ln, Warwick, RI 02886-6681
Tel (401) 827-2400 *Founded/Ownrshp* 1982
Sales NA *EMP* 2,634
SIC 6411 Insurance agents & brokers; Insurance agents & brokers
Pr: William Moore
Treas: John McSweeney
Ex VP: Mary Lovejoy
**VP:* Marvin A Beck
VP: Mike Ritchie
VP: Carol Stewart
VP: Mike Walsh
Prgrm Mgr: Shane Kirkland
Genl Mgr: Jeffrey Hebert
Advt Mgr: Greg Rosa

METROPOLITAN PUMP COMPANY
See METROPOLITAN INDUSTRIES INC

D-U-N-S 96-481-9093
METROPOLITAN REGIONAL COUNCIL UNITED BROTHERHOOD OF C&J OF A
1803 Spring Garden St, Philadelphia, PA 19130-3916
Tel (215) 569-1634 *Founded/Ownrshp* 2010
Sales 38.1MM *EMP* 18^E
Accts Gitomer & Berenholz Pc Huntin
SIC 8631 Labor unions & similar labor organizations
Prin: Joe Osbuchowicz

D-U-N-S 92-902-2937
METROPOLITAN REGIONAL INFORMATION SYSTEMS INC
MRIS
9707 Key West Ave Ste 200, Rockville, MD 20850-4079
Tel (301) 838-7100 *Founded/Ownrshp* 1993
Sales 20.4MM^E *EMP* 135
Accts Grant Thornton Llp Mclean Vi
SIC 6531 Multiple listing service, real estate
CEO: David Charron
Treas: Patricia Savani
VP: Danielle Davis
VP: Margaret O'Sullivan
VP: C Subramanian

Plnt Mgr: Greg Petch
Ql Cn Mgr: Jill Reynolds
Board of Directors: Terrence M McDermott

METROPOLITAN SALES COMPANY
See METROPOLITAN SALES DISTRIBUTORS INC

D-U-N-S 13-014-7291
METROPOLITAN SALES DISTRIBUTORS INC
METROPOLITAN SALES COMPANY
238 Atlantic Ave, Lynbrook, NY 11563-3554
Tel (516) 599-7900 *Founded/Ownrshp* 1981
Sales 59.1MM *EMP* 26
Accts Weisermazars Llp New York Ne
SIC 5045 5063 Computer peripheral equipment; Printers, computer; Motor controls, starters & relays: electric; Computer peripheral equipment; Printers, computer; Motor controls, starters & relays: electric
Pr: Jack Tawil
Genl Mgr: Alan Sweet
Mktg Mgr: Heather Schlichting

D-U-N-S 05-560-3427
METROPOLITAN SCHOOL DISTRICT OF DECATUR TOWNSHIP (IN)
MSD OF DECATUR TOWNSHIP
5275 Kentucky Ave, Indianapolis, IN 46221-3616
Tel (317) 856-5265 *Founded/Ownrshp* 1964
Sales 31.8MM^E *EMP* 800
SIC 8211 Public elementary school; Secondary school; Public elementary school; Secondary school

D-U-N-S 05-010-0130
METROPOLITAN SCHOOL DISTRICT OF LAWRENCE TOWNSHIP
6501 Sunnyside Rd, Indianapolis, IN 46236-9707
Tel (317) 423-8200 *Founded/Ownrshp* 1959
Sales 102.6MM^E *EMP* 2,500
SIC 8211 Public elementary & secondary schools; Public elementary & secondary schools
**CFO:* Robin Phelps
Treas: Dorothy Gaertner
Ex Dir: Cori Korn
Dir IT: Johnny McFarland
Psych: Beth Williams

D-U-N-S 02-042-9536
METROPOLITAN SCHOOL DISTRICT OF MOUNT VERNON
MSD OF MOUNT VERNON
1000 W 4th St, Mount Vernon, IN 47620-1626
Tel (812) 838-4471 *Founded/Ownrshp* 1920
Sales 25.4MM^E *EMP* 400
SIC 8211 9411 Public elementary & secondary schools; High school, junior or senior; Administration of educational programs; Public elementary & secondary schools; High school, junior or senior; Administration of educational programs
Dir IT: William Stein
Teacher Pr: Sara Batteiger

D-U-N-S 10-064-8369
METROPOLITAN SCHOOL DISTRICT OF STEUBEN COUNTY
400 S Martha St, Angola, IN 46703-1945
Tel (260) 665-2854 *Founded/Ownrshp* 1932
Sales 11.8MM^E *EMP* 343
SIC 8211 Public elementary & secondary schools; High school, junior or senior; Public elementary & secondary schools; High school, junior or senior

D-U-N-S 08-678-0053
METROPOLITAN SCHOOL DISTRICT OF WABASH COUNTY
204 N 300 W, Wabash, IN 46992-8689
Tel (260) 563-8050 *Founded/Ownrshp* 1959
Sales 20.7MM^E *EMP* 500
SIC 8211 Public elementary & secondary schools; Public elementary & secondary schools

D-U-N-S 07-204-1148
METROPOLITAN SCHOOL DISTRICT OF WAYNE TOWNSHIP
1220 S High School Rd, Indianapolis, IN 46241-3127
Tel (317) 988-8600 *Founded/Ownrshp* 1952
Sales 95.4MM^E *EMP* 2,200
SIC 8211 Public elementary & secondary schools; High school, junior or senior; Public elementary & secondary schools; High school, junior or senior
Pr: Rachel Cravens
Pr: Matt Good
CFO: Dennis J Tackitt
Genl Mgr: Aaron Moss
Snr Mgr: Wally Miller

D-U-N-S 07-207-1129
METROPOLITAN SCHOOL DISTRICT WASHINGTON TOWNSHIP
8550 Wdfld Xing Blvd, Indianapolis, IN 46240-2478
Tel (317) 845-9400 *Founded/Ownrsp* 1955
Sales 67.1MM^E *EMP* 1,294
SIC 8211 Public elementary & secondary schools; Public elementary & secondary schools
Teacher Pr: Thomas Oestreich

D-U-N-S 79-720-3932
METROPOLITAN SECURITY SERVICES INC
WALDEN SECURITY
100 E 10th St Ste 400, Chattanooga, TN 37402-4218
Tel (423) 702-8200 *Founded/Ownrshp* 1990
Sales 120.8MM *EMP* 2,500^E
Accts Lattimore Black Morgan & Cain
SIC 7381 Security guard service; Security guard service
Ch Bd: Amy S Walden
**Pr:* Michael S Walden
Ofcr: Abraham Awodi
Ofcr: Patrick Bull
Ofcr: Marvin Cook
Ofcr: Willie Core
Ofcr: Mark Lavender
Ofcr: Alan Lewis
Ofcr: Teresa Riverawilliams
Ofcr: Wanda Tyndall
Ofcr: Tim Whitaker
Ofcr: Lewis Wright

**Sr VP:* Curtis Casey
**VP:* Dick Wong

METROPOLITAN SERVICES
See YMCA OF NORTHWEST NORTH CAROLINA

D-U-N-S 15-590-4659
METROPOLITAN SEWERAGE DISTRICT OF BUNCOMBE COUNTY
2028 Riverside Dr, Asheville, NC 28804-3054
Tel (828) 225-8234 *Founded/Ownrshp* 1962
Sales 27.2MM^E *EMP* 152
SIC 4952 Sewerage systems; Sewerage systems
Genl Mgr: Thomas E Hartye

D-U-N-S 07-177-9532
METROPOLITAN SPORTS FACILITIES COMMISSION FOUNDATION INC
HHH METRODOME
900 S 5th St Ste A, Minneapolis, MN 55415-1563
Tel (612) 332-0386 *Founded/Ownrshp* 1954
Sales 20.5MM *EMP* 80
Accts James R Nobles/Cecile M Ferk
SIC 6512 Auditorium & hall operation; Auditorium & hall operation
Ex Dir: William Lester
**Ch Bd:* Roy Terwilliger
V Ch: Bill McCarthy
Ex VP: John Griffith
Comm Dir: Jenn Hathaway
Comm Dir: Jennifer Hathaway
Ex Dir: Bill Lester
Ex Dir: Ted Mondale
Admn Mgr: Stuart Lockwood
IT Man: Mike Clark
Mktg Dir: Dennis Alfton

D-U-N-S 04-637-3312
METROPOLITAN ST LOUIS SEWER DISTRICT
MSD
2350 Market St Ste 300, Saint Louis, MO 63103-2555
Tel (314) 768-6200 *Founded/Ownrshp* 1954
Sales 260.0MM *EMP* 976
Accts Rubinbrown Llp Saint Louis M
SIC 4952 Sewerage systems; Sewerage systems
Ex Dir: Brian Hoelscher
Ch Bd: James Buford
Treas: Edwin Dirck
Sec: Brenda Schaefer
Ofcr: Ken Lucas
Prgrm Mgr: Mike Buechter
Prgrm Mgr: Bill Ehrhard
Prgrm Mgr: Gary Moore
Div Mgr: Catherine Politte
Dir IT: Richard Unverferth
Tech Mgr: Jackie Weddington

D-U-N-S 05-909-4321
METROPOLITAN STATE UNIVERSITY OF DENVER
890 Auraria Pkwy, Denver, CO 80204-1806
Tel (303) 556-3030 *Founded/Ownrshp* 1965
Sales 159.3MM^E *EMP* 2,300
SIC 8221 Colleges universities & professional schools; Colleges universities & professional schools
Pr: Stephen Jordan
Ofcr: Judith Hilton
VP: Carrie A Besnette
VP: Kathleen A Mackay
VP: Carl R Powell
VP: Alberto Torres
VP: Jacob Welch
Dir Lab: Douglas Howey
Assoc Dir: Brooke Dilling
Assoc Dir: Marion Karanja
Assoc Dir: Daniel Parks
Assoc Dir: Chivonne Torres

D-U-N-S 04-523-1990
METROPOLITAN STEVEDORE CO
720 E E St, Wilmington, CA 90744-6014
Tel (310) 816-6500 *Founded/Ownrshp* 1967
Sales 29.4MM^E *EMP* 60
SIC 4491 Stevedoring; Waterfront terminal operation
CEO: James Callahan
Pr: Brian Johnson
COO: Al Garner
COO: Michael F Giove
CFO: John Hampton
Sr VP: Norm Hauser
VP: Boyette Fabio
VP: Stefano Pinna
Exec: Sam Ko
Dir Bus: Jamshid Pezeshk
Sfty Mgr: Craig Kappe

D-U-N-S 06-804-9543
METROPOLITAN SUBURBAN BUS AUTH
LONG ISLAND BUS
(*Suby of* M T A) ★
700 Commercial Ave Fl 2, Garden City, NY 11530-6410
Tel (516) 228-4000 *Founded/Ownrshp* 1972
Sales 46.4MM^E *EMP* 960
SIC 4111 Bus line operations; Bus line operations
Ch Bd: E Virgil Conway
**Pr:* Joe Smith
**VP:* James Campbell
**VP:* William Norwich
VP: Howard Permut
VP: Joseph Pokorny
Snr Mgr: Richard Jenkins

D-U-N-S 04-167-1173 IMP
METROPOLITAN THEATRES CORP
8727 W 3rd St Ste 301, Los Angeles, CA 90048-3897
Tel (310) 858-2800 *Founded/Ownrshp* 1936
Sales 25.3MM^E *EMP* 400
SIC 7832 Motion picture theaters, except drive-in; Motion picture theaters, except drive-in
CEO: Bruce C Corwin
**Pr:* David Corwin
COO: Dale Davison
MIS Dir: Victoria Uy

D-U-N-S 79-064-2029
■ **METROPOLITAN TOWER LIFE INSURANCE CO**
METLIFE
(*Suby of* METLIFE) ★
1 Netlife Plz 27 01 Qn Pl, New York, NY 10010
Tel (212) 578-2211 *Founded/Ownrshp* 1982
Sales NA *EMP* 249
SIC 6411 Insurance agents & brokers; Insurance agents & brokers
Ch: Robert Benmosche
Pr: Leonard L Kasendorf
**Pr:* David Alan Levene
CFO: Ron Manekofsky
Ofcr: Robert Sollmanm
Ex VP: Lisa M Weber
Ex VP: William J Wheeler
Sr VP: Virginia M Wilson
VP: Phillip Caponigro
VP: Gary Lineberry
VP: Mark Lonergan
VP: Abdou Terki-Hassaine
VP: Dave Zimmerman

METROPOLITAN TRANSIT
See DAVIDSON TRANSIT ORGANIZATION

D-U-N-S 09-483-4405
METROPOLITAN TRANSIT AUTHORITY OF HARRIS COUNTY
HOUSTON METRO TRNST AUTH
1900 Main St, Houston, TX 77002-8130
Tel (713) 635-4000 *Founded/Ownrshp* 1978
Sales 235.0MM^E *EMP* 3,700
Accts Kpmg Llp Austin Tx
SIC 4119 Local passenger transportation; Local passenger transportation
Pr: Thomas C Lambert
CFO: Suzzane Bailey
Ofcr: Ify Belonwu
Ofcr: John Ivey
Ofcr: Eric Lindbloom
Ofcr: Robert Lozano
Ofcr: Byron Nicholas
Ofcr: Roger Salazar
Ofcr: Robert Smith
Ofcr: Roger Trevino
Ofcr: John Truitt
Assoc VP: Danicel Whitaker
Ex VP: John M Sedlak
**Sr VP:* David W Couch
Sr VP: Bryan Pennington
Sr VP: Andrew Skabowski
VP: M Helen Cavazos
**VP:* Raul Luzarraga
**VP:* Rocky Marrero
VP: George F Smalley

D-U-N-S 04-544-5137 IMP/EXP
METROPOLITAN TRANSPORTATION AUTHORITY
M T A
2 Broadway Bsmt B, New York, NY 10004-3354
Tel (212) 878-7000 *Founded/Ownrshp* 1965
Sales 7.7MMM *EMP* 67,457
Accts Deloitte & Touche Llp New Yo
SIC 4111 Local & suburban transit; Local & suburban transit
Ch Bd: Thomas F Predergast
**Pr:* Howard R Permut
Bd of Dir: Bob Bickford
Bd of Dir: Doreen Frasca
Bd of Dir: Ira Greenberg
Bd of Dir: Norman Seabrook
Bd of Dir: Vincent Tessitore
Bd of Dir: Carl Wortendyke
Ofcr: Timothy Corcoran
Ofcr: Edward Meggett
VP: Ronnie Hakim
Assoc Dir: Jan Wells
Comm Man: Alonzo Williams

D-U-N-S 07-464-4501
METROPOLITAN TRANSPORTATION COMMISSION
M T C
101 8th St, Oakland, CA 94607-4700
Tel (510) 817-5700 *Founded/Ownrshp* 1970
Sales 305.4MM *EMP* 115^E
Accts Pricewaterhousecoopers Llp S
SIC 4111 Bus line operations; Bus line operations
Ex Dir: Steve Hieminger
**CFO:* Brian Mayhew
**V Ch Bd:* Jake Mackenzie
Exec: Bond Counsel
Exec: John Goodwin
**Ex Dir:* Therese McMillan
Ex Dir: Denise Rodrigues
Prgrm Mgr: Stephen Abbanat
Prgrm Mgr: Craig Bosman
Snr Ntwrk: James Hebert
Genl Couns: Adrienne Weil

METROPOLITAN TRNSP SVCS
See METRO TRANSPORT LLC

D-U-N-S 00-877-4432
METROPOLITAN TRUCKING INC
METROPOLITAN FREIGHT MGT
(*Suby of* MANGINO HOLDING CORP) ★
6675 Low St, Bloomsburg, PA 17815-8613
Tel (201) 843-5509 *Founded/Ownrshp* 1981
Sales 51.7MM^E *EMP* 417
SIC 4213 Contract haulers; Contract haulers
Ch Bd: Joseph Mangino Jr
**CFO:* Matthew Sullivan
**Ex VP:* Michael Maiore
**VP:* Wayne Beaudry
VP: Ken Bruno
Sfty Dirs: Andy Miller

D-U-N-S 00-697-0321
METROPOLITAN UTILITIES DISTRICT
M U D
1723 Harney St, Omaha, NE 68102-1960
Tel (402) 554-6666 *Founded/Ownrshp* 1913
Sales 341.9MM *EMP* 852
Accts Kpmg Llp Lincoln Ne
SIC 4932 Gas & other services combined; Gas & other services combined
Pr: Douglas R Clark
**Ch Bd:* Jack Frost
**Pr:* Daniel G Crouchley
**CFO:* Debra A Schneider
Ch: David J Friend
**Ch:* Michael W McGowan
Ex Ofcr: Kay Lange
**Sr VP:* Ron Bucher
Sls&Mrk Ex: Mike Corrigan

D-U-N-S 04-685-0208
METROPOLITAN UTILITIES DISTRICT
1723 Harney St, Omaha, NE 68102-1960
Tel (402) 554-6666 *Founded/Ownrshp* 2010
Sales 31.5MM^E *EMP* 163^E
SIC 4932 Gas & other services combined
Prin: Dan Crouchley
Sr VP: Daniel G Crouchley
Sr VP: William Freemel
Sr VP: Scott L Keep
VP: Roger Burmeister
VP: Rhonda Chantry
VP: Jason Stanek
VP: Raied Stanley
Snr Ntwrk: Frank Matras
CIO: Mark Doyle
Dir IT: Joe Dennick

D-U-N-S 11-620-3001
METROPOLITAN WASHINGTON AIRPORTS AUTHORITY
DULLES INTERNATIONAL AIRPORT
1 Aviation Cir, Washington, DC 20001-6000
Tel (703) 417-8600 *Founded/Ownrshp* 1987
Sales 234.6MM^E *EMP* 1,400
SIC 4581 4785 Airports, flying fields & services; Toll road operation; Airports, flying fields & services; Toll road operation
Ch: Frank Conner
**Pr:* John E Potter
**COO:* Margaret E McKeough
**CFO:* Andrew Rountree
Bd of Dir: Michael Curto
Chf Inves: Michelle Watson
Ofcr: Emmilie Cherry
Ofcr: Lewis Golladay
Ofcr: William Holman
Ofcr: Chris Humady
Ofcr: Edward Johnson
Ofcr: Ian Lauderdale
Ofcr: Matthew McDavid
Ofcr: Ryan McNeeley
Ofcr: Cheryl Patterson
Ofcr: Audrey Temple
Ofcr: Melanie Zinger
VP: Leslie Berkowitz
**VP:* Quince T Brinkley
VP: David Mould
VP: Roger Natsuhara

D-U-N-S 07-266-3115
METROPOLITAN WASHINGTON COUNCIL OF GOVERNMENTS
COG
777 N Capitol St Ne # 300, Washington, DC 20002-4239
Tel (202) 962-3200 *Founded/Ownrshp* 1957
Sales 46.3MM *EMP* 130
Accts Sb & Company Llc Cockeysville
SIC 8621 Professional membership organizations; Professional membership organizations
Pr: Kamilah Bunn
**Pr:* Judith Davis
**CFO:* Raymond Rawlins
Treas: Gabe Klein
Treas: Candice Quinn
**V Ch Bd:* G N Jay Fisette
Mng Dir: Mary McKown
CTO: George Danilovics

METROPOLITAN WASTE DISPOSAL
See CALMET INC

D-U-N-S 00-699-9011
METROPOLITAN WATER DISTRICT
700 N Alameda St Ste 1, Los Angeles, CA 90012-3353
Tel (213) 217-6000 *Founded/Ownrshp* 2011
Sales 21.6MM^E *EMP* 77^E
SIC 4941 Water supply
Prin: Reynaldo Reed
V Ch: John W Murray Jr

D-U-N-S 08-932-1459
METROPOLITAN WATER DISTRICT OF SALT LAKE & SANDY
3430 E Danish Rd, Cottonwood Heights, UT 84093-2139
Tel (801) 942-1391 *Founded/Ownrshp* 1935
Sales 24.9MM^E *EMP* 67
SIC 4941 Water supply
Genl Mgr: Mike Wilson
CFO: Michael Land
IT Man: Michael Devries
Opers Supe: Dallin Ewell

D-U-N-S 06-384-2975
METROPOLITAN WATER DISTRICT OF SOUTHERN CALIFORNIA
700 N Alameda St, Los Angeles, CA 90012-3352
Tel (213) 217-6000 *Founded/Ownrshp* 1928
Sales 1.1MMM^E *EMP* 2,000
SIC 4941

D-U-N-S 06-249-7441
METROPOLITAN WATER RECLAIMATION DISTRICT OF GREATER CHICAGO
MWRD
100 E Erie St, Chicago, IL 60611-2829
Tel (312) 751-5600 *Founded/Ownrshp* 1889
Sales NA *EMP* 2,259
Accts Baker Tilly Virchow Krause
SIC 9511 Sanitary engineering agency, government; ; Sanitary engineering agency, government;
Pr: Terrence J Obrien
Trst: Robert Regan
Ofcr: Allison Fore
Ofcr: Beverly Sanders

Ofcr: Tia Schrean
Ofcr: Helen Shields-Wright
VP: Kathleen Meany
Dir Risk M: Ruth Joplin
Prin: Jeff Weber
Ex Dir: David St Pierre
QA Dir: John McNamara

METROPOLITAN YMCA
See YOUNG MENS CHRISTIAN ASSOCIATION OF ORANGE COUNTY

D-U-N-S 07-930-7781
METROPOLITAN YMCA OF ORANGES INC (NJ)
Y M C A
139 E Mcclellan Ave, Livingston, NJ 07039-1320
Tel (973) 758-9622 Founded/Ownrshp 1885
Sales 14.0MM^E EMP 360
Accts Ra Fredericks & Company Llp M
SIC 8641 7991 8351 7032 8322 Youth organizations; Physical fitness facilities; Child day care services; Youth camps; Individual & family services; Youth organizations; Physical fitness facilities; Child day care services; Youth camps; Individual & family services
Pr: Richard Gorab
COO: Larry Lev
Trst: Bonnie Granatir
Exec: Sharon Czebotar
Ex Dir: Ernest Bryant
Ex Dir: Rick Gorab
Ex Dir: Justin Ihne
Off Mgr: Kathie Amato
Dir IT: Joe Penska
Mktg Dir: Greg Albers

D-U-N-S 82-680-0059
METROPOLITAN YMCA OF ORANGES INC
139 E Mcclellan Ave, Livingston, NJ 07039-1320
Tel (973) 758-9622 Founded/Ownrshp 2008
Sales 27.0MM EMP 2
Accts Ra Fredericks & Company Llp
SIC 8322 Individual & family services; Individual & family services
Pr: Richard Gorab
*COO: Larry Lev
*CFO: Alisa Vural

D-U-N-S 96-630-5315
METROPOLITAN YOUNG MENS CHRISTIAN ASSOCIATION OF GREATER FORT WAYNE
YMCA OF GREATER FORT WAYNE
347 W Berry St Ste 500, Fort Wayne, IN 46802-2241
Tel (260) 422-6488 Founded/Ownrshp 2009
Sales 15.0MM EMP 600
Accts Bkd Llp Fort Wayne In
SIC 8641 Youth organizations; Youth organizations
CEO: Martin Pastura
CFO: Mick Sokolowski

METROPOWER
See ESS INC

D-U-N-S 09-962-9602
METROPOWER INC
ALBANY ELECTRIC COMPANY
(Suby of PPC PARTNERS INC) ★
798 21st Ave, Albany, GA 31701-1137
Tel (229) 432-7345 Founded/Ownrshp 1979
Sales 128.9MM^E EMP 425
SIC 1731 Electrical work; Electrical work
CEO: Danny R Buck
*CFO: Kayanne Blackwell
VP: Arnold Geeslin Jr
Rgnl Mgr: Duane Howell
Dept Mgr: Dekalb Gibson
Dept Mgr: Greg Greenway
Off Mgr: Debra West

METROSTAR
See METROPOLITAN HOME HEALTH PRODUCTS INC

D-U-N-S 12-531-3051
METROSTAR SYSTEMS INC
1856 Old Reston Ave, Reston, VA 20190-3329
Tel (703) 481-9581 Founded/Ownrshp 1999
Sales 27.5MM EMP 150
Accts Miller Musmar Reston Virgini
SIC 7379 7371 Computer related consulting services; Software programming applications; Computer related consulting services; Software programming applications
CEO: Ali Manouchehri
*Pr: Robert Santos
*COO: Anthony Salvi
VP: Michael Belcher
VP: Vy Truong
Snr Sftwr: Gitendra Malla
Snr Sftwr: Dan Pick
Snr Sftwr: Jeff Zhang
Software D: Natasha Gorbatovskikh
Software D: Brandon Key
Software D: Marx Martin

D-U-N-S 06-070-1919 IMP
METROTECH CORP (CA)
VIVAX-METROTECH
3251 Olcott St, Santa Clara, CA 95054-3006
Tel (408) 734-3880 Founded/Ownrshp 1976, 1980
Sales 24.9MM^E EMP 180
SIC 3812 3599 3829 Detection apparatus: electronic/magnetic field, light/heat; Water leak detectors; Measuring & controlling devices; Detection apparatus: electronic/magnetic field, light/heat; Water leak detectors; Measuring & controlling devices
CEO: Christian Stolz
*Pr: Andrew Hoare
*VP: Mark Drew
VP: John Pelton
*VP: Mark Royle
VP: Jim Waite
Ex Dir: Lou Rossetti
IT Man: Kristin Lee

METROWEST MEDICAL CENTRE
See VHS ACQUISITION SUBSIDIARY NUMBER 9 INC

D-U-N-S 95-746-9927 IMP
METSA BOARD AMERICAS CORP
(Suby of METSA BOARD OYJ)
301 Merritt 7 Ste 2, Norwalk, CT 06851-1051
Tel (203) 229-0037 Founded/Ownrshp 1978
Sales 35.8MM^E EMP 69
SIC 2631 Paperboard mills
CEO: Lasse Wikstrom
*Ch Bd: Mika Paljakka
*Pr: Jorma Sahlstedt
Mill Mgr: Peter Kinell

D-U-N-S 11-064-2209
METSCHOOLS INC
80 Broad St Ste 1702, New York, NY 10004-2248
Tel (212) 867-2828 Founded/Ownrshp 1999
Sales 18.9MM^E EMP 650
SIC 8351 Preschool center; Preschool center
Pr: Michael Kofler
CFO: Kevin McCarthy

D-U-N-S 96-299-0284
METSO AUTOMATION
(Suby of METSO OYJ)
2425 Commerce Ave Ste 100, Duluth, GA 30096-8913
Tel (770) 476-3641 Founded/Ownrshp 2010
Sales 89.7MM^E EMP 142^E
SIC 5084 Industrial machinery & equipment
CEO: Matti Khknen
CFO: Neil Casale
*CFO: Harri Nikunen
VP: Mikko Karvinen
Area Mgr: Clayton Billey
Area Mgr: Bill Malak

D-U-N-S 10-489-5581 IMP
METSO AUTOMATION USA INC
FIELD SYTEMS DIVISION
(Suby of METSO USA INC) ★
44 Bowditch Dr, Shrewsbury, MA 01545-1719
Tel (508) 852-0200 Founded/Ownrshp 1954
Sales 96.2MM^E EMP 530^E
SIC 3592 Valves; Valves
Pr: John Quinlivan
Pr: David Bayreuther
Pr: Jerry Mitchell
CFO: Douglas Dunn
*Sec: Doug Dunn
Sr Cor Off: Jukka Tiitinen
Ex VP: Mike Mason
Ex VP: Robert Pape
VP: Rubens Costa
VP: Paul Gannon
VP: Yrj Norri
VP: Jouni Pyatsia

D-U-N-S 18-284-6063 IMP/EXP
METSO MINERALS INDUSTRIES INC
(Suby of METSO USA INC) ★
20965 Crossroads Cir, Waukesha, WI 53186-4083
Tel (262) 798-3994 Founded/Ownrshp 1990
Sales 389.9MM^E EMP 1,459
SIC 3321 3069 3561 3535 3532 Ductile iron castings; Linings, vulcanizable rubber; Hard rubber products; Pumps & pumping equipment; Bulk handling conveyor systems; Crushing, pulverizing & screening equipment; Ductile iron castings; Linings, vulcanizable rubber; Hard rubber products; Pumps & pumping equipment; Bulk handling conveyor systems; Crushing, pulverizing & screening equipment
CEO: Matti Khknen
*Pr: Perttu Louhiluoto
*Pr: Mike Phillips
CFO: Juha Sepp L
Treas: Debbie Trost
Sr VP: Pekka Pohjoism Ki
VP: Alvaro Braun
VP: Todd Dillmann
VP: Raymond N Koper
VP: Robert Lindstr M
VP: Kelly McCue
VP: Yrj Norri
VP: Helmut Zeipelt

D-U-N-S 80-473-9183 IMP/EXP
METSO MINERALS INDUSTRIES INC
1402 E Veterans Mem Pkwy, Warrenton, MO 63380-1316
Tel (636) 456-0035 Founded/Ownrshp 1987
Sales 26.4MM^E EMP 119
SIC 3496 3315 Wire cloth & woven wire products; Wire products, ferrous/iron: made in wiredrawing plants
VP: David Quail
COO: Mike Wendt
IT Man: Brendon Bardon
IT Man: Robert Brannock
IT Man: Fred Nothling
Mtls Mgr: Janet Edlen
Plnt Mgr: Chris Harrington
Plnt Mgr: Frank McCoy
Plnt Mgr: Bob Sutherland

D-U-N-S 80-154-2994 IMP/EXP
METSO USA INC
(Suby of METSO OYJ)
133 Federal St Ste 302, Boston, MA 02110-1703
Tel (770) 246-7237 Founded/Ownrshp 2000
Sales 537.7MM^E EMP 3,913
SIC 3554 5084 Paper industries machinery; Industrial machinery & equipment; Paper industries machinery; Industrial machinery & equipment
Pr: Mike Phillips
*Sec: Paul Gannon
Sr VP: Jukka Sampi
VP: Jouko Kauppila
VP: Jack Marmet
VP: Scott McGlothlin
VP: Jerry Mitchell
VP: Pekka Pajalahti
VP: Richard Parker
VP: Jouko Yli-Kauppila
Genl Mgr: Ismo Vaiste

D-U-N-S 13-052-6668
METSON MARINE INC
2060 Knoll Dr Ste 100, Ventura, CA 93003-7391
Tel (805) 658-2628 Founded/Ownrshp 1984
Sales 82.1MM^E EMP 120
SIC 4959 4499 Environmental cleanup services; Chartering of commercial boats; Environmental cleanup services; Chartering of commercial boats
Pr: Daniel G Randopoulos
*COO: Thanasi Randopoulos
COO: John Swift
*VP: Charlotte Randopoulos
*VP: Bruce Strong
Prgrm Mgr: Paul Laws
IT Man: Tessa Grant
IT Man: Scott Kopald
Opers Mgr: Chris Coons
Opers Mgr: Robert Golden

METTEL
See MANHATTAN TELECOMMUNICATIONS CORP

D-U-N-S 03-377-1288
METTERS INDUSTRIES INC
8200 Greensboro Dr # 500, Mc Lean, VA 22102-3871
Tel (703) 821-3300 Founded/Ownrshp 1981
Sales 40.0MM^E EMP 258
SIC 8711 7371 7373 7376 8742 8748 Engineering services; Custom computer programming services; Computer integrated systems design; Computer facilities management; Management consulting services; Business consulting; Engineering services; Custom computer programming services; Computer integrated systems design; Computer facilities management; Management consulting services; Business consulting
CEO: Dr Samuel Metters
CFO: Francine Devenoge
*CFO: David Thach
*Ex VP: Kim Metters
VP: Roger Houze
VP: Harold Robinson
Exec: Francine De Venoge
Dir Bus: Jack Koletty
Prgrm Mgr: James Bowser
Prgrm Mgr: Bonnie Kane
Brnch Mgr: Roy Willis

D-U-N-S 60-322-8909
■ **METTIKI COAL CORP**
(Suby of ALLIANCE COAL LLC) ★
293 Table Rock Rd, Oakland, MD 21550-5930
Tel (301) 334-3952 Founded/Ownrshp 1976
Sales 42.2MM^E EMP 245
SIC 1221 1222 Bituminous coal surface mining; Bituminous coal-underground mining; Bituminous coal surface mining; Bituminous coal-underground mining
Pr: Joseph W Craft III

METTLER TOLEDO
See METTLER-TOLEDO SAFELINE INC

D-U-N-S 86-770-0692
■ **METTLER-TOLEDO AUTOCHEM INC**
(Suby of METTLER-TOLEDO INTERNATIONAL INC) ★
7075 Samuel Morse Dr # 100, Columbia, MD 21046-3433
Tel (410) 910-8100 Founded/Ownrshp 1999
Sales 68.6MM^E EMP 206
SIC 5084 Industrial machinery & equipment; Industrial machinery & equipment
CEO: Olivier Filliol
*Pr: Henry Dupina
Genl Mgr: Roel Ferwerda
Genl Mgr: Jeff Sherman
Snr Sftwr: Dave Cook
IT Man: Andrea Eldridge
Sftwr Eng: Kenneth McKirahan
Netwrk Eng: Daniel Thompson
Sls Mgr: Elaine Kruse
Doctor: Julian Luescher
Snr Mgr: Felix Klebe

D-U-N-S 00-222-8229
■ **METTLER-TOLEDO INC**
(Suby of METTLER-TOLEDO LLC) ★
5 Barr Rd, Ithaca, NY 14850-9117
Tel (607) 257-6000 Founded/Ownrshp 1987
Sales 36.9MM^E EMP 135
SIC 3596 3537 Weighing machines & apparatus; Industrial trucks & tractors; Weighing machines & apparatus; Industrial trucks & tractors
CEO: Olivier Filliol
*Ch Bd: William P Donnelly
Genl Mgr: Gerald Liswoski
*Genl Mgr: Gerald Liswoski
Sls&Mrk Ex: Kyle Thomas
Sls Mgr: Aaron Rossi
Snr Mgr: Bill Rohde

D-U-N-S 09-069-6071 IMP
▲ **METTLER-TOLEDO INTERNATIONAL INC**
1900 Polaris Pkwy Fl 6, Columbus, OH 43240-4055
Tel (614) 438-4511 Founded/Ownrshp 1991
Sales 2.4MMM EMP 13,100^E
Accts Pricewaterhousecoopers Llp C
Tkr Sym MTD Exch NYS
SIC 3596 3821 3826 3823 Industrial scales; Laboratory measuring apparatus; Balances, laboratory; Analytical instruments; Industrial instrmnts msrmnt display/control process variable; Industrial scales; Laboratory measuring apparatus; Balances, laboratory; Analytical instruments; Industrial instrmnts msrmnt display/control process variable
Pr: Olivier A Filliol
*Ch Bd: Robert F Spoerry
CFO: Shawn P Vadala
Chf Mktg O: Martin Huber
Ex VP: William P Donnelly
Comm Dir: Lee Tompkins
Dir Bus: Dominic Connolly
Comm Man: Mike Donohoe
Area Mgr: Massimo Fiori
CIO: Mark Champlin
Opers Mgr: Todd Manifold
Board of Directors: Francis A Contino, Michael A Kelly, Martin D Madaus, Hans Ulrich Maerki, George M Milne Jr, Thomas Salice

D-U-N-S 19-464-9323 IMP/EXP
■ **METTLER-TOLEDO LLC**
(Suby of METTLER-TOLEDO INTERNATIONAL INC) ★
1900 Polaris Pkwy Fl 6, Columbus, OH 43240-4055
Tel (614) 438-4511 Founded/Ownrshp 1986
Sales 802.5MM^E EMP 9,500
SIC 3596 5049 7699 3821 3823 3826

D-U-N-S 60-416-7544 IMP
METTLER-TOLEDO SAFELINE INC
METTLER TOLEDO
(Suby of METTLER-TOLEDO SAFELINE X-RAY LIMITED)
6005 Benjamin Rd, Tampa, FL 33634-5145
Tel (614) 438-4511 Founded/Ownrshp 1989
Sales 36.9MM^E EMP 130
SIC 3844 3669 X-ray apparatus & tubes; Metal detectors; X-ray apparatus & tubes; Metal detectors
Pr: Viggo Nielsen
IT Man: Scott Watters
Sftwr Eng: Patrick Quigley
Mktg Mgr: Stephanie Coleman
Manager: Alan Zeng
Sls Mgr: Angie Benoit
Sls Mgr: Oscar Jeeter

D-U-N-S 01-269-2539
METTOWEE LUMBER & PLASTICS CO INC (NY)
(Suby of TELESCOPE CASUAL FURNITURE INC) ★
82 Church St, Granville, NY 12832-1662
Tel (518) 642-1100 Founded/Ownrshp 1936
Sales 20.2MM^E EMP 250
SIC 2421 0811 3089 Sawmills & planing mills, general; Timber tracts; Plastic processing; Sawmills & planing mills, general; Timber tracts; Plastic processing
Pr: Henry V Derminden IV
*VP: Robert Vanderminden Jr

D-U-N-S 96-344-1501
METUCHEN PUBLIC SCHOOL DISTRICT
16 Simpson Pl, Metuchen, NJ 08840-2535
Tel (732) 321-8700 Founded/Ownrshp 2010
Sales 10.0MM^E EMP 327^E
SIC 8211 Elementary & secondary schools
Pr: Mary P Kohl
HC Dir: Kristine Walters

METUCHEN-EDISON-WOODBRIDGE YMC
See YOUNG MENS CHRISTIAN ASSOCIATION OF METUCHEN NEW JERSEY

D-U-N-S 17-856-5565
■ **METWEST INC**
QUEST DIAGNOSTICS
(Suby of QUEST DIAGNOSTICS INC) ★
695 S Broadway, Denver, CO 80209-4003
Tel (303) 899-6000 Founded/Ownrshp 1990
Sales 33.6MM^E EMP 1,000
SIC 8071 Medical laboratories; Medical laboratories
Pr: Christine Shlagor
Dir Bus: Dave Brown
Sfty Mgr: Patrick Jenkins
Opers Mgr: Jo Dugan

D-U-N-S 93-924-2020
METZ CULINARY MANAGEMENT INC
2 Woodland Dr, Dallas, PA 18612-9159
Tel (570) 675-8100 Founded/Ownrshp 1994
Sales 97.8MM^E EMP 3,000
SIC 8299 Cooking school; Cooking school
Ch: John C Metz Sr
Pr: Jim Dickson
Pr: Kathy Gonzalez
*Pr: Jeffrey Metz
*CEO: John C Metz
*COO: Harold Leininger
VP: Grant Bennett
VP: Dennis Daley
*VP: John Geronimo
*VP: Craig Phillips
*VP: Greg Polk

D-U-N-S 60-248-7415
METZ ENTERPRISES INC
2 Woodland Dr, Dallas, PA 18612-9159
Tel (570) 675-8100 Founded/Ownrshp 1987
Sales 35.5MM^E EMP 990
SIC 6512 5812 Commercial & industrial building operation; Eating places; Commercial & industrial building operation; Eating places
Ch: John C Metz
*Pr: Jeff Metz
Genl Mgr: Tom Brocaglia
Sls Dir: John Geronimo

METZELER AUTO PROFILE SYSTEMS
See HENNIGES AUTOMOTIVE SEALING SYSTEMS NORTH AMERICA INC

D-U-N-S 07-418-3815
METZGER CONSTRUCTION CO
2055 Silber Rd Ste 100, Houston, TX 77055-2646
Tel (713) 956-0098 Founded/Ownrshp 1986
Sales 41.6MM^E EMP 50
Accts Mcconnell & Jones Llp Houston
SIC 1542 1541 Commercial & office building, new construction; Commercial & office buildings, renovation & repair; Industrial buildings & warehouses; Industrial buildings, new construction; Renovation, remodeling & repairs: industrial buildings; Commercial & office building, new construction; Commercial & office buildings, renovation & repair; Industrial buildings & warehouses; Industrial buildings, new construction; Renovation, remodeling & repairs: industrial buildings
Pr: James H Metzger
VP: Sue Henderson
*VP: Richard Metzger
*VP: Harold Thompson Sr
*VP: Harold D Thompson Jr
Snr Mgr: Rick Henderson
Snr Mgr: David Skaggs

D-U-N-S 78-704-2980 IMP
METZGERMEISTER & RESEARCH CORP
Carr 149 Km 155 Bo Jguas St Ca, Ciales, PR 00638
Tel (787) 871-3589 *Founded/Ownrshp* 2003
Sales 22.2MM^E *EMP* 160
SIC 2011 Meat packing plants; Meat packing plants
Pr: Jos R Rivera Ayala
**Sec:* Wilmet Pagan

D-U-N-S 15-114-3658
METZLER CONTRACTING CO LLC
57-1809 Kohala Mtn Rd, Hawi, HI 96719
Tel (808) 889-0581 *Founded/Ownrshp* 1976
Sales 33.1MM *EMP* 38
Accts Kmh Llp Honolulu Hawaii
SIC 1521 Single-family housing construction; Single-family housing construction

D-U-N-S 61-856-0460
MEURER RESEARCH INC
MRI
16133 W 45th Dr, Golden, CO 80403-1791
Tel (303) 279-8373 *Founded/Ownrshp* 1989
Sales 23.1MM^E *EMP* 40
SIC 3589 Water treatment equipment, industrial; Water treatment equipment, industrial
Pr: Charles L Meurer
VP: John Correa
Exec: Ron Dollar
VP Mktg: Joe Brauch
Board of Directors: Joseph Brauch

D-U-N-S 19-965-2145 IMP
MEVION MEDICAL SYSTEMS INC
300 Foster St Ste 3, Littleton, MA 01460-2017
Tel (978) 486-1006 *Founded/Ownrshp* 2004
Sales 78.1MM^E *EMP* 155
SIC 5047 Medical & hospital equipment; Medical & hospital equipment
CEO: Joseph K Jachinowski
**CFO:* Donald Melson
Ofcr: Ian Buchholz
Sr VP: Mike Cogswell
**VP:* Bill Alvord
VP: Earl Cleveland
VP: Thomas Faris
**VP:* Mark Jones
VP: Stanley Rosenthal
VP: George Rugg
Dir Bus: Stewart Pegrum
Board of Directors: Jay Moorin, Robert Wilson

MEVSA
See MITSUBISHI ELECTRIC VISUAL SOLUTIONS AMERICA INC

D-U-N-S 07-760-3595
MEWBOURNE HOLDINGS INC
3901 S Brdwy Ave, Tyler, TX 75701
Tel (903) 561-2900 *Founded/Ownrshp* 1965
Sales 313.0MM^E *EMP* 176
SIC 1311 Crude petroleum production; Natural gas production; Crude petroleum production
CEO: Curtis W Mewbourne
**COO:* Kenneth S Waits
**CFO:* J Roe Buckley
**CFO:* Roe Buckley
**Treas:* Alan Clark

D-U-N-S 04-783-9923
MEWBOURNE OIL CO
(*Suby of* MEWBOURNE HOLDINGS INC) ★
3620 Old Bullard Rd, Tyler, TX 75701-8644
Tel (903) 561-2900 *Founded/Ownrshp* 1991
Sales 312.8MM^E *EMP* 175
SIC 1311 Crude petroleum production; Natural gas production; Crude petroleum production; Natural gas production
Pr: Curtis W Mewbourne
**CFO:* J Roe Buckley
**CFO:* Roe Buckley
VP: Jerry Lebo
**VP:* Joseph F Odom
**VP:* Monty Whetstone
Dir IT: Bob Myers
Opers Mgr: Ronnie Howell

MEXCOR IMPORTERS & DISTRS
See MEXCOR INC

D-U-N-S 83-981-8536 IMP
MEXCOR INC
MEXCOR IMPORTERS & DISTRS
8950 Railwood Dr, Houston, TX 77078-4516
Tel (713) 979-0066 *Founded/Ownrshp* 1989
Sales 58.9MM^E *EMP* 60
SIC 5182 Liquor; Liquor
Pr: Eduardo J Morales
CFO: Brian Combs
**VP:* Jose Coioa
Rgnl Mgr: Mexcor Dickson
VP Opers: Stan Jimenez
Natl Sales: Mark Depugh
Sls Mgr: Chris Quintanilla

D-U-N-S 14-855-7734
MEXFIL HOTEL & BUILDING SERVICES INC
3506 Dunvale Rd, Houston, TX 77063-5711
Tel (713) 660-7678 *Founded/Ownrshp* 2002
Sales 7.9MM^E *EMP* 435
SIC 7011 Hotels; Hotels
Pr: Patty Martinez
**VP:* Marichu P Pasagui
**VP:* Rafael Perez

D-U-N-S 83-492-0811 IMP
MEXI-LAND INC
150 Russell St, City of Industry, CA 91744-3937
Tel (626) 330-5367 *Founded/Ownrshp* 1993
Sales 27.5MM^E *EMP* 42
SIC 5141 Groceries, general line
CEO: Eriberto Candelario
**Pr:* Ines Candelario
COO: Sixto Morales
VP: Cristina Candelario
VP Sls: Ron Kentish

D-U-N-S 09-350-8190
MEXIA INDEPENDENT SCHOOL DISTRICT
616 N Red River St, Mexia, TX 76667-2452
Tel (254) 562-4000 *Founded/Ownrshp* 1880
Sales 20.9MM^E *EMP* 375
SIC 8211 Public elementary & secondary schools; Public elementary & secondary schools
Schl Brd P: Richard Duncan

D-U-N-S 07-723-5091
MEXICAN AMERICAN OPPORTUNITY FOUNDATION
MAOF
401 N Garfield Ave, Montebello, CA 90640-2901
Tel (323) 890-9600 *Founded/Ownrshp* 1963
Sales 63.8MM *EMP* 710
Accts Vasin Heyn & Company Calabasa
SIC 8322 Social service center; Social service center
Pr: Martin Vasquez Castro
CFO: Orlando Sayson
VP: Vidal Pedro
**Prin:* Carlos J Viramontes
Prgrm Mgr: Maricela Covarrubias
IT Man: Rey Ladiona
Pgrm Dir: Zulema Andujo
Pgrm Dir: Claudia Arreola

D-U-N-S 94-571-6785
MEXICAN CHEESE PRODUCERS INC
(*Suby of* SIGMA ALIMENTOS EXTERIOR SLU)
11718 State Road 23, Darlington, WI 53530-9756
Tel (608) 776-8555 *Founded/Ownrshp* 2007
Sales 55.4MM *EMP* 120
Accts Pricewaterhousecoopers Llp H
SIC 2022 Cheese, natural & processed; Cheese, natural & processed
Genl Mgr: Lois Janssens
VP Opers: Dave Sandoval
Plnt Mgr: Nancy Lyon
Plnt Mgr: Randy Raymond

D-U-N-S 06-727-7947
■ **MEXICAN RESTAURANTS INC**
(*Suby of* WILLISTON HOLDINGS INC) ★
12000 Aerospace Ave # 400, Houston, TX 77034-5587
Tel (832) 300-5858 *Founded/Ownrshp* 2014
Sales 84.7MM^E *EMP* 1,950^E
Tkr Sym CASA *Exch* OTO
SIC 5812 6794 5046 Mexican restaurant; Franchises, selling or licensing; Restaurant equipment & supplies; Mexican restaurant; Franchises, selling or licensing; Restaurant equipment & supplies
CEO: Marcus Jundt
COO: Loic M Porry
COO: Loic Porry
CFO: Andrew J Dennard
CFO: Douglas Hipskind
CFO: Lawrence Neumann
Ofcr: Perry Brush

D-U-N-S 03-720-9442
MEXICAN SPECIALTY FOODS INC (NV)
LA PAZ
2295 Twn Lk Pkwy Ste 116, Woodstock, GA 30189-5520
Tel (770) 405-3220 *Founded/Ownrshp* 1979
Sales 10.4MM^E *EMP* 450
SIC 5812 Mexican restaurant; Mexican restaurant
Pr: Thomas W Nickoloff

MEXICANA AIRLINES
See COMPANIA MEXICANA DE AVIACION SA

D-U-N-S 80-562-4178 IMP/EXP
MEXICHEM FLUOR INC
(*Suby of* MEXICHEM FLUOR, S.A. DE C.V.)
4990b Ici Rd, Saint Gabriel, LA 70776
Tel (225) 642-0094 *Founded/Ownrshp* 2015
Sales 135.5MM^E *EMP* 81
SIC 2869 2833 2899 Olefins; Medicinal chemicals; Chemical preparations; Olefins; Medicinal chemicals; Chemical preparations
CEO: Andres Mugica Jimenez
**Pr:* Hector V Martin
**Pr:* Ricardo Gutierrez Munoz
**Treas:* Armando Vallejo Gomez
**VP:* Hector Jose Valle Martin
IT Man: Sean Cunningham
Sfty Mgr: Joel Hall

D-U-N-S 07-887-5792 IMP
MEXICHEM SPECIALTY RESINS INC
(*Suby of* MEXICHEM, S.A.B. DE C.V.)
33653 Walker Rd, Avon Lake, OH 44012-1044
Tel (440) 930-1435 *Founded/Ownrshp* 2013, 2014
Sales 103.8MM^E *EMP* 300
SIC 2822 2821 Ethylene-propylene rubbers, EPDM polymers; Polymethyl methacrylate resins (plexiglass); Ethylene-propylene rubbers, EPDM polymers; Polymethyl methacrylate resins (plexiglass)
Genl Mgr: Frank Tomaselli

D-U-N-S 07-160-1991
MEXICO CENTRAL SCHOOL DISTRICT INC
16 Fravor Rd Ste A, Mexico, NY 13114-3011
Tel (315) 963-8400 *Founded/Ownrshp* 1934
Sales 42.6MM *EMP* 354
Accts Paul W Schineible Cpa Oswego
SIC 8211 Public combined elementary & secondary school; Public combined elementary & secondary school
Pr: Janice Clark
VP: Kate Laduc
IT Man: Judy Perlet
Schl Brd P: James Emery

D-U-N-S 82-543-3266
MEXICO FOODS LLC
2600 Mccree Rd Ste 101, Garland, TX 75041-3901
Tel (972) 526-7200 *Founded/Ownrshp* 2007
Sales 202.4MM *EMP* 1,539
SIC 5411 Supermarkets; Supermarkets
Pr: Salah Nafal
**Treas:* Marwan Nafal
**VP:* Khaled Nafal

D-U-N-S 00-632-1640 IMP
MEXICO PLASTIC CO (MO)
CONTINENTAL PRODUCTS
2000 W Boulevard St, Mexico, MO 65265-1209
Tel (573) 581-4128 *Founded/Ownrshp* 1964
Sales 94.9MM^E *EMP* 200
SIC 2673 3089 2655 Plastic bags: made from purchased materials; Boxes, plastic; Fiber cans, drums & similar products; Plastic bags: made from purchased materials; Boxes, plastic; Fiber cans, drums & similar products
Pr: Carl Fuemmeler
**VP:* Thad Fisher
**VP:* Vincent F Fuemmeler Jr

MEXICO PUBLIC SCHOOLS
See MEXICO SCHOOL DISTRICT 59

D-U-N-S 10-004-1680
MEXICO SCHOOL DISTRICT 59
MEXICO PUBLIC SCHOOLS
2101 Lakeview Rd, Mexico, MO 65265-1358
Tel (573) 581-3773 *Founded/Ownrshp* 1870
Sales 24.8MM *EMP* 388
Accts Graves And Associates Cpas L
SIC 8211 Public elementary school; Public junior high school; Public senior high school; Public vocational/technical school; Public elementary school; Public junior high school; Public senior high school; Public vocational/technical school
Bd of Dir: Bethany Collins
Pr Dir: Jo Ann Diffenderfer

D-U-N-S 08-482-4734 EXP
MEXILINK INC
11767 Katy Fwy Ste 1040, Houston, TX 77079-1753
Tel (281) 754-8200 *Founded/Ownrshp* 2000
Sales 60.1MM *EMP* 100
SIC 5141 Food brokers; Food brokers
Pr: Jesus Salvador Escalona
**COO:* Francisco Morales
**CFO:* Clair Henkhaus
**VP:* Christopher Pye
**Prin:* Salvador Escalona
Admn Mgr: Eric Elcock
VP Opers: Carlos Escalona
Sales Exec: Nelson Rivera
VP Sls: Rafael Campuzano
Mktg Mgr: Lissette Barba
Mktg Mgr: Jacinto Esteban

D-U-N-S 12-056-0417
MEYER & NAJEM CONSTRUCTION LLC
(*Suby of* MEYER & NAJEM INC) ★
11787 Lantern Rd Ste 100, Fishers, IN 46038-2801
Tel (317) 577-0007 *Founded/Ownrshp* 1999
Sales 1.4MMM *EMP* 60
Accts Katz Sapper & Miller
SIC 1542 Nonresidential construction; Nonresidential construction
Pr: Tim Russell
Ch Bd: Karl Meyer
CEO: Anthony Najem
CFO: Robert Lawyer
VP: Toby Holcomb
VP: Sam Mishelow
VP: Paul Toddy

D-U-N-S 18-053-7425
MEYER & NAJEM INC
11787 Lantern Rd Ste 100, Fishers, IN 46038-2801
Tel (317) 577-0007 *Founded/Ownrshp* 1987
Sales 1.4MMM^E *EMP* 75
Accts Katz Sapper & Miller
SIC 1542 Commercial & office building, new construction; Commercial & office buildings, renovation & repair; Institutional building construction; Hospital construction
CEO: Karl Meyer
**Pr:* Anthony Najem
**CFO:* Robert Lawyer
Ex VP: Thomas Peck
Sr VP: Jim Boots
**VP:* Sam Mishelow
**VP:* Tim Russell
VP: Paul Toddy

D-U-N-S 00-418-8520
MEYER CO (OH)
TOMLINSON INDUSTRIES
13700 Broadway Ave, Cleveland, OH 44125-1945
Tel (216) 587-3400 *Founded/Ownrshp* 1897
Sales 37.7MM^E *EMP* 175
SIC 3556 Food products machinery; Food products machinery
Pr: H F Meyer
Pr: Jeff Labinski
**Sec:* Heidi Figas
Ex VP: Louis Castro
**VP:* Donald Calkins
**VP:* Michael E Figas
**VP:* H F Meyer III
Exec: Tomlinson Mark
Genl Mgr: Marianne Kives
Plnt Mgr: Ken Sidoi
Trfc Mgr: Alan Laskin

D-U-N-S 80-712-8546
MEYER COMPANIES INC
800 E 101st Ter Ste 120, Kansas City, MO 64131-5308
Tel (816) 246-4800 *Founded/Ownrshp* 2004
Sales 43.3MM *EMP* 56
SIC 1542 Commercial & office building contractors; Commercial & office building contractors
Ch Bd: Kasey Graham
**Sec:* Dave Meyer
**VP:* Rob Heise
**VP:* Mark Meyer

D-U-N-S 15-753-3308
MEYER CONTRACTING INC
11010 93rd Ave N Ste A, Maple Grove, MN 55369-4125
Tel (763) 391-5959 *Founded/Ownrshp* 1987
Sales 36.9MM^E *EMP* 60^E
SIC 1542 1799 Nonresidential construction; Hospital construction; Building site preparation
CEO: Paul Meyer
**Pr:* Verlyn Schoep
**Prin:* Kathleen Meyer
Sfty Mgr: Wilder Hoxie
Snr PM: Marc Allen

D-U-N-S 01-480-9511 IMP/EXP
MEYER CORP US
MEYER WINES
(*Suby of* MEYER INTERNATIONAL HOLDINGS LIMITED)
1 Meyer Plz, Vallejo, CA 94590-5925
Tel (707) 551-2800 *Founded/Ownrshp* 1982
Sales 78.4MM^E *EMP* 300
SIC 3469 3631 5023 Cooking ware, except porcelain enamelled; Household cooking equipment; Kitchenware; Cooking ware, except porcelain enamelled; Household cooking equipment; Kitchenware
CEO: Stanley Kin Sui Cheng
Pr: Robert Rae
COO: Ed Blackman
VP: Phil Barberi
VP: Barry Needleman
MIS Dir: Mike Marcotte

D-U-N-S 11-041-1209
MEYER DECORATIVE SURFACES USA INC
MAYER LAMINATES MA
(*Suby of* COMPAGNIE DE SAINT GOBAIN)
300 Executive Pkwy W # 100, Hudson, OH 44236-1690
Tel (800) 776-3900 *Founded/Ownrshp* 1990
Sales 54.5MM^E *EMP* 220
SIC 5031 Building materials, interior; Building materials, interior
Pr: David Sullivan

D-U-N-S 00-636-8914
MEYER DISTRIBUTING INC
560 E 25th St, Jasper, IN 47546-8117
Tel (812) 482-5102 *Founded/Ownrshp* 1937
Sales 216.0MM^E *EMP* 600
SIC 5013 5012

D-U-N-S 04-636-9450
MEYER ELECTRIC CO INC
3513 N Ten Mile Dr, Jefferson City, MO 65109-4991
Tel (573) 893-2335 *Founded/Ownrshp* 1968
Sales 36.7MM^E *EMP* 180
SIC 1731 General electrical contractor; General electrical contractor
Pr: Leon Keller
Pr: Jason Gruender
**VP:* Gary Heet
**VP:* Brian Keller
**VP:* Craig Linhardt
VP: Norma Meyer
VP: Victoria Meyer
Off Mgr: Marilyn Keller

D-U-N-S 03-915-5742
MEYER ENGLISH CIANCIULLI & PEIREZ P C
990 Stewart Ave Ste 300, Garden City, NY 11530-9882
Tel (516) 741-6565 *Founded/Ownrshp* 1961
Sales 23.1MM^E *EMP* 160
SIC 8111 General practice law office; General practice law office
Pt: John Klein
Pt: John H Byington
Pt: Murray D Schwartz
**VP:* Jeffery G Stark
**VP:* Joseph Suozzi
Mktg Dir: Jillian Eisman
Counsel: Richard Eisenberg
Counsel: Ira Warshawsky

D-U-N-S 12-986-8761
MEYER FC PACKAGING LLC
(*Suby of* MAFCOTE INC) ★
108 Main St Ste 3, Norwalk, CT 06851-4640
Tel (203) 847-8500 *Founded/Ownrshp* 2001
Sales 36.6MM^E *EMP* 200^E
SIC 3086 Packaging & shipping materials, foamed plastic; Packaging & shipping materials, foamed plastic
**CFO:* Steve Gilliand
Sales Exec: Matt Baryshyan

D-U-N-S 60-408-5399 EXP
MEYER HILL LYNCH CORP
1771 Indian Wood Cir, Maumee, OH 43537-4009
Tel (419) 897-9797 *Founded/Ownrshp* 1989
Sales 28.1MM^E *EMP* 40
SIC 5045 Computer peripheral equipment
Pr: D Stuart Lovee
**Pr:* D Stuart Love
**VP:* Robert Shick
DP Dir: Matt Farrington
Telecom Mg: Joe Perkins
Netwrk Eng: Herbert Bertz
Sls&Mrk Ex: Stuart Love
Mktg Mgr: Angel Belford

D-U-N-S 79-823-1189
MEYER JABARA HOTELS
7 Kenosia Ave Ste 2a, Danbury, CT 06810-7396
Tel (203) 798-1099 *Founded/Ownrshp* 1991
Sales 59.5MM^E *EMP* 509
SIC 7011 5813 5812 Hotels & motels; Cocktail lounge; Eating places; Hotels & motels; Cocktail lounge; Eating places
Pt: William Meyer
**Pt:* Richard Jabara
**CFO:* Henry Kelley
**Ex VP:* Kostas Kalogeropoulos
**Sr VP:* Kenneth R Conklin
Opers Mgr: Justin Jabara

D-U-N-S 88-455-3330
MEYER JABARA HOTELS LLC
1601 Belvedere Rd 407s, West Palm Beach, FL 33406-1518
Tel (561) 689-6602 *Founded/Ownrshp* 1989
Sales 20.1MM^E *EMP* 350
SIC 8741 Management services; Hotel or motel management; Management services; Hotel or motel management
Dir Risk M: Terri Stanganelli

D-U-N-S 02-120-6537
MEYER LABORATORY INC
2401 Nw Jefferson St, Blue Springs, MO 64015-7298
Tel (816) 228-4433 Founded/Ownrshp 1978
Sales 25.3MM^E EMP 65
SIC 2899 2842 2841 Chemical preparations; Specialty cleaning, polishes & sanitation goods; Soap & other detergents
Pr: Terry Oles
*Pr: Art Kurth
Exec: Sue Becker
*Prin: Russ Meyer
Sls Mgr: Hailey Dunham

D-U-N-S 02-320-5578 IMP
MEYER MANUFACTURING CORP
574 W Center Ave, Dorchester, WI 54425-9707
Tel (715) 654-5132 Founded/Ownrshp 1942
Sales 32.7MM^E EMP 120
SIC 3523 3433 Farm machinery & equipment; Spreaders, fertilizer; Balers, farm: hay, straw, cotton, etc.; Stoves, wood & coal burning; Farm machinery & equipment; Spreaders, fertilizer; Balers, farm: hay, straw, cotton, etc.; Stoves, wood & coal burning
Pr: Donald Meyer
*Sec: Judy Meyer
*VP: Larry Meyer
Off Mgr: Cheryl Sterzinger
Plnt Mgr: Michael Stock
Prd Mgr: John Andrew

D-U-N-S 02-540-6364
MEYER MATERIAL CO MERGER CORP
(Suby of AGGREGATE INDUSTRIES) ★
580 S Wolf Rd, Des Plaines, IL 60016-3139
Tel (815) 331-7200 Founded/Ownrshp 2006
Sales 61.8MM^E EMP 375
SIC 5032 3273 1771 1794

D-U-N-S 78-704-1961
MEYER MEMORIAL TRUST
425 Nw 10th Ave Ste 400, Portland, OR 97209-3128
Tel (503) 228-5512 Founded/Ownrshp 1982
Sales 51.5MM EMP 12
SIC 6732 Trusts: educational, religious, etc.; Trusts: educational, religious, etc.
Ex Dir: Doug Stamm
Ofcr: Sally Yee
Exec: James Rose
Software D: Jill Fuglister

D-U-N-S 14-928-9212 EXP
MEYER NATURAL ANGUS LLC
MEYER NATURAL FOODS
4850 Hahns Peak Dr, Loveland, CO 80538-6010
Tel (970) 292-5006 Founded/Ownrshp 2003
Sales 41.3MM^E EMP 38
SIC 5147 Meats & meat products
VP: Mike Pratt
VP: Bill Vanderbyl

MEYER NATURAL FOODS
See MEYER NATURAL ANGUS LLC

D-U-N-S 00-192-7516 IMP
MEYER PLASTICS INC
SILA SEAL
5167 E 65th St, Indianapolis, IN 46220-4816
Tel (317) 259-4131 Founded/Ownrshp 1950, 1931
Sales 24.9MM^E EMP 100
SIC 3089 5162 Thermoformed finished plastic products; Plastics materials & basic shapes
Pr: Ralph R Meyer
*CFO: Larry Pike
Mktg Mgr: Jason Williams
Sales Asso: Matt Muncie

MEYER PLUMBING SUPPLY
See AMERICAN INTERNATIONAL SUPPLY INC

MEYER PRODUCTS
See LOUIS BERKMAN CO

D-U-N-S 07-884-4997 IMP/EXP
MEYER PRODUCTS LLC
(Suby of LOUIS BERKMAN CO) ★
18513 Euclid Ave, Cleveland, OH 44112-1084
Tel (216) 486-1313 Founded/Ownrshp 2004
Sales 35.5MM^E EMP 86
SIC 3531 Construction machinery; Construction machinery; Blades for graders, scrapers, dozers & snow plows; Snow plow attachments
Pr: Andrew Outcalt
Exec: Craig Kemmerling
Dir IT: Carol Noell
IT Man: Chuck Cotter
Plnt Mgr: Ed Jakab
Natl Sales: Drew Aloisi
Manager: Greg Blankenheim
Manager: Mike Judson
Manager: Eric Sexton

MEYER REAL ESTATE
See PLEASURE ISLAND CORP

D-U-N-S 09-708-1608
MEYER SOUND LABORATORIES INC
2832 San Pablo Ave, Berkeley, CA 94702-2258
Tel (510) 486-1166 Founded/Ownrshp 1978
Sales 37.2MM^E EMP 170
SIC 3651 Loudspeakers, electrodynamic or magnetic; Loudspeakers, electrodynamic or magnetic
Pr: John D Meyer
*CFO: Brad Friedman
VP: Karen Ames
VP: David Beddingfield
Mng Dir: Jim Sides
QA Dir: Margarita Garza
Software D: Jeremy Friesner
VP Sls: Rick Coleman
Mktg Dir: Tim Chapman
Mktg Mgr: Jodi Hughes
Sls Mgr: Canada Franck-Olivier

D-U-N-S 08-535-0015 IMP
MEYER STEEL DRUM INC
IDEAL GERIT DRUM RING MFG
3201 S Millard Ave, Chicago, IL 60623-5078
Tel (773) 376-8376 Founded/Ownrshp 1976
Sales 70.0MM EMP 280
SIC 3412 5085 Drums, shipping: metal; Drums, new or reconditioned; Drums, shipping: metal; Drums, new or reconditioned
Pr: William Meyer
*Sec: Edward Meyer
Sls&Mrk Ex: Dan Burek
Sls Mgr: Michael Prack

D-U-N-S 00-425-0528 IMP/EXP
MEYER TOOL INC
3055 Colerain Ave, Cincinnati, OH 45225-1827
Tel (513) 681-7362 Founded/Ownrshp 1976
Sales 360.5MM^E EMP 800
SIC 3724 3599 Aircraft engines & engine parts; Machine shop, jobbing & repair; Aircraft engines & engine parts; Machine shop, jobbing & repair
Pr: Arlyn Easton
*VP: Larry Allen
VP: Beau Easton
*VP: Jerry Flyr
VP: Rick Kowalski
VP: Ed Mayer
IT Man: Doug Botle
Netwrk Mgr: Jim Hetcer
VP Mfg: Gary McGuire
Mfg Mgr: Rob Menzer
Ql Cn Mgr: Penny Carr

D-U-N-S 17-194-4721 IMP
MEYER U S A
(Suby of SAINT-GOBAIN BUILDING DISTRIBUTION LTD)
340 Patton Dr Sw, Atlanta, GA 30336-1843
Tel (404) 507-1200 Founded/Ownrshp 1987
Sales 24.5MM^E EMP 250
SIC 5031 Building materials, interior; Building materials, interior
CEO: Harry Fedden
*CEO: David Sullivan
*CFO: Jack Sable

MEYER WINES
See MEYER CORP US

MEYERPT
See WBC GROUP LLC

D-U-N-S 60-337-1915
MEYERS NAVE RIBACK SILVER & WILSON A PROFESSIONAL CORP
555 12th St Ste 1500, Oakland, CA 94607-4095
Tel (510) 351-4300 Founded/Ownrshp 1986
Sales 24.2MM^E EMP 107
SIC 8111 Legal services; Legal services
CEO: David W Skinner
Pr: Jo Barrington
Pr: Anabelle Cotapos
Pr: Patricia McNulty
*Pr: Steven R Meyers
Pr: Rhonda Simpson
Pr: Duyen Truong
*Sec: Elizabeth H Silver
Bd of Dir: Melissa Andrikopoulos
Bd of Dir: Robin Donoghue
Bd of Dir: Michael Hughes
Bd of Dir: Mara E Rosales
Bd of Dir: Linda Ross
Bd of Dir: Joanna M Smith
VP: Larry Cain
*VP: Michael S Riback

D-U-N-S 00-625-7026 IMP
MEYERS PRINTING COMPANIES INC (MN)
LABEL GROUP
7277 Boone Ave N, Minneapolis, MN 55428-1539
Tel (763) 533-9730 Founded/Ownrshp 1949
Sales 44.2MM^E EMP 235^E
SIC 2752

D-U-N-S 78-852-5553
MEYERS RV CENTERS LLC
MEYERS RV SUPERSTORES
(Suby of FREEDOMROADS LLC) ★
1000 Sanford Rd N, Churchville, NY 14428-9489
Tel (585) 293-3000 Founded/Ownrshp 2004
Sales 40.2MM^E EMP 250
SIC 5511 Automobiles, new & used; Automobiles, new & used
Reg Pr: Randy Thomson
VP: Mark Kalzone
Exec: Diane Pope

D-U-N-S 05-365-2079
MEYERS RV SUPERSTORE INC
MARK'S LEISURE TIME MARINE
5364 E Lake Rd, Conesus, NY 14435-9741
Tel (585) 346-2260 Founded/Ownrshp 1999
Sales 35.1MM^E EMP 135
SIC 5561 7538 Recreational vehicle dealers; Recreational vehicle parts & accessories; Recreational vehicle repairs
Pr: Mark D Meyer

MEYERS RV SUPERSTORES
See MEYERS RV CENTERS LLC

MEYERS SUPPLY
See ZWUSH LLC

D-U-N-S 16-175-0872 IMP
MEYERS-CARLISLE-LEAPLEY CONSTRUCTION CO INC
MCL CONSTRUCTION
14124 Industrial Rd, Omaha, NE 68144-3332
Tel (402) 339-2221 Founded/Ownrshp 1987
Sales 77.7MM EMP 85
Accts Lutz & Company Pc
SIC 1542 Commercial & office building, new construction; Commercial & office buildings, renovation & repair; Commercial & office building, new construction; Commercial & office buildings, renovation & repair
Pr: Robert Carlisle
*Sr VP: Anthony Fucinaro
*VP: Paul Beller
*VP: Nancy Benson
*VP: Gary Leapley
*VP: Greg Schwalb
Dir Bus: Travis Justice
Snr Mgr: Cathy Dugger
Snr Mgr: Joe Hebenstreit
Snr Mgr: Dennis Parr
Board of Directors: Robert Carlisle, Anthony Fucinaro, Gary Leapley

D-U-N-S 13-163-8830
MEYERTONS HOOD KIVLIN KOWERT & GOETZEL P C
MHKK&G
1120 S Capital Of Texas, West Lake Hills, TX 78746-6464
Tel (512) 853-8800 Founded/Ownrshp 2002
Sales 250.0MM EMP 72
SIC 8011 Offices & clinics of medical doctors

D-U-N-S 02-341-9570 IMP
■ **MEYN AMERICA LLC**
(Suby of MEYN LLC) ★
1000 Evenflo Dr, Ball Ground, GA 30107-4544
Tel (770) 967-0532 Founded/Ownrshp 1999
Sales 30.4MM^E EMP 150
SIC 3556 5083 Poultry processing machinery; Poultry equipment; Poultry processing machinery; Poultry equipment
CEO: Han Van Der Broek
*Pr: Han Defauwes
Opers Mgr: Jeremy Martin

D-U-N-S 96-328-5387
■ **MEYN LLC**
(Suby of MEYN BEHEER B.V.)
1000 Evenflo Dr, Ball Ground, GA 30107-4544
Tel (770) 967-0532 Founded/Ownrshp 1998
Sales 68.8MM^E EMP 412^E
SIC 3556 5083 Poultry processing machinery; Poultry equipment
Pr: Scott Russell
CFO: Marco Vanstraaten
Prgrm Mgr: Chris Massie
Genl Mgr: Carlos Pace

MEYNE COMPANY DIV , THE
See BULLEY & ANDREWS LLC

D-U-N-S 01-448-8215
■ **MEYOU HEALTH LLC**
(Suby of HEALTHWAYS INC) ★
27-43 Wormwood St Fl 6, Boston, MA 02210-1619
Tel (866) 885-2822 Founded/Ownrshp 2009
Sales 31.4MM^E EMP 1^E
SIC 5734 Software, computer games
Genl Mgr: Chris Carter

D-U-N-S 04-641-9382
MEZZ CAP
40 Wall St Fl 60, New York, NY 10005-1333
Tel (212) 250-2500 Founded/Ownrshp 2015
Sales NA EMP 370^E
SIC 6021 National commercial banks
Prin: Jeff Boyd
COO: Karen Bell
CFO: Mirek Lozinski
Chf Cred: Alan Delsman
Creative D: Anne-Katrin Mueldler
CTO: Yazad Patel

M.F. CACHAT COMPANY, THE
See M F CACHAT CO LLC

D-U-N-S 96-501-6830
MF GLOBAL HOLDINGS LTD
142 W 57th St Ste 401, New York, NY 10019-3462
Tel (646) 568-8114 Founded/Ownrshp 2010
Sales 313.6MM^E EMP 2,847^E
SIC 6211 Security brokers & dealers; Security brokers & dealers
Pr: Bradley I Abelow
COO: Karel F Harbour
*CFO: Henri J Steenkamp
*Ofcr: Michael G Stockman
Top Exec: Edward V Garlich Jr
Div VP: Patrick McClowry
*Genl Couns: Laurie R Ferber

D-U-N-S 05-059-3169
MF GLOBAL HOLDINGS USA INC
(Suby of MF GLOBAL HOLDINGS LTD) ★
717 5th Ave Fl 11, New York, NY 10022-8113
Tel (212) 589-6200 Founded/Ownrshp 2006
Sales 163.4MM^E EMP 982
SIC 6211 Security brokers & dealers; Security brokers & dealers
Pr: Ira Polk
COO: Bradley Abelow
Ex VP: Tom Harte
Board of Directors: David P Bolger, David Gelber

D-U-N-S 00-288-6799
MF LIGHTWAVE INC
CUSTOM CABLE
3221 Cherry Palm Dr, Tampa, FL 33619-8334
Tel (813) 623-2232 Founded/Ownrshp 1999
Sales 42.1MM^E EMP 200
SIC 3827 3357 Optical instruments & lenses; Fiber optic cable (insulated); Optical instruments & lenses; Fiber optic cable (insulated)
Pr: Stewart Saad
COO: Bradley Baylor
CFO: Ray Rowland
VP: M Olsen
Dist Mgr: Dave Ducharme
QA Dir: Steve Halbrook
Dir IT: James Turner
VP Sls: Davi Fox
Sls Dir: Robert Chipman
Sls Mgr: Phillip Rosatone
Sales Asso: Charles Merkey

D-U-N-S 08-008-4795
MF PARENT LP
16 New England Executive, Burlington, MA 01803-5217
Tel (781) 994-4800 Founded/Ownrshp 2014
Sales 62.5MM^E EMP 457^E
SIC 7359 Business machine & electronic equipment rental services

D-U-N-S 96-738-2511
MF SOUTHEASTERN HOLDING CORP
181 Security Pl, Spartanburg, SC 29307-5450
Tel (864) 582-8193 Founded/Ownrshp 2002
Sales NA EMP 3^E
Accts Elliott Davis Llc Greenville
SIC 6141 Personal credit institutions; Personal credit institutions
Pr: Susan Bridges

MFA AGRI SERVICES
See MFA INC

D-U-N-S 00-663-4211
MFA ENTERPRISES INC
FARMERS TRUCKING DIVISION
(Suby of MFA AGRI SERVICES) ★
201 Ray Young Dr, Columbia, MO 65201-3599
Tel (573) 874-5111 Founded/Ownrshp 1995
Sales 40.1MM^E EMP 95
SIC 5191 Farm supplies; Farm supplies
Pr: Bill Streeter
*Treas: Allen Floyd
Mktg Mgr: Jim Gesling

D-U-N-S 13-372-5676
MFA FINANCIAL INC
350 Park Ave Fl 20, New York, NY 10022-6054
Tel (212) 207-6400 Founded/Ownrshp 1998
Sales 463.8MM EMP 43^E
Accts Kpmg Llp New York New York
Tkr Sym MFA Exch NYS
SIC 6798 Real estate investment trusts; Real estate investment trusts
CEO: William S Gorin
Pr: Craig L Knutson
CFO: Stephen D Yarad
Sr VP: Kathleen A Hanrahan
Sr VP: Kathleen Hanrahan
Sr VP: Timothy W Korth
Sr VP: Terence Meyers
Sr VP: Matthew Ottinger
Sr VP: Harold E Schwartz
VP: Khalil Hraiche
VP: Shira Siry
Board of Directors: Stephen R Blank, James A Brodsky, Richard J Byrne, Laurie Goodman, Alan L Gosule, Robin Josephs, George H Krauss

D-U-N-S 00-696-5149
MFA INC
MFA AGRI SERVICES
201 Ray Young Dr, Columbia, MO 65201-3599
Tel (573) 874-5111 Founded/Ownrshp 1923
Sales 1.4MMM EMP 1,393
Accts Williams Keepers Llc Columbia
SIC 2875 2048 5191 5153 Fertilizers, mixing only; Prepared feeds; Farm supplies; Grains; Fertilizers, mixing only; Prepared feeds; Farm supplies; Grains
CEO: Ernie Verslues
Pr: Cassy Landewee
Treas: John Akridge
Treas: Patty Fuemmeler
*Sr VP: Janice Schuerman
*VP: Craig Childs
VP: Craig A Childs
*VP: Bill Coen
VP: Brian J Griffith
*VP: J Brian Griffith
VP: Dr Kent Haden
VP: David Moore
VP: Joe Powell
VP: Tom Staudt
*VP: Alan Wessler
Exec: Joe Weydert
Comm Dir: Chuck Lay
Board of Directors: Don Mills, Phillip Becker, John Moffitt, Glen Cope, R T Sloan, Joe Dent, Harry Thompson, Tim Engemann, David Cottrill Vice Chb, Lester Evans Chb, Kendall Kircher, Tim Lichte, Randy Ludwig, William McClure

D-U-N-S 00-696-5123 IMP
MFA OIL CO (MO)
1 Ray Young Dr, Columbia, MO 65201-3506
Tel (573) 442-0171 Founded/Ownrshp 1929
Sales 1.4MMM EMP 1,500
Accts Williams Keepers Llc Columbia
SIC 7549 5541 Lubrication service, automotive; Filling stations, gasoline; Lubrication service, automotive; Filling stations, gasoline
Ch Bd: Benny Farrell
CEO: Jerry Taylor
CFO: Robert Condron
VP: Curtis Chaney
Sls Mgr: Robert Burlbaugh

D-U-N-S 00-696-5131
MFA PETROLEUM CO
JIFFY LUBE
(Suby of MFA OIL CO) ★
1 Ray Young Dr, Columbia, MO 65201-3570
Tel (573) 442-0171 Founded/Ownrshp 1956
Sales 38.9MM^E EMP 800
SIC 7549 5531 7538 5984 Lubrication service, automotive; Automotive tires; Automobile & truck equipment & parts; General automotive repair shops; Liquefied petroleum gas dealers; Lubrication service, automotive; Automotive tires; Automobile & truck equipment & parts; General automotive repair shops; Liquefied petroleum gas dealers
CEO: Mark Fenner
*Pr: Jerome Taylor
Sr VP: Jerome Tayor
VP: James Belcher

MFC
See METAL FORMING & COINING CORP

MFC
See MINNESOTA FLEXIBLE CORP

MFC
See MEADVILLE FORGING CO LP

MFCP
See MOTION AND FLOW CONTROL PRODUCTS INC

D-U-N-S 12-720-5537 EXP
MFG COMPOSITE SYSTEMS CO
MFG CSC
(*Suby of* MOLDED FIBER GLASS COMPANIES) ★
2925 Mfg Pl, Ashtabula, OH 44004-9701
Tel (440) 997-5851 *Founded/Ownrshp* 1948
Sales 81.5MM^E *EMP* 350
SIC 3229 2823 Glass fiber products; Cellulosic manmade fibers; Glass fiber products; Cellulosic manmade fibers
Pr: Richard Morrison
**VP:* Andy Juhola

MFG CSC
See MFG COMPOSITE SYSTEMS CO

D-U-N-S 12-751-8855
MFG GALILEO COMPOSITES
(*Suby of* MOLDED FIBER GLASS COMPANIES) ★
18361 Galileo Dr, Opp, AL 36467-3774
Tel (334) 493-0014 *Founded/Ownrshp* 2003
Sales 81.4MM^E *EMP* 1,600^E
SIC 5731 3089 Antennas; Plastic processing; Antennas; Plastic processing
CEO: Richard Morrison
**CFO:* James G Irwin
IT Man: Alan Fletcher

D-U-N-S 96-815-5254
MFG HOLDINGS INC
1701 N Waverly St, Ponca City, OK 74601-2141
Tel (580) 762-5646 *Founded/Ownrshp* 2003
Sales 60.0MM^E *EMP* 302^E
SIC 5063 Power transmission equipment, electric; Power transmission equipment, electric
Pr: Steve Ballinger
**CFO:* John Soderstrom

D-U-N-S 02-316-4672
■ **MFI HOLDING CORP**
MICHAEL FOOD
(*Suby of* POST HOLDINGS INC) ★
301 Carlson Pkwy Ste 400, Minnetonka, MN 55305-5370
Tel (952) 258-4000 *Founded/Ownrshp* 2014
Sales 396.9MM^E *EMP* 3,596^E
SIC 6719 0252 Investment holding companies, except banks; Chicken eggs; Investment holding companies, except banks; Chicken eggs
Pr: Adrian M Jones
Pr: Michael Elliott
Ex VP: Deborah Laue
Sr VP: Thomas Jagiela
VP: Carol Morgan
VP: Thom Trace
VP: Adam Ziesel
IT Man: Mark Reimel
Mktg Mgr: Jacqueline Brown
Mktg Mgr: Sonia Johnson

D-U-N-S 05-433-9833 IMP
MFI INTERNATIONAL MANUFACTURING LLC (TX)
M F I INTERNATIONAL
9570 Pan American Dr, El Paso, TX 79927-2001
Tel (915) 858-0971 *Founded/Ownrshp* 1978
Sales 80.5MM^E *EMP* 500
SIC 2392 Household furnishings; Household furnishings
COO: Cecilia Levine
CFO: Larry Amrich
CFO: Christopher Santaguida
Dir Bus: Fatih Akben
Prgrm Mgr: Daniel Desperak
Prgrm Mgr: Gabriela Orozco
IT Man: Daniel Bohmer
Plnt Mgr: Miguel Cardona
Ql Cn Mgr: Ricardo Armendariz
VP Sls: Greg Freyermutn
Mktg Dir: Paola Ramos

D-U-N-S 11-211-1484 EXP
MFI PRODUCTS INC
(*Suby of* MCMURRAY FABRICS INC) ★
105 Vann Pl, Aberdeen, NC 28315-8612
Tel (910) 944-2128 *Founded/Ownrshp* 1999
Sales 35.2MM^E *EMP* 314
SIC 5013 2211 Automotive hardware; Apparel & outerwear fabrics, cotton; Automotive hardware; Apparel & outerwear fabrics, cotton
Pr: Brian McMurray

D-U-N-S 05-034-0819 IMP
MFM INC
BIG SAVE VALUE CENTER
4273 Rice St, Lihue, HI 96766-1330
Tel (808) 241-5222 *Founded/Ownrshp* 1926
Sales 39.4MM^E *EMP* 400
SIC 5411 5947 5541 Supermarkets, chain; Convenience stores, chain; Gift shop; Gasoline service stations; Supermarkets, chain; Convenience stores, chain; Gift shop; Gasoline service stations
Pr: Charles Kawakami
**Treas:* Yukie Murakami
**Sr VP:* Dennis Makiya
**VP:* Gary Furugen

D-U-N-S 14-839-8519
■ **MFOUNDRY INC**
(*Suby of* FIDELITY NATIONAL INFORMATION SERVICES INC) ★
60 E Sir Francis Drake Bl, Larkspur, CA 94939-1713
Tel (925) 254-6689 *Founded/Ownrshp* 2013
Sales 22.7MM^E *EMP* 200
SIC 7389 Financial services; Financial services
CEO: Drew Sievers
**CFO:* Kim Vogel
VP: Jon Squire
VP: Alex Yi
Snr Sftwr: Gary Fong
**CTO:* Rodney Aiglstorfer
QA Dir: Philip Ponsaran
QA Dir: John Walsenko
IT Man: Steven Gansemer
Sftwr Eng: Steven Donnelly
Sftwr Eng: Ricardo Reyna

D-U-N-S 62-541-4248
MFP AUTOMATION ENGINEERING INC
4404 Central Pkwy, Hudsonville, MI 49426-7831
Tel (616) 538-5700 *Founded/Ownrshp* 1991
Sales 33.1MM *EMP* 36
SIC 5084 3594 Industrial machinery & equipment; Pneumatic tools & equipment; Power plant machinery; Fluid power pumps & motors; Industrial machinery & equipment; Pneumatic tools & equipment; Power plant machinery; Fluid power pumps & motors
Pr: Roger L Betten Jr
**Pr:* David Grimm
**CEO:* Roger Betten
**VP:* Rod Kowalski
Sales Asso: Jill Paasch
Sales Asso: Jason Rogers
Sales Asso: Dave Spencer

MFP TECHNOLOGY SERVICES
See GLOBAL SOURCE LLC

D-U-N-S 79-297-2614
MFR TIRE SERVICES INC
ST LOUIS
5475 Brown Ave, Saint Louis, MO 63120-1709
Tel (314) 383-7300 *Founded/Ownrshp* 1992
Sales 50.8MM^E *EMP* 60^E
SIC 5014 Tires & tubes; Tires & tubes
Pr: Everette Slimp
**Treas:* Paul Weaver
**VP:* Michael Bajier
Sls Mgr: Jim Crandall

D-U-N-S 60-621-1977 IMP/EXP
▲ **MFRI INC**
7720 N Lehigh Ave, Niles, IL 60714-3491
Tel (847) 966-1000 *Founded/Ownrshp* 1993
Sales 194.8MM *EMP* 1,040^E
Tkr Sym MFRI *Exch* NGM
SIC 3677 3564 3569 Filtration devices, electronic; Blowers & fans; Filters & strainers, pipeline; Filtration devices, electronic; Blowers & fans; Filters & strainers, pipeline
Pr: Bradley E Mautner
**Ch Bd:* David S Barrie
CFO: Karl J Schmidt
Ofcr: Wayne Bosch
VP: Tom Benson
VP: Marilee Blackman
VP: Dhananjay Maslekar
VP: Billy E Rvin
Exec: Michael Gade
Exec: David Mautner
Sfty Mgr: Jon Bencheck
Board of Directors: David B Brown, Michael J Gade, Dennis Kessler, David Unger, Jerome T Walker, Mark A Zorko

D-U-N-S 95-836-2212
MFS INVESTMENT MANAGEMENT FOUNDATION INC
(*Suby of* M F S) ★
111 Huntington Ave # 200, Boston, MA 02199-7632
Tel (800) 343-2829 *Founded/Ownrshp* 2000
Sales 275.0MM^E *EMP* 722^E
SIC 6722 Mutual fund sales, on own account
Pr: John Ballen
Sr Pt: Thomas Ward
Pr: Paula Chapman
Pr: Rory Cowling
Pr: Christopher Grant
CFO: David A Antonelli
CFO: Amrit Kawal
**Ofcr:* Maria D Dwyer
Ofcr: Bob Emsing
Ofcr: Robyn Griffin
Ofcr: Stuart Lupton
Assoc VP: Gordon Forrest
Ex VP: Pat Zlotin
Sr VP: Mike Greene
Sr VP: David Rainville
Sr VP: John Riley
Sr VP: Brooks Taylor
Sr VP: Susan Unvarsky
Sr VP: Mark Weinburg
VP: Sal Barbagallo
VP: Matthew Barrett

MFS/YORK/STORMOR
See GLOBAL INDUSTRIES INC

D-U-N-S 78-882-7116
MG BUILDING MATERIALS LTD
(*Suby of* GROTHUES BROTHERS HOLDINGS LTD) ★
2651 Sw Military Dr, San Antonio, TX 78224-1048
Tel (210) 924-5131 *Founded/Ownrshp* 2005
Sales 211.5MM^E *EMP* 780
SIC 2421 4212 Sawmills & planing mills, general; Lumber (log) trucking, local
Pr: Alan Grothues
CFO: Kevin Sullivan
Sales Exec: Luis Ramos
Sls Mgr: Gary Miller

MG INDUSTRIES
See ALIG LLC

D-U-N-S 18-382-4655 IMP
MG INTERNATIONAL INC
(*Suby of* MG CO.,LTD.)
90 International Pkwy, Dallas, GA 30157-5738
Tel (770) 505-0004 *Founded/Ownrshp* 2003
Sales 31.6MM^E *EMP* 100
SIC 2821 Plastics materials & resins; Plastics materials & resins
CEO: Toshimichi Ito
**CFO:* Hironobu Shibuya
VP: Takatoshi Yamamoto

D-U-N-S 13-240-4042
MG LLC
Z-WIRELESS
(*Suby of* WHITE MOUNTAINS INSURANCE GROUP LTD) ★
2200 Fletcher Ave Ste 5, Fort Lee, NJ 07024-5016
Tel (201) 461-5665 *Founded/Ownrshp* 2014
Sales 33.3MM^E *EMP* 185^E
SIC 8742 Management consulting services; Management consulting services
Pr: David Graf
Pr: Anil Chappidi
**Ex VP:* Mercer Carlin
**Ex VP:* Mitchell Ginzburg
**Ex VP:* Andy Nelson
Sr VP: Lundgren Larry
VP: Jennifer Harbert
Mng Dir: Howard Sunkin
CIO: Jonathan Washburn
**CTO:* Fred Kauber

D-U-N-S 00-984-5397
MG MAHER & CO INC
(*Suby of* LIVINGSTON INTERNATIONAL INC)
365 Canal St Ste 1600, New Orleans, LA 70130-1133
Tel (504) 581-3320 *Founded/Ownrshp* 2012
Sales 27.2MM^E *EMP* 100
SIC 4731 Customhouse brokers; Freight forwarding; Transportation agents & brokers; Customhouse brokers; Freight forwarding; Transportation agents & brokers
Pr: David Schulingkamp
**Pr:* Peter Luit
**CFO:* Jill Floyd
**Ch:* Paula L Maher
**VP:* Robert Andru
**VP:* Joe Joseph
**VP:* Richard Kay

D-U-N-S 15-472-2326
MG MARKETS INC
MR GAS MARKETS
1817 W Lmar Alxander Pkwy, Maryville, TN 37801-3765
Tel (865) 983-4280 *Founded/Ownrshp* 1983
Sales 23.0MM^E *EMP* 95
SIC 5541 5411 7215 7542 Filling stations, gasoline; Convenience stores, independent; Laundry, coin-operated; Carwash, automatic
Ch Bd: Charles F Mc Nutt
**Pr:* Clara B Mc Nutt
**Sec:* Karen Mc Nutt Gale
**VP:* Pete Gale
**VP:* Susan E Mc Nutt

D-U-N-S 08-273-1993
MG OIL CO (SD)
FLYING J TRAVEL PLAZA
1180 Creek Dr, Rapid City, SD 57703-4111
Tel (605) 342-0527 *Founded/Ownrshp* 1976
Sales 355.5MM *EMP* 450
Accts Ketel Thorstenson Llp Rapid
SIC 5172 5541 5411 Gasoline; Diesel fuel; Lubricating oils & greases; Filling stations, gasoline; Convenience stores, independent; Gasoline; Diesel fuel; Lubricating oils & greases; Filling stations, gasoline; Convenience stores, independent
Pr: Marlyn G Erickson
**VP:* Troy Erickson
Genl Mgr: Dave Kulish
IT Man: Dan Davis
IT Man: Tami Hellendoorn
Sls Mgr: Ken Hutton
Sls Mgr: Todd Moe

D-U-N-S 83-117-5315
MG SECURITY SERVICES LLC
133 W 25th St Rm 8w, New York, NY 10001-7281
Tel (212) 242-6477 *Founded/Ownrshp* 2008
Sales 8.0MM^E *EMP* 300
SIC 7381 Protective services, guard; Protective services, guard
Pr: Manuel Gomez

D-U-N-S 00-727-8641 IMP/EXP
■ **MG WALDBAUM CO**
(*Suby of* MICHAEL FOODS OF DELAWARE INC) ★
301 Carlson Pkwy Ste 400, Minnetonka, MN 55305-5370
Tel (952) 258-4000 *Founded/Ownrshp* 2007
Sales 341.3MM^E *EMP* 2,694
SIC 2015 5153 5191 Egg processing; Eggs, processed: frozen; Eggs, processed: desiccated (dried); Grains; Feed; Egg processing; Eggs, processed: frozen; Eggs, processed: desiccated (dried); Grains; Feed
Pr: Mark D Whitmer
**CFO:* Mark Westther

MG2 ARCHITECTURE
See MG2 CORP

D-U-N-S 08-373-3428
MG2 CORP (WA)
MG2 ARCHITECTURE
1101 2nd Ave Ste 100, Seattle, WA 98101-2923
Tel (206) 962-6500 *Founded/Ownrshp* 1971
Sales 80.3MM^E *EMP* 460
SIC 8712 Architectural engineering; Architectural engineering
CEO: Mitch Smith
**Pr:* Russell Hazzard
**Ch:* Mitchell Smith
**Prin:* Brian Bonar
**Prin:* Patrick Kruger
**Prin:* Stan Laegreid
**Prin:* Mj Munsell
**Ex Dir:* Jerry Lee
CTO: Todd Enoki
Dir IT: Keith Martin
Snr PM: Tod Fukutomi

D-U-N-S 05-517-3959 IMP/EXP
MGA ENTERTAINMENT INC
16300 Roscoe Blvd Ste 150, Van Nuys, CA 91406-1257
Tel (818) 894-2525 *Founded/Ownrshp* 1980
Sales 417.9MM^E *EMP* 2,100
SIC 5092 Toys & games; Toys & games
Pr: Isaac Larian
Ex VP: Eli Makabi
VP: Lauren Conner
VP: Cathy Dean
VP: Terri Hauenstein
VP: Ninette Pembleton
VP Mktg: AME Cameron
VP Sls: Ann Maus

D-U-N-S 10-820-2854
■ **MGA INSURANCE CO INC**
(*Suby of* GAINSCO AUTO INSURANCE) ★
3333 Lee Pkwy, Dallas, TX 75219-5111
Tel (972) 629-4301 *Founded/Ownrshp* 1989
Sales NA *EMP* 2
SIC 6331 Automobile insurance
Pr: Glenn Anderson
Treas: Daniel Coots
Ex VP: Carolyn Ray
VP: John Graham
VP: Joseph Pitts

D-U-N-S 94-859-4890
MGA MANUFACTURING INC
2841 Pierce St, Dallas, TX 75233-1535
Tel (214) 467-4444 *Founded/Ownrshp* 1990
Sales NA *EMP* 700
SIC 2434

D-U-N-S 08-353-5385
MGA RESEARCH CORP
12790 Main Rd, Akron, NY 14001-9798
Tel (716) 542-5515 *Founded/Ownrshp* 1977
Sales 46.3MM *EMP* 130
SIC 8731 3829 8734 Commercial research laboratory; Physical property testing equipment; Testing laboratories; Commercial research laboratory; Physical property testing equipment; Testing laboratories
Pr: Patrick M Miller
VP: PM Miller II
Snr Mgr: Ali Kaafarani

D-U-N-S 06-108-7184
MGAGE LLC
3424 Peachtree Rd Ne # 400, Atlanta, GA 30326-1123
Tel (404) 942-5300 *Founded/Ownrshp* 2014
Sales 22.0MM *EMP* 50
SIC 7311 Advertising agencies; Advertising agencies

MGAM
See MUNICIPAL GAS AUTHORITY OF MISSISSIPPI

MGC
See MITSUBISHI GAS CHEMICAL AMERICA INC

D-U-N-S 10-281-8770
MGC CONTRACTORS INC
4110 E Elwood St, Phoenix, AZ 85040-1922
Tel (602) 437-5000 *Founded/Ownrshp* 2005
Sales 41.2MM *EMP* 150
Accts Alan Hoffmann Cpapc Phoeni
SIC 1629 Industrial plant construction; Waste water & sewage treatment plant construction; Industrial plant construction; Waste water & sewage treatment plant construction
Pr: Randy Gates
**VP:* Kurt Luvier

D-U-N-S 15-750-7237
▲ **MGC DIAGNOSTICS CORP**
350 Oak Grove Pkwy, Saint Paul, MN 55127-8507
Tel (651) 484-4874 *Founded/Ownrshp* 1986
Sales 30.0MM *EMP* 121^E
Accts Baker Tilly Virchow Krause Ll
Tkr Sym MGCD *Exch* NAS
SIC 3841 Surgical & medical instruments; Diagnostic apparatus, medical; Surgical & medical instruments; Diagnostic apparatus, medical
CEO: Todd M Austin
**Ch Bd:* Mark W Sheffert
Pr: Matthew S Margolies
COO: Wesley W Winnekins
Ex VP: Steve Lundeen
Sr VP: Jim Gaul
Dir Bus: Willy Martin
Mktg Dir: Patrick Burns
Board of Directors: John R Baudhuin, Terrence W Bunge, Wendy D Lynch, Robert E Munzenrider, Hendrik Struik

D-U-N-S 07-851-5545
MGC INC
6800 Sands Point Dr, Houston, TX 77074-3730
Tel (713) 800-7300 *Founded/Ownrshp* 2012
Sales 30.0MM *EMP* 120
SIC 2431 8734 Millwork; Testing laboratories; Millwork; Testing laboratories
CEO: David Mahood
**Pr:* Wes Furgerson

MGC LAW
See MCANGUS GOUDELOCK & COURIE LLC

D-U-N-S 95-994-8027 IMP/EXP
MGC PURE CHEMICALS AMERICA INC
(*Suby of* MITSUBISHI GAS CHEMICAL COMPANY,INC.)
6560 S Mountain Rd, Mesa, AZ 85212-9716
Tel (480) 987-9100 *Founded/Ownrshp* 1995
Sales 44.9MM^E *EMP* 70
SIC 2819 Chemicals, high purity: refined from technical grade; Chemicals, high purity: refined from technical grade
Pr: Yasuaki Matsumi
CFO: Eugene Tokraks
**Sec:* Akito Masunaga
**VP:* David Gallagher
Exec: Scott Hancock
**Prin:* Itaru Ikeya
Admn Mgr: Brenda Lenhardt
Sfty Mgr: Jene Tokraks
Ql Cn Mgr: Jim Kniery
Pdt Mgr: Yasuhiko Gamo
Sls Mgr: George Bacon

D-U-N-S 12-237-1599
▲ **MGE ENERGY INC**
133 S Blair St, Madison, WI 53788-0001
Tel (608) 252-7000 *Founded/Ownrshp* 1896
Sales 619.8MM *EMP* 695^E
Tkr Sym MGEE *Exch* NGS
SIC 4939 4911 4924 Combination utilities; Electric services; Natural gas distribution; Combination utilities; Electric services; Natural gas distribution
Ch Bd: Gary J Wolter
Pr: Gregory Bollom
CFO: Terry Hanson

CFO: Jeffrey C Newman
Sr VP: Lynn K Hobbie
VP: Kristine A Euclide
VP: Craig A Fenrick
VP: Mark T Maranger
VP: Gary Mathis
VP: Scott A Neitzel
VP: Peter J Waldron
VP: Mark C Williamson
Dir Bus: Jeff Ford
Board of Directors: Mark D Bugher, F Curtis Hastings, Regina M Millner, John R Nevin, James L Possin, Thomas R Stolper

D-U-N-S 07-834-2191 IMP
MGF SOURCING US LLC
MAST GLOBAL FASHIONS
(*Suby of* SYCAMORE PARTNERS MANAGEMENT LP) ★
4200 Regent St Ste 205, Columbus, OH 43219-6229
Tel (614) 904-3269 *Founded/Ownrshp* 2011
Sales 194.0MM^E *EMP* 750
SIC 5137 5136 Women's & children's clothing; Men's & boys' clothing; Women's & children's clothing; Men's & boys' clothing
Pr: James Schwartz

D-U-N-S 93-869-3652
MGH INC
M G H
100 Painters Mill Rd # 600, Owings Mills, MD 21117-7305
Tel (410) 902-5000 *Founded/Ownrshp* 1995
Sales 22.8MM^E *EMP* 85
SIC 8743 Public relations services
Pr: Andy Malis
**COO:* Jane Goldstrom
**Sec:* Terra Hopson
Ex VP: Mike Skandalis
Ex VP: Beth Willard
Sr VP: Dave Wassell
Sr VP: Shelley Welsh
VP: Daron Fisher
VP: Ryan Goff
VP: Chris McMurry
VP: Michael Obrien
VP: Genny Resch
Exec: Lindsay Novotny
Creative D: John Patterson

D-U-N-S 60-512-2258
MGH INSTITUTE OF HEALTH PROFESSIONS INC
NEUROENDOCRINE-UNIT
(*Suby of* GENERAL HOSPITAL) ★
36 1st Ave, Boston, MA 02129-4557
Tel (617) 726-8002 *Founded/Ownrshp* 1985
Sales 49.9MM *EMP* 150
SIC 8221 Professional schools; Professional schools
Pr: Janis Bellack
**Pr:* Ann W Caldwell
**CFO:* Atlas D Evans
**Treas:* Sally Boemer
Sr VP: Beatrice Thibedeau
Chf Nrs Of: Joanne Fucile
Prgrm Mgr: Christopher Lacerda
Off Admin: Laura Stengle
Opers Supe: Leah Jensen
Opers Supe: Margaret Rockcastle
Nrsg Dir: Lori Pugsley

D-U-N-S 78-938-8464
MGH PHYSICIANS
401 6th Ave, Montgomery, WV 25136-2116
Tel (304) 442-2613 *Founded/Ownrshp* 2006
Sales 25.4MM *EMP* 4^E
SIC 8011 Physical medicine, physician/surgeon; Neurologist; Physical medicine, physician/surgeon; Neurologist
Prin: Arturo Lim

MGI
See MINI GRAPHICS INC

D-U-N-S 62-337-4878
MGI HOLDINGS LP
(*Suby of* BLUE SAGE CAPITAL LP) ★
5912 Balcones Dr, Austin, TX 78731-4310
Tel (512) 459-4796 *Founded/Ownrshp* 2004
Sales 85.1MM^E *EMP* 800^E
SIC 5812 6794 Pizzeria, chain; Franchises, selling or licensing; Pizzeria, chain; Franchises, selling or licensing
CEO: Michael J Mrlik
Ch Bd: James D McBride
CFO: Steven B Burt

D-U-N-S 05-630-3956
MGI OF NC INC
2526 Ward Blvd, Wilson, NC 27893-1600
Tel (252) 243-7808 *Founded/Ownrshp* 2001
Sales 4.2MM^E *EMP* 500
SIC 8082 Home health care services; Home health care services
Pr: Terry Pilkington

MGIC INVESTMENT
See MORTGAGE GUARANTY INSURANCE CORP

D-U-N-S 10-829-5650
▲ MGIC INVESTMENT CORP
250 E Kilbourn Ave, Milwaukee, WI 53202-3102
Tel (414) 347-6480 *Founded/Ownrshp* 1984
Sales NA *EMP* 800^E
Tkr Sym MTG *Exch* NYS
SIC 6351 6411 Mortgage guarantee insurance; Insurance information & consulting services; Mortgage guarantee insurance; Insurance information & consulting services
Pr: Patrick Sinks
CFO: Michael Lauer
CFO: Timothy J Mattke
Ex VP: Jeffrey H Lane
Sr VP: Michael Meade
Sr VP: Joseph J Ziino
Sr VP: Michael Zimmerman
VP: Michael G Meade
VP: Paul Spiroff

VP: Dan Stilwell
Mng Dir: Robin Mallory
Board of Directors: Mark M Zandi, Daniel A Arrigoni, Cassandra C Carr, C Edward Chaplin, Curt S Culver, Timothy A Holt, Kenneth M Jastrow II, Michael E Lehman, Donald T Nicolaisen, Gary A Poliner

MGIS SERVICES,
See MEDICAL GROUP INSURANCE SERVICE INC

D-U-N-S 01-896-7183 IMP/EXP
MGK INTERNATIONAL INC
(*Suby of* MTC BUSINESS PRIVATE LIMITED)
13 Roszel Rd Ste C201, Princeton, NJ 08540-6384
Tel (201) 332-5645 *Founded/Ownrshp* 2007
Sales 65.2MM *EMP* 6
Accts Pandya Kapadia & Associates
SIC 5093 Ferrous metal scrap & waste; Nonferrous metals scrap; Ferrous metal scrap & waste; Nonferrous metals scrap
CEO: Hitendra Jain
**Prin:* Mahesh Navi
**Prin:* Arjun Vunnam

D-U-N-S 13-094-4361
MGL AMERICAS INC
1249 S River Rd Ste 102, Cranbury, NJ 08512-3633
Tel (609) 235-9632 *Founded/Ownrshp* 2001
Sales 41.6MM^E *EMP* 2,400
SIC 7379 7371 Computer related consulting services; Computer software development & applications; Computer related consulting services; Computer software development & applications
Ch: Sandy K Chandra
Ex Ofcr: Jaykar Krishnamurthy
S&M/Mgr: Amir Raza
S&M/Mgr: Ranga Sayee
Board of Directors: Sandy Chandra, Dr Nandu Thondavadi, Dr K S Vedantham

D-U-N-S 83-083-7089
MGL PARTNERS LLC
GOOD'S HOME FURNISHINGS
2220 Us Highway 70 Se # 220, Hickory, NC 28602-5192
Tel (828) 322-3471 *Founded/Ownrshp* 2009
Sales 20.1MM *EMP* 45^E
Accts Sledge And Company Pllc
SIC 5712 Furniture stores; Furniture stores
Owner: Scott Steven Lever
Owner: Randy Good

MGM
See METRO-GOLDWYN-MAYER STUDIOS INC

MGM
See TYSON DELI INC

MGM
See NATIONAL GRANGE MUTUAL INSURANCE CO

MGM
See METRO-GOLDWYN-MAYER INC

MGM BRAKES
See INDIAN HEAD INDUSTRIES INC

D-U-N-S 60-605-7180
MGM ENTERPRISES INC
APARTMENT GALLERY, THE
1 Waterford Pro Ctr, York, PA 17402-9280
Tel (717) 757-6638 *Founded/Ownrshp* 1984
Sales 26.1MM^E *EMP* 120
SIC 1522 Residential construction
Pr: Michael Groft
Rgnl Mgr: Dave Progelhof

MGM GRAND
See DESTRON INC

D-U-N-S 08-491-8791
■ MGM GRAND DETROIT LLC
(*Suby of* MGM RESORTS INTERNATIONAL) ★
1777 3rd St, Detroit, MI 48226-2561
Tel (313) 465-1777 *Founded/Ownrshp* 1999
Sales 500.0MM *EMP* 3,000
SIC 5812 7011 Eating places; Casino hotel; Eating places; Casino hotel
Ch: Jim Murren
**Pr:* Steve Zanella
Treas: Mike Gatten
VP: Juliette Eboh
VP: Marc Guastella
VP: Michael O'Connor
Info Man: Jeffrey Sauers
Secur Mgr: Ray McCullough
Advt Mgr: Tiffany Love
Mktg Mgr: Matt Buckley
Mktg Mgr: Lea Burnette

MGM GRAND HOTEL & CASINO
See MGM GRAND HOTEL LLC

D-U-N-S 80-744-9095 IMP
■ MGM GRAND HOTEL LLC
MGM GRAND HOTEL & CASINO
(*Suby of* MGM RESORTS INTERNATIONAL) ★
3799 Las Vegas Blvd S, Las Vegas, NV 89109-4319
Tel (702) 891-1111 *Founded/Ownrshp* 1993
Sales 369.1MM^E *EMP* 8,000
SIC 7011 Casino hotel; Casino hotel
Pr: Scot Sibella
**Pr:* Gamal Aziz
Sr Ex VP: Dave Cox
Ex VP: Mike Amie
**Ex VP:* Corey Sanders
Ex VP: Bill Scott
Ex VP: Myrna Soto
**Sr VP:* Tom Peterman
VP: Jeff Ellis
**VP:* Mark Huntley
VP: Brian Keenan
VP: Ann Krutchik
VP: Neil Lewis
VP: Patrick Lucas
VP: David McIntyre
VP: Cindy K Murphy
VP: Tom Reich
VP: Doug Seidenberg
VP: Richard Sturm

VP: London Swinney
VP: David Vera

D-U-N-S 19-835-2564
MGM HOLDINGS II INC
MGM STUDIOS
(*Suby of* M G M) ★
245 N Beverly Dr, Beverly Hills, CA 90210-5319
Tel (310) 449-3000 *Founded/Ownrshp* 2005
Sales 79.7MM^E *EMP* 1,465
SIC 7812 Motion picture & video production; Motion picture & video production
CEO: Daniel J Taylor
**CFO:* Steve Hendry
CFO: Tracy Reid
**Ex VP:* Charles Cohen
**Ex VP:* Scott Packman
VP: Cindy Wilford Perez
VP: Craig Ruby
Ex Dir: Marilyn Bernstein
CTO: Shannon Clark

D-U-N-S 19-396-9248
MGM HOLDINGS INC
M G M
245 N Beverly Dr, Beverly Hills, CA 90210-5319
Tel (310) 449-3000 *Founded/Ownrshp* 2010
Sales 79.9MM^E *EMP* 1,482^E
SIC 7812 Motion picture production & distribution
CEO: Gary Barber
**COO:* Ken Schapiro
**CFO:* Kenneth Kay

D-U-N-S 00-441-6608 IMP
MGM INDUSTRIES INC (TN)
(*Suby of* CUSTOM WINDOW SYSTEMS) ★
287 Free Hill Rd, Hendersonville, TN 37075-2136
Tel (615) 824-6572 *Founded/Ownrshp* 1990, 2015
Sales 61.4MM^E *EMP* 300
SIC 2591 Storm doors or windows, metal; Window blinds
Pr: Abe Gaskins
Treas: Joe Gaskins
VP: Richard Gaskins
VP Mfg: John Mackorell
Plnt Mgr: Ryan Blankenship

MGM LIQUOR WAREHOUSE
See MGM WINE & SPIRITS INC

D-U-N-S 78-201-8600
MGM PRODUCTS INC
1080 Culpepper Dr Sw, Conyers, GA 30094-5985
Tel (770) 483-0055 *Founded/Ownrshp* 1989
Sales 20.5MM^E *EMP* 50
SIC 3441 Fabricated structural metal
CEO: Wayne Raper
**Pr:* Robert W Wilkinson
**VP:* Carson Green
Genl Mgr: Carl Norris
Opers Mgr: Perry Parker
Snr Mgr: Rick Lanning

D-U-N-S 17-578-1913
▲ MGM RESORTS INTERNATIONAL
3600 Las Vegas Blvd S, Las Vegas, NV 89109-4303
Tel (702) 693-7120 *Founded/Ownrshp* 1986
Sales 10.0MMM *EMP* 68,100
Tkr Sym MGM *Exch* NYS
SIC 7011 Hotels & motels; Casino hotel; Resort hotel; Hotels & motels; Casino hotel; Resort hotel
Ch Bd: James J Murren
Pr: Bernard Efendi
Pr: William J Hornbuckle
Pr: D A Lin
Pr: Michael McBeath
COO: Corey I Sanders
CFO: Daniel J D'Arrigo
Chf Mktg O: Therese Bricknell
Ex VP: Richard C Harper
Ex VP: John M McManus
Ex VP: Andrew Schleimer
Ex VP: Robert C Selwood
Sr VP: Clark Dumont
Sr VP: Phyllis A James
Sr VP: Jenn Michaels
Sr VP: Cynthia K Murphy
Sr VP: Tom Peck
Sr VP: Richard Vosburgh
Sr VP: Bryan L Wright
Sr VP: Robert C Zapletal
VP: Christopher Henry
Board of Directors: William A Bible, Mary Chris Gay, William W Grounds, Alexis M Herman, Roland Hernandez, Rose McKinney-James, Anthony Mandekic, Gregory M Spierkel, Daniel J Taylor

D-U-N-S 84-895-3246 IMP
■ MGM RESORTS MISSISSIPPI INC
GOLD STRIKE CASINO RESORTS
(*Suby of* MANDALAY BAY RESORT AND CASINO) ★
1010 Casino Center Dr, Robinsonville, MS 38664-9758
Tel (662) 357-1111 *Founded/Ownrshp* 1993
Sales 13.1MM^E *EMP* 850
SIC 7999 Gambling establishment; Gambling establishment
CEO: Mike Hinson
**Pr:* George Corchis
**CFO:* Eric Wolfman
Genl Mgr: George Goldhoff

MGM STUDIOS
See MGM HOLDINGS II INC

D-U-N-S 06-089-9218 IMP/EXP
MGM TRANSFORMER CO
5701 Smithway St, Commerce, CA 90040-1583
Tel (323) 726-0888 *Founded/Ownrshp* 1975
Sales 43.0MM *EMP* 70
SIC 3612 Electrical apparatus & equipment; Transformers, except electric
Pr: Patrick Gogerchin
CFO: Don Trigillis
**VP:* Luis Otero
Genl Mgr: K D Tregillis
CIO: Chris Kaveh

D-U-N-S 19-428-8197
MGM WINE & SPIRITS INC
MGM LIQUOR WAREHOUSE
2550 University Ave W 201n, Saint Paul, MN 55114-1052
Tel (651) 487-1006 *Founded/Ownrshp* 1987
Sales 35.1MM^E *EMP* 250
SIC 5921 Hard liquor; Beer (packaged); Wine; Hard liquor
Pr: Terrence J Maglich
**VP:* Mike Maglich
Mktg Dir: Paul Setter

D-U-N-S 06-971-6736
MGMA-ACMPE
104 Inverness Ter E, Englewood, CO 80112-5313
Tel (303) 397-7869 *Founded/Ownrshp* 2011
Sales 24.3MM *EMP* 159
Accts Eks&H Denver Colorado
SIC 8621 8732 Medical field-related associations; Market analysis, business & economic research; Medical field-related associations; Market analysis, business & economic research
CEO: William F Jessee
**COO:* J Eric Cauble
**CFO:* Leah Brash
CFO: Wendy Rummler
Treas: Jeanie Cronrath
Treas: Amy Germann
Sr VP: Ann Vaughn
VP: Richard Hansen
VP: Kevin Spencer
Exec: Anna Bergstrom
Comm Dir: Cindy Hodges

D-U-N-S 07-008-2946
MGMNT DISTRICT SCHOOL BOARD OF BRADFORD COUNTY
501 W Washington St, Starke, FL 32091-2525
Tel (904) 966-6800 *Founded/Ownrshp* 1900
Sales 25.7MM^E *EMP* 600
SIC 8211 Public elementary & secondary schools; Elementary school; Secondary school; Vocational high school; Public elementary & secondary schools; Elementary school; Secondary school; Vocational high school
Prin: Robert Paterson Supt

MGMRESORTS
See MIRAGE RESORTS INC

D-U-N-S 62-307-2147
MGMT FIVE INC
SAXON, MIKE INVER GROVE FORD
4725 S Robert Trl, Inver Grove Heights, MN 55077-1108
Tel (651) 451-2201 *Founded/Ownrshp* 1990
Sales 32.9MM^E *EMP* 82
SIC 5511 Automobiles, new & used; Automobiles, new & used
CEO: Michael W Saxon
**VP:* James W Saxon
Genl Mgr: Jerry Bauer
Sls Mgr: Al Halcomb
Sls Mgr: Ken Hamen
Sls Mgr: R J Johnson
Sls Mgr: Tom Lisle

D-U-N-S 80-630-8529
MGO CAPITAL
5724 W 3rd St Ste 302, Los Angeles, CA 90036-3085
Tel (323) 658-3030 *Founded/Ownrshp* 2007
Sales 40.0MM *EMP* 18
SIC 6799 Commodity investors
Pr: Yehezkel Gurevitch
**VP:* Boaz Minitzer
**VP:* David Oscherowitz
**Prin:* Mali Gurevitch

D-U-N-S 04-833-1490
■ MGOC INC
(*Suby of* LIN TELEVISION CORP) ★
333 E Franklin St, Richmond, VA 23219-2213
Tel (804) 887-5000 *Founded/Ownrshp* 2014
Sales 674.9MM *EMP* 5,300^E
Tkr Sym MEG *Exch* NYS
SIC 4833 4841 Television broadcasting stations; Cable television services; Television broadcasting stations; Cable television services
Pr: George L Mahoney
CFO: James F Woodward
Ofcr: John McCarus
VP: Andrew C Carington
VP: James R Conschafter
VP: John R Cottingham
VP: Stephen Dickinson
VP: Robert E Macpherson
VP: Don Pratt
VP: Dan Ryan
Mktg Dir: Rose Dommer

D-U-N-S 83-879-1325 IMP
MGP HOLDING CORP
(*Suby of* GTCR GOLDER RAUNER LLC) ★
6451 Main St, Morton Grove, IL 60053-2633
Tel (847) 967-5600 *Founded/Ownrshp* 1995
Sales 39.0MM^E *EMP* 260
SIC 2834 Pharmaceutical preparations; Pharmaceutical preparations
Pr: William Goldberg
**Ch Bd:* Brian Tambi
**CEO:* Frank Leo

D-U-N-S 07-841-5272 IMP/EXP
▲ MGP INGREDIENTS INC (KS)
100 Commercial St, Atchison, KS 66002-2514
Tel (913) 367-1480 *Founded/Ownrshp* 1941
Sales 313.4MM *EMP* 268
Tkr Sym MGPI *Exch* NGS
SIC 2085 2041 2821 Distillers' dried grains & solubles & alcohol; Flour & other grain mill products; Plastics materials & resins; Distillers' dried grains & solubles & alcohol; Flour & other grain mill products; Plastics materials & resins
Pr: Augustus C Griffin
**Ch Bd:* Karen L Seaberg
Ofcr: Clodualdo Maningat
VP: Steve Glaser

VP Prd: Randy M Schrick
VP Sls: David E Dykstra
Board of Directors: John P Bridendall, Terrence P Dunn, Anthony P Foglio, George W Page Jr, Daryl R Schaller, M Jeannine Strandjord

D-U-N-S 00-712-8218 IMP/EXP
■ MGPI PROCESSING INC (KS)
(Suby of MGP INGREDIENTS INC) ★
100 Commercial St, Atchison, KS 66002-2514
Tel (913) 367-1480 Founded/Ownrshp 1941
Sales 89.1MM^E EMP 192^E
Accts Kpmg Llp Kansas City Missour
SIC 2085 2041 Distilled & blended liquors; Flour & other grain mill products; Distilled & blended liquors; Flour & other grain mill products
CEO: Gus Griffin
*CFO: Don Tracy
*VP: Scott B Phillips
*VP: Randy M Schrick
Board of Directors: Michael Braude, John E Byom, Gary Gradinger, Linda E Miller, Daryl R Schaller Phd, Karen Seaberg, John R Speirs

D-U-N-S 03-838-4348 IMP
MGR DESIGN INTERNATIONAL INC
1950 Williams Dr, Oxnard, CA 93036-2695
Tel (805) 981-6400 Founded/Ownrshp 2001
Sales 29.7MM^E EMP 200
SIC 3999 Potpourri; Candles; Potpourri; Candles
CEO: Michelle Bechard
*Pr: Rony Havive

D-U-N-S 03-629-4085 IMP/EXP
MGS GROUP NORTH AMERICA INC
TECXTAR
(Suby of MGS MFG GROUP INC) ★
W190n11701 Moldmakers Way, Germantown, WI 53022-2463
Tel (262) 250-2950 Founded/Ownrshp 1997
Sales 106.6MM^E EMP 425
SIC 3089 Plastic processing; Plastic processing
CEO: Mark G Sellers
*Pr: Craig Hall
*COO: Raig Hall
*Ex VP: Scott W Scampini
*VP: Kevin P Christ
*VP: Alan E Vick
Exec: Jeff Kolbow
Prgrm Mgr: Wade Schubert
Ql Cn Mgr: Keith Bates
VP Sls: Rudi Petrovic

D-U-N-S 00-300-4983 IMP
MGS INC (PA)
M G S TRAILERS
178 Muddy Creek Church Rd, Denver, PA 17517-9328
Tel (717) 336-7528 Founded/Ownrshp 1962, 1999
Sales 22.5MM EMP 120^E
Accts Weinhold Nickel & Company Ll
SIC 3443 3621 3799 5561 7539 3556 Fabricated plate work (boiler shop); Fuel tanks (oil, gas, etc.): metal plate; Motors & generators; Trailers & trailer equipment; Travel trailers: automobile, new & used; Trailer repair; Poultry processing machinery; Fabricated plate work (boiler shop); Fuel tanks (oil, gas, etc.): metal plate; Motors & generators; Trailers & trailer equipment; Travel trailers: automobile, new & used; Trailer repair; Poultry processing machinery
CEO: Andy Gehman
*VP: Joe Beatty
VP: Paul Gould
*VP: Phil Hornberger
*VP: Ted Miller
*VP: Chris Steinman
Div Mgr: Cory McQuate
Prd Mgr: Terry Burkholder
Sales Asso: Scott Shelley

D-U-N-S 03-628-7535 IMP/EXP
MGS MFG GROUP INC
W188n11707 Maple Rd, Germantown, WI 53022-2409
Tel (262) 255-5790 Founded/Ownrshp 1996
Sales 196.1MM^E EMP 450^E
SIC 3089 Plastic processing; Plastic processing
Pr: Mark G Sellers
Treas: Thomas Dunst
*Ex VP: Scott W Scampini
VP: Kenneth Eberle
VP: Pierre Lewis
*VP: Bruce Schneider
VP: Feliks Veysman
Exec: Laurel Herbst
Dir Bus: Bob Bordignon
Prgrm Mgr: Doug Hammond
Off Admin: Sarah Cummins

D-U-N-S 82-523-8707
MGS PLASTICS INC
(Suby of MGS MFG GROUP INC) ★
W188n11707 Maple Rd, Germantown, WI 53022-2409
Tel (262) 250-2950 Founded/Ownrshp 2003
Sales 36.4MM^E EMP 140
SIC 2821 Molding compounds, plastics; Molding compounds, plastics
Pr: Mark G Sellers
*VP: Paul E Manley

D-U-N-S 10-298-7666 IMP
MGT INDUSTRIES INC
CALIFORNIA DYNASTY
13889 S Figueroa St, Los Angeles, CA 90061-1025
Tel (310) 516-5900 Founded/Ownrshp 1983
Sales 60.8MM EMP 115^E
Accts Fineman West & Company Llp Lo
SIC 2339 Women's & misses' outerwear; Women's & misses' outerwear
CEO: Jeffrey P Mirvis
*Pr: Alessandra Strahl
*CFO: Phil Nathanson
*VP: Mike Brooks
VP: Tom Stevenson
VP Mfg: Lisa Grayson

MGWALGBAUMS
See MICHAEL FOODS INC

MH EBY TRAILERS
See M H EBY INC

D-U-N-S 02-574-3261 IMP
MH EQUIPMENT CORP
(Suby of M H EQUIPMENT COMPANY) ★
2001 Hartman, Chillicothe, IL 61523-9198
Tel (309) 579-8020 Founded/Ownrshp 2000
Sales 75.3MM^E EMP 140
SIC 5084 Industrial machinery & equipment; Materials handling machinery; Industrial machinery & equipment; Materials handling machinery
Pr: John S Wieland
Ex VP: Becky Czerkie
Brnch Mgr: Jeremy Burress
Brnch Mgr: Ted Nime
Brnch Mgr: Kevin Rodeman
Dir IT: James Gillis
IT Man: Matthew Lamb
Info Man: Margaret Zdanowski
Sls Dir: Violet Cook
Mktg Mgr: Jenny Fugate
Sls Mgr: Michael Kies

D-U-N-S 05-890-2644 IMP
MH EQUIPMENT CORP
(Suby of M H EQUIPMENT COMPANY) ★
3306 Gilmore Indus Blvd, Louisville, KY 40213-2173
Tel (309) 579-8020 Founded/Ownrshp 2000
Sales 54.3MM^E EMP 219
SIC 5084 Materials handling machinery; Materials handling machinery
Pr: John Wieland
Brnch Mgr: Brian Detrich
Brnch Mgr: Scott Revels

D-U-N-S 82-933-8743
MH EQUITY INVESTORS
(Suby of MHE PRIVATE EQUITY FUND LLC) ★
6270 Corporate Dr Ste 200, Indianapolis, IN 46278-2930
Tel (317) 582-2100 Founded/Ownrshp 2005
Sales 46.3MM^E EMP 810
SIC 6719 Investment holding companies, except banks; Investment holding companies, except banks
CEO: Stephen C Hilbert

D-U-N-S 96-502-3901
■ MH INC
(Suby of MGMRESORTS) ★
3950 Las Vegas Blvd S, Las Vegas, NV 89119-1005
Tel (702) 693-7120 Founded/Ownrshp 2010
Sales 12.5MM^E EMP 5,010^E
SIC 7011 Hotels & motels

D-U-N-S 13-555-7820 IMP
MH LOGISTICS CORP
M H EQUIPMENT COMPANY
2001 Hartman, Chillicothe, IL 61523-9198
Tel (309) 579-8030 Founded/Ownrshp 2000
Sales 218.5MM EMP 700
Accts Cliftonlarsonallen Peoria Il
SIC 5084 Industrial machinery & equipment; Materials handling machinery; Industrial machinery & equipment; Materials handling machinery
CEO: John S Wieland
*CFO: Bradley W Barrow
Brnch Mgr: Brian Michalec
Brnch Mgr: Ron Patterson
Trfc Dir: Valerie Correll
Opers Mgr: Amy Bailey
Opers Mgr: Brent Eiselstein
Sales Exec: Ken Mauch
Manager: Chad Ferry
Manager: Bob Lunt
Manager: David Manoni

D-U-N-S 04-074-2017
MHA LLC
MEADOWLANDS HOSPITAL MED CTR
55 Meadowlands Pkwy, Secaucus, NJ 07094-2977
Tel (201) 392-3200 Founded/Ownrshp 2010
Sales 468.1MM EMP 650
SIC 8062 General medical & surgical hospitals; General medical & surgical hospitals
Pr: Felicia Karsos
VP: Arturo Peralta
Dir Rx: Rosemary Bab
Genl Mgr: Marat Rysmendiev
CIO: Jim Yost
Dir IT: Olga Okonratev
Dir IT: William Regniault
Mktg Dir: Sally Deering
Ansthlgy: Michael E Tawfellos
Dir Health: Jenny Fernandez

MHA NATION
See THREE AFFILIATED TRIBES

MHAS
See OHIO DEPARTMENT OF MENTAL HEALTH & ADDICTION SERVICES

MHBT, A MARSH & MCLENNAN AGCY
See MHBT INC

D-U-N-S 10-730-7712
■ MHBT INC
MHBT, A MARSH & MCLENNAN AGCY
(Suby of MARSH & MCLENNAN AGENCY LLC) ★
8144 Walnut Hill Ln Fl 16, Dallas, TX 75231-4388
Tel (972) 770-1600 Founded/Ownrshp 2015
Sales NA EMP 206
SIC 6411 8741 Insurance agents, brokers & service; Insurance brokers; Financial management for business
CEO: Bill Henry
V Ch: Edward Troy
Pr: Dan Browning
COO: Robert C Smith
Ex VP: Brenda Smith
Sr VP: Danny Cox
Sr VP: Greg Rimling
Sr VP: Bryan Shofner
Sr VP: Matt Stadler
Sr VP: Brad Van Stavern
Sr VP: Brad Van Winkle
VP: Mike Buttrey
VP: Brett Herrington
VP: Marcus Humphrey
VP: Rick Koch

VP: Tiffany Parker
Creative D: Lauren Binkley
Board of Directors: Phil Brown, John D Fulkerson, Joe McQueary, Ted Troy

MHC HEALTHCARE
See MARANA HEALTH CENTER INC

D-U-N-S 07-465-5770
■ MHC INC
MIDAMERICAN
(Suby of MIDAMERICAN FUNDING LLC) ★
666 Grand Ave Ste 500, Des Moines, IA 50309-2511
Tel (515) 242-4300 Founded/Ownrshp 1996
Sales 3.8MMM^E EMP 3,500
Accts Deloitte & Touche Llp Des Moi
SIC 4924 4911 Natural gas distribution; Electric services; Natural gas distribution; Electric services
Ch Bd: David L Sokol
*Pr: Gregory E Abel
*Treas: Calvin D Haack
Netwrk Mgr: Solomon Egzi

MHC KENWORTH
See TEXAS KENWORTH CO

MHC KENWORTH
See OKLAHOMA KENWORTH INC

D-U-N-S 03-196-4653
MHC KENWORTH - KANSAS CITY
(Suby of MURPHY-HOFFMAN CO) ★
1524 N Corrington Ave, Kansas City, MO 64120-1944
Tel (816) 483-7035 Founded/Ownrshp 1986
Sales 199.7MM^E EMP 345
SIC 5012 Truck tractors; Truck tractors
Pr: Tim Murphy
*Ch Bd: Reed F Murphy Jr
*CFO: Jeff Johnson
*Ex VP: Kenneth Hoffman
Ex VP: Mike Murphy
VP: David Douglas
VP: Todd Harrington
VP: Steve Wisdom
Brnch Mgr: Bobby Bethune
Brnch Mgr: Bill Haworth
Brnch Mgr: Jason Mc Gehe

MHC KENWORTH - SAVANNAH
See GEORGIA KENWORTH INC

MHC KENWORTH- DURHAM
See CAROLINA NORTH KENWORTH INC

D-U-N-S 84-985-5788
■ MHC OPERATING LIMITED PARTNERSHIP
GOLF VISTA ESTATES
(Suby of EQUITY LIFESTYLE PROPERTIES INC) ★
2 N Riverside Plz Ste 800, Chicago, IL 60606-2682
Tel (312) 279-1400 Founded/Ownrshp 1996
Sales 83.1MM^E EMP 1,018
SIC 6515 6531 Mobile home site operators; Real estate agents & managers; Mobile home site operators; Real estate agents & managers
Mng Pt: Howard Walker
CIO: Joe McAdams

D-U-N-S 80-848-7602
MHC SERVICES LLC
201 Park Ave Ste 8, West Springfield, MA 01089-3368
Tel (413) 734-2148 Founded/Ownrshp 2006
Sales 17.0MM^E EMP 425
SIC 8741 Restaurant management; Restaurant management

D-U-N-S 10-250-9098
MHC TRUCK LEASING INC
(Suby of MURPHY-HOFFMAN CO) ★
1600 N Corrington Ave, Kansas City, MO 64120-1946
Tel (816) 483-0604 Founded/Ownrshp 1985
Sales 25.1MM^E EMP 131
SIC 7513 Truck leasing, without drivers; Truck rental, without drivers
Pr: Reed Murphy III
VP: Russell Laing
VP: Jared White
Brnch Mgr: Ron Jones
Sales Asso: Jimmy Wheeler

D-U-N-S 02-713-4979
MHE PRIVATE EQUITY FUND LLC
6270 Corporate Dr Ste 200, Indianapolis, IN 46278-2930
Tel (317) 582-2100 Founded/Ownrshp 2005
Sales 67.1MM^E EMP 825
SIC 6719 Investment holding companies, except banks; Investment holding companies, except banks
CEO: Stephen C Hilbert

MHESAC
See MONTANA HIGHER EDUCATION STUDENT ASSISTANCE CORP

D-U-N-S 16-259-5409
MHF PIT OPERATING IV LLC
HYATT REGEN PITTS INTER AIRPO
(Suby of MAGNA HOSPITALITY GROUP LC) ★
1111 Airport Blvd, Pittsburgh, PA 15231
Tel (724) 899-1234 Founded/Ownrshp 2013
Sales 20.4MM EMP 120
SIC 7011 5812 Hostels; Buffet (eating places)
CEO: Robert Indeglia
Genl Mgr: Chris Park

D-U-N-S 05-012-5434 IMP/EXP
MHH HOLDINGS INC
COFFEE BEAN & TEA LEAF
4580 Calle Alto, Camarillo, CA 93012-8509
Tel (805) 484-7924 Founded/Ownrshp 1963
Sales 74.3MM^E EMP 700
SIC 5499 Coffee; Tea; Coffee; Tea
Pr: Mona S Hyman
*Ch Bd: Herbert B Hyman
*Sec: Ann Hyman
*VP: Cori Connell
VP: Bill Robards

MHI HOTELS
See MARYLAND HOSPITALITY INC

D-U-N-S 79-063-9843 IMP
MHI PARTNERSHIP LTD
PLANTATION HOMES
7676 Woodway Dr Ste 104, Houston, TX 77063-1521
Tel (713) 952-6767 Founded/Ownrshp 1991
Sales 485.0MM^E EMP 350
Accts Ernst & Young Llp Houston Tx
SIC 1531 Speculative builder, single-family houses; Speculative builder, single-family houses
Ch Bd: Frank B McGuyer
Pr: Mike K Love
CFO: Gary Tesch
Ex Dir: Charles H Phillips

MHI SHIP REPAIR & SERVICES
See MARINE HYDRAULICS INTERNATIONAL INC

MHIA
See MITSUBISHI HEAVY INDUSTRIES AMERICA INC

MHKK&G
See MEYERTONS HOOD KIVLIN KOWERT & GOETZEL P C

D-U-N-S 79-981-0788
MHM CORRECTIONAL SERVICES INC
(Suby of MHM SERVICES INC) ★
1593 Spring Hill Rd # 610, Vienna, VA 22182-2249
Tel (703) 749-4600 Founded/Ownrshp 1997
Sales 15.9MM^E EMP 350
SIC 8093 Mental health clinic, outpatient; Mental health clinic, outpatient
Ch Bd: Michael S Pinkert
Pr: Deborah Crook
*Pr: Steven H Wheeler
CFO: Patrick Chunn
CFO: Susan Richie
*CFO: Susan Ritchie
Sr VP: Louie McKinney
Sr VP: David Westrate
Dir Bus: Andrew Sell
Off Mgr: Brenda Sloan
IT Man: Aliza Panitz

D-U-N-S 09-534-7357 IMP
MHM SERVICES INC
1593 Spring Hill Rd # 600, Vienna, VA 22182-2245
Tel (703) 749-4600 Founded/Ownrshp 1981
Sales 118.4MM^E EMP 2,143
Accts Pricewaterhousecoopers Llp Mc
SIC 8093 8361 8063 Mental health clinic, outpatient; Residential care; Psychiatric hospitals; Mental health clinic, outpatient; Residential care; Psychiatric hospitals
Pr: Steven H Wheeler
COO: David Lotocki
*CFO: John Campbell
CFO: Patrick Chunn
Sr VP: Michael Pinkert
VP: Gina Morris
VP: Rock Welch
Prgrm Mgr: Mike Hooper
Prgrm Mgr: Jeanne Jones
Prgrm Mgr: Vicki Love
Prgrm Mgr: Inez Tann

MHMR OF TARRANT COUNTY
See MENTAL HEALTH MENTAL RETARDATION OF TARRANT COUNTY

D-U-N-S 80-818-2559
■ MHN SERVICES
(Suby of HEALTH NET INC) ★
2370 Kerner Blvd, San Rafael, CA 94901-5546
Tel (415) 460-8300 Founded/Ownrshp 1988
Sales NA EMP 1,000
SIC 6324 8011 8742 8322 Hospital & medical service plans; Health maintenance organization; Management consulting services; Social service center; Hospital & medical service plans; Health maintenance organization; Management consulting services; Social service center
Pr: Juanell Hefner
Chf Mktg O: Ian Shaffer

D-U-N-S 96-502-4149
■ MHP INC
(Suby of COVENTRY HEALTH CARE INC) ★
14528 South Outer 40 Rd # 300, Chesterfield, MO 63017-5785
Tel (314) 214-8100 Founded/Ownrshp 2010
Sales 40.2MM^E EMP 400^E
SIC 6719 Investment holding companies, except banks; Investment holding companies, except banks
CEO: Chris Knackstedt
*COO: Mike Treash

MHQ MUNICIPAL VEHICLES
See NATICK AUTO SALES INC

MHRA
See PUBLIC HEALTH SOLUTIONS

D-U-N-S 82-998-8968
MHS LEGACY GROUP INC
1054 Central Indus Dr, Saint Louis, MO 63110-2304
Tel (314) 771-3080 Founded/Ownrshp 2009
Sales 49.3MM EMP 900
SIC 1742 1761 Insulation, buildings; Roofing, siding & sheet metal work; Insulation, buildings; Roofing, siding & sheet metal work
CEO: Walter O Hatfield
*Ch Bd: George Carlton McGrew
*CFO: John J Slattery
*VP: Carlton R Sumner
Genl Mgr: Tom Fleming
Plnt Mgr: Vern Hopley

MHS LIFT
See MATERIAL HANDLING SUPPLY INC

MHT LUXURY ALLOYS
See MOBILE HI-TECH WHEELS

D-U-N-S 00-253-6449 IMP/EXP
MHW LTD (NY)
MICHAEL LERNER SELECTION
1129 Nthrn Blvd Ste 312, Manhasset, NY 11030-3022
Tel (516) 869-9170 Founded/Ownrshp 1934, 1977

Sales 50.2MM^E *EMP* 86
SIC 5182 5181 Wine; Neutral spirits; Beer & ale; Wine; Neutral spirits; Beer & ale
CEO: John F Beaudette
**Ch Bd:* Peter K Warren
**CFO:* Hilary Grossman
**V Ch Bd:* Dr Edmund B Piccolino
**Ex VP:* Scott L Saul
Ex VP: Scott Saul
**VP:* Maryann Pisani
Opers Mgr: Philip Dunne
Opers Mgr: Jeanette Jankiewicz
Opers Mgr: Alexandra Morey

D-U-N-S 07-962-7697
MHWIRTH INC
(*Suby of* MHWIRTH AS)
3010 Briarpark Dr Ste 500, Houston, TX 77042-3755
Tel (713) 988-2002 *Founded/Ownrshp* 2014
Sales 24.9MM^E *EMP* 43^E
SIC 1381 Directional drilling oil & gas wells
CEO: Roy Dyrseth
**COO:* Andrew Bruce
**CFO:* Ole Falk Hansen
**Sr VP:* William Faubel
**Sr VP:* Thor Arne Hverstad

MI
See MERCHANDISE INC

D-U-N-S 09-027-9220
MI - DE - CON INC
3331 S 3rd St, Ironton, OH 45638-2863
Tel (740) 532-2277 *Founded/Ownrshp* 1999
Sales 25.0MM^E *EMP* 99
SIC 1542 Nonresidential construction; Nonresidential construction
Pr: Michael L Floyd
**Pr:* Dennis L Salyers

MI CMNTY BLOOD CTR-GRND RAPIDS
See MICHIGAN BLOOD

MI COSTENITA
See YOLI INC

MI GENTE ADULT DAY CARE CENTER
See DEL VALLE LAS MANITAS INC

D-U-N-S 19-760-9340 IMP/EXP
MI GROUP INC
MOVERS INTERNATIONAL
(*Suby of* MI GROUP LTD,THE)
118 Algonquin Pkwy, Whippany, NJ 07981-1602
Tel (905) 812-8900 *Founded/Ownrshp* 1988
Sales 50.3MM^E *EMP* 350
SIC 7389

MI HOTEL CINCINNATI
See CINCINNATI SI CO AN OHIO LIMITED PARTNERSHIP

D-U-N-S 02-319-2268
MI METALS INC
(*Suby of* BEAM ASSOCIATES LLC) ★
301 Commerce Blvd, Oldsmar, FL 34677-2806
Tel (813) 855-5695 *Founded/Ownrshp* 2013
Sales 414.2MM^E *EMP* 350^E
SIC 3585 Refrigeration & heating equipment; Aluminum extruded products; Refrigeration & heating equipment
Pr: Brook Massey
VP: Kevin Sponsler

D-U-N-S 06-011-0731
MI NURSING/RESTORATIVE CENTER INC
(*Suby of* COVENANT HEALTH INC) ★
172 Lawrence St, Lawrence, MA 01841-3849
Tel (978) 685-6321 *Founded/Ownrshp* 1875
Sales 19.3MM *EMP* 325
SIC 8051 8069 Skilled nursing care facilities; Specialty hospitals, except psychiatric; Skilled nursing care facilities; Specialty hospitals, except psychiatric
Pr: Barbara Grant
Nrsg Dir: Christine Pierre
HC Dir: Donna Brousseau

D-U-N-S 09-109-5786 IMP
MI PAN ASOCIADOS INC
Carr 866 Km 3/4 St Ca, Sabana Seca, PR 00952
Tel (787) 784-6604 *Founded/Ownrshp* 1974
Sales 20.0MM *EMP* 79
SIC 2051 Bread, all types (white, wheat, rye, etc): fresh or frozen; Bread, all types (white, wheat, rye, etc): fresh or frozen
Pr: Jose Luis Labeaga
**Treas:* Alfonso R Labeaga

MI PUEBLO FOOD CENTER
See MI PUEBLO LLC

D-U-N-S 02-745-7396
MI PUEBLO LATIN MARKET INC
MI PUEBLO MARKET
15421 E Batavia Dr, Aurora, CO 80011-4607
Tel (303) 531-2488 *Founded/Ownrshp* 2000
Sales 49.1MM^E *EMP* 400
SIC 5411 Grocery stores; Grocery stores
CEO: Jaime A Cueva

D-U-N-S 84-545-7063 IMP
MI PUEBLO LLC
MI PUEBLO FOOD CENTER
1775 Story Rd Ste 120, San Jose, CA 95122-1942
Tel (408) 928-1171 *Founded/Ownrshp* 1995
Sales 386.5MM^E *EMP* 1,500
SIC 5411 Grocery stores; Grocery stores
Pr: Javier Ramirez
**Ch Bd:* Juvenal Chavez
Pr: Sally Hernandez
**CFO:* Martin Cortes
VP: Greg Kare
**VP:* Perla A Rodriguez
**VP:* Hector Salas
VP: Guillermo Washington
Store Dir: Gabriel Arias
Store Dir: Jorge Fernandez
Pgrm Dir: Enrique Chavez

MI PUEBLO MARKET
See MI PUEBLO LATIN MARKET INC

MI RANCHO
See ROBERT BERBER & SON INC

MI RANCHO TORTILLA FACTORY
See BERBER FOOD MANUFACTURING INC

D-U-N-S 15-710-5185 IMP
MI TECHNOLOGIES INC
DISCOUNT MERCHANT.COM
2215 Pseo De Las Americas, San Diego, CA 92154-7908
Tel (619) 710-2637 *Founded/Ownrshp* 2004
Sales 21.6MM *EMP* 130
SIC 3672 3469 3089 Printed circuit boards; Metal stampings; Injection molding of plastics; Printed circuit boards; Metal stampings; Injection molding of plastics
CEO: Amir Tafreshi
**CFO:* John Celms
Comm Man: Angel Hodges
**Prin:* Ali Irani-Tehrani
Sls Mgr: Sam Shalchi

MI TIERRA CAFE & BAKERY
See MTC INC

D-U-N-S 00-829-7277 EXP
MI WINDOWS AND DOORS INC
650 W Market St, Gratz, PA 17030
Tel (717) 365-3300 *Founded/Ownrshp* 2013
Sales 651.1MM^E *EMP* 2,500
SIC 3089 3442 Window frames & sash, plastic; Screens, window, metal; Window frames & sash, plastic; Screens, window, metal
CEO: Peter Desoto
**Pr:* Jay K Poppleton
**CFO:* Sarah W Gutherie
**Treas:* Stan Sullivan
Sr VP: Jerry Meyer
**VP:* Matt Desoto
VP: Jeff Paradise
IT Man: Troy Liddick
IT Man: Mick Lower
Tech Mgr: Brent Sitlinger
Prd Mgr: Brett Erdman

D-U-N-S 12-127-0024 IMP/EXP
MI-JACK PRODUCTS INC
(*Suby of* LANCO INTERNATIONAL INC) ★
3111 167th St, Hazel Crest, IL 60429-0975
Tel (708) 596-5200 *Founded/Ownrshp* 1954
Sales 129.5MM^E *EMP* 450^E
SIC 3531 8711 Construction machinery; Designing: ship, boat, machine & product; Construction machinery; Designing: ship, boat, machine & product
Pr: Michael T Lanigan
**Ch Bd:* John J Lanigan Sr
**CFO:* Stephen J Bayers
Ex VP: Mike T Lanigan
VP: Grace Michael
Snr Sftwr: Eugene Zhukovsky
Dir IT: Jason Morris
IT Man: Alex Pawlicki
IT Man: John Wepfer
IT Man: Denise Werner
Netwrk Mgr: David Nagle

D-U-N-S 01-127-8724
MI-SHER FLEET SPECIALIST INC
2765 Florence Rd, Ponder, TX 76259-3406
Tel (940) 479-0414 *Founded/Ownrshp* 2008
Sales 28.9MM^E *EMP* 42^E
SIC 5013 Automotive brakes
Pr: Michael Baus
**Treas:* Sheryl Baus

D-U-N-S 06-324-2200 IMP/EXP
MI-T-M CORP (IA)
50 Mitm Dr, Peosta, IA 52068
Tel (563) 556-7484 *Founded/Ownrshp* 1971
Sales 156.2MM^E *EMP* 330
SIC 3569 Liquid automation machinery & equipment; Liquid automation machinery & equipment
CEO: A J Spiegel
**Pr:* Sam Humphrey
CFO: Tom Allendorf
**VP:* Dana Schrack
Admn Mgr: Becky Kremer
Ql Cn Mgr: Brian Ruden
Mktg Mgr: Karen Anderson

D-U-N-S 09-201-4901
MI-TECH METALS INC
4701 Massachusetts Ave, Indianapolis, IN 46218-3144
Tel (317) 549-4290 *Founded/Ownrshp* 1994
Sales 39.8MM^E *EMP* 100
SIC 3356 Tungsten, basic shapes; Tungsten, basic shapes
CEO: A J Bir
CTO: Kurt Kelso
Plnt Mgr: Eric Spoo

D-U-N-S 60-207-2357
MI-TECH SERVICES INC
46 S Rolling Meadows Dr, Fond Du Lac, WI 54937-9802
Tel (920) 924-3690 *Founded/Ownrshp* 2000
Sales 20.6MM^E *EMP* 150
Accts Evans & Race Co Llc Cpa S
SIC 8711 Consulting engineer
Pr: Dean Cline
**Treas:* John Schroeder
Mktg Mgr: Jim Walker

D-U-N-S 07-969-9271
MI9 RETAIL INC
12000 Biscayne Blvd # 600, North Miami, FL 33181-2735
Tel (647) 849-1101 *Founded/Ownrshp* 2014
Sales 28.9MM^E *EMP* 87^E
SIC 6719 Investment holding companies, except banks
Ch: James Zubok

MIAC
See MERRITT ISLAND AIR & HEAT INC

MIAC ANALYTICS
See MORTGAGE INDUSTRY ADVISORY CORP

MIAMI ACURA
See PUMA MANAGEMENT INC

D-U-N-S 04-341-1664 IMP/EXP
MIAMI AGROIMPORT INC
8298 Nw 21st St, Doral, FL 33122-1515
Tel (954) 442-9912 *Founded/Ownrshp* 1996
Sales 49.2MM^E *EMP* 15
SIC 5148 Fresh fruits & vegetables; Fresh fruits & vegetables
Pr: Tulio R Garcia
Off Admin: Soraya Londono

D-U-N-S 78-327-0317 IMP
MIAMI AIR INTERNATIONAL INC
(*Suby of* TSI HOLDING CO) ★
5000 Nw 36th St Ste 307, Miami, FL 33166-2763
Tel (305) 876-3600 *Founded/Ownrshp* 2004
Sales 55.3MM^E *EMP* 355
SIC 4522

D-U-N-S 03-609-4985
MIAMI AIRCRAFT SUPPORT INC
(*Suby of* AIRLINE SERVICES) ★
Palm Beach Intl Arprt, West Palm Beach, FL 33401
Tel (561) 689-0270 *Founded/Ownrshp* 1999
Sales 28.4MM^E *EMP* 930
Accts Kpmg Llp
SIC 4581 Air freight handling at airports; Air freight handling at airports
Pr: Anthony C Romeo
**Sec:* Paula Romeo
**VP:* Charles A Micale

D-U-N-S 62-334-3753 EXP
MIAMI AUTOMOTIVE RETAIL INC
BRICKELL HONDA, BUICK & GMC
665 Sw 8th St, Miami, FL 33130-3308
Tel (305) 856-3000 *Founded/Ownrshp* 2001
Sales 71.8MM^E *EMP* 115
SIC 5511 Automobiles, new & used; Automobiles, new & used
Pr: Mario Murgado
**VP:* Alexander Andreus
**VP:* Ricardo Barraza
Sls Mgr: Atif Latif

D-U-N-S 09-494-6183
MIAMI BEACH COMMUNITY HEALTH CENTER INC
11645 Biscayne Blvd # 103, North Miami, FL 33181-3138
Tel (305) 538-8835 *Founded/Ownrshp* 1977
Sales 43.9MM *EMP* 168
SIC 8011 Primary care medical clinic; Primary care medical clinic
CEO: Dr Mark Rabinowitz
Ex VP: Diego Martinez
VP: Rick Faria
VP: Orlando Taquechel
MIS Dir: Elieser Barrios
IT Man: Guillermo Fernandez
Doctor: Viviana Bilasano
Doctor: Jorge Rangel

MIAMI BEACH CONVENTION CENTER
See CITY OF MIAMI BEACH

D-U-N-S 07-386-9471
■ **MIAMI BEACH HEALTHCARE GROUP LTD**
AVENTURA HOSPITAL AND MED CTR
(*Suby of* HCA INC) ★
20900 Biscayne Blvd, Miami, FL 33180-1407
Tel (305) 682-7000 *Founded/Ownrshp* 1991
Sales 151.9MM^E *EMP* 1,100
SIC 8062 General medical & surgical hospitals; General medical & surgical hospitals
Ofcr: Dianne Goldenberg
Chf Rad: Reuven Porges
Chf Mktg O: Lester Eljack
Chf Mktg O: Alan Kutner
Dir Risk M: Patty Stover
Chf Nrs Of: Pam Hardesty
Doctor: Michael Bahrami
Doctor: Lawrence Berger
Doctor: Eugenio Bricio
Doctor: Henry Chua
Doctor: Aldo Coelho

MIAMI BEACH OCEAN RESORT
See PALMS SOUTH BEACH INC

D-U-N-S 05-133-7533 EXP
MIAMI BEEF CO INC
SPECIAL MEATS
4870 Nw 157th St, Miami Lakes, FL 33014-6486
Tel (305) 621-3252 *Founded/Ownrshp* 1972
Sales 28.4MM^E *EMP* 45
SIC 5142 5812 2011 Packaged frozen goods; Eating places; Meat packing plants
Pr: Michael Young
**Sec:* Jacqueline Young
**VP:* Betty Young

MIAMI BEHAVIORAL CENTER
See SPECTRUM FOUNDATION INC

D-U-N-S 09-720-1727 EXP
MIAMI BEHAVIORAL HEALTH CENTER INC (FL)
6100 Blue Lagoon Dr # 400, Miami, FL 33126-2080
Tel (305) 398-6101 *Founded/Ownrshp* 1977
Sales 19.2MM *EMP* 450
Accts Vizcaino Zomerfeld Llp Miami
SIC 8093 Mental health clinic, outpatient; Mental health clinic, outpatient
Ex Dir: Bruce Hayden
Exec: Ileana Garcia
**Prin:* Milagros Riveros
CIO: Martha Garcia
IT Man: Ileana Ruiz-Garcia

D-U-N-S 96-217-9607
MIAMI CHILDRENS HOSPITAL PRPG LLC
(*Suby of* NICKLAUS CHILDRENS HOSPITAL) ★
3100 Sw 62nd Ave, Miami, FL 33155-3009
Tel (305) 666-6511 *Founded/Ownrshp* 2003
Sales 71.6M *EMP* 540^E
SIC 8069 Children's hospital
Pr: Narendra M Kini MD

D-U-N-S 00-427-5533 IMP
MIAMI CORP
720 Anderson Ferry Rd, Cincinnati, OH 45238-4742
Tel (513) 451-6700 *Founded/Ownrshp* 1923
Sales 21.6MM *EMP* 66
Accts Clark Schaefer Hackett & Co
SIC 5131 5091 Upholstery fabrics, woven; Boat accessories & parts; Upholstery fabrics, woven; Boat accessories & parts
Pr: Timothy J Niehaus
**VP:* Dan Niehaus
Board of Directors: Daniel F Niehaus

D-U-N-S 03-393-6928
MIAMI CORRECTIONAL FACILITY
3038 W 850 S, Bunker Hill, IN 46914-9810
Tel (765) 689-8920 *Founded/Ownrshp* 1999
Sales 40.7MM^E *EMP* 700
SIC 8744 Correctional facility; Correctional facility

D-U-N-S 08-413-2125
MIAMI COUNTRY DAY SCHOOL INC
601 Ne 107th St, Miami, FL 33161-7199
Tel (305) 759-2843 *Founded/Ownrshp* 1938
Sales 35.2MM *EMP* 222
Accts Verdeja & De Armas Llp Coral
SIC 8211 Private elementary & secondary schools; Elementary school; Secondary school; Private elementary & secondary schools; Elementary school; Secondary school
Pr: Anne Paulk

D-U-N-S 08-932-1090
MIAMI COUNTY MEDICAL CENTER
PHARMACY EXPRESS
20375 W 151st St Ste 351, Olathe, KS 66061-7242
Tel (913) 791-4940 *Founded/Ownrshp* 2015
Sales 20.8MM *EMP* 2^E
SIC 8099 Blood related health services

D-U-N-S 03-064-4264
MIAMI COUNTY MEDICAL CENTER INC
(*Suby of* OLATHE HEALTH SYSTEM INC) ★
2100 Baptiste Dr, Paola, KS 66071-1314
Tel (913) 294-2327 *Founded/Ownrshp* 1955
Sales 20.9MM *EMP* 130
SIC 8062 General medical & surgical hospitals; General medical & surgical hospitals
Pr: Frank H Devocelle
CFO: Cheryl Sharp
**VP:* Meredith Drummond
**VP:* Heather McMurphey
**VP:* Nancy Schnegelberger
CTO: Tara Johnson
CTO: Jerry Wiegner

D-U-N-S 07-312-9249
MIAMI DADE COLLEGE
MDC
300 Ne 2nd Ave Rm 3116, Miami, FL 33132-2204
Tel (305) 237-3000 *Founded/Ownrshp* 1960
Sales 273.1MM^E *EMP* 9,172
Accts William O Monroe Cpa/State Of
SIC 8222 9411 8221 Community college; Administration of educational programs; ; Colleges universities & professional schools; Community college; Administration of educational programs; ; Colleges universities & professional schools
Pr: Eduardo J Padron
CFO: E H Lvring
Trst: Armando J Bucelo
Trst: Benjamin Le N
Ofcr: Demetrice Clay
Ofcr: Charlotte Fulton
Ofcr: Natasha Reeder
**Prin:* Cathlene Rodregez
Prgrm Mgr: Valerie Deangelis
Off Mgr: Elizabeth Samuels
Off Admin: Janice Carlo

MIAMI DADELAND MARRIOTT
See MDM HOTEL GROUP LTD

D-U-N-S 80-745-1067 EXP
MIAMI DIRECT INC
3650 Nw 82nd Ave Ste 501, Doral, FL 33166-6695
Tel (305) 597-3998 *Founded/Ownrshp* 1993
Sales 67.0MM *EMP* 9
SIC 5045 Computers; Computer peripheral equipment; Computers; Computer peripheral equipment
Ch Bd: Armando Gonzalez
**Treas:* Alfredo Darquea

D-U-N-S 07-698-5464 EXP
MIAMI DOLPHINS LTD
347 Don Shula Dr, Miami Gardens, FL 33056-2614
Tel (954) 452-7000 *Founded/Ownrshp* 1994
Sales 32.6MM^E *EMP* 200
SIC 7941 Football club
Pt: H Wayne Huizenga
Pt: Jeremy Gerson
Pr: Dawn Aponte
Pr: Stephen Ross
CEO: Mike Dee
CFO: Chris Clements
Bd of Dir: Marti Huizenga
Ofcr: Hal Talisman
Sr VP: Todd Boyan
Sr VP: Mark Brockelman
VP: Nick Forro
VP: Randy Mueller
VP: Stu Weinstein

D-U-N-S 03-999-8711
MIAMI INDUSTRIAL TRUCKS INC
2830 E River Rd, Moraine, OH 45439-1500
Tel (937) 293-4194 *Founded/Ownrshp* 1982
Sales 39.0MM^E *EMP* 150

SIC 5084 7359 7699 Materials handling machinery; Equipment rental & leasing; Industrial equipment services; Industrial truck repair; Materials handling machinery; Equipment rental & leasing; Industrial equipment services; Industrial truck repair
CEO: Mark Jones
Ch: George Malacos
Exec: Scott Zugelder
Opers Mgr: James Shriner
S&M/VP: Tony Argue

D-U-N-S 01-745-8610
MIAMI INTERNATIONAL FREIGHT SOLUTIONS LLC
MIFS
14100 Nw 60th Ave, Miami Lakes, FL 33014-3131
Tel (305) 685-0035 *Founded/Ownrshp* 2008
Sales 24.3MM^E^ *EMP* 65
SIC 4731 Freight transportation arrangement
**Pr:* Leonard C Roberts
COO: Jose Aguirre
Ex VP: George Creech
**VP:* Fred J Annunziata
**VP:* Charles B Siceloff
Sales Asso: Rosanna Leon-Pacheco

D-U-N-S 19-482-5055 EXP
MIAMI INTERNATIONAL MACHINERY & EQUIPMENT CORPO
MIMECO
7601 Nw 74th Ave, Medley, FL 33166-2424
Tel (305) 888-2405 *Founded/Ownrshp* 1987
Sales 35.4MM *EMP* 11
SIC 5084 5082 Industrial machinery & equipment; Road construction equipment; Industrial machinery & equipment; Road construction equipment
Pr: Joseph M Pimentel
**VP:* Thanh-Thuy Pimentel

D-U-N-S 13-309-8900
■ **MIAMI INTERNATIONAL UNIVERSITY OF ART & DESIGN**
MIAMI INTL UNIV ART & DESIGN
(*Suby of* EDUCATION MANAGEMENT CORP) ★
1501 Biscayne Blvd # 100, Miami, FL 33132-1449
Tel (305) 428-5700 *Founded/Ownrshp* 2001
Sales 17.6MM^E^ *EMP* 288
SIC 7336 Art design services; Art design services
Pr: Erika Fleming
**Treas:* Dorinda Pannozzo
Mktg Mgr: Marcia Gomez

MIAMI INTL UNIV ART & DESIGN
See MIAMI INTERNATIONAL UNIVERSITY OF ART & DESIGN

D-U-N-S 07-845-6712 IMP
MIAMI JEWISH HEALTH SYSTEMS INC
5200 Ne 2nd Ave, Miami, FL 33137-2706
Tel (305) 751-8626 *Founded/Ownrshp* 1945
Sales 70.8MM *EMP* 1,100
Accts Crowe Horwath Llp Fort Lauder
SIC 8051 Skilled nursing care facilities; Convalescent home with continuous nursing care; Extended care facility; Mental retardation hospital; Skilled nursing care facilities; Convalescent home with continuous nursing care; Extended care facility; Mental retardation hospital
Ch: Stephen H Cypen
**CEO:* Jeffrey P Freimark
CFO: Lisa Desmarteau
CFO: Barbara Salazar
**Treas:* Lisa J Desmarteau
Chf Mktg O: Wendie Nemeroff
**VP:* Morris Funk
VP: Mat Robie
Dir Sec: Zoe Alvarez
CIO: David Wolff
Dir IT: Bernardo Larralde

MIAMI LAKER
See GRAHAM COMPANIES

MIAMI LAKES AUTOMALL
See MIAMI LAKES AUTOMOTIVE LLC

D-U-N-S 96-364-3189 EXP
MIAMI LAKES AUTOMOTIVE LLC
MIAMI LAKES AUTOMALL
16600 Nw 57th Ave, Miami Lakes, FL 33014-6123
Tel (305) 558-1400 *Founded/Ownrshp* 1998
Sales 45.8MM^E^ *EMP* 66^E^
SIC 5511 5521 Automobiles, new & used; Used car dealers
Pr: Barry Frieder
**Pr:* Ali Ahmed
**Treas:* David Yusko
**VP:* Andrew Pfeifer
Genl Mgr: Fred Senra
Sls Mgr: Carlos Cabo
Sales Asso: Maritza Nodal

D-U-N-S 60-283-0010
MIAMI MANAGEMENT CO INC
WENDY'S
901 Adams Crossing Fl 1, Cincinnati, OH 45202-1693
Tel (513) 984-0061 *Founded/Ownrshp* 1989
Sales 10.2MM^E^ *EMP* 300
SIC 5812 Fast-food restaurant, chain; Fast-food restaurant, chain
Pr: James Fraley
**VP:* James Glass

D-U-N-S 78-641-4391 EXP
MIAMI MARLINS LP
501 Marlins Way, Miami, FL 33125-1121
Tel (305) 480-1300 *Founded/Ownrshp* 1999
Sales 55.0MM^E^ *EMP* 500
SIC 7941 Baseball club, professional & semi-professional; Baseball club, professional & semi-professional
Pt: David P Samson
**Genl Pt:* Jeffrey Loria
**CFO:* Michel Bussiere
Sr VP: Raul Striker Jr

D-U-N-S 19-732-8875
MIAMI OFFICE SYSTEMS INC
14791 Oak Ln, Hialeah, FL 33016-1518
Tel (954) 315-0580 *Founded/Ownrshp* 1986
Sales 41.1MM^E^ *EMP* 85^E^
SIC 5044 7699 Office equipment; Photocopy machines; Photocopy machine repair; Office equipment; Photocopy machines; Photocopy machine repair
Pr: Luis Gonzalez
**VP:* Luis Navarro
Sales Exec: Ricky Bolanos

MIAMI PERFORMING ARTS CENTER
See PERFORMING ARTS CENTER TRUST INC

D-U-N-S 96-520-8382
MIAMI PIZZA INC
PAPA JOHN'S
6264 Seven Springs Blvd, Greenacres, FL 33463-1643
Tel (561) 753-4500 *Founded/Ownrshp* 1993
Sales 11.1MM^E^ *EMP* 550
SIC 5812 Pizzeria, chain; Pizzeria, chain
Pr: Rene Prats
**Treas:* Henry R Szabo
**VP:* Jeff Roschman
**VP:* Robert Roschman

MIAMI PROJECT, THE
See BUONICONTI FUND TO CURE PARALYSIS INC

D-U-N-S 03-253-3044 EXP
MIAMI PURVEYORS INC
7350 Nw 8th St, Miami, FL 33126-2922
Tel (305) 262-6170 *Founded/Ownrshp* 1956
Sales 23.0MM^E^ *EMP* 50
SIC 5147 2011 5142 2013 Meats, fresh; Meat packing plants; Packaged frozen goods; Sausages & other prepared meats
Pr: Fredric Rosenberg

D-U-N-S 17-201-0357
MIAMI RADIOLOGY ASSOC
1400 Nw 12th Ave, Miami, FL 33136-1003
Tel (305) 325-5910 *Founded/Ownrshp* 1998
Sales 5.5MM^E^ *EMP* 300
SIC 8011 8071 8062 Radiologist; Medical laboratories; General medical & surgical hospitals; Radiologist; Medical laboratories; General medical & surgical hospitals
Pr: Allan Fishman

D-U-N-S 07-847-1471
MIAMI RESCUE MISSION INC
BROWARD OUTREACH CENTERS
2159 Nw 1st Ct, Miami, FL 33127-4814
Tel (305) 573-6340 *Founded/Ownrshp* 1975
Sales 24.4MM *EMP* 140
SIC 8322 Self-help organization; Self-help organization
Pr: Ronald Brummitt

D-U-N-S 10-006-6182
MIAMI SCHOOL DISTRICT I-23
26 N Main St, Miami, OK 74354-6323
Tel (918) 542-8455 *Founded/Ownrshp* 1800
Sales 12.4MM^E^ *EMP* 280
SIC 8211 Public elementary school; Public junior high school; Public senior high school; Kindergarten; Public elementary school; Public junior high school; Public senior high school; Kindergarten
Pr: Ted Kaufman
Schl Brd P: Larry Martin

MIAMI SUBS & GRILL
See MIAMI SUBS CORP

D-U-N-S 61-417-0538
MIAMI SUBS CORP
MIAMI SUBS & GRILL
(*Suby of* MIAMI SUBS CAPITAL PARTNERS I, INC.)
6300 Nw 31st Ave, Fort Lauderdale, FL 33309-1633
Tel (954) 973-0000 *Founded/Ownrshp* 2007
Sales 9.9MM^E^ *EMP* 282^E^
SIC 5812 Sandwiches & submarines shop
Ch Bd: Howard Lorber
Pr: Nancy Murphy
**COO:* Lawrence Austin
**CFO:* Jerry W Woda
Ex VP: Evan Friedman
Mktg Dir: Jaden Smith

D-U-N-S 03-302-5867
MIAMI TRACE LOCAL SCHOOL DISTRICT
3818 State Route 41 Nw, Wshngtn CT Hs, OH 43160-9184
Tel (740) 335-3010 *Founded/Ownrshp* 1960
Sales 30.6MM *EMP* 592
Accts Clark Schaefer Hackett & Co
SIC 8211 Public elementary & secondary schools; Public elementary & secondary schools
**Treas:* Debbie Black
Schl Brd P: Charlie Andrews
Schl Brd P: Rob Dawson

D-U-N-S 04-106-5129
MIAMI UNIVERSITY
501 E High St, Oxford, OH 45056-1846
Tel (513) 529-1809 *Founded/Ownrshp* 1809
Sales 443.0MM *EMP* 4,925^E^
Accts Mcgladrey Llp Cleveland Ohio
SIC 8221 University; University
Pr: David Hodge
Pr: Joe Bazeley
Pr: Scott Walter
Bd of Dir: Phyllis Wykoff
Ex VP: Bobby Gempesaw
VP: Brenden Clinton
VP: Deedie Dowdle
VP: Alan Ferrenberg
VP: Richard M Norman
Assoc Dir: Leng Hui
Assoc Dir: Felice Marcus

D-U-N-S 00-790-2588
■ **MIAMI VALLEY BROADCASTING CORP**
OLDIES 95
(*Suby of* COX ENTERPRISES INC) ★
1611 S Main St, Dayton, OH 45409-2547
Tel (937) 259-2111 *Founded/Ownrshp* 1964
Sales 41.3MM^E^ *EMP* 162
SIC 4833 Television broadcasting stations; Television broadcasting stations
Pr: Edrew Fichser
Tech Mgr: Steve Hardy

MIAMI VALLEY C T C
See MIAMI VALLEY CAREER TECHNOLOGY CENTER

D-U-N-S 07-127-3072
MIAMI VALLEY CAREER TECHNOLOGY CENTER
MIAMI VALLEY C T C
6800 Hoke Rd, Clayton, OH 45315-8975
Tel (937) 837-7781 *Founded/Ownrshp* 1968
Sales 21.4MM^E^ *EMP* 249^E^
Accts Plattenburg & Associates Inc
SIC 8211 Public elementary & secondary schools; Public elementary & secondary schools
CFO: Pamela Holdren
**Treas:* Debbie Jessup
Trst: Barbara Sommer
Ofcr: Greg Stephens
Exec: Helena Schlafman

D-U-N-S 07-470-1509
MIAMI VALLEY CHILD DEVELOPMENT CENTERS INC
MVCDC
215 Horace St, Dayton, OH 45402-8318
Tel (937) 226-5664 *Founded/Ownrshp* 1964
Sales 27.7MM *EMP* 430
Accts Clark Schaefer Hackett & Co M
SIC 8351 Head start center, except in conjunction with school; Head start center, except in conjunction with school
Pr: Marry Burn
**COO:* Dayvenia Chesney
CFO: Jeffrey Lakes
**CFO:* David Marker

D-U-N-S 07-127-1951
MIAMI VALLEY HOSPITAL
1 Wyoming St, Dayton, OH 45409-2711
Tel (937) 208-8000 *Founded/Ownrshp* 1982
Sales 630.4MM^E^ *EMP* 6,000
SIC 8062 General medical & surgical hospitals; General medical & surgical hospitals
Pr: Bobbie Gerhart
**Pr:* Mark Shaker
COO: Patti Clay
**COO:* Barbara Johnson
**CFO:* Lisa Bishop
CFO: Scott Shelton
Ex VP: Scott Schelton
**VP:* Makkie Clancy
VP: Diane Pleiman
Exec: William Linesch
Exec: T Reid
Exec: Anne Whetstone
Comm Man: Mike Jarvis

MIAMI VALLEY INSURANCE ASSOC
See NORMAN-SPENCER AGENCY INC

D-U-N-S 02-389-2078
MIAMI VALLEY INTERNATIONAL TRUCKS INC
MIAMI VALLEY ISUZU
7655 Poe Ave, Dayton, OH 45414-5811
Tel (937) 898-3660 *Founded/Ownrshp* 1982
Sales 45.8MM^E^ *EMP* 180
SIC 5511

MIAMI VALLEY ISUZU
See MIAMI VALLEY INTERNATIONAL TRUCKS INC

D-U-N-S 00-425-3308
MIAMI VALLEY PUBLISHING LLC (OH)
678 Yllow Sprng Frfeld Rd, Fairborn, OH 45324
Tel (937) 879-5678 *Founded/Ownrshp* 1867, 2009
Sales 40.6MM^E^ *EMP* 143
SIC 2752 Commercial printing, offset; Commercial printing, offset
Treas: Doug Boyle
Exec: Dan Stahl

D-U-N-S 10-148-6280 EXP
MIAMI VALLEY STEEL SERVICE INC
201 Fox Dr, Piqua, OH 45356-9265
Tel (937) 773-7127 *Founded/Ownrshp* 2012
Sales 200.4MM^E^ *EMP* 140
SIC 5051 Metals service centers & offices; Metals service centers & offices
CEO: Louis Moran
CFO: Jill Kendall
**CFO:* Jill Kindell
IT Man: Douglas Fenter
VP Opers: Ron Leak
Sfty Mgr: Tim McNally
Plnt Mgr: Chip Lameraue
Plnt Mgr: Chip Lamoreaux
Trfc Mgr: Dave Staley
VP Sls: Len Stahl
Manager: Jim Spence

MIAMI WABASH PAPER
See MAFCOTE INC

D-U-N-S 06-914-9011 IMP/EXP
MIAMI WALL SYSTEMS INC
701 W 25th St, Hialeah, FL 33010-2150
Tel (305) 888-2300 *Founded/Ownrshp* 1974
Sales 21.0MM^E^ *EMP* 110
SIC 3442 Window & door frames; Sash, door or window: metal
CEO: Larry D Johnson
**Pr:* Keith A Johnson
**VP:* Francisco Ortega

D-U-N-S 82-587-7991
MIAMI-DADE COUNTY PUBLIC SCHOOLS-158
1450 Ne 2nd Ave, Miami, FL 33132-1308
Tel (305) 995-1000 *Founded/Ownrshp* 2008
Sales 2.9MMM^E^ *EMP* 40,000^E^
SIC 8211 Elementary & secondary schools; Elementary & secondary schools
Bd of Dir: Reiner Diaz
Bd of Dir: Lawrence Feldman
Bd of Dir: Martin Karp
Bd of Dir: Ana Rivas-Logan
Ofcr: Beatriz Peraza
Adm Dir: Cyd Heyliger-Browne
Adm Dir: Addys Lopez
Adm Dir: Melanie Megias
Adm Dir: Dyann Rodriguez
Adm Dir: Ellen Wright
Adm Dir: Beatriz Zarraluqui

D-U-N-S 87-708-5634
MIAMI-DADE PUBLIC SCHOOL TRANSPORTATION
660 Sw 3rd Ave, Homestead, FL 33034-4826
Tel (305) 248-3380 *Founded/Ownrshp* 1998
Sales 8.2MM^E^ *EMP* 465
SIC 4151 School buses; School buses
VP: Kathy Price

D-U-N-S 01-797-0443
MIAMI-LUKEN INC
PARAMOUNT CONFECTION CO
265 S Pioneer Blvd, Springboro, OH 45066-3307
Tel (937) 743-7775 *Founded/Ownrshp* 1994
Sales 252.4MM^E^ *EMP* 275
Accts Dohner Louis & Stephens Inc
SIC 5122 Drugs, proprietaries & sundries; Drugs & drug proprietaries; Pharmaceuticals; Druggists' sundries; Drugs, proprietaries & sundries; Drugs & drug proprietaries; Pharmaceuticals; Druggists' sundries
CEO: Tony Rattini
Ch Bd: Joseph Mastandrea
Prin: Anthony V Rattini
Board of Directors: Steve Fullarton, Cindy Willet

D-U-N-S 08-474-9456
MIAMISBURG CITY SCHOOL DIST
540 Park Ave, Miamisburg, OH 45342-2854
Tel (937) 866-3381 *Founded/Ownrshp* 1820
Sales 31.9MM^E^ *EMP* 506
SIC 8211 Public elementary school; Public junior high school; Public senior high school; School board; Public elementary school; Public junior high school; Public senior high school; School board
Treas: Amy Twarek
Bd of Dir: Sharon Angel
Bd of Dir: Danielle Kuehnle
IT Man: Tammy Emrick
Psych: Steve Aylward
Psych: Chris Bennett
Psych: Brad Buzzell
Psych: Reva Pittman
Psych: Marty Sharts
Psych: Valerie Valdez
Psych: Rachelle Yakumithis

D-U-N-S 04-160-6869 IMP/EXP
MIAS FASHION MANUFACTURING CO INC
CALIFORNIA BASIC
12623 Cisneros Ln, Santa Fe Springs, CA 90670-3373
Tel (562) 906-1060 *Founded/Ownrshp* 1999
Sales 158.3MM *EMP* 252
Accts Kim & Lee Corporation Los Ang
SIC 5137 Women's & children's clothing; Women's & children's clothing
Pr: Peter D Anh
**CFO:* Brian Song

D-U-N-S 15-842-4445
MIASOLE
2590 Walsh Ave, Santa Clara, CA 95051-1315
Tel (408) 919-5700 *Founded/Ownrshp* 2001
Sales 97.2MM^E^ *EMP* 315
SIC 3674 Solar cells
CEO: Jeff Zhou
**CEO:* John Carrington
COO: Ramil Manzano
Bd of Dir: Michael Rotgin
Ex VP: Dennis Hollars
VP: Jason Corneille
VP: Shankar Pennathur
VP: David Smith
Genl Mgr: Cindy Peterson
Snr Sftwr: Chee Chan
Snr Sftwr: Steve Shi

D-U-N-S 07-923-9366
MIASOLE HI-TECH CORP
(*Suby of* HANERGY HOLDING (AMERICA) LLC) ★
2590 Walsh Ave, Santa Clara, CA 95051-1315
Tel (408) 919-5700 *Founded/Ownrshp* 2012
Sales 865.6M^E^ *EMP* 371^E^
SIC 3674 5074 Solar cells; Heating equipment & panels, solar
CEO: Jeffrey X Zhou
**CFO:* Merle McClendon
VP: Steven Berry
Sftwr Eng: Erik Nizenkoff
VP Mfg: Atiye Bayman
Opers Mgr: David Dileo

MIAT COLLEGE OF TECHNOLOGY
See MICHIGAN INSTITUTE OF AERONAUTICS INC

D-U-N-S 07-213-5692
MIB GROUP INC
50 Braintree Hill Park # 400, Braintree, MA 02184-8803
Tel (781) 751-6000 *Founded/Ownrshp* 1978
Sales NA *EMP* 150
SIC 6411 Information bureaus, insurance
CEO: Lee B Oliphant
Ch Bd: Joseph L Pray
Pr: Jay Cook
Pr: Cliff Toplis
CFO: Linda Barnes
CFO: Linda Daines
V Ch Bd: David P Wheeler
Ex VP: Robert Diangelo

Ex VP: Stacy J Gill
Ex VP: Jonathan W Sager
Snr Sftwr: Sreenivas Anupindi
Board of Directors: Thomas F English, Timothy A Walsh

D-U-N-S 82-859-3322
MIB INC
(*Suby of* MIB GROUP INC) ★
50 Braintree Hill Park # 400, Braintree, MA 02184-8803
Tel (781) 751-6000 *Founded/Ownrshp* 2008
Sales NA *EMP* 100
SIC 6411 Information bureaus, insurance; Information bureaus, insurance
Pr: Jay Cook
**CFO:* Linda Barnes
Ex VP: Paul Howman
VP: Thomas Ashley
VP: Thomas King
**VP:* Lee B Oliphant
Dir Surg: David Olson
Dir IT: Arthur S Loridas
Genl Couns: Jonathan Sager

D-U-N-S 03-806-8826 IMP
MIBA BEARINGS US LLC
(*Suby of* MITTERBAUER BETEILIGUNGS-AKTIENGESELLSCHAFT.)
5037 N State Route 60 Nw, McConnelsville, OH 43756-9218
Tel (740) 962-4242 *Founded/Ownrshp* 2001
Sales 104.8MM^E *EMP* 300
SIC 3799 Automobile trailer chassis; Automobile trailer chassis
Ch Bd: F Peter Mitterbauer
CFO: Markus Hofer
Plnt Mgr: Bernie Anderson
Plnt Mgr: Ted Mc Mc Connell

D-U-N-S 82-939-8390 IMP
MIBA SINTER USA LLC
(*Suby of* MITTERBAUER BETEILIGUNGS-AKTIENGESELLSCHAFT.)
5045 N State Route 60 Nw, McConnelsville, OH 43756-9640
Tel (740) 962-4242 *Founded/Ownrshp* 2008
Sales 27.2MM *EMP* 10
SIC 3312 Sinter, iron
Mng Dir: Peter Chudoba

D-U-N-S 05-719-6262
MIBO FRESH FOODS LLC
715 E 9th St, Fort Worth, TX 76102-5512
Tel (817) 882-9600 *Founded/Ownrshp* 2012
Sales 20.1MM^E *EMP* 81
SIC 2037 Frozen fruits & vegetables
Pr: Uzor Nwoko

D-U-N-S 14-558-1794
MIC CUSTOMS SOLUTIONS
MIC LOGISTICS
(*Suby of* MIC CUSTOMS SOLUTIONS HOLDING GMBH)
26555 Evergreen Rd # 1110, Southfield, MI 48076-4206
Tel (248) 304-4460 *Founded/Ownrshp* 2004
Sales 25.0MM *EMP* 160
SIC 7379 Computer related consulting services; Computer related consulting services
CEO: Klaus Hanisch
**Pr:* Alfred Hiebl

MIC FOOD DIVISION
See MERCADAGRO INTERNATIONAL CORP

D-U-N-S 05-316-8449
MIC INDUSTRIES INC
11911 Freedom Dr Ste 1000, Reston, VA 20190-5631
Tel (703) 318-1900 *Founded/Ownrshp* 1981
Sales 20.8MM^E *EMP* 125
SIC 3531 3549 Construction machinery; Metalworking machinery; Construction machinery; Metalworking machinery
Pr: Michael S Ansari
**Sec:* Eileen O Penland
**VP:* Syed Ahmed
**VP:* Lori Gray
**VP:* Domenico Oliva
Off Mgr: Beth Smith
Snr Sftwr: Christopher March

MIC LOGISTICS
See MIC CUSTOMS SOLUTIONS

D-U-N-S 00-480-4621 IMP
MICA CORP (TX)
5750 N Riverside Dr, Fort Worth, TX 76137-2430
Tel (817) 847-6121 *Founded/Ownrshp* 1962
Sales 55.9MM^E *EMP* 200
Accts Weaver & Tidwell Llp Fort Wor
SIC 1611 Highway signs & guardrails; Highway signs & guardrails
Pr: L C Tubb Jr
**Treas:* Jack L Davis
**VP:* Carla Danford
VP: Mike Tanner
**VP:* Kevin L Tubb
VP: Mike Walsh
Dir Risk M: Sarah Pratt
IT Man: Raun Deosarran

D-U-N-S 00-833-5502
MICAHTEK INC
8215 S Elm Pl, Broken Arrow, OK 74011-4330
Tel (918) 449-3300 *Founded/Ownrshp* 1994
Sales 34.9MM^E *EMP* 350
SIC 7374 Data processing service; Data processing service
Pr: Michael Conners
**VP:* Pam Conners
Mktg Dir: Jenna Vardeman

D-U-N-S 02-008-3457
MICALE MGT CORP
MCDONALD'S
11 Sayer Ave Ste 202, Cherry Hill, NJ 08002-2769
Tel (856) 665-8622 *Founded/Ownrshp* 1972
Sales 14.2MM^E *EMP* 305
SIC 5812 Fast-food restaurant, chain; Fast-food restaurant, chain
Pr: Anthony J Micale

MICATO SAFARIS
See TAICOA CORP

MICCOSUKEE TRAIL RESTAURANT
See MICCOSUKEE TRIBE OF INDIANS OF FLORIDA

D-U-N-S 03-253-3754 EXP
MICCOSUKEE TRIBE OF INDIANS OF FLORIDA
MICCOSUKEE TRAIL RESTAURANT
Sw 8th St & Us Hwy 41, Miami, FL 33194
Tel (305) 223-8380 *Founded/Ownrshp* 1962
Sales 56.1MM^E *EMP* 1,500
SIC 5812 5331 8412 5947 4489 Indian/Pakistan restaurant; Variety stores; Museum; Gift shop; Airboats; Indian/Pakistan restaurant; Variety stores; Museum; Gift shop; Airboats
Ch Bd: Colley Billie
**CFO:* Mike Hernandez
**Treas:* Max Billie
Exec: Risha Singh
Telecom Ex: Julio Martinez
DP Exec: Miguel Crispo
Dir IT: Miguel Crespo
Sls Mgr: Jodi Goldenberg

D-U-N-S 04-606-7021
MICELI & OLDFIELD INC
12250 Delta St, Taylor, MI 48180-6831
Tel (734) 946-4500 *Founded/Ownrshp* 1968
Sales 27.3MM^E *EMP* 30
SIC 5143 Dairy products, except dried or canned
Pr: Louis Miceli
**Sec:* Peter Miceli

D-U-N-S 00-422-5801 IMP
MICELI DAIRY PRODUCTS CO
2721 E 90th St, Cleveland, OH 44104-3396
Tel (216) 791-6222 *Founded/Ownrshp* 1946
Sales 74.8MM^E *EMP* 190
SIC 2022 0241 Natural cheese; Milk production; Natural cheese; Milk production
CEO: Joseph D Miceli
**Treas:* Rosemary Surace
**Ex VP:* John J Miceli Jr
**VP:* Joseph Lograsso
**VP:* Charles Surace
Plng Mgr: Keith Seman
IT Man: Melinda Yount
VP Opers: Brent Hare
Prd Mgr: Adam Csanyi
S&M/VP: Kevin Bresnahan

MICHAEL
See MANHATTAN SCHOOL OF MUSIC INC

D-U-N-S 14-467-2060 IMP
MICHAEL & SON SERVICES INC
5740 General Wash Dr, Alexandria, VA 22312-2407
Tel (703) 658-3998 *Founded/Ownrshp* 1988
Sales 113.0MM^E *EMP* 140^E
SIC 1521 1731 5074 Electrical work; Plumbing & hydronic heating supplies; General remodeling, single-family houses; Electrical work; Plumbing & hydronic heating supplies
Pr: Basim Mansour
**VP:* Joanna Mansour
Genl Mgr: Chris Thompson
Genl Mgr: George Vogt
IT Man: Molly Ahelet
Trfc Dir: Norbert Rancke
Opers Mgr: Michael Seton
Sales Asso: Charles Gibbs

D-U-N-S 09-808-0158
MICHAEL & SUSAN DELL FOUNDATION
4417 Westlake Dr, Austin, TX 78746-1437
Tel (512) 329-0799 *Founded/Ownrshp* 1999
Sales 111.4MM^E *EMP* 55
SIC 7389 Authors' agents & brokers; Authors' agents & brokers
Ch Bd: Susan Dell
**Prin:* Dr Alexander Dell
**Prin:* Michael Dell

MICHAEL ADOLESCENT PROGRAM
See HOPE NETWORK REHABILITATION SERVICES INC

MICHAEL ANGELO'S GOURMET FOODS
See BOTTOM LINE FOOD PROCESSORS INC

D-U-N-S 09-432-6493
■ **MICHAEL ANTHONY JEWELERS LLC**
(*Suby of* RICHLINE GROUP INC) ★
115 S Macquesten Pkwy, Mount Vernon, NY 10550-1724
Tel (914) 699-0000 *Founded/Ownrshp* 2005
Sales 26.5MM^E *EMP* 450
SIC 3911 5944 5094 Jewelry, precious metal; Earrings, precious metal; Rings, finger: precious metal; Bracelets, precious metal; Jewelry stores; Jewelry & precious stones; Jewelry, precious metal; Earrings, precious metal; Rings, finger: precious metal; Bracelets, precious metal; Jewelry stores; Jewelry & precious stones
**CFO:* Betty Sou
**Chf Mktg O:* Michael W Paolercio
**VP:* Anthony Paolercio Jr
CIO: Gregory Torski
Sales Exec: Terri Faber
VP Mktg: Mark Hanna

D-U-N-S 08-677-4309
MICHAEL BAKER GLOBAL SERVICES LLC (VA)
KASEMAN
(*Suby of* DC CAPITAL PARTNERS LLC) ★
3601 Eisenhower Ave # 600, Alexandria, VA 22304-6456
Tel (703) 676-3200 *Founded/Ownrshp* 1993, 2008
Sales 59.4MM *EMP* 170^E
Accts Mcgladrey Llp Mclean Virgini
SIC 8741 7363 8712 Management services; Help supply services; Management services; Help supply services; Architectural services; Architectural engineering
CEO: Kurt Bargman
Pr: Silvia M Park
CFO: Brian Arsenault
Ofcr: Don Healy
Prgrm Mgr: Hargrove Steve
Pgrm Dir: Amanda Austin
Pgrm Dir: David Banks
Board of Directors: Herbert J Lanese

D-U-N-S 00-791-6968
MICHAEL BAKER INTERNATIONAL HOLDCO CORP (PA)
(*Suby of* MICHAEL BAKER INTERNATIONAL LLC) ★
100 Airside Dr, Moon Township, PA 15108-4740
Tel (412) 269-6300 *Founded/Ownrshp* 1940, 2013
Sales 543.8MM^E *EMP* 3,200^E
SIC 8711 Civil engineering; Civil engineering
CEO: Kurt C Bergman
Mng Pt: Bill Hood
**COO:* Jeffrey S Hill
CFO: Ryan Goodliffe
**CFO:* Brian Lutes
**Ofcr:* Samuel C Knoch
**Ofcr:* Michael J Ziemianski
Assoc VP: Peter Hankovszky
**Ex VP:* John Kurgan
**Ex VP:* H James McKnight
Ex VP: James B Richards
Sr VP: Charles Russell
Sr VP: Thomas J Zagorski
**VP:* Jeremy N Gill
VP: Todd E Lynn
VP: John W Mentz
VP: Frederick Muncy
VP: George Perinis
VP: Roslyn G Trojan
VP: Raymond P Wattras
VP: Dennis Wiehl

D-U-N-S 07-917-1269
MICHAEL BAKER INTERNATIONAL LLC
100 Airside Dr, Coraopolis, PA 15108-4740
Tel (412) 269-6300 *Founded/Ownrshp* 2012
Sales 592.9MM *EMP* 3,280^E
Accts Mcgladrey Llp Mclean Virgini
SIC 8711 Civil engineering; Civil engineering
CFO: Brian Lutes
Chf Cred: Beth Foley
VP: Sairam Menon
CIO: Daniel Horton

D-U-N-S 09-733-6556
MICHAEL BEST & FRIEDRICH LLP
100 E Wisconsin Ave # 3300, Milwaukee, WI 53202-4108
Tel (414) 271-6560 *Founded/Ownrshp* 1997
Sales 95.2MM^E *EMP* 500
SIC 8111 General practice law office; General practice law office
Mng Pt: Dave Krutz
Mng Pt: David A Krutz
Mng Pt: Kerryann Minton
Mng Pt: John Sapp
Pr: Arlette Johnson
Pr: Jamie Kuehnel
COO: L Lentz
Ex Dir: Brian Wipperfurth
Off Mgr: Billie J Smith
CIO: Alan W Ciochon
MIS Dir: Jane Moberg

D-U-N-S 05-152-6911 IMP
MICHAEL C FINA CO INC
3301 Hunters Point Ave, Long Island City, NY 11101-2528
Tel (212) 557-2500 *Founded/Ownrshp* 1969
Sales 270.7MM^E *EMP* 325
SIC 5094 5947 Jewelry; Gifts & novelties; Jewelry; Gifts & novelties
Pr: Ashley Fina
**Ch:* George Fina
VP: Bill Fina
**VP:* Jeffrey Fina
VP: Jacqueline Hersch
VP: Rich Tuck
VP: Elliot Young
Exec: Jessica Geletez
Dir Bus: Exexa Orrange
Area Mgr: David Kovacovich
IT Man: Laura Salerno

D-U-N-S 09-398-2502
MICHAEL C STEAD INC
MICHAEL STEAD'S HILLTOP FORD
3280 Auto Plz, Richmond, CA 94806-1932
Tel (510) 222-4444 *Founded/Ownrshp* 1995
Sales 31.4MM^E *EMP* 85
SIC 5511 Automobiles, new & used; Pickups, new & used; Vans, new & used; Automobiles, new & used; Pickups, new & used; Vans, new & used
Pr: Michael Stead
IT Man: Kristina Guthrie

D-U-N-S 02-818-8076
MICHAEL CADILLAC INC
MICHAEL HUMMER
50 W Bullard Ave, Fresno, CA 93704-1700
Tel (559) 431-6000 *Founded/Ownrshp* 1985
Sales 118.7MM^E *EMP* 340
SIC 5511 Automobiles, new & used; Pickups, new & used; Vans, new & used; Automobiles, new & used; Pickups, new & used; Vans, new & used
CEO: Michael L Rosvold
Store Mgr: Andrew Thompson

MICHAEL CALLEN-AUDRE LORDE
See COMMUNITY HEALTH PROJECT INC

MICHAEL CASPERSON
See M CASPERSON ENTERPRISE LLC

D-U-N-S 18-527-2676
MICHAEL CUTLER CO
MICHAEL CUTLER OF NEW YORK
110 Terrace Dr Ste 5, Olyphant, PA 18447-2504
Tel (570) 291-5103 *Founded/Ownrshp* 2005
Sales 55.4MM *EMP* 30
SIC 5148 Vegetables; Vegetables
Pr: Michael Cutler

MICHAEL CUTLER OF NEW YORK
See MICHAEL CUTLER CO

D-U-N-S 07-152-9994
MICHAEL DUNN CENTER (TN)
629 Gallaher Rd, Kingston, TN 37763-4215
Tel (865) 376-1337 *Founded/Ownrshp* 1971
Sales 11.3MM *EMP* 300
SIC 8331 8361 Vocational rehabilitation agency; Home for the mentally retarded; Vocational rehabilitation agency; Home for the mentally retarded
Pr: Mike McElhinney
VP: Michaele Butler
VP: Roger Richmond
QA Dir: Tiffany Whittenbarger
Nrsg Dir: Denise Jandro

D-U-N-S 05-284-1269
MICHAEL F RONCA & SONS INC (PA)
179 Mikron Rd, Bethlehem, PA 18020-9476
Tel (610) 759-5100 *Founded/Ownrshp* 1978
Sales 37.4MM^E *EMP* 80
SIC 1629 1623 Waste water & sewage treatment plant construction; Water main construction
Pr: Frederick M Ronca
**Sec:* Lewis D Ronca
**VP:* Michael L Ronca
Genl Mgr: David Ronca
Sfty Dirs: Mike Vonelly

D-U-N-S 01-495-3939
MICHAEL FACCHIANO CONTRACTING INC
801 Mcneilly Rd Ste 4, Pittsburgh, PA 15226-2547
Tel (412) 344-5503 *Founded/Ownrshp* 1956
Sales 21.1MM^E *EMP* 80
SIC 1611 General contractor, highway & street construction
CEO: Michael Facchianoi Sr
VP: John Facchiano

MICHAEL FOOD
See MFI HOLDING CORP

MICHAEL FOODS
See PAPETTIS HYGRADE EGG PRODUCTS INC

D-U-N-S 36-155-3709
■ **MICHAEL FOODS GROUP INC**
(*Suby of* MFI MIDCO CORPORATION)
301 Carlson Pkwy Ste 400, Minnetonka, MN 55305-5370
Tel (952) 258-4000 *Founded/Ownrshp* 2011
Sales 1.9MMM *EMP* 3,596
SIC 0252 2015 5144 5143 5148 6719 Chicken eggs; Egg processing; Eggs; Eggs: cleaning, oil treating, packing & grading; Cheese; Butter; Potatoes, fresh; Investment holding companies, except banks; Chicken eggs; Egg processing; Eggs; Eggs: cleaning, oil treating, packing & grading; Cheese; Butter; Potatoes, fresh; Investment holding companies, except banks
Pr: James E Dwyer Jr
Treas: Mark Witmer
Sr VP: James G Mohr

D-U-N-S 01-807-6351 IMP/EXP
■ **MICHAEL FOODS INC**
MGWALGBAUMS
(*Suby of* POST HOLDINGS INC) ★
301 Carlson Pkwy Ste 400, Minnetonka, MN 55305-5370
Tel (507) 237-4600 *Founded/Ownrshp* 1928, 2015
Sales 643.0MM^E *EMP* 3,596
SIC 0252 2015 5144 5143 5148 5499 Chicken eggs; Egg processing; Eggs; Eggs: cleaning, oil treating, packing & grading; Cheese; Butter; Potatoes, fresh; Eggs & poultry; Chicken eggs; Egg processing; Eggs; Eggs: cleaning, oil treating, packing & grading; Cheese; Butter; Potatoes, fresh; Eggs & poultry
Pr: James E Dwyer Jr
Pr: Mark Anderson
Pr: S O'Brien
CFO: Debbie Laue
CFO: Mark W Westphal
CFO: Mark Witmer
Bd of Dir: Gregg Ostrander
Sr VP: Thomas J Jagiela
VP: Jim Healy
VP: Jonathan Merkle
VP: Carolyn V Wolski
Exec: Jackie Oliver
Exec: Matt Smith
Dir Bus: Kris Strathern
Board of Directors: Nicole V Agnew, Adrian M Jones, Leo F Mullin, Gregg A Ostrander, Oliver D Thymkent R Weldon

D-U-N-S 14-850-8716
■ **MICHAEL FOODS OF DELAWARE INC**
(*Suby of* MGWALGBAUMS) ★
301 Carlson Pkwy Ste 400, Minnetonka, MN 55305-5370
Tel (952) 258-4000 *Founded/Ownrshp* 1997
Sales 588.0MM^E *EMP* 3,596
SIC 0252 2015 5144 5143 5148 2024 Chicken eggs; Egg processing; Eggs; Eggs: cleaning, oil treating, packing & grading; Cheese; Butter; Potatoes, fresh; Ice milk, bulk; Ice cream, bulk; Chicken eggs; Egg processing; Eggs; Eggs: cleaning, oil treating, packing & grading; Cheese; Butter; Potatoes, fresh; Ice milk, bulk; Ice cream, bulk
CEO: James E Dwyer
Sec: Mark D Witmer
VP: John D Reedy

MICHAEL HOHL HONDA SUBARU
See TM&KKH INC

D-U-N-S 11-908-6650
MICHAEL HOHL MOTOR CO
2910 S Carson St, Carson City, NV 89701-5669
Tel (775) 883-5777 *Founded/Ownrshp* 1983
Sales 30.2MM^E *EMP* 70^E

SIC 5511 Automobiles, new & used; Pickups, new & used; Vans, new & used; Automobiles, new & used; Pickups, new & used; Vans, new & used
Pr: T Michael Hohl
**Sec:* Karen F Hohl
Genl Mgr: Katelyn Kuehner
Sls Mgr: David Clark
Board of Directors: Clifford O Findlay

MICHAEL HUMMER
See MICHAEL CADILLAC INC

D-U-N-S 01-967-3748
MICHAEL J CONNOLLY & SONS INC
609 Main St, Walpole, MA 02081-3733
Tel (508) 668-1530 *Founded/Ownrshp* 1960
Sales 23.7MM^E *EMP* 265
Accts Orcutt Pc
SIC 4151 School buses; School buses
Pr: Joseph E Connolly
**Treas:* Leo F Connolly

D-U-N-S 84-976-6068
MICHAEL J FOX FOUNDATION FOR PARKINSONS RESEARCH
498 Fashion Ave Fl 18, New York, NY 10018-6701
Tel (212) 509-0995 *Founded/Ownrshp* 2000
Sales 91.4MM *EMP* 34
SIC 7389 Fund raising organizations
CEO: Todd Sherer
**Pr:* Deborah Brooks
Ofcr: Eric Amanfu
Ofcr: Michelle Aquino
Ofcr: Alex Davidow
Sr VP: Sohini Chowdhury
VP: Sheila Kelly
VP: Karen Leies
VP: Emily Moyer
Assoc Dir: Shana Edwards
Assoc Dir: Leslie Fleisch
Assoc Dir: Sean Keating
Assoc Dir: Stephanie Paddock
Assoc Dir: Josh Weinstein
Assoc Dir: Nicole Willis
Comm Dir: Joyce Oberdorf

MICHAEL JON DESIGNS
See MORGAN FABRICS CORP

MICHAEL JORDAN NISSAN
See CAPITAL CITY NISSAN INC

MICHAEL KAIL
See STEPTOE & JOHNSON LLP

D-U-N-S 13-162-0630 IMP/EXP
MICHAEL KORS (USA) INC
(*Suby of* MICHAEL KORS HOLDINGS LIMITED)
11 W 42nd St Fl 20, New York, NY 10036-8002
Tel (212) 201-8100 *Founded/Ownrshp* 2002
Sales 648.4MM^E *EMP* 400
SIC 5137 5651 5621 Women's & children's clothing; Family clothing stores; Women's clothing stores; Women's & children's clothing; Family clothing stores; Women's clothing stores
Ch Bd: John Idol
**Ch Bd:* Silas Chou
**Ch Bd:* Michael Kors Hon
**Ch Bd:* Lawrence Stroll
Pr: Jennifer Jordano
**CFO:* Joseph Parsons
**Sr VP:* Laura Lentini
VP: Jill Francavilla
VP: Carole Hauer
VP: Ebrahim Hyder
VP: Ryan Jones
VP: Eleni Makriannis
VP: Joe Marotta
VP: Marie Robinson
VP: Nathan Serphos
VP: Jujuan Timberlake
VP: Jung Yoon
VP: Paul Zumbo

D-U-N-S 60-504-8409
MICHAEL KORS RETAIL INC
(*Suby of* MICHAEL KORS (USA) INC) ★
11 W 42nd St Fl 28, New York, NY 10036-8002
Tel (212) 201-8100 *Founded/Ownrshp* 2005
Sales 48.9MM^E *EMP* 200
SIC 5137 Women's & children's clothing; Women's & children's clothing
CEO: John Idol
**Ch Bd:* Silas Chou
**Ch Bd:* Michael Kors
**CFO:* Joseph Parsons
**Sr VP:* Laura Lentini

D-U-N-S 07-902-2893
MICHAEL L SHULAR
SHULAR COMPANIES
9475 Highway 49, Gulfport, MS 39503-4227
Tel (228) 868-1888 *Founded/Ownrshp* 1969
Sales 35.0MM^E *EMP* 600
SIC 7011 6531 5411 7312 Hotels & motels; Real estate brokers & agents; Convenience stores, independent; Billboard advertising; Hotels & motels; Real estate brokers & agents; Convenience stores, independent; Billboard advertising
Owner: Michael L Shular
Genl Mgr: Rosie Lowe
CIO: Doug Travis

MICHAEL LERNER SELECTION
See MHW LTD

D-U-N-S 00-512-0449 IMP/EXP
MICHAEL LEWIS CO
SIMON PRODUCTS CO
(*Suby of* SIMU LTD) ★
8900 W 50th St, Mc Cook, IL 60525-6005
Tel (708) 688-2200 *Founded/Ownrshp* 1933
Sales 390.3MM^E *EMP* 250
Accts Lipschultz Levin & Gray Nort
SIC 5113 5141 5142 2782 2759 2621 Industrial & personal service paper; Groceries, general line; Packaged frozen goods; Looseleaf binders & devices; Menus: printing; Packaging paper; Industrial & personal service paper; Groceries, general line; Packaged frozen goods; Looseleaf binders & devices; Menus: printing; Packaging paper
Pr: Michael L Simon
**VP:* Sheldon L Rosen
Mng Dir: Bob Frye
Off Mgr: Donna Bryant
Manager: Robert Wawrzaszeik
Sales Exec: Joe Bruzzino
Mktg Dir: Frank Kunz

D-U-N-S 10-311-5291 IMP/EXP
MICHAEL MADDEN CO INC
PAPER COMPANY, THE
2815 Warner Ave, Irvine, CA 92606-4443
Tel (800) 834-6248 *Founded/Ownrshp* 1982
Sales 64.4MM^E *EMP* 70
SIC 5113 Industrial & personal service paper; Industrial & personal service paper
Pr: Michael L Madden
CFO: Julie Scheibe
**VP:* Jody Madden
**VP:* Julie K Scheide
Sales Asso: Don Fogh

D-U-N-S 07-274-0285 IMP
MICHAEL MELNICKE
PARK NURSING HOME
353 Beach 48th St, Far Rockaway, NY 11691-1120
Tel (718) 471-5000 *Founded/Ownrshp* 1984
Sales 17.9MM^E *EMP* 400
SIC 8051 Convalescent home with continuous nursing care; Convalescent home with continuous nursing care
Owner: Michael Melnicke

D-U-N-S 05-817-6186 IMP
MICHAEL MILLER FABRICS LLC
118 W 22nd St Fl 5, New York, NY 10011-2416
Tel (212) 704-0774 *Founded/Ownrshp* 1999
Sales 34.5MM *EMP* 29
Accts Jh Cohn Llp New York New Y
SIC 5131 Textile converters; Textile converters
Co-Ownr: Michael Steiner
Dir IT: Karl Yang
Opers Mgr: Beverly Harris
Prd Mgr: Lisa Kang-Shaw

D-U-N-S 13-081-9923
MICHAEL P FRANK CO INC
BURGER KING
4374 W 52nd St, Indianapolis, IN 46254-3705
Tel (317) 817-4300 *Founded/Ownrshp* 1984
Sales 5.6MM^E *EMP* 340
SIC 5812 Fast-food restaurant, chain
Pr: Patrick Tilka
**Pr:* Patricia Tilka
**Treas:* Kim Tilka
**VP:* Richard Diegnan
**VP:* Fredrick Kaufman

D-U-N-S 04-551-0810
MICHAEL P MORRISON LAWYER
70 W Madison St Ste 4200, Chicago, IL 60602-4230
Tel (773) 251-4941 *Founded/Ownrshp* 1980
Sales 12.7MM^E *EMP* 500
SIC 8111 General practice attorney, lawyer; General practice attorney, lawyer
Pr: Michael P Morrison

MICHAEL REILLY DESIGN
See REILLY WORLDWIDE INC

MICHAEL SAUNDERS AND CO
See MICHAEL SAUNDERS SECURITIES CORP

D-U-N-S 18-648-6494
MICHAEL SAUNDERS SECURITIES CORP
MICHAEL SAUNDERS AND CO
1801 Main St, Sarasota, FL 34236-5911
Tel (941) 951-6660 *Founded/Ownrshp* 1991
Sales 20.0MM^E *EMP* 150
SIC 6211 Dealers, security; Dealers, security
Pr: Michael Saunders
Off Mgr: Jim Gorda
VP Opers: Paula Rees

D-U-N-S 60-408-3634 IMP
MICHAEL SKURNIK WINES INC
SKURNIK WINES AND SPIRITS
100 Jericho Quadrangle # 140, Jericho, NY 11753-2710
Tel (516) 677-9300 *Founded/Ownrshp* 1989
Sales 47.7MM^E *EMP* 90
SIC 5182 Wine
Ch Bd: Michael Skurnik
**Pr:* Harman Skurnik
COO: Jim Leskody
Natl Sales: Mark Hutchens
VP Sls: Andrew Shapiro
Sales Asso: Mike Higgins
Sales Asso: David Lancaster
Sales Asso: Ryan Lindsay
Sales Asso: Steven Meir
Sales Asso: David Newlin
Sales Asso: Douglas Rankin

D-U-N-S 60-915-2475
MICHAEL STAPLETON ASSOCIATES LTD
MSA SECURITY
9 Murray St Fl 2, New York, NY 10007-2258
Tel (212) 509-1336 *Founded/Ownrshp* 1987
Sales 24.4MM^E *EMP* 500^E
SIC 7382 8742 Security systems services; Training & development consultant
CEO: Patrick Timlin
**Pr:* Michael O'Neil
CFO: Peter Christenson
**CFO:* Michael Kennedy
VP: Patrick Devlin
**VP:* Keith Mulcahy
**Prin:* Jessica Hagstrom
Genl Mgr: Toni Scarito
Dir IT: Robert Correia
Dir IT: Robert Lamont
Dir IT: Marc Weathers
Board of Directors: Jessica Johnson

D-U-N-S 15-686-0249 IMP
MICHAEL STARS INC
12955 Chadron Ave, Hawthorne, CA 90250-5526
Tel (310) 263-7375 *Founded/Ownrshp* 1986
Sales 68.0MM^E *EMP* 140^E
SIC 5137

D-U-N-S 01-191-1398
MICHAEL STEADS AUTO DEPOT INC
HILLTOP CHRYSLER PLYMOUTH
3291 Auto Plz, Richmond, CA 94806-1931
Tel (510) 243-6100 *Founded/Ownrshp* 1996
Sales 71.8MM^E *EMP* 300
SIC 5511 Automobiles, new & used; Pickups, new & used; Trucks, tractors & trailers: new & used; Automobiles, new & used; Pickups, new & used; Trucks, tractors & trailers: new & used
CEO: Michael C Stead
Sls Mgr: Jimmy Carretta

MICHAEL STEAD'S HILLTOP FORD
See MICHAEL C STEAD INC

D-U-N-S 80-015-1953
MICHAEL T KLAK
MCDONALD'S
1180 Clock Tower Plz, Washington, MO 63090-5333
Tel (636) 239-7237 *Founded/Ownrshp* 1977
Sales 11.1MM^E *EMP* 401
SIC 5812 6512 0811 Fast-food restaurant, chain; Shopping center, property operation only; Tree farm; Fast-food restaurant, chain; Shopping center, property operation only; Tree farm
Owner: Michael T Klak

D-U-N-S 08-508-0497 IMP
MICHAEL WEINIG INC
(*Suby of* MICHAEL WEINIG AG)
124 Crosslake Park Dr, Mooresville, NC 28117-8016
Tel (704) 799-0100 *Founded/Ownrshp* 1976
Sales 97.5MM^E *EMP* 120
SIC 5084 Woodworking machinery; Woodworking machinery
Pr: Jeffrey H Davidson
Treas: Chad Starnes
Treas: Karl Wachter
VP: Dan Murphy
IT Man: Peter Fritsch
Ql Cn Mgr: David Lemasson
Sls Mgr: Penny Miller

D-U-N-S 05-686-3285
MICHAELS & ASSOCIATES INC
5470 Executive Pkwy Se, Grand Rapids, MI 49512-5510
Tel (616) 656-5100 *Founded/Ownrshp* 1981
Sales 26.7MM^E *EMP* 110
SIC 5141 Food brokers; Food brokers
Pr: Larry Brown
**Treas:* Louis Champine
**VP:* Cythia Holmes
**VP:* John Kotarski
**VP:* Marvin Miller
Mktg Dir: Darcy Rosely
Snr Mgr: Peter Manett

D-U-N-S 07-942-9778
▲ MICHAELS COMPANIES INC
8000 Bent Branch Dr, Irving, TX 75063-6023
Tel (972) 409-1300 *Founded/Ownrshp* 1983
Sales 4.7MMM *EMP* 51,000^E
Tkr Sym MIK *Exch* NGS
SIC 5945 3999 2273 Arts & crafts supplies; Framed artwork; Mats & matting; Door mats: paper, grass, reed, coir, sisal, jute, rags, etc.; Arts & crafts supplies; Framed artwork; Mats & matting; Door mats: paper, grass, reed, coir, sisal, jute, rags, etc.
CEO: Carl S Rubin
Pr: Bob Glinka
Ofcr: Charles M Sonsteby
Ex VP: Theodore J Bachmeier
Ex VP: Stephen J Carlotti
Ex VP: Philo T Pappas
Sr VP: Eric Gordon
Sr VP: Michael J Jones
Sr VP: Dennis A Mullahy
Sr VP: Michael J Veitenheimer
VP: Debbie Beadroux
VP: Lisa-Beth Galvin
VP: Anuradha Gupta
Board of Directors: Josh Bekenstein, Karen Kaplan, Lewis S Klessel, Matthew S Levin, John J Mahoney, James A Quella, Beryl B Raff, Peter F Wallace

D-U-N-S 92-652-7755
MICHAELS DEVELOPMENT GROUP INC
10 Blacksmith Dr, Ballston Spa, NY 12020-4428
Tel (518) 899-6311 *Founded/Ownrshp* 1992
Sales 23.0MM *EMP* 20
SIC 1522 Multi-family dwelling construction; Multi-family dwellings, new construction; Multi-family dwelling construction; Multi-family dwellings, new construction
CEO: John H Michaels
**Sec:* Heidi Harkins
**VP:* A David Michaels

D-U-N-S 00-896-8331
MICHAELS ELECTRICAL SUPPLY CORP
456 Merrick Rd, Lynbrook, NY 11563-2455
Tel (516) 593-7200 *Founded/Ownrshp* 1985
Sales 44.1MM^E *EMP* 45
SIC 5063 Electrical apparatus & equipment
Ch Bd: Marvin Greenberg
IT Man: Paul Baluyot
VP Sls: Alison Lozito

D-U-N-S 10-912-9775
MICHAELS ENTERPRISES INC
IRVING MICHAELS & COMPANY
150 Mattatuck Heights Rd # 3, Waterbury, CT 06705-3861
Tel (203) 597-4942 *Founded/Ownrshp* 1885
Sales 76.5MM^E *EMP* 120
Accts Blum Shapiro & Company Pc
SIC 5094 Jewelry; Jewelry
Pr: Paul Michaels
**Ch Bd:* John A Michaels
**VP:* Richard Michaels
**VP:* V Paul Michaels

D-U-N-S 88-330-5211
MICHAELS FAMILY RESTRAUNT IV INC
MICHAEL'S RESTAURANT
2991 Us Highway 1, Lawrenceville, NJ 08648-2413
Tel (609) 530-1676 *Founded/Ownrshp* 1994
Sales 1.0MM *EMP* 350
SIC 5812 Eating places; Eating places
Pr: Michael Petro
**Pr:* Michael Petrogiannis

D-U-N-S 07-947-7223
■ MICHAELS FINCO HOLDINGS LLC
(*Suby of* MICHAELS COMPANIES INC) ★
8000 Bent Branch Dr, Irving, TX 75063-6023
Tel (972) 409-1300 *Founded/Ownrshp* 2013
Sales 6.2MMM^E *EMP* 50,600^E
SIC 5945 Hobby, toy & game shops; Arts & crafts supplies
CEO: Carl S Rubin

D-U-N-S 00-448-9696
■ MICHAELS FINER MEATS LLC
(*Suby of* CHEFS WAREHOUSE INC) ★
3775 Zane Trace Dr, Columbus, OH 43228-3854
Tel (614) 527-4900 *Founded/Ownrshp* 1962
Sales 36.6MM^E *EMP* 110
SIC 5147 5146 5144

D-U-N-S 07-940-2542
■ MICHAELS FUNDING INC
(*Suby of* MICHAELS FINCO HOLDINGS LLC) ★
8000 Bent Branch Dr, Irving, TX 75063-6023
Tel (972) 409-1300 *Founded/Ownrshp* 2013
Sales 6.2MMM^E *EMP* 50,600^E
SIC 5945 Hobby, toy & game shops; Hobby & craft supplies; Hobby, toy & game shops; Hobby & craft supplies

D-U-N-S 07-610-4520
■ MICHAELS FURNITURE CO INC
(*Suby of* RESTORATION HARDWARE INC) ★
15 Koch Rd Ste J, Corte Madera, CA 94925-1231
Tel (916) 381-9086 *Founded/Ownrshp* 1998
Sales 26.5MM *EMP* 300
SIC 2511 Wood household furniture; Wood household furniture
CEO: Gary Friedman
**Genl Mgr:* Mike Bollum
Sfty Mgr: Clay Schmelling
Plnt Mgr: Bud Sciscio

D-U-N-S 18-051-7955
MICHAELS G L CONSTRUCTION INC
554 W Cedarwood Ave, West Terre Haute, IN 47885-8405
Tel (812) 478-3154 *Founded/Ownrshp* 1987
Sales 128.0MM *EMP* 10
SIC 1542 1541 Commercial & office building contractors; Industrial buildings, new construction; Commercial & office building contractors; Industrial buildings, new construction
Pr: Gary Lasure
**Sec:* Kimberly Lasure

D-U-N-S 79-006-4567 IMP
MICHAELS HOLDINGS LLC
8000 Bent Branch Dr, Irving, TX 75063-6023
Tel (972) 409-1300 *Founded/Ownrshp* 2006
Sales 2.2MMM^E *EMP* 89,000^E
SIC 5945 5999 5949 5947 5199 5099 Hobby, toy & game shops; Art, picture frames & decorations; Needlework goods & supplies; Party favors; Gifts & novelties; Novelties, durable; Hobby, toy & game shops; Art, picture frames & decorations; Needlework goods & supplies; Party favors; Gifts & novelties; Novelties, durable
Ofcr: Charles Sonsteby
Sr VP: Shawn Hearn
VP: Maria Mullen

MICHAEL'S RESTAURANT
See MICHAELS FAMILY RESTRAUNT IV INC

D-U-N-S 05-440-2896 IMP
■ MICHAELS STORES INC
(*Suby of* MICHAELS FUNDING INC) ★
8000 Bent Branch Dr, Irving, TX 75063-6023
Tel (972) 409-1300 *Founded/Ownrshp* 2013
Sales 6.2MMM^E *EMP* 50,600^E
SIC 5945 5999 5949 5947 5199 5099 Hobby, toy & game shops; Hobby & craft supplies; Arts & crafts supplies; Hobbies; Art, picture frames & decorations; Artificial flowers; Picture frames, ready made; Artists' supplies & materials; Needlework goods & supplies; Bridal fabrics; Gift, novelty & souvenir shop; Artcraft & carvings; Novelties; Party favors; Gifts & novelties; Novelties, durable; Souvenirs; Hobby, toy & game shops; Hobby & craft supplies; Arts & crafts supplies; Hobbies; Art, picture frames & decorations; Artificial flowers; Picture frames, ready made; Artists' supplies & materials; Needlework goods & supplies; Bridal fabrics; Gift, novelty & souvenir shop; Artcraft & carvings; Novelties; Party favors; Gifts & novelties; Novelties, durable; Souvenirs
CEO: Carl S Rubin
Bd of Dir: Jason Fries
Bd of Dir: Anthony Ricker
**Ofcr:* Charles M Sonsteby
Ex VP: Theodore J Bachmeier
Ex VP: Stephen Carlotti
Ex VP: Thomas C Decaro
Sr VP: Shawn E Hearn
Sr VP: Dennis A Mullahy
**Sr VP:* Michael J Veitenheimer
VP: Lance A Weibye
Exec: Linda Berquist
Exec: Dina Lackey
Creative D: Mick Murphy
Creative D: Joann Pearson

MICHAEL'S TOYOTA OF BELLEVUE
See SKYMATT AUTOMOTIVE GROUP INC

D-U-N-S 96-908-8855
MICHAELSON CONNOR & BOUL
5312 Bolsa Ave Ste 200, Huntington Beach, CA 92649-1062
Tel (714) 846-6099 Founded/Ownrshp 1994
Sales 20.4MM^E EMP 150
SIC 8742 Real estate consultant; Real estate consultant
Pr: Joan Heid
Mng Pt: Michel Bar
*Sec: Firmin Boul
Sr VP: Pam Santos
*VP: Michael Ryan
CTO: Dan Boul
Snr Mgr: Gail Savage

D-U-N-S 04-916-2118
MICHAUD DISTRIBUTORS INC
57 Spring Hill Rd, Saco, ME 04072-9650
Tel (207) 294-0441 Founded/Ownrshp 1981
Sales 43.7MM^E EMP 75
SIC 5145 5962 Snack foods; Potato chips; Candy & snack food vending machines
Pr: Richard Michaud Jr
Manager: Dave Dickey

D-U-N-S 93-787-3131
■ MICHCON PIPELINE CO
MCN
(Suby of DTE GAS CO) ★
500 Griswold St Fl 16th, Detroit, MI 48226-3480
Tel (313) 256-5505 Founded/Ownrshp 1995
Sales 325.0MM^E EMP 4,576
SIC 4922 Pipelines, natural gas
Pr: Stephen E Ewing
*Pr: Steven Kurmas
*Treas: Howard Dow
IT Man: Tom Motsinger

D-U-N-S 96-726-7845
MICHCON POST-RETIREMENT VEBA TRUST
1 Energy Plz, Detroit, MI 48226-1221
Tel (313) 235-1662 Founded/Ownrshp 2011
Sales 42.7MM EMP 2^E
Accts George Johnson & Company Detr
SIC 6733 Trusts

MICHELIN AIRCRAFT TIRE COMPANY
See MICHELIN NORTH AMERICA

D-U-N-S 03-010-3287
MICHELIN AMERICAS RESEARCH & DEVELOPMENT CORP
(Suby of MICHELIN NORTH AMERICA INC) ★
515 Michelin Rd, Greenville, SC 29605-6131
Tel (864) 422-4000 Founded/Ownrshp 1975
Sales 52.4MM^E EMP 900
SIC 8731 3011 Commercial physical research; Tires & inner tubes; Commercial physical research; Tires & inner tubes
Pr: Terry Gettys
Sec: Norman King
IT Man: Ronnie Engram

D-U-N-S 04-469-1848 IMP/EXP
MICHELIN CORP (NY)
(Suby of MICHELIN NORTH AMERICA INC) ★
1 Parkway S, Greenville, SC 29615-5095
Tel (864) 458-5000 Founded/Ownrshp 1907, 2014
Sales 2.5MMM^E EMP 23,000
SIC 3011 5014

D-U-N-S 07-874-2626 EXP
MICHELIN NORTH AMERICA
MICHELIN AIRCRAFT TIRE COMPANY
40589 S Stanly School Rd, Norwood, NC 28128-8752
Tel (704) 474-7634 Founded/Ownrshp 2013
Sales 45.0MM^E EMP 125^E
SIC 5531 Automotive tires
Prin: Jean-Dominique Senard
Pr: Jean Coulon
CFO: Art McDonald
VP: Maryanne Kuerzi
VP: Jan Skinner
CIO: Shafiq Anwar
QA Dir: Chris Morehouse
IT Man: Terry Greening
IT Man: Andreea Vance
Opers Mgr: Jim Dunbaugh
Plnt Mgr: Paul Cagle

D-U-N-S 00-166-7161 IMP
MICHELIN NORTH AMERICA INC
1 Parkway S, Greenville, SC 29615-5095
Tel (864) 458-5000 Founded/Ownrshp 2000
Sales 6.1MMM^E EMP 23,500
SIC 3011 Automobile tires, pneumatic; Truck or bus tires, pneumatic; Automobile tires, pneumatic; Truck or bus tires, pneumatic
Ch: Pete Selleck
COO: David Staffrod
CFO: Eric Le Le Corre
*CFO: Thomas Praktish
*Ch: Dick Wilkerson
*VP: Scott Clark
VP: Michael Fanning
VP: Craig Macgibbon
Exec: Ronald Musgnug
Admn Mgr: Bob Willmerdinger
Genl Mgr: Shawn McCullough

D-U-N-S 06-955-2750 IMP
■ MICHELLE STE WINE ESTATES LTD (WA)
DOMAINE STE MICHELLE
(Suby of INTERNATIONAL WINE & SPIRITS LTD) ★
14111 Ne 145th St, Woodinville, WA 98072-6981
Tel (425) 488-1133 Founded/Ownrshp 1930, 2009
Sales 29.1MM^E EMP 110
SIC 2084 Wines; Wines
Pr: Theodor P Baseler
Pr: Joe Gregg
Pr: Kari Leitch
Pr: Keith Love
*Treas: Daniel J Bryant
*Sr VP: Glen D Yaffa
VP: Michael Bobbett
VP: Lou Constant
VP: Joseph Fraser
*VP: Michael D Garvey
VP: Frank Genovese
VP: Dan Heller
VP: Steve Spadarotto
Dir Lab: Leslie Shannon
Dir: Steve Johnson
Creative D: Jenny Woyvodich
Comm Dir: Lynda Eller

D-U-N-S 82-501-8476
MICHELMAN-CANCELLIERE IRONWORKS INC
MC IRONWORKS
7230 Beth Bath Pike, Bath, PA 18014
Tel (610) 837-9914 Founded/Ownrshp 1992
Sales 32.6MM^E EMP 110
SIC 3441 Fabricated structural metal; Fabricated structural metal
CEO: John Cancelliere
*Treas: Donald C Smith
*VP: Lionel Michelman

D-U-N-S 00-629-7139
MICHELMANN STEEL CONSTRUCTION CO
MID-STATES DOOR AND HARDWARE
137 N 2nd St, Quincy, IL 62301-2999
Tel (217) 222-0555 Founded/Ownrshp 1865
Sales 24.4MM^E EMP 46^E
SIC 5051 3441 3443 3442 Structural shapes, iron or steel; Fabricated structural metal; Fabricated plate work (boiler shop); Metal doors, sash & trim
CEO: Laura Gerdes Ehrhart
*CFO: John Esselman
Genl Mgr: Mike Plant

D-U-N-S 00-226-9702
MICHELS BAKERY INC (PA)
5698 Rising Sun Ave, Philadelphia, PA 19120-1698
Tel (215) 742-3900 Founded/Ownrshp 1946
Sales 34.2MM^E EMP 130
SIC 2051 Bread, cake & related products; Bread, cake & related products
Pr: Jon Liss
*Pr: Jon H Liss
*VP: Betty Liss
VP: Jack Moran
VP: Stan Waloulek
VP: Stan Walulek
*VP: Stanley C Walulek
QC Dir: Jan Kleeman
Sfty Mgr: Jim Gallagher
Opers Mgr: Matt Rini

D-U-N-S 00-580-9868 IMP
MICHELS CORP (WI)
MICHELS MID-AMERICA LINE CABLE
817 W Main St, Brownsville, WI 53006-1439
Tel (920) 583-3132 Founded/Ownrshp 1960
Sales 4.0MMM^E EMP 5,000
Accts Grant Thornton Llp Appleton
SIC 1623 1771 1381 1629 3498 1794 Pipeline construction; Telephone & communication line construction; Foundation & footing contractor; Drilling oil & gas wells; Oil refinery construction; Fabricated pipe & fittings; Excavation work; Pipeline construction; Telephone & communication line construction; Foundation & footing contractor; Drilling oil & gas wells; Oil refinery construction; Fabricated pipe & fittings; Excavation work
Ch Bd: Ruth L Michels
*CEO: Patrick D Michels
*CFO: John Schroeder
*Ex VP: Brian P Johnson
*VP: Kevin Michels
*VP: Tim Michels
Dir Risk M: Alissa Dewar
Dir Lab: Charlie Walls
Genl Mgr: Dan Gellings
Genl Mgr: Brett Hurlburt
Genl Mgr: Landon Kluck

MICHELS MID-AMERICA LINE CABLE
See MICHELS CORP

D-U-N-S 79-452-6603
MICHELSEN PACKAGING CO
202 N 2nd Ave, Yakima, WA 98902-2625
Tel (509) 248-6270 Founded/Ownrshp 1953
Sales 30.5MM^E EMP 150
SIC 2657 5113 Folding paperboard boxes; Folding paperboard boxes; Folding paperboard boxes; Folding paperboard boxes
Pr: Dan Keck
*VP: Daniel L Beddeson

D-U-N-S 02-758-7716 IMP
MICHELSEN PACKAGING CO OF CALIFORNIA
202 N 2nd Ave, Yakima, WA 98902-2625
Tel (509) 248-6270 Founded/Ownrshp 1964
Sales 99.2MM^E EMP 175
SIC 5113 2653 Containers, paper & disposable plastic; Paper & products, wrapping or coarse; Pads, solid fiber: made from purchased materials; Containers, paper & disposable plastic; Paper & products, wrapping or coarse; Pads, solid fiber: made from purchased materials
Pr: Dan Keck
*Ex VP: Gary Gavin
Info Man: Dan Beddeson

D-U-N-S 78-656-3234
MICHELSON ORGANIZATION
7701 Forsyth Blvd Ste 900, Saint Louis, MO 63105-1813
Tel (314) 862-7080 Founded/Ownrshp 2003
Sales 26.1MM^E EMP 500^E
SIC 6531 Real estate agents & managers; Real estate agents & managers
VP: Robert Lazaroff
VP: Bruce Michelson
Area Mgr: Alicia Bush
Off Mgr: Jenn Estrada

D-U-N-S 07-029-2685
MICHIGAN AGRICULTURAL COMMODITIES INC
445 N Canal Rd, Lansing, MI 48917-7709
Tel (517) 627-0200 Founded/Ownrshp 1976
Sales 44.0MM^E EMP 100
SIC 5153

D-U-N-S 04-058-0938
MICHIGAN AIR PRODUCTS CO
MAP SERVICE
1185 Equity Dr, Troy, MI 48084-7108
Tel (248) 837-7000 Founded/Ownrshp 1986
Sales 54.8MM^E EMP 50
SIC 5074 Plumbing & hydronic heating supplies; Water heaters & purification equipment
Pr: James A Kutil
CEO: Donald H Kutil
VP: Paul D Joliat

D-U-N-S 00-656-9933
MICHIGAN ALUMINUM EXTRUSION & WINDOW CORP (MI)
MICHIGAN EXTRUDED ALUMINUM
205 Watts Rd, Jackson, MI 49203-2324
Tel (517) 764-5400 Founded/Ownrshp 1986
Sales 20.0MM^E EMP 75
SIC 3354 Aluminum extruded products
Pr: Jeffrey L Jacobs
*VP: Nancy J Jacobs

D-U-N-S 05-203-9625
MICHIGAN AUTOMATIC TURNING INC
AA GEAR & MANUFACTURING
1045 Durant Dr, Howell, MI 48843-9536
Tel (517) 552-3100 Founded/Ownrshp 2002
Sales 25.8MM^E EMP 94
SIC 3714 Transmission housings or parts, motor vehicle; Gears, motor vehicle
Pr: Pete Lazic

D-U-N-S 60-636-0444 IMP/EXP
MICHIGAN AUTOMOTIVE COMPRESSOR INC
MACI
(Suby of TOYOTA INDUSTRIES CORPORATION)
2400 N Dearing Rd, Parma, MI 49269-9415
Tel (517) 622-7000 Founded/Ownrshp 1989
Sales 109.6MM^E EMP 580^E
SIC 3585 3714 3568 3563 Air conditioning, motor vehicle; Motor vehicle parts & accessories; Power transmission equipment; Air & gas compressors; Air conditioning, motor vehicle; Motor vehicle parts & accessories; Power transmission equipment; Air & gas compressors
Pr: Yuji Ishizaki
CFO: David Pollack
Genl Mgr: Steve Sauter
MIS Dir: Eric Chaney
QA Dir: Patrick Flahie
QA Dir: Jason Hoover
QA Dir: Matt Kunesh
QA Dir: Bryant Powers
Plnt Mgr: Gary Dods
Snr Mgr: Jim Ludwig
Snr Mgr: Rafe Pierce

D-U-N-S 07-422-6556
MICHIGAN BASIC PROPERTY INSURANCE ASSOCIATION
3245 E Jefferson Ave, Detroit, MI 48207-4222
Tel (313) 877-7400 Founded/Ownrshp 1968
Sales NA EMP 76^E
SIC 6331 8611 Property damage insurance; Business associations; Property damage insurance; Business associations
Ex Dir: Richard Robertson
*CFO: Robert Hoffman
Genl Mgr: Dick Robertson
MIS Mgr: Sandra Schwartz
Software D: Chet Dunbar

D-U-N-S 00-695-8524
■ MICHIGAN BELL TELEPHONE CO
AT&T MICHIGAN
(Suby of AT&T MIDWEST) ★
444 Michigan Ave, Detroit, MI 48226-2517
Tel (313) 223-9900 Founded/Ownrshp 1904
Sales 836.1MM^E EMP 12,249
SIC 4813 8721 Local & long distance telephone communications; Local telephone communications; Billing & bookkeeping service; Local & long distance telephone communications; Local telephone communications; Billing & bookkeeping service
Pr: Gail Torreano

D-U-N-S 06-984-5139
MICHIGAN BLOOD (MI)
MI CMNTY BLOOD CTR-GRND RAPIDS
1036 Fuller Ave Ne, Grand Rapids, MI 49503-1304
Tel (616) 774-2300 Founded/Ownrshp 1955
Sales 40.8MM EMP 425
SIC 8099 8071

D-U-N-S 01-739-9411
MICHIGAN BLUEBERRY GROWERS ASSOCIATION (MI)
MBG MARKETING
O4726 Cr 215, Grand Junction, MI 49056
Tel (269) 434-6791 Founded/Ownrshp 1936, 1943
Sales 30.5MM^E EMP 28
Accts Cliftonlarsonallen Llp Steven
SIC 5142 5148 Fruits, frozen; Fruits, fresh
Pr: John Calsbeek
*CEO: Frank Bragg
VP: Larry Enfield

MICHIGAN BTNIC GRDN FOUNDATION
See WEST MICHIGAN HORTICULTURAL SOCIETY FOUNDATION

MICHIGAN CANCER FOUNDATION
See BARBARA ANN KARMANOS CANCER INSTITUTE

MICHIGAN CAT
See MACALLISTER MACHINERY CO INC

D-U-N-S 01-692-8657 EXP
MICHIGAN CHANDELIER CO INC
20855 Telegraph Rd, Southfield, MI 48033-4238
Tel (248) 353-0510 Founded/Ownrshp 1912
Sales 20.4MM^E EMP 32
Accts Croskey Lanni & Company Pc
SIC 5063 5719 Lighting fixtures; Wiring devices; Lighting fixtures; Lamps & lamp shades
Pr: Edward R Berne
*VP: Judith Berne
Sls Mgr: John Testasecca

D-U-N-S 06-976-1146
MICHIGAN CITY AREA SCHOOLS
408 S Carroll Ave, Michigan City, IN 46360-5345
Tel (219) 873-2000 Founded/Ownrshp 1966
Sales 76.3MM^E EMP 1,500
SIC 8211 Public elementary school; Public junior high school; Public senior high school; Public elementary school; Public junior high school; Public senior high school
COO: Joan M Corick
*Treas: Vincent Taylor
Prin: Richard Kirchner
Off Mgr: Linda Jones
Schl Brd P: Donald Dulaney

D-U-N-S 07-635-0024
MICHIGAN CLAIM SERVICE INC
ASU GROUP, THE
2120 University Park Dr, Okemos, MI 48864-3972
Tel (517) 349-2212 Founded/Ownrshp 1986
Sales NA EMP 60
SIC 6411 Insurance agents, brokers & service
CEO: Debra Claeys
COO: Dave Moscovick
*CFO: Sarah Hartman
Comm Man: Theresa Cooper
CIO: Duane Hershberger
VP Opers: Fred Jernigan
Snr Mgr: Michael Mulder
Board of Directors: Tara Larose Kim Pavlik Ric

D-U-N-S 10-154-6521
MICHIGAN COMMERCIAL INSURANCE MUTUAL CORP
MCIM
1044 Eastbury Dr, Lansing, MI 48917-9776
Tel (517) 886-3900 Founded/Ownrshp 1980
Sales NA EMP 65
SIC 6331 Workers' compensation insurance; Workers' compensation insurance
Ch: Donald Pratt
*CEO: Eleanor Powell-Yoder
*Sec: Andy Hofstra
VP: Donna Serdert
*VP: Laurie Zdanis
Brnch Mgr: Steve Baldwin

D-U-N-S 02-184-2463
MICHIGAN COMMUNITY ACTION AGENCY ASSOCIATION
MCAAA
2173 Commons Pkwy, Okemos, MI 48864-3987
Tel (517) 321-7500 Founded/Ownrshp 1975
Sales 24.0MM EMP 5
SIC 8399 Community action agency; Community action agency
Pr: Mary Trucks
*Treas: Art Fenrick
Ex Dir: Jim Crisp
Ex Dir: John Stephenson

D-U-N-S 05-282-1778
MICHIGAN COMMUNITY CREDIT UNION
1425 W Parnall Rd, Jackson, MI 49201-8610
Tel (517) 787-2060 Founded/Ownrshp 1986
Sales NA EMP 50
SIC 6351 Credit & other financial responsibility insurance
CEO: Tina Hamilton
Dir IT: Becca White

D-U-N-S 15-142-1732
MICHIGAN COMMUNITY SERVICES INC
5239 Morrish Rd Ste 2, Swartz Creek, MI 48473-7645
Tel (810) 635-4407 Founded/Ownrshp 1982
Sales 14.1MM EMP 375
SIC 8361 8331 Home for the mentally handicapped; Home for the physically handicapped; Job training services; Home for the mentally handicapped; Home for the physically handicapped; Job training services
Ex Dir: Greg Kirkland
IT Man: Jackie Easter

D-U-N-S 00-194-1715
MICHIGAN CONFERENCE ASSOCIATION OF SEVENTH DAY ADVENTISTS (MI)
(Suby of LAKE UNION CONF OF SDA) ★
320 W Saint Joseph St, Lansing, MI 48933-2319
Tel (517) 316-1500 Founded/Ownrshp 1929
Sales 9.2MM^E EMP 350
SIC 8661 Seventh Day Adventist Church; Seventh Day Adventist Church
Pr: Jay Gallimore
*Treas: Leroy Bruch
Bd of Dir: Evelyn Kissinger

D-U-N-S 08-546-4295
MICHIGAN CONFERENCE OF TEAMSTERS WELFARE FUND
2700 Trumbull St, Detroit, MI 48216-1269
Tel (313) 964-2400 Founded/Ownrshp 1949
Sales NA EMP 96
Accts Plante & Moran Pllc Auburn Hi
SIC 6371 Union welfare, benefit & health funds; Union welfare, benefit & health funds
Ex Dir: Richard Burker
Dir IT: Bill Deighton
Dir IT: Sue Hamilton
IT Man: Jason Brown

D-U-N-S 04-425-3243
MICHIGAN CREDIT UNION LEAGUE (MI)
38695 7 Mile Rd Ste 200, Livonia, MI 48152-7097
Tel (734) 793-1530 Founded/Ownrshp 1934, 1941
Sales 51.9MM EMP 46

Accts Rehmann Robson Troy Mi
SIC 8611 Trade associations; Trade associations
Ex Dir: David Adams
**COO:* Drew Egan
COO: Jenny Hoyle
Exec: Dana Reif
Mktg Mgr: Cathy Scoda
Counsel: Patricia Corkery

D-U-N-S 36-205-1398
■ MICHIGAN DAIRY LLC
(*Suby of* KROGER CO) ★
29601 Industrial Rd, Livonia, MI 48150-2012
Tel (734) 367-5390 *Founded/Ownrshp* 1999
Sales 199.7MM^E *EMP* 1^E
SIC 5143 Dairy products, except dried or canned
IT Man: Matt Heywood

MICHIGAN DEMOCRATIC PARTY
See MICHIGAN DEMOCRATIC STATE CENTRAL COMMITTEE

D-U-N-S 15-193-1862
MICHIGAN DEMOCRATIC STATE CENTRAL COMMITTEE
MICHIGAN DEMOCRATIC PARTY
606 Townsend St, Lansing, MI 48933-2313
Tel (517) 371-5410 *Founded/Ownrshp* 1900
Sales 23.0MM *EMP* 12
SIC 8651 Political campaign organization; Political campaign organization
Ex Dir: Garrett Arwa
**Ch:* Lon Johnson

D-U-N-S 80-533-5742
MICHIGAN DEPARTMENT OF ATTORNEY GENERAL
(*Suby of* EXECUTIVE OFFICE OF STATE OF MICHIGAN) ★
525 W Ottawa St Fl 7, Lansing, MI 48933-1067
Tel (517) 373-1110 *Founded/Ownrshp* 1837
Sales NA *EMP* 520^E
SIC 9222 Attorney General's office; ; Attorney General's office;
Prin: Bill Schuette

D-U-N-S 80-533-6278
MICHIGAN DEPARTMENT OF CIVIL SERVICE
(*Suby of* EXECUTIVE OFFICE OF STATE OF MICHIGAN) ★
400 S Pine St, Lansing, MI 48933-2250
Tel (517) 373-3048 *Founded/Ownrshp* 1937
Sales NA *EMP* 500^E
SIC 9199 Civil service commission, government; ; Civil service commission, government;
VP: Joyce Sweet
Comm Dir: Jessi Adler

D-U-N-S 80-534-0056
MICHIGAN DEPARTMENT OF COMMUNITY HEALTH
(*Suby of* EXECUTIVE OFFICE OF STATE OF MICHIGAN) ★
201 Townsend St Fl 7, Lansing, MI 48933-1554
Tel (517) 241-1193 *Founded/Ownrshp* 1965
Sales NA *EMP* 4,000
SIC 9431 Administration of public health programs; ; Administration of public health programs;
Exec: Nancy Houts

D-U-N-S 92-932-7880
MICHIGAN DEPARTMENT OF ENVIRONMENTAL QUALITY
MDEQ
(*Suby of* EXECUTIVE OFFICE OF STATE OF MICHIGAN) ★
525 W Allegan St, Lansing, MI 48933-1502
Tel (517) 284-6700 *Founded/Ownrshp* 1995
Sales NA *EMP* 1,100
SIC 9511 Air, water & solid waste management; ; Air, water & solid waste management;
Exec: Amy Peterson
IT Man: Sharon Maher

D-U-N-S 08-003-2707
MICHIGAN DEPARTMENT OF HEALTH & HUMAN SERVICES
MDHHS
(*Suby of* EXECUTIVE OFFICE OF STATE OF MICHIGAN) ★
201 Townsend St, Lansing, MI 48933-1551
Tel (517) 373-3740 *Founded/Ownrshp* 2015
Sales NA *EMP* 27,267^E
SIC 9431 9441 ; ; Administration of social & human resources

D-U-N-S 80-534-0163
MICHIGAN DEPARTMENT OF HUMAN SERVICES
(*Suby of* EXECUTIVE OFFICE OF STATE OF MICHIGAN) ★
235 S Grand Ave, Lansing, MI 48933-1805
Tel (517) 373-2000 *Founded/Ownrshp* 1965
Sales NA *EMP* 9,689
SIC 9441 8249 Administration of social & manpower programs; ; Vocational schools; Administration of social & manpower programs; ; Vocational schools
Netwrk Mgr: Carol Tierdney
Snr Mgr: Stanley Stewart

D-U-N-S 16-927-0662
MICHIGAN DEPARTMENT OF INFORMATION TECHNOLOGY
(*Suby of* EXECUTIVE OFFICE OF STATE OF MICHIGAN) ★
111 S Capitol Ave, Lansing, MI 48933-1555
Tel (517) 241-2000 *Founded/Ownrshp* 2003
Sales NA *EMP* 1,700
SIC 9111 City & town managers' offices; ; City & town managers' offices;
Prin: Teri Takai
Dir IT: Kenneth D Theis
IT Man: Sharita Hurst

D-U-N-S 80-533-9439 IMP
MICHIGAN DEPARTMENT OF MILITARY AND VETERANS AFFAIRS
(*Suby of* EXECUTIVE OFFICE OF STATE OF MICHIGAN) ★
3411 N Martin Luther King, Lansing, MI 48906-2934
Tel (517) 481-8083 *Founded/Ownrshp* 1837
Sales NA *EMP* 14,500
SIC 9711 9451 National security; ; Administration of veterans' affairs; ; National security; ; Administration of veterans' affairs;

D-U-N-S 80-533-9991
MICHIGAN DEPARTMENT OF NATURAL RESOURCES
(*Suby of* EXECUTIVE OFFICE OF STATE OF MICHIGAN) ★
525 W Allegan St, Lansing, MI 48933-1502
Tel (517) 284-5936 *Founded/Ownrshp* 1921
Sales NA *EMP* 1,800
SIC 9512

D-U-N-S 80-534-0247
MICHIGAN DEPARTMENT OF STATE POLICE
MICHIGAN STATE POLICE
(*Suby of* EXECUTIVE OFFICE OF STATE OF MICHIGAN) ★
333 S Grand Ave, Lansing, MI 48933-2108
Tel (517) 241-1075 *Founded/Ownrshp* 1965
Sales NA *EMP* 2,600
SIC 9221 State police; ; State police;
Sys/Dir: Jime Cook

D-U-N-S 80-534-0361
MICHIGAN DEPARTMENT OF TRANSPORTATION
(*Suby of* EXECUTIVE OFFICE OF STATE OF MICHIGAN) ★
425 W Ottawa St, Lansing, MI 48933-1516
Tel (517) 373-2090 *Founded/Ownrshp* 1978
Sales NA *EMP* 437
SIC 9621 Regulation, administration of transportation; ; Regulation, administration of transportation;
COO: Mark Van Port Fleet
Ofcr: Laura J Mester
VP: Neil Wilson
Comm Man: Ann Clery
Dept Mgr: Mike Blackledge
CIO: Doug Couto

D-U-N-S 80-534-0486
MICHIGAN DEPARTMENT OF TREASURY
(*Suby of* EXECUTIVE OFFICE OF STATE OF MICHIGAN) ★
430 W Allegan St, Lansing, MI 48933-1592
Tel (517) 373-3223 *Founded/Ownrshp* 1965
Sales NA *EMP* 1,200
SIC 9311 Finance, taxation & monetary policy; ; Finance, taxation & monetary policy;
Treas: Robert J Kleine
Comm Dir: Terry Stanton
IT Man: Jana Therrian

MICHIGAN DRILL
See REPUBLIC DRILL/APT CORP

D-U-N-S 80-903-7120
MICHIGAN ECONOMIC DEVELOPMENT CORP
(*Suby of* EXECUTIVE OFFICE OF STATE OF MICHIGAN) ★
300 N Washington Sq, Lansing, MI 48933-1244
Tel (517) 373-9808 *Founded/Ownrshp* 1993
Sales NA *EMP* 488
SIC 9611 Economic development agency, government; ; Economic development agency, government
Pr: Michael A Finney
COO: Jennifer Nelson
Bd of Dir: Mary Langhauser
Ofcr: Peter Morse
**Ex VP:* Steven H Hilfinger
Sr VP: Kathy Blake
Sr VP: Lynne Feldpausch
Sr VP: Gary Laroy
VP: Tricia Keith
Mng Dir: Emily Palsroke
CIO: Tilak Mohan

D-U-N-S 07-632-6651
MICHIGAN EDUCATION ASSOCIATION - NEA
M E A
1216 Kendale Blvd, East Lansing, MI 48823-2008
Tel (517) 332-6551 *Founded/Ownrshp* 1914
Sales 68.6MM *EMP* 295
SIC 8742

D-U-N-S 08-832-7440
MICHIGAN EDUCATION SPECIAL SERVICES ASSOCIATION (MI)
1475 Kendale Blvd, East Lansing, MI 48823-2011
Tel (517) 332-2581 *Founded/Ownrshp* 1960
Sales NA *EMP* 325
SIC 6411 6321 Insurance agents, brokers & service; Accident & health insurance; Insurance agents, brokers & service; Accident & health insurance
Ex Dir: Cynthia Williams
**Pr:* Sue Kelly
**VP:* Jeff Nyquist
Ex Dir: Cynthia Irwin
Ex Dir: Cynthia Irwing

D-U-N-S 11-104-2789
■ MICHIGAN ELECTRIC TRANSMISSION CO LLC
METC
(*Suby of* ITC HOLDINGS CORP) ★
27175 Energy Way, Novi, MI 48377-3639
Tel (248) 946-3000 *Founded/Ownrshp* 2006
Sales 40.5MM^E *EMP* 90
SIC 4911 Electric services; Electric services
Sr VP: Cameron M Bready
VP: Terry Harvill

MICHIGAN EXTRUDED ALUMINUM
See MICHIGAN ALUMINUM EXTRUSION & WINDOW CORP

D-U-N-S 62-334-6095
MICHIGAN FARM BUREAU FINANCIAL CORP
(*Suby of* MICHIGAN FARM BUREAU)
7373 W Saginaw Hwy, Lansing, MI 48917-1124
Tel (517) 323-7000 *Founded/Ownrshp* 1990
Sales NA *EMP* 100
Accts Patrick H Blanchett Lansing
SIC 6311 6331 Life insurance; Automobile insurance; Property damage insurance
Pr: Wayne Wood
Mng Pt: Patrick Carpenter
**Treas:* Thomas J Parker
**Treas:* John Stindt

D-U-N-S 96-227-0765
MICHIGAN FIDELITY ACCEPTANCE CORP
FRANKLIN MORTGAGE FUNDING
330 East St B, Rochester, MI 48307-2013
Tel (248) 799-4000 *Founded/Ownrshp* 1992
Sales NA *EMP* 330
Accts Doeren Mayhew Troy Michigan
SIC 6162 Mortgage bankers & correspondents; Mortgage bankers & correspondents
Pr: Robert Pilcowitz
CFO: Howard Morof
Board of Directors: Phyllis Pilcowitz Stockho, Hilary King Stockholder

D-U-N-S 07-478-0941
MICHIGAN FINANCIAL CORP
101 W Washington St, Marquette, MI 49855-4319
Tel (906) 228-8265 *Founded/Ownrshp* 1973
Sales NA *EMP* 657
SIC 6021 6311 National trust companies with deposits, commercial; Life reinsurance; National trust companies with deposits, commercial; Life reinsurance
Ch Bd: Howard L Cohodas
**Treas:* Kenneth F Beck
VP: Ward Rantala
Board of Directors: James L Smith, Alfred J Angli, James Smith, Gary L Butryn, Clarence Tisher, Willard M Carne, Willard L Cohodas, Hugh C Higley Jr, David Holli, Daniel H Lori, Louis S Paoli, Fred M Saigh

D-U-N-S 02-008-7458
MICHIGAN FIRST CREDIT UNION
27000 Evergreen Rd, Lathrup Village, MI 48076-3231
Tel (248) 443-4600 *Founded/Ownrshp* 1926
Sales NA *EMP* 162
SIC 6062 State credit unions, not federally chartered; State credit unions, not federally chartered
Pr: Michael Poulos
**Ch Bd:* Raymond Dudas
COO: Cassandra Harvey
Sr VP: Clifford Brown
VP: Cheryl Mallard
VP: Kelly McGrath
Exec: Barbara Coulter
Exec: Sandra Tomlin
Dir Risk M: Douglas Tour
Brnch Mgr: Megan Czar
Brnch Mgr: Rob Lokken

MICHIGAN FLAME HARDENING
See DETROIT EDGE TOOL CO

D-U-N-S 62-237-7096
■ MICHIGAN GAS UTILITIES CORP
(*Suby of* WEC ENERGY GROUP INC) ★
899 S Telegraph Rd, Monroe, MI 48161-4090
Tel (734) 457-6115 *Founded/Ownrshp* 2015
Sales 38.2MM^E *EMP* 182
SIC 4924 Natural gas distribution; Natural gas distribution
Pr: Gary W Erickson
**Treas:* Bradley A Johnson
**VP:* Thomas P Meinz
**VP:* Phillip M Mikulsky
VP Opers: Chuck Hauska

D-U-N-S 07-983-0013
MICHIGAN HEALTH & REHABILITATION SERVICES LLC
2630 Union Lake Rd # 300, Commerce Township, MI 48382-3585
Tel (248) 366-8839 *Founded/Ownrshp* 1998
Sales 2.0MM^E *EMP* 400
SIC 8049 Physical therapist
Ex VP: Janis Gregory-Geoffrey

MICHIGAN INDUSTRIAL TOOLS
See AMASH IMPORTS INC

D-U-N-S 78-548-6283
MICHIGAN INSTITUTE OF AERONAUTICS INC
MIAT COLLEGE OF TECHNOLOGY
2955 S Haggerty Rd, Canton, MI 48188-2533
Tel (734) 423-2100 *Founded/Ownrshp* 1989
Sales 5.7MM^E *EMP* 300
SIC 8249 Trade school
CEO: Charles Hawes
**Pr:* Kevin Burchett
**CFO:* Catherina A Vorst
VP Mktg: Mark Donahue

D-U-N-S 15-657-5805
MICHIGAN INSTITUTE OF UROLOGY P C
MIU
20952 E 12 Mile Rd # 200, Saint Clair Shores, MI 48081-3203
Tel (586) 771-4820 *Founded/Ownrshp* 1971
Sales 34.6MM^E *EMP* 450
SIC 8011 Urologist; Urologist
Pr: Alphonse M Santino MD
**Sec:* Robert Di Loreto MD
**VP:* James Boutrous MD
**VP:* Brian Guz MD
**VP:* Claude Rietelman MD
**VP:* Edward Schervais MD

MICHIGAN KITCHEN DISTRIBUTORS
See W S TOWNSEND CO

MICHIGAN LIBRARY CONSORTIUM
See MIDWEST COLLABORATIVE FOR LIBRARY SERVICES INC

D-U-N-S 07-929-2322
MICHIGAN MASONIC HOME
MASONIC PATHWAYS
1200 Wright Ave, Alma, MI 48801-1133
Tel (989) 463-3141 *Founded/Ownrshp* 1891
Sales 32.5MM *EMP* 350
SIC 8051 8322 Skilled nursing care facilities; Old age assistance; Skilled nursing care facilities; Old age assistance
CEO: Cindy Bosley
COO: Kevin Evans
CFO: Wanda Degase
**CFO:* Don Pray
Trst: Greg Mapes
VP: David Boring
Nurse Mgr: Amy Painter
HC Dir: Michelle Shaw
HC Dir: Aubrie Terwilliger

D-U-N-S 60-259-0457
MICHIGAN MEDICAL PATIENT CARE
MICHIGAN MEDICAL SPECIALISTS
(*Suby of* SPECTRUM HEALTH SYSTEM) ★
4100 Lake Dr Se Ste 300, Grand Rapids, MI 49546-8292
Tel (616) 954-0600 *Founded/Ownrshp* 2009
Sales 23.3MM^E *EMP* 650
SIC 8011 Specialized medical practitioners, except internal; Specialized medical practitioners, except internal
CEO: James V Buzzitta
**Treas:* Carol Montgomery
**VP:* Dan Grevengoed
Doctor: Sean Goodwin
Doctor: Michael Puff
Doctor: Glenn Van Otteren
Doctor: Yelena Yavich

MICHIGAN MEDICAL SPECIALISTS
See MICHIGAN MEDICAL PATIENT CARE

D-U-N-S 00-538-2460
MICHIGAN MILK PRODUCERS ASSOCIATION
41310 Bridge St, Novi, MI 48375-1302
Tel (248) 474-6672 *Founded/Ownrshp* 1916
Sales 854.0MM *EMP* 200
Accts Cliftonlarsonallen Llp
SIC 5143 2023 2021 8611 2026 Milk & cream, fluid; Dried milk; Condensed milk; Creamery butter; Business associations; Fluid milk; Milk & cream, fluid; Dried milk; Condensed milk; Creamery butter; Business associations; Fluid milk
CEO: John Dilland
**Pr:* Kenneth Nobis
**Treas:* C Velmar Green
**VP:* Bob Kran

D-U-N-S 00-696-0124
MICHIGAN MILLERS MUTUAL INSURANCE CO
2425 E Grand River Ave # 2, Lansing, MI 48912-3295
Tel (517) 482-6211 *Founded/Ownrshp* 1881
Sales NA *EMP* 115
SIC 6331 Fire, marine & casualty insurance: mutual; Fire, marine & casualty insurance: mutual
Ch Bd: James L Reutter
**Pr:* Thomas A Lindell
**CFO:* James Pratt
**Sr VP:* John Parsons
**VP:* Russ Clark
VP: Michael Dake
**VP:* William K Jamnik
VP: Dane Pickard
Software D: Greg Rochon
Sales Exec: Ed Jenkins
VP Sls: Maggie Ohara

D-U-N-S 15-417-7737
MICHIGAN MULTI-KING INC
BURGER KING
4897 Rochester Rd, Troy, MI 48085-4962
Tel (248) 528-2860 *Founded/Ownrshp* 1985
Sales 22.5MM^E *EMP* 500
SIC 5812 Fast-food restaurant, chain; Fast-food restaurant, chain
Pr: Anthony Versaci
**VP:* Michael Lucci

D-U-N-S 80-744-7909
MICHIGAN MUNICIPAL RISK MANAGEMENT AUTHORITY
14001 Merriman Rd, Livonia, MI 48154-4262
Tel (734) 261-9830 *Founded/Ownrshp* 1989
Sales NA *EMP* 34
Accts Plante & Moran Pllc Southfie
SIC 6411 Insurance agents, brokers & service; Insurance agents, brokers & service
Ex Dir: Tim Belanger
Off Mgr: Sharon Galvin

D-U-N-S 80-735-6464
MICHIGAN MUTUAL INC
FIRST PREFERRED MORTGAGE CO
800 Michigan St, Port Huron, MI 48060-3913
Tel (800) 700-5839 *Founded/Ownrshp* 1992
Sales NA *EMP* 100^E
Accts Plante & Moran Pllc Auburn H
SIC 6163 Mortgage brokers arranging for loans, using money of others; Mortgage brokers arranging for loans, using money of others
CEO: Mark Walker
**Pr:* Vince Parlove
VP: Martin Mercer
**VP:* Hale Walker
Mktg Dir: Julie Sakadales

D-U-N-S 01-707-7355
■ **MICHIGAN OFFICE SOLUTIONS INC**
(*Suby of* GLOBAL IMAGING SYSTEMS INC) ★
2859 Walkent Dr Nw, Grand Rapids, MI 49544-1400
Tel (616) 459-1161 *Founded/Ownrshp* 2002
Sales 138.6MM^E *EMP* 215
SIC 5044 5045 7629 Office equipment; Computers, peripherals & software; Business machine repair, electric; Office equipment; Computers, peripherals & software; Business machine repair, electric
Pr: Ralph Slider
**CFO:* Charles Wooding
**Ex VP:* Bill Orr III

D-U-N-S 05-205-2933 IMP
MICHIGAN PAVING AND MATERIALS CO (MI)
(*Suby of* OLDCASTLE MATERIALS GROUP) ★
2575 S Haggerty Rd # 100, Canton, MI 48188-2673
Tel (734) 397-2050 *Founded/Ownrshp* 1925, 1999
Sales 240.7MM^E *EMP* 600
SIC 1522 1541 2911 Residential construction; Industrial buildings, new construction; Asphalt or asphaltic materials, made in refineries; Residential construction; Industrial buildings, new construction; Asphalt or asphaltic materials, made in refineries
Pr: Dennis Rickard
CCO: Bill Brownell
CFO: Gregg Campbell
VP: Rick Becker
VP: James Lindstrom
VP: Robert Mayer
VP: Andrew Schulz
Mtls Mgr: Frank Azzopardi

D-U-N-S 06-587-9066
MICHIGAN PIZZA HUT INC
2053 Niles Rd, Saint Joseph, MI 49085-2505
Tel (269) 983-3888 *Founded/Ownrshp* 1970
Sales 45.2MM^E *EMP* 1,300
SIC 5812 Pizzeria, chain; Pizzeria, chain
Pr: Craig S Erickson
**COO:* John C Brinker
**VP:* Jeffrey White

D-U-N-S 92-927-6566
MICHIGAN PRIMARY CARE ASSN
VIRTUAL CHC
7215 Westshire Dr, Lansing, MI 48917-9764
Tel (517) 381-8000 *Founded/Ownrshp* 1980
Sales 28.3MM *EMP* 35
SIC 8399 Advocacy group; Advocacy group
Ex Dir: Kim Sibilsky
**Pr:* Anthony King
VP: Jeff Townes
Comm Man: Dana Hughes
Ex Dir: Donna Jaksic
Ex Dir: Jacqueline Tallman
IT Man: John Cahill
Pgrm Dir: Mouhanad Hammami

D-U-N-S 00-656-6723
MICHIGAN PRODUCE HAULERS INC
MPH TRANSPORTATION
1340 Locust St, Fremont, MI 49412-1468
Tel (231) 924-4600 *Founded/Ownrshp* 1962
Sales 22.3MM^E *EMP* 100
Accts Hendon & Slate Pc
SIC 4213 Contract haulers
Prin: Robert A Gilliland
**Pr:* Todd Gilliland
**VP:* Brad Gilliland
**VP:* Jon Gilliland

D-U-N-S 06-560-9430
MICHIGAN PRODUCTION MACHINING INC (MI)
16700 23 Mile Rd, Macomb, MI 48044-1100
Tel (586) 228-9700 *Founded/Ownrshp* 1973
Sales 76.0MM^E *EMP* 325^E
SIC 3599 Machine shop, jobbing & repair; Machine shop, jobbing & repair
VP: Kevin West
**CFO:* Dan Myers
CFO: Larie Smith
**Sec:* Mary Jane West
Plnt Mgr: Tony Anderson

D-U-N-S 19-424-4484
MICHIGAN PROPERTY & CASUALTY G
39810 Grand River Ave # 120, Novi, MI 48375-2139
Tel (248) 482-0381 *Founded/Ownrshp* 2005
Sales 29.6MM *EMP* 14
SIC 6512 Nonresidential building operators; Nonresidential building operators
Prin: Lori Rice

D-U-N-S 80-948-3670
MICHIGAN PUBLIC HEALTH INSTITUTE
MPHI
2436 Woodlake Cir Ste 300, Okemos, MI 48864-6002
Tel (517) 324-8300 *Founded/Ownrshp* 1990
Sales 77.9MM^E *EMP* 430
SIC 8733 Noncommercial research organizations; Noncommercial research organizations
CEO: Rene Branch Canady
**Pr:* Jean Chabut
**CFO:* Limin Kinsey
**Sec:* Dele Davies
**VP:* Dean Smith
Exec: Heather White
Dir Soc: Heather Hymes
**Prin:* Jeffrey R Taylor
Adm Dir: Kimberly Westmoreland
Off Mgr: Linda Johnson
CIO: Jeff Ott

D-U-N-S 06-946-4725
MICHIGAN PUBLIC POWER AGENCY
809 Centennial Way, Lansing, MI 48917-9277
Tel (517) 323-8346 *Founded/Ownrshp* 1978
Sales 166.2MM^E *EMP* 17
Accts Plante & Moran Pllc East Lans
SIC 4911 Distribution, electric power; Transmission, electric power; Distribution, electric power; Transmission, electric power
Ch: Annette Allen
CFO: Amy Deleeuw
CFO: David J Naberhuis
Sec: George Stojic
VP: Greg Pierce
Genl Mgr: David R Walters
Genl Mgr: Gary Zimmerman

MICHIGAN QUALITY COUNCIL
See CLEARY UNIVERSITY

D-U-N-S 05-796-5022 IMP
MICHIGAN ROD PRODUCTS INC
1326 Grand Oaks Dr, Howell, MI 48843-8579
Tel (517) 552-9812 *Founded/Ownrshp* 1998
Sales 20.6MM^E *EMP* 90^E
SIC 3496 3469 3452 3312 Miscellaneous fabricated wire products; Metal stampings; Bolts, nuts, rivets & washers; Blast furnaces & steel mills
Pr: Edward Lumm
**CFO:* Jerry A Bendert
CFO: Sam Sherman
**VP:* John Allen
**VP:* Timothy F Brown
Prin: Jerry Bendert
Ql Cn Mgr: Kevin Bell
Ql Cn Mgr: Scott Sherman

MICHIGAN RUBBER PRODUCTS
See ZHONGDING USA CADILLAC INC

MICHIGAN RUBBER PRODUCTS
See MRP INC

D-U-N-S 06-560-3375
MICHIGAN SCHOOLS & GOVERNMENT CREDIT UNION
40400 Garfield Rd, Clinton Township, MI 48038-4004
Tel (586) 263-8800 *Founded/Ownrshp* 1954
Sales NA *EMP* 170
SIC 6062 State credit unions; State credit unions
CEO: Pete Gates
**COO:* Lisa Burroughs
CFO: Steve Brewer
**Ch:* Milo J Perreault
**Treas:* James S McCann

D-U-N-S 12-131-1000
MICHIGAN SEAMLESS TUBE LLC
BLUE DIAMOND
(*Suby of* OPTIMA SPECIALTY STEEL INC) ★
400 Mcmunn St, South Lyon, MI 48178-1379
Tel (248) 486-0100 *Founded/Ownrshp* 2002
Sales 154.5MM^E *EMP* 280
SIC 3317 Tubes, seamless steel; Tubes, seamless steel
VP: Ted Fairley
**Mng Pt:* Mark Hommel
**VP:* Les Whitver
Genl Mgr: Mary Pollen
Sfty Dirs: Tonya Carrill
Manager: Allan Childs
Manager: Don Newcomb

MICHIGAN SEAT COMPANY
See JANESVILLE ACOUSTICS

D-U-N-S 09-479-8121
MICHIGAN SOUTH CENTRAL POWER AGENCY INC
MSCPA
720 Herring Rd, Litchfield, MI 49252-9510
Tel (517) 542-2346 *Founded/Ownrshp* 1978
Sales 55.6MM *EMP* 50
Accts Baker Tilly Virchow Krause Ll
SIC 4911 Generation, electric power; Generation, electric power
CEO: Glen White
Sfty Mgr: Michael Sprow
Plnt Mgr: Steve Flowers
Board of Directors: Lorna Nenciarini, Debbi Thiel

D-U-N-S 01-709-3691 IMP
MICHIGAN SPORTING GOODS DISTRIBUTORS INC (MI)
MC SPORTS
3070 Shaffer Ave Se, Grand Rapids, MI 49512-1710
Tel (616) 942-2600 *Founded/Ownrshp* 1963
Sales 195.5MM^E *EMP* 1,300
SIC 5941 Sporting goods & bicycle shops; Sporting goods & bicycle shops
Pr: Bruce Ullery
VP Opers: Irwin Wallach
Sls Mgr: John Mulligan

D-U-N-S 80-272-6265 IMP
MICHIGAN SPRING & STAMPING LLC
(*Suby of* HINES CORP) ★
2700 Wickham Dr, Muskegon, MI 49441-3532
Tel (231) 755-1691 *Founded/Ownrshp* 2008
Sales 26.5MM^E *EMP* 140
SIC 3495 Mechanical springs, precision; Mechanical springs, precision
CFO: Frank Verburg
Prgrm Mgr: Dave Meier
Ql Cn Mgr: Mike Hagye

MICHIGAN STATE POLICE
See MICHIGAN DEPARTMENT OF STATE POLICE

D-U-N-S 05-334-3976
MICHIGAN STATE UNIVERSITY
426 Auditorium Rd Rm 301, East Lansing, MI 48824-2600
Tel (517) 355-5029 *Founded/Ownrshp* 1855
Sales 1.6MMM *EMP* 11,100
Accts Plante & Moran Pllc Portage
SIC 8221 University; University
Ch: Joel I Ferguson
**Pr:* Lou Anna K Simon
COO: Dunlap Jim
**V Ch Bd:* Brian Breslin
VP: Robert Groves
Exec: Kristin Anderson
Assoc Dir: Donna Zischke
Comm Dir: Stephanie Motschenbacher
Ex Dir: Rachael Bergan
Ex Dir: Eric Doerr
Ex Dir: Irem Kiyak
Board of Directors: John Thelen

D-U-N-S 96-488-2786
MICHIGAN STATE UNIVERSITY COLLEGE OF LAW
368e College Law Bldg, East Lansing, MI 48824
Tel (517) 432-6813 *Founded/Ownrshp* 2010
Sales 38.7MM^E *EMP* 3^E
Accts Button Eddy Kolb & Sorrentino
SIC 8111 General practice law office; General practice law office
Prin: Joan Howath
VP: Cassie J Hare
VP: Nicholas Heberer
VP: Daniel Hilker
VP: Atheina Mansour
VP: Lauren Verbiscus

D-U-N-S 07-839-9219
MICHIGAN STATE UNIVERSITY FEDERAL CREDIT UNION
MSUFCU
3777 West Rd, East Lansing, MI 48823-8029
Tel (517) 333-2424 *Founded/Ownrshp* 1937
Sales NA *EMP* 371^E
Accts Crowe Horwath Llp Grand Rapid
SIC 6061 Federal credit unions; Federal credit unions
Pr: Patrick McPharlin
**Ch Bd:* Thomas Scarlett
**Treas:* Thomas Dutch
**V Ch Bd:* John Brick
Ofcr: Abbie Broughman
Ex VP: April Clobes
VP: Ronda Bennett
VP: Sarah Bohan
VP: Sara Dolan
VP: Catherine Lynch
VP: Ronda McCoy
VP: Diana McFadden
VP: Al Scheffler
VP: Daniel Vanhaften

D-U-N-S 11-033-7305 IMP
MICHIGAN STEEL INC
1148 W Western Ave, Muskegon, MI 49441-1621
Tel (231) 726-5177 *Founded/Ownrshp* 2002
Sales 25.0MM^E *EMP* 180
SIC 3325 Steel foundries
Pr: Vaughn McCary
**Pr:* Chris Moein
Prd Mgr: Tucker Theotis
Ql Cn Mgr: Jake Wilson

MICHIGAN SUGAR BEET GROWERS
See MICHIGAN SUGAR CO

D-U-N-S 10-320-4470 IMP
MICHIGAN SUGAR CO
MICHIGAN SUGAR BEET GROWERS
2600 S Euclid Ave, Bay City, MI 48706-3414
Tel (989) 686-0161 *Founded/Ownrshp* 1906
Sales 600.0MM *EMP* 430
SIC 2063 Beet sugar; Beet sugar
Pr: Mark Flegenheimer
**CFO:* Brian Haraga
**Ch:* Richard Gerstenberger
**Treas:* Eugene Meylan
**VP:* Charles Bauer
VP: Robert Braem
**VP:* Jerry Coleman
**VP:* David Noble
**VP:* Paul Pfenninger
**VP:* James Ruhlman
**VP:* Herb Wilson

D-U-N-S 06-545-3268
MICHIGAN TECHNOLOGICAL UNIVERSITY
1400 Townsend Dr, Houghton, MI 49931-1200
Tel (906) 487-1885 *Founded/Ownrshp* 1885
Sales 160.2MM *EMP* 1,939
Accts Rehmann Robson Llc Traverse C
SIC 8221 University; University
Pr: Glenn D Mroz
Pr: Beth Lunde
**Pr:* Dr Glenn Dmroz
CFO: Diane Nakkula
Ofcr: Ashley Cisa
Ofcr: Ben Larson
**VP:* William J Mc Garry
**VP:* Max Seel
**VP:* Dale R Tahtinen
Assoc Dir: James Hainault
Assoc Dir: Craig Pellizzaro
Creative D: Bill Tembreull
Comm Man: Briana Tucker

D-U-N-S 15-140-8416
MICHIGAN TITLE INSURANCE AGENCY INC
9333 Telegraph Rd Ste 100, Taylor, MI 48180-3386
Tel (313) 291-2323 *Founded/Ownrshp* 1985
Sales NA *EMP* 50
SIC 6361 Real estate title insurance
Pr: Richard S Smith
**VP:* Barbara Simpson
Admn Mgr: Kristy Spada

D-U-N-S 00-505-6437 IMP
MICHIGAN TUBE SWAGERS AND FABRICATORS INC (MI)
MTS SEATING
7100 Industrial Dr, Temperance, MI 48182-9105
Tel (734) 847-3875 *Founded/Ownrshp* 1955
Sales 70.0MM *EMP* 470
SIC 2522 Chairs, office: padded or plain, except wood; Tables, office: wood; Chairs, office: padded or plain, except wood
Pr: Paul Swy
**Pr:* Barton Kulish
**CFO:* Joseph Restivo
**Treas:* Peter D Swy
Ex VP: Greg Piper
Genl Mgr: Ken Auger
Natl Sales: Bo Freeman
Natl Sales: Ian King
Natl Sales: Eileen Kulish
Sls Dir: John Menas

D-U-N-S 11-479-0210
MICHIGAN TURKEY PRODUCERS COOPERATIVE INC
2140 Chicago Dr Sw, Wyoming, MI 49519-1215
Tel (616) 245-2221 *Founded/Ownrshp* 1998
Sales 109.7MM^E *EMP* 575
SIC 2015 Turkey processing & slaughtering; Turkey processing & slaughtering
Pr: Dan Lennon
**CFO:* Brian Boerigter
IT Man: Kevin Horner

D-U-N-S 96-480-8302
MICHIGAN UFCW HEALTH & WELFARE FUND
876 Horace Brown Dr, Madison Heights, MI 48071-1862
Tel (248) 658-0999 *Founded/Ownrshp* 2010
Sales 40.0MM *EMP* 3
SIC 8631 Labor unions & similar labor organizations
Prin: Andy Johnson

D-U-N-S 61-462-4682
MICHIGAN UFCW UNION & EMPLOYEES HEALTH WELFARE FUND
876 Horace Brown Dr, Madison Heights, MI 48071-1862
Tel (248) 585-9610 *Founded/Ownrshp* 1992
Sales NA *EMP* 34
Accts Dennis G Jenkins Cpa Llc Kenn
SIC 6371 Union welfare, benefit & health funds; Union welfare, benefit & health funds
Pr: Andy Johnson
**Pr:* Roger Robinson

D-U-N-S 80-832-2846
MICHIGAN WASTE ENERGY INC
DETROIT RENEWABLE POWER
5700 Russell St, Detroit, MI 48211-2545
Tel (313) 972-5700 *Founded/Ownrshp* 2013
Sales 49.0MM^E *EMP* 150
SIC 4953 1711 Recycling, waste materials; Solar energy contractor; Recycling, waste materials; Solar energy contractor

MICHIGAN WOODS CONSTRUCTION
See WOODS CONSTRUCTION INC

D-U-N-S 02-836-6755
■ **MICHIGANH1 LLC**
HONDA BLOOMFIELD
(*Suby of* PENSKE AUTOMOTIVE GROUP INC) ★
1819 S Telegraph Rd, Bloomfield Hills, MI 48302-0163
Tel (248) 333-3200 *Founded/Ownrshp* 2002
Sales 27.8MM^E *EMP* 72
SIC 5511 7515 7538 Automobiles, new & used; Passenger car leasing; General automotive repair shops; Automobiles, new & used; Passenger car leasing; General automotive repair shops
Genl Mgr: Jill Bernardi

D-U-N-S 02-561-0528
MICHLIG HOLDINGS INC
105 1st St, Manlius, IL 61338
Tel (815) 445-6921 *Founded/Ownrshp* 1983
Sales 30.4MM^E *EMP* 100
SIC 5191 5153 5984

D-U-N-S 96-487-7281
MICHOLS COLLEGE OF BUSINESS ADMINISTRATION
500 Federal St, Andover, MA 01810-1017
Tel (508) 213-1560 *Founded/Ownrshp* 2010
Sales 45.8MM *EMP* 0^E
Accts Bollus Lynch Llp Worcester M
SIC 8244

D-U-N-S 55-603-7349
MICI CORP
MATRIX INTERIORS
1206 Tappan Cir, Carrollton, TX 75006-6911
Tel (972) 245-1022 *Founded/Ownrshp* 1989
Sales 43.8MM^E *EMP* 185
SIC 1542 Commercial & office building, new construction; Commercial & office building, new construction
Pr: Brad Schmidt
**Sec:* Jeff Haley
Admn Mgr: Shannon Lasley
Opers Supe: Hershal Rogers
Opers Supe: Dan Trojanowski

D-U-N-S 00-779-9570 IMP
MICI INC
22320 130th Ave, Cadillac, MI 49601
Tel (231) 775-3478 *Founded/Ownrshp* 1961
Sales 23.3MM^E *EMP* 105
SIC 4833 Television broadcasting stations
Pr: Mario F Iacobelli
**Treas:* William Kring

D-U-N-S 00-510-5127
MICKELBERRY COMMUNICATIONS INC (DE)
405 Park Ave, New York, NY 10022-4405
Tel (212) 832-0303 *Founded/Ownrshp* 1926
Sales 50.1MM^E *EMP* 603
SIC 2752 7311 Commercial printing, lithographic; Advertising agencies; Commercial printing, lithographic; Advertising agencies
Ch Bd: James C Marlas
**Pr:* Gregory J Garville

D-U-N-S 14-318-4864
MICKEY HAGE INC
2308 E Robinson St, Orlando, FL 32803-6050
Tel (407) 897-8860 *Founded/Ownrshp* 2003
Sales 26.0MM *EMP* 12
SIC 6531 Real estate agents & managers; Real estate agents & managers
Pr: Michael Hage

D-U-N-S 17-404-3414
MICKEY PLYLER TRUCKING INC
1566 High Point Church Rd, Pageland, SC 29728-6441
Tel (843) 672-5553 *Founded/Ownrshp* 1986
Sales 41.0MM *EMP* 40

SIC 4212 4213 Local trucking, without storage; Trucking, except local; Local trucking, without storage; Trucking, except local
Pr: Dennis M Plyler
**VP:* Judith A Plyler

D-U-N-S 00-322-7188 EXP
MICKEY TRUCK BODIES INC (NC)
1305 Trinity Ave, High Point, NC 27260-8357
Tel (336) 882-6806 *Founded/Ownrshp* 1949
Sales 114.6MM^E *EMP* 400
SIC 3713 7532 3711 3715 Beverage truck bodies; Van bodies; Truck bodies (motor vehicles); Ambulance bodies; Body shop, trucks; Motor vehicles & car bodies; Truck trailers; Beverage truck bodies; Van bodies; Truck bodies (motor vehicles); Ambulance bodies; Body shop, trucks; Motor vehicles & car bodies; Truck trailers
Pr: H Dean Sink
**CFO:* Greg Fisher
**Ex VP:* Carl F Mickey Jr
VP: Tom Arland
VP: Tom Campbell
VP: Wayne Childress
VP: Jim Hiatt
**VP:* Kent Lapp
VP: Greg McLaughlin
Genl Mgr: Sid Merrill
Genl Mgr: Mike Parker

D-U-N-S 02-671-2729
MICKEYS ENTERPRISES INC
JASPER LAUNDRY & DRY CLEANING
1008 Illinois Ave, Killeen, TX 76541-9096
Tel (254) 258-7483 *Founded/Ownrshp* 1964
Sales 23.9MM^E *EMP* 200
SIC 5411 Convenience stores; Convenience stores
Pr: Thomas M Schroeder
**Treas:* Karen Walinder
**Sr VP:* Terecia Schroeder

D-U-N-S 02-522-8982
MICKEYS LINEN & TOWEL SUPPLY INC
MEDCLEAN
4601 W Addison St, Chicago, IL 60641-3702
Tel (773) 545-7211 *Founded/Ownrshp* 1930, 1984
Sales 19.1MM^E *EMP* 280
SIC 7213 7218 Linen supply; Table cover supply; Towel supply; Industrial launderers; Linen supply; Table cover supply; Towel supply; Industrial launderers
Pr: Gregory M Brown
**Treas:* Christopher P Brown
**VP:* Nicholas P Brown

MICKY MART
See COLES ENERGY INC

D-U-N-S 01-748-5632 IMP
MICNAN INC
ACE MITCHELL BOWLERS MART
3365 Cavalier Trl, Cuyahoga Falls, OH 44224-4905
Tel (330) 920-6200 *Founded/Ownrshp* 1973
Sales 33.7MM^E *EMP* 50
SIC 5091 Bowling equipment
Pr: David Grau
VP: Karen Grau
Prin: Mary E Limbach
Off Mgr: Tanja McCoy

MICO
See MOLLEN IMMUNIZATION CLINICS LLC

D-U-N-S 00-617-4353 IMP
MICO INC (MN)
MICO WEST
1911 Lee Blvd, North Mankato, MN 56003-2507
Tel (507) 625-6426 *Founded/Ownrshp* 1946, 1954
Sales 37.6MM^E *EMP* 320
SIC 3714 3561

D-U-N-S 10-163-3576
MICO INDUSTRIES INC
1425 Burlingame Ave Sw, Wyoming, MI 49509-1059
Tel (616) 245-6426 *Founded/Ownrshp* 1983
Sales 36.4MM^E *EMP* 150
SIC 3469 7692 3711 Stamping metal for the trade; Automotive welding; Automobile assembly, including specialty automobiles; Stamping metal for the trade; Automotive welding; Automobile assembly, including specialty automobiles
CEO: Terence Sammon
**Pr:* Henry Visser
**VP:* M Christina De La Garza

MICO WEST
See MICO INC

MICON
See EARTH SUPPORT SERVICES INC

D-U-N-S 12-245-2597 IMP
MICON PACKAGING INC
301 Commerce Blvd Bldg 1, Oldsmar, FL 34677-2806
Tel (813) 855-4651 *Founded/Ownrshp* 2013
Sales 49.3MM^E *EMP* 115
SIC 2653 Boxes, corrugated: made from purchased materials; Boxes, corrugated: made from purchased materials
Pr: Peter Tracey
Genl Mgr: Peter Tracy
Sls Mgr: Glen Morris

D-U-N-S 93-299-0807
MICOSA INTERNATIONAL INC
3415 N Kennicott Ave C, Arlington Heights, IL 60004-7819
Tel (847) 632-1200 *Founded/Ownrshp* 1986
Sales 36.0MM *EMP* 12
SIC 5142 5141 Packaged frozen goods; Food brokers; Packaged frozen goods; Food brokers
Pr: Gerald Goldman
**VP:* Bob Anderson

D-U-N-S 09-260-9585
MICREL INC
MICREL SEMICONDUCTOR
2180 Fortune Dr, San Jose, CA 95131-1815
Tel (408) 944-0800 *Founded/Ownrshp* 1978
Sales 247.5MM *EMP* 728^E
SIC 3674 Integrated circuits, semiconductor networks, etc.

D-U-N-S 07-995-3152
■ **MICREL LLC** (CA)
(*Suby of* MICROCHIP TECHNOLOGY INC) ★
2355 W Chandler Blvd, Chandler, AZ 85224-6199
Tel (480) 792-7200 *Founded/Ownrshp* 2015
Sales 92.4MM^E *EMP* 1,954^E
SIC 3674 Semiconductors & related devices
Pr: Steve Sanghi
COO: Ganesh Moorthy
CFO: J Eric Bjornholt
VP: Stephen V Drehobl
VP: Mitchell R Little
VP: Richard J Simoncic

MICREL SEMICONDUCTOR
See MICREL INC

D-U-N-S 06-456-3828 IMP
MICRO 100 TOOL CORP
1410 E Pine Ave, Meridian, ID 83642-5938
Tel (208) 888-7310 *Founded/Ownrshp* 1969
Sales 26.1MM^E *EMP* 110
Accts Travis Jeffries Pa Boise Ida
SIC 3545 Cutting tools for machine tools
Pr: Dale Newberry
**VP:* Michael D Armstrong Jr
VP: Randall J Nedrow
VP: E Wayne Newberry
VP Mfg: Craig C Graf
Sfty Mgr: Randy Niesen
Ql Cn Mgr: Doug Purcell
Sls&Mrk Ex: Max Steinback
Mktg Mgr: Cliff Conway
Manager: Scott Hegedus
Manager: Bob Jasmer

MICRO AIR - DIVISION METAL-FAB
See METAL-FAB INC

D-U-N-S 17-600-1956 IMP
MICRO ANALOG INC
1861 Puddingstone Dr, La Verne, CA 91750-5825
Tel (909) 392-8277 *Founded/Ownrshp* 1991
Sales 80.6MM^E *EMP* 230
SIC 3672 Printed circuit boards; Printed circuit boards
Pr: Hung T Nguyen
**CFO:* Khanh Van Nguyen
Genl Mgr: Tim Nguyn
Genl Mgr: Dat Vy

D-U-N-S 04-863-0839
■ **MICRO BEEF TECHNOLOGIES LTD**
MICRO DAIRY LOGIC
(*Suby of* MWI VETERINARY SUPPLY CO) ★
8701 Centerport Blvd, Amarillo, TX 79108-5731
Tel (806) 372-2369 *Founded/Ownrshp* 2011
Sales 37.2MM^E *EMP* 175
SIC 2048 Feed supplements; Feed supplements
Mng Pt: Mark Shaw
Pt: Bill Pratt
Store Mgr: Rhonda Bennett
CIO: Kenneth Berry
Info Man: Kyle Montgomery
Sls Mgr: Dick Travis

D-U-N-S 05-635-8138 IMP/EXP
■ **MICRO BIO-MEDICS INC**
CALIGOR
(*Suby of* HENRY SCHEIN INC) ★
135 Duryea Rd, Melville, NY 11747-3834
Tel (914) 738-9200 *Founded/Ownrshp* 1997
Sales 25.4MM^E *EMP* 300
SIC 5122 5047 Pharmaceuticals; Medical equipment & supplies; Physician equipment & supplies; Hospital equipment & supplies; Industrial safety devices: first aid kits & masks; Pharmaceuticals; Medical equipment & supplies; Physician equipment & supplies; Hospital equipment & supplies; Industrial safety devices: first aid kits & masks
Ch Bd: James P Breslawski
**Treas:* Gary L Butler

MICRO CENTER
See MICRO ELECTRONICS INC

D-U-N-S 07-912-1295
MICRO CENTER INC
(*Suby of* MICRO CENTER) ★
4119 Leap Rd, Hilliard, OH 43026-1117
Tel (614) 850-3000 *Founded/Ownrshp* 1997
Sales 14.1MM^E *EMP* 300
SIC 5734 5045 Computer & software stores; Computers, peripherals & software
CEO: Richard Mershad

D-U-N-S 05-528-9771
MICRO CHEMICAL INC
8701 Centerport Blvd, Amarillo, TX 79108-5731
Tel (806) 372-2369 *Founded/Ownrshp* 1971
Sales 20.0MM^E *EMP* 70
SIC 5191 5122 8742 Animal feeds; Animal medicines; Management consulting services
Pr: William C Pratt
**Sec:* Linda Pratt

D-U-N-S 06-745-9503
MICRO COMPUTER SYSTEMS INC
MICRO K12
12631 Beverly Park Rd, Lynnwood, WA 98087-1529
Tel (425) 778-7337 *Founded/Ownrshp* 1982
Sales 45.0MM *EMP* 27
SIC 5734 5045 Computer & software stores; Computer peripheral equipment; Printers & plotters: computers; Computers; Computer peripheral equipment; Printers, computer; Computer & software stores; Computer peripheral equipment; Printers & plotters: computers; Computers; Computer peripheral equipment; Printers, computer
Pr: Gary Gill
**Sec:* Patricia D Gill
**VP:* Richard Litchfield
IT Man: Gary Wagar
Mktg Dir: Ron Van Winkle

D-U-N-S 85-946-1865
MICRO COMPUTER SYSTEMS OF SOUTH WEST FLORIDA INC
2553 Longboat Dr, Naples, FL 34104-3327
Tel (239) 643-6672 *Founded/Ownrshp* 1984
Sales 24.5MM *EMP* 3
SIC 3679 Electronic circuits; Electronic loads & power supplies; Electronic switches; Electronic circuits; Electronic loads & power supplies; Electronic switches
Pr: Stephen Meek
**Sec:* Mary Meek

D-U-N-S 05-903-2607 IMP
MICRO CONTROL CO
7956 Main St Ne, Minneapolis, MN 55432-1898
Tel (763) 786-8750 *Founded/Ownrshp* 1972
Sales 58.3MM^E *EMP* 150
SIC 3825 Test equipment for electronic & electric measurement; Test equipment for electronic & electric measurement
CEO: Harold Hamilton
**Sec:* Eleanor Hamilton
VP Opers: Mike Odonnell
Sls Mgr: Kenneth Heiman

MICRO DAIRY LOGIC
See MICRO BEEF TECHNOLOGIES LTD

D-U-N-S 07-655-4864
MICRO DENTAL LABORATORIES
A DTI COMPANY
(*Suby of* HEALTHPOINT CAPITAL LLC) ★
5601 Arnold Rd Fl 100, Dublin, CA 94568-7726
Tel (925) 829-3611 *Founded/Ownrshp* 2007
Sales 23.3MM^E *EMP* 274^E
SIC 8072 Dental laboratories; Artificial teeth production; Denture production; Orthodontic appliance production
Pr: Kimberley Bradshaw
Pr: Mark Murphy
**CFO:* Bill Johnson
**CFO:* Jeffrey Zellmer
**Sr VP:* Laing Rikkers
VP: Jeff Guidie
VP: Randall Leininger
**VP:* Len Liptak
**VP:* Monica Yaksitch
Dir Lab: Steve Hoofard
Div Mgr: Eric Hill

D-U-N-S 16-101-3560
MICRO EAR TECHNOLOGY INC
MICRO-TECH
(*Suby of* MICRO TECH) ★
6425 Flying Cloud Dr, Eden Prairie, MN 55344-3305
Tel (952) 995-8800 *Founded/Ownrshp* 1986
Sales 22.5MM^E *EMP* 191
SIC 3842 5999 Hearing aids; Hearing aids; Hearing aids; Hearing aids
Pr: Larry Hagen
Pr: Mike Eckert
Exec: Steve Orvis
MIS Mgr: Harvey Morgan
Manager: Matt Davis
Doctor: Jennifer Anderson

D-U-N-S 09-972-3066 IMP
MICRO ELECTRONICS INC
MICRO CENTER
4119 Leap Rd, Hilliard, OH 43026-1117
Tel (614) 850-3000 *Founded/Ownrshp* 1979
Sales 3.4MMM^E *EMP* 3,000
SIC 5045 5734 Personal computers; Computer software & accessories; Computer peripheral equipment; Computers & accessories, personal & home entertainment; Computer peripheral equipment; Personal computers
Pr: Richard M Mershad
**COO:* Peggy Wolfe
**CFO:* John A Noble
CFO: Charlene Walker
Treas: Jeff Evanoff
Comm Dir: Dave Manring
Prgrm Mgr: Steve Curtis
Brnch Mgr: Colleen Niemiec
Dist Mgr: Bill Doering
Dist Mgr: Anthony Vio
Genl Mgr: Susan Bishop

D-U-N-S 04-076-0006
MICRO FOCUS (US) INC
(*Suby of* MICRO FOCUS INTERNATIONAL HOLDINGS LIMITED)
700 King Farm Blvd # 400, Rockville, MD 20850-5749
Tel (301) 838-5000 *Founded/Ownrshp* 2011
Sales 147.1MM^E *EMP* 400
SIC 7372 Business oriented computer software; Business oriented computer software
Ch: Kevin Loosemore
COO: David Taylor
CFO: Tony Muller
Treas: Martin Reed
Top Exec: Alison Baker
Sr VP: Luigi Bardelli
Sr VP: Mike Steinmetz
VP: Russell Baker
VP: Joseph Bell
VP: Jim Bladich
VP: Seth Braverman
VP: Susan Drennan
VP: Bill Errico
VP: Chris Livesey
VP: Eric Pan
VP: Hugo Pullen
VP: Roman Schubiger
VP: Michael Steinmetz
VP: Tod Tompkins
VP: Owen Williams
VP: Bg Willison
Board of Directors: Martin Reed, Tod Tompkins

D-U-N-S 06-558-2918
■ **MICRO GAUGE INC**
(*Suby of* MUELLER BRASS CO) ★
7350 Kensington Rd, Brighton, MI 48116-8354
Tel (248) 446-3720 *Founded/Ownrshp* 2000
Sales 33.0MM^E *EMP* 190
SIC 3599 Machine shop, jobbing & repair; Machine shop, jobbing & repair
Prin: Jim Rourke
Plnt Mgr: Bruce Bolyard

MICRO GLOBAL
See LEADING EDGE TECHNOLOGY SOLUTIONS INC

D-U-N-S 96-614-9887
MICRO HOLDING CORP
(*Suby of* HELLMAN & FRIEDMAN LLC) ★
1 Maritime Plz Fl 12, San Francisco, CA 94111-3502
Tel (415) 788-5111 *Founded/Ownrshp* 2010
Sales 17.9MM^E *EMP* 650
SIC 7374 7389 Computer graphics service; Advertising, promotional & trade show services; Computer graphics service; Advertising, promotional & trade show services
Pr: Warren Hellman

D-U-N-S 16-111-6546 IMP
MICRO INFORMATICA LLC
2020 Nw 114th Ave, Miami, FL 33172-3654
Tel (305) 418-3200 *Founded/Ownrshp* 1985
Sales 20.6MM^E *EMP* 35
SIC 5045 Computers; Computer software
Pr: Julia Dreyfus
Dept Mgr: Miriam Renzi
IT Man: Jose Gouveia
Mktg Mgr: Ming WEI
Pdt Mgr: David Gomez

D-U-N-S 00-221-1498
MICRO INSTRUMENT CORP (NY)
AUTOMATED SYSTEMS GROUP
1199 Emerson St, Rochester, NY 14606-3038
Tel (585) 458-3150 *Founded/Ownrshp* 1944, 1976
Sales 24.0MM^E *EMP* 100
SIC 3599 3613 7389 6552 3544 3365 Machine & other job shop work; Control panels, electric; Grinding, precision: commercial or industrial; Land subdividers & developers, commercial; Special dies, tools, jigs & fixtures; Aluminum foundries
Ch Bd: John Pfeffer
**Pr:* Anthony De Salvo
**Pr:* William Gunther
Mtls Mgr: Steve Hakes
Sls Mgr: Jeffrey Austill

MICRO K12
See MICRO COMPUTER SYSTEMS INC

D-U-N-S 11-269-3130 IMP
MICRO LITHOGRAPHY INC
1247 Elko Dr, Sunnyvale, CA 94089-2211
Tel (408) 747-1769 *Founded/Ownrshp* 1981
Sales 58.1MM^E *EMP* 225
SIC 3823 3674 Industrial instrmnts msrmnt display/control process variable; Semiconductors & related devices; Industrial instrmnts msrmnt display/control process variable; Semiconductors & related devices
CEO: Yung-Tsai Yen
**Pr:* Chris Yen
CFO: Joan Huang
**Ex VP:* Sandy Yen
Exec: John Liu

D-U-N-S 12-096-0414 IMP/EXP
MICRO MATIC USA INC
2386 Simon Ct, Brooksville, FL 34604-0751
Tel (352) 544-1081 *Founded/Ownrshp* 1984
Sales 32.7MM^E *EMP* 100
SIC 3491 5087 3585 Industrial valves; Liquor dispensing equipment & systems; Soda fountain & beverage dispensing equipment & parts
Pr: Peter J Muzzonigro
Ofcr: Cian Hickey
VP: Torber Toftegraard
Dir IT: Leo Murphy
Opers Supe: Kip Lohnes
Natl Sales: M M Scott
Manager: David Dixon
Sls Mgr: Barry Broughton
Sales Asso: Alexandra Maisel
Sales Asso: Andy Reed
Sales Asso: Megan Rojas

MICRO MEASUREMENTS
See VISHAY MEASUREMENTS GROUP INC

MICRO MEDICAL TECHNOLOGIES
See MICRO STAMPING CORP

D-U-N-S 83-100-0021
MICRO METL CORP
3035 N Shadeland Ave # 300, Indianapolis, IN 46226-6281
Tel (317) 543-5980 *Founded/Ownrshp* 1992
Sales 75.2MM^E *EMP* 328
SIC 3444 Sheet metalwork; Sheet metalwork
Pr: Gerald E Schultz
COO: Mike Wagner
CFO: Mark Cohlman
CFO: Mark Kolmer
**Prin:* Barbara E Schultz
Manager: Leeanne Shiller

D-U-N-S 06-578-9877 IMP
MICRO MO ELECTRONICS INC
MICROMO
14881 Evergreen Ave, Clearwater, FL 33762-3008
Tel (727) 572-0131 *Founded/Ownrshp* 1981
Sales 32.2MM^E *EMP* 80
SIC 5063 5084 Motors, electric; Motor controls, starters & relays: electric; Generators; Meters, consumption registering; Motors, electric; Motor controls, starters & relays: electric; Generators; Meters, consumption registering
Pr: Fritz Faulhaber
**COO:* Dodd M Disler
**Sec:* Ping Pan Faulhaber
Sls Mgr: Bob Kish

D-U-N-S 06-729-5808 IMP/EXP
■ MICRO MOTION INC
(*Suby of* EECO INC) ★
7070 Winchester Cir, Boulder, CO 80301-3566
Tel (303) 530-8400 *Founded/Ownrshp* 1984
Sales 1.0MMME *EMP* 1,023
SIC 5084 3824 Industrial machinery & equipment; Liquid meters; Industrial machinery & equipment; Liquid meters
Pr: Neal Ingram
VP: Andy Kolbeck
VP: Stanley Miller
VP: Jeff Nehr
VP: Paul Terry
VP: David Winder
CIO: Patrick Quinlan
Dir IT: Charles Stack
Tech Mgr: Geoffrey Lutz

MICRO P TECHNOLOGIES
See PCM SALES INC

D-U-N-S 00-514-2070 IMP
MICRO PLASTICS INC
111 Industry Ln, Flippin, AR 72634-8057
Tel (870) 453-8861 *Founded/Ownrshp* 1961
Sales 94.6MMME *EMP* 400
SIC 3965 Fasteners; Fasteners
Pr: Tom Hill
COO: Ed Chesney
* *Ex VP:* Marilyn H Hill
VP: Nueboch Vandermast
Mktg Dir: James Underwood

D-U-N-S 06-597-4404 IMP
MICRO PNEUMATIC LOGIC INC
MICROTECHNOLOGIES
2901 Gateway Dr, Pompano Beach, FL 33069-4326
Tel (954) 935-6821 *Founded/Ownrshp* 1973
Sales 49.4MMME *EMP* 145
SIC 3492 Control valves, aircraft: hydraulic & pneumatic; Control valves, aircraft: hydraulic & pneumatic
Pr: G F Tucci
* *Pr:* Michael F Tucci
CFO: Tony Bossiello
* *Treas:* Antonio Bossiello
Sls Mgr: Dan Bracewell

MICRO POWER ELECTRONICS
See GREATBATCH LTD

D-U-N-S 55-736-9782
MICRO RAM ELECTRONICS INC
222 Dunbar Ct, Oldsmar, FL 34677-2956
Tel (813) 854-5500 *Founded/Ownrshp* 1991
Sales 25.6MMME *EMP* 40
SIC 5065 Electronic parts
Pr: Mark A Wilson
* *COO:* Christine A Deferrari
Ex VP: Brian Wilson
Dir Soc: Nick Rees
Sales Exec: Cruz Roldan
Manager: Dan Hetnar
Sls Mgr: Joe Delegro
Sales Asso: Sarah Lemovitz

MICRO SOLUTIONS ENTERPRISES
See WBI INC

D-U-N-S 00-215-3484 IMP
MICRO STAMPING CORP
MICRO MEDICAL TECHNOLOGIES
140 Belmont Dr, Somerset, NJ 08873-5113
Tel (732) 302-0800 *Founded/Ownrshp* 1945
Sales 44.3MMME *EMP* 270
SIC 3841 3469 Surgical & medical instruments; Metal stampings; Surgical & medical instruments; Metal stampings
Pr: Brian Semcer
Pr: Thomas Rozmus
* *Ch:* Frank J Semcer
* *VP:* Charles Edwards
Genl Mgr: Christian Huapaya
Mfg Dir: Thomas Kitz
QC Dir: Emil Kallil
Sfty Mgr: Gayle Goldberg
Mfg Mgr: McCann Paige
Mfg Mgr: Thorsten Schluter
Opers Mgr: Jon Roever

D-U-N-S 15-378-4152
MICRO STRATEGIES INC
MICROSTRATEGIES
1140 Parsippany Blvd # 203, Parsippany, NJ 07054-1887
Tel (973) 625-7721 *Founded/Ownrshp* 1983
Sales 60.7MMME *EMP* 140
SIC 7371 5734 7379 Computer software development; Computer & software stores; Computer hardware requirements analysis
Pr: Anthony L Bongiovanni
* *Sr VP:* Scott D Smith
VP: Steve Deluca
* *VP:* Kelly A O'Neill
Snr Sftwr: Imran Majeed
IT Man: Letty Dempsey
IT Man: Kelly Krieger
IT Man: Keith Van Nortwick
Tech Mgr: Eileen Bobo
Software D: Joe Duvall
Sftwr Eng: Tim Bachmann

D-U-N-S 09-700-4576 IMP
MICRO SYSTEMS ENGINEERING INC
(*Suby of* MICRO SYSTEMS ENGINEERING GMBH)
6024 Jean Rd Ste B, Lake Oswego, OR 97035-8599
Tel (503) 635-4016 *Founded/Ownrshp* 2007
Sales 72.5MMME *EMP* 300E
SIC 3674 Semiconductor circuit networks; Semiconductor circuit networks
Pr: Joachim Langer
* *Pr:* Juergen Lindner
* *VP:* Bob Erb
Sftwr Eng: Rainer Grosskopf
Sftwr Eng: Wells Matthews
Sftwr Eng: Bill Rapoza

D-U-N-S 08-419-0594
MICRO SYSTEMS INC
(*Suby of* MSI ACQUISITION CORP) ★
35 Hill Ave Nw, Fort Walton Beach, FL 32548-3852
Tel (850) 244-2332 *Founded/Ownrshp* 2005
Sales 21.3MMME *EMP* 140
SIC 3823 Computer interface equipment for industrial process control; Computer interface equipment for industrial process control
Pr: Eric M Demarco
* *CFO:* Deanna Lund
VP: Thomas Ferguson
* *VP:* Michael Fink
* *VP:* Laura Siegal
Dir IT: Judy Griffin
IT Man: Tanya Kirby

MICRO TECH
See STARKEY LABORATORIES INC

D-U-N-S 61-105-8140
MICRO VOICE APPLICATIONS INC
5100 Gamble Dr Ste 400, Minneapolis, MN 55416-1587
Tel (612) 373-9300 *Founded/Ownrshp* 1989
Sales 57.0MMM *EMP* 45
SIC 5065 3661 Telephone equipment; Fiber optics communications equipment; Telephone equipment; Fiber optics communications equipment
Pr: Wayne Miller
* *Ex VP:* Steve Lazar
VP: Connie Nicholls
IT Man: Jim Ellison
VP Opers: Catherine Clary
VP Sls: Michael James

MICRO WORLD
See F A SYSTEMS INC

D-U-N-S 07-916-7938
MICRO-CLEAN INC
177 N Commerce Way, Bethlehem, PA 18017-8933
Tel (610) 691-3250 *Founded/Ownrshp* 1974
Sales 24.8MMME *EMP* 115
SIC 7389 Air pollution measuring service
Pr: John Wagner
* *Treas:* Julie Ann Harwick
Dir Lab: Ralph Evans
QA Dir: Crystal Wagner
Sfty Mgr: Ted Charles
Ql Cn Mgr: Tim Sunderland
Sales Asso: Paul Mark

D-U-N-S 08-700-2205
MICRO-COAX INC
206 Jones Blvd, Pottstown, PA 19464-3465
Tel (610) 495-4438 *Founded/Ownrshp* 1999
Sales 44.2MMME *EMP* 200E
SIC 3679 3677 3663 3612 3564 3357 Microwave components; Electronic coils, transformers & other inductors; Radio & TV communications equipment; Transformers, except electric; Blowers & fans; Nonferrous wiredrawing & insulating; Microwave components; Electronic coils, transformers & other inductors; Radio & TV communications equipment; Transformers, except electric; Blowers & fans; Nonferrous wiredrawing & insulating
Pr: Christopher I Kneizys
CIO: Tom Shultz
Mfg Mgr: Joe Joyce
Opers Mgr: Sean McDermott
Plnt Mgr: Edward Dampman
Ql Cn Mgr: Frank Cornwell

D-U-N-S 79-086-8678
MICRO-DATA SYSTEMS INC
71 Main St, Holmdel, NJ 07733-2349
Tel (732) 772-0200 *Founded/Ownrshp* 2007
Sales 21.5MMME *EMP* 190
SIC 7379 Computer related consulting services; Computer related consulting services
CEO: Michele Plenzo
* *Pr:* Dan Plenzo
* *VP:* Keeran Persaud

D-U-N-S 01-792-7620
MICRO-MECHANICS INC (CA)
(*Suby of* MICRO-MECHANICS (HOLDINGS) LTD.)
465 Woodview Ave, Morgan Hill, CA 95037-2800
Tel (408) 779-2927 *Founded/Ownrshp* 1997
Sales 24.1MMME *EMP* 50
SIC 5065 3674 Semiconductor devices; Semiconductors & related devices
Pr: Christopher R Borch
Prd Mgr: Mui Chiew

D-U-N-S 05-478-4277
MICRO-MODE PRODUCTS INC
1870 John Towers Ave, El Cajon, CA 92020-1193
Tel (619) 449-3844 *Founded/Ownrshp* 1971
Sales 23.6MMME *EMP* 110
SIC 3663 3678 7389 Microwave communication equipment; Electronic connectors; ; Microwave communication equipment; Electronic connectors;
Pr: Vincent De Marco
* *CEO:* Michael Cuban
* *Treas:* Ruby Marco

D-U-N-S 79-651-6461 IMP/EXP
■ MICRO-POISE MEASUREMENT SYSTEMS LLC
(*Suby of* AMETEK INC) ★
555 Mondial Pkwy, Streetsboro, OH 44241-4510
Tel (330) 541-9100 *Founded/Ownrshp* 2012
Sales 75.5MMME *EMP* 250
SIC 3559 Automotive maintenance equipment; Automotive maintenance equipment
Pr: Steve Harris
Prgrm Mgr: David Halco
CTO: Shaun Immel
VP Opers: Armand Massary
Sales Asso: Chris Price

D-U-N-S 05-824-4583 IMP
■ MICRO-PROBE INC
M P I
(*Suby of* FORMFACTOR INC) ★
627 River Oaks Pkwy, San Jose, CA 95134-1907
Tel (760) 603-0631 *Founded/Ownrshp* 2012
Sales 28.2MMME *EMP* 240
SIC 3825 Test equipment for electronic & electrical circuits; Test equipment for electronic & electrical circuits
CEO: Mike Slessor
Pr: Todd Swart
Off Mgr: Mel Fernandez
Plng Mgr: Hoehimm Tan
IT Man: Teresa Williams
Ql Cn Mgr: Michelle Guzdek
VP Mktg: Amy Leong
Snr Mgr: Ramesh Ramadoss

MICRO-TECH
See MICRO EAR TECHNOLOGY INC

D-U-N-S 61-342-8812
MICRO-TECHNOLOGY CONCEPTS INC
M T C
(*Suby of* MTC DIRECT INC) ★
17837 Rowland St, City of Industry, CA 91748-1122
Tel (626) 839-6800 *Founded/Ownrshp* 1989
Sales 54.3MMME *EMP* 85
SIC 5045 Computer peripheral equipment; Computer peripheral equipment
Pr: Roy Han
Sr VP: Richard Shyu
Mktg Dir: Alan Djen
Sales Asso: Raymond Cun

D-U-N-S 04-684-0310
MICRO-TRONICS INC
2905 S Potter Dr, Tempe, AZ 85282-3159
Tel (602) 437-8995 *Founded/Ownrshp* 2012
Sales 20.5MM *EMP* 140
SIC 3599 2822 3823 3624 3061 Electrical discharge machining (EDM); Silicone rubbers; Industrial instrmnts msrmnt display/control process variable; Carbon & graphite products; Mechanical rubber goods; Electrical discharge machining (EDM); Silicone rubbers; Industrial instrmnts msrmnt display/control process variable; Carbon & graphite products; Mechanical rubber goods
Pr: Mark Travis
* *Treas:* Edith Remaklus
Sfty Dirs: Jamie Beauvais

D-U-N-S 96-870-1479
■ MICRO-TUBE FABRICATORS INC
(*Suby of* HANDY & HARMAN) ★
250 Lackland Dr Ste 1, Middlesex, NJ 08846-2562
Tel (732) 469-7420 *Founded/Ownrshp* 1992
Sales 20.5MME *EMP* 57
SIC 3351 Tubing, copper & copper alloy
Pr: John Coates
* *Treas:* David Riposo
VP: Rick Kreppel

D-U-N-S 06-445-1917 IMP
MICRO-VU CORP OF CALIFORNIA
7909 Conde Ln, Windsor, CA 95492-9779
Tel (707) 838-6272 *Founded/Ownrshp* 1972
Sales 26.5MMME *EMP* 80
SIC 3827 Optical comparators
Pr: Edward P Amormino
* *Sec:* Virginia Amormino
Sftwr Eng: Dick Henke
Mfg Dir: Chuck Howard

MICROAGE
See FRONTIER TECHNOLOGY LLC

D-U-N-S 10-305-6420 IMP
MICROAIRE SURGICAL INSTRUMENTS LLC
(*Suby of* COLSON ASSOCIATES INC) ★
3590 Grand Forks Blvd, Charlottesville, VA 22911-9006
Tel (800) 722-0822 *Founded/Ownrshp* 1983
Sales 30.3MMME *EMP* 115
SIC 3841 3842 3546 Surgical & medical instruments; Surgical appliances & supplies; Power-driven handtools; Surgical & medical instruments; Surgical appliances & supplies; Power-driven handtools
Pr: George Saiz
* *Ch Bd:* Robert A Pritzker
* *Pr:* Francis I Lavin
* *VP:* Robert C Gluth
VP: Paul Skolnicic
* *VP:* Hank West
IT Man: Jane Stephens
VP Opers: Michael Williams
Natl Sales: Ryan Dailey
VP Sls: Theresa Johnson
Mktg Dir: Boli Emch

D-U-N-S 04-602-5217
MICROANALYSIS SOCIETY INC
3405 Scioto Run Blvd, Hilliard, OH 43026-3005
Tel (614) 256-8063 *Founded/Ownrshp* 1968
Sales 3.3MMME *EMP* 500
SIC 8299 7389 Educational services; ; Educational services;
Treas: Dan Kremser

D-U-N-S 04-819-2892
MICROBAC LABORATORIES INC
101 Bellevue Rd Ste 301, Pittsburgh, PA 15229-2132
Tel (412) 459-1060 *Founded/Ownrshp* 1969
Sales 151.7MMME *EMP* 650
SIC 8734 Testing laboratories; Testing laboratories
CEO: J Trevor Boyce
* *Pr:* James Nokes
* *COO:* Robert Morgan
VP: Ronald Sanders
Dir Lab: Nancy G Burnett
Dir Lab: Tom Zierenberg
Mng Dir: Rob Dermer
Dept Mgr: Ashley Malchow

D-U-N-S 92-902-2630 IMP
MICROBAN INTERNATIONAL LTD
(*Suby of* KLEAN-STRIP) ★
11400 Vanstory Dr, Charlotte, NC 28202
Tel (704) 875-0806 *Founded/Ownrshp* 2011
Sales 31.1MMME *EMP* 65
SIC 5169 Synthetic resins, rubber & plastic materials
CEO: William S Rubinstein
* *Ch Bd:* David J Meyers
* *Pr:* Andrew Rubinstein
Ex VP: Kevin Drake
* *Sr VP:* Steven Lukoskie
Mktg Dir: Max Ruckman

D-U-N-S 82-489-3671 IMP
MICROBAN PRODUCTS CO
(*Suby of* MICROBAN INTERNATIONAL LTD) ★
11400 Vanstory Dr, Huntersville, NC 28078-8147
Tel (704) 766-4267 *Founded/Ownrshp* 1987
Sales 31.1MMME *EMP* 65
SIC 2842 2819 2821 2899 2836 Specialty cleaning preparations; Sanitation preparations, disinfectants & deodorants; Industrial inorganic chemicals; Thermoplastic materials; Chemical preparations; Biological products, except diagnostic
Pr: David Mayers
* *CFO:* Tom Bowlds
* *VP:* Richard Chapman
VP: Lukoskie Stephens
VP: William Taylor

D-U-N-S 78-266-5046
MICROBAR INC
45473 Warm Springs Blvd, Fremont, CA 94539-6104
Tel (510) 659-9770 *Founded/Ownrshp* 1991
Sales 15.8MMME *EMP* 295
SIC 3559 Electronic component making machinery; Electronic component making machinery
Pr: Michael Lund

D-U-N-S 00-145-4099
MICROBEST INC (CT)
670 Captain Neville Dr # 1, Waterbury, CT 06705-3855
Tel (203) 597-0355 *Founded/Ownrshp* 1960
Sales 43.7MMME *EMP* 135
SIC 3451 3541 Screw machine products; Machine tools, metal cutting type; Screw machine products; Machine tools, metal cutting type
Pr: Steven Griffin
* *Pr:* Edward McNerney
Pr: Gregory Smith
* *VP:* Michael Altberg
* *VP:* Paul Lemay
* *VP:* Elaine M Studwell
* *VP:* Jim Tata

D-U-N-S 14-734-7400
MICROBLEND INC
MICROBLEND TECHNOLOGIES
1416 W San Pedro St # 101, Gilbert, AZ 85233-2409
Tel (480) 831-0757 *Founded/Ownrshp* 2002
Sales 30.6MMME *EMP* 46
SIC 5198 Paints
CEO: John E Tyson
* *Pr:* Melvin J Sauder
* *CFO:* Jon Steging
* *Ex VP:* John Bond
* *Ex VP:* Jennifer Haslip
* *Ex VP:* Dan Trevino
S&M/VP: David Philbrook

MICROBLEND TECHNOLOGIES
See MICROBLEND INC

D-U-N-S 07-491-7840
MICROBOARD PROCESSING INC
M P I
36 Cogwheel Ln, Seymour, CT 06483-3922
Tel (203) 881-1688 *Founded/Ownrshp* 1983
Sales 37.7MMME *EMP* 105
SIC 3672 7629 Printed circuit boards; Circuit board repair; Printed circuit boards; Circuit board repair
CEO: Craig Hoekenga
* *Pr:* Nicole Russo
* *VP:* Ted Labowski
* *VP:* Don Preziosi
* *Prin:* Mike Ellis
Prgrm Mgr: Sheri Macri
Prgrm Mgr: Kimberly Walsh
IT Man: Dane Wentworth
Snr Mgr: Shawn Roseboro

D-U-N-S 84-770-6504 IMP
MICROCAST TECHNOLOGIES CORP
1611 W Elizabeth Ave, Linden, NJ 07036-6342
Tel (908) 523-9503 *Founded/Ownrshp* 1995
Sales 23.8MMME *EMP* 116
SIC 3364 8711 3089 5051 7336 3369 Zinc & zinc-base alloy die-castings; Engineering services; Injection molding of plastics; Stampings, metal; Silk screen design; Zinc & zinc-base alloy castings, except die-castings; Zinc & zinc-base alloy die-castings; Engineering services; Injection molding of plastics; Stampings, metal; Silk screen design; Zinc & zinc-base alloy castings, except die-castings
Pr: Dean Fushcetti
* *Pr:* Leonard Cordaro
* *Treas:* Michael Fushcetti
VP: Susan Cordaro
* *VP:* Richard Fuschetti Jr
VP: Ann Fushcetti
QA Dir: Carlos Vega
VP Opers: Dean Fuschetti
Ql Cn Mgr: Elizabeth Fuschetti
Sls Dir: Kenny Oconnell

MICROCHASSIS
See SERRA CORP

D-U-N-S 18-691-7969 IMP
▲ MICROCHIP TECHNOLOGY INC
2355 W Chandler Blvd, Chandler, AZ 85224-6199
Tel (480) 792-7200 *Founded/Ownrshp* 1989
Sales 2.1MMM *EMP* 9,449
Accts Ernst & Young Llp Phoenix Ar
Tkr Sym MCHP *Exch* NGS
SIC 3674 Semiconductors & related devices; Semiconductors & related devices
Pr: Steve Sanghi

COO: Ganesh Moorthy
CFO: J Eric Bjornholt
VP: Stephen V Drehobl
VP: Mitchell R Little
VP: Richard J Simoncic
Dir Bus: Phil Kagel
CTO: Ken Farrow
IT Man: Stephen Cowden
IT Man: Thomas Lindner
Corp Couns: Michael Archiopoli
Board of Directors: Matthew W Chapman, L B Day, Esther L Johnson, Wade F Meyercord

MICRODERMAL
See SALESONE LLC

D-U-N-S 03-089-8449 IMP
MICRODYNAMICS CORP
MICRODYNAMICS GROUP
1400 Shore Rd, Naperville, IL 60563-8765
Tel (630) 276-0527 *Founded/Ownrshp* 1975
Sales 53.5MM^E *EMP* 150^E
SIC 7374 7389 2759 2752 Data processing & preparation; Data processing service; Microfilm recording & developing service; Laser printing; Commercial printing, lithographic; Data processing & preparation; Data processing service; Microfilm recording & developing service; Laser printing; Commercial printing, lithographic
CEO: Thomas Harter Sr
**CFO:* Dave Baker
**Sr VP:* Thomas Harter Jr
VP: Ivana Best
**VP:* Rick Schaltegger
VP: Jeremy Youngren
Exec: Tammy Shull
Dir Bus: Tom Bernardo
CIO: Adam Strack
Software D: Gary Goodman
Software D: Scott Walkowski

MICRODYNAMICS GROUP
See MICRODYNAMICS CORP

D-U-N-S 08-006-0874
MICRODYNE PLASTICS INC
1901 E Cooley Dr, Colton, CA 92324-6322
Tel (909) 503-4010 *Founded/Ownrshp* 1975
Sales 23.3MM^E *EMP* 100
SIC 3089 Blow molded finished plastic products; Injection molding of plastics
Pr: Ronald D Brown
COO: Harry Kline
CFO: Ed Housmann
Exec: Ed Day
MIS Dir: Debbie Martin

D-U-N-S 15-092-2490
■ **MICROEDGE LLC**
(*Suby of* BLACKBAUD INC) ★
619 W 54th St Fl 10, New York, NY 10019-3545
Tel (212) 757-1522 *Founded/Ownrshp* 2014
Sales 24.7MM^E *EMP* 100
SIC 7371 Computer software development
CEO: Kristin Nimsger
**COO:* Phil Montgomery
**CFO:* Todd Laddusaw
VP: Charlie Vanek
Snr Sftwr: Jody Grengs
**CTO:* Joel B Martins
QA Dir: Katelyn Parks
QA Dir: Matt Vaccaro
Software D: Christopher Franz
Software D: Chick Leiby
Sftwr Eng: Matthew Abbas

D-U-N-S 05-262-3548
MICROELECTRONICS ADVANCED RESEARCH CORP
S R C
(*Suby of* S R C) ★
1101 Slater Rd Ste 120, Durham, NC 27703-8447
Tel (919) 941-9400 *Founded/Ownrshp* 1996
Sales 33.2MM *EMP* 3
Accts Pricewaterhousecoopers Llp Wa
SIC 8733 Noncommercial research organizations; Noncommercial research organizations
Pr: Larry W Sumney

D-U-N-S 16-276-8167
MICROEXCEL INC
400 Plaza Dr Ste 102, Secaucus, NJ 07094-3605
Tel (201) 866-6789 *Founded/Ownrshp* 2001
Sales 25.8MM *EMP* 153
SIC 7379 7371 5045 7372 8243 Computer related maintenance services; Computer related consulting services; Custom computer programming services; Computers, peripherals & software; Prepackaged software; Data processing schools; Computer related maintenance services; Computer related consulting services; Custom computer programming services; Computers, peripherals & software; Prepackaged software; Data processing schools
Pr: Nirmal Mehta
**VP:* Paul Simon
CTO: Ravi Bose
Sls Mgr: Chris Jackman
Sls Mgr: Abdul Sattar

D-U-N-S 00-118-9935 IMP/EXP
MICROFIBRES INC
1 Moshassuck St, Pawtucket, RI 02860-4874
Tel (401) 725-4883 *Founded/Ownrshp* 1926
Sales 204.7MM^E *EMP* 1,080
SIC 2221 2295 5131 2262 Upholstery fabrics, manmade fiber & silk; Coated fabrics, not rubberized; Upholstery fabrics, woven; Printing: manmade fiber & silk broadwoven fabrics; Upholstery fabrics, manmade fiber & silk; Coated fabrics, not rubberized; Upholstery fabrics, woven; Printing: manmade fiber & silk broadwoven fabrics
Pr: James R McCulloch
COO: Bill Laird
**CFO:* Maryann Baron
VP: Judy Spivey
Opers Mgr: Garry Russ

D-U-N-S 17-721-8880
MICROFINANCIAL INC
(*Suby of* MF PARENT LP) ★
16 New England Executive, Burlington, MA 01803-5222
Tel (781) 994-4800 *Founded/Ownrshp* 2015
Sales 62.5MM *EMP* 457
SIC 7359 7377 6141 Business machine & electronic equipment rental services; Computer rental & leasing; Personal credit institutions; Business machine & electronic equipment rental services; Computer rental & leasing; Personal credit institutions
Pr: Richard F Latour
CFO: James R Jackson Jr
VP: Steven J Lacreta
CIO: John R Plumlee
Dir IT: Bob Gangi
Software D: Paul Reardon
Board of Directors: Steven Campbell, Douglas Greeff, David King, Scott Lustig, Hank Reeves

D-U-N-S 61-004-0388 IMP
MICROFLEX CORP
(*Suby of* BARRIERSAFE SOLUTIONS INTERNATIONAL INC) ★
2301 Robb Dr, Reno, NV 89523-1901
Tel (775) 746-6600 *Founded/Ownrshp* 2004
Sales 20.7MM^E *EMP* 97
SIC 3069 5047 Laboratory sundries: cases, covers, funnels, cups, etc.; Medical sundries, rubber; Medical & hospital equipment
Pr: Michael Mattos
**COO:* Mike Mattos
CFO: John Bailey
CFO: Lloyd Rogers
VP: Paul Bevilacua
**VP:* Steven Olechny
VP: Jim Tao

D-U-N-S 03-803-2280 IMP/EXP
MICROFLEX INC
1800 N Us Highway 1, Ormond Beach, FL 32174-2400
Tel (386) 677-8100 *Founded/Ownrshp* 1975
Sales 30.4MM *EMP* 120^E
SIC 3494 3599

D-U-N-S 12-215-3799 IMP
■ **MICROGENICS CORP**
(*Suby of* THERMO FISHER SCIENTIFIC INC) ★
46500 Kato Rd, Fremont, CA 94538-7310
Tel (510) 979-9147 *Founded/Ownrshp* 2006
Sales 410.5MM^E *EMP* 6,076
SIC 2834 Proprietary drug products; Proprietary drug products
CEO: Seth H Hoogasian
**Pr:* David Rubinfien
VP: Santiago Asuncion
VP: Azeem Syed
Genl Mgr: Macoy Heramia
Prd Mgr: Vienne Lee
Mktg Dir: Kathy Ruzich

D-U-N-S 02-171-7962
MICROGROUP INC
ALL TUBE DIV
(*Suby of* K C P) ★
7 Industrial Park Rd, Medway, MA 02053-1732
Tel (508) 533-4925 *Founded/Ownrshp* 2005
Sales 145.9MM^E *EMP* 150
SIC 5051 3312 3498 3494 3492 3317 Metals service centers & offices; Tubes, steel & iron; Fabricated pipe & fittings; Valves & pipe fittings; Fluid power valves & hose fittings; Steel pipe & tubes; Metals service centers & offices; Tubes, steel & iron; Fabricated pipe & fittings; Valves & pipe fittings; Fluid power valves & hose fittings; Steel pipe & tubes
Pr: William J Bergen
**CFO:* Geoff Holczer
Sr VP: Graeme Bennie
VP: Keith Miller
VP: Edward Perry
Genl Mgr: Patti-Jean Carchedi
QA Dir: Tony Tran
IT Man: John Sorgert
VP Opers: Alexander Magyar
Ql Cn Mgr: Nancy Litt
Ql Cn Mgr: Robert Pallotta

D-U-N-S 15-510-1637 IMP
MICROLAND ELECTRONICS CORP
1883 Ringwood Ave, San Jose, CA 95131-1721
Tel (408) 441-1688 *Founded/Ownrshp* 1986
Sales 52.9MM^E *EMP* 60
SIC 5045 3577 3572 3571 Computer peripheral equipment; Computer peripheral equipment; Computer storage devices; Electronic computers
Pr: Abraham Chen
COO: Jawahar Bekay
COO: Randy Yuen
Chf Mktg O: V M Kumar
Ex VP: Bala Palamadai
Mng Dir: Pradeep Kar
Netwrk Mgr: Eric Ko
VP Sls: Randy Yuan
Sls Mgr: Ellen Wang
Sales Asso: Doris Huang

MICROLEASE
See METRIC EQUIPMENT SALES INC

D-U-N-S 08-940-0977
MICROLEASE INC
(*Suby of* MICROLEASE PLC)
9221 Globe Center Dr # 105, Morrisville, NC 27560-6205
Tel (866) 520-0200 *Founded/Ownrshp* 2001
Sales 88.8MM^E *EMP* 250
SIC 7359 Equipment rental & leasing; Equipment rental & leasing
VP: Gordon Curwen
CEO: Michael E Clark
Natl Sales: Jim Carney

D-U-N-S 18-408-0570 IMP
MICROLINE SURGICAL INC
MSI
(*Suby of* HOYA CORPORATION)
50 Dunham Rd Ste 1500, Beverly, MA 01915-1882
Tel (978) 922-9810 *Founded/Ownrshp* 2008
Sales 58.4MM^E *EMP* 160
SIC 3841 Surgical & medical instruments; Surgical & medical instruments
Ch Bd: Dr Jean Luc Boulnois
Pr: Sharad H Joshi
CFO: Darlene Deptula-Hicks
Treas: Kengo Jojiki
Manager: John Egitto
Prd Mgr: Jason Williams
Mktg Mgr: Melissa Graves
Sls Mgr: Chris Lovely

D-U-N-S 18-537-6233
MICROLUMEN INC
1 Microlumen Way, Oldsmar, FL 34677-2983
Tel (813) 854-3070 *Founded/Ownrshp* 1987
Sales 20.3MM^E *EMP* 80
SIC 3082 3644 Tubes, unsupported plastic; Noncurrent-carrying wiring services
Pr: M Scott Roberds
**CEO:* Roger O Roberds
VP: Robin Reynolds
IT Man: Brian Labarbera
Prd Mgr: Rene Alvarado
Prd Mgr: Joe Slaven

D-U-N-S 06-683-9630
■ **MICROMEDICS INC**
NORDSON
(*Suby of* NORDSON CORP) ★
1270 Eagan Industrial Rd # 100, Saint Paul, MN 55121-1369
Tel (651) 452-1977 *Founded/Ownrshp* 2010
Sales 37.8MM^E *EMP* 130
SIC 3841 Instruments, microsurgical: except electromedical; Instruments, microsurgical: except electromedical
CEO: Michael F Hilton
**Pr:* Jeff Pembroke
**CFO:* Lorraine Duchene
**VP:* Bruce Brown
**VP:* Kevin Connelly
Dir Lab: Tom Kirk
Dir IT: Curtis Miller
Mfg Mgr: Mark Seuntjens
Sales Asso: Ben Johnson

D-U-N-S 14-813-1550
MICROMENDERS INC
1388 Sutter St Ste 650, San Francisco, CA 94109-5452
Tel (415) 344-0917 *Founded/Ownrshp* 1985
Sales 22.4MM^E *EMP* 55
SIC 5045 7373 7371 4813 Computers, peripherals & software; Local area network (LAN) systems integrator; Computer software systems analysis & design, custom;
CEO: Dave Sperry
**VP:* Corey Choi
IT Man: Stuart Bond
Netwrk Eng: Rodrigo Allegretti

MICROMERITICS ANALYTICAL SVCS
See MICROMERITICS INSTRUMENT CORP

D-U-N-S 00-348-3617 EXP
MICROMERITICS INSTRUMENT CORP (GA)
MICROMERITICS ANALYTICAL SVCS
4356 Communications Dr, Norcross, GA 30093-2901
Tel (770) 662-3620 *Founded/Ownrshp* 1962
Sales 56.7MM^E *EMP* 285
SIC 3826 8734

D-U-N-S 00-828-1792 IMP/EXP
MICROMETALS INC (CA)
5615 E La Palma Ave, Anaheim, CA 92807-2109
Tel (714) 970-9400 *Founded/Ownrshp* 1951
Sales 35.4MM^E *EMP* 250^E
SIC 3679 Cores, magnetic; Cores, magnetic
CEO: Richard H Barden
Admn Mgr: Chris Oliver
Dir IT: Steve Collier
Sfty Mgr: George Bradley
Mfg Mgr: Bill Kemper

D-U-N-S 78-765-2395 IMP/EXP
MICROMETALS/TEXAS INC
(*Suby of* MICROMETALS INC) ★
4825 Derrick Dr, Abilene, TX 79601-6701
Tel (325) 677-8753 *Founded/Ownrshp* 1991
Sales 35.4MM^E *EMP* 250
SIC 3679 Cores, magnetic; Cores, magnetic
Pr: Richard H Barden
VP: James R Cox

MICROMO
See MICRO MO ELECTRONICS INC

D-U-N-S 62-673-2213
MICRON HOLDINGS INC
4436 Broadmoor Ave Se, Kentwood, MI 49512-5305
Tel (616) 698-0707 *Founded/Ownrshp* 2004
Sales 103.2MM^E *EMP* 2,612
SIC 3714 Motor vehicle parts & accessories; Motor vehicle parts & accessories
VP: John F X Daly
Pr: John C Kennedy
COO: John R Buchan
COO: Eduardo Renner De Castilho
COO: Jonathan B Degaynor
CFO: Warren A Veltman
VP: Jack Daly
VP: James A Hislop
VP: Adrian Jones
VP: Thomas K O'Mara
VP: Richard J Peters

D-U-N-S 05-942-2261 IMP
MICRON INDUSTRIES CORP
MICRON POWER
1211 W 22nd St Ste 200, Oak Brook, IL 60523-3226
Tel (630) 516-1222 *Founded/Ownrshp* 1982
Sales 22.5MM^E *EMP* 105
SIC 3612 Control transformers; Power transformers, electric; Specialty transformers
Pr: Donald R Clark
VP: David Long
Ql Cn Mgr: Dale Wagner
VP Sls: Vincent Lamparelli

MICRON POWER
See MICRON INDUSTRIES CORP

D-U-N-S 05-901-8622
■ **MICRON PRODUCTS INC**
(*Suby of* ARRHYTHMIA RESEARCH TECHNOLOGY INC) ★
25 Sawyer Passway, Fitchburg, MA 01420-5702
Tel (978) 345-5000 *Founded/Ownrshp* 1992
Sales 38.5MM^E *EMP* 173^E
SIC 3845 Electromedical apparatus
Pr: James E Rouse
**Pr:* Salvatore Emma Jr
**CFO:* David Garrison
**Treas:* Derek T Welch
VP: Michael Collette
**VP:* Mark Laviolette
VP: Albert McGrath
IT Man: Michael Chiasson
Ql Cn Mgr: Kim Rice

D-U-N-S 03-648-0788 IMP
■ **MICRON SEMICONDUCTOR PRODUCTS INC**
(*Suby of* MICRON TECHNOLOGY INC) ★
8000 S Federal Way, Boise, ID 83716-9632
Tel (208) 368-4000 *Founded/Ownrshp* 1996
Sales 250.6MM^E *EMP* 550
SIC 5065 Semiconductor devices; Semiconductor devices
Pr: Michael W Sadler
Pr: Brian Kalisek
Pr: Michael Knapp
COO: Mark Duncan
Ex VP: Brian Klene
Ex Dir: Dee Mooney
Dir IT: Sharath Babu
Dir IT: Jeffrey King
Dir IT: Michael Zeigler
IT Man: Ryan Blanchard
IT Man: Dave Curtis

D-U-N-S 09-312-0871 IMP
▲ **MICRON TECHNOLOGY INC**
8000 S Federal Way, Boise, ID 83716-7128
Tel (208) 368-4000 *Founded/Ownrshp* 1978
Sales 16.1MMM *EMP* 31,800
Accts Pricewaterhousecoopers Llp Sa
Tkr Sym MU *Exch* NGS
SIC 3674 Semiconductors & related devices; Random access memory (RAM); Semiconductors & related devices; Random access memory (RAM)
CEO: D Mark Durcan
**Ch Bd:* Robert E Switz
Pr: Mark W Adams
CFO: Ernest E Maddock
VP: Scott J Deboer
VP: Joel L Poppen
VP: Brian M Shirley
VP: Steven L Thorsen Jr
Board of Directors: Robert L Bailey, Richard M Beyer, Patrick J Byrne, D Warren A East, Mercedes Johnson, Lawrence N Mondry

D-U-N-S 96-343-6667
MICRONET ENERTEC TECHNOLOGIES INC
28 W Grand Ave Ste 3, Montvale, NJ 07645-2100
Tel (201) 225-0190 *Founded/Ownrshp* 2002
Sales 34.2MM *EMP* 87^E
Tkr Sym MICT *Exch* NAS
SIC 3572 Computer storage devices; Computer storage devices
Ch Bd: David Lucatz
CFO: Eyal Leibovitz
Board of Directors: Jacob Berman, Jeffrey P Bialos

D-U-N-S 10-739-8224 IMP/EXP
MICRONICS INC
(*Suby of* VANCE STREET CAPITAL LLC) ★
200 West Rd, Portsmouth, NH 03801-8657
Tel (603) 433-1299 *Founded/Ownrshp* 2013
Sales 38.0MM *EMP* 55^E
SIC 5085 3569 Industrial supplies; Filters, general line: industrial
Pr: Richard E Weiler
**CEO:* Barry Hibble
**Treas:* Julie A Pugh
Rgnl Mgr: Robert Parks

MICRONUTRIENTS DIVISION
See HERITAGE TECHNOLOGIES LLC

MICROPACT
See IRON DATA SOLUTIONS INC

D-U-N-S 00-144-9354
MICROPHASE CORP
100 Trap Falls Road Ext # 400, Shelton, CT 06484-4655
Tel (203) 866-8000 *Founded/Ownrshp* 1955
Sales 21.9MM^E *EMP* 100
SIC 3663 3677 3674 3661 3651 3564 Microwave communication equipment; Electronic coils, transformers & other inductors; Semiconductors & related devices; Telephone & telegraph apparatus; Household audio & video equipment; Blowers & fans; Microwave communication equipment; Electronic coils, transformers & other inductors; Semiconductors & related devices; Telephone & telegraph apparatus; Household audio & video equipment
Ch Bd: Necdet Ergul
**CFO:* James Ashman
**Treas:* Jeffrey Peterson
**Chf Mktg O:* Michael Ghadaksaz
IT Man: William Blake
Mfg Mgr: Tony Siciliano
Board of Directors: Paul H Decoster

D-U-N-S 55-710-1367 IMP/EXP
MICROPOROUS LLC
AMERACE MICROPOROUS PRODUCTS
596 Industrial Park Rd, Piney Flats, TN 37686-4450
Tel (423) 926-7117 *Founded/Ownrshp* 2013

Sales 62.4MM^E *EMP* 153
SIC 3061 3443 Automotive rubber goods (mechanical); Fabricated plate work (boiler shop); Automotive rubber goods (mechanical); Fabricated plate work (boiler shop)
CEO: Jean-Luc Koch
Plnt Mgr: Sam Dettor
Plnt Mgr: Roger Eggleston

D-U-N-S 07-911-8736
MICROPORT ORTHOPEDICS INC
(*Suby of* SHANGHAI MICROPORT MEDICAL (GROUP) CO., LTD.)
5677 Airline Rd, Arlington, TN 38002-9501
Tel (866) 872-0211 *Founded/Ownrshp* 2014
Sales 221.8MM^E *EMP* 550
SIC 5047 Medical equipment & supplies; Orthopedic equipment & supplies; Medical equipment & supplies; Orthopedic equipment & supplies
Pr: Yan Zhang
CFO: Hongbin Sun
Treas: Xu Yimin
Ofcr: John Knighton
Sr VP: Kongrong Karl Pan
Sr VP: Edward Steiger
VP: Kamaal Anas
VP: Michael Carroll
VP: Ken Glatzer
VP: Jason Jones
Prd Mgr: Robert Phaneuf

D-U-N-S 15-386-4848
MICROPRECISION INC
1206 Ann St, Delavan, WI 53115-1983
Tel (262) 728-5262 *Founded/Ownrshp* 1950
Sales 42.2MM^E *EMP* 125
SIC 3469 3451 3541 Metal stampings; Screw machine products; Machine tools, metal cutting type; Metal stampings; Screw machine products; Machine tools, metal cutting type
Pr: Joseph Moser
VP: Brad Brown
Plnt Mgr: Ray Schilz

D-U-N-S 19-806-3257
MICROPULSE INC
5865 E State Road 14, Columbia City, IN 46725-9237
Tel (260) 625-3304 *Founded/Ownrshp* 1988
Sales 35.2MM^E *EMP* 240^E
SIC 3841 Surgical & medical instruments; Surgical & medical instruments
Pr: Brian G Emerick
COO: Larry Sutton
**CFO:* Brian More
VP: Abbott Kevin
QC Dir: Roger Stetzel

MICROS RETAIL
See DATAVANTAGE CORP

D-U-N-S 17-420-6508
MICROS RETAIL SYSTEMS INC
1200 Harbor Blvd Fl 10, Weehawken, NJ 07086-6728
Tel (201) 866-1000 *Founded/Ownrshp* 1986
Sales 36.1MM^E *EMP* 103
SIC 5045 5044 Accounting machines using machine readable programs; Cash registers; Accounting machines using machine readable programs; Cash registers
Pr: Lubodar Olesnycky
**Sec:* Ivanka Olesnycky
Snr Sftwr: Joe Devaasirvatham
Snr Sftwr: Anoumou Vossah
QA Dir: Shannon Paradise
Software D: Jonathan Warren
Sftwr Eng: Nuwan Wijekoon
Sls Dir: Tom Zerrenner
Art Dir: Hardy Hyppolite

D-U-N-S 09-240-2726
■ **MICROS SYSTEMS INC** (MD)
(*Suby of* OC ACQUISITION LLC) ★
7031 Columbia Gateway Dr # 1, Columbia, MD 21046-2583
Tel (443) 285-6000 *Founded/Ownrshp* 1977, 2014
Sales 718.1MM^E *EMP* 6,506
SIC 7373 7372 3577 3578 Computer integrated systems design; Business oriented computer software; Computer peripheral equipment; Calculating & accounting equipment; Computer integrated systems design; Business oriented computer software; Computer peripheral equipment; Calculating & accounting equipment
Pr: Peter A Altabef
Ch Bd: A L Giannopoulos
CFO: Cynthia A Russo
Ofcr: Carlos Echalar
Ex VP: Ed Chapel
Ex VP: John E Gularson
Ex VP: Jennifer M Kurdle
Ex VP: Thomas L Patz
Ex VP: Stefan M Piringer
Ex VP: Peter J Rogers Jr
Sr VP: Jay Upchurch
VP: Anthony Gherardini
VP: Michael P Russo
VP: Shawn Zudul
Exec: Hol Hustus

D-U-N-S 11-895-4718
MICROSCAN SYSTEMS INC
(*Suby of* SPECTRIS INC) ★
700 Sw 39th St Ste 100, Renton, WA 98057-2316
Tel (425) 226-5700 *Founded/Ownrshp* 1995
Sales 23.1MM^E *EMP* 146
SIC 3577

MICROSCOPES SYSTEMS
See M2 ASSOCIATES INC

D-U-N-S 13-090-6659 IMP
MICROSEISMIC INC
10777 Westheimer Rd # 500, Houston, TX 77042-3453
Tel (713) 781-2323 *Founded/Ownrshp* 2003
Sales 38.9MM^E *EMP* 53^E
SIC 1382 Oil & gas exploration services
Ch: Peter M Duncan
Pr: Jeff Foster
COO: Terry Jbeili
CFO: Rick Luke
Bd of Dir: Todd Wilson
VP: Indy Chakrabarti
VP: Sarah Groen
VP: Sudhendu Kashikar
VP: Malcolm Macaulay
VP: Ganesh Murdeshwar
VP: Mark Murphy
VP: Gary North
VP: Dave Oxford
VP: Rip Stringer
VP: Mike Thotnton

D-U-N-S 17-356-6738
■ **MICROSEMI COMMUNICATIONS INC**
VITESSE SEMICONDUCTOR CORP
(*Suby of* MICROSEMI CORP) ★
4721 Calle Carga, Camarillo, CA 93012-8541
Tel (805) 388-3700 *Founded/Ownrshp* 2015
Sales 97.6MM^E *EMP* 331^E
SIC 3674 Integrated circuits, semiconductor networks, etc.; Integrated circuits, semiconductor networks, etc.
Pr: Christopher R Gardner
**CFO:* Martin S McDermut
Ex VP: Vuong Nguyen
Prgrm Mgr: Sam Barnett
Prgrm Mgr: Pam Huggett
**CIO:* Jacob Nielsen
Ql Cn Mgr: Barbara Blick
Manager: Kevin Janssen

D-U-N-S 05-155-0838
▲ **MICROSEMI CORP**
1 Enterprise, Aliso Viejo, CA 92656-2606
Tel (949) 380-6100 *Founded/Ownrshp* 1960
Sales 1.1MMM *EMP* 3,400
Tkr Sym MSCC *Exch* NGS
SIC 3674 Semiconductors & related devices; Rectifiers, solid state; Zener diodes; Diodes, solid state (germanium, silicon, etc.); Semiconductors & related devices; Rectifiers, solid state; Zener diodes; Diodes, solid state (germanium, silicon, etc.)
Ch Bd: James J Peterson
Pr: Paul H Pickle
CFO: John W Hohener
Ex VP: Steve Litchfield
Ex VP: Steven G Litchfield
Sr VP: David Goren
Snr Ntwrk: Min Fang
Opers Mgr: Robert Wilcox
Sls Mgr: Fernando Serpa
Board of Directors: Thomas R Anderson, William E Bendush, Paul F Folino, William L Healey, Dennis R Leibel, Matthew E Massengill

D-U-N-S 80-772-8431
■ **MICROSEMI CORP - ANALOG MIXED SIGNAL GROUP**
LINFINITY MICROELECTRONICS
(*Suby of* MICROSEMI CORP) ★
11861 Western Ave, Garden Grove, CA 92841-2119
Tel (714) 898-8121 *Founded/Ownrshp* 1999
Sales 162.3MM^E *EMP* 1,300^E
SIC 3674 Semiconductor circuit networks; Semiconductor circuit networks
CEO: James Peterson
**COO:* Paul Pickle
**CFO:* John Hohener
**Ex VP:* Russ Garcia
**Dir Sec:* Steve Litchfield
**CTO:* Jim Aralis

D-U-N-S 05-694-2097
■ **MICROSEMI CORP - MASSACHUSETTS**
(*Suby of* MICROSEMI CORP) ★
6 Lake St Ste 1, Lawrence, MA 01841-3032
Tel (978) 794-1666 *Founded/Ownrshp* 1982
Sales 48.1MM^E *EMP* 220
SIC 3674 Semiconductors & related devices; Semiconductors & related devices
Pr: James Peterson
**CFO:* John Hohener
VP: Ethelda Hester
VP: Mick McKeighan
VP: Sven Nelson
Genl Mgr: Ron Davis

D-U-N-S 55-636-4230 IMP
■ **MICROSEMI CORP - MASSACHUSETTS**
(*Suby of* MICROSEMI CORP) ★
2381 Morse Ave, Irvine, CA 92614-6233
Tel (800) 713-4113 *Founded/Ownrshp* 1992
Sales 66.1MM^E *EMP* 645
SIC 3674 Semiconductors & related devices; Semiconductor diodes & rectifiers
Pr: Jim Peterson
**Ex VP:* Ralph Brandi
Software D: Jesse Does
Sls Mgr: Theresa Mazur-Lydon

D-U-N-S 00-506-9315 IMP
■ **MICROSEMI CORP - MEMORY AND STORAGE SOLUTIONS**
(*Suby of* MICROSEMI CORP) ★
3601 E University Dr, Phoenix, AZ 85034-7217
Tel (602) 437-1520 *Founded/Ownrshp* 1951, 2010
Sales 43.4MM^E *EMP* 160
SIC 3679 3575 3674 3643 Electronic circuits; Keyboards, computer, office machine; Microcircuits, integrated (semiconductor); Current-carrying wiring devices
CEO: Charles C Leader
Pr: Sumana Achar
Pr: Bjarne Heggli
**CFO:* Roger A Derse
CFO: Kevin Hanson
**CFO:* John W Hohener
Bd of Dir: Brian Kahn
VP: Dan Tarantine
**Ex VP:* Dante V Tarantine
VP: Willis Damkroger
**VP:* B J Heggli

D-U-N-S 13-196-8380
■ **MICROSEMI CORP - POWER PRODUCTS GROUP**
(*Suby of* MICROSEMI CORP) ★
405 Sw Columbia St, Bend, OR 97702-1087
Tel (541) 382-8028 *Founded/Ownrshp* 1992
Sales 38.2MM^E *EMP* 277
SIC 3674 3679 Semiconductors & related devices; Electronic circuits; Semiconductors & related devices; Electronic circuits
Pr: James J Peterson
COO: Ralph Brandi
CFO: John Hohener
VP: Charles C Leader
VP: John T Orvik
S&M/VP: George J Krausse

D-U-N-S 08-738-7759
MICROSEMI CORP-POWER MANAGEMENT GROUP
(*Suby of* BABCOCK) ★
11861 Western Ave, Garden Grove, CA 92841-2119
Tel (714) 994-6500 *Founded/Ownrshp* 1977
Sales 34.4MM^E *EMP* 250
SIC 3625 3677 3679 3613 3612 3577 Relays, for electronic use; Electronic transformers; Liquid crystal displays (LCD); Switchgear & switchboard apparatus; Transformers, except electric; Computer peripheral equipment; Relays, for electronic use; Electronic transformers; Liquid crystal displays (LCD); Switchgear & switchboard apparatus; Transformers, except electric; Computer peripheral equipment
Pr: James J Peterson
**CFO:* John W Hohener
**VP:* Rob Warren
Off Mgr: Julie Weber

D-U-N-S 05-285-1771
MICROSEMI CORP-POWER MANAGEMENT GROUP HOLDING (CA)
BABCOCK
11861 Western Ave, Garden Grove, CA 92841-2119
Tel (714) 994-6500 *Founded/Ownrshp* 1970
Sales 34.4MM^E *EMP* 250
SIC 3679 3625 Power supplies, all types: static; Liquid crystal displays (LCD); Relays, electric power; Power supplies, all types: static; Liquid crystal displays (LCD); Relays, electric power
Pr: Richard S Dixon
**VP:* Mike Dixon
IT Man: Guy Johnsen
Sls Mgr: Yuji Takeshita

D-U-N-S 00-824-8593 IMP
■ **MICROSEMI FREQUENCY AND TIME CORP**
(*Suby of* MICROSEMI CORP) ★
3870 N 1st St, San Jose, CA 95134-1702
Tel (408) 428-6993 *Founded/Ownrshp* 2001
Sales 180.6MM^E *EMP* 544
SIC 3625 7372 Timing devices, electronic; Business oriented computer software; Timing devices, electronic; Business oriented computer software
CEO: Steven G Litchfield
Pr: Lyle Smith
**CEO:* Liz Fetter
COO: Elizabeth Johnson
Ex VP: Bill Minor
Ex VP: Daniel L Scharre
VP: Sim Narashima
Exec: Suzanne Shanholtz
Rgnl Mgr: Christina Howe
Manager: Robin Doering
Sls Mgr: Tim Knight

D-U-N-S 14-822-2045 IMP
■ **MICROSEMI SOC CORP**
(*Suby of* MICROSEMI CORP) ★
3870 N 1st St, San Jose, CA 95134-1702
Tel (408) 643-6000 *Founded/Ownrshp* 1985
Sales 111.6MM^E *EMP* 550^E
SIC 3674 7371 Microcircuits, integrated (semiconductor); Computer software development; Microcircuits, integrated (semiconductor); Computer software development
CEO: James J Peterson
**CFO:* John W Hohener
**Sr VP:* Esmat Z Hamdy
**Sr VP:* Fares N Mubarak
VP: Rich Brossart
**VP:* David L Van De Hey
VP: David De Hey
VP: Esmat Dixon
VP: Doug Goodyear
VP: Dennis Nye
VP: Mike Pardini

D-U-N-S 08-146-6849
▲ **MICROSOFT CORP** (WA)
1 Microsoft Way, Redmond, WA 98052-8300
Tel (425) 882-8080 *Founded/Ownrshp* 1975
Sales 93.5MMM *EMP* 118,007
Accts Deloitte & Touche Llp Seattle
Tkr Sym MSFT *Exch* NGS
SIC 7372 7371 3577 7375 Prepackaged software; Operating systems computer software; Business oriented computer software; Application computer software; Computer software development; Computer peripheral equipment; Information retrieval services; Prepackaged software; Operating systems computer software; Business oriented computer software; Application computer software; Computer software development; Computer peripheral equipment; Information retrieval services
CEO: Satya Nadella
COO: B Kevin Turner
CFO: Amy E Hood
Chf Mktg O: Christopher C Capossela
Ex VP: Kathleen T Hogan
Ex VP: Margaret Johnson
Board of Directors: William H Gates III, Maria M Klawe, G Mason Morfit, Charles H Noski, Helmut Panke, Charles W Scharf, John W Stanton, Teri L List-Stoll, John W Thompson

D-U-N-S 00-952-2116
■ **MICROSOFT LICENSING GP**
(*Suby of* MICROSOFT CORP) ★
6100 Neil Rd Ste 100, Reno, NV 89511-1137
Tel (775) 823-5600 *Founded/Ownrshp* 2013
Sales 79.0MM^E *EMP* 165^E
SIC 7374 Data processing service; Data processing service
Pt: Tom Baumbach
Pt: Lloyd Brenner
Prgrm Mgr: Catherine Adams
Prgrm Mgr: Mark Anderson
Prgrm Mgr: Vanna Kumar
Prgrm Mgr: Tim Villareal

D-U-N-S 83-695-4123 IMP
■ **MICROSOFT NETWORK L L C**
(*Suby of* MICROSOFT CORP) ★
1 Microsoft Way, Redmond, WA 98052-8300
Tel (425) 538-2948 *Founded/Ownrshp* 1996
Sales 4.3MMM^E *EMP* 3,169^E
SIC 4813
Top Exec: Frank Shaw
Ex VP: Sarah Kennedy
VP: David Kubelka
Dir Bus: Sanjai Bijawat
Dir Sec: Ned Curic
Prgrm Mgr: Eric Fitzgerald
Prgrm Mgr: Diego Tamburini
Prgrm Mgr: Russell Wilson
CTO: Bryce Cogswell
Dir IT: Amanda McLain
Mktg Mgr: Justin Rice

MICROSS COMPONENTS
See CHIP SUPPLY INC

MICROSTRATEGIES
See MICRO STRATEGIES INC

D-U-N-S 62-289-5613
▲ **MICROSTRATEGY INC**
1850 Towers Crescent Plz # 700, Tysons Corner, VA 22182-6231
Tel (703) 848-8600 *Founded/Ownrshp* 1989
Sales 579.8MM *EMP* 2,470
Tkr Sym MSTR *Exch* NGS
SIC 7372 7371 Prepackaged software; Application computer software; Computer software systems analysis & design, custom; Prepackaged software; Application computer software; Computer software systems analysis & design, custom
Ch Bd: Michael J Saylor
Pr: Paul N Zolfaghari
COO: Andrew Rosen
CFO: Shirley Tan
CFO: Douglas K Thede
Chf Mktg O: Mark Gambill
Sr VP: Ram Ramachandran
Exec: Timothy E Lang
Board of Directors: Robert H Epstein, Stephen X Graham, Jarrod M Patten, Carl J Rickertsen

MICROSUN TECHNOLOGIES
See PALLADIUM ENERGY OF ILLINOIS LLC

MICROTECHNOLOGIES
See MICRO PNEUMATIC LOGIC INC

MICROTECHNOLOGIES
See M MICROTECHNOLOGIES INC

D-U-N-S 14-545-4182
MICROTECHNOLOGIES LLC
8330 Boone Blvd Ste 600, Vienna, VA 22182-2658
Tel (703) 891-1073 *Founded/Ownrshp* 2004
Sales 95.1MM *EMP* 425
SIC 7379 Computer related consulting services; Computer related consulting services
Pr: Anthony R Jimenez
CFO: David A Hinson
CFO: Lynn Wasylina
Sr VP: Roger Channing
Sr VP: Dave Coker
Sr VP: Aaron Drabkin
Sr VP: Preston Quick
VP: Ray Miles
IT Man: Fabio Rifici

MICROTEK
See MID VENTURES INC

D-U-N-S 06-432-1292 IMP
MICROTEK LAB INC
(*Suby of* MICROTEK INTERNATIONAL INC.)
13337 South St, Cerritos, CA 90703-7308
Tel (310) 687-5823 *Founded/Ownrshp* 1980, 1988
Sales 21.5MM^E *EMP* 170
SIC 5044 Copying equipment; Copying equipment
Pr: Clark Hsu
**Pr:* Stewart Chow

D-U-N-S 18-857-7050 IMP/EXP
■ **MICROTEK MEDICAL HOLDINGS INC**
(*Suby of* ECOLAB INC) ★
13000 Drfeld Pkwy Ste 300, Alpharetta, GA 30004
Tel (678) 896-4400 *Founded/Ownrshp* 2007
Sales 202.2MM^E *EMP* 1,863
SIC 3842 Surgical appliances & supplies; Surgical appliances & supplies; Sterilizers, hospital & surgical; Cotton & cotton applicators; Surgical appliances & supplies; Surgical appliances & supplies; Sterilizers, hospital & surgical; Cotton & cotton applicators
CEO: Martha Goldberg Aronson
COO: Mark J Alvarez
CFO: Ching Meng Chew
CFO: Roger G Wilson
Bd of Dir: Ronald Smorada
VP: Amy Levinson
VP: Peter Schmitt
VP: David Velmosky
Prin: Timothy Mulhere
Board of Directors: Kenneth F Davis, Michael E Glasscock III, Gene R McGrevin, Marc R Sarni, Ronald L Smorada

D-U-N-S 10-690-8437 IMP/EXP
■ MICROTEK MEDICAL INC
(*Suby of* MICROTEK MEDICAL HOLDINGS INC) ★
512 N Lehmberg Rd, Columbus, MS 39702-4464
Tel (662) 327-1863 *Founded/Ownrshp* 1996
Sales 202.0MM^E *EMP* 1,087
SIC 3841 Surgical & medical instruments; Surgical & medical instruments
Pr: Dan R Lee
COO: Mark J Alverez
VP: Tico Capote
VP: Robin Humble
VP: Gary Moses
VP: Debbie Wooley
Plng Mgr: Bert Rector
Natl Sales: Mark Gardner
Mktg Dir: Mary Ann Whitlock
Snr Mgr: Carol Pack-Walden

D-U-N-S 96-102-3777 IMP
MICROTUNE INC
(*Suby of* ZORAN CORP) ★
2201 10th St, Plano, TX 75074-8019
Tel (972) 673-1600 *Founded/Ownrshp* 2010
Sales 11.0MM^E *EMP* 276^E
SIC 3674 Semiconductors & related devices; Semiconductors & related devices
Pr: James A Fontaine
CFO: Justin M Chapman
CFO: Rob-Roy Graham
Ex VP: Barry F Koch
VP: Glenn Fraser
VP: Robert S Kirk
Ex Dir: Vincent Burleson
Ql Cn Mgr: Hark Felker
Mktg Mgr: Dewight Warren
Sls Mgr: Sharon Pearce
Genl Couns: Phillip D Peterson

D-U-N-S 00-326-3105
MICROVENTION INC
(*Suby of* TERUMO AMERICAS HOLDING INC) ★
1311 Valencia Ave, Tustin, CA 92780-6447
Tel (714) 258-8001 *Founded/Ownrshp* 1997, 2006
Sales 65.0MM^E *EMP* 737^E
SIC 8071 Neurological laboratory; Neurological laboratory
Pr: Richard Captetpa
**COO:* William R Hughes
Treas: William Hughes
**Sr VP:* Glenn Latham
VP: Bruce Canter
**VP:* Rob Green
**VP:* Philip Harvey
**VP:* Cherie Henket
**VP:* Jun Hoshino
Exec: Rosalie Jones
Prgrm Mgr: Kathleen McNeill

MICROWAVE RADIO COMMUNICATIONS
See VISLINK INC

D-U-N-S 18-633-3662
MICROWAVE TRANSMISSION SYSTEMS INC
MTSI
1751 Jay Ell Dr, Richardson, TX 75081-1835
Tel (972) 669-0591 *Founded/Ownrshp* 1987
Sales 53.8MM *EMP* 160
Accts Daniel L Lassiter Jr Richar
SIC 1731 Communications specialization; Communications specialization
Pr: Preston David Spurling
**VP:* Susan King

D-U-N-S 96-693-4259
■ MICRUS ENDOVASCULAR LLC
(*Suby of* JOHNSON & JOHNSON) ★
821 Fox Ln, San Jose, CA 95131-1601
Tel (408) 433-1400 *Founded/Ownrshp* 2010
Sales 35.7MM^E *EMP* 341
SIC 3841 Surgical instruments & apparatus; Surgical instruments & apparatus
Pr: P Laxminarain
Pr: Robert A Stern
CEO: John T Kilcoyne
CFO: Gordon T Sangster
Chf Cred: Edward F Ruppel Jr
VP: Carolyn M Bruguera
VP: Robert C Colloton
VP: Michael R Compton
VP: R Michael Crompton
VP: Richard J Snyder
CIO: Jacqueline DESA

MICUCCI GROCERY STORE
See MICUCCI WHOLESALE GROCERS

D-U-N-S 01-905-2687
MICUCCI WHOLESALE GROCERS (ME)
MICUCCI GROCERY STORE
961 Riverside St, Portland, ME 04103-1070
Tel (207) 775-1854 *Founded/Ownrshp* 1950
Sales 20.6MM^E *EMP* 43
SIC 5149 Macaroni
Pr: Bruce Micucci
**Treas:* Leo Micucci Jr
**VP:* Richard Micucci

MID AM
See MID-AM BUILDING SUPPLY INC

D-U-N-S 80-731-3296
MID AMERICA AGRI PRODUCTS/WHEATLAND LLC
76080 Road 338, Madrid, NE 69150-4014
Tel (308) 326-4570 *Founded/Ownrshp* 2005
Sales 55.6MM^E *EMP* 33
SIC 5172 Gasoline
Genl Mgr: Mike Kluthe
Prd Mgr: Marge Czaplewski
Prd Mgr: Richard Dike

MID AMERICA BUILDING PDTS DIV
See TAPCO HOLDINGS INC

D-U-N-S 07-392-2775
MID AMERICA CHRISTIAN UNIVERSITY (TX)
MACU
3500 Sw 119th St, Oklahoma City, OK 73170-4500
Tel (405) 691-3800 *Founded/Ownrshp* 1953, 1984
Sales 28.5MM *EMP* 139^E
Accts Hogantaylor Llp Oklahoma City
SIC 8221 University
Pr: John Fozard
CFO: Mici Sartin
CFO: Mici Sarton
**CFO:* Mickey Sirtin
Trst: Todd Braschler
Ofcr: Roy Anderson
Ofcr: Wesley Hinkston
Ofcr: Andrew Holt
VP: Sharon Lease
**VP:* Dr Ron Roddy
Assoc Dir: Amanda Harris

D-U-N-S 79-976-8361
MID AMERICA CLINICAL LABORATORIES LLC
MACL
2560 N Shadeland Ave B, Indianapolis, IN 46219-1706
Tel (317) 803-0056 *Founded/Ownrshp* 1997
Sales 38.6MM^E *EMP* 525
SIC 8071 8734 Medical laboratories; Medical laboratories; Testing laboratories
CEO: Dianne Vanness
CFO: Tom Kmetz
VP: Beth McCaslin
IT Man: Sue Word
Pathlgst: Indra F D

D-U-N-S 11-811-7522
MID AMERICA CORP
BURGER KING
2812 N Broadway St, Knoxville, TN 37917-3834
Tel (865) 524-3477 *Founded/Ownrshp* 1982
Sales 22.9MM^E *EMP* 1,000
SIC 5812 Fast-food restaurant, chain; Fast-food restaurant, chain
Pr: Merritt C Fore Jr
**Sec:* Gene B Camp
**VP:* Russ Seus

D-U-N-S 80-512-6307
MID AMERICA EYE & TISSUE BANK
MID AMERICA TRANPLANT SERIVCES
1110 Highlands Plaza Dr E, Saint Louis, MO 63110-1350
Tel (314) 735-8200 *Founded/Ownrshp* 1990
Sales 45.0MM *EMP* 2
SIC 8099 Organ bank; Organ bank
Ex Dir: Dean Kappel
**COO:* Diane Brockmeier

D-U-N-S 83-235-6203
MID AMERICA FREIGHT LOGISTICS LLC
900 S Highway Dr Ste 202, Fenton, MO 63026-2042
Tel (636) 226-4770 *Founded/Ownrshp* 2008
Sales 24.5MM^E *EMP* 52
SIC 4731 Brokers, shipping

D-U-N-S 09-152-7382
MID AMERICA HEALTH CARE LIMITED PARTNERSHIP
MARYMOUNT MANOR
1749 Gilsinn Ln, Fenton, MO 63026-2008
Tel (636) 349-2311 *Founded/Ownrshp* 1977
Sales 12.8MM^E *EMP* 450
SIC 8051 Convalescent home with continuous nursing care; Convalescent home with continuous nursing care
Pt: Charles Riley
Pt: Elaine Spence

D-U-N-S 07-990-3118 IMP
MID AMERICA MOTORWORKS INC
17082 N Us Hwy 45 Pl, Effingham, IL 62401
Tel (217) 540-4200 *Founded/Ownrshp* 1972
Sales 56.2MM^E *EMP* 80^E
SIC 5013 5961 Automotive supplies & parts; Catalog sales
Pr: Michael Yager
Snr Mgr: Josh Yager

D-U-N-S 62-101-8506
MID AMERICA NATIONAL BANCSHARES INC
100 W Elm St, Canton, IL 61520-2514
Tel (309) 647-5000 *Founded/Ownrshp* 1981
Sales NA *EMP* 136
SIC 6021 National commercial banks; National commercial banks
Pr: James Fassino
CFO: Ken Long

D-U-N-S 08-213-3604 IMP
MID AMERICA PIPE FABRICATING & SUPPLY LLC
2674 Nw Highway 102, Scammon, KS 66773-2222
Tel (620) 827-6121 *Founded/Ownrshp* 1983
Sales 44.7MM^E *EMP* 140
SIC 3498 3443 Fabricated pipe & fittings; Industrial vessels, tanks & containers; Fabricated pipe & fittings; Industrial vessels, tanks & containers

D-U-N-S 00-228-9449
MID AMERICA REHABILITATION HOSPITAL
5701 W 110th St, Overland Park, KS 66211-2503
Tel (913) 491-2482 *Founded/Ownrshp* 2007
Sales 33.4MM *EMP* 44^E
SIC 8049 8093 8322 Physical therapist; Rehabilitation center, outpatient treatment; Rehabilitation services; Physical therapist; Rehabilitation center, outpatient treatment; Rehabilitation services
CEO: Kristen De Hart
Dir Risk M: Kristin Barret
Dir Case M: Casandra Nuzic
Dir Soc: Casey Muzic
Phys Thrpy: Paul Matlack

D-U-N-S 00-616-0949
MID AMERICA STEEL INC (ND)
92 Np Ave N, Fargo, ND 58102-4832
Tel (701) 232-8831 *Founded/Ownrshp* 1905
Sales 42.0MM *EMP* 153
SIC 3443 3441 3599 1799 Fabricated plate work (boiler shop); Fabricated structural metal; Machine shop, jobbing & repair; Welding on site; Fabricated plate work (boiler shop); Fabricated structural metal; Machine shop, jobbing & repair; Welding on site
Pr: Lee Holsghuh
**Treas:* John Simonson
**VP:* Eric Rude
**VP:* James E Simonson
Prd Mgr: Dave Roth

MID AMERICA TRANPLANT SERIVCES
See MID AMERICA EYE & TISSUE BANK

MID AMERICA TRUSS
See INDEVCO INC

D-U-N-S 94-771-5686
MID AMERICAN RESTAURANTS INC
IKE'S
1650 Gladewood Dr, Alpharetta, GA 30005-7228
Tel (770) 752-9530 *Founded/Ownrshp* 1996
Sales 15.1MM^E *EMP* 550
SIC 5812 Restaurant, family: chain; Restaurant, family: chain
Pr: Haig Antranikian
CFO: Jon Girma

MID ATLANTIC CARS
See BROWN AUTOMOTIVE GROUP LTD

D-U-N-S 09-536-9393
MID ATLANTIC FARM CREDIT INC
411 W Roseville Rd, Lancaster, PA 17601-3129
Tel (717) 291-0618 *Founded/Ownrshp* 1933
Sales NA *EMP* 81
Accts Pricewater House Coopers Llp
SIC 6159 Agricultural credit institutions; Agricultural credit institutions
Pr: Philip W Kimmel
**CFO:* Dianne Spatcher
Sr VP: James Aird
Sr VP: Sonia Arteaga
**Sr VP:* James Jonik
IT Man: Danny Ross

D-U-N-S 05-672-8448
MID ATLANTIC INDUSTRIAL EQUIPMENT LTD
1231 Wallace St, York, PA 17403-1237
Tel (717) 846-2375 *Founded/Ownrshp* 2010
Sales 23.9MM^E *EMP* 35
SIC 5046 Commercial equipment
CEO: David Haight
**CFO:* David A Lang

D-U-N-S 10-795-5622
MID ATLANTIC LOGISTICS INC
8501 River Rd, Pennsauken, NJ 08110-3325
Tel (856) 665-1557 *Founded/Ownrshp* 2002
Sales 30.0MM *EMP* 4
SIC 4214 Local trucking with storage
Pr: Frank Stech Jr
**VP:* William Stech

D-U-N-S 18-854-7145
■ MID ATLANTIC MEDICAL SERVICES LLC
(*Suby of* UNITEDHEALTH GROUP INC) ★
800 King Farm Blvd # 600, Rockville, MD 20850-5979
Tel (301) 990-3844 *Founded/Ownrshp* 2004
Sales NA *EMP* 3,315
SIC 6324 Health maintenance organization (HMO), insurance only; Health maintenance organization (HMO), insurance only
Ch Bd: Mark D Groban MD
Pr: Thomas Barbera
Sr VP: Debbie J Hulen
Exec: Robert E Foss

MID ATLANTIC SPECIALITIES
See MAS MARKETING NETWORK

D-U-N-S 11-736-7201
MID ATLANTIC STORAGE SYSTEMS INC
1551 Robinson Rd Se, Wshngtn CT Hs, OH 43160-9201
Tel (740) 335-2019 *Founded/Ownrshp* 1984
Sales 27.5MM^E *EMP* 75
SIC 1791 Storage tanks, metal: erection
Pr: Jerry Morris
**Sec:* Jeanette Morris
**VP:* John Fox
VP: Gary Mann
Manager: Greg Mullins

D-U-N-S 02-081-7445
MID CENTRAL OPERATING ENGINEERS
1100 Poplar St Ste A, Terre Haute, IN 47807-4566
Tel (812) 232-4384 *Founded/Ownrshp* 2010
Sales 66.1MM *EMP* 12
SIC 8711 Engineering services

D-U-N-S 04-404-9740
MID CENTURY INSURANCE CO (CA)
(*Suby of* FARMERS INSURANCE EXCHANGE) ★
4680 Wilshire Blvd, Los Angeles, CA 90010-3807
Tel (323) 932-7116 *Founded/Ownrshp* 1953
Sales NA *EMP* 250
SIC 6331 6351 Automobile insurance; Fidelity insurance; Automobile insurance; Fidelity insurance
Sr VP: Ron Coble
**Pr:* Bob Woudstra

D-U-N-S 13-032-0427
MID CENTURY INSURANCE CO OF TEXAS
(*Suby of* FARMERS GROUP INC) ★
15700 Long Vista Dr, Austin, TX 78728-3822
Tel (512) 244-4400 *Founded/Ownrshp* 1992
Sales NA *EMP* 400
SIC 6331 Automobile insurance; Automobile insurance
Pr: Erik James Snikeris

D-U-N-S 03-712-6240
MID CITIES MOTOR FREIGHT INC
CHEROKEE CARGO
6006 Lake Ave, Saint Joseph, MO 64504-1413
Tel (816) 238-8000 *Founded/Ownrshp* 1977
Sales 24.6MM^E *EMP* 140^E
SIC 4213 4731 Trucking, except local; Freight consolidation; Trucking, except local; Freight consolidation
Pr: Robert T Whetsell
Treas: Mary Jow Marek
**VP:* Roger S Whetsell
Genl Mgr: Jill Atha

D-U-N-S 00-386-1960
MID CITY ELECTRIC CO (OH)
MID CITY TECH
1099 Sullivant Ave, Columbus, OH 43223-1447
Tel (614) 221-5153 *Founded/Ownrshp* 1960
Sales 48.9MM^E *EMP* 200
SIC 1731

D-U-N-S 11-550-3448
MID CITY MEDICAL CENTER
3600 Florida Blvd, Baton Rouge, LA 70806-3842
Tel (225) 387-7000 *Founded/Ownrshp* 1999
Sales 15.6MM^E *EMP* 3,000
SIC 8062 General medical & surgical hospitals; General medical & surgical hospitals
Pr: William Holman
**Ex VP:* Dionne Viator

D-U-N-S 10-333-9305
MID CITY NISSAN INC
MID CITY SUBARU
4444 W Irving Park Rd, Chicago, IL 60641-2848
Tel (773) 286-6000 *Founded/Ownrshp* 1988
Sales 26.9MM^E *EMP* 75
SIC 5511 Automobiles, new & used; Automobiles, new & used
Pr: Michael Berman
**VP:* Mike Puffer
Sls Mgr: Malcoy Phurman
Sls Mgr: Brent Sullivan

D-U-N-S 80-488-2058
MID CITY STEEL CORP
275 State Rd, Westport, MA 02790-3500
Tel (508) 646-9800 *Founded/Ownrshp* 1993
Sales 27.7MM^E *EMP* 51
SIC 5051 Steel
Pr: Louis D Gitlin
**CFO:* Steve Quinn
**VP:* Mark I Gitlin
Mktg Dir: Heather Ruszczyk

MID CITY SUBARU
See MID CITY NISSAN INC

MID CITY TECH
See MID CITY ELECTRIC CO

D-U-N-S 18-068-1488
MID COAST HEALTH SERVICES
123 Medical Center Dr # 800, Brunswick, ME 04011-2652
Tel (207) 729-0181 *Founded/Ownrshp* 1987
Sales 8.0M *EMP* 1,500
SIC 8062 8082 8051 General medical & surgical hospitals; Home health care services; Skilled nursing care facilities; General medical & surgical hospitals; Home health care services; Skilled nursing care facilities
Pr: Herbert Paris
Treas: Cindy Smith
VP: Joe Grant
**VP:* Robert McCue
**VP:* Philip Ortolani
VP: Louis Skillings
Dir Bus: Sue Frasier
Prac Mgr: Fran Fontanez
Prac Mgr: Celeste Moreau
Off Mgr: Kelly Gleason
Off Mgr: Leeann Smith

D-U-N-S 07-173-2523
MID COAST HOSPITAL
123 Medical Center Dr, Brunswick, ME 04011-2652
Tel (207) 373-6000 *Founded/Ownrshp* 1907
Sales 131.1MM *EMP* 1,000^E
Accts Baker Newman & Noyes Portland
SIC 8062 General medical & surgical hospitals; General medical & surgical hospitals
CEO: Herbert Paris
Chf Rad: Jaime Kline
Chf Rad: Joan Sucliffe
VP: Phil Ortolani
Dir Inf Cn: Lorna Mackinnon
Dir Rx: Sue Fraser
Prac Mgr: Karen Ludwig
Prac Mgr: Joan Ouellette
Prac Mgr: Marcia Smith
Off Mgr: Leeann Smith
Dir QC: Carolyn Koepke

D-U-N-S 06-059-0965
MID COLUMBIA BUS CO INC
M & A AUTO
73458 Bus Barn Ln, Pendleton, OR 97801-9113
Tel (541) 384-2292 *Founded/Ownrshp* 1956
Sales 31.5MM^E *EMP* 161
SIC 5251 5531 4151 4142 4141 Hardware; Automotive parts; School buses; Bus charter service, except local; Local bus charter service; Hardware; Automotive parts; School buses; Bus charter service, except local; Local bus charter service
Ch Bd: Bill Flatt
**CEO:* Lewis Barnhart
**CEO:* Tony Barnhart
**COO:* Bruce Flatt
**Ch:* William Flatt
**VP:* Jeff Flatt

D-U-N-S 09-983-6629
MID COLUMBIA ENGINEERING INC
(*Suby of* NUVISION ENGINEERING INC) ★
2155 Robertson Dr, Richland, WA 99354-5306
Tel (509) 943-6706 *Founded/Ownrshp* 2009
Sales 34.8MM^E *EMP* 100

SIC 3541 3532 8711 Machine tools, metal cutting type; Mining machinery; Engineering services
CEO: Van Walker
**Pr:* Fred Yapuncich
CFO: Karen Litts
VP: Andy Dallas
**VP:* Julie Lingle
Mng Dir: Jim Stull
Genl Mgr: Robert Willard
QA Dir: Ann Langevin
Sys Mgr: Mark McLeod

D-U-N-S 09-288-4949
MID COLUMBIA FORKLIFT INC (WA)
MIDCO MATERIAL HANDLING
1007 N 16th Ave, Yakima, WA 98902-1351
Tel (509) 454-0100 *Founded/Ownrshp* 1978
Sales 60.1MM^E *EMP* 104
SIC 5084 Materials handling machinery; Materials handling machinery
Pr: Terrance Bolinger
**Pr:* P Duane Bolinger
**VP:* Phillip H Hanford
MIS Dir: William Berry

MID COLUMBIA MEDICAL CENTER
See HEALTH CARE FOR MID-COLUMBIA REGION

MID CONTINENT CABINETRY
See NORCRAFT COMPANIES LP

D-U-N-S 08-296-9205
MID CONTINENT INSURANCE CO
(*Suby of* FETTEROLF GROUP INC) ★
209 Georgian Pl, Somerset, PA 15501-1610
Tel (814) 445-8905 *Founded/Ownrshp* 1969, 1978
Sales NA *EMP* 50
SIC 6331 Assessment associations: fire, marine & casualty insurance; Automobile insurance
Pr: John Windel
**Sec:* Donald L Fetterolf
Mktg Dir: Rick Leonard
Board of Directors: Richard Ely, M Mitchell Fetterolf, Peter Hervoyavich Jr, Duane Snyder, Frank Thomas

MID CONTINENT NAIL
See MID CONTINENT STEEL & WIRE INC

D-U-N-S 08-871-0744 IMP
MID CONTINENT STEEL & WIRE INC
MID CONTINENT NAIL
(*Suby of* D W R STRL CON REINFORCING) ★
2700 Central Ave, Poplar Bluff, MO 63901-7033
Tel (573) 785-1478 *Founded/Ownrshp* 2012
Sales 35.0MM^E *EMP* 240^E
SIC 3315

D-U-N-S 14-481-4006
MID COUNTRY FINANCIAL CORP
201 2nd St Ste 950, Macon, GA 31201-8259
Tel (478) 746-8222 *Founded/Ownrshp* 2002
Sales 147.7MM^E *EMP* 1,490^E
SIC 7389 Financial services
Pr: Robert F Hatcher
CFO: David L Hall
Ex VP: Charles G Davis
Ex VP: Richard A Hills
Ex VP: Alison Labruyere
Ex VP: Marian M Mackle
Ex VP: Lee B Murphey
Ex VP: Hills Richard
VP: Darren Cantlay
Dir Risk M: Sandra Laughlin
Dir IT: Monica Cole
Board of Directors: Richard W Carpenter, James L Clayton, C Lee Ellis, R Kirby Godsey, Robert F Hatcher, Robert F Hatcher Jr, Carol A Jackson, Sherry A Kellett, Jerry A Newby

D-U-N-S 09-095-7697 IMP
MID COUNTRY MACHINERY INC
3478 5th Ave S, Fort Dodge, IA 50501-6427
Tel (319) 234-8710 *Founded/Ownrshp* 1997
Sales 22.0MM^E *EMP* 34
SIC 5082 Construction & mining machinery
Pr: Bud Pecoy
**Sec:* Lucas Peed
**VP:* Mark Swedlund
Sls Mgr: Aaron Reicherts

D-U-N-S 07-150-3882
MID DAKOTA CLINIC PC
401 N 9th St Lbby Ste, Bismarck, ND 58501-4506
Tel (701) 530-6000 *Founded/Ownrshp* 1971
Sales 58.1MM^E *EMP* 250
SIC 8011 Clinic, operated by physicians; Clinic, operated by physicians
Ch: Bruce Hettand
CFO: Craig Schaaf
Surgeon: Derek Kane
Obsttrcn: Rhonda McLean
Plas Surg: Steven Yearsley
Podiatrist: Gregory Iwaasa
Doctor: John Botsford
Doctor: Beatriz Canete
Doctor: John Erickstad
Doctor: Lisa Kozel
Diag Rad: Andrew Wilder

D-U-N-S 08-471-9640
MID FLORIDA COMMUNITY SERVICES INC
820 Kennedy Blvd, Brooksville, FL 34601-5704
Tel (352) 796-1425 *Founded/Ownrshp* 1968
Sales 23.5MM *EMP* 305
Accts Carr Riggs Ingram Enterprise
SIC 8322 Individual & family services; Individual & family services
Pr: Tommy Blackmon
**VP:* Doug Childers
IT Man: Patricia Keelean
Pgrm Dir: Veronica Agle
Pgrm Dir: Brenda Mobley

D-U-N-S 80-202-6356
MID HUDSON MEDICAL GROUP PC
600 Westage Bus Ctr Dr, Fishkill, NY 12524-2281
Tel (845) 231-5585 *Founded/Ownrshp* 2007
Sales NA *EMP* 550
SIC 8011 Offices & clinics of medical doctors

D-U-N-S 00-530-0442
MID HUTSON VALLEY CREDIT UNION
GMAC INSURANCE
1099 Morton Blvd, Kingston, NY 12401-1503
Tel (845) 336-4444 *Founded/Ownrshp* 1963
Sales NA *EMP* 2
SIC 6411 State credit unions; Insurance agents, brokers & service
**Ex VP:* Wayne Winkler

D-U-N-S 02-202-1315
MID IOWA COOPERATIVE
201 S Main St, Conrad, IA 50621-7757
Tel (641) 366-2740 *Founded/Ownrshp* 1907
Sales 108.3MM^E *EMP* 60
Accts Meriwether Wilson And Company
SIC 5153 5191 2048 Grains; Seeds: field, garden & flower; Feed; Fertilizer & fertilizer materials; Prepared feeds; Grains; Seeds: field, garden & flower; Feed; Fertilizer & fertilizer materials; Prepared feeds
Pr: Hank Miller
**CFO:* Shane Coughenour
**Ex Dir:* Cliss Kitzman
IT Man: Mark Kistenmacher

D-U-N-S 84-741-0289
MID ISLAND DIE CUTTING CORP
77 Schmitt Blvd, Farmingdale, NY 11735-1403
Tel (631) 293-0180 *Founded/Ownrshp* 1991
Sales 32.5MM^E *EMP* 200
SIC 2675 Die-cut paper & board; Die-cut paper & board
Pr: Robert Geier
Ofcr: Joe Sferlazza

D-U-N-S 07-455-0260
MID MICHIGAN MEDICAL CENTER-CLARE
MIDMICHIGAN MEDICAL CENTERS
703 N Mcewan St, Clare, MI 48617-1440
Tel (989) 802-5000 *Founded/Ownrshp* 1936
Sales 45.1MM^E *EMP* 306
Accts Andrews Hooper Pavlik Plc Sag
SIC 8062 General medical & surgical hospitals; General medical & surgical hospitals
Pr: Lawrence Barco
CFO: Ray Stover

MID NEBRASKA LUBRICANTS
See COOPERATIVE PRODUCERS INC

D-U-N-S 10-412-2408
MID OAKS INVESTMENTS LLC
750 W Lake Cook Rd # 460, Buffalo Grove, IL 60089-2090
Tel (847) 215-3475 *Founded/Ownrshp* 1997
Sales 509.8MM^E *EMP* 1,655
SIC 6726 3089 Investment offices; Plastic kitchenware, tableware & houseware; Investment offices; Plastic kitchenware, tableware & houseware
CEO: Wayne C Kocourek
**Pr:* Michael A Kocourek
VP: Nicolas Gallo
VP: Christopher Willis

D-U-N-S 82-981-4735
MID OCEAN MARINE LLC
132 Water St Ste 3, Norwalk, CT 06854-3139
Tel (203) 299-0598 *Founded/Ownrshp* 2007
Sales 25.0MM *EMP* 2
SIC 4424 Deep sea domestic transportation of freight; Deep sea domestic transportation of freight

D-U-N-S 16-908-4790 EXP
■ **MID PAC PETROLEUM LLC**
(*Suby of* KOKO OHA INVESTMENTS INC) ★
1100 Alakea St Ste 800, Honolulu, HI 96813-2851
Tel (808) 535-5999 *Founded/Ownrshp* 2003
Sales 101.9MM^E *EMP* 650^E
SIC 5984 5172 Liquefied petroleum gas dealers; Gases, liquefied petroleum (propane); Liquefied petroleum gas dealers; Gases, liquefied petroleum (propane)
Dir Bus: Keith Yoshida
IT Man: Mike Miyashiro

D-U-N-S 78-959-3985
▲ **MID PENN BANCORP INC**
349 Union St, Millersburg, PA 17061-1654
Tel (866) 642-7736 *Founded/Ownrshp* 1991
Sales NA *EMP* 203^E
Tkr Sym MPB *Exch* NGM
SIC 6022 State commercial banks; State commercial banks
Pr: Rory G Ritrievi
CFO: Edward P Williams
VP: Leonard K Beasom
VP: Ernest P Kemper

D-U-N-S 09-422-8590
■ **MID PENN BANK**
(*Suby of* MID PENN BANCORP INC) ★
349 Union St, Millersburg, PA 17061-1654
Tel (717) 896-3140 *Founded/Ownrshp* 1991
Sales NA *EMP* 156^E
Accts Bdo Usa Llp Harrisburg Penn
SIC 6022 8721 Accounting, auditing & bookkeeping; State commercial banks; State commercial banks; Accounting, auditing & bookkeeping
Pr: Rory G Ritrievi
**Ch Bd:* Edwin D Schlegel
V Ch: William Specht
CFO: Edward Williams
Bd of Dir: Matthew Desoto
Assoc VP: Beverly S Hand
Sr VP: Roberta Hoffman
**Sr VP:* Randall Klinger
VP: Kathy Bordner
VP: Claudia Boyer
VP: Natalie Falatek
VP: Cortney Wilbert
Exec: Brittany Giberti
Board of Directors: Robert E Klinger, John E Noone

MID PLAINS INDUSTRIES
See CENTRAL CONFINEMENT SERVICE LTD

MID RIVERS CHRYSLER JEEP DODGE
See ROYAL OAKS CHRYSLER-JEEP INC

D-U-N-S 17-520-4051
MID ROGUE MANAGEMENT SERVICES ORGANIZATION LLC
740 Se 7th St, Grants Pass, OR 97526-3102
Tel (541) 471-4106 *Founded/Ownrshp* 2007
Sales NA *EMP* 85^E
SIC 6321 Health insurance carriers
CEO: Douglas Flow
Software D: John Eyman

D-U-N-S 60-737-8858
MID SOUTH AG EQUIPMENT INC
4517 S Mendenhall Rd, Memphis, TN 38141-6702
Tel (901) 794-1350 *Founded/Ownrshp* 1986
Sales 32.0MM *EMP* 40
SIC 5083 7699 Agricultural machinery & equipment; Agricultural equipment repair services; Agricultural machinery & equipment; Agricultural equipment repair services
Pr: Gary Reid
Genl Mgr: Craig Herring

D-U-N-S 15-853-7944
MID SOUTH AUTO SALES OF NORTH MISS INC
2505 S Green St, Tupelo, MS 38801-6501
Tel (662) 844-5502 *Founded/Ownrshp* 1973
Sales 40.0MM *EMP* 5
SIC 5012 Automobiles & other motor vehicles; Automobiles & other motor vehicles
Pr: Jeff McCalab

MID SOUTH BAKING COMPANY
See BRYAN BAKING INC

D-U-N-S 07-130-1337
MID SOUTH BUILDING SUPPLY OF MARYLAND INC
5640 Sunnyside Ave Ste P, Beltsville, MD 20705-2213
Tel (301) 513-9000 *Founded/Ownrshp* 1998
Sales 44.1MM^E *EMP* 87
SIC 5031 5033 1793 Kitchen cabinets; Siding, wood; Windows; Siding, except wood; Glass & glazing work; Kitchen cabinets; Siding, wood; Windows; Siding, except wood; Glass & glazing work
Ch: Timothy Flynn
**Pr:* John A Briggs
**VP:* Daniel Flynn
Sls Mgr: Bill Russell

D-U-N-S 15-474-7364 EXP
MID SOUTH EXTRUSION INC
2015 Jackson St, Monroe, LA 71202-2533
Tel (318) 322-7239 *Founded/Ownrshp* 1987
Sales 71.6MM^E *EMP* 125
SIC 3081 Polyethylene film; Polyethylene film
CEO: Mark Anderson
**Pr:* Ronald A Mason
**CFO:* Ken Upshaw
**VP:* Scott Anderson
Prd Mgr: Jeff Kennedy
Ql Cn Mgr: Tim Frost

D-U-N-S 16-681-9458
MID SOUTH FOOD BANK
239 S Dudley St, Memphis, TN 38104-3203
Tel (901) 527-0841 *Founded/Ownrshp* 1988
Sales 30.8MM *EMP* 35
Accts Zoccola Kaplan Pllc Germantow
SIC 8322 Helping hand service (Big Brother, etc.); Helping hand service (Big Brother, etc.)
Pr: Estella Mayhue-Greer
Dir Vol: Paula Rushing
Pr: Marcia Wells
COO: Tonya Bradley
CFO: Doug McDonald
VP: David Stephens
Mktg Mgr: Andrew Bell

D-U-N-S 12-464-9232
MID SOUTH LUMBER INC
1115 C St, Meridian, MS 39301-5436
Tel (601) 483-4389 *Founded/Ownrshp* 1999
Sales 600.0MM *EMP* 150
SIC 2411 Logging; Logging
CEO: Ross York

D-U-N-S 03-041-7349
MID SOUTH REGIONAL BLOOD CENTER
LIFEBLOOD
1040 Madison Ave, Memphis, TN 38104-2106
Tel (901) 522-8585 *Founded/Ownrshp* 1948
Sales 21.2MM *EMP* 200
Accts Dixon Hughes Goodman Llp Memp
SIC 8099 Blood bank; Blood bank
CEO: Suzanne Berry-Buckley
COO: Daniel Garrick
Bd of Dir: Lisa Taylor
VP: Sandra Dorothy
Dir Lab: Robert Knox
QA Dir: Daphne Jarvis
Dir IT: Rusty Jones
IT Man: Barry Baskin
IT Man: Gail Moore
Sfty Mgr: Renisa Hoskins
Mktg Dir: Jason Sykes

D-U-N-S 03-551-5162
MID SOUTH SALES INC (AR)
BULK WAREHOUSE
243 County Road 414, Jonesboro, AR 72404-7508
Tel (870) 933-6457 *Founded/Ownrshp* 1962
Sales 156.6MM *EMP* 60
Accts Mayer Hoffman Mccann Pc Mem
SIC 5172 Petroleum products; Petroleum products
Ch: William Benton
**Pr:* Murray R Benton
**CFO:* Allen Crisp
**Bd of Dir:* Helen R Benton
**VP:* Perry Byrd
Brnch Mgr: Chuck Preslar
Off Mgr: Leonard Sharp
IT Man: Victoria Livingston
Plnt Mgr: Thomas Handy
Sls Mgr: Jim Sugg

D-U-N-S 10-629-8342 IMP
MID SOUTH TRANSPORT INC
2765 Profit Dr, Memphis, TN 38132-2202
Tel (901) 332-8600 *Founded/Ownrshp* 1986
Sales 26.8MM^E *EMP* 135
SIC 4213 Trucking, except local; Contract haulers; Trucking, except local; Contract haulers
Ch Bd: Jack E Henry
**Pr:* Ronald E Lancaster
Off Mgr: Eric Vaccariello
IT Man: Vickie Hall

D-U-N-S 04-700-3165
■ **MID STATE AUTOMOTIVE DISTRIBUTORS INC**
THE PARTS DIVISION
(*Suby of* OREILLY AUTO PARTS) ★
485 Craighead St, Nashville, TN 37204-2333
Tel (615) 383-8566 *Founded/Ownrshp* 2001
Sales 58.7MM^E *EMP* 1,000
SIC 5013 5531 Automotive supplies & parts; Automotive parts; Automotive supplies & parts; Automotive parts
CEO: David O'Reilly
**Ch Bd:* Lawrence P O'Reilly
**CFO:* James R Batten
IT Man: Cliff Dunn

MID STATE MACHINE & FABG
See MID-STATE MACHINE AND FABRICATING CORP

D-U-N-S 05-657-0054 IMP
MID STATE MACHINE PRODUCTS INC (ME)
83 Verti Dr, Winslow, ME 04901-0727
Tel (207) 873-6136 *Founded/Ownrshp* 1967, 1998
Sales 53.1MM^E *EMP* 225
SIC 3599 3545 Machine shop, jobbing & repair; Machine tool attachments & accessories; Machine shop, jobbing & repair; Machine tool attachments & accessories
Pr: Duane Pekar
QA Dir: Michael Cianchette

MID STATE SUPPLY
See YELLOW THUNDER CORP

D-U-N-S 93-340-1309
MID STATES OIL REFINING CO
5501 Pennington Ave, Baltimore, MD 21226-1615
Tel (410) 354-9500 *Founded/Ownrshp* 1995
Sales 20.9MM^E *EMP* 50
SIC 4953 Recycling, waste materials
Sls Mgr: Rick Bender

D-U-N-S 10-340-2608
MID VALLEY AGRICULTURAL SERVICES INC
16401 E Highway 26, Linden, CA 95236-9746
Tel (209) 931-7600 *Founded/Ownrshp* 1983
Sales 189.4MM^E *EMP* 125
Accts Croce & Company Stockton Cal
SIC 5191 Chemicals, agricultural; Chemicals, agricultural
Pr: Larry Beck
**VP:* Pete Bulthuis
Opers Mgr: Todd Hudelson
Opers Mgr: Randy Northcutt
Opers Mgr: Gene Silveria

D-U-N-S 15-508-4028
MID VALLEY HEALTH SYSTEM
1401 E 8th St, Weslaco, TX 78596-6640
Tel (956) 969-5112 *Founded/Ownrshp* 1996
Sales 109.5MM *EMP* 1,000
Accts Bkd Llp Houston Tx
SIC 6719 Investment holding companies, except banks; Investment holding companies, except banks
Pr: Robert W Vanderveer
**CFO:* Curtis Haley

MID VALLEY I P A
See MID VALLEY IPA INC

D-U-N-S 96-572-2044
MID VALLEY INDUSTRIES LLC
1151 Delanglade St, Kaukauna, WI 54130-4122
Tel (920) 759-0314 *Founded/Ownrshp* 1997
Sales 35.1MM^E *EMP* 100
SIC 3599 Machine shop, jobbing & repair
Pr: Kevin Schmidt
VP: Dan Behnke
VP: John Mayer
**VP:* Jeff Nelson
VP: Doug Pribyl
CTO: Scott Verstegen
Dir IT: Mark Hostettler
Sales Exec: Tony Coats

D-U-N-S 83-138-3443
MID VALLEY IPA INC
MID VALLEY I P A
2995 Ryan Dr Se Ste 200, Salem, OR 97301-5157
Tel (503) 371-7701 *Founded/Ownrshp* 1976
Sales 245.4MM *EMP* 200
SIC 8011 Primary care medical clinic
Pr: Steven Paulissen
**CFO:* Dean Andretta

MID VALLEY PACKAGING & SUP CO
See GAHVEJIAN ENTERPRISES INC

D-U-N-S 01-461-5103
MID VALLEY PLASTERING INC
15300 Mckinley Ave, Lathrop, CA 95330-8782
Tel (209) 858-9766 *Founded/Ownrshp* 1998
Sales 31.1MM^E *EMP* 400
SIC 1742 Plastering, plain or ornamental; Plastering, plain or ornamental
Pr: Jeff Gann
**Sec:* Kevin Gann
**VP:* Jeremy Gann
Genl Mgr: Jorge Vera

MID VALLEY PRODUCTS
See EURPAC SERVICE INC

D-U-N-S 82-498-3860
MID VENTURES INC
MICROTEK
2001 Bttrfeld Rd Ste 1500, Downers Grove, IL 60515
Tel (630) 719-0211 *Founded/Ownrshp* 1991
Sales 35.0MM *EMP* 100
SIC 7389 7376 Convention & show services; Computer facilities management; Convention & show services; Computer facilities management
CEO: Donald Slivensky
**Pr:* Hugh McCullen
IT Man: Edwin Romero
Tech Mgr: Bob Moser
Tech Mgr: Kerrell Ray
Tech Mgr: Gilbert Roman

MID WEST BANK N.A.
See MIDWEST BANK NA

MID WEST FABRICATING CO
See MID-WEST FABRICATING CO

MID WEST HOLDINGS
See MIDAMERICA DIVISION INC

MID WEST RAILROAD TIE SALES
See NATIONAL SALVAGE & SERVICE CORP

MID WEST TERMINAL
See JSC TERMINAL LLC

D-U-N-S 07-642-7962
MID WILLAMETTE VALLEY COMMUNITY ACTION AGENCY INC
COMMUNITY ACTION HEADSTART
2475 Center St Ne, Salem, OR 97301-4520
Tel (503) 585-6232 *Founded/Ownrshp* 1965
Sales 22.2MM *EMP* 250
Accts Grove Mueller & Swank Pc Sale
SIC 8399 Antipoverty board; Antipoverty board
CFO: Nancy Cain
IT Man: Kathy Chase
Pgrm Dir: Susan Maxwell

D-U-N-S 02-991-7945 IMP/EXP
MID-AM BUILDING SUPPLY INC
MID AM
1615 Omar Bradley Rd, Moberly, MO 65270-9406
Tel (660) 263-2140 *Founded/Ownrshp* 1967
Sales 235.3MM^E *EMP* 400
SIC 5031 Building materials, exterior; Building materials, interior; Millwork; Building materials, exterior; Building materials, interior; Millwork
Pr: Joseph F Knaebel
CFO: John Rakers
**Treas:* James Deresinski
**VP:* Lilly Elliott
**VP:* Alan Knaebel
Sfty Dirs: Sean Evans
Mktg Mgr: Dave Elliott
Mktg Mgr: Gene Race
Sales Asso: Mallory Downing
Sales Asso: Tim Elliot
Sales Asso: Susie Hoffmeister

D-U-N-S 62-076-7533
MID-AM METAL FORMING INC
1108 Center Rd, Rogersville, MO 65742-7106
Tel (417) 753-2888 *Founded/Ownrshp* 1990
Sales 21.6MM^E *EMP* 95
SIC 3354 Aluminum extruded products; Aluminum extruded products
Pr: Dave Johnson
**Sec:* Michelle Williams
Genl Mgr: Chris Johnson

D-U-N-S 08-953-5694
■ **MID-AMERICA APARTMENT COMMUNITIES INC**
(*Suby of* MID-AMERICA APARTMENTS, L.P.)
6584 Poplar Ave Ste 340, Memphis, TN 38138-3687
Tel (901) 682-6600 *Founded/Ownrshp* 1994
Sales 989.3MM *EMP* 2,090^E
Tkr Sym MAA *Exch* NYS
SIC 6798 Real estate investment trusts; Real estate investment trusts
Ch Bd: H Eric Bolton Jr
COO: Thomas L Grimes Jr
CFO: Albert M Campbell III
Ex VP: Robert J Delpriore
Sr VP: Diane Chastain
Sr VP: Larry Davis
Sr VP: Mica Holton
Sr VP: Cynthia McMillion
Sr VP: Glenn Russell
VP: Tim Argo
VP: Doug Clark
VP: Robert Donnelly
VP: Dennis Duke
VP: Richard Hewitt
VP: Cynthia Thompson
VP: Linda Thompson
VP: Ray Thornton
Board of Directors: John W Spiegel, Alan B Graf Jr, Ralph Horn, James K Lowder, Thomas H Lowder, Claude B Nielsen, Philip W Norwood, W Reid Sanders, William B Sansom, Gary Shorb

MID-AMERICA COFFEE SERVICE
See ROSE COFFEE CO

D-U-N-S 62-638-8441 IMP
MID-AMERICA DOOR CO
1001 W Hartford Ave, Ponca City, OK 74601-1131
Tel (580) 765-9994 *Founded/Ownrshp* 1991
Sales 20.2MM^E *EMP* 90
SIC 3442 5072 Garage doors, overhead: metal; Rolling doors for industrial buildings or warehouses, metal; Hardware
Ch Bd: Myron Wilson
**Pr:* John Earnest
**CFO:* Carl Christensen
CFO: Corey Phipps
VP: Gregory Forton

MID-AMERICA FARM AND RANCH
See MID-AMERICA FEEDS INC

D-U-N-S 03-310-4746
MID-AMERICA FEEDS INC
MID-AMERICA FARM AND RANCH
101 E Sequoyah St, Talala, OK 74080-9401
Tel (918) 275-4292 *Founded/Ownrshp* 1984
Sales 40.0MM *EMP* 45^E
SIC 2048

D-U-N-S 96-715-1866
MID-AMERICA FOOD DISTRIBUTOR LLC
MAW
3101 S Van Buren St, Enid, OK 73703-8358
Tel (580) 237-1040 *Founded/Ownrshp* 2010
Sales 24.5MM^E *EMP* 40
SIC 5141 Groceries, general line

MID-AMERICA FUEL CENTER
See C C DILLON CO

D-U-N-S 18-456-8053
MID-AMERICA MANAGEMENT CORP
(*Suby of* INLAND PROPERTY MANAGEMENT INC) ★
2907 Butterfield Rd # 110, Oak Brook, IL 60523-1175
Tel (630) 574-2400 *Founded/Ownrshp* 1998
Sales 7.5MM^E *EMP* 500
SIC 6531 Real estate managers: Real estate managers
Pr: Joann Armenta
**Pr:* Thomas Mc Guinness
Sr VP: Richard E Kehoe
**Sr VP:* Sharen Mangiameli
**VP:* Robert M Barg
VP: Shari Juratovac

D-U-N-S 10-762-8158
MID-AMERICA OVERSEAS INC
M A O
650 E Devon Ave Ste 150, Itasca, IL 60143-1265
Tel (630) 285-9083 *Founded/Ownrshp* 1976
Sales 114.1MM^E *EMP* 200^E
SIC 4731 Foreign freight forwarding; Customhouse brokers; Foreign freight forwarding; Customhouse brokers
CEO: Minte Stienstra
**Pr:* Burkard Schmitt
**CFO:* Michael Mierwinski
Rgnl Mgr: Henrik Mikuta
Brnch Mgr: Imelda Abrigo
Brnch Mgr: Milo Ott
Brnch Mgr: Thorsten Scholz
Brnch Mgr: Resa Silcox
Brnch Mgr: Laura Yates
Opers Mgr: Bahar Bakhoda
Opers Mgr: Tanneshia Whigham

D-U-N-S 12-710-8715 IMP
MID-AMERICA PACKAGING LLC
2127 Reiser Ave Se, New Philadelphia, OH 44663-3331
Tel (330) 963-4199 *Founded/Ownrshp* 2002
Sales 81.4MM^E *EMP* 650
SIC 2674 Bags: uncoated paper & multiwall
CEO: James V Livingston
Plnt Mgr: Dave Tallarico

D-U-N-S 15-209-5253
MID-AMERICA PAPER RECYCLING CO INC
3865 W 41st St, Chicago, IL 60632-3401
Tel (773) 890-5454 *Founded/Ownrshp* 1973
Sales 25.0MM *EMP* 31
SIC 4953

D-U-N-S 06-395-4309
MID-AMERICA PARTS DISTRIBUTORS CORP
UNION AUTO PARTS
(*Suby of* DCA) ★
1901 I A C Dr, Memphis, TN 38116-3600
Tel (901) 395-0111 *Founded/Ownrshp* 2012
Sales 48.5MM^E *EMP* 142
SIC 5013 Automotive supplies & parts; Automotive supplies & parts
Pr: Mike Sneed
**Sec:* Bill Jorgensen
**VP:* Mike Langley

D-U-N-S 14-523-7876
■ **MID-AMERICA PIPELINE CO LLC**
(*Suby of* ENTERPRISE PRODUCTS CO) ★
1100 La St Ste 1000, Houston, TX 77002
Tel (713) 880-6500 *Founded/Ownrshp* 2002
Sales 95.7MM^E *EMP* 250^E
SIC 4922 Pipelines, natural gas; Pipelines, natural gas
Pr: J M Collingsworth
Treas: Bryan F Bulawa
Sr VP: Michael J Knesek

D-U-N-S 14-429-7129
MID-AMERICA PIPELINE CONSTRUCTION INC
5660 N 433 Rd, Adair, OK 74330-2739
Tel (918) 825-0075 *Founded/Ownrshp* 2003
Sales 36.9MM^E *EMP* 116
SIC 1623 Pipeline construction
Pr: Jim Boyles
**VP:* Randall Shultz

D-U-N-S 07-165-1988
MID-AMERICA RESTAURANT VENTURES INC (OH)
PONDEROSA STEAKHOUSE
601 E Main St, Jackson, OH 45640-2128
Tel (740) 288-1710 *Founded/Ownrshp* 1973
Sales 12.7MM^E *EMP* 600
SIC 5812 Steak restaurant; Steak restaurant
CEO: James M Delmore
**Pr:* Doug Robertson
**Ex VP:* Ervin P Campbell

MID-AMERICA STAINLESS
See MID-AMERICA STEEL CORP

D-U-N-S 05-581-2408
MID-AMERICA STEEL CORP
MID-AMERICA STAINLESS
20900 Saint Clair Ave, Cleveland, OH 44117-1020
Tel (216) 692-3800 *Founded/Ownrshp* 1971
Sales 65.5MM^E *EMP* 50
SIC 5051 3469 3316 3312 Metals service centers & offices; Sheets, metal; Metal stampings; Cold finishing of steel shapes; Blast furnaces & steel mills
Pr Dir: Jim Cash
VP: Jonathan Kaufman
IT Man: Raymond Cox

D-U-N-S 84-850-5582
■ **MID-AMERICA TELEPHONE INC**
TDS
(*Suby of* TDS TELECOMMUNICATIONS CORP) ★
110 W 5th St, Stonewall, OK 74871
Tel (608) 831-1000 *Founded/Ownrshp* 1992
Sales 853.0MM *EMP* 2,700
SIC 4813 Data telephone communications; Data telephone communications
Pr: David Wittwer
Sec: Debbie Meier

D-U-N-S 07-992-9857
MID-AMERICA TRANSPLANT SERVICES (MO)
MTS
1110 Highlands Plaza Dr E # 100, Saint Louis, MO 63110-1350
Tel (314) 735-8200 *Founded/Ownrshp* 1974
Sales 38.5MM *EMP* 100
SIC 8099 Medical services organization
Pr: Dean F Kappel

MID-AMERICA YACHT SALES
See BILL COLLINS FORD INC

D-U-N-S 79-617-1106
MID-AMERICAN CLEANING CONTRACTORS INC
447 N Elizabeth St, Lima, OH 45801-4336
Tel (419) 229-3899 *Founded/Ownrshp* 1991
Sales 22.9MM^E *EMP* 625
SIC 7349 Janitorial service, contract basis; Janitorial service, contract basis
Pr: John Whittacker
**CEO:* Harold Breidenbach
**Treas:* Troy Breidenbach
Genl Mgr: Ken Piercefield

D-U-N-S 06-994-9345 IMP
MID-AMERICAN ELEVATOR CO INC
USA HOIST COMPANY
820 N Wolcott Ave, Chicago, IL 60622-4937
Tel (773) 486-6900 *Founded/Ownrshp* 1985
Sales 57.5MM^E *EMP* 230
SIC 1796 7699 3823 3535 3534 Elevator installation & conversion; Elevators: inspection, service & repair; Controllers for process variables, all types; Conveyors & conveying equipment; Elevators & moving stairways; Elevator installation & conversion; Elevators: inspection, service & repair; Controllers for process variables, all types; Conveyors & conveying equipment; Elevators & moving stairways
Pr: Brian Selke
**Ch Bd:* Robert R Bailey Jr
**Pr:* Robert R Bailey III
**Sec:* Cullen Bailey
**VP:* Greg Selke
IT Man: Mark Callahan
Opers Mgr: Tim Moran

MID-AMERICAN GROUP
See MID-AMERICAN GUNITE INC

D-U-N-S 03-056-6780 IMP
MID-AMERICAN GROWERS INC
14240 Greenhouse Ave, Granville, IL 61326-9404
Tel (815) 339-6831 *Founded/Ownrshp* 1975
Sales NA *EMP* 280
SIC 0181 Ornamental nursery products; Bedding plants, growing of; Shrubberies grown under cover (e.g. greenhouse production); Flowers: grown under cover (e.g. greenhouse production)

D-U-N-S 10-840-7453
MID-AMERICAN GUNITE INC
MID-AMERICAN GROUP
8475 Port Sunlight Rd, Newport, MI 48166-9106
Tel (734) 586-8868 *Founded/Ownrshp* 1983
Sales 39.6MM^E *EMP* 325
SIC 1771 Gunite contractor; Gunite contractor
Ch Bd: Larry Masserant
CFO: Regan Morin
**VP:* Frank Kuderik
**VP:* Keith Masserant
**Prin:* Thomas Thompson

D-U-N-S 03-552-4487
MID-AMERICAN MOTORS INC
TIM PARKER CHRYSLER DODGE JEEP
4722 Central Ave, Hot Springs, AR 71913-7406
Tel (501) 525-0777 *Founded/Ownrshp* 1958
Sales 24.5MM^E *EMP* 60
SIC 5511 7532 7514 5531 5521 5013 Automobiles, new & used; Body shop, automotive; Passenger car rental; Automotive parts; Automobiles, used cars only; Automotive supplies & parts; Automobiles, new & used; Body shop, automotive; Passenger car rental; Automotive parts; Automobiles, used cars only; Automotive supplies & parts
Pr: Tim Parker
Off Mgr: Susie Croasdall

D-U-N-S 96-272-0525
MID-AMERICAN REAL ESTATE GROUP LLC
520 W 103rd St Ste 3, Kansas City, MO 64114-4503
Tel (816) 786-9273 *Founded/Ownrshp* 2010
Sales 55.8MM *EMP* 165
SIC 6798 Real estate investment trusts; Real estate investment trusts
V Ch: Kim Jackson

D-U-N-S 83-647-9261
MID-AMERICAN WATER & PLUMBING INC
5009 Murray Rd, Manhattan, KS 66503-9782
Tel (785) 537-1072 *Founded/Ownrshp* 1990
Sales 29.4MM^E *EMP* 45
SIC 5074 1711 Water softeners; Plumbing contractors
Pr: Robert Cansler
Exec: Kathy Burgess
**Prin:* Bruce Ewing

D-U-N-S 12-418-3844
MID-AMERICAN WATER OF WAUCONDA INC
1125 N Old Rand Rd Fl 1, Wauconda, IL 60084-1203
Tel (847) 487-7766 *Founded/Ownrshp* 1998
Sales 30.0MM *EMP* 12
SIC 5074 5085 5084 Plumbing fittings & supplies; Gaskets & seals; Machine tools & metalworking machinery; Plumbing fittings & supplies; Gaskets & seals; Machine tools & metalworking machinery
Pr: Charles J Dixon Jr
**Treas:* Richard Bennett
Sales Asso: Reg Rand

D-U-N-S 14-824-9357
MID-ATLANTIC AIR INC
MAAMECH
11111 Pepper Rd, Hunt Valley, MD 21031-1203
Tel (410) 329-1139 *Founded/Ownrshp* 2004
Sales 48.2MM^E *EMP* 139
SIC 1711 Heating & air conditioning contractors; Heating & air conditioning contractors
Pr: Richard Leeland
**COO:* Michael J Mohnacs
**CFO:* George Petty
VP: David Zeck
Exec: Michael McBain
Prd Mgr: Jim Edwards
Prd Mgr: Daniel Plona
Sls&Mrk Ex: Shannon Ruberry
Snr PM: John Kipferl
Snr Mgr: Michael Sharbaugh

D-U-N-S 10-911-7882
MID-ATLANTIC BAKING CO LLC
(*Suby of* AUTOMATIC ROLLS OF NEWYORK) ★
3800 E Baltimore St, Baltimore, MD 21224-1542
Tel (410) 649-1177 *Founded/Ownrshp* 2001
Sales 50.1MM^E *EMP* 200
SIC 2051 5149 Bread, cake & related products; Bread, all types (white, wheat, rye, etc): fresh or frozen; Rolls, bread type: fresh or frozen; Bakery products; Bread, cake & related products; Bread, all types (white, wheat, rye, etc): fresh or frozen; Rolls, bread type: fresh or frozen; Bakery products
Plnt Mgr: Grant West
Snr Mgr: Ned Dearden

D-U-N-S 96-837-1950
■ **MID-ATLANTIC CONVENIENCE STORES LLC**
MACS CHESTERFIELD CO
(*Suby of* SUNOCO INC) ★
1011 Boulder Springs Dr, North Chesterfield, VA 23225-4950
Tel (877) 468-7797 *Founded/Ownrshp* 2013
Sales 15.0MM^E *EMP* 400
SIC 5411 Convenience stores, chain; Convenience stores, chain
Prin: Brad Williams
**CFO:* Don Bassell
**Sr VP:* Lynn Lambrecht
**Sr VP:* Neil McCarthy
**Sr VP:* Liza Salaria
**Dir Sec:* Chad Lusk

D-U-N-S 02-155-1812
MID-ATLANTIC COOPERATIVE SOLUTIONS INC
AERO ENERGY
230 Lincoln Way E, New Oxford, PA 17350-1213
Tel (717) 624-4311 *Founded/Ownrshp* 2000
Sales 57.6MM^E *EMP* 104
Accts Adams Jenkins And Cheatham
SIC 5172 Petroleum brokers; Petroleum brokers
Pr: Frederick Hubbard
**Pr:* Thompson Washburn
**CFO:* James Sperry
**Treas:* Joseph Cole
**Sec:* Steve Rasmussen
**V Ch Bd:* A Joseph Slater
Brnch Mgr: John Smithson
Dir IT: Bryan Salsgiver
Mktg Mgr: Dawn Britcher
Sls Mgr: Joseph Mailey

D-U-N-S 05-474-5948 IMP
MID-ATLANTIC CRANE AND EQUIPMENT CO (NC)
3224 Northside Dr, Raleigh, NC 27615-4125
Tel (919) 790-3535 *Founded/Ownrshp* 1980
Sales 25.4MM^E *EMP* 25
SIC 5084 Materials handling machinery; Cranes, industrial
Pr: Mitchell E Filip
Dir IT: Dan Decremer

MID-ATLANTIC HEALTH CARE
See PARKHOUSE NURSING AND REHABILITATION CENTER LP

D-U-N-S 96-834-7281
MID-ATLANTIC HEALTH CARE LLC
1922 Greenspring Dr Ste 3, Lutherville Timonium, MD 21093-7603
Tel (410) 308-2300 *Founded/Ownrshp* 2003
Sales 1.0MM^E *EMP* 1,895^E
SIC 8062 General medical & surgical hospitals
COO: Michael Mahon
CFO: Howard Friner
CFO: Scott D Potter
VP: Donna Rooney

D-U-N-S 80-497-3295
MID-ATLANTIC HOME HEALTH NETWORK INC
25 Winchester St, Warrenton, VA 20186-2825
Tel (540) 347-4901 *Founded/Ownrshp* 1982
Sales 22.8MM^E *EMP* 2,000
SIC 8082 Home health care services; Home health care services
Ch Bd: Phillip Warman
CFO: Chich Gilpin

D-U-N-S 00-583-4242 IMP
MID-ATLANTIC INFRASTRUCTURE SYSTEMS INC (NC)
MIS
975 Pinebrook Knolls Dr, Winston Salem, NC 27105-5076
Tel (336) 251-1017 *Founded/Ownrshp* 2000
Sales 59.9MM^E *EMP* 142
SIC 1623 Underground utilities contractor; Underground utilities contractor
Pr: David T McGee
**VP:* Brad Boone

D-U-N-S 08-404-2605
MID-ATLANTIC MECHANICAL INC
307 Gravel Hill Rd, Monroe Township, NJ 08831-8823
Tel (732) 521-2150 *Founded/Ownrshp* 1977
Sales 22.7MM^E *EMP* 50
SIC 1711

D-U-N-S 00-443-6981 IMP
MID-ATLANTIC PETROLEUM PROPERTIES LLC (MD)
SUNOCO
12311 Middlebrook Rd, Germantown, MD 20874-2605
Tel (301) 972-4116 *Founded/Ownrshp* 1995
Sales 41.9MM^E *EMP* 75
SIC 5541 6512 Filling stations, gasoline; Property operation, retail establishment
COO: Pete Troilo
CFO: May Horcasitas
CFO: May M Au Huie

D-U-N-S 00-312-6943
MID-ATLANTIC PRINTERS LTD (VA)
503 3rd St, Altavista, VA 24517-1462
Tel (434) 369-6633 *Founded/Ownrshp* 1910, 1967
Sales 33.9MM^E *EMP* 110
SIC 2752 2741 Commercial printing, offset; Newsletter publishing; Commercial printing, offset; Newsletter publishing
Pr: Charles R Edwards
**Treas:* Nancy T Edwards
VP Mfg: Stanley Weeks
QC Dir: Tammy Shelhorse
Manager: Mark Peters

D-U-N-S 16-133-6305
MID-ATLANTIC RESTAURANTS LLC
275 Century Cir Ste 102, Louisville, CO 80027-9453
Tel (303) 396-0150 *Founded/Ownrshp* 2001
Sales 4.5MM^E *EMP* 325
SIC 5812 Eating places; Eating places

D-U-N-S 78-041-0676
■ **MID-ATLANTIC TRUCK CENTRE INC**
(*Suby of* NAVISTAR INC) ★
525 W Linden Ave, Linden, NJ 07036-6507
Tel (908) 862-2525 *Founded/Ownrshp* 1998
Sales 29.8MM^E *EMP* 60
SIC 5511 Trucks, tractors & trailers: new & used; Trucks, tractors & trailers: new & used
Pr: Eugene Sidor
**Sec:* Shaune Swift

MID-ATLANTIC WASTE SYSTEMS
See THC ENTERPRISES INC

MID-ATLNTIC CONVENIENCE STORES
See UPPYS CONVENIENCE STORES INC

MID-CAPE HOME CENTERS
See NICKERSON LUMBER CO

D-U-N-S 10-188-5366
MID-CAROLINA STEEL & RECYCLING CO INC
7425 Fairfield Rd, Columbia, SC 29203-9543
Tel (803) 786-9888 *Founded/Ownrshp* 1983
Sales 22.9MM *EMP* 48^E
Accts Burkett Burkett & Burkett Cpa
SIC 3341 3446 5051 Secondary nonferrous metals; Architectural metalwork; Stairs, fire escapes, balconies, railings & ladders; Fences, gates, posts & flagpoles; Ornamental metalwork; Steel; Secondary nonferrous metals; Architectural metalwork; Stairs, fire escapes, balconies, railings & ladders; Fences, gates, posts & flagpoles; Ornamental metalwork; Steel
Pr: Fred Seidenberg
**VP:* Kurt Richardson

D-U-N-S 07-888-5994
MID-CENTRAL ENERGY SERVICES LLC
727 N Morgan Rd, Oklahoma City, OK 73127-7142
Tel (405) 815-4041 *Founded/Ownrshp* 2013
Sales 51.8MM^E *EMP* 99
SIC 1389 Servicing oil & gas wells
Prin: Nick Armoudian
Prin: Antranik Armoudian

D-U-N-S 07-878-5993
MID-CENTRAL PRODUCTION LLC
(*Suby of* JBS UNITED INC) ★
4310 W State Road 38, Sheridan, IN 46069-9639
Tel (317) 758-2699 *Founded/Ownrshp* 1988
Sales 25.0MM *EMP* 4
SIC 5141 Food brokers

D-U-N-S 00-610-6496
MID-CITY FOUNDRY CO
UNITED DIVISION
1521 W Bruce St, Milwaukee, WI 53204-1224
Tel (414) 645-1327 *Founded/Ownrshp* 1992
Sales 23.1MM^E *EMP* 155
SIC 3543 3321 3369 Foundry patternmaking; Gray iron castings; Ductile iron castings; Nonferrous foundries; Foundry patternmaking; Gray iron castings; Ductile iron castings; Nonferrous foundries
Pr: Richard J Wieland
VP: Gary Baior

D-U-N-S 04-883-8916
MID-CITY LUMBER CO LTD
4709 Paris Rd, Columbia, MO 65202-3644
Tel (573) 474-6139 *Founded/Ownrshp* 1980
Sales 22.8MM^E *EMP* 85
SIC 5211 Lumber & other building materials
Pr: Michael Teel

D-U-N-S 03-418-7435
MID-CITY MOTORS INC
AUDUBON FORD
11455 Airline Hwy, Baton Rouge, LA 70816-6208
Tel (225) 293-8900 *Founded/Ownrshp* 2006
Sales 29.1MM^E *EMP* 165
SIC 5511 7515 7513 5012 Automotive repair shops; Automobiles, new & used; Pickups, new & used; Passenger car leasing; Truck rental & leasing, no drivers; Automobiles & other motor vehicles; Automobiles, new & used; Pickups, new & used; Passenger car leasing; Truck rental & leasing, no drivers; Automobiles & other motor vehicles
Pr: Gwin R Montgomery
**VP:* Steven Montgomery

D-U-N-S 06-477-0951
MID-CITY STEEL INC
115 Buchner Pl, La Crosse, WI 54603-3147
Tel (608) 782-0770 *Founded/Ownrshp* 1972
Sales 25.2MM^E *EMP* 70
SIC 3441 Fabricated structural metal
Pr: Kurt Bear
**CFO:* Paul Bagniefski
Plnt Mgr: Steve Beck
Sls Mgr: Dan Claussen
Snr Mgr: Andrew Fraser

D-U-N-S 09-864-3794
MID-CITY SUPPLY CO INC
940 Industrial Pkwy, Elkhart, IN 46516-5599
Tel (574) 294-5551 *Founded/Ownrshp* 1979
Sales 28.7MM^E *EMP* 70
SIC 5074

D-U-N-S 84-948-0293
MID-CITY TRUCK DRIVING ACADEMY INC
AUTOMOBILE DRIVING INSTRUCTIONS
6740 W Belmont Ave, Chicago, IL 60634-4649
Tel (773) 725-3000 *Founded/Ownrshp* 2007
Sales 12.7MM^E *EMP* 2,007
SIC 8299 5511 Automobile driving instruction; Trucks, tractors & trailers: new & used; Automobile driving instruction; Trucks, tractors & trailers: new & used
Pr: Jan Nikos

D-U-N-S 04-627-4452
MID-COAST ELECTRIC SUPPLY INC
3354 Nacogdoches Rd, San Antonio, TX 78217-3323
Tel (361) 575-6311 *Founded/Ownrshp* 1980
Sales 90.2MM^E *EMP* 95
SIC 5063 Electrical supplies; Electrical supplies
Pr: Steve Barker
**VP:* Thomas C Barker
Sls Dir: Glen Jamerson
Sales Asso: Melissa Adcox
Sales Asso: Carolyn Hamilton
Sales Asso: Huntleigh Harris
Sales Asso: Monica Huddleston
Sales Asso: Juanita Leal
Sales Asso: Modesto Paradero
Sales Asso: Colt Roberts

D-U-N-S 15-117-2244
MID-COLUMBIA HEALTH SERVICES CO INC
MID-COLUMBIA MEDICAL CENTER
(*Suby of* HEALTH CARE FOR MID-COLUMBIA REGION) ★
1700 E 19th St, The Dalles, OR 97058-3317
Tel (541) 296-1111 *Founded/Ownrshp* 1983
Sales 1.6MM^E *EMP* 500
SIC 8741 Hospital management; Nursing & personal care facility management; Hospital management; Nursing & personal care facility management
Pr: Duane Frances

MID-COLUMBIA MEDICAL CENTER
See MID-COLUMBIA HEALTH SERVICES CO INC

D-U-N-S 05-097-2314
MID-COLUMBIA MEDICAL CENTER
MCMC
1700 E 19th St, The Dalles, OR 97058-3398
Tel (541) 296-1111 *Founded/Ownrshp* 1944
Sales 107.1MM *EMP* 944
SIC 8062 8011 Hospital, affiliated with AMA residency; Offices & clinics of medical doctors; Hospital, affiliated with AMA residency; Offices & clinics of medical doctors
Pr: Duane W Francis
COO: Tracy Dugick
**VP:* Don Arbon
VP: William Hamilton
VP: Randy Skov
Exec: Marsha Davis
Dir OR: Dixon Ohnemus
Dir Risk M: Lisa Sosa
Dir Lab: Lois Corbett
Prac Mgr: Linda Compton
Off Mgr: Nyla Kent

D-U-N-S 96-908-0204
▲ **MID-CON ENERGY PARTNERS LP**
2501 N Harwood St # 2410, Dallas, TX 75201-1607
Tel (972) 479-5980 *Founded/Ownrshp* 2011
Sales 126.2MM *EMP* 75^E
Tkr Sym MCEP *Exch* NGM
SIC 1311 Crude petroleum & natural gas; Crude petroleum & natural gas
CEO: Jeffery R Olmstead
Genl Pt: Mid-Con Energy GP
**Ch Bd:* Charles R Olmstead
CFO: Michael D Peterson
Ex VP: Bradley Cox

D-U-N-S 00-790-7678
■ **MID-CONTINENT CASUALTY CO**
OKLAHOMA SURETY COMPANY
(*Suby of* GREAT AMERICAN INSURANCE CO) ★
1437 S Boulder Ave # 200, Tulsa, OK 74119-3693
Tel (918) 587-7221 *Founded/Ownrshp* 1947
Sales NA *EMP* 280
SIC 6331 Fire, marine & casualty insurance; Automobile insurance; Fire, marine & casualty insurance; Automobile insurance
Pr: Michael Coon
**CFO:* Greg Jones
Sr VP: Kirby Pancoast
**VP:* Todd Bazata
**VP:* Jim Davis
VP: John Gant
VP: Bob Martin
**VP:* Kirby Tancoast
Admn Mgr: Brian Garrett
**VP Mktg:* John Gent

D-U-N-S 00-586-0861 IMP/EXP
MID-CONTINENT COAL AND COKE CO
(*Suby of* MID-CONTINENT MINERALS CORP) ★
20600 Chagrin Blvd # 850, Cleveland, OH 44122-5374
Tel (216) 283-5700 *Founded/Ownrshp* 1922, 1980
Sales 28.9MM^E *EMP* 85
SIC 5052

D-U-N-S 00-722-2268
MID-CONTINENT CONCRETE CO INC
(*Suby of* HARDESTY CO INC) ★
431 W 23rd St, Tulsa, OK 74107-3005
Tel (918) 582-8111 *Founded/Ownrshp* 1963, 1980
Sales 38.8MM^E *EMP* 300
SIC 3273

D-U-N-S 06-815-6157
MID-CONTINENT ENGINEERING INC (MN)
405 35th Ave Ne Ste 1, Minneapolis, MN 55418-1154
Tel (612) 782-1330 *Founded/Ownrshp* 1950, 1977
Sales 20.9MM *EMP* 92
Accts Cliftonlarsonallen Llp Minnea
SIC 3599 3444 3479 7692 Machine shop, jobbing & repair; Sheet metal specialties, not stamped; Painting of metal products; Welding repair
CEO: Sanders Marvin
**Ch Bd:* Charles N Marvin
**Genl Mgr:* Melissa Sawin
Genl Mgr: Melissa Sawn
Sfty Mgr: Josh Wookeking

D-U-N-S 13-971-8993 IMP/EXP
MID-CONTINENT MINERALS CORP
4002 County Road 115, Glenwood Springs, CO 81601-9020
Tel (970) 947-9469 *Founded/Ownrshp* 1975
Sales 29.2MM^E *EMP* 100
SIC 3296 Insulation: rock wool, slag & silica minerals
Pr: Thomas G Gibbs
**Treas:* Harold Geiss

D-U-N-S 03-106-9412
MID-CONTINENT PAPER AND DISTRIBUTING CO INC
11809 Borman Dr, Saint Louis, MO 63146-4112
Tel (314) 989-0894 *Founded/Ownrshp* 1993
Sales 80.1MM^E *EMP* 65
SIC 5113 Paperboard & products; Paperboard & products
Pr: Robert S Grommet
**VP:* Cathy Grommet
Sales Exec: Bob Grommet

D-U-N-S 62-176-7979
MID-CONTINENT UNIVERSITY INC
99 E Powell Rd, Mayfield, KY 42066-9007
Tel (270) 247-8521 *Founded/Ownrshp* 1949
Sales 22.6MM *EMP* 125^E
Accts Dean Dorton Allen Ford Pll
SIC 8221 Colleges universities & professional schools; Colleges universities & professional schools
Pr: Robert Imhoff
VP: Jackie Imhoff
Mng Dir: Benetta Woods
Off Mgr: Trisha Vowell
IT Man: Cris Rogers
Psych: Tammy Webb
HC Dir: Jerry Muniz

D-U-N-S 00-879-2467
MID-CONTINENTAL RESTORATION CO INC
401 E Hudson St, Fort Scott, KS 66701-4611
Tel (620) 223-3700 *Founded/Ownrshp* 1946
Sales 51.2MM^E *EMP* 276
SIC 1741 Masonry & other stonework; Masonry & other stonework
Pr: Frank J Halsey
**CFO:* Steve Floyd
**Ex VP:* Scott Halsey
**VP:* Matt Deloney

D-U-N-S 07-822-8129
MID-CUMBERLAND COMMUNITY ACTION AGENCY INC
233 Legends Dr Ste 103, Lebanon, TN 37087-5306
Tel (615) 742-1113 *Founded/Ownrshp* 1972
Sales 11.5MM *EMP* 314
Accts Stone Rudolph & Henry Plc Cla
SIC 8399 8351 Community action agency; Head start center, except in conjunction with school; Community action agency; Head start center, except in conjunction with school
Ex Dir: Kevin Davenport

MID-DEL SCHOOL SYSTEM
See MIDWEST CITY PUBLIC SCHOOLS I-52

D-U-N-S 07-502-5197
MID-EAST CAREER AND TECHNOLOGY CENTERS
MUSKINGUM PERRY CAREER CENTER
400 Richards Rd, Zanesville, OH 43701-4645
Tel (740) 455-3111 *Founded/Ownrshp* 1969
Sales 15.0MM *EMP* 320
SIC 8211 Public vocational/technical school; Vocational high school; Public vocational/technical school; Vocational high school
**Pr:* Wendy Chamberlin
**Treas:* Richard White
MIS Dir: Penny Fletcher
Cmptr Lab: Jacqueline Gebhart
Pr Dir: Stacey Snider
Psych: Doug Bruner

D-U-N-S 01-115-6069
MID-FAB INC (LA)
(*Suby of* MIDLAND FABRICATORS & PROCESS SYSTEMS LLC) ★
6005 Port Rd, New Iberia, LA 70560-9664
Tel (337) 560-8645 *Founded/Ownrshp* 1997, 2005
Sales 20.6MM^E *EMP* 425
SIC 3441 1629 8711 Fabricated structural metal for ships; Industrial plant construction; Engineering services; Fabricated structural metal for ships; Industrial plant construction; Engineering services
Ch Bd: William A Hines
**CFO:* Frank J Cangelosi
Board of Directors: Frank J Cangelos

MID-FLORIDA MATERIALS DIVISION
See HUBBARD CONSTRUCTION CO

D-U-N-S 10-895-0312
MID-FLORIDA MEDICAL SERVICES INC
WINTER HEAVEN HOSPITAL
200 Avenue F Ne, Winter Haven, FL 33881-4131
Tel (863) 297-1895 *Founded/Ownrshp* 1983
Sales 254.7MM *EMP* 2,300
Accts Mcgladrey Llp Fort Lauderdale
SIC 8741 8062 8082 Hospital management; General medical & surgical hospitals; Home health care services; Hospital management; General medical & surgical hospitals; Home health care services
Pr: Lance W Anastasio

D-U-N-S 08-045-8573
MID-HUDSON VALLEY FEDERAL CREDIT UNION
M H V
1099 Morton Blvd, Kingston, NY 12401-1503
Tel (845) 336-4444 *Founded/Ownrshp* 1963
Sales NA *EMP* 170
SIC 6061 Federal credit unions; Federal credit unions
Pr: Wayne Winkler
**CFO:* Christopher Corallo
**Ch:* Gary Anderson
Ex VP: Candace Benedict
Sr VP: Robert Michaud
VP: Rick Dilorenzo
VP: John Dwyer
**VP:* Jill Hall
VP: Kyle Kragt
CTO: Dave Kellogg
IT Man: Scott Husta

D-U-N-S 08-113-1260
MID-IOWA TOOLS INC
METRO TOOL & ABRASIVES
3350 Square D Dr Sw, Cedar Rapids, IA 52404-3916
Tel (319) 366-1617 *Founded/Ownrshp* 1975
Sales 30.5MM^E *EMP* 27
Accts Voelschow & Associates Pc
SIC 5085 Tools; Mill supplies
Pr: Gregory L Harvieux
**Treas:* Louis Harvieux

MID-ISLAND ELECTRICAL SUPPLY
See MIE-TH HOLDINGS LLC

D-U-N-S 00-713-5395
MID-KANSAS COOPERATIVE ASSOCIATION
MKC
307 W Cole St, Moundridge, KS 67107-7533
Tel (620) 345-6328 *Founded/Ownrshp* 1965
Sales 403.0MM *EMP* 250
Accts Lindburg Vogel Pierce Faris H
SIC 5153 5191 Grain elevators; Farm supplies; Grain elevators; Farm supplies; Chemicals, agricultural; Fertilizer & fertilizer materials
Pr: Dave Christiansen
CFO: Danny Porch
**CFO:* Danny Posch
Dir IT: Matt Friesen
Sls&Mrk Ex: Liz McKim

D-U-N-S 03-127-4392
MID-KANSAS INVESTMENT INC
O'NEAL, JEFF TOYOTA
1100 E 30th Ave, Hutchinson, KS 67502-4229
Tel (620) 662-6631 *Founded/Ownrshp* 1950
Sales 27.4MM^E *EMP* 90
SIC 5511 Automobiles, new & used; Automobiles, new & used
Pr: Rusty Eck
**Pr:* B Jeff O'Neal
**Treas:* Richard E Smith
**VP:* Orestes L Eck

D-U-N-S 86-720-1360
■ **MID-MAINE COMMUNICATIONS INC**
OTT COMMUNICATIONS
(*Suby of* OTELCO INC) ★
890 Hammond St, Bangor, ME 04401-4328
Tel (207) 826-9911 *Founded/Ownrshp* 2006
Sales 24.0MM^E *EMP* 100
SIC 4813 Telephone communication, except radio
Sr VP: Nicholas A Winchester
**CFO:* Joseph Donato
**VP:* Curtis L Garner
Netwrk Mgr: Brian Starbird
Netwrk Eng: Frank Dorr
Netwrk Eng: Joe Wood
Mktg Mgr: Tracy Scheckel
Sls Mgr: Art Hanson
Sls Mgr: Jon Henderson

D-U-N-S 09-284-6534
MID-MISSOURI BANCSHARES INC
CENTRAL STATE BANCSHARES
1619 E Independence St, Springfield, MO 65804-3783
Tel (417) 877-0962 *Founded/Ownrshp* 1977
Sales NA *EMP* 323
SIC 6021 National commercial banks; National commercial banks
Ch Bd: Lee Gilbert
**Sec:* Donald B Russell

D-U-N-S 82-837-3337
MID-MISSOURI BANK
3546 E Sunshine St, Springfield, MO 65809-2813
Tel (417) 877-9191 *Founded/Ownrshp* 2008

Sales NA *EMP* 99^E
SIC 6022 State commercial banks; State commercial banks
Pr: Bob Ward
**Pr:* Eric McClure

D-U-N-S 17-596-3524
MID-MISSOURI ENERGY LLC
MME GRAIN
15311 N Saline 65 Hwy, Malta Bend, MO 65339-1310
Tel (660) 595-0144 *Founded/Ownrshp* 2001
Sales 150.0MM *EMP* 45
SIC 2869 Ethyl alcohol, ethanol
Pr: Ryland Utlaut
**CEO:* Chris Wilson
CFO: Art Madden
**Treas:* Ronald T Linneman
**VP:* Mark Casner
CIO: Matthew Endicott
Plnt Mgr: Tyler Edmundson

D-U-N-S 07-488-6771 IMP
MID-MOUNTAIN FOODS INC
MISTY MOUNTAIN SPRING WATER CO
(*Suby of* FOOD CITY) ★
26331 Hillman Hwy, Abingdon, VA 24210-7619
Tel (276) 623-5000 *Founded/Ownrshp* 1974
Sales 221.8MM^E *EMP* 500
SIC 5141 Groceries, general line; Groceries, general line
Pr: Jessee A Lewis
**Ch:* Dozier J Perry
**Treas:* Donald E Lay
Treas: Donald Lay
**VP:* K Sutton Rigg
VP: Sutton Rigg
IT Man: Ralph McCredy
Netwrk Mgr: Benjamin Lawson
Sfty Dirs: Jimmy Asbury
Sls&Mrk Ex: Mike Gilliam

D-U-N-S 08-461-9576
MID-NEBRASKA INDIVIDUAL SERVICES INC
216 N Denver Ave, Hastings, NE 68901-5138
Tel (402) 462-5107 *Founded/Ownrshp* 1970
Sales 9.9MM^E *EMP* 450
Accts Mcdermott And Miller Hasting
SIC 8331 Vocational training agency; Vocational training agency
CEO: Diane Campbell
Area Mgr: Cheri Murrell

D-U-N-S 05-444-5242
MID-OHIO CONTRACTING INC (OH)
1817 Horns Ln Nw, Dover, OH 44622-7314
Tel (330) 343-2925 *Founded/Ownrshp* 1981
Sales 34.7MM^E *EMP* 150
SIC 1623 Oil & gas pipeline construction; Oil & gas pipeline construction
Pr: Robert Kandle
**VP:* James E Hawk

D-U-N-S 03-753-2314
MID-OHIO FOODBANK
3960 Brookham Dr, Grove City, OH 43123-9741
Tel (614) 317-9400 *Founded/Ownrshp* 1980
Sales 75.6MM^E *EMP* 118
Accts Hemphill & Associates Columbu
SIC 8322 Meal delivery program; Meal delivery program
Pr: Mathew Habash
**COO:* Lyn Hang
**CFO:* Sharon Grunwell
VP: Evelyn Behm
VP: Bridget Decrane
VP: John Grunwell
**VP:* Marilyn Tomasi
**VP:* Greg Winslow
Exec: Fred Rutter
**Prin:* Kimberly Dorniden

D-U-N-S 06-598-1532
MID-OHIO IMPORTED CAR CO
KELLY BMW
4050 Morse Rd, Columbus, OH 43230-1448
Tel (614) 471-2277 *Founded/Ownrshp* 1976
Sales 20.8MM^E *EMP* 40
SIC 5511 5521 Automobiles, new & used; Used car dealers
CEO: Don F Marsh
**Pr:* Patrick M Marsh
Dir IT: David Migliore

D-U-N-S 05-413-4812
MID-OHIO PIPELINE CO INC
MID-OHIO PIPELINE SERVICES
2270 Eckert Rd, Mansfield, OH 44904-9742
Tel (419) 884-3772 *Founded/Ownrshp* 1970
Sales 23.3MM^E *EMP* 40
Accts Meaden & Moore Ltd Cpas Cl
SIC 1623 Oil & gas pipeline construction
Ch Bd: Brent Yates
**Pr:* Chuck Austin
**VP:* Thomas Lorenz
Mtls Mgr: C W Kick

MID-OHIO PIPELINE SERVICES
See MID-OHIO PIPELINE CO INC

MID-PAC DISTRIBUTORS
See PINT SIZE CORP

D-U-N-S 07-767-4984
MID-PACIFIC INSTITUTE
2445 Kaala St, Honolulu, HI 96822-2299
Tel (808) 973-5019 *Founded/Ownrshp* 1865
Sales 34.7MM *EMP* 200
Accts Kmh Llp Honolulu Hi
SIC 8211 Private junior high school; Private senior high school; Private junior high school; Private senior high school
Pr: Joe Rice
VP: Gary Cordova
VP: Kristy Tong
Comm Dir: Scot Allen
Cmptr Lab: Michael Krafft
Dir IT: Justin Goo
Snr Mgr: Brian Dote

D-U-N-S 08-676-7548
MID-PARK INC
1021 Salt River Rd, Leitchfield, KY 42754-1700
Tel (270) 259-3152 *Founded/Ownrshp* 1975
Sales 25.0MM *EMP* 100
SIC 3444 3441 3429 3452 Guard rails, highway: sheet metal; Bridge sections, prefabricated highway; Manufactured hardware (general); Bolts, nuts, rivets & washers; Guard rails, highway: sheet metal; Bridge sections, prefabricated highway; Manufactured hardware (general); Bolts, nuts, rivets & washers
Pr: Greg Bernnard
**CFO:* Larry Vott
VP: Roy Powell
**Prin:* G Alan Bernard
Opers Mgr: Mike Snell
Sales Exec: James Compton
Sales Exec: Steve Scott
Sales Asso: Joel Bernard

D-U-N-S 00-647-2179
MID-RIVERS TELEPHONE COOPERATIVE INC (MT)
904 C Ave, Circle, MT 59215
Tel (406) 485-3301 *Founded/Ownrshp* 1952
Sales 82.0MM^E *EMP* 170
SIC 4813 5731 5999 4841 Long distance telephone communications; Local telephone communications; Antennas, satellite dish; Telephone equipment & systems; Cable television services; Long distance telephone communications; Local telephone communications; Antennas, satellite dish; Telephone equipment & systems; Cable television services
Pr: Craig Johnson
**Pr:* Mark Robins
**CEO:* Robert Reukauf
**Sec:* Gene Engen
**VP:* Kevin Braun
Genl Mgr: Gerry Anderson
Manager: Scot Buerkle
Sales Exec: Debra Wagner

D-U-N-S 06-824-6990
MID-SHIP GROUP LLC (NY)
MID-SHIP MARINE
145 Main St, Port Washington, NY 11050-3239
Tel (516) 944-3500 *Founded/Ownrshp* 1974
Sales 36.0MM^E *EMP* 120^E
SIC 8742 4731 Management consulting services; Transportation agents & brokers; Management consulting services; Transportation agents & brokers
CEO: Matthew I Deluca Jr
Pr: Joseph Pontoli Sr
**Pr:* Steven Rzehak
CFO: Joseph Smith
**Ex VP:* Douglas M Aprahamina
**Ex VP:* Aysan Ay
**Ex VP:* George Catchmar
**Ex VP:* Robert C Diamond
**Ex VP:* Brian Malone
VP: Soren Winger
VP: Emmanouil Xidias

MID-SHIP MARINE
See MID-SHIP GROUP LLC

MID-SOUTH AG EQUIPMENT
See MID-SOUTH AGRICULTURAL EQUIPMENT INC

D-U-N-S 79-161-8171
MID-SOUTH AGRICULTURAL EQUIPMENT INC
MID-SOUTH AG EQUIPMENT
3044 Highway 302, Byhalia, MS 38611-6320
Tel (662) 890-3141 *Founded/Ownrshp* 1983
Sales 44.8MM^E *EMP* 45
SIC 5046 Commercial equipment
Pr: Gary M Reid
Ex VP: Gaylon Rogers
VP: Henry Shurlds
Genl Mgr: Kent Shaw
Mtls Mgr: Chris Kellum
Mktg Mgr: Charlie May
Sls Mgr: Sid Cameron
Sls Mgr: Dennis Perry
Sls Mgr: Victor Sample
Sales Asso: Kris Forman
Sales Asso: Kevin Mabry

D-U-N-S 04-967-9616 IMP
MID-SOUTH BUILDING SUPPLY INC
7940 Woodruff Ct, Springfield, VA 22151-2122
Tel (703) 321-8500 *Founded/Ownrshp* 1985
Sales 46.5MM *EMP* 126^E
Accts Mcgladrey Llp Baltimore Mary
SIC 5031 5033 Kitchen cabinets; Roofing, siding & insulation; Kitchen cabinets; Roofing, siding & insulation
Pr: Andrew R Tavss
**Ch Bd:* Melvin Rosenblatt
**Sec:* Gregory Mutchler
**Ex VP:* James Rowland
Brnch Mgr: Tim Bergen
Brnch Mgr: Kevin Dechristopher
Brnch Mgr: Stuart McCoy
IT Man: Mike Bowen
Sls Mgr: Tim Jarrell
Sls Mgr: Erich Leuck
Sls Mgr: Trent Overboe

D-U-N-S 07-823-1891
MID-SOUTH BUS CENTER INC (TN)
MID-SOUTH EMERGENCY EQUIPMENT
3512 Bill Smith Dr, Murfreesboro, TN 37129-4095
Tel (615) 890-6368 *Founded/Ownrshp* 1973
Sales 32.0MM *EMP* 35
SIC 5012 Buses
Pr: Steve Benefield
VP: Bucky Law

D-U-N-S 06-214-9646
MID-SOUTH DISTRIBUTING-USA INC (AR)
7501 Enmar Dr, Little Rock, AR 72209-3507
Tel (501) 565-4144 *Founded/Ownrshp* 1972
Sales 23.3MM^E *EMP* 37
SIC 5064 5722 Electrical appliances, major; Air conditioning appliances; Washing machines; Appliance parts, household; Appliance parts

Pr: Leonard Kremers Sr
**VP:* Leonard Kremers Jr

D-U-N-S 06-127-8594
MID-SOUTH ELECTRIC CO-OPERATIVE ASSOCIATION
MID-SOUTH SYNERGY
7625 Highway 6, Navasota, TX 77868-7478
Tel (936) 825-5100 *Founded/Ownrshp* 1940
Sales 65.1MM *EMP* 95
Accts Bolinger Segars Gilbert And Mo
SIC 4911 Distribution, electric power; Distribution, electric power
Pr: Marshall Shirley
Sec: Jack Shepherd
VP: James Morrison
Exec: Melanie Caballero
Genl Mgr: Kerry Kelton
Opers Mgr: Robert Taylor
Pr Mgr: Jeff Murski
Counsel: John Fultz
Snr Mgr: Kevin Diehl

D-U-N-S 09-077-9422 IMP/EXP
MID-SOUTH ELECTRONICS INC (AL)
(*Suby of* MID-SOUTH INDUSTRIES INC) ★
2463 Moores Creek Schl Rd, Annville, KY 40402-8906
Tel (606) 364-5142 *Founded/Ownrshp* 1978
Sales 21.1MM^E *EMP* 400
SIC 3672 3089 3824 3643 3613 3585 Printed circuit boards; Injection molding of plastics; Mechanical & electromechanical counters & devices; Current-carrying wiring devices; Switchgear & switchboard apparatus; Refrigeration & heating equipment; Printed circuit boards; Injection molding of plastics; Mechanical & electromechanical counters & devices; Current-carrying wiring devices; Switchgear & switchboard apparatus; Refrigeration & heating equipment
Ch Bd: Harold Weaver
**Pr:* Jerry Weaver
**CFO:* Bill Beshears
**Treas:* William Beshears
**VP:* John B Weaver
Ql Cn Mgr: Tom Greenhaw

MID-SOUTH EMERGENCY EQUIPMENT
See MID-SOUTH BUS CENTER INC

D-U-N-S 05-157-9001 IMP
MID-SOUTH EXTRUSION DIE CO INC
CED
(*Suby of* COCKBURN ENTERPRISES INC) ★
334 E Washington Dr, Muscle Shoals, AL 35661-2798
Tel (256) 381-3620 *Founded/Ownrshp* 1970
Sales 30.1MM^E *EMP* 200
SIC 3544 Extrusion dies; Extrusion dies
Pr: Terry Cockburn
**Sec:* Gary Cockburn

D-U-N-S 07-351-7682
MID-SOUTH FAIR INC
41 Union Ave Ste 1, Memphis, TN 38103-2419
Tel (901) 274-8800 *Founded/Ownrshp* 1856
Sales 699.6M *EMP* 300
SIC 7999 Fair; Fair
Pr: Eugene Smith

D-U-N-S 93-933-4041
MID-SOUTH HEALTH ENTERPRISES INC
REUNION PLAZA OF TYLER
(*Suby of* HSMTX/REUNION PLAZA LLC) ★
1401 Rice Rd, Tyler, TX 75703-3233
Tel (903) 561-6060 *Founded/Ownrshp* 1996
Sales 3.1MM^E *EMP* 303
SIC 8051 Convalescent home with continuous nursing care; Convalescent home with continuous nursing care

MID-SOUTH HEALTH SYSTEMS
See NORTHEAST ARKANSAS COMMUNITY MENTAL HEALTH CENTER INC

D-U-N-S 00-440-2301 IMP
MID-SOUTH INDUSTRIES INC (AL)
2620 E Meighan Blvd, Gadsden, AL 35903-1924
Tel (256) 492-8997 *Founded/Ownrshp* 1962
Sales 143.2MM^E *EMP* 1,474
SIC 3672 3089 3824 3714 Printed circuit boards; Injection molding of plastics; Mechanical & electromechanical counters & devices; Motor vehicle body components & frame; Printed circuit boards; Injection molding of plastics; Mechanical & electromechanical counters & devices; Motor vehicle body components & frame
Ch Bd: Harold Weaver
COO: Jerry Hawkins
**CFO:* Robert A Stringer
**VP:* John B Weaver
Prd Mgr: David Dobbs

D-U-N-S 00-816-7371
MID-SOUTH INDUSTRIES INC
THERMO-KOOL
723 E 21st St, Laurel, MS 39440-2457
Tel (601) 649-4600 *Founded/Ownrshp* 1970
Sales 46.2MM^E *EMP* 154
SIC 3585 Lockers, refrigerated; Lockers, refrigerated
Pr: M Randolph McLaughlin
**VP:* Teri Brewer
**VP:* Lee Thames
Plnt Mgr: Duane Eldridge
Sls Mgr: Frances Davis

D-U-N-S 00-336-3389
MID-SOUTH MANAGEMENT CO INC (SC)
172 E Main St Ste 300, Spartanburg, SC 29306-5182
Tel (864) 583-2907 *Founded/Ownrshp* 1961
Sales 36.4MM^E *EMP* 218
SIC 2711 Newspapers, publishing & printing; Newspapers, publishing & printing
Pr: Andrew Babb
Ex Dir: Vicki Lusk

D-U-N-S 08-374-0592
MID-SOUTH MECHANICAL INC
110 Airport Pkwy, Lagrange, GA 30240-5785
Tel (706) 884-3206 *Founded/Ownrshp* 1989
Sales 22.6MM^E *EMP* 99

SIC 1541 1611 3444 3441 Industrial buildings & warehouses; Highway & street construction; Sheet metalwork; Fabricated structural metal
CEO: Charles Arrington
**Pr:* Rex Grizzle
**Treas:* Sharon Arrington
**VP:* Gregory Arrington
IT Man: Celeste Woodson

D-U-N-S 60-393-3388
MID-SOUTH METALS LLC
637 Montgomery St, Shreveport, LA 71107-6931
Tel (318) 424-5002 *Founded/Ownrshp* 2005
Sales 22.9MM^E *EMP* 112^E
SIC 3322 Malleable iron foundries
Pr: Dwayne Defatta
VP: Vincent Defatta
Sls Mgr: Eric Zenter
Sales Asso: Josh Smith
Sales Asso: Zach Willoughby

D-U-N-S 00-704-5479
MID-SOUTH PLUMBING & ELECTRICAL SUPPLY CO INC (AR)
AMERICAN ELECTRIC
2600 E Highland Dr 2608, Jonesboro, AR 72401-6217
Tel (870) 932-4591 *Founded/Ownrshp* 1949
Sales 23.8MM^E *EMP* 30
SIC 5063 5074 Electrical apparatus & equipment; Plumbing fittings & supplies
Pr: James D Hunt
**Sec:* Juanita Latourette
Sls Mgr: Terry Gould
Board of Directors: Tom Hendrix

MID-SOUTH ROOF SYSTEMS
See MID-SOUTH SUBCONTRACTORS INC

D-U-N-S 00-629-3609
MID-SOUTH STEEL PRODUCTS INC (MO)
2071 Corporate Cir, Cape Girardeau, MO 63703-7671
Tel (573) 335-5529 *Founded/Ownrshp* 1954
Sales 26.7MM^E *EMP* 47
SIC 4925 1791 Liquefied petroleum gas, distribution through mains; Storage tanks, metal: erection
Pr: Albert L Underwood Jr
**VP:* Ronald L Underwood
Plnt Mgr: Chris Gockel

D-U-N-S 60-913-8961
MID-SOUTH SUBCONTRACTORS INC
MID-SOUTH ROOF SYSTEMS
5020 Old Dixie Hwy, Forest Park, GA 30297-2148
Tel (404) 361-5154 *Founded/Ownrshp* 1990
Sales 65.0MM *EMP* 215
SIC 1761 1541 1542 Roofing contractor; Renovation, remodeling & repairs: industrial buildings; Commercial & office buildings, renovation & repair; Roofing contractor; Renovation, remodeling & repairs: industrial buildings; Commercial & office buildings, renovation & repair
Pr: W Ronald Newton
CFO: Robert McManus
**Sec:* Pamela C Newton
Ex VP: Rob Wallace
Dir IT: Ron W Newton

MID-SOUTH SYNERGY
See MID-SOUTH ELECTRIC CO-OPERATIVE ASSOCIATION

D-U-N-S 00-498-7210 IMP/EXP
MID-SOUTH WIRE CO INC (TN)
1070 Visco Dr, Nashville, TN 37210-2208
Tel (615) 743-2850 *Founded/Ownrshp* 1966
Sales 68.9MM^E *EMP* 125
SIC 3315 Steel wire & related products; Engine electrical equipment; Steel wire & related products
Ch Bd: David L Rollins
**Pr:* John T Johnson Jr
CFO: Jeff McCann
**Sec:* Robert Rollins
VP: Todd Plate
VP: Andy Talbot
Sfty Mgr: Josh Backman
VP Sls: John T Son
Manager: Robert Knight

D-U-N-S 00-430-6445 IMP
MID-STATE BOLT AND NUT CO INC (OH)
1575 Alum Creek Dr, Columbus, OH 43209-2712
Tel (614) 253-8631 *Founded/Ownrshp* 1946, 2008
Sales 22.8MM^E *EMP* 43
SIC 5085 5072 Industrial supplies; Bolts
Pr: David R Broehm
**Treas:* David A Breault
**VP:* Stephen English
**VP:* Curt McCullough

D-U-N-S 09-138-3737 IMP
MID-STATE DISTRIBUTING CO
2600 Bell Ave, Des Moines, IA 50321-1121
Tel (515) 244-7231 *Founded/Ownrshp* 1987
Sales 27.5MM^E *EMP* 55
SIC 5065 Electronic parts & equipment
Pr: James L Hedden
**Treas:* Diane C Hedden

D-U-N-S 09-667-0914
MID-STATE DISTRIBUTING INC (AR)
T RICKS
2391 W Main St Ste C, Cabot, AR 72023-7670
Tel (501) 286-7960 *Founded/Ownrshp* 1979, 2008
Sales 50.0MM *EMP* 6
SIC 5541 6512 5172 Filling stations, gasoline; Property operation, retail establishment; Gasoline; Filling stations, gasoline; Property operation, retail establishment; Gasoline
Pr: Khirunissa Mandani
**VP:* Nuruddin Mandani

MID-STATE EQUIPMENT JANESVILLE
See MID-STATE GROUP INC

D-U-N-S 13-451-2644
MID-STATE FARMERS CO-OP INC
819 W Un, Rush Center, KS 67575
Tel (785) 372-4239 *Founded/Ownrshp* 1999
Sales 28.0MM *EMP* 30

SIC 0161 Vegetables & melons; Vegetables & melons
Pr: Craig Jecha

D-U-N-S 17-361-7291
MID-STATE GROUP INC
MID-STATE EQUIPMENT JANESVILLE
4323 E Us Highway 14, Janesville, WI 53546-9494
Tel (608) 754-8450 *Founded/Ownrshp* 2000
Sales 20.3MM[E] *EMP* 85
SIC 5999 5261 Farm equipment & supplies; Lawnmowers & tractors; Garden tractors & tillers
VP: Chris Hanson
IT Man: Marna Smith
Sls Mgr: Dean Pierce
Sls Mgr: Larry Schlender

MID-STATE HOSE & FITTINGS
See MID-STATE SALES INC

D-U-N-S 06-317-5087 IMP
MID-STATE LUMBER CORP
200 Industrial Pkwy, Branchburg, NJ 08876-3488
Tel (908) 725-4900 *Founded/Ownrshp* 1976
Sales 45.2MM[E] *EMP* 49
SIC 5031 Lumber: rough, dressed & finished; Plywood
Pr: Bernard Bernstein
**VP:* David Bernstein
Mktg Dir: Mike Kelly
Mktg Mgr: Helene Feinberg
Mktg Mgr: Elizabeth Ryan
Manager: Matt Veroneau
Sls Mgr: Drew Sienko
Sls Mgr: Lyle Tompkins
Sales Asso: Bill Artigliere
Sales Asso: Bob Obrien

D-U-N-S 07-320-3804
MID-STATE MACHINE AND FABRICATING CORP
MID STATE MACHINE & FABG
2730 Mine And Mill Rd, Lakeland, FL 33801-7006
Tel (863) 665-6233 *Founded/Ownrshp* 1972
Sales 26.6MM[E] *EMP* 250[E]
Accts Cross Fernandez & Riley Llp
SIC 3443 3599 7692 3444 Fabricated plate work (boiler shop); Machine & other job shop work; Welding repair; Sheet metalwork; Fabricated plate work (boiler shop); Machine & other job shop work; Welding repair; Sheet metalwork
CEO: Harold E Kersey
**Pr:* Jeff E Clyne
**Treas:* Lauren Jones
**Treas:* Laura Kersey
**VP:* John Hooten
**VP:* Steve Hutcheson
**VP:* Rick Rahn
Sfty Mgr: Josh Kersey
Sfty Mgr: Glenn Leewright
Board of Directors: Mike McGloro

D-U-N-S 80-097-7774
MID-STATE MACHINE CO LLC
294 W Plaza Dr Ste H8, Mooresville, NC 28117-6950
Tel (704) 636-7029 *Founded/Ownrshp* 2007
Sales 26.5MM[E] *EMP* 100
SIC 3549 Metalworking machinery
CEO: Larry Schwoeri
CFO: Mike Siddons
Dir Bus: Dave Templin
Genl Mgr: Ron Clair
VP Opers: Mike McKay
Plnt Mgr: Rick Rahn
Sls Mgr: Fred Kriger
Sls Mgr: Tim McCabe

D-U-N-S 07-851-1110
MID-STATE MANAGEMENT CORP
9777 Queens Blvd Ste 1008, Rego Park, NY 11374-3398
Tel (718) 459-9021 *Founded/Ownrshp* 1957
Sales 6.3MM[E] *EMP* 300
SIC 6531 Real estate managers; Real estate managers
Pr: Samuel J Lefrak
**VP:* Richard Lefrak

D-U-N-S 08-363-4329
MID-STATE PETROLEUM INC (NC)
4192 Mendenhall Oaks Pkwy, High Point, NC 27265-8034
Tel (336) 841-3000 *Founded/Ownrshp* 1992
Sales 76.5MM *EMP* 150
Accts Dixon Hughes Goodman Llp Hig
SIC 5541 5983 5411 Filling stations, gasoline; Fuel oil dealers; Convenience stores, independent; Filling stations, gasoline; Fuel oil dealers; Convenience stores, independent
Pr: Anthony L Perez
**Pr:* Tony Perez
**VP:* Jerry Rose

D-U-N-S 96-860-3956
MID-STATE RACEWAY INC
VERNON DOWNS
4229 Stuhlman Rd, Vernon, NY 13476-4516
Tel (315) 829-3400 *Founded/Ownrshp* 2006
Sales 10.5MM[E] *EMP* 300
SIC 7948 7011 Racing, including track operation; Hotels; Racing, including track operation; Hotels
Pr: Jeffery Gural

D-U-N-S 96-016-8532
MID-STATE RECLAMATION INC
21955 Grenada Ave, Lakeville, MN 55044-8055
Tel (952) 985-5555 *Founded/Ownrshp* 1991
Sales 30.0MM[E] *EMP* 25
SIC 4953 Refuse systems; Refuse systems
CEO: Tom Johnson
CFO: Ken Fechtner
**VP:* Vice President

D-U-N-S 04-964-6144 IMP
MID-STATE SALES INC
MID-STATE HOSE & FITTINGS
1101 Gahanna Pkwy, Columbus, OH 43230-6600
Tel (614) 864-1811 *Founded/Ownrshp* 1969
Sales 24.1MM[E] *EMP* 55[E]
SIC 5084 3494 3492

D-U-N-S 06-547-6582 EXP
MID-STATE SUPPLY CO LLC
(*Suby of* CREST OPERATIONS LLC) ★
3323 Broadway Ave, Alexandria, LA 71302-4412
Tel (318) 448-3411 *Founded/Ownrshp* 1973
Sales 25.0MM[E] *EMP* 35
SIC 5063 Electrical supplies; Motors, electric
Ch Bd: Kenneth L Robison
Pr: Eddie Milliner
Treas: Robert L Brinkerhoff
Sec: Brenda R Daenen
VP: Michael R Erwin
Ex Dir: Joe Robinson

D-U-N-S 15-212-2560
MID-STATE TANK CO INC
1357 Johnson Creek Rd, Sullivan, IL 61951
Tel (217) 728-8383 *Founded/Ownrshp* 1986
Sales 42.5MM[E] *EMP* 88
SIC 3443 Tanks, standard or custom fabricated: metal plate
Pr: Gery V Conlin
**VP:* Elmer Gingrich
**VP:* Gene Good
CIO: Elmer Gingerich
QI Cn Mgr: Jason Fleming

D-U-N-S 07-479-2789
MID-STATE TECHNICAL COLLEGE (INC)
WISCONSIN TECHNICAL COLLEGE SY
(*Suby of* WISCONSIN TECHNICAL COLLEGE SYSTEM BOARD) ★
500 32nd St N, Wisconsin Rapids, WI 54494-5599
Tel (715) 422-5300 *Founded/Ownrshp* 1911
Sales 16.0MM *EMP* 640
Accts Schenck Sc Green Bay Wiscons
SIC 8222 Technical institute; Technical institute
Ch: Lynneia Miller
**Pr:* John Clark
**Treas:* Patrick Costello
VP: Susan Budjac
Tech Mgr: Steven Eidenschink

D-U-N-S 04-179-1617
■ **MID-STATE TELEPHONE CO**
TDS TELECOMMUNICATIONS
(*Suby of* TDS TELECOMMUNICATIONS CORP) ★
7902 Chapin Dr Ne, New London, MN 56273
Tel (320) 354-7805 *Founded/Ownrshp* 1972
Sales 258.7MM[E] *EMP* 2,700
SIC 4813 Telephone communication, except radio; Telephone communication, except radio
Pr: David A Wittwer

D-U-N-S 02-334-1498
MID-STATE TRUCK SERVICE INC
IDEALEASE OF CENTRAL WISCONSIN
2100 E 29th St, Marshfield, WI 54449-5502
Tel (715) 591-2591 *Founded/Ownrshp* 1965
Sales 34.8MM[E] *EMP* 100
SIC 5012 5511

D-U-N-S 02-322-9123 IMP
MID-STATES ALUMINUM CORP
132 Trowbridge Dr, Fond Du Lac, WI 54937-9177
Tel (920) 922-7207 *Founded/Ownrshp* 1984
Sales 65.2MM[E] *EMP* 264
Accts Grant Thornton Llp Chicago
SIC 3471 3354 3499 Aluminum extruded products; Ammunition boxes, metal; Anodizing (plating) of metals or formed products; Anodizing (plating) of metals or formed products; Aluminum extruded products; Ammunition boxes, metal
CEO: Joseph Colwin
**CFO:* Bob Sippel
CIO: Tim Olig
Plnt Mgr: Leo Metivier
QI Cn Mgr: Kerri Feavel
QI Cn Mgr: Collin Krueger
Manager: Reggie Draheim
Manager: Jay Salzmann
Snr Mgr: Victor Blomstrom
Snr Mgr: Dan Chitwood
Snr Mgr: Henry Dixon

D-U-N-S 06-419-6199
MID-STATES BOLT & SCREW CO
4126 Somers Dr, Burton, MI 48529-2279
Tel (810) 744-0123 *Founded/Ownrshp* 1973
Sales 41.8MM[E] *EMP* 135
SIC 7389 5072 Packaging & labeling services; Bolts
Pr: Scott R Somers
CFO: Ken Rapoon
**VP:* Marc E Somers
VP: Ericw Williams
Sls Mgr: James P Baker
Sls Mgr: Jim Bourcier
Sls Mgr: Bernie Brown
Sls Mgr: Ken Charbonneau
Sls Mgr: Dale Chester
Sales Asso: Dewey Benson
Sales Asso: Bill Geiger

D-U-N-S 00-610-8013 IMP
MID-STATES CONCRETE INDUSTRIES LLC
500 S Park Ave 550, South Beloit, IL 61080-2099
Tel (815) 389-2277 *Founded/Ownrshp* 1946
Sales 21.2MM[E] *EMP* 55
SIC 3272 8711 Concrete products, precast; Engineering services
CEO: Charles H Harker
**Pr:* Hagen Harker
VP: Lynn Foster
Sfty Mgr: Mike Wolff
Opers Mgr: Kevin Wald
Plnt Mgr: Joel Purdy
Snr Mgr: Ian Lewellin
Snr Mgr: Neil Shaw

MID-STATES CONTRACTING COMPANY
See ALTHOFF INDUSTRIES INC

D-U-N-S 00-621-2369 IMP
MID-STATES DISTRIBUTING CO INC (ND)
1370 Mendota Hts Rd, Mendota, MN 55150
Tel (651) 698-8831 *Founded/Ownrshp* 1954
Sales 665.0MM[E] *EMP* 25[E]
SIC 5072 5013 5191 5091 5092 5136 Hardware; Automotive supplies & parts; Farm supplies; Sporting & recreation goods; Toys & games; Men's & boys' clothing
CEO: Thomas Mahlke
**Pr:* John W Atkins
**CFO:* Barbara Townsend
Dir Soc: Nelle Bing
Off Mgr: Pam Nord

MID-STATES DOOR AND HARDWARE
See MICHELMANN STEEL CONSTRUCTION CO

D-U-N-S 01-991-3182
■ **MID-STATES OILFIELD SUPPLY LLC**
(*Suby of* SEVENTY SEVEN OPERATING LLC) ★
777 Nw 63rd St, Oklahoma City, OK 73116-7601
Tel (405) 935-4478 *Founded/Ownrshp* 2005
Sales 27.2MM[E] *EMP* 35[E]
SIC 5099 Durable goods
CEO: Jerry Winchester

D-U-N-S 00-637-4938 IMP
MID-STATES RUBBER PRODUCTS INC
1232 S Race St, Princeton, IN 47670-3034
Tel (812) 385-3473 *Founded/Ownrshp* 1944
Sales 3.2MM[E] *EMP* 300
SIC 3061

D-U-N-S 00-385-4478 IMP
MID-STATES SUPPLY CO INC (MO)
CONTROLS MIDWEST
1716 Guinotte Ave, Kansas City, MO 64120-1480
Tel (816) 842-4290 *Founded/Ownrshp* 1956
Sales 351.4MM[E] *EMP* 450
Accts Kpmg Llp Kansas City Mo
SIC 5085 3545 Industrial supplies; Rubber goods, mechanical; Valves & fittings; Hose, belting & packing; Industrial supplies; Rubber goods, mechanical; Valves & fittings; Hose, belting & packing; Gauges (machine tool accessories)
CEO: Benjamin Hurst
Pr: Andrew Brown
Treas: Robert Brown
Brnch Mgr: David Ristau
Software D: Alex Mbuya
Mktg Dir: Bob Brown
Sls Mgr: Andy Hofmeier

D-U-N-S 12-202-1967
MID-STEP SERVICES INC
4303 Stone Ave, Sioux City, IA 51106-1998
Tel (712) 274-2252 *Founded/Ownrshp* 1977
Sales 16.8MM *EMP* 400
SIC 8361 Residential care for the handicapped; Residential care for the handicapped
CEO: Gary Turbes
CFO: Sandra Miller

D-U-N-S 02-684-4316
MID-TEX OF MIDLAND INC
5206 W Wadley Ave, Midland, TX 79707-5112
Tel (432) 697-2282 *Founded/Ownrshp* 1990
Sales 23.9MM *EMP* 40
Accts Beal & Wilkes Pc
SIC 1542 5713 Commercial & office building contractors; Floor covering stores; Commercial & office building contractors; Floor covering stores
Pr: Thomas White
**VP:* Paul Renz
**Prin:* Alan White
Sales Exec: Roger Copeland

D-U-N-S 78-432-0624
MID-VALLEY DISPOSAL
3444 W Whites Bridge Ave, Fresno, CA 93706-1130
Tel (559) 237-9425 *Founded/Ownrshp* 1996
Sales 56.4MM[E] *EMP* 80
SIC 4953 Refuse systems
Pr: John Kalpakoff
**VP:* Roy Mendrin
VP: William Winchester
**Genl Mgr:* Joseph Kalpakoff

MID-VALLEY GLASS & MILLWORK CO
See MID-VALLEY LLC

D-U-N-S 05-814-8305
MID-VALLEY HEALTHCARE INC
LEBANON COMMUNITY HOSPITAL
525 N Santiam Hwy, Lebanon, OR 97355-4363
Tel (541) 258-2101 *Founded/Ownrshp* 1950
Sales 85.9MM *EMP* 740
SIC 8062 8051 8011 8082 General medical & surgical hospitals; Skilled nursing care facilities; Offices & clinics of medical doctors; Home health care services; General medical & surgical hospitals; Skilled nursing care facilities; Offices & clinics of medical doctors; Home health care services
CEO: Larry Mullins
**Pr:* Bud Laurent
Dir Risk M: Kathy Guthrie
Dir Soc: Sandra Taylor
Dir Rx: Brant Krause
Sls&Mrk Ex: Brad Canfield
Mktg Dir: Evonne Walls
Obsttrcn: Kim James
Doctor: Leslie Pliskin

MID-VALLEY HOSPITAL
See OKANOGAN COUNTY PUBLIC HOSPITAL DISTRICT 3

D-U-N-S 06-857-3526
MID-VALLEY HOSPITAL ASSOCIATION
1400 Main St Ofc, Peckville, PA 18452-2098
Tel (570) 383-5500 *Founded/Ownrshp* 2001
Sales 25.5MM[E] *EMP* 180
SIC 8062 General medical & surgical hospitals; General medical & surgical hospitals
CEO: Harold A Anderson
COO: William Roe
**COO:* Emily Stevens
QA Dir: Katie Sunday
HC Dir: John Howells

D-U-N-S 80-331-7403
MID-VALLEY LABOR SERVICES INC
19358 Avenue 18 1/2, Madera, CA 93637-9709
Tel (559) 661-6390 *Founded/Ownrshp* 1988
Sales 27.0MM *EMP* 500
SIC 7361 Labor contractors (employment agency); Labor contractors (employment agency)
Pr: Samuel Mascarenas
**CFO:* Ben Mascarenas

D-U-N-S 06-344-0846
MID-VALLEY LLC
MID-VALLEY GLASS & MILLWORK CO
2630 W 7th Pl Ste A, Eugene, OR 97402-2682
Tel (541) 687-9112 *Founded/Ownrshp* 1973
Sales 62.5MM[E] *EMP* 125
SIC 5039 1793 Glass construction materials; Glass & glazing work; Glass construction materials; Glass & glazing work
CIO: Jim Lyerla
IT Man: Cheri Aiello
Mktg Dir: Steve Haner
Snr PM: Derek Rainer
Snr Mgr: Jeffrey Hansen

D-U-N-S 00-712-4977
MID-WEST CONVEYOR CO (DE)
DEARBORN MID-WEST
8245 Nieman Rd Ste 123, Lenexa, KS 66214-1509
Tel (913) 384-9950 *Founded/Ownrshp* 1946, 2007
Sales 26.0MM[E] *EMP* 335
SIC 3535 1796 3536

D-U-N-S 02-579-9586
MID-WEST DAIRYMENS CO (IL)
4313 W State St, Rockford, IL 61102-1339
Tel (815) 968-0504 *Founded/Ownrshp* 1924
Sales 115.5MM *EMP* 6[E]
SIC 5143 Milk & cream, fluid; Milk & cream, fluid
CEO: Dennis Tonak
**Ch Bd:* Daruis Simler

MID-WEST DIRECT
See MID-WEST PRESORT MAILING SERVICES INC

D-U-N-S 00-429-9418 IMP/EXP
MID-WEST FABRICATING CO (OH)
MID WEST FABRICATING CO
313 N Johns St, Amanda, OH 43102-9002
Tel (740) 969-4411 *Founded/Ownrshp* 1945, 1998
Sales 26.8MM[E] *EMP* 200
SIC 3714 3524 3452 Tie rods, motor vehicle; Lawn & garden tractors & equipment; Bolts, metal; Tie rods, motor vehicle; Lawn & garden tractors & equipment; Bolts, metal
Pr: Jennifer Johns Friel
**VP:* Ann Custer
Genl Mgr: David Gallimore
Dir IT: Kelly Wooddell
QI Cn Mgr: Roy Hoskins
Sls Mgr: Paul Strigle
Snr Mgr: Jim White

D-U-N-S 03-941-7696
MID-WEST FERTILIZER INC
1105 Baptiste Dr, Paola, KS 66071-1344
Tel (913) 294-5555 *Founded/Ownrshp* 1982
Sales 83.5MM[E] *EMP* 48
SIC 5191 Fertilizer & fertilizer materials
Pr: John Kershner
**VP:* Rod Silver
Dir IT: Harold Ackerly

D-U-N-S 00-418-7530
MID-WEST FORGE CORP
17301 Saint Clair Ave, Cleveland, OH 44110-2508
Tel (216) 481-3030 *Founded/Ownrshp* 1925
Sales 34.6MM[E] *EMP* 205
SIC 3462 Iron & steel forgings; Iron & steel forgings
Ch Bd: Robert I Gale III
Pr: Paul C Gum
Treas: Robert W Dems
V Ch Bd: Michael Sherwin
VP: John T Webster
Prd Mgr: Jerry Mejman
Board of Directors: Jim Rackley

MID-WEST HOMES FOR PETS
See MID-WEST METAL PRODUCTS CO INC

D-U-N-S 10-239-2925 IMP
MID-WEST HOSE & SPECIALTY INC
MIDWEST HOSE
3312 S I 35 Service Rd, Oklahoma City, OK 73129-6762
Tel (405) 670-6718 *Founded/Ownrshp* 1983
Sales 130.5MM[E] *EMP* 267
SIC 5085 Hose, belting & packing; Rubber goods, mechanical; Hose, belting & packing; Rubber goods, mechanical
Pr: W Harvey Sparkman
IT Man: Scotty Sparkman
VP Mktg: James Hatley

D-U-N-S 83-083-6321
MID-WEST INSTITUTIONAL FOOD DISTRIBUTORS INC
MIDWEST FOODS
3100 W 36th St, Chicago, IL 60632-2304
Tel (773) 927-8870 *Founded/Ownrshp* 1997
Sales 98.4MM[E] *EMP* 150
SIC 5142 5143 5144 5147 5148 Packaged frozen goods; Dairy products, except dried or canned; Poultry & poultry products; Meats & meat products; Fresh fruits & vegetables; Packaged frozen goods; Dairy products, except dried or canned; Poultry & poultry products; Meats & meat products; Fresh fruits & vegetables
Pr: Erin Fitzgerald

D-U-N-S 05-231-7435
MID-WEST MATERIALS INC
3687 Shepard Rd, Perry, OH 44081-9694
Tel (440) 259-5200 *Founded/Ownrshp* 1952
Sales 68.4MM[E] *EMP* 49
SIC 5051 Steel; Steel
CEO: Joseph Koppelman
**Pr:* Noreen Goldstein

*CFO: Michael Alley
*Treas: Sharon Koppelman
Exec: Vicki Stanfield
IT Man: Dale Niedzielski
Plnt Mgr: Mark Chabot
Manager: Paul Hollis
Manager: Rich McCarthy
Sales Asso: Howard Lake

D-U-N-S 00-641-8552 IMP
MID-WEST METAL PRODUCTS CO INC
MID-WEST HOMES FOR PETS
2100 W Mt Pleasant Blvd, Muncie, IN 47302-9101
Tel (888) 741-1044 Founded/Ownrshp 1921
Sales 42.9MM^E EMP 185
SIC 3496 Miscellaneous fabricated wire products; Grilles & grillework, woven wire; Mesh, made from purchased wire; Cages, wire; Miscellaneous fabricated wire products; Grilles & grillework, woven wire; Mesh, made from purchased wire; Cages, wire
CEO: Steven M Smith
*CFO: Carl Rolssen
Sr Cor Off: Larry Grass
*VP: Kevin P Smith
MIS Dir: Pam Besser
Sftwr Eng: Chris Smith
Plnt Mgr: Todd Strahan
Plnt Mgr: Martin Woolley
Ql Cn Mgr: Doug Campbell
Trfc Mgr: Eliza Schwer
Mktg Mgr: Tara King

D-U-N-S 06-909-5750
MID-WEST NATIONAL LIFE INSURANCE CO OFTENN (TN)
(Suby of HEALTHMARKETS LLC) ★
9151 Boulevard 26, Fort Worth, TX 76180-5600
Tel (817) 255-5200 Founded/Ownrshp 1965, 1986
Sales NA EMP 125
SIC 6311 6321 Life insurance; Accident insurance carriers
CEO: Kenneth J Fasola
*Ex VP: Scott R Donovan
*Ex VP: Derrick A Duke
*Sr VP: Richard E Bierman
*Sr VP: Connie Palacios

D-U-N-S 07-582-0613
MID-WEST PRESORT MAILING SERVICES INC
MID-WEST DIRECT
2222 W 110th St, Cleveland, OH 44102-3512
Tel (216) 251-2500 Founded/Ownrshp 1982
Sales 22.2MM^E EMP 250
SIC 7331

D-U-N-S 04-067-6348 IMP/EXP
MID-WEST TEXTILE CO
1600 E San Antonio Ave, El Paso, TX 79901-1726
Tel (915) 351-0231 Founded/Ownrshp 1988
Sales 121.2MM^E EMP 270
SIC 5093 5137 5136 Waste rags; Women's & children's clothing; Men's & boys' clothing; Waste rags; Women's & children's clothing; Men's & boys' clothing
Pr: James Maxfield
Treas: Tom Clark
VP: Sunny Hull
VP: John Paben

D-U-N-S 11-985-1611
MID-WEST TRUCK CENTER INC
801 N Main St Ste Q, Andrews, TX 79714-4030
Tel (432) 523-3451 Founded/Ownrshp 2002
Sales 20.4MM^E EMP 100
SIC 1389 Oil field services
Pr: Doyle Weishuhn
*VP: Max Mainord

D-U-N-S 19-704-8846
MID-WEST WHOLESALE HARDWARE CO INC
(Suby of SENTINEL CAPITAL PARTNERS LLC) ★
1000 Century Dr, Kansas City, MO 64120-1903
Tel (816) 241-5663 Founded/Ownrshp 2007
Sales 26.3MM^E EMP 72
SIC 5072 Builders' hardware
Pr: Jorge Echave
CFO: Mel Jay
Site Mgr: Fred Chubbuck
Sls Mgr: Joel Weimer
Sales Asso: Shane Anderson
Sales Asso: Larry Liggett

D-U-N-S 02-855-7874
MID-WEST WHOLESALE LIGHTING CORP
MIDWEST LIGHTING
5250 Hollywood Blvd, Los Angeles, CA 90027-4913
Tel (323) 469-1641 Founded/Ownrshp 1970
Sales 36.9MM^E EMP 50
SIC 5063 Lighting fixtures
CEO: David Frandzel
*Sec: Regina Frandzel
Genl Mgr: John Thies
Sales Asso: Martin Hernandez

D-U-N-S 03-622-3279
MID-WILLAMETTE LUMBER PRODUCTS INC
38054 Jefferson Scio Dr, Scio, OR 97374-9543
Tel (503) 394-2089 Founded/Ownrshp 1971
Sales 23.2MM^E EMP 150
SIC 2421 Resawing lumber into smaller dimensions; Resawing lumber into smaller dimensions
Pr: John Taylor
*Sec: Lynn Meier

D-U-N-S 00-612-7013
MID-WISCONSIN BEVERAGE INC (WI)
PEPSI COLA-7-UP
720 72nd Ave, Wausau, WI 54401
Tel (715) 842-0833 Founded/Ownrshp 1945, 1960
Sales 35.8MM EMP 90
SIC 2086 Carbonated soft drinks, bottled & canned
CEO: George D Wolff III
*COO: Robert W Wolff

D-U-N-S 78-239-3490
MID-WISCONSIN FINANCIAL SERVICES, INC
134 S 8th St, Medford, WI 54451-1518
Tel (715) 748-8300 Founded/Ownrshp 1986
Sales NA EMP 150^E
SIC 6022 State commercial banks; State commercial banks
CEO: Scot G Thompson
*Ch Bd: Kim A Gowey
Sec: William A Weiland
Bd of Dir: Norman Hatlestad
Ofcr: James R Tacey
VP: Sandra Lukas
DP Exec: Casey Jari
IT Man: Leif Chrisianson
Mktg Dir: Jennifer Normann
Mktg Mgr: Jennifer Norman

D-U-N-S 00-224-6734
MID-YORK PRESS INC (NY)
(Suby of MEDIA TENNEY GROUP) ★
2808 State Highway 80, Sherburne, NY 13460-4549
Tel (607) 674-4491 Founded/Ownrshp 1946, 1982
Sales 29.1MM^E EMP 70
SIC 2679 2752 2711 Paperboard products, converted; Commercial printing, offset; Newspapers, publishing & printing
Ch Bd: Robert W Tenney
COO: Pat Dowdall
*Prin: Jane Eaton
*Prin: Mary Mahoney
*Prin: Cynthia Tenney
Mktg Mgr: Thomas Revoir
Sls Mgr: John Zieno

D-U-N-S 80-313-4332
MIDAIRUSA INC
72 Macdill St Bldg 215, Rome, NY 13441-4008
Tel (315) 336-0715 Founded/Ownrshp 2007
Sales 57.2MM^E EMP 250^E
SIC 8711 7699 Aviation &/or aeronautical engineering; Aircraft & heavy equipment repair services

D-U-N-S 13-736-5136 IMP/EXP
MIDAMAR CORP
1105 60th Ave Sw, Cedar Rapids, IA 52404-7212
Tel (319) 362-3711 Founded/Ownrshp 1972
Sales 68.8MM^E EMP 50
SIC 5141 5046 5147 Food brokers; Restaurant equipment & supplies; Bakery equipment & supplies; Meats & meat products
Adm Dir: Jan Smith
Mng Dir: Tim Hyapt
Opers Mgr: Kent Vogel

D-U-N-S 15-209-5840
MIDAMERICA CARE FOUNDATION INC
HILLSBORO REHABILITATI
7611 State Line Rd, Kansas City, MO 64114-6801
Tel (816) 444-0900 Founded/Ownrshp 1983
Sales 57.9MM EMP 2,500
SIC 8051 8052 Skilled nursing care facilities; Intermediate care facilities; Skilled nursing care facilities; Intermediate care facilities
Pr: Mike Machaud
COO: Scott Gulledge

D-U-N-S 18-467-3775
MIDAMERICA DIVISION INC
MID WEST HOLDINGS
903 E 104th St Ste 500, Kansas City, MO 64131-3464
Tel (816) 508-4000 Founded/Ownrshp 2004
Sales 403.3MM^E EMP 15,040^E
SIC 8741 Hospital management; Hospital management
Pr: ML Lagarde
Chf Rad: Jeffrey Conaway
Pr: David Carnes
COO: Phil Buttell Fache
COO: Donald King III
COO: James Strieby
*CFO: Clifton Mills
VP: Amy Castillo
VP: Corrine Everson
*VP: Patrick Patterson
Dir Risk M: Jennifer Cross
Dir Rad: Tracy Miller

D-U-N-S 04-636-9930
MIDAMERICA HOTELS CORP (MO)
HOLIDAY INN
105 S Mount Auburn Rd, Cape Girardeau, MO 63703-4915
Tel (573) 334-0546 Founded/Ownrshp 1968
Sales 52.7MM^E EMP 1,000
SIC 5812 7011 Fast-food restaurant, chain; Hotels; Fast-food restaurant, chain; Hotels
Pr: Daniel M Drury
*Treas: Harold G Hale
*VP: John A Drury
VP: Diane Edwards
Exec: Larry Nelson
IT Man: Shawn Lowery
VP Opers: Joel Neikirk
Mktg Dir: Karla Drury
Sls Mgr: Brenda Newbern

D-U-N-S 06-794-8281
MIDAMERICA NAZARENE UNIVERSITY (KS)
2030 E College Way, Olathe, KS 66062-1851
Tel (913) 782-3750 Founded/Ownrshp 1966
Sales 32.1MM EMP 450
Accts Capin Crouse Llp Greenwood I
SIC 8221 5942 College, except junior; Book stores; College, except junior; Book stores
Pr: David J Spittal
*CFO: Kevin P Gilmore
Ofcr: Doug Ledbetter
*VP: Randy Beckum
VP: Jason Drummond
VP: Kevin Gilmore
*VP: Mary Jones
*VP: Jon North
Exec: Stan Hinshaw
HC Dir: Lisa Downs
HC Dir: Nicole Hodge

MIDAMERICAN
See MHC INC

MIDAMERICAN BUILDING SERVICES
See LEZK CORP

D-U-N-S 88-471-8768
■ **MIDAMERICAN ENERGY CO**
(Suby of MHC INC) ★
666 Grand Ave Ste 500, Des Moines, IA 50309-2511
Tel (515) 242-4300 Founded/Ownrshp 1996
Sales 3.7MMM EMP 2,100
SIC 4931 Electric & other services combined; Electric & other services combined
Pr: William J Fehrman
Pr: Ann Thelen
*CFO: Thomas B Specketer
Ofcr: Mark Hewett
Ex VP: Kelly Swenson
*Sr VP: Steven R Weiss
VP: Jodi Bacon
VP: Stefan Bird
VP: David Caris
VP: Stephen Dickas
VP: Jeffrey Gust
VP: Paul Priest

D-U-N-S 09-950-3943
■ **MIDAMERICAN FUNDING LLC**
(Suby of BERKSHIRE HATHAWAY ENERGY CO) ★
666 Grand Ave Ste 500, Des Moines, IA 50309-2511
Tel (515) 242-4300 Founded/Ownrshp 1999
Sales 3.7MMM EMP 3,600^E
SIC 4911 4924 Electric services; Distribution, electric power; Generation, electric power; Transmission, electric power; Natural gas distribution; Electric services; Distribution, electric power; Generation, electric power; Transmission, electric power; Natural gas distribution
Pr: William J Fehrman
Sr VP: David Levy
VP: Thomas B Specketer
Board of Directors: Douglas L Anderson, Sandra Hatfield Clubb, Patrick J Goodman

D-U-N-S 03-448-5645
MIDAS HOSPITALITY LLC (MO)
1804 Borman Circle Dr # 100, Saint Louis, MO 63146-4141
Tel (314) 692-0100 Founded/Ownrshp 2006
Sales 72.3MM^E EMP 700^E
SIC 8741 Hotel or motel management; Hotel or motel management
*CEO: David Robert
*Ex VP: Kurt Furlong
*VP: Jim Brueggemann
Exec: Stephanie Fischer
Genl Mgr: John Bremer
Genl Mgr: Michael Heater
Genl Mgr: Jackie Hubbard
Sls Dir: Jennifer Byerly
Sls Dir: Darlene Figlioli
Sls Dir: Kim Tolbert

D-U-N-S 00-812-8394 IMP
MIDAS INC
MIDAS MUFFLER
(Suby of TBC CORP) ★
4300 Tbc Way, Palm Beach Gardens, FL 33410-4281
Tel (630) 438-3000 Founded/Ownrshp 2012
Sales 98.5MM^E EMP 940
SIC 7533 6794 Muffler shop, sale or repair & installation; Franchises, selling or licensing; Muffler shop, sale or repair & installation; Franchises, selling or licensing
Pr: Alan D Feldman
*CFO: William M Guzik
*Chf Mktg O: Frederick W Dow Jr
Ofcr: Ronald J McEvoy
Sr VP: James D Hamrick
Sr VP: D Bruce Hutchison
Sr VP: Gerard M Klaisle
*Sr VP: Alvin K Marr
VP: Jeff Conner
VP: Peter Cooke
VP: Carl R Daniels Jr
VP: Timothy Garza
*VP: Michael J Gould
VP: James M Haeger Jr
VP: Robert Moschorak
VP: David C Perrin
VP: Wendell Province
VP: J Vought
Board of Directors: Thomas L Bindley, Archie R Dykes, Diane L Routson, Robert R Schoeberl

D-U-N-S 05-662-6237 IMP
MIDAS INTERNATIONAL CORP
MIDAS MUFFLER
(Suby of MIDAS INC) ★
4300 Tbc Way, Palm Beach Gardens, FL 33410-4281
Tel (561) 383-3100 Founded/Ownrshp 1998
Sales 29.3MM^E EMP 545
SIC 7533 5013 6794 3542 3714 6512 Muffler shop, sale or repair & installation; Springs, shock absorbers & struts; Automotive brakes; Automotive supplies & parts; Franchises, selling or licensing; Bending machines; Mufflers (exhaust), motor vehicle; Exhaust systems & parts, motor vehicle; Property operation, retail establishment; Muffler shop, sale or repair & installation; Springs, shock absorbers & struts; Automotive brakes; Automotive supplies & parts; Franchises, selling or licensing; Bending machines; Mufflers (exhaust), motor vehicle; Exhaust systems & parts, motor vehicle; Property operation, retail establishment
CEO: Alan Seodman
*Pr: Lawrence C Day
Pr: Jarred Klaisle
*CEO: Alan Feldman
*CFO: Willain Guzik
Sr VP: John A Warzecha
VP: Carl Daniels
VP: Cathy Hall
Board of Directors: Herbert M Baum, Thomas L Bindley, Archie R Dykes, Bob Troyer

D-U-N-S 83-155-8924
▲ **MIDAS MEDICI GROUP HOLDINGS INC**
445 Park Ave Frnt 5, New York, NY 10022-8603
Tel (212) 792-0920 Founded/Ownrshp 2009
Sales 89.6MM EMP 347
Tkr Sym MMED Exch OTO
SIC 7372 Prepackaged software; Prepackaged software
Ch Bd: Nana Baffour
*Pr: Johnson M Kachidza
*Ofcr: Frank Asante-Kissi
*Ex VP: Robert F McCarthy
Ex VP: John Roger
VP: Ricardo Giudice
VP: Mitch Lemons

MIDAS MUFFLER
See MIDAS INC

MIDAS MUFFLER
See AUTOMOTIVE SERVICE CENTERS INC

MIDAS MUFFLER
See MIDAS INTERNATIONAL CORP

D-U-N-S 82-696-2875
MIDASCO LLC
7121 Dorsey Run Rd, Elkridge, MD 21075-6884
Tel (410) 579-6700 Founded/Ownrshp 2005
Sales 74.7MM^E EMP 130^E
SIC 1611 Highway & street construction; Highway & street construction
Pr: Michael Filipczak
VP: Greg Gresko
Rgnl Mgr: Brandon Taylor
Off Mgr: Sheila Jones

D-U-N-S 09-656-3689
MIDATLANTIC FARM CREDIT
45 Aileeon Ct, Westminster, MD 21157-3022
Tel (410) 848-1033 Founded/Ownrshp 2000
Sales NA EMP 210
SIC 6159

D-U-N-S 80-594-6345
MIDATLANTIC REALTY PARTNERS LLC
MRP REALTY
3050 K St Nw Ste 125, Washington, DC 20007-5122
Tel (202) 719-9000 Founded/Ownrshp 2005
Sales 23.2MM^E EMP 85
SIC 1542 6513 Commercial & office building contractors; Apartment building operators
VP: Jennifer Demeo

D-U-N-S 83-055-3855
MIDATLANTICBROADBAND INC
PROTEL SERVICES
729 E Pratt St Ste 440, Baltimore, MD 21202-3329
Tel (410) 727-8250 Founded/Ownrshp 1999
Sales 25.0MM^E EMP 55
SIC 4813 ; ; ;
Pr: Willie Vereen
VP: Mike Piasecki
VP: Bob Steffen
VP: Jeff Weinel

MIDC
See METRO INFECTIOUS DISEASE CONSULTANTS LLC

D-U-N-S 00-506-5779
MIDCAP FINANCIAL TRUST
7255 Woodmont Ave Ste 200, Bethesda, MD 20814-7904
Tel (301) 760-7600 Founded/Ownrshp 2008
Sales 20.1MM^E EMP 55^E
SIC 6282 Investment advice
CEO: Steve Curwin
CFO: David Moore
VP: Jeff Shekell
Mng Dir: Thomas Couch
Mng Dir: Michael Levin
Mng Dir: Jason McMeen
Mng Dir: John Rosin

D-U-N-S 07-263-0010
MIDCO CALL CENTER SERVICES INC
MIDCO CONNECTIONS
(Suby of MIDCONTINENT MEDIA INC) ★
4901 E 26th St, Sioux Falls, SD 57110-6950
Tel (605) 330-4125 Founded/Ownrshp 1999
Sales 11.0MM EMP 300
SIC 7389 Telemarketing services; Telemarketing services
VP: Cordell Brooks
COO: John Kilene
Exec: Katie Roth
Dir Bus: Lance Fischer
Dir Bus: Jennifer Haskell
Genl Mgr: Chris Putzier
Genl Mgr: Doreen West
CTO: Kirk Dahl

MIDCO CONNECTIONS
See MIDCO CALL CENTER SERVICES INC

D-U-N-S 06-021-8266
■ **MIDCO FABRICATORS INC**
(Suby of FORUM ENERGY TECHNOLOGIES INC) ★
920 Mmrial Cy Way Ste 800, Houston, TX 77024
Tel (281) 949-2500 Founded/Ownrshp 2007
Sales 23.3MM^E EMP 365^E
SIC 3533 Oil field machinery & equipment; Drilling tools for gas, oil or water wells

D-U-N-S 02-522-9444
MIDCO INC (IL)
DIGICOMM
16w221 Shore Ct, Burr Ridge, IL 60527-5868
Tel (630) 887-1800 Founded/Ownrshp 1965, 1989
Sales 23.1MM^E EMP 80^E
SIC 7382 1731 Security systems services; Communications specialization; Safety & security specialization
Pr: Paul E Janik
*Treas: Sharon Macnab
*VP: Michael Janik
*VP: Jim Maertzig
Sls Mgr: Lynda Rudge

Board of Directors: Edwin Janik Jr, Sharon Mac Nab

MIDCO MATERIAL HANDLING
See MID COLUMBIA FORKLIFT INC

D-U-N-S 07-886-4088
■ MIDCOAST ENERGY PARTNERS LP
(*Suby of* ENBRIDGE ENERGY PARTNERS LP) ★
1100 La St Ste 3300, Houston, TX 77002
Tel (713) 821-2000 *Founded/Ownrshp* 2013
Sales 5.8MMM *EMP* 12
Accts Pricewaterhousecoopers Llp Ho
Tkr Sym MEP *Exch* NYS
SIC 1311 4923 Crude petroleum & natural gas; Gas transmission & distribution; Crude petroleum & natural gas; Gas transmission & distribution
CEO: Mark A Maki
Genl Pt: Midcoast Holdings
**Pr:* C Gregory Harper
COO: Terrance L McGill
Ofcr: R Poe Reed

D-U-N-S 05-841-7374
■ MIDCOAST OPERATING LP
(*Suby of* ENBRIDGE ENERGY PARTNERS LP) ★
1100 La St Ste 3400, Houston, TX 77002
Tel (713) 650-8900 *Founded/Ownrshp* 1999
Sales 423.6MM^E *EMP* 552^E
SIC 5172 1389 Gases, liquefied petroleum (propane); Processing service, gas; Gas field services
CEO: Curtis J Dufour
**Pr:* Dan Tutcher
**VP:* Mark A Maki
**VP:* Terry L McGill

D-U-N-S 03-410-2269
MIDCOM CORP (CA)
1275 N Manassero St, Anaheim, CA 92807-1933
Tel (714) 630-1999 *Founded/Ownrshp* 1979
Sales 27.7MM^E *EMP* 400
SIC 7361 Employment agencies; Employment agencies
Pr: Barbara Cepinko
COO: Anastacia Warunek
**CFO:* Paul Leone

D-U-N-S 60-613-6000
MIDCON CABLES CO INC
2500 Davis Blvd, Joplin, MO 64804-3225
Tel (417) 781-4331 *Founded/Ownrshp* 2001
Sales 41.8MM^E *EMP* 175
SIC 3679 Harness assemblies for electronic use: wire or cable; Harness assemblies for electronic use: wire or cable
Pr: Charles Wheeler
COO: Bobby Horn
**Sec:* Jack Walling
**VP:* Stan Proferi
Tech Mgr: Chuck Wheeler
Mtls Mgr: Jana Degraff
Ql Cn Mgr: Darrel Bilke
Ql Cn Mgr: Randy Durall
Manager: Matt Farris
Sls Mgr: Perry Stone

D-U-N-S 02-150-3340
■ MIDCON COMPRESSION LLC
(*Suby of* CHESAPEAKE ENERGY CORP) ★
6100 N Western Ave, Oklahoma City, OK 73118-1044
Tel (405) 935-4159 *Founded/Ownrshp* 2003
Sales 33.6MM^E *EMP* 360^E
SIC 7699 7353 Compressor repair; Oil equipment rental services; Compressor repair; Oil equipment rental services
CEO: Robert Doug Lawler
CFO: Marcus C Rowland

D-U-N-S 07-933-8582
MIDCON FUEL SERVICES LLC (AR)
8401 Lindsey Rd, Little Rock, AR 72206-3835
Tel (501) 708-2000 *Founded/Ownrshp* 2013
Sales 150.0MM *EMP* 7
SIC 5172 Engine fuels & oils; Engine fuels & oils
Pr: David Hightower

D-U-N-S 07-936-2662
MIDCON GATHERING LLC (TX)
4295 San Felipe St # 300, Houston, TX 77027-2942
Tel (713) 222-2330 *Founded/Ownrshp* 2013
Sales 30.0MM *EMP* 4
SIC 5172 Crude oil; Crude oil
Pr: David Hightower

D-U-N-S 93-002-3630
MIDCON INVESTORS INC
401 S Boston Ave Ste 3600, Tulsa, OK 74103-4020
Tel (918) 587-7325 *Founded/Ownrshp* 2000
Sales 156.6MM^E *EMP* 701
SIC 5084 Hydraulic systems equipment & supplies; Pneumatic tools & equipment; Hydraulic systems equipment & supplies; Pneumatic tools & equipment
Pr: Ian H Hill

D-U-N-S 01-773-4562
MIDCONTINENT COMMUNICATIONS
3600 Minnesota Dr Ste 700, Minneapolis, MN 55435-7918
Tel (952) 844-2600 *Founded/Ownrshp* 2000
Sales 350.2MM^E *EMP* 1,015
SIC 4841 4813 Cable & other pay television services; Telephone communication, except radio; ; Cable & other pay television services; Telephone communication, except radio;
Pt: Patrick McAdaragh
**Pt:* Richard Busch
**Pt:* Steven Grosser
CFO: Steven E Grosser
Sr VP: Tom Simmons
Snr Ntwrk: Jason Weber
IT Man: Kyle Norberg
Pgrm Dir: Wynne Haakenstad

D-U-N-S 15-894-4798
MIDCONTINENT INDEPENDENT SYSTEM OPERATOR INC
MISO
701 720 City Ctr Dr, Carmel, IN 46032
Tel (317) 249-5400 *Founded/Ownrshp* 1998
Sales 305.6MM *EMP* 700^E
Accts Ernst & Young Llp Indianapoli
SIC 4911 Distribution, electric power; Generation, electric power; Transmission, electric power; Distribution, electric power; Generation, electric power; Transmission, electric power
CEO: John R Bear
Sr Cor Off: J Evans
**Ex VP:* Richard Doying
**Ex VP:* Clair Moeller
**Sr VP:* John Goode
**VP:* Robert Berntsen
**VP:* Jo Biggers
VP: Michael Chiasson
**VP:* Jennifer Curran
VP: Michael J Gahagan
**VP:* Joseph Gardner
VP: Joseph J Gardner
**VP:* Todd Hillman
VP: Daniel L Jones
**VP:* Stephen G Kozey
**VP:* Keith Mitchell
**VP:* Greg Powell
**VP:* Todd Ramey
**VP:* Wayne Schug
VP: Robert A Sinclair
VP: Michael T Wander

D-U-N-S 00-792-0457
MIDCONTINENT MEDIA INC
3600 Minnesota Dr Ste 700, Minneapolis, MN 55435-7918
Tel (952) 844-2600 *Founded/Ownrshp* 1990
Sales 407.9MM^E *EMP* 1,300
SIC 4841 Cable television services; Cable television services
Ch Bd: Mark S Niblick
**Pr:* Patrick McAdaragh
**COO:* Richard Busch
**Sr VP:* Tom Simmons
VP: Scott Anderson
VP: Orville Frazier
VP: Wynne Haakenstad
CIO: Abdul Sofid
IT Man: Amy Lingbeck
Sfty Dirs: Jennifer Eichmann
Mtls Dir: Joe Mauss

MIDCONTINENT PUBLIC LIBRARY
See CONSOLIDATED LIBRARY DISTRICT NO 3

D-U-N-S 86-726-5118 IMP
MIDCONTINENTAL CHEMICAL CO INC
MCC
1802 E 123rd Ter, Olathe, KS 66061-5876
Tel (913) 390-5556 *Founded/Ownrshp* 1994
Sales 37.9MM^E *EMP* 40
SIC 5169 2911 8742 Chemical additives; Fuel additives; Management consulting services
Pr: Jim Elder
**Treas:* Rankin Hobbs
Area Mgr: Jeff Davidson
Dist Mgr: Ray Sparling
Mktg Dir: Everett Osgood
Sales Asso: Anju Singla

D-U-N-S 79-713-4157
MIDCOUNTRY BANK
(*Suby of* MID COUNTRY FINANCIAL CORP) ★
2611 Blue Heron Dr, Marion, IL 62959-4987
Tel (618) 998-4160 *Founded/Ownrshp* 2007
Sales NA *EMP* 565^E
SIC 6035 Savings institutions, federally chartered; Savings institutions, federally chartered
Prin: Larry Flowers
Sr VP: Karen Conrad
VP: Dean D Browning

D-U-N-S 17-842-4854
MIDCOUNTRY BANK INC
Investors Bldg 7 Ste 103, Minneapolis, MN 55402
Tel (952) 843-5200 *Founded/Ownrshp* 1933
Sales NA *EMP* 1,200
SIC 6035 Savings institutions, federally chartered; Savings institutions, federally chartered
Pr: Steve Meads
**COO:* Maureen O'Brien Wieser
CFO: Greg Christensen
Chf Cred: Greg Christianson
Chf Cred: Greg Drehmel
Sr VP: Tom Naughtin
**Sr VP:* Robin Roberts
VP: Sharon Bechtum
**VP:* Bob Calander
**VP:* Karen Conrad
VP: David Resch
VP: David Soukup
VP: Kathy Wachter
Dir Risk M: Sandra Laughlin

D-U-N-S 02-144-8501
MIDD-WEST SCHOOL DISTRICT (INC)
568 E Main St, Middleburg, PA 17842-1218
Tel (570) 837-0046 *Founded/Ownrshp* 1970
Sales 16.3MM^E *EMP* 321
SIC 8211 9411 Public combined elementary & secondary school; School board; Administration of educational programs; Public combined elementary & secondary school; School board; Administration of educational programs

D-U-N-S 05-396-4680
■ MIDDENDORF MEAT CO LLC
MIDDENDORF QUALITY FOODS
(*Suby of* P F G) ★
3737 N Broadway, Saint Louis, MO 63147-3496
Tel (314) 241-4800 *Founded/Ownrshp* 2002
Sales 83.4MM^E *EMP* 200
SIC 5147 5141 5148 5146 5113 2011 Meats, fresh; Groceries, general line; Fresh fruits & vegetables; Fish, frozen, unpackaged; Industrial & personal service paper; Meat packing plants; Meats, fresh; Groceries, general line; Fresh fruits & vegetables; Fish, frozen, unpackaged; Industrial & personal service paper; Meat packing plants
Pr: Orville Middendorf
**Treas:* Jeffery W Fender
VP: Donald Middendorf
Area Mgr: Shawn Nevins
Genl Mgr: Jerry Jones
Manager: Tom Maertz
Manager: Paul Witwer

MIDDENDORF QUALITY FOODS
See MIDDENDORF MEAT CO LLC

MIDDETOWN BOARD OF EDUCATION
See MIDDLETOWN CITY SCHOOL DISTRICT

D-U-N-S 10-124-2022 IMP/EXP
MIDDLE ATLANTIC PRODUCTS INC
DATATEL
(*Suby of* LEGRAND HOLDING INC) ★
300 Fairfield Rd, Fairfield, NJ 07004-1932
Tel (973) 839-1011 *Founded/Ownrshp* 2011
Sales 78.0MM^E *EMP* 339
SIC 3444 Casings, sheet metal; Casings, sheet metal
CEO: Bob Schluter
**Pr:* Michael L Baker
**Treas:* James Laperriere
**VP:* Robert Julian
Exec: Ross Leblanc
Rgnl Mgr: Carlo Coppola
IT Man: Tom Maglione
VP Opers: William Fuchs
Prd Mgr: Okan Esendemir
Pr Mgr: Rebeca Villareale
Manager: Blake Brubaker

D-U-N-S 01-374-8132
MIDDLE ATLANTIC WAREHOUSE DISTRIBUTOR INC
(*Suby of* UNI-SELECT INC)
20 Hazelwood Dr Ste 100, Amherst, NY 14228-2200
Tel (716) 531-9200 *Founded/Ownrshp* 1963
Sales 127.2MM^E *EMP* 1,600
SIC 5013 Automotive supplies & parts; Automotive supplies & parts
CEO: Jim Buzzard
**Ch:* Clay E Buzzard
**VP:* Robert C Buzzard
Plnt Mgr: Terry Johns

D-U-N-S 08-499-1348
MIDDLE ATLANTIC WHOLESALE LUMBER INC (MD)
2700 Lighthouse Pt E # 310, Baltimore, MD 21224-4777
Tel (410) 900-1290 *Founded/Ownrshp* 1977, 2002
Sales 27.0MM^E *EMP* 14
SIC 5031 Lumber, plywood & millwork; Lumber, plywood & millwork
Pr: Mary L Carlson
**VP:* Joel Winters

D-U-N-S 07-750-9438
MIDDLE COUNTRY CENTRAL SCHOOL DISTRICT
8 43rd St, Centereach, NY 11720-2325
Tel (631) 285-8000 *Founded/Ownrshp* 1930
Sales 222.3MM *EMP* 1,600
Accts Rs Abrams & Co Llp Island
SIC 8211 Public elementary & secondary schools; Public elementary & secondary schools

D-U-N-S 06-216-3993 IMP
MIDDLE EAST BAKERY INC
JOSEPH'S ONLINE BAKERY
30 International Way, Lawrence, MA 01843-1064
Tel (978) 688-2221 *Founded/Ownrshp* 1972
Sales 28.7MM^E *EMP* 85
SIC 2051 Bread, cake & related products
Prin: Joseph H Boghos
**Treas:* Joseph Ganem
**VP:* Tom Conomacos

D-U-N-S 13-839-3819
MIDDLE EAST BROADCASTING NETWORKS INC
MIDDLE EAST TELEVISION NETWORK
7600 Boston Blvd, Springfield, VA 22153-3136
Tel (703) 852-9000 *Founded/Ownrshp* 2003
Sales 107.3MM *EMP* 624
Accts Gelman Rosenberg & Freedman
SIC 4841 4832 Cable & other pay television services; Direct broadcast satellite services (DBS); Radio broadcasting stations; Cable & other pay television services; Direct broadcast satellite services (DBS); Radio broadcasting stations
Pr: Brian T Conniff
CFO: William Clancey
**Treas:* Kelley Sullivan
Ofcr: Mark Kozaki
VP: Daniel Nassif
CTO: Vijaykumar Mirchandani
IT Man: Ross Castle
IT Man: Dean Cowan

MIDDLE EAST TELEVISION NETWORK
See MIDDLE EAST BROADCASTING NETWORKS INC

MIDDLE GA COMMUNITY ACTION
See MIDDLE GEORGIA COMMUNITY ACTION AGENCY INC

D-U-N-S 07-248-3258
MIDDLE GEORGIA COMMUNITY ACTION AGENCY INC
MIDDLE GA COMMUNITY ACTION
121 Prince St, Warner Robins, GA 31093-0712
Tel (478) 922-4464 *Founded/Ownrshp* 1974
Sales NA *EMP* 410
Accts H Frank Erwin Jr Pc Eastm
SIC 9441 Administration of social & manpower programs; ; Administration of social & manpower programs;
Ex Dir: Nancy D Smith
Sr Cor Off: Dorothy Robinson
Exec: Carrol Phillips
Pgrm Dir: Patricia Evans

D-U-N-S 96-253-7622
MIDDLE GEORGIA CORP
309 Broad St, Ellaville, GA 31806
Tel (229) 937-2507 *Founded/Ownrshp* 2010
Sales NA *EMP* 88^E
SIC 6022 State commercial banks
Prin: John P Gill

D-U-N-S 87-903-2654
MIDDLE GEORGIA STATE UNIVERSITY
(*Suby of* BOARD OF REGENTS OF UNIVERSITY SYSTEM OF GEORGIA) ★
100 University Pkwy, Macon, GA 31206-5100
Tel (478) 471-2700 *Founded/Ownrshp* 1973
Sales 94.8MM^E *EMP* 1,125
Accts Russell W Hinton State Audit
SIC 8221 University; University
Pr: Chris Blake
Pr: David Sims
**Ex VP:* Nancy Stroud
**VP:* Martha Venn
Exec: Lee Polk
Dir Risk M: Ron Ardelean
Dir IT: Charles Warren
Opers Mgr: Alice Jane

D-U-N-S 09-669-3668
MIDDLE PENINSULA NORTHERN NECK COMMUNITY SERVICE BOARD INC
MIDDLE PENINSULA-NORTHERN NECK
Business Rte 17, Saluda, VA 23149
Tel (804) 758-5314 *Founded/Ownrshp* 1972
Sales 16.7MM^E *EMP* 980
SIC 8093 Mental health clinic, outpatient; Substance abuse clinics (outpatient); Mental health clinic, outpatient; Substance abuse clinics (outpatient)
Ex Dir: Charles Walsh

MIDDLE PENINSULA-NORTHERN NECK
See MIDDLE PENINSULA NORTHERN NECK COMMUNITY SERVICE BOARD INC

MIDDLE RIVER AIRCRAFT SYSTEMS
See MRA SYSTEMS INC

MIDDLE SCHOOL
See SKANEATELES CENTRAL SCHOOL DISTRICT

MIDDLE SCHOOL WEST
See ANGLETON SCHOOL DISTRICT

MIDDLE SCHOOLS EDUCATION OFF
See HILLSBOROUGH COUNTY SCHOOL DISTRICT

D-U-N-S 96-388-9063
MIDDLE TENNESSEE MEDICAL CENTER
1700 Medical Center Pkwy, Murfreesboro, TN 37129-2245
Tel (615) 396-4100 *Founded/Ownrshp* 1927
Sales 253.9MM *EMP* 9^E
Accts Deloitte Tax Llp Cincinnati
SIC 8062 General medical & surgical hospitals; General medical & surgical hospitals
Pr: Gordon B Ferguson
COO: Elizabeth Lemons
VP: Dr Andy Brown
Prin: Carol Bragdon
Prin: Kelly Miles

D-U-N-S 00-792-2321
MIDDLE TENNESSEE ELECTRIC MEMBERSHIP CORP
555 New Salem Hwy, Murfreesboro, TN 37129-3390
Tel (615) 890-9762 *Founded/Ownrshp* 1936
Sales 549.9MM *EMP* 410
Accts Winnett Associates Pllc Shelb
SIC 4911 Distribution, electric power; Distribution, electric power
Pr: Chris Jones
**Ch Bd:* Michael Woods
**V Ch:* Tom Purkey
**COO:* Tom Suggs
**CFO:* Bernie Steen
**Sec:* Steve Seger
**Sr VP:* Brad Gibson
**VP:* Keith Thomason
Prgrm Mgr: Kevin Collins
CTO: Marie Trott
Dir IT: Jeff Gill

D-U-N-S 62-649-3332
MIDDLE TENNESSEE MOTOR CARS INC
MERCEDES-BENZ OF NASHVILLE
630 Bakers Bridge Ave, Franklin, TN 37067-1686
Tel (615) 742-5250 *Founded/Ownrshp* 1991
Sales 30.0MM^E *EMP* 83
SIC 5511 Automobiles, new & used; Automobiles, new & used
CEO: Herald Hamilton
Sec: Ellis Hubbard
CTO: Tim Hillier
Sales Asso: Beatrix Mohsenin

D-U-N-S 04-293-8647
MIDDLE TENNESSEE NATURAL GAS UTILITY DISTRICT
MIDDLE TENNESSEE UTILITY DISTR
1030 W Broad St, Smithville, TN 37166-2501
Tel (615) 597-4300 *Founded/Ownrshp* 1955
Sales 69.5MM *EMP* 138
Accts Frazier & Deeter Nashville T
SIC 4924 Natural gas distribution; Natural gas distribution
CEO: James E Hodges
**CFO:* Daniel Hicks
VP: Jim Hodges
**VP:* Edward Kelley
Exec: Brenda Gay
CIO: Jason Morse

D-U-N-S 07-764-8780
MIDDLE TENNESSEE STATE UNIVERSITY
1301 E Main St, Murfreesboro, TN 37132-0002
Tel (615) 898-2300 *Founded/Ownrshp* 1972
Sales 182.9MM *EMP* 2,610
SIC 8221 University; University
Pr: Sidney A McPhee
Dir Recs: Teresa Thomas
COO: Sarah Bergemann
Ofcr: Vergena Forbes
VP: Michael D Allen
Ex Dir: Amanda Toney
Off Mgr: Francis Rich

MIDDLE TENNESSEE UTILITY DISTR
See MIDDLE TENNESSEE NATURAL GAS UTILITY DISTRICT

D-U-N-S 06-987-3818
MIDDLE TOWNSHIP PUBLIC SCHOOL
216 S Main St, Cape May Court House, NJ 08210-2273
Tel (609) 465-1802 *Founded/Ownrshp* 1950
Sales 20.5MM^E *EMP* 379
SIC 8211 Public elementary & secondary schools; Public elementary & secondary schools

D-U-N-S 07-979-9814
MIDDLEBOROUGH PUBLIC SCHOOLS
30 Forest St, Middleboro, MA 02346-4012
Tel (508) 946-2000 *Founded/Ownrshp* 2015
Sales 7.5MM^E *EMP* 435^E
SIC 8211 Public elementary & secondary schools
HC Dir: Laurie Perkins

D-U-N-S 03-583-7525
■ **MIDDLEBURG BANK**
(*Suby of* MIDDLEBURG FINANCIAL CORP) ★
111 W Washington St, Middleburg, VA 20117-2602
Tel (540) 687-6377 *Founded/Ownrshp* 1924
Sales NA *EMP* 103
SIC 6021 National commercial banks; National commercial banks
Pr: Gary R Shook
Sr VP: Gregory Baugher
Sr VP: Kathleen Croson
Sr VP: Tyler Harris
Sr VP: Richard Luttrell
Sr VP: Kevin Shaner
Sr VP: David Stalnaker
VP: Jeffrey Culver
VP: Patrick Heijmen
VP: Browning Herbert
VP: Jim Maki
VP: Jeff Milnes
VP: Rodney White
Exec: Michael Maddocks
Board of Directors: Mary Leigh McDaniel

D-U-N-S 04-878-2622
▲ **MIDDLEBURG FINANCIAL CORP**
111 W Washington St, Middleburg, VA 20117-2602
Tel (703) 777-6327 *Founded/Ownrshp* 1993
Sales NA *EMP* 352^E
Tkr Sym MBRG *Exch* NAS
SIC 6021 National commercial banks; National commercial banks
Pr: Gary R Shook
**Ch Bd:* Joseph L Boling
Pr: Carolyn Diprinzio
Pr: David L Hartley
COO: Jeffery H Culver
COO: Alice P Frazier
CFO: Kathleen Chappell
CFO: Rajesh Mehra
Bd of Dir: Howard Armfield
Ex VP: Suzanne K Withers
Sr VP: Andy McLean
VP: James E Abbe IV
VP: Reggie Dawson
VP: Efrsosine Tzaferis
VP: Jimmy Whirley

D-U-N-S 07-429-9710
MIDDLEBURY COMMUNITY SCHOOLS
56853 Northridge Dr, Middlebury, IN 46540-9536
Tel (574) 825-9425 *Founded/Ownrshp* 1964
Sales 34.1MM^E *EMP* 490
SIC 8211 Public elementary school; Public junior high school; Public senior high school; Public elementary school; Public junior high school; Public senior high school
Dir Rx: Mark Snyder
Dir IT: Chris Kratzer
Dir IT: Susan Parker

MIDDLEBURY TRAILERS
See LA EAST INC

MIDDLEBY COOKING SYSTEMS GROUP
See MARSHALL MIDDLEBY INC

D-U-N-S 08-893-2108 EXP
▲ **MIDDLEBY CORP**
1400 Toastmaster Dr, Elgin, IL 60120-9274
Tel (847) 741-3300 *Founded/Ownrshp* 1888
Sales 1.6MMM *EMP* 4,860
Tkr Sym MIDD *Exch* NGS
SIC 3556 3589 Food products machinery; Ovens, bakery; Mixers, commercial, food; Commercial cooking & foodwarming equipment; Cooking equipment, commercial; Food warming equipment, commercial; Food products machinery; Ovens, bakery; Mixers, commercial, food; Commercial cooking & foodwarming equipment; Cooking equipment, commercial; Food warming equipment, commercial
Ch Bd: Selim A Bassoul
CFO: Timothy J Fitzgerald
Treas: Martin M Lindsay
Board of Directors: Sarah Palisi Chapin, Robert B Lamb, Cathy McCarthy, John R Miller III, Gordon O'brien, Philip G Putnam

D-U-N-S 62-534-3579
▲ **MIDDLEFIELD BANC CORP**
15985 E High St, Middlefield, OH 44062-7229
Tel (440) 632-1666 *Founded/Ownrshp* 1988
Sales NA *EMP* 139
Tkr Sym MBCN *Exch* NAS
SIC 6022 State commercial banks; State commercial banks
Pr: Thomas G Caldwell
**Ch Bd:* Carolyn J Turk
**COO:* James R Heslop II
CFO: Donald L Stacy

D-U-N-S 01-976-8738
■ **MIDDLEFIELD BANKING CO INC** (OH)
(*Suby of* MIDDLEFIELD BANC CORP) ★
15985 E High St, Middlefield, OH 44062-7229
Tel (440) 632-1666 *Founded/Ownrshp* 1901, 1989
Sales NA *EMP* 55
SIC 6022 State commercial banks; State commercial banks
Pr: Tom Caldwell
**Ch Bd:* Carolyn J Turk
Bd of Dir: Joseph Thomas
Ofcr: Kristie Bond
Sr VP: Eric P Hollinger
VP: Courtney Erminio
VP: Joe Glassco
VP: Teresa Hetrick
**VP:* Nancy Snow
VP: Dave Stuthard
Brnch Mgr: Mary Gerbasi

D-U-N-S 04-283-3582
MIDDLEKAUFF AUTOMOTIVE GROUP INC (ID)
1243 Blue Lakes Blvd N, Twin Falls, ID 83301-3308
Tel (208) 736-2480 *Founded/Ownrshp* 1997
Sales 32.2MM *EMP* 110^E
SIC 5511 5531 7538 Automobiles, new & used; Automotive parts; General automotive repair shops; Automobiles, new & used; Automotive parts; General automotive repair shops
Genl Mgr: Dave Mace
**Pr:* Gregg O Middlekauff
Treas: Ken Bierman
**Treas:* Jeannette Bolton

MIDDLEOAK INSURANCE COMPANY
See MIDDLESEX MUTUAL ASSURANCE CO

D-U-N-S 00-636-4491
MIDDLESBORO COCA-COLA BOTTLING WORKS INC
1324 Cumberland Ave, Middlesboro, KY 40965-1116
Tel (606) 248-2660 *Founded/Ownrshp* 1904
Sales 28.7MM *EMP* 100
Accts Breazeale & Associates Pc
SIC 2086 Bottled & canned soft drinks; Bottled & canned soft drinks
Pr: Neil G Barry Jr
**CFO:* Patrick Forster
**VP:* Jill Barry
**VP:* Linvil D Day
Prd Mgr: Glenn Hoskins
Manager: Bobby Abbott

D-U-N-S 10-002-7622
MIDDLESBORO INDEPENDENT SCHOOLS TRUST FOUNDATION INC
220 N 20th St, Middlesboro, KY 40965-2808
Tel (606) 242-8800 *Founded/Ownrshp* 1880
Sales 14.9MM *EMP* 325
Accts Marr Miller & Myers Psc Corb
SIC 8211 Public elementary & secondary schools; Public elementary & secondary schools

D-U-N-S 07-832-5859
MIDDLESEX ASPHALT LLC (DE)
10801 Cosmonaut Blvd, Orlando, FL 32824-7627
Tel (407) 206-0078 *Founded/Ownrshp* 1975, 1998
Sales 22.3MM^E *EMP* 120^E
SIC 1611 1794 General contractor, highway & street construction; Highway & street paving contractor; Excavation & grading, building construction; General contractor, highway & street construction; Highway & street paving contractor; Excavation & grading, building construction
Pr: Alfred Aponas
**Treas:* Robert N Jacobson

D-U-N-S 07-844-2222
MIDDLESEX BANCORP MHC
6 Main St, Natick, MA 01760-4506
Tel (508) 653-0300 *Founded/Ownrshp* 2012
Sales NA *EMP* 547^E
SIC 6036 Savings institutions, not federally chartered
CEO: John Heerwagen
Chf Inves: Brian Stewart
Ex VP: Brian Lanigan
VP: Michael Hart
VP: Kevin Kane
VP: Bill Whelton
Mktg Dir: Laura Duncan

D-U-N-S 60-873-7615
MIDDLESEX COMMUNITY COLLEGE
591 Springs Rd, Bedford, MA 01730-1120
Tel (978) 656-3200 *Founded/Ownrshp* 1971
Sales 22.9MM^E *EMP* 500
SIC 8222 Junior college; Junior college
Ch: Royall M Mack Sr
Pr: Lura Smith
Pr: Carol Thomas
CFO: Michael Giles
CFO: James Linnehan
VP: Phil Sisson
Dir Lab: Randeane Tetu
Dir IT: Alan Keniston
IT Man: Ralph Cedrone
IT Man: Sandra Hill

D-U-N-S 06-218-5517
MIDDLESEX CORP (MA)
1 Spectacle Pond Rd, Littleton, MA 01460-1128
Tel (978) 742-4400 *Founded/Ownrshp* 1973
Sales 224.7MM^E *EMP* 500
SIC 1611 1794 1622 General contractor, highway & street construction; Excavation work; Bridge, tunnel & elevated highway; General contractor, highway & street construction; Excavation work; Bridge, tunnel & elevated highway
Pr: Robert Pereira II
**Pr:* Alfred S Aponas
**Pr:* Robert L Mabardy
**CFO:* Robert N Jacobson
**Sr VP:* David Skerrett
**Sr VP:* David Socci

D-U-N-S 06-870-7801
MIDDLESEX COUNTY COLLEGE
2600 Woodbridge Ave, Edison, NJ 08837-3675
Tel (732) 548-6000 *Founded/Ownrshp* 1964
Sales 39.4MM^E *EMP* 1,014
SIC 8222 9111 8221 8211 Community college; County supervisors' & executives' offices; Colleges universities & professional schools; Elementary & secondary schools; Community college; County supervisors' & executives' offices; Colleges universities & professional schools; Elementary & secondary schools
Pr: Joann La Perla-Morales
Ofcr: Cory Smith
VP: Laura Cahill
**VP:* Ronald Goldfarb
**VP:* Karen Hays
VP: Daniel Levine
VP: Patrick Madama
**VP:* Susan Perkins
Assoc Dir: Louis Marius
Ex Dir: Veronica Clinton
Ex Dir: Donald Drost

D-U-N-S 94-270-3885
MIDDLESEX COUNTY IMPROVEMENT AUTHORITY
101 Interchange Plz, Cranbury, NJ 08512-3716
Tel (609) 655-5141 *Founded/Ownrshp* 1991
Sales NA *EMP* 400
Accts Hodulik & Morrison Pa
SIC 9511 9512 Waste management program administration, government; ; Land management agency, government; Waste management program administration, government; ; Land management agency, government
Ex Dir: Richard Pucci
Ch: Leonard Rosman
Snr PM: Denise Nickel

D-U-N-S 07-313-3100
MIDDLESEX COUNTY OF (INC) (NJ)
75 Bayard St, New Brunswick, NJ 08901-2112
Tel (732) 745-3000 *Founded/Ownrshp* 1682
Sales NA *EMP* 2,100^E
Accts Hodulik & Morrison Pa High
SIC 9111 Executive offices; ; Executive offices;
CFO: Albert Kuchinskas
Treas: Jim Phillips
Ofcr: Doug Breen
Ofcr: Christopher Coen
Sr VP: John Stefani
IT Man: Kathy Borgen

MIDDLESEX COUNTY TREASURER
See COUNTY OF MIDDLESEX

D-U-N-S 07-041-2812
MIDDLESEX COUNTY UTILITIES AUTHORITY INC
2571 Main St, Sayreville, NJ 08872-1478
Tel (732) 721-3800 *Founded/Ownrshp* 1950
Sales 103.7MM^E *EMP* 185
Accts Parentebeard Llc Clark New J
SIC 4952 Sewerage systems; Sewerage systems
Ch: Ted Light
V Ch: John Pantalone
CFO: Victor Santamarna
**Treas:* Margaret M Brennan
Treas: William Burns
Treas: Karen Sissick
Exec: Robert Burner
Exec: Kathleen Guss
**Ex Dir:* Richard Fitamant
**Dist Mgr:* John F Wiley
Off Mgr: Theresa Gallagher

D-U-N-S 06-871-1159
MIDDLESEX COUNTY VOCATIONAL & TECHNICAL HIGH SCHOOLS (INC) (NJ)
BOARD OF EDUCATION
112 Rues Ln, East Brunswick, NJ 08816-4235
Tel (732) 257-3300 *Founded/Ownrshp* 1914
Sales 31.5MM^E *EMP* 409
SIC 8211 Public elementary & secondary schools; Public elementary & secondary schools
Prin: John F Bicsko Jr
IT Man: Francine Thompson

D-U-N-S 00-142-6311
MIDDLESEX GASES & TECHNOLOGIES INC (MA)
292 2nd St, Everett, MA 02149-4739
Tel (617) 387-5050 *Founded/Ownrshp* 1949
Sales 57.5MM^E *EMP* 63
SIC 5169 5084 Compressed gas; Industrial machinery & equipment; Compressed gas; Industrial machinery & equipment
Ch Bd: Joseph E Martin III
**Ex VP:* Thomas W Martin
**VP:* Albert R Reynolds
Opers Mgr: Steven Goncalves
Sales Exec: Ron Berry

D-U-N-S 96-676-1152
MIDDLESEX HEALTH SYSTEM INC
28 Crescent St, Middletown, CT 06457-3654
Tel (860) 358-6000 *Founded/Ownrshp* 1985
Sales 1.1MM *EMP* 2,664^E
Accts Kpmg Llp Boston Ma
SIC 8062 General medical & surgical hospitals
Pr: Vincent G Capece Jr
VP: Ludwig Johnson
**VP:* Susan M Martin
MIS Dir: Karen Kohler

D-U-N-S 06-925-7152
MIDDLESEX HOSPITAL FOUNDATION INC (CT)
(*Suby of* MIDDLESEX HEALTH SYSTEM INC) ★
28 Crescent St, Middletown, CT 06457-3654
Tel (860) 358-6000 *Founded/Ownrshp* 1895
Sales 366.5MM *EMP* 2,632
SIC 8062 Hospital, medical school affiliation; Hospital, medical school affiliation
Ch Bd: Arthur Mc Dowell III
Chf Rad: Michael Crain
**Pr:* Robert Kiely
**CFO:* Vincent G Capece Jr
Bd of Dir: Denise Byron
VP: Ludwig Johnson
VP: David J Miner
VP: Geg Nokes
Dir Lab: Jack Boehme
Dir Lab: Cheryl Mill
Assoc Dir: Stephanie Rosener
Dir Rx: Ann Calamari

D-U-N-S 00-691-7561
MIDDLESEX MUTUAL ASSURANCE CO
MIDDLEOAK INSURANCE COMPANY
213 Court St Fl 4, Middletown, CT 06457-3320
Tel (860) 347-4621 *Founded/Ownrshp* 1836
Sales NA *EMP* 250
SIC 6331 6411 Fire, marine & casualty insurance: mutual; Insurance agents, brokers & service; Fire, marine & casualty insurance: mutual; Insurance agents, brokers & service
Pr: Barbara Baurer
**CEO:* Gary J Vallo
VP: Bruce Hale
VP: Jonathan Herron
VP: Joseph Meagher
VP: Daniel Schwanke
VP: Sean Sweeney
VP: Anne Tarryk
Netwrk Eng: Robert Lynch
VP Opers: Karen Kolodziej
Natl Sales: John Barry

D-U-N-S 09-424-9026
MIDDLESEX REGIONAL EDUCATIONAL SERVICES COMMISSION (NJ)
1660 Stelton Rd, Piscataway, NJ 08854-4973
Tel (732) 777-9848 *Founded/Ownrshp* 1978
Sales NA *EMP* 800
Accts Ernst & Young Llp
SIC 9411 Administration of educational programs; Administration of educational programs
Dir IT: Bob Reinke

D-U-N-S 00-695-5181
MIDDLESEX SAVINGS BANK
(*Suby of* MIDDLESEX BANCORP MHC) ★
6 Main St, Natick, MA 01760-4534
Tel (508) 653-0300 *Founded/Ownrshp* 1835
Sales NA *EMP* 464
SIC 6036 Savings institutions, not federally chartered; Savings institutions, not federally chartered
CEO: John R Heerwagen
**Pr:* James A Lavoie
Pr: Madelyn Phelan
Pr: Timothy Wilson
**COO:* Brian D Lanigan
COO: Patricia Slaney
**CFO:* Paul M Totino
Ofcr: Jeffrey Kerl
Ex VP: Charles R Bauer
Ex VP: Karen M Curtis
Ex VP: Michael G McAuliffe
Ex VP: Dana M Neshe
Sr VP: David Shorey
**Sr VP:* Brian D Stewart
Sr VP: Bruce Weisberg
VP: Paul Adams
VP: David Bennett
VP: Carole Bernstein
VP: Cheryl Corman
VP: Keller David
VP: Timothy Fahey

D-U-N-S 07-659-5743
MIDDLESEX SCHOOL
1400 Lowell Rd, Concord, MA 01742-5255
Tel (978) 369-2550 *Founded/Ownrshp* 1901
Sales 37.8MM *EMP* 150
Accts Mcgladrey Llp Charlestown Ma
SIC 8211 Private senior high school
Pr: Richard M Burnes
**Treas:* Austin Olney
Ofcr: Sam Hoar
Ofcr: Matt Rawson
Ex Dir: Thomas J Hudner
Ex Dir: Heather Parker
Off Mgr: Terry Cunningham
Dir IT: Joe Alford
IT Man: Larry Buck

D-U-N-S 00-697-5122
▲ **MIDDLESEX WATER CO** (NJ)
1500 Ronson Rd, Iselin, NJ 08830-3020
Tel (732) 634-1500 *Founded/Ownrshp* 1896
Sales 117.1MM *EMP* 279^E
Accts Baker Tilly Virchow Krause Ll
Tkr Sym MSEX *Exch* NGS
SIC 4941 1623 Water supply; Water, sewer & utility lines; Water supply; Water, sewer & utility lines
Ch Bd: Dennis W Doll
COO: Richard M Risoldi
CFO: A Bruce O'Connor
Sr VP: Walter Brady
VP: Jay L Kooper
VP: Bernadette M Sohler
Exec: Joseph Baran
Board of Directors: James F Cosgrove Jr, John C Cutting, Steven M Klein, Amy B Mansue, John R Middleton, Walter G Reinhard, Jeffries Shein

MIDDLETON AEROSPACE
See MAGELLAN AEROSPACE USA INC

MIDDLETON AEROSPACE
See MAGELLAN AEROSPACE HAVERHILL INC

D-U-N-S 04-019-6354
MIDDLETON BRATRUD INSURANCE BROKERS INC
BRATRUD MIDDLETON INSURANCE
1201 Pacific Ave Ste 1000, Tacoma, WA 98402-4321
Tel (253) 759-2200 *Founded/Ownrshp* 1996
Sales NA *EMP* 175
SIC 6411 Insurance brokers; Insurance brokers
Pr: Kurt Carlson
**Pr:* Charles Miller
**CFO:* Stephen Feltus
VP: Cory Corye
VP: Kathy Fraley
VP: Nancy Frost
VP: Kyle Howat
Mng Dir: Max Hanley
Mng Dir: Kris Morimoto
Mng Dir: Charlie Morriss
Mng Dir: Sandi Paschall

D-U-N-S 80-950-4202 IMP
MIDDLETON BUILDING SUPPLY INC
DIPRIZIO PINES SALES
5 Kings Hwy, Middleton, NH 03887-6217
Tel (603) 473-2210 *Founded/Ownrshp* 1993
Sales 30.2MM^E *EMP* 139
SIC 5211 5099 2431 2421 Lumber & other building materials; Wood & wood by-products; Millwork; Sawmills & planing mills, general; Lumber & other building materials; Wood & wood by-products; Millwork; Sawmills & planing mills, general
Pr: Lawrence Huot
**Ch Bd:* Harold Lavalley
**Treas:* Marcella S Perry
Sales Asso: Greg Martin

D-U-N-S 00-896-0809
MIDDLETON FARMERS COOPERATIVE CO
1755 Pleasant View Rd, Middleton, WI 53562-4679
Tel (608) 831-5921 *Founded/Ownrshp* 1928
Sales 30.1MM *EMP* 40
Accts Cliftonlarsonallen Llp Middle
SIC 5191 5541 5171 5251 5172 Feed; Fertilizer & fertilizer materials; Seeds: field, garden & flower; Gasoline service stations; Petroleum bulk stations; Hardware; Petroleum products; Feed; Fertilizer & fertilizer materials; Seeds: field, garden & flower; Gasoline service stations; Petroleum bulk stations; Hardware; Petroleum products
Pr: Leo Acker
Sec: Henry Laufenberg
VP: Kevin Wagner
Genl Mgr: David Rischmueller
Board of Directors: Ivan Hellenbrand, Fred Laufenberg

MIDDLETON FORD
See MIDDLETON MOTORS INC

D-U-N-S 11-290-4057
MIDDLETON INC
MIDDLETON SHEET METAL
22039 Interstate 30 N, Bryant, AR 72022-4261
Tel (501) 224-4888 *Founded/Ownrshp* 1976
Sales 25.5MM^E *EMP* 100
SIC 1761 1711 1531 Speculative builder, single-family houses; Roofing, siding & sheet metal work; Heating & air conditioning contractors; Ventilation & duct work contractor; Roofing, siding & sheet metal work; Heating & air conditioning contractors; Speculative builder, single-family houses
Pr: Charles E Middleton
**VP:* Jeff Aldrich
Mng Dir: Mark Middleton
Genl Mgr: Gary Waddle
Sls&Mrk Ex: Wayne Kaller
Mktg Dir: Wayne Keller

D-U-N-S 00-779-5008
MIDDLETON INC E G (VA)
2510 Cromwell Rd, Norfolk, VA 23509-2306
Tel (757) 855-3351 *Founded/Ownrshp* 1920, 1987
Sales 21.5MM^E *EMP* 95
Accts Corbin & Company Pc Chesap
SIC 1731 Electrical work; Electrical work
Pr: Middleton III
**Treas:* Dawn R Middleton
**VP:* Carl J Gerlach
Off Mgr: Dawn Middleton
Sfty Mgr: Jacob Morton

D-U-N-S 02-335-6371
MIDDLETON MOTORS INC
MIDDLETON FORD
7520 Century Ave, Middleton, WI 53562-1480
Tel (608) 831-7725 *Founded/Ownrshp* 1947
Sales 26.8MM^E *EMP* 60
SIC 5511 Automobiles, new & used; Automobiles, new & used
Owner: Robert Hudson
**Treas:* Daniel S Hudson
Genl Mgr: Mike Bihun
Info Man: Hudson David
Sls Mgr: Chuck Polley
Sales Asso: Mike Burke
Sales Asso: Keith Norris

D-U-N-S 07-546-9122
MIDDLETON OIL CO INC
420 Bolling St, Greenville, AL 36037-2804
Tel (334) 382-2627 *Founded/Ownrshp* 1968
Sales 27.7MM^E *EMP* 62
Accts Willer Crook & Jones Pc Atmo
SIC 5171 5411 Petroleum bulk stations; Convenience stores, chain; Petroleum bulk stations; Convenience stores, chain
Pr: William L Coon Sr
**Sec:* Jane Bates
**VP:* William L Coon Jr

D-U-N-S 07-979-9411
MIDDLETON PUBLIC SCHOOLS
28 Middleton Rd, Boxford, MA 01921-2336
Tel (978) 887-0771 *Founded/Ownrshp* 2015
Sales 5.0MM^E *EMP* 436^E
SIC 8211 Public elementary & secondary schools

MIDDLETON SHEET METAL
See MIDDLETON INC

D-U-N-S 09-302-6367
MIDDLETON-CROSS PLAINS-AREA SCHOOL DISTRICT
7106 South Ave, Middleton, WI 53562-3263
Tel (608) 829-9000 *Founded/Ownrshp* 1968
Sales 80.4MM *EMP* 1,100
Accts Johnson Block And Company Inc
SIC 8211 Public elementary & secondary schools; Secondary school; High school, junior or senior; Public elementary & secondary schools; Secondary school; High school, junior or senior
Dir IT: Ruth Bachmeier
HC Dir: Blanche Baker-Vlask
Snr Mgr: Cathy Patton
Snr Mgr: Aaron Stutz

D-U-N-S 02-257-0170
MIDDLETOWN AREA SCHOOL DISTRICT (INC)
55 W Water St Ste 2, Middletown, PA 17057-1467
Tel (717) 948-3300 *Founded/Ownrshp* 1920
Sales 29.9MM^E *EMP* 450
SIC 8211 Public elementary & secondary schools; Secondary school; High school, junior or senior; Public elementary & secondary schools; Secondary school; High school, junior or senior
**Treas:* Gordon Einhorn
Dir Bus: David A Franklin

D-U-N-S 08-475-5297
MIDDLETOWN CITY SCHOOL DISTRICT
MIDDETOWN BOARD OF EDUCATION
1 Donham Plz 4, Middletown, OH 45042-1932
Tel (513) 423-0781 *Founded/Ownrshp* 1846
Sales 37.7MM^E *EMP* 675
Accts Balestra Harr & Scherer Cpas
SIC 8211 Public senior high school; Public junior high school; Public elementary school; Public senior high school; Public junior high school; Public elementary school
Bd of Dir: Katie McNeil
VP: Gregory Tyus
Exec: Brenda Long
Prin: Rose M Stiehl
IT Man: Don Gilgrist
IT Man: Laurie Wood
Info Man: Brenda Lansaw
Info Man: Andrea Long
Pr Dir: Gracie Gregory
Psych: Edna Caamano
Psych: Marie Galan

MIDDLETOWN HONDA
See ADEE MOTOR CARS LLC

D-U-N-S 07-888-7100
MIDDLETOWN MEDICAL PC
111 Maltese Dr, Middletown, NY 10940-2141
Tel (845) 342-3306 *Founded/Ownrshp* 1984
Sales 22.0MM^E *EMP* 250^E
SIC 8011 Physicians' office, including specialists; Physicians' office, including specialists
COO: Rajan Gulati
CFO: Gulbir Singh
Off Mgr: Lori Marl
Mktg Dir: Melissa Wolff
Obsttrcn: Rosa Atkinson
Doctor: Alexander Gapay
Doctor: Martin Palmer
Snr Mgr: David Kanters

D-U-N-S 93-189-6872
MIDDLETOWN NISSAN LLC
1153 Newfield St, Middletown, CT 06457-1817
Tel (860) 632-6550 *Founded/Ownrshp* 1995
Sales 45.2MM^E *EMP* 50
SIC 5511 Automobiles, new & used
IT Man: Allen Rundo
Sls Mgr: Jody Mitchell
Sales Asso: Amke Neii

MIDDLETOWN PARK REHABILITATION
See PARK MANOR ACQUISITION II LLC

D-U-N-S 18-424-6643
MIDDLETOWN PUBLIC SCHOOL DISTRICT
26 Oliphant Ln, Middletown, RI 02842-4659
Tel (401) 849-2122 *Founded/Ownrshp* 2010
Sales 14.7MM^E *EMP* 359^E
SIC 8211 Public elementary & secondary schools
Prin: Rosemarie Kraeger

D-U-N-S 02-348-6665
MIDDLETOWN PUBLIC SCHOOLS
311 Hunting Hill Ave, Middletown, CT 06457-4333
Tel (860) 638-1401 *Founded/Ownrshp* 1900
Sales 20.0MM^E *EMP* 485
SIC 8211 9111 Public elementary & secondary schools; Public elementary school; Public junior high school; Public senior high school; Mayors' offices; Public elementary & secondary schools; Public elementary school; Public junior high school; Public senior high school; Mayors' offices
MIS Dir: Michael Skott
Dir IT: Robert Polselli
Schl Brd P: Gene Nocera

D-U-N-S 06-869-7705
MIDDLETOWN TOWNSHIP BOARD OF EDUCATION
834 Leonardville Rd, Leonardo, NJ 07737-1751
Tel (732) 671-3850 *Founded/Ownrshp* 1900
Sales 56.0MM^E *EMP* 1,000
SIC 8211 9111 Public elementary & secondary schools; Mayors' offices; Public elementary & secondary schools; Mayors' offices
MIS Dir: Jay Attiya

D-U-N-S 07-979-9779
MIDDLETOWN TOWNSHIP PUBLIC SCHOOLS
834 Leonardville Rd, Middletown, NJ 07748
Tel (732) 671-3850 *Founded/Ownrshp* 2015
Sales 29.2MM^E *EMP* 1,158^E
SIC 8211 Public elementary & secondary schools
Teacher Pr: John D Covert

MIDDLETOWN TOYOTA AUTOBODY
See MIDDLETOWN TOYOTA INC

D-U-N-S 01-015-9481
MIDDLETOWN TOYOTA INC
MIDDLETOWN TOYOTA AUTOBODY
634 Newfield St, Middletown, CT 06457-1820
Tel (860) 347-7294 *Founded/Ownrshp* 1975
Sales 32.5MM^E *EMP* 70
SIC 5511 Automobiles, new & used; Trucks, tractors & trailers: new & used; Vans, new & used; Automobiles, new & used; Trucks, tractors & trailers: new & used; Vans, new & used
Pr: Joseph J Klimas Jr
Sls Mgr: Evan Douglas
Sls Mgr: Riz Haider
Sls Mgr: Charles Marella
Sales Asso: Bob Blakeslee
Sales Asso: Aurelio Figueroa
Sales Asso: Ben Podd

D-U-N-S 80-159-1058
MIDDLETOWN TUBE WORKS INC
2201 Trine St, Middletown, OH 45044-5766
Tel (513) 727-0080 *Founded/Ownrshp* 1993
Sales 23.4MM^E *EMP* 80
SIC 3312 Tubes, steel & iron
Pr: Angela Phillips
Sls Dir: Tammy Graham
Sls Mgr: Chris Barker

D-U-N-S 00-654-7566
MIDDLEVILLE TOOL & DIE CO INC (MI)
1900 Patterson Rd, Middleville, MI 49333-8410
Tel (269) 795-3646 *Founded/Ownrshp* 1966
Sales 28.2MM^E *EMP* 70
Accts Brickley Delong Muskegon Mi
SIC 3469 3544 3465 Metal stampings; Special dies & tools; Automotive stampings
CEO: Gary Middleton
**Pr:* Ross Martin
Genl Mgr: Greg Goodrich
VP Mfg: Mike Cornell
Ql Cn Mgr: Richard Thomas
Snr Mgr: Tom Konieczki

D-U-N-S 04-620-3444
MIDDOUGH INC
1901 E 13th St Ste 400, Cleveland, OH 44114-3507
Tel (216) 367-6000 *Founded/Ownrshp* 1963
Sales 142.2MM^E *EMP* 700
SIC 8711 8712 Consulting engineer; Architectural engineering; Consulting engineer; Architectural engineering
Pr: Ronald Ledin
**CFO:* Anthony Donofrio
**Sr VP:* Joseph S Cardile
**Sr VP:* Charles Dietz
Sr VP: Carl Wendell
VP: Steve Bogaert
**VP:* George Hlavacs
**VP:* Charles L Krzysiak
**VP:* Donald Majba
VP: Joseph Veselka
Dir Bus: David Derousse

D-U-N-S 60-406-3334 IMP
MIDEA AMERICA CORP
(*Suby of* MIDEA GROUP CO., LTD.)
5 Sylvan Way Ste 1, Parsippany, NJ 07054-3813
Tel (973) 539-5330 *Founded/Ownrshp* 2003
Sales 88.0MM^E *EMP* 30
SIC 5064 Refrigerators & freezers; Refrigerators & freezers
Pr: Eli Glanzberg
Genl Mgr: Raymond Garcia
Genl Mgr: Dave Michalik

MIDESSA RESTAURANT
See PRESTON FOODS INC

MIDFIELD BOARD OF EDUCATION
See MIDFIELD CITY SCHOOL SYSTEMS

D-U-N-S 00-208-5090
MIDFIELD CITY SCHOOL SYSTEMS
MIDFIELD BOARD OF EDUCATION
417 Parkwood St, Birmingham, AL 35228-2230
Tel (205) 923-2262 *Founded/Ownrshp* 1971
Sales 1,000.0M *EMP* 345
SIC 8211 Public elementary & secondary schools; Public elementary & secondary schools
Schl Brd P: John Ware
Snr Mgr: Aesha King

MIDFIELD CONCESSION ENTPS
See PHILLY CONCESSION ENTERPRISES INC

D-U-N-S 12-395-7524
MIDFIRST BANK
MIDLAND GROUP, THE
(*Suby of* MIDLAND FINANCIAL CO) ★
501 Nw Grand Blvd, Oklahoma City, OK 73118-6037
Tel (405) 767-7000 *Founded/Ownrshp* 1982
Sales NA *EMP* 1,336
SIC 6035 Federal savings & loan associations; Federal savings & loan associations
Ch Bd: G Jeffrey Records Jr
Owner: Ashley Grigsby
Mng Pt: Nicholas Powell
V Ch: Gerald Marshall
COO: Garland Wilkinson
**CFO:* Todd Dobson
Ex VP: Randy Roper
**Sr VP:* Ralph Farrar Jr
Sr VP: H James Holloman
Sr VP: Jim Holloman
Sr VP: Mary Przybyla
**Sr VP:* Betty L Rodgers
Sr VP: Doug Rutley
Sr VP: Tim Schneider
Sr VP: Glen Shipley
Sr VP: Marc Short
Sr VP: Donita Thomas
Sr VP: Chris Wertzberger
Sr VP: Scot Williams
VP: Scott Beermann
VP: Seth Bertram

D-U-N-S 08-194-4589
MIDFLORIDA FEDERAL CREDIT UNION
129 S Kentucky Ave # 100, Lakeland, FL 33801-5073
Tel (866) 913-3733 *Founded/Ownrshp* 1955
Sales 63.3MM *EMP* 278
SIC 6531 Real estate agent, residential; Real estate agent, residential
Pr: Kevin Jones
COO: Andy Hernan
**COO:* Dennis Pershing
Bd of Dir: Richard Isinghood
Bd of Dir: Gary Ruhle
Ofcr: Gayle O'Brien
Ofcr: Gail Obrien
Sr VP: Mark Gray
Sr VP: Richard Haggins
Sr VP: Chris Robertson
VP: Lori Katz
VP: John King
VP: Debra Lineberger

D-U-N-S 07-947-4270
MIDHUDSON REGIONAL HOSPITAL OF WESTCHESTER MEDICAL CENTER
(*Suby of* WESTCHESTER COUNTY HEALTH CARE CORP) ★
241 North Rd, Poughkeepsie, NY 12601-1154
Tel (845) 483-5000 *Founded/Ownrshp* 2014
Sales 34.2MM^E *EMP* 1,700^E
SIC 8062 8322 General medical & surgical hospitals; Individual & family services
Pr: Arthur Nizza
**Pr:* Mark Foster
**CFO:* Kristin Cash-Holland
**Chf Mktg O:* Keith Festa
**VP:* Joline Frey
**VP:* Barbara Naru
**VP:* George Prisco
Dir Rx: David Schaff
**CIO:* Joseph McCann
Sfty Dirs: Kent Amsden
QC Dir: Margaret Greenli

D-U-N-S 09-306-4731
MIDJIT MARKET INC
GREEN VALLEY GROCERY
1580 S Jones Blvd, Las Vegas, NV 89146-1237
Tel (702) 216-2154 *Founded/Ownrshp* 1978
Sales 137.3MM^E *EMP* 350
SIC 5541 5141 Filling stations, gasoline; Groceries, general line; Filling stations, gasoline; Groceries, general line
Pr: Richard Crawford
CFO: Mike Flinspach
Dist Mgr: Rhonda Knapp
Dist Mgr: Patricia Partridge
Genl Mgr: Ed Crawford

D-U-N-S 04-737-1463
MIDLAB INC
(*Suby of* KEL-SAN PRODUCTS) ★
140 Private Brand Way, Athens, TN 37303-1401
Tel (423) 337-3180 *Founded/Ownrshp* 1984
Sales 30.0MM *EMP* 85
SIC 2842 Specialty cleaning, polishes & sanitation goods
Ch Bd: Tillman J Keller III
**Prin:* Jorge Nieri
**Prin:* Michael B Ridley
Sales Exec: Matt Schenk
Mktg Mgr: Craig Dieter

D-U-N-S 00-210-2259 IMP
MIDLAND ASPHALT MATERIALS INC
(*Suby of* STRAWSER CONSTRUCTION INC) ★
640 Young St, Tonawanda, NY 14150-4103
Tel (716) 692-0730 *Founded/Ownrshp* 2000
Sales 54.4MM^E *EMP* 105
SIC 1611 2951 Surfacing & paving; Asphalt & asphaltic paving mixtures (not from refineries); Surfacing & paving; Asphalt & asphaltic paving mixtures (not from refineries)
Pr: Timothy Sanders
**Treas:* Fred Shelton
IT Man: Tim McNally

MIDLAND BUICK GMC CADILLAC
See BERG MOTOR CO

D-U-N-S 04-661-6918
MIDLAND CO
(*Suby of* MUNICH-AMERICAN HOLDING CORP) ★
7000 Midland Blvd, Amelia, OH 45102-2646
Tel (513) 947-5503 *Founded/Ownrshp* 2008
Sales NA *EMP* 1,200
SIC 6331 4449 Property damage insurance; Fire, marine & casualty insurance: stock; Intracoastal (freight) transportation; Property damage insurance; Fire, marine & casualty insurance: stock; Intracoastal (freight) transportation
Pr: John W Hayden
**Ch Bd:* Joseph P Hayden III
Pr: Kevin Morreale
**CFO:* W Todd Gray
Treas: Matthew McConnell
Bd of Dir: W Gray
**Ex VP:* Paul T Brizzolara
**Ex VP:* John I Von Lehman
Ex VP: John Lehman
VP: Patrick Law
Exec: Mary Pettit

D-U-N-S 07-636-0809
MIDLAND COMMUNITY CENTER INC (MI)
MIDLAND TENNIS CENTER
2205 Jefferson Ave, Midland, MI 48640-5679
Tel (989) 832-7937 *Founded/Ownrshp* 1916
Sales 30.1MM^E *EMP* 650^E
Accts Andrews Hooper Pavlik Plc Mid
SIC 8322 7999 Community center; Tennis courts, outdoor/indoor: non-membership; Community center; Tennis courts, outdoor/indoor: non-membership
CEO: Chris Tointon
CFO: Chris Pointon
Off Mgr: Paula Carr
Dir IT: Andrew Warren

MIDLAND CONSUMER RADIO
See MIDLAND RADIO CORP

D-U-N-S 09-161-0089
MIDLAND COUNTY
220 W Ellsworth St, Midland, MI 48640-4297
Tel (989) 832-6780 *Founded/Ownrshp* 1850
Sales NA *EMP* 300
Accts Rehmann Saginaw Mi
SIC 9111 County supervisors' & executives' offices; County supervisors' & executives' offices
Treas: Richard Enszer
Treas: Catherine Lunsford
IT Man: Randy Bunting
Board of Directors: Tony Stamos

D-U-N-S 07-314-9411
MIDLAND COUNTY HOSPITAL DISTRICT
MEMORIAL HOSPITAL AND MED CTR
400 R Redfern Grover Pkwy, Midland, TX 79701
Tel (432) 685-1111 *Founded/Ownrshp* 1942
Sales 268.1MM *EMP* 1,700
Accts Bkd Llp Waco Texas
SIC 8062 Hospital, affiliated with AMA residency; Hospital, affiliated with AMA residency
Pr: Russell Meyers
CFO: Stephen Bowerman
CFO: Lawrence Sanz
VP: Robert Dent
VP: Cory Edmondson
VP: Roberta Solorio
Exec: Ann Carter
Exec: Maria McAllister
Exec: Brian Middlebrook
Dir Case M: Barbara Wallace
Dir Lab: Denise Kemp
Assoc Dir: Tricia Cobb
Dir Rad: Mona Martinez
Dir Rx: John Harrington
Board of Directors: Robert Dimit, Pete Holder, Leigh Ann Lane, David Orr DDS, Jess Parrish, Jay Reynolds, Oral Williams

D-U-N-S 03-979-1061
■ **MIDLAND CREDIT MANAGEMENT INC**
(*Suby of* ENCORE CAPITAL GROUP INC) ★
2365 Northside Dr Ste 300, San Diego, CA 92108-2709
Tel (877) 240-2377 *Founded/Ownrshp* 1953
Sales NA *EMP* 1,800
SIC 6153 Short-term business credit
CEO: Kenneth A Vecchione
**Pr:* Carl Gregory
Ex VP: Sheryl Wright
Sr VP: Olivier Baudoux
**Sr VP:* Robin Pruitt
Sr VP: Manu Rikhye
Sr VP: Christopher Trepel
VP: Andrew Asch
VP: John Chalekian
Div Mgr: Katie Merrill
QA Dir: Miguel Avila

D-U-N-S 00-798-2549
MIDLAND DAVIS CORP
MIDLAND PAPER & PRODUCTS
3301 4th Ave, Moline, IL 61265-1605
Tel (309) 637-4491 *Founded/Ownrshp* 1892, 1991
Sales 34.8MM *EMP* 87
Accts Mcgladrey
SIC 5093 2679 3341 Scrap & waste materials; Pressed & molded pulp products, purchased material; Pressed fiber products from wood pulp: from purchased goods; Secondary nonferrous metals; Scrap & waste materials; Pressed & molded pulp products, purchased material; Pressed fiber products from wood pulp: from purchased goods; Secondary nonferrous metals
Pr: Martin H Davis
**VP:* Mitchell L Davis
IT Man: Kristine Clevenger
Mktg Dir: Leonard Zeid

MIDLAND ENGINEERING
See DECISION SYSTEMS INC

D-U-N-S 00-299-3772
MIDLAND ENGINEERING CO INC
52369 Ind St Rte 933, South Bend, IN 46637-3854
Tel (574) 272-0200 *Founded/Ownrshp* 1922
Sales 31.4MM *EMP* 140
Accts Crowe Horwath Llp South Bend
SIC 1761 1741 Roofing contractor; Architectural sheet metal work; Sheet metalwork; Stone masonry; Roofing contractor; Architectural sheet metal work; Sheet metalwork; Stone masonry
Pr: Frederick J Helmen
**Ex VP:* Michael Frahn
**VP:* Ryan J Haas
VP: Fred Helman
**VP:* Kenneth A Sage
**VP:* Greg R Seiss
Sfty Mgr: Bart Norville
Board of Directors: Michael W Frahn, Frederick J Helmen

D-U-N-S 00-477-3149
MIDLAND ENTERPRISES INC
(*Suby of* INGRAM INDUSTRIES INC) ★
4400 Harding Pike, Nashville, TN 37205-2204
Tel (615) 298-8200 *Founded/Ownrshp* 1917
Sales 35.7MM^E *EMP* 1,400
SIC 4449 4492 3731 4491 River transportation, except on the St. Lawrence Seaway; Intracoastal (freight) transportation; Marine towing services; Tugboat service; Shipbuilding & repairing; Barges, building & repairing; Waterfront terminal operation; River transportation, except on the St. Lawrence Seaway; Intracoastal (freight) transportation; Marine towing services; Tugboat service; Shipbuilding & repairing; Barges, building & repairing; Waterfront terminal operation
Ch Bd: Orrin H Ingram
Pr: Kaj Shah
CFO: Mary K Cavarra
Treas: R C Agricola
Ex VP: Eleanor McDonald
Board of Directors: Mary K Cavarra, Orrin H Ingram, Eleanor McDonald

D-U-N-S 13-656-5400
MIDLAND FABRICATORS & PROCESS SYSTEMS LLC
3636 N Causeway Blvd # 300, Metairie, LA 70002-7203
Tel (504) 837-5766 *Founded/Ownrshp* 2002
Sales 54.5MM^E *EMP* 925
SIC 3441 1629 Fabricated structural metal for ships; Industrial plant construction; Fabricated structural metal for ships; Industrial plant construction

D-U-N-S 11-536-6270
MIDLAND FINANCIAL CO
MIDLAND GROUP, THE
501 Nw Grand Blvd Ste 180, Oklahoma City, OK 73118-6037
Tel (405) 840-7600 *Founded/Ownrshp* 1981
Sales NA *EMP* 1,421
SIC 6035 6162 6531 Federal savings & loan associations; Mortgage bankers; Real estate brokers & agents; Real estate managers; Federal savings & loan associations; Mortgage bankers; Real estate brokers & agents; Real estate managers
Ch Bd: George J Records
Pr: Rachel Bloomer
Pr: Robin Perry
**COO:* Robert F Dilg Jr
**CFO:* Todd A Dobson
**Sr VP:* Betty L Rodgers
Sr VP: David Westman
VP: Daniel Adams
VP: Jeff Auchenbach
VP: Donny Hector
VP: Dana Kanady
VP: Virginia Kinon
VP: Nichole Lipps
VP: James Nield
VP: Cynthia Pearson

D-U-N-S 61-728-8766
MIDLAND FOOD SERVICES LLC
6200 Rockside Woods Blvd # 315, Independence, OH 44131-2333
Tel (216) 524-2251 *Founded/Ownrshp* 2012
Sales 69.6MM^E *EMP* 3,800
SIC 5812 Pizzeria, chain; Pizzeria, chain
CFO: Christopher Flocken
Ex Dir: Carol McMakin

D-U-N-S 16-106-8556
MIDLAND FORD LINCOLN INC
500 Joe Mann Blvd, Midland, MI 48642-7421
Tel (989) 631-0040 *Founded/Ownrshp* 1991
Sales 30.6MM^E *EMP* 55
SIC 5511 Automobiles, new & used; Pickups, new & used; Vans, new & used
Pr: James Wilson
Genl Mgr: Chad Wilson

D-U-N-S 10-731-3210
MIDLAND FORD TRUCKS AND SALES
330 County Ave, Secaucus, NJ 07094-2009
Tel (201) 617-0700 *Founded/Ownrshp* 2001
Sales 43.0MM *EMP* 65
SIC 5511 Automobiles, new & used; Automobiles, new & used
Pr: Roger Schlobohm

MIDLAND GROUP, THE
See MIDLAND FINANCIAL CO

MIDLAND GROUP, THE
See MIDFIRST BANK

D-U-N-S 19-674-5848
MIDLAND HOLDING CO
MIDLAND MEDICAL SUPPLY COMPANY
4850 Old Cheney Rd, Lincoln, NE 68516-3139
Tel (402) 423-8877 *Founded/Ownrshp* 1970
Sales 25.6MM^E *EMP* 55
Accts Hanigan Bjorkman Ecklund Llp
SIC 5047 Medical equipment & supplies; Hospital equipment & furniture
Pr: Aj Borchardt
**Pr:* Al J Borchardt

MIDLAND HOSPITAL
See MIDMICHIGAN MEDICAL CENTER-MIDLAND

D-U-N-S 00-890-9459
MIDLAND IMPLEMENT CO INC
402 Daniel St, Billings, MT 59101-3217
Tel (406) 248-7771 *Founded/Ownrshp* 1977
Sales 38.7MM^E *EMP* 61
SIC 5083 5064 5065 Farm & garden machinery; Lawn machinery & equipment; Irrigation equipment; Agricultural machinery; Television sets; Electric household appliances; Electronic parts & equipment; Farm & garden machinery; Lawn machinery & equipment; Irrigation equipment; Agricultural machinery; Television sets; Electric household appliances; Electronic parts & equipment
Pr: Gary Pates
**VP:* Randy Pates
Sales Asso: Jeano Picchioni

D-U-N-S 08-108-5391
MIDLAND INDEPENDENT SCHOOL DISTRICT
MIDLAND ISD
615 W Missouri Ave, Midland, TX 79701-5017
Tel (432) 689-1000 *Founded/Ownrshp* 1893
Sales 222.4MM *EMP* 2,760
Accts Weaver And Tidwell Llp Mi
SIC 8211 Public elementary school; Public junior high school; Public senior high school; Public elementary school; Public junior high school; Public senior high school
**Ch Bd:* Jay Issacs
**CFO:* David Garcia
Bd of Dir: Karen Fullen
Bd of Dir: Jordan Holmes
Trst: James Fuller
VP: Karen Nicholson
Exec: Nicole Gabriel
Comm Dir: Woodrow Bailey
Psych: Adolfo Chavez
Psych: Si Espanol
Psych: Betsy Faris

MIDLAND INDUSTRIAL PLASTICS
See MIDLAND PLASTICS INC

D-U-N-S 09-233-6945
MIDLAND INFORMATION RESOURCES CO
(*Suby of* ELANDERS GMBH)
5440 Corporate Park Dr, Davenport, IA 52807-2990
Tel (563) 359-3696 *Founded/Ownrshp* 1982
Sales 25.5MM *EMP* 160
SIC 2759 Commercial printing; Commercial printing
Pr: Thomas P Sheehan
**CFO:* Mary Gehrls
**Ch:* Magnus Nilsson
**VP:* Deb Cornelis
IT Man: Mark Wiseley
Mfg Dir: Don Singleton
Prd Mgr: Robert Johnson
**S&M/VP:* Jeff White

MIDLAND ISD
See MIDLAND INDEPENDENT SCHOOL DISTRICT

D-U-N-S 01-220-0585
■ **MIDLAND LOAN SERVICES A DIVISION OF PNC BANK NATIONAL ASSOCIATION**
(*Suby of* PNC FINANCIAL SERVICES GROUP INC) ★
10851 Mastin St Ste 700, Overland Park, KS 66210-1687
Tel (913) 253-9000 *Founded/Ownrshp* 1998
Sales NA *EMP* 475
SIC 6162 Mortgage bankers & correspondents; Mortgage bankers & correspondents
Pr: Steven W Smith
Pr: Jeremy Davis
**Sr VP:* Vince E Beckett
Sr VP: Cindy Bicknell
Sr VP: Sherry Ducarme
Sr VP: Greg McFarland
Sr VP: Jan Sternin
VP: Shelly Carrel
VP: Nenad Dordevic
VP: Chuck Hendricks
VP: Chad Milbrant
VP: Craig Mueller
VP: Dugger Schwartz
VP: Kellie Temple

D-U-N-S 96-898-0198
MIDLAND LUTHERAN COLLEGE
900 N Clarkson St, Fremont, NE 68025-4254
Tel (402) 721-5480 *Founded/Ownrshp* 2011
Sales 20.9MM *EMP* 1
Accts Baker Tilly Virchow Krause Llp
SIC 8661 Religious organizations; Religious organizations
Prin: Jodi Rinne
Dir IT: Shane Perrien
Dir IT: Carla Voelker

D-U-N-S 00-523-2558 IMP
■ **MIDLAND MANUFACTURING CORP**
(*Suby of* DOVER ARTIFICIAL LIFT INTERNATIONAL LLC) ★
7733 Gross Point Rd, Skokie, IL 60077-2615
Tel (847) 677-0333 *Founded/Ownrshp* 1994
Sales 45.2MM^E *EMP* 120
SIC 3494 3715 3731 3545 3491 Valves & pipe fittings; Truck trailers; Barges, building & repairing; Machine tool accessories; Industrial valves; Valves & pipe fittings; Truck trailers; Barges, building & repairing; Machine tool accessories; Industrial valves
Pr: Thomas Zant
**CFO:* Tom Noonan
**VP:* Kevin Cook

D-U-N-S 00-268-6715 IMP
MIDLAND MARBLE & GRANITE LLC (KS)
2077 Ne Rice Rd, Lees Summit, MO 64064-2142
Tel (816) 257-2000 *Founded/Ownrshp* 1996
Sales 20.7MM^E *EMP* 100
SIC 1743 Terrazzo, tile, marble, mosaic work
CEO: Bryan Caton
**VP:* Mike Caton
Sls Mgr: Ralph Goucher

D-U-N-S 00-694-2783
MIDLAND MARKETING CO-OP INC
219 E 9th St, Hays, KS 67601-4415
Tel (785) 625-5138 *Founded/Ownrshp* 1915
Sales 100.9MM *EMP* 2^E
Accts Lindburg Vogel Pierce Faris H
SIC 5153 5191 5541 5171 4221 Grains; Feed; Chemicals, agricultural; Fertilizer & fertilizer materials; Filling stations, gasoline; Petroleum bulk stations; Grain elevator, storage only; Grains; Feed; Filling stations, gasoline; Petroleum bulk stations; Grain elevator, storage only

MIDLAND MEDICAL SUPPLY COMPANY
See MIDLAND HOLDING CO

D-U-N-S 05-125-8648
MIDLAND MEDICAL SUPPLY CO
(*Suby of* MIDLAND HOLDING CO) ★
4850 Old Cheney Rd, Lincoln, NE 68516-3199
Tel (402) 423-8877 *Founded/Ownrshp* 1978
Sales 25.6MM^E *EMP* 50
SIC 5047 Medical equipment & supplies; Hospital equipment & furniture
Pr: Alex J Borchardt

D-U-N-S 11-910-0670
MIDLAND MEMORIAL HOSPITAL
400 Rsal Rdfern Gror Pkwy, Midland, TX 79701
Tel (432) 685-4952 *Founded/Ownrshp* 1950
Sales 260.1MM *EMP* 4^E
SIC 8049 Speech pathologist
Pr: Russell Meyers

D-U-N-S 87-310-1307
MIDLAND MEMORIAL HOSPITAL & MEDICAL CENTER
2200 W Illinois Ave, Midland, TX 79701-6407
Tel (432) 685-1111 *Founded/Ownrshp* 1969
Sales 11.7MM^E *EMP* 1,300
SIC 8062 General medical & surgical hospitals; General medical & surgical hospitals
Pr: Russel Meyers

D-U-N-S 00-720-5354
MIDLAND MORTGAGE CO
(*Suby of* MIDLAND FINANCIAL CO) ★
999 Nw Grand Blvd, Oklahoma City, OK 73118-6051
Tel (405) 426-1400 *Founded/Ownrshp* 1982
Sales NA *EMP* 426
SIC 6162 Mortgage bankers; Mortgage bankers
Ch: George J Records Sr
**Pr:* Ken Clark
CFO: Tim Tackett
**Sr VP:* Jim Nield
**Sr VP:* Tracy Yates
VP Mktg: Daniel Adams

D-U-N-S 00-792-0531
MIDLAND NATIONAL LIFE INSURANCE CO (IA)
(*Suby of* SAMMONS ENTERPRISES INC) ★
1 Sammons Plz, Sioux Falls, SD 57193-1001
Tel (605) 335-5700 *Founded/Ownrshp* 1906
Sales NA *EMP* 683
SIC 6311 Life insurance carriers; Life insurance carriers
Pr: Steven C Palmitier
Pr: Dan Cressman
Pr: Theresa Hagedorn
Pr: Debra Ourada
Pr: Douglas Schwartz
COO: Rob Tekolste
**CFO:* John J Craig II
CFO: Thomas M Eyer
CFO: Tom Myer
Treas: Alan H Spencer
**Ofcr:* Kevin Paulson
**Sr VP:* Esfandyar Dinshaw
Sr VP: John E Fromlt
**Sr VP:* Gary J Gaspar
**Sr VP:* Stephen P Horvat Jr
Sr VP: Dan Kiefer
**Sr VP:* Donald J Lyons
**Sr VP:* Brian P Rohr
VP: Spencer Bell
VP: Robert Buchanan
VP: Bob Coscarelli

D-U-N-S 03-727-2096
MIDLAND OIL CORP
6979 Hillsdale Ct, Indianapolis, IN 46250-2054
Tel (317) 291-2300 *Founded/Ownrshp* 2012
Sales 25.0MM^E *EMP* 5
SIC 5172 Crude oil; Crude oil
Pr: Manjit Singh

MIDLAND OPTICAL
See MOC ACQUISITION CORP

MIDLAND PAPER & PRODUCTS
See MIDLAND DAVIS CORP

D-U-N-S 00-798-0329 IMP
MIDLAND PAPER CO (IL)
101 E Palatine Rd, Wheeling, IL 60090-6512
Tel (847) 777-2700 *Founded/Ownrshp* 1907
Sales 769.6MM^E *EMP* 400
SIC 5111 Printing paper; Printing paper
Pr: E Stanton Hooker III
Pr: Michael Ratcliff
**COO:* Michael Graves
**CFO:* Ralph Deletto
Ex VP: Frank Morley
Sr VP: David Moore
VP: Hume Crawford
VP: Pam Mantor
VP: Patti Rank
VP: Bill Rojack
Genl Mgr: Keith Seeliger

D-U-N-S 00-658-1011
MIDLAND PLASTICS INC (WI)
MIDLAND INDUSTRIAL PLASTICS
5405 S Westridge Ct, New Berlin, WI 53151-7951
Tel (262) 938-7000 *Founded/Ownrshp* 1945
Sales 70.1MM^E *EMP* 120
SIC 5162 3089 Plastics sheets & rods; Plastics film; Plastic processing; Plastics sheets & rods; Plastics film; Plastic processing
Ch Bd: Clarence Hense Jr
**Pr:* Mark N Hense
VP: George Pesic
VP Mfg: Michael Crowley
Sales Exec: Roger Stoltenberg
Mktg Mgr: Jeff Smoot
Sales Asso: Maria Miller
Snr Mgr: Danielle Sciano

D-U-N-S 00-531-0479
MIDLAND POWER COOPERATIVE INC
1005 E Lincoln Way, Jefferson, IA 50129-2063
Tel (515) 386-4111 *Founded/Ownrshp* 1937
Sales 45.6MM *EMP* 39
Accts Keith C Germann Cpa Storm Lak
SIC 4911 Distribution, electric power; Distribution, electric power
Genl Mgr: William McKim
IT Man: Denny Kinsey

D-U-N-S 11-566-7248
MIDLAND PRESS CORP
(*Suby of* MIDLAND INFORMATION RESOURCES CO) ★
5440 Corporate Park Dr, Davenport, IA 52807-2990
Tel (563) 359-3696 *Founded/Ownrshp* 1999
Sales 21.5MM^E *EMP* 142
SIC 2759 Commercial printing; Commercial printing
CEO: Gene Blanc
**Pr:* Tom Sheehan
Sales Exec: Steve Christensen

D-U-N-S 07-424-7305
MIDLAND PUBLIC SCHOOL DISTRICT
600 E Carpenter St, Midland, MI 48640-5417
Tel (989) 923-5001 *Founded/Ownrshp* 1900
Sales 60.7MM^E *EMP* 1,396
Accts Yeo & Yeo Pc Saginaw Michig
SIC 8211 Public adult education school; Public combined elementary & secondary school; Public adult education school; Public combined elementary & secondary school
Dir IT: Steve Tacey
Teacher Pr: Brian Brutyn

D-U-N-S 92-683-4797 IMP
MIDLAND RADIO CORP
MIDLAND CONSUMER RADIO
5900 Parretta Dr, Kansas City, MO 64120-2134
Tel (816) 241-8500 *Founded/Ownrshp* 1995
Sales 45.6MM^E *EMP* 60
SIC 5065 Radio parts & accessories

Ch Bd: Baruch Shammah
Pr: Daniel M Devling
VP: Steve Koch
VP: Eric Schenck
Mktg Dir: Terry Mears

D-U-N-S 00-629-7170
MIDLAND RAILWAY SUPPLY INC (MO)
1815 W Delmar Ave, Godfrey, IL 62035-1352
Tel (618) 467-6305 *Founded/Ownrshp* 1946
Sales 21.5MM^E *EMP* 75^E
SIC 5088 3743 Railroad equipment & supplies; Railroad equipment; Railroad equipment & supplies; Railroad equipment
Pr: John Ferenbach
**VP:* Eric Ferenbach

D-U-N-S 02-314-2656
MIDLAND SERVICE INC
220 3rd Ave W, Ashland, WI 54806-1616
Tel (715) 682-2745 *Founded/Ownrshp* 1931
Sales 34.5MM *EMP* 60^E
Accts Clifton Larson Allen Llp Mars
SIC 5541 5171 7513 Gasoline service stations; Petroleum bulk stations; Truck rental & leasing, no drivers; Gasoline service stations; Petroleum bulk stations; Truck rental & leasing, no drivers
Pr: Richard Frostman
**VP:* Larry Ekholm

D-U-N-S 83-729-7923
MIDLAND STAMPING AND FABRICATING CORP
9521 Ainslie St, Schiller Park, IL 60176-1115
Tel (847) 678-7573 *Founded/Ownrshp* 2014
Sales 24.5MM^E *EMP* 62^E
SIC 3469 Metal stampings
Pr: Alan Blankshain

D-U-N-S 62-339-5068
MIDLAND STATES BANCORP INC
1201 Network Centre Dr, Effingham, IL 62401-4602
Tel (217) 342-7354 *Founded/Ownrshp* 1988
Sales NA *EMP* 428
SIC 6022 State commercial banks; State commercial banks
Pr: Leon Holschbach
CFO: Cindy Kremer
Treas: Michael Karibian
Chf Inves: John Culhane
Ofcr: Peter Del Real
VP: Eric Forguson
VP: Jan Woodward
Dir IT: Bradley Schaufenbuel
IT Man: Jeff McDevitt
Sls&Mrk Ex: Laura Dill
Mktg Mgr: Bruce Shumate
Board of Directors: Richard T Ramos, Thomas D Shaw

D-U-N-S 00-798-1616
MIDLAND STATES BANK
(*Suby of* MIDLAND STATES BANCORP INC) ★
1201 Network Centre Dr, Effingham, IL 62401-4602
Tel (217) 342-2141 *Founded/Ownrshp* 1881, 1989
Sales NA *EMP* 125
SIC 6022 State commercial banks; State commercial banks
Pr: Randall S Dempsey
Treas: Michael Karibian
Trst Ofcr: Jeri Madison
Sr VP: Leon Holschbach
Sr VP: Jeffrey Mefford
VP: Scott Denton
VP: Eric Forguson
VP: Ben Malsch
VP: Linda Perry
Exec: Dan Stevenson
Dir Risk M: James Stewart
Mng Ofcr: Pat Hartke
Board of Directors: Richard T Ramos, Thomas D Shaw

D-U-N-S 07-992-3512 IMP
MIDLAND STEEL WHSE CORP
1120 Leggett Ave, Bronx, NY 10474-6232
Tel (718) 328-4600 *Founded/Ownrshp* 1970
Sales 32.9MM^E *EMP* 45
Accts Chb Advisors Pc
SIC 5051 Steel; Steel
Ch Bd: Robert Allen
**VP:* Howard Allen
Off Mgr: Lisa Rodriguez

MIDLAND TENNIS CENTER
See MIDLAND COMMUNITY CENTER INC

D-U-N-S 07-674-6999
■ **MIDLAND TITLE SECURITY INC**
FIRST AMRCN TTLE MIDLAND TITLE
(*Suby of* FIRST AMERICAN TITLE INSURANCE CO) ★
1111 Superior Ave E # 700, Cleveland, OH 44114-2540
Tel (216) 241-6045 *Founded/Ownrshp* 1986
Sales NA *EMP* 500
SIC 6361 Title insurance; Title insurance
Pr: James Stipanovich
CFO: Norman Romansky
VP: Jeff Myers
Opers Mgr: Michael Koors

D-U-N-S 04-739-5629
MIDLAND TRACTOR CO
JOHN DEERE
1901 W Cleveland Ave, Madera, CA 93637-8705
Tel (559) 674-8757 *Founded/Ownrshp* 1969
Sales 47.0MM *EMP* 43
SIC 5999

D-U-N-S 78-660-4918
■ **MIDLAND UNITED CORP**
(*Suby of* CSX TRANSPORTATION INC) ★
8888 Keystone Xing # 1600, Indianapolis, IN 46240-4609
Tel (317) 262-5140 *Founded/Ownrshp* 1989
Sales 39.9MM^E *EMP* 180
SIC 4011 Railroads, line-haul operating; Railroads, line-haul operating
Pr: Thomas G Hoback
**CFO:* Michael Engle

D-U-N-S 07-802-0765
MIDLAND UNIVERSITY
900 N Clarkson St, Fremont, NE 68025-4254
Tel (402) 721-5480 *Founded/Ownrshp* 1883
Sales 40.2MM *EMP* 200
Accts Baker Tilly Virchow Krause Llp
SIC 8221 Colleges universities & professional schools; Colleges universities & professional schools
Pr: Stephen Fritz
Comm Dir: Nate Neufind
Ex Dir: Connie Kreikemeier
IT Man: Greg Clements
Snr Mgr: Steven Bullock

D-U-N-S 05-443-6118
MIDLAND-GUARDIAN CO (OH)
(*Suby of* MIDLAND CO) ★
7000 Midland Blvd, Amelia, OH 45102-2646
Tel (513) 943-7100 *Founded/Ownrshp* 1952, 1968
Sales NA *EMP* 1,080
SIC 6311 6331 Life insurance carriers; Fire, marine & casualty insurance: stock; Life insurance carriers; Fire, marine & casualty insurance: stock
Pr: John Hayden
**CFO:* Todd Gray
**Ch:* Joseph P Hayden III
**Treas:* Matt McConnell
**Ex VP:* John Von Lehman
**VP:* Jim Terney

MIDLANDS CARRIER TRANSICOLD
See REEFER SYSTEMS INC

D-U-N-S 83-783-2203
MIDLANDS CHOICE INC
8420 W Dodge Rd Ste 210, Omaha, NE 68114-3492
Tel (402) 390-8233 *Founded/Ownrshp* 1996
Sales NA *EMP* 120
SIC 6411 Insurance agents, brokers & service
CEO: Thomas E Press
VP: Greta Vaught
MIS Dir: Robert Hood
IT Man: Michael Shutts

D-U-N-S 02-018-4891
MIDLANDS HOSPITAL
(*Suby of* CHI) ★
11111 S 84th St, Papillion, NE 68046-4122
Tel (402) 593-3000 *Founded/Ownrshp* 1973
Sales 53.7MM^E *EMP* 535
SIC 8062 8011 General medical & surgical hospitals; Medical centers; General medical & surgical hospitals; Medical centers
Chf Path: Patrick J Bogart
**CFO:* Scott Wooten
VP: Kenneth Lawonn
VP: Richard Miller
**Exec:* Lisa Wilson
Dir Lab: Kristopher Mathews
Pathlgst: Jonathan Rouse
Pathlgst: Gregory Severson
Obsttrcn: Heather Taggart
Doctor: Richard Alarid
Doctor: Deb Feller

D-U-N-S 61-681-5122
■ **MIDLANDS MANAGEMENT CORP**
(*Suby of* PMA CAPITAL) ★
3817 Nw Expwy Ste 1000, Oklahoma City, OK 73112-1469
Tel (405) 840-0074 *Founded/Ownrshp* 2007
Sales NA *EMP* 190^E
SIC 6411 6331 6321 Insurance agents & brokers; Fire, marine & casualty insurance; Accident & health insurance; Insurance agents & brokers; Fire, marine & casualty insurance; Accident & health insurance
Pr: Charles Caldwell
**Sec:* Dennis Ottis
Sr Cor Off: Mark Davis
**VP:* Sheryl Case
Off Mgr: Janice Snyder
VP Mktg: Jake Harris
Manager: Bill Seal
Snr Mgr: Jackie Wood

D-U-N-S 02-163-4233
MIDLANDS MECHANICAL INC
8425 Wirt St, Omaha, NE 68134-4958
Tel (402) 571-4258 *Founded/Ownrshp* 1980
Sales 32.6MM^E *EMP* 120
SIC 1711 Mechanical contractor; Process piping contractor
CEO: Bill Kilmer
**Pr:* Chris Sills
VP: Adam Burns
**VP:* Mike Maryott
Rgnl Mgr: Matt Uerling
Sfty Dirs: Chris Hayes

D-U-N-S 78-331-8249 IMP
MIDLANDS MILLROOM SUPPLY INC
1911 36th St Ne, Canton, OH 44705-5023
Tel (330) 453-9100 *Founded/Ownrshp* 1991
Sales 20.4MM^E *EMP* 28
SIC 5084 3061 Industrial machinery & equipment; Mechanical rubber goods
Pr: Fred Clark
Mfg Mgr: Rod Cunningham
Sales Exec: Yoshi Terada

D-U-N-S 80-719-1796 IMP
■ **MIDLANDS NEWSPAPERS INC**
(*Suby of* OMAHA WORLD TIMES) ★
604 Fort Crook Rd N, Bellevue, NE 68005-4557
Tel (402) 537-2999 *Founded/Ownrshp* 1999
Sales 61.6MM^E *EMP* 800
SIC 2711 Newspapers: publishing only, not printed on site; Newspapers: publishing only, not printed on site
Pr: Doug Hiemstra

D-U-N-S 06-223-9611 IMP
MIDLANDS PACKAGING CORP
4641 N 56th St, Lincoln, NE 68504-1716
Tel (402) 464-9124 *Founded/Ownrshp* 1972
Sales 45.5MM^E *EMP* 153
SIC 2657 3086 2653 Folding paperboard boxes; Packaging & shipping materials, foamed plastic; Boxes, corrugated: made from purchased materials; Folding paperboard boxes; Packaging & shipping materials, foamed plastic; Boxes, corrugated: made from purchased materials
Pr: Steven R Warman
**Treas:* Elizabeth R Logan
Dir IT: Brent Lindquist
IT Man: Betty Logan
Ql Cn Mgr: Greg Hendrickson
Sales Asso: Deborah Pair

D-U-N-S 06-932-9753
MIDLANDS TECHNICAL COLLEGE FOUNDATION
316 Beltline Blvd, Columbia, SC 29205-3624
Tel (803) 738-8324 *Founded/Ownrshp* 1974
Sales 49.3MM^E *EMP* 1,186
Accts Stuart W Ford Cpa Columbia
SIC 8222 8221 Technical institute; Colleges universities & professional schools; Technical institute; Colleges universities & professional schools
Ch Bd: Mary H Wilkins
**Treas:* R Scott McClelland
Ofcr: Terrell White
**VP:* Van Gunter
**VP:* Sandy Oliver
**VP:* Starnell Williams
Dir Lab: Nicole Foster
Store Mgr: Bernice Holley
Dir IT: Anthony Hough
IT Man: Hampton Saussey
Pgrm Dir: Elaine Evans

D-U-N-S 09-997-6425
MIDLANTIC FOODS INC
7 Pembroke Dr, Voorhees, NJ 08043-3938
Tel (215) 289-2111 *Founded/Ownrshp* 1978
Sales 22.0MM^E *EMP* 40
SIC 5147 5144 5146 5142 Meats & meat products; Poultry & poultry products; Fish & seafoods; Packaged frozen goods
Pr: Bart Shipon

MIDLANTIC MACHINERY
See F AND M EQUIPMENT LTD

D-U-N-S 15-091-6989
MIDLANTIC RESTAURANTS INC
PONDEROSA STEAKHOUSE
(*Suby of* U S RESTAURANTS INC) ★
1780 Swede Rd, Blue Bell, PA 19422-3522
Tel (610) 277-4200 *Founded/Ownrshp* 1986
Sales 11.1MM^E *EMP* 600
SIC 5812 Steak restaurant; Steak restaurant
Pr: Steven M Lewis
**CFO:* Michael Kadelski
**Sec:* Vernon W Hill II
**VP:* Dike Stoe

D-U-N-S 07-701-5803
MIDLOTHIAN ENERGY LLC
(*Suby of* GDF SUEZ ENERGY INTERNATIONAL) ★
4601 Brookhollow Dr, Midlothian, TX 76065-5359
Tel (972) 923-7400 *Founded/Ownrshp* 2011
Sales 23.5MM^E *EMP* 46
SIC 5084 Power plant machinery
Pr: Herman Schopman

D-U-N-S 93-197-7417
MIDLOTHIAN INDEPENDENT SCHOOL DISTRICT
100 Walter Stephenson Rd, Midlothian, TX 76065-3418
Tel (972) 723-6290 *Founded/Ownrshp* 1989
Sales 81.8MM *EMP* 618
Accts Hankins Eastup Deaton Tonn
SIC 8221 Colleges universities & professional schools; Colleges universities & professional schools
Dir Sec: Rhonda Welch
IT Man: Julie Wood
Pr Dir: Jana Pongratz
Schl Brd P: Wayne Shuffield
Instr Medi: Nancy Bergvall
Psych: Andra Chapman
HC Dir: Diane Gossett

D-U-N-S 07-938-8445
MIDLOTHIAN LNG LLC
5091 Brookhollow Dr, Midlothian, TX 76065-5314
Tel (818) 450-3668 *Founded/Ownrshp* 2014
Sales 30.0MM *EMP* 15
SIC 1321 Natural gas liquids; Natural gas liquids
Pr: Cem Hacioglu
CFO: Edward McKenna Jr
VP: Frank Martelli

MIDLOTHIAN SCHOOL DIST 143
See MIDLOTHIAN SCHOOL DISTRICT 143

D-U-N-S 03-933-2986
MIDLOTHIAN SCHOOL DISTRICT 143
MIDLOTHIAN SCHOOL DIST 143
14959 Pulaski Rd, Midlothian, IL 60445-3436
Tel (708) 388-6450 *Founded/Ownrshp* 1989
Sales 18.1MM^E *EMP* 352
SIC 8211 Public elementary school; Public elementary school
Prin: Colleen Scholstrom
**Prin:* Mike W Hollinsworth
Board of Directors: A Seven Member Board

D-U-N-S 12-653-6247
MIDMARK CAPITAL II LP
177 Madison Ave Ste 2, Morristown, NJ 07960-6090
Tel (973) 971-9960 *Founded/Ownrshp* 2000
Sales 48.4MM^E *EMP* 242
SIC 6282 Investment advice; Investment advice
Pr: Denis Newman
Pt: Wayne L Clevenger
Pt: Joseph R Robinson
Mng Dir: Douglas Parker
Off Mgr: Julie McCartney

D-U-N-S 00-503-6025 IMP/EXP
MIDMARK CORP (OH)
1700 S Patterson Blvd, Kettering, OH 45409-2106
Tel (937) 526-3662 *Founded/Ownrshp* 1915
Sales 390.0MM *EMP* 1,500
SIC 3648 3842 3843 2542 3841 Lighting equipment; Stretchers; Dental equipment & supplies; Partitions & fixtures, except wood; Operating tables; Lighting equipment; Stretchers; Dental equipment & supplies; Partitions & fixtures, except wood; Operating tables
Pr: Anne E D
**COO:* Greg Blackmore
COO: Gregoire Blackmore
COO: Sue Hulsmeyer
**CFO:* Anthony Borzillo
CFO: Anthony Borzilo
**CFO:* Robert Morris
Ofcr: Sharyl S Gardner
VP: Anne Eiting Klamar
VP: Dick Moorman
VP: Eric Shirley
VP: Mike Walker
Exec: Lisa Beasley
Exec: Steve Cordonnier
Exec: Steve Davidson
Exec: Sue Huelsmeyer
Exec: Jamie Renner

D-U-N-S 18-335-4877
MIDMICHIGAN HEALTH
4000 Wellness Dr, Midland, MI 48670-2000
Tel (989) 839-3000 *Founded/Ownrshp* 1983
Sales 308.0MM *EMP* 6,500^E
SIC 8741 Hospital management; Hospital management
Pr: Terence F Moore
**Pr:* Richard M Reynolds
CFO: Francine Cadcagette
Trst: Robert Lofiego
VP: James Frye
VP: Dennis Knoss
Prac Mgr: Danielle Alward
Info Man: Gerald Wilhelm
Sls Dir: Shelli Wood
Psych: Lynn Simons
Surgeon: Jeffrey Bonacci

D-U-N-S 10-929-8471
MIDMICHIGAN HEALTH SERVICES
HOUGHTON LAKE HEALTH PARK
9249 W Lake City Rd, Houghton Lake, MI 48629-9602
Tel (989) 422-5148 *Founded/Ownrshp* 1977
Sales 8.9MM *EMP* 1,404
SIC 8011 Clinic, operated by physicians; Clinic, operated by physicians
**V Ch:* Jim Bischoff
**Ch:* Tom Moreau
**Sec:* Bev Budzynski
**Med Dir:* Jeffrey Strickler

MIDMICHIGAN HOME CARE
See MIDMICHIGAN VISITING NURSE ASSOCIATION

MIDMICHIGAN MEDICAL CENTER-GLA
See GLADWIN HOSPITAL INC

D-U-N-S 07-259-4997
MIDMICHIGAN MEDICAL CENTER-GRATIOT (MI)
GRATIOT COMMUNITY HOSPITAL
300 E Warwick Dr, Alma, MI 48801-1014
Tel (989) 463-1101 *Founded/Ownrshp* 1953
Sales 100.4MM *EMP* 1,000
Accts Andrews Hooper Pavlik Plc Sag
SIC 8062 General medical & surgical hospitals; General medical & surgical hospitals
CEO: Marc Bush
**CFO:* Scott Currie
VP: Carol Goffnett
Dir Lab: Larry Lashuay
CIO: Mike Larson
Doctor: Mary Stapelton
Pharmcst: Eric Dawson
HC Dir: Elizabeth Maxon

D-U-N-S 10-687-3698
MIDMICHIGAN MEDICAL CENTER-MIDLAND
MIDLAND HOSPITAL
(*Suby of* HOUGHTON LAKE HEALTH PARK) ★
4000 Wellness Dr, Midland, MI 48670-2000
Tel (989) 839-3000 *Founded/Ownrshp* 1940
Sales 348.9MM *EMP* 1,404
Accts Andrews Hooper Pavlik Plc Sag
SIC 8062 General medical & surgical hospitals; General medical & surgical hospitals
Pr: Richard M Reynolds
Chf Rad: Rick Ohle
**CFO:* Scott Currie
CFO: Deb Mills
VP: Cindy Fredrich
**VP:* Sandy Hermann
VP: Tom Lind
**VP:* Francine Padgett
**VP:* Greg Rogers
Dir Lab: Randy Wise
Dir Rad: Katie Mostek

MIDMICHIGAN MEDICAL CENTERS
See MID MICHIGAN MEDICAL CENTER-CLARE

D-U-N-S 00-748-3102
MIDMICHIGAN PHYSICIAN GROUP
2620 W Sugnet Rd, Midland, MI 48640-2647
Tel (989) 802-5000 *Founded/Ownrshp* 2009
Sales 68.2MM *EMP* 4
Accts Andrews Hooper Pavlik Plc Sag
SIC 8011 General & family practice, physician/surgeon; General & family practice, physician/surgeon
Prin: Adelberto J Adan

D-U-N-S 19-064-4930
MIDMICHIGAN VISITING NURSE ASSOCIATION
MIDMICHIGAN HOME CARE
3007 N Saginaw Rd, Midland, MI 48640-4555
Tel (989) 633-1400 *Founded/Ownrshp* 1986
Sales 21.3MM *EMP* 114

SIC 8082 5047 5999 5169 Visiting nurse service; Medical & hospital equipment; Telephone & communication equipment; Oxygen; Visiting nurse service; Medical & hospital equipment; Telephone & communication equipment; Oxygen
Pr: Chris Chesney
CFO: Lori Swarts

D-U-N-S 13-146-4927
MIDMOUNTAIN CONTRACTORS INC
(*Suby of* KONINKLIJKE VOLKER WESSELS STEVIN N.V.)
825 5th Ave, Kirkland, WA 98033-6391
Tel (425) 202-3600 *Founded/Ownrshp* 1993
Sales 53.9MM^E *EMP* 195^E
SIC 1611

D-U-N-S 08-538-4808
MIDNIGHT OIL AGENCY INC
LAGRAPHICO
3800 W Vanowen St Ste 101, Burbank, CA 91505-1173
Tel (818) 295-6100 *Founded/Ownrshp* 1989
Sales 81.6MM *EMP* 250
SIC 2752 8742

D-U-N-S 05-390-5589
MIDNIGHT OIL CO LLC
145 E 57th St Fl 12, New York, NY 10022-2190
Tel (212) 750-6361 *Founded/Ownrshp* 1998
Sales 21.8MM^E *EMP* 800
SIC 5812 Eating places; Eating places
CFO: Jim Walsh

D-U-N-S 78-862-3726
MIDNIGHT ROSE HOTEL & CASINO INC
256 Bennett Dr, Cripple Creek, CO 80813-9609
Tel (719) 689-0303 *Founded/Ownrshp* 1992
Sales 19.8MM^E *EMP* 320
SIC 7011 5812 Casino hotel; Eating places; Casino hotel; Eating places
Pr: Richard Holland
CFO: Ron Rosen
Genl Mgr: Richard Wenschlag
MIS Dir: Kevin O'Herron

D-U-N-S 10-651-8517
MIDNITE AIR CORP
MNX
(*Suby of* RIVERSIDE CO) ★
2132 Michelson Dr, Irvine, CA 92612-1304
Tel (310) 330-2300 *Founded/Ownrshp* 2012
Sales 73.5MM^E *EMP* 230
SIC 4513 Air courier services; Air courier services
CEO: Paul Martins
**COO:* Thomas Belmont
**CFO:* Sergio Palad
**Treas:* Steve Stubitz
Sr VP: Larry Glasscock
VP: David Cannon
Genl Mgr: Ed Rochat
Mktg Dir: Ken Ying
Board of Directors: Renzo Dicarlo Matt Dailey, Renzo Dicaro, Marty Graul, Joseph Kolshak, Paul Martins, Steven Stubitz, Peter Tsang

MIDOCEAN PARTNERS
See MIDOCEAN US ADVISOR LP

D-U-N-S 13-325-4438
MIDOCEAN US ADVISOR LP
MIDOCEAN PARTNERS
320 Park Ave Fl 16, New York, NY 10022-6815
Tel (212) 497-1400 *Founded/Ownrshp* 2003
Sales 467.3MM^E *EMP* 9,185
SIC 8742 Financial consultant; Financial consultant
CEO: Ted Virtue
CFO: Andrew Spring
Ofcr: Candice Richards
VP: Sam Goodyear
VP: Andrew Kuan
VP: Jonathan Marlow
VP: Sean O'Sullivan
VP: Daniel Penn
Mng Dir: Mike Apfel
Mng Dir: Christopher Cichella

D-U-N-S 96-539-9186
MIDPEN HOUSING CORP
303 Vintage Park Dr # 250, Foster City, CA 94404-1166
Tel (650) 356-2900 *Founded/Ownrshp* 1971
Sales 13.1MM^E *EMP* 300
Accts Lindquist Von Husen & Joyce Ll
SIC 6552 Land subdividers & developers, residential; Land subdividers & developers, residential
CEO: Mark Battey
**Pr:* Matthew O Franklin
Off Mgr: Jeff Gilkey
Snr PM: Mike Wiley

D-U-N-S 62-106-9280
MIDPEN RESIDENT SERVICES CORP
(*Suby of* STANFORD MID-PENINSULA URBAN COALITION) ★
303 Vintage Park Dr # 250, Foster City, CA 94404-1166
Tel (650) 356-2965 *Founded/Ownrshp* 2000
Sales 5.3MM *EMP* 300
Accts Lindquist Von Husen & Joyce Ll
SIC 6514 6513 Residential building, four or fewer units: operation; Apartment building operators; Residential building, four or fewer units: operation; Apartment building operators
Pr: Fran Wagstaff
**VP:* Lory Candelf

D-U-N-S 00-922-1656
MIDPENINSULA REGIONAL OPEN SPACE DISTRICT
330 Distel Cir, Los Altos, CA 94022-1404
Tel (650) 691-1200 *Founded/Ownrshp* 1972
Sales 36.0MM *EMP* 65
Accts Vavrinek Trine Day & Co Ll
SIC 8999 Natural resource preservation service; Natural resource preservation service
Pr: Craig Britton
Bd of Dir: Matt Freeman
Bd of Dir: Yoriko Kishimoto
Bd of Dir: Ira Ruskin
Plng Mgr: Meredith Manning

IT Man: Peggy Coats
IT Man: Benny Hsieh
IT Man: Penny Hsieh
Pr Mgr: Shelly Lewis
Genl Couns: Sheryl Schaffner

D-U-N-S 05-423-8022
MIDREX GLOBAL LOGISTICS INC
FORWARDING SERVICES INTL
2725 Water Ridge Pkwy # 100, Charlotte, NC 28217-4580
Tel (704) 424-9905 *Founded/Ownrshp* 1998
Sales 23.9MM^E *EMP* 72
SIC 4731 Freight forwarding
Pr: James D McClaskey

D-U-N-S 79-610-5930
MIDREX TECHNOLOGIES INC
(*Suby of* KOBE STEEL USA HOLDINGS INC) ★
2725 Water Ridge Pkwy # 100, Charlotte, NC 28217-4580
Tel (704) 373-1600 *Founded/Ownrshp* 1992
Sales 97.1MM^E *EMP* 215^E
SIC 8711 Engineering services; Engineering services
Pr: James D McClaskey
**CFO:* David Hamilton
**Ex VP:* Hiroshi Ishikawa
Ex VP: Akihiro Sawada
**VP:* Stephen Montague
VP: Eberhard Neumann
**VP:* Daniel J Sanford
VP: Masahiko Tetsumoto
Mng Dir: K C Woody
CTO: Antonio Eliot
IT Man: Bill Keiger

MIDSOUTH AGGREGATES
See MIDSOUTH PAVING INC

D-U-N-S 15-660-0710
▲ MIDSOUTH BANCORP INC
102 Versailles Blvd, Lafayette, LA 70501-6700
Tel (337) 237-8343 *Founded/Ownrshp* 1984
Sales NA *EMP* 604^E
Tkr Sym MSL *Exch* NYS
SIC 6021 National commercial banks; National commercial banks
Pr: C Rusty Cloutier
**Ch Bd:* Will Charbonnet Sr
CFO: James McLemore
Chf Cred: Jeffery L Blum
Ex VP: John Nichols
Sr VP: Jennifer S Fontenot
VP: Lorraine Miller
Exec: Troy M Cloutier
CIO: Lorin Lebla
Dir IT: Joy Duhon
Board of Directors: Leonard Q Abington, James R Davis Jr, Jake Delhomme, Clayton Paul Hillard, Milton B Kid III, Timothy J Lemone, R Glenn Pumpelly, William M Simmons, Joseph V Tortorice Jr

D-U-N-S 13-122-3273
■ MIDSOUTH BANK NA
(*Suby of* MIDSOUTH BANCORP INC) ★
102 Versailles Blvd # 100, Lafayette, LA 70501-6703
Tel (337) 366-9049 *Founded/Ownrshp* 1985
Sales NA *EMP* 600
SIC 6021 National commercial banks; National commercial banks
CEO: Rusty Cloutier
Pr: Troy Cloutier
Pr: Lynn Fowler
Pr: Gary W Junek
Pr: Blake McCaskill
Pr: John Wattinger
COO: Karen Hail
CFO: James McLemore
CFO: Terri Stelley
Chf Cred: John Nichols
Ofcr: Scott Borel
Ofcr: Brenda Jordan
Ofcr: Carolyn Lay
Ex VP: Donnie Landry
Sr VP: Jennifer Fontenot
Sr VP: Jem Fountenol
VP: David Bussell
VP: Ken Freeman
VP: Heather Hebert
VP: Lee F Hertel
VP: Lee Lightfoot
Board of Directors: Jake Delhomme

D-U-N-S 01-206-8977
MIDSOUTH DISTRICT IS A DISTRICT OF FOURSQUARE CHURCH
(*Suby of* FOURSQUARE INTERNATIONAL) ★
20825 Wilderness Oak, San Antonio, TX 78258-2627
Tel (210) 495-7600 *Founded/Ownrshp* 2010
Sales 6.4MM^E *EMP* 329^E
SIC 8661 Religious organizations; Churches, temples & shrines
Prin: David Coffey

D-U-N-S 12-650-9731
MIDSOUTH PAVING INC
MIDSOUTH AGGREGATES
(*Suby of* OLDCASTLE MATERIALS GROUP) ★
500 Rvrhills Bus Park, Birmingham, AL 35242-5039
Tel (205) 995-5900 *Founded/Ownrshp* 2002
Sales 5.8MM^E *EMP* 500
SIC 1475 1611 Phosphate rock; Highway & street construction; Phosphate rock; Highway & street construction
Pr: David M Church
**CFO:* Lamar Forsyth
VP: Sam Reeds
Ql Cn Mgr: Mike Fielding

D-U-N-S 05-380-8833
MIDSOUTH STEEL INC
4301 Roosevelt Hwy, Atlanta, GA 30349-2515
Tel (770) 465-3455 *Founded/Ownrshp* 2005
Sales 24.0MM^E *EMP* 50
SIC 3312 3446 Structural shapes & pilings, steel; Grillwork, ornamental metal
CEO: Charles M Staffins
**CFO:* Ashton Adams

D-U-N-S 05-508-3880
MIDSTATE BANCORP INC
LEGACY BANK
101 W Main St, Hinton, OK 73047-9160
Tel (405) 542-3101 *Founded/Ownrshp* 1966
Sales NA *EMP* 251
SIC 6712 Bank holding companies; Bank holding companies
Ch Bd: R Stephen Carmack
**Pr:* Michael Chaloner

D-U-N-S 14-487-8923
MIDSTATE BANKS INC
PLANTERSFIRST
131 N Jackson St, Hawkinsville, GA 31036-1547
Tel (478) 783-4017 *Founded/Ownrshp* 1979
Sales NA *EMP* 131
SIC 6022 State commercial banks; State commercial banks
Pr: Robert F Way
**Sec:* William E Shannon Jr
**VP:* Bobby Shepard

MIDSTATE BERKSHIRE
See MB WESTFIELD INC

D-U-N-S 19-597-4605
MIDSTATE CONSTRUCTION CORP
1180 Holm Rd, Petaluma, CA 94954-7120
Tel (707) 762-3200 *Founded/Ownrshp* 1987
Sales 29.8MM^E *EMP* 80
SIC 1521 1541 1542 New construction, single-family houses; General remodeling, single-family houses; Industrial buildings, new construction; Renovation, remodeling & repairs: industrial buildings; Commercial & office building, new construction; Commercial & office buildings, renovation & repair
Pr: Roger Nelson
**CFO:* Jim Debolt
CFO: Roger Treboutat
**VP:* Wesley Barry II
**VP:* Patrick Draeger
**VP:* Richard Oberdorfer

D-U-N-S 00-277-3638
MIDSTATE ELECTRIC COOPERATIVE INC (OR)
16755 Finley Butte Rd, La Pine, OR 97739-8884
Tel (541) 536-2126 *Founded/Ownrshp* 1948
Sales 29.9MM *EMP* 66
SIC 4911 Electric services; Electric services
Pr: Leland Smith
**Genl Mgr:* William A Kopacz
Dir IT: Shaun Lemar

D-U-N-S 08-431-3519
MIDSTATE MANUFACTURING CO INC
STEELWELD DIVISION
750 W 3rd St, Galesburg, IL 61401-5829
Tel (309) 342-9555 *Founded/Ownrshp* 1979
Sales 34.1MM^E *EMP* 150
SIC 3599 5084 Machine shop, jobbing & repair; Industrial machinery & equipment; Machine shop, jobbing & repair; Industrial machinery & equipment
Pr: Curtis A Pitman
**VP:* Russell Larson
VP Sls: Shawn Pitman

D-U-N-S 15-426-9195
MIDSTATE MECHANICAL INC
1850 E Riverview Dr, Phoenix, AZ 85034-6703
Tel (602) 452-8600 *Founded/Ownrshp* 1986
Sales 80.8MM^E *EMP* 250
SIC 1711 Warm air heating & air conditioning contractor; Mechanical contractor; Process piping contractor; Ventilation & duct work contractor; Warm air heating & air conditioning contractor; Mechanical contractor; Process piping contractor; Ventilation & duct work contractor
CEO: David Jones
**CFO:* Kevin Caroll
**Ex VP:* Ken Graul
Opers Mgr: Donald Humke

D-U-N-S 06-925-6618
MIDSTATE MEDICAL CENTER
RADIOLOGY ASSOCIATES
(*Suby of* HARTFORD HEALTHCARE CORP) ★
435 Lewis Ave, Meriden, CT 06451-2101
Tel (203) 694-8200 *Founded/Ownrshp* 1885
Sales 219.1MM *EMP* 900
SIC 8062 Hospital, medical school affiliation; Hospital, medical school affiliation
Pr: Lucille A Janatka
**CFO:* Ralph Becker
**VP:* Kenneth Cesca
VP: Harold P Kaplan
**VP:* Cindy Russo
VP Bus Dev: Maryanne Volkringer
Nurse Mgr: Beth Hackett
Pr Dir: Laura Spagnuolo
Doctor: Joyce Akhtar
Doctor: Rosamond Everard
Doctor: Inkwiy Kim

D-U-N-S 14-788-2286
MIDSTATE OIL CO (INC)
BREAK TIME
(*Suby of* MFA OIL CO) ★
1 Ray Young Dr, Columbia, MO 65201-3570
Tel (573) 442-0171 *Founded/Ownrshp* 1985
Sales 70.2MM *EMP* 365
SIC 5541 5411 Filling stations, gasoline; Convenience stores, independent; Filling stations, gasoline; Convenience stores, independent
Pr: Dale H Creach
**VP Admn:* Ron Benne

D-U-N-S 78-370-2418 IMP/EXP
MIDSTATE STEEL INC
2001 Jeffersonville Rd, Macon, GA 31217-4514
Tel (478) 743-4466 *Founded/Ownrshp* 1991
Sales 24.0MM^E *EMP* 85
SIC 3441 Fabricated structural metal
Pr: B L Slocumb III
**CFO:* Margaret M Slocumb
**Sec:* Judy Brown
**VP:* Robert Slocumb

VP: Wesley Solansky
Off Mgr: Glenda Sneed
Sfty Dirs: Tim Sparks
Prd Mgr: Terry Rainwater
VP Sls: Steve Burgamy

D-U-N-S 15-445-0969
MIDSTATES INC
QUALITY QUICKPRINT
4820 Capital Ave Ne, Aberdeen, SD 57401-8178
Tel (605) 225-5287 *Founded/Ownrshp* 1979
Sales 40.0MM^E *EMP* 289^E
SIC 2752 Commercial printing, lithographic; Commercial printing, lithographic
Pr: Roger Feickert
**VP:* Justin Feickert
Genl Mgr: David Bergard
Genl Mgr: Dave Hanson
IT Man: Chad Hoffman
IT Man: Chad Hoffmann
Sales Exec: Jeff Lagosh
Sls&Mrk Ex: Justin Feicker

MIDSTATES PETROLEUM
See MACS MINIT MART INC

D-U-N-S 07-839-8142
▲ MIDSTATES PETROLEUM CO INC
321 S Boston Ave Ste 1000, Tulsa, OK 74103-3322
Tel (918) 947-8550 *Founded/Ownrshp* 2011
Sales 794.1MM *EMP* 217
Tkr Sym MPO *Exch* NYS
SIC 1311 Crude petroleum & natural gas; Crude petroleum & natural gas
CEO: Frederic F Brace
**Ch Bd:* Thomas C Knudson
COO: Mark E Eck
CFO: Nelson M Haight
Ex VP: Mitchell G Elkins

D-U-N-S 15-345-2532
■ MIDSTATES PETROLEUM CO LLC
(*Suby of* MIDSTATES PETROLEUM CO INC) ★
321 S Boston Ave Ste 1000, Tulsa, OK 74103-3322
Tel (918) 947-8550 *Founded/Ownrshp* 2006
Sales 520.1MM^E *EMP* 163
SIC 1382 Oil & gas exploration services
Pr: Frederic Brace
**Pr:* Stephen J McDaniel
**CEO:* Robert McDaniel
VP: Brad Broekstra
VP: Kristen McDaniel

MIDSTATES SPIRAL
See SSM INDUSTRIES INC

D-U-N-S 15-211-8477
MIDSTATES VIDEO CORP
1022 E Adams St, Springfield, IL 62703-1028
Tel (217) 544-8433 *Founded/Ownrshp* 1985
Sales 307.4MM^E *EMP* 5,000
SIC 7389 7841 Coffee service; Video disk/tape rental to the general public; Coffee service; Video disk/tape rental to the general public
CEO: Charles R Hoogland
**Pr:* Keith Hoogland
CFO: Craig Hartner
**Treas:* Charles Eric Hoogland
Dist Mgr: Andra Morrissey

D-U-N-S 12-652-2940
MIDSUTH HOMEHEALTH
430 W Main St Ste 100, Dothan, AL 36301-1671
Tel (334) 618-2664 *Founded/Ownrshp* 2001
Sales 5.0MM *EMP* 700^E
SIC 8082 Home health care services

D-U-N-S 08-395-8371
MIDTEX OIL LP
PIT STOP FOOD MART
3455 S Interstate 35, New Braunfels, TX 78132-5270
Tel (830) 625-4214 *Founded/Ownrshp* 1966
Sales 112.7MM^E *EMP* 220
SIC 5541 5171 Filling stations, gasoline; Petroleum bulk stations; Filling stations, gasoline; Petroleum bulk stations
CEO: Maurice D Fischer
Pr: Rodney Fischer
CFO: Scott Schwind
VP: Russell Fischer
IT Man: Matt Curtis
Mktg Mgr: Katie Perera

D-U-N-S 84-582-5046
■ MIDTOWN EXPRESS LLC
(*Suby of* DYCOM INDUSTRIES INC) ★
5560 58th St, Maspeth, NY 11378-1117
Tel (718) 628-3420 *Founded/Ownrshp* 2008
Sales 40.6MM^E *EMP* 250^E
SIC 1731 7812 Telephone & telephone equipment installation; Cable television installation; Audio-visual program production; Telephone & telephone equipment installation; Cable television installation; Audio-visual program production
Pr: William Healy
VP: Michael Sicsko

D-U-N-S 05-399-2426
MIDTOWN FOOD STORES INC
GENE'S QUITO MARKET
18850 Cox Ave, Saratoga, CA 95070-4196
Tel (408) 379-8300 *Founded/Ownrshp* 1959
Sales 22.0MM^E *EMP* 154
SIC 5411 Grocery stores, independent; Grocery stores, independent
CEO: Richard Giomi
**Sec:* Sally Giomi
Off Mgr: Jeffy Cullati
Store Mgr: John Webber

MIDTOWN GROUP
See MIDTOWN PERSONNEL INC

D-U-N-S 15-763-3173
MIDTOWN MOTORS INC
JOHN HOWARD MOTORS
1730 Mileground Rd, Morgantown, WV 26505-3753
Tel (304) 296-3205 *Founded/Ownrshp* 1983
Sales 21.3MM^E *EMP* 50

SIC 5511 7538 7515 5521 7514 5531 Automobiles, new & used; General automotive repair shops; Passenger car leasing; Used car dealers; Rent-a-car service; Automotive parts
Pr: Randy W Buzzo
**VP:* James Howard
**VP:* Robert Meredith
Sls Mgr: Bud Regnier
Sales Asso: Joe Brown

D-U-N-S 79-358-6405
MIDTOWN PERSONNEL INC
MIDTOWN GROUP
900 7th St Nw Ste 725, Washington, DC 20001-4009
Tel (202) 887-4747 *Founded/Ownrshp* 1989
Sales 26.9MM *EMP* 22E
SIC 8742 Personnel management consultant
Pr: Helen Stefan Moreau
**Mng Pt:* David W Stefan
**VP:* Ward Howick

MIDTOWN TENNIS CLUB DIVISION
See TDA INDUSTRIES INC

D-U-N-S 04-129-4323 IMP/EXP
MIDTOWN TIRE INC
(*Suby of* TYLDIN CORP) ★
1771 Brighton Henrietta, Rochester, NY 14623-2505
Tel (585) 436-1410 *Founded/Ownrshp* 1974
Sales 40.9MME *EMP* 44
SIC 5014 Automobile tires & tubes
CEO: Tony Sagona
**Pr:* Richard J Henry
Opers Mgr: Dan Susa

D-U-N-S 15-175-2482 IMP
MIDTRONICS INC
7000 Monroe St, Willowbrook, IL 60527-5655
Tel (630) 323-2800 *Founded/Ownrshp* 1982
Sales 27.0MME *EMP* 130
SIC 3825 7622 3694 Battery testers, electrical; Meters: electric, pocket, portable, panelboard, etc.; Radio repair shop; Automotive electrical equipment; Battery testers, electrical; Meters: electric, pocket, portable, panelboard, etc.; Radio repair shop; Automotive electrical equipment
Pr: Stephen J McShane
Prgrm Mgr: Wayne Schindler
CTO: Wim Koster
Sls Mgr: Christopher Washburn
Board of Directors: C Richard Panico, Russ Smyth

D-U-N-S 00-693-1133
MIDVALE INDEMNITY CO (IL)
6000 American Pkwy, Madison, WI 53783-0001
Tel (847) 320-2000 *Founded/Ownrshp* 1912
Sales NA *EMP* 9,000
Accts Kpmg Llp
SIC 6331 8099 Workers' compensation insurance; Automobile insurance; Fire, marine & casualty insurance & carriers; Property damage insurance; Medical services organization; Workers' compensation insurance; Automobile insurance; Fire, marine & casualty insurance & carriers; Property damage insurance; Medical services organization
Pr: Douglas Andrews
**CFO:* Frederick T Griffith
Treas: Clark H Roberts
IT Man: Mike Gibbs
Board of Directors: John T Chain Jr, Peter B Hamilton, George R Lewis, Arthur J Massolo, David B Mathis

D-U-N-S 04-507-4010
MIDVALE INDUSTRIES INC
6310 Knox Industrial Dr, Saint Louis, MO 63139-3092
Tel (314) 647-5604 *Founded/Ownrshp* 1951
Sales 21.0MM *EMP* 29
SIC 5085 5051 5084 Industrial supplies; Abrasives; Refractory material; Foundry products; Ferroalloys; Cleaning equipment, high pressure, sand or steam; Metal refining machinery & equipment; Pollution control equipment, air (environmental); Conveyor systems; Industrial supplies; Abrasives; Refractory material; Foundry products; Ferroalloys; Cleaning equipment, high pressure, sand or steam; Metal refining machinery & equipment; Pollution control equipment, air (environmental); Conveyor systems
Pr: Gregory Kitzelman
Treas: Sergio Fernandez
VP: Karen Kane
Exec: Natalie Cox
IT Man: Mary Longo
Manager: Jon Sherman
Sls Mgr: Stan Mueller

D-U-N-S 08-177-8987
MIDVIEW LOCAL SCHOOL DISTRICT
13050 Durkee Rd, Grafton, OH 44044-1122
Tel (440) 926-3737 *Founded/Ownrshp* 1890
Sales 19.3MME *EMP* 320
SIC 8211 Public elementary school; Public junior high school; Public senior high school; Public elementary school; Public junior high school; Public senior high school
Treas: Nicole Spriggs
Bd of Dir: Brad Gross
Prin: Chuck Laubacher
Admn Mgr: Susan Bobola
IT Man: Denise Eslinger
Schl Brd P: Kathy Quintiliano
Psych: Lisa Montag

D-U-N-S 12-521-0492
MIDWAY AIRPORT CONCESSIONAIRE
SHIPWRECK KELLY'S BAR
5800 S Cicero Ave, Chicago, IL 60638
Tel (773) 582-4450 *Founded/Ownrshp* 1976
Sales 6.2MME *EMP* 300
SIC 5812 5461 5813 Ethnic food restaurants; Cafe; Pizzeria, independent; Snack bar; Bakeries; Bar (drinking places); Ethnic food restaurants; Cafe; Pizzeria, independent; Snack bar; Bakeries; Bar (drinking places)

D-U-N-S 08-691-7093
MIDWAY ARMS INC
MIDWAYUSA
5875 W Van Horn Tavern Rd, Columbia, MO 65203-9004
Tel (573) 445-6363 *Founded/Ownrshp* 1977
Sales 71.8MME *EMP* 185
SIC 5961 5091 Fishing, hunting & camping equipment & supplies: mail order; Hunting equipment & supplies; Fishing, hunting & camping equipment & supplies: mail order; Hunting equipment & supplies
Pr: Larry Potterfield
**Ex VP:* Brenda Potterfield
VP: Brian Felten
CTO: Joel Felten
IT Man: Steve Bayne
IT Man: Ricky Yates
Web Dev: Will Guldin
Web Dev: Amy Miller
Web Dev: Brandon Stallo
Software D: Jared Carlow
VP Opers: Stan Frink

D-U-N-S 03-591-5149
MIDWAY CHEVROLET CO
MIDWAY ISUZU
2323 W Bell Rd, Phoenix, AZ 85023-3298
Tel (602) 866-0102 *Founded/Ownrshp* 1966
Sales 98.4MME *EMP* 255E
SIC 5511 Automobiles, new & used; Automobiles, new & used
Pr: Larry Van Tuyl
**CFO:* John Bhatt
**Sec:* Allan M Cady
**VP:* Patricia Van Tuyl
Sls Mgr: David Camps
Sls Mgr: Richie Levingston
Sales Asso: Courtney O'Dell

D-U-N-S 06-152-9731
MIDWAY CHEVROLET INC
MIDWAY CHVROLET BUICK CADILLAC
515 2nd Ave, Kearney, NE 68847-7807
Tel (308) 234-2496 *Founded/Ownrshp* 1972, 1987
Sales 24.0MM *EMP* 41
SIC 5511 7538 5521 Automobiles, new & used; General automotive repair shops; Automobiles, used cars only; Automobiles, new & used; General automotive repair shops; Automobiles, used cars only
Pr: Brian Hamilton
**Treas:* Peggy Stabb
**VP:* Carie Hamilton
Genl Mgr: Wib Davenport
Genl Mgr: Ryan Davis

D-U-N-S 03-032-7902
MIDWAY CHEVROLET OLDSMOBILE CADILLAC PONTIAC BUICK INC
MIDWAY OLDSMOBILE
1337 Ocean Hwy, Pocomoke City, MD 21851-3015
Tel (410) 957-2222 *Founded/Ownrshp* 1976
Sales 23.3MME *EMP* 64
SIC 5511 5521 Automobiles, new & used; Pickups, new & used; Trucks, tractors & trailers: new & used; Vans, new & used; Used car dealers; Automobiles, new & used; Pickups, new & used; Trucks, tractors & trailers: new & used; Vans, new & used; Used car dealers
Pr: Glenn Ray Nordstrom
Top Exec: Eddie Mears
**VP:* Bonnie Nordstrom
Off Mgr: Sharon Worth
Sls Mgr: Clarence Campbell
Sales Asso: John Smith

MIDWAY CHRYSLER DODGE JEEP RAM
See PECK JEEP EAGLE INC

MIDWAY CHVROLET BUICK CADILLAC
See MIDWAY CHEVROLET INC

D-U-N-S 00-694-3476
MIDWAY CO-OP ASSOCIATION
MIDWAY COOP
210 W Harrison St, Osborne, KS 67473-1500
Tel (785) 346-5451 *Founded/Ownrshp* 1908
Sales 130.2MM *EMP* 90
Accts Lindburg Vogel Pierce Faris H
SIC 5153 5171 Grains; Petroleum bulk stations & terminals; Grains; Petroleum bulk stations & terminals
Genl Mgr: Dell Princ
Off Mgr: Scott Slabaugh
Sales Exec: Kenneth A Otte

D-U-N-S 07-407-4915
MIDWAY COLLEGE INC
512 E Stephens St, Midway, KY 40347-1120
Tel (859) 846-4421 *Founded/Ownrshp* 1847
Sales 22.8MM *EMP* 165
Accts Dean Dorton Allen Ford Pllc L
SIC 8222 Junior college; Junior college; Colleges universities & professional schools
Ch Bd: Donna R Moore
VP: Scott Fitzpatrick
VP: Ellen Gregory
VP: Judy Marcum
Exec: Anne Cockley
MIS Dir: Paula McGowen
Info Man: Capella McFarland
Pr Dir: Sheila Simpson
Psych: Shandra Irwin

MIDWAY COOP
See MIDWAY CO-OP ASSOCIATION

MIDWAY ENERGY SERVICES
See MIDWAY OILFIELD CONSTRUCTORS INC

D-U-N-S 78-739-8742
MIDWAY EQUIPMENT & SUPPLY CO
LES SCHWAB EQUIPMENT
20900 Cooley Rd, Bend, OR 97701-3406
Tel (541) 416-5233 *Founded/Ownrshp* 1988
Sales 21.2MME *EMP* 84E
SIC 5084 Industrial machinery & equipment; Recapping machinery, for tires; Industrial machinery & equipment; Recapping machinery, for tires
Pr: G Phillip Wick
**Pr:* John Britton
**CFO:* Jim Goad
**Ex VP:* Richard W Priday
**Exec:* Dick Borgman

MIDWAY FORD
See FORD MIDWAY MALL INC

D-U-N-S 05-342-5609
MIDWAY FORD CO INC
2777 Snelling Ave N, Saint Paul, MN 55113-1796
Tel (651) 636-8200 *Founded/Ownrshp* 1988
Sales 58.3MM *EMP* 63
SIC 5511 Automobiles, new & used; Pickups, new & used; Vans, new & used; Automobiles, new & used; Pickups, new & used; Vans, new & used
Pr: Ed Tichenor
**Treas:* John Tichenor
Ex VP: Mark Dinsen
VP Mktg: Tom Kulick

D-U-N-S 03-129-4283
MIDWAY FORD TRUCK CENTER INC (DE)
7601 Ne 38th St, Kansas City, MO 64161-9409
Tel (816) 455-3000 *Founded/Ownrshp* 1961, 1973
Sales 118.0MME *EMP* 235
SIC 5511 7538 Trucks, tractors & trailers: new & used; General automotive repair shops; Trucks, tractors & trailers: new & used; General automotive repair shops
CEO: Donald C Ahnger
**Pr:* Trey Meyer
**CFO:* Michael Doran
Ofcr: Mike Goebel
**Ex VP:* Michael Gaskill
**Ex VP:* Danny Warner
VP: Bill Hansen
VP: John Miller
VP: Larry Pasquini
**VP:* Terry Tyrrell
Exec: Kathy Mandacina
Board of Directors: Mark Graves

D-U-N-S 19-938-5147
MIDWAY GAMES INC
(*Suby of* ACQUISITION HOLDINGS SUBSIDIARY I LLC) ★
2704 W Roscoe St, Chicago, IL 60618-5910
Tel (773) 961-2222 *Founded/Ownrshp* 2008
Sales 27.6MME *EMP* 540E
Accts Ernst & Young Llp Chicago I
SIC 7372 Home entertainment computer software; Home entertainment computer software
Ch Bd: Matthew V Booty
Pr: Rosemary Hackett
CFO: Ryan G O'Desky
Sr VP: Deborah K Fulton
Sr VP: Miguel Iribarren
Dir IT: Ed Boon
Dir IT: Lupe Nunez

D-U-N-S 18-929-0807
MIDWAY GOLD CORP
8310 S Valley Hwy Ste 280, Englewood, CO 80112-5732
Tel (720) 979-0900 *Founded/Ownrshp* 1996
Sales 21.4MME *EMP* 49
SIC 1041 1044 Gold ores mining; Silver ores mining
Pr: William M Zisch
CFO: Bradley J Blacketor
VP: Tom Williams

D-U-N-S 61-185-1627
MIDWAY IMPORTING INC
1807 Brittmoore Rd, Houston, TX 77043-2213
Tel (713) 802-9363 *Founded/Ownrshp* 1989
Sales 161.9MME *EMP* 230
SIC 5122 Beauty shops; Cosmetics, perfumes & hair products
Pr: Christopher D Hartmann
**CFO:* Thomas J Schifanella Jr

D-U-N-S 01-820-1269 EXP
MIDWAY INC
MIDWAY TRUCK CENTER
220 Sandusky St, Monroeville, OH 44847-9506
Tel (419) 465-2551 *Founded/Ownrshp* 1978
Sales 24.4MME *EMP* 100
SIC 5013 5012 7538

D-U-N-S 00-126-2146
MIDWAY IND SCHOOL DISTRICT
12142 State Highway 148 S, Henrietta, TX 76365-7210
Tel (940) 476-2222 *Founded/Ownrshp* 1995
Sales 69.1MM *EMP* 70
SIC 8211 Public elementary & secondary schools; Public elementary & secondary schools
Prin: Dwight Mc New

D-U-N-S 10-261-3940
MIDWAY INDEPENDENT SCHOOL DISTRICT
13885 Woodway Dr, Woodway, TX 76712-7621
Tel (254) 761-5610 *Founded/Ownrshp* 1947
Sales 306.3M *EMP* 800
Accts Pattillo Brown & Hill Llp
SIC 8211 Public elementary school; Public junior high school; Public senior high school; Public elementary school; Public junior high school; Public senior high school

D-U-N-S 00-299-2261
MIDWAY INDUSTRIAL CONTRACTORS INC (IL)
MIDWAY WINDOWS AND DOORS
6750 S Belt Circle Dr, Bedford Park, IL 60638-4706
Tel (708) 594-2600 *Founded/Ownrshp* 1963, 1986
Sales 30.2MME *EMP* 120
SIC 3442 Metal doors; Window & door frames; Screen & storm doors & windows; Metal doors; Window & door frames; Screen & storm doors & windows
Pr: Arthur J Strauss Jr
Rgnl Mgr: Dennis Hart
Opers Mgr: Dick Baetzel
S&M/VP: Jerry Joseph

D-U-N-S 01-332-6038
MIDWAY INDUSTRIAL SUPPLY INC
SYMTH-DESPARD
51 Wurz Ave, Utica, NY 13502-2533
Tel (315) 797-6660 *Founded/Ownrshp* 1960
Sales 68.6MME *EMP* 80
Accts Moore & Hart Cpas Utica Ny
SIC 5085 Power transmission equipment & apparatus; Abrasives; Power transmission equipment & apparatus; Abrasives
Ch: Richard H Legro
**CEO:* Paul Rockwell
**VP:* Ken Smith
IT Man: David Leigh
Sales Asso: Frank Washicosky

D-U-N-S 60-605-1944
MIDWAY INFINITI INC
(*Suby of* I O D MOTORS INC)
2205 W Bell Rd, Phoenix, AZ 85023-3213
Tel (602) 866-6611 *Founded/Ownrshp* 2000
Sales 71.8MME *EMP* 460
SIC 5511 5521 Automobiles, new & used; Used car dealers; Automobiles, new & used; Used car dealers
Pr: Larry Van Tuyl
CFO: Ken Shaw
**Sec:* Allen Cade
**VP:* Stan Reed
Dir IT: Frankie Ruiz

MIDWAY ISUZU
See MIDWAY CHEVROLET CO

D-U-N-S 03-133-2372
MIDWAY MOTORS INC
2045 E Kansas Ave, McPherson, KS 67460-4005
Tel (620) 241-7737 *Founded/Ownrshp* 1960, 1991
Sales 31.2MME *EMP* 100
Accts Swindoll Janzen Hawk & Loyd
SIC 5511 7538 5531 5521 Automobiles, new & used; Trucks, tractors & trailers: new & used; General automotive repair shops; Automotive parts; Used car dealers; Automobiles, new & used; Trucks, tractors & trailers: new & used; General automotive repair shops; Automotive parts; Used car dealers
Pr: Jason Hoover
**Sec:* Jeanette James
VP: Steve Blomberg
Sls Mgr: Lesa Black
Sls Mgr: Kelly Hoover

D-U-N-S 60-470-6580
MIDWAY MOTORS OF HUTCHINSON LLC
1200 E 30th Ave, Hutchinson, KS 67502-4231
Tel (620) 662-4421 *Founded/Ownrshp* 1989
Sales 27.0MME *EMP* 100
SIC 5511 Automobiles, new & used; Automobiles, new & used
Owner: Gabe Goering
Genl Mgr: Danny Flynn

D-U-N-S 78-532-5056
MIDWAY MOTORS SUPERCENTER INC
MIDWAY MTRS FORD LNCOLN MRCURY
2075 E Kansas Ave, McPherson, KS 67460-4005
Tel (620) 241-0000 *Founded/Ownrshp* 2006
Sales 38.9MME *EMP* 100
SIC 5511 Automobiles, new & used; Automobiles, new & used
CEO: Jason Hoover
CFO: Craig Drucker
**VP:* Corey Hoover

MIDWAY MTRS FORD LNCOLN MRCURY
See MIDWAY MOTORS SUPERCENTER INC

D-U-N-S 15-994-6854
MIDWAY NISSAN INC
2201 W Bell Rd, Phoenix, AZ 85023-3213
Tel (602) 866-6600 *Founded/Ownrshp* 1997
Sales 71.8MME *EMP* 400
SIC 5511 5521 Automobiles, new & used; Used car dealers; Automobiles, new & used; Used car dealers
Pr: Tom Irwin
**Sec:* Joe Donofrio
**VP:* Frank Late
Genl Mgr: Jeff Anderson
Genl Mgr: Troy Matthews
Genl Mgr: Troy Methew
Sls Dir: Ed Brown
Sls Mgr: Brent Adkisson

D-U-N-S 01-912-6549
MIDWAY OIL CORP
217 N Main St, Rutland, VT 05701-2412
Tel (802) 775-5534 *Founded/Ownrshp* 1962
Sales 47.6MME *EMP* 150
SIC 5172 5541 5411 Gasoline; Filling stations, gasoline; Convenience stores, independent; Gasoline; Filling stations, gasoline; Convenience stores, independent
Pr: Francis M Trombetta
VP: Patrica Fettig
**VP:* Laura C Merone-Walsh
VP: Laura Walsh
Exec: Peter Longchamp
Dist Mgr: Matthew Pollock

D-U-N-S 06-797-2349
MIDWAY OILFIELD CONSTRUCTORS INC (TX)
MIDWAY ENERGY SERVICES
12627 State Highway 21 E, Midway, TX 75852-2833
Tel (936) 348-3721 *Founded/Ownrshp* 1981
Sales 292.6MME *EMP* 650
SIC 1389 1623 Oil field services; Oil & gas pipeline construction; Oil field services; Oil & gas pipeline construction
Pr: Billy A Smith Sr
VP: Jake Cain
Dir Bus: Landon Martin
Opers Mgr: Mil Clute

MIDWAY OLDSMOBILE
See MIDWAY CHEVROLET OLDSMOBILE CADILLAC PONTIAC BUICK INC

D-U-N-S 61-799-5527
MIDWAY PETROLEUM CO INC
5140 Midway Rd, Brandenburg, KY 40108-9683
Tel (270) 668-2070 Founded/Ownrshp 1990
Sales 24.5MM EMP 20
SIC 5171 Petroleum bulk stations & terminals; Petroleum bulk stations & terminals
Pr: Allen Hicks
*VP: Carol Hicks

MIDWAY PRODUCTS GROUP
See LAKEPARK INDUSTRIES INC

D-U-N-S 87-423-2465
MIDWAY PRODUCTS GROUP INC
1 Lyman Hoyt Dr, Monroe, MI 48161-9607
Tel (734) 241-7242 Founded/Ownrshp 1991
Sales 191.9MM^E EMP 352
SIC 8741 3469 Management services; Metal stampings; Management services; Metal stampings
Pr: James E Hoyt
*VP: Lloyd A Miller
Prgrm Mgr: Dana Gash
Prgrm Mgr: Ken Gove
Prgrm Mgr: Mike Gresko
CIO: Kendall Floyd
Mfg Dir: Bob Prucka
QC Dir: Christopher Aliapoulios
Mtls Mgr: Dave Devincentis
Sfty Mgr: Kent Downing
Opers Mgr: David Clawson

D-U-N-S 06-796-3736
MIDWAY SALES & DISTRIBUTING INC
MIDWAY WHOLESALE
218 Se Branner St, Topeka, KS 66607-1886
Tel (785) 233-7406 Founded/Ownrshp 1970
Sales 57.2MM^E EMP 100
SIC 5033 5031 Roofing & siding materials; Building materials, interior; Building materials, exterior; Roofing & siding materials; Building materials, interior; Building materials, exterior
CEO: Bruce H Myers
*VP: John Ossello
Sales Exec: Gary Weckbaugh
Sales Asso: Don Kellogg
Sales Asso: Cesar Rodriguez

D-U-N-S 03-243-7246 IMP
MIDWAY SERVICES INC
4677 118th Ave N, Clearwater, FL 33762-4444
Tel (727) 573-9500 Founded/Ownrshp 1957
Sales 34.4MM EMP 120
Accts Gregory Sharer & Stuart Pa
SIC 1711 1731 7623 Plumbing contractors; Warm air heating & air conditioning contractor; Electrical work; Refrigeration service & repair; Plumbing contractors; Warm air heating & air conditioning contractor; Electrical work; Refrigeration service & repair
Pr: William J Wolf
COO: John Baerg
*CFO: Ward Register
*Treas: Frances Wolf
Bd of Dir: Tonya Guldenpfennig
Genl Mgr: Jeff Vanscoyoc
Natl Sales: Dick Morris
Sls Dir: Joey Interrante
Snr PM: David Ortman
Snr PM: Manny Sanchez

MIDWAY SLOTS & SIMULCAST
See HARRINGTON RACEWAY INC

D-U-N-S 79-900-1644
MIDWAY STRUCTURAL PIPE AND SUPPLY INC
LANNIS FENCE SYSTEMS
1611 Clara St, Jackson, MI 49203-3471
Tel (517) 787-1350 Founded/Ownrshp 2007
Sales 20.4MM^E EMP 35
Accts Lally Group Pc Jackson Michi
SIC 5051 1799 3317 Pipe & tubing, steel; Exterior cleaning, including sandblasting; Steel pipe & tubes
Pr: Thomas Norton
*Sec: Edward J Adams III
Div Pres: Jack Adams
Div Pres: Phil Williams
*VP: Loeb Williams

MIDWAY TECHNOLOGY SOLUTIONS
See HUNT ELECTRIC CORP

MIDWAY TRUCK CENTER
See MIDWAY INC

D-U-N-S 80-678-3838 EXP
MIDWAY UNITED LIMITED
21a Highland Cir, Needham Heights, MA 02494-3011
Tel (781) 400-1742 Founded/Ownrshp 2006
Sales 29.7MM^E EMP 500
SIC 2491 Wood products, creosoted; Wood products, creosoted
Pr: Murphy Vandervelde
Pr: Trevor Larkan

D-U-N-S 96-933-5293
MIDWAY USA FOUNDATION INC
6001 W Van Horn, Columbia, MO 65203
Tel (573) 447-5957 Founded/Ownrshp 2011
Sales 29.1MM EMP 10
Accts Williams-Keepers Llc Columbia
SIC 8641 Civic social & fraternal associations
Ex Dir: Dick Leeper
*COO: Jay McClatchey
VP Opers: Stan Frink
Mktg Mgr: Sara Potterfield

MIDWAY WHOLESALE
See MIDWAY SALES & DISTRIBUTING INC

MIDWAY WINDOWS AND DOORS
See MIDWAY INDUSTRIAL CONTRACTORS INC

MIDWAYUSA
See MIDWAY ARMS INC

D-U-N-S 05-808-1373
MIDWESCO INDUSTRIES INC (OK)
2119 S Union Ave, Tulsa, OK 74107-2703
Tel (918) 446-6144 Founded/Ownrshp 1946, 1972
Sales 58.3MM^E EMP 242
SIC 5082 5085 General construction machinery & equipment; Industrial supplies; General construction machinery & equipment; Industrial supplies
Pr: James A Bost

D-U-N-S 09-973-3271
MIDWEST ACOUST-A-FIBER INC
M. A. I.
759 Pittsburgh Dr, Delaware, OH 43015-2862
Tel (740) 369-3624 Founded/Ownrshp 1979
Sales 72.7MM^E EMP 150^E
SIC 5531 Automotive parts; Automotive parts
Pr: Skip Allan
*CEO: Jerry M Wolf
*VP: Linda Wolf
*Prin: James E Hopple
Sls Mgr: Gary Ballard

D-U-N-S 92-846-7091
■ **MIDWEST AIR GROUP INC**
(Suby of REPUBLIC AIRWAYS HOLDINGS INC) ★
6744 S Howell Ave, Oak Creek, WI 53154-1422
Tel (414) 570-4000 Founded/Ownrshp 2009
Sales 91.1MM^E EMP 3,442
SIC 4512 Air transportation, scheduled; Air transportation, scheduled
Pr: Timothy E Hoeksema
COO: Joseph C Kolshak
CFO: Curtis E Sawyer
Treas: Dennis J O'Reilly
Chf Mktg O: Scott R Dickson
Sr VP: David Sislowski
Sr VP: Carol N Skoricka
CIO: Alex Yarmulnek
IT Man: Steve Mathwig
VP Opers: John Yowell
Natl Sales: Louise Habrack

D-U-N-S 13-937-4680 IMP/EXP
MIDWEST AIR TECHNOLOGIES INC
M A T
(Suby of MAT HOLDINGS INC) ★
6700 Wildlife Way, Long Grove, IL 60047
Tel (847) 821-9630 Founded/Ownrshp 1984
Sales 189.1MM^E EMP 75
Accts Bdo Seidman Llp
SIC 5072 5191 5063 5051 5031 Hardware; Garden supplies; Electrical apparatus & equipment; Nails; Fencing, wood; Hardware; Garden supplies; Electrical apparatus & equipment; Nails; Fencing, wood
Pr: George Ruhl
CFO: Gregory R Puse
Sr VP: Charles Walker
VP: Steven Rovtar
CIO: Edward Busse
Dir IT: Kevin Balster
IT Man: Manny Zavala
Opers Mgr: Patty Cate
Natl Sales: Christopher Clare
Mktg Dir: Donna Anderson

D-U-N-S 03-941-2275
MIDWEST AIR TRAFFIC CONTROL SERVICE INC
7285 W 132nd St Ste 340, Overland Park, KS 66213-1164
Tel (913) 782-7082 Founded/Ownrshp 1978
Sales 89.2MM EMP 12
SIC 4581 Airport control tower operation, except government; Airport control tower operation, except government
Pr: Shane Cordes
*CFO: Greg Schoofs
VP: Bill Ellis

D-U-N-S 17-561-1532
MIDWEST ASBESTOS ABATEMENT CORP
MIDWEST SERVICE GROUP
560 Turner Blvd, Saint Peters, MO 63376-1082
Tel (636) 926-7800 Founded/Ownrshp 1987
Sales 22.7MM^E EMP 120
SIC 1799 Asbestos removal & encapsulation
Pr: Jeff Blanton
*VP: Ben F Blanton
VP: Jay Giesler
Dir Bus: Todd Janson
Snr Mgr: Larry Shafer

D-U-N-S 03-634-7904
MIDWEST BANK NA
MID WEST BANK N.A.
(Suby of MIDWEST BANK NA)
2501 W Benjamin Ave, Norfolk, NE 68701-3119
Tel (402) 329-6221 Founded/Ownrshp 1969
Sales NA EMP 22
SIC 6021 National commercial banks; National commercial banks
CEO: Douglas Johnson
*CFO: Robert Schardt
*VP: Shannon Stuchlik
CTO: Peg Christensen

D-U-N-S 00-632-6995
MIDWEST BANKCENTRE
STUPP BRIDGE COMPANY
(Suby of STUPP BRIDGE COMPANY) ★
2191 Lemay Ferry Rd # 300, Saint Louis, MO 63125-2435
Tel (314) 544-8522 Founded/Ownrshp 1906
Sales NA EMP 220
SIC 6022 State commercial banks; State commercial banks
CEO: Jim Watson
Pr: Linda Hemmer
Pr: David Warning
Pr: Frank Ziegler Jr
Ch: Jack Biggs
Ofcr: Ben Anderson
Ofcr: Christopher Imming
Ofcr: John M Robinson
Ofcr: Mark Streeper
Sr VP: Laura Lehrmann
Sr VP: Timothy Reeves
Sr VP: Sarina Strack
VP: Don Fuller
VP: Randy Russell
VP: John Shivers
VP: Pete Zeiser

D-U-N-S 00-629-5018 IMP
MIDWEST BLOCK AND BRICK INC (MO)
2203 E Mccarty St, Jefferson City, MO 65101-4359
Tel (573) 635-7119 Founded/Ownrshp 1947, 1983
Sales 52.6MM^E EMP 150
SIC 5032 5031 3271 3272 Brick, except refractory; Cement; Lumber, plywood & millwork; Blocks, concrete or cinder: standard; Concrete products; Brick, except refractory; Cement; Lumber, plywood & millwork; Blocks, concrete or cinder: standard; Concrete products
CEO: Pat Dubbert
VP: Jason Gerling
VP: Mark Wilhelms
Genl Mgr: Darryl Winegar
Opers Mgr: Jeremy Winegar
Mktg Dir: Jamie Buffington
Sales Asso: Jason Carroll
Sales Asso: Cheynne Enyart
Sales Asso: Zach Kerr
Sales Asso: Klayton Labby
Sales Asso: Brian Rackers

D-U-N-S 02-329-7724
MIDWEST BOTTLE GAS CO INC
MIDWEST TV & APPLIANCE
3600 State Hwy 157, La Crosse, WI 54601
Tel (608) 781-1010 Founded/Ownrshp 1940
Sales 26.6MM EMP 70
SIC 5172 4924 5191 5722 Gases, liquefied petroleum (propane); Natural gas distribution; Fertilizer & fertilizer materials; Gas household appliances; Gases, liquefied petroleum (propane); Natural gas distribution; Fertilizer & fertilizer materials; Gas household appliances
Ch Bd: James Senty
Treas: Richard Linton
Ex Dir: Betsy Ahner

D-U-N-S 09-924-8171
MIDWEST BUS SALES INC
313 E Front St, Bonner Springs, KS 66012-1008
Tel (913) 422-1000 Founded/Ownrshp 1979
Sales 30.9MM^E EMP 100
SIC 5012 7513 Buses; Truck rental & leasing, no drivers; Buses; Truck rental & leasing, no drivers
Pr: Graydon J Kincaid Jr
*CFO: Linda Sinnett
*VP: Patricia Kincaid
Genl Mgr: Gary Whisenhunt
Off Mgr: Darlene Osman
IT Man: Dale Bohn
Opers Mgr: Lonnie Bruce
Sls Mgr: Scott Bruegge
Sls Mgr: Jeremy Messner

D-U-N-S 00-506-6873 IMP/EXP
MIDWEST CANVAS CORP (IL)
4635 W Lake St, Chicago, IL 60644-2798
Tel (773) 378-0741 Founded/Ownrshp 1947
Sales 85.7MM^E EMP 300^E
SIC 3081 3089 Plastic film & sheet; Laminating of plastic; Plastic film & sheet; Laminating of plastic
Pr: Barry A Handwerker
Plnt Mgr: Scott Kramer
Sls Mgr: Paul Wynn

D-U-N-S 04-314-5002
MIDWEST CAR CORP (WI)
INDEPENDENT NATIONAL CAR RENTL
1450 Delanglade St, Kaukauna, WI 54130-4128
Tel (414) 483-9800 Founded/Ownrshp 1957
Sales 75.1MM EMP 500
SIC 7514 Rent-a-car service; Rent-a-car service
Pr: James R Gustman
*CFO: Ray Leisgang
*Treas: Thomas P Gustman
*VP: Vance Herrings
*VP: James Maher
VP Mktg: Lee Vandersanden

D-U-N-S 05-209-8345
MIDWEST CASE MANAGEMENT INC
MIDWEST VOCATIONAL MANAGEMENT
2905 Lucerne Dr Se # 102, Grand Rapids, MI 49546-7160
Tel (616) 957-7796 Founded/Ownrshp 1988
Sales 1.0MMM^E EMP 8
SIC 8331 Job training & vocational rehabilitation services; Job training & vocational rehabilitation services
Pr: Nicole Phillips-Smith

D-U-N-S 18-088-4843
MIDWEST CHECK CASHING INC
EZ MONEY CHECK CASHING
2861 Capehart Rd Ste F, Bellevue, NE 68123-1786
Tel (402) 291-1175 Founded/Ownrshp 1988
Sales NA EMP 200
SIC 6099 Check cashing agencies; Check cashing agencies
Pr: Mike Medved

D-U-N-S 10-006-6190
MIDWEST CITY PUBLIC SCHOOLS I-52
MID-DEL SCHOOL SYSTEM
7217 Se 15th St, Oklahoma City, OK 73110-5235
Tel (405) 737-4461 Founded/Ownrshp 1944
Sales 81.0MM^E EMP 1,700
Accts Murrel Hall Mcintosh & Co
SIC 8211 Public elementary & secondary schools; Public elementary & secondary schools
Ofcr: Terry Tilley
Exec: Donna Cloud
Dir IT: Kevin Knauss
Software D: April Barney
Psych: Meagan Bryant
Psych: Kelly Collins
Psych: Becky Worth

D-U-N-S 00-981-4658
MIDWEST COAST TRANSPORT INC
(Suby of COMCAR INDUSTRIES INC) ★
1600 E Benson Rd, Sioux Falls, SD 57104-0822
Tel (605) 339-8400 Founded/Ownrshp 1994
Sales 34.8MM^E EMP 200
SIC 4213 Trucking, except local; Refrigerated products transport; Trucking, except local; Refrigerated products transport
Pr: Matt Staniszewski
*VP: Milton E Jacobs
Opers Mgr: Scott Wood

D-U-N-S 06-733-5869
MIDWEST COLLABORATIVE FOR LIBRARY SERVICES INC
MICHIGAN LIBRARY CONSORTIUM
1407 Rensen St Ste 1, Lansing, MI 48910-3657
Tel (517) 394-2420 Founded/Ownrshp 1974
Sales 25.9MM EMP 21
Accts Maner Costerisan Pc Lansing
SIC 8231 Libraries; Libraries
Ex Dir: Randy Dykhuis
Ex Dir: Gail Madziar
CTO: Mark Szidik

MIDWEST COMMERCIAL INTERIORS
See MIDWEST OFFICE INC

D-U-N-S 15-226-8058 IMP
MIDWEST COMPOSITE TECHNOLOGIES INC
1050 Walnut Ridge Dr, Hartland, WI 53029-8303
Tel (262) 367-8254 Founded/Ownrshp 1984
Sales 27.5MM^E EMP 45
SIC 5162 Plastics products
Pr: Helmut Keidl
*VP: Roberta Keidl

MIDWEST CONCRETE MATERIALS
See WAMEGO SAND CO

D-U-N-S 83-071-9360
MIDWEST CONSTRUCTION MATERIALS INC
220 Business Park Cir, Stoughton, WI 53589-3393
Tel (608) 205-6040 Founded/Ownrshp 2009
Sales 20.0MM^E EMP 37^E
SIC 5082 General construction machinery & equipment
Pr: Robert E Boettcher
*Sec: Jane M Shock
*Prin: John Leyden

D-U-N-S 80-909-8275
MIDWEST CONSTRUCTION SERVICES INC
TRILLIUM MARINE
5555 Gull Rd Ste 300, Kalamazoo, MI 49048-7640
Tel (269) 345-0150 Founded/Ownrshp 2007
Sales 45.4MM^E EMP 100
SIC 1542 Commercial & office building contractors; Commercial & office building, new construction; Commercial & office building, prefabricated erection; Commercial & office buildings, renovation & repair
CEO: Rene Poch
*Pr: Kate Spiegel
CFO: Kate Speigal
Area Mgr: Englert Gary
Brnch Mgr: Bob Erdmann
Brnch Mgr: Randy Fulton
Brnch Mgr: Dave Gurney
Opers Mgr: Jeffery Tendall

D-U-N-S 19-412-0754 EXP
MIDWEST COOLING TOWERS INC
1156 E Highway 19, Chickasha, OK 73018-6347
Tel (405) 224-4622 Founded/Ownrshp 2013
Sales 50.0MM EMP 190
SIC 2499 2452 Cooling towers, wood or wood & sheet metal combination; Prefabricated wood buildings; Cooling towers, wood or wood & sheet metal combination; Prefabricated wood buildings
Pr: Terry Ogburn
Genl Mgr: Bob Crozier Jr
Sfty Mgr: Gary Krupka
Sls Mgr: Shane Schmidt

D-U-N-S 02-435-6180
MIDWEST COOPERATIVES
1919 E Sioux Ave, Pierre, SD 57501-4079
Tel (605) 224-5935 Founded/Ownrshp 1956
Sales 65.7MM^E EMP 100
SIC 5153 5191 5172 Grain elevators; Feed; Seeds: field, garden & flower; Fertilizer & fertilizer materials; Chemicals, agricultural; Diesel fuel; Gasoline; Lubricating oils & greases; Grain elevators; Feed; Seeds: field, garden & flower; Fertilizer & fertilizer materials; Chemicals, agricultural; Diesel fuel; Gasoline; Lubricating oils & greases

D-U-N-S 19-581-3399
MIDWEST CURTAINWALLS INC
5171 Grant Ave, Cleveland, OH 44125-1031
Tel (216) 641-7900 Founded/Ownrshp 1986
Sales 20.9MM^E EMP 80
SIC 3449 3442 1751 Curtain wall, metal; Curtain walls for buildings, steel; Window & door frames; Window & door (prefabricated) installation
Pr: Donald F Kelly Jr
Pr: Jeremiah Sawyer

D-U-N-S 03-444-7680 IMP
MIDWEST CUSTOM CASE INC
MIDWEST STORE FIXTURES
425 Crossing Dr Unit A, University Park, IL 60484-4133
Tel (708) 672-2900 Founded/Ownrshp 1991
Sales 35.2MM EMP 210
Accts Joseph L Jimenez Ms Cpa
SIC 2541 Store fixtures, wood; Store fixtures, wood
Pr: Karen A Papiese
*CFO: Richard J Papiese
Sys/Mgr: Jeanine Zajeski

D-U-N-S 07-688-8929
MIDWEST DAIRY ASSOCIATION
MIDWEST DAIRY COUNCIL
2015 Rice St Ste 100, Saint Paul, MN 55113-6800
Tel (651) 488-0261 Founded/Ownrshp 1981
Sales 20.5MM EMP 75
Accts Wilkerson Guthmann & Johnson

SIC 8611 Business associations; Business associations
CEO: Mike Kruger
**CEO:* Mike Kriger
Dir IT: John McClerrey
Mktg Dir: Barb Luehmann

MIDWEST DAIRY COUNCIL
See MIDWEST DAIRY ASSOCIATION

MIDWEST DENTAL EQUIPMENT SUP
See FALLSTECH INC

D-U-N-S 79-428-6844
MIDWEST DIRECT MAILERS LLC
8711 S 77th Ave, Bridgeview, IL 60455-1805
Tel (708) 598-1212 *Founded/Ownrshp* 2006
Sales NA *EMP* 330
SIC 7331 Direct mail advertising services

D-U-N-S 03-134-1514 IMP
MIDWEST DISTRIBUTORS CO INC
6501 Kansas Ave, Kansas City, KS 66111-2396
Tel (913) 287-2020 *Founded/Ownrshp* 1986
Sales 22.3MM^E *EMP* 55
SIC 5181 Beer & other fermented malt liquors
Pr: Gary Marvine
VP: Tom Carter
**VP:* Tom White
VP: Thomas Wliite

D-U-N-S 08-929-7881
■ MIDWEST DIVISION - LSH LLC
HCA MIDWEST
(*Suby of* HCA HOLDINGS INC) ★
2100 Se Blue Pkwy, Lees Summit, MO 64063-1007
Tel (816) 282-5000 *Founded/Ownrshp* 2003
Sales 74.2MM *EMP* 411
SIC 8062 General medical & surgical hospitals; General medical & surgical hospitals
Chf Rad: John Eurich
Dir Vol: Shannon Pierce
CFO: Matthew Leary
Off Mgr: Erin Eskina

D-U-N-S 07-625-2659
■ MIDWEST DIVISION RMC LLC
COLUMBIA HCA
(*Suby of* HCA INC) ★
2316 E Meyer Blvd, Kansas City, MO 64132-1136
Tel (816) 276-4000 *Founded/Ownrshp* 2003
Sales 338.1MM *EMP* 2,400
SIC 8062 General medical & surgical hospitals; General medical & surgical hospitals
Dir Rx: Robert Bub
Dir Rx: Joe Burwinkle
CIO: Kent McAllister
Dir IT: William Schwab
Pathlgst: Larry Lawson
Ansthlgy: Dirk Davis
Pgrm Dir: Charlotte Haupt

D-U-N-S 05-996-6986
MIDWEST DRYWALL CO INC
MDC DRYWALL
1351 S Reca Ct Ste 101, Wichita, KS 67209-1815
Tel (316) 722-9559 *Founded/Ownrshp* 1972
Sales 123.2MM^E *EMP* 800
SIC 1742 Drywall; Acoustical & ceiling work; Plastering, plain or ornamental; Drywall; Acoustical & ceiling work; Plastering, plain or ornamental
Pr: Steven A Nienke
**CFO:* Denis Dieker
Sls Mgr: Esther Thiesing

D-U-N-S 09-480-8953 EXP
MIDWEST ELASTOMERS INC (OH)
MEI
700 Industrial Dr, Wapakoneta, OH 45895-9200
Tel (419) 738-8844 *Founded/Ownrshp* 1986
Sales 20.2MM^E *EMP* 65
SIC 2822 3069 Synthetic rubber; Reclaimed rubber (reworked by manufacturing processes)
Pr: George Wight
**Pr:* Ron Clark
**Treas:* Barbara Link
**Prin:* Bill Jacobs
**Prin:* Karen Jacobs
**Prin:* Evan Piland
**Prin:* LY SOO
Plnt Mgr: Mike Baker

MIDWEST ELECTRIC COMPANY
See MWMPC CORP

D-U-N-S 61-876-3676
MIDWEST EMERGENCY DEPARTMENT SERVICES INC
MEDS
320 E Highway 50, O Fallon, IL 62269-2704
Tel (618) 206-3398 *Founded/Ownrshp* 1983
Sales 40.3MM *EMP* 45
Accts Larson Allen Llp St Louis
SIC 8741 Management services
Pr: G Scott Dillon
COO: John D Cruzen
**Ch:* William Cruzen
**Chf Mktg O:* Carmon L Glover III
Ex VP: Carmon L Gover

D-U-N-S 15-020-1853
■ MIDWEST EMPLOYERS CASUALTY CO
MECC
(*Suby of* W R BERKLEY CORP) ★
14755 North Outer 40 Rd # 300, Chesterfield, MO 63017-6050
Tel (636) 449-7000 *Founded/Ownrshp* 2001
Sales NA *EMP* 112
SIC 6331 6399 Fire, marine & casualty insurance; Health insurance for pets
Pr: Timothy F Galvin
Pr: Philip Cordeiro
**Pr:* Melodee J Saunders
COO: Tim Galvin
**CFO:* Tom Lentz
**CFO:* Peter W Shaw
**VP:* Steven Link
**Ex VP:* Steven Link
**Sr VP:* Donna L Knowling
**VP:* Dan Asahl
VP: Andrew Cartwright
**VP:* Michael Foerst
VP: Mary McHugh
VP: Danielle Schroeder
VP: Mark Sidney
**VP:* Tom Vonderheid

D-U-N-S 13-449-4637
MIDWEST ENERGY COOPERATIV
901 E State St, Cassopolis, MI 49031-9339
Tel (269) 445-1000 *Founded/Ownrshp* 2003
Sales 79.4MM *EMP* 36^E
Accts Harris Group Cpa S Traverse C
SIC 3634 Electric housewares & fans
Ch: Clarence Barth
VP: David Allen
VP: Phil Goodell
Info Man: Bill McKenzie
Opers Supe: Todd Hartsell

D-U-N-S 00-881-4402
MIDWEST ENERGY COOPERATIVE
901 E State St, Cassopolis, MI 49031-9339
Tel (269) 445-1000 *Founded/Ownrshp* 1937
Sales 76.8MM *EMP* 90
Accts Harris Group Cpa S Trverse Ci
SIC 4911 Distribution, electric power; Distribution, electric power
Ex Dir: Bob Hance
V Ch: Jim Dickerson
**CFO:* John H Miner
**Ch:* Clarence Barth
**Treas:* Ben Russell
Board of Directors: Jerry Campbell

D-U-N-S 04-237-9594
MIDWEST ENERGY INC
1330 Canterbury Dr, Hays, KS 67601-2708
Tel (785) 625-3437 *Founded/Ownrshp* 1979
Sales 216.5MM *EMP* 274
Accts Bkd Llp Oklahoma Ok
SIC 4911 8611 Generation, electric power; Business associations; Generation, electric power; Business associations
Pr: Earnest A Lehman
**Treas:* Chuck Moore
VP: Bonnie Augustine
**VP:* Bill Dowling
**VP:* Sharon Dreher
**VP:* Tim Flax
VP: Lynn Horner
**VP:* Tom Meis
VP: Fred Taylor
Opers Mgr: Brett Albert
Opers Mgr: Don Augustine

D-U-N-S 01-087-7793
■ MIDWEST ENERGY RESOURCES CO
(*Suby of* DTE ELECTRIC CO) ★
2400 Winter St, Superior, WI 54880-1473
Tel (715) 392-9807 *Founded/Ownrshp* 1974
Sales 20.9MM^E *EMP* 92
SIC 4432 Freight transportation on the Great Lakes
Pr: Fred L Shusterich
**VP:* Jeff Papineau
Mng Dir: Ron Reckinger

D-U-N-S 78-772-8971
MIDWEST ENGINEERED SYSTEMS INC
W238n1800 Rockwood Dr, Waukesha, WI 53188-1113
Tel (262) 436-0381 *Founded/Ownrshp* 1993
Sales 43.3MM^E *EMP* 150
SIC 7373 8742 Systems engineering, computer related; Automation & robotics consultant; Systems engineering, computer related; Automation & robotics consultant
Pr: Scott J Woida
VP: Steve Bougie
VP: Terry Merrifield
VP: Dean Stefanac
Mfg Mgr: Jeff Cunha
Snr PM: Elmer Blachowiak

D-U-N-S 18-135-3806
MIDWEST ENVIROMENTAL SERVICES INC
420 1/2 S Francis St, Brownstown, IN 47220
Tel (812) 358-5160 *Founded/Ownrshp* 1982
Sales 35.4MM^E *EMP* 63
SIC 4953 Non-hazardous waste disposal sites; Hazardous waste collection & disposal
Pr: Nancy Sterling
VP: Ray Boyle
**VP:* Dennis Sterling

D-U-N-S 01-628-9282
MIDWEST EQUIPMENT & SUPPLY CO INC
IMPERIAL FASTENER
2145 Bergdolt Rd, Evansville, IN 47711-2845
Tel (812) 425-6216 *Founded/Ownrshp* 1963
Sales 48.6MM *EMP* 38
Accts Harding Shymanski & Company
SIC 5083 5084 Lawn & garden machinery & equipment; Chainsaws; Lawn & garden machinery & equipment; Chainsaws
Pr: Glenn Heseman
**Sec:* Michael Fendrich
VP: Robert Reynolds
Genl Mgr: Mike Benidict
IT Man: Tom Aull

D-U-N-S 18-340-3674
MIDWEST EXPRESS INC
(*Suby of* HONDA LOGISTICS NORTH AMERICA INC) ★
11590 Township Road 298, East Liberty, OH 43319-9450
Tel (937) 642-0335 *Founded/Ownrshp* 2008
Sales 145.1MM^E *EMP* 1,183
SIC 4226 Special warehousing & storage; Special warehousing & storage
Pr: Tamaki Hashimoto
Treas: Akio Nabuto
Sr VP: John Jenkins
**VP:* Ed Allison
**VP:* Robert Overbaugh
**Prin:* Tadao Endo
IT Man: Brian Beard
Tech Mgr: Tonya Wright
Opers Mgr: Jacqueline Wheeler
Sales Exec: Robert Charters
S&M/VP: Mike Meier

MIDWEST EYE BANK & TRANSPLANT
See EVERSIGHT

D-U-N-S 01-217-0478
MIDWEST EYE CONSULTANTS PC
GARNER & TRUMP EYECARE
833 N Cass St, Wabash, IN 46992-1613
Tel (260) 569-9244 *Founded/Ownrshp* 1992
Sales 21.4MM^E *EMP* 270
SIC 8042 8071 Offices & clinics of optometrists; Medical laboratories; Offices & clinics of optometrists; Medical laboratories
Pr: Gregory Garner
Sr VP: Bruce Trump
VP: Cathy Garrett
**VP:* Bruce Trumph

D-U-N-S 80-783-9464
MIDWEST FAMILY MUTUAL INSURANCE CO
3033 Campus Dr Ste E195, Minneapolis, MN 55441-2624
Tel (763) 951-7000 *Founded/Ownrshp* 2007
Sales NA *EMP* 80
SIC 6311 Life insurance
Pr: Ron Boid
CFO: Kristie Van Pelt
**Treas:* Richard Habstritt
Mktg Mgr: Rocky Kotter
Mktg Mgr: Brian Sloan
Manager: Steve Schleicher

MIDWEST FARMERS COOP
See GREENWOOD FARMERS COOPERATIVE

D-U-N-S 00-486-9442
MIDWEST FARMERS COOPERATIVE
304 S 3rd St, Elmwood, NE 68349-6114
Tel (402) 994-2585 *Founded/Ownrshp* 1919
Sales 170.7MM *EMP* 150
Accts Gardiner Thomsen Cpa Lincoln
SIC 5153 5191 5541 Grains; Fertilizer & fertilizer materials; Feed; Filling stations, gasoline; Grains; Fertilizer & fertilizer materials; Feed; Filling stations, gasoline
Pr: Dale Piper
**CFO:* Tim Junge
IT Man: Gayln Boesiger
Sales Exec: Reed Priess

D-U-N-S 02-088-7592 IMP
MIDWEST FASTENER CORP (MI)
9031 Shaver Rd, Portage, MI 49024-6179
Tel (269) 327-2829 *Founded/Ownrshp* 1971
Sales 47.3MM^E *EMP* 150
SIC 5072 Nuts (hardware); Bolts; Brads; Tacks; Nuts (hardware); Bolts; Brads; Tacks
Pr: Henry De Vries
COO: Fred Devries
**VP:* Robert De Vries
Dir IT: Brian Devries
Plnt Mgr: Kay Reynolds
Natl Sales: Glen Gevaart
Sls Mgr: Tiffanie Clawson

D-U-N-S 80-884-5911 IMP
MIDWEST FASTENERS INC
450 Richard St, Miamisburg, OH 45342-1863
Tel (937) 866-0463 *Founded/Ownrshp* 1987
Sales 22.1MM^E *EMP* 85
SIC 3548 Electric welding equipment; Electric welding equipment
Pr: Thomas Hartmann
**Sec:* Robert Fairbank
**VP:* Brian Waterhouse
Exec: Gloria Ramsey
Sales Exec: Bill Smith

MIDWEST FIBER - NORMAL
See MIDWEST FIBER INC

D-U-N-S 11-048-6482 EXP
MIDWEST FIBER INC
MIDWEST FIBER - NORMAL
422 S White Oak Rd, Normal, IL 61761-4328
Tel (309) 452-0064 *Founded/Ownrshp* 1990
Sales 21.4MM^E *EMP* 75
SIC 5093 4953 Waste paper; Recycling, waste materials
Pr: Ronald Shumaker
**VP:* Michael Shumaker
Genl Mgr: Chad Ijams

D-U-N-S 12-253-7798 IMP
MIDWEST FILTRATION LLC
9775 International Blvd, West Chester, OH 45246-4855
Tel (513) 874-6510 *Founded/Ownrshp* 2013
Sales 25.0MM^E *EMP* 65
SIC 3569 2653 Filters, general line: industrial; Corrugated & solid fiber boxes; Filters, general line: industrial; Corrugated & solid fiber boxes
CEO: Steven Vollmer
Pr: Frank Strittmatter
CFO: Bill Klien
VP: Russ Halstad
Exec: Carolyn Hughes
Opers Mgr: Dennis Logan
Plnt Mgr: James Valentine
Ql Cn Mgr: Larry Snyder

D-U-N-S 01-370-6601 IMP/EXP
■ MIDWEST FOLDING PRODUCTS CORP
(*Suby of* HNI CORP) ★
1302 Industrial Blvd, Temple, TX 76504-1126
Tel (312) 666-3366 *Founded/Ownrshp* 2011
Sales 29.6MM^E *EMP* 181
SIC 2531 5021 6512 5064 Public building & related furniture; Public building furniture; Shopping center, property operation only; Electric household appliances; Public building & related furniture; Public building furniture; Shopping center, property operation only; Electric household appliances
VP: Sam Thomas

D-U-N-S 62-352-6840
MIDWEST FOOD BANK NFP
1703 S Veterans Pkwy, Bloomington, IL 61701-7019
Tel (309) 663-5350 *Founded/Ownrshp* 2003
Sales 89.4MM *EMP* 2^E
Accts Heinold-Banwart Ltd East Pe
SIC 8322 Individual & family services; Individual & family services
Pr: David Kieser
**Treas:* Dave Hodel
**VP:* John Feit

MIDWEST FOODS
See MID-WEST INSTITUTIONAL FOOD DISTRIBUTORS INC

D-U-N-S 18-054-2573
MIDWEST FRESH FOODS INC
38 N Glenwood Ave, Columbus, OH 43222-1206
Tel (614) 469-1492 *Founded/Ownrshp* 1987
Sales 22.4MM^E *EMP* 35
SIC 5148 Fruits, fresh; Vegetables, fresh; Fruits, fresh; Vegetables, fresh
Pr: Charles Giller
**VP:* Stan Hunt
Genl Mgr: Taylor Hunt
Manager: Steve Walters
Sls Dir: Doug Dale
Sales Asso: Bob Hicks
Sales Asso: Jonathan Smith

D-U-N-S 02-329-4150
MIDWEST GARMENT INC (WI)
DESMOND'S MENS WEAR
620 Cass St, La Crosse, WI 54601-4753
Tel (608) 784-0513 *Founded/Ownrshp* 1949
Sales 7.9MM^E *EMP* 490
SIC 7299 5699 5136 Tuxedo rental; Formal wear; Men's & boys' suits & trousers; Tuxedo rental; Formal wear; Men's & boys' suits & trousers
Pr: John G Desmond

D-U-N-S 12-711-2931
■ MIDWEST GENERATION EME LLC
(*Suby of* EDISON MISSION ENERGY) ★
440 Suth La Salle St 3500, Chicago, IL 60605
Tel (312) 583-6000 *Founded/Ownrshp* 1999
Sales 1.8MMM^E *EMP* 1,000
SIC 4911 Electric services; Electric services
Rgnl VP: Charles Parnell
VP: Mark Clarke
VP: John Deshong
Dir IT: Jacqueline Trapp

D-U-N-S 11-446-6571 IMP
■ MIDWEST GENERATION LLC
(*Suby of* NRG ENERGY INC) ★
529 E Romeo Rd, Romeoville, IL 60446-1538
Tel (609) 524-4526 *Founded/Ownrshp* 2013
Sales 360.7MM^E *EMP* 586
SIC 4911 Electric services; Distribution, electric power; Generation, electric power; Transmission, electric power; Electric services; Distribution, electric power; Generation, electric power; Transmission, electric power
Pr: Douglas R McFarlan
CFO: Maria Rigatti
Ofcr: David Knox
VP: John C Kennedy
VP: Fred W McCluskey
VP: Daniel D McDevitt
Plng Mgr: Bryan Martinez
Snr PM: Todd Kollross

MIDWEST GLOVES AND GEAR
See MIDWEST QUALITY GLOVES INC

D-U-N-S 00-691-9476 IMP/EXP
MIDWEST HARDWOOD CORP
METRO HARDWOODS
9540 83rd Ave N, Maple Grove, MN 55369-4567
Tel (763) 425-8700 *Founded/Ownrshp* 1981
Sales 133.2MM^E *EMP* 385
SIC 5031 2421 Lumber: rough, dressed & finished; Plywood; Particleboard; Molding, all materials; Sawmills & planing mills, general; Kiln drying of lumber; Custom sawmill; Lumber: rough, dressed & finished; Plywood; Particleboard; Molding, all materials; Sawmills & planing mills, general; Kiln drying of lumber; Custom sawmill
Pr: Mike Flynn
Genl Mgr: Doug Hilber
Genl Mgr: Steve Koves
Off Admin: Wanda Blechschmidt
Off Admin: Diane Boley
Off Admin: Mary Brenner
Off Admin: Jeff Machovec
Off Admin: Robin McCallie
Off Admin: Melanie Niznik
Off Admin: Kristy Provost
Off Admin: Melissa Stowers

MIDWEST HAYWOOD
See HAYWOOD REGIONAL MEDICAL CENTER

D-U-N-S 04-919-5365
MIDWEST HEALTH CENTER PC
4700 Schaefer Rd Ste 340, Dearborn, MI 48126-3743
Tel (313) 581-2600 *Founded/Ownrshp* 1981
Sales 30.9MM^E *EMP* 267
SIC 8011 Clinic, operated by physicians; Clinic, operated by physicians
Ch Bd: Richard Poston
Pr: Mark B Saffer DPM
CFO: Allen Kessler
Treas: Robert Rubin
VP: Jack Shapiro
VP Opers: Jane Dehart
Sls Mgr: Randall Dervishi
Doctor: Suhail Banister
Doctor: Gerald Katzman
Doctor: Robert Orr MD
Pharmcst: Noelle Perkins

D-U-N-S 07-627-0610
MIDWEST HEALTH SERVICES INC
TOPEKA CONVALESCENT CENTER
3715 Sw 29th St Ste 200, Topeka, KS 66614-2100
Tel (785) 272-1535 *Founded/Ownrshp* 1977

Sales 21.0MM^E *EMP* 310
SIC 8051 8059

D-U-N-S 13-044-2853
MIDWEST HEALTH VENTURES INC
333 Dixie Hwy, Chicago Heights, IL 60411-1748
Tel (708) 756-0100 *Founded/Ownrshp* 1999
Sales 7.8MM^E *EMP* 450
SIC 8011 Freestanding emergency medical center; Freestanding emergency medical center
Pr: Peter J Murphy
Prin: Jeffrey Feeney

D-U-N-S 05-614-6744
MIDWEST HOME HEALTH CARE INC (MN)
2445 Park Ave, Minneapolis, MN 55404-3714
Tel (612) 343-3265 *Founded/Ownrshp* 2002
Sales 5.0MM^E *EMP* 400
SIC 8082 Home health care services; Home health care services
Pr: Mohamud K Hassan
**VP:* Bashir Mohamed

MIDWEST HOSE
See MID-WEST HOSE & SPECIALTY INC

D-U-N-S 82-755-3442
MIDWEST II INC
6194 Section Rd, Ottawa Lake, MI 49267-9526
Tel (734) 856-5200 *Founded/Ownrshp* 2008
Sales 60.7MM^E *EMP* 130
SIC 5198 Paints; Paints
Pr: Olin White
CFO: Richard Sands
Ql Cn Mgr: Mark Pawlaczyk

D-U-N-S 03-240-5649
MIDWEST INDUSTRIAL METALS CORP
615 Northwest Ave, Northlake, IL 60164-1301
Tel (773) 202-8202 *Founded/Ownrshp* 1980
Sales 21.4MM^E *EMP* 30
SIC 5093 Nonferrous metals scrap
Pr: Steven Cadkin
**Pr:* Mark Hewines
Bd of Dir: Michael Nanberg
Plnt Mgr: Jesus Solis
**VP Sls:* Chuck Dreyfuss

D-U-N-S 09-863-7473 IMP/EXP
MIDWEST INDUSTRIAL RUBBER INC
M I R
10431 Midwest Indus Dr, Saint Louis, MO 63132-1225
Tel (314) 890-0016 *Founded/Ownrshp* 1980
Sales 63.0MM^E *EMP* 145
SIC 5085 3535 3052 Hose, belting & packing; Power transmission equipment & apparatus; Rubber goods, mechanical; Conveyors & conveying equipment; Rubber & plastics hose & beltings; Hose, belting & packing; Power transmission equipment & apparatus; Rubber goods, mechanical; Conveyors & conveying equipment; Rubber & plastics hose & beltings
CEO: William Kuechler
**Ch Bd:* Don Schanche
**Pr:* Micheal Bruhn
**CFO:* Jean Timme
Exec: Mary Garavaglia
Exec: Kelly Hoierman
Rgnl Mgr: Sean Meyer
Tech Mgr: Clifford Atkinson
Snr Mgr: Greg Timme

D-U-N-S 08-177-7104 IMP
MIDWEST INDUSTRIAL SUPPLY INC
1101 3rd St Se, Canton, OH 44707-3230
Tel (330) 456-3121 *Founded/Ownrshp* 1975
Sales 35.5MM^E *EMP* 70
Accts Phillips Organization Canton
SIC 2899 Chemical preparations; Chemical preparations
Pr: Robert Vitale
**VP:* Steven Vitale
IT Man: Eric Ledwick
Mfg Mgr: Scott Weinstock
Prd Mgr: Michael Darke
Natl Sales: Adam Misurek
VP Sls: Lynn Edwards
Mktg Dir: Stephanie Cornell
Sls Dir: Marc Poirier
Mktg Mgr: Julie Mamula
Sls Mgr: Lynn Cielec

D-U-N-S 00-728-0290 EXP
MIDWEST INDUSTRIES INC
122 E State Highway 175, Ida Grove, IA 51445-1140
Tel (712) 364-3365 *Founded/Ownrshp* 1954
Sales 49.8MM^E *EMP* 235
SIC 3799 3536 Boat trailers; Boat lifts; Boat trailers; Boat lifts
Pr: Andy Brosius
**Ch Bd:* La June Godbersen
**CFO:* Daniel Dose
**VP:* Bruce Godbersen
VP: Kevin Rossiter
Exec: Jeff Orgen
Genl Mgr: Wendy Abts
CTO: Kipp Gebel
MIS Dir: Clifford Gebel
Dir IT: Renee Martin
Plnt Mgr: Jason Bones

MIDWEST INSPECTION SERVICES
See DESERT NDT LLC

D-U-N-S 16-737-5026
MIDWEST INTEGRATED COMPANIES LLC
MIDWEST MATERIAL MANAGEMENT
275 Sola Dr, Gilberts, IL 60136-9003
Tel (847) 426-6354 *Founded/Ownrshp* 2001
Sales 33.8MM^E *EMP* 150
SIC 2875 7699 2491 Compost; Waste cleaning services; Railroad cross-ties, treated wood; Compost; Waste cleaning services; Railroad cross-ties, treated wood
VP: David Pinter
**Exec:* Veronica Berglund

D-U-N-S 05-476-6563
MIDWEST JANITORIAL SERVICE INC (IA)
1395 N Center Point Rd, Hiawatha, IA 52233-1239
Tel (319) 393-6162 *Founded/Ownrshp* 1958, 1973
Sales 16.5MM^E *EMP* 500
SIC 7349 0782 Janitorial service, contract basis; Mowing services, lawn; Janitorial service, contract basis; Mowing services, lawn
Pr: Kimberly Hotchkiss
**Owner:* Craig Hotchkiss
**Prin:* Deborah Hotchkiss
Genl Mgr: Margo Rowland
IT Man: Mary Rubocki

D-U-N-S 08-712-9672
MIDWEST JANITORIAL SUPPLY
1395 N Center Point Rd, Hiawatha, IA 52233-1239
Tel (319) 393-6162 *Founded/Ownrshp* 1978
Sales 36.3MM^E *EMP* 87
SIC 5087 5999 Janitors' supplies; Cleaning equipment & supplies
Pr: Kimberly Hotchkiss
**Treas:* Bruce Hotchkiss
**Sec:* Craig Hotchkiss

MIDWEST KENWORTH
See OZARK KENWORTH INC

D-U-N-S 07-803-8403
MIDWEST LABORATORIES INC (NE)
13611 B St, Omaha, NE 68144-3617
Tel (402) 334-7770 *Founded/Ownrshp* 1975
Sales 22.7MM^E *EMP* 105
SIC 8734 Testing laboratories
Pr: Kennard Pohlman
**COO:* John Torpy
Dir Lab: Ken Johnson
Cmptr Lab: Charles Wasserburger
Info Man: Andrew Deboer
Sls Mgr: Matt Stukenholtz

D-U-N-S 03-106-9875
MIDWEST LIBRARY SERVICE INC
11443 St Charles Rock Rd, Bridgeton, MO 63044-2789
Tel (314) 739-3100 *Founded/Ownrshp* 1960
Sales 22.1MM^E *EMP* 94
SIC 5192

MIDWEST LIGHTING
See MID-WEST WHOLESALE LIGHTING CORP

D-U-N-S 06-510-6585
MIDWEST LIVESTOCK SYSTEMS INC
MLS
3600 N 6th St, Beatrice, NE 68310-1123
Tel (402) 223-5281 *Founded/Ownrshp* 1971
Sales 46.5MM^E *EMP* 70
SIC 5083 Poultry equipment; Livestock equipment; Poultry equipment; Livestock equipment
Pr: Bill J Reed
**Treas:* Klaus Dueck
**VP:* Dennis Boesinger
Genl Mgr: Janet Wasserman

D-U-N-S 10-677-0980
MIDWEST LOGISTICS SYSTEMS LTD
7021 State Route 703, Celina, OH 45822-2777
Tel (419) 584-1414 *Founded/Ownrshp* 1998
Sales 91.1MM^E *EMP* 389
SIC 4213 4212 Trucking, except local; Local trucking, without storage; Trucking, except local; Local trucking, without storage
Pr: F Edward Voelker
Trst: Andrew Roettger
Trst: Bill Russell
VP: Ellen Welker
Prin: James Duvall
IT Man: Cheryl Nicholas
Oper/Mgr: Floyd Sheaks

D-U-N-S 05-896-9056
MIDWEST MAINTENANCE CO INC
2901 Q St, Omaha, NE 68107-3426
Tel (402) 733-1114 *Founded/Ownrshp* 1995
Sales 11.0MM^E *EMP* 450
SIC 7349 Janitorial service, contract basis; Janitorial service, contract basis
CEO: Jamie Gutierrez
**Pr:* Christine Johnson
**VP:* Marylin Oldaker
VP Mktg: Esther Mejia
Sls Mgr: Frank Cano

MIDWEST MANAGEMENT COMPANY
See UNIFIED MANAGEMENT SERVICES LLC

MIDWEST MANUFACTURING
See MENARD INC

D-U-N-S 00-638-6468 IMP/EXP
MIDWEST MANUFACTURING AND MECHANICAL INC (MN)
M W M
515 E Platt Ave, Nashwauk, MN 55769-1168
Tel (218) 885-0061 *Founded/Ownrshp* 2007
Sales 24.6MM^E *EMP* 40
SIC 5511 Automobiles, new & used
CEO: Michael Anderson
**VP:* Mike Stiglich

D-U-N-S 07-950-1758
MIDWEST MANUFACTURING INC
(*Suby of* MENARD INC) ★
5311 Kane Rd, Eau Claire, WI 54703-9822
Tel (715) 876-5555 *Founded/Ownrshp* 1983
Sales 138.1MM^E *EMP* 200^E
SIC 5033 5031 3965 Roofing & siding materials; Building materials, exterior; Fasteners; Roofing & siding materials; Building materials, exterior; Fasteners
Pr: John Menard
Plnt Mgr: Brett Leith
Prd Mgr: Mike Grant

MIDWEST MATERIAL MANAGEMENT
See MIDWEST INTEGRATED COMPANIES LLC

D-U-N-S 10-426-5090
MIDWEST MECHANICAL GROUP INC
(*Suby of* MSHC INC) ★
801 Parkview Blvd, Lombard, IL 60148-3230
Tel (630) 850-2300 *Founded/Ownrshp* 2006
Sales 30.0MM *EMP* 94
SIC 1711 Warm air heating & air conditioning contractor
Pr: Tony Ponzo
**CFO:* John Caraher
Genl Mgr: Bob Hayes

D-U-N-S 06-285-2319
MIDWEST MECHANICAL SOLUTIONS
8125 Lewis Rd Ste 100, Golden Valley, MN 55427-4496
Tel (952) 525-2004 *Founded/Ownrshp* 1997
Sales 27.2MM^E *EMP* 25
SIC 5075 5064 Air filters; Air conditioning appliances
Prin: Matt Jacobsen
**Prin:* Nick Brecht
**Prin:* Tom Bresesen
**Prin:* Mark McCollough
**Prin:* Mick Miller
**Prin:* Brent Riemenschneider
**Prin:* Steve Sandim
Genl Mgr: Sue Vigliaturo
Sls Mgr: Todd Courneya

MIDWEST MED AIR
See PLATTE COUNTY AMBULANCE CO

MIDWEST MEDIA MANAGEMENT DIV
See RBC MINISTRIES

D-U-N-S 62-344-1029
MIDWEST MEDICAL HOLDINGS LLC
8400 Coral Sea St Ne # 200, Saint Paul, MN 55112-4397
Tel (763) 780-0100 *Founded/Ownrshp* 1990
Sales 53.0MM^E *EMP* 170
SIC 5912 Drug stores; Drug stores

D-U-N-S 03-958-2556
MIDWEST MEDICAL INSURANCE CO
(*Suby of* MMIC GROUP INC) ★
7701 France Ave S Ste 500, Minneapolis, MN 55435-3201
Tel (952) 838-6700 *Founded/Ownrshp* 1988
Sales NA *EMP* 106
SIC 6351 Liability insurance
Ch: Dr Richard Geier
**Pr:* David Bounk
**CFO:* Niles Cole
Sr Cor Off: Mark Odland
Sr VP: Steven Lacke
VP: Steve Heimel
**VP:* Elizabeth S Lincoln
VP: Gerald O'Connell
VP: John Woodward
VP: Jerry Zeitlin
Dir Risk M: Steven Dubois
Dir Bus: Robert Thompson
Comm Man: Rosalind Miller

D-U-N-S 94-158-1001
MIDWEST MEDICAL RECORDS ASSOCIATION INC
MMRA
1701 E Wdfeld Rd Ste 1100, Schaumburg, IL 60173
Tel (847) 413-9660 *Founded/Ownrshp* 1994
Sales 24.8MM^E *EMP* 160
SIC 7334 Photocopying & duplicating services
Pr: John Cardone
VP: Lawrence Koerner
Rgnl Mgr: Nisha Danawala
Rgnl Mgr: Carey Weaver
Sales Asso: Ben Gallagher

D-U-N-S 05-396-8590 IMP
MIDWEST MEDICAL SUPPLY CO LLC
MMS, A MEDICAL SUPPLY COMPANY
13400 Lakefront Dr, Earth City, MO 63045-1516
Tel (314) 291-2900 *Founded/Ownrshp* 1996
Sales 400.3MM^E *EMP* 440
SIC 5047 Medical equipment & supplies; Medical equipment & supplies
Pr: Gary Reeve
Pr: Anne Estes
Pr: Don Marchese
Pr: Ed Warren
CFO: John P Hoffman
VP: John Castberg
VP: Kelly Hart
**VP:* Rich Hawkins
**VP:* Tom Tenhula
**VP:* Bernie Thien
Rgnl Mgr: Howard Meade

D-U-N-S 83-033-6025
MIDWEST MEMORIAL GROUP LLC
31300 Southfield Rd Ste 1, Beverly Hills, MI 48025-5456
Tel (248) 290-0338 *Founded/Ownrshp* 2008
Sales 88.7MM^E *EMP* 400^E
SIC 5087 Cemetary supplies & equipment; Cemetary supplies & equipment
CEO: Jim Price
**COO:* Doug Miller
Off Mgr: Kathie Cronk
VP Sls: Aaron Shipper
Sls Dir: Linda Jankowski
Sls Mgr: Gilbert Clark
Sls Mgr: Anthony Covington

D-U-N-S 19-820-5114
MIDWEST MERCHANDISING INC
BIKESOURCE
2690 E County Line Rd, Highlands Ranch, CO 80126-7009
Tel (303) 221-4840 *Founded/Ownrshp* 1985
Sales 22.4MM^E *EMP* 200
SIC 5941 Bicycle & bicycle parts; Bicycle & bicycle parts
Pr: Marc Eisenberg
**VP:* James Hersey

D-U-N-S 04-219-2401
MIDWEST METAL PRODUCTS CO
800 66th Ave Sw, Cedar Rapids, IA 52404-4793
Tel (319) 366-6264 *Founded/Ownrshp* 1964
Sales 35.9MM^E *EMP* 120
SIC 3441 Fabricated structural metal; Fabricated structural metal
Pr: G Kevin Urban
Pr: Tom Parman
**CFO:* Dave Fritz
**Ex VP:* Rita Urban Jelinek
VP: Rita Jelinek
QA Dir: Guy Bangs
QA Dir: Dan Scearcy
Ql Cn Mgr: Ken Koffron

D-U-N-S 93-996-9044
MIDWEST MOLDING INC
1560 Hecht Ct, Bartlett, IL 60103-1691
Tel (224) 208-1110 *Founded/Ownrshp* 1996
Sales 23.8MM^E *EMP* 60
SIC 3089 Plastic processing
Pr: Pat Patel
VP: Hitesch Patel

D-U-N-S 06-418-7891
MIDWEST MOLE INC
6814 W 350 N, Greenfield, IN 46140-9617
Tel (317) 545-1335 *Founded/Ownrshp* 1982
Sales 22.1MM^E *EMP* 60
SIC 1623 Underground utilities contractor
Pr: Dan Liotti
**VP:* Jason D Miller
IT Man: Brent Hofer
IT Man: John Qualls
VP Opers: Steve Abernathy
Mtls Mgr: Eric Dudley

MIDWEST MOTIVE GEAR
See MIDWEST TRUCK & AUTO PARTS INC

D-U-N-S 00-386-8213
MIDWEST MOTOR EXPRESS INC (ND)
(*Suby of* MME INC) ★
5015 E Main Ave, Bismarck, ND 58501-9301
Tel (701) 223-1880 *Founded/Ownrshp* 1938
Sales 99.0MM *EMP* 695
SIC 4212 Local trucking, without storage; Local trucking, without storage
CEO: John T Roswick
**Pr:* Marlin Kling
**CFO:* Jodi Kary
**VP:* Joe Greenstein
Exec: Joleen Miller
Brnch Mgr: Ken Loken
**Genl Mgr:* Ron Martin
IT Man: Jim Sullivan
Opers Mgr: Chapman Law
Opers Mgr: Craig Ramsay
Trfc Mgr: Keith Becker

D-U-N-S 01-790-6231 IMP
MIDWEST MOTOR SUPPLY CO
KIMBALL MIDWEST
4800 Roberts Rd, Columbus, OH 43228-9791
Tel (800) 233-1294 *Founded/Ownrshp* 1955
Sales 163.2MM^E *EMP* 670
SIC 3965 3399 Industrial supplies; Automotive supplies & parts; Fasteners; Metal fasteners
Pr: Patrick J McCurdy Jr
**CFO:* Robert McCurdy
**VP:* Charles McCurdy
**Prin:* A Glenn McClelland
Dist Mgr: Jon Newton
Manager: Dale Tinkham
Sls Mgr: Zak Alzught
Sls Mgr: Michael Stavich
Sales Asso: Jerome Hancock

D-U-N-S 83-121-6036
MIDWEST MOTORS LLC
INVER GROVE TOYOTA
1037 Highway 110, Inver Grove Heights, MN 55077-1111
Tel (651) 455-6000 *Founded/Ownrshp* 2009
Sales 28.0MM^E *EMP* 75
SIC 5511 Automobiles, new & used
Sls Mgr: Tom Anderson
Sls Mgr: Tom Beedy
Sls Mgr: Craig Fuhs
Sls Mgr: Brandon Schliinz
Sls Mgr: Dan Schmitz
Sales Asso: Brad Bolz
Sales Asso: Bruce Brown

D-U-N-S 04-120-0809
MIDWEST NATURAL GAS INC
MIDWEST TV & APPLIANCE
(*Suby of* MIDWEST BOTTLE GAS CO INC) ★
3600 Hwy 157, La Crosse, WI 54602
Tel (608) 781-1011 *Founded/Ownrshp* 1964
Sales 22.3MM *EMP* 21
SIC 4924 Natural gas distribution; Natural gas distribution
Ch Bd: James A Senty
**Treas:* Richard A Linton CPA

MIDWEST NEUROSURGERY
See MIDWEST SURGICAL HOSPITAL LLC

D-U-N-S 03-537-3422
MIDWEST OFFICE INC
MIDWEST COMMERCIAL INTERIORS
987 S West Temple, Salt Lake City, UT 84101-2988
Tel (801) 359-7681 *Founded/Ownrshp* 1938
Sales 45.4MM^E *EMP* 60
SIC 5712

D-U-N-S 00-446-6939
MIDWEST OFFICE SUPPLY LLC (IL)
1999 Wabash Ave Ste 200, Springfield, IL 62704-5351
Tel (217) 753-5555 *Founded/Ownrshp* 2000
Sales 26.6MM^E *EMP* 32
SIC 5112 5021 5044 5113 5087 Office supplies; Office furniture; Copying equipment; Industrial & personal service paper; Service establishment equipment

D-U-N-S 02-027-4804
MIDWEST OPERATING ENGINEERS FRINGE BENEFIT FUND
6150 Joliet Rd, Countryside, IL 60525-3994
Tel (708) 482-0589 *Founded/Ownrshp* 1963
Sales NA *EMP* 80
SIC 6371 Union welfare, benefit & health funds; Union welfare, benefit & health funds

D-U-N-S 96-164-0682
MIDWEST OPERATING ENGINEERS WELFARE FUND
6150 Joliet Rd, Countryside, IL 60525-3994
Tel (708) 482-7300 *Founded/Ownrshp* 2010
Sales 331.0MM *EMP* 2
Accts Graff Ballauer & Blanski Pc N
SIC 6722 Management investment, open-end; Management investment, open-end
Prin: David Bodley

D-U-N-S 80-661-8976
MIDWEST OVERHEAD CRANE CORP
13900 Sunfish Lk Blvd Nw, Ramsey, MN 55303-4542
Tel (763) 566-8555 *Founded/Ownrshp* 2000
Sales 33.5MM^E^ *EMP* 52
SIC 5084 7699 Cranes, industrial; Hoists; Materials handling machinery; Industrial machinery & equipment repair
CEO: Carl Shaffer
Genl Mgr: Don Fenton

D-U-N-S 14-752-0563
MIDWEST PALLIATIVE & HOSPICE CARECENTER
2050 Claire Ct, Glenview, IL 60025-7635
Tel (847) 467-7423 *Founded/Ownrshp* 1978
Sales 33.1MM *EMP* 300^E^
SIC 8361 Residential care; Residential care
Pr: Mary K Sheehan
Pr: Heidi Schelling
CFO: David Bruce
VP: Cathleen Adams
CTO: Gary Novak
Obsttrcn: Sam Katz

D-U-N-S 03-288-2342
MIDWEST PANCAKE HOUSES INC
VILLAGE INN RESTAURANT
919 Se Frank Phillips Blvd, Bartlesville, OK 74003-4231
Tel (918) 336-3830 *Founded/Ownrshp* 1961
Sales 6.8MM^E^ *EMP* 400
SIC 5812 Restaurant, family: chain; Restaurant, family: chain
Pr: John C Hoyt

MIDWEST PATROL DIVISION
See GENERAL SECURITY SERVICES CORP

D-U-N-S 04-266-3781
MIDWEST PATTERNS INC (IL)
4901 N 12th St, Quincy, IL 62305-8751
Tel (217) 228-6900 *Founded/Ownrshp* 1956
Sales 21.2MM^E^ *EMP* 112
SIC 3543 Industrial patterns
Pr: Jeff Tushaus
**VP:* Dennis Frericks
**VP:* Richard Tushaus

D-U-N-S 10-221-9664
MIDWEST PERISHABLES INC
M P I
4850 Helgesen Dr, Madison, WI 53718-6773
Tel (608) 273-8000 *Founded/Ownrshp* 1993
Sales 30.9MM^E^ *EMP* 44
Accts Smith & Gesteland Madison Wi
SIC 5147 Meats, fresh
Pr: Daniel Roberts
**Sec:* Brian Regan

D-U-N-S 03-106-9941
MIDWEST PETROLEUM CO (MO)
6760 Southwest Ave, Saint Louis, MO 63143-2624
Tel (314) 647-5550 *Founded/Ownrshp* 1938
Sales 154.8MM^E^ *EMP* 450
Accts Bkd Llp St Louis Mo
SIC 5541 Gasoline service stations; Gasoline service stations
Pr: Don McNutt
COO: Brian Grotewiel
**VP:* Bernard Levin
**VP:* Mike McNutt
Dir IT: Paul Jeffries
Dir IT: Marty O'Brien
Tech Mgr: Ryan McNutt

D-U-N-S 05-358-9180
MIDWEST PHYSICIAN GROUP LTD
20110 Governors Hwy, Olympia Fields, IL 60461-1030
Tel (708) 747-7960 *Founded/Ownrshp* 1975
Sales 0.7 *EMP* 330
Accts Crowe Horwath Llp Chicago Il
SIC 8031 Offices & clinics of osteopathic physicians; Offices & clinics of osteopathic physicians
Pr: Lawrence Haspel
**Treas:* J Singh
**VP:* John Caneay
VP: Laura Sesol
**Ex Dir:* Dave Thomas
Surgeon: James Davis
Surgeon: Irene M Goldstein
Podiatrist: Randy Pachnik

D-U-N-S 04-028-3426
MIDWEST PIPE & STEEL INC
323 E Berry St, Fort Wayne, IN 46802-2707
Tel (260) 422-6541 *Founded/Ownrshp* 1980
Sales 55.1MM^E^ *EMP* 50
SIC 5051 Metals service centers & offices; Steel
Pr: Jerome F Henry Jr
**VP:* Douglas Ford

D-U-N-S 00-645-1520 IMP
MIDWEST PIPECOATING INC (MN)
(*Suby of* CS MCCROSSAN INC) ★
7865 Jefferson Hwy, Maple Grove, MN 55369-4900
Tel (763) 425-4167 *Founded/Ownrshp* 1962
Sales 20.0MM^E^ *EMP* 106
SIC 1799 Coating, caulking & weather, water & fireproofing
Pr: Charles Mc Crossan
**Treas:* Jane McCrossan
**VP:* Tom Hopkins

D-U-N-S 07-432-2959
MIDWEST PLASTIC ENGINEERING INC
1501 Progress St, Sturgis, MI 49091-8301
Tel (269) 651-5223 *Founded/Ownrshp* 1975
Sales 25.7MM^E^ *EMP* 100
SIC 3089 3544 Injection molded finished plastic products; Forms (molds), for foundry & plastics working machinery
Pr: Dennis E Baker
**Sec:* Judith A Baker

D-U-N-S 04-899-5484 IMP
MIDWEST POULTRY SERVICES LP
MIDWEST PULLET FARM
9951 W State Road 25, Mentone, IN 46539-9131
Tel (574) 353-7232 *Founded/Ownrshp* 1993
Sales 174.9MM *EMP* 350
Accts Haines Isenbarger & Skiba Ll
SIC 0751 2015 Poultry services; Egg processing; Poultry services; Egg processing
CEO: Robert Krouse
Genl Mgr: Dan Krouse
Sfty Mgr: Stacey Harsh
Sls Mgr: Mike Krouse
Sls Mgr: Jennifer Taylor

D-U-N-S 05-283-6285
MIDWEST PRO PAINTING INC (MI)
12845 Farmington Rd, Livonia, MI 48150-1607
Tel (734) 427-1040 *Founded/Ownrshp* 1981
Sales 15.0MM *EMP* 450
SIC 1721 Commercial painting; Industrial painting; Commercial painting; Industrial painting
Pr: Demetrios Livanos
**VP:* Steven H Lionas

MIDWEST PRO SERV
See PULMUONE FOODS USA INC

D-U-N-S 09-436-5541 IMP
MIDWEST PRODUCTS AND ENGINEERING INC (WI)
MPE
10597 W Glenbrook Ct, Milwaukee, WI 53224-1124
Tel (414) 355-0310 *Founded/Ownrshp* 1979, 2011
Sales 35.0MM *EMP* 110
SIC 3841 8731 Surgical & medical instruments; Surgical & medical instruments; Computer (hardware) development
CEO: Hank Kohl
CFO: Tom Groble
CFO: Thomas Jgroble
VP Mfg: Gary Pfannerstill
VP Sls: David Barta

D-U-N-S 08-121-1575
MIDWEST PRODUCTS FINISHING CO INC
6194 Section Rd, Ottawa Lake, MI 49267-9526
Tel (734) 856-5200 *Founded/Ownrshp* 2002
Sales 20.5MM^E^ *EMP* 200
SIC 3479 Painting of metal products; Painting of metal products
Pr: Mike Alcala
COO: Mark Pawlaczyk
Prd Mgr: Peter Schira

D-U-N-S 13-125-9277
MIDWEST PUBLISHING INC
10844 N 23rd Ave, Phoenix, AZ 85029-4924
Tel (602) 943-1244 *Founded/Ownrshp* 1974
Sales 20.7MM^E^ *EMP* 275
SIC 2721 Trade journals: publishing & printing; Trade journals: publishing & printing
Pr: Tina V Gerke
VP: Stan Burzynski

MIDWEST PULLET FARM
See MIDWEST POULTRY SERVICES LP

D-U-N-S 11-893-0577 IMP
MIDWEST QUALITY GLOVES INC
MIDWEST GLOVES AND GEAR
835 Industrial Rd, Chillicothe, MO 64601-3218
Tel (660) 646-2165 *Founded/Ownrshp* 1984
Sales 90.4MM^E^ *EMP* 215
Accts Bkd Llp Kansas City Missour
SIC 5199 3151 Leather goods, except footwear, gloves, luggage, belting; Leather gloves & mittens; Gloves, leather: work; Leather goods, except footwear, gloves, luggage, belting; Leather gloves & mittens; Gloves, leather: work
Pr: Stephen J Franke
**COO:* Karen Nichols
**Treas:* Jeremy Clevenger
IT Man: Jill Smith
Info Man: Annette Robinson
Opers Mgr: Mike Ward
Mktg Dir: Ann Whiteside

D-U-N-S 05-082-0955
MIDWEST RADIOLOGY LLP
ST PAUL RADIOLOGY
166 4th St E Ste 100, Saint Paul, MN 55101-1474
Tel (651) 292-2000 *Founded/Ownrshp* 1985
Sales 26.2MM^E^ *EMP* 150
SIC 8011 Radiologist
CFO: Jerry Gehling
Dir IT: Mike Kargel
Netwrk Eng: Chris Armstrong
Doctor: Martin Asis
Doctor: Diane Meath
Doctor: Nancy Morrissey
Diag Rad: Peter Bretzman
Diag Rad: Christopher Jackson
Diag Rad: Theodore Passe
Diag Rad: Vladimir Savcenko
Diag Rad: Mark Veldman

D-U-N-S 82-741-1146
MIDWEST REFRIGERATED TRANSPORT INC
M R S
11225 W County Line Rd, Milwaukee, WI 53224-1007
Tel (414) 410-8200 *Founded/Ownrshp* 2008
Sales 31.2MM^E^ *EMP* 209^E^
SIC 8741 Business management
CEO: Mike Pokel
**VP:* Jim Koeble
Sales Exec: Terry Swan

MIDWEST REGIONAL BLOOD SERVICE
See AMERICAN RED CROSS

D-U-N-S 14-826-7313
■ **MIDWEST REGIONAL MEDICAL CENTER LLC**
(*Suby of* HEALTH MANAGEMENT ASSOCIATES INC) ★
2825 Parklawn Dr, Midwest City, OK 73110-4201
Tel (405) 610-8807 *Founded/Ownrshp* 1961
Sales 124.5MM^E^ *EMP* 1,205
SIC 8011 8062 Medical centers; Hospital, affiliated with AMA residency; Medical centers; Hospital, affiliated with AMA residency
CEO: Damon Brown
Dir Risk M: Bernadette Burns
Dir Rx: Luann Young
Mktg Dir: Sheila Winn
Occ Thrpy: Tammy Cook
Diag Rad: Jason Pack

MIDWEST RESEARCH INSTITUTE
See MRIGLOBAL - KANSAS LLC

D-U-N-S 19-706-7234
MIDWEST ROLL FORMING & MFG INC
OMCO
(*Suby of* OHIO MOULDING CORP) ★
1 Arnolt Dr, Pierceton, IN 46562-9641
Tel (574) 594-2100 *Founded/Ownrshp* 1989
Sales 56.4MM^E^ *EMP* 150
SIC 3449 Custom roll formed products
CEO: Gary Schuster
**Treas:* Clint Cassese
**Prin:* Len Parker
Ql Cn Mgr: Jennie Skeens

D-U-N-S 13-022-6967
MIDWEST RUBBER CO
3525 Range Line Rd, Deckerville, MI 48427-9420
Tel (810) 376-2085 *Founded/Ownrshp* 2003
Sales 23.8MM^E^ *EMP* 165^E^
SIC 3061 Mechanical rubber goods; Mechanical rubber goods
Pr: Kenneth L Jehle
**VP:* Donald E Rose
Telecom Ex: Dan Thompson

D-U-N-S 06-047-2016 IMP
MIDWEST RUBBER SERVICE & SUPPLY CO (MN)
14307 28th Pl N, Minneapolis, MN 55447-4867
Tel (763) 557-2510 *Founded/Ownrshp* 1976
Sales 33.8MM^E^ *EMP* 50
SIC 5085 3052 Hose, belting & packing; Air line or air brake hose, rubber or rubberized fabric
CEO: H Charles Anderson
**Pr:* Doug Turk
Genl Mgr: Bill Weldon
MIS Dir: John Briesch
Dir IT: Dan Pence
Opers Mgr: Tommy Meijdam

MIDWEST SANITATION SERVICE
See KAL SERVICES INC

D-U-N-S 62-332-7434 IMP
MIDWEST SCRAP MANAGEMENT INC
4501 Packers Ave, Saint Joseph, MO 64504-3532
Tel (816) 214-9204 *Founded/Ownrshp* 1996
Sales 125.0MM *EMP* 35^E^
SIC 5093 Metal scrap & waste materials; Metal scrap & waste materials
CEO: Kenneth A Burgess Jr
**Sec:* Shirley Butcher
Off Mgr: Melanie Callen

D-U-N-S 83-538-7465
MIDWEST SCREW PRODUCTS INC
13426 B St, Omaha, NE 68144-3614
Tel (402) 333-6611 *Founded/Ownrshp* 1994
Sales 25.1MM^E^ *EMP* 50
SIC 5072 3599 Screws; Machine shop, jobbing & repair
Pr: Cereno Oddo
**Treas:* Sharmel V Farnsworth

MIDWEST SEC INSUR COMPANIES
See R W HOUSER INC

D-U-N-S 05-031-4996
MIDWEST SECURITY ADMINISTRATORS INC
(*Suby of* MIDWEST SEC INSUR COMPANIES) ★
2700 Midwest Dr, Onalaska, WI 54650-8763
Tel (608) 783-7130 *Founded/Ownrshp* 1981
Sales NA *EMP* 150
SIC 6411 Medical insurance claim processing, contract or fee basis
Pr: Ronald W Houser
**COO:* Frank Vierling
**CFO:* Jaron Johnson
**Sr VP:* Ed Hawley
**VP:* Robert W Burg
VP: Gregory Pavlic

D-U-N-S 18-917-3552
■ **MIDWEST SECURITY LIFE INSURANCE CO**
(*Suby of* UNITEDHEALTH GROUP INC) ★
2700 Midwest Dr, Onalaska, WI 54650-8763
Tel (608) 783-7130 *Founded/Ownrshp* 2002
Sales NA *EMP* 180
SIC 6321 6311 Health insurance carriers; Life insurance; Health insurance carriers; Life insurance
Pr: Ronald W Houser

D-U-N-S 96-725-0593
MIDWEST SENIOR MINISTRIES
622 Emerson Rd, Saint Louis, MO 63141-6727
Tel (314) 587-7903 *Founded/Ownrshp* 2011
Sales 27.2MM *EMP* 1
SIC 8661 Religious organizations

MIDWEST SERVICE CENTER
See SAFETY TODAY INC

MIDWEST SERVICE GROUP
See MIDWEST ASBESTOS ABATEMENT CORP

D-U-N-S 02-304-6501
MIDWEST SIGN & SCREEN PRINTING SUPPLY CO INC
45 Maryland Ave E, Saint Paul, MN 55117-4610
Tel (651) 489-9999 *Founded/Ownrshp* 1977
Sales 110.9MM^E^ *EMP* 187
SIC 5084 5063 Printing trades machinery, equipment & supplies; Electrical supplies; Printing trades machinery, equipment & supplies; Electrical supplies
CEO: Nancy J Peterson Anderson
VP: Craig Anderson
VP: Lyle Hanzal
VP: Russel May
VP: Roger Olson
Dept Mgr: Jim Higgins
Opers Mgr: Bob Dalpe
Manager: Mike Pingalore
Sales Asso: Jim Domingos
Sales Asso: Brian Phillips
Sales Asso: Tanya Russian

D-U-N-S 02-135-7728
MIDWEST SINGLE SOURCE INC
1501 E 1st St N, Wichita, KS 67214-4175
Tel (316) 267-6333 *Founded/Ownrshp* 1976
Sales 21.3MM^E^ *EMP* 46
Accts Allen Gibbs & Houlik Lc W
SIC 5112 5199 5044 5021 5045 2759 Business forms; Office supplies; Advertising specialties; Office equipment; Furniture; Computers, peripherals & software; Commercial printing
CEO: John H Osborne
**Pr:* Kevin Ulwelling
**CFO:* Angela Williams
Chf Mktg O: Sarah Strydom
**VP:* Chris Eckhoff
Off Mgr: Darlene Dunn
VP Mktg: Renee Osborne

D-U-N-S 07-175-1549
MIDWEST SPECIAL SERVICES INC
900 Ocean St, Saint Paul, MN 55106-3448
Tel (651) 778-1000 *Founded/Ownrshp* 1949
Sales 11.8MM *EMP* 600
Accts Wilkerson Guthmann & Johnson L
SIC 8331 Job training services; Vocational rehabilitation agency; Work experience center; Job training services; Vocational rehabilitation agency; Work experience center
Pr: Lyth L Hartz
VP: Will Aylward
VP: Tom Lyman
Dir: Candace Lopez
Plnt Mgr: Ed Selnes
Pgrm Dir: Heather Huff
Snr Mgr: Kevin McCaleb

D-U-N-S 19-807-2506
MIDWEST STAFFING GROUP INC
162 Pennsylvania Ave W, Saint Paul, MN 55103-1893
Tel (651) 641-0442 *Founded/Ownrshp* 1988
Sales 29.5MM^E^ *EMP* 4,018
SIC 7363 Temporary help service
Pr: Joseph Thoemke
**CFO:* Anna Marie Theissen

D-U-N-S 18-591-6749 IMP
MIDWEST STAINLESS TECHNOLOGIES LLC
5408 3m Dr Ste B, Menomonie, WI 54751-8502
Tel (715) 235-5472 *Founded/Ownrshp* 1986
Sales 29.8MM^E^ *EMP* 100
SIC 1751 Lightweight steel framing (metal stud) installation
CEO: K Kachadurian
Mktg Mgr: Rob Hesse

MIDWEST STEEL & ALUMINUM
See MIDWEST STEEL SUPPLY CO

D-U-N-S 60-408-2701
MIDWEST STEEL INC
2525 E Grand Blvd, Detroit, MI 48211-2001
Tel (313) 873-2220 *Founded/Ownrshp* 1989
Sales 130.0MM *EMP* 500
SIC 3441 1791 Fabricated structural metal; Structural steel erection; Fabricated structural metal; Structural steel erection
Pr: Gary R Broad
CFO: Ken Crismore
Sr VP: Ron Lewis
Mng Dir: Scott Stevens
Genl Mgr: Thomas Broad
IT Man: Peter Clinchoc
IT Man: Brad Swegles
Sfty Dirs: Mike Hall
VP Sls: Mark Cichy
Sls Dir: Mike Adkins
Snr PM: Jeff Curley

D-U-N-S 02-292-0748
MIDWEST STEEL SUPPLY CO
MIDWEST STEEL & ALUMINUM
9151 International Pkwy, New Hope, MN 55428-3607
Tel (763) 582-1925 *Founded/Ownrshp* 1983
Sales 26.4MM^E^ *EMP* 25
SIC 5051 Aluminum bars, rods, ingots, sheets, pipes, plates, etc.
Pr: Gerald I Rako
**VP:* Brandon Walton
Sls Mgr: Lynn Ambrose

D-U-N-S 00-725-7132
MIDWEST STEEL WORKS INC
749 N St, Lincoln, NE 68508-2237
Tel (402) 476-7545 *Founded/Ownrshp* 1999
Sales 30.2MM *EMP* 62
Accts Dana F Cole & Company Llp C
SIC 3441 Fabricated structural metal; Fabricated structural metal
Pr: Robert J Ediger
**Treas:* Douglas E Lienemann
VP: Robert Edgier
Plnt Mgr: Thomas Tidgn

MIDWEST STORE FIXTURES
See MIDWEST CUSTOM CASE INC

D-U-N-S 14-831-2895 IMP
MIDWEST SUBURBAN PUBLISHING INC
NEWS MARKETER
(*Suby of* SUN-TIMES MEDIA GROUP INC) ★
6901 159th St Unit 2, Tinley Park, IL 60477
Tel (708) 633-6880 *Founded/Ownrshp* 1994
Sales 22.8MM^E *EMP* 600
SIC 2711 2752 2741 Commercial printing & newspaper publishing combined; Publication printing, lithographic; Miscellaneous publishing; Commercial printing & newspaper publishing combined; Publication printing, lithographic; Miscellaneous publishing
Pr: Larry Kelly
COO: John Ardizzone
**VP:* John P Kern
IT Man: Rena Watson
Sls Mgr: Julie Barrett
Board of Directors: Bob Bong, Ed Czerwinski, Tom Finn, George Haas, Howard Ludwig, Mike Nolan, John Stein, Guy Tridgell, Steve Vansko

D-U-N-S 00-531-1708
MIDWEST SURGICAL HOSPITAL LLC
MIDWEST NEUROSURGERY
8005 Farnam Dr Ste 305, Omaha, NE 68114-3426
Tel (402) 398-9243 *Founded/Ownrshp* 2004
Sales 37.6MM *EMP* 2
SIC 8062 General medical & surgical hospitals; General medical & surgical hospitals
IT Man: Spencer Williamson

D-U-N-S 60-733-1498 IMP
MIDWEST TAPE LLC
6950 Hall St, Holland, OH 43528-9485
Tel (419) 868-9370 *Founded/Ownrshp* 2004
Sales 130.5MM^E *EMP* 330
SIC 7822 5099 8741 7389 5961 7374 Video tapes, recorded: wholesale; Motion picture distribution; Video cassettes, accessories & supplies; Administrative management; Packaging & labeling services; ; Data processing service; Video tapes, recorded: wholesale; Motion picture distribution; Video cassettes, accessories & supplies; Administrative management; Packaging & labeling services; ; Data processing service
Exec: Jeff Jankowski
Genl Mgr: Sue Bascuk
Dir IT: Victor Corral
Dir IT: Victor Panopoulos
Dir IT: Robert Wagener
Natl Sales: Ed Altwies
Sls Mgr: Eric Timm

D-U-N-S 00-692-8253
MIDWEST TELEVISION INC (DE)
KFMB 760 AM
100 W University Ave, Champaign, IL 61820-3910
Tel (217) 378-4201 *Founded/Ownrshp* 1952, 1966
Sales 41.3MM^E *EMP* 283
SIC 4833 4832

D-U-N-S 05-504-4853 IMP/EXP
MIDWEST TRANSATLANTIC LINES INC
MTA
1230 W Bagley Rd, Berea, OH 44017-2910
Tel (440) 243-1993 *Founded/Ownrshp* 1980
Sales 21.9MM^E *EMP* 61
SIC 4731 4412

D-U-N-S 04-756-5866 EXP
MIDWEST TRANSIT EQUIPMENT INC
146 W Issert Dr, Kankakee, IL 60901-7134
Tel (815) 933-2412 *Founded/Ownrshp* 1991
Sales 229.5MM^E *EMP* 100
SIC 5012 Buses; Trucks, commercial; Buses; Trucks, commercial
Pr: Barry Huebner
**Ch Bd:* James Bridgewater Sr
**Sec:* James R Bridgewater Jr
Opers Mgr: Jeff Burlison
Manager: Dan Hickman
Manager: Pete Pizzimenti
Manager: Denis Wiger
Sls Mgr: Tom Buhle
Sls Mgr: Joe Crabtree

D-U-N-S 07-303-2054
MIDWEST TRANSPLANT NETWORK INC
1900 W 47th Pl Ste 400, Shawnee Mission, KS 66205-1801
Tel (913) 262-1668 *Founded/Ownrshp* 1973
Sales 39.5MM *EMP* 95
Accts Bkd Llp Kansas City Mo
SIC 8099 Organ bank
Ex Dir: Robin Linderer
COO: Jan Finn
CFO: Judith Scott
CFO: Judy Scott
Dir Lab: Chris Bryan
Sfty Mgr: Tracy Morris
Doctor: Mark Reintjes MD

D-U-N-S 04-921-1089
MIDWEST TRANSPORT INC
11385 N Trimble Rd, Robinson, IL 62454-7206
Tel (618) 544-3399 *Founded/Ownrshp* 2003
Sales 94.1MM^E *EMP* 700
Accts Kemper Cpa Group Llc
SIC 4213 Trucking, except local; Trucking, except local
Pr: Mitch Ferree
CFO: Brian Garrard
Genl Couns: John Elmore

D-U-N-S 02-523-0921 IMP/EXP
MIDWEST TRUCK & AUTO PARTS INC
MIDWEST MOTIVE GEAR
1001 W Exchange Ave, Chicago, IL 60609-2531
Tel (773) 247-3400 *Founded/Ownrshp* 1964
Sales 53.8MM^E *EMP* 155
SIC 5013

D-U-N-S 80-949-2598
MIDWEST TUBE MILLS INC
2855 Michigan Rd, Madison, IN 47250-1814
Tel (812) 265-1553 *Founded/Ownrshp* 1993
Sales 50.3MM *EMP* 85
SIC 3312 Tubes, steel & iron
Pr: Richard L Russell
Genl Mgr: Larry Brown
Plnt Mgr: Lynn Pennington

MIDWEST TV & APPLIANCE
See MIDWEST BOTTLE GAS CO INC

MIDWEST TV & APPLIANCE
See MIDWEST NATURAL GAS INC

D-U-N-S 02-780-4421
MIDWEST UNDERGROUND TECHNOLOGY INC
MUTI
(*Suby of* SABRE COMMUNICATIONS) ★
2626 Midwest Ct, Champaign, IL 61822-8929
Tel (217) 819-3040 *Founded/Ownrshp* 2013
Sales 125.0MM^E *EMP* 400^E
SIC 1731 1623 Fiber optic cable installation; Water, sewer & utility lines; Fiber optic cable installation; Water, sewer & utility lines
Pr: Darrin M Peters
Pr: Patrick Cochran
VP: Geoff Bennett
VP: Jim Coleman
VP: Scott Kisting
Mtls Mgr: Tyler Mott

D-U-N-S 10-053-7096
MIDWEST UNITED ENERGY LLC
(*Suby of* MIDWEST ENERGY INC) ★
12687 W Cedar Dr Ste 200, Lakewood, CO 80228-2014
Tel (303) 989-7165 *Founded/Ownrshp* 2000
Sales 117.2MM *EMP* 7
Accts Ghp Horwath Pc
SIC 5172 Gases; Gases

D-U-N-S 12-128-2040 IMP
MIDWEST VALVE AND FITTING INC
20638 Amherst Ct, Joliet, IL 60433-9716
Tel (815) 727-9339 *Founded/Ownrshp* 1984
Sales 20.5MM^E *EMP* 27
SIC 5085 Valves & fittings
Pr: Rowland W Davies
**VP:* Joseph Davies

D-U-N-S 02-292-0821
MIDWEST VETERINARY SUPPLY INC
21467 Holyoke Ave, Lakeville, MN 55044-7303
Tel (952) 894-4350 *Founded/Ownrshp* 1960
Sales 311.0MM^E *EMP* 260
SIC 5122 5047 Animal medicines; Veterinarians' equipment & supplies; Animal medicines; Veterinarians' equipment & supplies
Pr: Guy G Flickinger
CFO: Janice Halvorsen
**Ex VP:* Cheryl Peterson
**VP:* Thomas Wheeler
Rgnl Mgr: Rick Zuber
Genl Mgr: Jeff Burkhamer
Dir IT: Stefan Lindberg
Dir IT: Brad Peterson
Mktg Dir: Cheryl Ahlquist
Sls Mgr: Paula Brennan
Sls Mgr: Gwen Dunn

MIDWEST VOCATIONAL MANAGEMENT
See MIDWEST CASE MANAGEMENT INC

D-U-N-S 00-727-4913 EXP
MIDWEST WALNUT CO IOWA
1914 Tostevin St, Council Bluffs, IA 51503-7749
Tel (712) 325-9191 *Founded/Ownrshp* 1987
Sales 31.9MM^E *EMP* 100
SIC 5031 2421 5099 Lumber: rough, dressed & finished; Kitchen cabinets; Sawmills & planing mills, general; Cut stock, softwood; Logs, hewn ties, posts & poles
Pr: James D Plowman
COO: Gerald Keller
**Treas:* Bruce R Severson
**VP:* Ted Hiers
Dir IT: Bob Moody
**VP Mktg:* Larry Mether

D-U-N-S 01-102-1839
MIDWEST WAREHOUSE AND DISTRIBUTION SYSTEM INC
2600 Internationale Pkwy, Woodridge, IL 60517-4804
Tel (630) 739-6760 *Founded/Ownrshp* 1982
Sales 35.6MM^E *EMP* 120
SIC 4225 General warehousing
Pr: Edward Borkowski
**VP:* John Borkowski
Dir IT: Ken Curry
Dir IT: Jonathon Ellis
Opers Mgr: Larry Duda

D-U-N-S 12-159-6993
MIDWEST WELL SERVICES INC
MUNCIPAL WELL & PUMP
1212 Storbeck Dr, Waupun, WI 53963-9691
Tel (920) 324-3400 *Founded/Ownrshp* 2000
Sales 7.1MM *EMP* 2,627
SIC 7699 1781

D-U-N-S 00-530-4134 IMP
MIDWEST WHEEL COMPANIES INC (IA)
AMERICAN DIESEL
1436 E Ovid Ave, Des Moines, IA 50316-1323
Tel (515) 265-1491 *Founded/Ownrshp* 1911
Sales 69.1MM^E *EMP* 170
SIC 5013 5531 Automotive supplies & parts; Truck parts & accessories; Automotive parts; Automotive accessories; Automotive supplies & parts; Truck parts & accessories; Automotive parts; Automotive accessories
Pr: Michael J Callison
**Treas:* Michael Laing
**VP:* John Mikkola
**VP:* John Minor

D-U-N-S 01-524-1954 IMP
MIDWEST WHOLESALE LLC
635 Cooper Ct Ste A, Schaumburg, IL 60173-4570
Tel (847) 519-1351 *Founded/Ownrshp* 2009
Sales 30.0MM *EMP* 15
SIC 5194 Tobacco & tobacco products; Tobacco & tobacco products

D-U-N-S 07-870-0589
MIDWEST-CBK LLC
(*Suby of* GANZ USA LLC) ★
32057 64th Ave, Cannon Falls, MN 55009-4340
Tel (800) 394-4225 *Founded/Ownrshp* 2012
Sales 36.3MM^E *EMP* 120
SIC 5199 5023 Gifts & novelties; Decorative home furnishings & supplies
Genl Mgr: Dick Duff
**Ex Dir:* Mike Palumbo
Mktg Dir: Paul Jacobson

MIDWESTERN AUTO GROUP
See BRENTLINGER ENTERPRISES

D-U-N-S 01-064-6511
MIDWESTERN BAPTIST THEOLOGICAL SEMINARY INC
5001 N Oak Trfy, Kansas City, MO 64118-4620
Tel (816) 414-3700 *Founded/Ownrshp* 1957
Sales 27.8MM^E *EMP* 150
SIC 8221 8661 Theological seminary; Religious organizations
Pr: R Philip Roberts
Top Exec: Judy Howie
Sr VP: Anthony W Allen
VP: Rodney A Harrison
VP: Jerry A Johnson
VP: Lyndal H Lovelace
VP: David M McAlpin
VP: N Ravi

MIDWESTERN CONTRACTORS DIV
See ELECTRIC CONDUIT CONSTRUCTION CO

D-U-N-S 00-679-2451
■ MIDWESTERN GAS TRANSMISSION CO
(*Suby of* ONEOK PARTNERS LP) ★
100 W 5th St, Tulsa, OK 74103-4279
Tel (918) 588-7000 *Founded/Ownrshp* 1951, 2001
Sales 21.1MM^E *EMP* 70
SIC 4923

D-U-N-S 10-212-5994
MIDWESTERN INSURANCE ALLIANCE INC
(*Suby of* K2 INSURANCE SERVICES LLC) ★
9520 Ormsby Station Rd # 300, Louisville, KY 40223-5019
Tel (502) 429-9990 *Founded/Ownrshp* 2012
Sales NA *EMP* 90
SIC 6411 Insurance agents
Pr: Marc Risen
**Sec:* Cathy New
**VP:* Kent Risen

D-U-N-S 07-495-4264
MIDWESTERN INTERMEDIATE UNIT IV
453 Maple St, Grove City, PA 16127-2324
Tel (724) 458-6700 *Founded/Ownrshp* 1971
Sales 7.6MM *EMP* 555
SIC 8211 Public elementary & secondary schools; Public elementary & secondary schools
Pr: Cedric Butchy
**VP:* Merle Glass
**Prin:* Joseph Boltz
**Ex Dir:* Cecelio Yauger
Mng Dir: Virginia Moore
IT Man: Dawn Book
IT Man: Kimberly Eaton

D-U-N-S 17-093-3274
MIDWESTERN MECHANICAL INC
COPPER COTTAGE
4105 N Lewis Ave, Sioux Falls, SD 57104-5572
Tel (605) 221-0958 *Founded/Ownrshp* 1991
Sales 37.4MM^E *EMP* 180
Accts Woltman Van Kekeriz & Stotz P
SIC 1711 Plumbing contractors; Plumbing contractors
Pr: Dwayne Klarenbeck
**CFO:* Karl Schlotman
**VP:* Randy Grotenhuis
Exec: Ken Amundson
Exec: Wendy Stocco

D-U-N-S 00-722-0791
MIDWESTERN PIPE LINE PRODUCTS CO
(*Suby of* MIDWESCO INDUSTRIES INC) ★
2119 S Union Ave, Tulsa, OK 74107-2703
Tel (918) 446-1587 *Founded/Ownrshp* 1950
Sales 26.6MM^E *EMP* 130
SIC 3533 3531 Oil & gas field machinery; Construction machinery; Oil & gas field machinery; Construction machinery
Pr: James A Bost

D-U-N-S 07-459-0969
MIDWESTERN REGIONAL MEDICAL CENTER INC
(*Suby of* CANCER TREATMENT CENTERS OF AMERICA INC) ★
2501 Emmaus Ave, Zion, IL 60099
Tel (847) 731-1364 *Founded/Ownrshp* 1975
Sales 92.7MM^E *EMP* 1,021
SIC 8069 Cancer hospital; Cancer hospital
CEO: Scott Jones
**Ch Bd:* Richard J Stephenson
Pr: Elizabeth Maribito
COO: Mike White
Ofcr: Janet Cheek
Ofcr: Sharon Day
Sr VP: Jacklynn Lesniak
VP: Joseph Coyne
Dir Rx: Gregg Helm
**Prin:* Anne Meisner
CTO: Elena Roman

D-U-N-S 07-314-9163
MIDWESTERN STATE UNIVERSITY
3410 Taft Blvd, Wichita Falls, TX 76308-2096
Tel (940) 397-4000 *Founded/Ownrshp* 1922
Sales 204.6M *EMP* 800
SIC 8221 University; University
Pr: Jesse Rogers
Pr: Amber Rawls
**Ch:* Munir Lalani
Ofcr: Chris Aten III
Assoc Dir: Chris Gore
Assoc Dir: Cindy Wood
CIO: Shauna Kennedy
IT Man: Chris Koetter
IT Man: Hayley Roach
Doctor: Stewart Carpenter
HC Dir: Barbara Merkle

D-U-N-S 18-177-8846
MIDWESTERN UNIVERSITY
555 31st St, Downers Grove, IL 60515-1235
Tel (630) 515-7145 *Founded/Ownrshp* 1985
Sales 318.2MM *EMP* 1,300
Accts Ernst & Young Llp Chicago Il
SIC 8221 University; University
Pr: Kathleen H Goeppinger
**CFO:* Gregory J Gaus
Treas: Melissa Davis
VP: George Caleel
**VP:* Karen D Johnson
**VP:* Mary Lee
VP: Dean Malon
**VP:* Dean Malone
**VP:* Angela Marty
**Exec:* Arthur G Dobbelaere
Exec: Susan Viselli
Assoc Dir: Suzanne Larson
Comm Dir: Dana Fay
Dir Rx: Susan R Winkler

D-U-N-S 00-694-1736
■ MIDWESTONE BANK
(*Suby of* MIDWESTONE FINANCIAL GROUP INC) ★
102 S Clinton St Ste 100, Iowa City, IA 52240-4024
Tel (319) 356-5800 *Founded/Ownrshp* 1934
Sales NA *EMP* 159^E
SIC 6022 State commercial banks; State commercial banks
Pr: Charles N Funk
Ofcr: Brad Amthauer
Ofcr: Scott Jamison
Ofcr: Teri Keenan
Ofcr: Tammy Moothart
Ofcr: Tammy Sauer
Ofcr: Christine Wilcox
VP: Cory Ahrendsen
VP: Sandy Bailey
VP: Mike Finlayson
VP: Luke Lesyshen
VP: Kim Ross
VP: Cathy Rottinghaus
**VP:* Kenneth Urmie
VP: Jerry Vanni
VP: Kevin Werner
VP: Thais Winkleblack

D-U-N-S 62-709-4675
▲ MIDWESTONE FINANCIAL GROUP INC
102 S Clinton St, Iowa City, IA 52240-4065
Tel (319) 356-5800 *Founded/Ownrshp* 1983
Sales NA *EMP* 374^E
Tkr Sym MOFG *Exch* NGS
SIC 6022 6331 State commercial banks; Assessment associations: fire, marine & casualty insurance; State commercial banks; Assessment associations: fire, marine & casualty insurance
Pr: Charles N Funk
**Ch Bd:* Kevin W Monson
V Ch: Charles S Howard
COO: Susan R Evans
CFO: Gary J Ortale
Ofcr: James M Cantrell
Ofcr: Holly Hankins
Ofcr: Kent L Jehle
VP: Allen Schneider
Exec: Ron Haines
Exec: Kathy Simon

D-U-N-S 07-434-3179
MIDWOOD AMBULANCE & OXYGEN SERVICE INC
2593 W 13th St, Brooklyn, NY 11223-5812
Tel (718) 645-1000 *Founded/Ownrshp* 1956
Sales 22.2MM *EMP* 85
Accts De Marco & Nesi Llc Garden C
SIC 4119 Ambulance service; Ambulance service
Ch: Al Rapisarda
Treas: Grace Rapisarda
**Treas:* Grace Rapisarda-Torres
**VP:* Anthony Rapisarda
IT Man: Chris Rapisarda

D-U-N-S 07-889-0102
MIE-TH HOLDINGS LLC
MID-ISLAND ELECTRICAL SUPPLY
(*Suby of* THIS) ★
59 Mall Dr, Commack, NY 11725-5703
Tel (631) 864-4242 *Founded/Ownrshp* 2013
Sales 35.3MM^E *EMP* 69
SIC 5063 Electrical supplies; Lighting fixtures; Light bulbs & related supplies; Motor controls, starters & relays: electric
Ch Bd: Suzanne T Millard
Pr: Richard Reffler Sr
CEO: Jayne Millard
COO: Kevin Doyle
CFO: Christopher Rausch
VP: William T Wresch Jr
Brnch Mgr: Kenny Kirsh
Brnch Mgr: Bill Rash
Genl Mgr: Margaret Stabile
VP Opers: Sebastian Gambino
Sales Asso: Paul Busardo

D-U-N-S 11-856-2412 IMP
MIECO INC
(*Suby of* MARUBENI CORPORATION)
301 E Ocean Blvd Ste 1100, Long Beach, CA 90802-4832
Tel (562) 435-0085 *Founded/Ownrshp* 1984
Sales 143.0MM *EMP* 50
SIC 5172 4925 Petroleum brokers; Mixed natural & manufactured gas, distribution; Petroleum brokers; Mixed natural & manufactured gas, distribution
CEO: Masahiro Yamazaki
**CEO:* Tomonari Sano
**Ex VP:* Doug Jeter
Exec: Karen Lyng
Dir Risk M: Kristin Seawright
Opers Mgr: Doris Steinbrecher

D-U-N-S 07-258-2117
MIEDEMA PRODUCE INC
GUN LAKE FARMS
5005 40th Ave, Hudsonville, MI 49426-9481
Tel (616) 669-9420 *Founded/Ownrshp* 1973
Sales 50.9MM *EMP* 100
SIC 5148 Vegetables, fresh; Vegetables, fresh
Pr: Ronald Schut
**VP:* Ronald T Miedema
Mktg Dir: Todd Miedema

D-U-N-S 11-534-8054 IMP/EXP
MIELE INC
MIELE PROFESSIONAL PRODUCTS
(*Suby of* MIELE & CIE. KG)
9 Independence Way, Princeton, NJ 08540-6621
Tel (609) 419-9898 *Founded/Ownrshp* 1984
Sales 82.5MM^E *EMP* 275
SIC 5064 Electric household appliances; Electric household appliances
Pr: Nick Ord
VP: Werner Goldbach
VP: Peggy Kotlarz
VP: Al Kramer
VP: Christian Schwartz
VP: Roland Weingartner
Exec: Ellie Jocham
Exec: Nurettin Selsil
Rgnl Mgr: Craig Leirvik
Rgnl Mgr: Justin Wagner
CTO: Ned Brigham

MIELE PROFESSIONAL PRODUCTS
See MIELE INC

D-U-N-S 07-121-0975
MIFFLIN COUNTY SCHOOL DISTRICT
201 8th St, Lewistown, PA 17044-1197
Tel (717) 242-0684 *Founded/Ownrshp* 1966
Sales 45.1MM^E *EMP* 800
SIC 8211 Public senior high school; Public junior high school; Public elementary school; Public senior high school; Public junior high school; Public elementary school
CFO: Sean Daubert
Prin: Carole A Auker
Prin: Marybeth D Irvin
Prin: Joseph P Maginnis
Prin: Daniel M McClenahen
Prin: Steven J Schaaf
Prin: Robert H Shinskie
Prin: Ronald L Varner

MIFS
See MIAMI INTERNATIONAL FREIGHT SOLUTIONS LLC

MIG
See MULTI IMAGE GROUP INC

D-U-N-S 80-994-8359
MIG CORP INC
1 Acton Pl Ste 200, Acton, MA 01720-3951
Tel (978) 264-4800 *Founded/Ownrshp* 1991
Sales 27.2MM *EMP* 80
Accts Cullen Murphy & Co Pc Nor
SIC 1611 1622 General contractor, highway & street construction; Bridge construction; General contractor, highway & street construction; Bridge construction
CEO: Donald Voghel
**Pr:* Robert Voghel
Opers Mgr: Lawrence Gordon
Opers Mgr: Rory Neubauer

D-U-N-S 07-230-5824
■ **MIGC INC**
(*Suby of* WESTERN GAS RESOURCES INC) ★
1099 18th St Ste 1200, Denver, CO 80202-1964
Tel (720) 929-6036 *Founded/Ownrshp* 1985
Sales 36.3MM^E *EMP* 300^E
SIC 4923 Gas transmission & distribution
CEO: Peter A DEA
**Ch Bd:* Brion Wise

MIGHTY DISTRIBUTING SYS AMER
See MDSA LLC

D-U-N-S 12-633-5988
MIGHTY DOLLAR LLC
132 Commercial Dr Ste 150, Forest City, NC 28043-2895
Tel (828) 245-1161 *Founded/Ownrshp* 2002
Sales 29.9MM^E *EMP* 340
SIC 5331 Variety stores; Variety stores

D-U-N-S 03-396-7944 IMP
MIGHTY ENTERPRISES INC
MIGHTY USA
19706 Normandie Ave, Torrance, CA 90502-1111
Tel (310) 516-7478 *Founded/Ownrshp* 1980
Sales 35.7MM^E *EMP* 55
SIC 5084 Industrial machinery & equipment
Pr: Peter Th Tsai
**VP:* Daniel Huang
Mktg Mgr: Nelson Duarte
Sls Mgr: Saim Kefeli

D-U-N-S 08-340-7283 IMP
MIGHTY FINE
2010 E 15th St, Los Angeles, CA 90021-2823
Tel (213) 627-2498 *Founded/Ownrshp* 1994
Sales 27.5MM^E *EMP* 120
SIC 2331 2253 T-shirts & tops, women's: made from purchased materials; Shirts, women's & juniors': made from purchased materials; T-shirts & tops, knit; T-shirts & tops, women's: made from purchased materials; Shirts, women's & juniors': made from purchased materials; T-shirts & tops, knit
CEO: Stacy L Kitchin
**VP:* Guy Brand
VP: Guy Brandwen
VP: Jan Sussman
Opers Mgr: Eric Opena
Mktg Dir: Sara Scargall

MIGHTY GOOD
See H & S BAKERY INC

D-U-N-S 18-704-3844 IMP
MIGHTY HURRICANE HOLDINGS INC
OXFORD
(*Suby of* GBG USA INC) ★
1359 Broadway Fl 21, New York, NY 10018-7824
Tel (646) 839-7000 *Founded/Ownrshp* 1998
Sales 24.5MM^E *EMP* 200
SIC 5137 Women's & children's clothing; Women's & children's clothing
CEO: Richard N Darling

D-U-N-S 94-619-7100 IMP
MIGHTY LEAF TEA
(*Suby of* PEETS COFFEE & TEA LLC) ★
100 Smith Ranch Rd # 120, San Rafael, CA 94903-1979
Tel (415) 491-2650 *Founded/Ownrshp* 2014
Sales 42.5MM^E *EMP* 65
SIC 5149 5499 Tea; Tea
Prin: Shiela Stanziale
**Pr:* Jill Portman
CFO: Gerald Hauprich
VP: Carol Cooper
VP: Bliss Dake
VP: Mick Sampson
Off Mgr: Donna Lahey
IT Man: Jim Lowry
Mktg Mgr: Robin Gonci
Mktg Mgr: Amanda Sonenberg
Sls Mgr: Charlie Woodruff

MIGHTY MIKES HOT STOP
See CAVALIER CONVENIENCE INC

D-U-N-S 08-353-0386
MIGHTY TACO INC
9362 Transit Rd, East Amherst, NY 14051-1495
Tel (716) 636-1151 *Founded/Ownrshp* 1973
Sales 10.3MM^E *EMP* 300
SIC 5812 Mexican restaurant; Mexican restaurant
Pr: Daniel Scepkowski
Pr: Russell Jasulevich
Off Mgr: Donna Scott

MIGHTY USA
See MIGHTY ENTERPRISES INC

D-U-N-S 07-937-9189
MIGHTYHIVE INC
1228 Folsom St Ste 100, San Francisco, CA 94103-3817
Tel (610) 737-7001 *Founded/Ownrshp* 2014
Sales 30.0MM *EMP* 35
SIC 5045 8742 7311 Computer software; Marketing consulting services; Advertising agencies
CEO: Peter Kim
Mng Pt: Ravi Belani
CFO: Chris Martin
VP: Lexi Viripaeff

D-U-N-S 96-422-0599
MIGRANT HEALTH CENTER WESTERN REGION INC
Ramon E Betances St 491, Mayaguez, PR 00680
Tel (787) 833-5890 *Founded/Ownrshp* 2010
Sales 30.4MM *EMP* 11^E
Accts Kreston Tlsr Llc San Juan Pr
SIC 8351 Child day care services
Ex Dir: Dolores Morales

D-U-N-S 14-994-6519
MII SERVICES INC
(*Suby of* M I I INC) ★
3535 Blue Cross Rd, Saint Paul, MN 55122-1154
Tel (651) 662-1506 *Founded/Ownrshp* 1984
Sales NA *EMP* 101
SIC 6411 Insurance claim processing, except medical
Pr: Chris Aasland

D-U-N-S 16-069-5008
MIINC LP
1960 W Northwest Hwy, Dallas, TX 75220-2314
Tel (214) 575-9600 *Founded/Ownrshp* 2004
Sales 28.0MM *EMP* 125
SIC 1796 Machinery installation; Machinery installation
Pr: Bill O Dwyer
Ex VP: Dennis Cowen
VP: Steve Hopkins
Off Mgr: Marcia Roades
Dir IT: Hal Clarridge
Snr PM: James Barnett
Snr PM: Geoff Sable

D-U-N-S 10-851-0934 IMP
MIKARA CORP
NATIONAL SALON RESOURCES DIV
3109 Louisiana Ave N, Minneapolis, MN 55427-2918
Tel (763) 541-1000 *Founded/Ownrshp* 1970
Sales 36.1MM^E *EMP* 100
SIC 5087 5999 Beauty parlor equipment & supplies; Barber shop equipment & supplies; Hair care products; Beauty parlor equipment & supplies; Barber shop equipment & supplies; Hair care products
CEO: Michael P Hicks
Off Mgr: Robin Sanders
Board of Directors: Richard E Christie

D-U-N-S 03-003-4847 IMP
MIKART INC (GA)
1750 Chattahoochee Ave Nw, Atlanta, GA 30318-2112
Tel (404) 352-0601 *Founded/Ownrshp* 1975
Sales 56.7MM^E *EMP* 165
Accts J Terry Gordon & Co Atlanta
SIC 2834 Pharmaceutical preparations; Pharmaceutical preparations
CEO: Miguel I Arteche
**Pr:* Cerie McDonald
CFO: Larry Gunnin
**CFO:* R Larry Gunnin
VP: Charles Chiao
VP: Czarina Mapua
Sfty Mgr: Sharon Warbington
Opers Mgr: Juan Lopez
Secur Mgr: William Brown
Mktg Mgr: Mitchell Tonik

D-U-N-S 11-857-5422 IMP
■ **MIKASA INC**
(*Suby of* LIFETIME BRANDS INC) ★
1 Century Way, Secaucus, NJ 07094-2532
Tel (866) 645-2721 *Founded/Ownrshp* 2008
Sales 115.1MM^E *EMP* 1,048
SIC 5023 5099 5719 Home furnishings; China; Glassware; Stainless steel flatware; Crystal goods; Kitchenware; Home furnishings; China; Glassware; Stainless steel flatware; Crystal goods; Kitchenware
Pr: Raymond B Dingman Jr
**Ch Bd:* George T Aratani
VP: Enrique Bernal
VP: Shannon M Erson
VP: James B Linsalata
VP: Shannon Merson
**VP:* Anthony F Santarelli
Creative D: Robert T Wheale
Mktg Mgr: Julie Lien

D-U-N-S 02-732-3580
MIKE ANDERSON CHEVROLET OF CHICAGO LLC
5333 W Irving Park Rd, Chicago, IL 60641-2529
Tel (773) 283-1874 *Founded/Ownrshp* 2008
Sales 21.1MM^E *EMP* 56^E
SIC 5511 Automobiles, new & used
Opers Mgr: Sandi Holeman
Sales Asso: Jesse Fakhoury

D-U-N-S 03-764-4739
MIKE BROWN ELECTRIC CO
561a Mercantile Dr, Cotati, CA 94931-3040
Tel (707) 792-8100 *Founded/Ownrshp* 1994
Sales 22.3MM *EMP* 65
Accts Johnston Gremaux & Rossi Llp
SIC 1731 Electrical work
Pr: James G Brown
**VP:* Tiffany Howe
Snr Mgr: Dave Dennis

D-U-N-S 60-978-2321 EXP
MIKE BROWN ENTERPRISES INC
AMERICAN INTERNATIONAL ALUM
2908 N Hoover Rd, Buckner, MO 64016-9123
Tel (816) 650-6101 *Founded/Ownrshp* 1989
Sales 31.8MM *EMP* 9
Accts Broadbent Houts & Co Pc
SIC 5051 7389 Metals service centers & offices;
Pr: Joseph M Brown
Sec: Brian Brown
VP: Linda Brown
Admn Mgr: Shani Dorsey

MIKE BROWN FORD CHRYSLER DODGE
See 3925 PARTNERS LTD

D-U-N-S 06-509-5044
MIKE CALVERT INC
MIKE CALVERT TOYOTA
2333 S Loop W, Houston, TX 77054-2811
Tel (713) 558-8282 *Founded/Ownrshp* 1983
Sales 71.8MM^E *EMP* 200
SIC 5511 Automobiles, new & used; Pickups, new & used; Vans, new & used; Automobiles, new & used; Pickups, new & used; Vans, new & used
Pr: Michael R Calvert
**Treas:* John J Davis
Genl Mgr: Johnny Gnemi
Genl Mgr: John Gnemy
Genl Mgr: Rick Rizzuto
IT Man: Brandon Dykes

MIKE CALVERT TOYOTA
See MIKE CALVERT INC

D-U-N-S 15-345-6488
MIKE CAMPBELL & ASSOCIATES LTD
MIKE CAMPBELL ASSOC LOGICTICS
13031 Temple Ave, City of Industry, CA 91746-1418
Tel (626) 369-3981 *Founded/Ownrshp* 1983
Sales 123.0MM^E *EMP* 1,000
SIC 4222 4225 4214 4213 Storage, frozen or refrigerated goods; General warehousing & storage; Local trucking with storage; Trucking, except local; Storage, frozen or refrigerated goods; General warehousing & storage; Local trucking with storage; Trucking, except local
CEO: Vickie J Campbell
**Pr:* James Heermans
**Pr:* Paul Trump
Mktg Dir: Ryan Campbell

MIKE CAMPBELL ASSOC LOGICTICS
See MIKE CAMPBELL & ASSOCIATES LTD

D-U-N-S 04-161-1406
MIKE CASTRUCCI CHEVROLET-OLDSMOBILE INC
MIKE CASTRUCCI OLDSMOBILE
1099 Lila Ave, Milford, OH 45150-1684
Tel (513) 831-5555 *Founded/Ownrshp* 1997
Sales 27.4MM^E *EMP* 72
SIC 5511 Automobiles, new & used; Automobiles, new & used
Pr: Mike Castrucci
**Sec:* Milissa Castrucci
Sales Asso: Lloyd Kitts

D-U-N-S 09-066-2883
MIKE CASTRUCCI FORD
1020 State Route 28, Milford, OH 45150-2002
Tel (513) 831-7010 *Founded/Ownrshp* 1995
Sales 38.3MM^E *EMP* 150
SIC 5511 7538 7532 5521 Automobiles, new & used; General automotive repair shops; Top & body repair & paint shops; Used car dealers; Automobiles, new & used; General automotive repair shops; Top & body repair & paint shops; Used car dealers
Owner: Mike Castrucci

MIKE CASTRUCCI OLDSMOBILE
See MIKE CASTRUCCI CHEVROLET-OLDSMOBILE INC

D-U-N-S 01-823-1902
MIKE COATES CONSTRUCTION CO INC
800 Summit Ave, Niles, OH 44446-3695
Tel (330) 652-0190 *Founded/Ownrshp* 1957
Sales 25.0MM *EMP* 150
Accts Cerimele Meyer & Wray Llc P
SIC 1542 1541 Institutional building construction; Commercial & office building contractors; Industrial buildings & warehouses; Institutional building construction; Commercial & office building contractors; Industrial buildings & warehouses
Pr: Michael J Coates Sr
**VP:* Michael J Coates Jr

D-U-N-S 00-623-1856
MIKE D DIMICH SONS (MT)
PEPSI-COLA BOTTLING CO. OF BIL
344 Howard Ave, Billings, MT 59101-3039
Tel (406) 255-0466 *Founded/Ownrshp* 1935
Sales 22.9MM *EMP* 60
SIC 2086 2087 Carbonated beverages, nonalcoholic: bottled & canned; Flavoring extracts & syrups; Mineral or spring water bottling
Pr: William M Dimich
**Sec:* Thomas W Dimich
Plnt Mgr: Ernie Brester
Plnt Mgr: Bill Dimich
**Sls Mgr:* Daniel W Dimich Jr
Sls Mgr: Mike W Dimich

D-U-N-S 12-793-5005
MIKE DAVIS BUILDERS INC
5236 Dumond Ct Ste A, Lansing, MI 48917-6001
Tel (517) 322-3800 *Founded/Ownrshp* 1968
Sales 32.0MM *EMP* 85
SIC 1542 Commercial & office building, new construction; Commercial & office building, new construction
Pr: Michael H Davis
**CFO:* Diane Weaver

D-U-N-S 01-686-3029
MIKE DORIAN FORD INC
35900 S Gratiot Ave, Clinton Township, MI 48035-1713
Tel (586) 792-4100 *Founded/Ownrshp* 1963
Sales 48.9MM^E *EMP* 110
SIC 5511 5521 Automobiles, new & used; Pickups, new & used; Vans, new & used; Used car dealers; Automobiles, new & used; Pickups, new & used; Vans, new & used; Used car dealers
Pr: Mike Dorian Jr
**VP:* Carolyn Dorian
**Prin:* Mark Chiamp
**Prin:* Tony McKheen
**Prin:* Gary Torrento
Sls Mgr: Rod Locricchio

D-U-N-S 80-928-8558
MIKE DUMAN AUTO SALES INC
2300 Godwin Blvd, Suffolk, VA 23434-8027
Tel (757) 539-1000 *Founded/Ownrshp* 1980
Sales 27.5MM^E *EMP* 73^E
SIC 5521 Automobiles, used cars only; Pickups & vans, used
Pr: Michael D Duman
**Sec:* Peggy Cornett
**VP:* Frances B Duman
VP: Karen Sale
Exec: Lynn Atkinson
Genl Mgr: Jim Pryne

D-U-N-S 03-802-3123
MIKE ERDMAN MOTORS INC
SUTHERLIN OLDS CADILLAC NSSN I
445 E Merritt Island Cswy, Merritt Island, FL 32952-3502
Tel (321) 453-2050 *Founded/Ownrshp* 1990
Sales 39.8MM^E *EMP* 100^E
SIC 5511 Automobiles, new & used; Automobiles, new & used
Pr: Michael Erdman
**Treas:* Paula Darby
**VP:* Fredrika Erdman
Plnt Mgr: Bobby Thomas
Sales Asso: Anton Qarana

D-U-N-S 80-161-3886
MIKE ERDMAN TOYOTA
EAST FLORIDA MOTOR SALES
1545 E Mrritt Island Cswy, Merritt Island, FL 32952-2611
Tel (321) 453-1313 *Founded/Ownrshp* 1989
Sales 40.5MM^E *EMP* 90
SIC 5511 7514 7515 7513 Automobiles, new & used; Rent-a-car service; Passenger car leasing; Truck rental & leasing, no drivers; Automobiles, new & used; Rent-a-car service; Passenger car leasing; Truck rental & leasing, no drivers
Pr: Michael H Erdman
Exec: Cindy Headly
Exec: Mike Toyota
Sls Mgr: Paula Darby
Sls Mgr: Joe Gallagher

D-U-N-S 04-368-9538
MIKE FINNIN FORD LLC
3600 Dodge St, Dubuque, IA 52003-5251
Tel (563) 556-1010 *Founded/Ownrshp* 1979
Sales 29.9MM^E *EMP* 70
SIC 5511 Automobiles, new & used; Pickups, new & used; Automobiles, new & used; Pickups, new & used
Pr: Michael L Finnin
**Sec:* Sharon Finnin
Exec: Susan Felton
Off Mgr: Mary Rollinger

Sls Mgr: Gabe Finnin
Sls Mgr: Amy Montgomery
Sales Asso: Diane Noble
Sales Asso: Kevin Wheaton

D-U-N-S 08-665-5982
MIKE FORD BASS INC
BASS TRUCK CENTER
5050 Detroit Rd, Sheffield Village, OH 44035-1464
Tel (440) 934-3673 *Founded/Ownrshp* 1977
Sales 35.0MM^E *EMP* 100
SIC 5511 Automobiles, new & used; Automobiles, new & used
Pr: James B Bass
**Sec:* Barbara Bass
**VP:* Mike Bass
Off Mgr: James M Wilsman

D-U-N-S 11-748-2851
MIKE FORD MURPHY INC
MIKE MURPHY AUTO ANNEX
565 W Jackson St, Morton, IL 61550-1556
Tel (309) 263-2311 *Founded/Ownrshp* 1984
Sales 25.6MM^E *EMP* 75
SIC 5511 Automobiles, new & used; Automobiles, new & used
Pr: Michael Murphy
**Sec:* Paul P Gilfillan
Sls Mgr: Nathan Noyes
Sales Asso: Paul Ekstam
Sales Asso: Richard Geiger
Sales Asso: Stan Saylor

D-U-N-S 18-616-9447 EXP
■ **MIKE FORD SHAD INC**
(*Suby of* AUTONATION INC) ★
7700 Blanding Blvd, Jacksonville, FL 32244-5114
Tel (904) 777-3673 *Founded/Ownrshp* 1997
Sales 57.3MM^E *EMP* 200
SIC 5511 Automobiles, new & used; Automobiles, new & used
Pr: Joe Key
Exec: Ike Ettinger

MIKE FOX TOYOTA
See FOX AUTOMOTIVE INC

D-U-N-S 02-794-3661
MIKE GARCIA MERCHANT SECURITY LLC
6000 Welch Ave Ste 11, El Paso, TX 79905-1836
Tel (915) 772-7047 *Founded/Ownrshp* 1941
Sales 10.9MM^E *EMP* 350
SIC 7381 Protective services, guard; Protective services, guard
Exec: Alfredo Rivera
IT Man: Yvette Garcia

D-U-N-S 02-569-6287
MIKE HAGGERTY BUICK GMC INC
MIKE HGGRTY PNTC-GMC-VLKSWAGEN
9301 S Cicero Ave, Oak Lawn, IL 60453-2517
Tel (708) 423-1630 *Founded/Ownrshp* 1988
Sales 29.7MM^E *EMP* 74^E
SIC 5511 Automobiles, new & used; Pickups, new & used; Vans, new & used; Automobiles, new & used; Pickups, new & used; Vans, new & used
Pr: Michael D Haggerty
**CFO:* Charlotte Beagle
VP: Tony Disalle
**VP:* Richard E Haggerty
Sls Mgr: Dan Fontana

D-U-N-S 00-190-8086 IMP/EXP
■ **MIKE HALL CHEVROLET INC**
CHAMPION CHEVROLET HIGHWAY 6
(*Suby of* AUTONATION INC) ★
8100 Highway 6 S, Houston, TX 77083-5701
Tel (281) 561-9900 *Founded/Ownrshp* 1998
Sales 1.6MMM^E *EMP* 8,000
SIC 5511 Automobiles, new & used; Automobiles, new & used
Pr: David Casto
**Treas:* Ian Swartz
**VP:* Ed Bailey
Exec: Melissa Hughes
Off Mgr: Amy Konstantin

MIKE HGGRTY PNTC-GMC-VLKSWAGEN
See MIKE HAGGERTY BUICK GMC INC

D-U-N-S 00-799-4106
MIKE HOOKS INC (LA)
409 Mike Hooks Rd, Westlake, LA 70669-5744
Tel (337) 436-6693 *Founded/Ownrshp* 1946, 1991
Sales 57.0MM^E *EMP* 275
SIC 1629 Dams, waterways, docks & other marine construction; Marine construction; Dredging contractor; Dams, waterways, docks & other marine construction; Marine construction; Dredging contractor
Pr: Mike P McMahon
**Treas:* Kim McMahon
**VP:* Ashley McMahon Kerns
**VP:* Mike McMahon
Opers Mgr: Arthur Sonnier

MIKE HUDSON DISTRIBUTING
See HDP ENTERPRISES INC

MIKE JOHNSON'S HICKORY TOYOTA
See TACK AUTOMOTIVE LLC

D-U-N-S 02-981-0660
MIKE KEHOE FORD INC
LINCOLN MERCURY
807 Southwest Blvd, Jefferson City, MO 65109-2657
Tel (573) 634-4444 *Founded/Ownrshp* 1992
Sales 27.5MM^E *EMP* 90
SIC 5511 7538 7532 5531 7359 5012 Automobiles, new & used; General automotive repair shops; Top & body repair & paint shops; Automotive & home supply stores; Equipment rental & leasing; Automobiles & other motor vehicles; Automobiles, new & used; General automotive repair shops; Top & body repair & paint shops; Automotive & home supply stores; Equipment rental & leasing; Automobiles & other motor vehicles
Pr: Michael Kehoe
Genl Mgr: Eric Heidt
Off Mgr: Donna Bloom

Store Mgr: Brian Gillmore
IT Man: Douglass Whitehead

MIKE MCGRATH AUTO CENTER
See MCGRATH AUTOMOTIVE GROUP INC

D-U-N-S 07-533-3732
■ **MIKE MILLER TOYOTA**
(*Suby of* MILLER AUTOMOTIVE GROUP INC) ★
9077 Washington Blvd, Culver City, CA 90232-2530
Tel (310) 559-3777 *Founded/Ownrshp* 1973, 1989
Sales 33.1MM^E *EMP* 120
SIC 5511 Automobiles, new & used; Automobiles, new & used
Pr: Mike Miller
**CFO:* Doug Stewart
**Sec:* Fred Miller

MIKE MURPHY AUTO ANNEX
See MIKE FORD MURPHY INC

MIKE NAUGHTON FORD
See MIKE NAUGHTON LEASING CO

D-U-N-S 03-189-4017
MIKE NAUGHTON LEASING CO
MIKE NAUGHTON FORD
150 S Havana St, Aurora, CO 80012-1025
Tel (303) 326-5652 *Founded/Ownrshp* 1978
Sales 61.5MM^E *EMP* 146
SIC 5511 7538 7532 5521 7515 5531 Automobiles, new & used; General automotive repair shops; Top & body repair & paint shops; Used car dealers; Passenger car leasing; Automotive & home supply stores; Automobiles, new & used; General automotive repair shops; Top & body repair & paint shops; Used car dealers; Passenger car leasing; Automotive & home supply stores
Pr: Michael D Naughton
**Sec:* Pacifico Gonzales
Sls Mgr: Brian Naughton

D-U-N-S 07-873-0857
MIKE PALMER PETROLEUM SERVICES INC (ND)
PETROLEUMSERVICES & TOOLS CO.
2502 4th Ave W, Williston, ND 58801-3431
Tel (701) 572-2487 *Founded/Ownrshp* 2003
Sales 91.7MM^E *EMP* 100
SIC 5172 Petroleum products; Petroleum products
Pr: Mike Palmer
**CFO:* Tricia McGlothlin
Genl Mgr: Wade Slater

D-U-N-S 01-742-8111
MIKE PIRRONE PRODUCE INC
15313 Bryce Rd, Mussey, MI 48014-2917
Tel (810) 395-4316 *Founded/Ownrshp* 1979
Sales 20.7MM^E *EMP* 7
SIC 5148 Fresh fruits & vegetables; Fresh fruits & vegetables
CEO: Donna Deblouw
**Pr:* Henry De Blouw

D-U-N-S 05-295-4294
MIKE RAISOR FORD INC
RAISOR MIKE FORD SALES & SVC
2051 Sagamore Pkwy S, Lafayette, IN 47905-5108
Tel (765) 447-9444 *Founded/Ownrshp* 1990
Sales 53.2MM^E *EMP* 135
SIC 5511 5521 5012 Automobiles, new & used; Pickups, new & used; Vans, new & used; Used car dealers; Automobiles & other motor vehicles; Automobiles, new & used; Pickups, new & used; Vans, new & used; Used car dealers; Automobiles & other motor vehicles
Pr: Michael V Raisor
**Treas:* Gene Bass
Sls Mgr: Steve Hyer

D-U-N-S 01-647-8026
MIKE RAISOR PONTIAC INC
2912 Main St, Lafayette, IN 47904-3354
Tel (765) 449-5400 *Founded/Ownrshp* 1986
Sales 41.1MM^E *EMP* 88
SIC 5511 5521 7538 Automobiles, new & used; Pickups, new & used; Trucks, tractors & trailers: new & used; Used car dealers; General automotive repair shops; Automobiles, new & used; Pickups, new & used; Trucks, tractors & trailers: new & used; Used car dealers; General automotive repair shops
Pr: Michael V Raisor
Off Mgr: Cathy Russell

D-U-N-S 83-316-9191
MIKE REICHENBACH FORD LINCOLN MERCURY INC
600 N Coit St, Florence, SC 29501-2822
Tel (843) 664-4141 *Founded/Ownrshp* 2006
Sales 50.0MM *EMP* 100
SIC 5511 Automobiles, new & used
Pr: Mike Reichenbach
Mktg Dir: Charisse Reichenbach
Sls Mgr: Sandra Brown
Sls Mgr: Wendell Gamble
Sls Mgr: James Welch

D-U-N-S 94-107-0864
MIKE ROVNER CONSTRUCTION INC
MRC
5400 Tech Cir, Moorpark, CA 93021-1792
Tel (805) 517-1968 *Founded/Ownrshp* 1991
Sales 119.4MM^E *EMP* 300
Accts Mayer Hoffman Mccann Pc Oxn
SIC 1522 Remodeling, multi-family dwellings; Remodeling, multi-family dwellings
Pr: Mike Rovner
VP: Dave Holland
Dir Bus: Thomas McBride
IT Man: Stephen Parks
Snr PM: David Grund

D-U-N-S 06-612-3696
MIKE ROZIER CONSTRUCTION CO INC
10474 Highway 82, Greenwood, MS 38930-7140
Tel (662) 453-8161 *Founded/Ownrshp* 1982
Sales 21.8MM^E *EMP* 45^E
SIC 1542 1541 Commercial & office building, new construction; Commercial & office buildings, renovation & repair; Industrial buildings, new construction; Renovation, remodeling & repairs: industrial buildings
Pr: Mike Rozier
**Sec:* Belinda Switzer
**VP:* Michael Rozier
Off Mgr: Chris Logan

D-U-N-S 01-675-7023
MIKE SAVOIE CHEVROLET INC
1900 W Maple Rd, Troy, MI 48084-7105
Tel (248) 643-8000 *Founded/Ownrshp* 1966
Sales 39.0MM^E *EMP* 85
SIC 5511 Automobiles, new & used; Automobiles, new & used
Pr: Myron P Savoie
Treas: Dave Miller
**VP:* Michael P Savoie
Sls Mgr: Chuck Martin
Sales Asso: Sandra McMenomay
Sales Asso: Ed Serwach
Sales Asso: Greg Zuelch

D-U-N-S 03-157-3702
MIKE SCHMITZ AUTOMOTIVE GROUP INC
2309 Ross Clark Cir, Dothan, AL 36301-4908
Tel (334) 794-6716 *Founded/Ownrshp* 1998
Sales 27.0MM^E *EMP* 70
SIC 5511 5521 New & used car dealers; Used car dealers; New & used car dealers; Used car dealers
Pr: Michael Schmitz
**VP:* Fred Faura
Sls Mgr: Carter Stegall

MIKE SHAD FORD AT THE AVENUES
See KINGS CROWN FORD INC

D-U-N-S 02-322-8224 IMP
MIKE SHANNON AUTOMOTIVE INC
HOLIDAY MAZDA
321 N Rolling Meadows Dr, Fond Du Lac, WI 54937-9726
Tel (920) 921-8898 *Founded/Ownrshp* 1979
Sales 144.5MM^E *EMP* 175
SIC 5511 Automobiles, new & used; Automobiles, new & used
Pr: Michael Shannon
**COO:* Rob Beane
CFO: Yvonne Loduha
**Sec:* Pat McCullough
Sr VP: Jeff Hopper
VP: Bill Agnew
Store Mgr: Richard Davies
Sls Mgr: Chad Guell
Sls Mgr: Chris Ingemann

D-U-N-S 03-192-8476
MIKE SHAW BUICK-PONTIAC-GMC INC
1313 Motor City Dr, Colorado Springs, CO 80905-7316
Tel (719) 636-3881 *Founded/Ownrshp* 2000
Sales 28.7MM^E *EMP* 65
SIC 5511 5531 Automobiles, new & used; Pickups, new & used; Automotive parts; Automobiles, new & used; Pickups, new & used; Automotive parts
Pr: Mike J Shaw
Genl Mgr: Craig Boyajian

MIKE SHAW CHEVROLET
See COLORADO BOULEVARD MOTORS INC

D-U-N-S 14-327-0952
MIKE SHAW TEXAS MOTORS INC
FERNANDEZ HONDA
8015 Interstate 35 S, San Antonio, TX 78224-1336
Tel (210) 928-1500 *Founded/Ownrshp* 2002
Sales 29.8MM^E *EMP* 70
SIC 5511 Automobiles, new & used; Automobiles, new & used
Pr: Mike Shaw
Genl Mgr: Adam Claiborne

D-U-N-S 05-222-5240
■ **MIKE SMITH AUTOPLAZA INC**
BMW OF BEAUMONT
(*Suby of* GROUP 1 AUTOMOTIVE INC) ★
1515 Interstate 10 S, Beaumont, TX 77701-4758
Tel (409) 833-7100 *Founded/Ownrshp* 1982
Sales 36.0MM^E *EMP* 137^E
SIC 5511 Automobiles, new & used; Pickups, new & used; Trucks, tractors & trailers: new & used; Vans, new & used; Automobiles, new & used; Pickups, new & used; Trucks, tractors & trailers: new & used; Vans, new & used
Pr: Michael G Smith
**Treas:* Cindy Powell
**VP:* Charles Smith
Sales Exec: Brian Kahla

D-U-N-S 06-752-7135
MIKE SMITH BUICK PONTIAC INC
MIKE SMITH PONTIAC
6014 S Transit Rd, Lockport, NY 14094-6397
Tel (716) 625-8235 *Founded/Ownrshp* 1993
Sales 24.0MM^E *EMP* 65
SIC 5511 Automobiles, new & used; Pickups, new & used; Automobiles, new & used; Pickups, new & used
Pr: Karen Smith

MIKE SMITH PONTIAC
See MIKE SMITH BUICK PONTIAC INC

D-U-N-S 15-424-1967
MIKE STUART ENTERPRISES INC
LAKELAND PHARMACY
18565 Business 13, Branson West, MO 65737-9659
Tel (417) 272-8064 *Founded/Ownrshp* 1998
Sales 155.9MM^E *EMP* 100
SIC 5122 Respirators; Pharmaceuticals
Pr: Mike Stuart
Off Mgr: Dan Priest
IT Man: Jim Parten
Cert Phar: Anne Lafferty
Cert Phar: Brenda Smith
Cert Phar: Heather Sutherland

D-U-N-S 03-707-4630
MIKE THOMPSON RECREATIONAL VEHICLES COLTON
MIKE THOMPSONS RV SUPER STORES
13940 Firestone Blvd, Santa Fe Springs, CA 90670-5808
Tel (562) 921-0955 *Founded/Ownrshp* 1979
Sales 66.7MM^E *EMP* 150
SIC 5561 Motor homes; Recreational vehicle parts & accessories; Motor homes; Recreational vehicle parts & accessories
Pr: Frank Degelas
Genl Mgr: Lonny Nicholson
Genl Mgr: Mark Rosenbaum
Sls&Mrk Ex: Calista Baldwin

MIKE THOMPSONS RV SUPER STORES
See MIKE THOMPSON RECREATIONAL VEHICLES COLTON

D-U-N-S 01-705-3844
MIKE YOUNG PONTIAC-GMC TRUCKS INC
312 N Main St, Frankenmuth, MI 48734-1114
Tel (989) 652-3271 *Founded/Ownrshp* 1976
Sales 24.2MM^E *EMP* 50
SIC 5511 7542 Automobiles, new & used; Pickups, new & used; Vans, new & used; Carwashes
Pr: Michael D Young
**Sec:* Anthony Young
**VP:* Terry Weiss

D-U-N-S 06-169-7397
MIKE-SELLS POTATO CHIP CO
(*Suby of* MIKE-SELLS WEST VIRGINIA INC) ★
333 Leo St, Dayton, OH 45404-1080
Tel (937) 228-9400 *Founded/Ownrshp* 1966
Sales 47.6MM^E *EMP* 270
SIC 2096 5145 Potato chips & other potato-based snacks; Snack foods; Pretzels; Corn chips; Potato chips & other potato-based snacks; Snack foods; Pretzels; Corn chips
CFO: Paul McNeil
Treas: Larry W Pounds
Ex VP: Philip Kazer
VP: Joe Gauthier
VP: Mary Mapp
VP: Bob Thompson
**Prin:* D W Mikesell
**Prin:* Martha J Mikesell
Rgnl Mgr: Dennis Franklin
MIS Dir: Jarrod Johnson
IT Man: Lily White

D-U-N-S 06-169-7215
MIKE-SELLS WEST VIRGINIA INC
333 Leo St, Dayton, OH 45404-1080
Tel (937) 228-9400 *Founded/Ownrshp* 1972
Sales 47.6MM^E *EMP* 270
SIC 2096 5145

D-U-N-S 15-736-3797
MIKE-TELL-CHAR INC
BASSETT'S MARKET
3994 East Harbor Rd B, Port Clinton, OH 43452-2671
Tel (419) 734-6506 *Founded/Ownrshp* 1985
Sales 23.0MM *EMP* 129
SIC 5411 Grocery stores, independent
Pr: Richard M Bassett
**Sec:* Kim Detzel
IT Man: Mike Kolhoff

MIKEN CLOTHING
See MIKEN SALES INC

D-U-N-S 87-464-9528 IMP
MIKEN SALES INC
MIKEN CLOTHING
539 S Mission Rd, Los Angeles, CA 90033-4228
Tel (323) 266-2560 *Founded/Ownrshp* 1991
Sales 38.9MM^E *EMP* 54
Accts Kaufman & Kabani Los Angeles
SIC 5137 Women's & children's clothing
CEO: Michael Bobbitt
**VP:* Kenny Landy
VP Opers: Jonathan Namm

D-U-N-S 96-502-9366
MIKEN SPECIALTIES LTD
BROCK GROUP, THE
(*Suby of* ATLANTIC HOLDINGS II INC) ★
10343 Sam Houston Park Dr, Houston, TX 77064-4656
Tel (979) 265-9599 *Founded/Ownrshp* 2008
Sales 57.7MM^E *EMP* 1,054
SIC 1721 1799 Industrial painting; Fireproofing buildings; Insulation of pipes & boilers; Industrial painting; Fireproofing buildings; Insulation of pipes & boilers
Pt: Mike Scarborough
Pt: Robert Hardy
Mtls Mgr: Dan Holy

D-U-N-S 04-263-5128
MIKES CAMERA INC
2500 Pearl St Ste Main, Boulder, CO 80302-3838
Tel (303) 443-1715 *Founded/Ownrshp* 1980
Sales 30.0MM *EMP* 135
SIC 5946 5043 Cameras; Photographic supplies; Cameras & photographic equipment; Cameras; Photographic supplies; Cameras & photographic equipment
Pr: Kaloust Christianian
**CFO:* Jirair Christianian
**VP:* Aroussiag Christianian
Store Mgr: Tito Roberts
Prd Mgr: David Lindquist
Sls Mgr: Mike Mitchell

D-U-N-S 08-134-9094
MIKES COLLIERVILLE BIG STAR NO 52 INC
BBA SUPERVALUE
1415 Goodman Rd W, Horn Lake, MS 38637-1404
Tel (662) 393-9708 *Founded/Ownrshp* 1992
Sales 25.0MM^E *EMP* 475
SIC 5411 Grocery stores, independent; Grocery stores, independent
Pr: Michael Gordin
**Sec:* Sherry Gordin

MIKE'S EXPRESS CAR WASH
See CREW CARWASH INC

MIKE'S FAMOUS HARLEY-DAVIDSON
See ROMMEL CYCLES LLC

MIKE'S TREE SERVICE
See BURFORDS TREE SURGEONS INC

D-U-N-S 11-298-4265 IMP
MIKIMOTO (AMERICA) CO LTD
(*Suby of* K.MIKIMOTO & CO.,LTD.)
680 5th Ave, New York, NY 10019-5429
Tel (212) 457-4500 *Founded/Ownrshp* 1978
Sales 41.8MM^E *EMP* 125
SIC 5094 Pearls; Pearls
CEO: Mitsuhiro Mitsui
Pt: Susumu Okuzono
COO: Meyer Hoffman
Sr VP: Robert Artelt
Sr VP: Hiroshi Inoue
VP: Joe Kakimoto
VP: Amy Kim
VP: Kano Kobayashi
VP: Aaron Reed
VP: Yugo Tsukikawa
Rgnl Mgr: Sharon Williams

D-U-N-S 79-513-0046
MIKOLSKY INC
CHARDON GIANT EAGLE 6383
351 Center St, Chardon, OH 44024-1103
Tel (440) 286-4949 *Founded/Ownrshp* 1990
Sales 36.5MM *EMP* 220
SIC 5411 5912 Supermarkets, chain; Drug stores & proprietary stores; Supermarkets, chain; Drug stores & proprietary stores
Pr: Charles W Mikolsky
*Sec: Edna Mikolsky
*VP: Steven Mikolsky

D-U-N-S 01-062-5309 IMP
MIKRON CORP DENVER
(*Suby of* MIKRON HOLDING AG)
8100 S Potomac St, Centennial, CO 80112-7156
Tel (303) 364-5222 *Founded/Ownrshp* 1981
Sales 28.8MM^E *EMP* 80
SIC 3535 3823 3825 3625

D-U-N-S 04-668-6622 IMP
MIKRON INDUSTRIES INC (WA)
1034 6th Ave N, Kent, WA 98032-2991
Tel (253) 854-8020 *Founded/Ownrshp* 2004
Sales NA *EMP* 1,000
SIC 3089

D-U-N-S 00-648-0297 IMP
MIKROS ENGINEERING INC (MN)
8755 Wyoming Ave N, Brooklyn Park, MN 55445-1832
Tel (763) 424-4642 *Founded/Ownrshp* 1963
Sales 24.4MM^E *EMP* 100
SIC 3089 Injection molding of plastics
Pr: James L Talmage
*VP: Johmn Mitlyn
*VP: Mary Talmage
*VP: William Talmage
Plnt Mgr: John Mitlyng

D-U-N-S 04-600-2572 IMP
MIKUNI AMERICAN CORP
M A C
(*Suby of* MIKUNI CORPORATION)
8910 Mikuni Ave, Northridge, CA 91324-3403
Tel (310) 676-0522 *Founded/Ownrshp* 1968
Sales 117.4MM^E *EMP* 214
SIC 5013 5088 Automotive hardware; Aircraft engines & engine parts; Aircraft & parts; Automotive hardware; Aircraft engines & engine parts; Aircraft & parts
Pr: Satoshi Fujimori
*CFO: Hirokazu Masahashi
*Ch: Masaki Ikuta
Ex VP: Ken Kaieda
Ex VP: Jun Suzuki
*VP: Shigeru Ikuta
VP: Hiroyuki Ono
VP: Robert Sein
Dir IT: Charlie Zhao
Sls Mgr: Steve Webb

D-U-N-S 16-157-9735
MIL CORP
4000 Mitchellville Rd R, Bowie, MD 20716-3104
Tel (301) 805-8500 *Founded/Ownrshp* 1980
Sales 98.3MM^E *EMP* 560
SIC 7371 7373 7374 7375 7376 8711 Computer software systems analysis & design, custom; Computer integrated systems design; Data processing & preparation; Information retrieval services; Computer facilities management; Engineering services; Computer software systems analysis & design, custom; Computer integrated systems design; Data processing & preparation; Information retrieval services; Computer facilities management; Engineering services
Pr: Maurice I Long
CFO: Michael Means
CFO: Brenda Pridgen
Ex VP: Marisa Daley
Ex VP: Jim McIntyre
Sr VP: William Dunkin
Sr VP: Dave Larson
VP: Martha Bailey
VP: Tom Clark
VP: Harvil Jenkins
VP: Peg Kendra
VP: Harvey Weiner

D-U-N-S 79-620-9963 IMP
MIL LTD
MYREX INDUSTRIES
9119 Weedy Ln, Houston, TX 77093-7006
Tel (713) 691-5200 *Founded/Ownrshp* 1990
Sales 35.3MM^E *EMP* 140
SIC 3441 Fabricated structural metal; Fabricated structural metal
Pt: Jim Moffa
Pt: R Kelly Boze
Genl Mgr: Carla Hawkins

MIL-CON
See MILITARY CONSTRUCTION CORP

MIL-SPEC. ENTERPRISES
See CARTER ENTERPRISES LLC

D-U-N-S 07-492-7708
MILABEL MOTORS INC
MILLER TOYOTA
8566 Sudley Rd, Manassas, VA 20110-3837
Tel (703) 369-3040 *Founded/Ownrshp* 1982
Sales 30.6MM^E *EMP* 80^E
SIC 5511 Automobiles, new & used; Automobiles, new & used
Pr: Jeff Abel Jr
Exec: John Strain
*Genl Mgr: Kenneth Shepherd
Dir IT: Chuck Seiders
Sls Mgr: Cecil Hager
Sls Mgr: Rob Jenkins
Sales Asso: Dale Erickson
Sales Asso: Lee Hall
Sales Asso: Jawed Ibrahimi
Sales Asso: Jose Prado
Sales Asso: Greg Tardif

D-U-N-S 07-979-3814 EXP
▲ MILACRON HOLDINGS CORP
3010 Disney St, Cincinnati, OH 45209-5028
Tel (513) 487-5000 *Founded/Ownrshp* 1860
Sales 1.2MMM *EMP* 5,368^E
Tkr Sym MCRN *Exch* NYS
SIC 3544 Industrial molds; Forms (molds), for foundry & plastics working machinery
Pr: Tom Goeke
*Ch Bd: Ira Boots
COO: John J Gallagher III
COO: Ron Krisanda
CFO: Bruce Chalmers
Ofcr: Mark Dixon
CTO: Bruce Catoen

D-U-N-S 07-984-3362
■ MILACRON INTERMEDIATE HOLDINGS INC
(*Suby of* MILACRON HOLDINGS CORP) ★
3010 Disney St, Cincinnati, OH 45209-5028
Tel (513) 536-2000 *Founded/Ownrshp* 2015
Sales 1.6MMM^E *EMP* 4,718^E
SIC 5962 8741 Merchandising machine operators; Industrial management

D-U-N-S 83-226-5602 IMP
■ MILACRON LLC
(*Suby of* MILACRON INTERMEDIATE HOLDINGS INC) ★
10200 Alliance Rd Ste 200, Blue Ash, OH 45242-4716
Tel (513) 487-5000 *Founded/Ownrshp* 2012
Sales 1.6MMM^E *EMP* 4,718
SIC 3549 2899 Metalworking machinery; Correction fluid; Metalworking machinery; Correction fluid
CEO: Tom Goeke
*COO: John Gallagher
*COO: Ron Krisanda
CFO: Ross A Anderson
*CFO: Bruce Chalmers
Exec: Lynn Miller
Dir Lab: Bill Downs
Off Mgr: Lynn Townsend
CIO: Dario Vettor
MIS Dir: Dennis Parish
QA Dir: Steve Allen

D-U-N-S 83-186-0494 IMP/EXP
■ MILACRON MARKETING CO LLC
(*Suby of* MILACRON LLC) ★
4165 Half Acre Rd, Batavia, OH 45103-3247
Tel (513) 458-8100 *Founded/Ownrshp* 2009
Sales 521.7MM^E *EMP* 4,700^E
SIC 3541 Machine tools, metal cutting type; Machine tools, metal cutting type
CEO: Tom Goeke
*CFO: John Francy
Exec: Roy Schweiger
Sftwr Eng: Andrei Bialevich
Sls Mgr: Umesh Pareek

D-U-N-S 83-226-5859 IMP
■ MILACRON PLASTICS TECHNOLOGIES GROUP LLC
(*Suby of* MILACRON LLC) ★
4165 Half Acre Rd, Batavia, OH 45103-3247
Tel (513) 536-2000 *Founded/Ownrshp* 2009
Sales 233.0MM^E *EMP* 777^E
SIC 3544 Forms (molds), for foundry & plastics working machinery; Forms (molds), for foundry & plastics working machinery
CEO: Tom Goeke
Pr: Dave Lawrence
COO: Ron Krisanda
CFO: John C Francy
VP: Mark Dixon
VP: Richard A Oleary
IT Man: Gary Smith
VP Opers: Mark Griffiths

MILAGRO MEZZ
See MILAGRO OIL & GAS INC

D-U-N-S 96-814-8523
MILAGRO OIL & GAS INC
MILAGRO MEZZ
(*Suby of* MILAGRO HOLDINGS LLC)
1301 Mckinney St Ste 500, Houston, TX 77010-3089
Tel (713) 750-1600 *Founded/Ownrshp* 1997
Sales 135.5MM *EMP* 19
Accts Deloitte & Touche Llp Houston
SIC 1382 Oil & gas exploration services; Oil & gas exploration services
Pr: Gary Mabie

D-U-N-S 04-866-3293
MILAGRO PACKAGING LLC
1585 Wells Rd, Dundee, MI 48131-9519
Tel (734) 777-1744 *Founded/Ownrshp* 2001
Sales 24.0MM *EMP* 43
SIC 5084 Processing & packaging equipment; Processing & packaging equipment

MILAM CONSTRUCTION CO
See MILAM OIL CORP

D-U-N-S 05-407-5130
MILAM OIL CORP
MILAM CONSTRUCTION CO
1605 Haynesville Hwy, El Dorado, AR 71730-6950
Tel (870) 862-4258 *Founded/Ownrshp* 1963
Sales 63.1MM^E *EMP* 275
SIC 1623 1796 1311 Oil & gas pipeline construction; Machinery installation; Crude petroleum production; Oil & gas pipeline construction; Machinery installation; Crude petroleum production
Ch Bd: John D Milam
*Pr: Johnny O'Pry
*CEO: David Atkins
*CFO: Tom Dunn
*Ch: Jim Etter
Sfty Dirs: D J Hargett

D-U-N-S 02-739-0525
MILAM OLDSMOBILE MAZDA JEEP INC
608 River Rd, Puyallup, WA 98371-4153
Tel (253) 845-1766 *Founded/Ownrshp* 1959
Sales 22.6MM *EMP* 45
SIC 5511 Automobiles, new & used; Automobiles, new & used
Pr: Glen Zevenbergen
*Treas: Harold Milam
*VP: Ken Dinsmore
Sales Exec: Mike Folk
Sales Asso: Alton Grounds
Sales Asso: Nick Kuzmick

MILAM'S MARKET
See B & R SUPERMARKET INC

D-U-N-S 07-841-0792
■ MILAN FCI
(*Suby of* BUREAU OF PRISONS) ★
4002 Arkona Rd, Milan, MI 48160
Tel (734) 439-1511 *Founded/Ownrshp* 1933, 2006
Sales NA *EMP* 320
SIC 9223 Prison, government; ; Prison, government;
CEO: C Eichenlaub
DP Exec: Bruce Fry

D-U-N-S 61-346-9100 IMP
MILAN METAL SYSTEMS LLC
(*Suby of* GLOBAL AUTOMOTIVE SYSTEMS LLC) ★
555 S Platt Rd, Milan, MI 48160-9303
Tel (734) 439-1546 *Founded/Ownrshp* 2005
Sales 43.2MM^E *EMP* 145
SIC 3465 Automotive stampings; Automotive stampings

D-U-N-S 05-024-1306
MILAN SUPPLY CHAIN SOLUTIONS INC
1091 Kefauver Dr, Milan, TN 38358-3412
Tel (731) 686-7428 *Founded/Ownrshp* 1969
Sales 50.9MM *EMP* 465
Accts Alexander Thompson Arnold Pllc
SIC 4212 4213 4731 Local trucking, without storage; Trucking, except local; Truck transportation brokers; Local trucking, without storage; Trucking, except local; Truck transportation brokers
Ch: Tommy Wayne Ross
*Pr: John W Ross
*CFO: Bruce F Kalem
*Treas: Linda Szopinski
VP: David Crean
VP: Barry Jones
Genl Mgr: Roy Mabry
CTO: David Moneypenny
DP Exec: Erika Long
DP Exec: Doug Taylor
Sales Exec: Tony Sneed

D-U-N-S 01-726-1579
MILAN SUPPLY CO
7125 E Pickard Rd, Mount Pleasant, MI 48858-7423
Tel (989) 773-9938 *Founded/Ownrshp* 1962
Sales 84.3MM^E *EMP* 50
SIC 5082 Wellpoints (drilling equipment); Wellpoints (drilling equipment)
Pr: John Gall
VP: Marty Derocco
*VP: Dean Dubay
*VP: Daniel Milan

D-U-N-S 02-820-1200
■ MILANO RESTAURANTS INTERNATIONAL CORP
ME-N-ED'S PIZZERIA
(*Suby of* AMERICAN REALTY INVESTORS INC) ★
6729 N Palm Ave Ste 200, Fresno, CA 93704-1077
Tel (559) 432-0399 *Founded/Ownrshp* 1996
Sales 18.1MM^E *EMP* 353
SIC 5812 Pizzeria, chain; Pizzeria, chain
Pr: John Ferdinandi
*COO: A Thomas Ferdinandi Jr
*CFO: Marta Gray
VP: Johannes Setyono
Sales Exec: Randy Christman

D-U-N-S 55-610-2994
MILARK INDUSTRIES INC
536 S Airport Rd, Mansfield, OH 44903-8067
Tel (419) 524-7627 *Founded/Ownrshp* 1986
Sales 20.8MM^E *EMP* 175^E
SIC 3465 3469 3751 3714

D-U-N-S 05-710-1677
■ MILBANK INSURANCE CO
(*Suby of* STATE AUTO FINANCIAL CORP) ★
107 Flynn Dr Ste 100, Milbank, SD 57252-1556
Tel (605) 432-5107 *Founded/Ownrshp* 1993
Sales NA *EMP* 160^E
SIC 6331 6411 Fire, marine & casualty insurance: stock; Insurance agents, brokers & service; Fire, marine & casualty insurance: stock; Insurance agents, brokers & service
Ch Bd: Robert L Restrepo

D-U-N-S 96-017-4795
MILBANK INSURANCE CO
518 E Broad St, Columbus, OH 43215-3901
Tel (614) 464-5000 *Founded/Ownrshp* 2014
Sales NA *EMP* 2^E
SIC 6411 Insurance agents, brokers & service

D-U-N-S 00-712-6378
MILBANK MANUFACTURING CO (MO)
4801 Deramus Ave, Kansas City, MO 64120-1180
Tel (816) 483-5314 *Founded/Ownrshp* 1913
Sales 132.0MM^E *EMP* 600
SIC 3825 3444 Meters: electric, pocket, portable, panelboard, etc.; Energy measuring equipment, electrical; Sheet metalwork; Meters: electric, pocket, portable, panelboard, etc.; Energy measuring equipment, electrical; Sheet metalwork
CEO: Lavon Winkler
*Ch Bd: R F Waldrop II
*CFO: James A Fitts
VP: Eric M Kirchbaum
*VP: W Dru Rachaner
*VP: John Siglock
Genl Mgr: Kris Johnson
Dir IT: Jonathen Hansen
Software D: Ray Grauberger
*VP Mfg: Shelley Jaderborg
Plnt Mgr: Ignacio Castro

D-U-N-S 07-526-0034
MILBANK TWEED HADLEY & MCCLOY LLP
28 Liberty St Fl 47, New York, NY 10005-1413
Tel (212) 530-5000 *Founded/Ownrshp* 1999
Sales 125.6MM^E *EMP* 900
SIC 8111 General practice law office; General practice law office
Pt: Trayton Davis
*Pt: Matthew S Barr
*Pt: Elizabeth A Besio
*Pt: Bruce Kale
CFO: Steven M Gacsik
CFO: Steven M Gamcsic
Ex VP: Ronald Freydberg
Dir Bus: Robert Gero
Mng Dir: Mel M Iergut
Plng Mgr: James Martin
IT Man: Heather Flaherty

D-U-N-S 08-164-5319
MILBAR HYDRO-TEST INC
651 Aero Dr, Shreveport, LA 71107-6943
Tel (318) 227-8210 *Founded/Ownrshp* 1977
Sales 26.1MM^E *EMP* 65
SIC 1389 Pipe testing, oil field service; Pipe testing, oil field service
Pr: Jerry L Acree
VP: Wayne May
*VP: J Stanton Woods
CTO: Layton Bryant

D-U-N-S 05-046-7810
MILBERG FACTORS INC
99 Park Ave Fl 21, New York, NY 10016-1589
Tel (212) 697-4027 *Founded/Ownrshp* 1969
Sales NA *EMP* 65^E
SIC 6153 Purchasers of accounts receivable & commercial paper
Ch Bd: Leonard L Milberg
Pr: David J Milberg
Treas: Stephen Murphy
Sr VP: Frank Derita
Sr VP: Barry Machowsky
Sr VP: Daniel R Milberg
Sr VP: James O'Lear
Sr VP: William A Zisfein
Sr VP: William Zisfein
VP: Neil R Desai
VP: Mark Equinda
VP: Paul Pagano
VP: David Reza
VP: Jeffrey S Sesko

D-U-N-S 06-825-7252
MILBERG LLP
1 Penn Plz Fl 49, New York, NY 10119-0033
Tel (212) 946-9442 *Founded/Ownrshp* 1967
Sales 33.4MM^E *EMP* 227
SIC 8111 General practice attorney, lawyer; Securities law; Antitrust & trade regulation law; Corporate, partnership & business law; General practice attorney, lawyer; Securities law; Antitrust & trade regulation law; Corporate, partnership & business law
Pt: Brad Friedman
Pt: Sanford P Dumain
Pt: Matt Gluck
Pt: Michael Spencer
Pt: Ariana Tadler
COO: Olivia Baldari
Ofcr: Paul H McVoy
Ofcr: Kathy Strozza
Ex Dir: Lois Silverman
Off Mgr: Billie Booth
CIO: Barry Weprin

D-U-N-S 00-656-5634
MILBOCKER AND SONS INC
1256 29th St, Allegan, MI 49010-9702
Tel (269) 673-2195 *Founded/Ownrshp* 1959
Sales 21.1MM^E *EMP* 80
Accts Yeo & Yeo Pc Kalamazoo Mich
SIC 1611 1629 1622 Grading; Drainage system construction; Bridge construction; Grading; Drainage system construction; Bridge construction
Pr: Bernard Milbocker
*Treas: Christopher Thomas
*VP: Scott Milbocker

D-U-N-S 15-735-4051
■ MILCARE INC
(*Suby of* HERMAN MILLER INC) ★
855 E Main Ave, Zeeland, MI 49464-1366
Tel (616) 654-8000 *Founded/Ownrshp* 1985
Sales 27.9MM^E *EMP* 486
SIC 2531 Public building & related furniture; Public building & related furniture
Pr: David Reid
VP: Tom Livengood

D-U-N-S 02-145-2313 IMP/EXP
MILCO INDUSTRIES INC
550 E 5th St, Bloomsburg, PA 17815-2300
Tel (570) 784-0400 Founded/Ownrshp 1979
Sales 72.5MM^E EMP 220
Accts Weisermazars Llp Edison Nj
SIC 2341 2258 2339 2384 2262 Nightgowns & negligees: women's & children's; Tricot fabrics; Women's & misses' outerwear; Maternity clothing; Robes & dressing gowns; Finishing plants, manmade fiber & silk fabrics; Nightgowns & negligees: women's & children's; Tricot fabrics; Women's & misses' outerwear; Maternity clothing; Robes & dressing gowns; Finishing plants, manmade fiber & silk fabrics
Ch: Norman Belmonte
*CFO: Anthony J Peluso
IT Man: David Mosteller
Sls&Mrk Ex: Joe Iurato

D-U-N-S 93-233-7363
MILCON CONSTRUCTION CORP
142 Dale St, West Babylon, NY 11704-1123
Tel (631) 756-9530 Founded/Ownrshp 1994
Sales 22.0MM^E EMP 220
SIC 1731 1761 Environmental system control installation; Roofing, siding & sheet metal work; Environmental system control installation; Roofing, siding & sheet metal work
Ch Bd: Scott Miller

MILE BLUFF MEDICAL CENTER
See HESS MEMORIAL HOSPITAL INC

D-U-N-S 60-945-2792
MILE DEVELOPMENT CORP
ROCKAWAY BEACH BOULEVARD CNSTR
200 Robbins Ln Unit D1, Jericho, NY 11753-2341
Tel (516) 935-5555 Founded/Ownrshp 1986
Sales 45.7MM^E EMP 125^E
SIC 1521 1542 8711 New construction, single-family houses; Commercial & office building, new construction; Building construction consultant; New construction, single-family houses; Commercial & office building, new construction; Building construction consultant
Ch Bd: Leslie A Lerner
VP: Michael Adler
*VP: Michael Dubb
VP: Christopher Gonzalez
VP: Kathy Sheck
Exec: Daniel Braff

MILE HI ACURA
See BRAMAN COLORADO IMPORTS INC

D-U-N-S 96-599-2501 IMP
MILE HI BAKERY INC
MILE HI FOODS
4770 E 51st Ave, Denver, CO 80216-3112
Tel (303) 399-6066 Founded/Ownrshp 2010
Sales 28.4MM^E EMP 55
SIC 5149 Bakery products
Pr: Tony Taddonio
*CFO: Stan Holzwart
*VP: Kristy Taddonio

MILE HI FOODS
See MILE HI BAKERY INC

D-U-N-S 03-044-3691 IMP
MILE HI FOODS CO
4701 E 50th Ave, Denver, CO 80216-3106
Tel (303) 399-6066 Founded/Ownrshp 1974
Sales 37.2MM^E EMP 180
SIC 4226 5087 Special warehousing & storage; Restaurant supplies; Special warehousing & storage; Restaurant supplies
Pr: Tony M Taddonio
VP: John Borowski
Trfc Dir: Ken Wagner

MILE HI FROZEN FOODS
See MILE HI SPECIALTY FOODS

D-U-N-S 06-961-8363
MILE HI SPECIALTY FOODS
MILE HI FROZEN FOODS
4770 E 51st Ave, Denver, CO 80216-3112
Tel (303) 399-6066 Founded/Ownrshp 2010
Sales 132.8MM^E EMP 130^E
SIC 5141 Food brokers; Food brokers
Pr: Tony M Taddonio
IT Man: Bob Dickerson
IT Man: Rick Julch

D-U-N-S 13-023-2163
MILE HI SPECIALTY FOODS INC
4701 E 50th Ave Ste 1, Denver, CO 80216-3106
Tel (303) 270-9883 Founded/Ownrshp 1998
Sales 35.1MM^E EMP 40
SIC 5141 Food brokers
Pr: Tony M Taddonio

MILE HI VALET SERVICE
See CIRI - STROUP INC

D-U-N-S 16-935-3724
MILE HIGH CONTRACTING INC
5568 S 300 W, Salt Lake City, UT 84107-5802
Tel (801) 916-7556 Founded/Ownrshp 1998
Sales 22.2MM^E EMP 70
SIC 5063 Telephone & telegraph wire & cable
Pr: Deric Shelley

D-U-N-S 00-743-4608 IMP/EXP
MILE HIGH EQUIPMENT LLC
ICE-O-MATIC
(Suby of SCOTSMAN INDUSTRIES INC) ★
11100 E 45th Ave, Denver, CO 80239-3029
Tel (303) 576-2940 Founded/Ownrshp 2012
Sales 135.5MM^E EMP 260
SIC 3585 Ice making machinery; Ice boxes, industrial; Ice making machinery; Ice boxes, industrial
Pr: George Parsons
CFO: Meg Collins
VP: Brian Bristol
CIO: Robert Crane
Mktg Dir: Scott Deshetler

Manager: David Swille
Sales Asso: Anna Howe

MILE HIGH GREYHOUND PARK
See MILE HIGH KENNEL CLUB INC

D-U-N-S 00-691-5813
MILE HIGH KENNEL CLUB INC
MILE HIGH GREYHOUND PARK
(Suby of MILE HIGH RACING AND ENTERTAINMENT) ★
6200 Dahlia St, Commerce City, CO 80022-3130
Tel (303) 751-5918 Founded/Ownrshp 1990
Sales 4.4MM^E EMP 300^E
SIC 7948 Dog race track operation; Dog race track operation
Pr: Bruce Fraser

D-U-N-S 55-643-9297
MILE HIGH RACING AND ENTERTAINMENT
WEMBLEY USA
(Suby of ROCKY MOUNTAIN POSTTIME) ★
26000 E Quincy Ave, Aurora, CO 80016-2026
Tel (303) 699-5724 Founded/Ownrshp 1990
Sales 6.8MM^E EMP 320^E
SIC 7948 Dog race track operation; Dog race track operation
VP: Bruce Faraser
COO: Bruce Seymour
CTO: Nonnie Pedraza

D-U-N-S 06-407-1343
MILE HIGH UNITED WAY INC
711 Park Ave W, Denver, CO 80205-2891
Tel (303) 433-8383 Founded/Ownrshp 1887
Sales 39.0MM EMP 165
Accts Eks&H Llp Denver Colorado
SIC 8399 United Fund councils; United Fund councils
CEO: Christine Benero
*COO: Ed Blair
*CFO: Leslie Hannon
VP: Richard Audsley
VP: Maria Cordero
VP: Jacqueline Hall
Prgrm Mgr: Marisol Cruz
Opers Mgr: Fermin Avila
Mktg Dir: Laura Esterly

MILE ONE
See ATLANTIC AUTOMOTIVE CORP

D-U-N-S 05-395-2792 IMP/EXP
■ **MILE ONE TIRE INC**
MR TIRE AUTO SERVICE CENTERS
(Suby of MONRO MUFFLER BRAKE INC) ★
1225 Bengies Rd Ste B, Baltimore, MD 21220-1928
Tel (410) 242-9187 Founded/Ownrshp 2004
Sales 64.9MM^E EMP 300
SIC 5531 7538 Automotive tires; General automotive repair shops; Automotive tires; General automotive repair shops
Pr: Fredric Tomarchio
*VP: Joseph Tomarchio Jr

MILE SQUARE BUS TRANSPORTATION
See MILE SQUARE TRANSPORTATION INC

D-U-N-S 78-822-1562
MILE SQUARE TRANSPORTATION INC
MILE SQUARE BUS TRANSPORTATION
15 Worth St, Yonkers, NY 10701-5507
Tel (914) 423-7777 Founded/Ownrshp 1989
Sales 20.1MM^E EMP 420
SIC 4151 School buses; School buses
Pr: Horacio Rodriguez
*VP: Joanne Rodriguez

D-U-N-S 78-533-0981 IMP
MILE-HI DR LLC
DEEP ROCK WATER COMPANY
2640 California St, Denver, CO 80205-2932
Tel (303) 292-2020 Founded/Ownrshp 2011
Sales 38.3MM^E EMP 185
SIC 5963 Bottled water delivery; Bottled water delivery
CEO: Tom Schwein
Ex VP: Jon Wittnebel
VP: Craig Dodd

D-U-N-S 18-690-5084 IMP
MILEGON LLC
MEC NORTHWEST
1140 Nw 3rd Ave, Canby, OR 97013-3441
Tel (503) 263-7300 Founded/Ownrshp 1999
Sales 69.6MM^E EMP 100
SIC 5065 Electronic parts & equipment; Electronic parts & equipment
CEO: P Michael Stoehr
Pr: Michael Stoehr
CFO: Jim Anzia
Genl Mgr: Rick McClain
Opers Mgr: Pam Kimbrough
Ql Cn Mgr: Jack Tanz
Sales Asso: Christine Schurpf

MILEN
See P2F HOLDINGS

D-U-N-S 13-007-5179
MILENDER WHITE CONSTRUCTION CO
MWCC
12655 W 54th Dr, Arvada, CO 80002-1343
Tel (303) 216-0420 Founded/Ownrshp 1997
Sales 73.6MM^E EMP 110^E
Accts Bauerle And Company Pc Den
SIC 1542 1522 Nonresidential construction; Residential construction; Nonresidential construction; Residential construction
Pr: Bryon White
Pr: Mike Milender
Sr VP: Shane Fobes
VP: Darren Hinton
VP: Adam Mack
VP: John Milender
VP: Tom Warchol
Area Mgr: Kevin Brattain
Sfty Dirs: Mike Falls
Ql Cn Mgr: Ryan Castillo
Snr PM: Trent Asbury

Board of Directors: Brian Shelton

D-U-N-S 07-828-5491
MILES & STOCKBRIDGE PC
100 Light St Fl 5, Baltimore, MD 21202-1153
Tel (410) 385-3671 Founded/Ownrshp 1993
Sales 97.5MM^E EMP 600
SIC 8111 General practice attorney, lawyer; General practice attorney, lawyer
Ch: John Frisch
*Pr: John Murray
COO: Katherine Hill
VP: Patrick Smith
Prin: David B Eberhardt
Adm Dir: William Psillas
Off Admin: Mari B Moulton
CIO: Ken Adams
Counsel: Katherine Lawler
Counsel: Adam Treiber

D-U-N-S 87-875-4043
MILES AUTOMOTIVE INC
CROWN TOYOTA
3400 Iowa St, Lawrence, KS 66046
Tel (785) 843-7700 Founded/Ownrshp 1994
Sales 25.8MM^E EMP 70
SIC 5511 Automobiles, new & used; Automobiles, new & used
Pr: Miles E Schnaer
Sls Mgr: John Laddusaw

D-U-N-S 07-058-8871 IMP
MILES CHEMICAL CO INC
12801 Rangoon St, Arleta, CA 91331-4322
Tel (818) 635-5538 Founded/Ownrshp 1996
Sales 36.5MM EMP 40^E
Accts W Bryan George Certified Pub
SIC 5169 Chemicals & allied products; Chemicals & allied products
Pr: Anthony Miles
*VP: Ray Sanchez
Exec: Jack Hardy
Exec: Gary Staszak
Genl Mgr: Mark Galser
Genl Mgr: Tony Rossi
Sales Asso: Steve Johnson

D-U-N-S 05-415-5601
MILES CHEVROLET INC
MILES NISSAN
150 W Pershing Rd, Decatur, IL 62526-3243
Tel (217) 877-4440 Founded/Ownrshp 1979
Sales 70.5MM^E EMP 170
SIC 5511 Automobiles, new & used; Automobiles, new & used
Pr: Cecil Van Tuyl
Chf Mktg O: Jay Hartman
Genl Mgr: Pat Dawson
Dir IT: Tim Fryman
Mktg Dir: Jim McNeely
Sls Mgr: Rob Evans
Sls Mgr: Todd Rogers
Sls Mgr: Scott Turner
Sales Asso: Justin Harriman

MILES CITY DAILY STAR
See STAR PRINTING CO

D-U-N-S 07-546-0758
MILES COLLEGE
5500 Myron Massey Blvd, Fairfield, AL 35064-2697
Tel (205) 929-1000 Founded/Ownrshp 1898
Sales 32.1MM EMP 300
Accts The Wesley Peachtree Group Cpa
SIC 8221 Colleges universities & professional schools; Colleges universities & professional schools
Pr: Dr George T French Jr
Recvr: Justin Brown
CFO: Diana Knighton
VP: Josna Mishra
Exec: Natasha Rogers
*Off Mgr: Shirley Epps
Store Mgr: Maxine Benns
Off Admin: Denae Beasley
Pr Dir: Ricky Lee
Psych: Deleon Francher

D-U-N-S 06-028-8016
MILES COMMUNITY COLLEGE (MT)
(Suby of MONTANA UNIVERSITY SYSTEM) ★
2715 Dickinson St, Miles City, MT 59301-4799
Tel (406) 874-6100 Founded/Ownrshp 1939
Sales 21.6MM^E EMP 145
Accts Independent
SIC 8222 Community college
Pr: Stefani Hicswa
Mktg Mgr: Sandy Myers

D-U-N-S 17-490-4516
MILES EXCAVATING INC
15063 State Ave, Basehor, KS 66007-3024
Tel (913) 724-1934 Founded/Ownrshp 1985
Sales 27.2MM EMP 180
Accts Bateson & Widerholt Pc North
SIC 1794 1611 1771 Excavation work; General contractor, highway & street construction; Concrete work; Excavation work; General contractor, highway & street construction; Concrete work
Pr: Steve M Miles
*Sec: Darla Miles
Sfty Dirs: David Redlin

D-U-N-S 06-832-2858
MILES FARM SUPPLY LLC
AGRI-MART
2760 Keller Rd, Owensboro, KY 42301-9600
Tel (270) 926-2420 Founded/Ownrshp 1970
Sales 66.4MM^E EMP 450
SIC 5261 5191 5083 Fertilizer; Farm supplies; Chemicals, agricultural; Fertilizer & fertilizer materials; Seeds: field, garden & flower; Agricultural machinery & equipment; Fertilizer; Farm supplies; Chemicals, agricultural; Fertilizer & fertilizer materials; Seeds: field, garden & flower; Agricultural machinery & equipment

D-U-N-S 00-905-9395 IMP
MILES FIBERGLASS & COMPOSITES INC
8855 Se Otty Rd, Happy Valley, OR 97086-2327
Tel (503) 775-7755 Founded/Ownrshp 1963
Sales 72.8MM^E EMP 200
SIC 3089 3714 Plastic & fiberglass tanks; Plastic hardware & building products; Plastic processing; Motor vehicle parts & accessories; Plastic & fiberglass tanks; Plastic processing; Motor vehicle parts & accessories
Pr: Lori Miles Luchak
*COO: Craig Hinkle
*CFO: Joe Luchak
*VP: Lori Luchak
Opers Mgr: Bob Kelso

MILES FOLDING BOX CO DIV
See SOBEL CORRUGATED CONTAINERS INC

D-U-N-S 12-135-4435
MILES HEALTH CARE INC
COVES EDGE
(Suby of LINCOLNHEALTH GROUP) ★
35 Miles St, Damariscotta, ME 04543-4047
Tel (207) 563-1234 Founded/Ownrshp 1981
Sales 1.0MMM EMP 800
SIC 8741 Hospital management; Nursing & personal care facility management; Hospital management; Nursing & personal care facility management
CEO: James Donavan
Mktg Dir: Janet Lee

MILES JENNINGS INDUSTRIAL SUP
See DILLON SUPPLY CO

MILES LUMBER
See N MILES JOE & SONS INC

D-U-N-S 07-948-0707
MILES MARINE INC
(Suby of VIGOR INDUSTRIAL LLC) ★
5555 N Channel Ave, Portland, OR 97217-7655
Tel (503) 247-1777 Founded/Ownrshp 2010
Sales 156.7MM^E EMP 1,110
SIC 3731 Shipbuilding & repairing; Combat vessels, building & repairing; Military ships, building & repairing; Commercial cargo ships, building & repairing; Shipbuilding & repairing; Combat vessels, building & repairing; Military ships, building & repairing; Commercial cargo ships, building & repairing
Pr: Frank J Foti
*COO: David R Whitcomb
*CFO: Lon V Leneve
*Sec: Julie Skirvin

D-U-N-S 03-273-1135 IMP
MILES MEDIA GROUP INC
SEE MAGAZINES
6751 Prof Pkwy W Ste 200, Sarasota, FL 34240
Tel (941) 342-2300 Founded/Ownrshp 1990
Sales 27.8MM^E EMP 135
SIC 2721 Magazines: publishing only, not printed on site; Statistical reports (periodicals): publishing only; Magazines: publishing only, not printed on site; Statistical reports (periodicals): publishing only
CEO: Roger W Miles
CFO: Dianne Gates
*CFO: Sandra Pioterek
*VP: Nate Huff
*VP: Jay Salyers
VP: Paul Winkle
Comm Dir: Camron Reid
Prgrm Mgr: Kerri Rebresh
Web Dev: Brian Anderson
Prd Mgr: Mike Tompkins
Advt Mgr: Samantha Davis

D-U-N-S 78-292-9249
MILES MEDIA GROUP LLLP
6751 Prof Pkwy W Ste 200, Sarasota, FL 34240
Tel (941) 342-2300 Founded/Ownrshp 1990
Sales 40.0MM EMP 170
SIC 8742 Marketing consulting services; Marketing consulting services
CFO: Dianne Gates
COO: David Burgess
Ofcr: Jim Praschak
VP: Nate Huff
VP: Doug Luciani
VP: Ben Miles
VP: Jay Salyers
VP: John Vitolo
IT Man: Kimberly Keller
Web Dev: Melissa Anderson
S&M/VP: Carrie Koenig

D-U-N-S 07-747-2652
MILES MEMORIAL HOSPITAL
(Suby of COVES EDGE) ★
35 Miles St, Damariscotta, ME 04543-4047
Tel (207) 563-1234 Founded/Ownrshp 1929
Sales 56.4MM EMP 800
Accts Mainehealth Portland Me
SIC 8062 General medical & surgical hospitals; General medical & surgical hospitals
CEO: James W Donovan
*Ch Bd: Peter Mundy
*CFO: Wayne Printy
*Treas: Robert Conn
VP: Judith McGuirre
IT Man: Bruce Hall

MILES NISSAN
See MILES CHEVROLET INC

D-U-N-S 96-167-8013
MILES RESOURCES LLC
400 Valley Ave Ne, Puyallup, WA 98372-2516
Tel (253) 383-3585 Founded/Ownrshp 2008
Sales 26.2MM^E EMP 200
SIC 1771 1611 2951 Blacktop (asphalt) work; Highway & street construction; Asphalt & asphaltic paving mixtures (not from refineries); Blacktop (asphalt) work; Highway & street construction; Asphalt & asphaltic paving mixtures (not from refineries)
*Pr: Cedric Brooks
*CFO: Bradley Deakins
IT Man: Angela Reis

Sfty Dirs: Doug Stiffarm
Snr Mgr: Mike Tollkuehn

D-U-N-S 00-948-0278
MILES SAND & GRAVEL CO
CONCRETE NOR'WEST DIVISION
400 Valley Ave Ne, Puyallup, WA 98372-2516
Tel (253) 833-3705 *Founded/Ownrshp* 1964
Sales 95.0MM^E *EMP* 300
SIC 3273 5032 Ready-mixed concrete; Sand, construction; Gravel; Ready-mixed concrete; Sand, construction; Gravel
Pr: Walter Miles
Pr: Gerard Pearson
**VP:* Lisa Kittilsby
**VP:* Frank Miles
Genl Mgr: Jerry Trudeau
Dir IT: Jarud Pierson
Plnt Mgr: Lars Ejde
Plnt Mgr: Richard North
Sls Mgr: Jeff Kushmaul
Sls Mgr: Scott Woodard

D-U-N-S 01-909-0273 IMP
MILES SUPPLY CO INC
143 Boynton St, Barre, VT 05641-4905
Tel (802) 476-3963 *Founded/Ownrshp* 1954
Sales 22.5MM^E *EMP* 34^E
SIC 5085 Abrasives; Diamonds, industrial: natural, crude
Pr: Adam C Martin
**Treas:* Doris Martin
VP: Kevin Spalding
Exec: Rob Donahue
**Prin:* Charles Martin
**Prin:* Sonia Spalding
Sls Mgr: Tom Meyer
Sales Asso: Larry Bessinger
Sales Asso: Eric Chaloux

D-U-N-S 80-462-7250
MILES TECHNOLOGIES INC
300 W Route 38 Ste 103, Moorestown, NJ 08057-3233
Tel (856) 439-0999 *Founded/Ownrshp* 1997
Sales 29.3MM^E *EMP* 150
SIC 7379 Computer related consulting services
CEO: Chris Miles
COO: John Bialous
**COO:* John Biolous
Off Mgr: Martha Richardson
CIO: Vaughn Johnson
Software D: Luquan Li
Software D: Suhit Pradhan
Software D: Pratic Sharma
Software D: Josh Tate
Sftwr Eng: Pinky Panjwani
Sftwr Eng: Pashupati Shrestha

D-U-N-S 09-216-2130
MILES-MCCLELLAN CONSTRUCTION CO INC
2100 Builders Pl, Columbus, OH 43204-4885
Tel (614) 487-7744 *Founded/Ownrshp* 1978
Sales 36.1MM^E *EMP* 100
SIC 1542 1541 Commercial & office building, new construction; Commercial & office buildings, renovation & repair; Industrial buildings, new construction; Renovation, remodeling & repairs: industrial buildings; Commercial & office building, new construction; Commercial & office buildings, renovation & repair; Industrial buildings, new construction; Renovation, remodeling & repairs: industrial buildings
CEO: Lonnie Miles
**Pr:* Matthew Q McClellan
**Sec:* Terry McClellan
**VP:* Tim McClellan
Opers Mgr: Steven Parsons
Sales Asso: David Berendt
Snr PM: Aubrey Harless
Snr PM: D J Hegarty
Snr Mgr: Steve Sausman

D-U-N-S 05-969-5080 IMP
MILESTEK CORP
(*Suby of* L-COM DATA PRODUCTS) ★
1506 Interstate 35 W, Denton, TX 76207-2402
Tel (940) 484-9400 *Founded/Ownrshp* 2013
Sales 32.5MM^E *EMP* 66^E
SIC 5065 Electronic parts & equipment
Pr: David B McCarthy
**COO:* Jake Ring
Prgrm Mgr: Robert Perez
Opers Mgr: Mike Greenhill
Prd Mgr: Ian Kincade
Sales Exec: Nick Engberg
Mktg Dir: Michel Guidry
Sls Mgr: Tammy Smith

D-U-N-S 08-611-5946 IMP
MILESTONE AV TECHNOLOGIES LLC
CHIEF
(*Suby of* PRITZKER GROUP- CHICAGO LLC) ★
6436 City West Pkwy, Eden Prairie, MN 55344-3245
Tel (952) 236-7231 *Founded/Ownrshp* 2013
Sales 140.7MM^E *EMP* 427
SIC 3669 Intercommunication systems, electric; Intercommunication systems, electric
Pr: Scott Gill
**CFO:* Troy Pfeiffer
VP: Keith T Pribyl
Comm Man: Katie Sillanpa
Genl Mgr: Matthew Teevan
Dir IT: Josh Barber
Prd Mgr: Tony Yerian
Ql Cn Mgr: Lakey He
Ql Cn Mgr: River Lee
Ql Cn Mgr: East Qi
Ql Cn Mgr: Luke Yin

D-U-N-S 07-499-2280
MILESTONE CENTERS INC
600 Ross Ave, Pittsburgh, PA 15221-2126
Tel (412) 243-3400 *Founded/Ownrshp* 1969
Sales 20.2MM^E *EMP* 350
Accts Maher Duessel Cpa S Pittsburg
SIC 8093 Mental health clinic, outpatient; Mental health clinic, outpatient
CEO: Barbara Conniff
**Pr:* Deborah Walrath
**COO:* Ken Wood
**CFO:* Gary Bell
**Treas:* Malcolm Blount
**VP:* Charles W Wise

D-U-N-S 05-092-6458
MILESTONE COMMUNITY BUILDERS LLC (TX)
9111 Jollyville Rd # 111, Austin, TX 78759-7411
Tel (512) 686-4986 *Founded/Ownrshp* 2009
Sales 23.8MM^E *EMP* 18^E
SIC 6552 1521 Subdividers & developers; Single-family housing construction; General remodeling, single-family houses
CEO: Garrett Martin
VP Opers: James Dimanoff

D-U-N-S 00-604-8912
MILESTONE CONTRACTORS LP
5950 S Belmont St, Indianapolis, IN 46217-9757
Tel (317) 788-6885 *Founded/Ownrshp* 1994
Sales 187.8MM^E *EMP* 300
SIC 1611 Highway & street paving contractor; Surfacing & paving; Highway & street paving contractor; Surfacing & paving
Pt: Ted Lucas
VP: Jim Delk
VP: Ralph Simpson
QA Dir: David Johnson
VP Opers: John Waechter
Trfc Dir: Bob Scaggs
Trfc Dir: Kathy Tanner
Mtls Mgr: Ron Rapp
Plnt Mgr: Ron Terrel
Prd Mgr: Mark McGaughey
Ql Cn Mgr: Brad Cruea

D-U-N-S 55-659-6039
■ **MILESTONE HEALTHCARE INC**
MILESTONE STAFFING SERVICE
(*Suby of* MANOR CARE INC) ★
2435 N Central Expy # 1420, Richardson, TX 75080-2791
Tel (800) 926-2388 *Founded/Ownrshp* 1997
Sales 12.6MM^E *EMP* 400
SIC 8049 Physical therapist; Physical therapist
Pr: Roger Jenkins
Pgrm Dir: Sue Blackburn

D-U-N-S 01-022-9854
MILESTONE INC
4060 Mcfarland Rd, Loves Park, IL 61111-4402
Tel (815) 654-6100 *Founded/Ownrshp* 1971
Sales 26.7MM *EMP* 570
Accts Wipfli Llp Rockford Illinois
SIC 8052 8361 Home for the mentally retarded, with health care; Home for the mentally handicapped; Home for the mentally retarded, with health care; Home for the mentally handicapped
CEO: Shawn Way
**CFO:* Hugh Lippitt
**VP:* Su Gilbert

D-U-N-S 82-745-1162
MILESTONE MANAGEMENTS LLC
5429 Lyndon B Johnson Fwy # 800, Dallas, TX 75240-2607
Tel (214) 561-1200 *Founded/Ownrshp* 2002
Sales 26.0MM^E *EMP* 1,100
SIC 6513 Apartment building operators; Apartment building operators
Pr: John B Bartling
**Pr:* Steve T Lamberti
**CFO:* Ryan Newberry
**CFO:* Christopher A Phillips
**Ch:* David B Deniger
**VP:* Monica Blankenship
**VP:* Jeffrey L Sherman
Ex Dir: Robert Honstein
Rgnl Mgr: Robert Correa
Rgnl Mgr: Ellyn Hanger
Rgnl Mgr: Ginny Williams

D-U-N-S 78-394-1698
MILESTONE PARTNERS II LP
595 E Lancaster Ave Ste 3, Wayne, PA 19087-5115
Tel (610) 526-2700 *Founded/Ownrshp* 2005
Sales 58.7MM^E *EMP* 300
SIC 6799 Investors; Investors
Pt: W Scott Warren
**Pt:* Robert G Levine
CFO: Mark Martinelli
VP: Geoffrey B Veale

D-U-N-S 01-816-9727
MILESTONE PARTNERS MANAGEMENT CO LP
MARINER FINANCE
555 E Lancaster Ave, Radnor, PA 19087-5158
Tel (610) 526-2700 *Founded/Ownrshp* 1994
Sales 82.3MM^E *EMP* 300^E
SIC 6799 Investors; Investors
Pt: W Scott Warren
Pt: Robert G Levine
Pt: John P Shoemaker
Prin: Patrick Hanaraty

MILESTONE STAFFING SERVICE
See MILESTONE HEALTHCARE INC

D-U-N-S 00-520-2754
MILESTONE TECHNOLOGIES INC (CA)
3101 Skyway Ct, Fremont, CA 94539-5910
Tel (510) 651-2454 *Founded/Ownrshp* 1997
Sales 172.7MM^E *EMP* 900^E
SIC 7373 7374 Computer integrated systems design; Data processing & preparation; Computer integrated systems design; Data processing & preparation
CEO: Prem Chand
COO: Jim Glueck
CFO: James Schultz
VP: Gary Bilovesky
VP: Kristi H Ledwein
VP: Rob Morris
VP: Tony Silveira
VP: Tara Spencer
Netwrk Eng: Chris Tate
VP Mktg: Jim Andersen
Sls Dir: Aida Johnson

D-U-N-S 36-108-6684
■ **MILFORD ANESTHESIA ASSOCIATES LLC**
(*Suby of* EMCARE INC) ★
831 Boston Post Rd # 203, Milford, CT 06460-3536
Tel (203) 783-1831 *Founded/Ownrshp* 2010
Sales 52.8MM^E *EMP* 3,358^E
SIC 8011 Anesthesiologist
Off Mgr: Nancy Ferguson
Anesthlgy: Ko Chan
Anesthlgy: Abhijit Desai
Anesthlgy: Terence Gray
Anesthlgy: Brian Reilly
Anesthlgy: Hemantha Sunkara
Anesthlgy: Scott Switzer
Anesthlgy: Rajeev Verma
Anesthlgy: Dino Zacharakos

MILFORD BOARD OF EDUCATION
See MILFORD EXEMPTED VILLAGE SCHOOL DISTRICT

D-U-N-S 06-911-2089
MILFORD BOARD OF EDUCATION
MILFORD SCHOOL DISTRICT
906 Lakeview Ave, Milford, DE 19963-1732
Tel (302) 422-1600 *Founded/Ownrshp* 1969
Sales 44.0MM *EMP* 450
SIC 8211 Public elementary & secondary schools; Public elementary & secondary schools
Pr: Marvin Schelhouse
Bd of Dir: Eugene Rust

D-U-N-S 19-309-0883
MILFORD CITY PUBLIC SCHOOLS
70 W River St, Milford, CT 06460-3317
Tel (203) 783-3400 *Founded/Ownrshp* 2000
Sales 37.5MM^E *EMP* 919
SIC 8211 9411 Public elementary & secondary schools; Administration of educational programs; Public elementary & secondary schools; Administration of educational programs
COO: Judy Jameson
COO: Lisa Streit
Bd of Dir: Suzanne Dibiase
Bd of Dir: Susan Glennon
Bd of Dir: Christopher Saley
Bd of Dir: Earl Whiskeyman
Pr Dir: Lori Hart

D-U-N-S 10-141-3524 IMP
MILFORD ENTERPRISES INC
450 Commerce Dr, Quakertown, PA 18951-3729
Tel (215) 538-2778 *Founded/Ownrshp* 1990
Sales 22.4MM^E *EMP* 100
Accts Geiger & Associates Allentown
SIC 2541 Store fixtures, wood; Store & office display cases & fixtures
Pr: Gary L Fetterman
Pr: Andrew Pierce
COO: Gary Young
**VP:* Jeffrey Adkins
**VP:* James F Dougherty
**VP:* Randall Hrabina
Plnt Mgr: Mike Hall
Sls Dir: Sal Gattuso

D-U-N-S 09-650-9641
MILFORD EXEMPTED VILLAGE SCHOOL DISTRICT
MILFORD BOARD OF EDUCATION
777 Garfield Ave, Milford, OH 45150-1607
Tel (513) 576-4175 *Founded/Ownrshp* 1900
Sales 54.7MM^E *EMP* 1,000^E
Accts Plattenburg & Associates Inc
SIC 8211 Public elementary & secondary schools; High school, junior or senior; Elementary school; Public elementary & secondary schools; High school, junior or senior; Elementary school
DP Exec: Vickie Parker
Dir IT: Sandy Soucek
Pr Dir: Meg Krascok

MILFORD FERTILIZER
See GROWMARK FS LLC

D-U-N-S 07-211-9241
MILFORD HOSPITAL INC
300 Seaside Ave, Milford, CT 06460-4600
Tel (203) 876-4000 *Founded/Ownrshp* 1920
Sales 63.5MM *EMP* 900
SIC 8062 General medical & surgical hospitals; General medical & surgical hospitals
Pr: Paul E Moss
COO: David Stahelski
Ofcr: George Poole
VP: Joan Demaio
**VP:* Linda Evanko
VP: John Oneil
**VP:* Joseph Pelaccia
**VP:* Laura Smith
VP: David Staaglski
Exec: Jeffrey Komornik
Dir Rad: Debra Mauriello

D-U-N-S 04-581-4365 IMP
MILFORD MANUFACTURING SERVICES LLC
4 Business Way, Hopedale, MA 01747-1540
Tel (508) 478-8544 *Founded/Ownrshp* 2002
Sales 21.7MM^E *EMP* 100
SIC 3672 7373 3577 3357 Printed circuit boards; Computer integrated systems design; Computer peripheral equipment; Nonferrous wiredrawing & insulating

MILFORD MEMORIAL HOSPITAL
See KENT GENERAL HOSPITAL INC

MILFORD PIPE AND SUPPLY
See MPS ENTERPRISES INC

D-U-N-S 07-324-7413
MILFORD PLAZA ASSOCIATES LLC
MILFORD PLAZA HOTEL
335 Madison Ave Ste 1500, New York, NY 10017-4611
Tel (212) 708-0800 *Founded/Ownrshp* 2010
Sales 9.8MM^E *EMP* 400
SIC 7011 Hotels; Hotels

MILFORD PLAZA HOTEL
See MILFORD PLAZA ASSOCIATES LLC

MILFORD PROPANE
See E OSTERMAN GAS SERVICE INC

D-U-N-S 13-502-0006
MILFORD PUBLIC SCHOOLS
31 W Fountain St, Milford, MA 01757-4027
Tel (508) 478-1101 *Founded/Ownrshp* 1780
Sales 7.7MM^E *EMP* 393
SIC 8211 Elementary school; High school, junior or senior

D-U-N-S 04-868-9637
MILFORD REGIONAL HEALTHCARE FOUNDATION INC
14 Prospect St, Milford, MA 01757-3003
Tel (508) 473-1190 *Founded/Ownrshp* 1984
Sales 187.7MM *EMP* 1,777^E
Accts Feeley & Driscoll Boston Ma
SIC 6733 8082 8011 Trusts; Visiting nurse service; Physicians' office, including specialists; Trusts; Visiting nurse service; Physicians' office, including specialists
CEO: Francis M Saba
**V Ch:* Harold Gould Jr
**Pr:* Edward J Kelly
**CFO:* Jeanne Lynskey
**Ch:* Roger Calarese
**Treas:* John Armstrong
Dir Rad: Brian Coolbaugh
CIO: Lawrence Fraize

D-U-N-S 07-534-6940
MILFORD REGIONAL MEDICAL CENTER INC
(*Suby of* MILFORD REGIONAL HEALTHCARE FOUNDATION INC) ★
14 Prospect St, Milford, MA 01757-3003
Tel (508) 473-1190 *Founded/Ownrshp* 1903
Sales 184.1MM *EMP* 1,159
SIC 8062 8082 General medical & surgical hospitals; Visiting nurse service; General medical & surgical hospitals; Visiting nurse service
CEO: Francis M Saba
**Pr:* Ed Kelly
**Treas:* Judge Francis J Larkin
VP: Linda Greason
VP: Sal Perla
Assoc Dir: Mary O'Neill
Assoc Dir: Mary Oneill
Dir Rx: Susan Otocki
Off Mgr: Nancy Macari
Telecom Mg: James Sullivan
IT Man: C Lyle

MILFORD SCHOOL DISTRICT
See MILFORD BOARD OF EDUCATION

D-U-N-S 04-024-1119
MILFORD SCHOOL DISTRICT
100 West St, Milford, NH 03055-4888
Tel (603) 673-2202 *Founded/Ownrshp* 1974
Sales 35.0MM *EMP* 412
SIC 8211 Public elementary & secondary schools; Public elementary & secondary schools
Dir IT: William Birch

D-U-N-S 07-979-9159
MILFORD SCHOOL DISTRICT
906 Lakeview Ave, Milford, DE 19963-1732
Tel (302) 422-1600 *Founded/Ownrshp* 2015
Sales 4.6MM^E *EMP* 319^E
SIC 8211 Public elementary & secondary schools
Bd of Dir: Mark Schanne

D-U-N-S 00-925-5068 IMP
■ **MILGARD MANUFACTURING INC**
MILGARD WINDOWS
(*Suby of* MASCO CORP) ★
1010 54th Ave E, Fife, WA 98424-2793
Tel (253) 922-2030 *Founded/Ownrshp* 2001
Sales 383.7MM^E *EMP* 2,037
SIC 3089 3442 Windows, plastic; Sash, door or window: metal; Windows, plastic; Sash, door or window: metal
Pr: Gary Gessel
**VP:* Kenneth Cole
VP: Beth Galliher-Ponce
**VP:* Lawrence Leaman
**VP:* David Maki
**VP:* Stephen Moore
**VP:* Mark Sturgis
QA Dir: Matt Boudrot
Mtls Mgr: Chad Boyd
Plnt Mgr: Scott Harcek
Ql Cn Mgr: Bradley Givens

MILGARD WINDOWS
See MILGARD MANUFACTURING INC

D-U-N-S 93-162-1270 IMP
MILIDAK USA INC
195 Bay 19th St 3, Brooklyn, NY 11214-4761
Tel (718) 965-2188 *Founded/Ownrshp* 1995
Sales 24.1MM^E *EMP* 325
SIC 5199 General merchandise, non-durable; General merchandise, non-durable
Ch: Steven Chen

D-U-N-S 06-110-8650 IMP
MILITARY AND COMMERCIAL FASTENERS CORP
11 Grumbacher Rd, York, PA 17406-8417
Tel (717) 767-6856 *Founded/Ownrshp* 1993
Sales 30.1MM^E *EMP* 70
SIC 5085 5072 3452 Fasteners, industrial: nuts, bolts, screws, etc.; Hardware; Bolts, nuts, rivets & washers; Fasteners, industrial: nuts, bolts, screws, etc.; Hardware; Bolts, nuts, rivets & washers
Pr: Craig Siewert
**Sec:* David Kin
**VP:* Ronald Kin
QA Dir: Audrey Hoff
IT Man: Michael Zambito
Opers Mgr: William Lighty
Ql Cn Mgr: Jason Siewert
Mktg Dir: Matthew Malkie

MILITARY AND VETERNS AFFAIRS
See HOLLIDAYSBURG VETERAN HOME

D-U-N-S 07-481-9798
MILITARY BENEFIT ASSOCIATION INC
14605 Avion Pkwy, Chantilly, VA 20151-1104
Tel (703) 968-6200 *Founded/Ownrshp* 1956
Sales 26.3MM *EMP* 2
Accts Homes Lowry Horn & Johnson
SIC 8621 6411 Health association; Insurance agents; Life insurance agents; Health association; Insurance agents; Life insurance agents
Pr: Roy L Gibson III
Off Mgr: Glenda Lee
Off Mgr: Judy Petrie

D-U-N-S 06-592-6917
MILITARY CAR SALES INC
INTERNATIONAL WARRANTY SVCS
175 Crossways Park Dr W, Woodbury, NY 11797-2002
Tel (516) 558-7556 *Founded/Ownrshp* 1967
Sales 21.4MM^E *EMP* 150
SIC 8741 Business management; Administrative management
Pr: David Goldring
Mng Dir: Neil Elliot
IT Man: Ralph Libby
Opers Mgr: Sue Lomangino

MILITARY COLLEGE OF SOUTH CARO
See CITADEL

D-U-N-S 13-195-5379
MILITARY CONSTRUCTION CORP
MIL-CON
6142 Lake Gray Blvd, Jacksonville, FL 32244-5895
Tel (904) 317-5601 *Founded/Ownrshp* 1984
Sales 33.3MM^E *EMP* 110
SIC 1542

D-U-N-S 96-910-8844
MILITARY DELI & BAKERY SERVICES INC
10600 N Trademark Pkwy, Rancho Cucamonga, CA 91730-5936
Tel (909) 373-1344 *Founded/Ownrshp* 1996
Sales 22.5MM^E *EMP* 1,000
SIC 5812 Commissary restaurant; Commissary restaurant
Pr: Timothy I Howard
**Ch:* Gunther Ditzel

MILITARY DEPARTMENT ARKANSAS
See ARKANSAS DEPARTMENT OF NATIONAL GUARD

D-U-N-S 80-748-1148
MILITARY DEPARTMENT CONNECTICUT
ADJUTANT GENERAL
(*Suby of* GOVERNORS OFFICE STATE OF CONNECTICUT) ★
360 Broad St, Hartford, CT 06105-3706
Tel (860) 524-4953 *Founded/Ownrshp* 1788
Sales NA *EMP* 5,000
SIC 9711 National security; ; National security;
Prin: Thad Martin
Store Dir: William Cugno

D-U-N-S 80-985-0050
MILITARY DEPARTMENT MISSISSIPPI
EXECUTIVE OFFC OF MISSISSIPPI
(*Suby of* EXECUTIVE OFFICE OF STATE OF MISSISSIPPI) ★
1410 Riverside Dr, Jackson, MS 39202-1271
Tel (601) 313-6209 *Founded/Ownrshp* 1817
Sales NA *EMP* 1,853
SIC 9711 ;
Pr: Harold Cross
Opers Supe: Kendrick Cager

D-U-N-S 80-888-3383
MILITARY DEPARTMENT WASHINGTON STATE
WASHINGTON NATIONAL GUARD
(*Suby of* EXECUTIVE OFFICE OF STATE OF WASHINGTON) ★
Bldg 1 Camp Murray, Tacoma, WA 98430-0001
Tel (253) 512-8000 *Founded/Ownrshp* 1895
Sales NA *EMP* 303^E
SIC 9711 ;

D-U-N-S 00-501-1544
MILITARY DIVISION OF STATE OF IDAHO
(*Suby of* EXECUTIVE OFFICE OF STATE OF IDAHO) ★
4040 W Guard St Bldg 600, Boise, ID 83705-5004
Tel (208) 422-5507 *Founded/Ownrshp* 1893
Sales NA *EMP* 3,681
SIC 9711 National security; ; National security;
Ofcr: David Dahle
Genl Mgr: Gary Sayler

D-U-N-S 80-988-8381
MILITARY NEVADA OFFICE OF
NEVADA NATIONAL GUARD
(*Suby of* EXECUTIVE OFFICE OF STATE OF NEVADA) ★
2460 Fairview Dr, Carson City, NV 89701-6807
Tel (775) 887-7302 *Founded/Ownrshp* 1864
Sales NA *EMP* 710
SIC 9711 National security; ; National security;
CEO: William Burks
CIO: Mike Lienert

D-U-N-S 78-885-5674
MILITARY ORDER OF PURPLE HEART SERVICE FOUNDATION INC
7008 Little River Tpke I, Annandale, VA 22003-3234
Tel (703) 256-6139 *Founded/Ownrshp* 1957
Sales 32.0MM *EMP* 6^E
Accts Raffa Pc Washington Dc
SIC 8641 Veterans' organization; Veterans' organization
Ex Dir: Richard Esau
COO: Rhea Kosar
IT Man: Stephen Ruckman

MILITARY PERISCOPE
See UCG INFORMATION SERVICES LLC

D-U-N-S 05-968-3727
MILITARY PERSONNEL SERVICES CORP
6066 Leesburg Pike # 900, Falls Church, VA 22041-2234
Tel (571) 481-4000 *Founded/Ownrshp* 1998
Sales NA *EMP* 1,550
SIC 9451 Employment agencies; Administration of veterans' affairs
Pr: Ross B Deblois
**COO:* Jonathan Tipa
**Treas:* Stanley Rubinstein
**VP:* Jeff Christi
**VP:* Duane Jahner
**VP:* Jackie Livingston
Prgrm Mgr: Julie Lofreddo
Prgrm Mgr: Myhre Lon
Rgnl Mgr: Jay Deutscher
Rgnl Mgr: Michele Harvard

D-U-N-S 07-998-1881
MILITARY RESTAURANT HOLDINGS LLC (TX)
7929 Brookriver Dr # 200, Dallas, TX 75247-4900
Tel (214) 353-3959 *Founded/Ownrshp* 2007
Sales 11.3MM^E *EMP* 700
SIC 5812 Fast-food restaurant, independent; Family restaurants

D-U-N-S 06-414-1518
MILITARY SALES & SERVICE CO
MSS
5301 S Westmoreland Rd, Dallas, TX 75237-1805
Tel (469) 221-4123 *Founded/Ownrshp* 1964
Sales 26.0MM^E *EMP* 750
SIC 7389 Brokers' services; Brokers' services
Pr: Roy M Barber Jr
**Ex VP:* Deryck Barber
**Ex VP:* Richard Krug
VP: David Krug
VP: Delores May
VP: Heather Taylor
Creative D: Darin Rowley
Rgnl Mgr: Stacy Butler
Rgnl Mgr: David Heath
Rgnl Mgr: Patti Klostermann
Rgnl Mgr: Robby Lewis

D-U-N-S 14-694-4855
■ **MILITARY SURFACE DEPLOYMENT & DISTRIBUTION COMMAND**
(SDDC)
(*Suby of* UNITED STATES DEPARTMENT OF THE ARMY) ★
200 Stovall St Fl 18, Alexandria, VA 22332-4013
Tel (703) 428-2753 *Founded/Ownrshp* 2015
Sales NA *EMP* 700^E
SIC 9711 Army;
Prin: Edna Lewis
Snr Mgr: Paul Denhup
Snr Mgr: Blair Duncan

D-U-N-S 01-173-6309
MILITARY WARRIORS SUPPORT FOUNDATION
2511 N Loop 1604 W, San Antonio, TX 78258-4633
Tel (210) 615-8973 *Founded/Ownrshp* 2008
Sales 43.1MM *EMP* 3
Accts Bdo Usa Llp San Antonio Tx
SIC 8641 Civic social & fraternal associations
Prin: Mouffa Nahhas

D-U-N-S 04-962-1519
MILK INDUSTRY MANAGEMENT CORP
BALFORD FARMS
4 Manhattan Dr, Burlington, NJ 08016-4120
Tel (609) 747-9542 *Founded/Ownrshp* 1969
Sales 222.6MM^E *EMP* 170
SIC 5143 Dairy products, except dried or canned; Milk & cream, fluid; Ice cream & ices; Dairy products, except dried or canned; Milk & cream, fluid; Ice cream & ices
Pr: Laurance Bowes
**Ch Bd:* George H Baldwin Sr
**Pr:* John F Baldwin
**CFO:* Robert Venafra
**Ex VP:* George H Baldwin Jr
Ex VP: Daniel Smith
Board of Directors: Marc N Levin, David Menard

D-U-N-S 60-810-5250
MILK PRODUCTS HOLDINGS (NORTH AMERICA) INC
(*Suby of* FONTERRA CO-OPERATIVE GROUP LIMITED)
9525 Bryn Mawr Ave, Rosemont, IL 60018-5249
Tel (847) 928-1600 *Founded/Ownrshp* 1987
Sales 28.9MM^E *EMP* 150
SIC 5143 2023 Dairy products, except dried or canned; Dry, condensed, evaporated dairy products; Dairy products, except dried or canned; Dry, condensed, evaporated dairy products
Pr: Martin Bates

D-U-N-S 05-973-4511
MILK PRODUCTS LLC
BORDEN DAIRY COMPANY
8750 N Central Expy # 400, Dallas, TX 75231-6436
Tel (214) 647-5717 *Founded/Ownrshp* 1997
Sales 26.1MM^E *EMP* 41^E
SIC 5143 Milk
Dir Surg: Laura Guevarra

D-U-N-S 11-571-5930 IMP/EXP
MILK SPECIALTIES CO
MSG
7500 Flying Cloud Dr # 500, Eden Prairie, MN 55344-3703
Tel (952) 942-7310 *Founded/Ownrshp* 1986
Sales 152.6MM^E *EMP* 250
SIC 2026 2834 5149 Prepared feeds; Feed supplements; Fermented & cultured milk products; Vitamin, nutrient & hematinic preparations for human use; Health foods
CEO: David Lenzmeier
COO: Brian Lundquist
Sr Cor Off: Garrett Dawes
VP: Paul Lombard
VP: Julian Price
CTO: Jeffrey Kegel
QA Dir: Amy Bolton
QA Dir: Dave Christel
QA Dir: Cheryl Jeske
Dir IT: Chuck Langdon
Opers Mgr: Tamara McDonnell

D-U-N-S 01-954-8853
MILK TRANSPORT SERVICES LP
910 Shelton Dr, Cabool, MO 65689-6310
Tel (417) 962-2373 *Founded/Ownrshp* 1998
Sales 31.0MM^E *EMP* 1,000
SIC 4213 4212 Trucking, except local; Local trucking, without storage; Trucking, except local; Local trucking, without storage
Pt: Regina Garrabrant
Pt: David Jones

D-U-N-S 06-262-2758
■ **MILKCO INC**
(*Suby of* INGLES MARKETS INC) ★
220 Deaverview Rd, Asheville, NC 28806-1710
Tel (828) 254-8428 *Founded/Ownrshp* 1982
Sales 57.7MM^E *EMP* 265
SIC 2026 2037 2086 Milk processing (pasteurizing, homogenizing, bottling); Fruit juices; Mineral water, carbonated: packaged in cans, bottles, etc.; Milk processing (pasteurizing, homogenizing, bottling); Fruit juices; Mineral water, carbonated: packaged in cans, bottles, etc.
Pr: Keith Collins
Off Mgr: Tony Estes
DP Dir: Donna Suggs

MILKEN COMMUNITY HIGH SCHOOL
See STEPHEN S WISE TEMPLE

D-U-N-S 19-198-0937
MILKEN FAMILY FOUNDATION
1250 4th St Fl 1, Santa Monica, CA 90401-1418
Tel (310) 570-4800 *Founded/Ownrshp* 1986
Sales 38.1MM *EMP* 200
SIC 8322 Individual & family services; Individual & family services
Pr: Lowell J Milken
**CFO:* Susan Fox
Trst: Mariano Guzm N
VP: C Crain
VP: Gary Panas
Ex Dir: Julius Lesner
CTO: Bill Prigge
Prd Dir: Jeffrey Gust

D-U-N-S 80-429-8107 IMP
MILKEN INSTITUTE
1250 4th St Fl 2, Santa Monica, CA 90401-1418
Tel (310) 570-4600 *Founded/Ownrshp* 1989
Sales 81.5MM *EMP* 50
Accts Green Hasson & Janks Llp Los A
SIC 8733 Economic research, noncommercial; Economic research, noncommercial
Pr: Michael L Klowden
**Ch Bd:* Michael Milken
**COO:* Paul H Irving
Mng Dir: Mindy Silverstein

MILKY WAY
See LTI INC

D-U-N-S 08-389-8916 IMP/EXP
MILKY WAY INTERNATIONAL TRADING CORP (CA)
MW POLAR
15203 Shoemaker Ave, Norwalk, CA 90650-6858
Tel (562) 921-2800 *Founded/Ownrshp* 1976
Sales 58.0MM^E *EMP* 30^E
SIC 5146 5148 5149

MILL BAY CASINO
See COLVILLE TRIBAL ENTERPRISE CORP

D-U-N-S 04-476-2370
MILL CREEK CARPET & TILE CO
(*Suby of* MILL CREEK LUMBER & SUPPLY CO INC) ★
6845 E 41st St, Tulsa, OK 74145-4501
Tel (918) 621-4000 *Founded/Ownrshp* 1976
Sales 23.6MM^E *EMP* 125
Accts Hogan Taylor Llp
SIC 5211 Flooring, wood; Flooring, wood
Pr: Jack Rodden
**Ex VP:* Jeff T Dunn
**VP:* James Dunn

D-U-N-S 00-893-3400 IMP
MILL CREEK LUMBER & SUPPLY CO INC
6974 E 38th St, Tulsa, OK 74145-3203
Tel (918) 794-3600 *Founded/Ownrshp* 1974
Sales 185.3MM^E *EMP* 500
SIC 3442 1771 5031 5211 Casements, aluminum; Flooring contractor; Lumber, plywood & millwork; Building materials, exterior; Building materials, interior; Lumber: rough, dressed & finished; Lumber & other building materials; Millwork & lumber; Doors, wood or metal, except storm; Windows, storm: wood or metal; Casements, aluminum; Flooring contractor; Lumber, plywood & millwork; Building materials, exterior; Building materials, interior; Lumber: rough, dressed & finished; Lumber & other building materials; Millwork & lumber; Doors, wood or metal, except storm; Windows, storm: wood or metal
Pr: Jeffrey T Dunn
Pr: Jeff Rill
COO: Kyle Brewer
COO: Arrington Tom
CTO: Adam Pancer
**VP:* Jim Cavanaugh
**VP:* James D Dunn
**Prin:* C E Burnett
CTO: Paul Cronin
Dir IT: Tom Arrington
Dir IT: Julie Schulte

D-U-N-S 96-443-7540
MILL CREEK RESIDENTIAL TRUST LLC
2255 Glades Rd Ste 423a, Boca Raton, FL 33431-8509
Tel (561) 998-4451 *Founded/Ownrshp* 2010
Sales 22.1MM^E *EMP* 70^E
SIC 6519 Real property lessors
CEO: Charles R Brindell Jr
COO: Michael M Hefley
CFO: Sheryl A Brown

D-U-N-S 00-417-6434
MILL DISTRIBUTORS INC (OH)
45 Aurora Industrial Pkwy, Aurora, OH 44202-8088
Tel (330) 995-9200 *Founded/Ownrshp* 1926
Sales 44.8MM^E *EMP* 53
SIC 5023 5021 Blankets; Bedspreads; Sheets, textile; Pillowcases; Furniture; Mattresses; Chairs
Pr: Thomas H Wieder
**Sec:* Douglas M Wieder
Mktg Dir: Kimberlee Franz
Sls Mgr: Timothy Koeth

MILL END TEXTILES
See STONE FABRICS INC

MILL METALS
See MILL STEEL CORP

MILL PRODUCTS DIVISION
See TC INDUSTRIES INC

MILL RESORT & CASINO
See COQUILLE ECONOMIC DEVELOPMENT CORP

D-U-N-S 96-616-3433
MILL RIVER COMMUNITY HOUSING CORP
249 Roosevelt Ave # 205, Pawtucket, RI 02860-2134
Tel (401) 724-8400 *Founded/Ownrshp* 2011
Sales 194.8M *EMP* 750
SIC 6513 Apartment building operators; Apartment building operators
Pr: Richard Leclerc

D-U-N-S 17-510-7965 IMP/EXP
MILL SERVICES CORP
(*Suby of* WELLSPRING CAPITAL MANAGEMENT LLC) ★
12 Monongahela Ave, Glassport, PA 15045-1315
Tel (412) 678-6141 *Founded/Ownrshp* 2004
Sales 121.4MM^E *EMP* 1,109^E
SIC 3295 1422 8742 3341 Slag, crushed or ground; Cement rock, crushed & broken-quarrying; Public utilities consultant; Secondary nonferrous metals
CEO: Michael Coslov
Genl Mgr: Tim Carmack

D-U-N-S 19-721-2400
MILL STEEL CORP
MILL METALS
62 Maple St, Manchester, NH 03103-5634
Tel (603) 626-7351 *Founded/Ownrshp* 1988
Sales 73.0MM^E *EMP* 80
SIC 5051 5719 Steel; Metalware; Steel; Metalware
Pr: Leo P Chasse Jr
Sales Asso: Nicole Hudon

D-U-N-S 00-555-3276
MILL SUPPLIES INC
MSI TOOL REPAIR
5105 Industrial Rd, Fort Wayne, IN 46825-5215
Tel (260) 484-8566 *Founded/Ownrshp* 1959, 1978
Sales 30.1MM^E *EMP* 41
SIC 5085 5072 7629 Industrial supplies; Builders' hardware; Tool repair, electric
CEO: Karen Beckstein
**Pr:* Andrew Beckstein
Sls Mgr: Tony Arnold
Sls Mgr: Jeremy White
Sales Asso: Earl Loveday
Sales Asso: Sean Ream
Sales Asso: Aimee Savieo

MILL TEK METALS
See MILLENIA PRODUCTS GROUP INC

D-U-N-S 04-503-1721 IMP
MILL VALLEY IMPORTS INC (CA)
SONNEN BMW
1599 Francisco Blvd E, San Rafael, CA 94901-5503
Tel (415) 482-2000 *Founded/Ownrshp* 1967
Sales 37.4MM^E *EMP* 85
SIC 5511 Automobiles, new & used; Automobiles, new & used
Pr: Lise Sonnen
Genl Mgr: Mark Blackshere
Sls Mgr: Brett Lynn
Sls Mgr: Darrin Mattice
Sls Mgr: Hans Wagner

D-U-N-S 12-051-6943
MILL VALLEY SCHOOL DISTRICT
411 Sycamore Ave, Mill Valley, CA 94941-2231
Tel (415) 389-7700 *Founded/Ownrshp* 1891
Sales 25.0MM *EMP* 220
SIC 8211 Public elementary & secondary schools; Public elementary & secondary schools
Sr VP: Carroll D Stevens
Prin: Jim Derich
Prin: Kit Gabbard

D-U-N-S 06-593-9902 IMP
MILL-MAX MFG CORP
190 Pine Hollow Rd, Oyster Bay, NY 11771-4711
Tel (516) 922-6000 *Founded/Ownrshp* 1971
Sales 50.7MM *EMP* 190
Accts Baker Tilly New York Ny
SIC 3678 5065 Electronic connectors; Electronic parts & equipment; Electronic connectors; Electronic parts & equipment
Ch Bd: Roger L Bahnik
**Pr:* James W Litke
CFO: Carolyn Simsac
CFO: Denise Vorgang
**VP:* Claude A Bahnik
**VP:* Bradley E Kuczinski
Ex Dir: Vreni Scheu
MIS Dir: Robert Laterra
QA Dir: Christopher Galasso
QA Dir: Patty Seaman
Sftwr Eng: Stephen Kelly

D-U-N-S 00-446-7064 IMP
MILL-ROSE CO
7995 Tyler Blvd, Mentor, OH 44060-4896
Tel (440) 255-9171 *Founded/Ownrshp* 1970

Sales 30.1MM^E *EMP* 200
SIC 3841 5085 3991 3624 3291 Surgical instruments & apparatus; Industrial supplies; Brushes, industrial; Brushes, household or industrial; Carbon & graphite products; Abrasive products; Surgical instruments & apparatus; Industrial supplies; Brushes, industrial; Brushes, household or industrial; Carbon & graphite products; Abrasive products
Pr: Paul M Miller
**VP:* Lawrence W Miller
Genl Mgr: Gregory Miller

D-U-N-S 09-612-8418
MILL-RUN TOURS INC
424 Madison Ave Fl 12, New York, NY 10017-1161
Tel (212) 486-9840 *Founded/Ownrshp* 1975
Sales 179.0MM *EMP* 82
SIC 4724 4725 Travel agencies; Tourist agency arranging transport, lodging & car rental; Arrangement of travel tour packages, wholesale; Travel agencies; Tourist agency arranging transport, lodging & car rental; Arrangement of travel tour packages, wholesale
Ch Bd: Issam N Sawaya
**Ofcr:* Pierre Azzi
**Ofcr:* Jalal Jafri
**Ofcr:* Abel Nunez
**VP:* Maricruz Sawaya

D-U-N-S 05-826-9648
MILLAR INC
6001 Gulf Fwy Ste A, Houston, TX 77023-5425
Tel (713) 923-9171 *Founded/Ownrshp* 1969
Sales 29.5MM^E *EMP* 120
SIC 3841 Catheters; Catheters
Ch: Huntley Millar
**Pr:* Tim Daugherty
**CEO:* Craig Thummel
**COO:* Anne Stoker

D-U-N-S 78-701-9483
MILLARD CHICAGO WINDOW CLEANING LLC
(*Suby of* MILLARD GROUP INC) ★
7301 N Cicero Ave, Lincolnwood, IL 60712-1613
Tel (847) 674-4100 *Founded/Ownrshp* 2002
Sales 15.8MM^E *EMP* 2,117^E
SIC 7349 Window blind cleaning; Window cleaning

D-U-N-S 09-931-4809
MILLARD COUNTY SCHOOL DISTRICT
285 E 450 N, Delta, UT 84624-9109
Tel (435) 864-1000 *Founded/Ownrshp* 1916
Sales 22.6MM^E *EMP* 420
Accts Gilbert & Stewart Cpa S Prov
SIC 8211 Public elementary & secondary schools; Public elementary & secondary schools
Bd of Dir: Ronald Draper
Schl Brd P: Carol Kimball

D-U-N-S 07-403-6476
MILLARD FILLMORE HOSPITALS
100 High St D1-588, Buffalo, NY 14203-1126
Tel (716) 859-5960 *Founded/Ownrshp* 1872
Sales 28.2MM^E *EMP* 1,605
SIC 8062 General medical & surgical hospitals; General medical & surgical hospitals
CEO: Carol Cassell
CFO: Anthony F Zito
**Treas:* Bryant H Prentice III
Prin: Maria Falbo
Ansthlgy: Daxin Chen
Doctor: Maciej Dryjski

D-U-N-S 02-523-1747
MILLARD GROUP INC (IL)
MILLARD METAL MAINTENANCE CO.
7301 N Cicero Ave, Lincolnwood, IL 60712-1613
Tel (847) 674-4100 *Founded/Ownrshp* 1920, 1958
Sales 219.9MM^E *EMP* 4,600
SIC 7349 Janitorial service, contract basis; Window cleaning; Janitorial service, contract basis; Window cleaning
Pr: Lawrence B Kugler
Sr VP: Vinton Lawson
VP: Bill Mathews
VP: Alberto Miranda
Dir Bus: Jerry Frym
Dir Bus: John Hucko
Dir Bus: Leeann Lynch
Rgnl Mgr: Randy Carollo
Rgnl Mgr: Jim English
Rgnl Mgr: George Stavrakis
Rgnl Mgr: Muharem Tafic

D-U-N-S 00-749-6193
MILLARD LUMBER INC
DO IT BEST
12900 I St, Omaha, NE 68137-1600
Tel (402) 896-2800 *Founded/Ownrshp* 1948
Sales 163.9MM^E *EMP* 220
SIC 5031 5211 Building materials, exterior; Building materials, interior; Millwork & lumber; Home centers; Building materials, exterior; Building materials, interior; Millwork & lumber; Home centers
Pr: G Richard Russell
**VP:* David M Anderson
**VP:* Don Rowe
**VP:* Joel R Russell
VP: Jeff D Taake

MILLARD METAL MAINTENANCE CO.
See MILLARD GROUP INC

D-U-N-S 08-021-3259
MILLARD PUBLIC SCHOOLS
SCHOOL DISTRICT 17
5606 S 147th St, Omaha, NE 68137-2647
Tel (402) 715-8200 *Founded/Ownrshp* 1938
Sales 225.1MM *EMP* 2,500
Accts Hsmc Orizon Llc Omaha Nebras
SIC 8211 Public elementary & secondary schools; High school, junior or senior; Public elementary & secondary schools; High school, junior or senior
**Treas:* Patrick Ricketts
Bd of Dir: Paul Meyer
**VP:* Linda Poole
Exec: Cindi Alberico
Exec: Peggy Silva
Prin: Connie Heinen
Prin: Mark Smith
Prin: Janet Wilson
Dir IT: Kent Kingston
IT Man: Jennifer Smith
Instr Medi: Donna Perkey

D-U-N-S 04-124-4153 IMP/EXP
MILLARD REFRIGERATED SERVICES LLC
13030 Pierce St, Omaha, NE 68144-1103
Tel (402) 896-6600 *Founded/Ownrshp* 2014
Sales NA *EMP* 2,000
SIC 4222 Refrigerated warehousing & storage

D-U-N-S 00-424-2657 IMP
MILLAT INDUSTRIES CORP
4901 Croftshire Dr, Dayton, OH 45440-1721
Tel (937) 434-6666 *Founded/Ownrshp* 1969
Sales 75.0MM^E *EMP* 140
SIC 3769 3599 3714 Guided missile & space vehicle parts & auxiliary equipment; Machine shop, jobbing & repair; Motor vehicle parts & accessories; Guided missile & space vehicle parts & auxiliary equipment; Machine shop, jobbing & repair; Motor vehicle parts & accessories
Ch: Robert Millat
**Pr:* Greg Millat
VP: Bill Barrows
Sfty Dirs: Joanie Dunkin
Ql Cn Mgr: John Blank
Ql Cn Mgr: Kerry Sykes

MILLBRAE EXPLORATION
See MILLBRAE NATURAL GAS DEVELOPMENT & EXPLORATION FUND 2002 LP

D-U-N-S 16-601-3644
MILLBRAE NATURAL GAS DEVELOPMENT & EXPLORATION FUND 2002 LP
MILLBRAE EXPLORATION
29 Upper Hook Rd, Katonah, NY 10536-3835
Tel (914) 232-1038 *Founded/Ownrshp* 2001
Sales 30.0MM *EMP* 2
SIC 6726 Investment offices; Investment offices
Pt: Stuart Reid
Pt: Millbrea Energy Corp

D-U-N-S 01-417-7760
MILLBRAE SCHOOL DISTRICT
555 Richmond Dr, Millbrae, CA 94030-1600
Tel (650) 697-5693 *Founded/Ownrshp* 1947
Sales 20.9MM^E *EMP* 458
Accts Boceta Macon Workman & Assoc
SIC 8211 Public elementary & secondary schools; Public elementary & secondary schools

D-U-N-S 15-037-4135
MILLBRAE WCP HOTEL I LLC
WESTIN SFO
(*Suby of* ULTIMA HOSPITALITY LLC) ★
335 Powell St, San Francisco, CA 94102-1804
Tel (415) 397-7000 *Founded/Ownrshp* 2013
Sales 41.5MM^E *EMP* 1,000
SIC 7011 Hotels & motels; Hotels & motels
Pr: Marc Swerdlow
**COO:* Mark Zettl
Exec: Richard Horshington

MILLBROOK COLONY
See MILLBROOK HUTTERIAN BRETHREN INC

D-U-N-S 00-625-4387
MILLBROOK DISTRIBUTION SERVICES INC (DE)
UNFI SPECIALTY DIST SERICES
Rr 56, Leicester, MA 01524
Tel (508) 892-8171 *Founded/Ownrshp* 2007
Sales NA *EMP* 1,300
SIC 5122 5023 5072 5112 5049 5199

D-U-N-S 05-150-2300
MILLBROOK HUTTERIAN BRETHREN INC (SD)
MILLBROOK COLONY
41659 256th St, Mitchell, SD 57301-7828
Tel (605) 996-6639 *Founded/Ownrshp* 1874
Sales 57.3MM^E *EMP* 38^E
SIC 0253 0723 3585 0191

D-U-N-S 02-066-2276
MILLBROOK SCHOOL
131 Millbrook School Rd, Millbrook, NY 12545-4932
Tel (845) 677-5510 *Founded/Ownrshp* 1932
Sales 28.7MM *EMP* 95
Accts Kirshon & Company Pc Pough
SIC 8211 Boarding school; Boarding school
Prin: Drew Casertano
Ofcr: Bonnie Lodevole
Info Man: Diane Massarone

D-U-N-S 08-921-0405
MILLBURN TOWNSHIP BOARD OF EDUCATION (INC)
434 Millburn Ave, Millburn, NJ 07041-1366
Tel (973) 376-3600 *Founded/Ownrshp* 1830
Sales 44.3MM^E *EMP* 500
SIC 8211 Public elementary & secondary schools; High school, junior or senior; School board; Public elementary & secondary schools; High school, junior or senior; School board
Pr: John Westfall-Kwong

D-U-N-S 07-979-9163
MILLBURN TOWNSHIP PUBLIC SCHOOLS
434 Millburn Ave, Millburn, NJ 07041-1366
Tel (973) 376-3600 *Founded/Ownrshp* 1830
Sales 3.6MM^E *EMP* 500
SIC 8211 Public elementary & secondary schools
Pr Dir: Nancy Dries
Teacher Pr: Candace Wildy
HC Dir: Harold Tarriff

D-U-N-S 92-796-7448
MILLCRAFT GROUP LLC
DELTACRAFT
6800 Grant Ave, Cleveland, OH 44105-5628
Tel (216) 441-5500 *Founded/Ownrshp* 1995
Sales 115.7MM^E *EMP* 275
SIC 5111 5113 2679 Printing & writing paper; Industrial & personal service paper; Paper products, converted; Printing & writing paper; Industrial & personal service paper; Paper products, converted
Ch Bd: Kay Mlakar
Ch Bd: Katherine Mlakar
Pr: Travis Mlakar
CFO: David Hegeman
CFO: Peter Mlakar
VP: Mike Davoran
VP: Bill Desantis
VP: Greg Lovensheimer
VP: John Orlando
VP: M Ortman
VP: Nicolas Piszko

D-U-N-S 05-929-6673
MILLCRAFT INDUSTRIES INC
95 W Beau St Ste 600, Washington, PA 15301-6827
Tel (724) 229-8800 *Founded/Ownrshp* 1971
Sales 31.9MM^E *EMP* 500
SIC 7699 3312 6799 Industrial equipment services; Blast furnace & related products; Real estate investors, except property operators; Industrial equipment services; Blast furnace & related products; Real estate investors, except property operators
Ch Bd: Jack B Piatt
COO: Lucas B Piatt
CFO: Brian R Walker
Sec: Charles D Boehm
VP: Jean McNeill
CIO: Lucas Piatt

D-U-N-S 00-790-0988 IMP
MILLCRAFT PAPER CO
6800 Grant Ave, Cleveland, OH 44105-5628
Tel (216) 441-5505 *Founded/Ownrshp* 1967
Sales 330.6MM^E *EMP* 250^E
SIC 5111 5113 Printing paper; Industrial & personal service paper; Printing paper; Industrial & personal service paper
Pr: Travis Mlakar
Ex VP: Peter Vogel Jr
**VP:* Mike Davoran
**VP:* Eric Michel
VP: Alastair Mitchell
**VP:* John Orlando
VP: John Shoup
Brnch Mgr: Steve Vusich
Div Mgr: Jack Oldiges
Store Mgr: Jim Kennedy
Sls Mgr: Mike Carr

D-U-N-S 07-498-8312
MILLCREEK COMMUNITY HOSPITAL INC
5515 Peach St, Erie, PA 16509-2695
Tel (814) 864-4031 *Founded/Ownrshp* 1948
Sales 52.7MM *EMP* 500
Accts Schaffner Knight Minnaugh & Co
SIC 8062 General medical & surgical hospitals; General medical & surgical hospitals
CEO: Mary L Eckert
**CFO:* Richard P Olinger
Ofcr: Martin Kelly
VP: Danielle Hansen
Dir OR: Brian Lock
Dir Risk M: Mary Ellen De Crapio
Dir Rx: Erin Brown
Dir Rx: Tim Dommermuth
Dir Rx: Tim Zurn
CIO: Cheryl Girardier
IT Man: Steven Inman

D-U-N-S 06-068-8975
MILLCREEK TOWNSHIP SCHOOL DISTRICT
3740 W 26th St, Erie, PA 16506-2039
Tel (814) 835-5673 *Founded/Ownrshp* 1955
Sales 70.2MM^E *EMP* 1,152
Accts Felix And Gloekler Pc Erie
SIC 8211 9111 Public elementary & secondary schools; Mayors' offices; Public elementary & secondary schools; Mayors' offices
Exec: Robert Howey
Teacher Pr: Liz Detich

D-U-N-S 04-348-2988
MILLE LACS BAND OF OJIBWE
CCLA
43408 Oodena Dr, Onamia, MN 56359-2236
Tel (320) 532-4181 *Founded/Ownrshp* 1899
Sales NA *EMP* 600
SIC 9131 Indian reservation; Indian reservation
Ch Bd: Melonie Benjamin
Plng Mgr: Don Wedll

D-U-N-S 00-779-0702
MILLE LACS ENERGY COOPERATIVE
36559 Us Hyw 169, Aitkin, MN 56431
Tel (218) 927-2191 *Founded/Ownrshp* 1939
Sales 24.8MM *EMP* 53
SIC 4911 Distribution, electric power; Distribution, electric power
Pr: Ralph Mykkannen
**VP:* Vern Watters
Genl Mgr: Jay Porter
Off Mgr: Carol Kyar
Opers Mgr: Steven Meld
Sls Mgr: Kris Milbradt

D-U-N-S 08-113-8992
MILLE LACS HEALTH SYSTEM
200 Elm St N, Onamia, MN 56359-7901
Tel (320) 532-3154 *Founded/Ownrshp* 1953
Sales 37.1MM *EMP* 425
SIC 8062 8051 8011 General medical & surgical hospitals; Skilled nursing care facilities; Offices & clinics of medical doctors; General medical & surgical hospitals; Skilled nursing care facilities; Offices & clinics of medical doctors
Pr: Bill Nelson
Chf Rad: Cathy Johnson
Pr: Del Yurick
**CFO:* John Unzen
**Ch:* Mark Tadych
**Treas:* Becky Houle
Dir Lab: Mark Loch
Dir Rad: Jennifer Connors
Ex Dir: Tina Chapman
IT Man: Michael Denda
IT Man: Ken Hayes

D-U-N-S 02-265-0376
MILLENIA CENTER
3902 Millenia Blvd, Orlando, FL 32839-6407
Tel (407) 690-9383 *Founded/Ownrshp* 2008
Sales 17.4MM^E *EMP* 300
SIC 5912 Drug stores

D-U-N-S 11-021-1757
MILLENIA HEALTHCARE INC
21400 Intl Blvd Ste 205, Seatac, WA 98198-6086
Tel (206) 878-0909 *Founded/Ownrshp* 1999
Sales 6.8MM^E *EMP* 280
SIC 8082 Home health care services; Home health care services

D-U-N-S 13-297-2758 IMP
MILLENIA PRODUCTS GROUP INC
MILL TEK METALS
1345 Norwood Ave, Itasca, IL 60143-1126
Tel (630) 458-0401 *Founded/Ownrshp* 1999
Sales 65.0MM *EMP* 100
SIC 3499 3469 Iron or steel flat products; Machine bases, metal; Metal stampings; Fire- or burglary-resistive products; Machine bases, metal; Metal stampings
CEO: Frank San Roman
**CFO:* James Carroll
**Treas:* Gerald Pines
VP: Tom Foust
**VP:* Patrick Milet
Manager: John Anderson

MILLENIUM GROUP, THE
See MILLENNIUM GROUP OF DELAWARE INC

D-U-N-S 12-671-4521
MILLENIUM HONDA
HEMPSTEAD AUTO SALES
286 N Franklin St, Hempstead, NY 11550-1304
Tel (631) 665-0005 *Founded/Ownrshp* 2005
Sales 36.2MM^E *EMP* 150
SIC 5511 Automobiles, new & used; Automobiles, new & used
Pr: Steve Sutton
**Genl Mgr:* Raval Mejia
Sls Mgr: Martin Kuzniak

MILLENIUM HOTEL MINNEAPOLIS
See TRIMARK HOTEL CORP

MILLENIUM HOTEL ST LOUIS
See GATEWAY HOTEL HOLDINGS INC

D-U-N-S 18-716-9230
MILLENIUM INC
SPORT DODGE OF PLEASANTVILLE
6831 Black Horse Pike, Egg Harbor Township, NJ 08234-4131
Tel (609) 646-1200 *Founded/Ownrshp* 1987
Sales 21.3MM^E *EMP* 50
SIC 5511 7515 7513 5521 Automobiles, new & used; Passenger car leasing; Truck rental & leasing, no drivers; Used car dealers; Automobiles, new & used; Passenger car leasing; Truck rental & leasing, no drivers; Used car dealers
Pr: Carlos Hozdevila
Pr: Richard C Porter II
CFO: Barry Hammond
**VP:* Peter Pollino
Sales Asso: Cathy Oleary

MILLENIUM KIA EAST
See TRIANGLE PRE OWNED LLC

D-U-N-S 93-248-1062 IMP
MILLENNIA STAINLESS INC
(*Suby of* CHAIN CHON INDUSTRIAL CO., LTD.)
10016 Romandel Ave, Santa Fe Springs, CA 90670-3424
Tel (562) 946-3545 *Founded/Ownrshp* 1996
Sales 26.5MM^E *EMP* 75
SIC 5085 5065 5051 Industrial supplies; Coils, electronic; Steel
CEO: Ching-PO LI
Snr Mgr: Charlie Wang

D-U-N-S 03-652-0922 IMP
MILLENNIA TECHNOLOGY INC
A MILLENNIA GROUP COMPANY
(*Suby of* 2862474 INC) ★
1105 Pittsburgh St, Cheswick, PA 15024-1330
Tel (724) 274-7741 *Founded/Ownrshp* 1997, 1979
Sales 22.4MM^E *EMP* 120
SIC 3679 Electronic circuits; Electronic circuits
Pr: Michael D'Ambrosio Sr
VP: Doug Harchick
VP Opers: Pat Sims
Prd Mgr: Chance Turner

D-U-N-S 79-052-6870 IMP
MILLENNIAL BRANDS LLC
ROCKET DOG BRANDS
2000 Crow Canyon Pl # 300, San Ramon, CA 94583-1367
Tel (866) 938-4806 *Founded/Ownrshp* 2007
Sales 54.7MM^E *EMP* 90^E
SIC 3144 Women's footwear, except athletic
Pr Mgr: Alison Lawton

D-U-N-S 01-004-4000
■ **MILLENNIAL MEDIA INC**
(*Suby of* AOL INC) ★
2400 Boston St Ste 300, Baltimore, MD 21224-4781
Tel (410) 522-8705 *Founded/Ownrshp* 2006, 2015
Sales 296.1MM *EMP* 636^E
Tkr Sym MM *Exch* NYS
SIC 7319 7371 Advertising agencies; Advertising consultant; Display advertising service; Computer software development & applications
CEO: Michael G Barrett
Pr: Jason Kelly
COO: Ernie Cormier
CFO: Andrew Jeanneret
CFO: Andrew J Jeanneret
Sr VP: Eric Hastings
Sr VP: Michael Kocorowski

Sr VP: Jeff Tennery
VP: Jim Butler
VP: Joseph Julian
VP: Frank Weishaupt
VP: Joe Wilkinson
Creative D: Sarah Jennings
Comm Man: Clare Lochary

MILLENNIUM
See CRISTAL USA INC

MILLENNIUM
See KYLE ENTERPRISES LLC

MILLENNIUM BILTMORE HOTEL, THE
See WHB CORP

MILLENNIUM BROADWAY HOTEL
See CDL WEST 45TH STREET LLC

D-U-N-S 06-939-5585
■ MILLENNIUM BUILDERS INC (CT)
(*Suby of* PPL ENERGY SERVICES NORTHEAST) ★
50 Inwood Rd Ste 2, Rocky Hill, CT 06067-3439
Tel (860) 571-0555 *Founded/Ownrshp* 1999
Sales 41.6MM^E *EMP* 122
SIC 1542 Nonresidential construction; Nonresidential construction
Pr: John J Mazzali
Treas: James E Abel
Genl Mgr: Ronald Stacy
Off Mgr: Robin Palen

D-U-N-S 14-279-7617
■ MILLENNIUM CHALLENGE CORP
MCC
(*Suby of* EXECUTIVE OFFICE OF UNITED STATES GOVERNMENT) ★
875 15th St Nw Ste 200, Washington, DC 20005-2227
Tel (202) 521-3600 *Founded/Ownrshp* 2004
Sales NA *EMP* 300
SIC 9611 Administration of general economic programs; ; Administration of general economic programs
CEO: Daniel Yohannes
Ofcr: Bethany Aquilina
Ofcr: Martha Bowen
Ofcr: Meredith Cabelka
Ofcr: Daniel Callahan
Ofcr: Sylvie Doutriaux
Ofcr: Melissa Griswold
Ofcr: Andria Hayes-Birchler
Ofcr: Myron Hirniak
Ofcr: Erin Kolodjeski
Ofcr: Catherine Marschner
Ofcr: Bradley Parks
Ofcr: Marcel Ricou
Ofcr: Ranjani Sankaran
Ofcr: Sonia Shahrigian
Ofcr: Geroldine Sicot
Ofcr: Amir Tejpar
Ofcr: Cynthia Waters
Ofcr: Victoria Willson
Ofcr: Tanya Young
VP: William G Anderson

D-U-N-S 93-252-8250
MILLENNIUM COMMUNICATIONS GROUP INC
11 Melanie Ln Unit 13e, East Hanover, NJ 07936-1100
Tel (973) 503-1313 *Founded/Ownrshp* 1995
Sales 21.1MM^E *EMP* 65^E
SIC 8711 Acoustical engineering
CEO: Ronald Cassel
**Pr:* Robert Ritchie
Pr: John Veninata
COO: Harish Nallabathula
**Sr VP:* Ken McLaughlin
VP: Suresh Nalla
VP: Suresh Nallabathula
VP: William Stark
Netwrk Eng: Andrew Cianciosi
Sfty Dirs: Doug Van Cauwenberge

MILLENNIUM COMPUTER PRODUCTS
See MCP COMPUTER PRODUCTS INC

MILLENNIUM DGTAL MEDIA SYSTEMS
See BROADSTRIPE LLC

D-U-N-S 78-557-0198 IMP
MILLENNIUM DISTRIBUTION LLC
(*Suby of* MILLENNIUM PACKAGING, LP)
4990 Eisenhauer Rd # 300, San Antonio, TX 78218-3716
Tel (210) 881-6850 *Founded/Ownrshp* 2006
Sales 32.6MM *EMP* 15
SIC 5141 7311 4731 7319 Food brokers; Food brokers; Advertising agencies; Freight transportation arrangement; Distribution of advertising material or sample services
Genl Mgr: Todd Smith
Genl Mgr: Robert Vogel
Opers Mgr: Marc Leclair

D-U-N-S 01-197-1939
MILLENNIUM ENGINEERING AND INTEGRATION CO
2231 Crystal Dr Ste 711, Arlington, VA 22202-3724
Tel (703) 413-7750 *Founded/Ownrshp* 1995, 2005
Sales 112.7MM^E *EMP* 300
SIC 8711 8731 Engineering services; Commercial physical research; Engineering services; Commercial physical research
CEO: Patrick Murphy
**CFO:* Dante Reeves
VP: Alfred Wassel

D-U-N-S 61-934-1188
MILLENNIUM GROUP OF DELAWARE INC
MILLENIUM GROUP, THE
106 Apple St Ste 207, Tinton Falls, NJ 07724-2670
Tel (732) 741-4870 *Founded/Ownrshp* 2003
Sales 59.8MM^E *EMP* 412
SIC 8744 Facilities support services; Facilities support services
CEO: Dermot Murphy
**Pr:* Timothy P Kerner
**CFO:* Christopher Trainor
**Ex VP:* Frank W Farnacci
Ex VP: Frank Farnacci
Div Mgr: Coy Dandridge

D-U-N-S 01-478-2231
MILLENNIUM HEALTH LLC
16981 Via Tazon Ste F, San Diego, CA 92127-1645
Tel (877) 451-3534 *Founded/Ownrshp* 2007
Sales 142.6MM^E *EMP* 258^E
SIC 8734 Testing laboratories; Testing laboratories
**Pr:* Howard Appel
**CEO:* Brock Hardaway
**COO:* David Cohen
**COO:* Mark A Winham
**CFO:* Timothy C Kennedy
**Chf Cred:* Darrell W Contreras
**Chf Mktg O:* Nikhil A Nayak
Chf Mktg O: Nikhil Nayak
**Ofcr:* Angela Huskey
Ex VP: Josh Benner
Sr VP: Rami Ben-Joseph
**Sr VP:* Charles Mikel
**Sr VP:* Janna Sipes
VP: Perla Almazan
VP: Michael E Flowers
VP: Brent Gibbs
VP: Nancy Lazarski

MILLENNIUM HOTELS & RESORTS
See M&C MANAGEMENT SERVICES (USA) INC

MILLENNIUM HOUSING
See WESTRIDGE GROUP THE LLC

D-U-N-S 96-477-9990
MILLENNIUM HOUSING CORP
20 Pacifica Ste 1470, Irvine, CA 92618-7468
Tel (949) 515-5100 *Founded/Ownrshp* 2010
Sales NA *EMP* 5
Accts Vavrinektrineday & Co Llp Ran
SIC 6331 Property damage insurance; Property damage insurance
Prin: George Turk

MILLENNIUM INDUSTIRES
See AMERICAN INDUSTRIAL PARTS

D-U-N-S 00-505-0463 IMP/EXP
MILLENNIUM INDUSTRIES CORP (MI)
925 N Main St, Ligonier, IN 46767-2060
Tel (260) 894-3163 *Founded/Ownrshp* 1990, 1998
Sales 115.6MM^E *EMP* 400
SIC 3469 Metal stampings; Metal stampings
Pr: Gary Vollmar
**VP:* Mike Zedroik
Ql Cn Mgr: Brent Firestone

D-U-N-S 82-657-1366
MILLENNIUM INFORMATION SERVICES INC
450 E Devon Ave Ste 310, Itasca, IL 60143-1263
Tel (630) 285-8282 *Founded/Ownrshp* 1991
Sales NA *EMP* 109
SIC 6411 Insurance agents, brokers & service
Pr: Steve Pietrzak
Genl Mgr: Scott Dismeier
Software D: Josh Meyers

MILLENNIUM LOGISITCS
See W J DONOVAN ENTERPRISES LLC

D-U-N-S 14-350-9276
MILLENNIUM MANAGEMENT LLC
666 5th Ave Frnt 8, New York, NY 10103-0025
Tel (212) 841-4132 *Founded/Ownrshp* 1994
Sales 36.0MM^E *EMP* 67^E
SIC 6726 Management investment funds, closed-end
Pr: Boris Twersky
COO: Ajay Nagpal
CFO: Bob Williams
Ch: Kunho Cho
VP: Rich Cappellano
VP: Drew Frahm
VP: Jamie Haire
VP: Rick Kohly
VP: Jitender Pal
VP: Sujendra Sawant
VP: Danielle Schaefer
VP: Maurice Schilder
VP: Michael Scrivo
VP: Fred Stone
VP: Lena Tamarkin
VP: Jonathan Tischio
VP: Mandar Vinod

D-U-N-S 06-834-1010 IMP
■ MILLENNIUM MAT CO LLC
(*Suby of* CINTAS CORP NO 2) ★
3200 Shawnee Indus Way, Suwanee, GA 30024-3617
Tel (678) 482-5623 *Founded/Ownrshp* 1999
Sales 50.6MM^E *EMP* 245^E
SIC 2273 Mats & matting; Mats & matting
Pr: Ian Malpass
Genl Mgr: Matt Williams
Off Mgr: Julie Bailey
Sls&Mrk Ex: Lyndsey Downs
Manager: Colleen Edington

D-U-N-S 78-742-2989
MILLENNIUM PARTNERS LP
1995 Broadway, New York, NY 10023-5882
Tel (212) 841-4100 *Founded/Ownrshp* 2002
Sales 33.0MM^E *EMP* 35
SIC 6211 Brokers, security
Pt: Israel Englander
VP: Michael Ounjian
Software D: Ed Bierly

D-U-N-S 61-195-5852 IMP
MILLENNIUM PARTNERS SPORTS CLUB MANAGEMENT LLC
SPORTS CLUB LA, THE
7 Water St Ste 200, Boston, MA 02109-4106
Tel (617) 476-8910 *Founded/Ownrshp* 2005
Sales 21.7MM^E *EMP* 1,500
SIC 7991 Athletic club & gymnasiums, membership; Athletic club & gymnasiums, membership
CEO: Smaiyra Million

D-U-N-S 80-414-8757
MILLENNIUM PHARMACEUTICALS INC
(*Suby of* TAKEDA AMERICA HOLDINGS INC) ★
40 Landsdowne St, Cambridge, MA 02139-4234
Tel (617) 679-7000 *Founded/Ownrshp* 2009
Sales 210.6MM^E *EMP* 947
SIC 8731 Biological research; Biological research
Pr: Deborah Dunsire
COO: Sherry Reynolds
**CFO:* Marsha H Fanucci
**Treas:* Todd Shegog
Ofcr: Joel Goldberg
Ofcr: Liz Lewis
**Ex VP:* Christophe Bianchi
**Sr VP:* Stephen M Gansler
Sr VP: Paul Hamelin
Sr VP: David Schenkein
Sr VP: Claire Thom
Sr VP: Susan J Ward
VP: Lisa Adler
VP: Janet Bush
VP: Alan Crane
VP: Sandra Dicesare
VP: John Ferguson
VP: Nick Galakatos
VP: Kyle Kuvalanka
VP: Clare Midgley
VP: Vincent Miles

D-U-N-S 10-564-9466
■ MILLENNIUM PHARMACY SYSTEMS INC
(*Suby of* PHARMERICA CORP) ★
100 E Kensinger Dr # 500, Cranberry Township, PA 16066-3557
Tel (724) 940-2490 *Founded/Ownrshp* 2014
Sales 95.1MM^E *EMP* 500^E
SIC 5912 Drug stores; Drug stores
Pr: Philip J Keough IV
**CFO:* J Chris Luthin
Chf Cred: A Jeffrey Newell
Ex VP: George Hepburn
**Ex VP:* Lena Sturgeon
Sr VP: Stephen Duvall
Sr VP: Anthony Gerardi
Sr VP: Gaile M Omori
VP: Thomas A Caneris

D-U-N-S 02-190-2891
MILLENNIUM PHYSICIAN GROUP LLC
19531 Cochran Blvd, Port Charlotte, FL 33948-2081
Tel (941) 255-3535 *Founded/Ownrshp* 2008
Sales 79.9MM^E *EMP* 775^E
SIC 8011 8049 Diabetes specialist, physician/surgeon; Nurses, registered & practical; Diabetes specialist, physician/surgeon; Nurses, registered & practical
CFO: David Koeninger
Nurse Mgr: Bridget Safron

D-U-N-S 94-439-3362
MILLENNIUM PRODUCTS INC
SYNERGY BEVERAGES
4646 Hampton St, Vernon, CA 90058-2116
Tel (323) 581-7787 *Founded/Ownrshp* 1994
Sales 50.0MM^E *EMP* 5
SIC 2086 Bottled & canned soft drinks; Bottled & canned soft drinks
Pr: GT Dave
**VP:* Jim Mancuso
Off Mgr: Alejandra Martinez

D-U-N-S 00-867-5423
MILLENNIUM RAIL INC
(*Suby of* WATCO COMPANIES LLC) ★
315 W 3rd St, Pittsburg, KS 66762-4706
Tel (620) 231-2230 *Founded/Ownrshp* 2007
Sales 36.0MM^E *EMP* 700
SIC 4789 3743 7699 Railroad car repair; Railroad car rebuilding; Railroad car customizing; Railroad car repair; Railroad car rebuilding; Railroad car customizing
CEO: William J Groos
Pr: Knut Hansen
**Pr:* David R Turner
**CFO:* Len Farrell
**Prin:* Rich Goldstein
**Prin:* Mike Herman
**Prin:* Steve Kaplan
**Rgnl Mgr:* Jim Moore
Dir Opers: Keith Egan
Plnt Mgr: Gary Campbell
Plnt Mgr: Jeff Maier

D-U-N-S 96-012-8346
MILLENNIUM SOFTWARE INC
2000 Town Ctr Ste 300, Southfield, MI 48075-1123
Tel (248) 213-1800 *Founded/Ownrshp* 1996
Sales 33.8MM^E *EMP* 280
SIC 7371 Custom computer programming services; Custom computer programming services
Pr: Anu Anand
IT Man: Arun Gupta
Tech Mgr: Jay Patel

D-U-N-S 06-291-1396
MILLENNIUM SUPER STORE LTD
MILLENNIUM TOYOTA
257 N Franklin St, Hempstead, NY 11550-1309
Tel (516) 485-1400 *Founded/Ownrshp* 1999
Sales 74.3MM^E *EMP* 200
SIC 5511 Automobiles, new & used; Automobiles, new & used
Pr: John Staluppi Sr
**Treas:* John Chmela

MILLENNIUM TOYOTA
See MILLENNIUM SUPER STORE LTD

D-U-N-S 11-789-4840
MILLENNIUM TRUST CO LLC
2001 Spring Rd Ste 700, Oak Brook, IL 60523-1890
Tel (630) 368-5600 *Founded/Ownrshp* 2000
Sales 51.6MM^E *EMP* 160
SIC 6733 Trusts, except educational, religious, charity: management; Trusts, except educational, religious, charity: management
**COO:* Gary Anetsberger
Sr VP: Kevin Clark
Sr VP: Dan Eastman
Sr VP: Scott Foster
Sr VP: Matthew Kiggins
Sr VP: Matthew Nitschke
Sr VP: Sandra Reese
Sr VP: Tommyjoe Valenzuela
VP: Chris Boyce
VP: David Braga
VP: Belinda Cheeks
VP: Jeremy Christensen
VP: Mary Corrigan
VP: Bob Hozian
VP: Mark Koeppen
VP: Joe Palumbo
VP: Lisa Powers
VP: Jeanne Reder
VP: Karin Stouffer
VP: David Turner
VP: David Vogt

D-U-N-S 00-386-3537
MILLER & ANDERSON INC
4150 Martinsburg Pike, Clear Brook, VA 22624-1534
Tel (540) 667-4757 *Founded/Ownrshp* 1911
Sales 22.4MM^E *EMP* 210
SIC 1711 Mechanical contractor; Mechanical contractor
Pr: John Dick
CFO: Trish Dick
**VP:* Thomas Dick

D-U-N-S 07-483-1793
MILLER & CHEVALIER CHARTERED
655 15th St Nw Ste 900, Washington, DC 20005-5799
Tel (202) 626-5800 *Founded/Ownrshp* 1920
Sales 48.3MM^E *EMP* 229
SIC 8111 Taxation law; Administrative & government law; Will, estate & trust law; Malpractice & negligence law; Taxation law; Administrative & government law; Will, estate & trust law; Malpractice & negligence law
Ch Bd: Anthony F Shelley
Pt: Richard H Abbey
Pt: Alan I Horowitz
Pt: Kathryn C Atkinson
Pt: Dennis P Bedell
Pt: James A Bensfield
Pt: Leonard Bickwit Jr
Pt: David B Blair
Pt: Kathleen E Carelis
Pt: Jay Michael Cornett
Pt: David B Cubeta
Pt: John E Davis
Pt: F Amanda Debusk
Pt: Warren J Devecchio
Pt: Adam P Feinberg
Pt: Rocco V Femia
Pt: F David Foster
Pt: Lawrence B Gibbs
Pt: Georges A Hani
Pt: Richard A Hibey
Pt: Robert K Huffman

D-U-N-S 00-339-7635
MILLER & CO INC (AL)
MILLER LUMBER
500 Hooper Dr, Selma, AL 36701-6444
Tel (334) 874-8271 *Founded/Ownrshp* 1929, 1987
Sales 10.5MM^E *EMP* 305
SIC 2426 2421 2431 Hardwood dimension & flooring mills; Sawmills & planing mills, general; Millwork; Hardwood dimension & flooring mills; Sawmills & planing mills, general; Millwork
Ch: Newton Anderson
**Pr:* William H Deramus
**Treas:* Kay Coley
**Treas:* Bremen Nedley
**VP:* Robert C Buchanan

D-U-N-S 00-890-4898
MILLER & HOLMES INC
M & H GAS
2311 Oneil Rd, Hudson, WI 54016-8168
Tel (715) 377-1730 *Founded/Ownrshp* 1896
Sales 27.6MM^E *EMP* 260
SIC 5411 5541 Convenience stores, independent; Filling stations, gasoline; Convenience stores, independent; Filling stations, gasoline
Ch Bd: Gerald T Peterson
Pr: Anthony W Holmes
Sec: Barbara Velasquez

D-U-N-S 00-285-2747 IMP
MILLER & LONG CO INC
4824 Rugby Ave, Bethesda, MD 20814-3070
Tel (301) 657-8000 *Founded/Ownrshp* 1947
Sales 278.9MM^E *EMP* 3,000
SIC 1771

D-U-N-S 02-670-9725
MILLER & MARTIN PLLC
832 Georgia Ave Ste 1200, Chattanooga, TN 37402-2285
Tel (423) 785-8232 *Founded/Ownrshp* 1867
Sales 38.8MM^E *EMP* 370
SIC 8111 General practice attorney, lawyer; General practice attorney, lawyer
Ch: Howard Levine
Pr: Heather Autry
CFO: Angela Wallace
**Ch:* James M Haley IV
Bd of Dir: Allen McCallie
Exec: Alfred Smith
Comm Man: Stella Shasteen
Ex Dir: David Hetzel
**Ex Dir:* Jay Markley
Genl Couns: Thomas Swafford
Counsel: Joel Richardson

D-U-N-S 01-214-9605
MILLER & RAVED INC
271 North Ave Ste 502, New Rochelle, NY 10801-5113
Tel (914) 632-3555 *Founded/Ownrshp* 1963
Sales 40.0MM *EMP* 5
SIC 1521 1522 1541 1542 Single-family housing construction; Residential construction; Industrial buildings & warehouses; Nonresidential construction; Single-family housing construction; Residential construction; Industrial buildings & warehouses; Nonresidential construction

Pr: A Charles Miller
**Treas:* Roy Raved

MILLER & SMITH
See MILLER AND SMITH INC

D-U-N-S 00-693-1513 IMP
MILLER AND CO LLC
(*Suby of* NIZI INTERNATIONAL SA)
9700 W Higgins Rd # 1000, Rosemont, IL 60018-4743
Tel (847) 696-2400 *Founded/Ownrshp* 1919, 2012
Sales 43.7MM^E *EMP* 57
SIC 5051 3313 Pig iron; Ferroalloys; Alloys, additive, except copper: not made in blast furnaces; Pig iron; Ferroalloys; Alloys, additive, except copper: not made in blast furnaces
CEO: John A Adcock
CFO: Dimitra Kotsinonos
Area Mgr: Michael Reesman
Dir IT: Fred Linebarger
Opers Mgr: James Li
VP Sls: Ryan Lacoursiere
Mktg Mgr: Sudhir Gupta

D-U-N-S 02-255-1667
MILLER AND SMITH INC
MILLER & SMITH
8401 Greensboro Dr # 450, Mc Lean, VA 22102-5113
Tel (703) 821-2500 *Founded/Ownrshp* 2008
Sales 187.0MM *EMP* 130
SIC 1799 1531 Speculative builder, single-family houses; Land preparation construction; Building mover, including houses;
Ch: Gordon V Smith
**Ch Bd:* Alvin D Hall
**Pr:* Doug Smith
**Sr VP:* Richard J North
**Sr VP:* Spencer R Stouffer
**Sr VP:* Charles Stuart Jr
MIS Mgr: L Reed
Corp Couns: Allyson McCarron

D-U-N-S 80-879-8342
MILLER APPLE LTD PARTNERSHIP
APPLEBEE'S
4488 W Bristol Rd Ste 3g, Flint, MI 48507-3134
Tel (810) 733-0663 *Founded/Ownrshp* 1993
Sales 33.2MM^E *EMP* 900
SIC 5812 5813 Restaurant, family: chain; Bar (drinking places); Restaurant, family: chain; Bar (drinking places)
Pt: William Wentworth

MILLER AUTO CENTER
See MILLER ENTERPRISES INC

MILLER AUTO CTR BODY SHOP
See MILLER PONTIAC-BUICK-GMC INC

D-U-N-S 02-400-7429
MILLER AUTO SALES INC (VA)
MILLER HND-VLKSWGN-SUZU-SUZUKI
3985 Valley Pike, Winchester, VA 22602-2474
Tel (540) 868-9921 *Founded/Ownrshp* 1955, 1966
Sales 22.5MM^E *EMP* 60
SIC 5511 Automobiles, new & used; Automobiles, new & used
Pr: George Miller
**VP:* John Miller
VP Sls: John Grist

D-U-N-S 01-864-3296
MILLER AUTOMOBILE CORP (CT)
LINCOLN-MERCURY DARIEN
1335 Post Rd, Darien, CT 06820-5417
Tel (203) 655-7451 *Founded/Ownrshp* 1930, 1958
Sales 27.8MM^E *EMP* 78
SIC 5511 Automobiles, new & used; Automobiles, new & used
Pr: William W Steinmetz
Sls Mgr: Robert Chien

D-U-N-S 78-535-5439 IMP
■ **MILLER AUTOMOTIVE GROUP INC**
MILLER NISSAN
(*Suby of* GROUP 1 AUTOMOTIVE INC) ★
6425 Van Nuys Blvd, Sherman Oaks, CA 91401-5628
Tel (818) 787-8400 *Founded/Ownrshp* 2002
Sales 157.6MM^E *EMP* 650
SIC 5511 7538 5521 Automobiles, new & used; General automotive repair shops; Automobiles, used cars only; Automobiles, new & used; General automotive repair shops; Automobiles, used cars only
Ch Bd: Fred Miller
**Pr:* Michael Miller
**CFO:* Doug Stewart
**VP:* Mark Miller
Genl Mgr: Tammy Weaver
MIS Dir: Jeff Boss
Sls Mgr: Marcelo Campiani

MILLER BEER DISTRIBUTING
See DIENST DISTRIBUTING CO

D-U-N-S 00-781-5905
MILLER BONDED INC
4538 Mcleod Rd Ne, Albuquerque, NM 87109-2219
Tel (505) 881-0220 *Founded/Ownrshp* 1956
Sales 37.8MM^E *EMP* 165
SIC 1731 1711 3444 7623 Energy management controls; Heating & air conditioning contractors; Sheet metalwork; Air conditioning repair; Energy management controls; Heating & air conditioning contractors; Sheet metalwork; Air conditioning repair
CEO: Keith Wilson
**Pr:* Kenneth E Otteni
**Treas:* Letitia J Hardwick
**VP:* Laura R Highfill

D-U-N-S 14-939-0416
MILLER BREWERIES EAST INC
(*Suby of* MILLERCOORS LLC) ★
3939 W Highland Blvd, Milwaukee, WI 53208-2816
Tel (414) 931-2000 *Founded/Ownrshp* 2004
Sales 248.3M *EMP* 2,889
SIC 2082 Beer (alcoholic beverage); Beer (alcoholic beverage)
Pr: Gavin Hattersley
VP: Gary Booher
VP: Thomas J Cardella
VP: Kevin Doyle
VP: Bill Dreger
VP: Erv Frederick
VP: David Goulet
VP: Paul Hansen
VP: Jeffrey Hembrock
VP: John C Radi
VP: Stephen D Rogers
VP: Jim Scheey
VP: Jerry Schiedt
VP: Jeffrey Schouten
VP: Denise Smith
VP: Charlie Teal
VP: David Zini

D-U-N-S 79-932-0106 IMP/EXP
MILLER BREWING INTERNATIONAL INC
(*Suby of* MILLERCOORS LLC) ★
3939 W Highland Blvd, Milwaukee, WI 53208-2866
Tel (414) 931-2000 *Founded/Ownrshp* 1987
Sales 35.7MM^E *EMP* 40
SIC 2082 Beer (alcoholic beverage)
Ex VP: David Zini
**Ex VP:* Charles S Frenette
Ex VP: Bob Mikulay
**Sr VP:* Mike Jones
Sr VP: Dick Strup
VP: Fred Hauser
VP: Juan Vergara
Mktg Mgr: Jeffrey Burrill
Mktg Mgr: Juan Contreras
Mktg Mgr: Cami Gregg
Sls Mgr: Mark L Denu

D-U-N-S 08-486-0162
MILLER BROS CONSTRUCTION INC (PA)
950 E Main St Ste 107, Schuylkill Haven, PA 17972-9720
Tel (570) 385-1662 *Founded/Ownrshp* 1976
Sales 33.1MM^E *EMP* 80
Accts Jones & Co Rottsville Penns
SIC 1541 1542 Industrial buildings & warehouses; Commercial & office buildings, renovation & repair
Pr: James L Miller
**Treas:* John P Stock
**VP:* Rick Lettich
Sales Exec: Dan Foose
Snr Mgr: Jeremy Hurst

MILLER BROS DIV WMPL-MLLER INC
See WAMPOLE-MILLER INC

D-U-N-S 12-849-8326
MILLER BROTHERS EXPRESS LC
560 W 400 N, Hyrum, UT 84319-1054
Tel (435) 245-6025 *Founded/Ownrshp* 1987
Sales 33.5MM^E *EMP* 125
SIC 4212 4213 Local trucking, without storage; Trucking, except local
Treas: Bruce Gittins
Snr Mgr: Miller Erni

D-U-N-S 19-088-4387
MILLER BUILDERS LLP
12813 Webercrest Rd, Houston, TX 77048-4304
Tel (713) 991-6767 *Founded/Ownrshp* 1987
Sales 33.3MM^E *EMP* 350
SIC 1771 Concrete work; Concrete work
Off Mgr: Mary Goodrich

MILLER BY HONEYWELL
See SPERIAN FALL PROTECTION INC

MILLER CANFIELD
See MILLER CANFIELD PADDOCK AND STONE PLC

D-U-N-S 07-635-2012
MILLER CANFIELD PADDOCK AND STONE PLC
MILLER CANFIELD
150 W Jefferson Ave # 2500, Detroit, MI 48226-4416
Tel (313) 963-6420 *Founded/Ownrshp* 1934
Sales 98.4MM^E *EMP* 700
SIC 8111 General practice law office; General practice law office
CEO: Michael P McGee
CFO: David Hoin
Counsel: Michael Allen
Counsel: Bob Baksi
Counsel: Bruce D Birgbauer
Counsel: Troy Harris
Counsel: Loren M Opper
Counsel: Loretta Stoyka

D-U-N-S 07-621-5466 IMP
MILLER CASTINGS INC
2503 Pacific Park Dr, Whittier, CA 90601-1680
Tel (562) 695-0461 *Founded/Ownrshp* 1973
Sales 59.4MM^E *EMP* 340^E
SIC 3324 Steel investment foundries; Steel investment foundries
Pr: Ralph Miller
**CEO:* Hadi Khandehroo
CFO: Roberta Baron
IT Man: Leah Stockton
QI Cn Mgr: Oscar Salazar
Mktg Dir: Frank Blank

MILLER CHILDREN'S HOSPITAL
See LONG BEACH MEMORIAL MEDICAL CENTER

D-U-N-S 09-257-0209
MILLER CO INC
11470 Bluegrass Pkwy, Louisville, KY 40299-2348
Tel (502) 254-5200 *Founded/Ownrshp* 1978
Sales 21.7MM^E *EMP* 42
SIC 5044 5065 Photocopy machines; Facsimile equipment
Ch Bd: Edward O Miller
**Pr:* Scott Miller
CFO: Debbie Kiefer
Ex VP: Chris Brown
VP: Mike Harris
**VP:* Sue Nally
CIO: Rick Masters

D-U-N-S 00-786-2964 IMP/EXP
MILLER COMPRESSING CO (WI)
(*Suby of* ALTER METAL RECYCLING) ★
1640 W Bruce St, Milwaukee, WI 53204-1140
Tel (414) 671-5980 *Founded/Ownrshp* 1903, 2012
Sales 87.2MM^E *EMP* 320
SIC 5093 Ferrous metal scrap & waste; Nonferrous metals scrap; Ferrous metal scrap & waste; Nonferrous metals scrap
Pr: John Busby
VP: Greg Kirkish
VP: Joseph Kovacich
VP: Philip Paley
CTO: Tom Carek
MIS Mgr: David Vogt
Snr Mgr: Brad Gahr
Board of Directors: Harold Paley

D-U-N-S 12-254-7284
MILLER CONSOLIDATED INDUSTRIES INC
2221 Arbor Blvd, Moraine, OH 45439-1521
Tel (937) 294-2681 *Founded/Ownrshp* 1982
Sales 25.1MM^E *EMP* 106
SIC 5051 3398 Steel; Metal heat treating; Steel; Metal heat treating
CFO: Tom Miller
Plnt Mgr: Nick Miller
Sales Exec: Carl Black

D-U-N-S 00-526-4544
MILLER CONTAINER CORP (IL)
3402 78th Ave W, Rock Island, IL 61201-7331
Tel (309) 787-6161 *Founded/Ownrshp* 1959
Sales 53.4MM^E *EMP* 250
SIC 2653 Boxes, corrugated: made from purchased materials; Boxes, corrugated: made from purchased materials
Pr: Michael Vonderhaa
**Ch Bd:* James Vonderhaa
**Ex VP:* Michael J Vanderhaar
Exec: Lynn Bickle
Genl Mgr: Tom Sivill
CTO: Sean McGuire
IT Man: Tracey Hitchcock
IT Man: Tracey Wisner
Plnt Mgr: Scott Copen

MILLER COUNTY SHERIFF DEPT
See COUNTY OF MILLER

D-U-N-S 06-387-5355
MILLER DISTRIBUTING INC
300 S 4th St, Saint Clair, PA 17970-1370
Tel (570) 429-1191 *Founded/Ownrshp* 1973
Sales 78.5MM *EMP* 38
SIC 5194 5145 5141 5147 Cigarettes; Cigars; Chewing tobacco; Confectionery; Groceries, general line; Meats & meat products; Cigarettes; Cigars; Chewing tobacco; Confectionery; Groceries, general line; Meats & meat products
Pr: William Miller
**Sec:* Elizabeth Miller
VP: Nan Merchant
VP: Jerry Watts
CTO: Allison Miller

D-U-N-S 02-194-0192 EXP
MILLER DISTRIBUTING OF FORT WORTH INC
1701 Pharr St, Fort Worth, TX 76102-1789
Tel (817) 877-5960 *Founded/Ownrshp* 1980
Sales 37.5MM^E *EMP* 215
SIC 5181 Beer & other fermented malt liquors; Beer & other fermented malt liquors
Pr: Dan Craine
**VP:* Joseph B Craine
**VP:* Pat Craine

D-U-N-S 01-924-9577
MILLER DON PONTIAC GMC TRUCK SUBARU INC
5802 Odana Rd, Madison, WI 53719-1212
Tel (608) 270-5000 *Founded/Ownrshp* 1977
Sales 25.6MM^E *EMP* 75
SIC 5511 Automobiles, new & used; Automobiles, new & used
Pr: Don Miller

D-U-N-S 78-206-8860 IMP/EXP
MILLER DRUCK SPECIALTY CONTRACTING INC
264 W 40th St, New York, NY 10018-1512
Tel (212) 343-3300 *Founded/Ownrshp* 1983
Sales 21.2MM *EMP* 125^E
Accts Citrincooperman Llp New York
SIC 1741 Marble masonry, exterior construction; Marble masonry, exterior construction
Pr: Barbara E Cohen
**Ofcr:* Frank Mizerik

D-U-N-S 01-898-4609
MILLER DRUG
LEADER DRUG STORE
210 State St, Bangor, ME 04401-5411
Tel (207) 947-8369 *Founded/Ownrshp* 1938
Sales 28.0MM *EMP* 90
SIC 5912 Drug stores; Drug stores
Pr: Bernard W Miller
**VP:* Gloria Miller
Admn Mgr: Brenda St Amand

D-U-N-S 00-287-4006
MILLER ELECTRIC CO (NE)
2501 Saint Marys Ave, Omaha, NE 68105-1696
Tel (402) 341-6479 *Founded/Ownrshp* 1912, 1977
Sales 150.7MM *EMP* 800
Accts Lutz & Company Pc Omaha Ne
SIC 1731 General electrical contractor; General electrical contractor
Pr: Ray Bruegman
**Treas:* William Henrichs
**VP:* Jeff Allen
VP: Brad Grate
**VP:* Ron Kohlmieer
Dir IT: Monte Watembach
Sales Exec: Don Fitzpatrick
Snr PM: Roger Knobbe Sr
Snr PM: John Kwyzla
Snr PM: Craig Langfeldt Sr

D-U-N-S 00-583-4205
MILLER ELECTRIC CO (FL)
2251 Rosselle St, Jacksonville, FL 32204-3125
Tel (904) 388-8000 *Founded/Ownrshp* 1928, 1966
Sales 260.5MM *EMP* 691
Accts Bishop And Draper Jacksonvill
SIC 1731 General electrical contractor; General electrical contractor
CEO: Henry K Brown
Pr: Thomas D Long
CFO: Susan A Walden
Sr VP: David Long
Sr VP: Ed Witt Jr
VP: Mike Brannen
VP: Daniel Brown
VP: Ngoc Lai
Exec: Scott Love
Exec: Kyle Paschal
CTO: Jonathan Matulevich

D-U-N-S 00-435-2837
MILLER ELECTRIC CONSTRUCTION INC (PA)
4377 William Flynn Hwy, Allison Park, PA 15101-1432
Tel (412) 487-1044 *Founded/Ownrshp* 1974, 2005
Sales 31.0MM^E *EMP* 150
Accts Mock Bosco & Associates Pc
SIC 1731 General electrical contractor; General electrical contractor
Ch Bd: Richard R Miller
**Pr:* William R Miller
Treas: Mariellie Mundy
**VP:* James Orchard
**VP:* Simon Reichbaum
**VP Opers:* Al Dicello

D-U-N-S 00-612-6379 IMP/EXP
■ **MILLER ELECTRIC MFG CO**
(*Suby of* ILLINOIS TOOL WORKS INC) ★
1635 W Spencer St, Appleton, WI 54914-4911
Tel (920) 734-9821 *Founded/Ownrshp* 1935, 1995
Sales 320.5MM^E *EMP* 1,500
SIC 3548 3621 Welding apparatus; Gas welding equipment; Arc welders, transformer-rectifier; Armatures, industrial; Welding apparatus; Gas welding equipment; Arc welders, transformer-rectifier; Armatures, industrial
Pr: Michael Weller
VP: Bill Henrichs
Rgnl Mgr: Keith Rzucidlo
Dist Mgr: Todd Stowell
Dist Mgr: Scott Wright
Genl Mgr: Jeff Schroeder
CIO: Cindy Lillge
CTO: Steve Clark
Dir IT: Keith King
Dir IT: Roy Miller
Sftwr Eng: Jeremy Overesch

D-U-N-S 84-753-6021
MILLER ELECTRICAL CONTRACTORS INC
613 Shallowford Rd, Chattanooga, TN 37411-1404
Tel (423) 698-4141 *Founded/Ownrshp* 2000
Sales 25.8MM^E *EMP* 100
SIC 1731 Electrical work
Pr: McKendree E Miller
**VP:* Chuck Wallen
Off Mgr: Lucy Russell

D-U-N-S 06-125-5543
▲ **MILLER ENERGY RESOURCES INC**
9721 Cogdill Rd Ste 302, Knoxville, TN 37932-3425
Tel (865) 223-6575 *Founded/Ownrshp* 1997
Sales 70.5MM *EMP* 84^E
Tkr Sym MILL *Exch* NYS
SIC 1311 Crude petroleum & natural gas; Crude petroleum & natural gas production; Crude petroleum & natural gas; Crude petroleum & natural gas production
CEO: Carl F Giesler Jr
**Ch Bd:* Scott M Boruff
COO: David M Hall
COO: Leland E Tate
CFO: Phillip G Elliott
Sr VP: Kurt C Yost
Dir IT: Chris Reneau
Counsel: Anya Corcoran
Board of Directors: Bob G Gower, Gerald E Hannahs Jr, William B Richardson, A Haag Sherman, Charles M Stivers

D-U-N-S 00-597-2674
MILLER ENGINEERING CO
MASTER SHEET METAL CONTRACTORS
1616 S Main St, Rockford, IL 61102-3598
Tel (815) 963-4878 *Founded/Ownrshp* 1960
Sales 27.9MM *EMP* 95
Accts Wipli Llp Freeport Il
SIC 1711 1731 Refrigeration contractor; Warm air heating & air conditioning contractor; Plumbing contractors; General electrical contractor; Refrigeration contractor; Warm air heating & air conditioning contractor; Plumbing contractors; General electrical contractor
Pr: Henry H Fortney
CFO: James E Brannick
VP: Bob Benen
VP: Steven Doonan
VP: James Fortney
VP: James Zweep
Genl Mgr: Cindy Broege
Sales Exec: Heather Landin
Sls Mgr: Todd Byxbe
Sls Mgr: Rob Quittschreiber

D-U-N-S 15-357-5618
MILLER ENGINEERS INC
SOUDER, MILLER & ASSOCIATES
3451 Cndlria Rd Ne Ste D, Albuquerque, NM 87107-1948
Tel (505) 325-7535 *Founded/Ownrshp* 1985
Sales 23.9MM^E *EMP* 120
SIC 8711 Consulting engineer; Consulting engineer
Ch Bd: Reid Allan
Pr: Peter Fant
COO: Karl Tonander

CFO: David Daffron
VP: Douglas Mize Sr
VP: James D Smith

MILLER ENTERPRISES
See MILLER HOLDING CO LLC

D-U-N-S 18-835-0482
MILLER ENTERPRISES INC
MILLER AUTO CENTER
2930 2nd St S, Saint Cloud, MN 56301-3809
Tel (320) 251-8900 *Founded/Ownrshp* 1998
Sales 56.4MM^E *EMP* 329
SIC 5511 5551 7514 7515 5531 5521 Automobiles, new & used; Trucks, tractors & trailers: new & used; Boat dealers; Passenger car rental; Passenger car leasing; Automotive & home supply stores; Automobiles, used cars only; Automobiles, new & used; Trucks, tractors & trailers: new & used; Boat dealers; Passenger car rental; Passenger car leasing; Automotive & home supply stores; Automobiles, used cars only
Pr: Thomas R Miller
**Sec:* Daniel R Dunn
**VP:* Barbara M Miller
Telecom Ex: Dan Diedrichs
Sls Mgr: Mike Mueller

D-U-N-S 07-578-8851
MILLER ENVIRONMENTAL GROUP INC (NY)
M E G
538 Edwards Ave, Calverton, NY 11933-1636
Tel (631) 369-4900 *Founded/Ownrshp* 1971
Sales 95.6MM^E *EMP* 145
SIC 4959 Oil spill cleanup; Oil spill cleanup
CEO: Mark Miller
CFO: Tom Horyczun
**VP:* George Wallace III

D-U-N-S 11-720-8293
MILLER ENVIRONMENTAL INC
1130 W Trenton Ave, Orange, CA 92867-3536
Tel (714) 385-0099 *Founded/Ownrshp* 1999
Sales 42.6MM^E *EMP* 150
SIC 1795 4953 Demolition, buildings & other structures; Hazardous waste collection & disposal; Demolition, buildings & other structures; Hazardous waste collection & disposal
Pr: Gregg Miller
**VP:* Rob Schaefer
Sfty Dirs: Eric Bdaniel

MILLER ENVIRONMENTAL SERVICES
See CKM INDUSTRIES INC

D-U-N-S 78-320-8130
MILLER ENVIRONMENTAL SERVICES LLC
401 Navigation Blvd, Corpus Christi, TX 78408-2747
Tel (361) 289-9800 *Founded/Ownrshp* 2014
Sales 95.5MM^E *EMP* 110
SIC 4953 7375 Hazardous waste collection & disposal; Data base information retrieval
Pr: Charles K Miller Jr
Dir IT: Joe Kramer
IT Man: Vincent Cotton
Mktg Dir: Paul Truax

D-U-N-S 61-171-8987
MILLER EXPEDITED FREIGHT INC
MILLER LOGISTICS
5777 Decatur Blvd Ste 300, Indianapolis, IN 46241-9609
Tel (317) 856-9240 *Founded/Ownrshp* 1998
Sales 21.0MM^E *EMP* 40
SIC 4731 Freight transportation arrangement
Pr: Lewis Miller
**CFO:* Robert Fair
**VP:* Joann Miller

D-U-N-S 00-615-0528 IMP
MILLER FELPAX CORP (MN)
MILLER INGENUITY
1155 E Sanborn St, Winona, MN 55987-4928
Tel (507) 452-2461 *Founded/Ownrshp* 1947
Sales 22.0MM *EMP* 55
SIC 3743 Lubrication systems, locomotive
Pr: Steve Blue
**CFO:* Paul Van Dyck
VP: Randy Skarlupka
Opers Mgr: Ron Papenfuss
VP Sls: Keith Gilbert
S&M/VP: Fred Gesell

MILLER FORD
See FORD MILLER SALES INC

D-U-N-S 87-692-2311
MILLER FORD INC
970 Kings Hwy E, Fairfield, CT 06825-5420
Tel (203) 335-7759 *Founded/Ownrshp* 1987
Sales 27.9MM^E *EMP* 150
SIC 5511 7515 7513 5531 5521 5013 Automobiles, new & used; Passenger car leasing; Truck rental & leasing, no drivers; Automotive & home supply stores; Used car dealers; Motor vehicle supplies & new parts; Automobiles, new & used; Passenger car leasing; Truck rental & leasing, no drivers; Automotive & home supply stores; Used car dealers; Motor vehicle supplies & new parts
Pr: Paul S Miller
**VP:* Kathleen Miller

MILLER FORD/MERCURY
See MILLER MOTOR SALES INC

MILLER FOREST PRODUCTS
See MILLER SHINGLE CO INC

D-U-N-S 02-169-5960
MILLER GLOBAL PROPERTIES LLC
4643 S Ulster St Ste 1500, Denver, CO 80237-2889
Tel (303) 773-0369 *Founded/Ownrshp* 1996
Sales 24.4MM^E *EMP* 25^E
SIC 6552 Land subdividers & developers, commercial
Ch: Myron Miller
**Pr:* Jim Miller
COO: Gary Roffe
Ex VP: Elisa Adam
Ex VP: Paul Hogan
Ex VP: William Lawrence
Ex VP: D Nickerson
Sr VP: Jason Kroll
VP: David Johnstone
VP: Gabrielle Keown
VP: Erin Onsager
VP: Mark Weston

D-U-N-S 12-256-9759
MILLER GROUP USA LLC
KSV
206 N Williamsburg Dr, Bloomington, IL 61704-3571
Tel (309) 662-8428 *Founded/Ownrshp* 1979
Sales 10.3MM^E *EMP* 300
Accts Reiser Chinski & Co Llp Cpas
SIC 5812 Fast-food restaurant, chain; Fast-food restaurant, chain

D-U-N-S 04-100-6628
MILLER HARDWARE CO LLC
211 E Hill Ave, Valdosta, GA 31601-5705
Tel (229) 244-0924 *Founded/Ownrshp* 1908
Sales 30.4MM^E *EMP* 69
SIC 5085 5251 Mill supplies; Hardware
CEO: Dutton Miller Sr
Genl Mgr: Arthur Barham

MILLER HILL JEEP EAGLE
See PEN INC

MILLER HND-VLKSWGN-SUZU-SUZUKI
See MILLER AUTO SALES INC

D-U-N-S 12-258-4204
MILLER HOLDING CO LLC
MILLER ENTERPRISES
105 N 8th Ave, Stroud, OK 74079-4407
Tel (918) 968-3584 *Founded/Ownrshp* 1983
Sales 50.4MM^E *EMP* 251^E
SIC 4213 Trucking, except local; Trucking, except local

D-U-N-S 00-110-0627
MILLER INDUSTRIES INC (ME)
EDWARDS HOME FURNISHINGS
Canal St Rr 196, Lisbon Falls, ME 04252
Tel (207) 353-4371 *Founded/Ownrshp* 1929, 2000
Sales 22.5MM^E *EMP* 290
SIC 2211 2282 Broadwoven fabric mills, cotton; Wool yarn: twisting, winding or spooling; Broadwoven fabric mills, cotton; Wool yarn: twisting, winding or spooling
Pr: Herbert A Miller

D-U-N-S 61-738-5208
▲ MILLER INDUSTRIES INC
JIGE
8503 Hilltop Dr, Ooltewah, TN 37363-6841
Tel (423) 238-4171 *Founded/Ownrshp* 1990
Sales 492.7MM *EMP* 820
Tkr Sym MLR *Exch* NYS
SIC 3713 Automobile wrecker truck bodies; Car carrier bodies; Automobile wrecker truck bodies; Car carrier bodies
Co-CEO: Jeffrey I Badgley
**Ch Bd:* William G Miller
CFO: J Vincent Mish
Ex VP: Frank Madonia
VP: John Hawkins
VP: Deborah Whitmire
IT Man: Samir Dhond
IT Man: Jonathan Freeland
VP Sls: Tom Luciano
Board of Directors: Theodore H Ashford III, A Russell Chandlier III, Richard H Roberts

D-U-N-S 07-904-2511
■ MILLER INDUSTRIES TOWING EQUIPMENT INC
(*Suby of* CENTURY HOLDINGS INC) ★
8503 Hilltop Dr, Ooltewah, TN 37363-6841
Tel (423) 238-4171 *Founded/Ownrshp* 1987
Sales 80.5MM^E *EMP* 425
SIC 3799 Towing & tugboat service; Towing bars & systems
Ch Bd: William G Miller
**Pr:* Jeffrey Badgley
**Pr:* Will Miller
**CFO:* J Vincent Mish
**VP:* Randy Olson

MILLER INDUSTRY
See CENTURY HOLDINGS INC

MILLER INGENUITY
See MILLER FELPAX CORP

D-U-N-S 05-904-0923
MILLER INSULATION CO INC
3520 E Century Ave, Bismarck, ND 58503-0739
Tel (701) 258-4323 *Founded/Ownrshp* 1984
Sales 87.6MM^E *EMP* 515
SIC 1742 1542 Insulation, buildings; Insulation, buildings; Nonresidential construction
Pr: Brad Miller
**VP:* Dwight Miller
Genl Mgr: Don Ell
Off Mgr: Karen Messer
Snr Mgr: Curt Heiser

D-U-N-S 82-491-4790 IMP
MILLER INTERMODAL LOGISTICS SERVICES INC
MILS
(*Suby of* DEWEY CORP) ★
371 Highland Colony Pkwy, Ridgeland, MS 39157-6035
Tel (601) 922-8331 *Founded/Ownrshp* 1993
Sales 31.5MM *EMP* 40
Accts Horne Llp Ridgeland Mississi
SIC 4213 Heavy hauling; Heavy hauling
Pr: Steve Haskins

D-U-N-S 00-705-9561 IMP
MILLER INTERNATIONAL INC
ROCKY MOUNTAIN CLOTHING CO
8500 Zuni St, Denver, CO 80260-5007
Tel (303) 428-5696 *Founded/Ownrshp* 1919
Sales 29.1MM^E *EMP* 150
SIC 2339 2325 2321 2331 Jeans: women's, misses' & juniors'; Jeans: men's, youths' & boys'; Men's & boys' furnishings; Shirts, women's & juniors': made from purchased materials; Jeans: women's, misses' & juniors'; Jeans: men's, youths' & boys'; Men's & boys' furnishings; Shirts, women's & juniors': made from purchased materials
CEO: David Dean
**Pr:* Ronald Schmitz
CFO: Pat Hurley
**CFO:* Thomas Whitten
VP: Cliff Peterson
VP: Chuck Winter
Dir IT: John Seville
IT Man: Charles Winter
Sls Dir: Matthew Schmitz
Sls Dir: Jeremy Weiss
Mktg Mgr: Chris Derrick

MILLER JOHNSON
See MILLER JOHNSON SNELL & CUMMISKEY PLC

D-U-N-S 07-927-6879
MILLER JOHNSON SNELL & CUMMISKEY PLC
MILLER JOHNSON
250 Monroe Ave Nw Ste 800, Grand Rapids, MI 49503-2283
Tel (616) 831-1700 *Founded/Ownrshp* 1959
Sales 33.8MM^E *EMP* 251
SIC 8111 General practice law office; General practice law office
CEO: Craig Mutch
V Ch: Richard Hillary
Pr: Caitlin Chamberlin
Pr: Jerusha Washington
COO: Betsy Raymond
CIO: Erik B Goltzer
Counsel: Harry Contos Jr
Counsel: Brent Rector

D-U-N-S 06-038-8576
MILLER KAPLAN ARASE LLP
CAHN, JSPH/MILLER KAPLAN ARASE
4123 Lankershim Blvd, North Hollywood, CA 91602-2828
Tel (818) 769-2010 *Founded/Ownrshp* 1940
Sales 21.2MM^E *EMP* 135
SIC 8721

MILLER KNAPP DIVISION
See TURTLE & HUGHES INC

D-U-N-S 08-323-5481
MILLER KREISCHER
100 Witmer Rd Ste 350, Horsham, PA 19044-2369
Tel (215) 441-4600 *Founded/Ownrshp* 1975
Sales 26.7MM^E *EMP* 190
SIC 8721 Certified public accountant; Certified public accountant
Pt: Stephen W Christian
**Pt:* Mark D Anderson
**Pt:* Michael A Coakley
**Pt:* Timothy A Dudek
**Pt:* John Heck
**Pt:* Sassan S Hejazi
**Pt:* Timothy C Hilbert
**Pt:* Mark G Metzler
**Pt:* John Schlechter
**Pt:* David E Shaffer
**Pt:* Richard Snyder
**Pt:* Mario O Vicari
Bd of Dir: Mark Metzler
Ofcr: Linda Larson
Ofcr: Roman Leshak
Dir Risk M: Laurie Murphy

D-U-N-S 83-600-3418
MILLER LARRY DODGE INC
LARRY MILLER DODGE
8665 W Bell Rd, Peoria, AZ 85382-3707
Tel (623) 815-2200 *Founded/Ownrshp* 1995
Sales 75.9MM^E *EMP* 200
SIC 5511 5531 7538 7532 5521 New & used car dealers; Automotive parts; General automotive repair shops; Top & body repair & paint shops; Used car dealers; New & used car dealers; Automotive parts; General automotive repair shops; Top & body repair & paint shops; Used car dealers
CEO: Greg Miller
**Pr:* Karen G Miller
**VP:* Roger Miller
Sls Mgr: Mark Mauer
Sales Asso: Sam Slater

MILLER LITTLE GIANT
See MILLER MANUFACTURING CO

MILLER LOGISTICS
See MILLER EXPEDITED FREIGHT INC

MILLER LUMBER
See MILLER & CO INC

D-U-N-S 04-671-2097 IMP
MILLER MANUFACTURING CO
MILLER LITTLE GIANT
(*Suby of* FRANDSEN CORP) ★
2910 Waters Rd Ste 150, Eagan, MN 55121-1654
Tel (651) 982-5100 *Founded/Ownrshp* 1996
Sales 89.8MM^E *EMP* 150
SIC 1542 5199 Farm building construction; Pet supplies; Farm building construction; Pet supplies
CEO: Dan Frandsen
**Pr:* Tom Botten
VP: Ron Barsalou
VP: Dan Gorowsky
Plnt Mgr: Tony Ebert
VP Mktg: Amy Scheel
**VP Sls:* James Thompson

MILLER, MARK TOYOTA
See MARK MILLER INC

MILLER MARTS
See MILLER OIL CO INC

MILLER MEAT POULTRY
See CRYSTAL VALLEY FARMS LLC

D-U-N-S 15-243-8417
MILLER MECHANICAL CONTRACTORS & ENGINEERS LLC
1976 Airport Ind Pk Dr Se, Marietta, GA 30060-9203
Tel (770) 952-3864 *Founded/Ownrshp* 2003
Sales 25.0MM *EMP* 160
SIC 1711 Plumbing contractors; Plumbing contractors
CFO: Alice Miller
Opers Mgr: Steve Sholl

D-U-N-S 05-454-5804
MILLER MEDICAL
4727 E Bell Rd Ste 45122, Phoenix, AZ 85032-2300
Tel (602) 773-1012 *Founded/Ownrshp* 2011
Sales 35.0MM *EMP* 2
SIC 5047 Hospital equipment & supplies; Hospital equipment & supplies
Owner: Cheryl Mercure

D-U-N-S 17-355-1094 IMP
MILLER METAL FABRICATION INC
16356 Sussex Hwy Unit 4, Bridgeville, DE 19933-3056
Tel (302) 337-2291 *Founded/Ownrshp* 1982
Sales 34.0MM^E *EMP* 68
SIC 3441 3542 Fabricated structural metal; Mechanical (pneumatic or hydraulic) metal forming machines
Pr: Martin W Miller Jr
**CFO:* Bruce Kelley
**VP Opers:* Dave Morris

D-U-N-S 05-055-8451
MILLER METALS SERVICE CORP (IL)
2400 Bond St, University Park, IL 60484-3102
Tel (708) 534-7200 *Founded/Ownrshp* 1969
Sales 23.9MM^E *EMP* 35
SIC 5051 Metals service centers & offices
CEO: Wayne J Miller
**Pr:* Brian R Miller
Plnt Mgr: Joel Sandoval

D-U-N-S 01-333-8934
MILLER MOTOR CAR CORP (NY)
MILLER'S BODY SHOP
4455 Vestal Pkwy E, Vestal, NY 13850-3559
Tel (607) 797-1221 *Founded/Ownrshp* 1945
Sales 37.9MM^E *EMP* 120
SIC 5511 7538 7515 7513 5531 Automobiles, new & used; General automotive repair shops; Passenger car leasing; Truck rental & leasing, no drivers; Automotive & home supply stores; Automobiles, new & used; General automotive repair shops; Passenger car leasing; Truck rental & leasing, no drivers; Automotive & home supply stores
Pr: Wendell H Miller
**VP:* Kenneth Miller
Sales Asso: Dave Petrolle

D-U-N-S 02-317-2372
MILLER MOTOR SALES INC
MILLER FORD/MERCURY
1196 Milwaukee Ave, Burlington, WI 53105-1367
Tel (888) 580-0957 *Founded/Ownrshp* 1939
Sales 22.8MM^E *EMP* 50
SIC 5511 7538 5521 5012 Automobiles, new & used; Pickups, new & used; General automotive repair shops; Used car dealers; Automobiles & other motor vehicles
Pr: Chris Miller
Pr: Heather Latham
**Sec:* Sally Miller
Store Mgr: Larry Hacker
Sales Asso: Ron Greiner

MILLER NISSAN
See MILLER AUTOMOTIVE GROUP INC

MILLER NISSAN, JEEP, VOLVO
See MCNAMARA MOTORS INC

D-U-N-S 02-686-4579 IMP
MILLER OF DENTON LTD
2421 N Interstate 35, Denton, TX 76207-2026
Tel (940) 566-6717 *Founded/Ownrshp* 1959
Sales 70.1MM^E *EMP* 214
SIC 5181 Beer & other fermented malt liquors; Beer & other fermented malt liquors
Pr: Richard J Fisher
**Sec:* Nancie A Lippe

D-U-N-S 08-629-2513 IMP
MILLER OIL CO INC
MILLER MARTS
1000 E City Hall Ave, Norfolk, VA 23504-4214
Tel (757) 623-6600 *Founded/Ownrshp* 1977
Sales 115.1MM^E *EMP* 550
SIC 5411 5172 5983 7549 Convenience stores, chain; Petroleum products; Fuel oil dealers; Lubrication service, automotive; Convenience stores, chain; Petroleum products; Fuel oil dealers; Lubrication service, automotive
CEO: Augustus C Miller
**Pr:* Jeffrey G Miller
**Sec:* Deanne Miller
VP: Colen Hodgson
Dist Mgr: Ron Reed
VP Opers: Wanda Sheffield

D-U-N-S 00-902-6659
MILLER PAINT CO INC
12812 Ne Whitaker Way, Portland, OR 97230-1110
Tel (503) 255-0190 *Founded/Ownrshp* 1890
Sales 81.0MM^E *EMP* 175
SIC 2851 5231 Paints: oil or alkyd vehicle or water thinned; Paints, waterproof; Wood stains; Paint; Paint brushes, rollers, sprayers & other supplies; Wallpaper; Paints: oil or alkyd vehicle or water thinned; Paints, waterproof; Wood stains; Paint; Paint brushes, rollers, sprayers & other supplies; Wallpaper
Pr: Stephen L Dearborn
**CFO:* Bill Cameron
**Sr VP:* Paul Sawyer
**VP:* Steve Serra
Store Mgr: Mike Appel
Sales Asso: Brian Brown
Sales Asso: Ray Rossi

MILLER PAPER & PACKAGING
See MILLER PAPER CO

D-U-N-S 87-875-4290
MILLER PAPER CO
MILLER PAPER & PACKAGING
6511 S Washington St, Amarillo, TX 79118-8347
Tel (806) 353-0317 *Founded/Ownrshp* 2006
Sales 23.7MM^E *EMP* 42
SIC 5113 5087 2621 5199 Industrial & personal service paper; Janitors' supplies; Packaging paper; Packaging materials
Pr: Joseph Earl Schmidt
**CFO:* Clay Robinett
**VP:* Corby Bleckert
**VP:* Beth Furgerson
**VP:* Charles Furgerson
**VP:* Cindy Schmidt
**VP:* Sean Wright
Opers Mgr: Greg Lane
Sls Mgr: Davis Estrange
Sls Mgr: David Strange
Sales Asso: Doug Smith

MILLER PARK
See MILWAUKEE SPORTSERVICE INC

MILLER, PAUL MAZDA
See PAUL MILLER FORD INC

D-U-N-S 18-469-5133
MILLER PAVING & CONSTRUCTION LLC
7150 Kaw Dr, Kansas City, KS 66111-2428
Tel (913) 334-5579 *Founded/Ownrshp* 2002
Sales 23.3MM^E *EMP* 250
SIC 1623 Underground utilities contractor; Underground utilities contractor

D-U-N-S 00-287-9294
■ **MILLER PIPELINE LLC**
(*Suby of* VECTREN CORP) ★
8850 Crawfordsville Rd, Indianapolis, IN 46234-1559
Tel (317) 293-0278 *Founded/Ownrshp* 1995
Sales 683.3MM^E *EMP* 2,000
SIC 1623 Pipeline construction; Pipeline construction
CEO: Douglas S Banning Jr
**Pr:* Kevin Miller
COO: Robert McCormick
**CFO:* Daniel Short
**Sec:* Nina Mann
**Ex VP:* Dale Anderson
VP: Greg Frazier
VP: Mark Hallett
VP: Scott Miller
VP: Greg Raver
VP: Dave Tucker

D-U-N-S 09-331-5489
MILLER PLACE UNION FREE SCHOOL DISTRICT (INC)
7 Memorial Dr, Miller Place, NY 11764-2802
Tel (631) 474-2700 *Founded/Ownrshp* 1920
Sales 19.5MM^E *EMP* 340
SIC 8211 Public elementary school; Public junior high school; Public senior high school; Public elementary school; Public junior high school; Public senior high school
Pr: Michael Unger
**VP:* Brian Neyland

D-U-N-S 02-301-7197
MILLER PONTIAC-BUICK-GMC INC
MILLER AUTO CTR BODY SHOP
(*Suby of* MILLER AUTO CENTER) ★
2930 2nd St S, Saint Cloud, MN 56301-3809
Tel (320) 251-1363 *Founded/Ownrshp* 1971
Sales 25.5MM^E *EMP* 100
Accts Mc Mahon Hartmann & Amundson
SIC 5511 7532 Automobiles, new & used; Trucks, tractors & trailers: new & used; Exterior repair services; Automobiles, new & used; Trucks, tractors & trailers: new & used; Exterior repair services
Pr: Thomas R Miller
**Treas:* Daniel R Dunn
**VP:* Barbara M Miller

MILLER POULTRY
See PINE MANOR INC

D-U-N-S 05-435-5755
MILLER PRODUCTS INC
M P I LABEL SYSTEMS
450 Courtney Rd, Sebring, OH 44672-1339
Tel (330) 938-2134 *Founded/Ownrshp* 1968
Sales 27.5MM^E *EMP* 160^E
SIC 2672

D-U-N-S 15-137-7736
MILLER PRODUCTS INC
596 Anderson Ave Ste 305, Cliffside Park, NJ 07010-1868
Tel (201) 943-7900 *Founded/Ownrshp* 1985
Sales 4.2MM^E *EMP* 355^E
SIC 5963 Direct selling establishments
Pr: Herb Miller

D-U-N-S 00-926-7592
MILLER SHINGLE CO INC (WA)
MILLER FOREST PRODUCTS
20820 Gun Club Rd, Granite Falls, WA 98252
Tel (360) 691-7727 *Founded/Ownrshp* 1946
Sales 26.8MM^E *EMP* 202
SIC 2411 7389 2429 2421 Logging camps & contractors; Log & lumber broker; Shingle & shingle mills; Sawmills & planing mills, general; Logging camps & contractors; Log & lumber broker; Shingle & shingle mills; Sawmills & planing mills, general
Pr: Bruce L Miller II
CFO: Tom Leach
**VP:* Barry R Miller

D-U-N-S 08-751-1817
MILLER SIERRA CONTRACTORS INC
MSC
1760 S Pipeline Rd W, Euless, TX 76040-6837
Tel (817) 358-1201 *Founded/Ownrshp* 1992
Sales 54.9MM^E *EMP* 200
Accts Sutton Frost Cary Llp Arlingt
SIC 1771 Concrete work; Concrete work
Pr: Robert H Miller
**VP:* Beth Bruner
**VP:* Terry Fowler
VP: Billy Hodges
**VP:* Jerry Seeley
**VP:* Robby Temple
VP Opers: Jim Semmens
Mtls Mgr: Daniel Garcia

D-U-N-S 05-202-0176
■ **MILLER SPRINGS MATERIALS LLC**
(*Suby of* JAMES CONSTRUCTION GROUP LLC) ★
6218 State Highway 317, Belton, TX 76513-5397
Tel (254) 780-9959 *Founded/Ownrshp* 2010
Sales 119.1MM^E *EMP* 716^E
SIC 5085 5999 Springs; Rock & stone specimens
Pr: Danny L Hester
CFO: Donald B Bonaventure
Off Mgr: Josey Taylor

D-U-N-S 07-490-6876
MILLER SUPPLY INC
29902 Avenida De Las Bnd, Rancho Santa Margari, CA 92688
Tel (949) 589-6033 *Founded/Ownrshp* 1980
Sales 22.6MM^E *EMP* 45^E
SIC 5113 5087 5085 Corrugated & solid fiber boxes; Moving equipment & supplies; Textile printers' supplies
Pr: Eric J Miller
**VP:* Susan Miller
Genl Mgr: Greg May

D-U-N-S 01-616-8379 IMP
MILLER SUPPLY OF WV INC
1537 Blachleyville Rd, Wooster, OH 44691-9752
Tel (330) 264-9146 *Founded/Ownrshp* 1964
Sales 28.2MM^E *EMP* 80
SIC 5084 Oil well machinery, equipment & supplies; Oil well machinery, equipment & supplies
Pr: Jack K Miller
CFO: Joe Sanders
**Sec:* Kenneth R Miller
**VP:* Max A Miller

D-U-N-S 11-867-5367
MILLER TECHNOLOGIES INTERNATIONAL
3928 Mcgregor Ct, Mobile, AL 36608-1832
Tel (251) 343-9101 *Founded/Ownrshp* 1989
Sales 23.1MM^E *EMP* 150
SIC 2671 Plastic film, coated or laminated for packaging; Plastic film, coated or laminated for packaging
Pr: Drayton Miller

MILLER TOYOTA
See MILABEL MOTORS INC

D-U-N-S 04-841-8487
MILLER TRANSFER AND RIGGING CO
(*Suby of* UNITED TRANSPORT INDUSTRIES INC) ★
3833 State Route 183, Rootstown, OH 44272-9799
Tel (330) 325-2521 *Founded/Ownrshp* 1968
Sales 36.7MM^E *EMP* 150
SIC 4213 Heavy machinery transport; Heavy machinery transport
Pr: Jim Unger
Pr: Norman Hartline
**Sec:* Kenneth H Rusinoff
**VP:* David Cochran
**VP:* Kevin Hohlefelder
**VP:* Mitchell Unger
Opers Mgr: Gordon Roe
Manager: Mike Raus

D-U-N-S 00-385-1409
MILLER TRANSPORTATION SERVICES INC (MS)
(*Suby of* DEWEY CORP) ★
5500 Highway 80 W, Jackson, MS 39209-3507
Tel (601) 856-6526 *Founded/Ownrshp* 1942, 1964
Sales 108.2MM *EMP* 1,000
Accts Horne Llp Ridgeland Mississi
SIC 4231 4213 Trucking terminal facilities; Trucking, except local; Trucking terminal facilities; Trucking, except local
Pr: Lee Miller
Ex VP: Hal Miller
Sfty Dirs: Ray Riley

MILLER TRANSPORTERS
See DEWEY CORP

D-U-N-S 10-788-3126
MILLER TRANSPORTERS EMPLOYEES
5500 Highway 80 W, Jackson, MS 39209-3507
Tel (601) 922-8331 *Founded/Ownrshp* 1950
Sales NA *EMP* 2
Accts Securities And Exchange Commis
SIC 6141 Personal credit institutions; Personal credit institutions
Pr: Scott Miller
**Treas:* James Smith

D-U-N-S 07-914-1630
MILLER TRANSPORTERS INC
(*Suby of* MILLER TRANSPORTATION SERVICES INC) ★
5500 Highway 80 W, Jackson, MS 39209-3507
Tel (601) 922-8331 *Founded/Ownrshp* 2013
Sales 110.0MM *EMP* 204^E
SIC 4213 Trucking, except local; Trucking, except local
Pr: Lee Miller

D-U-N-S 10-588-3102
MILLER TRUCK LINES LLC
(*Suby of* MILLER ENTERPRISES) ★
105 N 8th Ave, Stroud, OK 74079-4407
Tel (918) 968-3584 *Founded/Ownrshp* 1985
Sales 50.4MM^E *EMP* 250
SIC 4213 Trucking, except local; Trucking, except local
Pr: John Pinkston
CFO: Philip Vinson
Top Exec: James L Mier
Exec: Don Miller
Brnch Mgr: Bobby Miller

MILLER VALENTIN CONSTRUCTION
See MV COMMERCIAL CONSTRUCTION LLC

MILLER VALENTINE GROUP
See MILLER-VALENTINE OPERATIONS INC

D-U-N-S 00-642-0038 EXP
MILLER VENEERS INC
3724 E 13th St, Indianapolis, IN 46201-1502
Tel (317) 638-2326 *Founded/Ownrshp* 1930
Sales 25.4MM^E *EMP* 140
SIC 2435 Hardwood veneer & plywood; Hardwood veneer & plywood
Pr: Thomas A Miller
**Treas:* Benjamin R Miller
**VP:* Sally M Sando
Dir IT: Carla Carter
Plnt Mgr: Hugh Locke

D-U-N-S 00-615-0023 IMP
MILLER WASTE MILLS INC
RTP COMPANY
580 E Front St, Winona, MN 55987-4256
Tel (507) 454-6906 *Founded/Ownrshp* 1927
Sales 326.2MM^E *EMP* 650
SIC 3087 2821 Custom compound purchased resins; Fibers, textile: recovery from textile mill waste & rags; Custom compound purchased resins; Thermoplastic materials
CEO: Hugh L Miller
**CFO:* Brian Evenson
**Sec:* Jonathan Miller
**Ex VP:* Joe Kluck
VP: Mary Auna
**VP:* Steve Maki
VP: Steve Makia
VP: Peter Ploumidis
Exec: Jamey Erickson
Exec: Lance Sebo
Mng Dir: Jean Sirois

D-U-N-S 01-390-4628 IMP
MILLER WELDING AND MACHINE CO (PA)
111 2nd St, Brookville, PA 15825-2033
Tel (814) 849-3061 *Founded/Ownrshp* 1963
Sales 50.9MM^E *EMP* 200^E
Accts Smith Lewis Chess & Company Ll
SIC 7692 3599 3444 Welding repair; Machine shop, jobbing & repair; Sheet metalwork; Welding repair; Machine shop, jobbing & repair; Sheet metalwork
Pr: David K Miller
**Pr:* Pamela G Lindermuth
**Treas:* Sara G Miller
**Sr VP:* Bradley R Miller
**VP:* Jeffrey C Miller
Sales Asso: Dan Smith

D-U-N-S 03-354-4917
MILLER ZELL INC
(*Suby of* ISD HOLDINGS INC) ★
4715 Frederick Dr Sw, Atlanta, GA 30336-1809
Tel (404) 691-7400 *Founded/Ownrshp* 1999
Sales 102.1MM^E *EMP* 400
Accts Pricewaterhousecoopers Llp
SIC 7389 2542 2759 2752 Design services; Fixtures, store: except wood; Screen printing; Commercial printing, offset; Design services; Fixtures, store: except wood; Screen printing; Commercial printing, offset
CEO: Harmon B Miller III
Pr: Michael Leonhardi
**Pr:* Lucinda Williams
**CFO:* David Seem
**V Ch Bd:* Harmon Miller IV
Sr VP: Vera Litynsky
Sr VP: Brent Schilling
Sr VP: Amy Yuncker
VP: Rick Barrick
VP: Sam Dressler
VP: Tom Ertler
VP: Dave Feem
VP: D'Anna Hawthorne
VP: Robert Kapas
VP: Robert Kennedy
VP: Brian Kok
VP: Paul Nichols
VP: Paul Pizzini
VP: Dave Seem
VP: Craig Thompson
VP: Larry Wolfson

D-U-N-S 02-714-2892
MILLER-BOWIE SUPPLY CO
MBS
1007 W 3rd St, Texarkana, TX 75501-5435
Tel (903) 794-3631 *Founded/Ownrshp* 1950
Sales 64.6MM^E *EMP* 143
SIC 5191 5153 Farm supplies; Feed; Seeds & bulbs; Fertilizer & fertilizer materials; Grain elevators; Farm supplies; Feed; Seeds & bulbs; Fertilizer & fertilizer materials; Grain elevators
CEO: Ed R Smith
**Pr:* Charlie Starks
**Ch:* Dan York
**Treas:* Shep Gage
**VP:* Bill Goza

D-U-N-S 04-201-3227
MILLER-BRADFORD & RISBERG INC (WI)
W250n6851 State Road 164, Sussex, WI 53089-5510
Tel (262) 246-5710 *Founded/Ownrshp* 1969
Sales 47.9MM^E *EMP* 120
SIC 5082 General construction machinery & equipment; General construction machinery & equipment
Pr: Michael J Soley
Treas: William C Arnold
VP: Peter Kritch
VP: Dan Soley

D-U-N-S 10-752-5354
MILLER-CLAPPERTON PARTNERSHIP INC
7948 Second Flags Dr, Austell, GA 30168-7641
Tel (770) 941-8281 *Founded/Ownrshp* 1979
Sales 23.1MM^E *EMP* 65
SIC 3448 Trusses & framing: prefabricated metal
Pr: Ted S Miller
COO: William Coman
**Treas:* J David Clapperton
Dir IT: Rob Coker
Opers Mgr: Gene Lasey
Prd Mgr: Eric Harris
Mktg Dir: Zeke Miller

D-U-N-S 04-638-7809
MILLER-EADS CO INC
4125 N Keystone Ave, Indianapolis, IN 46205-2842
Tel (317) 495-6700 *Founded/Ownrshp* 1990
Sales 51.4MM^E *EMP* 120
Accts Bkd Llp Indianapolis In
SIC 1731 Electrical work; Electrical work
CEO: Thomas G Chastain
**Pr:* T Christopher Chastain
**Ex VP:* Daniel D Sparks
**VP:* Greg Costelow
Dir IT: Muegge Kyle
IT Man: Kyle Muegge
Sfty Dirs: Kevin Schrader

D-U-N-S 02-562-2845
MILLER-HFI LLC
428 N 2nd St, La Salle, CO 80645-3308
Tel (970) 785-2885 *Founded/Ownrshp* 2008
Sales 26.7MM^E *EMP* 51
SIC 1389 Oil field services; Oil field services

MILLER-KEYSTONE BLOOD CENTER
See HCSC BLOOD CENTER

D-U-N-S 00-895-7854
MILLER-NICHOLSON CO
HONDA OF SEATTLE
2005 Airport Way S, Seattle, WA 98134-1602
Tel (206) 382-8800 *Founded/Ownrshp* 1986
Sales 51.3MM^E *EMP* 135
SIC 5511

D-U-N-S 02-516-5359
MILLER-VALENTINE OPERATIONS INC
MILLER VALENTINE GROUP
137 N Main St Ste 900, Dayton, OH 45402-1846
Tel (937) 293-0900 *Founded/Ownrshp* 2004
Sales 153.0MM *EMP* 800
SIC 6552 6531 Subdividers & developers; Real estate managers
CEO: Bill Krul
**CFO:* Edward Blake
CFO: Al Schneider
**Ex VP:* Jack Goodwin
Ex VP: Clarice Hoffer
VP: Kevin Werner
Dir Bus: Peter Horton
Off Mgr: Lois Smith
Snr PM: Brooks Williams

D-U-N-S 00-618-6415
MILLERBERND MANUFACTURING CO (MN)
622 6th St S, Winsted, MN 55395-7721
Tel (320) 485-2111 *Founded/Ownrshp* 1933
Sales 145.8MM^E *EMP* 320
SIC 3312 Stainless steel; Structural shapes & pilings, steel; Stainless steel; Structural shapes & pilings, steel
Pr: Trevor S Millerbernd
**VP:* Stephen A Millerbernd
IT Man: Tad William
Sfty Dirs: Bill Krause
S&M/VP: Mark Wendt
Mktg Mgr: Cody Cuhel
Mktg Mgr: Mike Wendolek
Sls Mgr: Mitch Gaida
Sls Mgr: Jay Wilson
Sales Asso: Vicki Thonvold
Snr Mgr: Alan Barfknecht

D-U-N-S 06-285-2520 IMP
MILLERBERND SYSTEMS INC
330 6th St S, Winsted, MN 55395-1102
Tel (320) 485-2685 *Founded/Ownrshp* 1972
Sales 29.5MM^E *EMP* 70
SIC 3556 3599 Dairy & milk machinery; Machine shop, jobbing & repair
CEO: Ralph J Millerbernd
**Pr:* Brad Millenbrend
**Ex VP:* Farid Currimbhoy
VP: Terry Voigt
Genl Mgr: Brad Millerbernd
Opers Mgr: Sam Zimmerman

D-U-N-S 00-609-5251 IMP/EXP
MILLERCOORS LLC
(*Suby of* SABMILLER PLC)
250 S Wacker Dr Ste 800, Chicago, IL 60606-5888
Tel (312) 496-2700 *Founded/Ownrshp* 2008
Sales 1.5MMM^E *EMP* 4,500
SIC 2082 Beer (alcoholic beverage); Beer (alcoholic beverage)
CEO: Leo Kiely
**Pr:* Tom Long
**COO:* Dennis Puffer
**CFO:* Gavin Hattersley
CFO: Tracey Joubert
CFO: Reto Wittwer
Div Pres: Tom Cardella
Div Pres: Ed McBrien
**Chf Mktg O:* Andrew England
Ofcr: Cornell Boggs III
Ofcr: Tim Wolf
Ex VP: Fernando J Palacios
VP: Steve Pear
VP: Daniel Werth

D-U-N-S 80-018-8141
MILLERS ALE HOUSE INC
(*Suby of* ALE HOUSE MANAGEMENT INC) ★
5750 Major Blvd Ste 400, Orlando, FL 32819-7971
Tel (561) 743-2299 *Founded/Ownrshp* 2013
Sales 71.3MM^E *EMP* 1,307^E
SIC 5812 Restaurant, family: chain
CEO: John W Miller
**Pr:* Raymond Holden
VP: Doug Jackson
Rgnl Mgr: Paul Greenberg
Genl Mgr: Kevin Adams
Genl Mgr: Eric Dinsmore
Genl Mgr: Heather Gailey
Genl Mgr: Ken Garcia
Genl Mgr: Todd Goodman
Genl Mgr: Jon Holmes
Genl Mgr: Quentin Lapeyrouse

MILLER'S BODY SHOP
See MILLER MOTOR CAR CORP

D-U-N-S 00-791-1308
MILLERS CAPITAL INSURANCE CO (PA)
MILLERS MUTUAL GROUP
805 N Front St, Harrisburg, PA 17102-3418
Tel (717) 232-3211 *Founded/Ownrshp* 1890
Sales NA *EMP* 65
SIC 6331 Property damage insurance; Fire, marine & casualty insurance & carriers; Property damage insurance; Fire, marine & casualty insurance & carriers
CEO: Scott Orndoff
Treas: Karen Mashinski
Sr VP: J Michael Davis
VP: Lawrence Fortin
CIO: Larry Fortin
Counsel: Stephen Busch

D-U-N-S 60-684-7523
MILLERS HEALTH SYSTEMS INC
MILLER'S MERRY MANOR
1690 S County Farm Rd, Warsaw, IN 46580-8248
Tel (574) 267-7211 *Founded/Ownrshp* 1964
Sales 141.3MM^E *EMP* 3,000
SIC 8052 8051 8361 Intermediate care facilities; Skilled nursing care facilities; Residential care; Intermediate care facilities; Skilled nursing care facilities; Residential care
Pr: Patrick H Boyle
COO: Greg Spaulding
Sr VP: Mike Forgey
Chf Nrs Of: Krista Lickey
Ex Dir: Debbie Hale
Off Mgr: Barbara Green
Off Mgr: Cathy Rademaker
Dir IT: Brian Holdrread
Sls&Mrk Ex: Mary Chapman
Mktg Dir: Richard Hawley
Mktg Dir: Pam McMahan
Board of Directors: Brad Harris

D-U-N-S 03-136-9135
MILLERS INC
610 E Jefferson St, Pittsburg, KS 66762-5913
Tel (620) 231-8050 *Founded/Ownrshp* 1939
Sales 129.5MM *EMP* 380
SIC 7384 Film developing & printing; Film developing & printing
Ch Bd: Richard G Miller
**Pr:* Todd R Coleman
**CFO:* Marcia Sorrick
**VP:* H Richard Coleman
VP: Mark Ripley
Dir IT: Doug Berry
IT Man: Travis Bonine
Art Dir: Samae Claspill

MILLER'S MARKET
See SKICO INC

MILLER'S MERRY MANOR
See MILLERS HEALTH SYSTEMS INC

MILLERS MUTUAL GROUP
See MILLERS CAPITAL INSURANCE CO

D-U-N-S 00-791-7826
MILLERS PENN INSURANCE CO (PA)
ACE AGRIBUSINESS
(*Suby of* ACE AMERICAN INSURANCE CO) ★
72 N Franklin St, Wilkes Barre, PA 18701-1301
Tel (570) 822-8111 *Founded/Ownrshp* 1887
Sales NA *EMP* 116
SIC 6331 Fire, marine & casualty insurance: mutual; Fire, marine & casualty insurance: mutual
Ch: Harvey Sproul
**Pr:* John Lupica
**CFO:* Michael Banks
**Sr VP:* Kevin Higgins
**Sr VP:* Harold Roberts
**VP:* Joe Survilla
Board of Directors: F Kenneth Ackerman, Thomas Donnelley, John Randolph, James M Revee, James H Rockwell, J Harvey Sproul, William J Umphred

D-U-N-S 01-748-5491
MILLERS RENTAL AND SALES CO INC
2023 Romig Rd, Akron, OH 44320-3819
Tel (330) 753-8600 *Founded/Ownrshp* 1949
Sales 27.2MM^E *EMP* 95
SIC 5999 7352 Medical apparatus & supplies; Medical equipment rental
CEO: John J Miller
CFO: Steven C Bittel
VP: Kerry Klein
IT Man: Julie Houston

D-U-N-S 05-860-5775
MILLERS SUPPLIES AT WORK INC
8600 Cinder Bed Rd, Lorton, VA 22079-1470
Tel (703) 644-2200 *Founded/Ownrshp* 1974
Sales 81.7MM^E *EMP* 115
SIC 5112 5044 5021 Office supplies; Office equipment; Furniture; Office supplies; Office equipment; Furniture
Pr: Patricia Miller
**Ex VP:* Wayne Stillwagon
Sls Dir: Mike Colon

D-U-N-S 79-690-1205
MILLERSVILLE UNIVERSITY OF PENNSYLVANIA
STATE SYSTEM OF HGHR
(*Suby of* STATE SYSTEM HIGHER EDUCATN PA) ★
1 S George St, Millersville, PA 17551
Tel (717) 872-3011 *Founded/Ownrshp* 1983
Sales 99.0MM^E *EMP* 1,040^E
SIC 8221 9411 University; Administration of educational programs; ; University; Administration of educational programs;
Pr: Francine G McNairy
Pr: CarolY Phillips
CFO: Bernice Rydell
Ofcr: Corey Chivers
Ofcr: Brian Lefever
VP: Chip German
Exec: Thomas Miller
Exec: Jean Rineer
Assoc Dir: Katherine Kealey
Assoc Dir: Hiram Martinez
Admn Mgr: Barbara Havercamp

MILLIAGRO GROUP
See NUTRIMIX FEED CO INC

MILLICARE
See MILLIKEN DESIGN INC

D-U-N-S 00-194-5971
MILLIE AND SEVERSON INC (NV)
(*Suby of* SEVERSON GROUP INC) ★
3601 Serpentine Dr, Los Alamitos, CA 90720-2440
Tel (562) 493-3611 *Founded/Ownrshp* 1945, 1990
Sales 288.6MM *EMP* 75
SIC 1541 Industrial buildings, new construction; Renovation, remodeling & repairs: industrial buildings; Steel building construction; Warehouse construction
Pr: Scott Feest
**Ex VP:* Brian Cresap
**Sr VP:* Robert E Wissmann
VP: Robert Cavecche
**VP:* John Grossman
**VP:* Mark Huber
Exec: Roda Concetcion
Dir IT: Bob Severson
Sfty Mgr: Richard Wroble
Corp Couns: Clark Severson
Snr PM: Joseph Guaderrama

D-U-N-S 11-214-6290
MILLIES INC
MILLIE'S RESTAURANT & BAKERY
565 W Lambert Rd Ste C, Brea, CA 92821-3901
Tel (714) 671-0772 *Founded/Ownrshp* 2000
Sales 15.3MM^E *EMP* 465
SIC 5812 American restaurant; American restaurant
Pr: John R Bifone
CFO: Debbie Cowels
Brnch Mgr: Gus Rios

MILLIE'S RESTAURANT & BAKERY
See MILLIES INC

D-U-N-S 00-339-0580
MILLIGAN COLLEGE (TN)
1 Blowers Blvd, Milligan College, TN 37682
Tel (423) 461-8700 *Founded/Ownrshp* 1866
Sales 22.8MM *EMP* 170^E
Accts Blackburn Childers & Steagall
SIC 8221 College, except junior; College, except junior
Pr: William B Greer
VP: Mark Fox
VP: Jack Simpson
VP: Garland Young
Brnch Mgr: Joy Drinnon
Store Mgr: Jack Presnell
C/O: Pamela Day
CTO: Tracy Brinn
IT Man: Michael Bailey
Netwrk Mgr: Chris Haskins
VP Mktg: Lee Fierbaugh

D-U-N-S 00-201-7440 IMP/EXP
MILLIKEN & CO
MILLIKEN LIBRARY
920 Milliken Rd, Spartanburg, SC 29303-4995
Tel (864) 503-2020 *Founded/Ownrshp* 1865
Sales 1.4MMM^E *EMP* 9,140
SIC 2221 2211 2231 2273 2821 4911

D-U-N-S 07-280-9700
MILLIKEN DESIGN INC
MILLICARE
920 Milliken Rd, Spartanburg, SC 29303-4995
Tel (706) 880-5511 *Founded/Ownrshp* 1968
Sales 33.7MM^E *EMP* 240
SIC 2869 5131 2273 Industrial organic chemicals; Piece goods & notions; Carpets & rugs; Industrial organic chemicals; Piece goods & notions; Carpets & rugs
Pr: Joe Salley
Genl Mgr: Robert Baird

MILLIKEN LIBRARY
See MILLIKEN & CO

D-U-N-S 01-693-0976 IMP
MILLIKEN MILLWORK INC (MI)
6361 Sterling Dr N, Sterling Heights, MI 48312-4553
Tel (586) 264-0950 *Founded/Ownrshp* 1953
Sales 94.3MM^E *EMP* 400
SIC 5031 Lumber, plywood & millwork; Millwork; Door frames, all materials; Doors; Lumber, plywood & millwork; Millwork; Door frames, all materials; Doors
Ch Bd: Mary Lou Milliken
**COO:* Kevin T Milliken
**CFO:* Timothy Milliken
**Sec:* Maureen A Adams
**VP:* Keith M Milliken
**VP:* Terrance P Milliken
Genl Mgr: Paul Williams
Dir IT: Jerrod Rothey
Opers Mgr: Steve Saddler
Plnt Mgr: Mike Schorsch
Mktg Mgr: Jordan Buschmohle

D-U-N-S 07-710-2291 IMP
MILLIKEN NONWOVENS LLC
(*Suby of* MILLIKEN & CO) ★
370 Reed Rd Ste 200, Broomall, PA 19008-4018
Tel (610) 544-7117 *Founded/Ownrshp* 2013
Sales 21.5MM^E *EMP* 130
SIC 2299 2395 Batts & batting: cotton mill waste & related material; Quilted fabrics or cloth
CEO: Jeffrey Shapiro
**Pr:* Steven Derman
**Sr VP:* Joseph Ruffo
**VP Mfg:* Larry Wright

D-U-N-S 07-561-2747
MILLIKIN UNIVERSITY
1184 W Main St, Decatur, IL 62522-2084
Tel (217) 424-6211 *Founded/Ownrshp* 1900
Sales 64.0MM *EMP* 420
Accts Mcgladrey Llp Springfield Il
SIC 8221 University; University
Pr: Douglas Zemke
**VP:* Karen Bephel
Dir IT: Patricia Primmer
Pgrm Dir: Tisha Hess

D-U-N-S 07-183-5995
MILLIMAN INC
1301 5th Ave Ste 3800, Seattle, WA 98101-2635
Tel (206) 624-7940 *Founded/Ownrshp* 1947
Sales 838.0MM *EMP* 3,000^E
SIC 8742 8999 7389

D-U-N-S 08-170-4785
MILLING MACHINERY INC
1014 S Sirrine, Mesa, AZ 85210-8736
Tel (480) 964-9041 *Founded/Ownrshp* 1974
Sales 20.0MM *EMP* 125
Accts Schmidt Westergard & Company
SIC 1796 1791 1623 Machinery installation; Structural steel erection; Pipeline construction; Machinery installation; Structural steel erection; Pipeline construction
Pr: Dusty Pinckard
**Sec:* Betsie Pinckard
**VP:* Clifton R Pinckard

D-U-N-S 05-862-6617
MILLINGTON CATV INC
RITTER COMMUNICATIONS
4880 Navy Rd, Millington, TN 38053-2031
Tel (901) 872-0156 *Founded/Ownrshp* 2012
Sales 9.0MM *EMP* 350
SIC 4813 4841 ; Cable television services; ; Cable television services
Pr: Alan Morse
**COO:* David Adams
**CFO:* Gregg Smith
**Sec:* William Harrison
Exec: Peggy Cooper
IT Man: BeckyTyler

D-U-N-S 00-213-5093
MILLINGTON LOCKWOOD INC (NY)
RICHWAY REFINISHING
3901 Genesee St Ste 800, Buffalo, NY 14225-1954
Tel (716) 633-5600 *Founded/Ownrshp* 1884, 2002
Sales 25.7MM *EMP* 60
SIC 5021 7389

D-U-N-S 07-746-1705
MILLINOCKET REGIONAL HOSPITAL INC
200 Somerset St, Millinocket, ME 04462-1298
Tel (207) 723-5161 *Founded/Ownrshp* 1952
Sales 26.0MM *EMP* 220
SIC 8062 8322 General medical & surgical hospitals; Rehabilitation services; General medical & surgical hospitals; Rehabilitation services
CEO: Marie Vienneau
CFO: Catherine Lemay
CFO: Christine Mc Laughlin
Bd of Dir: Herbert Clark
Trst: Rose Hunt
VP: Shelly Drew
VP: Jason Fugleberg
VP: Missy Martin
VP: Stylianos Tsintzilonis
Dir Lab: Betsy Kelley
Dir Rad: Harry Cote

MILLION AIR DALLAS
See RR INVESTMENTS INC

MILLION DOLLAR BABY
See BEXCO ENTERPRISES INC

D-U-N-S 16-233-5074
MILLION DOLLAR ELM CASINO
(*Suby of* OSAGE NATION) ★
6128 E 38th St Ste 300, Tulsa, OK 74135-5814
Tel (918) 699-7740 *Founded/Ownrshp* 2004
Sales 9.2MM^E *EMP* 350^E
SIC 7011 Casino hotel; Casino hotel
Owner: David Hunter

MILLIPORESIGMA
See SIGMA-ALDRICH CORP

D-U-N-S 78-019-3038
MILLIS PUBLIC SCHOOLS
245 Plain St, Millis, MA 02054-1599
Tel (508) 376-7000 *Founded/Ownrshp* 2006
Sales 13.9MM^E *EMP* 319^E
SIC 8211 Public elementary & secondary schools
Netwrk Mgr: Don Tirell

D-U-N-S 06-048-1090
MILLIS TRANSFER INC
121 Gebhardt Rd, Black River Falls, WI 54615-9111
Tel (715) 284-4384 *Founded/Ownrshp* 1936
Sales 131.5MM^E *EMP* 750
SIC 4213 4231 4212 Contract haulers; Trucking terminal facilities; Local trucking, without storage; Contract haulers; Trucking terminal facilities; Local trucking, without storage
Pr: David Millis
**VP:* Steve Millis

D-U-N-S 12-787-6196
MILLITECH INC
(*Suby of* SMITHS INTERCONNECT) ★
29 Industrial Dr E, Northampton, MA 01060-2351
Tel (413) 582-9620 *Founded/Ownrshp* 2005
Sales 23.5MM^E *EMP* 100
SIC 4899 3663 Communication signal enhancement network system; Radio & TV communications equipment; Communication signal enhancement network system; Radio & TV communications equipment
Pr: Kent A Whitney
**Treas:* Michael G Whitcomb
VP: Robert Browning
VP: Joe Chandler
**VP:* Terri Marion Lemelin
Prgrm Mgr: Roger Allen
Genl Mgr: Richard Shepard
IT Man: David Leseige
IT Man: Robert White
VP Mfg: Cindy Peters
Plnt Mgr: Chris Uvrard

D-U-N-S 00-687-0703
MILLMAN LUMBER CO (MO)
FOREST PRODUCTS SUPPLY
9264 Manchester Rd, Saint Louis, MO 63144-2636
Tel (314) 961-6195 *Founded/Ownrshp* 1946
Sales 255.8MM *EMP* 80
SIC 5031 Lumber: rough, dressed & finished; Millwork; Plywood; Building materials, interior; Lumber: rough, dressed & finished; Millwork; Plywood; Building materials, interior
Ch Bd: Robert L Millman
Pr: Richard G Millman
Treas: Kenneth G Mains
Genl Mgr: Justin Dunlavy
Genl Mgr: Guy McGillivray
Dir IT: Mike Henson
Sales Exec: Patrick Sinclair

D-U-N-S 02-272-9016
MILLS AUTO ENTERPRISES INC
MILLS GM
14138 Dellwood Dr, Baxter, MN 56425-7441
Tel (218) 829-3504 *Founded/Ownrshp* 1996
Sales 23.6MM^E *EMP* 77
SIC 5511 Automobiles, new & used; Pickups, new & used; Automobiles, new & used; Pickups, new & used
Pr: Henry Mills
**Sec:* Stewart Mills
**VP:* Tom Green
Prin: Arnie Hunter
Genl Mgr: Brian Kopek
IT Man: Bret Mattheisen

D-U-N-S 02-565-0698
MILLS CHEVROLET CO
MILLS LEASING
1610 39th Ave, Moline, IL 61265-7256
Tel (309) 797-5555 *Founded/Ownrshp* 1952
Sales 25.3MM^E *EMP* 60
SIC 5511 7538 Automobiles, new & used; Trucks, tractors & trailers: new & used; General automotive repair shops; Automobiles, new & used; Trucks, tractors & trailers: new & used; General automotive repair shops
Pr: David Mills
Store Mgr: Ken Carpenter
Sls Mgr: Tim Harrington
Sls Mgr: Chad Ingwersen
Sls Mgr: Andy Maberry
Sls Mgr: Dean Wallarab
Sales Asso: Charlie Cox
Sales Asso: Ricardo Morales
Sales Asso: Robin Schrempf
Sales Asso: Jonathan Sens
Sales Asso: Ben Tarnish

D-U-N-S 07-392-9002
MILLS COLLEGE
5000 Macarthur Blvd, Oakland, CA 94613-1000
Tel (510) 430-2255 *Founded/Ownrshp* 1852
Sales 92.4MM *EMP* 211
Accts Grant Thornton Llp San Franci
SIC 8221 College, except junior; College, except junior
Pr: Alecia A Decoudreaux
**Pr:* Janet Holmgren
CFO: Peter Michell
Treas: Anne Cormia
Bd of Dir: Kristine Kaes
Trst: Lauriann Delay
Trst: James Fowler
Trst: Alexandra Moses
Trst: Jane Newhall
Trst: Cristine Russell
Trst: Clare Springs
Trst: Barbara Wolfe
Assoc VP: David Gin
Ex VP: Joan Braun
VP: Christi Chapman
Exec: Jaime Dominguez
Exec: Angela Gonsalves
Exec: Gayle Hall
Exec: Thea Hillman

D-U-N-S 08-350-3631
MILLS CORP
(*Suby of* SPG-FCM VENTURES LLC) ★
5425 Wisconsin Ave # 300, Chevy Chase, MD 20815-3581
Tel (301) 968-6000 *Founded/Ownrshp* 2007
Sales 115.5MM^E *EMP* 1,150
SIC 6798 Real estate investment trusts; Real estate investment trusts
Pr: Mark S Ordan
**CFO:* Richard J Nadeau
**Ex VP:* Gordon Glenn
VP: Norman Finbloom
VP: Bill Gilliland
CTO: Nelson Shimon
Dir IT: Sean Curran
Dir IT: Thomas Furness
Dir IT: Troy Sachs
Dir IT: Sylvie Williams
Info Man: Brent Pasanen

MILLS ELECTRIC CO
See HUNTLEY JOHN INC

MILLS FLEET FARM
See FLEET WHOLESALE SUPPLY CO INC

MILLS FLEET FARM
See FLEET AND FARM OF GREEN BAY INC

D-U-N-S 06-144-7272 IMP
MILLS FLEET FARM INC
512 Laurel St, Brainerd, MN 56401-3526
Tel (218) 829-3521 *Founded/Ownrshp* 1963
Sales 21.9MM^E *EMP* 5^E
SIC 5191 Farm supplies
CEO: Ronald Obeidzinski
**Pr:* Henry C Mills II
**VP:* Thomas W Green
**VP:* Stewart C Mills Jr
Genl Mgr: Don Griggs

MILLS FORD
See MCCOY MOTOR CO

MILLS FORD OF WILLMAR
See WILLMAR MOTORS LLC

MILLS GILBANE
See GILBANE BUILDING CO

MILLS GM
See MILLS AUTO ENTERPRISES INC

MILLS HEATING & AC
See MILLS HEATING & AIR CONDITIONING INC

D-U-N-S 11-866-4184
MILLS HEATING & AIR CONDITIONING INC
MILLS HEATING & AC
237 Bulldog Rd, Freeport, FL 32439-3168
Tel (850) 234-8177 *Founded/Ownrshp* 1984
Sales 21.1MM^E *EMP* 100
SIC 5075 1711 Warm air heating & air conditioning; Warm air heating & air conditioning contractor; Warm air heating & air conditioning; Warm air heating & air conditioning contractor
Pr: Larry Batchelor
**VP:* Kenneth Mills
Off Mgr: Beth Canterbury

D-U-N-S 00-838-2194
MILLS IRON WORKS
14834 S Maple Ave, Gardena, CA 90248-1936
Tel (323) 321-6520 *Founded/Ownrshp* 1905
Sales 20.2MM^E *EMP* 75
SIC 3494 Pipe fittings
CEO: Jeffrey Griffith
**Pr:* Kenneth E Berger
Telecom Mg: J Wang
Mfg Mgr: Robert Beard
Ql Cn Mgr: Jan Calderon

MILLS JAMES PRODUCTIONS
See MILLS/JAMES INC

MILLS LEASING
See MILLS CHEVROLET CO

D-U-N-S 00-316-1122
MILLS MANUFACTURING CORP (NC)
22 Mills Pl, Asheville, NC 28804-1216
Tel (828) 645-3061 *Founded/Ownrshp* 1934, 2009
Sales 28.4MM^E *EMP* 175
SIC 2399 2298 Parachutes; Twine, cord & cordage
Pr: James W Turner
**Ch Bd:* Pamela M Turner
**Pr:* John Oswald
IT Man: Cheryl Adkins
Mfg Mgr: Joel Guge

D-U-N-S 02-272-9602
MILLS MOTOR INC
14858 Dellwood Dr, Baxter, MN 56425-9746
Tel (218) 829-2893 *Founded/Ownrshp* 1922
Sales 47.3MM^E *EMP* 131
SIC 5511 Automobiles, new & used; Automobiles, new & used
CEO: Jeffry L Meek
**Treas:* Henry C Mills II
**VP:* Thomas W Green
Genl Mgr: Carney Shipman
Mktg Mgr: Bonnie Franke
Sls Mgr: Rob Baker
Sales Asso: Chuck Cole

D-U-N-S 00-371-8203
MILLS PENINSULA HOSPITAL INC
1635 Rollins Rd, Burlingame, CA 94010-2301
Tel (650) 652-3807 *Founded/Ownrshp* 2010
Sales 609.8MM *EMP* 11^E
SIC 8099 Health & allied services
Prin: Don McMahon

D-U-N-S 03-089-1310
MILLS POND NURSING AND REHABILIATION CENTER
273 Moriches Rd, Saint James, NY 11780-2117
Tel (631) 862-8990 *Founded/Ownrshp* 2011
Sales 30.5MM *EMP* 37^E
SIC 8059 8322 Nursing home, except skilled & intermediate care facility; Rehabilitation services
Nrsg Dir: Kathy Itzkowitz
HC Dir: Carol Smith

D-U-N-S 00-538-0829 IMP
MILLS PRODUCTS INC (MI)
PERMA-VIEW
7003 Chadwick Dr Ste 153, Brentwood, TN 37027-5288
Tel (615) 661-6570 *Founded/Ownrshp* 1952
Sales 26.6MM^E *EMP* 160
SIC 3479 3499 3469 Painting, coating & hot dipping; Metal household articles; Metal stampings
CEO: Bob D Mills
CFO: Gerald Drennan

D-U-N-S 07-876-9643
MILLS-PENINSULA HEALTH SERVICES (CA)
MILLS-PENINSULA HOSPITALS
(*Suby of* SUTTER C H S) ★
1501 Trousdale Dr, Burlingame, CA 94010-4506
Tel (650) 696-5400 *Founded/Ownrshp* 1906, 1998
Sales 609.8MM *EMP* 2,200
Accts Ernst & Young Llp Roseville
SIC 8062 General medical & surgical hospitals; General medical & surgical hospitals
Pr: Robert W Merwin
V Ch: Jordan Bloom
V Ch: Anita Hirsch
V Ch: Evelyn Khoo
V Ch: Michael Kohn
V Ch: Edward Sun
**CFO:* Iftikhar Hussaon
Treas: James Cody
Treas: Lorraine Massa
**VP:* Debbie Goodin
Exec: Ashani Chand
Dir Case M: Sheila Lyzwa
Dir Rx: Jeannette Hanni
Board of Directors: Anita Weiss

MILLS-PENINSULA HOSPITALS
See MILLS-PENINSULA HEALTH SERVICES

D-U-N-S 12-199-3653
MILLS/JAMES INC
MILLS JAMES PRODUCTIONS
3545 Fishinger Blvd, Hilliard, OH 43026-9550
Tel (614) 777-9933 *Founded/Ownrshp* 1984
Sales 21.3MM *EMP* 130
Accts Gbq Partners Llc Columbus Oh
SIC 7819 7812 Services allied to motion pictures; Motion picture production & distribution; Video tape production; Services allied to motion pictures; Motion picture production & distribution; Video tape production
CEO: Cameron James
**Pr:* Ken Mills
CFO: Steve Wenzlick
VP: John Aldrich
VP: Arthur James
VP: Joe Kurzer
VP: Dale McClintock
VP: Rodrick Pauley
VP: Bruce Reid
Exec: Leah Harper
Dir IT: Joe Armstrong

D-U-N-S 06-264-8100
MILLSAPS COLLEGE
1701 N State St, Jackson, MS 39210-0001
Tel (601) 974-1000 *Founded/Ownrshp* 2009
Sales 50.3MM *EMP* 357
Accts Bkd Llp Jackson Ms
SIC 8221 College, except junior; College, except junior
Prin: Howard L McMillan Jr
Pr: Penta Moore
Ofcr: Brad Ewing
Sr VP: S Dunn
VP: Robert Alexander
**VP:* Louise Burney
VP: Terri Hudson
VP: Michael Hutchison
VP: Brit Katz
VP: Susan Womack
Exec: Schetter Betsy
Comm Dir: John Sewell

D-U-N-S 14-482-1738 IMP
MILLSOURCE INC
WOODGRAIN DISTRIBUTION
(*Suby of* WOODGRAIN MILLWORK INC) ★
300 Nw 16th St, Fruitland, ID 83619-2218
Tel (208) 452-3801 *Founded/Ownrshp* 2004
Sales 48.2MM^E *EMP* 269
SIC 2431 Moldings, wood: unfinished & prefinished; Moldings, wood: unfinished & prefinished
Pr: Barry Dale
**CFO:* Greg Easton
Area Mgr: James Rouse
IT Man: Connie Dees
Board of Directors: Reed Dame

D-U-N-S 07-845-9579
MILLSTEIN & CO LP
1717 Penn Ave Nw Ste 333, Washington, DC 20006-1728
Tel (202) 800-2860 *Founded/Ownrshp* 2012
Sales 116.4MM^E *EMP* 254^E
SIC 8742 Banking & finance consultant
CEO: James Millstein
CFO: Jennie Main
VP: Adam Lavier

D-U-N-S 07-612-9477 IMP
■ **MILLSTONE COFFEE INC**
(*Suby of* J M SMUCKER CO) ★
1 Procter And Gamble Plz, Cincinnati, OH 45202-3315
Tel (513) 983-1100 *Founded/Ownrshp* 2008
Sales 67.9MM^E *EMP* 1,169
SIC 2095 Coffee roasting (except by wholesale grocers); Coffee roasting (except by wholesale grocers)
Pr: R Kerry Clark
**Pr:* G W Pric
**VP:* Clayton C Daley Jr
**VP:* S P Donovan Jr
**VP:* H J Kangis
**VP:* Alan G Lafley
**VP:* D R Walker

D-U-N-S 01-779-9847
MILLSTONE MEDICAL OUTSOURCING LLC
580 Commerce Dr, Fall River, MA 02720-4759
Tel (508) 679-8384 *Founded/Ownrshp* 2004
Sales 31.2MM^E *EMP* 160^E
SIC 7389 Packaging & labeling services; Packaging & labeling services
CEO: Chris Ramsden
Pr: Kelly Lucenti
Sr VP: Jonathan Tillman
VP: Peter Gerenz
VP: Victoria Hughes
Prgrm Mgr: Candy Bennett
Prgrm Mgr: Michael Caffee
Prgrm Mgr: Jasmine Cleary
Prgrm Mgr: Melissa Delk
Prgrm Mgr: Christine Lane
Prgrm Mgr: Ashleigh McAlpin

MILLSTONE POWER STATION
See DOMINION NUCLEAR CONNECTICUT INC

D-U-N-S 87-722-5193 EXP
MILLTOWN PAPER INC
1286 Ehlers Rd, Neenah, WI 54956-1451
Tel (920) 722-2112 *Founded/Ownrshp* 1994
Sales 26.5MM^E *EMP* 48^E
SIC 5111 2679 Printing & writing paper; Paper products, converted
Pr: Greg Duerr
**Ex VP:* Scott E Stadler
VP Sls: John McMinamin

D-U-N-S 06-654-0949 IMP
■ **MILLTRONICS MANUFACTURING CO INC**
(*Suby of* HURCO USA INC) ★
1400 Mill Ln, Waconia, MN 55387-1044
Tel (952) 442-1410 *Founded/Ownrshp* 2015
Sales 33.0MM^E *EMP* 113
SIC 3541 3823 Numerically controlled metal cutting machine tools; Computer interface equipment for industrial process control
CEO: Michael Fiterman
COO: Daniel Zdon
CFO: Byron Wieberdink
Ex VP: David Lenzen
VP: Ronda Bayer
CIO: Bill Bender
Dir IT: Jamie Morrow
IT Man: Benjamin Rashleger
Sftwr Eng: Tim Horgan

D-U-N-S 07-376-1355
MILLVILLE BOARD OF EDUCATION
110 N 3rd St, Millville, NJ 08332-3302
Tel (856) 293-2000 *Founded/Ownrshp* 1800
Sales 79.3MM^E *EMP* 1,100
SIC 8211 Public senior high school; Vocational high school; School board
Pr: Charles Flickinger
Pr: William Herman
Prin: Michael Calareso
Prin: Jennifer Lookabaugh
Prin: Fred Setser
Prin: William Sheridan
Prin: Harry Tillotson
IT Man: Linda Woodson
Netwrk Eng: John Law
Pr Dir: James Quinn

D-U-N-S 08-087-6394
MILLVILLE MUTUAL INSURANCE CO
215 S State St, Millville, PA 17846
Tel (570) 458-5517 *Founded/Ownrshp* 1875
Sales NA *EMP* 21
SIC 6331 Fire, marine & casualty insurance: mutual; Fire, marine & casualty insurance: mutual
Pr: M Paige Raski
IT Man: Paige Raski

D-U-N-S 55-658-0843
MILLVILLE PUBLIC SCHOOLS
110 N 3rd St, Millville, NJ 08332-3302
Tel (856) 293-2000 *Founded/Ownrshp* 1980
Sales 1.0MM^E *EMP* 1,100^E
SIC 8211 Public elementary & secondary schools

D-U-N-S 01-029-8628
MILLWARD BROWN LLC
(*Suby of* WPP GROUP USA INC) ★
11 Madison Ave Ste 1200, New York, NY 10010-3696
Tel (212) 548-7200 *Founded/Ownrshp* 2000
Sales 163.5MM^E *EMP* 1,632
SIC 8732 Market analysis or research; Market analysis or research
CEO: Mary Ann Packo
**Pr:* Eileen Cantbell
Pr: Stephen Dimarco
Pr: Scott Megginson
Pr: Lincoln Merrihew
CFO: Dave Sandberg
**CFO:* David Sandberg
Ofcr: George Donovan
Ofcr: Deepender Rana
Ex VP: Sue Elms
Ex VP: Brian Jacobs
Sr VP: Thomas O Neuman
Sr VP: Douglas Scott
Sr VP: Eric Villain
VP: Kelly Atkins
VP: Erika Bzdel
VP: Adrian Cruz
VP: Marco Forato
VP: Nik Gharekhan
VP: Irma Gonzalezclark
VP: Barbara Graham

D-U-N-S 00-934-7191
■ **MILLWOOD HOSPITAL LP**
(*Suby of* UNIVERSAL HEALTH SERVICES INC) ★
1011 N Cooper St, Arlington, TX 76011-5517
Tel (817) 303-7460 *Founded/Ownrshp* 2011
Sales 21.4MM^E *EMP* 150
SIC 8063 Psychiatric hospitals
Ch Bd: Nick Huhey
**CEO:* Jon Oshaughnessy
Dir Bus: Terri Haskett
Dir Bus: Rob Marsh
Dir Bus: Stacie York

D-U-N-S 94-850-4337 IMP
MILLWOOD INC
3708 International Blvd, Vienna, OH 44473-9796
Tel (330) 393-4400 *Founded/Ownrshp* 1993
Sales 364.7MM^E *EMP* 1,400
SIC 3565 4731 Packaging machinery; Freight transportation arrangement; Packaging machinery; Freight transportation arrangement
Pr: Steven J Miller
**Pr:* Lionel W Trebilcock
**CFO:* Craig Gretter
**Ex VP:* Ronald C Ringness
**CIO:* Tim Light
**VP Opers:* Brad Arnold
Plnt Mgr: Keith Ainsley
Plnt Mgr: Michael Cusack
Plnt Mgr: Emad Mana
Plnt Mgr: Chad Radke
Sales Asso: Janet Fleischer

D-U-N-S 18-629-8139 IMP
MILLWORK DISTRIBUTORS INC
2751 Universal St, Oshkosh, WI 54904
Tel (920) 235-8110 *Founded/Ownrshp* 1987
Sales 28.5MM^E *EMP* 54
SIC 5031 Millwork
COO: Michael C Huszar
**CFO:* Stephen R Huszar
IT Man: Nic Levy
Opers Mgr: Thomas Hoxie

MILLWORK HOLDINGS
See ALTON IRVINE INC

D-U-N-S 83-139-5343
MILLWORK HOLDINGS CO INC
(*Suby of* LI & FUNG LIMITED)
1359 Broadway Fl 16, New York, NY 10018-7116
Tel (646) 839-7000 *Founded/Ownrshp* 2008
Sales 40.0MM^E *EMP* 30^E
SIC 5092 7389 Toys & games; Advertising, promotional & trade show services
Pr: Richard Darling

D-U-N-S 03-837-7045 IMP
MILLWORK SALES OF ORLANDO LLC
(*Suby of* LIGHTEN UP LLC) ★
1925 Park Oaks Ave, Orlando, FL 32808-5668
Tel (770) 799-0345 *Founded/Ownrshp* 1998
Sales 34.0MM^E *EMP* 62
SIC 5031 Lumber, plywood & millwork
Genl Mgr: Ryan Stead

D-U-N-S 13-332-9719 EXP
MILLWORK SALES OF ROYAL PALM BEACH LLC
700 103rd Ave N Ste 100, Royal Palm Beach, FL 33411-4335
Tel (561) 472-6497 *Founded/Ownrshp* 2001
Sales 30.8MM^E *EMP* 50^E
SIC 5031 Building materials, exterior; Building materials, interior
CFO: Allen Bryan

D-U-N-S 19-667-4225 IMP
MILLY LLC
265 W 37th St Fl 20, New York, NY 10018-5769
Tel (212) 921-7800 *Founded/Ownrshp* 2000
Sales 41.1MM^E *EMP* 55
SIC 5137 5621 Women's & children's clothing; Women's clothing stores
Pr: Andrew Oshrin
CFO: Cotter Bruce
Mktg Dir: Beth Rothenberg
Mktg Mgr: Eileen Conlan

D-U-N-S 84-837-8431 IMP
MILMAR FOOD GROUP II LLC
1 6 1/2 Station Rd, Goshen, NY 10924-6777
Tel (845) 294-5400 *Founded/Ownrshp* 2000
Sales 69.6MM^E *EMP* 250
SIC 2038 8748 Frozen specialties; Business consulting; Frozen specialties; Business consulting
Ex VP: Roy Makinen
MIS Dir: Judah Koolyk

MILMOUR PRODUCTS
See INNOVATIVE HESS PRODUCTS LLC

D-U-N-S 05-124-4507 IMP/EXP
MILNE FRUIT PRODUCTS INC
(*Suby of* PEAK SEASON FOODS) ★
804 Bennett Ave, Prosser, WA 99350-1267
Tel (509) 786-0019 *Founded/Ownrshp* 1975
Sales 26.1MM^E *EMP* 80
SIC 2037 Fruit juice concentrates, frozen; Vegetables, quick frozen & cold pack, excl. potato products
Pr: Michael Sorenson
VP: Tim Chan
VP: David Luther
**VP:* John J Schroedder
VP: Jack Schroeder
Genl Mgr: Diane Moon
QA Dir: Sunil Kumar
IT Man: Sherri Pierce
IT Man: Jesse Taylor
Opers Supe: Gary McClure
Ql Cn Mgr: Ed Thomas

D-U-N-S 17-443-1601
MILNER INC
5125 Peachtree Indus Blvd, Norcross, GA 30092-3027
Tel (770) 458-0999 *Founded/Ownrshp* 1981
Sales 81.4MM^E *EMP* 228
SIC 7372 5999 7389 5065 5049 5044 Prepackaged software; Business machines & equipment; Microfilm recording & developing service; Facsimile equipment; Engineers' equipment & supplies; Duplicating machines; Prepackaged software; Business machines & equipment; Microfilm recording & developing service; Facsimile equipment; Engineers' equipment & supplies; Duplicating machines
Pr: Gene W Milner Jr
CFO: Jason Black
**Treas:* Eric W Daly
**VP:* Charles M Gibson
**VP:* Robert L Haverstick
VP: Tom Hintz
VP: Roger King
Snr Ntwrk: Juan Velasquez
Dir IT: Dave Gianndrez
Prd Mgr: Douglas Bogumill
Ql Cn Mgr: Jay Monson

MILNER MILLING
See GRAIN CRAFT INC

D-U-N-S 17-525-3095
MILNER VOICE & DATA INC
5125 Peachtree Indus Blvd, Norcross, GA 30092-3027
Tel (770) 454-6100 *Founded/Ownrshp* 1986
Sales 25.1MM^E *EMP* 115^E
SIC 5044 5065 Dictating machines; Telephone equipment; Facsimile equipment
CEO: Gene W Milner Jr
**Ch Bd:* Hicks L Milner
**Pr:* Steve Krengel
**CFO:* Eric Daily
CFO: Eric W Daly
Board of Directors: Hicks Lanier

MILNOR IRON & STEEL
See MORRIS IRON & STEEL CO INC

MILO GORDON AUTO MALL
See GREEN AUTOMOTIVE LP

D-U-N-S 03-296-9396
MILO GORDON CHRYSLER PLYMOUTH INC
5002 Nw Cache Rd, Lawton, OK 73505-3414
Tel (580) 355-2464 *Founded/Ownrshp* 1957
Sales 24.2MM^E *EMP* 62
SIC 5511 Automobiles, new & used; Pickups, new & used; Vans, new & used; Automobiles, new & used; Pickups, new & used; Vans, new & used
Pr: Mitchell Wyatt
**VP:* Michael T White
Sales Asso: Shaun Hamilton

Sales Asso: Tyler Martinez
Sales Asso: Cynthia Stauder

MILOSCH DODGE
See MILOSCHS PALACE CHRYSLER-JEEP-DODGE INC

D-U-N-S 96-719-8375
MILOSCHS PALACE CHRYSLER-JEEP-DODGE INC
MILOSCH DODGE
3800 S Lapeer Rd, Lake Orion, MI 48359-1325
Tel (248) 393-2222 *Founded/Ownrshp* 1996
Sales 32.4MM^E *EMP* 80^E
SIC 5511 7532 7539 Automobiles, new & used; Body shop, automotive; Automotive repair shops; Automobiles, new & used; Body shop, automotive; Automotive repair shops
Pr: Donald E Milosch
Rgnl Mgr: Tom Saigh
Store Mgr: Brian Boreo
Sales Asso: Ken Mumford

D-U-N-S 09-497-3922
MILPITAS UNIFIED SCHOOL DISTRICT
1331 E Calaveras Blvd, Milpitas, CA 95035-5707
Tel (408) 635-2600 *Founded/Ownrshp* 1969
Sales 71.7MM^E *EMP* 1,133
SIC 8211 8351 Public adult education school; Public elementary school; Public junior high school; Public senior high school; Preschool center; Public adult education school; Public elementary school; Public junior high school; Public senior high school; Preschool center
Pr: Daniel Bobay
Trst: Chris Norwood
**VP:* Marsha Grilli
Prin: Rita Scott
Dir IT: Richard Rose
Opers Mgr: Sucheta Gehani
Pr Dir: Tabitha Kappeler-Horle

D-U-N-S 02-341-5524
MILPORT ENTERPRISES INC
(*Suby of* ROWELL CHEMICAL CORP) ★
2829 S 5th Ct, Milwaukee, WI 53207-1458
Tel (414) 747-8384 *Founded/Ownrshp* 1994
Sales 32.8MM^E *EMP* 60
SIC 5169 2819 Chemicals, industrial & heavy; Sodium compounds or salts, inorg., ex. refined sod. chloride; Chemicals, industrial & heavy; Sodium compounds or salts, inorg., ex. refined sod. chloride
Pr: Warren Greisch
Sfty Mgr: Barry Coulter
VP Sls: Jon Denman
Sales Asso: Chris Dieckmann

MILPOWER SOURCE
See QUASAR POWER & TECHNOLOGIES INC

D-U-N-S 62-572-2939
MILROSE CONSULTANTS INC
498 Fashion Ave, New York, NY 10018-6798
Tel (212) 643-4545 *Founded/Ownrshp* 1987
Sales 26.5MM^E *EMP* 150^E
SIC 8742 Administrative services consultant; Administrative services consultant
Pr: Louis S Milo
CFO: Dave Hannaford
**VP:* Domenick A Chieco
VP: Gustavo Mazza
**VP:* William G Rose
Exec: Renee Tillie-Donald
Exec: Savita Vinas
Dist Mgr: Thomas Tabone
Off Mgr: Carleen Vilardi
CIO: Michael Richardson
Prd Mgr: Kathy Ragoo

MILS
See MILLER INTERMODAL LOGISTICS SERVICES INC

D-U-N-S 07-862-2802 IMP
■ **MILSCO MANUFACTURING CO**
(*Suby of* JASON INDUSTRIES INC) ★
9009 N 51st St, Milwaukee, WI 53223-2483
Tel (414) 354-0500 *Founded/Ownrshp* 2014
Sales 110.4MM^E *EMP* 902^E
SIC 2531 Vehicle furniture
VP: Tom Amherdt
Pr: Bruce Pate
VP: Steve Hall
VP: Mike Hynes
Prgrm Mgr: Dan Schoenberg
Dir IT: Steve Seroogy
VP Opers: Karen McDougall
VP Opers: Lowell Puls
Ql Cn Mgr: Jamie Hodgson

D-U-N-S 00-136-1906 IMP
■ **MILSO INDUSTRIES INC**
(*Suby of* MATTHEWS INTERNATIONAL CORP) ★
534 Union St, Brooklyn, NY 11215-1021
Tel (718) 624-4593 *Founded/Ownrshp* 1930, 2005
Sales 24.3MM^E *EMP* 150
SIC 5087 3995 Caskets; Burial caskets; Caskets; Burial caskets
Pr: Harry Pontone
**Treas:* Thomas Pontone Jr
**VP:* Louis Pontone

D-U-N-S 83-659-0232 IMP
MILSPEC INDUSTRIES INC
(*Suby of* GEHR INDUSTRIES INC) ★
5825 Greenwood Ave, Commerce, CA 90040-3846
Tel (213) 680-9690 *Founded/Ownrshp* 1981
Sales 23.7MM^E *EMP* 110
SIC 5072 5085 Hardware; Industrial supplies; Hardware; Industrial supplies
CFO: David Lifschitz
**Pr:* Galen Ho'o
**Ex VP:* Carl Rosenthal
**VP:* Saleem Baakza
**VP:* Anthony Batista
**VP Mktg:* Carl Tom

D-U-N-S 14-109-1582 IMP
MILSPRAY LLC
845 Towbin Ave, Lakewood, NJ 08701-5929
Tel (732) 886-2223 *Founded/Ownrshp* 2003
Sales 23.7MM^E *EMP* 57
SIC 5169 2851 3812 Aerosols; Paints & paint additives; Defense systems & equipment
Pr: Brian Feser
CFO: Elizabeth Deserio
VP: Peder Cox
VP: Jonathan Kalfus
VP: Chantel Robinson
Genl Mgr: Kyle Tierney
Site Mgr: Tyson Clymens
Ql Cn Mgr: Mark Ziegler
Pgrm Dir: Bill Morganti

MILSTEAD AUTOMOTIVE & TOWING
See MILSTEAD AUTOMOTIVE LTD

D-U-N-S 02-441-8998
MILSTEAD AUTOMOTIVE LTD
MILSTEAD AUTOMOTIVE & TOWING
29707 W Hawthorne Dr, Spring, TX 77386-2198
Tel (281) 367-3535 *Founded/Ownrshp* 2002
Sales 22.1MM^E *EMP* 150
SIC 7538 7549 7532 7515 General automotive repair shops; Towing service, automotive; Paint shop, automotive; Body shop, automotive; Passenger car leasing
Pt: Dick Milstead
**Pt:* Amy Milstead
**Pt:* Mark Orsack
**Pt:* Gabe Puentes

D-U-N-S 03-755-8442
MILT GUGGIA ENTERPRISES INC (CA)
JETTY RESTAURANT
376 Ave Of The Flags, Buellton, CA 93427
Tel (805) 688-0699 *Founded/Ownrshp* 1979
Sales 15.6MM^E *EMP* 500
SIC 5812

D-U-N-S 00-975-7360
■ **MILTEC CORP**
(*Suby of* DUCOMMUN INC) ★
678 Discovery Dr Nw, Huntsville, AL 35806-2802
Tel (256) 428-1300 *Founded/Ownrshp* 2006
Sales 66.2MM^E *EMP* 281
SIC 8711 Engineering services; Engineering services
Pr: James M Stanfield
Pr: Mike Dreessen
Pr: Scott McWhirter
**VP:* Charlotte Thompson
Sftwr Eng: Joshua Cassity

D-U-N-S 07-385-8982
MILTENBERGER OIL CO INC
JUMP OIL & PROPANE
17650 Garden Ridge Cir, Glencoe, MO 63038-2604
Tel (573) 353-3100 *Founded/Ownrshp* 1995
Sales 60.5MM^E *EMP* 500
SIC 5172 5541 Gasoline; Filling stations, gasoline
CEO: Steven Miltenberger
**VP:* Jason Miltenberger

D-U-N-S 80-860-5919
MILTENYI BIOTEC INC
(*Suby of* MILTENYI BIOTEC GMBH)
2303 Lindbergh St, Auburn, CA 95602-9562
Tel (530) 745-2800 *Founded/Ownrshp* 1992
Sales 39.4MM^E *EMP* 100^E
SIC 5047 8731 Medical & hospital equipment; Biotechnical research, commercial; Medical & hospital equipment; Biotechnical research, commercial
Pr: Stefan Miltenyi
Assoc Dir: George Cole
Genl Mgr: Tara Clark
Genl Mgr: Ira Marks
IT Man: Carmen Stemwedel
Mktg Mgr: Kirt Braun
Manager: Doug Bent
Manager: Riko Yamada
Sls Mgr: Jaymee Davis
Sales Asso: Rima Adler
Sales Asso: Diana Borenshtein

D-U-N-S 78-244-3696
■ **MILTEX HOLDINGS INC**
(*Suby of* INTEGRA LIFESCIENCES HOLDINGS CORP) ★
589 Davies Dr, York, PA 17402-8630
Tel (717) 840-9335 *Founded/Ownrshp* 1995
Sales 54.0MM^E *EMP* 201
SIC 5047 Medical equipment & supplies; Medical equipment & supplies
CEO: Kevin Breeden
Plnt Mgr: Lonnie Graybill

D-U-N-S 07-381-3743
MILTON ACADEMY INC
170 Centre St, Milton, MA 02186-3397
Tel (617) 898-1798 *Founded/Ownrshp* 1798
Sales 94.4MM *EMP* 345
Accts Mayer Hoffman Mccann Pc Bost
SIC 8211 Academy; Academy
Ch Bd: Brad Bloom
**CFO:* Steven Moore
**Treas:* Gide Zietlin
Ofcr: Matthew Fishbein
Ofcr: Abigail Grenon
Ofcr: Adam Leahy
Ofcr: Laura Wyrick
Exec: Benji Solivan
Assoc Dir: Amy Kirkcaldy
Assoc Dir: Katie Novak
Dir Soc: Jessica Kraus
Comm Dir: Erin Berg

D-U-N-S 07-598-6497
MILTON AREA SCHOOL DISTRICT
700 Mahoning St, Milton, PA 17847-2200
Tel (570) 742-7614 *Founded/Ownrshp* 2004
Sales 25.1MM^E *EMP* 331
SIC 8211 Public combined elementary & secondary school; School board; Public combined elementary & secondary school; School board
IT Man: Sean McDonough
IT Man: Tim Shade
IT Man: John Walter

D-U-N-S 01-398-0107
MILTON FREEWATER UNIFIED SCHOOL DISTRICT 7
1020 S Mill St, Milton Freewater, OR 97862-1112
Tel (541) 938-3551 *Founded/Ownrshp* 1994
Sales 20.0MM *EMP* 483
SIC 8211 Public elementary & secondary schools; Public elementary & secondary schools

D-U-N-S 06-979-5110
MILTON HERSHEY SCHOOL
1201 Homestead Ln, Hershey, PA 17033-8818
Tel (717) 520-2000 *Founded/Ownrshp* 1909
Sales 102.7MM^E *EMP* 873
SIC 8211 Private combined elementary & secondary school; Private combined elementary & secondary school
Pr: Anthony Colistra
**Pr:* Peter G Gurt
**Ch:* Robert F Cavanaugh
**Sec:* Robert C Vowler
VP: Steve Hanzelman
Div/Sub He: Robert Fehrs
VP Admn: Elliott Robinson
Snr Ntwrk: Dave Gattens
Cmptr Lab: Robert Johnston
IT Man: John Grab
Opers Mgr: Ron Meckley

D-U-N-S 96-685-2670
MILTON HERSHEY SCHOOL & SCHOOL TRUST
711 Crest Ln, Hershey, PA 17033-8903
Tel (717) 520-1100 *Founded/Ownrshp* 2011
Sales 386.3MM *EMP* 13^E
Accts Pricewaterhousecoopers Llp Ph
SIC 8211 Elementary & secondary schools; Elementary & secondary schools
Owner: Milton Hershey

D-U-N-S 07-381-7074
MILTON HOSPITAL INC
199 Reedsdale Rd, Milton, MA 02186-3900
Tel (617) 696-4601 *Founded/Ownrshp* 1903
Sales 77.6MM *EMP* 425
SIC 8062 8011 General medical & surgical hospitals; Offices & clinics of medical doctors; General medical & surgical hospitals; Offices & clinics of medical doctors
CEO: Joseph V Morrissey
Chf Path: Jon Keller
Chf Rad: Mark Lipsky
Dir Recs: Melinda Lee
Treas: Michael Brady
Ofcr: Jason Boussard
VP: Michael Conklin
VP: Doris Sinkevich
VP: Dennis Smith
Dir Rad: Donna Mendillo
CTO: Heather Brigham

D-U-N-S 00-508-6251 IMP/EXP
MILTON INDUSTRIES INC
4500 W Cortland St, Chicago, IL 60639-5193
Tel (773) 235-9400 *Founded/Ownrshp* 1944
Sales 22.2MM^E *EMP* 175^E
SIC 3491 3069 3423 3829 3569

MILTON J FLTCHER ELMNTARY SCHL
See JAMESTOWN CITY SCHOOL DISTRICT

D-U-N-S 05-077-2557 EXP
MILTON J WOOD CO
3805 Faye Rd, Jacksonville, FL 32226-2394
Tel (904) 353-5527 *Founded/Ownrshp* 1969
Sales 86.7MM^E *EMP* 300
SIC 1711 1542 Mechanical contractor; Commercial & office building contractors; Mechanical contractor; Commercial & office building contractors
CEO: Zarko Ognjenovic
**Ch Bd:* Mark S Wood
**Pr:* David W Tankersley
**CFO:* Annmarie M Nemeth
VP: Ed Steffen
Area Mgr: Jeff Jacks
Off Mgr: Shari Powers
IT Man: Josh Barker
IT Man: Justin Macdonald

MILTON MARTIN HONDA
See FOOTE & MILLER ENTERPRISES INC

D-U-N-S 13-221-5885
MILTON PUBLIC SCHOOLS
25 Gile Rd, Milton, MA 02186-3123
Tel (617) 696-5040 *Founded/Ownrshp* 2005
Sales 13.8MM^E *EMP* 451^E
SIC 8211 Public elementary & secondary schools
MIS Dir: Robert Patterson
Schl Brd P: Leroy Walker
HC Dir: Alex Campea
HC Dir: Steve Traister

MILTON ROY AMERICAS
See MILTON ROY LLC

D-U-N-S 00-409-7309 IMP
MILTON ROY LLC
MILTON ROY AMERICAS
(*Suby of* ACCUDYNE INDUSTRIES LLC) ★
201 Ivyland Rd, Ivyland, PA 18974-1706
Tel (215) 441-0800 *Founded/Ownrshp* 1936
Sales 108.8MM^E *EMP* 330
SIC 3561 3586 3826 Pumps & pumping equipment; Measuring & dispensing pumps; Spectroscopic & other optical properties measuring equipment; Mass spectrometers; Photometers; Pumps & pumping equipment; Measuring & dispensing pumps; Spectroscopic & other optical properties measuring equipment; Mass spectrometers; Photometers
Pr: Chris Krieps
CFO: James Englund
CFO: Jean-Louis Favre-Bully
**Treas:* Charles Gilstrap
**Ex VP:* Elmer Doty
**VP:* Kevin McGlinchey
Dir IT: Justin Foster
IT Man: Mike Connors
Mfg Dir: Greg Rees
Ql Cn Mgr: Eric Mensah
VP Sls: Miriam Clements

MILTON RUBEN
See RUBEN MILTON MOTORS INC

MILTON RUBEN CHEVROLET
See AUGUSTA ENTERPRISES INC

MILTON RUBEN CHEVROLET
See MILTON RUBEN PREOWNED CENTER

D-U-N-S 96-499-5229
MILTON RUBEN PREOWNED CENTER
MILTON RUBEN CHEVROLET
3514 Washington Rd, Augusta, GA 30907-2948
Tel (706) 854-1004 *Founded/Ownrshp* 1972
Sales 35.9MM^E *EMP* 200
SIC 5511 Automobiles, new & used; Automobiles, new & used
Pr: Milton Ruben
**VP:* Jim Burnstein
Sls Mgr: David Percival
Sales Asso: Don Heathman
Sales Asso: Robert Trinidad

MILTON RUBEN TOYOTA
See MJ AUTO SALES LLC

D-U-N-S 78-029-2681
MILTON S HERSHEY MED CTR PED
851 Spartan Ln, Hershey, PA 17033-8808
Tel (717) 531-8521 *Founded/Ownrshp* 2006
Sales 45.5MM^E *EMP* 403^E
SIC 8011 Offices & clinics of medical doctors
Prin: Milton Hershey
Doctor: Mark Cohen
Doctor: Niraja Rajan
Doctor: Jennifer Wallace
Doctor: Steven J Wassner

D-U-N-S 79-037-5088
MILTON S HERSHEY MEDICAL CENTER
PENN STATE HERSHEY MED CTR
500 University Dr, Hershey, PA 17033-2390
Tel (717) 531-8323 *Founded/Ownrshp* 2000
Sales 58.0MM^E *EMP* 245^E
SIC 8011 Medical centers
Ex Dir: Alan L Brechbill
COO: Robin Wittenstein
Sr VP: A Craig Hillemeier
VP: Lisa Abbott
VP: Kelly A Altland
Off Mgr: Deborah Null

D-U-N-S 07-829-8659
MILTON STEEL CO
(*Suby of* ACROW CORP OF AMERICA) ★
6 Canal St, Milton, PA 17847-1599
Tel (570) 742-9631 *Founded/Ownrshp* 2011
Sales 20.8MM^E *EMP* 130
SIC 3441 8711 Fabricated structural metal; Construction & civil engineering; Fabricated structural metal; Construction & civil engineering
Pr: Vell Holcombe

D-U-N-S 07-750-8810 IMP
MILTOPE CORP
VT MILTOPE
(*Suby of* VISION TECHNOLOGIES KINETICS INC) ★
3800 Richardson Rd, Hope Hull, AL 36043-4017
Tel (334) 284-8665 *Founded/Ownrshp* 2003
Sales 60.3MM^E *EMP* 210
SIC 3577 3572 3575 7378 Printers, computer; Computer storage devices; Computer terminals; Computer peripheral equipment repair & maintenance; Printers, computer; Computer storage devices; Computer terminals; Computer peripheral equipment repair & maintenance
Pr: Julie A Briggs
**CFO:* Tom B Dake
VP: Greg Broering
VP: John Cochran
VP: Tom Dake
VP: Robert Guidett
Dir Bus: Jeff Drader
Dir Bus: Markus Gilges
Dir Bus: Bill Kendrick
Dir Bus: Steve Rines
Prgrm Mgr: Manly Morgan

D-U-N-S 15-388-7773
MILVETS SYSTEMS TECHNOLOGY INC
11825 High Tech Ave # 150, Orlando, FL 32817-8475
Tel (407) 207-2242 *Founded/Ownrshp* 1986
Sales 32.6MM^E *EMP* 175
SIC 7373 7374 7378 Systems integration services; Data entry service; Computer maintenance & repair; Systems integration services; Data entry service; Computer maintenance & repair
Pr: Bobby J Daniels
**CFO:* Michael Adamcheck
**VP:* Roland Bradley
**VP:* Zahara Wadud
Prgrm Mgr: Bill Baran
Prgrm Mgr: Maurice Matthews

MILWAKEE AREA TCHNICAL COLLEGE
See MILWAUKEE AREA TECHNICAL COLLEGE FOUNDATION INC

D-U-N-S 04-118-8830
MILWAUKEE AREA TECHNICAL COLLEGE FOUNDATION INC
MILWAKEE AREA TCHNICAL COLLEGE
(*Suby of* WISCONSIN TECHNICAL COLLEGE SYSTEM BOARD) ★
700 W State St, Milwaukee, WI 53233-1419
Tel (414) 297-6792 *Founded/Ownrshp* 1970
Sales 7.0MM *EMP* 2,800
Accts Baker Tilly Virchow Krause Llp
SIC 8222 8221 Technical institute; Colleges universities & professional schools; Technical institute; Colleges universities & professional schools
Pr: Michael L Burke
Pr: Margie Kleineider

Bd of Dir: Ann Wilson
VP: Wilma Bonaparte
Ansthlgy: Gerald Wachowiak
Cert Phar: Sharon Skenandore

D-U-N-S 07-116-4370 IMP
MILWAUKEE BREWERS BASEBALL CLUB INC
1 Brewers Way, Milwaukee, WI 53214-3655
Tel (414) 902-4400 *Founded/Ownrshp* 1965
Sales 21.8MM^E *EMP* 125^E
SIC 7941 Baseball club, professional & semi-professional
Ch Bd: Mark Attanasio
**Pr:* Doug Melvin
**COO:* Rick Schlesinger
**Treas:* Robert J Quinn
**Ex VP:* Bob Quinn
VP: Gordon Ash
VP: Bob Hallas
VP: Jason Hartlund
VP: Tom Hecht
**VP:* Marti Wronski
Dir Sec: Randy Olewinski

D-U-N-S 07-895-0797
MILWAUKEE CATHOLIC HOME INC
2462 N Prospect Ave Ofc, Milwaukee, WI 53211-4462
Tel (414) 224-9700 *Founded/Ownrshp* 1913
Sales 17.8MM *EMP* 300
Accts Cliftonlarsonallen Llp Minnea
SIC 8051 8361 Skilled nursing care facilities; Geriatric residential care; Skilled nursing care facilities; Geriatric residential care
CEO: Dave Fulcher
**Pr:* Robert Leonhardt
**CFO:* Rohini Desai
**Ex Dir:* Paul Connelly
IT Man: Craig Niedringhaus
S&M/VP: Mary Cherniack

D-U-N-S 07-614-0680
MILWAUKEE CENTER FOR INDEPENDENCE INC
CHEF-LINE FOODS
2020 W Wells St, Milwaukee, WI 53233-2720
Tel (414) 937-2020 *Founded/Ownrshp* 1938
Sales 75.4MM *EMP* 230
Accts Grant Thornton Llp Milwaukee
SIC 8331 8322 Job training & vocational rehabilitation services; Sheltered workshop; Vocational rehabilitation agency; Adult day care center; Job training & vocational rehabilitation services; Sheltered workshop; Vocational rehabilitation agency; Adult day care center
Pr: Howard L Garber
COO: Alex Chou
**CFO:* Dick Zalewski
**Treas:* Tom Nelson
VP: Heidi Chada
**VP:* Randy Fare
**VP:* Tom Lutzow
VP: Tanya Posner
VP: Gerianne Prom
**VP:* Melinda Vernon
IT Man: Sandra Callaghan

D-U-N-S 04-113-0779
MILWAUKEE COUNTY BEHAVORIAL HEALTH DIVISION
9455 W Watertown Plank Rd, Milwaukee, WI 53226-3559
Tel (414) 257-6995 *Founded/Ownrshp* 1998
Sales 63.4MM^E *EMP* 1,000
SIC 8063 Psychiatric hospitals; Psychiatric hospitals
Psych: Sara Coleman
Psych: Steven Dykstra
Psych: Teri Kaczmarek
Psych: John Prestby
Psych: Laura Riggle
Psych: Shelly Silfven
Psych: Gary Stark

MILWAUKEE COUNTY TRANSIT SYS
See MILWAUKEE TRANSPORT SERVICES INC

D-U-N-S 78-990-0149
MILWAUKEE DRIVERS HEALTH WELFARE INC
10020 W Greenfield Ave, Milwaukee, WI 53214-3998
Tel (414) 258-2336 *Founded/Ownrshp* 1900
Sales 37.3MM *EMP* 10
SIC 8631 Labor union; Labor union
Ch: Paul Lovinus

D-U-N-S 00-609-4908 IMP/EXP
MILWAUKEE ELECTRIC TOOL CORP
MILWAUKEE TOOL
(*Suby of* TECHTRONIC INDUSTRIES NORTH AMERICA INC) ★
13135 W Lisbon Rd, Brookfield, WI 53005-2550
Tel (800) 729-3878 *Founded/Ownrshp* 1924
Sales 413.9MM^E *EMP* 2,000
SIC 3546 3425 Power-driven handtools; Saw blades for hand or power saws; Power-driven handtools; Saw blades for hand or power saws
Pr: Steven P Richman
Sr VP: Darrell Hendrix
Sr VP: Harry Peterson
VP: John Rushmer
**VP:* Joseph Smith
CTO: John Davis
Plnt Mgr: Robert Martenson
Manager: Brian Roglis
Genl Couns: Elizabeth Miller

D-U-N-S 15-186-1432 IMP
MILWAUKEE ELECTRONICS CORP
(*Suby of* MEC INTERNATIONAL CORP) ★
5855 N Glen Park Rd, Milwaukee, WI 53209-4435
Tel (414) 228-5000 *Founded/Ownrshp* 1985
Sales 25.0MM *EMP* 120
SIC 3625 3674 3825 Electric controls & control accessories, industrial; Industrial electrical relays & switches; Microprocessors; Test equipment for electronic & electrical circuits; Electric controls & control accessories, industrial; Industrial electrical relays & switches; Microprocessors; Test equipment for electronic & electrical circuits
CEO: P Michael Stoehr
**CFO:* James Anzia
**VP:* Susan B Stoehr
Genl Mgr: Hani Malek
IT Man: Tony Cieszynski
Ql Cn Mgr: Bob Schultz
Sls Dir: James Scholler

MILWAUKEE HAND TRUCK
See GLEASON INDUSTRIAL PRODUCTS INC

MILWAUKEE JOURNAL/SENTINEL
See JOURNAL SENTINEL INC

MILWAUKEE MEDICAL CLINIC
See ADVANCED HEALTHCARE INC

D-U-N-S 09-436-1409 IMP
MILWAUKEE METROPOLITAN SEWERAGE DISTRICT
M M S D
260 W Seeboth St, Milwaukee, WI 53204-1446
Tel (414) 272-5100 *Founded/Ownrshp* 1913
Sales 67.1MM^E *EMP* 240
Accts Baker Tilly Virchow Krause Ll
SIC 2873 4952 Fertilizers: natural (organic), except compost; Sewerage systems; Fertilizers: natural (organic), except compost; Sewerage systems
Ex Dir: Kevin Shafer
VP: Patrick Elliott
IT Man: Robert Schermeister
Snr PM: Bernadette Berdes
Snr PM: Jerome Flogel
Snr PM: Steve Franks
Snr PM: Scott Guzlecki
Snr PM: Flogel Jerome
Snr PM: Jim Kittleson
Snr PM: Micki Klappa-Sullivan
Snr PM: Ricardo Santiago

D-U-N-S 62-074-4888 IMP
MILWAUKEE PC INC A WISCONSIN CORP
4160 S 108th St, Greenfield, WI 53228-1906
Tel (414) 771-6965 *Founded/Ownrshp* 1989
Sales 53.1MM^E *EMP* 150
SIC 3575 5734 Computer terminals; Computer terminals; Computer peripheral equipment
Pr: James M Petr
**Pr:* Mary Petr
Brnch Mgr: Adam Armbruster
Brnch Mgr: Tom Canzoneri
Brnch Mgr: Paul Sawicki
Brnch Mgr: Curt Smith

D-U-N-S 55-593-3688
MILWAUKEE PRECISION CASTING INC
3400 S Nevada St, Milwaukee, WI 53207-3554
Tel (414) 483-7111 *Founded/Ownrshp* 2004
Sales 35.1MM^E *EMP* 140
SIC 3369 Castings, except die-castings, precision; Castings, except die-castings, precision
Owner: Tim Overmyer
Plnt Mgr: Jessica Rodic
VP Sls: Bob Reimer

D-U-N-S 07-616-9994
MILWAUKEE PSYCHIATRIC HOSPITAL INC
(*Suby of* AURORA HEALTH CARE INC) ★
12760 W North Ave, Brookfield, WI 53005-4628
Tel (414) 771-1309 *Founded/Ownrshp* 1946
Sales 22.1MM^E *EMP* 245
SIC 8063 Psychiatric hospitals; Psychiatric hospitals
Pr: William Jenkins
CFO: Jill Kahbaka
CFO: Larry Schwochert
Ofcr: Pete Carlson
Dir Bus: Larry Lenz

D-U-N-S 07-613-7892
MILWAUKEE PUBLIC SCHOOLS
M P S
5225 W Vliet St, Milwaukee, WI 53208-2698
Tel (414) 475-8393 *Founded/Ownrshp* 1846
Sales 605.2MM^E *EMP* 14,154
Accts Baker Tilly Virchow Krause Ll
SIC 8211 Public elementary & secondary schools; Public elementary & secondary schools
**CFO:* Gerald Pace
Bd of Dir: Kenneth Johnson
VP: Peter Blewett
Prin: Deborah Bell
Prin: Daniel J Donder
Prin: Jewell Riano
Prin: Martha Wheeler-Fair
IT Man: Roberto Surita
Psych: Kim Gulbrandson
Psych: Christopher Nyman

D-U-N-S 01-985-7153
MILWAUKEE SCHOOL OF ENGIINEERING
MSOE
1025 N Broadway, Milwaukee, WI 53202-3109
Tel (414) 277-6763 *Founded/Ownrshp* 2008
Sales 87.1MM *EMP* 161^E
Accts Baker Tilly Virchow Krause Llp
SIC 8221 Colleges & universities; Colleges & universities

D-U-N-S 00-643-3452
MILWAUKEE SCHOOL OF ENGINEERING (WI)
1025 N Broadway, Milwaukee, WI 53202-3109
Tel (414) 277-7300 *Founded/Ownrshp* 1903
Sales 130.8MM *EMP* 600^E
Accts Baker Tilly Virchow Krause Llp
SIC 8221 University; University
Pr: Hermann Viets
V Ch: Thomas Hauske
**CFO:* Mr Armund Janto
**Ch:* John Mellowes
**VP:* Roger Frankowski
**VP:* Mr Frank Habib
IT Man: James Blank
Sftwr Eng: Dan Fischer
Netwrk Eng: Tom Boshardy
Pgrm Dir: Richard Kelnhofer

D-U-N-S 02-345-0430
MILWAUKEE SPORTSERVICE INC
MILLER PARK
(*Suby of* DELAWARE NORTH COMPANIES SPORTSERVICE INC) ★
1 Brewers Way Stop 1, Milwaukee, WI 53214-3655
Tel (414) 902-4700 *Founded/Ownrshp* 1964
Sales 26.2MM^E *EMP* 800
SIC 5812 5813 5947 7941 Concessionaire; Drinking places; Souvenirs; Sports clubs, managers & promoters; Concessionaire; Drinking places; Souvenirs; Sports clubs, managers & promoters
CEO: Tom Olson
**Prin:* Jon Greenberg
IT Man: Chris Zwaska

MILWAUKEE TOOL
See MILWAUKEE ELECTRIC TOOL CORP

D-U-N-S 08-048-5402
MILWAUKEE TRANSPORT SERVICES INC
MILWAUKEE COUNTY TRANSIT SYS
1942 N 17th St, Milwaukee, WI 53205-1652
Tel (414) 344-6711 *Founded/Ownrshp* 1975
Sales 64.0MM^E *EMP* 1,130
SIC 4131 Intercity & rural bus transportation; Intercity & rural bus transportation
Pr: Anita Connelly
Mktg Dir: Joseph Caruso

MILWAUKEE TRUCK SALES
See MACK MILWAUKEE SALES INC

D-U-N-S 00-609-5616 IMP
MILWAUKEE VALVE CO INC
HAMMOND
16550 W Stratton Dr, New Berlin, WI 53151-7301
Tel (262) 432-2800 *Founded/Ownrshp* 1959
Sales 74.5MM^E *EMP* 450
SIC 3494 3492 3432 Valves & pipe fittings; Fluid power valves & hose fittings; Plumbing fixture fittings & trim; Valves & pipe fittings; Fluid power valves & hose fittings; Plumbing fixture fittings & trim
Ch Bd: Herschel L Seder
**Pr:* Rick Giannini
Ex VP: James Seder
Rgnl Mgr: Mike McKeever
Rgnl Mgr: Joe Noel
Rgnl Mgr: Chris Tarantello
Dist Mgr: Brett Prejean
Dist Mgr: Bob Rudman
Genl Mgr: John Labellarte
Dir IT: Dan Deaver
IT Man: John Flaig

D-U-N-S 02-046-1125
MILWAUKEE WORLD FESTIVAL INC
SUMMERFEST
114 N Jackson St, Milwaukee, WI 53202-6205
Tel (414) 273-2680 *Founded/Ownrshp* 1965
Sales 39.9MM *EMP* 1,200
Accts Coleman & Williams Ltd Milw
SIC 7999 Festival operation; Festival operation
Ch Bd: Howard Schnoll
**Pr:* Don Fimley
CFO: Sue Landry
**Treas:* Wally Mores
**VP:* Ann Minahan
**VP:* Howard Sosoff
Ex Dir: Donald Smiley
Dir Sec: Bill Wesley
Software D: Nick Volz

MIMA SERVICES, INC.
See HEALTH FIRST MEDICAL GROUP LLC

D-U-N-S 15-701-0955 IMP
MIMAKI USA INC
(*Suby of* MIMAKI ENGINEERING CO.,LTD.)
150 Satellite Blvd Ne A, Suwanee, GA 30024-7132
Tel (678) 730-0100 *Founded/Ownrshp* 1999
Sales 26.7MM^E *EMP* 60
SIC 5045 Printers, computer; Computer peripheral equipment
CEO: Masaaki Fujita
**Pr:* Hisauki Kobayashi
**CEO:* Akira Ikeda
**Ex VP:* Hiroyuki Nozawa
IT Man: Terence Waites
VP Sls: Naoya Kawagoshi
Sls Mgr: Scott Champeau
Sales Asso: Tiffany Patterson

D-U-N-S 80-915-0662
MIMECAST NORTH AMERICA INC
(*Suby of* MIMECAST LIMITED)
480 Pleasant St, Watertown, MA 02472-2463
Tel (781) 996-5340 *Founded/Ownrshp* 2007
Sales 27.2MM^E *EMP* 150
SIC 8748 Business consulting; Business consulting
Pr: Peter Bauer
**COO:* Ed Jennings
**Treas:* Peter Campbell
**Sr VP:* Joe Freitas
Sr VP: Jonathan Gale
Sr VP: Julian Martin
VP: Jim Steuterman
**Genl Mgr:* Alan Kenny
Off Mgr: Ellen Pierce
Sales Exec: Marc Albano
Sales Exec: Ben Darsigny
Board of Directors: Bernard Dalle

MIMECO
See MIAMI INTERNATIONAL MACHINERY & EQUIPMENT CORPO

D-U-N-S 87-648-5496
▲ MIMEDX GROUP INC
1775 W Oak Commons Ct, Marietta, GA 30062-2254
Tel (770) 651-9100 *Founded/Ownrshp* 2008
Sales 118.2MM *EMP* 386^E
Tkr Sym MDXG *Exch* NAS
SIC 3842 Surgical appliances & supplies; Surgical appliances & supplies
Ch Bd: Parker H Petit
**Pr:* William C Taylor
CFO: Marianne Barbour
CFO: Michael J Senken
Ofcr: Debbie Dean
Ex VP: Brent Miller
VP: Mike Carlton
VP: John Cranston
VP: Al Evans
VP: Lee Lawson
VP: David Mason
VP: Roberta McCaw
VP: Milena Ridl
VP: Travis Tucker
Board of Directors: Joseph G Blesser, J Terry Dewberry, Charles R Evans, Bruce L Hack, Charles E Koob, Larry W Papasan, Neil S Yeston

D-U-N-S 07-610-2602
MIMEO.COM INC
3 Park Ave Rm 22, New York, NY 10016-5902
Tel (212) 847-3000 *Founded/Ownrshp* 1998
Sales 236.2MM^E *EMP* 400^E
SIC 2759 Commercial printing; Commercial printing
CEO: Adam Slutsky
**COO:* John Delbridge
COO: Chuck Gehman
COO: Kenneth Trevathan
Treas: Paul Felber
Sr Cor Off: Scott Klemm
Ofcr: Nancy Ramirez
Ex VP: Wilfred Busby
Ex VP: Skip Trevathan
VP: Mike Barker
VP: Andy Berman
VP: Robert A Krauss
VP: Darren Lavelle
VP: Ben Shaw
Creative D: Douglas Jung

MIMG ENDOSCOPY
See MISSION INTERNAL MEDICAL GROUP INC

D-U-N-S 02-842-6638
MIMRX CO INC
SCRIP PHARMACY
2787 Charter St, Columbus, OH 43228-4607
Tel (614) 850-6672 *Founded/Ownrshp* 2000
Sales 41.1MM^E *EMP* 500
SIC 5122 Druggists' sundries; Druggists' sundries
Pr: Rich Friedman
**VP:* Al Corfera
Cert Phar: Ambu Patel
Cert Phar: Anita Roberts
Cert Phar: Shauna Setty
Cert Phar: Shelley Simund

D-U-N-S 02-475-3501 IMP
MIMS DISTRIBUTING CO INC (NC)
8605 Ebenezer Church Rd, Raleigh, NC 27617-4728
Tel (919) 872-8862 *Founded/Ownrshp* 1961, 1965
Sales 55.5MM^E *EMP* 125
Accts Batchelor Tillery & Roberts
SIC 5182 5181 Wine; Beer & other fermented malt liquors; Wine; Beer & other fermented malt liquors
CEO: Chip Mims
**Pr:* Joseph H Mims
**CFO:* John Dubois
**Treas:* Jeff B Mims
VP: Jim Bostic
VP: Michael Gunnells
**VP:* Roger Mackay
**VP:* H H Mims Jr
Area Mgr: Eric Cochran
Area Mgr: Scott Ray
Area Mgr: Gary Stadler

D-U-N-S 10-180-2254
MIMS OIL CO INC
SHELLGO
1600 1/2 Tallahatchie St, Greenwood, MS 38930
Tel (662) 453-5105 *Founded/Ownrshp* 1983
Sales 34.2MM^E *EMP* 250
SIC 5171 5541 5411 5172 Petroleum bulk stations; Filling stations, gasoline; Convenience stores; Petroleum products; Petroleum bulk stations; Filling stations, gasoline; Convenience stores; Petroleum products
Pr: J W Mims
**Sec:* Jewel Blakely
**VP:* Wayne Mims

MIN
See TREASURE ISLAND RESORT AND CASINO

D-U-N-S 79-962-8730
MINACS GROUP USA INC
(*Suby of* MINACS GROUP INC,THE)
34115 W 12 Mile Rd, Farmington Hills, MI 48331-3368
Tel (248) 553-8355 *Founded/Ownrshp* 1997
Sales 306.9MM^E *EMP* 2,600
SIC 7389 8742 Management consulting services; Marketing consulting services; Telephone services; Telephone services; Management consulting services; Marketing consulting services
Pr: Anil Bhalla
CFO: Ramesh Kamath
Sec: Kaveena Barretto
VP: Jim Kennig
Creative D: Mary Lebrato
IT Man: ARI LI
Sys Mgr: Steve Broughton
Site Mgr: Michael Scharrer
Sales Exec: Dave Livingway
Sls&Mrk Ex: Ann Willis
Snr Mgr: Nilanjan Chaudhuri

D-U-N-S 09-637-0655
MINACT INC
5220 Keele St, Jackson, MS 39206-4302
Tel (601) 362-1631 *Founded/Ownrshp* 1978
Sales 142.9MM *EMP* 1,100
Accts Carr Riggs & Ingram Llc Ridge
SIC 8331 8742 Job training services; Management consulting services; Job training services; Management consulting services
Ch: Reuben V Anderson
**V Ch:* Robert Smith

*Pr: Booker T Jones
Treas: Augustus Collins
Ex VP: Sam Devore
VP: Jacqueline Beasley
VP: Mark Brantley
VP: Cato Howard
Ex Dir: Gwendolyn Antoine
Ex Dir: David Grier
Ex Dir: Ilene Jones-Fraser

D-U-N-S 07-914-2090
MINAMI CORP US (HI)
870 Kawaiahao St, Honolulu, HI 96813-5208
Tel (808) 523-7873 Founded/Ownrshp 1991
Sales 33.4MM^E EMP 107^E
SIC 7389
Prin: Hatsuko Minami

MINARIK AUTOMATION & CONTROL
See MINARIK CORP

D-U-N-S 00-959-1033 IMP
■ MINARIK CORP
MINARIK AUTOMATION & CONTROL
(Suby of KAMAN INDUSTRIAL TECHNOLOGIES CORP) ★
1 Vision Way, Bloomfield, CT 06002-5321
Tel (860) 687-5000 Founded/Ownrshp 2010
Sales 55.2MM^E EMP 250
SIC 3625 Relays & industrial controls; Relays & industrial controls
Pr: Steven J Smidler
*Treas: Robert D Starr
Sr VP: Gary J Haseley
VP: Kyle Ahlfinger
VP: Roger S Jorgensen
VP Mktg: Tim Anderson
Board of Directors: Neal J Keating

D-U-N-S 08-607-4671 IMP
MINCEY MARBLE MFG INC
4321 Browns Bridge Rd, Gainesville, GA 30504-5333
Tel (770) 532-0451 Founded/Ownrshp 1977
Sales 22.5MM^E EMP 250
SIC 3261

D-U-N-S 15-782-5373 IMP/EXP
MINCHEM INTERNATIONAL INC
9999 Bellaire Blvd # 1088, Houston, TX 77036-3579
Tel (713) 266-8558 Founded/Ownrshp 1997
Sales 34.0MM EMP 7
SIC 5052 Coal & other minerals & ores; Coal & other minerals & ores
Pr: Jerry J Sun
*CFO: Johnathan Zou

D-U-N-S 79-817-6061 IMP/EXP
■ MINCO INC
(Suby of CERADYNE INC) ★
510 Midway Cir, Midway, TN 37809-3705
Tel (423) 422-6051 Founded/Ownrshp 2007
Sales 29.9MM^E EMP 259
SIC 3297 Alumina fused refractories; Castable refractories, nonclay; Alumina fused refractories; Castable refractories, nonclay
Pr: Bruce Lockhart
VP: Paul R Strunk
*VP: Mike Wilds
VP: Jim Wright
Sfty Mgr: Mike McCullough

D-U-N-S 00-647-8093 IMP
MINCO PRODUCTS INC (MN)
7300 Commerce Ln Ne, Minneapolis, MN 55432-3177
Tel (763) 571-3121 Founded/Ownrshp 1956
Sales 113.5MM^E EMP 700
SIC 3672 3823 3634 3829

D-U-N-S 10-159-7888
MINCORP INC
(Suby of SEVERSTAL PAO)
Rr 281, Friedens, PA 15541
Tel (814) 443-4668 Founded/Ownrshp 1998
Sales 43.4MM^E EMP 450^E
SIC 1221 Strip mining, bituminous; Strip mining, bituminous
Pr: David L Shanks
*Pr: Joseph Gallo
*CFO: Denis Kulichenko
*Treas: Dmitry Goryachev
*VP: Peter J Vuljanic

D-U-N-S 15-890-8637
MIND RESEARCH INSTITUTE
MUSIC INTLLGNCE NEURO DEV INST
111 Academy Ste 100, Irvine, CA 92617-3046
Tel (949) 345-8700 Founded/Ownrshp 2000
Sales 24.3MM EMP 160
Accts Guzman & Gray Long Beach Ca
SIC 8733 Noncommercial research organizations; Noncommercial research organizations
CEO: Matthew Peterson
Pr: Andrew R Coulson
VP: John Bishop
VP: Jim Lund
Board of Directors: Jim Mazzo

MIND SPRINGS HEALTH
See COLORADO WEST REGIONAL MENTAL HEALTH INC

D-U-N-S 80-817-5421
MINDBANK CONSULTING GROUP LLC
11800 Sunrise Valley Dr # 1450, Reston, VA 20191-5316
Tel (703) 893-4700 Founded/Ownrshp 1986
Sales 37.4MM^E EMP 202
SIC 7379 7373 8742 7371 Computer related consulting services; Computer integrated systems design; Financial consultant; Computer software writing services; Computer related consulting services; Computer integrated systems design; Financial consultant; Computer software writing services
Sr VP: Kurt Brient
Dir Bus: John Murray
Dir Bus: Stephanie Pritchett
Mng Dir: Scott Peikin

Prgrm Mgr: Trisha Herrera
DP Exec: Courtney Scott

D-U-N-S 78-441-0263
▲ MINDBODY INC
4051 Broad St Ste 220, San Luis Obispo, CA 93401-8723
Tel (877) 755-4279 Founded/Ownrshp 2001
Sales 70.0MM EMP 1,100
Tkr Sym MB Exch NGM
SIC 8741 7372 Business management; Business management; Business oriented computer software
Ch Bd: Richard L Stollmeyer
CFO: Brett White
*Chf Mktg O: Robert Murphy
Sr VP: Kimberly Lytikainen
CIO: William Donohue
Info Man: Brian Spolarich
Software D: Roberto Iraheta
Software D: Nestor Reyes
Software D: Michael Sanchez
Software D: Brett Wellman
Sales Exec: Kip Morais
Board of Directors: Katherine Blair Christie, Jeremy Levine, Eric Liaw, Tyler Newton, Graham Smith

MINDEN MEDICAL CENTER
See AHM MINDEN HOSPITAL INC

D-U-N-S 84-929-1620
MINDEX TECHNOLOGIES INC
3495 Winton Pl Ste E4, Rochester, NY 14623-2807
Tel (585) 424-3590 Founded/Ownrshp 1994
Sales 32.0MM^E EMP 180
SIC 7373 Systems software development services; Systems software development services
Pr: Marc Fiore
Pr: Steve Kull
VP: Dawn Millan
Exec: Andrea Fiore
Dir Bus: Karl Gielenfeldt
Snr Sftwr: Melissa Vick
Dir IT: Greg Wishart
IT Man: Barbara Larabee
IT Man: Gene Lockhart
Software D: Ted Greco
Sftwr Eng: Jack Hibit

D-U-N-S 62-145-3856
MINDJET CORP
1160 Battery St Fl 4, San Francisco, CA 94111-1216
Tel (415) 229-4200 Founded/Ownrshp 2005
Sales 71.2MM^E EMP 270^E
SIC 6719 Investment holding companies, except banks; Investment holding companies, except banks
CEO: Scott Raskin
*Pr: Robert Gordon
*CFO: Steve Anderson
*Chf Mktg O: Amy Millard
Ex VP: Todd Clyde
VP: Greg Brown
*VP: Valerie Burman
*VP: Ray Polanco
*VP: Uwe Richter
*VP: Abe Smith
VP: Mark Uicker
*VP: Felicity Wohltman

D-U-N-S 01-933-3199
MINDJET LLC
(Suby of MINDJET CORP) ★
1160 Battery St Fl 4, San Francisco, CA 94111-1216
Tel (415) 229-4200 Founded/Ownrshp 1998
Sales 37.0MM^E EMP 270^E
SIC 7372 Business oriented computer software; Educational computer software; Business oriented computer software; Educational computer software
CEO: Scott Raskin
*CFO: Steve Anderson
Chf Mktg O: Amy Millard
*Ex VP: Todd Clyde
*Sr VP: Valerie Burman
*Sr VP: James Gardner
VP: Doug Collins
VP: Steve Glass
VP: Gary Goelkel
VP: Bruce Sedlak
Off Admin: Stephanie Roder

D-U-N-S 17-241-8605
MINDLANCE INC
MINDLANCE INDIA PRIVATE LTD
80 River St Ste 4, Hoboken, NJ 07030-5619
Tel (201) 386-5400 Founded/Ownrshp 1999
Sales 103.3MM EMP 225^E
SIC 8742 Human resource consulting services; Human resource consulting services
VP: Vikram Kalra
Ex VP: Sumit Seth
*VP: Rajad Dhall
Exec: Raja Yalamanchi

MINDLANCE INDIA PRIVATE LTD
See MINDLANCE INC

D-U-N-S 82-629-3776 IMP
MINDRAY DS USA INC
MINDRAY NORTH AMERICA
(Suby of SHENZHEN MINDRAY BIO-MEDICAL ELECTRONICS CO., LTD.)
800 Macarthur Blvd, Mahwah, NJ 07430-2001
Tel (201) 995-8000 Founded/Ownrshp 2008
Sales 228.8MM^E EMP 4,050
SIC 3845 2835 3841 Electromedical equipment; Patient monitoring apparatus; In vitro diagnostics; Surgical & medical instruments; Electromedical equipment; Patient monitoring apparatus; In vitro diagnostics; Surgical & medical instruments
Pr: George Solomon
CFO: Chris Butfine
*Treas: Frank Gutworth
VP: Jim Fidacaro
VP: Michael Thompson
Rgnl Mgr: Bob Jevin
Rgnl Mgr: Bob Zhu
IT Man: Diane Steensma
VP Mktg: James Fidacaro
VP Sls: Wayne Quinn
Mktg Mgr: Todd Sawyer

MINDRAY NORTH AMERICA
See MINDRAY DS USA INC

MINDSHARE INTERACTION
See MINDSHARE USA LLC

D-U-N-S 84-397-5165
MINDSHARE USA LLC
MINDSHARE INTERACTION
(Suby of GROUP M WORLDWIDE LLC) ★
498 Fashion Ave, New York, NY 10018-6798
Tel (212) 297-7000 Founded/Ownrshp 2003
Sales 95.9MM^E EMP 800
SIC 7319 Media buying service; Media buying service
CEO: Kelly Clark
Sr Pt: Jane Barasch
Sr Pt: Kelly Foster
Sr Pt: Stacie Medley
Sr Pt: Chris Victor
Mng Pt: Paul Gibbins
Mng Pt: Gary Jones
Mng Pt: Jon Lefferts
Mng Pt: Joshua McTee
Mng Pt: Luigi Sorrentino
CEO: Jennie Caormina
CEO: Anthony Young
CFO: Joseph Scangamor
Ofcr: Arturo Ruiz
Top Exec: Kavitha Srinivasan
VP: Don Anderson
Exec: Joice Garcia
Exec: Elizabeth Takacs
Assoc Dir: Jayson Baron
Assoc Dir: Gretta Carlson
Assoc Dir: Matthew Denerstein

D-U-N-S 02-345-6101
MINDSHIFT TECHNOLOGIES INC
(Suby of RICOH JAPAN CORPORATION)
45610 Woodland Rd Ste 200, Sterling, VA 20166-4220
Tel (571) 643-7120 Founded/Ownrshp 2014
Sales 64.3MM^E EMP 148
SIC 7379 Computer related consulting services; Computer related consulting services
Ch Bd: Paul W Chisholm
*Pr: Mona Abutaleb
*CFO: Lawrence M Ingeneri
CFO: Mark Moore
*Ex VP: Cliff Chapman
*Ex VP: Jon Hallett
VP: Peter Diamond
VP: Jorge Restrepo
VP: Archie Seale
Dir Bus: Jamesen Gray
Dir Bus: Matt Salvatoriello
Dir Bus: Stephan Shackleton

D-U-N-S 78-510-4832 IMP
MINDSINSYNC INC
(Suby of MINDSINSYNC LTD)
276 5th Ave Rm 505, New York, NY 10001-4527
Tel (212) 228-1828 Founded/Ownrshp 2006
Sales 169.5MM EMP 50
SIC 5023 Sheets, textile
Pr: Iain Scorgie
*COO: Paul Cuthbertson
*CFO: Antony Pereira
Ofcr: Kathleen Huddy
Sr VP: Jill Fisher
VP: Angus Davidson
*VP: Jacqui Hatcher
VP: Larry Wilkins
Genl Mgr: Neil Dodds
Off Mgr: Dennys Franklin
Plng Mgr: Burcu Morkan

D-U-N-S 08-730-0526 IMP
■ MINDSPARK INTERACTIVE NETWORK INC
(Suby of ASK.COM) ★
29 Wells Ave Ste 300, Yonkers, NY 10701-8824
Tel (914) 591-2000 Founded/Ownrshp 1999, 2004
Sales 129.7MM^E EMP 210
SIC 4813 ;
CEO: Joey Levin
*Pr: Tim Allen
Pr: Sean Conrad
*CFO: Daniel Fossner
Ofcr: Timothy Allen
Ofcr: Mark Stein
Sr VP: Gregg Bernard
*Sr VP: Christopher Phillips
*Sr VP: Brad Simon
*VP: Adam Agensky
VP: Drew Berkowitz
VP: Damith Chandrasekara
VP: Roman Degtyur
*VP: Michelle Lee
VP: Ernest Wurzbach
Dir Bus: Jimmy Chin

D-U-N-S 00-803-6191
■ MINDSPEED TECHNOLOGIES INC
MACOM
(Suby of M/A-COM TECHNOLOGY SOLUTIONS HOLDINGS INC) ★
4000 Macarthur Blvd, Newport Beach, CA 92660-2558
Tel (949) 579-3000 Founded/Ownrshp 2002, 2013
Sales 120.1MM^E EMP 554^E
SIC 3674 Semiconductors & related devices; Semiconductors & related devices
CEO: Raouf Y Halim
COO: Juan Pacheco
*CFO: Stephen N Ananias
*Sr VP: Abdelnaser M Adas
Sr VP: Naser Adas
Sr VP: Stephen Ananias
Sr VP: Hasnain Bajwa
*Sr VP: Najabat H Bajwa
*Sr VP: Gerald J Hamilton
*Sr VP: Allison K Musetich
Sr VP: Thomas A Stites
Sr VP: Thomas Stites
Sr VP: Preet Virk
*Sr VP: Preetinder S Virk
VP: Atul Gupta
VP: David Rinke
*VP: Brandi R Steege
VP: Kevin Thornber

VP: Kevin Trosian
VP: James Watkins
Exec: Luis Farias
Board of Directors: Robert J Conrad, Dwight W Decker, Michael T Hayashi, Ming Louie, Thomas A Madden, Jerre L Stead

D-U-N-S 93-995-2230
MINDTECK INC
(Suby of MINDTECK (INDIA) LIMITED)
150 Corporate Center Dr # 200, Camp Hill, PA 17011-1759
Tel (717) 732-5692 Founded/Ownrshp 1995
Sales 30.6MM^E EMP 230
Accts Kpmg India Bangalore India
SIC 7371 7374 7373 Computer software development; Data processing & preparation; Computer integrated systems design; Computer software development; Data processing & preparation; Computer integrated systems design
Pr: Pankaj Agarwal
CFO: Anand Balakrishnan
Treas: Sudhindra Kowligi
Ex VP: Joe Underwood
Dir Bus: Ritesh Patel
Ex Dir: Meenaz Dhanani
Tech Mgr: Sajeev Thomas
VP Sls: Ranga Yeragudipati
Snr Mgr: Ramkumar Duraiswamy

D-U-N-S 06-384-9033
MINDTREE LIMITED
(Suby of MINDTREE LIMITED)
25 Independence Blvd # 401, Warren, NJ 07059-2706
Tel (732) 595-6432 Founded/Ownrshp 1999
Sales 30.8MMM EMP 235
SIC 7371 Computer software development; Computer software development
CEO: Krishnakumar Natarajan
Ch Bd: Subroto Bagchi
COO: N Krishnakumar
CFO: Rostow Ravanan
Ex VP: Ravi Shankar
Sr VP: Paul Gottsegen
VP: Raj Datta
VP: Vishweshwar Hegde
VP: Kamran Ozair
Assoc Dir: Joshua Fernando
Genl Mgr: Vijay Balakrishnan

MINE DEFENSE SYSTEMS
See EDO CORP

D-U-N-S 87-820-6838
■ MINE SAFETY AND HEALTH ADMINISTRATION
(Suby of UNITED STATES DEPARTMENT OF LABOR) ★
201 12th St S Ste 401, Arlington, VA 22202-5414
Tel (202) 693-9899 Founded/Ownrshp 1978
Sales NA EMP 2,419
SIC 9651 Inspection for labor standards & safety, government; ; Inspection for labor standards & safety, government;
*Prin: David J McAteer
*Prin: Merrifield Neal
Snr Mgr: Lawrence Trainor

D-U-N-S 00-432-1865 IMP
■ MINE SAFETY APPLIANCES CO LLC
(Suby of MSA SAFETY INC) ★
1000 Cranberry Woods Dr, Cranberry Township, PA 16066-5296
Tel (724) 776-8600 Founded/Ownrshp 2014
Sales 1.1MMM EMP 5,000
Tkr Sym MSA Exch NYS
SIC 3842 3826 3823 3648 3829 Personal safety equipment; Gas masks; Radiation shielding aprons, gloves, sheeting, etc.; Respiratory protection equipment, personal; Environmental testing equipment; Industrial process control instruments; Lighting equipment; Gas detectors; Personal safety equipment; Gas masks; Radiation shielding aprons, gloves, sheeting, etc.; Respiratory protection equipment, personal; Environmental testing equipment; Industrial process control instruments; Lighting equipment; Gas detectors
Pr: William M Lambert
Pr: Nish Vartanian
*CFO: Stacy McMahan
*Chf Cred: Joseph Bigler
VP: J M Barendt
VP: Steve Blanco
VP: Kerry Bove
VP: B V Demaria
VP: Ronald N Herring
*VP: Douglas K McClaine
VP: Paul Uhler
*VP: Markus H Weber

D-U-N-S 13-779-0044
MINE SERVICE LTD
855 E Us Highway 79, Rockdale, TX 76567-4541
Tel (512) 446-7011 Founded/Ownrshp 1984
Sales 45.8MM^E EMP 200
SIC 1794 1629 Excavation work; Land clearing contractor; Excavation work; Land clearing contractor
Mng Pt: Keith Debault
Pt: Rhonda Debault

D-U-N-S 01-487-1454 IMP
MINE SITE TECHNOLOGIES (USA) INC
13301 W 43rd Dr Unit 15, Golden, CO 80403-7250
Tel (303) 951-0570 Founded/Ownrshp 2002
Sales 25.3MM^E EMP 100^E
SIC 1629 Mine loading & discharging station construction
Pr: Annie Wang
Off Mgr: Stephanie Braselton

D-U-N-S 04-046-8464
MINEOLA UNION FREE SCHOOL DISTRICT
121 Jackson Ave, Mineola, NY 11501-2709
Tel (516) 237-2000 Founded/Ownrshp 1926
Sales 31.7MM^E EMP 600
SIC 8211 Public elementary & secondary schools; Public elementary & secondary schools
Schl Brd P: Artie Barnett

Board of Directors: Gia Hall, Juanita Maltese, Donna Martillo, Jane Valla

D-U-N-S 95-939-4750
MINER CORP
(*Suby of* MINER HOLDING CO INC) ★
11827 Tech Com Rd Ste 115, San Antonio, TX 78233-6015
Tel (210) 655-8600 *Founded/Ownrshp* 1994
Sales 174.1MM^E *EMP* 250
SIC 5084 Industrial machinery & equipment
CEO: Phillip T Miner III
* *Pr:* Matt Dirienzo
Pr: Benjie Hunt
* *CFO:* Steve Weaver
VP: Rhonda Lambert
* *VP:* Sue Ellen Miner
VP: Tra Tramonte
VP: Rick Upton
Genl Mgr: Colette Criss
CIO: Mirza Chughtai
CTO: Joanne Callahan

D-U-N-S 00-512-6115 IMP/EXP
MINER ENTERPRISES INC
W H MINER DIV
1200 E State St, Geneva, IL 60134-2493
Tel (630) 232-3000 *Founded/Ownrshp* 1970
Sales 69.5MM^E *EMP* 280
SIC 3743 Railroad equipment; Railroad equipment
Pr: David W Withall
Pr: Betty Carr
Pr: Robert Fischer
COO: Kris Jurasek
CFO: Gary E Bachman
Ex VP: Gary A Withall
Dir IT: Tom Bosko
Info Man: Jay Grams
Plnt Mgr: Erik Jensen
Mktg Dir: Mike Calvert
Mktg Dir: Mike Molitor
Board of Directors: Andrew W Withall, Gary A Withall

D-U-N-S 14-120-5265
MINER FLEET MANAGEMENT GROUP LLC
UNITED STATES EMERGENCY GLASS
(*Suby of* MINER CORP) ★
17319 San Pedro Ave # 500, San Antonio, TX 78232-1411
Tel (210) 892-1001 *Founded/Ownrshp* 2001
Sales 21.0MM^E *EMP* 120
SIC 7699 1799 Pallet repair; Dock equipment installation, industrial
CEO: Jeff Schmeck
Pr: Justin Steen
CFO: Patrick Aelvoet
VP: Chris Galvan
VP: Rhonda Lambert
VP: Fred Renteria
VP: Rick Upton

D-U-N-S 94-187-9715
MINER HOLDING CO INC
11827 Tech Com Rd Ste 115, San Antonio, TX 78233-6015
Tel (830) 627-8600 *Founded/Ownrshp* 2009
Sales 175.7MM^E *EMP* 250^E
SIC 1799 6719 Parking facility equipment & maintenance; Personal holding companies, except banks
Pr: Phillip T Miner III
VP: Steve Weaver
Dir IT: Justin Steen
Mktg Dir: Melissa Albright

D-U-N-S 02-151-4013
MINERAL AREA COLLEGE FACILITY DEVELOPMENT AUTHORITY INC
5270 Flat River Dr, Park Hills, MO 63601-2224
Tel (573) 783-7932 *Founded/Ownrshp* 1908
Sales 27.2MM^E *EMP* 250
Accts Thurman Shinn & Company Farm
SIC 8222 Junior college; Junior college
Pr: Steven Kurtz
Treas: Connie Holder
Ofcr: A C Walker
* *VP:* Gil Kennon
Store Mgr: Carol Whaley
CTO: Karen Groves
Dir IT: Judy East
IT Man: Ann Blanchfield

D-U-N-S 07-589-1135
■ **MINERAL AREA OSTEOPATHIC HOSPITAL INC**
(*Suby of* COMMUNITY HEALTH SYSTEMS INC) ★
1101 W Liberty St, Farmington, MO 63640-1921
Tel (573) 756-4581 *Founded/Ownrshp* 1952
Sales 25.1MM^E *EMP* 515
SIC 8062 General medical & surgical hospitals; General medical & surgical hospitals
CEO: Stephen L Crain
* *CFO:* Rick Jenkins
Dir Risk M: Marie Dealy
Dir Rx: Mark Trolinger
Software D: John Spurgin

D-U-N-S 10-067-5180
MINERAL COUNTY SCHOOL DISTRICT
1 Baker Pl, Keyser, WV 26726-2824
Tel (304) 788-4200 *Founded/Ownrshp* 1889
Sales 38.3MM^E *EMP* 825
SIC 8211 Public elementary & secondary schools; Public elementary & secondary schools
* *Treas:* Steve Peer
VP Admn: William Pratt
Pr Dir: Patricia Wagoner
Board of Directors: Rudy R Sites

D-U-N-S 09-180-8865
MINERAL FABRICATION & MACHINE CO INC
1 Waxler Rd, Keyser, WV 26726-9074
Tel (304) 788-5855 *Founded/Ownrshp* 1978
Sales 47.1MM^E *EMP* 100
SIC 1541 3441 Industrial buildings, new construction; Renovation, remodeling & repairs: industrial buildings; Fabricated structural metal; Industrial buildings, new construction; Renovation, remodeling & repairs: industrial buildings; Fabricated structural metal
Pr: John R Hale
* *Sec:* Melinda Hale
* *VP:* Jason Hale

D-U-N-S 19-706-1112 IMP
MINERAL PARK INC
8275 N Mineral Park Rd, Golden Valley, AZ 86413-8783
Tel (928) 565-2226 *Founded/Ownrshp* 2003
Sales 57.6MM^E *EMP* 105
SIC 1021 3331 Copper ores; Primary copper; Copper ores; Primary copper
Pr: D Bruce McLeod
* *CFO:* Mark W Distler
* *VP:* Michael J Broch
* *Genl Mgr:* Joseph Campbell
Sfty Mgr: Fedrick Thompson

D-U-N-S 96-270-4354
MINERAL RIDGE GOLD LLC
1515 7th St Ste 1, Elko, NV 89801-5084
Tel (775) 753-4778 *Founded/Ownrshp* 2010
Sales 52.0MM *EMP* 100
SIC 1081 Metal mining services

D-U-N-S 07-315-7877
MINERAL WELLS INDEPENDENT SCHOOL DISTRICT (INC)
906 Sw 5th Ave, Mineral Wells, TX 76067-8445
Tel (940) 325-6404 *Founded/Ownrshp* 1886
Sales 35.2MM^E *EMP* 545
Accts Crawford Carter & Thompson L
SIC 8211 Public senior high school; Public junior high school; Public elementary school; Public senior high school; Public junior high school; Public elementary school
Off Mgr: Wanda Voelcker
Dir IT: Greg Bird
Pr Dir: Caryn Bullock

D-U-N-S 00-506-8093 IMP
MINERALLAC CO
100 Gast Rd, Hampshire, IL 60140-7654
Tel (630) 543-7080 *Founded/Ownrshp* 1910
Sales 21.2MM^E *EMP* 90
SIC 3644 3496 Noncurrent-carrying wiring services; Electric conduits & fittings; Staples, made from purchased wire
Pr: James Hlavacek
Exec: Sonya Donald

MINERALS SERVICES DIVISION
See SGS NORTH AMERICA INC

MINERALS SERVICES DIVISION
See N A SGS INC

MINERALS TECH
See BARRETTS MINERALS INC

D-U-N-S 79-692-9313 IMP
▲ **MINERALS TECHNOLOGIES INC**
622 3rd Ave Fl 38, New York, NY 10017-6729
Tel (212) 878-1800 *Founded/Ownrshp* 1968
Sales 1.7MMM *EMP* 4,464
Accts Kpmg Llp New York New York
Tkr Sym MTX *Exch* NYS
SIC 3295 2819 3274 1411 3281 5032 Minerals, ground or treated; Minerals, ground or otherwise treated; Talc, ground or otherwise treated; Calcium compounds & salts, inorganic; Quicklime; Limestone & marble dimension stone; Limestone, cut & shaped; Limestone; Minerals, ground or treated; Minerals, ground or otherwise treated; Talc, ground or otherwise treated; Calcium compounds & salts, inorganic; Quicklime; Limestone & marble dimension stone; Limestone, cut & shaped; Limestone
Ch Bd: Joseph C Muscari
CFO: Douglas T Dietrich
Chf Cred: Thomas J Meek
Bd of Dir: Donald Winter
Sr VP: D Randy Harrison
Sr VP: Jonathan J Hastings
Sr VP: W Rand Mendez
VP: Michael A Cipolla
VP: Richard Hasselbusch
VP: Andrew Jones
VP: Alexander Masetti
Board of Directors: Joseph C Breunig, John J Carmola, Robert L Clark, Duane R Dunham, Marc E Robinson, Barbara Smith, Donald C Winter

D-U-N-S 80-819-5957
MINERGY LLC
12000 Westheimer Rd # 303, Houston, TX 77077-6681
Tel (832) 800-6336 *Founded/Ownrshp* 2005
Sales 7.9MM^E *EMP* 612
SIC 1382 Oil & gas exploration services; Oil & gas exploration services
Pr: Steve AMS

D-U-N-S 36-413-4254
MINERS COLFAX MEDICAL CENTER
203 Hospital Dr, Raton, NM 87740-2012
Tel (575) 445-3661 *Founded/Ownrshp* 1906
Sales 28.3MM^E *EMP* 225
SIC 8062 8052 8069 General medical & surgical hospitals; Intermediate care facilities; Specialty hospitals, except psychiatric; General medical & surgical hospitals; Intermediate care facilities; Specialty hospitals, except psychiatric
CEO: Charles Secora
* *Pr:* Mike Carter
CFO: Phillip Gonzales
CFO: Vicky REA
* *Treas:* Tom Ppoteste
* *VP:* Albino Martinez
Dir OR: Evelee Malespini
Dir Lab: Rob Bukovac
Dir Sec: Sam Serna
Off Mgr: Jana L Floersheim
Mktg Dir: Kandace Evans

D-U-N-S 02-280-6665
MINERS INC
COUNTY MARKET
5065 Miller Trunk Hwy, Hermantown, MN 55811-1442
Tel (218) 729-5882 *Founded/Ownrshp* 1957
Sales 530.6MM *EMP* 2,300
Accts Mcgladrey Llp Duluth Minneso
SIC 5411 Supermarkets, chain; Supermarkets, chain
Pr: James A Miner Sr
CFO: Greg Borash
* *Treas:* Theresa Lorentz
Dir Risk M: Michael Utecht
Dist Mgr: Tim Hill
Store Mgr: Mark McKenna
Dir IT: Bill Rulla
Genl Couns: Bruce Anderson
Snr Mgr: Gary Chilcote

D-U-N-S 00-421-2866
MINERVA DAIRY INC (OH)
MINERVA MAID
430 Radloff Ave, Minerva, OH 44657-1400
Tel (330) 868-4196 *Founded/Ownrshp* 1970
Sales 28.9MM^E *EMP* 65
SIC 2023 2021 2022 Dry, condensed, evaporated dairy products; Creamery butter; Processed cheese
Pr: Phillip Muller
* *Sec:* Venae Watts
* *VP:* Adam Muller
Sfty Mgr: Joan Raychech

D-U-N-S 83-144-2327
MINERVA LOCAL SCHOOLS
406 East St, Minerva, OH 44657-1429
Tel (330) 868-4942 *Founded/Ownrshp* 2009
Sales 20.4MM *EMP* 99^E
SIC 8249 Vocational schools; Vocational schools
Treas: Jason Schatzel

MINERVA MAID
See MINERVA DAIRY INC

D-U-N-S 62-548-4043
MINERVA NETWORKS INC
2150 Gold St, Alviso, CA 95002-3700
Tel (800) 806-9594 *Founded/Ownrshp* 1992
Sales 25.9MM^E *EMP* 100^E
SIC 7371 Software programming applications
Pr: Mauro Bonomi
Pr: George Bolonos
* *COO:* Dr Jean-Georges Fritsch
* *CFO:* John Doerner
Bd of Dir: Sebastiano Tevarotto
* *VP:* Todd Clayton
VP: Andy Crow
* *VP:* Randy Osborne
VP: Daniel Trangmar
Snr Sftwr: Francesco Emmi
QA Dir: Zina Kortava
Board of Directors:

D-U-N-S 00-420-9656
MINERVA WELDING AND FABRICATING INC (OH)
22133 Us Route 30, Minerva, OH 44657-9401
Tel (330) 868-7731 *Founded/Ownrshp* 1949
Sales 25.0MM^E *EMP* 40
SIC 5084 3599 Industrial machinery & equipment; Machine shop, jobbing & repair
Pr: James A Gram
* *Treas:* Stephen J Gram

MINERVAS RESTAURANT & BAR
See W R RESTAURANTS MANAGEMENT LLC

D-U-N-S 00-148-8915 IMP
MINES PRESS INC (NY)
231 Croton Ave, Cortlandt Manor, NY 10567-5284
Tel (914) 788-1800 *Founded/Ownrshp* 1933, 1952
Sales 37.9MM^E *EMP* 115
SIC 2752 2759 2789 2791 Commercial printing, offset; Letterpress printing; Gold stamping on books; Typesetting; Commercial printing, offset; Letterpress printing; Gold stamping on books; Typesetting
Ch Bd: Steven Mines
* *CFO:* Carl Hutt
* *Sec:* Cynthia Mines

D-U-N-S 07-281-8347
MING YANG AMERICA CORP
(*Suby of* YANG MING MARINE TRANSPORT CORPORATION)
1085 Raymond Blvd Fl 9, Newark, NJ 07102
Tel (201) 222-8899 *Founded/Ownrshp* 1974
Sales 40.0MM *EMP* 300
SIC 4731 Agents, shipping; Airports, flying fields & services; Agents, shipping
CEO: Spring Wu
Ch Bd: Wen Jen Lee
Pr: Frank Calvosa
Pr: Michelle KAO
Pr: Wenjin Lee
Treas: June Yeh
Sr VP: Adam Yeh
VP: Robert Bassillo
VP: Leo Chiang
VP: Charles Chiu
VP: Stephen Hsu
VP: Greg Krueger
VP: T R Lee
VP: Tony Micena
VP: Daniel Ni

D-U-N-S 00-318-7911
MINGES BOTTLING GROUP INC (NC)
128 Pepsi Way, Ayden, NC 28513-7599
Tel (252) 746-9700 *Founded/Ownrshp* 1932
Sales 62.5MM^E *EMP* 210
SIC 5149

D-U-N-S 03-354-5054
MINGLEDORFFS INC
JOHNSON CONTROLS
6675 Jones Mill Ct, Norcross, GA 30092-4394
Tel (770) 239-2100 *Founded/Ownrshp* 1945
Sales 152.7MM^E *EMP* 290
SIC 5075 Air conditioning equipment, except room units; Furnaces, warm air; Air conditioning equipment, except room units; Furnaces, warm air
Ch Bd: Robert M Kesterton
* *Pr:* Lindy B Mingledorff
* *CEO:* David R Kesterton
* *CFO:* Matthew Ranstead
* *Ch:* Bob Kesterton
VP: Ed Eckles
VP: Chris Weaver
Dir Soc: Carol Caldwell
Brnch Mgr: Scott Merwin
Brnch Mgr: Jessie Nantz
Brnch Mgr: Jeff Vetter

D-U-N-S 16-014-7398
MINGO AFFILIATES SERVICES INC
20900 Ne 30th Ave, Miami, FL 33180-2157
Tel (888) 788-2643 *Founded/Ownrshp* 2003
Sales 50.0MM *EMP* 4
SIC 1041 Gold ores mining; Gold ores mining
Pr: Timothy C Mingo
* *Sec:* Thelma Harper-Mingo

D-U-N-S 07-267-8162
MINGO COUNTY BOARD OF EDUCATION
Hc 2 Box 310, Williamson, WV 25661
Tel (304) 235-3333 *Founded/Ownrshp* 1895
Sales 68.6MM^E *EMP* 950
SIC 8211 Elementary & secondary schools; School board
Pr: James Farley
* *Pr:* Charles West
IT Man: Jim May

D-U-N-S 07-979-9038
MINGO COUNTY SCHOOLS
110 Cinderella Rd, Williamson, WV 25661
Tel (304) 235-3333 *Founded/Ownrshp* 2015
Sales 5.9MM^E *EMP* 950^E
SIC 8211 Public elementary & secondary schools

D-U-N-S 07-825-6650
MINGO LOGAN COAL CO
MOUNTAIN LAUREL COMPLEX
1 Mountain Laurel, Sharples, WV 25183
Tel (304) 369-7506 *Founded/Ownrshp* 1987
Sales 51.8MM^E *EMP* 400
SIC 1241 Coal mining services; Coal mining services
Pr: David Runyon
* *Treas:* James E Florczak
* *VP:* John T Drexler

D-U-N-S 86-948-0405
MINGS RESOURCE CORP
3316 47th Ave, Sacramento, CA 95824-2434
Tel (916) 421-5054 *Founded/Ownrshp* 2009
Sales 125.0MM *EMP* 25
Accts Gallina Llp Roseville Ca
SIC 4953 Recycling, waste materials
Pr: Kenny Eric Luong
* *CFO:* Kevin Luong

D-U-N-S 15-208-6997
MINI GRAPHICS INC
MGI
140 Commerce Dr, Hauppauge, NY 11788-3948
Tel (516) 223-6464 *Founded/Ownrshp* 1985
Sales 24.5MM^E *EMP* 100
SIC 2759 Commercial printing
CEO: James Delise
* *Prin:* Charles J Delise
Mng Dir: Chris Lapak
Tech Mgr: Rob Diekroger
Prd Mgr: Silvio Madonia

D-U-N-S 06-406-0452
■ **MINI MART INC**
LOAF 'N JUG
(*Suby of* KROGER CO) ★
442 Keeler Pkwy, Pueblo, CO 81001-4813
Tel (719) 948-3071 *Founded/Ownrshp* 1986
Sales 210.9MM^E *EMP* 1,600
SIC 5411 Convenience stores; Convenience stores
Pr: Arthur Stawski
* *CFO:* James Shiner
* *VP:* Robert Moeder
Dir IT: Norman Rupert
Site Mgr: Dave Wenger

MINI U STORAGE
See DAHN CORP

MINI-CIRCUITS
See SCIENTIFIC COMPONENTS CORP

D-U-N-S 08-178-8478
MINI-CIRCUITS FORT WAYNE LLC
13 Neptune Ave, Brooklyn, NY 11235-4404
Tel (718) 934-4500 *Founded/Ownrshp* 1969
Sales 72.8MM^E *EMP* 500
SIC 3679 3678 3677 3674 3663 3643 Attenuators; Electronic connectors; Electronic coils, transformers & other inductors; Semiconductors & related devices; Radio & TV communications equipment; Current-carrying wiring devices; Attenuators; Electronic connectors; Electronic coils, transformers & other inductors; Semiconductors & related devices; Radio & TV communications equipment; Current-carrying wiring devices

D-U-N-S 06-351-5605 IMP
MINIATURE PRECISION COMPONENTS INC
820 Wisconsin St, Walworth, WI 53184-9516
Tel (262) 275-5791 *Founded/Ownrshp* 1974
Sales 565.3MM^E *EMP* 1,700
SIC 3089 Injection molded finished plastic products; Molding primary plastic; Injection molded finished plastic products; Molding primary plastic
Ch: Jay Brost
* *Pr:* Dennis Konkol
* *CEO:* James Brost
* *CFO:* Nish Patel
VP: Ron Hardwick
* *Prin:* Dan Brost
Prgrm Mgr: Janet Pray
CTO: Rick Traeger
Plnt Mgr: Ing Arriola
Plnt Mgr: Chris Dunn
Plnt Mgr: Jose Maldonado

D-U-N-S 86-799-4261 IMP
MINIBAR NORTH AMERICA INC
MINIBAR SYSTEMS
(*Suby of* MINIBAR AG)
7340 Westmore Rd, Rockville, MD 20850-1260
Tel (301) 309-1100 *Founded/Ownrshp* 1994
Sales 26.5MM^E *EMP* 48
SIC 5064 7359 7623 Electrical appliances, television & radio; Appliance rental; Refrigerator repair service
Ch: Andreas Jacobs
**Pr:* Anthony J Torano
**CFO:* Pat Galgano
**CFO:* Patrick Galgano
**CFO:* Ralf Michael Rokoss
**Ex VP:* Walt Strasser
**Sr VP:* Espen Andersen

MINIBAR SYSTEMS
See MINIBAR NORTH AMERICA INC

D-U-N-S 61-337-2598
MINICHI INC
453 Ziegler St, Dupont, PA 18641-1947
Tel (570) 654-8332 *Founded/Ownrshp* 1989
Sales 50.8MM^E *EMP* 90
SIC 1081 1622 Preparing shafts or tunnels, metal mining; Bridge, tunnel & elevated highway
Pr: Marc Minichiello
Off Mgr: Joet Paticchi

D-U-N-S 07-381-5292
MINICHIELLO BROS INC
SCRAP IT
2 Dexter St, Everett, MA 02149-3230
Tel (617) 389-7213 *Founded/Ownrshp* 1957
Sales 37.2MM^E *EMP* 55
SIC 4953 Refuse systems; Refuse systems
Pr: Tanya Minichiello
**VP:* Frank Minichiello

D-U-N-S 10-001-5171
MINIDOKA COUNTY JOINT SCHOOL DISTRICT 331
MINIDOKA SCHOOLS
310 10th St, Rupert, ID 83350-1421
Tel (208) 436-0264 *Founded/Ownrshp* 1954
Sales 34.8MM^E *EMP* 677
SIC 8211 Public elementary & secondary schools; School board; Public elementary & secondary schools; School board
Prin: Dr Scott Rogers
**Treas:* Michelle Deluna
Bd of Dir: Jason Gibbons
IT Man: Jeremy Bywater
Teacher Pr: Margery Sneddon
HC Dir: Laurie Stimpson

D-U-N-S 08-182-5168
MINIDOKA MEMORIAL HOSPITAL INC
1224 8th St, Rupert, ID 83350-1599
Tel (208) 436-0481 *Founded/Ownrshp* 2009
Sales 25.2MM *EMP* 290^E
SIC 8062 8051 General medical & surgical hospitals; Skilled nursing care facilities; General medical & surgical hospitals; Skilled nursing care facilities
Ex Dir: Carl Hanson
**CFO:* Jason Gibbons
Ofcr: Tammy Day
**VP:* Kim Vega
Dir Lab: Anne Owens
Dir Rx: Wes Schow
Ex Dir: Joye Simpson
Dir Sec: Joel Rogers
QA Dir: Tammy Roger
Mtls Dir: Edith Castro
Pathlgst: Steve M Skoumal

MINIDOKA SCHOOLS
See MINIDOKA COUNTY JOINT SCHOOL DISTRICT 331

D-U-N-S 01-053-7492 IMP/EXP
MINIGRIP LLC
(*Suby of* AMTOPP DIV) ★
1650 N Heideke St, Seguin, TX 78155-2823
Tel (830) 433-6100 *Founded/Ownrshp* 2012
Sales 32.7MM^E *EMP* 52^E
SIC 5113 Bags, paper & disposable plastic
QA Dir: Lisa Moriarty

D-U-N-S 05-949-4146
MINIMATICS INC
433 Clyde Ave, Mountain View, CA 94043-2209
Tel (650) 969-5630 *Founded/Ownrshp* 1973
Sales 20.0MM^E *EMP* 57
SIC 5065 3599 Semiconductor devices; Machine shop, jobbing & repair
Pr: Walter Chew
Exec: Bud Coiner
Exec: Jenny Polozova

D-U-N-S 09-420-7545 IMP
MINING CONTROLS LLC
GILBERT/K & M ELEC SYSTEMS DIV
(*Suby of* ELGIN EQUIPMENT GROUP LLC) ★
214 Industrial Park Rd, Beaver, WV 25813-9306
Tel (304) 252-6243 *Founded/Ownrshp* 1988
Sales 44.4MM^E *EMP* 115
SIC 3612 3613 3629 3646 3699 3825 Transformers, except electric; Panelboards & distribution boards, electric; Circuit breakers, air; Switchgear & switchgear accessories; Capacitors & condensers; Commercial indusl & institutional electric lighting fixtures; Electrical equipment & supplies; Instruments to measure electricity; Transformers, except electric; Panelboards & distribution boards, electric; Circuit breakers, air; Switchgear & switchgear accessories; Capacitors & condensers; Commercial indusl & institutional electric lighting fixtures; Electrical equipment & supplies; Instruments to measure electricity
Pr: Mark Walker
CFO: Kerry Koch
**Sr VP:* Wayne J Conner
**Sr VP:* Charles D Hall
**Sr VP:* Fred Schulte
**Prin:* Randall L Hurst
VP Opers: Jack Miles

MINING JOY MACHINERY
See JOY GLOBAL UNDERGROUND MINING LLC

D-U-N-S 13-949-7820 IMP
MINING ROCK EXCAVATION AND CONSTRUCTION LLC
(*Suby of* ATLAS COPCO NORTH AMERICA LLC) ★
3700 E 68th Ave, Commerce City, CO 80022-2243
Tel (303) 287-8822 *Founded/Ownrshp* 1990
Sales 46.1MM^E *EMP* 188
SIC 3532 5084 Drills, bits & similar equipment; Drilling bits; Drills, bits & similar equipment; Drilling bits
CEO: Ronnie Leten
Pr: Brian Bieller
**Sec:* Mark Cohen
**Sr VP:* Stephan Kuhn
**VP:* Jim Levitt
Area Mgr: Daniel Lawrence
Genl Mgr: Torbjorn Redaelli
DP Dir: Boyd Funk
VP Sls: Alan Kurus
Mktg Dir: Stephen Nelson
Manager: Noyes Bakke

D-U-N-S 07-668-4182
MINISINK VALLEY CENTRAL SCHOOL DISTRICT
2320 Route 6, Slate Hill, NY 10973-3628
Tel (845) 355-5100 *Founded/Ownrshp* 1960
Sales 33.8MM^E *EMP* 615^E
SIC 8211 Public senior high school; Public senior high school
Pr: Joseph Flaherty
COO: Kimberly Jordan
Dir IT: Jason Patten
Psych: Shelly Matlofsky
Psych: Carol Schiavo

D-U-N-S 07-100-7173
MINISTERS AND MISSIONARIES BENEFIT BOARD OF AMERICAN BAPTIST CHURCHES
M & M B B
475 Riverside Dr Fl 17, New York, NY 10115-0035
Tel (212) 870-8088 *Founded/Ownrshp* 1913
Sales 66.0MM *EMP* 71
Accts Bdo Seidman Llp New York Ny
SIC 8661 Religious organizations; Religious organizations
Ex Dir: Louis P Barbarin
**Pr:* Gwynn Perlich
VP: Patricia Hunter
Comm Man: Noelle Durante
Dir IT: Karen Dubin
IT Man: Sharon McDowell
Netwrk Mgr: Rey Figueroa
Snr Mgr: Michael Lattis

D-U-N-S 15-731-6381
MINISTRY HEALTH CARE INC
(*Suby of* ASCENSION HEALTH ALLIANCE) ★
11925 W Lake Park Dr # 100, Milwaukee, WI 53224-3002
Tel (414) 359-1060 *Founded/Ownrshp* 2013
Sales 190.2MM *EMP* 5,000
Accts Deloitte Tax Llp Milwaukee W
SIC 8011 8051 Offices & clinics of medical doctors; Convalescent home with continuous nursing care; Offices & clinics of medical doctors; Convalescent home with continuous nursing care
Pr: Nicholas F Desien
Chf Mktg O: Larry Hegland
Ex VP: Theresa Richards
**Sr VP:* Sister Lois Bush
VP: Jerry Burke
VP: Dennis Kepchar
VP: Larry Sobal
Creative D: John Egan
Dir Rx: Amy Konop
IT Man: Brian Hanson
Opers Supe: Beth Sekerka

D-U-N-S 05-363-8941
MINISTRY HOME CARE INC
(*Suby of* MINISTRY HEALTH CARE INC) ★
611 N Saint Joseph Ave, Marshfield, WI 54449-1832
Tel (715) 389-3802 *Founded/Ownrshp* 1998
Sales 31.9MM *EMP* 315
SIC 8082 Home health care services; Home health care services
Pr: Jerry Cleveland
**VP:* Linda Bodien
VP: Gary Kusnierz
Genl Mgr: Hellen Mozuch
IT Man: Paul Thomas
IT Man: Todd Zieglmeier
Snr Mgr: Matthew Odland

D-U-N-S 36-102-3489
MINISTRY MEDICAL GROUP
2251 N Shore Dr Ste 200, Rhinelander, WI 54501-6712
Tel (715) 361-4700 *Founded/Ownrshp* 2005
Sales 113.0MM *EMP* 100
SIC 8011 Physicians' office, including specialists; Physicians' office, including specialists
Prin: Mike Jones
Doctor: Judith S Pagano MD

D-U-N-S 11-352-1405
MINISTRY MEDICAL GROUP INC
RICE CLINIC
(*Suby of* MINISTRY HEALTH CARE INC) ★
824 Illinois Ave, Stevens Point, WI 54481-3112
Tel (715) 342-7500 *Founded/Ownrshp* 2000
Sales 5.5MM^E *EMP* 500
SIC 8011 Clinic, operated by physicians; Clinic, operated by physicians
Pr: Jeff Martin
Dept Mgr: Linda Massopust
Off Mgr: Lori Ramczyk
Doctor: Lisa Jamison
Doctor: Thomas Omalley MD
Doctor: Steven Slezak MD
Doctor: Todd Williams
Doctor: Jessica Young

D-U-N-S 96-233-1596
MINISTRY MEDICAL GROUP INC
11925 W Lake Park Dr, Milwaukee, WI 53224-3002
Tel (414) 359-1060 *Founded/Ownrshp* 2010
Sales 126.9MM *EMP* 4
Accts Tax Llp Milwaukee Wi
SIC 8011 Offices & clinics of medical doctors; Offices & clinics of medical doctors
Pr: Donald Fasoli
V Ch: John Gauder
Doctor: Steven Brown
Doctor: Dhimant Patel

MINISTRY SAINT CLARES HOSPITAL
See SAINT CLARES HOSPITAL OF WESTON INC

MINIT MART
See RAMCO INC

D-U-N-S 10-732-6043
MINITAB INC
1829 Pine Hall Rd, State College, PA 16801-3008
Tel (814) 238-3280 *Founded/Ownrshp* 1988
Sales 85.5MM^E *EMP* 321
Accts Parentebeard Llc State Colleg
SIC 7372 Prepackaged software; Prepackaged software
Pr: Barbara F Ryan
**COO:* Yvette L Rauff
CFO: Bill Vesnesky
**CFO:* William J Vesnesky
**Sec:* Steven Pincus
VP: Jean Heck
VP: Peggy Snyder
Adv Bd Mbr: Cindy Nucciarone
Genl Mgr: Mary Zimmerman
Snr Sftwr: Steve Baird
Snr Sftwr: Denise Chester

MINKA GROUP
See MINKA LIGHTING INC

D-U-N-S 10-312-3956 IMP/EXP
MINKA LIGHTING INC
MINKA GROUP
1151 Bradford Cir, Corona, CA 92882-7166
Tel (951) 735-9220 *Founded/Ownrshp* 1982
Sales 83.2MM^E *EMP* 250
SIC 5063 Lighting fixtures; Lighting fixtures
CEO: Marian Tang
VP: Peter Decsy
**Prin:* Kurt Schulzman
Dir IT: Jason Yu
VP Opers: Dan Hitzeman
Natl Sales: Steve Cuttrell
Natl Sales: Jeff Lehman
Natl Sales: Martin Shepherd

D-U-N-S 00-383-6566
MINKOFF CO INC (DC)
11716 Baltimore Ave, Beltsville, MD 20705-1850
Tel (301) 652-8711 *Founded/Ownrshp* 1948
Sales 21.8MM *EMP* 75
SIC 1542 1521 Commercial & office building contractors; Repairing fire damage, single-family houses; Commercial & office building contractors; Repairing fire damage, single-family houses
Pr: Steven Gross

D-U-N-S 18-293-6984 IMP/EXP
MINMOR INDUSTRIES LLC
NOTABLES
6010 Earle Brown Dr, Minneapolis, MN 55430-4517
Tel (763) 504-5400 *Founded/Ownrshp* 2002
Sales 110.7MM^E *EMP* 306
SIC 2657 2673 2099 Commercial printing; Folding paperboard boxes; Bags: plastic, laminated & coated; Food preparations
CFO: Douglas Helm
VP: Mark Gubash
VP: Sarah Lindberg
VP: Richard Morehouse
VP: Mark Theno
Exec: Lori Anderson
Creative D: Scott Klingelhofer
CIO: Tim Wallace
IT Man: Connors Lau
Natl Sales: Jon Cleveland
Mktg Mgr: Margaret Vergeyle

D-U-N-S 79-420-5559
MINN-DAK CO
FARGO FREIGHTLINER
3440 36th St S, Fargo, ND 58104-8804
Tel (701) 293-9133 *Founded/Ownrshp* 1989
Sales 47.2MM *EMP* 72
Accts Eide Bailly Llp Fargo North
SIC 7538 5012 Truck engine repair, except industrial; Trucks, commercial
CEO: Ronald Ristvedt
Sls Mgr: Jeff Sedivy

D-U-N-S 06-653-2086 IMP
MINN-DAK FARMERS COOPERATIVE INC
7525 Red River Rd Ste 2, Wahpeton, ND 58075-9698
Tel (701) 671-1310 *Founded/Ownrshp* 1972
Sales 306.0MM *EMP* 455^E
SIC 2099 2063 Sugar; Yeast; Beet sugar; Beet pulp, dried: from beet sugar refinery; Powdered sugar from sugar beets; Molasses from sugar beets; Sugar; Yeast; Beet sugar; Beet pulp, dried: from beet sugar refinery; Powdered sugar from sugar beets; Molasses from sugar beets
Pr: Kurt Wickstrom
COO: Jeffrey Carlson
CFO: Steven M Caspers
CFO: Rick Kasper
Ex VP: Steven Caspers
VP: John R Haugen
VP: John Haugen
VP: Tom Knudsen
VP: Richard Richter
VP: Parker Thilmony
Comm Man: Sue Moffet
Board of Directors: Dennis Butenhoff, Douglas Etten, Dennis Klosterman, C Kevin Kutzer, Russell Mauch, Charles Steiner

D-U-N-S 15-168-1327
MINN-KOTA AG PRODUCTS INC
90 8th St N, Breckenridge, MN 56520-1556
Tel (218) 643-8464 *Founded/Ownrshp* 1990
Sales 37.1MM^E *EMP* 47
Accts Power Financial
SIC 5153 5191 Grain elevators; Fertilizer & fertilizer materials; Feed; Chemicals, agricultural; Grain elevators; Fertilizer & fertilizer materials; Feed; Chemicals, agricultural
CEO: Brian Arnhalt
**Pr:* George Schuler III

D-U-N-S 17-166-5052
MINNEAPOLIS COLLEGE OF ART & DESIGN
ART CELLAR BOOKSTORE
2501 Stevens Ave, Minneapolis, MN 55404-4347
Tel (612) 874-3700 *Founded/Ownrshp* 1883
Sales 30.7MM *EMP* 180
Accts Baker Tilly Virchow Krause Llp
SIC 8221 College, except junior; College, except junior
Pr: Jay Coogan
Pr: Pat Newsome
**Ch:* Clinton H Morrison
**VP:* Mary Lazarus
VP: Vince Leo
**VP:* Daniel L Sjoquist
Genl Mgr: Duke Shroot
Dir IT: Pamela Arnold
Dir IT: Matt Kiedrowski
IT Man: Greg Talmo

D-U-N-S 80-719-6985
MINNEAPOLIS COMMUNITY AND TECHNICAL COLLEGE FOUNDATION
(*Suby of* BEMIDJI STATE UNIVERSITY) ★
1501 Hennepin Ave, Minneapolis, MN 55403-1710
Tel (612) 659-6200 *Founded/Ownrshp* 2004
Sales 19.5MM^E *EMP* 600^E
SIC 8222 9199 Community college; ; Community college;
Pr: Phillip L Davis
Bd of Dir: Julie Chavez
VP: Lois Balman
VP: Scott Erickson
VP: Gail O'Kane
Telecom Ex: Emmanual Green
Psych: Melissa Perez
Psych: Russell Raczkowski
Pgrm Dir: Marnie Anderson
Pgrm Dir: Ninh Phan
Snr Mgr: Tara Martinez

D-U-N-S 83-278-4800
MINNEAPOLIS DIE CASTING LLC
METAL TECH - MNNPOLIS DIE CAST
(*Suby of* KEY 3 CASTING LLC) ★
5100 Boone Ave N, Minneapolis, MN 55428-4025
Tel (763) 536-5500 *Founded/Ownrshp* 2009
Sales 28.8MM^E *EMP* 116
SIC 3365 3321 Aluminum & aluminum-based alloy castings; Gray iron castings; Aluminum & aluminum-based alloy castings; Gray iron castings
Ofcr: Barry Onufrock
Sfty Mgr: Laurel Lashuay
Opers Mgr: Paul Karnowski

MINNEAPOLIS ENERGY CENTER
See NRG ENERGY CENTER MINNEAPOLIS LLC

D-U-N-S 07-179-2303
MINNEAPOLIS FOUNDATION
800 Ids Ctr 80 S 8th St, Minneapolis, MN 55402
Tel (612) 672-3878 *Founded/Ownrshp* 1915
Sales 121.9MM *EMP* 20^E
Accts Cliftonlarsonallen Llp Minnea
SIC 6732 Charitable trust management; Charitable trust management
Pr: Sandra Vargas
Ofcr: Robyn Schein
Sr VP: Beth Halloran
VP: Jean Adams
VP: Luz Frias
VP: Teresa Morrow
Ex Dir: Tawanna Black

D-U-N-S 02-292-1514
MINNEAPOLIS GLASS CO
14600 28th Ave N, Plymouth, MN 55447-4820
Tel (763) 559-0635 *Founded/Ownrshp* 1937
Sales 26.2MM^E *EMP* 60
SIC 5039 3231 1793 Exterior flat glass: plate or window; Interior flat glass: plate or window; Products of purchased glass; Glass & glazing work
CEO: Mike Horovitz
**Pr:* Jennifer Lang
**VP:* Thomas Stadler

MINNEAPOLIS INSTITUTE OF ARTS
See MINNEAPOLIS SOCIETY OF FINE ARTS

D-U-N-S 06-819-5064
MINNEAPOLIS MEDICAL RESEARCH FOUNDATION
(*Suby of* HENNEPIN FACULTY ASSOCIATES INC) ★
701 Park Ave, Minneapolis, MN 55415-1623
Tel (612) 873-5300 *Founded/Ownrshp* 1991
Sales 35.7MM *EMP* 200
Accts Eide Bailly Llp Minneapolis
SIC 8731 Medical research, commercial; Medical research, commercial
Pr: Paul R Pentel MD
Treas: Thomas Bloss
VP: Gaylan Rockswold
VP: Gaylan Rockwold
Prgrm Man: Lynne Burke
Info Man: Linda Hennings
Software D: Connie Lee
Orthpdst: Mark Lesage

D-U-N-S 19-080-4419
MINNEAPOLIS PUBLIC HOUSING AUTHORITY
1001 Washington Ave N, Minneapolis, MN 55401-1032
Tel (612) 342-1400 *Founded/Ownrshp* 1991
Sales NA *EMP* 287

SIC 9531 ;
CEO: Cora McCorvey
**CFO:* Tim Durose
Ex Dir: Alice Kindall
Ex Dir: Susan Seel

D-U-N-S 02-050-4114
MINNEAPOLIS PUBLIC SCHOOL DISTRICT
MINNEAPOLIS PUBLIC SCHOOLS
1250 W Broadway Ave, Minneapolis, MN 55411-2533
Tel (612) 668-0200 *Founded/Ownrshp* 1894
Sales 276.1MM^E *EMP* 9,000
Accts Larson Allen Llp Minneapolis
SIC 8211 Public elementary school; Public junior high school; Public senior high school; Public adult education school; Public elementary school; Public junior high school; Public senior high school; Public adult education school
CEO: Michael Goar
Bd of Dir: Lydia Lee
Exec: Sue Mortonsen
Exec: Vernon Rowe
Admn Mgr: Jill Pohtilla
Counsel: Kim Mesun

MINNEAPOLIS PUBLIC SCHOOLS
See MINNEAPOLIS PUBLIC SCHOOL DISTRICT

D-U-N-S 07-763-3840 IMP/EXP
MINNEAPOLIS SOCIETY OF FINE ARTS
MINNEAPOLIS INSTITUTE OF ARTS
2400 3rd Ave S, Minneapolis, MN 55404-3506
Tel (612) 870-3131 *Founded/Ownrshp* 1883
Sales 50.5MM *EMP* 300
Accts Cliftonlarsonallen Llp Minnea
SIC 8412 Art gallery, noncommercial; Art gallery, noncommercial
Pr: William M Grifwold
V Ch: Diane Lilly
**CFO:* Pat Grazzini
**Prin:* Kaywin Feldman
Dir IT: Douglas Hegley
IT Man: Steve Scidmor
Mktg Mgr: Kim Huskinson
Sls Mgr: Jessa Barron
Sales Asso: Jacquelyna Figueroa
Sales Asso: Allison Shilinski

D-U-N-S 08-611-5052
MINNEHAHA ACADEMY (MN)
3100 W River Pkwy, Minneapolis, MN 55406-1843
Tel (612) 729-8321 *Founded/Ownrshp* 1913
Sales 19.8MM *EMP* 407
Accts Scanlon Nietz & Murch Llc
SIC 8211 Private combined elementary & secondary school; Private combined elementary & secondary school
Pr: Donna Harris
Prin: Charice Deegan
Prin: Carey Erkel

D-U-N-S 15-065-3046
MINNEHAHA BANCSHARES INC
100 S Phillips Ave # 100, Sioux Falls, SD 57104-6745
Tel (605) 335-5100 *Founded/Ownrshp* 1981
Sales NA *EMP* 250^E
Accts Bkd Llp Lincoln/Omaha Nebras
SIC 6021 6022 National commercial banks; State commercial banks; National commercial banks; State commercial banks
Pr: William L Baker
**VP:* Richard J Corcoran
VP: Bert Olson
VP: Jan Ritter
**VP:* James Schnatterly
**VP:* Cal Willemssen

D-U-N-S 13-922-3239
MINNESOTA AG POWER INC
JOHN DEERE
1710 Franklin St N, Glenwood, MN 56334-2014
Tel (320) 634-5151 *Founded/Ownrshp* 2003
Sales 32.9MM^E *EMP* 150^E
SIC 5261 Lawnmowers & tractors
Pr: Curt Weber
**VP:* Andrew Swenson

D-U-N-S 93-269-3948
MINNESOTA AGRONOMY & PLANT PROTECTION DIVISION
(*Suby of* DEPARTMENT OF AGRICULTURE MINNESOTA) ★
90 Plato Blvd W, Saint Paul, MN 55107-2004
Tel (651) 644-0510 *Founded/Ownrshp* 1988
Sales NA *EMP* 400
SIC 9641 Regulation of agricultural marketing;

D-U-N-S 14-774-6080
MINNESOTA AIR INC
6901 W Old Shakopee Rd, Minneapolis, MN 55438-2683
Tel (952) 918-8000 *Founded/Ownrshp* 1999
Sales 60.9MM *EMP* 70
Accts Cliftonlarsonallen Llp Minne
SIC 5074 5075 Plumbing & hydronic heating supplies; Warm air heating & air conditioning; Plumbing & hydronic heating supplies; Warm air heating & air conditioning
Pr: Michael Metzger
**VP:* Wade Boelter
Opers Mgr: Randy Erickson
Advt Mgr: Laurie Janu
Sls Mgr: Glenn Dunham
Sales Asso: Kevin Kerrigan
Sales Asso: Curt Kunkel

MINNESOTA CENTRAL SCHOOL BUS
See ILLINOIS CENTRAL SCHOOL BUS LLC

MINNESOTA COMMUNITY FOUNDATION
See SAINT PAUL FOUNDATION INC

D-U-N-S 10-228-8396 IMP
MINNESOTA CORRUGATED BOX INC
2200 Yh Hanson Ave, Albert Lea, MN 56007-3440
Tel (507) 373-5006 *Founded/Ownrshp* 1983
Sales 42.3MM^E *EMP* 110
SIC 2653 Boxes, corrugated: made from purchased materials; Boxes, corrugated: made from purchased materials
CEO: Thomas J Krebsbach
**Pr:* Michael Moore
CFO: Noel Austin
**Prin:* Dar Nelson

D-U-N-S 02-136-5189
MINNESOTA COUNTIES INTERGOVERNMENTAL TRUST
MCIT
100 Empire Dr Ste 100, Saint Paul, MN 55103-1885
Tel (651) 209-6400 *Founded/Ownrshp* 2001
Sales 33.7MM *EMP* 37
Accts Eide Bailly Llp Minneapolis
SIC 8742 Compensation & benefits planning consultant; Compensation & benefits planning consultant
Ex Dir: Robyn Sykes
**Ch:* Denise Hegberk
Bd of Dir: Charles Enter
IT Man: Jeff Kulas

D-U-N-S 80-389-4021
MINNESOTA DEPARTMENT OF ADMINISTRATION
(*Suby of* EXECUTIVE OFFICE OF STATE OF MINNESOTA) ★
50 Sherburne Ave Ste 200, Saint Paul, MN 55155-1402
Tel (651) 493-4929 *Founded/Ownrshp* 1939
Sales NA *EMP* 910
SIC 9611 Economic development agency, government; ; Economic development agency, government;
Ofcr: Sara Turnbow

D-U-N-S 80-483-2640
MINNESOTA DEPARTMENT OF EMPLOYMENT AND ECONOMIC DEVELOPMENT
(*Suby of* EXECUTIVE OFFICE OF STATE OF MINNESOTA) ★
332 Minnesota St Ste E200, Saint Paul, MN 55101-1349
Tel (651) 259-7114 *Founded/Ownrshp* 2003
Sales NA *EMP* 1,700
SIC 9441 Administration of social & manpower programs; ; Administration of social & manpower programs;
CFO: Cindy Farrell
CIO: Henry May

D-U-N-S 80-389-4203
MINNESOTA DEPARTMENT OF HUMAN SERVICES
(*Suby of* EXECUTIVE OFFICE OF STATE OF MINNESOTA) ★
540 Cedar St, Saint Paul, MN 55164
Tel (651) 431-2000 *Founded/Ownrshp* 1953
Sales NA *EMP* 35,217
Accts Tautges Redpath Ltd White B
SIC 9441 Administration of social & manpower programs; ; Administration of social & manpower programs;
**Prin:* Lucinda Jesson

D-U-N-S 80-483-2129
MINNESOTA DEPARTMENT OF LABOR & INDUSTRY
(*Suby of* EXECUTIVE OFFICE OF STATE OF MINNESOTA) ★
443 Lafayette Rd N, Saint Paul, MN 55155-4301
Tel (651) 284-5005 *Founded/Ownrshp* 1967
Sales NA *EMP* 440
SIC 9651 Regulation, miscellaneous commercial sectors; ; Regulation, miscellaneous commercial sectors;
**CFO:* Cecelia Jackson
CIO: Cindy Valentine

D-U-N-S 80-533-6823
MINNESOTA DEPARTMENT OF MILITARY AFFAIRS
MINNESOTA NATIONAL GUARD
(*Suby of* EXECUTIVE OFFICE OF STATE OF MINNESOTA) ★
20 12th St W Fl 4, Saint Paul, MN 55155-2004
Tel (651) 268-8924 *Founded/Ownrshp* 1858
Sales NA *EMP* 322
SIC 9199 Personnel agency, government; ; Personnel agency, government;
Art Dir: Larry W Shellito
Snr Mgr: Melanie Nelson

D-U-N-S 80-488-6869
MINNESOTA DEPARTMENT OF NATURAL RESOURCES
D N R
(*Suby of* EXECUTIVE OFFICE OF STATE OF MINNESOTA) ★
500 Lafayette Rd N, Saint Paul, MN 55155-4002
Tel (651) 296-6157 *Founded/Ownrshp* 1931
Sales NA *EMP* 3,800
SIC 9512 Conservation & stabilization agency, government; ; Conservation & stabilization agency, government;
**CIO:* Robert Maki
MIS Dir: Michael Hager
Dir IT: Linda Randolph
Info Man: David Lent
Snr Mgr: Dirk Peterson

D-U-N-S 80-488-6729
MINNESOTA DEPARTMENT OF PUBLIC SAFETY
MINNESOTA DEPT -PUBLIC SAFETY
(*Suby of* EXECUTIVE OFFICE OF STATE OF MINNESOTA) ★
445 Minnesota St, Saint Paul, MN 55101-2190
Tel (651) 201-7000 *Founded/Ownrshp* 1970
Sales NA *EMP* 1,800
SIC 9229 Public order & safety statistics centers; ; Public order & safety statistics centers;

D-U-N-S 80-483-2327
MINNESOTA DEPARTMENT OF TRANSPORTATION
(*Suby of* EXECUTIVE OFFICE OF STATE OF MINNESOTA) ★
395 John Ireland Blvd, Saint Paul, MN 55155-1800
Tel (651) 296-3000 *Founded/Ownrshp* 1976
Sales NA *EMP* 4,900
SIC 9621 Regulation, administration of transportation; ; Regulation, administration of transportation;
VP: Wayne Brede
Exec: Dean Shaklee
Prgrm Mgr: Susan Mulvihill
Genl Mgr: Randy Christensen
IT Man: Michael Barnes
Netwrk Mgr: Lowell Schafer
Info Man: Tim Henkel
Info Man: Jeffrey Johnson

MINNESOTA DEPT -PUBLIC SAFETY
See MINNESOTA DEPARTMENT OF PUBLIC SAFETY

D-U-N-S 00-620-0836
MINNESOTA DIVERSIFIED PRODUCTS INC (MN)
DIVERSIFOAM PRODUCTS
9091 County Road 50, Rockford, MN 55373-9514
Tel (763) 477-5854 *Founded/Ownrshp* 1967, 1989
Sales 20.3MM^E *EMP* 100
SIC 3086 2821 2671 Insulation or cushioning material, foamed plastic; Packaging & shipping materials, foamed plastic; Plastics materials & resins; Packaging paper & plastics film, coated & laminated; Insulation or cushioning material, foamed plastic; Packaging & shipping materials, foamed plastic; Plastics materials & resins; Packaging paper & plastics film, coated & laminated
Pr: Benjamin G Sachs
VP: Carl Mura
CIO: Rebecca Coyle
IT Man: Mike Truebenbach
Opers Mgr: Deb Wick

D-U-N-S 07-134-0772
MINNESOTA ELEVATOR INC
MEI
19336 607th Ave, Mankato, MN 56001-8560
Tel (507) 245-3060 *Founded/Ownrshp* 1990
Sales 55.0MM^E *EMP* 230
SIC 3534 1796 7699 Elevators & equipment; Elevator installation & conversion; Elevators: inspection, service & repair; Elevators & equipment; Elevator installation & conversion; Elevators: inspection, service & repair
CEO: John Romnes
**Pr:* Rick Lowembry
CFO: Kurt Meyer
Mng Dir: Bobby Smith
Prgrm Mgr: Jeff Karvonen
CTO: Jane Krummel
IT Man: Roxie Weingartz
IT Man: Michelle Widmer
Natl Sales: Don Simons

D-U-N-S 78-006-2605
■ **MINNESOTA ENERGY RESOURCES CORP**
(*Suby of* WEC ENERGY GROUP INC) ★
2665 145th St W, Rosemount, MN 55068-4927
Tel (651) 322-8900 *Founded/Ownrshp* 2015
Sales 47.2MM^E *EMP* 225
SIC 4924 Natural gas distribution; Natural gas distribution
Pr: Barbara Nick
Pr: Charles A Cloninger

D-U-N-S 04-597-4680 IMP/EXP
MINNESOTA FLEXIBLE CORP
MFC
305 Bridgepoint Dr # 400, South Saint Paul, MN 55075-2491
Tel (651) 645-7522 *Founded/Ownrshp* 1987
Sales 25.0MM^E *EMP* 49
SIC 5085 3599 3492 3052 5162 Hose, belting & packing; Hose, flexible metallic; Hose & tube couplings, hydraulic/pneumatic; Rubber & plastics hose & beltings; Rubber hose; Plastic hose; Plastics materials & basic shapes
CEO: Terry Kelly
Pr: Will Stewart
Mtls Mgr: Brad Ferstan
Sls&Mrk Ex: Jeff Bush

D-U-N-S 83-552-7896
MINNESOTA FOOD BANK NETWORK
3585 Lexington Ave N # 246, Saint Paul, MN 55126-8064
Tel (651) 486-9860 *Founded/Ownrshp* 1983
Sales 56.2MM *EMP* 2
SIC 8699 Personal interest organization; Personal interest organization
Ex Dir: Diane Mack
Ex Dir: Christopher Morton

D-U-N-S 06-238-4965
MINNESOTA GASTROENTEROLOGY PA
MNGI
2550 University Ave W 423s, Saint Paul, MN 55114-8685
Tel (612) 871-1145 *Founded/Ownrshp* 2011
Sales 19.5MM^E *EMP* 500
SIC 8011 Internal medicine practitioners; Internal medicine practitioners
CEO: Scott Ketover

D-U-N-S 11-039-0135
MINNESOTA GASTROENTEROLOGY PA INC
MNGI ENDOSCOPY ASC
2550 University Ave W 423s, Saint Paul, MN 55114-8685
Tel (612) 871-1145 *Founded/Ownrshp* 1975
Sales 42.9MM^E *EMP* 475
SIC 8011 Clinic, operated by physicians; Clinic, operated by physicians
CEO: Scott Ketover
**Pr:* Sam Leon
**VP:* Tim Potter
Off Mgr: Dawn Cowle
Off Mgr: Dan Erickson
Site Mgr: Martha Carland
Doctor: Cecil Chally MD
Doctor: Paul Dickinson MD
Doctor: Arnold P Kalan MD
Doctor: Arnold Kaplan
Doctor: Scott Keeley

MINNESOTA HISTORICAL SOC PRESS
See MINNESOTA HISTORICAL SOCIETY

D-U-N-S 07-136-3253
MINNESOTA HISTORICAL SOCIETY
MINNESOTA HISTORICAL SOC PRESS
345 Kellogg Blvd W, Saint Paul, MN 55102-1903
Tel (651) 259-3000 *Founded/Ownrshp* 1849
Sales 88.1MM *EMP* 625
Accts Cliftonlarsonallen Llp Minnea
SIC 8412 Historical club; General government administration; ; Historical society
CEO: D Stephen Elliott
Pr: William R Stoeri
CFO: W Chuck Irrgang
Treas: Patricia Koenig
Comm Man: Laura Weber
Ex Dir: Nina M Archabal
Prgrm Mgr: Jeff Boorom
Prgrm Mgr: Nancy Cass
Prgrm Mgr: Tom Lalim
Prgrm Mgr: Erik Rogers
Pr Mgr: Megan Lawson

MINNESOTA LIFE INSURANCE CO
See SECURIAN FINANCIAL GROUP INC

D-U-N-S 00-696-3375
MINNESOTA LIFE INSURANCE CO
SECURIAN
(*Suby of* MINNESOTA LIFE INSURANCE CO) ★
400 And 401 Robert St N, Saint Paul, MN 55101
Tel (478) 314-3189 *Founded/Ownrshp* 1880
Sales NA *EMP* 2,000
Accts Kpmg Llp Minneapolis Mn
SIC 6311 Mutual association life insurance; Mutual association life insurance
Pr: Randy F Wallake
**CEO:* Christopher Michael Hilger
**CFO:* Warren Zaccaro
Sr VP: Maggie Jensen
Sr VP: Robert Olafson
**Sr VP:* Dwayne Radel
VP: George Battis
VP: Cameron Biberdorf
VP: Bruce Glider
VP: Peter Hobart
VP: Michael Kellett
VP: Daniel Kraus
VP: Richard Manke
VP: Kathleen Pinkett
VP: Vicki Shawn
VP: William Steffes
VP: Adam Swartz
Dir: Mary Streed

D-U-N-S 04-119-7369
MINNESOTA LIMITED LLC
18640 200th St, Big Lake, MN 55309
Tel (763) 262-7000 *Founded/Ownrshp* 1966
Sales 205.5MM^E *EMP* 350
SIC 1623 Oil & gas pipeline construction; Oil & gas pipeline construction
**Pr:* Reuben Leines
**VP:* Chris Leines
Sfty Dirs: Kurt Goossen
Sfty Dirs: Christopher Haux
Sfty Mgr: August Lafauci
Sfty Mgr: Brent Larson
Sfty Mgr: Basil Pottratz
Snr Mgr: Ted Crow

MINNESOTA LIVES
See SECURIAN FINANCIAL NETWORK INC

D-U-N-S 07-971-0232
MINNESOTA MASONIC HOME CARE CENTER
MASONIC HOME BLOOMINGTON
11501 Masonic Home Dr # 102, Minneapolis, MN 55437-3661
Tel (952) 948-7000 *Founded/Ownrshp* 1906
Sales 28.2MM *EMP* 500
Accts Cliftonlarsonallen Llp Minnea
SIC 8051 8052 Convalescent home with continuous nursing care; Personal care facility; Convalescent home with continuous nursing care; Personal care facility
Pr: Eric Jneetenbeek
**Pr:* Eric J Neetenbeek
**CFO:* Sue Mork
VP: Michael Hanson

D-U-N-S 12-119-1860
MINNESOTA MEDICAL FOUNDATION INC
University Of Minn Gtwy, Minneapolis, MN 55455
Tel (612) 625-1440 *Founded/Ownrshp* 1987
Sales 79.2MM *EMP* 55
Accts Kpmg Llp Minneapolis Mn
SIC 6732 Educational trust management; Educational trust management
Pr: Brad Choate
**CFO:* Cindy Kaiser
Ex Dir: Kay Christianson
Mktg Dir: Colleen Norton

D-U-N-S 10-866-4798
MINNESOTA MEDICAL SCANNING CORP
CENTER FOR DIAGNOSTIC IMAGING
5775 Wayzata Blvd Ste 190, Saint Louis Park, MN 55416-2627
Tel (952) 541-1840 *Founded/Ownrshp* 1981
Sales 43.5MM^E *EMP* 500
SIC 8071 Medical laboratories; Medical laboratories
CEO: Robert Baumgartner
Ch Bd: Robert V Baumgartner
Pr: Rick Long
COO: Jim Stanley
Ex VP: Pat Blank
Sr VP: Jim Varcarolis

VP: Terry Mitchell
Genl Mgr: Duane Hendrickson
CIO: Linda Bagley
VP Mktg: Thomas Rheineck
Surg Cl Rc: Renee M Devries
Board of Directors: Ken Heithoff

D-U-N-S 11-117-0283
MINNESOTA METHANE LLC
(*Suby of* FORTISTAR LLC) ★
1 N Lexington Ave Ste 620, White Plains, NY 10601-1721
Tel (914) 421-4900 *Founded/Ownrshp* 2008
Sales 29.8MM^{E} *EMP* 95
SIC 4911 Electric services; Electric services
Pr: Mark Comora
Genl Mgr: Trond Aschehoug

D-U-N-S 02-279-3103
MINNESOTA MOTOR CO
1108 Pebble Lake Rd, Fergus Falls, MN 56537-3851
Tel (218) 739-3331 *Founded/Ownrshp* 1922
Sales 40.0MM *EMP* 66
SIC 5511 Automobiles, new & used; Pickups, new & used; Automobiles, new & used; Pickups, new & used
Pr: Steve Brimhall
**Sec:* Tom Brimhall

D-U-N-S 01-963-4836 IMP
MINNESOTA MUNICIPAL POWER AGENCY (MN)
MMPA
220 S 6th St Ste 1300, Minneapolis, MN 55402-4525
Tel (612) 349-6868 *Founded/Ownrshp* 1992
Sales 106.1MM *EMP* 5^{E}
Accts Kpmg Llp Minneapolis Minneso
SIC 4911 Generation, electric power; Generation, electric power
Ch Bd: Steve Schmidt
**Prin:* Derick O Dahlen
**Prin:* Oncu H Er
**Prin:* Joseph V Fulliero
**Prin:* David W Niles
Snr PM: Randall W Porter

D-U-N-S 78-647-7278
MINNESOTA MUTUAL COMPANIES INC
400 Robert St N Ste A, Saint Paul, MN 55101-2099
Tel (651) 665-3500 *Founded/Ownrshp* 1998
Sales NA *EMP* 2,500
SIC 6311 Life insurance carriers; Life insurance carriers
CEO: Robert L Senkler
Sr VP: Charles Peterson
VP: Jerry Woelful

MINNESOTA NATIONAL GUARD
See MINNESOTA DEPARTMENT OF MILITARY AFFAIRS

D-U-N-S 00-696-3383
MINNESOTA PIPE LINE CO LLC
(*Suby of* KOCH INDUSTRIES INC) ★
4111 E 37th St N, Wichita, KS 67220-3203
Tel (316) 828-5500 *Founded/Ownrshp* 1953
Sales 101.5MM *EMP* 48
SIC 4612 Crude petroleum pipelines; Crude petroleum pipelines
Pr: Dave Stecher

D-U-N-S 61-723-2889
■ **MINNESOTA POWER**
(*Suby of* ALLETE INC) ★
30 W Superior St, Duluth, MN 55802-2093
Tel (218) 336-1800 *Founded/Ownrshp* 1986
Sales 25.4MM^{E} *EMP* 9
SIC 4911 5012 4941 4952 Generation, electric power; Transmission, electric power; Distribution, electric power; Automobiles & other motor vehicles; Water supply; Sewerage systems
Pr: Edwin L Russell
**Ch Bd:* Arend J Sandbulte
**COO:* Robert D Edwards
**CFO:* David G Gartzke
CFO: Thomas Oliveris
**Treas:* James K Vizanko
**VP:* Philip R Halverson
VP: Margaret Hodnik
VP: Josh Orhn
**VP:* Mark A Schober
VP: Timothy Thorp
Dir Bus: Greg Flanagan

D-U-N-S 06-478-2006
MINNESOTA PUBLIC RADIO
(*Suby of* AMERICAN PUBLIC MEDIA GROUP) ★
480 Cedar St, Saint Paul, MN 55101-2230
Tel (651) 290-1500 *Founded/Ownrshp* 2011
Sales 13.1MM^{E} *EMP* 320
Accts Mcgladrey Llp Minneapolis Mn
SIC 4832 Radio broadcasting stations; Radio broadcasting stations
Pr: Jon McTaggart
V Ch: Richard B Payne Jr
CFO: Mark Alfuth
Sr VP: Donald Creighton
Exec: Kathy Tischler
Dir Soc: Lynne Kasper
IT Man: Prem Kumar
Web Dev: Paul Wenzel
Pgrm Dir: Erik Nycklemoe

D-U-N-S 96-914-8795
MINNESOTA PUBLIC RADIO AMERICAN PUBLIC MEDIA
480 Cedar St, Saint Paul, MN 55101-2230
Tel (651) 290-1446 *Founded/Ownrshp* 2011
Sales 91.1MM *EMP* 217
Accts Mcgladrey Llp Minneapolis Mn
SIC 4832 Radio broadcasting stations; Radio broadcasting stations
Prin: Doug Roderick

MINNESOTA RESOURCE CENTER
See RESOURCE INC

MINNESOTA RUBBER & PLASTICS CO
See QUADION LLC

D-U-N-S 08-491-6654
MINNESOTA SOYBEAN PROCESSORS (MN)
121 Zeh Ave, Brewster, MN 56119-3009
Tel (507) 842-6677 *Founded/Ownrshp* 2003
Sales 500.0MM *EMP* 80
SIC 5153 2075 Soybeans; Soybean oil, cake or meal; Soybeans; Soybean oil, cake or meal
Ch Bd: Jim Sallstrom
**CEO:* Taryl Enderson
VP: Brad Louwagie
Dir Lab: Lyle Oberloh
Plnt Mgr: Wayne Faulkner

D-U-N-S 80-678-2330
MINNESOTA STATE COLLEGES AND UNIVERSITIES
ST. CLOUD STATE UNIVERSITY
(*Suby of* BEMIDJI STATE UNIVERSITY) ★
720 4th Ave S, Saint Cloud, MN 56301-4442
Tel (320) 308-0121 *Founded/Ownrshp* 1869
Sales 100.9MM *EMP* 1,583
Accts Cliftonlarsonallen Minneapoli
SIC 8221 9199 Colleges universities & professional schools; ; Colleges universities & professional schools;
Pr: Earl H Potter III
Dir Recs: Susan Bayer
Pr: Melissa M Krause
CFO: Nancy Anwary
CFO: Anne Chelin-Anderson
Treas: Nic Greer
Ofcr: Bill Kenyon
Assoc VP: Ann Radwan
Sr VP: Derrick Silvestri
VP: Nicolette Deason
VP: Greg Rosten
Dir Lab: Dien D Phan
Assoc Dir: Tyler Knudson

D-U-N-S 80-719-1432
MINNESOTA STATE COLLEGES AND UNIVERSITIES
BEMIDJI STATE UNIVERSITY
(*Suby of* EXECUTIVE OFFICE OF STATE OF MINNESOTA) ★
30 7th St E Ste 350, Saint Paul, MN 55101-4812
Tel (651) 296-8012 *Founded/Ownrshp* 1975
Sales 851.3MM *EMP* 15,000
Accts Cliftonlarsonallen Llp Minnea
SIC 8221 9411 Colleges universities & professional schools; Administration of educational programs; ; Colleges universities & professional schools; Administration of educational programs;
Pr: Devinder Malhotra
CFO: Laura M King
VP: Joan Costello
VP: Sharon Lacomb
Comm Man: Amy Yerkes
Ex Dir: R Dickhudt
Prgrm Mgr: Kent Dirks
Prgrm Mgr: James Morgan
Prgrm Mgr: Jeanne Qualley
Prgrm Mgr: Mary Rothchild
Web Dev: Neal Dawson

D-U-N-S 93-986-2686
MINNESOTA STATE COLLEGES AND UNIVERSITIES
BEMIDJI STATE UNIVERSITY
(*Suby of* BEMIDJI STATE UNIVERSITY) ★
501 W College Dr, Brainerd, MN 56401-3904
Tel (218) 855-8000 *Founded/Ownrshp* 1968
Sales 599.0M *EMP* 400^{E}
SIC 8222 9199 Community college; ; Community college;
Pr: Larry Lundblad
VP: Brian Kirkpatrick
Psych: Steve Jennisen

D-U-N-S 79-084-6299
MINNESOTA STATE COMMUNITY TECHNICAL COLLEGE
(*Suby of* BEMIDJI STATE UNIVERSITY) ★
150 2nd St Sw Ste B, Perham, MN 56573-1461
Tel (218) 347-6200 *Founded/Ownrshp* 1995
Sales 15.3MM^{E} *EMP* 500
SIC 8222 9199 Technical institute; ;Technical institute;
Ex Dir: Ann Valentine
CFO: Pat Nordick

MINNESOTA STATE CURB-GUTTER
See AVR INC

D-U-N-S 05-342-3133
MINNESOTA STATE UNIVERSITY MANKATO
(*Suby of* BEMIDJI STATE UNIVERSITY) ★
620 South Rd, Mankato, MN 56001-7013
Tel (507) 389-1866 *Founded/Ownrshp* 2004
Sales 123.5MM *EMP* 1,310
Accts Kern Dewenter Viere Ltd B
SIC 8221 9199 College, except junior; ; College, except junior;
Pr: Richard Davenport
Ofcr: Mavis Anderson
Ofcr: Brittney Gehrking
Ofcr: Paulette Kimber
Ofcr: Seth Whalen
Ofcr: Nhia Yang
VP: Mike Gustafson
VP: Rebecca McQuiston
Assoc Dir: Torin Akey
Assoc Dir: Joel Jensen
Off Mgr: Carol Alfson

D-U-N-S 80-719-7330
MINNESOTA STATE UNIVERSITY MOORHEAD
BEMIDJI STATE UNIVERSITY
(*Suby of* BEMIDJI STATE UNIVERSITY) ★
1104 7th Ave S, Moorhead, MN 56563-0002
Tel (218) 477-4000 *Founded/Ownrshp* 1888
Sales 6.6MM *EMP* 895
SIC 8221 9199 University; ; University;
Pr: Roland Barden
**Pr:* Anne Blackhurst
Pr: Kathleen McNabb
VP: Bette Midgarden
**VP:* Jan Mohoney
**VP:* Warren Wiese
**Ex Dir:* Joan Justesen
Mtls Mgr: Robin Abraham
Opers Mgr: David Lenard
Sls Mgr: Sandy Schob

D-U-N-S 00-389-8954 IMP
MINNESOTA SUPPLY CO (MN)
WISCONSIN MATERIAL HANDLING
6470 Flying Cloud Dr, Eden Prairie, MN 55344-3372
Tel (952) 828-7300 *Founded/Ownrshp* 1919, 1955
Sales 25.5MM *EMP* 90
Accts Cliftonlarsonallen Llp Minne
SIC 5084 7699 7359 Industrial machinery & equipment; Materials handling machinery; Industrial machinery & equipment repair; Equipment rental & leasing; Industrial machinery & equipment; Materials handling machinery; Industrial machinery & equipment repair; Equipment rental & leasing
Pr: Mark K Olsen
**VP:* Steven J Stromsness
Genl Mgr: Doug Remme
IT Man: Mary Wiczek
Mktg Dir: Stacey Lewandowski
Mktg Mgr: Neil Zimmerman
Sls Mgr: Terry Joos
Board of Directors: Douglas Remme

D-U-N-S 19-314-9556
MINNESOTA TEEN CHALLENGE INC
2240 7th Ave E Apt 2, Saint Paul, MN 55109-4963
Tel (612) 373-3366 *Founded/Ownrshp* 1984
Sales 28.0MM *EMP* 275^{E}
Accts Kern Dewenter Viere Ltd Minne
SIC 8361 Rehabilitation center, residential: health care incidental; Rehabilitation center, residential: health care incidental
CEO: Rich Scherber
**CFO:* Ronald Goodman
VP: Jeff Dye
VP: Vicki Jefferis
VP: Paul Lundeen
VP: Eric Vagle
Dir Soc: Melissa Varriano
Comm Man: Pati McConeghey
Dir IT: Kevin Brooks
IT Man: Cynthia Betz
IT Man: Kathy Jarve

D-U-N-S 95-820-9272
MINNESOTA TRANSITIONS CHTR SCH
2526 27th Ave S, Minneapolis, MN 55406-1310
Tel (612) 728-8915 *Founded/Ownrshp* 1996
Sales 31.0MM *EMP* 50
Accts Chuck Rinkey Ltd Minneapolis
SIC 8211 Elementary & secondary schools; Elementary & secondary schools
VP: Aaron Coe
VP: Rhonda EBY
VP: Tiffany Shively
VP: Deane Turner
Ex Dir: James Strait
CTO: Marc Guerrasio

D-U-N-S 07-149-7937 IMP
MINNESOTA TWINS BASEBALL CLUB
1 Twins Way, Minneapolis, MN 55403-1418
Tel (612) 659-3400 *Founded/Ownrshp* 1984
Sales 59.9MM^{E} *EMP* 900
SIC 7941 Baseball club, professional & semi-professional; Baseball club, professional & semi-professional
Owner: Karl Pohlad

MINNESOTA TWIST DRILL
See MTD ACQUISITION INC

D-U-N-S 07-867-5337
MINNESOTA VALLEY ACTION COUNCIL INC
706 N Victory Dr, Mankato, MN 56001-6803
Tel (507) 345-6822 *Founded/Ownrshp* 1966
Sales 23.6MM *EMP* 180
Accts Smith Schafer & Associates L
SIC 8322 Individual & family services; Individual & family services
Ex Dir: John Woodwick
CTO: Ruthie Corcoran

D-U-N-S 00-696-2856
MINNESOTA VALLEY COOPERATIVE LIGHT AND POWER ASSOCIATION (MN)
501 S 1st St, Montevideo, MN 56265-2103
Tel (320) 269-2163 *Founded/Ownrshp* 1938
Sales 20.3MM *EMP* 30
Accts Candice Jaenisch Ltd Maynard
SIC 4911 Transmission, electric power; Transmission, electric power
Genl Mgr: Patrick Carruth
IT Man: Candice Jaenisch

D-U-N-S 00-696-1445
MINNESOTA VALLEY ELECTRIC COOPERATIVE INC (MN)
MVEC
125 Minnesota Valley Dr, Jordan, MN 55352-9369
Tel (952) 492-2313 *Founded/Ownrshp* 1937
Sales 75.6MM *EMP* 94
Accts Brady Martz And Associates Pc
SIC 4911 Distribution, electric power; Distribution, electric power
Pr: Roger Geckler
**CFO:* Gerry Mareck
Bd of Dir: Jim Connelly
Bd of Dir: Bill Heinlein
**VP:* Marvin Denzer
**VP:* Ryan Hentges
**VP:* Daryl Hoffman
VP: Rod Nikula
VP: Kirk Wulf
Genl Mgr: Tom Kovalak

MINNESOTA VIKINGS FOOTBALL CLB
See MINNESOTA VIKINGS FOOTBALL CLUB LLC

D-U-N-S 07-103-5898
MINNESOTA VIKINGS FOOTBALL CLUB LLC
MINNESOTA VIKINGS FOOTBALL CLB
9520 Viking Dr, Eden Prairie, MN 55344-3825
Tel (952) 828-6500 *Founded/Ownrshp* 1998
Sales 63.5MM^{E} *EMP* 470
SIC 6799 7941 Investors; Football club; Investors; Football club
COO: Kevin Warren
Genl Mgr: Stephane Loesel
Mktg Mgr: Brian Harper
Snr PM: Jim Cima

D-U-N-S 07-867-9644
MINNESOTA VIKINGS FOOTBALL LLC
9520 Viking Dr, Eden Prairie, MN 55344-3898
Tel (952) 828-6500 *Founded/Ownrshp* 1961, 2005
Sales 26.4MM^{E} *EMP* 300
SIC 7941 Football club; Football club
Pr: Mark Wilf
**V Ch:* Leonard Wilf
Pr: Rick Spielman
Ex VP: Michael Kelly
VP: C J Rugh
Dir IT: Cheryl Nygaard
Sls Dir: Mike Slates
Sls Mgr: Peter Duggan
Sls Mgr: Doug Melnyk
Counsel: Josh Goldenberg
Snr PM: Jim Cima

D-U-N-S 07-178-7725
MINNESOTA WEST COMMUNITY & TECHNICAL COLLEGE
(*Suby of* BEMIDJI STATE UNIVERSITY) ★
1593 11th Ave, Granite Falls, MN 56241-1061
Tel (320) 564-4511 *Founded/Ownrshp* 1965
Sales 8.6MM^{E} *EMP* 300
SIC 8249 9199 Vocational schools; ; Vocational schools;
**Pr:* Richard Schrubb
VP: Diane Graber

D-U-N-S 02-379-7335
MINNESOTA WIRE & CABLE CO
1835 Energy Park Dr, Saint Paul, MN 55108-2721
Tel (651) 642-1800 *Founded/Ownrshp* 1972
Sales 35.8MM^{E} *EMP* 200
Accts Mcgladrey & Pullen Llp Minne
SIC 3643 Current-carrying wiring devices; Connectors & terminals for electrical devices; Current-carrying wiring devices; Connectors & terminals for electrical devices
Ch Bd: Paul J Wagner
**Pr:* Erik Wagner
**CFO:* Joan C Thompson
Exec: Steve Pape
Prgrm Mgr: Randi Lundell
Dir IT: Chuck Stenger
IT Man: Nate Martin
Ql Cn Mgr: Mark Thesenvitz
Mktg Mgr: Martin Handberg
Sales Asso: Joe Mustari
Board of Directors: Bob Pope - Sales Represent, Brad Steege - Sales Repres, Jon Jepko - Sales Represen, Bob Roberts - Sales Repres

MINNETONKA
See OLYMPIC COMPANIES INC

D-U-N-S 07-134-1358
MINNETONKA INDEPENDENT SCHOOL DISTRICT 276
5621 County Road 101, Minnetonka, MN 55345-4214
Tel (952) 401-5000 *Founded/Ownrshp* 1860
Sales 135.4MM *EMP* 16,000
Accts Cliftonlarsonallen Llp Minnea
SIC 8211 Public elementary school; Public junior high school; Public senior high school; Public elementary school; Public junior high school; Public senior high school
Dir Sec: Jim McCann
Pr Dir: Janet Swiecichowski
Instr Medi: Dave Eisennann

D-U-N-S 00-624-7381 IMP/EXP
MINNETONKA MOCCASIN CO INC (MN)
1113 E Hennepin Ave, Minneapolis, MN 55414-2396
Tel (612) 331-8493 *Founded/Ownrshp* 1946
Sales 28.1MM^{E} *EMP* 52
SIC 5139 3149 Footwear; Moccasins
CEO: Scott Sessa
**Pr:* David Miller
CFO: Tom Olson
VP: John Cardarella
CTO: Mark Bahn
Dir IT: Scott Anderson
IT Man: Tory Bahl
VP Sls: Mark Merritt
Mktg Dir: Kalyn Waters

D-U-N-S 16-101-9815
MINNETONKA MOTOR CAR SALES INC
MORRIE'S MAZDA
13700 Wayzata Blvd, Hopkins, MN 55305-1734
Tel (952) 977-7040 *Founded/Ownrshp* 1985
Sales 23.6MM^{E} *EMP* 55^{E}
SIC 5511 Automobiles, new & used; Automobiles, new & used
Pr: Maurice J Wagener
**Treas:* Peggy Monchap
**VP:* Arthur Wagener
Genl Mgr: Chris Morris
Off Mgr: Nancy Erikson
Sls Mgr: Ellen Schmidt
Sales Asso: Justin Moeller
Sales Asso: Douglas Sanchez

D-U-N-S 94-575-3622
MINNETRONIX INC
1635 Energy Park Dr, Saint Paul, MN 55108-2703
Tel (651) 917-4060 *Founded/Ownrshp* 1996
Sales 29.9MM^{E} *EMP* 135^{E}

SIC 3699 3845 3841 8711 8731 Electrical equipment & supplies; Electromedical equipment; Surgical & medical instruments; Engineering services; Electronic research; Electrical equipment & supplies; Electromedical equipment; Surgical & medical instruments; Engineering services; Electronic research
CEO: Richard Nazarian
**COO:* Jeremy Maniak
**COO:* Joe Renzetti
**CFO:* Phil Ankeny
**CFO:* Kevin Krumm
Chf Mktg O: Nandan Lad
**VP:* Stan Crossett
**VP:* Lynn Ihlenfeldt
**VP:* Jonathan Pierce
**VP:* Jim Reed
**VP:* Dirk Smith
Comm Man: Carolyn Baldus
Board of Directors: Mark Wagner

MINNEWASKA HOSPITALITY CORP
See HNA HUDSON VALLEY RESORT AND TRAINING CENTER LLC

D-U-N-S 15-140-1171
MINNIE HAMILTON HEALTH CARE CENTER
MINNIE HAMILTON HEALTH SYSTEM
186 Hospital Dr, Grantsville, WV 26147-7100
Tel (304) 354-9244 *Founded/Ownrshp* 1983
Sales 20.2MM *EMP* 230
Accts Arnett Foster Toothman Pllc C
SIC 8069 Specialty hospitals, except psychiatric; Specialty hospitals, except psychiatric
CEO: Steve Whited
**Pr:* Jean Simers
Bd of Dir: Randy Ball
Off Mgr: C Aya-Ay
Off Mgr: Becky Law
CIO: Brent Barr
QA Dir: Sandra Ellis
Mktg Dir: Jim Sullivan
Doctor: Suresh Balasubramony
Doctor: A Juanito
Doctor: Chadwick Smith

MINNIE HAMILTON HEALTH SYSTEM
See MINNIE HAMILTON HEALTH CARE CENTER

MINNIELAND ACADEMY
See MINNIELAND PRIVATE DAY SCHOOL INC

D-U-N-S 07-830-3435
MINNIELAND PRIVATE DAY SCHOOL INC
MINNIELAND ACADEMY
4300 Prince William Pkwy, Woodbridge, VA 22192-5361
Tel (703) 680-2548 *Founded/Ownrshp* 1972
Sales 45.5MM^E *EMP* 1,200
SIC 8351 8211 Child day care services; Private elementary school; Child day care services; Private elementary school
Pr: Jacqueline M Leopold
**VP:* Charles W Leopold

D-U-N-S 00-699-8082 IMP
MINNKOTA POWER COOPERATIVE INC
SQUARE BUTTE ELECTRIC COOPS
1822 Mill Rd, Grand Forks, ND 58203-1536
Tel (701) 795-4000 *Founded/Ownrshp* 1940
Sales 145.8MM *EMP* 355
Accts Brady Martz & Associates Pc
SIC 4911 Distribution, electric power; Generation, electric power; Distribution, electric power; Generation, electric power
CEO: Robert McLennan
**Sec:* Jeffrey Folland
**VP:* Russell Okeson
VP: David Sogard
CTO: Don Schempp
Sfty Mgr: Jason Uhlir
Counsel: Rick Stomberg

MINNKOTA RECYCLING
See BEVERAGE WHOLESALERS INC

D-U-N-S 00-682-2290
MINNOTTE CONTRACTING CORP (PA)
MC
Minnotte Sq, Pittsburgh, PA 15220
Tel (412) 922-1633 *Founded/Ownrshp* 1920
Sales 44.5MM^E *EMP* 300
SIC 1711 1791 1795 1541 Boiler maintenance contractor; Boiler setting contractor; Process piping contractor; Mechanical contractor; Structural steel erection; Wrecking & demolition work; Industrial buildings & warehouses; Boiler maintenance contractor; Boiler setting contractor; Process piping contractor; Mechanical contractor; Structural steel erection; Wrecking & demolition work; Industrial buildings & warehouses
Pr: David W Minno
**CFO:* Robert M Amic
CFO: Dave Frey
**Treas:* Richard S Galis
**VP:* Richard S Gal
**VP:* Erik Galis
IT Man: Gene Vezzani
IT Man: Gene Vezzoni
VP Opers: Charlie Hartman

D-U-N-S 00-433-6376
MINNOTTE MANUFACTURING CORP (PA)
Minnotte Sq, Pittsburgh, PA 15220
Tel (412) 922-2963 *Founded/Ownrshp* 1959
Sales 46.1MM^E *EMP* 285
SIC 3443 3599 3441

D-U-N-S 19-512-8905 IMP
MINNPAR LLC
5273 Program Ave, Saint Paul, MN 55112-4975
Tel (612) 379-0606 *Founded/Ownrshp* 1988
Sales 44.7MM^E *EMP* 60
SIC 5099 Firearms & ammunition, except sporting
CEO: Don Kemp
**VP:* Art Ashworth
VP: Donald Neudauer
Dir IT: Laurel Glewwe
Dir IT: Rashid Ibrahim
IT Man: John Gilbertson
Tech Mgr: Ted Osowski
Snr Mgr: Todd Schwarzrock

D-U-N-S 18-496-9020
MINNWEST BANK M V
(*Suby of* MINNWEST CORP) ★
300 S Washington St, Redwood Falls, MN 56283-1658
Tel (507) 637-5731 *Founded/Ownrshp* 1987
Sales NA *EMP* 105
SIC 6022 State commercial banks; State commercial banks
Pr: Douglas Karsky
COO: Sherri Schueller
Ofcr: Kirby Josephson
Ofcr: Beth Leopold
Ofcr: Elwood Phelps
Sr VP: Dan Koster
Sr VP: Gail J Ripka
VP: Richard Bales
VP: Al Larson
Brnch Mgr: Ben Hillesheim
Board of Directors: H A Dewolfe, Dr J B Flynn, K L Frederickson, D M Greene, Joe Malacek, J A McHugh, T T McVay, G Scherbing

D-U-N-S 78-439-1948
MINNWEST CORP
14820 Highway Ste 200, Minnetonka, MN 55345
Tel (952) 545-8815 *Founded/Ownrshp* 1986
Sales NA *EMP* 356
SIC 6022 State commercial banks; State commercial banks
Pr: T Todd McVay
**Ch Bd:* M D McVay
**CFO:* Lannon Brown
**Chf Cred:* Russ Bushman
VP: Greg Czerwinski
**VP:* Mary McVay
Dir Risk M: Nancy Snedeker
Off Mgr: Joyce Coulter
Sls Mgr: Sarah Sonstcby

MINOLTA BUSINESS SYSTEMS
See KONICA MINOLTA BUSINESS SOLUTIONS USA INC

D-U-N-S 04-677-3255
MINOOKA COMMUNITY HIGH SCHOOL DISTRICT 111
26655 W Eames St, Channahon, IL 60410-5380
Tel (815) 467-2557 *Founded/Ownrshp* 1941
Sales 16.5MM^E *EMP* 321
Accts Macchietto Roth & Company Pc
SIC 8211 Public elementary & secondary schools; Public elementary & secondary schools

D-U-N-S 07-185-3980
MINOR & JAMES MEDICAL PROFESSIONAL LIMITED LIABILITY CO
515 Minor Ave Ste 200, Seattle, WA 98104-2133
Tel (206) 386-9500 *Founded/Ownrshp* 1957
Sales 31.3MM^E *EMP* 350
SIC 8011 Primary care medical clinic; Primary care medical clinic
Telecom Ex: Kevin Port
Dir IT: Christopher Wisnoski
Doctor: Gina Chen
Doctor: Hugh Clark
Doctor: Derel Finch
Doctor: Christi Kenyon
Doctor: Eva Kojnok
Doctor: Steven Medwell
Doctor: James Sheffield
Doctor: Paul B Sytman
Doctor: Kent Ta

D-U-N-S 03-185-2221
MINOT AUTOMOTIVE CENTER INC
3615 S Broadway, Minot, ND 58701-7455
Tel (701) 852-0151 *Founded/Ownrshp* 1993
Sales 40.3MM^E *EMP* 81
SIC 5511 7532 New & used car dealers; Body shop, automotive; New & used car dealers; Body shop, automotive
Pr: Larry Durand
**Treas:* Sue Durand
Mktg Mgr: Tiffany Feist

D-U-N-S 00-786-2824
MINOT BUILDERS SUPPLY ASSOCIATION (MN)
EVERGREEN BUILDERS SUPPLY
2626 Burdick Expy W, Minot, ND 58701-5658
Tel (701) 852-1301 *Founded/Ownrshp* 1957, 1956
Sales 38.6MM^E *EMP* 100
SIC 5031 Building materials, exterior; Building materials, interior; Doors & windows; Building materials, exterior; Building materials, interior; Doors & windows
CEO: Dale Zarr
**CFO:* Thomas Philion
**Sec:* Jolene Graf
**VP:* Dick Winje

D-U-N-S 07-649-8799
MINOT CITY OF (INC)
515 2nd Ave Sw, Minot, ND 58701-3739
Tel (701) 857-4752 *Founded/Ownrshp* 1887
Sales NA *EMP* 350
Accts Eide Bailly Llp Bismarck Nor
SIC 9111 City & town managers' offices; ; City & town managers' offices;

D-U-N-S 10-227-1384
MINOT PUBLIC SCHOOLS
215 2nd St Se, Minot, ND 58701-3924
Tel (701) 857-4400 *Founded/Ownrshp* 1890
Sales 65.8MM^E *EMP* 1,400
SIC 8211 Public elementary & secondary schools; Public elementary & secondary schools
Dir IT: Craig Nansen

D-U-N-S 80-388-2174
MINOT STATE UNIVERSITY
(*Suby of* NORTH DAKOTA UNIVERSITY SYSTEM FOUNDATION) ★
500 University Ave W, Minot, ND 58707-0002
Tel (701) 858-3000 *Founded/Ownrshp* 1939
Sales 28.5MM *EMP* 26^E
Accts Robert R Peterson Fargo Nor
SIC 8221 Colleges universities & professional schools
Pr: David Fuller
CFO: Ron Dorn
VP: Kevin Harmon
VP: Richard Jenkins
VP: Cathy Reeve
VP: Shannon Schmidt
VP: Jamison Sheehan
VP: Codi Thomas
Genl Mgr: Martin Dahl
Off Mgr: Aubrey Stevens
Pgrm Dir: Susan Peterson

D-U-N-S 07-149-4967
MINOT VOCATIONAL ADJUSTMENT WORKSHOP INC
MINOT VOCATIONAL WORKSHOP
605 27th St Se, Minot, ND 58701-5169
Tel (701) 852-1014 *Founded/Ownrshp* 1960
Sales 23.4MM *EMP* 500
SIC 8331 Job training services; Job training services
Pr: Owen H Larson
Off Mgr: Connie Assels
IT Man: Sandi Myers

MINOT VOCATIONAL WORKSHOP
See MINOT VOCATIONAL ADJUSTMENT WORKSHOP INC

MINOVA AMERICAS
See ORICA GROUND SUPPORT INC

D-U-N-S 13-038-2588 IMP
MINOVA HOLDING INC
(*Suby of* ORICA US SERVICES INC) ★
150 Carley Ct, Georgetown, KY 40324-9303
Tel (502) 863-6800 *Founded/Ownrshp* 2003
Sales 159.3MM^E *EMP* 532^E
SIC 2821 3564 2439 Plastics materials & resins; Epoxy resins; Blowers & fans; Structural wood members; Plastics materials & resins; Epoxy resins; Blowers & fans; Structural wood members
CEO: Rory Harris
VP: Debbie Roberts
Opers Mgr: Mark Canapa

D-U-N-S 95-899-8973 IMP
MINSA CORP
(*Suby of* MATERIALES INDUSTRIALIZADOS, S.A. DE C.V.)
1972 County Road 1068, Muleshoe, TX 79347-9225
Tel (806) 272-5923 *Founded/Ownrshp* 1994
Sales 26.6MM^E *EMP* 115
SIC 2041 5149 Corn meal; Grain elevators; Corn meal; Groceries & related products
Pr: Rodrigo Ariceaga
**Pr:* Fernando Jimenez Gomez
**Treas:* Gary Mitchell
CIO: Ricky Rodriguez
Plnt Mgr: Jesus Ayala
Plnt Mgr: Gary Clark
Sales Exec: Lenin Vallecillo
VP Mktg: Luis Garcia

D-U-N-S 79-453-1236
MINSHEW BROTHERS STEEL CONSTRUCTION INC
12578 Vigilante Rd, Lakeside, CA 92040-1112
Tel (619) 561-5700 *Founded/Ownrshp* 1992
Sales 28.3MM^E *EMP* 105
Accts Douglas G Griffin San Diego
SIC 1541 1791 Steel building construction; Structural steel erection; Steel building construction; Structural steel erection
Pr: James Minshew
**Treas:* Daniel P Minshew
**VP:* John M Minshew

D-U-N-S 12-087-5034 IMP
MINSON CORP
MALLIN CASUAL FURNITURE
1 Minson Way, Montebello, CA 90640-6744
Tel (323) 513-1041 *Founded/Ownrshp* 1980
Sales 43.2MM^E *EMP* 300
Accts Kao & Kao Santa Monica Calif
SIC 2512 2514 Wood upholstered chairs & couches; Lawn furniture: metal; Backs & seats for metal household furniture; Household furniture: upholstered on metal frames; Bookcases, household: metal; Wood upholstered chairs & couches; Lawn furniture: metal; Backs & seats for metal household furniture; Household furniture: upholstered on metal frames; Bookcases, household: metal
Ch Bd: Jennifer Chen
Pr: Kenneth Chen
VP: Andy Chen
VP: Merv Conn
VP: Lee Honigsfeld
VP: Lee Honigsseld
Exec: Lee J Honigsseld
Exec: Brenda Pereyda
Admn Mgr: Allen Wang
Opers Mgr: Yung Chen

D-U-N-S 01-848-8796
MINTEL GROUP LTD
MINTEL INTERNATIONAL GROUP LTD
(*Suby of* MINTEL GROUP LTD)
333 W Wacker Dr Ste 1100, Chicago, IL 60606-1285
Tel (312) 932-0400 *Founded/Ownrshp* 1972
Sales 64.2MM^E *EMP* 498
SIC 8732 Market analysis or research; Market analysis or research
Pr: Jon Butcher
**Pr:* Pete Giannakopoulos
Pr: Pam McHugh
**CEO:* Nicholas William Berry
CFO: Sean Lim
**Ch:* John Weeks
Sr VP: Andrew Davidson
VP: Matt Hall
Dir Bus: Bora Kim
Genl Mgr: Susan He
IT Man: Aaron Smith

MINTEL INTERNATIONAL GROUP LTD
See MINTEL GROUP LTD

D-U-N-S 79-727-1186 IMP
■ **MINTEQ INTERNATIONAL INC**
(*Suby of* MINERALSTECHNOLOGIES INC) ★
35 Highland Ave, Bethlehem, PA 18017-9482
Tel (724) 794-3000 *Founded/Ownrshp* 1992
Sales 302.7MM^E *EMP* 1,800
SIC 3297 Nonclay refractories; Nonclay refractories
Ch Bd: Joseph C Muscari
**CFO:* Douglas Dietrick
VP: Rick Honey
**VP:* Johannes Schut
VP: Brian J Seelig
Dir Rx: Yves Dube
**Mng Dir:* Han Schut
Plnt Mgr: Michael Ashford
Sls Mgr: Ken Mueller

D-U-N-S 02-292-2207
■ **MINTER-WEISMAN CO**
(*Suby of* CORE-MARK INTERNATIONAL INC) ★
1035 Nathan Ln N Ste A, Minneapolis, MN 55441-5028
Tel (763) 545-3706 *Founded/Ownrshp* 2004
Sales 108.4MM^E *EMP* 320^E
SIC 5194 5149 5145 5013 5122 Cigarettes; Groceries & related products; Candy; Automotive supplies & parts; Cosmetics, perfumes & hair products; Cigarettes; Groceries & related products; Candy; Automotive supplies & parts; Cosmetics, perfumes & hair products
CEO: J Michael Walsh
VP: Audrey Fujimoto
VP: Paul Siegel
MIS Dir: Ron Vetch
Dir IT: Mark Jordan
VP Sls: Gary Christensen

D-U-N-S 80-864-8047
MINTO COMMUNITIES LLC
(*Suby of* MINTO HOLDINGS INC)
4400 W Sample Rd Ste 200, Coconut Creek, FL 33073-3473
Tel (954) 977-2061 *Founded/Ownrshp* 2005
Sales 44.6MM^E *EMP* 86^E
SIC 6513 Apartment building operators
Pr: Belmont Michael J
CFO: Doug Wallace
Ex VP: Mike Belmont
Sr VP: Craig Unger
Ql Cn Mgr: Scott Meyer
Sls Dir: Tonia Abrahamsson
Sls Dir: Tony Rodriguez
Sales Asso: Lynda S Julien

D-U-N-S 06-341-8180 EXP
MINTON AND ROBERSON INC
1100 International Plz, Chesapeake, VA 23323-1530
Tel (757) 351-1300 *Founded/Ownrshp* 1992
Sales 28.7MM^E *EMP* 150
SIC 1761 Sheet metalwork
CEO: G Royden Goodson III
**Ch Bd:* George R Goodson
**Pr:* William E Woodington
**Treas:* Pax A Goodson
VP: Royden G Goodson
**VP:* James Jarman
VP: William A Phelps
**VP:* Shane Stille
Genl Mgr: Adrienne Adams
VP Opers: Stacy Turpin

MINTZ LEVIN COHN
See MINTZ LEVIN COHN FERRIS GLOVSKY AND POPEO PC

D-U-N-S 07-380-4361
MINTZ LEVIN COHN FERRIS GLOVSKY AND POPEO PC
MINTZ LEVIN COHN
1 Financial Ctr Fl 39, Boston, MA 02111-2657
Tel (617) 348-4951 *Founded/Ownrshp* 1960
Sales 163.7MM^E *EMP* 1,100
SIC 8111 General practice law office; General practice law office
Ch: R R Popeo Jr
Owner: Pedro Suarez
COO: Robert D Kubic
CFO: John Palmer
Bd of Dir: Patrick Donnelly
Bd of Dir: Rick Macdonald
Bd of Dir: Danielle Mackinnon
Bd of Dir: Erin Manganello
Bd of Dir: Brian Pirri
Bd of Dir: Brendan Sheehan
Bd of Dir: Blake E Stuart
Bd of Dir: Shaun Thompson
Bd of Dir: Janet Tighe
Bd of Dir: John M Williams
Chf Inves: Mitch Dynan
Ex VP: Cary Geller
Sr VP: Gary E Bacher
Sr VP: David L O'Connor
Sr VP: Paul Scapicchio
Sr VP: Nancy J Sterling
VP: Bachergary E Bacher

MINUTE MAN FOOD MART
See GAS MART INC

D-U-N-S 01-863-4055
MINUTE MEN INC (CT)
600 Riverside Ave, Westport, CT 06880-5917
Tel (203) 227-6153 *Founded/Ownrshp* 1962
Sales 11.3MM^E *EMP* 450
SIC 7211 7216 7991 8099 8299 Power laundries, family & commercial; Drycleaning plants, except rugs; Physical fitness clubs with training equipment; Health screening service; Educational services; Power laundries, family & commercial; Drycleaning plants, except rugs; Physical fitness clubs with training equipment; Health screening service; Educational services
Pr: Kenneth Shepard
**Treas:* Daron Shepard

D-U-N-S 83-173-2735
■ MINUTECLINIC DIAGNOSTIC MEDICAL GROUP OF SAN DIEGO INC
(*Suby of* CVS HEALTH CORP) ★
1 Cvs Dr, Woonsocket, RI 02895-6146
Tel (401) 765-1500 *Founded/Ownrshp* 2009
Sales 43.3MM^E^ *EMP* 6^E^
SIC 5912 Drug stores & proprietary stores
Prin: Bernard J Katz

MINUTEMAN BIOCHEMICAL SERVICES
See MINUTEMAN SPILL RESPONSE INC

MINUTEMAN DIVISION
See ENI USA R & M CO INC

D-U-N-S 00-511-5852 IMP/EXP
MINUTEMAN INTERNATIONAL INC
(*Suby of* HAKO GMBH)
14n845 Us Highway 20, Pingree Grove, IL 60140-8893
Tel (630) 627-6900 *Founded/Ownrshp* 1951
Sales 29.1MM^E^ *EMP* 180
SIC 3589 2842 Commercial cleaning equipment; Cleaning or polishing preparations; Commercial cleaning equipment; Cleaning or polishing preparations
CEO: Steve Liew
**Pr:* Mario Schreiber
CFO: Steve Boebel
Div Mgr: Eugene Bene
Div Mgr: John Troy
Prd Mgr: Tim Vendegna

D-U-N-S 01-000-1626
MINUTEMAN PRESS INTERNATIONAL INC
61 Executive Blvd, Farmingdale, NY 11735-4710
Tel (631) 249-1370 *Founded/Ownrshp* 1975
Sales 22.2MM *EMP* 120
Accts Morris J Zakheim Co Llp New
SIC 6794 Franchises, selling or licensing; Franchises, selling or licensing
Ch Bd: Roy W Titus
**Pr:* Robert Titus
CFO: Stann Katz
VP: Clarice Barthel
VP: Doug Harlan
VP: Martha Landrigan
**VP:* Gary Rockwell
Exec: Melinda Kuhn
Mng Dir: Graham Moody
Area Mgr: Mark Jones
Genl Mgr: Cyndi Hurst

D-U-N-S 02-878-0523
MINUTEMAN SPILL RESPONSE INC
MINUTEMAN BIOCHEMICAL SERVICES
2435 Housels Run Rd, Milton, PA 17847-9047
Tel (570) 759-3658 *Founded/Ownrshp* 2001
Sales 51.3MM^E^ *EMP* 150^E^
SIC 4959 Environmental cleanup services; Environmental cleanup services
Pr: Brian Bolus

D-U-N-S 09-745-4821
MINUTEMAN TRUCKS INC
2181 Providence Hwy, Walpole, MA 02081-2528
Tel (508) 668-3112 *Founded/Ownrshp* 1997
Sales 67.6MM^E^ *EMP* 83
SIC 5012 Commercial vehicles; Commercial vehicles
CEO: Richard W Witcher
**COO:* William L Witcher
**CFO:* Sharon A Wood
Sls Mgr: Dennis Beausoleil
Sls Mgr: Dominick La Gambina
Sales Asso: Tom Fruzzetti

D-U-N-S 87-843-4752
MINWAX GROUP INC
10 Montinview Rd Ste N300, Upper Saddle River, NJ 07458
Tel (201) 818-7500 *Founded/Ownrshp* 1994
Sales 121.3MM^E^ *EMP* 990
SIC 2851 Stains: varnish, oil or wax; Stains: varnish, oil or wax
Pr: Peter Black
**Pr:* Stewart D Bill
**Pr:* Ridgely W Harrison III
**CFO:* Brian C Harriss
**Treas:* John C Zoephel
**VP:* Ann Allard
**VP:* Paul Gaynor
**VP:* Hank Holtermann
Board of Directors: Richard Mayer, Michael A Miles

D-U-N-S 11-634-2788
MINWIS ACQUISITION CO LLC
(*Suby of* AMERICAN MOTELS ACQUISITION CO LLC) ★
2101 4th Ave Ste 1020, Seattle, WA 98121-2313
Tel (206) 443-3550 *Founded/Ownrshp* 2002
Sales 2.4MM^E^ *EMP* 500
SIC 7011 Hotels & motels; Hotels & motels

MINYARD FOOD STORES, INC.
See AVT GROCERY INC

MINYARD GROUP
See ACQUISITION VEHICLE TEXAS II LLC

D-U-N-S 11-855-9517
MIO FRONTIERS
939 S Edward Dr, Tempe, AZ 85281-5221
Tel (480) 834-1500 *Founded/Ownrshp* 1982
Sales 29.7MM *EMP* 50
Accts Capin Crouse Llp Colorado Spr
SIC 8661 Religious organizations; Religious organizations
COO: Jeff Sloan

D-U-N-S 07-857-4008
MIPC LLC
4101 Post Rd, Marcus Hook, PA 19061-5052
Tel (610) 364-8660 *Founded/Ownrshp* 2012
Sales 29.9MM^E^ *EMP* 400
SIC 2911 Petroleum refining; Petroleum refining

D-U-N-S 80-383-1114
MIQ GLOBAL LLC
MIQ LOGISTICS
(*Suby of* MIQ HOLDINGS INC) ★
11501 Outlook St Ste 500, Overland Park, KS 66211-1808
Tel (913) 696-7100 *Founded/Ownrshp* 2010
Sales 23.2MM^E^ *EMP* 100
SIC 4731 4513 Freight transportation arrangement; Air courier services; Freight transportation arrangement; Air courier services
Pr: John E Carr
**CFO:* Brenda Stasiulis
**Sr VP:* Clint Dvorak
Sr VP: Erick Friendlander
Sr VP: Rich Hardt
**VP:* Tina Jansen
Dir Bus: David Hanley
Opers Mgr: Becky Zeller

D-U-N-S 96-455-4401
MIQ HOLDINGS INC
11501 Outlook St Ste 500, Overland Park, KS 66211-1808
Tel (913) 696-7363 *Founded/Ownrshp* 2010
Sales 323.5MM^E^ *EMP* 1,300
Accts Ernst & Young Llp Kansas City
SIC 4731 8741 4225 Freight transportation arrangement; Management services; General warehousing & storage; Freight transportation arrangement; Management services; General warehousing & storage
Pr: John Carr
**CFO:* Brenda Stasiulis
**Sr VP:* Dan Bentzinger
**VP:* Mike Collins

MIQ LOGISTICS
See MIQ GLOBAL LLC

D-U-N-S 11-641-9818
MIQ LOGISTICS LLC
(*Suby of* MIQ HOLDINGS INC) ★
11501 Outlook St Ste 500, Overland Park, KS 66211-1808
Tel (913) 696-7100 *Founded/Ownrshp* 2010
Sales 292.6MM^E^ *EMP* 1,300
SIC 4731 8741 Freight transportation arrangement; Management services; Freight transportation arrangement; Management services
Pr: John E Carr
COO: Reid Schultz
CFO: Brenda Stasiulis
Sr VP: Clint Dvorak
Dir Bus: Michael Brennan
Dir Bus: Kimberly Duca
Dir Bus: Rochelle Wilson
Genl Mgr: Yvonne Ll
Snr Sftwr: Kevin Tresenriter
Snr Sftwr: MEI Wong
CIO: Dan Bentzinger

D-U-N-S 13-680-4957
MIR3 INC
3398 Carmel Mountain Rd # 100, San Diego, CA 92121-1044
Tel (858) 724-1200 *Founded/Ownrshp* 1999
Sales 29.2MM^E^ *EMP* 90
SIC 4813 Telephone communication, except radio
Ch Bd: Massih Tayebi
**CEO:* Amir Moussavian
**COO:* Ann Pickren
**CFO:* Scott Neill
**Ex VP:* Ren Grossrieder
**VP:* Groff Bittner
VP: Robert Fink
**VP:* Maz Ghorban
VP: Stacey Giles
VP: Clifton McLellan
**Dir Sec:* Frank Mahdavi

MIRA
See MATERIALS INNOVATION AND RECYCLING AUTHORITY

D-U-N-S 96-502-3992
MIRABELLA AT SOUTH WATERFRONT
1200 Mira Mar Ave, Medford, OR 97504-8546
Tel (541) 857-7604 *Founded/Ownrshp* 2010
Sales 22.9MM *EMP* 5^E^
SIC 8361 Residential care
Prin: Rick Mazza

D-U-N-S 06-394-1827
MIRABILE INVESTMENT CORP
POPEYES CHICKEN & BISCUITS
1900 Whitten Rd, Memphis, TN 38133-7026
Tel (901) 873-1187 *Founded/Ownrshp* 1978
Sales 73.7MM^E^ *EMP* 2,000
SIC 5812 Fast-food restaurant, chain; Fast-food restaurant, chain
Pr: Joseph W Mirabile
**VP:* J J Mc Nelis
**VP:* Vivian Vaccaro
Mktg Dir: Kim Sabino

MIRABITO FUEL GROUP
See MIRABITO HOLDINGS INC

D-U-N-S 05-265-4006
MIRABITO HOLDINGS INC
MIRABITO FUEL GROUP
49 Court St Ste 1, Binghamton, NY 13901-4640
Tel (607) 561-2700 *Founded/Ownrshp* 1927
Sales 863.4MM^E^ *EMP* 765
SIC 5172 4925 5541 5411 5983 Petroleum products; Gas production and/or distribution; Gasoline service stations; Convenience stores, chain; Fuel oil dealers; Petroleum products; Gas production and/or distribution; Gasoline service stations; Convenience stores, chain; Fuel oil dealers
Ch Bd: William C Craine
**Ch Bd:* Joseph P Mirabito
**Pr:* Richard R Mirabito
**VP:* John Fitzsimmons
**VP:* Denny Mirabito
**CIO:* Ross Mirabito
Site Mgr: Kristie Lacey
Opers Mgr: Jared Fisher

D-U-N-S 95-898-3371
MIRACA LIFE SCIENCES INC
(*Suby of* CARIS MPI INC) ★
6655 N Macarthur Blvd, Irving, TX 75039-2443
Tel (214) 277-8700 *Founded/Ownrshp* 1998
Sales 26.8MM^E^ *EMP* 150^E^
SIC 8071 Pathological laboratory; Biological laboratory
Ch Bd: Gail Marcus
Pr: Frank Basile
Pr: Cindy Caccuro
Pr: Lisa Calabro
CFO: Margaret Bedgood
CFO: Jerry Martino
CFO: Haruhiko Shibuya
CFO: Everett K Truitt
Chf Mktg O: Richard H Lash
Chf Mktg O: Thomas T Spalding
VP: William McLaughlin
VP: Chris Roberts
Dir Bus: John Costelloe
Dir Bus: Kevin Eleeson
Dir Bus: Larry Obrien
Dir Bus: Jaime Riguez
Dir Bus: James Shea
Dir Bus: Dave Suarino
Dir Bus: Ken Vogel
Board of Directors: Jonathan Knowles, George Poste

MIRACLE MOTORS
See WEGNER AUTO CO INC

D-U-N-S 06-132-3358 IMP/EXP
MIRACLE RECREATION EQUIPMENT CO
(*Suby of* PLAYPOWER INC) ★
878 E Us Highway 60, Monett, MO 65708-9210
Tel (417) 235-6917 *Founded/Ownrshp* 2002
Sales 53.8MM^E^ *EMP* 252^E^
SIC 3949 2531 Playground equipment; Stadium seating
Pr: Keith Maib
**Pr:* Daniel Guthrie
Treas: Dave Finlon
**Sec:* Mike Pruss
Genl Mgr: Jim Pefferman
IT Man: Jerry Cramer
Info Man: Chris Hodgson
VP Mfg: Don Hemingway
Manager: David York

D-U-N-S 80-027-1467
MIRACLE RESTAURANT GROUP LLC
100 Mariners Blvd, Mandeville, LA 70448-6815
Tel (985) 674-5840 *Founded/Ownrshp* 2006
Sales 20.1MM^E^ *EMP* 400
SIC 5812 Fast-food restaurant, chain; Fast-food restaurant, chain
CFO: Patrick Burning

D-U-N-S 92-948-3550
MIRACLE SOFTWARE SYSTEMS INC
45625 Grand River Ave, Novi, MI 48374-1309
Tel (248) 350-1515 *Founded/Ownrshp* 1995
Sales 74.6MM^E^ *EMP* 185
Accts Uhy Llp Farmington Hills Mic
SIC 7371 7373 Custom computer programming services; Computer integrated systems design; Custom computer programming services; Computer integrated systems design
Pr: Prasad Lokam
VP: Satish Besetti
VP: Jithen Bondada
VP: Johnny Chandra
VP: Sudhakar Ghandikota
VP: Madhavi Lokam
**VP:* Steve Lokam
Dir Bus: Sankar Akula
Dir Bus: Joe Bontha
Dir Bus: Sam Hashmi
Dir Bus: Anil Pandey
Dir Bus: Gowtham Sala
Dir Bus: Mike Seerapu
Dir Bus: Priyanka Surampudi

D-U-N-S 05-560-9838
MIRACLE TOYOTA
37048 Hwy 27, Haines City, FL 33844-2300
Tel (863) 956-1123 *Founded/Ownrshp* 1982
Sales 21.4MM^E^ *EMP* 45
SIC 5511 Automobiles, new & used
Pr: Alton Wetteland
VP: Riley E Robert
Genl Mgr: Alan Murphy
Genl Mgr: Elton Wetteland
Sls Mgr: Steve Davis
Sls Mgr: Giovani Jesus
Sls Mgr: Dave Mulder

D-U-N-S 04-724-9925
MIRACLE-EAR INC
(*Suby of* AMPLIFON (USA) INC) ★
5000 Cheshire Pkwy N # 1, Minneapolis, MN 55446-3729
Tel (763) 268-4000 *Founded/Ownrshp* 1948
Sales 192.4MM^E^ *EMP* 800
SIC 5999 Hearing aids; Hearing aids
Pr: Heinz Ruch
**CFO:* Mario Riemma
Treas: Janet Halladay
Treas: Ester Porter
VP: Margaret McDonald
Exec: Deb Gran
Brnch Mgr: Doug Rice
Off Mgr: Paul Damico
Dir IT: Atul Dua
Nrsg Dir: Paul Erickson

D-U-N-S 60-447-9543 IMP/EXP
MIRACLECORP PRODUCTS
2425 W Dorothy Ln, Moraine, OH 45439-1827
Tel (937) 293-9994 *Founded/Ownrshp* 1999
Sales 20.0MM^E^ *EMP* 100^E^
SIC 3999 0752 5999 Pet supplies; Animal specialty services; Pet supplies
Pr: William M Sherk Jr
COO: Michael Viau
CFO: Patricia Weimer
CTO: Chris Bess
Dir IT: Scott Gibson
IT Man: Bryan Storlie
VP Opers: Blaine Bruner
Mktg Mgr: Tina Dailey
Sls Mgr: Kristin Schlegel

D-U-N-S 05-420-7449
MIRACLES CAN HAPPEN INC
1600 Church Ave, Brooklyn, NY 11226-2616
Tel (718) 693-2600 *Founded/Ownrshp* 2002
Sales 15.1MM^E^ *EMP* 700
SIC 7361 Employment agencies; Employment agencies
CEO: Claudette Berkel-Murray

D-U-N-S 07-875-3365
MIRACOSTA COMMUNITY COLLEGE DISTRICT
1 Barnard Dr, Oceanside, CA 92056-3820
Tel (760) 757-2121 *Founded/Ownrshp* 1934
Sales 12.5MM *EMP* 780
Accts Vavrinek Trine Day & Co Ll
SIC 8222 Community college; Community college
Pr: Dick Robertson
Pr: Fernando Lincoln
Pr: Carol Rodriguez
**Pr:* Francisco C Rodriguez
Ofcr: Dean Smith
Ofcr: William Waldrop
**VP:* James E Austin
**VP:* Jim Austin
**VP:* Mary Benard
VP: Julie Hatoff
**VP:* Charlie Ng
**VP:* Richard Robertson

MIRADA
See MOTION THEORY INC

D-U-N-S 60-322-9261
■ MIRAGE CASINO-HOTEL
(*Suby of* MGMRESORTS) ★
3400 Las Vegas Blvd S, Las Vegas, NV 89109-8923
Tel (702) 791-7111 *Founded/Ownrshp* 1986
Sales 247.0MM^E^ *EMP* 6,000
SIC 7011 Casino hotel; Casino hotel
Ch Bd: Stephen A Wynn
**Pr:* Felix Rappaport
**CFO:* Debbie Hottenson
**Treas:* Daniel J Darrigo
VP: Janice Fitzpatrick
**VP:* Christopher Nordling
VP: Graciela Olson
Snr Mgr: Edward Brents

MIRAGE IMPORT
See NONNS FLOORING INC

D-U-N-S 00-697-0883
■ MIRAGE RESORTS INC
MGMRESORTS
(*Suby of* MGM RESORTS INTERNATIONAL) ★
3400 Las Vegas Blvd S, Las Vegas, NV 89109-8923
Tel (702) 791-7111 *Founded/Ownrshp* 1949
Sales 538.1MM^E^ *EMP* 25,900
SIC 7011 Casino hotel; Casino hotel
Pr: James J Murren
Pr: Felix Rappaport
Pr: Frank P Visconti
CFO: Bobby Baldwin
CFO: Robert Baldwin
Treas: Daniel J D Arrigo
Sr VP: Cindy Ortega
Sr VP: Bryan Wright
VP: Brian Hardee
VP: Nicole Jourbadjian
VP: Franz Kallao
VP: Laura Lee
VP: Bruce A Levin
VP: Gary Mayo
VP: James E Pettis
VP: James M Powers
VP: John Schadler
VP: Robert C Selwood
VP: Joshua Soliz
VP: Kenneth R Wynn

D-U-N-S 01-915-3030
MIRAK CHEVROLET INC
MIRAK HYUNDAI
1125 Massachusetts Ave, Arlington, MA 02476-4316
Tel (781) 643-8000 *Founded/Ownrshp* 2003
Sales 42.1MM^E^ *EMP* 100
SIC 5511 Automobiles, new & used; Trucks, tractors & trailers: new & used; Automobiles, new & used; Trucks, tractors & trailers: new & used
Pr: Robert A Mirak
**Treas:* Mary Louise Longo
Sls Mgr: Norm Belzil

MIRAK HYUNDAI
See MIRAK CHEVROLET INC

MIRAMAR CONSTRUCTION CO
See ICA CONSTRUCCION URBANA SA DE CV

D-U-N-S 16-989-3281
MIRAMAR TRANSPORTATION INC
PILOT FREIGHT SERVICES
9340 Cabot Dr Ste I, San Diego, CA 92126-4397
Tel (858) 693-0071 *Founded/Ownrshp* 1993
Sales 32.6MM^E^ *EMP* 100
SIC 4731 Freight forwarding
Pr: Richard Evan Fore
VP: Robert Mirenda
**VP:* Bob Mirinda
Dist Mgr: Liz Beck
Dist Mgr: Keith Fauth
Dist Mgr: Fred Mackay
Genl Mgr: John Petree
Genl Mgr: John Savoia
Opers Mgr: Jessica Eastland
Opers Mgr: John McDonough
Opers Mgr: Russ Severs

D-U-N-S 05-529-1900
MIRAMAX FILM CORP
161 Avenue Of The America, New York, NY 10013-1205
Tel (917) 606-5500 *Founded/Ownrshp* 2010
Sales NA *EMP* 350
SIC 7822

D-U-N-S 80-774-3963
MIRAMED GLOBAL SERVICES INC
255 W Michigan Ave, Jackson, MI 49201-2218
Tel (866) 544-6647 *Founded/Ownrshp* 2006
Sales 81.3MM^E *EMP* 2,000
SIC 8742 Hospital & health services consultant; Hospital & health services consultant
Pr: Tony Mira
**COO:* Sue Mira
**CFO:* Alan Sugerman
**Ex VP:* Greg Fleckenstein
**Ex VP:* Joe Miserendino
Ansthlgy: Selma M Velilla

MIRANDA
See GRASS VALLEY

D-U-N-S 03-505-3219
MIRANTIS INC
VENTRA
525 Almanor Ave Fl 4, Sunnyvale, CA 94085-3542
Tel (650) 963-9828 *Founded/Ownrshp* 2000
Sales 59.3MM^E *EMP* 250
SIC 8742 Business consultant; Business consultant
CEO: Alexander Freedland
Pr: Georgy Okrokvertskhov
VP: Bob Albanese
VP: Craig Irons
VP: Ronen Kofman
VP: Amitabh Shah
Dir Bus: Boris Renski
Snr Sftwr: Sean Collins
Snr Sftwr: Alexander Sakhnov
Sftwr Eng: Ryan Moe
VP Mktg: David Fishman

D-U-N-S 06-521-9946
MIRASOL CLUB INC
COUNTRY CLUB AT MIRASOL
11600 Mirasol Blvd, West Palm Beach, FL 33418-6201
Tel (561) 775-7800 *Founded/Ownrshp* 2000
Sales 22.9MM^E *EMP* 320
SIC 7997 Membership sports & recreation clubs; Membership sports & recreation clubs
Pr: Stephen Kartf
**VP:* Patricia Russo
Dir Soc: Renee Hayes
Genl Mgr: Matt Lambert

MIRIAM HASKILL
See HASKELL JEWELS LLC

D-U-N-S 06-390-2704
MIRIAM HOSPITAL
164 Summit Ave, Providence, RI 02906-2894
Tel (401) 793-2500 *Founded/Ownrshp* 2010
Sales 379.7MM *EMP* 1,928^E
SIC 8062 General medical & surgical hospitals; General medical & surgical hospitals
CEO: Dr Timothy Babineau
**CEO:* Timothy J Babineau
**CFO:* Mary A Wakefield
Ofcr: Nicole Purcell
**VP:* Paul Pierannunzi
Dir Inf Cn: Nancy Vallande
Dir Risk M: Joan Flynn
Dir Rx: Cecilia Giambalvo
**Ex Dir:* Arthur Sampson
CTO: David Hemingder
Doctor: James Atkinson

D-U-N-S 07-270-2269
MIRIAM OSBORN MEMORIAL HOME ASSOCIATION
OSBORN RETIREMENT COMMUNITY
101 Theall Rd, Rye, NY 10580-1406
Tel (914) 925-8000 *Founded/Ownrshp* 1908
Sales 39.1MM *EMP* 500
Accts Loeb & Troper Llp New York N
SIC 8361 Home for the aged; Home for the aged
CEO: Mark Zwerger
**Ch Bd:* John Miller
**CFO:* Nathan Soffio
Ofcr: Matt Anderson
Off Mgr: Kathy Briotte
Nrsg Dir: Denise Taylor-Carey

D-U-N-S 15-926-3305
MIRIFEX SYSTEMS LLC
1383 Sharon Copley Rd, Sharon Center, OH 44274
Tel (440) 891-1210 *Founded/Ownrshp* 1999
Sales 21.2MM *EMP* 200
Accts Plante & Moran Pllc
SIC 7371 7375 Computer software development & applications; Remote data base information retrieval; Computer software development & applications; Remote data base information retrieval

D-U-N-S 13-767-3120
MIRION TECHNOLOGIES (GDS) INC
GLOBAL DOSIMETRY SOLUTIONS
(*Suby of* MIRION TECHNOLOGIES INC) ★
2652 Mcgaw Ave, Irvine, CA 92614-5840
Tel (949) 419-1000 *Founded/Ownrshp* 2003
Sales 40.0MM^E *EMP* 133
SIC 8734 Radiation dosimetry laboratory; Radiation dosimetry laboratory
CEO: Thomas Logan
**Pr:* Sander Perle
**CFO:* James Hippel
**CFO:* Jack Pacheco
**Ex VP:* Antony Besso
**Sr VP:* Mike Brumbaugh
VP: Louis Biacchi
VP: Luis Espada
Exec: Alison Ulrich
Mng Dir: Timo Salomaa
Off Admin: David Shia

D-U-N-S 18-639-9135
MIRION TECHNOLOGIES (IST) CORP
IMAGING AND SENSING TECHNOLOGY
(*Suby of* MIRION TECHNOLOGIES INC) ★
315 Daniel Zenker Dr # 204, Horseheads, NY 14845-1008
Tel (607) 562-4300 *Founded/Ownrshp* 2004
Sales 28.1MM^E *EMP* 190
SIC 3679 3861 3829 3812 3577 Electronic circuits; Photographic equipment & supplies; Nuclear radiation & testing apparatus; Search & navigation equipment; Computer peripheral equipment; Electronic circuits; Photographic equipment & supplies; Nuclear radiation & testing apparatus; Search & navigation equipment; Computer peripheral equipment
CEO: Thomas Logan
**Pr:* David Stewart
**CFO:* Jack Pacheco
**VP:* Tim Pelot
Board of Directors: Hilton Harrell, Sheldon Hunt, John Kennedy, Robert Klein, Thomas D Logan, Frank Witzel

D-U-N-S 78-871-2318
MIRION TECHNOLOGIES INC
3000 Executive Pkwy # 518, San Ramon, CA 94583-4355
Tel (925) 543-0800 *Founded/Ownrshp* 2015
Sales 87.2MM^E *EMP* 290
SIC 3829 Measuring & controlling devices; Measuring & controlling devices
CEO: Thomas Logan
CFO: Maggie S Yuen
Ex VP: Mike Brumbaugh
Ex VP: Seth Rosen
VP: Kip Bennett
VP: Louis Biacchi
VP: Alison Ulrich
Off Mgr: Judy Sims
QA Dir: Dominic Evans
QA Dir: Rachel Ronquillo
Dir IT: Craig Yurosko
Board of Directors: Brian S Graff

D-U-N-S 00-950-9950
MIRIXA CORP
11600 Sunrse Vly Dr # 100, Reston, VA 20191-1400
Tel (703) 683-1955 *Founded/Ownrshp* 2007
Sales 27.3MM *EMP* 2^E
SIC 8011 Group health association
CEO: Rick Solano
**Pr:* Paul J Miller
Sr VP: Kelly Besecker
**Sr VP:* Aaron Loutsch
Sr VP: Jim Vedder
VP: Ed Bissler
Ex Dir: Lonny Wilson
VP Sls: Stacey Lelko

D-U-N-S 13-929-3450 IMP
MIRKA ABRASIVES INC
(*Suby of* OY KWH MIRKA AB)
7950 Bavaria Rd, Twinsburg, OH 44087-2252
Tel (330) 963-6421 *Founded/Ownrshp* 2009
Sales 46.1MM^E *EMP* 80
SIC 5085 Abrasives
Pr: Mark Kush
Adm Dir: Goran Westerlund
CIO: Janice Fryman
IT Man: Matthew Hicks
IT Man: Fryman Jean
VP Opers: Kevin Snyder
Mktg Mgr: Jeff Fabian
Sls Mgr: Mike Burch
Sls Mgr: Israel Teran
Sales Asso: Tracy Burns

D-U-N-S 09-824-2480
■ **MIRO TECHNOLOGIES INC**
(*Suby of* BOEING CO) ★
5643 Copley Dr, San Diego, CA 92111-7903
Tel (858) 677-2100 *Founded/Ownrshp* 2012
Sales 20.3MM^E *EMP* 150
SIC 7373 Turnkey vendors, computer systems; Turnkey vendors, computer systems
Pr: Vincent Monteparte
**CFO:* Gregory Jasenovec
Ofcr: Steve Offen
Sys Eng: Jeff Kennedy

D-U-N-S 00-280-9804
MIRON CONSTRUCTION CO INC (WI)
1471 Mcmahon Rd, Neenah, WI 54956-6305
Tel (920) 969-7000 *Founded/Ownrshp* 1918, 1979
Sales 553.5MM^E *EMP* 1,200
SIC 1542 1541 1796

D-U-N-S 05-731-9476
MIRRIAM MARQUIS WASHINGTON DC
MARRIOTT
901 Massachusetts Ave Nw, Washington, DC 20001-4307
Tel (202) 962-4482 *Founded/Ownrshp* 2014
Sales 6.2MM^E *EMP* 600
SIC 7011 Hotels & motels
VP: Renee Werth

D-U-N-S 04-836-6353
MIRROR IMAGE ENVIRONMENTAL SERVICES INC
DYPEX
201 W Madison Ave Ste 200, Belgrade, MT 59714-3958
Tel (406) 388-8332 *Founded/Ownrshp* 2011
Sales 52.7MM^E *EMP* 90
SIC 5172 8744 Lubricating oils & greases; Facilities support services
CEO: Troy Butler
**CFO:* Mark Nichols
**VP:* Tyson Olson
Off Mgr: Bobbi Fox

D-U-N-S 01-442-9653
MIRUM INC
DIGITARIA INTERACTIVE INC
(*Suby of* J WALTER THOMPSON USA LLC) ★
350 10th Ave Ste 1200, San Diego, CA 92101-8702
Tel (619) 237-5552 *Founded/Ownrshp* 2010
Sales 30.9MM^E *EMP* 200
SIC 7336 Commercial art & graphic design; Commercial art & graphic design
CEO: Daniel Khabie
Pr: Doug Hecht
CFO: Gary Correia
VP: Karen Bellin
VP: Michael Brown
VP: Mark Newcomer
VP: Alice Shanaver
VP: John Spyk
VP: Andy Thwaite
VP Bus Dev: Doug Ruhl
Creative D: Oliver Duncan
Creative D: Jack Fahden
Creative D: Nattida Samanukorn
Creative D: A J Scherbring
Comm Man: Kristina Eastham

MIS
See MEDICAL IMAGING SOLUTIONS GROUP INC

MIS
See MID-ATLANTIC INFRASTRUCTURE SYSTEMS INC

MISA
See MARUBENI-ITOCHU STEEL AMERICA INC

D-U-N-S 60-939-3814
MISA METAL FABRICATING INC
(*Suby of* MARUBENI-ITOCHU STEEL AMERICA INC) ★
7101 International Dr, Louisville, KY 40258-2832
Tel (502) 933-5555 *Founded/Ownrshp* 1989
Sales 58.4MM^E *EMP* 240
SIC 3441 Fabricated structural metal; Fabricated structural metal
Pr: Mike Talis
**Prin:* Mac Makino

D-U-N-S 07-909-4197
MISA METAL PROCESSING INC
MARUBENI STEEL PROCESSING
(*Suby of* MARUBENI-ITOCHU STEEL AMERICA INC) ★
104 Western Dr, Portland, TN 37148-2017
Tel (615) 325-5454 *Founded/Ownrshp* 2013
Sales 48.7MM^E *EMP* 135
SIC 5051 Metals service centers & offices; Metals service centers & offices
CEO: Katsuya Masai

D-U-N-S 00-790-3073 IMP
MISA METALS INC
J R METALS
(*Suby of* MARUBENI-ITOCHU STEEL AMERICA INC) ★
9050 Centre Pointe Dr, West Chester, OH 45069-4874
Tel (212) 660-6000 *Founded/Ownrshp* 2001
Sales 256.2MM^E *EMP* 400
SIC 5051 Steel; Structural shapes, iron or steel; Steel; Structural shapes, iron or steel
CEO: Takeshi Mitomi
**VP:* John Hritz
**VP:* Jason Jamieson
VP: David Pratt
**VP:* Ronald P Roemer
VP: Eric Vogel
**VP:* Larry Wells
Genl Mgr: Tad Hayashi
Netwrk Mgr: Stephen Pate
Opers Mgr: Carol Suhich
Ql Cn Mgr: David Heberling

D-U-N-S 09-906-1681
MISCELLANEOUS DRIVERS & HELPERS WAREHOUSEMENS UNION LOCAL 638
TEAMSTERS LOCAL #638
3001 University Ave Se # 402, Minneapolis, MN 55414-3344
Tel (612) 379-1533 *Founded/Ownrshp* 1948
Sales 41.3MM *EMP* 11
Accts Legacy Professionals Llp Edi
SIC 8631 Labor unions & similar labor organizations; Labor unions & similar labor organizations
Pr: Brad Johnson
**Sec:* Mark Rime
**VP:* Jeff Eckman
**Prin:* Martin Lawrence

D-U-N-S 09-181-2073
MISCELLANEOUS METALS INC
5719 Industry Ln, Frederick, MD 21704-5126
Tel (301) 695-8820 *Founded/Ownrshp* 1977
Sales 23.4MM^E *EMP* 120
SIC 3446 Architectural metalwork; Gratings, tread: fabricated metal; Stairs, staircases, stair treads: prefabricated metal; Railings, bannisters, guards, etc.: made from metal pipe
Pr: Kenneth McCombs
**VP:* William James Kissner
Sfty Mgr: Andy Woodson
Sls Dir: Garry Spitzer
Snr PM: Joe Schiffer

MISCO
See MOORE IRON & STEEL CORP

MISCO ENTERPRISES
See MISSRY ASSOCIATES INC

D-U-N-S 00-233-6899
MISCO PRODUCTS CORP (PA)
1048 Stinson Dr, Reading, PA 19605-9440
Tel (610) 926-4106 *Founded/Ownrshp* 1882, 1962
Sales 25.4MM^E *EMP* 80
SIC 2842 2841 Floor waxes; Detergents, synthetic organic or inorganic alkaline; Soap: granulated, liquid, cake, flaked or chip; Floor waxes; Detergents, synthetic organic or inorganic alkaline; Soap: granulated, liquid, cake, flaked or chip
Pr: Steven Gable
**Treas:* Madeline Gable
**Sec:* Benjamin Gable
**VP:* Jeffrey Gable
VP: Joe Zhou
VP Opers: Dave Kutz
Mktg Dir: Nick Levandusky
Manager: John Albany
Manager: Jimmy Core
Manager: Robert Kluge

D-U-N-S 00-102-5530 IMP
MISCOR GROUP LTD
800 Nave Rd Se, Massillon, OH 44646-9476
Tel (330) 830-3500 *Founded/Ownrshp* 2004
Sales 49.7MM *EMP* 269^E
SIC 7629 7539 3519

MISD
See MARION INDEPENDENT SCHOOL DISTRICT

MISD
See MACOMB INTERMEDIATE SCHOOL DISTRICT

MISENER MARINE CONSTRUCTION
See ORION MARINE CONSTRUCTION INC

MISENER MARINE CONSTRUCTION
See MISENER MARINE INC

D-U-N-S 19-667-2232
MISENER MARINE INC
MISENER MARINE CONSTRUCTION
(*Suby of* FLATIRON CONSTRUCTION CORP) ★
5440 W Tyson Ave, Tampa, FL 33611-3228
Tel (813) 839-8441 *Founded/Ownrshp* 1999
Sales 70.8MM *EMP* 355
Accts Ernst & Young Llp Tampa Fl
SIC 1629 1622 Marine construction; Pile driving contractor; Bridge construction; Marine construction; Pile driving contractor; Bridge construction
CEO: Scott S Lynn
**Pr:* Eugene F Kelley
**CFO:* Simon Den Tuinder
**VP:* John Bolles
**VP:* Thomas E Boyle
**VP:* Paul R Driscoll
**VP:* John A Yaksh
Sfty Mgr: Robert P Caelli

MISERICORDIA HEART MERCY CTR
See MISERICORDIA HOME

D-U-N-S 19-390-4265 IMP
MISERICORDIA HOME
MISERICORDIA HEART MERCY CTR
6300 N Ridge Ave, Chicago, IL 60660-1099
Tel (773) 973-6300 *Founded/Ownrshp* 1921
Sales 87.4MM *EMP* 950^E
Accts Deloitte Tax Llp Chicago Il
SIC 8052 Home for the mentally retarded, with health care; Home for the mentally retarded, with health care
Ex Dir: SIS Rosemary Connelly
COO: John Tortorello
Act CFO: Kevin Connelly
Exec: Maureen Meter
Ex Dir: Rosemary Connelly
Dir IT: Jane Campbell
Dir IT: Timothy Campbell
Dir IT: Jane Guptill
Dir IT: A J Mahadevan
Dir IT: Hilda White
Telecom Mg: Jim Ahlfeld

D-U-N-S 06-564-6341
MISERICORDIA UNIVERSITY (PA)
301 Lake St, Dallas, PA 18612-7752
Tel (570) 674-6400 *Founded/Ownrshp* 1924
Sales 83.9MM *EMP* 503^E
SIC 8221 University; University
Pr: Thomas J Botzman
**Pr:* Michael A Mac Dowell
COO: Paul Krzywicki
CFO: Robert Cragle
**Treas:* John Risboskin
Exec: Dale Lent
CTO: William Daniels
CTO: James Waikem
Dir IT: Nora Blessner
Dir IT: Val Coney
Mktg Dir: Jim Roberts

MISHAWAKA MUNICIPAL UTILITIES
See CITY OF MISHAWAKA

D-U-N-S 96-256-3706 IMP
MISHIMA FOODS USA INC
2340 Plaza Del Amo # 105, Torrance, CA 90501-3451
Tel (310) 787-1533 *Founded/Ownrshp* 1988
Sales 20.6MM^E *EMP* 80
SIC 5141 Groceries, general line; Groceries, general line
Pr: Yutaka Mishima
**VP:* Tsukasa Hatsukade

D-U-N-S 09-354-1647 IMP
MISKELLY FURNITURE WAREHOUSE INC
101 Airport Rd S, Jackson, MS 39208-6686
Tel (601) 939-5303 *Founded/Ownrshp* 1978
Sales 63.6MM^E *EMP* 300
SIC 5712 Furniture stores; Furniture stores
Pr: Howard L Miskelly Jr
**COO:* Debra Watson
**Sec:* Tommy Miskelly
**VP:* Oscar S Miskelly
Mktg Dir: Betsy Tabor
Merch Mgr: Vicki Collums
Sales Asso: Mark Tullar

MISO
See MIDCONTINENT INDEPENDENT SYSTEM OPERATOR INC

D-U-N-S 06-596-3449 IMP
▲ **MISONIX INC**
1938 New Hwy, Farmingdale, NY 11735-1214
Tel (631) 694-9555 *Founded/Ownrshp* 1959
Sales 22.2MM *EMP* 80^E
Accts Grant Thornton Llp Melville
Tkr Sym MSON *Exch* NGM
SIC 3841 3845 3677 Surgical & medical instruments; Electromedical equipment; Filtration devices, electronic; Surgical & medical instruments; Electromedical equipment; Filtration devices, electronic
Pr: Michael A McManus Jr
CFO: Richard Zaremba
Sr VP: Robert S Ludecker
Sr VP: Michael C Ryan
VP: Bernhard Berger
VP: Joseph J Brennan
VP: Karen Fine
VP: Scott Ludecker
VP: Dan Voic
Exec: Andrea Zimmermann
CTO: Bill Gonzalez
Board of Directors: John W Gildea, Patrick McBrayer,

Charles Miner III, T Guy Minetti, Thomas M Patton, Stavros Vizirgianakis

MISS GALLERY
See JGL HOLDINGS LTD

MISS ME
See SWEET PEOPLE APPAREL INC

D-U-N-S 06-744-6385
MISS PAIGE LTD
PAIGE PERSONNEL SERVICES
8430 W Berwyn Ave Ste 625, Chicago, IL 60656-1453
Tel (773) 693-9070 *Founded/Ownrshp* 1964
Sales 24.0MM *EMP* 60
SIC 7361 7363 Employment agencies; Labor contractors (employment agency); Help supply services; Employment agencies; Labor contractors (employment agency); Help supply services
Pr: Karen Rae Horwitz
**Pr:* Richard Schuster
Treas: Janet O'Malley

D-U-N-S 07-731-8095
MISS PORTERS SCHOOL INC
60 Main St, Farmington, CT 06032-2232
Tel (860) 409-3500 *Founded/Ownrshp* 1843
Sales 33.7MM *EMP* 151
Accts Blum Shapiro & Company Pc Cpas
SIC 8211 Boarding school; Boarding school
Ch Bd: Diana Terlato
Dir Vol: Ann Fromherz
**Ch Bd:* Barbara Episanio
COO: Chris Noll
**Treas:* J Michael McQuade
Comm Dir: Siobhan Federici

D-U-N-S 08-879-3146 IMP
MISSA BAY LLC
(*Suby of* READY PAC FOODS INC) ★
2339 Center Square Rd, Swedesboro, NJ 08085-1700
Tel (856) 241-0900 *Founded/Ownrshp* 2015
Sales 41.7MM[E] *EMP* 200[E]
SIC 2099 5142 Food preparations; Packaged frozen goods; Food preparations; Packaged frozen goods
Pr: Frank C Pollera
Netwrk Mgr: Paul Albano
Ql Cn Mgr: Bill Cousins

D-U-N-S 00-696-4407
MISSCO CORP OF JACKSON (MS)
2001 Airport Rd N Ste 102, Flowood, MS 39232-8846
Tel (601) 987-8600 *Founded/Ownrshp* 1919
Sales 30.9MM[E] *EMP* 151
SIC 5021 2531 2599 3821

MISSICIPPIE X RAY
See H & H X-RAY SERVICES INC

D-U-N-S 01-131-3314
■ MISSILE DEFENSE AGENCY
(*Suby of* OFFICE OF THE SECRETARY OF DEFENSE) ★
7100 Defense Pentagon, Washington, DC 20301-7100
Tel (256) 705-8561 *Founded/Ownrshp* 2006
Sales NA *EMP* 500[E]
SIC 9711 National security;
Ofcr: Henry Trey Obering III
Ofcr: Henry A Trey Obering III
CIO: James Armstrong

MISSION ARCHERY
See MATHEWS INC

D-U-N-S 06-311-7279
MISSION AVIATION FELLOWSHIP (CA)
M A F
112 N Pilatus Ln, Nampa, ID 83687-9635
Tel (208) 498-0800 *Founded/Ownrshp* 1945
Sales 46.0MM *EMP* 110[E]
Accts Smith Marion & Co
SIC 4522 Flying charter service
Ch Bd: Bob Swanson
**Ch Bd:* Ron Pritz
**Pr:* Kevin Swanson
**Treas:* Wiliam Southworth
Ex VP: William Yantiss
VP: Bill Southworth
IT Man: Brent Palmer
Sls&Mrk Ex: John Woodberry

D-U-N-S 03-941-1806
MISSION BANK INC
(*Suby of* VALLEY VIEW BANCSHARES INC) ★
5201 Johnson Dr, Shawnee Mission, KS 66205-2925
Tel (913) 831-2400 *Founded/Ownrshp* 1980
Sales NA *EMP* 86
SIC 6022 State commercial banks; State commercial banks
Pr: Clay E Coburn Jr
Ofcr: Clay Coburn Jr
Trst Ofcr: James S O'Ullivan
Sr VP: Ron Bradbury
Sr VP: David Shepherd
VP: Jeffery Forgey
VP: Duane L Patton
Dir Bus: Blake Morgan
VP Mktg: Charles Weldon
Board of Directors: James S Lewis, Larry G Mc Lemon

MISSION BARGAIN CENTER
See RESCUE MISSION ALLIANCE

MISSION BAY AQUATIC CENTER
See ASSOCIATED STUDENTS OF SAN DIEGO STATE UNIVERSITY

D-U-N-S 04-876-1639
MISSION BAY IMPORT AUTO SALES LLC
PACIFIC NISSAN
4433 Mission Bay Dr, San Diego, CA 92109-5731
Tel (858) 581-3200 *Founded/Ownrshp* 2013
Sales 36.6MM[E] *EMP* 73
SIC 5511 Automobiles, new & used; Automobiles, new & used
CFO: John Cracas
Sls Dir: Ron Houston
Sls Dir: Steve Paladino
Sls Mgr: Hugo Solorzano

Sls Mgr: Gabriela Wagner
Sales Asso: Brian Groves
Sales Asso: Nader Suliman

D-U-N-S 04-522-8467 IMP
MISSION BEVERAGE CO
(*Suby of* TOPA EQUITIES LTD) ★
550 S Mission Rd, Los Angeles, CA 90033-4256
Tel (323) 266-6238 *Founded/Ownrshp* 1956
Sales 81.1MM[E] *EMP* 240
SIC 5181 5149 Beer & other fermented malt liquors; Soft drinks; Beer & other fermented malt liquors; Soft drinks
Ch Bd: John E Anderson Sr
**Pr:* Don Holland
**Sec:* Therese D Curtis

D-U-N-S 12-065-5977
MISSION BROADCASTING INC
30400 Detroit Rd Ste 304, Westlake, OH 44145-1855
Tel (440) 526-2227 *Founded/Ownrshp* 1998
Sales 78.5MM *EMP* 38
SIC 4833 Television broadcasting stations; Television broadcasting stations
Pr: Dennis Thatcher
**Ch Bd:* Nancie J Smith
Treas: David Smith

MISSION CANDLE COMPANY
See REED CANDLE CO

D-U-N-S 02-639-7364 IMP
MISSION CHEVROLET LTD
MISSION ISUZU TRUCK
1316 George Dieter Dr, El Paso, TX 79936-7408
Tel (915) 594-1700 *Founded/Ownrshp* 1999
Sales 33.6MM[E] *EMP* 95[E]
SIC 5511 5521 Automobiles, new & used; Used car dealers; Automobiles, new & used; Used car dealers
Ltd Pt: Ron Wallace
Off Mgr: Mary Alvidrez
Sls Mgr: Jerry Slaughter

D-U-N-S 96-159-5456
MISSION CLAY PRODUCTS LLC
(*Suby of* MCP INDUSTRIES INC) ★
23835 Temescal Canyon Rd, Corona, CA 92883-6000
Tel (951) 277-4600 *Founded/Ownrshp* 2009
Sales 45.1MM[E] *EMP* 76
SIC 3259 Clay sewer & drainage pipe & tile
Plnt Mgr: Dean Padgett
Sls Mgr: Garrett Richardson

D-U-N-S 02-880-5351
MISSION COMMUNITY BANCORP
3380 S Higuera St, San Luis Obispo, CA 93401-6926
Tel (805) 782-5000 *Founded/Ownrshp* 2000
Sales NA *EMP* 111
SIC 6021

MISSION COMMUNITY HOSPITAL
See DEANCO HEALTHCARE LLC

D-U-N-S 01-053-1739
MISSION CONSOLIDATED INDEPENDENT SCHOOL DISTRICT
1201 Bryce Dr, Mission, TX 78572-4311
Tel (956) 323-5500 *Founded/Ownrshp* 1908
Sales 127.1MM[E] *EMP* 2,000
Accts Reyna & Garza Pllc Edinburg
SIC 8211 Public elementary school; Public junior high school; Public senior high school; Public elementary school; Public junior high school; Public senior high school
Dir Sec: Sylvia Cruz
Cmptr Lab: Nora Cavazos
IT Man: Luis Rocha
Schl Brd P: Sonia Trevino
Board of Directors: Oscar Rodirguez Sup

MISSION CRITICAL SOLUTION
See MCS OF TAMPA INC

D-U-N-S 00-950-8698
MISSION CRITICAL SYSTEMS INC
1347 E Sample Rd Ste 3, Pompano Beach, FL 33064-6278
Tel (954) 788-7110 *Founded/Ownrshp* 1997
Sales 32.0MM *EMP* 28[E]
SIC 7379 Computer related consulting services
Pr: Susan Crabtree
**VP:* Frank Darden
CTO: Michael Nash
Mktg Dir: Brad Haizlett
Sls Dir: Dave Doebler

D-U-N-S 08-932-6453
■ MISSION ENERGY HOLDING CO
(*Suby of* EDISON MISSION GROUP INC) ★
2600 Michelson Dr # 1700, Irvine, CA 92612-1550
Tel (949) 752-5588 *Founded/Ownrshp* 2001
Sales NA *EMP* 1,890
SIC 6719 Personal holding companies, except banks; Personal holding companies, except banks
CEO: Mark C Clarke
Pr: Thomas R McDaniel
CFO: W James Scilacci
Board of Directors: Jacob A Bouknight Jr

D-U-N-S 14-242-3990
MISSION ESSENTIAL PERSONNEL LLC
M E P
6525 W Campus Oval # 101, New Albany, OH 43054-8831
Tel (614) 416-2345 *Founded/Ownrshp* 2004
Sales 65.3MM[E] *EMP* 250
SIC 7389 8748 Translation services; Safety training service; Translation services; Safety training service
CFO: Albert Campbell
VP: John Doran
VP: David Larocca
VP: David Slovina
VP: Peter Tirinnanzi
VP: Susan Zidek
Exec: Mary Harmer
Exec: Barbara Nelson
Comm Dir: Sean Rushton
Prgrm Mgr: Jonathan Havens
IT Man: Reeves Bill

D-U-N-S 07-992-2052
MISSION FEDERAL CREDIT UNION
5785 Oberlin Dr Ste 312, San Diego, CA 92121-3752
Tel (858) 546-2184 *Founded/Ownrshp* 2015
Sales NA *EMP* 550[E]
SIC 6061 Federal credit unions
CEO: Debra Schwartz
**CFO:* Ron Araujo

D-U-N-S 02-021-9077
MISSION FEDERAL SERVICES LLC
5785 Oberlin Dr Ste 333, San Diego, CA 92121-3752
Tel (800) 500-6328 *Founded/Ownrshp* 1961
Sales NA *EMP* 325
SIC 6061 Federal credit unions; Federal credit unions
CEO: Debra Schwartz
COO: Rose Hartley
COO: Monica Hoolsema
CFO: Peter Sainato
Ofcr: Nancy Morris
Ofcr: Frank Poole
Sr VP: Neville Billimoria
Sr VP: Monica Cones
Sr VP: John Cooke
Sr VP: Gary M Devan
Sr VP: Richard Hartley
Sr VP: Rob Miller
Sr VP: Ron Petroskey
Sr VP: Elaine Ziegler
VP: Sherry Carr
VP: Dan Colt
VP: Jeanine Dodman
VP: Corinne Grandgirard
VP: Donna Handwerger
VP: Mique Kee
VP: Linda Kramer
Board of Directors: Jim Abbott, Melanie R Branca, Lupe Buell, Ken Clark, John J Daily, Shirley J Mills, G Wayne Oetken, Richard L Pepper, Len Servetter

MISSION FOODS
See GRUMA CORP

MISSION GOLF CARS
See RIVER CITY MARKETING INC

D-U-N-S 12-514-3383
MISSION GROCERS INC
CANTWELL'S MARKET & DELI
915 Elm Ave, Carpinteria, CA 93013-1926
Tel (805) 966-3902 *Founded/Ownrshp* 1999
Sales 25.0MM *EMP* 27
SIC 5411 Grocery stores, independent; Grocery stores, independent
Pr: James Gally
**VP:* Jim Gally
VP: Dean Murray

MISSION GROUP, THE
See MEDILODGE GROUP INC

D-U-N-S 02-301-2573
MISSION GROUP KANSAS INC
WRIGHT BUSINESS SCHOOL
405 5th Ave S Ste 6, Naples, FL 34102-6515
Tel (239) 435-9299 *Founded/Ownrshp* 1994
Sales 38.3MM *EMP* 200
Accts Salmon Sims Thomas & Assoc Pll
SIC 8244 Business college or school; Business college or school
CEO: James Miller Jr
**Pr:* John Mucci
**VP:* Gayle Miller

D-U-N-S 04-213-3398
MISSION GROUP KANSAS INC
WRIGHT CAREER COLLEGE
10700 Metcalf Ave, Overland Park, KS 66210-1616
Tel (913) 381-2577 *Founded/Ownrshp* 2011
Sales 33.0MM *EMP* 420
SIC 8299 Educational services
Pr: James Miller Jr
**Prin:* John L Mucci
IT Man: Jesse Graglia
Nrsg Dir: Kimbra Rosenberg
HC Dir: Sally Atchity

D-U-N-S 06-256-8209
MISSION HEALTH SYSTEM INC
509 Biltm Ave Aka Hwy 25, Asheville, NC 28801
Tel (828) 213-1111 *Founded/Ownrshp* 1998
Sales 574.6MM[E] *EMP* 5,500
SIC 8062 General medical & surgical hospitals; General medical & surgical hospitals
CEO: Ronald A Paulus MD
COO: Jill Hoggard-Green
CFO: Charles Aysques
Treas: Carol Goodrun
Chf Mktg O: William R Hathaway
Ofcr: Jeri Williams
Sr VP: Sonya B Greck
Sr VP: William Maples
Sr VP: Rowena Timms
Sr VP: Marc B Westle
VP: Richard Arwood
VP: Monica Collins
VP: Melody Dunlop
VP: Dale Fell
VP: Tara Lewis
VP: John Maher
VP: Rhonda Miller
VP: Ann Ray
VP: Angela Wills

D-U-N-S 96-635-3505
MISSION HEALTH SYSTEM INC
400 Ridgefield Ct, Asheville, NC 28806-2213
Tel (828) 257-7004 *Founded/Ownrshp* 1981
Sales 66.8MM *EMP* 24[E]
Accts Grant Thornton Llp Charlotte
SIC 8062 General medical & surgical hospitals; General medical & surgical hospitals
Pr: Ronald A Paulus

MISSION HILLS MORTGAGE BANKERS
See MISSION HILLS MORTGAGE CORP

D-U-N-S 07-604-9865
MISSION HILLS MORTGAGE CORP
MISSION HILLS MORTGAGE BANKERS
(*Suby of* TARBELL FINANCIAL CORP) ★
18500 Von Karman Ave # 1100, Irvine, CA 92612-0546
Tel (714) 972-3832 *Founded/Ownrshp* 1982
Sales NA *EMP* 380
SIC 6163 Mortgage brokers arranging for loans, using money of others; Mortgage brokers arranging for loans, using money of others
Pr: Jay Ledbetter
CFO: Melinda Davis
VP: Marsha Boniti
Site Mgr: Tim Cooper
Site Mgr: Renee Jones
Site Mgr: Dave Raffi
Site Mgr: Mark Wauge
Mktg Mgr: Collin Cobb

D-U-N-S 01-272-2138
MISSION HOSPITAL INC (TX)
MISSION REGIONAL MEDICAL CENTE
900 S Bryan Rd, Mission, TX 78572-6613
Tel (956) 323-9000 *Founded/Ownrshp* 1954
Sales 105.3MM *EMP* 1,100
SIC 8062 General medical & surgical hospitals; General medical & surgical hospitals
CEO: Javier Iruegas
V Ch: Alicia Requenez
**CFO:* Timothy McVey
CFO: Sandra Yanez
Chf Mktg O: Desi Canad
VP: Kathleen Mowery
Dir Lab: Carlos Gonzalez
Mng Dir: Laura Cavazos
Dir IT: Emundo Ortega
Sfty Dirs: Michael Cerna
Pharmcst: Bianca Cruz

D-U-N-S 07-452-6690 IMP
MISSION HOSPITAL INC
509 Biltmore Ave, Asheville, NC 28801-4601
Tel (828) 213-1111 *Founded/Ownrshp* 1998
Sales 936.2MM *EMP* 5,400[E]
SIC 8062 General medical & surgical hospitals; General medical & surgical hospitals
Pr: Joseph Damore
Chf Path: Michael Teaford
**CEO:* Ronald A Paulus
COO: Bryan Astin
Ex VP: Paul Thomas
**Sr VP:* Charles F Ayscue
VP: Karen Lemieux
VP: John Maher
VP: Sheila Meadows
VP: Rowena Timms
VP: Angie Wills
VP: Ann Young
Dir Lab: Janet Colvin
Dir Rad: Michael R Boene
Dir Rx: Mollie A Scott

D-U-N-S 06-445-7005
MISSION HOSPITAL REGIONAL MEDICAL CENTER INC
27700 Medical Center Rd, Mission Viejo, CA 92691-6426
Tel (949) 364-1400 *Founded/Ownrshp* 1941
Sales 511.1MM *EMP* 2,600
Accts Ernst & Young Us Llp San Dieg
SIC 8062 General medical & surgical hospitals; General medical & surgical hospitals
CEO: Kenn Nicfaralnd
CFO: Ken McFarland
Dir Lab: Jarren Bell
Dir Lab: Don White
Ex Dir: Victoria McKinney
Mng Dir: William Losee
Dir Sec: Scott Odonnell
Genl Mgr: Paul Gausman
CIO: Gary Fybel
MIS Dir: Marsha Defrofierf
Opers Mgr: Leyla Davijani

MISSION IMPORTS A CALIFORNIA
See MERCEDES-BENZ OF LAGUNA NIGUEL

D-U-N-S 87-875-1106 IMP
MISSION IMPRINTABLES INC
MISSIONIMPRINTABLES.COM
6060 Bus Ctr Ct Ste 200, San Diego, CA 92154-6625
Tel (619) 623-3200 *Founded/Ownrshp* 1994
Sales 54.2MM[E] *EMP* 38[E]
SIC 5136 5137 Men's & boys' clothing; Women's & children's clothing
Pr: Lisa Coy

MISSION INDUSTRIES
See MISSION OF NEVADA INC

MISSION INN HOTEL AND SPA, THE
See HISTORIC MISSION INN CORP

D-U-N-S 11-025-5734
MISSION INTERNAL MEDICAL GROUP INC
MIMG ENDOSCOPY
26522 La Alameda Ste 120, Mission Viejo, CA 92691-6330
Tel (949) 282-1600 *Founded/Ownrshp* 1972
Sales 20.1MM[E] *EMP* 227
SIC 8011 Cardiologist & cardio-vascular specialist; Gastronomist; Internal medicine, physician/surgeon; Pulmonary specialist, physician/surgeon; Cardiologist & cardio-vascular specialist; Gastronomist; Internal medicine, physician/surgeon; Pulmonary specialist, physician/surgeon
CEO: Dennis Wolin
**Pr:* Daniel Kulick
COO: Trissa Wheat

D-U-N-S 78-686-8687
MISSION INVESTMENT FUND OF EVANGELICAL LUTHERAN CHURCH IN AMERICA (INC)
8765 W Higgins Rd Ste 600, Chicago, IL 60631-4100
Tel (773) 380-2700 *Founded/Ownrshp* 1987
Sales NA *EMP* 46
Accts Kpmg Llp Chicago Il

SIC 6036 Savings & loan associations, not federally chartered; Savings & loan associations, not federally chartered
Pr: Christina Jackson-Skelton
**Pr:* C Jackson-Skelton
Ex VP: Eva Roby

MISSION ISUZU TRUCK
See MISSION CHEVROLET LTD

D-U-N-S 06-448-5154
MISSION LANDSCAPE COMPANIES INC
536 E Dyer Rd, Santa Ana, CA 92707-3737
Tel (714) 545-9962 *Founded/Ownrshp* 1973
Sales 20.3MM^E *EMP* 200
SIC 0782 Landscape contractors; Landscape contractors
CEO: David Dubois
Pr: Kristen Parkins
**Treas:* Beth Du Boise
VP: Beatrice Campos

MISSION LINEN & UNIFORM SVC
See MISSION LINEN SUPPLY

D-U-N-S 03-494-6574 IMP
MISSION LINEN SUPPLY
MISSION LINEN & UNIFORM SVC
717 E Yanonali St, Santa Barbara, CA 93103-3235
Tel (805) 730-3620 *Founded/Ownrshp* 1973
Sales 154.3MM^E *EMP* 3,000
SIC 7218 7213 Industrial launderers; Linen supply; Industrial launderers; Linen supply
CEO: John Ross
**CFO:* Anne Wilson
**Ex VP:* Nick Katzenstein
**Ex VP:* Joe Plowman
**VP:* Mark Whitten
Exec: Carolyn Alexander
Info Man: Mike Daymude
Software D: Joel Schiffer

MISSION OF MERCY
See BETHESDA MINISTRIES

D-U-N-S 00-289-7333
MISSION OF NEVADA INC
MISSION INDUSTRIES
1 W Mayflower Ave, North Las Vegas, NV 89030-3951
Tel (702) 639-2500 *Founded/Ownrshp* 1995
Sales 23.4MM^E *EMP* 2,100
SIC 7213 Linen supply; Linen supply
Pr: Grover W Ferguson
**Pr:* D W Doc Wiener
**CFO:* Andrew Zimmerman
**Ch:* James B Page

MISSION PACKING COMPANY
See GRIFFIN PRODUCE CO INC

MISSION PARK FUNERAL CHAPELS
See MPII INC

D-U-N-S 00-814-3588
MISSION PETROLEUM CARRIERS INC
(*Suby of* TETCO INC) ★
8450 Mosley Rd, Houston, TX 77075-1114
Tel (210) 821-5900 *Founded/Ownrshp* 1983
Sales 10.0MM *EMP* 830
SIC 4213

D-U-N-S 00-811-7095 IMP
MISSION PHARMACAL CO
10999 W Interstate 10 # 1000, San Antonio, TX 78230-1300
Tel (210) 696-8400 *Founded/Ownrshp* 1946
Sales 157.2MM *EMP* 495
Accts Ernst & Young Llp San Antoni
SIC 2834 Vitamin preparations; Vitamin preparations
Ch Bd: Neill B Walsdorf Sr
**Pr:* Neill B Walsdorf Jr
COO: Max Martin
**CFO:* Tom Dooley
**Treas:* Beverly A Walsdorf
Ofcr: Marshall Hayward
Ofcr: Anita Scott
VP: Darryl Johnson
VP: John Simonick
VP: Natalie Sirjuesingh
VP: Jon Taylor
Dir Lab: Stephanie Lowe

MISSION PHARMACY SERVICES
See PROFESSIONAL SPECIALIZED PHARMACIES LLC

D-U-N-S 07-659-1072 IMP
MISSION PLASTICS INC
1930 S Parco Ave, Ontario, CA 91761-8312
Tel (909) 947-7287 *Founded/Ownrshp* 1982
Sales 33.1MM^E *EMP* 120
SIC 3089 Injection molding of plastics; Injection molding of plastics
CEO: Patrick Dauphinee
**Sec:* Charles Montes
IT Man: Brian Wilberding
Sfty Mgr: Kenneth Miles
Plnt Mgr: Louie Castaneda
Ql Cn Mgr: William Cypert
Ql Cn Mgr: Tom Hileman

D-U-N-S 19-705-4505 IMP
MISSION PLASTICS OF ARKANSAS INC
(*Suby of* PETERSON MANUFACTURING CO) ★
102 Mission Dr, Nashville, AR 71852-3400
Tel (870) 845-4085 *Founded/Ownrshp* 1987
Sales 31.8MM^E *EMP* 200
SIC 3089 Injection molding of plastics; Injection molding of plastics
Pr: David S Armacost
**Sec:* O Nelson Auer
**Sec:* Stephen K Hickerson
**VP:* Don R Armacost
Exec: Charlene Wright
Genl Mgr: Jim Rash
Sfty Dirs: Elaine Pannell

D-U-N-S 08-757-7433
MISSION POOLS OF ESCONDIDO
755 W Grand Ave, Escondido, CA 92025-2594
Tel (760) 743-2605 *Founded/Ownrshp* 1977
Sales 25.9MM^E *EMP* 130
SIC 1799 Swimming pool construction; Swimming pool construction
Pr: Bruce Dunn
**CEO:* G Bruce Dunn
**Treas:* Jeff Dunn
**VP:* Jack Tone Jr
Snr PM: Mike Roudebush

D-U-N-S 10-304-6736 IMP/EXP
MISSION PRODUCE INC
2500 E Vineyard Ave # 300, Oxnard, CA 93036-1377
Tel (805) 981-3650 *Founded/Ownrshp* 1983
Sales 139.3MM^E *EMP* 300
SIC 5148

MISSION REGIONAL MEDICAL CENTE
See MISSION HOSPITAL INC

MISSION RESTAURANT SUPPLY CO
See SOUTHWEST TEXAS EQUIPMENT DISTRIBUTORS INC

D-U-N-S 06-892-9517
MISSION RESTAURANTS INC
PIZZA HUT
171 Brooks St Se Ste F, Fort Walton Beach, FL 32548-3718
Tel (850) 244-6130 *Founded/Ownrshp* 1998
Sales 7.5MM^E *EMP* 300
SIC 5812 Pizzeria, chain; Pizzeria, chain
Pr: Chuck Cooper
Off Mgr: Amanda McArdle

MISSION RUBBER CO
See MCP INDUSTRIES INC

D-U-N-S 13-925-5397 IMP
MISSION RUBBER CO LLC
(*Suby of* MCP INDUSTRIES INC) ★
1660 Leeson Ln, Corona, CA 92879-2061
Tel (951) 736-1313 *Founded/Ownrshp* 2009
Sales 34.4MM^E *EMP* 200^E
SIC 3494 Couplings, except pressure & soil pipe; Couplings, except pressure & soil pipe
VP: Thomas Garrett
**VP:* Chris Vansell
Exec: Carol Holt
Mng Dir: Marco Buoninfante
Dir IT: Bob Hurley
Mtls Mgr: Janel Alvarez
Mfg Mgr: Andy Chavez
Plnt Mgr: Jay Clark
Plnt Mgr: Richard Posiviata
Ql Cn Mgr: Don Wrixon
Manager: Dan Girton
Board of Directors: Joe Watso

D-U-N-S 01-207-0981 IMP
MISSION SOLAR ENERGY LLC
(*Suby of* NEXOLON CO., LTD.)
8303 S New Braunfels, San Antonio, TX 78235-1068
Tel (210) 787-1225 *Founded/Ownrshp* 2012
Sales 22.7MM^E *EMP* 60
SIC 3674 Photovoltaic devices, solid state; Solar cells; Silicon wafers, chemically doped
CEO: Alex Kim
**Ex VP:* Brad Miles
Prgrm Mgr: Mike Parry
Off Mgr: Patricia Garza

MISSION SOLUTIONS ENGINEERING
See MISSION SOLUTIONS LLC

D-U-N-S 83-138-9353
MISSION SOLUTIONS LLC
MISSION SOLUTIONS ENGINEERING
(*Suby of* ASRC FEDERAL HOLDING CO LLC) ★
121 Whittendale Dr Ste A, Moorestown, NJ 08057-1373
Tel (856) 291-2468 *Founded/Ownrshp* 2010
Sales 31.5MM^E *EMP* 599^E
SIC 8711 Engineering services; Engineering services
Pr: Michael Knowles
VP: Charles Zimmerman
Comm Dir: Christine Courard
Prgrm Mgr: Harry Rose
Snr Sftwr: Bob Fitzsimmons
Snr Sftwr: Roger Ladd
Snr Sftwr: Eric Landrieu
Snr Sftwr: Joanis Ploumitsakos
Snr Sftwr: Karl Schraut
QA Dir: Sue Goldberg
Software D: Michael McCloskey

D-U-N-S 01-060-5464
MISSION SUPPORT ALLIANCE LLC
MSA
2490 Garlick Blvd, Richland, WA 99354-1786
Tel (509) 376-6770 *Founded/Ownrshp* 2009
Sales 98.4MM^E *EMP* 1,945
SIC 8741 Business management
Pr: William Johnson
QA Dir: Steve Peterson
QA Dir: Mike Wingfield
IT Man: Jennifer Jahner
IT Man: Christopher Luke
Tech Mgr: Richard Grantham

MISSION SUPPORT SERVICES
See PRESBYTERIAN CHURCH U S A

MISSION SYSTEMS AND TRAINING
See LOCKHEED MARTIN CORP

MISSION TO THE AMERICAS
See CONSERVATIVE BAPTIST HOME MISSION SOCIETY

D-U-N-S 82-513-1998
MISSION TO WORLD (PCA) INC
MTW
1600 N Brown Rd, Lawrenceville, GA 30043-8141
Tel (678) 823-0004 *Founded/Ownrshp* 1973
Sales 63.6MM *EMP* 500
Accts Capincrouse Llp Atlanta Geo
SIC 8399 8661 8322 Social change association; Religious organizations; Individual & family services; Social change association; Religious organizations; Individual & family services
Mktg Dir: Amy Glass

D-U-N-S 15-509-5748
MISSION VALLEY FORD TRUCK SALES INC
MISSION VLY FORD STRLNG TRCKS
780 E Brokaw Rd, San Jose, CA 95112-1007
Tel (408) 933-2300 *Founded/Ownrshp* 1986
Sales 52.9MM^E *EMP* 80
SIC 5511 5531 7513 7538 Automobiles, new & used; Truck equipment & parts; Truck leasing, without drivers; Truck rental, without drivers; General truck repair; Automobiles, new & used; Truck equipment & parts; Truck leasing, without drivers; Truck rental, without drivers; General truck repair
Pr: Ernest A Speno
**Treas:* Yuliko Hopkins
**VP:* Jeffrey A Speno
Sales Exec: Mike Creech

D-U-N-S 10-476-9208
MISSION VALLEY POWER
36079 Pablo Rd W, Pablo, MT 59855
Tel (406) 883-7900 *Founded/Ownrshp* 1987
Sales 54.3MM^E *EMP* 86
SIC 4911 4939 Electric services; Combination utilities; Electric services; Combination utilities
Genl Mgr: Ralph Goode
IT Man: Jean Matt
IT Man: Dalene Morrison

MISSION VIEW HEALTH CENTER
See COMPASS HEALTH INC

MISSION VLY FORD STRLNG TRCKS
See MISSION VALLEY FORD TRUCK SALES INC

D-U-N-S 87-292-2208
MISSION VOLKSWAGEN INC
CAPISTRANO VOLKSWAGEN
32922 Valle Rd, San Juan Capistrano, CA 92675-4802
Tel (949) 493-4511 *Founded/Ownrshp* 1997
Sales 30.5MM^E *EMP* 80
SIC 5511 7538 Automobiles, new & used; General automotive repair shops; Automobiles, new & used; General automotive repair shops
Pr: Miles Braden
**Pr:* Miles Brandon
Brnch Mgr: Vance Perierra
Off Mgr: Barbara Edwards
IT Man: Steve Skinner
Mktg Dir: Gary Willenborg
Mktg Mgr: Brooke Campos
Sls Mgr: Tom Deering

D-U-N-S 06-311-5372
MISSION WEST PROPERTIES INC
10050 Bandley Dr, Cupertino, CA 95014-2102
Tel (408) 725-0700 *Founded/Ownrshp* 1969
Sales 104.8MM *EMP* 6^E
SIC 6798

D-U-N-S 10-438-9085
MISSION WITHOUT BORDERS INC
CHILD RESCUE INTERNATIONAL
711 E Daily Dr Ste 120, Camarillo, CA 93010-6082
Tel (805) 987-8891 *Founded/Ownrshp* 1960
Sales 29.5MM *EMP* 3
Accts Fanning & Karrh Ventura Ca
SIC 8361 Orphanage; Orphanage
Pr: Harry Graham
Ch Bd: William Temlett
Off Mgr: Tami Soria

D-U-N-S 55-557-0576
MISSION1ST GROUP INC
155 Village Blvd Ste 203, Princeton, NJ 08540-5765
Tel (609) 520-1900 *Founded/Ownrshp* 2005
Sales 23.6MM^E *EMP* 150
SIC 8742 Management consulting services; Management consulting services
CEO: Richard Zareck
**Pr:* Augustine Zareck
**COO:* Dr Robert T Ashe
**CFO:* Michael Farissier
**VP:* Brent Hursey
Sales Exec: Steve Giamos
Genl Couns: Douglas Walsh

D-U-N-S 07-430-4437
MISSIONARY CHURCH INC
WORLD PARTNERS
3811 Vanguard Dr, Fort Wayne, IN 46809-3304
Tel (260) 747-2027 *Founded/Ownrshp* 1969
Sales 8.0MM *EMP* 400
Accts Krouse Kern & Co Inc Cpas
SIC 8661 5999 Miscellaneous denomination church; Religious goods; Miscellaneous denomination church; Religious goods
Pr: Steve Jones
Treas: Dan Bridges
Ex Dir: Eric Smith

MISSIONIMPRINTABLES.COM
See MISSION IMPRINTABLES INC

MISSIONS PROPOGATION FAITH
See DIOCESE OF COLUMBUS

D-U-N-S 07-207-6664
MISSISSINEWA COMMUNITY SCHOOLS
424 E South A St, Gas City, IN 46933-1902
Tel (765) 674-8528 *Founded/Ownrshp* 1950
Sales 20.0MM^E *EMP* 300
SIC 8211 Public elementary & secondary schools; Public elementary & secondary schools
VP: Wayne Gaskin
Cmptr Lab: Mendy Hussong
Psych: Libby Anderson
Psych: Carol Mannix
HC Dir: Tami Corbin

D-U-N-S 07-945-8287
MISSISSIPPI ACTION FOR PROGRESS INC
HEAD START SCHOOL
1751 Morson Rd, Jackson, MS 39209-6546
Tel (601) 923-4100 *Founded/Ownrshp* 1966
Sales 41.8MM *EMP* 1,250
Accts Watkins Ward & Stafford Pllc
SIC 8099 8211 Health screening service; Preparatory school; Health screening service; Preparatory school
Ex Dir: Bobby E Brown
**Prin:* Hodding Carter III
**Prin:* Owen Cooper
**Prin:* Leroy Percy
**Ex Dir:* Dorothy S Foster
Dir IT: George Bartley

D-U-N-S 04-574-9256
MISSISSIPPI AG CO
JOHN DEERE
441 Haley Barbour Pkwy, Yazoo City, MS 39194-9412
Tel (662) 746-6208 *Founded/Ownrshp* 2004
Sales 180.0MM^E *EMP* 240
SIC 5083 Farm implements; Tractors, agricultural; Farm implements; Tractors, agricultural
Pr: G Leyden Pugh
**Sec:* Gus Pugh
**VP:* Frank Pugh

D-U-N-S 16-961-8241
MISSISSIPPI ARTS AND ENTERTAINMENT CENTER
212 Constitution Ave, Meridian, MS 39301-5101
Tel (601) 581-1550 *Founded/Ownrshp* 2003
Sales 21.6MM *EMP* 1
SIC 8412 Arts or science center; Arts or science center
Pr: Tommy Dulaney
Off Mgr: Laura Gidden

D-U-N-S 07-764-6446
MISSISSIPPI BAND OF CHOCTAW INDIANS
101 Industrial Rd, Choctaw, MS 39350-4224
Tel (601) 650-1845 *Founded/Ownrshp* 1945
Sales NA *EMP* 8,500
SIC 9131 Indian reservation; Indian reservation
CFO: Larry Kovach
CFO: Lawrene J Kovneh
**Treas:* Lola Parkerson
Ofcr: Kirby Willis
Comm Dir: Misty Dreifuss
Ex Dir: Billy Robertson
QA Dir: Penny Wells
Netwrk Mgr: Ledale Reynolds

D-U-N-S 06-954-0123
MISSISSIPPI BAPTIST HEALTH SYSTEMS INC
1225 N State St Ofc, Jackson, MS 39202-2069
Tel (601) 968-1000 *Founded/Ownrshp* 2008
Sales 76.5MM *EMP* 3,000
Accts Bkd Llp Jackson Ms
SIC 8741 8721 8069 Hospital management; Accounting, auditing & bookkeeping; Specialty hospitals, except psychiatric; Hospital management; Accounting, auditing & bookkeeping; Specialty hospitals, except psychiatric
CEO: Mark F Slyter
**Pr:* Mark Slider
**CFO:* Russell York
Dir Lab: Pat Herrington
**Prin:* Eric McVey
Doctor: Michael R Byers MD
Doctor: Luther H Fulcher MD
Doctor: Paul D Van Landingham MD

D-U-N-S 01-038-4659
MISSISSIPPI BAPTST MEDICAL CENTER INC
(*Suby of* MISSISSIPPI BAPTIST HEALTH SYSTEMS INC) ★
1225 N State St, Jackson, MS 39202-2064
Tel (601) 968-1000 *Founded/Ownrshp* 1912
Sales 396.3MM *EMP* 3,000
SIC 8062 8069 8051

D-U-N-S 87-814-1548
MISSISSIPPI BEND AREA EDUCATION AGENCY
729 21st St, Bettendorf, IA 52722-5004
Tel (563) 359-1371 *Founded/Ownrshp* 1974
Sales NA *EMP* 348
SIC 9411 ;
**Pr:* David Swim
IT Man: Joy Huffman
Pr Dir: Whitney Smith
Psych: James Ott

D-U-N-S 07-789-3030
MISSISSIPPI BLOOD SERVICES INC
115 Tree St, Flowood, MS 39232-7661
Tel (601) 981-3232 *Founded/Ownrshp* 1979
Sales 24.1MM *EMP* 184
Accts Matthews Cutrer & Lindsay Pa
SIC 8099 Blood bank; Blood bank
Pr: David Allen
**COO:* Janet Herman
**CFO:* Dona Mitchell
**V Ch Bd:* Nehemiah Flowers
VP: Shelia Allen
VP: Todd Sing
VP: Linda Wagner
VP: Diana Wyrick
Off Mgr: Chad Vestal
Dir IT: Calvin Robinson
Mktg Mgr: Tammy Bouchillon

D-U-N-S 02-497-5062
MISSISSIPPI BOULEVARD CHRISTIAN CHURCH
DISCIPLE OF CHRIST
70 N Bellevue Blvd, Memphis, TN 38104-2221
Tel (901) 729-6222 *Founded/Ownrshp* 2000
Sales 50.0MM *EMP* 70
SIC 5942 8661 Books, religious; Miscellaneous denomination church; Books, religious; Miscellaneous denomination church
Store Mgr: Tiffany Lewis

MISSISSIPPI BRAVES
See ATLANTA NATIONAL LEAGUE BASEBALL CLUB INC

D-U-N-S 18-058-7362
■ MISSISSIPPI COCA COLA BOTTLING CO INC
(*Suby of* COCA-COLA REFRESHMENTS USA INC) ★
191 Devereaux Dr, Natchez, MS 39120-3754
Tel (601) 442-1641 *Founded/Ownrshp* 1996
Sales 34.5MM^E *EMP* 100
SIC 5149 Soft drinks
Pr: Moe Leblanc
Treas: Charles L Wiiams
**Sec:* Charles L Williams
**VP:* Morse Strickland

D-U-N-S 07-263-0874
MISSISSIPPI COLLEGE
200 Capitol St, Clinton, MS 39056-4026
Tel (601) 925-3000 *Founded/Ownrshp* 1826
Sales 75.4MM *EMP* 482^E
Accts Cherry Bekaert Llp Charlotte
SIC 8221 College, except junior; College, except junior
Pr: Lee G Royce
**CFO:* Donna Lewis
**VP:* Ron Howard
VP: Mark Hughes
**VP:* Debbie C Norris PHD
**VP:* Eric Pratt
**VP:* Danny Rutland
**VP:* Steve Stanford PHD
VP: Bill Townsend
**VP:* James Turcotte
Genl Mgr: Doug Amacker

D-U-N-S 00-705-3556
MISSISSIPPI COUNTY ELECTRIC COOPERATIVE INC
510 N Broadway St, Blytheville, AR 72315-2732
Tel (870) 763-4563 *Founded/Ownrshp* 1938
Sales 157.2MM *EMP* 16
SIC 4911 Distribution, electric power; Distribution, electric power
Pr: Larry Hellums
**Sec:* Steve West
VP: Keeley Wheeler

D-U-N-S 02-269-9380
MISSISSIPPI COUNTY HOSPITAL SYSTEM
GREAT RIVER PHYSICIANS GROUP
1520 N Division St, Blytheville, AR 72315-1448
Tel (870) 838-7300 *Founded/Ownrshp* 2009
Sales 21.2MM *EMP* 330^E
SIC 8062 General medical & surgical hospitals; General medical & surgical hospitals
CEO: Ralph Beaty
**COO:* Chris Raymer
**CFO:* Randy Nichols
HC Dir: Anntricia Strivner
Snr Mgr: Ronald Smith

D-U-N-S 07-354-3639
MISSISSIPPI DELTA COMMUNITY COLLEGE (INC)
MDCC
Hwy 3 Cherry St, Moorhead, MS 38761
Tel (662) 246-6322 *Founded/Ownrshp* 1928
Sales 18.1MM^E *EMP* 325
Accts Ellis & Hirsberg Cpa Pllc Cla
SIC 8222 8221 Community college; Colleges universities & professional schools; Community college; Colleges universities & professional schools
Pr: Larry Nabors
**Ex VP:* Charles Barnett
**VP:* D Reed Abraham
**VP:* Magdalene Abraham
VP: Reed Abraham
**VP:* Mary Anne Brocato
VP: J Gregory
VP: Edward Rice
**VP:* Linda Steelle
**VP:* Carol Walden
**Prin:* Larry G Bailey

D-U-N-S 87-819-3150
MISSISSIPPI DEPARTMENT OF EMPLOYMENT SECURITY
JOB SERVICE
(*Suby of* EXECUTIVE OFFICE OF STATE OF MISSISSIPPI) ★
1235 Echelon Pkwy, Jackson, MS 39213-8220
Tel (601) 321-6000 *Founded/Ownrshp* 1995
Sales NA *EMP* 800
SIC 9441 Administration of social & human resources; Administration of social & human resources
COO: Les Range
Exec: Theodora Anderson
Off Mgr: Joanna Boss
Pr Dir: Wayne Gasson
Snr Mgr: Karen Prideaux

D-U-N-S 80-939-9876
MISSISSIPPI DEPARTMENT OF ENVIROMENTAL QUALITY
(*Suby of* EXECUTIVE OFFICE OF STATE OF MISSISSIPPI) ★
515 E Amite St, Jackson, MS 39201-2709
Tel (601) 961-5171 *Founded/Ownrshp* 1979
Sales NA *EMP* 440
SIC 9511 Air, water & solid waste management; ; Air, water & solid waste management;
Ex Dir: Gary Rikard
Comm Dir: Robbie Wilbur

D-U-N-S 80-939-9918
MISSISSIPPI DEPARTMENT OF HUMAN SERVICES
MDHS FAMILY AND CHILDRENS SVCS
(*Suby of* EXECUTIVE OFFICE OF STATE OF MISSISSIPPI) ★
750 N State St, Jackson, MS 39202-3033
Tel (601) 359-5131 *Founded/Ownrshp* 1989
Sales NA *EMP* 4,000
SIC 9441 Administration of social & manpower programs; ; Administration of social & manpower programs;
Ex Dir: Richard Berry
CIO: Mark Allen

D-U-N-S 80-939-9926
MISSISSIPPI DEPARTMENT OF MENTAL HEALTH
(*Suby of* EXECUTIVE OFFICE OF STATE OF MISSISSIPPI) ★
239 N Lamar St Ste 1101, Jackson, MS 39201-1325
Tel (601) 359-1288 *Founded/Ownrshp* 1974
Sales NA *EMP* 8,800
SIC 9431 Mental health agency administration, government; ; Mental health agency administration, government;
Ex Dir: Edwin Legrand G III
**CFO:* Glynn Kegley
Ofcr: Leslie Smith

D-U-N-S 80-985-0076
MISSISSIPPI DEPARTMENT OF PUBLIC SAFETY
STATE HIGHWAY PATROL
(*Suby of* EXECUTIVE OFFICE OF STATE OF MISSISSIPPI) ★
1900 E Woodrow Wilson Ave, Jackson, MS 39216-5118
Tel (601) 987-1212 *Founded/Ownrshp* 1938
Sales NA *EMP* 1,014
SIC 9229 9221 Public order & safety statistics centers; Police protection; Public order & safety statistics centers; Police protection
Ch: Robert Latham

D-U-N-S 80-985-0100
MISSISSIPPI DEPARTMENT OF REHABILITATION SERVICES
(*Suby of* EXECUTIVE OFFICE OF STATE OF MISSISSIPPI) ★
1281 Highway 51, Madison, MS 39110-9092
Tel (601) 853-5281 *Founded/Ownrshp* 1921
Sales NA *EMP* 753
SIC 9441 ;

D-U-N-S 61-455-3816
MISSISSIPPI DEPARTMENT OF REVENUE
(*Suby of* EXECUTIVE OFFICE OF STATE OF MISSISSIPPI) ★
500 Clinton Center Dr # 2100, Clinton, MS 39056-5673
Tel (601) 923-7000 *Founded/Ownrshp* 1932
Sales NA *EMP* 800
SIC 9311 State tax commission; ; State tax commission;
Comm Dir: Kathy Waterbury

D-U-N-S 80-939-4067
MISSISSIPPI DEPARTMENT OF TRANSPORTATION
TRANSPORTATION COMMISSION
(*Suby of* EXECUTIVE OFFICE OF STATE OF MISSISSIPPI) ★
401 N West St, Jackson, MS 39201-1010
Tel (601) 359-7001 *Founded/Ownrshp* 1916
Sales NA *EMP* 3,300
SIC 9621 Regulation, administration of transportation; ; Regulation, administration of transportation;
Ex Dir: Larry L Brown
Ex Dir: Melinda McGrath
MIS Dir: John M Sipson
IT Man: Janet Lee
Opers Mgr: Denise Jones
Opers Mgr: Sherry Milner

D-U-N-S 95-641-5764
MISSISSIPPI DEPT OF FINANCE & ADMINISTRATION
(*Suby of* EXECUTIVE OFFICE OF STATE OF MISSISSIPPI) ★
501 N West St, Jackson, MS 39201-1001
Tel (601) 359-3402 *Founded/Ownrshp* 1996
Sales NA *EMP* 380
SIC 9199 General government administration; ; General government administration;

D-U-N-S 07-640-1483
MISSISSIPPI DEPT OF VOCATIONAL REHABILITATION
1281 Highway 51, Madison, MS 39110-9092
Tel (601) 853-5152 *Founded/Ownrshp* 1999
Sales 7.7MM^E *EMP* 405
SIC 8093 Rehabilitation center, outpatient treatment; Rehabilitation center, outpatient treatment
Ex Dir: H S McMillan

D-U-N-S 80-939-9686
MISSISSIPPI DEVELOPMENT AUTHORITY
M D A
(*Suby of* EXECUTIVE OFFICE OF STATE OF MISSISSIPPI) ★
501 N West St, Jackson, MS 39201-1001
Tel (601) 359-3449 *Founded/Ownrshp* 1989
Sales NA *EMP* 340
SIC 9611 Administration of general economic programs; ; Administration of general economic programs;
Ex Dir: Brent Christensen
**CFO:* Kathy Gelston
**CFO:* Jay McCarthy
Ofcr: Manning McPhillips
Exec: Cathey Jackson
MIS Dir: Donald Thurman
Software D: Lamar Frazier

D-U-N-S 02-102-1431
MISSISSIPPI FARM BUREAU MUTUAL INSURANCE CO
FARM BUREAU INSURANCE
6311 Ridgewood Rd, Jackson, MS 39211-2035
Tel (601) 957-3200 *Founded/Ownrshp* 1952
Sales NA *EMP* 325
SIC 6331 Fire, marine & casualty insurance: mutual; Fire, marine & casualty insurance: mutual
Pr: David W Waide
**Sec:* Robert Arnold

MISSISSIPPI FILING
See VRC OF MS LLC

D-U-N-S 15-550-3410
MISSISSIPPI FOOD NETWORK
440 Beatty St, Jackson, MS 39201-6215
Tel (601) 353-7286 *Founded/Ownrshp* 1983
Sales 22.4MM *EMP* 13
Accts Bkd Llp Jackson Ms
SIC 8699 Charitable organization; Charitable organization
Prin: Walker Satterwhite
COO: Marilyn Blackledge
IT Man: Charles Beady

D-U-N-S 05-145-2027
MISSISSIPPI FORESTRY COMMISSION (INC) (MS)
(*Suby of* EXECUTIVE OFFICE OF STATE OF MISSISSIPPI) ★
660 North St Ste 300, Jackson, MS 39202-3105
Tel (601) 359-1386 *Founded/Ownrshp* 1926, 1999
Sales NA *EMP* 459
SIC 9512 Land, mineral & wildlife conservation; ; Land, mineral & wildlife conservation
Prin: Charlie Morgan
Ofcr: Meacham Harlow
Snr Mgr: Scott Miles

D-U-N-S 07-944-8973
MISSISSIPPI GULF COAST COMMUNITY COLLEGE
PERKINSTON CAMPUS
51 Main St, Perkinston, MS 39573-3374
Tel (601) 928-5211 *Founded/Ownrshp* 1915
Sales 117.0MM *EMP* 980
Accts Culumber Fletcher Harvey & A
SIC 8222 Community college; Community college
Pr: Willis H Lott
VP: Jay Allen
VP: Mary Graham
VP Admn: Billy Stewart
Dir IT: David Beascon
Netwrk Mgr: Raymond Hutton
Pr Mgr: Brenda Donahoe
HC Dir: Nichol Green
Snr Mgr: Greg Hartley

D-U-N-S 11-741-8046
MISSISSIPPI HIGHER EDUCATION ASSISTANCE CORP
2600 Lakeland Ter, Jackson, MS 39216-4726
Tel (601) 321-5555 *Founded/Ownrshp* 1980
Sales NA *EMP* 40
Accts Haddox Reid Burkes & Calhoun P
SIC 6111 Student Loan Marketing Association; Student Loan Marketing Association
Ex Dir: Kenneth L Smith Jr
**Ch Bd:* Jack L Woodward
**Sec:* William M Jones
**V Ch Bd:* Alvis T Hunt

D-U-N-S 00-815-1326 IMP
MISSISSIPPI INDUSTRIES FOR BLIND (INC)
M I B
2501 N West St, Jackson, MS 39216-3840
Tel (601) 984-3200 *Founded/Ownrshp* 1942
Sales 46.4MM^E *EMP* 225
SIC 2515 Mattresses & foundations; Mattresses & foundations
Ex Dir: Michael Chew
**CFO:* Brack Schloemer
Tech Mgr: David Brister
Sls Mgr: Karen Chen

MISSISSIPPI LIGNITE MINING
See LIBERTY FUELS CO LLC

D-U-N-S 16-530-2345
■ MISSISSIPPI LIGNITE MINING CO
(*Suby of* NORTH AMERICAN COAL CORP) ★
1000 Mcintire Rd, Ackerman, MS 39735-4524
Tel (662) 387-5200 *Founded/Ownrshp* 1997
Sales 23.8MM^E *EMP* 120
SIC 1221 Bituminous coal & lignite-surface mining; Bituminous coal & lignite-surface mining
Ch: Alfred M Rankin Jr
**Pr:* Robert L Benson
**VP:* J C Butler Jr Sr
**VP:* Michael J Gregory
Counsel: Bob Benson

D-U-N-S 00-628-5225 EXP
MISSISSIPPI LIME CO
FALCO LIME COMPANY
3870 S Lindbergh Blvd # 200, Saint Louis, MO 63127-1398
Tel (314) 543-6300 *Founded/Ownrshp* 1907
Sales 292.7MM^E *EMP* 750
SIC 3274 2819 2879 1422 Quicklime; Industrial inorganic chemicals; Agricultural chemicals; Limestones, ground; Quicklime; Industrial inorganic chemicals; Agricultural chemicals; Limestones, ground
CEO: Michael A Decola
**CFO:* Don Roberts
Sr Cor Off: Harry Mathews
VP: William H Ayers
**VP:* Bruce L Baggio
VP: Kris Schuster
Genl Mgr: Tom Siedhoff
Sfty Mgr: Rick Donovan
VP Sls: Eric V Rens
Mktg Mgr: Robert Rasche
Sls Mgr: Mark Free

D-U-N-S 08-285-4548
MISSISSIPPI METHODIST HOSPITAL AND REHABILITATION CENTER INC (MS)
METHODIST REHABILITATION CTR
1350 E Woodrow Wilson Ave, Jackson, MS 39216-5112
Tel (601) 364-3381 *Founded/Ownrshp* 1969
Sales 49.7MM *EMP* 590
Accts Horne Llp Ridgeland Ms
SIC 8062 General medical & surgical hospitals; General medical & surgical hospitals
Pr: Mark Adams
COO: Jim Macfarquar
COO: Joseph Morette
Exec: Kristy Sessions
Exec: Jessica White
Ex Dir: Chris Wallace
Dir Sec: Hoot Gibson
Mtls Mgr: Archie Henderson
Psych: Clea Evans
Doctor: Guy Vise
HC Dir: Mary Palmertree

D-U-N-S 06-771-7959
MISSISSIPPI METHODIST SENIOR SERVICES INC (MS)
109 S Brdwy St, Tupelo, MS 38802
Tel (662) 844-8977 *Founded/Ownrshp* 1962
Sales 13.0MM *EMP* 616
Accts Watkins Ward And Stafford Pllc
SIC 8051 6513 Skilled nursing care facilities; Apartment building operators; Skilled nursing care facilities; Apartment building operators
CEO: Steve McAlilly
**COO:* Alan Brown
**CFO:* Christie Vance
**VP:* Ed Allen
**VP:* Bernice Thompson

D-U-N-S 62-308-2963 IMP
MISSISSIPPI PHOSPHATES CORP
601 Industrial Rd, Pascagoula, MS 39581-3233
Tel (228) 762-3210 *Founded/Ownrshp* 1990
Sales 126.7MM^E *EMP* 225
SIC 2874 Diammonium phosphate

D-U-N-S 08-650-7365 IMP/EXP
MISSISSIPPI POLYMERS INC
2733 S Harper Rd, Corinth, MS 38834-9272
Tel (662) 287-1401 *Founded/Ownrshp* 2003
Sales 83.5MM^E *EMP* 300
SIC 3089 Plastic hardware & building products; Plastic hardware & building products
Pr: Jerry Waxman
**Prin:* Jerold Waxman
Plnt Mgr: Whisenant Ron

D-U-N-S 00-696-4118 IMP
■ MISSISSIPPI POWER CO
(*Suby of* SOUTHERN CO) ★
2992 W Beach Blvd, Gulfport, MS 39501-1907
Tel (228) 864-1211 *Founded/Ownrshp* 1972
Sales 1.2MMM *EMP* 1,344
Accts Deloitte & Touche Llp Atlanta
SIC 4911 Electric services; Distribution, electric power; Generation, electric power; Electric services; Distribution, electric power; Generation, electric power
Pr: G Edison Holland Jr
CFO: Moses H Feagin
CFO: A Southern
Bd of Dir: Carl J Chaney
Ofcr: Michelle Kinsey
VP: Tom Anderson
VP: John W Atherton
VP: Jeff G Franklin
VP: F Kuester
VP: Don E Mason
VP: R Allen Reaves
VP: Billy Thornton
VP: Emile Troxclair
Board of Directors: Carl J Chaney, L Royce Cumbest, Thomas A Dews, Mark D Kleemum, L Pickering, Philip J Terrel, Marion L Waters

D-U-N-S 06-547-5527
MISSISSIPPI RIVER BRIDGE AUTHORITY
2001 Mardi Gras Blvd, New Orleans, LA 70114-4637
Tel (504) 361-6565 *Founded/Ownrshp* 1952
Sales 11.4MM^E *EMP* 360
SIC 4785 4482 Highway bridge operation; Ferries; Highway bridge operation; Ferries
Ex Dir: Thomas E Short
**V Ch:* Hugh O'Connor
**Ch:* Arthur T Screen
**Ch:* W Richard White
**Treas:* Louis Munster

D-U-N-S 92-725-5534
MISSISSIPPI SAND LLC
2320 Creve Coeur Mill Rd, Maryland Heights, MO 63043-4207
Tel (314) 678-7840 *Founded/Ownrshp* 2006
Sales 25.8MM^E *EMP* 40
SIC 1442 Construction sand & gravel
Pr: Tony Giordano
CFO: Charlie Kamper
VP: Jason Bish
VP: Mike Cochran
VP: Martin Goolsby
VP: Patrick Kellerman
VP: Rob Meyer
VP Opers: Tom Greco

D-U-N-S 80-939-9694
MISSISSIPPI STATE DEPARTMENT OF EDUCATION
(*Suby of* EXECUTIVE OFFICE OF STATE OF MISSISSIPPI) ★
359 N West St, Jackson, MS 39201-1502
Tel (601) 359-3513 *Founded/Ownrshp* 1817
Sales NA *EMP* 750
SIC 9411 Administration of educational programs; ; Administration of educational programs;
Ofcr: Rana Hood

D-U-N-S 07-546-1814
MISSISSIPPI STATE UNIVERSITY
245 Barr Ave Mcrthur Hl Mcrthur Hall, Mississippi State, MS 39762
Tel (662) 325-2302 *Founded/Ownrshp* 1878
Sales 392.8MM *EMP* 8,000
SIC 8221 University; University
Pr: Mark E Keenum
Treas: Brandi Cunningham
Top Exec: Bill Epperson
VP: Bill Broyles
VP: Brad Carter
VP: John Rush
Ex Dir: Jonathan Adams
Ex Dir: Adam Thigpen
Dir IT: Tom Ritter
Web Dev: Cindy Callahan
Snr Mgr: Ronald Tiffin

D-U-N-S 07-875-1875
MISSISSIPPI STATE UNIVERSITY
250 Mccain Hl, Mississippi State, MS 39762
Tel (662) 325-2323 *Founded/Ownrshp* 2013
Sales 20.9MM^E *EMP* 294^E
SIC 7389
Pr: Mark E Keenum
Ofcr: Neal Grogan
Assoc VP: C Herndon
VP: Katie Echols
VP: David Shaw
Assoc Dir: Mitzy Johnson
Assoc Dir: Pamela Stafford
Assoc Dir: Allen Ulmer
Ex Dir: Wesley Reed
Ex Dir: Jason Townsend
CTO: Sherry Smith

D-U-N-S 62-746-3003
MISSISSIPPI STATE UNIVERSITY EXTENSION SERVICE
COOPERATIVE EXTENSION SERVICE
201 Bost Ext Ctr Ste A, Mississippi State, MS 39762
Tel (662) 325-3036 *Founded/Ownrshp* 1996
Sales 5.6MM^E *EMP* 650
SIC 8299 Educational services; Educational services

D-U-N-S 08-374-2593
MISSISSIPPI STATE UNIVERSITY FOUNDATION INC
1 Hunter Henry Blvd, Mississippi State, MS 39762
Tel (662) 325-7000 *Founded/Ownrshp* 1962
Sales 76.5MM *EMP* 35
Accts Kpmg Llp Jackson Ms
SIC 8399 Fund raising organization, non-fee basis; Fund raising organization, non-fee basis
CEO: John Rush
**CFO:* David Easley
Ex Dir: James V Hemphill

D-U-N-S 11-277-9970 EXP
MISSISSIPPI TANK AND MANUFACTURING CO
MISSISSIPPI TANK COMPANY
3000 W 7th St, Hattiesburg, MS 39401-5617
Tel (601) 264-1800 *Founded/Ownrshp* 2009
Sales 49.9MM^E *EMP* 205
SIC 3443 Tanks, standard or custom fabricated: metal plate; Process vessels, industrial: metal plate; Tanks for tank trucks, metal plate; Tanks, standard or custom fabricated: metal plate; Process vessels, industrial: metal plate; Tanks for tank trucks, metal plate
Ch Bd: Robert O Tatum
**Pr:* Charles Daniel Miller
**Sec:* Joe F Tatum Jr
**VP:* Joseph Michael Pitts
IT Man: Bob Ezell
Sfty Mgr: Danny Miller

MISSISSIPPI TANK COMPANY
See MISSISSIPPI TANK AND MANUFACTURING CO

D-U-N-S 15-204-8682
MISSISSIPPI VALLEY BANCSHARES INC
13205 Manchester Rd, Saint Louis, MO 63131-1733
Tel (314) 543-3512 *Founded/Ownrshp* 1984
Sales NA *EMP* 50
SIC 6022 6712 State commercial banks; Bank holding companies; State commercial banks; Bank holding companies
Ch Bd: Andrew N Baur
**Pr:* Linn H Bealke
CFO: Paul M Strieker
Sec: Carol B Dolenz
Assoc VP: Paula Evans
Sr VP: Daniel Fridrich
VP: Dennis Hunter
VP: Steve Sanden
Board of Directors: G Watts Humphrey Jr, John Baumstark, Donna D Lambert, Andrew S Baur, Michael D Latta, Andrew N Baur, Louis B Shipley, Alice C Behan, William H T Bush, Franklin J Cornwell Jr, Theodore P Desloge Jr, Louis N Goldring, Richard T Grote, Frederick O Hanser

D-U-N-S 08-414-7268
MISSISSIPPI VALLEY REALTORS
736 Lake Park Blvd, Muscatine, IA 52761-5466
Tel (563) 263-5130 *Founded/Ownrshp* 1999
Sales 36.8MM *EMP* 3
SIC 6531 Real estate agents & managers; Real estate agents & managers
Owner: Marsha Schenkel

D-U-N-S 07-807-9332
MISSISSIPPI VALLEY REGIONAL BLOOD CENTER INC
M V R B C
5500 Lakeview Pkwy, Davenport, IA 52807-3481
Tel (563) 359-5401 *Founded/Ownrshp* 1974
Sales 61.9MM *EMP* 510
Accts Mcgladrey Llp Davenport Iowa
SIC 8099 Blood bank; Blood bank
CEO: David Green
**Pr:* Susan Blaskovich
**CFO:* Darren Klocke
Ex VP: Louis M Katz
**VP:* Jeff Bryant
VP: Laura Pena

D-U-N-S 07-353-8654
MISSISSIPPI VALLEY STATE UNIVERSITY EDUCATIONAL BUILDING CORP
14000 Highway 82 W 7265, Itta Bena, MS 38941-1400
Tel (662) 254-3597 *Founded/Ownrshp* 1950
Sales 59.7MM^E *EMP* 583
SIC 8221 University; University
Pr: William B Bynum Jr
VP Bus: Jmaes Washburn
Opers Supe: Lester Adams

D-U-N-S 07-869-1540 IMP
MISSISSIPPI WELDERS SUPPLY CO INC
5150 W 6th St, Winona, MN 55987-1248
Tel (507) 454-5231 *Founded/Ownrshp* 1959
Sales 74.5MM^E *EMP* 140
SIC 5084 5999 Welding machinery & equipment; Welding supplies; Welding machinery & equipment; Welding supplies
Ch: Bradley Peterson
VP: Donna Peterson
Brnch Mgr: Todd Folz
Brnch Mgr: Jim Hanson
Store Mgr: Rick Jackson
Dir IT: Linda Haney
Sales Asso: Leroy Kiecker
Sales Asso: Pat Savage

D-U-N-S 18-931-2705
MISSISSIPPI WILDLIFE FISHERIES AND PARKS FOUNDATION
1505 Eastover Dr, Jackson, MS 39211-6322
Tel (601) 213-8111 *Founded/Ownrshp* 2004
Sales 567.1M *EMP* 400
SIC 0921 Fish hatcheries & preserves; Fish hatcheries & preserves
CEO: George Gordin
**Prin:* John Taylor

D-U-N-S 07-842-4789
MISSISSIPPIAN SANDRIDGE TRUST II
919 Congress Ave Ste 500, Austin, TX 78701-2153
Tel (512) 236-6599 *Founded/Ownrshp* 2012
Sales 84.3MM *EMP* 2^E
SIC 6733 Trusts; Trusts

D-U-N-S 04-591-3787
MISSOULA COUNTY PUBLIC SCHOOLS
215 S 6th St W, Missoula, MT 59801-4081
Tel (406) 728-2400 *Founded/Ownrshp* 1910
Sales 35.8MM^E *EMP* 1,500
SIC 8299 8211 Educational service, nondegree granting: continuing educ.; School board; Educational service, nondegree granting: continuing educ.; School board
Pr Dir: Lesli Brassfield
Pr Dir: Hatton Littman
Teacher Pr: David Rott
Psych: Mary Archer
Psych: Camille Barraclough
Psych: Katie Boynton
Psych: Aine Franczyk
Psych: Carol Holte
Psych: Starla Klevenberg
Psych: Janet Metcalf
Psych: Nancy Ventresca

D-U-N-S 00-682-7547
MISSOULA ELECTRIC COOPERATIVE INC
1700 W Broadway St, Missoula, MT 59808-2099
Tel (406) 541-6339 *Founded/Ownrshp* 1939
Sales 21.2MM *EMP* 50
Accts Summers Mcnea & Co Pc Billing
SIC 4911 Distribution, electric power; Distribution, electric power
Pr: Sharon Jacobson
Genl Mgr: Mark Hayden
**Genl Mgr:* Anthony Sinclar
Counsel: Edward T Dussault

D-U-N-S 00-888-7684
MISSOURI ACADEMY OF SCIENCE
(*Suby of* TRUMAN STATE UNIVERSITY) ★
100 E Normal Ave, Kirksville, MO 63501-4200
Tel (660) 785-4635 *Founded/Ownrshp* 2001
Sales 1.6MM^E *EMP* 774^E
SIC 8221 Colleges universities & professional schools
Prin: Jasck Magruder

D-U-N-S 00-787-2203
MISSOURI ATHLETIC CLUB (MO)
405 Washington Ave, Saint Louis, MO 63102-2183
Tel (314) 231-7220 *Founded/Ownrshp* 1903, 1986
Sales 16.4MM *EMP* 300
Accts Bkd Llp St Louis Mo
SIC 8641 7997 5812 7011 Social club, membership; Membership sports & recreation clubs; Eating places; Hotels & motels; Social club, membership; Membership sports & recreation clubs; Eating places; Hotels & motels
Pr: John Bugh
**Pr:* Philip Schwarz
**CFO:* Larry Absheer
**Treas:* Troy W Robertson
Genl Mgr: Larry Thompson

MISSOURI BANK
See MBT BANCSHARES INC

D-U-N-S 00-890-7149
MISSOURI BANK AND TRUST CO OF KANSAS CITY
(*Suby of* MBT BANCSHARES INC) ★
1044 Main St Ste 700, Kansas City, MO 64105-2404
Tel (816) 881-8200 *Founded/Ownrshp* 1933, 1984
Sales NA *EMP* 30^E
SIC 6022 State commercial banks; State commercial banks
CEO: J Thomas Burcham
**Pr:* Jim Getz
**VP:* Charles Benson
VP: Michelle Freed

D-U-N-S 12-174-6697
MISSOURI BAPTIST HOSPITAL OF SULLIVAN
751 Sappington Bridge Rd, Sullivan, MO 63080-2354
Tel (573) 468-4186 *Founded/Ownrshp* 1994
Sales 45.7MM *EMP* 400
SIC 8062 8011 Hospital, AMA approved residency; Offices & clinics of medical doctors; Hospital, AMA approved residency; Offices & clinics of medical doctors
Chf Rad: Jerry Vanover
Dir Lab: Sherry Munsick
Info Man: Gayle Peebles
Nrsg Dir: Carmen Wacker
Pharmcst: Tara Schreit
Mngd Care: Laura Boyd
Snr Mgr: Jaroslaw Michalik

D-U-N-S 07-588-6358
MISSOURI BAPTIST MEDICAL CENTER
3015 N Ballas Rd, Saint Louis, MO 63131-2374
Tel (314) 996-5000 *Founded/Ownrshp* 1994
Sales 413.7MM^E *EMP* 1,670
SIC 8062 General medical & surgical hospitals; General medical & surgical hospitals
Pr: Joan Magruder
Chf Rad: John Niemeyer
**CFO:* Gary McLaughlin
CFO: Tony Noronha
**VP:* Douglas Black
**VP:* Tim Mislan
**VP:* Timothy Ranney
**VP:* Sandra Young
Dir Lab: Cynthia M Kling
Dir Rad: Dennis Balfe
Dir Rad: Gene Davis
Dir Rad: Lawrence Kotner
Dir Rad: Maxwell Lazinger
Dir Rad: Christine Menias
Dir Rad: Vijay Sadhu
Dir Rx: Tom Hall

D-U-N-S 07-196-6519
MISSOURI BAPTIST UNIVERSITY
1 College Park Dr, Saint Louis, MO 63141-8698
Tel (314) 434-1115 *Founded/Ownrshp* 1968
Sales 41.7MM *EMP* 300
Accts Bkd Llp Saint Louis Mo
SIC 8221 College, except junior; College, except junior
Pr: R Alton Lacey
Ofcr: Minoi Okai
**VP:* Andy Chambers
**VP:* Arlen Dykstra
VP: Keith Ross
VP: Julia Schroeder
Adm Dir: Marie Tudor
Off Mgr: Edie Beamer
Off Mgr: Cheryl Schwartz
Off Mgr: Jessica Stone
Store Mgr: Kristen Peebles

D-U-N-S 06-511-5263
MISSOURI BASIN MUNICIPAL POWER AGENCY
MISSOURI RIVER ENERGY SERVICES
3724 W Avera Dr, Sioux Falls, SD 57108-5750
Tel (605) 338-4042 *Founded/Ownrshp* 1965
Sales 60.7MM^E *EMP* 75
SIC 4911 Generation, electric power; Generation, electric power
CEO: Thomas J Heller
**CFO:* Merlin Sawyer
Off Admin: Geraldyne Shumaker
Mktg Dir: Jeff Peters

D-U-N-S 05-297-1405
MISSOURI BASIN WELL SERVICE INC
MBI ENERGY SERVICES
12980 35th St Sw, Belfield, ND 58622-9703
Tel (701) 575-8242 *Founded/Ownrshp* 1981
Sales 253.2MM^E *EMP* 1,900
SIC 4213 1389 Contract haulers; Servicing oil & gas wells; Contract haulers; Servicing oil & gas wells
CEO: James Arthaud
Pr: Jeff Kostelecky
**CFO:* David Wanner
**Treas:* Bob Arthaud
Sr VP: Charles Steffan
VP: Tim Brown
**VP:* Don Hecker
VP: Jason Homiston
VP: Nathan Jorgensen
Off Admin: Sue Berger
Dir IT: Brent Pringle

D-U-N-S 03-430-1940
MISSOURI BOARD OF PROBATION & PAROLE
(*Suby of* DEPARTMENT OF CORRECTIONS MISSOURI) ★
3400 Knipp Dr, Jefferson City, MO 65109-5701
Tel (573) 751-8488 *Founded/Ownrshp* 1821
Sales 8.9MM^E *EMP* 315^E
SIC 8322 9223 Probation office; Correctional institutions; ; Probation office; Correctional institutions;
Ch: Ellis McSwain

D-U-N-S 07-591-4887 IMP
MISSOURI BOTANICAL GARDEN
BOARD OF TRUSTEES OF MISSOURI
4344 Shaw Blvd, Saint Louis, MO 63110-2291
Tel (314) 577-5100 *Founded/Ownrshp* 1859
Sales 44.7MM *EMP* 470^E
SIC 8422 Botanical garden; Botanical garden
Pr: Peter Wyse Jackson
Ofcr: Chuck Miller
**VP:* Richard F Angevine
VP: Olga Montiel
Software D: Mike Latzel
Mktg Mgr: Glenda Abney
Snr Mgr: Lindsay Myers
Assoc Ed: Laura Slown

D-U-N-S 07-313-4231
MISSOURI CITY OF KANSAS CITY
414 E 12th St Ste 105, Kansas City, MO 64106-2705
Tel (816) 513-1313 *Founded/Ownrshp* 1853
Sales NA *EMP* 8,000
Accts Bkd Llp Kansas City Missour
SIC 9111 City & town managers' offices; ; City & town managers' offices;
CFO: Jeffrey A Yates
Sr Cor Off: Ronnell Simpson Sr
Ofcr: Mary Charles
Ofcr: Kevin Guthrie
Ofcr: Matt McKinley
Ofcr: Mark Runge
**Prin:* Silvester James
Ex Dir: Ron Goold
CTO: Kay Barnes

D-U-N-S 80-985-9010
MISSOURI CONSOLIDATED HEALTH CARE PLAN
832 Weathered Rock Ct, Jefferson City, MO 65101-1824
Tel (573) 751-8881 *Founded/Ownrshp* 1994
Sales NA *EMP* 78
SIC 6321 Health insurance carriers; Health insurance carriers
Ex Dir: Ron Meyer

D-U-N-S 96-100-7440 IMP
MISSOURI COOPERAGE CO INC
(*Suby of* INDEPENDENT STAVE CO LLC) ★
1078 S Jefferson Ave, Lebanon, MO 65536-3601
Tel (417) 588-4151 *Founded/Ownrshp* 1992
Sales 48.7MM^E *EMP* 400
SIC 2449 5947 2499 Barrels, wood: coopered; Gift shop; Kitchen, bathroom & household ware: wood; Barrels, wood: coopered; Gift shop; Kitchen, bathroom & household ware: wood
Ch Bd: John Boswell
**Pr:* Brad Boswell

D-U-N-S 07-195-6247
MISSOURI DELTA MEDICAL CENTER
MDMC
1008 N Main St, Sikeston, MO 63801-5044
Tel (573) 471-1600 *Founded/Ownrshp* 1968
Sales 83.5MM *EMP* 750
Accts Kerber Eck & Braeckel Llp Car
SIC 8062 General medical & surgical hospitals; General medical & surgical hospitals
CEO: Jason Schrumps
**CEO:* Jason Schrumpf
**CFO:* Greg Carda
Ofcr: Linda Culbertson
**Sr VP:* Jim Henson
VP: John Runastedler
VP: Earl Sisk
VP: Julie Young
Dir OR: Libby Klipfel
Dir Lab: Joanie Delisle
Dir Rad: Debbie Nichols

D-U-N-S 87-901-6764
MISSOURI DEPARTMENT OF CONSERVATION
(*Suby of* EXECUTIVE OFFICE OF STATE OF MISSOURI) ★
2901 W Truman Blvd, Jefferson City, MO 65109-4999
Tel (573) 751-4115 *Founded/Ownrshp* 1937
Sales NA *EMP* 1,550
SIC 9512 Conservation & stabilization agency, government; ; Conservation & stabilization agency, government;
**CFO:* Margie Miller
Sr Cor Off: Jim Price
**Prin:* Robert Zeihmer
Dir IT: Sandy Dorge
IT Man: Doyle Brown
IT Man: James Poole
Sys Mgr: Jack Quade
VP Opers: Cathy Adams
Counsel: David McAllister
Art Dir: Cliff White
Snr Mgr: Jacob Careaga

D-U-N-S 87-901-4686
MISSOURI DEPARTMENT OF ECONOMIC DEVELOPMENT
(*Suby of* EXECUTIVE OFFICE OF STATE OF MISSOURI) ★
301 W High St, Jefferson City, MO 65101-1517
Tel (573) 751-4962 *Founded/Ownrshp* 1821
Sales NA *EMP* 1,000
SIC 9611 Economic development agency, government; ; Economic development agency, government;
Brnch Mgr: Mike Downing
Ofcr: Sarah Reid
Comm Man: Jill Kline
**Prin:* Jay Nixon
IT Man: Stacey Hirst
Mktg Mgr: Jonathon Mack
Counsel: Julia Grus
Pgrm Dir: Brenda Wilbers

D-U-N-S 87-901-6624
MISSOURI DEPARTMENT OF ELEMENTARY AND SECONDARY EDUCATION
(*Suby of* EXECUTIVE OFFICE OF STATE OF MISSOURI) ★
205 Jefferson St, Jefferson City, MO 65101-2901
Tel (573) 751-4212 *Founded/Ownrshp* 1821
Sales NA *EMP* 1,693
SIC 9411 State education department; ; State education department;
**CFO:* Andrea Beck
Pr Dir: Sarah Potter
Schl Brd P: Victor Lenz

D-U-N-S 87-809-2600
MISSOURI DEPARTMENT OF HEALTH AND SENIOR SERVICES
(*Suby of* EXECUTIVE OFFICE OF STATE OF MISSOURI) ★
920 Wildwood Dr, Jefferson City, MO 65109-5796
Tel (573) 751-6014 *Founded/Ownrshp* 1821
Sales NA *EMP* 1,200
SIC 9431

D-U-N-S 87-814-1076
MISSOURI DEPARTMENT OF LABOR AND INDUSTRIAL RELATIONS
(*Suby of* EXECUTIVE OFFICE OF STATE OF MISSOURI) ★
421 E Dunklin St, Jefferson City, MO 65101-3138
Tel (573) 751-3978 *Founded/Ownrshp* 1821
Sales NA *EMP* 876
SIC 9651 Labor regulatory agency; ; Labor regulatory agency;
CFO: Rebecca Voss
**Prin:* Todd Smith
Pgrm Dir: William Benzel

D-U-N-S 87-814-3742
MISSOURI DEPARTMENT OF MENTAL HEALTH
MENTAL HEALTH STATE OF MO DEPT
(*Suby of* EXECUTIVE OFFICE OF STATE OF MISSOURI) ★
1706 E Elm St, Jefferson City, MO 65101-4130
Tel (573) 751-4122 *Founded/Ownrshp* 1972
Sales NA *EMP* 8,000
SIC 9431 Mental health agency administration, government; ; Mental health agency administration, government;
Dir IT: Larry Bradley
Dir IT: Bob Curran
Dir IT: Virginia Rowe
Dir IT: Michelle Yahnig
IT Man: Dan Haug

D-U-N-S 87-814-4757
MISSOURI DEPARTMENT OF NATURAL RESOURCES
(*Suby of* EXECUTIVE OFFICE OF STATE OF MISSOURI) ★
1101 Riverside Dr, Jefferson City, MO 65101-4272
Tel (573) 751-3443 *Founded/Ownrshp* 1974
Sales NA *EMP* 1,800
SIC 9512 Land, mineral & wildlife conservation; ; Land, mineral & wildlife conservation;

D-U-N-S 87-804-7364
MISSOURI DEPARTMENT OF PUBLIC SAFETY
(*Suby of* EXECUTIVE OFFICE OF STATE OF MISSOURI) ★
1101 Riverside Dr 4w, Jefferson City, MO 65101-4272
Tel (573) 751-4905 *Founded/Ownrshp* 1821
Sales NA *EMP* 4,971
SIC 9229 Criminal justice statistics center, government; ; Criminal justice statistics center, government;
**Prin:* Jay Nixon

D-U-N-S 87-804-8008
MISSOURI DEPARTMENT OF SOCIAL SERVICES
(*Suby of* EXECUTIVE OFFICE OF STATE OF MISSOURI) ★
221 W High St Ste 240, Jefferson City, MO 65101-1516
Tel (573) 751-4815 *Founded/Ownrshp* 1999
Sales NA *EMP* 9,216
SIC 9441 8322

D-U-N-S 02-528-0335
MISSOURI DEPARTMENT OF TRANSPORTATION
(*Suby of* EXECUTIVE OFFICE OF STATE OF MISSOURI) ★
105 W Capitol Ave, Jefferson City, MO 65101-6811
Tel (573) 751-2551 *Founded/Ownrshp* 1821
Sales NA *EMP* 6,295
Accts Bkd Llp Springfield Mo
SIC 9621 Bureau of public roads; Bureau of public roads

MISSOURI DEPT OF INS, FIN & PR
See DEPARTMENT OF INSURANCE MISSOURI

D-U-N-S 07-099-5865
MISSOURI EAGLE LLC
242 Highway Mm, Lebanon, MO 65536-7019
Tel (417) 532-6157 *Founded/Ownrshp* 1962
Sales 26.3MM^E *EMP* 60
SIC 5181 Beer & other fermented malt liquors
Rgnl Mgr: Teresa Rector

D-U-N-S 87-792-8002
MISSOURI EMPLOYERS MUTUAL INSURANCE CO
101 N Keene St, Columbia, MO 65201-6619
Tel (573) 499-9714 *Founded/Ownrshp* 1994
Sales NA *EMP* 250
SIC 6331 Workers' compensation insurance; Workers' compensation insurance
Pr: Jim Owen
COO: Dina Schultz
CFO: Doug Phillips
VP: Jennifer Barth
VP: David Fischhoff
VP: Robert Gibson
VP: Timothy D Jackman
VP: Timothy Jackman
VP: Michael Kravchick
VP: Steven Millikan
Plng Mgr: Larry Earley

MISSOURI FARM BUREAU FED
See MISSOURI FARM BUREAU SERVICES INC

D-U-N-S 07-196-5982
MISSOURI FARM BUREAU FEDERATION AND AFFILIATED COMPANIES
FARM BUREAU LIFE INSURANCE
701 S Country Club Dr # 3, Jefferson City, MO 65109-4571
Tel (573) 893-1400 *Founded/Ownrshp* 1922
Sales NA *EMP* 885
Accts Williams-Keepers Llc Jefferso
SIC 6311 6331 8732 8699 6411 2711 Life insurance; Fire, marine & casualty insurance & carriers; Market analysis or research; Farm bureau; Insurance agents, brokers & service; Insurance agents; Newspapers; Life insurance; Fire, marine & casualty insurance & carriers; Market analysis or research; Farm bureau; Insurance agents, brokers & service; Insurance agents; Newspapers
Pr: Charles Kruse
**Treas:* Randy Campbell
Treas: Jane Peters
IT Man: Justin Baker
IT Man: Mickey Martin
Mktg Dir: Jeff Carr
Mktg Dir: Dexter McIntyre
Mktg Dir: Kelly Smith

D-U-N-S 07-034-1607
MISSOURI FARM BUREAU SERVICES INC (MO)
MISSOURI FARM BUREAU LIFE INSURANCE
(*Suby of* FARM BUREAU LIFE INSURANCE) ★
701 S Country Club Dr, Jefferson City, MO 65109-4571
Tel (573) 893-1400 *Founded/Ownrshp* 1974
Sales NA *EMP* 350
SIC 6311 6331 8732 6411 8699 Life insurance; Fire, marine & casualty insurance & carriers; Market analysis or research; Insurance agents, brokers & service; Farm bureau; Life insurance; Fire, marine & casualty insurance & carriers; Market analysis or research; Insurance agents, brokers & service; Farm bureau
Pr: Blake Hurst
Pr: Debbie Johnston
**CFO:* Randall Campbell
Ofcr: Lowell Mohler
Ex VP: Dan Cassidy
IT Man: Christy Clark
Mktg Mgr: James Perch
Sls Mgr: Quenten Coon
Sales Asso: Justin Strong

D-U-N-S 55-643-8083
MISSOURI FIESTA INC
910 S Kirkwood Rd Ste 100, Saint Louis, MO 63122-6047
Tel (314) 821-7635 *Founded/Ownrshp* 1988
Sales 8.5MM^E *EMP* 300
SIC 5812 Fast-food restaurant, chain; Fast-food restaurant, chain
Pr: David Freese

D-U-N-S 09-863-6947 EXP
MISSOURI FORGE INC
500 Loyal Hood Indl Park, Doniphan, MO 63935
Tel (573) 996-7177 *Founded/Ownrshp* 1984
Sales 29.3MM^E *EMP* 100
SIC 3462 Iron & steel forgings; Iron & steel forgings
Pr: Michael A Wicklund
**Treas:* Mike Wicklund
QA Dir: Nick Wellborn

D-U-N-S 10-517-4846
MISSOURI FOUNDATION FOR HEALTH
415 S 18th St Ste 400, Saint Louis, MO 63103-2269
Tel (314) 345-5500 *Founded/Ownrshp* 2000
Sales 140.7MM *EMP* 43
SIC 8399 Health systems agency; Health systems agency
Ch Bd: Wentzville J Brown
**Pr:* Dr Jim Kimmey
**Treas:* Jay D Auner
Ofcr: Amy Stringer Heffel
VP: Martha Gragg

D-U-N-S 80-972-7399
■ **MISSOURI GAMING CO**
ARGOSY RIVERSIDE CASINO
(*Suby of* PENN NATIONAL GAMING INC) ★
777 Argosy Pkwy, Riverside, MO 64150-1512
Tel (816) 746-3171 *Founded/Ownrshp* 2013
Sales 35.2MM^E *EMP* 1,000
Accts Ernst & Young Llp Kansas City
SIC 7999 7011 Gambling & lottery services; Eating places; Delicatessen (eating places); Gambling & lottery services; Casino hotel
Ch Bd: Peter Carlino
**Pr:* Tim Wilmott
**VP:* Robert Ippolito
Dir IT: Cassie Yates

D-U-N-S 18-939-6138
MISSOURI HIGHER EDUCATION LOAN AUTHORITY
MOHELA
633 Spirit Dr, Chesterfield, MO 63005-1243
Tel (636) 733-3830 *Founded/Ownrshp* 1981
Sales NA *EMP* 209
SIC 6111 Student Loan Marketing Association; Student Loan Marketing Association
Ex Dir: Raymond Bayer Jr
VP: Susan Crump

D-U-N-S 15-619-7303
MISSOURI HISTORICAL SOCIETY (INC)
MUSEUM SHOP, THE
5700 Lindell Blvd, Saint Louis, MO 63112-1004
Tel (314) 746-4599 *Founded/Ownrshp* 1866
Sales 27.3MM^E *EMP* 200
SIC 8412 Museum; Museum
Pr: Frances Levine
**Pr:* Robert R Archibald
**CFO:* Harry Rich
Ex Dir: Karen Goering
Mng Dir: Katherine Allen
Mng Dir: Vicki Kaffenberger
Web Dev: David Henry

D-U-N-S 15-390-4024
MISSOURI HOME CARE OF ROLLA INC
1026 Kingshighway St, Rolla, MO 65401-2921
Tel (573) 341-8164 *Founded/Ownrshp* 1975
Sales 7.8MM^E *EMP* 431
SIC 8082 Home health care services; Home health care services
Pr: Margaret Cossette
**VP:* Terry Cossette

D-U-N-S 92-647-0832
MISSOURI HOSPITAL PLAN
4700 Country Club Dr, Jefferson City, MO 65109-4541
Tel (573) 893-5300 *Founded/Ownrshp* 1986
Sales NA *EMP* 2
SIC 6411 Insurance agents, brokers & service; Insurance agents, brokers & service
Pr: Mike Delaney
Treas: Richard Anderson

D-U-N-S 62-520-4854
MISSOURI JOINT MUNICIPAL ELECTRIC UTILITY COMMISSION
MOPEP ENRGY SCHEDULING TAGGING
1808 Interstate 70 Dr Sw, Columbia, MO 65203-1032
Tel (573) 445-3279 *Founded/Ownrshp* 1983
Sales 352.2MM *EMP* 29
SIC 4911 ;
CEO: Duncan Kincheloe
**CFO:* Michael Loethen

MISSOURI OFFC OF STATE CRT ADM
See JUDICIARY COURTS OF STATE OF MISSOURI

D-U-N-S 87-804-6036
MISSOURI OFFICE OF ADMINISTRATION
CAPITAL BUILDING
(*Suby of* EXECUTIVE OFFICE OF STATE OF MISSOURI) ★
201 W Capitol Ave Rm125, Jefferson City, MO 65101-1556
Tel (573) 751-1851 *Founded/Ownrshp* 2000
Sales NA *EMP* 1,100
SIC 9199 General government administration; . ; General government administration;
Prin: Barb Shimmens

D-U-N-S 02-150-6878
MISSOURI PETROLEUM PRODUCTS CO LLC
(*Suby of* LIONMARK CNSTR COMPANIES) ★
1620 Woodson Rd, Saint Louis, MO 63114-6179
Tel (314) 991-2180 *Founded/Ownrshp* 1932
Sales 144.7MM^E *EMP* 334
SIC 5033 1611 2951 Asphalt felts & coating; Highway & street maintenance; Asphalt paving mixtures & blocks; Asphalt felts & coating; Highway & street maintenance; Asphalt paving mixtures & blocks
Ex VP: Joe Rideout
Ex Dir: Teresa Gier

D-U-N-S 05-171-7205
MISSOURI POWER TRANSMISSION INC
3226 Blair Ave, Saint Louis, MO 63107-3799
Tel (314) 421-0919 *Founded/Ownrshp* 1970
Sales 31.7MM^E *EMP* 55
SIC 5085 Industrial supplies; Bearings; Sprockets; Chains, power transmission
CEO: Alfred Dressing
**CFO:* Mitchell Stierwalt
**Ex VP:* Chad Dressing
VP: Mitch Stierwald
Brnch Mgr: Jerry Nixon
Brnch Mgr: Shirley Phillips

MISSOURI RIVER ENERGY SERVICES
See MISSOURI BASIN MUNICIPAL POWER AGENCY

MISSOURI RIVER MARINE
See W B INC

D-U-N-S 96-488-3685
MISSOURI SLOPE LUTHERAN CARE CENTER INC
2425 Hillview Ave, Bismarck, ND 58501-3056
Tel (701) 223-9407 *Founded/Ownrshp* 2010
Sales 28.6MM *EMP* 54^E
Accts Eide Bailly Llp Bismarck Nd
SIC 8351 Child day care services; Child day care services
Prin: Robert R Thompson
Ofcr: Sheryl Terry
Dir IT: Ben Crawford
Doctor: Vicki Butler

D-U-N-S 07-868-0311
MISSOURI SLOPE LUTHRAN
2425 Hillview Ave, Bismarck, ND 58501-3056
Tel (701) 223-9407 *Founded/Ownrshp* 1962
Sales 27.2MM *EMP* 400
SIC 8051 Skilled nursing care facilities; Skilled nursing care facilities
Pr: Robert R Thompson
**CFO:* Jeffery Wanek

D-U-N-S 83-582-0341
MISSOURI SOUTHERN STATE UNIVERSITY ALUMNI ASSOCIATION
M.S.S.U.
3950 Newman Rd, Joplin, MO 64801-1512
Tel (417) 625-9300 *Founded/Ownrshp* 1937
Sales 30.1MM *EMP* 6^E
Accts Bkd Llp Springfield Missour
SIC 8221 University; University
VP: Rob Yust
CFO: Terri Agee
**Treas:* Linda Eis

D-U-N-S 01-695-7701
MISSOURI STATE EMPLOYEES RETIREMENT SYSTEM (MO)
MOSERS
(*Suby of* EXECUTIVE OFFICE OF STATE OF MISSOURI) ★
907 Wildwood Dr, Jefferson City, MO 65109-5798
Tel (573) 632-6100 *Founded/Ownrshp* 1957
Sales NA *EMP* 71
SIC 6371 9441 Pension funds; Administration of social & manpower programs;
Ex Dir: Gary Findlay
Bd of Dir: Larry Schepker
Ofcr: Meg Cline
Ofcr: Derrick Griffin
Ofcr: M Yoakum
IT Man: Stacy Gillmore

D-U-N-S 07-625-5876
MISSOURI STATE UNIVERSITY
901 S National Ave, Springfield, MO 65897-0001
Tel (417) 836-5000 *Founded/Ownrshp* 1905
Sales 190.3MM *EMP* 2,066
Accts Bkd Llp Springfield Mo
SIC 8221 8211 University; Elementary & secondary schools; University; Elementary & secondary schools
Pr: Clif Smart
Pr: Andrew Wright
CFO: Nila Hayes
Treas: Lenord McGownd
Ex Ofcr: Ardeshir Dallal
Ex Ofcr: Judi Smith
Top Exec: April Reno
VP: Thomas Allen
VP: Jim Baker
VP: Tessa Friedman
VP: Ken McClure
VP: Kent Thomas

MISSOURI STAVE PRODUCTS CO
See MISSOURI WALNUT LLC

MISSOURI TASK FORCE ONE
See BOONE COUNTY FIRE PROTECTION DISTRICT

D-U-N-S 85-930-0519
MISSOURI UNITED SCHOOLS INSURANCE COUNCIL
MUSIC
12444 Powerscort Dr # 500, Saint Louis, MO 63131-3660
Tel (314) 800-2220 *Founded/Ownrshp* 1985
Sales NA *EMP* 12
SIC 6411 Education services, insurance
**Ex Dir:* Gary Vanmeter

D-U-N-S 02-121-2246
MISSOURI VALLEY COLLEGE
500 E College St, Marshall, MO 65340-3109
Tel (660) 886-6924 *Founded/Ownrshp* 1889
Sales 34.7MM *EMP* 250
Accts Williams-Keepers Llc Columbia
SIC 8221 College, except junior; College, except junior
Pr: Bonnie Humphrey
**CFO:* Amy Roe
**CFO:* Greg Silvey
Treas: Karl Caldwell

D-U-N-S 80-386-5369
MISSOURI VALLEY LINE CONTRUCTORS
7505 Nw Tffany Sprng Pkwy, Kansas City, MO 64153-1386
Tel (816) 891-9066 *Founded/Ownrshp* 2001
Sales 166.8MM *EMP* 3
SIC 8742 8631 Labor & union relations consultant; Trade union; Labor & union relations consultant; Trade union

D-U-N-S 12-513-6015
MISSOURI VALLEY PETROLEUM INC
1722 Mandan Ave, Mandan, ND 58554-2203
Tel (701) 663-5091 *Founded/Ownrshp* 1978
Sales 321.9MM *EMP* 200
Accts Eidebailly Llp Bismarck Nort
SIC 5172 3443 Gasoline; Diesel fuel; Lubricating oils & greases; Gases, liquefied petroleum (propane); Gasoline; Diesel fuel; Lubricating oils & greases; Gases, liquefied petroleum (propane);Tank towers, metal plate
Pr: Dave Froelich
CFO: Lance Olson
Sec: Kathy Nilles
VP: Jim Froelich

D-U-N-S 16-978-5792 IMP/EXP
MISSOURI WALNUT LLC
MISSOURI STAVE PRODUCTS CO
11417 Oak Rd, Neosho, MO 64850-5345
Tel (417) 455-0972 *Founded/Ownrshp* 2004
Sales 21.6MM^E *EMP* 150^E
SIC 2421 5211 Sawmills & planing mills, general; Lumber & other building materials; Sawmills & planing mills, general; Lumber & other building materials
Genl Mgr: Spacy Martin
Plnt Mgr: Yimin Ding

D-U-N-S 01-064-8814
MISSOURI WESTERN STATE UNIVERSITY
4525 Downs Dr, Saint Joseph, MO 64507-2246
Tel (816) 271-4464 *Founded/Ownrshp* 1969
Sales 35.3MM *EMP* 1,300
Accts Cliftonlarsonallen Llp St Lo
SIC 8221 College, except junior; College, except junior
CEO: Robert Vartabedian
Assoc VP: Douglas Davenport
VP: Ronald Olinger
Off Admin: Jamie Willis
Art Dir: Nathanael May

D-U-N-S 00-696-8374 IMP
■ **MISSOURI-AMERICAN WATER CO** (MO)
(*Suby of* AMERICAN WATER WORKS CO INC) ★
727 Craig Rd, Saint Louis, MO 63141-7175
Tel (314) 991-3404 *Founded/Ownrshp* 1925, 1999
Sales 69.3MM^E *EMP* 200^E
SIC 4941 Water supply; Water supply
Pr: Robert Maclean
**VP:* Jim Jenkins
VP Opers: Phil Wood

D-U-N-S 05-355-2964 IMP
MISSRY ASSOCIATES INC
MISCO ENTERPRISES
100 S Washington Ave, Dunellen, NJ 08812-1692
Tel (732) 752-7500 *Founded/Ownrshp* 1974
Sales 26.6MM^E *EMP* 150
SIC 5193 2874 Artificial flowers; Phosphatic fertilizers; Artificial flowers; Phosphatic fertilizers
Pr: Morris Missry
**VP:* Ezra Missry

D-U-N-S 00-150-4463 IMP
MISTDODA INC (NY)
CROSCILL HOME FASHIONS
(*Suby of* CROSCILL HOME LLC) ★
261 5th Ave Fl 25, New York, NY 10016-7601
Tel (212) 213-8000 *Founded/Ownrshp* 1925, 2008
Sales 58.3MM^E *EMP* 600
SIC 2391 2392 Curtains & draperies; Blankets, comforters & beddings; Sheets, fabric: made from purchased materials; Curtains & draperies; Blankets, comforters & beddings; Sheets, fabric: made from purchased materials
CEO: Douglas Kahn

*Pr: Marc Navarre
*CFO: Clifford F Campbell
Sr VP: Michelle L Rovere
VP: Pegeen Cooper
VP: Debbie Powell
VP: Dave Roman
Exec: Charlene Walter
Off Mgr: Maribel Melendez
VP Sls: William Heisler
S&M/VP: Michelle Larovere

D-U-N-S 80-749-3887 IMP
MISTEQUAY GROUP LTD
1156 N Niagara St, Saginaw, MI 48602-4741
Tel (989) 752-7700 Founded/Ownrshp 2014
Sales 41.3MM^E EMP 140
SIC 3812 3544 3714 3545 Search & navigation equipment; Special dies, tools, jigs & fixtures; Motor vehicle parts & accessories; Machine tool accessories; Search & navigation equipment; Special dies, tools, jigs & fixtures; Motor vehicle parts & accessories; Machine tool accessories
Pr: R James Paas
*CFO: Gary L Steele
VP: Sherry Carpenter
MIS Dir: Sally Ader
Plnt Mgr: Tom Crook
Plnt Mgr: Bamberg Wayne

D-U-N-S 05-202-0610
MISTER - E - LIQUID LLC
MISTER-E'S
632 Plymouth Ave Ne, Grand Rapids, MI 49505-6032
Tel (517) 262-9950 Founded/Ownrshp 2010
Sales 26.7MM^E EMP 66^E
SIC 5194 Tobacco & tobacco products; Cigarettes
Prin: Daniel Lawitzke

MISTER CAR WASH
See CAR WASH PARTNERS INC

D-U-N-S 80-884-0623
MISTER COOKIE FACE INC
MRS FIELDBROOK FOOD
(Suby of FIELDBROOK FOODS CORP) ★
1989 Rutgers Blvd, Lakewood, NJ 08701-4538
Tel (732) 370-5533 Founded/Ownrshp 1992
Sales 33.5MM^E EMP 125
SIC 2024 Ice cream & ice milk; Ice cream & ice milk
Pr: Frank R Koenemund
CFO: Suzanne Crovo
VP: Nora Schmidt
IT Man: Ed Grosso
Sfty Mgr: Miguel Minasian
Prd Mgr: Mahesh Khemraj

D-U-N-S 09-239-2315
MISTER KLEEN MAINTENANCE CO INC
7302 Beulah St, Alexandria, VA 22315-3522
Tel (703) 719-6900 Founded/Ownrshp 1976
Sales 7.5MM^E EMP 350
SIC 7349

MISTER MONEY FINANCIAL SVCS
See MISTER MONEY HOLDINGS INC

D-U-N-S 60-426-6630
MISTER MONEY HOLDINGS INC
MISTER MONEY FINANCIAL SVCS
351 Linden St Unit 140, Fort Collins, CO 80524-4416
Tel (970) 493-0574 Founded/Ownrshp 2002
Sales 34.0MM EMP 250
SIC 7389 Financial services; Financial services
Pr: Ralph Douglas Will
*COO: Timothey S Lanham

D-U-N-S 62-106-5015
MISTER SWEEPER LP
3522 Doug Dr, Dallas, TX 75247-6414
Tel (214) 688-4444 Founded/Ownrshp 1965
Sales 45.7MM^E EMP 82^E
SIC 4959 Sweeping service: road, airport, parking lot, etc.
Pr: Jodie Thompson
*Genl Pt: Master Sweeper LLC
*VP: Scott Henderson

MISTER-E'S
See MISTER - E - LIQUID LLC

D-U-N-S 07-948-6131
MISTICA FOODS LLC
50 W Commercial Ave, Addison, IL 60101-4502
Tel (630) 543-5409 Founded/Ownrshp 2014
Sales 98.3MM^E EMP 120
SIC 5147 Meats, fresh; Meats, fresh
Pr: Monika Rose Walas
*COO: Daniel Waligora
*CFO: David Prill
*CFO: Geraldine A Smrcina

D-U-N-S 82-853-0381
MISTICK CONSTRUCTION CO
1300 Brighton Rd Ste 1, Pittsburgh, PA 15233-1630
Tel (412) 322-1121 Founded/Ownrshp 2005
Sales 20.3MM^E EMP 57
SIC 1522 1542 Residential construction; Commercial & office building, new construction
Pr: M Robert Mistick
*Prin: Robert Mistick

MISTLIN HONDA
See MISTLIN MOTORS

D-U-N-S 02-868-7739
MISTLIN MOTORS
MISTLIN HONDA
4754 Mchenry Ave, Modesto, CA 95356-9523
Tel (209) 549-5000 Founded/Ownrshp 1964
Sales 49.5MM EMP 62^E
SIC 5511 Automobiles, new & used; Automobiles, new & used
Pr: Anthony A Mistlin
*Treas: Kimberly Chaves
*VP: Joan Mistlin
Sls Mgr: Jim Lemmons

D-U-N-S 93-983-2494
MISTRAL EQUITY PARTNERS LP
650 5th Ave Fl 31, New York, NY 10019-6108
Tel (212) 616-9600 Founded/Ownrshp 2008
Sales 137.8MM^E EMP 871^E
SIC 6211 Investment bankers; Investment bankers
Mng Pt: Andrew Heyer
Mng Dir: Bill Phoenix

D-U-N-S 93-261-7434
▲ MISTRAS GROUP INC
195 Clarksville Rd Ste 2, Princeton Junction, NJ 08550-5392
Tel (609) 716-4000 Founded/Ownrshp 1978
Sales 711.2MM EMP 5,300
Tkr Sym MG Exch NYS
SIC 8711 7372 3829 3825 Engineering services; Prepackaged software; Measuring & controlling devices; Instruments to measure electricity; Engineering services; Prepackaged software; Measuring & controlling devices; Instruments to measure electricity
Ch Bd: Sotirios J Vahaviolos
COO: Ned Cunningham
CFO: Peter Peterik
CFO: Jonathan H Wolk
Ofcr: Daryl Istre
Ofcr: Alfred Medina
Ofcr: Greg Sullivan
Ex VP: Mark F Carlos
Ex VP: Phillip T Cole
Ex VP: Michael C Keefe
*Ex VP: Michael J Lange
VP: Richard Hilyard
VP: Chris Smith
Dir Lab: Robert Labelle
Board of Directors: James J Forese, Richard H Glanton, Ellen T Ruff, Manuel N Stamatakis, W Curtis Weldon

MISTY HARBOR
See KEVCON CORP

MISTY MOUNTAIN SPRING WATER CO
See MID-MOUNTAIN FOODS INC

D-U-N-S 07-884-8218
MISUMI INVESTMENT USA CORP
(Suby of MISUMI GROUP INC.)
500 Progress Rd, Dayton, OH 45449-2326
Tel (937) 859-5111 Founded/Ownrshp 2013
Sales 106.2MM^E EMP 1,402
SIC 6719 3544 Investment holding companies, except banks; Die sets for metal stamping (presses)
Pr: Ryusei Ono

D-U-N-S 18-722-2559 IMP
MISUMI USA INC
(Suby of MISUMI GROUP INC.)
1717 N Penny Ln Ste 200, Schaumburg, IL 60173-5627
Tel (847) 843-9057 Founded/Ownrshp 1988
Sales 77.7MM^E EMP 180^E
SIC 5084 Machine tools & metalworking machinery; Machine tools & metalworking machinery
Pr: Nobu Ashida

D-U-N-S 80-839-7137
MISYS INTERNATIONAL BANKING SYSTEMS INC
(Suby of MISYS LTD)
1180 Avenue Of The Amer, New York, NY 10036-8401
Tel (914) 428-7200 Founded/Ownrshp 1997
Sales 80.5MM^E EMP 350
SIC 7378 7372 Computer maintenance & repair; Prepackaged software; Computer maintenance & repair; Prepackaged software
Ch Bd: Richard Salk
*Pr: Edward Ho
*CEO: Nadeem Syed
*Ex VP: M H Herskovits
*VP: Shaye Mozes
VP: Donald Sunderland
Assoc Dir: Lina Shenker
Sales Exec: Peter Martin
Sales Asso: Darryl Bernstein
Sales Asso: Britney Pope
Snr PM: Kevin Dono

D-U-N-S 01-610-6069
MISYS IQ LLC
(Suby of MISYS LTD)
1180 Ave Of The Amrcas, New York, NY 10036-8401
Tel (212) 898-9500 Founded/Ownrshp 2004
Sales 20.1MM^E EMP 99
SIC 7371 Computer software development & applications
VP: Rick Bernard
VP: Joanne Felix
Exec: Andrew Darby
Assoc Dir: Tat Fung
Dir Bus: Holli McCaffery
Prgrm Mgr: Keith Brown
Snr Sftwr: Radu Talmaciu
CIO: Christina Parkinson
Netwrk Mgr: Diogenes Morales
Sftwr Eng: Kalpana Nitzsche
VP Opers: Shaye Mozes

MIT
See MASSACHUSETTS INSTITUTE OF TECHNOLOGY

D-U-N-S 96-478-4099 IMP
MITAC INFORMATION SYSTEMS CORP
MITAC USA
(Suby of MITAC INTERNATIONAL CORPORATION)
39889 Eureka Dr, Newark, CA 94560-4811
Tel (510) 668-3679 Founded/Ownrshp 2010
Sales 40.1MM^E EMP 156
SIC 3572 Computer storage devices; Computer storage devices
Pr: Charlotte Chou
*CFO: Karen Soong

MITAC USA
See MITAC INFORMATION SYSTEMS CORP

D-U-N-S 03-819-1058 IMP
MITAS TIRES NORTH AMERICA INC
1200 Rove Ave, Charles City, IA 50616-3420
Tel (641) 228-8151 Founded/Ownrshp 2000
Sales 35.5MM^E EMP 175
SIC 3011 Motorcycle tires, pneumatic; Agricultural tires, pneumatic; Industrial tires, pneumatic; Motorcycle tires, pneumatic; Agricultural tires, pneumatic; Industrial tires, pneumatic
Pr: Parvel Charvat
*Treas: Vladimir Dusanek
Exec: Josef Heigl
Exec: Gaetano Mellia
Exec: Gerd Schulterobben
Area Mgr: Vladimir Bartl
Area Mgr: Belarus Poland
Manager: Tomas Hanacek

D-U-N-S 15-472-9388
MITCH COX CONSTRUCTION INC
801 Sunset Dr Bldg D, Johnson City, TN 37604-3033
Tel (423) 282-6582 Founded/Ownrshp 1979
Sales 26.3MM^E EMP 85
SIC 1542 1541 6531 1531 1521 Commercial & office building, new construction; Commercial & office buildings, renovation & repair; Industrial buildings, new construction; Renovation, remodeling & repairs: industrial buildings; Real estate agents & managers; Operative builders; Single-family housing construction
Pr: J Mitch Cox Jr
*Treas: Tracey Fleenor

D-U-N-S 02-648-5250 IMP
▲ MITCHAM INDUSTRIES INC
8141 Sh 75 S, Huntsville, TX 77342
Tel (936) 291-2277 Founded/Ownrshp 1987
Sales 83.1MM EMP 187^E
Accts Hein & Associates Llp Houston
Tkr Sym MIND Exch NGS
SIC 7359 Equipment rental & leasing; Geophysical equipment rental; Equipment rental & leasing; Geophysical equipment rental
Pr: Billy F Mitcham Jr
*CFO: Robert P Capps
CFO: Michael Pugh
Ex VP: Guy Malden
Ex VP: Bill Sheppard
VP: Paul Guy Rogers
VP: Gustavo Solorzano
Board of Directors: Robert J Albers, Peter H Blum, R Dean Lewis, John F Schwalbe

MITCHEL & SCOTT MACHINE CO
See MITCHEL GROUP INC

D-U-N-S 00-642-2182
MITCHEL & SCOTT MACHINE CO INC
BAR STEEL SERVICE CENTER
1841 Ludlow Ave, Indianapolis, IN 46201-1035
Tel (317) 639-5331 Founded/Ownrshp 1956
Sales 19.9MM^E EMP 300
SIC 3451 Screw machine products; Screw machine products
Ch Bd: Thomas L Mitchel
Pr: Richard G Siler
Treas: Gary Williams
Bd of Dir: James Edwards
Bd of Dir: Otto Frenzel
Bd of Dir: Brett Pheffer
Bd of Dir: Jerry Wraley
VP: Stephen Mitchel
Genl Mgr: Chuck Jaskiewicz
Genl Mgr: Jim Lee
MIS Mgr: John Mitchel
Board of Directors: James Edwards, Otto Frenzel IV Are Outsid, Jerry Wraley

D-U-N-S 00-606-5643 IMP
MITCHEL GROUP INC (IN)
MITCHEL & SCOTT MACHINE CO
1841 Ludlow Ave, Indianapolis, IN 46201-1035
Tel (317) 639-5331 Founded/Ownrshp 1933, 2000
Sales 39.7MM^E EMP 215
SIC 3451 Screw machine products; Screw machine products
Pr: Bradley Smith
Dir IT: John Mitchel
VP Mfg: David Mitchel
Plnt Mgr: Pat Mitchel
VP Mktg: Dave Grande
Board of Directors: Ann Bastianelli, Otto Frenzel IV, Dave Mitchel, Steve Mitchel, Tom Mitchel

D-U-N-S 00-784-5555
MITCHELL & STARK CONSTRUCTION CO INC
170 W 1st St, Medora, IN 47260
Tel (812) 966-2151 Founded/Ownrshp 1955, 1986
Sales 86.9MM^E EMP 250
Accts Kb Parrish & Co Llp Indian
SIC 1623 1629 Water & sewer line construction; Waste water & sewage treatment plant construction; Water & sewer line construction; Waste water & sewage treatment plant construction
Pr: Fred C Harrison
*VP: Brian R Penner

D-U-N-S 06-497-7002
MITCHELL & TITUS LLP
1 Battery Park Plz Fl 27, New York, NY 10004-1431
Tel (212) 709-4500 Founded/Ownrshp 1973
Sales 24.2MM^E EMP 175
Accts Bert Mitchell Chairman-Ceo By
SIC 8721 Certified public accountant; Certified public accountant
CEO: Anthony S Kendall
Pt: Tim Carty
Pt: Tonny Dekker
Pt: Davis Frederick
Mng Pt: Williams H Oneil
Mng Pt: Alan Pateman
CFO: Steven Becker
CFO: Jeffrey Dworken
CFO: Ashley Gardner
Bd of Dir: Bert Mitchell
Exec: Margie Williams
Assoc Dir: Catherine Pulley-Dennison

Board of Directors: Andre J Clarke, Herbert Harriott

D-U-N-S 18-476-4009 IMP
MITCHELL AIRCRAFT SPARES INC
1160 Alexander Ct, Cary, IL 60013-1892
Tel (847) 516-3773 Founded/Ownrshp 1987
Sales 48.3MM^E EMP 45
SIC 5088 Aircraft & parts
Ch: Richard C Sebion
*Pr: Gavin Gallogly
Ex VP: Jim Glockner
Rgnl Mgr: Patrick Armstrong
Ql Cn Mgr: William Gallacher
Ql Cn Mgr: Cory Reisenbigler
Manager: Chris Dundas
Manager: Chris Irwin
Manager: Brett Kaether
Manager: Ash Raupp
Manager: Chris Robertson

D-U-N-S 00-588-3322
MITCHELL AIRPORT-GENERAL INTERNATIONAL AIRPORT
6744 S Howell Ave, Oak Creek, WI 53154-1422
Tel (414) 570-7000 Founded/Ownrshp 1941
Sales 20.9MM^E EMP 400
SIC 4581 Airports, flying fields & services; Airports, flying fields & services
Pr: Timothy Hoeksema
*VP: Carol Skornika

D-U-N-S 01-886-5493
MITCHELL AUTO GROUP (CT)
384 Hopmeadow St, Weatogue, CT 06089-9731
Tel (860) 408-6003 Founded/Ownrshp 1922, 1956
Sales 50.6MM^E EMP 160
SIC 5511 Automobiles, new & used; Automobiles, new & used
Ch Bd: Walter Mitchell
*Pr: Mark Mitchell
*VP: Steven Mitchell
Dir IT: Joe Baril

D-U-N-S 07-944-7331
MITCHELL BEVERAGE OF MARYLAND LLC
CHESAPEAKE BEVERAGE
7001 Quad Ave, Baltimore, MD 21237-2441
Tel (410) 646-5500 Founded/Ownrshp 2014
Sales 167.9MM^E EMP 225^E
SIC 5181 5182 Beer & other fermented malt liquors; Liquor

D-U-N-S 18-055-8140
MITCHELL BROS TRUCK LINE INC
600 Se Marit Ave Brg Bldg 3 Ste 100, Vancouver, WA 98661
Tel (360) 693-7477 Founded/Ownrshp 1987
Sales 27.0MM EMP 175^E
SIC 4213 4212 Trucking, except local; Trailer or container on flat car (TOFC/COFC); Local trucking, without storage; Trucking, except local; Trailer or container on flat car (TOFC/COFC); Local trucking, without storage
Pr: Betty Cooke
*Sec: Jill Turner
Admn Mgr: Glenn Roberts
VP Sls: John Sullivan

D-U-N-S 03-098-8760
MITCHELL BUCKMAN INC
KEMPER INSURANCE
500 N Santa Fe St, Visalia, CA 93292-5065
Tel (559) 733-1181 Founded/Ownrshp 1964
Sales NA EMP 90
Accts Pine Pedroncelli & Aguilar In
SIC 6411 Insurance agents
Ch Bd: Clifford Dunbar
*Pr: Jeffrey Boyle
*Pr: Judy A Fussel
*Pr: Brent Swanson
Ex VP: Todd Williams
*Sr VP: Linda N Loflin

MITCHELL BUICK-PONTIAC-GMC
See MITCHELL MOTORS INC

D-U-N-S 78-279-6932
MITCHELL CO INC
JOEL COURT APTS
Bbnt Bank Ctr 41 W I 65 S, Mobile, AL 36608
Tel (251) 380-2929 Founded/Ownrshp 1992
Sales 35.3MM^E EMP 200
SIC 1531 6512 6513 Operative builders; Shopping center, property operation only; Apartment building operators; Operative builders; Shopping center, property operation only; Apartment building operators
Pr: John B Saint
CFO: Lindsey Boney
Ex VP: Don Kelly
VP: Ken Kvalheim
VP: Alex Pate
IT Man: Harry Brislin

D-U-N-S 01-018-2236
MITCHELL COLLEGE (INC)
437 Pequot Ave, New London, CT 06320-4498
Tel (860) 701-5000 Founded/Ownrshp 1938
Sales 32.4MM EMP 196
Accts Blum Shapiro & Company Pc Cpa
SIC 8222 8221 Junior college; Colleges universities & professional schools; Junior college; Colleges universities & professional schools
Pr: Mary Ellen Jukoski Edd
CFO: Diane Baker
Treas: Daniel Weekley
VP: Kevin Mayne
VP: Richard Milnet
VP: Kathleen Rice
Exec: George Wezner
Off Admin: Julie Church
IT Man: Kristin Lambert
HC Dir: Kim Hodge

MITCHELL COMPANIES
See MITCHELL DISTRIBUTING CO INC

D-U-N-S 07-904-9490
MITCHELL COUNTY BOARD OF EDUCATION
72 Ledger School Rd, Bakersville, NC 28705-7260
Tel (828) 688-4432 Founded/Ownrshp 1925
Sales 19.4MM^E EMP 410
SIC 8211 Public elementary school; School board; Public elementary school; School board

D-U-N-S 10-001-4133
MITCHELL COUNTY BOARD OF EDUCATION
108 S Harney St, Camilla, GA 31730-2065
Tel (229) 336-2100 Founded/Ownrshp 1900
Sales 26.1MM EMP 500
SIC 8211 Public elementary & secondary schools; Public elementary & secondary schools
Pr Dir: Ruth Lee

D-U-N-S 07-878-5100
MITCHELL COUNTY HOSPITAL HEALTH SYSTEMS
400 W 8th St, Beloit, KS 67420-1605
Tel (785) 738-2266 Founded/Ownrshp 2005
Sales 24.3MM EMP 300
SIC 8062 General medical & surgical hospitals; General medical & surgical hospitals
CEO: David Dick
*CFO: Eldon Koepke
Dir Lab: Jolene Albert
Dir Rx: Lance Cheney
Dir IT: Mark Marihugh
Mtls Dir: Janet Fischer
HC Dir: Teri Henningsen

D-U-N-S 07-952-9083
MITCHELL COUNTY SCHOOL DISTRICT
108 S Harney St, Camilla, GA 31730-2065
Tel (229) 336-2100 Founded/Ownrshp 2014
Sales NA EMP 462^E
SIC 9111
Netwrk Mgr: Darryl Burley

D-U-N-S 07-979-8988
MITCHELL COUNTY SCHOOLS
72 Ledger School Rd, Bakersville, NC 28705-7260
Tel (828) 766-2220 Founded/Ownrshp 2015
Sales 5.6MM^E EMP 301^E
SIC 8211 Public elementary & secondary schools
Exec: Billi Hollifield
Schl Brd P: Sam Blivens
Teacher Pr: Lisa McKinney

D-U-N-S 02-662-7380 EXP
MITCHELL CRANE RENTAL INC
1611 Crosswind Dr, Bryan, TX 77808-9697
Tel (979) 778-2057 Founded/Ownrshp 1955
Sales 23.4MM^E EMP 55
SIC 5084 7699 Cranes, industrial; Industrial machinery & equipment repair
Pr: Don Mitchell
*Treas: Julie Stokes
*VP: Marilyn Mitchell

D-U-N-S 05-081-2585
▲ **MITCHELL DETWILER & CO**
100 High St Ste 2800, Boston, MA 02110-1761
Tel (617) 451-0100 Founded/Ownrshp 1983
Sales 75.4MM^E EMP 564
Tkr Sym DMCD Exch OTO
SIC 7389 6211 Financial services; Investment bankers; Financial services; Investment bankers
CEO: Peter Fenton
Pr: Robert Detwiler
CFO: Stephen D Martino
Ex VP: Alex Arnold

D-U-N-S 07-912-5449 IMP
MITCHELL DISTRIBUTING CO INC
MITCHELL COMPANIES
100 James E Chaney Dr, Meridian, MS 39307-6720
Tel (601) 482-6161 Founded/Ownrshp 1972
Sales 36.3MM^E EMP 54
SIC 5181 Beer & ale
Pr: John Mitchell Jr
*CFO: Kent Davis
*VP: Melanie M Mitchell

D-U-N-S 04-759-6085
MITCHELL ELECTRIC MEMBERSHIP CORP
E M C
475 Cairo Rd, Camilla, GA 31730-3800
Tel (229) 336-5221 Founded/Ownrshp 1973
Sales 56.9MM EMP 86
Accts Mcnair Mclemore Middlebrooks
SIC 4911 Distribution, electric power; Distribution, electric power
Ch Bd: Lucius Adkins
V Ch: Leonard J Eubanks
*V Ch: John Johnson
*Pr: Tony Tecker
Bd of Dir: Max Lewis
VP: Evera Moye
VP: Tammy Prince

D-U-N-S 62-211-4288
MITCHELL ENTERPRISES LTD
700 N Crockett St, Sherman, TX 75090-4978
Tel (903) 893-6593 Founded/Ownrshp 2002
Sales 20.8MM^E EMP 88^E
SIC 1542 Commercial & office building, new construction; Commercial & office buildings, renovation & repair
Pt: Steve Mitchell
Pt: Shane Mitchell
Pt: Tim Mitchell

MITCHELL GOLD BOB WILLIAMS
See MITCHELL GOLD CO

D-U-N-S 05-793-1024 IMP/EXP
MITCHELL GOLD CO (NC)
MITCHELL GOLD BOB WILLIAMS
135 One Comfortable Pl, Taylorsville, NC 28681-3783
Tel (828) 632-9200 Founded/Ownrshp 1989
Sales 199.2MM^E EMP 750^E
SIC 2512 Upholstered household furniture; Upholstered household furniture
Ch Bd: Mitchell Gold
*Pr: George Ackerman
Pr: Garrett Barr
CFO: John Bannons
*CFO: Bob Williams
VP: Kim Caraballo
VP: Eloise Goldman
VP: Marjorie Hall
VP: Ken Hipp
VP: Lewis Kohnle
Comm Dir: Mindy Drucker

D-U-N-S 03-146-7350
MITCHELL GROCERY CORP
FOODLAND ALBERTVILLE
550 Railroad Ave, Albertville, AL 35950-1485
Tel (256) 878-4211 Founded/Ownrshp 1965
Sales 638.7MM^E EMP 550
SIC 5141 5411 Groceries, general line; Grocery stores; Groceries, general line; Grocery stores
CEO: Jack Mitchell
*Pr: David Mitchell
CFO: Jennifer Amos
*Sec: Bill Woodham
Exec: Gary Cameron
MIS Dir: Doug Masters
IT Man: Glenda Kilpatrick
IT Man: Eileen Walls
Sfty Dirs: Larry Skelton
Sls&Mrk Ex: William Woodham
Mktg Dir: Kirk Clark

D-U-N-S 04-297-1663
MITCHELL INC GRAYSON
2462 Sussex Dr, Emporia, VA 23847-6312
Tel (434) 634-3212 Founded/Ownrshp 1976
Sales 31.8MM EMP 350
SIC 4213 Trucking, except local; Trucking, except local; Building materials transport
Pr: H Grayson Mitchell Jr
*Sec: Loretta Mitchell
*VP: Raymond Bricker
*VP: Beth Childrey
*VP: John R Rawls

D-U-N-S 15-537-6916
■ **MITCHELL INTERNATIONAL INC**
(Suby of KKR & CO LP) ★
6220 Greenwich Dr, San Diego, CA 92122-5913
Tel (858) 368-7000 Founded/Ownrshp 2013
Sales 358.3MM^E EMP 1,084^E
SIC 7371 Computer software development & applications; Computer software development & applications
V Ch Bd: James Lindner
Pr: Jack Farnan
Pr: Alex Sun
CFO: Arthur J Long
Ex VP: Nina Smith Garmon
Ex VP: Jesse Herrera
VP: Erika James
VP: W McCraken
VP: John Pontarola
Exec: Dominic Early
Exec: Jim O'Leary
Creative D: Kelly Eismann

D-U-N-S 00-893-4242
MITCHELL LEWIS & STAVER CO (OR)
9935 Sw Commerce Cir, Wilsonville, OR 97070-8608
Tel (503) 682-1800 Founded/Ownrshp 1882, 1976
Sales 35.6MM^E EMP 55
SIC 3561 4941 Pumps & pumping equipment; Water supply
Pr: D C Brown
VP: Mike Eglidis
Rgnl Mgr: Jim Schlabach
Opers Mgr: Kenny Fitzgerald
Prd Mgr: Lou Marie
Sales Exec: Clint Eshelman
Mktg Dir: Kevin Brooks
Sls Dir: Matt Johnson
Mktg Mgr: Jason Oliver
Manager: Reed Stewart
Sls Mgr: Joe Montoya

D-U-N-S 07-915-3605
MITCHELL MANAGEMENT CO
5440 L St, Omaha, NE 68117-1366
Tel (402) 850-5555 Founded/Ownrshp 2013
Sales 35.2MM^E EMP 350
SIC 6794 Franchises, selling or licensing; Franchises, selling or licensing
Owner: Mark W Mitchell

D-U-N-S 12-108-0287
MITCHELL MANOR CONVALESCENT HOME INC
315 W Electric Ave, McAlester, OK 74501-3600
Tel (918) 423-4661 Founded/Ownrshp 1974
Sales 251.4MM EMP 60
SIC 8051 8059 Skilled nursing care facilities; Convalescent home with continuous nursing care; Convalescent home; Skilled nursing care facilities; Convalescent home with continuous nursing care; Convalescent home
VP: Joe Wayne-Mitchell

D-U-N-S 02-700-1239
MITCHELL MOTORS INC
MITCHELL BUICK-PONTIAC-GMC
1500 Knickerbocker Rd, San Angelo, TX 76904-5517
Tel (325) 653-8728 Founded/Ownrshp 1987
Sales 23.0MM^E EMP 70
SIC 5511 Automobiles, new & used; Automobiles, new & used
Pr: Michael D Mitchell
*Treas: Linda Pellegrin
Sls Mgr: Mike O'Connor

MITCHELL OIL
See NORBERT E MITCHELL CO INC

D-U-N-S 01-832-3238
MITCHELL PETERSON INC (OH)
PERKINS FAMILY RESTAURANT
1170 Upper Valley Pike, Springfield, OH 45504-4018
Tel (937) 325-8744 Founded/Ownrshp 1958
Sales 11.8MM^E EMP 400
Accts Mesarvey Russel & Co
SIC 5812 Restaurant, family: chain; Restaurant, family: chain
Pr: Rudy Mosketti

MITCHELL PLASTICS
See K&M INDIANA LLC

MITCHELL PLASTICS
See ULTRA MANUFACTURING (USA) INC

D-U-N-S 02-023-4105
■ **MITCHELL REPAIR INFORMATION CO LLC** (UT)
MRIC
(Suby of SNAP-ON INC) ★
14145 Danielson St Ste A, Poway, CA 92064-8827
Tel (858) 391-5000 Founded/Ownrshp 1996, 1999
Sales 34.9MM^E EMP 244
SIC 2741 2731 5251 Technical manuals: publishing only, not printed on site; Book publishing; Hardware; Technical manuals: publishing only, not printed on site; Book publishing; Hardware
CFO: Patrick Sell
Ex VP: Ken Young
VP: Randy Bislew
VP: David Niemiec
VP: Ray Yankowski
Dir Bus: Matt Krimple
Ex Dir: Randy Dislew
Brnch Mgr: Jim Lindner
Genl Mgr: Scott Degiorgio
Genl Mgr: David Rady
Snr Sftwr: Phillip Castaneda

D-U-N-S 04-309-0109 IMP
MITCHELL RUBBER PRODUCTS INC
VALLEY PROCESSING DIVISION
491 Wilson Way, City of Industry, CA 91744-3935
Tel (626) 961-0311 Founded/Ownrshp 1967
Sales 60.0MM^E EMP 235
SIC 3069 2891 2822 Mats or matting, rubber; Floor coverings, rubber; Rubber automotive products; Custom compounding of rubber materials; Adhesives & sealants; Synthetic rubber; Mats or matting, rubber; Floor coverings, rubber; Rubber automotive products; Custom compounding of rubber materials; Adhesives & sealants; Synthetic rubber
CEO: Ted C Ballou
Pr: James Wood

D-U-N-S 08-020-4324
MITCHELL SCHOOL DISTRICT
800 W 10th Ave, Mitchell, SD 57301-4931
Tel (605) 995-3010 Founded/Ownrshp 1890
Sales 22.7MM^E EMP 400
SIC 8211 Public combined elementary & secondary school; Public vocational/technical school; Public combined elementary & secondary school; Public vocational/technical school

D-U-N-S 07-018-9360
MITCHELL SILBERBERG & KNUPP LLP
11377 W Olympic Blvd Fl 2, Los Angeles, CA 90064-1683
Tel (310) 312-2000 Founded/Ownrshp 1908
Sales 39.6MM^E EMP 300^E
SIC 8111 General practice law office; Real estate law; Taxation law; Labor & employment law; General practice law office; Real estate law; Taxation law; Labor & employment law
Mng Pt: Thomas P Lambert
COO: Kevin E Gaut
COO: Bonnie Norwood
Exec: Gerald Hathaway
Exec: Nahla Rajan
Ex Dir: Jerry Kaufman
Counsel: Steven Krone
Counsel: Mary Lane
Counsel: Joan Lanigan
Counsel: Marvin Leon
Counsel: Alan Pepper

D-U-N-S 01-158-3580
MITCHELL SUPREME FUEL CO
532 Freeman St, Orange, NJ 07050-1312
Tel (973) 678-1800 Founded/Ownrshp 1921
Sales 21.0MM^E EMP 100
SIC 5983 7699 1711

D-U-N-S 17-281-8593
MITCHELL/MARTIN INC
ESSENTIAL STAFFING ASSOCIATES
307 W 38th St Rm 1305, New York, NY 10018-9521
Tel (212) 943-1404 Founded/Ownrshp 1984
Sales 31.6MM^E EMP 195
SIC 7361 7379 7389 Placement agencies; Computer related maintenance services; Personal investigation service; Placement agencies; Computer related maintenance services; Personal investigation service
Pr: Eugene Holtzman
*COO: Brian Delle Donne
*COO: Joseph Schimpf
VP: Stephen Comando

MITCHELLS NEWSPAPERS
See AM NEWSPAPER DELIVERY SERVICE INC

MITCHELLS OF WESTPORT
See ED MITCHELL INC

D-U-N-S 08-951-0234
MITCHELLS OILFIELD SERVICE INC
(Suby of JOHN WOOD GROUP P.L.C.)
409 N Central Ave, Sidney, MT 59270-4219
Tel (406) 482-4927 Founded/Ownrshp 2012
Sales 153.2MM^E EMP 135
Accts Chms Pc Sidney Montana
SIC 1389 3273 Oil field services; Haulage, oil field; Ready-mixed concrete; Oil field services; Haulage, oil field; Ready-mixed concrete
Pr: Todd Appel
*CFO: Patrick Sameulson
*Treas: Andrea Davidson
*VP: Dan Boulds
*VP: Duane Mitchell
Opers Mgr: Shayn Mitchell
Opers Mgr: Alton Smith
Opers Mgr: Dennis Twedt

D-U-N-S 05-661-1973
MITCHELLS SALON & DAY SPA INC (OH)
5901 E Galbraith Rd # 230, Cincinnati, OH 45236-2230
Tel (513) 793-0900 Founded/Ownrshp 1983
Sales 8.7MM^E EMP 397
SIC 7231 7991 Beauty shops; Spas; Beauty shops; Spas
Pr: Deborah M Schmidt
VP: Vivian Moore
Mktg Dir: Logan Schmidt

D-U-N-S 04-858-8169
MITCHEM ENTERPRISES INC
202 Lyons Ave, Tazewell, VA 24651-1118
Tel (276) 326-3877 Founded/Ownrshp 1997
Sales 45.1MM EMP 60
SIC 5411 Convenience stores, independent; Convenience stores, independent
Pr: Don Mitchem

D-U-N-S 10-684-2545 IMP
MITEK CORP
M T X
4545 E Baseline Rd, Phoenix, AZ 85042-6400
Tel (602) 438-4545 Founded/Ownrshp 1986
Sales 78.4MM^E EMP 350
SIC 3651 2517 3769 Loudspeakers, electrodynamic or magnetic; Speaker systems; Audio electronic systems; Amplifiers: radio, public address or musical instrument; Stereo cabinets, wood; Guided missile & space vehicle parts & auxiliary equipment; Loudspeakers, electrodynamic or magnetic; Speaker systems; Audio electronic systems; Amplifiers: radio, public address or musical instrument; Stereo cabinets, wood; Guided missile & space vehicle parts & auxiliary equipment
CEO: Loyd L Ivey
*Pr: Steve Favory
COO: Steve Avery
CFO: Ann Frey
*Ex VP: Rod Boyer
VP: Bernie Boland
VP: Bruce Marlin
VP: John Welch
Plnt Mgr: Travis Pranschke
Natl Sales: Jason Fickas
Natl Sales: Jamie Trentacoste

D-U-N-S 00-413-0415
■ **MITEK INDUSTRIES INC**
(Suby of BERKSHIRE HATHAWAY INC) ★
14515 North Outer 40 Rd # 300, Chesterfield, MO 63017-5746
Tel (314) 434-1200 Founded/Ownrshp 1947, 2001
Sales 757.9MM^E EMP 1,500
SIC 8711 8748 Engineering services; Systems analysis & engineering consulting services; Engineering services; Systems analysis & engineering consulting services
Ch Bd: Eugene M Toombs
*CFO: Ronald S Burkhardt
VP: Joseph Arr
*VP: Joseph C Carr Jr

D-U-N-S 00-492-4841
▲ **MITEK SYSTEMS INC**
8911 Balboa Ave Ste B, San Diego, CA 92123-6503
Tel (858) 309-1700 Founded/Ownrshp 1986
Sales 25.3MM EMP 85^E
Accts Mayer Hoffman Mccann Pc San
Tkr Sym MITK Exch NAS
SIC 7372 Prepackaged software; Business oriented computer software; Prepackaged software; Business oriented computer software
Pr: James B Debello
*Ch Bd: John M Thornton
CFO: Russell C Clark
Sr VP: Michael Diamond
Sr VP: David Pintsov PHD
VP: Julie Cunningham
VP: Fritz Hesse
Dir Bus: Cate Schumacher
Mng Dir: Michael Hagen
Off Mgr: Erika Farmer
Netwrk Eng: Chris Preston
Board of Directors: Bill Aulet, Vinton P Cunningham, James C Hale, Bruce E Hansen, Alex W Hart

D-U-N-S 84-999-5725
■ **MITEK USA INC**
(Suby of MITEK INDUSTRIES INC) ★
14515 North Outer 40 Rd # 300, Chesterfield, MO 63017-5791
Tel (314) 434-1200 Founded/Ownrshp 1987
Sales 515.6MM^E EMP 740
SIC 3443 3429 3542 8711 5051 5085 Truss plates, metal; Metal fasteners; Presses: hydraulic & pneumatic, mechanical & manual; Consulting engineer; Steel; Industrial supplies; Truss plates, metal; Metal fasteners; Presses: hydraulic & pneumatic, mechanical & manual; Consulting engineer; Steel; Industrial supplies
CEO: Thomas Manenti
*VP: Joseph C Carr Jr
VP: Eric Eversgerd
VP: Bill Howard
VP: Richard Marriott
VP: Terry McGrath
VP: David A McQuinn
Dir IT: Lynnea Daleiden
IT Man: Nancy Dahl
Netwrk Mgr: Ron Lewis
VP Mktg: David Cattapan

D-U-N-S 04-838-4143
MITEL (DELAWARE) INC
(Suby of MITEL US HOLDINGS, INC)
1146 N Alma School Rd, Mesa, AZ 85201-3000
Tel (480) 449-8900 Founded/Ownrshp 2007
Sales 571.0MM^E EMP 1,949

SIC 3661 5045 4813 5065 1731 7359 Telephone & telegraph apparatus; Telephones & telephone apparatus; PBX equipment, manual or automatic; Computer software; Long distance telephone communications; Telephone equipment; Telephone & telephone equipment installation; Equipment rental & leasing; Telephone & telegraph apparatus; Telephones & telephone apparatus; PBX equipment, manual or automatic; Computer software; Long distance telephone communications; Telephone equipment; Telephone & telephone equipment installation; Equipment rental & leasing
CEO: Richard McBee
**Pr:* Craig W Rauchle
**CFO:* Kurt R Kneip
**CFO:* Steve Spooner
**Ex VP:* Graham Bevington
**Ex VP:* Joe Vitalone
**Ex VP:* Ron Wellard
**Sr VP:* Jeffrey T Ford
**Sr VP:* John L Gardner
Software D: Mark Strickland
VP Opers: Todd West

D-U-N-S 60-317-1658
MITEL MOBILITY INC
MAVENIR SYSTEMS, INC.
(*Suby of* BAYART DAVID)
1700 Intl Pkwy Ste 200, Richardson, TX 75081
Tel (469) 916-4393 *Founded/Ownrshp* 2015
Sales 129.8MM^E *EMP* 700
Accts Bdo Usa Llp Dallas Texas
SIC 4813 Voice telephone communications; Voice telephone communications
CEO: Pardeep Kohli
Ch Bd: Ben Scott
CFO: Terry Hungle
Ex VP: Bahram Jalalizadeh
VP: Alex Garbuz
VP: Ashok Khuntia
VP: Dick Van Der Kwaak
VP: Edgar Mendoza
VP: Brett Wallis
Dir Bus: Gagan Bhalla
Off Mgr: Stacy Priddy

D-U-N-S 03-869-7942 IMP
MITEL NETWORKS INC
(*Suby of* MITEL NETWORKS LIMITED)
1146 N Alma School Rd, Mesa, AZ 85201-3000
Tel (480) 961-9000 *Founded/Ownrshp* 2001
Sales 335.0MM^E *EMP* 2,000
SIC 3661 7359 1731 7373 Telephones & telephone apparatus; Switchboards, telephone or telegraph; PBX equipment, manual or automatic; Electronic equipment rental, except computers; Telephone & telephone equipment installation; Systems integration services; Telephones & telephone apparatus; Switchboards, telephone or telegraph; PBX equipment, manual or automatic; Electronic equipment rental, except computers; Telephone & telephone equipment installation; Systems integration services
CEO: Richard McBee
CFO: Souglas McCarthy
**CFO:* Steve Spooner
VP: Robert Anderson
**VP:* Tim Gaines
VP: Doug Michaelides
**VP:* Charles Oakley
VP: John Uehling
**VP:* Joe Vitalon
Exec: Bob Darmody
Exec: Mark Donnelly
Exec: Brad Ross

D-U-N-S 10-348-4783
MITEL TECHNOLOGIES INC
(*Suby of* MITEL (DELAWARE) INC) ★
1146 N Alma School Rd, Mesa, AZ 85201-3000
Tel (480) 449-8900 *Founded/Ownrshp* 1969
Sales 200.1MM^E *EMP* 1,900
SIC 5065 Electronic parts & equipment; Electronic parts & equipment
Pr: Martyn Etherington
CFO: Kurt Kneip
**Treas:* Paul Ciaramitaro
Treas: Susan K Sherman
**VP:* Steven E Spooner

D-U-N-S 05-058-4101 EXP
■ **MITEQ INC** (DE)
(*Suby of* L-3 COMMUNICATIONS CORP) ★
100 Davids Dr, Hauppauge, NY 11788-2034
Tel (631) 436-7400 *Founded/Ownrshp* 1969, 2015
Sales 9.2MM^E *EMP* 680
SIC 3663 3769 3661 3651 3643

D-U-N-S 07-430-5863 IMP
MITO CORP
213 County Road 17 Th, Elkhart, IN 46516-5449
Tel (574) 295-2441 *Founded/Ownrshp* 1982
Sales 24.8MM *EMP* 42
Accts Mcgladrey Llp Elkhart Indian
SIC 5065 5015 Sound equipment, electronic; Automotive parts & supplies, used; Sound equipment, electronic; Automotive parts & supplies, used
Pr: Marvin Metzler
**Ch Bd:* Michael Stock
VP: Daniel Maloney
VP: Ken Smith
**VP:* Kenneth W Smith
Sls Mgr: Ben Bontrager
Sales Asso: Steve Putman

D-U-N-S 18-313-0079
MITRATECH HOLDINGS INC
(*Suby of* VISTA EQUITY PARTNERS LLC) ★
5001 Plaza On The Lk # 111, Austin, TX 78746-1084
Tel (512) 382-7322 *Founded/Ownrshp* 2011
Sales 25.8MM^E *EMP* 172^E
SIC 7371 Computer software writers, freelance
CEO: Jason Parkman
**CFO:* Samuel Monti
CFO: David Morton
Sr VP: Ralph Carter
Sr VP: Michael Schmitt
VP: George Wedana
Software D: Justin Forman

VP Sls: Shawn Lane
Sales Asso: Jeanne Kuennen

D-U-N-S 00-787-2690
MITRE CORP (DE)
202 Burlington Rd, Bedford, MA 01730-1420
Tel (781) 271-2000 *Founded/Ownrshp* 1958
Sales 1.6MM^E *EMP* 7,000
Accts Pricewaterhousecoopers Llp Mc
SIC 8733 8711 Noncommercial research organizations; Engineering services; Noncommercial research organizations; Engineering services
CEO: Alfred Grasso
**Treas:* Mark Kontos
**Sec:* Sol Glasner
Ex Ofcr: Stuart Matthews
Trst: Nicholas M Donofrio
Trst: Jane C Garvey
Trst: Edmund P Giambastiani Jr
Trst: John J Hamre
Trst: Elizabeth J Keefer
Trst: Donald M Kerr
Trst: Cleve L Killingsworth Jr
Trst: Montgomery C Meigs
Trst: Cathy E Minehan
**VP:* Julie Gravallese
VP: Jane Hall
VP: Stephen D Huffman

D-U-N-S 15-403-2585 IMP
MITSUBA BARDSTOWN INC
AMERICAN MITSUBA
901 Withrow Ct, Bardstown, KY 40004-2605
Tel (502) 348-1409 *Founded/Ownrshp* 2007
Sales 129.2MM *EMP* 200
SIC 3714 Motor vehicle parts & accessories

D-U-N-S 79-045-1231
MITSUBISHI CATERPILLAR FORKLIFT AMERICA INC
MCFA
(*Suby of* MITSUBISHI NICHIYU FORKLIFT CO.,LTD.)
2121 W Sam Houston Pkwy N, Houston, TX 77043-2305
Tel (713) 365-1000 *Founded/Ownrshp* 1992
Sales 257.5MM^E *EMP* 1,100
SIC 3537 5084 Forklift trucks; Lift trucks & parts; Forklift trucks; Lift trucks & parts
Pr: Hiroshi Nagai
**Treas:* Michiaki Nakamura
Ex VP: Kent Eudy
**Ex VP:* Hiroki Oikawa
**VP:* Kent E Eudy
**VP:* Jack Sipola
**VP:* Michael Veillete
**VP Admn:* John Hansen
Genl Mgr: Ed Sikora
Software D: Kushal Paudyal
VP Opers: Jay Gusler
Board of Directors: Richard A Benson

D-U-N-S 19-607-2334 IMP
MITSUBISHI CEMENT CORP
(*Suby of* MITSUBISHI MATERIALS CORPORATION)
151 Cassia Way, Henderson, NV 89014-6616
Tel (702) 932-3900 *Founded/Ownrshp* 1988
Sales 123.4MM^E *EMP* 619
SIC 3297 5032 Cement refractories; Cement; Cement refractories; Cement
Pr: Kimball P McCloud
**Treas:* H Kubota
**Treas:* Naoki Shigeta
**VP:* Lndaro Galeg
**VP:* Michael Jasberg
**VP:* William Mein

D-U-N-S 62-236-9101
MITSUBISHI CHEMICAL HOLDINGS AMERICA INC
(*Suby of* MITSUBISHI CHEMICAL CORPORATION)
655 3rd Ave Fl 15, New York, NY 10017-9135
Tel (212) 672-9400 *Founded/Ownrshp* 2006
Sales 26.7MM^E *EMP* 95
SIC 8721 8741 Accounting, auditing & bookkeeping; Management services
Pr: Yoshimitsu Kobayashi
**Ch Bd:* Shoji Yoshisato
Ex VP: Hideki Tsubota
**Sr VP:* John Canfield
**VP:* Donna Costa
**VP:* Jeff Kuropatkin
Off Mgr: Ming Chen
Software D: Brian Doyle

D-U-N-S 61-165-9447 IMP
MITSUBISHI CHEMICAL PERFORMANCE POLYMERS INC
(*Suby of* MITSUBISHI CHEMICAL CORPORATION)
2001 Hood Rd, Greer, SC 29650-1014
Tel (864) 879-5487 *Founded/Ownrshp* 2005
Sales 42.3MM^E *EMP* 155
SIC 2821 2891 Plastics materials & resins; Adhesives; Plastics materials & resins; Adhesives
Pr: Mike Gragtmans
**Treas:* Shinichiro Iguchi

MITSUBISHI CLIMATE CONTROL
See MITSUBISHI HEAVY INDUSTRIES CLIMATE CONTROL INC

D-U-N-S 07-834-6382 IMP
MITSUBISHI CORP (AMERICAS)
(*Suby of* MITSUBISHI CORPORATION)
655 3rd Ave Fl 15, New York, NY 10017-9135
Tel (212) 605-2000 *Founded/Ownrshp* 2012
Sales 1.2MMM^E *EMP* 810
SIC 5051 5172 5141 5153 5169 5084 Ferrous metals; Nonferrous metal sheets, bars, rods, etc.; Steel; Petroleum products; Crude oil; Fuel oil; Gasoline; Groceries, general line; Grains; Industrial chemicals; Alkalines; Synthetic rubber; Aromatic chemicals; Industrial machinery & equipment; Ferrous metals; Nonferrous metal sheets, bars, rods, etc.; Steel; Petroleum products; Crude oil; Fuel oil; Gasoline; Groceries, general line; Grains; Industrial chemicals; Alkalines; Synthetic rubber; Aromatic chemicals; Industrial machinery & equipment
Pr: Seiei Ono

CFO: Hiroshi Kizaki
Ex VP: Hideto Nishimura
Sr VP: Makoto Okawara
Sr VP: Yu Sato
VP: Cheng Chun-Hsiung

MITSUBISHI EDM/LASER
See MC MACHINERY SYSTEMS INC

MITSUBISHI ELECT ELECTRNCS USA
See MITSUBISHI ELECTRIC US HOLDINGS INC

D-U-N-S 61-872-6079 IMP
MITSUBISHI ELECTRIC AUTOMATION INC
MEAU
(*Suby of* MITSUBISHI ELECT ELECTRNCS USA) ★
500 Corporate Woods Pkwy, Vernon Hills, IL 60061-3108
Tel (847) 478-2512 *Founded/Ownrshp* 2005
Sales 46.1MM^E *EMP* 300
SIC 3625 3566 3612 3613 3822 3829 Relays & industrial controls; Speed changers, drives & gears; Transformers, except electric; Switchgear & switchboard apparatus; Auto controls regulating residntl & coml environmt & applncs; Measuring & controlling devices; Relays & industrial controls; Speed changers, drives & gears; Transformers, except electric; Switchgear & switchboard apparatus; Auto controls regulating residntl & coml environmt & applncs; Measuring & controlling devices
CEO: Toshio Kawai
**CFO:* David Rebmann
Ofcr: Jason Stevens
VP: Matthew Lopinski
VP: Kazuhiko Tsutsui
VP: Tony Verissimo
Area Mgr: Steve Benedict
QA Dir: Steve Dietzel
Dir IT: Jeremy Bartusch
Info Man: Shingaku Kochi
Web Dev: Sal Salvador

D-U-N-S 18-311-7860 IMP
MITSUBISHI ELECTRIC AUTOMOTIVE AMERICA INC
(*Suby of* MITSUBISHI ELECT ELECTRNCS USA) ★
4773 Bethany Rd, Mason, OH 45040-8344
Tel (513) 573-6614 *Founded/Ownrshp* 2005
Sales 154.3MM^E *EMP* 754
SIC 3694 3651 3714 Motors, starting: automotive & aircraft; Alternators, automotive; Household audio & video equipment; Motor vehicle parts & accessories; Motors, starting: automotive & aircraft; Alternators, automotive; Household audio & video equipment; Motor vehicle parts & accessories
Pr: Takeo Sasaki
Pr: Richard Krieger
VP: Chris Gerdes
VP: Koichi Kawabata
Exec: Mike Delano
Plng Mgr: Carrie Grayson
Prd Mgr: Dominic Kroth
Ql Cn Mgr: Josiah Coleman
Sls&Mrk Ex: Bill Mondillo

MITSUBISHI ELECTRIC ELEVATORS
See MITSUBISHI ELECTRIC US INC

D-U-N-S 15-374-7456 IMP
MITSUBISHI ELECTRIC POWER PRODUCTS INC
MEPPI
(*Suby of* MITSUBISHI ELECT ELECTRNCS USA) ★
530 Keystone Dr, Warrendale, PA 15086-7537
Tel (724) 772-2555 *Founded/Ownrshp* 2005
Sales 168.2MM^E *EMP* 700
SIC 3613 Power circuit breakers; Power circuit breakers
Pr: Brian Herry
**CFO:* Bruce J Hampton
Ex VP: Masahiro Oya
VP: Carolyn Gerber
VP: Tammy Savoie
VP: Noah Tai
Genl Mgr: Hari Cheema
Genl Mgr: George Danbury
Genl Mgr: Dean Datre
Genl Mgr: Arthur Nagy
IT Man: Kevin Beamer

D-U-N-S 06-779-2481 EXP
MITSUBISHI ELECTRIC US HOLDINGS INC
MITSUBISHI ELECT ELECTRNCS USA
(*Suby of* MITSUBISHI ELECTRIC CORPORATION)
5900 Katella Ave Ste A, Cypress, CA 90630-5019
Tel (714) 220-2500 *Founded/Ownrshp* 2002
Sales 1.5MMM^E *EMP* 3,900
SIC 5065 5045 3651 3663 Electronic parts & equipment; Semiconductor devices; Computer peripheral equipment; Television receiving sets; Cellular radio telephone; Electronic parts & equipment; Semiconductor devices; Computer peripheral equipment; Television receiving sets; Cellular radio telephone
Pr: Katsuya Takamiya
Pr: Kyle Martin
**Treas:* Hiroshi Ishikawa
Treas: Peter Salavantis
**Ex VP:* Alan Olschwang
Area Mgr: George Carrera
Brnch Mgr: Chris Coll
Dir IT: Masami Ikeda
Opers Mgr: John Spalding
Sales Exec: Kristofor Ahuja
Sls&Mrk Ex: Rachel Ferguson

D-U-N-S 09-141-8897 IMP/EXP
MITSUBISHI ELECTRIC US INC
MITSUBISHI ELECTRIC ELEVATORS
(*Suby of* MITSUBISHI ELECT ELECTRNCS USA) ★
5900 Katella Ave Ste A, Cypress, CA 90630-5019
Tel (714) 220-2500 *Founded/Ownrshp* 2002
Sales 438.1MM^E *EMP* 750

SIC 5065 5045 1796 3534 Electronic parts & equipment; Semiconductor devices; Computer peripheral equipment; Elevator installation & conversion; Escalators, passenger & freight; Electronic parts & equipment; Semiconductor devices; Computer peripheral equipment; Elevator installation & conversion; Escalators, passenger & freight
CEO: Katsuya Takamiya
**CEO:* Masaki Sakuyama
**Treas:* Ittetsu Mori
**Ex VP:* Perry Pappous
**Sr VP:* Akira Kurishima
**VP:* Bruce Brenizer
VP: Don Lee
**VP:* Yuri Nakagawa
Genl Mgr: Mike Corbo
QA Dir: Steve Guyton
Dir IT: William Lucy

D-U-N-S 96-834-9006 IMP
MITSUBISHI ELECTRIC VISUAL SOLUTIONS AMERICA INC
MEVSA
(*Suby of* MITSUBISHI ELECTRIC CORPORATION)
10833 Valley View St # 300, Cypress, CA 90630-5051
Tel (714) 252-7801 *Founded/Ownrshp* 2011
Sales 55.8MM^E *EMP* 150
SIC 3679 Liquid crystal displays (LCD); Liquid crystal displays (LCD)
CEO: Tadashi Hiraoka
Pr: Kent Lofthouse
CFO: Hiroyuki Usami
**Ch:* Kenichiro Yamanishi
Treas: Hirohide Iwashita
Ex VP: Max Wasinger
Ex VP: Max Wassinger
Sr VP: Shoichi Suwa
VP: Akihiro Kambara
VP: Jim Landrum
Rgnl Mgr: David Gilles

D-U-N-S 12-129-0365 IMP
MITSUBISHI ENGINE NORTH AMERICA INC
M E N A
(*Suby of* MITSUBISHI HEAVY INDUSTRIES, LTD.)
2 Pierce Pl Ste 1100, Itasca, IL 60143-3133
Tel (630) 625-1875 *Founded/Ownrshp* 2006
Sales 21.8MM^E *EMP* 46
SIC 5084 Industrial machinery & equipment; Industrial machine parts
Pr: Yasushi Nio
VP: Sung Choi
Genl Mgr: Aki Kobuta
Dir IT: Sherman Ladd
VP Sls: Warren Roth

D-U-N-S 17-552-1079 IMP
MITSUBISHI FUSO TRUCK OF AMERICA INC
(*Suby of* MITSUBISHI FUSO TRUCK AND BUS CORPORATION)
2015 Center Square Rd, Swedesboro, NJ 08085-1683
Tel (856) 467-4500 *Founded/Ownrshp* 2004
Sales 39.0MM *EMP* 82
SIC 5012 5013 Trucks, commercial; Truck parts & accessories; Trucks, commercial; Truck parts & accessories
Pr: R E McDowell
Pr: Kevin Murray
CFO: Cynthia Koerner
Genl Mgr: Joshua Tregear
IT Man: Tom Hotham
Sls Mgr: Paul Overton

D-U-N-S 17-511-4909 IMP
MITSUBISHI GAS CHEMICAL AMERICA INC
MGC
(*Suby of* MITSUBISHI GAS CHEMICAL COMPANY,INC.)
655 3rd Ave Fl 24, New York, NY 10017-9105
Tel (212) 687-9030 *Founded/Ownrshp* 1984
Sales 231.1MM *EMP* 18
Accts Kiso & Tanaka Llp New York
SIC 5169 8742 Chemicals & allied products; Marketing consulting services; Chemicals & allied products; Marketing consulting services
Ch Bd: Kinji Hiramoto
**CFO:* Shuichi Murai
**Treas:* Hajime Fujaita
**Ex VP:* Tracy Austin
VP: Yoshikazu Nose
Genl Mgr: Hiroshi Hasegawa
Tech Mgr: Yusuke Yamataka

MITSUBISHI HEAVY INDS AMER
See PRIMETALS TECHNOLOGIES USA HOLDINGS INC

D-U-N-S 14-785-2636 IMP
MITSUBISHI HEAVY INDUSTRIES AMERICA INC
MHIA
(*Suby of* MITSUBISHI HEAVY INDUSTRIES, LTD.)
630 5th Ave Ste 2650, New York, NY 10111-2696
Tel (212) 969-9000 *Founded/Ownrshp* 1979
Sales 887.6MM *EMP* 1,030
Accts Ernst & Young Llp New York
SIC 5084 Industrial machinery & equipment; Petroleum industry machinery; Machine tools & metalworking machinery; Engines & transportation equipment; Industrial machinery & equipment; Petroleum industry machinery; Machine tools & metalworking machinery; Engines & transportation equipment
Pr: Yoshiyuki Ishii
**Pr:* Kenji Ando
**Treas:* Naohisa Higashida
**Ex VP:* Michihisa Yoshida
**Sr VP:* Nobutoshi Hanai
**VP:* Robert Allen Evers
VP: Ichiro Hagiwara
Opers Mgr: Dick Reinke
Counsel: Michael Bacon
Snr Mgr: Gaku Nakamura

D-U-N-S 95-616-5161 IMP/EXP
MITSUBISHI HEAVY INDUSTRIES CLIMATE CONTROL INC
MITSUBISHI CLIMATE CONTROL
(*Suby of* MITSUBISHI HEAVY INDUSTRIES, LTD.)
1200 N Mitsubishi Pkwy, Franklin, IN 46131-7560
Tel (317) 346-5000 *Founded/Ownrshp* 1995
Sales 37.6MM^E *EMP* 237
SIC 3585 7519 Air conditioning, motor vehicle; ; Air conditioning, motor vehicle;
Pr: Tetsuzo Ukai
**Sec:* Tenko Ikeea
**Sec:* Yasuaki Kubota
Sr VP: Scott Casalino
Genl Mgr: Tom Macfarland
IT Man: George Watson
Plnt Mgr: Kazuya Watanabe
Ql Cn Mgr: Gill Gallegos
Ql Cn Mgr: Maho Hasken

D-U-N-S 60-913-3744 IMP
MITSUBISHI HITACHI POWER SYSTEMS AMERICA-ENERGY AND ENVIRONMENT LTD
HPSA
645 Martinsville Rd, Basking Ridge, NJ 07920-4701
Tel (908) 542-9101 *Founded/Ownrshp* 2005
Sales 150.0MM *EMP* 100
SIC 8711 Engineering services; Electrical or electronic engineering

D-U-N-S 02-792-7958 IMP
MITSUBISHI HITACHI POWER SYSTEMS AMERICAS INC
MITSUBSHI PWR SYSTEMS AMERICAS
(*Suby of* MITSUBISHI HITACHI POWER SYSTEMS,LTD.)
400 Colonial Center Pkwy # 400, Lake Mary, FL 32746-7682
Tel (407) 688-6100 *Founded/Ownrshp* 2014
Sales 444.2MM^E *EMP* 600
SIC 5084 1796 Industrial machinery & equipment; Petroleum industry machinery; Machine tools & metalworking machinery; Engines & transportation equipment; Power generating equipment installation; Industrial machinery & equipment; Petroleum industry machinery; Machine tools & metalworking machinery; Engines & transportation equipment; Power generating equipment installation
CEO: Henry E Bartoli
**Pr:* Koji Hasegawa
**CFO:* Arunava Mitra
Treas: Haruo Nishio
**Treas:* Tomonari Takahashi
**Ex VP:* Tanc King
**Ex VP:* Mani Seshamani
**Sr VP:* William Buffa
**Sr VP:* Rick Inskeep
**VP:* David Brozek
VP: Michio Hara
VP: Chris Jensen
VP: Richard Sidkoff
VP: Shinichi Ueki

D-U-N-S 00-698-7770 IMP/EXP
MITSUBISHI INTERNATIONAL CORP (NY)
M I C
(*Suby of* MITSUBISHI CORP (AMERICAS)) ★
655 3rd Ave Ste 800, New York, NY 10017-9122
Tel (212) 605-2500 *Founded/Ownrshp* 1954, 2000
Sales 1.0MMM^E *EMP* 752
SIC 5051 5172 5141 5153 5169 5084 Ferrous metals; Nonferrous metal sheets, bars, rods, etc.; Steel; Petroleum products; Crude oil; Fuel oil; Gasoline; Groceries, general line; Grains; Industrial chemicals; Alkalines; Synthetic rubber; Aromatic chemicals; Industrial machinery & equipment; Ferrous metals; Nonferrous metal sheets, bars, rods, etc.; Steel; Petroleum products; Crude oil; Fuel oil; Gasoline; Groceries, general line; Grains; Industrial chemicals; Alkalines; Synthetic rubber; Aromatic chemicals; Industrial machinery & equipment
Ch Bd: Seiei Ono
**Ch Bd:* Hidemoto Mizuhara
Pr: Niel Taitt
CFO: Katsuhiro Ito
CFO: Hiroshi Kizaki
CFO: Yoichi Tamagawa
**CFO:* Naoki Tsuruta
Ex VP: Katsuhiko Hiyama
Ex VP: Osamu Tanaka
Ex VP: Hiroyuki Tarumi
Ex VP: Kazumi Yashimora
**Sr VP:* Jil Galloway
**Sr VP:* Jason Stevens
VP: Kazuki Haginoya
VP: Nobuo Mio
VP: Bill Ono
VP: Toshiro Sakai
VP: Atsushi Takahashi
VP: George Takahashi
VP: Takatoshi Wako

D-U-N-S 16-855-1443
MITSUBISHI INTERNATIONAL FOOD INGREDIENTS INC
(*Suby of* MITSUBISHI CORP (AMERICAS)) ★
5080 Tuttle Crossing Blvd, Dublin, OH 43016-3540
Tel (614) 652-1111 *Founded/Ownrshp* 2004
Sales 150.0MM *EMP* 83
SIC 5169 Food additives & preservatives; Food additives & preservatives
Ch Bd: Nobiuhiro Shirasu
Ofcr: Gerry McKiernan

D-U-N-S 80-701-9070 IMP/EXP
MITSUBISHI INTERNATIONAL POLYMERTRADE CORP
M I P
(*Suby of* M I C) ★
2 Penn Plz E Fl 11, Newark, NJ 07105-2251
Tel (732) 357-2000 *Founded/Ownrshp* 2010
Sales 800.0MM^E *EMP* 45^E
Accts Deloitte & Touche Llp New Yor
SIC 5169 Chemicals & allied products; Chemicals & allied products
Pr: Motoi Azumi
Dept Mgr: Dion Mahase
Div Mgr: Takahiro Tokuda
Div Mgr: Akito Watanabe
Mktg Mgr: Scott Goodell
Mktg Mgr: Takahiro Matsui
Sls Mgr: Takanori Ishii

D-U-N-S 36-136-1462 IMP/EXP
MITSUBISHI KAGAKU IMAGING CORP
FUTURE GRAPHICS
(*Suby of* MITSUBISHI CHEMICAL CORPORATION)
655 N Central Ave # 1550, Glendale, CA 91203-1451
Tel (818) 837-8100 *Founded/Ownrshp* 2010
Sales 309.1MM^E *EMP* 277
SIC 5044 3699 Laser systems & equipment; Office equipment; Office equipment; Laser systems & equipment
Pr: Hiromitsu Takayama
**Pr:* Yoshinobu Ikeda
**Ex VP:* Jimmy Simba

D-U-N-S 04-462-6885
MITSUBISHI LOGISTICS AMERICA CORP
(*Suby of* MITSUBISHI LOGISTICS CORPORATION)
61 Broadway Rm 1115, New York, NY 10006-2726
Tel (212) 968-0610 *Founded/Ownrshp* 1972
Sales 66.0MM *EMP* 22
Accts Wagner Ferber Fine & Ackerma
SIC 4731 4225 Freight forwarding; General warehousing; Freight forwarding; Customhouse brokers; General warehousing
Pr: Akio Miura
**Pr:* Mitsuaki Takada
**Treas:* Mayumi Tsujimura
**Treas:* Midori Yamamoto
**VP:* Ryoichi Furukawa
**VP:* Arata Kawada
**VP:* Robert Wallace
Admn Mgr: Elsie Meza
Sls Mgr: Spencer Kashiwagi

D-U-N-S 11-838-3330 IMP/EXP
MITSUBISHI MATERIALS USA CORP
(*Suby of* MITSUBISHI MATERIALS CORPORATION)
11250 Slater Ave, Fountain Valley, CA 92708-5421
Tel (714) 352-6100 *Founded/Ownrshp* 1984
Sales 73.5MM^E *EMP* 170
SIC 5085 5084 Industrial tools; Machine tools & accessories; Industrial tools; Machine tools & accessories
CEO: Motoharu Yamamoto
**Sec:* Niro Odani
VP: Dan Muldowney
Rgnl Mgr: Mike Bjerke
Sls Mgr: Ricardo Colon

D-U-N-S 62-697-3218
MITSUBISHI MOTORS CREDIT OF AMERICA INC
(*Suby of* MITSUBISHI MOTORS NORTH AMERICA INC) ★
6400 Katella Ave, Cypress, CA 90630-5208
Tel (714) 799-4730 *Founded/Ownrshp* 1990
Sales NA *EMP* 474
SIC 6141 6159 Automobile loans, including insurance; Truck finance leasing; Finance leasing, vehicles: except automobiles & trucks; Automobile loans, including insurance; Truck finance leasing; Finance leasing, vehicles: except automobiles & trucks
Pr: Dan Booth
**Treas:* Hideyuki Kitamura
**Ex VP:* Charles Tredway
Genl Mgr: Don Wright
MIS Dir: Angie Reynolds
Web Dev: Chris Patam

D-U-N-S 05-817-8583 IMP/EXP
MITSUBISHI MOTORS NORTH AMERICA INC
MMNA
(*Suby of* MITSUBISHI MOTORS CORPORATION)
6400 Katella Ave, Cypress, CA 90630-5208
Tel (714) 799-4730 *Founded/Ownrshp* 1981
Sales 1.5MMM^E *EMP* 3,600
SIC 5511 5013 6159 6512 Automobiles, new & used; Motor vehicle supplies & new parts; Automobile finance leasing; Truck finance leasing; Nonresidential building operators; Automobiles, new & used; Motor vehicle supplies & new parts; Automobile finance leasing; Truck finance leasing; Nonresidential building operators
Ch: Gayu Uesugi
**COO:* Jerry Berwanger
**Ex VP:* Takashi Kawasaki
Ex VP: Daniel P Kuhnert
Ex VP: Kazuki Sato
Ex VP: Kazuhiro Yamana
Sr VP: Dick Rinehimer
VP: John McElroy
VP: Mitsunobu Orihara
VP: Gary Shultz
**Exec:* Dan Booth
Comm Dir: Dan Irvin
Board of Directors: Dan Booth, Richard Gilligan, Hiroshi Harunari, Takashi Kawasaki

D-U-N-S 04-941-3693 IMP/EXP
MITSUBISHI MOTORS SALES OF CARIBBEAN INC
(*Suby of* MITSUBISHI MOTORS CORPORATION)
Road 2 K M 20 H M 1, TOA Baja, PR 00949
Tel (787) 251-8715 *Founded/Ownrshp* 1982
Sales 25.7MM^E *EMP* 90
SIC 5511 5013 Automobiles, new & used; Automotive supplies & parts; Automobiles, new & used; Automotive supplies & parts
Pr: Eduardo Mayoral
**Treas:* Shunichi Kihara
Mktg Mgr: Josephine Garcia
Sls Mgr: Wilbur Irizarry

D-U-N-S 78-812-4399 IMP/EXP
MITSUBISHI PLASTICS COMPOSITES AMERICA INC
M C H C
(*Suby of* MITSUBISHI PLASTICS,INC.)
401 Volvo Pkwy, Chesapeake, VA 23320-4611
Tel (757) 548-7850 *Founded/Ownrshp* 2005
Sales 35.7MM^E *EMP* 100
SIC 2819 5063 5051 Aluminum compounds; Electrical apparatus & equipment; Aluminum bars, rods, ingots, sheets, pipes, plates, etc.; Aluminum compounds; Electrical apparatus & equipment; Aluminum bars, rods, ingots, sheets, pipes, plates, etc.
Pr: Eiichi Sato
**Pr:* Eisaku Kakikura
**Treas:* Kohei Ichiya
**Treas:* Shinichi Iguchi
VP: Katsuya Serizawa
Sls Mgr: Chris Alvares

D-U-N-S 94-868-2695 IMP
MITSUBISHI POLYCRYSTALLINE SILICON AMERICA CORP
MITSUBISHI POLYSILICON
(*Suby of* MITSUBISHI MATERIALS CORPORATION)
7800 Mitsubishi Ln, Theodore, AL 36582-7204
Tel (251) 443-6440 *Founded/Ownrshp* 2002
Sales 20.7MM^E *EMP* 125
SIC 2869 3339 Silicon, epitaxial (silicon alloy); Minerals, ground or treated; Industrial organic chemicals; Industrial organic chemicals; Silicon, epitaxial (silicon alloy)
CEO: Hiro Ohta
**Pr:* Katsutoshi Ueda
**CEO:* Hashimoto Mayuki
**CFO:* Rob Howell
CFO: Howell Rob
**Sr VP:* K Ueda
VP: Rick Deckbar
VP: Seiichi Kirii
VP: Matt Wilson
Sfty Mgr: Chris Hicks
Snr Mgr: Rex Hudson

D-U-N-S 09-411-9133 IMP/EXP
MITSUBISHI POLYESTER FILM INC
(*Suby of* MITSUBISHI PLASTICS,INC.)
2001 Hood Rd, Greer, SC 29650-1014
Tel (864) 879-5000 *Founded/Ownrshp* 1999
Sales 228.8MM^E *EMP* 500
SIC 3081 2671 Unsupported plastics film & sheet; Packaging paper & plastics film, coated & laminated; Unsupported plastics film & sheet; Packaging paper & plastics film, coated & laminated
VP: Bill Wells
COO: Dennis Trice
**CFO:* Rick Mizuno
**Treas:* Dave Etherington
VP: Bill Radlein
Genl Mgr: Steven Yurich
QA Dir: Amy Lister
Dir IT: Kevin Shafer
IT Man: Jimmy Deyoung
Mfg Mgr: Ted Higgins
Sls Mgr: Matt Crandall

MITSUBISHI POLYSILICON
See MITSUBISHI POLYCRYSTALLINE SILICON AMERICA CORP

D-U-N-S 92-858-6312 IMP
MITSUBISHI RAYON AMERICA INC
(*Suby of* MITSUBISHI RAYON COMPANY,LIMITED)
655 3rd Ave Fl 15, New York, NY 10017-9135
Tel (212) 223-3043 *Founded/Ownrshp* 1983
Sales 120.7MM^E *EMP* 187
SIC 5169 Chemicals & allied products; Chemicals & allied products
Ch Bd: Hakaru Inaokam
**Ch Bd:* Hakaru Inaoka
**Pr:* Hiroyuki Sugao
**Treas:* D Ohyama
VP: Ryozo Nishioka
VP: Ward Urban
Mktg Mgr: Tats Iwai
Mktg Mgr: Mark Vassar

D-U-N-S 78-572-0798 IMP
MITSUBISHI RAYON CARBON FIBER AND COMPOSITES INC
CARBON FIBER DIVISION
(*Suby of* MITSUBISHI RAYON COMPANY,LIMITED)
5900 88th St, Sacramento, CA 95828-1109
Tel (916) 386-1733 *Founded/Ownrshp* 1991
Sales 28.4MM^E *EMP* 130
SIC 3624 Fibers, carbon & graphite; Fibers, carbon & graphite
CEO: Susumu Sasaki
**CFO:* Donald Carter
**VP:* Masayoshi Ozeki
**VP:* Takeshi Sasaki
Sls Dir: Steven Carmicheal

D-U-N-S 96-184-2825
MITSUBISHI TANABE PHARMA HOLDINGS AMERICA INC
(*Suby of* MITSUBISHI TANABE PHARMA CORPORATION)
525 Wshngton Blvd Fl 1400, Jersey City, NJ 07310
Tel (908) 607-1950 *Founded/Ownrshp* 2010
Sales 73.4MM^E *EMP* 78^E
SIC 5169 Chemicals & allied products
Top Exec: Michael Cooreman
VP: Doug Dobak
Info Man: Robbin Boccanfuso
Snr Mgr: Yosuke Kimura
Snr Mgr: Koji Takei

D-U-N-S 18-761-6982
MITSUBISHI UFJ SECURITIES (USA) INC
(*Suby of* MITSUBISHI UFJ SECURITIES HOLDINGS CO.,LTD.)
1221 Avenue Of The Flr 6, New York, NY 10020
Tel (212) 405-7000 *Founded/Ownrshp* 2003
Sales 34.3MM^E *EMP* 300
SIC 6211 Brokers, security; Dealers, security
Pr: William Mansfield
Ch Bd: Geoffrey Coley
VP: Cara Adler
VP: Marc Platizky
VP: Ranjan RAO
VP: Yasutaka Suehiro
VP: Damien Walters
Assoc Dir: Brian Young
Ex Dir: Maheen Baig
Ex Dir: Natsuki Kaijima
Ex Dir: Edward Todd

D-U-N-S 78-448-1392 IMP
MITSUBISHI UFJ TRUST AND BANKING CORP USA
(*Suby of* MITSUBISHI UFJ TRUST AND BANKING CORPORATION)
666 5th Ave Fl 33, New York, NY 10103-0001
Tel (212) 891-8500 *Founded/Ownrshp* 2006
Sales NA *EMP* 71^E
SIC 6021 National trust companies with deposits, commercial; National trust companies with deposits, commercial
Pr: Shigeru Tsukada
**VP:* Heidi Brown
VP: Ann Nolan

MITSUBSHI LITHOGRAPHIC PRESSES
See MLP USA INC

MITSUBSHI PWR SYSTEMS AMERICAS
See MITSUBISHI HITACHI POWER SYSTEMS AMERICAS INC

D-U-N-S 00-166-4523 IMP
MITSUI & CO (USA) INC (NY)
(*Suby of* MITSUI & CO., LTD.)
200 Park Ave Fl 35, New York, NY 10166-3599
Tel (212) 878-4000 *Founded/Ownrshp* 1966
Sales NA *EMP* 4,488
Accts Deloitte & Touche Llp New Yor
SIC 5051 5094 5084 5153 5172 5169 Ferrous metals; Nonferrous metal sheets, bars, rods, etc.; Steel; Bullion, precious metals; Industrial machinery & equipment; Machine tools & accessories; Grains; Petroleum products; Crude oil; Gases, liquefied petroleum (propane); Industrial chemicals; Ferrous metals; Nonferrous metal sheets, bars, rods, etc.; Steel; Bullion, precious metals; Industrial machinery & equipment; Machine tools & accessories; Grains; Petroleum products; Crude oil; Gases, liquefied petroleum (propane); Industrial chemicals
CEO: Motomu Takahashi
Pr: Taro Kondo
Pr: David Matsushita
Pr: Masamutsu Shinozaki
**CFO:* Kazuma Umehara
Treas: Eiji Imamura
Bd of Dir: Hiroko Kubota
**Ofcr:* Keiichi Furihata
Sr VP: Katsunori Aikyo
**Sr VP:* Susumu Katagiri
Sr VP: Isao Kuroda
Sr VP: Itaru Nishimura
Sr VP: Kazuki Okamura
Sr VP: Katagiri Susumu
Sr VP: Katsurao Yoshimori
VP: Keith Ewing
VP: Daiji Kojima
VP: Toru Tanaka
Exec: Makoto Koto

D-U-N-S 62-730-4108 IMP/EXP
MITSUI CHEMICALS AMERICA INC
(*Suby of* MITSUI CHEMICALS,INC.)
800 Westchester Ave N607, Rye Brook, NY 10573-1328
Tel (914) 253-0777 *Founded/Ownrshp* 1988
Sales 235.0MM^E *EMP* 830
SIC 2821 2865 3082 8731 5169 6159 Plastics materials & resins; Plasticizer/additive based plastic materials; Cyclic crudes & intermediates; Unsupported plastics profile shapes; Computer (hardware) development; Chemical additives; Loan institutions, general & industrial; Plastics materials & resins; Plasticizer/additive based plastic materials; Cyclic crudes & intermediates; Unsupported plastics profile shapes; Computer (hardware) development; Chemical additives; Loan institutions, general & industrial
Pr: Naoto Tani
**Treas:* Tsuneo Shibacaki
Ex VP: Toshikazu Tanaka
VP: Furukawa Manabu
Dir Bus: Yasuhiro Higuchi
Dir Bus: Takayuki Onogi
Dir Bus: Hiroshi Tsukuemoto
Mng Dir: Keiichi Sano
Off Mgr: Joan McLaughlin
Tech Mgr: Tamotsu Harada
Tech Mgr: Shige Yasui

D-U-N-S 05-666-7983 IMP
MITSUI FOODS INC
M F I
(*Suby of* MITSUI & CO (USA) INC) ★
35 Maple St, Norwood, NJ 07648-2003
Tel (201) 750-0500 *Founded/Ownrshp* 1972
Sales 71.0MM^E *EMP* 140
SIC 5142 5499 5149

D-U-N-S 15-124-6147
MITSUI FUDOSAN AMERICA INC
1251 AMERICAS ASSOCIATES
(*Suby of* MITSUI FUDOSAN CO., LTD.)
1251 Ave Of Americas 800, New York, NY 10020
Tel (212) 403-5600 *Founded/Ownrshp* 2000
Sales 82.0MM^E *EMP* 17^E
SIC 6519 6552 Landholding office; Land subdividers & developers, commercial
CEO: Yukio Yoshida
**COO:* Graham Bond
**CFO:* Iden Bentata
Treas: George Tietjen
**Sr VP:* Ian J Bentata
**Sr VP:* Christopher N Perez
Sr VP: Gregory Sutherland
Sr VP: Kaoru Yamaoka
VP: Breslin Anita

D-U-N-S 96-428-3287 IMP/EXP
MITSUI OSK LINES (AMERICA) INC
(*Suby of* MITSUI O.S.K. LINES, LTD.)
160 Fieldcrest Ave, Edison, NJ 08837-3642
Tel (201) 395-5800 *Founded/Ownrshp* 1990
Sales 28.8MM^E^ *EMP* 300
SIC 8611 Shipping & steamship company association; Shipping & steamship company association
Pr: Tsuyohi Yoshida
Ex VP: Raymond Keene
VP: Bill Daniels
VP: Alan Elman
**Prin:* Paul L Carlton
Opers Supe: Marty Wooley
Sls Mgr: John O'Brien

D-U-N-S 19-536-4260 IMP/EXP
MITSUI PLASTICS INC
(*Suby of* MITSUI & CO (USA) INC) ★
11 Martine Ave Ste 1175, White Plains, NY 10606-4026
Tel (914) 287-6800 *Founded/Ownrshp* 1988
Sales 116.6MM *EMP* 62
Accts Deloitte & Touche Llp Stamfor
SIC 5162 Plastics materials; Plastics materials
Pr: Fumitaka Tasaka
**COO:* David Matsushita
**CFO:* Kevi Siladi
Chf Cred: Naoto Kihara

D-U-N-S 02-484-8251 IMP
MITSUI SEIKI (USA) INC
(*Suby of* MITSUI SEIKI KOGYO CO.,LTD.)
563 Commerce St, Franklin Lakes, NJ 07417-1309
Tel (201) 337-1300 *Founded/Ownrshp* 1982
Sales 53.2MM *EMP* 34
SIC 5084 Industrial machinery & equipment; Machine tools & accessories; Industrial machinery & equipment; Machine tools & accessories
Pr: Scott Walker
**Ex VP:* Howard Hong H Lee
VP: Tom Dolan
Rgnl Mgr: James Previti
Sales Exec: Bill Malanche

D-U-N-S 12-365-1817
MITSUI SUMITOMO INSURANCE CO OF AMERICA
(*Suby of* MSIG HOLDINGS (AMERICAS) INC) ★
560 Lexington Ave Fl 20, New York, NY 10022-6828
Tel (212) 446-3600 *Founded/Ownrshp* 2002
Sales NA *EMP* 24^E^
SIC 6331 Fire, marine & casualty insurance; Fire, marine & casualty insurance
Prin: Tetsuro Kihara
VP: Takehisa Chiba
**VP:* Koji Oki
VP: Tatsuya Sudou
Brnch Mgr: Yasuhisa Tsukada

D-U-N-S 88-440-8956
MITSUI SUMITOMO INSURANCE CO OF AMERICA
MSIG
(*Suby of* MSIG HOLDINGS (AMERICAS) INC) ★
15 Independence Blvd 1100a, Warren, NJ 07059-2721
Tel (908) 604-2900 *Founded/Ownrshp* 2001
Sales NA *EMP* 197
SIC 6331 Fire, marine & casualty insurance; Fire, marine & casualty insurance
Pr: Koji Yoshida
Treas: Joseph L Farrell
Treas: Hisatoshi Saito
Ofcr: Robert B Miller
VP: Hiroshi Yamashita

D-U-N-S 10-159-5341
MITSUI SUMITOMO MARINE MANAGEMENT (USA) INC
(*Suby of* MSIG HOLDINGS (AMERICAS) INC) ★
15 Independence Blvd # 1, Warren, NJ 07059-2721
Tel (908) 604-2900 *Founded/Ownrshp* 2001
Sales 48.7MM^E^ *EMP* 350
SIC 8741 Administrative management; Administrative management
Ch Bd: Maki Kumagai
**COO:* Gary Garcia
**CFO:* Joseph Farrell
VP: Makoto Iida
VP: David Leskauskas
VP: Cheryl Lowden
VP: Eugene Wawer
Ql Cn Mgr: Tina O'Conner
Mktg Mgr: Shinji Tanaka

D-U-N-S 10-327-4759
MITSUI-SOKO (USA) INC
(*Suby of* MITSUI-SOKO HOLDINGS CO.,LTD.)
1651 Glenn Curtiss St, Carson, CA 90746-4014
Tel (310) 900-3004 *Founded/Ownrshp* 1983
Sales 26.9MM^E^ *EMP* 70
SIC 4731 Brokers, shipping; Freight forwarding
CEO: Masafumi Inoue
**Ch Bd:* Ryuji Ikeda
**Pr:* H Chijiiwa
VP: Ginny Blasnick
VP: Tak Sakamoto
Trfc Mgr: Eddie Sasaki
Trfc Mgr: Sharon Thomas

D-U-N-S 09-179-3620 IMP
MITSUKAWA US A INC
12 E 49th St Fl 17, New York, NY 10017-8287
Tel (212) 753-5580 *Founded/Ownrshp* 1977
Sales NA *EMP* 315
SIC 5199 5094 5812 5944

D-U-N-S 06-665-5614 IMP
MITSUWA CORP
MITSUWA MARKETPLACE
(*Suby of* KAMEI CORPORATION)
21515 S Western Ave, Torrance, CA 90501-3048
Tel (310) 782-6800 *Founded/Ownrshp* 1998
Sales 75.3MM^E^ *EMP* 652
SIC 5411 Grocery stores, chain; Grocery stores, chain
CEO: Takeshi Izuma
**CFO:* Kazuhiko Hori
VP: Noriyoshi Miyata
Store Mgr: Yasuaki Kishimoto

MITSUWA MARKETPLACE
See MITSUWA CORP

MITTAL STEEL -IHW- 3 SP
See ARCELORMITTAL MINORCA MINE INC

MITTEN FLUID POWER
See MITTEN FLUIDPOWER INC

D-U-N-S 05-938-6680 IMP
MITTEN FLUIDPOWER INC
MITTEN FLUID POWER
5960 Court Street Rd, Syracuse, NY 13206-1706
Tel (315) 437-7563 *Founded/Ownrshp* 1971
Sales 39.5MM^E^ *EMP* 50^E^
SIC 5085 3569 5084 Industrial supplies; Pistons & valves; Jacks, hydraulic; Industrial machinery & equipment
Co-Pr: John Mitten
**VP:* Robert Mitten
IT Man: John Buczek
S&M/VP: Brent Weicht
Sls Mgr: Gene Waggoner
Sales Asso: Tony Calarese
Sales Asso: Terry Smith

D-U-N-S 03-060-6693
MITTEN INC
MITTEN TRAVEL CENTER
1001 Highway 40, Oakley, KS 67748-6061
Tel (785) 672-3062 *Founded/Ownrshp* 1966
Sales 42.6MM^E^ *EMP* 100
Accts Williams Consulting Chartered
SIC 5541 Truck stops; Filling stations, gasoline; Truck stops; Filling stations, gasoline
Pr: Gary L Johnson
**Sec:* Toni S Johnson
**VP:* James Mildenberger
Store Mgr: Greg Klein

MITTEN TRAVEL CENTER
See MITTEN INC

MITTERA
See ROCK ACQUISITION HOLDINGS LLC

D-U-N-S 07-961-3433
MITTERA CREATIVE SERVICES LLC
CATCHFIRE MEDIA, LLC
(*Suby of* MITTERA GROUP INC) ★
1312 Locust St Ste 202, Des Moines, IA 50309-2920
Tel (800) 348-9044 *Founded/Ownrshp* 2014
Sales 43.6MM^E^ *EMP* 200^E^
SIC 4899 Data communication services; Data communication services
Pr: Jon Troen
Chf Mktg O: Al Tramontina
VP: Perry Klein
VP Opers: Dave Fehrer

D-U-N-S 00-527-5870
MITTERA GROUP INC
ROCK COMMUNICATIONS LTD.
1312 Locust St Ste 202, Des Moines, IA 50309-2920
Tel (515) 343-5353 *Founded/Ownrshp* 1974
Sales 207.1MM^E^ *EMP* 410
SIC 2752 Commercial printing, offset; Commercial printing, offset
Pr: Jon Troen
IT Man: Rich May
Mktg Dir: Todd Johnson
Genl Couns: Thomas Slaughter

D-U-N-S 00-815-0765 EXP
MITTERNIGHT BOILER WORKS INC
5301 Highway 43 N, Satsuma, AL 36572
Tel (251) 675-2550 *Founded/Ownrshp* 1946
Sales 34.1MM^E^ *EMP* 75
SIC 3443 3559 Vessels, process or storage (from boiler shops): metal plate; Chemical machinery & equipment
CEO: F Todd Burkhalter
**Pr:* Lance Covan
**CFO:* Norbert F Long
**VP:* Thomas T Rogers
QC Dir: Mike Estes
Sfty Mgr: John Harrington

D-U-N-S 00-185-4892 IMP
MITUTOYO AMERICA CORP (NY)
(*Suby of* MITUTOYO CORPORATION)
965 Corporate Blvd, Aurora, IL 60502-9176
Tel (630) 820-9666 *Founded/Ownrshp* 1963
Sales 151.6MM *EMP* 250
Accts Etsuko Neupame
SIC 5084 7373 Measuring & testing equipment, electrical; Computer systems analysis & design; Measuring & testing equipment, electrical; Computer systems analysis & design
Pr: Shigeyuki Sasaki
VP: Doug Atkins
VP: Matt Dye
Admn Mgr: Norman McHan
Dir IT: Bob Brown
IT Man: Jackie Macshane
Manager: Alan Jackson
Sls Mgr: Robert Dillon
Sales Asso: Betsy Modaff

D-U-N-S 84-812-5659 IMP/EXP
MITY ENTERPRISES INC
MITYLITE
(*Suby of* M L E HOLDINGS INC) ★
1301 W 400 N, Orem, UT 84057-4442
Tel (801) 224-0589 *Founded/Ownrshp* 2007
Sales 35.0MM^E^ *EMP* 392
SIC 2531 2522 2521 Public building & related furniture; Office desks & tables: except wood; Panel systems & partitions, office: except wood; Chairs, office: padded or plain, except wood; Tables, office: except wood; Wood office furniture; Wood office chairs, benches & stools; Chairs, office: padded, upholstered or plain: wood; Panel systems & partitions (free-standing), office: wood; Public building & related furniture; Office desks & tables: except wood; Panel systems & partitions, office: except wood; Chairs, office: padded or plain, except wood; Tables, office: except wood; Wood office furniture; Wood office chairs, benches & stools; Chairs, office: padded, upholstered or plain: wood; Panel systems & partitions (free-standing), office: wood
Pr: Randall Hales
**VP:* Fraser Bullock
**VP:* Paul R Killpack
Snr Mgr: Paul Killpack

D-U-N-S 18-107-2521 IMP/EXP
MITY-LITE INC
(*Suby of* SULLIVAN UNIVERSITY SYSTEM INC) ★
1301 W 400 N, Orem, UT 84057-4442
Tel (801) 224-0589 *Founded/Ownrshp* 2007
Sales 73.7MM *EMP* 280
Accts Deloitte & Touche Llp Salt La
SIC 2531 2522 7359 Public building & related furniture; Tables, office: except wood; Dishes, silverware, tables & banquet accessories rental; Public building & related furniture; Tables, office: except wood; Dishes, silverware, tables & banquet accessories rental
Pr: John Dudash
**COO:* Brian Bowers
**CFO:* Paul Kilpack
**CFO:* Jim Yostrum
**Ex VP:* Dennis Claspell
**Ex VP:* Brandon Ross
VP: Mark Hoffman

MITYLITE
See MITY ENTERPRISES INC

MITZEL'S AMERICAN KITCHENS
See ELMERS RESTAURANTS INC

D-U-N-S 08-689-4433 IMP/EXP
MITZI INTERNATIONAL HANDBAG & ACCESSORIES LTD
250 Passaic St, Newark, NJ 07104-3700
Tel (212) 686-4666 *Founded/Ownrshp* 1976
Sales 60.3MM^E^ *EMP* 255
SIC 5137 5199

MIU
See MICHIGAN INSTITUTE OF UROLOGY P C

MIU MIU
See PRADA USA CORP

D-U-N-S 83-151-3564 IMP/EXP
MIURA MANUFACTURING AMERICA CO LTD
2200 Steven B Smith Blvd, Rockmart, GA 30153-3662
Tel (678) 685-0929 *Founded/Ownrshp* 2009
Sales 31.0MM^E^ *EMP* 110^E^
SIC 3443 Boilers: industrial, power, or marine
Pt: Mark Utzinger
IT Man: Bethany Patty
Plnt Mgr: Brad Wood

D-U-N-S 06-106-7823 IMP
MIVILA CORP
MIVILA FOODS
226 Getty Ave, Paterson, NJ 07503-2690
Tel (973) 278-4148 *Founded/Ownrshp* 1972
Sales 43.7MM^E^ *EMP* 112
SIC 5141

MIVILA FOODS
See MIVILA CORP

D-U-N-S 79-037-1269
■ **MIX HOLDINGS INC**
(*Suby of* HALLMARK CARDS INC) ★
2501 Mc Gee Traffic Way, Kansas City, MO 64108
Tel (816) 274-5111 *Founded/Ownrshp* 2000
Sales 1.0MMM^E^ *EMP* 5,650^E^
SIC 3952 3951 3295 3944 Lead pencils & art goods; Crayons: chalk, gypsum, charcoal, fusains, pastel, wax, etc.; Chalk: carpenters', blackboard, marking, tailors', etc.; Paints, except gold & bronze: artists'; Markers, soft tip (felt, fabric, plastic, etc.); Clay, ground or otherwise treated; Games, toys & children's vehicles; Craft & hobby kits & sets; Lead pencils & art goods; Crayons: chalk, gypsum, charcoal, fusains, pastel, wax, etc.; Chalk: carpenters', blackboard, marking, tailors', etc.; Paints, except gold & bronze: artists'; Markers, soft tip (felt, fabric, plastic, etc.); Clay, ground or otherwise treated; Games, toys & children's vehicles; Craft & hobby kits & sets
Ofcr: Tim Malcomvetter
VP: Michael Goodwin
Dir IT: Danyel Bischof-Forsyth
IT Man: Ken Cameron
IT Man: Steve Eikos
IT Man: Jerry Wolfe
IT Man: Joel Zigelstein

D-U-N-S 14-484-3976
MIXON SEED CO INC
1438 Joe Jeffords Hwy, Orangeburg, SC 29115
Tel (803) 531-1777 *Founded/Ownrshp* 1985
Sales 89.4MM^E^ *EMP* 34
SIC 5191 Seeds: field, garden & flower
Pr: Daniel A Mixon

D-U-N-S 03-604-8635
MIXSON OIL CO INC
TIGER EXPRESS
4301 Allndale Fairfax Hwy, Allendale, SC 29810-5909
Tel (803) 584-2398 *Founded/Ownrshp* 1924
Sales 51.6MM *EMP* 33
Accts Steven D Murdaugh Pa Walterb
SIC 5171 Petroleum bulk stations; Petroleum bulk stations
Pr: David M Mixson
**Sec:* Robert R Mixson
**VP:* Richard H Mixson Jr

D-U-N-S 09-768-6356
MIYAKE CONCRETE ACCESSORIES INC
250 Waiehu Beach Rd Ste N, Wailuku, HI 96793-1462
Tel (808) 244-7988 *Founded/Ownrshp* 1979
Sales 25.8MM^E^ *EMP* 64
SIC 5032 5031 5211 Concrete building products; Lumber: rough, dressed & finished; Concrete & cinder block; Lumber products
CEO: David Miyake
**Pr:* Myron M Nakamura
**COO:* Tyson K Miyake
**CFO:* Michelle Miyake- Duquero
**VP:* Stacie K Miyake

D-U-N-S 04-895-1842 IMP
MIZAR HOLDING CO INC
BERNINA OF AMERICA
(*Suby of* BERNINA INTERNATIONAL AG)
3702 Prairie Lake Ct, Aurora, IL 60504-3135
Tel (630) 978-2500 *Founded/Ownrshp* 2002
Sales 79.5MM^E^ *EMP* 425
SIC 5064 Sewing machines, household: electric; Sewing machines, household: electric
Ch Bd: H P Ueltschi
**Pr:* Paul Ashworth
**Pr:* Michael Perich
CFO: Mike Parish
VP: Hermann Kuhn
Dist Mgr: Therese Canfield
Dist Mgr: John Carr
Dist Mgr: Joyce Douglas
Dist Mgr: Dan Robbins
Mktg Dir: Amy Gutierrez
Mktg Mgr: Gayle Schliemann

D-U-N-S 83-032-5619 IMP
MIZCO INTERNATIONAL INC
CELLULAR INNOVATIONS
80 Essex Ave E, Avenel, NJ 07001-2020
Tel (732) 912-2000 *Founded/Ownrshp* 1987
Sales 46.2MM^E^ *EMP* 100
SIC 5043 3629 3663 3661 3691 Photographic cameras, projectors, equipment & supplies; Battery chargers, rectifying or nonrotating; Mobile communication equipment; Telephone cords, jacks, adapters, etc.; Batteries, rechargeable; Photographic cameras, projectors, equipment & supplies; Battery chargers, rectifying or nonrotating; Mobile communication equipment; Telephone cords, jacks, adapters, etc.; Batteries, rechargeable
Pr: Albert Mizrahi
**CFO:* Joseph Mizrahi
Ex VP: David Strumeier
VP: Chris Flaharty
**VP:* Sam Mizarahi
**VP:* Isaac Mizrahi
Software D: Michael Shamalow
Sftwr Eng: Jim Kugit
VP Opers: Joe Schonfeld
Sales Exec: Elliot Dabah
Sls Dir: Jennifer Schroeder

D-U-N-S 19-474-6988
MIZE IMPORT GROUP INC
O HARE HYUNDI
1533 S River Rd, Des Plaines, IL 60018-1760
Tel (847) 297-5700 *Founded/Ownrshp* 1987
Sales 28.7MM^E^ *EMP* 80
SIC 5511 Automobiles, new & used; Automobiles, new & used
Prin: Joe Griff
Dir IT: Rodney Niewinski

D-U-N-S 18-505-0002 IMP/EXP
MIZKAN AMERICA HOLDINGS INC
NAKANO FOODS
(*Suby of* MIZKAN J PLUS HOLDINGS CO.,LTD.)
1661 Feehanville Dr # 300, Mount Prospect, IL 60056-6087
Tel (847) 590-0059 *Founded/Ownrshp* 1982
Sales 141.9MM^E^ *EMP* 350
SIC 2099 Vinegar
Pr: Hiroyasu Nakano
**VP:* Kenji Sano
**VP:* Ichiro Suzuki
IT Man: Richard Bugna
Natl Sales: Tim Marvin

D-U-N-S 06-237-8401 IMP
MIZKAN AMERICAS INC
(*Suby of* MIZKAN AMERICAS INC) ★
4065 J St Se, Deming, NM 88030-7164
Tel (575) 546-8863 *Founded/Ownrshp* 2011
Sales 20.8MM^E^ *EMP* 150
SIC 2099 2037 2038 2032 Chili pepper or powder; Vegetables, quick frozen & cold pack, excl. potato products; Frozen specialties; Canned specialties; Chili pepper or powder; Vegetables, quick frozen & cold pack, excl. potato products; Frozen specialties; Canned specialties
CEO: Randy Clark
**Pr:* Craig M Smith
**Treas:* Mark E Majewski
**Sr VP:* Bob Gats
**VP:* Kazuya Kawamura
**VP:* Robert Lampert
**VP:* Jesus Torres
VP: Barry Zelickson
Prd Mgr: Robert Ramos

D-U-N-S 06-832-6164 IMP/EXP
MIZKAN AMERICAS INC (MI)
NAKANO FOODS
(*Suby of* MIZKAN AMERICA HOLDINGS INC) ★
1661 Feehanville Dr # 300, Mount Prospect, IL 60056-6031
Tel (847) 590-0059 *Founded/Ownrshp* 1902, 1987
Sales 141.9MM^E^ *EMP* 350
SIC 2099 2035 Vinegar; Dressings, salad: raw & cooked (except dry mixes); Mustard, prepared (wet); Vinegar; Dressings, salad: raw & cooked (except dry mixes); Mustard, prepared (wet)
CEO: Kazuhide M Nakano Viii
Pr: Craig Smith
CFO: Mark Majewski

CFO: Michael McGuire
Sr VP: Matt Moore
VP: Peter Marsing
Off Mgr: Beryle Martin
Off Mgr: Jessica Ruiz
Off Admin: Patricia Alexander
Off Admin: Sharon Brotzge
Off Admin: Lori May

D-U-N-S 80-138-7445
MIZUHO ALTERNATIVE INVESTMENTS LLC
(*Suby of* MIZUHO BANK,LTD.)
757 3rd Ave Fl 8, New York, NY 10017-2013
Tel (212) 282-3871 *Founded/Ownrshp* 2007
Sales 22.0MM *EMP* 54
SIC 6282 Investment advice; Investment advice
CEO: Nasatoshi Mugo
**COO:* Sagoshi Iwanaga
COO: Jun Nozaki
Sr VP: Kazuhiro Shimbo

D-U-N-S 06-020-3957
MIZUHO BANK LTD
(*Suby of* MIZUHO BANK,LTD.)
1251 Ave Of The Americas, New York, NY 10020-1104
Tel (212) 282-3000 *Founded/Ownrshp* 2002
Sales NA *EMP* 500ᴱ
SIC 6022 6082 7359 State commercial banks; Foreign trade & international banking institutions; Equipment rental & leasing; State commercial banks; Foreign trade & international banking institutions; Equipment rental & leasing
Ex Dir: Masathuga Nagato
CFO: Koji Mimura
Treas: Ashok Kapoor
Ofcr: Luis Baltodano
Ofcr: Katori Hanada
Ofcr: Michelle Kim
Ofcr: Hiroshi Suehiro
Ofcr: Temannis Tay
Sr VP: Masatoshi Abe
Sr VP: Carl Benzinger
Sr VP: Brian Caldwell
Sr VP: Paul Chew
Sr VP: Bobby Dixit
Sr VP: Palrick Doyle
Sr VP: Richard Dunning
Sr VP: James Ecock
Sr VP: Tetsuya Fujita
Sr VP: Yasuo Fukai
Sr VP: Christian Hammerbeck
Sr VP: Kevin Holmes
Sr VP: Masatoshi Imaeda

D-U-N-S 08-452-7241 IMP
MIZUHO ORTHOPEDIC SYSTEMS INC
MIZUHO OSI
(*Suby of* MIZUHO CORPORATION)
30031 Ahern Ave, Union City, CA 94587-1234
Tel (510) 429-1500 *Founded/Ownrshp* 2002
Sales 49.6MMᴱ *EMP* 300ᴱ
SIC 3841 Surgical & medical instruments; Operating tables; Surgical & medical instruments; Operating tables
CEO: Takashi Nemoto
**Pr:* Steve Lamb
CFO: Randha Lata
**Treas:* Yosup Kim
Treas: Dean Yamamura
VP: Mark Lane
VP: Jon Levenson
VP: Greg Neukirch
VP: Larry Waters
Genl Mgr: Maxima Cordero
**Genl Mgr:* Patrick Rimroth

MIZUHO OSI
See MIZUHO ORTHOPEDIC SYSTEMS INC

D-U-N-S 08-308-6298
MIZUHO SECURITIES USA INC
(*Suby of* MIZUHO SECURITIES CO.,LTD.)
320 Park Ave Fl 12, New York, NY 10022-6848
Tel (212) 282-3000 *Founded/Ownrshp* 1979, 2007
Sales 170.2MMᴱ *EMP* 290
SIC 6211 Traders, security; Traders, security
Ch Bd: Bernard Jensen
COO: Patrick Fay
Bd of Dir: Yasuo Agemura
Bd of Dir: Keisuke Yokoo
Ofcr: Shigeru Akiyoshi
Ofcr: Masahiro Miyamoto
Ofcr: Ikuo Shimayoshi
Ofcr: Glenn Visco
Ofcr: Hiroshi Yuki
Sr VP: Naosuke Abe
Sr VP: David Evans
Sr VP: Jeffrey Lynch
Sr VP: David McNeela
VP: Franklin Amoo
VP: Sandy Bidon
VP: Andrew Buenaventura
VP: Jeffrey Connolly
VP: Joao Costa
VP: Babak Ghatan
VP: Vanessa Goodger
VP: Paul Hughes

D-U-N-S 78-842-3770
MIZUHO TRUST & BANKING CO (USA)
(*Suby of* MIZUHO TRUST & BANKING CO., LTD.)
135 W 50th St Fl 16, New York, NY 10020-1201
Tel (212) 373-5900 *Founded/Ownrshp* 2007
Sales NA *EMP* 100
SIC 6021 National trust companies with deposits, commercial; National trust companies with deposits, commercial
Ch Bd: Masakzu Hirosawa
**Pr:* R Ban
**V Ch Bd:* Anthony C Howkins
**Ex VP:* Toshihiro Uehara
**Sr VP:* Paul Schneider
VP: Glen Banta
VP: Brian Casey
VP: Vincent Esposito
VP: Julia Minnemeyer
VP: John Vogel
VP: Scott Wozny

D-U-N-S 78-479-7169 IMP
MIZUNO USA INC
(*Suby of* MIZUNO CORPORATION)
4925 Avalon Ridge Pkwy, Peachtree Corners, GA 30071-1571
Tel (770) 441-5553 *Founded/Ownrshp* 1996
Sales 69.3MMᴱ *EMP* 285
SIC 3949 5091 Sporting & athletic goods; Golf equipment; Athletic goods; Sporting & athletic goods; Golf equipment; Athletic goods
CEO: Robert S Puccini
COO: Robert White
CFO: Marsha King
VP: Josh Creasman
**VP:* Katsuyoki Makino
VP: Peter Moore
**VP:* Bruce Riccio
VP: Bob White
Rgnl Mgr: Chuck Gartner
CTO: Bill Price
Mfg Dir: Curtis Brown

D-U-N-S 07-881-8533
MJ AUTO SALES LLC
MILTON RUBEN TOYOTA
3510 Washington Rd, Augusta, GA 30907-2948
Tel (706) 868-5454 *Founded/Ownrshp* 2009
Sales 42.9MMᴱ *EMP* 300
SIC 5511 Automobiles, new & used; Automobiles, new & used
Genl Mgr: Robbie Newman

MJ CARE FOR KIDS
See MJ CARE INC

D-U-N-S 14-774-2993
MJ CARE INC
MJ CARE FOR KIDS
2448 S 102nd St Ste 340, Milwaukee, WI 53227-2147
Tel (414) 329-2500 *Founded/Ownrshp* 2002
Sales 20.0MMᴱ *EMP* 400
SIC 8049 Occupational therapist; Physical therapist; Occupational therapist; Physical therapist
CEO: Mary Van Lare
**Pr:* Curt Klade
**Ch:* Mary Cavicchi
**VP:* Jane Beisser
**VP:* Norbert H Kurth
VP: Mary Schwenke
VP: Keith Wilson
CTO: Anne Stoner
Occ Thrpy: Christy Anderson
Occ Thrpy: Jenny Gfall
Occ Thrpy: Suzanne Weigman

D-U-N-S 06-761-5471 IMP/EXP
■ **MJ ELECTRIC LLC**
(*Suby of* QUANTA SERVICES INC) ★
200 W Frank Pipp Dr, Iron Mountain, MI 49801-1419
Tel (906) 774-0185 *Founded/Ownrshp* 2007
Sales 63.1MMᴱ *EMP* 198
SIC 1731 Electrical work; Electrical work
Pr: Steve J Reiten
Treas: Terence R Montgomery
Sr VP: Tony Broccolo
Sr VP: Jeff Campbell
Sr VP: Ed Farrington
VP: Dale Ebert
VP: William Nagy
Mtls Mgr: Jared Keller
Opers Mgr: Andy Gardner
Snr PM: Harry Laski

D-U-N-S 07-463-9584
MJ HALL & CO INC
709 N Center St Ste 2k, Stockton, CA 95202-1641
Tel (209) 948-8108 *Founded/Ownrshp* 1973
Sales NA *EMP* 55
SIC 6411 Insurance brokers
Pr: Rupert C Hall
**Ch:* Michael J Hall
**Treas:* John A Quattrin

D-U-N-S 88-341-8378
MJ HARRIS CONSTRUCTION SERVICES LLC
1 Riverchase Rdg Ste 300, Hoover, AL 35244-2910
Tel (205) 380-6800 *Founded/Ownrshp* 2012
Sales 96.9MMᴱ *EMP* 135
SIC 1542 Commercial & office building contractors; Commercial & office building contractors
Pr: Michael J Harris
CFO: Robbie Egan
Sec: Bobby J Harris
Sr VP: Tommy Yeager
VP: Matt Hall
VP: Blair Hayes
VP: Kevin Hicks
Mtls Mgr: Paul Ealy
Snr PM: Lance Couch
Snr PM: Ralph Crumpton

D-U-N-S 78-106-8440
MJ HOLDING CO LLC
7001 S Harlem Ave, Bedford Park, IL 60638-4713
Tel (708) 793-5800 *Founded/Ownrshp* 1990
Sales 35.6MMᴱ *EMP* 73ᴱ
SIC 5099 5091 Novelties, durable; Sporting & recreation goods
CEO: Matthew Bayer
Pr: David Stickney
COO: Charles Barerther
CFO: Lew Dewalt
Sr Cor Off: Bruce Azuma
Software D: Todd Demantes
VP Opers: Alan Wojak
VP Opers: Ryan Wright
Opers Mgr: David Hodgson
Plnt Mgr: Jaime Delgadillo
Natl Sales: Mike Berin

D-U-N-S 07-206-4447
MJ INSURANCE INC
9225 Priority Way West Dr # 100, Indianapolis, IN 46240-1572
Tel (317) 805-7500 *Founded/Ownrshp* 1964
Sales NA *EMP* 101ᴱ
SIC 6411 Insurance agents
CEO: Michael H Bill
**Pr:* Jon Loftin
**Ch:* Michael M Bill
Sr Cor Off: Cindy Williams
Bd of Dir: Ruth Knauer
Ex VP: Donna Bender
**VP:* Jan R Bednarz
**VP:* Frank Crossland
**VP:* Brian P Friend
**VP:* J Colin Mac Nab
VP: Colin Macnab
**VP:* Ed Mournighan
Dir Bus: Mike Schmidt

MJ KELLNER FOODSERVICE
See M J KELLNER CO INC

D-U-N-S 14-071-4648
MJ LAWNS INC
761 Leonardo Ct, Kissimmee, FL 34758-3350
Tel (407) 729-1122 *Founded/Ownrshp* 2001
Sales 70.0MM *EMP* 5
SIC 0782 Lawn care services; Lawn care services
Pr: Mark Feliciano

D-U-N-S 08-033-5383
■ **MJ MECHANICAL SERVICES INC**
(*Suby of* COMFORT SYSTEMS USA INC) ★
2040 Military Rd, Tonawanda, NY 14150-6776
Tel (716) 874-9200 *Founded/Ownrshp* 1977, 1998
Sales 56.8MMᴱ *EMP* 205
SIC 1711 Mechanical contractor; Warm air heating & air conditioning contractor; Mechanical contractor; Warm air heating & air conditioning contractor
CEO: Michael D Poole
**CFO:* Nancy Pohlman
**VP:* John E Bergmann

D-U-N-S 19-368-7563
■ **MJ RESEARCH INC**
(*Suby of* BIO-RAD LABORATORIES INC) ★
245 Winter St Ste 100, Waltham, MA 02451-8709
Tel (510) 724-7000 *Founded/Ownrshp* 1987
Sales 20.4MMᴱ *EMP* 325
SIC 3823 Industrial process measurement equipment
Pr: John D Finney
**Treas:* Michael J Finney

D-U-N-S 85-857-7364
MJ RESURRECTION INC
FRESH WAREHOUSING
4300 Church Rd, Centreville, IL 62207-1378
Tel (618) 271-5500 *Founded/Ownrshp* 1991
Sales 26.0MMᴱ *EMP* 85
SIC 4225 General warehousing & storage
CEO: Mark Cusumano
**Pr:* Mary Jane Cusumano
VP: Micheal Cusama
**VP:* Micheal Cusumano
VP: Jason Overbey
IT Man: Mary Cusamano
IT Man: Andy Suchanek
Opers Mgr: Bill Volkamer
Opers Mgr: Scott Zitnick
Mktg Mgr: Kelly Sullivan

M.J. SCHNEIDER PLUMBING & MECH
See CHAS ROBERTS AIR CONDITIONING INC

D-U-N-S 05-182-5347 IMP/EXP
■ **MJ SOFFE LLC**
COTTON EXCHANGE, THE
(*Suby of* DELTA APPAREL INC) ★
1 Soffe Dr, Fayetteville, NC 28312-5262
Tel (910) 435-3138 *Founded/Ownrshp* 2003
Sales 163.5MMᴱ *EMP* 1,190
SIC 2339 2329 2369 2321 Athletic clothing: women's, misses' & juniors'; Athletic (warmup, sweat & jogging) suits: men's & boys'; Girls' & children's outerwear; Men's & boys' furnishings; Athletic clothing: women's, misses' & juniors'; Athletic (warmup, sweat & jogging) suits: men's & boys'; Girls' & children's outerwear; Men's & boys' furnishings
Pr: Steve Cochran
VP: Tony Augustine
**VP:* Keith Bilyeu
VP: Jeff Bradford
Store Mgr: Matthew Anderson
IT Man: Lori Herring
IT Man: Laura Howell
MIS Mgr: Carla Autry
QC Dir: Teresa Jones
VP Sls: Elisa Palefsky
S&M/VP: Steve Wheeler

D-U-N-S 18-181-6562 IMP
■ **MJ SOFFE LLC**
TCX, LLC
(*Suby of* COTTON EXCHANGE) ★
115 E Third St, Wendell, NC 27591-9791
Tel (910) 483-2500 *Founded/Ownrshp* 2010
Sales 18.0MM *EMP* 290
SIC 5136 5137 2339 2331 Sportswear, men's & boys'; Sportswear, women's & children's; Women's & misses' outerwear; Women's & misses' blouses & shirts; Sportswear, men's & boys'; Sportswear, women's & children's; Women's & misses' outerwear; Women's & misses' blouses & shirts
Ch Bd: Robert Humphreys
CFO: Deborah H Miller
Div Pres: Ken Spires
Ex VP: Keith Bilyeu
VP: Bill Howard
VP: Martha M Watson
VP Opers: Scott Reynolds
VP Mktg: Dottie Dye

D-U-N-S 80-598-8474 IMP
MJ SYSTEMS INC
17050 Evergreen Pl, City of Industry, CA 91745-1819
Tel (626) 964-2000 *Founded/Ownrshp* 1992
Sales 25.0MM *EMP* 20
SIC 5045 5065 Computer peripheral equipment; Diskettes, computer
Pr: Michael Jen

D-U-N-S 07-842-9017 EXP
MJ VISALIA PRODUCE LLC
VISALIA PRODUCE SALES
201 W Stroud Ave, Kingsburg, CA 93631-9531
Tel (559) 897-6652 *Founded/Ownrshp* 2011
Sales 50.0MM *EMP* 25
SIC 5148 Fresh fruits & vegetables; Fresh fruits & vegetables
COO: Stephen Biswell
Sales Exec: Aron Gularte

D-U-N-S 03-613-4807
MJB OF EASLEY INC
CRANE OLDSMOBILE
1600 E Main St, Easley, SC 29640-3790
Tel (864) 859-3286 *Founded/Ownrshp* 1923
Sales 20.8MM *EMP* 43
SIC 5511 Automobiles, new & used; Automobiles, new & used
Pr: William C Crane Jr
**VP:* William C Crane III

D-U-N-S 04-324-2606 IMP
MJB WOOD GROUP INC (TX)
MJB WORLD TRADE DIVISION
2201 W Royal Ln Ste 250, Irving, TX 75063-3210
Tel (972) 401-0005 *Founded/Ownrshp* 1998
Sales 250.0MM *EMP* 165
SIC 5031 Lumber, plywood & millwork; Lumber, plywood & millwork
CEO: Joe A Caldwell
**Pr:* Jeffrey L Messick
**CFO:* Charles A Little
VP: Dale Arnold
**VP:* Amy G Quaid
Div Mgr: Steve Daugherty
Mfg Dir: Mike Trostle
Manager: Robert Poston
Sls Mgr: Sue-Ann Clemons
Sls Mgr: Trevor Cowell
Sls Mgr: Vincent Fergen

MJB WORLD TRADE DIVISION
See MJB WOOD GROUP INC

D-U-N-S 80-490-7236 IMP
MJC INTERNATIONAL GROUP LLC
(*Suby of* BOLERO USA) ★
5 Thomas Mellon Cir # 303, San Francisco, CA 94134-2501
Tel (415) 467-9500 *Founded/Ownrshp* 2008
Sales 40.2MMᴱ *EMP* 40
SIC 5136 Neckwear, men's & boys'
VP: Mark Siegel

D-U-N-S 05-377-7517
■ **MJD VENTURES INC**
(*Suby of* FAIRPOINT COMMUNICATIONS INC) ★
521 E Morehead St Ste 500, Charlotte, NC 28202-2861
Tel (704) 344-8150 *Founded/Ownrshp* 1995
Sales 71.2MMᴱ *EMP* 297
SIC 4813 5999 4812 Telephone communication, except radio; Local telephone communications; Telephone equipment & systems; Paging services; Telephone communication, except radio; Local telephone communications; Telephone equipment & systems; Paging services
CEO: Paul H Sunu
**CFO:* Lisa Hood
**CFO:* Walter Leach Jr
**Ch:* David Hauser
**VP:* Shirley Linn
**VP:* Peter Nixon
Genl Mgr: Gabrielle Stevens
**CIO:* Kathleen McLean

D-U-N-S 09-937-2120
MJG CORP
DAIRY QUEEN
204 W 4th St, Roswell, NM 88201-4629
Tel (575) 622-8711 *Founded/Ownrshp* 1979
Sales 35.6MMᴱ *EMP* 900
SIC 5812 Ice cream stands or dairy bars; Ice cream stands or dairy bars
Pr: Jay Gluck

D-U-N-S 06-828-9867
MJG NURSING HOME CO INC (NY)
METROPOLITAN JEWISH HOSPICE
6323 7th Ave Ste 2, Brooklyn, NY 11220-4742
Tel (718) 851-3700 *Founded/Ownrshp* 1971
Sales 129.0MM *EMP* 730
Accts Loeb & Troper Llp New York N
SIC 8051 Skilled nursing care facilities; Skilled nursing care facilities
Pr: Eli S Feldman
**CFO:* Alexander Balko
CFO: Daniel Kasle
Ex VP: Maxine Hochhauser
Ex VP: Barry Volin
Sr VP: Erin O'Connor
Sr VP: Robert Sideli
VP: Harold Baron
VP: Elliot Brooks
VP: John Levitt
VP: Janet Rothman

MJHS HOSPICE AND PALLIATIVE CA
See METROPOLITAN JEWISH HOME CARE INC

MJJ BRILLIANT
See BRILLIANT JEWELERS/MJJ INC

D-U-N-S 09-286-5679
MJKL ENTERPRISES LLC
5210 S Priest Dr, Tempe, AZ 85283-1431
Tel (480) 897-7777 *Founded/Ownrshp* 2000
Sales 46.2MMᴱ *EMP* 1,200
SIC 5812 Eating places; Eating places
CEO: Jason Levecke

MJLM ENGRG & TECHNICAL SVCS
See MCCONNELL JONES LANIER & MURPHY LLP

D-U-N-S 00-115-5670
MJM HOLDINGS INC (NH)
130 N Main St, Lisbon, NH 03585-6603
Tel (603) 838-6624 *Founded/Ownrshp* 1871, 1985

Sales 75.0MM *EMP* 576
SIC 3357 Nonferrous wiredrawing & insulating; Nonferrous wiredrawing & insulating
Pr: Wendell W Jesseman
**VP:* Richard C Johns
**VP:* Robert F Meserve
Prd Mgr: Felix Paneto

D-U-N-S 00-430-6288
MJO INDUSTRIES INC
HUGHES-PETERS
8000 Technology Blvd, Huber Heights, OH 45424-1573
Tel (937) 235-7100 *Founded/Ownrshp* 1999
Sales 69.5MM *EMP* 80
SIC 5063 5065

D-U-N-S 83-014-1359
MJP EMPIRE INC
1682 Langley Ave Fl 2, Irvine, CA 92614-5620
Tel (714) 564-7900 *Founded/Ownrshp* 2004
Sales 15.8MM^E *EMP* 300^E
SIC 1721 Painting & paper hanging; Painting & paper hanging
Pr: Jason Reid
CFO: Nancy Meloni
**CFO:* Tracy Meneses
**VP:* Jeff Gunhus
**VP:* Matt Stewart

D-U-N-S 78-553-3423
MJPT II & ASSOCIATES LTD
MCDONALD'S
1333 Oakview Dr, Columbus, OH 43235-1134
Tel (614) 431-5774 *Founded/Ownrshp* 1989
Sales 10.5MM^E *EMP* 300
SIC 5812 6513

D-U-N-S 88-446-1674
MJV JANITORIAL INC
TEAM MJV
115 Farabee Dr N Ste E, Lafayette, IN 47905-5933
Tel (765) 449-8641 *Founded/Ownrshp* 1992
Sales 19.3MM^E *EMP* 600
SIC 7349 Cleaning service, industrial or commercial; Cleaning service, industrial or commercial
Pr: Mark Vaughn
**Ex Dir:* Marc Vaughn
Sls Mgr: Lori Bauerle

MK BATTERY
See KCM MARKETING INC

D-U-N-S 01-924-0659
MK MANAGEMENT INC
COMPUDIRECT 3000
23052 Lake Forest Dr D1, Laguna Hills, CA 92653-1325
Tel (949) 581-3036 *Founded/Ownrshp* 2000
Sales 26.0MM *EMP* 16
SIC 5045 Computers, peripherals & software
Pr: Mike Kiani

MK MANUFACTURING
See M K PRODUCTS INC

D-U-N-S 80-450-6319
MK WEEDEN CONSTRUCTION INC
2 Miles W Hwy 87, Lewistown, MT 59457
Tel (406) 538-3726 *Founded/Ownrshp* 1991
Sales 31.9MM^E *EMP* 150
SIC 1794 Excavation work; Excavation work
Pr: Monte K Weeden
**CFO:* Karlene Weeden

D-U-N-S 04-367-3136
MKA ENTERPRISES INC
SCION
10100 Parallel Pkwy, Kansas City, KS 66109-3635
Tel (913) 299-8600 *Founded/Ownrshp* 1966
Sales 20.4MM^E *EMP* 52
SIC 5511 5521 Automobiles, new & used; Pickups, new & used; Vans, new & used; Used car dealers
Pr: Duce Lett
**Prin:* Roger Smith
Genl Mgr: Jon Tucker
Sls Mgr: Chevis Reid
Sls Mgr: Phil Ulrich
Sales Asso: Leo Bernal

MKB REALTORS
See MASTIN KIRKLAND BOLLING INC

MKC
See MID-KANSAS COOPERATIVE ASSOCIATION

D-U-N-S 03-690-3045
MKD ELECTRIC INC
1450 N Mclean Blvd Ste A, Elgin, IL 60123-1235
Tel (847) 608-8244 *Founded/Ownrshp* 1995
Sales 23.8MM *EMP* 116
SIC 1731 Electrical work; Electrical work
Pr: Mark E Wesa
CFO: Mary Kuehl
**VP:* Michael Bowman
Exec: John Burck
Off Mgr: Wendy Loftus
Sales Asso: Keith Lichthardt
Snr PM: Marv Baar

D-U-N-S 01-692-8947 IMP/EXP
MKI OLD CO INC
7393 Expressway Ct Sw, Grand Rapids, MI 49548-7967
Tel (616) 281-8610 *Founded/Ownrshp* 1965, 1979
Sales 34.1MM^E *EMP* 85
SIC 5511 5531 Trucks, tractors & trailers: new & used; Truck equipment & parts; Trucks, tractors & trailers: new & used; Truck equipment & parts
Ch Bd: Ronald V Nordstrom Sr
**Pr:* Joel Love
**Treas:* Vicki Love
**VP:* Brian Arens

D-U-N-S 79-231-0133
MKM AUTOMOTIVE INC
MCGRATH CITY HONDA
6720 W Grand Ave, Chicago, IL 60707-2212
Tel (773) 889-3030 *Founded/Ownrshp* 2006
Sales 20.0MM^E *EMP* 70
SIC 5511 Automobiles, new & used; Automobiles, new & used
Pr: Michael J McGrath
IT Man: Chad Benner

D-U-N-S 13-110-7435 IMP
MKM DISTRIBUTION SERVICES INC
8256 Zionsville Rd, Indianapolis, IN 46268-1627
Tel (317) 334-7900 *Founded/Ownrshp* 1981
Sales 48.9MM^E *EMP* 424^E
SIC 4213 4225 Trucking, except local; General warehousing; Trucking, except local; General warehousing
Pr: William J Hurley
Ofcr: Beth Frank
**VP:* Kathleen Hurlwy
VP Bus Dev: William Mancuso
Prgrm Mgr: John Severson
IT Man: John Williams
VP Opers: Ted Baggesen

D-U-N-S 83-048-8156
MKMB RESTAURANT PARTNERS LLC
BURGER KING
17 N Loomis St Ste 1a, Chicago, IL 60607-1914
Tel (312) 433-0300 *Founded/Ownrshp* 2008
Sales 16.8MM^E *EMP* 710
SIC 5812 Fast-food restaurant, chain; Fast-food restaurant, chain
CEO: Martin L King

MKMG
See MOUNT KISCO MEDICAL GROUP PC

MKNI
See KLEPPE & NASH MORGAN

D-U-N-S 00-619-5908
MKRB LIQUIDATION INC (PA)
L S I
1645 W Chester Pike, West Chester, PA 19382-7955
Tel (888) 808-6111 *Founded/Ownrshp* 2000
Sales 30.2MM^E *EMP* 93^E
SIC 4813 Local telephone communications
CEO: Michael Miller
**Pr:* Raymond Fireman
**CEO:* Kevin McGeary
**Treas:* Barry Fireman
**Ex VP:* Warren Reyburn
**VP:* John West
Sales Exec: Carl O'Brien

D-U-N-S 00-105-3982 IMP
▲ MKS INSTRUMENTS INC (MA)
2 Tech Dr Ste 201, Andover, MA 01810-2434
Tel (978) 645-5500 *Founded/Ownrshp* 1961
Sales 780.8MM *EMP* 2,377
Accts Pricewaterhousecoopers Llp Bo
Tkr Sym MKSI *Exch* NGS
SIC 3823 3491 3494 Pressure measurement instruments, industrial; Flow instruments, industrial process type; Pressure valves & regulators, industrial; Valves & pipe fittings; Pressure measurement instruments, industrial; Flow instruments, industrial process type; Industrial valves; Pressure valves & regulators, industrial; Valves & pipe fittings
Pr: Gerald G Colella
Treas: William Donlan
Ofcr: Seth H Bagshaw
Sr VP: John R Abrams
Sr VP: John T C Lee
Sr VP: Brian C Quirk
Sr VP: John A Smith
VP: Jian Ding
Prin: Roger Wu
Mng Dir: Terry Moore
Mng Dir: Ole Wenzel
Board of Directors: Cristina H Amon, Robert R Anderson, Gregory R Beecher, John R Bertucci, Peter R Hanley, Elizabeth A Mora

D-U-N-S 12-672-8448
■ MKS MSC INC
(*Suby of* MKS INSTRUMENTS INC) ★
90 Industrial Way, Wilmington, MA 01887-4610
Tel (978) 284-4000 *Founded/Ownrshp* 1986
Sales 64.3MM^E *EMP* 700
Accts Pricewaterhousecoopers Llp Bo
SIC 3823 3491 3494 Pressure measurement instruments, industrial; Flow instruments, industrial process type; Pressure valves & regulators, industrial; Valves & pipe fittings; Pressure measurement instruments, industrial; Flow instruments, industrial process type; Pressure valves & regulators, industrial; Valves & pipe fittings
Pr: John R Bertucci
Treas: Joe Tocci
VP: Jack Abrams
Dir IT: Lance Lambert

D-U-N-S 01-351-1770
MKS SERVICES LLC (TX)
6389 N Us Highway 79, Palestine, TX 75801-2418
Tel (903) 727-0105 *Founded/Ownrshp* 2007
Sales 28.6MM^E *EMP* 48^E
SIC 5984 Liquefied petroleum gas dealers

D-U-N-S 07-834-4911
MKTECHNICALSUPPORT CA INC (NY)
1855 Five Mile Line Rd, Penfield, NY 14526-1007
Tel (585) 267-7084 *Founded/Ownrshp* 2012
Sales 31.9MM^E *EMP* 279
SIC 3571 Electronic computers; ; Electronic computers
CEO: Kevin Whitman
**VP:* Casey Vanetri
**Ex Dir:* Marie Hoffman

D-U-N-S 07-998-9822
MKTG INC
32 Avenue Of The Americas, New York, NY 10013-2473
Tel (212) 366-3481 *Founded/Ownrshp* 2015
Sales 33.0MM^E *EMP* 6,000
SIC 8742 Marketing consulting services
Pr: Rachelle McDonough

D-U-N-S 83-569-5453
▲ MKTG INC
75 9th Ave Fl 3, New York, NY 10011-7027
Tel (212) 366-3400 *Founded/Ownrshp* 1972
Sales 139.0MM *EMP* 6,840^E
Tkr Sym CMKG *Exch* OTC
SIC 7311 7389 8743 Advertising agencies; Advertising, promotional & trade show services; Sales promotion; Advertising agencies; Advertising, promotional & trade show services; Sales promotion
Ch Bd: Charles Horsey
COO: Michael Price
CFO: Paul Trager
Bd of Dir: Richard L Feinstein
Chf Mktg O: Frank Dudley
Chf Mktg O: Feliz Morin
Ex VP: Bryan Duffy
Ex VP: John Mousseau
Sr VP: James R Haughton
VP: Leslie Brennan
VP: Richard Gifford
VP: Kerry Lange
VP: Rachelle McDonnel
VP: Rachelle McDonough
VP: Ben Roth
VP: Ken Zick
Exec: Peter Rozie
Dir Soc: Victoria Hilger
Dir Soc: Nicholas Knapic
Dir Soc: Mischelle Maurer
Dir Soc: Alexis Thomas
Board of Directors: Scott Hughes

D-U-N-S 07-869-8215 EXP
ML AUTOMOTIVE GROUP LLC
PALMETTO57 NISSAN
16725 Nw 57th Ave, Miami Gardens, FL 33055-3919
Tel (305) 474-4045 *Founded/Ownrshp* 2012
Sales 63.6MM^E *EMP* 158
SIC 5511 Automobiles, new & used; Automobiles, new & used
Dir IT: Eric Mund
Sls Mgr: Antonio Cantu

D-U-N-S 07-867-7609
ML INDUSTRIES INC
605 W Austin St, Fredericksburg, TX 78624-3211
Tel (956) 279-8678 *Founded/Ownrshp* 2008
Sales 45.2MM^E *EMP* 3,850
SIC 7549 Automotive maintenance services
Pr: Mickey T Dunn
CFO: Gary Dunham

D-U-N-S 05-600-9160
ML MCDONALD SALES CO LLC
50 Oakland St, Watertown, MA 02472-2202
Tel (617) 923-4071 *Founded/Ownrshp* 1923
Sales 35.0MM *EMP* 250^E
SIC 1721 1742 1799 Painting & paper hanging; Drywall; Fireproofing buildings; Window treatment installation; Painting & paper hanging; Drywall; Fireproofing buildings; Window treatment installation
Pr: Peter Towsend
**CFO:* Stephen O'Donnell
VP: Glenn Alexander
MIS Dir: Roger Cram
Mfg Dir: Anthony Gallonio

D-U-N-S 04-036-1370
MLADEN BUNTICH CONSTRUCTION CO INC
1500 W 9th St, Upland, CA 91786-5636
Tel (909) 920-9977 *Founded/Ownrshp* 1975
Sales 24.7MM^E *EMP* 60
SIC 1623 Sewer line construction; Pipeline construction; Sewer line construction; Pipeline construction
Ch Bd: Mladen Buntich Jr
VP: Lee Rocsncr
**VP:* Lee Roesner
Exec: Mladen Griffith
**Exec:* Scott Peterson

M'LADY, JIM OLDSMOBILE, NISSA
See JIM MLADY OLDSMOBILE INC

D-U-N-S 00-767-3671
MLB ADVANCED MEDIA LP
M L B
(*Suby of* M L B) ★
75 9th Ave Fl 5, New York, NY 10011-7076
Tel (212) 485-3444 *Founded/Ownrshp* 2001
Sales 21.6MM^E *EMP* 300^E
SIC 4841 7313 7929 Subscription television services; Subscription television services; Electronic media advertising representatives; Entertainment service
Prin: Robert Bowman
**CFO:* Edward Weber Jr
Bd of Dir: David James
Ofcr: Joe Choti
Sr VP: Tony Santomauro
VP: Andy Butters
VP: John Fisher
VP: Matthew A Gould
VP: Raymond Maccio
VP: Bernadette McDonald
VP: Keith Stoler
Exec: Bill Morningstar
Assoc Dir: Aleksandar Kolundzija
Assoc Dir: Ariana Soba
Dir Bus: Rebecca Shaw

D-U-N-S 15-390-2676
MLB CONSTRUCTION SERVICES LLC
1 Stonebreak Rd, Ballston Spa, NY 12020-4425
Tel (518) 289-1371 *Founded/Ownrshp* 2002
Sales 36.5MM^E *EMP* 85
SIC 1542 Commercial & office building, new construction
**VP:* Scott A Shepherd
Dir Bus: Brian R Akley

D-U-N-S 82-756-9711
MLB NETWORK LLC
(*Suby of* M L B) ★
40 Hartz Way Ste 1, Secaucus, NJ 07094-2403
Tel (201) 974-2470 *Founded/Ownrshp* 2008
Sales 46.4MM^E *EMP* 180
SIC 4833 Television broadcasting stations; Television broadcasting stations
CEO: Tony Petitti
Ex VP: Rob McGlarry
Ex VP: Bill Morningstar
Sr VP: Mary Beck
Sr VP: Steve Miller
Sr VP: Jennifer Shaw
VP: Andy Butters
VP: Chris Mallory
VP: Keith Stoler
Info Man: Don Schulze
Mktg Mgr: Dan Robins

D-U-N-S 02-938-4476
MLC AUTOMOTIVE INC
MEL CLAYTON FORD
1550 E Camelback Rd, Phoenix, AZ 85014-3496
Tel (602) 266-2415 *Founded/Ownrshp* 1988
Sales 26.1MM^E *EMP* 120
SIC 5511 Automobiles, new & used; Automobiles, new & used
Pr: Gary L Clayton
**VP:* M L Clayton
Sls Mgr: Jerry Schwelling

D-U-N-S 11-191-9205
MLC THEMING INC
2700 Bonnet Creek Rd, Lake Buena Vista, FL 32830-8513
Tel (407) 812-6616 *Founded/Ownrshp* 2008
Sales 44.8MM^E *EMP* 150
SIC 1542 Nonresidential construction; Nonresidential construction
Pr: John Lynch
**CFO:* Niall Connolly

D-U-N-S 02-121-3918
MLF DISTRIBUTING INC
SUN OFFICE PRODUCTS
1 Environmental Way, Broomfield, CO 80021-3415
Tel (720) 484-5555 *Founded/Ownrshp* 2001
Sales 67.1MM^E *EMP* 40
SIC 5112 5113 Stationery & office supplies; Industrial & personal service paper
Prin: Michael Fikany
**VP:* Roger Dieckhaus
Dir IT: Dustin Armbrust

D-U-N-S 62-240-5723 IMP
MLG IMPORTS LLC
4841 Summer Ave, Memphis, TN 38122-4733
Tel (901) 345-8525 *Founded/Ownrshp* 2005
Sales 21.4MM^E *EMP* 50
SIC 5137 Women's & children's clothing
**CFO:* Jeffrey B Presley
**Opers Mgr:* Keith A Thweatt

D-U-N-S 07-939-0255
MLG LAW LLC
1425 K St Nw Ste 350, Washington, DC 20005-3514
Tel (813) 574-1852 *Founded/Ownrshp* 2012
Sales 30.0MM *EMP* 12
SIC 8111 General practice attorney, lawyer; General practice attorney, lawyer
Prin: Tim Jordan

D-U-N-S 62-036-6310
MLH INC
GARBO'S
120 Regency Pkwy Ste 139, Omaha, NE 68114-4399
Tel (402) 391-2333 *Founded/Ownrshp* 1988
Sales 7.7MM^E *EMP* 335
Accts Bkd Llp Omaha Ne
SIC 7231 Hairdressers; Hairdressers
Pr: Mary L Walker
**Sec:* Linda Mixon
**VP:* Mark Constantino

MLI INTGRTED GRAPHIC SOLUTIONS
See MARTIN LITHOGRAPH INC

D-U-N-S 07-887-7217
MLIM HOLDINGS LLC
350 Camino De La Reina, San Diego, CA 92108-3003
Tel (619) 299-3131 *Founded/Ownrshp* 2011
Sales NA *EMP* 768
SIC 6719 Investment holding companies, except banks; Investment holding companies, except banks
Ch: Douglas Manchester
CEO: John Lynch

D-U-N-S 07-887-7191
■ MLIM LLC
(*Suby of* TRIBUNE PUBLISHING CO) ★
350 Camino De La Reina, San Diego, CA 92108-3003
Tel (619) 299-3131 *Founded/Ownrshp* 2015
Sales 155.0MM^E *EMP* 766^E
SIC 2711 Newspapers; Newspapers
Ch: Douglas Manchester
CEO: John Lynch
CFO: Ryan Kiesel

D-U-N-S 03-409-7489
MLN ADVERTISING INC
1608 Bush St, Baltimore, MD 21230-2021
Tel (443) 449-7564 *Founded/Ownrshp* 2009
Sales 50.6MM *EMP* 4
SIC 7311 Advertising agencies; Advertising agencies
CEO: Justin Musterman
**Pr:* Sundararajan Nathikudic
**COO:* Stephen Williams
Snr Mgr: Sundar Nathikudi

D-U-N-S 61-737-5464 IMP/EXP
MLN CO
3931 Ann Arbor Dr, Houston, TX 77063-6301
Tel (713) 784-7353 *Founded/Ownrshp* 1988
Sales 40.3MM^E *EMP* 250^E
SIC 1711

D-U-N-S 62-698-7069 IMP
MLP USA INC
MITSUBSHI LITHOGRAPHIC PRESSES
(*Suby of* MHIA) ★
11204 Mccormick Rd South, Hunt Valley, MD 21031-1115
Tel (410) 584-7990 *Founded/Ownrshp* 2004

Sales 26.7MM^E *EMP* 120
SIC 5084 Printing trades machinery, equipment & supplies; Printing trades machinery, equipment & supplies
Pr: K G Katayama
**Ex VP:* Tak Uchiu
Sales Exec: Ken Ono

MLS
See MIDWEST LIVESTOCK SYSTEMS INC

D-U-N-S 83-599-0573
MLS FREIGHT LOGISTICS LLC
1802 S Expressway 281, Edinburg, TX 78542-7201
Tel (956) 292-2700 *Founded/Ownrshp* 1993
Sales 34.0MM^E *EMP* 68
SIC 4731 Truck transportation brokers
CEO: Ray Villareal Jr
**Pr:* David Rowland
**CFO:* Aaron Heller
**Ex VP:* Mike Castillo
IT Man: Ray Reyna
Opers Mgr: Nick Cuevas

MLS SOLUTIONS
See MARKETLINX INC

MLT INC.
See MLT VACATIONS LLC

D-U-N-S 05-073-6644
■ **MLT VACATIONS LLC**
MLT INC.
(*Suby of* DELTA AIR LINES INC) ★
700 S Central Ave, Atlanta, GA 30354-1923
Tel (651) 289-8500 *Founded/Ownrshp* 1989
Sales 700.0MM^E *EMP* 500
SIC 4725 Arrangement of travel tour packages, wholesale; Arrangement of travel tour packages, wholesale
Pr: John Caldwell
**CEO:* James J Cron
Sr VP: Tina Iglio
VP: Terry Williams
IT Man: Kim Boesen
Mktg Mgr: Kate Gregory
Mktg Mgr: Sarah Leaf

MM
See MORLEY-MURPHY CO

MM ADVERTISING
See MONEY MAILER LLC

D-U-N-S 14-331-6920
MM HOLDINGS I LLC
MANCHESTER METALS
205 Wabash Rd, North Manchester, IN 46962-1418
Tel (260) 982-2191 *Founded/Ownrshp* 2003
Sales 39.7MM^E *EMP* 135
SIC 3321 Gray & ductile iron foundries; Gray & ductile iron foundries
Pr: David Boyd
Sales Exec: Richards Steve

D-U-N-S 08-656-4960
MM LOUISIANA INC
HOLIDAY INN
(*Suby of* MMI HOTEL GROUP INC) ★
1000 Red Fern Pl, Jackson, MS 39232-8879
Tel (601) 936-3666 *Founded/Ownrshp* 1977
Sales 6.8MM^E *EMP* 300
SIC 7011 8741 Hotels & motels; Restaurant management; Hotels & motels; Restaurant management
Co-Ch Bd: Mike P Sturdivant
**Pr:* Gaines P Sturdivant
**Co-Ch Bd:* Earle F Jones Jr
**Treas:* Michael J Hart

D-U-N-S 94-306-1085
MM PACKAGING PRODUCTS INC
MM SOLUTIONS
3915 N Garfield Ave, Loveland, CO 80538-2239
Tel (970) 203-0393 *Founded/Ownrshp* 1994
Sales 20.9MM^E *EMP* 31
SIC 5085 7389 2449 Packing, industrial; Relocation service; Rectangular boxes & crates, wood
Pr: David Yowell
Exec: Shannon Johnson
Mktg Mgr: Trevor Trout

MM SOLUTIONS
See MM PACKAGING PRODUCTS INC

D-U-N-S 05-141-1130
MM USA HOLDINGS INC
780 Township Line Rd, Yardley, PA 19067-4200
Tel (267) 685-2300 *Founded/Ownrshp* 1976
Sales 536.8MM^E *EMP* 1,500
SIC 2741 8732 Miscellaneous publishing; Market analysis or research; Miscellaneous publishing; Market analysis or research
CEO: William Goldberg
**CFO:* Puneet Sapra
Ex VP: Sue Lewis
Sr VP: Gloria Cross
Sr VP: Beth Nergard
Sr VP: Jennifer Thompson
Sr VP: Sean P Wagner
VP: Sharon Aquaro
VP: Jennifer Cressman
VP: Camm Epstein
VP: Ben Etherington
VP: Maureen Liberti
VP: Jodie McVan
VP: Timothy Murphy
Exec: Christopher Labarthe
Exec: Laurie Telsey
Creative D: Sean Kelly

MMA
See MARSHALL MILLER & ASSOCIATES INC

D-U-N-S 08-815-6799
▲ **MMA CAPITAL MANAGEMENT LLC**
621 E Pratt St Ste 600, Baltimore, MD 21202-3147
Tel (443) 263-2900 *Founded/Ownrshp* 1995
Sales NA *EMP* 49^E
Tkr Sym MMAC *Exch* NAS
SIC 6162 6722 6799 Mortgage bankers & correspondents; Bond & mortgage companies; Management investment, open-end; Real estate investors, except property operators; Mortgage bankers & correspondents; Bond & mortgage companies; Management investment, open-end; Real estate investors, except property operators
Pr: Michael L Falcone
**Ch Bd:* Francis X Gallagher Jr
CFO: David C Bjarnason
CFO: Lisa M Roberts
Ex VP: Frank Creamer
Ex VP: William S Harrison
Ex VP: Gary A Mentesana
Sr VP: Keith J Gloeckl
VP: Stephen Goldberg
VP: Kevin Panzica
Mng Dir: Roxanne Walton
Board of Directors: Steven S Bloom, J P Grant, Frederick W Puddester

D-U-N-S 16-823-9882
■ **MMA FINANCIAL WAREHOUSING LLC**
(*Suby of* MMA CAPITAL MANAGEMENT LLC) ★
101 Arch St Ste 1600, Boston, MA 02110-1106
Tel (617) 439-3911 *Founded/Ownrshp* 2002
Sales 80.5MM^E *EMP* 100^E
SIC 6799 6282 Real estate investors, except property operators; Investment advice
Off Mgr: Trish Gator

D-U-N-S 60-750-8913
■ **MMA RENEWABLE VENTURES LLC**
(*Suby of* MMA CAPITAL MANAGEMENT LLC) ★
44 Montgomery St Ste 2200, San Francisco, CA 94104-4709
Tel (415) 229-8817 *Founded/Ownrshp* 2006
Sales 80.5MM^E *EMP* 100
SIC 5074 Heating equipment & panels, solar
VP: Peter Conklin
VP: Davis Kastner
Genl Couns: Steve Holman

MMC
See MARSH RISK & INSURANCE SERVICES INC

MMC
See MEDICAL MANAGEMENT CONSULTANTS INC

MMC
See MEADVILLE MEDICAL CENTER

MMC ARMORY
See MENNIES MACHINE CO

MMC BEHAVIORAL HEALTH SERVICES
See MEMORIAL MEDICAL CENTER INC

D-U-N-S 00-716-8214
MMC CONTRACTORS NATIONAL INC (MO)
(*Suby of* MMC CORP) ★
13800 Wyandotte St, Kansas City, MO 64145-1518
Tel (816) 215-3422 *Founded/Ownrshp* 1932
Sales 108.3MM^E *EMP* 500
SIC 1711 Mechanical contractor; Mechanical contractor
CEO: William F McDermott
CFO: David Cimpl
Treas: Michael J Teahan
**Treas:* Michael J Tehan
**VP:* Keith E Andrews
VP: Kim Caddell
VP: Mike Chick
VP: Daniel Christensen
VP: John Duncan
VP: Brent Leed
VP: David Leibowitz
VP: Mike Teahan

D-U-N-S 10-758-9129
MMC CONTRACTORS NORTHEAST INC
(*Suby of* MWM GROUP INC) ★
144 Belmont Dr, Somerset, NJ 08873-1204
Tel (973) 560-0100 *Founded/Ownrshp* 1990
Sales 37.1MM^E *EMP* 175
Accts Bkd Llp Kansas City Mo
SIC 1711 Mechanical contractor; Process piping contractor; Mechanical contractor; Process piping contractor
CEO: William McDermott
**Pr:* Thomas Powers
**CFO:* David Cimpl
**Treas:* Michael J Teahan
**VP:* Jane Zelazny Belz
**VP:* Daniel V Kearney
**VP:* David M Liebowitz
VP: Jacob Vogel
VP Opers: Brent Hawley
Snr PM: Mark Couret
Snr PM: Vance Hall

D-U-N-S 00-965-5929
MMC CONTRACTORS WEST INC
(*Suby of* MMC CONTRACTORS NATIONAL INC) ★
5080 Cameron St, Las Vegas, NV 89118-1553
Tel (702) 889-6800 *Founded/Ownrshp* 1970
Sales 32.9MM^E *EMP* 100
SIC 1711

D-U-N-S 62-221-1712
MMC CORP
10955 Lowell Ave Ste 350, Shawnee Mission, KS 66210-2408
Tel (913) 469-0101 *Founded/Ownrshp* 2005
Sales 475.7MM^E *EMP* 790
SIC 1542 1711 Commercial & office building contractors; Mechanical contractor; Commercial & office building contractors; Mechanical contractor
Pr: Tim Chadwick
**Pr:* Bill McDermott
**CFO:* Dave Cimpl
Ex VP: Keith E Andrews
**VP:* Robin Broder
**VP:* Erica Jones
**VP:* Harold Mitts
**VP:* Craig Woodson
Dir IT: Jim Scales

D-U-N-S 01-914-0834
MMC GROUP LP (TX)
105 Decker Ct Ste 1100, Irving, TX 75062-2777
Tel (972) 893-0100 *Founded/Ownrshp* 2000
Sales 90.8MM^E *EMP* 750
SIC 7374 Data processing service; Data processing service
Genl Pt: C Douglas Mitchell
Pt: Tabitha Bagwell
Pt: Tamerlane Carter
Pt: Robert Cruise
Pt: Kelly Davis
Pt: Allen Griffin
Pt: Karen Merriweather
Pt: Gary Miglicco
Pt: Chris Mitchell
Pt: Teresa Rich
Pt: Michelle Smallwood
Pt: Pamela Young
CFO: Gary Golden
Ofcr: Chris Damron
Dir Bus: Cristi Dey

D-U-N-S 13-131-6259
MMC HOLDING OF BROOKLYN INC
(*Suby of* MAIMONIDES HEALTH RESOURCES INC) ★
4510 16th Ave Fl 2, Brooklyn, NY 11204-1101
Tel (718) 283-8720 *Founded/Ownrshp* 1990
Sales 38.4MM *EMP* 150
SIC 5912 6531 7359 8721 8742 8082 Drug stores; Real estate managers; Equipment rental & leasing; Accounting, auditing & bookkeeping; Billing & bookkeeping service; Management consulting services; Home health care services
Ex Dir: Maryann Ferrari
**Pr:* Robert Naldi
**Sec:* Joyce Leahy

D-U-N-S 00-817-7180
MMC MATERIALS INC (MS)
(*Suby of* DUNN INVESTMENT CO) ★
1052 Highland Colony Pkwy # 201, Ridgeland, MS 39157-8764
Tel (601) 898-4000 *Founded/Ownrshp* 1927
Sales 70.1MM^E *EMP* 450
SIC 3273 Ready-mixed concrete; Ready-mixed concrete
Pr: James Overstreet Jr
**Pr:* Rodney Grogan
Pr: Mike Pepper
**VP:* Butch Bailess
VP: Eliza Henderson
**VP:* Chris Hoyt
**VP:* J Shane Huff
**VP:* Shane Huff
Area Mgr: Rocky McBride
Genl Mgr: Brian McDonald
CIO: Jonathan Huff

D-U-N-S 85-925-3742
MMC MEDICAL SERVICES CORP
MMC OUTPATIENT DIAGNOSTIC SVCS
(*Suby of* MAINE MEDICAL CENTER) ★
22 Bramhall St, Portland, ME 04102-3134
Tel (207) 662-0111 *Founded/Ownrshp* 1988
Sales 14.7MM^E *EMP* 300
SIC 8062 8071 8093 General medical & surgical hospitals; X-ray laboratory, including dental; Specialty outpatient clinics; General medical & surgical hospitals; X-ray laboratory, including dental; Specialty outpatient clinics
Pr: Richard Peterson
**Treas:* William L Caron Jr
Sr VP: Andy Crowder
Prin: Vincent Conti

D-U-N-S 14-964-4754
■ **MMC OF NEVADA LLC**
MESA VIEW REGIONAL HOSPITAL
(*Suby of* COMMUNITY HEALTH SYSTEMS INC) ★
1299 Bertha Howe Ave, Mesquite, NV 89027-7500
Tel (702) 345-4315 *Founded/Ownrshp* 2002
Sales 33.3MM^E *EMP* 158
SIC 8062 General medical & surgical hospitals
CFO: Latibeaudiere Jorge
Dir Recs: Victoria Cassady
Ofcr: Patty Holden
Dir Risk M: Lisa Cook
Dir Risk M: Mary Lyman
Dir Lab: William Spatz
Mktg Dir: Robert Fuller
Pharmcst: Renate Cavalcanti
HC Dir: Barbara Templeton

MMC OUTPATIENT DIAGNOSTIC SVCS
See MMC MEDICAL SERVICES CORP

D-U-N-S 80-848-2983
MMC PRECISION HOLDINGS CORP
1021 W Birchwood St, Morton, IL 61550-9617
Tel (309) 266-7176 *Founded/Ownrshp* 2006
Sales 110.5MM^E *EMP* 1,370^E
SIC 3449 Miscellaneous metalwork; Miscellaneous metalwork
Pr: Frank C Lukacs

D-U-N-S 80-181-8592
MMCO LLC
DON ROSEN IMPORTS
1312 W Ridge Pike, Conshohocken, PA 19428-1022
Tel (610) 279-4100 *Founded/Ownrshp* 2004
Sales 48.3MM^E *EMP* 75
SIC 5511 Automobiles, new & used; Automobiles, new & used
VP: Frank Roman
Genl Mgr: Tim Hedrick
IT Man: David Stevenson

MMD EQUIPMENT
See RAJYSAN INC

MME GRAIN
See MID-MISSOURI ENERGY LLC

D-U-N-S 15-159-5535
MME INC
5015 E Main Ave, Bismarck, ND 58501-9301
Tel (701) 223-1880 *Founded/Ownrshp* 1984
Sales 203.6M *EMP* 800
SIC 4213 Trucking, except local; Trucking, except local
Pr: John Roswick
**Treas:* Jodi Kary
**VP:* Joe Greenstein
Off Mgr: Kimberly Newland

D-U-N-S 78-321-1035
MMETRO.COM LLC
THRILLIST.COM
568 Broadway Rm 507, New York, NY 10012-3225
Tel (646) 786-1938 *Founded/Ownrshp* 2006
Sales 102.3MM^E *EMP* 113^E
SIC 7371 Custom computer programming services; Custom computer programming services
Pr: Mike Rothman
CFO: Jeff Farnath
Ex VP: Ryan McIntyre
Creative D: Benjamin Gelinas
Comm Dir: Devon Giddon
CTO: Mark O'Neill
Prd Dir: Jacob Gilmore
Advt Dir: Jeffrey Cohen
Mktg Mgr: Andrew Yung
Snr Mgr: Ben Lerer

D-U-N-S 07-173-8629
MMG INSURANCE CO
MAINE MUTUAL GROUP
44 Maysville Rd, Presque Isle, ME 04769-3220
Tel (207) 764-6611 *Founded/Ownrshp* 1897
Sales NA *EMP* 160
SIC 6331

MMG STONE SUPPLY
See MODERN METHOD GUNITE INC

D-U-N-S 07-856-9452
MMGY GLOBAL LLC
4601 Madison Ave, Kansas City, MO 64112-1268
Tel (816) 472-5988 *Founded/Ownrshp* 2012
Sales 30.4MM^E *EMP* 150
SIC 7311 Advertising agencies; Advertising agencies
CEO: Clayton Reid
Ex VP: Stewart Colovin
Ex VP: Chris Davidson
Ex VP: Julie Freeman
VP: Claire Bishop
VP: Katie Briscoe
VP: Steve Cohen
VP: Bob Frohoff
VP: Calep Howard
VP: Robert Patterson
VP: Wayne South
VP: Ted Sullivan
Creative D: Christian Conte
Creative D: Rick Dunn

D-U-N-S 01-501-9255
MMH AMERICAS INC
(*Suby of* MMH HOLDINGS INC) ★
4401 Gateway Blvd, Springfield, OH 45502-9339
Tel (414) 764-6200 *Founded/Ownrshp* 1998
Sales 150.0MM^E *EMP* 350
SIC 3536 5084 6719 Hoists, cranes & monorails; Cranes, overhead traveling; Boat lifts; Materials handling machinery; Cranes, industrial; Investment holding companies, except banks; Hoists, cranes & monorails; Cranes, overhead traveling; Boat lifts; Materials handling machinery; Cranes, industrial; Investment holding companies, except banks
Pr: Tom Sothard
**Treas:* Steve Mayes
VP: Ross Smith
Sfty Mgr: Bob Kotecki

D-U-N-S 02-515-7061 IMP/EXP
MMH HOLDINGS INC
MORRIS MATERIAL HANDLING
(*Suby of* KONECRANES INC) ★
4401 Gateway Blvd, Springfield, OH 45502-9339
Tel (937) 525-5533 *Founded/Ownrshp* 2006
Sales 150.0MM^E *EMP* 350
SIC 3536 5084 Hoists, cranes & monorails; Cranes, overhead traveling; Boat lifts; Materials handling machinery; Cranes, industrial
Pr: Tom Sothard
CFO: Fran Kelch
Treas: Amy Corbisier
**Treas:* Steve Mayes
VP: Peter A Kerrick
Brnch Mgr: John Snyder
Genl Mgr: Bob Locasale
Sfty Mgr: Bob Kotecki
Prd Mgr: Kenneth Lindstrom
Sales Exec: Kim Hall
Sales Exec: Joe Manis

MMI AGENCY
See MONTGOMERY MARION INC

D-U-N-S 00-538-4144 IMP
MMI ENGINEERED SOLUTIONS INC (MI)
DRAYTON PLAINS TOOL COMPANY
(*Suby of* TOMSONS INC) ★
1715 Woodland Dr, Saline, MI 48176-1614
Tel (734) 429-4664 *Founded/Ownrshp* 1983
Sales 21.0MM *EMP* 86^E
SIC 3089 8711 Injection molding of plastics; Engineering services
Pr: Doug Callahan
**CFO:* Paul Larson
Dir Bus: Michael Rosser

D-U-N-S 07-193-7437
MMI HOTEL GROUP INC
1000 Red Fern Pl, Jackson, MS 39232-8879
Tel (601) 936-3666 *Founded/Ownrshp* 1965
Sales 59.7MM^E *EMP* 1,627
SIC 7011 Hotels & motels; Motel, franchised; Hotels & motels; Motel, franchised
Ch Bd: Earle F Jones
**Pr:* Gaines P Sturdivant
**Treas:* Michael J Hart
VP: Ken O'Keefe
Dist Mgr: Cynde Houston

MMI OF KENTUCKY
See CONTRACTORS MATERIALS CO

D-U-N-S 16-128-2611
MMI SERVICES INC
4042 Patton Way, Bakersfield, CA 93308-5030
Tel (661) 589-9366 Founded/Ownrshp 2006
Sales 51.8MM^E EMP 250
Accts Daniells Phillips Vaughan &
SIC 1389 Oil field services; Oil field services
Pr: Steve McGowan
*CEO: Mel McGowan
*VP: Eric Olson
Dir IT: Roxanne Campbell
Sfty Mgr: Matthew Kennedy

D-U-N-S 36-444-5312
MMIC GROUP INC
7701 France Ave S Ste 500, Minneapolis, MN 55435-3201
Tel (952) 838-6700 Founded/Ownrshp 1988
Sales 138.3MM EMP 120^E
SIC 6719 Investment holding companies, except banks; Investment holding companies, except banks
CEO: David P Bounk
Mng Pt: Dave Kenady
Pr: Lori Berreman
COO: Bill McDonough
*CFO: Niles Cole
Bd of Dir: Richard Geier
VP: Steve Heimel
VP: Woodward John
VP: Steve Lacke
*VP: Elizabeth Lincoln
VP: Debra McBride
*VP: Jerry O'Connell
VP: Jeff Pearson
*VP: Julie Stafford
VP: Lori Trygg
VP: Peggy Wagner
*VP: Peggy Warner
*VP: Jerry Zeitlin
Comm Man: Jane Rodriguez

D-U-N-S 94-639-4533
MMJ INDUSTRIES INC
C E I
11298 Florida Blvd, Walker, LA 70785-5947
Tel (225) 667-1707 Founded/Ownrshp 1995
Sales 20.9MM^E EMP 180
SIC 4212 Local trucking, without storage; Local trucking, without storage
Pr: George Lockhart
Ex VP: Tom Gioia
*VP: Kevin Juneau
*VP: Derk Lockhart
*VP: John Lockhart
Sfty Mgr: J J Barnes
Sales Exec: Kevin Junau

MMMM
See 4M BUILDING SOLUTIONS INC

MMNA
See MITSUBISHI MOTORS NORTH AMERICA INC

D-U-N-S 96-685-9188
MMODAL INC
M MODAL
(Suby of LEGEND PARENT, INC.)
5000 Meridian Blvd, Franklin, TN 37067-6667
Tel (888) 840-4050 Founded/Ownrshp 2012
Sales 692.2MM^E EMP 12,000
SIC 7374 Data processing & preparation; Data processing & preparation
CEO: Scott Mackenzie
Pr: Michael Finke
COO: Ronald L Scarboro
CFO: David Woodworth
Ex VP: Mike Etue
Sr VP: William J Donovan
Sr VP: Matt Jenkins
Sr VP: Shasank Yellamanchali
VP: Bill Donovan
Snr Sftwr: Bret Bailey
Snr Sftwr: Dennis Graham
Board of Directors: William Allen, Eugene Davis, Jeffrey Goldberg, Michael O'boyle

MMODAL MQ INC
See MMODAL SERVICES INC

D-U-N-S 01-643-9999
MMODAL SERVICES INC
MMODAL MQ INC
(Suby of M MODAL) ★
5000 Meridian Blvd # 200, Franklin, TN 37067-6667
Tel (615) 261-1500 Founded/Ownrshp 2008
Sales 289.8MM^E EMP 5,382^E
SIC 7372 7371 Prepackaged software; Custom computer programming services; Prepackaged software; Custom computer programming services
CIO: Kevin Piltz
Pr: Adell Bareato
*COO: Anthony D James
CFO: Ethan Cohen
*Sr VP: Michael F Clark
*Sr VP: Alan Gold
VP: Frank Digiambattista
VP: Deeann Logan
VP: Toni Maldonado
VP: Chris Spring
Ex Dir: Quirino Micua
Board of Directors: Robert Aquilina, Frank Baker, Peter E Berger, John F Jastrem, Colin J O'brien, Warren E Pinckert II, Michael Seedman, Andrew E Vogel

D-U-N-S 04-716-7556
MMODAL SERVICES LTD INC
(Suby of MMODAL MQ INC) ★
5000 Meridian Blvd # 200, Franklin, TN 37067-6667
Tel (800) 233-3030 Founded/Ownrshp 1965
Sales 206.2MM^E EMP 5,000
SIC 8999 Communication services; Communication services
Pr: Michael Finke
*COO: Ronald L Scarboro
*CFO: David Woodworth
*Ex VP: Mike Etue
CIO: Kevin M Piltz

D-U-N-S 82-886-5217
MMODAL SERVICES LTD INC
(Suby of MMODAL MQ INC) ★
5430 Metric Pl Ste 200, Norcross, GA 30092-2517
Tel (678) 824-3000 Founded/Ownrshp 2000
Sales 25.3MM^E EMP 500
SIC 7371 8748 7373 1731 7372 Software programming applications; Business consulting; Computer integrated systems design; Electrical work; Prepackaged software; Software programming applications; Business consulting; Computer integrated systems design; Electrical work; Prepackaged software
CFO: Vern Davenport
Board of Directors: Vern Davenport

MMP
See MONTANA METAL PRODUCTS LLC

MMPA
See MINNESOTA MUNICIPAL POWER AGENCY

MMR
See MCMORAN EXPLORATION CO

MMR
See MATERIAL MANAGEMENT RESOURCES INC

MMR CONSTRUCTORS
See MMR GROUP INC

D-U-N-S 14-450-1798
MMR CONSTRUCTORS INC
MMR OFFSHORE SERVICES
(Suby of MMR CONSTRUCTORS) ★
15961 Airline Hwy, Baton Rouge, LA 70817-7412
Tel (225) 756-5090 Founded/Ownrshp 1985
Sales 700.0MM EMP 2,500
Accts Maddox & Associates Apc Bato
SIC 1731 Computerized controls installation; General electrical contractor; Computerized controls installation; General electrical contractor
Pr: James B Rutland
*CFO: Donald Fairbanks
VP: Thomas B Rutland
*VP: Tom Welborn
Dist Mgr: Scoff Kerr
Netwrk Mgr: Dustin Landry

D-U-N-S 84-720-7057 EXP
MMR GROUP INC
MMR CONSTRUCTORS
15961 Airline Hwy, Baton Rouge, LA 70817-7412
Tel (225) 756-5090 Founded/Ownrshp 1985
Sales 674.7MM EMP 2,500
Accts Maddox & Associates Apc Bato
SIC 1731 Computerized controls installation; General electrical contractor; Computerized controls installation; General electrical contractor
Pr: James B Rutland
CFO: Donald Fairbanks
*Sec: Donald W Fairbanks
VP: Darryl Clark
VP: Ken Friedman
VP: Jeff Smith
*VP: Thomas O Welborn
Off Mgr: Anita Lewis
Sfty Dirs: Juan Leon
Sfty Dirs: Justin Leyva
Opers Mgr: Jason Racca

MMR OFFSHORE SERVICES
See MMR CONSTRUCTORS INC

MMRA
See MIDWEST MEDICAL RECORDS ASSOCIATION INC

D-U-N-S 17-849-6373
MMRC GIFT SHOP
METHODIST REHABILITAION CENTER
1350 E Woodrow Wilson Ave, Jackson, MS 39216-5112
Tel (601) 364-3304 Founded/Ownrshp 2000
Sales 52.8MM EMP 1
SIC 5947 Gift shop; Gift shop
Prin: Mark A Adams
Doctor: David Gandy

MMREM
See CHRONOS SOLUTIONS LLC

MMRF
See MULTIPLE MYELOMA RESEARCH FOUNDATION INC

MMS
See MARITIME MANAGEMENT SERVICES

MMS, A MEDICAL SUPPLY COMPANY
See MIDWEST MEDICAL SUPPLY CO LLC

D-U-N-S 62-140-2531
MMS HOLDINGS INC
6880 Commerce Blvd, Canton, MI 48187-4457
Tel (734) 245-0310 Founded/Ownrshp 2005
Sales 28.0MM^E EMP 250
SIC 8731 Commercial physical research; Commercial physical research
Pr: Madan M Sharma
*VP: Prasad Koppolu
*Prin: Uma Sharma
IT Man: Don McLean

D-U-N-S 79-111-1854
MMS USA HOLDINGS INC
(Suby of PUBLICIS GROUPE S A)
35 W Wacker Dr Lbby 5, Chicago, IL 60601-1726
Tel (800) 933-3622 Founded/Ownrshp 2002
Sales 189.5MM^E EMP 1,740^E
SIC 8742 Marketing consulting services
Pr: John Betley
*CEO: Monica Gasby
*COO: Jose Rosario
*Prin: Maurice Levy
Mng Dir: St Phane Buisseret
Board of Directors: Maurice Levy

D-U-N-S 80-187-7952
MMS USA INVESTMENTS INC
(Suby of PUBLICIS GROUPE S A)
41 Madison Ave, New York, NY 10010-2202
Tel (212) 463-2000 Founded/Ownrshp 2001
Sales 49.4MM^E EMP 1,000
SIC 7311 Advertising agencies; Advertising agencies
CEO: Kevin Roberts
CFO: Johann Xavier
Ofcr: Jay Benjamin
Ofcr: Brett Stover
Ex VP: Vaughan Emsley
Ex VP: Paul Meiter
Ex VP: Ed Nathan
Ex VP: Jennifer Shirley
VP: Diana Bosniack
VP: Marcia Gold
VP: Dan Gonda
VP: Jaclyn Krongold
VP: Tom Larkin
VP: Nicole Lobkowicz
VP: Carol Plunkett
VP: Roger Poirier
VP: April Portner
VP: Tina Sperber
VP: Maggie Sumner
Dir: Tom Lanktree
Creative D: Ben Barney

MMSD
See MADISON METROPOLITAN SCHOOL DISTRICT

MMSI
See MARKETING & MEDIA SERVICES LLC

D-U-N-S 02-954-4033
MMW FAB LTD
MMW INDUSTRIES
1155 W Hurst Blvd, Hurst, TX 76053-7403
Tel (817) 589-0881 Founded/Ownrshp 1997
Sales 41.7MM^E EMP 80
SIC 3441 Fabricated structural metal for bridges
Genl Pt: Miller Bros
VP: Terry Miller
Sls Mgr: Paul Jacobs

MMW INDUSTRIES
See MMW FAB LTD

D-U-N-S 80-260-1265
MN AIRLINE HOLDINGS INC
SUN COUNTRY AIRLINES
1300 Mendota Heights Rd, Saint Paul, MN 55120-1128
Tel (651) 905-2737 Founded/Ownrshp 2008
Sales 91.1MM^E EMP 800
Accts Deloite & Touche Llp Minneapo
SIC 4512 Air cargo carrier, scheduled; Air passenger carrier, scheduled; Air cargo carrier, scheduled; Air passenger carrier, scheduled
Pr: Stanley J Gadek
CFO: Shawn Nugent
Treas: Jill Molnar
Ofcr: Kurt Amundson
VP: Eric Curry
VP: Bob Hinkley
Exec: Katie Bellows
Genl Mgr: Glenn Nordling
MIS Dir: Jane Garske
Dir IT: Rocky Wiggins
IT Man: Kevin Bottemiller
Board of Directors: John S Fredericksen, Stanley J Gadek

D-U-N-S 11-437-0096
MN AIRLINES LLC
SUN COUNTRY AIRLINES
(Suby of CAMBRIA CO LLC) ★
1300 Mendota Heights Rd, Mendota Heights, MN 55120-1128
Tel (651) 681-3900 Founded/Ownrshp 2011
Sales 91.1MM^E EMP 950
SIC 4512 Air cargo carrier, scheduled; Air passenger carrier, scheduled; Air cargo carrier, scheduled; Air passenger carrier, scheduled
Bd of Dir: Stanley J Gadek
Ex VP: Ron Jacobs
VP: Jim Olsen
VP: Tim Wise
Admn Mgr: Madison Fri
MIS Dir: Mark Osterberg
Dir IT: Gary Elwood
Dir IT: Mario Garcia
IT Man: Jae Ljiyode
Sales Exec: Jennifer Lien
Mktg Mgr: Pete Heunisch
Board of Directors: Robert R Fafinski Jr, Michael J Opat

D-U-N-S 02-300-9475 IMP
MN EQUIPMENT SOLUTIONS INC
JOHN DEERE
13725 Main St, Rogers, MN 55374-9589
Tel (763) 428-4107 Founded/Ownrshp 2007
Sales 31.8MM EMP 65
Accts Gordon L Duncombe
SIC 5261 5531 Lawnmowers & tractors; Truck equipment & parts; Lawnmowers & tractors; Truck equipment & parts
Pr: Michael S Scharber
Treas: Pat Scharber
*Sec: Dan Scharber
*VP: Michael Bell
*VP: Robert Kraft
*VP: Mark Nordrum
Sls Mgr: Doug Anderson
Sales Asso: Jonathan Nordrum

D-U-N-S 02-636-6046
MN GROUP INC
3625 Swiftwater Park Dr, Suwanee, GA 30024-2188
Tel (770) 831-0760 Founded/Ownrshp 2010
Sales 22.2MM^E EMP 86^E
SIC 6531 Real estate brokers & agents
CEO: Michael Nance II

D-U-N-S 79-880-2000
MNB BANCORP
300 E Main St, Milford, MA 01757-2806
Tel (508) 634-4100 Founded/Ownrshp 2007
Sales NA EMP 101^E
SIC 6712 Bank holding companies
Prin: Roger R Lavallee

D-U-N-S 78-639-4692
MND HOSPITALITY SERVICES CORP
(Suby of WOODLANDS OPERATING CO L P) ★
2301 N Millbend Dr, Spring, TX 77380-1360
Tel (281) 367-1100 Founded/Ownrshp 1988
Sales 29.0MM EMP 400
SIC 8721 Payroll accounting service; Payroll accounting service
Genl Mgr: Kent Johnson

D-U-N-S 83-675-1826
MNDUSTRIES INC
(Suby of MN GROUP INC) ★
3625 Swiftwater Park Dr, Suwanee, GA 30024-2188
Tel (770) 831-0760 Founded/Ownrshp 1995
Sales 22.2MM^E EMP 80
SIC 3441 Fabricated structural metal
CEO: Michael E Nance II

D-U-N-S 09-665-6368
MNEMONICS INC
3900 Dow Rd Ste J, Melbourne, FL 32934-9291
Tel (321) 254-7300 Founded/Ownrshp 1976
Sales 45.1MM^E EMP 103
SIC 8711 3825 Engineering services; Test equipment for electronic & electric measurement; Engineering services; Test equipment for electronic & electric measurement
Pr: Harry B Thompson Jr
*COO: Harry Thompson III
Ofcr: Lisa Beach
*VP: Ellen C Durso
VP: Ed Struble
VP: Robert Thompson
Exec: Maryanna Brushe
Dir Bus: Troy Didier
IT Man: Woody Bramblett
IT Man: David James
IT Man: Caroline Peterson

MNG NEWSPAPERS
See CALIFORNIA NEWSPAPERS PARTNERSHIP

MNGI
See MINNESOTA GASTROENTEROLOGY PA

MNGI ENDOSCOPY ASC
See MINNESOTA GASTROENTEROLOGY PA INC

D-U-N-S 04-252-6087
MNI ENTERPRISES INC
NICHOLAS HOMES
8080 E Gelding Dr Ste 108, Scottsdale, AZ 85260-6983
Tel (480) 505-4600 Founded/Ownrshp 1963
Sales 123.1MM^E EMP 500
SIC 1521 Single-family housing construction; Single-family housing construction
Pr: Michael G Nicholas
CEO: Christopher Lombardi
CFO: Harry Griffith
VP: Ken Christopherson
VP: Bob Dalton
Dir IT: Sean Wegele
Sls Mgr: Karen Smith

D-U-N-S 08-362-0633
■ **MNI TARGETED MEDIA INC**
(Suby of TIME INC) ★
225 High Ridge Rd Ste 2, Stamford, CT 06905-3035
Tel (877) 275-4664 Founded/Ownrshp 1997
Sales 21.0MM^E EMP 150
SIC 7311 Advertising agencies; Advertising agencies
Pr: Robert Reif
Treas: Julie Bonner
*Sr VP: Robert Moore
*VP: Matthew Fanelli
*VP: Mark Glatzhofer
*VP: John Kenyon
IT Man: Lauren Burkhart
IT Man: Casey Cunnife
*VP Sls: Laura West

D-U-N-S 10-797-8954
MNJ TECHNOLOGIES DIRECT INC
1025 Busch Pkwy, Buffalo Grove, IL 60089-4504
Tel (847) 634-0700 Founded/Ownrshp 2002
Sales 103.8MM EMP 78
SIC 5734 7373 5045 Personal computers; Printers & plotters: computers; Modems, monitors, terminals & disk drives: computers; Value-added resellers, computer systems; Printers, computer; Personal computers; Printers & plotters: computers; Modems, monitors, terminals & disk drives: computers; Value-added resellers, computer systems; Printers, computer
Pr: Susan Kozak
Mng Pt: David Pfau
*VP: Paul Kozak
Snr Sftwr: Jason Chapman
Dir IT: Jim Brice
IT Man: Vincent Yarmoska
Sales Exec: Bob Kerr
Sls Mgr: Patrick Barnes
Snr Mgr: Patrick Sullivan

D-U-N-S 12-338-6596
MNL INC
RALPH SCHOMP CHEVY OLDS
5700 S Broadway, Littleton, CO 80121-8007
Tel (303) 798-1500 Founded/Ownrshp 1997
Sales 44.5MM^E EMP 200
SIC 5511 Automobiles, new & used; Automobiles, new & used
Pr: Mark Wallace
*VP: Lisa Schomp
Dir Bus: Michael Dunlap
Off Mgr: Amos Depuy
Telecom Ex: Dewayne Barker

D-U-N-S 05-145-9568
MNM GROUP INC (PA)
2421 Wyandotte Rd Ste A, Willow Grove, PA 19090-1202
Tel (215) 672-9600 Founded/Ownrshp 1975, 1992
Sales 35.5MM^E EMP 50

SIC 5063 Wire & cable
Pr: Gregory Carson
**Treas:* Francis Miller
IT Man: Nicole Carson

D-U-N-S 07-029-9268 IMP
MNP CORP
STEEL AND WIRE
44225 Utica Rd, Utica, MI 48317-5464
Tel (586) 254-1320 *Founded/Ownrshp* 1970
Sales 195.4MM *EMP* 1,000
Accts Baker Tilly Virchow Krause Ll
SIC 3452 5051 5072 3714 Bolts, metal; Screws, metal; Washers, metal; Steel; Wire; Bolts; Screws; Washers (hardware); Miscellaneous fasteners; Motor vehicle parts & accessories; Bolts, metal; Screws, metal; Washers, metal; Steel; Wire; Bolts; Screws; Washers (hardware); Miscellaneous fasteners; Motor vehicle parts & accessories
CEO: Terri Chapman
**Pr:* Thomas Klein
COO: Bernie Cell
**CFO:* Craig L Stormer
**VP:* Chad Clifford
**VP:* David Cronovich
VP: Janice Kelin
VP: Janice Klein
Dir Bus: Gerald Lorenz
CIO: Scott Greenlay
Dir IT: Steve Rowan

D-U-N-S 62-690-8839
MNP PRECISON PARTS LLC
(*Suby of* MNP CORP) ★
1111 Samuelson Rd, Rockford, IL 61109-3620
Tel (815) 397-5151 *Founded/Ownrshp* 2006
Sales 21.0MM^E *EMP* 190
SIC 3452 3465 3469 Bolts, metal; Automotive stampings; Electronic enclosures, stamped or pressed metal; Bolts, metal; Automotive stampings; Electronic enclosures, stamped or pressed metal
VP: Karen Leary
VP: Martin Schnurr

D-U-N-S 03-319-6387 IMP/EXP
MNS LTD
ABC STORES
766 Pohukaina St, Honolulu, HI 96813-5307
Tel (808) 591-2550 *Founded/Ownrshp* 1955
Sales 123.1MM^E *EMP* 700
SIC 5411

D-U-N-S 79-452-0226
MNTRY PNSUA CLGE FUNDTION
980 Fremont St, Monterey, CA 93940-4704
Tel (831) 646-4000 *Founded/Ownrshp* 1947
Sales 1.0MM *EMP* 350
SIC 8221 Colleges universities & professional schools; Colleges universities & professional schools
Pr: Pam Lehman
VP: Carsbia Anderson
VP: Joe Bissell
VP: John Gonzalez
VP: H E Ihn
VP: Kim Panis
VP: Arthur St Laurent
Sys Mgr: Gabino Valladares
Mktg Dir: Richard Montori

MNX
See MIDNITE AIR CORP

D-U-N-S 82-530-2904
■ **MO INDUSTRIES LLC**
ELLA MOSS
(*Suby of* V F) ★
777 S Alameda St Fl 4, Los Angeles, CA 90021-1633
Tel (213) 745-0155 *Founded/Ownrshp* 2009
Sales 39.1MM^E *EMP* 225
SIC 2339 Women's & misses' outerwear; Women's & misses' outerwear
CFO: Jonathan Saven

D-U-N-S 09-555-1099 IMP/EXP
MO MONEY ASSOCIATES LLC
3838 N Palafox St, Pensacola, FL 32505-5222
Tel (850) 432-6301 *Founded/Ownrshp* 1979
Sales 50.2MM^E *EMP* 155
SIC 5199 2396 2395 Advertising specialties; Screen printing on fabric articles; Embroidery & art needlework; Advertising specialties; Screen printing on fabric articles; Embroidery & art needlework
Ch: Mowe Wayne
**Pr:* Cliff Mowe
Pr: Bill Reid
VP: Emory Bell
**VP:* Bell Emory
VP: Travis Hall
VP: Tom McVoy
**VP:* Hall Travis
Exec: Kim McDole
IT Man: Gloria Ellington

D-U-N-S 09-010-1338
MO-KA SHOE CORP (DE)
Km 0 Hm 9 Zona Rr 459, Aguadilla, PR 00603
Tel (787) 891-1975 *Founded/Ownrshp* 1962, 2000
Sales 34.5MM^E *EMP* 550
SIC 3143 Boots, dress or casual: men's; Boots, dress or casual: men's
VP: David Lutz
Genl Mgr: Herb Bolin

D-U-N-S 00-680-1369
MO-VAC SERVICE CO
3721 S Mccoll Rd, Edinburg, TX 78539-9618
Tel (956) 682-6381 *Founded/Ownrshp* 1960
Sales 241.5MM^E *EMP* 315
SIC 1389 4959 Mud service, oil field drilling; Environmental cleanup services; Mud service, oil field drilling; Environmental cleanup services
Pr: Glynn Andrews
VP Opers: Arnold Perez
Opers Mgr: Erick McLaughlin
Manager: Mike Flanagan

D-U-N-S 78-894-5640 IMP
■ **MOA ENTERTAINMENT CO LLC**
CAMP SNOOPY
(*Suby of* SIMON PROPERTY GROUP LP) ★
5000 Center Ct, Bloomington, MN 55425-5505
Tel (952) 883-8810 *Founded/Ownrshp* 1990
Sales 20.0MM^E *EMP* 561
SIC 7999 7996 Tourist attractions, amusement park concessions & rides; Theme park, amusement; Tourist attractions, amusement park concessions & rides; Theme park, amusement
**Ex VP:* Maureen Bausch

MOAB REGIONAL HOSPITAL
See MOAB VALLEY HEALTHCARE INC

D-U-N-S 06-198-0178
MOAB VALLEY HEALTHCARE INC
MOAB REGIONAL HOSPITAL
450 Williams Way, Moab, UT 84532-2065
Tel (435) 719-3500 *Founded/Ownrshp* 1995
Sales 23.1MM *EMP* 118
Accts Eide Bailly Llp Fargo North
SIC 8062 General medical & surgical hospitals; General medical & surgical hospitals
Pr: Michael Bynum
CFO: Craig Daniels
**V Ch Bd:* Kyle Bailey
Info Man: Mike Foster
Surgeon: Juan Vasquez
Genl Couns: Robert Sherlock

D-U-N-S 79-679-7012
MOAC MALL HOLDINGS LLC
MALL OF AMERICA
(*Suby of* TRIPLE FIVE GROUP LTD)
60 E Broadway, Bloomington, MN 55425-5550
Tel (952) 883-8810 *Founded/Ownrshp* 1992
Sales 54.5MM^E *EMP* 600
SIC 6512 Shopping center, property operation only; Shopping center, property operation only
Ofcr: Pat Bendel
Ofcr: Barb Kanter
**Ex VP:* Maureen Bausch
VP: Carrie Charleston
VP: Jill Renslow
VP: Mike Tvrdik
Dir Sec: Doug Reynolds
Dir IT: Chris Lake-Smith
Sfty Dirs: Michael Zondervan
Trfc Dir: Nick Baldwin
Pr Dir: Dan Jasper

D-U-N-S 02-992-7662 IMP
MOARK LLC
(*Suby of* LAND OLAKES INC) ★
28 Under The Mountain Rd, North Franklin, CT 06254-1421
Tel (951) 332-3300 *Founded/Ownrshp* 2000
Sales 710.6MM^E *EMP* 1,000
SIC 5144 2048 0252 2015 Eggs; Poultry feeds; Chicken eggs; Started pullet farm; Poultry slaughtering & processing; Eggs; Poultry feeds; Chicken eggs; Started pullet farm; Poultry slaughtering & processing
CFO: Craig Wells
VP: Donald Brown
VP: Nyle McAnally
Opers Mgr: Alex Onyshchenko

MOASIS TRUCKSTOP
See VAN ZEELAND OIL CO INC

D-U-N-S 07-713-1753
MOBERLY AREA COMMUNITY COLLEGE
101 College Ave, Moberly, MO 65270-1304
Tel (660) 263-4110 *Founded/Ownrshp* 1927
Sales 13.7MM *EMP* 400^E
SIC 8222 Community college; Community college
Pr: Dr Evelyn Jorgenson
**CFO:* Gary Steffes
Ofcr: Shannon Crist
VP: Keith Chrisman
VP: Jeffery Lashley
DP Exec: Heather Lawery
Dir IT: Lloyd Marchant
Sftwr Eng: Deanna Blickhan

D-U-N-S 05-615-3398 IMP
■ **MOBERLY HOSPITAL INC**
CHS
(*Suby of* COMMUNITY HEALTH SYSTEMS INC) ★
1515 Union Ave, Moberly, MO 65270-9407
Tel (660) 269-3280 *Founded/Ownrshp* 1993
Sales 67.5MM *EMP* 511
SIC 8062 General medical & surgical hospitals; General medical & surgical hospitals
CEO: Kevin Clement
Dir Lab: Anita Smith

D-U-N-S 02-991-8042
MOBERLY MOTOR CO
FORD LINCOLN MERCURY
1520 N Morley St, Moberly, MO 65270-3633
Tel (660) 263-6000 *Founded/Ownrshp* 1943
Sales 23.6MM^E *EMP* 50
SIC 5511 Automobiles, new & used; Pickups, new & used; Vans, new & used
Pr: Dean Miller Jr
**Treas:* Ann Miller
VP: Calvin Vilt
Sales Exec: Richard White
Sales Asso: Erik Davidson

D-U-N-S 02-692-7319
MOBERLY SCHOOL DISTRICT
926 Kwix Rd, Moberly, MO 65270-3813
Tel (660) 269-2610 *Founded/Ownrshp* 1867
Sales 25.3MM *EMP* 300
Accts Gerding Korte & Chitwood Pc
SIC 8211 Public elementary & secondary schools; Public elementary & secondary schools
**Prin:* Rebecca Bartolacci
**Prin:* Tim Jefferies
Ex Dir: Bobbi Martin
MIS Dir: Alan West

MOBERN LIGHTING COMPANY
See SAYLITE LLC

D-U-N-S 94-699-4274
MOBI CORP
600 Congress Ave Ste 1600, Austin, TX 78701-2974
Tel (512) 617-5300 *Founded/Ownrshp* 1996
Sales 31.1MM^E *EMP* 85
SIC 7371 7372 Custom computer programming services; Prepackaged software
CEO: Benjamin Bromberg
CFO: Robert S Smith
**VP:* Eric Anderson
**VP:* Grey Gray
**VP:* Bryan Karp
VP: Ken Kolchier
VP: Doug White
Dir IT: Chase Clear
IT Man: Jay Inman
Sls Dir: Stuart Nolley
Sls Dir: Bill White

D-U-N-S 07-881-0964
MOBICA US INC (CA)
(*Suby of* MOBICA LIMITED)
2570 N 1st St Fl 2, San Jose, CA 95131-1035
Tel (650) 450-6654 *Founded/Ownrshp* 2012
Sales 329.4M^E *EMP* 900
SIC 7373 Systems software development services
CEO: Marcin Kloda
**COO:* Rafael Janczyk

MOBIL
See TRAVEL MART INC

MOBIL
See BOLLA OPERATING CORP

MOBIL
See CHASE INC

D-U-N-S 80-377-8034
■ **MOBIL EXPLORATION & PRODUCING US INC**
(*Suby of* MOBIL CORPORATION)
22777 Sprngwoods Vlg Pkwy, Spring, TX 77389-1425
Tel (281) 288-4545 *Founded/Ownrshp* 1987
Sales 266.9MM^E *EMP* 2,800
SIC 1311 Crude petroleum production; Natural gas production; Crude petroleum production; Natural gas production
Pr: P J Hoenmans
CFO: Mohammed Ghannam

D-U-N-S 60-779-4690 IMP
■ **MOBIL HOLDINGS (UK) LIMITED**
EXXONMOBIL DOWNSTREAM OPERTN
(*Suby of* EXXONMOBIL OIL CORP) ★
22777 Sprngwoods Vlg Pkwy, Spring, TX 77389-1425
Tel (281) 288-4545 *Founded/Ownrshp* 2006
Sales 160.2MM^E *EMP* 4,000^E
SIC 1311 Crude petroleum & natural gas; Crude petroleum & natural gas
Pr: Lee Raymonds
**Pr:* Eugene A Renna
Dir Soc: Kelly Nealon

D-U-N-S 18-311-0840 IMP/EXP
■ **MOBIL INTERNATIONAL PETROLEUM CORP**
(*Suby of* EXXONMOBIL OIL CORP) ★
22777 Sprngwoods Vlg Pkwy, Spring, TX 77389-1425
Tel (281) 288-4545 *Founded/Ownrshp* 1935
Sales 363.6MM^E *EMP* 343
SIC 5172 Petroleum brokers; Petroleum brokers
Pr: Eugene A Renna
**Treas:* George Broadhead
**VP:* R H Gardner
**VP:* Joe B Hinton
**VP:* Paul J Hoenmans
VP: N S Kyburg
**VP:* Robert J Mc Cool
**VP:* Robert O Swanson
Advt Dir: Paula Chen
Sls Dir: Tim Hinchman
Sls Dir: Connie Shao

MOBIL MART
See REX OIL CO

D-U-N-S 06-492-7486
■ **MOBIL PETROLEUM CO INC**
(*Suby of* EXXON MOBIL CORP) ★
22777 Sprngwoods Vlg Pkwy, Spring, TX 77389-1425
Tel (703) 846-3000 *Founded/Ownrshp* 1960
Sales 33.2MM^E *EMP* 77^E
SIC 5541 Filling stations, gasoline
CEO: Rex Tillerson
**Pr:* W M Colton
Treas: Hartwell Gardner
**Treas:* David Levy
Sr VP: Harold Kramer
VP: Rob Franklin
VP: Edward Galante
**VP:* H H Hubble
VP: T F Lemons Jr
VP: Senior Vice Stuart
Telecom Mg: Kevin Citizen

D-U-N-S 03-776-6813
■ **MOBIL PRODUCING TEXAS AND NEW MEXICO INC**
(*Suby of* EXXON MOBIL CORP) ★
9 Greenway Plz 2700, Houston, TX 77046-0905
Tel (713) 871-5000 *Founded/Ownrshp* 2014
Sales 30.9MM^E *EMP* 2,400
SIC 1311 Crude petroleum & natural gas; Crude petroleum & natural gas
Pr: Fines F Martin

D-U-N-S 05-666-5136
■ **MOBIL RESEARCH AND DEVELOPMENT CORP**
(*Suby of* EXXONMOBIL OIL CORP) ★
600 Billingsport Rd, Paulsboro, NJ 08066-1034
Tel (856) 224-2134 *Founded/Ownrshp* 1967
Sales 79.5MM^E *EMP* 2,300
SIC 8731 Commercial research laboratory; Commercial physical research; Commercial research laboratory; Commercial physical research
Pr: J E Crawford
**VP:* R H Gardner
**VP:* J R Green
**VP:* J R Katzer
**VP:* K D Kroupa
**VP:* R J McGowan
**VP:* A J Silvestri
**VP:* J J Wise
IT Man: Rick Burns
IT Man: Steve Goldman

D-U-N-S 61-474-4998 IMP
MOBIL STEEL INTERNATIONAL INC
13830 S Wayside Dr, Houston, TX 77048-5210
Tel (713) 991-0450 *Founded/Ownrshp* 2005
Sales 20.3MM^E *EMP* 41
Accts Pannell Kerr Forster Of Texas
SIC 3441 Fabricated structural metal
Pr: Leonard A Bedell
**Treas:* Ray Guillory
VP: Bobby Mitchell
**Prin:* Clark A Gunderson
Genl Mgr: Mark Scott
Sls Mgr: Bruce Kenner
Board of Directors: Ray Guillory

D-U-N-S 13-116-6696
MOBILE AIRPORT AUTHORITY
MOBILE REGIONAL AIRPORT
1891 9th St, Mobile, AL 36615-4201
Tel (251) 438-7334 *Founded/Ownrshp* 1980
Sales 25.8MM^E *EMP* 125
Accts Prichard Dewberry & Hodges P
SIC 4581 6512 Airport; Nonresidential building operators
Ex Dir: William Sisson
Bd of Dir: Patricia Edington
**Ex Dir:* Roger Wehner
Pr Mgr: Buddy Rice

D-U-N-S 55-695-4501
MOBILE ASPHALT CO LLC
3151 Hamilton Blvd, Theodore, AL 36582-8500
Tel (251) 408-0770 *Founded/Ownrshp* 1995
Sales 36.9MM^E *EMP* 105
SIC 2951 1611 Asphalt & asphaltic paving mixtures (not from refineries); Highway & street paving contractor; Asphalt & asphaltic paving mixtures (not from refineries); Highway & street paving contractor
VP: John Whitman
VP Mktg: Lisa King

MOBILE AUTO GLASS
See DAKOTALAND AUTOGLASS INC

D-U-N-S 03-128-3187 IMP
MOBILE CLIMATE CONTROL CORP
MCC
(*Suby of* MOBILE CLIMATE CONTROL GROUP HOLDING AB)
17103 State Road 4, Goshen, IN 46528-6674
Tel (574) 534-1516 *Founded/Ownrshp* 1987, 2008
Sales 73.1MM^E *EMP* 117
Accts William B Schmidt Cpa Llc
SIC 5075 3714 Compressors, air conditioning; Air conditioner parts, motor vehicle; Compressors, air conditioning; Air conditioner parts, motor vehicle
CEO: Clas Genneberg
VP: Tim Hested
Ql Cn Mgr: David Boyen
Sls Mgr: John Volkerding
Board of Directors: Timothy Hested

D-U-N-S 04-912-4688
MOBILE COMMUNITY ACTION INC
461 Donald St, Mobile, AL 36617-3327
Tel (251) 457-5700 *Founded/Ownrshp* 1966
Sales 18.7MM *EMP* 380
Accts Robert A Headrick Jr Cpa
SIC 8322 Temporary relief service; Temporary relief service
Ex Dir: Elige Jones
CFO: Loretta Faxx
IT Man: Janet Buckley

D-U-N-S 07-979-8929
MOBILE COUNTY PUBLIC SCHOOLS
1 Magnum Pass, Mobile, AL 36618-3412
Tel (251) 221-4394 *Founded/Ownrshp* 2015
Sales 36.3MM^E *EMP* 7,052^E
SIC 8211 Public elementary & secondary schools

D-U-N-S 62-013-5611
MOBILE ENERGY SERVICES CO LLC
414 S Main St Ste 600, Ann Arbor, MI 48104-2398
Tel (734) 302-4800 *Founded/Ownrshp* 2004
Sales 27.4MM^E *EMP* 77^E
SIC 4931
Ch Bd: Jarred Anderson

MOBILE EQUIPMENT REPAIR
See DRIVETRAIN INDUSTRIES INC

D-U-N-S 07-508-2198
MOBILE EYE EAR NOSE & THROAT CENTER PC
2880 Dauphin St, Mobile, AL 36606-2457
Tel (251) 473-1900 *Founded/Ownrshp* 1997
Sales 8.9MM^E *EMP* 335
SIC 8011 Ears, nose & throat specialist: physician/surgeon; Ears, nose & throat specialist: physician/surgeon
Pr: Jim Spires
**CFO:* James Hartman
Doctor: Mark J Douglas

D-U-N-S 00-796-0859 IMP
MOBILE FIXTURE AND EQUIPMENT CO INC (AL)
1155 Montlimar Dr, Mobile, AL 36609-1710
Tel (800) 345-6458 *Founded/Ownrshp* 1927
Sales 38.2MM^E *EMP* 66
Accts Mostellar & Shreve Llp Mobil
SIC 5046 Commercial cooking & food service equipment; Commercial cooking & food service equipment

Pr: Walne W Donald Jr
**Sec:* Carol E Payne
**VP:* Keith Murray
**VP:* Tom Watson
**VP:* Ben Whitlock
Sls Dir: Chris Pacey
Sales Asso: Barry Crigler
Sales Asso: John Hass
Sales Asso: Doug Revere
Sales Asso: Tim Sirmon
Sales Asso: Reggie Williams

D-U-N-S 11-916-2340 IMP
MOBILE FLEET SERVICE INC
BUY BIG TIRES
1682 Frazier Rd, Spring Hope, NC 27882-8200
Tel (919) 300-7224 *Founded/Ownrshp* 2002
Sales 25.0MM *EMP* 7
SIC 7538 General automotive repair shops; General automotive repair shops
Pr: Lavonne White
**VP:* Brad Johnson
**VP:* Tom White

D-U-N-S 14-458-2954 IMP/EXP
MOBILE FOREST PRODUCTS & BIOMASS INC
3151b Midtown Park S, Mobile, AL 36606-4146
Tel (251) 476-8184 *Founded/Ownrshp* 1984
Sales 32.4MM^E *EMP* 95
SIC 5099 4212 Timber products, rough; Pulpwood; Lumber & timber trucking; Timber products, rough; Pulpwood; Lumber & timber trucking
Pr: John Zukley
**Sec:* Robert Sharp

D-U-N-S 00-690-1094
■ **MOBILE GAS SERVICE CORP**
(*Suby of* SEMPRA ENERGY) ★
2828 Dauphin St, Mobile, AL 36606-2493
Tel (251) 476-2720 *Founded/Ownrshp* 2008
Sales 151.6MM^E *EMP* 259^E
SIC 4924 5722 Natural gas distribution; Gas household appliances; Natural gas distribution; Gas household appliances
Pr: Mike Fine
**Pr:* John Davis
**CEO:* Gregory H Welch
CFO: Faith McInnis
VP: Bruce Ellis
VP: Gerald Keen
VP: Susan Stringer
IT Man: Sherry Garner
IT Man: Suzanne Hunt
IT Man: Russell Kendrick
IT Man: Angela McNulty

MOBILE HELP
See INTEGRITY TRACKING LLC

D-U-N-S 19-385-3959 IMP
MOBILE HI-TECH WHEELS
MHT LUXURY ALLOYS
19200 S Reyes Ave, Compton, CA 90221-5812
Tel (714) 228-7460 *Founded/Ownrshp* 1983
Sales 41.7MM^E *EMP* 80^E
SIC 5531 5013

D-U-N-S 15-352-9110
MOBILE HOME DEPOT INC
232 Pedro St, Venice, FL 34285-2322
Tel (863) 467-6080 *Founded/Ownrshp* 1992
Sales 45.9MM^E *EMP* 35
SIC 5039 5271 Mobile homes; Mobile homes
Pr: Stephen L Guzman
**VP:* Richard Guzman

MOBILE HOSE AND HYDRAULIC SUP
See CONTROLLED MOTION SOLUTIONS INC

D-U-N-S 08-205-8918
MOBILE HOUSING BOARD
151 S Claiborne St, Mobile, AL 36602-2323
Tel (251) 434-2200 *Founded/Ownrshp* 1935
Sales 23.7MM^E *EMP* 215
Accts Yeager & Boyd Llc Birmingham
SIC 8748 Urban planning & consulting services; Urban planning & consulting services
Ex Dir: Dwayne C Vaughn
**CFO:* Lori Shackleford
**Ch:* Clarence M Ball Jr
**Prin:* Anthony Cooper
**Ex Dir:* Dwayne Vaughn

D-U-N-S 07-260-8367
MOBILE INFIRMARY ASSOCIATION
MOBILE INFIRMARY MEDICAL CTR
5 Mobile Infirmary Cir, Mobile, AL 36607-3513
Tel (251) 435-2400 *Founded/Ownrshp* 1910
Sales 413.6MM *EMP* 2,938
SIC 8062 General medical & surgical hospitals; General medical & surgical hospitals
Ch Bd: David Cooper
Ofcr: Katherine Shiver
VP: Donald J Kirby
Exec: William J McLaughlin Jr
Off Mgr: Barry Sanders
Dir IT: Ricardo Souza
Obsttrcn: John Ives
Ansthlgy: Ryan Neil
Doctor: Chandler E Bramitt
Pharmcst: John Childs
Pharmcst: Hong Duong

MOBILE INFIRMARY MEDICAL CTR
See MOBILE INFIRMARY ASSOCIATION

D-U-N-S 13-560-8891
MOBILE LIFE SUPPORT SERVICES INC
3188 Us Route 9w, New Windsor, NY 12553-6754
Tel (845) 562-4368 *Founded/Ownrshp* 1981
Sales 31.0MM^E *EMP* 250^E
SIC 4119 Ambulance service; Ambulance service
Pr: Gayle M Metzger
COO: Scott Woebse
**VP:* Edward H Horton
**VP:* Scott F Woebse

D-U-N-S 80-455-7502 IMP
MOBILE LINE COMMUNICATIONS CORP
1402 Morgan Cir, Tustin, CA 92780-6423
Tel (877) 247-2544 *Founded/Ownrshp* 1991
Sales 31.5MM^E *EMP* 75
SIC 5065 Telephone & telegraphic equipment; Paging & signaling equipment
Pr: Dennis Curtis
Sales Exec: Dan Husband
Sls Mgr: Alex Mente

D-U-N-S 61-844-2784
MOBILE LUMBER & BUILDING MATERIALS INC
MOBILE LUMBER & MILLWORK
5229 Highway 90 W, Mobile, AL 36619-4201
Tel (251) 661-8000 *Founded/Ownrshp* 1990
Sales 29.0MM^E *EMP* 130^E
SIC 5211 Lumber & other building materials; Lumber & other building materials
Pr: James Henderson Sr
Treas: Kaye Barr
**VP:* Jim Henderson Jr
VP: Scott Henderson
Sales Asso: Bill Daniel

MOBILE LUMBER & MILLWORK
See MOBILE LUMBER & BUILDING MATERIALS INC

MOBILE MEDIA GROUP
See MOBILE MEDIA INC

D-U-N-S 60-309-2677
MOBILE MEDIA INC
MOBILE MEDIA GROUP
12675 W Townsend St, Brookfield, WI 53005-3130
Tel (262) 373-3330 *Founded/Ownrshp* 1984
Sales 18.9MM^E *EMP* 300
SIC 7311 3993 Advertising agencies; Signs & advertising specialties; Advertising agencies; Signs & advertising specialties
Pr: Larry Anthony
**VP:* Terrence Murphy
Dir IT: Dan Crawford

MOBILE MEDIC
See AMR AMBULANCE SERVICE

D-U-N-S 07-261-2922
■ **MOBILE MEDIC AMBULANCE SERVICE INC**
(*Suby of* AMERICAN MEDICAL RESPONSE INC) ★
12020 Intraplex Pkwy, Gulfport, MS 39503-4602
Tel (228) 897-1196 *Founded/Ownrshp* 1992
Sales 14.7MM^E *EMP* 500
SIC 4119 Ambulance service; Ambulance service
IT Man: Bradford Chase

D-U-N-S 88-409-1620
MOBILE MEDICAL INDUSTRIES LLC
CAREADVANTAGE
2400 High Ridge Rd # 103, Boynton Beach, FL 33426-8710
Tel (561) 893-0163 *Founded/Ownrshp* 2000
Sales 25.5MM^E *EMP* 750
SIC 8748 Business consulting; Business consulting
CEO: Greg Bellomy
**COO:* Kim Myrick
**CFO:* James M Douthitt
MIS Dir: Edward A Etchell

D-U-N-S 87-289-6618
MOBILE MEDICAL RESPONSE INC
MEDCONNECTION
834 S Washington Ave, Saginaw, MI 48601-2577
Tel (989) 758-2900 *Founded/Ownrshp* 1994
Sales 34.6MM^E *EMP* 350
Accts Yeo & Yeo Pc Saginaw Mi
SIC 4119 8721 5999 Ambulance service; Billing & bookkeeping service; Alarm signal systems; Ambulance service; Billing & bookkeeping service; Alarm signal systems
Ch Bd: Raymond G Little
**Pr:* Mark Thompson
**V Ch Bd:* Edward Bruff
**VP:* Mike Barrow
**VP:* Michelle McGill
Comm Man: Mark Baringer
**Prin:* James Van Tiflin
Mng Dir: Marianne King
Dir IT: Jay Cooper
Dir IT: Rob George
VP Opers: Michael Blyakher

D-U-N-S 85-958-3341
MOBILE MESSENGER AMERICAS INC
6601 Center Dr W Ste 700, Los Angeles, CA 90045-1545
Tel (310) 957-3300 *Founded/Ownrshp* 2005
Sales 22.2MM^E *EMP* 154^E
SIC 7389 Courier or messenger service
CEO: Darcy Wedd
**CFO:* Daniel Machock
Sr VP: Amy Dudman
Sr VP: Edward McCormick
Sr VP: Israel Niezen
Sr VP: Alan Sege
VP: Larry Robiner

D-U-N-S 11-806-2157
▲ **MOBILE MINI INC**
4646 E Van Buren St # 400, Phoenix, AZ 85008-6927
Tel (480) 894-6311 *Founded/Ownrshp* 1983
Sales 445.4MM *EMP* 1,921
Tkr Sym MINI *Exch* NGS
SIC 4225 3448 3441 3412 7359 Miniwarehouse, warehousing; Buildings, portable: prefabricated metal; Fabricated structural metal; Drums, shipping: metal; Shipping container leasing; Miniwarehouse, warehousing; Buildings, portable: prefabricated metal; Fabricated structural metal; Drums, shipping: metal; Shipping container leasing
Pr: Erik Olsson
**Ch Bd:* Michael L Watts
CFO: Mark E Funk
Ex VP: Phillip H Hobson
Ex VP: Kelly Williams
Sr VP: Ron Halchishak
Sr VP: Ronald Halchishak
Sr VP: Ruth Hunter
Sr VP: Ruth L Hunter
Sr VP: Patrick Lowry
Sr VP: Ron Marshall
Sr VP: Christopher J Miner
VP: William Armstead
VP: Peter C Buchner
VP: Gil Gomez
VP: Brian P Kavanagh
VP: Audra L Taylor
VP: Joseph Wagner
Board of Directors: Sarah R Dial, Jeffrey S Goble, James J Martell, Stephen A McConnell, Frederick G McNamee III, Kimberly J McWaters, Lawrence Trachtenberg

D-U-N-S 00-816-3115 IMP/EXP
MOBILE PAINT MANUFACTURING CO OF DELAWARE INC
B L P MOBILE PAINT STORES
4775 Hamilton Blvd, Theodore, AL 36582-8509
Tel (251) 443-6110 *Founded/Ownrshp* 1921
Sales 92.5MM^E *EMP* 240
Accts Wilkins Miller Hieronymus Llc
SIC 2851 5198 5231 Paints & allied products; Paints; Varnishes; Lacquers; Enamels; Paint & painting supplies; Wallcoverings; Paints & allied products; Paints; Varnishes; Lacquers; Enamels; Paint & painting supplies; Wallcoverings
CFO: John Wilson
**Pr:* William Miles Tunno
Ex VP: Louis Petit
Plnt Mgr: Curtis Polk
VP Sls: Tony McDonald

D-U-N-S 00-815-0294
MOBILE PRESS REGISTER INC (AL)
(*Suby of* ADVANCE PUBLICATIONS INC) ★
401 N Water St, Mobile, AL 36602-4015
Tel (251) 219-5400 *Founded/Ownrshp* 1813, 1966
Sales 37.8MM^E *EMP* 475
SIC 2711 2752 Newspapers; Commercial printing, lithographic; Newspapers; Commercial printing, lithographic
Pr: Howard Bronson Jr
**Treas:* Vickie Catlett
VP: Michael Marshall
Dir IT: Deniane Ocin
Opers Mgr: Mel Balch
Mktg Dir: Randy Granger
Mktg Mgr: Debra Casciano

MOBILE REGIONAL AIRPORT
See MOBILE AIRPORT AUTHORITY

D-U-N-S 62-005-9766 EXP
■ **MOBILE STORAGE GROUP INC**
A BETTER MOBILE STORAGE
(*Suby of* MOBILE MINI INC) ★
7420 S Kyrene Rd Ste 101, Tempe, AZ 85283-4610
Tel (480) 894-6311 *Founded/Ownrshp* 2008
Sales 100.0MM^E *EMP* 700^E
SIC 5999 7359 Packaging materials: boxes, padding, etc.; Shipping container leasing; Packaging materials: boxes, padding, etc.; Shipping container leasing
Pr: Douglas A Waugaman
Ch Bd: Ronald F Valenta
Treas: Allan A Villegas

MOBILE SYSTEMS INTERNATIONAL
See METAPATH SOFTWARE INTERNATIONAL

D-U-N-S 94-649-2055
MOBILE SYSTEMS WIRELESS INC
3195 Independence Dr, Livermore, CA 94551-7595
Tel (925) 344-7200 *Founded/Ownrshp* 1997
Sales 26.0MM *EMP* 180
SIC 5999 Telephone & communication equipment; Telephone & communication equipment
Pr: Joseph Howeth
**VP:* Paul Dubia
Rgnl Mgr: Sean Oco
IT Man: Gregory Jones
IT Man: Carl Matthias

D-U-N-S 78-434-5535 IMP
MOBILE TECH INC
MTI
1050 Nw 229th Ave, Hillsboro, OR 97124-6575
Tel (503) 648-6500 *Founded/Ownrshp* 2013
Sales 70.8MM^E *EMP* 237^E
SIC 3699 7389 Security devices; Security devices; Personal service agents, brokers & bureaus
CEO: Chris Remy
Pr: Thaine Allison
COO: Wayne Zentgraf
CFO: Philip Brown
VP: Lori Andersen
VP: Hsu Chang
VP: Gerry Demple
VP: Pete Johnson
VP: Farouk Kassier
VP: Hunter Wylie
Creative D: Alex Vera

MOBILE WATER SERVICE SYSTEM
See BOARD OF WATER AND SEWER COMMISSIONERS OF CITY OF MOBILE

D-U-N-S 02-562-6944
▲ **MOBILEIRON INC**
415 E Middlefield Rd, Mountain View, CA 94043-4005
Tel (650) 919-8100 *Founded/Ownrshp* 2007
Sales 132.3MM *EMP* 783^E
Accts Deloitte & Touche Llp San Jos
Tkr Sym MOBL *Exch* NGS
SIC 7372 Prepackaged software; Prepackaged software
Pr: Robert Tinker
**Ch Bd:* Tae Hea Nahm
**CFO:* Simon Biddiscombe
**CFO:* Todd Ford
Ofcr: Jared Lucas
Sr VP: Damian Artt
**Sr VP:* Suresh Batchu
**Sr VP:* John Donnelly
VP: Matt Bennett
**VP:* Laurel Finch
VP: David Hawk
VP: Mike Morrissey
VP: Kees Van Veenendaal
VP: Vittorio Viarengo
Comm Dir: Clarissa Horowitz
Dir Bus: Kevin White
Comm Man: Sara Nixon
Board of Directors: Matthew Howard, Frank Marshall, Bob Tinker, James Tolonen

D-U-N-S 11-834-5920
MOBILENET SERVICES INC
18 Morgan Ste 200, Irvine, CA 92618-2074
Tel (949) 951-4444 *Founded/Ownrshp* 2002
Sales 48.9MM^E *EMP* 360
SIC 8711 4813 Engineering services; Telephone communication, except radio
Pr: Richard Grant
**VP:* Eugene Powell

D-U-N-S 87-285-1568
MOBILEUM INC
2880 Lakeside Dr Ste 135, Santa Clara, CA 95054-2830
Tel (408) 844-6600 *Founded/Ownrshp* 2000
Sales 95.6MM^E *EMP* 180^E
SIC 4899 7373 Data communication services; Computer systems analysis & design; Data communication services; Computer systems analysis & design
CEO: Ori Sasson
**CFO:* Stephen Baker
**CFO:* Neil Laird
Bd of Dir: Craig Ehrlich
**Ex VP:* Avnish Chauhan
**Ex VP:* John Jiang
Ex VP: Gregory S Wood
**Sr VP:* Bishal Bisht
VP: Richard Grohot
VP: Rob McMillen
**Prin:* Julie Kondo
Board of Directors: Craig Ehrlich, Scott Fox, David Kaplan, Rob Theis, Mohan Uttarwar

MOBILEX USA
See SYMPHONY DIAGNOSTIC SERVICES NO 1 LLC

MOBILEXUSA
See SYMPHONY DIAGNOSTIC SERVICES NO 1 LLC

MOBILIA TECHNOLOGY
See AGREEYA MOBILITY INC

D-U-N-S 10-676-2750
MOBILITY SERVICES INTERNATIONAL LLC
MSI
1 Liberty Ln E, Hampton, NH 03842-1809
Tel (603) 274-9100 *Founded/Ownrshp* 1981
Sales 25.9MM^E *EMP* 100^E
SIC 7389 Relocation service
CEO: Timm Runnion
Pr: Andrew Brombosz
CFO: Liz Schulze
**CFO:* Elizabeth Schulze-Smith
VP: Elizabeth Bilek-Portalla
VP: Nellie Bogart
VP: Barbara Casiere
VP: Thomas Colucci
VP: Liz Portalla
VP: Gail Rabasca
VP: Susan Rose
VP: Rob Vickery

MOBILITYWORKS
See WMK INC

MOBILLCASH
See BOKU INC

D-U-N-S 09-248-1373
MOBILOIL FEDERAL CREDIT UNION INC
4285 Treadway Rd, Beaumont, TX 77706-7126
Tel (409) 892-1111 *Founded/Ownrshp* 1935
Sales NA *EMP* 82
SIC 6061 6062 Federal credit unions; State credit unions; Federal credit unions; State credit unions
Pr: Robert Hammer
**CEO:* Chris McDonald
**Ch:* Richard Hegele
VP: Sam James
VP: Pete Johnson
**VP:* Clint Walters
Dir Risk M: Catherine Bishop
IT Man: Tim Beard
Mktg Dir: Lisa Miller
Mktg Mgr: Alyson Kirchner

D-U-N-S 07-834-2793
MOBILUTION INTERNATIONAL INC
5655 W Howard St, Niles, IL 60714-4011
Tel (847) 763-7717 *Founded/Ownrshp* 2009
Sales 22.0MM^E *EMP* 13
SIC 5999 Mobile telephones & equipment; Mobile telephones & equipment
Prin: Sang Won Yum

D-U-N-S 13-098-1710 IMP
MOBIS ALABAMA LLC
GEORGIA PLANT
(*Suby of* MOBIS AMERICA INC) ★
1395 Mitchell Young Rd, Montgomery, AL 36108-5818
Tel (334) 387-4800 *Founded/Ownrshp* 2002
Sales 403.5MM^E *EMP* 1,655
SIC 3714 Motor vehicle body components & frame; Motor vehicle body components & frame
CEO: Chul SOO
CFO: Jay Kim
**CFO:* Beom Seo Koo
QA Dir: Shakerha Sturdivant
QA Dir: Eric Young
Ql Cn Mgr: Steve Choi
Ql Cn Mgr: Robert Hanson
Snr Mgr: Won Kim
Snr Mgr: Robbie Rasberry

D-U-N-S 62-129-7691 IMP
MOBIS AMERICA INC
(*Suby of* HYUNDAI MOBIS CO., LTD.)
1395 Mitchell Young Rd, Montgomery, AL 36108-5818
Tel (334) 387-4840 *Founded/Ownrshp* 2006

Sales 403.5MM^E *EMP* 951^E
SIC 3714 Motor vehicle body components & frame
CEO: Chul SOO Kim
COO: Manuel Maldonado

D-U-N-S 16-397-6512 IMP
MOBIS NORTH AMERICA LLC
MOBIS PARTS DETRIOT
(*Suby of* HYUNDAI MOBIS CO., LTD.)
46501 Commerce Dr, Plymouth, MI 48170
Tel (248) 426-5577 *Founded/Ownrshp* 2004
Sales 242.2MM^E *EMP* 62^E
SIC 5013 8731 Automotive supplies; Commercial physical research
Pr: James Lee

D-U-N-S 16-426-2656 IMP
MOBIS PARTS AMERICA LLC
(*Suby of* HYUNDAI MOBIS CO., LTD.)
10550 Talbert Ave Fl 4, Fountain Valley, CA 92708-6031
Tel (786) 515-1101 *Founded/Ownrshp* 2015
Sales 245.7MM^E *EMP* 300
SIC 5012 Automobiles & other motor vehicles; Automobiles & other motor vehicles
QA Dir: Joshua York
Ql Cn Mgr: Timothy Song
Snr Mgr: David Gault

MOBIS PARTS DETRIOT
See MOBIS NORTH AMERICA LLC

D-U-N-S 01-758-4959
MOBITV INC
6425 Christie Ave Fl 5, Emeryville, CA 94608-1091
Tel (510) 981-1303 *Founded/Ownrshp* 2000
Sales 45.3MM^E *EMP* 100^E
SIC 4813 4899 ; Data communication services
Ch Bd: Charlie Nooney
**Pr:* Paul Scanlan
COO: Anders Norstr M
**COO:* Anders Norstrom
**COO:* Bill Routt
CFO: William E Losch
**CFO:* Terri Stevens
**Chf Mktg O:* Ray Derenzo
Chf Mktg O: Raymond A Derenzo
Sr VP: Paul Burmester
Sr VP: Richard C Herman
**VP:* David Brubeck
VP: Terri M Falcone
VP: Ellen McDonald
VP Bus Dev: Desiree Rodriguez
Board of Directors: Phillip Alvelda, Jeff Annison, Jeff Brody, Steven R Goodbarn, B R Inman, John Jarve, William T Morrow, Paul Scanlan, Vern Stevenson

D-U-N-S 07-914-9264
MOBIUS IMAGING LLC
2 Shaker Rd, Shirley, MA 01464-2525
Tel (978) 796-5068 *Founded/Ownrshp* 2008
Sales 23.0MM *EMP* 53
SIC 3841 Surgical & medical instruments

D-U-N-S 60-253-0169
MOBIUS INDUSTRIES USA INC
READY PORTION MEAT
550 Kirkland Way Ste 400, Kirkland, WA 98033-6240
Tel (425) 558-1690 *Founded/Ownrshp* 2005
Sales 26.1MM^E *EMP* 250
SIC 8748 Business consulting; Business consulting
Pr: Jeffrey Balentine
Dir IT: Josh Owen

D-U-N-S 02-468-3880
MOBIUS MANAGEMENT SYSTEMS INC (DE)
(*Suby of* ALLEN SYSTEMS GROUP INC) ★
287 Bowman Ave Ste 401, Purchase, NY 10577-2517
Tel (914) 921-7200 *Founded/Ownrshp* 1981
Sales 33.5MM^E *EMP* 443
SIC 7372 Business oriented computer software; Business oriented computer software
Ch Bd: Mitchell Gross
CFO: Raymond F Kunzmann
Treas: David J Gordon
Sr VP: Mauricio Barberi
Sr VP: David Barton
VP: David B Barton
VP: James C Biggs
VP: John Murphy
Dir Bus: Anne Korb
QA Dir: Art Celestini
Sftwr Eng: Alan Carter

D-U-N-S 09-667-4205
MOBLEY CONTRACTORS INC
952 Highway 287, Morrilton, AR 72110-9417
Tel (501) 354-2510 *Founded/Ownrshp* 1978
Sales 43.3MM^E *EMP* 160
SIC 1611 General contractor, highway & street construction; General contractor, highway & street construction
Pr: Ronald F Mobley
**Treas:* Janice Mobley
**VP:* Don Depriest
**VP:* Kenny French
**VP:* Ronnie Mobley Jr
**Prin:* Ment Dollar
Sls Mgr: Kathy Lawrence

D-U-N-S 09-767-2182
MOBLEY INDUSTRIAL SERVICES INC
(*Suby of* SAFWAY GROUP HOLDING LLC) ★
1220 Miller Cut Off Rd, La Porte, TX 77571-9799
Tel (281) 470-9120 *Founded/Ownrshp* 2015
Sales 130.0MM^E *EMP* 1,400
SIC 1721 1799 5033 Residential painting; Fireproofing buildings; Insulation of pipes & boilers; Sandblasting of building exteriors; Scaffolding construction; Insulation materials; Residential painting; Fireproofing buildings; Insulation of pipes & boilers; Sandblasting of building exteriors; Scaffolding construction; Insulation materials
Pr: Chuck Mobley
Sec: Bernice L Mobley
VP: Charles Mobley
VP: Kirk Mobley
VP: Bob Yates
VP: Blake Young
Area Mgr: Pedro Infante
Area Mgr: William Patterson
Off Mgr: Angela Outlaw
Off Mgr: Pat Strange
IT Man: Justin Meeks

MOBLEY OILFIELD SERVICES
See TERVITA LLC

D-U-N-S 00-894-7095
MOBLEY-SPEED CEMENT CONTRACTORS
4699 Production Dr, Dallas, TX 75235-8015
Tel (214) 637-3270 *Founded/Ownrshp* 1950
Sales 21.1MM^E *EMP* 150
SIC 1771 Concrete work; Concrete work
Genl Mgr: Lonnie Williams

D-U-N-S 01-050-0056
MOBRO MARINE INC
ARLINGTON MARINA
606 Leonard C Taylor Pkwy, Green Cove Springs, FL 32043-8335
Tel (866) 313-9670 *Founded/Ownrshp* 1964
Sales 28.9MM^E *EMP* 106
SIC 4492 7699 4449 Marine towing services; Nautical repair services; Canal barge operations
Pr: John Rowland
**CFO:* Stephen T Cumella
**VP:* John Hall
VP: Boyd Moody
**VP:* T Boyd Moody
Sls Mgr: Trish Kramer

D-U-N-S 03-106-9461
MOC ACQUISITION CORP
MIDLAND OPTICAL
(*Suby of* DUFFENS OPTICAL) ★
2360 59th St, Saint Louis, MO 63110-2812
Tel (314) 533-2020 *Founded/Ownrshp* 1989
Sales 27.7MM^E *EMP* 150
Accts Hoffman Bricker & Adams Pc
SIC 3851 5049 Lens grinding, except prescription: ophthalmic; Optical goods; Lens grinding, except prescription: ophthalmic; Optical goods
Pr: Matt Iovaldi
VP: Bill Browne
VP: William Browne
VP: Craig Hausmann
**VP:* Susan Iovaldi
S&M/VP: Kim Clynes
Sales Asso: Lisa Flanagan
Sales Asso: Mike Jobe

D-U-N-S 08-179-3945 EXP
MOC PRODUCTS CO INC
AUTO EDGE SOLUTIONS
12306 Montague St, Pacoima, CA 91331-2279
Tel (818) 794-3500 *Founded/Ownrshp* 1975
Sales 175.6MM^E *EMP* 250
SIC 5169 7549 Chemicals & allied products; Automotive maintenance services; Chemicals & allied products; Automotive maintenance services
CEO: Mark Waco
**Sec:* Nadelin Waco
**VP:* Dave Waco
Off Mgr: Neetu Salwan
Mtls Mgr: Jerry Wesserling
Opers Mgr: Valari Harrell
Manager: Paul Borrelli
Manager: Duane Crewse
Manager: John Frederick
Manager: Dean Josey
Manager: Ed Love

D-U-N-S 01-966-9621
MOCAP LLC (MO)
409 Parkway Dr, Park Hills, MO 63601-4435
Tel (573) 431-4610 *Founded/Ownrshp* 1981
Sales 38.0MM^E *EMP* 175
SIC 3089 Caps, plastic; Novelties, plastic; Caps, plastic; Novelties, plastic
**CFO:* Tom Heckert
VP: Paul T Miller
IT Man: Jason Froidcoeur
Sfty Mgr: Wayne Stringer
Plnt Mgr: Glen Weibel
VP Sls: Gregory Miller
Mktg Dir: Jim Boehm
Art Dir: Randy Stone

D-U-N-S 00-667-1106
MOCEAN LLC (CA)
2440 S Sepulveda Blvd # 150, Los Angeles, CA 90064-1786
Tel (310) 481-0808 *Founded/Ownrshp* 2000
Sales 24.5MM^E *EMP* 200
SIC 7374 7822 Computer graphics service; Motion picture distribution; Computer graphics service; Motion picture distribution
Pr: Michael McIntyre
VP: Roshone Harmon
VP: Alan Ireland
VP: Jeremy Keeler
VP: Adam Rosenblatt
Dir Bus: Candace Reid
Mng Dir: Kevin Aratari
Art Dir: Craig Oelrich
Snr Mgr: Beth Bradmon

MOCERI PRODUCE
See SEA BREEZE FOODS INC

D-U-N-S 05-102-4735
MOCK PLUMBING AND MECHANICAL INC
67 Ross Rd, Savannah, GA 31405-1660
Tel (770) 449-4445 *Founded/Ownrshp* 1971
Sales 29.6MM *EMP* 125
Accts Thombley & Simmons Pc Mariet
SIC 1711 Plumbing contractors; Warm air heating & air conditioning contractor; Plumbing contractors; Warm air heating & air conditioning contractor
Pr: William H Mock Jr
**CFO:* William G Cail
**VP:* Ronald A Tucker
Exec: Jack Cooey

D-U-N-S 06-180-2518 IMP
MOCK TIRE & AUTOMOTIVE INC
4752 Country Club Rd, Winston Salem, NC 27104-3599
Tel (336) 768-1010 *Founded/Ownrshp* 1973
Sales 43.9MM^E *EMP* 150
SIC 5531 7539 7534 Automotive tires; Automotive accessories; Front end repair, automotive; Brake repair, automotive; Tire repair shop; Automotive tires; Automotive accessories; Front end repair, automotive; Brake repair, automotive; Tire repair shop
Pr: Floyd L Mock
**Sec:* Cecil G Mock
**VP:* Carey W Mock

D-U-N-S 03-419-4845
MOCKLER BEVERAGE CO LP
MOCKLER BEVERAGE/BUDWEISER
11811 Reiger Rd, Baton Rouge, LA 70809-4925
Tel (225) 408-4283 *Founded/Ownrshp* 1988
Sales 88.0MM *EMP* 156
Accts Hannis T Bourgeois Llp Denh
SIC 5181 Beer & other fermented malt liquors; Beer & other fermented malt liquors
Pt: Gary W Mockler
**Pt:* Michael A Coon
**Pt:* Douglas F Mackey
**Pt:* Patrick E Mockler
**Pt:* William C Ruiz
VP: Mary Lewis
IT Man: Keith Dahlgreen
VP Sls: Chris Davis
Mktg Dir: John Schiller
Snr Mgr: Dan Palmer

MOCKLER BEVERAGE/BUDWEISER
See MOCKLER BEVERAGE CO LP

MOCON
See SPS CORP

D-U-N-S 00-644-8112
▲ MOCON INC
7500 Mendelsohn Ave N, Minneapolis, MN 55428-4045
Tel (763) 493-6370 *Founded/Ownrshp* 1966
Sales 64.4MM *EMP* 250^E
Accts Kpmg Llp Minneapolis Minneso
Tkr Sym MOCO *Exch* NGM
SIC 3829 Measuring & controlling devices; Measuring & controlling devices
Ch Bd: Robert L Demorest
**COO:* Donald N Demorett
CFO: Elissa Lindsoe
**Ex VP:* Daniel W Mayer
VP: Bruce Bauer
Adv Bd Mbr: Ryan Holland
MIS Dir: Roger Oestreich
Natl Sales: Betty Kauffman
Mktg Mgr: Guy Wray
Plas Surg: Bill Halvorson
Board of Directors: Robert F Gallagher, Bradley D Goskowicz, Kathleen P Iverson, Tom C Thomas, David J Ward, Paul R Zeller

D-U-N-S 05-995-9429 EXP
MOD-PAC CORP
1801 Elmwood Ave Ste 1, Buffalo, NY 14207-2496
Tel (716) 873-0640 *Founded/Ownrshp* 1968
Sales 59.2MM *EMP* 370^E
SIC 2657 2759 Folding paperboard boxes; Commercial printing; Invitations: printing; Business forms: printing; Folding paperboard boxes; Commercial printing; Invitations: printing; Business forms: printing
Pr: Daniel G Keane
**Ch Bd:* Kevin T Keane
COO: David B Lupp
Prin: Robert J McKenna
Prin: Howard Zemsky
CTO: Marie L Smith
IT Man: Steve Anderson
VP Sls: Philip C Rechin
Sales Asso: Donald J Coppola
Board of Directors: William G Gisel Jr, Robert J McKenna, Howard Zemsky

D-U-N-S 05-584-2462
MOD-U-KRAF HOMES LLC
(*Suby of* ALL AMERICAN GROUP, INC.)
260 Weaver St, Rocky Mount, VA 24151-2251
Tel (540) 482-0273 *Founded/Ownrshp* 1971
Sales 27.7MM^E *EMP* 250^E
SIC 2452 1521 Prefabricated wood buildings; Modular homes, prefabricated, wood; Single-family housing construction; Prefabricated wood buildings; Modular homes, prefabricated, wood; Single-family housing construction
Treas: Thomas Martini
Treas: Tom Martini
VP: Jeff Towell
Plnt Mgr: Ricky Adkins

MODA EXPRESS
See MODAEXPRESS OF USA INC

MODA FABRICS AND UNITED NOT
See UNITED NOTIONS INC

D-U-N-S 95-990-7411
MODA HEALTH PLAN INC
ODS COMPANIES
(*Suby of* ODS COMPANIES) ★
601 Sw 2nd Ave, Portland, OR 97204-3199
Tel (503) 228-6554 *Founded/Ownrshp* 1984
Sales NA *EMP* 741^E
SIC 6321 Accident & health insurance; Accident & health insurance
Pr: William Johnson
VP: Marty Stewart
Dir IT: Bill Howell
IT Man: Jerry Beagle
Sls Mgr: C J McLeod

D-U-N-S 96-797-5546
MODA OPERANDI INC
315 Hudson St Fl 5r, New York, NY 10013-1025
Tel (917) 688-3711 *Founded/Ownrshp* 2010
Sales 45.0MM *EMP* 100
SIC 5621 Women's clothing stores
Pr: Deborah Nicodemus
**Sr VP:* Hoddi Hafsteinsson
Exec: Amanda Farbish
CTO: Matt Pavelle
Dir IT: George Alexandrakis
Prd Mgr: Francesca Del Balzo

D-U-N-S 07-874-8493
MODAEXPRESS OF USA INC
MODA EXPRESS
900 Secaucus Rd Unit A, Secaucus, NJ 07094-2423
Tel (201) 325-8808 *Founded/Ownrshp* 1993
Sales 21.6MM^E *EMP* 70
SIC 4731 Freight transportation arrangement
Pr: Giovanni Gaetani
IT Man: Eddie Smolenskiy

D-U-N-S 06-439-6104
MODAGRAFICS INC
5300 Newport Dr, Rolling Meadows, IL 60008-3702
Tel (847) 392-3980 *Founded/Ownrshp* 1973
Sales 22.1MM^E *EMP* 80
SIC 2759 3993 7389 Screen printing; Signs, not made in custom sign painting shops; Interior decorating
Pr: Atul Anand
**CFO:* Michael Antongiovanni
**VP:* Howard Baden
**VP:* Jack Masters
VP: Ed Peek
Creative D: Ben Berning
Opers Mgr: Len Carlson
Plnt Mgr: Marty Dorner
VP Sls: Bob Jurgens
Sls Dir: Bob Jergens
Sales Asso: Christina Mulligan
Board of Directors: Robert J Browne, Andrew Filipowski, William O'connor, H E Olson, Dr Leonard Smith, Roger Stedronsky, Bruno Seghin of Navis Capi

D-U-N-S 62-443-5491
MODAL SHOP INC
T M S
(*Suby of* PCB GROUP INC) ★
3149 E Kemper Rd, Cincinnati, OH 45241-1516
Tel (513) 351-9919 *Founded/Ownrshp* 1990
Sales 49.0MM^E *EMP* 70
SIC 5084 7359 8711 Instruments & control equipment; Electronic equipment rental, except computers; Engineering services
Pr: Michael J Lally
IT Man: Gayle Haarmeyer
Opers Mgr: Kevin McCluskey

D-U-N-S 80-921-6323 IMP
MODCLOTH INC
MODCLOTH.COM
115 Sansome St Ste 900, San Francisco, CA 94104-3624
Tel (412) 587-4938 *Founded/Ownrshp* 2002
Sales 26.1MM^E *EMP* 123^E
SIC 5621 Women's clothing stores
CEO: Matt Kaness
**CFO:* Antonio Nieves
**Chf Cred:* Susan Gregg Koger
VP: Shawn Davis
VP: Jennifer Grasso
VP: Leo Haryono
Comm Dir: Rebecca Silliman
Dir IT: Jason Santarcangelo
Advt Mgr: Stephanie Lim
Snr PM: Simon Darken

MODCLOTH.COM
See MODCLOTH INC

D-U-N-S 17-633-5420
■ MODCOMP INC
(*Suby of* CSP INC) ★
1500 S Powerline Rd Ste A, Deerfield Beach, FL 33442-8185
Tel (954) 571-4600 *Founded/Ownrshp* 1997
Sales 43.6MM^E *EMP* 106
SIC 7378 7373 Computer maintenance & repair; Systems integration services
CEO: Alexander R Lupinetti
VP: Nick Monfreda
Exec: Christina Ally
Dir IT: Frank Special
Sales Asso: Jay Ledesma

D-U-N-S 61-978-4353
MODE MEDIA CORP
PROJECTY
2000 Sierra Point Pkwy # 10, Brisbane, CA 94005-1866
Tel (650) 244-4000 *Founded/Ownrshp* 2004
Sales 57.4MM^E *EMP* 240^E
SIC 7313 7311 Electronic media advertising representatives; Advertising agencies; Electronic media advertising representatives; Advertising agencies
Ch Bd: Samir Arora
CFO: Stephen E Recht
CFO: Jeanne Seeley
Ofcr: Dan Lagani
Ex VP: Ernie Cicogna
Ex VP: Fernando Ruarte
Ex VP: John Trimble
Sr VP: Jill Byron
Sr VP: Erin Matts
Sr VP: Victor Zaud
VP: Mark Boxer
VP: Lane Buschel
VP: Leah Corselli
VP: Bernard Desarnauts
VP: Christian Galindo
VP: Marianne Goode
VP: Karin Marke
VP: Wendy Mazzoni
VP: Christine McNicholas
VP: Jack Rotolo
VP: Matthew Schulte
Board of Directors: Marc Andreessen, Gary R Effren, David Saltzman

D-U-N-S 10-249-3418
■ MODE TRANSPORTATION LLC
(Suby of HUB GROUP INC) ★
17330 Preston Rd Ste 200c, Dallas, TX 75252-6035
Tel (800) 434-8881 Founded/Ownrshp 2011
Sales 64.5MM^E EMP 119
SIC 4731 Trucking, except local; Brokers, shipping; Agents, shipping; Air cargo carriers, nonscheduled; Brokers, shipping; Agents, shipping
CEO: David P Yeager
*Pr: James Damman
*CFO: Terri Pizzuto
*Ch: Mark A Yeager
*Treas: Thomas Foster
Ex VP: David Gordon
*Sr VP: William Todd Thompson Jr
VP: Terrence Sweeney
VP: Brad Young
Brnch Mgr: Omar Younis
Genl Mgr: Bill Balsley

D-U-N-S 83-433-4463
MODEC (USA) INC
INC, MODEC INTERNATIONAL
(Suby of MODEC,INC.)
15011 Katy Fwy, Houston, TX 77094-1905
Tel (281) 529-8100 Founded/Ownrshp 1968
Sales 35.0MM^E EMP 200
Accts Uhy Llp Houston Tx
SIC 3533 Oil & gas drilling rigs & equipment; Oil & gas drilling rigs & equipment
Pr: Kenji Yamada
Ofcr: Ross Little
Off Admin: Theini Suppiah

D-U-N-S 09-603-2545
MODEC INTERNATIONAL INC
(Suby of MODEC,INC.)
15011 Katy Fwy Ste 500, Houston, TX 77094-0010
Tel (281) 529-8306 Founded/Ownrshp 1999, 2008
Sales 3.0MMM^E EMP 1,000
SIC 8711 2499 3731 Professional engineer; Floating docks, wood; Commercial cargo ships, building & repairing; Professional engineer; Floating docks, wood; Commercial cargo ships, building & repairing
Pr: Toshiro Miyazaki
*COO: Shigeru Usami
*CFO: Bruce John Beever
CFO: Bruce Beever
Ex VP: John Gremp
Exec: Jeffrey Carr
*Prin: Norihisa Fukuda
*Prin: Ricky Alan Hall
*Prin: Takashi Nashino
*Prin: Kensuke Taniguchi
Genl Mgr: Kazunari Miwa
Board of Directors: M Mokumoto, N Yaji

MODEC SOFEC
See SOFEC INC

D-U-N-S 03-495-4131
■ MODEL DAIRY LLC
(Suby of DEAN FOODS CO) ★
500 Gould St, Reno, NV 89502-1466
Tel (775) 788-7900 Founded/Ownrshp 1996
Sales 95.4MM^E EMP 324
SIC 2026 5143 Fluid milk; Dairy products, except dried or canned; Fluid milk; Dairy products, except dried or canned
Genl Mgr: Jim Breslin
Genl Mgr: Neila Collins
Plnt Mgr: Art Schermerhorn
Sls Mgr: Derek Allbee

D-U-N-S 04-741-1541
MODEL DRUG INC
MODEL HEALTHCARE
1506 Draper St, Kingsburg, CA 93631-1909
Tel (559) 897-5111 Founded/Ownrshp 1989
Sales 21.8MM^E EMP 48
SIC 5912 Drug stores
CEO: Russ Zakarian
*Pr: Patricia Zakarian
Pharmcst: Jim Antaramian

D-U-N-S 07-096-0976
MODEL ELECTRONICS INC
615 E Crescent Ave, Ramsey, NJ 07446-1220
Tel (201) 961-9200 Founded/Ownrshp 1976
Sales 22.1MM^E EMP 135^E
SIC 3679 5064 5731 Recording & playback apparatus, including phonograph; Radios; Sound equipment, automotive; Recording & playback apparatus, including phonograph; Radios; Sound equipment, automotive
Pr: Matthew Sasso
*Pr: Peter Maroccia
*VP: Thomas Churchill
Sls Mgr: Bryan Caglione
Sls Mgr: T J Churchill

MODEL HEALTHCARE
See MODEL DRUG INC

D-U-N-S 03-899-0537
MODEL HOME INTERIORS INC
7700 Port Capital Dr, Elkridge, MD 21075-6504
Tel (443) 899-0200 Founded/Ownrshp 1980
Sales 33.9MM^E EMP 150
SIC 5712 7359 7389 Office furniture; Furniture rental; Interior designer; Office furniture; Furniture rental; Interior designer
Pr: Carl Mc Williams
*Ex VP: William F Carroll
*VP: Jerry Bayshore
*VP: Vince Florenzo

MODELL'S SPORTING GOODS
See HENRY MODELL & CO INC

D-U-N-S 96-897-3037
MODELLS SPORTING GOODS INC
(Suby of HENRY MODELL & CO INC) ★
498 Fashion Ave Fl 20, New York, NY 10018-6704
Tel (212) 822-1000 Founded/Ownrshp 1999
Sales 58.1MM^E EMP 174^E
SIC 5941 Sporting goods & bicycle shops
Ch Bd: Mitchell B Modell

D-U-N-S 07-424-4088
MODELS & TOOLS INC
51400 Bellestri Ct, Shelby Township, MI 48315-2749
Tel (586) 580-6900 Founded/Ownrshp 2011
Sales 35.5MM^E EMP 165
SIC 3544 Special dies & tools; Special dies, tools, jigs & fixtures
Pr: Philip Neale
*CFO: Rick Faubert
IT Man: Jason Neale

D-U-N-S 00-806-8603 IMP/EXP
MODERN AG PRODUCTS LTD
DRAGON ESP
1655 Louisiana St, Beaumont, TX 77701-1120
Tel (409) 833-2665 Founded/Ownrshp 1963
Sales 286.5MM^E EMP 1,900
SIC 7359 6792 0161 Equipment rental & leasing; Oil royalty traders; Artichoke farm; Equipment rental & leasing; Oil royalty traders; Artichoke farm
CEO: Will Crenshaw
Pr: Casey Crenshaw
CFO: Brian Balmer

D-U-N-S 16-027-1508
MODERN ALLOYS INC
11172 Western Ave, Stanton, CA 90680-2994
Tel (714) 893-0551 Founded/Ownrshp 1987
Sales 29.3MM^E EMP 91
SIC 5039 Metal guardrails; Metal guardrails
Pr: Ronald B Grey
*VP: Scott Metko
*VP: John D Rehoreg
*VP: Scott R Squires

D-U-N-S 01-568-2503
MODERN AMERICAN RECYCLING SERVICE INC
MARS
499 Powhatten Ct, Gibson, LA 70356
Tel (985) 845-8618 Founded/Ownrshp 1995
Sales 60.0MM EMP 415
SIC 5093 Metal scrap & waste materials; Metal scrap & waste materials
Pr: Dwight Caton Sr
VP: Khristie Caton
VP: Khristie Yates

D-U-N-S 00-167-3177
MODERN BANK
(Suby of MODERN FINANCIAL INC.)
250 W 55th St Fl 15, New York, NY 10019-7599
Tel (212) 323-1100 Founded/Ownrshp 1976, 1985
Sales NA EMP 33
SIC 6021 National commercial banks; National commercial banks
CEO: Jeff Lane
CFO: Steven Sabitini
*Chf Cred: Dennis Kennedy
Ofcr: Valerie Swaya
Sr VP: Nora Pinilla-Shapiro
VP: Doug Gardner
VP: Michael Halloran
VP: Donnie Shir
VP: Bippy Siegal
VP: Reynold Tan
VP: Christopher Terlik
VP: Kitty Yen

MODERN BANKING SYSTEMS
See INTERSTATE BUSINESS EQUIPMENT INC

D-U-N-S 15-133-7201
MODERN BUILDERS SUPPLY INC
POLARIS TECHNOLOGIES
302 Mcclurg Rd, Youngstown, OH 44512-6401
Tel (330) 729-2690 Founded/Ownrshp 1986
Sales 328.6MM^E EMP 750
SIC 5032 3089 3446 3442 Brick, stone & related material; Windows, plastic; Doors, folding: plastic or plastic coated fabric; Architectural metalwork; Metal doors, sash & trim; Brick, stone & related material; Windows, plastic; Doors, folding: plastic or plastic coated fabric; Architectural metalwork; Metal doors, sash & trim
CEO: Kevin Leggett
*Ch Bd: Larry Leggett
*Treas: G Taylor Evans III
*VP: Eric Leggett
*VP: Jack Marstellar
VP: Tony Puntel
Rgnl Mgr: Brian Balasko
Genl Mgr: Kevin Buchholtz
Manager: Clint Hulse
Manager: Kevin Kuligowski
Manager: Dave Reynolds

D-U-N-S 06-781-0689
MODERN BUILDING INC
3083 Southgate Ln, Chico, CA 95928-7427
Tel (530) 891-4533 Founded/Ownrshp 1973
Sales 22.5MM^E EMP 50
SIC 1541 1542 Industrial buildings & warehouses; Commercial & office building, new construction
CEO: L Gage Chrysler
*Sec: Gary Fowler
*VP: James Seegert

MODERN BUSINESS MACHINES
See MERIZON GROUP INC

D-U-N-S 00-699-7787
MODERN CHEVROLET CO OF WINSTON - SALEM
5955 University Pkwy, Winston Salem, NC 27105-1341
Tel (336) 722-4191 Founded/Ownrshp 1933
Sales 38.0MM^E EMP 168
SIC 5511 Automobiles, new & used; Automobiles, new & used
Pr: Omnia Fowler
*VP: Robert Fowler

D-U-N-S 14-794-1082
MODERN CLASSIC MOTORS INC
HILTON HEAD ISLAND HONDA
355 William Hilton Pkwy, Hilton Head Island, SC 29926-2432
Tel (843) 681-8500 Founded/Ownrshp 1985
Sales 20.6MM^E EMP 56
Accts Wilson & Lunder
SIC 5511 Automobiles, new & used; Automobiles, new & used
Pr: Gordon Faulkner

D-U-N-S 06-666-4566
MODERN DEVELOPMENT CO A LIMITED PARTNERSHIP
PARAMOUNT SWAPMEET
3333 W Coast Hwy Ste 400, Newport Beach, CA 92663-4042
Tel (949) 646-6400 Founded/Ownrshp 1992
Sales 22.7MM^E EMP 176
SIC 7389 2084 5812 6512 Flea market; Wines; Concessionaire; Commercial & industrial building operation; Flea market; Wines; Concessionaire; Commercial & industrial building operation
Genl Pt: Glenn A Bianchi
Pt: Beau Bianchi
Pt: Donald J Ransom

D-U-N-S 04-346-8768
MODERN DISPERSIONS INC
302 Ed Ward Rd, Fitzgerald, GA 31750-8813
Tel (229) 423-9141 Founded/Ownrshp 1967
Sales 21.3MM^E EMP 70
SIC 3087 Custom compound purchased resins
Pr: Janos Kozma Sr
*Treas: Janos Kozma Jr
Off Mgr: Darlene Willard

D-U-N-S 60-952-4835 IMP/EXP
MODERN DISPERSIONS SOUTH INC
302 Ed Ward Rd, Fitzgerald, GA 31750-8813
Tel (229) 423-9141 Founded/Ownrshp 2005
Sales 63.3MM^E EMP 185
SIC 3089 Extruded finished plastic products; Extruded finished plastic products
Pr: Marton Kozma
VP Sls: Jim Kanan

D-U-N-S 03-537-3927 IMP
MODERN DISPLAY SERVICE INC
MODERN EXPOSITION SERVICES
424 S 700 E, Salt Lake City, UT 84102-2864
Tel (801) 355-7427 Founded/Ownrshp 1940
Sales 58.8MM^E EMP 125
SIC 5193 7389 5046 5113 Flowers & florists' supplies; Convention & show services; Display equipment, except refrigerated; Industrial & personal service paper; Flowers & florists' supplies; Convention & show services; Display equipment, except refrigerated; Industrial & personal service paper
Pr: William C Vriens Jr
*Pr: Aaron Bludworth
VP: Tim Taylor
*VP: Spencer Vriens
*VP: W Taylor Vriens
Exec: Rob Racker
Opers Mgr: Eddie Novak

D-U-N-S 05-181-7682
MODERN DISPOSAL SERVICES INC
4746 Model City Rd, Model City, NY 14107-9800
Tel (716) 692-1272 Founded/Ownrshp 1964
Sales 27.2MM^E EMP 177^E
SIC 4953 Refuse collection & disposal services; Refuse collection & disposal services
Ch: Sonia Washuta
*Pr: Richard Washuta
*Sec: Lorie Washuta
*VP: Gary Smith
CTO: Kevin Doyle
VP Opers: Robert Trunzo

D-U-N-S 02-418-4525
MODERN DISTRIBUTORS INC (TN)
817 W Columbia St, Somerset, KY 42501-1729
Tel (606) 679-1178 Founded/Ownrshp 1961, 1965
Sales 80.7MM^E EMP 170
SIC 5194 5962 5145 5064 Cigarettes; Cigarettes vending machines; Sandwich & hot food vending machines; Candy; Electrical entertainment equipment
Pr: Gerald D Ray
*Sec: Robert Mickey Ray
IT Man: J C Meece
Sls&Mrk Ex: Raymond Hranicky
Mktg Dir: Elizabeth Tuttle
Sales Asso: Cindi Burgette

D-U-N-S 15-384-0574
MODERN DOOR AND EQUIPMENT SALES INC
J & L CONSTRUCTION
4301 Charles Crossing Dr, White Plains, MD 20695-3027
Tel (301) 843-5255 Founded/Ownrshp 1998
Sales 23.5MM EMP 59
SIC 5046 5091 Partitions; Gymnasium equipment
Pr: William Dotson
*Treas: Janice Haupt
*VP: Phil Pasini

D-U-N-S 09-458-2533
MODERN DOOR CORP
(Suby of PLYCO CORP) ★
1300 Virginia St, Walkerton, IN 46574-1073
Tel (574) 586-3117 Founded/Ownrshp 1977
Sales 32.4MM^E EMP 100
SIC 3442 3444 Metal doors; Sheet metalwork
Pr: Garry L Matz
*CFO: Thomas R Blend
Plnt Mgr: Dave Kaiser

D-U-N-S 00-545-5597 IMP
MODERN DROP FORGE CO
13810 Western Ave, Blue Island, IL 60406-3249
Tel (708) 388-1806 Founded/Ownrshp 1948
Sales 7.1MM EMP 610
Accts Coope Ltd Deerfield Il
SIC 3462 3544 Iron & steel forgings; Special dies & tools; Iron & steel forgings; Special dies & tools
CEO: Gregory Heim
*CFO: Patrick Thompson
VP: Ron Macari
MIS Dir: Ronald Rotondi

D-U-N-S 01-185-1573
MODERN ELECTRIC CO (INC)
71 Crooks Ave Ste 1, Clifton, NJ 07011-1074
Tel (973) 478-1222 Founded/Ownrshp 1972
Sales 21.2MM^E EMP 100
SIC 1731 General electrical contractor
Pr: Alan M Golub
*VP: Matthew T Glennon

D-U-N-S 00-727-6355
MODERN EQUIPMENT CO INC
MECO OMAHA
6161 Abbott Dr, Omaha, NE 68110-2806
Tel (402) 341-4939 Founded/Ownrshp 1907
Sales 42.6MM^E EMP 137
SIC 3537 2542 3411 Lift trucks, industrial: fork, platform, straddle, etc.; Shelving, office & store: except wood; Metal cans; Lift trucks, industrial: fork, platform, straddle, etc.; Shelving, office & store: except wood; Metal cans
Pr: Richard W Johnson Jr
*CFO: Mitch Schlater
VP Opers: Bill Singer
VP Sls: Jim Bullock
Sls Mgr: Dennis McClintock

MODERN EXPOSITION SERVICES
See MODERN DISPLAY SERVICE INC

D-U-N-S 04-610-8452
MODERN FACILITIES SERVICES INC
733 Ridgedale Ave Ste 201, East Hanover, NJ 07936-3157
Tel (973) 599-9393 Founded/Ownrshp 1979
Sales 32.3MM^E EMP 525
Accts Amper Politziner & Mattia Ll
SIC 7349 Building cleaning service; Building cleaning service
Pr: Sergio Benvenuto Jr
*Sec: Oriana Benvenuto
*Exec: Rick Lomonaco
Opers Mgr: Fernando Arias
Sls Mgr: Dave Pittenger

MODERN FREE NORTH CAROLINA
See LUXOR GRAND LODGE 44 CROWN & SCEPTER GRAND CHAPTER OES

MODERN GRAPHIC ARTS
See SANDY-ALEXANDER INC

MODERN GROCERY
See MARKET GROCERY CO

D-U-N-S 05-074-5876 IMP/EXP
MODERN GROUP LTD
2501 Durham Rd, Bristol, PA 19007-6999
Tel (215) 943-9100 Founded/Ownrshp 2003
Sales 206.8MM^E EMP 570
SIC 5084 7353 7699 Industrial machinery & equipment; Materials handling machinery; Heavy construction equipment rental; Earth moving equipment, rental or leasing; Industrial equipment services; Industrial machinery & equipment; Materials handling machinery; Heavy construction equipment rental; Earth moving equipment, rental or leasing; Industrial equipment services
Pr: Dave Griffith
Pr: Paul Farrell
CFO: Brian Bommer
Ex VP: George S Wilkinson
Sr VP: Thomas Callahan
VP: Nancy Lee
VP: Stephen Seminack
Brnch Mgr: Dave Devanzo
IT Man: Rosalie Storti
Podiatrist: Ellen Altenburg

D-U-N-S 93-272-0139
MODERN GROUP LTD
1655 Louisiana St, Beaumont, TX 77701-1120
Tel (800) 231-8198 Founded/Ownrshp 1980
Sales 276.0MM^E EMP 1,500
SIC 7359 3441 Equipment rental & leasing; Fabricated structural metal; Equipment rental & leasing; Fabricated structural metal
CEO: Will Crenshaw
Pr: Casey Crenshaw
COO: Doug Pierce
CFO: Brian Bommer

D-U-N-S 00-232-2071 IMP
MODERN HANDLING EQUIPMENT CO (PA)
(Suby of MODERN GROUP LTD) ★
2501 Durham Rd Ste G, Bristol, PA 19007-6923
Tel (215) 943-9100 Founded/Ownrshp 1955, 1979
Sales 170.7MM^E EMP 203
SIC 5084 7353 Materials handling machinery; Cranes & aerial lift equipment, rental or leasing; Materials handling machinery; Cranes & aerial lift equipment, rental or leasing
Pr: Paul Farrell
*CFO: Stephen Seminack
*Treas: George S Wilkinson
*VP: Thomas P Callahan
VP: Lawrence Norton
*Prin: Gerald Couch
IT Man: Nancy Lee
Mtls Mgr: Larry Gower
Board of Directors: Steve Lecatsas, John F Smith

D-U-N-S 01-476-4088 EXP
MODERN HANDLING EQUIPMENT OF N J INC
(Suby of MODERN GROUP LTD) ★
75 New St, Edison, NJ 08837-3563
Tel (732) 738-9200 Founded/Ownrshp 1966
Sales 22.4MM^E EMP 57
SIC 5084 Materials handling machinery
Pr: Carl P Rathemacher
*CFO: Steven Seminack

*Treas: George S Wilkinson
*VP: Thomas P Callahan

D-U-N-S 07-939-6092
MODERN HC HOLDINGS INC
6435 Hazeltine National, Orlando, FL 32822-5158
Tel (626) 932-1600 Founded/Ownrshp 2012
Sales 850.0MM EMP 140
SIC 6719 Investment holding companies, except banks; Investment holding companies, except banks
CEO: Dominic Meffe
*CFO: Vincent Cook

D-U-N-S 08-837-5472
MODERN HEALTHCARE INC
P X DRUG STORE
110 E Huntington Dr, Monrovia, CA 91016-3415
Tel (626) 932-1600 Founded/Ownrshp 1976
Sales 71.8MM^E EMP 350
SIC 5912 Drug stores; Drug stores
Pr: Ira Halpern
Pr: Brenda Goodman
*CFO: Denny Kon
*CFO: Mark C Russell
*Sec: Richard I Katz
Netwrk Mgr: Amanda Xu

D-U-N-S 06-558-5470
MODERN HOME HEALTH CARE INC
3130 Bonita Rd Ste 103, Chula Vista, CA 91910-3263
Tel (619) 476-6619 Founded/Ownrshp 2010
Sales 25.0MM EMP 30
SIC 8082 Home health care services
Prin: Rosalind Ong
*CEO: Tita T Manglicmot

MODERN HONDA OF CONCORD
See MODERN NISSAN OF CONCORD INC

D-U-N-S 61-737-7270 IMP/EXP
MODERN ICE EQUIPMENT AND SUPPLY CO
MODERN TOUR
5709 Harrison Ave, Cincinnati, OH 45248-1601
Tel (513) 367-2101 Founded/Ownrshp 1990
Sales 21.4MM^E EMP 50
SIC 5078 3444 Refrigeration equipment & supplies; Sheet metalwork
Pr: Gary E Jerow
*VP: John Murphy
IT Man: Brian Ballman

D-U-N-S 04-837-9077 IMP
MODERN INDUSTRIES INC
4747 E Beautiful Ln, Phoenix, AZ 85044-5318
Tel (602) 267-7248 Founded/Ownrshp 1969
Sales 103.6MM^E EMP 380
SIC 3599 3769 Machine shop, jobbing & repair; Guided missile & space vehicle parts & auxiliary equipment; Machine shop, jobbing & repair; Guided missile & space vehicle parts & auxiliary equipment
CEO: Andrew W Yahraus
*Pr: Daniel L Yahraus
*Treas: Jean A Lashinske
Dir Bus: Steven Cropper
Div Mgr: Darrin Smiley
CIO: Mark Lashinske
Ql Cn Mgr: Sisto Tarquino

D-U-N-S 01-363-7921
MODERN ITALIAN BAKERY OF WEST BABYLON INC
301 Locust Ave, Oakdale, NY 11769-1652
Tel (631) 589-7300 Founded/Ownrshp 1982
Sales 43.8MM^E EMP 170
SIC 2051 5142 5149 Bread, all types (white, wheat, rye, etc): fresh or frozen; Bakery products, frozen; Bakery products; Bread, all types (white, wheat, rye, etc): fresh or frozen; Bakery products, frozen; Bakery products
Ch Bd: Edward R Otis
Ofcr: Michael Dunne
VP: Ken Burke
VP: Jerry Yllanes
Plnt Mgr: Julio Llovet

MODERN JEWELER MAGAZINE
See CYGNUS BUSINESS MEDIA INC

D-U-N-S 06-747-0955
MODERN LANDFILL INC
4746 Model City Rd, Model City, NY 14107-9800
Tel (716) 754-8226 Founded/Ownrshp 1979
Sales 30.4MM^E EMP 61^E
SIC 4953 Sanitary landfill operation
Pr: Richard Washuta
*Sec: Lorie Washuta
*VP: Gary Smith
Sfty Mgr: Joann Tremble
Opers Mgr: Brent Minet

D-U-N-S 13-120-4427
MODERN LITHO INC
6009 Stertzer Rd, Jefferson City, MO 65101-4528
Tel (573) 635-6119 Founded/Ownrshp 1999
Sales 25.0MM^E EMP 101^E
SIC 2752 6719 Commercial printing, lithographic; Investment holding companies, except banks
Prin: Jeanie Moore
*Prin: Dick Moore
Plnt Mgr: Larry Bexten

D-U-N-S 06-243-3891
MODERN LITHO-PRINT CO
(Suby of MODERN LITHO INC) ★
6009 Stertzer Rd, Jefferson City, MO 65101-4528
Tel (573) 635-6119 Founded/Ownrshp 1937
Sales 25.0MM EMP 101
SIC 2752 2789 2759 Commercial printing, lithographic; Bookbinding & related work; Commercial printing
CEO: Jeanie Moore
Pr: Darrell Moore
VP: Dale Auffenberg
VP: Greg Meeker
VP: Dick Moore
VP: Darla Porter
VP: Jim Tomblinson
Creative D: Kathleen Parvis

IT Man: Regina Durr
Sfty Mgr: Andrew Millard

D-U-N-S 00-585-4070 IMP
MODERN MACHINERY CO INC
(Suby of WASHINGTON COMPANIES) ★
101 International Dr, Missoula, MT 59808-1549
Tel (406) 523-1100 Founded/Ownrshp 1944
Sales 214.6MM^E EMP 450
SIC 5082 Construction & mining machinery; General construction machinery & equipment; Mining machinery & equipment, except petroleum; Logging equipment & supplies; Construction & mining machinery; General construction machinery & equipment; Mining machinery & equipment, except petroleum; Logging equipment & supplies
Pr: Brian Sheridan
*Sec: Paul W Keiper
*Sec: Helen B Miller
*VP: William G Brandall
VP: William Crandall
VP: Chris Johnson
Brnch Mgr: Kory Bladt
IT Man: Christian Davidson
Sales Exec: Tom Wackler
Sls Mgr: Allen Ball
Sls Mgr: Robert Jacobs

D-U-N-S 10-859-2700
MODERN MAINTENANCE INC
14400 W 96th Ter, Shawnee Mission, KS 66215-4710
Tel (913) 345-9777 Founded/Ownrshp 1990
Sales 13.0MM^E EMP 400
SIC 7349 Janitorial service, contract basis; Janitorial service, contract basis
Pr: Nasi Zarinkia
*VP: Michael Zarinkia

D-U-N-S 00-647-7335 IMP
MODERN MANUFACTURING & ENGINEERING INC (MN)
9380 Winnetka Ave N, Brooklyn Park, MN 55445-1617
Tel (612) 781-3347 Founded/Ownrshp 1950
Sales 22.7MM EMP 145
Accts Clifton Larson Allen Llp Minn
SIC 3599 Machine & other job shop work; Machine & other job shop work
Pr: Hue Van Lien
*VP: Elroy Cady
Ql Cn Mgr: Dan Lopez

D-U-N-S 17-435-2583
MODERN MARKETING CONCEPTS INC
29 Industrial Park Dr, Binghamton, NY 13904-3201
Tel (607) 754-7473 Founded/Ownrshp 1986
Sales 56.0MM^E EMP 250
SIC 8742 Marketing consulting services; Marketing consulting services
Ch Bd: Daniel R Babcock
*Pr: Scott Kay
VP: Chris Fouts
VP: Kathryn Kellam
VP: Joe Mele
VP Bus Dev: Bob Moretz
Exec: Lucas Vallet
Creative D: Joe Mallory
Prgrm Mgr: Michael McDonald
Genl Mgr: Richard Scott
CTO: Katie Meier

D-U-N-S 18-506-2585
■ **MODERN MEDICAL INC**
(Suby of HEALTHCARE SOLUTIONS INC) ★
7840 Graphics Way, Lewis Center, OH 43035-8002
Tel (800) 547-3330 Founded/Ownrshp 2013
Sales 22.6MM^E EMP 130
SIC 5999 5912 5047 Medical apparatus & supplies; Drug stores & proprietary stores; Medical & hospital equipment
Pr: Joseph G Favazzo
Bd of Dir: Blake Peelman
Bd of Dir: Brian Sheskey
VP: Raymond Black
Dir Rx: Rebecca Potter
CIO: Ron Carter
Ql Cn Mgr: Tik Chan
Mktg Mgr: Lori Warner
Manager: Eric Kirk
Manager: J J McIntyre
Pharmcst: Ben Link

MODERN MEDICAL SYSTEMS CO
See A KINGSBURY CO INC

D-U-N-S 03-106-5022
MODERN METHOD GUNITE INC
MMG STONE SUPPLY
3334 Brownie Campbell Rd, Houston, TX 77086-1508
Tel (281) 847-1855 Founded/Ownrshp 1981
Sales 26.6MM^E EMP 140
SIC 1771 Gunite contractor; Gunite contractor
Pr: Cesareo Sanchez
*CFO: Edgar Sanchez
*VP: Carmin Sanchez
*VP: Cesar Sanchez Jr

D-U-N-S 06-572-5434
MODERN MUSHROOM FARMS INC
1330 Newark Rd, Toughkenamon, PA 19374-1034
Tel (610) 268-3535 Founded/Ownrshp 1970
Sales 67.1MM^E EMP 500
SIC 0182 2033 2099 Mushrooms grown under cover; Canned fruits & specialties; Food preparations; Mushrooms grown under cover; Canned fruits & specialties; Food preparations
Pr: Charles J Ciarrocchi Jr
COO: Jack Reitnauer
CFO: Ben Lazar
*Treas: Charles J Ciarrocchi Sr
Sfty Mgr: Will Rechuiti
Plnt Mgr: Bruce Broomalli
Prd Mgr: Willie Recchuiti

D-U-N-S 09-333-6147
MODERN NISSAN OF CONCORD INC (NC)
MODERN HONDA OF CONCORD
967 Concord Pkwy S, Concord, NC 28027-9061
Tel (704) 788-2110 Founded/Ownrshp 1978, 2001
Sales 20.0MM^E EMP 45

SIC 5511 Automobiles, new & used
CEO: Joe Fulk
Genl Mgr: Gary Fazier
Sls Mgr: Dan Vickery

D-U-N-S 01-766-0697
MODERN OFFICE METHODS INC (OH)
M.O.M.
4747 Lake Forest Dr # 200, Blue Ash, OH 45242-3853
Tel (513) 791-0909 Founded/Ownrshp 1957
Sales 27.6MM^E EMP 189
SIC 7359 7629 5044 Office machine rental, except computers; Business machine repair, electric; Office equipment; Office machine rental, except computers; Business machine repair, electric; Office equipment
Ch Bd: Robert J McCarthy
*Pr: Kevin P McCarthy
COO: Mark Merkel
*Treas: Ron Slageter
*VP: Steven Bandy
VP: Rod Randall
*VP: Silas P Rose
VP: Daniel Vail
Dir Bus: Brandon Bellamy
VP Admn: Chris Shersky
Info Man: Peggy Sullivan

D-U-N-S 83-547-0808
MODERN PARKING INC
MPI
1200 Wilshire Blvd # 300, Los Angeles, CA 90017-1931
Tel (213) 482-8400 Founded/Ownrshp 1994
Sales 55.4MM^E EMP 700
SIC 7521 Automobile parking; Automobile parking
CEO: Mohammed Islam
Pr: Gary Pitts
Ex VP: Donald Palmieri
Sr VP: Lori Pinson
IT Man: Alvin Esguerra
Mktg Dir: Melody Perkins

D-U-N-S 00-281-7914
MODERN PIPING INC (IA)
500 Walford Rd, Cedar Rapids, IA 52404-8921
Tel (319) 364-0131 Founded/Ownrshp 1939, 1967
Sales 38.6MM^E EMP 190
SIC 7699 1711 Industrial machinery & equipment repair; Mechanical contractor; Industrial machinery & equipment repair; Mechanical contractor
CEO: David D Brown
*Pr: Ken Brown
*Treas: Matthew T Huber
*VP: Ken Burns
*VP: Mike Shive
Dir Bus: Britton Langdon
Genl Mgr: Dan Wille
Sls Mgr: Don Magee

MODERN PLASTICS
See WISCONSIN PLASTICS INC

D-U-N-S 78-097-9407
MODERN PORTABLE TOILETS INC
4746 Model City Rd, Model City, NY 14107-9800
Tel (716) 754-8226 Founded/Ownrshp 1996
Sales 563.0M EMP 350
SIC 7359 Portable toilet rental; Portable toilet rental
Pr: Steve Washuta
*VP: Gary Smith

MODERN POSTCARD
See IRIS GROUP INC

D-U-N-S 87-627-6759 IMP
MODERN SILICONE TECHNOLOGIES INC
2345 Waukegan Rd Ste 155, Bannockburn, IL 60015-1592
Tel (727) 507-9800 Founded/Ownrshp 2000
Sales 26.0MM^E EMP 142
SIC 3053 3061 2822 Gaskets, packing & sealing devices; Mechanical rubber goods; Synthetic rubber; Gaskets, packing & sealing devices; Mechanical rubber goods; Synthetic rubber
CEO: Rachel Grunfeld
*Pr: Aron Grunfeld
COO: William McFadden

D-U-N-S 00-338-8303
MODERN SUPPLY CO (TN)
MODERN SUPPLY LIGHTING STUDIO
525 Lovell Rd, Knoxville, TN 37932-3216
Tel (865) 966-4567 Founded/Ownrshp 1949
Sales 26.9MM^E EMP 84
SIC 5074 5075 5031 5064 5063

MODERN SUPPLY LIGHTING STUDIO
See MODERN SUPPLY CO

D-U-N-S 62-065-4335 IMP
MODERN TECHNOLOGIES GROUP INC
MT G
3 Reeves Station Rd, Medford, NJ 08055-9630
Tel (609) 953-4031 Founded/Ownrshp 1990
Sales 24.4MM^E EMP 118
SIC 5013 Motor vehicle supplies & new parts; Motor vehicle supplies & new parts
CEO: Iric Cohen
*Pr: Eric Alpert
*CFO: Sharon Ronchetti

D-U-N-S 80-745-4640
MODERN TECHNOLOGY SOLUTIONS INC
MTSI
5285 Shawnee Rd Ste 400, Alexandria, VA 22312-2328
Tel (703) 564-3800 Founded/Ownrshp 1993
Sales 109.0MM EMP 615
Accts Cherry Bekaert Llp Tysons Cor
SIC 8711 8742 8731 7379 Engineering services; Management consulting services; Commercial physical research; Computer related maintenance services; Engineering services; Management consulting services; Commercial physical research; Computer related maintenance services
Pr: Kevin M Robinson
*Ch Bd: Phil Soucy
COO: Angel Garcia
Treas: Valerie Underhill
Prgrm Mgr: Greg Green

Prgrm Mgr: Michael Hague
Prgrm Mgr: Sean Hayes
Genl Mgr: Molly James
Snr Sftwr: Mark Krutz
Snr Sftwr: Paul Phillips
Snr Sftwr: Tim Sloane
Board of Directors: Frank Backes, Pamela Little, Tom McMahan, Kevin Robinson, Phil Soucy

D-U-N-S 00-625-3322
MODERN TOOL INC
1200 Northdale Blvd Nw, Minneapolis, MN 55448-3141
Tel (763) 754-7337 Founded/Ownrshp 2014
Sales 49.0MM^E EMP 212
SIC 3444 Sheet metalwork; Sheet metalwork
Pr: Richard Mark Hamlin Jr
Prin: Suzanne C Nolan
Prin: Mary Elizabeth Shannon
IT Man: Bob Morgan

MODERN TOUR
See MODERN ICE EQUIPMENT AND SUPPLY CO

D-U-N-S 87-916-8086 IMP
■ **MODERN TRANSMISSION DEVELOPMENT CO**
(Suby of MTD PRODUCTS INC) ★
2555 Brandenburg Rd, Leitchfield, KY 42754-7501
Tel (270) 259-2600 Founded/Ownrshp 1994
Sales 50.3MM^E EMP 250
SIC 3714 Motor vehicle transmissions, drive assemblies & parts; Motor vehicle transmissions, drive assemblies & parts
CEO: Curtis E Moll
*Pr: Robert T Moll
*Treas: James M Milinski
*VP: Jeffrey C V Deuch
*VP: Jean H Hlay
Opers Mgr: Doug Myers
Plnt Mgr: Derek Clemons
Prd Mgr: Joe Daley
Ql Cn Mgr: Christopher Haynes
Snr Mgr: Jason Williams

D-U-N-S 01-070-9356
MODERN TRANSPORTATION SERVICES
2605 Nicholson Rd # 2301, Sewickley, PA 15143-7609
Tel (412) 489-4800 Founded/Ownrshp 2009
Sales 10.8MM^E EMP 323
SIC 4213

D-U-N-S 17-503-5302
MODERN TRANSPORTATION SERVICES INC
2605 Nicholson Rd # 2301, Sewickley, PA 15143-7609
Tel (724) 935-8180 Founded/Ownrshp 1987
Sales 74.5MM^E EMP 350
SIC 4212 4213 Local trucking, without storage; Steel hauling, local; Trucking, except local; Local trucking, without storage; Steel hauling, local; Trucking, except local
CEO: Neil Neil Strosnider
*Pr: Patrick Cousins
Ex VP: Patrick Cozzens
VP: Bill Doyle
Opers Mgr: Jim Shafer

D-U-N-S 09-898-9551
MODERN VIDEOFILM INC
MVF WORLD WIDE SERVICES
2300 W Empire Ave, Burbank, CA 91504-3341
Tel (818) 840-1700 Founded/Ownrshp 1979
Sales 46.8MM^E EMP 500
SIC 7819 Video tape or disk reproduction; Film processing, editing & titling: motion picture; TV tape services: editing, transfers, etc.; Video tape or disk reproduction; Film processing, editing & titling: motion picture; TV tape services: editing, transfers, etc.
CEO: Scott Avila
*Pr: Cooper Crouse
CFO: Hugh Miller
*CFO: Roxanna Sassanian
Ex VP: Alan Hart
Ex VP: John Johnson
Ex VP: Mark Smirnoff
Ex VP: Bill Watt
Sr VP: Frank Bluestein
Sr VP: Tal Fiala
VP: Damon Blake
VP: Marvin Hall

D-U-N-S 00-637-0712
MODERN WELDING CO INC (KY)
2880 New Hartford Rd, Owensboro, KY 42303-1321
Tel (270) 685-4400 Founded/Ownrshp 1932, 1946
Sales 104.0MM^E EMP 430
SIC 3443 5051 7692 3441 5085

D-U-N-S 06-104-8450
MODERN WOODMEN OF AMERICA
1701 1st Ave, Rock Island, IL 61201-8779
Tel (309) 793-5537 Founded/Ownrshp 1883
Sales NA EMP 480
SIC 6311 Life insurance; Life insurance
Pr: W Kenneth Massey
Mng Pt: Michael Farris
Mng Pt: Brad Keltner
Mng Pt: Mark Wiggington
COO: Thaddeus Crass
COO: Mark Sperfslage
*Treas: Nick S Coin
Chf Cred: Pamela Fritz
Ofcr: Josh Butler
Ofcr: John Cauley
Ofcr: Kenny Chilton
Ofcr: John Escobar
Ofcr: Louise Jones
Ofcr: Norman Kohn
Ofcr: Kim Lacy
Ofcr: Matt Monroe
Ofcr: Gerald Steffen
Ofcr: Tyler Whitaker
VP: Crewe Chamber
Exec: Tom Haertjens

D-U-N-S 05-553-9639 IMP
MODERNE GLASS CO INC (PA)
1000 Industrial Blvd, Aliquippa, PA 15001-4871
Tel (724) 857-5700 *Founded/Ownrshp* 1967, 1978
Sales 43.3MM^E *EMP* 280
SIC 3231 Decorated glassware: chipped, engraved, etched, etc.; Decorated glassware: chipped, engraved, etched, etc.
Pr: Thomas J McKnight
VP: LI Bates
VP: Kris Fredericks
VP: Jay Saymansky
Genl Mgr: Lynn Gartley
DP Exec: Brian Thyen
Dir IT: Sandy Jonas
Dir IT: David Timczyk
IT Man: Joe Snyder
Plnt Mgr: John Bailey
Sales Exec: Ray Wayt

D-U-N-S 14-708-5930 IMP
MODERNFOLD INC
(*Suby of* DORMA USA INC) ★
215 W New Rd, Greenfield, IN 46140-1095
Tel (317) 468-6700 *Founded/Ownrshp* 1990
Sales 44.2MM^E *EMP* 204^E
SIC 2542 2522 Partitions for floor attachment, prefabricated: except wood; Panel systems & partitions, office: except wood; Partitions for floor attachment, prefabricated: except wood; Panel systems & partitions, office: except wood
Pr: Lewis N Stryke
**Pr:* Brian Hurley
CFO: Richard Haffey
VP Sls: David Smith
Sls Dir: Dan Popplewell
Manager: Diana Frankowski

D-U-N-S 07-939-6605
MODERNHEALTH SPECIALTY (AD-RX) LLC
AD-RX PHARMACY
6240 Wilshire Blvd, Los Angeles, CA 90048-5104
Tel (323) 936-8221 *Founded/Ownrshp* 2012
Sales 80.0MM *EMP* 25
SIC 5912 Proprietary (non-prescription medicine) stores; Proprietary (non-prescription medicine) stores
CEO: Dominic Meffe
CFO: Vincent Cook

D-U-N-S 83-887-2377
MODERNHEALTH SPECIALTY (PX) LLC
PX DRUG STORE
7373 Lincoln Way, Garden Grove, CA 92841-1428
Tel (818) 769-0313 *Founded/Ownrshp* 2012
Sales 115.0MM *EMP* 70
SIC 5912 Drug stores & proprietary stores; Drug stores & proprietary stores
CEO: Dominic Meffe
CFO: Vincent Cook
Pharmcst: Phillip Sirois

D-U-N-S 14-427-7014
MODERNISTIC CARPET CLEANING CO
1460 Rankin Dr, Troy, MI 48083-4021
Tel (248) 589-1700 *Founded/Ownrshp* 1980
Sales 22.2MM^E *EMP* 102^E
SIC 5713 Carpets
CEO: Bob McDonald
VP: Bill Wurtzbacher
Creative D: Nathan Malecki
Ex Dir: Rachel Hitow

D-U-N-S 00-619-0722
MODERNISTIC INC
1987 Industrial Blvd S, Stillwater, MN 55082-6049
Tel (651) 291-7650 *Founded/Ownrshp* 1932
Sales 50.6MM^E *EMP* 135
SIC 2679 2675 2759 3993 2796 2672 Paper products, converted; Cutouts, paper or paperboard: made from purchased materials; Screen printing; Signs & advertising specialties; Platemaking services; Coated & laminated paper; Paper products, converted; Cutouts, paper or paperboard: made from purchased materials; Screen printing; Signs & advertising specialties; Platemaking services; Coated & laminated paper
Co-CEO: James Schulte
**Pr:* Tim Beres
**Co-CEO:* John S Schulte
IT Man: Rob Wales
VP Opers: Mark Gorski
Prd Mgr: Ken Hall
S&M/VP: Sharon Johnson
Mktg Dir: Deann Straenke
Mktg Mgr: Brenda Persyn
Mktg Mgr: Deann Strenke

D-U-N-S 03-022-9542
MODERNIZING MEDICINE INC
3600 Fau Blvd Ste 202, Boca Raton, FL 33431-6474
Tel (561) 544-0906 *Founded/Ownrshp* 2010
Sales 72.2MM^E *EMP* 385^E
SIC 7372 Application computer software
Pr: Daniel Cane
COO: Robert Nagro
CFO: Karen Obyrne
Chf Mktg O: Michael Sherling
Ex VP: Brooks James
Sr VP: Patric Edmondson
Sr VP: Maria Hernandez
VP: Thom Schildmeyer
Exec: Brad Rennick
Dir Bus: Scott Ponder
Off Mgr: Alison Murray
Board of Directors: Mark Delaar

D-U-N-S 07-937-0968
MODEST BILLIONAIRES LLC (TX)
3815 Martha Ln, Dallas, TX 75229-6126
Tel (972) 672-0755 *Founded/Ownrshp* 2014
Sales 1.0MMM *EMP* 3
SIC 7374 7371 7389 Computer graphics service; Computer software development & applications; ; Computer graphics service; Computer software development & applications;
Pr: Thomas Richard

D-U-N-S 06-012-5051
MODESTO CITY OF (INC)
1010 10th St Ste 2100, Modesto, CA 95354-0861
Tel (209) 577-5200 *Founded/Ownrshp* 1884
Sales NA *EMP* 1,200
Accts Brown Armstrong Bakersfield
SIC 9111 City & town managers' offices; ; City & town managers' offices;
Ofcr: Adam Foster
VP: Kay Maksoud
Comm Man: Cheryl Detmar
Comm Man: Firoz Vohra
Ex Dir: Regan Wilson
Brnch Mgr: Mike Milich
Plng Mgr: Patrick Kelly
Plng Mgr: Cindy Van Empel
IT Man: Mark Avila
IT Man: Steve Dittrich
Sys Mgr: Vicky Dion

D-U-N-S 07-467-5844
MODESTO CITY SCHOOL DISTRICT FINANCING CORP
MODESTO CITY SCHOOLS
426 Locust St, Modesto, CA 95351-2631
Tel (209) 576-4011 *Founded/Ownrshp* 1871
Sales 306.5MM *EMP* 3,000
Accts Vavrinek Trine Day & Co Ll
SIC 8211 Public senior high school; Elementary school; Public junior high school; Public senior high school; Elementary school; Public junior high school
CFO: Pamela Able
**Pr:* Cindy Marks
Bd of Dir: David Allan
Trst: Jordan Dickson
**VP:* Amy Elliott Neumann
MIS Dir: Andy Minter
Web Dev: David Buell
Pr Dir: Becky Fortuna
Teacher Pr: Craig Rydquist
Psych: Sonia Ambriz
Psych: Marvin Greener

MODESTO CITY SCHOOLS
See MODESTO CITY SCHOOL DISTRICT FINANCING CORP

D-U-N-S 02-868-7937
MODESTO INDUSTRIAL ELECTRICAL CO INC
1417 Coldwell Ave, Modesto, CA 95350-5703
Tel (209) 495-1597 *Founded/Ownrshp* 2004
Sales 51.8MM^E *EMP* 180^E
SIC 1731 5063 7694 General electrical contractor; Motors, electric; Electric motor repair; General electrical contractor; Motors, electric; Electric motor repair
CEO: David Howell
VP: Jim Hodge
**VP:* Michelle Howell
Dir IT: Dave Jones
VP Opers: Paul Swanson
VP Sls: Ron Forthun
Sls Mgr: Randy Bowerman
Sls Mgr: Curt Dyer
Sls Mgr: Chuck Fleming
Sls Mgr: Grant Gaskill
Sls Mgr: Alton Mullis

D-U-N-S 04-131-9419
MODESTO IRRIGATION DISTRICT (INC)
1231 11th St, Modesto, CA 95354-0701
Tel (209) 526-7337 *Founded/Ownrshp* 1887
Sales 416.7MM *EMP* 440
Accts Baker Tilly Virchow Krause Llp
SIC 4911 4971 ; Water distribution or supply systems for irrigation; ; Water distribution or supply systems for irrigation
Pr: Allen Short
Bd of Dir: Roger Vanhoy
Dir Risk M: Scott Vuren
CTO: Erick Davis
Tech Mgr: Toxie Burris
Trfc Dir: Tim Fisher
Sfty Mgr: Jeff Fairbanks
Plnt Mgr: Richard Smith
VP Mktg: Tracy Herbeck
VP Mktg: Bob Root
Pr Mgr: Melissa Williams

MODESTO SCION WORLD
See STINSON ENTERPRISES INC

D-U-N-S 05-188-8873
MODICA BROTHERS LTD (TX)
MODICA BROTHERS TIRE & WHL CTR
3615 Washington Blvd, Beaumont, TX 77705-1135
Tel (409) 842-1794 *Founded/Ownrshp* 1970, 1996
Sales 21.6MM^E *EMP* 65
SIC 5531 5013 5014 Automotive parts; Automotive tires; Automotive supplies & parts; Automobile tires & tubes; Truck tires & tubes
Pr: John Calvin Modica
**VP:* Lanny Graham

MODICA BROTHERS TIRE & WHL CTR
See MODICA BROTHERS LTD

D-U-N-S 87-691-8616
■ **MODINE AFTERMARKET HOLDINGS INC**
(*Suby of* MODINE MANUFACTURING CO INC) ★
1500 De Koven Ave, Racine, WI 53403-2540
Tel (262) 636-1200 *Founded/Ownrshp* 1983
Sales 55.8MM^E *EMP* 700
SIC 3443 3444 3714 Heat exchangers, condensers & components; Sheet metalwork; Radiators & radiator shells & cores, motor vehicle; Heat exchangers, condensers & components; Sheet metalwork; Radiators & radiator shells & cores, motor vehicle
Pr: David Rayburn
CFO: Bradley Richardson
VP: M A Denker
VP: J E Drone
VP: D J Roble
**VP:* Dean Zakos

D-U-N-S 00-609-2555 IMP/EXP
▲ **MODINE MANUFACTURING CO INC** (WI)
1500 De Koven Ave, Racine, WI 53403-2552
Tel (262) 636-1200 *Founded/Ownrshp* 1916
Sales 1.5MMM *EMP* 6,900^E
Accts Pricewaterhousecoopers Llp Mi
Tkr Sym MOD *Exch* NYS
SIC 3443 3714 3433 3585 Heat exchangers, condensers & components; Heat exchangers: coolers (after, inter), condensers, etc.; Air coolers, metal plate; Air conditioner parts, motor vehicle; Radiators & radiator shells & cores, motor vehicle; Heating equipment, except electric; Refrigeration & heating equipment; Heating equipment, complete; Air conditioning equipment, complete; Refrigeration equipment, complete; Heat exchangers, condensers & components; Heat exchangers: coolers (after, inter), condensers, etc.; Air coolers, metal plate; Air conditioner parts, motor vehicle; Radiators & radiator shells & cores, motor vehicle; Heating equipment, except electric; Refrigeration & heating equipment; Heating equipment, complete; Air conditioning equipment, complete; Refrigeration equipment, complete
Pr: Thomas A Burke
COO: Thomas F Marry
CFO: Michael B Lucareli
Bd of Dir: Frank Jones
VP: Scott Bowser
VP: Klaus Feldmann
VP: Margaret C Kelsey
VP: Holger Schwab
VP: Scott Wollenberg
Dir Bus: Stephen Dicks
Mng Dir: Jerry Kapoor
Board of Directors: David J Anderson, David G Bills, Charles P Cooley, Suresh V Garimella, Larry O Moore, Christopher W Patterson, Marsha C Williams, Christine Y Yan

D-U-N-S 00-553-7469
MODINEER CO (MI)
2190 Industrial Dr, Niles, MI 49120-1233
Tel (269) 683-2550 *Founded/Ownrshp* 1940
Sales 104.2MM^E *EMP* 500
SIC 3469 3599 3544 Stamping metal for the trade; Machine shop, jobbing & repair; Special dies & tools; Stamping metal for the trade; Machine shop, jobbing & repair; Special dies & tools
Ch: Michael J Dreher
CFO: Roger Kluge
CFO: Shawn Schimpa
VP: Gary Dreher
Prgrm Mgr: Jason Hamilton
Prgrm Mgr: Erick Nelson
Genl Mgr: Ed Hamilton
Genl Mgr: Jonathon Stough
CIO: Todd Kankel
Plnt Mgr: Brian McClure
Snr Mgr: Scott Grice

D-U-N-S 19-660-8905
MODIS INC
(*Suby of* ADECCO TECHNICAL) ★
10151 Deerwood Pkwy Bldg, Jacksonville, FL 32256
Tel (904) 360-2000 *Founded/Ownrshp* 1994
Sales 665.7MM^E *EMP* 9,000
SIC 7371 Computer software systems analysis & design, custom; Computer software systems analysis & design, custom
Pr: John P Pcoo Cullen
**Pr:* Jack Cullen
Pr: Craig Hollenbaugh
**CEO:* Theron Ceod Gilliam
CFO: Robert Crouch
VP: Scott Baughman
VP: Howard Medow
VP: Sarah Sample-Reif
VP: Mike Telatovich
VP: James Wolf
Mng Dir: Jana Bergman

D-U-N-S 04-902-8608
MODJESKI AND MASTERS INC
100 Sterling Pkwy Ste 302, Mechanicsburg, PA 17050-2903
Tel (717) 766-2852 *Founded/Ownrshp* 1980
Sales 29.8MM^E *EMP* 175
SIC 8711 Consulting engineer; Consulting engineer
Ch Bd: William B Conway
**Pr:* John Kulicki
**Treas:* H Eugene Waldner
**Sr VP:* Donald F Sorgenfrei
VP: Jeff Egenrieder
**VP:* Leon K Huang
VP: BT Martin Jr
VP: Barney Martin

MODOC MEDICAL CENTER
See LAST FRONTIER HEALTHCARE DISTRICT

MODPOWER
See EEG POWER DISTRIBUTION CORP

MODRALL SPERLING
See MODRALL SPERLING ROEHL HARRIS & SISK PA

D-U-N-S 09-414-8020
MODRALL SPERLING ROEHL HARRIS & SISK PA (NM)
MODRALL SPERLING
500 4th St Nw Ste 1000, Albuquerque, NM 87102-2186
Tel (505) 848-1800 *Founded/Ownrshp* 1940
Sales 20.3MM^E *EMP* 180
SIC 8111 General practice attorney, lawyer; General practice attorney, lawyer
Pr: R E Thompson
**Sec:* Ruth M Schifani
**VP:* Kenneth Harrigan
Ex Dir: Eva Carter
Dir IT: Ken Brown
Dir IT: Stephen Moule
Mktg Mgr: Darla Humphreys
Genl Couns: Chris Muirhead

MODROTO
See MEESE INC

MODSPACE
See MODULAR SPACE CORP

MODU-LINE WINDOWS
See OLDCASTLE GLASS ENGINEERED PRODUCTS INC

D-U-N-S 13-795-4413 IMP
MODULAR AUTOMOTIVE SYSTEMS LLC
(*Suby of* LOGISTICS HOLLINGSWORTH GROUP LLC) ★
12200 Oakland Pkwy, Highland Park, MI 48203-3543
Tel (586) 498-5561 *Founded/Ownrshp* 2000
Sales 20.0MM *EMP* 110
SIC 5013 Automotive supplies & parts; Automotive supplies & parts
Pr: R J La Pointe

D-U-N-S 82-528-7662
MODULAR DOCUMENT SOLUTIONS LLC
12320 Crystal Cmmrce Loop, Fort Myers, FL 33966-1082
Tel (239) 210-9940 *Founded/Ownrshp* 2006
Sales 49.8MM^E *EMP* 84^E
SIC 5044 Office equipment
Pr: Marty R Maddox

D-U-N-S 05-384-7711
MODULAR METAL FABRICATORS INC
24600 Nandina Ave, Moreno Valley, CA 92551-9537
Tel (951) 242-3154 *Founded/Ownrshp* 1973
Sales 24.7MM^E *EMP* 130
SIC 3444 Pipe, sheet metal; Ducts, sheet metal
CEO: E E Gearing
**Pr:* Don Gearing
**Treas:* John Wingate
**Ex VP:* Mike Beam
IT Man: Hugh Poole

D-U-N-S 03-954-6114 IMP
MODULAR MINING SYSTEMS INC
(*Suby of* KOMATSU AMERICA CORP) ★
3289 E Hemisphere Loop, Tucson, AZ 85706-5028
Tel (520) 746-9127 *Founded/Ownrshp* 2000
Sales 26.3MM^E *EMP* 270
SIC 3823

D-U-N-S 16-951-3108
MODULAR SPACE CORP
MODSPACE
1200 Swedesford Rd, Berwyn, PA 19312-1172
Tel (610) 232-1200 *Founded/Ownrshp* 1986
Sales 278.8MM^E *EMP* 730
SIC 7359 1542 Equipment rental & leasing; Nonresidential construction; Equipment rental & leasing; Nonresidential construction
Pr: Charles R Paquin
**Sr VP:* Marc Boily
**VP:* Ron Wagner
Brnch Mgr: Tricia Ryhorchuk
Sls Dir: Mark Meyers
Manager: Matthew Schafer
Manager: Marc Shandro
Sales Asso: Jay Carrion
Sales Asso: Michael Dempsey
Sales Asso: Michelle Jordan
Sales Asso: Sean Smith

D-U-N-S 05-367-1392
MODULAR TRANSPORTATION CO
393 Mart St Sw, Grand Rapids, MI 49548-1014
Tel (616) 241-2060 *Founded/Ownrshp* 1969
Sales 37.9MM^E *EMP* 200
SIC 4213 Contract haulers; Contract haulers
Ch Bd: Robert Stouten
**Pr:* Evan Stouten
COO: Scott Hooper
Off Mgr: Clara Young
Netwrk Mgr: Mark Malone
Sfty Mgr: Larry Archer
Sfty Mgr: Michel Stemler
Sfty Mgr: Jamie White
Opers Mgr: Vince Cruse

D-U-N-S 93-980-5284
MODULO SECURITY LLC
(*Suby of* MODULO SECURITY SOLUTIONS S/A.)
41 Perimeter Ctr E # 610, Atlanta, GA 30346-1910
Tel (973) 744-1617 *Founded/Ownrshp* 2010
Sales 3.0MM^E *EMP* 400
SIC 7376 7372 7371 Computer facilities management; Business oriented computer software; Computer software systems analysis & design, custom; Computer facilities management; Business oriented computer software; Computer software systems analysis & design, custom
CEO: Sergio Thompson-Flores
VP: Portia Mills
Mng Dir: Stephen Gant
Mktg Mgr: Rachel Trignano
Snr Mgr: Antnio Rangel

D-U-N-S 06-022-8965
MODUS EDISCOVERY INC
2 Ravinia Dr Ste 1570, Atlanta, GA 30346-2116
Tel (678) 822-5600 *Founded/Ownrshp* 2010
Sales 29.0MM^E *EMP* 163
SIC 2752 Commercial printing, lithographic; Commercial printing, lithographic
CEO: Mark Marmon
**Pr:* Ron Self
**Sec:* R Patrick Weston

D-U-N-S 92-613-5666 IMP
MODUS FURNITURE INTERNATIONAL
M F I
(*Suby of* F E A) ★
5410 Mcconnell Ave, Los Angeles, CA 90066-7028
Tel (310) 827-2129 *Founded/Ownrshp* 1994
Sales 32.0MM^E *EMP* 16
SIC 2511 5021 Wood bedroom furniture; Dining room furniture: wood; Furniture; Wood bedroom furniture; Dining room furniture: wood; Furniture
CEO: Oliver SC Wong
IT Man: Bruce Peterson

D-U-N-S 17-852-5879 IMP
■ **MODUSLINK CORP**
(*Suby of* MODUSLINK GLOBAL SOLUTIONS INC) ★
1601 Trapelo Rd Ste 170, Waltham, MA 02451-7353
Tel (781) 663-5000 *Founded/Ownrshp* 2004
Sales 561.6MM^E *EMP* 2,900
SIC 7379 7389 5045 Computer related maintenance services; Telemarketing services; Telephone answering service; Computers, peripherals & software; Computer related maintenance services; Telemarketing services; Telephone answering service; Computers, peripherals & software
Pr: John J Boucher
Pr: Bill McLennan
COO: Matt Farber
COO: Hardy Luo
CFO: Lorraine Buffman
CFO: Mark Catizone
**CFO:* Steven G Crane
**Treas:* Brian O'Donnell
Bd of Dir: Bob Joyce
Bd of Dir: Dennis Schropp
**Ofcr:* Scott D Smith
**Ex VP:* Peter L Gray
Ex VP: James Herb
Ex VP: Michael Mortson
Sr VP: Phil Radnidge
Sr VP: Pat Ring
Sr VP: Lorcan Sheehan
VP: Eric Ammon
VP: Glenn Brower
VP: Thomas Collins
VP: Glenn Grube
Board of Directors: Anthony J Bay, Virginia Bonker, Francis J Jules, Jonathan A Kraft, Michael J Mardy, David S Wetherell

D-U-N-S 13-620-6000
▲ **MODUSLINK GLOBAL SOLUTIONS INC**
1601 Trapelo Rd Ste 170, Waltham, MA 02451-7353
Tel (781) 663-5000 *Founded/Ownrshp* 1986
Sales 561.6MM *EMP* 2,500^E
Accts Bdo Usa Llp Boston Massachu
Tkr Sym MLNK *Exch* NGS
SIC 7379 Computer related consulting services; Computer related consulting services
Pr: John Boucher
CFO: Mark Catizone
CFO: Joseph B Sherk
Ofcr: Glen M Kassan
Ex VP: Robert Dechant
Ex VP: Patrick Donnellan
Ex VP: Michael Mortson
Ex VP: Scott D Smith
Sr VP: Alan R Cormier
VP: Enright Harold
VP: Richard Lucey
VP: Janet Scott
Board of Directors: Anthony Bergamo, Jeffrey J Fenton, Glen M Kassan, Philip E Lengyel, Warren G Lichtenstein, Jeffrey S Wald

D-U-N-S 62-048-7017
■ **MODUSLINK PTS INC**
PTS ELECTRONICS
(*Suby of* MODUSLINK GLOBAL SOLUTIONS INC) ★
5233 S Old State Road 37, Bloomington, IN 47401-7569
Tel (812) 824-9931 *Founded/Ownrshp* 2008
Sales 87.1MM^E *EMP* 450
SIC 7629 Electronic equipment repair
CEO: Jack Craig
**Pr:* Jeffrey A Hamilton
**Treas:* Amy Ketcham
**Ex VP:* Michael Craig
VP: Gary Noone
Telecom Ex: Matt McGhee
Plnt Mgr: Phillip Collier
Sls Mgr: David Melwid

MODUTEC
See JEWELL INSTRUMENTS LLC

D-U-N-S 02-508-6797
MODWAY INC (NY)
138 Georges Rd, Dayton, NJ 08810-1514
Tel (908) 368-1025 *Founded/Ownrshp* 2010
Sales 34.7MM^E *EMP* 140
Accts Hirsch Oelbaum Bram Hanover &
SIC 5021 Furniture; Furniture
Pr: Menachem T Greisman
**COO:* Zalman M Melamed
**VP:* Smuly Senzweig

D-U-N-S 07-995-3819
MODWORXX LLC
244 5th Ave Ste M205, New York, NY 10001-7604
Tel (646) 395-1216 *Founded/Ownrshp* 2013
Sales 25.0MM *EMP* 44
SIC 8712 7389 Architectural services; Interior design services
Pr: Scott Lesizza
CFO: Ali Shah
**Treas:* Jon Kessler
**VP:* Bill Corey

D-U-N-S 02-212-7153
MOEHL MILLWORK INC
KANSAS CITY MILLWORK
5150 Se Rio Ct, Ankeny, IA 50021-4001
Tel (515) 276-6791 *Founded/Ownrshp* 1999
Sales 46.7MM^E *EMP* 105
SIC 5031 5072 Millwork; Windows; Doors; Kitchen cabinets; Hardware; Millwork; Windows; Doors; Kitchen cabinets; Hardware
Pr: Don E Rudd
**Sec:* Michael Ryerson
**VP:* Robert D Lane
Opers Mgr: Justin Douds

D-U-N-S 07-936-9610
MOELIS & CO
399 Park Ave Fl 5, New York, NY 10022-4416
Tel (212) 883-3800 *Founded/Ownrshp* 2007
Sales 62.6MM^E *EMP* 550
SIC 6282 Investment advice; Investment advice
Ch Bd: Kenneth Moelis
Pr: Navid Mahmoodzadegan
Pr: Jeff Raich
COO: Elizabeth Crain
CFO: Joseph Simon
**V Ch Bd:* Eric Cantor
Genl Couns: Osamu R Watanabe
Board of Directors: John A Allison IV, Eric Cantor, Yvonne Greenstreet, J Richard Leaman III, Jeffrey Raich, Kenneth L Shropshire

D-U-N-S 82-757-4331
▲ **MOELIS & CO HOLDINGS LLC**
1999 Ave Of The Ste 1900, Los Angeles, CA 90067
Tel (310) 443-2300 *Founded/Ownrshp* 2007
Sales 201.7MM^E *EMP* 23
SIC 6733 6282 Private estate, personal investment & vacation fund trusts; Investment advisory service
CEO: Kenneth Moelis

MOELIS & COMPANY INTERNATIONAL
See MOELIS & CO LLC

D-U-N-S 80-781-9565
■ **MOELIS & CO LLC**
MOELIS & COMPANY INTERNATIONAL
(*Suby of* MOELIS & CO HOLDINGS LLC) ★
399 Park Ave Fl 5, New York, NY 10022-4416
Tel (212) 883-3800 *Founded/Ownrshp* 2007
Sales 201.7MM^E *EMP* 470
Tkr Sym MC *Exch* NYS
SIC 6733 6282 Private estate, personal investment & vacation fund trusts; Investment advisory service; Private estate, personal investment & vacation fund trusts; Investment advisory service
COO: Elizabeth Crain
Mng Pt: Edward Yun
V Ch: David Cheyne
CFO: Joseph W Simon
Sr VP: Andrew Gitkin
Sr VP: Andrew Goldfarb
Sr VP: Matt Hughes
Sr VP: Robert Roeder
Sr VP: Frank Sellman
VP: Ashish Ajmera
VP: Azad Badakhsh
VP: Carlo Girolamo
VP: Demetra Lordi
VP: David McDermott
VP: Christian Root
VP: Demetra Stellas

D-U-N-S 07-852-3551
MOELIS ASSET MANAGEMENT LP
399 Park Ave Fl 5, New York, NY 10022-4416
Tel (212) 883-3800 *Founded/Ownrshp* 2007
Sales 71.3MM^E *EMP* 597^E
SIC 6726 Investment offices; Investment offices
CEO: Kenneth Moelis
V Ch: David Cheyne
COO: Elizabeth Crain
CFO: Joseph Simon
CFO: Joseph W Simon
VP: Ryan Taulbee
Mng Dir: Navid Mahmoodzadegan
Mng Dir: Dominick Petrosino

D-U-N-S 96-179-0529
MOELIS CAPITAL PARTNERS LLC
399 Park Ave Fl 5, New York, NY 10022-4416
Tel (212) 883-3800 *Founded/Ownrshp* 2007
Sales 275.2MM^E *EMP* 1,535
SIC 6726 Investment offices; Investment offices
Mng Pt: Kurt Larsen
VP: Andrew Goldfarb

D-U-N-S 60-547-9393
MOELLER AEROSPACE TECHNOLOGY INC
8725 Moeller Dr, Harbor Springs, MI 49740-9583
Tel (231) 347-9575 *Founded/Ownrshp* 1988
Sales 46.6MM^E *EMP* 225
SIC 3724 Aircraft engines & engine parts; Aircraft engines & engine parts
Pr: Daniel Moellering
COO: Joe Baker
**Sec:* Adriene Moellering

MOELLER, DADE
See DADE MOELLER & ASSOCIATES INC

D-U-N-S 00-539-0083 IMP
MOELLER MFG CO INC (MI)
30100 Beck Rd, Wixom, MI 48393-2827
Tel (248) 960-3999 *Founded/Ownrshp* 1963
Sales 73.6MM^E *EMP* 550
SIC 3724 3728

D-U-N-S 19-144-0148
MOELLER TRUCKING INC
8100 Industrial Dr, Maria Stein, OH 45860-9544
Tel (419) 925-4799 *Founded/Ownrshp* 1980
Sales 22.2MM^E *EMP* 90
SIC 4213 4212 Trucking, except local; Local trucking, without storage
Pr: Gary Moeller
**Treas:* Art Moeller Jr
Opers Mgr: Dan Moeller

D-U-N-S 00-114-4237 IMP/EXP
■ **MOEN INC**
(*Suby of* FORTUNE BRANDS HOME & SECURITY INC) ★
25300 Al Moen Dr, North Olmsted, OH 44070-5619
Tel (440) 962-2000 *Founded/Ownrshp* 1969, 2011
Sales 60.2MM^E *EMP* 400
SIC 3429

D-U-N-S 04-006-7670 IMP
MOET HENNESSY USA INC
(*Suby of* LVMH MOET HENNESSY LOUIS VUITTON)
85 10th Ave Fl 2, New York, NY 10011-4753
Tel (212) 888-7575 *Founded/Ownrshp* 1980
Sales 453.9MM^E *EMP* 3,442
SIC 0172 2844 6153 5182 5122 Grapes; Perfumes, natural or synthetic; Short-term business credit; Wine; Neutral spirits; Perfumes; Grapes; Perfumes, natural or synthetic; Short-term business credit; Wine; Neutral spirits; Perfumes
Pr: James Clerkin
Ex VP: Jon Potter
Sr VP: Bruce Scott
VP: Samantha Barnes
VP: Laurent Boidevezi
VP: Christopher O'Rourke
VP: Gene Robinson
VP: Gilles Rousseau
VP: Cathy Steen
VP: Rodney Williams
VP: Cristian Yanez
Exec: Tracy Carlson
Exec: Cassondra Hall
Exec: John James
Exec: Brooks Jorgensen
Exec: Scott Ridlen
Dir Soc: Hannah Levitz
Comm Dir: Christine Kaculis
Comm Dir: Korinne Munson

MOFFAT
See CHAMPION INDUSTRIES INC

D-U-N-S 08-265-9574
MOFFAT COUNTY SCHOOL DISTRICT 1
775 Yampa Ave, Craig, CO 81625-2517
Tel (970) 826-4249 *Founded/Ownrshp* 1959
Sales 17.9MM^E *EMP* 380
Accts Gregory A Hamilton Cpa
SIC 8211 Public elementary & secondary schools; Public elementary & secondary schools
Treas: Julie Sperl
**Prin:* Christine Villard

D-U-N-S 07-941-1861
MOFFAT COUNTY SCHOOL DISTRICT RE1
775 Yampa Ave, Craig, CO 81625-2517
Tel (970) 824-3268 *Founded/Ownrshp* 2014
Sales 9.0MM^E *EMP* 314^E
SIC 8211 Public elementary & secondary schools
Prin: Marlene Knez
Instr Medi: Joe Padon
HC Dir: Karie Fisher

D-U-N-S 05-486-0010
MOFFATT & NICHOL
3780 Kilroy Arprt Way, Long Beach, CA 90806-2457
Tel (562) 590-6500 *Founded/Ownrshp* 1946
Sales 167.1MM^E *EMP* 450
SIC 8711 Structural engineering; Civil engineering; Mechanical engineering; Marine engineering; Structural engineering; Civil engineering; Mechanical engineering; Marine engineering
CEO: Eric Nichol
**CFO:* Olie Abbamonto
Bd of Dir: Ric Cruz
Chf Mktg O: Randy Paulson
VP: Shaun McFarlane
VP: Bruce Ostbo
VP: Kerry Simpson
Admn Mgr: Kathleen Gillion
Off Admin: Celeste Fontenelle
IT Man: Nhan Truong
Snr PM: Bob Beasley
Board of Directors: Mark Faeth, Pierce Homer, Michael Johnson, Ralph Larison, Eric Nichol, Richard Steinke

D-U-N-S 80-595-4232
MOFFITT GENETICS CORP
M2GEN
(*Suby of* H LEE MOFFITT CANCER CENTER & RESEARCH INSTITUTE HOSPITAL INC) ★
10902 N Mckinley Dr, Tampa, FL 33612-6471
Tel (813) 745-4261 *Founded/Ownrshp* 2007
Sales 64.2MM^E *EMP* 1,148^E
SIC 8731 Medical research, commercial
Ch: Theodore J Couch Sr
CEO: William S Dalton
VP: Naveen Kumar

MOFFITT VLKSWGN-PRSCH-DI-MAZDA
See MOFFITT VOLKSWAGEN INC

D-U-N-S 03-420-7944
MOFFITT VOLKSWAGEN INC (LA)
MOFFITT VLKSWGN-PRSCH-DI-MAZDA
1960 Old Minden Rd, Bossier City, LA 71111-4999
Tel (318) 746-2175 *Founded/Ownrshp* 1964
Sales 25.0MM^E *EMP* 60
SIC 5511 Automobiles, new & used; Automobiles, new & used
Pr: Fred L Moffitt
**Treas:* Michael Moffitt
**VP:* John P Moffitt
**VP:* Susan Moffitt
**VP:* Willetta Moffitt
Exec: Larry Bowers
IT Man: Mike Guy
Sls Mgr: Ray Sledge

MOFO
See MORRISON & FOERSTER LLP

D-U-N-S 01-529-3123
MOG INC
(*Suby of* BEATS BY DRE) ★
2607 7th St Ste C, Berkeley, CA 94710-2571
Tel (510) 883-7100 *Founded/Ownrshp* 2010, 2012
Sales 20.9MM^E *EMP* 373^E
SIC 7371 Custom computer programming services
Prin: David Rotenberg
Pr: Tyler Lenane
Mtls Mgr: Don Proctor
Snr Mgr: Martin Zacharias

MOGAMI
See MARSHALL ELECTRONICS INC

MOGAN DAVID WINE
See WINE GROUP INC

D-U-N-S 07-415-6209 IMP/EXP
MOGAS INDUSTRIES INC
14330 E Hardy Rd, Houston, TX 77039-1405
Tel (281) 449-0291 *Founded/Ownrshp* 1973
Sales 67.3MM^E *EMP* 250^E
SIC 3491 Industrial valves; Industrial valves
CEO: Matthew Mogas
Pr: John Williams
COO: Carey Lorenz
**Treas:* V Louis Mogas
VP: Shelton Suter
VP Bus Dev: Duke Tran
CTO: Stan Hicks
QA Dir: Imelda Hernandez
IT Man: Jason Bennett
Tech Mgr: Joel Perry
QC Dir: Hashimali Merchant

D-U-N-S 01-886-5091
MOHANLAL KAPADIA CORP (TX)
TELE CONCEPTS TEXAS
2727 Lbj Fwy Ste 824, Dallas, TX 75234-7437
Tel (972) 877-8075 *Founded/Ownrshp* 2008
Sales 45.0MM *EMP* 5
SIC 4813 Telephone communication, except radio
Pr: Shilpin Kapadia

D-U-N-S 00-900-2130
MOHAVE COUNTY MINER INC
KINGMAN DAILY MINER
(*Suby of* WESTERN NEWSPAPERS INC) ★
3015 N Stockton Hill Rd, Kingman, AZ 86401-4162
Tel (928) 753-6397 *Founded/Ownrshp* 1978
Sales 50.0MM^E *EMP* 497
SIC 2711 Newspapers: publishing only, not printed on site; Newspapers: publishing only, not printed on site
Pr: Donald Soldwedel
**Sec:* Robert McCord
**VP:* Joseph Soldwedel

D-U-N-S 00-279-3438
MOHAVE ELECTRIC CO-OPERATIVE INC (AZ)
928 Hancock Rd, Bullhead City, AZ 86442-5159
Tel (928) 763-4115 *Founded/Ownrshp* 1946
Sales 83.3MM *EMP* 80
Accts Dreyer & Kelso Pc Pa Mission
SIC 4911 1731 Distribution, electric power; Electrical work; Distribution, electric power; Electrical work
Pr: Lyn R Opalka
**Treas:* Carlos Tejeda
**VP:* John B Nelssen
Opers Mgr: Bob Hancock

D-U-N-S 11-443-6025
MOHAVE MENTAL HEALTH CLINIC INC
1743 Sycamore Ave, Kingman, AZ 86409-0927
Tel (928) 757-8111 *Founded/Ownrshp* 2001
Sales 31.7MM *EMP* 275
Accts Cbiz Mhm Llc Phoenix Az
SIC 8063 Psychiatric hospitals; Psychiatric hospitals
CEO: Dawn Abbott
**Pr:* Sally Walker
**CFO:* Janet Rettman

MOHAWK
See ALADDIN MANUFACTURING CORP

D-U-N-S 13-384-7512
■ **MOHAWK CARPET DISTRIBUTION INC**
(*Suby of* MOHAWK INDUSTRIES INC) ★
160 S Industrial Blvd, Calhoun, GA 30701-3030
Tel (706) 695-9743 *Founded/Ownrshp* 2001
Sales 116.3MM^E *EMP* 500
SIC 2273 Carpets & rugs; Carpets & rugs
CEO: Frank H Boykin
**CEO:* Jeff Lorberbaum
**CFO:* James Brunk

D-U-N-S 96-947-5516 IMP/EXP
■ **MOHAWK CARPET LLC**
(*Suby of* MOHAWK INDUSTRIES INC) ★
160 S Industrial Blvd, Calhoun, GA 30701-3030
Tel (706) 629-7721 *Founded/Ownrshp* 1995
Sales 2.6MMM^E *EMP* 20,431
SIC 2273 Finishers of tufted carpets & rugs; Smyrna carpets & rugs, machine woven; Finishers of tufted carpets & rugs; Smyrna carpets & rugs, machine woven
VP: Antony Patti
Site Mgr: Carl Hilger

D-U-N-S 03-793-7182
MOHAWK CONSTRUCTION AND SUPPLY CO INC
108 W Mcmurray Rd, Mc Murray, PA 15317-2428
Tel (724) 941-5700 *Founded/Ownrshp* 1980
Sales 21.2MM *EMP* 12
SIC 1761

D-U-N-S 80-792-2935 IMP/EXP
MOHAWK CUSTOMS & SHIPPING CORP
MOHAWK GLOBAL LOGISTICS
123 Air Cargo Rd, North Syracuse, NY 13212-3917
Tel (315) 455-3003 *Founded/Ownrshp* 1993
Sales 101.0MM *EMP* 117
SIC 4731

D-U-N-S 00-207-0076 IMP
MOHAWK FINE PAPERS INC (NY)
465 Saratoga St, Cohoes, NY 12047-4626
Tel (518) 237-1740 *Founded/Ownrshp* 1876, 1986
Sales 276.5MM^E *EMP* 725
SIC 2672 2621 Coated & laminated paper; Paper mills; Uncoated paper; Coated & laminated paper; Paper mills; Uncoated paper
Ch Bd: Thomas D O'Connor Jr
Pr: John F Haren
COO: Kevin P Richard
CFO: Jack Haren
Treas: John Macy
V Ch Bd: Walter Duignan
Sr VP: Bill Milton
VP: Paul Bourgeois
VP: John O'Connor
VP Bus Dev: Chris Harrold
Exec: Paul Strobell
Board of Directors: George William Wurtz III

D-U-N-S 00-958-1103 IMP
■ **MOHAWK FLUSH DOORS**
(*Suby of* MASONITE CORP) ★
980 Point Township Dr, Northumberland, PA 17857-8886
Tel (570) 473-3557 *Founded/Ownrshp* 2009
Sales 193.9MM^E *EMP* 1,430^E
SIC 2431 Doors & door parts & trim, wood; Door trim, wood; Door frames, wood; Doors, wood

Prin: Gary Willow
Plnt Mgr: Bill Freeman

D-U-N-S 04-722-7942 IMP
MOHAWK GAMING ENTERPRISES LLC
AKWESASNE MOHAWK CASINO
(*Suby of* ST REGIS MHAWK TRIBE FOR AGING) ★
837 State Rt 37, Hogansburg, NY 13655
Tel (518) 358-2222 *Founded/Ownrshp* 2009
Sales 37.1MM^E *EMP* 900
SIC 7929 Entertainment service; Entertainment service
CTO: Shiela King

MOHAWK GLOBAL LOGISTICS
See MOHAWK CUSTOMS & SHIPPING CORP

D-U-N-S 10-860-7672
MOHAWK GROUP LIMITED PARTNERSHIP
295 Main St Rm 210, Buffalo, NY 14203-2402
Tel (716) 854-0060 *Founded/Ownrshp* 1983
Sales 2.3MM^E *EMP* 416^E
SIC 6512

D-U-N-S 01-332-6384
MOHAWK HOSPITAL EQUIPMENT INC (NY)
335 Columbia St, Utica, NY 13502-4270
Tel (315) 797-0570 *Founded/Ownrshp* 1946, 1986
Sales 44.4MM *EMP* 76
Accts Fitzgerald Depietro Wojnas C
SIC 5047 Hospital equipment & supplies; Hospital equipment & supplies
Ch Bd: Thomas Spellman
CEO: Matthew J Ross
Ex VP: Paul Holehan
VP: Holly Burke
Mtls Mgr: Michael Sullivan

D-U-N-S 61-275-7070 IMP/EXP
▲ **MOHAWK INDUSTRIES INC**
160 S Industrial Blvd, Calhoun, GA 30701-3030
Tel (706) 629-7721 *Founded/Ownrshp* 1988
Sales 7.8MMM *EMP* 32,300
Accts Kpmg Llp Atlanta Georgia
Tkr Sym MHK *Exch* NYS
SIC 2273 3253 Finishers of tufted carpets & rugs; Smyrna carpets & rugs, machine woven; Ceramic wall & floor tile; Carpets & rugs; Finishers of tufted carpets & rugs; Smyrna carpets & rugs, machine woven; Ceramic wall & floor tile
Ch Bd: Jeffrey S Lorberbaum
**Pr:* W Christopher Wellborn
CFO: Frank Boykein
CFO: Frank H Boykin
CFO: David Repp
Bd of Dir: Mark Ruppert
Ofcr: David Mohler
VP: Bobby Berrier
VP: Scott Harkins
VP: R David Patton
VP: Edward Schleper
Comm Dir: Stephen Grass
Comm Dir: Robertbob Webb
Board of Directors: Karen A Smith Bogart, Bruce C Bruckmann, Frans G De Cock, John F Fiedler, Richard C III, Joseph A Onorato, William H Runge III

D-U-N-S 02-523-5490 IMP
MOHAWK MFG & SUPPLY CO (IL)
7200 N Oak Park Ave, Niles, IL 60714-3822
Tel (847) 647-2269 *Founded/Ownrshp* 1958
Sales 20.8MM^E *EMP* 44
SIC 5013 Automotive supplies & parts
Pr: John W Brown
VP: Bob Brown
Manager: Thomas Gramly
Manager: Bob Pinet
Sls Mgr: Roger Hristovski
Sls Mgr: Terry Muellner

D-U-N-S 05-131-9689
MOHAWK NORTHEAST INC
170 Canal St, Plantsville, CT 06479-1754
Tel (860) 621-1451 *Founded/Ownrshp* 1987
Sales 48.9MM *EMP* 80
Accts Cohn Reznick Llp Hartford Co
SIC 1622 1623 1629 Bridge construction; Highway construction, elevated; Pipeline construction; Marine construction; Bridge construction; Highway construction, elevated; Pipeline construction; Marine construction
Pr: Allan R Heinke III
**VP:* Andrew S Clarke
Sfty Mgr: Bruce McAllister

D-U-N-S 05-731-3033 IMP
MOHAWK NORTHERN PLASTICS INC
(*Suby of* AMPAC HOLDINGS LLC) ★
701 A St Ne, Auburn, WA 98002-4026
Tel (253) 939-8206 *Founded/Ownrshp* 2007
Sales 41.0MM^E *EMP* 150
SIC 3081 Polyethylene film; Plastic film & sheet; Packing materials, plastic sheet; Polyethylene film; Plastic film & sheet; Packing materials, plastic sheet
Pr: John Baumann
CFO: Dan McFarlan
**VP:* Joe Browder
Off Mgr: Lorraine Stamps
VP Opers: Paul Nemechek
VP Sls: Stephen Barrett

D-U-N-S 10-128-9916 IMP
MOHAWK RESOURCES LTD
65 Vrooman Ave, Amsterdam, NY 12010-5321
Tel (518) 842-1431 *Founded/Ownrshp* 1981
Sales 31.2MM^E *EMP* 70
SIC 3536 Hoists
Pr: Rick Wells
**Ch Bd:* Steven Perlstein
**Genl Mgr:* Andrea Baldomar
IT Man: Janet Chardavoyne
Opers Mgr: Patrick Ofarrell
Sales Exec: Timothy Malone
Mktg Mgr: Gretchen Smith
Sls Mgr: Sherri Abell
Sls Mgr: Buck Gasner
Sls Mgr: Ray Pedrick
Sls Mgr: Mitch Weller

D-U-N-S 00-176-9223 IMP
MOHAWK RUBBER SALES OF N E INC (MA)
65a Industrial Park Rd, Hingham, MA 02043-4306
Tel (781) 741-6000 *Founded/Ownrshp* 1932, 2008
Sales 52.8MM^E *EMP* 75
SIC 5013 Motor vehicle supplies & new parts; Motor vehicle supplies & new parts
Pr: Brian McGeoghehan
Exec: Mark Paquette
Dir IT: Peter Laprade
Sales Asso: Brian Bufis
Sales Asso: Lonnie Hunter

D-U-N-S 19-216-9829
MOHAWK TRAIL REGIONAL SCHOOL DISTRICT
24 Ashfield Rd, Shelburne Falls, MA 01370-9416
Tel (413) 625-0192 *Founded/Ownrshp* 1985
Sales 14.8MM^E *EMP* 305^E
Accts Melanson Health & Company Pc
SIC 8211 Public junior high school; Public senior high school; Public junior high school; Public senior high school
HC Dir: Susan Mitchell

D-U-N-S 09-990-3189
MOHAWK VALLEY COMMUNITY ACTION AGENCY INC
9882 River Rd, Utica, NY 13502-2304
Tel (315) 624-9930 *Founded/Ownrshp* 1966
Sales 16.2MM *EMP* 360
Accts Bonadio & Co Llp Syracuse
SIC 8351 8399 Head start center, except in conjunction with school; Community action agency; Head start center, except in conjunction with school; Community action agency
Ex Dir: Amy Turner
Bd of Dir: Stephen Reeves
Pgrm Dir: Venice Ervin

D-U-N-S 05-596-1718
MOHAWK VALLEY COMMUNITY COLLEGE
MVCC
(*Suby of* STATE UNIVERSITY OF NEW YORK) ★
1101 Sherman Dr, Utica, NY 13501-5394
Tel (315) 792-5400 *Founded/Ownrshp* 1946
Sales 30.7MM^E *EMP* 650^E
SIC 8222 9411 Community college; Administration of educational programs; ; Community college; Administration of educational programs;
Pr: Randall J Vanwagoner
**VP:* Ralph Feola
**Prin:* Michael I Schafer
Dir IT: Karen Maggio
IT Man: Tania Bader
Mktg Dir: Matthew Snyder
Pgrm Dir: Pattina Keniston
Snr Mgr: Jason Carpenter

D-U-N-S 80-269-4455
MOHAWK VALLEY HEALTH SYSTEM
MOHAWK VALLEY NETWORK, INC.
1710 Burrstone Rd, New Hartford, NY 13413-1002
Tel (315) 624-5116 *Founded/Ownrshp* 1991
Sales 49.2MM^E *EMP* 35
SIC 8062 General medical & surgical hospitals
Pr: Scott Perra
**Pr:* Keith Fenstemacher

MOHAWK VALLEY NETWORK
See LITTLE FALLS HOSPITAL

MOHAWK VALLEY NETWORK, INC.
See MOHAWK VALLEY HEALTH SYSTEM

D-U-N-S 36-111-0273
MOHAWK VALLEY NURSING HOME INC
99 6th Ave, Ilion, NY 13357-1500
Tel (315) 895-4050 *Founded/Ownrshp* 1972
Sales 21.2MM^E *EMP* 300
SIC 8051 Skilled nursing care facilities; Skilled nursing care facilities
CEO: Ralph Reed
HC Dir: Janet Harwick

MOHEGAN SUN CASINO
See MTIC LLC

D-U-N-S 07-994-6033
MOHEGAN SUN CASINO
MOHEGAN TRIBAL GAMING AUTH
1 Mohegan Sun Blvd, Uncasville, CT 06382-1372
Tel (888) 226-7711 *Founded/Ownrshp* 1996
Sales 4.1MM^E *EMP* 7,000
SIC 7011 Casino hotel

MOHEGAN TRIBAL GAMING AUTH
See MOHEGAN SUN CASINO

D-U-N-S 00-897-7480
MOHEGAN TRIBAL GAMING AUTHORITY
(*Suby of* MOHEGAN SUN CASINO) ★
1 Mohegan Sun Blvd, Uncasville, CT 06382-1355
Tel (860) 862-0777 *Founded/Ownrshp* 1995
Sales 1.2MMM *EMP* 9,220^E
Accts Pricewaterhousecoopers Llp Ha
SIC 7011 7999 Hotels; Casino hotel; Gambling & lottery services; Hotels; Casino hotel; Gambling & lottery services
CEO: Mitchell Grossinger Etess
**CFO:* Mario C Kontomerkos
**Ch:* Kevin P Brown
VP Mktg: Donald Chapman
Board of Directors: Bruce S Bozsum, Mark F Brown, Ralph James Gessner Jr, Kathleen M Reagan-Pyne, William Quidgeon, Mark M Sperry, Cheryl A Todd

MOHEGAN TRIBE, THE
See MOHEGAN TRIBE OF INDIANS OF CONNECTICUT

D-U-N-S 96-303-5428
MOHEGAN TRIBE OF INDIANS OF CONNECTICUT
MOHEGAN TRIBE, THE
13 Crow Hill Rd, Uncasville, CT 06382-1118
Tel (860) 862-6100 *Founded/Ownrshp* 1994
Sales 38.7MM^E *EMP* 400

SIC 7389 Personal service agents, brokers & bureaus; Personal service agents, brokers & bureaus
Ch Bd: Kevin Brown
V Ch: Stephanie Fielding
MIS Dir: Daniel Przybyl

MOHELA
See MISSOURI HIGHER EDUCATION LOAN AUTHORITY

D-U-N-S 02-386-9498
MOHENIS SERVICES INC
875 E Bank St, Petersburg, VA 23803-3470
Tel (804) 722-3038 *Founded/Ownrshp* 1934
Sales 20.9MM^E *EMP* 238
SIC 7211 7213 Power laundries, family & commercial; Linen supply; Power laundries, family & commercial; Linen supply
Ch Bd: Donald L Struminger
**Pr:* David M Struminger
**Treas:* Nancy P Alley
VP: John Crockford

D-U-N-S 00-699-1442
MOHICAN MILLS INC
(*Suby of* FAB INDUSTRIES CORP) ★
1419 E Gaston St, Lincolnton, NC 28092-4401
Tel (704) 735-3343 *Founded/Ownrshp* 2000
Sales 58.4MM^E *EMP* 307
SIC 2258 Cloth, warp knit; Cloth, warp knit
Pr: Steven Myers
**VP:* Jerry Deese
**VP:* Jim Sitterly
Ql Cn Mgr: Al Heywood

MOHONK MOUNTAIN HOUSE
See SMILEY BROTHERS INC

MOHR ENGINEERING DIVISION
See STRESS ENGINEERING SERVICES INC

D-U-N-S 02-547-2549
MOHR OIL CO (IL)
7340 Harrison St, Forest Park, IL 60130-2081
Tel (708) 366-2900 *Founded/Ownrshp* 1950, 1978
Sales 21.7MM *EMP* 10^E
Accts Poulos & Bayer Chicago Illin
SIC 5172 5983 Gasoline; Diesel fuel; Fuel oil; Fuel oil dealers; Gasoline; Diesel fuel; Fuel oil; Fuel oil dealers
Pr: Michael H Mohr Jr
**VP:* Donald Stange

D-U-N-S 10-145-9402 IMP
MOI INC
2923 Lord Baltimore Dr, Baltimore, MD 21244-2634
Tel (410) 265-5600 *Founded/Ownrshp* 1983
Sales 78.3MM *EMP* 150
Accts Ellin & Tucker Chartered Balt
SIC 5021 Office furniture; Office furniture
Pr: David Noel

D-U-N-S 82-507-7316
MOISHES MOVING SYSTEMS INC
227 Coles St, Jersey City, NJ 07310-1007
Tel (201) 659-2801 *Founded/Ownrshp* 1992
Sales 29.9MM^E *EMP* 229^E
SIC 4213 Trucking, except local
Pr: Eugene Lemay
Opers Mgr: Nissim Fadida
VP Mktg: Micha Lang

D-U-N-S 96-181-7579
MOISTURE FESTIVAL
4301 Leary Way Nw, Seattle, WA 98107-4538
Tel (206) 297-1405 *Founded/Ownrshp* 2005
Sales 351.1M *EMP* 282
SIC 7999 Festival operation; Festival operation
Pr: Ron Bailey
Bd of Dir: Mike Bailey
Bd of Dir: Katherine Bragdon
Bd of Dir: Maque Davis
Bd of Dir: Sandy Neale
Bd of Dir: Phil O'Brien

MOJAVE ELECTRIC
See EDNA WEST ASSOCIATES LTD

D-U-N-S 00-837-3946 IMP/EXP
■ **MOJAVE FOODS CORP**
(*Suby of* MCCORMICK & CO INC) ★
6200 E Slauson Ave, Commerce, CA 90040-3012
Tel (323) 890-8900 *Founded/Ownrshp* 1991
Sales 43.0MM^E *EMP* 200
SIC 2099 Butter, renovated & processed; Butter, renovated & processed
CEO: Richard D Lipka
**CFO:* Craig M Berger
Genl Mgr: Robert Horn

D-U-N-S 12-867-4579
MOJAVE UNIFIED SCHOOL DISTRICT
3500 Douglas Ave, Mojave, CA 93501-1199
Tel (661) 824-4001 *Founded/Ownrshp* 1953
Sales 12.7MM^E *EMP* 300
SIC 8211 Public elementary & secondary schools; Public junior high school; Public senior high school; Public elementary & secondary schools; Public junior high school; Public senior high school

D-U-N-S 13-193-6668
MOJAVE WATER AGENCY
MWA
13846 Conference Ctr Dr, Apple Valley, CA 92307-4309
Tel (760) 247-3316 *Founded/Ownrshp* 1960
Sales 24.7MM^E *EMP* 43^E
SIC 4941 Water supply
Genl Mgr: Kirbi Brill
**CFO:* Ken Weel
Exec: Kate Beyer
CTO: Jesse Shelby
IT Man: Lorrie Steely
Board of Directors: Bill Christopher, Carl Dalton, Thomas Irwin, George Parker, John Russell, Donaldibrendle

MOJO
See STRATASYS INC

D-U-N-S 61-146-1153 IMP/EXP
MOL (AMERICA) INC
(*Suby of* MITSUI O.S.K. LINES, LTD.)
700 E Bttrfeld Rd Ste 250, Lombard, IL 60148
Tel (630) 424-3480 *Founded/Ownrshp* 1991
Sales 94.9MM^E *EMP* 389
SIC 4731 7373 4412 Agents, shipping; Railroad freight agency; Truck transportation brokers; Computer integrated systems design; Deep sea foreign transportation of freight; Agents, shipping; Railroad freight agency; Truck transportation brokers; Computer integrated systems design; Deep sea foreign transportation of freight
CEO: Tsuyashi Yoshida
**Ch:* Noboru Kitazawa
Bd of Dir: Akimitsu Ashida
Bd of Dir: Tomonobu Hada
Bd of Dir: Yoshinori Hama
Bd of Dir: Hidehiro Harada
Bd of Dir: Kentaro Hino
Bd of Dir: Tokinao Hojo
Bd of Dir: Noriaki Hori
Bd of Dir: Tsutomu Iizuka
Bd of Dir: Kazuo Iwamoto
Bd of Dir: Makoto Iwata
Bd of Dir: Toshifumi Kato
Bd of Dir: Tsuneo Kawahara
Bd of Dir: Saburo Koide
Bd of Dir: Kazuaki Konishi
Bd of Dir: Makoto Kuroishi
Bd of Dir: Kenji Machino
Bd of Dir: Kazuki Mori
Bd of Dir: Chikanobu Nomura
Bd of Dir: Yutaka Okamoto

D-U-N-S 07-937-6453
MOL INFORMATION TECHNOLOGY AMERICA INC
MOL IT AMERICA
(*Suby of* MOL INFORMATION TECHNOLOGY INDIA PRIVATE LIMITED)
10 Woodbridge Center Dr, Woodbridge, NJ 07095-1152
Tel (732) 512-5100 *Founded/Ownrshp* 1988
Sales 32.5MM^E *EMP* 300
SIC 7371 Computer software development & applications; Computer software development & applications
CEO: Kazuhisa Kaneta
**Sr VP:* Toshitaka Sunayama

MOL IT AMERICA
See MOL INFORMATION TECHNOLOGY AMERICA INC

D-U-N-S 06-625-7361 IMP/EXP
MOL LOGISTICS (USA) INC
(*Suby of* MOL LOGISTICS(JAPAN) CO.,LTD.)
380 N Brdwy Ste 202, Jericho, NY 11753
Tel (516) 403-2100 *Founded/Ownrshp* 1969, 2006
Sales 28.9MM^E *EMP* 83
SIC 4731

D-U-N-S 12-208-5327
MOL-SON INC
WESTERN DIVERSIFIED
53196 N Main St, Mattawan, MI 49071-8305
Tel (269) 668-3377 *Founded/Ownrshp* 1984
Sales 51.2MM^E *EMP* 100
SIC 3544 Special dies & tools
Pr: Ronald A Molitor
COO: John Switzer
Genl Mgr: John Flach
Dir IT: Jim Horton
Mfg Mgr: Dean Weurding

D-U-N-S 61-497-8083 IMP
MOLA INC
2957 E 46th St, Vernon, CA 90058-2423
Tel (323) 582-0088 *Founded/Ownrshp* 2003
Sales 45.2MM^E *EMP* 150
SIC 5137 Women's & children's clothing

D-U-N-S 03-179-4050
MOLALLA RIVER SCHOOL DISTRICT 35
412 S Swiegle Ave, Molalla, OR 97038-8113
Tel (503) 651-2128 *Founded/Ownrshp* 1998
Sales 21.3MM^E *EMP* 350
SIC 8211 Public elementary & secondary schools; Public elementary & secondary schools
Ex Dir: Tony Mann
Schl Brd P: Cyndie Hobart
Schl Brd P: Neal Lucht

D-U-N-S 05-423-3101
MOLALLA UNION HIGH SD U-4
434 S Molalla Ave, Molalla, OR 97038-9113
Tel (503) 829-2359 *Founded/Ownrshp* 1920
Sales 5.7MM^E *EMP* 314
SIC 8211 9411 Public elementary & secondary schools; School board; Administration of educational programs; Public elementary & secondary schools; Administration of educational programs

D-U-N-S 01-020-2190 IMP
MOLBAKS LLC
13625 Ne 175th St, Woodinville, WA 98072-8558
Tel (425) 483-5000 *Founded/Ownrshp* 2002
Sales 34.3MM^E *EMP* 150
SIC 5261 0181 5947 Nursery stock, seeds & bulbs; Garden supplies & tools; Ornamental nursery products; Gift shop; Nursery stock, seeds & bulbs; Garden supplies & tools; Ornamental nursery products; Gift shop
CFO: Robert McNamara
Genl Mgr: Mark Bradbury
IT Man: Jens Molbak
Mktg Mgr: Kurt Dicus

MOLD MAKER
See MOLDMAKERS INC

D-U-N-S 06-560-2807 IMP
MOLD MASTERS CO
1455 Imlay City Rd, Lapeer, MI 48446-3142
Tel (810) 245-4100 *Founded/Ownrshp* 1973
Sales 50.6MM^E *EMP* 150
SIC 3544 Industrial molds; Industrial molds

CEO: Hugo Leonardi
Prgrm Mgr: Jeff Palmateer
Prgrm Mgr: Karen Yank
**Genl Mgr:* Robert Swiatkowski
Ql Cn Mgr: Brian Boike
Ql Cn Mgr: Paul Rogers
Ql Cn Mgr: Susan Smith
Ql Cn Mgr: Mary Szelog

D-U-N-S 05-837-5346
MOLD MASTERS INTL INC
7500 Clover Ave, Mentor, OH 44060-5296
Tel (440) 953-0220 *Founded/Ownrshp* 1972
Sales 29.9MM^E *EMP* 170
SIC 3544 3324 2842 Special dies & tools; Steel investment foundries; Specialty cleaning, polishes & sanitation goods; Special dies & tools; Steel investment foundries; Specialty cleaning, polishes & sanitation goods
CEO: Jim Allen
**Pr:* George Goodrich
**VP:* Robert Soltis
**Prin:* Ron Kern
**Prin:* Vic Sirotek

D-U-N-S 06-052-3156 IMP/EXP
MOLD-RITE PLASTICS LLC
(*Suby of* IRVING PLACE CAPITAL LLC) ★
1 Plant St, Plattsburgh, NY 12901-3788
Tel (518) 324-4859 *Founded/Ownrshp* 2010
Sales 115.6MM^E *EMP* 481^E
SIC 3089 Closures, plastic; Closures, plastic
Pr: Brian Bauerbach
**CFO:* Tom Rency
CFO: Robert Rohde
Sr VP: Keith Keible
VP: Bhojraj Naveen
Dept Mgr: Mark Lucas
Dir IT: Nathan Durland
Ql Cn Mgr: Chris McLear
VP Sls: Troy Rinke
VP Sls: Jeff Titherington
Sales Asso: Erin Soule

D-U-N-S 78-469-8250
MOLDED ACOUSTICAL PRODUCTS OF EASTON INC
MAP OF EASTON
3 Danforth Dr, Easton, PA 18045-7821
Tel (610) 253-7135 *Founded/Ownrshp* 1973
Sales 81.5MM^E *EMP* 400
SIC 3296

D-U-N-S 86-140-2808
MOLDED FIBER GLASS CO/NORTH CAROLINA
(*Suby of* MOLDED FIBER GLASS COMPANIES) ★
213 Reep Dr, Morganton, NC 28655-8253
Tel (828) 584-4974 *Founded/Ownrshp* 1994
Sales 74.8MM^E *EMP* 215
SIC 3713 Truck & bus bodies; Truck & bus bodies
Pr: Richard S Morrison
**Treas:* Joseph A Cotman
Sr VP: Nicol Connor
Prgrm Mgr: Jorge Trevino
Genl Mgr: Joe Wilk
Ql Cn Mgr: Larry Parker

D-U-N-S 04-841-4098 EXP
MOLDED FIBER GLASS COMPANIES
2925 Mfg Pl, Ashtabula, OH 44004-9445
Tel (440) 997-5851 *Founded/Ownrshp* 1946
Sales 639.9MM^E *EMP* 1,917
SIC 3089 Molding primary plastic; Boxes, plastic; Injection molding of plastics; Molding primary plastic; Boxes, plastic; Injection molding of plastics
CEO: Richard Morrison
**Pr:* Dave Denny
**COO:* Greg Tilton
**CFO:* Darren Schwede
Ex VP: J McKenzie
Sr VP: Peter Emrich
Sr VP: David M Giovannini
**Sr VP:* Carl Lafrance
Exec: Perry Bennett
Exec: Glen Warner
Genl Mgr: Pete Emrich

D-U-N-S 92-955-7726
■ **MOLDED FIBER TECHNOLOGY INC**
(*Suby of* UFP TECHNOLOGIES INC) ★
1521 Windsor Dr, Clinton, IA 52732-6611
Tel (563) 242-2444 *Founded/Ownrshp* 1993
Sales 37.5MM^E *EMP* 600^E
SIC 3086 4953 Packaging & shipping materials, foamed plastic; Refuse systems; Packaging & shipping materials, foamed plastic; Refuse systems
Pr: Bailly R Jeffrey
Genl Mgr: Darrell Rollerson

MOLDED PARTS DIVISION
See PREMIX INC

MOLDED PRODUCTS DIVISION
See COOPER CROUSE- HINDS LLC

D-U-N-S 00-607-4652
MOLDED RUBBER & PLASTIC CORP
M R P C
13161 W Glendale Ave, Butler, WI 53007-1806
Tel (262) 781-7122 *Founded/Ownrshp* 1957
Sales 25.5MM^E *EMP* 157^E
SIC 3069 3089 Molded rubber products; Injection molded finished plastic products; Molded rubber products; Injection molded finished plastic products
Pr: Greg Riemer
Pr: Jeff Randall
CFO: Thomas Brunner
CFO: John Schlump
VP: Tom Hartman
QA Dir: Eric Powers
IT Man: Marianne Elmer
VP Mfg: Ken Simatic
Ql Cn Mgr: Susan Lloyd
Ql Cn Mgr: Cindy Zimmerman
Mktg Mgr: Corey Wentz

D-U-N-S 06-623-7736 IMP/EXP
MOLDEX-METRIC INC
10111 Jefferson Blvd, Culver City, CA 90232-3509
Tel (310) 837-6500 *Founded/Ownrshp* 1960
Sales 144.2MM^E *EMP* 500
SIC 3842 Personal safety equipment; Ear plugs; Personal safety equipment; Ear plugs
CEO: Mark Magidson
CFO: Meiling Hsu
VP: Jeffrey Birkner
VP: James Hornstein
VP: Paul Zaitz
Rgnl Mgr: Bill Schwab
CIO: Carlos Acosta
Dir IT: Steve Wooley
Mfg Dir: Gabe Guerra
Mfg Dir: Robert Sanchez
Ql Cn Mgr: Dennis Wickline

D-U-N-S 02-353-9876
MOLDING ACQUISITION CORP
ROTOPLAS
(*Suby of* GRUPO ROTOPLAS, S.A. DE C.V.)
2651 Cooper Ave, Merced, CA 95348-4315
Tel (209) 723-5000 *Founded/Ownrshp* 2013
Sales 6.0MM *EMP* 4,000
SIC 2822 Polyethylene, chlorosulfonated (hypalon)

MOLDING PRODUCTS
See INTERPLASTIC CORP

D-U-N-S 96-523-7597 IMP
MOLDMAKERS INC
MOLD MAKER
(*Suby of* MGS MFG GROUP INC) ★
W188 N 11707 Maple Rd W 188 N, Germantown, WI 53022
Tel (262) 255-5790 *Founded/Ownrshp* 2002
Sales 44.0MM^E *EMP* 250
SIC 3544 Special dies, tools, jigs & fixtures; Special dies, tools, jigs & fixtures
CEO: Mark G Sellers
**Pr:* Jeff E Callen
Pr: John Hahn
**Sr VP:* Brian P Conrad
**VP:* Jeffrey A Kolbow
IT Man: Jeffrey Riopelle

D-U-N-S 09-148-7140 IMP/EXP
■ **MOLECULAR BIOPRODUCTS INC**
(*Suby of* FISHER SCIENTIFIC INTERNATIONAL LLC) ★
9389 Waples St, San Diego, CA 92121-3903
Tel (858) 453-7551 *Founded/Ownrshp* 2006
Sales 282.3MM^E *EMP* 470
SIC 4953 Medical waste disposal; Medical waste disposal
CEO: Seth H Hoogasian
**VP:* Verner Andersen

D-U-N-S 12-512-3125 IMP
■ **MOLECULAR DEVICES LLC**
(*Suby of* DANAHER CORP) ★
1311 Orleans Dr, Sunnyvale, CA 94089-1136
Tel (408) 747-1700 *Founded/Ownrshp* 2010
Sales 118.9MM^E *EMP* 543
SIC 3826 3841 Analytical instruments; Surgical & medical instruments; Analytical instruments; Surgical & medical instruments
Pr: Kevin Chance
VP: Gillian M Huphries
Plng Mgr: Mike Nersesian
VP Sls: Greg Milosevich
VP Sls: Tom Olenic
S&M/VP: Thomas Olenic

MOLECULAR IMPRINTS, INC.
See CANON NANOTECHNOLOGIES INC

MOLECULAR STRUCTURE
See RIGAKU AMERICAS CORP

D-U-N-S 00-524-6673 IMP
MOLEX LLC
(*Suby of* KOCH INDUSTRIES INC) ★
2222 Wellington Ct, Lisle, IL 60532-1682
Tel (630) 969-4550 *Founded/Ownrshp* 2013
Sales 7.0MMM^E *EMP* 41,000
SIC 3679 3643 3357 Electronic connectors; Connectors & terminals for electrical devices; Communication wire; Fiber optic cable (insulated); Electronic circuits; Antennas, receiving; Electronic circuits; Connectors & terminals for electrical devices; Communication wire; Fiber optic cable (insulated)
CEO: Martin P Slark
Ch Bd: Frederick A Krehbiel
Ch Bd: John H Krehbiel Jr
Pr: Graham Brock
Pr: Liam McCarthy
CFO: Travis George
CFO: David D Johnson
Div Pres: J Michael Nauman
Bd of Dir: Darren Young
Ex VP: Gary J Matula
VP: Aldo Lopez
Exec: Kevin Delaney
Exec: Joel Eurich
Exec: John Luthy
Exec: Terra Maher
Exec: Bruce Nicholas
Exec: Scott Reynolds
Exec: John Rochford
Exec: Christian Slinkman

D-U-N-S 19-476-1490
MOLEX U S INC
(*Suby of* MOLEX LLC) ★
2222 Wellington Ct, Lisle, IL 60532-1682
Tel (630) 969-4550 *Founded/Ownrshp* 1986
Sales 108.7MM^E *EMP* 2,200^E
SIC 3678 3679 3643 3357 Electronic connectors; Electronic switches; Electronic circuits; Connectors & terminals for electrical devices; Communication wire; Electronic connectors; Electronic switches; Electronic circuits; Connectors & terminals for electrical devices; Communication wire
Pr: John H Krehbiel Jr
Ex VP: James Fleischhacker
Ex VP: Charles Graham

D-U-N-S 05-904-3950
MOLIN CONCRETE PRODUCTS CO INC
LINO LAKES
415 Lilac St, Circle Pines, MN 55014-1098
Tel (651) 786-7722 *Founded/Ownrshp* 1897
Sales 44.1MM *EMP* 130
SIC 3272 Concrete products; Prestressed concrete products; Columns, concrete; Concrete products; Prestressed concrete products; Columns, concrete
CEO: Thomas Molin
**CFO:* Mark Groff
**VP:* Robert Flood
**VP:* Daniel Molin
**VP:* Randall Molin
**VP:* Ricky Rule
**VP:* John Saccoman
Sfty Dirs: Jerome Schmitz
Plnt Mgr: Dan Knudsen
Sls Mgr: Stephen Brawthen
Sls Mgr: Bob Clauson

D-U-N-S 11-017-5023
▲ **MOLINA HEALTHCARE INC**
200 Oceangate Ste 100, Long Beach, CA 90802-4317
Tel (562) 435-3666 *Founded/Ownrshp* 1980
Sales 9.6MMM *EMP* 10,500
Tkr Sym MOH *Exch* NYS
SIC 8011 6324 Health maintenance organization; Hospital & medical service plans; Health maintenance organization (HMO), insurance only; Health maintenance organization; Hospital & medical service plans; Health maintenance organization (HMO), insurance only
Ch Bd: J Mario Molina
Pr: Craig Bass
Pr: Richard Chambers
Pr: Stephen Harris
Pr: Norman Nichols
Pr: Jesse L Thomas
Pr: Chad Westover
CEO: Ann Wehr
COO: Terry P Bayer
**CFO:* John C Molina
Chf Mktg O: Keith Wilson
Ofcr: Daniel Barzman
Ofcr: Joseph W White
Sr VP: Michael Steele
Board of Directors: Daniel Cooperman, Charles Z Fedak, Steven G James, Frank E Murray, Steven J Orlando, Ronna E Romney, Richard M Schapiro, Dale B Wolf

D-U-N-S 03-381-6864
■ **MOLINA HEALTHCARE OF MICHIGAN**
(*Suby of* MOLINA HEALTHCARE INC) ★
880 W Long Lake Rd, Troy, MI 48098-4504
Tel (248) 925-1700 *Founded/Ownrshp* 1997
Sales NA *EMP* 84^E
SIC 6411 Insurance agents, brokers & service
CEO: Roman T Kulich
Pr: Stephen Harris

D-U-N-S 00-519-9018
MOLINA HEALTHCARE OF NEW MEXICO INC (NM)
400 Tijeras Ave Nw 200, Albuquerque, NM 87102-3234
Tel (505) 342-4660 *Founded/Ownrshp* 1992, 2004
Sales NA *EMP* 53^E
Accts Kpmg Albuquerque Nm
SIC 6321 8741 6324 Health insurance carriers; Management services; Hospital & medical service plans
CFO: Anita Mullins
Board of Directors: Irvin Diamond, David Sachs Phd, James Tryon MD, John Wills MD

D-U-N-S 82-800-0096
■ **MOLINA HEALTHCARE OF TEXAS INC**
(*Suby of* MOLINA HEALTHCARE INC) ★
84 Ne Loop 410 Ste 200, San Antonio, TX 78216-8419
Tel (210) 366-6500 *Founded/Ownrshp* 2004
Sales 18.6MM^E *EMP* 555^E
SIC 8399 Health systems agency
Pr: J Mario Molina
COO: Terry Bayer
CFO: John Molia
VP: Bryce Berg
Prgrm Mgr: Gwendolyn Sowa

D-U-N-S 80-377-7671
■ **MOLINA HEALTHCARE OF WASHINGTON INC**
(*Suby of* MOLINA HEALTHCARE INC) ★
21540 30th Dr Se Ste 400, Bothell, WA 98021-7015
Tel (425) 424-1100 *Founded/Ownrshp* 2000
Sales 600.0MM *EMP* 320
SIC 8011 Health maintenance organization; Health maintenance organization
CEO: Dael Ahlskog
Pr: Bela Biro
Pr: Janeen Tarrow
Ofcr: John Robinson
Assoc VP: Claudia Stclair
VP: Julie Lindberg
VP: Johnna Perry
VP: Michael Siegel
Dir Rx: Shea Wilson
IT Man: Alberto Laveaga
VP Mktg: Jeannie Koontz

D-U-N-S 83-228-0973
■ **MOLINA HELATHCARE OF CALIFORNIA PARTNER PLAN INC**
(*Suby of* MOLINA HEALTHCARE INC) ★
200 Oceangate Ste 100, Long Beach, CA 90802-4317
Tel (562) 435-3666 *Founded/Ownrshp* 1980
Sales NA *EMP* 2,800
SIC 6321 8011 Health insurance carriers; Clinic, operated by physicians; Health insurance carriers; Clinic, operated by physicians
CEO: Richard Chambers
**Pr:* Dr J Mario Molina
**COO:* Terry Bayer
**Ofcr:* Dr James Howatt

D-U-N-S 03-550-1633
MOLINA INFORMATION SYSTEMS LLC
200 Oceangate Ste 100, Long Beach, CA 90802-4317
Tel (562) 435-3666 *Founded/Ownrshp* 2010
Sales 7.2MM^E *EMP* 1,022
SIC 8011 Medical insurance plan; Medical insurance plan

D-U-N-S 96-582-6865
■ **MOLINA INFORMATION SYSTEMS LLC**
MOLINA MEDICAL SOLUTIONS
(*Suby of* MOLINA HEALTHCARE INC) ★
200 Oceangate Ste 100, Long Beach, CA 90802-4317
Tel (916) 561-8540 *Founded/Ownrshp* 2011
Sales NA *EMP* 1,200^E
SIC 6411 Medical insurance claim processing, contract or fee basis; Medical insurance claim processing, contract or fee basis

MOLINA MEDICAL SOLUTIONS
See MOLINA INFORMATION SYSTEMS LLC

D-U-N-S 04-730-0363
MOLINE DISPATCH PUBLISHING CO
ROCK ISLAND ARGUS
(*Suby of* JOURNAL) ★
1720 5th Ave, Moline, IL 61265-7907
Tel (309) 764-4344 *Founded/Ownrshp* 1983
Sales 72.6MM^E *EMP* 1,000
SIC 2711 2752 Newspapers, publishing & printing; Commercial printing, lithographic; Newspapers, publishing & printing; Commercial printing, lithographic
Exec: Stephanie Hoffstatter
Advt Dir: Nick Norman

D-U-N-S 80-541-5262 IMP
MOLINE MACHINERY LLC
114 S Central Ave, Duluth, MN 55807-2302
Tel (218) 624-5734 *Founded/Ownrshp* 1991
Sales 23.0MM^E *EMP* 80
SIC 3556 Bakery machinery
Pr: Gary Molin
COO: Kevin Boreen
Ch: Don Moline
Sr VP: Gary Moline
IT Man: Colin Anderson
IT Man: Bob Gulcin
IT Man: Deborah Pallas
IT Man: Paul Silverberg
Sfty Mgr: Ralph Johnson
Opers Mgr: Mike Plaunt
Natl Sales: Mike Gentile

D-U-N-S 09-875-0813
MOLINE-COAL VALLEY COMMUNITY UNIT SCHOOL DISTRICT 40
1619 11th Ave, Moline, IL 61265-3143
Tel (309) 743-1600 *Founded/Ownrshp* 1871
Sales 87.6MM *EMP* 1,000
Accts Mcgladrey Llp Davenport Iowa
SIC 8211 School board; School board
Ofcr: Rick Sanchez
VP: Keith Lindbloom
MIS Dir: Craig Reid
Psych: Danelle Lyon
Snr Mgr: Angie Curnyn

D-U-N-S 62-418-6933
MOLLE AUTOMOTIVE GROUP LLC
MOLLE VOLKSWAGEN
10344 Summit St, Kansas City, MO 64114-4522
Tel (816) 941-9500 *Founded/Ownrshp* 2005
Sales 30.0MM *EMP* 56^E
SIC 5511 Automobiles, new & used; Automobiles, new & used
CEO: Frank Molle
Off Mgr: Cindy Tailor
Mktg Dir: Kelly Hodges

D-U-N-S 04-956-4461
MOLLE CHEVROLET INC (MO)
411 Nw Mock Ave, Blue Springs, MO 64014-2512
Tel (816) 228-1121 *Founded/Ownrshp* 1950, 1969
Sales 35.6MM^E *EMP* 84
SIC 5511 5521 5531 7539 Automobiles, new & used; Pickups, new & used; Vans, new & used; Used car dealers; Automotive parts; Automotive repair shops; Automobiles, new & used; Pickups, new & used; Vans, new & used; Used car dealers; Automotive parts; Automotive repair shops
Pr: Frank Molle
**VP:* Joanne Molle
Store Mgr: Don Vantrees
Sls Mgr: Drew Anderson
Sls Mgr: Bruce Phelps
Sales Asso: Marcus Thornton

D-U-N-S 02-984-8082
MOLLE TOYOTA INC
601 W 103rd St, Kansas City, MO 64114-4504
Tel (816) 942-5200 *Founded/Ownrshp* 1986
Sales 44.1MM^E *EMP* 130
SIC 5511 5521 Automobiles, new & used; Used car dealers; Automobiles, new & used; Used car dealers
Pr: Frank Molle
VP: Becky Reece
Genl Mgr: Mike Mansour
Mktg Dir: Jim Seaman
Sls Mgr: John Sanson
Sales Asso: Rick McPherson

MOLLE VOLKSWAGEN
See MOLLE AUTOMOTIVE GROUP LLC

D-U-N-S 84-900-2787
MOLLEN IMMUNIZATION CLINICS LLC
MICO
8324 E Hartford Dr # 200, Scottsdale, AZ 85255-5466
Tel (480) 214-2000 *Founded/Ownrshp* 1978
Sales 22.5MM^E *EMP* 414
SIC 8011 Specialized medical practitioners, except internal; Specialized medical practitioners, except internal
Ch Bd: Arthur J Mollen Do
VP: Paul Fishburn
VP: Beverly Watts

D-U-N-S 07-861-3006
MOLLENBERG-BETZ HOLDINGS LLC
300 Scott St, Buffalo, NY 14204-2268
Tel (716) 614-7473 *Founded/Ownrshp* 2010
Sales 48.1MM *EMP* 273
Accts Chiampou Travis Besaw & Kershn
SIC 1711 Plumbing, heating, air-conditioning contractors; Mechanical contractor; Ventilation & duct work contractor; Warm air heating & air conditioning contractor; Plumbing, heating, air-conditioning contractors; Mechanical contractor; Ventilation & duct work contractor; Warm air heating & air conditioning contractor
Pr: Henry Van Mollenberg
CFO: James P Camarre
Ex VP: Joseph Kilijanski

D-U-N-S 00-210-9981
MOLLENBERG-BETZ INC
(*Suby of* MOLLENBERG-BETZ HOLDINGS LLC) ★
300 Scott St, Buffalo, NY 14204-2268
Tel (716) 614-7473 *Founded/Ownrshp* 1910
Sales 29.8MM^E *EMP* 105^E
SIC 1711 Plumbing, heating, air-conditioning contractors; Mechanical contractor; Ventilation & duct work contractor; Warm air heating & air conditioning contractor; Plumbing, heating, air-conditioning contractors; Mechanical contractor; Ventilation & duct work contractor; Warm air heating & air conditioning contractor
CEO: Henry Van Mollenberg
CFO: James P Camarre
Bd of Dir: Adam Mollenberg
Ex VP: Joseph Kilijanski
Trfc Dir: Christopher Comstock
Sfty Mgr: Paul Schiffhauer

D-U-N-S 13-057-1743 IMP
MOLLER GROUP NORTH AMERICA INC
MEGAPLAST NORTH AMERICA
(*Suby of* MOLLERTECH INTERNATIONAL GMBH)
13877 Teresa Dr, Shelby Township, MI 48315-2929
Tel (586) 532-0860 *Founded/Ownrshp* 1998
Sales 68.2MM^E *EMP* 146^E
SIC 3089 Injection molding of plastics; Injection molding of plastics
Pr: Peter Von Moller

D-U-N-S 82-677-6684
MOLLER INVESTMENT GROUP INC
6591 Collins Dr Ste E11, Moorpark, CA 93021-1493
Tel (805) 299-8200 *Founded/Ownrshp* 1991
Sales 109.1MM *EMP* 120
SIC 5541 Filling stations, gasoline; Filling stations, gasoline
Ch: John Moller
**Treas:* Christian Driscoll

D-U-N-S 08-589-7601 IMP
MOLLERS NORTH AMERICA INC
(*Suby of* BIRKENFELD HOLDING GMBH)
5215 52nd St Se, Grand Rapids, MI 49512-9702
Tel (616) 942-6504 *Founded/Ownrshp* 1978, 2015
Sales 25.0MM *EMP* 65
SIC 3537 7389 Palletizers & depalletizers; Packaging & labeling services
Ex VP: Thomas Wagner

D-U-N-S 03-628-1710 IMP
MOLLERTECH LLC
(*Suby of* MEGAPLAST NORTH AMERICA) ★
13877 Teresa Dr, Shelby Township, MI 48315-2929
Tel (586) 532-0860 *Founded/Ownrshp* 1998
Sales 56.3MM^E *EMP* 125
SIC 3089 Injection molding of plastics; Injection molding of plastics
Pr: Dietmar Huebsch
Prgrm Mgr: Vic Sarpolus
Tech Mgr: D Azuara
Opers Mgr: Kevin Adams
Snr PM: Michael Sweet

MOLLIE STONE'S MARKET
See ALBECO INC

D-U-N-S 07-239-0198
MOLLOY COLLEGE (NY)
1000 Hempstead Ave Unit 1, Rockville Centre, NY 11570-1135
Tel (516) 678-5733 *Founded/Ownrshp* 1955
Sales 117.3MM *EMP* 700^E
SIC 8221 Colleges universities & professional schools; Colleges universities & professional schools
Pr: Drew Bogner
**Ch Bd:* Daniel T Henry
**Treas:* Michael A McGovern
Bd of Dir: Janet Knipfing
Bd of Dir: Lynne Nordone
Bd of Dir: Susan Pickering
Bd of Dir: Chris Sedlacek
Ofcr: William Hempstead
**VP:* Valerie Collins
VP: Valerie Hawkes-Collins
VP: Jackie Meli-Rizzo
VP: Robert Paterson
VP: Edward J Thompson
Exec: Dawn Egan
Exec: Sharion Scott

D-U-N-S 16-530-1032 IMP
MOLNLYCKE HEALTH CARE US LLC
(*Suby of* MOLNLYCKE HEALTH CARE AB)
5550 Peachtree Pkwy # 500, Norcross, GA 30092-2825
Tel (678) 250-7900 *Founded/Ownrshp* 2004
Sales 120.2MM^E *EMP* 230
SIC 5047 Surgical equipment & supplies; Surgical equipment & supplies
Area Mgr: Mary Hippern
Genl Mgr: Benjamin Vicuaa
Manager: Jacqueline Morrison

D-U-N-S 07-924-1181 IMP
MOLNLYCKE MANUFACTURING US LLC
192 Admiral Fitch Ave, Brunswick, ME 04011-2795
Tel (207) 607-4900 *Founded/Ownrshp* 2011
Sales 30.0MM *EMP* 41
SIC 5199 First aid supplies; First aid supplies

D-U-N-S 02-214-5668
MOLO OIL CO
BIG 10 MART
123 Southern Ave, Dubuque, IA 52003-8786
Tel (563) 557-7540 *Founded/Ownrshp* 1927
Sales 51.7MM^E *EMP* 250
SIC 5411 5171

D-U-N-S 00-510-1464 IMP
MOLON MOTOR & COIL CORP
300 N Ridge Ave, Arlington Heights, IL 60005-1376
Tel (847) 253-6000 *Founded/Ownrshp* 1954
Sales 25.0MM *EMP* 300
SIC 3621

D-U-N-S 00-705-7342 EXP
▲ MOLSON COORS BREWING CO
1801 Calif St Ste 4600, Denver, CO 80202-2664
Tel (303) 927-2337 *Founded/Ownrshp* 1873
Sales 4.1MMM *EMP* 9,100
Accts Pricewaterhousecoopers Llp De
Tkr Sym TAP *Exch* NYS
SIC 2082 Malt beverages; Beer (alcoholic beverage); Near beer; Malt liquors; Malt beverages; Beer (alcoholic beverage); Near beer; Malt liquors
Pr: Mark R Hunter
Pr: Christopher Jackson
CEO: Mark Hunter
Bd of Dir: Catherine Boilard
Ofcr: Karen Ripley
Ofcr: Nigel Tordoff
Ofcr: Samuel D Walker
Ofcr: Samuel Walker
Ofcr: Celso L White
Sr VP: William H Weintraub
VP: David G Barnes
Exec: Bob Johnston
Dir Lab: David Jang
Dir Lab: Mike Walsh
Board of Directors: Douglas D Tough, Peter H Coors, Louis Vachon, Roger G Eaton, Charles M Herington, Franklin W Hobbs, Mary Lynn Ferguson-Mchugh, Andrew T Molson, Geoffrey W Molson, Iain J G Napier, H Sanford Riley

D-U-N-S 03-518-1841
MOLT MANUFACTURING CO INC
81819 Mill Rd, Spalding, NE 68665-6077
Tel (308) 497-2301 *Founded/Ownrshp* 1969
Sales 35.7MM^E *EMP* 300
SIC 3523 7692 Farm machinery & equipment; Welding repair; Farm machinery & equipment; Welding repair
Pr: Robert Molt
**VP:* Sherri Molt

D-U-N-S 14-265-9213 IMP
MOLTEN (NORTH AMERICA) CORP
(*Suby of* MOLTEN CORPORATION)
1835 Industrial Dr, Findlay, OH 45840-5440
Tel (419) 425-2700 *Founded/Ownrshp* 1990
Sales 21.9MM^E *EMP* 190
SIC 3089 Automotive parts, plastic; Automotive parts, plastic
Pr: Hiddaki Miyamoto
**VP:* Toshikazu Yamate
Dir IT: Justine Brown
QI Cn Mgr: Guy Crawford
Snr Mgr: Brian Smith

D-U-N-S 60-171-1856
MOLTZ CONSTRUCTION INC
8807 County Road 175, Salida, CO 81201-9522
Tel (719) 539-7319 *Founded/Ownrshp* 1989
Sales 48.8MM *EMP* 170
SIC 1629

D-U-N-S 12-392-3141 IMP
MOLY-COP USA LLC
(*Suby of* ARRIUM LIMITED)
8116 Wilson Rd, Kansas City, MO 64125-1327
Tel (816) 231-9191 *Founded/Ownrshp* 2004
Sales 23.1MM^E *EMP* 40
SIC 3399 Steel balls
Pr: Steve Ornduff
VP: Michael McGrath
**Genl Mgr:* Martin Meulendyke
**VP Sls:* James Purdue

D-U-N-S 00-129-4719 IMP
▲ MOLYCORP INC
5619 Denver Tech Ste, Greenwood Village, CO 80111
Tel (303) 843-8040 *Founded/Ownrshp* 2010
Sales 475.6MM *EMP* 2,650^E
Accts Kpmg Llp Toronto Canada
Tkr Sym MCP *Exch* NYS
SIC 1099 Rare-earth ores mining; Zirconium ore mining; Rare-earth ores mining; Zirconium ore mining
Pr: Geoffrey R Bedford
**Ch Bd:* Constantine E Karayannopoulos
CFO: Michael F Doolan
Ofcr: Masood Inayat
Ex VP: Jeffrey Hogan
Ex VP: Kevin W Johnson
Sr VP: Kevin D Morris
VP: John F Ashburn Jr
Genl Mgr: Julie Forman
Off Mgr: Missy Wilson
IT Man: Doug Bonnefoy
Board of Directors: Russell D Ball, Brian T Dolan, John Graell, Charles R Henry, James J Jackson, Mark S Kristoff, Alec Machiels, Michael Schwarzkopf

D-U-N-S 00-406-3168
■ MOLYCORP MINERALS LLC
(*Suby of* MOLYCORP INC) ★
5619 Dtc Pkwy Ste 1000, Greenwood Village, CO 80111-3075
Tel (303) 843-8040 *Founded/Ownrshp* 2008
Sales 47.4MM^E *EMP* 70
SIC 1081 1099 Metal mining services; Rare-earth ores mining
Ch: Ross Bhappu
Pr: Jonathan Coleman
Pr: Carl Hassler
**Pr:* Constantine Karayannopoulos
Pr: Brock O'Kelley
**Ex VP:* Geoffrey R Bedford
**Ex VP:* Michael F Doolan
**Ex VP:* Douglas J Jackson
**Sr VP:* James S Allen
Dir IT: Sam Maddox
IT Man: James Camacci

D-U-N-S 06-405-1097
MOLYE CHEVROLET BUIK SALES CORP
115 W Main St, Honeoye Falls, NY 14472-1103
Tel (585) 624-2818 *Founded/Ownrshp* 1982
Sales 25.0MM *EMP* 39
SIC 5511 Automobiles, new & used; Automobiles, new & used
Pr: Tom Rosati
**VP:* Vito Arbore
Sls Dir: Jeff Knickerbocker
Sls Mgr: Michael Contestable

M.O.M.
See MODERN OFFICE METHODS INC

D-U-N-S 00-625-4312 EXP
■ MOM BRANDS CO
MALT-O-MEAL
(*Suby of* POST HOLDINGS INC) ★
20802 Kensington Blvd, Lakeville, MN 55044-8052
Tel (952) 322-8000 *Founded/Ownrshp* 2015
Sales 450.2MM^E *EMP* 1,400
SIC 2043 Cereal breakfast foods; Oatmeal: prepared as cereal breakfast food; Oats, rolled: prepared as cereal breakfast food; Corn flakes: prepared as cereal breakfast food; Cereal breakfast foods; Oatmeal: prepared as cereal breakfast food; Oats, rolled: prepared as cereal breakfast food; Corn flakes: prepared as cereal breakfast food
CEO: Christopher J Neugen
**CFO:* John Gappa
Bd of Dir: Missy Plante
VP: Paul Holzhueter
VP: Paul Reppenhagen
VP: Grant Stallknecht
IT Man: Raymond Picl
Mtls Mgr: Jane Saberon
Opers Mgr: Alan Zoeller
Mktg Dir: Linda Fisher
Mktg Dir: Dan O'Connor

D-U-N-S 96-683-6467 EXP
■ MOM BRANDS SALES LLC
(*Suby of* MALT-O-MEAL) ★
20802 Kensington Blvd, Lakeville, MN 55044-8052
Tel (952) 322-8000 *Founded/Ownrshp* 2010
Sales 52.3MM^E *EMP* 110
SIC 5141 Food brokers; Food brokers
Pr: Chris Neugent
**Treas:* John Gappa
IT Man: Tim Rossini
**VP Sls:* Jesse Garcia

D-U-N-S 02-710-1963
MOM365 INC
(*Suby of* FALCONHEAD CAPITAL PARTNERS II LP) ★
3613 Mueller Rd, Saint Charles, MO 63301-0005
Tel (636) 946-5115 *Founded/Ownrshp* 2006
Sales 30.6MM^E *EMP* 275
SIC 7221 7335 Photographic studios, portrait; Commercial photography; Photographic studios, portrait; Commercial photography
CEO: David Yarnell
Pt: Maria Paguirigan
**Pr:* Laura Klein
**Pr:* Mary Jo Romeo
CFO: Max S Barnett
VP: Jim Cambell
Dist Mgr: Todd Stewart
VP Opers: Janna Alford

MOMA
See MUSEUM OF MODERN ART

D-U-N-S 00-326-6616
MOMAR INC
AQUATROL WATER TREATMENT CHEM
1830 Ellswrth Indstrl Blv, Atlanta, GA 30318-3792
Tel (404) 355-4580 *Founded/Ownrshp* 1947
Sales 74.7MM^E *EMP* 300
SIC 2842 Specialty cleaning, polishes & sanitation goods; Specialty cleaning, polishes & sanitation goods
CEO: Julian B Mohr Sr
Pr: Jason French
Pr: Julian Mohr Jr
COO: Donna Ray
CFO: Matt Herndon
Sr VP: Beau Black
Sr VP: William S Buckley Jr
Sr VP: John Hostetler
Sr VP: Darryl Jones
Sr VP: Cliff Kaczmarek
Sr VP: Bill Latouche
Sr VP: Farrell Odom
Sr VP: Edd Pruett
Sr VP: Charlie Yancey
VP: Dick Arensberg
VP: Toby Cook
VP: Billy Davidson
VP: Richard King
VP: Rick Kramer
VP: Mike Renegar
VP: Jim Shore

D-U-N-S 05-422-6626
MOMENCE PACKING CO
334 W North St, Momence, IL 60954-1157
Tel (815) 472-6485 *Founded/Ownrshp* 1982
Sales 38.2MM^E *EMP* 300
SIC 2013 2011 Sausages & other prepared meats; Meat packing plants; Sausages & other prepared meats; Meat packing plants
Pr: Robert Salzwedel

MOMENI AND SONS
See MOMENI INC

D-U-N-S 07-888-6850 IMP
MOMENI INC
MOMENI AND SONS
60 Broad St, Carlstadt, NJ 07072-2006
Tel (201) 549-7220 *Founded/Ownrshp* 1975
Sales 22.2MM *EMP* 52
SIC 5023 Rugs
Owner: Reza Momeni
**CFO:* Aria Momeni
**VP:* Ali Reza Momeni
**Prin:* Haji Momeni
VP Sls: Stephen Hoberman

D-U-N-S 11-795-5422
MOMENTA PHARMACEUTICALS INC
675 W Kendall St, Cambridge, MA 02142-1110
Tel (617) 491-9700 *Founded/Ownrshp* 2002
Sales 52.2MM *EMP* 256
Tkr Sym MNTA *Exch* NGS
SIC 2834 Pharmaceutical preparations; Pharmaceutical preparations
Pr: Craig A Wheeler
**Ch Bd:* James R Sulat
Pr: Michael Franken
COO: Matt Ottmer
CFO: Richard P Shea
Chf Mktg O: James M Roach
Sr VP: Lakshmi Jayaraman
Sr VP: Ganesh V Kaundinya
Sr VP: Bruce A Leicher
VP: James Anderson
VP: Marcio Voloch
Board of Directors: John K Clarke, Bruce Downey, Marsha H Fanucci, George Gemayel, Bennett M Shapiro, Elizabeth Stoner

MOMENTIVE
See MPM SILICONES LLC

D-U-N-S 96-219-2279
MOMENTIVE PERFORMANCE MATERIALS HOLDINGS INC
MOMENTIVE PRFMCE MTLS HOLDINGS
22 Corporate Woods Blvd, Albany, NY 12211-2374
Tel (518) 533-4600 *Founded/Ownrshp* 2010
Sales NA *EMP* 9,270^E
SIC 2869 3479 Silicones; Coating of metals with silicon

D-U-N-S 96-521-4146 EXP
MOMENTIVE PERFORMANCE MATERIALS HOLDINGS LLC
180 E Broad St, Columbus, OH 43215-3707
Tel (614) 986-2495 *Founded/Ownrshp* 2010
Sales 5.1MMM^E *EMP* 10,000^E
SIC 2821 2899 2869 Chemical preparations; Silicones; Thermosetting materials; Thermosetting materials; Chemical preparations; Silicones
CEO: Craig O Morrison
**Pr:* Dale N Plante
**CFO:* William H Carter
Treas: George F Knight
Top Exec: Deepak Kumar
Ex VP: Nathan E Fisher
Ex VP: Anthony B Greene
Ex VP: Douglas A Johns
Ex VP: Kevin W McGuire
**Ex VP:* Judith A Sonnett
Sr VP: Raymond Baran
VP: Colette Barricks
VP: Nancy Brown
VP: Peter F Loscocco
Board of Directors: Robert T Seminara, Kenneth Cordell, Jordan C Zaken, Robert J Duffy, Joshua J Harris, William H Joyce, Scott M Kleinman, Stan Parker, Jonathan Rich, David B Sambur, Marvin O Schlanger

D-U-N-S 78-999-4014 IMP/EXP
MOMENTIVE PERFORMANCE MATERIALS INC
(*Suby of* MPM INTERMEDIATE HOLDINGS INC) ★
260 Hudson River Rd, Waterford, NY 12188-1910
Tel (518) 237-3330 *Founded/Ownrshp* 2014
Sales 1.6MMM^E *EMP* 4,600
Accts Pricewaterhousecoopers Llp C
SIC 2869 3479 3679 Silicones; Coating of metals with silicon; Electronic crystals; Quartz crystals, for electronic application; Silicones; Coating of metals with silicon; Electronic crystals; Quartz crystals, for electronic application
Pr: John G Boss
CFO: Erick R Asmussen
**CFO:* Brian D Berger
CFO: William H Carter
CFO: Wolf Lehmann
Treas: George F Knight
**Ex VP:* Nathan E Fisher
Ex VP: Kevin W McGuire
**VP:* Craig R Branchfield
IT Man: Steve Dorn
Mktg Mgr: Steve Carbone

D-U-N-S 82-856-7342 IMP/EXP
MOMENTIVE PERFORMANCE MATERIALS QUARTZ INC
(*Suby of* MOMENTIVE PERFORMANCE MATERIALS INC) ★
22557 Lunn Rd, Strongsville, OH 44149-4871
Tel (440) 878-5700 *Founded/Ownrshp* 1996
Sales 102.5MM^E *EMP* 200
SIC 2869 3479 3446 Silicones; Coating of metals with silicon; Architectural metalwork; Silicones; Coating of metals with silicon; Architectural metalwork
Pr: Raymond Kolberg
**CFO:* William L Torrence
Snr Mgr: Chad McKnight
Snr Mgr: Imad Qashou
Snr Mgr: Rachel Roberts
Snr Mgr: Daniel Weinmann

MOMENTIVE PRFMCE MTLS HOLDINGS
See MOMENTIVE PERFORMANCE MATERIALS HOLDINGS INC

D-U-N-S 93-905-4768
MOMENTOUS INSURANCE BROKERAGE INC
5990 Sepulvda Blvd # 550, Van Nuys, CA 91411-2536
Tel (818) 933-2700 *Founded/Ownrshp* 2008
Sales NA *EMP* 99^E
SIC 6411 Insurance agents, brokers & service
Pr: Diane Brinson Schiele
COO: David Toth

Ex VP: Pam Weiser
Sr VP: Susan Brien
**Sr VP:* Erin Gaston
**Sr VP:* David Oliver
VP: Jeff Davis
VP: Mitula Patel
VP: Lisa Rocha
VP: Lisa Samler
VP: Sherrie Zenter
Exec: Dominique Butler

MOMENTUM AUDI
See SONIC MOMENTUM VOLKSWAGEN LP

D-U-N-S 07-849-5191
MOMENTUM AUTO GROUP
MOMENTUM TOYOTA OF FAIRFIELD
2575 Auto Mall Pkwy, Fairfield, CA 94533-5803
Tel (707) 402-3100 *Founded/Ownrshp* 2010
Sales 24.3MM^E *EMP* 35^E
SIC 5511 Automobiles, new & used
Pr: Rahim Hassanally
VP Opers: Kraig Quisenberry

D-U-N-S 02-664-4526
■ **MOMENTUM BMW LTD**
(*Suby of* LONE STAR FORD) ★
10002 Southwest Fwy, Houston, TX 77074-1202
Tel (713) 596-3100 *Founded/Ownrshp* 2004
Sales 60.9MM^E *EMP* 200
SIC 5511 Automobiles, new & used; Automobiles, new & used
Mng Pt: Ricardo Weitz
Genl Mgr: George Ault
Sls Mgr: Marianna Brasel
Sls Mgr: Tom Herald
Sls Mgr: Maria Moncada
Sales Asso: Jason Gonzales
Sales Asso: Tracy Turner

D-U-N-S 80-233-0808
MOMENTUM BMW WEST SALES
20822 Katy Fwy, Katy, TX 77449-7765
Tel (832) 772-9000 *Founded/Ownrshp* 2004
Sales 23.7MM^E *EMP* 95^E
SIC 5511 Automobiles, new & used
Prin: Michael Rouch
Sls Mgr: Dan KAO
Sales Asso: Dylan Godesteanu

D-U-N-S 09-092-1917
MOMENTUM FOR MENTAL HEALTH
438 N White Rd, San Jose, CA 95127-1439
Tel (408) 254-6828 *Founded/Ownrshp* 1997
Sales 33.6MM *EMP* 300
Accts Nichols Rick & Company Morgan
SIC 8399 Health systems agency; Health systems agency
CEO: David K Mineta
**Ch Bd:* Nancy Flannigan
**Pr:* Mary Williams
**CFO:* Melinda Golden
**CFO:* Jack Smelser
Treas: Larry Burns
**Treas:* Dan Woodward
CTO: Howard Smith
Sls&Mrk Ex: Elsa Dahl
Mktg Dir: Alicia Ramirez
Psych: Teodora Goltiao

D-U-N-S 01-887-0549
MOMENTUM PAYMENT SYSTEMS LLC
(*Suby of* EVO PAYMENTS INTERNATIONAL LLC) ★
3801 Arapaho Rd, Addison, TX 75001-4314
Tel (214) 442-1700 *Founded/Ownrshp* 2008, 2013
Sales NA *EMP* 337^E
SIC 6099 Check cashing agencies

D-U-N-S 00-773-2568 IMP
MOMENTUM PLASTICS LLC
5631 Old Clinton Rd, Houston, TX 77020-7345
Tel (713) 678-7741 *Founded/Ownrshp* 1999
Sales 21.9MM^E *EMP* 150
SIC 3089 2673 Plastic containers, except foam; Bags: plastic, laminated & coated; Plastic containers, except foam; Bags: plastic, laminated & coated
Pr: Pi-Chee Chen

D-U-N-S 79-951-3192
MOMENTUM TELECOM INC
880 Montclair Rd Ste 400, Birmingham, AL 35213-1979
Tel (205) 978-4400 *Founded/Ownrshp* 2000
Sales 71.3MM^E *EMP* 210^E
SIC 4813 4215 Local telephone communications; Long distance telephone communications; ; Courier services, except by air; Local telephone communications; Long distance telephone communications; ; Courier services, except by air
Pr: William Fox
CFO: Matthew Conroy
Sr VP: Alan Creighton
VP: David M Benck
VP: Hilaire B DESA
VP: Dennis E Lipford
VP: Auri Vizgaitis
Exec: Ashley Smith
Snr Ntwrk: Paul Bentley
IT Man: Melissa Gilbert
Sftwr Eng: Mike Dawson
Board of Directors: Alan Creighton

D-U-N-S 16-160-7460 IMP/EXP
MOMENTUM TEXTILES LLC
TEXTUS GROUP
17811 Fitch, Irvine, CA 92614-6001
Tel (949) 833-8886 *Founded/Ownrshp* 1993
Sales 94.5MM^E *EMP* 140
SIC 5131 2221 Upholstery fabrics, woven; Broadwoven fabric mills, manmade; Upholstery fabrics, woven; Broadwoven fabric mills, manmade
Pr: John Wilkinson
**CFO:* Joanne Corrao
VP: Roger Arciniega
**VP:* Kathy Gowdy
Sales Asso: Madeleine Hobbins

MOMENTUM TOYOTA OF FAIRFIELD
See MOMENTUM AUTO GROUP

MOMENTUM WORLDWIDE
See MOMENTUM-NA INC

D-U-N-S 10-802-4191
■ **MOMENTUM-NA INC**
MOMENTUM WORLDWIDE
(*Suby of* INTERPUBLIC GROUP OF COMPANIES INC) ★
7930 Clayton Rd Ste 400, Saint Louis, MO 63117-1331
Tel (314) 646-6200 *Founded/Ownrshp* 1998
Sales 65.1MM^E *EMP* 520
SIC 8743 7311 8732 Sales promotion; Advertising consultant; Commercial nonphysical research; Sales promotion; Advertising consultant; Commercial nonphysical research
Pr: Chris Weil
CFO: Philippe Touzot
Chf Cred: Omid Farhang
Ex VP: Robert McQueen
**Ex VP:* Denny Reed
VP: David Bannecke
VP: Shaun Brown
VP: Jeff Coburn
Creative D: Chris Aguirre
Creative D: Daniel Chu
Creative D: Matt Glarner
Creative D: Sue Sylvia
Creative D: Dean Weiler

D-U-N-S 60-413-6119
MOMI PALI MEDICAL CENTER
(*Suby of* HAWAI I PACIFIC HEALTH) ★
98-1079 Moanalua Rd # 680, Aiea, HI 96701-4725
Tel (808) 486-6000 *Founded/Ownrshp* 1989
Sales 16.6MM^E *EMP* 618
SIC 8011 Medical centers; Medical centers
CEO: Jen Chahanovich
Ex VP: David Okabe
VP: Terry Long
VP: Herbert Uesara
Exec: Kyle Kanemura
Dir OR: Christi Kaliipio
Dir Rad: Wendell Woo
Opers Supe: Robyn Kalahiki
Ansthlgy: Mark Nishijo
Ansthlgy: Jeffrey Sullivan
Doctor: Jeffrey Killeen

MOM'S MEALS
See PURFOODS LLC

D-U-N-S 09-392-8062
MOMS MEALS LTD
PURE FOODS
3210 Se Corp Woods Dr, Ankeny, IA 50021
Tel (515) 382-8888 *Founded/Ownrshp* 1999
Sales 21.6MM^E *EMP* 200
SIC 2099 Ready-to-eat meals, salads & sandwiches; Ready-to-eat meals, salads & sandwiches
Pr: Rick Anderson

MOMS PHARMACY
See ALLION HEALTHCARE INC

D-U-N-S 62-802-7351 IMP
MON CHERI BRIDALS LLC
1018 Whitehead Road Ext # 1, Ewing, NJ 08638-2429
Tel (609) 530-1900 *Founded/Ownrshp* 2004
Sales 38.3MM^E *EMP* 65
SIC 5131 Bridal supplies
CEO: Stephen Lang
VP: Walter Soltys
Off Mgr: Gail Salewski
Ql Cn Mgr: Melanie De La Cruz
Sales Exec: Yolanda Carita
Natl Sales: John Amato

D-U-N-S 13-135-7642
MON CHONG LOONG TRADING CORP
5672 49th Pl, Maspeth, NY 11378-2022
Tel (718) 417-1668 *Founded/Ownrshp* 1985
Sales 56.4MM^E *EMP* 75
SIC 5141 Groceries, general line
CEO: Myint J Kyaw
**Pr:* Jeffrey Wu

MON GENERAL HOSPITAL
See MONONGALIA HEALTH SYSTEM INC

MON VALLEY HOSPITAL
See MONONGAHELA VALLEY HOSPITAL INC

D-U-N-S 15-652-1221
MON-VALE HEALTH RESOURCES INC
1163 Country Club Rd, Monongahela, PA 15063-1013
Tel (724) 258-1000 *Founded/Ownrshp* 1982
Sales 162.9MM *EMP* 1,024^E
Accts Carbis Walker Llp New Castle
SIC 8062 General medical & surgical hospitals; General medical & surgical hospitals
Pr: Louis Panza Jr
Sr VP: Daniel Simmons
VP: Lawrence J Rusnock
Genl Mgr: Veronica Vamivakas
Sls Mgr: Silver Hawk

D-U-N-S 06-376-6158
MON-VALLEY FOODS INC
FISHER HEIGHTS GIANT EAGLE
1300 Country Club Rd, Monongahela, PA 15063-1018
Tel (724) 258-5011 *Founded/Ownrshp* 1973
Sales 34.3MM^E *EMP* 250
SIC 5411 Supermarkets, chain; Supermarkets, chain
Pr: Aldo Bartolotta
**Treas:* Toni Jo Allridge
**VP:* Bruce Bartolotta

D-U-N-S 06-069-0575
MON-YOUGH COMMUNITY SERVICES CENTER INC
500 Walnut St Fl 3, McKeesport, PA 15132-2801
Tel (412) 675-8530 *Founded/Ownrshp* 1969
Sales 19.3MM *EMP* 370
Accts Mckeever Varga & Senko Pittsb
SIC 8093 Mental health clinic, outpatient; Drug clinic, outpatient; Alcohol clinic, outpatient; Mental health clinic, outpatient; Drug clinic, outpatient; Alcohol clinic, outpatient
Ex Dir: Noreen Fredrick

D-U-N-S 61-921-9736
MONA ELECTRIC GROUP INC
7915 Malcolm Rd Ste 400w, Clinton, MD 20735-1768
Tel (301) 868-8400 *Founded/Ownrshp* 1966
Sales 99.2MM^E *EMP* 400
SIC 1731 Electrical work; Electrical work
Ch Bd: Vincent P Mona
CFO: Barbara Gordon
Ex VP: John Kurty
Ex VP: Paul Warren
Sr VP: Douglas Bailey
Sr VP: Ron Michael
VP: Doris Daye
VP: Al Dimuzio
VP: Randy Kurty
VP: Janet Miller
VP: Brian Moorefield
VP: Kenneth Robertson
Exec: Richard Carmona

MONA SHORES PUBLIC SCHOOLS
See MONA SHORES SCHOOL DISTRICT

D-U-N-S 07-927-8727
MONA SHORES SCHOOL DISTRICT
MONA SHORES PUBLIC SCHOOLS
121 Randall Rd, Norton Shores, MI 49441-4944
Tel (231) 780-4751 *Founded/Ownrshp* 1959
Sales 28.8MM^E *EMP* 490
SIC 8211 Public elementary & secondary schools; Public elementary & secondary schools
Sr VP: Ryan Portenga
Pr Dir: Renee Doan
Psych: Danielle Smith

D-U-N-S 01-866-2114
MONACO & SONS MOTOR SALES INC (CT)
MONACO FORD
767 New London Tpke, Glastonbury, CT 06033-3077
Tel (860) 652-3000 *Founded/Ownrshp* 1942
Sales 27.5MM^E *EMP* 85
SIC 5511 5013 5531 5541 5521

MONACO BAKING COMPANY
See PHENIX GOURMET LLC

MONACO FORD
See MONACO & SONS MOTOR SALES INC

MONACO HOTEL
See HOTEL MONACO

MONACO RIDGE
See WASHOE MEDICAL CENTER SOUTH MEADOW

D-U-N-S 83-099-9715
MONACO RV LLC
(*Suby of* ALLIED SPECIALTY VEHICLES INC) ★
91320 Coburg Indus Way, Coburg, OR 97408-9492
Tel (541) 501-8011 *Founded/Ownrshp* 2013
Sales 74.3MM^E *EMP* 600^E
SIC 3799 Recreational vehicles; Recreational vehicles

D-U-N-S 00-119-5585
MONADNOCK CO (CA)
LISI AEROSPACE
(*Suby of* HI-SHEAR CORP) ★
16728 Gale Ave, City of Industry, CA 91745-1803
Tel (626) 964-6581 *Founded/Ownrshp* 1987
Sales 50.0MM *EMP* 190
SIC 3429 Aircraft hardware; Metal fasteners; Aircraft hardware; Metal fasteners
CEO: Christian Darville
**VP:* Michael Reyes
Mfg Mgr: Armando Mendoza
Opers Mgr: Eddie Diaz

D-U-N-S 07-396-9438
MONADNOCK COMMUNITY HOSPITAL
452 Old Street Rd, Peterborough, NH 03458-1295
Tel (603) 924-4699 *Founded/Ownrshp* 1919
Sales 75.5MM *EMP* 360^E
Accts Baker Newman & Noyes Manchest
SIC 8062 8011 General medical & surgical hospitals; Offices & clinics of medical doctors; General medical & surgical hospitals; Offices & clinics of medical doctors
Ch: Robert Taft
**Pr:* Benjamin J Wheeler
**CEO:* Peter L Gosline
CFO: Richard Scheinblum
**Treas:* David A Reilly
VP: Andrew Macdonald
VP: Elvin Ramey
Dir Rad: Mark Luedke
Dir Rx: Michael Flynn
Dir Pat Ac: Janet Willis
Genl Mgr: Michael Faber
Board of Directors: John Bryan, Richard Carvalho, Joseph M De Vera

D-U-N-S 08-045-4804 IMP
MONADNOCK CONSTRUCTION INC
155 3rd St, Brooklyn, NY 11231-4822
Tel (718) 875-8160 *Founded/Ownrshp* 1975
Sales 34.6MM^E *EMP* 100
SIC 1522 1542 Apartment building construction; Remodeling, multi-family dwellings; Commercial & office building, new construction; Commercial & office buildings, renovation & repair
Pr: Nicholas Lembo
CFO: John D'Ambrosio
**VP:* Greg Bauso
**VP:* Jens Peter Hansen
**VP:* Peter Hansen
**VP:* Jose Martinez
Exec: Anthony Ohaire
Sfty Mgr: Marco Carcich

D-U-N-S 15-855-6217
MONADNOCK DEVELOPMENTAL SERVICES INC
121 Railroad St, Keene, NH 03431-3747
Tel (603) 352-1304 *Founded/Ownrshp* 1983
Sales 27.4MM^E *EMP* 300
SIC 8322 Individual & family services; Individual & family services
Ex Dir: Alan Greene

Sls&Mrk Ex: Joel Fitzpatrick
Sls&Mrk Ex: Susan Reilly

D-U-N-S 87-836-8505
MONADNOCK HEALTH SERVICES INC
MONADNOCK INTERNISTS
452 Old Street Rd, Peterborough, NH 03458-1263
Tel (603) 924-7191 *Founded/Ownrshp* 1987
Sales 18.2MM^E *EMP* 600
Accts Berry Dunn Mcneil & Parker
SIC 8011 Offices & clinics of medical doctors; Offices & clinics of medical doctors
Pr: Peter Gosline
**COO:* Sarah Taylor
CFO: Deborah Shipman
**VP:* Dr Ross Ramey

MONADNOCK INTERNISTS
See MONADNOCK HEALTH SERVICES INC

MONADNOCK LEDGER
See NEWSPAPERS OF NEW HAMPSHIRE INC

D-U-N-S 00-107-8427 EXP
MONADNOCK PAPER MILLS INC (NH)
117 Antrim Rd, Bennington, NH 03442-4205
Tel (603) 588-8633 *Founded/Ownrshp* 1819, 1948
Sales 54.3MM^E *EMP* 235
SIC 2621 Specialty papers; Cover paper; Text paper; Specialty papers; Cover paper; Text paper
Pr: Richard G Verney
CFO: Andrew Manns
VP: Chris Benincasa
VP: Paul Ciccone
VP: Joseph A Fletcher
Dir IT: Matt Crandall
Mfg Dir: Norman Tomlinson
Sfty Mgr: Norman Provencher
VP Sls: James Clemente
Snr PM: Tom Graczyk

D-U-N-S 07-979-9238
MONADNOCK REGIONAL SCHOOL DISTRICT
600 Old Homestead Hwy, Swanzey, NH 03446-2311
Tel (603) 352-6955 *Founded/Ownrshp* 2015
Sales 3.7MM^E *EMP* 393^E
SIC 8211 Public elementary & secondary schools

D-U-N-S 79-157-0612 IMP
MONAHAN FILAMENTS LLC
SPECIALTY FILAMENTS
(*Suby of* THOMAS MONAHAN CO) ★
215 Egyptian Trl, Arcola, IL 61910-1904
Tel (217) 268-4957 *Founded/Ownrshp* 2007
Sales 30.1MM^E *EMP* 90
SIC 3089 Molding primary plastic
Plnt Mgr: Mike Arsenalut

D-U-N-S 06-015-5694
MONAHANS-WICKETT-PYOTE INDEPENDENT SCHOOL DISTRICT
606 S Betty Ave, Monahans, TX 79756-5018
Tel (432) 943-6711 *Founded/Ownrshp* 1931
Sales 26.0MM *EMP* 313
Accts Smith & Rives Pc Monahans T
SIC 8211 Public elementary school; Public junior high school; Public senior high school; Public special education school; Public elementary school; Public junior high school; Public senior high school; Public special education school
Dir Sec: Tommy King
IT Man: Allen Fox

D-U-N-S 78-580-1069
MONARC CONSTRUCTION INC
2781 Hartland Rd, Falls Church, VA 22043-3529
Tel (703) 641-8500 *Founded/Ownrshp* 1991
Sales 37.8MM^E *EMP* 75
SIC 1542 Nonresidential construction
Pr: John D Bellingham
**VP:* Lynne Bellingham
**VP:* Byron Kassing
**VP:* Sara Lawrence
VP: Randall Mullen
**VP:* Gene Prichard
**VP:* William Stepanick
IT Man: Bill Brummitt
Snr Mgr: Peter Forster

MONARCH
See ELTREX INDUSTRIES INC

D-U-N-S 07-062-2592
MONARCH
350 Pee Dee Ave Ste 101, Albemarle, NC 28001-4945
Tel (704) 986-1500 *Founded/Ownrshp* 1958
Sales 76.6MM *EMP* 1,200
Accts Davidson Holland Whitesell & C
SIC 8322 8049 8331 8052 Association for the handicapped; Psychotherapist, except M.D.; Vocational rehabilitation agency; Home for the mentally retarded, with health care; Association for the handicapped; Psychotherapist, except M.D.; Vocational rehabilitation agency; Home for the mentally retarded, with health care
CEO: Dr Peggy S Terhune
**COO:* James Kelley
CFO: Cindy Jones
Treas: Brenda Hinson
Adm Dir: Sylvia Hancock
Prgrm Mgr: Damon Heath
Prgrm Mgr: Reginald Marshall
CIO: Crisc Basinger
IT Man: Troy Connell
Opers Mgr: Pat Carpenter
Opers Mgr: Cynthia Fewell

D-U-N-S 05-331-9740
■ **MONARCH BANK INC** (VA)
(*Suby of* MONARCH FINANCIAL HOLDINGS INC) ★
1101 Executive Blvd, Chesapeake, VA 23320-3634
Tel (757) 222-2100 *Founded/Ownrshp* 1998
Sales NA *EMP* 52
SIC 6029 Commercial banks; Commercial banks
CEO: Brad E Schwartz
Pr: William H Carr
**Pr:* E Neal Crawford
**Pr:* Neal Crawford

Pr: Adam Goldblatt
Pr: Jack H Lane
Pr: W Craig Reilly
CEO: William T Morrison
COO: William Morrison
*CFO: Lynette P Harris
Ofcr: Christopher Preston
Ofcr: Jay Siegfried
*Ex VP: Denys Diaz
*Ex VP: Andrew Lock
Sr VP: Tim Miller
Sr VP: Dennis Napier
Sr VP: Katherine Nowell
Sr VP: Andrew Proctor
VP: Terri Trotman

D-U-N-S 01-643-0407 IMP
MONARCH BEVERAGE CO INC
WORLD CLASS BEVERAGE DIV
9347 Pendleton Pike, Indianapolis, IN 46236-2768
Tel (317) 612-1310 Founded/Ownrshp 1947, 1983
Sales 127.2MM^E EMP 360
SIC 5181 5182 Beer & other fermented malt liquors; Wine; Beer & other fermented malt liquors; Wine
Pr: Edwin T French Jr
CFO: Fred Dufor
*VP: Phil Terry
Mng Dir: Wayne Miller
Dist Mgr: Matt Love
Genl Mgr: John E Xnos
VP Mktg: Dave Rogers
Sls Mgr: Robert Shoulders
Sales Asso: Chad Leidolf
Sales Asso: Matthew Thomas

D-U-N-S 80-755-0280
▲ MONARCH CASINO & RESORT INC
3800 S Virginia St, Reno, NV 89502-6005
Tel (775) 335-4600 Founded/Ownrshp 1993
Sales 187.7MM EMP 2,100^E
Tkr Sym MCRI Exch NGS
SIC 7011 Hotels & motels; Casino hotel; Resort hotel; Hotels & motels; Casino hotel; Resort hotel
Ch Bd: John Farahi
*Ch Bd: Bob Farahi
COO: David Farahi
CFO: Ronald M Rowan
Genl Mgr: Darlyne Sullivan
Manager: Bert Johnson
Board of Directors: Paul Andrews, Yvette E Landau, Craig F Sullivan

D-U-N-S 00-714-4884 IMP/EXP
▲ MONARCH CEMENT CO
449 1200th St, Humboldt, KS 66748-1785
Tel (620) 473-2222 Founded/Ownrshp 1913
Sales 147.0MM EMP 510
Tkr Sym MCEM Exch OTC
SIC 3241 3273 Portland cement; Ready-mixed concrete; Portland cement; Ready-mixed concrete
Ch Bd: Walter H Wulf Jr
CFO: Debra P Roe
*Treas: Byron K Radcliff
*VP: Robert M Kissick
Telecom Ex: Karen Emerson
Dir IT: Steve Bulk
VP Opers: Roy Owens
Opers Mgr: Dennis Osborn
Plnt Mgr: Gary Stalder
VP Sls: Joan Perez
Sls Mgr: Jay Taff
Board of Directors: Jack R Callahan, Ronald E Callaway, David L Deffner, Gayle C McMillen, Byron J Radcliff, Michael R Wachter, Walter H Wulf III

D-U-N-S 02-949-1870 IMP
■ MONARCH CERAMIC TILE INC
(Suby of AMERICAN MARAZZI TILE INC) ★
359 Clay Rd, Mesquite, TX 75182-9710
Tel (972) 226-0110 Founded/Ownrshp 1998
Sales 27.4MM^E EMP 180
SIC 3253 Ceramic wall & floor tile; Ceramic wall & floor tile
CEO: Gianni Mattioli
*Sec: David Carlile

MONARCH CONSTRUCTION COMPANY
See MONARCH ENTERPRISES INC

D-U-N-S 06-162-9150
MONARCH CONSTRUCTION CO
1654 Sherman Ave, Cincinnati, OH 45212-2598
Tel (513) 351-6900 Founded/Ownrshp 1963
Sales 65.6MM^E EMP 200
SIC 1542 1541 Commercial & office building, new construction; Commercial & office buildings, renovation & repair; Institutional building construction; School building construction; Industrial buildings & warehouses; Commercial & office building, new construction; Commercial & office buildings, renovation & repair; Institutional building construction; School building construction; Industrial buildings & warehouses
CEO: Ronald A Koetters
*Pr: Thomas P Butler
*CFO: Jerome J Corbett Jr
Treas: William C Otte

D-U-N-S 94-570-4823
MONARCH DENTAL CORP
(Suby of BRIGHT NOW DENTAL) ★
7989 Belt Line Rd Ste 90, Dallas, TX 75248-5728
Tel (972) 720-9017 Founded/Ownrshp 2003
Sales 51.6MM^E EMP 2,300
SIC 8021 Dental clinics & offices; Dental clinics & offices
Pr: Steven Bilt
CFO: Bradley Schmidt
Ofcr: Roy D Smith III DDS
Sr VP: Dennis Fratt
Board of Directors: Glenn E Hemmerle, Allan S Huston, John E Maupin Jr DDS, Warren F Melamed DDS

MONARCH DOOR
See HOJ ENGINEERING & SALES CO INC

D-U-N-S 00-445-6836 IMP/EXP
MONARCH ELECTRIC SERVICE CO (OH)
(Suby of I P S) ★
5325 W 130th St, Cleveland, OH 44130-1034
Tel (216) 433-7800 Founded/Ownrshp 1958
Sales 25.9MM^E EMP 165
SIC 7699 5063 Industrial machinery & equipment repair; Electrical apparatus & equipment; Industrial machinery & equipment repair; Electrical apparatus & equipment
CEO: John Zuleger
*CEO: George E Roller
*COO: Richard Mintern
*Ch: Tim Jeans
Sec: Neil Gurney
*VP: Brad Roller
Sls Mgr: Bill Oros

D-U-N-S 10-400-0039
MONARCH ENTERPRISES INC
MONARCH CONSTRUCTION COMPANY
117 Lively Blvd, Elk Grove Village, IL 60007-1620
Tel (847) 439-4223 Founded/Ownrshp 1980
Sales 24.9MM^E EMP 240
SIC 1751 Carpentry work; Carpentry work
Pr: Roger A Monaco
*Treas: Noelle D'Ambrosio
VP: Patrick Waite

D-U-N-S 78-961-7029
▲ MONARCH FINANCIAL HOLDINGS INC
1435 Crossways Blvd, Chesapeake, VA 23320-2896
Tel (757) 389-5111 Founded/Ownrshp 2006
Sales NA EMP 631^E
Tkr Sym MNRK Exch NAS
SIC 6022 State commercial banks; State commercial banks
CEO: Brad E Schwartz
*Ch Bd: Jeffrey F Benson
V Ch: Lawton Baker
*Pr: E Neal Crawford Jr
CFO: Lynette P Harris
*V Ch Bd: Lawton H Baker
Ex VP: Denys J Diaz
Ex VP: Andrew N Lock

D-U-N-S 07-848-5795
■ MONARCH GROWTH INC
(Suby of MONARCH CASINO & RESORT INC) ★
3800 S Virginia St, Reno, NV 89502-6005
Tel (775) 335-4600 Founded/Ownrshp 2012
Sales 1.5MM^E EMP 285^E
SIC 7011 Casino hotel
Pr: David Farahi
*Treas: Ronald Rowan

D-U-N-S 78-213-1692
MONARCH HEALTHCARE A MEDICAL GROUP INC
11 Technology Dr, Irvine, CA 92618-2302
Tel (949) 923-3200 Founded/Ownrshp 1986
Sales 43.8MM^E EMP 450^E
SIC 8011 Group health association
CEO: Bartley Asner
CEO: Marcie Greene
COO: Ray Chicoine
*CFO: Marvin Gordon MD
CFO: Amy Park
*VP: Jay J Cohen MD
*VP: Steven Rudy MD
Ex Dir: Colin Leclair
Snr Ntwrk: Bryant Marsh
CIO: Wayne Sass
*CIO: James Selevan MD

MONARCH LANDING
See SENIOR NAPERVILLE CARE LLC

D-U-N-S 08-432-1462
MONARCH LITHO INC (CA)
1501 Date St, Montebello, CA 90640-6324
Tel (323) 727-0300 Founded/Ownrshp 1974
Sales 57.1MM^E EMP 275
SIC 2752 Commercial printing, offset; Advertising posters, lithographed; Commercial printing, offset; Advertising posters, lithographed
Pr: Robert Lopez
Sec: Victor Neri
VP: George Lopez
MIS Dir: Gary Sakata
Dir IT: Mariano Balbuena
Plnt Mgr: Carlos Lopez
Sales Exec: Alejandro Estevez
Sales Exec: Maia Giordani
Sales Exec: Javier Gomez
Sales Exec: Debbie Hughes
Sls&Mrk Ex: Marquita Clark

D-U-N-S 82-827-0996
MONARCH LLC
7050 N 76th St, Milwaukee, WI 53223-5006
Tel (414) 353-8820 Founded/Ownrshp 2007
Sales 24.4MM^E EMP 78
SIC 3315 Steel wire & related products; Steel wire & related products
Pr: David Mitchell
Sls Mgr: Paul Schultz

D-U-N-S 03-183-0112
MONARCH MONTESSORI OF DENVER
4895 Peoria St, Denver, CO 80239-2847
Tel (303) 565-4165 Founded/Ownrshp 2010
Sales 30.4MM EMP 35^E
Accts John Cutler & Ssociates Llc D
SIC 8351 Montessori child development center
Owner: Jessica Bidlingmaier
Assoc Dir: Noel Giametta
Pgrm Dir: Tammi Mobley

D-U-N-S 95-708-7146
MONARCH MORTGAGE
300 32nd St Ste 200, Virginia Beach, VA 23451-2968
Tel (757) 390-2200 Founded/Ownrshp 2008
Sales NA EMP 640
SIC 6162 Mortgage bankers & correspondents; Mortgage bankers & correspondents
CEO: Will Morrison
Pr: Jack Lane
Ofcr: Dan Hughes
Manager: R Lindley

MONARCH MOUNTAIN
See POWDER MONARCH LLC

D-U-N-S 03-660-4478 IMP/EXP
MONARCH NUT CO LLC (CA)
MUNGER FARMS
786 Road 188, Delano, CA 93215-9508
Tel (661) 720-2746 Founded/Ownrshp 1986
Sales 50.5MM^E EMP 250
SIC 0723 Tree nuts (general) hulling & shelling services; Tree nuts (general) hulling & shelling services
Owner: David Munger
CFO: Albert Arkush
*VP: Kamie Munger
QA Dir: Andy Garcia
Opers Mgr: Maz Ahmadi

D-U-N-S 93-291-5242
■ MONARCH PHARMACEUTICALS INC
(Suby of KING PHARMACEUTICALS LLC) ★
501 5th St, Bristol, TN 37620-2304
Tel (423) 989-6200 Founded/Ownrshp 1994
Sales 39.6MM^E EMP 667
SIC 5961 Pharmaceuticals, mail order; Pharmaceuticals, mail order
Pr: Joe Gregory
Pr: Michael Davis
Treas: Randy Sharrow
VP: Dean Slack

D-U-N-S 03-066-4619 IMP
MONARCH PLASTICS INC
1205 65th St, Kenosha, WI 53143-5076
Tel (262) 652-4444 Founded/Ownrshp 1982
Sales 21.4MM^E EMP 90
SIC 3085 Plastics bottles
Pr: Hemang Mehta
*Pr: Eric De Souza
*CEO: Kristal Gideon
*Sec: Rui Pinto
VP: Debra N Caskey
VP: Raj Desai
Exec: Eric Desouza
VP Sls: Sheldon Hirshman

D-U-N-S 00-254-0438 IMP
MONARCH STEEL CO INC (OH)
(Suby of AMERICAN CONSOLIDATED INDUSTRIES INC) ★
4650 Johnston Pkwy, Cleveland, OH 44128-3219
Tel (216) 587-8000 Founded/Ownrshp 1934, 1986
Sales 43.3MM^E EMP 40
SIC 5051 Metals service centers & offices
CEO: Josh Kaufman
*Pr: Robert L Meyer
CFO: Sue Freedland
*CFO: Steve Lefkowitz
Mtls Mgr: Nino Frostino
Plnt Mgr: Phil Stidham
Ql Cn Mgr: Mark Yahraus
Sls Mgr: Jon Campbell

D-U-N-S 55-659-7693
MONARCH STEEL OF ALABAMA INC
(Suby of AMERICAN CONSOLIDATED INDUSTRIES INC) ★
1425 Red Hat Rd, Decatur, AL 35601-7588
Tel (256) 301-5730 Founded/Ownrshp 1999
Sales 28.5MM^E EMP 55
SIC 5051 Metals service centers & offices
CEO: Josh Kaufman
*Pr: Robert L Meyer
*CFO: Steve Lefkowitz

D-U-N-S 00-801-4862 IMP/EXP
MONARCH TILE INC
834 Rickwood Rd, Florence, AL 35630-1372
Tel (256) 764-6181 Founded/Ownrshp 1946, 2011
Sales 31.5MM^E EMP 240
SIC 3253 Wall tile, ceramic; Wall tile, ceramic
Ch Bd: Garrison Kitchen
Pr: Daniel Lasky
VP: John N Turley
Exec: Mike Willis
Board of Directors: Edwin A Wahlen Jr

MONARCH WINDOW
See WINDSOR WINDOW CO

MONARK MARINE
See STARCRAFT MARINE LLC

D-U-N-S 61-341-3934 IMP/EXP
MONAVIE LLC
(Suby of JEUNESSE GLOBAL HOLDINGS LLC) ★
10855 S River Front Pkwy # 100, South Jordan, UT 84095-5763
Tel (801) 748-3100 Founded/Ownrshp 2015
Sales 94.0MM^E EMP 400^E
SIC 5963 Juices; Direct selling establishments
Pr: Mauricio Bellora
*V Ch: Randy Larsen
*COO: Dell Brown
*COO: Walter Noot
CFO: Sandy Darlington
*CFO: James Marsh
*Ch: Henry Marsh
*Chf Mktg O: Paul Muehlmann
VP: Doug Allen
VP: Jeff Graham
VP: Katy Holt-Larsen
VP: Lance Smith
VP: Shawn Talbott
Exec: Tate Tinley
Dir Soc: Kim Parkinson
Creative D: Kurt Gray

D-U-N-S 96-751-0400
MONCLA MARINE OPERATIONS LLC
2107 Carmel Dr, Lafayette, LA 70501-5449
Tel (337) 456-8799 Founded/Ownrshp 2010
Sales 40.0MM EMP 200
SIC 7699 Boat repair; Boat repair

D-U-N-S 96-751-5177
MONCLA WORKOVER & DRILLING OPERATIONS LLC
2107 Carmel Dr, Lafayette, LA 70501-5449
Tel (337) 456-8799 Founded/Ownrshp 2010
Sales 34.6MM^E EMP 200
SIC 3533 Drill rigs; Drill rigs

D-U-N-S 09-901-8244
MONCO ENTERPRISES INC
1507 Kuntz Rd, Dayton, OH 45404-1232
Tel (937) 461-0034 Founded/Ownrshp 1970
Sales 326.9M EMP 850
SIC 8331 2789 Sheltered workshop; Community service employment training program; Bookbinding & related work; Sheltered workshop; Community service employment training program; Bookbinding & related work
Genl Mgr: Phil Hartje
IT Man: Tom Digiovanna

D-U-N-S 61-035-1913
MONDAY PROPERTIES SERVICES LLC
667 Madison Ave Fl 19, New York, NY 10065-8029
Tel (212) 490-7100 Founded/Ownrshp 2005
Sales 57.8MM^E EMP 250
SIC 6531

D-U-N-S 07-860-5713 EXP
■ MONDELEZ GLOBAL LLC
(Suby of MONDELEZ INTERNATIONAL INC) ★
3 Parkway N Ste 300, Deerfield, IL 60015-2565
Tel (847) 943-4000 Founded/Ownrshp 2012
Sales 3.8MMM^E EMP 14,430
SIC 2022 Processed cheese; Processed cheese

D-U-N-S 87-714-7228 IMP/EXP
▲ MONDELEZ INTERNATIONAL INC
3 Parkway N Ste 300, Deerfield, IL 60015-2565
Tel (847) 943-4000 Founded/Ownrshp 2000
Sales 34.2MMM EMP 107,000
Tkr Sym MDLZ Exch NGS
SIC 2022 2013 2095 2043 2035 2087 Processed cheese; Natural cheese; Spreads, cheese; Dips, cheese-based; Sausages & other prepared meats; Bacon, side & sliced: from purchased meat; Frankfurters from purchased meat; Luncheon meat from purchased meat; Coffee roasting (except by wholesale grocers); Freeze-dried coffee; Instant coffee; Cereal breakfast foods; Dressings, salad: raw & cooked (except dry mixes); Powders, drink; Processed cheese; Natural cheese; Spreads, cheese; Dips, cheese-based; Sausages & other prepared meats; Bacon, side & sliced: from purchased meat; Frankfurters from purchased meat; Luncheon meat from purchased meat; Coffee roasting (except by wholesale grocers); Freeze-dried coffee; Instant coffee; Cereal breakfast foods; Dressings, salad: raw & cooked (except dry mixes); Powders, drink
CEO: Irene B Rosenfeld
COO: Roberta Phillippi
CFO: B Chiasson
*CFO: Brian T Gladden
Bd of Dir: Karel Culik
Ex VP: Marc S Firestone
Ex VP: Marc S Firestone
*Ex VP: Karen J May
Ex VP: Michael Osanloo
*Ex VP: Gerhard W Pleuhs
*Ex VP: Mary Beth West
Sr VP: Richard A Bailey
Sr VP: John J Becker
Sr VP: Douglas A Burns
Sr VP: Gary Chan
Sr VP: Piet Claus
Sr VP: Marcia E Glenn
Sr VP: Philip A Hodges
Sr VP: Rhonda L Jordon
Sr VP: Robert M Levi
Sr VP: Frederick Schaeffer
Board of Directors: Ruth J Simmons, Stephen F Bollenbach, Lewis W K Booth, Lois D Juliber, Mark D Ketchum, Jorge S Mewquita, Joseph Neubauer, Nelson Peltz, Fredric G Reynolds, Patrick T Siewert

D-U-N-S 09-003-6302 IMP/EXP
■ MONDELEZ PUERTO RICO LLC
KRAFT FOODS
(Suby of MONDELEZ GLOBAL LLC) ★
9615 Ave Los Romeros # 801, San Juan, PR 00926-7036
Tel (787) 522-9810 Founded/Ownrshp 1959, 2012
Sales 74.9MM^E EMP 150
SIC 5141 Groceries, general line; Groceries, general line

D-U-N-S 61-828-6889 IMP
MONDI AKROSIL LLC
(Suby of MONDI FRANTSCHACH GMBH)
7201 108th St, Pleasant Prairie, WI 53158-2912
Tel (262) 947-3371 Founded/Ownrshp 2005
Sales 59.6MM^E EMP 180^E
SIC 2679 Paper products, converted; Paper products, converted
CEO: David Hathorn
CFO: Andrew King
Exec: Monica Askelson

D-U-N-S 07-950-3347
MONDI BAGS USA LLC
(Suby of MONDI FRANTSCHACH GMBH)
281 Hemphill Blvd, Eastman, GA 31023-8293
Tel (478) 374-7032 Founded/Ownrshp 2014
Sales 349.9MM^E EMP 2,000
SIC 2393 2621 Textile bags; Paper mills; Textile bags; Paper mills
Pr: Allen Ennis
*COO: Thomas Ott
VP: Peter Ritten

D-U-N-S 07-980-0940
MONDI BAGS USA LLC
MONDI PAPER SALES NORTH AMER
1230 Peachtree St Ne # 19, Atlanta, GA 30309-3574
Tel (770) 243-5410 Founded/Ownrshp 2002
Sales 553.1MM^E EMP 1,288^E

SIC 2621 Packaging paper
CEO: David Hathorn
*CFO: Andrew King

D-U-N-S 61-162-6524 IMP/EXP
MONDI JACKSON LLC
(Suby of MONDI GRONAU GMBH)
14591 State Highway 177, Jackson, MO 63755-8309
Tel (573) 335-4900 Founded/Ownrshp 2014
Sales 201.6MM^E EMP 415
SIC 2671 Plastic film, coated or laminated for packaging; Wrapping paper, waterproof or coated; Plastic film, coated or laminated for packaging; Wrapping paper, waterproof or coated
Pr: Kevin Young
V Ch: Andreas Picolin
*VP: David Gonzales
Ex Dir: Fred Himpelmann
CIO: Chris Davis
Web Dev: Jim Ostergaard
VP Opers: Pat Klein
VP Opers: Patrick Pat
Opers Mgr: Mark Higgins
Opers Mgr: Jeff Kitzner
Ql Cn Mgr: Kent Zimmerman

MONDI PAPER SALES NORTH AMER
See MONDI BAGS USA LLC

D-U-N-S 01-312-1335 IMP/EXP
MONDI ROMEOVILLE INC
(Suby of MONDI FRANTSCHACH GMBH)
1140 Arbor Dr, Romeoville, IL 60446-1188
Tel (630) 378-9886 Founded/Ownrshp 2003, 2005
Sales 23.2MM^E EMP 67^E
SIC 2674 Bags: uncoated paper & multiwall
Opers Mgr: Rick Jones

MONDIAL RISK MANAGEMENT CO
See PAX MONDIAL LLC

D-U-N-S 07-963-0173
MONDO INTERNATIONAL LLC
(Suby of BLUE WOLF GROUP LLC) ★
102 Madison Ave Fl 7, New York, NY 10016-7417
Tel (212) 257-5111 Founded/Ownrshp 2000, 2014
Sales 6.6MM^E EMP 450
SIC 7363 Help supply services; Help supply services
CEO: Michael Kirven

D-U-N-S 07-987-1390
MONEERO INC
1900 Addison St Ste 200, Berkeley, CA 94704-1161
Tel (702) 859-9402 Founded/Ownrshp 2015
Sales 50.0MM EMP 1
SIC 7371 7389 Computer software development & applications;
Pr: Steven Morell

D-U-N-S 00-456-9047
MONERIS SOLUTIONS INC
(Suby of MONERIS SOLUTIONS CORPORATION)
150 N Martingale Rd # 900, Schaumburg, IL 60173-2081
Tel (847) 240-6600 Founded/Ownrshp 2000
Sales NA EMP 102
SIC 6153 Credit card services, central agency collection
CEO: James Baumgartner
*Pr: Larry Wine
*CFO: Claudio Debon
CFO: Samir Zabaneh
*Sr VP: Patrick Albright
*Sr VP: Deb Koontz
Sr VP: Gregory A Leos
Sr VP: David Magley
*Sr VP: J Brian Merena
Sr VP: Joseph Radest
VP Sls: Jeff Fogel

D-U-N-S 86-781-4444 IMP/EXP
■ **MONESSEN HEARTH SYSTEMS CO**
VERMONT CASTINGS GROUP
(Suby of HNI CORP) ★
149 Cleveland Dr, Paris, KY 40361-9782
Tel (859) 987-0740 Founded/Ownrshp 2014
Sales 159.5MM^E EMP 500
SIC 3433 Logs, gas fireplace; Room & wall heaters, including radiators; Logs, gas fireplace; Room & wall heaters, including radiators
Pr: Ricardo Leon
COO: Michael Carr
*CFO: Jacob Reuben

D-U-N-S 07-857-9871 IMP
MONESSEN HOLDING CO LLC
149 Cleveland Dr, Paris, KY 40361-9782
Tel (859) 987-0740 Founded/Ownrshp 1997
Sales 56.0MM^E EMP 750
SIC 3433 Heating equipment, except electric; Heating equipment, except electric; Logs, gas fireplace; Room & wall heaters, including radiators
CEO: Daniel Clifford
*Pr: Ricardo Leon

D-U-N-S 04-859-8879
MONETA GROUP INVESTMENT ADVISORS INC
100 S Brentwood Blvd # 500, Saint Louis, MO 63105-1649
Tel (314) 726-2300 Founded/Ownrshp 1991
Sales 21.1MM^E EMP 142
SIC 6282 Investment advisory service; Investment advisory service
Pr: Peter Schick
*COO: Joseph Sheehan

D-U-N-S 06-965-0075
MONETA GROUP LLC
100 S Brentwood Blvd # 500, Saint Louis, MO 63105-1649
Tel (314) 726-2300 Founded/Ownrshp 2005
Sales 69.2MM EMP 240
SIC 8742 Financial consultant; Financial consultant
CEO: Gene Diederich
COO: Chris Whiting
CFO: Julie Sward
Ofcr: Nathan Howard
Comm Man: Emily Barlean
Off Mgr: Leslie Hahn
Sftwr Eng: Julia Shah
Sftwr Eng: Matt Turner
Opers Mgr: Kate Parker
Opers Mgr: Teresa Spring

D-U-N-S 87-980-5299
MONETARY MANAGEMENT OF CA INC
MONEY MART
(Suby of DOLLAR FINANCIAL GROUP INC) ★
1436 Lancaster Ave, Berwyn, PA 19312-1200
Tel (610) 296-3400 Founded/Ownrshp 1990
Sales NA EMP 510
SIC 6099 Check cashing agencies; Check cashing agencies
Pr: Gary Wheihart
*Ch Bd: Randy Underwood
*CFO: Jeffrey Weiss

D-U-N-S 02-636-1066
MONETATE INC
951 E Hector St, Conshohocken, PA 19428-2307
Tel (877) 666-3828 Founded/Ownrshp 2008
Sales 21.0MM^E EMP 65^E
SIC 7374 Computer graphics service
CEO: Lucinda Duncalfe
Ch Bd: David Brussin
COO: John Healy
CFO: Bob Lawson
CFO: Collin McHugh
Sr VP: Scott Rogers
VP: Steve Brescia
VP: Michelle Curless
VP: Bruce Ernst
VP: Mike Harris
VP: Dave Swarthout
Exec: Eric Palumbo
Exec: Jessica Ruth
Board of Directors: Tim Kopp, Tim Maudlin

D-U-N-S 05-339-3088
MONETT R-1 SCHOOL DISTRICT
900 E Scott St, Monett, MO 65708-1782
Tel (417) 235-7422 Founded/Ownrshp 1911
Sales 14.5MM^E EMP 300
SIC 8211 School board; School board
Schl Brd P: Doug Childress
HC Dir: Kristen Earnest
HC Dir: Carol Hamm

MONEY BACK
See MCDONALD OIL CO INC

MONEY BOX, THE
See MONEY STORE L P

D-U-N-S 09-822-8810
MONEY MAILER LLC
MM ADVERTISING
(Suby of ROARK CAPITAL GROUP INC) ★
12131 Western Ave, Garden Grove, CA 92841-2914
Tel (714) 889-3800 Founded/Ownrshp 2011
Sales 57.6MM^E EMP 445
SIC 7331 6794 Mailing service; Franchises, selling or licensing; Mailing service; Franchises, selling or licensing
Pr: Joe Craciun
Sr VP: Mike Hiskett
Sr VP: John Sabo
VP: Brandy Barney
VP: Tom Cimino
VP: Doug Cunningham
VP: Stephen Lee
VP: Holly Riley
Dir Bus: Mike Lacombe
Area Mgr: Rick Christman
Area Mgr: Vicky Evans

D-U-N-S 01-023-6532
MONEY MANAGEMENT INTERNATIONAL INC
M M I
14141 Southwest Fwy # 1000, Sugar Land, TX 77478-3494
Tel (713) 923-2227 Founded/Ownrshp 1997
Sales 73.6MM EMP 1,100
SIC 7389 Financial services; Financial services
Pr: Ivan L Hand Jr
*Ch Bd: Scot Sheldon
*CFO: David Juengel
Ex VP: Ann Morris
*VP: Chuck Stanley
VP Opers: Kandee Jahns
S&M/VP: Alan Olinger

D-U-N-S 02-053-2836
MONEY MAP PRESS LLC (MD)
(Suby of AGORA INC) ★
16 W Madison St, Baltimore, MD 21201-5231
Tel (410) 864-0154 Founded/Ownrshp 2007
Sales 35.0MM EMP 55
SIC 2741 Miscellaneous publishing; Miscellaneous publishing
VP: Alex Williams
Ex Dir: Bret Holmes
Mktg Dir: Danielle O'Dell
Assoc Ed: Christopher Skokna

MONEY MART
See MONETARY MANAGEMENT OF CA INC

D-U-N-S 14-444-6556
■ **MONEY STORE INVESTMENT CORP**
(Suby of HOMEQ SERVICING CORP) ★
707 3rd St, West Sacramento, CA 95605-2811
Tel (916) 441-7700 Founded/Ownrshp 1979
Sales NA EMP 1^E
SIC 6163 Agents, farm or business loan
CEO: Bill Templeton
*Pr: Paul Leliakov
*Ex VP: Morton Dear
Ex VP: Sumit Sen
Sr VP: Daryl Carlson
VP: Jim Teufel

D-U-N-S 08-253-7598
MONEY STORE L P
MONEY BOX, THE
(Suby of SPEEDY CASH HOLDINGS CORP) ★
1114 Lost Creek Blvd # 125, Austin, TX 78746-6175
Tel (512) 306-0341 Founded/Ownrshp 2013
Sales NA EMP 285
SIC 6099 Check cashing agencies; Money order issuance; Check cashing agencies; Money order issuance
CEO: James Rickenbacker

D-U-N-S 18-853-1532
MONEY TREE INC
114 S Broad St, Bainbridge, GA 39817-3614
Tel (229) 246-6536 Founded/Ownrshp 1984
Sales NA EMP 300^E
SIC 6141 Personal credit institutions; Personal credit institutions
Ch Bd: Bradley D Bellville
CFO: Steven P Morrison
VP: Karen V Harrell
VP: Clayton Penhallegon
VP Admn: D Michael Wallace

MONEYGRAM INTERNATIONAL
See MONEYGRAM PAYMENT SYSTEMS INC

D-U-N-S 14-579-1997
▲ **MONEYGRAM INTERNATIONAL INC**
2828 N Harwood St Fl 15, Dallas, TX 75201-1518
Tel (214) 999-7552 Founded/Ownrshp 1940
Sales NA EMP 2,727^E
Tkr Sym MGI Exch NGS
SIC 6099 Electronic funds transfer network, including switching; Money order issuance; Electronic funds transfer network, including switching; Money order issuance
Ch Bd: Pamela H Patsley
COO: W Alexander Holmes
Treas: Jeff Shonty
Chf Cred: Phyllis J Skene-Stimac
Chf Mktg O: Juan Agualimpia
Ofcr: Jack Chau
Ofcr: Pablo Rivera
Ofcr: William Shen
Ofcr: Alvaro Velez
Ex VP: Francis Aaron Henry
Ex VP: W Alexander Hoffmann
Ex VP: Alice V Kirk
Ex VP: Grant A Lines
Ex VP: Peter E Ohser
Ex VP: Steven Piano
Sr VP: Larry Angelilli
Sr VP: Kim Heavey-Garner
Sr VP: Angela M McQuien
VP: Ruth Dessel
VP: Nick Flint
VP: Aaron Henry
Board of Directors: J Coley Clark, Victor W Dahir, Antonio O Garza, Seth W Lawry, W Bruce Turner, Peggy Vaughan

D-U-N-S 00-645-4151
■ **MONEYGRAM PAYMENT SYSTEMS INC**
MONEYGRAM INTERNATIONAL
(Suby of MONEYGRAM INTERNATIONAL INC) ★
1550 Utica Ave S Ste 100, Minneapolis, MN 55416-5300
Tel (952) 591-3000 Founded/Ownrshp 1940
Sales NA EMP 1,650
SIC 6099 7389 Money order issuance; Electronic funds transfer network, including switching; Financial services; Money order issuance; Electronic funds transfer network, including switching; Financial services
CEO: Philip Milne
*CEO: Pamela H Patsley
*COO: Anthony Ryan
Bd of Dir: Victor Dahir
Bd of Dir: W Turner
Chf Mktg O: Juan Agualimpia
Ofcr: Deb Guertin
Ex VP: David Albright
Ex VP: Timothy C Everett
Ex VP: Teresa H Johnson
Ex VP: Daniel J Omalley
Ex VP: Steve Piano
VP: Massimo Canovi
VP: Michael Daugherty
VP: Keith Fulton
VP: Robert W Glaus
VP: Joe Steiger
VP: Dennis Wildsmith
VP: J Wimer
Exec: Eleni Chanioti
Board of Directors: Robert H Bohannon, Ronald G Nelson

MONEYLINE LENDING SERVICES
See GENPACT MORTGAGE SERVICES INC

D-U-N-S 10-288-4194
MONEYTREE INC
6720 Fort Dent Way # 230, Tukwila, WA 98188-8508
Tel (206) 246-3500 Founded/Ownrshp 1983
Sales NA EMP 750
SIC 6099 Check cashing agencies; Check cashing agencies
Pr: Agartha Sylvia Clark
*CEO: Dennis Bassford
COO: Chris Kiely
*CFO: Rob Grover
Treas: Sara Bassford
*Ex VP: David Bassford
Sr VP: Tom King
Dept Mgr: Philip Clark
Brnch Mgr: Danny Arguello
Brnch Mgr: Sarah Barker
Brnch Mgr: Richard Baze

D-U-N-S 19-358-7925
MONGIELLOS ITALIAN CHEESE SPECIALTIES LLC
FORMAGGIO ITALIAN CHEESE
250 Hilldale Rd, Hurleyville, NY 12747-5301
Tel (845) 436-4200 Founded/Ownrshp 2001
Sales 25.6MM EMP 150
SIC 2022 Natural cheese; Natural cheese
CEO: Anthony Mongiello
COO: John Mongiello
CTO: Chris Lokke

D-U-N-S 00-377-0532
MONGODB INC
(Suby of MONGODB AUSTRALIA PTY LTD)
229 W 43rd St Fl 5, New York, NY 10036-3982
Tel (866) 237-8815 Founded/Ownrshp 2007
Sales 34.1MM^E EMP 100
SIC 7373 Systems software development services; Systems software development services
CEO: Max Schireson
*Ch Bd: Dwight Merriman
*CFO: Michael Gordon
*Ofcr: Carlos Delatorre
*Ofcr: Meagen Eisenberg
*Sr VP: Philip Carty
Sr VP: Michael Cohn
Sr VP: Carol Glover
Sr VP: Dennis Wall
*VP: Matt Asay
*VP: Ron Avnur
VP: Kevin Cox
VP: Paul Cross
*VP: Kurt Daniel
VP: Andrew Erlichson
VP: Darren Linscott
VP: Jason Little
VP: David Perry
Exec: Dev Ittycheria
Dir Soc: Katie Chapin
Board of Directors: Tom Killalea

D-U-N-S 79-689-2362
MONGOLIAN OPERATING CO LLC
BD'S MONGOLIAN GRILL
200 E Travelers Trl # 235, Burnsville, MN 55337-4192
Tel (952) 288-2363 Founded/Ownrshp 1992
Sales 29.6MM^E EMP 950^E
SIC 5812 6794 Buffet (eating places); Buffet (eating places); Franchises, selling or licensing
CFO: William T Downs III
COO: Todd Pahl
CFO: Becky Moldenhauer

D-U-N-S 10-218-7408
MONICAL PIZZA CORP
530 N Kinzie Ave, Bradley, IL 60915-1225
Tel (815) 937-1890 Founded/Ownrshp 1982
Sales 45.3MM^E EMP 1,000
SIC 5812 Pizzeria, chain; Pizzeria, chain
Pr: Janelle L Reents
*Pr: Harry Bond
COO: Donna Jakob
CTO: Todd Hallberg
MIS Dir: Dawn Savoie
IT Man: Mike Pelletier
Opers Mgr: Doug Davis

D-U-N-S 09-838-4647 IMP/EXP
MONICO ALLOYS INC
3039 E Ana St, Compton, CA 90221-5604
Tel (310) 928-0168 Founded/Ownrshp 1979
Sales 46.0MM^E EMP 98
SIC 5051 Metals service centers & offices; Metals service centers & offices
CEO: Barbara Zenk
*Pr: Jason D Zenk
*CFO: Saul Zenk
*Sr VP: Ken Larson
*VP: Bruce Botansky
Plnt Mgr: Ramon Barajas

D-U-N-S 16-197-8440
MONICO INC
2703 Bernice Rd, Lansing, IL 60438-1011
Tel (708) 474-8300 Founded/Ownrshp 1969
Sales 75.5MM^E EMP 150^E
Accts Mcgladrey & Pullen
SIC 1711 1731 Mechanical contractor; General electrical contractor; Mechanical contractor; General electrical contractor
Pr: John D Curran
*Sec: Stephen Curran

MONIN GOURMET FLAVORINGS
See MONIN INC

D-U-N-S 80-525-2459 IMP/EXP
MONIN INC
MONIN GOURMET FLAVORINGS
(Suby of GEORGES MONIN SAS)
2100 Range Rd, Clearwater, FL 33765-2125
Tel (727) 461-3033 Founded/Ownrshp 1912
Sales 68.0MM EMP 123
SIC 2087 Flavoring extracts & syrups; Flavoring extracts & syrups
CEO: William Lombardo
*Pr: Olivier Monin
CFO: Greg Grabau
Sr VP: Terri Casey
VP: J J Jones
VP: John Koch
Genl Mgr: Jeremy Coulbeck
Software D: Steve Sirulnick
Opers Mgr: Ty Hartigan
Opers Mgr: Doug Pray
Natl Sales: Steven Bishop

D-U-N-S 95-864-0047
MONIQUE LHUILLIER INC
4533 Pacific Blvd, Vernon, CA 90058-2207
Tel (213) 747-8811 Founded/Ownrshp 1996
Sales 22.5MM^E EMP 120
SIC 2335 Bridal & formal gowns; Bridal & formal gowns
Pr: Tom Bugbee
VP: Dawn Bromander
VP: Gwen Thayer
Opers Mgr: Christin Anonuevo
Opers Mgr: Hannah Ham
Sales Exec: Brieanne Cameron
VP Sls: Stephanie Mah
Sls Mgr: Rachel Zimmermann
Sales Asso: Alison Hinkley
Sales Asso: Midori Inoue
Sales Asso: Sharon Sless

D-U-N-S 83-511-7698
MONITECH INC
215 Southport Dr Ste 400, Morrisville, NC 27560-8439
Tel (919) 459-1700 *Founded/Ownrshp* 1989
Sales 28.3MM^E *EMP* 70
SIC 5084 Instruments & control equipment; Instruments & control equipment
Pr: Jerry Mobley
**Pr:* John S Stump
Snr Mgr: M P Hariharan

MONITOR, THE
See AIM MEDIA TEXAS OPERATING LLC

D-U-N-S 18-645-1431
MONITOR BUILDERS INC
225 Friend St Fl 3, Boston, MA 02114-1897
Tel (617) 523-9300 *Founded/Ownrshp* 1988
Sales 21.0MM *EMP* 11
Accts Mcgladrey & Pullen Llp Burli
SIC 8741 8742 Construction management; Construction project management consultant; Construction management; Construction project management consultant
Pr: John Hughes
**Treas:* John Weaver
**VP:* Michael Kessler
**VP:* Marie Lesperance
**VP:* John Zychowicz Jr

D-U-N-S 96-536-8421
MONITOR CLIPPER PARTNERS LLC
116 Huntington Ave Ste 9, Boston, MA 02116-5749
Tel (617) 638-1100 *Founded/Ownrshp* 2004
Sales 103.5MM^E *EMP* 406^E
SIC 6799 Investors
CFO: April Evans
**VP:* Julia Monfrini Peev
**VP:* Matt Stone
Mng Dir: Peter S Laino

D-U-N-S 79-447-4320
■ **MONITOR LIABILITY MANAGERS INC**
(*Suby of* W R BERKLEY CORP) ★
233 S Wacker Dr Ste 3900, Chicago, IL 60606-6380
Tel (847) 806-6590 *Founded/Ownrshp* 1992
Sales NA *EMP* 115
SIC 6331 Fire, marine & casualty insurance
CEO: Douglas J Powers
**Pr:* Joseph G Shores
**CFO:* Peter A Lindquist
Ex VP: Diane Cummings
VP: Valerie Foster
VP: Todd Hampton
**VP:* James E Hill
VP: Craig Musgrave
**VP:* Paul E Sowadski
Snr Sftwr: Kevin Sheasgreen

D-U-N-S 19-645-7873
■ **MONITRONICS INTERNATIONAL INC**
(*Suby of* ASCENT CAPITAL GROUP INC) ★
1990 Wittington Pl, Dallas, TX 75234-1904
Tel (972) 243-7443 *Founded/Ownrshp* 2010
Sales 534.4MM *EMP* 923^E
SIC 7382 1731 Burglar alarm maintenance & monitoring; Electrical work; Burglar alarm maintenance & monitoring; Electrical work
Pr: Mike Haislip
Pr: Monica Taylor
**CFO:* Michael Meyers
**Treas:* David Verret
**VP:* Darin Anderson
VP: Rick Hudson
VP: Rick L Hudson
**VP:* Frank McGhee
VP: John Mejia
**VP:* Bruce Mungiguerra
VP: Robert N Sherman
VP: Phyllis Turner

D-U-N-S 96-922-3929
MONMOUTH COLLEGE
700 E Broadway, Monmouth, IL 61462-1998
Tel (309) 457-2124 *Founded/Ownrshp* 1857
Sales 56.8MM *EMP* 280
Accts Clifton Gunderson Peoria Ill
SIC 8221 Colleges universities & professional schools; Colleges universities & professional schools
Pr: Mauri Ditzler
**Ch:* David Byrnes
**VP:* Donald Gladfelter

D-U-N-S 05-423-5259
MONMOUTH COLLEGE ALUMNI ASSOCIATION
700 E Broadway, Monmouth, IL 61462-1998
Tel (309) 457-2345 *Founded/Ownrshp* 1853
Sales 60.3MM *EMP* 300
SIC 8221 University; University
Pr: Mauri Dizler
**VP:* Don Gladfelder
Prd Mgr: Kim Fornero

MONMOUTH COUNTY
See COUNTY OF MONMOUTH

D-U-N-S 10-060-5807
MONMOUTH COUNTY VOCATIONAL SCHOOL DISTRICT
4000 Kozloski Rd, Freehold, NJ 07728-4364
Tel (732) 431-7942 *Founded/Ownrshp* 1960
Sales 44.5MM *EMP* 520
SIC 8211 9111 Public vocational/technical school; County supervisors' & executives' offices; Public vocational/technical school; County supervisors' & executives' offices
Teacher Pr: Arlene Foreman

D-U-N-S 04-987-5636
MONMOUTH MEDICAL CENTER INC
300 2nd Ave, Long Branch, NJ 07740-6395
Tel (732) 222-5200 *Founded/Ownrshp* 1889
Sales 355.2MM *EMP* 2,400
Accts Withumsmithbrown Pc Morristow
SIC 8062 Hospital, AMA approved residency; Hospital, AMA approved residency
Ex Dir: Frank Vozos
CFO: David McClung
VP: Tara Kelly
Dir Risk M: Patricia Keating
Dir Rad: Patricia Derosa
Dir Rx: Julie Saleh
Adm Dir: Shirley S Hwang
CIO: Kathryn Collins
CTO: Thomas Bartiromo
Telecom Mg: Brian Keene
IT Man: Dominic Hart

D-U-N-S 00-530-1721
MONMOUTH MEDICAL GROUP PC (NJ)
223 Monmouth Rd Ste 1a, West Long Branch, NJ 07764-1024
Tel (732) 229-3838 *Founded/Ownrshp* 1995
Sales 38.1MM *EMP* 27
Accts Withum Smith Brown Pc Morrist
SIC 8011 Internal medicine, physician/surgeon; Internal medicine, physician/surgeon
Pr: Eric N Burkett MD
CFO: Ivette Yatcilla

D-U-N-S 10-169-3844
MONMOUTH OCEAN EDUCATIONAL SERVICES COMMISSION
M-OESC
100 Tornillo Way Ste 1, Tinton Falls, NJ 07712-7512
Tel (732) 389-5555 *Founded/Ownrshp* 1979
Sales 34.0MM *EMP* 500
SIC 8299 8211 8741 Educational services; Elementary & secondary schools; Management services; Educational services; Elementary & secondary schools; Management services

MONMOUTH PARK RACETRACK
See NEW JERSEY SPORTS & EXPOSITION AUTHORITY

D-U-N-S 06-313-7061
MONMOUTH REAL ESTATE INVESTMENT CORP
3499 Route 9 N Ste 3d, Freehold, NJ 07728-3277
Tel (732) 577-9996 *Founded/Ownrshp* 1968
Sales 78.0MM *EMP* 15
Accts Pkf O Connor Davies Llp New Y
SIC 6798 Real estate investment trusts; Real estate investment trusts
Pr: Michael P Landy
**Ch Bd:* Eugene W Landy
CFO: Kevin S Miller
**Treas:* Anna T Chew
VP: Susan M Jordan
VP: Richard P Molke
Genl Couns: Allison Nagelberg

D-U-N-S 03-719-1152
MONMOUTH REGIONAL HIGH SCHOOL BOARD OF EDUCATION
MONMOUTH RGIONAL HIGH SCHL DST
1 Norman J Field Way, Tinton Falls, NJ 07724-3299
Tel (732) 542-5815 *Founded/Ownrshp* 1957
Sales 25.0MM *EMP* 180
SIC 8211 Public senior high school; Public senior high school
Prin: Charles Ford Jr
Prin: William George
**Prin:* Andy Teeple

MONMOUTH RGIONAL HIGH SCHL DST
See MONMOUTH REGIONAL HIGH SCHOOL BOARD OF EDUCATION

D-U-N-S 36-186-7088
MONMOUTH UNIVERSITY
400 Cedar Ave, West Long Branch, NJ 07764-1898
Tel (732) 571-3400 *Founded/Ownrshp* 1948
Sales 171.1MM *EMP* 1,000^E
Accts Kpmg Llp Short Hills Nj
SIC 8221 Colleges universities & professional schools; Colleges universities & professional schools
Pr: Paul G Gaffney II
V Ch: Alfred J Schiavetti
**Pr:* Paul Brown PHD
Trst: Monica M Sweeney
Ofcr: Tracy Turner
VP: William Craig
VP: Thomas S Pearson
VP: John Sonn
Exec: Barbara Growney
Admn Mgr: Nikki Reed
DP Exec: Barbara Nitzberg

D-U-N-S 11-921-5580
MONMOUTH-OCEAN HOSPITAL SERVICE CORP
MONOC
4806 Megill Rd, Wall Township, NJ 07753-6926
Tel (732) 919-3045 *Founded/Ownrshp* 1984
Sales 42.5MM *EMP* 400
Accts Withumsmithbrown Pc New Bruns
SIC 4119 8742 Local passenger transportation; Hospital & health services consultant; Local passenger transportation; Hospital & health services consultant
Pr: Vincent Robbins
**Ch Bd:* Joseph Coyle
**CFO:* Brian Hector
**Treas:* Frank Vozos
**V Ch Bd:* John Gribbin
Ofcr: Laurie Rovan
VP: Phil Bryant
Trfc Dir: Nick Bissel

D-U-N-S 80-892-8688
MONMOUTH-ROSEVILLE SCHOOL DISTRICT 238
105 N E St, Monmouth, IL 61462-1667
Tel (309) 734-4712 *Founded/Ownrshp* 2007
Sales 100.1M *EMP* 392^E
SIC 8211 Elementary & secondary schools

MONOC
See MONMOUTH-OCEAN HOSPITAL SERVICE CORP

D-U-N-S 06-201-9088 IMP/EXP
MONOFLO INTERNATIONAL INC
882 Baker Ln, Winchester, VA 22603-5722
Tel (540) 665-1691 *Founded/Ownrshp* 1973
Sales 110.4MM^E *EMP* 170
SIC 3089 3523 Plastic containers, except foam; Plastic hardware & building products; Barn, silo, poultry, dairy & livestock machinery; Plastic containers, except foam; Plastic hardware & building products; Barn, silo, poultry, dairy & livestock machinery
Pr: Henning Rader
Board of Directors: Gisela Rader, Helmut Rader Jr

D-U-N-S 80-005-0577 IMP
■ **MONOGRAM AEROSPACE FASTENERS INC**
(*Suby of* TRIMAS CORP) ★
3423 Garfield Ave, Commerce, CA 90040-3103
Tel (323) 722-4760 *Founded/Ownrshp* 1990
Sales 45.0MM^E *EMP* 250^E
SIC 3429 3452 Manufactured hardware (general); Bolts, metal; Rivets, metal; Screws, metal; Manufactured hardware (general); Bolts, metal; Rivets, metal; Screws, metal
Pr: David Adler
Pr: Jim Eastwood
Pr: Behrouz Khodnegah
Ofcr: Christian Perron
IT Man: Mike Belcher
IT Man: Oscar Gonzales
IT Man: Michelle Mullin
VP Opers: Brian McGuire
Mfg Mgr: Ramiz Sipilovic
Ql Cn Mgr: Greg Bermel
Ql Cn Mgr: Eloise Ramclam

D-U-N-S 94-549-4490
■ **MONOGRAM BIOSCIENCES INC**
(*Suby of* LABORATORY CORP OF AMERICA HOLDINGS) ★
345 Oyster Point Blvd, South San Francisco, CA 94080-1913
Tel (650) 635-1100 *Founded/Ownrshp* 1995
Sales 65.7MM^E *EMP* 382
SIC 2835 In vitro & in vivo diagnostic substances; In vitro & in vivo diagnostic substances
CEO: Floyd S Eberts III
**CFO:* Alfred G Merriweather
**Ofcr:* Michael J Dunn
Assoc VP: Sarah Irwin
**Sr VP:* Kathy L Hibbs
**Sr VP:* William J Welch
VP: Susan Owens
VP: Gregory Toft
Dir Lab: Cindy Lee
Assoc Dir: Mojgan Haddad
Snr Sftwr: Yalin Jiang
Board of Directors: William Jenkins MD, Cristina H Kepner, John D Mendlein Phd, David H Persing Phd, Christine A White MD

D-U-N-S 78-101-2005
MONOGRAM FOOD SOLUTIONS LLC
530 Oak Court Dr Ste 400, Memphis, TN 38117-3735
Tel (901) 685-7167 *Founded/Ownrshp* 2004
Sales 321.5MM *EMP* 790
Accts Mayer Hoffman Mccann Pc Mem
SIC 5142 2013 Packaged frozen goods; Pigs' feet, cooked & pickled: from purchased meat; Beef, dried: from purchased meat; Snack sticks, including jerky: from purchased meat; Packaged frozen goods; Pigs' feet, cooked & pickled: from purchased meat; Beef, dried: from purchased meat; Snack sticks, including jerky: from purchased meat
CFO: Joey Stoner
VP: Joan Vanness
VP Sls: Tom Keim

D-U-N-S 02-553-8026 IMP
MONOGRAM FROZEN FOODS LLC
605 Kesco Dr, Bristol, IN 46507-8980
Tel (574) 848-0344 *Founded/Ownrshp* 2012
Sales 63.7MM^E *EMP* 250
SIC 2013 Sausages & other prepared meats; Sausages & related products, from purchased meat; Frozen meats from purchased meat; Sausages & other prepared meats; Sausages & related products, from purchased meat; Frozen meats from purchased meat
VP: Phillip M Smith

D-U-N-S 78-101-1882
MONOGRAM MEAT SNACKS LLC
(*Suby of* MONOGRAM FOOD SOLUTIONS LLC) ★
530 Oak Court Dr Ste 400, Memphis, TN 38117-3735
Tel (800) 852-1863 *Founded/Ownrshp* 2006
Sales 136.0MM^E *EMP* 132^E
SIC 5147 Meats & meat products

D-U-N-S 96-736-6969
MONOGRAM RESIDENTIAL TRUST INC
5800 Gran Pkwy Ste 1000, Plano, TX 75024
Tel (469) 250-5500 *Founded/Ownrshp* 2006
Sales 209.0MM *EMP* 370
SIC 6798 Real estate investment trusts; Real estate investment trusts
Pr: Mark T Alfieri
**Ch Bd:* E Alan Patton
CFO: Howard S Garfield
Ex VP: Margaret M Daly
Ex VP: Robert T Poynter
Sr VP: Daniel J Rosenberg
Board of Directors: Sami S Abbasi, Robert S Aisner, Roger D Bowler, David D Fitch, Jonathan L Kempner, Murray J McCabe

D-U-N-S 83-202-9651
MONOGRAM SNACKS MARTINSVILLE LLC
(*Suby of* MONOGRAM FOOD SOLUTIONS LLC) ★
200 Knauss Dr, Martinsville, VA 24112-1958
Tel (901) 685-7167 *Founded/Ownrshp* 2009
Sales 140.1MM^E *EMP* 514
SIC 5147 Meats & meat products; Meats & meat products

MONOGRAM SYSTEMS
See MAG AEROSPACE INDUSTRIES INC

D-U-N-S 79-996-8680
▲ **MONOLITHIC POWER SYSTEMS INC**
79 Great Oaks Blvd, San Jose, CA 95119-1311
Tel (408) 826-0600 *Founded/Ownrshp* 1997
Sales 282.5MM *EMP* 1,105^E
Accts Deloitte & Touche Llp San Jos
Tkr Sym MPWR *Exch* NGS
SIC 3674 8711 Semiconductors & related devices; Engineering services; Semiconductors & related devices; Engineering services
Ch Bd: Michael R Hsing
CFO: Meera P RAO
Sr VP: C R Neely Jr
Sr VP: Maurice Sciammas
VP: Josip Huljev
VP: Saria Tseng
Mng Dir: Dave Baker
Area Mgr: Karl Kopp
Area Mgr: Roger Straight
Dist Mgr: Rob Martell
QA Dir: Julia Chu
Board of Directors: Karen A Smith Bogart, Herbert Chang, Eugen Elmiger, Victor K Lee, Jeff Zhou

D-U-N-S 60-194-4072
MONOMOY CAPITAL PARTNERS LLC
142 W 57th St Fl 17, New York, NY 10019-3300
Tel (212) 699-4000 *Founded/Ownrshp* 2005
Sales NA *EMP* 780
SIC 6371 Pension, health & welfare funds; Pension, health & welfare funds

D-U-N-S 79-106-7080
MONOMOY CAPITAL PARTNERS LP
142 W 57th St Fl 17, New York, NY 10019-3300
Tel (212) 699-4000 *Founded/Ownrshp* 2005
Sales 1.1MMM^E *EMP* 3,775
SIC 6799 Venture capital companies; Venture capital companies
Genl Pt: Stephen Presser
Pt: Kareem Aktar
Pt: Andrea Cipriani
Pt: Daniel Collin
Pt: Justin Hillenbrand
Pt: Jaime McKenzie
Pt: Nathan Richey
Pt: Loren Roseman
Pt: Earl Dos Santos
Pt: Mayank Singh
Pt: Philip Von Burg
VP: Lauren Mulholland

MONONA GROVE ALTERNATIVE HS
See GROVE MONONA SCHOOL DISTRICT INC

D-U-N-S 95-861-1774
■ **MONONA HOLDINGS LLC**
(*Suby of* COMMERCIAL VEHICLE GROUP INC) ★
1952 Mc Dowell Rd Ste 207, Naperville, IL 60563-6506
Tel (630) 946-0630 *Founded/Ownrshp* 2005
Sales 175.6MM^E *EMP* 1,200
SIC 3694 5063 Harness wiring sets, internal combustion engines; Wire & cable; Harness wiring sets, internal combustion engines; Wire & cable
MIS Mgr: Dan Hurley

D-U-N-S 08-281-2991
MONONA PLUMBING AND FIRE PROTECTION INC
3126 Watford Way, Madison, WI 53713-3251
Tel (608) 273-4556 *Founded/Ownrshp* 1977
Sales 27.7MM^E *EMP* 110
Accts Mcgladrey & Pullen Llp Madis
SIC 1711 Plumbing contractors; Plumbing contractors
CEO: Phillip McManamy
**Pr:* Brent Williams
VP: Kevin Klug
Genl Mgr: Michael Tolley
Snr PM: Dave Bartolerio
Snr PM: Jeremy Maguire

D-U-N-S 04-856-2664
■ **MONONA WIRE CORP**
(*Suby of* MONONA HOLDINGS LLC) ★
301 W Spruce St, Monona, IA 52159-8035
Tel (563) 539-2012 *Founded/Ownrshp* 2002
Sales 175.6MM^E *EMP* 1,100
SIC 3679 3694 Harness assemblies for electronic use: wire or cable; Harness wiring sets, internal combustion engines; Harness assemblies for electronic use: wire or cable; Harness wiring sets, internal combustion engines
CFO: Timothy Trenary
VP: Kevin Frailey
IT Man: Tim West

D-U-N-S 00-794-4812
■ **MONONGAHELA POWER CO** (OH)
FIRST ENERGY
(*Suby of* FIRSTENERGY CORP) ★
1310 Fairmont Ave, Fairmont, WV 26554-3526
Tel (800) 686-0022 *Founded/Ownrshp* 1924, 2012
Sales 2.1MMM^E *EMP* 4,000
SIC 4911 Generation, electric power; Distribution, electric power; Transmission, electric power; Generation, electric power; Distribution, electric power; Transmission, electric power
Ch Bd: Paul J Evanson
**Pr:* David E Flitman
COO: Arthur Erskine
**CFO:* Jeffrey David Serkes
**VP:* Philip L Goulding
**VP:* Hyun Park
CIO: Gary Benz
CTO: Keith March
Mktg Dir: Trent Smith

D-U-N-S 06-872-8773
MONONGAHELA VALLEY HOSPITAL INC
MON VALLEY HOSPITAL
1163 Country Club Rd, Monongahela, PA 15063-1095
Tel (724) 258-1000 *Founded/Ownrshp* 1982
Sales 134.6MM *EMP* 1,200
Accts Carvis Walker Llp New Castle

SIC 8062 8063 8069 General medical & surgical hospitals; Psychiatric hospitals; Specialty hospitals, except psychiatric; General medical & surgical hospitals; Psychiatric hospitals; Specialty hospitals, except psychiatric
CEO: Anthony M Lombardi
Chf Rad: Abdul Chaudry
CFO: Anthony Lombardi
CFO: Daniel Simmons
**Treas:* John G Schaeffer
Sr VP: Mary Murt
VP: Larry Rusnock
Comm Dir: Corinne Laboon
Dir Rad: Jan Forlini
Ex Dir: Walter Young
Cmptr Lab: Betty Ritzer

D-U-N-S 01-179-9830
MONONGALIA COUNTY BOARD OF EDUCATION (WV)
13 S High St, Morgantown, WV 26501-7546
Tel (304) 291-9210 *Founded/Ownrshp* 1933
Sales 116.3MM^E *EMP* 1,400
SIC 8211 Public elementary & secondary schools; School board
Pr: Barbara Parsons
**Treas:* William T Hawkins
Board of Directors: Jean Schmalzried

D-U-N-S 07-748-3154 IMP
MONONGALIA COUNTY GENERAL HOSPITAL CO
MONONGALIA GENERAL HOSPITAL
1200 J D Anderson Dr, Morgantown, WV 26505-3494
Tel (304) 598-1200 *Founded/Ownrshp* 1982
Sales 241.2MM *EMP* 1,100
Accts Dixon Hughes Goodman Llp Morg
SIC 8062 General medical & surgical hospitals; General medical & surgical hospitals
Pr: Thomas J Senker
**Pr:* Darryl Duncan
**COO:* Linda Ollis
**CFO:* Nicholas Grubbs
CFO: Shannon Wissmar
**Treas:* Sister Nancy White
**Ex VP:* Robert P Ritz
VP: Linda Allen
VP: Mary Edwards
VP: Steven A Mariner
**VP:* Daris Rosencrance

MONONGALIA GENERAL HOSPITAL
See MONONGALIA COUNTY GENERAL HOSPITAL CO

D-U-N-S 15-377-1936
MONONGALIA HEALTH SYSTEM INC
MON GENERAL HOSPITAL
1200 J D Anderson Dr, Morgantown, WV 26505-3494
Tel (304) 598-1200 *Founded/Ownrshp* 1982
Sales 4.8MM *EMP* 1,500
Accts Dixon Hughes Goodman Llp Morg
SIC 8062 8011 General medical & surgical hospitals; Offices & clinics of medical doctors; General medical & surgical hospitals; Offices & clinics of medical doctors
Pr: Daris Rosencrance
Dir Vol: Christina Brown
COO: Darryl Duncan
CFO: Nick Grubbs
CFO: Daris Rosencran
**Sec:* Terry Shaffer
Ofcr: Amy Rockis
VP: Michael Ferrebee
VP: Brian Hawthorne
Dir Risk M: Denice Myers
Dir Rad: Peggy Pust

D-U-N-S 14-950-4917 IMP/EXP
■ **MONOPRICE INC**
MONOPRICE.COM
(*Suby of* BLUCORA INC) ★
11701 6th St, Rancho Cucamonga, CA 91730-6030
Tel (877) 271-2592 *Founded/Ownrshp* 2013
Sales 123.3MM^E *EMP* 160
SIC 5099 Video & audio equipment; Video & audio equipment
Pr: Jong Lee
**CEO:* Ajay Kumar
**VP:* Julie Hong
VP: Jeovahna Vazquez
Exec: Larry Chong
Software D: Brandi Bailes
Natl Sales: Darin Stout
Mktg Dir: Larry Jones
Manager: Eric Krause
Manager: Daniel Leuciuc

MONOPRICE.COM
See MONOPRICE INC

D-U-N-S 04-245-5845 IMP
MONOSOL LLC
(*Suby of* KAI) ★
707 E 80th Pl Ste 301, Merrillville, IN 46410-5683
Tel (219) 762-3165 *Founded/Ownrshp* 2011
Sales 74.1MM^E *EMP* 200
SIC 2671 Plastic film, coated or laminated for packaging; Plastic film, coated or laminated for packaging
CEO: P Scott Bening
CFO: Stephanie Baker
VP: David Devoll
VP: Robert McGreal
Mng Ofcr: Jonathan Gallagher
IT Man: Mike Kelly
Mtls Mgr: Denise Holzhauser
Opers Supe: Chuck Jones
Prd Mgr: Cassie Schaufele
VP Sls: Matt Scearce
Mktg Mgr: Carl Simpson

D-U-N-S 17-622-8419
MONOTECH OF MISSISSIPPI
(*Suby of* PSP ENGINEERING) ★
27 County Road 342, Iuka, MS 38852-8448
Tel (662) 423-2033 *Founded/Ownrshp* 1985
Sales 25.2MM^E *EMP* 200
SIC 3569 Filters; Filters
Ch Bd: Roger Schwab
**Pr:* Andrew Easton
**VP:* Dennis Stirm
**VP:* Roy Stokes

D-U-N-S 80-704-5732
▲ **MONOTYPE IMAGING HOLDINGS INC**
600 Unicorn Park Dr, Woburn, MA 01801-3376
Tel (781) 970-6000 *Founded/Ownrshp* 2005
Sales 184.5MM *EMP* 435^E
Tkr Sym TYPE *Exch* NGS
SIC 7371 7372 Custom computer programming services; Prepackaged software; Custom computer programming services; Prepackaged software
Pr: Douglas J Shaw
**Ch Bd:* Robert L Lentz
COO: Scott E Landers
CFO: Joseph Hill
CFO: Joseph D Hill
Ex VP: John L Seguin
Ex VP: Ben Semmes
Sr VP: Steven R Martin
VP: Janet M Dunlap
VP: Daniel T Gerron
VP: Lisa A Landa
VP: John H McCallum
VP: Jennifer H Peterson
VP: Christopher J Roberts
Board of Directors: Gay W Gaddis, Roger J Heinen Jr, Pamela F Lenehan, Peter J Simone, Timothy B Yeaton

D-U-N-S 82-752-6286
■ **MONOTYPE IMAGING INC**
(*Suby of* MONOTYPE IMAGING HOLDINGS INC) ★
500 Unicorn Park Dr, Woburn, MA 01801-3377
Tel (781) 970-6000 *Founded/Ownrshp* 2004
Sales 67.7MM^E *EMP* 300
SIC 7372 7371 Prepackaged software; Custom computer programming services; Prepackaged software; Custom computer programming services
Pr: Douglas Shaw
**Ch Bd:* Robert Givens
Pr: Dawn Demars
CFO: Scott Landers
Sr VP: Steve Martin
VP: Geoffrey W Greve
VP: Lisa Landa
VP: John McCallum
VP: Dave McCarthy
VP: Tim McManus
VP: Ira Mirochnick
VP: Michael Osborn
Creative D: Dennis Dimos
Board of Directors: Roger Heinen, Pamela F Lenehan, Peter J Simone

D-U-N-S 01-313-5058 IMP
▲ **MONRO MUFFLER BRAKE INC**
200 Holleder Pkwy, Rochester, NY 14615-3808
Tel (585) 647-6400 *Founded/Ownrshp* 1957
Sales 894.4MM *EMP* 6,557
Accts Pricewaterhousecoopers Llp Ro
Tkr Sym MNRO *Exch* NGS
SIC 7539 7533 7534 7549 Wheel alignment, automotive; Powertrain components repair services; Automotive brake lining, installation; Shock absorber replacement; Muffler shop, sale or repair & installation; Tire retreading & repair shops; Emissions testing without repairs, automotive; Inspection & diagnostic service, automotive; Wheel alignment, automotive; Powertrain components repair services; Automotive brake lining, installation; Shock absorber replacement; Muffler shop, sale or repair & installation; Tire retreading & repair shops; Emissions testing without repairs, automotive; Inspection & diagnostic service, automotive
Pr: John W Van Heel
**Ch Bd:* Robert G Gross
CFO: Catherine D'Amico
CFO: Patty Merlau
Ex VP: Joseph Tomarchio Jr
VP: Dave Baier
VP: Craig L Hoyle
VP: Paulette Kuehnert
VP: Barbara Ross
VP: Joel Zaleski
Exec: Ray Pickens
Board of Directors: Frederick M Danziger, Donald Glickman, Stephen C McCluski, Robert E Mellor, Peter J Solomon, James R Wilen, Elizabeth A Wolszon

D-U-N-S 06-198-4709
■ **MONRO SERVICE CORP**
(*Suby of* MONRO MUFFLER BRAKE INC) ★
200 Holleder Pkwy, Rochester, NY 14615-3808
Tel (585) 647-6400 *Founded/Ownrshp* 1992
Sales 21.7MM^E *EMP* 414^E
SIC 7538 General automotive repair shops
Ch Bd: David Baier
VP Mktg: James Prinzi

D-U-N-S 14-105-7385
MONROE 1 BOCES EDUCATIONAL FOUNDATION INC
41 Oconnor Rd, Fairport, NY 14450-1327
Tel (585) 377-4660 *Founded/Ownrshp* 2000
Sales 89.6MM^E *EMP* 2,000
SIC 8299 Educational services; Educational services
Pr: Eugene Kinney
Treas: Elizabeth Hartley
**Treas:* Sheila Wallenhorst
**VP:* Frederick Shippey
IT Man: Doug Evans
IT Man: Christine Osadciw
Psych: Doreen Massie

MONROE 2-ORLEANS BOCES
See BOARD OF COOP EDUC SERVICES FOR 2ND SUPERVISORY DIST OF MONROE & ORLEANS COUNTIES

D-U-N-S 15-060-6580
MONROE BANCORP
210 E Kirkwood Ave, Bloomington, IN 47408-3551
Tel (812) 336-0201 *Founded/Ownrshp* 1984
Sales NA *EMP* 16^E
SIC 6022 State commercial banks; State commercial banks
Pr: Mark D Bradford
Pr: Anissa Veon
CFO: Gordon M Dyott
Ofcr: Jennifer McCloud
VP: Nathan Bean
VP: Bill Compton
VP: Scot Davidson
Brnch Mgr: Timothy Frazier

D-U-N-S 01-975-4548
■ **MONROE BANK**
(*Suby of* OLD NATIONAL BANK) ★
2801 E Bick Cadillac Blvd, Bloomington, IN 47401-5441
Tel (812) 331-3444 *Founded/Ownrshp* 2011
Sales NA *EMP* 225
SIC 6163 6022 Loan brokers; State commercial banks; Loan brokers; State commercial banks
Pr: Mark Bradford
**CFO:* Gordon M Dyott
**Sr VP:* R Scott Walters

D-U-N-S 00-696-0355
■ **MONROE BANK & TRUST** (MI)
(*Suby of* MBT FINANCIAL CORP) ★
510 N Monroe St, Monroe, MI 48162-2933
Tel (734) 241-0070 *Founded/Ownrshp* 1890
Sales NA *EMP* 102^E
SIC 6022 State commercial banks; State commercial banks
Pr: H Douglas Chaffin
CFO: John L Skibski
Ch: Michael J Miller
Ofcr: Christopher Cosby
Trst Ofcr: James E Morr
Ex VP: Donald M Lieto
Ex VP: Thomas G Myers
Sr VP: Jim Arnold
Sr VP: Mike Irvin
Sr VP: T Maddox
VP: Bruce Benton
VP: Vicki Franzen
VP: Darron Lalonde
VP: Susan Mehregan
VP: Dean Moening
VP: Terry Nisley
VP: Angela Szuma
VP: Wendy Timmins

D-U-N-S 09-383-2483 IMP
MONROE CABLE CO INC (NY)
14 Commercial Ave, Middletown, NY 10941-1444
Tel (845) 692-2800 *Founded/Ownrshp* 1978, 1993
Sales 41.5MM^E *EMP* 104
SIC 3357 Shipboard cable, nonferrous; Coaxial cable, nonferrous; Shipboard cable, nonferrous; Coaxial cable, nonferrous
Pr: Isaac Wieder
COO: Mendel Wieder

D-U-N-S 07-863-7161
MONROE CAPITAL CORP
311 S Wacker Dr Ste 6400, Chicago, IL 60606-6710
Tel (312) 258-8300 *Founded/Ownrshp* 2011
Sales 29.9MM *EMP* 2^E
Tkr Sym MRCC *Exch* NGM
SIC 6726 7389 Management services; Management investment funds, closed-end; Financial services
Ch Bd: Theodore L Koenig
**CFO:* Aaron D Peck

D-U-N-S 83-324-9738
MONROE CAPITAL LLC
311 S Wacker Dr Ste 6400, Chicago, IL 60606-6710
Tel (312) 258-8300 *Founded/Ownrshp* 1999
Sales 29.9MM *EMP* 29^E
SIC 7389 Financial services
Pr: Theodore Koenig
Chf Inves: Aaron Peck
Sr VP: Mike Kempel
Sr VP: Mark Nowak
VP: Jeffrey K Williams
Prin: Alex Franky
Mng Dir: Andrew Cozewith
Off Mgr: Briget Brew

MONROE CAROL JR CHILDREN HOSPT
See VANDERBILT CHILDRENS HOSPITAL

MONROE CHRYSLER
See MONROE DODGE-CHRYSLER INC

MONROE CITY SCHOOL BOARD
See MONROE CITY SCHOOLS INC

D-U-N-S 02-032-8662
MONROE CITY SCHOOLS INC
MONROE CITY SCHOOL BOARD
2006 Tower Dr, Monroe, LA 71201-5036
Tel (318) 325-0601 *Founded/Ownrshp* 1900
Sales 81.2MM^E *EMP* 1,405
SIC 8211 Public elementary & secondary schools; Public elementary & secondary schools
Teacher Pr: Phedra Brantley

D-U-N-S 07-115-3951
MONROE CLINIC INC
515 22nd Ave, Monroe, WI 53566-1598
Tel (608) 324-2775 *Founded/Ownrshp* 1963
Sales 172.9MM *EMP* 1,100
Accts Wipfli Llp Wausau Wisconsin
SIC 8062 8011 General medical & surgical hospitals; Offices & clinics of medical doctors; General medical & surgical hospitals; Offices & clinics of medical doctors
Pr: Michael Sanders
V Ch: Bill Oemichen
COO: Amy Sweeney
**CFO:* James Nemeth
Ofcr: Julie Allemagne
VP: Jane Monahan
VP: Karen Thomas
VP: Jane Weldon
Prac Mgr: Dawn Hill
Off Admin: Ann Kloepping
Off Admin: Christine Lindh

MONROE CNTY MDDLE COLLEGE SCHL
See MONROE COUNTY INTERMEDIATE SCHOOL DISTRICT

D-U-N-S 07-326-0986
MONROE COLLEGE LTD
2501 Jerome Ave, Bronx, NY 10468-4305
Tel (718) 220-0017 *Founded/Ownrshp* 1933
Sales 33.4MM^E *EMP* 600
SIC 8244 Business college or school; Business college or school
Pr: Stephen J Jerome
COO: Roberta Greenberg
CFO: Stu Freiman
**Ex VP:* Marc Jerome
Sr VP: Alex Ephrem
**Sr VP:* Alan Mintz
VP: Anthony Allen
VP: Stephen Waldow
Exec: Villin Cruz
Exec: Conrad Goldberg
Exec: Shawn Kaba

D-U-N-S 06-792-1585
MONROE COMMUNITY COLLEGE (NY)
(*Suby of* STATE UNIVERSITY OF NEW YORK) ★
1000 E Henrietta Rd, Rochester, NY 14623-5780
Tel (585) 292-2000 *Founded/Ownrshp* 1962
Sales 67.8MM *EMP* 1,800
Accts Bonadio & Co Llp Pittsford
SIC 8222 9411 Community college; Administration of educational programs; ; Community college; Administration of educational programs;
Pr: Anne M Kress
**Pr:* Thomas Flynn
Exec: Donna Pogroszewski
Assoc Dir: Kimberley Willis
Dir Sec: Sal Simonetti

D-U-N-S 07-369-7732
MONROE COMMUNITY COLLEGE ASSOCIATION INC
MONROE COMMUNITY COLLEGE BOOKS
1000 E Henrietta Rd, Rochester, NY 14623-5780
Tel (585) 292-2500 *Founded/Ownrshp* 1962
Sales 20.5MM *EMP* 50
Accts Efp Rotenberg Llp Rochester
SIC 5942 8641 Book stores; Civic social & fraternal associations; Book stores; Civic social & fraternal associations
Ex Dir: Jenny Geer
Pgrm Dir: Susan Gunther

MONROE COMMUNITY COLLEGE BOOKS
See MONROE COMMUNITY COLLEGE ASSOCIATION INC

D-U-N-S 06-791-0356
MONROE COMMUNITY HOSPITAL (INC)
(*Suby of* COUNTY OF MONROE) ★
435 E Henrietta Rd, Rochester, NY 14620-4684
Tel (585) 760-6500 *Founded/Ownrshp* 1933
Sales 80.4M *EMP* 1,000
Accts Rizzo Digiacco & Hern Cpas P
SIC 8051 Skilled nursing care facilities; Skilled nursing care facilities
Ex Dir: Todd Spring
Pr: Dixie Schaedel
Pr: Matt Schwasman
**CFO:* Tom Anderson
VP: Ken Allaire
Exec: John Veneron
Dir Rx: Julie Olschewski
Nurse Mgr: Christine McCracken
CIO: Joel Snyder
CTO: James Wheaton
Dir IT: Joel Snider

D-U-N-S 05-179-9864
MONROE COUNTY BOARD OF EDUCATION
9875 Willow Bend Rd, Union, WV 24983-9739
Tel (304) 772-3094 *Founded/Ownrshp* 1934
Sales 7.9MM^E *EMP* 300
SIC 8299 Educational services; Educational services

D-U-N-S 10-001-4141
MONROE COUNTY BOARD OF EDUCATION
MONROE COUNTY SCHOOLS
25 Brooklyn Ave Ste A, Forsyth, GA 31029-1987
Tel (478) 994-7060 *Founded/Ownrshp* 1940
Sales 42.5MM *EMP* 517
Accts Russell W Hinton Cpa Cgfm
SIC 8211 Public elementary & secondary schools; Public elementary & secondary schools
CFO: Becky Firster

D-U-N-S 09-726-6787
MONROE COUNTY BOARD OF EDUCATION
309 Emberton St, Tompkinsville, KY 42167-1431
Tel (270) 487-6772 *Founded/Ownrshp* 1915
Sales 19.2MM^E *EMP* 430
SIC 8211 Public elementary & secondary schools; High school, junior or senior; Public vocational/technical school; Public elementary & secondary schools; High school, junior or senior; Public vocational/technical school
**Prin:* Mike Gee
**Prin:* James Graves
Adm Dir: Larry Moore

D-U-N-S 19-320-8741
MONROE COUNTY BOARD OF EDUCATION
109 Pickens St, Monroeville, AL 36460-1890
Tel (251) 575-3672 *Founded/Ownrshp* 1900
Sales 60.9M *EMP* 545
SIC 8211 Public elementary & secondary schools; Public elementary & secondary schools

D-U-N-S 03-955-3060
MONROE COUNTY CHAPTER NYSARC INC
ARCWORKS
(*Suby of* NYSARC INC) ★
2060 Brighton Henrietta, Rochester, NY 14623-2792
Tel (585) 271-0660 *Founded/Ownrshp* 1956
Sales 38.6MM *EMP* 825
Accts Bonadio & Co Llp Pittsford

SIC 8093 8331 8322 Rehabilitation center, outpatient treatment; Job training & vocational rehabilitation services; Individual & family services; Rehabilitation center, outpatient treatment; Job training & vocational rehabilitation services; Individual & family services
CEO: Barbara S Wale
**Pr:* James G Mroczek
**COO:* Barbara Wale
Treas: David Rizzari
Ofcr: Pete Dancer
**VP:* Tracy Petrichick
MIS Dir: Nathan Lucier

MONROE COUNTY COMMISIONERS OFF
See COUNTY OF MONROE

D-U-N-S 08-098-2606
MONROE COUNTY COMMUNITY COLLEGE FACULTY ASSOCIATION
1555 S Raisinville Rd, Monroe, MI 48161-9047
Tel (734) 242-7300 *Founded/Ownrshp* 1964
Sales 19.8MM^E *EMP* 325
SIC 8222 Community college; Community college
Pr: Dr David Nixon
Ch Bd: Margery Kreps
Pgrm Dir: Anthony Quinn

D-U-N-S 07-206-2342
MONROE COUNTY COMMUNITY SCHOOL CORP
MCCSC
315 E North Dr, Bloomington, IN 47401-6595
Tel (812) 330-7700 *Founded/Ownrshp* 1968
Sales 65.6MM *EMP* 2,300
SIC 8211 Public elementary & secondary schools; Elementary school; Public elementary & secondary schools; Elementary school
Bd of Dir: Jim Muehling
Dir Sec: John Carter
Pr Dir: Tim Pritchett
Teacher Pr: Vick Chambers
Teacher Pr: April Underwood

MONROE COUNTY EMERGENCY MGT
See COUNTY OF MONROE

MONROE COUNTY GOVERNMENT
See COUNTY OF MONROE

D-U-N-S 13-953-0492
MONROE COUNTY HEALTH CARE AUTHORITY
MONROE COUNTY HOSPITAL
2016 S Alabama Ave, Monroeville, AL 36460-3044
Tel (251) 575-3111 *Founded/Ownrshp* 1959
Sales 20.4MM *EMP* 245
SIC 8062 8011 General medical & surgical hospitals; General & family practice, physician/surgeon
CEO: Jeffrey Brannon
CFO: Michael Vaughn
Ex VP: Andy Weaver
Dir OR: Lisa Watson
Dir Rx: Cynthia Martens
Ex Dir: Ernistine Howard
Off Mgr: Rita Kelly
QA Dir: Emilie Martin
Nrsg Dir: Barbara Harned
HC Dir: Jeane Simmons

MONROE COUNTY HIGHWAY ENGINEER
See COUNTY OF MONROE

MONROE COUNTY HOSPITAL
See MONROE COUNTY HEALTH CARE AUTHORITY

D-U-N-S 07-809-2319
MONROE COUNTY HOSPITAL
6580 165th St, Albia, IA 52531-8893
Tel (641) 932-2134 *Founded/Ownrshp* 1956
Sales 25.0MM *EMP* 130
SIC 8062 General medical & surgical hospitals; General medical & surgical hospitals
CEO: Todd Willert
**CEO:* Greg Paris
**CFO:* Heather Cain
Dir OR: Brian Teeter
Doctor: Alex Curiel
Occ Thrpy: Megan Irving

D-U-N-S 02-027-8065
MONROE COUNTY INTERMEDIATE SCHOOL DISTRICT (MI)
MONROE CNTY MDDLE COLLEGE SCHL
1101 S Raisinville Rd, Monroe, MI 48161-9047
Tel (734) 242-5799 *Founded/Ownrshp* 1946
Sales 22.5MM^E *EMP* 450
SIC 8211 Public elementary & secondary schools; Public elementary & secondary schools;
**Pr:* Dale Desloover
**CFO:* Nancy Swanson
**VP:* Larry Hammons
Netwrk Mgr: Mark Samp

D-U-N-S 07-368-5034
MONROE COUNTY LIBRARY SYSTEM
CENTRAL LIB RCHSTER MNROE CNTY
115 South Ave, Rochester, NY 14604-1817
Tel (585) 428-7300 *Founded/Ownrshp* 1952
Sales 9.6MM^E *EMP* 420
SIC 8231 Libraries; Libraries

D-U-N-S 07-979-9751
MONROE COUNTY PUBLIC SCHOOLS
109 Pickens St 967, Monroeville, AL 36460-1915
Tel (251) 743-2150 *Founded/Ownrshp* 2015
Sales 19.2MM^E *EMP* 606^E
SIC 8211 Public elementary & secondary schools

D-U-N-S 79-115-4185
MONROE COUNTY SCHOOL DISTRICT
241 Trumbo Rd, Key West, FL 33040-6684
Tel (305) 293-1400 *Founded/Ownrshp* 2007
Sales 80.0MM^E *EMP* 1,000
SIC 8211 Elementary & secondary schools; Public elementary & secondary schools
**CFO:* Michael Kinneer
MIS Dir: David Richardson
Psych: Heather Jennings

MONROE COUNTY SCHOOLS
See MONROE COUNTY BOARD OF EDUCATION

D-U-N-S 07-979-8770
MONROE COUNTY SCHOOLS
25 Brooklyn Ave, Forsyth, GA 31029-1910
Tel (478) 994-2031 *Founded/Ownrshp* 2015
Sales 6.1MM^E *EMP* 535^E
SIC 8211 Public elementary & secondary schools
MIS Dir: Valerie Mercer
Teacher Pr: Mike Hickman

D-U-N-S 07-979-8797
MONROE COUNTY SCHOOLS
205 Oak Grove Rd, Madisonville, TN 37354-5930
Tel (423) 442-2373 *Founded/Ownrshp* 2015
Sales 6.7MM^E *EMP* 628^E
SIC 8211 Public elementary & secondary schools

D-U-N-S 07-982-7388
MONROE COUNTY SCHOOLS
1209 N Main St, Tompkinsville, KY 42167-9471
Tel (270) 487-5456 *Founded/Ownrshp* 2015
Sales 9.4MM^E *EMP* 296^E
SIC 8211 Public elementary & secondary schools

D-U-N-S 04-129-0925
MONROE COUNTY WATER AUTHORITY
475 Norris Dr, Rochester, NY 14610-2498
Tel (585) 442-2000 *Founded/Ownrshp* 1959
Sales 60.0MM *EMP* 225
Accts Bonadio & Co Llp Pittsford
SIC 4941 Water supply; Water supply
Ex Dir: Nicholas Noce

D-U-N-S 04-134-9937
MONROE DODGE-CHRYSLER INC
MONROE CHRYSLER
15160 S Dixie Hwy, Monroe, MI 48161-3792
Tel (734) 242-6370 *Founded/Ownrshp* 1966
Sales 25.4MM^E *EMP* 60
SIC 5511 Automobiles, new & used; Automobiles, new & used
Pr: Ralph Mahalak Jr
VP: JP Mahalak
Sls Mgr: John Akens

D-U-N-S 07-852-2170 IMP
■ **MONROE ENERGY LLC**
(*Suby of* DELTA AIR LINES INC) ★
4101 Post Rd, Trainer, PA 19061-5052
Tel (610) 364-8000 *Founded/Ownrshp* 2012
Sales 228.8MM^E *EMP* 445
SIC 2911 Petroleum refining; Petroleum refining
Pr: Jeffrey Warmann
VP: Rodney Smith
VP: Coby Stewart
VP: Jeff Warman
Dir Lab: Don Bobal
Area Supr: Frank Kofeldt
Sfty Mgr: Mel Scavicio
Opers Mgr: Tim Carter
Opers Mgr: Edward Ernst
Opers Mgr: Steve Hamilton
Snr Mgr: Adam Gattuso

MONROE EQUIPMENT
See MONROE GAS EQUIPMENT INC

D-U-N-S 04-901-9649
MONROE GAS EQUIPMENT INC
MONROE EQUIPMENT
N50w13941 Overview Dr, Menomonee Falls, WI 53051-7038
Tel (262) 783-8190 *Founded/Ownrshp* 2009
Sales 21.3MM^E *EMP* 30
SIC 5075 Electrical heating equipment; Air conditioning equipment, except room units; Ventilating equipment & supplies
Pr: Randy Schneider
VP Opers: Matt Schneider
VP Sls: Ron Lutz

D-U-N-S 00-699-7076 IMP
MONROE HARDWARE CO (NC)
101 N Sutherland Ave, Monroe, NC 28110-3601
Tel (704) 289-3121 *Founded/Ownrshp* 1886, 1900
Sales 130.9MM^E *EMP* 220
SIC 5072 5083 Shelf or light hardware; Farm implements; Shelf or light hardware; Farm implements
Pr: James G Allred
Ch Bd: Carl G Belk
Exec: Agnes Frodge
IT Man: Adam Dotsey
Mktg Dir: Keith Driscoll
Mktg Mgr: Brooks Gornto
Sls Mgr: Rick Swaim
Sales Asso: Todd Burr

D-U-N-S 06-647-4008
■ **MONROE HMA INC**
WALTON REGIONAL MEDICAL CENTER
(*Suby of* HEALTH MANAGEMENT ASSOCIATES INC) ★
330 Alcovy St, Monroe, GA 30655-2140
Tel (770) 267-8461 *Founded/Ownrshp* 2003
Sales 51.5MM^E *EMP* 400
SIC 8062 8051 General medical & surgical hospitals; Skilled nursing care facilities; General medical & surgical hospitals; Skilled nursing care facilities
CEO: Gary Lang
CFO: Barbara Duncan
**CFO:* Jeff Grimsley
CFO: Kevin Rinks
**Sr VP:* Parry Timothy
Dir Rx: Maria Gray
**Prin:* Alan George
Web Dev: Shannon Delchamts
Sfty Mgr: Reinhold Werzner
Pr Mgr: Cynthia Baynes
Pathlgst: Jeffrey Cohenour

D-U-N-S 78-100-4663
MONROE HOSPITAL LLC
DIGESTIVE DISEASES CENTER
4011 S Monroe Med Pk Blvd, Bloomington, IN 47403-8000
Tel (812) 825-1111 *Founded/Ownrshp* 2005
Sales 41.6MM *EMP* 350^E
SIC 8062 General medical & surgical hospitals; General medical & surgical hospitals
CEO: Joe Roche
**VP:* Donetta Breeden
Dir Lab: Ashley Everett
Dir Pat Ac: Dion Beaty
CIO: Carrie Silvers
Sfty Dirs: Steve Sharp
Doctor: Tom Sharp
Cert Phar: Tanalee Chapman
Phys Thrpy: Renae Cartwright
Diag Rad: Steven Strickler

D-U-N-S 03-880-1791
MONROE IRON & METAL CO INC
AUTO SHRED OF LOUISIANA
(*Suby of* THE MEYER CRYSTAL FAMILY FOUNDATION)
411 N 9th St, Monroe, LA 71201-6964
Tel (318) 325-4636 *Founded/Ownrshp* 1979
Sales 20.7MM^E *EMP* 54
SIC 5093 Scrap & waste materials; Junk & scrap; Ferrous metal scrap & waste; Nonferrous metals scrap
Pr: Clayton A Crystal
**Ch Bd:* Gerald Crystal
**VP:* Edward Erlich
VP: Norman Paulson

D-U-N-S 78-598-1510
MONROE LLC
4490 44th St Se, Grand Rapids, MI 49512-4011
Tel (616) 942-9820 *Founded/Ownrshp* 2006
Sales 73.1MM^E *EMP* 285
SIC 3089 3542 3714 3544 Molding primary plastic; Machine tools, metal forming type; Motor vehicle parts & accessories; Special dies, tools, jigs & fixtures; Molding primary plastic; Machine tools, metal forming type; Motor vehicle parts & accessories; Special dies, tools, jigs & fixtures
QA Dir: Lorri McCrary

D-U-N-S 11-098-9618
MONROE LOCAL SCHOOL DISTRICT
500 Yankee Rd, Monroe, OH 45050-1068
Tel (513) 539-2536 *Founded/Ownrshp* 2000
Sales 22.4MM *EMP* 220^E
Accts Clark Schaefer Hackett & Co C
SIC 8211 Public elementary & secondary schools; Public elementary & secondary schools
**Treas:* Kelley Thorpe
Bd of Dir: Bob Hunt
Bd of Dir: Gayle Martz
Bd of Dir: Michael Oster
Bd of Dir: Leslie Stone
VP: Tim Carpenter
IT Man: Holly Cahall

MONROE MANNOR
See GRAND UNION HEALTHCARE LLC

MONROE MANOR NURSING HOME
See MANAGEMENT CO INC

D-U-N-S 01-069-5646
MONROE MANUFACTURING INC
2813 Desiard St, Monroe, LA 71201-7205
Tel (318) 388-4916 *Founded/Ownrshp* 1990
Sales 20.9MM^E *EMP* 300
SIC 3085 3069 Plastics bottles; Baby pacifiers, rubber; Plastics bottles; Baby pacifiers, rubber
CEO: Nouri Ed Hakim
**Pr:* Joseph Hakim

D-U-N-S 05-794-1205
MONROE MOTOR PRODUCTS CORP
PARTS PLUS
40 Joseph Ave, Rochester, NY 14605-3032
Tel (585) 546-6633 *Founded/Ownrshp* 2004
Sales 26.0MM *EMP* 180
SIC 5013 5531

D-U-N-S 02-470-5238
MONROE OIL CO INC (NC)
519 E Franklin St, Monroe, NC 28112-5701
Tel (704) 289-5438 *Founded/Ownrshp* 1951, 2003
Sales 85.6MM *EMP* 32
Accts Spangler Inc Pa Charlotte
SIC 5541 5172 5411 Gasoline service stations; Petroleum products; Convenience stores; Gasoline service stations; Petroleum products; Convenience stores
Pr: Olin Furr
**VP:* Amy Furr

D-U-N-S 08-275-0571
MONROE PLAN FOR MEDICAL CARE INC
1120 Pittsford Victor Rd, Pittsford, NY 14534-3818
Tel (585) 244-5550 *Founded/Ownrshp* 1970
Sales NA *EMP* 180
Accts Robinson & Gordon Cpas Pc Roc
SIC 6324 Hospital & medical service plans; Hospital & medical service plans
CEO: Dennis Graziano
CFO: Michael Messier
Dir IT: Scott Ferris
IT Man: Laura Weisbein

D-U-N-S 02-027-7489
MONROE PUBLIC SCHOOLS
1275 N Macomb St, Monroe, MI 48162-3196
Tel (734) 265-3000 *Founded/Ownrshp* 1827
Sales 60.8MM *EMP* 803
Accts Cooley Hehl Wohlgamuth & Carlo
SIC 8211 Public elementary & secondary schools; Public elementary & secondary schools
VP: Lawrence Vanwasshenova
Prin: Randall Monday
Dir IT: Connie Payne
Dir IT: Peggy Rapai

D-U-N-S 07-662-8569
MONROE PUBLIC SCHOOLS
200 E Fremont St, Monroe, WA 98272-2336
Tel (360) 804-2500 *Founded/Ownrshp* 1900
Sales 44.7M *EMP* 750
SIC 8211 Public elementary & secondary schools; Public senior high school; Public junior high school; Public elementary school; Public elementary & secondary schools; Public senior high school; Public junior high school; Public elementary school
MIS Dir: Carl Velez
Schl Brd P: Katy Woods

D-U-N-S 10-380-1072
MONROE PUBLIC SCHOOLS
375 Monroe Tpke, Monroe, CT 06468-2201
Tel (203) 452-2860 *Founded/Ownrshp* 1823
Sales 26.8MM^E *EMP* 500
SIC 8211 Public elementary & secondary schools; Public elementary & secondary schools
**Ch Bd:* Thomas Taylor
Dir IT: Paul Koorse
IT Man: Heather Ross
Psych: Lance Berndlmaier
Psych: Melissa Costanzo
Psych: Sean McDonald
Psych: Lisa Melillo
HC Dir: Kay Moser

D-U-N-S 01-806-4845
MONROE REGIONAL HEALTH SYSTEM
131 Sw 15th St, Ocala, FL 34471-6529
Tel (352) 351-7200 *Founded/Ownrshp* 1996
Sales 372.3M *EMP* 2,500
SIC 8011 Medical centers; Medical centers
Prin: R Cyrus Huffman
VP: Carl Candullo Jr
VP: Sharon Jones
Ex Dir: Sharon Stuckey

D-U-N-S 19-249-6990
MONROE STAFFING SERVICES LLC
35 Nutmeg Dr Ste 1, Trumbull, CT 06611-5495
Tel (203) 268-8624 *Founded/Ownrshp* 2010
Sales 74.1MM^E *EMP* 1,700
SIC 7361 Employment agencies; Employment agencies
Pr: Matt Briand
**CFO:* Steve Miller
Treas: Sophia H Huang
Sr VP: Michelle Crispino
**VP:* Paul Polito
**VP:* Erik Schwartz
**VP:* Steve Thompson
Opers Mgr: Melissa Franklin
Manager: Josh Iadarola

D-U-N-S 05-793-8995
■ **MONROE TITLE INSURANCE CORP** (NY)
(*Suby of* STEWART TITLE INSURANCE CO) ★
47 W Main St, Rochester, NY 14614-1416
Tel (585) 232-4950 *Founded/Ownrshp* 1922
Sales 21.0MM *EMP* 200
SIC 6541 6361 Title abstract offices; Real estate title insurance; Title abstract offices; Real estate title insurance
Pr: Thomas A Podsiadlo
CFO: Scott Deverell
**VP:* Barry C Balonek
VP: Peter Bryant
IT Man: Judith Heath

MONROE TOWNSHIP - MUNICIPALITY
See TOWNSHIP OF MONROE

MONROE TOWNSHIP BOARD EDUCATN
See MONROE TOWNSHIP SCHOOL DISTRICT

D-U-N-S 02-077-7785
MONROE TOWNSHIP BOARD OF EDUCATION (NJ)
423 Buckelew Ave, Jamesburg, NJ 08831-2976
Tel (732) 521-2111 *Founded/Ownrshp* 1895
Sales 107.3MM *EMP* 900
SIC 8211 9111 Public elementary & secondary schools; Mayors' offices; Public elementary & secondary schools
Pr: Doug Poye
VP: Tom Nothstein

D-U-N-S 01-226-1020
MONROE TOWNSHIP SCHOOL DISTRICT
MONROE TOWNSHIP BOARD EDUCATN
75 E Academy St, Williamstown, NJ 08094-1663
Tel (856) 629-6400 *Founded/Ownrshp* 1895
Sales 27.4M^E *EMP* 500
Accts James J Descano Cpa Pc Penn
SIC 8211 Public elementary & secondary schools; Public elementary & secondary schools
Bd of Dir: Carol Fox
VP: Roberta Braverman
Ex Dir: Janet Chen
IT Man: Jo Matienko

D-U-N-S 01-272-3128 IMP
MONROE TRACTOR & IMPLEMENT CO INC (NY)
1001 Lehigh Station Rd, Henrietta, NY 14467-9311
Tel (585) 334-3867 *Founded/Ownrshp* 1951
Sales 108.9MM^E *EMP* 200
SIC 5082 5083 7353

D-U-N-S 02-694-6211
MONROE TRACTOR IMPLEMENT CO INC
1508 Lehigh Station Rd, Henrietta, NY 14467-9236
Tel (585) 334-3867 *Founded/Ownrshp* 2010
Sales 27.1MM^E *EMP* 200
SIC 7353 Cranes & aerial lift equipment, rental or leasing; Cranes & aerial lift equipment, rental or leasing
CEO: Janet Felosky

D-U-N-S 00-608-1863 EXP
MONROE TRUCK EQUIPMENT INC (WI)
M T E
1051 W 7th St, Monroe, WI 53566-9100
Tel (608) 328-8127 *Founded/Ownrshp* 1958
Sales 247.2MM^E *EMP* 678

SIC 5013 3441 3599 Truck parts & accessories; Fabricated structural metal for bridges; Building components, structural steel; Machine & other job shop work; Machine shop, jobbing & repair; Custom machinery; Truck parts & accessories; Fabricated structural metal for bridges; Building components, structural steel; Machine & other job shop work; Machine shop, jobbing & repair; Custom machinery
Pr: David Quade
**Treas:* Richard Rufenacht
**VP:* Gregory Krahenbuhl
VP: Dan Nommensen
Off Mgr: Lisa Smith
Off Admin: Stacy Bailey
Dir IT: Teresa Johnson
Opers Mgr: Andy Knake
Ql Cn Mgr: Jon Briggs
Ql Cn Mgr: Gary Hess
Natl Sales: Jim Blodgett

D-U-N-S 01-495-8797
MONROE-WOODBURY CENTRAL SCHOOL DISTRICT
278 Route 32, Central Valley, NY 10917-3226
Tel (845) 460-6200 *Founded/Ownrshp* 1951
Sales 57.1MM^E *EMP* 1,200
Accts Nugent & Haeussler Pc Mont
SIC 8211 Public elementary & secondary schools; High school, junior or senior; Public elementary & secondary schools; High school, junior or senior
**Pr:* Michael J Digeronimo
Treas: Mike Henry
**VP:* Erich Tusch
Mktg Dir: Elisabeth Hellwege
Schl Brd P: John Huberth
Psych: Christine Ricker

MONROEVILLE DODGE THE
See NEW MONROEVILLE DODGE INC

MONROVIA GROWES
See MONROVIA NURSERY CO

MONROVIA MEMORIAL HOSPITAL
See ALAKOR HEALTHCARE LLC

D-U-N-S 00-690-4049
MONROVIA NURSERY CO
MONROVIA GROWES
817 E Monrovia Pl, Azusa, CA 91702-6297
Tel (626) 334-9321 *Founded/Ownrshp* 1926
Sales 443.1MM^E *EMP* 2,000
SIC 0181 5193 5261 Nursery stock, growing of; Flowers & florists' supplies; Nurseries & garden centers; Nursery stock, growing of; Flowers & florists' supplies; Nurseries & garden centers
CEO: Miles R Rosedale
Pr: William B Usrey
Pr: Richard Van Landinghan
CFO: Jason Matsuura
VP: Dennis Conner
VP Bus Dev: Jonathan Pedersen
Exec: Sylvia Lopez
Genl Mgr: Rick Wells
Tech Mgr: Reiner Kruger
VP Sls: Phil Harley
Sls Mgr: Gregory Estes
Board of Directors: Harry E Rosedale Jr Direc, Lance H Rosedale, Miles R Rosedale, Martin W Usrey

D-U-N-S 07-230-6137
MONROVIA UNIFIED SCHOOL DISTRICT
325 E Huntington Dr, Monrovia, CA 91016-6419
Tel (626) 471-2000 *Founded/Ownrshp* 1961
Sales 45.0MM *EMP* 700
Accts Nigro Nigro & White Llp
SIC 8211 Public elementary & secondary schools; Public elementary & secondary schools
Prin: Al Clegg
Prin: Larry Fitzgibbons
Prin: Manny Gonzales
Prin: Byron Greer
Prin: Dianne Lahti
Prin: Ron Letourneau
Prin: Esther McDonald
Prin: Jill Selak
Prin: Marco Villegas
MIS Dir: Jason Buchanan
Dir IT: Paul Dols

D-U-N-S 03-346-9967 IMP
■ **MONSANTO CO**
(*Suby of* MONSANTO CO) ★
Hwy 34 N, Soda Springs, ID 83276
Tel (208) 547-4300 *Founded/Ownrshp* 2000
Sales 23.9MM^E *EMP* 72^E
SIC 2819 Phosphorus, elemental
Plnt Mgr: Sheldon Alber
Prgrm Mgr: Scott Elsmore
Netwrk Eng: Lonnie Brown
Prd Mgr: Jason Cunningham

D-U-N-S 16-842-8287 IMP/EXP
▲ **MONSANTO CO**
800 N Lindbergh Blvd, Saint Louis, MO 63167-0001
Tel (314) 694-1000 *Founded/Ownrshp* 2000
Sales 15.8MMM *EMP* 21,400
Tkr Sym MON *Exch* NYS
SIC 2879 0181 Agricultural chemicals; Seeds, vegetable: growing of; Agricultural chemicals; Seeds, vegetable: growing of
Ch Bd: Hugh Grant
Pr: Brett Begemann
CFO: Pierre C Courduroux
CFO: Gary Crittden
Bd of Dir: Steve Levine
Ex VP: Brett D Begemann
Ex VP: Robert T Fraley
Ex VP: David F Snively
Sr VP: Sarah S Hull
VP: Karen Wishart
Dir Bus: Paul Flynn
Board of Directors: William U Parfet, Gregory H Boyce, George H Poste, David L Chicoine, Robert J Stevens, Janice L Fields, Patricia Verduin, Arthur H Harper, Laura K Ipsen, Gwendolyn S King, Marcos M Lutz, C Steven McMillan, Jon R Moeller

MONSIEUR HENRI WINE
See SAZERAC CO INC

D-U-N-S 12-082-4180 IMP
MONSIEUR TOUTON SELECTION LTD
(*Suby of* TOUTON HOLDINGS LTD) ★
129 W 27th St Fl 9, New York, NY 10001-6206
Tel (212) 255-0674 *Founded/Ownrshp* 1983
Sales 47.2MM^E *EMP* 65
SIC 5182 Wine; Wine
Pr: Guillame Touton
Pr: Dan Salvucci
**VP:* Neil Amoruso
Brnch Mgr: Mario Alvarez
VP Sls: Allan Trelford
Mktg Dir: Andy Healey
Mktg Mgr: Timothe Cousins

D-U-N-S 01-708-4443
MONSMA MARKETING CORP (MI)
2450 Buchanan Ave Sw, Grand Rapids, MI 49548-1005
Tel (616) 245-8714 *Founded/Ownrshp* 1930, 1963
Sales 35.1MM^E *EMP* 59
SIC 7389 Artists' agents & brokers; Artists' agents & brokers
Ch Bd: Jane Lovell
**Pr:* George Brightrall
**Treas:* Kendal K Lovell
Opers Mgr: Jim Oosterman
Sls Mgr: Craig Vandervlies
Sales Asso: Mike Bonney
Sales Asso: Chip Johnson
Sales Asso: Scott Lapoint
Sales Asso: Brent Patterson
Sales Asso: Rod Seely
Sales Asso: Fred Vail

D-U-N-S 04-941-9682 IMP
MONSON COMPANIES INC
(*Suby of* KODA DISTRIBUTION GROUP INC) ★
154 Pioneer Dr, Leominster, MA 01453-3474
Tel (978) 840-7007 *Founded/Ownrshp* 1987
Sales 97.7MM^E *EMP* 76
SIC 5169 5172 2899 2842 Industrial chemicals; Anti-freeze compounds; Lubricating oils & greases; Chemical preparations; Specialty cleaning, polishes & sanitation goods; Industrial chemicals; Anti-freeze compounds; Lubricating oils & greases; Chemical preparations; Specialty cleaning, polishes & sanitation goods
Pr: Charles P Walkovich
**Pr:* Steven Barney
Pr: Doug Hiple
Pr: Eric Nowicki
Sr VP: Jules Brandes
Genl Mgr: Retta-Jo Madore
VP Opers: Hal Chevalier

D-U-N-S 18-904-7434
MONSON FRUIT CO INC
252 N Rushmore Rd, Selah, WA 98942-9313
Tel (509) 697-9175 *Founded/Ownrshp* 1988
Sales 51.8MM^E *EMP* 250
SIC 0723

D-U-N-S 05-298-7130
MONSOON COMMERCE INC
(*Suby of* ALIBRIS, INC.)
520 Nw Davis St Ste 300, Portland, OR 97209-3620
Tel (503) 239-1055 *Founded/Ownrshp* 2006, 2010
Sales 42.1MM^E *EMP* 276^E
SIC 7371 ; Computer software development
CEO: Tommaso Trionfi
CFO: Liz Murray
VP: Peter Bohnert
VP: Rob Teichman
VP Bus Dev: Sean Moran
Genl Mgr: Jeanie Bunker
Genl Mgr: Madhav Mehra
CTO: William Aegerter
VP Mktg: Casey Carey
Mktg Mgr: Robin Carter

D-U-N-S 62-543-7488 IMP
■ **MONSTER BEVERAGE 1990 CORP**
(*Suby of* MONSTER BEVERAGE CORP) ★
1 Monster Way, Corona, CA 92879-7101
Tel (951) 739-6200 *Founded/Ownrshp* 1985
Sales 2.4MMM *EMP* 2,001^E
Tkr Sym MNST *Exch* NGS
SIC 2086 Bottled & canned soft drinks; Iced tea & fruit drinks, bottled & canned; Bottled & canned soft drinks; Carbonated beverages, nonalcoholic: bottled & canned; Iced tea & fruit drinks, bottled & canned
Ch Bd: Rodney C Sacks
**Pr:* Hilton H Schlosberg
COO: Nick R Gagliardi
Ofcr: Mark J Hall
Sr VP: Thomas J Kelly
VP: Gareth Bowen
VP: Neil Calvesbert
VP: Alan Clark
VP: Marc De Beffort
VP: Emelie Tirre
VP Bus Dev: Dan Lamb
Board of Directors: Norman C Epstein, Gary P Fayard, Mark J Hall, Benjamin M Polk, Sydney Selati, Harold C Taber Jr, Mark S Vidergauz, Kathy N Waller

D-U-N-S 96-274-2412
■ **MONSTER BEVERAGE CO**
(*Suby of* MONSTER BEVERAGE 1990 CORP) ★
1990 Pomona Rd, Corona, CA 92880-6955
Tel (866) 322-4466 *Founded/Ownrshp* 2010
Sales 40.1MM^E *EMP* 860^E
SIC 2086 Bottled & canned soft drinks
Prin: Mark Hall

D-U-N-S 07-992-4394
▲ **MONSTER BEVERAGE CORP**
1 Monster Way, Corona, CA 92879-7101
Tel (951) 739-6200 *Founded/Ownrshp* 2015
Sales 2.4MMM^E *EMP* 2,019^E
SIC 2086 Bottled & canned soft drinks; Carbonated beverages, nonalcoholic: bottled & canned
Ch Bd: Rodney C Sacks
Ch Bd: Dennis Quinn
**Pr:* Hilton H Schlosberg
COO: Hilton Schlosberg
Sr VP: Thomas J Kelly
Sr VP: Emelie Tirre
VP: Alan Clark
VP: Marc De Beffort
VP: Tom Kelly
VP: Scott Lewis
VP: Sam Pontrelli
Exec: Kay Collins
Dir Soc: Tammi Collier
Dir Soc: Denise Hixson

D-U-N-S 79-310-6956 EXP
■ **MONSTER ENERGY CO**
(*Suby of* MONSTER BEVERAGE 1990 CORP) ★
1 Monster Way, Corona, CA 92879-7101
Tel (951) 739-6200 *Founded/Ownrshp* 1992
Sales 1.2MMM^E *EMP* 1,000^E
SIC 5149 Juices; Soft drinks; Juices; Soft drinks
CEO: Rodney C Sacks
Pr: Ray La Rue
**V Ch Bd:* Hilton H Scholsberg
Ex VP: Keith Riley
Sr VP: Thomas Hicks
VP: Darlene Barrett
VP: Michael Cucchiara
VP: Paul Dechary
VP: Steve Edgar
VP: Rich Frediani
VP: Heidi Hand
VP: Terrence Hughes
VP: Ron Kane
VP: Tom Kelly
VP: Sam Pontrelli
VP: Gui Weaver
VP: Carl Willis
Exec: Annemarie McKeown
Exec: Kristen Purdy

D-U-N-S 96-174-6984
MONSTER HEAVY HAULERS LLC
222 Lexington Dr, Rayne, LA 70578-7535
Tel (337) 873-3085 *Founded/Ownrshp* 2009
Sales 35.6MM^E *EMP* 75
SIC 1623 1389 Oil & gas pipeline construction; Haulage, oil field

D-U-N-S 08-452-9171 IMP/EXP
MONSTER INC (CA)
MONSTER MUSIC
455 Valley Dr, Brisbane, CA 94005-1209
Tel (415) 840-2000 *Founded/Ownrshp* 1978
Sales 178.0MM^E *EMP* 700
SIC 3357 5999 3679 Nonferrous wiredrawing & insulating; Video & audio equipment; Cable & other pay television services; Headphones, radio
CEO: Noel Lee
CFO: Leo Lin
Sr VP: Deena Ghazarian
**VP:* Irene Baron
VP: Chaka Zulu
CIO: Oded Haner
Dir IT: Amir Shafi
Natl Sales: Michael Davis
Natl Sales: Stephanie Nordhaus

MONSTER MUSIC
See MONSTER INC

MONSTER TOOL COMPANY
See CARBIDE CO LLC

D-U-N-S 05-047-1754
▲ **MONSTER WORLDWIDE INC**
133 Boston Post Rd # 15, Weston, MA 02493-2525
Tel (978) 461-8000 *Founded/Ownrshp* 1967
Sales 770.0MM *EMP* 4,000
Accts Bdo Usa Llp New York New Yo
Tkr Sym MWW *Exch* NYS
SIC 7311 7361 Advertising agencies; Employment agencies; Advertising agencies; Employment agencies
CEO: Timothy T Yates
Pr: Mark Stoever
CFO: Michael B McGuinness
Ofcr: Lise Poulos
Ex VP: Steven M Cooker
Sr VP: Phillip Bond
Sr VP: Jeffrey Fleischman
Sr VP: Susan J Hayden
Sr VP: Kathy Paladino
Sr VP: Faye Palmacci
Sr VP: Linda Soldatos
VP: John Kinsella
VP: Michael Lonigro
Board of Directors: Gillian Munson

D-U-N-S 16-365-1545 IMP
MONT DOR OF AMERICA LLC
ALLIANCE TIME COMPANY
545 Broadway Ste 3, Brooklyn, NY 11206-2962
Tel (212) 308-5580 *Founded/Ownrshp* 1998
Sales 40.7MM^E *EMP* 25
SIC 5094 Clocks, watches & parts
CEO: Hoch Mozes
Ex VP: Simon Zelman
VP: Jeffrey Rabinovich
CTO: Kent Helbig
Dir IT: Khalid Maqsudi
VP Opers: Akiva Goldstein

D-U-N-S 00-546-4060
MONT EAGLE MILLS INC
804 W Main St, Oblong, IL 62449-1164
Tel (618) 592-4211 *Founded/Ownrshp* 1979
Sales 37.2MM^E *EMP* 35
SIC 5153 5191 Grain elevators; Fertilizer & fertilizer materials; Chemicals, agricultural
Owner: Robert Glezen
**VP:* Harold Eubank

D-U-N-S 02-151-3820 IMP/EXP
MONTACHEM INTERNATIONAL INC
200 S Andrews Ave Ste 702, Fort Lauderdale, FL 33301-2066
Tel (954) 385-9908 *Founded/Ownrshp* 2004
Sales 284.5MM^E *EMP* 41
SIC 5169 Synthetic resins, rubber & plastic materials
CEO: Murcia Jerry
**Pr:* Liston Steve
**Treas:* Valentina Webel
**Prin:* Steven Liston
**Genl Mgr:* Juan Carlos Avila

D-U-N-S 07-536-7243
MONTACHUSETT OPPORTUNITY COUNCIL INC
133 Prichard St, Fitchburg, MA 01420-7539
Tel (978) 343-0185 *Founded/Ownrshp* 1966
Sales 16.5MM *EMP* 329
SIC 8399 Council for social agency; Council for social agency
Ex Dir: Kathy Mc Dormett
Ex Dir: Cathlene McDermott
Sls Mgr: Patricia Pistone

D-U-N-S 87-932-8094
MONTACHUSETT REGIONAL TRANSIT AUTHORITY
1427 Water St, Fitchburg, MA 01420-7266
Tel (978) 345-7711 *Founded/Ownrshp* 1979
Sales 77.0MM *EMP* 72
SIC 4119 Local passenger transportation; Local passenger transportation
Prin: Mohammed H Khan

D-U-N-S 07-345-8622
MONTAG & CALDWELL LLC
3455 Peachtree Rd Ne # 1200, Atlanta, GA 30326-4202
Tel (404) 262-0100 *Founded/Ownrshp* 2010
Sales 46.7MM *EMP* 60
SIC 6282 Investment counselors; Investment counselors
CEO: Bill Vogel
Pr: Ann Pusieko
**CFO:* Brian W Stahl
**Ch:* Ronald E Canakaris
Sr VP: Charles Hagood
VP: Sandra Barker
VP: Jane Davenport
VP: James M Francis IV
**VP:* Rebecca Keister
VP: William E Long III
VP: Charles Markwalter
VP: Kurt Momand
VP: George Northrop
VP: Carla Phillips
VP: David Watson
VP: Jeff Wilson
Exec: John Whitney

MONTAGE DEER VALLEY
See DV LUXURY RESORT LLC

D-U-N-S 12-285-5120
MONTAGE HOTELS & RESORTS LLC
MONTAGE LAGUNA BEACH
1 Ada Ste 250, Irvine, CA 92618-5340
Tel (949) 715-5002 *Founded/Ownrshp* 2002
Sales 464.4MM^E *EMP* 1,770
SIC 6531 Real estate managers; Real estate managers
CEO: Alan Fuerstman
**Pr:* Jason Herthel
**VP:* Iqbal Bashir
**VP:* James D Bermingham
**VP:* Bill Claypool
**VP:* Monica Digilio
VP: Edgar Gasparyan
**VP:* Greg Villeneuve
Dir Risk M: Andrew Flor
Mng Dir: Rick Riess
Dir Sec: Chad Pohle

MONTAGE INN
See PALMETTO BLUFF LODGE LLC

MONTAGE LAGUNA BEACH
See MONTAGE HOTELS & RESORTS LLC

D-U-N-S 00-915-2877 IMP
MONTAGUE CO (CA)
1830 Stearman Ave, Hayward, CA 94545-1018
Tel (510) 785-8822 *Founded/Ownrshp* 1932
Sales 32.2MM^E *EMP* 105
SIC 3589 Cooking equipment, commercial; Commercial cooking & foodwarming equipment; Cooking equipment, commercial; Commercial cooking & foodwarming equipment
Pr: Thomas M Whalen
**Ch:* Robert M Whalen
Sls&Mrk Ex: Steve Vassau

D-U-N-S 00-796-8415
MONTALBANO INC (CA)
STEWART CHEVROLET
780 Serramonte Blvd, Colma, CA 94014-3220
Tel (650) 994-2400 *Founded/Ownrshp* 1933
Sales 26.2MM^E *EMP* 60^E
SIC 5511 Automobiles, new & used; Pickups, new & used; Automobiles, new & used; Pickups, new & used
Pr: Paul Montalbano
**Sec:* Conchetta Shutt

D-U-N-S 00-493-0012
MONTALBANO LUMBER CO INC (TX)
1309 Houston Ave, Houston, TX 77007-6296
Tel (713) 228-9011 *Founded/Ownrshp* 1900, 1960
Sales 52.0MM *EMP* 103
SIC 5211 5031 Lumber & other building materials; Lumber products; Lumber: rough, dressed & finished; Building materials, exterior; Building materials, interior; Lumber & other building materials; Lumber products; Lumber: rough, dressed & finished; Building materials, exterior; Building materials, interior
Pr: Michael J Montalbano
**VP:* John J Montalbano

D-U-N-S 80-979-0546
MONTANA DEPARTMENT OF ADMINISTRATION
(*Suby of* EXECUTIVE OFFICE OF STATE OF MONTANA) ★
125 N Roberts St Rm 155, Helena, MT 59601-4558
Tel (406) 444-2032 *Founded/Ownrshp* 1971
Sales NA *EMP* 700
SIC 9199 General government administration; ; General government administration;

Ofcr: Brad Sanders
**CIO:* Ronald Baldwin

D-U-N-S 11-248-1648
MONTANA DEPARTMENT OF ENVIRONMENTAL QUALITY
(*Suby of* EXECUTIVE OFFICE OF STATE OF MONTANA) ★
1520 E 6th Ave Rm 3, Helena, MT 59601-4541
Tel (406) 444-0201 *Founded/Ownrshp* 1996
Sales NA *EMP* 438
SIC 9511 Air, water & solid waste management; ; Air, water & solid waste management;

D-U-N-S 80-979-1007
MONTANA DEPARTMENT OF FISH WILDLIFE AND PARKS
(*Suby of* EXECUTIVE OFFICE OF STATE OF MONTANA) ★
1420 E 6th Ave, Helena, MT 59601-3872
Tel (406) 444-3186 *Founded/Ownrshp* 1903
Sales NA *EMP* 450
SIC 9512 Land, mineral & wildlife conservation; ; Land, mineral & wildlife conservation;
Ch: Dan Vermillion
IT Man: Marjorie Gilbert

D-U-N-S 80-979-1031
MONTANA DEPARTMENT OF LABOR AND INDUSTRY
(*Suby of* EXECUTIVE OFFICE OF STATE OF MONTANA) ★
1327 Lockey Ave, Helena, MT 59601-5195
Tel (406) 444-3555 *Founded/Ownrshp* 1893
Sales NA *EMP* 671
SIC 9651 Labor regulatory agency; ; Labor regulatory agency;

D-U-N-S 80-979-1056
MONTANA DEPARTMENT OF MILITARY AFFAIRS
MONTANA NAT GRD/VTRANS AFFAIRS
(*Suby of* EXECUTIVE OFFICE OF STATE OF MONTANA) ★
1900 Williams St, Fort Harrison, MT 59636
Tel (406) 324-3000 *Founded/Ownrshp* 1889
Sales NA *EMP* 383
SIC 9711 National security; ; National security;
Prin: Mg Randall D Mosley
**Prin:* Karen Revious
IT Man: Peter Schaefer

D-U-N-S 94-962-6444
MONTANA DEPARTMENT OF PUBLIC HEALTH AND HUMAN SERVICES
(*Suby of* EXECUTIVE OFFICE OF STATE OF MONTANA) ★
111 N Sanders St Rm 6, Helena, MT 59601-4520
Tel (406) 444-4228 *Founded/Ownrshp* 1930
Sales NA *EMP* 2,900
SIC 9431 ;

D-U-N-S 80-979-1320
MONTANA DEPARTMENT OF TRANSPORTATION
(*Suby of* EXECUTIVE OFFICE OF STATE OF MONTANA) ★
2701 Prospect Ave, Helena, MT 59601-9746
Tel (406) 444-6201 *Founded/Ownrshp* 1991
Sales NA *EMP* 1,725
SIC 9621 Regulation, administration of transportation; ; Regulation, administration of transportation;
Ofcr: Margaret Souza
Comm Dir: Casey Kyler-West
Prgrm Mgr: Alice Flesch
Prgrm Mgr: Kathy Terrio
Off Mgr: Larry Murolo
Mktg Mgr: Angela Wong

D-U-N-S 80-958-8726
MONTANA DEPT OF JUSTICE
(*Suby of* EXECUTIVE OFFICE OF STATE OF MONTANA) ★
215 N Sanders St, Helena, MT 59601-4522
Tel (406) 444-2026 *Founded/Ownrshp* 2000
Sales NA *EMP* 1,124
SIC 9222 Attorney General's office; ; Attorney General's office;
Prin: Mike McGrath
Ofcr: Kevin Downs
Plnt Mgr: CT Reap
**Counsel:* Chris Tweeten

D-U-N-S 80-979-1304
MONTANA DEPT OF NATURAL RESOURCES & CONSERVATION
(*Suby of* EXECUTIVE OFFICE OF STATE OF MONTANA) ★
1625 11th Ave Ste 2, Helena, MT 59601-4668
Tel (406) 444-2074 *Founded/Ownrshp* 1927
Sales NA *EMP* 500
SIC 9512 9511 Land conservation agencies; ; Water control & quality agency, government; Land conservation agencies; ; Water control & quality agency, government

MONTANA GROUP
See MONTANA SILVERSMITHS INC

D-U-N-S 04-156-8492
MONTANA HEALTHCARE FOUNDATION
777 E Main St Ste 206, Bozeman, MT 59715-3809
Tel (406) 451-7060 *Founded/Ownrshp* 2014
Sales 23.3MM *EMP* 4
SIC 8641 Civic social & fraternal associations
CEO: Aaron Wernham

D-U-N-S 12-205-9611
MONTANA HIGHER EDUCATION STUDENT ASSISTANCE CORP
MHESAC
2500 E Broadway St, Helena, MT 59601-4901
Tel (406) 495-7800 *Founded/Ownrshp* 1980
Sales NA *EMP* 80
SIC 6111 Student Loan Marketing Association; Student Loan Marketing Association

Ex Dir: Jim Stipcich
**Pr:* Richard A Crofts
Treas: Rolf Groseth
**Treas:* Arlene Hannawalt
**VP:* Rodney Sundsted
CIO: Tim Donahue

D-U-N-S 00-523-1873
MONTANA METAL PRODUCTS LLC (IL)
MMP
25 Howard Ave, Des Plaines, IL 60018-1901
Tel (847) 803-6600 *Founded/Ownrshp* 1957, 1996
Sales 23.5MM^E *EMP* 115^E
SIC 3444 Sheet metalwork
**CFO:* Michael Faten

MONTANA NAT GRD/VTRANS AFFAIRS
See MONTANA DEPARTMENT OF MILITARY AFFAIRS

D-U-N-S 80-958-8700
MONTANA OFFICE OF PUBLIC INSTRUCTION
(*Suby of* EXECUTIVE OFFICE OF STATE OF MONTANA) ★
1227 11th Ave, Helena, MT 59601-3910
Tel (406) 444-7362 *Founded/Ownrshp* 1889
Sales NA *EMP* 342
SIC 9411 Administration of educational programs; ; Administration of educational programs;

D-U-N-S 82-876-0764
MONTANA PETERBILT LLC
3255 N Frontage Rd, Billings, MT 59101-7427
Tel (406) 896-6640 *Founded/Ownrshp* 2008
Sales 49.9MM *EMP* 67
Accts Galusha Higgins & Galusha Pc
SIC 5511 Trucks, tractors & trailers: new & used; Trucks, tractors & trailers: new & used

D-U-N-S 18-063-0378
MONTANA RAIL LINK INC
M R L
101 International Dr, Missoula, MT 59808-1598
Tel (406) 523-1288 *Founded/Ownrshp* 2015
Sales 120.7MM^E *EMP* 1,150
SIC 4011 Switching & terminal services; Railroads, line-haul operating; Railroads, line-haul operating
Pr: Tom Walsh
Pr: Lynda Frost
CFO: Dave Koerner
Bd of Dir: Rick Shelley
VP: David Koerner
Exec: Clint Hammer
CTO: Steve Larance
Snr Mgr: Richard Keller

D-U-N-S 14-418-0304 IMP/EXP
MONTANA RESOURCES INC
600 Shields Ave, Butte, MT 59701-2799
Tel (406) 496-3200 *Founded/Ownrshp* 1985
Sales NA *EMP* 335
SIC 1061 1021 Molybdenum ores mining; Open pit copper ore mining; Molybdenum ores mining; Open pit copper ore mining
Prin: Dennis Washington
VP: Keith Graham
CIO: Thomas Dale
Sfty Dirs: Pete Steelman

D-U-N-S 02-081-8337
MONTANA ROCKWORKS INC
1107 Rose Xing, Kalispell, MT 59901-6634
Tel (406) 752-7625 *Founded/Ownrshp* 2006
Sales 22.2MM^E *EMP* 115
SIC 5032 Building stone
Pr: Brad Mercord
**VP:* Bill Carter
Sfty Mgr: Mark Halbur
Natl Sales: Beth Dewbre
Natl Sales: Beth McBride
Mktg Mgr: Tristan Taylor

D-U-N-S 07-141-2340
MONTANA SILVERSMITHS INC
MONTANA GROUP
(*Suby of* GROUP MONTANA INC) ★
1 Sterling Ln, Columbus, MT 59019-7611
Tel (406) 322-4902 *Founded/Ownrshp* 1973
Sales 21.9MM^E *EMP* 200^E
SIC 3965 3911 Buckles & buckle parts; Jewelry, precious metal; Buckles & buckle parts; Jewelry, precious metal
Pr: George Branca
**CFO:* David Stimmel
Dir IT: Steve Anderson
IT Man: Lorie Adkins
VP Sls: Steve Miller

D-U-N-S 15-780-3784 IMP
MONTANA SPECIALTY MILLS LLC
701 2nd St S, Great Falls, MT 59405-1852
Tel (406) 761-2338 *Founded/Ownrshp* 1997
Sales 30.9MM^E *EMP* 20
SIC 2076 2099 4221 Vegetable oil mills; Food preparations; Grain elevator, storage only
Genl Mgr: Gordon Svenby
Plng Mgr: Gordon Mattern

D-U-N-S 07-884-8042
MONTANA STATE FUND
855 Front St, Helena, MT 59601
Tel (406) 444-6500 *Founded/Ownrshp* 1990
Sales NA *EMP* 287
SIC 6331 Workers' compensation insurance; Workers' compensation insurance
Pr: Laurence Hubbard
Snr Sftwr: Darren Munson
CIO: Sandy Leyva
CTO: Pam Byers
Netwrk Mgr: Wes Winden
Sftwr Eng: Gary Brewer
Sftwr Eng: Bryan Flynn
Sftwr Eng: Darin Holloway
Sftwr Eng: Beth Richardson
Snr Mgr: Maura Fleetwood
Snr Mgr: Dennis Lee

MONTANA STATE UNIV - BOZEMAN
See MONTANA STATE UNIVERSITY INC

D-U-N-S 06-556-9048
MONTANA STATE UNIVERSITY INC
MONTANA STATE UNIV - BOZEMAN
(*Suby of* MONTANA UNIVERSITY SYSTEM) ★
901 W Garfield St, Bozeman, MT 59717
Tel (406) 994-4361 *Founded/Ownrshp* 1893
Sales 341.8MM *EMP* 2,500^E
Accts Legislative Audit Division Ci
SIC 8221 University; University
Pr: Waded Cruzado
**Treas:* Laura Humberger
Ofcr: Donald Bolick
Ofcr: Thomas Bonnell
Ofcr: Ronald Brekke
Ofcr: Naomi Woienski
VP: Brittany Nickolay
VP: Craig Oloff
Prgrm Mgr: Julie Clay
Prgrm Mgr: Signe Lahren
Prgrm Mgr: Andrea Rankin

D-U-N-S 07-971-3608
MONTANA STATE UNIVERSITY-BILLINGS (MT)
CITY COLLEGE
(*Suby of* MONTANA STATE UNIV - BOZEMAN) ★
1500 University Dr, Billings, MT 59101-0245
Tel (406) 657-2011 *Founded/Ownrshp* 1927
Sales 35.4MM *EMP* 1,109
Accts Cindy Jorgensen Helena Mt
SIC 4832 5942 8221 Radio broadcasting stations; Book stores; Colleges & universities; Radio broadcasting stations; Book stores; Colleges & universities
Pr: Tim Schruth
**Treas:* Curt Starr
Ofcr: Don Cetrone
Ofcr: Ryan Endres
Ofcr: Ashley Picard
Ofcr: Charles Smith
Ofcr: Bruce Wakefield
**VP:* Bobby Anner-Hughes
Comm Dir: Evan O'Kelly
**Prin:* Dean John Cech
Adm Dir: Sarah Brockel

D-U-N-S 07-140-8496
MONTANA TECH OF UNIVERSITY OF MONTANA
(*Suby of* RESEARCH & SPONSORED PROGRAMS) ★
1300 W Park St Ste A, Butte, MT 59701-8997
Tel (406) 496-4101 *Founded/Ownrshp* 1893, 2000
Sales 64.2MM^E *EMP* 709
SIC 8221 College, except junior; College, except junior
CEO: Donald M Blackkatter
**CEO:* W Franklin Gilmore
Sr VP: Ed Metesh
Assoc Dir: Ruthanne Shope
IT Man: Jeff Johnson
Pr Dir: Dave Scott
HC Dir: Antoni Campeau

D-U-N-S 03-889-3972
MONTANA UNIFIED SCHOOL TRUST
MUST
P.O. Box 4579 (59604-4579)
Tel (406) 457-4400 *Founded/Ownrshp* 2011
Sales 30.6MM *EMP* 10
Accts Anderson Zurmuehlen & Co Pc H
SIC 8211 School board
Prin: Montana School

D-U-N-S 07-960-2596
MONTANA UNIVERSITY SYSTEM
2500 E Broadway St, Helena, MT 59601-4901
Tel (406) 444-6570 *Founded/Ownrshp* 1994
Sales 627.6MM^E *EMP* 2,500^E
SIC 8221 University; University
Ofcr: Tina Bright
Ofcr: Karl Kruger
Ofcr: Susan Witte
Assoc Dir: Mary Lachenbruch

D-U-N-S 94-868-6894 IMP
MONTAPLAST OF NORTH AMERICA INC
(*Suby of* MONTAPLAST GESELLSCHAFT MIT BESCHRANKTER HAFTUNG)
2011 Hoover Blvd, Frankfort, KY 40601-8213
Tel (502) 695-7766 *Founded/Ownrshp* 1992
Sales 91.1MM^E *EMP* 284^E
SIC 3714 3089 Motor vehicle parts & accessories; Plastic processing; Motor vehicle parts & accessories; Plastic processing
Pr: Christian A Stulz
**CFO:* Holger Ramcke
VP: Sanford Roth
**Prin:* Albert Stulz Jr
Prgrm Mgr: Derek Johnson
VP Mfg: Dave Burnett
VP Opers: Karlheinz Poehlmann
QC Dir: Tom Nimrick
Opers Mgr: Anthony Moore
Plnt Mgr: Thomas Shuck
Ql Cn Mgr: Scott Kutnick
Board of Directors: John Phillips

D-U-N-S 02-491-6640
MONTAUK BUS SERVICE INC (NY)
242 W Montauk Hwy, Hampton Bays, NY 11946-3510
Tel (631) 723-1439 *Founded/Ownrshp* 1998, 1999
Sales 19.3MM^E *EMP* 400^E
SIC 4151 School buses; School buses
Pr: John Mensch

D-U-N-S 87-663-7336
MONTAUK ENERGY CAPITAL LLC
(*Suby of* HOSKEN CONSOLIDATED INVESTMENTS LTD)
680 Andersen Dr Ste 500, Pittsburgh, PA 15220-2775
Tel (412) 747-8700 *Founded/Ownrshp* 2006
Sales 47.4MM^E *EMP* 52^E
SIC 4931 4924 ; Natural gas distribution
CEO: David Herrman
**CFO:* Sean McClain
Ex VP: Marshall Morris

**VP:* Marty Ryan
Rgnl Mgr: Joe Sziveri
VP Opers: Scott Hill
VP Opers: George O'Mahony
Plnt Mgr: John Babineaux

D-U-N-S 79-057-2655
MONTBLANC NORTH AMERICA LLC
(*Suby of* COMPAGNIE FINANCIERE RICHEMONT SA)
645 5th Ave Fl 6, New York, NY 10022-5944
Tel (800) 995-4810 *Founded/Ownrshp* 1994
Sales 60.6MM^E *EMP* 200
SIC 5511 5943 New & used car dealers; Writing supplies; New & used car dealers; Writing supplies
CEO: Mike Giannattasio
Pr: Jan-Patrick Schmitz
CFO: Anthony Gruber
Merch Mgr: Toni Mitek

D-U-N-S 04-140-7750
MONTBLEAU & ASSOCIATES INC
555 Raven St, San Diego, CA 92102-4523
Tel (619) 263-5550 *Founded/Ownrshp* 1980
Sales 22.8MM^E *EMP* 90
Accts Leone Huffman & Associates I
SIC 2521 1751 2434 Wood office furniture; Cabinet building & installation; Wood kitchen cabinets
Pr: Ron P Montbleau
**Ex VP:* Barton Ward
**VP:* David Zammit
Rgnl Mgr: Bob Geyer
Sls&Mrk Ex: Tom Zeman
Sls Dir: Mike Bonde
Sales Asso: Ana Rothman
Snr PM: Steve Paul

D-U-N-S 04-073-1119
MONTCLAIR BOARD OF EDUCATION (INC)
22 Valley Rd, Montclair, NJ 07042-2709
Tel (973) 509-4000 *Founded/Ownrshp* 1890
Sales 101.7MM *EMP* 1,100
SIC 8211 Public elementary school; Public junior high school; Public senior high school; School board
Pr: Jessica Dekoninck
VP: Wilford Adkins
IT Man: Abagale Adams
IT Man: Samantha Morra

MONTCLAIR HOSPITAL MEDICAL CTR
See PRIME HEALTHCARE SERVICES III LLC

D-U-N-S 83-854-9392
MONTCLAIR HOTELS MB LLC
6600 Mannheim Rd, Rosemont, IL 60018-3625
Tel (847) 457-3900 *Founded/Ownrshp* 1995
Sales 32.0MM^E *EMP* 1,500
SIC 7011 Hotels & motels; Hotels & motels

D-U-N-S 06-427-5282 IMP
MONTCLAIR KIMBERLEY ACADEMY
INDEPENDENT EDUCATION PRE K-12
201 Valley Rd, Montclair, NJ 07042-2335
Tel (973) 746-9800 *Founded/Ownrshp* 2005
Sales 34.5MM *EMP* 250
Accts Eisneramper Llp Iselin New J
SIC 8211 Private combined elementary & secondary school; Private combined elementary & secondary school
CFO: Richard Sunshine
Comm Dir: Deborah Kozak
Dir IT: William Stites
IT Man: Erica Budd
Snr Mgr: Cherylanne Amendola
Board of Directors: John Garippa, Larry Gaydos, Newton Schott, Anne Muenster-Sinton, Jodi Smith

D-U-N-S 07-979-9162
MONTCLAIR PUBLIC SCHOOLS
22 Valley Rd, Montclair, NJ 07042-2709
Tel (973) 509-4000 *Founded/Ownrshp* 2015
Sales 11.0MM^E *EMP* 1,173^E
SIC 8211 Public elementary & secondary schools
Teacher Pr: Felice A Harrison

D-U-N-S 05-350-6184
MONTCLAIR STATE UNIVERSITY
825 8th Ave Fl 14, New York, NY 10019-7416
Tel (973) 655-4000 *Founded/Ownrshp* 1908
Sales 280.3MM *EMP* 2,000
Accts O Connonr Davies Llp Paramus
SIC 8221 University; University
Ch: George Hiltzik
**Pr:* Susan Cole
**V Ch Bd:* Dougla Kennedy
Ex VP: James Wassel
VP: Gregory Bressler
**VP:* Willard Gingerich
VP: Karen Pennington
VP: John T Shannon
Ex Dir: Julie Adams
Prd Mgr: Jeffrey Rosolen
Psych: Doris V Reavis

D-U-N-S 19-377-3249
MONTCO OFFSHORE INC
17751 Highway 3235, Galliano, LA 70354-3578
Tel (985) 325-7157 *Founded/Ownrshp* 1981
Sales 20.7MM^E *EMP* 150
SIC 7359 4499 Equipment rental & leasing; Boat rental, commercial; Equipment rental & leasing; Boat rental, commercial
Pr: Lee Orgeron
Treas: Melvin Gisclair
**Sec:* Derek Boudreaux
**VP:* Wayne Tyler
Off Mgr: Christie Orgeron
**CTO:* Joseph Orgeron

MONTE CARLO HOTEL AND CASINO
See VICTORIA PARTNERS

D-U-N-S 03-212-1386
MONTE VISTA COOPERATIVE
1901 Us Highway 160 E, Monte Vista, CO 81144-9350
Tel (719) 852-5181 *Founded/Ownrshp* 1949
Sales 53.0MM *EMP* 105
Accts Scofield & Scofield Pc Cen

SIC 5191 5541 5153 Fertilizer & fertilizer materials; Filling stations, gasoline; Barley; Wheat; Fertilizer & fertilizer materials; Filling stations, gasoline; Barley; Wheat
CEO: Mike Boothe
**CEO:* Micheal Boothe
**CFO:* Judi Neufeld

D-U-N-S 96-802-7966 IMP/EXP
MONTEBELLO PACKAGING INC
(*Suby of* GREAT PACIFIC ENTERPRISES INC)
650 Industrial Dr, Lebanon, KY 40033-1953
Tel (270) 692-5760 *Founded/Ownrshp* 1991
Sales 35.0MM *EMP* 150E
SIC 3354 Aluminum pipe & tube
Pr: Betty Pilon
**Pr:* James E Reilly
**VP:* Michael Korenberg
Plnt Mgr: Betty J Pilon

D-U-N-S 07-694-9197
MONTEBELLO UNIFIED SCHOOL DISTRICT PROTECTIVE LEAGUE
123 S Montebello Blvd, Montebello, CA 90640-4729
Tel (323) 887-7900 *Founded/Ownrshp* 1933
Sales 296.9MM *EMP* 4,000
Accts Vasquez & Company Llp Los Ang
SIC 8211 Public elementary & secondary schools; Public elementary & secondary schools
CEO: Howard Stuckey Commander
**Pr:* David Bela
**Pr:* Edwin Chau
Exec: Grace Loya
Off Admin: Helen Babb
Off Admin: Maria Gonzalez
Off Admin: Renata Hernandez
Off Admin: Barbara Williams
Snr Ntwrk: Terry Moore
CIO: Bob Geiger
IT Man: Gabriela Orozco

MONTEBELLO WELLNESS CENTER
See OAKBEND MEDICAL CENTER

D-U-N-S 07-528-7219
MONTECITO BANK & TRUST
(*Suby of* MONTECITO BANCORP)
1010 State St, Santa Barbara, CA 93101-2711
Tel (805) 963-7511 *Founded/Ownrshp* 1974
Sales NA *EMP* 170
SIC 6022 State commercial banks; State commercial banks
CEO: Janet A Garufis
COO: Janel Smit
**CFO:* Bruce A Stevens
**Ch:* Michael Towbes
Ex VP: Robert Skinner
Sr VP: John Franklin
Sr VP: Jud Guillermonewton
Sr VP: Jeff Paul
Sr VP: Michelle Richardson
VP: Terease Chin
VP: Heidi Cougoule
VP: Scott Estby
VP: Brad Holt
VP: Darla Kot
VP: Robert Mislang
VP: Heather Olivera
VP: Ben Scott
Dir Risk M: Laurel Sykes

D-U-N-S 61-762-3876
MONTECITO PORTLAND LLC
KOIN 6 TV
222 Sw Columbia St, Portland, OR 97201-6600
Tel (503) 464-0600 *Founded/Ownrshp* 2012
Sales 21.3MME *EMP* 91
SIC 4833 Television broadcasting stations; Television broadcasting stations
Sls&Mrk Ex: Mike Henry

D-U-N-S 07-694-0352
MONTECITO RETIREMENT ASSOCIATION
CASA DORINDA
300 Hot Springs Rd # 300, Santa Barbara, CA 93108-2037
Tel (805) 969-8011 *Founded/Ownrshp* 1973
Sales 23.3MM *EMP* 250
Accts Bartlett Pringle & Wolf Llp
SIC 8051 8052 8361 Skilled nursing care facilities; Personal care facility; Rest home, with health care incidental; Skilled nursing care facilities; Personal care facility; Rest home, with health care incidental
Pr: George Kolva
Exec: Thomas Abrahamsson
Opers Mgr: Tim Gallagher

D-U-N-S 01-740-9452 IMP
MONTEFERRO USA INC LLC
258 Global Dr, Orangeburg, SC 29115-8236
Tel (803) 531-1352 *Founded/Ownrshp* 2008
Sales 40.0MM *EMP* 5
SIC 7699 Industrial equipment services
Pr: Bill Welch

D-U-N-S 78-877-6685
MONTEFIORE HEALTH SYSTEM INC
MONTIFIORE NORTH MEDICAL CTR
555 S Broadway, Tarrytown, NY 10591-6301
Tel (718) 920-9000 *Founded/Ownrshp* 2004
Sales 4.1MM *EMP* 13,295E
Accts Ernst & Young Us Llp New York
SIC 8062 General medical & surgical hospitals; General medical & surgical hospitals
Pr: Steven M Safyer
**CFO:* Philip O Ozuah
**Ex VP:* Joel A Perlman
**Sr VP:* Alfredo Cabrera
**Sr VP:* Richard T Celiberti
Pathlgst: Lucia Wolgast
Obsttrcn: Cassandra E Henderson
Obsttrcn: Clelia Moline
Obsttrcn: Kristin Patzkowsky
Anesthlgy: Shafiq A Bazaz
Podiatrist: Bijou M Dennis-Nfor

D-U-N-S 07-775-9207
MONTEFIORE HOME
1 David N Myers Pkwy, Beachwood, OH 44122
Tel (216) 360-9080 *Founded/Ownrshp* 1881
Sales 27.4MME *EMP* 450
SIC 8051 Skilled nursing care facilities; Skilled nursing care facilities
CEO: Lauren B Rock
**CFO:* Mark Weiss
Snr Mgr: Barbara Gonick

D-U-N-S 83-316-3442
MONTEFIORE INFORMATION TECHNOLOGY LLC
(*Suby of* MONTEFIORE MEDICAL CENTER) ★
3 Odell Plz, Yonkers, NY 10701-1405
Tel (914) 457-3448 *Founded/Ownrshp* 2001
Sales 48.9MME *EMP* 431
SIC 7361 7379 Executive placement; Computer related consulting services; Executive placement; Computer related consulting services
Off Mgr: Kawana Hart
IT Man: Patrick Sevcik

D-U-N-S 04-158-1026 IMP
MONTEFIORE MEDICAL CENTER
111 E 210th St, Bronx, NY 10467-2401
Tel (718) 920-4321 *Founded/Ownrshp* 1884
Sales 2.3MMM *EMP* 11,000
Accts Ernst & Young Us Llp New York
SIC 8062 General medical & surgical hospitals; General medical & surgical hospitals
CEO: Steven M Safyer MD
COO: Susan Green
Treas: Tammi Reel
Assoc VP: Jeannine McCormack
**Ex VP:* Philip O Ozuah
**Ex VP:* Joel A Perlman
**Sr VP:* Alfredo Cabrera
**Sr VP:* Lynn Richmond
VP: Audre Bagnall
VP: Marjory Karlin
VP: Joanne Ritter-Teitel
VP: Peter Semczuk
Assoc Dir: Ronald Walsh

D-U-N-S 07-923-0100
MONTEFIORE MOUNT VERNON HOSPITAL
(*Suby of* MONTEFIORE MEDICAL CENTER) ★
12 N 7th Ave, Mount Vernon, NY 10550-2026
Tel (914) 664-8000 *Founded/Ownrshp* 2013
Sales 50.0MME *EMP* 600
SIC 8062 General medical & surgical hospitals; General medical & surgical hospitals
Pr: Steven M Safyer
**COO:* Philip O Ozuah
**CFO:* Joel A Perlman

D-U-N-S 07-923-0105
MONTEFIORE NEW ROCHELLE HOSPITAL
(*Suby of* MONTEFIORE MEDICAL CENTER) ★
16 Guion Pl, New Rochelle, NY 10801-5502
Tel (914) 632-5000 *Founded/Ownrshp* 2013
Sales 120.1MME *EMP* 1,200E
SIC 8062 General medical & surgical hospitals; General medical & surgical hospitals
Pr: Steven M Safyer
**COO:* Philip O Ozuah
**CFO:* Joel A Perlman

D-U-N-S 07-499-7545
MONTEFIORE UNIVERSITY HOSPITAL
(*Suby of* UNIVERSITY OF PITTSBURGH MEDICAL CENTER) ★
3459 5th Ave, Pittsburgh, PA 15213-3236
Tel (412) 647-2345 *Founded/Ownrshp* 1990
Sales 54.2MME *EMP* 1,500
SIC 8062 General medical & surgical hospitals; General medical & surgical hospitals
Pr: Jeffrey A Romoff
CFO: Robert Demichiei
Doctor: T C Gamblin MD

D-U-N-S 07-303-2232
MONTEITH CONSTRUCTION CORP
32 N Front St, Wilmington, NC 28401-4482
Tel (704) 405-1011 *Founded/Ownrshp* 2012
Sales 25.8MME *EMP* 40
SIC 1542 Nonresidential construction
Pr: John Monteith
**Mng Pt:* Denise Brandon
**VP:* Michael Montieth
VP: Bryan Thomas
Off Admin: Meagan Hutchings

D-U-N-S 82-847-7195
MONTELUCIA RESORT & SPA LLC
OMNI SCOTTSDALE RESORT
(*Suby of* KSL CAPITAL PARTNERS LLC) ★
4949 E Lincoln Dr, Scottsdale, AZ 85253-4108
Tel (480) 627-3200 *Founded/Ownrshp* 2011
Sales 25.6MME *EMP* 475
SIC 7011 Resort hotel; Resort hotel
Dir IT: Stefan Sbiera

MONTENAY POWER
See VEOLIA ES WASTE-TO-ENERGY INC

MONTEREAU IN WARREN WOODS
See MONTEREAU INC

D-U-N-S 12-572-9470
MONTEREAU INC
MONTEREAU IN WARREN WOODS
6800 S Granite Ave, Tulsa, OK 74136-7039
Tel (918) 491-5200 *Founded/Ownrshp* 1999
Sales 31.6MM *EMP* 240
Accts Cliftonlarsonallen Llp St Lou
SIC 8051 8361 Skilled nursing care facilities; Residential care; Skilled nursing care facilities; Residential care
Prin: William K Warren
**CEO:* Mark Fried
CFO: Angela Larson
**Ch:* John-Kelly C Warren
**VP:* Thomas E Cooper
**Ex Dir:* William A Major
Nrsg Dir: Diane Reagle

D-U-N-S 05-866-3162
MONTEREY BAY AQUARIUM FOUNDATION
886 Cannery Row, Monterey, CA 93940-1023
Tel (831) 648-4800 *Founded/Ownrshp* 1978
Sales 86.5MM *EMP* 380E
Accts Grant Thornton Llp San Franci
SIC 8422 Aquarium; Aquarium
CEO: Julie Packard
**Ch Bd:* Peter Bing
Pr: Hank Armstrong
Pr: Justin Skinner
**CFO:* Edward Prohaska
Ofcr: James Bonovich
Ofcr: Scott Chapman
Ofcr: Elaine Tobosa
VP: Margaret Spring
VP: Cynthia Vernon
Mng Dir: James Hekkers

D-U-N-S 17-834-1772 IMP
MONTEREY BAY AQUARIUM RESEARCH INSTITUTE
MBARI
7700 Sandholdt Rd, Moss Landing, CA 95039-9644
Tel (831) 775-1700 *Founded/Ownrshp* 1987
Sales 47.0MM *EMP* 220
SIC 8731 Commercial physical research; Commercial physical research
Pr: Christopher A Scholin
**Pr:* Marcia McNutt
COO: Keith Raybould
Bd of Dir: Eric Hartwig
Ofcr: Dan Chamberlain
**VP:* Julie Packard
Exec: Judith Connor
Exec: Jason Felton
Dir Lab: William Kirkwood
Prgrm Mgr: David Anderson
Snr Sftwr: Andrew Pearce

MONTEREY BOATS
See SEABRING MARINE INDUSTRIES INC

D-U-N-S 80-016-5933
MONTEREY COUNTY OFFICE OF EDUCATION
MCOE
901 Blanco Cir, Salinas, CA 93901-4401
Tel (831) 755-0301 *Founded/Ownrshp* 2007
Sales 46.6MME *EMP* 820E
SIC 8211 Public elementary & secondary schools; Public elementary & secondary schools
**Pr:* Harvey Kuffner
**VP:* John McPherson
Exec: Barry Brown
Pgrm Dir: Charles Parker

MONTEREY HOMES
See MERITAGE HOMES OF FLORIDA INC

D-U-N-S 00-178-2952 IMP
MONTEREY INC
MONTEREY MILLS
(*Suby of* ROLLER FABRICS) ★
1725 E Delavan Dr, Janesville, WI 53546-2704
Tel (608) 754-2866 *Founded/Ownrshp* 2005
Sales 26.1MME *EMP* 100
SIC 2221 2392 2257 Pile fabrics, manmade fiber & silk; Household furnishings; Weft knit fabric mills
Pr: Daniel Sinykin
VP: Brent Birkhoss
VP: Walt Oakley
Natl Sales: Cheryl Marchek
Sls Dir: Dan Koopmann

D-U-N-S 36-267-8547
MONTEREY LIGHTING SOLUTIONS INC
1151 N Del Rio Pl, Ontario, CA 91764-4505
Tel (909) 397-8000 *Founded/Ownrshp* 2003
Sales 21.8MME *EMP* 25
SIC 5063 Lighting fixtures
CEO: Steven Spitzer
**Pr:* Clark Longhurst
Sales Asso: Oscar Sanchez

D-U-N-S 03-764-0844
MONTEREY MECHANICAL CO
CONTRA COSTA METAL FABRICATORS
8275 San Leandro St, Oakland, CA 94621-1972
Tel (510) 632-3173 *Founded/Ownrshp* 1942
Sales 79.0MME *EMP* 150
SIC 1629 1711 1761 3444 3441 1542 Waste disposal plant construction; Waste water & sewage treatment plant construction; Mechanical contractor; Boiler setting contractor; Boiler maintenance contractor; Sheet metalwork; Sheet metalwork; Fabricated structural metal; Nonresidential construction; Waste disposal plant construction; Waste water & sewage treatment plant construction; Mechanical contractor; Boiler setting contractor; Boiler maintenance contractor; Sheet metalwork; Sheet metalwork; Fabricated structural metal; Nonresidential construction
CEO: Milton C Burleson
**Pr:* Jim Troup
**CFO:* Paul Moreira
Sr VP: Mark Alvarez
Exec: Vy Nguyen
Div Mgr: Karl Hosier
CIO: Bob Giovannonni
IT Man: Mark Elvest
Sales Exec: Doug Baker

MONTEREY MILLS
See MONTEREY INC

D-U-N-S 08-859-5186 IMP
MONTEREY MUSHROOMS INC
260 Westgate Dr, Watsonville, CA 95076-2452
Tel (831) 763-5300 *Founded/Ownrshp* 1988
Sales 748.8MME *EMP* 3,500
SIC 0182 Mushrooms grown under cover; Mushrooms grown under cover
Pr: Shah Kazemi
**CFO:* Ray Selle
VP: Joe Caldwell
Exec: Terry Marler
Exec: Edward Stoll
Genl Mgr: Wayne Bautista
CTO: Laurie Heath

Dir IT: Michael Matelli
Software D: Julie Williams
Opers Mgr: Bob Emery

MONTEREY PARK HOSPITAL
See PARK MONTEREY HOSPITAL

MONTEREY PASTA COMPANY
See PULMUONE FOODS USA INC

D-U-N-S 07-631-1547
MONTEREY PENINSULA COLLEGE
MONTEREY PNNSULA CMNTY COLLEGE
(*Suby of* CALIFORNIA COMMUNITY COLLEGES SYSTEM) ★
980 Fremont St, Monterey, CA 93940-4799
Tel (831) 646-4010 *Founded/Ownrshp* 1945
Sales 18.1MME *EMP* 660
SIC 8222 Community college; Community college
Prin: Walter Britley
**Pr:* Dr Carl Ehmann
**VP:* Joe Bissell

D-U-N-S 07-717-0983
MONTEREY PENINSULA COUNTRY CLUB
MPCC
3000 Club Rd, Pebble Beach, CA 93953-2542
Tel (831) 373-1556 *Founded/Ownrshp* 1925
Sales 21.7MM *EMP* 130
Accts Pkf Certified Public Accountan
SIC 7997 Country club, membership
CEO: Robert Perry Smith
**Ex Dir:* Michael Bowhay

D-U-N-S 02-401-0530
MONTEREY PENINSULA ENGINEERING
192 Healy Ave, Marina, CA 93933-2203
Tel (831) 384-4081 *Founded/Ownrshp* 1980
Sales 27.3MME *EMP* 150
SIC 1611 1623

D-U-N-S 83-242-3375 IMP/EXP
MONTEREY PENINSULA HORTICULTURE INC
360 Espinosa Rd, Salinas, CA 93907-8895
Tel (831) 449-3440 *Founded/Ownrshp* 1982
Sales 56.6MME *EMP* 267
SIC 0181 5193 Ornamental nursery products; Flowers & nursery stock; Ornamental nursery products; Flowers & nursery stock
CEO: Charles Kosmont
**Pr:* Sergio Silva
**VP:* Marc Clark

D-U-N-S 07-718-6302
MONTEREY PENINSULA UNIFIED SCHOOL DISTRICT
700 Pacific St, Monterey, CA 93940-2815
Tel (831) 392-3915 *Founded/Ownrshp* 1933
Sales 52.7MME *EMP* 1,400
SIC 8211 Public elementary & secondary schools; Public elementary & secondary schools
Trst: Bettye Lusk
VP: Tom Jennings
Dir IT: Gerardo Z Ceja
Dir IT: Antonio Navarro
Site Mgr: Sylvia Covarrubias
Site Mgr: Latonya Glover
Site Mgr: Amanda Newman
Site Mgr: Paya Vang
Pr Dir: Marcy McFadden

MONTEREY PLAZA HOTEL & SPA
See MONTEREY PLAZA HOTEL LIMITED PARTNERSHIP

D-U-N-S 83-643-5214
MONTEREY PLAZA HOTEL LIMITED PARTNERSHIP
MONTEREY PLAZA HOTEL & SPA
400 Cannery Row, Monterey, CA 93940-7501
Tel (800) 334-3999 *Founded/Ownrshp* 1993
Sales 24.4MME *EMP* 360
SIC 7011 Hotels; Hotels
Genl Pt: John V Narigi

MONTEREY PNNSULA CMNTY COLLEGE
See MONTEREY PENINSULA COLLEGE

D-U-N-S 08-143-8236
MONTEREY REGIONAL WASTE MANAGEMENT DISTRICT
14201 Del Monte Blvd, Marina, CA 93933
Tel (831) 384-5313 *Founded/Ownrshp* 1951
Sales 26.1MME *EMP* 120
SIC 4953 4911 4931 Sanitary landfill operation; Recycling, waste materials; Generation, electric power; Electric & other services combined; Sanitary landfill operation; Recycling, waste materials; Generation, electric power; Electric & other services combined
Pr: William Merry
**CFO:* Charles Rees
**Ch:* Leo Laska
Exec: Richard Norton

D-U-N-S 10-277-2860
MONTEREY REGIONAL WATER POLLUTION CONTROL AGENCY
MRWPCA
5 Harris Ct Bldg D, Monterey, CA 93940-5756
Tel (831) 372-3367 *Founded/Ownrshp* 1972
Sales 47.6MME *EMP* 80
Accts Vavrinek Trine Day & Co Ll
SIC 4952 Sewerage systems; Sewerage systems
Genl Mgr: Keith Israel
Ofcr: James Coleman
Dir IT: Richard Gilliam
Sls Mgr: Garrett Haertel

D-U-N-S 86-720-3697
■ **MONTEREYS ACQUISITION CORP**
TORTUGA CANTINA
(*Suby of* MEXICAN RESTAURANTS INC) ★
12000 Aerospace Ave # 400, Houston, TX 77034-5587
Tel (832) 300-5858 *Founded/Ownrshp* 1994
Sales 17.3MME *EMP* 750
SIC 5812 Carry-out only (except pizza) restaurant; Carry-out only (except pizza) restaurant

VP: Andrew Dennard
CEO: Curt Glowacki
COO: Loic M Porry
VP: Nancy Croff

D-U-N-S 78-814-3191
MONTERREY IRON & METAL LTD
TOUCAN RECYCLING
2300 Frio City Rd, San Antonio, TX 78226-1520
Tel (210) 927-2727 *Founded/Ownrshp* 1994
Sales 41.7MM^E *EMP* 100
SIC 5093 Scrap & waste materials; Scrap & waste materials
CEO: Jack Vexler
**COO:* Jordan Vexler

MONTERREY THE NATURAL CHOICE
See MONTERREY PROVISION CO INC

D-U-N-S 06-447-8381 IMP
MONTERREY PROVISION CO INC (CA)
MONTERREY THE NATURAL CHOICE
7850 Waterville Rd, San Diego, CA 92154-8219
Tel (619) 294-2222 *Founded/Ownrshp* 1972
Sales 162.0MM *EMP* 130^E
SIC 5147 5143 5148 5113 Meats, fresh; Cheese; Fresh fruits & vegetables; Disposable plates, cups, napkins & eating utensils; Boxes & containers; Meats, fresh; Cheese; Fresh fruits & vegetables; Disposable plates, cups, napkins & eating utensils; Boxes & containers
Pr: Thomas Luke Abbott
Pr: John Verbeek
**VP:* Colleen Goodloe
Dir Soc: Amanda Rubio
IT Man: Grant Fisher
Opers Mgr: Carrie Craig
Opers Mgr: Cory Roughton
VP Sls: Paul Miller
Sls Dir: David Singh
Sales Asso: Barbara Hanmer
Sales Asso: Dave Ruiz

D-U-N-S 15-839-0158
MONTERREY SECURITY CONSULTANTS INC
2232 S Blue Island Ave, Chicago, IL 60608-4412
Tel (773) 843-0120 *Founded/Ownrshp* 1999
Sales 95.5MM^E *EMP* 1,150
SIC 8742 Management consulting services; Management consulting services
Pr: Juan Gaytan
Pr: Caesar Gaytan
COO: Anthony Casa
VP Opers: Steve Gaytan
Opers Mgr: Alfredo Guerra

D-U-N-S 05-865-6450 IMP
MONTERREY TILE CO
225 W Baseline Rd, Gilbert, AZ 85233-1014
Tel (480) 507-7966 *Founded/Ownrshp* 1991
Sales 32.1MM^E *EMP* 76
SIC 5023 Resilient floor coverings: tile or sheet
Pr: Ed York
**Pr:* Carl Lancaster
**VP:* Carla Lancaster
**VP:* Edward York
Opers Mgr: Steve Stierstorfer

D-U-N-S 80-534-5295 IMP
MONTESQUIEU CORP
MONTESQUIEU VINS & DOMAINES
8221 Arjons Dr Ste F, San Diego, CA 92126-6319
Tel (877) 705-5669 *Founded/Ownrshp* 1991
Sales 41.9MM^E *EMP* 100
SIC 5182 8743 Wine & distilled beverages; Promotion service; Wine & distilled beverages; Promotion service
Pr: Fonda Hopkins

MONTESQUIEU VINS & DOMAINES
See MONTESQUIEU CORP

D-U-N-S 08-657-9752
MONTEVIDEO SCHOOL DISTRICT 129
INDEPENDENT SCHOOL DST 129
2001 Williams Ave, Montevideo, MN 56265-2200
Tel (320) 269-6446 *Founded/Ownrshp* 1900
Sales 15.5MM^E *EMP* 290
SIC 8211 Public elementary & secondary schools; Public elementary & secondary schools
Bd of Dir: Carl Vanravensway
IT Man: Scott Ripley

MONTEVISTA HOSPITAL
See SBH-MONTEVISTA LLC

D-U-N-S 02-247-3342
MONTEZUMA-CORTEZ SCHOOL DISTRICT RE-1
400 N Elm St, Cortez, CO 81321-2736
Tel (970) 565-7282 *Founded/Ownrshp* 1967
Sales 21.0MM^E *EMP* 458
SIC 8211 Public combined elementary & secondary school; Public combined elementary & secondary school
CFO: Melissa Brunner
Teacher Pr: Dan Porter
Psych: Donnetta Dehart
Psych: Cindy Ryan

D-U-N-S 96-756-2281
MONTEZUMAS REVENGE INC
TOLTECA FOODS
4305 Steve Reynolds Blvd, Norcross, GA 30093-3362
Tel (770) 263-0490 *Founded/Ownrshp* 1995
Sales 26.9MM^E *EMP* 25
SIC 5141 Food brokers
CEO: Silvia V Gonzalez
**Pr:* Silvia Garcia
**CFO:* Javier Macias

MONTGMERY HOSP PHYSCN RFERRALS
See MONTGOMERY HOSPITAL

MONTGOMERY ADVERTISER
See ADVERTISER CO

D-U-N-S 80-178-3374
MONTGOMERY AREA FOOD BANK INC
521 Trade Center St, Montgomery, AL 36108-2107
Tel (334) 262-1157 *Founded/Ownrshp* 1986
Sales 34.2MM *EMP* 27
Accts Parker Gill Eisen & Stevenson
SIC 8699 Food co-operative; Food co-operative
VP: Clynt Hart
Ex Dir: E Hinman

D-U-N-S 78-409-6976
MONTGOMERY BANCORPORATION INC
1 First National Plz, Sikeston, MO 63801
Tel (573) 471-2275 *Founded/Ownrshp* 1984
Sales NA *EMP* 115
SIC 6022 State commercial banks; State commercial banks
Pr: Troy Wilson
**Ch Bd:* Joel A Montgomery Sr
**VP:* Richard H Montgomery

D-U-N-S 00-890-9236
MONTGOMERY BANK NATIONAL ASSOCIATION
FIRST NATIONAL BANK, THE
(*Suby of* MONTGOMERY BANCORPORATION INC) ★
1 Montgomery Bank Plz St, Sikeston, MO 63801-3069
Tel (573) 471-2275 *Founded/Ownrshp* 1984
Sales NA *EMP* 115^E
SIC 6021 National commercial banks; National commercial banks
CEO: Kenneth A Witbrodt Jr
**Pr:* Richard H Montgomery III
COO: Donna Evans
**CFO:* Gary Pewitt
Chf Cred: Ralph Green
Ofcr: Diane Eberhard
Ofcr: Brian Harper
Sr VP: Bob Cockrell
Brnch Mgr: August Kirn
Dir IT: Steven Ward
Mktg Mgr: Michelle Boldrey

D-U-N-S 07-824-4142
MONTGOMERY BELL ACADEMY INC
4001 Harding Pike, Nashville, TN 37205-1998
Tel (615) 298-5514 *Founded/Ownrshp* 1867
Sales 31.4MM *EMP* 135
Accts Rayburn Bates & Fitzgerald Pc
SIC 8211 Academy; Private senior high school; Academy; Private senior high school
Exec: Bradford Gioia
Treas: Michael Marro
Exec: Carrie Lund
Dir IT: Marc Ardisson
IT Man: Mark Ardisson
Sls Mgr: Peggy Jordan
Assoc Ed: Vicki Mayhew

MONTGOMERY, BOB HONDA
See BOB MONTGOMERY CHEVROLET HONDA INC

MONTGOMERY CHEVROLET
See TWO M CO INC

D-U-N-S 00-339-6421 IMP
MONTGOMERY COCA-COLA BOTTLING CO LTD (AL)
300 Coca Cola Rd, Montgomery, AL 36105-5401
Tel (334) 284-9555 *Founded/Ownrshp* 1934
Sales 73.1MM^E *EMP* 500
SIC 2086 5149 5499 5087 Soft drinks: packaged in cans, bottles, etc.; Soft drinks; Soft drinks; Vending machines & supplies; Soft drinks: packaged in cans, bottles, etc.; Soft drinks; Soft drinks; Vending machines & supplies
Exec: Tony Young
CTO: Adrianne Finch

D-U-N-S 07-482-0978
MONTGOMERY COLLEGE
900 Hungerford Dr, Rockville, MD 20850-1728
Tel (301) 279-5000 *Founded/Ownrshp* 1982
Sales 91.6MM *EMP* 3,600
Accts Cliftonlarsonallen Llp Balti
SIC 8222 Community college; Community college
Pr: Derionne Pollard
**VP:* Cathy Jones
Exec: Vivian Lawyer
Brnch Mgr: Charlene Nunley
Off Admin: Homa Arabshahi
Pgrm Dir: Liliana Arango
Snr Mgr: Michelle Santiago

D-U-N-S 18-397-5015
MONTGOMERY COSCIA GREILICH LLP
2500 Dallas Pkwy Ste 300, Plano, TX 75093-4872
Tel (972) 748-0300 *Founded/Ownrshp* 2001
Sales 42.9MM^E *EMP* 250
SIC 8742 7291 8721 Financial consultant; Tax return preparation services; Accounting, auditing & bookkeeping; Financial consultant; Tax return preparation services; Accounting, auditing & bookkeeping

MONTGOMERY COUNTY BD EDUCATN
See MONTGOMERY PUBLIC SCHOOLS

D-U-N-S 09-325-7475
MONTGOMERY COUNTY CHAPTER NYSARC INC
LIBERTY ENTERPRISES
(*Suby of* NYSARC INC) ★
43 Liberty Dr, Amsterdam, NY 12010-5635
Tel (518) 842-5080 *Founded/Ownrshp* 1954
Sales 42.7MM *EMP* 800
Accts Bdo Usa Llp New York Ny
SIC 8331 2841 0723 Sheltered workshop; Soap & other detergents; Fruit (fresh) packing services; Sheltered workshop; Soap & other detergents; Fruit (fresh) packing services
CEO: Frank Capone
**COO:* Mike Becker
**CFO:* Jennifer Saunders
VP: Kelly Swart
Ex Dir: Dan Jepsen
Ex Dir: Bruce Wilhelm
IT Man: Bernard Harman

MONTGOMERY COUNTY COMMISSION
See COUNTY OF MONTGOMERY

D-U-N-S 06-988-6679
MONTGOMERY COUNTY COMMUNITY COLLEGE FOUNDATION
MCCC
340 Dekalb Pike, Blue Bell, PA 19422-1412
Tel (215) 641-6300 *Founded/Ownrshp* 1964
Sales 2.8MM *EMP* 2,000^E
SIC 8222

D-U-N-S 03-974-5591
MONTGOMERY COUNTY EDUCATIONAL SERVICE CENTER
200 S Keowee St, Dayton, OH 45402-2242
Tel (937) 224-8087 *Founded/Ownrshp* 1916
Sales 18.4MM^E *EMP* 331
SIC 8211 Public elementary & secondary schools; Public elementary & secondary schools

D-U-N-S 08-187-3614
MONTGOMERY COUNTY INTERMEDIATE UNIT
MCIU
2 W Lafayette St, Norristown, PA 19401-4758
Tel (610) 755-9313 *Founded/Ownrshp* 1970
Sales 55.1M *EMP* 500
Accts Maillie Llp Oaks Pa
SIC 8299 Educational services; Educational services
CEO: John George
**CFO:* Stan H Wisler
Bd of Dir: Donna Kelly
Bd of Dir: Jane Mansuy
Bd of Dir: Monica Weber
Comm Dir: Kristen Rawlings
Ex Dir: Allan Moore
CIO: Larry Konig
MIS Dir: Joan Evans
MIS Dir: Taffy Wolfe
Teacher Pr: Jack Hurd

D-U-N-S 04-090-7123
MONTGOMERY COUNTY MEMORIAL HOSPITAL
2301 Eastern Ave, Red Oak, IA 51566-1305
Tel (712) 623-7000 *Founded/Ownrshp* 1940
Sales 56.5MM^E *EMP* 305
SIC 8062 General medical & surgical hospitals; General medical & surgical hospitals
CEO: Allen E Pohren
**CFO:* Richard J Leinen
**Ch:* Sarah Smith
CIO: Ronald Kloewer

D-U-N-S 02-735-6614
MONTGOMERY COUNTY PRIMARY CARE CORP
155 Memorial Dr, Pinehurst, NC 28374-8710
Tel (910) 576-6222 *Founded/Ownrshp* 2009
Sales 30.4MM *EMP* 4
Accts Dixon Hughes Goodman Llp Ashe
SIC 8011 Offices & clinics of medical doctors
Prin: David Kilarski
Dir IT: Mitch Walker

D-U-N-S 07-482-1505 EXP
MONTGOMERY COUNTY PUBLIC SCHOOLS
MCPS
850 Hungerford Dr Rm 149, Rockville, MD 20850-1718
Tel (301) 279-3617 *Founded/Ownrshp* 1858
Sales 2.6MMM *EMP* 11,500
SIC 8211

D-U-N-S 94-321-5830
MONTGOMERY COUNTY PUBLIC SCHOOLS
750 Imperial St, Christiansburg, VA 24073-5309
Tel (540) 382-5100 *Founded/Ownrshp* 1929
Sales 95.7MM^E *EMP* 1,700^E
SIC 8211 Public elementary & secondary schools; Public elementary & secondary schools
Bd of Dir: Drema Foster
Bd of Dir: Penny Franklin
Bd of Dir: Wendell Jones
Ofcr: Jason West
VP: Robin Grove
Prgrm Mgr: Larry Lowe
MIS Dir: Harvey Goodwin
Sls&Mrk Ex: Anne Guthrie
Pr Dir: Brenda Drake
Teacher Pr: Joe Makolandra
Teacher Pr: Roberta Snelling

D-U-N-S 07-984-0010
MONTGOMERY COUNTY R-II SCHOOL DISTRICT
418 N Highway 19, Montgomery City, MO 63361-5217
Tel (573) 564-2278 *Founded/Ownrshp* 2015
Sales 9.1MM^E *EMP* 344^E
SIC 8211 Public elementary & secondary schools

D-U-N-S 03-095-4341
MONTGOMERY COUNTY SCHOOL DISTRICT
640 Woodford Dr, Mount Sterling, KY 40353-9504
Tel (859) 497-8760 *Founded/Ownrshp* 1930
Sales 53.3MM^E *EMP* 600
Accts White L Associates Psc Rich
SIC 8211 Public elementary & secondary schools; High school, junior or senior; Public elementary & secondary schools; High school, junior or senior
CTO: John Porter
HC Dir: Shada Brewer
HC Dir: Shonda Brewer

D-U-N-S 18-419-4884
MONTGOMERY COUNTY SCHOOL DISTRICT
OFFICE OF SUPERINTENDENT
441 Page St, Troy, NC 27371-2839
Tel (910) 576-6511 *Founded/Ownrshp* 1926
Sales 40.3MM^E *EMP* 725^E

SIC 8211 9411 Public elementary & secondary schools; School board; Administration of educational programs; Public elementary & secondary schools; School board; Administration of educational programs
**Treas:* Kathy Johnson
Pr Dir: Katie Hursey

D-U-N-S 61-726-6275 IMP
■ **MONTGOMERY COVANTA INC**
(*Suby of* COVANTA ENERGY LLC) ★
21204 Martinsburg Rd, Dickerson, MD 20842-9406
Tel (301) 691-9000 *Founded/Ownrshp* 2013
Sales 48.1MM^E *EMP* 80^E
SIC 4953 Refuse collection & disposal services
CEO: Anthony J Orlando
**COO:* Seth Myones
**CFO:* Edward W Moneypenny
**Treas:* Louis M Walters
**Ex VP:* Brad Helgeson
**Ex VP:* John Klett
**Ex VP:* Derek Veenhof
Sfty Mgr: Matt Kossick

D-U-N-S 03-459-3558
MONTGOMERY FARMERS COOPERATIVE
1801 Wilma Rudolph Blvd, Clarksville, TN 37040-6795
Tel (931) 645-9628 *Founded/Ownrshp* 1945
Sales 26.0MM^E *EMP* 58
SIC 5191 5251 Farm supplies; Hardware
Pr: Jerry Albright
**Treas:* Chris Schmidt
Exec: Joel Baggett
Opers Mgr: Gary Lowe

MONTGOMERY GENERAL HOME CARE
See MONTGOMERY GENERAL HOSPITAL INC

D-U-N-S 05-556-9701
MONTGOMERY GENERAL HOSPITAL INC
MONTGOMERY GENERAL HOME CARE
401 6th Ave, Montgomery, WV 25136-2199
Tel (304) 442-4585 *Founded/Ownrshp* 1940
Sales 20.5MM *EMP* 260
Accts Arnett & Foster Pllc Charlest
SIC 8062 8051 General medical & surgical hospitals; Skilled nursing care facilities; General medical & surgical hospitals; Skilled nursing care facilities
CEO: Vickie Gay
**Pr:* Randolph G Mills
**CFO:* Sherri Murray
**Sec:* Patsy Tucker
Ofcr: Vicki Gay
Sr VP: Donna Raynes
Dir Lab: Pam Arthur
Dir Rx: Valerie Hughes
CIO: Denzil Blevins
QA Dir: Betty Edelman
Opers Mgr: Luann Bowen

D-U-N-S 07-780-6669 IMP
MONTGOMERY GENERAL HOSPITAL INC
MEDSTAR HEALTH VNA
(*Suby of* MEDSTAR HEALTH INC) ★
18101 Prince Philip Dr, Olney, MD 20832-1512
Tel (301) 774-8882 *Founded/Ownrshp* 1984
Sales 148.7MM *EMP* 1,500
Accts Kpmg Llp Mc Lean Va
SIC 8062 General medical & surgical hospitals; General medical & surgical hospitals
Pr: Peter W Monge
Pr: Inder Pahwar
COO: Robert Gancayco
COO: Frederick Guckes
COO: Adele Henderson
COO: John Kennedy
COO: Michelle Kosci
COO: Samuel Maller
COO: Curtis Ollayos
CFO: David Havrilla
Sr VP: Kiersten Henry
VP: Roger Leonard
VP: Kevin Mell
VP: Betty Anne Secrist
VP: Linda Winger
Exec: Karen Hardart
Exec: Owen Horne
Exec: Rong Huang
Exec: Julia Kariya
Exec: Alberto Rotsztain
Exec: Annemarie Steetin

D-U-N-S 00-796-5775
MONTGOMERY HARDWARE CO (CA)
8777 Lanyard Ct, Rancho Cucamonga, CA 91730-0804
Tel (909) 204-4000 *Founded/Ownrshp* 1917
Sales 23.0MM^E *EMP* 40
SIC 5072 5031 Builders' hardware; Doors; Builders' hardware; Doors
CEO: Stephen F Montgomery
Pr: Johnny J Wilson
Ex VP: Denise M Wilson
VP: Rick Meyers

D-U-N-S 36-370-7519
MONTGOMERY HOSPICE INC
MONTGY HOSPICE SOCIETY
1355 Piccard Dr Ste 100, Rockville, MD 20850-4317
Tel (301) 921-4400 *Founded/Ownrshp* 1979
Sales 22.1MM *EMP* 6
SIC 8052 Personal care facility; Personal care facility
Pr: Ann Mitchell
VP: Millicent Higgins
VP: Lisa Morris
VP: Gerry Vent
Dir Soc: Donna McKinney
Comm Dir: Susan Burket
IT Man: Nick Worthington
Doctor: Caren Glassman

D-U-N-S 07-365-8981
MONTGOMERY HOSPITAL
MONTGMERY HOSP PHYSCN RFERRALS
(*Suby of* ALBERT EINSTEIN HEALTHCARE NETWORK) ★
559 W Germantown Pike, Norristown, PA 19403-4250
Tel (610) 270-2000 *Founded/Ownrshp* 1874
Sales 65.1MM^E *EMP* 1,200^E

SIC 8062 General medical & surgical hospitals; Hospital, affiliated with AMA residency; General medical & surgical hospitals; Hospital, affiliated with AMA residency
Pr: Tim Casey
Dir Lab: Paul Belser
Doctor: Samuel Puleo

MONTGOMERY HOSPITAL PHYSICIAN
See FORNANCE PHYSICIAN SERVICES

D-U-N-S 09-483-4108
MONTGOMERY INDEPENDENT SCHOOL DISTRICT
13159 Walden Rd, Montgomery, TX 77356-5383
Tel (936) 582-1333 Founded/Ownrshp 1925
Sales 70.9MM EMP 750
Accts Weaver & Tidwell Llp Houston
SIC 8211 Public elementary & secondary schools; Public elementary & secondary schools
*CFO: Sharon Fields
Bd of Dir: Skip Stanberry
*Prin: Duane McFadden
*Prin: Bobby Morris
Dir IT: Jerry Krusleski
Netwrk Mgr: George Thornton
Opers Mgr: Sylvia Adam
Schl Brd P: Trish Mayne

D-U-N-S 01-766-1141
MONTGOMERY INN INC
BOATHOUSE
9440 Montgomery Rd, Cincinnati, OH 45242-7683
Tel (513) 791-3482 Founded/Ownrshp 1979
Sales 24.6MM^E EMP 550
SIC 5812 5813 Eating places; Drinking places; Eating places; Drinking places
Pr: Thomas Gregory
*Ex VP: Margaret Andrews
*Ex VP: Dean Gregory
*Ex VP: Victoria Gregory

MONTGOMERY IRON & METAL
See SABEL STEEL SERVICE INC

MONTGOMERY JEEP EAGLE
See LINCOLN MERCURY OF KINGS AUTO MALL

D-U-N-S 18-112-5337
MONTGOMERY MARION INC
MMI AGENCY
1712 Pease St, Houston, TX 77003-5040
Tel (713) 929-6900 Founded/Ownrshp 1986
Sales 23.4MM^E EMP 80
SIC 7311 8743 Advertising agencies; Public relations services; Advertising agencies; Public relations services
CEO: Benjamin Spiegel
*Pr: Cindy Marion
*Sr VP: Kelly Bright
*Sr VP: Jung Choi
*Sr VP: Lesa Sorrentino
VP: Brooks Boeing
*VP: Amanda Hansen

D-U-N-S 03-855-2246
MONTGOMERY MAZDA INC
2520 Sardis Rd N Ste 206, Charlotte, NC 28227-6744
Tel (704) 563-1510 Founded/Ownrshp 1980
Sales 25.0MM EMP 45
SIC 5511 Automobiles, new & used; Pickups, new & used; Automobiles, new & used; Pickups, new & used
Pr: Charles Montgomery

MONTGOMERY MCCRACKEN
See MONTGOMERY MCCRACKEN WALKER & RHOADS LLP

D-U-N-S 07-709-1429
MONTGOMERY MCCRACKEN WALKER & RHOADS LLP
MONTGOMERY MCCRACKEN
123 S Broad St Fl 24, Philadelphia, PA 19109-1023
Tel (215) 772-1500 Founded/Ownrshp 1912
Sales 36.2MM^E EMP 366
SIC 8111 General practice law office; General practice law office
Ch: Richard L Scheff
Pt: Jeanne Baker
Pt: Timothy Bergere
Pt: Ellen Brotman
Pt: Julie Chelius
Pt: Gregory Fox
Pt: Catherine Gillespie
Pt: Jeremy Mishkin
Pt: Katherine O'Brien
Pt: Joanne Semeister
Mng Pt: Daniel O'Meara
Mng Pt: Lee Unterman
Pr: Charmaine Butler
Pr: Kathy Lemma

MONTGOMERY MEDICAL EQUIPMENT
See TRICOUNTY MEDICAL EQUIPMENT AND SUPPLY LLC

MONTGOMERY MEDICAL EQUIPMENT
See QMES LLC

D-U-N-S 08-206-5442
MONTGOMERY PUBLIC SCHOOLS
MONTGOMERY COUNTY BD EDUCATN
307 S Decatur St, Montgomery, AL 36104-4305
Tel (334) 223-6873 Founded/Ownrshp 1910
Sales 229.6MM^E EMP 4,500
SIC 8211 Public elementary & secondary schools; Public elementary & secondary schools
Ex VP: Anna Willis
VP: Carol Doucet
*Prin: Gary Adams
*Prin: Ronald Glover
*Prin: Michael Lenhart
*Prin: Deborah Thomas
Dir Sec: Bobby Crew
Genl Mgr: Carlinda Percell
Dir IT: Drew Douglas
Dir IT: Gaynelle Harris-Jackson
IT Man: Steve Blair

D-U-N-S 61-723-2236
MONTGOMERY PULBIC SCHOOLS EDUCATIONAL FOUNDATION
850 Hungerford Dr, Rockville, MD 20850-1718
Tel (301) 517-5099 Founded/Ownrshp 1998
Sales 1.9MM EMP 1,900^E
SIC 8621 8741 Education & teacher association; Management services; Education & teacher association; Management services

D-U-N-S 09-355-8864 IMP
■ **MONTGOMERY REGIONAL HOSPITAL INC**
LEWISGALE HOSP AT MONTGOMERY
(Suby of HCA INC) ★
3700 S Main St, Blacksburg, VA 24060-7081
Tel (540) 951-1111 Founded/Ownrshp 1995
Sales 84.9MM EMP 437
SIC 8062 General medical & surgical hospitals; General medical & surgical hospitals
CEO: Scott Hill
*Pr: Samuel N Hazen
*Sr VP: Donald W Stinnett
*VP: David G Anderson
VP: Gege Beall
*VP: Dora A Blackwood
*VP: John M Franck II
CTO: Maggie Ratcliff
Dir IT: Dan Cheverton
IT Man: George Snyder
Obsttrcn: Robert J Young

MONTGOMERY SAND
See SCRUGGS CO

MONTGOMERY SEED & SUPPLY
See GROSOUTH INC

MONTGOMERY WATER WORKS
See WATER WORKS AND SANITARY SEWER BOARD OF MONTGOMERY ALABAMA

MONTGOMERY-HAGGLUND
See PACIFIC MOTION LLC

MONTGOMERYVILLE ACURA
See 309 AUTOMART INC

MONTGY HOSPICE SOCIETY
See MONTGOMERY HOSPICE INC

D-U-N-S 05-839-6557 IMP
MONTI INC
4510 Reading Rd, Cincinnati, OH 45229-1230
Tel (513) 761-7775 Founded/Ownrshp 1971
Sales 38.0MM^E EMP 150
SIC 3644 3599 Insulators & insulation materials, electrical; Machine shop, jobbing & repair; Insulators & insulation materials, electrical; Machine shop, jobbing & repair
Pr: Gavin J Narburgh
*VP: Beverly Narburgh

MONTICELLO
See THOMAS JEFFERSON FOUNDATION INC

MONTICELLO BANKING CO
See MONTICELLO BANKSHARES INC

D-U-N-S 00-687-0760
MONTICELLO BANKING CO (KY)
(Suby of MONTICELLO BANKING CO) ★
50 N Main St, Monticello, KY 42633-2851
Tel (606) 340-3159 Founded/Ownrshp 1894, 1982
Sales NA EMP 150
SIC 6022 State commercial banks; State commercial banks
CEO: Mack Butler
*Pr: Kenny Ramsey
*VP: Kevin R Mullins
CTO: Randy Parsons
IT Man: Kelley Rader

D-U-N-S 79-298-6242
MONTICELLO BANKSHARES INC
MONTICELLO BANKING CO
50 N Main St, Monticello, KY 42633-2851
Tel (606) 348-8411 Founded/Ownrshp 1982
Sales NA EMP 150
Accts Mountjoy & Bressler Llp Lexi
SIC 6022 State commercial banks; State commercial banks
Pr: Mack Butler
*CFO: Kevin Mullins
*Sec: Barbara Rice

MONTICELLO BIG LAKE NURSING HM
See CENTRACARE HEALTH-MONTICELLO SERVICES LLC

D-U-N-S 08-045-8714
MONTICELLO CENTRAL SCHOOL DISTRICT
237 Forestburgh Rd, Monticello, NY 12701-2649
Tel (845) 794-7702 Founded/Ownrshp 1956
Sales 28.0MM^E EMP 500
SIC 8211 Public elementary & secondary schools; Elementary school; Public elementary & secondary schools; Elementary school
HC Dir: Tanya Duryea

MONTICELLO HOUSE
See COMMUNITY LTC INC

D-U-N-S 18-934-8337
MONTICELLO INDEPENDENT SCHOOL DISTRICT 882
302 Washington St, Monticello, MN 55362-8812
Tel (763) 271-0300 Founded/Ownrshp 1900
Sales 55.0MM EMP 425
Accts Kern Dewenter Viere Ltd S
SIC 8211 Public elementary & secondary schools; Public elementary & secondary schools

D-U-N-S 82-532-1438
MONTICELLO PUBLIC SCHOOLS
302 Washington St, Monticello, MN 55362-8812
Tel (763) 272-2000 Founded/Ownrshp 2008
Sales 15.1MM^E EMP 396^E
SIC 8211 Public elementary & secondary schools

MONTIFIORE NORTH MEDICAL CTR
See MONTEFIORE HEALTH SYSTEM INC

D-U-N-S 01-399-8091 IMP
MONTOUR INDUSTRIAL SUPPLY INC
1400 2nd Ave, Coraopolis, PA 15108-1400
Tel (412) 262-7460 Founded/Ownrshp 1995
Sales 20.2MM^E EMP 47
SIC 5074 5251 5084 5085 Plumbing & hydronic heating supplies; Plumbing fittings & supplies; Plumbing & heating valves; Hardware; Water pumps (industrial); Fasteners, industrial: nuts, bolts, screws, etc.
Pr: William R Ondrasik
CFO: Howard Holmes
*Sec: Glenn Ondrasik
VP Sls: Rich Somplatsky
Sls Mgr: Joe Zuccarelli

D-U-N-S 14-497-3083 IMP
■ **MONTOUR LLC**
(Suby of TALEN ENERGY SUPPLY LLC) ★
835 Hamilton St, Allentown, PA 18101-2426
Tel (610) 774-5151 Founded/Ownrshp 2011
Sales 39.3MM^E EMP 114
SIC 4911 Distribution, electric power; Distribution, electric power
Pr: Paul A Farr

D-U-N-S 08-891-0922
MONTOUR SCHOOL DISTRICT (INC)
225 Clever Rd, Mc Kees Rocks, PA 15136-4015
Tel (412) 490-6500 Founded/Ownrshp 1950
Sales 26.7MM^E EMP 350
SIC 8211 Public elementary school; Public junior high school; Public senior high school; Public elementary school; Public junior high school; Public senior high school
VP: Cynthia J Morrow
Teacher Pr: Terri Testa

D-U-N-S 01-100-5314
MONTPELIER RE US HOLDINGS LTD
(Suby of MONTPELIER RE HOLDINGS LTD.)
6263 N Scottsdale Rd # 300, Scottsdale, AZ 85250-5413
Tel (480) 306-8300 Founded/Ownrshp 2007
Sales NA EMP 122
SIC 6331 Fire, marine & casualty insurance
Pr: Glen W Anderson
*Ch Bd: Jack Byrnes
Brnch Mgr: Susan Edwards
Opers Mgr: Tracy Davis

MONTPELIER STEELWORKS
See SSAB IOWA INC

MONTRAIL
See MOUNTAIN HARDWEAR INC

D-U-N-S 05-238-7362
MONTRAN CORP
60 E 42nd St Ste 464, New York, NY 10165-6250
Tel (212) 684-5214 Founded/Ownrshp 1979
Sales 20.7MM EMP 120
Accts Adelman Katz & Mond Llp New Y
SIC 7371 Computer software development; Computer software development
Pr: Kaye E Marron
*Ex VP: Alex Esca
*Ex VP: Sanford Faden
*VP: Charles P Walsh
Web Dev: Alex Bughiu
Sftwr Eng: Prahalad Babu
Sftwr Eng: Adrian Carcu
Sftwr Eng: Miguel Espinoza
Sftwr Eng: George Voina

D-U-N-S 12-652-2692
MONTREAL MAINE & ATLANTIC RAILWAY LTD
15 Iron Rd, Hermon, ME 04401-1179
Tel (207) 848-4200 Founded/Ownrshp 2003
Sales 24.9MM^E EMP 230
SIC 4011 Railroads, line-haul operating; Railroads, line-haul operating
Ch: Edward A Burkhardt
*Pt: Frederick Jones
*CEO: Robert C Grindrod
VP: Yocum Frederic
VP: Donald Gardner Jr
Sls&Mrk Ex: Rushmore Dick
VP Mktg: Bob D Thomas

MONTROSE ADMINISTRATION SERVIC
See COUNTY OF MONTROSE

D-U-N-S 08-320-4586
MONTROSE COUNTY SCHOOL DISTRICT RE-1J
930 Colorado Ave, Montrose, CO 81401-4835
Tel (970) 249-2653 Founded/Ownrshp 1962
Sales 47.8MM EMP 750
Accts Chadwick Steinkirchner Davis
SIC 8211 Public elementary & secondary schools; Public elementary & secondary schools

D-U-N-S 86-094-3401
MONTROSE ENVIRONMENTAL CORP
1 Park Plz Ste 1000, Irvine, CA 92614-8507
Tel (949) 988-3500 Founded/Ownrshp 2013
Sales 20.2MM^E EMP 600
SIC 8734 5084 Pollution testing; Pollution control equipment, air (environmental)
CEO: Jeremiah Yu
Sr VP: Leslie Johnson
VP: Jason Wirth
VP Mktg: Ginger Stringer
Snr PM: Joe Adamiak
Snr PM: Wayne Johnson
Snr PM: Kevin Kawainui

D-U-N-S 01-063-3667
MONTROSE MEMORIAL HOSPITAL INC
800 S 3rd St, Montrose, CO 81401-4212
Tel (970) 249-2211 Founded/Ownrshp 1951
Sales 83.4MM EMP 514
SIC 8062 8011 General medical & surgical hospitals; Offices & clinics of medical doctors; General medical & surgical hospitals; Offices & clinics of medical doctors
CEO: Dave Hample
Chf Rad: Thomas Davis
Dir Vol: Dale Cracraft
CFO: Connie Pruitt
CFO: Al White
VP: Patricia Dickinson
VP: Burt Hatter
Dir Lab: Bryan Evensen
Dir Lab: Charolette Schendel
Mng Ofcr: Richard Shannon
Off Mgr: Ann Rivera

MONTROY SIGN AND GRAPHIC PDTS
See MONTROY SUPPLY CO

MONTROY SUPPLY
See JDW MANAGEMENT CO

D-U-N-S 00-964-0723
MONTROY SUPPLY CO
MONTROY SIGN AND GRAPHIC PDTS
(Suby of JDW MANAGEMENT CO) ★
2674 Raymond Ave, Signal Hill, CA 90755-2128
Tel (562) 997-2920 Founded/Ownrshp 1989
Sales 38.6MM^E EMP 103
SIC 5046 5199 5085

D-U-N-S 10-001-1816
MONTVILLE PUBLIC SCHOOLS
800 Old Colchester Rd # 2, Oakdale, CT 06370-2608
Tel (860) 848-1228 Founded/Ownrshp 1950
Sales 21.8MM^E EMP 477
SIC 8211 Public elementary & secondary schools; Public elementary & secondary schools
Instr Medi: Christy Foss

D-U-N-S 17-800-4859
MONTVILLE TOWNSHIP BOARD OF EDUCATION
MONTVILLE TWP SCHOOL DIST
123 Changebridge Rd, Montville, NJ 07045-8933
Tel (973) 331-7140 Founded/Ownrshp 1950
Sales 13.2MM^E EMP 400
SIC 8211 9111 Public elementary & secondary schools; Mayors' offices
Pr: Jeneene Norman

MONTVILLE TWP SCHOOL DIST
See MONTVILLE TOWNSHIP BOARD OF EDUCATION

MONUMENT CAR PARTS
See TRIMON INC

D-U-N-S 00-966-4247 IMP/EXP
MONUMENT CHEMICAL KENTUCKY LLC
2450 Olin Rd, Brandenburg, KY 40108-9508
Tel (270) 422-2101 Founded/Ownrshp 2013
Sales 160.9MM^E EMP 169^E
SIC 2911 Fractionation products of crude petroleum, hydrocarbons
Prgrm Mgr: Matt Kriech
IT Man: Kaye Redmon
Mtls Mgr: Craig Foster
Sfty Mgr: Earl Fitzgerald
Opers Mgr: David Spalt
Snr Mgr: Jacobus Sinnema

D-U-N-S 83-308-8284
MONUMENT CHEMICALS INC
6510 Telecom Dr Ste 425, Indianapolis, IN 46278-6330
Tel (270) 422-6307 Founded/Ownrshp 2010
Sales 47.0MM^E EMP 253^E
SIC 2821 5033 2951 Thermoplastic materials; Asphalt felts & coating; Asphalt paving mixtures & blocks
Snr Mgr: Peter Jacobs

D-U-N-S 03-207-9105
MONUMENT OIL CO
GO FER FOOD
560 Colorado Ave, Grand Junction, CO 81501-2606
Tel (970) 245-3440 Founded/Ownrshp 1963
Sales 94.8MM EMP 60
SIC 5172 Diesel fuel; Gasoline; Diesel fuel; Gasoline
CEO: Cullen R Brown
*Pr: C Paul Brown

D-U-N-S 04-389-9603
MONUMENT REALTY LLC
1700 K St Nw Ste 600, Washington, DC 20006-3816
Tel (202) 777-2000 Founded/Ownrshp 1998
Sales 39.7MM^E EMP 70^E
SIC 6552 Land subdividers & developers, commercial; Land subdividers & developers, residential
Pr: F Russell Hines
*CFO: Debra Volpicelli
*Ex VP: Douglas D Olson
Sr VP: Mike Blum
Sr VP: Robert Brumm
*Sr VP: Joshua A Olsen
Sr VP: Kirk Salpini
Sr VP: Joseph Wasilewski
VP: Tatiana Banicevic
VP: Eric May
Off Mgr: Christina Combs

D-U-N-S 93-273-8214
MONUMENT SECURITY INC
4926 43rd St Ste 10, McClellan, CA 95652-2618
Tel (916) 564-4234 Founded/Ownrshp 1995
Sales 24.9MM^E EMP 600
SIC 7381 Security guard service; Security guard service
Pr: Scott Mc Donald
Opers Mgr: Jack Llorens

D-U-N-S 00-511-5654 EXP
■ **MONUMENTAL INVESTMENT CORP**
(Suby of EMCOR CONSTRUCTION SERVICES) ★
2207 Monumental Ave, Baltimore, MD 21227
Tel (410) 247-2200 Founded/Ownrshp 1999
Sales 44.9MM^E EMP 100
SIC 1711 8711 Mechanical contractor; Construction & civil engineering

Pr: M Delmar Ritchie Jf
Pr: M Delmar Ritchie Jr
VP: Adelberto Perez

MONUMENTAL SPORTS & ENTRMT
See WASHINGTON SPORTS & ENTERTAINMENT LIMITED PARTNERSHIP

MONUMENTAL SPORTS & ENTRMT
See LINCOLN HOLDINGS LLC

D-U-N-S 00-886-0033 IMP
MONUMENTAL SUPPLY CO INC (MD)
401 S Haven St, Baltimore, MD 21224-5294
Tel (410) 732-9300 *Founded/Ownrshp* 1950
Sales 37.4MM[E] *EMP* 45
SIC 5085 5051 Valves & fittings; Pipe & tubing, steel
CEO: Susan Kirchner
**Ex VP:* Stacie Sauzer
**VP:* David Coarts
**VP:* Ross Hall
**VP:* Rob Mechalske
Sls Mgr: Paul Nickles
Sales Asso: Paul Carr
Sales Asso: Dave Paul

D-U-N-S 04-231-6997
MONY GROUP INC
(*Suby of* AXA FINANCIAL INC) ★
1740 Broadway Ste 202, New York, NY 10019-4315
Tel (212) 708-2000 *Founded/Ownrshp* 2004
Sales NA *EMP* 2,288
SIC 6411 Insurance agents, brokers & service; Insurance agents, brokers & service
CEO: Michael I Roth
Pr: Samuel J Foti
CFO: Richard Daddario
Ex VP: Kenneth M Levine
Sr VP: Bart R Schwartz
VP: Eileen Forrest
Dir IT: Cosimo Pagano

D-U-N-S 00-698-7960
MONY LIFE INSURANCE CO (NY)
(*Suby of* PROTECTIVE LIFE INSURANCE CO) ★
1740 Broadway, New York, NY 10019-4315
Tel (800) 487-6669 *Founded/Ownrshp* 1843, 2013
Sales NA *EMP* 1,900
SIC 6411 6321 6211 6282 6531 Insurance agents, brokers & service; Accident insurance carriers; Health insurance carriers; Disability health insurance; Distributors, security; Mutual funds, selling by independent salesperson; Investment advisory service; Manager of mutual funds, contract or fee basis; Real estate managers; Insurance agents, brokers & service; Accident insurance carriers; Health insurance carriers; Disability health insurance; Distributors, security; Mutual funds, selling by independent salesperson; Investment advisory service; Manager of mutual funds, contract or fee basis; Real estate managers
Pr: Samuel J Foti
CFO: Richard Daddario
Treas: Tamara Bronson
Ex VP: Kenneth M Levine
Ex VP: Steven G Orluck
Sr VP: Stephen J Hall
Sr VP: Thomas McCahill
Sr VP: Evelyn L Peos
Sr VP: Ernest P Rogers
Sr VP: Bart Schwartz
Sr VP: Michael Slipowitz
Sr VP: Robert O Wright Jr
VP: Debbie Udicious
Board of Directors: Daniel G Kaye, Kristi A Matus

D-U-N-S 07-872-4681
MOOD MEDIA CORP
1703 W 5th St Ste 600, Austin, TX 78703-4894
Tel (800) 345-5000 *Founded/Ownrshp* 2013
Sales 494.0MM *EMP* 2,000[E]
SIC 7319 7389 Media buying service; Media buying service; Music & broadcasting services
CEO: Steve Richards
**COO:* Ken Eissing
**CFO:* Dodd Haynes
**Ex VP:* Jim McFelea
**Sr VP:* Trey Courtney
VP: John Walker

D-U-N-S 08-508-1268
MOOD MEDIA NORTH AMERICA LIMITED
(*Suby of* MOOD MEDIA CORPORATION)
1703 W 5th St Ste 600, Austin, TX 78703-4894
Tel (512) 380-8500 *Founded/Ownrshp* 2011
Sales 355.1MM[E] *EMP* 950
SIC 6794 7389 Franchises, selling or licensing; Music & broadcasting services; Franchises, selling or licensing; Music & broadcasting services
CEO: Stephen P Richards
COO: Ken Eissing
**CFO:* R Dodd Haynes
Ex VP: Randal Rudniski
VP: Troy Cooper
VP: Jaime Kane
VP: John Walker
Mng Dir: Mick Bennett
Mktg Dir: Mike Kelly
Manager: Maryanne Baker
Snr PM: Andrew Koehler

D-U-N-S 80-564-8961
MOODIE IMPLEMENT INC
3701 Us Highway 14, Pierre, SD 57501-5747
Tel (605) 224-1631 *Founded/Ownrshp* 1992
Sales 23.2MM *EMP* 35
Accts Palmercurrier&Hoffertllp Pi
SIC 5083 5261 Farm implements; Farm equipment parts & supplies; Lawnmowers & tractors; Farm implements; Farm equipment parts & supplies; Lawnmowers & tractors
Pr: Robert Moodie

D-U-N-S 13-756-0983
MOODY BANCSHARES INC
2302 Post Office St # 704, Galveston, TX 77550-1935
Tel (409) 765-5561 *Founded/Ownrshp* 1982
Sales NA *EMP* 112
SIC 6021 National commercial banks; National commercial banks
Pr: Robert Moody
Treas: Victoria Chen
VP: Walter Syers

D-U-N-S 00-175-2252
MOODY BIBLE INSTITUTE OF CHICAGO (IL)
820 N La Salle Dr, Chicago, IL 60610-3263
Tel (312) 329-4000 *Founded/Ownrshp* 1886
Sales 123.5MM *EMP* 605
Accts Crowe Horwath Llp Chicago Il
SIC 8661 8299 8221 4832 2731 Religious organizations; Bible school; Professional schools; Radio broadcasting stations; Books: publishing only; Religious organizations; Bible school; Professional schools; Radio broadcasting stations; Books: publishing only
Pr: Paul Nyquist
Ch Bd: Jerry Jenkins
Pr: Janet Steven
CFO: Kenneth D Heulitt
CFO: Delmar Mohler
Ex VP: Steven Mogck
Sr VP: Greg Thornton
VP: Elizabeth Brolon
VP: Elizabeth Brown
VP: Larry Davidhizer
VP: Jim Elliott
VP: Christine Gorz
VP: John Jelinek
VP: Colin Lambert
VP: Tom Shaw
VP: James Spencer
VP: Gregory Thornton
Exec: Laurie Campbell
Assoc Dir: Lindsey Crystal
Dir Soc: Ruth Dinwiddie

D-U-N-S 00-338-0524
MOODY DUNBAR INC
2000 Waters Edge Dr # 21, Johnson City, TN 37604-8312
Tel (423) 952-0100 *Founded/Ownrshp* 1933
Sales 36.6MM[E] *EMP* 150
SIC 2033 2035 Vegetables: packaged in cans, jars, etc.; Vegetables, brined; Vegetables: packaged in cans, jars, etc.; Vegetables, brined
Pr: Stanley Dunbar
**Sec:* Christina Dunbar
QA Dir: David Adkins
IT Man: Steve Turner
Sls Mgr: Mary Cullen
Sls Mgr: Bill McConnell

D-U-N-S 96-314-9674
MOODY ENDOWMENT
1528 Post Office St, Galveston, TX 77550-4833
Tel (409) 762-6661 *Founded/Ownrshp* 2010
Sales 22.3MM *EMP* 2
SIC 8699 Charitable organization; Charitable organization

D-U-N-S 17-758-6880
MOODY GARDENS INC
PALM BEACH AT MOODY GARDENS
1 Hope Blvd, Galveston, TX 77554-8928
Tel (409) 744-4673 *Founded/Ownrshp* 1986
Sales 103.3MM *EMP* 650
Accts Pannell Kerr Forster Of Texas
SIC 8412 8422 7999 7011 Museum; Arboreta & botanical or zoological gardens; Golf services & professionals; Hotels; Museum; Arboreta & botanical or zoological gardens; Golf services & professionals; Hotels
Ch: E Douglas McLeod
**Treas:* John Peterson Jr
Ofcr: Elizabeth Foster
Snr Mgr: John Sinegal

D-U-N-S 06-971-6025
MOODY INSURANCE AGENCY INC
8055 E Tufts Ave Ste 1000, Denver, CO 80237-2861
Tel (303) 824-6600 *Founded/Ownrshp* 1972
Sales NA *EMP* 45[E]
SIC 6411 6351 Insurance agents; Surety insurance
CEO: Evan Moody
Ofcr: Kim Burkhardt
VP: Jeff Giltner
**VP:* Brad Moody
**VP:* Karen Moody
CIO: Patience McQuade
Snr Mgr: Don Collins

D-U-N-S 17-790-2483
MOODY NATIONAL 1715 OST HOUSTON S LLC
1715 Old Spanish Trl, Houston, TX 77054-1909
Tel (713) 797-0040 *Founded/Ownrshp* 1997
Sales 40.0MM *EMP* 35
SIC 7011 Hotels & motels; Hotels & motels
Genl Mgr: Michael Giangrosso

D-U-N-S 00-793-0456
MOODY NATIONAL BANK (TX)
(*Suby of* MOODY BANCSHARES INC) ★
2302 Post Office St 23, Galveston, TX 77550-1935
Tel (409) 765-5561 *Founded/Ownrshp* 1907, 1982
Sales NA *EMP* 50
SIC 6021 National commercial banks; National commercial banks
Pr: Victor Pierson
CFO: Jo Tang
Chf Cred: George Casseb
Bd of Dir: Bruse Farmer
Ofcr: Sonya Burnett
Ofcr: Steve Spits
**Ex VP:* Craig Barker
Ex VP: Owen Cheney
Ex VP: Rick Price
**Ex VP:* Katherine Rodriguez
Ex VP: John Smith
Ex VP: Dan Walsh
**Ex VP:* Mark Wilson
**Ex VP:* Michael Wisner
Sr VP: Mary Kantara
Sr VP: Michael Lerner
Sr VP: C Owen
VP: Vicki Charles
VP: Jason Eversole
**Exec:* Richard Cardner

D-U-N-S 00-654-1358
MOODY NATIONAL MORTGAGE CORP
HP BEDFORD HOUS
6363 Woodway Dr Ste 110, Houston, TX 77057-1714
Tel (713) 977-7500 *Founded/Ownrshp* 1996
Sales 20.1MM[E] *EMP* 160
SIC 7011 6162 Hotels & motels; Mortgage bankers & correspondents
CEO: Brett C Moody
**Pr:* Philip A McRae
**VP:* David Gould
**VP:* Diana Larson
VP: W Lee
**VP:* Stephen B Woods

D-U-N-S 96-250-9738
MOODY NATIONAL REIT I INC
6363 Woodway Dr Ste 110, Houston, TX 77057-1714
Tel (713) 977-7500 *Founded/Ownrshp* 2010
Sales NA *EMP* 34[E]
SIC 6162 Mortgage bankers
Prin: Brett C Moody

D-U-N-S 60-914-7996
MOODY-NOLAN INC
300 Spruce St Ste 300, Columbus, OH 43215-1175
Tel (614) 221-5216 *Founded/Ownrshp* 1987
Sales 26.1MM[E] *EMP* 169
SIC 8712 8711 Architectural engineering; Engineering services; Architectural engineering; Engineering services
CEO: Curtis J Moody
**CFO:* David King
**Treas:* Robert K Larimer
VP: Quentin Elliott
**Prin:* John William Miller
**Prin:* Paul F Pryor
Admn Mgr: Clyde Seidle
Dir IT: Renauld Mitchell
Telecom Mg: Chris Schwanekamp
Opers Mgr: Kathleen Dussault
Sls&Mrk Ex: John Ensign

D-U-N-S 03-418-8052
MOODY-PRICE LLC
18320 Petroleum Dr, Baton Rouge, LA 70809-6123
Tel (225) 751-7001 *Founded/Ownrshp* 1954, 1985
Sales 90.6MM[E] *EMP* 90
SIC 5084 Industrial machinery & equipment; Instruments & control equipment; Industrial machinery & equipment; Instruments & control equipment
Treas: Danny Daniel Jr
Genl Mgr: Mike Leggett
Dir IT: Kendall Ducote
Opers Mgr: Matt Humble
S&M/VP: Kenneth Lebleu
Sls Dir: Jimmy Sandifer
Sales Asso: Doug Dover
Snr Mgr: Darryl Pabst

D-U-N-S 61-964-8199
■ **MOODYS ANALYTICS INC**
(*Suby of* MOODYS CORP) ★
250 Greenwich St 7w, New York, NY 10007-2140
Tel (415) 874-6368 *Founded/Ownrshp* 2002
Sales 229.5MM[E] *EMP* 9,900[E]
SIC 7323 Credit reporting services; Credit reporting services
CEO: Mark E Almeida
Pr: Ton Brown
Pr: Teresa Stok
COO: Jacob Grotta
Treas: Randolph Roy
**Ex VP:* Geoff Fite
VP: Robert Fauber
VP: Trevor Pijper
VP: Peter Smith
Snr Sftwr: Ryan Wibawa
Software D: Andrew Terekhov

D-U-N-S 04-997-7473
▲ **MOODYS CORP**
250 Greenwich St, New York, NY 10007-2140
Tel (212) 553-0300 *Founded/Ownrshp* 1900
Sales 3.3MMM *EMP* 9,900[E]
Accts Kpmg Llp New York New York
Tkr Sym MCO *Exch* NYS
SIC 7323 6282 Credit reporting services; Investment advisory service; Credit reporting services; Investment advisory service
Ch Bd: Henry A McKinnell Jr
**Pr:* Raymond W McDaniel Jr
CEO: G V Mani
COO: Michel Madelain
CFO: Linda S Huber
Treas: Steve Maire
Ofcr: Richard Cantor
Ofcr: Lisa S Westlake
Ex VP: Jeanne Dering
Ex VP: Jane Eddy
Ex VP: John J Goggins
Ex VP: Chester Murray
Ex VP: Gil Zeilberger
Sr VP: Lisa Goldstein
Sr VP: Scott Kenney
Sr VP: Joseph McCabe
Sr VP: Steven Oman
Sr VP: Debra Perry
Sr VP: Dennis Saputo
Sr VP: Arthur N Skelskie
Sr VP: Tony Stoupas
Board of Directors: Basil L Anderson, Jorge A Bermudez, Darrell Duffie, Kathryn M Hill, Ewald Kist, Leslie F Seidman, John K Wulff

D-U-N-S 00-192-2178
■ **MOODYS INVESTORS SERVICE INC**
(*Suby of* MOODYS CORP) ★
250 Greenwich St, New York, NY 10007-2140
Tel (212) 553-0300 *Founded/Ownrshp* 1900, 1962
Sales 105.3MM[E] *EMP* 1,950
SIC 7323 Credit reporting services; Credit reporting services
CEO: Raymond McDaniel
Pr: Betty Ng
**COO:* Michel Madelain
**Treas:* Jeff Hare
Chf Mktg O: Sherry Rashkovsky
**Ofcr:* James Bodovitz
Assoc VP: Sarah Glendon
Ex VP: Chester Murray
Sr VP: Laura Baird
Sr VP: Kent Becker
Sr VP: Susan Fitzgerald
Sr VP: Randall Gordon
Sr VP: Robert Jankowitz
Sr VP: Andris Kalnins
Sr VP: Marie Menendez
Sr VP: Christina Pedicone
Sr VP: Maya Penrose
Sr VP: Algis Remeza
Sr VP: Natalie Wells
VP: Michael Agranoff
VP: Scott Bosch
Board of Directors: Clifford L Alexander Jr

D-U-N-S 03-528-4967
MOODYS MARKET INC
50389 Us Highway 93, Polson, MT 59860-7046
Tel (406) 883-1500 *Founded/Ownrshp* 1966
Sales 46.0MM *EMP* 240
Accts James M Oates Pc Polson
SIC 5411 Grocery stores, independent; Grocery stores, independent
Pr: Gregory Hertz
**Sec:* Tim McGreevey
Off Mgr: Kitty Starke

D-U-N-S 02-391-5754
MOOERS MOTOR CAR CO INC
7211 W Broad St, Richmond, VA 23294-3601
Tel (804) 755-6666 *Founded/Ownrshp* 1924
Sales 25.6MM[E] *EMP* 80
SIC 5511 Automobiles, new & used; Automobiles, new & used
Pr: Ronald J Ferguson
**VP:* Lori M Ferguson

D-U-N-S 00-210-3166 IMP/EXP
▲ **MOOG INC** (NY)
400 Jamison Rd, East Aurora, NY 14052
Tel (716) 652-2000 *Founded/Ownrshp* 1951
Sales 2.5MMM *EMP* 10,691
Accts Ernst & Young Llp Buffalo Ne
Tkr Sym MOGA *Exch* NYS
SIC 3812 3492 3625 3769 3728 3841 Aircraft control systems, electronic; Fluid power valves for aircraft; Relays & industrial controls; Actuators, industrial; Guided missile & space vehicle parts & auxiliary equipment; Aircraft parts & equipment; Surgical & medical instruments; Aircraft control systems, electronic; Fluid power valves for aircraft; Relays & industrial controls; Actuators, industrial; Guided missile & space vehicle parts & auxiliary equipment; Aircraft parts & equipment; Surgical & medical instruments
Ch Bd: John R Scannell
CFO: Donald R Fishback
Treas: Mike Wooline
**V Ch Bd:* Richard A Aubrecht
VP: Maureen M Athoe
VP: R Eric Burghardt
VP: R Burghardt
VP: Glenn Dorsey
Exec: Joe Alfieri
Exec: Bond David
Exec: Ann Everts
Exec: John Grabon
Exec: Nielson Lori
Board of Directors: William G Gisel Jr, Peter K Gundermann, Kraig J Kayser, Brian J Lipke, Robert J Maskrey

D-U-N-S 02-407-5111
MOOG LOUISVILLE WAREHOUSE INC (KY)
TOOL PRO
1421 Magazine St, Louisville, KY 40203-2063
Tel (502) 583-7795 *Founded/Ownrshp* 1960
Sales 71.0MM[E] *EMP* 175
SIC 5013 Automotive supplies & parts; Automotive supplies; Automotive batteries; Automotive supplies & parts; Automotive supplies; Automotive batteries
VP: Glenn Hardin
Genl Mgr: Brian Osborn
IT Man: Gregg Williams
VP Sls: Bill Grover

D-U-N-S 07-846-7641
MOOG MEDICAL DEVICES
4314 S Zevex Park Ln, Salt Lake City, UT 84123-7881
Tel (801) 264-1001 *Founded/Ownrshp* 2012
Sales 32.1MM[E] *EMP* 52[E]
SIC 5047 Medical equipment & supplies
CFO: Andy Kotlarz
Treas: Timothy Balkin
VP: David Gray
VP: Paul Murphy
Exec: Nancy Ott
Ex Dir: Mike Henderson
Area Mgr: Paul Lovoi
Netwrk Eng: Paul Gyergyek
Ql Cn Mgr: Chris Hecht
Ql Cn Mgr: Jon Morningstar
Snr Mgr: Debbie Lyons

MOOG MEDICAL DEVICES GROUP
See ZEVEX INTERNATIONAL INC

D-U-N-S 07-498-6597
MOON AREA SCHOOL DISTRICT
8353 University Blvd, Coraopolis, PA 15108-2597
Tel (412) 264-9440 *Founded/Ownrshp* 1975
Sales 60.3MM *EMP* 550
Accts Hosack Specht Muetzel & Wood
SIC 8211 Public elementary school; Public junior high school; Public senior high school; Public elementary school; Public junior high school; Public senior high school

D-U-N-S 00-690-3488 IMP
MOON DISTRIBUTORS INC
2800 Vance St, Little Rock, AR 72206-3338
Tel (501) 375-8291 *Founded/Ownrshp* 1935
Sales 30.6MM[E] *EMP* 65
SIC 5182 Neutral spirits; Bottling wines & liquors

CEO: Stan Hastings
**Ch Bd:* Harry L Hastings Jr
**Pr:* Harry Lee Hastings IV
**Pr:* Mickey Nottingham
**VP:* Andrew Hastings
**VP:* Lee Hastings
Genl Mgr: Jerry Harrod
VP Opers: Mike Phillips

MOON MOUNTAIN FARMS
See NOON VALLEY NURSERY INC

D-U-N-S 95-742-0730
MOON NURSERIES INC
145 Moor Rd, Chesapeake City, MD 21915
Tel (410) 755-6600 *Founded/Ownrshp* 2003
Sales 24.7MM^E *EMP* 100
SIC 0181 Nursery stock, growing of
Pr: John Pursell
Sls Mgr: Kraig O'Keefe

D-U-N-S 05-753-5148
MOON SECURITY SERVICES INC
515 W Clark St, Pasco, WA 99301-5521
Tel (509) 545-1881 *Founded/Ownrshp* 1984
Sales 34.5MM^E *EMP* 206
SIC 1731 7382 7381 Fire detection & burglar alarm systems specialization; Burglar alarm maintenance & monitoring; Fire alarm maintenance & monitoring; Security guard service; Burglary protection service; Protective services, guard; Fire detection & burglar alarm systems specialization; Burglar alarm maintenance & monitoring; Fire alarm maintenance & monitoring; Security guard service; Burglary protection service; Protective services, guard
Pr: Michael A Miller
**Sec:* Jolene Nelson
**VP:* Laurel Heinemann
Rgnl Mgr: Nathan Bogar
Dept Mgr: Monica Quigley
Genl Mgr: Tom Pitcher
Tech Mgr: Jade Kozelisky

D-U-N-S 93-850-8215
MOON VALLEY NURSERY INC
MOON MOUNTAIN FARMS
18047 N Tatum Blvd, Phoenix, AZ 85032-1506
Tel (602) 493-0403 *Founded/Ownrshp* 1995
Sales 263.8MM^E *EMP* 365
SIC 5193 5261 Flowers & florists' supplies; Nurseries; Flowers & florists' supplies; Nurseries
Pr: Les Blake
VP: John Marshall

D-U-N-S 10-539-8544
MOONEY AIRPLANE CO INC
165 Al Mooney Rd, Kerrville, TX 78028-8388
Tel (830) 896-6000 *Founded/Ownrshp* 2002
Sales 62.8MM^E *EMP* 400
SIC 3721 3724 Aircraft; Aircraft engines & engine parts; Aircraft; Aircraft engines & engine parts
Pr: Solomon Mayer
**CEO:* Dennis E Ferguson
COO: William Rickard
**CFO:* Jon Greenwood
VP: Chad Nelson
Ex Dir: So Jos

D-U-N-S 60-251-8086 IMP
MOONEY FARMS
1220 Fortress St, Chico, CA 95973-9029
Tel (530) 899-2661 *Founded/Ownrshp* 1988
Sales 33.6MM^E *EMP* 50
SIC 0723 2034 2033 Fruit crops market preparation services; Dried & dehydrated fruits; Canned fruits & specialties
Pr: Mary Mooney
**VP:* Steve Mooney

D-U-N-S 00-177-5097
MOONEY GENERAL PAPER CO INC
M G P
1451 Chestnut Ave, Hillside, NJ 07205-1195
Tel (973) 926-1085 *Founded/Ownrshp* 1917
Sales 48.9MM^E *EMP* 70
SIC 5087 5113 Janitors' supplies; Industrial & personal service paper; Janitors' supplies; Industrial & personal service paper
Pr: Richard D Ribakove
**Ch Bd:* Gary Riemer
**Ex VP:* Andrea Ribakove
Sls Mgr: Kathy Kennedy

D-U-N-S 01-965-4389
MOONLIGHT BASIN LLC
66 Mountain Loop Rd, Big Sky, MT 59716
Tel (406) 993-6000 *Founded/Ownrshp* 2002
Sales 11.9MM^E *EMP* 500
SIC 7011 Ski lodge; Ski lodge
Genl Mgr: Gregg Pack

MOONLIGHT COMPANIES
See MOONLIGHT PACKING CORP

D-U-N-S 84-786-0939
MOONLIGHT PACKING CORP
MOONLIGHT COMPANIES
17719 E Huntsman Ave, Reedley, CA 93654-9205
Tel (559) 638-7799 *Founded/Ownrshp* 1992
Sales 490.6MM^E *EMP* 2,000
SIC 5148 4783 Frozen vegetables & fruit products; Packing & crating; Fruits, fresh; Packing & crating
Pr: Russell Tavlan
**CFO:* Ty Tavlan

MOONPIE
See CHATTANOOGA BAKERY INC

D-U-N-S 11-900-0730 IMP
MOONS INDUSTRIES AMERICA INC
1113 N Prospect Ave, Itasca, IL 60143-1401
Tel (630) 833-5940 *Founded/Ownrshp* 2000
Sales 74.1MM^E *EMP* 520
SIC 3621 Motors, electric; Motors, electric
Pr: James Chang
Genl Mgr: William Chen
Off Mgr: Karen Ostendof
Mktg Dir: Rich Lenzing

MOONSTONE HOTEL PROPERTIES
See MOONSTONE MANAGEMENT CORP

D-U-N-S 96-506-6772
MOONSTONE MANAGEMENT CORP
MOONSTONE HOTEL PROPERTIES
2905 Burton Dr, Cambria, CA 93428-4001
Tel (805) 927-4200 *Founded/Ownrshp* 1995
Sales 14.1MM^E *EMP* 500
SIC 6531 Real estate managers; Real estate managers
Pr: Dirk Winter
CIO: Matthhew Holder
Sls Mgr: Sue Krug

D-U-N-S 09-920-8444
MOOR INNOVATIVE TECHNOLOGIES LLC
4812 64th St E, Tacoma, WA 98443-2345
Tel (253) 343-2216 *Founded/Ownrshp* 2000
Sales 100.0MM *EMP* 2^E
SIC 2326 Work uniforms; Work uniforms

D-U-N-S 08-371-9674 IMP
MOOR PRODUCTS INC (AZ)
GREENLEAF/A PPR CONVERTING CO
4850 W Jefferson St, Phoenix, AZ 85043-3807
Tel (602) 269-9640 *Founded/Ownrshp* 1977, 1987
Sales 35.2MM^E *EMP* 60
SIC 2679 Adding machine rolls, paper: made from purchased material
CEO: Gregg R Mosby Sr
**Pr:* Gregg Mosby Jr
Opers Mgr: Lorenzo Gutierrez
VP Mktg: Greg Solloway

D-U-N-S 06-505-9446
MOORE & BALLIEW OIL CO INC
2903 Rutherford Rd, Taylors, SC 29687-2123
Tel (864) 268-3484 *Founded/Ownrshp* 2003
Sales 24.6MM^E *EMP* 19
SIC 5172 5983 5541 Lubricating oils & greases; Fuel oil dealers; Filling stations, gasoline
Pr: Jerry L Moore
**Treas:* Mary W Balliew
**VP:* Buddy Balliew

D-U-N-S 84-749-8532 IMP
MOORE & GILES INC
1081 Tannery Row, Forest, VA 24551-3920
Tel (434) 846-5281 *Founded/Ownrshp* 1992
Sales 37.1MM^E *EMP* 75
SIC 5199 Leather, leather goods & furs
Ch: Donald M Giles
**Pr:* R Sackett Wood
**VP:* Erin Foltz
VP: B J Kavanaugh
**VP:* David T Petty III
**VP:* Patricia Stover
IT Man: Daniel Cope
IT Man: Brian Hillsman
VP Mktg: Brooks Tyree
Pr Dir: Brooks Morrison

D-U-N-S 09-546-1141
MOORE & VAN ALLEN PLLC
100 N Tryon St Ste 4700, Charlotte, NC 28202-4003
Tel (704) 331-1000 *Founded/Ownrshp* 1933
Sales 99.7MM^E *EMP* 575
SIC 8111 General practice law office; General practice law office
Pt: W B Hawfield
**Pt:* Hal A Levinson
**Pt:* Peter J McGrath
**Pt:* Randel E Phillips
Ex Dir: Matthew F Gillespie
Mng Dir: Walter S Price
IT Man: Kevin Benjamin
Netwrk Mgr: Jonathan Littlepage
Mktg Mgr: Shelly Hefner
Counsel: Jay S Bilas
Counsel: Karen A Dean

D-U-N-S 05-332-2095
MOORE - TROSPER CONSTRUCTION CO (MI)
4224 Keller Rd, Holt, MI 48842-1212
Tel (517) 694-6310 *Founded/Ownrshp* 1982
Sales 30.3MM *EMP* 44
Accts Layton & Richardson Pc Eas
SIC 1542 Commercial & office building, new construction; Commercial & office buildings, renovation & repair; Commercial & office building, new construction; Commercial & office buildings, renovation & repair
CEO: Harold V Moore
**Pr:* Brian M Moore
**Co-Pr:* Theron E Moore

MOORE AUTOMOTIVE GROUP
See MOORE CHRYSLER-JEEP INC

D-U-N-S 18-568-4966
MOORE AUTOMOTIVE GROUP INC
MOORE JAGUAR
14116 Manchester Rd, Ballwin, MO 63011-4523
Tel (314) 394-0900 *Founded/Ownrshp* 1988
Sales 30.8MM^E *EMP* 135
SIC 5511 Automobiles, new & used
Pr: Ronald Moore
Off Mgr: Connie Givens

D-U-N-S 02-863-7643
MOORE BUICK CORP
MOORE BUICK G M C
15500 Los Gatos Blvd, Los Gatos, CA 95032-2511
Tel (408) 356-8111 *Founded/Ownrshp* 1951
Sales 34.5MM^E *EMP* 65
SIC 5511 Automobiles, new & used; Automobiles, new & used
CEO: John Moore
**VP:* Mary Ann Moore
Store Mgr: Jim Hopkins
Sls Mgr: Bret Moore

MOORE BUICK G M C
See MOORE BUICK CORP

D-U-N-S 06-267-5236
MOORE BUICK-PONTIAC-GMC TRUCK INC
MOORE PONTIAC
2445 N Marine Blvd, Jacksonville, NC 28546-6929
Tel (910) 455-1414 *Founded/Ownrshp* 1987
Sales 34.5MM^E *EMP* 101
SIC 5511 Automobiles, new & used; Pickups, new & used; Automobiles, new & used; Pickups, new & used
Pr: Donald C Williamson
**VP:* Betty Williamson
Store Mgr: Kevin Wynne

MOORE CADILLAC
See SEVILLE CORP

D-U-N-S 08-492-3242
MOORE CADILLAC CO (VA)
25450 Pleasant Valley Rd, Chantilly, VA 20152-1307
Tel (703) 674-5900 *Founded/Ownrshp* 1965
Sales 43.4MM^E *EMP* 110
SIC 5511 Automobiles, new & used; Automobiles, new & used
Pr: Jacques Moore III
**VP:* Blanche Moore
Store Mgr: Jackie Orr
Sls Mgr: Ken Bell
Sls Mgr: Jeff Doughty
Sls Mgr: Tom Horton
Sls Mgr: Stephanie Parker
Sales Asso: John Dorazio

D-U-N-S 61-484-4533 IMP
MOORE CADILLAC- HUMMER OF DULLES CO
25440 Pleasant Valley Rd, Chantilly, VA 20152-1307
Tel (703) 674-5900 *Founded/Ownrshp* 2005
Sales 31.9MM^E *EMP* 99
SIC 5511 Automobiles, new & used; Automobiles, new & used
VP: Joe Moore

D-U-N-S 61-521-7056 IMP
MOORE CAPITAL MANAGEMENT LP
11 Times Sq Ste 36, New York, NY 10036-6622
Tel (212) 782-7000 *Founded/Ownrshp* 2008
Sales 39.1MM^E *EMP* 100^E
SIC 8741 Management services
CEO: Louis Moore Bacon

D-U-N-S 07-397-8223
MOORE CENTER SERVICES INC
195 Mcgregor St Ste 400, Manchester, NH 03102-3779
Tel (603) 206-2700 *Founded/Ownrshp* 1960
Sales 41.6MM *EMP* 632
Accts Howe Riley & Howe Pllc Manche
SIC 8322 8331 8361 Multi-service center; Family counseling services; Job training & vocational rehabilitation services; Vocational training agency; Residential care; Multi-service center; Family counseling services; Job training & vocational rehabilitation services; Vocational training agency; Residential care
Pr: Paul Boynton
**Ch:* Maureen Donovan
**Treas:* Mark Lore
Chf Mktg O: Rick Elwell
**Ofcr:* Janet Bamberg
VP: David Jenkins
VP: Ellen Roposa
CTO: Tim McGinnin
Dir IT: Tom Duer
Pgrm Dir: Philip Valley

D-U-N-S 83-451-3074
MOORE CHARITABLE FOUNDATION
1251 Avenue Of The Americ, New York, NY 10020-1104
Tel (212) 782-7324 *Founded/Ownrshp* 1994
Sales 51.5MM *EMP* 2
SIC 8699 Charitable organization
Ex Dir: Ann Stevenson Colley

MOORE CHRYSLER DODGE JEEP
See MOORE CHRYSLER INC

D-U-N-S 83-580-5698
MOORE CHRYSLER INC
MOORE CHRYSLER DODGE JEEP
1523 W 3rd Ave, Williamson, WV 25661-3407
Tel (304) 235-8040 *Founded/Ownrshp* 1994
Sales 22.0MM^E *EMP* 80
SIC 5511 Automobiles, new & used; Automobiles, new & used
Pr: Betty Jo Moore
**VP:* Dan Moore
Ex Dir: Cecil E Hatfild
**Genl Mgr:* Daniel Moore

D-U-N-S 78-640-7098 IMP
MOORE CHRYSLER-JEEP INC
MOORE AUTOMOTIVE GROUP
8600 W Bell Rd, Peoria, AZ 85382-3708
Tel (623) 972-6004 *Founded/Ownrshp* 1991
Sales 39.3MM^E *EMP* 100
SIC 5511 Automobiles, new & used; Automobiles, new & used
CEO: Fred Moore
**Pr:* Connie R Moore
Treas: Tim Elridge
**VP:* Clifton Matt Roe
Genl Mgr: Matt Moore
Store Mgr: Kevin Caruso
Sls Dir: Trevor Underwood
Sales Asso: Henry Ajiboye
Sales Asso: Wally Illsley
Sales Asso: Roy Morris
Sales Asso: Bob Shotwell

D-U-N-S 00-119-9926 EXP
MOORE CO (RI)
36 Beach St, Westerly, RI 02891-2771
Tel (401) 596-2816 *Founded/Ownrshp* 1909
Sales 243.0MM^E *EMP* 1,000
SIC 2258 2241 3069 3061 2821 Fabric finishing, warp knit; Manmade fiber narrow woven fabrics; Tape, pressure sensitive: rubber; Thread, rubber; Appliance rubber goods (mechanical); Battery separators, wood; Molding compounds, plastics; Fabric finishing, warp knit; Manmade fiber narrow woven fabrics; Tape, pressure sensitive: rubber; Thread, rubber; Appliance rubber goods (mechanical); Molding compounds, plastics
Pr: Dana Barlow
Pr: Pete Johnson
**Pr:* Alexandra Moore
Treas: Janet Robidoux
VP: Jim Oconnor
IT Man: George Watts
Board of Directors: Lee Judd, Nicholas Moore, Peter Moore, Thomas F Moore, James Murphy

D-U-N-S 07-548-3982
MOORE COLLEGE OF ART & DESIGN (PA)
20th Str And The Pkwy, Philadelphia, PA 19103
Tel (215) 965-4000 *Founded/Ownrshp* 1848
Sales 23.3MM^E *EMP* 182
SIC 8221 College, except junior; College, except junior
Pr: Happy Craven Fernandez
**VP:* William L Hill II
Telecom Ex: Charles Duquesne
CTO: Kirk Widra
IT Man: Dennis Dawton
Mktg Dir: Susan Penn
Mktg Dir: Roy Wilbur

D-U-N-S 06-030-6917
MOORE COUNTY BOARD OF EDUCATION
MOORE COUNTY SCHOOLS
5227 Us 15 501 Hwy, Carthage, NC 28327-8665
Tel (910) 947-2976 *Founded/Ownrshp* 2004
Sales 109.7MM *EMP* 1,900
Accts Dixon Hughs Goodman Llp Pine
SIC 8211 Public elementary & secondary schools; Public elementary & secondary schools

D-U-N-S 06-638-9693
MOORE COUNTY HOSPITAL DISTRICT
MEMORIAL HOSPITAL
224 E 2nd St, Dumas, TX 79029-3808
Tel (806) 935-4946 *Founded/Ownrshp* 1948
Sales 49.4MM^E *EMP* 350^E
SIC 8062 8052 General medical & surgical hospitals; Intermediate care facilities; General medical & surgical hospitals; Intermediate care facilities
CEO: Jeff Turner
**CEO:* Theron Park
CFO: John Bailey
**CFO:* Lawrence Phillips
Ofcr: Carol Cadenhead
Dir Rx: Ken George
CIO: Chris Killion
Dir IT: Gerard Carter
Ansthlgy: Stella Tan
Doctor: Pramoda K Mohapatra MD
Pharmcst: Irma Soliz

MOORE COUNTY SCHOOLS
See MOORE COUNTY BOARD OF EDUCATION

D-U-N-S 07-979-8903
MOORE COUNTY SCHOOLS
5277 Hwy 15 501 S, Carthage, NC 28327
Tel (910) 947-2976 *Founded/Ownrshp* 2015
Sales 48.8MM^E *EMP* 1,474^E
SIC 8211 Public elementary & secondary schools
Dir Sec: Sammy McNeill
Pr Dir: Amber Rach
Teacher Pr: Anita Alpenfels

D-U-N-S 02-774-1248
MOORE EXCAVATION INC
MEI GROUP
5501 Ne 223rd Ave, Fairview, OR 97024-8703
Tel (503) 252-1180 *Founded/Ownrshp* 1957
Sales 31.0MM^E *EMP* 100
SIC 1623

D-U-N-S 19-431-1189
MOORE FAMILY REALTY INC
GV MOORE LUMBER CO
22 W Main St, Ayer, MA 01432-1211
Tel (978) 772-0900 *Founded/Ownrshp* 1984
Sales 20.8MM^E *EMP* 150
SIC 6512 Commercial & industrial building operation
Pr: Calvin E Moore

D-U-N-S 04-187-4488
MOORE FOOD DISTRIBUTORS INC
9910 Page Ave, Saint Louis, MO 63132-1431
Tel (314) 426-1300 *Founded/Ownrshp* 1986
Sales 23.8MM^E *EMP* 46
SIC 5148 5143 5142 5149 Fruits, fresh; Vegetables, fresh; Dairy products, except dried or canned; Packaged frozen goods; Canned goods: fruit, vegetables, seafood, meats, etc.
Pr: Alwal B Moore
Opers Mgr: Jim Grasso
Sls Dir: Skip Salzenstein
Sls Mgr: Kevin Tiggard

D-U-N-S 60-664-2952
MOORE FREIGHT SERVICE INC
2000 Eastbridge Pkwy, Mascot, TN 37806-1500
Tel (865) 932-2660 *Founded/Ownrshp* 2001
Sales 33.4MM^E *EMP* 70
SIC 4731 Transportation agents & brokers
CEO: Dan Moore
**Pr:* Randy Moore
VP: Steve Sparks

D-U-N-S 15-464-1435
MOORE IACOFANO GOLTSMAN INC
M I G
800 Hearst Ave, Berkeley, CA 94710-2018
Tel (510) 845-7549 *Founded/Ownrshp* 1981
Sales 21.1MM^E *EMP* 70
SIC 8748 Environmental consultant; Communications consulting
Pr: Susan M Goltsman
**CEO:* Daniel Iacofano

**COO:* Carolyn Verheyen
Adm Dir: Jeff Baker
Snr Sftwr: Dave Banks
Prd Mgr: Kimberly Donahue
Mktg Dir: Serena Sidmore
Mktg Mgr: Brian Boecking
Snr PM: Ryan Mottau
Snr PM: Ray Pendro

D-U-N-S 02-070-7881
MOORE INDEPENDENT SCHOOL DISTRICT NO 2
MOORE SCHOOL FOOD SERVICE
1500 Se 4th St, Moore, OK 73160-8266
Tel (405) 735-4200 *Founded/Ownrshp* 1908
Sales 104.8MM^E *EMP* 2,000
Accts Sanders Bledsoe & Hewett Cpa
SIC 8211 Public elementary school; Public junior high school; Public senior high school; Specialty education; Public elementary school; Public junior high school; Public senior high school; Specialty education
VP: Pauline Caldwell
Adm Dir: Kerry Cooter
Off Admin: Gina Henry
Off Admin: Cathy Wright
IT Man: Suzanne Cheshier
Mtls Mgr: Heather Azbell
Mtls Mgr: Virginia Shepherd
Board of Directors: Larry Leemaster

D-U-N-S 08-718-7852 IMP
MOORE INDUSTRIES-INTERNATIONAL INC
16650 Schoenborn St, North Hills, CA 91343-6106
Tel (818) 830-5518 *Founded/Ownrshp* 1965
Sales 72.7MM^E *EMP* 260
SIC 5084 3823

D-U-N-S 13-019-1518
MOORE IRON & STEEL CORP
MISCO
201 W Charleston Ave, Yale, OK 74085-6001
Tel (918) 387-2639 *Founded/Ownrshp* 2002
Sales 45.6MM^E *EMP* 90
SIC 3448 Prefabricated metal buildings
Pr: David Moore
**CFO:* Mike McCull
**VP:* Matthew Moore
Sfty Dirs: Cindy Ross

MOORE JAGUAR
See MOORE AUTOMOTIVE GROUP INC

D-U-N-S 05-142-0107 EXP
■ **MOORE MEDICAL LLC**
(*Suby of* MCKESSON MEDICAL-SURGICAL INC) ★
1690 New Britain Ave, Farmington, CT 06032-3361
Tel (860) 826-3600 *Founded/Ownrshp* 1949
Sales 103.2MM^E *EMP* 305
SIC 5047 5122 Medical equipment & supplies; Surgical equipment & supplies; Instruments, surgical & medical; Physician equipment & supplies; Pharmaceuticals; Medical equipment & supplies; Surgical equipment & supplies; Instruments, surgical & medical; Physician equipment & supplies; Pharmaceuticals
Pr: J Richard Frey
**VP:* Tim Bidwell
VP: Rick Frey
VP: Charles Valentino
Creative D: Jason Benson
Rgnl Mgr: Robert Piscal
CIO: Tom Garro
VP Inf Sys: Michelle Solomon
IT Man: Bonnie Irish
Opers Mgr: Mike Swoboda
Sales Exec: Don Silk

MOORE MOTOR SALES
See FORD BURTON-MOORE INC

D-U-N-S 07-075-7682
MOORE NANOTECHNOLOGY SYSTEMS LLC
NANOTECHSYS
(*Suby of* MOORE TOOL CO INC) ★
230 Old Homestead Hwy, Swanzey, NH 03446-2120
Tel (603) 352-3030 *Founded/Ownrshp* 1997
Sales 23.8MM *EMP* 63^E
SIC 3827 5084 Optical instruments & lenses; Machine tools & accessories
Pr: Len Chaloux
**COO:* Tom Dupell
**VP:* Bob Cassin

D-U-N-S 02-026-7280
MOORE NURSES LLC
2425 West Loop S Ste 200, Houston, TX 77027-4208
Tel (713) 344-1336 *Founded/Ownrshp* 2009
Sales 19.1MM^E *EMP* 519
SIC 7361 Nurses' registry; Nurses' registry
CEO: Johnny Moore

D-U-N-S 00-177-9313
MOORE OIL CO INC (WI)
4033 W Custer Ave, Milwaukee, WI 53209-4600
Tel (414) 462-3200 *Founded/Ownrshp* 1936, 1977
Sales 39.4MM^E *EMP* 75
SIC 5169 5172

D-U-N-S 00-820-4711
MOORE OIL CO INC
STOP & SAVE FOOD MART
1705 Washington St, Monroe, LA 71201-7046
Tel (318) 388-2111 *Founded/Ownrshp* 1941
Sales 42.7MM^E *EMP* 220
SIC 5541 5172 Gasoline service stations; Petroleum products; Gasoline service stations; Petroleum products
Pr: James W Moore Jr
**Treas:* Lynn W Moore
MIS Dir: Becky Gomilla

D-U-N-S 03-152-3269
MOORE OIL CO INC
1800 Center Point Pkwy, Birmingham, AL 35215-4510
Tel (205) 853-1533 *Founded/Ownrshp* 1956
Sales 56.7MM^E *EMP* 50
SIC 5172 Petroleum products; Petroleum products
Pr: Ronald J Moore Sr
**Sec:* Elizabeth J Moore
**VP:* Ronald J Moore Jr
Off Mgr: Steve Paul

D-U-N-S 03-414-3032
MOORE PETROLEUM CO INC (AL)
630 Midway Dr, Winfield, AL 35594-4524
Tel (205) 487-2960 *Founded/Ownrshp* 1951, 1975
Sales 25.8MM^E *EMP* 61
SIC 5171 Petroleum bulk stations; Petroleum bulk stations
Pr: Thomas W Moore
**Sec:* Peggy C Moore

MOORE PONTIAC
See MOORE BUICK-PONTIAC-GMC TRUCK INC

MOORE PUBLIC WORKS AUTHORITY
See CITY OF MOORE

MOORE REGIONAL HOSPITAL
See FIRSTCAROLINACARE INSURANCE CO

MOORE REGIONAL HOSPITAL
See FIRSTHEALTH OF CAROLINAS INC

D-U-N-S 07-156-2060
MOORE REGIONAL HOSPITAL
20 Page Dr, Pinehurst, NC 28374-8847
Tel (910) 295-7888 *Founded/Ownrshp* 1929
Sales 468.1MM *EMP* 1,400
SIC 8062 General medical & surgical hospitals; General medical & surgical hospitals
Ch Bd: Walker Morris
**Treas:* Norris L Hodgins Jr

MOORE SCHOOL FOOD SERVICE
See MOORE INDEPENDENT SCHOOL DISTRICT NO 2

D-U-N-S 00-118-0686 IMP/EXP
MOORE TOOL CO INC (CT)
(*Suby of* PMT GROUP INC) ★
800 Union Ave, Bridgeport, CT 06607-1137
Tel (203) 366-3224 *Founded/Ownrshp* 1924, 1993
Sales 24.4MM^E *EMP* 63^E
SIC 3541 3544 3545 Machine tools, metal cutting: exotic (explosive, etc.); Dies & die holders for metal cutting, forming, die casting; Gauges (machine tool accessories)
Pr: Newman Marsilius III
Dir IT: Tony Koch
IT Man: Gayle Griffin
Manager: Beat Ries

D-U-N-S 00-310-4851
MOORE TRANSPORT OF TULSA LIMITED LIABILITY CO (OK)
661 N Plano Rd Ste 319, Richardson, TX 75081-2960
Tel (972) 907-3688 *Founded/Ownrshp* 2005
Sales 43.0MM *EMP* 100
SIC 4731 Freight transportation arrangement
CEO: Gary Moore
COO: Dan Faircloth

D-U-N-S 61-691-3349
MOORE-DAVIS MOTORS INC
TOYOTA OF ROSWELL
11130 Alpharetta Hwy, Roswell, GA 30076-1420
Tel (770) 594-8696 *Founded/Ownrshp* 1990
Sales 70.5MM^E *EMP* 300
SIC 5511 Automobiles, new & used; Automobiles, new & used
Pr: Jerry Gresham
Exec: Cecilia Waites
Genl Mgr: Dave Berg
Genl Mgr: Dewayne Fairchild
Genl Mgr: Robert Gagliardi
Sls Mgr: Michael Rampey

D-U-N-S 78-216-5984 IMP
MOORECO INC
BALT BEST RITE MFG TRNTY FURN
(*Suby of* MOORECO INTERNATIONAL HOLDINGS INC) ★
2885 Lorraine Ave, Temple, TX 76501-7402
Tel (254) 778-4727 *Founded/Ownrshp* 2007
Sales 25.9MM^E *EMP* 140^E
SIC 2522 Office furniture, except wood; Office furniture, except wood
CEO: Gregory C Moore
**COO:* Brian Wilkinson
**CFO:* Russell Chupik
**VP:* Jeanne Swift
**VP:* Trudy Vollmer
IT Man: Wayne Thompson
Trfc Mgr: Diane Oliver
Natl Sales: Bret Doyle

D-U-N-S 96-188-4272 IMP
MOORECO INTERNATIONAL HOLDINGS INC
2885 Lorraine Ave, Temple, TX 76501-7402
Tel (254) 778-4727 *Founded/Ownrshp* 2007
Sales 25.9MM^E *EMP* 141
SIC 2522 Office furniture, except wood
Prin: Russell Chupik
CFO: Russell L Chupik

D-U-N-S 05-923-5333
MOOREFIELD CONSTRUCTION INC
600 N Tustin Ave Ste 210, Santa Ana, CA 92705-3781
Tel (714) 972-0700 *Founded/Ownrshp* 1957
Sales 118.5MM *EMP* 52
Accts Glenn M Gelman & Associates
SIC 1542 Shopping center construction; Shopping center construction
CEO: Ann Moorefield
**Pr:* Mike Moorefield
**VP:* Hal Moorefield
VP Opers: Don Hamann
Snr Mgr: Claudio Celis

MOOREFIELD HIGH SCHOOL
See HARDY COUNTY BOARD OF EDUCATION

D-U-N-S 15-121-6371
MOORES ELECTRICAL & MECHANICAL CONSTRUCTION INC
101 Edgewood Ave, Altavista, VA 24517-1051
Tel (434) 369-4374 *Founded/Ownrshp* 1985
Sales 87.7MM *EMP* 275
Accts Shelton & Company Cpas Pc L
SIC 1731 1711 General electrical contractor; Plumbing, heating, air-conditioning contractors; General electrical contractor; Plumbing, heating, air-conditioning contractors
Pr: Dale Moore
**Treas:* Linnie W Barr
**VP:* Michael Booth
**VP:* George J Coleman Jr
VP: Susan Foster
VP: Buzz Layne
VP: Donald Shelton
**VP:* Troy Shelton
Dir IT: Alan Adams
IT Man: Steve Fahed
IT Man: Scott Francis

MOORE'S FEED MILL
See MOORES II INC

D-U-N-S 03-342-7295
MOORES II INC
MOORE'S FEED MILL
157 Highway 15 S, Pontotoc, MS 38863-3103
Tel (662) 489-1411 *Founded/Ownrshp* 1988
Sales 24.2MM^E *EMP* 80
SIC 0723 5999 5261 5191 5699 Feed milling custom services; Feed & farm supply; Nursery stock, seeds & bulbs; Fertilizer; Farm supplies; Feed; Seeds: field, garden & flower; Fertilizer & fertilizer materials; Western apparel; Feed milling custom services; Feed & farm supply; Nursery stock, seeds & bulbs; Fertilizer; Farm supplies; Feed; Seeds: field, garden & flower; Fertilizer & fertilizer materials; Western apparel
Pr: Johnny Moore
**Sec:* Sherria Waldrop
**VP:* John Moore Jr

D-U-N-S 05-407-1071 IMP
MOORES RETREAD & TIRE OF ARK-LA-TEX INC
GOODYEAR
8901 Linwood Ave, Shreveport, LA 71106-6507
Tel (318) 687-7777 *Founded/Ownrshp* 1990
Sales 37.2MM^E *EMP* 150
SIC 5014 5531 7538

D-U-N-S 15-430-6534
MOORES SERVICE CENTER LLC
82 Winfield Rd, Saint Albans, WV 25177-1558
Tel (304) 722-1175 *Founded/Ownrshp* 1974
Sales 350.4MM *EMP* 4
SIC 7538 General automotive repair shops; General automotive repair shops

D-U-N-S 01-280-3532
MOORES TIRE SALES INC
REIDS TIRES
1436 Taylor Rd, Owego, NY 13827-1833
Tel (607) 687-3275 *Founded/Ownrshp* 1967
Sales 32.8MM^E *EMP* 140
SIC 5014 5531

MOORES TOWN VISITING NURSE ASS
See PARTNERS IN HOME CARE INC

MOORESTOWN TOWNSHIP OF PUBLIC
See BOARD OF EDUCATION OF TOWNSHIP OF MOORESTOWN

D-U-N-S 80-809-4015
MOORESTOWN TOWNSHIP SCHOOL DISTRICT
803 N Stanwick Rd, Moorestown, NJ 08057-2034
Tel (856) 778-6600 *Founded/Ownrshp* 1840
Sales 71.5MM *EMP* 400
SIC 8211 Public elementary & secondary schools; Public elementary & secondary schools

D-U-N-S 61-163-9084
MOORESTOWN VISITING NURSE ASSOCIATION INC
300 Harper Dr, Moorestown, NJ 08057-3208
Tel (856) 552-1300 *Founded/Ownrshp* 2005
Sales 22.7MM *EMP* 99
SIC 8082 Visiting nurse service; Visiting nurse service
CEO: Charlotte Holcombe

MOORESTOWN VNA
See VISITING NURSE ASSOCIATION HOME CARE INC

D-U-N-S 02-737-9952
MOORESVILLE COMMUNITY DEV
413 N Main St, Mooresville, NC 28115-2455
Tel (704) 662-7040 *Founded/Ownrshp* 1980
Sales 9.5MM^E *EMP* 300
SIC 4785 Inspection & fixed facilities; Inspection & fixed facilities

D-U-N-S 07-595-3703
MOORESVILLE CONSOLIDATED SCHOOL CORP
11 W Carlisle St, Mooresville, IN 46158-1558
Tel (317) 834-9192 *Founded/Ownrshp* 1920
Sales 43.2MM^E *EMP* 520
SIC 8211 Public elementary school; Public junior high school; Public senior high school; Public elementary school; Public junior high school; Public senior high school
Prin: Brad Lindsay
VP: Mark Meadows
Dir Sec: Rex Cook
Pr Dir: Susan Haynes
Schl Brd P: William Roberson

D-U-N-S 02-470-7812
MOORESVILLE FORD MERCURY INC
151 E Plaza Dr, Mooresville, NC 28115-8042
Tel (704) 664-1300 *Founded/Ownrshp* 1959
Sales 31.9MM^E *EMP* 85
SIC 5511 Automobiles, new & used; Pickups, new & used; Trucks, tractors & trailers: new & used; Automobiles, new & used; Pickups, new & used; Trucks, tractors & trailers: new & used
Pr: Jeff Shoe
**Sec:* Chester A Michael
Exec: Laurann Alley
Sls Mgr: John Keyes

D-U-N-S 10-005-8841
MOORESVILLE GRADED SCHOOL DISTRICT
305 N Main St, Mooresville, NC 28115-2453
Tel (704) 664-5553 *Founded/Ownrshp* 1905
Sales 32.0MM^E *EMP* 560
SIC 8211 Public elementary & secondary schools; School board; Public elementary & secondary schools; School board
Bd of Dir: Leon Pridgen
Bd of Dir: Greg Whitfield
Dir IT: Jeff Martin
Dir IT: Berry Williams
HC Dir: Yvonne Nicopoulos

D-U-N-S 78-848-8518
■ **MOORESVILLE HOSPITAL MANAGEMENT ASSOCIATES LLC**
LAKENORMAN REGIONAL MED CTR
(*Suby of* HEALTH MANAGEMENT ASSOCIATES INC) ★
170 Medical Park Rd # 208, Mooresville, NC 28117-8540
Tel (704) 660-4000 *Founded/Ownrshp* 1986
Sales 137.7MM *EMP* 900^E
SIC 8062 General medical & surgical hospitals; General medical & surgical hospitals
CEO: Jill Gibson
**COO:* Todd Dixson
COO: Jaylene Fultz
**CFO:* Jamie Stoner
Ofcr: Rusty Eldridge
Sr VP: Glenn Silverman
Dir Rx: Reggie Faulkner
Dir Sec: Chuck Ball
MIS Dir: Brian Bissonnette
Doctor: Sylvia Whitmire MD

D-U-N-S 94-146-2889
MOORETOWN RANCHERIA
FEATHER FALLS CASINO
1 Alverda Dr, Oroville, CA 95966-9379
Tel (530) 533-3625 *Founded/Ownrshp* 1989
Sales 21.4MM^E *EMP* 525
SIC 7999 5993 Gambling establishment; Cigar store; Gambling establishment; Cigar store
Ch Bd: Gary Archuleta
**Treas:* Kayla Lobo
**VP:* Melvin Jackson
**Prin:* Julie McIntosh

MOORHEAD PUBLIC SCHOOLS
See INDEPENDENT SCHOOL DISTRICT 152

D-U-N-S 17-085-9909
MOORING RECOVERY SERVICES INC
MOORING USA
2110 113th St, Grand Prairie, TX 75050-1240
Tel (888) 293-9953 *Founded/Ownrshp* 2004
Sales 25.8MM^E *EMP* 75
SIC 1521 1541 1542 1799 Single-family home remodeling, additions & repairs; Repairing fire damage, single-family houses; Renovation, remodeling & repairs: industrial buildings; Commercial & office buildings, renovation & repair; Post-disaster renovations
Pr: Richard J Linahan
**CEO:* John Scott Mooring
**CFO:* Mike Howell
VP: Jay Stephenson
Opers Mgr: Joe Quintero

MOORING USA
See MOORING RECOVERY SERVICES INC

MOORINGS, THE
See MARINER INTERNATIONAL TRAVEL INC

D-U-N-S 82-520-2190
MOORINGS INC
120 Moorings Park Dr, Naples, FL 34105-2122
Tel (239) 261-1616 *Founded/Ownrshp* 2010
Sales 60.7MM *EMP* 65^E
SIC 8062 General medical & surgical hospitals
Ch Bd: Denise C Heinemann
**Pr:* Daniel J Lavender
**COO:* Kent L McRae
**CFO:* Tim Buist
**Treas:* Kathryn Chair M E Smith
**VP:* Steve Brinkert
Ex Dir: Joanne Wallace

D-U-N-S 02-141-7399
MOORINGS PARK FOUNDATION INC
120 Moorings Park Dr, Naples, FL 34105-2122
Tel (239) 261-1616 *Founded/Ownrshp* 1977
Sales 33.8MM^E *EMP* 620
Accts Hill Barth & King Llc Naples
SIC 8361 Residential care; Residential care
Ch: Daniel C Maclea
**CEO:* Dan Lavender
COO: Kent McCray
CFO: Tim Buist
**Ch:* Stevan Brinkert
**Treas:* David Sweeney

D-U-N-S 09-562-8715
MOORPARK UNIFIED SCHOOL DISTRICT
5297 Maureen Ln, Moorpark, CA 93021-7125
Tel (805) 378-6300 *Founded/Ownrshp* 1900
Sales 62.8MM *EMP* 575
SIC 8211 Public elementary & secondary schools; Public elementary & secondary schools
**Pr:* Ute Van Dam
**VP:* Bruce Thomas

*Prin: Greg Barker
*Prin: Nathan Sweet
Dir IT: Julie Judd

D-U-N-S 05-178-9212
MOORS & CABOT INC
111 Devonshire St Ste 100, Boston, MA 02109-5483
Tel (617) 426-0500 Founded/Ownrshp 1991
Sales 53.3MM^E EMP 215
SIC 6211 6282 Security brokers & dealers; Investment advisory service; Security brokers & dealers; Investment advisory service
Ch Bd: Herbert A Sarkisian Jr
*Pr: Daniel M Joyce
CFO: George Clarke
CFO: Paul Maisch
CFO: William Teuber
Treas: Charles Turner
Ex VP: Scott Eisler
Ex VP: Michael Hildreth
*Ex VP: John Mulcahy
Ex VP: Peter Raskind
Sr VP: Victor Berman
Sr VP: Scott Bundy
Sr VP: Todd Clark
Sr VP: Gray Dalton
Sr VP: Stephen Denapoli
Sr VP: Anthony Dorval
Sr VP: Sondria Eure
Sr VP: Jason Facey
Sr VP: Dave Farbman
Sr VP: Aaron Foley
Sr VP: Dennett Goodrich

D-U-N-S 19-875-7809
MOOSE INC
310 Lewers St, Honolulu, HI 96815-2343
Tel (808) 923-0751 Founded/Ownrshp 1982
Sales 6.4MM^E EMP 315
SIC 5812 5813 American restaurant; Cocktail lounge; American restaurant; Cocktail lounge
Pr: Lee De Shong
*VP: George E Watson
Genl Mgr: Antonio Payton

D-U-N-S 06-401-9995
MOOSE INTERNATIONAL INC
LOYAL ORDER OF THE MOOSE
155 S International Dr, Mooseheart, IL 60539-1169
Tel (630) 859-2000 Founded/Ownrshp 1888
Sales 53.7MM EMP 430
Accts Moose International Moosehear
SIC 8641 Veterans' organization; Veterans' organization
CEO: Scott D Hart
Treas: Joe Mech
VP: Leonard J Solfa
Rgnl Mgr: Bill Cavanaugh
Rgnl Mgr: Robert Longchamps
Rgnl Mgr: Ron Trygstad
Genl Couns: T Leuer
Assoc Ed: Darryl Mellema

D-U-N-S 06-099-6139
MOOSE RIVER LUMBER CO INC
25 Talpey Rd, Moose River, ME 04945-4016
Tel (207) 668-4426 Founded/Ownrshp 1976
Sales 34.6MM EMP 75
Accts Perry Fits Boulette & Fitton
SIC 2421 Lumber: rough, sawed or planed; Chipper mill; Lumber: rough, sawed or planed; Chipper mill
Pr: Charles Lumbert
*VP: Jeff Defjardins
Plnt Mgr: Tom Sylvester

MOPAC
See JBS SOUDERTON INC

MOPEP ENRGY SCHEDULING TAGGING
See MISSOURI JOINT MUNICIPAL ELECTRIC UTILITY COMMISSION

D-U-N-S 83-255-9996 IMP
MOPHIE LLC
6244 Technology Ave, Kalamazoo, MI 49009-8113
Tel (269) 415-0217 Founded/Ownrshp 2006
Sales 40.4MM^E EMP 99
SIC 3692 4812 8999 Primary batteries, dry & wet; Cellular telephone services; Communication services
CEO: Daniel Huang

D-U-N-S 05-658-7512 IMP
MOR FURNITURE FOR LESS INC
8996 Miramar Rd Ste 300, San Diego, CA 92126-4463
Tel (858) 547-1616 Founded/Ownrshp 1987
Sales 154.9MM^E EMP 600
SIC 5712 Furniture stores; Furniture stores
CEO: Richard D Haux
*Ch Bd: Rick Haux Sr
*Pr: Jeff Haux
Pr: George Meier
Genl Mgr: Jeffrey Allen
Genl Mgr: Derek Riedlinger
Genl Mgr: Nick Wilkin
Site Mgr: Jenna Rivera
*S&M/VP: Robert Kelley
Mktg Mgr: Don Smith
Mktg Mgr: David Stiff

D-U-N-S 00-386-8932
MOR GRAN SOU ELECTRIC COOPERATIVE
202 6th Ave W, Flasher, ND 58535-7131
Tel (701) 597-3301 Founded/Ownrshp 1946
Sales 21.4MM EMP 35^E
SIC 4911 Distribution, electric power; Distribution, electric power
Genl Mgr: Don Franklund
Treas: Pam Geiger
Bd of Dir: Mark Doll
Bd of Dir: Robert Gaebe
Bd of Dir: Chad Harrison
Bd of Dir: Robert Leingang
Board of Directors: Robert Gripp V Chmn, William Gerger, Gary Jochim, Delores Olsen, Delwin Patrick, David Schmidt Sec-Treas, Robert Tomac

D-U-N-S 13-473-5294
■ **MOR PPM INC**
(Suby of EMCOR GROUP INC) ★
1127 S Main St, Society Hill, SC 29593-8990
Tel (843) 378-4700 Founded/Ownrshp 2008
Sales 158.5MM^E EMP 1,000
SIC 1731 General electrical contractor; General electrical contractor
Pr: Henry B Moree
*VP: Hank Moree
*VP: Bobby L Ollis

MOR-RYDE SERVICE CENTER
See MOR/RYDE INC

D-U-N-S 01-627-2494
MOR/RYDE INC
MOR-RYDE SERVICE CENTER
1966 Moyer Ave, Elkhart, IN 46516-4230
Tel (574) 293-1581 Founded/Ownrshp 1966
Sales 26.1MM^E EMP 115
SIC 3714 Motor vehicle transmissions, drive assemblies & parts; Frames, motor vehicle; Motor vehicle body components & frame; Motor vehicle transmissions, drive assemblies & parts; Frames, motor vehicle; Motor vehicle body components & frame
Pr: Robert G Moore Jr
*Ch Bd: Robert Moore Sr
*Sec: Rodney A Moore
Dir: Jan Freer

D-U-N-S 80-442-5002
MOR/RYDE INTERNATIONAL INC
1966 Moyer Ave, Elkhart, IN 46516-4230
Tel (574) 266-0053 Founded/Ownrshp 1982
Sales 42.3MM^E EMP 260^E
SIC 3449 3714 Bars, concrete reinforcing: fabricated steel; Motor vehicle transmissions, drive assemblies & parts; Frames, motor vehicle; Motor vehicle body components & frame; Bars, concrete reinforcing: fabricated steel; Motor vehicle transmissions, drive assemblies & parts; Frames, motor vehicle; Motor vehicle body components & frame
Ch Bd: Robert Moore Sr
*Pr: Robert Moore Jr
COO: Jack Enfield
VP: Jan Freers
VP: Josh Moore
Dir IT: Billy Fink
Plnt Mgr: Dale Bennet
Mktg Mgr: Becca Carpenter
Sales Asso: Todd Obergfell

D-U-N-S 14-298-0478 IMP
MORADA PRODUCE CO LP
500 N Jack Tone Rd, Stockton, CA 95215-9725
Tel (209) 546-0426 Founded/Ownrshp 2003
Sales 57.6MM^E EMP 1,500
SIC 0723 Fruit (fresh) packing services; Vegetable packing services; Fruit (fresh) packing services; Vegetable packing services
Pt: Henry Foppiano

MORAINE PARK TECHNICAL COLLEGE
See PARK MORAINE TECHNICAL COLLEGE

D-U-N-S 06-620-8398
MORAINE VALLEY COMMUNITY COLLEGE (IL)
COMMUNITY COLLEGE DST 524
9000 W College Pkwy, Palos Hills, IL 60465-2478
Tel (708) 974-4300 Founded/Ownrshp 1967
Sales 40.4MM EMP 1,200
Accts Crowe Horwath Llp Oak Brook
SIC 8222 Community college; Community college
CEO: Dr Sylvia Jenkins
COO: Sarah Bales
IT Man: Jack Lifel
Secur Mgr: John Wagrowski
Psych: Matthew Cullen

D-U-N-S 07-974-9561
MORALE WELFARE AND RECREATION DEPT
5th St Bldg 219, Kaneohe, HI 96744
Tel (808) 257-0372 Founded/Ownrshp 2014
Sales NA EMP 900^E
SIC 9532

D-U-N-S 07-884-9062
MORALE WELFARE RECREATION ACTIVITY
MARINE CORPS COMMUNITY SVCS
1401 West Rd, Camp Lejeune, NC 28547-2539
Tel (910) 451-2861 Founded/Ownrshp 1989
Sales 71.0MM^E EMP 2,500
SIC 5311 5812 8322 7999 9711 Department stores; Eating places; Individual & family services; Recreation center; ; Department stores; Eating places; Individual & family services; Recreation center;
Prin: Michael Smith
Secur Mgr: Dusty Carven

D-U-N-S 14-005-1470
MORAN CHEVROLET INC
35500 S Gratiot Ave, Clinton Township, MI 48035-2847
Tel (586) 791-1010 Founded/Ownrshp 2003
Sales 42.3MM^E EMP 80
SIC 5511 Automobiles, new & used; Automobiles, new & used
Pr: Patrick J Moran
CFO: Carol Lucas
*Treas: Debbie L Stein
Exec: Lisa Horetski
Store Mgr: Tom Barczak
IT Man: Jomarie Ruggeri
Mktg Dir: Brian Moran
Sls Mgr: Terry Pickelhaupt
Sls Mgr: Gary Sommer
Sales Asso: Sean Pavlik
Sales Asso: Dave Sengstock

MORAN DISTRIBUTION CENTERS
See MORAN TRANSPORTATION CORP

MORAN DRY BULK
See MORAN TOWING CORP

D-U-N-S 11-048-7076 IMP
MORAN ENVIRONMENTAL RECOVERY LLC
75 York Ave Ste D, Randolph, MA 02368-1841
Tel (781) 815-1100 Founded/Ownrshp 2007
Sales 62.9MM^E EMP 191
SIC 8744 ;
VP: John Silva
Genl Mgr: Paul Laflamme
Sfty Dirs: Krystal Weaver
VP Sls: John Mahoney

D-U-N-S 09-548-4572 EXP
■ **MORAN FOODS LLC**
(Suby of SUPERVALU HOLDINGS INC) ★
100 Corporate Office Dr, Earth City, MO 63045-1511
Tel (314) 592-9100 Founded/Ownrshp 1992
Sales 2.3MMM^E EMP 5,000
SIC 5141 5411 Groceries, general line; Grocery stores; Groceries, general line; Grocery stores
Pr: Bill Shaner
Pr: Brian Thiemann
*CFO: Rob Anderson

D-U-N-S 36-271-8108 IMP
MORAN INDUSTRIES INC
MORAN LOGISTICS
202 E 7th St Ste 1, Watsontown, PA 17777-1146
Tel (570) 538-5558 Founded/Ownrshp 1975
Sales 33.0MM^E EMP 105
SIC 4225 General warehousing
Ch: Jack D Moran
*Pr: John D Moran Jr
VP: Jeff Stroehmann
Opers Mgr: Jeff Gummo
Snr Mgr: Sara Kaskie

MORAN LOGISTICS
See MORAN INDUSTRIES INC

MORAN MAZDA
See MORAN OLDSMOBILE-CADILLAC-GMC TRUCK INC

D-U-N-S 10-650-9425
MORAN OLDSMOBILE-CADILLAC-GMC TRUCK INC
MORAN MAZDA
4511 24th Ave, Fort Gratiot, MI 48059-3401
Tel (810) 385-8500 Founded/Ownrshp 1987
Sales 20.7MM^E EMP 50
SIC 5511 5521 Automobiles, new & used; Pickups, new & used; Automobiles, used cars only; Pickups & vans, used
Pr: Patrick J Moran
*Sec: Deborah L Stein

D-U-N-S 78-213-2179
MORAN PRINTING INC
EMPRINT DOCUMENT SOLUTIONS
5425 Florida Blvd, Baton Rouge, LA 70806-4132
Tel (225) 923-2550 Founded/Ownrshp 1991
Sales 28.0MM EMP 193
Accts Hawthorn Waymouth & Carroll
SIC 2752 2789 2791 Commercial printing, offset; Bookbinding & related work; Typesetting; Commercial printing, offset; Bookbinding & related work; Typesetting
Pr: Rebecca Vance
*CEO: Courtney Westbrook
VP: Keith Page
VP: John Phillips
Dir IT: Jonathan Brown
IT Man: Jonathan Brand
Prd Mgr: Trisha Higdon
Prd Mgr: Greg Thompson
Mktg Mgr: Nicky Taylor

D-U-N-S 00-698-7846
MORAN TOWING CORP (NY)
MORAN DRY BULK
(Suby of MORAN TRANSPORTATION CO) ★
50 Locust Ave Ste 10, New Canaan, CT 06840-4741
Tel (203) 442-2800 Founded/Ownrshp 1860, 1994
Sales 61.4MM^E EMP 335
SIC 4492 Marine towing services; Tugboat service; Docking of ocean vessels; Undocking of ocean vessels; Marine towing services; Tugboat service; Docking of ocean vessels; Undocking of ocean vessels
Ch Bd: Paul R Tregurtha
Pr: Aislinn Pitchford
Pr: Edward J Tregurtha
COO: Mark Koenig
CFO: Jeffrey J McAulay
Treas: Joseph A De Angelo
Sr VP: Gregory McGinty
Sr VP: William P Muller
Sr VP: Edmond J Murand Jr
Sr VP: Peter J Nistad
VP: David Beardsley
VP: Jeff Beech
VP: James Coyne
VP Bus Dev: Robert Barry
Exec: Janice Daiuto
Dir Risk M: Daniel Klaben

D-U-N-S 87-445-4705
MORAN TRANSPORTATION CO
50 Locust Ave Ste 3, New Canaan, CT 06840-4737
Tel (203) 442-2800 Founded/Ownrshp 1996
Sales 70.6MM^E EMP 550
SIC 4492 Marine towing services; Tugboat service; Docking of ocean vessels; Undocking of ocean vessels; Marine towing services
CEO: Paul R Tregurtha
Sec: Alan Marchisotto
V Ch Bd: James R Baker
VP: Jeffrey J McAulay
Off Mgr: Judy Enrigh

D-U-N-S 14-636-1845
MORAN TRANSPORTATION CORP
MORAN DISTRIBUTION CENTERS
2401 Arthur Ave, Elk Grove Village, IL 60007-6016
Tel (847) 439-0000 Founded/Ownrshp 1980
Sales 23.2MM^E EMP 135
SIC 4214 4225 Local trucking with storage; General warehousing & storage
Pr: Michael J Moran

*CFO: Jerome Gayda
Opers Mgr: Robert J Petzold

D-U-N-S 09-553-6124
MORANDE FORD INC
MORANDE LINCOLN MERCURY, MAZDA
250 Webster Square Rd, Berlin, CT 06037-2329
Tel (860) 828-3546 Founded/Ownrshp 1979
Sales 38.2MM^E EMP 125
SIC 5511 Automobiles, new & used; Trucks, tractors & trailers: new & used; Automobiles, new & used; Trucks, tractors & trailers: new & used
Ch Bd: Robert J Morande
*Treas: Paula Morande
*VP: William R Morande

MORANDE LINCOLN MERCURY, MAZDA
See MORANDE FORD INC

D-U-N-S 06-149-8416 IMP
MORASCH MEATS INC (OR)
MORASCH'S QUALITY MEATS
4050 Ne 158th Ave, Portland, OR 97230-5003
Tel (503) 257-9821 Founded/Ownrshp 1956
Sales 50.0MM EMP 170
SIC 5142 2013 5147 Packaged frozen goods; Meat, frozen: packaged; Sausages & other prepared meats; Meats, cured or smoked
Pr: Michael N Morasch
*Sec: Steven J Morasch
*VP: Melissa G Morasch

MORASCH'S QUALITY MEATS
See MORASCH MEATS INC

D-U-N-S 08-202-5099
MORAVIAN ACADEMY
11 W Market St, Bethlehem, PA 18018-5702
Tel (610) 868-4744 Founded/Ownrshp 2007
Sales 20.2MM EMP 174
Accts Campbell Rappold & Yurasits Ll
SIC 8211 Private elementary school; Private junior high school; Private senior high school; Private elementary school; Private junior high school; Private senior high school
Ch: Judy Waldman
Treas: Nicholas Zumas
HC Dir: Christine Murphy

D-U-N-S 07-361-9405
MORAVIAN COLLEGE
MORAVIAN COLLEGE BOOKSTORE
1200 Main St, Bethlehem, PA 18018-6650
Tel (610) 861-1300 Founded/Ownrshp 1742
Sales 54.5MM EMP 450^E
Accts Baker Tilly Virchow Krause Ll
SIC 8221 College, except junior; Theological seminary; College, except junior; Theological seminary
Pr: Bryon L Grigsby
V Ch: Ann Claussen
COO: Amy Saul
Treas: Sharon Maus
*Treas: Anne Reid
Trst: Frederick P Sutliff
*VP: Dennis Domchek
*VP: Curtis Keim
*VP: Beverly Koshard
VP: Steven Soba
VP: Gordon Weil
Exec: Beverly Kochard
Exec: Mike Kostalis
Dir Soc: Bertie Knisely

MORAVIAN COLLEGE BOOKSTORE
See MORAVIAN COLLEGE

D-U-N-S 14-428-7703
MORAVIAN HALL SQUARE OF NAZARETH PA INC
175 W North St, Nazareth, PA 18064-1410
Tel (610) 746-1000 Founded/Ownrshp 1985
Sales 21.9MM^E EMP 355
SIC 6513 8052 8051 Retirement hotel operation; Intermediate care facilities; Skilled nursing care facilities; Retirement hotel operation; Intermediate care facilities; Skilled nursing care facilities
CEO: Susan C Drabic
CFO: Chris Hunt
Dir IT: Monica Bustemante

D-U-N-S 07-144-3626
MORAVIAN MANORS INC (PA)
300 W Lemon St, Lititz, PA 17543-2398
Tel (717) 626-0214 Founded/Ownrshp 1975
Sales 17.7MM EMP 325
SIC 8051 Skilled nursing care facilities; Skilled nursing care facilities
Pr: J David Swartley
*Ch: Richard A Minnich
Treas: Richard Minnich
VP: Joyce Krushinski
Exec: Debra Hoffstead
Exec: Dan Snyder
Dir Soc: Lisa Dorsey
CIO: Eric Palabay
QC Dir: Donna Gerofsky
HC Dir: Stacy Frey
HC Dir: Liz Hewitt

D-U-N-S 96-353-6003
MORAVIAN SPRINGS HEALTH CENTER
175 W North St, Nazareth, PA 18064-1410
Tel (610) 746-1000 Founded/Ownrshp 2010
Sales 1.3MMM EMP 10^E
SIC 8051 Skilled nursing care facilities; Skilled nursing care facilities
Owner: Susan C Drabic

D-U-N-S 80-116-9496
MORAVIAN VILLAGE OF BETHLEHEM
526 Wood St, Bethlehem, PA 18018-4453
Tel (610) 625-4885 Founded/Ownrshp 1999
Sales 21.2MM EMP 250
SIC 8059 Personal care home, with health care; Personal care home, with health care
CEO: David Roth
*CFO: Tracy Patton
CFO: Daniel Soos
Mktg Dir: Valerie Stumer-Heller

Nrsg Dir: Susan Newhard
HC Dir: Theresa Benner

D-U-N-S 19-558-6185 IMP/EXP
MORBARK INC
8507 S Winn Rd, Winn, MI 48896
Tel (989) 866-2381 *Founded/Ownrshp* 1988
Sales 89.9MME *EMP* 414
SIC 3599 3553 3549 3523 Machine shop, jobbing & repair; Woodworking machinery; Metalworking machinery; Farm machinery & equipment; Machine shop, jobbing & repair; Woodworking machinery; Metalworking machinery; Farm machinery & equipment
CEO: Lon Morey
* *Treas:* Debra Lehmann
Ofcr: Kerry Noch
* *VP:* Miland Robinson
VP: Jim Shoemaker
* *Exec:* Larry H Noch
Off Mgr: Kelly Pung
Dir IT: Nick Mullin
Opers Supe: Ben Schanck
Mktg Mgr: Jeanne Maddox
Manager: Chris Edmonds

D-U-N-S 02-145-8018
MORC REHABILITATION SERVICES
16200 19 Mile Rd, Clinton Township, MI 48038-1103
Tel (586) 739-5792 *Founded/Ownrshp* 2001
Sales 198.2MM *EMP* 8
SIC 8322 Rehabilitation services

D-U-N-S 06-682-7346
MORCON CONSTRUCTION CO INC
5905 Golden Valley Rd # 231, Minneapolis, MN 55422-4475
Tel (763) 546-3314 *Founded/Ownrshp* 1982
Sales 34.5MME *EMP* 75
SIC 1542 Commercial & office building contractors
CEO: Jerry Jullie
* *VP:* Stan Thom

D-U-N-S 17-402-3564 IMP
MORCON INC
879 State Rte 22, Cambridge, NY 12816
Tel (518) 677-8511 *Founded/Ownrshp* 2013
Sales 28.4MME *EMP* 148
SIC 2679 Paper products, converted; Paper products, converted
Pr: Joseph F Raccuia

D-U-N-S 12-159-7231
MORE THAN COMPUTERS INC
3001 W Beltline Hwy Lbby, Madison, WI 53713-2891
Tel (608) 661-7700 *Founded/Ownrshp* 1984
Sales 25.3MME *EMP* 150
Accts Smith & Gesteland Llp Madiso
SIC 5045 7372 7378 Computers; Business oriented computer software; Computer & data processing equipment repair/maintenance; Computers; Business oriented computer software; Computer & data processing equipment repair/maintenance
Pr: Laurie Benson
* *Treas:* Barbara Mortenson
Chf Mktg O: Stacie Bogan
* *VP:* Frank Albi
* *VP:* Bryan Bechtoldt
* *VP:* Teri Bruns
* *VP:* Gary Hoffman
VP: Julie Jolliffe
* *VP:* Loren Mortenson
Brnch Mgr: Phil Heaton
MIS Dir: Jim Exendine

D-U-N-S 17-640-5090 IMP
MORE THAN GOURMET INC
929 Home Ave, Akron, OH 44310-4107
Tel (330) 762-6652 *Founded/Ownrshp* 1996
Sales 26.0MM *EMP* 45
SIC 2032 Soups & broths: canned, jarred, etc.
CEO: Brad Sacks
VP: Emily Maglott
Dir Bus: Barry Donovan
QA Dir: Chris Balthis
Plnt Mgr: Todd McFarland

D-U-N-S 85-926-0317 IMP
■ **MOREDIRECT INC**
(*Suby of* PC CONNECTION INC) ★
1001 Yamato Rd Ste 200, Boca Raton, FL 33431-4403
Tel (561) 237-3300 *Founded/Ownrshp* 2002
Sales 563.9MME *EMP* 316
SIC 5045 7373 7376 Computers; Computer software; Systems software development services; Computer facilities management; Computers; Computer software; Systems software development services; Computer facilities management
Pr: John Thomas
CFO: Jack Ferguson
* *VP:* Kerri Chiappone
* *VP:* Carlos Covarrubias
VP: Sylvia Diamant
VP: Paul Geiss
* *VP:* Sylvia Johe
Exec: Jennifer Wood
Dir Bus: Kay Childs
Dir Bus: George Hartlein
IT Man: Cory Fisher

D-U-N-S 01-392-2059
MOREFIELD COMMUNICATIONS INC
35 N 35th St, Camp Hill, PA 17011-2797
Tel (717) 761-6170 *Founded/Ownrshp* 1957
Sales 30.2MME *EMP* 105
SIC 4813

D-U-N-S 78-192-0954
MOREHEAD ASSOCIATES INC
(*Suby of* PRESS GANEY ASSOCIATES INC) ★
700 E Morehead St Ste 200, Charlotte, NC 28202-2742
Tel (704) 522-0776 *Founded/Ownrshp* 2013
Sales 27.3MME *EMP* 500
SIC 8732 8742 Survey service: marketing, location, etc.; Opinion research; Training & development consultant
Pr: Larry Tilson
CEO: Joe Greskoviak
Sr VP: Sue Knight
VP: Greg Johns
VP: Megan Medvedeff
VP: Barbara Reilly
Snr Sftwr: Michael Linnert
Software D: Mike Linnen
Mktg Mgr: Anna Vordermark

D-U-N-S 07-783-2418
MOREHEAD MEMORIAL HOSPITAL INC
117 E Kings Hwy, Eden, NC 27288-5201
Tel (336) 623-9711 *Founded/Ownrshp* 1924
Sales 81.1MM *EMP* 850
Accts Cliftonlarsonallen Llp Charl
SIC 8062 8051 General medical & surgical hospitals; Skilled nursing care facilities; General medical & surgical hospitals; Skilled nursing care facilities
Pr: W Carl Martin
* *Pr:* Cynthia Bradley
Treas: Emma Jennings
Trst: Edwin Wilson
Exec: Jeanette Light
Dir Inf Cn: Teresa Johnson
Dir Lab: Sandra Clark
Dir Rad: David Brown
Dir Pat Ac: Sarah Stokes
CIO: B Williams
CTO: Jane Younts

D-U-N-S 04-195-7010
MOREHEAD STATE UNIVERSITY
207 Hal Mcdowell, Morehead, KY 40351-1683
Tel (606) 783-2053 *Founded/Ownrshp* 1922
Sales 77.5MM *EMP* 1,200
Accts Dean Dorton Allen Ford Pllc
SIC 8221 University; University
Pr: Wayne D Andrews
* *Assoc VP:* Gary Holeman
VP: Kevin Koett
VP: Brenda Porter

D-U-N-S 07-887-7419
MOREHOUSE BIOENERGY LLC
7070 Carl Rd, Bastrop, LA 71220-6584
Tel (770) 743-4300 *Founded/Ownrshp* 2012
Sales 100.0MM *EMP* 50
SIC 2493 Reconstituted wood products
Treas: Tamara Richards
Board of Directors: Charles Davis

D-U-N-S 07-586-1773
MOREHOUSE COLLEGE (INC)
830 Westview Dr Sw, Atlanta, GA 30314-3776
Tel (404) 681-2800 *Founded/Ownrshp* 1867
Sales 114.3MM *EMP* 700E
SIC 8221 College, except junior; College, except junior
CEO: John Silvanus Wilson Jr
* *Pr:* Robert Franklin
* *CFO:* Shelia B Jacobs
* *CFO:* Gwendolyn Sykes
* *Treas:* John Whllace
Trst: Garrett Auzenne
Trst: Susan Buffett
Trst: Dawud Crooms
Trst: Chester Davenport
Trst: Walter E Massey
Trst: Phillip H McCall Jr
Trst: Otis Moss
Sr VP: Garikai Campbell
Sr VP: Karen Miller
VP: Andr Bertrand
VP: John Brown
VP: David Connor
VP: Nashon Hornsby
VP: Phillip Howard
VP: Willis B Sheftall Jr
VP: Shytall Willis

D-U-N-S 06-973-3574
MOREHOUSE GENERAL HOSPITAL (INC)
323 W Walnut Ave, Bastrop, LA 71220-4521
Tel (318) 283-3662 *Founded/Ownrshp* 1955
Sales 28.7MME *EMP* 300E
Accts La Porte Apac Metairie La
SIC 8062 General medical & surgical hospitals; General medical & surgical hospitals
Ch: Mike Wooden
* *CEO:* Stephen Pitts
* *CFO:* Jim Allbritton
Dir Inf Cn: Cheryl McCrary
Dir Rx: Beverly Jones
* *CIO:* Robert Woods
IT Man: B J Vail
Sfty Dirs: Dee Robinson
Obsttrcn: Janos Guoth
Doctor: Ernest M Mak
Doctor: Brett McDonald

D-U-N-S 55-645-1219
MOREHOUSE PARISH SCHOOL BOARD
4099 Naff Ave, Bastrop, LA 71220-7486
Tel (318) 281-5784 *Founded/Ownrshp* 1891
Sales 38.8MME *EMP* 645
Accts Allen Green & Williamson Llp
SIC 8211 Public elementary & secondary schools; Public elementary & secondary schools
Schl Brd P: Loe Dun

D-U-N-S 10-200-5451
MOREHOUSE SCHOOL OF MEDICINE INC
720 Westview Dr Sw, Atlanta, GA 30310-1458
Tel (404) 752-1500 *Founded/Ownrshp* 1980
Sales 142.8MM *EMP* 700E
Accts Bdo Usa Llp Atlanta Ga
SIC 8322 8221 Drug abuse counselor, nontreatment; College, except junior; Drug abuse counselor, nontreatment; College, except junior
Pr: John E Maupin Jr
Ofcr: Brian Byars
Ofcr: Jason Camp
Ofcr: Mfon Essien
Ofcr: Rufus Hunley
Ofcr: Lonon Norwood
Ofcr: Howard Rodgers
Ofcr: Daphine Seay
Sr VP: John Case
Div/Sub He: Sisi Arango
Ex Dir: Daniel Dawes

D-U-N-S 18-291-5470
MORELAND ALTOBELLI ASSOCIATES INC
2450 Commerce Ave Ste 100, Duluth, GA 30096-8910
Tel (770) 263-5945 *Founded/Ownrshp* 1987
Sales 32.0MM *EMP* 312
SIC 8711 Consulting engineer; Consulting engineer
Pr: Thomas D Moreland
* *CFO:* Vickie Moreland
* *Ex VP:* Buddy Gratton
* *VP:* Stephen T Moreland
Prgrm Mgr: Russell Small
Off Admin: Jennifer Rhodes
Info Man: David Phillips
Manager: Maurice Sheehan
Sls&Mrk Ex: Wayne Hill
Mktg Dir: Michael Gill
Genl Couns: Alexander Kass

D-U-N-S 10-064-4574
MORELAND SCHOOL DISTRICT
4711 Campbell Ave, San Jose, CA 95130-1790
Tel (408) 874-2900 *Founded/Ownrshp* 1993
Sales 26.1MME *EMP* 421
SIC 8211 Public elementary & secondary schools; Kindergarten; School board; Public elementary & secondary schools; Kindergarten; School board
Bd of Dir: Robert Varich
Dir IT: Jenny Mendoza
Dir IT: Linh Vu

D-U-N-S 00-139-1044
MORENG METAL FAB INC
100 W End Rd, Totowa, NJ 07512-1407
Tel (973) 256-2001 *Founded/Ownrshp* 1902
Sales 27.8MME *EMP* 85
SIC 3444 3644 Sheet metalwork; Noncurrent-carrying wiring services
CEO: James R Moreng
* *VP:* Joseph H Moreng Jr
VP Opers: Thomas Signore

MORENO PETROLEUM
See STURDY OIL CO

D-U-N-S 08-913-9257 IMP
MORENO VALLEY UNIFIED SCHOOL DISTRICT
25634 Alessandro Blvd, Moreno Valley, CA 92553-4916
Tel (951) 571-7500 *Founded/Ownrshp* 1962
Sales 16.4MM *EMP* 3,500
SIC 8211 Public elementary & secondary schools; High school, junior or senior; Public elementary & secondary schools; High school, junior or senior
VP: Cleveland Johnson
Bd of Dir: Maria Lozano
Exec: Tim McGillivray
Dir Rx: Bertha Bravo
Admn Mgr: Tammy Guzzetta
CIO: Steve Jones
CTO: Steven Morford
IT Man: Abdul Kamara
Software D: Roxanne Mummert
Schl Brd P: Tracie Vackar
Psych: Karla Aguirre

D-U-N-S 83-539-8538
■ **MOREQUITY INC**
(*Suby of* SPRINGLEAF FINANCE CORP) ★
7116 Eagle Crest Blvd, Evansville, IN 47715-8152
Tel (800) 345-0187 *Founded/Ownrshp* 1994
Sales NA *EMP* 125
SIC 6162 Mortgage bankers; Mortgage bankers
Pr: George D Roach
Assoc Dir: Darell Pennington

D-U-N-S 84-901-5425 IMP
MORESCO DISTRIBUTING CO
1450 Tech Ln Ste 150, Petaluma, CA 94954
Tel (707) 773-2500 *Founded/Ownrshp* 1994
Sales 35.5MME *EMP* 33
SIC 5113 Containers, paper & disposable plastic; Paper & products, wrapping or coarse; Sanitary food containers
Pr: Ronald S Moresco
* *COO:* Eileen Lott
* *CFO:* Kim Marshall

D-U-N-S 00-215-4607 IMP
MORETRENCH AMERICAN CORP (GA)
FREEZ WALL
100 Stickle Ave, Rockaway, NJ 07866-3146
Tel (262) 652-4444 *Founded/Ownrshp* 1911
Sales 118.2MM *EMP* 600
SIC 1629

D-U-N-S 78-771-6414
MORETRENCH ENVIRONMENTAL SERVICES INC
(*Suby of* FREEZ WALL) ★
100 Stickle Ave, Rockaway, NJ 07866-3146
Tel (973) 627-2100 *Founded/Ownrshp* 1985
Sales 46.2MME *EMP* 150
SIC 4959

D-U-N-S 15-532-1441 EXP
MOREX INC
1609 Cross Beam Dr, Charlotte, NC 28217-2809
Tel (704) 423-0102 *Founded/Ownrshp* 1986
Sales 22.9MM *EMP* 30
Accts Peter Bell Pllc Charlotte N
SIC 5075 5074 5087 Ventilating equipment & supplies; Heating equipment (hydronic); Firefighting equipment
Ch Bd: Rudolph Mazigi
* *VP:* Albert Isaac
* *VP:* Edgar Mazigi

D-U-N-S 02-541-5266 IMP
MOREY CORP
100 Morey Dr, Woodridge, IL 60517-8135
Tel (630) 754-2300 *Founded/Ownrshp* 1934
Sales 58.7MME *EMP* 386
SIC 3672 3999

D-U-N-S 00-382-2152
MOREY INDUSTRIES INC
WESTMONT ENGINEERING COMPANY
2000 Beach St, Broadview, IL 60155-2833
Tel (708) 343-3220 *Founded/Ownrshp* 1958
Sales 29.0MME *EMP* 110
SIC 3441 1796 1791 Fabricated structural metal; Machinery installation; Structural steel erection; Fabricated structural metal; Machinery installation; Structural steel erection
Pr: Douglas Morey
* *Sec:* Scott Morey

D-U-N-S 04-263-4944
MOREYS SEAFOOD INTERNATIONAL LLC
115 N Michigan, Chicago, IL 60601
Tel (218) 352-2137 *Founded/Ownrshp* 1998
Sales 61.6MME *EMP* 400
SIC 5146 Fish & seafoods; Fish & seafoods

D-U-N-S 16-196-2428 IMP
MOREYS SEAFOOD INTERNATIONAL LLC
742 Decatur Ave N, Minneapolis, MN 55427-4323
Tel (763) 541-0129 *Founded/Ownrshp* 1998
Sales 209.0MME *EMP* 400
SIC 5146 2091 Fish, cured; Fish, fresh; Fish, frozen, unpackaged; Seafoods; Fish, smoked; Fish, cured; Fish, pickled; Seafood products: packaged in cans, jars, etc.; Fish, cured; Fish, fresh; Fish, frozen, unpackaged; Seafoods; Fish, smoked; Fish, cured; Fish, pickled; Seafood products: packaged in cans, jars, etc.
* *CFO:* Gary Ziolkowski
Ex VP: Heyman Justin
VP: Tom Daly
CIO: Ann Walstrom
Dir IT: Tom Pfluger
IT Man: Kevin Becklin
Tech Mgr: Forest Reichel
Opers Supe: Tony Turner
VP Mktg: Tracy Wiese
VP Sls: Scott Wickert
Mktg Dir: Paul Clemensen

MORFLEX
See VERTELLUS PERFORMANCE MATERIALS INC

D-U-N-S 00-430-1099 IMP
MORGAL MACHINE TOOL CO (OH)
MCGREGOR METALWORKING
2100 S Yellow Springs St, Springfield, OH 45506-3369
Tel (937) 325-5561 *Founded/Ownrshp* 1939
Sales 29.1MME *EMP* 90
SIC 3469 3568 3544 3451 3429 Metal stampings; Stamping metal for the trade; Power transmission equipment; Special dies, tools, jigs & fixtures; Screw machine products; Manufactured hardware (general)
Pr: Tom Wright
* *Ch Bd:* Daniel P Mc Gregor
* *Pr:* James B Mc Gregor
* *COO:* Dwight Kent
* *CFO:* Seth Powers
* *Ch:* James McGregor
VP: Rick Hemmelgarn
VP: Mike Molar
* *Prin:* Dane A Belden
Prgrm Mgr: Dave Myers
Genl Mgr: Jeff Powell

D-U-N-S 62-273-8458
MORGAN & BROTHER HOLDING INC
16 Bruce Park Ave, Greenwich, CT 06830-6314
Tel (203) 869-8700 *Founded/Ownrshp* 1989
Sales 39.8MME *EMP* 250
SIC 6719 Investment holding companies, except banks; Investment holding companies, except banks
Pr: Jeffrey S Morgan
* *Treas:* Charles S Morgan

D-U-N-S 00-394-9906
MORGAN & BROTHER MANHATTAN STORAGE CO INC (NY)
MORGAN MANHATTAN
(*Suby of* MORGAN & BROTHER HOLDING INC) ★
16 Bruce Park Ave, Greenwich, CT 06830-6314
Tel (203) 869-8700 *Founded/Ownrshp* 1851, 1989
Sales 37.7MME *EMP* 250
SIC 6719 Investment holding companies, except banks; Investment holding companies, except banks
Pr: Jeffrey S Morgan
VP: Doug Spelman

D-U-N-S 61-782-5468
MORGAN & MORGAN PA
20 N Orange Ave Ste 1607, Orlando, FL 32801-4645
Tel (407) 420-1414 *Founded/Ownrshp* 1988
Sales 98.0MME *EMP* 400
SIC 8111 General practice law office; General practice law office
Pr: John B Morgan
COO: Tim Morgan
CFO: Bernardo Garcia
* *VP:* Scott H Bates

D-U-N-S 00-381-2435
MORGAN & THORNBURG INC
4076 Hatcher Cir, Memphis, TN 38118-6837
Tel (901) 365-4936 *Founded/Ownrshp* 1976
Sales 35.7MME *EMP* 140
SIC 1711 1761 Warm air heating & air conditioning contractor; Sheet metalwork; Warm air heating & air conditioning contractor; Plumbing contractors; Sheet metalwork
Pr: Wes Thornburg
* *Treas:* Randy Thornburg
* *VP:* Steve Thornburg

D-U-N-S 00-415-5347 IMP
MORGAN ADHESIVES CO LLC
MACTAC
4560 Darrow Rd, Stow, OH 44224-1898
Tel (330) 688-1111 *Founded/Ownrshp* 2014
Sales 657.3MME *EMP* 1,600

SIC 2891 3565 2672 2823 Adhesives; Labeling machines, industrial; Adhesive papers, labels or tapes: from purchased material; Cellulosic manmade fibers; Adhesives; Labeling machines, industrial; Adhesive papers, labels or tapes: from purchased material; Cellulosic manmade fibers
Pr: Ed T Laforge
**CFO:* Jerry S Krempa
**VP:* Sheri S Edison
VP: Gary McMaster
VP: Thierry Van Doosselaere
VP: William Vandeparre
Comm Man: Sandy Syme
Genl Mgr: Clarence Chan
Genl Mgr: Ingrid V Cluyzen
QA Dir: Lindsay Shaheen
Tech Mgr: George Matalenas

D-U-N-S 61-476-2664 IMP
MORGAN ADVANCED CERAMICS INC
(*Suby of* MORGANITE INDUSTRIES INC) ★
13079 Earhart Ave, Auburn, CA 95602-9536
Tel (530) 823-3401 *Founded/Ownrshp* 1986
Sales 28.8MM^E *EMP* 167
SIC 2819 3356 3264 Aluminum oxide; Zirconium & zirconium alloy bars, sheets, strip, etc.; Porcelain electrical supplies; Aluminum oxide; Zirconium & zirconium alloy bars, sheets, strip, etc.; Porcelain electrical supplies
CEO: John Stang
**Pr:* James A West

D-U-N-S 78-708-5901 IMP
MORGAN ADVANCED CERAMICS INC
M C
(*Suby of* MORGANITE INDUSTRIES INC) ★
2425 Whipple Rd, Hayward, CA 94544-7807
Tel (510) 491-1100 *Founded/Ownrshp* 1991
Sales 76.5MM^E *EMP* 572
SIC 2899 3251 3264

MORGAN ADVANCED MATERIALS
See THERMAL CERAMICS INC

D-U-N-S 80-181-0078 IMP/EXP
MORGAN ADVANCED MATERIALS AND TECHNOLOGY INC
(*Suby of* MORGANITE INDUSTRIES INC) ★
441 Hall Ave, Saint Marys, PA 15857-1400
Tel (814) 781-1573 *Founded/Ownrshp* 1996
Sales 78.9MM^E *EMP* 555
SIC 3624 3291 3592 3568 3264 3053 Carbon & graphite products; Silicon carbide abrasive; Carburetors, pistons, rings, valves; Power transmission equipment; Porcelain electrical supplies; Gaskets, packing & sealing devices; Carbon & graphite products; Silicon carbide abrasive; Carburetors, pistons, rings, valves; Power transmission equipment; Porcelain electrical supplies; Gaskets, packing & sealing devices
CEO: John Stang
**Pr:* Don Klas
VP: Steve Coppella
**VP:* Susan Georgino
Dir IT: Steven Coppella
Mfg Mgr: Keith McManus
Ql Cn Mgr: Erica Bower
Manager: Jerry Lipski

D-U-N-S 04-967-4773
MORGAN AUTO PARTS
NAPA AUTO PARTS
817 Morgantown Ave, Fairmont, WV 26554-4333
Tel (304) 366-3860 *Founded/Ownrshp* 1952
Sales 29.7MM^E *EMP* 100
SIC 5531 Automotive & home supply stores; Automobile & truck equipment & parts
Pr: Jay L Morgan
**Sec:* Delia Morgan
**VP:* Marty Morgan

MORGAN BORSZCZ CONSULTING
See MORGAN BUSINESS CONSULTING LLC

D-U-N-S 00-509-0980 IMP
MORGAN BRONZE PRODUCTS INC
340 E Il Route 22, Lake Zurich, IL 60047-2572
Tel (847) 526-6000 *Founded/Ownrshp* 2010
Sales 25.4MM *EMP* 85
Accts Plante & Moran Pllc Chicago
SIC 3599 5051 Machine shop, jobbing & repair; Metals service centers & offices; Machine shop, jobbing & repair; Metals service centers & offices
Pr: Ron Rogers
Sfty Mgr: Paul Swanson
Prd Mgr: Dave Eakins
Sales Exec: Ben Chelini
Board of Directors: Len Harder

D-U-N-S 80-823-5373
MORGAN BROSUPPLY INC
7559 W Gulf To Lake Hwy, Crystal River, FL 34429-7804
Tel (386) 255-2200 *Founded/Ownrshp* 1980
Sales 91.3MM^E *EMP* 75
SIC 5074 Plumbing & hydronic heating supplies
Pr: Peter Morgan
Sls Mgr: Richard Formel
Sales Asso: Eric Campbell
Sales Asso: Dave Turner

D-U-N-S 15-721-9437
MORGAN BROTHERS MILLWORK INC
Bruce Ave Ste 1, Laurel, MS 39440
Tel (601) 649-9188 *Founded/Ownrshp* 1980
Sales 28.8MM^E *EMP* 230
SIC 2431 Doors, wood; Doors, wood
Pr: Steve Morgan
**Sec:* Mark Morgan
**VP:* Alan Morgan

D-U-N-S 62-128-2656
MORGAN BUILDING & SPA MANUFACTURING CORP
(*Suby of* GHM CORP) ★
12700 Hillcrest Rd # 291, Dallas, TX 75230-2033
Tel (972) 864-7300 *Founded/Ownrshp* 1968
Sales 24.9MM^E *EMP* 364
SIC 2452 3999 Prefabricated buildings, wood; Hot tubs; Prefabricated buildings, wood; Hot tubs
Pr: Guy H Morgan
**Treas:* Hicks B Morgan
IT Man: Scott Turner

D-U-N-S 09-971-5344
MORGAN BUILDINGS & SPAS INC
(*Suby of* GHM CORP) ★
12700 Hillcrest Rd # 291, Dallas, TX 75230-2161
Tel (972) 864-7300 *Founded/Ownrshp* 1978
Sales 83.1MM^E *EMP* 350
SIC 5211 5999 5561 3448 Prefabricated buildings; Spas & hot tubs; Recreational vehicle dealers; Prefabricated metal buildings; Prefabricated buildings; Spas & hot tubs; Recreational vehicle dealers; Prefabricated metal buildings
Pr: Guy H Morgan
**VP:* Megan Spanitz
**VP:* Glenn Stevens
**Prin:* Karen Belans
**Prin:* Elisa Stevenson
Rgnl Mgr: Steven McFadden
Mfg Mgr: Mark White
Sls&Mrk Ex: Michael Morgan
Sls Mgr: Jim Schilligo
Pgrm Dir: Robert Luce

D-U-N-S 18-941-0215
MORGAN BUSINESS CONSULTING LLC
MORGAN BORSZCZ CONSULTING
1401 S Clark St Ste 600, Arlington, VA 22202-4141
Tel (866) 455-2424 *Founded/Ownrshp* 2001
Sales 30.7MM^E *EMP* 145
Accts Baker Tilly Virchow Krause Ll
SIC 7379 Computer related consulting services; Computer related consulting services
**VP:* Alex Amenabar
**VP:* Matthew Borszcz
**VP:* Michael Morgan

MORGAN CITY RENTALS
See T & J ENTERPRISES LLC

MORGAN CO SCHOOL DISTRICT
See MORGAN COUNTY BOARD OF EDUCATION

D-U-N-S 05-591-6241
MORGAN CORP (SC)
1800 E Main St, Duncan, SC 29334-9785
Tel (864) 433-8800 *Founded/Ownrshp* 1945
Sales 166.5MM^E *EMP* 508
SIC 1629

MORGAN COUNTY BOARD EDUCATION
See MORGAN COUNTY SCHOOL DISTRICT INC

D-U-N-S 08-101-6388
MORGAN COUNTY BOARD OF EDUCATION
MORGAN CO SCHOOL DISTRICT
212 University Dr, West Liberty, KY 41472-2150
Tel (606) 743-8002 *Founded/Ownrshp* 1890
Sales 24.0MM^E *EMP* 408
SIC 8211 Public elementary & secondary schools; Public elementary & secondary schools

D-U-N-S 07-210-5547
MORGAN COUNTY BOARD OF EDUCATION (INC)
302 Fourth Ave, Decatur, AL 35601
Tel (256) 552-3000 *Founded/Ownrshp* 1910
Sales 75.0MM *EMP* 1,000
Accts Ronald L Jones Montgomery A
SIC 8211 Public elementary & secondary schools; School board
Pr: Karen Duke
Bd of Dir: Jeff McLemore
Prin: William Ellinger
Ex Dir: George Crawford
IT Man: Sharey Adams
Psych: Chuck Smith
Psych: Heather Steadham
HC Dir: Brenda Caudle
Board of Directors: Gary Cobb, Tom Earwood, Kenneth Henson, Kevin Murphy, Carolyn Wallace, Dora Woodard

MORGAN COUNTY COMMISSION
See COUNTY OF MORGAN

D-U-N-S 07-206-2060
MORGAN COUNTY MEMORIAL HOSPITAL FOUNDATION INC
IU HELTH MRGAN HOSP FOUNDATION
2209 John R Wooden Dr, Martinsville, IN 46151-1840
Tel (765) 349-6500 *Founded/Ownrshp* 1924
Sales 13.4M *EMP* 390
Accts Blue & Co Llc Louisville Ky
SIC 8699 Charitable organization; Charitable organization
Pr: Garry Lindboe
Chf Rad: Barry Allen
**Pr:* Thomas Laux
CFO: Susan Havers
Dir Rad: John Macbeth
Chf Nrs Of: Robin Nelson
Ex Dir: Amy Wozniak
Off Mgr: Sharon Britton
CIO: Jim Riley
Opers Mgr: Patrick Downey
Sls&Mrk Ex: Larry McKee

D-U-N-S 01-750-8771
MORGAN COUNTY SCHOOL DISTRICT (UT)
240 E Young St, Morgan, UT 84050-9924
Tel (801) 829-3411 *Founded/Ownrshp* 1900
Sales 21.7MM *EMP* 215
Accts Gilbert & Stewart Cpas Provo
SIC 8211 Public elementary school; Public junior high school; Public senior high school; Public elementary school; Public junior high school; Public senior high school
Dir IT: Terry Allen
Dir IT: Lawana Tarpley

D-U-N-S 10-064-6199
MORGAN COUNTY SCHOOL DISTRICT INC
MORGAN COUNTY BOARD EDUCATION
1065 East Ave, Madison, GA 30650-1468
Tel (706) 752-4600 *Founded/Ownrshp* 1890
Sales 25.3MM^E *EMP* 475
Accts Department Of Audits And Accou
SIC 8211 Public elementary & secondary schools; Public elementary & secondary schools

D-U-N-S 08-264-9674
MORGAN COUNTY SCHOOL DISTRICT RE3 (INC)
715 W Platte Ave, Fort Morgan, CO 80701-2942
Tel (970) 867-5633 *Founded/Ownrshp* 1876
Sales 20.8MM^E *EMP* 500
Accts Anderson Lee & Company Cpas
SIC 8211 Public elementary & secondary schools; Public elementary & secondary schools
Pr: Brian Amack

D-U-N-S 07-839-1318
MORGAN COUNTY SCHOOLS
1325 Pt Mallard Pkwy Se, Decatur, AL 35601-6542
Tel (256) 309-2100 *Founded/Ownrshp* 2012
Sales 24.3MM^E *EMP* 1,218^E
SIC 8211 Public elementary & secondary schools
Teacher Pr: Ann Nolton
Instr Medi: Beverly Burfield

D-U-N-S 03-055-6674
MORGAN DISTRIBUTING INC
3425 N 22nd St, Decatur, IL 62526-2107
Tel (217) 877-3579 *Founded/Ownrshp* 1976
Sales 96.9MM *EMP* 55
Accts May Cocagne & King Pc Decat
SIC 5171 Petroleum bulk stations; Petroleum bulk stations
CEO: Gary R Morgan
**Pr:* Daniel E Butler
**CFO:* Beverly D Evitt
VP: David Morgan
IT Man: Kim Grant
Opers Mgr: Brad Pugh
Sales Exec: Jim Potthast
Mktg Dir: Kenny Copenbarger
Manager: Beth Medlen
Manager: Rebekah Miller
Manager: Jeff Wehner

D-U-N-S 02-769-9875 IMP
MORGAN DISTRIBUTING INC
15125 S Lake Ridge Way, Oregon City, OR 97045-8025
Tel (503) 656-2961 *Founded/Ownrshp* 1959
Sales 26.1MM^E *EMP* 83
SIC 5181 Beer & other fermented malt liquors; Beer & other fermented malt liquors
Pr: Don Aughenbaugh
**VP:* David Morgan
Genl Mgr: Wolfgang Werner
Off Mgr: Patty Benington

D-U-N-S 05-469-3718
MORGAN DISTRIBUTION INC
4930 Maumee Rd, Fort Wayne, IN 46803-1719
Tel (260) 748-2300 *Founded/Ownrshp* 1971
Sales 25.0MM^E *EMP* 35
SIC 5198 Paints; Paint brushes, rollers, sprayers
Pr: Perry Morgan
Ex VP: Chris Morgan
Ex VP: Keith Morgan
Genl Mgr: Ron Garing
VP Mktg: Tonia Morgan
Sls Mgr: Gordie Hoeft

D-U-N-S 00-966-1313
MORGAN DREXEN INC
MORGAN DRXEN INTGRATED SYSTEMS
675 Anton Blvd Ste 100, Costa Mesa, CA 92626-7012
Tel (800) 868-1458 *Founded/Ownrshp* 2007
Sales 21.1MM^E *EMP* 330
SIC 7299 7389 8111 Debt counseling or adjustment service, individuals; ; Specialized legal services; Debt counseling or adjustment service, individuals; ; Specialized legal services
CEO: Walter Ledda
Pr: Staffen Megan
COO: Rita Augusta
CFO: David Walker
Prin: Joseph Lizura
CTO: AVI Gupta
Mktg Mgr: Elizabeth Stone
Genl Couns: Jeffrey Katz

MORGAN DRXEN INTGRATED SYSTEMS
See MORGAN DREXEN INC

D-U-N-S 36-178-5210
MORGAN ELECTRIC SOUTHEAST LLC
3047 Nw 60th St, Fort Lauderdale, FL 33309-2254
Tel (954) 756-6025 *Founded/Ownrshp* 2005
Sales 27.0MM^E *EMP* 300
SIC 3679 Electronic crystals; Electronic crystals
Genl Mgr: Oscar Morales

D-U-N-S 18-974-5086 EXP
MORGAN ENGINEERING SYSTEMS INC
1049 S Mahoning Ave, Alliance, OH 44601-3212
Tel (330) 823-6130 *Founded/Ownrshp* 2012
Sales 25.0MM^E *EMP* 120
SIC 3536

D-U-N-S 00-969-8010 IMP
MORGAN FABRICS CORP
MICHAEL JON DESIGNS
4265 Exchange Ave, Vernon, CA 90058-2604
Tel (323) 583-9981 *Founded/Ownrshp* 1956
Sales 56.3MM^E *EMP* 122
SIC 5131 Piece goods & notions; Upholstery fabrics, woven; Piece goods & notions; Upholstery fabrics, woven
Ch Bd: Arnold Gittelson
**Pr:* Michael Gittelson
**CFO:* Sam Yung
VP: Bob Gittelson
**VP:* Robert Gittelson
VP: David Young
Exec: Lourdes Carlos
Genl Mgr: Terry Thorn
Off Mgr: Chasity Turner
DP Dir: Sunary Chau
QA Dir: Keith Wiltbank

D-U-N-S 00-638-6809 IMP
MORGAN FOODS INC
90 W Morgan St, Austin, IN 47102-1741
Tel (812) 794-1170 *Founded/Ownrshp* 1901
Sales 201.5MM^E *EMP* 550
SIC 2032 Soups, except seafood: packaged in cans, jars, etc.; Soups, except seafood: packaged in cans, jars, etc.
Ch Bd: John S Morgan
V Ch: Kelly Maciejak
**VP:* Lawrence M Higdon
Dir Sec: Ken McDonald
IT Man: Tom McCormick
Software D: Robert Wormley
Sfty Dirs: Dwayne Bratcher
S&M/VP: Bryan Flowers
Mktg Dir: Kim Hannaford

D-U-N-S 18-571-5877
MORGAN FUEL & HEATING CO INC
BOTTINI FUEL
2785 W Main St, Wappingers Falls, NY 12590-1576
Tel (845) 297-5580 *Founded/Ownrshp* 1936
Sales 53.3MM^E *EMP* 260
SIC 5983 1711 5984 Fuel oil dealers; Heating & air conditioning contractors; Propane gas, bottled; Fuel oil dealers; Heating & air conditioning contractors; Propane gas, bottled
CEO: Brian Bottini
**VP:* Rick Bottini
IT Man: Patrick Ladd
Sales Exec: Dana Capuano
Sales Exec: Charlene Flood
Sales Exec: John Hughes
Sales Exec: Samantha Juliano-Starego

D-U-N-S 02-296-3763
MORGAN GRAIN & FEED CO
MORGAN GRAIN AND FEED
260 State Highway 68, Morgan, MN 56266-1431
Tel (507) 249-3157 *Founded/Ownrshp* 1953
Sales 34.0MM *EMP* 15
SIC 5153 5191 Grain & field beans; Feed; Seeds: field, garden & flower; Fertilizer & fertilizer materials; Chemicals, agricultural; Grain & field beans; Feed; Seeds: field, garden & flower; Fertilizer & fertilizer materials; Chemicals, agricultural
Pr: Scott Potter
**Sec:* Kathy Potter

MORGAN GRAIN AND FEED
See MORGAN GRAIN & FEED CO

D-U-N-S 18-717-9262
MORGAN GROUP INC
5606 S Rice Ave, Houston, TX 77081-2118
Tel (713) 361-7200 *Founded/Ownrshp* 1986
Sales 61.5MM^E *EMP* 200
SIC 8742 6513 Management consulting services; Apartment building operators; Management consulting services; Apartment building operators
CEO: Michael S Morgan
Pr: Alan Patton
COO: Sandra Morgan
Ex VP: Brian Hebert
Sr VP: Carter Bechtol
Sr VP: Michael Born
Sr VP: Rosalind McLeroy
Sr VP: Kim Small
Sr VP: Shelley Watson
VP: Richard A Buck
Prin: Ronnie Morgan

D-U-N-S 07-716-4804 IMP
MORGAN HILL UNIFIED SCHOOL DISTRICT
PARADISE VLY ELEMENTARY SCHL
15600 Concord Cir, Morgan Hill, CA 95037-7110
Tel (408) 201-6000 *Founded/Ownrshp* 1966
Sales 55.0MM *EMP* 805
Accts Vavrinek Trine Day & Co Ll
SIC 8211 School board; School board
CEO: William Agler
VP: Matt Taylor
Dir IT: Denis Guerrero
Trfc Dir: Rosana Almeida
Trfc Dir: Brandon Maillo
Teacher Pr: Fawn Myers

D-U-N-S 78-237-3344 IMP
MORGAN INDUSTRIAL INC
OMEGA MORGAN MACHINERY MOVING
23810 Nw Huffman St, Hillsboro, OR 97124-5987
Tel (503) 647-7474 *Founded/Ownrshp* 1991
Sales 83.1MM^E *EMP* 250^E
SIC 1796 4213 Machine moving & rigging; Machinery dismantling; Heavy machinery transport; Machine moving & rigging; Machinery dismantling; Heavy machinery transport
CEO: Greg Tansey
**Ch Bd:* Vic Petroff
CFO: Aaron Wilkins
VP: Tom Walker
Genl Mgr: Mark Turner
Off Mgr: Lisa Simmons
Trfc Dir: Damion Brian
Sls Mgr: Meghan Murphy
Sales Asso: Austin Hope
Snr PM: Ron Sachowsky
Snr PM: Mark Shanholtzer
Board of Directors: Erik Krieger, Jeff Morgan, Vic Petroff, Dennis Pixton, Peter Stott

D-U-N-S 62-077-2012 IMP/EXP
MORGAN INDUSTRIES CORP
255 Diesel Rd, Saint Augustine, FL 32084-4271
Tel (904) 829-0500 *Founded/Ownrshp* 1969
Sales NA *EMP* 775
SIC 3732

D-U-N-S 03-537-4198
MORGAN JEWELERS OF SALT LAKE CITY INC
11 S Rio Grande St, Salt Lake City, UT 84101-1151
Tel (801) 328-8511 *Founded/Ownrshp* 1914

Sales 20.1MM^E EMP 150
SIC 5944 Jewelry stores; Jewelry stores
CEO: Nate Morgan
*Pr: Brad Campbell
CFO: Monika Griff
*VP: Vince Roth
*VP: Steven L Sharp
*VP: Jim Van Bree
*Prin: Mike Marzo

D-U-N-S 04-911-9803
■ MORGAN KEEGAN & CO LLC
(Suby of RAYMOND JAMES FINANCIAL INC) ★
50 N Front St, Memphis, TN 38103-1199
Tel (901) 524-4100 Founded/Ownrshp 2012
Sales 463.7MM^E EMP 3,217
SIC 6211 Brokers, security; Dealers, security; Brokers, security; Dealers, security
Pr: John C Carson Jr
COO: Sanjay C Arora
COO: Ted Cashion
COO: R Patrick Kruczek
COO: Allen B Morgan
COO: Dennis Zank
CFO: Charles D Maxwell
Ofcr: Brent Nicks
Ofcr: Michele Wood
Assoc VP: Brock Griffin
Assoc VP: Ryan Luzod
Assoc VP: Michael Revilla
Assoc VP: Ryan J Schrift
Ex VP: Bella Allaire
Ex VP: Chet Helck
Ex VP: Jeffrey P Julien
Ex VP: Jeffrey Trocin
Ex VP: William Wells
Sr VP: Neil F Adams
Sr VP: Euriah Bennett
Sr VP: Jason Bernstein

D-U-N-S 02-258-4215
■ MORGAN KINDER TREATING LP
(Suby of KINDER MORGAN ENERGY PARTNERS LP) ★
407 Holt Rd, Victoria, TX 77905-5575
Tel (361) 578-1312 Founded/Ownrshp 1999
Sales 36.0MM^E EMP 70^E
SIC 1311 Gas & hydrocarbon liquefaction from coal
CFO: Kimberly A Dang
Genl Couns: Joseph Listengart

MORGAN LEWIS
See MORGAN LEWIS & BOCKIUS LLP

D-U-N-S 06-886-6292
MORGAN LEWIS & BOCKIUS LLP
(Suby of MORGAN LEWIS) ★
1 Market St Ste 500, San Francisco, CA 94105-1306
Tel (415) 393-2000 Founded/Ownrshp 2014
Sales 92.7MM^E EMP 696
SIC 8111 General practice law office; General practice law office
Pt: Donn Pickett
Pt: Dale Barnes
Pt: Michael Begert
Pt: Charles Crompton
Pt: Anne Deibert
Pt: Debra Fischer
Pt: Matthew Fisher
Pt: David Heilbron
Pt: Stephen Hibbard
Pt: Holly House
Pt: Mary Huser
Pt: Karen Kennard
Pt: Anne Knowles
Pt: James Rockett
Pt: R Raymond Rothman
Pt: Stephen Ryan
Pt: Neil Shapiro
Pt: Cecily Talbert

D-U-N-S 07-695-9279
MORGAN LEWIS & BOCKIUS LLP
MORGAN LEWIS
1701 Market St Ste Con, Philadelphia, PA 19103-2987
Tel (215) 963-5000 Founded/Ownrshp 1873
Sales 637.5MM^E EMP 3,100
SIC 8111 General practice law office; General practice law office
Pt: Francis M Milone
Pt: Neal Aizenstein
Pt: Paul Huey- Burns
Pt: Steven M Cohen
Pt: J Gordon Cooney Jr
Pt: Bonnie L Dixon
Pt: Mark P Edwards
Pt: Fred F Fielding
Pt: Brady L Green
Pt: J Pat Heptig
Pt: Stephen A Jannetta
Pt: Thomas P Lemke
Pt: Morgan Lewis
Pt: Michael J Macaluso
Pt: Edward S Mazurek
Pt: John J McAleese
Pt: Carol Merchasin
Pt: Francis M Milone
Pt: John M Ramsay
Pt: Thomas J Sharbaugh
Pt: Mari M Shaw

MORGAN LIBRARY & MUSEUM, THE
See PIERPONT MORGAN LIBRARY

MORGAN LINEN
See MORGAN SERVICES INC

D-U-N-S 00-121-2620
MORGAN LOCAL SCHOOL DISTRICT
65 W Union Ave, McConnelsville, OH 43756-1218
Tel (740) 962-2510 Founded/Ownrshp 1957
Sales 24.2MM EMP 380
SIC 8211 9411 Public elementary school; Public junior high school; Public senior high school; Administration of educational programs; Public elementary school; Public junior high school; Public senior high school; Administration of educational programs
*Treas: Susan Gable
Ex Dir: Cary White

D-U-N-S 10-044-1682
MORGAN LOCAL SCHOOL DISTRICT
65 W Union Ave, McConnelsville, OH 43756-1218
Tel (740) 962-2782 Founded/Ownrshp 1994
Sales 7.7MM^E EMP 350
SIC 8211 Public elementary & secondary schools; Public elementary & secondary schools

D-U-N-S 02-473-5768
MORGAN MANAGEMENT LLC
1080 Pittsford Victor Rd # 201, Pittsford, NY 14534-3805
Tel (585) 419-9630 Founded/Ownrshp 1998
Sales 32.7MM^E EMP 49
SIC 8741 Administrative management
CFO: Larry Hill
IT Man: Frank Van Deusen

MORGAN MANHATTAN
See MORGAN & BROTHER MANHATTAN STORAGE CO INC

MORGAN MARINE
See CATALINA YACHTS INC

D-U-N-S 04-838-9621 IMP/EXP
MORGAN MATERIALS INC
380 Vulcan St, Buffalo, NY 14207-1324
Tel (716) 873-2000 Founded/Ownrshp 1963
Sales 30.2MM^E EMP 40
SIC 5162 5169 5199 Plastics materials; Organic chemicals, synthetic; Rubber, crude
CEO: Donald Sadkin

D-U-N-S 03-598-8542 IMP
MORGAN MECHANICAL CONTRACTORS INC
204 W Stadium Dr, Eden, NC 27288-3332
Tel (336) 623-1144 Founded/Ownrshp 1990
Sales 20.5MM^E EMP 75
SIC 1711 1731 Plumbing, heating, air-conditioning contractors; Electrical work
Pr: Zane Gauldin
*Sec: Jeff Morgan

D-U-N-S 00-253-9062
MORGAN MEMORIAL GOODWILL INDUSTRIES INC
1010 Harrison Ave, Boston, MA 02119-2540
Tel (617) 445-1010 Founded/Ownrshp 1895
Sales 22.3MM^E EMP 500
SIC 8331 7032 5932 Vocational rehabilitation agency; Youth camps; Used merchandise stores; Vocational rehabilitation agency; Youth camps; Used merchandise stores
Ch: Steven Pogorzelski
*Pr: Joanne Hilferty
COO: Jay Carney
CFO: Patrick Duff
*Treas: Nancy Aubrey
Sr Cor Off: Robert Hart
Sr Cor Off: Michael Rodrigues
VP: Joy Burghardt
VP: Jason Marshall
Exec: Linda Makris
Exec: Mary Rahal

MORGAN MURPHY MEDIA
See TELEVISION WISCONSIN INC

D-U-N-S 02-686-9123
MORGAN OIL CO INC
MORGAN OIL CO-CHEVRON
3023 Appleby Sand Rd, Nacogdoches, TX 75965-3763
Tel (936) 564-4801 Founded/Ownrshp 1965
Sales 32.0MM^E EMP 85
Accts Halls Johnson Mclemore Redf
SIC 5171 5411 Petroleum bulk stations; Grocery stores, independent; Petroleum bulk stations; Grocery stores, independent
VP: Douglas Jordan
*VP: J Ed Morgan Jr

MORGAN OIL CO-CHEVRON
See MORGAN OIL CO INC

D-U-N-S 13-577-2668 IMP/EXP
MORGAN OLSON LLC
(Suby of J B POINDEXTER & CO INC) ★
1801 S Nottawa St, Sturgis, MI 49091-8723
Tel (269) 659-0200 Founded/Ownrshp 2003
Sales NA EMP 500
SIC 3713 Truck bodies (motor vehicles); Truck bodies (motor vehicles)
Pr: Michael Ownbey
Pr: Robert Zeaton
*CFO: Greg Pairitz
*VP: Robert Burnham
VP: Joyce Delong
VP: John Engebretson
VP: Steve Hart
VP: Mark Hope
VP: Stu McGowan
VP: Stuart McGowen
*VP: Stephen Miller

D-U-N-S 17-658-1627 IMP
MORGAN POLYMER SEALS LLC
2475 A Paseo De Las, San Diego, CA 92154
Tel (858) 679-4946 Founded/Ownrshp 2009
Sales 19.0MM EMP 500^E
SIC 3053 Gaskets & sealing devices; Gaskets & sealing devices
Admn Mgr: Isela Garcia

D-U-N-S 15-748-6044
MORGAN PONTIAC INC
SATURN
8757 Business Park Dr, Shreveport, LA 71105-5612
Tel (318) 798-1800 Founded/Ownrshp 1986
Sales 46.9MM^E EMP 130
SIC 5511 Automobiles, new & used; Automobiles, new & used
Pr: Michael I Morgan
*VP: Keith Marcotte

MORGAN PROPERTIES
See KBF ASSOCIATES LP

D-U-N-S 18-907-1368
MORGAN RESEARCH CORP
(Suby of STANLEY INC) ★
7067 Old Madison Pike Nw # 100, Huntsville, AL 35806-2177
Tel (703) 739-7419 Founded/Ownrshp 2006
Sales 21.4MM^E EMP 480
SIC 8711 Engineering services; Engineering services
CEO: Sharon D Morgan
*Sr VP: Albert Killen
VP: Mike Sapenter

D-U-N-S 05-662-6922
MORGAN SERVICES INC
MORGAN LINEN
323 N Michigan Ave, Chicago, IL 60601-3701
Tel (312) 346-3181 Founded/Ownrshp 1976
Sales 31.8MM^E EMP 900
SIC 7213 7218

D-U-N-S 06-118-2234
■ MORGAN SOUTHERN INC
(Suby of ROADRUNNER TRANSPORTATION SYSTEMS INC) ★
1500 Cedar Grove Rd, Conley, GA 30288-1204
Tel (404) 366-1345 Founded/Ownrshp 1982, 2011
Sales 65.4MM^E EMP 350
SIC 4213 Trucking, except local; Trucking, except local
CEO: Benjamin G Kirkland
*CFO: Mark Diblasi
*VP: Jim Morgan
*VP: Lance Spencer
*VP Sls: Jeff Hershey

MORGAN STANLEY
See MS FINANCING INC

MORGAN STANLEY
See STANLEY MORGAN CREDIT CORP

D-U-N-S 10-114-7130
▲ MORGAN STANLEY
1585 Broadway, New York, NY 10036-8200
Tel (212) 761-4000 Founded/Ownrshp 1924
Sales 37.9MMM EMP 55,802
Accts Deloitte & Touche Llp New Yor
Tkr Sym MS Exch NYS
SIC 6211 State commercial banks; Investment advisory service; Futures brokers & dealers, commodity; Credit card service; Consumer finance companies; Security brokers & dealers; Brokers, security; Dealers, security; Stock option dealers; Security brokers & dealers
Ch Bd: James P Gorman
Mng Pt: Patrick McDonough
V Ch: Thomas R Nides
COO: Scott Ince
COO: Russell Napurano
COO: James A Rosenthal
COO: Stan Zlotsky
CFO: Jeffrey Gelfand
CFO: Robert Giegerich
CFO: Ruth Porat
CFO: Jonathan Pruzan
CFO: Paul C Wirth
Treas: James Gillis
Co-COO: Andy Saperstein
Co-COO: Clare Woodman
Chf Mktg O: Maura Rose
Ofcr: Keishi Hotsuki
Assoc VP: Harrison Hill
Assoc VP: Timothy Logan
Assoc VP: Paul Urbanek
Assoc VP: Brian Wiese

D-U-N-S 00-698-7879 IMP/EXP
■ MORGAN STANLEY & CO LLC
(Suby of MORGAN STANLEY) ★
1585 Broadway, New York, NY 10036-8200
Tel (212) 761-4000 Founded/Ownrshp 1935
Sales 8.9MMM^E EMP 27,838
SIC 6211 Brokers, security; Dealers, security; Investment bankers; Brokers, security; Dealers, security; Investment bankers
Ch Bd: Richard B Fisher
*Pr: Peter Karches
*CEO: James P Gorman
COO: Andrew S Hawkyard
*Treas: Eileen K Murray
Chf Inves: Edward Kerschner
Sr VP: David Sherman
VP: Mike P Bouros
VP: Angela Di Martino
Ex Dir: Sergio Alvarez-Mena
Ex Dir: Rebecca Doede

D-U-N-S 36-155-5282
■ MORGAN STANLEY BANK
(Suby of STANLEY MORGAN DOMESTIC HOLDINGS INC) ★
680 W 10000 S Fl 2, South Jordan, UT 84095-3970
Tel (801) 902-4089 Founded/Ownrshp 1990
Sales NA EMP 39^E
SIC 6022 State commercial banks; State commercial banks
Ch Bd: James P Gorman
*Pr: Robert D Myrick
Mktg Mgr: Karyn Dobin

D-U-N-S 13-019-8013
■ MORGAN STANLEY CAPITAL GROUP INC
(Suby of MORGAN STANLEY) ★
1585 Broadway, New York, NY 10036-8200
Tel (212) 761-4000 Founded/Ownrshp 1984
Sales 358.9MM^E EMP 749
SIC 6221 Commodity dealers, contracts; Commodity dealers, contracts
Ch Bd: Simon T W Greenshields
*Pr: John A Shapiro
*VP: Ralph Pellecchio

D-U-N-S 18-337-2721
■ MORGAN STANLEY DEAN WITTER & CO
(Suby of MORGAN STANLEY) ★
1585 Broadway Lowr B, New York, NY 10036-8293
Tel (212) 761-4000 Founded/Ownrshp 1997
Sales 278.3MM^E EMP 4,500
SIC 6211 Brokers, security; Dealers, security; Brokers, security; Dealers, security
CEO: Phillip Purcell
*Ch Bd: Richard B Fisher
Ex VP: Frank Cooke
VP: Matthew Bush
Ex Dir: Bruce Sandberg
IT Man: Meryl Klein
IT Man: Clement Lee
IT Man: James Peer

D-U-N-S 17-725-5320
■ MORGAN STANLEY INVESTMENT MANAGEMENT INC
(Suby of MORGAN STANLEY) ★
1585 Broadway, New York, NY 10036-8200
Tel (888) 454-3965 Founded/Ownrshp 1997
Sales 341.8MM^E EMP 870
SIC 6282 Investment advisory service; Investment advisory service
Ch: Barton Biggs
*Pr: James M Allwin
*Pr: Gregory J Fleming
Ex VP: Christina Carroll
VP: John Lowry
VP: Tracy Solley
Exec: A Smith
Ex Dir: Kevin Brown
Ex Dir: Sharon Cannon
Ex Dir: Pramod Chivate
Ex Dir: Barry Kirkman

D-U-N-S 12-157-0758
■ MORGAN STANLEY MORTGAGE CAPITAL HOLDINGS LLC
(Suby of MORGAN STANLEY) ★
1585 Broadway Lowr B, New York, NY 10036-8200
Tel (212) 761-4000 Founded/Ownrshp 1997
Sales NA EMP 1,627
SIC 6162 Mortgage bankers & correspondents; Mortgage bankers & correspondents
Prin: Robert Scott
*VP: James R Gross

D-U-N-S 96-908-3323
■ MORGAN STANLEY SMITH BARNEY HOLDINGS LLC
(Suby of MORGAN STANLEY) ★
1585 Broadway, New York, NY 10036-8200
Tel (212) 761-4000 Founded/Ownrshp 2009
Sales 661.8MM^E EMP 16,040^E
SIC 6211 Security brokers & dealers
Pr: Joseph B Parrish

D-U-N-S 83-261-4502
■ MORGAN STANLEY SMITH BARNEY LLC
(Suby of MORGAN STANLEY SMITH BARNEY HOLDINGS LLC) ★
2000 Westchester Ave, Purchase, NY 10577-2530
Tel (914) 225-5510 Founded/Ownrshp 2009
Sales 661.6MM^E EMP 16,000^E
SIC 6211 Security brokers & dealers
Pr: Gregory Fleming
*CEO: James P Gorman
*COO: Jim Rosenthal
*CFO: Ruth Porat
Chf Inves: Jeffrey M Applegate
Sr VP: Clifford Topol
Sr VP: Eric Villamater
VP: Wenton Camporin
VP: Sarah Tan
VP: John Thompson
Software D: Raymond Lau

D-U-N-S 87-994-1318
MORGAN STATE UNIVERSITY
1700 E Cold Spring Ln, Baltimore, MD 21251-0002
Tel (443) 885-3015 Founded/Ownrshp 1970
Sales 100.1MM EMP 1,500
Accts Sb & Company Llc Hunt Valley
SIC 8221 University; University
Ofcr: Octavio Villodas
VP: George I Glenn
VP: Ken Xavier
Prgrm Mgr: Levi Lipscomb
Off Mgr: Patricia Burgess
Off Mgr: Merlyn R Morgan
Off Admin: Chanelle Goods
Off Admin: Wanda Hedgepeth
Off Admin: Lavaughn Leach
DP Exec: Joyce Wilkins
IT Man: Duane Jackson

D-U-N-S 07-936-1347
MORGAN STEEL LLC
1207 Riverside Blvd, Memphis, TN 38106-2502
Tel (901) 774-5444 Founded/Ownrshp 2014
Sales 38.2MM^E EMP 44
SIC 5051 1541 Steel; Steel building construction

D-U-N-S 05-845-2814 IMP
MORGAN TIRE & AUTO LLC
TEAM TIRES PLUS
(Suby of BRIDGESTONE AMERICAS INC) ★
2021 Sunnydale Blvd, Clearwater, FL 33765-1202
Tel (727) 441-3727 Founded/Ownrshp 2007
Sales 249.4MM^E EMP 6,500
SIC 7539 5531 5014

D-U-N-S 00-236-0485 IMP
MORGAN TRUCK BODY LLC
(Suby of J B POINDEXTER & CO INC) ★
111 Morgan Way, Morgantown, PA 19543-7714
Tel (610) 286-5025 Founded/Ownrshp 1952, 1990
Sales 200.5MM^E EMP 600
SIC 3713 7532 5013 5084 Truck bodies (motor vehicles); Body shop, trucks; Truck parts & accessories; Materials handling machinery; Truck bodies (motor vehicles); Body shop, trucks; Truck parts & accessories; Materials handling machinery
Pr: Corby Stover
CFO: Bill Pearcey
Ex VP: Steve Constable
VP: Mark Albertson
VP: Cathy Clark
Exec: Angelica Banuelos
Div/Sub He: Peter Hunt
Genl Mgr: Paul Jarossy

MIS Dir: Doug Ward
Dir IT: Michael McPhee
Dir IT: Lisa Owens

MORGAN WHOLESALE
See APPLE OIL CO

D-U-N-S 12-134-5008 IMP/EXP
MORGAN WOOD PRODUCTS INC
9761 Fairway Blvd, Powell, OH 43065-6947
Tel (614) 336-4000 *Founded/Ownrshp* 2002
Sales 30.0MM *EMP* 12
SIC 2448 Wood pallets & skids; Wood pallets & skids
Pr: Luke Reinstetle
Genl Mgr: Dwight Reinstetle

MORGAN-KELLER CONSTRUCTION
See MORGAN-KELLER INC

D-U-N-S 04-101-4598
MORGAN-KELLER INC
MORGAN-KELLER CONSTRUCTION
70 Thomas Johnson Dr # 200, Frederick, MD 21702-4306
Tel (301) 663-0626 *Founded/Ownrshp* 1981
Sales 95.7MM^E *EMP* 225
SIC 1542 1541 Institutional building construction; Commercial & office building, new construction; Commercial & office building, renovation & repair; Industrial buildings & warehouses; Industrial buildings, new construction; Institutional building construction; Commercial & office building, new construction; Commercial & office buildings, renovation & repair; Industrial buildings & warehouses; Industrial buildings, new construction
Pr: Bradley C Guyton
CFO: Joy Watt
**Ch:* Gail T Guyton
**Treas:* Joy A Watt
**Ex VP:* Jerry L Bowman
**VP:* Charlie Clark
**VP:* Darrell Guyton
**VP:* Karl Morris
VP: Bob Rininger
Genl Mgr: Robert Rininger
Dir IT: Joanne Desantis

D-U-N-S 02-369-7048
MORGAN-MCCLURE CHEVROLET BUICK CADILLAC INC
11147 Norton Coeburn Rd, Coeburn, VA 24230-6412
Tel (276) 395-3333 *Founded/Ownrshp* 1980
Sales 21.5MM *EMP* 48
SIC 5511 Automobiles, new & used; Pickups, new & used; Vans, new & used; Automobiles, new & used; Pickups, new & used; Vans, new & used
Pr: Larry Mc Clure
**CFO:* Vickie Oliver
**Sec:* Timothy Morgan

D-U-N-S 10-345-3044
MORGAN-WHITE GROUP INC
5722 I 55 N, Jackson, MS 39211-2638
Tel (601) 956-2028 *Founded/Ownrshp* 1997
Sales NA *EMP* 190
Accts Carr Riggs & Ingram Llc Ridg
SIC 6411 Insurance agents, brokers & service; Insurance agents, brokers & service
Pr: David R White
**CFO:* Richard L Eaton
**VP:* John J Morgan
Comm Man: Andi Davis
Web Dev: Adam Wislocki
Mktg Dir: Ed Buchanan
Mktg Mgr: Frank Impastato
Snr Mgr: Gwen Webster

D-U-N-S 04-900-3812
MORGANFRANKLIN CONSULTING LLC
1753 Pinnacle Dr Ste 1200, Mc Lean, VA 22102-3853
Tel (703) 564-7525 *Founded/Ownrshp* 2006
Sales 65.1MM^E *EMP* 255
SIC 8742 Financial consultant; Financial consultant
CEO: Robert Morgan
Pr: Robert Franklin
CFO: Jeff Pagano
Sr VP: Hannah Griffith
VP: Ashley Baquie
VP: Ronald Morgan
Mng Dir: Howie Cohen
Mng Dir: Shawn Degnan
Mng Dir: Amy Hover
Mng Dir: Charlie Price
VP Mktg: Erik Ayers

D-U-N-S 00-893-6460 IMP/EXP
MORGANITE INDUSTRIES INC
(*Suby of* MORGAN ADVANCED MATERIALS PLC)
4000 Westchase Blvd # 170, Raleigh, NC 27607-3971
Tel (919) 821-1253 *Founded/Ownrshp* 1979
Sales 556.5MM^E *EMP* 3,260
SIC 3674 3255 3699 3264 3299 3624 Semiconductors & related devices; Clay refractories; Electrical equipment & supplies; Porcelain electrical supplies; Ceramic fiber; Carbon & graphite products; Semiconductors & related devices; Clay refractories; Electrical equipment & supplies; Porcelain electrical supplies; Ceramic fiber; Carbon & graphite products
Pr: Fred Wollman

D-U-N-S 00-446-9771
■ **MORGANS FOODS INC**
(*Suby of* APEX RESTAURANT MANAGEMENT INC) ★
4829 Galaxy Pkwy Ste S, Cleveland, OH 44128-5955
Tel (216) 359-9000 *Founded/Ownrshp* 2014
Sales 55.6MM^E *EMP* 1,495
Tkr Sym MRFD *Exch* OTO
SIC 5812 Fast-food restaurant, chain; Family restaurants; Pizza restaurants; Fast-food restaurant, chain; Family restaurants; Pizza restaurants
Pr: James J Liguori
CFO: Kenneth L Hignett
VP: Ramesh J Gursahaney
VP: Ramesh Gursahaney
VP: Bob McLaughlin
VP: Vincent J Oddi
Exec: Alex Gionta

D-U-N-S 79-610-4297
■ **MORGANS FOODS OF MISSOURI INC**
(*Suby of* MORGANS FOODS INC) ★
24200 Chagrin Blvd # 126, Cleveland, OH 44122-5550
Tel (216) 360-0471 *Founded/Ownrshp* 1988
Sales 9.7MM^E *EMP* 300
SIC 5812 Fast-food restaurant, independent; Fast-food restaurant, independent
Ch Bd: Leonard Stein-Sapir
**Pr:* James L Liguori
VP: Ramesh Gursahaney
IT Man: Srinivas Thakkilapati

D-U-N-S 61-910-1608
▲ **MORGANS HOTEL GROUP CO**
475 10th Ave Fl 11, New York, NY 10018-9716
Tel (212) 277-4100 *Founded/Ownrshp* 2005
Sales 234.9MM *EMP* 2,600^E
Tkr Sym MHGC *Exch* NGM
SIC 7011 Hotels & motels; Hotels; Hotels & motels; Hotels
CEO: Richard T Szymanski
**Ch Bd:* Howard M Lorber
COO: Joshua Fluhr
Chf Mktg O: Alan Philips
Ex VP: Meredith L Deutsch
VP: Roger Casalengo
VP: Jason Harper
Exec: Jesus Melendez
Exec: Luke Rayment
Exec: Geoff Rudaw
Exec: Thomas Weibull
Board of Directors: Andrew Broad, Kenneth E Cruse, John J Dougherty, Jason T Kalisman, Jonathan A Langer, Bradford B Nugent, Michael Olshan, Michelle S Russo, Adam Stein

D-U-N-S 93-189-1725
■ **MORGANS HOTEL GROUP MANAGEMENT LLC**
(*Suby of* MORGANS HOTEL GROUP CO) ★
475 10th Ave Fl 11, New York, NY 10018-9716
Tel (212) 277-4100 *Founded/Ownrshp* 1997
Sales 91.7MM^E *EMP* 2,000
SIC 7011 Hotels; Hotels
CEO: Jason Kalisman
**CEO:* Michael Gross

D-U-N-S 15-146-9608
MORGANS OF WASHINGTON INC
DOUBLE DIAMOND FRUIT
1801 F St Sw, Quincy, WA 98848-8928
Tel (509) 787-4644 *Founded/Ownrshp* 1986
Sales 28.5MM^E *EMP* 70
SIC 5148 Fruits; Fruits
Pr: Rex Morgan
**VP:* Warren Morgan

D-U-N-S 07-774-8663
■ **MORGANS RESTAURANT OF PENNSYLVANIA INC**
KFC
(*Suby of* MORGANS FOODS INC) ★
24200 Chagrin Blvd # 126, Cleveland, OH 44122-5550
Tel (216) 360-7500 *Founded/Ownrshp* 1977
Sales 27.2MM^E *EMP* 1,200
SIC 5812 Fast-food restaurant, chain; Fast-food restaurant, chain
Pr: James J Ligouri
**Ch Bd:* Leonard Stein-Sapir
COO: James J Liguori
**CFO:* Kenneth Hignett
**VP:* Ramesh Gursahaney
**VP:* Vincent Oddi

D-U-N-S 14-493-3744
MORGANTI GROUP INC
(*Suby of* CONSOLIDATED CONTRACTORS INTERNATIONAL COMPANY SAL)
100 Mill Plain Rd Ste 400, Danbury, CT 06811-5189
Tel (203) 743-2675 *Founded/Ownrshp* 1985
Sales 40.7MM^E *EMP* 130
SIC 8741 1542 1541 Construction management; Commercial & office building, new construction; Specialized public building contractors; Industrial buildings, new construction
CEO: Nabil M Takla
**VP:* Ghassan Antonios
**VP:* Melody Douglas
**VP:* Tom Ennis
**VP:* Joseph Kummer
**VP:* Michael Olenick
Dir Bus: Robert Tripi
CTO: Christine Braunger
MIS Mgr: Don Esbjornson
MIS Mgr: Kevork Toroyan
Snr PM: Chuck Kerns
Board of Directors: Berge Setrakian

D-U-N-S 07-452-4554
MORGANTON CITY OF (INC) (NC)
305 E Union St Ste A100, Morganton, NC 28655-3475
Tel (828) 438-5376 *Founded/Ownrshp* 1784
Sales NA *EMP* 406
Accts S Eric Bowman Pa Cpa Morga
SIC 9111 ;
Dir Risk M: Andy Smith
Ex Dir: Jim Cotherman
Dir IT: Greg Branch

D-U-N-S 04-207-6190
MORGANTON EYE PHYSICIANS PA INC (NC)
335 E Parker Rd, Morganton, NC 28655-5112
Tel (828) 433-1000 *Founded/Ownrshp* 1974
Sales 25.1MM^E *EMP* 200
SIC 8011 Ophthalmologist; Ophthalmologist
Pr: Philip Kath MD
Off Mgr: Dennis Lee
Doctor: Larry Willis

D-U-N-S 79-141-0652 IMP
MORGANTON PRESSURE VESSELS LLC
(*Suby of* BAGLIONI SPA)
1 Alfredo Baglioni Dr, Marion, NC 28752-5104
Tel (828) 652-3704 *Founded/Ownrshp* 2006
Sales 32.6MM^E *EMP* 85
SIC 3491 Pressure valves & regulators, industrial
Genl Mgr: Alberto Giardina
Mfg Mgr: Derrick Fairchild

MORGANTOWN HONDA
See AUTO SOURCE OF WEST VIRGINIA INC

D-U-N-S 13-152-7780
■ **MORGANTOWN PLASTICS CO INC**
(*Suby of* MASCO CORP) ★
113 Delta Way, Morgantown, KY 42261-7345
Tel (270) 526-5745 *Founded/Ownrshp* 1984
Sales 43.7MM^E *EMP* 250
SIC 3089 Injection molding of plastics; Injection molding of plastics
Pr: Ronald D Smith
Ql Cn Mgr: Teresa Gravil

D-U-N-S 13-944-5811
MORGANTOWN UTILITY BOARD
M U B
278 Greenbag Rd, Morgantown, WV 26501-7158
Tel (304) 292-8443 *Founded/Ownrshp* 1950
Sales 22.4MM *EMP* 140
Accts Perry & Associates Cpas Ac
SIC 4941 Water supply; Water supply
Pr: Tim Ball

D-U-N-S 08-176-6636 IMP
MORGENTHALER MANAGEMENT PARTNERS VI LLC
MORGENTHALER MGT PARTNERS
50 Public Sq Ste 2700, Cleveland, OH 44113-2236
Tel (216) 416-7500 *Founded/Ownrshp* 1999
Sales 159.7MM^E *EMP* 2,324
SIC 1731 5065 7622 7373 5999 Telephone & telephone equipment installation; Telephone & telegraphic equipment; Communication equipment repair; Local area network (LAN) systems integrator; Telephone & communication equipment; Telephone & telephone equipment installation; Telephone & telegraphic equipment; Communication equipment repair; Local area network (LAN) systems integrator; Telephone & communication equipment
Pr: David T Morgenthaler
Pt: Hank Plain

MORGENTHALER MGT PARTNERS
See MORGENTHALER MANAGEMENT PARTNERS VI LLC

D-U-N-S 96-301-8184
MORGRIDGE FAMILY FDN
501 Silverside Rd Ste 123, Wilmington, DE 19809-1377
Tel (800) 839-1754 *Founded/Ownrshp* 2010
Sales 20.3MM *EMP* 2
SIC 8699 Charitable organization; Charitable organization

D-U-N-S 01-242-0082
MORGRIDGE INSTITUTE FOR RESEARCH INC
330 N Orchard St, Madison, WI 53715-1119
Tel (608) 316-4300 *Founded/Ownrshp* 2007
Sales 41.7MM *EMP* 81
Accts Mcgladrey Llp Madison Wisco
SIC 8733 Noncommercial research organizations; Noncommercial research organizations
CEO: Brad Schwartz
CFO: Kathi Stanek

MORI CLASSICS
See MORI LUGGAGE AND GIFTS INC

D-U-N-S 06-142-5047 IMP
MORI LUGGAGE AND GIFTS INC
MORI CLASSICS
3595 Mccall Pl, Atlanta, GA 30340-2801
Tel (770) 451-6674 *Founded/Ownrshp* 1971
Sales 23.9MM *EMP* 300
Accts Ethridge & Miller Cpa
SIC 5948 5947 Luggage, except footlockers & trunks; Gift shop; Luggage, except footlockers & trunks; Leather goods, except luggage & shoes; Gift shop
CEO: Jean A Mori
**Pr:* John Mori
**VP:* Betty Mori
Brnch Mgr: Paul Whites

D-U-N-S 80-681-1253
MORIAH INC
EISENHOWER CENTER
3200 E Eisenhower Pkwy, Ann Arbor, MI 48108-3231
Tel (734) 677-0070 *Founded/Ownrshp* 1993
Sales 31.0MM^E *EMP* 450
SIC 8093 8069 Rehabilitation center, outpatient treatment; Specialty hospitals, except psychiatric; Rehabilitation center, outpatient treatment; Specialty hospitals, except psychiatric
Pr: John Cornack
CFO: Linda Mound
Assoc Dir: Bonnie Holt

D-U-N-S 01-122-4219
MORIARTY-EDGEWOOD SCHOOL DISTRICT
200 Center St, Moriarty, NM 87035
Tel (505) 832-4471 *Founded/Ownrshp* 1920
Sales 28.7MM^E *EMP* 543
SIC 8211 Public elementary school; Public junior high school; Public senior high school; Public elementary school; Public junior high school; Public senior high school
HC Dir: Natalie Romero

D-U-N-S 60-334-7782 IMP
MORIDEN AMERICA INC
(*Suby of* MORIDEN CO.,LTD.)
9760 Mayflower Park Dr # 100, Carmel, IN 46032-7940
Tel (317) 484-5555 *Founded/Ownrshp* 2002
Sales 22.6MM^E *EMP* 47
SIC 5013 Automotive supplies & parts
Prin: Ken-Ichi Morita
**VP:* Okihiro Yokoyama
Mtls Mgr: Richard Gonzalez

D-U-N-S 00-713-5387 IMP
MORIDGE MANUFACTURING INC
GRASS HOPPER COMPANY
105 Old Us Highway 81, Moundridge, KS 67107-7110
Tel (620) 345-6301 *Founded/Ownrshp* 1958
Sales 127.4MM^E *EMP* 290
SIC 3524 3523 Lawnmowers, residential: hand or power; Driers (farm): grain, hay & seed; Lawnmowers, residential: hand or power; Driers (farm): grain, hay & seed
Pr: E Guyer
COO: Don Schiavone
**Treas:* Dwayne Guyer
Exec: Donald Moore
Sfty Dirs: Ryan Wiebe
Sls Mgr: Jon Shiverdecker

D-U-N-S 60-400-4077 IMP
MORIN CORP
MORIN EAST
(*Suby of* KINGSPAN-MEDUSA INC) ★
685 Middle St, Bristol, CT 06010-8416
Tel (860) 584-0900 *Founded/Ownrshp* 2008
Sales 24.6MM^E *EMP* 100
SIC 3448 Prefabricated metal buildings; Prefabricated metal buildings
Pr: Russell Shiels
**VP:* Ilhan Eser
**VP:* George McDuffee
Prd Mgr: Scott Evans
Sls&Mrk Ex: Lori Morrow
VP Mktg: Dave Milewski
Mktg Mgr: John Boccuzzi
Board of Directors: Delano Morin, Michael Morin

MORIN EAST
See MORIN CORP

MORINDA BIOACTIVES
See MORINDA HOLDINGS INC

D-U-N-S 16-175-6643
MORINDA BIOACTIVES INC
(*Suby of* MORINDA BIOACTIVES) ★
737 E 1180 S, American Fork, UT 84003-3395
Tel (801) 234-1000 *Founded/Ownrshp* 1997
Sales 128.0MM^E *EMP* 1,150
SIC 6719 Investment holding companies, except banks; Investment holding companies, except banks
Pr: Kerry Asay
CFO: Randall Smith
VP: Charlie Smith
VP: Shon Whitney
Mng Dir: Brandon Groves
Mng Dir: Michael Olsen
Mng Dir: Howard Silverman
Dir IT: Shane Golding
VP Opers: Joel Neilsen
Plnt Mgr: Larry Knight
Mktg Dir: Adam Olsen

D-U-N-S 95-792-6140 IMP/EXP
MORINDA HOLDINGS INC
MORINDA BIOACTIVES
333 River Park Dr, Provo, UT 84604-5787
Tel (801) 234-1000 *Founded/Ownrshp* 1996
Sales 264.3MM^E *EMP* 1,164
SIC 5149 8099 3999 Health foods; Health foods; Nutrition services; Bleaching & dyeing of sponges
Pr: Kerry O Asay
**Treas:* Randall N Smith
**VP:* Kim S Asay
**VP:* Stephen P Story
Rgnl Mgr: Shane Greer
Plnt Mgr: Larry Knight
Mktg Dir: Bruce Call
Sls Mgr: Arcenio Gomez
Genl Couns: Richard Rife

D-U-N-S 04-176-3855
MORING DISPOSAL INC
FREEPORT RECYCLING CENTER
306 E Main St, Forreston, IL 61030-7701
Tel (815) 938-3602 *Founded/Ownrshp* 1977
Sales 33.5MM^E *EMP* 60
SIC 4953 Refuse collection & disposal services; Recycling, waste materials
Pr: Larry Moring
**Sec:* Sharon Moring
IT Man: Lisa Keller

D-U-N-S 06-862-4493 IMP
MORITANI AMERICA INC
(*Suby of* MORITANI & CO.,LTD.)
300 Park Blvd Ste 320, Itasca, IL 60143-2631
Tel (630) 250-9898 *Founded/Ownrshp* 1970
Sales 40.0MM^E *EMP* 8
SIC 5084 Industrial machinery & equipment
Pr: Mitsunori Akiyama
VP: Hiro Yamamoto
Genl Mgr: Toru Hatsumi

D-U-N-S 86-831-1978
MORITZ AEROSPACE INC
(*Suby of* CARLING TECHNOLOGIES INC) ★
123 N Main St Ste 257-258, Dublin, PA 18917-2107
Tel (215) 249-1300 *Founded/Ownrshp* 2004
Sales 164.4M^E *EMP* 500
SIC 3728 Aircraft parts & equipment; Aircraft parts & equipment
Pr: Claude Mercier
**CFO:* Richard Nace
**VP:* Simon Cordner
Ql Cn Mgr: David Strauss

D-U-N-S 00-803-8408
MORITZ CHEVROLET LTD (TX)
MORITZ FORWORTH TEXAS
9101 Camp Bowie West Blvd, Fort Worth, TX 76116-6095
Tel (817) 696-2000 *Founded/Ownrshp* 1952, 1996
Sales 68.5MM^E *EMP* 225
SIC 5511 Automobiles, new & used; Pickups, new & used; Vans, new & used; Automobiles, new & used; Pickups, new & used; Vans, new & used
Genl Pt: John David Moritz
Pt: David L Moritz
Sales Exec: Jim Hardick
Sls Mgr: Robert Sanders

Sls Mgr: Dick Titterington
Sales Asso: Roberto Arevalo
Sales Asso: Derek Johnson
Sales Asso: Robert Marshall
Sales Asso: Lisa Vinecke

D-U-N-S 15-743-5587
MORITZ CHRYSLER JEEP LTD
9101 Camp Bowie West Blvd, Fort Worth, TX 76116-6095
Tel (817) 696-2000 *Founded/Ownrshp* 1996
Sales 51.1MM^E *EMP* 280
SIC 5511 Automobiles, new & used; Pickups, new & used; Vans, new & used; Automobiles, new & used; Pickups, new & used; Vans, new & used
Mng Pt: John David Moritz
**Pt:* David L Moritz
Sales Asso: James Honeycutt

MORITZ FORWORTH TEXAS
See MORITZ CHEVROLET LTD

D-U-N-S 06-424-2977
MORITZ PARTNERS LP
DISCOUNT MOTORS
2111 N Collins St Ste 323, Arlington, TX 76011-2810
Tel (817) 461-9222 *Founded/Ownrshp* 2002
Sales 94.6MM^E *EMP* 300^E
SIC 5511 Automobiles, new & used; Automobiles, new & used

D-U-N-S 01-905-0813
MORLAN CHRYSLER LLC
374 Siemers Dr, Cape Girardeau, MO 63701-8476
Tel (573) 388-3331 *Founded/Ownrshp* 2009
Sales 30.0MM *EMP* 35
SIC 5511 Automobiles, new & used; Automobiles, new & used

D-U-N-S 11-857-5000
MORLEY BUILDERS INC
BENCHMARK CONTRACTORS
3330 Ocean Park Blvd # 101, Santa Monica, CA 90405-3211
Tel (310) 399-1600 *Founded/Ownrshp* 1984
Sales 166.0MM^E *EMP* 350
SIC 1541 1522 1542 1771

D-U-N-S 00-539-7500 IMP
MORLEY CANDY MAKERS INC (MI)
SANDERS
23770 Hall Rd, Clinton Township, MI 48036-1275
Tel (586) 468-4300 *Founded/Ownrshp* 1919, 1948
Sales 54.3MM^E *EMP* 172
SIC 2064 2066 5441 Candy & other confectionery products; Chocolate & cocoa products; Candy; Candy & other confectionery products; Chocolate & cocoa products; Candy
Pr: Ronald Rapson
**Ch:* Brian Jefferson
**VP:* Karen Jefferson
**VP:* Michael Koch
Exec: Niki Pherson
Telecom Ex: Ed Kammer
Sls&Mrk Ex: Paul Pavaelich
Mktg Mgr: Diane Lynch
Board of Directors: Karl Lapeer, Erwin O Morley

D-U-N-S 07-386-3946
MORLEY COMPANIES INC
MORLEY TRAVEL
1 Morley Plz, Saginaw, MI 48603-1363
Tel (989) 791-2550 *Founded/Ownrshp* 1982
Sales 168.5MM^E *EMP* 1,200
SIC 8742 4724 Marketing consulting services; Travel agencies; Marketing consulting services; Travel agencies
CEO: Paul W Furlo
Ch Bd: Louis J Furlo Sr
Pr: Sam Jundi
CFO: Richard Mott
VP: Thomas C Fay
VP: Christopher J Furlo
VP: Louis J Furlo Jr
VP: Robert Reindel
Prgrm Mgr: Becky Forrest
Prgrm Mgr: Steve Mulvaney
Prgrm Mgr: Michael Quiroz
Board of Directors: John Armstrong, cass Ferris

D-U-N-S 00-685-3527
MORLEY CONSTRUCTION CO
(*Suby of* BENCHMARK CONTRACTORS) ★
3330 Ocean Park Blvd # 101, Santa Monica, CA 90405-3211
Tel (310) 399-1600 *Founded/Ownrshp* 1947
Sales 32.8MM^E *EMP* 200
SIC 1771 1522 1542 Concrete work; Condominium construction; Commercial & office building, new construction; Concrete work; Condominium construction; Commercial & office building, new construction
CEO: Jeff Simonson
**Ch Bd:* Mark Benjamin
**CFO:* Tod Paris
**Ex VP:* Bert Lewitt
**VP:* Arun Asher
**VP:* Reginald Jackson
MIS Dir: Racquel Espiritusanto
VP Mktg: Charlie Muttillo
Snr PM: Audre Kleven

MORLEY TRAVEL
See MORLEY COMPANIES INC

MORLEY-MOSS ELECTRICAL CONTRS
See MORLEY-MOSS INC

D-U-N-S 11-331-6897
MORLEY-MOSS INC
MORLEY-MOSS ELECTRICAL CONTRS
430 S Aston Dr, Mesquite, TX 75182-9104
Tel (214) 388-1177 *Founded/Ownrshp* 1984
Sales 33.5MM^E *EMP* 120
Accts Travis Wolff & Company Llp
SIC 1731 General electrical contractor
Pr: William L Morley
**Sec:* Mark Westbrook
**VP:* Michael G Oltean
Snr PM: Charlie Green
Snr PM: Les Smith
Snr PM: Ben Sumbera

D-U-N-S 00-794-5991
MORLEY-MURPHY CO (WI)
MM
200 S Washington St # 305, Green Bay, WI 54301-4200
Tel (920) 499-3171 *Founded/Ownrshp* 1904
Sales 22.0MM^E *EMP* 40
SIC 5063

MORMON HANDICRAFT
See DESERET BOOK CO

D-U-N-S 00-239-4666
■ **MORNING CALL INC**
UPPER BUCKS PUBLISHING COMPANY
(*Suby of* TRIBUNE MEDIA CO) ★
101 N 6th St, Allentown, PA 18101-1480
Tel (610) 820-6500 *Founded/Ownrshp* 1905
Sales NA *EMP* 878
SIC 2752 2711 Commercial printing, lithographic; Newspapers, publishing & printing; Commercial printing, lithographic; Newspapers, publishing & printing
CEO: Tim Ryan
Sls&Mrk Ex: Mary Bishop
Pr Dir: Matt Provence
Mktg Mgr: Chris Cleaver
Manager: Kay McLane
Manager: Jason Wilson

D-U-N-S 08-867-4775 IMP
MORNING FRESH FARMS INC
15121 County Road 32, Platteville, CO 80651-8199
Tel (970) 785-2889 *Founded/Ownrshp* 2009
Sales 22.9MM^E *EMP* 85
SIC 5144 2875

D-U-N-S 00-427-7034 IMP
■ **MORNING PRIDE MFG LLC**
HONEYWELL FIRST RESPONDER PDTS
(*Suby of* SAFETY PRODUCTS HOLDINGS INC) ★
1 Innovation Ct, Dayton, OH 45414-3967
Tel (937) 264-2662 *Founded/Ownrshp* 2008
Sales 228.8MM^E *EMP* 521
SIC 3842 2326 Respirators; Men's & boys' work clothing; Respirators; Men's & boys' work clothing
Pr: William L Grilliot
QA Dir: John Hodac
IT Man: Ron Stone
Sls&Mrk Ex: Gary Mc Evoy
Mktg Mgr: Tammy Wells

MORNING STAR COMPANY THE
See LIBERTY PACKING CO LLC

D-U-N-S 09-706-5734 IMP/EXP
MORNING STAR CO
724 Main St Ste 202, Woodland, CA 95695-3492
Tel (530) 666-6600 *Founded/Ownrshp* 1970
Sales 63.2MM^E *EMP* 570
SIC 7363 8741 4212 2033

D-U-N-S 10-382-5381
MORNING STAR PUBLISHING CO
(*Suby of* 21ST CENTURY NEWSPAPERS INC) ★
711 W Pickard St, Mount Pleasant, MI 48858-1585
Tel (989) 779-6000 *Founded/Ownrshp* 2002
Sales 22.9MM^E *EMP* 300
SIC 2759 Newspapers: printing; Newspapers: printing
Pr: Bill McHugh
Netwrk Mgr: Ray Pike
Plnt Mgr: Paul Gunderson

MORNING SUN
See BALTIMORE SUN CO

MORNING VIEW CARE CENTER
See DEARTH MANAGEMENT CO

D-U-N-S 07-801-3232
MORNINGSIDE COLLEGE
1501 Morningside Ave, Sioux City, IA 51106-1717
Tel (712) 274-5000 *Founded/Ownrshp* 1894
Sales 52.5MM *EMP* 448^E
SIC 8221 College, except junior; College, except junior
Pr: John C Reynders
VP: Ron Jorgensen

D-U-N-S 10-328-6316
MORNINGSIDE HOUSE NURSING HOME CO INC
1000 Pelham Pkwy S, Bronx, NY 10461-1099
Tel (718) 409-8200 *Founded/Ownrshp* 1974
Sales 33.0MM^E *EMP* 500
SIC 8051 Skilled nursing care facilities; Skilled nursing care facilities
Pr: William T Smith PHD
Dir Recs: Susie Lee
**CFO:* Mitchell Defrin
**Ex VP:* Linda Martin

D-U-N-S 05-756-4148
MORNINGSIDE MINISTRIES FOUNDATION INC
700 Babcock Rd, San Antonio, TX 78201-2600
Tel (210) 734-1000 *Founded/Ownrshp* 1959
Sales 43.8MM *EMP* 625
Accts Paul J Fitzgeral Pc San A
SIC 8361 8082 Rest home, with health care incidental; Home health care services; Rest home, with health care incidental; Home health care services
Pr: Alvin A Loewenberg Jr
**CFO:* Joan E Dixon
**Sec:* Jerry Ash
**Ex VP:* Leo M Cutcliff Jr
**VP:* Beth Keough
VP: Jack Rodgers
IT Man: Christian Burt
Board of Directors: Robert Kesl

D-U-N-S 78-746-7687 EXP
MORNINGSTAR FELLOWSHIP CHURCH
HERITAGE INTL MINISTRIES
375 Starlight Dr, Fort Mill, SC 29715-8397
Tel (803) 802-5544 *Founded/Ownrshp* 1985
Sales 22.8MM^E *EMP* 165
SIC 2721 8661 Periodicals; Non-denominational church; Periodicals; Non-denominational church
Pr: Rick Joyner
**VP:* Steve Thompson
Sls Mgr: Erika Robinson

D-U-N-S 12-147-7160
▲ **MORNINGSTAR INC**
22 W Washington St # 600, Chicago, IL 60602-1607
Tel (312) 696-6000 *Founded/Ownrshp* 1984
Sales 760.0MM *EMP* 3,760^E
Tkr Sym MORN *Exch* NGS
SIC 6282 6722 7375 Investment advice; Management investment, open-end; Money market mutual funds; Information retrieval services; Data base information retrieval; On-line data base information retrieval; Investment advice; Management investment, open-end; Money market mutual funds; Information retrieval services; Data base information retrieval; On-line data base information retrieval
Ch Bd: Joe Mansueto
Pr: Andreas Hetland
Pr: Thomas Idzorek
Pr: Kunal Kapoor
Pr: Christopher Meyer
CEO: Anthony Serhan
CFO: Stephane Biehler
Chf Mktg O: Rob Pinkerton
Ofcr: Denver Ignacio
Ex VP: Davide Frattini
Assoc Dir: Nicolas Owens
Assoc Dir: Banita Radia
Dir Bus: Matt Cox
Dir Bus: Rick Schmehl
Dir Bus: Lisa Terwilliger
Board of Directors: Robin Diamonte, Cheryl Francis, Steven Kaplan, Gail Landis, Bill Lyons, Jack Noonan, Donald J Phillips II, Paul Sturm, Hugh Zentmyer

D-U-N-S 03-555-4744
MORNINGSTAR PARTNERS LP
400 W 7th St, Fort Worth, TX 76102-4701
Tel (817) 334-7800 *Founded/Ownrshp* 2012
Sales 48.4MM^E *EMP* 150^E
SIC 1381 Drilling oil & gas wells

D-U-N-S 12-133-5611
▲ **MORO CORP**
994 Old Eagle School Rd # 1000, Wayne, PA 19087-1802
Tel (484) 367-0300 *Founded/Ownrshp* 1992
Sales 71.5MM^E *EMP* 212
Tkr Sym MRCR *Exch* OTO
SIC 1711 3444 5051 Mechanical contractor; Ducts, sheet metal; Metals service centers & offices; Mechanical contractor; Ducts, sheet metal; Metals service centers & offices
Ch Bd: David W Menard
**VP:* Lawrence J Corr
**VP:* Peter D Menard

D-U-N-S 05-301-7701 IMP/EXP
MOROCCANOIL INC
16311 Ventura Blvd # 1200, Encino, CA 91436-2124
Tel (888) 700-1817 *Founded/Ownrshp* 2010
Sales 69.0MM^E *EMP* 200^E
SIC 5122 Cosmetics, perfumes & hair products
CEO: Carmen Tal
**Pr:* Ofer Tal

D-U-N-S 02-329-8912
MOROCH HOLDINGS INC
MOROCH PARTNERS
3625 N Hall St Ste 1100, Dallas, TX 75219-5113
Tel (214) 520-9700 *Founded/Ownrshp* 1981
Sales 97.4MM^E *EMP* 580
SIC 7311 Advertising agencies; Advertising agencies
Pr: Rob Boswell
Mng Pt: Glenn Geller
Mng Pt: Jerrie Vangelder
**Ch Bd:* Tom Moroch
Pr: Rob Boswell
COO: Melinda Yoder
CFO: Mark Stepanek
Chf Mktg O: Jack Phifer
Ofcr: Brad B McCormick
VP: Carol Dodson
VP: Chip Gorman
Exec: Joseph Salazar
Exec: Laura Theut
Exec: Chris White
Creative D: Barbara Barnes
Creative D: Galen Greenwood
Creative D: Thomas Hripko
Creative D: Ray Sturdivant
Creative D: Kathleen Torres

MOROCH PARTNERS
See MOROCH HOLDINGS INC

D-U-N-S 01-905-2919 EXP
MORONG BROTHERS VOLKSWAGEN
MORONG-FALMOUTH
187 Us Route 1 Ste 1, Falmouth, ME 04105-1315
Tel (207) 781-4020 *Founded/Ownrshp* 1950
Sales 23.7MM^E *EMP* 55
SIC 5511 Automobiles, new & used; Automobiles, new & used
Pr: H William Sowles
**VP:* Peter Sowles
Sls Mgr: Anne Cote
Sls Mgr: David Menapace
Sales Asso: Phillip Chouinard
Sales Asso: Ted Ciancette
Sales Asso: Gregg Copenhagen

MORONG-FALMOUTH
See MORONG BROTHERS VOLKSWAGEN

D-U-N-S 09-192-6220
MORONGO BAND OF MISSION INDIANS
12700 Pumarra Rd, Banning, CA 92220-6977
Tel (951) 849-4697 *Founded/Ownrshp* 1976
Sales NA *EMP* 653
SIC 9131 Indian reservation; ; Indian reservation;
Ch: Robert Martin
**Ch Bd:* Maurice Lyons
CFO: Dan Lynch
Ofcr: Julia Cloninger
Ofcr: Michael Milhiser
Snr Mgr: Steve Garwood

D-U-N-S 92-843-4117
MORONGO UNIFIED SCHOOL DISTRICT
5715 Utah Trl, Twentynine Palms, CA 92277-6917
Tel (760) 367-9191 *Founded/Ownrshp* 1914
Sales 79.6MM *EMP* 1,000
Accts Vavrinek Trine Day & Co Ll
SIC 8211 Public elementary school; Public junior high school; Public senior high school; Public special education school; Public elementary school; Public junior high school; Public senior high school; Public special education school
IT Man: Glenn Williams
Sfty Mgr: Donna Wendt
HC Dir: Kathy Papp

D-U-N-S 00-909-5498
MORONI FEED CO
TRUE VALUE
15 E 1900 S Feed Mill Rd, Moroni, UT 84646
Tel (435) 436-8221 *Founded/Ownrshp* 1938
Sales NA *EMP* 660
SIC 2015 2048 0254 Turkey, processed: fresh; Poultry feeds; Poultry hatcheries

D-U-N-S 04-517-2079 IMP
MOROSO PERFORMANCE PRODUCTS INC
80 Carter Dr, Guilford, CT 06437-2116
Tel (203) 453-5200 *Founded/Ownrshp* 1968
Sales 23.6MM^E *EMP* 190
SIC 3714 Motor vehicle parts & accessories; Motor vehicle parts & accessories
Pr: Richard B Moroso
CFO: John Ferretti
VP: Ronald Johnson
Sales Exec: Manos Kazakidis
Natl Sales: Frank Thibadeau

D-U-N-S 61-791-8057
MORPACE INC
31700 Middlebelt Rd # 200, Farmington Hills, MI 48334-2375
Tel (248) 737-5300 *Founded/Ownrshp* 1975
Sales 52.0MM^E *EMP* 335
SIC 8732 Market analysis or research; Market analysis or research
Pr: Duncan Lawrence
**Pr:* John McDonald
**COO:* Sharna Morelli
**Ch:* Frank Ward
**Treas:* Charles Haffey
VP: Ed Knopp
VP: David Myhrer
VP: Steve Nemeth
VP: Sue Prieur
VP: Chris Winkler
Exec: Kimberly Lindsay
Board of Directors: Peter Haag, Steve Johnson, James M Leiman, Keith Woods

D-U-N-S 62-392-4651 IMP
MORPHO DETECTION LLC
(*Suby of* SAFRAN)
7151 Gateway Blvd, Newark, CA 94560-1012
Tel (510) 739-2400 *Founded/Ownrshp* 2009
Sales 272.0MM^E *EMP* 1,009
SIC 3812 Detection apparatus: electronic/magnetic field, light/heat; Detection apparatus: electronic/magnetic field, light/heat
Pr: Karen Bomba
CFO: Greg Eyink
**Treas:* Linda Hildebrant
Ofcr: Scott Weiss
Ex VP: Brad Buswell
VP: Mel Kirk
VP: Monty Lutzker
VP: Lilia Ramirez
Prgrm Mgr: Collin Nwachukwu
Rgnl Mgr: Jennifer Herrmann
Genl Mgr: Michael Cavanaugh

D-U-N-S 14-855-3712 IMP
MORPHOTRAK LLC
SAFRAN
(*Suby of* MORPHO)
5515 E La Palma Ave # 100, Anaheim, CA 92807-2116
Tel (714) 238-2000 *Founded/Ownrshp* 2014
Sales 98.5MM^E *EMP* 400
SIC 7373 Computer integrated systems design; Computer integrated systems design
CEO: Celeste Thomasson
CFO: Florian Hebras
VP: Nelson Clark
VP: Daniel Danciu
VP: Clark Nelson
VP: Steve Vinsik
Snr Mgr: James Haluska
Snr Mgr: Doug Meier

MORPHOTRUST
See IDENTIX INC

D-U-N-S 96-905-5321
MORPHOTRUST USA LLC
(*Suby of* SAFRAN)
296 Concord Rd Ste 300, Billerica, MA 01821-3487
Tel (978) 215-2400 *Founded/Ownrshp* 1996
Sales 360.4MM^E *EMP* 1,100^E
SIC 7374 Data entry service; Data entry service
CEO: Robert Eckel
**Treas:* Greg Magoon
Chf Mktg O: Joseph Paresi
Ex VP: Doni Fordyce
VP: John Caffrey
VP: Benjamin Mallen
Dir Rx: Gina Clough
Dir Bus: Bradley Honl
Prgrm Mgr: Amanda Bondi
Prgrm Mgr: Michaela Bowers
Prgrm Mgr: Bruce Charles

D-U-N-S 01-820-2630
MORRAL COMPANIES LLC
(*Suby of* CENTRAL OHIO FARMERS CO-OP INC) ★
132 Postle St, Morral, OH 43337
Tel (740) 465-3251 *Founded/Ownrshp* 2001
Sales 25.5MM^E *EMP* 100
SIC 4783 5191 Packing & crating; Fertilizer & fertilizer materials
CEO: Daryl Gates
CFO: Joe Cunningham
Sr VP: Sandy Wampler
Sfty Mgr: Bill Corthers
Plnt Mgr: Jay Hildreth
Ql Cn Mgr: Jon Hartshorn

MORRELL CONTROL TECHNOLOGY
See MORRELL INC

D-U-N-S 60-521-5987
MORRELL GROUP INC
270 Congress St, Boston, MA 02210-1003
Tel (770) 662-8775 *Founded/Ownrshp* 2007
Sales 3.9MM^E *EMP* 300
SIC 0782 0781 Lawn care services; Landscape counseling & planning; Lawn care services; Landscape counseling & planning
CEO: Cottril Dick
**VP:* Mark Allen
**VP:* Don C Smith

D-U-N-S 01-742-3997 IMP/EXP
MORRELL INC
MORRELL CONTROL TECHNOLOGY
3333 Bald Mountain Rd, Auburn Hills, MI 48326-1808
Tel (248) 373-1600 *Founded/Ownrshp* 1979
Sales 101.1MM^E *EMP* 325
SIC 5084 5065 3621 3643 3559 3357 Hydraulic systems equipment & supplies; Electronic parts; Motors & generators; Power line cable; Metal finishing equipment for plating, etc.; Nonferrous wiredrawing & insulating; Hydraulic systems equipment & supplies; Electronic parts; Motors & generators; Power line cable; Metal finishing equipment for plating, etc.; Nonferrous wiredrawing & insulating
Pr: Steven L Tallman
VP: James E Cook
Dir IT: Matt Endres
IT Man: Ruthanne Dudley
Sales Exec: Brett Sevon
Mktg Dir: Dawn Hall
Sls Mgr: Ty Huser
Sales Asso: Terry Whiting

D-U-N-S 19-946-8179
MORRELL INTERNATIONAL INC
14901 S Heritagecrest Way, Riverton, UT 84065-4894
Tel (801) 495-3111 *Founded/Ownrshp* 2005
Sales 106.9MM^E *EMP* 370
SIC 4213 5039 4226 Trucking, except local; Structural assemblies, prefabricated: non-wood; Special warehousing & storage
CEO: Paul Jeffries
**Ch Bd:* Phil Morrell
**CFO:* Neil Vos

D-U-N-S 00-521-3772 EXP
MORRELL JOHN & CO
(*Suby of* SMITHFIELD FOODS INC) ★
805 E Kemper Rd, Cincinnati, OH 45246-2515
Tel (513) 782-3800 *Founded/Ownrshp* 1957, 1995
Sales 1.2MMM^E *EMP* 6,565
SIC 2011 Meat packing plants; Pork products from pork slaughtered on site; Bacon, slab & sliced from meat slaughtered on site; Hams & picnics from meat slaughtered on site; Meat packing plants; Pork products from pork slaughtered on site; Bacon, slab & sliced from meat slaughtered on site; Hams & picnics from meat slaughtered on site
Pr: Joseph B Sebring
VP: Jeff Crowley
VP: Ronald Easterday
VP: Terry Wendt
VP Bus Dev: Joe Laws
**Prin:* Mark Dorsey
Off Admin: Pamela Brinkman
Manager: Matt Rzepka

MORRELL NURSING CENTER
See MORRELLS NURSING CENTER

D-U-N-S 08-470-8197
MORRELLS NURSING CENTER
MORRELL NURSING CENTER
(*Suby of* SENIOR WILSON CARE INC) ★
900 N Marquis Hwy, Hartsville, SC 29550-3526
Tel (843) 383-5164 *Founded/Ownrshp* 1996
Sales 24.1MM *EMP* 130
SIC 8051 Skilled nursing care facilities; Skilled nursing care facilities
CEO: Dennis Lofe
**Pr:* Dr John M Wilson
**Treas:* Dr Thomas G Wilson
Ex Dir: Ron Hendrix
Off Mgr: Ashley Clark
Nrsg Dir: Dawn Alexander
Nrsg Dir: Anna Byrd
HC Dir: Leslie Carter
HC Dir: Elizabeth Frazer

D-U-N-S 03-495-8694 IMP
MORREY DISTRIBUTING CO
1850 E Lincoln Way, Sparks, NV 89434-8945
Tel (775) 352-6000 *Founded/Ownrshp* 1995
Sales 21.6MM^E *EMP* 64
SIC 5181 Beer & other fermented malt liquors
Pr: J John Morrey III
Genl Mgr: Nye Smoley
IT Man: Dave Peel
Board of Directors: Dave Peel

D-U-N-S 02-310-6016
MORRIES IMPORTS INC
MORRIE'S SUBARU
12550 Wayzata Blvd, Hopkins, MN 55305-1937
Tel (952) 544-0376 *Founded/Ownrshp* 1962
Sales 23.7MM^E *EMP* 61
SIC 5511 Automobiles, new & used; Automobiles, new & used
Pr: Maurice J Wagener
COO: Karl Schmidt
**VP:* Arthur Wagener
Genl Mgr: Natasha George
Off Mgr: Jennifer Zuniga
Dir IT: Scott Putnam
Sls Mgr: Dave Ahlm
Sls Mgr: Michael Iverson
Sls Mgr: Noah Joseph

MORRIE'S MAZDA
See MINNETONKA MOTOR CAR SALES INC

MORRIE'S MINNETONKA FORD
See RIDGEDALE AUTOMOTIVE INC

MORRIE'S SUBARU
See MORRIES IMPORTS INC

MORRIES USED CAR & TRUCK CTR
See BROOKLYN PARK AUTOMOTIVE INC

D-U-N-S 10-251-8917
■ **MORRILL & JANES BANK AND TRUST CO**
(*Suby of* HEARTLAND FINANCIAL USA INC) ★
6740 Antioch Rd Ste 100, Overland Park, KS 66204-1261
Tel (913) 677-4500 *Founded/Ownrshp* 2013
Sales NA *EMP* 85
SIC 6022 State commercial banks
CEO: Kurt Saylor
CFO: Steeve Cowman
Sr VP: Kurt Fischer

D-U-N-S 07-954-5073
MORRILL MOTORS INC
(*Suby of* REGAL BELOIT AMERICA, INC)
229 S Main Ave, Erwin, TN 37650-1110
Tel (423) 735-2000 *Founded/Ownrshp* 2014
Sales 17.2MM^E *EMP* 311
SIC 3585 Refrigeration & heating equipment; Refrigeration & heating equipment
Pr: Tim Neal

D-U-N-S 00-547-2824 IMP
■ **MORRILL MOTORS LLC**
(*Suby of* REGAL BELOIT AMERICA INC) ★
112 Giles Morrill Ln, Erwin, TN 37650-4517
Tel (423) 743-7000 *Founded/Ownrshp* 2007
Sales 53.4MM^E *EMP* 380
SIC 3585 3089 Refrigeration & heating equipment; Injection molded finished plastic products; Refrigeration & heating equipment; Injection molded finished plastic products
Pr: Mark Gliebe
**CFO:* David Barta
**Prin:* Peter Underwood

D-U-N-S 00-799-5079 IMP
MORRIS & DICKSON CO LLC
410 Kay Ln, Shreveport, LA 71115-3611
Tel (318) 797-7900 *Founded/Ownrshp* 1918
Sales 633.7MM^E *EMP* 120^E
SIC 5122 Drugs & drug proprietaries; Drugs & drug proprietaries
Pr: Markham A Dickson
CFO: Skipper Dickson
**VP:* C Markham Dickson Jr
Telecom Ex: Clara Guin
CIO: Eileen Ferguson
IT Man: Thien Vo
Mktg Dir: Russell Henry
Mktg Mgr: Walter Howell
Sls Mgr: Mike La Combe
Sales Asso: Mark Bivins

D-U-N-S 07-795-2711
MORRIS & GARRITANO INSURANCE AGENCY INC
1122 Laurel Ln, San Luis Obispo, CA 93401-5895
Tel (805) 543-6887 *Founded/Ownrshp* 1958
Sales NA *EMP* 85
SIC 6411 Insurance agents, brokers & service; Insurance brokers
CEO: Brendan Morris
**CFO:* Gabe Garcia
**Sec:* Gene Garritano
Ofcr: Jackie Stringfield
MIS Mgr: Michael Por
Sales Exec: Ben Hoover
Sales Exec: Pam Hummel
S&M/VP: Dorthy Maino
Mktg Mgr: Domingues Martine

D-U-N-S 17-859-7027
MORRIS & GWENDOLYN CAFRITZ FOUNDATION
1825 K St Nw Lbby, Washington, DC 20006-1206
Tel (202) 223-3100 *Founded/Ownrshp* 1950
Sales 48.9MM *EMP* 14^E
Accts Grossberg Company Llp Bethesd
SIC 8699 Charitable organization; Charitable organization
Pr: Calvin Cafritz
Ofcr: Michael Bigley
Ofcr: Karen Kinney
Ofcr: Carolynn Mambu
Ofcr: Mardell Moffett
VP: Ed McGeogh
VP: Rohan Rodrigo
Ex Dir: Rose Cleveland

D-U-N-S 83-876-9768
MORRIS AVENUE ASSOCIATES
(*Suby of* CHILDRENS HOSPITAL NEW JERSEY) ★
201 Lyons Ave, Newark, NJ 07112-2027
Tel (973) 926-7000 *Founded/Ownrshp* 1998
Sales 13.6MM^E *EMP* 903^E
SIC 8741 Nursing & personal care facility management
Pr: Lester Bornstein

D-U-N-S 00-424-1071
MORRIS BEAN & CO (OH)
777 E Hyde Rd, Yellow Springs, OH 45387-9726
Tel (937) 767-7301 *Founded/Ownrshp* 1932
Sales 37.1MM^E *EMP* 175
SIC 3365 3769 3369 Aluminum & aluminum-based alloy castings; Guided missile & space vehicle parts & auxiliary equipment; Nonferrous foundries; Aluminum & aluminum-based alloy castings; Guided missile & space vehicle parts & auxiliary equipment; Nonferrous foundries
Pr: Edward Myers
**CFO:* William Magro
Opers Mgr: Debbie Whitt
Snr Mgr: Brian Roos

D-U-N-S 00-251-8611
MORRIS BLACK & SONS INC (PA)
MORRIS BLACK DESIGN STUDIOS
984 Marcon Blvd, Allentown, PA 18109-9557
Tel (610) 264-2700 *Founded/Ownrshp* 1908
Sales 27.4MM^E *EMP* 100
SIC 5031 5211 5033

MORRIS BLACK DESIGN STUDIOS
See MORRIS BLACK & SONS INC

D-U-N-S 14-166-1772
MORRIS CAPITAL MANAGEMENT LLC
2120 Northgate Park Ln, Chattanooga, TN 37415-6937
Tel (423) 870-0800 *Founded/Ownrshp* 2002
Sales 63.5MM^E *EMP* 456
SIC 8741 Management services; Management services

D-U-N-S 05-730-1764 IMP
MORRIS COMMUNICATIONS CO LLC (GA)
BESTREADGUIDE.COM
(*Suby of* SHIVERS TRADING & OPERATING CO) ★
725 Broad St, Augusta, GA 30901-1336
Tel (706) 724-0851 *Founded/Ownrshp* 1970, 2011
Sales 417.7MM^E *EMP* 2,000
SIC 2711 7312 2721 2731 Newspapers; Newspapers, publishing & printing; Outdoor advertising services; Periodicals; Books: publishing only; Newspapers; Newspapers, publishing & printing; Outdoor advertising services; Periodicals; Books: publishing only
CEO: William S Morris III
**Pr:* William S Morris IV
CFO: Trimble Carol
Sr Cor Off: Raymond Dallman
Sr Cor Off: Amelia Patrie
Ex VP: Gay Ketchum
Ex VP: Michael Romaner
Ex VP: Haines Wilkerson
**Sr VP:* Craig S Mitchell
**Sr VP:* Steve K Stone
VP: John Bock
VP: Christopher Caldwell
VP: Dick Cheney
VP: Steven R Guchawka
VP: Jeffrey Hartley
**VP:* Derek May
VP: Steven B Strout
Exec: Brian Brooker
Dir Soc: Akagi Greg

D-U-N-S 15-428-5373
MORRIS COUNTY MUNICIPAL UTILITIES AUTHORITY
MCMUA
214a Center Grove Rd, Randolph, NJ 07869-2044
Tel (973) 285-8383 *Founded/Ownrshp* 1958
Sales 37.2MM^E *EMP* 86
SIC 4941 Water supply
Ex Dir: Glenn Schweizer
**Treas:* Larry Kaletcher
Exec: Helen O'Keefe
Opers Mgr: Bobby Ross
Opers Mgr: Fred Wilson

D-U-N-S 00-502-8949
MORRIS COUPLING CO (PA)
TENNESSEE TUBEBENDING DIVISION
2240 W 15th St, Erie, PA 16505-4510
Tel (814) 459-1741 *Founded/Ownrshp* 1941, 1960
Sales 29.3MM^E *EMP* 132
SIC 3568 3498 Couplings, shaft: rigid, flexible, universal joint, etc.; Tube fabricating (contract bending & shaping); Couplings, shaft: rigid, flexible, universal joint, etc.; Tube fabricating (contract bending & shaping)
CEO: John Whiteman
**Sec:* Barbara Pollock
**VP:* George Shabla
Exec: Howard Pollock
S&M/VP: Bob Shreve
Manager: John McUmber
Sls Mgr: Karen Shaw
Sales Asso: Amy Fisher
Sales Asso: Karenann Siemieniak
Sales Asso: Melissa Steele

MORRIS DAILY HERALD PUBLISHER
See MORRIS PUBLISHING CO

D-U-N-S 16-474-1449
MORRIS DRYWALL SYSTEMS INC
500 State Highway 110 N, Whitehouse, TX 75791-3040
Tel (903) 839-6500 *Founded/Ownrshp* 1979
Sales 22.7MM^E *EMP* 130
Accts Stephen L Hundnall Pc Tyler
SIC 1742 Drywall
Pr: Charles A Morris
**VP:* Belinda Morris

D-U-N-S 05-817-5233
MORRIS FORD & MERCURY INC
MORRIS KIA
872 State Route 50, Burnt Hills, NY 12019-2006
Tel (518) 399-9188 *Founded/Ownrshp* 1972
Sales 23.2MM^E *EMP* 58
SIC 5511 Automobiles, new & used; Automobiles, new & used
Pr: Terrance Morris
**Pr:* Charles Morris
**VP:* Noeloa Morris
Sales Asso: Dennis Enright

D-U-N-S 01-797-1540 IMP
MORRIS FURNITURE CO INC
MORRIS HOME FURNISHING
2377 Commerce Center Blvd, Fairborn, OH 45324-6377
Tel (937) 874-7080 *Founded/Ownrshp* 1998
Sales 106.9MM^E *EMP* 450^E
SIC 5722 5712 5731

D-U-N-S 00-342-9107
MORRIS GINSBERG & CO LLC
(*Suby of* HANDY CO N B) ★
65 10th St, Lynchburg, VA 24504-1621
Tel (410) 732-3200 *Founded/Ownrshp* 1930, 2007
Sales 32.1MM^E *EMP* 60^E
SIC 5033 Roofing, asphalt & sheet metal; Roofing, asphalt & sheet metal

D-U-N-S 80-117-7523 IMP
MORRIS GROUP INC
910 Day Hill Rd, Windsor, CT 06095-5727
Tel (860) 687-3300 *Founded/Ownrshp* 2004
Sales 117.6MM^E *EMP* 337
SIC 5084 Industrial machinery & equipment; Industrial machinery & equipment
Ch: Lee B Morris
Pr: Bradley Morris
CFO: John B Bowen
Chf Mktg O: Jeff Boulden
VP: Robert Bauer
VP: Chris Stine
IT Man: Eileen Martin
Mktg Mgr: Tina Carnelli
Sls Mgr: Tom Cauley
Snr Mgr: Michael Whitney

MORRIS GROUP INTERNATIONAL
See ACORN ENGINEERING CO

D-U-N-S 10-653-8788
MORRIS HALL ST LAWRENCE INC
2381 Lawrenceville Rd, Lawrenceville, NJ 08648-2025
Tel (609) 896-0006 *Founded/Ownrshp* 1971
Sales 49.9MM *EMP* 400
Accts Pricewaterhouse Coopers Llp P
SIC 8051 8059 Skilled nursing care facilities; Personal care home, with health care; Skilled nursing care facilities; Personal care home, with health care
CEO: Darlene S Hanley
COO: Linda Doran
**CFO:* Thomas Boyle
Exec: John Levi
Dir Risk M: Donna Sears
Obsttrcn: Joseph Castronuovo
Doctor: Madhu Jain
Phys Thrpy: Andrea Higginbottom

D-U-N-S 03-821-0373
MORRIS HEIGHTS HEALTH CENTER INC
85 W Burnside Ave, Bronx, NY 10453-4015
Tel (718) 299-3494 *Founded/Ownrshp* 1981
Sales 63.6MM *EMP* 300^E
Accts Cohnreznick Llp New York Ny
SIC 8011 Medical centers; Medical centers
Pr: Verona Greenland
**CFO:* Frank Kploanyi
**Sr VP:* Yvette Walker
VP: Wanda McCoy
VP: Alida Quinones
VP: Alida Quinones-Reyes
**VP:* Pamella Smith
Dir Case M: Latanya Kemp
Dir: Dana Lennon
CTO: Elissa Macklin
MIS Dir: Rachael Liu

D-U-N-S 15-911-1954
MORRIS HILLS REGIONAL HIGH SCHOOL DISTRICT
48 Knoll Dr, Rockaway, NJ 07866-4088
Tel (973) 664-2291 *Founded/Ownrshp* 1954
Sales 23.7MM^E *EMP* 400
SIC 8211 9411 Public senior high school; Administration of educational programs; Public senior high school; Administration of educational programs
Prin: Ernest Palestis
IT Man: Mathew Jusinski

D-U-N-S 92-607-8874
MORRIS HOLDING CO LLC
1015 E Mechanic St, Brazil, IN 47834-3321
Tel (812) 446-6141 *Founded/Ownrshp* 1995
Sales 66.2MM^E *EMP* 205
SIC 3714 3599 Motor vehicle transmissions, drive assemblies & parts; Machine shop, jobbing & repair; Motor vehicle transmissions, drive assemblies & parts; Machine shop, jobbing & repair

D-U-N-S 05-534-4097
MORRIS HOLDINGS INC
SUBWAY
1650 County Road 210 W, Jacksonville, FL 32259-2011
Tel (904) 829-3946 *Founded/Ownrshp* 1971
Sales 93.3MM *EMP* 350
Accts Erwin Fountain & Jackson Pa
SIC 5541 5812 5411 Truck stops; Filling stations, gasoline; Eating places; Grocery stores; Convenience stores, independent; Truck stops; Filling stations, gasoline; Eating places; Grocery stores; Convenience stores, independent
Pr: George R Morris
Sls Dir: Geoffrey Willoughby

MORRIS HOME FURNISHING
See MORRIS FURNITURE CO INC

MORRIS HOSP & HEALTHCARE CTRS
See MORRIS HOSPITAL

D-U-N-S 07-559-9308
MORRIS HOSPITAL
MORRIS HOSP & HEALTHCARE CTRS
150 W High St, Morris, IL 60450-1497
Tel (815) 942-2932 *Founded/Ownrshp* 1906
Sales 137.8MM *EMP* 525
Accts Kpmg Llp Chicago Il

SIC 8011 8062 Offices & clinics of medical doctors; General medical & surgical hospitals; Offices & clinics of medical doctors; General medical & surgical hospitals
Pr: Mark Steadham
Dir Recs: Joan Naines
Bd of Dir: John Scala
VP Bus Dev: Cindy Dupler
Exec: Coiff Corbett
Dir Risk M: Linda Petrick
Dir Lab: Kimberly Wolfer
Dir Rad: Liz Bates
Dir Rx: Alyssa Urbasek
Off Mgr: Sandra Pierce
Nurse Mgr: Theresa Reece

D-U-N-S 05-760-7566 IMP
MORRIS INC
306 W Highway 14/34, Fort Pierre, SD 57532-2091
Tel (605) 224-8089 *Founded/Ownrshp* 1970
Sales 70.8MM^E *EMP* 170
SIC 1623 3273 1611 Water & sewer line construction; Pipeline construction; Ready-mixed concrete; Surfacing & paving; Water & sewer line construction; Pipeline construction; Ready-mixed concrete; Surfacing & paving
Pr: Milton Morris
**Prin:* Jean Morris
**Prin:* John Morris
**Prin:* Julie Morris-Holter
**Prin:* Nancy Ronning
**Prin:* Mary Weinheimer
Genl Mgr: Doug Smith
IT Man: Jamie Kerr
IT Man: Nancy Morris
Sls&Mrk Ex: Dave Hufford

D-U-N-S 00-191-5735 IMP
MORRIS INDUSTRIES INC
777 State Rt 23, Pompton Plains, NJ 07444-1498
Tel (973) 835-6600 *Founded/Ownrshp* 1959
Sales 41.7MM^E *EMP* 58
SIC 5051 5084 5074 3317 5087 Pipe & tubing, steel; Drilling equipment, excluding bits; Drilling bits; Pumps & pumping equipment; Pipes & fittings, plastic; Steel pipe & tubes; Well casing, wrought: welded, lock joint or heavy riveted; Service establishment equipment; Pipe & tubing, steel; Drilling equipment, excluding bits; Drilling bits; Pumps & pumping equipment; Pipes & fittings, plastic; Steel pipe & tubes; Well casing, wrought: welded, lock joint or heavy riveted; Service establishment equipment
Pr: Robert Nochenson

D-U-N-S 10-218-6892 IMP
MORRIS IRON & STEEL CO INC
MILNOR IRON & STEEL
7345 Milnor St Ste 1, Philadelphia, PA 19136-4286
Tel (215) 624-6526 *Founded/Ownrshp* 1943
Sales 25.3MM^E *EMP* 40
SIC 5093 Metal scrap & waste materials
Pr: Stanton R Greller
**Treas:* Ronald W Greller
**Sec:* Sidney Greller
**VP:* Michael Pallotti

D-U-N-S 09-286-1715
MORRIS JAMES LLP
MARS JAMES HITCHENS & WILLIAMS
500 Delaware Ave Ste 1500, Wilmington, DE 19801-1494
Tel (302) 888-6863 *Founded/Ownrshp* 1932
Sales 20.3MM^E *EMP* 142
SIC 8111 General practice attorney, lawyer; General practice attorney, lawyer
Genl Pt: Noris P Wright
Pt: Richard Gallperin
Pt: Morris James
Pt: Edward M McNally
Pt: Stepeh M Miller
Pt: D P Mucollough
Pt: Laura S Murphy
Pt: David H Williams
Bd of Dir: Kevin G Healy
Ex Dir: Thomas C Herweg
Mktg Dir: Joanne Owens

MORRIS KIA
See MORRIS FORD & MERCURY INC

MORRIS LEVIN RENTL & PARTS CTR
See LEVIN MORRIS AND SON

D-U-N-S 00-641-3637
MORRIS MACHINE CO INC
6480 S Belmont St, Indianapolis, IN 46217-9767
Tel (317) 788-0371 *Founded/Ownrshp* 1957
Sales 31.1MM^E *EMP* 70
Accts Mid-America Audit & Tax Inc
SIC 3724 Aircraft engines & engine parts; Aircraft engines & engine parts
CEO: Robert J Chylaszek
**CFO:* Cecil Williams
Plnt Mgr: Tom Gregory

D-U-N-S 08-282-7551
MORRIS MANNING & MARTIN LLP
1600 Atlanta Financial Ct, Atlanta, GA 30326
Tel (404) 233-7000 *Founded/Ownrshp* 1976
Sales 60.2MM^E *EMP* 350
SIC 8111 General practice law office; General practice law office
Pt: John G Morris
Pt: Frank B Bazzel
Pt: Charles R Beaudrot Jr
Pt: T Daniel Brannan
Pt: Gina Brannon
Pt: Oby T Brewer III
Pt: Brian Casey
Pt: Lewis Hassett
Pt: Richard Haury
Pt: James Hunter
Pt: Randal Johnson
Pt: Jefferson D Kirby III
Pt: Donald Loft
Pt: Joseph R Manning
Pt: John P McNaughton
Pt: Thomas Player
Pt: Timothy Pollack
Pt: Gerald L Pouncey Jr
Pt: David A Rabin
Pt: Robert E Saudek
Pt: Nicholas N Sears

D-U-N-S 00-604-5306
MORRIS MANUFACTURING AND SALES CORP
(*Suby of* MORRIS HOLDING CO LLC) ★
1015 E Mechanic St, Brazil, IN 47834-3321
Tel (812) 446-6141 *Founded/Ownrshp* 1962
Sales 66.2MM^E *EMP* 200
SIC 3714 3599 Motor vehicle transmissions, drive assemblies & parts; Machine shop, jobbing & repair; Motor vehicle transmissions, drive assemblies & parts; Machine shop, jobbing & repair
Pr: Michael L Morris
CFO: Kerry Allen
Exec: Rick Whitlock
Prd Mgr: Todd Swearingen
Ql Cn Mgr: Mike Deakins

MORRIS MART
See DEGROOD OIL INC

MORRIS MATERIAL HANDLING
See MMH HOLDINGS INC

D-U-N-S 11-551-9188 IMP/EXP
MORRIS MATERIAL HANDLING INC
(*Suby of* PHMH HOLDING CO) ★
4401 Gateway Blvd, Springfield, OH 45502-9339
Tel (937) 525-5520 *Founded/Ownrshp* 1998
Sales 150.0MM^E *EMP* 350
SIC 3625 3443 7699 Crane & hoist controls, including metal mill; Crane hooks, laminated plate; Construction equipment repair; Crane & hoist controls, including metal mill; Crane hooks, laminated plate; Construction equipment repair
Pr: Tom Sothard
**Treas:* Steve Mayes
**VP:* Bernard D'Ambrosi Jr
**VP:* Keith King
**VP:* Steve Kosir
**VP:* Kim Sullivan
**Prin:* Tom Berringer
IT Man: Doug Weber

D-U-N-S 78-095-6020
MORRIS MIDWEST LLC
9300 W Heather Ave, Milwaukee, WI 53224-2425
Tel (414) 586-0450 *Founded/Ownrshp* 2006
Sales 28.1MM^E *EMP* 125^E
SIC 8742 Management consulting services
Pr: John Murphy
VP Sls: Jim Gondeck
Mktg Mgr: Jeff Boulden
Sls Mgr: Vince Hebein
Sls Mgr: Jeff Houghtaling
Sls Mgr: Andy Sharafinski

D-U-N-S 05-247-2222
MORRIS MOORE CHEVROLET-BUICK INC
COWBOY CHEVROLE
1415 96 Buypass, Silsbee, TX 77656
Tel (409) 385-5221 *Founded/Ownrshp* 1975
Sales 34.7MM^E *EMP* 100
SIC 5511 5521 Automobiles, new & used; Used car dealers; Automobiles, new & used; Used car dealers
Pr: Morris H Moore

D-U-N-S 04-755-6824
MORRIS MOTORS INC
MORRIS NISSAN
1113 River Rd, Johns Island, SC 29455-8703
Tel (843) 571-2810 *Founded/Ownrshp* 1962
Sales 26.8MM^E *EMP* 52
SIC 5511 Automobiles, new & used; Automobiles, new & used
Owner: Bucky Morris
**Owner:* David P Morris III
**Pr:* David P Morris Jr
**Treas:* Pam M Hanckel
**VP:* W B Morris
VP: Carrie Rogers
Store Mgr: Danny Servello
Sls Dir: Gill Morris

D-U-N-S 05-102-9890
MORRIS MULTIMEDIA INC
27 Abercorn St, Savannah, GA 31401-2715
Tel (912) 233-1281 *Founded/Ownrshp* 1970
Sales 185.5MM^E *EMP* 1,005
SIC 2711 4833 2752 Newspapers, publishing & printing; Television broadcasting stations; Lithographing on metal; Newspapers, publishing & printing; Television broadcasting stations; Lithographing on metal
Pr: Charles H Morris
COO: Michael Sunderman
**VP:* Alden M Maier
Dir IT: Charles Joiner

D-U-N-S 07-299-5681
MORRIS MURDOCK LLC
MORRIS MURDOCK TRAVEL
515 S 700 E Ste 1b, Salt Lake City, UT 84102-2820
Tel (801) 483-6441 *Founded/Ownrshp* 2000
Sales 99.0MM *EMP* 125
SIC 4724 Travel agencies; Travel agencies
Pr: Becky Potts
CFO: BJ Mendenhall
VP: Dick Jensen
Exec: Kathy Hirst
Dir IT: Cari Stewart
IT Man: Kerri Stewart
Opers Mgr: Janice Park
Advt Mgr: Brittany Piotrowski

MORRIS MURDOCK TRAVEL
See MORRIS MURDOCK LLC

D-U-N-S 10-703-5404 IMP/EXP
MORRIS NATIONAL INC
MCGREEVER AND DANLEE VERY
(*Suby of* MORRIS NATIONAL INC)
760 N Mckeever Ave, Azusa, CA 91702-2349
Tel (626) 385-2000 *Founded/Ownrshp* 1974
Sales 159.8MM^E *EMP* 330
Accts Ernst & Young Llp Toronto C
SIC 5145 5149 Chocolate; Confectionery; Confectionery; Chocolate
CEO: Gerry Morris Zubatoff
**Pr:* Gerald Morris
**CFO:* David Pistole
VP: Al Herpt
Exec: Alejandra Jaytan

D-U-N-S 07-549-1654
MORRIS NICHOLS ARSHT & TUNNELL LLP
1201 N Market St Fl 16, Wilmington, DE 19801-1147
Tel (302) 658-9200 *Founded/Ownrshp* 1932, 2004
Sales 35.8MM^E *EMP* 200
SIC 8111 General practice attorney, lawyer; General practice attorney, lawyer
Pt: Walter C Tuthill
Pt: Jack Blumenfeld
Pt: Donna Culver
Pt: Rob Dehney
Pt: Andrew Johnston
Pt: A Gilchrist Sparks
Pt: Alan Stone
COO: Albert Conti
MIS Dir: Frank Lawler
Dir IT: Wade Goldt
Genl Couns: Rachel A Dwares

MORRIS NISSAN
See MORRIS MOTORS INC

D-U-N-S 02-101-7314
MORRIS P HEBERT INC (LA)
283 Corporate Dr, Houma, LA 70360-2769
Tel (985) 879-2731 *Founded/Ownrshp* 1980
Sales 35.3MM *EMP* 207
SIC 8713 8711 8748 Surveying services; Engineering services; Environmental consultant; Surveying services; Engineering services; Environmental consultant
Pr: Morris P Hebert
**Sec:* Brian P Hebert
VP: Michael Capello
**VP:* John M Hebert
VP: Miccah Richie
Admn Mgr: Caroline Binnings
IT Man: Greg Pitre
Mktg Dir: John Speice
Snr PM: Anthony Garofalo

D-U-N-S 07-622-1670
MORRIS POLICH & PURDY LLP
1055 W 7th St Ste 2400, Los Angeles, CA 90017-2550
Tel (213) 891-9100 *Founded/Ownrshp* 1969
Sales 24.3MM^E *EMP* 110
SIC 8111 General practice attorney, lawyer
Pt: Theodore D Levin
Pt: Jeff Barron
Pt: William M Betley
Pt: Anthony Brazil
Pt: James Chantland
Pt: Gary Hoffman
Pt: Gary Jacobsen
Pt: Beth Kahn
Pt: Marc S Katz
Pt: Randall F Koenig
Pt: Theodore Levin
Pt: Walter Lipsman
Pt: Dean Olson
Pt: Douglas C Purdy
Pt: Janet Richardson
Pt: Gerald P Schneeweis
Pt: D Creighton Sebra
Pt: Nicholas Wieczorek
Mng Pt: Donald Ridge

MORRIS PRESS
See MORRIS PRINTING GROUP INC

D-U-N-S 00-726-2033 IMP
MORRIS PRINTING GROUP INC (NE)
MORRIS PRESS
3212 Highway 30 E, Kearney, NE 68847-9792
Tel (308) 237-7037 *Founded/Ownrshp* 1933, 1975
Sales 20.8MM^E *EMP* 150
SIC 2752 Commercial printing, lithographic; Commercial printing, lithographic
Pr: Scott D Morris
**Sec:* Maxine Lillis
VP Opers: Ryan Morris
Plnt Mgr: Randy Humston

D-U-N-S 07-159-5581
MORRIS PROTECTIVE SERVICE INC
1723 Burnet Ave, Syracuse, NY 13206-3341
Tel (315) 437-3475 *Founded/Ownrshp* 1947
Sales 11.3MM^E *EMP* 550
SIC 7381 Security guard service; Security guard service
CEO: Richard W Morris Jr
**Pr:* Michael Morris
**Ex VP:* Harold S Dibble
Opers Mgr: Cyle Farwell

D-U-N-S 00-545-9730
MORRIS PUBLISHING CO
MORRIS DAILY HERALD PUBLISHER
(*Suby of* THE B F SHAW PRINTING COMPANY)
1804 N Division St, Morris, IL 60450-1127
Tel (815) 942-3221 *Founded/Ownrshp* 1987
Sales 25.0MM^E *EMP* 516
SIC 2711 Newspapers; Newspapers
CEO: Thomas D Shaw
CFO: Phil Metka
CFO: Terri Swegle
Exec: Becky Eartoy
Genl Mgr: Bob Wall
Dir IT: Lisa Stroner
Advt Dir: Tim Stacy
Advt Mgr: John Ringer
Assoc Ed: Mark Malone

D-U-N-S 83-318-4182
MORRIS PUBLISHING FINANCE CO
(*Suby of* MORRIS PUBLISHING GROUP LLC) ★
725 Broad St, Augusta, GA 30901-1336
Tel (706) 724-0851 *Founded/Ownrshp* 2010
Sales 77.7M^E *EMP* 296^E
SIC 2711 Newspapers; Newspapers, publishing & printing
CEO: William S Morris IV

D-U-N-S 14-125-0188
MORRIS PUBLISHING GROUP LLC
(*Suby of* MPG NEWSPAPER HOLDING LLC) ★
725 Broad St, Augusta, GA 30901-1336
Tel (706) 724-0851 *Founded/Ownrshp* 2009
Sales 225.2MM *EMP* 1,722^E
SIC 2711 Newspapers; Newspapers, publishing & printing; Newspapers; Newspapers, publishing & printing
Pr: William S Morris IV
CFO: Steve K Stone
**Treas:* Craig S Mitchell
Ex VP: Derek J May
VP: Tony Bernados
VP: James Currow
VP: Lee Leschper
Dir IT: Tilden Leigh
Sls Mgr: Lindsay Randall
Snr Mgr: Heather Nagel-Doughtie
Board of Directors: William S Morris III

D-U-N-S 07-563-1317
MORRIS ROBERT UNIVERSITY ILLINOIS
401 S State St Fl 2, Chicago, IL 60605-1234
Tel (312) 935-6800 *Founded/Ownrshp* 1965
Sales 99.1MM *EMP* 800
Accts Mcclintock & Associates Pc P
SIC 8221 Colleges universities & professional schools; Colleges universities & professional schools
Pr: Michael P Viollt
VP: Leigh Brinson
MIS Dir: Depak Patel
HC Dir: Erin Ginn
HC Dir: Veronica Saucedo
Snr Mgr: Loretta Jeter
Snr Mgr: Lynn Rodgers

D-U-N-S 00-180-0770 IMP
MORRIS ROTHENBERG & SON INC (NY)
ROTHCO
3015 Veterans Mem Hwy, Ronkonkoma, NY 11779-7612
Tel (631) 585-9446 *Founded/Ownrshp* 1953
Sales 96.0MM^E *EMP* 165
SIC 5199 5091 5139 5136 General merchandise, non-durable; Camping equipment & supplies; Shoes; Men's & boys' clothing; General merchandise, non-durable; Camping equipment & supplies; Shoes; Men's & boys' clothing
Ch Bd: Milton Somberg
**Pr:* Howard Somberg
**CFO:* Richard Fleishman
Dir IT: Anthony Prossi
IT Man: Anthony Anthon
Mktg Mgr: Kristy Dineen
Sls Mgr: Tonimarie Anselmo
Sls Mgr: Hans Blechschmidt
Sls Mgr: John Brucculeri
Sls Mgr: Chuck Moore
Sales Asso: Andrew Rotolo

D-U-N-S 09-495-2595
MORRIS SCHOOL DISTRICT
31 Hazel St, Morristown, NJ 07960-3121
Tel (973) 292-2300 *Founded/Ownrshp* 1972
Sales 35.3MM^E *EMP* 535
Accts Hodulik & Morrison Pa Cpas
SIC 8211 Public elementary & secondary schools; Public elementary & secondary schools
Off Mgr: Dorothy Thomas
Cmptr Lab: Karen Andre
IT Man: Christine Kelly
Sls&Mrk Ex: Susan Young

D-U-N-S 02-913-7965
MORRIS SILVERMAN MANAGEMENT CORP
M S MANAGEMENT
790 Estate Dr Ste 100, Deerfield, IL 60015-4884
Tel (847) 919-4800 *Founded/Ownrshp* 1977
Sales 28.1MM^E *EMP* 300
SIC 8741 Business management; Business management
Pr: Jeffrey D Silverman
**Ch Bd:* Morris Silverman
**Pr:* Jeffrey Silverman
Mktg Dir: Mark Leboyer

D-U-N-S 09-840-4197
MORRIS SOUTH LLC
MORRIS SOUTH M T S
12428 Sam Neely Rd Ste A, Charlotte, NC 28278-7756
Tel (704) 523-6008 *Founded/Ownrshp* 2005
Sales 21.7MM^E *EMP* 38
SIC 5084 Machine tools & accessories
Pr: Jerry Rex
COO: Dan Danese
Ex VP: Mark Elmore
CTO: Richard Long
Sls Mgr: Tom O'Toole

MORRIS SOUTH M T S
See MORRIS SOUTH LLC

D-U-N-S 03-633-7210
MORRIS STATE BANK
(*Suby of* MORRIS STATE BANCSHARES, INC.)
301 Bellevue Ave, Dublin, GA 31021-6105
Tel (478) 272-2828 *Founded/Ownrshp* 1954, 1989
Sales NA *EMP* 43
SIC 6022 State commercial banks; State commercial banks
Ch: Louie Livingston
Pr: Spencer Mollies
CEO: Melton Tyson
COO: Ann Mickler
CFO: Ashlee Torpy
Ofcr: Bucky Dixon
Ofcr: Kimberly Ely
Ex VP: Susan Brandon
Sr VP: Jeff Palmer
VP: Brian Bazemore
VP: Linda Furer

D-U-N-S 04-786-3212 IMP
MORRIS-SHEA BRIDGE CO INC
609 20th St S, Irondale, AL 35210-2025
Tel (205) 956-9518 *Founded/Ownrshp* 1969

Sales 74.4MM *EMP* 145
SIC 1629 1794 1771

D-U-N-S 62-706-1781
MORRIS-UNION JOINTURE COMMISSION SCHOOL DISTRICT
340 Central Ave, New Providence, NJ 07974-2322
Tel (908) 464-7625 *Founded/Ownrshp* 1977
Sales 27.2MM^E *EMP* 600
SIC 8211 School board; Specialty education; School board; Specialty education
Prin: Terry Foppert
Prin: Barbara Starling
Teacher Pr: Jane Gorman-Mendez

D-U-N-S 01-533-8471
MORRISANIA DIAGNOSTIC & TREATMENT CENTER
(*Suby of* LINCOLN MEDICAL AND MENTAL HEALTH CENTER) ★
1225 Gerard Ave, Bronx, NY 10452-8001
Tel (718) 960-2777 *Founded/Ownrshp* 2010
Sales 69.4MM^E *EMP* 440^E
SIC 8011 Medical centers

D-U-N-S 02-459-5951 IMP/EXP
MORRISETTE PAPER CO INC
5925 Summit Ave, Browns Summit, NC 27214-9704
Tel (336) 375-1515 *Founded/Ownrshp* 1962
Sales 114.0MM^E *EMP* 200
Accts Davenport Marvin Joyce & Co
SIC 5113 5111 5087 Industrial & personal service paper; Printing & writing paper; Janitors' supplies; Industrial & personal service paper; Printing & writing paper; Janitors' supplies
Pr: William Morrisette Jr
**Ex VP:* Marie Morrisette Sartin
**VP:* Jim Dawson
**VP:* Henry B Harwell
Brnch Mgr: Randy Butler
Brnch Mgr: Rick Gilliam
Off Mgr: Gina Clark
MIS Dir: Phyllis Bilal
Ql Cn Mgr: Dennis Fagge

D-U-N-S 09-039-3260
MORRISON & FOERSTER LLP
MOFO
425 Market St Fl 30, San Francisco, CA 94105-2482
Tel (415) 268-7000 *Founded/Ownrshp* 1883
Sales 390.1MM^E *EMP* 2,150
SIC 8111 Specialized law offices, attorneys; Specialized law offices, attorneys
Mng Pt: Philip T Besirof
Pt: Jay Baris
COO: Pat Cavaney
COO: Cathy Flight
Ch: Larren Nashelsky
Admn Mgr: Debra Mendez
VP Inf Sys: Mark Pahlavan
IT Man: Tim Frogner
Counsel: Kathleen K Bryski
Counsel: Tushna Gamadia
Counsel: Thomas Kostic

D-U-N-S 00-510-3825
MORRISON BROTHERS CO
570 E 7th St, Dubuque, IA 52001-2378
Tel (563) 583-5701 *Founded/Ownrshp* 1997
Sales 20.2MM^E *EMP* 130
SIC 3366 3365 3321 Brass foundry; Aluminum foundries; Gray iron castings; Brass foundry; Aluminum foundries; Gray iron castings
Pr: Charles Glab
Pr: Tim Weiss
COO: Rick Treanor
**Treas:* David S Cushman
Bd of Dir: John Freund
IT Man: Tom Ertmer
Sfty Dirs: Paul Gregory
Sls Mgr: Rich Stevens
Snr Mgr: Michael Lattner

D-U-N-S 07-129-6065
MORRISON BROWN ARGIZ & FARRA LLC
1450 Brickell Ave # 1800, Miami, FL 33131-4913
Tel (305) 373-5500 *Founded/Ownrshp* 1969
Sales 58.3MM^E *EMP* 455
SIC 8721 Accounting, auditing & bookkeeping; Certified public accountant; Accounting, auditing & bookkeeping; Certified public accountant
CEO: Antonio L Argiz
CFO: Ed Torgas
Prin: Ed Blum
Prin: Marc S Dickler
Prin: Marjorie A Horwin
Prin: Ira Rubenstein
IT Man: Kenneth Saltzman
Mktg Mgr: Valeria Sanchez

MORRISON CENTER
See MORRISON CHILD AND FAMILY SERVICES

D-U-N-S 07-642-4720
MORRISON CHILD AND FAMILY SERVICES
MORRISON CENTER
11035 Ne Sandy Blvd, Portland, OR 97220-2553
Tel (503) 258-4200 *Founded/Ownrshp* 1947
Sales 23.7MM *EMP* 400
Accts Gary Mcgee & Co Llp Portland
SIC 8322 Child guidance agency; Child guidance agency
CEO: Tia Gray Stecher
Prgrm Mgr: Jodie Teitelbaum
Dir IT: Mark Arcuri
Opers Supe: Scott Brown
Opers Mgr: Scott Montgomery
Psych: Minal Patel
Pgrm Dir: Alfonso Ramirez

D-U-N-S 07-563-1614
MORRISON COMMUNITY HOSPITAL
303 N Jackson St, Morrison, IL 61270-3042
Tel (815) 772-2161 *Founded/Ownrshp* 1942
Sales 23.0MM^E *EMP* 180
SIC 8062 General medical & surgical hospitals
CEO: Pamela Pfister
Dir OR: Debb Hanson
Dir Soc: Neil Cooperrider
Dir Health: Leslie Wagenecht

D-U-N-S 00-693-7577
MORRISON CONSTRUCTION CO INC
1834 Summer St, Hammond, IN 46320-2236
Tel (219) 932-5036 *Founded/Ownrshp* 1925, 1948
Sales 153.6MM^E *EMP* 300
SIC 1541 Industrial buildings & warehouses; Industrial buildings & warehouses
CEO: James M Morrison
**Pr:* Daniel Sharpe
VP: Mike Skura
**VP:* Mark Winter

D-U-N-S 11-476-2482
MORRISON EKRE & BART MANAGEMENT SERVICES INC
MEB MANAGEMENT SERVICES
120 E Congress St, Tucson, AZ 85701-1708
Tel (520) 620-1640 *Founded/Ownrshp* 1998
Sales 17.0MM^E *EMP* 500
SIC 6531 Real estate managers; Real estate managers
CFO: Melanie Morrison
Sr VP: Mark Schilling
VP: Suzanne Lavergne
VP: Andrew Titche
Dist Mgr: Luz Bruscini
Dist Mgr: Monica Franzi
Dist Mgr: Carol Murray
Sales Exec: Shawn Mazon

D-U-N-S 92-810-0259
MORRISON ENERGY GROUP
16285 Park Ten Pl, Houston, TX 77084-5070
Tel (281) 616-8405 *Founded/Ownrshp* 2011
Sales 20.6MM^E *EMP* 1,000
SIC 1389 Oil field services; Oil field services
Pr: Chad Morrison

D-U-N-S 08-539-5846
MORRISON EXPRESS CORP (USA)
2000 S Hughes Way, El Segundo, CA 90245-4730
Tel (310) 322-8999 *Founded/Ownrshp* 1977
Sales 74.0MM^E *EMP* 154
Accts Deloitte & Touche Llp Los Ang
SIC 4731 Freight forwarding; Freight forwarding
CEO: Danny Chiu
Pr: Wilson Lee
**V Ch Bd:* Jackson C CHI
VP: Paul Fu
VP: Hannspeter Jansen
VP: Henry Lim
Rgnl Mgr: Janis Mullman
Dist Mgr: Emmanuel Desbats
Dist Mgr: Teddy Hsu
Dist Mgr: William Wu
Dist Mgr: Changyao Zhu

D-U-N-S 62-803-5545
MORRISON GROUP INC
3601 S Broadway Ste 1000, Edmond, OK 73013-4140
Tel (405) 242-5200 *Founded/Ownrshp* 1991
Sales 24.3MM^E *EMP* 30
SIC 5113 Disposable plates, cups, napkins & eating utensils
Pr: Michael Morrison
IT Man: Jeff Garlington
Opers Mgr: Denitra Knox

D-U-N-S 03-843-0885
MORRISON HERSHFIELD CORP
1455 Lincoln Pkwy E # 500, Atlanta, GA 30346-2229
Tel (770) 379-8500 *Founded/Ownrshp* 1946
Sales 27.5MM^E *EMP* 130
SIC 8741 Construction management
CEO: Anthony Karakatsanis
**Pr:* Edward Gazzola
**CFO:* David Pavey
VP: Al Bhanji
VP: Kevin Pask
VP: Jim Warren
Dept Mgr: Jeff Siddall
Snr PM: Robert Blakeney
Snr PM: Mark Lucuik
Snr PM: Blakeney Robert

D-U-N-S 02-227-8220
MORRISON HOMES INC
3655 Brookside Pkwy # 400, Alpharetta, GA 30022-1430
Tel (770) 360-8700 *Founded/Ownrshp* 1978
Sales NA *EMP* 800^E
SIC 1521 6552

D-U-N-S 03-861-6587 IMP
MORRISON INDUSTRIAL EQUIPMENT CO
(*Suby of* MORRISON INDUSTRIES INC) ★
1825 Monroe Ave Nw, Grand Rapids, MI 49505-6240
Tel (616) 447-3800 *Founded/Ownrshp* 1981
Sales 73.6MM^E *EMP* 225
Accts Plante & Moran
SIC 5084 7699 7359 Materials handling machinery; Industrial machinery & equipment repair; Equipment rental & leasing; Materials handling machinery; Industrial machinery & equipment repair; Equipment rental & leasing
Pr: Roger Troost
**CFO:* Greg Vanderlande
**VP:* Dale Monticello
**VP:* Greg Morrison
VP: Greg Vanderlende
Brnch Mgr: Sandy Evers
Brnch Mgr: Sue Sturtevant
Opers Mgr: Steven White

D-U-N-S 00-656-6376
MORRISON INDUSTRIES INC (MI)
1825 Monroe Ave Nw, Grand Rapids, MI 49505-6240
Tel (616) 361-2673 *Founded/Ownrshp* 1953
Sales 102.1MM^E *EMP* 350
SIC 5084 7699 7359 Materials handling machinery; Compressor repair; Industrial truck rental; Materials handling machinery; Compressor repair; Industrial truck rental
CEO: Dick Morrison
**Pr:* Richard G Morrison
**CEO:* Roger Troost
**VP:* Dale Monticello
VP: Greg Morrison

D-U-N-S 07-536-0305
MORRISON MAHONEY LLP
250 Summer St Fl 1, Boston, MA 02210-1181
Tel (617) 439-0542 *Founded/Ownrshp* 1998
Sales 36.8MM^E *EMP* 340
SIC 8111 Specialized law offices, attorneys; Specialized law offices, attorneys
Pt: Michael F Aylward
Sr Pt: Mark Granger
Pt: Nicholas P Alexander
Pt: David A Bakst
Pt: Steven J Bolotin
Pt: Nancy Dindinger
Pr: Maria McKinnon
Netwrk Mgr: Robert Yates
Counsel: Patrick Day
Counsel: William Wynne

D-U-N-S 93-753-4295
MORRISON MANAGEMENT SPECIALISTS INC
(*Suby of* COMPASS GROUP USA INC) ★
5801 Pachtree Dunwoody Rd, Atlanta, GA 30342-1503
Tel (404) 845-3330 *Founded/Ownrshp* 2001
Sales 229.1MM^E *EMP* 4,000
SIC 8099 Nutrition services; Nutrition services
CEO: Scott Maclellan
**Pr:* Tim Pierce
CFO: Jerry D Underhill
Ex VP: Daniel Kingsbury
Sr VP: Gary L Gaddy
**Sr VP:* Jim Rathburn
VP: Marty Cawley
**VP:* John E Fountain
VP: Chip Kent
VP: Jeffrey Massey
VP: Joe O'Brien
VP: Richard Roberson
Exec: Rodney Booker
Exec: Waverly Overton
Exec: Tim Spain

D-U-N-S 00-731-9429 IMP
MORRISON MILLING CO (TX)
(*Suby of* C H GUENTHER & SON INC) ★
319 E Prairie St, Denton, TX 76201-6109
Tel (940) 387-6111 *Founded/Ownrshp* 1886, 2006
Sales 63.3MM^E *EMP* 165^E
SIC 2041 Wheat flour; Flour mixes; Corn meal; Wheat flour; Flour mixes; Corn meal
Pr: Dale W Tremblay
**Ch Bd:* Scott Petty Jr
**Pr:* J Steven Stroud
**CFO:* Janelle M Sykes
**Sr VP:* Thomas A McRae
**Sr VP:* Stephen T Phillips
**Sr VP:* Chris Redkey
**VP:* Kenneth Newton
VP: Gus Wallgren

D-U-N-S 00-417-2888 EXP
MORRISON PRODUCTS INC (OH)
16900 S Waterloo Rd, Cleveland, OH 44110-3895
Tel (216) 486-4000 *Founded/Ownrshp* 1923, 1960
Sales 88.7MM *EMP* 390
SIC 3564

D-U-N-S 61-388-7442
MORRISON SECURITY CORP
12334 S Keeler Ave, Alsip, IL 60803-1813
Tel (773) 779-1000 *Founded/Ownrshp* 1999
Sales 17.6MM^E *EMP* 350^E
SIC 7381 Security guard service; Security guard service
Pr: Sean M Morrison
Sr VP: Tony Martin
Opers Mgr: Joel Cruz

D-U-N-S 00-792-9938 IMP
MORRISON SUPPLY CO
JOHNSON CONTROLS
(*Suby of* MORSCO INC) ★
311 E Vickery Blvd, Fort Worth, TX 76104-1385
Tel (817) 336-0451 *Founded/Ownrshp* 1995, 2011
Sales 399.3MM^E *EMP* 300
SIC 5074 Plumbing & hydronic heating supplies; Plumbing & hydronic heating supplies
**Pr:* Stan Allen
**CEO:* Chip Hornsby
**COO:* Kevin Moore
**CFO:* Kerry Warren
VP: Charlie Allen
VP: Tim Bevins
VP: Ron Bohannon
VP: Dan Filler
VP: Mark Kirby
**VP:* Joe Lacik
VP: Phil Osborn

D-U-N-S 92-748-4949
■ **MORRISON-KNUDSEN ENGINEERS INC**
WASHINGTON GROUP
(*Suby of* URS ENERGY & CONSTRUCTION INC) ★
720 E Park Blvd, Boise, ID 83712-7758
Tel (208) 386-5000 *Founded/Ownrshp* 1945
Sales 30.2MM^E *EMP* 600
SIC 1622 1611 1623 Bridge construction; Highway construction, elevated; Highway & street paving contractor; Water, sewer & utility lines; Bridge construction; Highway construction, elevated; Highway & street paving contractor; Water, sewer & utility lines
Pr: Stephen Hanks
Genl Mgr: Stephen Depew

D-U-N-S 06-372-6665
MORRISON-MAIERLE INC
1 Engineering Pl, Helena, MT 59602-0241
Tel (406) 442-3050 *Founded/Ownrshp* 1946
Sales 31.7MM *EMP* 275
Accts Anderson Zurmuehlen & Co Pc
SIC 8711 8748 7374 Consulting engineer; Environmental consultant; Data processing & preparation; Consulting engineer; Environmental consultant; Data processing & preparation
Ch Bd: John R Schunke
**Pr:* James A Maierle
**Pr:* Robert Morrison
**COO:* Kenneth C Hill
**Sr VP:* John H Morrison Jr
VP: Carl Anderson
VP: Scott T Bell
VP: Michael F Cummings
VP: Deborah Johnston
VP: Kurt W Keith
VP: Scott Murphy
VP: P D Rensmon
VP: Terry Richmond
**VP:* Kenneth Salo
VP: Eugene D Wasia
VP: Gene Wasia

D-U-N-S 09-548-0893
MORRISSEY CONSTRUCTION CO
705 Southmoor Pl, Godfrey, IL 62035-1871
Tel (618) 467-3400 *Founded/Ownrshp* 1953
Sales 24.9MM^E *EMP* 71
SIC 1542 1522

D-U-N-S 11-303-9515
MORRISTOWN DRIVERS SERVICE INC
M D S
1111 Gateway Svc Pk Rd, Morristown, TN 37813
Tel (423) 581-6048 *Founded/Ownrshp* 1993
Sales 48.8MM^E *EMP* 220
SIC 4213 Trucking, except local; Trucking, except local
Pr: Bob Jenkins
**CFO:* Mike Long
**VP:* Tim McKinnish
Dir IT: David Hensley
Opers Mgr: Tracy Cutshall
Manager: Steve Davidson

MORRISTOWN MEMORIAL HOSPITAL
See DELAIRE NURSING AND CONVALESCENT CENTER INC

MORRISTOWN MEMORIAL HOSPITAL
See ATLANTIC HEALTH SYSTEM INC

MORRISTOWN MEMORIAL HOSPITAL
See AHS HOSPITAL CORP

MORRISTOWN POWER SYSTEM
See MORRISTOWN UTILITY COMMISSION

D-U-N-S 06-671-7992
MORRISTOWN UTILITY COMMISSION
MORRISTOWN POWER SYSTEM
441 W Main St, Morristown, TN 37814-4615
Tel (423) 317-8845 *Founded/Ownrshp* 1901
Sales 95.2MM^E *EMP* 105
Accts Coulter & Justus Pc Knoxville
SIC 4931 Electric & other services combined; Electric & other services combined
CEO: Joseph Wigington
**Ch:* George B Mc Guffin
**Sec:* Harold Nichols
Exec: Marie Morgan
Genl Mgr: Clark Rucker
Telecom Mg: George Benjamin

MORRISTOWN WESTIN
See INK ACQUISITION VI LLC

D-U-N-S 05-812-5949
MORRISTOWN-BEARD SCHOOL
70 Whippany Rd, Morristown, NJ 07960-4523
Tel (973) 539-3032 *Founded/Ownrshp* 1971
Sales 23.3MM *EMP* 100
Accts Suplee Clooney & Company West
SIC 8211 Secondary school; Secondary school
Prin: Peter Caldwell
Ofcr: Janet Crowley

D-U-N-S 07-152-3823
MORRISTOWN-HAMBLEN HOSPITAL ASSOCIATION
908 W 4th North St, Morristown, TN 37814-3894
Tel (423) 492-9000 *Founded/Ownrshp* 1955
Sales 89.4MM^E *EMP* 848
SIC 8062 Hospital, affiliated with AMA residency; Hospital, affiliated with AMA residency
CEO: Richard Clark
COO: Michael Pierce
**CFO:* Maz Owens
CTO: Tim Krieger
Pharmcst: Cheryl Wallace
Phys Thrpy: Jackie Murray
Dir Health: Peggy Brown

D-U-N-S 06-926-9509
MORRISVILLE STATE COLLEGE
(*Suby of* STATE UNIVERSITY OF NEWYORK) ★
80 Eaton St, Morrisville, NY 13408-2608
Tel (315) 684-6083 *Founded/Ownrshp* 2006
Sales 28.8MM^E *EMP* 628
SIC 8221 9411 Colleges universities & professional schools; Administration of educational programs; ; Colleges universities & professional schools; Administration of educational programs;
Pr: Raymond W Cross
**Pr:* William J Murabito

D-U-N-S 03-992-1333
MORROW CONSTRUCTION CO INC
DAVIS DEVELOPMENT
403 Corporate Center Dr # 201, Stockbridge, GA 30281-9023
Tel (770) 474-4345 *Founded/Ownrshp* 1976
Sales 41.9MM^E *EMP* 60
SIC 1542 1521 Commercial & office buildings, renovation & repair; General remodeling, single-family houses
CEO: Mike B Davis
**CFO:* Fred S Hazel

MORROW COUNTY COMMISIONERS
See COUNTY OF MORROW

D-U-N-S 00-790-8403
MORROW COUNTY GRAIN GROWERS INC (OR)
GREEN FEED
350 E Main St, Lexington, OR 97839
Tel (541) 989-8221 *Founded/Ownrshp* 1930

Sales 89.0MM *EMP* 55
Accts Barnett & Moro Pc Hermiston
SIC 5153 5083 Grains; Barley; Farm implements; Agricultural machinery & equipment; Farm equipment parts & supplies; Grains; Barley; Farm implements; Agricultural machinery & equipment; Farm equipment parts & supplies
CFO: Lisanne Currin
**Genl Mgr:* John Ripple

D-U-N-S 09-215-7403
MORROW COUNTY HOSPITAL
MORROW COUNTY HOSPITAL HM HLTH
651 W Marion Rd, Mount Gilead, OH 43338-1096
Tel (419) 947-9127 *Founded/Ownrshp* 1952
Sales 25.0MM *EMP* 320ᴱ
SIC 8062 General medical & surgical hospitals; General medical & surgical hospitals
CEO: Christopher Traux
IT Man: Nicholas Lawyer
Sfty Dirs: Kelley Shealy
Mktg Dir: Lois Peoples
Nrsg Dir: Lorelei Heineman
Pharmcst: Laura Morris

MORROW COUNTY HOSPITAL HM HLTH
See MORROW COUNTY HOSPITAL

D-U-N-S 04-830-7862
MORROW COUNTY SCHOOL DISTRICT
235 Stansbury St, Heppner, OR 97836-2104
Tel (541) 989-8202 *Founded/Ownrshp* 1959
Sales 26.0MM *EMP* 320
Accts Oster Professional Group Cpa
SIC 8211 Public elementary & secondary schools; Public elementary & secondary schools
Sys Mgr: Dave Fowler
Schl Brd P: Thad Killingdeck

D-U-N-S 87-978-9410
MORROW EQUIPMENT CO LLC
3218 Pringle Rd Se, Salem, OR 97302-6313
Tel (503) 385-0122 *Founded/Ownrshp* 1994
Sales 43.3MMᴱ *EMP* 230
SIC 7353 7699 5082 Heavy construction equipment rental; Cranes & aerial lift equipment, rental or leasing; Construction equipment repair; General construction machinery & equipment; Cranes, construction; Heavy construction equipment rental; Cranes & aerial lift equipment, rental or leasing; Construction equipment repair; General construction machinery & equipment; Cranes, construction
V Ch: John Morrow
Brnch Mgr: Jerry Sykes
Web Dev: Jeff Allman
Sfty Dirs: Brian Silbernagel
Opers Mgr: Donn Trotter
Sls Mgr: Mark Forbes

D-U-N-S 04-106-4312
MORROW GRAVEL CO INC (OH)
11641 Mosteller Rd Ste 2, Cincinnati, OH 45241-1520
Tel (513) 771-0820 *Founded/Ownrshp* 1958
Sales 35.3MMᴱ *EMP* 120
SIC 1442 1771 2951 Construction sand mining; Gravel mining; Blacktop (asphalt) work; Asphalt & asphaltic paving mixtures (not from refineries); Construction sand mining; Gravel mining; Blacktop (asphalt) work; Asphalt & asphaltic paving mixtures (not from refineries)
Pr: James P Jurgensen
**CFO:* Tim St Clair

D-U-N-S 03-371-4502
MORROW MOTOR SALES INC
TOYOTA SOUTH
6865 Jonesboro Rd, Morrow, GA 30260-2902
Tel (770) 961-0225 *Founded/Ownrshp* 1999
Sales 55.9MMᴱ *EMP* 120
SIC 5511 Automobiles, new & used; Automobiles, new & used
Pr: Jerry Gresham
COO: Derak Rawlings
**Sec:* Cheryl Wise
VP: Shannon Ingram
Genl Mgr: Rich Mahon
Sales Exec: David Curtis
Sls Mgr: Erik Anderson
Sls Mgr: Zach Dunn
Sls Mgr: John Gibson

D-U-N-S 00-969-4779
MORROW-MEADOWS CORP
CHERRY CITY ELECTRIC
231 Benton Ct, City of Industry, CA 91789-5213
Tel (858) 974-3650 *Founded/Ownrshp* 1964
Sales 306.9MMᴱ *EMP* 1,200
SIC 1731 General electrical contractor; General electrical contractor
CEO: Karen V Price
**Ch Bd:* Elizabeth Meadows
CFO: Tim Langley
**CFO:* Timothy D Langley
**Ch:* J Robert Meadows
**Ex VP:* Robert E Meadows
VP: Joseph Babcock
VP: Ray Ellis
VP: Rick Jarvis
VP: Rick Lane
VP: Ed Slingluff
Exec: Ken Freeman
Exec: Dan Gleason

D-U-N-S 07-991-1315
MORSCO INC
100 E 15th St Ste 200, Fort Worth, TX 76102-6567
Tel (877) 709-2227 *Founded/Ownrshp* 2005
Sales 371.2MMᴱ *EMP* 300ᴱ
SIC 5074 1711 Plumbing & hydronic heating supplies; Plumbing, heating, air-conditioning contractors; Heating & air conditioning contractors
CEO: Chip Hornsby
CFO: Kerry Warren
Chf Mktg O: Darren Taylor
VP: Dan Filler
VP: Mark Kirby
VP: Joe Lacik
VP: Philip K Osborn

D-U-N-S 78-450-8897 IMP
MORSE AUTOMOTIVE CORP
MORSE HEAVY DUTY
750 W Lake Cook Rd # 480, Buffalo Grove, IL 60089-2074
Tel (773) 843-9000 *Founded/Ownrshp* 1992
Sales 116.2MMᴱ *EMP* 1,500
SIC 3714 Motor vehicle brake systems & parts; Motor vehicle brake systems & parts
CEO: Peter Morse
Pr: Bob Wilkes
**CFO:* Robert Kurasz
CFO: Robert Murasz
**Ex VP:* Jay McCrory
CIO: John Giardina

D-U-N-S 87-793-7219
MORSE COMMUNICATIONS INC
395 East Dr, Melbourne, FL 32904-1030
Tel (321) 259-8469 *Founded/Ownrshp* 1994
Sales 24.4MMᴱ *EMP* 82
SIC 5999 Telephone & communication equipment
Pr: Annette Costello
**VP:* Michael J Costello
Sls Mgr: Patrick Copeland

D-U-N-S 00-895-7235 IMP
MORSE DISTRIBUTION INC
MORSE STEEL SERVICE
3002 W Illinois St, Bellingham, WA 98225-1572
Tel (360) 756-6200 *Founded/Ownrshp* 1884
Sales 24.4MMᴱ *EMP* 63
SIC 5051

D-U-N-S 00-783-4914
MORSE ELECTRIC INC (IL)
500 W South St, Freeport, IL 61032-6836
Tel (815) 266-4200 *Founded/Ownrshp* 1944, 1977
Sales 91.2MMᴱ *EMP* 400
SIC 1731 General electrical contractor; General electrical contractor
CEO: Donald Morse
**Pr:* Lou Rotello
CFO: Janey Morse
Treas: Sarah Scheider
**Treas:* Brian Scott
**Ex VP:* David Morse
VP: Wanda Gast
Sfty Mgr: Mike Daniel
Board of Directors: Jane Morse

D-U-N-S 82-947-1312
MORSE GROUP INC
500 W South St, Freeport, IL 61032-6836
Tel (815) 266-4200 *Founded/Ownrshp* 2007
Sales 138.5MMᴱ *EMP* 500
SIC 1731 Electrical work; Electrical work
Pr: Lou Rotello
**Treas:* Brian Scott

MORSE HEAVY DUTY
See MORSE AUTOMOTIVE CORP

D-U-N-S 04-546-6083 EXP
MORSE OPERATIONS INC
ED MORSE AUTOMOTIVE GROUP
2850 S Federal Hwy, Delray Beach, FL 33483-3216
Tel (561) 276-5000 *Founded/Ownrshp* 1960
Sales 863.2MM *EMP* 1,295
Accts Crowe Horwath Llp Fort Lauder
SIC 5511 Automobiles, new & used; Automobiles, new & used
Pr: Edward J Morse Jr
**CEO:* Edward Ted Morse Jr
**CFO:* Dennis Macinnes
**Ch:* Edward J Morse Sr
**VP:* Elizabeth A Beaver
**VP:* Richard Beaver Sr
VP: Beaver Richard
Creative D: Scott Reynolds
Web Prj Mg: Vic Parra
MIS Mgr: C Roth
Sls Mgr: Tommy Davis

MORSE STEEL SERVICE
See MORSE DISTRIBUTION INC

D-U-N-S 00-701-4442
MORSEY CONSTRUCTORS LLC
(*Suby of* HARPER INDUSTRIES INC) ★
777 Dr Smith Ln, Calvert City, KY 42029-8934
Tel (270) 448-5731 *Founded/Ownrshp* 1959, 1976
Sales 56.0MMᴱ *EMP* 250
SIC 1629 1541 Industrial plant construction; Power plant construction; Industrial buildings, new construction; Industrial plant construction; Power plant construction; Industrial buildings, new construction
Ql Cn Mgr: Richard Dilaura

D-U-N-S 02-127-0269
MORSTAN GENERAL INSURANCE AGENCY INC
GMAC INSURANCE
600 Community Dr, Manhasset, NY 11030-3802
Tel (516) 488-4747 *Founded/Ownrshp* 1980
Sales NA *EMP* 250
SIC 6411 Insurance agents, brokers & service; Insurance agents, brokers & service
Pr: Jay Levy
VP: Jim Cusick
**VP:* Al Eskanazy
VP: Joseph Esposito
VP: Robert Goldfarb
VP: Michael Gottdank
Brnch Mgr: Helen Palumbo
CTO: Craig Caparelli
VP Opers: Jennifer Zelin
VP Prd: Bob Finkel
Opers Mgr: Marcia Clapman

D-U-N-S 14-690-5125
MORTAGE WAREHOUSE
3 Huntington Quad Ste 303, Huntington Station, NY 11747-4602
Tel (631) 773-5175 *Founded/Ownrshp* 2007
Sales NA *EMP* 420
SIC 6162 Mortgage bankers & correspondents; Mortgage bankers & correspondents
CEO: David Peskin
CFO: Nicholas Hahn

D-U-N-S 06-204-6149
MORTARA INSTRUMENT INC (WI)
7865 N 86th St, Milwaukee, WI 53224-3431
Tel (414) 354-1600 *Founded/Ownrshp* 1982
Sales 78.6MMᴱ *EMP* 180ᴱ
SIC 8731 3845 Medical research, commercial; Electrocardiographs; Medical research, commercial; Electrocardiographs
CEO: Justin Mortara
Pr: Maurizio Fumigalli
**Pr:* David W Mortara
COO: Paul Andress
COO: Frank Schmidt
COO: Tom Schmitz
**CFO:* Brian Brenegan
Sr VP: Chuck Webster
VP: Joe Austin
VP: Merat Bagha
VP: Ted Johnston

D-U-N-S 19-044-4620 EXP
MORTECH MANUFACTURING CO INC
411 N Aerojet Dr, Azusa, CA 91702-3253
Tel (626) 334-1471 *Founded/Ownrshp* 1986
Sales 20.3MMᴱ *EMP* 42
SIC 5087 Funeral directors' equipment & supplies
CEO: Benny Joseph
Off Mgr: Rachel Sequeida
VP Opers: Paul Joseph
Mktg Mgr: John Joseph

D-U-N-S 19-640-9965 IMP
MORTENSEN WOODWORK INC
4920 Baker St, Union City, GA 30291-1984
Tel (770) 969-1475 *Founded/Ownrshp* 1987
Sales 25.3MMᴱ *EMP* 125
SIC 2511 2431 5211 2521 Wood household furniture; Millwork; Millwork & lumber; Wood office furniture; Wood household furniture; Millwork; Millwork & lumber; Wood office furniture
CEO: Frederick J Mortensen
**Pr:* Greg Kasten
Admn Mgr: Richark Pakdo
Prd Mgr: Charlie Bowlden
Mktg Dir: Erin Cole
Manager: David Goudy
Snr PM: Terry Tews

MORTENSON CONSTRUCTION
See M A MORTENSON CO

D-U-N-S 07-316-1317 IMP
MORTEX PRODUCTS INC
SUMMIT
501 Terminal Rd, Fort Worth, TX 76106-1954
Tel (817) 624-0820 *Founded/Ownrshp* 1957
Sales 111.3MMᴱ *EMP* 300
SIC 3585 3433 1711 3999 Parts for heating, cooling & refrigerating equipment; Heating equipment, except electric; Parts for heating, cooling & refrigerating equipment; Heating equipment, except electric; Heating & air conditioning contractors; Atomizers, toiletry
CEO: Terrell J Small III
**Pr:* Joe McCorkle
Exec: Michelle Dye
IT Man: Sagun Joshi
Opers Mgr: Gilbert Cedirco
S&M/VP: Stephen Small
Sls Mgr: John Stoltz

D-U-N-S 13-048-8133
MORTGAGE ACCESS CORP
WEICHERT FINANCIAL SERVICES
225 Littleton Rd, Morris Plains, NJ 07950-2927
Tel (973) 605-1515 *Founded/Ownrshp* 1984
Sales NA *EMP* 285
SIC 6162 Mortgage bankers; Mortgage bankers
Ch Bd: James Weichert
Pr: Stephen E Adamo
Pr: John Mahoney
CFO: Al Dwojewski
CFO: Larry Jackson
Ofcr: Marlenis Rivera
Sr VP: N Crocetto
Sr VP: Carolyn Hoffman
Sr VP: David McCormick
VP: Carolee Boles
VP: Jobi Decker
VP: Jacqueline Vila
VP: Laura Williamson
Exec: Sandy Epstein
Dir Risk M: Ben Niles

MORTGAGE ADVISORY GROUP
See GLOBAL ADVISORY GROUP INC

D-U-N-S 02-031-1973
MORTGAGE BANKERS ASSOCIATION
1919 M St Nw Fl 5, Washington, DC 20036-3572
Tel (202) 557-2719 *Founded/Ownrshp* 1912
Sales 45.5MM *EMP* 125
Accts Tate And Tryon Washington Dc
SIC 8611 Trade associations; Trade associations
CEO: David Stevens
**CFO:* Rich Pirrotta
Assoc VP: Tamara King
Assoc VP: Heather Messam
Ex VP: Michael Brady
Sr VP: Gail Davis
Sr VP: John Golden
Sr VP: Thomas Kim
Sr VP: Steve O'Connor
VP: Andrea Bona
VP: Lynn M Fisher
VP: Jen Griege
VP: Drew Luning
VP: Ken Markison
VP: Kevin Michno
Dir Bus: Brendan Barry

D-U-N-S 07-955-5275
MORTGAGE CAPITAL ADVISORS II LLC
2293 Fairhaven Cir Ne, Atlanta, GA 30305-4316
Tel (404) 308-8809 *Founded/Ownrshp* 2014
Sales NA *EMP* 3ᴱ
SIC 6162 Mortgage bankers & correspondents; Mortgage bankers & correspondents
Pr: Mark Dodson

MORTGAGE CAPITAL INVESTORS
See UNION MORTGAGE GROUP INC

D-U-N-S 55-675-1634
MORTGAGE CENTER LC
29621 Northwestern Hwy, Southfield, MI 48034-1033
Tel (248) 353-4449 *Founded/Ownrshp* 1997
Sales NA *EMP* 84
Accts Doeren Mayhew Troy Michigan
SIC 6162 Bond & mortgage companies; Bond & mortgage companies
CEO: Thoms N Teeple
**VP:* Vernita Glenn
**VP:* Kristine M Kline
**VP:* Kenneth Martin
**VP:* Jacqueline Normandeau
**VP:* Brigitte Stowell

D-U-N-S 09-412-5536
MORTGAGE CONSULTING GROUP INC
16991 Timber Ridge Dr, Granada Hills, CA 91344-1137
Tel (818) 425-6001 *Founded/Ownrshp* 1999
Sales NA *EMP* 1
SIC 6163 Mortgage brokers arranging for loans, using money of others; Mortgage brokers arranging for loans, using money of others
Pr: Vahe Der Gevorkian
**VP:* Carol Hazarian

D-U-N-S 82-528-4370
MORTGAGE CONTRACTING SERVICES LLC
4890 Kenne Blvd Fl 5 50, Tampa, FL 33609
Tel (813) 387-1100 *Founded/Ownrshp* 2013
Sales 98.0MMᴱ *EMP* 400
SIC 4785 Inspection & fixed facilities; Inspection & fixed facilities
CEO: Caroline Reaves
CFO: Paul Lee
CFO: Bart R Vincent
Sr VP: John Maxwell
Sr VP: Chad Mosley
Sr VP: Andrew Rowlands
Sr VP: Dave Sunlin
VP: Nickie Bigenho
VP: Tracy Hager
VP: Elspeth Spransy
CTO: Robert Colbeck
Board of Directors: Jim Goetz

D-U-N-S 08-901-9058
MORTGAGE EXPRESS LLC
10260 Sw Greenburg Rd # 830, Portland, OR 97223-5518
Tel (503) 520-1141 *Founded/Ownrshp* 1999
Sales NA *EMP* 100
SIC 6162 Mortgage brokers, using own money; Mortgage brokers, using own money
CFO: David Brown
VP: Travis Wallis
Sls Mgr: Curt Vanderzanden

D-U-N-S 10-829-5718
■ **MORTGAGE GUARANTY INSURANCE CORP**
MGIC INVESTMENT
(*Suby of* MGIC INVESTMENT CORP) ★
270 E Kilbourn Ave, Milwaukee, WI 53202-3199
Tel (414) 347-6480 *Founded/Ownrshp* 1985
Sales NA *EMP* 877ᴱ
SIC 6351 Mortgage guarantee insurance; Mortgage guarantee insurance
CEO: Curt S Culver
**Pr:* Patrick Sinks
CEO: Chuck Wilson
**COO:* Heidi A Heyrman
**CFO:* J Michael Lauer
Chf Mktg O: Carolyn Omelina
**Ofcr:* Kurt Thomas
**Ex VP:* Lawrence J Pierzchalski
**Sr VP:* Gregory CHI
Sr VP: Sean Dilweg
**Sr VP:* Jeffrey H Lane
VP: Gail Andrich
VP: Gary Antonovich
VP: Mark Conrad
VP: Stephen M Dempsey
VP: Sandra Dunst
VP: Mary Elkins
**VP:* Susan Friedrich
VP: David A Greco
VP: Mark Krauter
VP: Todd Pittman
Board of Directors: C Edward Chaplin

D-U-N-S 14-995-4224
■ **MORTGAGE GUARANTY REINSURANCE CORP**
(*Suby of* MGIC INVESTMENT CORP) ★
250 E Kilbourn Ave 270, Milwaukee, WI 53202-3102
Tel (414) 347-6480 *Founded/Ownrshp* 1985
Sales NA *EMP* 1,093
SIC 6351 Mortgage guarantee insurance; Mortgage guarantee insurance
CEO: Curt Culver
Mktg Mgr: Kyle Bensen

D-U-N-S 78-120-0977
MORTGAGE INDUSTRY ADVISORY CORP
MIAC ANALYTICS
521 5th Ave Fl 9, New York, NY 10175-0999
Tel (212) 233-1250 *Founded/Ownrshp* 1989
Sales 21.0MMᴱ *EMP* 51
SIC 7371 8742 Custom computer programming services; Management consulting services; Custom computer programming services; Management consulting services
CEO: Robert Husted Jr
Pr: Paul Van Valkenburg
Sr VP: Bruce Benzley
Sr VP: John Easton
Sr VP: K Daniel Libby
Sr VP: Tina Reid
Sr VP: Daniel Thomas
VP: Heidi Fuchs
VP: Danielle Roper

VP: Alexander Samuel
Mng Dir: Dan Thomas

D-U-N-S 78-675-2048
MORTGAGE INFORMATION SERVICES INC
4877 Galaxy Pkwy Ste I, Cleveland, OH 44128-5952
Tel (216) 514-7480 *Founded/Ownrshp* 1990
Sales NA *EMP* 320
Accts Deloitte & Touche Llp
SIC 6361 6531 Title insurance; Appraiser, real estate; Title insurance; Appraiser, real estate
Ch Bd: Leonard R Stein-Sapir
**Treas:* Kenneth Hignett
VP: David Bortolotto
VP: Brian Schorr
VP: Randi Tormollen
VP: Dawn Wolf
CIO: Ryan Falkofsky
CTO: Scott Crawford
IT Man: Steve Freeman

D-U-N-S 78-131-2525
MORTGAGE INVESTMENT GROUP INC
8320 E Walker Springs Ln # 200, Knoxville, TN 37923-3120
Tel (865) 691-8910 *Founded/Ownrshp* 1984
Sales NA *EMP* 200
SIC 6162 Mortgage bankers; Mortgage bankers
Pr: Christine Rhea
**Pr:* Charles Tonkin
**Ex VP:* Jesse A Lehn

D-U-N-S 00-541-8306
MORTGAGE INVESTORS CORP (OH)
AMERIGROUP
6090 Central Ave, Saint Petersburg, FL 33707-1622
Tel (727) 347-1930 *Founded/Ownrshp* 1938
Sales NA *EMP* 1,200
Accts Grant Thornton Llp Tampa Fl
SIC 6162 Mortgage bankers; Mortgage bankers
Ch Bd: William L Edwards
Pr: Jeffrey Crilley
Pr: Jean Talley
CFO: David L Lattner
Dir IT: Andrew Cleaveland

D-U-N-S 86-780-5079
MORTGAGE LOAN SPECIALISTS INC
REALTY SPECIALISTS
514 Via De La Valle, Solana Beach, CA 92075-2750
Tel (858) 481-3600 *Founded/Ownrshp* 1994
Sales NA *EMP* 345
Accts Richey May & Co Englewood
SIC 6163 Mortgage brokers arranging for loans, using money of others; Mortgage brokers arranging for loans, using money of others
Pr: Myles Hubers
**VP:* Michelle Hubers

MORTGAGE MASTER
See CALM INC

D-U-N-S 05-317-8526
MORTGAGE NOW INC (OH)
9700 Rockside Rd Ste 295, Cleveland, OH 44125-6267
Tel (800) 245-1050 *Founded/Ownrshp* 1997
Sales NA *EMP* 245
SIC 6162 Mortgage bankers; Mortgage bankers
Pr: James Marchese
**VP:* Michael Perry
Dir IT: Jeff Worden

D-U-N-S 87-920-4113
MORTGAGE RESOURCE GROUP INC
8620 Ne 2nd Ave, El Portal, FL 33138-3004
Tel (305) 893-2353 *Founded/Ownrshp* 1994
Sales NA *EMP* 5
SIC 6163 Mortgage brokers arranging for loans, using money of others; Mortgage brokers arranging for loans, using money of others
Pr: Jeanette A Alonso

D-U-N-S 88-437-7995
MORTGAGE RESULTS CORP
195 Hanover St, Hanover, MA 02339-2247
Tel (781) 826-9999 *Founded/Ownrshp* 1996
Sales 76.0MM *EMP* 15
SIC 6211 Mortgages, buying & selling; Mortgages, buying & selling
Pr: Craig Good

D-U-N-S 79-703-1759
MORTGAGE SERVICES III LLC
(*Suby of* FIRST STATE BANK (INC)) ★
502 N Hershey Rd, Bloomington, IL 61704-3753
Tel (630) 705-4220 *Founded/Ownrshp* 2005
Sales 38.1MM^E *EMP* 150^E
Accts Wipfli Sterling Il
SIC 6798 Mortgage investment trusts; Mortgage investment trusts
CEO: Mark Young
**CFO:* Brian Everett
Ofcr: Frank Ybarra
Sr VP: Rebecca Crain
**Sr VP:* Adam Rieke
**Sr VP:* Rene Shaffer
**Sr VP:* Jeff Young
VP: Katie Bottrell
VP: Brian Busch
VP: Karen Frazee
**VP:* Bob Swords
VP: Sue Verplank

D-U-N-S 00-668-0487
MORTGAGE SOLUTIONS OF COLORADO LLC
FREEDOM FINANCIAL SERVICES
5455 N Union Blvd, Colorado Springs, CO 80918-2077
Tel (719) 447-0325 *Founded/Ownrshp* 2000
Sales NA *EMP* 220^E
SIC 6163 Mortgage brokers arranging for loans, using money of others; Mortgage brokers arranging for loans, using money of others
CEO: Alan Kalell
**COO:* Christina Baker
**VP:* Robert Clennan
**VP:* Greg Grandchamp
**VP:* Jesse Lopez
**VP:* Thomas Michel
Exec: Wendy Heffner
Brnch Mgr: Tandi Bolt
Dir IT: Jeremy Betterson
Info Man: Barbara Klinger
Opers Mgr: Brian Neuwirth

D-U-N-S 12-236-8942
MORTGAGE SOURCE LLC
600 Old Country Rd Rm 210, Garden City, NY 11530-2011
Tel (516) 487-3111 *Founded/Ownrshp* 2002
Sales NA *EMP* 70
SIC 6162 Mortgage bankers & correspondents; Mortgage bankers & correspondents

D-U-N-S 94-558-7579
MORTGAGE SPECIALISTS INTERNATIONAL LLC
MSI
500 Grapevine Hwy Ste 400, Hurst, TX 76054-2796
Tel (817) 428-0000 *Founded/Ownrshp* 2008
Sales NA *EMP* 65
SIC 6162 Mortgage bankers & correspondents
Pr: Stacey Baumann

MORTGAGE WORKS FINANCIAL
See MOUNTAIN WEST FINANCIAL INC

D-U-N-S 08-997-4745
MORTGAGEAMERICA INC
1800 Intl Pk Dr Ste 100, Birmingham, AL 35243
Tel (205) 970-3000 *Founded/Ownrshp* 1978
Sales NA *EMP* 150
SIC 6162 Mortgage bankers; Mortgage bankers
Pr: John B Johnson
**Ex VP:* Maurice F Wilhelm Jr
Sls&Mrk Ex: Mike Boyd
Counsel: Faiyaz Hussain

D-U-N-S 00-890-2884
MORTIMER AND SON LUMBER CO INC (MI)
ORGILL
2307 Lapeer Ave, Port Huron, MI 48060-4159
Tel (810) 987-3020 *Founded/Ownrshp* 1919
Sales 25.0MM^E *EMP* 52
SIC 5211 5251 Lumber & other building materials; Builders' hardware; Lumber & other building materials; Builders' hardware
Pr: Franklin J Mortimer II
CFO: Bill Bedard

D-U-N-S 96-709-7945
MORTON AND BARBARA MANDEL FAMILY FOUNDATION
2829 Euclid Ave, Cleveland, OH 44115-2413
Tel (216) 875-6500 *Founded/Ownrshp* 2011
Sales 27.1MM *EMP* 2
SIC 8699 Charitable organization; Charitable organization
Prin: Arthur L Dougan

D-U-N-S 06-847-8197
MORTON ARBORETUM
4100 Lincoln Ave, Lisle, IL 60532-1293
Tel (630) 968-0074 *Founded/Ownrshp* 1922
Sales 56.4MM *EMP* 170^E
Accts Plante & Moran Pllc Chicago
SIC 8412 5812 Museum; Eating places; Museum; Eating places
Pr: Gerard Donnelly
**Pr:* Gerard T Donnelly
Pr: Susan Ross
**Ch:* W Robert Reum
**Treas:* John Oleniczak
Ofcr: Kelly Vantine
VP: Nicole Cavender
VP: Susan Wagner
VP: Suzanne Wegener
Dir Soc: Jenelle Hardtke
Dir IT: SAI Ravichandran

D-U-N-S 00-516-3753
MORTON BUILDINGS INC (IL)
252 W Adams St, Morton, IL 61550-1804
Tel (309) 263-7474 *Founded/Ownrshp* 1903
Sales 380.2MM^E *EMP* 2,200
SIC 2452

D-U-N-S 05-320-1653
MORTON COLLEGE
COMMUNITY COLLEGE DST 527
(*Suby of* ILLINOIS COMMUNITY COLLEGE BD) ★
3801 S Central Ave, Cicero, IL 60804-4398
Tel (708) 656-8000 *Founded/Ownrshp* 1924
Sales 59.4MM^E *EMP* 412
SIC 8222 9411 Junior college; Administration of educational programs; Junior college; Administration of educational programs
Pr: Dana Grove
Assoc VP: Mario Moreno
**VP:* Raquel Martinez
Exec: Kabria Cummings
Exec: Eugene Suire
MIS Dir: Phillip Pena
IT Man: Esteban Cruz

D-U-N-S 05-994-7317
MORTON COMMUNITY BANK INC
721 W Jackson St, Morton, IL 61550-1537
Tel (309) 263-8126 *Founded/Ownrshp* 1961
Sales NA *EMP* 132
SIC 6022 6021 State commercial banks; National commercial banks; State commercial banks; National commercial banks
Pr: James Mamer
CFO: John Gregg
Chf Mktg O: Bruce Huber
Ofcr: Joseph Borrelli
Sr VP: Laura Bouchard
Sr VP: Steve Freeze
Sr VP: Cliff Haelbacher
**Sr VP:* Clifford Hasselbacher
VP: Laura Elam
VP: Josh Graber
VP: John Lacy
VP: Anita Oberle

MORTON COMPANIES
See MANGUM OIL AND GAS CO

MORTON COUNTY HEALTH SYSTEM
See MORTON COUNTY HOSPITAL

D-U-N-S 07-982-6020
MORTON COUNTY HOSPITAL
MORTON COUNTY HEALTH SYSTEM
445 Hilltop St, Elkhart, KS 67950
Tel (620) 697-2141 *Founded/Ownrshp* 1957
Sales 29.1MM^E *EMP* 230
SIC 8062 8052 General medical & surgical hospitals; Personal care facility; General medical & surgical hospitals; Personal care facility
**CFO:* Jeff Weaver
Dir Soc: Rosa Mitchell
DP Dir: Rachel Stiver
IT Man: Joel Garcia
Mtls Mgr: Angie Lutters
Doctor: Dominador Perido
Nrsg Dir: Kelly Whisennand
Cert Phar: Tracie Bowker
Phys Thrpy: Amanda Aranda

D-U-N-S 02-346-4035
MORTON DRUG CO
MORTON PHARMACY
706 Midway Rd, Menasha, WI 54952-1014
Tel (920) 727-3853 *Founded/Ownrshp* 1970
Sales 33.8MM^E *EMP* 175
SIC 5912 Drug stores; Drug stores
CEO: Steve Morton
**Sr VP:* David J Morton
**VP:* Jeffrey Blank
Pharmcst: Ellen Courtney
Pharmcst: Jan Helwig
Cert Phar: Jacqueline Bolwerk
Cert Phar: Bo Chang
Cert Phar: Jeneen Liebergen
Cert Phar: Rebecca Manske

D-U-N-S 05-825-1463
MORTON ELECTRIC INC
3625 W State Road 46, Sanford, FL 32771-8853
Tel (407) 830-1000 *Founded/Ownrshp* 1971
Sales 46.2MM^E *EMP* 300
SIC 1731 Electrical work; Electrical work
Pr: Duane H Pitts
**Sec:* Sharon Pitts
**VP:* John Armstrong
**VP:* Duane Jason Pitts

MORTON GENERAL HOSPITAL
See LOUIS COUNTY HOSPITAL DISTRICT NUMBER 1

D-U-N-S 04-441-8820
MORTON GRINDING INC
MORTON MANUFACTURING
201 E Avenue K 15, Lancaster, CA 93535
Tel (661) 298-0895 *Founded/Ownrshp* 1991
Sales 23.4MM^E *EMP* 110
SIC 3965 3769 3452 Fasteners; Guided missile & space vehicle parts & auxiliary equipment; Bolts, nuts, rivets & washers; Fasteners; Guided missile & space vehicle parts & auxiliary equipment; Bolts, nuts, rivets & washers
Ch Bd: Yolanda A Morton
Pr: Frank Morton
**Pr:* Wallace Morton
**Sec:* Patrick Dansby
**VP:* John Morton
IT Man: Arcee Tricerri
Sales Exec: Shawn Martin

D-U-N-S 80-189-7505 IMP
MORTON GROVE PHARMACEUTICALS INC
(*Suby of* WOCKHARDT HOLDING CORP) ★
6451 Main St, Morton Grove, IL 60053-2633
Tel (847) 967-5600 *Founded/Ownrshp* 2007
Sales 148.2MM^E *EMP* 300
SIC 2834 Pharmaceutical preparations; Pharmaceutical preparations
Pr: Sunil Khera
Sr Cor Off: Prakash Chainani
Snr Mgr: Amani Alak

D-U-N-S 06-985-4495
MORTON HOSPITAL & MEDICAL CENTER INC
(*Suby of* CARITAS CHRISTI HEALTH CARE) ★
72 Washington St, Taunton, MA 02780-2491
Tel (508) 828-7000 *Founded/Ownrshp* 1888
Sales 13.8MM^E *EMP* 850
Accts Feeley & Driscoll Pc Boston
SIC 8062 General medical & surgical hospitals; General medical & surgical hospitals
Pr: Kim Bassett
Chf OB: Maria Molina
**Ch Bd:* Joseph Quinn
**COO:* Donna L Maher
**CFO:* Carmen Acker
**Treas:* Lawrence Seck
VP: Jane Metzger
Dir Rx: Ann Viall
CIO: Michael Shea

D-U-N-S 16-134-7315
MORTON HOSPITAL AND MEDICAL CENTER INC
88 Washington St, Taunton, MA 02780-2499
Tel (508) 828-7000 *Founded/Ownrshp* 1888
Sales 857.5MM^E *EMP* 14,000^E
Accts Feeley & Driscoll Pc Boston
SIC 6733 8062 Trusts; General medical & surgical hospitals; Trusts; General medical & surgical hospitals
Pr: Kim Bassett
Chf Path: Paul Ferbend
**COO:* Donna L Maher
**CFO:* Carmen Acker
**CFO:* Richard Jeffcote
**VP:* Kelly Hoye
**VP:* Harvey Kowaloff
VP: Roger Ruth
Dir Lab: William Auerbach
Dir Rx: Joseph Andrade
Off Mgr: Deborah Costa

D-U-N-S 00-520-3828 IMP
MORTON INDUSTRIAL GROUP INC (GA)
(*Suby of* MMC PRECISION HOLDINGS CORP) ★
1021 W Birchwood St, Morton, IL 61550-9617
Tel (309) 266-7176 *Founded/Ownrshp* 1998
Sales 110.5MM^E *EMP* 1,370
SIC 3449 Miscellaneous metalwork; Miscellaneous metalwork
Pr: Frank C Lukacs
**Ch Bd:* William D Morton
**Sr VP:* Brian Doolittle
**Sr VP:* Brian Geiger
**Sr VP:* Daryl R Lindemann
IT Man: Robert Johnson
Board of Directors: Patrick K McGee

D-U-N-S 02-566-1075 IMP
MORTON INDUSTRIES LLC
(*Suby of* NELSON GLOBAL PRODUCTS INC) ★
70 Commerce Dr, Morton, IL 61550-9198
Tel (309) 263-2590 *Founded/Ownrshp* 2011
Sales 107.6MM^E *EMP* 400
SIC 3498 Fabricated pipe & fittings; Fabricated pipe & fittings
CFO: Jan Christiansan
IT Man: Rod Miller

D-U-N-S 03-646-1556 IMP/EXP
MORTON INTERNATIONAL LLC
MORTON SALT
(*Suby of* K+S AG)
100 N Independence Mall W, Philadelphia, PA 19106-1521
Tel (312) 807-2696 *Founded/Ownrshp* 2009
Sales 528.6MM^E *EMP* 2,900
SIC 2891 2851 2822 1479 2899 Adhesives; Lacquers, varnishes, enamels & other coatings; Polysulfides (thiokol); Salt & sulfur mining; Salt; Adhesives; Lacquers, varnishes, enamels & other coatings; Polysulfides (thiokol); Salt & sulfur mining; Salt
Pr: Mark L Roberts
COO: James Swanson
**CFO:* Andrew J Kotlarz
Treas: Charlie Thacker
Dir IT: Kurt Berghofer
Dir IT: Chris Carbaugh
Dir IT: Ben Caruso
Dir IT: Brian Cook
Dir IT: Grooms David
Dir IT: Keven Longfellow
Dir IT: Tom Lusha

MORTON MANUFACTURING
See MORTON GRINDING INC

MORTON PHARMACY
See MORTON DRUG CO

D-U-N-S 11-550-0191
MORTON PLANT HOSPITAL ASSOCIATION INC
(*Suby of* MORTON PLANT MEASE HEALTH CARE INC) ★
300 Pinellas St, Clearwater, FL 33756-3892
Tel (727) 462-7000 *Founded/Ownrshp* 1914
Sales 598.3MM *EMP* 3,000
Accts Ernst & Young Us Llp Atlanta
SIC 8062 8051 General medical & surgical hospitals; Skilled nursing care facilities; General medical & surgical hospitals; Skilled nursing care facilities
Pr: Phil Beauchant
CFO: David O"neil
**VP:* Hal Ziecheck
Dir Lab: Pam Pound
Dir Rad: Craig A Bnull
Dir Rad: Barbara J Bourland
Nurse Mgr: Lashelle Leftheris
CIO: Neal Brown
Pathlgst: Michael Linden
Pathlgst: Ryan Olson
Pathlgst: Jason Savell

D-U-N-S 60-247-7192
MORTON PLANT MEASE HEALTH CARE INC
(*Suby of* BAYCARE EDUCATION SERVICES) ★
300 Pinellas St, Clearwater, FL 33756-3804
Tel (727) 462-7777 *Founded/Ownrshp* 1983
Sales 83.3MM *EMP* 3,950
SIC 8741 8721 Hospital management; Billing & bookkeeping service; Hospital management; Billing & bookkeeping service
Pr: Philip K Beauchamp
Doctor: William C Brown MD

D-U-N-S 06-088-2425
MORTON PLANT NORTH BAY HOSPITAL
6600 Madison St, New Port Richey, FL 34652-1971
Tel (727) 842-8468 *Founded/Ownrshp* 1999
Sales 107.0MM *EMP* 400
SIC 8062 General medical & surgical hospitals; General medical & surgical hospitals
CEO: Glen Waters
CFO: Carl Tremonti
Dir OR: Jennifer Downing
Dir Lab: Dale Scutro
Dir Rad: Lauren Witmer
Dir Sec: Mohammad Ali
IT Man: Nick Rayas
Pathlgst: Neila Alvarez
Nrsg Dir: Robin Lapham

MORTON SALT
See MORTON INTERNATIONAL LLC

D-U-N-S 96-477-8299 IMP/EXP
MORTON SALT INC
CHICAGO SALT SERVICE
(*Suby of* K+S SALT LLC) ★
123 N Wacker Dr Fl 24, Chicago, IL 60606-1760
Tel (800) 725-8847 *Founded/Ownrshp* 2010
Sales 835.6MM^E *EMP* 2,900
SIC 2891 2851 2822 1479 2899 Adhesives & sealants; Paints & allied products; Synthetic rubber; Salt & sulfur mining; Chemical preparations; Adhesives & sealants; Paints & allied products; Synthetic rubber; Salt & sulfur mining; Chemical preparations
CEO: Christian Herrmann

CFO: Andrew J Kotlarz
CFO: Tim McKean
CFO: Andy Totlerz
Bd of Dir: Walt Bryant
VP: Robert Alberico
VP: Guy Leblanc
VP: Elizabeth Nohe
VP: Dan Thompson
VP: Chad E Walker
VP: Shayn Wallace
VP: Lisa Zumbach

D-U-N-S 14-437-2810 IMP
MORTON TRUCKING INC
121 Garnet Ln, Jacksonville, NC 28546-8801
Tel (910) 346-9068 *Founded/Ownrshp* 1987
Sales 29.3MM *EMP* 85
Accts Williams Scarborough Smith Gra
SIC 1794 1521 1623 Excavation work; Single-family housing construction; Water, sewer & utility lines; Excavation work; Single-family housing construction; Water, sewer & utility lines
Pr: Elijah Morton
**VP:* Violet Morton
IT Man: Tim Morton
IT Man: Mary Vaughan

D-U-N-S 09-257-8111
MORTON UNIT SCHOOL DISTRICT 709
1050 S 4th Ave Ste 200, Morton, IL 61550-2502
Tel (309) 266-9093 *Founded/Ownrshp* 1970
Sales 17.5MM^E *EMP* 296
SIC 8211 Public elementary school; Public junior high school; Public senior high school; Public elementary school; Public junior high school; Public senior high school
Pr Dir: Carol Jankowski
Schl Brd P: Michelle Vernier

MORTONS OF CHICAGO
See MORTONS OF CHICAGO/BOCA RATON INC

D-U-N-S 04-687-4277
MORTONS OF CHICAGO/BOCA RATON INC
MORTONS OF CHICAGO
(*Suby of* LANDRYS INC) ★
350 W Hubbard St, Chicago, IL 60654-5798
Tel (713) 850-1010 *Founded/Ownrshp* 1989
Sales 81.5MM^E *EMP* 3,950
SIC 5812 Steak restaurant; Steak restaurant
V Ch Bd: Klaus Fritsch
**Pr:* Edi Ames
**Pr:* John T Bettin
Pr: Peggy Reilly
**CFO:* Ronald M Dinella
Sr VP: Scott Levin
VP: Kate Shehan
**VP:* E Nichols Wagner
Rgnl Mgr: Ralph Cook
Genl Mgr: Christopher Goss
Genl Mgr: Cory Mason

D-U-N-S 19-982-4822
MORTONS STEAKHOUSE
325 N Lasalle St Ste 500, Chicago, IL 60654
Tel (312) 923-0030 *Founded/Ownrshp* 2012
Sales NA *EMP* 4,154^E
SIC 5812

D-U-N-S 05-041-0455 IMP
MORTY-PRIDE MEATS INC
3603 Clinton Rd, Fayetteville, NC 28312-9271
Tel (910) 483-6004 *Founded/Ownrshp* 1969
Sales 22.3MM^E *EMP* 35
Accts Florence Black & Associates F
SIC 5147 Meats, fresh
Pr: Mickey Hudson
**VP:* Chris Hudson
Plnt Mgr: Lance Lewis

D-U-N-S 86-903-3191
MORVEN PARTNERS LP
ORIGINAL NUT HOUSE, THE
11 Leigh Fisher Blvd, El Paso, TX 79906-5240
Tel (915) 772-5871 *Founded/Ownrshp* 1995
Sales 38.1MM^E *EMP* 338
SIC 6799 Commodity investors; Commodity investors
Pt: Joseph P Patten

D-U-N-S 16-911-0165 IMP/EXP
■ **MOS HOLDINGS INC**
MOSAIC COMPANY
(*Suby of* MOSAIC CO) ★
3033 Campus Dr Ste E490, Plymouth, MN 55441-2655
Tel (763) 577-2700 *Founded/Ownrshp* 2004
Sales 1.2MMM^E *EMP* 7,700
SIC 2874 1475 2819 1094 1481 Phosphatic fertilizers; Phosphate rock; Sulfuric acid, oleum; Uranium ore mining; Nonmetallic mineral services; Phosphatic fertilizers; Phosphate rock; Sulfuric acid, oleum; Uranium ore mining; Nonmetallic mineral services
Pr: James T Prokopanko
CFO: Lawrence W Stranghoener
Ex VP: Richard L Mack
Sr VP: Stephen P Malia
Sr VP: Corrine D Ricard
VP: Norman Beug
VP: Anthony T Brausen
VP: Jeff Clyne
VP: Laura C Gagnon
VP: Mark E Kaplan
VP: Mark Kaplan
Board of Directors: David T Seaton, Phyllis E Cochran, Steven M Seibert, William R Graber, Emery N Koenig, Robert L Lumpkins, Harold H Mackay, David B Mathis, William T Monahan, James L Popowich, Sergio Rial

MOSAIC
See FONTANA LITHOGRAPH INC

D-U-N-S 07-804-1035
MOSAIC (NE)
4980 S 118th St, Omaha, NE 68137-2200
Tel (402) 896-3884 *Founded/Ownrshp* 1912, 2002
Sales 221.0MM *EMP* 5,000
SIC 8361 8741 Administrative management; Home for the mentally handicapped; Home for the mentally handicapped; Administrative management
CEO: Linda Timmons
**COO:* Raul Saldivar
**CFO:* Cindy Schroeder
**Treas:* Cynthia L Schroeder
**Sr VP:* Keith Schmode
**Sr VP:* Donna Werner
VP: Paula Burton
VP: David Defreese
VP: Yvette Gillett
VP: Kristin Rossow
VP: Keith H Schmode
VP: Brenda Solomon
VP: Amy Stevens
Assoc Dir: Michelle McFadden
Assoc Dir: Paul Weber
Comm Dir: Tracie Klassen

MOSAIC ANSTHSIA PRPRATIVE SVCS
See AMERICAN ANESTHESIOLOGY INC

MOSAIC COMPANY
See MOS HOLDINGS INC

D-U-N-S 96-955-3820 IMP/EXP
▲ **MOSAIC CO**
3033 Campus Dr Ste E490, Plymouth, MN 55441-2655
Tel (763) 577-2700 *Founded/Ownrshp* 2004
Sales 9.0MMM *EMP* 9,100^E
Accts Kpmg Llp Minneapolis Minneso
Tkr Sym MOS *Exch* NYS
SIC 2874 1475 Phosphatic fertilizers; Phosphate rock; Phosphatic fertilizers; Phosphate rock
Pr: James T Prokopanko
Pr: Courtney Mattson
**COO:* James C O'Rourke
CFO: Richard L Mack
Sr VP: Anthony T Brausen
Sr VP: Gary Davis
Sr VP: Mark E Kaplan
Sr VP: Walter F Precourt III
VP: Floris Bielders
VP: Mark J Isaacson
VP: Todd Madden
VP: Dennis Orke
VP: Katie Stokes
VP: Ben Vasquez
VP Bus Dev: Bob Everett
Board of Directors: David T Seaton, Nancy E Cooper, Steven M Seibert, Gregory L Ebel, Timothy S Gitzel, William R Graber, Denise C Johnson, Emery N Koenig, Robert L Lumpkins, William T Monahan, James L Popowich

D-U-N-S 78-933-4422
MOSAIC COMMUNITY SERVICES INC
DULANEY STATION
1925 Greenspring Dr, Lutherville Timonium, MD 21093-4128
Tel (410) 453-9553 *Founded/Ownrshp* 1984
Sales 33.5MM *EMP* 500
Accts Sc&H Tax & Advisory Services L
SIC 8322 8093 Individual & family services; Mental health clinic, outpatient; Individual & family services; Mental health clinic, outpatient
Ex Dir: Jeff Richardson
**CFO:* Janet Deal
**Treas:* Rob Williams
Ofcr: Spencer Gear
**VP:* Ellen Callegary
VP: Debbie Scoblick
Pgrm Dir: Caitlin Carlson
Snr Mgr: Andrea Dyson

D-U-N-S 00-892-2187
■ **MOSAIC CROP NUTRITION LLC**
(*Suby of* MOS HOLDINGS INC) ★
3033 Campus Dr, Minneapolis, MN 55441-2651
Tel (763) 577-2700 *Founded/Ownrshp* 2004
Sales 73.7MM^E *EMP* 240^E
SIC 2874 1474 Phosphatic fertilizers; Potash, soda & borate minerals; Phosphatic fertilizers; Potash, soda & borate minerals
CFO: Lawrence W Stranghoener

D-U-N-S 06-469-6107 EXP
■ **MOSAIC FERTILIZER LLC**
(*Suby of* MOSAIC CO) ★
13830 Circa Crossing Dr, Lithia, FL 33547-3953
Tel (813) 500-6300 *Founded/Ownrshp* 2004
Sales 646.3MM^E *EMP* 1,300
SIC 2874 Phosphatic fertilizers; Phosphatic fertilizers
CEO: James T Prokopanko
**Ex VP:* Richard L Mack
**Sr VP:* Gary Davis
**VP:* Mark E Kaplan
**Prin:* Jason Vanvleet

D-U-N-S 17-765-7095
■ **MOSAIC GLOBAL HOLDINGS INC**
(*Suby of* MOS HOLDINGS INC) ★
3033 Campus Dr Ste E490, Minneapolis, MN 55441-2655
Tel (763) 577-2700 *Founded/Ownrshp* 2004
Sales 515.8MM^E *EMP* 5,017
SIC 2874 1474 1475 2875 2819 Phosphatic fertilizers; Potash mining; Phosphate rock; Fertilizers, mixing only; Chemicals, high purity: refined from technical grade; Phosphatic fertilizers; Potash mining; Phosphate rock; Fertilizers, mixing only; Chemicals, high purity: refined from technical grade
CFO: Lawrence Stranghoener
CFO: Lawrence W Stranghoener

D-U-N-S 60-760-5227 IMP/EXP
■ **MOSAIC GLOBAL OPERATIONS INC**
FITZGERALD RAILCAR SERVICES
(*Suby of* MOSAIC GLOBAL HOLDINGS INC) ★
1 Overlook Pt Ste 110, Lincolnshire, IL 60069-4303
Tel (847) 478-0850 *Founded/Ownrshp* 1987
Sales 228.8MM^E *EMP* 5,017
SIC 2874 2875 2873 Phosphatic fertilizers; Fertilizers, mixing only; Nitrogenous fertilizers; Phosphatic fertilizers; Fertilizers, mixing only; Nitrogenous fertilizers
Ch Bd: Douglas A Pertz
Treas: E Paul Dunn Jr
VP: Robert F Clark
VP: C Steven Hoffman
VP: John U Huber
VP: Mary A Hynes
VP: Stephen P Malia
VP: Kermit E McCormack
VP: Anne M Scavone
Board of Directors: Douglas A Pertz

D-U-N-S 07-956-5069
■ **MOSAIC GLOBAL SALES LLC**
(*Suby of* MOSAIC CROP NUTRITION LLC) ★
3033 Campus Dr Ste E490, Plymouth, MN 55441-2655
Tel (763) 577-2700 *Founded/Ownrshp* 2014
Sales 29.6MM^E *EMP* 115
SIC 2874 Phosphatic fertilizers; Phosphatic fertilizers
Sr VP: Rick McLellan

D-U-N-S 80-791-7526
MOSAIC RESIDENTIAL INC
LAUREL RIDGE APARTMENTS
15021 Katy Fwy Ste 580, Houston, TX 77094-1900
Tel (281) 647-6400 *Founded/Ownrshp* 2007
Sales 74.2MM^E *EMP* 240^E
SIC 6726 8741 Investment offices; Management services
Pr: Robert M Weber

D-U-N-S 13-676-0811
MOSAIC SALES SOLUTIONS US OPERATING CO LLC
(*Suby of* ACOSTA INC) ★
220 Las Colinas Blvd E, Irving, TX 75039-5500
Tel (972) 870-4800 *Founded/Ownrshp* 2012
Sales 580.6MM^E *EMP* 8,000
SIC 8742 8743 7374 Merchandising consultant; Sales promotion; Computer graphics service; Merchandising consultant; Sales promotion; Computer graphics service
Pr: Aidan Tracey
**Pr:* Brian Kava
**CFO:* Kelly Parsons
CFO: Bob Vesely
**Sr VP:* Dick Doyle
Sr VP: Tim Hauser
**Sr VP:* Ed Slavin
Sr VP: Jeff Stelmach
VP: Chad Grenier
Exec: Tracie Carter
Prgrm Mgr: Elyse Erickson

D-U-N-S 83-881-9092 IMP
MOSAIC TECHNOLOGY CORP
23 Northwestern Dr, Salem, NH 03079-4809
Tel (603) 898-5966 *Founded/Ownrshp* 1994
Sales 35.4MM^E *EMP* 38
SIC 5045 7373 7379 Computers, peripherals & software; Value-added resellers, computer systems; Computer related consulting services
Pr: Thomas J Desmet
COO: Dean Kacos
Ex VP: Agnes Desmet
VP: Herb Hamblen
VP: Bill Moulin
Netwrk Mgr: Matt Shamitoff

MOSAIC TELECOM
See CHIBARDUN TELEPHONE COOPERATIVE INC

D-U-N-S 07-779-7629 IMP
MOSAIC TILE CO OF VIRGINIA INC
3935 Stonecroft Blvd, Chantilly, VA 20151-1032
Tel (703) 631-4848 *Founded/Ownrshp* 1972
Sales 56.9MM^E *EMP* 60
SIC 5032 Tile & clay products
Pr: Robert J Hughes
**Sec:* Bernice Hughes
**VP:* Christopher M Hughes
**VP:* James Igoe
**VP:* Sean Schaefer

D-U-N-S 96-500-1048
MOSAIC US HOLDINGS INC
220 E Las Coli Blvd St Ste 300, Irving, TX 75038
Tel (877) 870-4800 *Founded/Ownrshp* 2004
Sales 56.0MM^E *EMP* 293^E
SIC 6799 Tax liens: holding, buying & selling
Prin: Jeff Rogers
Pr: Dave Martella
VP: Greg Oakes
VP: Steve Paxton
Exec: Mollie Coleman
Exec: Nina Madrack
Creative D: Seth Gable
Ex Dir: Sally Montgomery
Rgnl Mgr: Elisabeth Hillyer
Dist Mgr: Nicole Gillespie
Dist Mgr: Kathy Hewitt

D-U-N-S 07-919-5435
■ **MOSAIC USA LLC**
(*Suby of* MOS HOLDINGS INC) ★
3033 Campus Dr Ste E170, Plymouth, MN 55441-2715
Tel (800) 918-8270 *Founded/Ownrshp* 2004
Sales 27.3MM^E *EMP* 421^E
SIC 1743 Mosaic work

D-U-N-S 01-032-7679
MOSAICA GROUP LLC
N53w24615 S Corporate Cir, Sussex, WI 53089-4360
Tel (262) 820-9025 *Founded/Ownrshp* 1999
Sales 35.0MM^E *EMP* 32
Accts Kosler & Company Sc Waukes
SIC 5111 Printing & writing paper
Genl Mgr: Melanie Bond
CIO: Thomas Kelly
Dir IT: Matt Fehn
Opers Mgr: Karen Seidl

MOSAK ADVERTISING & INSIGHTS
See MOSAK INC

D-U-N-S 15-812-6537
MOSAK INC
MOSAK ADVERTISING & INSIGHTS
3809 Juniper Trce Ste 100, Austin, TX 78738-5534
Tel (512) 374-2800 *Founded/Ownrshp* 1999
Sales 29.1MM *EMP* 50
SIC 7311 Advertising agencies; Advertising agencies
Pr: Monique Threadgill
**VP:* Kelly E Clancy
VP: Craig Foster
**VP:* David C Martin
Exec: Teri Morales
Creative D: Lauren Clancy
Creative D: Greg Needham
Creative D: Ralph Yznaga
CIO: Sean Ryan
CTO: Safa Movassaghi
IT Man: Amy Raymond

D-U-N-S 60-866-1083
MOSBY HOLDINGS CORP
(*Suby of* REED ELSEVIER INC) ★
125 Park Ave, New York, NY 10017-5529
Tel (212) 309-8100 *Founded/Ownrshp* 1998
Sales 120.8MM^E *EMP* 2,000^E
SIC 2741 8999 Technical manuals: publishing only, not printed on site; Writing for publication
Pr: Ron Mobed

D-U-N-S 00-629-4391 IMP
MOSBY INC
ELSEVIER SCIENCE
(*Suby of* REED ELSEVIER INC) ★
360 Park Ave S, New York, NY 10010-1710
Tel (314) 447-8000 *Founded/Ownrshp* 1900, 2010
Sales 137.9MM^E *EMP* 263^E
SIC 2731 2721 Books: publishing only; Trade journals: publishing only, not printed on site
CEO: Erik Engstrom
**Pr:* Virgil L Mette
**CEO:* Ron Mobed
**Ex VP:* A Jerome Freeland
**VP:* Tom Reller
**Prin:* Michael Riley

D-U-N-S 00-383-1617
MOSCOW BUILDING SUPPLY INC (ID)
MOSCOW PULLMAN BUILDING SUPPLY
760 N Main St, Moscow, ID 83843-8512
Tel (208) 882-4716 *Founded/Ownrshp* 1957, 1993
Sales 58.2MM^E *EMP* 110
SIC 5031 5211 Doors; Fencing, wood; Lumber: rough, dressed & finished; Molding, all materials; Doors, storm: wood or metal; Fencing; Millwork & lumber; Doors; Fencing, wood; Lumber: rough, dressed & finished; Molding, all materials; Doors, storm: wood or metal; Fencing; Millwork & lumber
Pr: Pat Garrett

D-U-N-S 80-813-3925
MOSCOW CAMDEN AND SAN AUGUSTINE RAILROAD LLC
(*Suby of* GEORGIA-PACIFIC WOOD PRODUCTS SOUTH LLC) ★
133 Peachtree St Ne, Atlanta, GA 30303-1804
Tel (404) 652-4000 *Founded/Ownrshp* 2007
Sales 61.2MM^E *EMP* 1,543^E
SIC 2656 Paper cups, plates, dishes & utensils

MOSCOW PULLMAN BUILDING SUPPLY
See MOSCOW BUILDING SUPPLY INC

D-U-N-S 02-978-5391
MOSCOW SCHOOL DISTRICT 281
650 N Cleveland St, Moscow, ID 83843-3600
Tel (208) 882-1120 *Founded/Ownrshp* 1948
Sales 19.8MM *EMP* 334
Accts Hayden & Ross Pa Moscow I
SIC 8211 Public elementary & secondary schools; Public elementary & secondary schools
Psych: Robert Allenger

D-U-N-S 05-890-7353
MOSELEY ARCHITECTS PC
3200 Norfolk St, Richmond, VA 23230-4428
Tel (804) 794-7555 *Founded/Ownrshp* 1986
Sales 28.3MM^E *EMP* 182
SIC 8712 Architectural services; Architectural services
Pr: Robert L Mills
**VP:* James N Copeland
**VP:* John W Hasten
VP: John Hasten
VP: Michael Hurd
VP: Jeff Hyder
VP: Jason Kunkel
VP: Harold Lanna
VP: Dan Mace
**VP:* John J Moore III
VP: George Nasis
VP: EKA Rahardjo
VP: Matthew Shirk

D-U-N-S 00-833-7545 IMP
MOSELEY ASSOCIATES INC
82 Coromar Dr, Santa Barbara, CA 93117-3024
Tel (805) 968-9621 *Founded/Ownrshp* 1977
Sales 107.3MM^E *EMP* 350^E
SIC 3663 Radio & TV communications equipment; Radio & TV communications equipment
Pr: Jamal N Hamdani
**CFO:* Bruce Tarr
Tech Mgr: Matthew Coon

D-U-N-S 86-871-9592
MOSELEY TECHNICAL SERVICES INC
MTSI
7500 Memorial Pkwy Sw 215r, Huntsville, AL 35802-2227
Tel (256) 880-0446 *Founded/Ownrshp* 1994
Sales 40.7MM *EMP* 125
SIC 8711 Engineering services; Engineering services
Pr: Jerry L Moseley

D-U-N-S 04-850-9157
MOSER CONSULTING INC
6220 Castleway West Dr, Indianapolis, IN 46250-1910
Tel (317) 596-8022 *Founded/Ownrshp* 1996
Sales 27.0MM *EMP* 185
SIC 7379 Computer related consulting services
Pr: Tyron Moser
**Ch:* Paula Moser

MOSER ENERGY SYSTEMS
See MOSER ENGINE SERVICE INC

D-U-N-S 07-646-2472
MOSER ENGINE SERVICE INC
MOSER ENERGY SYSTEMS
5180 W Yellowstone Hwy, Casper, WY 82604-2231
Tel (307) 234-7833 *Founded/Ownrshp* 1973
Sales 28.8MM *EMP* 50
Accts Leo Riley & Co Casper Wyomi
SIC 7353 7699 5084 Oil field equipment, rental or leasing; Industrial machinery & equipment repair; Industrial machinery & equipment; Oil field equipment, rental or leasing; Industrial machinery & equipment repair; Industrial machinery & equipment
Pr: Randall J Moser
CFO: John Bean
**Sec:* Katherine Moser

MOSERS
See MISSOURI STATE EMPLOYEES RETIREMENT SYSTEM

MOSES AUTO MALL
See MOSES INC

D-U-N-S 07-571-6399
MOSES BROWN SCHOOL INC
250 Lloyd Ave, Providence, RI 02906-2398
Tel (401) 831-7350 *Founded/Ownrshp* 1784
Sales 24.7MM^E *EMP* 200
SIC 8211 Private combined elementary & secondary school; Private combined elementary & secondary school
Prin: Matthew Glendinning

MOSES BUICK
See MOSES CADILLAC BUICK GMCTRUCK INC

D-U-N-S 03-723-7500
MOSES CADILLAC BUICK GMCTRUCK INC
MOSES BUICK
1406 Washington St E, Charleston, WV 25301-1937
Tel (304) 343-5534 *Founded/Ownrshp* 1964
Sales 28.7MM^E *EMP* 77
SIC 5511 Automobiles, new & used; Automobiles, new & used
Pr: Robert L Moses
**Treas:* Jackson F Moses II
**VP:* J Steven Moses

D-U-N-S 96-628-7521
MOSES CONE AFFILIATED PHYSICIANS INC
1200 N Elm St, Greensboro, NC 27401-1004
Tel (336) 832-7000 *Founded/Ownrshp* 2011
Sales 51.6MM *EMP* 4
Accts Pricewaterhousecoopers Llp Gr
SIC 8011 Physical medicine, physician/surgeon; Physical medicine, physician/surgeon
Prin: Robert B Carter

D-U-N-S 79-110-2713
MOSES CONE MEDICAL SERVICES INC
1200 N Elm St Ste 1049, Greensboro, NC 27401-1004
Tel (336) 832-8145 *Founded/Ownrshp* 2007
Sales 56.8MM *EMP* 3
Accts Pricewaterhousecoopers Llp Gr
SIC 8011 Offices & clinics of medical doctors; Offices & clinics of medical doctors
Pr: Tim Rice

D-U-N-S 80-617-8468
MOSES CONE-WESLEY LONG COMMUNITY HEALTH FOUNDATION INC
CONE HEALTH FOUNDATION
1200 N Elm St, Greensboro, NC 27401-1004
Tel (336) 832-9555 *Founded/Ownrshp* 1997
Sales 4.2MM *EMP* 2,105^E
Accts Pricewaterhousecoopers Llp Gr
SIC 8699 Charitable organization; Charitable organization
Pr: Susan Fitzgibbon Shumaker
COO: Terrence Akin
Ex VP: Maryjo Cangle
Ex VP: Bob Goldstein
Ex VP: Jim Roskelly
**VP:* Sandra Welch Boren
VP: John Jenkins
VP: Grace Moffitt
VP: William Porter
**VP:* Antonia Reaves
VP: Brian Romig
VP: Melissa Shearer
VP: Annette Smith
Assoc Dir: Alan Champ

D-U-N-S 03-335-3715
MOSES ELECTRIC INC
1207 Pin Oak Dr, Flowood, MS 39232-9715
Tel (601) 939-9473 *Founded/Ownrshp* 1991
Sales 30.5MM^E *EMP* 153
SIC 1731 General electrical contractor; General electrical contractor
Pr: William Hux
**VP:* Russel Brock
**VP:* Pete Morrison
**VP:* Robert Powers
**VP:* Larry Wilemon
**VP:* Henry Williams
Sfty Dirs: Gibby Myers

D-U-N-S 05-703-6071
MOSES H CONE MEMORIAL HOSPITAL
ANNIE PENN HOSPITAL
1200 N Elm St, Greensboro, NC 27401-1020
Tel (336) 832-7000 *Founded/Ownrshp* 1911
Sales 906.3MM *EMP* 7,000
SIC 8062 General medical & surgical hospitals; Offices & clinics of medical doctors; General medical & surgical hospitals
CEO: Terry Akin
Chf Rad: James Maxwell
V Ch: Craven E Williams
Pr: Frank Aluisio
**COO:* Judy Schanel
**CFO:* Jeff Jones
Trst: Dwight M Davidson
Trst: Lily Kelly-Radford
Trst: William V Nutt
Trst: Henry W Smith
Trst: William R Soles
Ex VP: Mary Cagle
Ex VP: Mike Simms
VP: Andy Barrow
VP: Skip Hislop
VP: Rich Lundy
VP: Anette Smith
VP: Cheryl Somers
Dir Inf Cn: Beth Cable
Dir Risk M: Cheryl Koob
Dir Risk M: Sue Yow

D-U-N-S 83-209-7336
MOSES H CONE MEMORIAL HOSPITAL OPERATING CORP
1200 N Elm St, Greensboro, NC 27401-1020
Tel (336) 832-7000 *Founded/Ownrshp* 1985
Sales 893.9MM *EMP* 37^E
Accts Pricewaterhousecoopers Llp Gr
SIC 8062 General medical & surgical hospitals
Ex Dir: R Timothy Rice
COO: Tim Rice
Ofcr: Mary J Cagle

D-U-N-S 01-607-8172
MOSES INC
MOSES AUTO MALL
5200 Us Route 60, Huntington, WV 25705-2023
Tel (304) 736-5291 *Founded/Ownrshp* 1949
Sales 24.4MM^E *EMP* 53
SIC 5511 New & used car dealers; New & used car dealers
Pr: Jackson F Moses II
**VP:* Joel Goldy
Sls Mgr: Lance Daniels

D-U-N-S 79-025-8859
MOSES LAKE COMMUNITY HEALTH CENTER
QUINCY COMMUNITY HEALTH CENTER
605 S Coolidge St, Moses Lake, WA 98837-1893
Tel (509) 765-0674 *Founded/Ownrshp* 1991
Sales 21.9MM *EMP* 210
Accts Clark Nuber Ps Bellevue Wa
SIC 8011 8021 Offices & clinics of medical doctors; Dental clinics & offices; Offices & clinics of medical doctors; Dental clinics & offices
Ex Dir: John Browne
**CEO:* Sheila Chilson
Dir Lab: Josie Bean
CIO: John Gamble
QC Dir: Kathy Smith
Doctor: Steven Rubinstein

MOSES LAKE HIGH SCHOOL
See MOSES LAKE SCHOOL DIST 161

D-U-N-S 10-008-0795
MOSES LAKE SCHOOL DIST 161
MOSES LAKE HIGH SCHOOL
920 W Ivy Ave, Moses Lake, WA 98837-2047
Tel (509) 766-2650 *Founded/Ownrshp* 1935
Sales 57.8MM^E *EMP* 1,000
SIC 8211 Elementary & secondary schools; High school, junior or senior; Elementary & secondary schools; High school, junior or senior
Pr: Kevin Donovan
MIS Dir: Marlin Howell
Teacher Pr: Patty Laughery

MOSES LAKES FARMS
See WILLAMETTE EGG FARMS LLC

MOSES TAYLOR HOSPITAL
See QUINCY SCRANTON HOSPITAL LLC

D-U-N-S 00-606-1576
MOSEY MANUFACTURING CO INC
262 Fort Wayne Ave, Richmond, IN 47374-2392
Tel (765) 983-8800 *Founded/Ownrshp* 1946
Sales 91.0MM^E *EMP* 450
SIC 3541 Machine tools, metal cutting type; Machine tools, metal cutting type
Pr: George N Mosey
**Ex VP:* Stephen A Mosey
**VP:* Dan Kindley
**VP:* Kenneth L Mackey
Plnt Mgr: Scott Griffin

D-U-N-S 18-066-2256
MOSHER ENTERPRISES INC
4441 Anaheim Ave Ne, Albuquerque, NM 87113-1664
Tel (505) 828-1008 *Founded/Ownrshp* 1984
Sales 24.7MM^E *EMP* 120
SIC 1731 General electrical contractor; General electrical contractor
Pr: Jerry Mosher
**Treas:* Lynn Mosher
**VP:* Mike Barnes
**VP:* Paceson Neel

MOSHI
See AEVOE CORP

D-U-N-S 10-223-5975
MOSIER AUTOMATION INC
9851 Park Davis Dr, Indianapolis, IN 46235-2393
Tel (317) 895-6200 *Founded/Ownrshp* 1993
Sales 31.5MM^E *EMP* 46
Accts Dunbar Cook & Shepard Pc
SIC 5065 8299 5084 Electronic parts & equipment; Arts & crafts schools; Pneumatic tools & equipment; Hydraulic systems equipment & supplies
Pr: James R McMillan
**Treas:* Christie Hasseld
VP: Larry Cooper
VP: Jeff Hardwick
Mfg Mgr: Rick Colee
S&M/VP: Rob McMillan
Sales Asso: Steve Cooper

D-U-N-S 00-613-0926 EXP
■ **MOSINEE PAPER CORP**
(*Suby of* WAUSAU PAPER CORP) ★
100 Paper Pl, Kronenwetter, WI 54455-9099
Tel (715) 693-4470 *Founded/Ownrshp* 1910
Sales 40.0MM^E *EMP* 530
SIC 2621 2631 3444 Paper mills; Specialty or chemically treated papers; Towels, tissues & napkins: paper & stock; Linerboard; Metal housings, enclosures, casings & other containers; Paper mills; Specialty or chemically treated papers; Towels, tissues & napkins: paper & stock; Linerboard; Metal housings, enclosures, casings & other containers
Pr: Thomas J Howatt
**Sr VP:* Scott P Doescher

D-U-N-S 00-479-8443
■ **MOSINEE TELEPHONE CO LLC**
TDS
(*Suby of* TDS TELECOMMUNICATIONS CORP) ★
410 4th St, Mosinee, WI 54455-1199
Tel (715) 693-2622 *Founded/Ownrshp* 1947
Sales 853.0MM *EMP* 2,700
Accts Kiesling Associates Llp
SIC 4813 Local telephone communications; Local telephone communications
Pr: David Wittwer
**Ofcr:* Noel Hutton
VP: Jack Koss
**VP:* William J Megan

D-U-N-S 00-682-2324
MOSITES CONSTRUCTION CO (PA)
4839 Campbells Run Rd, Pittsburgh, PA 15205-1386
Tel (412) 923-2255 *Founded/Ownrshp* 1959
Sales 138.6MM^E *EMP* 250
SIC 1542 1611 Commercial & office building contractors; Highway & street construction; Commercial & office building contractors; Highway & street construction
CEO: Donald A Mosites
**Pr:* Steven T Mosites
**CFO:* Joe Pazicni
VP: Mark Edgar
**VP:* M Dean Mosites
VP: David N Rubis
Genl Mgr: Dale Short
VP Opers: Joe Wattick
Sfty Mgr: Jason Malatok

D-U-N-S 00-273-3439
MOSLEY HOLDINGS INC (AR)
101a S Oak St, Sheridan, AR 72150-2436
Tel (870) 942-2662 *Founded/Ownrshp* 2000, 2001
Sales NA *EMP* 95
SIC 6712 2893 Bank holding companies; Printing ink; Bank holding companies; Printing ink
Pr: Jerry Mosley
**Sec:* Margaret Mosley
**VP:* Micheal Mosley

D-U-N-S 14-123-6237 IMP/EXP
MOSS & ASSOCIATES LLC
2101 N Andrews Ave # 300, Wilton Manors, FL 33311-3940
Tel (954) 524-5678 *Founded/Ownrshp* 2004
Sales 313.7MM^E *EMP* 350^E
SIC 1542 Nonresidential construction; Commercial & office building, new construction; Commercial & office buildings, renovation & repair; Hospital construction; Nonresidential construction; Commercial & office building, new construction; Commercial & office buildings, renovation & repair; Hospital construction
Pr: Bob L Moss
**Pr:* Scott Moss
**Ex VP:* Ted Adams
**Ex VP:* Joe Harris
**Ex VP:* Mike Little
**Ex VP:* Bruce Moldow
Ex VP: W Trethewey
**Sr VP:* Chad Moss
Sr VP: Anderson Russell
VP: Steven McNeely
Dir IT: William Snow

D-U-N-S 07-573-4889
MOSS ADAMS LLP
999 3rd Ave Ste 3300, Seattle, WA 98104-4002
Tel (206) 302-6500 *Founded/Ownrshp* 1913
Sales 251.4MM^E *EMP* 1,215
SIC 8721 Certified public accountant; Certified public accountant
CEO: Chris Schmidt
Pt: Rick Anderson
Pt: Carol Suruki
Mng Pt: Wayne Brown
Mng Pt: Paul Farkas
Mng Pt: Randy Fenich
Mng Pt: Dick Fohn
Mng Pt: Kerry Gordon
Mng Pt: Jeff Green
Mng Pt: Rob Greenspan
Mng Pt: Bob Hinton
Mng Pt: Joe Karas
Mng Pt: Steve Keene
Mng Pt: Ed Kitrosser
Mng Pt: Tom Krippaehne
Mng Pt: Mike Lynch
Mng Pt: Tony Maki
Mng Pt: Curtis Matthews
Mng Pt: Ty Pforsich
Mng Pt: Bob Ryker
Mng Pt: David W Schilling

MOSS BROS DODGE
See MOSS BROS INC

D-U-N-S 02-900-1526
MOSS BROS HON INC
MOSS BROS HONDA
8146 Auto Center Dr, Riverside, CA 92504
Tel (951) 688-6200 *Founded/Ownrshp* 1938
Sales 70.2MM^E *EMP* 150
SIC 5511 Automobiles, new & used; Automobiles, new & used
Pr: Glenn L Moss Sr
**CFO:* Bill Camp
**VP:* J A Moss Jr
Genl Mgr: Mike Rewley
Dir IT: Tim Johnson
IT Man: Maritza Roman

MOSS BROS HONDA
See MOSS BROS HON INC

D-U-N-S 02-890-8630
MOSS BROS INC
MOSS BROS DODGE
1100 S E St, San Bernardino, CA 92408-1915
Tel (909) 884-8255 *Founded/Ownrshp* 1981
Sales 71.8MM^E *EMP* 185
SIC 5511

D-U-N-S 14-912-9160 IMP
MOSS HOLDING CO
(*Suby of* CENTURY PARK CAPITAL PARTNERS LLC) ★
2600 Elmhurst Rd, Elk Grove Village, IL 60007-6312
Tel (847) 238-4200 *Founded/Ownrshp* 2000
Sales 52.8MM^E *EMP* 250
SIC 2399 2541 2211 Banners, pennants & flags; Store & office display cases & fixtures; Stretch fabrics, cotton; Banners, pennants & flags; Store & office display cases & fixtures; Stretch fabrics, cotton
Pr: Dan Patterson
CFO: Mark Ollinger
Ex VP: Bob Frey

D-U-N-S 09-859-4120
MOSS MOTORS INC
1401 Surrey St, Lafayette, LA 70501-7751
Tel (337) 235-9086 *Founded/Ownrshp* 1989
Sales 57.9MM^E *EMP* 150
SIC 5511 5521 New & used car dealers; Used car dealers; New & used car dealers; Used car dealers
Pr: Sharon K Moss
**Sec:* Julie Landry
Sls Mgr: Missy Hughes

D-U-N-S 00-833-9129 IMP/EXP
MOSS MOTORS LTD
400 Rutherford St, Goleta, CA 93117-3702
Tel (805) 967-4546 *Founded/Ownrshp* 1998
Sales 55.6MM^E *EMP* 150
SIC 5531 5013

MOSS POINT ALTERNATIVE SCHOOL
See MOSS POINT SCHOOL DISTRICT

D-U-N-S 17-479-1046
MOSS POINT MUNICIPAL SEPARATE SCHOOL DISTRICT
MOSS POINT SCHOOL DISTRICT
4924 Church St, Moss Point, MS 39563-2600
Tel (228) 474-2269 *Founded/Ownrshp* 1901
Sales NA *EMP* 520
Accts Cunningham Cpas Pllc Belzoni
SIC 9111 8211 Mayors' offices; Public combined elementary & secondary school; Mayors' offices; Public combined elementary & secondary school
Pr: Charles Wesley
Pr Dir: Myya Robinson

MOSS POINT SCHOOL DISTRICT
See MOSS POINT MUNICIPAL SEPARATE SCHOOL DISTRICT

D-U-N-S 80-047-2032
MOSS POINT SCHOOL DISTRICT
MOSS POINT ALTERNATIVE SCHOOL
4924 Church St, Moss Point, MS 39563-2600
Tel (228) 474-2269 *Founded/Ownrshp* 2007
Sales 26.0MM^E *EMP* 500
SIC 8211 Public elementary & secondary schools
Prin: Dennis Thomas
Prin: Toletha Cook
Dir Sec: Troy Brown
Pr Dir: Stephanie Packer
HC Dir: Harriet Wilkinsion

D-U-N-S 00-315-0893
MOSS SUPPLY CO (NC)
5001 N Graham St, Charlotte, NC 28269-4826
Tel (704) 596-8717 *Founded/Ownrshp* 1961
Sales 90.2MM^E *EMP* 350
SIC 3442 Screen & storm doors & windows; Screen & storm doors & windows
CEO: Robert Moss Jr
**Pr:* Gregory B Smith
**Pr:* Ralph Wearsch
**CFO:* Gregory Smith
**Sec:* Cassandra Nott
Sr Cor Off: Terry Massey
IT Man: Lisa Jackson
Opers Mgr: Vance Almonde
Plnt Mgr: Fred Rymer

D-U-N-S 00-547-9316
MOSSBERG & CO INC
301 E Sample St, South Bend, IN 46601-3547
Tel (574) 289-9253 *Founded/Ownrshp* 1930
Sales 32.7MM^E *EMP* 140^E
SIC 2752 2759 Commercial printing, lithographic; Letterpress printing; Commercial printing, lithographic; Letterpress printing
Ch: Charles W Hillman
**CEO:* James W Hillman
**CFO:* Gary Belting
**VP:* William Knight
VP: Bill Lutton
Off Mgr: Melinda Steinke
Plnt Mgr: Shawn Welch
Ql Cn Mgr: Dennis Feece
Natl Sales: Jim Rigney
S&M/VP: Rhonda Perry

D-U-N-S 85-987-9256 IMP
MOSSBERG CORP
7 Grasso Ave, North Haven, CT 06473-3259
Tel (203) 230-5300 *Founded/Ownrshp* 1991
Sales 205.8MM^E *EMP* 550
SIC 3484 Shotguns or shotgun parts, 30 mm. & below; Shotguns or shotgun parts, 30 mm. & below
Ch Bd: Alan Iver Mossberg
Pr: Bill Lutton
CFO: Paul Chartier
Dir IT: Jacques Frantz
IT Man: Bhavesh Patel
Plnt Mgr: Chad Drake
Ql Cn Mgr: Aaron Summers
Mktg Dir: Pete Angle
Mktg Dir: David Miles
Sls Mgr: Stephen Wright

D-U-N-S 06-370-7699
MOSSER CONSTRUCTION INC
(*Suby of* MOSSER GROUP) ★
122 S Wilson Ave, Fremont, OH 43420-2725
Tel (419) 334-3801 *Founded/Ownrshp* 1974
Sales 80.1MM *EMP* 200
SIC 1541 1542

MOSSER GROUP, THE
See WMOG INC

D-U-N-S 85-918-1901
MOSSY AUTOMOTIVE GROUP INC
MOSSY TOYOTA
(*Suby of* MOSSY HOLDING CO INC) ★
4555 Mission Bay Dr, San Diego, CA 92109-4920
Tel (858) 581-4000 *Founded/Ownrshp* 2002
Sales 51.3MM^E *EMP* 125
SIC 5511 7538 Automobiles, new & used; General automotive repair shops; Automobiles, new & used; General automotive repair shops
Pr: Philip Mossy
VP: Peter Mossy
Genl Mgr: Owen Mossy
Genl Mgr: Simon Soaf
Sls Dir: Jason Mozisek
Sls Dir: Ray Smith
Sls Mgr: Oscar Garcia
Sls Mgr: Jason Mossy
Sales Asso: Joe Amendola
Sales Asso: Peter Fletcher

MOSSY BUICK-PONTIAC-GMC
See MOSSY MOTORS INC

D-U-N-S 62-608-0915
MOSSY HOLDING CO INC
MOSSY OLDSMOBILE
12150 Old Katy Rd, Houston, TX 77079
Tel (281) 558-9970 *Founded/Ownrshp* 1946
Sales 393.8MM^E *EMP* 1,090
SIC 5511 6159 7532 Automobiles, new & used; Pickups, new & used; Vans, new & used; Automobile finance leasing; Body shop, automotive; Automobiles, new & used; Pickups, new & used; Vans, new & used; Automobile finance leasing; Body shop, automotive
Ch Bd: Wiley Mosay
**Pr:* David Mossy
**Pr:* Philip Mossy
CFO: Amy Gladys
Sls Mgr: Jason Jaffe

D-U-N-S 00-820-8252
MOSSY MOTORS INC
MOSSY BUICK-PONTIAC-GMC
1331 S Broad St, New Orleans, LA 70125-2016
Tel (504) 822-2050 *Founded/Ownrshp* 1957
Sales 25.7MM^E *EMP* 50
SIC 5511 5521 7538 Automobiles, new & used; Used car dealers; General automotive repair shops; Automobiles, new & used; Used car dealers; General automotive repair shops
Pr: R Joseph Mossy Jr
CFO: Keith Jarrett
**Ex VP:* Michael Gonzales
Sls Dir: David Carritelli
Sales Asso: Michael Collins
Sales Asso: David Martz
Sales Asso: Kenneth Simms

D-U-N-S 19-716-8045
MOSSY MOTORS OF MISSISSIPPI LLP
241 Frontage Rd, Picayune, MS 39466-7587
Tel (601) 798-7575 *Founded/Ownrshp* 2004
Sales 20.2MM^E *EMP* 46^E
SIC 5511 Automobiles, new & used
Mng Pr: Roger A Bacon Jr
Sls Mgr: Jim Eastridge

MOSSY NISSAN KEARNY MESA
See NISSAN MOSSY INC

MOSSY NISSAN OLDSMOBILE
See MOSSY OLDSMOBILE INC

MOSSY OAK
See HAAS OUTDOORS INC

MOSSY OLDSMOBILE
See MOSSY HOLDING CO INC

D-U-N-S 05-362-1645
MOSSY OLDSMOBILE INC
MOSSY NISSAN OLDSMOBILE
12150 Old Katy Rd, Houston, TX 77079
Tel (281) 496-4555 *Founded/Ownrshp* 1970
Sales 27.4MM^E *EMP* 150^E
SIC 5511 Automobiles, new & used; Pickups, new & used; Vans, new & used; Automobiles, new & used; Pickups, new & used; Vans, new & used
Pr: Wiley Mossy
**VP:* David Mossy
Genl Mgr: David Hruska
Store Mgr: Phil Hahn
Sls Mgr: Bryan Bothwell
Sales Asso: Armando Flores
Sales Asso: Jerry Waddy

MOSSY TOYOTA
See MOSSY AUTOMOTIVE GROUP INC

D-U-N-S 01-684-4040
MOST INC (MO)
(*Suby of* TOYOTA TSUSHO AMERICA INC) ★
50 Cherry Blossom Way, Troy, MO 63379-2527
Tel (636) 528-3013 *Founded/Ownrshp* 1997
Sales 40.6MM^E *EMP* 66
SIC 3334 3341 Primary aluminum; Aluminum smelting & refining (secondary)
Pr: Van Anthony
**Sec:* Atsushi Shimizu
Ex VP: Mark Baffa
Plnt Mgr: Mark Chadbourne
Plnt Mgr: Randy McElroy

MOST VALUABLE PERSONNEL
See PERSONNEL STAFFING GROUP LLC

D-U-N-S 19-562-9584
MOTC LP
2821 Turtle Creek Blvd, Dallas, TX 75219-4802
Tel (214) 520-5807 *Founded/Ownrshp* 1997
Sales 3.6MM^E *EMP* 300
SIC 7011 Hotels; Hotels

D-U-N-S 03-427-9948 IMP/EXP
MOTCO INC (FL)
7900 Sw 57th Ave Ste 10, South Miami, FL 33143-5545
Tel (305) 662-8814 *Founded/Ownrshp* 1975
Sales 127.3MM^E *EMP* 424
SIC 5182 5122 5199 Liquor; Toiletries; Gifts & novelties; Liquor; Toiletries; Gifts & novelties
Pr: Harold M Rifas
**Treas:* Mary Crawley
**VP:* David Granick

D-U-N-S 05-120-1481
MOTE FARM SERVICE
8531 E 100 S, Union City, IN 47390-8409
Tel (765) 964-3941 *Founded/Ownrshp* 1985
Sales 20.2MM *EMP* 7
Accts Peterson & Stachler Pc Cpas
SIC 5191 Fertilizers & agricultural chemicals; Seeds & bulbs; Fertilizers & agricultural chemicals; Seeds & bulbs
Pt: Derrick Mote

MOTE MARINE AQUARIUM
See MOTE MARINE LABORATORY INC

D-U-N-S 07-919-4080
MOTE MARINE LABORATORY INC (FL)
MOTE MARINE AQUARIUM
1600 Ken Thompson Pkwy, Sarasota, FL 34236-1096
Tel (941) 388-4441 *Founded/Ownrshp* 1955
Sales 21.2MM *EMP* 220
Accts Kerkering Barberio & Co Saras
SIC 8733 Scientific research agency; Scientific research agency
CEO: Michael P Crosby
**Pr:* Kumar Mahadevan
**CFO:* Dena Smith
**Treas:* Howard G Crowell

D-U-N-S 14-569-4803
MOTECH AMERICAS LLC
GE ENERGY
(*Suby of* MOTECH INDUSTRIES INC.)
1300 Valley Vista Dr # 207, Diamond Bar, CA 91765-3940
Tel (302) 451-7500 *Founded/Ownrshp* 2009
Sales 32.7MM^E *EMP* 320
SIC 8731 3674 Energy research; Solar cells; Energy research; Solar cells
CEO: Peng Heng Chang
Pr: Eric Kuo
Pr: Dr Alan Wu

D-U-N-S 04-177-8705 IMP
MOTEK-TEAM INDUSTRIES INC
(*Suby of* TEAM INDUSTRIES INC) ★
625 2nd Ave Se, Cambridge, MN 55008-1710
Tel (763) 691-2385 *Founded/Ownrshp* 1967
Sales 70.0MM *EMP* 209
Accts Peffer & Wallace Ltd Cambri
SIC 3599 Machine shop, jobbing & repair; Machine & other job shop work; Machine shop, jobbing & repair; Machine & other job shop work
CEO: David W Ricke
**CFO:* Steven Kast
**VP:* Michael Matthews
**VP:* Robert G Skawski

MOTEL 6
See G6 HOSPITALITY LLC

D-U-N-S 15-277-2463
MOTEL 6 OPERATING LP
(*Suby of* G6 HOSPITALITY LLC) ★
4001 Intl Pkwy Ste 500, Carrollton, TX 75007
Tel (972) 360-9000 *Founded/Ownrshp* 2012
Sales 151.4MM^E *EMP* 2,000
SIC 7011 Hotels & motels; Hotels & motels
CEO: Jim Amorosia
**Geni Pt:* Emmett Gossen
VP: Jeff Winslow
Genl Mgr: Jack Gillinghan
Netwrk Mgr: Adel Habashy
Secur Mgr: Elco Voorhaar
Sls Dir: Joanna Stevenson

D-U-N-S 06-530-6342
MOTEL SLEEPERS INC
101 Morgan Keegan Dr B, Little Rock, AR 72202-2210
Tel (501) 666-4800 *Founded/Ownrshp* 1968
Sales 24.9MM^E *EMP* 250
SIC 8741 7021 Administrative management; Dormitory, commercially operated; Administrative management; Dormitory, commercially operated
Pr: Leon B Catlett IL
**Pr:* Leon B Catlett II
CFO: Lisa Ware

D-U-N-S 02-656-7875 IMP
MOTENG INC
RAX ALAR PRODUCTS
12220 Parkway Centre Dr, Poway, CA 92064-6867
Tel (858) 715-2500 *Founded/Ownrshp* 1980
Sales 20.2MM^E *EMP* 70^E
SIC 5136 5137 5072 5139 5091 Men's & boys' clothing; Women's & children's clothing; Hardware; Security devices, locks; Footwear; Watersports equipment & supplies; Diving equipment & supplies; Surfing equipment & supplies; Swimming pools, equipment & supplies
CEO: Leslie R Edelstein
**CFO:* Neville Berman

D-U-N-S 96-927-5036
MOTENG NA LLC
MOTENG NORTH AMERICA
7220 Trade St Ste 100, San Diego, CA 92121-2325
Tel (858) 715-2500 *Founded/Ownrshp* 2011
Sales 36.8MM^E *EMP* 40^E
SIC 5091 5072 Sporting & recreation goods; Cutlery
CEO: Kassie Fraser
**CFO:* James Call
Sales Exec: Thomas Pistole

MOTENG NORTH AMERICA
See MOTENG NA LLC

D-U-N-S 08-655-4862
MOTHE LIFE INSURANCE CO INC
401 Whitney Ave Ste 303, Gretna, LA 70056-2502
Tel (504) 398-0777 *Founded/Ownrshp* 1932
Sales NA *EMP* 208
SIC 6311 Life insurance carriers; Life insurance carriers
Pr: Charles J Gerrets III
VP: Joseph Saltaformaggio

D-U-N-S 04-074-6430
MOTHER FRANCES HOSPITAL REGIONAL HEALTH CARE CENTER
800 E Dawson St, Tyler, TX 75701-2093
Tel (903) 593-8441 *Founded/Ownrshp* 1937
Sales 196.3MM^E *EMP* 2,747
Accts Bkd Llp Houston Tx
SIC 8062 General medical & surgical hospitals; General medical & surgical hospitals
Pr: Lindsey Bradely
Chf Rad: Robert Sanchez
CFO: William Bellenfant
CFO: Joyce Hester
VP: Chris Gleeney
VP: Ray Thompson
CIO: Lee Portwood
Dir IT: Jobe Marshal
Dir IT: Becky Wester
IT Man: Robert Hilliard
Obsttrcn: Ann H Abrameit

D-U-N-S 18-551-0570
MOTHER INDUSTRIES LLC
(*Suby of* MOTHER LONDON LIMITED)
595 11th Ave, New York, NY 10036-2101
Tel (212) 254-2800 *Founded/Ownrshp* 2003
Sales 29.3MM^E *EMP* 150
SIC 7311 Advertising agencies; Advertising agencies
COO: Pernilla Ammann
CFO: Daniel Tucker
Creative D: Daniel Carlsson

D-U-N-S 62-803-6600
MOTHER LODE HOLDING CO
189 Fulweiler Ave, Auburn, CA 95603-4507
Tel (530) 887-2410 *Founded/Ownrshp* 1987
Sales NA *EMP* 480
SIC 6361 6531 7389 Title insurance; Escrow agent, real estate; Courier or messenger service; Title insurance; Escrow agent, real estate; Courier or messenger service
CEO: Jerry Adams
**Pr:* Marsha Emmett
**CFO:* David Philipp
Exec: Jane Donovan

D-U-N-S 11-251-6539
MOTHER MCAULEY LIBERAL ARTS HIGH SCHOOL
3737 W 99th St, Chicago, IL 60655-3133
Tel (773) 881-6500 *Founded/Ownrshp* 1956
Sales 20.0MM^E *EMP* 150
Accts Mulcahy Pauritsch Salvador &
SIC 8211 Catholic senior high school
Prin: Dr Christine Melone
**CFO:* Gordon Brannon
**VP:* SIS Lois Bromark
VP: Carey Harrington
Exec: Linda Porter
Mktg Dir: Jennifer Busk
Psych: Nicole Hynes

MOTHER MESQUITE'S RESTAURANT
See GOOD EATS RESTAURANT GROUP INC

D-U-N-S 00-321-3071
MOTHER MURPHYS LABORATORIES INC (NC)
2826 S Elm Eugene St, Greensboro, NC 27406-4435
Tel (336) 273-1737 *Founded/Ownrshp* 1946
Sales 42.9MM *EMP* 120
Accts Mcgladrey Llp Greensboro Nor
SIC 2087 Extracts, flavoring; Extracts, flavoring
Ch: Robert B Murphy
Pr: Gigi Melton
**Pr:* David Murphy
Pr: Brian Schreiber
Pr: Roger Stark
**CFO:* Timothy Hansen
**Sr VP:* James A Murphy
VP: Suzanne Johnson
VP: James Murphy
**VP:* Janet Murphy
**VP:* R Bruce Murphy
VP: David Sholty
Exec: John Worsley

D-U-N-S 13-026-0826 IMP
MOTHER PARKERS TEA & COFFEE USA LTD
MOTHER PARKER'S TEA AND COFFEE
(*Suby of* MOTHER PARKER'S TEA & COFFEE INC)
7800 Will Rogers Blvd, Fort Worth, TX 76140-6026
Tel (817) 551-5500 *Founded/Ownrshp* 1912
Sales 96.8MM^E *EMP* 155
SIC 5149 2095 2099 Coffee & tea; Roasted coffee; Food preparations; Coffee & tea; Roasted coffee; Food preparations
Mng Pt: Paul Higgins
**Pr:* Michael Higgins
VP: Dennis Paynter
VP: Bill Vandenbygaart
Natl Sales: Mario Cappella
Natl Sales: Laura Rutherford
Natl Sales: Don Scott
Mktg Mgr: Deetricha Younger
Manager: Carolyn Bowers
Manager: Buffy Day
Manager: Dirk Gunderson

MOTHER PARKER'S TEA AND COFFEE
See MOTHER PARKERS TEA & COFFEE USA LTD

MOTHERAL PRINTING COMPANY
See F L MOTHERAL CO

D-U-N-S 88-419-1842
MOTHERBOARD EXPRESS CO
MBX SYSTEMS
1200 Technology Way, Libertyville, IL 60048-5369
Tel (847) 487-2700 *Founded/Ownrshp* 1996
Sales 56.7MM^E *EMP* 150^E
SIC 7373

D-U-N-S 03-475-7575
MOTHERS AGAINST DRUNK DRIVING INC
MADD
511 E John Carpenter Fwy # 700, Irving, TX 75062-3983
Tel (214) 744-6233 *Founded/Ownrshp* 1980
Sales 33.4MM *EMP* 320
Accts Bruce E Bernstien & Assoc Pc
SIC 8699 Personal interest organization; Personal interest organization
CEO: Debbie Weir
**Pr:* Jan Withers
CFO: Lista Hightower
Ofcr: Adam Vanek
Ex Dir: Ericka Espino
Ex Dir: Abigail Nickell
Ex Dir: Jennifer Northway

MOTHER'S MARKET & KITCHEN
See AVA RUHA CORP

MOTION AND FLOW CONTROL PDTS
See MCCOY SALES CORP

D-U-N-S 07-180-5592
MOTION AND FLOW CONTROL PRODUCTS
2929 Nw 31st Ave, Portland, OR 97210-1721
Tel (503) 228-0190 *Founded/Ownrshp* 1995
Sales 41.5MM^E *EMP* 107
Accts Mack Roberts & Co Llc Port
SIC 5084 Hydraulic systems equipment & supplies; Pneumatic tools & equipment; Hydraulic systems equipment & supplies; Pneumatic tools & equipment
Pr: Darrell Sabin
**Pr:* John Niemy
**VP:* Steve Robinson
Brnch Mgr: Dustin Todd
Genl Mgr: Nick Kennelly
Store Mgr: Kerry Lang
Sales Asso: David Grigsby
Sales Asso: Craig Tietje

D-U-N-S 03-879-4762
MOTION AND FLOW CONTROL PRODUCTS INC
MFCP
7941 Shaffer Pkwy, Littleton, CO 80127-3734
Tel (888) 254-2571 *Founded/Ownrshp* 2006
Sales 46.4MM^E *EMP* 13^E
SIC 5085 Industrial supplies
Pr: John Niemi
IT Man: Steve Bohn
Manager: Jake Hahn
Manager: Donnie Loerwald
Sales Asso: Brandon Smith

MOTION AUTO SUPPLY
See PARTS WHOLESALERS INC

D-U-N-S 11-370-6597
■ **MOTION COMPUTING INC**
(*Suby of* XPLORE TECHNOLOGIES CORP OF AMERICA) ★
8601 Rr 2222 Bldg Ii, Austin, TX 78730-2304
Tel (512) 637-1100 *Founded/Ownrshp* 2015
Sales 32.1MM^E *EMP* 200
SIC 7371 Computers; Software programming applications
CEO: Philip S Sassower
Pr: Mark Holleran
COO: Rob Karsch
CFO: Michael J Rapisand
Chf Mktg O: Peter M Poulin
VP: Guy Allen
VP: Bryan J Bell
VP: Ron Harter
VP: Lee Hinkle
VP: Jerry Mayfield
VP: Valerie Walden
VP: Michael Zimmerman
Exec: Bill Getchell
Dir Soc: John Honning

D-U-N-S 10-754-0726 IMP/EXP
MOTION CONTROL ENGINEERING INC
(*Suby of* KINETEK INC) ★
11380 White Rock Rd, Rancho Cordova, CA 95742-6522
Tel (916) 638-4011 *Founded/Ownrshp* 2010
Sales 88.1MM^E *EMP* 400^E
SIC 3534 3613 Elevators & equipment; Switchgear & switchboard apparatus; Elevators & equipment; Switchgear & switchboard apparatus
Ch Bd: Thomas H Quinn
**CEO:* Dennis R Bays
**CFO:* Daniel D Drury
CFO: Courtney Enghauser
VP: Mohamed Ezzeddine
VP: Jed Shapiro
Snr Sftwr: Brian Freeman
DP Exec: Sammy Ghattas
IT Man: Rutu Shah
IT Man: Greg Thiesen
IT Man: Sheila Villarreal

D-U-N-S 00-796-0446 IMP
■ **MOTION INDUSTRIES INC**
(*Suby of* GENUINE PARTS CO) ★
1605 Alton Rd, Birmingham, AL 35210-3770
Tel (205) 956-1122 *Founded/Ownrshp* 1946
Sales 3.5MMM^E *EMP* 5,200
SIC 5085 Industrial supplies; Bearings; Power transmission equipment & apparatus; Industrial supplies; Bearings; Power transmission equipment & apparatus
Pr: Timothy P Breen
**Ch Bd:* William J Stevens
Pr: Doug Osborne

Pr: Pamela Sims
**COO:* Bob Summerlin
**Treas:* Michael D Harper
**VP:* G Harold Dunaway
**VP:* Ellen Holladay
**VP:* Wayne Law
**VP:* Joe Limbaugh
Exec: Anthony G Cefalu
Exec: Randy R Till
Exec: Kala Williamson

D-U-N-S 07-412-8380
MOTION PICTURE AND TELEVISION FUND
BOB HOPE HEALTH CENTER
23388 Mulholland Dr # 200, Woodland Hills, CA 91364-2733
Tel (818) 876-1888 *Founded/Ownrshp* 1924
Sales 31.1MM *EMP* 850
Accts Pricewaterhousecoopers Llp Lo
SIC 8062 8051 8011 8351 8322 6513 General medical & surgical hospitals; Convalescent home with continuous nursing care; Medical centers; Child day care services; Individual & family services; Retirement hotel operation; General medical & surgical hospitals; Convalescent home with continuous nursing care; Medical centers; Child day care services; Individual & family services; Retirement hotel operation
CEO: Robert Beitcher
**Ch Bd:* Bob Pisano
COO: David Asplund
CFO: Frank Guarrera
**Treas:* Jay Roth
Exec: Tara Piazza
Exec: Sue Schubert
Dir Inf Cn: Suzanne Hackett
Adm Dir: Sandra Danburg
Adm Dir: Lea Pipes
Dir Sec: Mike Spalinger
Board of Directors: Frank Mancuso

D-U-N-S 07-525-8590
MOTION PICTURE ASSOCIATION OF AMERICA INC (NY)
1600 I St Nw, Washington, DC 20006-4010
Tel (202) 293-1966 *Founded/Ownrshp* 1922
Sales 24.7MM^E *EMP* 200
SIC 8611 6512 Trade associations; Commercial & industrial building operation; Trade associations; Commercial & industrial building operation
CEO: Christopher J Dodd
Ofcr: David M Corwin
Sr Ex VP: Henry Hoberman
Ex VP: Steven Fabrizio
Sr VP: Marilyn Gordon
Sr VP: Brad Hunt
Sr VP: Jim C Williams
VP: Paul Egge
VP: Howard Gantman
VP: Patrick Kilcur
Exec: Joan Graves

D-U-N-S 03-086-9010
MOTION PICTURE HEALTH & WELFARE FUND
11365 Ventura Blvd # 300, Studio City, CA 91604-3148
Tel (818) 769-0007 *Founded/Ownrshp* 1952
Sales NA *EMP* 215
SIC 6371 Union welfare, benefit & health funds; Union welfare, benefit & health funds
Ex Dir: Thomas Zimmerman
**CFO:* Theodre Friesen
Opers Mgr: Mitch Field
Snr Mgr: Celso Perez

D-U-N-S 96-658-7797
MOTION PICTURE INDUSTRY HEALTH PLAN
11365 Ventura Blvd, Studio City, CA 91604-3148
Tel (818) 769-0007 *Founded/Ownrshp* 2011
Sales 732.4MM *EMP* 21^E
Accts Miller Kaplan Arase Llp North
SIC 8099 Health & allied services; Health & allied services
Prin: David Wescoe

D-U-N-S 18-760-0259
MOTION PICTURE INDUSTRY PENSION & HEALTH PLANS
11365 Ventura Blvd # 300, Studio City, CA 91604-3148
Tel (818) 769-0007 *Founded/Ownrshp* 1954
Sales NA *EMP* 150
SIC 6371 Pension, health & welfare funds
CEO: David Wescoe
CFO: Chuck Gordon
**CFO:* Chuck Killian
Bd of Dir: Ronald Kutak
Comm Man: Marc Schwartz
CIO: Paul Egge
Dir IT: Patrick Carmona
Snr Mgr: Wynnette Legaspi

D-U-N-S 87-970-5317
MOTION RECRUITMENT PARTNERS INC
131 Clarendon St Fl 3, Boston, MA 02116-5179
Tel (617) 585-6500 *Founded/Ownrshp* 1994
Sales 75.4MM^E *EMP* 580
SIC 7361 Placement agencies; Placement agencies
Pr: Beth Gilfeather
**CFO:* Anthony J M Groves
Sr VP: Bethann G Gilfeather
VP: Jason Berkowitz
**VP:* Krista Weeks
Prac Mgr: Brett Sturgill
Dir IT: Matt Giarratnia

MOTION SOLUTIONS
See BEARING ENGINEERS INC

D-U-N-S 61-483-8233
MOTION TECH AUTOMATION LLC
7166 4th St N, Saint Paul, MN 55128-7082
Tel (651) 730-9010 *Founded/Ownrshp* 1987
Sales 27.2MM^E *EMP* 85
SIC 5063 Motor controls, starters & relays: electric
Pr: Fred Stutter
Sec: Cindy Vilks
IT Man: Allan Flinn

D-U-N-S 02-477-2886
MOTION THEORY INC (CA)
MIRADA
4235 Redwood Ave, Los Angeles, CA 90066-5605
Tel (310) 396-9433 *Founded/Ownrshp* 2000
Sales 27.0MM *EMP* 110
SIC 7336 7371 7812 Graphic arts & related design; Computer software development & applications; Motion picture production
CFO: Janell Perez
Bd of Dir: Christopher Leone
Art Dir: Jesus Defrancisco
Art Dir: Jesus Francisco
Art Dir: Mark Kudsi

D-U-N-S 36-428-9574
MOTIONPOINT CORP
4661 Johnson Rd Unit 14, Coconut Creek, FL 33073-4363
Tel (954) 421-0890 *Founded/Ownrshp* 2000
Sales 29.7MM^E *EMP* 190^E
SIC 7389 Translation services; Translation services
CEO: William S Fleming
**COO:* Adam Rubenstein
**Sr VP:* Charles Whiteman
**VP:* Arcadio Andrade
**VP:* Ben Field
Dir Bus: Joseph Bley
Snr Sftwr: Meena Radhakrishnan
**CTO:* Enrique Travieso
DP Exec: Eugenio Alvarez
Tech Mgr: Ed Ruano
Natl Sales: Dave Jukich

D-U-N-S 00-871-6441
MOTIR SERVICES INC (DC)
1508 E Capitol St Ne, Washington, DC 20003-1507
Tel (202) 371-9393 *Founded/Ownrshp* 1994
Sales 32.1MM^E *EMP* 400
SIC 8744 Facilities support services; Facilities support services
Pr: Emmanuel O Irono
**CFO:* Mark Peter
Ex Dir: Deborah Washington

D-U-N-S 02-383-8670 IMP
MOTIVA ENTERPRISES LLC
MOTIVA SALES TERMINAL
500 Dallas St, Houston, TX 77002-4800
Tel (713) 241-6161 *Founded/Ownrshp* 1998
Sales 1.6MMM^E *EMP* 3,000
SIC 2911 5541 Petroleum refining; Filling stations, gasoline; Petroleum refining; Filling stations, gasoline
CEO: Dan Romasko
**CEO:* Robert W Pease
**CFO:* Marcel P Luijten
**Treas:* James B Castles
Genl Mgr: Gerry Jackson
Genl Mgr: Don Jasperson
MIS Dir: Frank Doyle
**VP Mfg:* Tom Purves
Trfc Mgr: Diane Arvey
Sls Mgr: Don Hill
Sls Mgr: David McMahon

MOTIVA SALES TERMINAL
See MOTIVA ENTERPRISES LLC

D-U-N-S 08-237-5577
MOTIVACTION LLC
16355 36th Ave N Ste 100, Minneapolis, MN 55446-4600
Tel (763) 412-3000 *Founded/Ownrshp* 2001
Sales 36.4MM^E *EMP* 100^E
SIC 8742 5091 5064 Incentive or award program consultant; Sporting & recreation goods; Electrical entertainment equipment
CFO: Mike Simon
VP: Greg Mazzuco
VP: Kari Vrba
Exec: Jan Brown
Exec: Tyler Gentry
Exec: Venessa Grant
Exec: Eric Heining
Exec: Kathryn McCreary
Exec: Lisa Myers
Exec: Marlyn Sjaarda
Exec: Pete Windahl
Dir Soc: Jodi Hilgers
Dir Soc: Mary Macgregor
Dir Bus: Debbie Disch
Dir Bus: Scott McKone
Dir Bus: Matt Robb
Dir Bus: Rhonda Sucharda

D-U-N-S 78-900-8653
MOTIVATED SECURITY SERVICES INC
34 W Main St Ste 204, Somerville, NJ 08876-2218
Tel (908) 526-1140 *Founded/Ownrshp* 1991
Sales 14.9MM^E *EMP* 500
Accts Maffei Masiello & Company P
SIC 7381 7361 Detective & armored car services; Employment agencies; Detective & armored car services; Employment agencies
Ch Bd: Kathleen M Kavanaugh
CFO: Anthony Lapolla
VP: Daniel E Kavanaugh III
VP: Gerard Leahy
Opers Mgr: Scot Schroeder
VP Sls: Sheref Shahid

MOTIVATIONAL FULFILLMENT
See MOTIVATIONAL MARKETING INC

D-U-N-S 95-604-1750
MOTIVATIONAL MARKETING INC
MOTIVATIONAL FULFILLMENT
15820 Euclid Ave, Chino, CA 91708-9162
Tel (909) 517-2200 *Founded/Ownrshp* 1975
Sales 32.5MM^E *EMP* 400^E
SIC 7389 8748 8742 Telephone services; Mailing & messenger services; Business consulting; Management consulting services; Telephone services; Mailing & messenger services; Business consulting; Management consulting services
CEO: Hal Altman
**Ex VP:* Andrea Stuhley
**Sr VP:* Anthony Altman
**VP:* Tony Altman
**VP:* Cheryl Nataren
**VP:* Jessie Ortiz
Exec: Jeff Landon
Dir Soc: Melanie Altman
IT Man: Carlos Flores

D-U-N-S 02-051-9864
MOTIVATIONAL SYSTEMS INC (CA)
2200 Cleveland Ave, National City, CA 91950-6412
Tel (619) 474-8246 *Founded/Ownrshp* 1975
Sales 24.8MM^E *EMP* 130
SIC 7336 3993 Commercial art & graphic design; Signs & advertising specialties
CEO: Robert D Yound
**Treas:* Joe Jordan
Ex VP: Tony Young
VP: Debra Bennett
**VP:* David Cowan
VP: Mark McClure
Off Mgr: Linda Forman
IT Man: Guen Okano

D-U-N-S 10-352-9632 IMP/EXP
MOTIVATORS INC
123 Frost St Ste 201, Westbury, NY 11590-5027
Tel (516) 735-9600 *Founded/Ownrshp* 1980
Sales 24.7MM^E *EMP* 53
SIC 5199 Advertising specialties
Pr: Kenneth Laffer
Genl Mgr: D Naidu
IT Man: Khurram Khan
Mktg Dir: Bill Shea
Sls Mgr: Alison Strauss

D-U-N-S 07-288-0511 EXP
MOTIVE ENERGY INC
125 E Coml St Bldg B, Anaheim, CA 92801
Tel (714) 888-2525 *Founded/Ownrshp* 1982
Sales 68.9MM^E *EMP* 85
SIC 5063 Storage batteries, industrial; Storage batteries, industrial
Pr: Robert J Istwan
Brnch Mgr: Jeffrey Gilliland
Genl Mgr: Chris Glade
Sfty Dirs: Jesse Moreno
VP Sls: Tony Capolino
Mktg Dir: Allen Tanner

D-U-N-S 11-030-6115
MOTIVE INC
(*Suby of* ALCATEL-LUCENT USA INC) ★
12515 Res Blvd Bldg 5, Austin, TX 78759
Tel (512) 339-8335 *Founded/Ownrshp* 2008
Sales 32.6MM^E *EMP* 350
SIC 7372 Prepackaged software; Prepackaged software
CEO: Alfred Mockett
**COO:* Rick Hanna
**CFO:* Michael Fitzpatrick
Ex VP: Kenny Zant
**Sr VP:* Aramis Alvarez
**VP:* Anna Clepper
VP: Tom Donnellan
VP: David Stevenson
VP: Raj Tummala
Exec: Pat Obrien
Prac Mgr: Russ Keveryn

MOTIVE NATION
See ROCKVIEW DAIRIES INC

D-U-N-S 11-475-9124 IMP/EXP
■ **MOTIVEPOWER INC**
(*Suby of* WABTEC) ★
4600 S Apple St, Boise, ID 83716-5505
Tel (208) 947-4800 *Founded/Ownrshp* 1972
Sales 157.3MM^E *EMP* 750
SIC 3743 Railroad car rebuilding; Railroad car rebuilding
Pr: Albert J Neupaver
**COO:* Raymond T Betler
**Ex VP:* Alvaro Garcia-Tunon
**Sr VP:* Patrick D Dugan
**Sr VP:* Charles F Kovac
**VP:* Robert C Bourg
**VP:* Mark Warner
Manager: Joseph Karnes

D-U-N-S 08-077-5836
MOTLEY RICE LLC
28 Bridgeside Blvd, Mount Pleasant, SC 29464-4375
Tel (843) 216-9000 *Founded/Ownrshp* 2002
Sales 70.0MM^E *EMP* 450
SIC 8111 General practice law office; General practice law office
V Ch: Robert McConnell
Pr: Marvetta Holmes
Pr: Alice Janelle
Comm Dir: Erin Watson
Snr Ntwrk: Josh Brantley
Sftwr Eng: Jason Quinton

D-U-N-S 19-712-6089
MOTMANCO INC
MCDONALD'S
319 Rosedale Pl, Valdosta, GA 31602-3044
Tel (229) 247-7889 *Founded/Ownrshp* 1988
Sales 12.7MM^E *EMP* 460
SIC 5812 Fast-food restaurant, chain; Fast-food restaurant, chain
Pr: David Motley

D-U-N-S 06-852-7027
MOTO INC
721 W Main St, Belleville, IL 62220-1514
Tel (618) 233-6754 *Founded/Ownrshp* 1974
Sales 500.0MM^E *EMP* 850
SIC 5541 5411 1221 Filling stations, gasoline; Convenience stores; Bituminous coal & lignite-surface mining; Filling stations, gasoline; Convenience stores; Bituminous coal & lignite-surface mining
Ch: Gerald Justafson
**Pr:* James G Forsyth III
Advt Dir: Jeff Faulkner

D-U-N-S 07-988-5038
MOTOIR LTD
MOTOROLA IRRIGATION
23272 Mill Creek Dr, Laguna Hills, CA 92653-1641
Tel (949) 552-6552 *Founded/Ownrshp* 2015
Sales 28.0MM *EMP* 120
SIC 4971 5049 Water distribution or supply systems for irrigation; Engineers' equipment & supplies
COO: Eric Schmidt

MOTOMART CONVENIENCE STORES
See FKG OIL CO

MOTOMCO
See BELL LABORATORIES INC

D-U-N-S 00-629-6230 IMP
MOTOR APPLIANCE CORP (MO)
MAC
601 International Ave, Washington, MO 63090-3535
Tel (636) 231-6100 *Founded/Ownrshp* 1946
Sales 31.5MM^E *EMP* 150
SIC 3621 3694 Motors, electric; Battery charging generators, automobile & aircraft; Motors, electric; Battery charging generators, automobile & aircraft
Pr: Evan Ballman
Dir IT: Ray Shea
Plnt Mgr: Steffan Nadler
Sls Mgr: James Blomberg

D-U-N-S 07-311-5065
■ **MOTOR CARGO**
(*Suby of* UPS GROUND FREIGHT INC) ★
845 W Center St, North Salt Lake, UT 84054-2916
Tel (801) 936-1111 *Founded/Ownrshp* 2005
Sales 91.1MM^E *EMP* 1,726
SIC 4213 Contract haulers; Contract haulers
Co-Pr: Pete Morrow
Co-Pr: Lynn H Wheeler
Sr VP: Marvin Friedland
Netwrk Mgr: Jared Roper

D-U-N-S 12-239-2616
MOTOR CARRIER SERVICE INC
815 Lemoyne Rd, Northwood, OH 43619-1815
Tel (419) 693-6207 *Founded/Ownrshp* 1979
Sales 35.4MM^E *EMP* 110
SIC 4213 Contract haulers
Pr: Keith A Tuttle
COO: John Fritzius
Genl Mgr: John Fritziuf

MOTOR CARS HONDA
See MOTOR CARS INC

D-U-N-S 16-727-2009 IMP
MOTOR CARS INC
MOTOR CARS HONDA
2953 Mayfield Rd, Cleveland, OH 44118-1634
Tel (216) 932-2400 *Founded/Ownrshp* 1973
Sales 63.4MM^E *EMP* 140
SIC 5511 Automobiles, new & used; Automobiles, new & used
Pr: Chuck Gile
CFO: Debbie Housholder
Exec: Linda Lisy
IT Man: Mike Buehner
Sls Mgr: Gloria Shirilla
Sls Mgr: Brian Zent
Sales Asso: Michael Mastropietro
Sales Asso: James Petitt

D-U-N-S 00-608-4073
MOTOR CASTINGS CO (WI)
(*Suby of* MOTORCASTING INC) ★
1323 S 65th St, Milwaukee, WI 53214-3251
Tel (414) 476-1434 *Founded/Ownrshp* 1919
Sales 25.7MM^E *EMP* 200^E
SIC 3321 5051 Ductile iron castings; Gray iron castings; Copper sheets, plates, bars, rods, pipes, etc.; Ductile iron castings; Gray iron castings; Copper sheets, plates, bars, rods, pipes, etc.
Ch Bd: James J O'Sullivan
**Pr:* Joseph Kempen
VP: Rebecca Goss
Plnt Mgr: Tim Eilers
Plnt Mgr: John Wasikowski

MOTOR CITY CASINO & HOTEL
See DETROIT ENTERTAINMENT LLC

D-U-N-S 00-481-7490 IMP
MOTOR CITY ELECTRIC CO (MI)
9440 Grinnell St, Detroit, MI 48213-1151
Tel (313) 567-5300 *Founded/Ownrshp* 1952
Sales 156.9MM^E *EMP* 500
SIC 1731 General electrical contractor; Lighting contractor; Telephone & telephone equipment installation; General electrical contractor; Lighting contractor; Telephone & telephone equipment installation
Pr: Dale Wieczorek
**Ex VP:* Thomas McGrail
**Sr VP:* Paul Gillespie
**VP:* Denise Hodgins
Exec: Courteney Zagacki
Dir Bus: Richard Miller
Snr Ntwrk: Jim Vallee
Opers Mgr: Dan Reske
Snr Mgr: Russ Craig

D-U-N-S 15-142-7507
MOTOR CITY ELECTRIC TECHNOLOGIES INC
(*Suby of* MOTOR CITY ELECTRIC CO) ★
9440 Grinnell St, Detroit, MI 48213-1151
Tel (313) 921-5300 *Founded/Ownrshp* 1993
Sales 21.6MM^E *EMP* 95
SIC 3613 8711 Control panels, electric; Engineering services; Control panels, electric; Engineering services
Pr: Dale M Wieczorek
**VP:* Denise Hodgins

D-U-N-S 01-693-4259 IMP
MOTOR CITY FASTENER INC
1600 E 10 Mile Rd, Hazel Park, MI 48030-1208
Tel (248) 399-2830 *Founded/Ownrshp* 1968
Sales 21.0MM^E *EMP* 48

SIC 5072 Nuts (hardware); Bolts
Pr: Robert J Puskas
Off Mgr: Linda Danhousen

MOTOR CITY GMC BUICK PONTIAC
See MOTOR CITY SALES & SERVICE

MOTOR CITY GROWLERS
See SRC INC

D-U-N-S 02-788-0319
MOTOR CITY SALES & SERVICE
MOTOR CITY GMC BUICK PONTIAC
3101 Pacheco Rd, Bakersfield, CA 93313-3214
Tel (661) 836-9000 *Founded/Ownrshp* 1954
Sales 71.8MM^E *EMP* 220
SIC 5511 7538

D-U-N-S 04-243-9265 IMP
MOTOR CITY STAMPINGS INC
47783 Gratiot Ave, Chesterfield, MI 48051-2721
Tel (586) 949-8420 *Founded/Ownrshp* 1969
Sales 74.8MM^E *EMP* 330^E
SIC 3465 3544 Body parts, automobile: stamped metal; Special dies, tools, jigs & fixtures; Body parts, automobile: stamped metal; Special dies, tools, jigs & fixtures
Pr: Judith Kucway
**VP:* Roger Kucway
Genl Mgr: Lou Thumm
CTO: Charlie Karam
Plnt Mgr: Bob Ritter
Plnt Mgr: Steve Saunders

D-U-N-S 07-290-3826
MOTOR CLUB INSURANCE ASSOCIATION INC
AAA INSURANCE
910 N 96th St Ste 100, Omaha, NE 68114-2573
Tel (402) 390-1000 *Founded/Ownrshp* 1948
Sales NA *EMP* 150
SIC 6331 6411 Automobile insurance; Insurance agents, brokers & service; Automobile insurance; Insurance agents, brokers & service
Pr: Mark E Grieb
Ch: Robert Stubblefield
Treas: Paul A Andersen
Treas: Paul A Ndersen
Exec: Mary Wagner
Board of Directors: Richard M Hudson, Lloyd Vincent

D-U-N-S 00-594-3873
MOTOR COACH INDUSTRIES INC
VERIZON BUSINESS
(*Suby of* MCII) ★
552 W Stutsman St, Pembina, ND 58271-4308
Tel (701) 825-6234 *Founded/Ownrshp* 1962
Sales 228.6MM^E *EMP* 600
SIC 3711 Motor buses, except trackless trollies, assembly of; Motor buses, except trackless trollies, assembly of
Pr: Steven Clough
CFO: Sandra Morrison
VP: Patricia Ziska
Ex Dir: Carlos Godinez
Sfty Mgr: Rick Anderson
Manager: Robert Lessor

D-U-N-S 79-819-4171
MOTOR COACH INDUSTRIES INTERNATIONAL INC
MCII
(*Suby of* MCII HOLDINGS INC) ★
200 E Oakton St, Des Plaines, IL 60018-1948
Tel (847) 285-2000 *Founded/Ownrshp* 1932
Sales NA *EMP* 1,500
SIC 3713 3711 3714 Bus bodies (motor vehicles); Buses, all types, assembly of; Motor vehicle parts & accessories; Bus bodies (motor vehicles); Buses, all types, assembly of; Motor vehicle parts & accessories
Pr: Richard A Heller
**CFO:* Horst O Sieben
**Treas:* William M Murray
**Ex VP:* Mario Gonzalez
VP: Sam S Amour
**VP:* Timothy J Nalepka
**VP:* Allan D Swanson
VP: Peter Tully
VP: Patricia Ziska
Genl Mgr: Doug Michie
Dir IT: Grant Mushumanski
Board of Directors: Juan Jaime Peterson Farah, Ramsey Frank, Paul Levy, Jeffrey Lightcap, Francisco Rodriquez

D-U-N-S 11-048-6813 IMP
MOTOR COMPONENTS LLC
(*Suby of* BAM ENTERPRISES INC) ★
2243 Corning Rd, Elmira Heights, NY 14903-1031
Tel (607) 737-8011 *Founded/Ownrshp* 2002
Sales 23.2MM^E *EMP* 68
SIC 3714 Motor vehicle wheels & parts
**CFO:* Shel Alfiero
IT Man: Chris Miller

D-U-N-S 14-493-7331
MOTOR CONTROLS INC
STEELINE ENCLOSURE SOLUTIONS
2818 Virgo Ln, Dallas, TX 75229-4718
Tel (972) 247-4440 *Founded/Ownrshp* 1980
Sales 55.1MM^E *EMP* 170
SIC 3444 3561 3625 3565 Metal housings, enclosures, casings & other containers; Pumps & pumping equipment; Industrial controls: push button, selector switches, pilot; Packaging machinery; Metal housings, enclosures, casings & other containers; Pumps & pumping equipment; Industrial controls: push button, selector switches, pilot; Packaging machinery
CEO: James Carter
**Pr:* Craig Carter
**Treas:* Vicki Carter
**VP:* Jeff Hains
**VP:* Roger Vowell
**VP Sls:* Carson Keifer
Sales Asso: David Tucker

D-U-N-S 02-269-9680
MOTOR INN CO
2114 E Main St, Albert Lea, MN 56007-3919
Tel (507) 373-2341 *Founded/Ownrshp* 1962
Sales 21.1MM^E *EMP* 46
SIC 5511 New & used car dealers
Pr: David Christensen
Store Mgr: Jim Kortz
Sls Mgr: Brad Hegwood

D-U-N-S 09-572-8226
MOTOR OIL SUPPLY CO (WA)
1123 4th Ave N, Kent, WA 98032-2941
Tel (253) 854-5454 *Founded/Ownrshp* 1979
Sales 25.4MM^E *EMP* 27
SIC 5172 Lubricating oils & greases
Pr: Saundra J Ruth
**VP:* Philip Maasen
Sls Mgr: Dave Bennett
Sales Asso: Steve Hansen
Sales Asso: Bob Woodruff

D-U-N-S 02-580-0103
MOTOR PARTS & EQUIPMENT CORP
NAPA AUTO PARTS
1696 Northrock Ct, Rockford, IL 61103-1203
Tel (815) 963-6481 *Founded/Ownrshp* 1989
Sales 52.5MM^E *EMP* 110
SIC 5531 Automotive & home supply stores
Pr: Joseph D Hansberry

MOTOR PARTS BARRINGS
See INDUSTRIAL MACHINE & MANUFACTURING CORP

D-U-N-S 00-647-2427
MOTOR POWER EQUIPMENT CO (MT)
4941 Midland Rd, Billings, MT 59101-6311
Tel (406) 657-9440 *Founded/Ownrshp* 1947
Sales 24.1MM^E *EMP* 60^E
SIC 5012 5013 7538 Trucks, commercial; Trailers for trucks, new & used; Truck parts & accessories; Truck engine repair, except industrial; Trucks, commercial; Trailers for trucks, new & used; Truck parts & accessories; Truck engine repair, except industrial
Pr: Bruce Sunwall
**COO:* Brian Sunwall
Ex VP: Marilyn Sunwell
**VP:* Marilyn P Sunwall
Sales Exec: Dave Hardy
Sales Asso: Layne Martin

D-U-N-S 11-296-3590 IMP/EXP
MOTOR SERVICES HUGO STAMP INC
3190 Sw 4th Ave, Fort Lauderdale, FL 33315-3017
Tel (954) 763-3660 *Founded/Ownrshp* 1983
Sales 44.2MM *EMP* 142
Accts Howard N Fink Cpa Pa
SIC 5084 7699 Engines & transportation equipment; Marine engine repair; Engines & transportation equipment; Marine engine repair
Pr: Are Friesecke
**VP:* Frank Friesecke
VP: Stefan Lehmann
VP: Rodrigo Quilula
IT Man: Aliccia Forsythe
Sls Dir: Alberto Cordero
Sls Dir: Marcus Platt

D-U-N-S 03-537-6151
MOTOR SPORTSLAND INC
4001 S State St, Salt Lake City, UT 84107-1590
Tel (801) 262-2921 *Founded/Ownrshp* 1961
Sales 43.2MM *EMP* 55
SIC 5561

MOTOR STATE DISTRIBUTING
See LANE AUTOMOTIVE INC

MOTOR SUPPLY
See GRAFFMANS INC

D-U-N-S 13-776-7570
MOTOR TRANSPORTATION DIVISION NEW MEXICO
(*Suby of* NEW MEXICO DEPARTMENT OF PUBLIC SAFETY) ★
1100 S Saint Francis Dr, Santa Fe, NM 87505-4147
Tel (505) 827-0321 *Founded/Ownrshp* 2000
Sales NA *EMP* 402
SIC 9621 Regulation, administration of transportation; ; Regulation, administration of transportation;
Exec: Rich Williams
IT Man: Jacque Geoffrion
Snr Mgr: Tony Hoffman

D-U-N-S 82-574-4493 IMP
MOTOR TRIKE INC
22667 Fm 15, Troup, TX 75789-6221
Tel (903) 842-3094 *Founded/Ownrshp* 1994
Sales 28.2MM^E *EMP* 132
SIC 3621 3751 Motors & generators; Motorcycles, bicycles & parts; Motors & generators; Motorcycles, bicycles & parts
Pr: Jeffrey L Vey
**Sec:* Diane D Vey

D-U-N-S 01-418-7470 IMP
MOTOR TRUCK EQUIPMENT CO INC
KENWORTH OF PENNSYLVANIA
198 Kost Rd, Carlisle, PA 17015-8534
Tel (717) 766-8000 *Founded/Ownrshp* 1969
Sales 54.5MM^E *EMP* 100
SIC 5012 5013 7538 Commercial vehicles; Trailers for trucks, new & used; Truck tractors; Motor vehicle supplies & new parts; General automotive repair shops; Commercial vehicles; Trailers for trucks, new & used; Truck tractors; Motor vehicle supplies & new parts; General automotive repair shops
Pr: Gareth Mitchell
**CFO:* Marsha Hoy
Genl Mgr: Melissa Motter
Genl Mgr: Mike Wiseman
Sls Mgr: Frank Miller
Sales Asso: Charlie Brown
Sales Asso: Bob Zenker

D-U-N-S 07-770-8709
MOTOR VEHICLE ACCIDENT INDEMNIFICATION CORP
M V A I C
110 William St Fl 19, New York, NY 10038-3937
Tel (212) 791-1280 *Founded/Ownrshp* 1959
Sales NA *EMP* 85
SIC 6331 Assessment associations: fire, marine & casualty insurance
Pr: Jeffrey R Rubinton
**Ch Bd:* V Daniel Robinson II
Treas: Victor Fetaya

MOTOR WERKS OF BARRINGTON
See MOTOR WERKS PARTNERS LP

D-U-N-S 05-784-6966
MOTOR WERKS PARTNERS LP
MOTOR WERKS OF BARRINGTON
1475 S Barrington Rd, Barrington, IL 60010-5205
Tel (847) 842-1352 *Founded/Ownrshp* 1981
Sales 138.6MM^E *EMP* 308
SIC 5511 7515 Automobiles, new & used; Passenger car leasing; Automobiles, new & used; Passenger car leasing
Pt: Paul D Tamraz
Pt: Nick Pontikes

MOTOR WORKS
See DUNDEE & BARRINGTON LLC

D-U-N-S 96-581-6713
MOTOR WORLD GROUP
(*Suby of* M. W. IMPORTS INC.)
150 Motorworld Dr, Wilkes Barre, PA 18702-7009
Tel (570) 829-3500 *Founded/Ownrshp* 1987
Sales 42.0MM^E *EMP* 162^E
Accts Parente Randolph Orlando Ca
SIC 5511 New & used car dealers
Pr: Jerald O Donald

D-U-N-S 09-004-5550 IMP
MOTORAMBAR INC
(*Suby of* GRUPO AMBAR LTD)
Westgate Industrial Park, Catano, PR 00962
Tel (787) 620-0900 *Founded/Ownrshp* 1965, 1969
Sales 48.4MM^E *EMP* 160
SIC 5012 Automobiles & other motor vehicles; Automobiles & other motor vehicles
Pr: Miguel Barleta
**Treas:* David Firpo
**Treas:* Elena Lugo
**VP:* Luis M Machado
**VP:* Jose Ordeix

MOTORCADE AUTOMOTIVE GROUP
See BIG BANK PRODUCTIONS INC

D-U-N-S 04-447-7123 IMP/EXP
▲ MOTORCAR PARTS OF AMERICA INC
2929 California St, Torrance, CA 90503-3914
Tel (310) 212-7910 *Founded/Ownrshp* 1968
Sales 301.7MM *EMP* 2,270
Accts Ernst & Young Llp Los Angeles
Tkr Sym MPAA *Exch* NGS
SIC 3714 3694 3625 5013 Motor vehicle parts & accessories; Alternators, automotive; Starter, electric motor; Motor vehicle supplies & new parts; Motor vehicle parts & accessories; Alternators, automotive; Starter, electric motor; Motor vehicle supplies & new parts
Ch Bd: Selwyn Joffe
COO: Steve Kratz
CFO: David Lee
VP: Gary Delgreco
VP: Ron Namias
VP: Michael Umansky
VP: Michael M Umansky
Opers Mgr: Pedro Hernandez
Manager: Wayne Golonka
Board of Directors: Scott J Adelson, Rudolph J Borneo, Philip Gay, Mel Marks, Duane Miller, Jeffrey Mirvis

D-U-N-S 14-798-0903
MOTORCARS ACQUISITION IV LLC
MERCEDES-BENZ OF BEDFORD
18122 Rockside Rd, Bedford, OH 44146-2040
Tel (440) 439-0100 *Founded/Ownrshp* 2000
Sales 32.1MM^E *EMP* 100
SIC 5511 Automobiles, new & used; Automobiles, new & used
Pr: Jed Hunter
Genl Mgr: Peter Mapp
Genl Mgr: Jamie Pilla
Sales Asso: Jonathan Betlejewski
Sales Asso: Bill Robertson
Snr Mgr: David Kovell
Snr Mgr: Jeremy Zenk

D-U-N-S 06-462-0396 IMP
MOTORCARS WEST L L C
21301 Ventura Blvd, Woodland Hills, CA 91364-2007
Tel (818) 884-4411 *Founded/Ownrshp* 1965
Sales 26.8MM^E *EMP* 89
SIC 5511 5531 7539 Automobiles, new & used; Automobile & truck equipment & parts; Tune-up service, automotive; Automobiles, new & used; Automobile & truck equipment & parts; Tune-up service, automotive
Pr: Harry Gray
**Pr:* Tony Schwertz

D-U-N-S 55-622-5480
MOTORCASTING INC
1323 S 65th St, Milwaukee, WI 53214-3251
Tel (414) 476-1434 *Founded/Ownrshp* 1919
Sales 25.7MM^E *EMP* 200^E
SIC 3321 Ductile iron castings; Gray iron castings; Ductile iron castings; Gray iron castings
Pr: Joseph Kemfton

D-U-N-S 02-291-7699 IMP
MOTORCYCLE SUPERSTORE INC
(*Suby of* MOTORSPORT AFTERMARKET GROUP INC) ★
931 Chevy Way, Medford, OR 97504-4127
Tel (541) 842-4496 *Founded/Ownrshp* 2012
Sales 62.5MM^E *EMP* 140
SIC 5571 5699 Motorcycles; Riding apparel
CEO: Don Becklin
**CFO:* John Warekois
VP: Jay Friedland
VP: John Lloyd
**CIO:* Jason Miller
IT Man: Raul Villagomez
VP Opers: Kevin Murry
Sales Exec: Jay Ogg
Mktg Dir: Erick Barney
Mktg Dir: REA McLean
Pr Mgr: Cheryl Coburn

D-U-N-S 93-359-0697 IMP
MOTORCYCLES TIRES & ACCESSORIES INC
MTA LOUISIANA
6469 Highway 33, Choudrant, LA 71227-3473
Tel (318) 255-0049 *Founded/Ownrshp* 1994
Sales 50.0MM *EMP* 13^E
SIC 5014

D-U-N-S 07-135-1233
MOTORISTS COMMERCIAL MUTUAL INSURANCE CO
MOTORISTS INSURANCE GROUP
471 E Broad St Bsmt, Columbus, OH 43215-3852
Tel (614) 225-8211 *Founded/Ownrshp* 1899
Sales NA *EMP* 32
SIC 6331 Fire, marine & casualty insurance: mutual; Fire, marine & casualty insurance: mutual
Ch Bd: John J Bishop
**Pr:* David L Kaufman
**CFO:* Susan E Haack
VP: Joel Kratzer
Board of Directors: Charles Stapleton, John Bishop, Michael Wiseman, Larry Forrester, Robert Western, Susan Haack, Sandra Harbrecht, David Kaufman, David Lemon, Robert McCracken, Thomas Ogg, Robert Smith

MOTORISTS INSURANCE GROUP
See MOTORISTS MUTUAL INSURANCE CO

MOTORISTS INSURANCE GROUP
See CONSUMERS INSURANCE USA INC

MOTORISTS INSURANCE GROUP
See MOTORISTS LIFE INSURANCE CO

MOTORISTS INSURANCE GROUP
See MOTORISTS COMMERCIAL MUTUAL INSURANCE CO

D-U-N-S 05-285-8636
MOTORISTS LIFE INSURANCE CO
MOTORISTS INSURANCE GROUP
(*Suby of* MOTORISTS INSURANCE GROUP) ★
471 E Broad St Ste 200, Columbus, OH 43215-3842
Tel (614) 225-8211 *Founded/Ownrshp* 1965
Sales NA *EMP* 48
SIC 6311 Life insurance; Life insurance
CEO: David Kaufman
Ch Bd: John Bishop
Pr: Michael Agan
CFO: Susan Haack
Bd of Dir: Michael Wiseman
Board of Directors: Yvette McGee Brown, Larry Forrester, Susan Haack, Sandra Harbrecht, David Kaufman, Charles Stapleton, Michael Wiseman, Johnykessler L

D-U-N-S 00-790-2018
MOTORISTS MUTUAL INSURANCE CO
MOTORISTS INSURANCE GROUP
471 E Broad St Ste 200, Columbus, OH 43215-3805
Tel (614) 225-8211 *Founded/Ownrshp* 1928
Sales NA *EMP* 736
SIC 6331 Fire, marine & casualty insurance: mutual; Automobile insurance; Property damage insurance; Burglary & theft insurance; Fire, marine & casualty insurance: mutual; Automobile insurance; Property damage insurance; Burglary & theft insurance
Ch Bd: John Bishop
Pr: Steven Entenmann
Pr: Teresa King
Pr: Mel Pryor
Pr: Austin Slattery
**CEO:* David Kaufman
**CFO:* Susan Haack
**CFO:* Michael L Wiseman
VP: Michael Agan
VP: Grady Campbell
VP: Daniel L Crawford
VP: Chuck Gaskill
VP: John Huey
VP: Dan Jeffers
VP: Jeff Kirkey
VP: Randy Rudowicz
VP: Karen Schwartz
VP: Rick Stelzer
VP: Pete Weisenberger
Board of Directors: Yvette McGee Brown, Sandra Harbrecht, Robert McCracken, Thomas Ogg, Robert Smith, Michael Wiseman

MOTOROLA
See CINRAM WIRELESS LLC

D-U-N-S 10-634-4898
MOTOROLA EMPLOYEES CREDIT UNION
1205 E Algonquin Rd, Schaumburg, IL 60196-4040
Tel (847) 576-5199 *Founded/Ownrshp* 1939
Sales NA *EMP* 106
SIC 6062 State credit unions; State credit unions
Pr: John C Fiore
**COO:* Michael Murphy
**CFO:* Larry Rosin
Ofcr: Helen Glover
Ofcr: Christine Stotland
VP: Keith Brook
VP: Erin Hennessy
VP Mktg: Sue Nolan

D-U-N-S 77-992-0701
■ MOTOROLA INTERNATIONAL DEVELOPMENT CORP
(*Suby of* MOTOROLA SOLUTIONS INC) ★
1303 E Algonquin Rd, Schaumburg, IL 60196-1079
Tel (847) 576-5000 *Founded/Ownrshp* 1968

Sales NA *EMP* 100
SIC 6159 Loan institutions, general & industrial; Loan institutions, general & industrial
CFO: Carl Koenemann
**Pr:* Garth Milne
VP: James Langrock
IT Man: Hari Bayyea
IT Man: Richard Dalton

MOTOROLA IRRIGATION
See MOTOIR LTD

D-U-N-S 96-342-0638 IMP
MOTOROLA MOBILITY HOLDINGS LLC
(*Suby of* LENOVO GROUP LIMITED)
222 Merchandise Mart Plz # 1600, Chicago, IL 60654-4262
Tel (800) 668-6765 *Founded/Ownrshp* 2014
Sales 1.8MMM^E^ *EMP* 20,500^E^
SIC 3663 Radio & TV communications equipment; Mobile communication equipment; Radio & TV communications equipment; Mobile communication equipment
Pr: Rick Osterloh
**CFO:* Vanessa Wittman
Chf Mktg O: Bill Ogle
**Sr VP:* Iqbal Arshad
Sr VP: Adrienne Hayes
Sr VP: Steve Horowitz
**Sr VP:* Kouji Kodera
Sr VP: Bill Morgan
**Sr VP:* D Scott Offer
Sr VP: Scott Offer
Sr VP: Geoff Roman
**Sr VP:* Geoffrey S Roman
VP: John Bucher
VP: Jayesh Patel
VP: Michael Pencek
Exec: Man Mohan
Dir Rx: B J Marwaha

D-U-N-S 96-342-7765 IMP
MOTOROLA MOBILITY LLC
(*Suby of* MOTOROLA MOBILITY HOLDINGS LLC) ★
222 Merchandise Mart Plz # 1600, Chicago, IL 60654-4262
Tel (800) 866-6765 *Founded/Ownrshp* 2007
Sales 659.0MM^E^ *EMP* 1,996
SIC 3663 4812 Radio & TV communications equipment; Mobile communication equipment; Semiconductors & related devices; Mobile communication equipment; Cellular telephone services
CEO: Rick Osterloh
**Pr:* Sanjay Jha
**Sr VP:* Iqbal Arshad
Sr VP: Adrienne Hayes
Sr VP: Bill Morgan
**Sr VP:* Mark Randall
**VP:* Magnus Ahlqvist
VP: Patrick Beattie
**VP:* Sergio Buniac
VP: Ruth Hennigar
VP: Jeffrey Lutz
**VP:* Jeff Millerv

D-U-N-S 00-552-7247 IMP/EXP
■ **MOTOROLA SALES AND SERVICES INC**
(*Suby of* MOTOROLA SOLUTIONS INC) ★
1303 E Algonquin Rd, Schaumburg, IL 60196-1079
Tel (847) 576-1000 *Founded/Ownrshp* 1952
Sales 522.7MM^E^ *EMP* 2,500
SIC 5065 Electronic parts; Mobile telephone equipment; Electronic parts; Mobile telephone equipment
Pr: Edward Fitzpatrick
**CEO:* Greg Brown
**CFO:* David Devonshire
**Treas:* Garth Milne
**Ex VP:* Gino A Bonanotte
**Ex VP:* Mark Moon
**Sr VP:* Eduardo Conrado
**Sr VP:* Mark S Hacker
Opers Mgr: Reggie Barnes

D-U-N-S 02-951-8649
MOTOROLA SATELLITE COMMUNICATIONS INC
(*Suby of* MOTOROLA MOBILITY LLC) ★
2900 S Diablo Way, Tempe, AZ 85282-3201
Tel (480) 732-2000 *Founded/Ownrshp* 1998, 2011
Sales 57.6MM^E^ *EMP* 1,650
SIC 3674 Semiconductors & related devices; Semiconductors & related devices
Pr: Christopher B Galvin

D-U-N-S 00-132-5463 IMP/EXP
▲ **MOTOROLA SOLUTIONS INC**
1303 E Algonquin Rd, Schaumburg, IL 60196-1079
Tel (847) 576-5000 *Founded/Ownrshp* 1928
Sales 5.8MMM *EMP* 15,024
Accts Kpmg Llp Chicago Illinois
Tkr Sym MSI *Exch* NYS
SIC 3663 3661 Radio & TV communications equipment; Mobile communication equipment; Pagers (one-way); Cellular radio telephone; Modems; Multiplex equipment, telephone & telegraph; Radio & TV communications equipment; Mobile communication equipment; Pagers (one-way); Cellular radio telephone; Modems; Multiplex equipment, telephone & telegraph
Ch Bd: Gregory Q Brown
Pr: Scott Anderson
Pr: Joseph M Guglielmi
Pr: Adrian R Nemcek
CFO: Gino A Bonanotte
Ofcr: Mark S Hacker
Ex VP: Glenn A Gienko
Sr VP: Eduardo F Conrado
VP: Debora Courtright
VP: Jonathan Meyer
VP: John K Wozniak
Comm Man: Chantal Montsion
Board of Directors: Kenneth C Dahlberg, David W Dorman, Egon P Durban, Michael V Hayden, Judy C Lewent, Greg K Mondre, Anne R Pramaggiore, Samuel C Scott III, Bradley E Singer

D-U-N-S 04-920-4936 IMP
MOTORS & ARMATURES INC
MARS
250 Rabro Dr, Hauppauge, NY 11788-4255
Tel (631) 348-0200 *Founded/Ownrshp* 1946
Sales 74.4MM^E^ *EMP* 100
SIC 5078 5075 5064 Refrigeration equipment & supplies; Air conditioning equipment, except room units; Vacuum cleaners; Refrigeration equipment & supplies; Air conditioning equipment, except room units; Vacuum cleaners
CEO: Edward A Chernoff
**CFO:* Therese D'Angelis
**VP:* Ray Mohr
Dir IT: Artie Cennamo
Mktg Mgr: Fred Baron

D-U-N-S 07-209-6857
■ **MOTORS HOLDING SAN FERNANDO VALLEY INC**
(*Suby of* GENERAL MOTORS LLC) ★
300 Renaissance Ctr, Detroit, MI 48243-1402
Tel (313) 556-5000 *Founded/Ownrshp* 2009
Sales 56.4MM^E^ *EMP* 456
SIC 5511 New & used car dealers; New & used car dealers
CEO: Daniel F Akerson
Pr: Richard Wagoner
VP: Bill Farmer
VP: Steve Kovauch
VP: Ron Sobrerro
VP: Doug Stevens

D-U-N-S 05-455-0371
■ **MOTORS INSURANCE CORP**
M I C
(*Suby of* ALLY INSURANCE HOLDINGS INC) ★
300 Galleria Officentre, Southfield, MI 48034-4700
Tel (248) 263-6000 *Founded/Ownrshp* 2008
Sales NA *EMP* 2,260
SIC 6331

D-U-N-S 03-251-9117 EXP
MOTORS JIDD INC
855 Rand Rd, Des Plaines, IL 60016-2336
Tel (224) 250-2222 *Founded/Ownrshp* 2011
Sales 22.1MM^E^ *EMP* 48
SIC 5511 Automobiles, new & used
Owner: Sam Jidd

D-U-N-S 13-154-2979
MOTORS MANAGEMENT CORP
3701 Alabama Ave S, St Louis Park, MN 55416-5156
Tel (952) 258-8800 *Founded/Ownrshp* 1981
Sales 27.2MM^E^ *EMP* 315
SIC 8741 5611 8742 Management services; Men's & boys' clothing stores; Management consulting services; Management services; Men's & boys' clothing stores; Management consulting services
Pr: C David Luther
**VP:* Owen A Parr
Dir IT: Brian Kenny
IT Man: Dan Johnson
Sls Mgr: Alex Mohanna
Sls Mgr: Debbie Tufts

D-U-N-S 11-921-8147
MOTORS MANAGEMENT CORP
90 Us Highway 1 100, Avenel, NJ 07001-1630
Tel (732) 815-0500 *Founded/Ownrshp* 1981
Sales 4.0MM *EMP* 315
SIC 8741 Management services; Management services
Pr: John Pugliese
**Ch:* Paul J Sansone Sr

D-U-N-S 10-651-1199
MOTORS MANAGEMENT INC
TROY HONDA
1835 Maplelawn Dr, Troy, MI 48084-4617
Tel (248) 649-0202 *Founded/Ownrshp* 1983
Sales 20.8MM^E^ *EMP* 47
SIC 5511 5531 Automobiles, new & used; Automotive parts
Pr: William E Fuller
Sales Exec: Dan Amell
Mktg Dir: Jim Corn
Sls Mgr: Tom Rzeppa
Sales Asso: Randy Leong

D-U-N-S 05-249-9873
MOTORSPORT AFTERMARKET GROUP INC
(*Suby of* LDI LTD., LLC)
17771 Mitchell N Ste A, Irvine, CA 92614-6028
Tel (949) 440-5500 *Founded/Ownrshp* 2014
Sales 1.0MMM^E^ *EMP* 1,150
SIC 3751 Motorcycle accessories; Motorcycle accessories
CEO: J A Lacy
Pr: Brian Etter
Pr: Mike Walz
Software D: Vy Le
Mktg Dir: Shane Halstead

D-U-N-S 85-899-9329 IMP
MOTORSPORTS AUTHENTICS INC
6301 Performance Dr Sw, Concord, NC 28027-3426
Tel (704) 454-4000 *Founded/Ownrshp* 1992
Sales 96.7MM^E^ *EMP* 200^E^
SIC 5099 5136 5137 5947 5611 5621 Souvenirs; Sportswear, men's & boys'; Women's & children's sportswear & swimsuits; Gifts & novelties; Clothing, sportswear, men's & boys'; Women's sportswear; Souvenirs; Sportswear, men's & boys'; Women's & children's sportswear & swimsuits; Gifts & novelties; Clothing, sportswear, men's & boys'; Women's sportswear
CEO: Don Hawk
**CFO:* David Riddiford
**CFO:* Melodee L Volosin
**VP:* Jim Morris
**VP:* Tommy Warlick

D-U-N-S 60-543-9707 IMP
MOTORSPORTS AUTHENTICS LLC
(*Suby of* MOTORSPORTS AUTHENTICS INC) ★
6301 Performance Dr Sw, Concord, NC 28027-3426
Tel (704) 454-4000 *Founded/Ownrshp* 2005
Sales 56.5MM^E^ *EMP* 200^E^
SIC 5099 5947 5136 5137 5611 5621 Souvenirs; Souvenirs; Sportswear, men's & boys'; Women's & children's sportswear & swimsuits; Clothing, sportswear, men's & boys'; Women's sportswear; Souvenirs; Souvenirs; Sportswear, men's & boys'; Women's & children's sportswear & swimsuits; Clothing, sportswear, men's & boys'; Women's sportswear
VP: Jim Morris
**VP Bus:* Tommy Warlick
Sales Asso: Michael Barrows

D-U-N-S 80-020-0250
MOTORSPORTS MANAGEMENT INC
MOTORSPORTS SOLUTIONS
12271 Towne Lake Dr, Fort Myers, FL 33913-8012
Tel (239) 690-4647 *Founded/Ownrshp* 2004
Sales 35.8MM^E^ *EMP* 292
SIC 5571 Motorcycle dealers; Motorcycle dealers
Pr: Jeffery S Fischer
**COO:* Glorita Cuiffi
**CFO:* Wolf Tschaikowksy

MOTORSPORTS SOLUTIONS
See MOTORSPORTS MANAGEMENT INC

MOTORTRONICS
See PHASETRONICS INC

MOTORWAY AUTO GROUP
See JD AUTO CORP

MOTORWERKS BMW
See MOTORWERKS INC

D-U-N-S 18-876-1290
MOTORWERKS INC
MOTORWERKS BMW
1300 American Blvd W, Minneapolis, MN 55420-1039
Tel (952) 830-4800 *Founded/Ownrshp* 1992
Sales 30.9MM^E^ *EMP* 85
SIC 5511 Automobiles, new & used; Automobiles, new & used
Ch: Robert Walser
**Pr:* Paul Walser
**VP:* Peter Hasselquist
**VP:* Andrew Walser
Sls Mgr: Dale Stinar

D-U-N-S 13-075-6760
MOTORWORLD AUTOMOTIVE GROUP INC
150 Motorworld Dr, Wilkes Barre, PA 18702-7009
Tel (570) 821-3735 *Founded/Ownrshp* 1999
Sales 75.3MM^E^ *EMP* 745
SIC 7515 7377 Passenger car leasing; Computer rental & leasing; Passenger car leasing; Computer rental & leasing
Pr: Gerald T Odonnel
**CFO:* Richard J Osick
Sr VP: Marc Diamand
Sr VP: Dino Martincic
Sr VP: Dave Triplett
VP: Brian Maher
**VP:* Lonnie L Swiger
Genl Mgr: Chris Lark
MIS Dir: Rich Gibbons
Sls Dir: Wayne Geare
Mktg Mgr: Dorie Fader

D-U-N-S 07-194-5906 IMP/EXP
MOTOSPORT INC
15353 Sw Sequoia Pkwy # 140, Portland, OR 97224-7283
Tel (503) 783-5600 *Founded/Ownrshp* 2005
Sales 85.7MM^E^ *EMP* 200
SIC 5571 Motorcycle parts & accessories; Motorcycle parts & accessories
Dir: Ian Griffith
Sales Asso: Kent Reynolds

D-U-N-S 80-386-4461 IMP
MOTOSTAR TIRE & AUTO PRODUCTS INC
4 Webb Dr, Merrimack, NH 03054-4803
Tel (603) 281-5114 *Founded/Ownrshp* 1993
Sales 43.7MM^E^ *EMP* 25^E^
SIC 5013 5014 Automotive supplies & parts; Tires & tubes
Pr: Eugene T Bova Jr

D-U-N-S 05-881-5911
MOTOWN AUTOMOTIVE DISTRIBUTING CO INC
24701 Hallwood Ct, Farmington Hills, MI 48335-1606
Tel (248) 427-0910 *Founded/Ownrshp* 1971
Sales 50.1MM^E^ *EMP* 100
SIC 5013 Automotive supplies & parts; Automotive supplies & parts
Pr: James Sechrist
**Sec:* Mary M Sechrist
**VP:* Paul Sechrist
Genl Mgr: Paul Clunis

MOTOWORLD OF EL CAJON
See ACME CYCLES INC

D-U-N-S 00-193-9826
MOTT CHARLES STEWART FOUNDATION INC (MI)
503 S Saginaw St Ste 1200, Flint, MI 48502-1807
Tel (810) 238-5651 *Founded/Ownrshp* 1926
Sales 106.7MM *EMP* 106
SIC 6732 Charitable trust management; Charitable trust management
Ch Bd: William S White
Ch Bd: William S Flint
Ofcr: Maggie Potter
VP: Maureen H Flint
VP: Marilyn Stein Lefeber
**VP:* Phillip Peters
**VP:* Maureen Smyth
**VP:* Robert E Swaney Jr
CTO: John Brown
Pgrm Dir: Sam Passmore

MOTT COMMUNITY COLLEGE
See CHARLES STEWART MOTT COLLEGE COMMUNITY

D-U-N-S 00-115-0739 IMP/EXP
MOTT CORP (CT)
84 Spring Ln, Farmington, CT 06032-3142
Tel (800) 289-6688 *Founded/Ownrshp* 1959, 2009
Sales 59.6MM^E^ *EMP* 326
SIC 3569 Filters; Filters
CEO: Boris F Levin
**VP:* Thomas Fahey
**VP:* Franklin J Hubbell
**VP:* Kenneth L Robow
**VP:* Susanne D Spargo
**VP:* Jeanine Wilmot
**CTO:* Ken Rubow
Dir IT: Bill Bergamo
IT Man: Sylvia Hall
Mfg Mgr: Cindy Lovejoy
Mfg Mgr: Jamie Stringer

MOTTS
See MOTTS LLP

D-U-N-S 06-987-1200 IMP/EXP
■ **MOTTS LLP**
MOTTS
(*Suby of* DR PEPPER SNAPPLE GROUP INC) ★
55 Hunter Ln, Elmsford, NY 10523-1334
Tel (972) 673-8088 *Founded/Ownrshp* 2008
Sales 215.9MM^E^ *EMP* 1,000
SIC 2033 5149 2087 Fruit juices: packaged in cans, jars, etc.; Apple sauce: packaged in cans, jars, etc.; Beverage concentrates; Cocktail mixes, nonalcoholic; Fruit juices: packaged in cans, jars, etc.; Apple sauce: packaged in cans, jars, etc.; Beverage concentrates; Cocktail mixes, nonalcoholic
MIS Dir: Jeff Morgan
**Genl Couns:* Jim Baldwin

MOTUS INTEGRATED TECHNOLOGIES
See MOTUS LLC

D-U-N-S 07-921-5669
MOTUS LLC
MOTUS INTEGRATED TECHNOLOGIES
(*Suby of* ACR II MOTUS INTEGRATED TECHNOLOGIES COOPERATIEF U.A.)
88 E 48th St, Holland, MI 49423-9307
Tel (616) 422-7479 *Founded/Ownrshp* 2013, 2015
Sales 271.3MM^E^ *EMP* 760
SIC 3465 Body parts, automobile: stamped metal; Body parts, automobile: stamped metal
CEO: Shannon White
COO: Kevin Kernan
VP: Thomas Eickhoff
VP: Chris Hall
VP: Craig Lorraine
VP: Carol Stewart

MOULDING & MILLWORK
See METRIE INC

D-U-N-S 02-011-5747
MOULTON LOGISTICS MANAGEMENT
7850 Ruffner Ave, Van Nuys, CA 91406-1619
Tel (818) 997-1800 *Founded/Ownrshp* 1969
Sales 57.0MM^E^ *EMP* 175
SIC 7389 4822 Subscription fulfillment services: magazine, newspaper, etc.; Electronic mail; Subscription fulfillment services: magazine, newspaper, etc.; Electronic mail
Pr: Lawrence Moulton
Pr: Shane Bradford
**VP:* Tom Moulton
CIO: Elaine Hattendorf
IT Man: Ernie Marsalis
Netwrk Mgr: Oscar Orozco

D-U-N-S 00-329-2620 IMP
MOULTRIE MANUFACTURING CO (GA)
1403 Ga Highway 133 S # 3, Moultrie, GA 31788-2199
Tel (229) 985-1312 *Founded/Ownrshp* 1952
Sales 31.3MM^E^ *EMP* 95
SIC 3355 2514 3446 3443 3369 3365 Structural shapes, rolled, aluminum; Rails, rolled & drawn, aluminum; Lawn furniture: metal; Architectural metalwork; Fabricated plate work (boiler shop); Nonferrous foundries; Aluminum foundries; Structural shapes, rolled, aluminum; Rails, rolled & drawn, aluminum; Lawn furniture: metal; Architectural metalwork; Fabricated plate work (boiler shop); Nonferrous foundries; Aluminum foundries
CEO: William Edward Smith
Genl Mgr: Tim Carpenter
Genl Mgr: Peter Dillard

D-U-N-S 07-770-3726
MOUND COTTON WOLLAN & GREENGRASS
1 New York Plz Ste 4510, New York, NY 10004-1960
Tel (212) 804-4200 *Founded/Ownrshp* 1981
Sales 25.2MM^E^ *EMP* 150
SIC 8111 General practice law office; Corporate, partnership & business law; Securities law; General practice law office; Corporate, partnership & business law; Securities law
Pt: Stuart Cotton
Pt: Lawerence S Greengrass
Pr: Angelika Wawrzyszko
Ex Dir: Edward Bale
Ex Dir: Ed Bayle
IT Man: Roger Eichenour
Counsel: Leonard Dome
Assoc Ed: Christine Wong

D-U-N-S 96-301-6535
MOUNDS VIEW PUBLIC SCHOOL DISTRICT
350 Highway 96 W, Shoreview, MN 55126-1951
Tel (651) 621-6017 *Founded/Ownrshp* 1952
Sales 298.8M *EMP* 1,500^E^
SIC 8211 Elementary & secondary schools; Elementary & secondary schools
CEO: Dan Hooverman
CFO: Carol Neilsen

MOUNDS VIEW SCHOOL DISTRICT 62
See IND SCHOOL DIST 621

D-U-N-S 10-005-8858
MOUNT AIRY CITY SCHOOL DISTRICT
130 Rawley Ave, Mount Airy, NC 27030-3529
Tel (336) 786-8355 *Founded/Ownrshp* 1895
Sales 17.8MM *EMP* 300
SIC 8211 Public elementary & secondary schools; Public elementary & secondary schools
Dir IT: Carrie Venable
Pr Dir: Jamie Martin

MOUNT AIRY RESORT AND CASINO
See POCONO ASSOCIATES LP

D-U-N-S 03-007-1633
MOUNT ALOYSIUS COLLEGE (PA)
7373 Admiral Peary Hwy, Cresson, PA 16630-1999
Tel (814) 886-6412 *Founded/Ownrshp* 1939
Sales 30.2MM *EMP* 278
Accts Parente Beard Llc State Colle
SIC 8221 College, except junior; College, except junior
Pr: Thomas Foley
Ofcr: Michael Greer
Ofcr: Donald Shay
Sr VP: Suzanne Campbell
VP: Frank C Crouse Jr
VP: Jennifer Dubuque
VP: Jane Grassadonia
VP: Amy Oberholtzer
Comm Dir: John Coyle
Dir Sec: William Trexler
CTO: Beth Sharp

D-U-N-S 10-711-2856
MOUNT ALVERNA HOME INC
6765 State Rd Ofc, Cleveland, OH 44134-4597
Tel (440) 843-7800 *Founded/Ownrshp* 1936
Sales 15.5MM^E *EMP* 320
SIC 8051 Skilled nursing care facilities; Skilled nursing care facilities
Mktg Dir: Debbie Rapp
HC Dir: Marylou Fleck

MOUNT ANTHONY HIGH SCHOOL
See MOUNT ANTHONY UNION HIGH SCHOOL DISTRICT 14

D-U-N-S 19-361-3551
MOUNT ANTHONY UNION HIGH SCHOOL DISTRICT 14
MOUNT ANTHONY HIGH SCHOOL
301 Park St, Bennington, VT 05201-5011
Tel (802) 447-7541 *Founded/Ownrshp* 1930
Sales 23.4MM^E *EMP* 800
SIC 8211 Public junior high school; Public senior high school; Public junior high school; Public senior high school

D-U-N-S 07-381-2125
MOUNT AUBURN HOSPITAL
(*Suby of* CAREGROUP INC) ★
330 Mount Auburn St, Cambridge, MA 02138-5597
Tel (617) 492-3500 *Founded/Ownrshp* 1871
Sales 321.5MM *EMP* 1,700
SIC 8062 General medical & surgical hospitals; General medical & surgical hospitals
CEO: Jeanette G Clough
COO: John Patrick
CFO: Peter Semaneza
CFO: William Sullivan
Chf Mktg O: Philip Wu
VP: John Bridgeman
VP: Denis Bustin
Dir Rx: Greg Sophis
Dir Sec: Norman Colling
Prgrm Mgr: Margie McGlone
Off Mgr: Jean Burns

D-U-N-S 07-656-8476
MOUNT AUBURN PATHOLOGISTS INC
330 Mount Auburn St, Cambridge, MA 02138-5502
Tel (617) 492-3500 *Founded/Ownrshp* 1971
Sales 60.7MM *EMP* 5
SIC 8071 Pathological laboratory; Pathological laboratory
Pr: Gregory Kauvin

D-U-N-S 03-851-8767
MOUNT BAKER KIDNEY CENTER INC
410 Birchwood Ave Ste 100, Bellingham, WA 98225-1783
Tel (360) 734-4243 *Founded/Ownrshp* 1980
Sales 32.2MM *EMP* 45
SIC 8092 Kidney dialysis centers; Kidney dialysis centers
Ex Dir: Jeff Lehman

MOUNT CARMEL CEMETARY
See CATHOLIC CEMETERIES

D-U-N-S 95-884-2643
MOUNT CARMEL EAST HOSPITAL
(*Suby of* NIAGARA HEALTH CORP) ★
6001 E Broad St, Columbus, OH 43213-1570
Tel (614) 234-6000 *Founded/Ownrshp* 1995
Sales 161.5MM^E *EMP* 1,100
SIC 8062 General medical & surgical hospitals; General medical & surgical hospitals
CEO: Joseph Calvaruso
Dir Inf Cn: Karen Swecker
Dir Rx: Jenni Wai
QA Dir: Katie Barga
Pr Mgr: Robby Channell
Surgeon: Aaron Kulwicki
Doctor: Thomas Brady
Pharmcst: Tracy Morris
HC Dir: Tiffany Anderson
HC Dir: Peggy Sadowski

D-U-N-S 07-504-0121
MOUNT CARMEL HEALTH
(*Suby of* NIAGARA HEALTH CORP) ★
793 W State St, Columbus, OH 43222-1551
Tel (614) 234-5000 *Founded/Ownrshp* 1995
Sales 289.9MM^E *EMP* 3,507
SIC 8062 General medical & surgical hospitals; Hospital, professional nursing school; General medical & surgical hospitals; Hospital, professional nursing school
Prin: Marcia Ladue
Chf Path: Steven Tuttle
COO: Sloan A Fache
CFO: Jackie Prineau
VP: Dina Bush
VP: Brian Smith
VP: Larry Swanner
Dir Risk M: Rebecca Smith
Dir Risk M: Billie Watson
Dir Lab: Randy Clark
Dir Rx: Sherry Haberkern
Dir Rx: Natalie Malone

D-U-N-S 07-975-8372
MOUNT CARMEL HEALTH PLAN MEDIG
6150 E Broad St, Columbus, OH 43213-1574
Tel (614) 546-3138 *Founded/Ownrshp* 2013
Sales 423.5MM *EMP* 3^E
SIC 8099 Health & allied services

D-U-N-S 04-965-3066
MOUNT CARMEL HEALTH SYSTEM
CATHOLIC HEALTH EAST
(*Suby of* CATHOLIC HEALTH EAST) ★
6150 E Broad St, Columbus, OH 43213-1574
Tel (614) 234-6000 *Founded/Ownrshp* 1995
Sales 1.2MMM *EMP* 8,000
SIC 8062 General medical & surgical hospitals; General medical & surgical hospitals
CEO: Claus Von Zychlin
**Pr:* Douglas H Stine
COO: Ronald E Whiteside
Treas: Michael Cooney
VP: Chris Browning
VP: Tessa Burke
VP: Dina Bush
VP: P E Cozier
VP: Lyn Flanagan
VP: Hugh Jones
VP: Dawn Sorensen

D-U-N-S 00-805-5935
MOUNT CARMEL LAB SERVICE CENTERS
495 Cooper Rd Ste 100, Westerville, OH 43081-8710
Tel (614) 882-2581 *Founded/Ownrshp* 2007
Sales 423.5MM *EMP* 20^E
SIC 8071 Medical laboratories
Prin: Carol M Wilson

D-U-N-S 83-111-5464
MOUNT CARMEL LLC
MOUNT CARMEL REHABILITATION
5700 W Layton Ave, Milwaukee, WI 53220-4016
Tel (414) 281-7200 *Founded/Ownrshp* 1953
Sales 8.8MM^E *EMP* 700
SIC 8049 8051 Nurses & other medical assistants; Skilled nursing care facilities; Nurses & other medical assistants; Skilled nursing care facilities

D-U-N-S 96-489-7487
MOUNT CARMEL NEW ALBANY SURGICAL HOSPITAL
7333 Smiths Mill Rd, New Albany, OH 43054-9291
Tel (614) 775-6600 *Founded/Ownrshp* 2010
Sales 113.5MM *EMP* 41^E
SIC 8062 General medical & surgical hospitals; General medical & surgical hospitals
Prin: Gregory Beham
CFO: Kellie Risser
Chf Nrs Of: Lynda Yonker
Pharmcst: Amanda Parker

MOUNT CARMEL REHABILITATION
See MOUNT CARMEL LLC

MOUNT CLEMENS MEDICAL CENTER
See MOUNT CLEMENS REGIONAL MEDICAL CENTER INC

D-U-N-S 07-635-7946
MOUNT CLEMENS REGIONAL MEDICAL CENTER INC
MOUNT CLEMENS MEDICAL CENTER
(*Suby of* MCLAREN FLINT) ★
1000 Harrington St, Mount Clemens, MI 48043-2920
Tel (586) 493-8000 *Founded/Ownrshp* 1944
Sales 303.5MM *EMP* 2,249
Accts Plante & Moran Pllc Portage
SIC 8062 General medical & surgical hospitals; General medical & surgical hospitals
CEO: Tom Brisse
**Pr:* Mark O'Halla
Trst: Monroe Adams
VP: David Klinger
Off Mgr: Bridget Berlin
VP Opers: Susan Durst
Sfty Dirs: Bruce Anderson
Surgeon: Andrea Gerber
Surgeon: Joel Strehl
Obsttrcn: Brandon Freel
Diag Rad: Roshan Pai

D-U-N-S 85-919-4904
MOUNT CONSTRUCTION CO INC
427 S White Horse Pike, Berlin, NJ 08009-9003
Tel (856) 767-3897 *Founded/Ownrshp* 1986
Sales 55.5MM^E *EMP* 140
SIC 1623 1611 Underground utilities contractor; Highway & street construction; Underground utilities contractor; Highway & street construction
Pr: Dave Smith
IT Man: Jennifer Cantlin

MOUNT DESERT ISLAND
See AOS 91

MOUNT DESERT ISLAND HLTH CTRS
See MOUNT DESERT ISLAND HOSPITAL INC

D-U-N-S 07-746-8445
MOUNT DESERT ISLAND HOSPITAL INC
MOUNT DESERT ISLAND HLTH CTRS
10 Wayman Ln, Bar Harbor, ME 04609-1625
Tel (207) 288-5081 *Founded/Ownrshp* 1897
Sales 49.9MM *EMP* 310
SIC 8011 8062 Offices & clinics of medical doctors; General medical & surgical hospitals; Offices & clinics of medical doctors; General medical & surgical hospitals
CEO: Arthur Blank
Dir Vol: Brenda Sprague
CFO: Christina Harding
VP: Barbara Hannon
VP: Bradley Parken
VP: Louise Soucy
Dir Rx: Trevor Casey
Dir Rx: Bill Kenausis
Off Mgr: Lisa Dewitt
Dir IT: Bruce Donlin
Psych: Alan Graff

MOUNT DEVELOPMENT SERVICES
See MDS COMMUNICATIONS CORP

D-U-N-S 06-238-6883 IMP
MOUNT FRANKLIN FOODS LLC (TX)
ELAMF
1800 Northwestern Dr, El Paso, TX 79912-1122
Tel (915) 877-4079 *Founded/Ownrshp* 1914, 2006
Sales 357.0MM^E *EMP* 980
SIC 5145 2068 2064

D-U-N-S 08-009-9566
MOUNT HEALTHY CITY SCHOOLS
7615 Harrison Ave, Mount Healthy, OH 45231-3107
Tel (513) 729-0077 *Founded/Ownrshp* 1875
Sales 828.9M^E *EMP* 400
SIC 8211 Public elementary & secondary schools

D-U-N-S 09-792-8675
MOUNT HEALTHY CITY SCHOOLS
MT HEALTHY SCHOOL DISTRICT
7615 Harrison Ave, Mount Healthy, OH 45231-3107
Tel (513) 729-0077 *Founded/Ownrshp* 1875
Sales 23.3MM^E *EMP* 400
SIC 8211 Public elementary & secondary schools; Secondary school; Public elementary & secondary schools; Secondary school
**Treas:* Rebecca Brooks
Teacher Pr: Karen Green
HC Dir: Sarah Gahring

D-U-N-S 17-325-8641
MOUNT HOOD SKI PATROL
Government Camp Loop Rd, Portland, OR 97208
Tel (866) 828-9205 *Founded/Ownrshp* 1937
Sales 92.2M *EMP* 420
SIC 8699 Personal interest organization; Personal interest organization
Pr: Jim Trett
**Pr:* Floyd Hunsaker
**Sec:* Joel Stevens

D-U-N-S 19-307-8177
MOUNT HOREB AREA SCHOOL DISTRICT
1304 E Lincoln St, Mount Horeb, WI 53572-2077
Tel (608) 437-2400 *Founded/Ownrshp* 1960
Sales 20.6MM^E *EMP* 300
SIC 8211 Public elementary & secondary schools; Finishing school, secondary; High school, junior or senior; Public elementary & secondary schools; Finishing school, secondary; High school, junior or senior
CFO: Michelle Denk
Treas: Diana Rothamer
MIS Dir: Ryan Curless
IT Man: Mae Magnuson
Teacher Pr: Kris Sutterparent

D-U-N-S 07-380-4866
MOUNT IDA COLLEGE
NATIONAL CENTER FOR DEATH EDUC
777 Dedham St, Newton, MA 02459-3310
Tel (617) 928-4500 *Founded/Ownrshp* 1927
Sales 47.3MM *EMP* 350
Accts Cliftonlarsonallen Llp Quincy
SIC 8221 College, except junior; College, except junior
Pr: Barry Brown
**Pr:* Carol J Matteson
Ofcr: Joe Pappagallo
VP: Philip A Conroy Jr
**VP:* David G Healy
VP: Cheryl Sleboda
Assoc Dir: Steve Peters IV
Ex Dir: Kenneth Spritz
Pgrm Dir: Jacqueline Palmer

D-U-N-S 78-222-0370 IMP
MOUNT JOY WIRE CORP
1000 E Main St, Mount Joy, PA 17552-9332
Tel (717) 653-1461 *Founded/Ownrshp* 1991
Sales 81.2MM^E *EMP* 150
SIC 3315 Wire & fabricated wire products; Wire & fabricated wire products
CEO: Tom R Duff
**Pr:* Ty Krieger
MIS Dir: Paul Bucher
Plnt Mgr: Byron Shiffer
Plnt Mgr: John Steine
Board of Directors: Fredrick R Krieger

D-U-N-S 00-578-6965
MOUNT KELLETT CAPITAL MANAGEMENT LP
1345 6th Ave Fl 46, New York, NY 10105-0302
Tel (212) 588-6100 *Founded/Ownrshp* 2008
Sales 20.3MM^E *EMP* 38^E
SIC 6799 Investors
CFO: Richard Frapart
Assoc Dir: Ben Roberts
Counsel: David Sandler
Snr Mgr: Cody Donnan
Snr Mgr: Joseph Hartswell
Snr Mgr: Michael Linahan
Snr Mgr: Gregg Montanaro

D-U-N-S 07-668-6435
MOUNT KISCO MEDICAL GROUP PC
MKMG
90 S Bedford Rd, Mount Kisco, NY 10549-3422
Tel (914) 241-1050 *Founded/Ownrshp* 1989
Sales 133.1MM^E *EMP* 900
SIC 8011 Physicians' office, including specialists; Physicians' office, including specialists
Ch Bd: Scott Hayworth MD
Ofcr: Amy Fleming
QA Dir: Rosemarie White
Mktg Mgr: Sonia Young
Orthpdst: Eric Grossman
Doctor: Deborah Cerar
Doctor: Claire Hibbard
Doctor: Michele McLeod
Doctor: Emily Puntillo
Doctor: Ronald Wallach
Doctor: Robert Wolfson MD

D-U-N-S 10-060-4768
MOUNT LAUREL TOWNSHIP PUBLIC SCHOOLS
330 Mount Laurel Rd, Mount Laurel, NJ 08054-9521
Tel (856) 235-3387 *Founded/Ownrshp* 1890
Sales 35.8MM^E *EMP* 730
SIC 8211 Public elementary & secondary schools; Public elementary & secondary schools
Schl Brd P: Diane Blair
Teacher Pr: Susan Henry

D-U-N-S 15-857-3683
MOUNT LAUREL TWP MUA
1201 S Church St, Mount Laurel, NJ 08054-2909
Tel (856) 234-0062 *Founded/Ownrshp* 1950
Sales 64.9MM^E *EMP* 126
Accts Bowman & Company Llp Voorhee
SIC 4971 ; Water distribution or supply systems for irrigation
Ch: Geraldine Nardello
**Ex Dir:* Pamela J Carolan
MIS Dir: Joseph Lehmann
Snr Mgr: William Jack

D-U-N-S 07-384-1595
MOUNT MARY UNIVERSITY INC
2900 N Menomonee Rvr Pkwy, Milwaukee, WI 53222-4545
Tel (414) 258-4810 *Founded/Ownrshp* 1913
Sales 32.4MM *EMP* 280
Accts Schenck Sc Green Bay Wi
SIC 8221 College, except junior; College, except junior
Pr: Eileen Schwalbach
COO: Sandra Ruesink
**Sr VP:* Robert I Crombie

D-U-N-S 07-349-9584
MOUNT MERCY UNIVERSITY
1330 Elmhurst Dr Ne, Cedar Rapids, IA 52402-4797
Tel (319) 363-1323 *Founded/Ownrshp* 1928
Sales 41.2MM *EMP* 180
Accts Mcgladrey Llp Davenport Iow
SIC 8221 University; University
Pr: Laurie M Hamen JD
**Pr:* Christopher Blake
**VP:* Buelaad Doaugherty
VP: Megan Hall
VP: Lisa Lafler
**VP:* Barbara Pooley
VP: Taylor Zumbach
Dir Lab: Sharon Lutgens
CTO: Wade Kooiman
Psych: Karol White
Pgrm Dir: Candace Chihak

D-U-N-S 05-292-1079
MOUNT MORRIS CNSOLIDATED SCHOOLS (MI)
12356 Walter St, Mount Morris, MI 48458-1749
Tel (810) 591-7100 *Founded/Ownrshp* 1958
Sales 17.0MM^E *EMP* 310^E
SIC 8211 Public elementary & secondary schools; Public elementary & secondary schools
IT Man: Ben McGuire

D-U-N-S 00-783-6462
MOUNT NITTANY HEALTH SYSTEM (PA)
1800 E Park Ave, State College, PA 16803-6709
Tel (814) 231-7040 *Founded/Ownrshp* 2011
Sales 387.7MM^E *EMP* 1,541^E
SIC 8062 General medical & surgical hospitals
Pr: Steven Brown
Owner: Robert Foust
COO: Debbie Linnes

D-U-N-S 06-979-6241 IMP
MOUNT NITTANY MEDICAL CENTER
(*Suby of* MOUNT NITTANY HEALTH SYSTEM) ★
1800 E Park Ave, State College, PA 16803-6797
Tel (814) 231-7000 *Founded/Ownrshp* 1902
Sales 325.9MM *EMP* 902
SIC 8062 General medical & surgical hospitals; General medical & surgical hospitals
CEO: Richard Wisniewski
CFO: Richard Wiesensky
Bd of Dir: Julie Charnosky
Ofcr: Steven Brown
**Ex VP:* David B Peterson
Sr VP: Tom Charles
**Sr VP:* Janet Schachtner
Sr VP: Wayne Thompson
VP: Robert Wunar
Comm Dir: Maureen Karstetter
Dir Rad: Jenny Foreman
Dir Rad: Dana Miller
Dir Rx: Angela Rickabaugh
Dir Rx: John Rossi

D-U-N-S 07-984-1992
MOUNT NITTANY MEDICAL CENTER HEALTH SERVICES INC
MOUNT NITTANY PHYSICIAN GROUP
(*Suby of* MOUNT NITTANY HEALTH SYSTEM) ★
1800 E Park Ave, State College, PA 16803-6797
Tel (814) 234-8800 *Founded/Ownrshp* 2002
Sales 61.7MM *EMP* 54^E
Accts Baker Tilly Virchow Krause Llp
SIC 8011 General & family practice, physician/surgeon
Ch: Pete Roy III
**V Ch:* Craig Collison MD
**Treas:* Paul Guillard MD

MOUNT NITTANY PHYSICIAN GROUP
See MOUNT NITTANY MEDICAL CENTER HEALTH SERVICES INC

D-U-N-S 04-207-1118
MOUNT OLIVE BOARD OF EDUCATION (INC)
89 Us Highway 46, Budd Lake, NJ 07828-1703
Tel (973) 691-4000 *Founded/Ownrshp* 1920
Sales 45.7MM^E *EMP* 800
SIC 8211 Public elementary & secondary schools; Public elementary & secondary schools
Adm Dir: Donald Todd

D-U-N-S 00-318-3902 IMP
MOUNT OLIVE PICKLE CO INC (NC)
THAT'S PICKLICIOUS
1 Cucumber Blvd, Mount Olive, NC 28365-1210
Tel (919) 658-2535 *Founded/Ownrshp* 1926
Sales 198.6MM^E *EMP* 600
SIC 2035 Pickles, vinegar; Relishes, vinegar; Pickles, vinegar; Relishes, vinegar
Pr: William H Bryan
COO: Doug Brock
CFO: Dan Bowen
**VP:* Richard D Bowen
**VP:* A Douglas Brock
**VP:* Robert D Frye Jr
VP: Rich Gerber
Dir Bus: Robert Springer
Telecom Ex: Sheila Coats
Sfty Dirs: Gordon Bennett
Opers Mgr: Bob Quinn

D-U-N-S 07-979-9160
MOUNT OLIVE SCHOOL DISTRICT
89 Us Rte 46, Budd Lake, NJ 07828
Tel (973) 691-4000 *Founded/Ownrshp* 2015
Sales 5.4MM^E *EMP* 412^E
SIC 8211 Public elementary & secondary schools

D-U-N-S 07-135-6638
MOUNT OLIVET ROLLING ACRES INC (MN)
18986 Lake Dr E, Chanhassen, MN 55317-9348
Tel (952) 474-5974 *Founded/Ownrshp* 1966
Sales 19.1MM *EMP* 400
Accts Malloy Montague Karnowski R
SIC 8361 Children's home; Home for the mentally retarded; Children's home; Home for the mentally retarded
Ex Dir: Bruce Torgerson
**Treas:* Wayne Neubarth
**VP:* Thomas Macnally
Pgrm Dir: Steven Anderson
Pgrm Dir: Karen Brantner

D-U-N-S 04-708-3662
MOUNT PLEASANT INDEPENDENT SCHOOL DISTRICT
2230 N Edwards Ave, Mount Pleasant, TX 75455-2036
Tel (903) 575-2000 *Founded/Ownrshp* 1851
Sales 54.2MM *EMP* 1,050
Accts Arnold Walker Arnold & Co
SIC 8211 Public elementary & secondary schools; Public elementary & secondary schools
Bd of Dir: Mary Hearron
Bd of Dir: Lance Hinson
Trst: Ray Brown
Trst: Palmore Currey
Trst: Vivian Fowler
Trst: J A Petty
Trst: Mark Traylor
Pr Dir: Judi Saxton
HC Dir: Debra Malone

D-U-N-S 01-694-9158
MOUNT PROSPECT SCHOOL DISTRICT 57 (IL)
701 W Gregory St Fl 1, Mount Prospect, IL 60056-2220
Tel (847) 394-7300 *Founded/Ownrshp* 1881, 2002
Sales 29.3MM *EMP* 330
Accts Miller Cooper & Co Ltd De
SIC 8211 8741 Public elementary school; Public junior high school; Public senior high school; School board; Management services; Public elementary school; Public junior high school; Public senior high school; School board; Management services
Bd of Dir: Eileen Kowalczyk
Bd of Dir: Joe Leane
Bd of Dir: Karen Nejdl
Dir IT: Trevor Hope
Schl Brd P: Michael V Berry
HC Dir: Cathy Black

D-U-N-S 00-297-1612 EXP
MOUNT PROSPECTS NORTHWEST ELECTRICAL SUPPLY CO INC
600 E Rand Rd, Mount Prospect, IL 60056-2533
Tel (847) 818-5234 *Founded/Ownrshp* 1956
Sales 20.1MM^E *EMP* 48
SIC 5063

MOUNT RODGERS CMNTY SVCS BD
See CARROLL HOUSE RESIDENTIAL SERVICE

D-U-N-S 08-305-4601
MOUNT ROGERS COMMUNITY SERVICES BOARD
ADMINISTRATIVE OFFICE
770 W Ridge Rd, Wytheville, VA 24382-1187
Tel (276) 223-3200 *Founded/Ownrshp* 1972
Sales 39.6MM *EMP* 805^E
Accts Robinson Farmer Cox Associat
SIC 8322 8331 Individual & family services; Vocational rehabilitation agency; Individual & family services; Vocational rehabilitation agency
Ex Dir: Alisa Moore

D-U-N-S 07-272-1632
MOUNT SAINT MARY COLLEGE
330 Powell Ave, Newburgh, NY 12550-3412
Tel (845) 561-0800 *Founded/Ownrshp* 1954
Sales 55.8MM *EMP* 550^E
Accts Crowe Horwath Llp New York
SIC 8221 Colleges & universities; Colleges & universities
Pr: Father Kevin E Mackin
**CFO:* Richard S Morgan
VP: Mary Hinton
VP: James Raimo
**VP:* Iris Turkenkopf
CIO: Dennis Rush
IT Man: Sandy Fisher
Info Man: Barbara Connolly
Sfty Mgr: Carl Truffi
Plnt Mgr: Robert Herder
Pr Mgr: Michelle Iacuessa

MOUNT SAINT MARY'S SEMINARY
See MOUNT SAINT MARYS UNIVERSITY INC

MOUNT SAINT MARY'S UNIVERSITY
See MOUNT ST MARYS COLLEGE

D-U-N-S 07-495-0254
MOUNT SAINT MARYS UNIVERSITY INC
MOUNT SAINT MARY'S SEMINARY
16300 Old Emmitsburg Rd, Emmitsburg, MD 21727-7702
Tel (301) 447-3723 *Founded/Ownrshp* 1808
Sales 101.9MM^E *EMP* 890
Accts Mcgladrey & Pullen Llp Gaith
SIC 8221 College, except junior; College, except junior
Pr: Simon Newman
Trst: Thomas Mullelly
Ofcr: Matthew Lewis
Ofcr: Andrew Marfo
Ofcr: Catherine Miller
Ofcr: Tracy Reagan
Ofcr: Ryan Spevak
**Ex VP:* Dan Soller
**VP:* John Butler
**VP:* Paulie Engelsphaperr
**VP:* Michael Malewicki
**VP:* David Rehm

MOUNT SAN RAFAEL HOSPITAL
See TRINIDAD AREA HEALTH ASSOCIATION

MOUNT SCRAP MATERIAL COMPANY
See WASTE RECYCLING INC

D-U-N-S 96-630-1884
MOUNT SINAI COMMUNITY FOUNDATION
2750 W 15th Pl, Chicago, IL 60608-1704
Tel (708) 786-2900 *Founded/Ownrshp* 2011
Sales 76.0MM^E *EMP* 3
SIC 8641 Civic social & fraternal associations; Civic social & fraternal associations
Prin: Robert C Parker

D-U-N-S 94-645-9583
MOUNT SINAI HEALTH SYSTEM INC
150 E 42nd St Bsmt 2, New York, NY 10017-5642
Tel (646) 605-4750 *Founded/Ownrshp* 2013
Sales 819.9MM^E *EMP* 20,000^E
SIC 8011 Health maintenance organization; Group health association; Health maintenance organization; Group health association
Pr: Kenneth L Davis
Ch Bd: Peter W May
CFO: Donald Scanlon
Chf Mktg O: Jeremy Boal
Ex VP: Jeffrey Silberstein
Doctor: Rica Arnon

MOUNT SINAI HOSPITAL
See SINAI CHILDRENS HOSPITAL

MOUNT SINAI HOSPITAL, THE
See ICAHN SCHOOL OF MEDICINE AT MOUNT SINAI

D-U-N-S 05-830-2266 IMP
MOUNT SINAI HOSPITAL
(*Suby of* MOUNT SINAI HEALTH SYSTEM INC) ★
1 Gustave L Levy Pl Fl 12, New York, NY 10029-6574
Tel (212) 241-6500 *Founded/Ownrshp* 1852
Sales 304.7MM *EMP* 12,559
Accts Ernst & Young Llp New York N
SIC 8062 General medical & surgical hospitals; General medical & surgical hospitals
Pr: Kenneth L Davis MD
Chf Rad: Burton Dryer
Act CFO: Stephen Harvey
Chf Mktg O: Deborah Marin
VP: Diane Adams
Assoc Dir: Alma Azua-Cassady
Assoc Dir: Jeffery Beck
Dir Bus: Sean Healy
Comm Man: Juan Badimon
Adm Dir: Matthew Baney
Off Mgr: Necauri Fabian

D-U-N-S 07-443-3046 IMP
MOUNT SINAI HOSPITAL MEDICAL CENTER OF CHICAGO
FRIENDS OF SINAI CHILDREN
1501 S California Ave, Chicago, IL 60608-1732
Tel (773) 542-2000 *Founded/Ownrshp* 1918
Sales 311.9MM^E *EMP* 1,700
SIC 8062 Hospital, AMA approved residency; Hospital, AMA approved residency
Pr: Alan Channing
Pr: Karen Teitelbaum
**CFO:* Charles Weis
Treas: Linda Manning
**Ex VP:* Rachel Dvorken
**VP:* David Berkey
CIO: Peter Ingram
Surgeon: Don Teed
Doctor: Toby Efferen
Phys Thrpy: Brenda Koverman

MOUNT SINAI MEDICAL CENTER
See ICAHN MEDICAL INSTITUE

D-U-N-S 08-689-8855
MOUNT SINAI MEDICAL CENTER INC
(*Suby of* MOUNT SINAI HEALTH SYSTEM INC) ★
1 Gustave L Levy Pl Fl 12, New York, NY 10029-6500
Tel (212) 731-3200 *Founded/Ownrshp* 1967
Sales 26.9MM^E *EMP* 20
Accts Ernst & Young Us Llp Indianap
SIC 8399 Fund raising organization, non-fee basis
CEO: Kenneth L Davis
**CFO:* Donald Scanlon
Chf Mktg O: Ann Marie Gothard
**Ex VP:* Dennis S Charney
Ex VP: Wayne E Keathley
**Sr VP:* Stephen Harvey
**VP:* Jean Ford
**VP:* Michelle Gelber
VP: Lynn Vogel
Exec: Lori Dempsey
Dir Teleco: Michelle Larue
Dir Lab: Rong Wang
Dir Rad: Robert A Lookstein
Dir Env Sv: David Loverin

D-U-N-S 04-602-5144
MOUNT SINAI MEDICAL CENTER OF FLORIDA INC
4300 Alton Rd, Miami Beach, FL 33140-2948
Tel (305) 674-2121 *Founded/Ownrshp* 1946
Sales 584.7MM *EMP* 3,225^E
Accts Deloitte Tax Llp Tampa Fl
SIC 8062 8741 General medical & surgical hospitals; Management services; General medical & surgical hospitals; Management services
Pr: Steven Sonenreich
Chf Rad: Jose Pizarro
**Ch Bd:* Wayne Chaplain
COO: Amy Perry
**CFO:* Alex Mendez
Ofcr: Norman Gomez
Sr VP: Robert Goldszer
VP: Wayne Chukan
**VP:* Angel Pallin
Dir Case M: Olga Atienza
Dir Lab: Robert Poppiti
Dir Rad: Karin Knesaurek
Dir Rx: Mukush Shah

D-U-N-S 80-822-6372
MOUNT SINAI REHABILITATION HOSPITAL INC
490 Blue Hills Ave, Hartford, CT 06112-1513
Tel (860) 714-2647 *Founded/Ownrshp* 1995
Sales 35.2MM^E *EMP* 23^E
Accts Marcum Llp Hartford Ct
SIC 8093 Rehabilitation center, outpatient treatment; Rehabilitation center, residential: health care incidental; Rehabilitation center, outpatient treatment
Pr: Christopher M Dadlez
**Ch:* Howard W Orr
**Treas:* Jeannine Mara
Doctor: Raymond Chagnon
Phys Thrpy: Joan Page

D-U-N-S 09-331-5547
MOUNT SINAI UNION FREE SCHOOL DISTRICT
118 N Country Rd, Mount Sinai, NY 11766-1525
Tel (631) 473-1991 *Founded/Ownrshp* 1920
Sales 339.5M *EMP* 326
Accts Rizzi Scwarz & Taraskao Llp
SIC 8211 Public elementary school; Public junior high school; Public senior high school; Public elementary school; Public junior high school; Public senior high school
Pr: John Wittpenn
**Treas:* Lynne Kirchenko
**Prin:* John Gentilcore
DP Exec: Ken Jockers
IT Man: Andrew Matthews
HC Dir: Scott Reh

MOUNT ST FRANCIS
See SISTERS OF ST FRANCIS OF DUBUQUE IOWA

D-U-N-S 03-288-7056
MOUNT ST JOSEPH UNIVERSITY
5701 Delhi Rd, Cincinnati, OH 45233-1669
Tel (513) 244-4200 *Founded/Ownrshp* 1962
Sales 53.6MM *EMP* 400
Accts Ernst & Young Us Llp Columbus
SIC 8221 College, except junior; College, except junior
Pr: Tony Aretz
VP: Joel Thierstein
Pr Mgr: Jeanette Bryson
HC Dir: Peggy Minnich

D-U-N-S 06-992-7150
MOUNT ST MARYS COLLEGE
MOUNT SAINT MARY'S UNIVERSITY
12001 Chalon Rd, Los Angeles, CA 90049-1599
Tel (310) 954-4000 *Founded/Ownrshp* 1925
Sales 63.2MM^E *EMP* 400
Accts Baker Tilly Virchow Krause Llp
SIC 8221 College, except junior; College, except junior
Pr: Ann McElaney
**Pr:* Ann McElaney-Johnson PHD
**Sec:* Chris McAlary
Ex VP: Maryann Bonino
VP: Larry Smith
Assoc Dir: Chinako Belanger
Tech Mgr: Frank Hwang
Psych: Alexandra Faubel
Psych: David Luna
Psych: William Martinez
Psych: Shawn Peters

MOUNT ST MARY'S HOSPITAL AND H
See MOUNT ST MARYS HOSPITAL OF NIAGARA FALLS

D-U-N-S 07-147-4316
MOUNT ST MARYS HOSPITAL OF NIAGARA FALLS
MOUNT ST MARY'S HOSPITAL AND H
5300 Military Rd, Lewiston, NY 14092-1903
Tel (716) 297-4800 *Founded/Ownrshp* 1909
Sales 92.1MM *EMP* 832
Accts Deloitte Tax Llp Cincinnati
SIC 8062 Hospital, medical school affiliated with nursing & residency; Hospital, medical school affiliated with nursing & residency
Pr: Judith A Maness
**Pr:* Judy Maness
**CFO:* Michael Ickowski
Treas: Denise Dorato
Sr VP: Gary Tucker
**VP:* Deborah Serafin
Dir Lab: Angela Kostuk
Dir Lab: Paul Meade
Dir Sec: Joe Callara
CIO: Dick Witkowski
Sfty Dirs: Wayne Lynch

MOUNT ST RITA'S HEALTH CENTER
See SISTERS OF MERCY OF PROVIDENCE INC

MOUNT ST VINCENT NURSING HOME
See SISTERS OF PROVIDENCE CARE CENTERS INC

D-U-N-S 10-006-9848
MOUNT UNION AREA SCHOOL DISTRICT
603 N Industrial Dr, Mount Union, PA 17066-1700
Tel (814) 542-8631 *Founded/Ownrshp* 1963
Sales 13.9MM^E *EMP* 300
SIC 8211 Elementary & secondary schools; Public elementary & secondary schools; School board; Elementary & secondary schools; Public elementary & secondary schools; School board

D-U-N-S 82-986-2387 EXP
MOUNT VERNON CHEMICALS LLC
APOLLO CHEMICAL
(*Suby of* MOUNT VERNON MILLS INC) ★
2001 Willow Spring Ln, Burlington, NC 27215-8854
Tel (336) 226-1161 *Founded/Ownrshp* 2007
Sales 46.4MM^E *EMP* 108
SIC 5169 Chemicals & allied products; Chemicals & allied products
IT Man: Tracy Kivett
Mtls Mgr: Steven Horne
Plnt Mgr: Jim Corradini
Plnt Mgr: Bill O'Dell

D-U-N-S 11-391-3925
MOUNT VERNON CITY SCHOOL DIST 80
2710 North St, Mount Vernon, IL 62864-2317
Tel (618) 244-8080 *Founded/Ownrshp* 1889
Sales 20.9MM *EMP* 237
Accts Krehbiel & Associates Llc Mt
SIC 8211 Public elementary & secondary schools; Public elementary & secondary schools
Sls Mgr: Linda Cruser

D-U-N-S 05-556-4546
MOUNT VERNON CITY SCHOOL DISTRICT
300 Newark Rd, Mount Vernon, OH 43050-4510
Tel (740) 397-7422 *Founded/Ownrshp* 1968
Sales 11.6MM *EMP* 500
SIC 8211 Public elementary school; Public junior high school; Public senior high school; Public elementary school; Public junior high school; Public senior high school
Treas: Barbara Donohue
Schl Brd P: Margie Bennett

D-U-N-S 00-982-0119
MOUNT VERNON COMMUNITY SCHOOL DISTRICT
525 Palisades Rd Sw, Mount Vernon, IA 52314-1761
Tel (319) 895-6254 *Founded/Ownrshp* 1873
Sales 318.4M *EMP* 300
SIC 8211 Public elementary & secondary schools; Public elementary & secondary schools
**Treas:* Matt Burke
VP: Lori Merlak
**Prin:* Dennis Walsh
IT Man: Ericka Johnson
Schl Brd P: Darrin Gage
Psych: Heidi Hassen
HC Dir: Missy Howser

D-U-N-S 07-708-9886
■ **MOUNT VERNON FIRE INSURANCE CO**
(*Suby of* UNITED STATES LIABILITY INSURANCE CO INC) ★
190 S Warner Rd Ste 200, Wayne, PA 19087
Tel (610) 688-2535 *Founded/Ownrshp* 1958
Sales NA *EMP* 136
Accts Pricewater House Coopers Llp
SIC 6331 Fire, marine & casualty insurance; Fire, marine & casualty insurance
Pr: Thomas P Nerney
**Ch Bd:* Robert B Berry
**Treas:* Louis Rivituso
**VP:* Henry Mitchell
**VP:* Theodore Ziffer

D-U-N-S 07-869-6242
MOUNT VERNON HOSPITAL RADIOLOGY ASSOCIATES PC
12 N 7th Ave, Mount Vernon, NY 10550-2098
Tel (914) 664-8000 *Founded/Ownrshp* 1983
Sales 59.9MM^E *EMP* 725
SIC 8062 General medical & surgical hospitals; General medical & surgical hospitals
CEO: Paul L Novotny MD
**Ch Bd:* Vincent Bufano
**COO:* George Haskins
**CFO:* Frank Vutrano
**Sec:* Charles Rasher
Sr VP: Amy Cassidy
DP Dir: Barbara Cook
HC Dir: Robin Arterberry
HC Dir: Kristen Whalen

D-U-N-S 07-779-3248
MOUNT VERNON LADIES ASSOCIATION OF UNION
GEORGE WASHINGTON'S MT VERNON
3200 Mount Vernon Mem Hwy, Mount Vernon, VA 22121
Tel (703) 780-2000 *Founded/Ownrshp* 1853
Sales 51.5MM *EMP* 500
Accts Raffa Pc Washington Dc
SIC 8412 5947 5812 Historical society; Souvenirs; Restaurant, lunch counter; Snack bar; Historical society; Souvenirs; Restaurant, lunch counter; Snack bar
Pr: James Rees
CFO: Phil Manno
Mktg Dir: Kris Blanchette

D-U-N-S 00-308-2203 IMP/EXP
MOUNT VERNON MILLS INC (MD)
(*Suby of* R B PAMPLIN CORP) ★
503 S Main St, Mauldin, SC 29662-2204
Tel (864) 688-7100 *Founded/Ownrshp* 1847, 1982
Sales 268.9MM^E *EMP* 2,700

SIC 2221 2281 2211

D-U-N-S 07-165-3398
MOUNT VERNON NAZARENE UNIVERSITY
800 Martinsburg Rd, Mount Vernon, OH 43050-9500
Tel (740) 392-6868 Founded/Ownrshp 1966
Sales 51.3MM EMP 540
Accts Crowe Horwath Llp Columbus O
SIC 8221 University; University
Pr: Henry W Spaulding II
CFO: Richard Raymond
Treas: Donald Cobb
VP: Chris Hudson
VP: Scott Peterson
VP: Brock Schroeder
VP: Lanette Sessink
VP: Richard Sutherland
VP: Randie Timpe
VP: Brooke Whetsell
Ex Dir: Kathleen Clark

D-U-N-S 06-254-5918
MOUNT VERNON NEIGHBORHOOD HEALTH CENTER INC
107 W 4th St, Mount Vernon, NY 10550-4002
Tel (914) 699-7200 Founded/Ownrshp 1978
Sales 17.6MM^E EMP 300
SIC 8093

D-U-N-S 05-919-7954
MOUNT VERNON NEON SIGN CO
(Suby of EVERBRITE LLC) ★
1 Neon Dr, Mount Vernon, IL 62864-6723
Tel (618) 242-0645 Founded/Ownrshp 1972
Sales 23.2MM^E EMP 125
SIC 3993 Neon signs
Pr: Bill Fritz
*Treas: David Heger
Plnt Mgr: Dave Meador

D-U-N-S 84-839-4763
MOUNT WACHUSETT COMMUNITY COLLEGE
444 Green St, Gardner, MA 01440-1378
Tel (978) 632-6600 Founded/Ownrshp 1971
Sales 394.9M EMP 300
Accts O Connor & Drew Pc Braintree
SIC 8222 Community college; Community college
Pr: Daniel M Asquino
Ofcr: Michael Braley
Ofcr: Paul Grunditz
Ofcr: Marlon Medero
Ofcr: Ed Ramos
Ex VP: Jane Gustowski
*Ex VP: Ann McDonald
VP: Robin Duncan
VP: Jacqueline Feldman
VP: John Rearson
Ex Dir: Alida Cogswell

D-U-N-S 11-243-4803
MOUNT WASHINGTON PEDIATRIC HOSPITAL INC
UMMS
(Suby of UMMS) ★
1708 W Rogers Ave, Baltimore, MD 21209-4545
Tel (410) 578-8600 Founded/Ownrshp 2005
Sales 56.8MM EMP 500
Accts Grant Thornton Llp Baltimore
SIC 8069 Children's hospital; Children's hospital
CEO: Sheldon J Stein
VP: Jenny Bowie
*VP: Mary Miller
Dir Risk M: Denise Pudinski
Dir Rad: Terri Spinks
MIS Dir: Tim Brady
Mtls Dir: James Maddock
Mktg Dir: Tom Paullin
Psych: Kendra Battaglia
Psych: Melissa Lee
Doctor: Kamana Verma

D-U-N-S 06-797-5318
MOUNT WHEELER POWER INC
M W SERVICES
1600 Great Basin Blvd, Ely, NV 89301
Tel (775) 289-8981 Founded/Ownrshp 1963
Sales 34.5MM EMP 37
SIC 4911 Distribution, electric power; Distribution, electric power
CEO: Randy Ewell
Treas: Donnell Doty
IT Man: Euelene Twitchell
Opers Mgr: Bill Ricci

D-U-N-S 01-322-5677
MOUNTAIN / SERVICE DISTRIBUTORS
40 Lake St, South Fallsburg, NY 12779-5417
Tel (845) 434-5674 Founded/Ownrshp 1962
Sales 27.2MM^E EMP 75^E
SIC 5194 5145 5149 Cigarettes; Confectionery; Fountain supplies; Syrups, fountain; Groceries & related products; Sandwiches; Cigarettes; Confectionery; Fountain supplies; Syrups, fountain; Groceries & related products; Sandwiches
Pr: Steve Altman
*COO: Mark Gandulla
*Sec: Josh Altman
*VP: Michele Elliott
Mfg Mgr: Ed Rausch
Sls Mgr: Jerry Beaulieu

D-U-N-S 10-178-8636
■ **MOUNTAIN AIR CARGO INC**
(Suby of T AIR INC) ★
3524 Airport Rd, Maiden, NC 28650-9056
Tel (828) 464-8741 Founded/Ownrshp 1983
Sales 34.8MM^E EMP 340
SIC 4513 Package delivery, private air; Package delivery, private air
Pr: Robert Norton
*VP: Walter Clark
VP: Paul Simpson
Opers Mgr: Alan Knollmeyer

MOUNTAIN ALARM
See FIRE PROTECTION SERVICE CORP

MOUNTAIN AMERICA CREDIT UNION
See MOUNTAIN AMERICA FEDERAL CREDIT UNION

D-U-N-S 07-311-5537
MOUNTAIN AMERICA FEDERAL CREDIT UNION
MOUNTAIN AMERICA CREDIT UNION
7181 S Campus View Dr, West Jordan, UT 84084-4312
Tel (801) 325-6228 Founded/Ownrshp 1952
Sales NA EMP 1,033
SIC 6062 State credit unions, not federally chartered; State credit unions, not federally chartered
Pr: Sterling Nielsen
CFO: Chad Curtis
Bd of Dir: John Holt
Ofcr: Dale Fisher
Ofcr: Chelsie Larsen
Sr VP: Dennis Bromley
Sr VP: Tony Rasmussen
Sr VP: Jason Rogers
Sr VP: Catherine Smoyer
VP: Jade Beckman
VP: Jonathan Brouse
VP: Tammy Bryant
VP: David Glod
Exec: Marshall Paepke

D-U-N-S 07-905-0613
MOUNTAIN AREA HEALTH EDUCATION CENTER INC
MAHEC
121 Hendersonville Rd, Asheville, NC 28803-2868
Tel (828) 257-4400 Founded/Ownrshp 1973
Sales 39.3MM EMP 420
Accts Dixon Hughes Goodman Llp Char
SIC 8299 Educational service, nondegree granting: continuing educ.; Educational service, nondegree granting: continuing educ.
Ch: Dale E Fell
*Pr: Jeffery E Heck
*CFO: George Wike
*Sec: William G Lapsley
Assoc Dir: Joyce Jolly

D-U-N-S 01-630-9368 IMP
MOUNTAIN BEVERAGE CO LLC
712 Springbuck Rd, Gypsum, CO 81637
Tel (970) 777-4000 Founded/Ownrshp 2008
Sales 27.4MM EMP 44
Accts Chilton Wilcox & Fortenberry
SIC 5182 Wine & distilled beverages; Wine & distilled beverages

MOUNTAIN BROADCASTING
See NORTHWEST BROADCASTING INC

D-U-N-S 55-660-5145
MOUNTAIN BROADCASTING LLC
KAYU
(Suby of MOUNTAIN BROADCASTING) ★
4600 S Regal St, Spokane, WA 99223-7960
Tel (509) 448-2828 Founded/Ownrshp 1995
Sales 22.6MM^E EMP 125
SIC 4833 Television broadcasting stations; Television broadcasting stations

D-U-N-S 12-702-6367
MOUNTAIN BROOK BOARD OF EDUCATION
32 Vine St, Mountain Brk, AL 35213-3716
Tel (205) 871-4608 Founded/Ownrshp 2010
Sales 58.5MM EMP 603
Accts Potter Bryant & Moore Pc Bi
SIC 8211 Public elementary & secondary schools; Public elementary & secondary schools
*CFO: Karen Lusk Smith

D-U-N-S 06-970-8758
MOUNTAIN CASCADE INC (CA)
555 Exchange Ct, Livermore, CA 94550-2400
Tel (925) 373-8370 Founded/Ownrshp 1982
Sales 60.0MM^E EMP 250
SIC 1623 Pipeline construction; Water & sewer line construction; Pipeline construction; Water & sewer line construction
CEO: Michael L Fuller
*Pr: Michael Duke Fuller
*CFO: William W Whelan
*Treas: Schelly Frades
*Ex VP: Bill E Williams Jr
*VP: Mike Nelson
*VP: Roger Williamson
Sfty Dirs: Rickey Arslanian
QI Cn Mgr: Paul Golden

D-U-N-S 15-178-2406 IMP
■ **MOUNTAIN CEMENT CO**
(Suby of EAGLE MATERIALS INC) ★
5 Sand Creek Rd, Laramie, WY 82070-6865
Tel (307) 745-2600 Founded/Ownrshp 1927
Sales 23.3MM^E EMP 134
SIC 3241 5032 Natural cement; Cement; Natural cement; Cement
CEO: Steve Rowley
Pr: David Challacomb
Pr: Tom Hamp
*CFO: Arthur Zunker
Ex VP: Paul Anderson
VP: Chael Fox
VP: Ey Mendenhall
Genl Mgr: Danny Cutler
Genl Mgr: Al Swain
Sfty Mgr: Steve Adkins
Sfty Mgr: Charles Murphy
Board of Directors: Steve Rowley, Arthur Zunker

D-U-N-S 03-200-5555 IMP
MOUNTAIN CITY MEAT CO INC
5905 E 42nd Ave, Denver, CO 80216-4613
Tel (303) 320-1116 Founded/Ownrshp 1987
Sales 19.0MM^E EMP 300
SIC 5142 5147

D-U-N-S 00-434-7654
MOUNTAIN CO (OH)
166 60th St, Parkersburg, WV 26105-8002
Tel (304) 295-0036 Founded/Ownrshp 1951, 1923
Sales 50.3MM^E EMP 368
SIC 1761 1711 Roofing contractor; Sheet metalwork; Plumbing, heating, air-conditioning contractors; Roofing contractor; Sheet metalwork; Plumbing, heating, air-conditioning contractors
Ch: Harry H Esbenshade III
CFO: Brian Ream
*VP: Michael D Cain
VP: Gary Paschen
*VP: M Michael Richardson
IT Man: Eric Brown

D-U-N-S 09-163-5693
■ **MOUNTAIN COAL CO LLC** (CO)
WEST ELK MINE
(Suby of ARCH COAL INC) ★
1 Mile E Of Somerset On H, Somerset, CO 81434
Tel (970) 929-5015 Founded/Ownrshp 1981
Sales 43.2MM^E EMP 320
SIC 1222 1241 Bituminous coal-underground mining; Coal mining services; Bituminous coal-underground mining; Coal mining services
Sfty Mgr: Bill Olsen
Sfty Mgr: Lavon Turpin

MOUNTAIN COIN MACHINE DISTRS
See WORLD ENTERPRISES INC

D-U-N-S 06-813-5607
MOUNTAIN COMPREHENSIVE CARE CENTER INC
104 S Front Ave, Prestonsburg, KY 41653-1614
Tel (606) 886-8572 Founded/Ownrshp 1966
Sales 30.5MM EMP 324
Accts Strothman & Company Psc Loui
SIC 8093 Mental health clinic, outpatient; Detoxification center, outpatient; Mental health clinic, outpatient; Detoxification center, outpatient
CEO: Promod Bishnoi
*CFO: Durward Hale
*CFO: Rebecca Hall
Treas: Vickie Hall
Exec: Linda Craft
Ex Dir: Darlene Starnes
Dir IT: David Webb

D-U-N-S 07-409-3915
MOUNTAIN COMPREHENSIVE HEALTH CORP
MCHC
226 Medical Plaza Ln, Whitesburg, KY 41858-7425
Tel (606) 633-4823 Founded/Ownrshp 1972
Sales 23.9MM EMP 233
SIC 8011 Clinic, operated by physicians; Clinic, operated by physicians
CEO: L M Caudill
*CFO: Teresa Fleming
VP: Zach Sturgill

D-U-N-S 36-074-6226
MOUNTAIN COMPREHENSIVE HEALTH CORP
226 Medical Plaza Ln, Whitesburg, KY 41858-7425
Tel (606) 633-4871 Founded/Ownrshp 1990
Sales 22.7MM EMP 119^E
SIC 8011 Offices & clinics of medical doctors; Offices & clinics of medical doctors
CEO: Mike Cauvill
Sls Mgr: Wanda Lamaster
Doctor: Larry Quillen

D-U-N-S 14-860-9589 EXP
MOUNTAIN CORP
59 Optical Ave, Keene, NH 03431-4320
Tel (603) 355-2272 Founded/Ownrshp 1998
Sales 25.0MM^E EMP 180
SIC 2253 T-shirts & tops, knit; T-shirts & tops, knit
Pr: Michael Krinsky
CFO: Peter H Friedman
*VP: Michael Gallen

MOUNTAIN COUNTRY DISTRIBUTING
See LEHRKINDS INC

D-U-N-S 10-688-2020
MOUNTAIN COUNTRY FOODS LLC
195 E 1600 N, Spanish Fork, UT 84660-1013
Tel (801) 798-8634 Founded/Ownrshp 1974
Sales 52.5MM^E EMP 300
SIC 2047

D-U-N-S 17-251-6150
MOUNTAIN CRANE SERVICE LLC
393 S 2650 W, Salt Lake City, UT 84104-3907
Tel (801) 282-3330 Founded/Ownrshp 2004
Sales 37.6MM EMP 100^E
SIC 7353

MOUNTAIN CY NRSING RHBLITATION
See OAK HRC MOUNTAIN CITY LLC

D-U-N-S 06-671-8198
MOUNTAIN ELECTRIC COOPERATIVE INC
604 S Church St, Mountain City, TN 37683-1844
Tel (423) 727-1800 Founded/Ownrshp 1941
Sales 61.1MM EMP 83
SIC 4911 Distribution, electric power; Distribution, electric power
Pr: Harry Smith
*VP: David Atwood
*VP: Ross Dowell
Genl Mgr: Joseph Thacker

D-U-N-S 03-467-6981
MOUNTAIN EMPIRE OIL CO
ROADRUNNER MARKETS
282 Christian Church Rd, Johnson City, TN 37615-4475
Tel (423) 928-7241 Founded/Ownrshp 1977
Sales 130.3MM^E EMP 450
SIC 5541 5411 Filling stations, gasoline; Convenience stores; Filling stations, gasoline; Convenience stores
Pr: Ryan Broyles
*Sec: Ralph Fellars
*VP: John Kelly
Trfc Dir: Lee Stanley
Opers Mgr: Mike Hernandez

D-U-N-S 02-109-8231
MOUNTAIN ENERGY CORP
288 Riverside Dr, Asheville, NC 28801-3139
Tel (828) 253-2321 Founded/Ownrshp 2002
Sales 42.3MM^E EMP 250
SIC 5983 5411 5984 Fuel oil dealers; Convenience stores, independent; Liquefied petroleum gas dealers; Fuel oil dealers; Convenience stores, independent; Liquefied petroleum gas dealers
Pr: Thomas R Morgan

D-U-N-S 05-019-5361
MOUNTAIN ENTERPRISES INC
(Suby of OLDCASTLE MATERIALS GROUP) ★
2257 Executive Dr, Lexington, KY 40505-4809
Tel (859) 299-7001 Founded/Ownrshp 2005
Sales 60.0MM^E EMP 200
SIC 1611 1771 2951 Highway & street paving contractor; Blacktop (asphalt) work; Asphalt & asphaltic paving mixtures (not from refineries); Highway & street paving contractor; Blacktop (asphalt) work; Asphalt & asphaltic paving mixtures (not from refineries)
CFO: Charles Herman
*Ex VP: James York
*VP: Phil Annis
Sales Exec: Buzz Tharte

D-U-N-S 55-560-4537
MOUNTAIN F ENTERPRISES INC
4110 Pleasant Ranch Rd, Placerville, CA 95667-8956
Tel (530) 626-4127 Founded/Ownrshp 1989
Sales 21.9MM^E EMP 40
SIC 5099 2411 0851 0783 Firewood; Logging; Forestry services; Tree trimming services for public utility lines; Arborist services
CEO: Marcos A Gomez
COO: Raul Gomez
CFO: Jake Wolf

D-U-N-S 02-326-2277
MOUNTAIN FORESTRY INC
4570 Independence Hwy, Independence, OR 97351-9679
Tel (503) 606-3503 Founded/Ownrshp 1986
Sales 4.3MM^E EMP 323
SIC 0851 Reforestation services; Reforestation services
Pr: Francisco Cisneros
*VP: Penny Cox

D-U-N-S 96-837-2594
■ **MOUNTAIN GATHERING LLC**
(Suby of XTO ENERGY INC) ★
395 Airport Rd, Indiana, PA 15701-8914
Tel (724) 349-0600 Founded/Ownrshp 2008
Sales 39.5MM^E EMP 14^E
SIC 5172 Gasoline

D-U-N-S 61-618-2473 IMP
MOUNTAIN GEAR CORP
TRI-MOUNTAIN
4889 4th St, Irwindale, CA 91706-2194
Tel (626) 851-2488 Founded/Ownrshp 1994
Sales 60.3MM^E EMP 125
SIC 5136 Men's & boys' sportswear & work clothing; Men's & boys' sportswear & work clothing
CEO: Daniel Tsai
VP: Jennifer Tsai
*VP: Rosie Tsai
CTO: Olga Duran
IT Man: Niem Thai

D-U-N-S 60-747-7960 IMP
MOUNTAIN GROUP INC
6600 High Ridge Rd, Boynton Beach, FL 33426-9380
Tel (561) 450-7394 Founded/Ownrshp 2001
Sales 22.0MM EMP 19
SIC 5013 Automotive supplies & parts
Pr: Joseph Ende
*Treas: Alex Ende

D-U-N-S 80-884-5473 IMP
■ **MOUNTAIN HARDWEAR INC**
MONTRAIL
(Suby of COLUMBIA SPORTSWEAR USA CORP) ★
1414 Harbour Way S, Richmond, CA 94804-3694
Tel (510) 558-3000 Founded/Ownrshp 1993
Sales 6.8MM^E EMP 1,500
SIC 2399 2394 5651

MOUNTAIN HEALTH & WELLNESS
See HORIZON HEALTH AND WELLNESS INC

D-U-N-S 17-959-2613
MOUNTAIN HIGH RESORT ASSOCIATES LLC
24512 Highway 2, Wrightwood, CA 92397
Tel (760) 249-5808 Founded/Ownrshp 2010
Sales 43.8MM^E EMP 900
SIC 6531 Real estate managers; Real estate managers

D-U-N-S 11-889-0847
MOUNTAIN HOME BANCSHARES INC
FIRST NATIONAL BANK
502 Hickory St, Mountain Home, AR 72653-3534
Tel (870) 425-2101 Founded/Ownrshp 1980
Sales NA EMP 145
Accts Erwin & Company Little Rock
SIC 6021 National trust companies with deposits, commercial; National trust companies with deposits, commercial
CEO: Denny Williams
Bd of Dir: Mona Blankenship

D-U-N-S 07-622-7797
MOUNTAIN HOME HEALTH CARE
RAVENSWOOD
8527 W Colfax Ave Ste 201, Lakewood, CO 80215-4028
Tel (303) 424-2420 Founded/Ownrshp 1999
Sales 9.1MM^E EMP 400^E
SIC 8059 Personal care home, with health care; Personal care home, with health care
Pr: Louis Colaianaia
Sls&Mrk Ex: Louis Colaiannia

D-U-N-S 07-564-8634
MOUNTAIN HOME PUBLIC SCHOOLS
2465 Rodeo Dr, Mountain Home, AR 72653-4501
Tel (870) 425-1201 Founded/Ownrshp 1875
Sales 19.8MM^E EMP 550
SIC 8211 Public elementary & secondary schools; Public combined elementary & secondary school; Public junior high school; Public elementary & secondary schools; Public combined elementary & secondary schools; Public junior high school
*CFO: Ann Harned

D-U-N-S 80-016-6519
MOUNTAIN HOME SCHOOL DIST 9
2465 Rodeo Dr, Mountain Home, AR 72653-4501
Tel (870) 425-1201 Founded/Ownrshp 2007
Sales 11.9MM^E EMP 419^E
SIC 8211 Elementary & secondary schools

D-U-N-S 07-300-2495
MOUNTAIN HOME SCHOOL DISTRICT 193
470 N 3rd E, Mountain Home, ID 83647-2737
Tel (208) 587-2580 Founded/Ownrshp 1893
Sales 18.8MM^E EMP 327
Accts Eide Bailly Llp Boise Idaho
SIC 8211 9411 Public elementary & secondary schools; Administration of educational programs; Public elementary & secondary schools; Administration of educational programs
Ch: James Alexander
CIO: Kerri Reynolds

MOUNTAIN LAKE SERVICES
See ESSEX COUNTY CHAPTER NYSARC INC

D-U-N-S 07-932-8639
MOUNTAIN LAKES BOARD OF EDUCATION (INC)
400 Boulevard Ste 3, Mountain Lakes, NJ 07046-1520
Tel (973) 334-8280 Founded/Ownrshp 1914
Sales 16.5MM^E EMP 300
SIC 8211 Public elementary & secondary schools; Public elementary & secondary schools

D-U-N-S 07-810-1599
MOUNTAIN LAKES MEDICAL CENTER AUXILIARY INC
196 Ridgecrest Cir, Clayton, GA 30525-4111
Tel (706) 782-3100 Founded/Ownrshp 1951
Sales 25.1MM^E EMP 153
SIC 8062 General medical & surgical hospitals
CEO: Sheila Wells
*CFO: Susan Fisher
*Prin: Vicky Lawrenson

MOUNTAIN LAKES SENIOR LIVING
See SENIOR NORTHSTAR LIVING INC

D-U-N-S 18-477-4735
MOUNTAIN LAND DESIGN INC
2345 S Main St, Salt Lake City, UT 84115-2760
Tel (801) 466-0990 Founded/Ownrshp 1994
Sales 22.7MM^E EMP 78
SIC 5064 5072 5074 Electric household appliances; Hardware; Plumbing & hydronic heating supplies; Electric household appliances; Hardware; Plumbing & hydronic heating supplies
Pr: Danny S Devenport
Genl Mgr: Jerri Longo
Genl Mgr: Martina Midgley
Off Mgr: Jon Davis
Store Mgr: Dave Cook
IT Man: Ben Devenport
Sls Mgr: Paul Beasley
Sls Mgr: Stephanie Dahle
Sls Mgr: Jessica Roberts
Sls Mgr: Candice Tanner

MOUNTAIN LAUREL COMPLEX
See MINGO LOGAN COAL CO

D-U-N-S 78-237-6248
MOUNTAIN MANAGEMENT SERVICES INC
5600 Brainerd Rd Ste 500, Chattanooga, TN 37411-5371
Tel (423) 495-8659 Founded/Ownrshp 1994
Sales 10.6MM^E EMP 500
SIC 8741 8742 Office management; Office management; Management consulting services
Pr: Glyn Hughes
Mng Dir: John Tressler
Off Mgr: Ladonna Howard

MOUNTAIN MANOR BALTIMORE
See MARYLAND TREATMENT CENTERS INC

D-U-N-S 00-285-1483
MOUNTAIN MEADOWS LAMB CORP
(Suby of SUPERIOR FARMS) ★
4900 Clarkson St, Denver, CO 80216-2086
Tel (303) 296-1801 Founded/Ownrshp 1982
Sales 32.5MM^E EMP 308
SIC 2011 Lamb products from lamb slaughtered on site; Lamb products from lamb slaughtered on site
Pr: Jerry Dotson
*CEO: Dennis Breen

MOUNTAIN METROPOLITAIN TRANSIT
See COLORADO SPRINGS CITY GOVERNMENT

D-U-N-S 84-013-1577
MOUNTAIN MOBILE TV LIMITED LIABILITY CO
8455 Highfield Pkwy, Englewood, CO 80112-7141
Tel (303) 388-8500 Founded/Ownrshp 1994
Sales 9.0MM^E EMP 300
SIC 7812 Television film production; Television film production

MOUNTAIN MOTOR SPORTS CONYERS
See SOUTHERN MOUNTAIN ADVENTURES LLC

D-U-N-S 14-039-0936
MOUNTAIN NATIONAL BANCSHARES INC
300 E Main St, Sevierville, TN 37862-3518
Tel (865) 428-7990 Founded/Ownrshp 2002
Sales NA EMP 143
Accts Crowe Horwath Llp Brentwood
Tkr Sym MNBT Exch OTO
SIC 6021 National commercial banks; National commercial banks
Pr: Michael L Brown
Ex VP: Grace D McKinzie
VP: James Forrester
VP: James Huffman
VP: Roy Owen
VP: Michael Patterson
Board of Directors: Gary A Helton, Charlie R Johnson, Sam L Large, Jeffrey J Monson, Linda N Ogle, Michael C Ownby, John M Parker Sr, Ruth A Reams

D-U-N-S 61-004-9686
MOUNTAIN PARK HEALTH CENTER
2702 N 3rd St Ste 4020, Phoenix, AZ 85004-4608
Tel (602) 323-3344 Founded/Ownrshp 1980
Sales 54.5MM EMP 530
Accts Fester & Chapman Pc Scottsdal
SIC 8011 Primary care medical clinic; Primary care medical clinic
CEO: John Swagart
*COO: Rachel Lambert
*CFO: Chris Hewett
Ofcr: Stella Xenakis
Sr VP: Cecelia Hofberger
Comm Dir: Michelle Hernandez

D-U-N-S 00-386-9898
MOUNTAIN PARKS ELECTRIC INC
321 W Agate Ave, Granby, CO 80446
Tel (970) 887-3378 Founded/Ownrshp 1946
Sales 37.2MM EMP 62
SIC 4911 Transmission, electric power; Transmission, electric power
CEO: Joe Pandy
*CFO: Tom Sifers
CTO: Kayci Green
Opers Mgr: Ronald Mettler
Mktg Dir: Rob Taylor

D-U-N-S 06-405-6823
MOUNTAIN PRODUCTIONS INC
REGAN
80 New Frederick St, Wilkes Barre, PA 18702-6104
Tel (570) 826-5566 Founded/Ownrshp 1979
Sales 66.1MM^E EMP 79
SIC 5084 7359 Hoists; Equipment rental & leasing; Hoists; Equipment rental & leasing
Pr: Ronald W Simms
*Pr: James B Evans
*Treas: Richard A Rose Jr
Sls Dir: Timothy Evans

D-U-N-S 01-079-2922
MOUNTAIN RANGE RESTAURANTS LLC
825 S 48th St, Tempe, AZ 85281-5101
Tel (480) 829-5090 Founded/Ownrshp 2001
Sales 51.8MM^E EMP 2,500
SIC 5812 Restaurant, family: chain; Restaurant, family: chain

D-U-N-S 61-249-9822
MOUNTAIN REGIONAL SERVICES INC
50 Allegiance Cir, Evanston, WY 82930-3804
Tel (307) 789-3710 Founded/Ownrshp 1985
Sales 11.6MM EMP 288
Accts Jones Simkins Llc Logan Utah
SIC 8093 Rehabilitation center, outpatient treatment; Rehabilitation center, outpatient treatment
Pr: John Holderegger
*Ch: Glenna Calmes
Mktg Mgr: John Knopf
Psych: Mikaela Bernthaler
Psych: Adam Fuller
Psych: Suzanne Petren

D-U-N-S 19-602-2651
MOUNTAIN RIVER TRUCKING CO INC
207 Direct Ln, Mount Airy, NC 27030-9856
Tel (336) 374-3106 Founded/Ownrshp 2006
Sales 31.7MM^E EMP 120
SIC 4213 Contract haulers
Pr: James H Smith

D-U-N-S 00-877-3657
MOUNTAIN RURAL TELEPHONE COOPERATIVE CORP INC
MOUNTAIN TELEPHONE
425 Main St, West Liberty, KY 41472-1013
Tel (606) 738-0100 Founded/Ownrshp 1950
Sales 24.3MM EMP 83
Accts Alan Zumstein Lexington Ky
SIC 4813 Local & long distance telephone communications; Local & long distance telephone communications
Pr: Jimmie Jones
*VP: Katie Ison
Mng Dir: Sharon Salyers
Genl Mgr: W A Gillum
Sls&Mrk Ex: Lisa Fannin

D-U-N-S 61-553-3148
MOUNTAIN STATE AUTO AUCTION INC
5546 Benedum Dr, Shinnston, WV 26431-7340
Tel (304) 592-5300 Founded/Ownrshp 1987
Sales 73.7MM^E EMP 200
Accts Rudy Dzadony
SIC 5012 5521 Automobile auction; Used car dealers; Automobile auction; Used car dealers
Pr: Joseph R Pyle
*VP: Charlotte Pyle
Genl Mgr: Chad Garrison
Off Mgr: Amy Gerau
Natl Sales: Felicity Lemon
Sls Mgr: Allyson Correale
Sls Mgr: Amber Finch
Sls Mgr: Brett Miller
Sls Mgr: Melissa Reedy

D-U-N-S 61-489-8661 IMP
MOUNTAIN STATE CARBON LLC
1851 Main St, Follansbee, WV 26037-1266
Tel (304) 527-5626 Founded/Ownrshp 2005
Sales 35.8MM^E EMP 67^E
SIC 2999 Coke
CFO: Lawrence Hermes

D-U-N-S 03-960-9151
MOUNTAIN STATE UNIVERSITY INC
609 S Kanawha St, Beckley, WV 25801-5624
Tel (304) 253-7351 Founded/Ownrshp 1933
Sales 10.2MM EMP 718
Accts Dixon Hughes Goodman Llp Cha
SIC 8221 College, except junior; College, except junior
Pr: Charles H Polk
*Treas: Michele Sarrett
*VP: James G Silosky
Genl Mgr: Ronald Thomure

D-U-N-S 00-727-8877
MOUNTAIN STATES CONSTRUCTORS INC
3601 Pan American Fwy Ne # 111, Albuquerque, NM 87107-4789
Tel (505) 344-5030 Founded/Ownrshp 2012
Sales 35.2MM^E EMP 150
SIC 1611 Highway & street construction; Highway & street construction
Pr: David Otoski
*Sec: Karen Pace
Mtls Mgr: Rick Cartwright
Board of Directors: Michael Brayman, Neil Jackson, Karen Pace, Henry Smith

D-U-N-S 10-280-2196
MOUNTAIN STATES CONTRACTING INC
4001 S 34th St, Phoenix, AZ 85040-1820
Tel (602) 595-1575 Founded/Ownrshp 1982
Sales 25.4MM^E EMP 95
SIC 1629 Railroad & railway roadbed construction
Pr: Joseph Van De Loo
*Treas: Terry Vanderplas
*VP: Blake Van De Loo

D-U-N-S 14-033-4496
MOUNTAIN STATES CONTRACTORS LLC
5760 Old Lebanon Dirt Rd, Mount Juliet, TN 37122-3393
Tel (615) 773-3137 Founded/Ownrshp 2003
Sales 23.8MM^E EMP 260
SIC 1611 1622 1623 Highway & street construction; Surfacing & paving; Bridge construction; Highway construction, elevated; Water, sewer & utility lines; Water & sewer line construction; Highway & street construction; Surfacing & paving; Bridge construction; Highway construction, elevated; Water, sewer & utility lines; Water & sewer line construction

D-U-N-S 07-340-9518
MOUNTAIN STATES EMPLOYERS COUNCIL INC
MSEC
1799 N Pennsylvania St, Denver, CO 80203-1310
Tel (303) 839-5177 Founded/Ownrshp 1939
Sales 20.9MM EMP 200
Accts Eks&H Lllp Denver Colorado
SIC 8631 Employees' association; Employees' association
Pr: Michael G Severns
*CFO: Julie A McLaughlin
*Ex VP: Barbara A Thompson
*VP: Deborah Dale Brackney
*VP: William Smith Jr
Exec: Jodi Thompson
Ex Dir: James M Sullivan II
Off Admin: Pam Massett
Sls&Mrk Ex: Bill Smith
Mktg Mgr: Kharyl Grajczyk
Sales Asso: David Murphy

D-U-N-S 06-318-9898
MOUNTAIN STATES HEALTH ALLIANCE
400 N State Of Frnklin Rd, Johnson City, TN 37604-6035
Tel (423) 431-6111 Founded/Ownrshp 1945
Sales 707.3MM EMP 5,978
SIC 8741 Management services; Management services
Pr: Dennis Vonderfecht
Pr: Tamera Fields
*CFO: Marvin Eichorn
Exec: Charles Dugger
Dir Lab: Chris Hall
Dir Rx: Henry Ferguson
Dir Rx: Lea Mullins
Comm Man: Teresa Hicks
Prac Mgr: Kimberly Hunt
Prgrm Mgr: Hunter Ledbetter
Nurse Mgr: Lisa Carter

D-U-N-S 62-139-6514
MOUNTAIN STATES HEALTH ALLIANCE
JOHNSON CITY MEDICAL CENTER
(Suby of MOUNTAIN STATES HEALTH ALLIANCE) ★
400 N State Of Frnklin Rd, Johnson City, TN 37604-6035
Tel (423) 431-6111 Founded/Ownrshp 1978
Sales 311.3MM^E EMP 2,300
SIC 8062 General medical & surgical hospitals; General medical & surgical hospitals
*Sr VP: Marvin Eichorn
VP: Ed Herbert
VP: Kenneth E Marshall
Dir Rx: Trish Tanner
Psych: Grace Pereira
Pharmcst: Richard Mackin

MOUNTAIN STATES INSURANCE GROU
See MOUNTAIN STATES MUTUAL CASUALTY CO INC

D-U-N-S 04-299-7148
MOUNTAIN STATES MUTUAL CASUALTY CO INC (NM)
MOUNTAIN STATES INSURANCE GROU
5051 Journal Ctr Blvd Ne, Albuquerque, NM 87109-5903
Tel (505) 764-1400 Founded/Ownrshp 1937
Sales NA EMP 80^E
SIC 6331 Fire, marine & casualty insurance; Fire, marine & casualty insurance
Ch: Julia Stafford
*Pr: William F Davis
*Treas: Julie Nicolaysen
*Bd of Dir: Bill Armstrong Jr
*VP: Pam Kaufmann
Exec: Valerie Pollock
*Dir Risk M: William Irwin

D-U-N-S 03-192-9607 IMP
MOUNTAIN STATES PIPE & SUPPLY CO INC (CO)
US METERING & TECHNOLOGY
111 W Las Vegas St, Colorado Springs, CO 80903-4247
Tel (719) 634-5555 Founded/Ownrshp 1955, 1986
Sales 22.6MM EMP 130
Accts Osborne Parsons & Rosacker L
SIC 5074 5085 Plumbing & hydronic heating supplies; Water heaters & purification equipment; Gas equipment, parts & supplies; Plumbing & hydronic heating supplies; Water heaters & purification equipment; Gas equipment, parts & supplies
CEO: Paul T Carroll
*Pr: Elizabeth Carroll
COO: Scott Wateylingen
COO: Scott Zanteylinger
*CFO: Clinton Knowles
*VP: Jerry Uhlman
Sales Asso: Steve Sloan

D-U-N-S 18-208-6835
MOUNTAIN STATES STEEL INC
325 S Geneva Rd Ste 1, Lindon, UT 84042-1698
Tel (801) 785-5085 Founded/Ownrshp 1987
Sales 83.1MM^E EMP 170
Accts Squire & Company Orem Utah
SIC 3441 Fabricated structural metal for bridges; Building components, structural steel; Fabricated structural metal for bridges; Building components, structural steel
Pr: J Chris Olsen
VP: Darrin Barney
VP: Bruce Dastrup
VP: Chris Olsen
*VP: Jack Olsen
IT Man: Robert Condie
QC Dir: Jeff Perry
Sfty Mgr: Brad Olsen
Opers Mgr: Cade Sargent
VP Sls: Grady Southwick

D-U-N-S 03-537-4578
MOUNTAIN STATES SUPPLY INC
MOUNTAIN STATES WATERWORKS
184 W 3300 S, Salt Lake City, UT 84115-3704
Tel (801) 487-8265 Founded/Ownrshp 1974
Sales 64.5MM^E EMP 90
Accts Hawkins Cloward & Simister Cp
SIC 5074 Plumbing & hydronic heating supplies; Plumbing & hydronic heating supplies
Pr: John I Heslop
*Prin: Bob Rasmussen
Sales Asso: Ken Konopka

D-U-N-S 19-003-8989
MOUNTAIN STATES TOYOTA
201 W 70th Ave, Denver, CO 80221-2916
Tel (303) 302-8888 Founded/Ownrshp 2005
Sales 24.2MM^E EMP 56^E
SIC 5511 Automobiles, new & used
Prin: Tim Van Binsbergen
Pr: Sean Robertson
CFO: Jeffrey Jenkin
Genl Mgr: Kim Vanbinsbergen
Genl Mgr: Timothy Vanbinsbergen
Sls Mgr: Matt Marr
Sales Asso: Bayard Bliss

D-U-N-S 07-298-2929
MOUNTAIN STATES TUMOR INSTITUTE INC
190 E Bannock St, Boise, ID 83712-6241
Tel (208) 381-2222 Founded/Ownrshp 1969
Sales 116.5MM EMP 80
SIC 8093 Specialty outpatient clinics; Specialty outpatient clinics
*Treas: Clarence Pomeroy
*VP: Gary Fletcher

MOUNTAIN STATES WATERWORKS
See MOUNTAIN STATES SUPPLY INC

D-U-N-S 83-127-2880
MOUNTAIN SUPPLY AND SERVICE LLC
1512 Colony Cir, Longview, TX 75604-4454
Tel (903) 753-2400 Founded/Ownrshp 2009
Sales 51.7MM EMP 115
SIC 5082 Oil field equipment; Oil field equipment
Pr: Jimmy D Pleasant
Sr VP: Tc Waln
VP: Ben Arens
VP: Raegan Quesenberry
VP: Jr Royce
Sales Asso: Kevin Heater

D-U-N-S 00-624-0667
MOUNTAIN SUPPLY CO (MT)
2101 Mullan Rd, Missoula, MT 59808-1845
Tel (406) 543-8255 Founded/Ownrshp 1960, 1987
Sales 34.6MM^E EMP 55
SIC 5074 5999 Plumbing & hydronic heating supplies; Plumbing & heating supplies
Pr: Michael C Rubie
*Sec: Vickie P Rubie
Sales Exec: Eric Hendricksen
Mktg Mgr: Ryan Rubie

MOUNTAIN TELEPHONE
See MOUNTAIN RURAL TELEPHONE COOPERATIVE CORP INC

D-U-N-S 01-288-8670 IMP
MOUNTAIN TOP ENTERPRISES LLC (TX)
SARATOGA ROOFING & CNSTR
209 Nw 132nd St, Oklahoma City, OK 73114-2305
Tel (405) 692-6100 Founded/Ownrshp 1999
Sales 32.1MM^E EMP 360^E
Accts Bledsoe & Assoc Pllc Edmond
SIC 5033 1761 Roofing, siding & insulation; Roofing contractor; Roofing, siding & insulation; Roofing contractor
Pr: Denver Green
*Ex VP: Craig Dallas
Ex VP: Kerry Degener

*Ex VP: Patrick Hansen
Ex VP: Andy Lacks
*Ex VP: Jason Nowell
*VP: Kelly Heathington
*Prin: Danny Green
Off Mgr: Jeremy Houchin
Natl Sales: Evan Grobe
Snr PM: Jack Vaughn

D-U-N-S 96-352-4587
MOUNTAIN TOWERS HEALTHCARE & REHAB
3128 Boxelder Dr, Cheyenne, WY 82001-5808
Tel (307) 634-7901 Founded/Ownrshp 2010
Sales 890.6MM EMP 5E
SIC 8051 Skilled nursing care facilities; Skilled nursing care facilities
Prin: Paul Diaz

D-U-N-S 06-013-9961
MOUNTAIN VALLEY EXPRESS CO INC
6750 Longe St Ste 100, Stockton, CA 95206-4938
Tel (209) 823-2168 Founded/Ownrshp 1976
Sales 40.0MME EMP 306
SIC 4213 Trucking, except local; Trucking, except local
Pr: James Scott Blevins
VP: Dick McIntosh
Off Mgr: Penny Regelman
VP Sls: Mark Hoherd
S&M/VP: Ken Brandon

D-U-N-S 00-634-8890
MOUNTAIN VALLEY SPRING CO LLC
150 Central Ave, Hot Springs, AR 71901-3528
Tel (501) 623-6671 Founded/Ownrshp 1871, 2008
Sales 499.7MME EMP 2,600
SIC 5084 Industrial machinery & equipment; Industrial machinery & equipment
Ch: James Speed
Ql Cn Mgr: Ashley Haberer
Ql Cn Mgr: Karen Malone
Ql Cn Mgr: Jo Russell-Price
VP Sls: Don Simmons
Mktg Dir: Collins Pugh
Manager: Kelly Davidson
Sls Mgr: Tom Gorman

D-U-N-S 18-850-7974
MOUNTAIN VALLEY SPRING CO LLC
CLEAR MTN NATURAL SPRING WTR
283 Mountain Vly Wtr Pl, Hot Springs, AR 71909-9559
Tel (501) 624-7329 Founded/Ownrshp 2014
Sales 107.1MME EMP 148
SIC 5149 5499 Mineral or spring water bottling; Water: distilled mineral or spring; Mineral or spring water bottling; Water: distilled mineral or spring
CEO: Breck Speed
*CFO: Brad Frieberg
*VP: John Speed

D-U-N-S 82-550-6756
MOUNTAIN VIEW AG SERVICES INC
13281 Avenue 416, Orosi, CA 93647-9405
Tel (559) 528-6004 Founded/Ownrshp 2009
Sales 6.2MM EMP 1,200
SIC 0761 Farm labor contractors; Farm labor contractors
Pr: Leonard Hutchinson
*Sec: Sonya Hutchinson

MOUNTAIN VIEW CHEVROLET
See MTW ACQUISITION INC

D-U-N-S 02-956-7799
MOUNTAIN VIEW CHEVROLET INC
1079 W Foothill Blvd, Upland, CA 91786-3731
Tel (909) 985-2866 Founded/Ownrshp 2001
Sales 26.1MME EMP 54
SIC 5511 7532 Automobiles, new & used; Top & body repair & paint shops; Automobiles, new & used; Top & body repair & paint shops
Pr: Christopher Leggio
CFO: Loretta Holtz
*VP: Nick Cacucciolo
Mktg Dir: Darren Davis
Sls Mgr: Tony Ahmed
Sls Mgr: Manuel Chaij
Sls Mgr: Robert Fernandez
Sls Mgr: Rick Mignanelli

D-U-N-S 80-873-7902
MOUNTAIN VIEW CHILD CARE INC
TOTALLY KIDS RHBILITATION HOSP
1720 Mountain View Ave, Loma Linda, CA 92354-1799
Tel (909) 796-6915 Founded/Ownrshp 1993
Sales 56.6MME EMP 490
SIC 8062 8052 8051 General medical & surgical hospitals; Intermediate care facilities; Skilled nursing care facilities; General medical & surgical hospitals; Intermediate care facilities; Skilled nursing care facilities
CEO: Doug Pagett
*CFO: Cynthia Capetillo
*VP: Donald Nydam
*Prin: Loma Linda
*Prin: Sun Valley

D-U-N-S 16-873-5116
MOUNTAIN VIEW CO-OP
2200 Old Havre Hwy, Black Eagle, MT 59414-1043
Tel (406) 453-5900 Founded/Ownrshp 2002
Sales 75.5MME EMP 175E
SIC 5541 5153 2875 5191 Filling stations, gasoline; Grain elevators; Fertilizers, mixing only; Farm supplies; Filling stations, gasoline; Grain elevators; Fertilizers, mixing only; Farm supplies
Pr: Del Styren
*VP: Terry Allen
Sales Exec: Dave Douglas

D-U-N-S 07-526-8318
MOUNTAIN VIEW ELEMENTARY SCHOOL DISTRICT
MOUNTAIN VIEW SCHOOL DISTRICT
3320 Gilman Rd, El Monte, CA 91732-3201
Tel (626) 652-4000 Founded/Ownrshp 1898
Sales 57.8MME EMP 1,013
Accts Vicenti Lloyd & Stutzman Llp
SIC 8211 Public elementary school; Public elementary school
*Pr: Patsy Sutley
*CFO: Steve Thomas
Bd of Dir: Robert Griffith
Rgnl Mgr: George Schonborn
MIS Dir: Joy Ramirez
IT Man: Michael Coughlin
IT Man: Sandra Montoya
Pr Dir: Michele Earle
Schl Brd P: Mary Espinoza

D-U-N-S 05-503-0191
MOUNTAIN VIEW EQUIPMENT CO INC
700 W Overland Rd, Meridian, ID 83642-6510
Tel (208) 888-1593 Founded/Ownrshp 1981
Sales 42.0MM EMP 91
SIC 5999 Farm equipment & supplies; Farm equipment & supplies
Pr: Tom Nicholson
*Treas: Kathy Boehlke
*VP: Randy Stewart
Sls Mgr: John Canine

D-U-N-S 09-673-5584
MOUNTAIN VIEW FABRICATING INC
300 Hunter Ave, Saint Louis, MO 63124-2081
Tel (314) 725-0100 Founded/Ownrshp 1978, 2005
Sales 27.4MME EMP 250E
SIC 3581 Mechanisms for coin-operated machines; Mechanisms for coin-operated machines
Pr: Jack Thomas

MOUNTAIN VIEW FORD LINCOLN
See MTN VIEW FORD INC

D-U-N-S 08-680-8110
■ **MOUNTAIN VIEW HOSPITAL INC**
COLUMBIA HCA
(Suby of HCA INC) ★
1000 E 100 N, Payson, UT 84651-1600
Tel (801) 465-9201 Founded/Ownrshp 1979
Sales 7.9M EMP 400
SIC 8062 General medical & surgical hospitals; General medical & surgical hospitals
CEO: Kevin Johnson
*Pr: Samuel N Hazen
*COO: Kimball Anderson
*CFO: Steven R Schramm
*Treas: David G Anderson
*VP: Natalie H Cline
Dir Lab: Steve Hancock
Telecom Ex: Richard Brunson
QA Dir: Elaine Hoagland
QA Dir: Joan Rowbottom
Dir IT: Jason Coward

D-U-N-S 12-115-6983
MOUNTAIN VIEW HOSPITAL LLC
READYCARE
2325 Coronado St, Idaho Falls, ID 83404-7407
Tel (208) 557-2700 Founded/Ownrshp 1999
Sales 121.8MME EMP 420E
SIC 8062 General medical & surgical hospitals; General medical & surgical hospitals
Pr: Jeffery L Sayer
Ofcr: James Adamson
VP: Joshua Tolman
Dir Lab: Amanda Tinsley
Brnch Mgr: Scott Nelson
Off Admin: Jennifer Winterbottom
Phys Thrpy: Casey Jackman

MOUNTAIN VIEW REGIONAL HOSP
See CASPER MEDICAL CENTER LLC

MOUNTAIN VIEW SCHOOL DISTRICT
See MOUNTAIN VIEW ELEMENTARY SCHOOL DISTRICT

D-U-N-S 02-145-3238
MOUNTAIN VIEW SCHOOL DISTRICT
11748 State Route 106, Kingsley, PA 18826-6941
Tel (570) 434-2180 Founded/Ownrshp 1955
Sales 19.6MME EMP 390
SIC 8211 Public elementary school; Public senior high school; Public elementary school; Public senior high school
*Pr: William Beaman
VP: Ellen Aherne
*VP: Garry Foltc
Prin: Collin Furneaux
Schl Brd P: Thomas Stoddard

MOUNTAIN VIEW SEEDS
See PRATUM CO-OP

D-U-N-S 19-739-5635
MOUNTAIN VIEW TIRE & SERVICE INC
GOODYEAR
8548 Utica Ave, Rancho Cucamonga, CA 91730-4868
Tel (909) 484-9497 Founded/Ownrshp 1987
Sales 34.0MME EMP 255
SIC 7538 5531 General automotive repair shops; Automotive tires; General automotive repair shops; Automotive tires
CEO: Nicholas Mitsos
*Sec: Irene Mitsos
*VP: Chris Mitsos
*VP: Michael Mitsos

D-U-N-S 10-000-7491
MOUNTAIN VIEW-LOS ALTOS UNION HIGH SCHOOL DISTRICT
M V L A
1299 Bryant Ave, Mountain View, CA 94040-4527
Tel (650) 940-4650 Founded/Ownrshp 1900
Sales 24.0MME EMP 300
SIC 8211 Public elementary & secondary schools; Public elementary & secondary schools
Psych: Marti McGuirk
Psych: Judy Prothro

D-U-N-S 78-476-1780
MOUNTAIN VISTA MEDICAL CENTER LP
(Suby of IASIS HEALTHCARE CORP) ★
1301 S Crismon Rd, Mesa, AZ 85209-3767
Tel (480) 358-6100 Founded/Ownrshp 2015
Sales 68.4MME EMP 600
SIC 8062 General medical & surgical hospitals
CEO: Anthony R Marinello
CFO: Darryl Linnington
Dir Rx: Kal Stiles
Cmptr Lab: Davin Pang

MOUNTAIN W FRM BUR MUTL INSRAN
See MOUNTAIN WEST FARM BUREAU MUTUAL INSURANCE CO INC

D-U-N-S 18-055-5187
MOUNTAIN WATER DISTRICT
UTILITY MANAGEMENT GROUP
6332 Zebulon Hwy, Pikeville, KY 41501-6512
Tel (606) 631-9162 Founded/Ownrshp 1986
Sales 37.8MME EMP 62
SIC 4941 Water supply
IT Man: Tammy Olson
Sfty Mgr: Kevin Hamilton

D-U-N-S 88-478-0164
MOUNTAIN WEST CORRAL
GOLDEN CORRAL
302 S Main St, Centerville, UT 84014-2266
Tel (801) 295-8807 Founded/Ownrshp 1994
Sales 13.7MME EMP 300
SIC 5812 Restaurant, family: chain; Restaurant, family: chain
Sr VP: James Laverty
Off Mgr: Kris Prinster

D-U-N-S 00-942-7154
MOUNTAIN WEST DISTRIBUTORS INC
2889 S 900 W, South Salt Lake, UT 84119-2419
Tel (801) 487-5694 Founded/Ownrshp 1964
Sales 23.6MME EMP 33
SIC 5065 5064 Telephone equipment; Sound equipment, electronic; Electrical appliances, television & radio; High fidelity equipment; Radios, motor vehicle; Television sets
Pr: Rick Reynolds
*Sec: Debra Breinholt
VP: Craig Breinholt
*VP: J Craig Breinholt
Off Mgr: Lexi Dubelo
Sls Mgr: Eric Barker
Sls Mgr: Don Bell
Sls Mgr: Dave Clawson
Sls Mgr: John Collier
Sls Mgr: Lehi Herrin
Sls Mgr: Brent Stanley

D-U-N-S 07-644-1856
MOUNTAIN WEST FARM BUREAU MUTUAL INSURANCE CO INC
MOUNTAIN W FRM BUR MUTL INSRAN
931 Boulder Dr, Laramie, WY 82070-5131
Tel (307) 745-4835 Founded/Ownrshp 1948
Sales NA EMP 117
SIC 6331 Fire, marine & casualty insurance
Pr: Karen Henry
Pr: Perry Livingston
Treas: Roy Schmett
Ex VP: Ken Hamilton
VP: David L Mc Clure
VP: Jeff Suloff
CIO: Dave Sewell
Ql Cn Mgr: Sharon Howa
Sales Asso: Colleen Sylvester

D-U-N-S 79-718-2482
MOUNTAIN WEST FINANCIAL INC
MORTGAGE WORKS FINANCIAL
1209 Nevada St Ste 200, Redlands, CA 92374-4581
Tel (909) 793-1500 Founded/Ownrshp 1990
Sales NA EMP 400
Accts Streit & Peters Redlands Ca
SIC 6162 Mortgage bankers & correspondents; Mortgage bankers & correspondents
Pr: Gary H Martell Jr
*CFO: Michael W Douglas

D-U-N-S 13-234-5120 EXP
MOUNTAIN WEST LLC
4212 S Highway 191, Rexburg, ID 83440-4251
Tel (208) 359-5640 Founded/Ownrshp 1999
Sales 121.8MME EMP 150
SIC 1429 Basalt, crushed & broken-quarrying; Basalt, crushed & broken-quarrying
Pt: Ernest Johnson
Treas: David Wolfe
Genl Mgr: Byron Morgan
Sls Mgr: Lyle Jeppesen

MOUNTAIN WEST MEDICAL CENTER
See TOOELE HOSPITAL CORP

D-U-N-S 62-282-3586
MOUNTAIN WEST PIPE AND SUPPLY INC
3001 S 300 W, Salt Lake City, UT 84115-3406
Tel (801) 484-3500 Founded/Ownrshp 2005
Sales 36.0MME EMP 100
SIC 5085 Valves & fittings; Valves & fittings
Pr: Jed Chamberlain
*Sec: Wesley Fisher
Ofcr: Ann Fisher
*VP: Jay A Chamberlain
Sales Asso: Gary Evans
Sales Asso: Mark Johnson

D-U-N-S 00-845-5995
MOUNTAIN WEST RETIREMENT CORP
BONAVENTURE SENIOR LIVING
3425 Boone Rd Se, Salem, OR 97317-9336
Tel (503) 566-5715 Founded/Ownrshp 1999
Sales 30.5MME EMP 135
SIC 8741 Nursing & personal care facility management
Pr: Kelley D Hamilton
Dir IT: Cameron Memmott

MOUNTAIN WEST TRUCK CENTER
See SALT LAKE CITY MACK SALES & SERVICE INC

D-U-N-S 00-436-8452
MOUNTAINEER CONTRACTORS INC
15237 Soutrh Preston Hwy, Kingwood, WV 26537
Tel (304) 329-2129 Founded/Ownrshp 1965
Sales 69.8MME EMP 125
SIC 1611 Surfacing & paving; Grading; Surfacing & paving; Grading
Pr: John T Boyle II
*Treas: Denise Good
*VP: Robert E Leigh

D-U-N-S 11-274-6458
MOUNTAINEER GAS CO
2401 Sissonville Dr, Charleston, WV 25387-1336
Tel (800) 834-2070 Founded/Ownrshp 1957
Sales 310.7MME EMP 489E
SIC 4924 Natural gas distribution; Natural gas distribution
Pr: Tom M Tylor
CFO: George Behrens
*Treas: Scott F Klemm
Sr VP: Moses Skaff
*VP: Danny Chandler
*VP: Michael N Trusty
Dir IT: Shaun Conley
Dir IT: Brady Hunt
IT Man: James Meadows

D-U-N-S 05-590-9328
MOUNTAINEER KEYSTONE LLC
6031 Wallace Road Ext # 300, Wexford, PA 15090-3430
Tel (724) 940-1100 Founded/Ownrshp 2011
Sales 45.5MME EMP 36E
SIC 1381 Drilling oil & gas wells
Pr: Gregory R Wrightstone
*Pr: Len Paugh

MOUNTAINEER RACE TRACK RESORT
See PARK MOUNTAINEER INC

MOUNTAINKING POTATOES
See FARMING TECHNOLOGY CORP

D-U-N-S 04-369-8299 IMP
MOUNTAINLAND SUPPLY CO
1505 W 130 S, Orem, UT 84058-5161
Tel (801) 224-6050 Founded/Ownrshp 2013
Sales 33.7MME EMP 55E
SIC 5074 5085 5083

D-U-N-S 00-695-5454
MOUNTAINONE BANK
(Suby of MOUNTAINONE FINANCIAL, INC.)
93 Main St, North Adams, MA 01247-3405
Tel (413) 663-5353 Founded/Ownrshp 1848, 2002
Sales NA EMP 49
SIC 6036 Savings & loan associations, not federally chartered; Savings & loan associations, not federally chartered
Pr: Thomas W Kelly
COO: Cynthia Noyes
*Treas: Edward Nimmons
Chf Mktg O: Liz Bissell
*VP: Marilyn De Rosa
Exec: Jeff Polucci

D-U-N-S 03-059-6654
MOUNTAINS COMMUNITY HOSPITAL FOUNDATION INC
29101 Hospital Rd, Lake Arrowhead, CA 92352-9706
Tel (909) 336-3651 Founded/Ownrshp 1957
Sales 32.1MME EMP 180
Accts Wipfli Llp Wausau Wi
SIC 8062 8051 General medical & surgical hospitals; Skilled nursing care facilities; General medical & surgical hospitals; Skilled nursing care facilities
CEO: Don Willerth
Ofcr: Tandi Orangetree
Dir Rad: Allan Maneje
CIO: Patrick Miller
Doctor: John Gonzalez
Phys Thrpy: Ginny Dunn
Snr Mgr: Terry Pena

D-U-N-S 14-567-2051
MOUNTAINSIDE COAL CO INC
(Suby of WHITE ENERGY COMPANY LIMITED)
7692 S Highway 25 W, Williamsburg, KY 40769-9779
Tel (606) 786-7217 Founded/Ownrshp 2013
Sales 51.8MME EMP 125
SIC 1221 Bituminous coal & lignite-surface mining; Bituminous coal & lignite-surface mining
Pr: Dan Chambers
VP: Dean Chambers

MOUNTAINSIDE HOSPITAL
See HACKENSACKUMC MOUNTAINSIDE

D-U-N-S 83-817-7129
MOUNTAINVIEW HOSPITAL INC
SUNRISE MOUNTAIN VIEW HOSPITAL
3100 N Tenaya Way, Las Vegas, NV 89128-0436
Tel (702) 255-5000 Founded/Ownrshp 1995
Sales 134.1MME EMP 1,051
SIC 8062 8011 4119 General medical & surgical hospitals; Offices & clinics of medical doctors; Ambulance service; General medical & surgical hospitals; Offices & clinics of medical doctors; Ambulance service
CEO: Chris Mowan
*COO: JD Melchiode
COO: J D Melchioe
COO: Tad Morley
*CFO: Steve Killian
Dir Lab: Janet Genter
Nurse Mgr: Cammy Goodwin
CIO: Gary Sharp
Dir IT: Donna Forrester
Dir IT: Gary Sharpe
QC Dir: Antoinette Prefto-Sparkuhl

MOUNTAINVIEW REGIONAL MED CTR
See NORTON HMA INC

MOUNTAINVIEW REGIONAL MED CTR
See LAS CRUCES MEDICAL CENTER LLC

D-U-N-S 06-977-5468
■ **MOUNTAINVIEW THOROUGHBRED RACING ASSOCIATION**
HOLLYWOOD CASINO
(Suby of PENN NATIONAL GAMING INC) ★
At I 81 Rr 743, Grantville, PA 17028
Tel (717) 469-2211 Founded/Ownrshp 1995

Sales 2.1MM^E *EMP* 300
SIC 7948 Thoroughbred horse racing; Thoroughbred horse racing
CEO: Peter M Carlino
Pr: William Bork
**Sec:* Robert Ippolito
**VP:* Gary Ludertz

D-U-N-S 11-112-9115
MOUNTAINVIEW THOROUGHBRED RACING ASSOCIATION LLC
HOLLYWOOD CASINO
777 Hollywood Blvd, Grantville, PA 17028-9237
Tel (717) 469-2211 *Founded/Ownrshp* 1986
Sales 58.3MM^E *EMP* 1,100
SIC 7999 Off-track betting; Off-track betting
Pr: Peter Carlino
CFO: Tim Ebling
VP: Garlon Banks
VP: Frank Quigley

D-U-N-S 01-645-2388
MOUNTAINWOOD PET HOSPITAL PC
1200 W Ash St Unit A, Windsor, CO 80550-4610
Tel (970) 460-9070 *Founded/Ownrshp* 2008
Sales 8.6MM^E *EMP* 392^E
SIC 8062 General medical & surgical hospitals
Prin: Arun Rustgi

D-U-N-S 00-634-3958 IMP/EXP
MOUNTAIRE CORP
1901 Napa Valley Dr, Little Rock, AR 72212-3913
Tel (501) 372-6524 *Founded/Ownrshp* 1964
Sales 1.3MMM^E *EMP* 6,079
SIC 2015 Poultry slaughtering & processing; Poultry slaughtering & processing
Pr: Ronald M Cameron
**CFO:* Dabbs Cavin
**Treas:* Gina Risberg
**Ex VP:* Dee Ann Landreth
**VP:* Alan Duncan
Genl Mgr: Andrew Cobb
Snr Mgr: Joey Lister

D-U-N-S 09-181-2669 IMP/EXP
MOUNTAIRE FARMS INC
(*Suby of* MOUNTAIRE CORP) ★
1901 Napa Valley Dr, Little Rock, AR 72212-3913
Tel (501) 372-6524 *Founded/Ownrshp* 1977
Sales 938.8MM^E *EMP* 4,100
SIC 2015 Poultry slaughtering & processing; Poultry slaughtering & processing
Pr: Paul Downes
**Ch Bd:* Ronald Cameron
**CFO:* Dabbs Cavin
**Treas:* Gina Risberg
**VP:* Alan Duncan
**VP:* Dee A Landreth
VP: Larry Sagwell
CTO: Charles Wallace
Pr Dir: Roger Marino

D-U-N-S 00-101-8816 EXP
MOUNTAIRE FARMS OF DELAWARE INC
(*Suby of* MOUNTAIRE CORP) ★
1901 Napa Valley Dr, Little Rock, AR 72212-3913
Tel (501) 372-6524 *Founded/Ownrshp* 2000
Sales 34.3MM^E *EMP* 1,500
SIC 0751 Poultry services; Poultry services
Pr: Paul Downes
**Ch Bd:* Ronald Cameron
**CFO:* Dabbs Cavin
**Treas:* Gina Risberg
**Sr VP:* Dee Ann Landreth
**VP:* Alan H Duncan

D-U-N-S 01-250-1922 IMP/EXP
MOUNTAIRE FARMS OF DELAWARE INC
(*Suby of* MOUNTAIRE CORP) ★
29005 John J Williams Hwy, Millsboro, DE 19966-4095
Tel (302) 934-1100 *Founded/Ownrshp* 2000
Sales 359.3MM^E *EMP* 1,698
SIC 2015 Poultry slaughtering & processing; Poultry slaughtering & processing
CEO: Paul Downs
**COO:* Joe Moran
**CFO:* Jim Lecates
**VP:* Phil Plylar
VP: Lou Rascona
**VP:* Larry Saywell
Dir IT: Bill Saulsbury
IT Man: Chad Elliott
IT Man: Michael Taylor
Sfty Mgr: Bob Kendall
Plnt Mgr: Randall Bostic

D-U-N-S 17-259-6272
MOUNTIAN VIEW-WHISMAN SCHOOL DISTRICT
750a San Pierre Way, Mountain View, CA 94043-3133
Tel (650) 526-3500 *Founded/Ownrshp* 1865
Sales 34.0MM *EMP* 450
SIC 8211 Public elementary & secondary schools; Public elementary & secondary schools
Trst: Ellen Wheeler
Genl Mgr: Jenni Cummings
Schl Brd P: Bill Lambert

MOUNTIANKING POTATOES
See FARMING TECHNOLOGY INC

D-U-N-S 08-869-8097
MOUNTRAIL-WILLIAMS ELECTRIC COOPERATIVE
218 58th St W, Williston, ND 58801
Tel (701) 577-3765 *Founded/Ownrshp* 1944
Sales 183.2MM *EMP* 86^E
Accts Eide Bailly Llp Fargo Nd
SIC 4911 Distribution, electric power; Distribution, electric power
IT Man: Cole Arndt
IT Man: Jay Lux
IT Man: Jerry Rehak

D-U-N-S 00-330-8558 IMP
MOUNTVILLE MILLS INC (GA)
ANDRESON COMPANY, THE
1729 S Davis Rd, Lagrange, GA 30241-6172
Tel (706) 882-2961 *Founded/Ownrshp* 1963
Sales 138.7MM^E *EMP* 500
SIC 2273 2211 2221 Door mats: paper, grass, reed, coir, sisal, jute, rags, etc.; Broadwoven fabric mills, cotton; Broadwoven fabric mills, manmade; Door mats: paper, grass, reed, coir, sisal, jute, rags, etc.; Broadwoven fabric mills, cotton; Broadwoven fabric mills, manmade
CEO: Emmett David Jr Hart
**Ch Bd:* David Hart
**CFO:* Susan H Ekkebus
**VP:* David Watterson
Genl Mgr: Suzy Phillips
Off Admin: Brenda Toney
Dir IT: Michael Eastman
IT Man: Artie Todd
IT Man: Arnold Wolfe
Sftwr Eng: Caleb Duncan
Natl Sales: Joe Rubbelke

D-U-N-S 16-119-4410 IMP/EXP
■ MOUSER ELECTRONICS INC
(*Suby of* TTI INC) ★
1000 N Main St, Mansfield, TX 76063-1514
Tel (817) 804-3800 *Founded/Ownrshp* 1964
Sales 772.2MM^E *EMP* 500
SIC 5065 Electronic parts; Electronic parts
CEO: Glenn Smith
**Ch Bd:* Paul Andrews
**Ch Bd:* Warren Buffett
Sr VP: Jeff Newell
VP: Barry McConnell
VP: Kristin Schuetter
VP: Tina Sears
VP: Stephanie Sorrell
VP: Dan Troutt
VP: Misti Webb
QA Dir: Todd Dearman

D-U-N-S 02-232-1335
MOUW MOTOR CO INC
FORD MERCURY
1245 N Main Ave, Sioux Center, IA 51250-2105
Tel (712) 722-0085 *Founded/Ownrshp* 1960
Sales 23.0MM *EMP* 25
SIC 5511 Automobiles, new & used; Automobiles, new & used
Pr: Marion Mouw
**Sec:* Neil Van Schouwen

MOV N STORE
See PIONEER PACKAGING INC

D-U-N-S 04-619-5103 IMP
▲ MOVADO GROUP INC
650 From Rd Ste 375, Paramus, NJ 07652-3556
Tel (201) 267-8000 *Founded/Ownrshp* 1967
Sales 586.9MM *EMP* 1,110^E
Accts Pricewaterhousecoopers Llp Ne
Tkr Sym MOV *Exch* NYS
SIC 3873 3915 5094 5944 7631 Watches, clocks, watchcases & parts; Jewel preparing: instruments, tools, watches & jewelry; Watches & parts; Watches; Watch repair; Watches, clocks, watchcases & parts; Jewel preparing: instruments, tools, watches & jewelry; Watches & parts; Watches; Watch repair
Ch Bd: Efraim Grinberg
V Ch: Richard J Cot
Pr: Julian Addison
Pr: Ricardo Quintero
**COO:* Richard J Cote
CFO: Sallie A Demarsilis
Chf Mktg O: Mary Leach
Sr VP: Rob Cherrington
Sr VP: Harvey Driansky
**Sr VP:* Alex Grinberg
Sr VP: Frank A Morelli
Sr VP: Joe Zanone
VP: Kristen Cavagnuolo
VP: Luis Conde
VP: Kaitlyn Fischer
VP: Joseph Nici
VP: Everett Rashotsky
Creative D: Richard Tassone
Board of Directors: Margaret Hayes Adame, Peter A Bridgman, Alan H Howard, Richard Isserman, Nathan Leventhal, Maurice Reznik

D-U-N-S 03-535-7768
■ MOVE INC
(*Suby of* NEWS CORP) ★
10 Almaden Blvd Ste 800, San Jose, CA 95113-2238
Tel (408) 558-7100 *Founded/Ownrshp* 2014
Sales 227.0MM *EMP* 913
SIC 6531 7375 Real estate listing services; Multiple listing service, real estate; On-line data base information retrieval; Real estate listing services; Multiple listing service, real estate; On-line data base information retrieval
CEO: Steven H Berkowitz
Pr: Sunil Mehrotra
Pr: Eric Thorkilsen
**CFO:* Bryan Charap
**CFO:* Rachel C Glaser
**Chf Mktg O:* Nate Johnson
**Ex VP:* James S Caulfield
Ex VP: Jeremy R Lent
Ex VP: Ray Picard
Ex VP: Raymond Picard
Sr VP: M Jeffrey Charney
Sr VP: Michael Kane
Sr VP: Hahn Lee
VP: Julie Karafiath
VP: Mark Langsfeld
VP: Betty Li
VP: Anthony Perry
VP: Celeste Starchild
VP: Leza Vanbeuren
VP: Yi-Fang Yen

D-U-N-S 07-940-0908
MOVE LOOT INC
3825 S Willow Ave, Fresno, CA 93725-9025
Tel (415) 590-0640 *Founded/Ownrshp* 2014
Sales 27.5MM^E *EMP* 92

SIC 5961 Catalog & mail-order houses
CEO: William Bobbitt
**COO:* Sharuti Shah
**Chf Mktg O:* Jenny Karin Morrill
**CTO:* Ryan Smith

D-U-N-S 18-125-0432
MOVE SOLUTIONS-DALLAS LTD
1473 Terre Colony Ct, Dallas, TX 75212-6220
Tel (214) 630-3607 *Founded/Ownrshp* 2000
Sales 13.0MM^E *EMP* 300
SIC 4212 Moving services; Moving services
Genl Pt: Michael A Monette
Pt: Linda Monette
Genl Mgr: Amy Linton
Dir IT: James Nugeness
Opers Mgr: Randy Moore
Opers Mgr: Shane Williams

D-U-N-S 00-414-1981
MOVEMBER FOUNDATION (CA)
8559 Higuera St, Culver City, CA 90232-2535
Tel (310) 450-3331 *Founded/Ownrshp* 2007
Sales 20.1MM *EMP* 15
SIC 7389 Fund raising organizations; Fund raising organizations
CEO: Adam Garone
Opers Mgr: Brooke Bastain

MOVERS INTERNATIONAL
See MI GROUP INC

D-U-N-S 09-371-0135
MOVERS SPECIALTY SERVICE INC (PA)
M S S
211 Commerce Dr, Montgomeryville, PA 18936-9641
Tel (215) 393-1900 *Founded/Ownrshp* 1978
Sales 21.8MM^E *EMP* 140
SIC 4212 4783 Moving services; Containerization of goods for shipping
CEO: Timothy P Hughes
**CFO:* Suzann Torpey
**VP:* Maria Bunch
**VP:* Aurora Hughes
**VP:* Christopher Hughes
VP: Dick McDonald
**VP:* Michael Muddit
Sftwr Eng: Matt Hasson
Trfc Dir: Wayde Craig
Sales Exec: Steve Brown
Mktg Dir: Rob Uriso

D-U-N-S 12-463-1305
MOVIE BRANDS INC
MR MOVIES
1523 Nicollet Ave, Minneapolis, MN 55403-2723
Tel (952) 835-3321 *Founded/Ownrshp* 2011
Sales 7.2MM^E *EMP* 325
SIC 7841 Video tape rental; Video tape rental
Pr: Lonnie Strong
**VP:* Doug Dunn
**VP:* Paula Kinney
VP Opers: Leslie Davis
Mktg Mgr: Judy Corey

D-U-N-S 86-945-2177 IMP/EXP
MOVIE GALLERY INC
9275 Sw Peyton Ln, Wilsonville, OR 97070-9200
Tel (503) 570-1700 *Founded/Ownrshp* 1994
Sales 1.3MMM^E *EMP* 36,250
SIC 7841 5735 Video tape rental; Film or tape rental, motion picture; Video tapes, prerecorded; Video discs, prerecorded; Video tape rental; Film or tape rental, motion picture; Video tapes, prerecorded; Video discs, prerecorded
Pr: Clarence J Gabriel Jr
**CFO:* Lucinda M Baier
**Chf Mktg O:* Wes Sand
**Chf Mktg O:* Clifford Torng
Ex VP: Guy Marsala
**Ex VP:* Craig J Miller
Ex VP: Pamela R Schneide
**Ex VP:* Pamela R Schneider
VP: Sherif J Mityas
Dist Mgr: Karen Osborn
Dist Mgr: Mel Phillips
Board of Directors: Robert Fiorella, Mark E Holliday, Thomas B McGrath, Steven D Scheiwe, Richard L Shorten Jr, Neil S Subin

D-U-N-S 00-266-2364
MOVIE GRILL CONCEPTS I LTD
STUDIO MOVIE GRILL
8350 N Central Expy # 400, Dallas, TX 75206-1600
Tel (972) 388-7888 *Founded/Ownrshp* 1998
Sales 38.9MM^E *EMP* 192^E
SIC 7832 5812 Motion picture theaters, except drive-in; Eating places; Motion picture theaters, except drive-in; Eating places
CEO: Brian Schultz
VP: Jim Gdula
Area Mgr: John Elliott
Genl Mgr: Joseph Diggs
Genl Mgr: Mike Dingess
Genl Mgr: Ron Hahn
Genl Mgr: Adam Kennedy
Genl Mgr: Michael McCreary
VP Opers: Christopher Gainey
Mktg Dir: Gary Frank
Mktg Dir: Tearlach Hutcheson

MOVIE MADNESS
See PAXTON & BALL INC

MOVIE STAR
See FREDERICKS OF HOLLYWOOD INC

MOVIE STAR
See FOH GROUP INC

MOVIE STARZ VIDEO
See ADVENTURE ENTERTAINMENT INC

D-U-N-S 79-060-7605 IMP
MOVIE TAVERN INC
(*Suby of* GRAND THEATER) ★
12400 Coit Rd Ste 800, Dallas, TX 75251-2067
Tel (214) 751-8277 *Founded/Ownrshp* 2013
Sales 81.0MM^E *EMP* 200^E

SIC 7832 Motion picture theaters, except drive-in; Motion picture theaters, except drive-in
CEO: George Solomon
**CEO:* John Hersker
Rgnl Mgr: Gary Van Gundy
Area Mgr: Roy Van Horn
Genl Mgr: Mike Eller
Genl Mgr: Kenny Perry
Genl Mgr: Mark Pool
Dir IT: Timothy Douglas
Opers Mgr: Larry White
Mktg Dir: Danny Digiacomo
Sls Mgr: Nick Vedda

MOVIE TRADING COMPANY
See VINTAGE STOCK INC

D-U-N-S 96-809-1483
MOVIESTOP LLC
(*Suby of* DRAW ANOTHER CIRCLE LLC) ★
1300 Cobb Intl Dr Nw, Kennesaw, GA 30152-4398
Tel (770) 590-1765 *Founded/Ownrshp* 2014
Sales 47.0MM^E *EMP* 500^E
SIC 5735 Video discs & tapes, prerecorded; Video discs & tapes, prerecorded
CEO: Russel Howard
Dist Mgr: James Coburn

D-U-N-S 15-161-4393
MOVING SOLUTIONS INC
NORTH AMERICAN VAN LINES
927 Wrigley Way, Milpitas, CA 95035-5407
Tel (408) 920-0110 *Founded/Ownrshp* 1984
Sales 32.6MM^E *EMP* 150
SIC 4214 8742 7376 1799 Local trucking with storage; Construction project management consultant; Computer facilities management; Office furniture installation
CEO: Rick S Philpott
**VP:* Janet Philpott
VP: Pam Welsh

D-U-N-S 79-119-4652
MOVIUS INTERACTIVE CORP
11360 Lakefield Dr, Johns Creek, GA 30097-1569
Tel (770) 283-1000 *Founded/Ownrshp* 2006
Sales 54.6MM^E *EMP* 154^E
SIC 7371 Computer software development; Computer software development
Ch Bd: Augustine Cruciotti
**CEO:* Dominic Gomez
CFO: Kathleen Eichelroth
**CFO:* Stacy Kilgore
Sr Cor Off: Jim Caparro
Sr VP: John Boden
**Sr VP:* Steve Summers
VP: Fabio Almeida
VP: Javier Garcia
VP: John Green
VP: Wayne Greenberg
VP: Lynn Herrick
VP: Bill Mastrototaro
VP: Chuck Mitchell
VP: Bill Pettit
**VP:* Brad Reeves
VP: Howard Shaw
VP: Shandton Williams
Dir Lab: Eric Huff
Creative D: Paul Grosso

D-U-N-S 82-585-2189
MOWAT CONSTRUCTION CO
20210 142nd Ave Ne, Woodinville, WA 98072-4477
Tel (425) 398-0205 *Founded/Ownrshp* 1994
Sales 100.0MM^E *EMP* 180
Accts Moss Adams Llp Everett Washi
SIC 1611 General contractor, highway & street construction; General contractor, highway & street construction
Ch Bd: Mark Mowat
**Pr:* John Sandstrom
VP: Janifer Hays
**VP:* Doug Smith
Board of Directors: Mark Mowat

D-U-N-S 07-332-5383
MOWERY CLINIC LLC
737 E Crawford St, Salina, KS 67401-5103
Tel (785) 827-7261 *Founded/Ownrshp* 1994
Sales 30.6MM^E *EMP* 150
SIC 8011 Clinic, operated by physicians
Pr: Bob Gaekwad MD
Cmptr Lab: Valerie Kasselman
Surgeon: Christopher Rupe
Obsttrcn: Leslie Ablard
Obsttrcn: Steven Sebree
Doctor: David Battin
Doctor: Lavelle Ellis MD
Doctor: Brad Stuewe

D-U-N-S 12-769-4045 IMP
MOXA AMERICAS INC
(*Suby of* MOXA INC.)
601 Valencia Ave Ste 100, Brea, CA 92823-6357
Tel (714) 528-6777 *Founded/Ownrshp* 2002
Sales 23.3MM^E *EMP* 50
SIC 3577 Input/output equipment, computer
CEO: Tein Shun
**Pr:* Ben Chen
Ex VP: Steve Won
VP: Clark Ko
VP: C C Peng
Prgrm Mgr: Joe Matsumoto
Genl Mgr: Steve Lin
Sftwr Eng: Jay Yan
Opers Mgr: Sylvia Ho
Sls Dir: Jacky Chang
Mktg Mgr: Amanda Wu

MOXEE RANCH
See ZIRKLE FRUIT CO

D-U-N-S 01-018-7081
MOXIE INTERACTIVE INC
NORTHYARDS, THE
(*Suby of* ZENITH MEDIA SERVICES INC) ★
384 Northyards Blvd Nw, Atlanta, GA 30313-2440
Tel (404) 601-4500 *Founded/Ownrshp* 2000
Sales 35.8MM^E *EMP* 102^E
SIC 8742 4813 Management consulting services;

CEO: Suzy Deering
COO: Solange Claudio
CFO: Chris Walker
Ex VP: Adam Albrecht
Ex VP: Christine Bensen
Ex VP: Kristina Jonathan
Ex VP: Alyse Schwartz
Ex VP: Steve Swanson
Sr VP: Jane Matthews
Sr VP: Paul Santello
VP: Sara Francis
VP: Andrew Lovasz
VP: Brian Mathena
VP: Chris Pickett
VP: Michael Winter

D-U-N-S 83-120-0493
MOXIE SOFTWARE CIM CORP
(*Suby of* MOXIE SOFTWARE INC) ★
15 Lake Bellevue Dr # 200, Bellevue, WA 98005-2485
Tel (425) 467-5000 *Founded/Ownrshp* 2008
Sales 35.0MM *EMP* 60
SIC 7372 7371 Prepackaged software; Custom computer programming services
Pr: Rebecca Ward
COO: Alan Heitmann

D-U-N-S 80-137-3403
MOXIE SOFTWARE INC
1250 Bayhill Dr Ste 200, San Bruno, CA 94066-3049
Tel (650) 294-4680 *Founded/Ownrshp* 2006
Sales 35.0MM *EMP* 150
SIC 7373 Systems software development services; Computer systems analysis & design; Systems software development services; Computer systems analysis & design
Pr: Rebecca Ward
COO: Alan Heitmann
VP: Tom Hresko
VP: David Lowy
VP: Dennis Omalley
VP: Tara Sporrer
VP Sls: Troy Tackett
Manager: Craig Hambelton
Manager: Kieran McDonogh
Manager: Jerry Philips
Manager: Jason Westman
Board of Directors: James I Cash Jr, Ken Goldman, Thomas Kelly, Susan Whiting

D-U-N-S 17-531-9805 IMP
MOXTEK INC
(*Suby of* POLATECHNO CO.,LTD.)
452 W 1260 N, Orem, UT 84057-2941
Tel (801) 225-0930 *Founded/Ownrshp* 1986
Sales 51.3MM^E *EMP* 160
SIC 3827 3826 Optical instruments & lenses; Analytical instruments; Optical instruments & lenses; Analytical instruments
Ch: Sanji Arisawa
**CEO:* Hiroyuki Iseki
**CFO:* Nathan West
VP: Bill Hansen
VP: Raymond Perkins
CTO: Roger Crist
CTO: Clark Turner
Dir IT: Puman Punuchuburd
IT Man: Brian Halls
IT Man: Amy Swain
Prd Mgr: Nathan Wendt

MOXY
See DRFIRST.COM INC

D-U-N-S 03-754-9383
MOYE WHITE LLP
1400 16th St Ste 600, Denver, CO 80202-1486
Tel (303) 292-2900 *Founded/Ownrshp* 1976
Sales 20.6MM *EMP* 85
SIC 8111 General practice law office; General practice law office
Mng Pt: Thomas List
Pr: Carolyn Lux
Pr: Glenna McKelvy
Pr: Lisa Oliver
COO: Lorri Salyards
Ex Dir: Moye White
IT Man: Brad Crook
Mktg Mgr: Cassandra Bohn
Counsel: Ken Tolle

D-U-N-S 01-458-8107 EXP
MOYER & SON INC
113 E Reliance Rd, Souderton, PA 18964-1308
Tel (215) 799-2000 *Founded/Ownrshp* 1869
Sales 110.5MM^E *EMP* 240
SIC 5191 5983 2875 0782 1711 Animal feeds; Fuel oil dealers; Fertilizers, mixing only; Lawn care services; Plumbing, heating, air-conditioning contractors; Animal feeds; Fuel oil dealers; Fertilizers, mixing only; Lawn care services; Plumbing, heating, air-conditioning contractors
Pr: John Moyer
**VP:* Jon Clemmer
**VP:* David A Moyer
Opers Mgr: John Haley
Sls Mgr: Amy Rullo

D-U-N-S 02-436-3376
MOYLE PETROLEUM CO (SD)
COMMON CENTS STORES
2504 W Main St, Rapid City, SD 57702-2424
Tel (605) 343-1966 *Founded/Ownrshp* 1957
Sales 149.3MM^E *EMP* 400
SIC 5541 5411 Filling stations, gasoline; Convenience stores; Filling stations, gasoline; Convenience stores
CEO: Gilbert D Moyle III
**Pr:* Gilbert D Moyle
CFO: Steve Mentele
**Treas:* E Steve Mentele
**VP:* Clark Moyle
Exec: Jack Sullivan
Telecom Ex: Derek Budahl
IT Man: Andy Foster

D-U-N-S 12-899-4485
MOYLES CENTRAL VALLEY HEALTH CARE INC
999 N M St, Tulare, CA 93274-2019
Tel (559) 688-0288 *Founded/Ownrshp* 1990
Sales 8.5MM^E *EMP* 340
SIC 8051 Skilled nursing care facilities; Skilled nursing care facilities
Pr: Ken Moyel III

MOYNA, C J & SONS CONSTRUCTION
See C J MOYNA & SONS INC

MOYNIHAN LUMBER
See READING MOYNIHAN-NORTH LUMBER INC

D-U-N-S 16-361-0384 IMP
■ **MOYNO INC**
NOV PROCESS & FLOWTECH
(*Suby of* ROBBINS & MYERS INC) ★
1895 W Jefferson St, Springfield, OH 45506-1115
Tel (937) 327-3111 *Founded/Ownrshp* 1998
Sales 25.1MM^E *EMP* 200^E
SIC 7699 Industrial equipment services; Industrial equipment services
Pr: Aaron Ravenscroft
**Prin:* Norman Shearer

D-U-N-S 03-963-1554
MOZIDO INC
1601 S Mopac Expy Ste 200, Austin, TX 78746
Tel (512) 518-2200 *Founded/Ownrshp* 2010
Sales 36.4MM^E *EMP* 99
SIC 8743 Promotion service
CEO: R Todd Bradley
Ch Bd: Michael Liberty
Pr: Ron Hynes
COO: Ed N Collazo
COO: Dan O'Malley
Ex VP: Ira Levy
Ex VP: Mike Love
Ex VP: David Luther
Ex VP: Minaz Saragi
Ex VP: Minaz Sarangi
Sr VP: Steve Bacastow
Sr VP: Pat Downing
Sr VP: Charlie Wiggs
VP: Mitchell Dillard
VP: Lynn Eslick
VP: Teri Harwood

D-U-N-S 62-325-1852
MOZILLA CORP
(*Suby of* MOZILLA FOUNDATION) ★
331 E Evelyn Ave Ste 100, Mountain View, CA 94041-1538
Tel (650) 903-0800 *Founded/Ownrshp* 2005
Sales 93.8MM^E *EMP* 425
SIC 7373 Systems software development services; Systems software development services
Ch Bd: Mitchell Baker
CEO: Chris Beard
CFO: James Cook
Top Exec: Robert O'Callahan
Ex VP: Christopher Beard
VP: David Ascher
Prgrm Mgr: Diane Bisgeier
Prgrm Mgr: Kathleen Wilson
Snr Sftwr: Dan Callahan
Snr Sftwr: Randell Jesup
Snr Sftwr: Chris Peterson

D-U-N-S 19-227-1984
MOZILLA FOUNDATION
331 E Evelyn Ave, Mountain View, CA 94041-1550
Tel (650) 903-0800 *Founded/Ownrshp* 2003
Sales 93.9MM^E *EMP* 425^E
Accts Deloitte Tax Llp San Francisc
SIC 7371 Computer software development; Computer software development
CEO: Mark Surman
Snr Sftwr: Laura Thomson
CTO: Andreas Gal
Sftwr Eng: Zach Carter
Snr Mgr: Winston Bowden

MOZY
See DECHO CORP

D-U-N-S 10-292-5849 IMP
MP ASSOCIATES INC
M P A
6555 Jackson Valley Rd, Ione, CA 95640-9630
Tel (209) 274-4715 *Founded/Ownrshp* 1981
Sales 33.5MM^E *EMP* 170
SIC 2892 2899 Explosives; Pyrotechnic ammunition: flares, signals, rockets, etc.; Explosives; Pyrotechnic ammunition: flares, signals, rockets, etc.
Pr: Thaine Morris
**Treas:* David Pier
Sfty Mgr: Mike Buck
Sfty Mgr: Raul Rodriguez

D-U-N-S 13-782-5928 IMP
MP BIOMEDICALS LLC
3 Hutton Cntre Dr Ste 100, Santa Ana, CA 92707
Tel (949) 833-2500 *Founded/Ownrshp* 2003
Sales 63.0MM *EMP* 500
SIC 5047 Diagnostic equipment, medical; Diagnostic equipment, medical
COO: Ralph Seeberger
CFO: Steve Perrone
VP: Jeffrey Hillman
Exec: Jim Mahacek
CTO: Merl Hoekstra
Dir IT: Bill Jones
Prd Mgr: Jeffrey White
Natl Sales: Tom Glickman
VP Mktg: Gerard David
VP Sls: Steven Reynolds
S&M/VP: Brian Conkle

D-U-N-S 05-112-2146 IMP
MP DIRECT INC
TALK2US
4800 126th Ave N, Clearwater, FL 33762-4709
Tel (727) 572-8443 *Founded/Ownrshp* 2000
Sales 85.8MM^E *EMP* 530
SIC 5094 5944 5091 Clocks, watches & parts; Clock & watch stores; Golf equipment; Clocks, watches & parts; Clock & watch stores; Golf equipment
Pr: Kenneth W Byers

D-U-N-S 62-278-9923
MP ENVIRONMENTAL SERVICES INC
3400 Manor St, Bakersfield, CA 93308-1451
Tel (800) 458-3036 *Founded/Ownrshp* 1991
Sales 117.5MM^E *EMP* 225
SIC 4953 4213 8748 7699 Hazardous waste collection & disposal; Radioactive waste materials, disposal; Trucking, except local; Environmental consultant; Tank repair & cleaning services; Hazardous waste collection & disposal; Radioactive waste materials, disposal; Trucking, except local; Environmental consultant; Tank repair & cleaning services
Pr: Dawn Calderwood
Opers Mgr: Shawn Calderwood

D-U-N-S 10-753-3218 IMP
MP EQUIPMENT
2395 Murphy Blvd, Gainesville, GA 30504-6001
Tel (770) 503-7605 *Founded/Ownrshp* 1971
Sales 34.5MM^E *EMP* 40
SIC 5084 Food product manufacturing machinery
CEO: Jerrill Sprinkle
**Pr:* Mark Phillips
**Sec:* Nadine Sprinkle
VP: Gary Cowart
Manager: Scott Ladd

D-U-N-S 17-645-1748 IMP
MP GLOBAL PRODUCTS LLC
2500 Old Hadar Rd, Norfolk, NE 68701-1122
Tel (402) 379-9695 *Founded/Ownrshp* 1997
Sales 50.0MM^E *EMP* 100
SIC 2299 Padding & wadding, textile
Pr: Alan B Collison
**VP:* Chad A Collison
Mktg Dir: Jack Boesch

D-U-N-S 77-994-4896
■ **MP MASK TECHNOLOGY CENTER LLC**
(*Suby of* MICRON TECHNOLOGY INC) ★
8000 S Federal Way, Boise, ID 83716-9632
Tel (208) 368-4839 *Founded/Ownrshp* 2006
Sales 50.0MM *EMP* 144
SIC 3674 Semiconductors & related devices; Semiconductors & related devices

D-U-N-S 12-960-8126 IMP
MP NEXLEVEL LLC
500 County Road 37, Maple Lake, MN 55358-2864
Tel (320) 963-2400 *Founded/Ownrshp* 2002
Sales 259.6MM^E *EMP* 600^E
Accts Larsonallen Llp Minneapolis
SIC 1623 Water & sewer line construction; Gas main construction; Cable television line construction; Electric power line construction
Pr: Larry Pribyl
**VP:* Robbi Pribyl
**VP:* Timothy Pribyl

D-U-N-S 04-758-7832
MP SYSTEMS INC
PIEPER ELECTRIC
53 S Owasso Blvd W, Saint Paul, MN 55117-1029
Tel (651) 484-9632 *Founded/Ownrshp* 2002
Sales 37.6MM^E *EMP* 132
SIC 1623 Water, sewer & utility lines; Water, sewer & utility lines
Ch: Richard R Pieper Sr

D-U-N-S 15-629-9716
MP TECHNOLOGIES LLC
M P
9938 State Highway 55 Nw, Annandale, MN 55302-3031
Tel (320) 963-2499 *Founded/Ownrshp* 2004
Sales 82.0MM^E *EMP* 153
SIC 4911 Electric services; Electric services
Pr: Karen Pribyl
**VP:* Pam Pribyl
**VP:* Rob Pribyl

D-U-N-S 87-906-9458
MP TOTALCARE SUPPLY INC
(*Suby of* MPTC HOLDINGS INC) ★
14255 49th St N Ste 301, Clearwater, FL 33762-2813
Tel (614) 855-6300 *Founded/Ownrshp* 2002
Sales 23.1MM^E *EMP* 713^E
SIC 5961 5047 Pharmaceuticals, mail order; Medical & hospital equipment
Pr: Kevin Pawlowski
**CEO:* Howard Deutsch
**CFO:* Ron Drabik
**Ex VP:* Michael O'Connor

D-U-N-S 03-119-4447
MP&E INC
MEDICAL PROFILES & ENGINEERING
6271 Bury Dr, Eden Prairie, MN 55346-1720
Tel (952) 835-1468 *Founded/Ownrshp* 1997
Sales 20.0MM^E *EMP* 75
SIC 3559 3061 Electronic component making machinery; Medical & surgical rubber tubing (extruded & lathe-cut)
Pr: William P Ryan
Mtls Mgr: Andrea Geiger
Sls Mgr: Kent Kramer

MPA
See MARINE PRESERVATION ASSOCIATION INC

D-U-N-S 00-108-2908 IMP
■ **MPB CORP**
TIMKEN SUPER PRECISION
(*Suby of* TIMKEN CO) ★
7 Optical Ave, Keene, NH 03431-4348
Tel (603) 352-0310 *Founded/Ownrshp* 1941, 1990
Sales 202.3MM^E *EMP* 1,820
SIC 3562 Ball bearings & parts; Roller bearings & parts; Ball bearings & parts; Roller bearings & parts
Pr: Erik Paulhardt
**Sec:* Wayne F Crowell

Exec: Bill Kellher
Genl Mgr: Cengiz Kurkcu
Genl Mgr: Gerald Levesque
Dir IT: Eric Gibson
Snr Mgr: Steven Carey
Snr Mgr: Jin Xia

D-U-N-S 13-129-0173
■ **MPB GROUP LLC**
BERYL COMPANIES, THE
(*Suby of* STERICYCLE INC) ★
3600 Harwood Rd Ste A, Bedford, TX 76021-4011
Tel (817) 355-5040 *Founded/Ownrshp* 1984
Sales 24.0MM^E *EMP* 450
SIC 8082 Telephone answering service; Oxygen tent service
CEO: Paul Spiegelman
VP: George Benson
VP: F Joshua Hall
VP: Dennis Nasto
VP: Steven Nickerson
VP: Mary L Vonderau
Off Mgr: Dianne Hopper
Dir IT: Darren Anderson
Mktg Dir: Melissa Brooks

D-U-N-S 01-719-6510
MPC CASH-WAY LUMBER CO (MI)
5401 W Grand River Ave, Lansing, MI 48906-9117
Tel (517) 321-7766 *Founded/Ownrshp* 1963, 1981
Sales 26.5MM *EMP* 60
SIC 5211 5031

MPC ENVIRONMENTAL
See MARINE POLLUTION CONTROL CORP

D-U-N-S 62-383-2503
MPC GROUP LLC
4834 S Oakley Ave, Chicago, IL 60609-4036
Tel (773) 927-4120 *Founded/Ownrshp* 2006
Sales 29.2MM^E *EMP* 112
SIC 2394 3089 Canvas & related products; Plastic processing
CEO: Benjamin Beiler

D-U-N-S 00-545-1240 IMP/EXP
■ **MPC PRODUCTS CORP** (IL)
WOODWARD MPC
(*Suby of* WOODWARD INC) ★
6300 W Howard St, Niles, IL 60714-3406
Tel (847) 673-8300 *Founded/Ownrshp* 1962, 2008
Sales 171.0MM *EMP* 963
SIC 3728 3621 3676 3812 3625 Aircraft body & wing assemblies & parts; Aircraft assemblies, subassemblies & parts; Relays & industrial controls; Electronic resistors; Aircraft/aerospace flight instruments & guidance systems; Motors & generators; Fluid power cylinders & actuators; Aircraft body & wing assemblies & parts; Aircraft assemblies, subassemblies & parts; Motors & generators; Electronic resistors; Aircraft/aerospace flight instruments & guidance systems; Relays & industrial controls
CEO: Thomas Gendron
Pr: Martin Glass
CFO: Robert Webber Jr
Prgrm Mgr: Christopher Wall
IT Man: Indrajeet Rai

D-U-N-S 00-799-2779
MPC PROMOTIONS LLC (KY)
M P C LOUISVILLE PROMOTIONS
4300 Produce Rd, Louisville, KY 40218-3062
Tel (502) 451-4900 *Founded/Ownrshp* 1915
Sales 35.5MM^E *EMP* 55
SIC 5199 5137 5136 3993 2396 2395 Advertising specialties; Sportswear, women's & children's; Sportswear, men's & boys'; Signs & advertising specialties; Automotive & apparel trimmings; Pleating & stitching
Pr: Donald V Dobina
**CFO:* Sara Shanks
Sls Mgr: Gary Garrison
Sales Asso: Conrad Kissel
Art Dir: Tony Poynter

MPC SURPLUS
See MATERIALS PROCESSING CORP

MPCC
See MONTEREY PENINSULA COUNTRY CLUB

D-U-N-S 17-350-2824
MPD INC
316 E 9th St, Owensboro, KY 42303-3513
Tel (270) 685-6200 *Founded/Ownrshp* 1997
Sales 135.6MM^E *EMP* 897
SIC 3671 3829 3812 3663 3643 3053 Electron tubes; Breathalyzers; Radar systems & equipment; Radio & TV communications equipment; Current-carrying wiring devices; Gaskets, packing & sealing devices; Electron tubes; Breathalyzers; Radar systems & equipment; Radio & TV communications equipment; Current-carrying wiring devices; Gaskets, packing & sealing devices
Pr: Gary J Braswell
**CFO:* Michael D Robinson
**Treas:* Randy L Roos
**VP:* Janice Tomblinson
VP: Robert White
IT Man: David Blythe
MIS Mgr: Terry Horn
Ql Cn Mgr: Byron Cason
Board of Directors: Anthony Lewis, John P Olson, Frederick S Perry, David A York

MPE
See MIDWEST PRODUCTS AND ENGINEERING INC

D-U-N-S 80-965-9402
■ **MPE AEROENGINES INC**
ENGINETICS
(*Suby of* STANDEX INTERNATIONAL CORP) ★
7700 New Carlisle Pike, Huber Heights, OH 45424-1512
Tel (937) 878-3800 *Founded/Ownrshp* 2014
Sales 26.6MM^E *EMP* 140^E
SIC 3365 Aerospace castings, aluminum

CEO: Dale Pelfrey

D-U-N-S 83-133-8616
MPG NEWSPAPER HOLDING LLC
(Suby of SHIVERS TRADING & OPERATING CO) ★
725 Broad St, Augusta, GA 30901-1336
Tel (706) 724-0851 Founded/Ownrshp 2009
Sales 225.2MM^E EMP 2,500^E
SIC 2711 Newspapers; Newspapers, publishing & printing; Newspapers; Newspapers, publishing & printing
Pr: William S Morris IV

D-U-N-S 08-717-2532
MPG OFFICE TRUST INC
355 S Grand Ave Ste 3300, Los Angeles, CA 90071-1592
Tel (213) 626-3300 Founded/Ownrshp 2003
Sales 231.1MM EMP 70^E
SIC 6798

D-U-N-S 82-710-9005
MPG PIPELINE CONTRACTORS LLC
16770 Imperial Valley Dr # 105, Houston, TX 77060-3400
Tel (713) 904-1168 Founded/Ownrshp 2008
Sales 120.1MM EMP 40^E
Accts Laporte Cpas Houston Tx
SIC 1623 Pipeline construction; Pipeline construction
Pr: Jimmy Fontenot
*COO: Aaron Simon
*VP: Ken McDougall

D-U-N-S 84-740-5656
MPGWEST LLC
WESTERN PRODUCE GROUP
79440 Corp Ctr Dr Ste 114, La Quinta, CA 92253
Tel (760) 399-5750 Founded/Ownrshp 2008
Sales 26.1MM EMP 20
SIC 5148 Fresh fruits & vegetables; Fresh fruits & vegetables
Pr: William Penny
CFO: Gary Lutes
CIO: Jason Wesner
Sls&Mrk Ex: Bill Penny

MPH TRANSPORTATION
See MICHIGAN PRODUCE HAULERS INC

D-U-N-S 04-780-9350
MPHASIS CORP
(Suby of MPHASIS LIMITED)
460 Park Ave S Rm 1101, New York, NY 10016-7315
Tel (212) 686-6655 Founded/Ownrshp 1998
Sales 567.2MM^E EMP 2,000
SIC 7371 Custom computer programming services; Custom computer programming services
Pr: Vikas Gurugunti
*CFO: Ganesh Murthy
Top Exec: Michelle Kumar
Top Exec: Deepa Nagaraj
Assoc VP: Abdij Bhat
Assoc VP: Sunil Jain
Assoc VP: Deepak Manjarekar
Assoc VP: Soumendu Mukhopadhyay
Sr VP: Rajeev Jamburao
Sr VP: Ajay Jotwani
Sr VP: Rich Mock
Sr VP: Donald Morrison
VP: Murty Chennubhotla
VP: Vijay Gupta
VP: Girish Nair
VP: Rajan Nalawade
VP: Jane Plant
VP: Kumail Tyebjee
Dir Risk M: Murali Soundar
Assoc Dir: Puneet Bhirani
Comm Man: Daphne Jacob

MPHI
See MICHIGAN PUBLIC HEALTH INSTITUTE

MPI
See MODERN PARKING INC

D-U-N-S 00-397-5078
MPI GLOBAL HOLDINGS CORP
(Suby of WINGATE PARTNERS V LP) ★
2129 Austin Ave, Rochester Hills, MI 48309-3668
Tel (248) 237-3007 Founded/Ownrshp 2014
Sales 181.8MM^E EMP 747^E
SIC 1761 Sheet metalwork
Pr: Steven Crain
Prin: Brad Brenneman

D-U-N-S 01-657-7264
MPI HOLDINGS INC
MARBURGER FOODS
3311 S State Road 19, Peru, IN 46970-7476
Tel (765) 473-3086 Founded/Ownrshp 1956
Sales 20.9MM^E EMP 225
SIC 2011 2013 Meat packing plants; Sausages & other prepared meats; Meat packing plants; Sausages & other prepared meats
Pr: John A Marburger

D-U-N-S 06-369-3116
MPI PRODUCTS HOLDINGS LLC
(Suby of MPI GLOBAL HOLDINGS CORP) ★
2129 Austin Ave, Rochester Hills, MI 48309-3668
Tel (248) 237-3007 Founded/Ownrshp 2014
Sales 181.8MM^E EMP 744^E
SIC 3448 Prefabricated metal components
Pr: Steven Crain
CFO: Mike Putz

D-U-N-S 83-007-0962 EXP
MPI PRODUCTS LLC
(Suby of MPI PRODUCTS HOLDINGS LLC) ★
2129 Austin Hills Ave, Rochester Hills, MI 48309
Tel (248) 237-3007 Founded/Ownrshp 2014
Sales 181.8MM^E EMP 750
SIC 3469 Boxes: tool, lunch, mail, etc.: stamped metal; Boxes: tool, lunch, mail, etc.: stamped metal
CEO: Steve Crain
*CFO: Michael Putz
VP: Franz Boos
QA Dir: Sue Schroeder
QA Dir: Dennis Snowdy
VP Sls: David Crisp

D-U-N-S 83-736-3605
MPI RESEARCH INC
54943 N Main St, Mattawan, MI 49071-8353
Tel (269) 668-3336 Founded/Ownrshp 1995
Sales 240.7MM^E EMP 1,300
SIC 8731 Commercial research laboratory; Commercial research laboratory
Ch Bd: William U Parfet
COO: Andy Dumpis
CFO: Paul R Sylvester
Ex VP: James Lavaglia
Sr VP: David G Serota
VP: Ed Amat
VP: Roger Hayes
Assoc Dir: Steve Denham
Assoc Dir: Thomas Stahl
Dir Bus: Gary Oliff
QA Dir: Mary Edgerly

D-U-N-S 07-460-6906
MPII INC (TX)
MISSION PARK FUNERAL CHAPELS
23645 Us Highway 281 N, San Antonio, TX 78258-7318
Tel (210) 224-0999 Founded/Ownrshp 1907
Sales 37.3MM^E EMP 145
SIC 6553 7261 Cemeteries, real estate operation; Funeral home
Pr: Robert D Tips

D-U-N-S 07-854-2035
MPLX LP
200 E Hardin St, Findlay, OH 45840-4963
Tel (419) 672-6500 Founded/Ownrshp 2012
Sales 548.3MM EMP 700
Tkr Sym MPLX Exch NYS
SIC 4612 4613 Crude petroleum pipelines; Refined petroleum pipelines; Crude petroleum pipelines; Refined petroleum pipelines
Ch Bd: Gary R Heminger
Genl Pt: Mplx GP LLC
Pr: Pamela K M Beall

MPM EAST
See MPM FARMS

D-U-N-S 95-614-4109
MPM FARMS
MPM EAST
811 Brooke Dr, Wayne, NE 68787-1248
Tel (402) 375-4823 Founded/Ownrshp 1996
Sales 21.5MM EMP 40
Accts Genske Mulder & Co Llp Ont
SIC 0241 Dairy farms; Dairy farms
Pt: Bud Mouw
Pt: Kent Pulfer

D-U-N-S 07-974-6031
MPM HOLDINGS INC
260 Hudson River Rd, Waterford, NY 12188-1910
Tel (518) 237-3330 Founded/Ownrshp 2014
Sales 1.6MMM^E EMP 4,605
SIC 2869 3479 3679 Silicones; Coating of metals with silicon; Electronic crystals; Quartz crystals, for electronic application
Pr: John G Boss
CFO: Brian D Berger
Ex VP: Douglas A Johns
Sr VP: John D Moran
VP: George F Knight
Genl Couns: Stephen J Psutka

D-U-N-S 07-974-6051
MPM INTERMEDIATE HOLDINGS INC
(Suby of MPM HOLDINGS INC) ★
260 Hudson River Rd, Waterford, NY 12188-1910
Tel (518) 237-3330 Founded/Ownrshp 2014
Sales 1.6MMM^E EMP 4,602
SIC 2869 3479 3679 Silicones; Coating of metals with silicon; Electronic crystals; Quartz crystals, for electronic application
Pr: John G Boss
CFO: Brian D Berger

D-U-N-S 82-585-6151
MPM SILICONES LLC
MOMENTIVE
(Suby of MOMENTIVE PERFORMANCE MATERIALS INC) ★
260 Hudson River Rd, Waterford, NY 12188-1910
Tel (518) 233-3330 Founded/Ownrshp 2000
Sales 185.0MM^E EMP 4,600
SIC 2869 Silicones
Ex VP: Joseph Bevilaqua
VP: Jose Conde
Prgrm Mgr: Matthew Haley
Netwrk Eng: Stan Popov
Snr Mgr: Wendell Ellis

D-U-N-S 96-700-1801 IMP
MPOWER COMMUNICATIONS CORP
(Suby of MPOWER HOLDING CORP) ★
515 S Flower St, Los Angeles, CA 90071-2201
Tel (213) 213-3000 Founded/Ownrshp 1996
Sales 124.4MM^E EMP 750
SIC 4813 Telephone communication, except radio; Telephone communication, except radio
Ch Bd: Rolla P Huff
Pr: Joseph M Wetzel
CFO: S Gregory Clevenger
CFO: Tim Medina
Treas: Michael J Tschiderer
Sr VP: Russell I Zuckerman
VP: Dan Blank
VP: Gary Durbin
VP: Kent F Heyman
VP: Mark Magarian
VP: Linda Sunbury

D-U-N-S 03-010-4140
MPOWER HOLDING CORP
(Suby of US TELEPACIFIC HOLDINGS CORP) ★
515 S Flower St Fl 36, Los Angeles, CA 90071-2221
Tel (213) 213-3000 Founded/Ownrshp 2006
Sales 124.4MM^E EMP 825^E
SIC 4813 Telephone communication, except radio; ; Telephone communication, except radio;
CEO: Richard A Jalkut
Pr: James E Ferguson
CFO: Timothy J Medina
Ofcr: Russell A Shipley
Sr VP: Roger A Pachuta
Sr VP: Steven A Reimer
VP: Anthony J Marion Jr
VP: Michele D Sadwick

MPOWERLABS
See REV WORLDWIDE INC

D-U-N-S 04-727-1358
MPR ASSOCIATES INC
320 King St Ste 400, Alexandria, VA 22314-3230
Tel (703) 519-0200 Founded/Ownrshp 1964
Sales 65.7MM EMP 235
SIC 8711 Engineering services; Engineering services
CEO: Paul Damerell
COO: Danielle Harrison
Bd of Dir: Alexander Zarechnak
VP: Ryan Downs
*VP: Jacqueline McMullen
*Prin: Robert Coward
Off Admin: Nancy G Svites

D-U-N-S 18-920-1379 IMP
MPR CORP
FABRIC SERVICES
103 Hinsdale Farm Rd, Bristol, IN 46507-9167
Tel (574) 848-5100 Founded/Ownrshp 1988
Sales 30.0MM EMP 60
SIC 5131 2295 Upholstery fabrics, woven; Plastic piece goods, woven; Piece goods & other fabrics; Laminating of fabrics
Pr: John Wuori
Pr: Don Wade

D-U-N-S 00-516-4199 IMP
MPS CHICAGO INC
JET LITHOCOLOR, INC.
(Suby of MULTI PACKAGING SOLUTIONS INC) ★
1500 Centre Cir, Downers Grove, IL 60515-1019
Tel (630) 932-9000 Founded/Ownrshp 1962, 2014
Sales 55.8MM^E EMP 195
SIC 2752 3499 Color lithography; Novelties & giftware, including trophies; Color lithography; Novelties & giftware, including trophies
Pr: George Bogdanovic
CFO: David Bertram
VP: Michael McNeil
IT Man: Ron Pufahl
Ql Cn Mgr: Tonya Sothen
Mktg Mgr: Andrea Plachy
Mktg Mgr: Greg Wood

D-U-N-S 05-886-8811
MPS ENTERPRISES INC
MILFORD PIPE AND SUPPLY
1224 W Broadway Pl, Hobbs, NM 88240-5568
Tel (432) 563-3332 Founded/Ownrshp 2011
Sales 105.9MM^E EMP 60
SIC 5169 Polyurethane products; Polyurethane products
CEO: Shawn Beard
*CFO: Scott Brown
*VP: Cody Tippy
Sales Asso: Melissa Wimer

D-U-N-S 83-882-9760
MPS GROUP INC
38755 Hills Tech Dr, Farmington Hills, MI 48331-3408
Tel (313) 841-7588 Founded/Ownrshp 1995
Sales 77.0MM^E EMP 350
SIC 1799 Refuse systems; Cleaning new buildings after construction
Ch Bd: Charlie Williams
*Pr: Edward L Schwartz
*COO: Darrin Stafford
*CFO: Brian Susko
Sls Mgr: Bill Sinzheimer

MPS HOLDINGS
See JOHN HENRY HOLDINGS INC

MPS HOLLAND
See STEKETEE-VAN HUIS INC

D-U-N-S 83-056-9807
MPS HRL LLC
CHESAPEAKE PHARMACEUTICAL
(Suby of MULTI PACKAGING SOLUTIONS INC) ★
325 Duffy Ave Unit 1, Hicksville, NY 11801-3644
Tel (516) 277-8639 Founded/Ownrshp 2014
Sales 58.7MM^E EMP 500
SIC 7389 Packaging & labeling services; Packaging & labeling services
CEO: Marc Shore
*Co-Pr: Mike Cheetham
*Co-Pr: Dennis Kaltman

D-U-N-S 07-955-8265
■ **MPS INTERNATIONAL LTD**
(Suby of MONOLITHIC POWER SYSTEMS INC) ★
79 Great Oaks Blvd, San Jose, CA 95119-1311
Tel (408) 826-0660 Founded/Ownrshp 2014
Sales 238.0MM EMP 1,000
SIC 3674 Semiconductors & related devices; Semiconductors & related devices
CEO: Michael R Hsing
Snr Mgr: Wingfield Liu

D-U-N-S 79-560-2890
MPT OPERATING PARTNERSHIP LP
(Suby of MEDICAL PROPERTIES TRUST INC) ★
3500 Colonnade Pkwy # 540, Birmingham, AL 35243-8300
Tel (205) 969-3755 Founded/Ownrshp 2003
Sales 312.5MM EMP 6,000^E
SIC 6798 Real estate investment trusts

D-U-N-S 55-757-9864
MPTC HOLDINGS INC
615 S Ware Blvd, Tampa, FL 33619-4444
Tel (813) 621-4800 Founded/Ownrshp 2003
Sales 49.3MM^E EMP 850
SIC 5961 Mail order house; Mail order house
CEO: Howard Deutsch
*Pr: Kevin Pawlowski
*CFO: Ron Drabik

MPU POWER GROUP
See M D HENRY CO INC

D-U-N-S 03-126-8464
MPW INDUSTRIAL SERVICES GROUP INC (OH)
9711 Lancaster Rd, Hebron, OH 43025-9764
Tel (740) 927-8790 Founded/Ownrshp 1972
Sales 201.5MM^E EMP 1,700^E
SIC 7349 8744 3589 Cleaning service, industrial or commercial; Facilities support services; Cleaning service, industrial or commercial; Facilities support services; Commercial cleaning equipment
Ch Bd: Monte R Black
COO: Robert Valentine
Treas: Sarah D Pemberton
VP: Adam Black
VP: Kristen N Black
VP: Rick Roth
Dir Bus: Joe Novello
Prin: Theodore G Gudorf
Area Mgr: Blake Byers
Area Mgr: Nathan Chandler
Genl Mgr: Jimmy Peck
Board of Directors: Pete A Klisares, Timothy A Walsh

D-U-N-S 07-503-7747
MPW INDUSTRIAL SERVICES INC
(Suby of MPW INDUSTRIAL SERVICES GROUP INC) ★
9711 Lancaster Rd, Hebron, OH 43025-9764
Tel (740) 927-8790 Founded/Ownrshp 1997
Sales 145.7MM^E EMP 1,200
SIC 7349 Building maintenance services; Building maintenance services
CEO: Monte Black
VP: Kristen Hargus
Dir Soc: Haley Black
Opers Mgr: Allen Hawkins
Mktg Dir: Bryan Whitehead
Sls Dir: Dale Campion

D-U-N-S 80-910-8678
MPW INDUSTRIAL WATER SERVICES INC
(Suby of MPW MANAGEMENT SERVICES CORP) ★
9711 Lancaster Rd, Hebron, OH 43025-9764
Tel (800) 827-8790 Founded/Ownrshp 1998
Sales 45.0MM EMP 176
SIC 4499 Water transportation cleaning services; Water transportation cleaning services
Pr: Monte R Black

D-U-N-S 94-515-2759
MPW MANAGEMENT SERVICES CORP
(Suby of MPW INDUSTRIAL SERVICES INC) ★
9711 Lancaster Rd, Hebron, OH 43025-9764
Tel (740) 927-8790 Founded/Ownrshp 1997
Sales 45.0MM^E EMP 176
SIC 8742 Management consulting services; Management consulting services
Pr: Monte R Black
*Treas: Sarah D Pemberton
*VP: Adam Black
*VP: Kristen N Black

D-U-N-S 92-890-3699 IMP
MQ ASSOCIATES INC
(Suby of LAKESIDE FAMILY PHYSICIANS) ★
3480 Preston Ridge Rd # 600, Alpharetta, GA 30005-2028
Tel (770) 300-0101 Founded/Ownrshp 2007
Sales 59.8MM^E EMP 1,604
SIC 8099 Physical examination & testing services; Physical examination & testing services
CEO: Chris Winkle
*Ch Bd: Donald C Tomasso
*COO: Daniel J Schaefer
COO: Jennifer Swearinger
COO: Michael A Vill
*CFO: Todd Andrews
Board of Directors: John R Belk, Benjamin B Edmands, Anthony R Masso, Stephen P Murray

D-U-N-S 08-875-2993 IMP
MR ALANS MENS BOOTERY INC
POGO
14177 Telegraph Rd Ste A, Redford, MI 48239-2854
Tel (313) 387-4000 Founded/Ownrshp 1974
Sales 23.1MM EMP 200
Accts Patel & Associates Plc Bi
SIC 5661 5611 Men's shoes; Men's boots; Footwear, athletic; Clothing, sportswear, men's & boys'; Men's shoes; Men's boots; Footwear, athletic; Clothing, sportswear, men's & boys'
Pr: Alan I Bishop
*CFO: Roger G Karnow

MR BILL'S PERENNIALS
See SAWYER NURSERY INC

MR BUG
See EMPI INC

D-U-N-S 36-061-6817 IMP
MR CHIPS INC
1380 Gateway Dr Ste 7, Elgin, IL 60124-7891
Tel (847) 468-9000 Founded/Ownrshp 1988
Sales 893.7M EMP 1,013
SIC 5092 5047 Bingo games & supplies; Board games; Medical equipment & supplies; Bingo games & supplies; Board games; Medical equipment & supplies
Pr: Natalia Kovari
Treas: Natasha Kovari
*VP: Andrew J Kovari

MR CLEAN MAINTENANCE SYSTEMS
See CHIRO INC

D-U-N-S 96-593-3455
■ **MR COPY INC**
MRC, SMARTTECH SOLUTIONS
(Suby of GLOBAL IMAGING SYSTEMS INC) ★
5657 Copley Dr, San Diego, CA 92111-7903
Tel (858) 573-6300 Founded/Ownrshp 2009

Sales 155.6MM^E *EMP* 120
SIC 5044 Office equipment; Photocopy machines
Pr: Bob Leone
CFO: Kevin McCarty
Ex VP: John Taumoepeau
Sls Mgr: Steve Campos
Sls Mgr: Desiree Medina

D-U-N-S 07-443-8078 IMP
MR DAVIDS CARPET SERVICE LTD
MR. DAVID'S FLOORING INTL
865 W Irving Park Rd, Itasca, IL 60143-2021
Tel (847) 250-4600 *Founded/Ownrshp* 1976
Sales 75.0MM^E *EMP* 500
SIC 1752 Carpet laying; Carpet laying
CEO: Leonard Zmijewski
**Co-Ownr:* David Zmijewski
VP Opers: Tom Nowicki
Mktg Dir: Peter Standish

MR. DAVID'S FLOORING INTL
See MR DAVIDS CARPET SERVICE LTD

D-U-N-S 83-195-2536
MR DEALS INC
MR DEALS SUPERMARKET
689 S Miami St, West Milton, OH 45383-1415
Tel (937) 698-4535 *Founded/Ownrshp* 1994
Sales 30.0MM *EMP* 25
SIC 5411 Grocery stores
Pr: Daniel Oman
**Prin:* John Oman

MR DEALS SUPERMARKET
See MR DEALS INC

MR D'S FRESH FOOD MARKETS
See DIETELS INC

D-U-N-S 01-759-9648
MR EXCAVATOR INC
8616 Euclid Chardon Rd, Kirtland, OH 44094-9586
Tel (440) 256-2008 *Founded/Ownrshp* 1962
Sales 26.4MM^E *EMP* 85
SIC 1794 Excavation work
Pr: William A Flesher
**VP:* Tim Flesher
**Prin:* Patricia Flesher

D-U-N-S 03-078-8616
MR FORMAL INC
TUX SHOP, THE
1205 Se Grand Ave, Portland, OR 97214-3435
Tel (503) 232-1542 *Founded/Ownrshp* 1976
Sales 9.9MM^E *EMP* 350
SIC 7299 5699 Tuxedo rental; Formal wear; Tuxedo rental; Formal wear
Pr: Edwin E Honeycutt I
VP: Nancy Fox

MR FUEL
See AROGAS INC

MR FUEL
See ARO SYSTEMS INC

MR GAS MARKETS
See MG MARKETS INC

D-U-N-S 04-701-6787
MR GATTIS LP
GATTI'S PIZZA
(*Suby of* MGI HOLDINGS LP) ★
5912 Balcones Dr Ste 200, Austin, TX 78731-4202
Tel (512) 459-4796 *Founded/Ownrshp* 2015
Sales 85.1MM^E *EMP* 500
SIC 6794 5812 Franchises, selling or licensing; Pizzeria, chain; Franchises, selling or licensing; Pizzeria, chain
Pr: Michael Poates
CFO: Steven B Burt
Dir IT: Scott Kelly
VP Mktg: Ronnie Steck
Mktg Mgr: Christina Acosta
Board of Directors: James D McBride III

MR HEATER
See ENERCO GROUP INC

MR. HEATER
See ENERCO TECHNICAL PRODUCTS INC

MR JOHN
See RUSSELL REID WASTE HAULING AND DISPOSAL SERVICE CO INC

D-U-N-S 00-714-4611 IMP
MR LONGARM INC (MO)
(*Suby of* SPECIALTY PRODUCTS OF GREENWOOD MISSOURI INC) ★
400 Walnut St, Greenwood, MO 64034-9678
Tel (816) 537-6777 *Founded/Ownrshp* 1958, 1986
Sales 40.7MM^E *EMP* 100
SIC 3423 3999 Hand & edge tools; Window squeegees; Hand & edge tools; Window squeegees
CEO: Robert D Newman
**Pr:* Dere Newman
CTO: Bill Gulledge

MR MIKE'S MINI MART
See PETERBOROUGH OIL CO INC

MR MOVIES
See MOVIE BRANDS INC

MR PAYROLL
See EXCHANGE SERVICES INC

D-U-N-S 55-758-3742
MR PITTMAN GROUP LLC
171 I-310 Service Rd, Saint Rose, LA 70087-3135
Tel (504) 733-3040 *Founded/Ownrshp* 2004
Sales 27.2MM^E *EMP* 100
SIC 1623 Water main construction
**Sls&Mrk Ex:* Chris Laiche

D-U-N-S 09-251-6327 IMP
MR RJC INC
R J R FASHION FABRICS
2610 Columbia St B, Torrance, CA 90503-3802
Tel (310) 222-8782 *Founded/Ownrshp* 1978
Sales 36.3MM^E *EMP* 45
SIC 5131 Cotton goods
Pr: Richard J Cohan
**Sec:* Bobby Ramos

D-U-N-S 09-008-0649 IMP
MR SPECIAL SUPERMARKETS INC
620 Ave Sta Tresa Journet, Mayaguez, PR 00682-1342
Tel (787) 834-2695 *Founded/Ownrshp* 1966
Sales 268.6MM *EMP* 1,707
Accts Rodriguez Rivera & Toro Psc
SIC 5411 Supermarkets, 55,000-65,000 square feet (superstore); Supermarkets, 55,000-65,000 square feet (superstore)
Pr: Santos Alonso
**CFO:* Edwin Alonso
**Treas:* Iris Alonso
Ex VP: Ernesto Quinones
**VP:* Richard Alonso
Dir IT: David Vega
Mktg Dir: Debbie Alonso
Mktg Dir: Victor Caban

D-U-N-S 08-469-9834
MR STAX INC
25060 Ave Stnford Ste 200, Valencia, CA 91355
Tel (661) 294-8877 *Founded/Ownrshp* 1977
Sales 28.7MM^E *EMP* 780
SIC 8742 Management consulting services; Management consulting services
Pr: Richard Sandnes

MR TIRE
See VESPIA TIRE CENTERS INC

MR TIRE AUTO SERVICE CENTERS
See MILE ONE TIRE INC

MR ZIP FOOD STORES
See MR ZIP INC OF TENNESSEE

D-U-N-S 02-157-2847
MR ZIP INC OF TENNESSEE (TN)
MR ZIP FOOD STORES
1510 Stuart Rd Ne Ste 202, Cleveland, TN 37312-5869
Tel (423) 476-3261 *Founded/Ownrshp* 1974
Sales 34.6MM^E *EMP* 150
SIC 5541 ;
Pr: Calvin Zuber
**Sec:* K J Coleman Jr
**VP:* Kent Zuber

MRA - INSTITUTE OF MANAGEMENT
See MRA-MANAGEMENT ASSOCIATION INC

D-U-N-S 96-796-4466
MRA HOLDINGS INC
3445 Box Hill Crp Ctr Dra, Abingdon, MD 21009
Tel (410) 515-9000 *Founded/Ownrshp* 2008
Sales 22.4MM^E *EMP* 120^E
Accts Weyrich Cronin & Sorra Chart
SIC 6719 Investment holding companies, except banks
Pr: Frank Hertsch
**CFO:* David Quaranta
**Sec:* Brian Silverling
**VP:* Paul Muddiman

D-U-N-S 00-509-5000 IMP
■ **MRA SYSTEMS INC**
MIDDLE RIVER AIRCRAFT SYSTEMS
(*Suby of* GE AIRCRAFT ENGINES HOLDINGS INC) ★
103 Chesapeake Park Plz, Baltimore, MD 21220-4201
Tel (410) 682-1500 *Founded/Ownrshp* 1997
Sales 199.3MM^E *EMP* 700
SIC 3728 Aircraft assemblies, subassemblies & parts; Aircraft assemblies, subassemblies & parts
Ex VP: David Calhoun
**CFO:* William Heskett
**Ex VP:* Michael Chanatry
Ex VP: Sagar A Patel
**VP:* Pupinder Bhutiani
**VP:* Bernard Grossman
**VP:* Doug Mallon
**VP:* Christopher Wright

D-U-N-S 02-047-0084
MRA-MANAGEMENT ASSOCIATION INC
MRA - INSTITUTE OF MANAGEMENT
N19w24400 Riverwood Dr # 100, Waukesha, WI 53188-1166
Tel (262) 523-9090 *Founded/Ownrshp* 1997
Sales 20.4MM *EMP* 210
Accts Wegner Cpas Llp Pewaukee Wi
SIC 8611 Trade associations; Trade associations
CEO: Susan Fronk
**CFO:* Bill Budzien
**VP:* Patricia Staaden
**VP:* Vicki Vought
**VP:* Nancy Warren
Web Prj Mg: Dorit Liberman
Opers Mgr: Doree Kaforski
Pr Dir: George Blomgren
Mktg Mgr: Michael O'Connor

MRC
See MCLAUGHLIN RESEARCH CORP

MRC
See MIKE ROVNER CONSTRUCTION INC

D-U-N-S 14-414-8371
■ **MRC ENERGY CO**
MATADOR RESOURCES COMPANY
(*Suby of* MATADOR RESOURCES CO) ★
5400 L B Johnson Fwy Ste 1500, Dallas, TX 75240
Tel (972) 371-5200 *Founded/Ownrshp* 2003
Sales 20.9MM^E *EMP* 40
SIC 1382 Oil & gas exploration services
Ch Bd: Joseph Wm Foran
**COO:* David E Lancaster
**Treas:* Kathy Wayne
Ex VP: Craig N Adams
Ex VP: Ryan C London
**VP:* Craig Adams
VP: Billy E Goodwin
**VP:* Matthew Hairford
**VP:* Scott King
**VP:* Bradley M Robinson
Mktg Mgr: Robert Muth
Board of Directors: David M Laney, Michael C Ryan, Edward R Scott, Stephen A Holditch, steven

D-U-N-S 00-794-4580 IMP/EXP
■ **MRC GLOBAL (US) INC**
MCJUNKIN RED MAN CORPORATION
(*Suby of* MRC GLOBAL INC) ★
909 Fannin St Ste 3100, Houston, TX 77010-1011
Tel (877) 294-7574 *Founded/Ownrshp* 2007
Sales 656.9MM^E *EMP* 280
SIC 5051 5085 Pipe & tubing, steel; Industrial supplies; Valves & fittings; Pipe & tubing, steel; Industrial supplies; Valves & fittings
Ch Bd: Andrew Lane
Ofcr: Gary Ittner
**Ex VP:* James E Braun
Sr VP: Mike Chamberlain
Sr VP: David A Fox
VP: Rob Bliton
Brnch Mgr: John Jones
Sfty Mgr: Bob Boggess
Opers Mgr: Larry Shank
VP Mktg: Elaine Michael
Sales Asso: Wendy Harbin

D-U-N-S 82-871-0348 IMP
▲ **MRC GLOBAL INC**
2 Houston Ctr 9093100, Houston, TX 77010-1015
Tel (877) 294-7574 *Founded/Ownrshp* 2006
Sales 5.9MMM *EMP* 4,900^E
Tkr Sym MRC *Exch* NYS
SIC 5051 5085 Pipe & tubing, steel; Industrial supplies; Valves & fittings; Pipe & tubing, steel; Industrial supplies; Valves & fittings
Ch Bd: Andrew R Lane
CFO: James E Braun
Ex VP: Daniel J Churay
Sr VP: Steiner Aasland
Sr VP: Elton Bond
Sr VP: John Bowhay
Sr VP: Nasser A Farshchian
Sr VP: Rory M Isaac
Sr VP: Gary A Ittner
VP: Stuart Bailey
VP: Grant Bates
VP: Cinda Bowling
VP: Dave Dillon
VP: Stuart Spears
Board of Directors: Leonard M Anthony, Rhys J Best, Barbara J Duganier, Craig Ketchum, Gerard P Krans, Cornelis A Linse, John A Perkins, H B Wehrle III, Robert L Wood

D-U-N-S 03-851-4881 IMP
MRC POLYMERS INC
3307 S Lawndale Ave, Chicago, IL 60623-5007
Tel (773) 890-9000 *Founded/Ownrshp* 1980
Sales 21.5MM^E *EMP* 100^E
SIC 2821 Polycarbonate resins; Polypropylene resins; Polyesters; Polycarbonate resins; Polypropylene resins; Polyesters
Pr: Paul Binks
**CFO:* Steve Sola
Exec: Brenda Gamboa
**Ex Dir:* David Lawson
Genl Mgr: Brett Miller
Off Mgr: Jane Favia
Sfty Dirs: Brendon Parrish
Plnt Mgr: Sergio Cabrales
S&M/VP: Jane Horal

MRC, SMARTTECH SOLUTIONS
See MR COPY INC

MRCI WORKSOURCE
See MANKATO REHABILITATION CENTER INC

MRD SERVICES
See MUELLER ROOFING DISTRIBUTORS INC

D-U-N-S 14-546-3225
MRE CONSULTING LTD
3800 Buffalo Spdwy # 200, Houston, TX 77098-3725
Tel (713) 844-6400 *Founded/Ownrshp* 2004
Sales 25.0MM *EMP* 120
SIC 7379 Computer related consulting services; Computer related consulting services
Genl Pt: K Michael Short
Pt: Shane Merz
Pt: Dru Neikirk
COO: Bjorn Hagelmann
Treas: Scott Heflin
Top Exec: Mike Berry
VP: Robert Panico
Dir Bus: Becky Galli
CTO: Stephen Webster
Dir IT: Micah Robinson
IT Man: Stephen Burgess

D-U-N-S 04-269-4323
MRF CORP (WV)
Us Route 119 S, Chapmanville, WV 25508
Tel (304) 855-8200 *Founded/Ownrshp* 1967, 1982
Sales 26.0MM *EMP* 36
SIC 5511 Automobiles, new & used; Pickups, new & used; Automobiles, new & used; Pickups, new & used
Pr: Michael R Ferrell
Sec: Gladys L Ferrell
VP: Joe C Ferrell

D-U-N-S 06-689-9569
MRG MARKETING & MANAGEMENT INC
RAISING CANE'S CHICKEN FINGERS
1215 S Fort Apache Rd # 240, Las Vegas, NV 89117-5491
Tel (702) 365-9221 *Founded/Ownrshp* 2005
Sales 13.3MM^E *EMP* 319^E
SIC 5812 Eating places
Pr: Joseph II Micatrotto

D-U-N-S 07-956-7374
MRGB HOLD CO
382 Greenwich Ave Apt 1, Greenwich, CT 06830-6501
Tel (203) 987-3500 *Founded/Ownrshp* 2014
Sales 24.9MM^E *EMP* 154^E
SIC 6719 Investment holding companies, except banks
CEO: Scott Scharfman

MRHC
See MCALESTER REGIONAL HEALTH CENTER AUTHORITY

MRI
See MARKETING REPRESENTATIVES INC

MRI
See MANUFACTURING RESOURCES INTERNATIONAL INC

MRI
See MEURER RESEARCH INC

D-U-N-S 06-604-4827
MRI SOFTWARE LLC
28925 Fountain Pkwy, Solon, OH 44139-4356
Tel (800) 327-8770 *Founded/Ownrshp* 2015
Sales 123.2MM^E *EMP* 405^E
SIC 7374 7371 6531 Computer software development; Data processing & preparation; Data processing & preparation; Computer software development; Real estate managers
CEO: Patrick Ghilani
CFO: Bill Roselli
Ofcr: Brian Zrimsek
VP: Stephen Baker
VP: Marc Dicapua
VP: Chuck McDowell
VP: Oren Rosen
VP: Phil Trudeau
Snr Sftwr: Doug Obojski
QA Dir: Michelle Golden
Sftwr Eng: Brenna Anderson

MRIC
See MITCHELL REPAIR INFORMATION CO LLC

D-U-N-S 00-717-3453
MRIGLOBAL - KANSAS LLC (KS)
MIDWEST RESEARCH INSTITUTE
425 Volker Blvd, Kansas City, MO 64110-2241
Tel (816) 753-7600 *Founded/Ownrshp* 1943
Sales 466.8MM *EMP* 2,547
Accts Kpmg Llp Kansas City Missour
SIC 8731 6794 Commercial physical research; Patent owners & lessors; Commercial physical research; Patent owners & lessors
Pr: Thomas M Sack
CFO: R Thomas Fleener
Ofcr: David Easton
Ofcr: Kyle Eslinger
Ofcr: James Fyler
Ofcr: Matthew O'Callaghan
Ofcr: Lisa Read
Ofcr: Lolly Robinson
Ex VP: Dan E Arvizu PH D
Sr VP: Dan Arvizu
Sr VP: Tom Sack
VP: John Barsa
VP: Robert P Casillas
VP: Robert A Conklin
VP: Linda D Evans
VP: David Franz
VP: Roger Harris
VP: Roger K Harris
Dir Lab: Keven Welch
Dir Soc: Ward Wheeler
Comm Dir: Nancy Shawver
Board of Directors: David B Dillon, David Field Oliver

MRIS
See METROPOLITAN REGIONAL INFORMATION SYSTEMS INC

D-U-N-S 04-440-9402
MRM HOLDINGS LLC
DRAKE MATERIALS
5745 N Scottsdale Rd # 110, Scottsdale, AZ 85250-5902
Tel (480) 607-3999 *Founded/Ownrshp* 1998
Sales 38.8MM^E *EMP* 200
SIC 3273 Ready-mixed concrete; Ready-mixed concrete

D-U-N-S 07-868-5343
MRM MCCANN
60 E South Temple # 1400, Salt Lake City, UT 84111-1001
Tel (801) 257-7700 *Founded/Ownrshp* 2012
Sales 75.0MM^E *EMP* 309^E
SIC 7311 Advertising agencies
Pr: Hank Summy
Pr: Marcy Q Samet
Sr VP: Sue Geramian
Sls&Mrk Ex: Kelly Hindley

MRMSCO
See METRO ROOFING & METAL SUPPLY CO INC

MRO DISTRIBUTION
See UR HOLDINGS LP

D-U-N-S 06-514-1517
■ **MRO SOFTWARE INC**
MROI
(*Suby of* IBM) ★
550 King St, Littleton, MA 01460-6245
Tel (781) 280-2000 *Founded/Ownrshp* 2006
Sales 34.6MM^E *EMP* 924
SIC 7372 Application computer software; Application computer software
Pr: Norman E Drapeau Jr
Pt: Steve Caslick
Pt: Bill Coakley
Ch Bd: Robert L Daniels
CFO: Peter J Rice
Ex VP: Patricia C Foye
Ex VP: William J Sawyer
VP: Gary Freeman
VP: Edward Gledhill
VP: Craig Newfield
VP: Walt Vanderlaan
Board of Directors: David N Campbell, Richard P Fishman, John A McMullen, Stephen B Sayre, Alan L Stanzler

MROI
See MRO SOFTWARE INC

D-U-N-S 10-581-7303
MRP AUTO INC
PHILLIPS AUTO
1220 W Coast Hwy, Newport Beach, CA 92663-5025
Tel (949) 574-7777 *Founded/Ownrshp* 1984
Sales 30.0MM *EMP* 10
SIC 5511 New & used car dealers; New & used car dealers
Pr: Malcolm Phillips

D-U-N-S 07-829-5036
MRP INC
MICHIGAN RUBBER PRODUCTS
1600 Holman St, Cadillac, MI 49601-9183
Tel (248) 320-6352 *Founded/Ownrshp* 1972
Sales 36.4MM^E *EMP* 400
SIC 3069 Rubber hardware; Rubber hardware
Pr: Francisco Neto

D-U-N-S 60-401-2703
MRP LLC
AMSINO MEDICAL USA
5209 Linbar Dr Ste 640, Nashville, TN 37211-1026
Tel (615) 833-2633 *Founded/Ownrshp* 2009
Sales 23.6MM^E *EMP* 150
SIC 3841 Hypodermic needles & syringes; Hypodermic needles & syringes
CEO: Timir Patel
IT Man: Shirley Bell

MRP REALTY
See MIDATLANTIC REALTY PARTNERS LLC

D-U-N-S 96-456-0309
MRRC HOLD CO
382 Greenwich Ave Apt 1, Greenwich, CT 06830-6501
Tel (203) 987-3500 *Founded/Ownrshp* 2010
Sales 430.6MM^E *EMP* 3,800^E
SIC 6719 Investment holding companies, except banks; Investment holding companies, except banks
Pr: Scott Scharfman

D-U-N-S 55-630-2453
MRS ASSOCIATES INC
1930 Olney Ave, Cherry Hill, NJ 08003-2016
Tel (856) 667-5566 *Founded/Ownrshp* 1991
Sales 32.0MM^E *EMP* 700
SIC 7322 Collection agency, except real estate; Collection agency, except real estate
Pr: Saul Freedman
**Pr:* Jeffrey Freedman
CFO: Darren Schulman
Genl Mgr: John-Jack Daniels

D-U-N-S 02-001-7286 IMP
MRS BAIRDS BAKERIES BUSINESS TRUST (DE)
(*Suby of* BIMBO BAKERIES USA INC) ★
14401 Statler Blvd, Fort Worth, TX 76155-2861
Tel (817) 864-2500 *Founded/Ownrshp* 1997
Sales 228.8MM^E *EMP* 7,000
SIC 2051 Bread, cake & related products; Bread, cake & related products
Pr: Reynaldo Reyna
**Sr VP:* Jim Brennan
**Sr VP:* Joe Dangelmaier
**Sr VP:* Andy Lang
**VP:* H Darrell Miller
**VP:* Greg Stehr
Dir IT: Natalie Newby
Sls&Mrk Ex: Reid Stinnett

D-U-N-S 01-689-0616
MRS BPO LLC
(*Suby of* MRS ASSOCIATES INC) ★
1930 Olney Ave, Cherry Hill, NJ 08003-2016
Tel (856) 988-0004 *Founded/Ownrshp* 2008
Sales 32.0MM *EMP* 475
SIC 7322 Adjustment & collection services; Adjustment & collection services
VP: Daphne Burkhalter

MRS. CLARK'S FOODS
See MCF OPERATING LLC

MRS FIELDBROOK FOOD
See MISTER COOKIE FACE INC

D-U-N-S 13-615-3553
MRS FIELDS COMPANIES INC
FAMOUS BRANDS INTERNATIONAL
8001 Arista Pl Unit 600, Broomfield, CO 80021-4135
Tel (720) 599-3350 *Founded/Ownrshp* 2001
Sales 805.0MM^E *EMP* 6,614
SIC 6794 5461 5499 Franchises, selling or licensing; Cookies; Food gift baskets; Franchises, selling or licensing; Cookies; Food gift baskets
Pr: James Zenni
Pr: Greg Berglund
CFO: Gregory K Barber
CFO: Michael Chao
Ex VP: Michael Ward
Sr VP: David Bloom
VP: Dustin Finkel
VP: Brandon Fitzgerald
VP: Belinda Oakley
VP: Evelyn Romero
Prin: Jon M Biotti
Board of Directors: Jon M Biotti, Alexander Coleman, John D Collins, George N Fugelsang, Peter W Mullin, Don Rice, John D Shafer, Christopher Wright

D-U-N-S 60-876-0117
MRS FIELDS FAMOUS BRANDS LLC
MRS. FIELDS ORIGINAL COOKIES
(*Suby of* MRS FIELDS ORIGINAL COOKIES INC) ★
8001 Arista Pl Unit 600, Broomfield, CO 80021-4135
Tel (720) 599-3350 *Founded/Ownrshp* 2004
Sales 37.4MM^E *EMP* 200^E
SIC 5461 Cookies; Cookies
Pr: Jeffrey P Werner
**CFO:* Brian Johnson
**Chf Cred:* Kimberly Aylward
Sr VP: David Bloom
Opers Mgr: Gail Harper
Board of Directors: Tim Clayton, John Dupy, Joyce Hrinya, Christopher J Kipley, James J Zenni

D-U-N-S 96-213-0472
MRS FIELDS HOLDING CO INC
(*Suby of* FAMOUS BRANDS INTERNATIONAL) ★
8001 Arista Pl Unit 600, Broomfield, CO 80021-4135
Tel (720) 599-3350 *Founded/Ownrshp* 1996
Sales 124.6MM^E *EMP* 2,326
Accts Kpmg Llp Salt Lake City Ut
SIC 5461 6794 Cookies; Franchises, selling or licensing; Cookies; Franchises, selling or licensing
Pr: Stephen Russo
**Ch:* Herbert S Winokur Jr
**Sr VP:* Garry Remington
VP: John Lauck
**VP:* Michael R Ward
Board of Directors: Richard Ferry, Debbi Fields, Nat Gregory, Walker Lewis, Peter Mullin, Gilbert Osnos

MRS. FIELDS ORIGINAL COOKIES
See MRS FIELDS FAMOUS BRANDS LLC

D-U-N-S 96-055-7460
MRS FIELDS ORIGINAL COOKIES INC
TCBY
8001 Arista Pl Unit 600, Broomfield, CO 80021-4135
Tel (720) 599-3350 *Founded/Ownrshp* 2011
Sales 77.1MM^E *EMP* 200
SIC 5149 5961 5812 Crackers, cookies & bakery products; Catalog & mail-order houses; Frozen yogurt stand; Crackers, cookies & bakery products; Catalog & mail-order houses; Frozen yogurt stand
Pr: Jeffrey P Werner
**CFO:* Brian Johnson
Treas: Mark McBride
**Chf Cred:* Kimberly Aylward
Sr VP: Sandra Buffa
Sr VP: Garry Remington
Sr VP: John Rogers
Comm Man: John Fahey
Admn Mgr: Paula Butler
Brnch Mgr: Heather Reynolds
Brnch Mgr: Kevin Scott
Board of Directors: Tim Clayton, John Dupuy, Joyce Hrinya, Christopher J Kipley, James J Zenni

MRS. FRIDAY'S
See KING & PRINCE SEAFOOD CORP

D-U-N-S 09-172-5135
MRS GERRYS KITCHEN INC
2110 Yh Hanson Ave, Albert Lea, MN 56007-3406
Tel (507) 373-6384 *Founded/Ownrshp* 1973
Sales 40.4MM^E *EMP* 150
SIC 2099 5812 Food preparations; Salads, fresh or refrigerated; Ready-to-eat meals, salads & sandwiches; Sauces: gravy, dressing & dip mixes; Eating places; Food preparations; Salads, fresh or refrigerated; Ready-to-eat meals, salads & sandwiches; Sauces: gravy, dressing & dip mixes; Eating places
VP: Geraldine Vogt
**Sec:* Gerald Vogt

MRS GOOCHES
See WHOLE FOODS MARKET SOPAC

D-U-N-S 02-707-6459
MRS GREENS MANAGEMENT CORP (NY)
MRS GREEN'S NATURAL MARKET
(*Suby of* RICHTREE MARKET RESTAURANTS INC)
780 Post Rd, Scarsdale, NY 10583-5005
Tel (914) 472-0111 *Founded/Ownrshp* 1997, 2010
Sales 49.3MM^E *EMP* 300
SIC 5499 Health & dietetic food stores; Health & dietetic food stores
Pr: Harold Hochberger
**Ch:* Matt Williams

MRS GREEN'S NATURAL MARKET
See MRS GREENS MANAGEMENT CORP

D-U-N-S 00-403-8014
MRS GRISSOMS SALADS INC
2500 Bransford Ave, Nashville, TN 37204-2810
Tel (615) 255-4137 *Founded/Ownrshp* 1955
Sales 27.7MM^E *EMP* 60
SIC 2099 2035 Food preparations; Pickles, sauces & salad dressings
Pr: Grace G Grissom
**Ex VP:* Ken Funger
VP: Alan Casey
**VP:* Jack Mc Gee
**VP:* Herberta Moore
Sls Mgr: Tommy Heath

D-U-N-S 02-176-9617 IMP
MRS GROSSMANS PAPER CO (CA)
PARAGON LABEL
3810 Cypress Dr, Petaluma, CA 94954-5613
Tel (707) 763-1700 *Founded/Ownrshp* 1975
Sales 30.1MM^E *EMP* 100
SIC 2678 2679 2759 2752 Stationery: made from purchased materials; Gift wrap & novelties, paper; Commercial printing; Commercial printing, lithographic; Stationery: made from purchased materials; Gift wrap & novelties, paper; Commercial printing; Commercial printing, lithographic
CEO: Jason H Grossman
**Pr:* Andrea Grossman
Genl Mgr: Sean Downing
Sfty Mgr: Nash Alvarez
Sfty Mgr: Brett Mathews
Mktg Dir: Lara Starr

MRS LUMBER
See MANUFACTURERS RESERVE SUPPLY INC

D-U-N-S 00-260-1003
MRS RESSLERS FOOD PRODUCTS CO (PA)
PCI
5501 Tabor Ave, Philadelphia, PA 19120-2127
Tel (215) 744-4004 *Founded/Ownrshp* 1954
Sales 63.0MM *EMP* 140^E
Accts Brinker Simpson & Company Ll
SIC 2015 2013 Turkey, processed: cooked; Chicken, processed: cooked; Spreads, sandwich: poultry; Corned beef from purchased meat; Roast beef from purchased meat; Spiced meats from purchased meat; Turkey, processed: cooked; Chicken, processed: cooked; Spreads, sandwich: poultry; Corned beef from purchased meat; Roast beef from purchased meat; Spiced meats from purchased meat
CEO: Joseph Israeli
**Pr:* David Israeli
**Sec:* Edith Ressler
**VP:* Michael Israeli
Prd Mgr: Fred Burke
Ql Cn Mgr: Flor Negron
Manager: Bill Gregor

D-U-N-S 06-114-3962
MRS STRATTONS SALADS INC
380 Industrial Ln, Birmingham, AL 35211-4462
Tel (205) 940-9640 *Founded/Ownrshp* 1972
Sales 44.3MM^E *EMP* 125
SIC 2035 2099 Pickles, sauces & salad dressings; Salads, fresh or refrigerated; Pickles, sauces & salad dressings; Salads, fresh or refrigerated
Pr: George Bradford
**CFO:* Tim Mask
Sls Mgr: Lanny Baker

MRS. T'S
See ATEECO INC

D-U-N-S 00-515-4133
MRT SUREWAY INC
SUREWAY TOOL & ENGINEERING CO
2959 Hart Ct, Franklin Park, IL 60131-2213
Tel (847) 801-3010 *Founded/Ownrshp* 1962, 1996
Sales 23.1MM^E *EMP* 109
SIC 3441 Fabricated structural metal; Fabricated structural metal
Pr: M Richard Tetrault
**VP:* Julian Burnley
Exec: Betts Siwy
Mfg Dir: Marcelo Buenrostro
Ql Cn Mgr: Bobbie Braczko
Sales Exec: Chris Maxson
Sales Exec: Steve Schommer

D-U-N-S 19-202-1608 IMP
▲ **MRV COMMUNICATIONS INC**
20415 Nordhoff St, Chatsworth, CA 91311-6112
Tel (818) 773-0900 *Founded/Ownrshp* 1988
Sales 172.0MM *EMP* 420^E
Accts Grant Thornton Llp Los Angele
Tkr Sym MRVC *Exch* NAS
SIC 3674 5049 Semiconductors & related devices; Switches, silicon control; Optical goods; Semiconductors & related devices; Switches, silicon control; Optical goods
Pr: Mark J Bonney
**Ch Bd:* Kenneth H Traub
CFO: Stephen Krulik
**V Ch Bd:* Robert M Pons
Ex VP: Paul Trunfio
Sr VP: Adam Scheer
VP: Koby Bergman
VP: Zeev Draer
VP: Scott John
VP: Jack Yocum
Genl Mgr: Nye Liu
Board of Directors: Jeannie H Diefenderfer, Matthew Stecker

MRWPCA
See MONTEREY REGIONAL WATER POLLUTION CONTROL AGENCY

D-U-N-S 15-162-5498
MRY US LLC
LBI US
(*Suby of* LBI INTERNATIONAL N.V.)
11 W 19th St Fl 3, New York, NY 10011-4280
Tel (212) 206-6270 *Founded/Ownrshp* 2000
Sales 48.0MM^E *EMP* 250^E
SIC 7379 ;
CEO: Matt Britton
**Pr:* Judith Carr
Pr: Vishal Sapra
**COO:* Richard Tan
CFO: Scott Heydt
**CFO:* Dan Lafontaine
**Chf Mktg O:* David Berkowitz
**Ofcr:* Ian Chee
VP: Jesper Andersen
Assoc Dir: Kapil Bahadur
Creative D: Stefanie Gunning

MS
See MURPHY & SONS INC

MS
See METALS AND SERVICES INC

D-U-N-S 79-110-1413
MS AEROSPACE INC
13928 Balboa Blvd, Sylmar, CA 91342-1086
Tel (818) 833-9095 *Founded/Ownrshp* 1992
Sales 105.3MM^E *EMP* 302
SIC 3452 3728 Bolts, nuts, rivets & washers; Aircraft parts & equipment; Bolts, nuts, rivets & washers; Aircraft parts & equipment
CEO: Michel Szostak
**CFO:* Jerome Taieb
**VP:* Jim Cole
DP Exec: Louis Hernandez
QA Dir: Gregg Ferguson
QA Dir: Kevin Jones
IT Man: Davina Lamb
IT Man: Charles Nissen
Sfty Dirs: Joe Herbison
QC Dir: Alex Rodriguez
Prd Mgr: Adrien Szsostak

D-U-N-S 09-210-9222
■ **MS CARRIERS INC**
(*Suby of* SWIFT TRANSPORTATION CO) ★
1940 E Brooks Rd Ste 20, Memphis, TN 38116-3645
Tel (901) 332-2500 *Founded/Ownrshp* 2001
Sales 80.2MM^E *EMP* 3,336
SIC 4213 Trucking, except local; Trucking, except local
Pr: Michael S Starnes
**Treas:* M J Barrow
**Sr VP:* James W Welch
VP: John M Hudson
**VP:* Robert P Hurt
VP: Azmi B Ujang

MS COMPANIES
See ABC EMPLOYMENT HOLDINGS LLC

D-U-N-S 96-179-3374
MS COMPANIES LLC
916 E Westfield Blvd # 300, Indianapolis, IN 46220-1996
Tel (317) 322-9311 *Founded/Ownrshp* 2006
Sales 42.6MM^E *EMP* 600
SIC 7389 Inspection & testing services
COO: Scott Haller
CFO: Nick Vandergrift
Chf Mktg O: Warren Wilkinson
Area Supr: Amanda Holloway
VP Sls: Courtney Jones

D-U-N-S 06-102-4220
MS CONSULTANTS INC
333 E Federal St, Youngstown, OH 44503-1821
Tel (330) 744-5321 *Founded/Ownrshp* 1965
Sales 33.5MM^E *EMP* 173
SIC 8711 8712 Consulting engineer; Architectural services; Consulting engineer; Architectural services
Pr: Thomas E Mosure
**COO:* Michael D Kratofil
VP: Don Killmeyer
VP: Jason Longbrake
VP: John Pierko
VP: Brian Szuch
VP: Bill Wilson
Exec: George Tomich
CIO: Thomas Dundics

D-U-N-S 10-819-5801
■ **MS DIVERSIFIED CORP**
AMERICAN BANKERS INSUR GROUP
(*Suby of* AMERICAN BANKERS INSURANCE GROUP INC) ★
1501 Lakeland Dr Ste 350, Jackson, MS 39216-4849
Tel (601) 420-4909 *Founded/Ownrshp* 1998
Sales NA *EMP* 274
SIC 6311 6321 6331 6351 6411 Life insurance; Accident & health insurance; Fire, marine & casualty insurance; Credit & other financial responsibility insurance; Warranty insurance, home; Insurance agents & brokers; Life insurance; Accident & health insurance; Fire, marine & casualty insurance; Credit & other financial responsibility insurance; Warranty insurance, home; Insurance agents & brokers
Pr: Robert S Furman
Sr VP: James D Mc Brayer
Sr VP: Bob F Norsworthy Jr
VP: John E Gough
Board of Directors: C Harrell Schaeffer, Bert Allen, Robert B Briscoe, Edmund L Brunini Jr, J Kane Ditto Jr, R B Dossett Jr, Hap Hederman, Gerald Lane, Paul G Moak, W E Powell Sr

MS ENERGY SERVICES
See MULTI-SHOT LLC

D-U-N-S 78-372-5773
■ **MS FINANCING INC**
MORGAN STANLEY
(*Suby of* MORGAN STANLEY) ★
1585 Broadway, New York, NY 10036-8200
Tel (212) 761-4000 *Founded/Ownrshp* 1994
Sales NA *EMP* 148^E
SIC 6159 Farm mortgage companies
CEO: James P Gorman
**COO:* Roy J Bostock

D-U-N-S 04-233-6243 IMP
MS INDUSTRIES INC
(*Suby of* MS SPAICHINGEN GMBH)
1101 Highview Dr, Webberville, MI 48892-9290
Tel (517) 223-1059 *Founded/Ownrshp* 1997
Sales 35.8MM^E *EMP* 96
SIC 5084 Welding machinery & equipment; Welding machinery & equipment
Pr: Volker Amann
**Treas:* Rouven Muell
**VP:* Frank Jedele
VP: Mark Pucel
Off Mgr: Christine Greck

D-U-N-S 01-594-6163
MS INET LLC
(*Suby of* CORPORATE OFFICE) ★
270 Davidson Ave Fl 8, Somerset, NJ 08873-4140
Tel (732) 469-2866 *Founded/Ownrshp* 1998
Sales 12.2MM^E *EMP* 400
SIC 7373 Systems software development services; Systems software development services
CEO: James Desilver

D-U-N-S 07-830-6424
MS INSPECTION & LOGISTICS INC
6325 Guilford Ave Ste 208, Indianapolis, IN 46220-1741
Tel (317) 730-4646 *Founded/Ownrshp* 2005
Sales 45.0MM *EMP* 98
SIC 4785 7389 Transportation inspection services; Packaging & labeling services
Pr: Leticia Snoddy

D-U-N-S 78-266-6895
MS PAWN LIMITED PARTNERSHIP
1901 Capital Pkwy, Austin, TX 78746-7613
Tel (512) 314-3400 *Founded/Ownrshp* 1989
Sales 276.2MM^E *EMP* 7,500
SIC 5932 6141 Pawnshop; Personal credit institutions; Pawnshop; Personal credit institutions
Prin: Jason Duma

D-U-N-S 82-862-7153 IMP
MS PRECISION COMPONENTS LLC
(*Suby of* MS INDUSTRIES INC) ★
1101 Highview Dr, Webberville, MI 48892-9290
Tel (517) 223-1059 *Founded/Ownrshp* 2007
Sales 28.8MM^E *EMP* 95
SIC 3519 Internal combustion engines

Sec: Chris Greck
Ql Cn Mgr: Marcus Buffler

D-U-N-S 36-070-4613
MS SUPREME COURT
(*Suby of* STATE OF MISSISSIPPI) ★
450 High St Ste 300, Jackson, MS 39201-1082
Tel (601) 359-3694 Founded/Ownrshp 1817
Sales NA EMP 1,050
SIC 9211 State courts; ; State courts;
IT Man: Carol Allgood

MS TECHNOLOGIES
See STINE SEED CO

MS&L
See MSLGROUP AMERICAS INC

MSA
See MISSION SUPPORT ALLIANCE LLC

MSA
See MAGNET-SCHULTZ OF AMERICA INC

D-U-N-S 55-542-8366
MSA GROUP INC
CROWN LOGISTICS
2839 Charter St, Columbus, OH 43228-4607
Tel (614) 334-0400 Founded/Ownrshp 1992
Sales 6.0MM EMP 300
SIC 5087 5122 Beauty parlor equipment & supplies; Drugs & drug proprietaries; Beauty parlor equipment & supplies; Drugs & drug proprietaries
CEO: Jeff Hoover
**COO:* James Carmody Jr

D-U-N-S 06-650-7864
MSA INC
410 Spring St, Chattanooga, TN 37405-3849
Tel (423) 756-0334 Founded/Ownrshp 1974
Sales 22.5MM^E EMP 77
SIC 5065 5044 Facsimile equipment; Photocopy machines; Facsimile equipment; Photocopy machines
Pr: Richard D Morrison
**Ex VP:* Michael R Morrison
**Ex VP:* Robert A Morrison III
VP: Bobby Morrison
Sales Exec: Joe Littlejohn

D-U-N-S 04-803-4433
MSA PROFESSIONAL SERVICES INC
1230 South Blvd, Baraboo, WI 53913-2791
Tel (608) 355-8881 Founded/Ownrshp 1991
Sales 32.1MM EMP 280
SIC 8711 8999 8732

D-U-N-S 07-935-8187
▲ MSA SAFETY INC
1000 Cranberry Woods Dr, Cranberry Township, PA 16066-5207
Tel (724) 776-8600 Founded/Ownrshp 1914
Sales 1.1MMM EMP 5,000^E
SIC 3842 3826 3823 3648 3829 Surgical appliances & supplies; Personal safety equipment; Environmental testing equipment; Industrial process control instruments; Lighting equipment; Gas detectors; Surgical appliances & supplies; Personal safety equipment; Environmental testing equipment; Industrial process control instruments; Lighting equipment; Gas detectors
Ch Bd: William M Lambert
CFO: Stacy McMahan
Ofcr: Dave McNulty
VP: Steve Blanco
VP: Kerry M Bove
VP: Douglas K McClaine
VP: Mary McGinley
VP: Michael Taucher
VP: Paul R Uhler
VP: Markus Weber
Snr Sftwr: Eric Rose
Board of Directors: Robert A Bruggeworth, Thomas B Hotopp, Diane M Pearse, Rebecca B Roberts, John T Ryan III, L Edward Shaw Jr, Alvaro Garcia-Tunon, Thomas H Witmer

MSA SECURITY
See MICHAEL STAPLETON ASSOCIATES LTD

D-U-N-S 12-914-8909
MSA SYSTEMS INTEGRATION INC
ACCESS SYSTEMS INTEGRATION
1 Indll Wy W Bldg D Ste C, Eatontown, NJ 07724
Tel (732) 544-8444 Founded/Ownrshp 2015
Sales 22.6MM^E EMP 38
SIC 7382 Security systems services
Pr: James Hennessy
**Prin:* Edward Gleason
Genl Mgr: Edward Adams
VP Opers: Pat Lyons
Snr PM: Salvatore Sarrecchia

MSAD 1
See REGIONAL SCHOOL UNIT 88/MAINE SCHOOL ADMINISTRATIVE DISTRICT 1

MSAD 22
See REGIONAL SCHOOL UNIT 22

MSAD 29
See SCHOOL ADMIN DISTRICT 29

M.S.A.D. 35
See REGIONAL SCHOOL UNIT 35/MAINE SCHOOL ADMINISTRATIVE DISTRICT 35

MSB
See MARYLAND SCHOOL FOR BLIND

MSBSD
See MATANUSKA SUSITNA BOROUGH SCHOOL DISTRICT

MSC
See MILLER SIERRA CONTRACTORS INC

D-U-N-S 80-370-4550
MSC CARE MANAGEMENT INC
MSC-MEDICAL SVC ATKINS PHARM
(*Suby of* ONE CALL CARE MANAGEMENT) ★
841 Prudential Dr Ste 900, Jacksonville, FL 32207-8371
Tel (904) 646-0199 Founded/Ownrshp 2012
Sales 22.6MM^E EMP 200^E
SIC 7352 5047 Medical equipment rental; Medical & hospital equipment; Medical equipment rental; Medical & hospital equipment
CEO: Joseph P Delaney
Ch Bd: Patrick G Dills
Pr: Guy Jackson
Sr VP: Linda D Lane
Sr VP: Linda Lane
Sr VP: Joe McCullough
VP: Marty Ovens
VP: Dawn Phillips
Exec: Alyssa Murray
QA Dir: Wendy Frederico
Opers Mgr: Brad Dickinson

D-U-N-S 82-920-6452
MSC GROUP INC
EXPRESS SCRIPTS
841 Prudential Dr Ste 900, Jacksonville, FL 32207-8371
Tel (904) 646-0199 Founded/Ownrshp 2008
Sales 22.1MM^E EMP 100
SIC 7352 5047 Medical equipment rental; Medical & hospital equipment
Pr: Joseph Delaney
Ch Bd: Robert J Bunker
Pr: Sam Hillman
Pr: Linda Hirschi
Pr: Dawn Phillips
Sr VP: Ed Finney
Sr VP: Guy Jackson
Sr VP: Linda Lane
Sr VP: Joe McCullough
VP: Jeffrey Edelson
VP: Jill Lawson
VP: Joel McMains
VP: Jay Wilson

D-U-N-S 93-261-9265 IMP
▲ MSC INDUSTRIAL DIRECT CO INC
75 Maxess Rd, Melville, NY 11747-3151
Tel (516) 812-2000 Founded/Ownrshp 1941
Sales 2.9MMM EMP 6,642
Accts Ernst & Young Llp Jericho Ne
Tkr Sym MSM Exch NYS
SIC 5084 5085 5063 5072 Industrial machinery & equipment; Machine tools & metalworking machinery; Measuring & testing equipment, electrical; Safety equipment; Industrial supplies; Abrasives & adhesives; Fasteners & fastening equipment; Electrical apparatus & equipment; Hardware; Industrial machinery & equipment; Machine tools & metalworking machinery; Measuring & testing equipment, electrical; Safety equipment; Industrial supplies; Abrasives & adhesives; Fasteners & fastening equipment; Electrical apparatus & equipment; Hardware
Pr: Erik Gershwind
CFO: Rustom Jilla
Treas: John G Chironna
Ofcr: Kari Heerdt
Sr VP: Ross Anker
Sr VP: Steve Armstrong
Sr VP: Charles Bonomo
VP: Shelley M Boxer
VP: John Chironna
Board of Directors: Jonathan Byrnes, Roger Fradin, Louise Goeser, Mitchell Jacobson, Michael Kaufmann, Denis Kelly, Steven Paladino, Philip Peller

MSC METALWORKING
See RUTLAND TOOL & SUPPLY CO

D-U-N-S 05-663-9883
MSC PRE FINISH METALS (EGV) INC
(*Suby of* MATERIAL SCIENCES CORP) ★
2200 Pratt Blvd, Elk Grove Village, IL 60007-5917
Tel (847) 439-2210 Founded/Ownrshp 1971
Sales 63.1MM^E EMP 436
SIC 3479 3471 3399 Coating of metals & formed products; Electroplating of metals or formed products; Laminating steel; Coating of metals & formed products; Electroplating of metals or formed products; Laminating steel
Ch Bd: Gerald G Nadig
**Pr:* Douglas M Rose
**CFO:* James Waclawik Sr
VP Sls: Michael Mooney

MSC-MEDICAL SVC ATKINS PHARM
See MSC CARE MANAGEMENT INC

MSCC
See ARKANSAS STATE UNIVERSITY MID-SOUTH

D-U-N-S 07-922-4771
MSCI 2007-IQ16 LODGING 100 LLC
DAYTONA HILTON
100 N Atlantic Ave, Daytona Beach, FL 32118-4204
Tel (386) 254-8200 Founded/Ownrshp 2013
Sales 18.5MM^E EMP 350
SIC 7011 Hotels & motels; Hotels & motels
Genl Mgr: Rich Larkin
Genl Mgr: Dan Willis

D-U-N-S 80-809-5793
▲ MSCI INC
250 Greenwich St Fl 49, New York, NY 10007-2340
Tel (212) 804-3900 Founded/Ownrshp 1969
Sales 996.6MM EMP 2,926^E
Tkr Sym MSCI Exch NYS
SIC 7389 7371 6282 8742 Financial services; Software programming applications; Investment advice; Management consulting services; Business consultant; Financial services; Software programming applications; Investment advice; Management consulting services; Business consultant
Ch Bd: Henry A Fernandez
COO: CD Baer Pettit
CFO: Robert Qutub
Ofcr: Scott A Crum
VP: Edward Allen
VP: Andrew Demond
VP: Altaf Mubaraki
VP: Bryan Murphy
VP: Geraldo Paris
VP: Henry Sharr
VP: Aaron Young
Board of Directors: Patrick Tierney, Robert G Ashe, Rodolphe M Vallee, Benjamin F Dupont, Wayne Edmunds, D Robert Hale, Alice W Handy, Catherine R Kinney, Wendy E Lane, Linda H Riefler, George W Siguler

MSCITX.COM
See MEDICAL & SURGICAL CLINIC OF IRVING P A

MSCPA
See MICHIGAN SOUTH CENTRAL POWER AGENCY INC

D-U-N-S 00-965-3148
MSCSOFTWARE CORP
(*Suby of* MAXIMUS HOLDINGS INC) ★
4675 Macarthur Ct Ste 900, Newport Beach, CA 92660-1845
Tel (714) 540-8900 Founded/Ownrshp 1963, 2009
Sales 177.3MM^E EMP 1,006
SIC 7372 Prepackaged software; Prepackaged software
Pr: Dominic Gallello
Pr: Douglas Lubben
CFO: Kevin Rubin
Sr VP: Kais Bouchiba
Sr VP: Douglas W Peterson
VP: Leslie Bodnar
VP: Stephen Bodnar
VP: Jeffrey Graff
VP: John Howaniec
VP: John Janevic
VP: Bert Knops
VP: Doug Neill
Board of Directors: Frank Cappuccio

MSD
See MECHANICAL SYSTEMS OF DAYTON INC

MSD
See METROPOLITAN ST LOUIS SEWER DISTRICT

D-U-N-S 02-822-5196
MSD CAPITAL LP
645 5th Ave Fl 21, New York, NY 10022-5922
Tel (212) 230-2560 Founded/Ownrshp 1998
Sales 32.5MM^E EMP 70^E
SIC 6799 Venture capital companies; Real estate investors, except property operators; Security speculators for own account
Mng Pt: Glenn R Fuhrman
Pt: Howard M Berk
Pt: Jonathan Esfandi
Pt: Brian L Frank
Mng Pt: Glenn Fuhrman
Mng Pt: John C Phelan
CFO: MEI-Ying Tsai
VP: Richard Borchers
VP: Pankaj Chandhok
Exec: Alan Epstein
Mng Dir: Chris Evison
Board of Directors: Joel Alsfine

D-U-N-S 00-701-7452 IMP
MSD CONSUMER CARE INC
(*Suby of* BAYER HEALTHCARE LLC) ★
3030 Jackson Ave, Memphis, TN 38112-2020
Tel (866) 360-3226 Founded/Ownrshp 1923, 2014
Sales 28.8MM^E EMP 51^E
SIC 2844 Toilet preparations; Suntan lotions & oils
CEO: Kenneth C Frazier
VP: John Clayton
IT Man: Linda Risby
MIS Mgr: Susan Guarino

MSD IGNITIONS
See MSD LLC

D-U-N-S 07-929-0152
MSD LLC
MSD IGNITIONS
1350 Pullman Dr Ste 200, El Paso, TX 79936-7738
Tel (915) 857-5200 Founded/Ownrshp 2013
Sales 78.1MM^E EMP 308
SIC 3694 Ignition systems, high frequency; Ignition systems, high frequency
CEO: Ron Turcotte
Pr: Russell Stephens

MSD MARTINSVILLE
See MSD OF MARTINSVILLE SCHOOLS

MSD OF DECATUR TOWNSHIP
See METROPOLITAN SCHOOL DISTRICT OF DECATUR TOWNSHIP

D-U-N-S 11-266-1160
MSD OF MARTINSVILLE SCHOOLS
MSD MARTINSVILLE
389 E Jackson St, Martinsville, IN 46151-1503
Tel (765) 342-6641 Founded/Ownrshp 1949
Sales 38.8MM^E EMP 867
SIC 8211 Public elementary & secondary schools; Public elementary & secondary schools
**Treas:* Sandy Hart

MSD OF MOUNT VERNON
See METROPOLITAN SCHOOL DISTRICT OF MOUNT VERNON

D-U-N-S 05-010-0395
MSD OF WARREN TOWNSHIP
WARREN TWP SCHOOL DISTRICT
975 N Post Rd, Indianapolis, IN 46219-5545
Tel (317) 869-4300 Founded/Ownrshp 1956
Sales 91.3MM^E EMP 1,400
SIC 8211 Public combined elementary & secondary school; Public vocational/technical school; Public combined elementary & secondary school; Public vocational/technical school
Pr: Julie A French
**CFO:* David Holt
**VP:* Anthony R Mendez
Ex Dir: Mary McKinley
Sls Mgr: Lisa Hedge
Psych: Cathleen Leganza

MSD PERFORMANCE
See MSDP GROUP LLC

D-U-N-S 07-969-4557
MSDP GROUP LLC
MSD PERFORMANCE
(*Suby of* HOLLEY PERFORMANCE PRODUCTS INC) ★
1350 Pullman Dr Dr14, El Paso, TX 79936-7737
Tel (915) 857-5200 Founded/Ownrshp 2013, 2015
Sales 72.9MM^E EMP 300^E
SIC 3694 Ignition systems, high frequency
CEO: Rick Ruebusch
Mktg Mgr: Jill Metsala

D-U-N-S 11-248-8007
■ MSDSONLINE INC
(*Suby of* ACTUA CORP) ★
350 N Orleans St Ste 950, Chicago, IL 60654-1616
Tel (312) 881-2000 Founded/Ownrshp 2012
Sales 25.3MM^E EMP 240^E
SIC 7389 7375 Document storage service; Information retrieval services; Document storage service; Information retrieval services
CEO: Glenn Trout
**Pr:* Douglas States
VP: Ron Deger
VP: Chuck Haling
Genl Mgr: Patricia Owens
IT Man: Peter Hake
IT Man: Jeff Johns
Software D: Reed Rawhouser
Sales Exec: Keith Anderson
Sales Exec: Ryan Chappell
Sales Exec: Jake Furey

D-U-N-S 80-674-1851 IMP/EXP
MSEAFOOD CORP
17934 Point Sur St, Fountain Valley, CA 92708-5042
Tel (714) 842-7900 Founded/Ownrshp 2001
Sales 101.4MM EMP 5^E
SIC 5146 Fish & seafoods; Fish & seafoods
Prin: Quang Van Le
Sls Mgr: Ned Ligenza

MSEC
See COUNCIL EMPLOYERS SERVICES INC

MSEC
See MOUNTAIN STATES EMPLOYERS COUNCIL INC

D-U-N-S 17-775-5329 IMP
MSEI INC
MADER SOUTHEAST
2300 E Landstreet Rd, Orlando, FL 32824-7974
Tel (813) 628-5566 Founded/Ownrshp 1994
Sales 65.5MM^E EMP 650
SIC 1742 Drywall; Drywall
Pr: Thomas M Johnson Sr
**VP:* James C Coddington
**VP:* Thomas M Johnson Jr
**VP:* James Morehead
Div Mgr: Paul Daniel
Genl Mgr: Jeff Dowd
Sfty Dirs: Timothy Bernardi
Snr PM: Kevin Watkins
Snr Mgr: Karl Pearson

MSEO.COM
See GLOBAL VIBRATION INC

D-U-N-S 79-064-3725
MSF ELECTRIC INC
M S F
10455 Fountaingate Dr, Stafford, TX 77477-3154
Tel (281) 494-4700 Founded/Ownrshp 2006
Sales 22.6MM^E EMP 150
Accts Melton & Melton Llp Houston
SIC 1731 General electrical contractor; General electrical contractor
Pr: John Paschal
**VP:* Henry Ossowski
Div Mgr: Mike Jennings
Div Mgr: Jim Wandland
Dir IT: Alex Adarmis
Snr PM: Fred Herron

MSG
See MILK SPECIALTIES CO

MSG
See MERCHANDISING SOLUTIONS GROUP INC

MSG HOLDINGS, L.P.
See MSGN HOLDINGS LP

D-U-N-S 83-283-1999
▲ MSG NETWORKS INC
11 Penn Plz, New York, NY 10001-2006
Tel (212) 465-6000 Founded/Ownrshp 1879
Sales 1.6MMM EMP 9,300^E
Accts Kpmg Llp New York New York
Tkr Sym MSG Exch NYS
SIC 4841 7922 7941 4832 Cable & other pay television services; Television program, including commercial producers; Entertainment promotion; Sports clubs, managers & promoters; Sports; Cable & other pay television services; Television program, including commercial producers; Entertainment promotion; Sports clubs, managers & promoters; Sports
Pr: David O'Connor
**Ch Bd:* James L Dolan
Pr: Andrea Greenberg
Pr: Kai Haasler
CFO: Donna Coleman
CFO: Bret Richter
Ex VP: Lawrence J Burian
Ex VP: Robin Korn
Ex VP: Joseph Lhota
Dir Risk M: Debbie Sturniolo
Genl Mgr: Sal Federico
Board of Directors: Brian G Sweeney, William J Bell, John L Sykes, Eugene F Demark, Charles F Dolan, Paul J Dolan, Quentin F Dolan, Thomas C Dolan, Wilt Hildenbrand, Joel M Litvin, Hank J Ratner

D-U-N-S 08-004-9921
MSG SPORTS & ENTERTAINMENT LLC
MADISON SQUARE GARDEN COMPANY
2 Penn Plz Fl 15, New York, NY 10121-1700
Tel (212) 465-6000 *Founded/Ownrshp* 2015
Sales 4.3MMM *EMP* 1,020
SIC 7941 Stadium event operator services; Sports field or stadium operator, promoting sports events
CEO: David O'Connor
CFO: Donna Coleman
Treas: Robert Lynn
VP: Brian Krisburg

D-U-N-S 96-731-4977
MSGE LLC
546 Hamilton St Ste 313, Allentown, PA 18101-1521
Tel (610) 704-9056 *Founded/Ownrshp* 2011
Sales 101.2MM^E *EMP* 400
SIC 4911 4925 Distribution, electric power; Gas production and/or distribution; Distribution, electric power; Gas production and/or distribution

D-U-N-S 01-415-2057
MSGI CORP (FL)
5426 Bay Center Dr # 100, Tampa, FL 33609-3415
Tel (813) 769-8060 *Founded/Ownrshp* 2000
Sales 28.7MM^E *EMP* 155
SIC 7379 Computer related consulting services; Computer related consulting services
Pr: Angel E Cintron
Pr: Jim Kelley
VP: Tom Baxter
VP: Pedro Gomez
Off Mgr: Mitchel McNalley

D-U-N-S 83-553-4694 IMP
■ **MSGN HOLDINGS LP**
MSG HOLDINGS, L.P.
(*Suby of* MSG NETWORKS INC) ★
4 Penn Plz, New York, NY 10121-0078
Tel (212) 465-6000 *Founded/Ownrshp* 2011
Sales 228.6MM^E *EMP* 500
SIC 4832 7922 Sports; Television program, including commercial producers; Entertainment promotion; Sports; Television program, including commercial producers; Entertainment promotion
Genl Pt: James Dolan
Pr: Al Coates
Pr: Michael Guth
Ex VP: Seth Abrham
Ex VP: David Clark
Ex VP: Joe Gangone
Ex VP: Howard Handler
Ex VP: Robert Pollichino
Ex VP: Don Simpson
Sr VP: Sean Barror
Sr VP: Glen Grunwald
Sr VP: Kristina Heney
Sr VP: Chris Moseley
Sr VP: Cathy Murray
Sr VP: Lewis Sherr
Sr VP: Billie Streets
Sr VP: Art Ventura
VP: Joseph Ali
VP: Kris Elvgren
VP: Joe Favorito
VP: Eric Gelfang

D-U-N-S 07-977-7755
MSHC INC
SERVICE LOGIC
12005 E 45th Ave, Denver, CO 80239-3111
Tel (303) 455-2825 *Founded/Ownrshp* 2006
Sales 200.0MM *EMP* 1,000^E
SIC 8741 Administrative management
CEO: Craig A Steinke
COO: Timothy Ridel
CFO: Matthew W Austin

M.S.H.D.A.
See HOUSING DEVELOPMENT AUTHORITY MICHIGAN STATE

MSI
See MANAGEMENT SYSTEMS INTERNATIONAL INC

MSI
See M S INTERNATIONAL INC

MSI
See MOBILITY SERVICES INTERNATIONAL LLC

MSI
See MICROLINE SURGICAL INC

MSI
See MULTI-SYSTEMS INC

MSI
See MORTGAGE SPECIALISTS INTERNATIONAL LLC

D-U-N-S 06-751-8095
MSI ACQUISITION CORP
(*Suby of* HERLEY INDUSTRIES INC) ★
3061 Industry Dr Ste 200, Lancaster, PA 17603-4025
Tel (717) 397-2777 *Founded/Ownrshp* 2011
Sales 21.3MM^E *EMP* 148^E
SIC 3812 Search & navigation equipment
Pr: Eric Demarco
**CEO:* Deanna Lund
**Treas:* Laura Siegal
**Sec:* Deborah Butera
**Sec:* Edward Lake
**VP:* Michael Fink

D-U-N-S 62-353-8071
MSI BENEFITS GROUP INC
245 Townpark Dr Nw # 100, Kennesaw, GA 30144-5888
Tel (770) 425-1231 *Founded/Ownrshp* 1983
Sales NA *EMP* 14^E
SIC 6411 Insurance agents, brokers & service; Insurance agents, brokers & service
Pr: Les Szabolcsi
VP: Matt Bidwell

D-U-N-S 79-543-5197 IMP/EXP
MSI COMPUTER CORP
(*Suby of* MICRO-STAR INTERNATIONAL CO., LTD.)
901 Canada Ct, City of Industry, CA 91748-1136
Tel (626) 913-0828 *Founded/Ownrshp* 1986
Sales 25.8MM^E *EMP* 100
SIC 5045 Computer peripheral equipment; Computer peripheral equipment
CEO: Daniel WEI Ming Wang
**CEO:* Andy Tung
**CFO:* Connie Chang
VP: David Wu
Mktg Mgr: Angela Lan
Sls Mgr: Mark Chen

MSI CONSTRUCTION CO
See MULTIPLE SYSTEMS INDUSTRIAL CONSTRUCTION CO INC

MSI HVAC
See MATERIAL SUPPLY INC

D-U-N-S 16-080-9513
MSI INVENTORY SERVICE CORP
I-FRAN
105 Katherine Dr Bldg D, Flowood, MS 39232-8857
Tel (601) 939-0130 *Founded/Ownrshp* 1983
Sales 25.6MM^E *EMP* 350
SIC 7389 Inventory computing service; Inventory computing service
Pr: James McClain
**Sec:* Melinda Gordin
**VP:* Sandra McClain

MSI MERCHANT SERVICES
See CREDIT CARD PROCESSING USA INC

MSI OILFIELD PRODUCTS
See ESSENTRA PIPE PROTECTION TECHNOLOGIES INC

D-U-N-S 19-952-9033
MSI PACKAGING INC
MARKETING SPECIALTIES
352 N Enterprise Blvd, Lebanon, IN 46052-8191
Tel (765) 485-0145 *Founded/Ownrshp* 2003
Sales 22.4MM^E *EMP* 40
SIC 5113 5199 Shipping supplies; Packaging materials
Pr: Patrick Fitzgerald
**VP:* Tyler Dill

D-U-N-S 87-800-2880
MSI SYSTEMS INTEGRATORS INC
14301 Fnb Pkwy Ste 400, Omaha, NE 68154-5299
Tel (402) 965-2300 *Founded/Ownrshp* 2010
Sales NA *EMP* 700
SIC 7373

MSI TOOL REPAIR
See MILL SUPPLIES INC

MSIG
See MITSUI SUMITOMO INSURANCE CO OF AMERICA

D-U-N-S 80-998-8764
MSIG HOLDINGS (AMERICAS) INC
(*Suby of* MITSUI SUMITOMO INSURANCE COMPANY, LIMITED)
560 Lexington Ave Fl 20, New York, NY 10022-6828
Tel (212) 446-3600 *Founded/Ownrshp* 1988
Sales 389.4MM^E *EMP* 600
SIC 8741 6331 Administrative management; Fire, marine & casualty insurance; Administrative management; Fire, marine & casualty insurance
Ch Bd: Tetsuro Kihara
**Treas:* Shinichiro Nakayama

D-U-N-S 07-836-3630
MSIP-SSCC HOLDINGS LLC
1585 Broadway, New York, NY 10036-8200
Tel (270) 852-5000 *Founded/Ownrshp* 2005
Sales 216.1MM^E *EMP* 498^E
SIC 4923 Gas transmission & distribution; Gas transmission & distribution
Pr: Jerry L Morris

D-U-N-S 96-717-4256
MSJ FOUNDATION
333 Bridge St Nw Ste 800, Grand Rapids, MI 49504-5320
Tel (616) 732-1706 *Founded/Ownrshp* 2011
Sales 27.6MM *EMP* 2
SIC 8699 Charitable organization

D-U-N-S 07-328-6817
MSLGROUP AMERICAS INC
MS&L
(*Suby of* PUBLICIS GROUPE S A)
375 Hudson St Fl 14, New York, NY 10014-7457
Tel (646) 500-7600 *Founded/Ownrshp* 2002
Sales 52.6MM^E *EMP* 200
SIC 8743 Public relations & publicity; Public relations & publicity
CFO: Maury Shapiro
Pt: Pal Jebsen
CEO: Ron Guirguis
COO: Don Lee
Sr VP: David Chamberlin
Sr VP: Larry Larsen
VP: Brian Burgess
VP: Allyson Clarke
VP: Kim Friedman
VP: Trish Gannon
VP: Lawrence Haas
VP: Ellen Schneidau
Assoc Dir: Angie Shen
Dir Bus: Mike Echter

D-U-N-S 96-726-1640
MSMC RESIDENTIAL REALTY LLC
1425 Madison Ave, New York, NY 10029-6514
Tel (212) 243-9090 *Founded/Ownrshp* 2011
Sales 25.8MM *EMP* 2
Accts Ernst & Young Us Llp Indianap
SIC 6531 Real estate brokers & agents; Real estate brokers & agents

Prin: Mahendra Jagmohan
Dir IT: Bruce B Levin

MSNBC.COM
See M S N B C INTERACTIVE NEWS L L C

MSOE
See MILWAUKEE SCHOOL OF ENGIINEERING

D-U-N-S 82-995-8938
MSOLUTIONS LLC
MEDIA SOLUTIONS
(*Suby of* MEDIA SOLUTIONS LLC) ★
661 Fitzhugh Blvd Ste 129, Smyrna, TN 37167-2078
Tel (615) 836-0058 *Founded/Ownrshp* 2008
Sales 22.6MM^E *EMP* 78
SIC 5192 Periodicals
Genl Mgr: Joe Wilhelm
VP Mktg: Rich Coccaro
Sls Dir: Lisa Brown
Sales Asso: Denise Rimmer

MSOUTH EQUITY PARTNERS
See EQUITY MSOUTH PARTNERS L P

MSP
See MAILING SERVICES OF PITTSBURGH INC

MSP
See MACHINE SOLUTION PROVIDERS INC

D-U-N-S 05-749-2290 IMP
■ **MSP INDUSTRIES CORP**
(*Suby of* AAMCO TRANSMISSIONS) ★
45 W Oakwood Rd, Oxford, MI 48371-1631
Tel (248) 628-4150 *Founded/Ownrshp* 1999
Sales 39.0MM^E *EMP* 250
SIC 3462 Automotive forgings, ferrous: crankshaft, engine, axle, etc.; Automotive forgings, ferrous: crankshaft, engine, axle, etc.
Pr: Micheal North
**Prin:* Ronald Kramer

MSPCA/ANGELL MEM ANIMAL HOSP
See MASSACHUSETTS SOCIETY FOR PREVENTION CRUELTY ANIMALS

D-U-N-S 60-358-4848
MSQUARED CONSULTING INC
235 Montgomery St Ste 760, San Francisco, CA 94104-2918
Tel (415) 391-1038 *Founded/Ownrshp* 1988
Sales 64.0MM *EMP* 31
SIC 8742 Management consulting services; Management consulting services
CEO: Alex Dodd

D-U-N-S 03-346-8583
■ **MSR HOTELS & RESORTS INC**
CNL HOSPITALITY PROPERTIES
(*Suby of* MORGAN STANLEY) ★
450 S Orange Ave, Orlando, FL 32801-3383
Tel (407) 650-1000 *Founded/Ownrshp* 2007
Sales 94.6MM^E *EMP* 2,640
SIC 7011 Hotels & motels; Hotels & motels
CEO: John R Klopp
**Ch Bd:* James N Seneff Jr
**Pr:* John A Griswold
**CEO:* Thomas J Hutchison III
**CEO:* Klopp John R
Chf Inves: Sean McLaughlin
**Ex VP:* C Brian Strickland
Sr VP: Justin Ruby
Sr VP: Steve Wortman
VP: Brian Brooks
VP: Chris Bury
VP: Ron Olstad
VP: Tommy Trimble
VP: Ted Watson
VP: Patrick Willis
VP: William Wyatt

D-U-N-S 06-671-1156
MSR PROPERTIES LLC
HOTEL VALLEY HO
6850 E Main St, Scottsdale, AZ 85251-4310
Tel (480) 248-2000 *Founded/Ownrshp* 2002
Sales 22.4MM^E *EMP* 275
SIC 7011 Hotels; Hotels
CEO: Scott B Lyon
Genl Mgr: Andrew Chipendall
Natl Sales: Abigail Betts

D-U-N-S 13-160-5636 IMP
MSR PUBLIC POWER AGENCY
1231 11th St, Modesto, CA 95354-0701
Tel (209) 526-7473 *Founded/Ownrshp* 1980
Sales 87.8MM *EMP* 4
Accts Pricewaterhousecoopers Llp Sa
SIC 4911 Generation, electric power; Generation, electric power
Genl Mgr: Merchant Hopper
**Treas:* Lou Hampel

D-U-N-S 61-435-7460
■ **MSR RESORT LODGING TENANT LLC**
PGA WEST BY WLDORF ASTORIA MGT
(*Suby of* HILTON WORLDWIDE INC) ★
49499 Eisenhower Dr, La Quinta, CA 92253-2722
Tel (760) 564-4111 *Founded/Ownrshp* 2004
Sales 72.1MM^E *EMP* 900
SIC 7011 Hotels & motels; Hotels & motels
**CFO:* Michael Aflory
Exec: Jimmy Schmidt
Dir Teleco: Lorena Alvarez
Mng Dir: Paul Cherrett
Mng Dir: Gary Sims
Genl Mgr: April Shute
Off Mgr: Jonathan Longoria
IT Man: Ray Castro
Mktg Dir: Bob Buttaro
Mktg Mgr: Samantha Swadish
Sls Mgr: Jeane Snavely

MSRC
See MARINE SPILL RESPONSE CORP

MSS
See MILITARY SALES & SERVICE CO

MSS
See MECHANICAL SERVICE & SYSTEMS INC

D-U-N-S 02-028-8296
MSS INC (VA)
SHELL
3201 Germantown Rdste 320, Fairfax, VA 22030
Tel (703) 425-3684 *Founded/Ownrshp* 1978
Sales 97.8MM^E *EMP* 260
SIC 5531 5541 7538 Gasoline service stations; General automotive repair shops; Automotive tires; Automotive tires; Gasoline service stations; General automotive repair shops
Ch: Myron Boncarosky
CFO: Chris Crough
Sec: Carole Boncarosky
VP: Julie Boncarosky Holmes
VP: Michael Bradley Holmes

D-U-N-S 00-340-4451 IMP
MSSC US INC
MERITOR SUSPENSION SYSTEMS COM
(*Suby of* MITSUBISHI STEEL MFG. CO., LTD.)
102 Bill Bryan Blvd, Hopkinsville, KY 42240-6800
Tel (270) 887-3000 *Founded/Ownrshp* 2000, 2010
Sales 42.2MM^E *EMP* 185
SIC 3493 Automobile springs; Automobile springs
Pr: John Trapp
**Sec:* Charles Weisbaum
**Ex VP:* Tsutomu Murayama
VP: Rebekah Hutton
Exec: Eugene Finch
Exec: Rob Holiway
Exec: Tim Johnson
Dir IT: Mark Velva
IT Man: Chuck Longo
Mtls Mgr: Brian Bechard
Sfty Mgr: Marcus Grey

D-U-N-S 07-947-9012
MSSL WIRING SYSTEM INC
(*Suby of* MOTHERSON SUMI SYSTEMS LIMITED)
8640 E Market St, Warren, OH 44484-2346
Tel (330) 856-3344 *Founded/Ownrshp* 2014
Sales 41.5MM^E *EMP* 99^E
SIC 3679 Harness assemblies for electronic use: wire or cable
Pr: Jitender Mahajan
COO: Duncan Reid

MSSS
See MANAGEMENT SSS INC

D-U-N-S 96-498-5167
■ **MSSTAFF LLC**
(*Suby of* CROSS COUNTRY HEALTHCARE INC) ★
901 Nw 51st St Ste 110, Boca Raton, FL 33431-4415
Tel (561) 322-1300 *Founded/Ownrshp* 2014
Sales 46.4MM^E *EMP* 950
SIC 7363 7361 Help supply services; Medical help service; Employment agencies
Pr: Brian Poplin MD

M.S.S.U.
See MISSOURI SOUTHERN STATE UNIVERSITY ALUMNI ASSOCIATION

MST
See PRECIOUS LKQ METALS INC

D-U-N-S 08-393-2582 IMP
MST STEEL CORP
24417 Groesbeck Hwy, Warren, MI 48089-4786
Tel (586) 773-5460 *Founded/Ownrshp* 1977
Sales 42.0MM^E *EMP* 95
SIC 5051 Steel; Steel
Pr: Richard Thompson
VP: Wally Wilson
Genl Mgr: Greg Tavalire
Trfc Mgr: Robert Peplinski
VP Sls: Tom Moseley
Sls Mgr: Adam Roush
Sales Asso: Rhonda Nichols

D-U-N-S 96-952-7808
MSTREET ENTERTAINMENT LLC
1207 Mcgavock St Ste D, Nashville, TN 37203-3154
Tel (615) 942-5591 *Founded/Ownrshp* 2011
Sales 5.0MM *EMP* 300
SIC 6719 Personal holding companies, except banks; Personal holding companies, except banks
CFO: Hartman King
Mktg Dir: Jennifer McMakin

MSU/KCMS
See WESTERN MICHIGAN UNIVERSITY SCHOOL OF MEDICINE

MSUFCU
See MICHIGAN STATE UNIVERSITY FEDERAL CREDIT UNION

MSW
See MAHOMED SALES & WAREHOUSING LLC

D-U-N-S 07-749-9853
MSW RESEARCH INC
1111 Marcus Ave Ste Mz200, New Hyde Park, NY 11042-2037
Tel (516) 394-6000 *Founded/Ownrshp* 1968
Sales 22.7MM^E *EMP* 360^E
SIC 8732 Market analysis or research; Market analysis or research
Ch Bd: Peter R Klein
**CEO:* Harold M Spielman
Ex VP: Steven Jagger
Ex VP: Karl Rosenberg
Sr VP: Pat Brennan
VP: Rachel Day
VP: Frank Findley
Snr Ntwrk: Emily Taub
Snr Mgr: Enrique Guemez

MSX AMERICAS
See MSX INTERNATIONAL INC

D-U-N-S 13-947-0009
MSX INTERNATIONAL INC
MSX AMERICAS
26555 Evergreen Rd # 122, Southfield, MI 48076-4206
Tel (248) 829-6300 *Founded/Ownrshp* 1996
Sales 844.9MM^E *EMP* 4,000
SIC 8748 7363 8742 8711 Test development & evaluation service; Labor resource services; Management consulting services; Engineering services; Test development & evaluation service; Labor resource services; Management consulting services; Engineering services
Pr: Frederick K Minturn
CFO: R Michael Muraske
Ch: Erwin H Billig
VP: Jim Bazner
VP: Michael Bowe
VP: Richard Calmes
VP: Leslie Cooney
VP: Shawn Coyle
VP: Cynthia Dauphinais
VP: Sam Del Mar
VP: David Graff
VP: Frederick Minturn
VP: Charles Streeter
VP: Margaret Turner
VP: Pieter Van Rosmalen
VP: Brendan Walsh
VP: Susan West
Board of Directors: Richard Puricelli

D-U-N-S 82-903-2114
MSX INTERNATIONAL PLATFORM SERVICES LLC
M S X INTERNATIONAL
(*Suby of* MSX AMERICAS) ★
1950 Concept Dr, Warren, MI 48091-1385
Tel (248) 829-6300 *Founded/Ownrshp* 2001
Sales 20.6MM^E *EMP* 200^E
SIC 8711 Engineering services; Engineering services
Prin: Ralph Miller
Ex VP: John Miller
IT Man: Juergen Funke
**Plnt Mgr:* Brian Chambers

MT ASCUTNEY HOSPITAL AND HEALT
See WINDSOR HOSPITAL CORP

MT BAKER PLYWOOD
See MT BAKER PRODUCTS INC

D-U-N-S 80-703-3774 IMP
MT BAKER PRODUCTS INC
MT BAKER PLYWOOD
(*Suby of* SWANER HARDWOOD CO INC) ★
2929 Roeder Ave, Bellingham, WA 98225-2065
Tel (360) 733-3960 *Founded/Ownrshp* 1993
Sales 40.0MM^E *EMP* 157
SIC 2435 Plywood, hardwood or hardwood faced; Plywood, hardwood or hardwood faced
Pr: Rod Remington
**Ch:* Keith Swaner
**Treas:* Steven G Haag
**VP:* Gary Keith Swaner
Exec: Shawn Goenen
Plnt Mgr: Tim Shannon
Sales Exec: Steve King

D-U-N-S 08-657-7850
MT BLUE REGIONAL SCHOOL DISTRICT
RSU 9
115 Learning Ln, Farmington, ME 04938-7039
Tel (207) 778-6571 *Founded/Ownrshp* 1959
Sales 14.0MM^E *EMP* 300
SIC 8211 Public elementary & secondary schools; Public elementary & secondary schools
Prin: Michael Corminer
Dir Vol: Pauline Rodrigue

D-U-N-S 01-814-8379
MT BUSINESS TECHNOLOGIES INC (OH)
1150 National Pkwy, Mansfield, OH 44906-1911
Tel (419) 529-6100 *Founded/Ownrshp* 1930, 1975
Sales 60.0MM *EMP* 273
SIC 5044 Office equipment; Computer maintenance & repair; Computer integrated systems design; Office equipment
CEO: Carlton Fernyak
Area Mgr: William Forrester
Area Mgr: Joe Monastra
Off Mgr: Melissa James
Dir IT: Jerry Duewel
Opers Mgr: Mark Keiper
Sls Dir: Tim Cusic
Mktg Mgr: Tammy Runion
Manager: Kevin Schwede
Sls Mgr: Pete Gori
Sls Mgr: Kraig Hoffmann

D-U-N-S 80-983-9322 IMP
MT CARMEL COGEN INC
1226 Park Ave, Marion Heights, PA 17832
Tel (570) 373-3999 *Founded/Ownrshp* 1987
Sales 40.8MM^E *EMP* 52
SIC 4911 Generation, electric power
Pr: Joseph Prociak
**Ch Bd:* Kenneth M Pollock
**Sec:* Connie P Rado
**VP:* Paul R Freeman
Plnt Mgr: Paul Freeman

D-U-N-S 00-629-7584
MT CARMEL STABILIZATION GROUP INC
1611 College Dr, Mount Carmel, IL 62863-2614
Tel (618) 262-5118 *Founded/Ownrshp* 1928
Sales 86.0MM^E *EMP* 60
Accts Kemper Cpa Group Llp Vincenne
SIC 1611 3273 Highway & street construction; Construction sand & gravel; Ready-mixed concrete; Highway & street construction; Ready-mixed concrete
Pr: Mike McPherson
**Sec:* Phil Hipsher
**VP:* Douglas Mc Pherson
VP: Douglas Pherson
IT Man: Donna Cundiff
Sfty Mgr: Jack Fowler
Mktg Mgr: Neil Ryan

MT. CLEMENS KIA
See SUMMIT PLACE MOTORS III INC

MT DIABLO MEDICAL PAVILION
See JOHN MUIR MEDICAL PAVILION

D-U-N-S 08-616-6576
MT DIABLO UNIFIED SCHOOL DISTRICT
1936 Carlotta Dr, Concord, CA 94519-1358
Tel (925) 682-8000 *Founded/Ownrshp* 1948
Sales 330.5MM *EMP* 3,800
Accts Christy White Associates San
SIC 8211 Public elementary & secondary schools; Public elementary & secondary schools
Pr: Richard Nicoll
**CFO:* Bryan Richards
Treas: Ramn Hoekwater
Bd of Dir: Linda Mayo
VP: Brian Lawrence
VP: Debra Mason
Ex Dir: Jonathan Eagan
Off Mgr: Val Bostwick
Off Mgr: Kathy Enemark
Off Mgr: Nola Pace
Off Mgr: Elisa Pierson

MT EDGECUMBE HOSPITAL
See SOUTHEAST ALASKA REGIONAL HEALTH CONSORTIUM

MT EPHRAIM DODGE
See FOULKE MANAGEMENT CORP

D-U-N-S 08-420-3439
MT EPHRAIM DODGE INC
620 N Black Horse Pike, Mount Ephraim, NJ 08059-1380
Tel (856) 931-2000 *Founded/Ownrshp* 1977
Sales 21.5MM^E *EMP* 68
SIC 5511 Automobiles, new & used; Automobiles, new & used
Pr: Joseph H Mc Erlean
**Sec:* Edward Mc Erlean

D-U-N-S 82-639-4926
MT FOOD SERVICE INC
M.T. FOODSERVICE
400 N Noble St Ste Rear, Chicago, IL 60642-6697
Tel (312) 733-7028 *Founded/Ownrshp* 1990
Sales 43.9MM^E *EMP* 92
SIC 5143 5148 5144 Dairy products, except dried or canned; Fresh fruits & vegetables; Poultry & poultry products; Dairy products, except dried or canned; Fresh fruits & vegetables; Poultry & poultry products
Pr: Marc Troop
**Treas:* Bill Sullivan
**VP:* Gary Levinson

M.T. FOODSERVICE
See MT FOOD SERVICE INC

D-U-N-S 07-445-9603
MT GRAHAM REGIONAL MEDICAL CENTER FOUNDATION INC
1600 S 20th Ave, Safford, AZ 85546-4011
Tel (928) 348-4000 *Founded/Ownrshp* 1970
Sales 65.8MM *EMP* 512
Accts Eide Bailly Llp Oklahoma City
SIC 8062 General medical & surgical hospitals; General medical & surgical hospitals
CEO: Patrick Peters
**CFO:* Keith Bryce
Bd of Dir: Frank Granberg
Bd of Dir: Susan Jones
Bd of Dir: Charlie Owen
Bd of Dir: Carl Vessels
VP: Becky Johnson
Dir Lab: Lillian Durham
Dir Lab: Cindy Hinton
Dir Rx: Jade Ashby
CTO: Kathy McQueen

D-U-N-S 00-984-9373
MT HAMILL ELEVATOR AND LUMBER INC
DONELLSON ELEVATOR
1564 143rd St, Donnellson, IA 52625-9239
Tel (319) 469-2531 *Founded/Ownrshp* 1947
Sales 25.3MM^E *EMP* 54
SIC 5153 5211 5191 5251 Grains; Lumber & other building materials; Fertilizer & fertilizer materials; Animal feeds; Seeds & bulbs; Hardware; Grains; Lumber & other building materials; Fertilizer & fertilizer materials; Animal feeds; Seeds & bulbs; Hardware
Pr: Barbara Bentler

D-U-N-S 06-025-3275
■ **MT HAWLEY INSURANCE CO**
(*Suby of* RLI INSURANCE CO (INC)) ★
9025 N Lindbergh Dr, Peoria, IL 61615-1499
Tel (309) 692-1001 *Founded/Ownrshp* 1979
Sales NA *EMP* 12^E
SIC 6331 Property damage insurance; Fire, marine & casualty insurance: stock; Property damage insurance; Fire, marine & casualty insurance: stock
Ch: Gerald D Stephens
**CEO:* Jon E Michael
CFO: Dondanville Joe
VP: Richard W Quehl
VP: David C Sandoz
Ex Dir: Don M Intyre

MT HEALTHY SCHOOL DISTRICT
See MOUNT HEALTHY CITY SCHOOLS

MT HEBRON CEMETERY
See CEDAR GROVE CEMETERY ASSOCIATION

D-U-N-S 00-902-0108
MT HOOD CAPITAL CORP
SWISHER
14546 N Lombard St, Portland, OR 97203-6462
Tel (503) 227-3505 *Founded/Ownrshp* 1961
Sales 36.9MM^E *EMP* 114
SIC 2841 Soap & other detergents; Soap & other detergents
Pr: Tom Mulflur

D-U-N-S 05-096-4063
MT HOOD COMMUNITY COLLEGE DISTRICT FOUNDATION INC
26000 Se Stark St, Gresham, OR 97030-3300
Tel (503) 491-6422 *Founded/Ownrshp* 1966
Sales 45.6MM^E *EMP* 1,100
SIC 8222 8221 Community college; Colleges universities & professional schools; Community college; Colleges universities & professional schools
Pr: Nancy Jaksich
CFO: Jay Crowthers
**Prin:* William Becker
CIO: Linda Vigesaa
CTO: Ilya Babiy
IT Man: Zack Custovic
IT Man: Michelle Solberg

MT HOREB LUMBER
See PREMIER COOPERATIVE

D-U-N-S 00-190-7120
MT LEBANON OFFICE EQUIPMENT CO INC (PA)
1817 Banksville Rd, Pittsburgh, PA 15216-3199
Tel (412) 344-4300 *Founded/Ownrshp* 1960
Sales 26.1MM^E *EMP* 34
SIC 5021 5044 5712 5943 Office furniture; Office equipment; Office furniture; Office forms & supplies
VP: James M Droney Jr
Pr: Tim Bosack
**Pr:* James M Droney
**Treas:* John Silvestre
IT Man: Rosemary Droney
IT Man: Karen Parent
VP Sls: Jeff Pinney

D-U-N-S 06-874-8078
MT LEBANON SCHOOL DISTRICT
7 Horsman Dr, Pittsburgh, PA 15228-1107
Tel (412) 344-2077 *Founded/Ownrshp* 1912
Sales 67.0MM^E *EMP* 1,269
Accts Maher Duessel Pittsburgh Pen
SIC 8211 Public elementary & secondary schools; High school, junior or senior; Public elementary & secondary schools; High school, junior or senior
Ex Dir: Alyssa Beluca
Bd of Dir: Beth Evans
Bd of Dir: Nora Nealon
Bd of Dir: Thomas Peterson
Bd of Dir: Karen Wolowski
VP: Donna Dinardo
VP: Robert Mallery
VP: Kelly Szesterniak
Dir Bus: Janice Klien
Prin: David Zolkowski
Pr Dir: Cissy Bowman

D-U-N-S 00-896-4835
■ **MT MANSFIELD CO INC**
STOWE MOUNTAIN RESORT
(*Suby of* NATIONAL UNION FIRE INSURANCE CO OF PITTSBURGH PA) ★
5781 Mountain Rd, Stowe, VT 05672-4803
Tel (802) 253-3000 *Founded/Ownrshp* 1973
Sales 47.2MM^E *EMP* 400
SIC 7011 5812 5941 5813 Ski lodge; American restaurant; Skiing equipment; Drinking places; Ski lodge; American restaurant; Skiing equipment; Drinking places
Pr: C Robert McEleney
**Ch Bd:* M R Greenberg
**Pr:* Henry Lundi
**V Ch Bd:* Thomas J Amidon
**VP:* Barry Pius
VP: Scott Reeves
Dir Risk M: Joshua Klevans
Comm Dir: Jeff Weis
Dir IT: Ric Schaaf
Dir IT: Karen Secon
VP Mktg: Mike Colburn

D-U-N-S 87-715-1654
MT PLEASANT BAPTIST CHURCH
505 S Church St, Swansea, SC 29160-8533
Tel (803) 568-2722 *Founded/Ownrshp* 2003
Sales 6.0MM^E *EMP* 500
SIC 8661 Baptist Church; Baptist Church

D-U-N-S 11-278-4939
MT PLEASANT CENTRAL SCHOOL DISTRICT
825 Westlake Dr Ste 3, Thornwood, NY 10594-1946
Tel (914) 769-5500 *Founded/Ownrshp* 1972
Sales 42.6MM *EMP* 300
SIC 8211 Public elementary & secondary schools; Public elementary & secondary schools
Bd of Dir: Eric Schulze
Dir IT: Nasrin Rouzati
IT Man: Lisa Zareski

D-U-N-S 08-887-3070
MT PLEASANT PUBLIC SCHOOLS INC
720 N Kinney Ave, Mount Pleasant, MI 48858-1757
Tel (989) 775-2250 *Founded/Ownrshp* 1929
Sales 3.2M *EMP* 481
SIC 8211 Public elementary & secondary schools; Public elementary & secondary schools
CFO: Ginger Faber
Adm Dir: Dee Kenny

D-U-N-S 08-530-5050
MT PLEASANT SCHOOL DISTRICT
3434 Marten Ave, San Jose, CA 95148-1300
Tel (408) 223-3700 *Founded/Ownrshp* 1865
Sales 18.2MM^E *EMP* 300
SIC 8211 Public elementary school; Public elementary school
**Prin:* Mariann Engle
**Prin:* Sandy Meyer
**Prin:* Laura Pham
Adm/Dir: Phuong Le
Genl Mgr: Mike Osicka
Schl Brd P: Betty Martinez
HC Dir: Laurie Breton

MT RAINIER BRANCH
See PRINCE GEORGE COUNTY MEMORIAL LIBRARY SYSTEM

MT RUBIDOUX CONVALESCENT HOSP
See WATERMAN CONVALESCENT HOSPITAL INC

MT RUSHMORE BLACK HILLS GOLD
See RIDDLES GROUP INC

MT SAN ANTONIO COLLEGE
See MT SAN ANTONIO COMMUNITY COLLEGE DISTRICT

D-U-N-S 10-298-5108
MT SAN ANTONIO COMMUNITY COLLEGE DISTRICT
MT SAN ANTONIO COLLEGE
(*Suby of* CALIFORNIA COMMUNITY COLLEGES SYSTEM) ★
1100 N Grand Ave, Walnut, CA 91789-1341
Tel (909) 594-5611 *Founded/Ownrshp* 1946
Sales 86.7MM^E *EMP* 1,500
SIC 8222 Community college; Community college
Pr: William Scroggins
**Pr:* Rosa Royce
**CFO:* Michael D Gregoryk
**Bd of Dir:* Manuel Baca
**Bd of Dir:* Rosanne Bader
**Bd of Dir:* Fred Chyr
**Bd of Dir:* Judy Chen Haggerty
**Bd of Dir:* Dr David K Hall
**VP:* James Czaja
**VP:* Irene Malmgren
**VP:* Dr Audrey Yamagata-

D-U-N-S 07-815-0968
MT SAN JACINTO COLLEGE FOUNDATION
1499 N State St, San Jacinto, CA 92583-2325
Tel (951) 487-6752 *Founded/Ownrshp* 1963
Sales 32.4MM^E *EMP* 517
SIC 8222 Community college; Community college
CEO: Richard Giese
**Pr:* Roger Schultz
VP: Becky Elam
VP: Patrick Schwerdtfeger
Exec: Ella Hornback
CTO: Theodora King
Psych: Rosalva Amezcua
Psych: April Vrtis
Pgrm Dir: Ketmani Kouanchao
Snr Mgr: Rosemary Soto

D-U-N-S 06-068-0147
MT SAVAGE SPECIALTY REFRACTORIES CO INC
736 W Ingomar Rd, Ingomar, PA 15127-2000
Tel (412) 367-9100 *Founded/Ownrshp* 1975
Sales 28.9MM^E *EMP* 45
SIC 3255 5033

MT SINAI MEM PK & MORTUARY
See TEMPLE SINAI

D-U-N-S 18-126-1439
MT SUPPLY INC
MACHINE TOOLS SUPPLY
3505 Cadillac Ave Ste K2, Costa Mesa, CA 92626-1432
Tel (714) 434-4748 *Founded/Ownrshp* 1987
Sales 168.9MM^E *EMP* 140
SIC 5085 5084 Industrial supplies; Materials handling machinery; Industrial supplies; Materials handling machinery
CEO: George H Ponce Jr
COO: Bryan Rigney
Prin: Joseph Custer
Prin: Steve Gurley
Prin: Steve Pixley
Brnch Mgr: Mike Hodges
Brnch Mgr: Galo Martinez
Genl Mgr: Scott Shimel
IT Man: Victor Santiago
Site Mgr: Jill Grochala
S&M/VP: Scott Beardshear

D-U-N-S 36-125-1361
MT TRANSPORTATION AND LOGISTICS SERVICES INC
470 Commack Rd, Deer Park, NY 11729-4510
Tel (631) 392-4124 *Founded/Ownrshp* 2006
Sales 20.4MM^E *EMP* 213
SIC 4213 4225

D-U-N-S 07-095-4904
MT VERNON CITY SCHOOL DISTRICT
165 N Columbus Ave, Mount Vernon, NY 10553-1101
Tel (914) 665-5000 *Founded/Ownrshp* 1894
Sales 99.4MM^E *EMP* 1,951
SIC 8211 Public elementary & secondary schools; Public elementary & secondary schools
**Treas:* Shaji Zacharia
Ofcr: Dawn Jackson
Ofcr: Alice Patterson
Dir Sec: Carl Barchus
Schl Brd P: Gerald Whiteside
Psych: Francine Silvestri

D-U-N-S 08-704-1216
MT VERNON COMMUNITY SCHOOL CORP
1776 W State Road 234, Fortville, IN 46040-9562
Tel (317) 485-3100 *Founded/Ownrshp* 1964
Sales 27.6MM^E *EMP* 380^E
SIC 8211 Public elementary & secondary schools; High school, junior or senior; School board; Public elementary & secondary schools; High school, junior or senior; School board
Pr: Jan Cochard
Schl Brd P: Tony May

MT VERNON NRSING RHBLTTION CTR
See EXTENDICARE HEALTH SERVICES INC

D-U-N-S 01-020-5169
MT VERNON SCHOOL DISTRICT 320 INC
124 E Lawrence St, Mount Vernon, WA 98273-2999
Tel (360) 428-6110 *Founded/Ownrshp* 1900
Sales 46.3MM^E *EMP* 800
SIC 8211 Public elementary & secondary schools; School board; Public elementary & secondary schools; School board
Dir Vol: Jodeen Gilpatrick
**Pr:* Robert Coffey
**VP:* Luanne Burkhart

Ex Dir: Yoshihiro Okamoto
Dir IT: Lucila Ayon
Dir IT: Ken Gray
IT Man: Melea Medrano
Psych: Karen Bertsch

D-U-N-S 07-493-4241
MT WASHINGTON PEDIATRIC HEALTH SYSTEM INC
MT WASHINGTON PHYSICIANS
1708 W Rogers Ave, Baltimore, MD 21209-4545
Tel (410) 578-8600 *Founded/Ownrshp* 1922
Sales 53.0MM *EMP* 500
SIC 8069 Children's hospital; Children's hospital
Pr: James Walker
**Pr:* Sheldon Stein
VP: Tom Paullin
DP Dir: Heather Dewan
Mktg Dir: Jill Feinberg

MT WASHINGTON PHYSICIANS
See MT WASHINGTON PEDIATRIC HEALTH SYSTEM INC

MT&L CARD PRODUCTS
See MAGNETIC TICKET & LABEL CORP

D-U-N-S 60-384-2337
MTA BUS CO
12815 28th Ave, Flushing, NY 11354-1138
Tel (718) 445-3100 *Founded/Ownrshp* 2004
Sales 40.2MM^E *EMP* 800
SIC 4131 Intercity bus line; Intercity bus line
Ch Bd: Myra Burke
**Pr:* Tom Savage
**Treas:* Joseph Nocera
Plnt Mgr: William Norwich

D-U-N-S 00-759-3910
MTA CAPITAL CONSTRUCTION CO
(*Suby of* M T A) ★
2 Broadway Bsmt B, New York, NY 10004-3357
Tel (212) 878-7000 *Founded/Ownrshp* 2003
Sales 25.9MM^E *EMP* 1^E
SIC 1521 Single-family housing construction
Ch: Fernando Ferrer
Opers Mgr: Martina Mercaldo
Snr Mgr: Ronaldo Edralin

D-U-N-S 04-562-6223 IMP
MTA DISTRIBUTORS INC
555 Hickory Hills Blvd, Whites Creek, TN 37189-9287
Tel (615) 299-8777 *Founded/Ownrshp* 1980
Sales 23.8MM^E *EMP* 48^E
SIC 5082 General construction machinery & equipment
Pr: David Harrington
**VP:* Charles W Dunn

MTA LEASING
See FORD MONTROSE INC

MTA LONG ISLAND RAIL ROAD
See LONG ISLAND RAIL ROAD CO

MTA LOUISIANA
See MOTORCYCLES TIRES & ACCESSORIES INC

D-U-N-S 09-191-9394 IMP
MTC DIRECT INC
17837 Rowland St, City of Industry, CA 91748-1122
Tel (626) 839-6800 *Founded/Ownrshp* 1989
Sales 94.9MM^E *EMP* 106^E
SIC 5045 Computers, peripherals & software; Computers, peripherals & software
CEO: Roy Han
VP Sls: Brian Wang

D-U-N-S 00-886-0967
MTC DISTRIBUTING (CA)
4900 Stoddard Rd, Modesto, CA 95356-9389
Tel (209) 523-6449 *Founded/Ownrshp* 1921
Sales 170.9MM^E *EMP* 200
SIC 5194 5145 5149 Tobacco & tobacco products; Candy; Groceries & related products; Tobacco & tobacco products; Candy; Groceries & related products
Ch Bd: Thomas Eakin
CFO: Todd Manss
IT Man: Robert Bettencourt
VP Mktg: Roe Edwards
Mktg Dir: Tom Kennedy
Sls Dir: Noel Chavez
Sls Mgr: Doug Ramos
Snr Mgr: Kathy Olivera

D-U-N-S 02-701-9249
MTC INC
MI TIERRA CAFE & BAKERY
800 Dolorosa Ste 204, San Antonio, TX 78207-4561
Tel (210) 225-1262 *Founded/Ownrshp* 1941
Sales 29.7MM^E *EMP* 600
SIC 5812 Mexican restaurant; Mexican restaurant
Pr: George Cortez
**CFO:* Joe M Guerra
**Sec:* Micheal Cortez
VP: Roben Cartiz
**VP:* David Cortez
**VP:* Roslinda Pouya
Site Mgr: Pete Cortez

MTC WHOLESALE
See MARTIN TIRE CO

D-U-N-S 86-925-7758 IMP
MTC WORLDWIDE CORP
(*Suby of* MTC DIRECT INC) ★
17837 Rowland St, City of Industry, CA 91748-1122
Tel (626) 839-6800 *Founded/Ownrshp* 1992
Sales 40.6MM^E *EMP* 79
SIC 5045 3577 Computer peripheral equipment; Computer peripheral equipment; Computer peripheral equipment
Pr: Roy Han

D-U-N-S 17-604-1127
■ **MTCSC INC**
(*Suby of* MANTECH INTERNATIONAL CORP) ★
925 Corporate Dr Ste 401, Stafford, VA 22554-4881
Tel (703) 221-7400 *Founded/Ownrshp* 1997
Sales 18.1MM^E *EMP* 300
Accts Mayer Hoffman Mccann Pc San
SIC 8711 Consulting engineer; Consulting engineer
Pr: David Camarata
**CFO:* Marguerite Camarata
Prgrm Mgr: Mark Hevel
IT Man: Matt Ingermen
IT Man: John Roehl
Netwrk Eng: John Gellios

D-U-N-S 13-046-0371
MTD ACCEPTANCE CORP INC
5965 Grafton Rd, Valley City, OH 44280-9329
Tel (330) 225-2600 *Founded/Ownrshp* 2012
Sales NA *EMP* 300
SIC 6159 Loan institutions, general & industrial; Loan institutions, general & industrial
CEO: Curt Moll
**Pr:* Dieter Kaesgen
**Treas:* Jim Milinski
Opers Mgr: Jason Belsito

D-U-N-S 15-177-4049 IMP
MTD ACQUISITION INC
MINNESOTA TWIST DRILL
1 7th St Sw, Chisholm, MN 55719
Tel (218) 254-3362 *Founded/Ownrshp* 2003
Sales 27.5MM^E *EMP* 100
SIC 3545 Drills (machine tool accessories)
Pr: Scott Allison
Off Mgr: Jenny Noben
Natl Sales: Brent White
Sls Mgr: Terry Bergum

D-U-N-S 16-860-4598
MTD AMERICA LTD
METAL TEK DEVELOPMENT
111 Hollow Tree Ln Sw, Atlanta, GA 30354-2600
Tel (404) 767-3185 *Founded/Ownrshp* 2004
Sales 43.6MM^E *EMP* 75^E
SIC 5084 Recycling machinery & equipment; Recycling machinery & equipment
Pr: John J Camozzi
**VP:* Mark Ashley Day
**CTO:* Thomas Valerio

D-U-N-S 18-408-2118 EXP
▲ **MTD HOLDINGS INC**
5965 Grafton Rd, Valley City, OH 44280-9329
Tel (330) 225-2600 *Founded/Ownrshp* 2002
Sales 2.8MMM^E *EMP* 6,000
SIC 3524 3544 3469 6141 Lawn & garden equipment; Lawnmowers, residential: hand or power; Special dies & tools; Metal stampings; Financing: automobiles, furniture, etc., not a deposit bank; Lawn & garden equipment; Lawnmowers, residential: hand or power; Special dies & tools; Metal stampings; Financing: automobiles, furniture, etc., not a deposit bank
Ch Bd: Curtis E Moll
**Treas:* Jeff Deuch
Genl Mgr: Glen Stringfield

D-U-N-S 00-419-6515 IMP/EXP
■ **MTD PRODUCTS INC**
(*Suby of* MTD HOLDINGS INC) ★
5965 Grafton Rd, Valley City, OH 44280-9329
Tel (330) 225-2600 *Founded/Ownrshp* 1932, 2002
Sales 1.9MMM^E *EMP* 5,614
SIC 3524 Lawn & garden equipment; Lawnmowers, residential: hand or power; Lawn & garden equipment; Lawnmowers, residential: hand or power
CEO: Robert T Moll
**Pr:* Jean Hlay
CFO: Craig Boyd
**CFO:* Jeffery C V Deuch
CFO: David Duckhouse
**Treas:* James M Milinski
Ex VP: James Milinsky
Dir Bus: Luis Garza
Prgrm Mgr: Pete Sadosky
Prgrm Mgr: Andrew Ziemba
Rgnl Mgr: Ian Rogers

D-U-N-S 08-066-8163
■ **MTD SOUTHWEST INC**
(*Suby of* MTD PRODUCTS INC) ★
9235 S Mckemy St, Tempe, AZ 85284-2938
Tel (480) 961-1002 *Founded/Ownrshp* 2000
Sales 192.9MM^E *EMP* 650
SIC 3524 3546 3423 Lawn & garden equipment; Blowers & vacuums, lawn; Hedge trimmers, electric; Power-driven handtools; Hand & edge tools; Lawn & garden equipment; Blowers & vacuums, lawn; Hedge trimmers, electric; Power-driven handtools; Hand & edge tools
Pr: Phil Clouse
Genl Mgr: Gene Elefane
Genl Mgr: Randy Parrish
Mfg Dir: Domingo Rodriguez
Board of Directors: Robert T Moll

MTDC WELFARE FUND
See MASON TENDER DISTRICT COUNCIL TRUST FUND

MTE HYDRAULICS
See MECHANICAL TOOL & ENGINEERING CO INC

D-U-N-S 11-352-1061
MTECH MECHANICAL TECHNOLOGIES GROUP INC
12300 Pecos St, Westminster, CO 80234-3426
Tel (303) 650-4000 *Founded/Ownrshp* 2002
Sales 69.3MM^E *EMP* 210
SIC 1711 Mechanical contractor; Mechanical contractor
Pr: Thomas E Dean
**Ex VP:* Marco Capitelli
**Ex VP:* Steve Kugler
Snr Mgr: Toby Howling

MTEQ
See MANUFACTURING TECHNIQUES INC

MTG
See MACHINE TOOL & GEAR INC

D-U-N-S 08-008-4059
MTG ACQUISITIONS LLC
DAV EL WOLDWIDE
69 Norman St, Everett, MA 02149-1951
Tel (800) 922-0343 *Founded/Ownrshp* 2002
Sales 11.4MM^E *EMP* 2,500
SIC 4789 Transportation services
Ch: David Marcu
VP Sls: Steve Patel

D-U-N-S 17-388-2056
MTGLQ INVESTORS LP
200 West St, New York, NY 10282-2102
Tel (212) 902-1000 *Founded/Ownrshp* 1993
Sales 35.5MM^E *EMP* 203^E
SIC 6221 6282 6153 6211 Commodity traders, contracts; Commodity brokers, contracts; Investment advisory service; Purchasers of accounts receivable & commercial paper; Brokers, security; Dealers, security; Underwriters, security; Investment bankers

D-U-N-S 13-140-5581
MTH HOLDINGS CORP
823 Fairview Rd, Wytheville, VA 24382-4507
Tel (276) 228-7943 *Founded/Ownrshp* 1998
Sales 30.2MM^E *EMP* 100
SIC 5063 3612 Transformers, electric; Power transformers, electric; Transformers, electric; Power transformers, electric
Pr: Thomas M Hough

MTI
See MOBILE TECH INC

D-U-N-S 36-075-0616 IMP
MTI BATHS INC
MTI WHIRLPOOLS
670 N Price Rd, Sugar Hill, GA 30518-4722
Tel (770) 271-8228 *Founded/Ownrshp* 1988
Sales 29.6MM^E *EMP* 110
SIC 3088 2821 Tubs (bath, shower & laundry), plastic; Plastics materials & resins; Tubs (bath, shower & laundry), plastic; Plastics materials & resins
CEO: Katherine Adams
**Pr:* Russell Adams
CFO: Roy Harris
Genl Mgr: Lee Lock
IT Man: Ryan Witt
Sfty Mgr: Janet Clark
Opers Mgr: John Coleman
Opers Mgr: Ross Williams
Natl Sales: Dori Adams
Natl Sales: Chris Hawreluk
S&M/VP: Jeff Sherrill

D-U-N-S 08-051-0167
MTI ELECTRONICS INC
MTI INTERNATIONAL
W133n5139 Campbell Dr, Menomonee Falls, WI 53051-7068
Tel (262) 783-6080 *Founded/Ownrshp* 1995
Sales 54.1MM^E *EMP* 130
SIC 3672 Printed circuit boards; Printed circuit boards
CEO: Brad Heath
Dir Bus: Charlie Ketelhohn
Prgrm Mgr: John Kautsky
Prgrm Mgr: Beverly Ronge
IT Man: Linda Schieble

MTI INTERNATIONAL
See MTI ELECTRONICS INC

D-U-N-S 03-485-1535
MTI TECHNOLOGY CORP
15461 Red Hill Ave # 200, Tustin, CA 92780-7314
Tel (949) 251-1101 *Founded/Ownrshp* 1977
Sales 54.8MM^E *EMP* 361
SIC 3572 3571 7372 3674 3577 Computer storage devices; Computer disk & drum drives & components; Computer tape drives & components; Electronic computers; Prepackaged software; Application computer software; Semiconductors & related devices; Computer peripheral equipment

MTI WHIRLPOOLS
See MTI BATHS INC

MTI-SALINE
See CRESCIVE DIE AND TOOL INC

D-U-N-S 87-282-3109
MTIC LLC
MOHEGAN SUN CASINO
1 Mohegan Sun Blvd, Uncasville, CT 06382-1355
Tel (860) 862-6100 *Founded/Ownrshp* 1995
Sales 1.3MMM^E *EMP* 10,745^E
SIC 7011 Hotels & motels; Casino hotel; Hotels & motels; Casino hotel
Ch Bd: Marilynn Malerba
Ch Bd: Kevin Brown
Treas: Thayne Hutchins
VP: Harry Coldreck
VP: Jenifer Rainvelle
Dir Soc: Linda Klein
Snr Mgr: Michael Murtha

D-U-N-S 15-969-4194
MTL GROUP INC
MTL INSTRUMENTS GROUP
(*Suby of* COOPER CROUSE HINDS ELEC PDTS) ★
17314 State Highway 249 # 310, Houston, TX 77064-1138
Tel (281) 571-8065 *Founded/Ownrshp* 2008
Sales 22.2MM^E *EMP* 52^E
SIC 5084 Instruments & control equipment
Prin: Jerry Haney

MTL INSTRUMENTS GROUP
See MTL GROUP INC

D-U-N-S 00-693-1653
MTL INSURANCE CO
MUTUAL TRUST FINANCIAL GROUP
1200 Jorie Blvd Ste 100, Oak Brook, IL 60523-2274
Tel (630) 990-1000 *Founded/Ownrshp* 1904
Sales NA *EMP* 144
SIC 6311

MTM
See MANITOWOC TOOL AND MACHINING LLC

MTM
See MANITOWOC TOOL & MANUFACTURING LLC

D-U-N-S 06-544-6577 IMP
MTM RECOGNITION CORP
3201 Se 29th St, Oklahoma City, OK 73115-1605
Tel (405) 609-6900 *Founded/Ownrshp* 1971
Sales 87.3MM^E *EMP* 500
SIC 3911 3873 2499 2389 3499 2791 Jewelry, precious metal; Watches, clocks, watchcases & parts; Trophy bases, wood; Men's miscellaneous accessories; Trophies, metal, except silver; Typesetting; Jewelry, precious metal; Watches, clocks, watchcases & parts; Trophy bases, wood; Men's miscellaneous accessories; Trophies, metal, except silver; Typesetting
Owner: Dave Smith
**Pr:* Roger Mashore
**CFO:* Mark Landes
**Treas:* Linda Smith
**VP:* Darrel Davis
**VP:* Monica Finley
**VP:* Guy Manley
**VP:* Molly Martin
**VP:* David Smith Jr
**VP:* Bob Thomas
Software D: Joe Young

D-U-N-S 15-772-7991
■ **MTM TECHNOLOGIES INC**
(*Suby of* FIRSTMARK CAPITAL LLC) ★
4 High Ridge Park Ste 102, Stamford, CT 06905-1325
Tel (203) 588-1981 *Founded/Ownrshp* 1986
Sales 122.8MM^E *EMP* 250
Tkr Sym MTMC *Exch* OTO
SIC 5045 7379 Computers, peripherals & software; Computer peripheral equipment; Computers & accessories, personal & home entertainment; Computer software; Computer related consulting services
Pr: Steven Stringer
Pr: Jerry Mattey
Pr: Shawn Patterson
CFO: Jay Braukman
CFO: John W Braukman
CFO: Michael El-Hillow
CFO: Michael Elhillow
**CFO:* Rosemarie Milano
Bd of Dir: Howard A Pavony
Ex VP: Howard Cohen
Ex VP: Steven Rothman
**Sr VP:* Stephen Hicks
**VP:* Jason Bernstein
VP: Rodney Callum
VP: John Centinaro
VP: John Cross
VP: Greg Galanos
VP: Steve Hartenstein
VP: Chris Harvey
VP: Kevin Langan
VP: Dean J Maire

D-U-N-S 83-006-1094
MTN GOVERNMENT SERVICES INC
(*Suby of* EMC) ★
161 Fort Evans Rd Ne # 220, Leesburg, VA 20176-3372
Tel (703) 443-6738 *Founded/Ownrshp* 2015
Sales 30.0MM *EMP* 42
SIC 3448 Prefabricated metal buildings
Pr: Peg Grayson
Pr: Quais Hassan
Pr: Ty Narkmon
Ofcr: Benjamin Shaw
**VP:* Catherine Melquist
**VP:* Michael Shakarji
VP: Robert Turner
Creative D: Will Agranoff
Mng Dir: Christopher D Brady Jr

D-U-N-S 03-457-4368
MTN VIEW FORD INC
MOUNTAIN VIEW FORD LINCOLN
301 E 20th St, Chattanooga, TN 37408-2797
Tel (423) 756-1331 *Founded/Ownrshp* 1962
Sales 73.0MM *EMP* 110
SIC 5511 7538 5012 Automobiles, new & used; Pickups, new & used; General automotive repair shops; Automobiles & other motor vehicles; Automobiles, new & used; Pickups, new & used; General automotive repair shops; Automobiles & other motor vehicles
Pr: David Watson
**Sec:* Donald Watson
VP: Jeanine Clark
**VP:* Clay Watson
Mng Dir: Shaun Kesler
Genl Mgr: Mike Thornton
Mktg Mgr: Carla Cawood
Sls Mgr: Rodney Grimes
Sales Asso: Kenny Cone
Sales Asso: Ron Elliott
Sales Asso: Kenny Epple
Board of Directors: David Watson

D-U-N-S 02-132-4108
MTNT LTD
10 Main St, Mc Grath, AK 99627
Tel (907) 524-3391 *Founded/Ownrshp* 2008
Sales 49.0MM *EMP* 36
Accts Mcgladrey & Pullen Llp Frede
SIC 6211 5983 6512 4911 6514 Security brokers & dealers; Fuel oil dealers; Nonresidential building operators; Distribution, electric power; Residential building, four or fewer units: operation; Security brokers & dealers; Fuel oil dealers; Nonresidential building operators; Distribution, electric power; Residential building, four or fewer units: operation
Pr: Donne Fleagle
**CEO:* Vicki Otte
CFO: Sandra Culver

D-U-N-S 62-522-5946
MTPCS LLC
CELLULAR ONE
1170 Devon Park Dr # 104, Wayne, PA 19087-2128
Tel (610) 688-1334 *Founded/Ownrshp* 2005
Sales 171.5MM^E *EMP* 500

SIC 4812 Cellular telephone services; Cellular telephone services
VP: Angela Tufte

MTR
See MEMBRANE TECHNOLOGY AND RESEARCH INC

D-U-N-S 18-200-0430
■ MTR GAMING GROUP INC
(*Suby of* ELDORADO RESORTS INC) ★
Hc 2 Box S, Chester, WV 26034
Tel (304) 387-8000 *Founded/Ownrshp* 2014
Sales 351.8MM *EMP* 2,600ᴱ
SIC 7011 7948 Casino hotel; Horse race track operation; Casino hotel; Horse race track operation
Ch Bd: Gary L Carano
**Pr:* Thomas R Reeg
COO: Joseph L Billhimer Jr
COO: William Robinson
CFO: Robert M Jones
Ex VP: John W Bittner
Ex VP: Anthony L Carano
VP: Chris Kern
Sls Dir: Rich House
Genl Couns: Thomas Diehl

D-U-N-S 06-462-3255
MTROIZ INTERNATIONAL INC
24932 Avenue Kearny, Santa Clarita, CA 91355-3424
Tel (310) 734-9486 *Founded/Ownrshp* 2011
Sales 62.0MM *EMP* 63
SIC 3699 Electrical equipment & supplies
CEO: Eun H Chae
**VP:* Hong Chae

D-U-N-S 18-324-1454 IMP
MTRONICS.COM INC
325 Electronics Blvd Sw F, Huntsville, AL 35824-2221
Tel (256) 461-8883 *Founded/Ownrshp* 1987
Sales 24.3MM *EMP* 70
SIC 3679 Electronic circuits; Electronic circuits
Pr: Ashok Mahbubani
**Sec:* Amrita Mahbubani

MTRONPTI
See M-TRON INDUSTRIES INC

MTS
See MID-AMERICA TRANSPLANT SERVICES

MTS
See MERGENTHALER TRANSFER & STORAGE CO INC

D-U-N-S 13-583-7776
MTS HEALTH INVESTORS LLC
623 5th Ave 16, New York, NY 10022-6831
Tel (212) 887-2100 *Founded/Ownrshp* 1999
Sales NA *EMP* 412
SIC 7299 Personal financial services; Personal financial services
Ofcr: Lucy Darita
VP: Curtis Lane
VP: Michael Ludwig
VP: Daniel O'Keefe
Mng Dir: Peter Collum
Mng Dir: Andrew Fineberg

D-U-N-S 00-768-1633
MTS LOGISTICS INC (NY)
5 W 37th St Rm 300, New York, NY 10018-5352
Tel (212) 594-3117 *Founded/Ownrshp* 2000
Sales 79.4MM *EMP* 29ᴱ
SIC 4731 Freight forwarding
Pr: Sedat Saka
Sls Mgr: Amelia Jardine

MTS MEDICATION TECHNOLOGIES
See MTS PACKAGING SYSTEMS INC

D-U-N-S 13-177-1446 IMP
■ MTS MEDICATION TECHNOLOGIES INC
(*Suby of* OMNICELL INC) ★
2003 Gandy Blvd N Ste 800, Saint Petersburg, FL 33702-2167
Tel (727) 576-6311 *Founded/Ownrshp* 1986
Sales 78.9MMᴱ *EMP* 271
SIC 3565 3089 Packaging machinery; Blister or bubble formed packaging, plastic; Packaging machinery; Blister or bubble formed packaging, plastic
CEO: Todd E Siegel
**Pr:* William G Shields
**COO:* Michael D Stevenson
CFO: Jamie Conroy
**Sec:* Matthew C Hicks
Ofcr: Michael Stevenson
**VP:* Robert A Martin
QA Dir: Brett Smith
IT Man: Sandra Beiter
IT Man: Rick Maher
Sls Mgr: Linda Jones

D-U-N-S 83-764-9243 EXP
MTS PACKAGING SYSTEMS INC
MTS MEDICATION TECHNOLOGIES
2003 Gandy Blvd N Ste 800, Saint Petersburg, FL 33702-2167
Tel (727) 576-6311 *Founded/Ownrshp* 2011
Sales 24.3MMᴱ *EMP* 145
SIC 3089 Blister or bubble formed packaging, plastic; Blister or bubble formed packaging, plastic
Pr: Todd E Siegel
**COO:* Michael Stevenson
**CFO:* Michael P Conroy
VP: Robert Berratt
**Prin:* Selm Robin E

MTS SEATING
See MICHIGAN TUBE SWAGERS AND FABRICATORS INC

D-U-N-S 19-442-6896
MTS SERVICES INC
13 Delta Dr Unit 7, Londonderry, NH 03053-2372
Tel (603) 845-1100 *Founded/Ownrshp* 1988
Sales 40.6MMᴱ *EMP* 200
SIC 1731 1799 Electrical work; Electrical work; Appliance installation
CEO: Thomas R Banks
**Pr:* Judith B Bergeron
**CFO:* Craig Gilroy
**CFO:* David Petropulos
Div Mgr: Fred Bartlett
Sfty Dirs: Anthony Baker
Opers Mgr: Brad Bergstrom
Sales Exec: Jim Desousa
Snr PM: Bill Barry
Snr PM: Daniel Donithan

D-U-N-S 14-003-9392
MTS SOFTWARE SOLUTIONS INC
PMI IMAGING OF FLORIDA
225 Executive Dr Ste 4, Moorestown, NJ 08057-4237
Tel (856) 642-1188 *Founded/Ownrshp* 2003
Sales 64.6MMᴱ *EMP* 157
SIC 5045 5072 7378 Computers, peripherals & software; Hardware; Computer maintenance & repair; Computers, peripherals & software; Hardware; Computer maintenance & repair
Pr: Gary Schwartz
Sr VP: Andy Schwartz
VP: Ken Galanaugh
VP: Bhavik Patel
VP: Larry Schwartz
Dir Bus: Matt Skinner
Prd Mgr: Eric Smith

D-U-N-S 00-645-2312 IMP/EXP
▲ MTS SYSTEMS CORP
14000 Technology Dr, Eden Prairie, MN 55344-2247
Tel (952) 937-4000 *Founded/Ownrshp* 1966
Sales 563.9MM *EMP* 2,180
Tkr Sym MTSC *Exch* NGS
SIC 3829 3825 Measuring & controlling devices; Testing equipment: abrasion, shearing strength, etc.; Stress, strain & flaw detecting/measuring equipment; Vibration meters, analyzers & calibrators; Instruments to measure electricity; Measuring & controlling devices; Testing equipment: abrasion, shearing strength, etc.; Stress, strain & flaw detecting/measuring equipment; Vibration meters, analyzers & calibrators; Instruments to measure electricity
Pr: Jeffrey A Graves MD
CFO: Jeffrey P Oldenkamp
Treas: Thomas Minneman
Ofcr: Kristin E Trecker
Sr VP: William Bachrach
Sr VP: Rich Baker
Sr VP: John Emholz
Sr VP: Michael B Jost
Sr VP: Mark D Losee
Sr VP: Steven G Mahon
VP: Bill Beduhn
VP: Kelly Donaldson
VP: Maurice Mergeay
Exec: Patrick Dhommee
Exec: Kevin Hendricks
Board of Directors: David J Anderson, David D Johnson, Emily M Liggett, Randy J Martinez, Barb J Samardzich, Michael V Schrock, Gail P Steinel

D-U-N-S 79-886-4393
MTS TECHNOLOGIES INC
M T S
2800 S Shirlington Rd # 1000, Arlington, VA 22206-3601
Tel (703) 575-2900 *Founded/Ownrshp* 1991
Sales 26.8MMᴱ *EMP* 99
SIC 8742 8711 8748 Management consulting services; Business consultant; Engineering services; Testing service, educational or personnel
CEO: Daniel T Perkins
CFO: Timothy Schimkus
CFO: Stephen Tobash
**Ex VP:* Barton W Whitman
**Sr VP:* Lowell J Berry
VP: Beverly Baly
VP: Rene Belanger
VP: Redmond Dennis
VP: Berry Lowell
VP: Susan Ovalle
**VP:* Dennis K Redmond
VP Bus Dev: Beverly Bev

D-U-N-S 80-954-2959
MTS TITAN ELECTRIC LLC
1050 Spring Lake Dr, Itasca, IL 60143-2064
Tel (630) 530-4422 *Founded/Ownrshp* 2006
Sales 20.7MMᴱ *EMP* 50
SIC 1731 Electrical work
Owner: Michael M Mc Inerney
**Owner:* Alex C Guillen
**Owner:* Daniel J Neswold
CFO: Jane Klass
VP: Derek Olenek
Off Mgr: Virginia Alvarez
Snr PM: John Finn
Snr PM: Bryant Jessen

MTSI
See MCDANIEL TECHNICAL SERVICES INC

MTSI
See MICROWAVE TRANSMISSION SYSTEMS INC

MTSI
See MODERN TECHNOLOGY SOLUTIONS INC

MTSI
See MOSELEY TECHNICAL SERVICES INC

D-U-N-S 02-001-6718 IMP
MTU AMERICA INC
(*Suby of* MTU FRIEDRICHSHAFEN GMBH)
39525 Mackenzie Dr, Novi, MI 48377-1602
Tel (248) 560-8000 *Founded/Ownrshp* 1978
Sales 154.1MMᴱ *EMP* 518
SIC 3519 Diesel engine rebuilding; Diesel engine rebuilding
CEO: Joachim Coers
CFO: Otto Figel
Treas: Anke Lorscheid
VP: Bernard Bentgen
VP: David Oliphant
Prgrm Mgr: Larry Benedict
Rgnl Mgr: John Houp
Genl Mgr: Joanna Vardas
Plng Mgr: Joe Adamo
QA Dir: Jesse Harris
IT Man: Paul Lee

D-U-N-S 00-617-5954
MTU ONSITE ENERGY CORP (MN)
(*Suby of* ROLLS-ROYCE POWER SYSTEMS AG)
100 Power Dr, Mankato, MN 56001-4790
Tel (507) 625-7973 *Founded/Ownrshp* 1952, 2007
Sales 91.4MMᴱ *EMP* 300
SIC 3621 Power generators; Power generators
CEO: Todd Riemann
**CFO:* Markus Hentschel
Plng Mgr: Joe Adamo
IT Man: William Gernentz
Mtls Mgr: John Griebel
Mtls Mgr: Bob Walker
Plnt Mgr: Jeff Scholten
Ql Cn Mgr: Paul Mehltretter
Ql Cn Mgr: Drew Miller
Mktg Mgr: Jennifer Heimer
Manager: Matthew Graham

D-U-N-S 80-488-1340 IMP
MTV FOODS INC
AUSTIN MEAT COMPANY
355 Food Ctr Dr Hunt Pt C, Bronx, NY 10474
Tel (718) 842-6767 *Founded/Ownrshp* 1993
Sales 51.6MMᴱ *EMP* 75
SIC 5147 Meats & meat products; Meats & meat products
Ch Bd: Timothy Decamp
**Sec:* Vincent Pacifico
**VP:* Mike Johnson
Natl Sales: Nuno Fernandes

MTV NETWORKS
See VIACOM NETWORKS

D-U-N-S 13-444-4442
MTV NETWORKS INC
COUNTRY MUSIC TELEVISON
330 Commerce St, Nashville, TN 37201-1821
Tel (615) 335-8395 *Founded/Ownrshp* 2005
Sales 27.8MMᴱ *EMP* 250
SIC 4841 Cable television services; Cable television services
Pr: Tom Freston
Sr VP: Dario Spina
VP: Michael Bivona
VP: Mark Cohen
VP: Brian Philips
VP: Don Steele
IT Man: Larry Boshers
Mktg Mgr: Tamika Blockett
Sls Mgr: John McInnes

D-U-N-S 19-586-0770 IMP
■ MTV NETWORKS INC
(*Suby of* C B S) ★
1515 Broadway Fl 31, New York, NY 10036-5797
Tel (212) 258-8000 *Founded/Ownrshp* 2006
Sales 185.1MMᴱ *EMP* 329
SIC 4833 Television broadcasting stations; Television broadcasting stations
CEO: Judy McGrath
V Ch: Herb Scannell
Pr: Sean Atkins
Pr: Hank Close
Pr: Larry Divney
Pr: Kevin Kay
Pr: Mika Salmi
COO: Long Ellis
COO: Sarah Levy
CFO: Jacques Tortoroli
Treas: George S Smith Jr
Ofcr: Colleen Fahey Rush
Ex VP: Gideon Bierer
Ex VP: Houser Catherine
Ex VP: Colette Chestnut
Ex VP: Rich Eigendorff
Ex VP: Sahar Elhabashi
Ex VP: Alex Ferrari
Ex VP: Scott Guthrie
Ex VP: Douglas Herzog
Ex VP: Michael Hirschorn

D-U-N-S 80-765-2649
■ MTV NETWORKS LATIN AMERICA INC
(*Suby of* C B S) ★
1111 Lincoln Rd Fl 6, Miami Beach, FL 33139-2402
Tel (305) 534-9936 *Founded/Ownrshp* 2006
Sales 40.1MMᴱ *EMP* 125ᴱ
SIC 4841 4833 Cable television services; Television broadcasting stations; Cable television services; Television broadcasting stations
Pr: Bill Roedy
**CFO:* Scott McBride
Treas: Jennifer Segarra
Ex VP: Rich Eigendorff
**Sr VP:* Linda Alexander
VP: Maria Badillo
VP: Mario Cader-Frech
VP: Pierliugi Gazzolo
VP: Sean Saylor
VP: Charlie Singer
VP: Vicente Solis
Creative D: Jose Carmona

D-U-N-S 82-707-6204
MTW ACQUISITION INC
MOUNTAIN VIEW CHEVROLET
301 E 20th St, Chattanooga, TN 37408-2722
Tel (423) 266-0181 *Founded/Ownrshp* 2007
Sales 21.2MMᴱ *EMP* 53
SIC 5511 Automobiles, new & used
Pr: Andrew Watson
**Sec:* David Watson
**VP:* Don Thomas
Genl Mgr: Jason Whittle
Off Mgr: Tandalea Stephenson

D-U-N-S 79-681-2233
MU SIGMA INC
3400 Dundee Rd Ste 160, Northbrook, IL 60062-2333
Tel (847) 919-0445 *Founded/Ownrshp* 2004
Sales 116.3MMᴱ *EMP* 360
SIC 7378 7374 Computer & data processing equipment repair/maintenance; Computer & data processing equipment repair/maintenance; Data processing & preparation
Pr: Dhiraj C Rajaram
VP: Mukund Raghunath
Snr Mgr: Sumit Bajaj

D-U-N-S 04-448-9110 IMP
MUBEA INC
(*Suby of* MUHR UND BENDER KG)
6800 Industrial Rd, Florence, KY 41042-3090
Tel (859) 746-5300 *Founded/Ownrshp* 1981
Sales 313.7MMᴱ *EMP* 1,300
SIC 3493 3312 3495 3429 3714 Automobile springs; Bar, rod & wire products; Wire springs; Clamps & couplings, hose; Motor vehicle parts & accessories; Automobile springs; Bar, rod & wire products; Wire springs; Clamps & couplings, hose; Motor vehicle parts & accessories
CEO: Byrd Douglas Cain III
Pr: Juan Dominguez
**Pr:* Dr Thomas Muhr
CFO: Doug Cain
VP: Peter Lohage
**VP:* Rudolph Muhr
Prgrm Mgr: Anton Reinhart
Genl Mgr: Andrew Farris
Genl Mgr: Frederick Klein PHD
Mtls Mgr: Justin Belew
Opers Mgr: Josh Lawson

D-U-N-S 06-849-8864
MUCH SHELIST PC
191 N Wacker Dr Ste 1800, Chicago, IL 60606-1631
Tel (312) 521-2000 *Founded/Ownrshp* 1970
Sales 49.7MMᴱ *EMP* 150ᴱ
SIC 8111 General practice law office; General practice law office
Pr: Mitchell S Roth
Pt: Louis G Apostol
Pt: David B Goodman
Pt: James P Hanrath
Pt: Vernon A Kowal
Pt: Michael L O'Shaughnessy
Pt: Oran F Whiting
**Ch Bd:* David T Brown
Pr: Janice Bednarz
Pr: Catherine Leeper
Pr: Monica Macklin
Pr: Nancy Sulak
**VP:* Scott L David
**VP:* Michael B Hyman
**VP:* Jeffrey C Rubenstein
**VP:* Steven Schwartz

D-U-N-S 07-665-5851
MUCKLESHOOT INDIAN TRIBE
MUCKLESHOOT TRIBAL ENTERPRISES
39015 172nd Ave Se, Auburn, WA 98092-9763
Tel (253) 333-8741 *Founded/Ownrshp* 1934
Sales NA *EMP* 2,000
SIC 9131 Indian reservation; ; Indian reservation;
Ch: Louie Ungaro
**Ch Bd:* John Daniels Jr
Ofcr: Kenneth Lewis
Dir Risk M: Phillip Brooke
Ex Dir: Isabel Tinoco
Brnch Mgr: Judith Zelter
Dir IT: Pius Oleskey
IT Man: Jeff Songster
Netwrk Eng: Doug Newell
Pr Mgr: Linda Freed
Snr Mgr: Angelica Wellman

MUCKLESHOOT TRIBAL ENTERPRISES
See MUCKLESHOOT INDIAN TRIBE

D-U-N-S 06-114-8896 IMP/EXP
MUD PIE LLC
4893 Lewis Rd, Stone Mountain, GA 30083-1120
Tel (678) 937-9696 *Founded/Ownrshp* 1982
Sales 43.8MMᴱ *EMP* 82
Accts Windham Brannon Pc
SIC 5199 5023 Gifts & novelties; Decorative home furnishings & supplies
CEO: Marcia Miller
**Pr:* Fred Pannek
**CFO:* Mark Miller
**Ex VP:* Adrienne Boyer
**VP:* Dale Doss
Off Mgr: Vicki Westbrook
Natl Sales: Amy Taylor
VP Sls: Michael Chiu
Pr Dir: Ellen Fruchtman
Board of Directors: Mark Sullivan, Brian Sykora

MUDD ADVERTISING
See MUDD INC

D-U-N-S 10-454-9043
MUDD INC
MUDD ADVERTISING
915 Technology Pkwy, Cedar Falls, IA 50613-6938
Tel (319) 277-2003 *Founded/Ownrshp* 1981
Sales 24.4MMᴱ *EMP* 182
SIC 7311

MUEBLERIA BERRIOS
See EMPRESAS BERRIOS INC

D-U-N-S 14-187-4870
MUEHLHAN SURFACE PROTECTION INC
(*Suby of* MUEHLHAN AG)
2320 Cordelia Rd, Fairfield, CA 94534-1600
Tel (707) 639-4421 *Founded/Ownrshp* 2001
Sales 26.2MMᴱ *EMP* 325
Accts Bowman & Company Llp Stockton
SIC 1721 1799 Industrial painting; Ship painting; Commercial painting; Decontamination services; Sandblasting of building exteriors
CEO: Dr Wulf-Dieter Greverath
**CFO:* Tim A Taylor
**Treas:* Bernd Janssen

MUEHLSTEIN COMPOUNDED PRODUCTS
See H MUEHLSTEIN & CO INC

D-U-N-S 10-113-3361
MUEHLSTEIN HOLDING CORP
800 Connecticut Ave, Norwalk, CT 06854-1631
Tel (203) 855-8087 Founded/Ownrshp 1996
Sales NA EMP 500
SIC 5162 5169 Plastics materials; Synthetic rubber

D-U-N-S 00-589-3029 IMP/EXP
MUEHLSTEIN INTERNATIONAL LTD
(Suby of MUELSTEIN) ★
10 Westport Rd Ste 200, Wilton, CT 06897-4548
Tel (203) 855-6000 Founded/Ownrshp 1959
Sales 275.3MM^E EMP 115^E
SIC 5169 5162 Synthetic rubber; Plastics materials & basic shapes; Synthetic rubber; Plastics materials & basic shapes
CEO: Fernando Montenegro
*Pr: James Duffy
*CFO: Ron Restivo
*Treas: Ronald J Nardozzi
*VP: Jerrold Johnston
*VP: Mark Lux
*VP: Oscar Novo
Genl Mgr: Franz Apel

MUELLER BRASS
See EXTRUDED METALS INC

D-U-N-S 00-535-7504 IMP
■ **MUELLER BRASS CO** (MI)
MUELLER BRASS PRODUCTS
(Suby of MUELLER BRASS HOLDING CO INC) ★
8285 Tournament Dr # 150, Memphis, TN 38125-1745
Tel (901) 753-3200 Founded/Ownrshp 1917, 1974
Sales 208.8MM^E EMP 740
SIC 3351 3463 3354 3494 Copper rolling & drawing; Copper pipe; Pipe, brass & bronze; Tubing, copper & copper alloy; Nonferrous forgings; Plumbing fixture forgings, nonferrous; Aluminum extruded products; Valves & pipe fittings; Plumbing & heating valves; Copper rolling & drawing; Copper pipe; Pipe, brass & bronze; Tubing, copper & copper alloy; Nonferrous forgings; Plumbing fixture forgings, nonferrous; Aluminum extruded products; Valves & pipe fittings; Plumbing & heating valves
Pr: Steffen Sigloch
*Treas: Kent A McKee

D-U-N-S 85-847-5908
■ **MUELLER BRASS FORGING CO INC**
(Suby of MUELLER BRASS CO) ★
2199 Lapeer Ave, Port Huron, MI 48060-4155
Tel (810) 987-7770 Founded/Ownrshp 1991
Sales 20.1MM^E EMP 90
SIC 3463 Nonferrous forgings; Aluminum forgings; Nonferrous forgings; Aluminum forgings
Pr: James H Rourke
CFO: Kent A Mc Kee

D-U-N-S 82-894-7783
■ **MUELLER BRASS HOLDING CO INC**
(Suby of MUELLER INDUSTRIES INC) ★
8285 Tournament Dr # 150, Memphis, TN 38125-1745
Tel (901) 753-3200 Founded/Ownrshp 2007
Sales 208.8MM^E EMP 1,942^E
SIC 3351 3463 3494 Copper rolling & drawing; Copper pipe; Pipe, brass & bronze; Tubing, copper & copper alloy; Nonferrous forgings; Plumbing fixture forgings, nonferrous; Valves & pipe fittings; Plumbing & heating valves
Pr: Gregory Christopher

MUELLER BRASS PRODUCTS
See MUELLER BRASS CO

D-U-N-S 00-516-2102 IMP
■ **MUELLER CO LLC**
(Suby of MUELLER WATER PRODUCTS INC) ★
633 Chestnut St Ste 1200, Chattanooga, TN 37450-1202
Tel (423) 209-4800 Founded/Ownrshp 1857, 2008
Sales 490.5MM^E EMP 2,685
SIC 3823 3533 7699 Flow instruments, industrial process type; Drilling tools for gas, oil or water wells; Pumps & pumping equipment repair; Flow instruments, industrial process type; Drilling tools for gas, oil or water wells; Pumps & pumping equipment repair
Pr: Greg Rogowski
*Treas: Walt Smith
VP: Mark Gingerich
VP Opers: John Van Gerwen

D-U-N-S 85-847-6120 IMP
■ **MUELLER COPPER TUBE CO INC**
MUELLER INDUSTRIES
(Suby of MUELLER BRASS CO) ★
404 Mueller Brass Rd, Fulton, MS 38843-8594
Tel (662) 862-1700 Founded/Ownrshp 1991
Sales 5.0MM^E EMP 400
SIC 3351 Copper & copper alloy pipe & tube
Pr: Gregory Christopher
*CFO: Kent A McKee
*VP: Karl J Bambas
*Genl Mgr: Bruce Clements
Plnt Mgr: Michael Simmerman
VP Sls: Jeffrey Harris

D-U-N-S 00-433-5519 IMP
■ **MUELLER COPPER TUBE PRODUCTS INC**
(Suby of MUELLER INDUSTRIES INC) ★
8285 Tournament Dr # 150, Memphis, TN 38125-1743
Tel (901) 753-3200 Founded/Ownrshp 1998
Sales 400.6MM^E EMP 3,925
SIC 3351 Tubing, copper & copper alloy; Tubing, copper & copper alloy
CEO: Gregory L Christopher
*Ex VP: Brian Caufield
*VP: Kent McKee

D-U-N-S 00-100-3128 IMP
MUELLER CORP (MA)
530 Spring St, East Bridgewater, MA 02333-1834
Tel (508) 456-4500 Founded/Ownrshp 1955, 1984
Sales 21.0MM^E EMP 160
SIC 3471 Plating & polishing
Pr: Mark D Svizzero
*VP: Glenn Mueller
Genl Mgr: Rob Anthony
Prd Mgr: Kim Quill

D-U-N-S 00-200-1550 IMP
MUELLER DIE CUT SOLUTIONS INC (NJ)
9201 Stockport Pl, Charlotte, NC 28273-4565
Tel (704) 588-3900 Founded/Ownrshp 1940, 1961
Sales 22.2MM^E EMP 84^E
SIC 3053 5084 2675 Gaskets, all materials; Conveyor systems; Die-cut paper & board
Pr: Ken Stober
*CFO: James Brazas
*Ex VP: Brian Stober

D-U-N-S 09-469-5314
■ **MUELLER GROUP LLC**
(Suby of MUELLER WATER PRODUCTS INC) ★
1200 Abernathy Rd, Atlanta, GA 30328-5662
Tel (770) 206-4200 Founded/Ownrshp 2005
Sales 486.3MM^E EMP 4,015
SIC 3823 3321 3533 7699 Flow instruments, industrial process type; Gray & ductile iron foundries; Drilling tools for gas, oil or water wells; Pumps & pumping equipment repair; Flow instruments, industrial process type; Gray & ductile iron foundries; Drilling tools for gas, oil or water wells; Pumps & pumping equipment repair

D-U-N-S 85-847-6096 EXP
■ **MUELLER IMPACTS CO INC**
(Suby of MUELLER BRASS CO) ★
2409 Wills St, Marysville, MI 48040-1979
Tel (810) 364-3700 Founded/Ownrshp 1991
Sales 22.5MM^E EMP 125
SIC 3469 3354 3463 Metal stampings; Aluminum extruded products; Nonferrous forgings
Pr: James H Rourke
VP: David Lockhart
Plnt Mgr: Tony Kamendat
Ql Cn Mgr: Brian Darby

D-U-N-S 04-398-4277
MUELLER INC PETER (VA)
INTERNATIONAL MOTORS
551 N Washington St, Falls Church, VA 22046-3536
Tel (703) 534-0770 Founded/Ownrshp 1960, 1992
Sales 23.5MM^E EMP 74^E
SIC 5511 7538 Automobiles, new & used; General automotive repair shops; Automobiles, new & used; General automotive repair shops
Pr: Kurt Schirm
*Sec: Allan Hillman

D-U-N-S 85-847-5973
■ **MUELLER INDUSTRIAL REALTY CO**
(Suby of MUELLER BRASS CO) ★
2199 Lapeer Ave, Port Huron, MI 48060-4155
Tel (810) 987-7770 Founded/Ownrshp 1919
Sales 28.9MM^E EMP 300
SIC 3312 Rods, iron & steel: made in steel mills; Rods, iron & steel: made in steel mills
Pr: James R Rourke
Treas: Kent A McKee
VP: Karl J Bambas
VP Legal: William H Hensley
Board of Directors: William O'hagan

MUELLER INDUSTRIES
See MUELLER COPPER TUBE CO INC

D-U-N-S 62-203-1748
▲ **MUELLER INDUSTRIES INC**
8285 Tournament Dr # 150, Memphis, TN 38125-1743
Tel (901) 753-3200 Founded/Ownrshp 1917
Sales 2.3MMM EMP 3,850
Tkr Sym MLI Exch NYS
SIC 3463 3494 3089 Nonferrous forgings; Aluminum forgings; Valves & pipe fittings; Plumbing & heating valves; Fittings for pipe, plastic; Nonferrous forgings; Aluminum forgings; Valves & pipe fittings; Plumbing & heating valves; Fittings for pipe, plastic
CEO: Gregory L Christopher
CFO: Robert Goodwin
CFO: Jeffrey A Martin
VP: Bob Cook
VP: Daniel R Corbin
VP: Daniel Corbin
VP: Richard W Corman
VP: Jack Mueller
VP: Gary C Wilkerson
Opers Mgr: Collin Schafer
Trfc Mgr: Tim Jones
Board of Directors: Paul J Flaherty, Gennaro J Fulvio, Gary S Gladstein, Scott J Goldman, John B Hansen, Terry Hermanson

D-U-N-S 11-435-2602 IMP
MUELLER METALS LLC
2152 Schwartz Rd, San Angelo, TX 76904-4137
Tel (325) 651-9558 Founded/Ownrshp 1984
Sales 43.6MM^E EMP 50
Accts Oliver Rainey & Wojtek Llp
SIC 5051 Steel; Tubing, metal
Pr: Fred Mueller

D-U-N-S 01-762-2770
MUELLER ROOFING DISTRIBUTORS INC (OH)
MRD SERVICES
327 E Wyoming Ave, Cincinnati, OH 45215-3027
Tel (513) 679-8540 Founded/Ownrshp 1977
Sales 153.4MM^E EMP 120
SIC 5033 5099 Roofing & siding materials; Containers: glass, metal or plastic; Roofing & siding materials; Containers: glass, metal or plastic
CEO: Herbert J Mueller
CFO: Brad Schwartz
*Ex VP: Terry J Powell
*VP: Robert P Marini
Brnch Mgr: Donna Mueller
VP Sls: Scott Fritsch

D-U-N-S 00-504-5898
MUELLER SERVICES INC
63 Main St, Tonawanda, NY 14150-2133
Tel (716) 691-4344 Founded/Ownrshp 1998
Sales NA EMP 200
SIC 6331 Fire, marine & casualty insurance; Fire, marine & casualty insurance
Ch Bd: John F Noe
Pr: John Armstrong
*Pr: Thomas R Noe
CFO: Phillip Arp
VP: Ken Clark
VP: Jeff Fisher
VP: John Holbrook
VP: Mat Huftalen
VP: Chad Mize
Dir Bus: Carlton Chamberlain
Dist Mgr: Mike Doody

D-U-N-S 00-642-6316 IMP/EXP
MUELLER SPORTS MEDICINE INC (WI)
1 Quench Dr, Prairie Du Sac, WI 53578-2100
Tel (608) 643-6450 Founded/Ownrshp 1957, 2010
Sales 57.4MM^E EMP 140
SIC 2834 3842 Pharmaceutical preparations; Braces, elastic; Braces, orthopedic; Tape, adhesive: medicated or non-medicated; Pharmaceutical preparations; Braces, elastic; Braces, orthopedic; Tape, adhesive: medicated or non-medicated
CEO: Curt Mueller
*Pr: Brett Mueller
*Treas: Stanley Johnson
*Sr VP: Herb Raschka
Sr VP: John Swafford
*VP: Ginger Mueller-Mann
Dir IT: Ann Leonard
Opers Mgr: Brad Keith
Sales Exec: Lori Pulvermacher
Mktg Dir: Eric Boyer
Sls Dir: Dave Beal

D-U-N-S 78-326-0458 IMP
■ **MUELLER STREAMLINE CO**
(Suby of MUELLER BRASS CO) ★
8285 Tournament Dr # 150, Memphis, TN 38125-1745
Tel (901) 753-3200 Founded/Ownrshp 1991
Sales 31.6MM^E EMP 150
SIC 3351 Copper rolling & drawing; Copper rolling & drawing
Pr: Gregory L Christopher
*Treas: Kent A McKee
*Prin: Jeffrey Martin
Sls Mgr: Grant Hajek

D-U-N-S 00-804-0743 IMP
MUELLER SUPPLY CO INC
1913 Hutchins Ave, Ballinger, TX 76821-4401
Tel (325) 365-3555 Founded/Ownrshp 2014
Sales 205.6MM^E EMP 359
SIC 3448 3496 5039 Metal buildings; Prefabricated metal components; Prefabricated metal buildings; Miscellaneous fabricated wire products; Prefabricated metal components; Miscellaneous fabricated wire products; Metal buildings
Pr: Bryan Davenport
*CFO: Phillip Arp
*VP: Joel Davenport
Brnch Mgr: Ben Albarado
Brnch Mgr: Tyler Jones
DP Exec: Evanet Gallant
IT Man: Stephen Hamons
IT Man: Mike Hoten
IT Man: Mark Ussery
Tech Mgr: Brian Campbell
Software D: Joey Rodriguez

D-U-N-S 00-350-1079
▲ **MUELLER WATER PRODUCTS INC** (DE)
1200 Abernathy Rd # 1200, Atlanta, GA 30328-5670
Tel (770) 206-4200 Founded/Ownrshp 2005
Sales 1.1MMM EMP 4,200^E
Accts Ernst & Young Llp Atlanta G
Tkr Sym MWA Exch NYS
SIC 3491 3492 3494 3443 3321 3823 Industrial valves; Fluid power valves & hose fittings; Valves & pipe fittings; Pipe, standpipe & culverts; Gray & ductile iron foundries; Industrial flow & liquid measuring instruments; Industrial valves; Fluid power valves & hose fittings; Valves & pipe fittings; Pipe, standpipe & culverts; Gray & ductile iron foundries; Industrial flow & liquid measuring instruments
Ch Bd: Gregory E Hyland
CFO: Evan L Hart
CFO: Kim Macinnis
Chf Cred: Keith L Belknap
Ex VP: Robert Leggett
Sr VP: Robert P Keefe
Sr VP: Walt Smith
Sr VP: Marietta Edmunds Zakas
VP: Tim Holcombe
VP: Greg Hollod
VP: Jim Lambert
VP: Kevin G McHugh
VP: Steve Mead
VP: Donna Raines
VP: Gary Wilbanks
Dir Risk M: Diane Markel
Board of Directors: Shirley C Franklin, Thomas J Hansen, Jerry W Kolb, Joseph B Leonard, Mark J O'brien, Bernard G Rethore, Neil A Springer, Lydia W Thomas, Michael T Tokarz

D-U-N-S 08-030-4280
MUELLER-YURGAE ASSOCIATES INC (IA)
1055 Se 28th St, Grimes, IA 50111-4958
Tel (515) 986-0491 Founded/Ownrshp 1975
Sales 37.7MM^E EMP 128^E
Accts Denman & Company Llp West De
SIC 5141 5143 5199 5145 Groceries, general line; Cheese; Pet supplies; General merchandise, non-durable; Confectionery; Candy; Groceries, general line; Cheese; Pet supplies; General merchandise, non-durable; Confectionery; Candy
Pr: Phillip Yurgae
*Treas: Bob Mueller
VP: Justin Heidenreich
VP: John Walker
*VP Sls: Jeffrey Yurgae

MUELSTEIN
See RAVAGO AMERICAS LLC

D-U-N-S 07-103-2692
MUESER RUTLEDGE CONSULTING ENGINEERS
225 W 34th St Fl 6, New York, NY 10122-0610
Tel (917) 339-9300 Founded/Ownrshp 1910
Sales 30.2MM EMP 140
Accts Raich Ende Malter & Co Llp
SIC 8711 Consulting engineer; Structural engineering; Consulting engineer; Structural engineering
Pt: Walter Kaeck
Pt: Fransis J Arland
Pt: David M Cacoilo
Pt: Peter W Deming
Pt: Roderick A Ellman Jr
CFO: Joseph Courtade
Off Mgr: Christine Malave
Dir IT: Milton Terrell
Dir IT: Milton Teruel

MUFFIN TOWN
See J S B INDUSTRIES INC

D-U-N-S 00-691-1770
MUFG AMERICAS HOLDINGS CORP (CA)
(Suby of BANK OF TOKYO-MITSUBISHI UFJ, LTD., THE)
1251 Ave Of The Americas, New York, NY 10020-1104
Tel (212) 782-5911 Founded/Ownrshp 1996, 2008
Sales NA EMP 12,550^E
Accts Deloitte & Touche Llp San Fra
SIC 6021 National commercial banks; National commercial banks
Pr: Masashi Oka
*Pr: Katsumi Hatao
CFO: John F Woods
Ofcr: Arthur G Smith
Ex VP: Mary A Curran
Ex VP: Ronald H Kendrick
Ex VP: Joseph M Petitti
Ex VP: Michael A C Spilsbury
Sr VP: Mark L Stevenson
Board of Directors: Michael D Fraizer, Christine Garvey, Ann F Jaedicke, Henry R Keizer, Takashi Morimura, Barbara L Rambo, Dean A Yoost

D-U-N-S 00-691-1754
MUFG UNION BANK NA
(Suby of MUFG AMERICAS HOLDINGS CORP) ★
400 California St, San Francisco, CA 94104-1302
Tel (415) 765-2000 Founded/Ownrshp 1864
Sales NA EMP 9,676
SIC 6021 National commercial banks; National commercial banks
Pr: Norimichi Kanari
Ch Bd: Kyota Omori
V Ch: Mark W Midkiff
V Ch: Timothy H Wennes
COO: Philip B Flynn
Ch: Patrick M Fahey
Ch: Takashi Morimura
Bd of Dir: Richard Farman
Bd of Dir: Standley Farrar
Bd of Dir: Michael Gillfillan
Bd of Dir: Steven Glaser
Bd of Dir: Ronald Havner
Bd of Dir: Carl Robertson
Chf Mktg O: Arthur G Smith
Ofcr: Tammie Klink
Ofcr: Annemieke Van Der Werff
Ex VP: Linda Betzer
Ex VP: John M Edmonston
Ex VP: Morris W Hirsch
Ex VP: John H McGuckin Jr
Ex VP: Dennis J Mooradian

D-U-N-S 17-644-5539
MUGO GRAVEL & GRADING INC
2600 Concord Pkwy S, Concord, NC 28027-9045
Tel (704) 782-3478 Founded/Ownrshp 2004
Sales 34.4MM^E EMP 85
SIC 1442 1794 Construction sand & gravel; Excavation work
Pr: Karen Moore Christy

D-U-N-S 04-735-2836
MUHLENBERG COLLEGE
2400 Chew St, Allentown, PA 18104-5586
Tel (484) 664-3100 Founded/Ownrshp 1864
Sales 152.0MM EMP 758^E
Accts Tait Weller & Baker Llp Phi
SIC 8221 Colleges & universities; Colleges & universities
Ch Bd: Richard Bruekner
Pr: Mark Brewer
*Pr: Peyton R Helm
Pr: Sarah Hunt-Barron
COO: Nicole Hammel
*CFO: Kent A Dyer
VP: Michael Krouse
Exec: Sharon Albert
Exec: Kathleen Harring
Exec: Steve Nemes
Assoc Dir: Laura Garland

D-U-N-S 07-405-3679
MUHLENBERG COUNTY BOARD OF EDUCATION
510 W Main St, Powderly, KY 42367-5487
Tel (270) 338-2871 Founded/Ownrshp 1900
Sales 33.8MM^E EMP 777
Accts Alexander & Company Psc Owen
SIC 8211 Public elementary & secondary schools; Public elementary & secondary schools
*Treas: Jeff Travis

D-U-N-S 96-922-4679
MUHLENBERG COUNTY SCHOOL DISTRICT
510 W Main St, Powderly, KY 42367-5487
Tel (270) 338-2871 Founded/Ownrshp 2011
Sales 14.2MM^E EMP 1,043^E
SIC 8211 Elementary & secondary schools
Prin: Don Richey

D-U-N-S 07-753-9708
MUHLENBERG REGIONAL MEDICAL CENTER INC
JFK MEDICAL CENTER
(Suby of JFK HEALTH SYSTEM INC) ★
Park Ave & Randolph Rd, Plainfield, NJ 07060
Tel (908) 668-2000 Founded/Ownrshp 1997
Sales 675.8M EMP 1,400E
Accts Parente Beard Llc Clark New
SIC 8062 General medical & surgical hospitals; General medical & surgical hospitals
Pr: John McGee
Dir Rad: Fred Wishner
Phys Thrpy: Lynn Stallworth

D-U-N-S 03-766-5437
MUHLENBERG SCHOOL DISTRICT
801 E Bellevue Ave, Reading, PA 19605-1701
Tel (610) 921-8000 Founded/Ownrshp 1925
Sales 48.6MM EMP 440
SIC 8211 Public combined elementary & secondary school; School board; Public combined elementary & secondary school; School board
Ofcr: Michele Calvaresi
VP: Lori Potteiger
IT Man: Daniel Houck
Psych: Sharawn Hall
Psych: Christina Marco-Fies
Doctor: Joseph Macharola

D-U-N-S 86-012-6879
MUHLER CO INC
630 Skylark Dr Ste U, Charleston, SC 29407-1718
Tel (843) 572-9727 Founded/Ownrshp 1996
Sales 46.4MME EMP 125
SIC 5031 Windows; Windows
Pr: Henry M Hay III

MUIR COPPER CANYON FARMS
See MUIR ENTERPRISES INC

D-U-N-S 03-537-4628
MUIR ENTERPRISES INC
MUIR COPPER CANYON FARMS
3575 W 900 S, Salt Lake City, UT 84104-4543
Tel (801) 363-7695 Founded/Ownrshp 1998
Sales 27.9MM EMP 64
SIC 5148 Fresh fruits & vegetables; Fresh fruits & vegetables
Pr: Phil Muir
*CFO: Chuck Madsen
CIO: Adam Jenson
Opers Mgr: Jacob Lawes

D-U-N-S 94-855-0421
MUIR LABS
MUIRLAB
1601 Ygnacio Valley Rd, Walnut Creek, CA 94598-3122
Tel (925) 947-3335 Founded/Ownrshp 1960
Sales 5.0MME EMP 400
SIC 8071 Medical laboratories; Medical laboratories

D-U-N-S 02-073-7391
MUIR-CHASE PLUMBING CO INC (CA)
M C
4530 Brazil St Ste 1, Los Angeles, CA 90039-1000
Tel (818) 500-1940 Founded/Ownrshp 1975, 1991
Sales 24.5MME EMP 90
SIC 1711 7699 Plumbing contractors; Sewer cleaning & rodding; Plumbing contractors; Sewer cleaning & rodding
Pr: Don Chase
*VP: Jay Chase
*VP: Grant Muir

D-U-N-S 03-286-2476
MUIRFIELD INC
HERITAGE FORD
State Road 54, Zephyrhills, FL 33543
Tel (813) 907-7800 Founded/Ownrshp 1984
Sales 25.6MME EMP 90
SIC 5511 5521 Automobiles, new & used; Pickups, new & used; Used car dealers; Automobiles, new & used; Pickups, new & used; Used car dealers
Pr: Ronald R Parks
*VP: Steve Couey
*VP: Jack W Parks
Sls Mgr: John Baker

MUIRLAB
See MUIR LABS

D-U-N-S 09-288-5516
MUKILTEO SCHOOL DISTRICT
9401 Sharon Dr, Everett, WA 98204-2699
Tel (425) 356-1274 Founded/Ownrshp 1952
Sales 101.3MME EMP 1,800
SIC 8211 Public elementary school; Public junior high school; Public senior high school; Public elementary school; Public junior high school; Public senior high school
Off Admin: Karen Ebel
Pr Dir: Andy Muntz
Teacher Pr: Bruce Hobert
Teacher Pr: Joan Steiner
HC Dir: Ruth Pesckarsky

D-U-N-S 07-893-6119
MUKWONAGO AREA SCHOOL DISTRICT
385 County Road Nn E, Mukwonago, WI 53149-2038
Tel (262) 363-6300 Founded/Ownrshp 1971
Sales 33.7MME EMP 586
SIC 8211 Public elementary school; Public junior high school; Public senior high school; Public elementary school; Public junior high school; Public senior high school
*Treas: Todd Clemens
*VP: Paul Wysocki
HC Dir: Laura Heidelmeier

D-U-N-S 60-680-2445
MULBERRY CHILD CARE CENTERS INC
(Suby of KINDERCARE LEARNING CENTERS LLC) ★
990 Washington St Ste 104, Dedham, MA 02026-6715
Tel (781) 320-9222 Founded/Ownrshp 2001
Sales 21.0MME EMP 2,100
SIC 8351 Preschool center; Preschool center
VP: Deann Besch
VP Opers: Diane Driscoll
Doctor: Roderick Fletcher
Doctor: Clare Onorato

D-U-N-S 03-027-3697
MULBERRY CHILDCARE CENTERS INC
KINDERCARE
650 Ne Holladay St # 1400, Portland, OR 97232-2045
Tel (503) 872-1300 Founded/Ownrshp 2001
Sales 56.2MME EMP 2,000
SIC 8351 Child day care services; Child day care services
Pr: Tom Heymann
Treas: Dan R Jackson
*Sr VP: Edward Brewington
*Sr VP: Eva Kripalani
*Sr VP: Bruce Walters
*VP: David Benedict
VP: Lauren Klein
Dist Mgr: Bill Leger
Dist Mgr: Michelle Mazzulo

D-U-N-S 00-214-0101
MULBERRY METAL PRODUCTS INC
2199 Stanley Ter, Union, NJ 07083-4399
Tel (908) 688-8850 Founded/Ownrshp 1927
Sales 24.0MM EMP 90E
SIC 3644 5065 Face plates (wiring devices); Outlet boxes (electric wiring devices); Switch boxes, electric; Semiconductor devices; Face plates (wiring devices); Outlet boxes (electric wiring devices); Switch boxes, electric; Semiconductor devices
Pr: Richard Horn
*Ex VP: Richard E Mueller
*VP: Kristina Hom
VP: Kristina Horn
Exec: Victor Perez
Plnt Mgr: Sam Valente
Sls Mgr: Robert Walker
Sls Mgr: Robert Walker

D-U-N-S 03-258-3502 EXP
MULBERRY MOTOR PARTS INC
160 S Broadway Ave, Bartow, FL 33830-4601
Tel (863) 533-0788 Founded/Ownrshp 1962
Sales 35.8MME EMP 87
SIC 5531 Automobile & truck equipment & parts; Automotive parts
Pr: William A Read
*VP: Dennis Barnhart
*Prin: Kevin Stanaback

D-U-N-S 10-432-0408
MULBERRY STREET MANAGEMENT SERVICES INC
COORDNTING CNCIL FOR IND LVING
1097 Greenbag Rd, Morgantown, WV 26508-1532
Tel (304) 291-3996 Founded/Ownrshp 2002
Sales 14.0MM EMP 600
SIC 8082 Home health care services; Home health care services
Pr: Dennis Parrucci
CFO: Mary Plevich

D-U-N-S 13-189-3794 IMP
MULCH MANUFACTURING INC
6747 Taylor Rd Sw, Reynoldsburg, OH 43068-9649
Tel (614) 864-4004 Founded/Ownrshp 1985
Sales 37.1MME EMP 180
SIC 2499

MULCOA
See C-E MINERALS INC

MULE BARN
See HENSON MOTOR CO INC

D-U-N-S 05-171-4314
MULE-HIDE MANUFACTURING CO INC
(Suby of ABC SUPPLY CO) ★
50 Bridge St, Cornell, WI 54732-8376
Tel (715) 239-6424 Founded/Ownrshp 2002
Sales 24.8MME EMP 85
SIC 2621 Felts, building
Pr: Diane Hendricks
Genl Mgr: Sheri Johnson

D-U-N-S 15-513-2780
MULE-HIDE PRODUCTS CO INC
(Suby of ABC SUPPLY CO) ★
1195 Prince Hall Dr, Beloit, WI 53511-5481
Tel (608) 365-3111 Founded/Ownrshp 1985
Sales 31.2MME EMP 55
SIC 2952 5033 Roofing materials; Roofing & siding materials
Pr: Dan Piche
Treas: Kendra Story
Chf Mktg O: Kate Baumann
VP: Diane Hendricks
Manager: James Fountain
Sls Mgr: Jim Lessig
Sls Mgr: Rick Mason
Sls Mgr: Charlie Miller
Sls Mgr: Bob Mueller
Sls Mgr: Marshall Powell
Sls Mgr: Lou Ramos
Board of Directors: David Luck

D-U-N-S 06-639-7522
MULESHOE AREA MEDICAL CENTER
708 S 1st St, Muleshoe, TX 79347-3627
Tel (806) 272-4524 Founded/Ownrshp 1968
Sales 21.0MME EMP 200
SIC 8062 8051 General medical & surgical hospitals; Convalescent home with continuous nursing care; General medical & surgical hospitals; Convalescent home with continuous nursing care
Dir Lab: Brian Rambow
Dir Rad: Joy Elivarraraz
Dir Rad: Brenda B Kirk
Off Mgr: Brian Rambo
Dir IT: Bobby Turner
Dir IT: Bolan You
Nrsg Dir: Cody Kitchen
Nrsg Dir: Coddy Kitchens
Board of Directors: Roy Anzaldua, Christine Isaacson, Tonya Lookingbill, Missy Shultz,eileen Morton, Suzanne Nichols, Lajuana Renfro, Mike Richards, Robert Turner

D-U-N-S 79-746-4810
MULESOFT INC
77 Geary St Fl 400, San Francisco, CA 94108-5707
Tel (415) 229-2009 Founded/Ownrshp 2003
Sales 26.8MME EMP 500
SIC 7371 Computer software development
Pr: Greg Schott
Pr: James Donelan
Pr: Nick Trombetta
*Pr: Ken Yagen
*CFO: Matt Langdon
*Sr VP: Rob Horton
*Sr VP: Simon Parmett
*VP: Ed Dubrawski
*VP: Jim Emerich
VP: Chris Erickson-King
VP: Stephen Hallowell
VP: Sarvesh Jagannivas
VP: Matthew Kilguss
VP: Erich Leipold
*VP: Ross Mason
*VP: Chris Purpura
VP: Hollie Wegman
VP: David Wyatt
Creative D: Michael Hindman
Comm Dir: Melissa Czapiga
Board of Directors: Michael Capellas, Steve Collins

D-U-N-S 02-214-5767
MULGREW OIL CO
PERFECTION OIL
10314 Silverwood Dr, Dubuque, IA 52003-8477
Tel (563) 583-7386 Founded/Ownrshp 1955
Sales 199.6MM EMP 48
SIC 5171 5172 5541

MULHALLS DESIGN
See MULHALLS NURSERY INC

D-U-N-S 15-064-8517
MULHALLS NURSERY INC
MULHALLS DESIGN
3615 N 120th St, Omaha, NE 68164-2599
Tel (402) 496-0700 Founded/Ownrshp 1983
Sales 31.0MME EMP 125
SIC 5261 0781 Lawn & garden supplies; Landscape services
Pr: Sean Mulhall
*Sec: Maureen Mulhall
*VP: Daniel Mulhall
IT Man: Kamin Beavers
Sls&Mrk Ex: Jay Genoa

D-U-N-S 03-358-2131
MULHERIN LUMBER CO
705 Industrial Park Rd, Evans, GA 30809-3680
Tel (706) 863-6070 Founded/Ownrshp 1937
Sales 23.2MM EMP 65
Accts Jones Jones Davis Cpa Pc Augu
SIC 5031 2431 5072 2439 Lumber: rough, dressed & finished; Building materials, exterior; Building materials, interior; Door frames, wood; Louver windows, glass, wood frame; Builders' hardware; Trusses, wooden roof; Lumber: rough, dressed & finished; Building materials, exterior; Building materials, interior; Door frames, wood; Louver windows, glass, wood frame; Builders' hardware; Trusses, wooden roof
Pr: Louis Mulherin
*Treas: Michael Grady
VP: Amber Bodnar
*VP: Sean Grady
*VP: Mark Mulherin

D-U-N-S 00-127-3556 IMP
MULHERN BELTING INC (NJ)
148 Bauer Dr, Oakland, NJ 07436-3187
Tel (201) 337-5700 Founded/Ownrshp 1932
Sales 21.0MM EMP 90
SIC 3535 3052

D-U-N-S 18-960-2175
MULHOLLAND SECURITY AND PATROL INC
CENTURION GROUP, THE
11454 San Vicente Blvd Fl, Los Angeles, CA 90049-6208
Tel (818) 755-0202 Founded/Ownrshp 2004
Sales 8.4MME EMP 350
SIC 7381 Protective services, guard; Protective services, guard
Pr: David Rosenberg
*VP: Daniel Campbell
*VP: Steven Lemmer

D-U-N-S 11-328-8815
MULKEY ENTERPRISES INC
904 Kennesaw Ave Nw, Marietta, GA 30060-1005
Tel (770) 428-2968 Founded/Ownrshp 1983
Sales 25.2MM EMP 80
Accts Mobley & Company Atlanta Ga
SIC 1799 Home/office interiors finishing, furnishing & remodeling
Pr: Ron Mulkey
*CFO: Janice Pace Mazur
*VP: David Crace

D-U-N-S 05-469-0227
MULLEN & FILIPPI LLP
1435 River Park Dr # 300, Sacramento, CA 95815-4510
Tel (916) 442-4503 Founded/Ownrshp 1949
Sales 22.2MME EMP 165
SIC 8111 Labor & employment law; Labor & employment law
Mng Pt: Jerome Young
Mng Pt: Anne Hernandez
Mng Pt: Robert Sherman
Pr: Shelley King
Dir Risk M: Daniel Staub

D-U-N-S 84-535-7750
MULLEN ADVERTISING INC
JAMES X. MULLEN
40 Broad St, Boston, MA 02109-4316
Tel (617) 226-9000 Founded/Ownrshp 1975
Sales 54.0MME EMP 337E
SIC 7311 Advertising agencies
Ch: Joe Grimaldi
Ex VP: Sheila Leyne
Sr VP: Denise Ambrosio
Sr VP: Christy Blain
Sr VP: Sean Corcoran
Sr VP: Chere Furman
Sr VP: Steve Kalb
Sr VP: Tony Labriola
Sr VP: Liza Near
Sr VP: John Wolfarth
VP: Justin Baum
VP: Laurel Boyd
VP: Chip Cook
VP: James Gledhill
VP: Dustin Johnson
VP: Norm Shupe
Creative D: John Kearse

D-U-N-S 05-180-2866
■ **MULLEN COMMUNICATIONS INC**
(Suby of INTERPUBLIC GROUP OF COMPANIES INC) ★
40 Broad St Fl 10, Boston, MA 02109-4316
Tel (978) 468-1155 Founded/Ownrshp 1999
Sales 46.0MME EMP 600
SIC 7311 8743 8742 8732 Advertising agencies; Public relations & publicity; Marketing consulting services; Commercial nonphysical research; Advertising agencies; Public relations & publicity; Marketing consulting services; Commercial nonphysical research
Ch: Joe Grimaldi
*CEO: Alex Leikikh
*COO: Paul Slack
*Chf Cred: Edward Boches
Ofcr: Kristen Cavallo
Ex VP: Anne Elwell
Ex VP: Marc Kempter
Sr VP: Susanna Gates-Rose
Sr VP: Heidi Grassi
Sr VP: Rebekah Pagis
Sr VP: Ruth E Winig
VP: Debbie Basham
VP: Zeke Bowman
VP: Jeannie Houchins
VP: Steve Kalb
VP: Alison Kaplan
VP: Don Lorenzet
VP: Keith Lusby
VP: Seton McGowen
VP: David Morse
VP: Cindy Parker
Board of Directors: Nicholas J Camera

D-U-N-S 01-326-0450 IMP
MULLEN INDUSTRIAL HANDLING CORP
6245 Fly Rd, East Syracuse, NY 13057-9338
Tel (315) 437-3386 Founded/Ownrshp 1980
Sales 30.1MME EMP 45
SIC 5084 7359 Materials handling machinery; Equipment rental & leasing
Pr: Francis G Fay
*CFO: Kathleen Fay
*VP: William Wright
Sfty Mgr: Phillip Clarke
Sales Exec: Billy Wright

D-U-N-S 02-178-9128
MULLER CO
MULLROCK TOWER 17
18881 Von Karman Ave # 400, Irvine, CA 92612-1500
Tel (949) 476-9800 Founded/Ownrshp 1979
Sales 27.1MME EMP 85
SIC 6552 6531 Subdividers & developers; Real estate managers
Pr: Stephen J Muller
*COO: Timothy M Gooch
*CFO: George F Derrington
VP: Hugh Fast
*VP: Jon M Muller
IT Man: Laura Nhu

MULLER HONDA
See HIGHLAND PARK MOTORS INC

D-U-N-S 01-466-1680 IMP
MULLER INC (PA)
2800 Grant Ave, Philadelphia, PA 19114-2302
Tel (215) 676-7575 Founded/Ownrshp 1954
Sales 27.3MME EMP 156
SIC 2082 5181 Beer & other fermented malt liquors; Malt beverages; Malt beverages; Beer & other fermented malt liquors
Pr: Sandy Muller
CFO: Joel Shafer
*VP: Ed Odonnell
Board of Directors: Barbara - Offc Mgr

D-U-N-S 05-773-0764 IMP/EXP
MULLER MARTINI CORP
MULLER MARTINI HOLDING AG
(Suby of GRAPHA-HOLDING AG)
456 Wheeler Rd, Hauppauge, NY 11788-4343
Tel (631) 582-4343 Founded/Ownrshp 1967
Sales 96.1MME EMP 150
SIC 5084 7699 Industrial machinery & equipment; Industrial machinery & equipment repair; Industrial machinery & equipment; Industrial machinery & equipment repair
Pr: Werner Naegeli
CFO: Richard Slattery
Ex Dir: Kris Organ
Off Mgr: Tom Duckett
Dir IT: Carrington Herbert
Dir IT: Elie Saliba
IT Man: David Brown
IT Man: Judy Pollock
Info Man: Daniel Denue
Plnt Mgr: Fred Jones
VP Sls: Wolfgang Hanzl
Board of Directors: Kasper F Meier

MULLER MARTINI HOLDING AG
See MULLER MARTINI CORP

D-U-N-S 08-230-1284 EXP
MULLER MARTINI MAILROOM SYSTEMS INC
(*Suby of* GRAPHA-HOLDING AG)
4444 Innovation Way, Allentown, PA 18109-9404
Tel (610) 266-7000 *Founded/Ownrshp* 1992
Sales 49.0MM^E *EMP* 300
SIC 3555 3535 Printing trades machinery; Conveyors & conveying equipment; Printing trades machinery; Conveyors & conveying equipment
Pr: Amrish Thaker
**Ch Bd:* Rudolf Mller
**Treas:* Charles A Spierto
IT Man: Thomas George
IT Man: Daryl Gregory

D-U-N-S 07-872-9484 IMP
MULLER QUAKER DAIRY LLC
(*Suby of* TM UK PRODUCTION LIMITED)
5140 Agi Business Pk Dr W, Batavia, NY 14020
Tel (585) 409-2200 *Founded/Ownrshp* 2011
Sales 20.0MM^E *EMP* 52^E
SIC 2023 Dried & powdered milk & milk products
VP: Kevin Williams
Plnt Mgr: David Sharma
Ql Cn Mgr: Michael Kuemmerle

D-U-N-S 05-533-2316
MULLER TOYOTA INC
2019 Rt 31 S, Clinton, NJ 08809
Tel (908) 638-4100 *Founded/Ownrshp* 1980
Sales 32.7MM^E *EMP* 80
SIC 5511 5521 7515 7513 Automobiles, new & used; Used car dealers; Passenger car leasing; Truck rental & leasing, no drivers; Automobiles, new & used; Used car dealers; Passenger car leasing; Truck rental & leasing, no drivers
Pr: William J Muller Jr

D-U-N-S 05-317-7911
MULLICA HILL COLD STORAGE INC
554 Franklinville Rd, Mullica Hill, NJ 08062-4706
Tel (856) 478-6300 *Founded/Ownrshp* 1981
Sales 38.2MM^E *EMP* 101
Accts Rowland Johnson & Co Pa Wi
SIC 4222 Warehousing, cold storage or refrigerated
CEO: Fred Sorbello
**Pr:* Dan Sorbello
**COO:* Peter Tobey
**VP:* Ethan Graff
**VP:* Anthony Kimsal
**VP:* Andy Lugo

MULLICAN CARE CENTER
See MULLICAN SCC LLC

D-U-N-S 13-951-9151 IMP
MULLICAN FLOORING LP
(*Suby of* AMERICAN LUMBER CO) ★
655 Woodlyn Rd, Johnson City, TN 37601-3837
Tel (423) 262-8440 *Founded/Ownrshp* 1995
Sales 68.4MM^E *EMP* 380
SIC 2426 2421 Flooring, hardwood; Sawmills & planing mills, general; Flooring, hardwood; Sawmills & planing mills, general
Pr: Neil Poland
**VP:* Jim Dills
**VP:* Doris Meyer
QA Dir: Shane Smith
Plnt Mgr: Joe Ratliff
Natl Sales: Pat Oakley
Mktg Mgr: Amber Stringer

D-U-N-S 83-093-6881
MULLICAN SCC LLC
MULLICAN CARE CENTER
105 N Main, Savoy, TX 75479-2133
Tel (903) 965-0200 *Founded/Ownrshp* 2009
Sales 6.1MM *EMP* 1,888
SIC 8051 Skilled nursing care facilities; Skilled nursing care facilities

D-U-N-S 36-258-9277
MULLIGAN SECURITY CORP
2 Penn Plz Rm 2495, New York, NY 10121-2495
Tel (212) 563-0500 *Founded/Ownrshp* 1992
Sales 19.1MM^E *EMP* 900
SIC 7381 Detective & armored car services; Private investigator; Security guard service; Detective & armored car services; Private investigator; Security guard service
CEO: Kevin Mulligan
**Pr:* William P Mulligan Sr
Ex Dir: Robert Salafia

D-U-N-S 84-883-2663
■ **MULLIN TBG INSURANCE AGENCY SERVICES LLC**
MULLINTBG
(*Suby of* PRUDENTIAL INSURANCE CO OF AMERICA) ★
100 N Sepulveda Blvd, El Segundo, CA 90245-4359
Tel (310) 203-8770 *Founded/Ownrshp* 2008
Sales NA *EMP* 260
SIC 6411 Insurance agents, brokers & service; Insurance agents, brokers & service
CEO: Michael R Shute
COO: Yong Lee
**CFO:* Michael Glickman
Ex VP: Dan Banis
Ex VP: Deanna B McMahon
Sr VP: Dave Buckalew
Sr VP: Jason Burlie
Sr VP: Victor Palmieri
VP: John Antonio
VP: Jamie Bosley
VP: Matthew Cobb
VP: Janet Garcia
VP: Kerry George
VP: Carl Greene
VP: Lorraine Grod
VP: Peter H Lester
VP: Harry Levitt
VP: Holly Lifson
VP: Laura Malafronte
VP: Andrew McGinnis
VP: Rhonda Miller

MULLINAX FORD EAST
See FORD AUTONATION EAST

D-U-N-S 79-102-0258
■ **MULLINAX FORD NORTH CANTON INC**
(*Suby of* AUTONATION INC) ★
5900 Whipple Ave Nw, Canton, OH 44720-7614
Tel (330) 238-3206 *Founded/Ownrshp* 1992
Sales 40.8MM^E *EMP* 125
SIC 5511 5521 7515 Automobiles, new & used; Pickups, new & used; Vans, new & used; Used car dealers; Passenger car leasing; Automobiles, new & used; Pickups, new & used; Vans, new & used; Used car dealers; Passenger car leasing
Pr: Charles E Mullinax
**Treas:* Larry Mullinax
Exec: Rick Otani
MIS Dir: Dale Greagory

D-U-N-S 18-545-3800 EXP
MULLINAX FORD OF CENTRAL FLORIDA INC
1551 E Semoran Blvd, Apopka, FL 32703-5603
Tel (407) 889-7600 *Founded/Ownrshp* 2000
Sales 50.8MM^E *EMP* 87
SIC 5511 Automobiles, new & used; Automobiles, new & used
Pr: Jerry Mullinax
**Sec:* Ed Mullinax
**VP:* Larry Mullinax
IT Man: Brian Winn
Sls Mgr: Shannon Moore
Sales Asso: Sean Cahill
Sales Asso: Frankie Juliano
Sales Asso: Tonia Wheeler

D-U-N-S 60-408-3022 EXP
■ **MULLINAX FORD SOUTH INC**
MAROONE FORD OF MARGATE
(*Suby of* ED MULLINAX FORD LLC) ★
5401 W Copans Rd, Margate, FL 33063-7739
Tel (954) 935-8311 *Founded/Ownrshp* 1989
Sales 52.1MM^E *EMP* 200
SIC 5511 Automobiles, new & used; Automobiles, new & used
Pr: James R Bender
**Treas:* Ronald J Eberhardt
**VP:* Johnathan Ferrado

D-U-N-S 13-164-0349 EXP
MULLINAX FORD-MERCURY INC
2317 State Road 44, New Smyrna Beach, FL 32168-8205
Tel (888) 261-1363 *Founded/Ownrshp* 2003
Sales 21.5MM^E *EMP* 50
SIC 5511 5521 7538 Automobiles, new & used; Used car dealers; General automotive repair shops
Pr: Lawrence E Mullinax

D-U-N-S 08-286-8423 IMP
MULLINIX PACKAGES INC
3511 Engle Rd, Fort Wayne, IN 46809-1117
Tel (260) 747-3149 *Founded/Ownrshp* 1970, 2011
Sales 83.3MM^E *EMP* 350^E
SIC 3089 Plastic containers, except foam; Plastic containers, except foam
Pr: Gene Gentili
**CFO:* Belinda Glenn
VP: Valdez German
**VP:* Luther Gross
**VP:* Robert Inlow
**VP:* Timothy Love
**VP:* Herman Valbez
CIO: Robert Beckley
Dir IT: Jonathan Fry
VP Opers: Victor Rimkevicius
Ql Cn Mgr: Doug Dark

D-U-N-S 00-512-5786
MULLINS FOOD PRODUCTS INC
2200 S 25th Ave, Broadview, IL 60155-4584
Tel (708) 344-3224 *Founded/Ownrshp* 1957
Sales 146.2MM^E *EMP* 405
SIC 2033 2035 Tomato products: packaged in cans, jars, etc.; Barbecue sauce: packaged in cans, jars, etc.; Catsup: packaged in cans, jars, etc.; Dressings, salad: raw & cooked (except dry mixes); Tomato products: packaged in cans, jars, etc.; Barbecue sauce: packaged in cans, jars, etc.; Catsup: packaged in cans, jars, etc.; Dressings, salad: raw & cooked (except dry mixes)
Pr: Jeanne Gannon
**COO:* Michael Mullins
**CFO:* Arthur Clausen
Genl Mgr: Ed Mullins
QA Dir: Jamie Krystofiak
Dir IT: Joe Sands
IT Man: Nelson Powell
Sfty Dirs: Gary Saatkamp
Sfty Dirs: Rich Vlach
Opers Mgr: Mike Mazur
Opers Mgr: Terry McCarthy

MULLINS HIGH SCHOOL
See MARION SCHOOL DISTRICT 2

MULLINS NURSING CENTER
See CAROLINA HOSPITAL SYSTEM OF MARION

MULLINTBG
See MULLIN TBG INSURANCE AGENCY SERVICES LLC

MULLROCK TOWER 17
See MULLER CO

D-U-N-S 87-687-8554 IMP
MULTALLOY INC
(*Suby of* FLOWORKS INTERNATIONAL LLC) ★
8511 Monroe Rd, Houston, TX 77061-4816
Tel (800) 568-9551 *Founded/Ownrshp* 2012
Sales 73.0MM^E *EMP* 106^E
SIC 5051 Iron & steel (ferrous) products; Iron & steel (ferrous) products
Pr: Michael L Stanwood
Brnch Mgr: Kelly Bradshaw

D-U-N-S 11-950-0101 IMP
MULTEK FLEXIBLE CIRCUITS INC
(*Suby of* FLEXTRONICS INTERNATIONAL PA INC) ★
1150 Sheldahl Rd, Northfield, MN 55057-9444
Tel (507) 663-8000 *Founded/Ownrshp* 2004
Sales 118.2MM^E *EMP* 450
SIC 3672 Printed circuit boards; Printed circuit boards
CEO: Franck Lize
**CFO:* Alan Wadleigh
Bd of Dir: Stewart Auerbach
Bd of Dir: Kenneth Roering
**VP:* Jim Drass
VP: Luiz Guerra
VP: Alex Liew
Prgrm Mgr: Jim Clark
Genl Mgr: Ho Chan
Genl Mgr: Michael Kissel
IT Man: Tim Seitz

MULTI CARE STAFFING
See MULTICARE SKILLED HOME HEALTH CARE INC

D-U-N-S 04-579-9657
MULTI CHEVROLET INC
2675 Us Highway 22 W, Union, NJ 07083-8505
Tel (908) 686-2727 *Founded/Ownrshp* 1969
Sales 37.8MM^E *EMP* 89^E
SIC 5511 7515 5521 7539 Automobiles, new & used; Passenger car leasing; Used car dealers; Automobiles, new & used; Passenger car leasing; Used car dealers; Tune-up service, automotive
Pr: James V Tino Sr
Treas: John Amendola
**VP:* James V Tino Jr
Genl Mgr: David Alesso
Trfc Dir: Bryan Cullen
Sls Mgr: Tony Izzo
Sales Asso: Jonathan Andrade
Sales Asso: Mike Bielinski
Sales Asso: Nick Elkashab
Sales Asso: Randy McCloud
Sales Asso: Luis Rivera

MULTI CONSUMER ITEMS
See COSMOPOLITAN COSMETICS INC

D-U-N-S 83-624-9706 IMP
MULTI FITTINGS CORP
LASAINT LOGISTICS
(*Suby of* IPEX INC)
4507 Le Saint Ct, West Chester, OH 45014-5486
Tel (513) 942-9910 *Founded/Ownrshp* 1995
Sales 20.3MM^E *EMP* 156
SIC 3432 4226 Plumbing fixture fittings & trim; Special warehousing & storage; Plumbing fixture fittings & trim; Special warehousing & storage
Ch Bd: Thomas Torokvei
**Pr:* Paul Graddon
Genl Mgr: Laval Fong

D-U-N-S 14-368-3832
MULTI GROUP LOGISTICS INC
10900 Belmont Ave Ste 400, Franklin Park, IL 60131-1416
Tel (847) 621-3333 *Founded/Ownrshp* 2004
Sales 88.7MM^E *EMP* 550
SIC 4213 Trucking, except local; Trucking, except local
Pr: Vassil R Bayraktarov
VP: James Ogilvy
VP: Pete Ricciardone

MULTI HOUSING DEPOT
See APPLIANCE REPLACEMENT INC

D-U-N-S 06-380-1591
MULTI IMAGE GROUP INC
MIG
1701 Clint Moore Rd, Boca Raton, FL 33487-2755
Tel (561) 994-3515 *Founded/Ownrshp* 1979
Sales 37.8MM *EMP* 120
Accts Multi Image Group Inc
SIC 7812 Audio-visual program production; Audio-visual program production
CEO: Arlene J Sclafani
**Pr:* James V Sclafani
**Pr:* Robert J Sclafani
**CFO:* John Reitzes
**Treas:* Regina S O Neil
Treas: Regina O'Neil
**Treas:* Jonathan S Reitzes

MULTI MEDIA SERVICES
See UNIFIED AV SYSTEMS INC

D-U-N-S 78-874-9872
MULTI PACKAGING SOLUTIONS INC
1703 S Brook St, Louisville, KY 40208-1933
Tel (502) 635-7465 *Founded/Ownrshp* 2004
Sales 86.7MM^E *EMP* 383
SIC 2657 2752 2759 Folding paperboard boxes; Commercial printing, offset; Advertising literature: printing; Folding paperboard boxes; Commercial printing, offset; Advertising literature: printing
CEO: Marc Shore
Sr VP: Chris Turk
VP: Randy Bloch
VP: Brit Davis
Exec: Larry Beckham
Genl Mgr: Steven Bass
CIO: John Serbetzian
CTO: Steve Wolfe
QA Dir: Dee Abbott
IT Man: Lisa Lindsey
IT Man: Eric Pullen

D-U-N-S 79-128-9742 IMP/EXP
MULTI PACKAGING SOLUTIONS INC
150 E 52nd St Ste 2800, New York, NY 10022-6240
Tel (646) 885-0157 *Founded/Ownrshp* 2013
Sales 1.3MMM^E *EMP* 2,415
SIC 2759 2731 2761 3089 5092 2671 Commercial printing; Screen printing; Letterpress printing; Tags: printing; Books: publishing & printing; Continuous forms, office & business; Identification cards, plastic; Arts & crafts equipment & supplies; Packaging paper & plastics film, coated & laminated; Commercial printing; Screen printing; Letterpress printing; Tags: printing; Books: publishing & printing; Continuous forms, office & business; Identification cards, plastic; Arts & crafts equipment & supplies; Packaging paper & plastics film, coated & laminated
CEO: Marc Shore
**Pr:* Dennis Kaltman
Pr: Nancy Smith
**CFO:* William Hogan
Treas: Ed Gasper
Ex VP: Arthur Kern
Sr VP: Tim Klewicki
VP: Jim Ferrel
VP: Kristi Huffman
IT Man: Robert Cundy
VP Opers: Jody Arrington

MULTI PURE DRNKING WTR - DISTR
See CERTIFIED WATER FILTERS.COM

MULTI RESTAURANTS GROUP
See MULTIRESTAURANTS CONCEPTS LTD

D-U-N-S 09-675-4882 IMP
MULTI SERVICE CORP
8650 College Blvd, Overland Park, KS 66210-1886
Tel (913) 451-2400 *Founded/Ownrshp* 1988
Sales 48.4MM^E *EMP* 300
SIC 7389 Credit card service; Credit card service
CEO: Mark O Connell
Bd of Dir: Christopher Combest
**Sr VP:* Rutger Gassner
**Sr VP:* Michele Urness
**VP:* Molly Hundley
**VP:* Doretta Watson
VP: Michele Wills
Exec: Carol Lytle
Dir IT: Victoria Walworth
IT Man: James Hambrick
Sys Mgr: Luis Miranda

D-U-N-S 07-873-0188
■ **MULTI SERVICE TECHNOLOGY SOLUTIONS INC** (FL)
(*Suby of* WORLD FUEL SERVICES CORP) ★
8650 College Blvd, Overland Park, KS 66210-1886
Tel (913) 663-9694 *Founded/Ownrshp* 2012
Sales 35.2MM^E *EMP* 300
SIC 7389 Credit card service; Credit card service
Pr: Mark M O'Connell
**CFO:* Molly Hundley
**Sr VP:* Rutger Gassner
**Sr VP:* Michele Urness
**VP:* Elizabeth Benditt
**VP:* Martha Salinas
**VP:* Doretta Watson
Plnt Mgr: Steve Ruoff

MULTI SPECIALTY GROUP PRACTICE
See NORTH SUTTER MEDICAL FOUNDATION

MULTI SPECIALTY MEDICAL SVC
See VISALIA MEDICAL CLINIC INC

D-U-N-S 00-547-0265
MULTI-AD SERVICES INC
KWIKEE
1720 W Detweiller Dr, Peoria, IL 61615-1695
Tel (309) 690-5231 *Founded/Ownrshp* 1945
Sales 31.6MM^E *EMP* 238^E
SIC 2741 7374 3993 Miscellaneous publishing; Computer graphics service; Signs & advertising specialties

D-U-N-S 83-512-2672
MULTI-BANK SECURITIES INC
(*Suby of* MULTI-BANK SERVICES LTD) ★
1000 Town Ctr Ste 2300, Southfield, MI 48075-1239
Tel (248) 291-1100 *Founded/Ownrshp* 1987
Sales 38.1MM *EMP* 70
Accts Carnaghi & Schwark Pllc Rose
SIC 6211 Security brokers & dealers; Security brokers & dealers
CEO: David Maccagnone
Pr: Michael Drews
CFO: Mark Cleland
CFO: Michael Karsner
Ofcr: Merlin Elsner
Ex VP: James Schneider
Sr VP: John Coban
Sr VP: Tim Peacock
Sr VP: Amy Wheatley
VP: Jeffrey Jaworski
VP: John Korody
VP: Paul Lukasiewicz
VP: Krista Martin
VP: Bill Morris
VP: Robert Samples
VP: Gail Schaumann
VP: Alex Silva
VP: Bob Thomas

D-U-N-S 15-737-1626
MULTI-BANK SERVICES LTD
1000 Town Ctr Ste 2300, Southfield, MI 48075-1239
Tel (248) 291-1100 *Founded/Ownrshp* 1985
Sales 45.0MM *EMP* 100
Accts Carnaghi & Schwark Pllc Cpas
SIC 6211 Investment firm, general brokerage; Investment firm, general brokerage
Ch Bd: David T Maccagnone
CFO: Mark Cleland
CFO: Mark Coulmbu
**Ch:* Michael Drews

D-U-N-S 96-479-8508 IMP
■ **MULTI-CHEM GROUP LLC**
(*Suby of* HALLIBURTON CO) ★
424 S Chadbourne St, San Angelo, TX 76903-6926
Tel (325) 223-6200 *Founded/Ownrshp* 2011
Sales 1.0MMM^E *EMP* 1,024
SIC 1389 Oil field services; Servicing oil & gas wells; Oil field services; Servicing oil & gas wells
Pr: David J Lesar

**Treas:* Jon Grottis
**VP:* James Archer
VP: Cade Bourque
VP: Don Hallett
VP: Don Leatherwood
VP: Thane Schaffer
Dir IT: Jim Russum
IT Man: Fernando Coronado
IT Man: Jorge Velarde
Plnt Mgr: Randy Harris

D-U-N-S 80-110-2489 IMP/EXP
MULTI-CHEM INC
HOUSTON TECHNOLOGY CENTER
15865 Intl Plz Dr Ste 200, Houston, TX 77032-2594
Tel (281) 442-1222 *Founded/Ownrshp* 1993
Sales 21.8MM^E^ *EMP* 50
SIC 5169 Chemicals & allied products
Pr: James B Archer
VP: Danny Durham
VP: Don Hallett
**VP:* Jorge Velarde
Dir IT: Curtis Conkle
Opers Mgr: Glenn Drysdale
Snr Mgr: Michael Harless
Snr Mgr: Ying Jiang
Snr Mgr: Lionel Karber
Snr Mgr: Nihal Obeyesekere

D-U-N-S 96-635-8074
■ **MULTI-COLOR AUSTRALIA LLC**
(*Suby of* MULTI-COLOR CORP) ★
4053 Clough Woods Dr, Batavia, OH 45103-2587
Tel (513) 381-1480 *Founded/Ownrshp* 2010
Sales 13.6MM^E^ *EMP* 388
SIC 2754 2752 2759 Commercial printing, gravure; Commercial printing, lithographic; Advertising literature: printing; Laser printing; Commercial printing, gravure; Commercial printing, lithographic; Advertising literature: printing; Laser printing
CEO: Nigel A Vinecombe
CFO: Sharon E Birkett
VP: Mary T Fetch

D-U-N-S 12-129-8590 IMP
▲ **MULTI-COLOR CORP**
4053 Clough Woods Dr, Batavia, OH 45103-2587
Tel (513) 381-1480 *Founded/Ownrshp* 1985
Sales 810.7MM *EMP* 3,550
Accts Grant Thornton Llp Cincinnati
Tkr Sym LABL *Exch* NGS
SIC 2759 2679 2672 Labels & seals: printing; Labels, paper: made from purchased material; Labels (unprinted), gummed: made from purchased materials; Labels & seals: printing; Labels, paper: made from purchased material; Labels (unprinted), gummed: made from purchased materials
Pr: Nigel A Vinecombe
Ch Bd: Robert R Buck
COO: Floyd E Needham
COO: Vadis A Rodato
CFO: Sharon E Birkett
VP: Greg Myers
VP: Stephen Riccardi

D-U-N-S 60-836-2760
MULTI-CONVEYOR LLC
25 Industrial Dr, Winneconne, WI 54986-8534
Tel (920) 582-7960 *Founded/Ownrshp* 1994
Sales 30.1MM^E^ *EMP* 73
SIC 3535 5084 Conveyors & conveying equipment; Industrial machinery & equipment
Mktg Dir: Cheryl Miller

D-U-N-S 05-964-1266
MULTI-CRAFT CONTRACTORS INC
AIRWORKS
2300 N Lowell Rd, Springdale, AR 72764-1842
Tel (479) 751-4330 *Founded/Ownrshp* 1986
Sales 79.7MM^E^ *EMP* 392
SIC 1711 3441 1731

D-U-N-S 13-556-3695
MULTI-FAMILY BUILDING PRODUCTS
DIRECT LUMBER & DOOR COLORADO
8000 E 40th Ave, Denver, CO 80207-1711
Tel (303) 778-7650 *Founded/Ownrshp* 2000
Sales 23.1MM^E^ *EMP* 29^E^
SIC 5031 Building materials, interior
Pr: Tom Kospelecky
**Ch:* Russ Brown
Sls Mgr: Pat Scheurer

D-U-N-S 93-167-4360
MULTI-FAMILY PROPERTIES LTD
EMBREYPARTNERSLTD.COM
1020 Ne Loop 410 Ste 700, San Antonio, TX 78209-1220
Tel (210) 824-6044 *Founded/Ownrshp* 1992
Sales 29.5MM^E^ *EMP* 60^E^
SIC 6552 1522 Subdividers & developers; Apartment building construction
Pr: Walter M Embrey Jr
**COO:* Michael L Elder
**Sr VP:* Douglas A Koch
**VP:* Suzanne White

MULTI-FINANCIAL
See PLASTIPAK PACKAGING INC

D-U-N-S 13-184-4185
▲ **MULTI-FINELINE ELECTRONIX INC**
8659 Research Dr, Irvine, CA 92618-4291
Tel (949) 453-6800 *Founded/Ownrshp* 1984
Sales 633.1MM^E^ *EMP* 6,290
Tkr Sym MFLX *Exch* NGS
SIC 3672 Printed circuit boards; Printed circuit boards
Pr: Reza Meshgin
CFO: Thomas Kampfer
CFO: Thomas D Kampfer
Treas: Craig Riedel
Ex VP: Christine Besnard
Ex VP: Lance Jin
Ex VP: Thomas Lee
Prgrm Mgr: Chris Jong
Prgrm Mgr: Sukhjiwan Tiwana
Prgrm Mgr: Hao Zhou
Genl Mgr: Sam Tabarani

Board of Directors: Philippe Lemaitre, Linda Yuen-Ching Lim, James McCluney, Donald K Schwanz, Roy Chee Keong Tan, Sam Yau

D-U-N-S 04-571-3625
MULTI-FLOW DISPENSERS OF OHIO INC
4705 Van Epps Rd, Brooklyn Heights, OH 44131-1013
Tel (216) 641-0200 *Founded/Ownrshp* 1963
Sales 51.3MM^E^ *EMP* 100
SIC 5145 7359 Syrups, fountain; Vending machine rental; Syrups, fountain; Vending machine rental
Pr: Stanley Klein
VP: Bill Fazzone

D-U-N-S 18-114-0658
MULTI-MANAGEMENT SERVICES INC
(*Suby of* BAPTIST HEALTH) ★
904 Autumn Rd Ste 500, Little Rock, AR 72211-3738
Tel (501) 202-4366 *Founded/Ownrshp* 1984
Sales 13.5MM^E^ *EMP* 800
SIC 8082 8071 7011 7349 Visiting nurse service; Testing laboratories; Hotels; Chemical cleaning services; Cleaning service, industrial or commercial; Visiting nurse service; Testing laboratories; Hotels; Chemical cleaning services; Cleaning service, industrial or commercial
Pr: Larry Lazenby

D-U-N-S 06-286-9383
MULTI-METAL & MFG CO INC
1500 E Interstate 30, Rockwall, TX 75087-6235
Tel (972) 771-1376 *Founded/Ownrshp* 1973
Sales 23.1MM^E^ *EMP* 97
SIC 3444 Sheet metalwork
Ch: Avos E Wicker
**Pr:* Kevin Fite
**CFO:* Erin Walker
VP: Kevin Crawford
**VP:* Juan Carlos Luna
Sls Mgr: Josh Buckner

MULTI-METALS
See TKW LLC

MULTI-PACK CHICAGO
See MULTI-PACK SOLUTIONS LLC

D-U-N-S 04-098-6426
MULTI-PACK SOLUTIONS LLC
MULTI-PACK CHICAGO
1804 W Central Rd, Mount Prospect, IL 60056-2230
Tel (847) 635-6772 *Founded/Ownrshp* 2010
Sales 71.4MM^E^ *EMP* 250^E^
SIC 7389 2844 Packaging & labeling services; Towelettes, premoistened; Packaging & labeling services; Towelettes, premoistened
Pt: Les Teague
**Pt:* Brian McInerney
VP Sls: Don Fritz

D-U-N-S 02-615-6662 IMP/EXP
MULTI-PLASTICS EXTRUSIONS INC
(*Suby of* MULTI-PLASTICS INC) ★
600 Dietrich Ave, Hazleton, PA 18201-7754
Tel (570) 455-2021 *Founded/Ownrshp* 2009
Sales 60.2MM^E^ *EMP* 175
SIC 2821 Plastics materials & resins; Plastics materials & resins
Pr: John Parsio Jr
VP: Paul Hinspeter
Dir IT: Joanne Cragen
Opers Mgr: Michael Abboud
Opers Mgr: Juan Escobar
Plnt Mgr: Tom Hughes
Ql Cn Mgr: Edward Lengen
VP Sls: Wesley Hall

D-U-N-S 09-754-0397 IMP
MULTI-PLASTICS INC
7770 N Central Dr, Lewis Center, OH 43035-9404
Tel (740) 548-4894 *Founded/Ownrshp* 1979
Sales 210.1MM^E^ *EMP* 300
SIC 5162 Plastics film; Plastics film
Pr: John R Parsio
**CFO:* Michael T Hickey
**Ex VP:* John Parsio Jr
**VP:* Wesley Hall
**VP:* Steven Parsio
Exec: Kim Chalmers
CTO: Jim Lintz
Mfg Dir: Juan Escobar
Plnt Mgr: Larry Wright
Natl Sales: Robert Weber
Sls Dir: Don Hillman

D-U-N-S 00-965-5622
MULTI-SALES CO
MULTI-SLES/HARRISON DOORMASTER
5600 Fresca Dr, La Palma, CA 90623-1008
Tel (562) 803-3552 *Founded/Ownrshp* 1997
Sales 21.3MM^E^ *EMP* 53
SIC 5063 Electrical apparatus & equipment
Pr: Glenn Harrison
**VP:* Bob Laher
Brnch Mgr: Donald Aragon
Sales Exec: Todd Howard

D-U-N-S 83-570-2127
MULTI-SHOT LLC
MS ENERGY SERVICES
3335 Pollok Dr, Conroe, TX 77303-5702
Tel (936) 441-6630 *Founded/Ownrshp* 2004
Sales 322.8MM^E^ *EMP* 468^E^
SIC 1389 1381 Servicing oil & gas wells; Drilling oil & gas wells; Servicing oil & gas wells; Drilling oil & gas wells
Snr Mgr: Allen Neel
CFO: Scot Bork
Dir IT: Chris Cole
Sftwr Eng: Philip Stanley
VP Opers: Paul Culbreth
VP Opers: Paul Motley

MULTI-SLES/HARRISON DOORMASTER
See MULTI-SALES CO

D-U-N-S 78-329-8813
MULTI-SYSTEMS INC
MSI
7600 N 15th St Ste 250, Phoenix, AZ 85020-4337
Tel (602) 870-4200 *Founded/Ownrshp* 1991
Sales 26.7MM^E^ *EMP* 170
SIC 7371 5045 7372 Computer software development; Computer software; Prepackaged software; Computer software development; Computer software; Prepackaged software
Pr: Richard Munson
**Sec:* Joni Munson
Chf Mktg O: Laura Kirby-Meck
**Ex VP:* Gene Sullivant Cha
**Ex VP:* Charles Haaker
VP: Robert Bansfield
**VP:* Joel Soderbeg
CTO: Ted Warring
QA Dir: April Cheek
Sftwr Eng: Antoinette Silago
Sftwr Eng: Bismarck Soto

D-U-N-S 05-274-7987 IMP
MULTI-TECH SYSTEMS INC (MN)
2205 Woodale Dr, Saint Paul, MN 55112-4973
Tel (763) 785-3500 *Founded/Ownrshp* 1970, 2007
Sales 46.1MM^E^ *EMP* 241^E^
Accts Olsen Thielen & Co Ltd Min
SIC 3661 Modems; Multiplex equipment, telephone & telegraph; Telephones & telephone apparatus; Modems; Multiplex equipment, telephone & telegraph; Telephones & telephone apparatus
CEO: Stefan Lindvall
**Pr:* Patricia Sharma
**COO:* Del Palacheck
**CFO:* Bruce Richardson
VP: Mike Kydd
VP Bus Dev: Bryan Eagle
Snr Sftwr: Carol Almquist
**CTO:* Scott Wilken
Dir IT: Ian Schwartzman
IT Man: Steven Husby
IT Man: Laurie Permaloff

D-U-N-S 00-463-8750
MULTI-VIEW INC (TX)
MULTIVIEW
7701 Las Colinas Rdg, Irving, TX 75063-8081
Tel (972) 402-7070 *Founded/Ownrshp* 2000
Sales 116.7MM^E^ *EMP* 700^E^
SIC 7313 Electronic media advertising representatives; Electronic media advertising representatives
CEO: Scott Bedford
COO: Cathy Breden
**COO:* Steve Fullbright
COO: Edward F Haye
**CFO:* Omar Choucair
**Chf Mktg O:* Todd Ebert
VP: Joe Brannon
Creative D: Jonny Hill
Comm Man: Callie Cady
**Prin:* Mark Colodny
**Prin:* Raj Gajwani

D-U-N-S 00-223-5726
■ **MULTI-WALL PACKAGING CORP**
(*Suby of* NATIONAL PACKING SUPPLY) ★
1 N Bridge St, Gary, IN 46404-1073
Tel (219) 882-0070 *Founded/Ownrshp* 2009
Sales 24.6MM^E^ *EMP* 100
SIC 5199 Packaging materials
CEO: Charles Dunn

D-U-N-S 05-244-3439
■ **MULTI-WALL PACKAGING CORP**
(*Suby of* NATIONAL PACKING SUPPLY) ★
130 S 20th St, Irvington, NJ 07111
Tel (973) 374-0704 *Founded/Ownrshp* 1950
Sales 75.3MM^E^ *EMP* 550
SIC 2631 2671 2653 Packaging board; Packaging paper & plastics film, coated & laminated; Corrugated & solid fiber boxes; Packaging board; Packaging paper & plastics film, coated & laminated; Corrugated & solid fiber boxes
Pr: Charles Dunn
**VP:* Jeffrey Dunn
Plnt Mgr: Shakar Dyal

MULTI-WAY LIFE PLUS
See LIFE PLUS INTERNATIONAL

D-U-N-S 03-001-6992
MULTIBAND CORP
(*Suby of* GOODMAN NETWORKS INC) ★
5605 Green Circle Dr # 100, Minnetonka, MN 55343-4525
Tel (763) 504-3000 *Founded/Ownrshp* 2013
Sales 725.1MM^E^ *EMP* 3,612^E^
SIC 4841 4813 Cable & other pay television services; Cable television services; ; Cable & other pay television services; Cable television services;
CEO: James Mandel
**COO:* Kent Whitney
CFO: Jeff Tillman
Bd of Dir: Jonathan Dodge
**Ofcr:* Steven M Bell
Ex VP: Mitch Clarke
VP: Roy Henry
VP: Ryan Kemp
VP: J B Mattingly
VP: Larry Zucchero
Exec: Razvan Tomsa

D-U-N-S 07-915-3655
MULTIBAND SUBSCRIBER SERVICES INC
(*Suby of* MULTIBAND CORP) ★
5605 Green Circle Dr, Minnetonka, MN 55343-4523
Tel (763) 504-3000 *Founded/Ownrshp* 2013
Sales 13.1MM^E^ *EMP* 350
SIC 4841 Subscription television services; Subscription television services
CEO: James L Mandel

D-U-N-S 08-234-0415 IMP
MULTIBASE INC
(*Suby of* DOW CORNING CORP) ★
3835 Copley Rd, Copley, OH 44321-1671
Tel (330) 666-0505 *Founded/Ownrshp* 1988
Sales 29.3MM^E^ *EMP* 85
SIC 2821 Plastics materials & resins; Plastics materials & resins
Pr: Brian Schell
**Pr:* Gifford Shearer
**Treas:* Joseph Rinaldi
**VP:* Thomas G Tangney
Exec: Gifford Sheare

D-U-N-S 13-384-9450 IMP/EXP
MULTICAM INC
(*Suby of* ROSEWOOD PRIVATE INVESTMENTS INC) ★
1025 W Royal Ln, Dallas, TX 75261
Tel (972) 929-4070 *Founded/Ownrshp* 2014
Sales 82.5MM^E^ *EMP* 252^E^
SIC 3545 Machine tool attachments & accessories
Pr: Kris Hachette
CFO: Douglas Trinh
Netwrk Mgr: Richard Humphrey
Opers Mgr: Tony McGrew
VP Sls: David Scheffrahn
Mktg Dir: Kelsey Smith
Sls Dir: Kris Hanchette
Sls Mgr: John Harris

D-U-N-S 08-025-4246
MULTICARE ASSOCIATES OF TWIN CITIES PA
FRIDLEY MEDICAL CENTER
480 Osborne Rd Ne Ste 100, Minneapolis, MN 55432-2781
Tel (763) 785-4500 *Founded/Ownrshp* 1964
Sales 24.2MM^E^ *EMP* 250
SIC 8011 Medical centers; Medical centers
CEO: Kevin Bailey
CFO: Kurt Neil
Dir IT: Peter Pha
Surgeon: Jens Strand
Obsttrcn: Stacy Noyes
Doctor: Joy Anderson MD
Doctor: Eleanor Beltran
Doctor: Janis Dimants MD
Doctor: Christopher Luhman
Doctor: Allan Olson
Doctor: Phillip Schiller

D-U-N-S 19-512-8640
MULTICARE HEALTH SYSTEM
ALLENMORE HOSPITAL
316 M L King Jr Way # 314, Tacoma, WA 98405-4260
Tel (253) 403-1000 *Founded/Ownrshp* 1986
Sales 1.5MMM^E^ *EMP* 6,510
Accts Kpmg Llp Seattle Washington
SIC 8062 8093 8069 General medical & surgical hospitals; Specialty outpatient clinics; Children's hospital; General medical & surgical hospitals; Specialty outpatient clinics; Children's hospital
Pr: Diane Cecchettini
Mng Pt: Andrea L Hartley
**Pr:* Theresa M Boyle
**CFO:* Vince Schmitz
CFO: Vincent Schmitz
Ofcr: Claire Spain-Remy
Ofcr: Catherine Wakefield
**Ex VP:* Florence Chang
**Sr VP:* Sarah M Horsman
**Sr VP:* Lois I Bernstein
Sr VP: Erik Rasmussen
Sr VP: Lester Reed
Exec: Kate Bechtold
Exec: Ginger Fraley
Exec: Pamela A Hannah
Dir Rad: Jim Sapienza

D-U-N-S 14-833-9765
MULTICARE HOME HEALTH
710 Fawcett Ave, Tacoma, WA 98402-5504
Tel (253) 459-8355 *Founded/Ownrshp* 1977
Sales 5.9MM^E^ *EMP* 280
SIC 8082 Home health care services; Home health care services
CEO: Dave Larson
IT Man: Rick Neumann

D-U-N-S 01-193-0984
MULTICARE SKILLED HOME HEALTH CARE INC (ID)
MULTI CARE STAFFING
324 S Meridian Rd Ste 14, Meridian, ID 83642-2900
Tel (208) 887-7719 *Founded/Ownrshp* 1996
Sales 6.6MM^E^ *EMP* 300
SIC 8082 Home health care services; Home health care services
Pr: Robin Wallis

D-U-N-S 61-140-0938
MULTICORP INC
69 W Main St, Westminster, MD 21157-4839
Tel (410) 876-5000 *Founded/Ownrshp* 2002
Sales 15.6MM^E^ *EMP* 500^E^
SIC 7349 Building maintenance services; Building cleaning service; Hospital housekeeping; Janitorial service, contract basis; Building maintenance services; Building cleaning service; Hospital housekeeping; Janitorial service, contract basis
Pr: Philip Maffei
**VP:* Robert Merena

D-U-N-S 03-375-6628
MULTICORP MANAGEMENT GROUP INC
SHELL FOOD MARTS
205 N Lewis St, Lagrange, GA 30240-2756
Tel (706) 837-0599 *Founded/Ownrshp* 1985
Sales 22.7MM^E^ *EMP* 200^E^
SIC 5171 5411 Petroleum terminals; Convenience stores, independent; Petroleum terminals; Convenience stores, independent
Pr: Needham C Mallory

D-U-N-S 09-269-0833 IMP
MULTICRAFT INTERNATIONAL LIMITED PARTNERSHIP
4341 Highway 80, Pelahatchie, MS 39145-2918
Tel (601) 854-8801 *Founded/Ownrshp* 1991
Sales 33.6MM^E^ *EMP* 130

SIC 3699 3711 Electrical equipment & supplies; Automobile assembly, including specialty automobiles; Electrical equipment & supplies; Automobile assembly, including specialty automobiles
Genl Pt: Andrew Mallinson
Ql Cn Mgr: Randall Hott
Ql Cn Mgr: Larry Savell

D-U-N-S 08-745-1712
MULTICULTURAL COMMUNITY SERVICE OF PIONEER VALLEY INC
WEST STREET INN
1000 Wilbraham Rd, Springfield, MA 01109-2050
Tel (413) 782-2500 *Founded/Ownrshp* 1979
Sales 10.7MM^E *EMP* 317
Accts James Lowe Cpa Inc Chicopee
SIC 8322 Social service center; Social service center
**Treas:* Bernard S Cohen
Sr Cor Off: Sadie Murray
Brnch Mgr: Karl Krueger
MIS Dir: David Chambers

D-U-N-S 01-075-8716
MULTICULTURAL KIDS INC
6332 Franklin Bluff Dr, El Paso, TX 79912-8155
Tel (877) 686-7357 *Founded/Ownrshp* 2006
Sales 45.0MM *EMP* 2
SIC 5961 Educational supplies & equipment, mail order
**Prin:* Lynne Raspet

D-U-N-S 10-113-0755
MULTICULTURAL RADIO BROADCASTING INC
WAY BROADCASTING
207 William St Fl 11, New York, NY 10005
Tel (212) 966-1059 *Founded/Ownrshp* 1991
Sales 67.2MM^E *EMP* 300
SIC 4832 Radio broadcasting stations; Radio broadcasting stations
CEO: Arthur Liu
**COO:* Gene Heinamyer
**CFO:* Sean Kim
**CFO:* Young C Kim
**VP:* Yvonne Liu
Admn Mgr: Regina Leuag
Genl Mgr: Sherman Ngan
CTO: Jim Glogowski
IT Man: Bing Chen
Pgrm Dir: Sunny Chan
Pgrm Dir: Gene Heinemeyer

D-U-N-S 88-406-9915 IMP
MULTIEXPORT FOODS INC
AQUAFARMS INTERNATIONAL
703 Nw 62nd Ave Ste 510, Miami, FL 33126-4688
Tel (305) 364-0009 *Founded/Ownrshp* 1994
Sales 194.0MM *EMP* 15
SIC 5146 Seafoods; Seafoods
CEO: Jose Ramon Gutierrez
**VP:* Andres Lyon
**VP:* Jason Paine

MULTIFAB
See MULTILINK INC

D-U-N-S 18-351-9099 IMP
MULTIFAB INC
3808 N Sullivan Rd Bldg 6, Spokane Valley, WA 99216-1618
Tel (509) 924-6631 *Founded/Ownrshp* 1987
Sales 77.5MM^E *EMP* 145^E
SIC 5085 2542 Fasteners, industrial: nuts, bolts, screws, etc.; Staplers & tackers; Packing, industrial; Partitions & fixtures, except wood; Office & store showcases & display fixtures; Racks, merchandise display or storage: except wood; Fasteners, industrial: nuts, bolts, screws, etc.; Staplers & tackers; Packing, industrial; Partitions & fixtures, except wood; Office & store showcases & display fixtures; Racks, merchandise display or storage: except wood
Pr: Timothy B Smith
COO: Al Boschma
Plnt Mgr: Mike Veale
Plnt Mgr: Toffer Wise
Sales Asso: Don Burnet
Sales Asso: Brian Marchant

D-U-N-S 04-767-7224 IMP
MULTIFILM PACKAGING CORP
1040 N Mclean Blvd, Elgin, IL 60123-1709
Tel (847) 695-7600 *Founded/Ownrshp* 2008
Sales 25.8MM^E *EMP* 55
Accts Plante & Moran Pllc Elgin I
SIC 3081 Packing materials, plastic sheet
CEO: Olle Mannertorp
**Pr:* Christopher Rogers
VP: Robert Tate
IT Man: Dan Acevedo
Sales Asso: Ida Mannertorp

D-U-N-S 60-973-9115
MULTIFRESH INC
CROOK BROTHERS
250 Grey Flats Rd, Beckley, WV 25801-5873
Tel (304) 252-7711 *Founded/Ownrshp* 1989
Sales 30.8MM^E *EMP* 50
SIC 5148 Fresh fruits & vegetables
Pr: Kenneth Crook
VP: Keith Crook

D-U-N-S 14-468-3042
MULTIGON INDUSTRIES INC
525 Executive Blvd # 140, Elmsford, NY 10523-1240
Tel (914) 376-5200 *Founded/Ownrshp* 1985
Sales 22.5MM *EMP* 85
SIC 5047 Medical equipment & supplies; Medical equipment & supplies
Pr: William Stern
VP: Fidel Howard
Off Mgr: Michelle Montoya

MULTIGRAINS BAKERY
See MULTIGRAINS INC

D-U-N-S 00-998-9815 IMP
MULTIGRAINS INC
MULTIGRAINS BAKERY
117 Water St, Lawrence, MA 01841-4720
Tel (978) 691-6100 *Founded/Ownrshp* 1996
Sales 38.0MM^E *EMP* 205
SIC 2051 Bread, cake & related products; Bread, cake & related products
Pr: Joseph A Faro
VP: Joseph Holovach
QC Dir: Rachael Popek
Sls Mgr: Elie Cohen
Sls Mgr: Darren Gaiero

D-U-N-S 06-191-1483 IMP
MULTILINE TECHNOLOGY INC
75 Roebling Ct, Ronkonkoma, NY 11779-9202
Tel (631) 249-8300 *Founded/Ownrshp* 1979
Sales 28.1MM^E *EMP* 160
SIC 3559 Electronic component making machinery; Electronic component making machinery
Pr: Michael Angelo
CFO: John A Karcher
**VP:* David Angelo
IT Man: Lynn McCann
Sls Mgr: Mary Endres

D-U-N-S 10-786-2732 IMP
MULTILINK INC
MULTIFAB
580 Ternes Ln, Elyria, OH 44035-6252
Tel (440) 366-6966 *Founded/Ownrshp* 1983
Sales 134.0MM^E *EMP* 140
SIC 5063 3829 Wire & cable; Cable testing machines; Wire & cable; Cable testing machines
Pr: Steven Kaplan
COO: Bernadette Golas
**VP:* Kathy Kaplan
VP: Michael Shaw
Off Mgr: Julie Prenatt
QA Dir: Chris Slivka
Sales Exec: Steve Pribula
VP Sls: Matt Ternes
Mktg Mgr: Brad Setliff
Manager: Mike Walsh
Sls Mgr: Sam Belfiore-Smith

D-U-N-S 17-403-4611
MULTIMEDIA CABLEVISION OF CHICAGO RIDGE INC
COX COMMUNICATIONS
901 S George Wash Blvd, Wichita, KS 67211-3901
Tel (316) 262-4270 *Founded/Ownrshp* 1995
Sales NA *EMP* 850
SIC 4841 4813 1731

D-U-N-S 80-321-2356 IMP
■ **MULTIMEDIA GAMES HOLDING CO INC**
(*Suby of* EVERI HOLDINGS INC) ★
206 Wild Basin Rd B400, West Lake Hills, TX 78746-3309
Tel (512) 334-7500 *Founded/Ownrshp* 2014
Sales 104.5MM^E *EMP* 280^E
SIC 3944 Electronic game machines, except coin-operated; Video game machines, except coin-operated; Electronic game machines, except coin-operated; Video game machines, except coin-operated
Pr: Ram V Chary
CFO: Adam Chibib
Sr VP: Mickey D Roemer
VP: Jason Kremer
VP: Clint Owen
VP: Valerie Siegrist
Sftwr Eng: Richard Dalfonso
Sls&Mrk Ex: Tommy Gassick
Sls Dir: Jesse Debruin

MULTIMEDIA GAMES, INC.
See EVERI GAMES INC

D-U-N-S 60-331-7447 IMP
MULTIMETCO INC
1610 Frank Akers Rd, Anniston, AL 36207-6763
Tel (800) 824-5092 *Founded/Ownrshp* 1982
Sales 21.4MM^E *EMP* 52
SIC 3341 3339 Recovery & refining of nonferrous metals; Primary nonferrous metals
Pr: James B Robert
VP: Pat Sullivan
Dept Mgr: Lyn Johnston

D-U-N-S 09-004-7283
MULTINATIONAL INSURANCE CO INC
(*Suby of* ASEGURADORA ANCON S.A.)
510 Ave Munoz Rivera, San Juan, PR 00918-3354
Tel (787) 758-0909 *Founded/Ownrshp* 1961, 2011
Sales NA *EMP* 81
SIC 6331 Fire, marine & casualty insurance
Pr: Edgardo Banrhyn
**Treas:* Maria Julia Garcia
**VP:* Lois Reivere

D-U-N-S 09-119-3235
MULTINATIONAL LIFE INSURANCE CO
510 Ave Munoz Rivera, San Juan, PR 00918-3354
Tel (787) 758-8080 *Founded/Ownrshp* 1969
Sales NA *EMP* 100
SIC 6311 Life insurance
CEO: Fernando Rivera Munoz
**Treas:* Maria Julia Garcia
**Sr VP:* Fernando Rivera Arroyo
Sr VP: Rolando M Rivera
**VP:* Armando Andujar
**VP:* Livia Flores
**VP:* Edgardo R Martinez
**VP:* Jose M Morillo
**VP:* Carmin Munoz
**VP:* Jorge E Seda

D-U-N-S 84-893-2554 IMP
MULTIPET INTERNATIONAL INC
MULTIPLUSH
245 W Commercial Ave, Moonachie, NJ 07074-1609
Tel (201) 935-2974 *Founded/Ownrshp* 1994
Sales 41.6MM *EMP* 40
Accts Cohnreznick Llp Roseland Nj
SIC 5199 Pet supplies; Gifts & novelties; Pet supplies; Gifts & novelties
Pr: Mark Hirschberg
**Ex VP:* Leslie Yellin
**VP:* Richard Koliner
**VP:* Stephen Misovic
Opers Mgr: Perry Figueroa
VP Sls: Rich Rivlin

D-U-N-S 07-301-9465
MULTIPLAN INC
115 5th Ave Fl 7, New York, NY 10003-1004
Tel (212) 780-2000 *Founded/Ownrshp* 2014
Sales 314.8MM^E *EMP* 506
SIC 8742 Hospital & health services consultant; Hospital & health services consultant
CEO: Mark Tabak
V Ch: Rubin Shelly
Pr: Rudy Gontek
COO: Kevin Williams
CFO: David Redmond
Ex VP: Marcy Feller
Ex VP: Michael Ferrante
Ex VP: Dale White
VP: Frank Budzisz
VP: Andrew Hoffmann
VP: Dave Manning
Exec: Julia Hilliard
Exec: Bill Kirsch
Exec: Brenda Lalande
Exec: Barbara Miller
Exec: Deanna Parker
Exec: Tony Pettigrew
Exec: Linda Rockford
Exec: Brenda Steinle
Exec: Ricki Wilkey

D-U-N-S 02-297-7484
MULTIPLE MYELOMA RESEARCH FOUNDATION INC
MMRF
383 Main Ave Fl 5, Norwalk, CT 06851-1586
Tel (203) 229-0464 *Founded/Ownrshp* 1998
Sales 28.6MM *EMP* 21
SIC 8733 Medical research; Medical research
Pr: Walter Capone
**Ch Bd:* Kathy Giusti
VP: Daniel Auclair
VP: Robert Lucas
VP: Anne Quinn Young
Dir Rx: Jeremy Carmichael
Comm Man: Jeffrey Spiegel
Prgrm Mgr: Stefanie Kasven
Pgrm Dir: Anne Young

D-U-N-S 13-092-9862
MULTIPLE SCLEROSIS ASSOCIATION OF AMERICA
375 Kings Hwy N, Cherry Hill, NJ 08034-1013
Tel (856) 488-4500 *Founded/Ownrshp* 1970
Sales 26.4MM *EMP* 54
Accts Raffa Pc Washington Dc
SIC 8699 Charitable organization; Charitable organization
Pr: Douglas G Franklin
**Ch Bd:* James M Anderson
COO: Robert Rapp
CFO: Gary Wallace
Treas: Robert Reichenbach

D-U-N-S 06-933-2443
MULTIPLE SYSTEMS INDUSTRIAL CONSTRUCTION CO INC (SC)
MSI CONSTRUCTION CO
745 Greenwood Rd, West Columbia, SC 29169-5320
Tel (803) 796-3324 *Founded/Ownrshp* 1974
Sales 20.8MM^E *EMP* 95^E
SIC 1711 3441 Mechanical contractor; Fabricated structural metal
Pr: Damon Walker
**Sec:* Esther S Walker
**VP:* Grant Hunter
Dir Risk M: Jesse Strong

MULTIPLUSH
See MULTIPET INTERNATIONAL INC

D-U-N-S 06-089-5679 IMP/EXP
MULTIQUIP INC
(*Suby of* ITOCHU INTERNATIONAL INC) ★
18910 Wilmington Ave, Carson, CA 90746-2820
Tel (310) 537-3700 *Founded/Ownrshp* 1991
Sales 278.8MM^E *EMP* 383
SIC 5063 5082 3645 Generators; General construction machinery & equipment; Garden, patio, walkway & yard lighting fixtures: electric; Generators; General construction machinery & equipment; Garden, patio, walkway & yard lighting fixtures: electric
CEO: Tom Yasuda
**Pr:* Gary Moskovitz
**CFO:* Jim Henehan
**Sr VP:* Bob Graydon
**Sr VP:* Mike Howlett
VP: Michael Ferguson
Rgnl Mgr: Ken Bartelli
Rgnl Mgr: Todd Jones
Ql Cn Mgr: Preston Adams

D-U-N-S 00-801-6078
MULTIRESTAURANTS CONCEPTS LTD
MULTI RESTAURANTS GROUP
8008 Cedar Springs Rd # 27, Dallas, TX 75235-2852
Tel (214) 353-3959 *Founded/Ownrshp* 1994
Sales 13.5MM^E *EMP* 500
SIC 5812 5947 Eating places; Gift, novelty & souvenir shop; Eating places; Gift, novelty & souvenir shop
Pr: Danny Bruce
**CFO:* Rosemary Roberts
**VP:* Vicki Allen

D-U-N-S 78-626-0190
MULTISEAL INC
4320 Hitch Peters Rd, Evansville, IN 47711-2831
Tel (812) 428-3422 *Founded/Ownrshp* 1991
Sales 29.6MM^E *EMP* 120
SIC 2891 Sealants; Adhesives; Sealants; Adhesives
Pr: Gary M Rust
**VP:* Robert C Rust

D-U-N-S 00-211-3744 IMP/EXP
MULTISORB TECHNOLOGIES INC (NY)
325 Harlem Rd, Buffalo, NY 14224-1893
Tel (716) 824-8900 *Founded/Ownrshp* 1961
Sales 78.8MM^E *EMP* 500
SIC 2819

D-U-N-S 83-042-4185
MULTISORB TECHNOLOGIES INTERNATIONAL LLC
325 Harlem Rd, Buffalo, NY 14224-1825
Tel (716) 824-8900 *Founded/Ownrshp* 2008
Sales 31.4MM^E *EMP* 400
SIC 2819 Industrial inorganic chemicals; Industrial inorganic chemicals
Pr: James Renda
Off Admin: Sean Laughlin
Dir IT: Jim Lines
Mktg Mgr: Paige Weis
Snr Mgr: Jeff Brown
Snr Mgr: Rick Cellich
Snr Mgr: Michael Crisanti
Snr Mgr: Russell D'Anna
Snr Mgr: Joseph Dennis
Snr Mgr: Dave Elliason
Snr Mgr: Samuel Incorvia

D-U-N-S 06-476-6827
MULTISOURCE MANUFACTURING LLC (MN)
MULTISOURCE MINNETONKA DIV
10300 Bren Rd E, Minnetonka, MN 55343-9048
Tel (952) 456-5550 *Founded/Ownrshp* 1986, 1998
Sales 44.8MM *EMP* 243
SIC 3599

MULTISOURCE MINNETONKA DIV
See MULTISOURCE MANUFACTURING LLC

MULTISPECIALTY MEDICAL CLINIC
See MEDICAL ASSOCIATES CLINIC PC

D-U-N-S 18-108-2470 EXP
MULTISTACK LLC
1065 Maple Ave, Sparta, WI 54656-2379
Tel (608) 366-2400 *Founded/Ownrshp* 2002
Sales 65.4MM^E *EMP* 145
SIC 3585 Parts for heating, cooling & refrigerating equipment; Parts for heating, cooling & refrigerating equipment
**CFO:* Charles Kenyon
CFO: Kathy Mathison
Manager: Scott Degier
Sls Mgr: Dan Pabst
Sales Asso: Andy Patton
Snr Mgr: David Longacre

D-U-N-S 87-993-8595
MULTISYSTEMS RESTAURANTS INC
SIZZLER
1155 Ave Ponce De Leon, San Juan, PR 00907-3803
Tel (787) 273-3180 *Founded/Ownrshp* 1991
Sales 35.5MM *EMP* 900
SIC 5812 Steak restaurant; Steak restaurant
Pr: Carlos Trigo
**Ch Bd:* Jorge Colon Jerena

D-U-N-S 82-677-7609 IMP
MULTITECH INDUSTRIES INC
350 Village Dr, Carol Stream, IL 60188-1828
Tel (630) 784-9200 *Founded/Ownrshp* 1993
Sales 74.9MM *EMP* 70
SIC 5013 Automotive supplies & parts; Automotive supplies & parts
Pr: Rahul Parikh
Sales Exec: Anthony Falcone

D-U-N-S 18-264-8600 IMP
■ **MULTITEST ELECTRONIC SYSTEMS INC**
(*Suby of* XCERRA CORP) ★
3021 Kenneth St, Santa Clara, CA 95054-3416
Tel (408) 988-6544 *Founded/Ownrshp* 2013
Sales 76.3MM^E *EMP* 300
SIC 3825 3674 3624 Semiconductor test equipment; Semiconductors & related devices; Brushes & brush stock contacts, electric; Semiconductor test equipment; Semiconductors & related devices; Brushes & brush stock contacts, electric
Pr: Dave Tacelli

D-U-N-S 84-420-3914
MULTITRONICS INC
325 Electronics Blvd Sw B, Huntsville, AL 35824-2221
Tel (256) 461-8883 *Founded/Ownrshp* 1989
Sales 28.8MM *EMP* 6
SIC 4225 General warehousing & storage; General warehousing & storage
Pr: Ashok Mahbubani
**Treas:* Amrita Mahbubani

D-U-N-S 17-844-4147 IMP/EXP
MULTIVAC INC
(*Suby of* MULTIVAC EXPORT AG)
11021 N Pomona Ave, Kansas City, MO 64153-1146
Tel (816) 891-0555 *Founded/Ownrshp* 1988
Sales 72.0MM^E *EMP* 185^E
SIC 5084

MULTIVIEW
See MULTI-VIEW INC

D-U-N-S 18-859-7889
MULTIVISION INC
10565 Fairfax Blvd # 301, Fairfax, VA 22030-3135
Tel (703) 225-1000 *Founded/Ownrshp* 2003
Sales 37.9MM^E *EMP* 300
SIC 7379 ;
Pr: Srikanth Ramachandran
COO: Ashwin Bharath
**VP:* Ravi Addepalli
Snr Mgr: Shoban Babu

D-U-N-S 05-597-3192
MULTNOMAH ATHLETIC CLUB
1849 Sw Salmon St, Portland, OR 97205-1794
Tel (503) 223-6251 *Founded/Ownrshp* 1891
Sales 33.8MM *EMP* 500
Accts Moss Adams Llp Portland Or

SIC 7997 Tennis club, membership; Swimming club, membership; Racquetball club, membership; Tennis club, membership; Swimming club, membership; Racquetball club, membership
Ex Dir: Norm Rich
**Pr:* Carl Burnham III
**CFO:* Tim Arbogast
Treas: Alex Nikitin
Bd of Dir: Mary Jubitz
Exec: Philippe Boulot
Comm Dir: Kelly Harris
Comm Man: Michole Jensen
Ex Dir: Lisa Bendt
Genl Mgr: Norman Rich
Art Dir: Gregory Barrett

MULTNOMAH COUNTY
See COUNTY OF MULTNOMAH

D-U-N-S 83-146-8454
MULTNOMAH COUNTY LIBRARY
COUNTY LIBRARY ADMINISTRATION
(*Suby of* COUNTY OF MULTNOMAH) ★
205 Ne Russell St, Portland, OR 97212-3708
Tel (503) 988-5402 *Founded/Ownrshp* 2009
Sales 14.2MM^E *EMP* 699
SIC 8231 Libraries; Libraries
Comm Dir: Shawn Cunningham

D-U-N-S 09-129-5832
MULTNOMAH EDUCATION SERVICE DISTRICT (OR)
11611 Ne Ainsworth Cir, Portland, OR 97220-9017
Tel (503) 255-1841 *Founded/Ownrshp* 1947
Sales 70.3MM *EMP* 606
Accts Talbot Korvola & Warwick Llp
SIC 8211 Public elementary & secondary schools; Public elementary & secondary schools
COO: Edward Schmitt
Off Admin: Jill Seiler
CTO: Eric Gustafson
IT Man: Don Hicks
Snr Mgr: Kathryn Skimas

D-U-N-S 06-288-0539
MULVANE UNIFIED SCHOOL DISTRICT 263
628 E Mulvane St, Mulvane, KS 67110-1663
Tel (316) 777-1102 *Founded/Ownrshp* 1885
Sales NA *EMP* 280
SIC 9411 8211 Administration of educational programs; School board; Administration of educational programs; School board
Schl Brd P: Steve Fry

D-U-N-S 00-639-7566
MULZER CRUSHED STONE INC
TELL CITY CONCRETE SUPPLY
534 Mozart St, Tell City, IN 47586-2446
Tel (812) 547-7921 *Founded/Ownrshp* 1939
Sales 495.1MM^E *EMP* 450
SIC 1422 3273 5191 5085 Crushed & broken limestone; Ready-mixed concrete; Limestone, agricultural; Industrial supplies; Crushed & broken limestone; Ready-mixed concrete; Limestone, agricultural; Industrial supplies
Pr: Kenneth Mulzer Jr
IT Man: Patty Hawhoose
Mtls Mgr: Don Gengelbach
Site Mgr: Steve Speedy
Sfty Mgr: Matthew Bunner
Sales Exec: Ed Hagedorn
Mktg Dir: Natalie Maasberg
Sls Mgr: Russ Woosley
Sales Asso: Carlyn Greene

MUM
See MAHARISHI UNIVERSITY OF MANAGEMENT

D-U-N-S 02-196-7880
MUMFORD AND MILLER CONCRETE INC
1005 Industrial Rd, Middletown, DE 19709-1097
Tel (302) 378-7736 *Founded/Ownrshp* 1976
Sales 28.4MM^E *EMP* 140
SIC 1629 1611 1771 Land preparation construction; Highway & street construction; Concrete work; Land preparation construction; Highway & street construction; Concrete work
Pr: Richard L Mumford
**Sec:* Bernadette Mumford

D-U-N-S 02-655-3909
MUMMES INC
120 Hwy 173 N, Hondo, TX 78861
Tel (830) 426-3313 *Founded/Ownrshp* 1977
Sales 31.4MM *EMP* 46
Accts Parr & Associates San Antonio
SIC 5191 5261 Farm supplies; Fertilizer & fertilizer materials; Feed; Seeds & bulbs; Nurseries & garden centers; Fertilizer; Lawn & garden supplies; Farm supplies; Fertilizer & fertilizer materials; Feed; Seeds & bulbs; Nurseries & garden centers; Fertilizer; Lawn & garden supplies
Pr: Russell Meyer
**Sec:* Annette Billings
**VP:* Wade Swanson

D-U-N-S 78-702-6855 IMP
MUNCHKIN INC
7835 Gloria Ave, Van Nuys, CA 91406-1822
Tel (818) 893-5000 *Founded/Ownrshp* 1991
Sales 39.5MM^E *EMP* 133
SIC 3085 3069 5999 Plastics bottles; Teething rings, rubber; Bibs, vulcanized rubber or rubberized fabric; Infant furnishings & equipment; Plastics bottles; Teething rings, rubber; Bibs, vulcanized rubber or rubberized fabric; Infant furnishings & equipment
CEO: Steven B Dunn
Pr: Mark Hatherill
Pr: Tony Hu
Pr: Andrew Keimach
COO: Jeff Hale
CFO: Gary Rolfes
Ch: David J Dunn
VP: Marc Hayes
VP: John Lika
Comm Man: Jennifer Campana
Dir IT: Philippe Brisset
Board of Directors: Lisa Licht

D-U-N-S 02-555-7281
MUNCHS SUPPLY LLC
1901 Ferro Dr, New Lenox, IL 60451-3505
Tel (815) 723-1111 *Founded/Ownrshp* 1956
Sales 40.7MM^E *EMP* 100^E
SIC 5075

D-U-N-S 12-157-9734
MUNCIE AVIATION CO
5201 N Walnut St, Muncie, IN 47303-9778
Tel (765) 289-7141 *Founded/Ownrshp* 1932
Sales 36.7MM *EMP* 56
Accts Whitinger & Company Llc Munci
SIC 4581 Aircraft maintenance & repair services; Hangars & other aircraft storage facilities; Aircraft maintenance & repair services; Hangars & other aircraft storage facilities
Pr: Martin W Ingram
Ch Bd: Frank Ball
**CFO:* Rebecca Stansberry
VP: Stephen J Larrimore
**VP:* Richard D Manes
**VP:* William Roundtree
Sales Asso: Todd Shoup

D-U-N-S 17-259-0168
MUNCIE CHEVROLET CADILLAC INC
AMERICAN CHVRLET CDLLAC MUNCIE
6580 W Hometown Blvd, Muncie, IN 47304-5957
Tel (765) 289-1801 *Founded/Ownrshp* 2003
Sales 24.2MM^E *EMP* 70
SIC 5511 7538 7532 Automobiles, new & used; General automotive repair shops; Body shop, automotive; Automobiles, new & used; General automotive repair shops; Body shop, automotive
Pr: Steve Deanda
Sls Mgr: Rod Huffman
Sls Mgr: Lee Robbins

D-U-N-S 07-206-1641
MUNCIE COMMUNITY SCHOOLS
2501 N Oakwood Ave, Muncie, IN 47304-2399
Tel (765) 747-5205 *Founded/Ownrshp* 1958
Sales 75.7MM^E *EMP* 1,600
SIC 8211 Public senior high school; Public junior high school; Public elementary school; Public senior high school; Public junior high school; Public elementary school
CFO: Mark Burnhardt
Ex Dir: Julie A Bailey

D-U-N-S 00-603-9655
MUNCIE NOVELTY CO INC
INDIANA TICKET COMPANY
9610 N State Road 67, Muncie, IN 47303-9123
Tel (765) 288-8301 *Founded/Ownrshp* 1936
Sales 26.5MM^E *EMP* 100
SIC 2791 2759 2752 Typesetting; Schedule, ticket & tag printing & engraving; Commercial printing, lithographic
Pr: David Broyles
**Sec:* Joseph Broyles
**VP:* James Broyles
Off Mgr: Connie Nauck
Off Admin: Jo Dunnington
Plnt Mgr: Ted Shockley
Plnt Mgr: Sonny Stahl

D-U-N-S 00-603-9523 IMP
MUNCIE POWER PRODUCTS INC
(*Suby of* INTERPUMP GROUP SPA)
201 E Jackson St Ste 500, Muncie, IN 47305-2838
Tel (765) 284-7721 *Founded/Ownrshp* 1935
Sales 67.3MM^E *EMP* 300
SIC 3714 5013 Motor vehicle parts & accessories; Motor vehicle supplies & new parts; Motor vehicle parts & accessories; Motor vehicle supplies & new parts
CEO: Terry L Walker
**CEO:* Ray Chambers
**CEO:* Terry L Walker
Treas: Connie Gregory
VP: Chris Fancher
VP: George Halleck
Off Mgr: Melissa Melton
VP Opers: Bill Moore
Mfg Dir: Larry Kouval
Manager: Jasen Combs
Sls Mgr: Gregg Henricks
Board of Directors: Terry L Walker

D-U-N-S 60-583-7970 IMP
MUNCIE RECLAMATION AND SUPPLY CO
MUNCIE TRANSIT SUPPLY
3720 S Madison St, Muncie, IN 47302-5757
Tel (765) 288-1971 *Founded/Ownrshp* 2007
Sales 25.1MM^E *EMP* 54
SIC 5013 Automotive supplies & parts
Pr: Timothy Wayland
**CEO:* Dane Cornell
**CFO:* Dan Axelson
**VP:* Shaun Huxford

MUNCIE TRANSIT SUPPLY
See MUNCIE RECLAMATION AND SUPPLY CO

MUNCIPAL WELL & PUMP
See MIDWEST WELL SERVICES INC

D-U-N-S 88-453-3373
MUNCY HOMES INC
1567 Route 442 Hwy, Muncy, PA 17756-6853
Tel (570) 546-2264 *Founded/Ownrshp* 1973
Sales 74.4MM^E *EMP* 450
SIC 2452 Modular homes, prefabricated, wood; Modular homes, prefabricated, wood
Pr: Thomas M Saltsgiver
**Sec:* Jo Ann Saltsgiver
Ex VP: Mike Clementoni
**VP:* Bill Huber
**VP:* William F Huber
Exec: Kim Rager
Genl Mgr: Dennis Morgan
Genl Mgr: Dick Shives

D-U-N-S 08-522-0614
MUNDELEIN CONSOLIDATED HIGH SCHOOL DISTRICT
DISTRICT 120
1350 W Hawley St, Mundelein, IL 60060-1504
Tel (847) 949-2200 *Founded/Ownrshp* 2008
Sales 42.4MM *EMP* 152^E
Accts Miller Cooper & Co Ltd Dee
SIC 8211 Public senior high school; Public senior high school
Bd of Dir: Patrick Browne
Bd of Dir: Al Hitzke
Bd of Dir: Paul Lohr
Bd of Dir: Laura Mellon
Bd of Dir: Gerald Munley
VP: Joanne Anderson
Exec: Ron Girard
Comm Dir: Matt Farmer
Instr Medi: Doug Lillydahl
Instr Medi: Rebecca Plaza
Psych: George Kaider

D-U-N-S 80-488-3411
MUNDET INC
919 E Main St Ste 1130, Richmond, VA 23219-4622
Tel (804) 644-3970 *Founded/Ownrshp* 2012
Sales 45.9MM^E *EMP* 160
SIC 2621 2952 Cigarette paper; Asphalt felts & coatings; Cigarette paper; Asphalt felts & coatings
Pr: Stephen Young
VP: Harvey Robert C L
Plnt Mgr: Larry Humbert
Sls Dir: Philip James

MUNDI WESTPORT GROUP
See WESTPORT CORP

MUNDY COMPANY
See MUNDY PLANT MAINTENANCE INC

D-U-N-S 18-602-1093
MUNDY CONTRACT MAINTENANCE INC
11150 S Wilcrest Dr # 300, Houston, TX 77099-4388
Tel (281) 530-8711 *Founded/Ownrshp* 1985
Sales 38.1MM^E *EMP* 1,200
SIC 7349 Building maintenance services; Building maintenance services
Pr: David A Mundy
**VP:* John Mundy
Dir IT: Scott Bratton

D-U-N-S 04-034-2321
MUNDY PLANT MAINTENANCE INC
MUNDY COMPANY
11150 S Wilcrest Dr # 300, Houston, TX 77099-4388
Tel (281) 530-8711 *Founded/Ownrshp* 1955
Sales 345.9M *EMP* 322
SIC 7699 Industrial equipment services; Industrial equipment services
Pr: Edward W Foster
**COO:* Peter Sciles
**CFO:* David Hartsell
Ex VP: Erich Stolz
**VP:* Andy Beard
**VP:* Scott Bratton
Area Mgr: Donald Coley
Off Mgr: Rebecca Buckner
Off Mgr: Lisa Montemayor
Off Mgr: Stephanie Scott
Software D: Rodney Adams

D-U-N-S 36-204-5338 IMP
MUNEKATA AMERICA INC
(*Suby of* MUNEKATA CO.,LTD.)
2320 Paseo Delas Amer 1 Ste 112, San Diego, CA 92154
Tel (619) 661-8080 *Founded/Ownrshp* 2008
Sales 38.5MM *EMP* 500
SIC 3089 Plastic hardware & building products; Plastic hardware & building products
CEO: Nobumitsu Endo
**Sec:* Koji Yanagida
Genl Mgr: Masamichi Nagasawa

D-U-N-S 17-404-6495
MUNGER BROS LLC
MUNGER FARM
786 Road 188, Delano, CA 93215-9508
Tel (661) 721-0390 *Founded/Ownrshp* 1998
Sales 10.0MM *EMP* 600
SIC 0179 Avocado orchard; Avocado orchard
Genl Mgr: Cynthia Klein

MUNGER FARM
See MUNGER BROS LLC

MUNGER FARMS
See MONARCH NUT CO LLC

D-U-N-S 01-071-1661
MUNGER TOLLES & OLSON FOUNDATION
355 S Grand Ave Ste 3500, Los Angeles, CA 90071-3161
Tel (213) 683-9100 *Founded/Ownrshp* 1962
Sales 25.9MM^E *EMP* 470
Accts Dreyer Edmonds & Robbins Los
SIC 8111 General practice attorney, lawyer; General practice attorney, lawyer
CEO: O'Malley M Miller
**Pr:* Robert Johnson
**CFO:* Larry Kleinberg
**VP:* Mark Helm
**VP:* Steven B Weisburd
**VP:* Bart Williams

D-U-N-S 03-841-5555
MUNGER TOLLES & OLSON LLP
355 S Grand Ave Fl 35, Los Angeles, CA 90071-3161
Tel (213) 683-9100 *Founded/Ownrshp* 2001
Sales 30.1MM^E *EMP* 124^E
SIC 8111 Specialized law offices, attorneys
Pt: Sandra Seville-Jones
Ex Dir: Thomas B Edwards
IT Man: Ted Dane

D-U-N-S 05-248-8140
MUNGO HOMES INC (SC)
441 Western Ln, Irmo, SC 29063-9230
Tel (803) 749-9000 *Founded/Ownrshp* 1974, 1998
Sales 24.2MM^E *EMP* 55
SIC 1531 1521

MUNIC
See INFINITE DIAMONDS & JEWELLERY INC

D-U-N-S 05-620-2625
MUNICH AMERICAN REASSURANCE CO PAC INC
MARC LIFE
(*Suby of* MUNICH-AMERICAN HOLDING CORP) ★
56 Perimeter Ctr E # 200, Atlanta, GA 30346-2290
Tel (770) 350-3200 *Founded/Ownrshp* 1995
Sales NA *EMP* 230
SIC 6331 Fire, marine & casualty insurance & carriers; Fire, marine & casualty insurance & carriers
Pr: Michael G Dekoning
Pr: Gregory Brandner
Pr: David Bruggeman
Pr: Leo Tinkham
COO: James Sweeney
CFO: Michael W Farley
Treas: Steven K Thompson
Sr VP: Paige S Freeman
Sr VP: ARI J Lindner
Sr VP: Michael Taht
Sr VP: Michael S Taht
VP: Skowronnek Bill
VP: Andrew Carroll
VP: Mark Costello
VP: Melinda Dressler
VP: Dieter S Gaubatz
VP: Scott Gilliam
VP: Kevin Glasgow
VP: Gina Guzman
VP: D Hintz
VP: Robert Lund

D-U-N-S 96-274-5555
MUNICH HEALTH NORTH AMERICA INC
(*Suby of* MUNICH-AMERICAN HOLDING CORP) ★
555 College Rd E, Princeton, NJ 08540-6616
Tel (609) 243-4200 *Founded/Ownrshp* 2010
Sales NA *EMP* 4^E
SIC 6331 Fire, marine & casualty insurance & carriers
Prin: Luigi Lupo
Pr: Scott Machut
Pr: Travis Micucci
COO: Donna Peterson
Sr VP: Jim Acker
Sr VP: Michael Shevlin
VP: Bill Udzienski
Snr Mgr: Nicholas Potenza

D-U-N-S 15-737-8407
MUNICH RE AMERICA BROKERS INC
(*Suby of* MUNICH-AMERICAN HOLDING CORP) ★
685 College Rd E, Princeton, NJ 08540-6625
Tel (609) 243-4900 *Founded/Ownrshp* 1994
Sales NA *EMP* 1,100
SIC 6321 6311 Reinsurance carriers, accident & health; Life insurance; Reinsurance carriers, accident & health; Life insurance
CEO: John Phelan
**Pr:* Anthony Kuczinski
**Pr:* George Roberts
**Ch:* Edward J Noonan
VP: Denise Ambrogio
**VP:* Donald F Merkel Jr
VP: Vincent Raspa
VP Mktg: Joseph Stuhl
VP Mktg: John Tracey

D-U-N-S 79-689-0044 IMP
MUNICH RE AMERICA CORP
(*Suby of* MUNICH-AMERICAN HOLDING CORP) ★
555 College Rd E, Princeton, NJ 08540-6616
Tel (609) 243-4200 *Founded/Ownrshp* 1991
Sales NA *EMP* 1,450
SIC 6331 Fire, marine & casualty insurance & carriers; Fire, marine & casualty insurance & carriers
CEO: Anthony J Kuczinski
**Pr:* Pina C Albo
Pr: James B Couch
Pr: Blaine Desmond
Pr: Joe Dintrone
Pr: John Vasturia
Pr: Peter J Walker
COO: Michael McMonagle
COO: Kari Parker
COO: Nick Young
CFO: Mike Farley
CFO: Anthony Kuczinski
CFO: George Oshaughnessey
CFO: Herma Pohlchristoph
Ofcr: Charlie Shamieh
**Ex VP:* Albert J Beer
**Ex VP:* Wolfgang Engshuber
Sr VP: Ashish Agarwal
Sr VP: Jill Beggs
Sr VP: Warren Britt
Sr VP: Arm Crouse

D-U-N-S 82-984-5325
MUNICH RE AMERICA HEALTHCARE
(*Suby of* MUNICH REINSURANCE AMERICA INC) ★
555 College Rd E, Princeton, NJ 08540-6616
Tel (609) 243-4893 *Founded/Ownrshp* 2009
Sales NA *EMP* 48^E
SIC 6321 Reinsurance carriers, accident & health
Pr: Robert Trainer
VP: James Camerino

D-U-N-S 00-698-0031
MUNICH REINSURANCE AMERICA INC
MUNICH-AMERICA GLOBAL SERVICES
(*Suby of* MUNICH RE AMERICA CORP) ★
555 College Rd E, Princeton, NJ 08540-6616
Tel (609) 243-4200 *Founded/Ownrshp* 1996
Sales NA *EMP* 1,200
SIC 6331 6311 Fire, marine & casualty insurance & carriers; Life insurance; Fire, marine & casualty insurance & carriers; Life insurance
Pr: Steven Levy
Pr: Anthony J Kuczinski
Pr: John Vasturia
CFO: M Steven Levy
Treas: Ray Cox
Ex VP: Wolfgang Engshuber

Sr VP: Jill Beggs
Sr VP: David Brown
Sr VP: Patrick Collins
Sr VP: Chris Daley
Sr VP: Daniel Fisher
Sr VP: Oliver Frase
Sr VP: Jim Higgins
Sr VP: Kenneth Jenkins
Sr VP: Edward Lang
Sr VP: Kevin McDermott
Sr VP: David O'Keefe
Sr VP: Peter Poshepny
Sr VP: Boccitto Princeton-Mram
Sr VP: Alden Provost
Sr VP: Michael Shevlin

D-U-N-S 04-197-9162 IMP
MUNICH WELDING CO INC
211 Eastern Blvd, Jeffersonville, IN 47130-2897
Tel (812) 282-0488 *Founded/Ownrshp* 1967
Sales 20.9MM^E *EMP* 70
SIC 3441 7692 Fabricated structural metal; Welding repair
Pr: Paul Ernstberger
**Sec:* F Laverne Ernstberger
**VP:* Dean Collins

MUNICH-AMERICA GLOBAL SERVICES
See MUNICH REINSURANCE AMERICA INC

D-U-N-S 12-887-3671 IMP/EXP
MUNICH-AMERICAN HOLDING CORP
(*Suby of* MUNCHENER RUCKVERSICHERUNGS-GESELLSCHAFT AG IN MUNCHEN)
555 College Rd E, Princeton, NJ 08540-6616
Tel (609) 243-4876 *Founded/Ownrshp* 2000
Sales NA *EMP* 3,912
SIC 6331 Fire, marine & casualty insurance & carriers; Fire, marine & casualty insurance & carriers
Pr: John P Phelan
CFO: Guy Perinotti
Treas: Steven Thompson
Sr VP: Michael Davis
VP: Raymond Cox
VP: Glenn Fogarty
VP: Gary Greene
VP: Eric Herbst
VP: Amy Klicker
VP: Gregory Lang
VP: Brian McCormick
VP: Stephen J Morello
VP: Douglas Paige
VP: Joseph Peppelman
VP: Edward Ryan
VP: Michael Shevlin
VP: Howard Taylor
VP: Frank Turner
VP: Bruce Weisgerber
VP: Kenneth Welsh

D-U-N-S 07-748-0432
MUNICIPAL AUTHORITY OF BOROUGH OF WEST VIEW
WEST VIEW WATER AUTHORITY
210 Perry Hwy, Pittsburgh, PA 15229-1862
Tel (412) 931-3292 *Founded/Ownrshp* 1942
Sales 27.7MM *EMP* 100
Accts Goff Backa Alfera & Company L
SIC 4941 8734 5087 4971 1623 Water supply; Testing laboratories; Service establishment equipment; Irrigation systems; Water, sewer & utility lines; Water supply; Testing laboratories; Service establishment equipment; Irrigation systems; Water, sewer & utility lines
Ch Bd: Thomas Witherel
**Ch:* Dennis Watson
**Treas:* Joseph Nowark
**V Ch Bd:* William King
Brnch Mgr: John Shuey
IT Man: John Devine
IT Man: David Hay

D-U-N-S 05-554-3425
MUNICIPAL AUTHORITY OF WESTMORELAND COUNTY
WESTMORELAND WATER AUTHORITY
124 Park N Pool Dr, New Stanton, PA 15672-2404
Tel (724) 834-6500 *Founded/Ownrshp* 1942
Sales 71.2MM *EMP* 272
Accts Deluzio & Company Llp Greens
SIC 4941 Water supply; Water supply
Ch: Randy Roadman
**Treas:* Jawdat Nikoula
Board of Directors: Dr Anthony Bompiani, Jerome Defabo Sr, Joseph Dreskler, A Keith Staso, Peter Wast

D-U-N-S 07-871-2546
MUNICIPAL CAPITAL APPRECIATION PARTNERS III (VA) LP
437 Madison Ave Ste 33c, New York, NY 10022-7049
Tel (212) 715-6090 *Founded/Ownrshp* 2012
Sales 21.0MM *EMP* 2
SIC 6798 Real estate investment trusts; Real estate investment trusts
Pt: Richard Corey
CFO: Jay Johnson

MUNICIPAL CENTER
See CITY OF LIMA

D-U-N-S 07-683-8143
MUNICIPAL CREDIT UNION
22 Cortlandt St Fl 24, New York, NY 10007-3153
Tel (212) 238-3300 *Founded/Ownrshp* 1917
Sales NA *EMP* 430
SIC 6062 State credit unions, not federally chartered; State credit unions, not federally chartered
CEO: William Porter
Pr: Corey Fernandes
**COO:* Norman Kohn
CFO: Shirley Laliberte
**CFO:* Kam Wong
Treas: Mick Lamedola
Ofcr: Eric Gong
Ofcr: Timothy Wheeler
Sr VP: Carole Porter
VP: John Beeson
VP: Richard Casamassa
VP: Katherine Dugmore
VP: Willie James
VP: Latosha McCoy
VP: Vincent Miller
VP: Leon Smith
VP: Jean Suffak

D-U-N-S 08-282-4566
MUNICIPAL ELECTRIC AUTHORITY OF GEORGIA
MEAG POWER
1470 Riveredge Pkwy, Atlanta, GA 30328-4640
Tel (770) 563-0300 *Founded/Ownrshp* 1975
Sales 748.5MM *EMP* 150^E
SIC 1623 Electric power line construction; Electric power line construction
Pr: Robert P Johnston
**Treas:* Steve A Rentfrow
VP: Daryl Ingram
VP: Scott Jones
VP: Gary Schaeff
**VP:* William J Yearta
Dir IT: Ron King
Dir IT: Nantambu Starks
Opers Mgr: Fred Shelby
Snr Mgr: Dale Dyer

D-U-N-S 18-215-7214
MUNICIPAL ELECTRIC UTILITY OF CITY OF CEDAR FALLS IOWA
CEDAR FALLS UTILITIES
1 Utility Pkwy, Cedar Falls, IA 50613-3358
Tel (319) 266-1761 *Founded/Ownrshp* 1913
Sales 269.0MM^E *EMP* 184
Accts Baker Tilly Virchow Krause Ll
SIC 4911 Electric services; Electric services
CEO: James Krieg
**Ch:* Roger A Kuete
Ofcr: Katie Burkhardt
Dir Bus: Steve Bernard
Netwrk Eng: Charles Dostale
Opers Supe: Ed Olthoff
Opers Mgr: Trent Hill
Plnt Mgr: Tom Risse

D-U-N-S 04-816-7923
MUNICIPAL EMERGENCY SERVICES INC
7 Poverty Rd Ste 85h, Southbury, CT 06488-2273
Tel (203) 364-0620 *Founded/Ownrshp* 2001
Sales 174.9MM^E *EMP* 330
SIC 5087 Firefighting equipment; Firefighting equipment
CEO: Thomas Hubregsen
**VP:* Jeff Johnson
**VP:* John Skaryak
Sls Mgr: Brian Alsup
Sales Asso: Dick Gorham

D-U-N-S 07-494-4935
MUNICIPAL EMPLOYEES CREDIT UNION OF BALTIMORE INC
MECU
7 E Redwood St Ste 1400, Baltimore, MD 21202-1106
Tel (410) 752-8313 *Founded/Ownrshp* 1936
Sales NA *EMP* 110
SIC 6062 9111 State credit unions, not federally chartered; Mayors' offices; State credit unions, not federally chartered; Mayors' offices
Ch Bd: Herman William
**Pr:* Burt Hash Jr
COO: Andrew Pataki
**V Ch Bd:* William Brown
Bd of Dir: Carey Dassatti
Bd of Dir: Mark Valentine
VP: William Copper
VP: Phillip Domzalski
VP: Eric Kapusinski
VP: Gary Martin
VP: Frank Richter
VP: Patricia Roberts
VP: Gaela Wilson

D-U-N-S 01-441-1420
MUNICIPAL EMPLOYEES RETIREMENT SYSTEM OF MICHIGAN
1134 Municipal Way, Lansing, MI 48917-7886
Tel (517) 703-9030 *Founded/Ownrshp* 1996
Sales NA *EMP* 126
SIC 6371 Pension funds
CEO: Anne Wagner
Pr: Ganesh Sundaram
**CFO:* Luke Huelskamp
Bd of Dir: Michael Brown
**VP:* Jeb Burns
VP: Judith Jarvis
Comm Dir: Lisa Brewer
Comm Man: Ann Cool
Rgnl Mgr: Marne Carlson
Rgnl Mgr: Sue Feinberg
Rgnl Mgr: Michael Overley

D-U-N-S 10-629-6296
MUNICIPAL ENERGY AGENCY OF MISSISSIPPI
6000 Lakeover Rd, Jackson, MS 39213-8011
Tel (601) 362-2252 *Founded/Ownrshp* 1978
Sales 37.8MM *EMP* 7
Accts Bkd Llp Jackson Ms
SIC 4911 Distribution, electric power; Distribution, electric power
Ex Dir: Geoffrey Wilson
**Ch:* James Quinn

D-U-N-S 17-550-3770
MUNICIPAL ENERGY AGENCY OF NEBRASKA (INC)
M E A N
8377 Glynoaks Dr, Lincoln, NE 68516-6304
Tel (402) 474-4759 *Founded/Ownrshp* 1981
Sales 139.2MM *EMP* 50
Accts Bkd Llp Lincoln Nebraska
SIC 4911 Distribution, electric power; Generation, electric power; Transmission, electric power; Distribution, electric power; Generation, electric power; Transmission, electric power
CEO: J Gary Stauffer
**COO:* Tim Sutherland
Genl Mgr: Larry Marquis

D-U-N-S 18-390-9514
MUNICIPAL GAS AUTHORITY OF GEORGIA
PUBLIC GAS PARTNERS
104 Townpark Dr Nw, Kennesaw, GA 30144-5556
Tel (770) 590-1000 *Founded/Ownrshp* 1987
Sales 390.1MM *EMP* 50
Accts Ernst & Young Llp Atlanta Ge
SIC 5172 Petroleum products
Pr: Arthur C Corbin
Treas: Carter Crawford

D-U-N-S 04-353-6940
MUNICIPAL GAS AUTHORITY OF MISSISSIPPI
MGAM
6000 Lakeover Rd, Jackson, MS 39213-8011
Tel (601) 362-2252 *Founded/Ownrshp* 1987
Sales 61.7MM *EMP* 7
Accts Bkd Llp Jackson Ms
SIC 4924 Natural gas distribution; Natural gas distribution
Ex Dir: Geoffrey Wilson

MUNICIPAL HALL
See GLOUCESTER TOWNSHIP (INC)

MUNICIPAL REVENUE COLLECTN CTR
See PUERTO RICO DEPARTMENT OF TREASURY

D-U-N-S 07-011-4368
MUNICIPAL SECURITIES RULEMAKING BOARD
1900 Duke St Ste 600, Alexandria, VA 22314-3461
Tel (703) 767-6600 *Founded/Ownrshp* 1975
Sales 31.9MM *EMP* 64
Accts Deloitte & Touch Llp Mclean
SIC 8611 Business associations; Business associations
Ex Dir: Lynnette Kelly
**CFO:* Elizabeth Wolfe
**Ofcr:* Robert Fippinger
Comm Man: Leah Szarek
CIO: Al Morisato
Genl Couns: Michael Post
Genl Couns: Larry Sandor
Counsel: Ben Tecmire
Pgrm Dir: Margaret Boorom
Snr Mgr: Jennifer Galloway

D-U-N-S 10-180-3666
MUNICIPAL SEPARATE SCHOOL DISTRICT TISHOMANGO COUNTY
TISHOMANGO COUNTY SPECIAL MUNI
1620 Paul Edmondson Dr, Iuka, MS 38852-1212
Tel (662) 423-3206 *Founded/Ownrshp* 1991
Sales 22.8MM^E *EMP* 450
SIC 8211 Specialty education; School board; Specialty education; School board
**Prin:* Nancy Parker

D-U-N-S 12-032-3696
MUNICIPAL UTILITIES BOARD OF DECATUR MORGAN COUNTY ALABAMA
DECATUR UTILITIES
1002 Central Pkwy Sw, Decatur, AL 35601-4848
Tel (256) 552-1400 *Founded/Ownrshp* 1933
Sales 32.3MM^E *EMP* 173
SIC 4939 Combination utilities; Combination utilities
Ch: Neal Holland
CFO: Steve Pinkle
**Genl Mgr:* Ray Hardin
Sales Exec: Anena Maxwell

D-U-N-S 79-430-7686
MUNICIPAL UTILITIES BOARD OF DECATUR MORGAN COUNTY ALABAMA
DECATUR UTILITIES
1002 Central Pkwy Sw, Decatur, AL 35601-4848
Tel (256) 552-1440 *Founded/Ownrshp* 1938
Sales 146.8MM *EMP* 157
Accts Alexander Thompson Arnold Pllc
SIC 4911 1321 1623 Distribution, electric power; Natural gas liquids; Water, sewer & utility lines; Distribution, electric power; Natural gas liquids; Water, sewer & utility lines
Ch: Neal Holland
**CFO:* Steve Pirkle

MUNICIPAL WATER DEPARTMENT
See CITY OF SAN BERNARDINO

MUNICIPALITY
See CITY OF SHERIDAN

D-U-N-S 09-105-9964
MUNICIPALITY OF GUANICA
MUNICIPIO DE GUANICA
Carretera Industrial Ramal 116, Guanica, PR 00653
Tel (787) 821-0402 *Founded/Ownrshp* 1898
Sales NA *EMP* 320^E
SIC 9111 Mayors' offices; Mayors' offices

D-U-N-S 12-068-0009
MUNICIPALITY OF HATILLO
Calle Frnklin D Roosevelt, Hatillo, PR 00659
Tel (787) 262-1504 *Founded/Ownrshp* 1925
Sales NA *EMP* 577
SIC 9111

D-U-N-S 13-606-9648
MUNICIPALITY OF LUQUILLO
14 De Julio St, Luquillo, PR 00773
Tel (787) 889-6228 *Founded/Ownrshp* 1895
Sales NA *EMP* 300
SIC 9111 Mayors' offices

D-U-N-S 09-110-6013
MUNICIPALITY OF MANATI
10 Calle Quinones, Manati, PR 00674-5013
Tel (787) 854-2024 *Founded/Ownrshp* 1732
Sales NA *EMP* 870
SIC 9111 Mayors' offices; Mayors' offices

D-U-N-S 09-280-3089
MUNICIPALITY OF MONROEVILLE
2700 Monroeville Blvd, Monroeville, PA 15146-2359
Tel (412) 856-1000 *Founded/Ownrshp* 1951
Sales NA *EMP* 311
Accts Hosack Specht Muetzel & Wood
SIC 9111 Mayors' offices; ; Mayors' offices;
Comm Dir: Henry Hoffman
Dir IT: Tina Mular

D-U-N-S 02-497-6649
MUNICIPALITY OF MOUNT LEBANON
710 Washington Rd Ste 1, Pittsburgh, PA 15228-2018
Tel (412) 343-3745 *Founded/Ownrshp* 1912
Sales NA *EMP* 585
Accts Maher Duessel Pittsburgh Pen
SIC 9111 City & town managers' offices; ; City & town managers' offices;
Ofcr: Josh Chops
Ofcr: Phil Quattrone
Snr Mgr: Mike Gallagher
Snr Mgr: Rodger Ricciuti

D-U-N-S 09-106-0020
MUNICIPALITY OF SABANA GRANDE
MUNICIPIO DE SABANA GRANDE
60 Esq Betances, Sabana Grande, PR 00637
Tel (787) 873-2060 *Founded/Ownrshp* 1993
Sales NA *EMP* 350
SIC 9111 Mayors' offices; Mayors' offices

D-U-N-S 15-692-6669
MUNICIPALITY OF TRUJILLO ALTO
212 Calle Dr Fernandez, Trujillo Alto, PR 00976-5938
Tel (787) 908-3107 *Founded/Ownrshp* 1801
Sales NA *EMP* 525
SIC 9111 Mayors' offices; ; Mayors' offices;

D-U-N-S 09-109-0266
MUNICIPIO DE ARECIBO
Jose De Diego St, Arecibo, PR 00612
Tel (787) 879-1561 *Founded/Ownrshp* 1616, 1898
Sales NA *EMP* 1,480
SIC 9199 Personnel agency, government; Personnel agency, government

D-U-N-S 09-058-4798
MUNICIPIO DE BAYAMON
Road 2 Km 11 Hm 3 St Ro, Bayamon, PR 00959
Tel (787) 780-5552 *Founded/Ownrshp* 1772
Sales NA *EMP* 3,300
SIC 9111 Mayors' offices; ; Mayors' offices;

D-U-N-S 09-109-9382
MUNICIPIO DE CATANO
129 Ave Barbosa, Catano, PR 00962-6070
Tel (787) 788-0404 *Founded/Ownrshp* 1927
Sales NA *EMP* 470
SIC 9111 City & town managers' offices; ; City & town managers' offices;
**Prin:* Edwin Rivera Sierra

D-U-N-S 10-409-8975
MUNICIPIO DE CAYEY
Calle Nunz Rom Esq Mnz Ri, Cayey, PR 00736
Tel (787) 738-2581 *Founded/Ownrshp* 1850
Sales NA *EMP* 800
SIC 9111 City & town managers' offices; ; City & town managers' offices;

D-U-N-S 04-953-4498
MUNICIPIO DE COMERIO
13 Calle Jose De Diego, Comerio, PR 00782-2531
Tel (787) 875-2300 *Founded/Ownrshp* 1806
Sales NA *EMP* 372
SIC 9111 Mayors' offices; Mayors' offices

MUNICIPIO DE GUANICA
See MUNICIPALITY OF GUANICA

D-U-N-S 82-715-2633
MUNICIPIO DE GUARBO
5 Carr 189 Km, Gurabo, PR 00778-3037
Tel (787) 712-1100 *Founded/Ownrshp* 1948
Sales NA *EMP* 300
SIC 9111

D-U-N-S 01-717-2623
MUNICIPIO DE JAYUYA
18 Calle Figuera, Jayuya, PR 00664-1409
Tel (787) 828-0900 *Founded/Ownrshp* 1911
Sales NA *EMP* 365
SIC 9111 ;

D-U-N-S 09-113-6168
MUNICIPIO DE JUNCOS
Paseo Escute, Juncos, PR 00777
Tel (787) 734-0335 *Founded/Ownrshp* 1797
Sales NA *EMP* 600
SIC 9111 City & town managers' offices; ; City & town managers' offices;

D-U-N-S 13-497-2710
MUNICIPIO DE MAYAGUEZ
Betances St Crnr Mckinley Corner Mckinley, Mayaguez, PR 00680
Tel (787) 834-8585 *Founded/Ownrshp* 1760
Sales NA *EMP* 1,555
SIC 9111 Mayors' offices; ; Mayors' offices;

D-U-N-S 09-112-7365
MUNICIPIO DE PONCE
Calle Comercio Frente, Ponce, PR 00731
Tel (787) 284-4141 *Founded/Ownrshp* 1692
Sales NA *EMP* 3,000
SIC 9111 City & town managers' offices; City & town managers' offices
Pr: Francisco Zayas Seijo
Pr: Rafael Santiago
Ex Dir: Jorge Hernandez

MUNICIPIO DE SABANA GRANDE
See MUNICIPALITY OF SABANA GRANDE

D-U-N-S 13-144-8151
MUNICIPIO DE SAN GERMAN
Luna St, San German, PR 00683
Tel (787) 892-3500 *Founded/Ownrshp* 1898
Sales NA *EMP* 400
SIC 9111

D-U-N-S 09-036-2773
MUNICIPIO DE SAN JUAN
SAN JUAN CITY HALL
1306 Ave Fernandez Juncos, San Juan, PR 00909-2521
Tel (787) 724-7171 *Founded/Ownrshp* 1898
Sales NA *EMP* 3,171^E
SIC 9111 Executive offices; Executive offices
Pr: Laura Del Carmen
**Prin:* Carlos A Acevedo

D-U-N-S 13-922-0714
MUNICIPIO DE SAN JUAN
EMPRESAS MUNICIPALES DEPT.
(*Suby of* MUNICIPIO DE SAN JUAN) ★
1205 Ave Ponce De Leon, San Juan, PR 00907-3916
Tel (787) 289-0310
Sales NA *EMP* 2,854^E
SIC 9611

D-U-N-S 09-117-5521
MUNICIPIO DE TOA ALTA
MAYOR'S OFFICE
Antonio R Barcelo St, TOA Alta, PR 00954
Tel (787) 873-8496 *Founded/Ownrshp* 1851
Sales NA *EMP* 300
SIC 9111

D-U-N-S 10-409-4545
MUNICIPIO DE UTUADO
27 Calle Betances, Utuado, PR 00641-2862
Tel (787) 894-3505 *Founded/Ownrshp* 1898
Sales NA *EMP* 325
SIC 9111 Mayors' offices; Mayors' offices

D-U-N-S 09-111-3944
MUNICPALITY OF GUAYNABO
Jose De Diego St Final, Guaynabo, PR 00969
Tel (787) 720-4040 *Founded/Ownrshp* 1912
Sales NA *EMP* 2,577^E
SIC 9111 Mayors' offices; ; Mayors' offices;

D-U-N-S 83-621-8479 IMP
MUNIRE FURNITURE CO INC
PERSONAL TOUCH FURNITURE
91 New England Ave, Piscataway, NJ 08854-4142
Tel (732) 339-6070 *Founded/Ownrshp* 2000
Sales 61.6MM *EMP* 55
Accts Ram Associates Cpas Hamilton
SIC 2511 Wood household furniture; Wood household furniture
Pr: Munir Hussain
VP: Norman Desouza
**VP:* Bill Wagner
CTO: Lavine D'Souza
Sales Exec: Robert Omansky
Natl Sales: Jeff Maken
Snr Mgr: Henry Duran

D-U-N-S 06-213-9076 IMP
MUNRO & CO INC (AR)
LAKE CATHERINE FOOTWEAR CO
3770 Malvern Rd, Hot Springs, AR 71901-6744
Tel (501) 262-6000 *Founded/Ownrshp* 1971, 1972
Sales 50.2MM^E *EMP* 1,200
SIC 3144 3149 Women's footwear, except athletic; Children's footwear, except athletic; Sandals, except rubber or plastic: children's; Women's footwear, except athletic; Children's footwear, except athletic; Sandals, except rubber or plastic: children's
CEO: Bruce Munro
Pr: Buddy Eoff
**CFO:* Jane Adams
**Ex VP:* Mollie Munro
Natl Sales: Ron Dillehay
VP Mktg: Molly Munro
Snr Mgr: David Swan

MUNRO COMPANIES
See ECLECTIC INDUSTRIES INC

D-U-N-S 01-045-9097
MUNROE INC (PA)
(*Suby of* SHELBURNE CORP)
1820 N Franklin St, Pittsburgh, PA 15233-2253
Tel (412) 231-0600 *Founded/Ownrshp* 1835
Sales 58.9MM^E *EMP* 336
SIC 3443 3634 3444 Boiler & boiler shop work; Electric housewares & fans; Sheet metalwork; Boiler & boiler shop work; Electric housewares & fans; Sheet metalwork
Ch Bd: Philip F Muck
**VP:* Stephen E Zemba
Genl Mgr: Frank Jeffrey
IT Man: Tim Scott
VP Mfg: Frank Massaro
Opers Supe: Randy Partridge
Plnt Mgr: John Kikta

MUNROE REGIONAL MEDICAL CENTER
See OCALA HEALTHCARE ASSOCIATES LLP

D-U-N-S 07-998-9869
MUNROE REGIONAL MEDICAL CENTER INC (FL)
1500 Sw 1st Ave, Ocala, FL 34471-6559
Tel (352) 351-7200 *Founded/Ownrshp* 1927
Sales 317.6MM^E *EMP* 2,179
SIC 8062 General medical & surgical hospitals; General medical & surgical hospitals
CEO: Richard D Mutarelli
Chf Rad: Rolando Prieto
**Sr VP:* Paul Clark
Sr VP: Lon Mc Pherson
**Sr VP:* Lon H McPherson
**Sr VP:* Marc J Miller
VP: Beth NC Call
VP: Cy Huffman
VP: Kathy Hurley
VP: Rich Muteralli
Dir Lab: Joy Nunez
Dir Rad: Ralf Barckhausen

D-U-N-S 17-779-2843
MUNSCH HARDT KOPF & HARR PC
3800 Lincoln Plz, Dallas, TX 75201-3429
Tel (214) 855-7588 *Founded/Ownrshp* 1985
Sales 61.0MM *EMP* 215
SIC 8111 Legal services; Legal services
Ch Bd: Glenn Callison
Mng Pt: James Jordan
**CFO:* Sharon Price
**Prin:* Jeff Dunn
Prd Mgr: Tim Reichert

MUNSON HALTHCARE GRAYLING HOSP
See MUNSON HEALTHCARE GRAYLING

D-U-N-S 15-193-0278
MUNSON HEALTHCARE
MUNSON HOSPICE HOUSE
1105 Sixth St, Traverse City, MI 49684-2349
Tel (800) 252-2065 *Founded/Ownrshp* 1985
Sales 6.5MM *EMP* 4,000
SIC 8062 General medical & surgical hospitals; General medical & surgical hospitals
CEO: Ed Ness
**Pr:* Al Pilong
COO: Derk Pronger
**Ch:* John Pelizzari
**Ch:* Dan Wolf
**Treas:* Connie Deneweth
**Treas:* Christina Macinnes
**Treas:* Dan McDavid
Ofcr: Rochelle Steimel
Sr VP: Mark R Anthony
VP: Cristen Dingman
VP: Kenneth Eike
VP: Jim P Fischer
VP: David S McGreaham
VP: Christopher J Podges
Exec: Ruth Bloomer
Dir: Heidi Gustine
Dir Rx: Clare Coles

D-U-N-S 07-977-1661
MUNSON HEALTHCARE GRAYLING (MI)
MUNSON HALTHCARE GRAYLING HOSP
(*Suby of* MUNSON HEALTHCARE) ★
1100 E Michigan Ave, Grayling, MI 49738-1312
Tel (989) 348-5461 *Founded/Ownrshp* 2014
Sales 15.4MM^E *EMP* 600^E
SIC 8062 General medical & surgical hospitals
Pr: Stephanie Riemer

MUNSON HOSPICE HOUSE
See MUNSON HEALTHCARE

D-U-N-S 06-017-9595 IMP
MUNSON MEDICAL CENTER
(*Suby of* MUNSON HEALTHCARE) ★
1105 Sixth St, Traverse City, MI 49684-2386
Tel (231) 935-6000 *Founded/Ownrshp* 1985
Sales 510.9MM *EMP* 3,100
SIC 8062 General medical & surgical hospitals; General medical & surgical hospitals
CEO: Edwin A Ness
Chf Rad: C Williams
**COO:* Derk Pronger
**CFO:* Edward Carlson
Ofcr: Kathy Warnes
VP: Eugene Lyons
VP: Paul Shirilla
Dir Lab: Julie Richards
Dir Rad: Frederick Brodeur
Dir Rad: Charlie Dziedzic
Chf Nrs Of: Kathleen Glaza

D-U-N-S 06-949-0167
MUNSTER MEDICAL RESEARCH FOUNDATION INC
COMMUNITY HOSPITAL
901 Macarthur Blvd, Munster, IN 46321-2901
Tel (219)-836-1600 *Founded/Ownrshp* 1985
Sales 465.4MM *EMP* 2,000
Accts Ernst & Young Us Llp Indianap
SIC 8062 General medical & surgical hospitals; General medical & surgical hospitals
Pr: Donald S Powers
CFO: Maryann Schalett
CFO: Marianne Shacklett
**Ch:* Frankie L Fesko
**Treas:* George E Watson
**Treas:* David E Wickland
Ofcr: Nancy Lund
**VP:* Joseph Morrow
Dir Risk M: Nancy Moser
Dir Rx: Elizabeth Clements
Dir Rx: Joan Miller

MUNTERS CARGOCAIRE
See MUNTERS USA INC

D-U-N-S 95-799-6341 IMP
MUNTERS CORP
(*Suby of* AB CARL MUNTERS)
79 Monroe St, Amesbury, MA 01913-3204
Tel (978) 241-1100 *Founded/Ownrshp* 1965
Sales 135.2MM^E *EMP* 500
SIC 3585 3822 3569 3564 Humidifiers & dehumidifiers; Air flow controllers, air conditioning & refrigeration; Filters, general line: industrial; Blowers & fans; Humidifiers & dehumidifiers; Air flow controllers, air conditioning & refrigeration; Filters, general line: industrial; Blowers & fans
Pr: Maj Britt Hallmark
CFO: Don Driscoll
**VP:* Mark Collins
VP: Paul Dinnage
VP: Britt Hallmark
VP: Hansi Krugei
Rgnl Mgr: Len Bosman
Genl Mgr: Camille Camasso
Off Mgr: Pernilla Karlsson
IT Man: Michael Rabkin
IT Man: Deborah Vandeberghe

D-U-N-S 04-416-8888 IMP
MUNTERS USA INC
MUNTERS CARGOCAIRE
(*Suby of* MUNTERS AB)
79 Monroe St, Amesbury, MA 01913-3204
Tel (978) 241-1100 *Founded/Ownrshp* 1978
Sales 57.0MM^E *EMP* 700
SIC 3585 Refrigeration & heating equipment; Refrigeration & heating equipment
Pr: Lennart Lindquist
Opers Mgr: Michele Waugh
Natl Sales: Russ Brown

D-U-N-S 07-235-0317 IMP/EXP
MUNTZ INDUSTRIES INC
AFC MACHINING DIVISION
710 Tower Rd, Mundelein, IL 60060-3818
Tel (847) 949-8280 *Founded/Ownrshp* 1974
Sales 41.0MM^E *EMP* 50
SIC 5084 3677 Metalworking machinery; Electronic coils, transformers & other inductors
Pr: David Muntz
**VP:* Steven Muntz

D-U-N-S 78-125-4792 IMP
MURAD INC
2121 Park Pl 1, El Segundo, CA 90245-4705
Tel (310) 726-0600 *Founded/Ownrshp* 1990
Sales 108.5MM^E *EMP* 169
SIC 5122 Cosmetics; Cosmetics
Pr: Howard Murad
COO: Beverly Parsons
CFO: Fred Gysi
Chf Mktg O: Elizabeth Ashmun
Ex VP: Jamie Thomas
VP: Ju Wong

D-U-N-S 02-478-0061 IMP
MURAKAMI MANUFACTURING USA INC (KY)
(*Suby of* MURAKAMI CORPORATION)
575 Watertower Byp, Campbellsville, KY 42718-8693
Tel (270) 469-3939 *Founded/Ownrshp* 2000
Sales 84.0MM *EMP* 275
SIC 3231 Mirrors, truck & automobile: made from purchased glass; Mirrors, truck & automobile: made from purchased glass
CEO: Masaharu Okuno
**Pr:* Michael Rodenberg
Sr VP: Toru Komatsu
Admn Mgr: Angie Miller
Genl Mgr: Eric Thompson
IT Man: Masaki Suzuki
Ql Cn Mgr: Jeff Hall
Ql Cn Mgr: Dana Mattingly
Ql Cn Mgr: Naoto Yoshimura
Sales Asso: Jason Wheat

D-U-N-S 00-146-8255 IMP
MURALO CO INC
ELDER & JENKS CO DIV
148 E 5th St, Bayonne, NJ 07002-4252
Tel (201) 437-0770 *Founded/Ownrshp* 1924, 1981
Sales 46.5MM^E *EMP* 250
SIC 2851 Paints & allied products; Paints & allied products
Pr: James S Norton
**CFO:* Chuck Lee Jr
VP: Chitra Jeurkar
**VP:* Edward Norton III
**VP:* Shashi Patel
**VP:* Peter Seaborg
MIS Mgr: Jim Harris
Plnt Mgr: Michael Norton

D-U-N-S 05-080-6447 IMP
MURANAKA FARM
11018 E Los Angeles Ave, Moorpark, CA 93021
Tel (805) 529-6692 *Founded/Ownrshp* 1966
Sales 148.6MM^E *EMP* 250
SIC 5148 Vegetables, fresh; Vegetables, fresh
Ch Bd: Roy Muranaka
**CEO:* Harry Muranaka
**Ex VP:* Charles Muranaka
**Prin:* Carolyn Muranaka
Prin: Frank Saltzman

D-U-N-S 06-258-7324 IMP
MURATA ELECTRONICS NORTH AMERICA INC (TX)
(*Suby of* MURATA MANUFACTURING CO.,LTD.)
2200 Lake Park Dr Se, Smyrna, GA 30080-7604
Tel (770) 436-1300 *Founded/Ownrshp* 1973
Sales 301.1MM^E *EMP* 1,200
SIC 5065 3675 3679 Electronic parts; Electronic capacitors; Electronic circuits; Electronic parts; Electronic capacitors; Electronic circuits
Pr: David Kirk
**Pr:* Hiroshi Jozuka
**Treas:* Hidekazu Tachikawa
Treas: Toshiyuki Yasutaka
**Ex VP:* Tom Yamamoto
**VP:* Tony Coalson
**VP:* John F Denslinger
VP: Farlin Halsey
**VP:* David McGinnis
Genl Mgr: Horacio Flores
IT Man: Tony Garcia

D-U-N-S 12-673-9320 IMP/EXP
MURATA MACHINERY USA HOLDINGS INC
MURATATEC
(*Suby of* MURATA MACHINERY,LTD.)
2120 Queen City Dr, Charlotte, NC 28208-2709
Tel (704) 394-8331 *Founded/Ownrshp* 2002
Sales 115.6MM^E *EMP* 220^E
SIC 3542 3552 5065 Punching & shearing machines; Textile machinery; Facsimile equipment; Punching & shearing machines; Textile machinery; Facsimile equipment
Pr: Masahiko Hattori

D-U-N-S 60-620-4030 IMP
MURATA MACHINERY USA INC
MURATEC
(*Suby of* MURATA MACHINERY USA HOLDINGS INC) ★
2120 Queen City Dr, Charlotte, NC 28208-2709
Tel (704) 875-9280 *Founded/Ownrshp* 2002
Sales 91.5MM^E *EMP* 220
SIC 5084 5085 3542 Textile & leather machinery; Metal refining machinery & equipment; Clean room supplies; Punching & shearing machines; Textile & leather machinery; Metal refining machinery & equipment; Clean room supplies; Punching & shearing machines
Pr: Masahiko Hattori
**CFO:* Dale R Mitchell
VP: Jim Cicora
Exec: Threse Scott
Rgnl Mgr: Sergio Tondato
Tech Mgr: Tom Matsui
Mtls Mgr: Mark Lindley
Trfc Mgr: Steven Pressley
Sales Exec: Larry Pellegrini
Natl Sales: Lloyd Keller
Mktg Mgr: Alisa Criswell

D-U-N-S 17-816-0560 IMP
MURATA POWER SOLUTIONS INC
(*Suby of* MURATA ELECTRONICS NORTH AMERICA INC) ★
11 Cabot Blvd, Mansfield, MA 02048-1137
Tel (508) 339-3000 *Founded/Ownrshp* 2007
Sales 65.1MM^E *EMP* 300^E
SIC 3679 3672 3629 3825 3674 3625 Electronic circuits; Wiring boards; Power conversion units, a.c. to d.c.: static-electric; Volt meters; Semiconductors & related devices; Relays & industrial controls; Electronic circuits; Wiring boards; Power conversion units, a.c. to d.c.: static-electric; Volt meters; Semiconductors & related devices; Relays & industrial controls
Pr: Tatsuo Bizen
**Pr:* William E Bachrach
**Treas:* Neil Daniels
**Treas:* Dawn Hattan
**Treas:* Trieu H Tran
**VP:* Ian J Harvie
**VP:* Yoshitaka Kotera
**VP:* Chris Viola
Genl Mgr: Tony Khazen
Genl Mgr: Walter Wong
Dir IT: Wayne McKay

MURATATEC
See MURATA MACHINERY USA HOLDINGS INC

MURATEC
See MURATA MACHINERY USA INC

D-U-N-S 07-259-7636 IMP
MURATEC AMERICA INC
(*Suby of* MURATA MACHINERY USA HOLDINGS INC) ★
3301 E Plano Pkwy Ste 100, Plano, TX 75074-7226
Tel (469) 429-3300 *Founded/Ownrshp* 2002
Sales 21.4MM^E *EMP* 50
SIC 5065 Facsimile equipment
CEO: James D'Emidio
**CFO:* Masahiko Hattori
Area Mgr: Richard Courtney
Area Mgr: Craig Ott
Sls Dir: Gregg Ross
Sls Mgr: Chris Wilson

D-U-N-S 07-412-7168
MURCHISON & CUMMING LLP
M & C
801 S Grand Ave Ste 900, Los Angeles, CA 90017-4624
Tel (213) 623-7400 *Founded/Ownrshp* 1974
Sales 20.1MM^E *EMP* 150
SIC 8111 General practice law office; General practice law office
Pt: Friedrich W Seitz
Sr Pt: Edmund G Farrell
Sr Pt: Guy R Gruppie
Sr Pt: Jean M Lawler
Sr Pt: Michael Lawler
Sr Pt: Don L Longo
Sr Pt: Michael D Mc Evoy
Sr Pt: Kenneth Moreno
Sr Pt: Steven L Smilay
Counsel: Joseph Fox

MURDER MYSTERY COMPANY, THE
See MURDER MYSTERY CO L L C

D-U-N-S 96-736-1752
MURDER MYSTERY CO L L C
MURDER MYSTERY COMPANY, THE
2424 Whspering Meadows Ct, Kentwood, MI 49512-3703
Tel (888) 643-2583 *Founded/Ownrshp* 2009
Sales 6.8MM^E *EMP* 500
SIC 5812 7922 Dinner theater; Theatrical companies; Dinner theater; Theatrical companies
Pr: Scott Cramton

D-U-N-S 00-265-9688
MURDOCH CENTER FOUNDATION INC
1600 E C St, Butner, NC 27509-2530
Tel (919) 575-1000 *Founded/Ownrshp* 1957
Sales 32.4M *EMP* 1,700
SIC 8699 Charitable organization; Charitable organization

MURDOCH'S RANCH & HOME SUPPLY
See RANCH AND HOME SUPPLY LLC

D-U-N-S 04-464-7022
MURDOCK CHEVROLET INC
2375 S 625 W, Woods Cross, UT 84010-8182
Tel (801) 298-8090 *Founded/Ownrshp* 1982
Sales 54.4MM^E *EMP* 100
SIC 5511 Automobiles, new & used; Pickups, new & used; Automobiles, new & used; Pickups, new & used
Pr: Kent Murdock
**VP:* J Blake Murdock

D-U-N-S 01-665-0564
MURDOCK HYUNDAI MURRAY LLC
4646 S State St, Murray, UT 84107-3816
Tel (801) 262-6401 *Founded/Ownrshp* 2012
Sales 30.5MM^E *EMP* 99^E
SIC 5511 Automobiles, new & used; Automobiles, new & used

D-U-N-S 00-119-3002 IMP
MURDOCK WEBBING CO INC (RI)
27 Foundry St, Central Falls, RI 02863-2348
Tel (401) 724-3000 *Founded/Ownrshp* 1936, 1954
Sales 33.0MM^E *EMP* 175
SIC 2241 Webbing, woven; Fabric tapes; Webbing, woven; Fabric tapes
CEO: Craig Pilgrim

**Pr:* Don A De Angelis
**CFO:* Ed Brodeur
**Off Mgr:* Vann Cummings
VP Sls: Raymond Clarke

D-U-N-S 16-142-9253 EXP
MUREX LLC
NA MUREX
7160 Dallas Pkwy Ste 300, Plano, TX 75024-7112
Tel (972) 702-0021 *Founded/Ownrshp* 1995
Sales 143.4MM^E *EMP* 35
SIC 5172 Petroleum products
Pr: Robert Wright
**CFO:* Rick Bartel
**CFO:* Richard J Patel
**Sec:* Charles E Senn
**VP:* Chris Wall
Mng Dir: Marc Travillian

D-U-N-S 96-263-8107
MUREX NORTH AMERICA INC
(*Suby of* MUREX)
810 7th Ave Fl 14, New York, NY 10019-5839
Tel (212) 381-4300 *Founded/Ownrshp* 1994
Sales 33.3MM^E *EMP* 40
SIC 5045 Computer software
Ch Bd: Maroon Edde
Pr: Jean-Gabriel Edde
Top Exec: Pierre Spatz
Off Mgr: Jadie Aponte
CTO: Antoine Mourad
Software D: Igor Racic
Opers Mgr: Aaron Tang

D-U-N-S 12-791-3080
MUREX PETROLEUM CORP
363 N Sam Houston Pkwy E # 200, Houston, TX 77060-2437
Tel (281) 590-3313 *Founded/Ownrshp* 1996
Sales 108.6MM *EMP* 100
Accts Hein & Associates Llp Houston
SIC 1382 Oil & gas exploration services; Oil & gas exploration services
Pr: Waldo J Ackerman
**COO:* Jason Leeper
**Treas:* Angela Wolsey
**Sr VP:* Donald A Kessel
**VP:* Rob Foss
Mng Dir: Ola Andersen
Snr Mgr: Geir Olsen
Board of Directors: Waldo Ackerman, Donald Kessel, Chris Latimer

D-U-N-S 82-505-9280 EXP
MURFIN DRILLING CO INC
250 N Water St Ste 300, Wichita, KS 67202-1299
Tel (316) 267-3241 *Founded/Ownrshp* 1991
Sales 196.6MM^E *EMP* 303
SIC 1381 1382 5082 6512 6514 Directional drilling oil & gas wells; Aerial geophysical exploration oil & gas; General construction machinery & equipment; Commercial & industrial building operation; Dwelling operators, except apartments; Directional drilling oil & gas wells; Aerial geophysical exploration oil & gas; General construction machinery & equipment; Commercial & industrial building operation; Dwelling operators, except apartments
Pr: David Murfinis
**CFO:* Richard Koll
**Treas:* Robert D Young
**VP:* Jerry Abels
**VP:* David Doyel
**VP:* Leon Rodak

MURFIN'S QUALITY MARKET
See OZARK SUPERMARKET INC

D-U-N-S 12-436-1783
MURFREESBORO CITY SCHOOLS
2552 S Church St Ste 100, Murfreesboro, TN 37127-7135
Tel (615) 893-2313 *Founded/Ownrshp* 1968
Sales 59.4MM^E *EMP* 1,000
SIC 8211 Elementary & secondary schools; School board; Elementary & secondary schools; School board
Ex Dir: Linda Gilbert
**Treas:* Golena Bell
Top Exec: Aaron Thompson
Comm Dir: Lisa Trail
Snr Ntwrk: Scott Campbell
Board of Directors: Phil Huddleson

D-U-N-S 06-074-7557
MURFREESBORO MEDICAL CLINIC P A
SURGE CTR OF MURFREB MED CL PA
1272 Garrison Dr Ste 308, Murfreesboro, TN 37129-2598
Tel (615) 893-4480 *Founded/Ownrshp* 1965
Sales 23.7MM^E *EMP* 108
SIC 8011 Clinic, operated by physicians
Pr: James A Nunnery MD
COO: Denise Flannigan
Dir Lab: Cathy Barnes
Off Mgr: Gina Wilson
CIO: Robert Jackson
Dir IT: Don Gray
IT Man: John Grey
Mktg Dir: Kimberly Smith
Surgeon: Ramesh Narayanagowda
Obsttrcn: Colleen Bratsch
Doctor: Kecia Badem

D-U-N-S 03-481-8609
MURFREESBORO PURE MILK CO INC
PURITY
2450 Southgate Blvd, Murfreesboro, TN 37128-5531
Tel (615) 893-3810 *Founded/Ownrshp* 1929
Sales 26.7MM^E *EMP* 65
SIC 5143 Butter; Cheese; Milk & cream, fluid
Pr: Herbert D Young Sr
**Sec:* Margaret P Young
**VP:* Brad Young

D-U-N-S 01-974-2444 IMP
MURIDA FURNITURE CO INC
ROTMANS FURNITURE & CARPET
725 Southbridge St, Worcester, MA 01610-2998
Tel (508) 755-5276 *Founded/Ownrshp* 1956
Sales 29.3MM^E *EMP* 164^E
SIC 5712 5713 5731

D-U-N-S 02-535-6614
MURKEL ENTERPRISES LLC
MCDONALD'S
3051 S Church St Ste 2, Burlington, NC 27215-5154
Tel (336) 584-1382 *Founded/Ownrshp* 2002
Sales 6.9MM^E *EMP* 350
SIC 5812 Fast-food restaurant, chain; Fast-food restaurant, chain

D-U-N-S 07-099-0270
MURKS VILLAGE MARKET INC (MI)
VILLAGE MARKET FOOD CENTERS
514 Huron St, South Haven, MI 49090-1436
Tel (269) 637-8655 *Founded/Ownrshp* 1964, 1967
Sales 60.8MM^E *EMP* 450
SIC 5411

D-U-N-S 62-662-1783
MURNANE BUILDING CONTRACTORS INC
104 Sharron Ave, Plattsburgh, NY 12901-3803
Tel (518) 561-4010 *Founded/Ownrshp* 1986
Sales 81.1MM^E *EMP* 120
SIC 1542 1541 Commercial & office building contractors; Industrial buildings, new construction; Commercial & office building contractors; Industrial buildings, new construction
Pr: Patrick T Murnane
**Treas:* Darcy M Mousseau
VP: James Hogel
Off Mgr: Peggy Demers
Off Mgr: Anne Homer
IT Man: Maria Martino

D-U-N-S 06-583-5845 IMP
MURNANE PAPER CO
MARQUETTE PAPER COMPANY
345 W Fischer Farm Rd, Elmhurst, IL 60126-1432
Tel (630) 530-8222 *Founded/Ownrshp* 1982
Sales 40.7MM^E *EMP* 50
SIC 5111 5112 Printing paper; Photocopying supplies
Pr: Robert Hunt
**Pr:* Frank J Murnane Jr
**Treas:* John Ostry
Netwrk Mgr: Bob Hunt
Plnt Mgr: Ken Preze
Mktg Mgr: Sarah Stelzel

D-U-N-S 01-253-1104
MURNEY ASSOCIATES REALTORS
1625 E Primrose St, Springfield, MO 65804-7929
Tel (417) 823-2300 *Founded/Ownrshp* 1997
Sales 23.2MM^E *EMP* 400^E
SIC 6531 Real estate brokers & agents; Rental agent, real estate; Real estate brokers & agents; Rental agent, real estate
Exec: Mary Wilson
CTO: Twila Hillme
Dir IT: Jim Roberts
Sales Asso: Joyce Branstetter
Sales Asso: Michael Cataldo
Sales Asso: James Turner
Sales Asso: Melody Ward
Sales Asso: Terri Woody

D-U-N-S 07-723-2692
MUROC JOINT UNIFIED SCHOOL DISTRICT
17100 Foothill Ave, Edwards, CA 93523-3533
Tel (661) 258-4356 *Founded/Ownrshp* 1951
Sales 15.6MM^E *EMP* 300^E
SIC 8211 Public combined elementary & secondary school; Public combined elementary & secondary school
IT Man: Trevor Walker
HC Dir: Lynette Traynor
Board of Directors: Paula Harper, Chuck James, Ronnie Toy, Karen Webster, Steve Wiser

D-U-N-S 10-711-6860 IMP
MUROTECH OHIO CORP
M T O
550 Mckinley Rd, Saint Marys, OH 45885-1803
Tel (419) 394-6529 *Founded/Ownrshp* 1998
Sales 21.0MM^E *EMP* 60
SIC 3465 Body parts, automobile: stamped metal
Pr: N Matsushima
**Pr:* Naonobu Kenmoku
**Pr:* H Taguchi
Prd Mgr: Nathan Gates
Prd Mgr: Pam Haffey

D-U-N-S 05-863-1094
MURPHCO OF FLORIDA INC
HOLIDAY INN
360 Corporate Way, Orange Park, FL 32073-6290
Tel (904) 217-5191 *Founded/Ownrshp* 1972
Sales 25.3MM^E *EMP* 300
SIC 7011 5812 5813 Hotels & motels; Family restaurants; Cocktail lounge; Hotels & motels; Family restaurants; Cocktail lounge
Pr: Philip W Murphey
**VP:* Josh Harrison
**VP:* Lynn K Murphy
**VP:* Patrick Papa
IT Man: Susan Suggs

D-U-N-S 07-342-8435
MURPHEY TAYLOR & ELLIS PROPERTIES INC
PERSONS FAMILY HOLDINGS
3095 Vineville Ave, Macon, GA 31204-2460
Tel (478) 743-2671 *Founded/Ownrshp* 1930
Sales 25.0MM^E *EMP* 55
SIC 6512 Nonresidential building operators; Nonresidential building operators
Pr: Henry P Persons III
**Sec:* Elizabeth C Persons
**VP:* Bryan B Persons

D-U-N-S 01-215-8275
MURPHY & DURIEU LP
355 S End Ave Apt 30n, New York, NY 10280-1059
Tel (212) 618-0900 *Founded/Ownrshp* 1929, 1972
Sales 41.4MM^E *EMP* 160
Accts Mcgladrey & Pullen Llp New Y
SIC 6211 Dealers, security
Genl Pt: Richard J Murphy
Pt: Gloria Murphy
VP Opers: Joseph Timpone

D-U-N-S 00-514-5677
MURPHY & MILLER INC (DE)
600 W Taylor St, Chicago, IL 60607-4491
Tel (312) 427-8900 *Founded/Ownrshp* 1935, 1979
Sales 25.0MM^E *EMP* 125
SIC 1711 Heating systems repair & maintenance; Heating & air conditioning contractors; Heating systems repair & maintenance; Heating & air conditioning contractors
Pr: James J Miller
**Ch:* Patricia O Rielly Miller
VP: Russ Miemczewski
VP: Bill Zitzka
Mktg Mgr: Carl Wigginton

D-U-N-S 08-326-7211 IMP
MURPHY & SONS INC (MS)
MS
9148 Corporate Dr, Southaven, MS 38671-1242
Tel (662) 393-3130 *Founded/Ownrshp* 1977
Sales 55.4MM^E *EMP* 123
SIC 1542 1541 5084 1799 Commercial & office building, new construction; Industrial buildings, new construction; Petroleum industry machinery; Service station equipment installation, maintenance & repair; Commercial & office building, new construction; Industrial buildings, new construction; Petroleum industry machinery; Service station equipment installation, maintenance & repair
Pr: David G Murphy
**VP:* Stephen M Gross
Sfty Mgr: Steve Williams

D-U-N-S 01-024-4586
MURPHY ADAMS RESTAURANT GROUP INC
512 E Rverside Dr Ste 250, Austin, TX 78704
Tel (512) 949-3220 *Founded/Ownrshp* 2007
Sales 11.6MM^E *EMP* 330
SIC 5812 Eating places; Eating places
Pr: Randy Murphy

D-U-N-S 00-291-6252 IMP
MURPHY AND NOLAN INC (NY)
340 Peat St, Syracuse, NY 13210-1352
Tel (315) 474-8203 *Founded/Ownrshp* 1953
Sales 37.0MM^E *EMP* 58
SIC 5051 Metals service centers & offices; Metals service centers & offices
Pr: John J Murphy III
**VP:* Edward Dera
**VP:* John J Murphy IV
**VP:* William Murphy
Area Mgr: Michael Duxbury
Off Mgr: Greg Diehl
Board of Directors: Eileen Murphy, Erica Reeners

D-U-N-S 04-145-9418
MURPHY AUDIE VA HOSPITAL
CARDIOLOGY DEPT
7400 Merton Minter St, San Antonio, TX 78229-4404
Tel (210) 617-5300 *Founded/Ownrshp* 2004
Sales 26.6MM^E *EMP* 113^E
SIC 8011 Medical centers
Prin: Gregory Freeman
COO: Richard Bauer
Pharmcst: Terri Nguyen

D-U-N-S 18-143-8693
MURPHY AUTO GROUP INC
TOYOTA OF WINTER HAVEN
37048 Hwy 27, Haines City, FL 33844-2300
Tel (888) 318-2623 *Founded/Ownrshp* 2004
Sales 27.8MM^E *EMP* 70
SIC 5511 Automobiles, new & used; Automobiles, new & used
Pr: Dennis L Murphy
CFO: Matt Forenza
Genl Mgr: Louis Hernandez
Sls Mgr: Brian McClary
Sls Mgr: David Mulder
Sls Mgr: Sandy Sanderson
Sales Asso: Cassidy Morales
Sales Asso: Luis A Velasco

D-U-N-S 06-104-4566
MURPHY BROS INC
3150 5th Ave, East Moline, IL 61244-9534
Tel (309) 752-1227 *Founded/Ownrshp* 1971
Sales 28.5MM^E *EMP* 150
SIC 1623 Oil & gas pipeline construction; Oil & gas pipeline construction
Pr: William Murphy
**CFO:* Gene Pavinato
VP: Larry Ernst
**VP:* Rick Mosokowitz
**VP:* Karen Murphy
**VP:* Michael D Murphy

D-U-N-S 95-692-0821
MURPHY BUSINESS & FINANCIAL SERVICES
MURPHY BUSINESS BROKERS
513 N Belcher Rd Ste A, Clearwater, FL 33765-2636
Tel (727) 725-7090 *Founded/Ownrshp* 1995
Sales 20.5MM^E *EMP* 80
SIC 7389 Personal service agents, brokers & bureaus
Pr: Roger Murphy
Ex VP: Tom Miller
**VP:* Kathy Murphy
**VP:* Len Russek
Mng Dir: Mark Davis
Mng Dir: Malena Meazell

MURPHY BUSINESS BROKERS
See MURPHY BUSINESS & FINANCIAL SERVICES

D-U-N-S 62-513-7716 IMP
MURPHY CO
MURPHY PLYWOOD
2350 Prairie Rd, Eugene, OR 97402-9742
Tel (541) 461-4545 *Founded/Ownrshp* 1986
Sales 92.0MM^E *EMP* 450
SIC 2435 2436 Hardwood veneer & plywood; Softwood veneer & plywood; Hardwood veneer & plywood; Softwood veneer & plywood
Pr: John Murphy
**Sr VP:* Tim Perderson
VP: Knox Marshall
Exec: Greg Gassner
Exec: Scott Prowell
**Prin:* Dennis Murphy
IT Man: Keith Hurlic
Mtls Mgr: Matt Smith
Mfg Mgr: Bill Day
VP Sls: Tim Lewis
Sales Asso: Robin Heide
Board of Directors: Dennis Murphy Edward J Mur

D-U-N-S 00-383-3365 IMP
MURPHY CO MECHANICAL CONTRACTORS AND ENGINEERS (MO)
1233 N Price Rd, Saint Louis, MO 63132-2303
Tel (314) 997-6600 *Founded/Ownrshp* 1907
Sales 212.2MM *EMP* 550
Accts Rubin Brown Llp Saint Louis
SIC 1711 Mechanical contractor; Plumbing contractors; Warm air heating & air conditioning contractor; Mechanical contractor; Plumbing contractors; Warm air heating & air conditioning contractor
Ch Bd: James J Murphy Jr
Pr: Gary Miller
Pr: Patrick J Murphy Jr
COO: Donald D Hardin
CFO: Robert L Koester
Treas: Kent Decker
Sr VP: Lawrence Dicicco
Sr VP: Michael J Knapp
Sr VP: Larry Kruse
Sr VP: Robert Mathisen
VP: Edward Becker
VP: Mark L Bengard
VP: David Book
VP: Bob Breth
VP: Christopher Carter
VP: Kevin Cook
VP: Tim Dace
VP: Greg Hackl
VP: Thomas Hegger
VP: Christopher Hiemenz
VP: Christopher B Hiemenz

MURPHY CONSTRUCTION COMPANY
See MCC INC

D-U-N-S 02-733-6890 IMP
MURPHY CORMIER GENERAL CONTRACTOR INC
HOOT AEROBIC SYSTEMS
2885 Highway 14 E, Lake Charles, LA 70607-7629
Tel (337) 474-2804 *Founded/Ownrshp* 1971
Sales 20.9MM^E *EMP* 55
SIC 3589 1542 Sewage treatment equipment; Commercial & office building, new construction
Pr: Murphy Jude Cormier
**Sec:* Charlene Aguillard
**VP:* Todd Cormier

D-U-N-S 94-477-0361
MURPHY ELECTRIC INC
7155 Bermuda Rd Ste A, Las Vegas, NV 89119-4372
Tel (702) 597-2403 *Founded/Ownrshp* 1989
Sales 28.0MM^E *EMP* 180
SIC 1731 Electrical work; Electrical work
Pr: Joseph A Murphy
**VP:* Michael Frye
VP: Mark Ortega

D-U-N-S 87-954-0193
MURPHY ENERGY CORP
2250 E 73rd St Ste 600, Tulsa, OK 74136-6835
Tel (918) 743-7979 *Founded/Ownrshp* 1993
Sales 144.6MM^E *EMP* 129^E
SIC 5172 Petroleum products; Petroleum products
CEO: Matthew J Murphy
**Pr:* Carter Simmons
Ofcr: Ed Paitsel
**Ex VP:* Gregory A Westfall
**VP:* Patrick Johndrow
VP: Grant Simmons
**VP:* Glen Smith
VP: Shane Wittig
IT Man: Sarah Habiger
Ql Cn Mgr: Ryan Rogers

D-U-N-S 00-885-1479 IMP
■ **MURPHY EXPLORATION & PRODUCTION CO - USA**
(*Suby of* MURPHY OIL CORP) ★
9805 Katy Fwy Ste G200, Houston, TX 77024-1269
Tel (281) 599-8145 *Founded/Ownrshp* 1953
Sales 775.3MM^E *EMP* 611
Accts Kpmg By Fax On September 20 2
SIC 1382 1311 Oil & gas exploration services; Crude petroleum & natural gas production; Oil & gas exploration services; Crude petroleum & natural gas production
Pr: R W Jenkins
**Treas:* Miendy K West
VP: Dale Bradford
VP: Steven A Coss
VP: Ron Manz
Genl Mgr: Glenn Bixler
Genl Mgr: Kevin Gottshall
Genl Mgr: Bob Lamond
Genl Mgr: Chris Lorino
Genl Mgr: Bert Terry
Genl Mgr: Paul Thayer

D-U-N-S 18-811-6750
■ **MURPHY EXPLORATION (ALASKA) INC**
MURPHY OIL
(*Suby of* MURPHY EXPLORATION & PRODUCTION CO - USA) ★
200 E Peach St, El Dorado, AR 71730-5836
Tel (870) 862-6411 *Founded/Ownrshp* 1990
Sales 18.4MM^E *EMP* 325
SIC 1311 Crude petroleum & natural gas; Crude petroleum & natural gas
Pr: R W Jenkins
**Treas:* M K West

VP: S Carboni
**VP:* W K Compton

D-U-N-S 06-529-1981
MURPHY FARMS LLC
CHIEF FEED MILL
(*Suby of* MURPHY-BROWN LLC) ★
600 Rte Hwy A, Rose Hill, NC 28458
Tel (910) 289-6439 *Founded/Ownrshp* 1962
Sales 113.2MM^E *EMP* 2,100
SIC 0213 Hogs; Hogs
Pr: Dr M Terry Coffey

MURPHY FOODSERVICE
See BADGER FARMS INC

D-U-N-S 94-483-4407
MURPHY FORD CO
MURPHY FORD-LINCOLN MERCURY
3310 Township Line Rd, Chester, PA 19013-1498
Tel (610) 494-8800 *Founded/Ownrshp* 1942
Sales 33.4MM^E *EMP* 90
SIC 5511 Automobiles, new & used; Automobiles, new & used
Pr: Dan Murphy Jr
**VP:* Daniel G Murphy III
Genl Mgr: Carylin Riak
Sales Asso: Kevin McLaughlin

MURPHY FORD-LINCOLN MERCURY
See MURPHY FORD CO

D-U-N-S 02-166-0303 IMP/EXP
MURPHY INDUSTRIES LLC
FW MURPHY
(*Suby of* ENOVATION CONTROLS LLC) ★
5311 S 122nd East Ave, Tulsa, OK 74146-6006
Tel (918) 317-4100 *Founded/Ownrshp* 2009
Sales 33.0MM^E *EMP* 392
SIC 3829

D-U-N-S 84-744-9857
MURPHY MARINE SERVICES INC
1 Hausel Rd Ste 103, Wilmington, DE 19801-5876
Tel (302) 571-4700 *Founded/Ownrshp* 1994
Sales 27.3MM^E *EMP* 300
SIC 4491 Marine loading & unloading services; Stevedoring; Marine loading & unloading services; Stevedoring
Pr: John Coulahan
**Pr:* Mark Murphy
CFO: Dennis Monahan
VP: Edward Heinlein

D-U-N-S 08-914-7524
MURPHY MEDICAL CENTER
3990 E Us 64 Alt, Murphy, NC 28906-8707
Tel (828) 837-8161 *Founded/Ownrshp* 1985
Sales 61.7MM *EMP* 525
SIC 8062 8051 8052 General medical & surgical hospitals; Skilled nursing care facilities; Intermediate care facilities; General medical & surgical hospitals; Skilled nursing care facilities; Intermediate care facilities
CEO: Mike Stevenson
CFO: Steve Gilgen
Dir Rx: Angie Moss
Off Mgr: Jennifer Rogers
QA Dir: Kim Williams
Mktg Dir: Paul Demichael
Doctor: Mark Gilbert MD
Nrsg Dir: Monique Matheny
Pharmcst: Rachel Snow
Cert Phar: Belinda Gaddis
HC Dir: Cindy Buchanan

MURPHY OIL
See MURPHY EXPLORATION (ALASKA) INC

D-U-N-S 10-891-7493 IMP
▲ MURPHY OIL CORP
200 E Peach St, El Dorado, AR 71730-5890
Tel (870) 862-6411 *Founded/Ownrshp* 1950
Sales 5.4MMM *EMP* 1,712
Tkr Sym MUR *Exch* NYS
SIC 1311 4612 2911 Crude petroleum production; Natural gas production; Crude petroleum pipelines; Petroleum bulk stations; Petroleum terminals; Petroleum refining; Crude petroleum & natural gas; Crude petroleum production; Natural gas production; Crude petroleum pipelines; Petroleum refining
Pr: Roger W Jenkins
CFO: John W Eckart
Treas: John B Gardner
Ofcr: Michael Donnella
Ex VP: Walter K Compton
Sr VP: Kelli M Hammock
VP: E Ted Botner
VP: Tim F Butler
VP: John W Dumas
VP: Allan J Misner
VP: K Todd Montgomery
VP: Kelly L Whitley
Exec: Leona Ralph

D-U-N-S 00-805-3712 IMP
■ MURPHY OIL USA INC
MURPHY USA
(*Suby of* MURPHY USA INC) ★
200 E Peach St, El Dorado, AR 71730-5836
Tel (870) 862-6411 *Founded/Ownrshp* 2013
Sales 17.2MMM *EMP* 7,350
Accts Kpmg Llp Houston Texas
SIC 2911 8742 1311 4213 Gasoline; Liquefied petroleum gases, LPG; Industry specialist consultants; Crude petroleum production; Liquid petroleum transport, non-local; Gasoline; Liquefied petroleum gases, LPG; Industry specialist consultants; Crude petroleum production; Liquid petroleum transport, non-local
Pr: R Andrew Clyde
**Treas:* Kevin Fitzgerald
Sr VP: Henry J Heithaus
VP: Ijaz Iqbal
Genl Mgr: Gil Reath
VP Mfg: Kevin Melnyk
Opers Mgr: Sharolyn Givens
VP Mktg: Charles Ganus

MURPHY PLYWOOD
See MURPHY CO

D-U-N-S 02-165-2672
MURPHY SCHOOL DISTRICT 21
2615 W Buckeye Rd, Phoenix, AZ 85009-5743
Tel (602) 353-5000 *Founded/Ownrshp* 1886
Sales 18.4MM^E *EMP* 300
Accts Heinfeld & Meech Pc
SIC 8211 Elementary & secondary schools; Elementary & secondary schools
**Pr:* Eric Buckmaster
**Prin:* William E Grimes
**Prin:* Arthur V Murillo
**Prin:* Raymond M Rodriguez

D-U-N-S 14-492-9825
MURPHY SECURITY SERVICE LLC
230 Oak St, New Britain, CT 06051-1226
Tel (860) 229-7727 *Founded/Ownrshp* 1977
Sales 6.5MM^E *EMP* 400
SIC 7381 Security guard service; Security guard service
Off Mgr: Linda Leiss
Opers Mgr: Martin Muzzey

MURPHY TOMATOES
See E A BROWN TOMATOES INC

D-U-N-S 06-293-6075 IMP/EXP
MURPHY TRACTOR & EQUIPMENT CO INC
JOHN DEERE
(*Suby of* MURFIN DRILLING CO INC) ★
5375 N Deere Rd, Park City, KS 67219-3307
Tel (855) 246-9124 *Founded/Ownrshp* 1982
Sales 123.8MM^E *EMP* 300
SIC 5082 General construction machinery & equipment; General construction machinery & equipment
Pr: Thomas A Udland
**Sec:* Robert D Young
VP: Mike Slinger
Area Mgr: Chris Seta
Brnch Mgr: Ken Geoghegan
Mktg Mgr: Candace Jindra
Manager: Travis Clinesmith
Manager: Darrell Dupree
Manager: Dick Evans
Manager: Luke Fanshler
Manager: Christopher Grimes

MURPHY TRANSPORTATION SERVICES
See MURPHY WAREHOUSE CO

MURPHY USA
See MURPHY OIL USA INC

D-U-N-S 96-566-6824
▲ MURPHY USA INC
200 E Peach St, El Dorado, AR 71730-5836
Tel (870) 875-7600 *Founded/Ownrshp* 2013
Sales 17.2MMM *EMP* 9,450^E
Accts Kpmg Llp Houston Texas
Tkr Sym MUSA *Exch* NYS
SIC 5531 5541 Investment holding companies, except banks; Automotive & home supply stores; Gasoline service stations
Pr: R Andrew Clyde
CFO: Mindy K West
Ex VP: John Rudolfs
Sr VP: Marn K Cheng
Sr VP: John A Moore
VP: Walter K Compton
VP: Joseph Henderson III
VP: Angelos Lambis
VP: Donnie Smith
Dist Mgr: Nadim Azad
Div Mgr: Scott Woodward
Board of Directors: Claiborne P Deming, Thomas M Gattle Jr, Robert A Hermes, Fred L Holliger, Christoph Keller III, James W Keyes, Diane N Landen, R Madison Murphy, Jack T Taylor

D-U-N-S 06-138-5084 EXP
MURPHY WALL PRODUCTS INTERNATIONAL INC
201 Ne 21st St, Fort Worth, TX 76164-8527
Tel (817) 626-1987 *Founded/Ownrshp* 2007
Sales 24.9MM^E *EMP* 54
SIC 3272 5198 3563 3423 3275 2851 Wall & ceiling squares, concrete; Paints, varnishes & supplies; Air & gas compressors; Hand & edge tools; Gypsum products; Paints & allied products
Pr: Joan Benton

D-U-N-S 06-653-8349
MURPHY WAREHOUSE CO
MURPHY TRANSPORTATION SERVICES
701 24th Ave Se, Minneapolis, MN 55414-2691
Tel (612) 746-3491 *Founded/Ownrshp* 1956
Sales 53.3MM^E *EMP* 200
SIC 4225 General warehousing; General warehousing
CEO: Richard T Murphy Jr
**CFO:* D Thomas Griep
**Ch:* Richard T Murphy Sr
**VP:* Michael Butchert
IT Man: Jean Parupsky
Info Man: Richard Larson
**VP Opers:* Paul Welna
Sfty Mgr: Wendy Pigorsch
Opers Mgr: Alex Geister
Opers Mgr: Eric Glennie
Opers Mgr: Adam Sokoll

D-U-N-S 03-905-5368 IMP/EXP
MURPHY-BROWN LLC
SMITHFIELDS HOG PRODUCTION DIV
(*Suby of* SMITHFIELD FOODS INC) ★
2822 W Nc 24 Hwy, Warsaw, NC 28398-7952
Tel (910) 293-3434 *Founded/Ownrshp* 2001
Sales 1.3MMM^E *EMP* 5,000
SIC 0213 Hogs; Hogs
Ex VP: Richard Kiger
VP: Russ Collingwood

D-U-N-S 15-559-0128
MURPHY-HOFFMAN CO
11120 Tomahawk Creek Pkwy, Leawood, KS 66211-2695
Tel (816) 483-6444 *Founded/Ownrshp* 1985
Sales 890.0MM^E *EMP* 1,998
SIC 5012 7513 7538 6159 5511 Truck tractors; Truck leasing, without drivers; General truck repair; Truck finance leasing; Pickups, new & used; Truck tractors; Truck leasing, without drivers; General truck repair; Truck finance leasing; Pickups, new & used
Pr: Timothy R Murphy
**CFO:* Jeff Johnson
**Treas:* Reed F Murphy Jr
**Ex VP:* Kenneth A Hoffman
Ex VP: David Stroop
VP: Jay Lang
Brnch Mgr: Lance Miller
IT Man: Edward Zuniga
Sls Mgr: Richard Pim

D-U-N-S 10-295-9681
MURPHY-TRUE INC
JIM MURPHY & ASSOCIATES
464 Kenwood Ct Ste B, Santa Rosa, CA 95407-5709
Tel (707) 576-7337 *Founded/Ownrshp* 1968
Sales 35.1MM *EMP* 60
SIC 1542 1521 Commercial & office building, new construction; New construction, single-family houses; Commercial & office building, new construction; New construction, single-family houses
CEO: Jim M Murphy
**VP:* Leighton J True III
Mktg Mgr: Audrey Giroux

D-U-N-S 02-624-2982 IMP
MURRAY A GOLDENBERG TEXTILES INC
GOLDEN D'OR FABRICS
10795 Harry Hines Blvd, Dallas, TX 75220-1327
Tel (214) 351-6651 *Founded/Ownrshp* 1959
Sales 45.2MM^E *EMP* 60
Accts Philip Vogel & Co Pc Dallas
SIC 5131 Piece goods & other fabrics
Pr: Ted Butler
**VP:* Charles Tryon
**VP:* Sylvia Villamizar
IT Man: Daniel Aboudara

D-U-N-S 12-095-7097 IMP
■ MURRAY BISCUIT CO LLC
(*Suby of* KELLOGG SALES CO) ★
1550 Marvin Griffin Rd, Augusta, GA 30906-3853
Tel (706) 798-8600 *Founded/Ownrshp* 2001
Sales 109.0MM^E *EMP* 1,000
SIC 2052 2051 Cookies; Crackers, dry; Saltine crackers; Cakes, pies & pastries; Cookies; Crackers, dry; Saltine crackers; Cakes, pies & pastries
Pr: William G Bayer
CFO: Byron Russell
VP: Jerry Cavitt
VP: Gerald Defalco

MURRAY BMW OF DENVER
See SAI DENVER B INC

D-U-N-S 79-275-8823
MURRAY BRESKY CONSULTANTS LTD
MURRAY'S CHICKEN
5190 Main St, South Fallsburg, NY 12779
Tel (845) 436-5001 *Founded/Ownrshp* 1994
Sales 48.2MM^E *EMP* 300
SIC 2015 Poultry slaughtering & processing; Poultry slaughtering & processing
Pr: Murray Bresky
**Sec:* Ellen Gold
**VP:* Dean Koplik
Opers Mgr: Allen Schwartz

D-U-N-S 07-312-6542
MURRAY CITY CORP
5025 S State St 118, Salt Lake City, UT 84107-4824
Tel (801) 264-2600 *Founded/Ownrshp* 1902
Sales NA *EMP* 880
Accts Keddington & Christensen Llc
SIC 9121 Legislative bodies; ; Legislative bodies;
Dir IT: David Larsen
IT Man: Brenda Moore

MURRAY CITY DISTRICT
See MURRAY SCHOOL DISTRICT (INC)

MURRAY COMPANY
See MURRAY PLUMBING AND HEATING CORP

D-U-N-S 00-306-7816 IMP
MURRAY CORP
260 Schilling Cir Ste 1, Hunt Valley, MD 21031-1109
Tel (410) 771-0380 *Founded/Ownrshp* 1964
Sales 24.9MM^E *EMP* 70
SIC 3429 Clamps & couplings, hose
Pr: Thorne Gould
**Ch Bd:* Kingdon Gould Jr
IT Man: Cathy Mellor
VP Opers: Thad Schippereit
Plnt Mgr: Tom Branch
Sales Exec: Joe Schindler

D-U-N-S 15-929-5203
MURRAY COUNTY BOARD OF EDUCATION
MURRAY COUNTY SCHOOLS
1006 Green Rd, Chatsworth, GA 30705-2012
Tel (706) 695-4531 *Founded/Ownrshp* 1996
Sales 33.2MM^E *EMP* 1,000
SIC 8211

D-U-N-S 04-254-8206
MURRAY COUNTY CENTRAL DISRICT 2169
2420 28th St, Slayton, MN 56172-1457
Tel (507) 836-6183 *Founded/Ownrshp* 1890
Sales 15.6MM^E *EMP* 412
SIC 8211 Public elementary & secondary schools; Public elementary & secondary schools

D-U-N-S 07-593-9876
MURRAY COUNTY HOSPITAL AUTHORITY
MURRAY MEDICAL CENTER
707 Old Dalton Ellijay Rd, Chatsworth, GA 30705-2060
Tel (706) 695-4564 *Founded/Ownrshp* 1998
Sales 47.3MM *EMP* 155^E
SIC 8062 General medical & surgical hospitals
Pr: Mickey Rabuka
Dir Lab: Kerry Coefield
Pathlgst: Kathryn Knight

D-U-N-S 88-482-8224
MURRAY COUNTY MEDICAL CENTER
2042 Juniper Ave, Slayton, MN 56172-1017
Tel (507) 836-6111 *Founded/Ownrshp* 2006
Sales NA *EMP* 140
SIC 6324 Hospital & medical service plans
CFO: John Osse
Off Mgr: Ann Lubben

MURRAY COUNTY SCHOOLS
See MURRAY COUNTY BOARD OF EDUCATION

D-U-N-S 04-799-7501
MURRAY COUNTY SCHOOLS
2239 Bowers Rd Ne, Dalton, GA 30721-7161
Tel (706) 259-8682 *Founded/Ownrshp* 2010
Sales 32.3MM^E *EMP* 1,260^E
SIC 8211 Elementary & secondary schools
Prin: Michelle Nelms

MURRAY DODGE KIA
See MURRAY MOTORS CO INC

D-U-N-S 00-161-6184
MURRAY DRYWALL AND INSULATION OF TEXAS INC
11105 Sapp Brothers Dr, Omaha, NE 68138-3829
Tel (402) 332-0466 *Founded/Ownrshp* 1980
Sales 23.9MM^E *EMP* 45
Accts Darst Brune & Associates Llc
SIC 1742 Drywall; Drywall
Pr: James L Murray
**Treas:* Corey Price
**Sr VP:* Greg Williamsen
**VP:* Greg Murray

D-U-N-S 79-044-2649 IMP/EXP
MURRAY EDGEN CORP
(*Suby of* EDGEN GROUP INC) ★
18444 Highland Rd, Baton Rouge, LA 70809-6105
Tel (225) 756-9868 *Founded/Ownrshp* 2007
Sales 290.5MM^E *EMP* 280
SIC 5051 Iron & steel (ferrous) products; Environmental consultant; Iron & steel (ferrous) products
Ch Bd: Daniel J O'Leary
**Pr:* Craig S Kiefer
**CFO:* Erika Fortenberry
Sr VP: Douglas J Daly
**Sr VP:* Daniel Keaton
**VP:* Graeme Cad
**VP:* Craig Doel
**VP:* Rob Fishbein
**VP:* David Kemp
**VP:* John Nicholas
CIO: Randy Harless

D-U-N-S 82-855-8978
MURRAY EDGEN II L P
(*Suby of* EDGEN GROUP INC) ★
18444 Highland Rd, Baton Rouge, LA 70809-6105
Tel (225) 756-9868 *Founded/Ownrshp* 2007
Sales 204.8MM^E *EMP* 1,038
Accts Kpmg Llp Baton Rouge Louisia
SIC 5051 Iron & steel (ferrous) products; Iron & steel (ferrous) products
CEO: Daniel J O Leary
Pr: Craig S Kiefer
CFO: David L Laxton III
Sr VP: Dan Keaton
Sr VP: Daniel D Keaton
VP: Graeme Cadger
VP: David Mullaney
VP: John Nicholas
IT Man: Randy Harlis
Mtls Mgr: Ralph B Lawrence

MURRAY ELC SYSTEM/CATV DIV
See MURRAY ELECTRIC SYSTEM PLANT BOARD

D-U-N-S 01-261-2651
MURRAY ELECTRIC SYSTEM PLANT BOARD
MURRAY ELC SYSTEM/CATV DIV
401 Olive St, Murray, KY 42071-2066
Tel (270) 753-3324 *Founded/Ownrshp* 1942
Sales 30.3MM^E *EMP* 27
SIC 4911 Distribution, electric power
Bd of Dir: John Weatherly
VP: Max Cleaver
VP: Mitchell Moss
Ex Dir: Debi Danislon
Genl Mgr: June Cunningham
Genl Mgr: David Rogers
Sales Asso: Mike Lovins
Surg Cl Rc: Scott Foster

D-U-N-S 11-487-0509
MURRAY ENERGY CORP
46226 National Rd W, Saint Clairsville, OH 43950-8742
Tel (740) 338-3100 *Founded/Ownrshp* 2003
Sales 3.5MMM^E *EMP* 3,000
SIC 1222 Bituminous coal-underground mining; Bituminous coal-underground mining
CEO: Robert E Murray
**COO:* Robert D Moore
**Treas:* Michael Loiacono
**Ex VP:* Moore Robert D
**Sr VP:* McKown Michael O
**VP:* Cornelius BJ
**VP:* Murray Ryan
**Prin:* Paul Piccolini

D-U-N-S 01-631-4288 IMP
MURRAY EQUIPMENT INC
TOTAL CONTROL SYSTEMS
2515 Charleston Pl, Fort Wayne, IN 46808-1397
Tel (260) 484-0382 *Founded/Ownrshp* 1951
Sales 77.5MM^E *EMP* 60
Accts Baden Gage & Schroeder Llc Fo
SIC 5084 3594 Industrial machinery & equipment; Materials handling machinery; Pumps & pumping equipment; Fluid power pumps & motors; Industrial machinery & equipment; Materials handling machinery; Pumps & pumping equipment; Fluid power pumps & motors
Pr: Stephen Murray
**Treas:* F David Musselman
**VP:* Daniel Murray
S&M/VP: Shawn Kiefer
Sls Mgr: Chris Ravenscraft
Board of Directors: Daniel Murray, Stephen Murray, F David Musselman

D-U-N-S 00-151-5634 IMP
MURRAY FEISS IMPORT LLC
FEISS INDUSTRIES
555 Theodore Fremd Ave B101, Rye, NY 10580-1456
Tel (718) 742-8200 *Founded/Ownrshp* 2004, 2006
Sales 35.4MM^E *EMP* 230
SIC 5063 Lighting fixtures; Lighting fixtures, residential; Lighting fixtures; Lighting fixtures, residential
Pr: Maria Scutaro
VP Admn: Joe Belkevich
Natl Sales: Christy Mutino

D-U-N-S 03-479-7860
MURRAY GUARD INC
58 Murray Guard Dr, Jackson, TN 38305-3625
Tel (731) 668-3400 *Founded/Ownrshp* 1968
Sales 62.5MM^E *EMP* 2,030
Accts Horne Cpas Jackson Tn
SIC 7381 Protective services, guard; Security guard service; Protective services, guard; Security guard service
Ch Bd: Roger G Murray Jr
**Pr:* Gerald P Ferguson Jr
**Ex VP:* James L Exum
**Ex VP:* James A Ward
**VP:* Bruce K Burch
VP: John Carter
**VP:* David Harris
**VP:* Claude Kelly
VP: Claude H Kelly Jr
**VP:* Blair Ross
**VP:* Rick Shackleford
VP: David Tremblay

MURRAY HEAD START
See MURRAY INDEPENDENT SCHOOL DISTRICT

D-U-N-S 04-836-0598
MURRAY HILL OFFICE MAINTENANCE INC
200 Park Ave S Ste 1510, New York, NY 10003-1553
Tel (212) 254-1320 *Founded/Ownrshp* 1968
Sales 5.8MM^E *EMP* 300
SIC 7349 Building maintenance, except repairs; Janitorial service, contract basis; Building maintenance, except repairs; Janitorial service, contract basis
Pr: Joseph Uslip
**Sec:* Michael Uslip
IT Man: Evelyn Torres-Lowe

D-U-N-S 95-997-7414
MURRAY INC
MEDICAL MURRAY
400 N Rand Rd, North Barrington, IL 60010-1496
Tel (847) 620-7990 *Founded/Ownrshp* 1996
Sales 21.7MM^E *EMP* 100
SIC 3841 Medical instruments & equipment, blood & bone work; Medical instruments & equipment, blood & bone work
Pr: Phillip M Leopold
**VP:* Paul Maoka
Sales Exec: Brent Roland

D-U-N-S 04-803-9911
MURRAY INDEPENDENT SCHOOL DISTRICT
MURRAY HEAD START
208 S 13th St, Murray, KY 42071-2302
Tel (270) 753-6031 *Founded/Ownrshp* 1900
Sales 15.8MM^E *EMP* 300
SIC 8211 Public elementary & secondary schools; Public elementary & secondary schools
CIO: Rusty Back
MIS Dir: Michael Back
Pr Dir: Sherry Perdom
HC Dir: Pamela Oakley

D-U-N-S 06-978-1516
MURRAY INSURANCE ASSOCIATES INC
MURRAY SECURUS
39 N Duke St, Lancaster, PA 17602-2842
Tel (717) 735-3088 *Founded/Ownrshp* 1983
Sales NA *EMP* 136
SIC 6411 Insurance brokers
Pr: Richard M Rankin
COO: David E Hosler
CFO: Holly Murray Kutz
Ch: Joseph P Nolt
Ex VP: Ryan Neff
Sr VP: David R Bradbury
Sr VP: Stephen V Riley
Sr VP: Peter Wengrenovich
VP: Mark R Bennett
VP: Bruce G Cannon
VP: David M Dvorchak
VP: Timothy C Hoagland
VP: James L Landis
VP: Anthony M Macinanti
VP: R Miller
VP: Matt K Pfeiffenberger
VP: Sheri C Riley
VP: Arthur H Stoner Jr
Board of Directors: Clarence C Kegel, Richard D Poole, Robert A Saul

D-U-N-S 05-538-2295
MURRAY LOGAN CONSTRUCTION INC
313 65th Trl N, West Palm Beach, FL 33413-1792
Tel (561) 686-3948 *Founded/Ownrshp* 1968
Sales 21.9MM *EMP* 100
SIC 1622 1623 Bridge construction; Pumping station construction; Bridge construction; Pumping station construction
Pr: David A Logan
**VP:* Edward O Leary
**VP:* Andrew Logan
Sfty Dirs: Matthew Portilla

MURRAY MEDICAL CENTER
See MURRAY COUNTY HOSPITAL AUTHORITY

D-U-N-S 08-643-2796
MURRAY MOTORS CO INC (PA)
MURRAY DODGE KIA
1402 W Ridge Pike, Conshohocken, PA 19428-1024
Tel (610) 279-3020 *Founded/Ownrshp* 1976
Sales 26.5MM^E *EMP* 70
Accts Source By Fax On June 26 2001
SIC 5511 Automobiles, new & used; Trucks, tractors & trailers: new & used; Automobiles, new & used; Trucks, tractors & trailers: new & used
Pr: Bernard I Murray
**VP:* Bernard Murray III
**VP:* David T Murray
Sls Mgr: Murray Kia
Sls Mgr: Roger O'Kane
Sales Asso: Steven Fulmer

D-U-N-S 06-624-6133
MURRAY PLUMBING AND HEATING CORP
MURRAY COMPANY
18414 S Santa Fe Ave, E Rncho Dmngz, CA 90221-5612
Tel (310) 637-1500 *Founded/Ownrshp* 1972
Sales 136.1MM^E *EMP* 500^E
SIC 1711 Plumbing contractors; Warm air heating & air conditioning contractor; Plumbing contractors; Warm air heating & air conditioning contractor
CEO: Kevan Steffey
Pr: Jim Deflavio
Pr: John Odom
CFO: Barbara Braymajor
Brnch Mgr: Douglas Orban
Genl Mgr: Jenee Dixon
Snr PM: Trung Vuong

D-U-N-S 02-338-5359
MURRAY REGIONAL HOSPITAL
GENTRY, SHAWN MD
1605 Nashville Hwy # 200, Columbia, TN 38401-2071
Tel (931) 540-4210 *Founded/Ownrshp* 1994
Sales 37.7MM^E *EMP* 12
SIC 8011 General & family practice, physician/surgeon; General & family practice, physician/surgeon

D-U-N-S 07-075-2399
MURRAY RIDGE PRODUCTION CENTER INC
1091 Infirmary Rd, Elyria, OH 44035-4804
Tel (440) 329-3734 *Founded/Ownrshp* 1970
Sales 11.7MM^E *EMP* 500
Accts Anthony R Keys Cpa Inc Elyria
SIC 8331 8322 Vocational rehabilitation agency; Social services for the handicapped; Vocational rehabilitation agency; Social services for the handicapped
Dir Rx: John Bonko

D-U-N-S 07-299-1953
MURRAY SCHOOL DISTRICT (INC)
MURRAY CITY DISTRICT
5102 S Commerce Dr, Salt Lake City, UT 84107
Tel (801) 264-7400 *Founded/Ownrshp* 1890
Sales 40.3MM^E *EMP* 826
Accts Squire & Company Pc Orem Ut
SIC 8211 Public elementary & secondary schools; School board; Public elementary & secondary schools; School board
COO: Marsha Wallin
Bd of Dir: Belinda Johnson
Bd of Dir: Marjorie Tuckett
VP: Laura S Baker
VP: Laura Baker
Exec: Kaylee Schatten
Ex Dir: Jeanne Habel
CTO: Gloria Merrill
Dir IT: John Nielson
Teacher Pr: Darren Dean
Psych: Earl Kauffman

MURRAY SECURUS
See MURRAY INSURANCE ASSOCIATES INC

D-U-N-S 07-429-0743
MURRAY STATE COLLEGE
1 Murray Campus St, Tishomingo, OK 73460-3122
Tel (580) 371-2371 *Founded/Ownrshp* 1908
Sales 190.5M *EMP* 300
SIC 8222 8221 Junior college; Colleges universities & professional schools; Junior college; Colleges universities & professional schools
Pr: Joy McDaniel
VP: Michaelle Gray
VP: Judy Rowland
VP: Roger Stacy
VP: Phillip J Traughber
Exec: Erin Knight
**Prin:* Clyde R Kindell
**Prin:* J A Nichols
Psych: Bridget Hilburn

D-U-N-S 04-198-0632
MURRAY STATE UNIVERSITY
102 Curris Ctr, Murray, KY 42071-3369
Tel (270) 809-3774 *Founded/Ownrshp* 1922
Sales 110.2MM *EMP* 1,250
Accts Rubin Brown Llp Saint Louis
SIC 8221 University; University
Pr: Robert Davies
Bd of Dir: Stephanie REA
Ofcr: Teresa Groves
Assoc Dir: Katie Payne
Opers Supe: Bob Scales
Opers Mgr: Scott Thile
Pr Dir: Dana Starnes

D-U-N-S 07-965-1162
MURRAY-CALLOWAY COUNTY HOSPITAL CORP (KY)
803 Poplar St, Murray, KY 42071-2432
Tel (270) 762-1100 *Founded/Ownrshp* 1948
Sales 108.4MM *EMP* 1,110
SIC 8062 General medical & surgical hospitals; General medical & surgical hospitals
Pr: Keith Bailey
Chf Path: Dewey L Dean
Chf OB: Charles G Cook
Chf Rad: Henry C Hines
**CFO:* Brad Bloemer
CFO: Vicki H Parks
Chf Mktg O: Richard Crouch
Ofcr: Don Futrell
VP: Sandra Dick
**VP:* Lisa Ray
**VP:* Keith Travis
**VP:* John Wilson
Dir OR: Jill Asher
Dir Lab: Linda Cavitt
Dir Rad: Heidi Hordyk
Dir Rx: Sheila Walker
Dir Env Sv: Mark Torsak

D-U-N-S 04-668-9154
MURRAY-FRANKLYN INC
14410 Bellevue Redmond Rd, Bellevue, WA 98007
Tel (425) 644-2323 *Founded/Ownrshp* 1966
Sales 21.5MM^E *EMP* 220
SIC 8741 Administrative management; Administrative management
Pr: Donald Kline
**Sec:* Donald Jasper
**VP:* Dawn Jasper
**VP:* Janice Kline

D-U-N-S 03-319-9514
MURRAYAIR LTD
Hilo International Arprt, Hilo, HI 96720
Tel (808) 961-6601 *Founded/Ownrshp* 1943
Sales 36.7MM^E *EMP* 74
SIC 5172 8249 0721 Aircraft fueling services; Aviation school; Crop dusting services; Aircraft fueling services; Aviation school; Crop dusting services
Pr: Mike Markov
**VP:* Alderine Pascua
**VP:* William W Stearns

MURRAY'S AUTO PART
See MURRAYS DISCOUNT AUTO STORES INC

MURRAY'S CHICKEN
See MURRAY BRESKY CONSULTANTS LTD

D-U-N-S 05-880-1507 IMP
■ **MURRAYS DISCOUNT AUTO STORES INC**
MURRAY'S AUTO PART
(*Suby of* CSK AUTO CORP) ★
8080 Haggerty Rd, Belleville, MI 48111-1643
Tel (734) 957-8080 *Founded/Ownrshp* 2005
Sales 268.9MM^E *EMP* 2,200
SIC 5531 Automotive parts; Automotive accessories; Automotive parts; Automotive accessories
Pr: Thomas McFall
CFO: Fred Tinfey
VP: Jim Mangiapane
VP: George Sutherland
VP: Brian Woodworth
VP Admn: John Broses

D-U-N-S 04-431-0027
MURRAYS FORD INC
3007 Blinker Pkwy, Du Bois, PA 15801-5323
Tel (814) 371-6600 *Founded/Ownrshp* 1968
Sales 42.4MM^E *EMP* 122
SIC 5012 5511 Trucks, commercial; Automobiles, new & used; Trucks, commercial; Automobiles, new & used
Pr: Greg Murray
**Ch Bd:* Harvey Murray
**Sec:* Genevieve Murray
Sls Dir: Meagan Thomas

D-U-N-S 04-221-9345 IMP
MURRAYS IRON WORKS INC (FL)
7355 E Slauson Ave, Commerce, CA 90040-3626
Tel (323) 521-1100 *Founded/Ownrshp* 1966
Sales 29.6MM^E *EMP* 167
SIC 2514 3446 5021 5961 1791

D-U-N-S 01-612-5346
MURRAYS SHEET METAL CO INC
3112 7th St, Parkersburg, WV 26104-3846
Tel (304) 422-5431 *Founded/Ownrshp* 2004
Sales 36.5MM^E *EMP* 150
SIC 3444 1761 Sheet metalwork; Roofing contractor; Sheet metalwork; Sheet metalwork; Roofing contractor; Sheet metalwork
Pr: Christopher Campbell
**VP:* Randall Rogers

D-U-N-S 13-960-1371
MURRIETA DEVELOPMENT CO INC
42540 Rio Nedo, Temecula, CA 92590-3727
Tel (951) 719-1680 *Founded/Ownrshp* 1981
Sales 30.8MM^E *EMP* 126
SIC 1623

D-U-N-S 61-693-8809
MURRIETA VALLEY UNIFIED SCHOOL DISTRICT
41870 Mcalby Ct, Murrieta, CA 92562-7036
Tel (951) 696-1600 *Founded/Ownrshp* 1989
Sales 103.5MM^E *EMP* 2,000
Accts Vavrinek Trine Day & Co Ll
SIC 8211 Public elementary & secondary schools; Public elementary & secondary schools
Bd of Dir: Robin Crist
Dir IT: Ken Balliger
Teacher Pr: Faythe Mutchnisk-Jayk

MURRY'S FAMILY OF FINE FOODS
See MURRYS INC

D-U-N-S 00-281-2550
MURRYS INC
MURRY'S FAMILY OF FINE FOODS
(*Suby of* MENDELSON HOLDING CO LTD INC) ★
7852 Walker Dr Ste 420, Upper Marlboro, MD 20772
Tel (301) 967-4802 *Founded/Ownrshp* 1948
Sales 88.5MM^E *EMP* 800
SIC 5421 5142

D-U-N-S 06-119-0187
MURRYS OF MARYLAND INC
(*Suby of* MURRYS FAMILY OF FINE FOODS) ★
7852 Walker Dr Ste 420, Greenbelt, MD 20770-3262
Tel (301) 420-6400 *Founded/Ownrshp* 1948
Sales 88.5MM^E *EMP* 800
SIC 5421 Food & freezer plans, meat; Food & freezer plans, meat
Ch Bd: Ira Mendelson
**Treas:* Matthew Young
Bd of Dir: Richard Meyer
**VP:* Gary Gold

D-U-N-S 61-015-1755 IMP
MURSIX CORP
TWOSON TOOL COMPANY
2401 N Executive Park Dr, Yorktown, IN 47396-9806
Tel (765) 282-2221 *Founded/Ownrshp* 1990
Sales 81.6MM^E *EMP* 200
Accts Crawford & Associates Carmel
SIC 3469 3679 Metal stampings; Harness assemblies for electronic use: wire or cable; Metal stampings; Harness assemblies for electronic use: wire or cable
Ch Bd: Steve Murray
**Pr:* Todd A Murray
**VP:* Karen Beard
VP: Robert Neville
Telecom Ex: Patty Mahoney
Dir IT: David Jones
QC Dir: Duane Werling
Mtls Mgr: Shelley Sheagley
Sfty Mgr: Cheryl Brewer
Opers Mgr: Ryan Reed
Prd Mgr: Mike Oliver

D-U-N-S 06-066-5304
MURTHA CULLINA LLP (CT)
185 Asylum St Fl 29, Hartford, CT 06103-3455
Tel (860) 240-6000 *Founded/Ownrshp* 1998
Sales 47.7MM^E *EMP* 260
SIC 8111 General practice law office; General practice law office
Pt: Elizabeth J Stewart
**Pt:* Paul L Baccari
**Pt:* Susan J Baronoff
**Pt:* Heather O Berchem
**Pt:* Marcel J Bernier
**Pt:* Francis J Brady
**Pt:* George A Dagon Jr
**Pt:* Thomas M Daniells
**Pt:* John W Gahan III
**Pt:* Robert V Giunta Jr
**Pt:* H Kennedy Hudner
**Pt:* Dwight A Johnson
**Pt:* William J Keenan Jr
**Pt:* Mark F Korber
**Pt:* Timothy L Largay
**Pt:* Paul R McCary
**Pt:* Martha Everett Meng
**Pt:* Lissa J Paris
**Pt:* Willard F Pinney Jr
**Pt:* David Platt
**Pt:* Frank J Saccomondi III

D-U-N-S 08-523-0837
MURTIS TAYLOR HUMAN SERVICES SYSTEM
13422 Kinsman Rd, Cleveland, OH 44120-4410
Tel (216) 283-4400 *Founded/Ownrshp* 1954
Sales 21.4MM *EMP* 400
Accts Maloney & Novotny Llc Clevela
SIC 8093 8322 Mental health clinic, outpatient; Community center; Social service center; Child related social services; Emergency social services; Mental health clinic, outpatient; Community center; Social service center; Child related social services; Emergency social services
CEO: Lovell J Custard
CFO: John Chen
**Ch:* Muqit Sabur
**Treas:* Annetta L Fisher
**Sr VP:* John Chan
VP: Roberta Taliaferro
Off Mgr: Orlean Grant
Info Man: Robert Cerny
Snr Mgr: Elbert Clark

D-U-N-S 02-850-0007 IMP
MUSASHI AUTO PARTS MICHIGAN INC
TECHNICAL AUTO PARTS
(*Suby of* MUSASHI SEIMITSU INDUSTRY CO., LTD.)
195 Brydges Dr, Battle Creek, MI 49037-7340
Tel (269) 965-0057 *Founded/Ownrshp* 1980
Sales 94.6MM^E *EMP* 330
SIC 3714 Motor vehicle transmissions, drive assemblies & parts; Motor vehicle transmissions, drive assemblies & parts
Pr: Mr Takayuki Miyata
Ofcr: Sanders Carl

MUSCATELL SUBARU
See WARD MUSCATELL AUTOMOTIVE GROUP INC

D-U-N-S 04-748-5495
MUSCATINE COMMUNITY SCHOOL DISTRICT
2900 Mulberry Ave, Muscatine, IA 52761-2757
Tel (563) 263-7223 *Founded/Ownrshp* 1900
Sales 60.4MM^E *EMP* 1,000
SIC 8211 Public elementary & secondary schools; Public elementary & secondary schools
**Pr:* Penny Jones
Treas: Charles Domer
**VP:* Mary Wildermuth
Schl Brd P: Nathan Mather

D-U-N-S 06-104-4160
MUSCATINE POWER & WATER (INC)
MACHLINK-MUSCATINE POWER & WAT
3205 Cedar St, Muscatine, IA 52761-2287
Tel (563) 263-2631 *Founded/Ownrshp* 1900
Sales 117.9MM *EMP* 302
SIC 4911 4941 Electric services; Water supply; Electric services; Water supply
CEO: D Scott Ingstad
**Pr:* Doyle D Tubandt
**Ch:* Warren Heidbreder
**VP:* Tracy McGinnis
**Genl Mgr:* Salvatore L Lobiancо
Off Mgr: Terri Anderson
Opers Supe: Mark Costello
Sfty Mgr: Jeff Hedrington
Opers Mgr: Jay Freese
Snr Mgr: Mark Nelson
Snr Mgr: Dennis Riedel

D-U-N-S 15-315-0701
MUSCHLITZ EXCAVATING INC
615 Moorestown Dr, Bath, PA 18014-9716
Tel (610) 759-0525 *Founded/Ownrshp* 1990
Sales 21.3MM^E *EMP* 85
SIC 1794 1711 Excavation work; Septic system construction
Pr: Ron Muschlitz
**CFO:* Mitchell Sherman
**Sec:* David Muschlitz
**VP:* Jack Muschlitz

MUSCLE & FITNESS FLEX M&F HERS
See WEIDER PUBLICATIONS LLC

D-U-N-S 10-000-0710
MUSCLE SHOALS CITY SCHOOL DISTRICT
MUSCLE SHOALS HIGH SCHOOL
3200 S Wilson Dam Rd, Muscle Shoals, AL 35661-2746
Tel (256) 389-2600 *Founded/Ownrshp* 1958
Sales 17.2MM *EMP* 288
SIC 8211 Public elementary school; Public senior high school; Public elementary school; Public senior high school
Prin: Hal Horton
HC Dir: Pam Russell

D-U-N-S 18-565-2542
MUSCLE SHOALS ELECTRICAL BOARD
1015 Avalon Ave, Muscle Shoals, AL 35661-2401
Tel (256) 386-9290 *Founded/Ownrshp* 1962
Sales 24.0MM *EMP* 33
SIC 4911 Distribution, electric power; Distribution, electric power
Genl Mgr: Rickey Thomas
**Ch:* Rodney Howard
**VP:* Charles Ricks
Genl Mgr: Matt Bernauer
Off Mgr: Dan Burns

MUSCLE SHOALS HIGH SCHOOL
See MUSCLE SHOALS CITY SCHOOL DISTRICT

D-U-N-S 96-041-8036
MUSCLEBOUND INC
GOLDS GYM
19835 Nordhoff St, Northridge, CA 91324-3331
Tel (818) 349-0123 *Founded/Ownrshp* 1990
Sales 13.5MM^E *EMP* 350
SIC 7991 Physical fitness facilities; Physical fitness facilities
Pr: Angel J Banos
**VP:* William Banos
VP: Michelle McLemore

D-U-N-S 85-927-8132 IMP
MUSCLEDRIVER USA LLC
587 Greenway Indus Dr, Fort Mill, SC 29708-8100
Tel (803) 802-3238 *Founded/Ownrshp* 2007
Sales 36.6MM^E *EMP* 78^E
SIC 5091 Fitness equipment & supplies
Pr: Eric Carpenter
VP: Glenn Pendlay
VP: Lisa Strump

D-U-N-S 82-968-0276 EXP
▲ MUSCLEPHARM CORP
4721 Ironton St Unit A, Denver, CO 80239-2422
Tel (303) 396-6100 *Founded/Ownrshp* 2006
Sales 177.3MM *EMP* 273^E
Tkr Sym MSLP *Exch* OTO
SIC 2023 Dietary supplements, dairy & non-dairy based; Dietary supplements, dairy & non-dairy based
CEO: Bradley J Pyatt
**Ch Bd:* Ryan Drexler
**Pr:* Richard F Estalella
COO: Michael Wingate
CFO: John Price
Ex VP: Cory J Gregory
Sr VP: Brian Cavanaugh
VP: Brent Baker
VP: Kyle Gosnell
VP: Mark Miller
VP: Derek West
VP: Debi Wilson
Board of Directors: William Bush, Michael J Doron, Stacey Jenkins, Noel Thompson

D-U-N-S 00-526-4718
MUSCO CORP (IA)
MYCRO GROUP CO
100 1st Ave W, Oskaloosa, IA 52577-3244
Tel (641) 676-1746 *Founded/Ownrshp* 1978, 1988
Sales 134.7MM^E *EMP* 672
SIC 7359 3648 3646 3641 3545 3423 Sound & lighting equipment rental; Area & sports luminaries; Commercial indusl & institutional electric lighting fixtures; Electric lamps; Machine tool accessories; Hand & edge tools; Sound & lighting equipment rental; Area & sports luminaries; Commercial indusl & institutional electric lighting fixtures; Electric lamps; Machine tool accessories; Hand & edge tools
Pr: Joe P Crookham
Pr: Walter Tippett
COO: Jeff Rogers
**Treas:* Christopher K Hyland
VP: Louann Ferreira
**VP:* Myron K Gordin
Exec: Greg Gilley
VP Admn: Diane Crookham
CTO: Dave McCumber
QA Dir: Kevin Yerington
Dir IT: Bret Nelson

MUSCO FAMILY OLIVE CO
See OLIVE MUSCO PRODUCTS INC

D-U-N-S 08-259-3369 IMP/EXP
MUSCO FOOD CORP (NY)
VANTIA BRAND
5701 49th St, Maspeth, NY 11378-2020
Tel (718) 366-4256 *Founded/Ownrshp* 1926, 1976
Sales 39.9MM^E *EMP* 45
SIC 5143 5141 Cheese; Groceries, general line
Pr: Philip Musco
Opers Mgr: Jim Pellegrino
Sales Asso: Joe Diperna
Sales Asso: Giuseppe Sindoni

D-U-N-S 03-791-9701
MUSCO SPORTS LIGHTING INC
MARV SMITH SIGNS
200 1st Ave W, Oskaloosa, IA 52577-3246
Tel (641) 673-0411 *Founded/Ownrshp* 1995
Sales 27.1MM^E *EMP* 400
SIC 7389 2261 Sign painting & lettering shop; Screen printing of cotton broadwoven fabrics; Sign painting & lettering shop; Screen printing of cotton broadwoven fabrics
Pr: Joe Crookam
Counsel: Melinda Walter

D-U-N-S 13-525-9000 IMP/EXP
MUSCO SPORTS LIGHTING LLC
(*Suby of* MUSCO CORP) ★
100 1st Ave W, Oskaloosa, IA 52577-3244
Tel (641) 673-0411 *Founded/Ownrshp* 1988
Sales 122.3MM^E *EMP* 550
SIC 3648 Lighting equipment; Lighting equipment
Mktg Dir: Joe P Crookham
VP: Mike Foster
Dir IT: Tony Rivera
Dir IT: Jane Ryder
Manager: Jeff Omer
Sls Mgr: Tim Imhoff
Sls Mgr: Mike Marchetti
Sls Mgr: Doug Miller
Snr Mgr: Vaughn Blythe

MUSCOGEE COUNTY
See COLUMBUS GEORGIA CONSOLIDATED GOVERNMENT

D-U-N-S 07-812-5408
MUSCOGEE COUNTY SCHOOL DISTRICT
2960 Macon Rd, Columbus, GA 31906-2204
Tel (706) 748-2000 *Founded/Ownrshp* 1950
Sales 239.6MM^E *EMP* 6,000
Accts Robinson Grimes & Company P
SIC 8211 Public elementary & secondary schools; Public elementary & secondary schools
Bd of Dir: Patricia Green
Bd of Dir: Norene Marvets
Exec: Carmen Negron
Dir Risk M: Tracy Fox
MIS Dir: Andy Canady
MIS Dir: Ron Pleasant
Pr Dir: Don Hall
Schl Brd P: Mary S Polleys
Schl Brd P: Robert Varner
Psych: Laurie Wylie
HC Dir: Darlene Shirley

D-U-N-S 07-240-6150
MUSCOGEE CREEK NATION
AGRI-BUSINESS COMPLEX DIVISION
1008 E Eufaula St, Okmulgee, OK 74447-7939
Tel (918) 756-8700 *Founded/Ownrshp* 1907
Sales NA *EMP* 1,200
Accts Finance Office Of Muscogee (Cr
SIC 9131 Indian reservation; ; Indian reservation;
CEO: Perry Beaver
Ofcr: Sonya McIntosh
**Prin:* Susanna Barnett
**Prin:* George Tiger
Off Mgr: Ryan Logan
IT Man: Cindy Freiling
Web Dev: Sonya Rock

MUSCOGEE MNOR NRSING RHAB CNTR
See HOSPITAL AUTHORITY OF COLUMBUS GEORGIA

D-U-N-S 07-963-1222
MUSCOLINO INVENTORY SERVICE INC
(*Suby of* PHYLE INVNTORY CTRL SPCIALISTS) ★
320 W Chestnut Ave, Monrovia, CA 91016-3318
Tel (626) 357-8600 *Founded/Ownrshp* 2007
Sales 8.7MM^E *EMP* 375
SIC 7389 Inventory computing service; Inventory computing service
Pr: William Calderwood
COO: Christian Okandey
Ex VP: Joseph P Balli

D-U-N-S 07-324-9625
MUSCULAR DYSTROPHY ASSOCIATION INC
MDA
222 S Riverside Plz # 1500, Chicago, IL 60606-6000
Tel (520) 529-2000 *Founded/Ownrshp* 1950
Sales 139.7MM *EMP* 950
Accts Bdo Usa Llp Phoenix Arizona
SIC 8733 Medical research; Medical research
Pr: Steven M Derks
Sr Pt: Alfred Schrader
CFO: Bruce Neufeld
Ch: R Rodney Howell
**Treas:* Suzanne Lowden
Sr VP: Ronald Schenkenberger
VP: Brad Barghols
VP: Louis Benzak
VP: John F Crowley
VP: Brenda Davis
VP: Stephen P Evans
VP: Patricia A Laus
VP: Amy Mitchell
VP: Kristin Stephenson
Dir Bus: Danielle Etter
Board of Directors: Maureen McGovern, Stanley H Appel, Ed McMahon, Robert M Bennett, Olin F Morris, Leon I Charash MD, Christopher J Rosa Phd, Bart Conner, Jeanne Y Russell, Harold C Crump, Charles D Schoor, Joseph S Dimartino, Lois R West, Daniel G Fries, David L Hutton, Suzanne L Lowden

D-U-N-S 60-366-3691
MUSCULOSKELETAL INSTITUTE CHARTERED
FLORIDA ORTHOPEDIC INSTITUTE
13020 N Telecom Pkwy, Temple Terrace, FL 33637-0925
Tel (813) 978-9700 *Founded/Ownrshp* 1989
Sales 62.3MM^E *EMP* 330
SIC 8011 Orthopedic physician; Orthopedic physician
Pr: Roy Sanders MD
COO: Grant Garlick
CFO: Nick Marsala
Treas: Mark Frankle MD
Exec: Carol Serwatke
Off Mgr: Angelo Setta
QA Dir: Karen Denemark
Dir IT: Daniel Pressner
IT Man: Chad Maynord
Orthpdst: Mark Davis
Surgeon: Brigham Au

D-U-N-S 18-756-0545 IMP
MUSCULOSKELETAL TRANSPLANT FOUNDATION INC
M T F
125 May St Ste 300, Edison, NJ 08837-3264
Tel (732) 661-0202 *Founded/Ownrshp* 1987
Sales 404.8MM *EMP* 1,000
SIC 2836 8099 Biological products, except diagnostic; Medical services organization; Biological products, except diagnostic; Medical services organization
Pr: Bruce W Stroever
**CFO:* Michael J Kawas
**Ch:* William Tomford
**Ex VP:* Martha Anderson
Ex VP: Arthur Gertzman
**Ex VP:* Mark Spilker
VP: Michael Oleck
**VP:* Michael Schuler
Exec: George Herrera
Exec: David Paul
Dir Soc: Laura Dey
Dir Bus: Carey Markey

D-U-N-S 18-531-4432
MUSE COMMUNICATIONS INC
9543 Culver Blvd Fl 2, Culver City, CA 90232-2618
Tel (310) 945-4100 *Founded/Ownrshp* 1987
Sales 35.0MM^E *EMP* 20^E
SIC 7311 Advertising consultant; Advertising consultant
Ch Bd: J Melvin Muse
VP: Alex Perez
IT Man: Jeff Bernstein
VP Mktg: Wanda Melendez
Mktg Mgr: Walter Reynolds

D-U-N-S 83-137-4892
MUSEUM ASSOCIATES
LA COUNTY MUSEUM OF ART
5905 Wilshire Blvd, Los Angeles, CA 90036-4504
Tel (323) 857-6172 *Founded/Ownrshp* 1938
Sales 81.7MM *EMP* 400
SIC 8412 Museum; Museum
CEO: Michael Gavin
Ofcr: Diana Vesga
IT Man: CHI-Young Kim

D-U-N-S 11-085-7039
MUSEUM CO INC
695 Us Highway 46 Ste 400, Fairfield, NJ 07004-1592
Tel (973) 575-4446 *Founded/Ownrshp* 2006
Sales 23.0MM^E *EMP* 1,000
SIC 5947 Gifts & novelties; Gifts & novelties
Ch: Joel Kier

D-U-N-S 07-856-9897 IMP/EXP
MUSEUM OF BIBLE INC
7701 Sw 44th St, Oklahoma City, OK 73179-4808
Tel (405) 745-1100 *Founded/Ownrshp* 2012
Sales 73.5MM *EMP* 5
Accts Cole & Reed Pc Oklahoma Cit
SIC 8412 Museum; Museum
Ch: Steven Green
IT Man: Cary Summers

D-U-N-S 02-912-1696 IMP
MUSEUM OF CONTEMPORARY ART
250 S Grand Ave, Los Angeles, CA 90012-3021
Tel (213) 626-6222 *Founded/Ownrshp* 1979
Sales 91.5MM *EMP* 200
Accts Singerlewak Llp Los Angeles
SIC 8412 Museums & art galleries; Museums & art galleries
CEO: Charles Young
**CEO:* Jeffrey Deitch
**CFO:* Michael Harrison
Store Mgr: Matti Allison
Mktg Dir: Angelique Power
Sales Asso: Lydia Terlo
Snr Mgr: Helen Molesworth
Assoc Ed: Jane Hyun
Board of Directors: Grant Breding

D-U-N-S 07-236-2916 IMP
MUSEUM OF CONTEMPORARY ART
MUSEUM OF CONTEMPORARY ART STO
220 E Chicago Ave, Chicago, IL 60611-2644
Tel (312) 280-2660 *Founded/Ownrshp* 1964
Sales 20.8MM *EMP* 340
SIC 8412 Museum; Museum
CEO: Madeleine Grynsztejn
Bd of Dir: Richard Shapiro
Ofcr: Willie Lin
Assoc Dir: Yolanda Cesta
Ex Dir: Jeanne Shoaff
Dir Sec: Eddie Sallie
Telecom Ex: Jared Sheldon
Prd Mgr: Joe Iverson
Sales Asso: Stefanie Greisbach
Snr Mgr: Susan Chun
Snr Mgr: Kathryn Kanjo

MUSEUM OF CONTEMPORARY ART STO
See MUSEUM OF CONTEMPORARY ART

D-U-N-S 07-658-0638 IMP
MUSEUM OF FINE ARTS (MA)
465 Huntington Ave, Boston, MA 02115-5597
Tel (617) 369-3861 *Founded/Ownrshp* 1867
Sales 184.8MM *EMP* 1,000
Accts Cbiz Tofias Boston Ma
SIC 8412 5961 8299 Museum; Clothing, mail order (except women's); Art school, except commercial; Museum; Clothing, mail order (except women's); Art school, except commercial
Ch Bd: Richard Lubin
**Pr:* Sandra Moose
CFO: Peter Gerondeau
**CFO:* Mark B Kerwin
**Treas:* Stephen Fine
Trst: Roger Servison
VP: John B Adams
**VP:* Bettina Burr
Ex Dir: John Schroder
Ex Dir: Richard Woodward
Genl Mgr: Jordana Weiss

D-U-N-S 07-415-5219 IMP
MUSEUM OF FINE ARTS OF HOUSTON
GLASSELL SCHOOL OF ART
1001 Bissonnet St, Houston, TX 77005-1896
Tel (713) 639-7300 *Founded/Ownrshp* 1913
Sales 163.4MM *EMP* 494
Accts Deloitte Tax Llp Houston Tx
SIC 8412 Museum; Museum
Assoc Dir: Jennifer Cronin
Ex Dir: Gwen Goffee
Snr Mgr: Dale Benson
Snr Mgr: Mayrav Fisher

D-U-N-S 01-925-6627
MUSEUM OF FLIGHT FOUNDATION (WA)
9404 E Marginal Way S, Tukwila, WA 98108-4097
Tel (206) 764-5720 *Founded/Ownrshp* 1965
Sales 24.0MM *EMP* 156
SIC 8412 Museum; Museum
CEO: Douglas R King
**CFO:* Edward Waale
**Treas:* James Farmer
**VP:* Michael Hallman
MIS Dir: Alison Lee
S&M/Mgr: Bill Hayes

D-U-N-S 07-327-3559 IMP/EXP
MUSEUM OF MODERN ART
MOMA
11 W 53rd St, New York, NY 10019-5497
Tel (212) 708-9400 *Founded/Ownrshp* 1929
Sales 85.1MM^E *EMP* 825
SIC 8412 5942

D-U-N-S 07-660-6334 IMP
MUSEUM OF SCIENCE
1 Science Park, Boston, MA 02114-1099
Tel (617) 723-2500 *Founded/Ownrshp* 1830
Sales 65.9MM *EMP* 350
Accts Mayer Hoffman Mccann Pc Bos
SIC 8412 Museum; Museum
CEO: Ioannis N Miaoulis
CFO: Nancy McKee
Bd of Dir: Barbara Feldman
**VP:* Jonathan Burke
Prgrm Mgr: Karen Ellis

D-U-N-S 06-847-4337
MUSEUM OF SCIENCE & INDUSTRY
5700 S Lake Shore Dr, Chicago, IL 60637-2093
Tel (773) 684-1414 *Founded/Ownrshp* 1926
Sales 48.5MM *EMP* 500^E
Accts Grant Thornton Llp Chicago I
SIC 8412 Museum; Museum
Pr: David Mosena
Bd of Dir: James R Kackley
VP: Shannon Alexander
VP: Sheila Cawley
VP: Kurt Haunfelner
VP: Allyson Laackman
VP: Nancy Wright
Exec: Jeff Buonomo
Exec: Elizabeth Keating
Assoc Dir: Julie Haymon
CTO: Austin Pope

D-U-N-S 07-387-7037
MUSEUM OF SCIENCE INC
PATRICIA / PHILLIP FROST MSM
3280 S Miami Ave, Miami, FL 33129-2899
Tel (305) 646-4200 *Founded/Ownrshp* 1949
Sales 71.1MM *EMP* 90
Accts Verdeja De Armas Coral Gables
SIC 8412 Museum; Planetarium; Museum; Planetarium
CEO: Gillian Thomas
Dir Vol: Vanessa Herrero
**COO:* Frank Steslow
**CFO:* Roxanne Ortiz
CFO: Raj Sarangapani
Trst: Lance Aylsworth
Ex VP: Jonah Pruitt
Sr VP: Jennifer Gibbs
Sr VP: Sheldon Roy
VP: Sean Duran
VP: Tony Lima
VP: Margaret Machado
VP: Ron Nuce
Exec: Vanessa Florio

MUSEUM SHOP, THE
See MISSOURI HISTORICAL SOCIETY (INC)

D-U-N-S 00-236-8231 IMP
MUSHROOM CO
902 Woods Rd, Cambridge, MD 21613-9470
Tel (410) 221-8970 *Founded/Ownrshp* 1931
Sales 20.2MM^E *EMP* 75
SIC 2033 Mushrooms: packaged in cans, jars, etc.
CEO: Dennis G Newhard
Natl Sales: Dan Davis

Natl Sales: Ruth Newhard
Sls Mgr: Bonni Young

MUSIC
See MISSOURI UNITED SCHOOLS INSURANCE COUNCIL

MUSIC & ARTS CENTERS
See GUITAR CENTER STORES INC

D-U-N-S 83-920-7743 IMP
MUSIC AND DANCE THEATER CHICAGO INC
205 E Randolph St, Chicago, IL 60601-6530
Tel (312) 629-8696 *Founded/Ownrshp* 1994
Sales 22.9MM *EMP* 10
Accts Mcgladrey Llp Chicago Il
SIC 7929 Entertainers & entertainment groups
Ch Bd: James L Alexander
**Pr:* Michael Tiknis
**Ch:* Joan W Harris
Ex VP: Laura Hanssel
**Prin:* Caryn Harris
**Prin:* Alexandra Nichols
**Prin:* Mary Kay Sullivan
IT Man: Catherine Miller

D-U-N-S 96-966-3868
MUSIC AND EVENT MANAGEMENT INC
1241 Elm St, Cincinnati, OH 45202-7531
Tel (513) 621-1919 *Founded/Ownrshp* 2011
Sales 23.9MM *EMP* 2
Accts Clark Schaefer Hackett And Co
SIC 7231 Beauty shops; Beauty shops
Prin: Douglas D Thomson

MUSIC CENTER
See PERFORMING ARTS CENTER OF LOS ANGELES COUNTY

D-U-N-S 78-197-0017
MUSIC CHOICE
650 Dresher Rd, Horsham, PA 19044-2204
Tel (215) 784-5840 *Founded/Ownrshp* 1993
Sales 38.5MM^E *EMP* 90
SIC 5063 Transformers & transmission equipment
CEO: David J Del Beccaro
Pr: Matt Turner
VP: Donna O'Neill

D-U-N-S 09-212-4890
MUSIC EXPRESS INC (CA)
2601 W Empire Ave, Burbank, CA 91504-3225
Tel (818) 845-1502 *Founded/Ownrshp* 1973, 1975
Sales 60.8MM^E *EMP* 391
SIC 4119

MUSIC INTLLGNCE NEURO DEV INST
See MIND RESEARCH INSTITUTE

D-U-N-S 06-704-2713
MUSIC MOUNTAIN WATER CO LLC
305 Stoner Ave, Shreveport, LA 71101-4118
Tel (318) 425-4400 *Founded/Ownrshp* 1980
Sales 50.3MM^E *EMP* 120^E
SIC 5149 5499

D-U-N-S 02-181-7051 IMP
MUSIC PEOPLE INC
ON-STAGE STANDS
154 Woodlawn Rd Ste C, Berlin, CT 06037-1500
Tel (860) 829-9229 *Founded/Ownrshp* 1979
Sales 42.0MM *EMP* 54
SIC 5099

D-U-N-S 01-084-7978 IMP
MUSICAL ARTS ASSOCIATION (OH)
BLOSSOM MUSIC CENTER
11001 Euclid Ave, Cleveland, OH 44106-1796
Tel (216) 231-7300 *Founded/Ownrshp* 1925
Sales 58.0MM *EMP* 205
Accts Ernst & Young Us Llp Chicago
SIC 7929 6512 Musical entertainers; Orchestras or bands; Auditorium & hall operation; Musical entertainers; Orchestras or bands; Auditorium & hall operation
Ex Dir: Gary Hanson
Dir Vol: Lori Cohen
COO: Mell Csicsila
Bd of Dir: Frank Bianchi
Ofcr: Timothy Mann
Ofcr: Pratima Raju
VP: Alfred Rankin
Genl Mgr: Jennifer Barlament
Dir IT: Kevin Lawlor
Info Man: George Kradel
Merch Mgr: Larry Fox

MUSICAL FULFILLMENT SERVICES
See AMERICAN MUSICAL SUPPLY INC

D-U-N-S 07-873-7673 IMP/EXP
MUSICIANS FRIEND INC
LMI
(*Suby of* GUITAR CENTER INC) ★
5795 Lindero Canyon Rd, Westlake Village, CA 91362-4013
Tel (818) 735-8800 *Founded/Ownrshp* 1997
Sales 28.6MM^E *EMP* 137^E
SIC 5736 Musical instrument stores; Musical instrument stores
Ex VP: Tim Martin
**Treas:* John Unger
Sr Cor Off: Deanna Eastman
Ex VP: John Bagan
Ex VP: Eugene Joly
VP: Dennis Haffeman
Dir IT: John Owen
Sls Dir: Eric Breeze

D-U-N-S 07-623-1950
MUSICK PEELER & GARRETT LLP
624 S Grand Ave Ste 2000, Los Angeles, CA 90017-3321
Tel (213) 629-7600 *Founded/Ownrshp* 1945
Sales 32.3MM^E *EMP* 232
SIC 8111 General practice law office; Taxation law; Corporate, partnership & business law; Labor & employment law; General practice law office; Taxation law; Corporate, partnership & business law; Labor & employment law
Mng Pt: R Joseph De Briyn
Pt: Peter J Diedrich
Pt: Edward Landrey
Pt: Wayne Littlefield
Pt: Gary Overstreet
Mng Pt: R De Briyn
Pr: Alayne Farrell

MUSICMAGPIE.COM
See ENTERTAINMENT MAGPIE INC

MUSICTODAY C D REPLICATION
See MUSICTODAY LLC

D-U-N-S 10-269-5710
■ **MUSICTODAY LLC**
MUSICTODAY C D REPLICATION
(*Suby of* LIVE NATION WORLDWIDE INC) ★
5391 Three Notch D Rd, Crozet, VA 22932-3181
Tel (434) 823-2226 *Founded/Ownrshp* 1993
Sales 43.1MM^E *EMP* 225
SIC 7373 7922 Computer integrated systems design; Theatrical producers & services; Computer integrated systems design; Theatrical producers & services
CEO: Gorgan Vance
Mktg Mgr: John Hanna

D-U-N-S 00-977-1692
MUSKA ELECTRIC CO
1985 Oakcrest Ave, Saint Paul, MN 55113-2686
Tel (651) 636-5820 *Founded/Ownrshp* 1919
Sales 50.0MM *EMP* 214^E
SIC 1731 General electrical contractor; General electrical contractor
CEO: Ron Von Bank
**Pr:* Gary D Nelson
COO: Becky Munson
**CFO:* Nathan Stein
Brnch Mgr: Don Edel
MIS Dir: Chad Armstrong
MIS Dir: Larry EBY
Snr Mgr: Ted Olson

D-U-N-S 02-862-5044
MUSKEGO-NORWAY SCHOOL DISTRICT
S87w18763 Woods Rd, Muskego, WI 53150-7904
Tel (262) 971-1800 *Founded/Ownrshp* 1960
Sales 36.6MM^E *EMP* 477
Accts Hawkins Ash Baptie & Company
SIC 8211 Public combined elementary & secondary school; Public combined elementary & secondary school
Dir IT: Marie Cimpl

D-U-N-S 94-224-1373
MUSKEGON CAR CREDIT INC
CAR CITY
1515 28th St Sw, Grand Rapids, MI 49509-2707
Tel (616) 249-2000 *Founded/Ownrshp* 1999
Sales 25.0MM *EMP* 50
SIC 5521 Automobiles, used cars only; Automobiles, used cars only
Ch Bd: Jeff Baker
**Sec:* Donald Kolehouse

D-U-N-S 93-110-5811 IMP
MUSKEGON CASTINGS CORP
PORT CITY GROUP
(*Suby of* PORT CITY GROUP HOLDINGS) ★
1985 E Laketon Ave, Muskegon, MI 49442-6127
Tel (231) 777-3941 *Founded/Ownrshp* 1998
Sales 24.1MM^E *EMP* 127
SIC 3363 Aluminum die-castings; Aluminum die-castings
CEO: John Essex
**Pr:* Mark Pickett
**CFO:* Dale Keyser
Prgrm Mgr: Greg Klimowicz
Plnt Mgr: Joe Grevious
Plnt Mgr: Scott Maus
Ql Cn Mgr: Kevin Hysell
Ql Cn Mgr: Ron Shoemaker

D-U-N-S 02-090-2391
MUSKEGON COMMUNITY COLLEGE
221 S Quarterline Rd, Muskegon, MI 49442-1493
Tel (231) 773-9131 *Founded/Ownrshp* 1926
Sales 21.6MM^E *EMP* 360^E
SIC 8222 Community college; Community college
Pr: Dale K Nesbary
Trst: Sean Mullally
VP: John Selmon
Store Mgr: Kim Oakes
Snr Mgr: Pamela Cengiz

D-U-N-S 04-798-1808
MUSKEGON HEIGHTS PUBLIC SCHOOLS
2603 Leahy St, Muskegon, MI 49444-2121
Tel (231) 830-3200 *Founded/Ownrshp* 1891
Sales 16.2MM^E *EMP* 360
SIC 8211 Public combined elementary & secondary school; Public combined elementary & secondary school

D-U-N-S 07-258-2877
MUSKEGON PUBLIC SCHOOLS
349 W Webster Ave, Muskegon, MI 49440-1208
Tel (231) 720-2000 *Founded/Ownrshp* 1890
Sales 37.4MM^E *EMP* 900
SIC 8211 8331 8412 8231 8741 Public elementary school; Public junior high school; Public senior high school; Kindergarten; Skill training center; Museum; Public library; Management services; Public elementary school; Public junior high school; Public senior high school; Kindergarten; Skill training center; Museum; Public library; Management services
**Ch:* Charles Poole
Prin: Greg Hazard
Pr Dir: Dee Carlson

D-U-N-S 62-607-4066 IMP
MUSKET CORP
LOVE'S TRVL STOPS CNTRY STORES
(*Suby of* LOVES TRAVEL STOPS & COUNTRY STORES INC) ★
10601 N Pennsylvania Ave, Oklahoma City, OK 73120-4108
Tel (713) 332-5726 *Founded/Ownrshp* 1964
Sales 489.9MM^E *EMP* 64
SIC 5172 Gasoline; Gasoline
Pr: Frank Love
**Ch Bd:* Tom E Love
Pr: Roger Griffin
Pr: Jenny Meyer
**Treas:* Doug Stussi
**Ex VP:* Gregory M Love
**VP:* Brad Jenkins
Exec: Dave Coburn
Dir Risk M: Larry Dixon
**Prin:* Daniel P Kavanaugh
**Prin:* Judith M Love

D-U-N-S 01-911-9595
MUSKIE PROPPANT LLC
14301 Caliber Dr Ste 210, Oklahoma City, OK 73134-1032
Tel (405) 233-3558 *Founded/Ownrshp* 2011
Sales 30.9MM^E *EMP* 23
SIC 1442 Sand mining

MUSKINGUM COUNTY JUVENILE CRT
See MUSKINGUM COUNTY OHIO

D-U-N-S 07-943-5137
MUSKINGUM COUNTY OHIO
MUSKINGUM COUNTY JUVENILE CRT
401 Main St, Zanesville, OH 43701-3519
Tel (740) 455-7100 *Founded/Ownrshp* 1800
Sales NA *EMP* 900
Accts Dave Yost Athens Ohio
SIC 9221 County police; County police
Prin: James Porter
**Prin:* Stephen Strauss

D-U-N-S 01-848-6761
MUSKINGUM IRON & METAL CO (OH)
345 Arthur St, Zanesville, OH 43701-5850
Tel (740) 452-9351 *Founded/Ownrshp* 1929
Sales 20.7MM^E *EMP* 36
SIC 5093 Nonferrous metals scrap
Pr: Jack Joseph
**VP:* Joshua Joseph
**Prin:* Arthur L Joseph
**Prin:* Shirley L Joseph
**Prin:* Stanley I Joseph
Genl Mgr: Brian Ferguson

MUSKINGUM PERRY CAREER CENTER
See MID-EAST CAREER AND TECHNOLOGY CENTERS

D-U-N-S 07-502-7516
MUSKINGUM UNIVERSITY
163 Stormont St, New Concord, OH 43762-1118
Tel (740) 826-8211 *Founded/Ownrshp* 1837
Sales 38.1MM *EMP* 305
Accts Crowe Horwath Llp Columbus O
SIC 8221 College, except junior; College, except junior
Pr: Anne Steele
Pr: Margaret Brown
**CFO:* James R Wilson
Treas: Stephen Fondriest
**VP:* James Callaghan
**VP:* Kathleen Fitzgerald
VP: Amber Gump
VP: Teresa Riley
VP: Mark Sanford
Assoc Dir: Marcy Ritzert
Ex Dir: Sheila Ellenberger

D-U-N-S 06-890-6452
MUSKINGUM WATERSHED CONSERVANCY DISTRICT
1319 3rd St Nw, New Philadelphia, OH 44663-1305
Tel (330) 343-6647 *Founded/Ownrshp* 1933
Sales NA *EMP* 350
SIC 9512 Conservation & stabilization agency, government; Conservation & stabilization agency, government
Ex Dir: John M Hoopingarner
**Treas:* James Cugliari

D-U-N-S 83-304-7751
MUSKOGEE MUNICIPAL AUTHORITY
229 W Okmulgee St, Muskogee, OK 74401-7033
Tel (918) 684-6290 *Founded/Ownrshp* 1977
Sales NA *EMP* 450^E
SIC 9111 Mayors' offices; Mayors' offices
**Treas:* Jean Kingston

MUSKOGEE PUBLIC SCHOOLS
See MUSKOGEE SCHOOL DISTRICT I-20

D-U-N-S 07-241-0111
MUSKOGEE REGIONAL MEDICAL CENTER LLC
EASTAR HEALTH SYSTEM
300 Rockefeller Dr, Muskogee, OK 74401-5075
Tel (918) 682-5501 *Founded/Ownrshp* 2007
Sales 147.5MM^E *EMP* 1,003
SIC 8062 General medical & surgical hospitals; General medical & surgical hospitals
CEO: Kevin Fowler
Chf OB: David Whatley
**COO:* James Davidson
**CFO:* Matthew Romero
Chf Mktg O: Gary Lambert
Chf Nrs Of: Diane Feder
Doctor: Evan Cole
Doctor: Jewell Daniels
Doctor: Jason Dansby
Doctor: Jackie Dean
Doctor: Lori Ford

D-U-N-S 09-664-7847
MUSKOGEE SCHOOL DISTRICT I-20
MUSKOGEE PUBLIC SCHOOLS
202 W Broadway St, Muskogee, OK 74401-6651
Tel (918) 684-3700 *Founded/Ownrshp* 1907
Sales 53.3MM^E *EMP* 841
SIC 8211 Public combined elementary & secondary school; Public combined elementary & secondary school
Prin: Mike Garde
IT Man: Eric Wells
Pr Dir: Wendy Burton
Teacher Pr: Martha Brians

D-U-N-S 06-184-6937
MUSS DEVELOPMENT LLC
11835 Queens Blvd # 1600, Forest Hills, NY 11375-7251
Tel (718) 263-3800 *Founded/Ownrshp* 1906
Sales 77.6MM^E *EMP* 150
SIC 1522 1542 Multi-family dwellings, new construction; Commercial & office building, new construction; Multi-family dwellings, new construction; Commercial & office building, new construction
**COO:* Jeffrey A Kay
Sr VP: W Cadogan
Sr VP: Michael Seidenwar
Sr VP: Robert Stern
VP: William Bergman
VP: Michael Cinamon
VP: Bob Machado
VP: Ross Spitalnick
**VP:* Ronald Zeccardi
Genl Couns: Joseph McKillop

D-U-N-S 02-985-8305
MUSSELMAN AND HALL CONTRACTORS LLC
M & H
4922 Blue Banks Ave, Kansas City, MO 64130-2346
Tel (816) 861-1234 *Founded/Ownrshp* 1996
Sales 28.0MM^E *EMP* 200
Accts Marks Nelson Vohland Campbell
SIC 4789 1771 1611 Railroad maintenance & repair services; Concrete work; Surfacing & paving; Railroad maintenance & repair services; Concrete work; Surfacing & paving
CEO: Douglas H Hall
**CFO:* Mark S Weese
Ofcr: Erin Wright
**Ex VP:* Dexter Phillips
VP: Kyle Slyke
Sftwr Eng: Michael Morris

D-U-N-S 85-846-0694
MUSSELMANS DODGE INC
5717 Baltimore Nat Pike, Catonsville, MD 21228-1785
Tel (410) 744-7400 *Founded/Ownrshp* 1992
Sales 22.0MM^E *EMP* 55
SIC 5511 Automobiles, new & used; Pickups, new & used; Vans, new & used; Automobiles, new & used; Pickups, new & used; Vans, new & used
Pr: Robert P Musselman Sr
Sec: Terry Vacek
**VP:* Kenneth Musselman Jr
Store Mgr: J D McDaniels

D-U-N-S 80-994-9563 EXP
MUSSER LUMBER CO INC
RURAL RETREAT TRANSPORT
200 Shoal Ridge Dr, Rural Retreat, VA 24368-3132
Tel (276) 686-5113 *Founded/Ownrshp* 1993
Sales 39.6MM^E *EMP* 90^E
SIC 5031 Lumber, plywood & millwork; Lumber, plywood & millwork
CEO: Musser Ronald Edward
**Pr:* Ronald M Musser
**Treas:* Helen Musser
**VP:* Michael G Musser

D-U-N-S 07-943-2793
MUSSER PARK HOLDINGS CORP (PA)
120 N Lime St, Lancaster, PA 17602-2923
Tel (717) 399-5290 *Founded/Ownrshp* 2013
Sales 35.8MM^E *EMP* 380
Accts Baker Tilly Virchow Krause Ll
SIC 1742 1721 Drywall; Painting & paper hanging; Drywall; Acoustical & ceiling work; Painting & paper hanging
Pr: Benjamin Dicarlo

D-U-N-S 01-448-9983
MUSSERS INC (PA)
MUSSER'S MARKETS
35 Friendly Dr, Quarryville, PA 17566-9794
Tel (717) 284-4147 *Founded/Ownrshp* 1967, 1979
Sales 29.2MM^E *EMP* 200
Accts Trout Ebersole & Groff Llp
SIC 5411 Supermarkets, independent; Supermarkets, independent
Pr: Michael Musser
**Treas:* Abner Musser III
**Treas:* Greg Musser
**VP:* Mike J Musser

MUSSER'S MARKETS
See MUSSERS INC

D-U-N-S 00-613-1304
MUSSON BROS INC
909 Boyce Dr, Rhinelander, WI 54501-3836
Tel (715) 365-8700 *Founded/Ownrshp* 1955
Sales 50.8MM^E *EMP* 155
SIC 1611 3273 General contractor, highway & street construction; Ready-mixed concrete; General contractor, highway & street construction; Ready-mixed concrete
Pr: Timothy Musson
VP: Jack David
VP: Mike Sickma
Sfty Dirs: Darren Muljo

D-U-N-S 03-436-2251
MUSSON-PATOUT AUTOMOTIVE GROUP INC
(*Suby of* DEALER MANAGEMENT AGENCY INC) ★
1200 E Main St, New Iberia, LA 70560-3922
Tel (337) 365-3411 *Founded/Ownrshp* 1994

Sales 37.5MM^E *EMP* 93^E
SIC 5511 New & used car dealers; New & used car dealers
Pr: Diane Musson
**Sec:* Jessamine Musson
**VP:* Barton Romero

MUSSON-PATUT AUTOMOTIVE GROUP
See DEALER MANAGEMENT AGENCY INC

MUST
See MONTANA UNIFIED SCHOOL TRUST

D-U-N-S 19-407-7228 IMP
MUSTAD CONNECTICUT INC
CAPEWELL HORSE NAILS
(*Suby of* MUSTAD INTERNATIONAL GROUP N.V.)
5195 Scandia Trl N, Forest Lake, MN 55025-8112
Tel (651) 287-8289 *Founded/Ownrshp* 1984
Sales 36.3MM^E *EMP* 140^E
SIC 3315 5051 5084 Nails, steel: wire or cut; Nails; Paper, sawmill & woodworking machinery; Nails, steel: wire or cut; Nails; Paper, sawmill & woodworking machinery
Pr: Carlos Lara

MUSTANG CAT
See MUSTANG MACHINERY CO LTD

D-U-N-S 78-602-6492
MUSTANG CLAIM SERVICE
(*Suby of* FRONTIER GENERAL INSURANCE AGENCY INC) ★
6801 Calmont Ave, Fort Worth, TX 76116-4108
Tel (817) 732-2111 *Founded/Ownrshp* 1988
Sales NA *EMP* 38
SIC 6411 Insurance agents, brokers & service; Insurance agents, brokers & service
Pr: Al Johnston
**Pr:* Robert Hudson
**VP:* Don Bauman

MUSTANG DYNAMOMETER
See GANZCORP INVESTMENTS INC

D-U-N-S 15-396-6721
MUSTANG ENGINEERS AND CONSTRUCTORS LP
(*Suby of* WOOD GROUP MUSTANG INC) ★
16001 Park Ten Pl, Houston, TX 77084-5135
Tel (713) 215-8000 *Founded/Ownrshp* 2000
Sales NA *EMP* 3,500
SIC 1542 1541 Construction project management consultant; Consulting engineer; Commercial & office building contractors; Industrial buildings & warehouses
VP: Meg Lassart
Dir Bus: Mike Martinez
Software D: Samer Saleh
Sales Asso: Travis Hansen

D-U-N-S 15-202-5045 IMP
MUSTANG FUEL CORP
9800 N Oklahoma Ave, Oklahoma City, OK 73114-7406
Tel (405) 884-2092 *Founded/Ownrshp* 1969
Sales 169.4MM^E *EMP* 124
Accts Grant Thornton Llp Oklahoma
SIC 1311 4923 Crude petroleum production; Natural gas production; Gas transmission & distribution; Crude petroleum production; Natural gas production; Gas transmission & distribution
Ch Bd: Carey Joullian IV
Ch Bd: E Carey Joullian IV
CFO: Scott M Chapline
Sr VP: Rand Phipps
VP: Paul Belflower
VP: Thomas Bennett
VP: Carrie Brower
VP: Gary Sump
Exec: Eric Rice
VP Opers: Gary Stump

D-U-N-S 00-490-8916
MUSTANG GAS COMPRESSION LLC (TX)
14825 Saint Marys Ln # 200, Houston, TX 77079-2991
Tel (281) 973-6201 *Founded/Ownrshp* 2007
Sales 30.1MM^E *EMP* 97^E
SIC 1389 Gas compressing (natural gas) at the fields
Pr: John Mark Story
**Treas:* M S Chapline
**VP:* R Phipps

D-U-N-S 36-097-9913
MUSTANG GROUP LLC
339 Auburn St Ste 11, Auburndale, MA 02466-1907
Tel (617) 467-6800 *Founded/Ownrshp* 2005
Sales 20.3MM^E *EMP* 109
SIC 6799 5045 Investors; Computer software
**Mng Pt:* Carson Biederman

D-U-N-S 78-507-1882
MUSTANG HEAVY HAUL LLC
LATSHAW DRILLING
(*Suby of* LATSHAW DRILLING & EXPLORATION CO) ★
4905 S Perkins Rd, Stillwater, OK 74074-7554
Tel (405) 743-0085 *Founded/Ownrshp* 2012
Sales 57.6MM^E *EMP* 1,100
SIC 1381 Drilling oil & gas wells; Drilling oil & gas wells
COO: Mike Brown
CFO: Rich Goode
Ofcr: Roff Duke
VP: Steve Owen
Sfty Dirs: Dusty Stasyszen
Trfc Dir: Troy Holman
Opers Mgr: Jason Burke
Opers Mgr: Sonny Marsalia

MUSTANG INDUSTRIAL EQUIPMENT
See FORKLIFT SYSTEMS OF TEXAS LTD

D-U-N-S 00-793-2163 IMP/EXP
MUSTANG MACHINERY CO LTD (TX)
MUSTANG CAT
12800 Northwest Fwy, Houston, TX 77040-6302
Tel (713) 861-1440 *Founded/Ownrshp* 1952
Sales 677.7MM^E *EMP* 1,340
SIC 5082 5084 General construction machinery & equipment; Industrial machinery & equipment; Engines & transportation equipment; General construction machinery & equipment; Industrial machinery & equipment; Engines & transportation equipment
Pr: Bradford Tucker
Sr Cor Off: Steve Ross
**Ex VP:* Douglas R Fisk
Off Mgr: Peggy Gexler
QC Dir: Joseph Russo
Mtls Mgr: Roy Escamilla
VP Mktg: Melody Bizego
Mktg Mgr: Scott Bowen
Sls Mgr: Ken Rickett
Sales Asso: Dale Couvillon
Sales Asso: Mike Otis

D-U-N-S 87-426-3036
MUSTANG PROCESS AND INDUSTRIAL INC
30 Patewood Dr Ste 200, Greenville, SC 29615-6812
Tel (864) 288-3009 *Founded/Ownrshp* 2008
Sales 98.4MM^E *EMP* 4,500
SIC 8741 Management services
Pr: Steve Knowles
**Prin:* Gordon Gibson

D-U-N-S 09-614-8267
MUSTANG PUBLIC SCHOOLS
906 S Heights Dr, Mustang, OK 73064-3542
Tel (405) 376-2461 *Founded/Ownrshp* 1923
Sales 52.6MM^E *EMP* 1,000
SIC 8211 Public combined elementary & secondary school; Public elementary school; Public junior high school; Public combined elementary & secondary school; Public elementary school; Public junior high school
Dir IT: Geromy Schrick
IT Man: Carol Scott
Pr Dir: Shannon Rigsby
**Schl Brd P:* Chad Fulton
Teacher Pr: Tracy Skinner
Psych: Amy Hill
HC Dir: Karen Wilson

D-U-N-S 02-434-0697
MUSTANG SEEDS INC
306 S Washington Ave, Madison, SD 57042-3053
Tel (605) 256-1065 *Founded/Ownrshp* 1961
Sales 27.1MM^E *EMP* 42
SIC 5191 5261 Seeds: field, garden & flower; Nursery stock, seeds & bulbs; Garden supplies & tools
Pr: Terry Schultz
**Sec:* Marlys Schultz
**VP:* Tim Schultz

D-U-N-S 06-987-1502
■ **MUSTANG TECHNOLOGY GROUP LP** (TX)
L-3 MUSTANG TECHNOLOGY
(*Suby of* L-3 COMMUNICATIONS CORP) ★
6900 K Ave, Plano, TX 75074-2527
Tel (972) 747-0707 *Founded/Ownrshp* 1999, 2013
Sales 34.4MM^E *EMP* 115
SIC 3812 Radar systems & equipment; Radar systems & equipment
Pr: Kent Lowder
CFO: Rob Byers
Exec: Patricia Manalo
VP Mktg: Howard Witt
Snr Mgr: Heath Keene

D-U-N-S 19-386-1650
MUSTANG VACUUM SYSTEMS INC
7135 16th St E, Sarasota, FL 34243-6818
Tel (941) 377-1440 *Founded/Ownrshp* 2005
Sales 20.5MM^E *EMP* 50
SIC 3569 Industrial shock absorbers
CEO: Dean Ganzhorn
**Pr:* Richard Greenwell
**VP:* Robert Choquette
Dir Bus: Todd Komanetsky
Sales Exec: Jan Kirchner

D-U-N-S 09-553-0580 IMP
MUSTANGS UNLIMITED INC
440 Adams St, Manchester, CT 06042-2767
Tel (860) 647-1965 *Founded/Ownrshp* 1976
Sales 26.1MM^E *EMP* 60
SIC 5531 5961 5015 5013 Automotive parts; Automotive supplies & equipment, mail order; Motor vehicle parts, used; Automotive supplies & parts
Pr: Christopher Hoverman
Dir Lab: Nathan Sosna
Sales Exec: Mike Malignaggi

D-U-N-S 01-743-2576
MUSTARD SEED HEALTH FOOD MARKET INC
MUSTARD SEED MARKET & CAFE
3885 Medina Rd, Akron, OH 44333-2449
Tel (330) 666-7333 *Founded/Ownrshp* 1981
Sales 54.3MM^E *EMP* 350
SIC 5499 5999 5421 5921 5431 5812 Health foods; Gourmet food stores; Cosmetics; Seafood markets; Beer (packaged); Wine; Fruit & vegetable markets; Delicatessen (eating places); Health foods; Gourmet food stores; Cosmetics; Seafood markets; Beer (packaged); Wine; Fruit & vegetable markets; Delicatessen (eating places)
CEO: Margaret S Kanfer
**Pr:* Phillips Nabors
COO: Jon Fiume
Genl Mgr: Art Watkins
Off Mgr: Mary Graham
CIO: Vicki Shepler
**VP Opers:* Barbara Schenk

MUSTARD SEED MARKET & CAFE
See MUSTARD SEED HEALTH FOOD MARKET INC

D-U-N-S 12-984-3020 IMP
MUSTARD SEED TECHNOLOGIES INC
P K C
3000 W Warner Ave, Santa Ana, CA 92704-5311
Tel (714) 556-7007 *Founded/Ownrshp* 2002
Sales 47.2MM^E *EMP* 134
SIC 3679 5065 Harness assemblies for electronic use: wire or cable; Electronic parts & equipment; Harness assemblies for electronic use: wire or cable; Electronic parts & equipment
Pr: Bruce T McCleave Sr
**VP:* Roger Litz
Prgrm Mgr: Maribel Alday
Sales Exec: Roger Metcalfe
Natl Sales: Joel Longoria

MUSUEM OF TOLERANCE
See SIMON WIESENTHAL CENTER INC

D-U-N-S 15-163-3781
MUTANG HOLDINGS INC
VALTRONICS SOLUTIONS
43 Ritmore Dr, Ravenswood, WV 26164-8801
Tel (304) 273-5356 *Founded/Ownrshp* 1985
Sales 61.4MM^E *EMP* 50
SIC 5085 5084 Valves & fittings; Controlling instruments & accessories
Pr: Kenneth Thompson
CFO: James Rossi
**VP:* Brenda Thompson
Sales Asso: Ruami Dyck
Sales Asso: Walt Gerhold

D-U-N-S 07-289-1435
MUTH ELECTRIC INC
MUTH TECHNOLOGY
1717 N Sanborn Blvd, Mitchell, SD 57301-1025
Tel (605) 996-3983 *Founded/Ownrshp* 2002
Sales 75.7MM *EMP* 380
SIC 1731 General electrical contractor; General electrical contractor
Pr: Richard Muth
**CFO:* Terry Sabers
VP: Gaylord Grieve
**VP:* Paul Muth
VP: Jon Pollock
Genl Mgr: Stacy Schuman
CIO: Scott Kahre

MUTH TECHNOLOGY
See MUTH ELECTRIC INC

MUTI
See MIDWEST UNDERGROUND TECHNOLOGY INC

D-U-N-S 19-536-7669 IMP
MUTSUTECH LTD
3130 Bonita Rd Ste 107, Chula Vista, CA 91910-3263
Tel (619) 691-7056 *Founded/Ownrshp* 1988
Sales 276.4MM^E *EMP* 700
SIC 5064 Electrical appliances, major; Electrical appliances, major
CEO: Nobutoshi Mutsuki
**Pr:* Hiro Hamamatsu

MUTUAL BENEFIT GROUP
See MUTUAL BENEFIT INSURANCE CO

D-U-N-S 07-283-7677
MUTUAL BENEFIT INSURANCE CO
MUTUAL BENEFIT GROUP
409 Penn St, Huntingdon, PA 16652-1601
Tel (814) 643-3000 *Founded/Ownrshp* 1908
Sales NA *EMP* 160
SIC 6331 Fire, marine & casualty insurance; Fire, marine & casualty insurance
Pr: Steven C Sliver
**CFO:* John Coursen
CFO: Joseph L Soan
**Treas:* Joseph L Sloan
Sr VP: Kevin O'Brien
VP: Pat Bangs
VP: John Hanna
VP: Donna Patterson
Comm Man: Amy Miller
CIO: Jeff Smeltzer
Dir IT: Steven J Phillips

MUTUAL DISTRIBUTING COMPANY
See BJT INC

MUTUAL DROPCLOTH
See DUNN MANUFACTURING CORP

MUTUAL DRUG
See NORTH CAROLINA MUTUAL WHOLESALE DRUG CO

MUTUAL FLAVORS
See AMERICAN FRUITS AND FLAVORS

D-U-N-S 36-462-6515 IMP
MUTUAL INDUSTRIES NORTH INC
BILT-RITE MASTEX
707 W Grange Ave Ste 1, Philadelphia, PA 19120-2298
Tel (215) 927-6000 *Founded/Ownrshp* 1910
Sales 83.5MM^E *EMP* 300
SIC 3842 2221 Personal safety equipment; Broadwoven fabric mills, manmade; Personal safety equipment; Broadwoven fabric mills, manmade
CEO: Edmund Dunn
**Pr:* Andrew Dunn

D-U-N-S 08-372-2041
MUTUAL INSURANCE CO OF ARIZONA (AZ)
2602 E Thomas Rd, Phoenix, AZ 85016-8202
Tel (602) 956-5276 *Founded/Ownrshp* 1976
Sales NA *EMP* 100
SIC 6411 Medical insurance claim processing, contract or fee basis
Ch Bd: James Carland
Pr: David Palmer
CFO: Ed Marley
VP: Mary Hedin
VP: Julie Ritzman
CTO: Ron Brun
IT Man: Sonia Gosz

D-U-N-S 07-554-3116
■ **MUTUAL INSURANCE CO(INC)** (NJ)
(*Suby of* UFG) ★
10 Route 31 N, Pennington, NJ 08534-1606
Tel (609) 737-0426 *Founded/Ownrshp* 1844, 2011
Sales NA *EMP* 200
SIC 6331 Property damage insurance; Workers' compensation insurance; Burglary & theft insurance; Automobile insurance; Property damage insurance; Workers' compensation insurance; Burglary & theft insurance; Automobile insurance
Pr: Andrew R Speaker
**CFO:* David B Merclean
**Treas:* Gordon Coleman

D-U-N-S 06-764-7883
MUTUAL LIQUID GAS AND EQUIPMENT CO INC (CA)
MUTUAL PROPANE
17117 S Broadway, Gardena, CA 90248-3191
Tel (310) 515-0553 *Founded/Ownrshp* 1934, 1978
Sales 20.0MM^E *EMP* 50
SIC 5084 3549 Propane conversion equipment; Metalworking machinery
CEO: Melvin Moore
VP: Tom Boerum
Sls&Mrk Ex: Tom Boerom

D-U-N-S 00-924-4377 IMP
MUTUAL MATERIALS CO INC
605 119th Ave Ne, Bellevue, WA 98005-3073
Tel (425) 455-2869 *Founded/Ownrshp* 1900
Sales 33.6MM^E *EMP* 200^E
SIC 3251 3271 5032

D-U-N-S 83-286-8728
MUTUAL MOBILE INC
206 E 9th St Ste 1400, Austin, TX 78701-4412
Tel (512) 615-1800 *Founded/Ownrshp* 2009
Sales 65.0MM^E *EMP* 500
SIC 7371 7379 Computer software development; Computer related consulting services; Computer software development; Computer related consulting services
CEO: John Arrow
Pr: Russell Buyse
**COO:* Tarun Nimmagadda
Chf Mktg O: Sam Gaddis
Dir Bus: Jason Story
QA Dir: Quynh Pham
Dir IT: Ajay Pali
Web Dev: Holden Christiansen
VP Sls: Paul Ristroph

D-U-N-S 82-762-1942
MUTUAL OF AMERICA CAPITAL MANAGEMENT CORP
(*Suby of* MUTUAL OF AMERICA CORP) ★
320 Park Ave Fl 9, New York, NY 10022-6815
Tel (212) 224-1600 *Founded/Ownrshp* 1993
Sales 66.2MM^E *EMP* 375^E
SIC 6282 Investment advisory service
Prin: Manfred Altstadt
Pr: Ben Bartel
Ex VP: Stephen Rich
VP: Duygu Akyatan
VP: Sharonn Itliong
**VP:* Alex Kotlyar
VP: Joseph O'Reilly

D-U-N-S 78-337-2709
MUTUAL OF AMERICA CORP
(*Suby of* MUTUAL OF AMERICA LIFE INSURANCE CO) ★
320 Park Ave Fl 5, New York, NY 10022-6839
Tel (212) 224-1147 *Founded/Ownrshp* 1985
Sales NA *EMP* 1,000
SIC 6311 7389 Life insurance; Financial services; Life insurance; Financial services
Pr: Thomas J Moran
**Ch Bd:* William J Flynn
V Ch: Ted Herman
Pr: Jim Tiensvold
**CFO:* Manfred Altstadt
Ofcr: Jared Gutman
Ex VP: Andrew Altstadt
Ex VP: Kimberly Curiale
Ex VP: Thomas Dillman
Ex VP: Frida Maiorana
Ex VP: Robert Siedlecki
Ex VP: Marguerite Wagner
Sr VP: Jeffrey Angelo
Sr VP: Kola Angelo
Sr VP: Dick Brozovich
Sr VP: Katherine Cannizzaro
Sr VP: Sean Carroll
Sr VP: Susan Ferber
Sr VP: Chris Festog
Sr VP: Gordon Gaspard
Sr VP: Andrew Gutman

D-U-N-S 07-330-0337
MUTUAL OF AMERICA LIFE INSURANCE CO
320 Park Ave Fl 5, New York, NY 10022-6839
Tel (212) 224-1600 *Founded/Ownrshp* 1945
Sales NA *EMP* 1,100
Accts Kpmg Llp New York New York
SIC 6311 Mutual association life insurance; Mutual association life insurance
CEO: Thomas J Moran
**Ch Bd:* William J Flynn
**Pr:* John R Greed
**COO:* William S Conway
COO: Amir Lear
**CFO:* Manfred Altstadt
**CFO:* Thomas Gilliam
Treas: Chris W Festog
Treas: George L Medlin
Ex VP: Diane M Aramony
**Ex VP:* Jeremy J Brown
Ex VP: William A Demilt
Ex VP: Joseph R Gaffoglio
Ex VP: Robert Giaquinto
Ex VP: Thomas E Gilliam
Ex VP: Andrew L Heiskill
Ex VP: Theodore L Herman
Ex VP: Kathryn Lu
**Ex VP:* James J Roth
Ex VP: Scott H Rothstein
Ex VP: Marguerite H Wagner
Board of Directors: Wayne A I Frederick

D-U-N-S 07-664-0028
MUTUAL OF ENUMCLAW INSURANCE CO
1460 Wells St, Enumclaw, WA 98022-3098
Tel (360) 825-2591 *Founded/Ownrshp* 1898
Sales NA *EMP* 573
SIC 6331 6311 Fire, marine & casualty insurance: mutual; Automobile insurance; Burglary & theft insurance; Property damage insurance; Life insurance carriers; Fire, marine & casualty insurance: mutual; Automobile insurance; Burglary & theft insurance; Property damage insurance; Life insurance carriers
Pr: Gerald P Schmidt
**Ch Bd:* Vance O Fredrickson
CFO: Bradley Gipson
**Treas:* Larry Edlund
Chf Inves: Anthony Baruffi
VP: John Engel
VP: Rich Hundven
VP: Matthew L Picinich

D-U-N-S 09-468-4107
MUTUAL OF OMAHA BANK
(*Suby of* OMAHA FINANCIAL HOLDINGS, INC.)
3333 Farnam St Ste 10, Omaha, NE 68131-3406
Tel (402) 351-5118 *Founded/Ownrshp* 1927, 2007
Sales NA *EMP* 200
SIC 6035 Savings institutions, federally chartered; Savings institutions, federally chartered
CEO: Jeffrey R Schmid
Pr: John Clark
**CEO:* Marjorie J Heller
**Chf Cred:* Tod R Ellis
Ofcr: Ronald Cheffer
Ofcr: Terry McBride
Ofcr: Larry Weisinger
Ex VP: Kevin C Hale
Ex VP: Barry S Major
Sr VP: Philip Potamitis
VP: William Creekmur

D-U-N-S 02-398-6156
MUTUAL OF OMAHA HEALTH PLANS INC
(*Suby of* MUTUAL OF OMAHA INSURANCE CO) ★
3301 Dodge St, Omaha, NE 68131-3416
Tel (402) 342-7600 *Founded/Ownrshp* 1994
Sales NA *EMP* 354
SIC 6411 Insurance agents & brokers; Insurance agents & brokers
Pr: Dan Neary
Treas: James T Blackledge

D-U-N-S 00-697-0347
MUTUAL OF OMAHA INSURANCE CO
Mutual Of Omaha Plaza, Omaha, NE 68175-0001
Tel (402) 342-7600 *Founded/Ownrshp* 1909
Sales NA *EMP* 5,392
SIC 6311 6211 8748 Life insurance carriers; Mutual funds, selling by independent salesperson; Business consulting; Life insurance carriers; Mutual funds, selling by independent salesperson; Business consulting
CEO: Daniel P Neary
Owner: Rachelle Bruning
Pr: James T Blackledge
Pr: Jeffrey R Schmid
CFO: David A Diamond
CFO: Tommy Thomason
Treas: Tommie D Thompson
Ofcr: Richard Leeberg
Ofcr: James Schema
Ex VP: Richard C Anderl
Ex VP: Cecil D Bykerk
Ex VP: Richard L Frederick
Ex VP: James L Hanson
Ex VP: Randall C Horn
Ex VP: Daniel P Martin
Ex VP: Stacy A Scholtz
Ex VP: Tommie Thompson
Sr VP: David Ahrendt
Sr VP: Devon Fischer
Sr VP: Gil Peers
Sr VP: Mark Prauner
Board of Directors: Samuel L Foggie Sr, Carol B Hallett, Jeffrey M Heller, Hugh W Hunt, Derek R McClain, James G McFarlane, Richard W Mies, Anthony J Principi

D-U-N-S 55-654-0920
MUTUAL OF OMAHA MARKETING CORP
(*Suby of* MUTUAL OF OMAHA INSURANCE CO) ★
3301 Dodge St, Omaha, NE 68131-3416
Tel (402) 342-7600 *Founded/Ownrshp* 1987
Sales 90.6MM^E *EMP* 600
SIC 6722 Management investment, open-end; Management investment, open-end
MIS Mgr: William Harrold

D-U-N-S 00-142-1221
MUTUAL OIL CO INC (MA)
863 Crescent St, Brockton, MA 02302-3488
Tel (508) 583-5777 *Founded/Ownrshp* 1937, 1983
Sales 53.5MM^E *EMP* 48^E
SIC 5172 Petroleum brokers; Petroleum brokers
Pr: Edward A Rachins
**CFO:* David Weber
**Ex VP:* Stephen Shaer
**VP:* Jonathan Shaer
Sls Dir: Cecila Lally
Mktg Mgr: Paul Labrecque

D-U-N-S 12-173-5955 IMP
■ **MUTUAL PHARMACEUTICAL CO INC**
URL PHARMA
(*Suby of* SUN PHARMACEUTICAL INDUSTRIES INC) ★
1100 Orthodox St, Philadelphia, PA 19124-3199
Tel (215) 288-6500 *Founded/Ownrshp* 2012
Sales 100.7MM^E *EMP* 520^E
SIC 2834 Pharmaceutical preparations; Pharmaceutical preparations
Sr VP: Donald L Evans
**Treas:* Whitney K Stearns Jr
**Ex VP:* Kurt R Nielsen
Sr VP: Nicholas J Hart
**Sr VP:* Gerald E Monigle
**VP:* Scott Delancy
**VP:* Richard P Foster
**VP:* Brendan Magrab
Ql Cn Mgr: Maril Cifolelli
Ql Cn Mgr: Adnan Wasim
Mktg Mgr: Nicole M Bailey

MUTUAL PROPANE
See MUTUAL LIQUID GAS AND EQUIPMENT CO INC

D-U-N-S 00-690-0674
■ **MUTUAL SAVINGS LIFE INSURANCE CO**
(*Suby of* KEMPER CORP) ★
12115 Lackland Rd, Saint Louis, MO 63146-4003
Tel (888) 847-1879 *Founded/Ownrshp* 1998
Sales NA *EMP* 650
SIC 6311 Life insurance; Life insurance
Pr: Edward James Konar
CFO: Ronald Koch

D-U-N-S 00-696-3425
MUTUAL SERVICE COOPERATIVE (MN)
COUNTRY INSURANCE & FINCL SVCS
2 Pine Tree Dr, Saint Paul, MN 55112-3754
Tel (651) 631-7000 *Founded/Ownrshp* 1949
Sales 17.3MM^E *EMP* 325
Accts Kpmg Peat Marwick Llp
SIC 8741 Administrative management; Administrative management
CEO: John Blackburn

D-U-N-S 79-554-1184
■ **MUTUAL TELECOM SERVICES INC**
BLACK BOX NETWORK SERVICES
(*Suby of* BLACK BOX CORP) ★
250 1st Ave Ste 301, Needham, MA 02494-2888
Tel (781) 449-1900 *Founded/Ownrshp* 2008
Sales NA *EMP* 300
SIC 4813 4822 Telephone communication, except radio; Telegraph & other communications; Telephone communication, except radio; Telegraph & other communications
Pr: Michael McAndrew
**CFO:* Elizabeth Steffick
IT Man: Liz Steffick

D-U-N-S 07-487-2516
MUTUAL TELEPHONE CO OF SIOUX CENTER IOWA
PREMIER COMMUNICATIONS
339 1st Ave Ne, Sioux Center, IA 51250-1801
Tel (712) 722-3451 *Founded/Ownrshp* 1906
Sales 23.7MM^E *EMP* 56
SIC 4813 4841

D-U-N-S 02-856-3443 IMP
MUTUAL TRADING CO INC
M T C
431 Crocker St, Los Angeles, CA 90013-2180
Tel (213) 626-9458 *Founded/Ownrshp* 1963
Sales 79.0MM^E *EMP* 181
SIC 5149 5141 5023 Groceries & related products; Groceries, general line; Home furnishings; Groceries & related products; Groceries, general line; Home furnishings
CEO: Kosei Yamamoto
**Pr:* Noritoshi Kanai
Pr: Katsumata Yasuo
CFO: Kendra Ikeda
**VP:* Seicho Fujikawa
**Prin:* Kotaro Hoshizaki
Dir IT: Keita Scarola
Dir IT: Keita Yagai
IT Man: Taksahi Hamamoto
Mktg Dir: Seicho Fujikawa
Mktg Mgr: Atsuko Kanai

MUTUAL TRUST FINANCIAL GROUP
See MTL INSURANCE CO

D-U-N-S 07-597-7157
■ **MUTUALBANK**
(*Suby of* MUTUALFIRST FINANCIAL INC) ★
110 E Charles St, Muncie, IN 47305-2468
Tel (765) 747-2800 *Founded/Ownrshp* 2000
Sales NA *EMP* 204
SIC 6163 6035 Loan brokers; Federal savings banks; Loan brokers; Federal savings banks
Ch Bd: Will Davis
**Pr:* Pat Botts
Pr: Charles Viater
**CEO:* David Heeter
**CFO:* Chris Cook
Ofcr: Karen Bock
Ofcr: Scott Green
Ofcr: Samantha Rowe
Ofcr: Tessa Trigg
Sr VP: Sharon Ferguson
VP: Torey Cook
VP: Dorothy Douglass
VP: Tim Goldy
VP: Dianne Harris
VP: James Martindale
VP: David Neeser
VP: Martha Oprea
VP: Michael Portolese
VP: Tina Rabel
VP: Jeffrey Remble
VP: James Ryan

D-U-N-S 09-030-9464
▲ **MUTUALFIRST FINANCIAL INC**
110 E Charles St, Muncie, IN 47305-2468
Tel (765) 747-2800 *Founded/Ownrshp* 1999
Sales NA *EMP* 412^E
Tkr Sym MFSF *Exch* NGM
SIC 6022 State commercial banks; State commercial banks
Pr: David W Heeter
**Ch Bd:* Wilbur R Davis
V Ch: Julie Skinner
Pr: Lesley Neal
CFO: Christopher D Cook
**Ex VP:* Patrick C Botts
Sr VP: Sharon L Ferguson
**Sr VP:* Charles J Viater
VP: Kathy Balser
VP: Amanda Hill
VP: Thomas Mohler
Board of Directors: Linn A Crull, William V Hughes, Jonathan E Kintner, Richard J Lashley, Edward C Levy, Michael J Marien, Jerry D McVicker, James D Rosema, James R Schrecongost

D-U-N-S 79-232-7095
MUTUALINK INC
1269 S Broad St, Wallingford, CT 06492-1737
Tel (203) 949-1800 *Founded/Ownrshp* 2006
Sales 27.1MM^E *EMP* 92^E
SIC 4813 Telephone communication, except radio
Ch Bd: Mark Hatten
Pr: David Long
**Pr:* Colin McWay
Bd of Dir: Barry McCaffrey
Dir Bus: Joe Marinich
Dir Bus: David Verbrugge
Dir Bus: Robert Wright
CTO: Joseph Boucher
QA Dir: Sean Horton
QA Dir: Ted Mayers
Sftwr Eng: Sanmathi Bharamgouda

D-U-N-S 07-660-9569
MUTUALONE BANK
160 Cochituate Rd, Framingham, MA 01701-7800
Tel (508) 820-4000 *Founded/Ownrshp* 1889
Sales NA *EMP* 70
SIC 6022 State commercial banks; State commercial banks
Pr: Mark Haranas
**Ch Bd:* Charles W Hickson
**Treas:* Robert P Lamprey
Ex VP: Steven Sousa
Sr VP: Kurt Bischoff
Sr VP: Brady Connors
Sr VP: Andrew Zelman
**VP:* Roland J Bunnell
VP: Garth Chapman
**VP:* Lawrence E Erickson
VP: Nick Kefalas
**VP:* Nick Kefalis
VP: Brien Kmaginnis
**VP:* Steve Rowan
**VP:* Joseph M Vincent

D-U-N-S 06-327-5176 EXP
MUTZ MOTORS LTD PARTNERSHIP
LAKELAND AUTO MALL
1430 W Memorial Blvd, Lakeland, FL 33815-1231
Tel (863) 682-1100 *Founded/Ownrshp* 1967
Sales 106.4MM^E *EMP* 240
SIC 5511 7538 7532 7515 5531 5521 Automobiles, new & used; General automotive repair shops; Top & body repair & paint shops; Passenger car leasing; Automotive & home supply stores; Used car dealers; Automobiles, new & used; General automotive repair shops; Top & body repair & paint shops; Passenger car leasing; Automotive & home supply stores; Used car dealers
Pt: Oscar Mutz
Pr: Marsey Wickenkamp
Off Mgr: Peggy Chambers
Store Mgr: Emmi Jburkett
IT Man: Nelson Moreles
Sales Asso: Lee Gonczy
Sales Asso: Ken Ramka

MUVICO ENTERTAINMENT
See MUVICO THEATERS INC

D-U-N-S 82-825-8454
MUVICO ENTERTAINMENT LLC
MUVICO THEATERS
2929 E Coml Blvd Ste 408, Fort Lauderdale, FL 33308
Tel (954) 564-6550 *Founded/Ownrshp* 1996
Sales 5.1MM^E *EMP* 800
SIC 7832 Motion picture theaters, except drive-in; Motion picture theaters, except drive-in

MUVICO THEATERS
See MUVICO ENTERTAINMENT LLC

D-U-N-S 80-228-0024
MUVICO THEATERS INC
MUVICO ENTERTAINMENT
2929 E Coml Blvd Ste 408, Fort Lauderdale, FL 33308
Tel (954) 564-6550 *Founded/Ownrshp* 1984
Sales 36.9MM^E *EMP* 1,200
SIC 7832 8741 Motion picture theaters, except drive-in; Management services; Motion picture theaters, except drive-in; Management services
Pr: Neil F Bretan
**Pr:* Michael Melvin
COO: Hank Linghstone
CFO: Dennis Jones
**Ch:* Joseph Amaturo
**VP:* Alan Rainbeau
**Exec:* Mary Ann Majni
Admn Mgr: Irene Pierpont

D-U-N-S 07-870-0753
MUY HAMBURGER PARTNERS LLC
17890 Blanco Rd Ste 401, San Antonio, TX 78232-1031
Tel (210) 408-2400 *Founded/Ownrshp* 2012
Sales 23.3MM^E *EMP* 656^E
SIC 5812 Hamburger stand

D-U-N-S 05-368-5194
MUZA METAL PRODUCTS LLC
606 E Murdock Ave, Oshkosh, WI 54901-2352
Tel (920) 236-3535 *Founded/Ownrshp* 2011
Sales 52.8MM^E *EMP* 200
SIC 3469 3699 3444 2542 2522 Metal stampings; Electrical equipment & supplies; Sheet metalwork; Partitions & fixtures, except wood; Office furniture, except wood; Metal stampings; Electrical equipment & supplies; Sheet metalwork; Partitions & fixtures, except wood; Office furniture, except wood
Pr: Tom Muza
Genl Mgr: Randy Shawman
Dir IT: Dave Pritzl
IT Man: Brad Oxton
IT Man: Jeff Paulus
Info Man: Judy Boyce
Plnt Mgr: Jim Shank
Ql Cn Mgr: Jason Stenz

D-U-N-S 05-932-8922
MUZAK LLC
(*Suby of* MOOD MEDIA CORPORATION)
3318 Lakemont Blvd, Fort Mill, SC 29708-8309
Tel (803) 396-3000 *Founded/Ownrshp* 2011
Sales 130.2MM^E *EMP* 950
SIC 7389 6794 Music & broadcasting services; Franchises, selling or licensing; Music & broadcasting services; Franchises, selling or licensing
CEO: Stephen Villa
Pr: Dan Kath
**COO:* Thomas Gantert
**CFO:* Dodd Hynes
Ex VP: Robert Finigan
Ex VP: Christopher Williams
VP: Jeff Mullarkey
VP: Dave Thompson
VP: David Vance
**VP:* Michael F Zendan II
VP: Paul Ziegler

D-U-N-S 15-123-3194
MUZAK LLC - ATLANTA
(*Suby of* MOOD MEDIA NORTH AMERICA LIMITED) ★
4754 N Royal Atlanta Dr, Tucker, GA 30084-3821
Tel (800) 313-3340 *Founded/Ownrshp* 1999
Sales 13.8MM^E *EMP* 543
SIC 7389 Music & broadcasting services; Music & broadcasting services
Pr: Joe Koff
Pr: Bill Boyd
CFO: Brad Bodenman
Genl Mgr: Mike Hoeltke

MUZI FORD CITY
See MUZI MOTORS INC

D-U-N-S 01-950-4992
MUZI MOTORS INC (MA)
MUZI FORD CITY
557 Highland Ave, Needham Heights, MA 02494-2203
Tel (781) 455-9274 *Founded/Ownrshp* 1932, 2000
Sales 66.2MM^E *EMP* 175
SIC 5511 7538 7532 Automobiles, new & used; Pickups, new & used; Vans, new & used; General automotive repair shops; Body shop, automotive; Automobiles, new & used; Pickups, new & used; Vans, new & used; General automotive repair shops; Body shop, automotive
CEO: Neal Cammarano
**Treas:* Glen Cammarano
Sls Mgr: Jeff Cutler
Sls Mgr: James Jubb
Sales Asso: Vadim Iablonovski

D-U-N-S 78-422-8285 IMP/EXP
MV & SONS-TEXAS LP
TIANTIAN
1515 Hebert St, Houston, TX 77012-3421
Tel (281) 657-6628 *Founded/Ownrshp* 2005
Sales 21.8MM^E *EMP* 50
SIC 5142 Frozen fish, meat & poultry
Pt: Marty Valderrama

D-U-N-S 03-992-6311
MV COMMERCIAL CONSTRUCTION LLC
MILLER VALENTIN CONSTRUCTION
137 N Main St Ste 900, Dayton, OH 45402-1846
Tel (937) 293-0900 *Founded/Ownrshp* 2000
Sales 125.0MM *EMP* 125
SIC 1541 Industrial buildings & warehouses; Industrial buildings & warehouses
Pr: Christopher Knueven
VP: Nick Beach

D-U-N-S 78-755-5002
MV LAND DEVELOPMENT CO
VALENTINE GROUP
137 N Main St Ste 900, Dayton, OH 45402-1846
Tel (937) 293-0900 *Founded/Ownrshp* 1963
Sales 9.3MM^E *EMP* 450
SIC 6531 Real estate agent, commercial; Real estate agent, commercial
CEO: Bill Krul

D-U-N-S 36-322-9373
MV PARTNERS LLC
250 N Water St Ste 300, Wichita, KS 67202-1216
Tel (316) 267-3241 *Founded/Ownrshp* 2006
Sales 51.0MM *EMP* 6
Accts Grant Thornton Llp
SIC 1381 Drilling oil & gas wells; Drilling oil & gas wells
Pt: David L Murfin
**Pt:* J Michael Vess

D-U-N-S 82-912-7542
MV PURCHASING LLC
8301 E 21st St N Ste 370, Wichita, KS 67206-2955
Tel (316) 262-2819 *Founded/Ownrshp* 2008
Sales 40.1MM^E *EMP* 27^E
SIC 5172 Crude oil
Dir IT: Stephen Sims

D-U-N-S 82-521-0958
MV RESIDENTIAL CONSTRUCTION INC
9349 Waterstone Blvd # 200, Cincinnati, OH 45249-8325
Tel (513) 588-1000 *Founded/Ownrshp* 1963
Sales 120.3MM^E *EMP* 750
SIC 1522 Residential construction; Residential construction
CEO: Mike Green
**Pr:* Randy Humbert

D-U-N-S 11-580-0968
■ **MVB BANK INC**
(*Suby of* MVB FINANCIAL CORP) ★
301 Virginia Ave, Fairmont, WV 26554-2777
Tel (304) 363-0883 *Founded/Ownrshp* 1999
Sales NA *EMP* 50^E
SIC 6022 State commercial banks; State commercial banks
Pr: Larry Mazza
Pr: Herman Deprospero
Pr: Samuel Gallo
Pr: Jim Rodgers

Chf Mktg O: Gary M Cox
Ofcr: Ken Ash
Ofcr: Eric L Tichenor
Sr VP: Joy Knight
VP: Deborah Davis
VP: George Johnston
VP: Butch Phillips
VP: Brenda Poston
VP: Roger Turner
VP: Susan Walls

D-U-N-S 79-128-4602
▲ MVB FINANCIAL CORP
301 Virginia Ave, Fairmont, WV 26554-2777
Tel (304) 363-4800 *Founded/Ownrshp* 2003
Sales NA *EMP* 72
Tkr Sym MVBF *Exch* OTO
SIC 6712 Bank holding companies
Pr: Larry Nazza
Ch Bd: Stephen R Brooks
COO: Donald Robinson
CFO: Bret S Price
V Ch Bd: David B Alvarez
Sr VP: Robert J Bardusch
VP: Deborah Davis
VP: Roger Turner

MVC
See MCKECHNIE VEHICLE COMPONENTS USA INC

D-U-N-S 62-713-2298
MVC CONST CO INC
2908 Southfield Rd, Heber City, UT 84032-3712
Tel (435) 657-9671 *Founded/Ownrshp* 2006
Sales 22.8MM *EMP* 80
SIC 1611 General contractor, highway & street construction; Concrete construction: roads, highways, sidewalks, etc.; General contractor, highway & street construction; Concrete construction: roads, highways, sidewalks, etc.
Pr: Mark Lloyd
**Treas:* Erik M Sugerman
**VP:* John C Cook

D-U-N-S 83-137-6830
MVC HOLDINGS LLC
27087 Gratiot Ave Fl 2, Roseville, MI 48066-2947
Tel (586) 491-2600 *Founded/Ownrshp* 2008
Sales 47.4MM *EMP* 400
Accts Cenco Vendittelli & Haynes P
SIC 3714 3498 3465 3429 3471 Motor vehicle wheels & parts; Fabricated pipe & fittings; Automotive stampings; Manufactured hardware (general); Plating & polishing; Motor vehicle wheels & parts; Fabricated pipe & fittings; Automotive stampings; Manufactured hardware (general); Plating & polishing
Pr: Linda Torakis
**CEO:* Michael Torakis
**CFO:* Steve Aretakis

MVCC
See MOHAWK VALLEY COMMUNITY COLLEGE

MVCDC
See MIAMI VALLEY CHILD DEVELOPMENT CENTERS INC

D-U-N-S 13-585-9176
MVD COMMUNICATIONS LLC
5188 Cox Smith Rd, Mason, OH 45040-9005
Tel (513) 683-4711 *Founded/Ownrshp* 1992
Sales 41.1MM^E *EMP* 110
SIC 4813 Data telephone communications; Voice telephone communications; Data telephone communications; Voice telephone communications
Chf Mktg O: Maureen Schaller
CTO: Craig Allen
Opers Mgr: Tom Taylor
Sls&Mrk Ex: Mary Wilson
Sales Asso: Meghan Murray

MVEC
See MINNESOTA VALLEY ELECTRIC COOPERATIVE INC

D-U-N-S 17-274-3085
MVENTIX INC
25129 The Old Rd Ste 112, Stevenson Ranch, CA 91381-2293
Tel (661) 263-1768 *Founded/Ownrshp* 2004
Sales 23.2MM^E *EMP* 386
SIC 7389 Advertising, promotional & trade show services; Advertising, promotional & trade show services
CEO: Kristian Fatzov
Exec: Troy Elwood
Prgrm Mgr: Marian Krebbers
Prgrm Mgr: Andrey Lyutykh
Off Mgr: Margaret Aragon
**CTO:* Pavel Monev
Sls Dir: Renee McLafferty
Board of Directors: Kristian Fatzov

MVF WORLD WIDE SERVICES
See MODERN VIDEOFILM INC

D-U-N-S 82-614-0618
MVHE INC
(*Suby of* MIAMI VALLEY HOSPITAL) ★
110 N Main St Ste 370, Dayton, OH 45402-3729
Tel (937) 499-8211 *Founded/Ownrshp* 1986
Sales 23.5MM^E *EMP* 550
Accts Ernst & Young Llp Dayton Ohi
SIC 8099 8011 Medical services organization; Offices & clinics of medical doctors
Pr: Ken Prunier
**CFO:* David Sturgeon

D-U-N-S 15-811-2230
MVL GROUP INC
1061 E Indiantown Rd # 300, Jupiter, FL 33477-5104
Tel (561) 748-0931 *Founded/Ownrshp* 1999
Sales 17.9MM^E *EMP* 550
SIC 8732 7374 Market analysis or research; Data processing & preparation; Market analysis or research; Market analysis, business & economic research; Survey service: marketing, location, etc.; Data processing & preparation

Pr: Adam Rogers
**Treas:* Edward W Dean
**Prin:* M Van Lefferdink

D-U-N-S 04-306-5825 IMP
MVP GROUP INTERNATIONAL INC (KY)
TLC
(*Suby of* PRIMACY INDUSTRIES LIMITED)
1031 Legrand Blvd, Charleston, SC 29492-7673
Tel (843) 216-8380 *Founded/Ownrshp* 1998
Sales 306.3MM^E *EMP* 900
SIC 3999 5122 Candles; Perfumes; Candles; Perfumes
CEO: Mary V Propes
**Pr:* Troy R Propes
Pr: Scott Wehrs
VP: Pat Autore
VP: Amy Finstad
VP: Susan Fisher
VP: Tuck McConnell
VP: Katherine Vermette
Creative D: Joyce Barbati
Brnch Mgr: Ken Marcoon
IT Man: Ben Steele

MVP HEALTH CARE
See MVP HEALTH PLAN INC

MVP HEALTH CARE
See HUDSON HEALTH PLAN INC

D-U-N-S 82-638-7466
MVP HEALTH CARE INC
(*Suby of* MVP HEALTH CARE) ★
259 Monroe Ave, Rochester, NY 14607-3632
Tel (585) 325-3920 *Founded/Ownrshp* 2006
Sales 13.6MM^E *EMP* 400^E
SIC 8011 6321 6411 Health maintenance organization; Accident & health insurance; Insurance agents, brokers & service; Health maintenance organization; Accident & health insurance; Insurance agents, brokers & service
Pr: John Urban
IT Man: Gerry Arndt

D-U-N-S 10-868-9787
MVP HEALTH PLAN INC
MVP HEALTH CARE
625 State St, Schenectady, NY 12305-2260
Tel (518) 370-4793 *Founded/Ownrshp* 1982
Sales 0.3 *EMP* 1,500
Accts Pricewaterhousecoopers Llp Ha
SIC 8011 Health maintenance organization; Health maintenance organization
Pr: David Oliker
**Pr:* Patrick Glavey
**Pr:* Denise Gonick
Pr: Dale Hockel
Bd of Dir: Jon Jarrett
Bd of Dir: Jeff Kuberka
Ofcr: Laura Wenzel
**Ex VP:* Karla Austen
Ex VP: Scott W Averill
Ex VP: David Crosby
Ex VP: Christopher Delvecchio
**Ex VP:* Mark Fish
**Ex VP:* Allen J Hinkle
VP: Dennis L Allen
VP: James Hester
VP: George Thomson

D-U-N-S 07-974-6886
MVP HOLDINGS LLC
8301 E 21st St N Ste 370, Wichita, KS 67206-2955
Tel (316) 262-2819 *Founded/Ownrshp* 2013
Sales 3.0MMM *EMP* 50
SIC 6719 Investment holding companies, except banks

MVS
See MERRITT VETERINARY SUPPLIES INC

MVSB
See MEREDITH VILLAGE SAVINGS BANK

D-U-N-S 01-240-5506
MVT SERVICES INC
3750 Stewarts Ln, Nashville, TN 37218-3300
Tel (615) 251-0169 *Founded/Ownrshp* 2009
Sales 11.6MM^E *EMP* 300
SIC 7359 Industrial truck rental; Industrial truck rental
Pr: Royal Jones

D-U-N-S 15-295-6504
MVT SERVICES LLC
MESILLA VALLEY TRANSPORTATION
3590 W Picacho Ave, Las Cruces, NM 88007-4725
Tel (575) 524-2835 *Founded/Ownrshp* 1981
Sales 202.7MM^E *EMP* 850
SIC 4213 Trucking, except local; Trucking, except local
**VP:* Jimmy Ray
Exec: Jose Rocha
Sftwr Eng: Kim C Hayes
Netwrk Eng: Jason Gaume
Sfty Mgr: Raul Garcia
Natl Sales: Arminda Neyland
Sls&Mrk Ex: Dennis Sherman
Sls Dir: John Kelley
Snr Mgr: Noemi Aldana
Snr Mgr: Mike Kelly
Snr Mgr: Dean Rigg

D-U-N-S 78-436-8982
MW BUILDERS GROUP INC
(*Suby of* MMC CORP) ★
10955 Lowell Ave Ste 350, Shawnee Mission, KS 66210-2408
Tel (913) 345-0007 *Founded/Ownrshp* 2002
Sales 162.0MM^E *EMP* 700
SIC 1542 Nonresidential construction; Nonresidential construction
Pr: William McDermott
Treas: David A Burt
**Sec:* David Cimpl
**VP:* Harold W Mitts Jr

D-U-N-S 10-671-7353
MW BUILDERS INC
(*Suby of* MW BUILDERS GROUP INC) ★
1701 N General Bruce Dr, Temple, TX 76504-2474
Tel (254) 778-4241 *Founded/Ownrshp* 2001
Sales 83.7MM^E *EMP* 140
SIC 1542 Nonresidential construction; Nonresidential construction
CEO: William McDermott
Pr: Robin Broder
**Pr:* Tim Chadwick
**Pr:* R Jason Evelyn
**VP:* David Burt
**VP:* Todd Winnerman
VP: Craig Woodson
Off Mgr: Allison Laird
Sfty Mgr: John Francis
Opers Mgr: Sparky Campbell
Opers Mgr: Jason Evelyn

D-U-N-S 85-945-8663
MW FINANCIAL GROUP LTD
GUARDIAN LIFE INSURANCE THE
197 Scott Swamp Rd, Farmington, CT 06032-3149
Tel (860) 677-2600 *Founded/Ownrshp* 1991
Sales NA *EMP* 50
SIC 6311 Life insurance
Pr: Bob Worgaftik
Ofcr: Francis King
Ofcr: Jonathan Lipson
Ofcr: Matthew Spielman
**VP:* Rich Gribinas
Mng Dir: Morris Mete

MW INDUSTRIES
See MATTHEW WARREN INC

MW INDUSTRIES
See MATTHEW WARREN INC

D-U-N-S 00-576-1445
MW LOGISTICS LLC (TX)
5429 Lyndon B Johnson Fwy, Dallas, TX 75240-2607
Tel (972) 669-4259 *Founded/Ownrshp* 2001
Sales 61.1MM *EMP* 45
Accts Grant Thornton Llp Dallas T
SIC 4731 Freight transportation arrangement
CFO: Kimberly Singeleton
VP: Andrew Ringgold
Dir Bus: Gregg Walton
Natl Sales: Denaus Eddings
S&M/VP: Mark Howard

D-U-N-S 13-054-0719 IMP
■ MW MANUFACTURERS INC
(*Suby of* PLY GEM INDUSTRIES INC) ★
433 N Main St, Rocky Mount, VA 24151-1165
Tel (540) 483-0211 *Founded/Ownrshp* 2004
Sales 204.9MM^E *EMP* 1,600
SIC 2431 Window frames, wood; Window sashes, wood; Window trim, wood; Doors, wood; Window frames, wood; Window sashes, wood; Window trim, wood; Doors, wood
Pr: Art Steinhafel
**Treas:* Shawn K Poe
**Prin:* Lynn Morstad

MW MIELKE
See MARVIN W MIELKE INC

MW POLAR
See MILKY WAY INTERNATIONAL TRADING CORP

D-U-N-S 62-422-7091
MW UNIVERSAL INC
2008 Cypress St Ste 100, Paris, KY 40361-1380
Tel (859) 333-5953 *Founded/Ownrshp* 2006
Sales 62.9MM^E *EMP* 500^E
SIC 3462 Iron & steel forgings
Pr: George Hofmeister
**VP:* L F Wolf Jr

D-U-N-S 36-391-8140 IMP
MW/MB LLC
1900 Corporate Pkwy Blvd, Clarksville, TN 37040-5342
Tel (931) 245-5050 *Founded/Ownrshp* 2005
Sales 35.7MM^E *EMP* 104^E
SIC 3443 Fabricated plate work (boiler shop)
Plnt Mgr: John Smith
Snr Mgr: Arthur Iverson
Snr Mgr: Greg Separk

MWA
See MOJAVE WATER AGENCY

D-U-N-S 09-336-6839
■ MWB COPY PRODUCTS INC
SOCAL OFFICE TECHNOLOGIES
(*Suby of* GLOBAL IMAGING SYSTEMS INC) ★
5700 Warland Dr, Cypress, CA 90630-5030
Tel (800) 736-7979 *Founded/Ownrshp* 1985
Sales 41.3MM^E *EMP* 197
SIC 5999 5044 Photocopy machines; Typewriters; Photocopy machines; Duplicating machines; Typewriters; Photocopy machines; Typewriters; Photocopy machines; Duplicating machines; Typewriters
CEO: David Riener
**Pr:* Joseph Payne
**CFO:* Juan Salcedo
VP: Dane Medley
Exec: Alitt Marroquin
Sls Dir: Tom Figlio
Sls Dir: Chris Hoffie
Sls Dir: Dean Reiber
Sls Dir: Jonathan Rubic
Sls Dir: Martin Yi

MWCC
See MILENDER WHITE CONSTRUCTION CO

MWCI ROOFING
See MARK WRIGHT CONSTRUCTION INC

D-U-N-S 00-459-5265
MWD LOGISTICS INC
245 E 4th St, Mansfield, OH 44902-1519
Tel (419) 522-3510 *Founded/Ownrshp* 1999
Sales 29.1MM^E *EMP* 272
Accts Kleshinski Morrison & Morris
SIC 4225 4213 General warehousing; Trucking, except local; General warehousing; Trucking, except local
Ch Bd: Stuart Lichter
**Pr:* Brian Glowaski

D-U-N-S 17-566-3566
MWE INC
SERVICE REFRIGERATION COMPANY
(*Suby of* SOURCE REFRIGERATION & HVAC INC) ★
1208 1st St E Ste B, Humble, TX 77338-5915
Tel (281) 446-4355 *Founded/Ownrshp* 2014
Sales 40.3MM^E *EMP* 165
SIC 1711 Refrigeration contractor; Refrigeration contractor
Pr: W L Edmonds Jr
COO: Jeff Jenskins
VP: Les Edmonds
VP: Gary McCorquodale
VP: Stephen Weaver
IT Man: Eric Barkmann

D-U-N-S 04-523-2204
MWH AMERICAS INC
(*Suby of* MWH GLOBAL INC) ★
370 Interlocken Blvd, Broomfield, CO 80021-8009
Tel (303) 410-4000 *Founded/Ownrshp* 1992
Sales 515.1MM^E *EMP* 3,000
SIC 8711 Engineering services; Engineering services
CEO: Alan Krause
**Pr:* Daniel McConville
**CFO:* David Barnes
**Treas:* Thomas Payne

D-U-N-S 87-863-5176
MWH CONSTRUCTORS INC
(*Suby of* MWH GLOBAL INC) ★
370 Interlocken Blvd # 300, Broomfield, CO 80021-8012
Tel (303) 439-2800 *Founded/Ownrshp* 1993
Sales 85.0MM^E *EMP* 330
Accts Deloitte & Touche Llp
SIC 8711 1629 Pollution control engineering; Waterway construction; Pollution control engineering; Waterway construction
Pr: Blair Lavoie
**Ch Bd:* Alan Krause
**CFO:* David Barnes
**Treas:* Thomas Payne
VP: Ron Evans
VP: Joseph Willich Jr
Snr PM: Randy Helzer

D-U-N-S 80-192-7492
MWH GLOBAL INC
380 Inter Cres Ste 200, Broomfield, CO 80021
Tel (303) 533-1900 *Founded/Ownrshp* 1970
Sales 1.3MMM^E *EMP* 6,700
SIC 8711 8741 Engineering services; Water & sewer line construction; Engineering services; Management services
Pr: Alan J Krause
COO: Rich Wankmuller
**CFO:* David G Barnes
**Treas:* Thomas Payne
Sr Cor Off: Vic Gualas
Ex VP: Michael Bruen
VP: Luis Casado
VP: Edwin Cryer
VP: Peter Dickson
VP: Bill Gauntt
VP: Raymond Hartley
VP: Eugene Minnick
VP: Nora Okusu
VP: Bob Parent
VP: Philip Smith
VP: Philip Waller
VP: Timothy Wolfe
Dir Risk M: Ian Cartwright
Board of Directors: Janet Linden Cooper, Catherine Schefer

D-U-N-S 00-413-1512 IMP/EXP
MWI CORP (FL)
MWI PUMPS
33 Nw 2nd St, Deerfield Beach, FL 33441-2013
Tel (954) 426-1500 *Founded/Ownrshp* 1927
Sales 45.5MM^E *EMP* 140
SIC 7359 3561 Equipment rental & leasing; Pumps & pumping equipment; Equipment rental & leasing; Pumps & pumping equipment
Ch Bd: J David Eller
**Pr:* Dana J Eller
CFO: Tom Rogers
**Sec:* Tom Roegiers
**VP:* Daren J Eller
Genl Mgr: John Springer
VP Mktg: Corey Blake
Sls Dir: Marc Buodet
Manager: Billy Wing

D-U-N-S 06-425-4212 IMP
MWI INC
1269 Brighton Henrietta T, Rochester, NY 14623-2485
Tel (585) 424-4200 *Founded/Ownrshp* 1993
Sales 23.4MM^E *EMP* 133
SIC 3624 Carbon & graphite products; Carbon & graphite products
Ch Bd: David Mc Mahon
**Pr:* Kevin Mc Mahon
**COO:* Brian Mc Mahon
**CFO:* Josh Stern
**VP:* Ryan Mc Mahon
VP: Ryan McMahon
Manager: Matt Witherow
Sls Mgr: Richard Chown
Sls Mgr: Carmy Marchese
Sls Mgr: Rocky Reitano
Sales Asso: Theresa Pierson

MWI PUMPS
See MWI CORP

D-U-N-S 01-992-6120 IMP
■ MWI VETERINARY SUPPLY CO (ID)
(*Suby of* MWI VETERINARY SUPPLY INC) ★
3041 W Pasadena Dr, Boise, ID 83705-4776
Tel (208) 955-8930 *Founded/Ownrshp* 1981, 2002
Sales 661.6MM^E *EMP* 558

SIC 5047 2834 2835 2836 Veterinarians' equipment & supplies; Veterinary pharmaceutical preparations; Veterinary diagnostic substances; Vaccines; Veterinarians' equipment & supplies; Veterinary pharmaceutical preparations; Veterinary diagnostic substances; Vaccines
Ch Bd: John F McNamara
**Pr:* James Cleary
**CFO:* Mary Patricia Thompson
**Treas:* Tracy Huettl
Treas: Tracy Tucker
VP Admn: John L Francis
**CIO:* James S Hay
Sls Mgr: Eric Scott
Board of Directors: William Robison

D-U-N-S 55-556-7721 IMP
■ MWI VETERINARY SUPPLY INC
(*Suby of* AMERISOURCEBERGEN CORP) ★
3041 W Pasadena Dr, Boise, ID 83705-4776
Tel (208) 955-8930 *Founded/Ownrshp* 2015
Sales 661.6MM^{E} *EMP* 1,732^{E}
SIC 5047 5149 Veterinarians' equipment & supplies; Pet foods; Veterinarians' equipment & supplies; Pet foods
Pr: James F Cleary Jr
**CFO:* Richard Dubois
Ofcr: Charlie Diaz
Sr VP: Mary Patricia B Thompson
VP: John L Francis
VP: Jeremy C Ouchley
**VP:* Alden J Sutherland
Dist Mgr: Chris Vouk
IT Man: Stephanie Wyatt
Software D: Joseph Caufield
Software D: Josef Wagner

D-U-N-S 13-184-2481
MWM GROUP INC
(*Suby of* MMC CORP) ★
11100 Ash St Ste 100, Shawnee Mission, KS 66211-1700
Tel (913) 469-0101 *Founded/Ownrshp* 2002
Sales 37.1MM^{E} *EMP* 180
SIC 1711 Plumbing, heating, air-conditioning contractors; Plumbing, heating, air-conditioning contractors
Ch Bd: Michael W Gossman

D-U-N-S 19-027-5016
MWMPC CORP
MIDWEST ELECTRIC COMPANY
(*Suby of* CAPPADONNA ELECTRICAL MANAGEMENT CORP) ★
3828 Pinemont Dr, Houston, TX 77018-1222
Tel (713) 681-0627 *Founded/Ownrshp* 1987
Sales 47.6MM *EMP* 222
Accts Ron Kirby Cpa Odessa Texas
SIC 1731 General electrical contractor; General electrical contractor
Pr: Mitchell P Cappadonna
**VP:* Matthew Cappadonna

D-U-N-S 00-160-6131
MWP LLC
4212 S Highway 191, Rexburg, ID 83440-4251
Tel (208) 356-4571 *Founded/Ownrshp* 1981
Sales 21.2MM^{E} *EMP* 140
SIC 5191 2875 2421 Garden supplies; Fertilizers, mixing only; Sawmills & planing mills, general; Garden supplies; Fertilizers, mixing only; Sawmills & planing mills, general

MWRA
See MASSACHUSETTS WATER RESOURCES AUTHORITY

MWRA
See MASSACHUSETTS WATER RESOURCES AUTHORITY

MWRD
See METROPOLITAN WATER RECLAIMATION DISTRICT OF GREATER CHICAGO

D-U-N-S 06-400-4948
MWS ENTERPRISES INC
A PLUS MINI MARKET
5701 Transit Rd Ste B, East Amherst, NY 14051-1898
Tel (716) 689-0600 *Founded/Ownrshp* 1981
Sales 43.4MM^{E} *EMP* 275
SIC 5411 5541 5921 Convenience stores, chain; Filling stations, gasoline; Beer (packaged); Convenience stores, chain; Filling stations, gasoline; Beer (packaged)
Pr: Mark W Sidebottom
**Sec:* Patti W Sidebottom

D-U-N-S 05-012-4957
MWS PRECISION WIRE INDUSTRIES INC
MWS WIRE INDUSTRIES
31200 Cedar Valley Dr, Westlake Village, CA 91362-4035
Tel (818) 991-8553 *Founded/Ownrshp* 1968
Sales 43.8MM^{E} *EMP* 52
SIC 5051 3351 3357 Copper sheets, plates, bars, rods, pipes, etc.; Wire, copper & copper alloy; Nonferrous wiredrawing & insulating; Copper sheets, plates, bars, rods, pipes, etc.; Wire, copper & copper alloy; Nonferrous wiredrawing & insulating
Pr: Darrell H Friedman
**Pr:* Alan Friedman
IT Man: Tomm Carlson
Netwrk Mgr: Leonard Agoado
Mktg Dir: Mike McClure

MWS WIRE INDUSTRIES
See MWS PRECISION WIRE INDUSTRIES INC

D-U-N-S 01-617-9272
MWSTAR WASTE HOLDINGS CORP
F/K/A VEOLIA ES SOLID WASTE
(*Suby of* ADS WASTE HOLDINGS INC) ★
90 Fort Wade Rd Ste 200, Ponte Vedra, FL 32081-5112
Tel (904) 737-7900 *Founded/Ownrshp* 1992
Sales 1.2MMM^{E} *EMP* 2,984^{E}
SIC 1629 4953 Waste disposal plant construction; Hazardous waste collection & disposal
CEO: Richard Burke
**CFO:* Steven Carn
**VP:* Jaime Marini
Off Mgr: John Perugia

MWU PEMCO ACQUISITION
See WILL-PEMCO INC

MWW
See MASSEY WOOD & WEST INC

D-U-N-S 60-522-8592
MWW GROUP LLC
1 Meadowlands Plz Ste 600, East Rutherford, NJ 07073-2232
Tel (201) 507-9500 *Founded/Ownrshp* 1986
Sales 83.1MM^{E} *EMP* 233
SIC 8743

D-U-N-S 80-656-6068 IMP
MX ELECTRONICS MANUFACTURING INC
INTERCONNECT SOLUTIONS
(*Suby of* EXPERTS EN MEMOIRE INTERNATIONALE INC, LES)
1651 E Saint Andrew Pl, Santa Ana, CA 92705-4932
Tel (714) 258-0200 *Founded/Ownrshp* 2000
Sales 20.9MM^{E} *EMP* 58
SIC 3357 Aluminum wire & cable
Pr: Lawrence Reusing
**CFO:* Mike Anderson
CFO: Robert S Jean

D-U-N-S 83-006-6721
MX HOLDINGS US INC
CFP FIRE PROTECTION
153 Technology Dr Ste 200, Irvine, CA 92618-2461
Tel (949) 727-3277 *Founded/Ownrshp* 1997
Sales 334.0MM^{E} *EMP* 1,790
SIC 1711 1731 5999 Fire escape installation; Fire sprinkler system installation; Fire detection & burglar alarm systems specialization; Fire extinguishers
CEO: Klaus Hoffmann
CFO: Ted Carrier

D-U-N-S 60-650-8588
MX PETROLEUM CORP
22 Center St, Massena, NY 13662-1437
Tel (315) 769-9500 *Founded/Ownrshp* 1989
Sales 23.8MM^{E} *EMP* 20
SIC 5172 5983 Petroleum products; Fuel oil dealers
Ch Bd: W Allan Macewen
VP: Robert French

D-U-N-S 05-386-2777 IMP/EXP
MXD GROUP INC
(*Suby of* PLATINUM EQUITY LLC) ★
7795 Walton Pkwy Ste 400, New Albany, OH 43054-8246
Tel (614) 895-1959 *Founded/Ownrshp* 2013
Sales 272.6MM^{E} *EMP* 800
SIC 4214 4213 Local trucking with storage; Household goods transport; Local trucking with storage; Household goods transport
CEO: Terry Solvedt
**Pr:* David Vieira
**CFO:* Renee Albarano
Sr VP: W T Thompson
VP: Mike Agey
VP: Frank Gaura
VP: Marvin T Larger
Dir Bus: Kim Banton
Genl Mgr: Matt Robinson

MXR SOURCEONE
See SOURCEONE HEALTHCARE TECHNOLOGIES INC

D-U-N-S 04-602-8697
MY AUTO IMPORT CENTER LLC
TOYOTA OF MUSKEGON
1860 E Sternberg Rd, Muskegon, MI 49444-9704
Tel (231) 799-2886 *Founded/Ownrshp* 1993
Sales 21.1MM^{E} *EMP* 60
SIC 5511 Automobiles, new & used
Sls Mgr: Rocky Rycenga
Sls Mgr: Dave Sedgley

D-U-N-S 86-848-2964
MY COMMUNITY DENTAL CENTERS INC
1 Water St Ste 200, Boyne City, MI 49712-1811
Tel (877) 313-6232 *Founded/Ownrshp* 2006
Sales 34.8MM *EMP* 300
Accts Crowe Horwath Llp Chicago Il
SIC 8021 Dental clinic; Dental clinic
CEO: Thomas J Veryser
**CFO:* Keith Sherwood
Off Admin: Leslie Videki
Dir IT: Larry Keys
Dir IT: Luke Whitley
Opers Mgr: Tracy Cedar
Opers Mgr: Wendie Rodriguez

D-U-N-S 11-226-5595
MY COMPADRE LLC
SYDCOR
1909 W Braker Ln Ste 100e, Austin, TX 78758-4087
Tel (512) 334-1000 *Founded/Ownrshp* 2003
Sales 47.9MM^{E} *EMP* 146
SIC 5131 Labels; Labels
CEO: Chris Horton
**VP:* Keith Jacoby
IT Man: Marion Robertson
VP Opers: Bill Porth

MY DIAMOND STORY
See HK DESIGNS

MY EXPRESS FREIGHT
See G KATEN & PARTNERS LIMITED LIABILITY CO

D-U-N-S 00-554-8943
MY FIT FOODS INC (TX)
5000 Plaza On The Lk # 380, Austin, TX 78746-1092
Tel (512) 400-0600 *Founded/Ownrshp* 2009
Sales 21.5MM^{E} *EMP* 60^{E}
SIC 5999 Toiletries, cosmetics & perfumes
CEO: David Goronkin
Pr: Sarah Desmarais
**CFO:* Michael Lubitz
Sr VP: Miranda Pulliam
**Prin:* Eric Garcia
Genl Mgr: Michael Lipsey

MY FLOORING AMERICA
See MY FLOORING TEXAS LLC

D-U-N-S 96-204-1674
MY FLOORING TEXAS LLC
MY FLOORING AMERICA
16800 N Texas Ave, Webster, TX 77598-4044
Tel (281) 338-1345 *Founded/Ownrshp* 2009
Sales 24.0MM^{E} *EMP* 100
SIC 5713 Floor covering stores

MY GOODS MARKET
See CONVENIENCE RETAILERS LLC

D-U-N-S 19-576-7988 IMP/EXP
MY IMPORTS USA LLC
75 Ethel Rd, Edison, NJ 08817-2209
Tel (732) 662-3622 *Founded/Ownrshp* 2008
Sales 20.3MM^{E} *EMP* 30
SIC 5199 Variety store merchandise
Pr: Judy Wong
VP: Fahim Ibrahimi
**VP:* Jimmy Zahng

MY MICHELLE
See MYMICHELLE CO LLC

D-U-N-S 11-279-0097 IMP
MY OFFICE INC
6060 Nncy Rdge Dr Ste 100, San Diego, CA 92121
Tel (858) 549-6700 *Founded/Ownrshp* 1990
Sales 21.0MM^{E} *EMP* 100
SIC 1799 Office furniture installation
CEO: Shaun Alger
**Pr:* Ronald D Harrell

D-U-N-S 02-037-1285
MY PILLOW INC
MYPILLOW
343 E 82nd St Ste 102, Chaska, MN 55318-2354
Tel (952) 826-8611 *Founded/Ownrshp* 2009
Sales 40.0MM^{E} *EMP* 70
SIC 5719 Bedding (sheets, blankets, spreads & pillows); Bedding (sheets, blankets, spreads & pillows)
CEO: Michael James Lindell

MY PROJECTOR STORE
See INTERNATIONAL AUDIO VISUAL INC

D-U-N-S 62-562-6119
MY WAY HOLDINGS LLC
1200 Futurity Dr, Sunland Park, NM 88063-9057
Tel (575) 874-5200 *Founded/Ownrshp* 2000
Sales 13.8MM^{E} *EMP* 500
SIC 7948 7011 Horse race track operation; Casino hotel; Horse race track operation; Casino hotel

MY-CAP VENDORS
See MYERS-COX CO

D-U-N-S 11-185-1742
MYBUYS INC
MAGNETIC
167 2nd Ave, San Mateo, CA 94401-3801
Tel (650) 544-2400 *Founded/Ownrshp* 2001
Sales 21.4MM^{E} *EMP* 113
SIC 8742 Marketing consulting services
Pr: Rita Brogley
**Ch Bd:* Robert Cell
Pr: Charizza Mallard
**CFO:* Ainslie Mayberry
**Ch:* Anu Shukla
**Sr VP:* Chip Overstreet
**Sr VP:* Mark Weiler
VP: Joe Recchia
**VP:* Paul Rosenblum
**VP:* Lisa Joy Rosner
**VP:* Shaun Schooley
VP: Jason Shriver

D-U-N-S 02-913-4772
MYCLES CYCLES INC
SAN DIEGO HARLEY-DAVIDSON
4645 Morena Blvd, San Diego, CA 92117-3650
Tel (858) 616-6999 *Founded/Ownrshp* 1993
Sales 32.4MM^{E} *EMP* 90^{E}
SIC 5571 Motorcycle dealers; Motorcycle parts & accessories; Motorcycle dealers; Motorcycle parts & accessories
Pr: Michael Shelby
**Sec:* Paula Shelby
Genl Mgr: Ty Miller
Mktg Mgr: Dawn Hockaday
Sls Mgr: Mike Willer

D-U-N-S 04-252-4041
MYCO INC
1122 Milford Ave, Rockford, IL 61109-3636
Tel (815) 395-8500 *Founded/Ownrshp* 1967
Sales 32.2MM^{E} *EMP* 220
SIC 3496 Miscellaneous fabricated wire products; Shelving, made from purchased wire; Miscellaneous fabricated wire products; Shelving, made from purchased wire
Pr: Robert Yedor
Plnt Mgr: Jim Musick

D-U-N-S 03-391-3182
MYCO MECHANICAL INC
1 N Washington St, Telford, PA 18969-1846
Tel (267) 382-0267 *Founded/Ownrshp* 1996
Sales 30.0MM *EMP* 85
SIC 1711 Mechanical contractor
Pr: Brian L Myers
Treas: Merrill Myers

D-U-N-S 10-315-7442 EXP
■ MYCOGEN CORP
(*Suby of* ROFAN SERVICES INC) ★
9330 Zionsville Rd, Indianapolis, IN 46268-1053
Tel (317) 337-3000 *Founded/Ownrshp* 1998
Sales 145.9MM^{E} *EMP* 300
SIC 5191 2879 0721 8731 Seeds & bulbs; Seeds: field, garden & flower; Agricultural chemicals; Crop protecting services; Crop disease control services; Crop related entomological services (insect control); Agricultural research; Seeds & bulbs; Seeds: field, garden & flower; Agricultural chemicals; Crop protecting services; Crop disease control services; Crop related entomological services (insect control); Agricultural research
Pr: Jerome Periberie
Treas: Geoffrey E Merszer
VP: W Pete Siggelko
VP: William W Wales

D-U-N-S 13-911-8306
■ MYCOGEN PLANT SCIENCE INC
(*Suby of* MYCOGEN CORP) ★
9330 Zionsville Rd, Indianapolis, IN 46268-1053
Tel (317) 337-3000 *Founded/Ownrshp* 2004
Sales 142.9MM^{E} *EMP* 325^{E}
SIC 5191 Seeds: field, garden & flower
Pr: Jerome Peribere

D-U-N-S 00-464-0715
MYCOM NORTH AMERICA INC
(*Suby of* MYCOM INTERNATIONAL INC)
1080 Holcomb Bridge Rd # 200210, Roswell, GA 30076-4348
Tel (770) 776-0000 *Founded/Ownrshp* 2000
Sales 81.8MM^{E} *EMP* 250
SIC 4899 Data communication services; Data communication services
Pr: Richard Hessler
CFO: Dave Winters
**VP:* Brian Arabi
Dir Bus: Moe Fayaz
Dir IT: Marc Froemelt
IT Man: Gilbert Fong
IT Man: Brett Ullman
Board of Directors: Brian Arabi, Richard Hessler

D-U-N-S 18-410-7845
MYCON GENERAL CONTRACTORS INC
208 E La St Ste 200, Mc Kinney, TX 75069
Tel (972) 529-2444 *Founded/Ownrshp* 1987
Sales 104.5MM *EMP* 47
SIC 1542

D-U-N-S 01-476-9301 IMP
MYCONE DENTAL SUPPLY CO INC
POLYCHROMATIC COATINGS
480 S Democrat Rd, Gibbstown, NJ 08027-1239
Tel (856) 663-4700 *Founded/Ownrshp* 1983
Sales 120.0MM^{E} *EMP* 250
SIC 5047 3843 2844 Dental equipment & supplies; Dental equipment & supplies; Toilet preparations; Dental equipment & supplies; Dental equipment & supplies; Toilet preparations
Ch Bd: Fred Robinson
Pr: Sam Nelson
**Pr:* Cary Robinson
COO: Steve Katz
CFO: Tim Cryan
Ex VP: Gloria Berger
VP: Jeffrey Diblasi
VP: David Leeming
VP: George Lein
VP: Chris McDevitt
VP: Monica Rocco
VP: Marina Van Sligter
Exec: Michelle Bender
Exec: John Fetterolf

MYCRO GROUP CO
See MUSCO CORP

D-U-N-S 60-690-2641
MYCROFT INC
12655 Olive Blvd Ste 500, Saint Louis, MO 63141-6362
Tel (314) 317-7500 *Founded/Ownrshp* 1988
Sales 24.8MM^{E} *EMP* 130
SIC 7379 Computer related consulting services; Computer related consulting services
Pr: Jonathan Freeman
Ch Bd: Robert Smith
COO: Glendy Yeung
CFO: Jeffrey Sanders
Mng Dir: Sebastien Fouillade
Netwrk Mgr: Ken Bruening
Netwrk Eng: Kurt Boyle
Netwrk Eng: Wayne Rolwes
S&M/VP: Shanley Stern
Mktg Dir: Ashley Weaver
Board of Directors: Terry Jost

MYELIN COMMUNICATIONS
See MYELIN HEALTH COMMUNICATIONS INC

D-U-N-S 07-950-0822
MYELIN HEALTH COMMUNICATIONS INC
MYELIN COMMUNICATIONS
25 Drydock Ave Fl 8, Boston, MA 02210-2369
Tel (617) 330-9393 *Founded/Ownrshp* 2013
Sales 82.2MM^{E} *EMP* 172^{E}
SIC 8742 8099 8731 Hospital & health services consultant; Blood related health services; Biological research
CEO: Bill O'Donell
Snr Mgr: Kris Coombs

D-U-N-S 14-852-2444
MYERS & CHAPMAN INC
1101 Wdrdg Ctr Dr Ste 160, Charlotte, NC 28217-1763
Tel (704) 529-6661 *Founded/Ownrshp* 1986
Sales 75.0MM *EMP* 49
Accts Bgw Cpa Pllc Charlotte Nor
SIC 1542 1541 Commercial & office building, new construction; Shopping center construction; Industrial buildings & warehouses
CEO: Robert M Webb
**Pr:* Richard C Handford
**VP:* H Derek Carpenter
**VP:* Scott Hinson
**VP:* Marcus Rabun
**VP:* Bo South
Sfty Dirs: Mike Ussery
Board of Directors: Larry Atkins

D-U-N-S 96-202-0090
MYERS & SONS CONSTRUCTION LP
4600 Northgate Blvd # 100, Sacramento, CA 95834-1121
Tel (916) 283-9950 *Founded/Ownrshp* 2010
Sales 144.8MM *EMP* 250
Accts Grant Thornton Llp Houston T
SIC 1611 Highway & street construction; Highway & street construction
Pt: Clinton C Myers
Pt: Clinton W Myers
Sfty Dirs: Edward Garcia
Opers Mgr: Kurtis Frailey
Snr Mgr: Michael Lewis

D-U-N-S 05-283-6459 IMP
MYERS & SONS HI-WAY SAFETY INC (CA)
13310 5th St, Chino, CA 91710-5125
Tel (909) 591-1781 *Founded/Ownrshp* 1975
Sales 35.1MM^E^ *EMP* 120
SIC 3669 Pedestrian traffic control equipment; Pedestrian traffic control equipment
CEO: Michael Rodgers
*Ex VP: Brandon Myer
Sales Exec: Scott Jargin

D-U-N-S 04-498-6685
MYERS AND STAUFFER LC
700 W 47th St Ste 1100, Kansas City, MO 64112-2050
Tel (816) 945-5300 *Founded/Ownrshp* 1995
Sales 107.2MM *EMP* 650
SIC 8721 Accounting, auditing & bookkeeping; Accounting, auditing & bookkeeping
VP: Jeanne Tomisser
DP Dir: Donald Byrd
DP Dir: Charles Schreiner

D-U-N-S 07-922-3882
MYERS AUTO GROUP LLC
PALM BEACH MOTOR CARS
915 S Dixie Hwy, West Palm Beach, FL 33401-6401
Tel (561) 659-6206 *Founded/Ownrshp* 2012
Sales 120.0MM *EMP* 53
SIC 5511 New & used car dealers; New & used car dealers

D-U-N-S 18-632-6112
MYERS AUTO PARTS INC
NAPA AUTO PARTS
1915 2nd Ave W, Williston, ND 58801-3403
Tel (701) 577-2900 *Founded/Ownrshp* 1987
Sales 25.0MM^E^ *EMP* 80^E^
SIC 5531 7538 Automotive & home supply stores; Automobile & truck equipment & parts; General automotive repair shops; Automotive & home supply stores; Automobile & truck equipment & parts; General automotive repair shops
Pr: W Darroll Myers
*Sec: Joan E Myers
Site Mgr: Shon Johnson

D-U-N-S 05-015-6819
MYERS CO INC
MYERS PLUMBING & UTILITY CONTR
2810 Whites Creek Pike, Nashville, TN 37207-3709
Tel (615) 356-8811 *Founded/Ownrshp* 1978
Sales 20.0MM^E^ *EMP* 80
SIC 1711 Plumbing contractors
Pr: Charles G Myers
*CFO: Stokley Donelson
VP: Calvin Bell
*VP: Cliff Myers

MYERS CONTAINER
See IMACC CORP

D-U-N-S 80-974-6261
MYERS CONTAINER LLC
8435 Ne Killingsworth St, Portland, OR 97220-4660
Tel (503) 255-0557 *Founded/Ownrshp* 2007
Sales 35.6MM^E^ *EMP* 203
SIC 3412 Metal barrels, drums & pails; Metal barrels, drums & pails
Plnt Mgr: Frank Risco

D-U-N-S 36-267-3373 IMP
MYERS CONTROLLED POWER LLC
(*Suby of* MYERS FSI) ★
219 E Maple St 100-200e, North Canton, OH 44720-2586
Tel (330) 834-3200 *Founded/Ownrshp* 2005
Sales 25.3MM^E^ *EMP* 105^E^
SIC 3613 Switchgear & switchboard apparatus; Switchgear & switchboard apparatus
Pr: James Owens
Natl Sales: Jack Hastings
Snr Mgr: Daniel Marchak

D-U-N-S 83-229-4540
MYERS FAMILY LIMITED PARTNERSHIP
CAMANO PLAZA TEXACO & EX LUBE
14485 State Route 525, Langley, WA 98260-8517
Tel (360) 387-0631 *Founded/Ownrshp* 1995
Sales 32.0MM *EMP* 180
SIC 5961 5541 5411 Tools & hardware, mail order; Gasoline service stations; Grocery stores; Tools & hardware, mail order; Gasoline service stations; Grocery stores; Convenience stores
Pt: Kent Myers
Pt: Jonathan Stoverud-Myers

MYERS FSI
See MYERS POWER PRODUCTS INC

MYERS GROUP, THE
See PATIENT SATISFACTION PLUS LLC

D-U-N-S 01-744-0715 IMP/EXP
MYERS GROUP L L C
SOGIMEX
74 Blanchard Rd, South Orange, NJ 07079-1341
Tel (973) 761-6414 *Founded/Ownrshp* 2005
Sales 87.0MM *EMP* 1,380
SIC 3111 Tanneries, leather; Tanneries, leather
VP: Benjamin Myers
Sls Dir: Ted Salomon

D-U-N-S 00-195-0849 IMP/EXP
▲ **MYERS INDUSTRIES INC**
1293 S Main St, Akron, OH 44301-1339
Tel (330) 253-5592 *Founded/Ownrshp* 1955
Sales 623.6MM *EMP* 3,241
Accts Ernst & Young Llp Akron Ohio
Tkr Sym MYE *Exch* NYS
SIC 3089 3086 3069 3052 5013 5014 Pallets, plastic; Stock shapes, plastic; Boxes, plastic; Blow molded finished plastic products; Plastics foam products; Packaging & shipping materials, foamed plastic; Insulation or cushioning material, foamed plastic; Padding, foamed plastic; Rubber automotive products; Automobile hose, rubber; Tools & equipment, automotive; Tire & tube repair materials; Pallets, plastic; Stock shapes, plastic; Boxes, plastic; Blow molded finished plastic products; Plastics foam products; Packaging & shipping materials, foamed plastic; Insulation or cushioning material, foamed plastic; Padding, foamed plastic; Rubber automotive products; Automobile hose, rubber; Tools & equipment, automotive; Tire & tube repair materials
Pr: John C Orr
*Ch Bd: Richard P Johnston
*CFO: Greggory W Branning
Treas: Monica Vinay
Ex VP: David Smith
VP: Jeff Gervais
VP: Bill Iovino
VP: Michael Valentino
VP: Alex Williamson
Exec: Cindy Dawson
Dir Risk M: Scott James
Comm Dir: Stephen Durinsky
Board of Directors: Vincent C Byrd, Sarah R Coffin, John B Crowe, William A Foley, Robert B Heisler Jr, Edward W Kissel, Robert A Stefanko

MYERS PLUMBING & UTILITY CONTR
See MYERS CO INC

D-U-N-S 06-122-0583 IMP
MYERS POWER PRODUCTS INC
MYERS FSI
2950 E Philadelphia St, Ontario, CA 91761-8545
Tel (909) 923-1800 *Founded/Ownrshp* 2003
Sales 115.6MM^E^ *EMP* 305
SIC 3629 Inverters, nonrotating: electrical; Inverters, nonrotating: electrical
CEO: Diana Grootonk
CFO: Jose Cudal
VP: Anoosh Farbod
VP: Barnet Rogers
Genl Mgr: Bruce Steigerwald
Dir IT: Greg Odion
S&M/VP: Chris Boehm
Mktg Dir: Nancy Gordon-Brooks
Snr Mgr: John Pantaleo

MYERS SELECT MATERIAL HANDLING
See SELECT EQUIPMENT SALES INC

MYERS SHEET METAL DIVISION
See KAMPEL ENTERPRISES INC

D-U-N-S 03-970-5343 EXP
■ **MYERS TIRE SUPPLY DISTRIBUTION INC**
MYERS TIRE SUPPLY INTL
(*Suby of* MYERS INDUSTRIES INC) ★
1293 S Main St, Akron, OH 44301-1302
Tel (330) 253-5592 *Founded/Ownrshp* 1999
Sales 123.1MM^E^ *EMP* 410
SIC 5531 Automotive & home supply stores; Automotive & home supply stores
CEO: John C Orr
*COO: David Knowles
*CFO: Donald Merril
VP: Linda Carter
*VP: Todd Smith
Brnch Mgr: Larry Nester
Genl Mgr: Richard Nunez
Sls Mgr: Michael Smith

D-U-N-S 15-133-1642 IMP/EXP
■ **MYERS TIRE SUPPLY INTERNATIONAL INC**
(*Suby of* MYERS INDUSTRIES INC) ★
1293 S Main St, Akron, OH 44301-1302
Tel (330) 253-5592 *Founded/Ownrshp* 1970
Sales 39.6MM^E^ *EMP* 150
SIC 5014 Tires & tubes; Tires & tubes
Pr: John Orr
Treas: Mark Watkins
Dir Soc: Scott James
Brnch Mgr: Ralph Stoll
Genl Mgr: Richard Nunez
CIO: Byron Spilker
IT Man: Anthony Derusso
IT Man: John Kraus
IT Man: Tim Smith
IT Man: Ernie Surnegie
Mktg Dir: Jeff Jobe

MYERS TIRE SUPPLY INTL
See MYERS TIRE SUPPLY DISTRIBUTION INC

D-U-N-S 02-214-5809
MYERS-COX CO
MY-CAP VENDORS
8797 Kapp Dr, Peosta, IA 52068-9448
Tel (563) 556-5369 *Founded/Ownrshp* 1967
Sales 24.7MM^E^ *EMP* 52^E^
SIC 5194 5145 5113 Tobacco & tobacco products; Cigarettes; Cigars; Confectionery; Candy; Chewing gum; Industrial & personal service paper; Tobacco & tobacco products; Cigarettes; Cigars; Confectionery; Candy; Chewing gum; Industrial & personal service paper
Pr: Rob Apel
CFO: Kim Ellis
*Sec: Marie Carew
VP: Chris Dempsey
Sls Mgr: David Flanagan

MYERSVILLE BANK
See FIRST UNITED BANK AND TRUST

D-U-N-S 18-562-6475
■ **MYFONTS.COM INC**
BITSTREAM
(*Suby of* MONOTYPE IMAGING INC) ★
500 Unicorn Park Dr # 200, Woburn, MA 01801-3377
Tel (781) 970-6000 *Founded/Ownrshp* 1999
Sales 11.5MM^E^ *EMP* 300
SIC 7374 Data processing & preparation; Data processing & preparation
Pr: Douglas Shaw

D-U-N-S 02-796-7793 IMP
MYGRANT GLASS CO INC
3271 Arden Rd, Hayward, CA 94545-3901
Tel (510) 786-1425 *Founded/Ownrshp* 1971
Sales 198.1MM^E^ *EMP* 600
SIC 5013 Automobile glass; Automobile glass
CEO: Michael R Mygrant
Treas: Cathy Mygrant
*Sec: Kathy Mygrant
Rgnl Mgr: Vincent Burger
Rgnl Mgr: Tom Dresbach
Brnch Mgr: Robert Alvarez
Brnch Mgr: David Maclean
Brnch Mgr: Donald Rommell
Brnch Mgr: Brent Sell
Dir IT: Dan Parkinson
Opers Mgr: Michael Dattilo

D-U-N-S 05-929-8141 IMP
■ **MYLAN INC**
(*Suby of* MYLAN N.V.)
1000 Mylan Blvd, Canonsburg, PA 15317-5853
Tel (724) 514-1800 *Founded/Ownrshp* 2015
Sales 8.3MMM^E^ *EMP* 30,000
Tkr Sym MYL *Exch* NGS
SIC 2834 Pharmaceutical preparations; Analgesics; Antibiotics, packaged; Tranquilizers or mental drug preparations; Pharmaceutical preparations; Analgesics; Antibiotics, packaged; Tranquilizers or mental drug preparations
CEO: Heather Bresch
*Ch Bd: Robert J Coury
V Ch: Rodney L Goldhahn
*V Ch: Rodney L Piatt
Pr: Rakesh Bamzai
Pr: Roger Graham
*Pr: Rajiv Malik
Pr: John Thievon
COO: S Rinivaan
CFO: Edward Borkowski
CFO: Daniel Caron
*CFO: John D Sheehan
Chf Mktg O: Debra O'Brien
Ex VP: Adele Gulfo
Ex VP: Jolene Varney
Sr VP: John Deiriggi
Sr VP: Joseph F Haggerty
Sr VP: James Hood
Sr VP: Roderick Jackson
Sr VP: M Lacerca
Sr VP: David F Mulder

D-U-N-S 03-961-5992
■ **MYLAN INSTITUTIONAL INC**
(*Suby of* MYLAN INC) ★
1718 Northrock Ct, Rockford, IL 61103-1201
Tel (815) 282-1201 *Founded/Ownrshp* 2009
Sales 32.7MM^E^ *EMP* 300
SIC 7389 5122 Pharmaceuticals; Packaging & labeling services; Packaging & labeling services; Pharmaceuticals
Pr: Matthew Erick
Sr VP: Greg Sheldon
Genl Mgr: Jodi Eichelberger
QA Dir: Sue Powers
Dir IT: William Snyder
IT Man: Jaime Catbagan
IT Man: Shirley Falk
Sfty Mgr: Ken Darty
Opers Mgr: Dan Peters
Mktg Dir: Fran Skaug

D-U-N-S 15-692-7717 IMP
■ **MYLAN LLC**
(*Suby of* MYLAN INC) ★
Caguas West Indust Rr 156, Caguas, PR 00725
Tel (787) 746-0003 *Founded/Ownrshp* 1987
Sales 41.8MM^E^ *EMP* 123
SIC 2834 Proprietary drug products; Proprietary drug products
Pr: Carlos R Machin
Off Mgr: Zaida Dides
QA Dir: Linda Navarro-Lugo
QA Dir: Hernan Rodriguez

D-U-N-S 05-929-5980 IMP
■ **MYLAN PHARMACEUTICALS INC**
(*Suby of* MYLAN INC) ★
781 Chestnut Ridge Rd, Morgantown, WV 26505-2772
Tel (304) 599-2595 *Founded/Ownrshp* 1976
Sales 1.0MMM^E^ *EMP* 7,500^E^
SIC 2834 Proprietary drug products; Druggists' preparations (pharmaceuticals); Proprietary drug products; Druggists' preparations (pharmaceuticals)
Pr: Robert Tighe
V Ch: Rodney L Piatt
*Pr: Joseph Duda
*COO: John Deiriggi
*CFO: Gary Sphar
Bd of Dir: Prasad Nimmagadda
*Ex VP: Mark Fitch
Ex VP: Ray Patterson
VP: Derek Glover
VP: Eric Goodwin
VP: Chuck Koone
VP: Michael J Monroe
*VP: John P O'Donnell
*VP: Brian Roman
VP: Dan Snider
VP: D Witt
Assoc Dir: Chris Benson
Assoc Dir: Keith Giunta
Assoc Dir: Andrew Shaw

D-U-N-S 19-477-5557
■ **MYLAN SPECIALTY LP**
(*Suby of* MYLAN INC) ★
781 Chestnut Ridge Rd, Morgantown, WV 26505-2772
Tel (304) 554-4519 *Founded/Ownrshp* 2007
Sales 117.7MM^E^ *EMP* 1,000
SIC 2834 8731 Drugs acting on the respiratory system; Commercial physical research; Drugs acting on the respiratory system; Commercial physical research
Pr: Roger Graham
*Pt: Imtiaz Chaundry
VP: David Jones
Snr Mgr: James Lugo
Snr Mgr: Deendayal Reddy

D-U-N-S 06-379-0265 IMP
■ **MYLAN TECHNOLOGIES INC**
(*Suby of* MYLAN INC) ★
110 Lake St, Saint Albans, VT 05478-2287
Tel (802) 527-7792 *Founded/Ownrshp* 1993
Sales 64.3MM^E^ *EMP* 250^E^
SIC 2834 2833 2675 2891 Dermatologicals; Medicinals & botanicals; Die-cut paper & board; Adhesives; Dermatologicals; Medicinals & botanicals; Die-cut paper & board; Adhesives
Pr: Harry Korman
*Treas: Brian Byala
VP: Michael Houghton
*VP: David Kennedy
Dir Lab: Jeff Lloyd
Dir Bus: Martin Fletcher
*Prin: Matthew Erick
Mng Dir: Andy McMillan
Dir IT: William Coseo
IT Man: Deidra Losaw
Mfg Mgr: Miles Herbert

MYLIBERTYCLAIM
See LIBERTY LIFE ASSURANCE CO OF BOSTON

D-U-N-S 10-797-5810
MYLIFE.COM INC
REUNION ONLINE
1100 Glendon Ave Ste 1800, Los Angeles, CA 90024-3522
Tel (310) 571-3144 *Founded/Ownrshp* 2001
Sales 22.4MM^E^ *EMP* 75
SIC 7375 On-line data base information retrieval
CEO: Jeffrey Tinsley
COO: Rachel C Glaser
Ofcr: Ian Siegel
Sr VP: Sharyn Eles
Sr VP: Thod Nguyen
VP: K C Brotherton
VP: Richard Rosenblatt
VP: Todd Schlosser
VP: Aaron Taylor
CTO: Paul Onnen
QA Dir: John Coanda

D-U-N-S 09-989-8066
MYLLYKOSKI NORTH AMERICA
2 S Main St, Madison, ME 04950-4501
Tel (207) 696-3307 *Founded/Ownrshp* 2011
Sales 35.6MM^E^ *EMP* 286
SIC 6719 Personal holding companies, except banks; Personal holding companies, except banks
Pr: Rebecca Norris
*VP: Christopher Bean
VP: Mike Ostrowski

MYMATRIXX
See MATRIX HEALTHCARE SERVICES INC

D-U-N-S 00-913-2200 IMP
MYMICHELLE CO LLC
MY MICHELLE
(*Suby of* KELLWOOD CO LLC) ★
13077 Temple Ave, La Puente, CA 91746-1418
Tel (626) 934-4166 *Founded/Ownrshp* 1998
Sales 23.3MM^E^ *EMP* 350
SIC 2331 2337 2335 2361 2369 2339 Blouses, women's & juniors': made from purchased material; Shirts, women's & juniors': made from purchased materials; Skirts, separate: women's, misses' & juniors'; Dresses, paper: cut & sewn; Blouses: girls', children's & infants'; Shirts: girls', children's & infants'; Girls' & children's outerwear; Women's & misses' athletic clothing & sportswear; Blouses, women's & juniors': made from purchased material; Shirts, women's & juniors': made from purchased materials; Skirts, separate: women's, misses' & juniors'; Dresses, paper: cut & sewn; Blouses: girls', children's & infants'; Shirts: girls', children's & infants'; Girls' & children's outerwear; Women's & misses' athletic clothing & sportswear
Pr: Arthur Gordon
Pr: Caren Belair
Pr: Perri Cohen
Pr: Susan Stokes
*Treas: Roger D Joseph
VP: Nathan E Burrow
VP: Staphenie Trailo

D-U-N-S 62-038-1538
MYMTMP CORP
TEXAS MEAT PACKERS
401 N Grove Rd Ste 200, Richardson, TX 75081-2788
Tel (469) 916-3343 *Founded/Ownrshp* 2003
Sales 50.5MM^E^ *EMP* 150
SIC 5147 Meats & meat products; Meats & meat products
CEO: Andrew Fisk
*Pr: Gary Meixelsperger

D-U-N-S 11-269-9025 IMP
MYOFFICEPRODUCTS INC
(*Suby of* HITOUCH BUSINESS SERVICES LLC) ★
22 Century Blvd Ste 420, Nashville, TN 37214-3724
Tel (615) 507-3515 *Founded/Ownrshp* 2010
Sales 537.7MM^E^ *EMP* 359
SIC 5112 5943 Stationery & office supplies; Office forms & supplies; Stationery & office supplies; Office forms & supplies
CEO: Michael Brown
*Pr: John Frisk
Pr: Debbie Lafferty

*CFO: Jeff Sammons
*Ch: Howard Brown
*Ex VP: Joseph Aiello
*Ex VP: Anthony Cavalieri
Ex VP: Butch Johnson
*Ex VP: Earlis Johnson Jr
*Ex VP: Michael Palmer
VP: Lisa Black
VP: Lane Thomas
Exec: Lenny Morella

MYOTCSTORE.COM
See DARISI INC

MYPILLOW
See MY PILLOW INC

D-U-N-S 04-534-8588
▲ MYR GROUP INC
1701 Golf Rd Ste 3-1012, Rolling Meadows, IL 60008-4210
Tel (847) 290-1891 Founded/Ownrshp 1891
Sales 943.9MM EMP 3,650[E]
Accts Ernst & Young Llp Chicago Il
Tkr Sym MYRG Exch NGS
SIC 1623 1731 Electric power line construction; General electrical contractor; Electric power line construction; General electrical contractor
Ch Bd: William A Koertner
COO: Richard S Swartz Jr
CFO: Paul J Evans
CFO: Betty R Johnson
Sr VP: Tod M Cooper
Sr VP: William H Green
VP: Michael Cooper
VP: Michael D Cooper
VP: Norberto Cruz
VP: Marco Martinez
VP: Robert E McDaniel
VP: Brian L Smolinski
VP: Steven T Theis
Board of Directors: Jack L Alexander, Larry F Altenbaumer, Henry W Fayne, Betty R Johnson, Gary R Johnson, Maurice E Moore, William D Patterson

MYREX INDUSTRIES
See MIL LTD

D-U-N-S 96-259-2424
■ MYRIAD GENETIC LABORATORIES INC
(Suby of MYRIAD GENETICS INC) ★
320 S Wakara Way, Salt Lake City, UT 84108-1214
Tel (801) 584-3600 Founded/Ownrshp 1993
Sales 36.3MM[E] EMP 500
SIC 8731 Biotechnical research, commercial; Biotechnical research, commercial
Pr: Gregory Critchfield
*COO: Pete Meldrum
*Treas: James Evans
VP: Bob Davis
*VP: Jay Moyes
Off Mgr: Karen Wooldridge
DP Exec: Rob Harrison
Dir IT: Gregory Ward
IT Man: Keith Wilson
Sls&Mrk Ex: William Rusconi

D-U-N-S 79-757-1668
▲ MYRIAD GENETICS INC
320 S Wakara Way, Salt Lake City, UT 84108-1214
Tel (801) 584-3600 Founded/Ownrshp 1992
Sales 723.1MM EMP 2,038[E]
Accts Ernst & Young Llp Salt Lake C
Tkr Sym MYGN Exch NGS
SIC 2835 8731 In vitro & in vivo diagnostic substances; In vitro diagnostics; In vivo diagnostics; Biological research; Biotechnical research, commercial; In vitro & in vivo diagnostic substances; In vitro diagnostics; In vivo diagnostics; Biological research; Biotechnical research, commercial
Pr: Mark C Capone
*Ch Bd: John T Henderson
CFO: Bryan Riggsbee
CFO: R Bryan Riggsbee
*V Ch Bd: Walter Gilbert
Bd of Dir: Lynne Daugirda
Ex VP: Michael Brawer
Ex VP: Gary A King
Ex VP: Richard M Marsh
Exec: Sara Masters
Dir Lab: Debbie Dinardo
Dir Lab: Priscilla Fernandes
Dir Lab: Ya-Ping Qian
Dir Bus: Patrick Burke
Dir Bus: Troy Tremaine
Board of Directors: Lawrence C Best, Walter Gilbert, Dennis Langer, S Louise Phanstiel

D-U-N-S 12-981-6877
MYRIAD SUPPLY CO LLC
22 W 19th St Ste 4l, New York, NY 10011-4204
Tel (212) 366-6996 Founded/Ownrshp 2003
Sales 58.5MM[E] EMP 43
SIC 7373 Value-added resellers, computer systems; Value-added resellers, computer systems
CEO: Andrew Fisher
CFO: Mark Hosny

D-U-N-S 83-130-8577 IMP
MYRIANT CORP
3 Batterymarch Park Fl 3, Quincy, MA 02169-7541
Tel (617) 657-5234 Founded/Ownrshp 2009
Sales 24.8MM[E] EMP 92
SIC 2869 Industrial organic chemicals; Industrial organic chemicals
Pr: Dennis McCullough
CFO: Chris Tewell
*Treas: Eric Conlin
Ex VP: Cenan Ozmeral
Sr VP: Montgomery Alger
Sr VP: Arne Philipp Duss
*Sr VP: Regina Detore Paglia
VP: Paglia Detore
VP: Susan Hager
VP: David Leblanc
VP: Detore Paglia
VP: Alif Saleh
*VP: Mark Shmorhun

D-U-N-S 04-545-7025
MYRICK CONSTRUCTION INC
101 Shady Oak Dr, Biscoe, NC 27209-9590
Tel (910) 428-2106 Founded/Ownrshp 1995
Sales 29.8MM[E] EMP 100
SIC 1542 1541 1623 1629 Commercial & office building, new construction; Industrial buildings, new construction; Water & sewer line construction; Waste water & sewage treatment plant construction
Pr: Bonny H Myrick
*Ch Bd: Bobby H Myrick
*VP: Frank Burrell III
*VP: Otis Morris
*VP: Bobby H Myrick III

D-U-N-S 00-904-0494
MYRMO & SONS INC
3600 Franklin Blvd, Eugene, OR 97403-2300
Tel (541) 747-4565 Founded/Ownrshp 1925
Sales 34.6MM[E] EMP 75
SIC 5531 7538 3599 7692 3594 Truck equipment & parts; Automobile & truck equipment & parts; Truck engine repair, except industrial; Machine shop, jobbing & repair; Welding repair; Fluid power pumps & motors
CEO: Eric Myrmo
*Pr: George Myrmo

D-U-N-S 00-200-2228 IMP
MYRON CORP
205 Maywood Ave, Maywood, NJ 07607-1000
Tel (201) 843-6464 Founded/Ownrshp 1949
Sales 293.5MM[E] EMP 700
SIC 5199 Advertising specialties; Advertising specialties
Ch: Myron Adler
*Pr: Hal Korman
*CEO: Donald J Adler
COO: David Chun
*CFO: William Byrne
CFO: Saul Kravecas
Treas: Robert Lack
Ex VP: Jim Odowd
VP: Edward Hohnecker
VP: Mark Pepin
VP: Andrew Perelson
Board of Directors: Jackie Ward

D-U-N-S 05-363-4234
MYRON F STEVES & CO
3131 Eastside St Ste 600, Houston, TX 77098-1947
Tel (713) 522-1100 Founded/Ownrshp 1955
Sales NA EMP 203
SIC 6411 Insurance agents, brokers & service; Insurance agents, brokers & service
Pr: Fred Steves
Ex VP: Ron Balcar
Exec: Jane Chisholm
Assoc Dir: Veronica Smith
*Prin: Teresa Skinner
*Prin: Myron F Steves Jr
Sls Mgr: Lisa Mitchell

D-U-N-S 84-800-5104
MYRON F STEVES CO
3131 Eastside St Ste 600, Houston, TX 77098-1947
Tel (713) 522-1100 Founded/Ownrshp 1980
Sales NA EMP 200
SIC 6331 Fire, marine & casualty insurance; Fire, marine & casualty insurance
Pt: Teresa S Skinner
Pt: Frederick B Steves
Pt: Myron F Steves Jr

D-U-N-S 78-723-0051
MYRON GREEN CORP
TREAT AMERICA FOOD SERVICES
8500 Shawnee Mission Pkwy, Merriam, KS 66202-2967
Tel (913) 384-4900 Founded/Ownrshp 2001
Sales 84.7MM[E] EMP 900
Accts Mayer Hoffman Mccann Pc Lea
SIC 5962 Food vending machines; Beverage vending machines; Food vending machines; Beverage vending machines
CEO: John Mitchell Sr
*CFO: Mike Meurer
Genl Mgr: Michael Ortyl
IT Man: Brian Sarbaugh

D-U-N-S 06-446-8689 IMP
MYRON L CO
2450 Impala Dr, Carlsbad, CA 92010-7226
Tel (760) 438-2021 Founded/Ownrshp 1957
Sales 28.7MM[E] EMP 80
SIC 3823 3825 3613 Electrodes used in industrial process measurement; Instruments to measure electricity; Switchgear & switchboard apparatus
Pr: Gary O Robinson
*VP: Jerry Adams
IT Man: Jonathan Rekalske
VP Mktg: Kathryn Robinsin
Mktg Dir: Kathy Robinson
Manager: Jeremy Robinson
Manager: Willie Stuart
Manager: Ron Triplett
Sls Mgr: Johneo Morgan

D-U-N-S 96-438-8875
MYRTLE BEACH AREA CHAMBER OF COMMERCE EDUCATIONAL FOUNDATION
1200 N Oak St, Myrtle Beach, SC 29577-3558
Tel (843) 626-7444 Founded/Ownrshp 2010
Sales 39.0MM EMP 2
Accts Smith Sapp Myrtle Beach Sc
SIC 8611 Chamber of Commerce; Chamber of Commerce
Prin: Brad Dean

D-U-N-S 03-170-8923
MYRTLE BEACH BUILDING SUPPLY CO INC
9326 Hwy 90, Conway, SC 29528
Tel (843) 347-3325 Founded/Ownrshp 2001
Sales 22.0MM[E] EMP 40
SIC 5031 Building materials, exterior
Pr: Bobby Smith
*VP: Joe Kenkins
Genl Mgr: Joe Jenkins

D-U-N-S 60-793-1581
MYRTLE BEACH CHEVROLET INC
1785 Highway 501, Myrtle Beach, SC 29577-9751
Tel (843) 448-3105 Founded/Ownrshp 1993
Sales 35.0MM EMP 65
SIC 5511 Automobiles, new & used; Automobiles, new & used
Pr: Luis Rodguiez

D-U-N-S 85-858-3404
MYRTLE BEACH FARMS CO INC
(Suby of BURROUGHS & CHAPIN CO INC) ★
8820 Marina Pkwy, Myrtle Beach, SC 29572-8101
Tel (843) 448-5123 Founded/Ownrshp 1990
Sales 165.1MM[E] EMP 1,000[E]
SIC 6552 7996 6512 Subdividers & developers; Theme park, amusement; Commercial & industrial building operation; Subdividers & developers; Theme park, amusement; Commercial & industrial building operation
Pr: Douglas P Wendell
Ch Bd: James Egerton Burroughs
Pr: Jim Rosenburg
CFO: Barry Spivey
Sr VP: Tanya Greenlee
Sr VP: William F Pritchard
VP: Mary E Basden
VP: Tony Cox
VP: Franklin J Long

D-U-N-S 03-009-2407
■ MYRTLE BEACH HOSPITAL INC
(Suby of HCA INC) ★
809 82nd Pkwy, Myrtle Beach, SC 29572-4607
Tel (843) 692-1000 Founded/Ownrshp 1994
Sales 23.4MM[E] EMP 875
SIC 8062 8011 General medical & surgical hospitals; Offices & clinics of medical doctors; General medical & surgical hospitals; Offices & clinics of medical doctors
Chf Rad: Richard Wonder
Dir Risk M: David Brooks
Dir Rx: Connie Williams

D-U-N-S 07-805-1943
MYRTLE BEACH NATIONAL CO
1203 48th Ave N Ste 200, Myrtle Beach, SC 29577-5425
Tel (843) 497-5488 Founded/Ownrshp 1971
Sales 33.8MM[E] EMP 900
SIC 7992 7011 Public golf courses; Resort hotel; Public golf courses; Resort hotel
CEO: Robert J Mauragas
*Ch Bd: H E Pearce Jr
*Pr: Matthew J Brittain
*Ex VP: Thomas W Hale

D-U-N-S 02-418-8948
MYRTLE HILLIARD DAVIS COMPREHENSIVE HEALTH CENTERS INC (MO)
ST. LOUIS COMP HEALTH CENTER
5471 Dr M L King Dr, Saint Louis, MO 63112-4265
Tel (314) 367-5820 Founded/Ownrshp 1968
Sales 19.0MM EMP 466
Accts Schmersahl Treloar & Co Pc St
SIC 8082 Home health care services; Home health care services
Pr: Archie Griffin
*CFO: Angela Archibald
CFO: Kahn Raisat
Chf Cred: Corliss White
Dir Rx: Robert Seigal
Dir Rx: Curtis Young
CIO: Renee Brooks
IT Man: Angela Clabon
IT Man: Rene Gregson
Nutrtnst: Sandra Rice
Podiatrist: Henry Bradford

MYRTUE MEDICAL CENTER
See SHELBY COUNTY CHRIS A MYRTUE MEMORIAL HOSPITAL

D-U-N-S 13-596-1774 IMP/EXP
MYSTIC APPAREL LLC
KIDS WITH CHARACTER
1333 Broadway Fl 6, New York, NY 10018-7268
Tel (212) 704-0424 Founded/Ownrshp 2003
Sales 92.7MM[E] EMP 19[E]
SIC 2339 Bathing suits: women's, misses' & juniors'; Bathing suits: women's, misses' & juniors'
Pr: Charles Mizrahi

MYSTIC AQUARIUM
See SEA RESEARCH FOUNDATION INC

D-U-N-S 08-933-1263 IMP
MYSTIC INC
HERMAN KAY
463 7th Ave Fl 12, New York, NY 10018-7499
Tel (212) 239-2025 Founded/Ownrshp 1989
Sales 62.3MM[E] EMP 240
Accts Citrin Cooperman & Co Llp Cp
SIC 2339 Women's & misses' outerwear; Women's & misses' outerwear
Pr: Richard Kringstein
CFO: Lawrence Peltz
Snr Mgr: Harold Weiss

MYSTIC LAKE CASINO
See SMSC GAMING ENTERPRISE

D-U-N-S 03-633-8916
MYSTIC LOGISTICS HOLDINGS LLC (CT)
2187 New London Tpke C, South Glastonbury, CT 06073-2636
Tel (860) 657-4300 Founded/Ownrshp 1998
Sales 36.1MM[E] EMP 48
SIC 4731 4213 Truck transportation brokers; Contract haulers
Ch Bd: Samuel J Campbell
*CFO: William D Morehead
VP: Robert Depaolo
*VP: Joanne V Sproull
*VP Sls: Charlene Dufresne-Achatz

D-U-N-S 60-324-4492
MYSTIC LOGISTICS INC
(Suby of MYSTIC LOGISTICS HOLDINGS LLC) ★
2187 New London Tpke C, South Glastonbury, CT 06073-2636
Tel (860) 659-1566 Founded/Ownrshp 1997
Sales 36.1MM[E] EMP 45
SIC 4731 4213 Truck transportation brokers; Contract haulers
CEO: Charlene Dufresne-Achatz
*CFO: William Morehead
Dir IT: Donald Labarre
Trfc Dir: Anthony Young

D-U-N-S 14-425-2210
MYSTIC LTD
SHEETS UNLIMITED
301 Sw 27th St, Renton, WA 98057-3381
Tel (425) 251-5959 Founded/Ownrshp 1984
Sales 41.6MM[E] EMP 93
SIC 2653 Sheets, corrugated: made from purchased materials; Sheets, corrugated: made from purchased materials
Ch Bd: Gordon Younger
*Pr: Todd Thompson
Sfty Dirs: Grace Gustafson
Mktg Mgr: Stefanie Toth

D-U-N-S 04-510-4882 IMP
MYSTIC SEAPORT MUSEUM INC
75 Greenmanville Ave, Mystic, CT 06355-1972
Tel (860) 572-0711 Founded/Ownrshp 1929
Sales 17.4MM EMP 340
SIC 8412 5947 2731

D-U-N-S 06-680-1309 IMP
MYSTIC STAMP CO INC
9700 Mill St, Camden, NY 13316-9111
Tel (315) 245-2690 Founded/Ownrshp 1974
Sales 21.0MM[E] EMP 150
SIC 5961 Stamps, mail order; Catalog sales; Stamps, mail order; Catalog sales
Pr: Donald Sundman
Genl Mgr: Mark Fox
MIS Dir: Cynthia Wiard
Dir IT: Don Arsenault
Advt Dir: Jessica Johnson

D-U-N-S 09-587-3832
MYSTIC VALLEY ELDER SERVICES INC
HOME CARE
300 Commercial St Ste 19, Malden, MA 02148-7311
Tel (781) 324-7705 Founded/Ownrshp 1975
Sales 35.9MM EMP 155
Accts Steven P Richer Cpa Millbur
SIC 8322 Old age assistance
Off Mgr: Deb Pelletier
QA Dir: Sandy Fall
Dir IT: Alex Jurkevich

D-U-N-S 00-418-9853
MYSTICK KREWE OF LOUISIANIANS INC
8941 Jefferson Hwy # 200, Baton Rouge, LA 70809-2407
Tel (225) 216-1911 Founded/Ownrshp 2004
Sales 4.2MM[E] EMP 500
SIC 7997 Membership sports & recreation clubs; Membership sports & recreation clubs
Sec: Ted Jones

D-U-N-S 01-335-8002
MYTHICS INC
1439 N Great Neck Rd, Virginia Beach, VA 23454-1347
Tel (757) 965-6756 Founded/Ownrshp 2000
Sales 352.6MM[E] EMP 222[E]
SIC 5045 Computers; Computers
CEO: Robert S Larose
*Pr: Gary Newman
CFO: Barbara Darr
*CFO: Rick Welborn
*VP: Sloan Frey
VP: Jennifer Ladd
VP: Zeb Mellett
VP: Dave Miller
*VP: Chris Richards
*VP: Brent Seaman
VP: Brian Wickum

D-U-N-S 19-654-2740
MYTREX INC
RESCUE ALERT
10321 S Beckstead Ln, South Jordan, UT 84095-8801
Tel (801) 571-4121 Founded/Ownrshp 1986
Sales 45.0MM EMP 100
SIC 7363 8711 Medical help service; Electrical or electronic engineering; Medical help service; Electrical or electronic engineering
Pr: Richard M Bangerter
Sec: Max E Bangerter
VP: Ron L Hardy
Genl Mgr: Ernest Wessman
IT Man: Jared Wood

MYUS.COM
See ACCESS USA SHIPPING INC

D-U-N-S 01-192-2176 IMP
MZ BERGER & CO INC (NY)
ELGIN WATCH
2976 Northern Blvd Fl 4, Long Island City, NY 11101-2829
Tel (718) 472-7500 Founded/Ownrshp 1963, 1953
Sales 69.8MM[E] EMP 135
SIC 5094 3873 Watches & parts; Watches, clocks, watchcases & parts; Watches & parts; Watches, clocks, watchcases & parts
Ch Bd: Bernard Mermelstein
*Pr: Joseph Mermelstein
CFO: Patrick Carlsen
VP: Jackie Leathem
VP: Steve Schachtel
CIO: Rudy Adametz
VP Sls: Chris Smith

N

D-U-N-S 04-647-1397 IMP
N & A ENTERPRISES INC
BIG "D FLOOR COVERING SUPPLIES
7412 Anaconda Ave, Garden Grove, CA 92841-2912
Tel (714) 894-3934 *Founded/Ownrshp* 1984
Sales 23.0MM^E *EMP* 58
SIC 5087 Carpet & rug cleaning equipment & supplies, commercial
CEO: Stephen Kleinhans
**Pr:* Wade Jackson
**CFO:* Dody Brennan
Genl Mgr: Kyle Jackson
Store Mgr: Ben Kaufman
Sls Mgr: Raul Mateus

D-U-N-S 03-024-1336
N & D HEALTHCARE INC
10101 Harwin Dr Ste 293, Houston, TX 77036-1688
Tel (281) 408-4530 *Founded/Ownrshp* 2012
Sales 22.5MM *EMP* 12
SIC 5047 5999 Medical equipment & supplies; Medical apparatus & supplies

D-U-N-S 60-221-7742 IMP
N & F LOGISTIC INC
1300 Edwards Ave, New Orleans, LA 70123-2232
Tel (504) 733-0880 *Founded/Ownrshp* 2006
Sales 34.3MM^E *EMP* 50
SIC 5141 4789 5153 Food brokers; Cargo loading & unloading services; Grains
Pr: Jin Zhang

N & K INC AUTO CARE CENTER
See N AND K INC

D-U-N-S 09-634-3421
N & M TRANSFER CO INC (WI)
630 Muttart Rd, Neenah, WI 54956-9764
Tel (920) 722-7760 *Founded/Ownrshp* 1963
Sales 80.0MM^E *EMP* 850
SIC 4212 4213 Local trucking, without storage; Trucking, except local; Local trucking, without storage; Trucking, except local
Pr: Thomas Pawlacyk
**VP:* Eileen Pawlacyk
**VP:* Dave Williams
Genl Mgr: Larry Briski
Trfc Dir: Christine Dietzen
Trfc Dir: Josh Huelsbeck
Sls Mgr: Keith Gowdy
Sales Asso: Ron Walters

N & S SUPPLY
See CENTRAL PURCHASING CORP

D-U-N-S 02-867-2046
N & S TRACTOR CO
600 S St 59, Merced, CA 95341-6543
Tel (209) 944-5500 *Founded/Ownrshp* 1954
Sales 30.7MM^E *EMP* 65
SIC 5083 7699 Agricultural machinery & equipment; Farm machinery repair; Agricultural machinery & equipment; Farm machinery repair
CEO: Arthur R Nutcher
**Sec:* Mary Wallace
**VP:* Stephanie Nutcher
Plnt Mgr: Matt Nutcher

N A B
See NATIONAL ASSOCIATION OF BROADCASTERS

D-U-N-S 83-173-0382
■ **N A BANKUNITED**
(*Suby of* BANKUNITED INC) ★
14817 Oak Ln, Miami Lakes, FL 33016-1517
Tel (305) 231-6400 *Founded/Ownrshp* 2009
Sales NA *EMP* 1,100
SIC 6035 6163 6111 Federal savings & loan associations; Loan brokers; Federal savings & loan associations; Loan brokers; Federal National Mortgage Association
CEO: John A Kanas
Pr: Thomas M Cornish
Pr: Ingrid Mason
**Pr:* Ramiro A Ortiz
Pr: Dan Overbey
**COO:* Rajinder P Singh
**CFO:* Leslie Lunak
**CFO:* Douglas J Pauls
Ofcr: Lissette Cantillo
Ofcr: John Coles
Ofcr: Lisa Katz
Ofcr: Helen Varela
Ofcr: Ryan Wikel
Ex VP: Mark Bagnoli
Ex VP: Michael Dunigan
Ex VP: Frank Fernandez
**Ex VP:* Felix M Garcia
**Ex VP:* Robert Green
Ex VP: Thomas Harris
Ex VP: Eric Hibbert
**Ex VP:* Abel L Iglesias
Board of Directors: Sue Cobb

D-U-N-S 03-101-5399
N A BUFFEN CO INC
2550 Harley Dr, Maryland Heights, MO 63043-3513
Tel (314) 567-3340 *Founded/Ownrshp* 1951
Sales 22.5MM^E *EMP* 3
Accts Fiehler & Marcus Pc St Loui
SIC 5122 5131 5141 Toiletries; Cosmetics; Druggists' sundries; Toilet articles; Piece goods & notions; Groceries, general line; Toiletries; Cosmetics; Druggists' sundries; Toilet articles; Piece goods & notions; Groceries, general line
Pr: Larry Buffen
**Pr:* Andrew Buffen

N A C
See NORTHERN AIR CARGO INC

N A C
See NORTH AMERICAN COMMUNICATIONS INC

N A C S
See NATIONAL ASSOCIATION OF COLLEGE STORES INC

N. A. D. E.
See NATIONAL AUTO DEALERS EXCHANGE (INC)

D-U-N-S 06-098-8706
■ **N A FIRST**
FIRST NATIONAL BANK
(*Suby of* FIRST BANCORP INC) ★
223 Main St, Damariscotta, ME 04543-4651
Tel (207) 563-3195 *Founded/Ownrshp* 1864
Sales NA *EMP* 210
SIC 6021 National commercial banks; National commercial banks
Pr: Daniel R Daigneault
CFO: Matthew Graves
**CFO:* F Stephen Ward
**Ch:* Robert B Gregory
Ofcr: Stacy Brann
Ofcr: Richard Elder
Sr VP: Susan Norton
Sr VP: Steven Poulin
**Sr VP:* Charles A Wootton
**VP:* Petrea Allen
VP: R Buthy
VP: Jon Nicholson
VP: Stephen Staples
VP: Walter Vietze
VP: Thomas M Wilhel
Exec: Carl S Poole Jr
Exec: Amy Rollins

D-U-N-S 04-030-6821
N A FIRST BANK RICHMOND
(*Suby of* RICHMOND MUTUAL BANCORPORATION INC) ★
20 N 9th St, Richmond, IN 47374-3170
Tel (765) 962-2581 *Founded/Ownrshp* 1887
Sales NA *EMP* 150
SIC 6021 National commercial banks; National commercial banks
Pr: Garry D Kleer
**Ch Bd:* Thomas L Holthouse
**COO:* Donald Benziger
**COO:* John Rusie
Bd of Dir: Mike Blum
Ofcr: Niles Richards
**Ofcr:* Paul Witte
**Trst Ofcr:* Alan Spears
**VP:* Albert Fullerton Jr
**VP:* Lynette Lafuse
**Prin:* Donald A Benziger
Board of Directors: E Michael Blum, Lindley Mann, Carol B McKee, W Ray Stevens III

N A I
See NORRIS BEGGS & SIMPSON NORTHWEST LIMITED PARTNERSHIP

N A I BT COMMERCIAL
See BLICKMAN TURKUS LP

D-U-N-S 01-742-2254
N A MANS & SONS INC
MANS LUMBER AND MILL WORK
3300 W Jefferson Ave, Trenton, MI 48183-2939
Tel (734) 676-3000 *Founded/Ownrshp* 1900
Sales 67.0MM *EMP* 110
SIC 5211 Lumber & other building materials; Lumber & other building materials
Pr: Douglas Mans
COO: Peter Mans
**CFO:* Anna Motschall
**VP:* Christopher Mans

N A P
See NAP INDUSTRIES INC

N A S
See NATIONAL ACADEMY OF SCIENCES OF UNITED STATES OF AMERICA

N A S
See NORTH AMERICAN STAINLESS

N A S S
See NATIONAL AGRICULTURAL STATISTICS SERVICE

D-U-N-S 13-839-0450
N A SGS INC
MINERALS SERVICES DIVISION
1919 S Highland Ave, Lombard, IL 60148-6153
Tel (630) 953-9300 *Founded/Ownrshp* 2007
Sales 30.7MM^E *EMP* 650
SIC 8734 Testing laboratories; Testing laboratories
Pr: Christian Cilch
Sfty Mgr: Douglas Leeber

D-U-N-S 07-847-8664
N A SODECIA INC
SODECIA GROUP
(*Suby of* SODECIA GROUP) ★
24331 Sherwood, Center Line, MI 48015-1060
Tel (586) 879-8969 *Founded/Ownrshp* 2010
Sales 27.5MM^E *EMP* 300
SIC 3465 Body parts, automobile: stamped metal; Body parts, automobile: stamped metal
CEO: Rui Montero
**Treas:* Sheryl McGowan
**VP:* Gary Easterly
Snr Mgr: Brian Wawrzynski

D-U-N-S 19-670-7707 IMP
N A TEADIT INC
NORTH LOOP IMPORTS
(*Suby of* TEADIT INDUSTRIA E COMERCIO LTDA.)
10545 Red Bluff Rd, Pasadena, TX 77507-1073
Tel (281) 476-3900 *Founded/Ownrshp* 2003
Sales 31.0MM *EMP* 130
SIC 5085 5084 Industrial supplies; Gaskets; Seals, industrial; Industrial machinery & equipment; Industrial supplies; Gaskets; Seals, industrial; Industrial machinery & equipment
Pr: Chris Day
**CFO:* Craig Neel
VP Opers: Marco Calzini
Plnt Mgr: Chris Channell

Sls Mgr: Paul Vileno
Sales Asso: Debbie McMillin
Sales Asso: Pauline Perry

D-U-N-S 05-219-5641
N A WATER SYSTEMS LLC
(*Suby of* VEOLIA WATER TECHNOLOGIES) ★
250 Airside Dr, Moon Township, PA 15108-2793
Tel (412) 809-6000 *Founded/Ownrshp* 2004
Sales 30.0MM^E *EMP* 175
SIC 1629 8711 Waste water & sewage treatment plant construction; Engineering services; Waste water & sewage treatment plant construction; Engineering services
CEO: Anthony F Lisanti
**CFO:* Rich Cashdollar
CFO: Rich Cashtollr
**VP:* Craig Yendell
Tech Mgr: Mohan Badami
VP Opers: Kirk Schwab
Mktg Mgr: Carla Robinson

N A WHITTENBURG
See DESIGN WORKS BY TECH PRODUCTS INC

D-U-N-S 06-648-8057
N A WILLIAMS CO INC
2900 Paces Ferry Rd Se A100, Atlanta, GA 30339-5771
Tel (770) 433-2282 *Founded/Ownrshp* 1934
Sales 21.0MM^E *EMP* 130^E
SIC 5013 Automotive supplies & parts; Automotive supplies & parts
Pr: Roger McCollum
**CFO:* Glenn D Rainbow
**VP:* Chris Williams
**VP:* Ridley Williams

D-U-N-S 17-022-3606
N ALAMO WATER SUPPLY CO CORP
420 S Doolittle Rd, Edinburg, TX 78542-9707
Tel (956) 383-4744 *Founded/Ownrshp* 1968
Sales 22.3MM *EMP* 3
SIC 4941 Water supply; Water supply
Genl Mgr: Charles Browning

D-U-N-S 04-441-4642
N AND K INC
N & K INC AUTO CARE CENTER
15701 E Valley Blvd, City of Industry, CA 91744-3934
Tel (818) 968-9204 *Founded/Ownrshp* 1998
Sales 22.0MM *EMP* 15
SIC 5541 Gasoline service stations; Gasoline service stations
Pr: Sam Khoury
**Pr:* Nasif Khoury

N B A
See NATIONAL BASKETBALL ASSOCIATION INC

N B T
See ENOBLE INC

N B T BANK
See NBT BANK NA

D-U-N-S 03-111-1537
N B WEST CONTRACTING CO
2780 Mary Ave, Saint Louis, MO 63144-2726
Tel (314) 962-3145 *Founded/Ownrshp* 1955
Sales 21.8MM^E *EMP* 160
SIC 2951 1611 Asphalt paving mixtures & blocks; Highway & street paving contractor; Asphalt paving mixtures & blocks; Highway & street paving contractor
Pr: Larry West
**VP:* Harvey Alderson

N C B
See NATIONAL CONSUMER COOPERATIVE BANK

N C B
See NCB FSB

D-U-N-S 04-439-7156
N C B SAVINGS BANK FSB
(*Suby of* N C B) ★
139 S High St Ste 1, Hillsboro, OH 45133-1442
Tel (937) 393-4246 *Founded/Ownrshp* 1890, 1988
Sales NA *EMP* 125^E
SIC 6035 Federal savings banks; Federal savings banks
Pr: Deb Shoemaker
Pr: Chris Goettke
Sr VP: Liz White

D-U-N-S 04-111-0750 IMP
N C BRIGHTON MACHINE CORP
7300 Whitmore Lake Rd, Brighton, MI 48116-8558
Tel (810) 227-6190 *Founded/Ownrshp* 1965
Sales 35.8MM^E *EMP* 140
SIC 3599 Machine shop, jobbing & repair; Machine shop, jobbing & repair
Pr: Jack Clausnitzer
**CFO:* Shirley Barton
**Prin:* Bill Barton
**Prin:* Tim Clausnitzer
Off Mgr: Billie Barton

N C C
See NEW COMMUNITY CORP

N C C D
See NATIONAL COUNCIL ON CRIME AND DELINQUENCY

N C D M V
See NORTH CAROLINA DIVISION OF MOTOR VEHICLES

N C FARM BUREAU MUTUAL INSUR
See NORTH CAROLINA FARM BUREAU INSURANCE AGENCY INC

N C H
See NORTHWEST COMMUNITY HOSPITAL FOUNDATION

D-U-N-S 96-520-8036 IMP
N C HOLDINGS
NORMACK
10395 Yellow Circle Dr, Hopkins, MN 55343-9101
Tel (952) 933-7060 *Founded/Ownrshp* 1995
Sales 41.6MM^E *EMP* 76
SIC 5091 3949 Sporting & recreation goods; Fishing tackle; Hunting equipment & supplies; Bait, artificial: fishing

N C I
See NCI MFG INC

N C L R
See NATIONAL COUNCIL OF LA RAZA

D-U-N-S 79-708-8627 IMP
N C MACHINERY CO
CATERPILLAR
(*Suby of* HARNISH GROUP INC) ★
17025 W Valley Hwy, Tukwila, WA 98188-5552
Tel (425) 251-9800 *Founded/Ownrshp* 2000
Sales 316.2MM^E *EMP* 1,000
SIC 5082 5013 5083 Construction & mining machinery; Tractors, construction; Front end loaders; Graders, motor; Automotive engines & engine parts; Agricultural machinery & equipment; Tractors, agricultural; Cultivating machinery & equipment; Planting machinery & equipment; Construction & mining machinery; Tractors, construction; Front end loaders; Graders, motor; Automotive engines & engine parts; Agricultural machinery & equipment; Tractors, agricultural; Cultivating machinery & equipment; Planting machinery & equipment
Pr: John Harnish
CTO: Dale Buzitis
Mktg Mgr: Scott Field

N C PARTNERSHIP FOR CHILDREN
See NORTH CAROLINA PARTNERSHIP FOR CHILDREN INC

D-U-N-S 79-708-8734 IMP
N C POWER SYSTEMS CO
CATERPILLAR
(*Suby of* HARNISH GROUP INC) ★
17900 W Valley Hwy, Tukwila, WA 98188-5533
Tel (425) 251-5877 *Founded/Ownrshp* 1999
Sales 87.6MM^E *EMP* 200
SIC 5013 5082 5083 Automotive engines & engine parts; Construction & mining machinery; Agricultural machinery & equipment; Automotive engines & engine parts; Construction & mining machinery; Agricultural machinery & equipment
Pr: John Harnish
**VP:* Richard Bellin
**VP:* Joseph Huley
Exec: Sally Hausken
Brnch Mgr: William Ring
Sls Mgr: Warren Hull
Sales Asso: Darrel Vail

N C R A
See CHS MCPHERSON REFINERY INC

N C S
See NCS TECHNOLOGIES INC

N C T A
See NATIONAL CABLE & TELECOMMUNICATIONS ASSOCIATION

D-U-N-S 15-973-8595
N COMPASS INTERNATIONAL INC
NCOMPASS INTERNATIONAL
8223 Santa Monica Blvd, West Hollywood, CA 90046-5912
Tel (323) 785-1700 *Founded/Ownrshp* 2003
Sales 37.7MM *EMP* 138
Accts Meloni Hribal Tratner Llp Woo
SIC 8742 Marketing consulting services; Marketing consulting services
CEO: Donna Direnzo Graves
**COO:* Kae Erickson
VP: Michaela McCoy
VP: Aaron Miller
Mktg Mgr: Jatera Mayo

N D C
See NATIONAL DISTRIBUTION & CONTRACTING INC

N D C
See NDCHEALTH CORP

N D C
See NITINOL DEVELOPMENT CORPORATIO

N D I
See NASHVILLE DENTAL INC

N D I A
See NATIONAL TRAINING SYSTEMS ASSOCIATION INC

N E A
See NATIONAL EDUCATION ASSOCIATION OF UNITED STATES

N E A
See NEW YORK STATE UNITED TEACHERS

D-U-N-S 08-587-6360
N E A ALASKA HEALTH PLAN
4003 Iowa Dr, Anchorage, AK 99517-2539
Tel (907) 274-7526 *Founded/Ownrshp* 1996
Sales NA *EMP* 3
SIC 6411 Insurance agents, brokers & service; Insurance agents, brokers & service
Pr: Teri Burke
**Treas:* Rhonda Kitter

N E C
See NEC ENERGY SOLUTIONS INC

N E C COLUMBUS
See NATIONAL ELECTRIC COIL INC

N E I
See NUCLEAR ENERGY INSTITUTE INC

N E I
See NORTHWEST EARTHMOVERS INC

N E PRESTRESSED PRODUCTS
See NORTHEAST PRESTRESSED PRODUCTS LLC

N E R C
See NORTH AMERICAN ELECTRIC RELIABILITY CORP

D-U-N-S 15-448-0859
N E WHERE TRANSPORT INC
3808 E Dr M L King Jr Blv Martin Luther, Tampa, FL 33610
Tel (813) 363-0959 *Founded/Ownrshp* 1983
Sales 320.0MM *EMP* 13
SIC 4212 Delivery service, vehicular; Delivery service, vehicular
Pr: John E Amato
**VP:* Lenore L Amato

N F A
See NATIONAL FUTURES ASSOCIATION (INC)

N F C
See NIX-FOWLER CONSTRUCTORS INC

N F I B
See NATIONAL FEDERATION OF INDEPENDENT BUSINESS

N F L
See NATIONAL FOOTBALL LEAGUE INC

D-U-N-S 18-350-1014
N F L CHARITIES INC
280 Park Ave, New York, NY 10017-1216
Tel (212) 450-2000 *Founded/Ownrshp* 1972
Sales 32.7MM *EMP* 4
SIC 8699 Charitable organization; Charitable organization
Pr: Paul Tagliabue

N F M
See NFM INC

N F M
See NFM/WELDING ENGINEERS INC

N F P SECURITIES
See NFP INSURANCE SERVICES INC

N F R
See KROLL FACTUAL DATA LLC

D-U-N-S 87-889-2884
N F S HOLDINGS INC
1205 Banner Hill Rd, Erwin, TN 37650-9318
Tel (423) 743-9141 *Founded/Ownrshp* 1994
Sales 55.3MM^E *EMP* 400
SIC 4959 Environmental cleanup services; Environmental cleanup services
Pr: Paul F Schutt
**CFO:* Glen Jones
Board of Directors: Charles R Johnson

D-U-N-S 11-738-2457 IMP
N F SMITH & ASSOCIATES LP
5306 Hollister St, Houston, TX 77040-6120
Tel (713) 430-3000 *Founded/Ownrshp* 1984
Sales 748.1MM *EMP* 400
SIC 5065

N G A
See NATIONAL GEOSPATIAL-INTELLIGENCE AGENCY

N G B
See GEORGIA NORTH BRICK CO INC

N G I
See NEVELL GROUP INC

N G L
See NETWORK GLOBAL LOGISTICS LLC

D-U-N-S 09-860-8375
N G P MOTORS INC
SUNRISE FORD
5500 Lankershim Blvd, North Hollywood, CA 91601-2724
Tel (818) 980-9800 *Founded/Ownrshp* 1987
Sales 53.1MM^E *EMP* 131
SIC 5511 7539 Automobiles, new & used; Automotive repair shops; Automobiles, new & used; Automotive repair shops
Pr: Robert Burncati
**VP:* Maureen Burncati
Exec: Mike Mayberry

D-U-N-S 04-371-3445
N G PURVIS FARMS INC
2504 Spies Rd, Robbins, NC 27325-7213
Tel (910) 948-2297 *Founded/Ownrshp* 1949
Sales 39.9MM^E *EMP* 100
SIC 0213 Hogs
Pr: Jerry M Purvis Sr
**Treas:* Jerry Purvis
Prd Mgr: Kelly Lambert

D-U-N-S 00-301-5489
N GLANTZ & SON LLC (TX)
(*Suby of* GLANTZ HOLDINGS INC) ★
2501 Constant Comment Pl, Louisville, KY 40299-6324
Tel (502) 426-4473 *Founded/Ownrshp* 1988
Sales 134.8MM^E *EMP* 156
SIC 5046 Neon signs; Neon signs
CEO: Davey Glantz
Ch: Joe Hartman
Brnch Mgr: Tim Cunningham
Brnch Mgr: Mike Davis
Brnch Mgr: Toni Fajardo
Brnch Mgr: Brett Kerley
Opers Supe: Michael Crepeault
Opers Supe: Ed Haddick
Opers Mgr: Tim Markert
Opers Mgr: Ted Mayfield
Natl Sales: Larry Markert

D-U-N-S 00-819-0282 IMP
N GOLDRING CORP
MAGNOLIA LIQUORS
675 S Pace Blvd, Pensacola, FL 32502-5098
Tel (850) 429-7000 *Founded/Ownrshp* 1934
Sales 20.2MM^E *EMP* 115
SIC 5181 5182 Beer & other fermented malt liquors; Liquor; Beer & other fermented malt liquors; Liquor
Pr: William Goldring
**CFO:* Paul L Fine
**VP:* Joseph Wanek

N H
See NORTHSIDE HOSPITAL - CHEROKEE INC

N H
See NEWBURGH METALS INC

N H A
See NEIGHBORHOOD HOUSE ASSOCIATION

N H A
See NATIONAL HERITAGE ACADEMIES INC

D-U-N-S 00-799-5319
N H BRAGG & SONS (ME)
BRAGG'S AUTO PARTS
92 Perry Rd Ste A, Bangor, ME 04401-6741
Tel (207) 947-8611 *Founded/Ownrshp* 1854
Sales 33.5MM^E *EMP* 70
SIC 5085 5084 5531

D-U-N-S 10-469-8720
N H C O P LP
100 E Vine St, Murfreesboro, TN 37130-3734
Tel (615) 890-2020 *Founded/Ownrshp* 1997
Sales 148.1MM^E *EMP* 3,000
SIC 8051 Skilled nursing care facilities; Skilled nursing care facilities
Pr: W Andrew Adams

D-U-N-S 06-446-8655 IMP
N H RESEARCH INC
16601 Hale Ave, Irvine, CA 92606-5049
Tel (949) 474-3900 *Founded/Ownrshp* 1978
Sales 20.3MM^E *EMP* 75
SIC 3825 3829 Test equipment for electronic & electrical circuits; Measuring & controlling devices
Pr: Peter Swartz
Ofcr: Mary Roell

N I C
See NICUSA INC

N I C T D
See NORTHERN INDIANA COMMUTER TRANSPORTATION DISTRICT

N I D
See NEVADA IRRIGATION DISTRICT

N I H
See NATIONAL INSTITUTES OF HEALTH

D-U-N-S 78-750-5965
N J B OPERATIONS INC
TACO BELL
231 Olde Half Day Rd, Lincolnshire, IL 60069-2906
Tel (847) 955-1000 *Founded/Ownrshp* 1984
Sales 15.1MM^E *EMP* 315
SIC 5812 Fast-food restaurant, chain; Fast-food restaurant, chain
Pr: Neil Borkan

D-U-N-S 09-163-5623
N J PROTOCALL INC
1 Mall Dr Ste 100, Cherry Hill, NJ 08002-2102
Tel (856) 667-9003 *Founded/Ownrshp* 1965
Sales 118.5MM^E *EMP* 7,000
SIC 7363 Temporary help service; Temporary help service
Pr: Janis Le Bude
Pr: Zach Fazio
VP: Roy Fazio
VP: Priscilla Mascuilli
VP: Darlene Melfi
VP: Lois Weidhaas

D-U-N-S 00-230-6231 IMP
N JONAS & CO INC (PA)
4525 Adams Cir, Bensalem, PA 19020-3927
Tel (215) 639-8071 *Founded/Ownrshp* 1948, 1994
Sales 44.4MM^E *EMP* 70
SIC 5169 Swimming pool & spa chemicals; Swimming pool & spa chemicals
Pr: Shelia Wexler
**VP:* Edward Wexler

N K H S
See NORTHEAST KINGDOM HUMAN SERVICES INC

D-U-N-S 02-577-0264
N KOHL GROCER CO
KOHL WHOLESALE
130 Jersey St, Quincy, IL 62301-3831
Tel (217) 222-5000 *Founded/Ownrshp* 1873
Sales 207.8MM^E *EMP* 175
SIC 5141 5113 5046 Groceries, general line; Industrial & personal service paper; Restaurant equipment & supplies; Groceries, general line; Industrial & personal service paper; Restaurant equipment & supplies
Pr: R A Ehrhart
**Treas:* Richard Ehrhart
**VP:* Mark J Ehrhart
Sls Mgr: Kurt Dudenhoeffer

N L C
See NATIONS LENDING CORP

N M H
See NORTHFIELD MOUNT HERMON SCHOOL INC

D-U-N-S 00-815-7430
N MILES JOE & SONS INC
MILES LUMBER
21501 Highway 21 N, Bogalusa, LA 70427
Tel (985) 732-7111 *Founded/Ownrshp* 1971, 1940
Sales 33.7MM^E *EMP* 200
SIC 2421 2426

D-U-N-S 12-818-7221
▲ N MODEL INC
1600 Seaport Blvd Ste 400, Redwood City, CA 94063-5564
Tel (650) 610-4600 *Founded/Ownrshp* 1999
Sales 93.7MM *EMP* 589^E
Accts Pricewaterhousecoopers Llp Sa
Tkr Sym MODN *Exch* NYS
SIC 7371 Computer software development & applications; Computer software development & applications
Ch Bd: Zack Rinat
COO: Kirk Bowman
CFO: Mark Tisdel
Chf Mktg O: Shail Khiyara
Ofcr: Christopher Larsen
Sr VP: Eric Carrasquilla
Sr VP: Michael Laroche
VP: Manish Dalmia
VP: Gary Fine
VP: Vasanta Palakodety
VP: Harman Singh
VP: Alex Wakefield
VP: Steve Zocchi
Assoc Dir: Ashokraj Janarthanan
Assoc Dir: Samuel Kim
Assoc Dir: Nitish Pargal
Assoc Dir: Mahesh Thapa
Board of Directors: David Bonnette, Mark Garrett, Alan Henricks, Mark Leslie, Charles Robel

N O I T U INSURANCE TRUST FUND
See NATIONAL ORGANIZATION OF INDUSTRIAL TRADE UNIONS INSURANCE TRUST FUND

N O V E C
See NORTHERN VIRGINIA ELECTRIC COOPERATIVE

N P C
See NEWSPAPER PRINTING CO

D-U-N-S 00-486-9491
N P DODGE CO (NE)
13321 California St # 300, Omaha, NE 68154-5258
Tel (402) 397-4900 *Founded/Ownrshp* 1921
Sales NA *EMP* 450
SIC 6531 6552 6211 Real estate brokers & agents; Subdividers & developers; Brokers, security; Real estate brokers & agents; Subdividers & developers; Brokers, security
Ch Bd: N P Dodge Jr
**CFO:* N P Dodge III
**Treas:* Leslie A Delperdang
**Ex VP:* Kathleen C Dodge
Sales Asso: Ryan Adle
Sales Asso: Jill Anderson
Sales Asso: Vanessa Arndt
Sales Asso: Linda Ciochon-Lichter
Sales Asso: Greg Eades
Sales Asso: Elizabeth Freshman
Sales Asso: Dana Gill

N P G
See NATIONAL POSTERS INC

N P R
See NATIONAL PUBLIC RADIO INC

N P S
See NATIONAL PACKAGING SPECIALISTS INC

N P S
See NATIONAL PRODUCTS SALES INC

N P S SERVICES
See DAY & ZIMMERMANN NPS INC

D-U-N-S 07-916-2939
N PENN COMPREHENSIVE HEALTH SVCS
101b West Ave, Wellsboro, PA 16901-1358
Tel (570) 723-0500 *Founded/Ownrshp* 1972
Sales 19.9MM *EMP* 465
SIC 8322 8099 Family service agency; Youth self-help agency; Medical services organization; Family service agency; Youth self-help agency; Medical services organization
Ex Dir: Elaine Herstek
**CFO:* Ronald Gilbert

N R H
See NATIONAL REHABILITATION HOSPITAL INC

D-U-N-S 00-384-7894
N R HAMM QUARRY INC (KS)
(*Suby of* HAMM INC) ★
609 Perry Pl, Perry, KS 66073-4201
Tel (785) 597-5111 *Founded/Ownrshp* 1948
Sales 60.9MM^E *EMP* 300
SIC 1422 4953 Crushed & broken limestone; Sanitary landfill operation; Crushed & broken limestone; Sanitary landfill operation
Pr: Rodney Hamm
**CFO:* C Scott Anderson
**Sec:* Delores Meyers
**VP:* Bradley T Hamm
Off Mgr: Dee Myers
IT Man: Ramon Gonzalez
Sfty Mgr: Kent Miller

N R I
See NATIONAL REFRIGERANTS INC

N R M
See NEVADA RAILROAD MATERIALS INC

N R S
See NATIONAL RETIREMENT SERVICES INC

N R S
See NATIONAL RETAIL SYSTEMS INC

N S I
See NOTABLE SOLUTIONS INC

D-U-N-S 06-380-2151 IMP
N S INTERNATIONAL LTD
(*Suby of* NIPPON SEIKI CO.,LTD.)
600 Wilshire Dr, Troy, MI 48084-1625
Tel (248) 362-8570 *Founded/Ownrshp* 1977
Sales 83.9MM^E *EMP* 174^E
SIC 5013 Automotive supplies & parts; Motorcycle parts; Automotive supplies & parts; Motorcycle parts
CEO: Teruyuki Matsui
Prgrm Mgr: John Ogger
Prgrm Mgr: Yuka Pearl
Prgrm Mgr: Stacy Schaeffler
Snr Sftwr: Balaji RAO
IT Man: John Gauthier
Opers Mgr: Therissa Allen

N S M G
See NORTHSTAR MEMORIAL GROUP LLC

N S S INDUSTRIES
See NSS TECHNOLOGIES INC

N S U
See NICHOLLS STATE UNIVERSITY

N T
See NT WINDOW INC

N T B
See NATIONWIDE TRUCK BROKERS INC

N T C
See NEBRASKA TRANSPORT CO INC

N T C
See NTC AMERICA CORP

N T G
See NOLAN TRANSPORTATION GROUP INC

N T H P
See NATIONAL TRUST FOR HISTORIC PRESERVATION IN UNITED STATES

N T M
See NEWTECH MACHINERY CORP

D-U-N-S 04-662-6727 IMP
N T RUDDOCK CO (OH)
26123 Broadway Ave, Cleveland, OH 44146-6512
Tel (440) 439-4976 *Founded/Ownrshp* 1952, 1967
Sales 26.8MM^E *EMP* 17
SIC 5085 5051 Abrasives; Ferrous metals
Ch Bd: Neil T Ruddock
**Pr:* Kevin Ruddock
**VP:* Jim Ruddock

N T S
See NETWORK TELEPHONE SERVICES INC

N T S
See NETWORKING TECHNOLOGIES AND SUPPORT INC

N T T
See NTT USA INC

N V B
See NORTH VALLEY BANK

D-U-N-S 55-620-0095
N V CAST STONE LLC
NAPA VALLEY CAST STONE
1111 Green Island Rd, Vallejo, CA 94503-9639
Tel (707) 261-6615 *Founded/Ownrshp* 1991
Sales 32.9MM^E *EMP* 100
SIC 3272 3281 Concrete products, precast; Cut stone & stone products; Concrete products, precast; Cut stone & stone products
CFO: Jody Hansen

N V E PHARMACEUTICALS
See V E N INC

D-U-N-S 96-817-0089
N V NIELSEN
85 Broad St, New York, NY 10004-2434
Tel (646) 654-5000 *Founded/Ownrshp* 1923
Sales 6.2MMM *EMP* 42,000^E
SIC 7389 Process serving service; Process serving service
CEO: Mitch Barns
**Ch Bd:* David L Calhoun
COO: Brian J West
CFO: Jamere Jackson
Ofcr: Mary Elizabeth Finn
Ex VP: Karen Kornbluh
Sr VP: Jeffrey R Charlton
Sls Mgr: Carol Nassif

N W BUYERS
See N W BUYERS & JOBBERS INC

D-U-N-S 02-292-3981
N W BUYERS & JOBBERS INC
N W BUYERS
3525 Plymouth Blvd # 108, Minneapolis, MN 55447-1395
Tel (763) 450-2000 *Founded/Ownrshp* 1920
Sales 29.9MM *EMP* 4
SIC 7389 Purchasing service; Purchasing service
Ex Dir: Brian Schuette
**Pr:* Brian Kaufman
**Pr:* Allan Kurtzman

D-U-N-S 04-826-0418 IMP
N W ELECTRIC POWER COOPERATIVE INC
1001 W Grand Ave, Cameron, MO 64429-1116
Tel (816) 632-2121 *Founded/Ownrshp* 1949
Sales 99.2MM *EMP* 60
SIC 4911 Transmission, electric power; Transmission, electric power
Genl Mgr: Donald R McQuitty
Genl Mgr: R McQuitty
IT Man: Kent Brown
IT Man: Jennifer Hill

D-U-N-S 80-204-5930
N W HOLDING CO
NU-WAY
620 Doddridge St Ste C, Saint Louis, MO 63147-2355
Tel (314) 383-6100 *Founded/Ownrshp* 1991
Sales 52.6MM^E *EMP* 85
SIC 5172 7513 7538 Petroleum products; Truck rental & leasing, no drivers; Truck engine repair, except industrial; Petroleum products; Truck rental & leasing, no drivers; Truck engine repair, except industrial

Pr: Marion Costello
**Sec:* Donald Costello

N W R
See NORTHWEST RESEARCH INC

N W U
See NEBRASKA WESLEYAN UNIVERSITY INC

D-U-N-S 00-428-9864 EXP
N WASSERSTROM & SONS INC (OH)
WASSERSTROM MARKETING DIVISION
(*Suby of* NATIONAL SMALLWARES) ★
2300 Lockbourne Rd, Columbus, OH 43207-6111
Tel (614) 737-8543 *Founded/Ownrshp* 1933
Sales 103.8MM^E *EMP* 460
SIC 3556 5046 3444 Food products machinery; Restaurant equipment & supplies; Sheet metalwork; Food products machinery; Restaurant equipment & supplies; Sheet metalwork
Pr: William Wasserstrom
Sr VP: John H Mc Cormick
VP: Craig Dietz
Mktg Dir: Adam Caltrider
Sls Dir: Eric Wasserstrom
Board of Directors: Leonard Wasserstrom, Stanley Wasserstrom

NY B
See NEW YORK BLOWER CO

D-U-N-S 78-321-2772
■ **NY MCG INC**
MERIDIAN
(*Suby of* SANTANDER HOLDINGS USA INC) ★
1 Battery Park Plz Fl 26, New York, NY 10004-1432
Tel (212) 972-3600 *Founded/Ownrshp* 1991
Sales NA *EMP* 124
SIC 6163 Mortgage brokers arranging for loans, using money of others
Pr: J Jay Lobell
Ex VP: Terry Baydala
VP: Alan Blank
VP: Jonathan Bodner
VP: Robert Corso
VP: Michael Diaz
VP: Catherine EBY
VP: Eliezer Finkel
VP: Jacob Fischer
VP: Alan Friedman
VP: Ben Friedman
VP: Jason Goldstein
VP: Judah Hammer
**VP:* Tara Heal
VP: Luke Hingson
VP: Keith Kurland
**VP:* Marcia Larson
VP: Joseph Lazar
VP: Benjamin Lukasiewicz
VP: Joseph Melohn
**VP:* Gaffar Mohamed

D-U-N-S 87-795-0295
NY STEAMSTER HEALTH PENSION & RETIREMENT FUND
151 Northern Concourse, Syracuse, NY 13212-4065
Tel (315) 455-9790 *Founded/Ownrshp* 1994
Sales 192.8MM *EMP* 3
SIC 8631 Labor unions & similar labor organizations; Labor unions & similar labor organizations

NY U
See NEW YORK UNIVERSITY

D-U-N-S 04-210-7854
N&M COOLING AND HEATING INC
COOL TODAY
6143 Clark Center Ave, Sarasota, FL 34238-2723
Tel (941) 921-5581 *Founded/Ownrshp* 2004
Sales 22.2MM^E *EMP* 105
SIC 1711 1731 Plumbing contractors; General electrical contractor
Pr: Jaime V Didomenico
Div Mgr: Charles Blum

D-U-N-S 01-129-2294
N-LINK CORP
550 Nw Franklin Ave, Bend, OR 97703-2892
Tel (541) 617-0011 *Founded/Ownrshp* 1995
Sales 21.0MM^E *EMP* 80
SIC 7373 Systems software development services; Computer systems analysis & design; Systems engineering, computer related; Systems software development services; Computer systems analysis & design; Systems engineering, computer related
CEO: Sandra Green
Ofcr: John Anderson
VP: Vic Cordell
Netwrk Eng: Dustin Abey

D-U-N-S 10-663-9193 IMP
N-M VENTURES LLC
NINE GROUP
4321 W Flamingo Rd, Las Vegas, NV 89103-3903
Tel (702) 938-9999 *Founded/Ownrshp* 1999
Sales 13.1MM^E *EMP* 350
SIC 7999 7929 5813 Swimming pool, non-membership; Entertainment service; Night clubs; Swimming pool, non-membership; Entertainment service; Night clubs
Genl Mgr: Sean Crowley
Sls Mgr: Annales Cable
Sls Mgr: Rocco Gonzalez

N/A
See UTAH DEPARTMENT OF PUBLIC SAFETY

D-U-N-S 96-351-0578
N2GRATE GOVERNMENT TECHNOLOGY SOLUTIONS LLC
9111 Edmonston Rd Ste 303, Greenbelt, MD 20770-1552
Tel (855) 508-2476 *Founded/Ownrshp* 2010
Sales 28.0MM^E *EMP* 12
SIC 7379 Computer related consulting services

N9305-192
See WELLS FARGO FOUNDATION MINNESOTA

D-U-N-S 79-882-5886
NA ACQUISITION CO
3400 Northern Cross Blvd, Fort Worth, TX 76137-3600
Tel (817) 231-1300 *Founded/Ownrshp* 1999
Sales 31.7MM^E *EMP* 130
SIC 3841 5047 Surgical & medical instruments; Medical & hospital equipment
Pr: Kevin W Kile

D-U-N-S 00-881-1960
NA DEGERSTROM INC (WA)
3303 N Sullivan Rd, Spokane Valley, WA 99216-1676
Tel (509) 928-3333 *Founded/Ownrshp* 1904, 1949
Sales 124.7MM *EMP* 230
Accts Anatasi Moore & Martin Spoka
SIC 1041 1475 1622 Open pit gold mining; Phosphate rock; Bridge, tunnel & elevated highway; Open pit gold mining; Phosphate rock; Bridge, tunnel & elevated highway
Pr: Christopher Myers
**Sec:* Michael Cannon
**VP:* Mike Coleman
**VP:* Joan B Degerstrom
**VP:* Chris Myers
**VP:* Richard Stager
Div Mgr: Lee Bernardi
IT Man: Michele Munson
Sfty Dirs: Phillip Saderup
Mtls Mgr: Jeremy Morago

D-U-N-S 00-923-0863 IMP
NA HOKU INC
3049 Ualena St Fl 12, Honolulu, HI 96819-1954
Tel (808) 833-7772 *Founded/Ownrshp* 1924
Sales 65.4MM^E *EMP* 491
SIC 5944 Jewelry, precious stones & precious metals; Jewelry, precious stones & precious metals
Pr: Scherer Roschelle
**CEO:* Edward D Sultan III
**COO:* Steven Bookatz
Store Mgr: Julia Macdonald
Store Mgr: Magie Palalay
Dir IT: Matt Dickson
Software D: David Gallatin
VP Sls: Paul Sato

D-U-N-S 60-295-9587 IMP/EXP
NA INDUSTRIES INC
(*Suby of* NIPPON SHOKUBAI CO., LTD.)
2651 Riverport Rd, Chattanooga, TN 37406-1723
Tel (423) 624-6496 *Founded/Ownrshp* 1997
Sales 41.2MM^E *EMP* 167
SIC 2891 Adhesives & sealants; Adhesives & sealants
Pr: Yuji Noma
Treas: A Hamilton
**Treas:* Shinichi Ota

NA MUREX
See MUREX LLC

NAACP
See NATIONAL ASSOCIATION FOR ADVANCEMENT OF COLORED PEOPLE

NAAG
See NATIONAL ASSOCIATION OF ATTORNEYS GENERAL

D-U-N-S 95-969-2984 IMP
NAARTJIE CUSTOM KIDS INC
3676 W Ca Ave Ste D100, Salt Lake City, UT 84104-6516
Tel (801) 973-7988 *Founded/Ownrshp* 2001
Sales 79.1MM^E *EMP* 912^E
SIC 5641 Children's & infants' wear stores
Pr: Glenn Wood

D-U-N-S 00-279-5763
NAB CONSTRUCTION CORP (NY)
11401 14th Ave, College Point, NY 11356-1411
Tel (718) 762-0001 *Founded/Ownrshp* 1954
Sales 47.7MM^E *EMP* 400
SIC 1541 1611 3441 1791 Industrial buildings & warehouses; Highway & street construction; Fabricated structural metal; Structural steel erection; Industrial buildings & warehouses; Highway & street construction; Fabricated structural metal; Structural steel erection
Ch Bd: Edward Simpson
**Pr:* Gary Simpson
**V Ch Bd:* Harvey Simpson
Ex Dir: Michael Lembo
MIS Dir: Bhaskar Anant
Dir IT: Joseph Acosta

D-U-N-S 04-726-1979 IMP
NABCO ENTRANCES INC
(*Suby of* NABTESCO CORPORATION)
S82w18717 Gemini Dr, Muskego, WI 53150-9222
Tel (262) 679-7532 *Founded/Ownrshp* 1992
Sales 49.4MM^E *EMP* 100
SIC 3699 3442 Door opening & closing devices, electrical; Window & door frames; Door opening & closing devices, electrical; Window & door frames
Pr: Philip Stuckey
**VP:* Taka Tanaka
S&M/VP: Larry Grassmann
Manager: Neal Stob
Sls Mgr: Oskar Garza
Sls Mgr: Chuck Linehan

D-U-N-S 09-667-8115
NABCO MECHANICAL & ELECTRICAL INC (AR)
NABCO SERVICE CO
1750 S Amity Rd, Conway, AR 72032-9097
Tel (501) 753-5777 *Founded/Ownrshp* 1961
Sales 22.3MM^E *EMP* 125
Accts Engelkes & Felts Ltd Conway
SIC 1711 1731 Heating & air conditioning contractors; Mechanical contractor; General electrical contractor; Heating & air conditioning contractors; Mechanical contractor; General electrical contractor
Ch Bd: Robert Unwer
**VP:* Alan Hacke
**VP:* Steve Watts

NABCO SERVICE CO
See NABCO MECHANICAL & ELECTRICAL INC

D-U-N-S 00-635-9277
NABHOLZ CONSTRUCTION CORP (AR)
NABHOLZ CONSTRUCTION-OZARK DIV
612 Garland St, Conway, AR 72032-4418
Tel (501) 505-5800 *Founded/Ownrshp* 1949
Sales 421.4MM^E *EMP* 900
SIC 1541

NABHOLZ CONSTRUCTION-OZARK DIV
See NABHOLZ CONSTRUCTION CORP

NABHOLZ CRANES & RIGGINGS
See NABHOLZ INC

D-U-N-S 09-341-4555
NABHOLZ INC (AR)
NABHOLZ CRANES & RIGGINGS
612 Garland St, Conway, AR 72032-4418
Tel (501) 327-7781 *Founded/Ownrshp* 1951
Sales 109.0MM^E *EMP* 410
SIC 5084 7359

D-U-N-S 07-888-8322
NABI BUS LLC
(*Suby of* NEW FLYER INDUSTRIES INC)
106 National Dr, Anniston, AL 36207-8339
Tel (888) 452-7871 *Founded/Ownrshp* 2013
Sales 195.7MM^E *EMP* 633
SIC 3711 5012 Buses, all types, assembly of; Automobiles & other motor vehicles; Buses, all types, assembly of; Automobiles & other motor vehicles
Prin: Jim Marcotuli
Sr VP: Bill Doig
Sr VP: David Warren
Ql Cn Mgr: Steve Giordano
Ql Cn Mgr: Mack Johnson
Mktg Mgr: Ruth Richeson
Sls Mgr: Karen Dhanie

D-U-N-S 07-911-3348
NABI PARTS LLC
(*Suby of* NEW FLYER INDUSTRIES INC)
2338 Us Highway 42 S, Delaware, OH 43015-9502
Tel (888) 333-6224 *Founded/Ownrshp* 2013
Sales 171.8MM^E *EMP* 1,059^E
SIC 5013 Motor vehicle supplies & new parts; Automotive brakes
Pr: Jim Marcotuli

D-U-N-S 04-569-6499
■ **NABORS ALASKA DRILLING INC**
(*Suby of* NABORS INDUSTRIES INC) ★
2525 C St Ste 200, Anchorage, AK 99503-2632
Tel (907) 263-6000 *Founded/Ownrshp* 1980
Sales 270.2MM^E *EMP* 800^E
SIC 1381 Drilling oil & gas wells; Drilling oil & gas wells
Pr: Anthony G Petrello
**Pr:* Jerry C Shanklin
**Treas:* Jenia Jarrett
**VP:* Ben Kent
**Genl Mgr:* David Hebert
Genl Mgr: Dave Herbert
CIO: SRI Vallaru
Dir IT: Dan Hamcher
Dir IT: Dan Hammocker
Sfty Mgr: John Haynes
Opers Mgr: Norm Haynes

D-U-N-S 79-695-6019
■ **NABORS CORPORATE SERVICES INC**
(*Suby of* NABORS INDUSTRIES INC) ★
515 W Greens Rd Ste 1100, Houston, TX 77067-4511
Tel (281) 874-0035 *Founded/Ownrshp* 1991
Sales 57.6MM^E *EMP* 200
SIC 1389 1381 Servicing oil & gas wells; Drilling oil & gas wells; Servicing oil & gas wells; Drilling oil & gas wells
Pr: Anthony G Petrello
COO: Larry Heidt
**CFO:* William Restrepo
**Ex VP:* Jerry Long
Sr VP: Mark Bedford
Sr VP: Padira Reddy
Sr VP: Ronnie Witherspoon
VP: Derryl Cleaveland
VP: Derryl Cleveland
VP: Gil Gayaut
VP: Mark Horner
VP: Bruce McConnell
VP: Dave Werner

NABORS DRILLING INTERNATIONAL
See NABORS INTERNATIONAL INC

D-U-N-S 00-790-7603 IMP/EXP
■ **NABORS DRILLING USA LP**
(*Suby of* NABORS INDUSTRIES INC) ★
515 W Greens Rd Ste 1200, Houston, TX 77067-4536
Tel (281) 874-0035 *Founded/Ownrshp* 1911, 1990
Sales 1.8MMM^E *EMP* 1,637
SIC 1381 Directional drilling oil & gas wells; Directional drilling oil & gas wells
Pt: Joe Hudson
Pr: Larry Heidt
Sr VP: Joey Husband
VP: Randy Clark
VP: Clyde Hebert
VP: Saj Shapiro
Area Mgr: Larry Jaramillo
Dir IT: Joe Zmarzly
IT Man: Michelle Brown
Sfty Dirs: David Darling
Sfty Dirs: Jim Rich
Board of Directors: James H Denney

D-U-N-S 07-887-4351 IMP
■ **NABORS INDUSTRIES INC**
(*Suby of* NABORS INDUSTRIES LTD.)
515 W Greens Rd Ste 1200, Houston, TX 77067-4599
Tel (281) 874-0035 *Founded/Ownrshp* 1987
Sales 7.0MMM^E *EMP* 16,847
SIC 1381 1389 Drilling oil & gas wells; Servicing oil & gas wells; Drilling oil & gas wells; Servicing oil & gas wells
CEO: Eugene M Isenberg
**Ch Bd:* Anthony G Petrello
CFO: Bruce P Koch
CFO: William Restrepo
CFO: Kevin White
Sr VP: Dan Arnold
Sr VP: Ronnie Witherspoon
VP: G Arms
**VP:* Jose S Cadena
**VP:* Laura W Doerre
VP: Kim Unerfusser
Assoc Dir: William Conroy

D-U-N-S 00-691-5748 IMP/EXP
■ **NABORS INTERNATIONAL INC** (DE)
NABORS DRILLING INTERNATIONAL
(*Suby of* NABORS INDUSTRIES INC) ★
515 W Greens Rd Ste 600, Houston, TX 77067-4510
Tel (281) 874-0035 *Founded/Ownrshp* 1947
Sales 2.4MMM^E *EMP* 1,689
SIC 1381 7353 Drilling oil & gas wells; Oil well drilling equipment, rental or leasing; Drilling oil & gas wells; Oil well drilling equipment, rental or leasing
CEO: Anthony G Petrello
**CFO:* William Restrepo
**VP:* Jose Cadena
**VP:* Derryl W Cleaveland
**VP:* Christopher Papouras
**VP:* Bob Supopin
VP: Richard Ward
Opers Mgr: Kerry Kunz

D-U-N-S 96-988-0012 IMP
■ **NABORS OFFSHORE CORP**
(*Suby of* NABORS INDUSTRIES INC) ★
515 W Greens Rd Ste 1200, Houston, TX 77067-4536
Tel (281) 874-0406 *Founded/Ownrshp* 1996
Sales 311.7MM^E *EMP* 700
SIC 1381 1389 Reworking oil & gas wells; Directional drilling oil & gas wells; Servicing oil & gas wells; Oil field services; Reworking oil & gas wells; Directional drilling oil & gas wells; Servicing oil & gas wells; Oil field services
Pr: Jerry C Shanklin
Sr VP: Subodh Saxena
**VP:* Ronnie L Gaspard
**VP:* Daniel McLachlin
**VP:* Lonnie Mills
**VP:* Earney White
Sls Mgr: Beau Davis
Board of Directors: Jose Cadena, Anthony G Petrello

NABORS OIL TOOLS
See NABORS WELL SERVICES CO

D-U-N-S 00-571-7228 IMP
■ **NABORS WELL SERVICES CO**
NABORS OIL TOOLS
(*Suby of* NABORS INDUSTRIES INC) ★
515 W Greens Rd Ste 1000, Houston, TX 77067-4536
Tel (281) 874-0035 *Founded/Ownrshp* 1999
Sales 1.7MMM^E *EMP* 4,740
SIC 1389 Oil field services; Oil field services
Ch: Eugene M Isenberg
Pr: Johnson Jeff
**CEO:* Anthony G Petrello
**CFO:* William Restrepo
VP: Jim Denney
VP: Frank Labrenz
VP: Ron Morrison
Area Mgr: Ronnie Munoz
Area Mgr: Albino Reyes
Dir IT: Jill Gregory
Mtls Mgr: Russell Pickrel

D-U-N-S 18-273-0440
■ **NABORS WELL SERVICES LTD**
(*Suby of* NABORS OIL TOOLS) ★
515 W Greens Rd Ste 1200, Houston, TX 77067-4536
Tel (281) 874-0035 *Founded/Ownrshp* 1987
Sales 540.5MM^E *EMP* 1,668
SIC 1389 7353 Servicing oil & gas wells; Oil equipment rental services; Servicing oil & gas wells; Oil equipment rental services
Ch Bd: Anthony G Petrello
Pr: Nicholas Petronio

NABP
See NATIONAL ASSOCIATION OF BOARDS OF PHARMACY

NABRICO
See TRINITY MARINE PRODUCTS INC

D-U-N-S 01-020-3842 IMP
NABTESCO AEROSPACE INC (WA)
(*Suby of* NABTESCO CORPORATION)
12413 Willows Rd Ne, Kirkland, WA 98034-8766
Tel (425) 602-8400 *Founded/Ownrshp* 1976, 2003
Sales 90.0MM *EMP* 48
SIC 3728 3812 3593 Aircraft parts & equipment; Search & navigation equipment; Fluid power cylinders & actuators; Aircraft parts & equipment; Search & navigation equipment; Fluid power cylinders & actuators
Pr: Isao Ohashi
QA Dir: Tim Kent

D-U-N-S 94-950-6646 IMP/EXP
NAC GROUP INC
NAC-DIVISION
10001 16th St N, Saint Petersburg, FL 33716-4228
Tel (727) 576-0550 *Founded/Ownrshp* 1997
Sales 42.7MM^E *EMP* 51
SIC 5065 Electronic parts & equipment; Electronic parts & equipment
Pr: Jonathan Stanton
**Ex VP:* John Connolly
**VP:* Joseph Sanders
Off Mgr: Peggy Mitchell

D-U-N-S 00-907-7371
NAC INC
4770 S 5600 W, West Valley City, UT 84118-7400
Tel (801) 204-6500 *Founded/Ownrshp* 1952
Sales 74.7MM^E *EMP* 385

SIC 2759 7313 5963 7322 2711 Newspapers: printing; Newspaper advertising representative; Newspapers, home delivery, not by printers or publishers; Collection agency, except real estate; Newspapers; Newspapers: printing; Newspaper advertising representative; Newspapers, home delivery, not by printers or publishers; Collection agency, except real estate; Newspapers
Ch Bd: Brent J Low
Pr: Dan Hartman
**Treas:* James E Shelledy
Sr VP: Harry Whipple
**VP:* Judd Alvord
VP: Steve Mugleston
VP: Tony Traven
Exec: Eric Salway
Dist Mgr: Suzie Curran
Genl Mgr: Bob Burns
IT Man: Kim Mugleston

D-U-N-S 78-945-1692
NAC MARKETING CO LLC
NEW VITALITY
95 Executive Dr Ste 14, Edgewood, NY 11717-8326
Tel (631) 777-7767 *Founded/Ownrshp* 2010
Sales 20.0MM^E *EMP* 110
SIC 7331 5499 Addressing service; Vitamin food stores
CEO: John Greenhut
**Pr:* Jonathan Flicker
**CFO:* Bill Sarr
Ex VP: Luc Vannhal
VP: David Goldberg
Creative D: Ralph Suarez
CIO: Thierry Dessertenne
VP Mktg: Jennifer Haus
Sls Mgr: Rafia Ali
Sls Mgr: Steven Foley
Sls Mgr: Kevin McClure

NAC MECHANICAL & ELEC SVCS
See NORTHERN AIR CORP

NAC-DIVISION
See NAC GROUP INC

D-U-N-S 03-233-0909 IMP/EXP
NACA HOLDINGS INC
DIRECT CONTAINER LINE
5000 Arprt Plz Dr Ste 100, Long Beach, CA 90815
Tel (650) 872-0800 *Founded/Ownrshp* 2000
Sales 232.2MM^E *EMP* 685
SIC 4731 Freight consolidation; Freight consolidation
CEO: Charles Brennan
**CFO:* J Thurso Barendse
**VP:* Therese Groff

D-U-N-S 07-912-9011
NACARATO TRUCKS INC
NACARATO VOLVO & GMC TRUCKS
519 New Paul Rd, La Vergne, TN 37086-4958
Tel (615) 259-9500 *Founded/Ownrshp* 1976
Sales 73.3MM^E *EMP* 132^E
SIC 5511 5012 Automobiles, new & used; Trucks, commercial; Automobiles, new & used; Trucks, commercial
Pr: Michael J Nacarato Jr
VP: Dennis Boswinkle
**VP:* Bob Nacarato

NACARATO VOLVO & GMC TRUCKS
See NACARATO TRUCKS INC

D-U-N-S 14-720-4127 IMP/EXP
▲ NACCO INDUSTRIES INC
5875 Landerbrook Dr # 300, Cleveland, OH 44124-4069
Tel (440) 229-5151 *Founded/Ownrshp* 1913
Sales 896.7MM *EMP* 1,900
Tkr Sym NC *Exch* NYS
SIC 3634 1221 5719 3631 Electric household cooking appliances; Toasters, electric: household; Irons, electric: household; Coffee makers, electric: household; Surface mining, lignite; Kitchenware; Cookware, except aluminum; Household cooking equipment; Microwave ovens, including portable: household; Electric household cooking appliances; Toasters, electric: household; Irons, electric: household; Coffee makers, electric: household; Surface mining, lignite; Kitchenware; Cookware, except aluminum; Household cooking equipment; Microwave ovens, including portable: household
Ch Bd: Alfred M Rankin Jr
CFO: Elizabeth I Loveman
Treas: J C Butler Jr
Ex VP: Frederick Kuester
Ex VP: Donald L Perlyn
Sr VP: Gregory E Salyers
VP: Robert L Benson
VP: Jennifer M Langer
VP: John D Neumann
VP: Kristine Rappac
Dir IT: Ted Gilchrist
Board of Directors: Scott S Cowen, John P Jumper, Dennis W Labarre, Richard De J Osborne, James A Ratner, Britton T Taplin, David F Taplin, David B H Williams

D-U-N-S 00-902-1429 IMP/EXP
■ NACCO MATERIALS HANDLING GROUP INC
HYSTER
(*Suby of* HYSTER-YALE MATERIALS HANDLING INC)
4000 Ne Blue Lake Rd, Fairview, OR 97024-8710
Tel (503) 721-6000 *Founded/Ownrshp* 2012
Sales 1.3MMM^E *EMP* 5,100
SIC 3537 Lift trucks, industrial: fork, platform, straddle, etc.; Trucks, tractors, loaders, carriers & similar equipment; Lift trucks, industrial: fork, platform, straddle, etc.; Trucks, tractors, loaders, carriers & similar equipment
Pr: Michael P Brogan
COO: Colin Wilson
Treas: G Decker
Sr VP: Lauren E Miller
VP: Glen Baunsgard
VP: I Bergen
VP: Darrell Cross
VP: Frank Muller
VP: Victoria L Rickey
Mng Dir: Yoshinori Ohno
CIO: John Bartho

NACCRRA
See NATIONAL ASSOCIATION OF CHILD CARE RESOURCE AND REFERRAL AGENCIES

NACDS
See NATIONAL ASSOCIATION OF CHAIN DRUG STORES INC

D-U-N-S 07-418-9820
NACE INTERNATIONAL
15835 Park Ten Pl, Houston, TX 77084-5145
Tel (281) 228-6200 *Founded/Ownrshp* 1945
Sales 37.2MM *EMP* 112
SIC 8621 2721 8748

D-U-N-S 00-167-2096 IMP
NACHI AMERICA INC
(*Suby of* NACHI-FUJIKOSHI CORP.)
715 Pushville Rd, Greenwood, IN 46143-9782
Tel (317) 535-5527 *Founded/Ownrshp* 1962
Sales 59.2MM^E *EMP* 97^E
SIC 5084 Industrial machinery & equipment; Industrial machinery & equipment
Pr: Tony Inoue
**Pr:* Noel Segawa
**Treas:* Sue Deaton
Treas: Roy Takie
Ex VP: Francis Wisner
VP: Iwao Kodera
VP: Masafumi Minami
Rgnl Mgr: Don Kosal
Dist Mgr: Bill Busbee
Genl Mgr: Nobu Tsurumaki
IT Man: Kumiko Martin

D-U-N-S 19-727-2263 IMP
NACHI ROBOTIC SYSTEMS INC
(*Suby of* NACHI AMERICA INC) ★
42775 W 9 Mile Rd, Novi, MI 48375-4113
Tel (248) 305-6545 *Founded/Ownrshp* 1992
Sales 32.0MM^E *EMP* 62
SIC 5084 Robots, industrial; Robots, industrial
CEO: Toru Inoue
**Pr:* Michael J Bomya
**Treas:* Masanobu Tsuruga
QC Dir: Weylan Stricklin
Mktg Dir: Kerry Ferrazza
Sales Asso: Christopher Lorente
Snr PM: Charles Hemlock
Board of Directors: Michael J Bomya

D-U-N-S 60-603-3025 IMP/EXP
NACHI TECHNOLOGY INC
(*Suby of* NACHI AMERICA INC) ★
713 Pushville Rd, Greenwood, IN 46143-9782
Tel (317) 535-5000 *Founded/Ownrshp* 1974
Sales 21.8MM^E *EMP* 66
SIC 3714 Bearings, motor vehicle
Pr: Eiichi Nishio
Rgnl Mgr: Geoffery Hong
Rgnl Mgr: Don Ritter
Dir IT: Jeff Maczuga
IT Man: Phil Caves
Sfty Mgr: Joe Schmidt

D-U-N-S 06-694-1808
NACHON ENTERPRISES INC
NACHON LUMBER
2477 W 4th Ave 350w, Hialeah, FL 33010-1422
Tel (305) 888-5236 *Founded/Ownrshp* 1975
Sales 23.6MM^E *EMP* 115^E
SIC 5251 5031 5211 5072 Hardware; Lumber, plywood & millwork; Lumber & other building materials; Hardware
Pr: Carlos J Nachon
**Sec:* Fabiola Nachon
**VP:* Adela B Nachon

NACHON LUMBER
See NACHON ENTERPRISES INC

NACHRI
See NATIONAL ASSOCIATION OF CHILDRENS HOSPITALS AND RELATED INSTITUTIONS INC

D-U-N-S 04-901-3811 IMP/EXP
NACHURS ALPINE SOLUTIONS CORP
(*Suby of* TRANS-RESOURCES INC) ★
421 Leader St, Marion, OH 43302-2225
Tel (740) 382-5701 *Founded/Ownrshp* 1998
Sales 35.9MM^E *EMP* 100
SIC 2875 2869 2819 Fertilizers, mixing only; Industrial organic chemicals; Industrial inorganic chemicals; Fertilizers, mixing only; Industrial organic chemicals; Industrial inorganic chemicals
CEO: Jeffrey Barnes
VP: Bob Hopp
**VP:* Robert Hopp
**VP:* Reiny Packull
**VP:* David Rose
VP: Murray Vanzeggelaar
MIS Dir: Joseph C Du Polo
IT Man: Frank Shelby
VP Opers: Mac Duncan
Sls Mgr: Brad King

NACKARD BEVERAGE
See NACKARD FRED WHOLESALE LIQUOR CO

D-U-N-S 03-586-0626 IMP
NACKARD FRED WHOLESALE LIQUOR CO
NACKARD BEVERAGE
5660 E Penstock Ave, Flagstaff, AZ 86004-2914
Tel (928) 522-2103 *Founded/Ownrshp* 1934
Sales 32.8MM^E *EMP* 105
SIC 5182 5181 Liquor; Wine; Beer & other fermented malt liquors
Pr: Patrick M Nackard
**VP:* P Jewel Nackard

NAC.NET
See NET ACCESS LLC

NACO
See NATIONAL ASSOCIATION OF COUNTIES

NACOG
See NORTHERN ARIZONA COUNCIL OF GOVERNMENTS

NACOGDOCHES CNTY LAW ENFRCEMENT
See COUNTY OF NACOGDOCHES

D-U-N-S 10-382-6558
NACOGDOCHES COMMERCIAL BANCSHARES INC
COMMERCIAL BANK OF TEXAS
215 E Main St, Nacogdoches, TX 75961-5257
Tel (936) 569-8251 *Founded/Ownrshp* 1983
Sales NA *EMP* 175
SIC 6021 National commercial banks; National commercial banks
CEO: Thomas Ellison
**Treas:* Matt Jacoby
**VP:* David Shofner
Mktg Dir: April Salagaj

D-U-N-S 07-420-4470
NACOGDOCHES COUNTY HOSPITAL DISTRICT
NACOGDOCHES MEMORIAL HOSPITAL
1204 N Mound St, Nacogdoches, TX 75961-4027
Tel (936) 564-4611 *Founded/Ownrshp* 1968
Sales 0.7 *EMP* 750
Accts Bkd Llp Houston Tx
SIC 8062 8093 8011 General medical & surgical hospitals; Rehabilitation center, outpatient treatment; Occupational & industrial specialist, physician/surgeon; General medical & surgical hospitals; Rehabilitation center, outpatient treatment; Occupational & industrial specialist, physician/surgeon
CEO: Tim Hayward
COO: Scott Christopher
CFO: Ann Bridges
**CFO:* Jane Ann Bridges
Exec: Lisa King
Dir Inf Cn: Jessica Rodgers
Dir Lab: Russell Maness
Dir Lab: Julie Wright
Dir Rad: Carl Davis
Dir QC: Chris Ryan
IT Man: Daniel Whatley

D-U-N-S 09-602-8659
NACOGDOCHES INDEPENDENT SCHOOL DISTRICT
420 S Shawnee St, Nacogdoches, TX 75961-5696
Tel (936) 569-5000 *Founded/Ownrshp* 1850
Sales 66.3MM *EMP* 927
Accts Axley & Rode Llp Lufkin Tex
SIC 8211 Public elementary & secondary schools; Public elementary school; Public junior high school; Public senior high school; Public elementary & secondary schools; Public elementary school; Public junior high school; Public senior high school
Off Mgr: Wanda Yates
Schl Brd P: Tom Davis
Teacher Pr: Michael Martin
Genl Couns: Coby Wilbanks

D-U-N-S 80-081-1499
■ NACOGDOCHES MEDICAL CENTER
TENT HEALTH
(*Suby of* TENET HEALTHSYSTEM HOSPITALS INC) ★
4920 Ne Stallings Dr, Nacogdoches, TX 75965-1254
Tel (936) 569-9481 *Founded/Ownrshp* 1987
Sales 57.6MM^E *EMP* 400
SIC 8062 General medical & surgical hospitals; General medical & surgical hospitals
CEO: Gary L Stokes
**COO:* Clay Farell
**CFO:* Frank Malek
**Ch:* Francis Spruiell
VP: Randy Prentice
Dir OR: Joan Hill
**Prin:* Shannon Smith
Dir IT: Kathy Welch
Surgeon: Brandon Jones
Doctor: Gerard Ventura
Snr Mgr: Ed Price

NACOGDOCHES MEMORIAL HOSPITAL
See NACOGDOCHES COUNTY HOSPITAL DISTRICT

NACR
See NORTH AMERICAN COMMUNICATIONS RESOURCE INC

NACS
See NATIONAL ASSOCIATION OF CONVENIENCE STORES

NADA
See NATIONAL AUTOMOBILE DEALERS ASSOCIATION

NADA'S USED CAR GUIDE
See JD POWER AND ASSOCIATES

NADEL & GUSSMAN ANADARKO
See NADEL AND GUSSMAN LLC

D-U-N-S 00-790-7744
NADEL AND GUSSMAN LLC
NADEL & GUSSMAN ANADARKO
15 E 5th St Ste 3200, Tulsa, OK 74103-4313
Tel (918) 583-3333 *Founded/Ownrshp* 2000
Sales 233.8MM^E *EMP* 110
SIC 1311 Crude petroleum production; Natural gas production; Crude petroleum production; Natural gas production
Pr: James F Adelson
CFO: Wayne Hamilton
Genl Mgr: Stephen Heyman
IT Man: Steve Short

D-U-N-S 00-297-8534 IMP
NADEX OF AMERICA CORP
W T C
24775 Crestview Ct, Farmington Hills, MI 48335-1507
Tel (248) 477-3900 *Founded/Ownrshp* 1939, 1989
Sales 21.9MM^E *EMP* 165
SIC 3625 3825 8711 3548 Control equipment, electric; Current measuring equipment; Electrical or electronic engineering; Welding apparatus; Control equipment, electric; Current measuring equipment; Electrical or electronic engineering; Welding apparatus
Pr: Durrell G Miller
**VP:* David Androvich
**VP:* Steve Connors
Mng Ofcr: Matt Smith

D-U-N-S 61-453-0111 IMP
NADINE FOOD CORP
TRADE FAIR 6
3012 30th Ave, Astoria, NY 11102-2267
Tel (718) 721-2437 *Founded/Ownrshp* 1989
Sales 31.8MM^E *EMP* 219
Accts Sax Macy Fromm & Co Pc Clif
SIC 5411 5921 Supermarkets, independent; Beer (packaged); Supermarkets, independent; Beer (packaged)
Ch Bd: Frank Jaber
Comm Dir: Debra Eschmeyer

D-U-N-S 79-084-8464
NADONAH MEDICAL SUPPLY
5021 Columbia Way, Quartz Hill, CA 93536-3010
Tel (661) 718-3870 *Founded/Ownrshp* 2014
Sales 213.6MM *EMP* 4
SIC 5999 Medical apparatus & supplies
CEO: Donald Nnamdi Iwuagwu

NAE
See NORTH AMERICAN ENCLOSURES INC

NAEC
See NORTH ALABAMA ELECTRIC COOPERATIVE

NAEIR
See NATIONAL ASSOCIATION FOR EXCHANGE OF INDUSTRIAL RESOURCES INC

D-U-N-S 05-044-4603
NAES CORP
(*Suby of* ITOCHU INTERNATIONAL INC) ★
1180 Nw Maple St Ste 200, Issaquah, WA 98027-8106
Tel (425) 961-4700 *Founded/Ownrshp* 2001
Sales 514.7MM *EMP* 2,210
Accts Pricewaterhousecoopers Llp Se
SIC 4911 Electric services; Electric services
Pr: Robert E Fishman
**Pr:* John Brewster
COO: John Meyer
COO: John Stender
**CFO:* Stuart Neale
VP: Robert C Faull
**VP:* Mark R Iraola
**VP:* Debra A Olson
**VP:* George Wackerhagen
Dir Risk M: Robert Holmes
Genl Mgr: Terrence Kurtz

NAEYC
See NATIONAL ASSOCIATION FOR EDUCATION OF YOUNG CHILDREN

D-U-N-S 07-827-8835 IMP
■ NAF BUSINESS AND SUPPORT SERVICES DIVISION
(*Suby of* UNITED STATES DEPARTMENT OF THE NAVY) ★
3044 Catlin Ave, Quantico, VA 22134-5003
Tel (703) 432-0109 *Founded/Ownrshp* 1903
Sales 642.4MM^E *EMP* 12,000
SIC 7997 Marine Corps; ; Membership sports & recreation clubs; Membership sports & recreation clubs
Ofcr: Paula Hevner
Ofcr: Joe Schumacher
Ofcr: Rebecca Wilkinson
VP: Jessica Bradley
Dir Soc: Gary Karr
**Prin:* Amanda Ayers
Admn Mgr: Sheila Dabrowski
Dept Mgr: Vendella Davis
Genl Mgr: Cedric Overton
CIO: Len Jacaruso
DP Exec: Rycourt Freeman

NAFCO PLANT
See TARKETT ALABAMA INC

NAFCO WHOLESALE FISH DEALERS
See STANLEY PEARLMAN ENTERPRISES INC

NAFCU
See NEW MEXICO EDUCATORS FEDERAL CREDIT UNION (INC)

NAFECO
See NORTH AMERICA FIRE EQUIPMENT CO INC

NAFI
See NORTH AMERICAN FAMILY INSTITUTE INC

D-U-N-S 14-065-1931
NAFI CONNECTICUT INC
20 Batterson Park Rd # 301, Farmington, CT 06032-4502
Tel (860) 284-1177 *Founded/Ownrshp* 2003
Sales 19.9MM *EMP* 297
Accts Kpmg Llp Boston Ma
SIC 8322 Individual & family services; Individual & family services
Ex Dir: Jim Isenberg
**CFO:* Pamela Bruce
**Treas:* Daniel Nakamoto
Pgrm Dir: Megan Graham

D-U-N-S 01-941-7856 IMP
NAFP INC
983 Riverside Dr, Methuen, MA 01844-6703
Tel (978) 682-1855 *Founded/Ownrshp* 1984
Sales 48.6MM^E *EMP* 60
SIC 5145 Confectionery
Pr: Thomas M Reilly
**Ch Bd:* John Morrissey
**VP:* Robin Birch
VP Opers: Gary Less

D-U-N-S 08-635-2093
NAFSA ASSOCIATION OF INTERNATIONAL EDUCATORS
1307 New York Ave Nw Fl 8, Washington, DC 20005-4715
Tel (202) 737-3699 *Founded/Ownrshp* 1948
Sales 20.9MM *EMP* 63E
Accts P C Hnreznick Llp Bethesda
SIC 8621 Education & teacher association; Education & teacher association
CEO: Marlene Johnson
**CFO:* William Newman
Treas: Maria Sophocleous
Creative D: Ana Foreman
Mktg Dir: Kathleen Post

D-U-N-S 87-916-8540
NAFTA DISTRIBUTORS
5120 Santa Ana St, Ontario, CA 91761-8632
Tel (909) 605-7515 *Founded/Ownrshp* 1994
Sales 36.4MME *EMP* 50
SIC 5141 Groceries, general line
CEO: Samuel Madikians
VP: Bashar Hallak

D-U-N-S 86-726-4806 EXP
NAFTA TRADERS INC
520 N Wildwood Dr, Irving, TX 75061-8800
Tel (972) 438-7253 *Founded/Ownrshp* 1993
Sales 42.7MME *EMP* 135
SIC 5139 5136 5137 Footwear; Men's & boys' clothing; Women's & children's clothing; Footwear; Men's & boys' clothing; Women's & children's clothing
CEO: Robert Schlachter
**CFO:* Adam Fenster
**VP:* Marc Schlachter

D-U-N-S 87-626-1025 IMP
NAGAKURA ENGINEERING WORKS CO INC
N.E.W. INDIANA CO.,
(*Suby of* NAGAKURA MFG.CO.,LTD.)
630 S Mapleton St, Columbus, IN 47201-7360
Tel (812) 375-1382 *Founded/Ownrshp* 1994
Sales 31.4MME *EMP* 169
SIC 3714 3462 Motor vehicle transmissions, drive assemblies & parts; Iron & steel forgings; Motor vehicle transmissions, drive assemblies & parts; Iron & steel forgings
Pr: Shuji Nagakura
VP: Kay Hawkins
Genl Mgr: John Bailey
Genl Mgr: Masashi Ito

D-U-N-S 00-220-5727
NAGARRO INC
PROJISTICS
226 Airport Pkwy Ste 390, San Jose, CA 95110-1026
Tel (408) 436-6170 *Founded/Ownrshp* 1999
Sales 35.0MME *EMP* 2,000E
SIC 7373 Computer-aided system services; Computer-aided system services
CEO: Vikas Sehgal
Pr: Manmohan Gupta

D-U-N-S 07-326-5449 IMP
NAGASE AMERICA CORP
(*Suby of* NAGASE & CO., LTD.)
546 5th Ave Fl 16, New York, NY 10036-5000
Tel (212) 703-1340 *Founded/Ownrshp* 1971
Sales 90.6MME *EMP* 96
SIC 5169 5162 5122 5065 5047 Industrial chemicals; Plastics materials & basic shapes; Pharmaceuticals; Electronic parts & equipment; Medical equipment & supplies; Industrial chemicals; Plastics materials & basic shapes; Pharmaceuticals; Electronic parts & equipment; Medical equipment & supplies
Pr: Gen Hirao
**Ch:* Ryuichi Uchida
**Treas:* Keiichiro Yamashita
**Sr VP:* Kazuyuki Sato
**Sr VP:* Takuya Tomomura
Exec: Kamal Hossain
Dir Bus: Bradley Hilborn
Genl Mgr: Masao Hidaka
Sales Exec: Jeremy Smith
Sls Mgr: Mitsuaki Murashige
Sls Mgr: Kazuki Sumino
Board of Directors: Jessica Chan

N.A.G.E.
See NATIONAL ASSOCIATION OF GOVERNMENT EMPLOYEES INC

D-U-N-S 06-762-0104 IMP/EXP
NAGEL PRECISION INC
288 Dino Dr, Ann Arbor, MI 48103-9502
Tel (734) 426-5650 *Founded/Ownrshp* 1987
Sales 45.8MME *EMP* 130
SIC 3541 3545 Honing & lapping machines; Honing heads; Honing & lapping machines; Honing heads
Pr: Peter Nagel
**VP:* Rolf Bochsler
VP: Tim Furgason
**VP:* Willi Koch
**VP:* Wolf Nagel
Ql Cn Mgr: Kurt Marcum

D-U-N-S 07-848-0146 IMP
NAGL MANUFACTURING CO (INC) (NE)
(*Suby of* TEAM TECHNOLOGIES INC) ★
3626 Martha St, Omaha, NE 68105-3156
Tel (402) 342-2006 *Founded/Ownrshp* 2012
Sales 27.5MME *EMP* 1E
SIC 3991 Brooms & brushes
Plnt Mgr: Craig Peters
Mktg Dir: Richard Keating

D-U-N-S 00-655-7763
NAGLE PAVING CO
39525 W 13 Mile Rd # 300, Novi, MI 48377-2361
Tel (248) 553-0600 *Founded/Ownrshp* 1999
Sales 51.1MME *EMP* 140
SIC 1611 2951 Highway & street construction; Asphalt & asphaltic paving mixtures (not from refineries); Highway & street construction; Asphalt & asphaltic paving mixtures (not from refineries)
Pr: Michael Santi
**VP:* Lawrence Brennan
**VP:* Robert Nagle
**VP:* James P Oliver

NAGRA
See OPENTV INC

D-U-N-S 86-900-8334
NAGRA USA INC
(*Suby of* KUDELSKI S.A.)
841 Apollo St Ste 300, El Segundo, CA 90245-4769
Tel (310) 335-5225 *Founded/Ownrshp* 2008
Sales 54.9MME *EMP* 285
SIC 5084 Safety equipment; Safety equipment
Pr: Virginio Trevisan
Prgrm Mgr: Dale Hoefer
Prgrm Mgr: Rolf Keller
Prgrm Mgr: Hani Khairallah
Prgrm Mgr: Emmet Odonnell
IT Man: Chris Beechler
IT Man: Jack Mixer
Sls Dir: Lindy Shallcross
Manager: Richard Horner

D-U-N-S 00-621-4464 IMP
NAHAN PRINTING INC (MN)
7000 Saukview Dr, Saint Cloud, MN 56303-0814
Tel (320) 217-7700 *Founded/Ownrshp* 1972
Sales 161.9MME *EMP* 505
SIC 2759 2752 Commercial printing; Commercial printing, lithographic; Commercial printing, offset; Commercial printing; Commercial printing, lithographic; Commercial printing, offset
CEO: Michael Nahan
Pr: Kurt Brintlinge
Pr: Dan Sand
**COO:* Kent Gilmore
Sr VP: Alicia Andres
VP: Daniel Carlo
**VP:* Steve Kirk
**VP:* Dale Kopel
**VP:* Tim Wolfe
CTO: Jim Nahan
Dir IT: Steve Burns

NAHB
See NATIONAL ASSOCIATION OF HOME BUILDERS

D-U-N-S 05-634-9541
NAI CAPITAL INC
16001 Ventura Blvd # 200, Encino, CA 91436-4482
Tel (818) 905-2400 *Founded/Ownrshp* 1979
Sales 36.9MME *EMP* 197
SIC 6531 Real estate brokers & agents
Ch Bd: Michael A Zugsmith
**Pr:* Rachel Howitt
Ex VP: Lee Black
Ex VP: Ryan Campbell
Sr VP: Brian Bethea
Sr VP: Robert Davis
Sr VP: Alan Deszcz
Sr VP: Chris Fitzgerald
Sr VP: Bob Harrison
Sr VP: James Houghton
Sr VP: Parham Khoshbakhtian
Sr VP: Stephen Lim
Sr VP: Chris Shea
VP: Steve Body
VP: Billy Choi
VP: Adam Comora
VP: Randy Cude
VP: Michael Lanzarotta
VP: Steven Lewallen
VP: Ben Mark
VP: Ryan Ramage

D-U-N-S 01-864-5625
NAI GROUP LLC
7975 N Hayden Rd Ste D105, Scottsdale, AZ 85258-3247
Tel (480) 556-6066 *Founded/Ownrshp* 2002
Sales 271.3MME *EMP* 1,500E
Accts Bdo Usa Llp Phoenix Az
SIC 3679 Harness assemblies for electronic use: wire or cable; Harness assemblies for electronic use: wire or cable
CEO: Preston Speers
**CFO:* Kevin Dye
**Ex VP:* Wayne Harrison

NAI-HIFFMAN
See HIFFMAN SHAFFER ASSOCIATES INC

NAIC
See NATIONAL ASSOCIATION OF INSURANCE COMMISSIONERS

NAICO
See NATIONAL AMERICAN INSURANCE CO

NAILITE
See EXTERIA BUILDING PRODUCTS LLC

D-U-N-S 19-369-4213 IMP
NAILOR INDUSTRIES OF TEXAS INC
(*Suby of* NAILOR INDUSTRIES INC)
4714 Winfield Rd, Houston, TX 77039-6016
Tel (702) 648-5400 *Founded/Ownrshp* 1981
Sales 47.7MME *EMP* 230
SIC 3822 Hardware for environmental regulators; Thermostats & other environmental sensors; Hardware for environmental regulators; Thermostats & other environmental sensors
Pr: Michael Nailor
Pr: Gus Faris
COO: Dave Soden
**Treas:* William Byrne
**VP:* Lance Nailor
DP Exec: Phong Tran
IT Man: Will Yin
Web Prj Mg: Lorin Williams
Prd Mgr: Gerardo Suarez
Sls&Mrk Ex: Julian Rochester
S&M/VP: Jerri Sealy

NAIR AND CO., INC.
See RADIUS GGE INC

NAIS
See NATIONAL ASSOCIATION OF INDEPENDENT SCHOOLS INC

D-U-N-S 80-197-9340
NAJAFI COMPANIES LLC
2525 E Camelback Rd, Phoenix, AZ 85016-4219
Tel (602) 476-0600 *Founded/Ownrshp* 2003
Sales 515.0MME *EMP* 2,335
SIC 3695 Magnetic disks & drums; Magnetic disks & drums
CEO: Jahm Najafi
CFO: Tina Rhodes
Snr Mgr: Gary McRae

D-U-N-S 14-469-3561 IMP/EXP
NAJARIAN FURNITURE CO INC
ITALIAN CONCEPTS
265 N Euclid Ave, Pasadena, CA 91101-1594
Tel (626) 839-8700 *Founded/Ownrshp* 1986
Sales 200.0MM *EMP* 100
SIC 5021 5023 Household furniture; Home furnishings; Household furniture; Home furnishings
Pr: Antranik Najarian
**Pr:* Mike Najarian
**VP:* George Najarian
S&M/VP: Michael Lawrence
Board of Directors: Michael Lawrence

D-U-N-S 79-649-2593
NAJJAR LUBE CENTERS INC
JIFFY LUBE
490 W Arrow Hwy Ste D, San Dimas, CA 91773-2920
Tel (909) 592-8484 *Founded/Ownrshp* 1997
Sales 22.0MME *EMP* 225
SIC 7549 Lubrication service, automotive; Lubrication service, automotive
CEO: Elias Najjar
**CFO:* Martha Villalobos

D-U-N-S 19-327-5641 IMP
NAKANISHI MANUFACTURING CORP
(*Suby of* NAKANISHI METAL WORKS CO.,LTD.)
1225 Voyles Rd, Winterville, GA 30683-2510
Tel (706) 353-0006 *Founded/Ownrshp* 1987
Sales 111.4MME *EMP* 150
SIC 5085 3562 Bearings; Ball & roller bearings; Bearings; Ball & roller bearings
Pr: Junji Tokuume
**Ch Bd:* Tatsuo Nakanishi
**CFO:* Naoshi Shimamura
**VP:* Hirotaka Nakanishi
Ex Dir: Shuji Miwa
Opers Mgr: Mitsu Takimoto
Board of Directors: Kazuo Nakanishi

D-U-N-S 62-320-3601 IMP
NAKANO AVIATION INC
(*Suby of* HAYAKAWA & CO., LTD.)
375 Van Ness Ave Ste 1105, Torrance, CA 90501-7204
Tel (310) 212-1480 *Founded/Ownrshp* 1991
Sales 31.9MM *EMP* 9
Accts Two Miles
SIC 5088 Aircraft & space vehicle supplies & parts; Aircraft & space vehicle supplies & parts
Pr: Tadaaki Nakaji
**Ex VP:* Kenji Ishizuka
**Sr VP:* Kikuzo Sato

NAKANO FOODS
See MIZKAN AMERICAS INC

NAKANO FOODS
See MIZKAN AMERICA HOLDINGS INC

D-U-N-S 04-364-8864 IMP
NAKASE BROTHERS WHOLESALE NURSERY
9441 Krepp Dr, Huntington Beach, CA 92646-2799
Tel (714) 962-6604 *Founded/Ownrshp* 1965
Sales 79.8MME *EMP* 300
SIC 5193 Nursery stock; Nursery stock
Prin: Shigeo Gary Nakase

D-U-N-S 96-823-6021
NAKASH FIVE POINTS LLC
NAKASH HOLDINGS
1400 Broadway Fl 15, New York, NY 10018-5300
Tel (646) 383-8124 *Founded/Ownrshp* 2011
Sales 24.9MME *EMP* 82E
SIC 6719 Investment holding companies, except banks
Mng Dir: Jonathan Bennett

NAKASH HOLDINGS
See NAKASH FIVE POINTS LLC

D-U-N-S 19-282-1937
■ **NAKED JUICE CO OF GLENDORA INC**
(*Suby of* PEPSICO INC) ★
1333 S Mayflower Ave # 100, Monrovia, CA 91016-5265
Tel (626) 873-2600 *Founded/Ownrshp* 2007
Sales 34.6MME *EMP* 400
SIC 5499 2033 Juices, fruit or vegetable; Fruit juices: fresh; Juices, fruit or vegetable; Fruit juices: fresh
CEO: Monty Sharma
**Pr:* Tom Hicks
**VP:* Paul Travis

NAKOMA GROUP OF COLORADO
See DENOVO VENTURES LLC

D-U-N-S 14-109-0170
NAKUURUQ SOLUTIONS LLC
(*Suby of* AKIMA LLC) ★
13873 Park Center Rd 400n, Herndon, VA 20171-3223
Tel (571) 323-5970 *Founded/Ownrshp* 2003
Sales 24.5MME *EMP* 130E
SIC 4812 Radio telephone communication; Radio telephone communication

D-U-N-S 07-938-7030
■ **NAL OHIO HOLDINGS LLC**
(*Suby of* CAESARS ENTERTAINMENT CORP) ★
1 Caesars Palace Dr, Las Vegas, NV 89109-8969
Tel (702) 407-6000 *Founded/Ownrshp* 2014
Sales 1.1MME *EMP* 411E
SIC 7011 Casino hotel
Prin: Gary W Loveman

D-U-N-S 96-818-0666
NAL WORLDWIDE HOLDINGS INC
NAL.SYNCREON ADDISON
(*Suby of* NALSYNCREON) ★
1200 N Greenbriar Dr A, Addison, IL 60101-1049
Tel (630) 261-3100 *Founded/Ownrshp* 2009
Sales 72.3MME *EMP* 398E
SIC 3559 Automotive related machinery
Sr VP: Chris Lennon
Ex Dir: Robert Frusolone
Genl Couns: Gwendolyn L Hassan

NALC
See NATIONAL ASSOCIATION OF LETTER CARRIERS

NALCO CHAMPION - AN ECOLAB CO
See NALCO CO

D-U-N-S 00-496-2403 IMP/EXP
■ **NALCO CO**
NALCO CHAMPION - AN ECOLAB CO
(*Suby of* ECOLAB INC) ★
1601 W Diehl Rd, Naperville, IL 60563-1198
Tel (630) 305-1000 *Founded/Ownrshp* 1928, 2011
Sales 3.6MMME *EMP* 10,560
SIC 3559 2899 2992 2891 Chemical machinery & equipment; Corrosion preventive lubricant; Lubricating oils; Adhesives; Chemical machinery & equipment; Corrosion preventive lubricant; Lubricating oils; Adhesives
Ch: Douglas M Baker
COO: William Roe
CFO: Bradley Bell
CFO: Robert Glaza
Bd of Dir: Paul J Norris
Sr VP: Scott Mason
VP: Jeff Dickens
VP: Lee Josey
VP: Jeannie Shimer
VP: Denise Wright
Rgnl Mgr: Lucky Braimoh

D-U-N-S 86-815-9013 IMP/EXP
■ **NALCO ENERGY SERVICES LP**
(*Suby of* NALCO CHAMPION - AN ECOLAB CO) ★
7705 Highway 90a, Sugar Land, TX 77478-2121
Tel (281) 263-7000 *Founded/Ownrshp* 1994
Sales 309.7MME *EMP* 1,500
SIC 2899 Chemical preparations; Chemical preparations
Pt: Mark L Bosanko
Pt: Gary Aman
Pt: David Johnson
Pt: Bruno Lavandier
Pt: Steve Taylor
Bd of Dir: Chinh E Chu
Bd of Dir: Joshua J Harris
Bd of Dir: Sanjeev K Mehra
Bd of Dir: Paul H O'Neill
Bd of Dir: Daniel S Sanders
Ex VP: William J Roe
VP: Lisa Curran
VP: Michael Gibson
VP: John L Gigerich
VP: Deborah C Hockman
VP: J K Long
VP: Mary T Manupella
VP: Manian Ramesh
Exec: Dave Larson

D-U-N-S 13-203-1571 EXP
■ **NALCO FAB-TECH LLC**
(*Suby of* NALCO CHAMPION - AN ECOLAB CO) ★
4500 33 Mile Rd, Casper, WY 82604
Tel (307) 472-9740 *Founded/Ownrshp* 2010
Sales 38.5MME *EMP* 97
SIC 3441 3444 3491 Fabricated structural metal; Sheet metalwork; Pressure valves & regulators, industrial; Fabricated structural metal; Sheet metalwork; Pressure valves & regulators, industrial
CEO: Bruno Lavandier
Pr: Larry Rubis

D-U-N-S 16-707-5113
■ **NALCO HOLDING CO**
(*Suby of* ECOLAB INC) ★
1601 W Diehl Rd, Naperville, IL 60563-1198
Tel (630) 305-1000 *Founded/Ownrshp* 2003
Sales 2.1MMME *EMP* 12,400E
SIC 2899 2992 Chemical preparations; Corrosion preventive lubricant; Water treating compounds; Lubricating oils & greases; Chemical preparations; Corrosion preventive lubricant; Water treating compounds; Lubricating oils & greases
Ch Bd: J Erik Fyrwald
Pr: David E Flitman
Pr: Terrence M Gallagher
CFO: Kathryn A Mikells
Treas: Todd Hacker
Chf Mktg O: Mary Kay Kaufmann
Ofcr: Lori F Arnold
Ex VP: David Johnson
Ex VP: John Macleod
Ex VP: Scott Mason
Ex VP: Eric G Melin
Sr VP: R J Allain
VP: Richard A Bendure
VP: Lisa Curran
VP: C Deborah
VP: Matthew Knight
VP: Stephen N Landsman
VP: Chris Moore
VP: Pete Nassos
VP: Mark Stoll
Dir Risk M: James Smaga

D-U-N-S 15-442-9620 IMP
■ **NALCO HOLDINGS LLC**
(*Suby of* NALCO HOLDING CO) ★
1601 W Diehl Rd, Naperville, IL 60563-1198
Tel (630) 305-1000 *Founded/Ownrshp* 2004
Sales 532.9MME *EMP* 11,590

SIC 2899 2992 3559 Corrosion preventive lubricant; Water treating compounds; Antiscaling compounds, boiler; Lubricating oils; Chemical machinery & equipment; Corrosion preventive lubricant; Water treating compounds; Antiscaling compounds, boiler; Lubricating oils; Chemical machinery & equipment
Ch: J Eric Fyrwald
Pr: Richard Bendure
Pr: David Flitman
Pr: David Johnson
Pr: Eric Melin
Pr: Steve Taylor
CFO: Kathryn Mikells
Bd of Dir: Richard B Marchese
Chf Mktg O: Mary Kay Kaufmann
Sr VP: Daniel M Harker
Snr Ntwrk: Eugene Dvoretsky
Board of Directors: Carl M Casale, Paul J Norris, Douglas A Pertz, Daniel S Sanders

D-U-N-S 19-408-2517 IMP/EXP
■ NALGE NUNC INTERNATIONAL CORP
(*Suby of* FISHER SCIENTIFIC INTERNATIONAL LLC) ★
75 Panorama Creek Dr, Rochester, NY 14625-2303
Tel (585) 586-8800 *Founded/Ownrshp* 1995
Sales 265.3MM^E *EMP* 1,519
SIC 3089 3949 3821 3085 3083 Plastic processing; Plastic & fiberglass tanks; Sporting & athletic goods; Laboratory apparatus & furniture; Plastics bottles; Laminated plastics plate & sheet; Plastic processing; Plastic & fiberglass tanks; Sporting & athletic goods; Laboratory apparatus & furniture; Plastics bottles; Laminated plastics plate & sheet
Prin: Michaeline Reed
Area Mgr: Debbie O'Donley
Sls Mgr: Debbie Miller

D-U-N-S 07-590-9130
NALLATECH INC
(*Suby of* I S I) ★
759 Flynn Rd, Camarillo, CA 93012-8056
Tel (805) 383-8997 *Founded/Ownrshp* 2008
Sales 34.0MM^E *EMP* 64
SIC 5065 Electronic parts & equipment
Ch: Colin Rutherford
**Pr:* Allan Cantle
**CEO:* William P Miller
**VP:* Ed Hennessy
Manager: Paul Houlihan
Manager: Jim Mazzola
Manager: Jon Mudrick
Board of Directors: Ian Robertson

D-U-N-S 07-905-2262
NALLE CLINIC CO INC
1918 Randolph Rd, Charlotte, NC 28207-1100
Tel (704) 342-8000 *Founded/Ownrshp* 1921
Sales 11.5MM^E *EMP* 600
SIC 8011 Clinic, operated by physicians; Clinic, operated by physicians
**Pr:* Jeremiah H Holleman Jr
**Treas:* Lawrence Fleishman MD
**VP:* Donald Kamerer
**Ex Dir:* Suzanne Savard
Med Dir: Ophelia Garmon-Brown

NALLEY
See ASBURY AUTOMOTIVE ATLANTA LLC

D-U-N-S 03-367-7709
NALLEY BMW (GA)
CHRIS BMW
1606 Church St, Decatur, GA 30033-5996
Tel (404) 292-1400 *Founded/Ownrshp* 1965
Sales 36.6MM^E *EMP* 94
SIC 5511 7538 7515 7513 5521 Automobiles, new & used; General automotive repair shops; Passenger car leasing; Truck rental & leasing, no drivers; Used car dealers; Automobiles, new & used; General automotive repair shops; Passenger car leasing; Truck rental & leasing, no drivers; Used car dealers
Pr: C V Nalley III
**VP:* Joyce Christman
**VP:* Theo Christman
Genl Mgr: Paul Maza
Sls Mgr: Thomas Dragoo
Sls Mgr: Willie James

D-U-N-S 18-511-1861
NALLEY BRUNSWICK AUTOMOBILES INC
NALLEY HONDA
178 Altama Connector, Brunswick, GA 31525-2222
Tel (912) 267-7000 *Founded/Ownrshp* 1988
Sales 34.7MM^E *EMP* 73
SIC 5511 Automobiles, new & used; Automobiles, new & used
CEO: C V Nalley III
**CFO:* Ann Nigro
**VP:* Mark D Hall
Genl Mgr: Leighton Johnson
CIO: Al Lim
Sls Dir: John Bozza
Sls Mgr: Linda Ganas
Sls Mgr: David Hunt
Sls Mgr: James Stevenot
Sls Mgr: Jeff Wentworth
Sales Asso: Chip Anderson

NALLEY FORD SANDY SPRINGS
See ASBURY ATLANTA FORD LLC

NALLEY HONDA
See NALLEY BRUNSWICK AUTOMOBILES INC

NALLEY HONDA
See ATLANTA ASBURY HONDA LLC

NALLEY INFINITI
See NISSAN TRONCALLI INC

NALLEY LEXUS
See ASBURY ATLANTA LEX LLC

NALLEY MOTOR TRUCKS
See ASBURY AUTOMOTIVE ATLANTA LLC

NALLEY MOTOR TRUCKS
See ATLANTA IDEAL LEASE INC

D-U-N-S 07-133-3314
NALLY & HAMILTON ENTERPRISES INC (KY)
109 S 4th St, Bardstown, KY 40004-1005
Tel (502) 348-0084 *Founded/Ownrshp* 1974
Sales 51.8MM^E *EMP* 200
SIC 1221 Bituminous coal surface mining; Bituminous coal surface mining
Pr: Thomas R Hamilton
**Sec:* Stephen Hamilton
**VP:* Leo Hamilton

D-U-N-S 05-567-9096 IMP
NALPAC ENTERPRISES LTD (MI)
1111 E 8 Mile Rd Ste 1, Ferndale, MI 48220-2656
Tel (248) 541-1140 *Founded/Ownrshp* 1971
Sales 32.3MM^E *EMP* 90
SIC 5199 5099 3993 2759 2396 Gifts & novelties; Advertising specialties; Sunglasses; Signs & advertising specialties; Commercial printing; Automotive & apparel trimmings
Pr: Ralph S Caplan
Dir IT: Mike Cali
Sls Mgr: Jane Kubiski
Sls Mgr: Thomas Rafferty
Sls Mgr: Ken Sahn

NAL.SYNCREON
See SYNCREON TECHNOLOGY (USA) LLC

NAL.SYNCREON ADDISON
See NAL WORLDWIDE HOLDINGS INC

NAM
See NATIONAL ASSOCIATION OF MANUFACTURERS OF UNITED STATES OF AMERICA INC

D-U-N-S 16-014-2055 EXP
NAMASTE LABORATORIES LLC
(*Suby of* DABUR INDIA LIMITED)
310 S Racine Ave Ste 8, Chicago, IL 60607-2841
Tel (708) 824-1393 *Founded/Ownrshp* 2011
Sales 98.0MM^E *EMP* 90
SIC 2844 Hair preparations, including shampoos; Hair preparations, including shampoos
CEO: Clarisa Wilson
COO: Clyde Burks
**Sls Dir:* Vikram Bali
Genl Couns: Byrdie Tucker

D-U-N-S 80-577-8821
NAMBE INC
2891 Cooks Rd, Santa Fe, NM 87507-3129
Tel (505) 471-2912 *Founded/Ownrshp* 2003
Sales 22.0MM *EMP* 85
SIC 8748 Business consulting; Business consulting
Pr: Daniel Hillenbrand
**Pr:* Robert Barakian

D-U-N-S 00-221-4393 IMP
NAMBE LLC (NM)
2891 Cooks Rd, Santa Fe, NM 87507-3129
Tel (505) 471-2912 *Founded/Ownrshp* 1953, 2005
Sales 20.9MM^E *EMP* 116
SIC 2514 5712 5999 3469 3645 5944 Tables, household: metal; Furniture stores; Stones, crystalline: rough; Table tops, porcelain enameled; Residential lighting fixtures; Jewelry stores
CIO: Richard Rieckenberg

NAMCO
See NORTH AMERICAN MARKETING CORP

NAMCO
See NORTH ATLANTIC CORP

D-U-N-S 06-618-8509 IMP/EXP
NAMCO ENTERTAINMENT INC
NEI
(*Suby of* BANDAI NAMCO HOLDINGS USA INC) ★
712 N Central Ave Ste B, Wood Dale, IL 60191-1263
Tel (630) 238-2200 *Founded/Ownrshp* 1993
Sales 29.8M^E *EMP* 400
SIC 7993 Coin-operated amusement devices; Coin-operated amusement devices
Pr: Hitoshi Yoshida
Dist Mgr: John Moody
Dist Mgr: Kurt Wyndham
MIS Dir: George Boyle
Natl Sales: Marty Smith
Mktg Dir: James Whattam
Board of Directors: David Bishop, Chris Krakow

D-U-N-S 00-122-6943
NAMDAR INC (NY)
(*Suby of* GRISTEDES FOODS INC) ★
823 11th Ave Fl 3, New York, NY 10019-3557
Tel (212) 956-5770 *Founded/Ownrshp* 1946, 1984
Sales 113.5MM^E *EMP* 1,700^E
SIC 5411 Supermarkets; Supermarkets
Ch Bd: John Catsimatidis

NAME BRANDS CLOTHING
See NAME BRANDS INC

D-U-N-S 04-312-9022
NAME BRANDS INC
NAME BRANDS CLOTHING
7215 S Memorial Dr, Tulsa, OK 74133-2943
Tel (918) 307-0289 *Founded/Ownrshp* 1968
Sales 29.7MM *EMP* 300
SIC 5651 Family clothing stores; Family clothing stores
Pr: Russell Gaddy
**Sec:* James S Bryden
VP: Joe Gaddy
VP: Steve Harrison
**VP:* James Stevenson
VP: Paul Venamon
Dir IT: Sean Cross
Mktg Dir: Jeremy Aldrich

NAMEBRAND OUTLET
See DOWNEAST OUTFITTERS INC

NAMES AND NUMBERS
See K W BROCK DIRECTORIES INC

NAMF
See NEW AGE METAL FABRICATING CO INC

D-U-N-S 02-917-4344 IMP
NAMIFY LLC
BADGE BOSS
280 W 900 N, Springville, UT 84663-1096
Tel (801) 491-8068 *Founded/Ownrshp* 2001
Sales 48.6MM^E *EMP* 90^E
SIC 5131 Labels
CEO: Bryan L Welton Jr
VP: Joe Brown
VP: Tyler Kimball
Web Dev: Matthew Gardiner
Sales Exec: Carina Rivas
Sales Exec: Tessa Toth
VP Sls: Kevin Wright

NAMM
See NATIONAL ASSOCIATION OF MUSIC MERCHANTS INC

D-U-N-S 78-374-5396
NAMM HOLDINGS INC
(*Suby of* INNOVACARE SERVICES CO LLC) ★
3281 E Guasti Rd Ste 700, Ontario, CA 91761-7643
Tel (909) 605-8000 *Founded/Ownrshp* 2005
Sales NA *EMP* 240
SIC 6324 8741 Health maintenance organization (HMO), insurance only; Hospital management; Nursing & personal care facility management; Health maintenance organization (HMO), insurance only; Hospital management; Nursing & personal care facility management
CEO: Timothy J O'Donnell
**Pr:* Wayne Aardsma
**Pr:* Richard A Shinto
**CEO:* Gloria Leavitt Austin
VP: Trisha Daniels

D-U-N-S 83-554-1236
NAMMO COMPOSITE SOLUTIONS LLC
(*Suby of* NAMMO TALLEY INC) ★
1020 S 500 W, Salt Lake City, UT 84101-3064
Tel (801) 350-6120 *Founded/Ownrshp* 2009
Sales 23.5MM^E *EMP* 105
SIC 3599 Machine shop, jobbing & repair; Machine shop, jobbing & repair
Pr: Brian T Lundy
**Opers Mgr:* Daniel Buck
Prd Mgr: Nick Furness
Prd Mgr: Chad Heward
Ql Cn Mgr: Pier Calacino

D-U-N-S 02-013-2502 IMP/EXP
NAMMO TALLEY INC
(*Suby of* NAMMO AS)
4051 N Higley Rd, Mesa, AZ 85215-1210
Tel (480) 898-2200 *Founded/Ownrshp* 1975, 2007
Sales 58.4MM^E *EMP* 324^E
SIC 3764 3489 3483 Guided missile & space vehicle propulsion unit parts; Ordnance & accessories; Ammunition, except for small arms; Guided missile & space vehicle propulsion unit parts; Ordnance & accessories; Ammunition, except for small arms
Pr: Steven M Wegener
Pr: John Hill
**CFO:* Hassan A Mirza
Sr VP: Dee Swartz
VP: Dave Chapman
VP: Marcie Franklin
Prgrm Mgr: Rebecca Cote
Prgrm Mgr: Nick Duke
Prgrm Mgr: Gary Ostendorf
Prgrm Mgr: Buck Willow
Prgrm Mgr: Ed Woodruff

D-U-N-S 02-964-6478
NAMPA SCHOOL DISTRICT 131
619 S Canyon St, Nampa, ID 83686-6634
Tel (208) 468-4600 *Founded/Ownrshp* 1900
Sales 98.6MM *EMP* 1,800
SIC 8211 Public combined elementary & secondary school; Public elementary school; Public junior high school; Public senior high school; Public combined elementary & secondary school; Public elementary school; Public junior high school; Public senior high school
Prin: Nancy Chopko
Prin: William Deakins
Prin: John Emerson
Prin: Vicki McNeal
Teacher Pr: Rachelle Armstrong
Psych: Jessica McCarty

NAMPAC
See NORTH AMERICA PACKAGING CORP

NAMSA
See NORTH AMERICAN SCIENCE ASSOCIATES INC

D-U-N-S 09-154-7505 IMP
NAMSCO PLASTICS INDS INC
100 Hunt Valley Rd, New Kensington, PA 15068-7072
Tel (724) 339-3591 *Founded/Ownrshp* 1978
Sales 20.4MM^E *EMP* 80
SIC 3089 Injection molding of plastics
Pr: David Namey
**Sec:* David Johns
Plnt Mgr: Terry Hixson

D-U-N-S 86-773-7348 IMP
NAN FANG DISTRIBUTION GROUP INC
2100 Williams St, San Leandro, CA 94577-3225
Tel (510) 297-5382 *Founded/Ownrshp* 1994
Sales 32.6MM^E *EMP* 100
SIC 5084 Engines & parts, diesel; Engines & parts, diesel
CEO: Ze Pan
**VP:* Zhen Poon

D-U-N-S 62-161-0278 IMP/EXP
NAN INC
OCEAN HOUSE BUILDERS
636 Laumaka St, Honolulu, HI 96819-2312
Tel (808) 842-4929 *Founded/Ownrshp* 1995
Sales 240.0MM^E *EMP* 350
SIC 1542 Commercial & office buildings, renovation & repair; Commercial & office buildings, renovation & repair
Pr: Fooney Freestone

**VP:* Ryan Nakaima
**VP:* Frank Okimoto
Off Mgr: Jocelyn Peralta

D-U-N-S 17-366-2222
NAN MCKAY AND ASSOCIATES INC
1810 Gillespie Way # 202, El Cajon, CA 92020-0920
Tel (619) 258-1855 *Founded/Ownrshp* 1980
Sales 20.4MM *EMP* 58
Accts Wade Howard & Associates Cpa
SIC 8742 7371 2731 Training & development consultant; Computer software development; Textbooks: publishing & printing; Training & development consultant; Computer software development; Textbooks: publishing & printing
Pr: Nan McKay
**CEO:* John McKay
**VP:* Raymond Adair
**VP:* Dorian Jenkins
**VP:* James McKay
VP: Holly St Hilaire
**VP:* Carrol Vaughan
Exec: Adair Ray
Creative D: Nikolai Bokolichvili
IT Man: Chad Coalier
IT Man: Mike Ordonez

D-U-N-S 61-812-4507 IMP/EXP
NAN YA PLASTICS CORP AMERICA
(*Suby of* NAN YA PLASTICS CORPORATION)
9 Peach Tree Hill Rd, Livingston, NJ 07039-5702
Tel (973) 992-2090 *Founded/Ownrshp* 1989
Sales 1.3MMM *EMP* 1,300
SIC 2824 2869 3083 Polyester fibers; Ethylene glycols; Laminated plastics plate & sheet; Polyester fibers; Ethylene glycols; Laminated plastics plate & sheet
CEO: William Wong
**Pr:* Chia-Chau Wu
**Treas:* Gino Way

D-U-N-S 08-062-5106 IMP
NAN YA PLASTICS CORP USA
(*Suby of* NAN YA PLASTICS CORPORATION)
9 Peach Tree Hill Rd, Livingston, NJ 07039-5702
Tel (718) 578-1286 *Founded/Ownrshp* 1979
Sales 124.9MM *EMP* 300
SIC 3081 Vinyl film & sheet; Vinyl film & sheet
Pr: Chia-Chau Wu
**Ch Bd:* William Wong

NANA CORPORATE SERVICES
See NANA MANAGEMENT SERVICES LLC

D-U-N-S 07-925-6996
NANA DEVELOPMENT CORP
(*Suby of* NANA REGIONAL CORP INC) ★
909 W 9th Ave, Anchorage, AK 99501-3322
Tel (907) 265-4100 *Founded/Ownrshp* 1974
Sales 1.7MMM^E *EMP* 3,000^E
Accts Kpmg Llp Anchorage Ak
SIC 7381 1389 Security guard service; Oil field services; Security guard service; Oil field services
Pr: Helvi Sandvik
**Ch Bd:* Lester Hadley
**Pr:* Sandvik Helvi K
**Ch:* Luke Sampson
**Treas:* Henry Horner
Bd of Dir: Levi Cleveland
Bd of Dir: Rosa Horner
Sr VP: Barry Coleman
**Sr VP:* Stan Fleming
**Sr VP:* Jacquelyn R Luke
**Sr VP:* David W Mrquez
**Sr VP:* Lawrence Mucciarelli
**VP:* Thomas Kevin E
**VP:* Charles J Greene
**VP:* Selina Moose
**VP:* Kornfield Robin

D-U-N-S 09-782-6176
NANA MANAGEMENT SERVICES LLC
NANA CORPORATE SERVICES
(*Suby of* NANA DEVELOPMENT CORP) ★
1001 E Benson Blvd, Anchorage, AK 99508-4298
Tel (907) 273-2400 *Founded/Ownrshp* 1978
Sales 89.7MM^E *EMP* 2,234
SIC 5812 7349 7021 7033 7381

D-U-N-S 01-020-9724
NANA OILFIELD SERVICES INC
(*Suby of* NANA DEVELOPMENT CORP) ★
1800 W 48th Ave Ste G, Anchorage, AK 99517-3195
Tel (907) 265-4100 *Founded/Ownrshp* 1975
Sales 71.7MM^E *EMP* 101
Accts Kpmg Llp Anchorage Ak
SIC 5172 Petroleum products; Petroleum products
Pr: Marie Greene

D-U-N-S 07-925-3761
NANA REGIONAL CORP INC
Shore Ave Bldg 100, Kotzebue, AK 99752
Tel (907) 442-3301 *Founded/Ownrshp* 1972
Sales 2.1MMM^E *EMP* 4,650
SIC 1389 Oil field services; Oil field services
CEO: Marie Green
**Pr:* Wayne Westlake
**COO:* Lori Henry
**CFO:* Jens Becks
CFO: Marsh Gross
**Prin:* Kevin Thomas
VP Admn: Sandy Shroyer
Mktg Dir: Carol Richards

D-U-N-S 00-782-1635
NANA SERVICES LLC
3150 C St Ste 250, Anchorage, AK 99503-3980
Tel (253) 661-9608 *Founded/Ownrshp* 2008
Sales 24.6MM *EMP* 450
Accts Ernst & Young Llp Seattle Wa
SIC 8744 Facilities support services; Facilities support services
CFO: Steve Pence

D-U-N-S 60-334-6214 IMP/EXP
NANA WALL SYSTEMS INC
100 Madowcreek Dr Ste 250, Corte Madera, CA 94925
Tel (415) 383-3148 *Founded/Ownrshp* 1989
Sales 27.4MM^E *EMP* 47

SIC 5031 3089 2431 5211 5039 Doors & windows; Fiberglass doors; Doors, wood; Doors, wood or metal, except storm; Doors, sliding
Pr: Ebrahim M Nana
**Treas:* Ilyas Nana
**VP:* Ahmad M Nana
Natl Sales: Norm Schwingel
Sales Asso: Mark Galloro

D-U-N-S 05-528-3696
NANA WORLEYPARSONS LLC
3700 Centerpoint Dr Fl 7, Anchorage, AK 99503-5800
Tel (907) 273-3900 *Founded/Ownrshp* 2001
Sales 66.7MM^E *EMP* 425
SIC 8711 Consulting engineer; Consulting engineer
Pr: Rock Hengen
**VP:* Craig Morrison
**VP:* Stuart Parks
**VP:* Gary Powell
VP: Jim Steward
Ql Cn Mgr: Steven Walstrom
Snr Mgr: Nick Rodes

D-U-N-S 79-101-7577 IMP
NANAKS LANDSCAPING GROUNDS MAINTENANCE INC
1174 Florida Central Pkwy, Longwood, FL 32750-4257
Tel (407) 831-8101 *Founded/Ownrshp* 1986
Sales 33.9MM *EMP* 430
SIC 0781 0782 Landscape counseling & planning; Landscape contractors; Landscape counseling & planning; Landscape contractors
Pr: Sampuran Singh Khalsa
CFO: Frank E Lubinskas
**VP:* Mahan Kalpa Singh Khalsa
VP: Mahan S Khalsa

D-U-N-S 07-999-3127
NANAKS LANDSCAPING OF ORLANDO INC
1174 Florida Central Pkwy, Longwood, FL 32750-4257
Tel (407) 831-8101 *Founded/Ownrshp* 1974
Sales 36.7MM *EMP* 400
SIC 8741 Business management; Business management
Pr: Sampuran Singh Khalsa
**CFO:* Frank E Lubinskas
**Sec:* Swarn S Khalsa
**VP:* Mahan Kalpa Singh Khalsa

D-U-N-S 06-650-8623 IMP
NANCE CARPET & RUG INC
PRESTIGE MILLS
201 Nance Rd Ne, Calhoun, GA 30701-8812
Tel (706) 629-7731 *Founded/Ownrshp* 1973
Sales 64.9MM^E *EMP* 120
SIC 5023 Carpets; Rugs; Carpets; Rugs
**VP:* Bob Nance
Mktg Dir: Tyler Arnold
Sales Asso: Frankie Beck

D-U-N-S 02-605-6671
NANCE INTERNATIONAL INC
NANCE MARINE & INDUSTRIAL AC
2915 Milam St, Beaumont, TX 77701-4816
Tel (409) 838-6127 *Founded/Ownrshp* 1954
Sales 25.5MM^E *EMP* 55
SIC 3585 Refrigeration & heating equipment
Pr: R D Nance
**Sec:* Tara Holland
VP: Curtis McGuirt
**VP:* John Trescott

NANCE MARINE & INDUSTRIAL AC
See NANCE INTERNATIONAL INC

NANCO
See NANCY SALES CO INC

D-U-N-S 02-550-8433
NANCOR CORP
TACO BELL
7155 E Thomas Rd Ste 105, Scottsdale, AZ 85251-6330
Tel (480) 947-4463 *Founded/Ownrshp* 1980
Sales 12.8MM^E *EMP* 650
SIC 5812 Fast-food restaurant, chain; Fast-food restaurant, chain
Pr: Jerry Lee

D-U-N-S 00-416-3184
NANCY BAER TRUCKING INC
3137 Virginia Ave, Jasper, IN 47546-1375
Tel (812) 482-2936 *Founded/Ownrshp* 1978
Sales 20.4MM^E *EMP* 120
SIC 4213 4212 Trucking, except local; Local trucking, without storage
Pr: Nancy Baer

D-U-N-S 00-176-8332 IMP/EXP
NANCY SALES CO INC
NANCO
22 Willow St, Chelsea, MA 02150-3506
Tel (617) 884-1700 *Founded/Ownrshp* 1937
Sales 23.3MM^E *EMP* 100
SIC 5099 5199 5092 3942 Souvenirs; Gifts & novelties; Toys; Dolls & stuffed toys; Souvenirs; Gifts & novelties; Toys; Dolls & stuffed toys
Pr: Stephen B Lipkin
CFO: Ron Makovsky
**Treas:* Peter J Seresky
VP: Patrick Wavershack
Dir IT: Jim Conrad
Opers Mgr: Harvey Stone
Sls Mgr: James Ho

NANCY'S
See SPRINGFIELD CREAMERY INC

D-U-N-S 79-392-1156 IMP
NANCYS BEAUTY WAREHOUSE INC
ULTIMATE BEAUTY SUPPLY
5901 Maywood Ave, Huntington Park, CA 90255-3209
Tel (323) 303-3551 *Founded/Ownrshp* 1992
Sales 21.3MM^E *EMP* 34
SIC 5122 5087 7231 Cosmetics; Hair preparations; Beauty parlor equipment & supplies; Beauty shops
Pr: Morad Zahabian

D-U-N-S 09-564-5057
■ **NANCYS SPECIALTY FOODS**
(*Suby of* HEINZ KRAFT FOODS CO) ★
1763 Tice Valley Blvd, Walnut Creek, CA 94595-1632
Tel (510) 494-1100 *Founded/Ownrshp* 2005
Sales 31.2MM^E *EMP* 375
SIC 2038 Frozen specialties; Frozen specialties
COO: Adam Ferrif
Pr: Nancy S Mueller
Treas: Paul Smith
VP: R Larry Booth
VP: David M Joiner
Plnt Mgr: Aaron Jakubowicz
Sales Exec: Larry Booth

D-U-N-S 09-950-0944 IMP
NANDANSONS INTERNATIONAL INC
NN
55 Mayfield Ave, Edison, NJ 08837-3820
Tel (908) 561-2400 *Founded/Ownrshp* 1979
Sales 117.0MM^E *EMP* 48
SIC 5122 Perfumes
CEO: Ajay Gupta
**Pr:* Ankur Gupta
**CFO:* Ankit Gupta
**Sec:* Nutan Gupta
**Genl Couns:* Anuj Gupta

D-U-N-S 06-998-1009
NANDORF INC
UNIQUE THRIFT STORES
(*Suby of* APOGEE RETAIL LLC) ★
4700 Proviso Dr, Melrose Park, IL 60163-1305
Tel (708) 371-4242 *Founded/Ownrshp* 1969
Sales 82.1MM^E *EMP* 550
SIC 5932 Homefurnishings & appliances, secondhand; Homefurnishings & appliances, secondhand
Pr: Allan Ellison
Genl Mgr: Otto Bonomo
Opers Mgr: Frances MA

NANETTE LEPORE
See ROBESPIERRE INC

D-U-N-S 02-465-6786
NANIGANS INC
60 State St Fl 12, Boston, MA 02109-1800
Tel (857) 277-0364 *Founded/Ownrshp* 2010
Sales 27.8MM^E *EMP* 150
SIC 7371 7389 Computer software development & applications; Computer software development; Advertising, promotional & trade show services; Computer software development & applications; Computer software development; Advertising, promotional & trade show services
CEO: Ric Calvillo
Pr: Nick Gianos
Pr: Derek Yimoyines
**COO:* Marc Grabowski
Sr VP: John Marsland
Sr VP: Benjamin Tregoe
Sr VP: Scott Ward
VP: Dave Carroll
VP: John Dobrowolski
VP: Mike Earls
VP: Antonio Garcia-Martinez
VP: Jon Palmer
VP: Per Sandell
Board of Directors: Jim Payne

D-U-N-S 94-982-8248 IMP
NANKAI ENVIRO-TECH CORP
(*Suby of* KURODA ELECTRIC CO., LTD.)
9765 Marconi Dr Ste 107, San Diego, CA 92154-7242
Tel (619) 754-2250 *Founded/Ownrshp* 2014
Sales 48.7MM^E *EMP* 168
SIC 3089 Molding primary plastic; Molding primary plastic
CEO: Kan Kaneko
**Pr:* Takayoshi Hirayama
**VP:* Hitoshi Nakamura

D-U-N-S 18-145-7391 IMP
■ **NANOFILM LTD**
(*Suby of* PEN INC)
10111 Sweet Valley Dr, Cleveland, OH 44125-4249
Tel (216) 447-1137 *Founded/Ownrshp* 1985
Sales 37.8MM^E *EMP* 114^E
SIC 8731 5995 Commercial physical research; Biological research; Chemical laboratory, except testing; Optical goods stores
CEO: Scott Rickert
**Pr:* Bruce Vereecken
CFO: Bruce Bereeckes
**VP:* Krish RAO

D-U-N-S 60-386-3015
NANOLUMENS INC
4900 Avalon Ridge Pkwy, Peachtree Corners, GA 30071-1572
Tel (678) 974-1544 *Founded/Ownrshp* 2005
Sales 20.0MM^E *EMP* 46
SIC 3823 7311 Digital displays of process variables; Advertising consultant
CEO: Richard Cope
Ch Bd: Fran Dramis
COO: Paul Schaefer
Ex VP: Rick Bortle
Ex VP: Karen Robinson
Ex VP: Burt Smith
VP: Rick Bortles
VP: Karen Cope
VP: Jeff Crowley
VP: Jorge Perez
VP: Nathan Remmes
VP: Mitchell Rosenberg

D-U-N-S 07-630-3858 IMP
▲ **NANOMETRICS INC**
1550 Buckeye Dr, Milpitas, CA 95035-7418
Tel (408) 545-6000 *Founded/Ownrshp* 1975
Sales 166.4MM *EMP* 536^E
Accts Pricewaterhousecoopers Llp Sa
Tkr Sym NANO *Exch* NGS
SIC 3829 3559 Measuring & controlling devices; Geophysical or meteorological electronic equipment; Semiconductor manufacturing machinery; Measuring & controlling devices; Geophysical or meteorological electronic equipment; Semiconductor manufacturing machinery
Pr: Timothy J Stultz
**Ch Bd:* Bruce C Rhine
Pr: Yaron Ish-Shalom
COO: Bruce A Crawford
CFO: Jeffrey Andreson
VP: Nagesh Avadhany
VP: Michael Fischer
VP: Kevin Heidrich
VP: Dawn Laplante
VP: David Pangburn
VP: Azmat Siddiqi
VP: Michael Weber
Board of Directors: J Thomas Bentley, Edward J Brown Jr, Stephen G Newberry, Christine Tsingos

D-U-N-S 14-388-8712 IMP
▲ **NANOSTRING TECHNOLOGIES INC**
530 Frview Ave N Ste 2000, Seattle, WA 98109
Tel (206) 378-6266 *Founded/Ownrshp* 2003
Sales 47.5MM *EMP* 276^E
Tkr Sym NSTG *Exch* NGM
SIC 2899 8731 Chemical preparations; Medical research, commercial; Chemical preparations; Medical research, commercial
Pr: R Bradley Gray
**Ch Bd:* William D Young
COO: Sean Ferree
CFO: James A Johnson
Sr VP: Joseph M Beechem
Sr VP: Wayne Burns
Sr VP: David W Ghesquiere
Sr VP: Barney Saunders
Sr VP: Bruce J Seeley
VP: Dale Levitzke
Manager: Michael Morin
Board of Directors: Nicholas Galakatos, Robert M Hershberg, Gregory Norden, Charles P Waite

D-U-N-S 10-251-1842
NANOSYS INC
233 S Hillview Dr, Milpitas, CA 95035-5417
Tel (408) 240-6700 *Founded/Ownrshp* 2001
Sales 37.7MM^E *EMP* 130^E
SIC 8733 Research institute
CEO: Jason Hartlove
Ex VP: Noland Granberry
**Sr VP:* John Hanlow
VP: Catherine Cotell
VP: Andrew Filler
VP: Charlie Hotz
VP: Matthew Murphy
Ex Dir: Matthew Bigge
Mfg Dir: Paul Altamirano
Ql Cn Mgr: Tina Arruabarrena

NANOTECHSYS
See MOORE NANOTECHNOLOGY SYSTEMS LLC

D-U-N-S 07-343-8462
NANOTHERAPEUTICS INC
13859 Progress Blvd # 300, Alachua, FL 32615-9403
Tel (386) 462-9663 *Founded/Ownrshp* 1999
Sales 38.9MM^E *EMP* 103^E
SIC 8731 Commercial physical research; Commercial physical research
Pr: James D Talton
Pr: Gary Ascani
**CFO:* James M Matthew
**Sr VP:* Robert V House
**Sr VP:* Dennis Tomisaka
VP: Ron Cobb
VP: Brbel Eppler
**VP:* James F Kirk
VP: James Kirk
VP: Simone Zwiercan
QA Dir: Sabine Abramson

D-U-N-S 02-189-0562 IMP
NANSHAN AMERICA ADVANCED ALUMINUM TECHNOLOGIES LLC (IN)
(*Suby of* SHANDONG NANSHAN ALUMINIUM CO., LTD.)
3600 Us Highway 52 S, Lafayette, IN 47905-7706
Tel (765) 838-8645 *Founded/Ownrshp* 2011
Sales 68.7MM^E *EMP* 110
SIC 3334 3341 Primary aluminum; Aluminum smelting & refining (secondary); Primary aluminum; Aluminum smelting & refining (secondary)
Pr: Lijun Du
Genl Mgr: Eric Angermeier
Manager: Bryce Wilson
Sls Mgr: Michael Patty
Snr Mgr: Brad Lewis

NANSTON DENTAL
See NANSTON INC

D-U-N-S 11-852-7712
NANSTON INC
NANSTON DENTAL
(*Suby of* GREAT EXPRESSIONS DENTAL CENTERS PC) ★
1590 Oakbrook Dr Ste 200, Norcross, GA 30093-2388
Tel (770) 242-3260 *Founded/Ownrshp* 2010
Sales 10.6MM^E *EMP* 415
SIC 8021 Specialized dental practitioners; Specialized dental practitioners
Pr: Kyle Anderson
**VP:* Chris Johnston
**VP:* Steve Johnston

D-U-N-S 96-340-6652
NANTICOKE HEALTH SERVICES INC
801 Middleford Rd, Seaford, DE 19973-3636
Tel (302) 629-6611 *Founded/Ownrshp* 1985
Sales 138.0MM *EMP* 950^E
Accts Cliftonlarsonallen Llp Plymo
SIC 8099 Medical services organization; Medical services organization
Prin: E Hancock
CFO: Douglas Connell
Dir IT: Susan Godeski
Dir IT: Susan Godesky
Doctor: Georgianna Mitchell
Doctor: Anthony Policastro

D-U-N-S 07-162-0025
NANTICOKE MEMORIAL HOSPITAL INC (DE)
(*Suby of* NANTICOKE HEALTH SERVICES INC) ★
801 Middleford Rd, Seaford, DE 19973-3636
Tel (302) 629-6611 *Founded/Ownrshp* 1945
Sales 139.8MM *EMP* 706
SIC 8062

D-U-N-S 62-252-7026
NANTUCKET ALLSERVE INC
NANTUCKET NECTARS
55 Hunter Ln, Elmsford, NY 10523-1334
Tel (914) 612-4000 *Founded/Ownrshp* 2009
Sales 17.9MM^E *EMP* 400
SIC 2086 5499 Fruit drinks (less than 100% juice): packaged in cans, etc.; Juices, fruit or vegetable
Pr: Mark Hellendrung
**Co-Ch Bd:* Thomas First
**Co-Ch Bd:* Thomas Scott
**Treas:* Tim Chan

D-U-N-S 01-976-0602
■ **NANTUCKET BANK**
(*Suby of* SANTANDER BANK NA) ★
104 Pleasant St, Nantucket, MA 02554-4004
Tel (508) 825-1152 *Founded/Ownrshp* 1834
Sales NA *EMP* 1^E
SIC 6036 State savings banks, not federally chartered
Pr: William P Houriham Jr
Ofcr: Albert Fuller

D-U-N-S 07-953-0432
NANTUCKET COTTAGE HOSPITAL
(*Suby of* PARTNERS HEALTHCARE SYSTEM INC) ★
57 Prospect St Unit 1, Nantucket, MA 02554-4396
Tel (508) 825-8100 *Founded/Ownrshp* 1911
Sales 37.0MM *EMP* 200
SIC 8062 General medical & surgical hospitals; General medical & surgical hospitals
CEO: Margot Hartmann
**Ch Bd:* Michael A F Roberts
**Treas:* Robert H Brust
Exec: Janice Ellsworth
Exec: Jason Graziadei
Dir Lab: Allyson Silverthorne
Assoc Dir: Courtney O'Neill
Dir Pat Ac: Kenneth Winders
Sfty Dirs: Oliver Murray
Opers Mgr: Dan Pace
Surgeon: Raymond R Monto

D-U-N-S 18-616-9207 IMP/EXP
■ **NANTUCKET DISTRIBUTING CO INC**
(*Suby of* CHRISTMAS TREE SHOPS INC) ★
64 Leona Dr, Middleboro, MA 02346-1433
Tel (508) 394-1225 *Founded/Ownrshp* 1978
Sales 37.7MM^E *EMP* 30
SIC 5199 Gifts & novelties
Pr: Todd Johnson
**Pr:* Charles G Bilezikian
**Sec:* Susan E Lattmann
VP: Ed Kopil
Rgnl Mgr: Mark Agruso
Plng Mgr: Sarah Gagne
Plng Mgr: Kimie McBride
Plng Mgr: Pauline Savastinuk
Plng Mgr: Dick Tibbetts
Store Mgr: Susan Hurley
Store Mgr: Suzanne Kjoller

D-U-N-S 96-660-5573
NANTUCKET ISLAND MANAGEMENT LLC
NANTUCKET ISLAND RESORTS
1 Wells Ave Fl 4, Newton, MA 02459-3211
Tel (508) 638-2475 *Founded/Ownrshp* 1998
Sales 7.8MM^E *EMP* 500
SIC 7011 Hotels & motels; Hotels & motels
CFO: Jim Crosby
Sls Dir: Aoife Owens

NANTUCKET ISLAND RESORTS
See NANTUCKET ISLAND MANAGEMENT LLC

NANTUCKET NECTARS
See NANTUCKET ALLSERVE INC

D-U-N-S 07-831-1051
NANTWORKS LLC
9920 Jefferson Blvd, Culver City, CA 90232-3506
Tel (310) 405-7539 *Founded/Ownrshp* 2011
Sales 77.2MM^E *EMP* 194^E
SIC 7373 Computer-aided system services; Computer-aided system services
Pr: Phillip Yang

D-U-N-S 61-898-3316 EXP
NANTZE SPRINGS INC
156 W Carroll St, Dothan, AL 36301-4316
Tel (229) 725-3616 *Founded/Ownrshp* 1991
Sales 54.6MM^E *EMP* 150
SIC 5149 Mineral or spring water bottling; Water, distilled; Mineral or spring water bottling; Water, distilled
Ch Bd: Fred Garrett
**Pr:* Malone Garrett
**Sec:* Dr Ben Garrett
**VP:* Bill Garrett
VP Sls: Ralph Grasso

NANUET PUBLIC SCHOOLS
See NANUET UNION FREE SCHOOL DISTRICT

D-U-N-S 03-824-9371
NANUET UNION FREE SCHOOL DISTRICT
NANUET PUBLIC SCHOOLS
101 Church St, Nanuet, NY 10954-3030
Tel (845) 627-9880 *Founded/Ownrshp* 1812
Sales 64.0MM *EMP* 494
Accts O Connor Davies Munns & Dobbin
SIC 8211 Public elementary & secondary schools; Public elementary & secondary schools
**Treas:* William Gavin
**Dir Bus:* Philip Sions

Pr Dir: Kathleen Maier
Schl Brd P: Ron Hansen

NANZ COMPANY, THE
See NANZ CUSTOM HARDWARE INC

D-U-N-S 62-765-4338
NANZ CUSTOM HARDWARE INC
NANZ COMPANY, THE
20 Vandam St Fl 5l, New York, NY 10013-1277
Tel (212) 367-7000 *Founded/Ownrshp* 1988
Sales 26.3MM^E *EMP* 150^E
SIC 3429 5031 Door opening & closing devices, except electrical; Building materials, interior; Door opening & closing devices, except electrical; Building materials, interior
CEO: Carl Sorenson
**Pr:* Steve Nanz
Sls Dir: Liz Hall
Snr Mgr: Michelle Lynch
Board of Directors: Alyson Dick, Michelle Lynch, Samuel Michelson, Todd Puckett

D-U-N-S 00-636-8088 IMP
NAP ASSET HOLDINGS LTD
NAP GLADU
1180 Wernsing Rd, Jasper, IN 47546-8171
Tel (812) 482-2000 *Founded/Ownrshp* 2012
Sales 44.5MM^E *EMP* 378
SIC 7699 3541 3545 Knife, saw & tool sharpening & repair; Saws, power (metalworking machinery); Tools & accessories for machine tools; Knife, saw & tool sharpening & repair; Saws, power (metalworking machinery); Tools & accessories for machine tools
Pr: Bradley Stack
Plnt Mgr: Patrick Stoflet
Mktg Dir: Karl Wagner

NAP GLADU
See NAP ASSET HOLDINGS LTD

D-U-N-S 04-360-0212
NAP INDUSTRIES INC (NY)
N A P
667 Kent Ave, Brooklyn, NY 11249-7500
Tel (718) 625-4948 *Founded/Ownrshp* 1961
Sales 20.2MM^E *EMP* 90
SIC 2673 Plastic bags: made from purchased materials; Plastic bags: made from purchased materials
Pr: Leopold Lowy
**VP:* Jack Freund
Ex Dir: Ram Sirupurapu

NAPA
See AUTO TIRE AND PARTS CO INC

NAPA
See NORTH AMERICAN PARTNERS IN ANESTHESIA LLP

NAPA
See NATIONAL AUTOMOTIVE PARTS ASSOCIATION INC

NAPA AUTO PARTS
See RIDGE CO

NAPA AUTO PARTS
See GENUINE PARTS CO

NAPA AUTO PARTS
See QUAKER CITY MOTOR PARTS CO

NAPA AUTO PARTS
See AUTOMOTIVE OF YORK INC

NAPA AUTO PARTS
See HASLER OIL CO INC

NAPA AUTO PARTS
See BARNES MOTOR & PARTS CO INC

NAPA AUTO PARTS
See MOTOR PARTS & EQUIPMENT CORP

NAPA AUTO PARTS
See WHITENER ENTERPRISES INC

NAPA AUTO PARTS
See BROOKS AUTO PARTS INC

NAPA AUTO PARTS
See FINLEY INDUSTRIES INC

NAPA AUTO PARTS
See MORGAN AUTO PARTS

NAPA AUTO PARTS
See AUTOPARTSPROS LLC

NAPA AUTO PARTS
See BARRON SERVICE PARTS CO

NAPA AUTO PARTS
See SPRINGFIELD AUTO SUPPLY INC

NAPA AUTO PARTS
See COLKITT INC

NAPA AUTO PARTS
See CENTRAL MOTOR PARTS INC

NAPA AUTO PARTS
See MYERS AUTO PARTS INC

NAPA AUTO PARTS
See UNITED COMMERCE CENTERS INC

NAPA AUTO PARTS
See DYSONS INC

NAPA AUTO SUPPLY AND EQUIPMENT
See ASEC INC

NAPA BALKAMP
See BALKAMP INC

NAPA DIST CENTER-HAWAII
See GENUINE PARTS CO

D-U-N-S 09-308-1958
NAPA SANITATION DISTRICT
1515 Soscol Ferry Rd, NAPA, CA 94558-6247
Tel (707) 254-9231 *Founded/Ownrshp* 1945
Sales 21.1MM *EMP* 50
Accts Gallina Llp Roseville Califo
SIC 4952 Sewerage systems; Sewerage systems
Genl Mgr: Tim Healy
CFO: John Cuevas
VP: Michael Abramson
Dir Lab: Mark Koekenoer
Opers Supe: Frank Ziliotto
Plnt Mgr: Jim Keller
Plnt Mgr: Sharleen Maglione
Sls&Mrk Ex: Darcy Aston

D-U-N-S 78-559-6263
NAPA TRANSPORTATION INC
4800 E Trindle Rd, Mechanicsburg, PA 17050-3617
Tel (717) 920-9840 *Founded/Ownrshp* 1991
Sales 37.8MM^E *EMP* 358
SIC 4213 Trucking, except local; Trucking, except local
Pr: Ronald G Accomando
**Sec:* Debra H Accomando
**VP:* Nicolas R Accomando
VP Opers: Kevin Hite
Natl Sales: Steven Schreffler
VP Sls: Ed Perry
Manager: Sarah Walsh

NAPA VALLEY CAST STONE
See N V CAST STONE LLC

D-U-N-S 07-393-0299
NAPA VALLEY COMMUNITY COLLEGE DISTRICT
2277 Napa Vallejo Hwy, NAPA, CA 94558-6236
Tel (707) 253-3000 *Founded/Ownrshp* 1942
Sales 20.9MM^E *EMP* 515
SIC 8222 Community college; Junior college; Community college; Junior college
Pr: Ronald Kraft
CFO: Scott Miller
VP: Ed Shenk
VP: Sonia Wright
Exec: Kirk Berger
**Prin:* Diane Carey Woodruff
Ofcr: Sable Howard
Dir IT: Vanessa Davis

D-U-N-S 17-651-4545
■ **NAPA VALLEY FORD LINCOLN MERCURY INC**
(*Suby of* LITHIA MOTORS INC) ★
570 Soscol Ave, NAPA, CA 94559-3439
Tel (707) 255-2580 *Founded/Ownrshp* 2003
Sales 27.5MM^E *EMP* 55
SIC 5511 Automobiles, new & used; Automobiles, new & used
CEO: Kevin D Massie
**Sec:* Linda Walston
Sls Mgr: Kevin Carpenter
Sls Mgr: George Love
Sales Asso: Justo Alvarez
Sales Asso: Christopher Drumm
Sales Asso: Michael E Henry

NAPA VALLEY MEDICAL CENTER
See QUEEN OF VALLEY MEDICAL CENTER

D-U-N-S 07-653-0807
NAPA VALLEY UNIFIED SCHOOL DISTRICT
2425 Jefferson St, NAPA, CA 94558-4931
Tel (707) 253-3715 *Founded/Ownrshp* 1965
Sales 428.1M *EMP* 1,800
SIC 8211 Public elementary & secondary schools; Public elementary & secondary schools
Dir Sec: Ken Spencer
MIS Dir: Elizabeth Emett
Teacher Pr: Joe Alvarez
Teacher Pr: Ashley Halliday

NAPCO COPY GRAPHICS CENTER
See R S KNAPP CO INC

D-U-N-S 16-196-2824 IMP
NAPCO INTERNATIONAL LLC
(*Suby of* JATA LLC) ★
11055 Excelsior Blvd, Hopkins, MN 55343-3429
Tel (952) 931-2400 *Founded/Ownrshp* 2003
Sales 46.0MM^E *EMP* 65
SIC 5065 5013 Security control equipment & systems; Truck parts & accessories; Security control equipment & systems; Truck parts & accessories
Pr: Theunis Botha
**CFO:* Gerald Theisen
**CFO:* Jerry Tyson
**VP:* Joann Lindgren
Opers Mgr: Trish Pham

D-U-N-S 82-595-0129
NAPCO PRECAST LLC
6949 Low Bid Ln, San Antonio, TX 78250-4632
Tel (210) 509-9100 *Founded/Ownrshp* 2008
Sales 45.3MM^E *EMP* 230
Accts Baird Kurtz & Dobson
SIC 1791 Precast concrete structural framing or panels, placing of; Precast concrete structural framing or panels, placing of
Pr: Jay E Miller
**Pr:* Todd Davidson
**CFO:* Douglas Funk
CTO: Joey Espinoza
Plnt Mgr: Cipriano Deluna
Snr Mgr: Guillermo Rodriguez

D-U-N-S 05-497-9125 IMP/EXP
▲ **NAPCO SECURITY TECHNOLOGIES INC**
333 Bayview Ave, Amityville, NY 11701-2801
Tel (631) 842-9400 *Founded/Ownrshp* 1969
Sales 77.7MM *EMP* 1,013^E
Accts Baker Tilly Virchow Krause Ll
Tkr Sym NSSC *Exch* NGS
SIC 3669 3699 3429 1731 7373 Emergency alarms; Fire alarm apparatus, electric; Security control equipment & systems; Door locks, bolts & checks; Safety & security specialization; Systems software development services; Emergency alarms; Fire alarm apparatus, electric; Security control equipment & systems; Door locks, bolts & checks; Safety & security specialization; Systems software development services
Ch Bd: Richard L Soloway
**Treas:* Kevin S Buchel
Sr VP: Michael Carrieri
Sr VP: Jorge Hevia
VP: Charlie Buccola
VP: Alfred Depierro
VP: Raymond Gaudio
VP: Kenny Stetz
VP: Craig Szmania
VP: Harvinder Vasir
CIO: George McBride
Board of Directors: Paul Stephen Beeber, Randy B Blaustein, Arnold Blumenthal, Donna A Soloway, Andrew J Wilder

NAPERVILLE COLLEGE
See NORTH CENTRAL COLLEGE

D-U-N-S 07-442-5547
NAPERVILLE COMMUNITY UNIT SCHOOL DISTRICT 203
203 W Hillside Rd, Naperville, IL 60540-6500
Tel (630) 420-6300 *Founded/Ownrshp* 1972
Sales 309.4MM *EMP* 2,000
Accts Klein Hall Cpas Aurora Illi
SIC 8211 Public elementary & secondary schools; Public elementary & secondary schools
CFO: Brad Cauffman
Bd of Dir: Jim Dennison
Bd of Dir: Mike Jaensch
Bd of Dir: Jackie Romberg
Bd of Dir: Terry Tamblyn
Trst: Debbie Shipley
VP: Kristin Fitzgerald
Exec: Gayle Wahlin
DP Exec: Josh Mika
IT Man: Lisa Dalton
Pr Dir: Julie Carlsen

NAPERVILLE JEEP EAGLE
See BURKE AUTOMOTIVE GROUP INC

D-U-N-S 88-417-7999
NAPERVILLE PSYCHIATRIC VENTURES
LINDEN OAKS HOSPITAL
(*Suby of* EDWARD HEALTH VENTURES) ★
801 S Washington St, Naperville, IL 60540-7430
Tel (630) 305-5500 *Founded/Ownrshp* 2011
Sales 49.8MM *EMP* 200
Accts Crowe Horwath Llp Chicago Il
SIC 8063 8093 8361 Psychiatric hospitals; Specialty outpatient clinics; Residential care; Psychiatric hospitals; Specialty outpatient clinics; Residential care
COO: Paul Teodo
CFO: Robert Rosenberger
Nurse Mgr: Trish Jones-Bendel
Mktg Dir: Charla Waxman
Doctor: Tahmineh Abbasian
Doctor: Lina Abujamra
Nrsg Dir: Jaimon Nanthikkattu

NAPERVILLE YMCA
See HERITAGE YMCA GROUP

D-U-N-S 00-467-7399
NAPHCARE INC
2090 Columbiana Rd # 4000, Vestavia, AL 35216-2158
Tel (205) 536-8400 *Founded/Ownrshp* 1989
Sales 66.9MM^E *EMP* 918
SIC 8099 Medical services organization; Medical services organization
CEO: James S McLane
**Pr:* B Lee Harrison
**CFO:* Connie Young
Ex VP: Susanne Moore
VP: Richard Apollo
VP: Jason Douglas
VP: Donna Dowling
VP: Jeff McIntyre
Exec: Katherine Tarin
Dir Rx: Kerry Kelley
Dir Bus: John Donahue

NAPI
See NAVAJO AGRICULTURAL PRODUCTS INDUSTRY

D-U-N-S 07-882-2139
NAPIER HEALTHCARE SOLUTIONS INC
(*Suby of* NAPIER HEALTHCARE SOLUTIONS PTE. LTD.)
3673 Quakerbridge Rd, Trenton, NJ 08619-1207
Tel (732) 742-5526 *Founded/Ownrshp* 2011
Sales 19.1MM^E *EMP* 450
SIC 8742 Management consulting services; Management consulting services
CEO: Karthik Tirutaphi
**VP:* Manish Mehta

D-U-N-S 07-878-9439
NAPIER PARK GLOBAL CAPITAL LLC
280 Park Ave Fl 3w, New York, NY 10017-1312
Tel (212) 559-0223 *Founded/Ownrshp* 2012
Sales 29.9MM^E *EMP* 69^E
SIC 6799 Security speculators for own account
CEO: James Michael O'Brien
Mng Pt: James Duplessie
**Ch Bd:* John Havens
Mng Dir: Rajesh Agarway
Mng Dir: Lisa Anderson
Mng Dir: William Jacoby
Mng Dir: Donald Leitch
Mng Dir: Peter Manion
Mng Dir: Manu Rana
Mng Dir: Walter Thorman
Mng Dir: Jeffrey Traum

D-U-N-S 03-258-5846
NAPLES BEACH HOTEL & GOLF CLUB
851 Gulf Shore Blvd N, Naples, FL 34102-5397
Tel (239) 261-2222 *Founded/Ownrshp* 1946
Sales 31.9MM^E *EMP* 285
SIC 7011 7997 7992 Hotels; Golf club, membership; Public golf courses; Hotels; Golf club, membership; Public golf courses
Pr: Michael E Watkins
**Treas:* Mohammed Azami
**Ex VP:* Henry B Watkins III
**VP:* Azi Azami
Exec: Patsy Carbone
Genl Mgr: Jason Parsons
Genl Mgr: Leanne Pawlowski
CTO: Karen Naccarato
IT Man: Irving Rushworth
Sls Mgr: Jennifer Brinkman

NAPLES CHILDREN & EDUCATION FO
See NAPLES CHILDREN FOUNDATION INC

D-U-N-S 03-051-7192
NAPLES CHILDREN FOUNDATION INC
NAPLES CHILDREN & EDUCATION FO
4305 Exchange Ave, Naples, FL 34104-7021
Tel (239) 514-2239 *Founded/Ownrshp* 2001
Sales 20.3MM *EMP* 7
Accts Phillips Harvey Group Naples
SIC 7389 Fund raising organizations; Fund raising organizations
Ch: Bob Clifford
**Prin:* Scott Lutgert
**Ex Dir:* Pamela Nesheim

D-U-N-S 07-847-2818
NAPLES COMMUNITY HOSPITAL INC
NCH HEALTHCARE SYSTEM
350 7th St N, Naples, FL 34102-5754
Tel (239) 436-5000 *Founded/Ownrshp* 1956
Sales 398.8MM *EMP* 3,300
SIC 8062 General medical & surgical hospitals; General medical & surgical hospitals
Ch: Carl E Westman
**Pr:* Allen S Weiss MD
COO: Gail Dolan
**CFO:* Vicki Hale
**Sec:* Edwin Stedem
Chf Mktg O: Aurora Estevez
Mtls Mgr: David Mobley
Doctor: Reisha Brown
Doctor: Karen Henrichsen
Doctor: Marchelle K Hofeldt MD
Doctor: Obayedur Khan
Board of Directors: Daniel Baer, Jay Baker

D-U-N-S 06-361-9100 EXP
NAPLES DODGE INC
6381 Airport Pulling Rd N, Naples, FL 34109-2015
Tel (239) 594-2100 *Founded/Ownrshp* 1972
Sales 32.0MM^E *EMP* 66
SIC 5511 Automobiles, new & used; Automobiles, new & used
Pr: Jon Myers
**VP:* Tom Myers
Exec: Trena McGill
**Prin:* Richard C Myers
Genl Mgr: Wayne Gratkowski

NAPLES FORT MEYERS GROUNDHOUND
See SOUTHWEST FLORIDA ENTERPRISES INC

D-U-N-S 87-642-8970
NAPLES ITALIAN AMERICAN CLUB
ITALIAN AMERICAN CLUB OF NAPLE
7035 Airport Pulling Rd N, Naples, FL 34109-1709
Tel (239) 597-5210 *Founded/Ownrshp* 1965
Sales 297.5M *EMP* 417
SIC 5812 Italian restaurant; Italian restaurant
Pr: Edith Coleman
**Treas:* Ronald Tenaro
**VP:* Joe Delfino

NAPLES MITSUBISHI
See OBRIEN IMPORTS OF FT MYERS INC

NAPLES PHILHARMONIC LEAGUE
See ARTIS-NAPLES INC

D-U-N-S 60-122-3241
NAPLETON ED DODGE INC
ED DODGE NAPLETON
17225 Torrence Ave, Lansing, IL 60438-1016
Tel (708) 636-5800 *Founded/Ownrshp* 1991
Sales 22.5MM^E *EMP* 65
SIC 5511 Automobiles, new & used; Automobiles, new & used
Pr: Ray Czarnik
**VP:* Edward F Napleton
Trfc Dir: Justin Hauser
Sls Mgr: MO Muhsen
Sls Mgr: George Obas
Sales Asso: Keith McKinney

NAPLETON, ED HONDA
See ED NAPLETON HONDA

D-U-N-S 96-716-9751
NAPLETON ENTERPRISES LLC
1460 E Osceola Pkwy, Kissimmee, FL 34744-1602
Tel (407) 483-7700 *Founded/Ownrshp* 2005
Sales 22.1MM^E *EMP* 70
SIC 5511 New & used car dealers; New & used car dealers
Genl Mgr: Vincent Ferrara

NAPLETON FORD IN LIBERTYVILLE
See FORD SESSLER INC

NAPLETON NORTHLAKE AUTO PARK
See NAPLETONS NORTH PALM AUTO PARK INC

D-U-N-S 36-060-4961
NAPLETON SCHAUMBURG MOTORS INC
NAPLETONS SCHAUMBURG MAZDA
110 W Golf Rd, Schaumburg, IL 60195-3604
Tel (847) 882-9000 *Founded/Ownrshp* 1988
Sales 28.3MM^E *EMP* 72
SIC 5511 7538 7532 5521 New & used car dealers; Automobiles, new & used; General automotive repair shops; Top & body repair & paint shops; Used car dealers; Automobiles, new & used; General automotive repair shops; Top & body repair & paint shops; Used car dealers
Pr: Stephen Napleton
**Sec:* C A Panek
**VP:* Carol Napleton
**VP:* Charles Weck

D-U-N-S 06-799-1554
NAPLETONS AUTO WERKS INC
JAGUAR
6600 E Riverside Blvd, Loves Park, IL 61111-4426
Tel (815) 636-6600 *Founded/Ownrshp* 1996
Sales 44.9MM^E *EMP* 100

SIC 5511 Automobiles, new & used; Automobiles, new & used
Pr: William F Napleton
**VP:* Paul Napleton

D-U-N-S 15-465-6896 EXP
NAPLETONS NORTH PALM AUTO PARK INC
NAPLETON NORTHLAKE AUTO PARK
3703 Northlake Blvd, Palm Beach Gardens, FL 33403-1629
Tel (561) 622-0101 *Founded/Ownrshp* 2001
Sales 33.2MM^E *EMP* 100
SIC 5511 Automobiles, new & used; Automobiles, new & used
Pr: Edward Napleton
**Treas:* Bruce Etheridge
**VP:* Kathy Napleton
Genl Mgr: Oe Wyers

NAPLETONS SCHAUMBURG MAZDA
See NAPLETON SCHAUMBURG MOTORS INC

D-U-N-S 61-110-7871
NAPOLEON BAKERY INC
MELROSE BAKERY
7356 Melrose Ave, Los Angeles, CA 90046-7527
Tel (323) 651-3822 *Founded/Ownrshp* 1989
Sales 21.1MM^E *EMP* 80
SIC 2051 Bakery: wholesale or wholesale/retail combined
Pr: Kevin Chapchin

D-U-N-S 06-337-3047 IMP/EXP
NAPOLEON CO
310 120th Ave Ne Ste A203, Bellevue, WA 98005-3013
Tel (425) 455-3776 *Founded/Ownrshp* 1903
Sales 20.1MM *EMP* 10
SIC 5149 5141 Specialty food items; Food brokers; Specialty food items; Food brokers
Pr: Joseph A Magnano
**VP:* Roger Thorson
Exec: Milo Magnano

D-U-N-S 62-214-5191 IMP
NAPOLI FOODS INC
10 Knotter Dr, Cheshire, CT 06410-1103
Tel (860) 276-4000 *Founded/Ownrshp* 1980
Sales 37.4MM^E *EMP* 75
SIC 5149 Specialty food items
Pr: Mark Cipriano
**Treas:* Angelo Farisello
**VP:* Michael Cipriano
Opers Mgr: Bill Nowak

D-U-N-S 01-871-9807
NAPOLI MOTORS INC (CT)
NAPOLI PONTIAC-NISSAN
688 Bridgeport Ave, Milford, CT 06460-3196
Tel (203) 877-5141 *Founded/Ownrshp* 1959
Sales 36.1MM *EMP* 43
SIC 5511 Automobiles, new & used; Automobiles, new & used
Pr: Leonard Napoli Jr
Genl Mgr: Scott Haverl
Off Mgr: Candace Miller
Sales Exec: John Ming
Sls Mgr: Lou Etemi

NAPOLI PONTIAC-NISSAN
See NAPOLI MOTORS INC

NAPOLI'S PIZZA
See WAL-BON OF OHIO INC

D-U-N-S 05-718-6231 IMP/EXP
NAPPCO FASTENER CO
11260 Hempstead Rd, Houston, TX 77092-7617
Tel (713) 688-2521 *Founded/Ownrshp* 1995
Sales 29.6MM^E *EMP* 65
SIC 5085

D-U-N-S 05-276-5542 IMP
NAPPI DISTRIBUTORS (ME)
615 Main St, Gorham, ME 04038-2676
Tel (207) 887-8200 *Founded/Ownrshp* 1959
Sales 76.1MM^E *EMP* 165
SIC 5182 5181 Wine; Beer & other fermented malt liquors; Wine; Beer & other fermented malt liquors
Pr: Frank Nappi
CFO: Elmer Alcott
**Ex VP:* Savitino Nappi
VP: Jim Bourque
Genl Mgr: Paul Carr
IT Man: Peter Pagilo
IT Man: Peter Paglio
Sls Dir: Tim Coffee
Sls Mgr: Pat Hazlett

NAPPIE'S FOOD SERVICE
See NAPPIES FRESH & FROZEN FOOD CO

D-U-N-S 01-399-8182 IMP
NAPPIES FRESH & FROZEN FOOD CO
NAPPIE'S FOOD SERVICE
8051 Steubenville Pike, Oakdale, PA 15071-9376
Tel (724) 695-3500 *Founded/Ownrshp* 1995, 1983
Sales 30.7MM^E *EMP* 50
SIC 5141 Groceries, general line
Pt: Edward Napoleone

D-U-N-S 94-649-4747
NAPROTEK INC
90 Rose Orchard Way, San Jose, CA 95134-1356
Tel (408) 830-5000 *Founded/Ownrshp* 1995
Sales 21.2MM^E *EMP* 61
SIC 3672 Printed circuit boards
CEO: Najat Badriyeh
VP: Geri Hehir
Prgrm Mgr: Nikki Hawkins
QI Cn Mgr: Arlis Greco

NAR-DAR/KC ST LOUIS
See PROCESS SUPPLY CO INC

NARC
See NOBLE AMERICAS RESOURCES CORP

D-U-N-S 07-684-2319
NARCO FREEDOM INC
250 Grand Concourse, Bronx, NY 10451-5430
Tel (718) 292-2240 *Founded/Ownrshp* 1971
Sales 46.1MM *EMP* 353
Accts Rosenblatt Levittan Vulpis Goe
SIC 8093 8011 Detoxification center, outpatient; Drug clinic, outpatient; Medical centers; Detoxification center, outpatient; Drug clinic, outpatient; Medical centers
CEO: Alan Brand
CFO: Brenda Vazquez
IT Man: Sam Levenson
Nrsg Dir: Jennifer Bowland

D-U-N-S 02-304-0900
NARDINI FIRE EQUIPMENT CO INC
405 County Road E W, Saint Paul, MN 55126-7093
Tel (651) 483-6631 *Founded/Ownrshp* 1955
Sales 34.7MM^E *EMP* 75
SIC 5099 7699 Fire extinguishers; Safety equipment & supplies; Fire control (military) equipment repair
Pr: Tom Nardini
Exec: Terry Palumbo
Dept Mgr: Zach Wilson
Genl Mgr: Dave Sorenson

NARDONE BROS
See NARDONE BROTHERS BAKING CO INC

D-U-N-S 00-305-2214 IMP
NARDONE BROTHERS BAKING CO INC
NARDONE BROS
420 New Commerce Blvd, Hanover Township, PA 18706-1445
Tel (570) 823-0141 *Founded/Ownrshp* 1915
Sales 50.0MM^E *EMP* 225
SIC 2038 5812 2099 Pizza, frozen; Eating places; Food preparations; Pizza, frozen; Eating places; Food preparations
Pr: Vincent Nardone
CFO: Louis J Nardone
**Treas:* Mario Nardone
**VP:* Frank Nardone

NARDY HONDA
See CENTURY MOTORS INC

NAREIT
See NATIONAL ASSOCIATION OF REAL ESTATE INVESTMENT TRUSTS INC

NARENCO
See NATIONAL RENEWABLE ENERGY CORP

NARH
See NORTHERN BERKSHIRE HEALTHCARE INC

NARMCO
See PRINCE METAL STAMPING USA INC

NARON CANDY COMPANY
See RUXTON CHOCOLATES LLC

D-U-N-S 01-061-3396
NAROPA UNIVERSITY
BOULDER COLLEGE OF MASSAGE THE
2130 Arapahoe Ave, Boulder, CO 80302-6602
Tel (303) 444-0202 *Founded/Ownrshp* 1974
Sales 26.4MM *EMP* 394
Accts Ehrhardt Keefe Steiner & Hottm
SIC 8221 College, except junior; College, except junior
Pr: Charles G Lief
Ofcr: Erin Farrell
**VP:* Sue Evans
Adm Dir: Genet Simone
Ex Dir: Gene Hooley
CIO: Harvey Nichols
IT Man: Janet Guidici

D-U-N-S 80-986-4002
NARRAGANSETT BAY INSURANCE CO
PAWTUCKET
25 Maple St, Pawtucket, RI 02860-2104
Tel (401) 725-5600 *Founded/Ownrshp* 2005
Sales NA *EMP* 48
SIC 6331 Fire, marine & casualty insurance & carriers; Automobile insurance; Property damage insurance
CEO: Todd C Hart
**CFO:* Kirk Lusk
**Ch:* Stewart H Steffey Jr
Bd of Dir: Dale Hammond
**Ofcr:* Richard Grisolia
**Ofcr:* Bob Khosropur
**Sr VP:* Timothy Moura
**Sr VP:* John Rafferty
**Sr VP:* Jose Trasancos
**Sr VP:* Brendan Voss
VP: Nicole Perrault
VP: John Siano

NARRAGANSETT CREAMERY
See PROVIDENCE SPECIALTY PRODUCTS INC

D-U-N-S 00-119-3655
NARRAGANSETT ELECTRIC CO (RI)
(*Suby of* NATIONAL GRID USA) ★
280 Melrose St, Providence, RI 02907-2157
Tel (401) 784-7000 *Founded/Ownrshp* 1926, 1969
Sales 339.9MM^E *EMP* 800
SIC 4911 Generation, electric power; Transmission, electric power; Distribution, electric power; Generation, electric power; Transmission, electric power; Distribution, electric power
Pr: Timothy F Horan
**Treas:* Malcolm Charles Cooper
**Ex VP:* Ellen Smith
**Sr VP:* James B Howe
**Sr VP:* Colin Owyang
VP: Tim Horan
VP: Charles Meunier
VP: Sharon Partridge
VP: Jeffrey Polucha
**VP:* Michael F Ryan
**VP:* Martin Wheatcroft
VP: Ed White
Exec: Lynda Scannell
Board of Directors: James B Howe, Thomas B King, Paul R Renaud, Michael F Ryan, Ellen Smith

D-U-N-S 00-680-7911
NARRAGANSETT IMPROVEMENT CO (RI)
223 Allens Ave, Providence, RI 02903-4937
Tel (401) 331-0051 *Founded/Ownrshp* 1893
Sales 38.4MM^E *EMP* 100^E
SIC 6552 1611 1794 2951 Subdividers & developers; Highway & street construction; Excavation work; Asphalt paving mixtures & blocks
Pr: John E Everson
**Treas:* Dustin J Everson
Treas: Dustin Everson
**VP:* Jon Toegemann

D-U-N-S 93-392-9069 IMP/EXP
NARROFLEX INC
UNITED ELASTIC-A NARROFLEX CO
201 S Main St, Stuart, VA 24171-3960
Tel (276) 694-7171 *Founded/Ownrshp* 2011
Sales 25.7MM^E *EMP* 165
SIC 2241 Elastic narrow fabrics, woven or braided; Elastic narrow fabrics, woven or braided
Pr: Xavier Joseph
CFO: Bruce Baden

NARS
See NORTH AMERICAN RISK SERVICES INC

NARS
See INTEGRITY SOLUTION SERVICES INC

D-U-N-S 83-736-3571 IMP
NARS COSMETICS INC
(*Suby of* SHISEIDO AMERICAS CORP) ★
900 3rd Ave Fl 17, New York, NY 10022-4792
Tel (212) 941-0890 *Founded/Ownrshp* 1994
Sales 197.1MM^E *EMP* 390
SIC 5122 Cosmetics; Cosmetics
Ch: Kuninori Veno
**CEO:* Louis Desazars
**Ch:* Suichi Tanaka
Genl Mgr: Carlos Alcazar

D-U-N-S 14-353-5255 IMP
NARSTCO INC
300 Ward Rd, Midlothian, TX 76065-9646
Tel (972) 775-5560 *Founded/Ownrshp* 2002
Sales 22.3MM^E *EMP* 70
SIC 3312 Rails, steel or iron
CEO: Sean Keightley
**VP:* John Coulam
**Prin:* Matt Violin
**Prin:* Kristin Ward
Opers Mgr: Darwyn Cornwell

D-U-N-S 09-331-3823 IMP
NAS-TRA AUTOMOTIVE INDUSTRIES INC (NY)
NASTRA AUTOMOTIVE
3 Sidney Ct, Lindenhurst, NY 11757-1011
Tel (631) 225-1225 *Founded/Ownrshp* 1978
Sales 24.4MM^E *EMP* 150
SIC 3714 3694 3625 Motor vehicle parts & accessories; Engine electrical equipment; Relays & industrial controls; Motor vehicle parts & accessories; Engine electrical equipment; Relays & industrial controls
Ch Bd: James Lambert
**Pr:* Americo De Rocchis
**Sec:* Antonio Abbatiello
Off Mgr: Mary Smith
Plnt Mgr: Tim Nolan

NASA
See NATIONAL AERONAUTICS AND SPACE ADMINISTRATION

NASA
See JOHN F KENNEDY SPACE CENTER

D-U-N-S 00-923-1648
■ **NASA AMES RESEARCH CENTER**
(*Suby of* NASA) ★
Moffet Fld, Moffett Field, CA 94035
Tel (650) 604-5000 *Founded/Ownrshp* 1939
Sales NA *EMP* 958^E
SIC 9661 Space flight operations, government; Space research & development, government; ; Space flight operations, government; Space research & development, government;
**CFO:* Paul Agnew
Exec: Ruth Marlaire
Rgnl Mgr: Julia Horner
Software D: Vinay Suri
Sftwr Eng: Steve Elkins
Sftwr Eng: Vu Tran
QI Cn Mgr: Bob Mohlenhoff
Snr Mgr: Kevin Kouba

D-U-N-S 16-486-2935
NASA ELECTRONICS CORP
2330 Nw 102nd Pl, Doral, FL 33172-2517
Tel (305) 716-7706 *Founded/Ownrshp* 2002
Sales 100.0MM *EMP* 8
SIC 5065 Electronic parts & equipment; Electronic parts & equipment
Owner: Hussein M Alawieh
**Pr:* Mohammad I Ghaddar
**Pr:* Diya Salame
**VP:* Mohammad Hteit

D-U-N-S 08-107-4510
NASA FEDERAL CREDIT UNION
500 Prince Georges Blvd, Upper Marlboro, MD 20774-8732
Tel (301) 249-1800 *Founded/Ownrshp* 1949
Sales NA *EMP* 200
SIC 6061 Federal credit unions; Federal credit unions
Pr: Douglas M Allman
CFO: Rhonda Bazey
VP: Bill White
Brnch Mgr: Stesan Bradham

D-U-N-S 02-761-3459
■ **NASA LANGLEY RESEARCH CENTER**
(*Suby of* NASA) ★
11 Langley Blvd, Hampton, VA 23681-2143
Tel (757) 864-1000 *Founded/Ownrshp* 1917
Sales NA *EMP* 4,000^E
SIC 9661 Space flight operations, government; Space research & development, government; ; Space flight operations, government; Space research & development, government;
Ofcr: Les Kagey
Ofcr: Nora Normandy
Top Exec: Stanley Cole
Top Exec: William Cooke
Top Exec: Gary Gibson
Top Exec: Larry Leavitt
Top Exec: William Winfree
Assoc Dir: Frank Jones
Comm Man: T Memory
Prgrm Mgr: Bill Copeland
Prgrm Mgr: Chris Holloway

D-U-N-S 01-999-1694
■ **NASA/ARMSTRONG FLIGHT RESEARCH CENTER**
NASA/DRYDEN FLIGHT RES CTR
(*Suby of* NASA) ★
4800 Lilly Dr Ms 4839 4839 Ms, Edwards, CA 93523
Tel (661) 276-3449 *Founded/Ownrshp* 2005
Sales NA *EMP* 498^E
SIC 9661 Space flight operations, government; Space research & development, government; ; Space flight operations, government; Space research & development, government;
**CFO:* Robert Gardner
Ofcr: CAM Martin
Off Admin: Glenda Almeida
QA Dir: Steven Spandorf
Netwrk Eng: Edwin Koshimoto

NASA/DRYDEN FLIGHT RES CTR
See NASA/ARMSTRONG FLIGHT RESEARCH CENTER

D-U-N-S 00-452-3320
■ **NASA/GLENN RESEARCH CENTER**
(*Suby of* NASA) ★
21000 Brookpark Rd, Cleveland, OH 44135-3191
Tel (216) 433-4000 *Founded/Ownrshp* 1941
Sales NA *EMP* 3,359^E
SIC 9661 Space flight operations, government; Space research & development, government; ; Space flight operations, government; Space research & development, government;
Prin: Arlene Holbert
Adm Dir: Victoria Anzalone
Adm Dir: Linda Yavoich
IT Man: Richard Czentorycki
IT Man: Chuck Trefny
IT Man: Allison Walker
Netwrk Eng: Bilal Bomani
Netwrk Eng: Jason Edwards
Netwrk Eng: Brian Frantz
Netwrk Eng: Alessandro Geist
Netwrk Eng: James Griner

D-U-N-S 00-496-8611
■ **NASA/GODDARD SPACE FLIGHT CENTER**
(*Suby of* NASA) ★
8800 Greenbelt Rd, Greenbelt, MD 20771-0002
Tel (301) 286-2000 *Founded/Ownrshp* 2002
Sales NA *EMP* 7,000^E
SIC 9661 Space flight operations, government; Space research & development, government; ; Space flight operations, government; Space research & development, government;
**CFO:* Nancy Abell
Assoc Dir: Mitchell Brown
Assoc Dir: Frederick Huegel
Assoc Dir: Eric Isaac
Comm Man: Amy Johnson
Prgrm Mgr: Kenneth Anderson
Prgrm Mgr: Robert Bartlett
Prgrm Mgr: Sherri Panciera
Off Admin: Bruce Gentry
IT Man: Mark McInerney
IT Man: William Pence

D-U-N-S 06-037-5672
■ **NASA/JET PROPULSION LABORATORY INC**
(*Suby of* NASA) ★
4800 Oak Grove Dr, La Canada Flintridge, CA 91011
Tel (818) 354-4321 *Founded/Ownrshp* 2003
Sales NA *EMP* 5,000
SIC 9661 Space flight operations, government; Space research & development, government; ; Space flight operations, government
Assoc Dir: Thomas Gavin
Prgrm Mgr: Larry Bergman
Prgrm Mgr: Fuk LI
CIO: Tom Soderstrom
Sftwr Eng: Cara Cheung
Sftwr Eng: Edith Parrott
Genl Couns: Harry Yohalem
Snr Mgr: Timothy Corn
Snr Mgr: Paul Dimotakis
Snr Mgr: Steven Jones
Snr Mgr: Jonathan Pettus

D-U-N-S 01-945-3930
■ **NASA/MARSHALL SPACE FLIGHT CENTER RETIREES ASSOCIATION**
(*Suby of* NASA) ★
Nasa Marshall Space, Huntsville, AL 35812
Tel (256) 544-2121 *Founded/Ownrshp* 1994
Sales NA *EMP* 3,000
SIC 9661 Space flight operations, government; Space research & development, government; ; Space flight operations, government; Space research & development, government;
Exec: Willard McFarland
Brnch Mgr: Doris Jallice
Brnch Mgr: Cynthia Jarvis
Genl Mgr: Don Beckmeyer
Dir IT: Lisa Roberts
IT Man: Cassandra Robinson
IT Man: Belinda Triplett
Sftwr Eng: Rodney Grubbs
Netwrk Eng: Tim Baldridge
Netwrk Eng: Darren Bedell
Netwrk Eng: Ron Newby

D-U-N-S 03-700-9581
▲ NASB FINANCIAL INC
12498 S Us Highway 71, Grandview, MO 64030-1733
Tel (816) 765-2200 Founded/Ownrshp 1998
Sales NA EMP 463E
Accts Bkd Llp Kansas City Missour
Tkr Sym NASB Exch OTO
SIC 6035 Savings institutions, federally chartered; Savings institutions, federally chartered
CEO: Paul L Thomas
*Ch Bd: David H Hancock
CFO: Rhonda Nyhus
Ex VP: Bruce J Thielen
Sr VP: Bruce Thielen
VP: Roger Campbell
VP: Pat Cox
VP: Wade Hall
VP: Jennie Harris
VP: Rachel Jones
VP: Lisa Lillard
VP: Marquise Mansaw
VP: Luke Miller
VP: Dan Morton
VP: Lori West
VP: Donna Williams
Exec: Shauna Olson
Adv Bd Mbr: Susan Bustamante
Board of Directors: Frederick V Arbanas, Barrett Brady, Laura Brady, Linda S Hancock, W Russell Welsh

NASC
See NAVMAR APPLIED SCIENCES CORP

NASCAR
See NATIONAL ASSOCIATION FOR STOCK CAR AUTO RACING INC

NASCAR MEDIA GROUP
See NASCAR PRODUCTIONS LLC

D-U-N-S 02-722-1621
NASCAR PRODUCTIONS LLC
NASCAR MEDIA GROUP
550 S Caldwell St # 2000, Charlotte, NC 28202-2633
Tel (704) 348-7131 Founded/Ownrshp 2000
Sales 27.2MME EMP 200
SIC 7812 7922 Video tape production; Television program, including commercial producers; Video tape production; Television program, including commercial producers
COO: Jay Abraham
Snr Mgr: Colleen Young

NASCENT FOODSERVICE
See NASCENT WINE CO INC

D-U-N-S 61-485-7048
NASCENT WINE CO INC
NASCENT FOODSERVICE
12055 E Broadway Blvd, Tucson, AZ 85748-6944
Tel (619) 730-1604 Founded/Ownrshp 2002
Sales 20.6MME EMP 300
Tkr Sym NCTW Exch OTO
SIC 5182 8742 Wine & distilled beverages; Food & beverage consultant; Wine & distilled beverages; Food & beverage consultant
CEO: Sandro Piancone
*CFO: Peter V White
Board of Directors: Thomas J Soucy

NASCO
See NATIVE AMERICAN SERVICES CORP

NASCO
See ARISTOTLE CORP

NASCO
See NATIONAL ACCOUNT SERVICE CO LLC

D-U-N-S 10-113-2038
NASCO AEROSPACE AND ELECTRONICS LLC
NASCO DISTRIBUTORS SALES
150 2nd Ave N Ste 550, Saint Petersburg, FL 33701-3340
Tel (727) 344-7554 Founded/Ownrshp 2001
Sales 27.7MME EMP 31E
SIC 5088 5065 Aeronautical equipment & supplies; Connectors, electronic
QI Cn Mgr: Woody Hewett
*Sls Mgr: Frank Bagnasco
Sls Mgr: Brad Yazell

D-U-N-S 12-087-1892
NASCO AIRCRAFT BRAKE INC
MEGGITT ARCFT BRAKING SYSTEMS
(Suby of MABSC) ★
13300 Estrella Ave, Gardena, CA 90248-1519
Tel (310) 532-4430 Founded/Ownrshp 2006
Sales 22.5MME EMP 100
SIC 3728 Brakes, aircraft
Pr: Daniel Aron
*Sec: Phil Friedman
Opers Mgr: Matthew Aron
QI Cn Mgr: Yousef Youesi

NASCO DISTRIBUTORS SALES
See NASCO AEROSPACE AND ELECTRONICS LLC

NASCO FORT ATKINSON
See NASCO INTERNATIONAL INC

D-U-N-S 61-465-8664
NASCO GOURMET FOODS INC
PLATINUM DISTRIBUTION
(Suby of NASSER CO INC) ★
22720 Savi Ranch Pkwy, Yorba Linda, CA 92887-4608
Tel (714) 279-2100 Founded/Ownrshp 1990
Sales 21.4MME EMP 65
SIC 2033 Seasonings, tomato: packaged in cans, jars, etc.
Pr: Burhan Nasser
*Sec: Mary Beth Nasser
*VP: Jerry Pascoe
Dir IT: Lorynn Mason
IT Man: Gregory Dapkus

D-U-N-S 09-537-7107
NASCO INDUSTRIES INC
3 Ne 21st St, Washington, IN 47501-3111
Tel (812) 254-7393 Founded/Ownrshp 1979
Sales 26.5MME EMP 120
Accts Kemper Cpa Group Llc Washingt
SIC 2385 Waterproof outerwear
Pr: Todd N Smith
*CFO: John Richardson
*Ch: Neil A Smith
IT Man: Marcus Brashear
Board of Directors: Joe Kilps, Dick Mc Clure, Jeff Smith

D-U-N-S 00-177-9008 IMP/EXP
NASCO INTERNATIONAL INC
NASCO FORT ATKINSON
901 Janesville Ave, Fort Atkinson, WI 53538-2497
Tel (920) 563-2446 Founded/Ownrshp 1941
Sales NA EMP 600E
SIC 5961 3999

D-U-N-S 16-276-3820 IMP
NASCOTE INDUSTRIES INC
(Suby of MAGNA INTERNATIONAL INC)
18310 Enterprise Ave, Nashville, IL 62263-1619
Tel (618) 327-3286 Founded/Ownrshp 2006
Sales 254.4MME EMP 800
SIC 3714 Bumpers & bumperettes, motor vehicle; Bumpers & bumperettes, motor vehicle
Pr: Andrew Barban
*Pr: Alan J Power
CIO: Brian Mense
Mtls Dir: Art Stolle
QI Cn Mgr: Greg Kasban
QI Cn Mgr: Ziegler Mark
QI Cn Mgr: Vinny Pagano
Snr Mgr: Josh Milburn

NASDA
See NATIONAL ASSOCIATION OF STATE DEPARTMENTS OF AGRICULTURE INC

D-U-N-S 83-107-7578
■ NASDAQ GLOBAL INC
(Suby of NASDAQ INC) ★
9600 Blackwell Rd Ste 500, Rockville, MD 20850-3783
Tel (301) 978-8008 Founded/Ownrshp 2009
Sales 54.5MME EMP 79E
SIC 6231 Security & commodity exchanges
Prin: E Bruce
*Assoc VP: Gregory Pelosi
VP: Lucien Foster
VP: Jeannie Merritt
VP: Gary Sundick
Assoc Dir: Brie Charles
Assoc Dir: Anahi Pilarz
DP Dir: Eugene Jennings
Dir IT: Robert Vilardo
Genl Couns: Alex Kogan
Counsel: Erika Moore

D-U-N-S 12-655-4732
▲ NASDAQ INC
1 Liberty Plz Ste 4900, New York, NY 10006-1400
Tel (212) 401-8700 Founded/Ownrshp 1971
Sales 3.5MMM EMP 3,687E
Accts Ernst & Young Llp New York N
Tkr Sym NDAQ Exch NGS
SIC 6231 8742 Security & commodity exchanges; Financial consultant; Security & commodity exchanges; Financial consultant
CEO: Robert Greifeld
*Ch Bd: Borje Ekholm
Pr: Brian Kreider
Pr: John Oboyle
Pr: Dominick Paniscotti
Pr: Michael Pelliccia
CFO: Lee Shavel
Assoc VP: Steven Bump
Assoc VP: Kenneth Hawley
Assoc VP: Bill Nosal
Assoc VP: Ira Reiss
Assoc VP: Jim Wee
Ex VP: Chris Concannon
Ex VP: Christopher R Concannon
Ex VP: Salil Donde
Ex VP: Anna M Ewing
Ex VP: Edward S Knight
Ex VP: Bradley J Peterson
Ex VP: Denise B Stires
Ex VP: Brian Tock
Ex VP: Thomas A Wittman
Board of Directors: Charlene T Begley, Steven D Black, Glenn H Hutchins, Thomas A Kloet, John D Markese, Ellyn A McColgan, Thomas F O'neill, Michael R Splinter, Lars R Wedenborn

NASDAQ OMX
See OMX (US) INC

NASDAQ OMX BXSM
See BOSTON STOCK EXCHANGE INC

D-U-N-S 07-916-4212
■ NASDAQ OMX CORPORATE SOLUTIONS LLC
(Suby of NASDAQ INC) ★
1 Liberty Plz Ste 4900, New York, NY 10006-1400
Tel (212) 231-5369 Founded/Ownrshp 2013
Sales 229.1MME EMP 2,009
SIC 6231 Security exchanges; Security exchanges
VP: Demetrios Skalkotos

D-U-N-S 00-232-3087
■ NASDAQ OMX PHLX LLC
(Suby of NASDAQ INC) ★
1900 Market St Fl 2, Philadelphia, PA 19103-3510
Tel (215) 496-5000 Founded/Ownrshp 1790, 2008
Sales 328.6MM EMP 130E
Accts Ernst & Young Llp New York N
SIC 6231 Security & commodity exchanges; Management services; Security & commodity exchanges
Pr: Thomas Wittman
Treas: Tom Kelly
Ofcr: Charles Roger
Ex VP: William N Briggs
Ex VP: Lanny Schwartz
VP: Lynda Caravello
VP: Bernie Donnally
VP: Robert Grant
VP: Edith Hallahan
VP: Robert Intartaglio
VP: Kevin J Kennedy
VP: Amy Kitzen
VP: Ken Meaden
VP: Richard Rudolph
VP: Walt Smith
VP: Tom Wittman

D-U-N-S 82-626-0163
■ NASDAQ STOCK MARKET LLC
(Suby of NASDAQ INC) ★
1 Liberty Plz Ste 4900, New York, NY 10006-1400
Tel (301) 978-4144 Founded/Ownrshp 2011
Sales 67.0MME EMP 169E
SIC 6231 Security & commodity exchanges
CEO: Robert Greifeld
CFO: Lee Shavel
Ex VP: Anna Ewing
Sr VP: Joan Conley
VP: Bruce E Aust
VP: Terry Campbell
VP: Thomas Fay
VP: Magnus Haglind
VP: Tom Kucinski
VP: Stefan Lemos
VP: Peter Manzella
VP: Jeannie Merritt
VP: John Zecca
Dir Risk M: Jesper Bruzelius
Assoc Dir: Meagan Brady
Assoc Dir: Jeff Preusse

D-U-N-S 08-714-1370
NASDI LLC
39 Olympia Ave, Woburn, MA 01801-2035
Tel (781) 250-6600 Founded/Ownrshp 2014
Sales 37.6MME EMP 150
Accts Deloitte Touche Llp Chicago
SIC 1795 1799 1794 Demolition, buildings & other structures; Asbestos removal & encapsulation; Excavation & grading, building construction; Demolition, buildings & other structures; Asbestos removal & encapsulation; Excavation & grading, building construction
CEO: Jonathan Berger
*CFO: William Steckel
*Treas: Katherine Hayes

D-U-N-S 04-106-7013
NASG TENNESSEE NORTH 1 LLC
NORTH AMERICAN STAMPING GROUP
(Suby of NORTH AMERICAN STAMPING GROUP LLC) ★
119 Kirby Dr, Portland, TN 37148-2004
Tel (615) 323-0500 Founded/Ownrshp 1998
Sales 38.6MME EMP 220
SIC 3465 Automotive stampings; Automotive stampings
Pr: Mike Haughey
Opers Mgr: Leo Lublac

D-U-N-S 07-925-1912
NASG TENNESSEE NORTH 2 LLC (TN)
(Suby of NORTH AMERICAN STAMPING GROUP LLC) ★
160 Kirby Dr, Portland, TN 37148-2003
Tel (615) 323-0500 Founded/Ownrshp 2013
Sales 225.0MME EMP 165
SIC 3465 Automotive stampings; Automotive stampings
Ch: Jana Haughey
CFO: David Hannah

D-U-N-S 03-376-0539
NASH CHEVROLET CO
630 Scenic Hwy, Lawrenceville, GA 30046-6363
Tel (770) 963-9266 Founded/Ownrshp 1955
Sales 52.9MME EMP 115
SIC 5511 Automobiles, new & used; Automobiles, new & used
Pr: Coy T Nash
CFO: Gary Ernest
*VP: Mark Nash
Sls Mgr: Clinton Sisco

D-U-N-S 14-436-2423
NASH COMMUNITY COLLEGE FOUNDATION INC
(Suby of NORTH CAROLINA COMMUNITY COLLEGE SYSTEM) ★
522 N Old Carriage Rd, Rocky Mount, NC 27804-9708
Tel (252) 443-4011 Founded/Ownrshp 1967
Sales 56.8MME EMP 400
SIC 8222 9411 Community college; Administration of educational programs; ; Community college; Administration of educational programs;
Pr: William S Carver II
Store Mgr: Lindsey Schulte
Dir IT: Andy Castillo
Dir IT: Jonathan Vester
Psych: Charlene Bell

D-U-N-S 01-156-3301 IMP
NASH DISTRIBUTORS INC (NJ)
801 Washington Ave, Carlstadt, NJ 07072-3002
Tel (201) 896-1330 Founded/Ownrshp 1904, 1959
Sales 36.9MME EMP 100
SIC 5181 Beer & other fermented malt liquors; Beer & other fermented malt liquors
CEO: Mike Nash
*VP: Beverly Nash

NASH GENERAL HOSPITAL
See NHCS INC

D-U-N-S 80-386-1186
NASH HEALTH CARE SYSTEMS
2460 Curtis Ellis Dr, Rocky Mount, NC 27804-2237
Tel (252) 962-8000 Founded/Ownrshp 1983
Sales 163.5MME EMP 1,850E
SIC 8011 8741 Clinic, operated by physicians; Management services; Clinic, operated by physicians; Management services
Ch: Vincent C Andracchio II
*Pr: Larry Chewning
*Pr: Mary Chewning
*COO: Bradd Weisner
*CFO: Leslie Hall
*CFO: Al Hooks
*Treas: James Lilley
*Sr VP: CAM Blalock
VP: Brian Agan
Exec: Pam Owens
Dir Inf Cn: Wanda Lamm
Dir Rx: Michael Lamonds

D-U-N-S 83-076-2576
NASH HOLDINGS LLC
1403 Hamlin St Ne, Washington, DC 20017-2944
Tel (202) 334-6727 Founded/Ownrshp 2013
Sales 1.7MMME EMP 10,000E
SIC 2711 2721 Newspapers, publishing & printing; Periodicals: publishing & printing

D-U-N-S 00-319-9692 IMP/EXP
NASH JOHNSON & SONS FARMS INC
Hwy 117 N, Rose Hill, NC 28458
Tel (910) 289-3113 Founded/Ownrshp 1950
Sales 1.0MMM EMP 6,000
SIC 2015 0254 0253 0251 2048 Poultry, slaughtered & dressed; Poultry hatcheries; Turkey farm; Broiler, fryer & roaster chickens; Poultry feeds; Poultry, slaughtered & dressed; Poultry hatcheries; Turkey farm; Broiler, fryer & roaster chickens; Poultry feeds
CEO: Robert C Johnson
*Ch Bd: E Marvin Johnson
*COO: Don Taber
Genl Mgr: Dennis Beasley
Dir IT: Chuck Robison
VP Sls: Robert Johnson

D-U-N-S 13-110-7757
NASH KENSEY CORP
DSM BIOMEDICAL
(Suby of KONINKLIJKE DSM N.V.)
735 Pennsylvania Dr, Exton, PA 19341-1130
Tel (484) 713-2100 Founded/Ownrshp 2012
Sales 86.7MME EMP 307E
SIC 3841 Surgical & medical instruments; Surgical & medical instruments
Pr: Joseph W Kaufmann
*COO: Douglas G Evans
*CFO: Michael Celano
VP: Simon Coles
VP: Donald Daveer
VP: Donald Daveler
*VP: Todd W Dewitt
VP: Tom Maguire
*VP: John E Nash
VP: John Nash
VP: Ted Rauth
VP: Cynthia Rose
Dir Bus: Jediah White
Board of Directors: Robert J Bobb, Lisa Earnhardt, C McCollister Evarts MD, Walter R Maupay Jr, Donald E Morel Jr Phd

D-U-N-S 09-658-7332
NASH PLUMBING AND MECHANICAL LLC
3494 N Us Highway 301, Wildwood, FL 34785-8373
Tel (352) 748-1454 Founded/Ownrshp 1999
Sales 52.2MM EMP 250
Accts Mixner & Company Orlando Fl
SIC 1711 1611 Plumbing contractors; Warm air heating & air conditioning contractor; Mechanical contractor; Plumbing contractors; Warm air heating & air conditioning contractor; Mechanical contractor; General contractor, highway & street construction
CEO: James C Nash
*Pr: David J Mears III
*Sec: Susan E Nash
*VP: Ryan Nash
*VP: Monte Wilson

D-U-N-S 16-185-2665
NASH PRODUCE LLC
6160 S Nc Highway 58, Nashville, NC 27856-8642
Tel (252) 443-6011 Founded/Ownrshp 2006
Sales 43.9MM EMP 50
Accts Rabon & Dailey Llp Cpa Rale
SIC 0723 Fruit (farm-dried) packing services; Fruit (fresh) packing services; Vegetable packing services; Fruit (farm-dried) packing services; Fruit (fresh) packing services; Vegetable packing services
*VP: Richard Joyner

D-U-N-S 00-696-2294 IMP
■ NASH-FINCH CO
(Suby of SPARTANNASH CO) ★
7600 France Ave S Ste 200, Minneapolis, MN 55435-5920
Tel (952) 832-0534 Founded/Ownrshp 1885, 2013
Sales 3.9MMME EMP 8,134
SIC 5141 5148 5142 5147 5411 Groceries, general line; Fruits, fresh; Vegetables, fresh; Packaged frozen goods; Meats, fresh; Meats, cured or smoked; Supermarkets, chain; Groceries, general line; Fruits, fresh; Vegetables, fresh; Packaged frozen goods; Meats, fresh; Meats, cured or smoked; Supermarkets, chain
Pr: Dennis Eidson
CFO: Robert B Dimond
Treas: David M Staples
Bd of Dir: Doug Hacker
Ex VP: Kathleen M Mahoney
Ex VP: Jeffrey E Poore
Ex VP: Calvin S Sihilling
Sr VP: Howard Befort
Sr VP: Terri Belene
Sr VP: Edward L Brunot
Sr VP: Lonnie Eggers
Sr VP: Keith Erickson
Sr VP: Tom Swanson
Sr VP: Denise M Wilson
VP: Alex J Deyonker
VP: Terry Littrell
Exec: Steve Brougham
Dir Risk M: Bill Weisbrod

D-U-N-S 80-832-8306
NASH-ROCKY MOUNT SCHOOLS
NRMS
930 Eastern Ave, Nashville, NC 27856-1716
Tel (252) 459-5220 Founded/Ownrshp 1992

Sales 102.0MM^E *EMP* 2,670
SIC 8211 Public elementary & secondary schools; Public elementary & secondary schools
VP: Jim Albright
Exec: Sharon Spain
MIS Dir: Lisa Ballance
IT Man: Sharon Braswell
Pr Dir: Patricia Hollingsworth
Instr Medi: Danny Plyler

D-U-N-S 05-231-9001 IMP/EXP
NASHBAR DIRECT INC
BIKE NASHBAR
(*Suby of* PERFORMANCE BICYCLE) ★
6103 State Route 446, Canfield, OH 44406-9428
Tel (330) 533-1989 *Founded/Ownrshp* 2000
Sales 26.6MM^E *EMP* 200
SIC 5961

D-U-N-S 07-661-6598
NASHOBA COMMUNITY HOSPITAL INC
NASHOBA VALLEY MEDICAL CENTER
(*Suby of* CARITAS CHRISTI HEALTH CARE) ★
200 Groton Rd, Ayer, MA 01432-1168
Tel (978) 784-9000 *Founded/Ownrshp* 2003
Sales 61.2MM^E *EMP* 365
SIC 8062 General medical & surgical hospitals; General medical & surgical hospitals
CEO: Steve Roach
**Pr:* Salvatore Perla
**COO:* Doreen Thomas
Dir Rx: Dick Oakley
CIO: Armen Arajelian
Pr Dir: Rosanna Casavecchia
Pathlgst: Magdy Salama
Obsttrcn: Zoe Gillis
Doctor: John P Katzenberg MD
Doctor: James E Tat MD
Pharmcst: Joe McLaughlin

D-U-N-S 10-003-2440
NASHOBA REGIONAL SCHOOL DISTRICT INC
50 Mechanic St, Bolton, MA 01740-1327
Tel (978) 779-0539 *Founded/Ownrshp* 1953
Sales 27.3MM^E *EMP* 500
SIC 8211 Public elementary & secondary schools; Public elementary & secondary schools

NASHOBA VALLEY MEDICAL CENTER
See NASHOBA COMMUNITY HOSPITAL INC

D-U-N-S 06-675-8343
NASHUA CITY OF (INC)
229 Main St, Nashua, NH 03060-9220
Tel (603) 589-3000 *Founded/Ownrshp* 1853
Sales NA *EMP* 919
Accts Melanson Heath & Company Pc
SIC 9111 Executive offices; City & town managers' offices; Mayors' offices; Executive offices; City & town managers' offices; Mayors' offices

D-U-N-S 00-107-9433 EXP
■ **NASHUA CORP**
NASHUA SPECIALTY COATED PDTS
(*Suby of* CENVEO INC) ★
59 Daniel Webster Hwy A, Merrimack, NH 03054-4831
Tel (603) 880-1100 *Founded/Ownrshp* 2009
Sales 178.9MM^E *EMP* 761
SIC 2672 2754 2679 2621 2782 Thermoplastic coated paper: made from purchased materials; Adhesive papers, labels or tapes: from purchased material; Gummed paper: made from purchased materials; Labels (unprinted), gummed: made from purchased materials; Tickets: gravure printing; Tags & labels, paper; Specialty papers; Receipt, invoice & memorandum books; Thermoplastic coated paper: made from purchased materials; Adhesive papers, labels or tapes: from purchased material; Gummed paper: made from purchased materials; Labels (unprinted), gummed: made from purchased materials; Tickets: gravure printing; Tags & labels, paper; Specialty papers; Receipt, invoice & memorandum books
Pr: Thomas G Brooker
**Pr:* Robert G Burton Sr
**CFO:* Scott Goodwin
**CFO:* John L Patenaude
**Treas:* David Jacoboski
VP: William Todd McKeown
Sls Mgr: Helen Duquette

D-U-N-S 17-673-1412
■ **NASHUA HOLLIS CVS INC**
(*Suby of* CVS HEALTH CORP) ★
1 Cvs Dr, Woonsocket, RI 02895-6146
Tel (401) 765-1500 *Founded/Ownrshp* 1989
Sales 386.1MM^E *EMP* 3,195
SIC 5912 Drug stores & proprietary stores; Drug stores & proprietary stores
Prin: Thomas Ryan

D-U-N-S 02-154-1206
NASHUA HOMES OF IDAHO INC
5200 S Federal Way, Boise, ID 83716-9638
Tel (208) 345-0222 *Founded/Ownrshp* 1961
Sales 26.0MM^E *EMP* 130
SIC 2451 Mobile homes; Mobile homes
VP: Milt Barningham
**Treas:* Bryan S Norby
Exec: Ron Zenor

D-U-N-S 10-005-0327
NASHUA SCHOOL DISTRICT
141 Ledge St, Nashua, NH 03060-3073
Tel (603) 966-1000 *Founded/Ownrshp* 1853
Sales 90.0MM^E *EMP* 2,000
SIC 8211 8741 Elementary & secondary schools; Management services; Elementary & secondary schools; Management services
Treas: Amy Tefft
Dir Bus: Julie Simons

NASHUA SPECIALTY COATED PDTS
See NASHUA CORP

D-U-N-S 07-930-1304
NASHVILLE AUTOMOTIVE LLC
SERRA CHEVROLET BUICK GMC
2340 Gallatin Pike N, Madison, TN 37115-2008
Tel (615) 851-8000 *Founded/Ownrshp* 2013
Sales 100.0MM *EMP* 138
SIC 5511 Automobiles, new & used; Automobiles, new & used
Pr: Joseph O Serra
VP: Barry K Carver

D-U-N-S 10-336-8549
NASHVILLE BUN CO LLC
NBC
2975 Armory Dr, Nashville, TN 37204-3768
Tel (615) 256-6500 *Founded/Ownrshp* 1999
Sales 25.7MM *EMP* 120
SIC 2051

NASHVILLE CHRY
See PREMIER AUTOMOTIVE OFTN LLC

NASHVILLE, CITY OF
See METROPOLITAN GOVERNMENT OF NASHVILLE & DAVIDSON COUNTY

D-U-N-S 19-853-6406
NASHVILLE CONVENTION & VISITORS CORP
150 4th Ave N Ste G250, Nashville, TN 37219-2425
Tel (615) 259-4700 *Founded/Ownrshp* 1976
Sales 22.4MM *EMP* 80^E
SIC 7389 Convention & show services; Tourist information bureau; Convention & show services; Tourist information bureau
Pr: Christopher Spyridon
Pr: Scott Parenteau
**CFO:* Jeff Mefford
VP: Laura Moore
VP: Whitney Weeks
Exec: Camara Randolph
Comm Dir: Mark Drury

D-U-N-S 00-403-7719
NASHVILLE DENTAL INC (TN)
N D I
1229 Northgte Bus Pkwy, Madison, TN 37115-2475
Tel (615) 868-3911 *Founded/Ownrshp* 1905, 1966
Sales 35.8MM *EMP* 104
Accts Frasier Dean Howard Plcc N
SIC 5047 Dental equipment & supplies; Dental equipment & supplies
Pr: Michael V Brown
**Sec:* Susan E Brock
**VP:* Kirk Brown
VP: Todd Brown
**VP:* Randy Reeder
IT Man: Paul Jacobsen

NASHVILLE ELECTRIC SERVICE
See ELECTRIC POWER BOARD OF METROPOLITAN GOVERNMENT OF NASHVILLE & DAVIDSON COUNTY

NASHVILLE INTERNATIONAL AIRPOR
See METROPOLITAN NASHVILLE AIRPORT AUTHORITY

D-U-N-S 00-405-0746
NASHVILLE MACHINE CO INC (TN)
(*Suby of* CVE INC) ★
530 Woodycrest Ave, Nashville, TN 37210-4394
Tel (615) 244-2030 *Founded/Ownrshp* 1887
Sales 52.1MM^E *EMP* 300
SIC 1796 1711 3599 3444

D-U-N-S 18-328-6152
NASHVILLE READY MIX INC
NASHVILLE READY MIX MT JULIET
605 Cowan St, Nashville, TN 37207-5619
Tel (615) 256-2071 *Founded/Ownrshp* 1987
Sales 24.3MM^E *EMP* 88
SIC 3273 Ready-mixed concrete; Ready-mixed concrete
Pr: Steve Meadows
Genl Mgr: Jeff Bryant

NASHVILLE READY MIX MT JULIET
See NASHVILLE READY MIX INC

D-U-N-S 03-484-1007 IMP
NASHVILLE RUBBER AND GASKET CO INC
DIXIE PACKING & SEALING DIV
1900 Elm Tree Dr, Nashville, TN 37210-3725
Tel (615) 883-5592 *Founded/Ownrshp* 1967
Sales 27.7MM^E *EMP* 47^E
SIC 5085 Gaskets; Hose, belting & packing
Pr: Don Garner
**Ch Bd:* Walter Bates
IT Man: Kathy Wilson
Sales Asso: Kerry Chamberlain

D-U-N-S 62-077-9934
NASHVILLE SCHOOL DISTRICT 1
600 N 4th St, Nashville, AR 71852-3911
Tel (870) 845-3425 *Founded/Ownrshp* 1928
Sales 21.5MM *EMP* 252
SIC 8211 Public elementary & secondary schools; Public elementary & secondary schools
**Treas:* Dana Newburg

NASHVILLE STATE CMNTY COLLEGE
See NASHVILLE STATE TECHNICAL COMMUNITY COLLEGE

D-U-N-S 94-198-7075
NASHVILLE STATE TECHNICAL COMMUNITY COLLEGE
NASHVILLE STATE CMNTY COLLEGE
120 White Bridge Pike, Nashville, TN 37209-4515
Tel (615) 353-3333 *Founded/Ownrshp* 1970
Sales 24.8MM *EMP* 880
SIC 8222 Technical institute; Technical institute
Pr: George H Van Allen
**VP:* Mary Cross

D-U-N-S 00-441-2128
NASHVILLE STEEL CORP (TN)
7211 Centennial Blvd, Nashville, TN 37209-1037
Tel (615) 350-7933 *Founded/Ownrshp* 1960
Sales 32.3MM^E *EMP* 56
SIC 5051 Steel; Steel
Ch Bd: Okey B Johnson Jr
**Pr:* Okey B Johnson III
Pr: Richard Johnson
**VP:* Brandt H Johnson
VP Sls: Brandt Johnson

D-U-N-S 14-763-1923
NASHVILLE SYMPHONY ASSOCIATION
SCHERMERHORN SYMPHONY CENTER
1 Symphony Pl, Nashville, TN 37201-2031
Tel (615) 687-6500 *Founded/Ownrshp* 1946
Sales 21.1MM *EMP* 205
Accts Crowe Horwath Llp Brentwood
SIC 7929 Symphony orchestras; Symphony orchestras
Pr: Alan D Valentine
**CFO:* Michael Kirby
**Sr VP:* Mark A Blakeman
VP: Andrea Dillenburg
**VP:* James Gooch
**VP:* Jonathan Norris
Board of Directors: Craig Colunga, Kimberly Darlington, Kent Henderson, George Mabry, Jonathan Marx, Kristen Oliver, Steve Perdue, Dan Sanders

D-U-N-S 00-403-5168 IMP
NASHVILLE WIRE PRODUCTS MFG CO (TN)
199 Polk Ave, Nashville, TN 37210-4629
Tel (615) 244-8001 *Founded/Ownrshp* 1934, 2009
Sales 300.7MM^E *EMP* 800
Accts Lattimore Black Morgan & Cain
SIC 3496 3471 3643 Miscellaneous fabricated wire products; Plating & polishing; Lightning protection equipment; Miscellaneous fabricated wire products; Plating & polishing; Lightning protection equipment
CEO: Steven Rollins
**CFO:* Brad Hunter
VP: Kent Rollins
Exec: Cindy Tilson
Genl Mgr: Michael Diers
Genl Mgr: Bin Liu
IT Man: Denise Alves
Plnt Mgr: Raul Delapena
Plnt Mgr: Nick Phy
S&M/VP: Geof Wigner

D-U-N-S 08-955-7714 IMP/EXP
NASHVILLE WRAPS LLC
242 Molly Walton Dr, Hendersonville, TN 37075-2154
Tel (615) 338-3200 *Founded/Ownrshp* 1978
Sales 57.9MM^E *EMP* 100
SIC 5113 Bags, paper & disposable plastic; Boxes, paperboard & disposable plastic; Paper & products, wrapping or coarse; Bags, paper & disposable plastic; Boxes, paperboard & disposable plastic; Paper & products, wrapping or coarse
Pr: Robert Meadows
Genl Mgr: Buffie Baril
Off Mgr: Sue Wright
Dir IT: Glen Batson
Opers Mgr: Bear Golightly
VP Sls: Chris Wilson

D-U-N-S 04-927-3626
NASON CO
1307 S Highway 11, Walhalla, SC 29691-5115
Tel (864) 638-5506 *Founded/Ownrshp* 1987
Sales 24.7MM^E *EMP* 110
SIC 3822 3643 3613 Thermostats & other environmental sensors; Static pressure regulators; Current-carrying wiring devices; Switchgear & switchboard apparatus; Thermostats & other environmental sensors; Static pressure regulators; Current-carrying wiring devices; Switchgear & switchboard apparatus
CEO: Steve Mihaly Sr
**Sec:* Robert D Capell Jr
IT Man: Tim Taylor
Mfg Dir: Bill Sanders
Sfty Dirs: Carl Wulff
Sales Asso: Danny Dehler

D-U-N-S 87-981-7674
NASON CONSTRUCTION INC
3411 Silverside Rd # 200, Wilmington, DE 19810-4803
Tel (302) 529-2510 *Founded/Ownrshp* 2000
Sales 32.3MM^E *EMP* 70
Accts Joseph P Melvin Company Pc
SIC 1542 1541 Commercial & office building, new construction; Industrial buildings & warehouses
Ch Bd: Thomas W Nason II
**Pr:* Michael B Berardi
**Sec:* Deborah P Nason
Exec: Robert Coppins
Exec: Erik Fay
Opers Mgr: John Gorecki
Opers Mgr: Joby McCormick

D-U-N-S 09-219-1899
NASOYA FOODS INC
(*Suby of* VITASOY USA INC) ★
1 New England Way, Ayer, MA 01432-1514
Tel (978) 772-6880 *Founded/Ownrshp* 1990
Sales 25.6MM^E *EMP* 159
SIC 2099 5149 Tofu, except frozen desserts; Specialty food items; Tofu, except frozen desserts; Specialty food items
Pr: Robert Jones
Board of Directors: Winston Lo

NASS
See NORTH AMERICAN SUBSTATION SERVICES LLC

D-U-N-S 19-397-8699 IMP
NASSAL CO
415 W Kaley St, Orlando, FL 32806-3942
Tel (407) 648-0400 *Founded/Ownrshp* 1984
Sales 31.8MM *EMP* 85^E
Accts Hhcbr Altamonte Springs Fl
SIC 1542 8742 Commercial & office building, new construction; Custom builders, non-residential; Management consulting services; Commercial & office building, new construction; Custom builders, non-residential; Management consulting services
Ch Bd: William A Nassal Sr
**Pr:* William P Nassal
**CFO:* Michael Nendza
**VP:* Matthew S Brown
**VP:* Dennis S Butler
VP: Iain McGillivray
IT Man: Denni Vendemaele

D-U-N-S 95-972-6555
NASSAU ASSOCIATION FOR HELP OF RETARDED CHILDREN INC
189 Wheatley Rd, Glen Head, NY 11545-2641
Tel (516) 626-1000 *Founded/Ownrshp* 2002
Sales 9.6MM^E *EMP* 1,500
SIC 8093 8322 Mental health clinic, outpatient; Child related social services; Mental health clinic, outpatient; Child related social services
Pr: Jack Garofalo

D-U-N-S 05-497-9992
NASSAU BOCES SCHOOL DISTRICT
71 Clinton Rd Ste 100, Garden City, NY 11530-4728
Tel (516) 396-2500 *Founded/Ownrshp* 1967
Sales 137.9MM^E *EMP* 3,059
Accts Rs Abrams And Co Llp Island
SIC 8211 Public elementary & secondary schools; Public elementary & secondary schools
Pr: Eric B Schultz
**Treas:* Charles Carollo
Ex Dir: Lucinda Hurley
Dir IT: Muhammad Khan
Dir IT: Karen Murtha
Sfty Dirs: Wendy Richter
Schl Brd P: Stephen Witt

D-U-N-S 83-982-4992
NASSAU BROADCASTING PARTNERS LP
619 Alexander Rd Fl 3, Princeton, NJ 08540-6000
Tel (609) 452-9696 *Founded/Ownrshp* 1995
Sales 92.7MM^E *EMP* 500
SIC 4832 Radio broadcasting stations; Radio broadcasting stations
Pr: Louis F Mercatanti Jr
VP: Tim Gatz
Ex Dir: Laurena Gilbert
Dir IT: Man Chan
Sls Mgr: Stacey Geelan
Pgrm Dir: Dave McKay

D-U-N-S 10-120-6456 IMP/EXP
NASSAU CANDY DISTRIBUTORS INC
NASSAU CANDY SPECIALTY
(*Suby of* NASSAU-SOSNICK DISTRIBUTION CO LLC) ★
530 W John St, Hicksville, NY 11801-1039
Tel (516) 433-7100 *Founded/Ownrshp* 1984
Sales 126.8MM^E *EMP* 260
SIC 5145 Candy; Candy
Pr: Les Stier
**CFO:* Joe Vanella
Treas: Michael Pritchett
VP: Randy Goldbaum
VP: Torben Hansen
**VP:* Barry Rosenbaum
Off Mgr: Jennifer Collins
CTO: Michael Cohen
IT Man: Pat Chiapuzzi
Mfg Dir: Garrett Stier
Sfty Dirs: Maria Adames

NASSAU CANDY SPECIALTY
See NASSAU CANDY DISTRIBUTORS INC

D-U-N-S 13-926-7728
NASSAU COMMUNITY COLLEGE
NCC
(*Suby of* STATE UNIVERSITY OF NEW YORK) ★
1 Education Dr, Garden City, NY 11530-6793
Tel (516) 572-7501 *Founded/Ownrshp* 1959
Sales 204.5MM^E *EMP* 2,965
Accts Deloitte & Touche Llp New Yor
SIC 8222 9411 Community college; Administration of educational programs; ; Community college; Administration of educational programs;
Pr: Sean A Fanelli
Pr: Donna Haugen
Assoc VP: Lynette Brown
VP: Alla Brodsky
VP: Dorlena Dunbar
VP: Janice Grackin
VP: James Hoyt
Exec: Chuck Cutolo
Exec: Jeanne McCarthy
DP Exec: Les Frimerman
Prd Mgr: Cheryl McBride

D-U-N-S 06-593-9225
NASSAU COUNTY A H R C
AHRC-NASSAU COUNTY CHAPTER
(*Suby of* NYSARC INC) ★
189 Wheatley Rd, Glen Head, NY 11545-2641
Tel (516) 626-1000 *Founded/Ownrshp* 1948
Sales 60.7MM^E *EMP* 1,225
SIC 8331 8322 Vocational training agency; Individual & family services; Vocational training agency; Individual & family services
Pr: Terrence Ullrich
**Pr:* Paul Giordano
**CFO:* Will Derr
**Treas:* Kenneth Fpulick
Assoc Dir: Stanfort Perry
**Ex Dir:* Michael Mascari
Site Mgr: Shaun Weathers

NASSAU COUNTY DETECTIVES
See NASSAU COUNTY POLICE DEPARTMENT ASSOCIATION

D-U-N-S 18-853-1425
NASSAU COUNTY POLICE DEPARTMENT ASSOCIATION
NASSAU COUNTY DETECTIVES
777 Old Country Rd # 202, Plainview, NY 11803-4992
Tel (516) 681-8442 *Founded/Ownrshp* 1943

Sales 728.3M *EMP* 400
Accts Mcenerney Brady & Company Llc
SIC 7381 Detective services; Detective services
Pr: Glenn T Ciccone
**Pr:* Thomas Willdig

D-U-N-S 19-304-6778
NASSAU COUNTY SCHOOL DISTRICT
NASSAU DISTRICT SCHOOL BOARD
1201 Atlantic Ave, Fernandina Beach, FL 32034-3403
Tel (904) 491-9900 *Founded/Ownrshp* 1869
Sales 103.8MM *EMP* 1,500
SIC 8211 Public combined elementary & secondary school; Kindergarten; Public combined elementary & secondary school; Kindergarten
Ch: Donna Martin
Treas: Laurye Ray
Bd of Dir: Kathy Burns
IT Man: Theresa Milligan
Netwrk Mgr: Dana Whicker
Opers Mgr: Tim Groat

NASSAU DISTRICT SCHOOL BOARD
See NASSAU COUNTY SCHOOL DISTRICT

NASSAU DOWNS OTB
See NASSAU REGIONAL OFF-TRACK BETTING CORP

D-U-N-S 08-151-9548
NASSAU EDUCATORS FEDERAL CREDIT UNION
NEFCU
1000 Corporate Dr, Westbury, NY 11590-6648
Tel (516) 561-0030 *Founded/Ownrshp* 1938
Sales NA *EMP* 250
SIC 6061 Federal credit unions; Federal credit unions
Pr: Edward P Paternostro
Pr: Mark Head
**Ch:* Francis A De Mita
**Treas:* Alfred J Lewis
Ofcr: John Beneri
Ofcr: Andrew Saluk
**Ex VP:* Mike Egan
VP: Susan Becker
VP: Valerie Garguilo
VP: Eric Oterson
Brnch Mgr: Mary Aller
Board of Directors: Lawrence Lerner, Saul Mines, Dr George Papaioannou, Dr William Russo

D-U-N-S 62-803-8317
NASSAU ENERGY CORP
(*Suby of* GDF SUEZ ENERGY INTERNATIONAL) ★
185 Chrles Lindbergh Blvd, Garden City, NY 11530-4819
Tel (516) 222-1022 *Founded/Ownrshp* 2011
Sales 20.2MM^E *EMP* 35
SIC 4911 Electric services
Ch: Herman Schopman
**Pr:* Nicholas J Cavagnaro

NASSAU EXTENDED CARE FACILITY
See NASSAU OPERATING CO LLC

D-U-N-S 01-112-5825
NASSAU HEALTH CARE CORP
NASSAU UNIVERSITY MEDICAL CTR
2201 Hempstead Tpke, East Meadow, NY 11554-1859
Tel (516) 572-0123 *Founded/Ownrshp* 1999
Sales 333.5MM^E *EMP* 3,500
Accts Cerini & Associates Llp Bohem
SIC 8399 Health systems agency; Health systems agency
Pr: Arthur A Gianelli
COO: Michael M Deluca
**CFO:* John Maher
**CFO:* Richard Perrotti
Ofcr: Bruce Emmer
Ofcr: Bruce Laplante
**Ex VP:* Robert S Heatley
Ex VP: Robert Heatley
**Ex VP:* Larry I Slatky
Ex VP: Maureen Roarty
**Ex VP:* Steven J Walerstein
**Sr VP:* Kathy Skarka
VP: Sharon Popper
VP: James Senterfitt
**VP:* Ronald Tomo
Exec: Justin Biel
Dir Lab: Adele Wilson
Dir Rad: Shari Lobel
Dir Rx: Martine Eliconte
Dir Rx: Marcelle Levy-Santoro
Dir Rx: Marcelle Santoror
Board of Directors: Arthur Gianelli

D-U-N-S 05-061-7893 IMP
NASSAU LENS CO INC
NASSAU VISION GROUP
(*Suby of* ESSILOR OF AMERICA INC) ★
160 Legrand Ave, Northvale, NJ 07647-2484
Tel (201) 767-8033 *Founded/Ownrshp* 1932
Sales 174.5MM^E *EMP* 440
SIC 5048 Frames, ophthalmic; Lenses, ophthalmic; Frames, ophthalmic; Lenses, ophthalmic
Pr: Francois Bezberc
**CFO:* Irwin Kaufman
VP: Paul Keppler
IT Man: Scott Falkenstern
Sales Asso: Joe Lombardo

D-U-N-S 83-858-8614
NASSAU MANAGEMENT GROUP INC
RE/MAX
88 Orchard Rd, Skillman, NJ 08558-2642
Tel (609) 466-4499 *Founded/Ownrshp* 1997
Sales 11.6MM^E *EMP* 350^E
SIC 6531 Real estate agent, residential; Real estate agent, residential
Pr: Rob Lyszczarz
**VP:* Brent Franklin

D-U-N-S 02-665-2771
NASSAU OPERATING CO LLC
NASSAU EXTENDED CARE FACILITY
1 Greenwich St, Hempstead, NY 11550-5624
Tel (516) 565-0085 *Founded/Ownrshp* 1994
Sales 34.3MM *EMP* 275
SIC 8051 Skilled nursing care facilities; Skilled nursing care facilities
CEO: Ben Philipson
**Prin:* Lynwana Johnson

D-U-N-S 96-649-4218
NASSAU PARADISE ISLAND DESTINATION PROMOTION BOARD LLC
1200 S Pine Island Rd # 700, Plantation, FL 33324-4441
Tel (954) 648-6097 *Founded/Ownrshp* 2013
Sales 20.1MM *EMP* 2
Accts Daszkal Bolton Llp Boca Raton
SIC 8743 Promotion service

D-U-N-S 93-753-5961
NASSAU PROVISIONS KOSHER FOODS INC
200 Albany Ave, Freeport, NY 11520-4712
Tel (516) 378-5921 *Founded/Ownrshp* 1983
Sales 26.5MM^E *EMP* 26
SIC 5141 Groceries, general line
Ch Bd: Scott Horowitz

D-U-N-S 07-578-5683
NASSAU REGIONAL OFF-TRACK BETTING CORP
NASSAU DOWNS OTB
139 Liberty Ave, Mineola, NY 11501-3510
Tel (516) 572-2800 *Founded/Ownrshp* 1974
Sales 12.9MM^E *EMP* 350
SIC 7999 Off-track betting; Off-track betting
Pr: Dino Amoroso
Exec: William Funk
IT Man: Carol Chapman
Genl Couns: Dianne Malone

D-U-N-S 05-497-9885
NASSAU SUFFOLK LUMBER & SUPPLY CORP
3800 Vtrans Mem Hwy Ste 1, Bohemia, NY 11716-1070
Tel (631) 467-2020 *Founded/Ownrshp* 1971
Sales 44.6MM^E *EMP* 160
SIC 5031 5211 2431 Lumber, plywood & millwork; Building materials, exterior; Building materials, interior; Millwork; Lumber & other building materials; Lumber, plywood & millwork; Building materials, exterior; Building materials, interior; Lumber & other building materials; Millwork
Ch Bd: William H Van Tuyl III
**Pr:* Christopher Van Tuyl
**CFO:* John Sturmer
Mktg Dir: Sharon Govern
Sls Mgr: Dorothy Cunningham

NASSAU UNIVERSITY MEDICAL CTR
See NASSAU HEALTH CARE CORP

D-U-N-S 02-687-5906
NASSAU VETERANS MEMORIAL COLISEUM
(*Suby of* SMG HOLDINGS INC) ★
1255 Hempstead Tpke, Uniondale, NY 11553-1200
Tel (516) 794-9300 *Founded/Ownrshp* 1988
Sales 18.0MM^E *EMP* 400
SIC 6531 7311 Real estate managers; Advertising agencies; Real estate managers; Advertising agencies
Genl Mgr: Scott Mullen
Dir Soc: David Kapsack
Dir Soc: Jaime Taylor
Genl Mgr: Jerry Goldman
Store Mgr: Denise Farnacci

NASSAU VISION GROUP
See NASSAU LENS CO INC

D-U-N-S 08-004-2284
NASSAU-SOSNICK DISTRIBUTION CO LLC
258 Littlefield Ave, South San Francisco, CA 94080-6922
Tel (650) 952-2226 *Founded/Ownrshp* 2015
Sales 126.8MM^E *EMP* 262^E
SIC 5149 5145 5182 Groceries & related products; Candy; Wine
CEO: Jeff Sosnick
**Pr:* Martin Sosnick
**VP:* Wayne Sosnick

NASSCO
See NATIONAL STEEL & SHIPBUILDING CO

NASSCO
See INTERNATIONAL MANUFACTURING TECHNOLOGIES INC

D-U-N-S 60-206-5989 IMP
■ NASSCO HOLDINGS INC
(*Suby of* GENERAL DYNAMICS CORP) ★
2798 Harbor Dr, San Diego, CA 92113-3650
Tel (619) 544-3400 *Founded/Ownrshp* 1998
Sales 581.6MM^E *EMP* 3,500
SIC 3731 Shipbuilding & repairing; Shipbuilding & repairing
Pr: Frederick J Harris
Pr: Matthew Luxton
**CFO:* Eric Murray
**VP:* Michael Askew
**VP:* Tom Brown
**VP:* David J Carver
**VP:* William Cuddy
**VP:* Kevin M Graney
Exec: Jenie Farotte
IT Man: Teresa Duberg
Opers Mgr: Andy Jenkins

D-U-N-S 02-341-8544 IMP
NASSCO INC
5365 S Moorland Rd, New Berlin, WI 53151-7925
Tel (414) 422-9960 *Founded/Ownrshp* 1968
Sales 46.8MM^E *EMP* 100^E
SIC 5087 5113

D-U-N-S 13-051-7287
NASSER CO INC
NASSER COMPANY OF ARIZONA
22720 Savi Ranch Pkwy, Yorba Linda, CA 92887-4614
Tel (714) 279-2100 *Founded/Ownrshp* 1984
Sales 143.2MM^E *EMP* 150
SIC 5141 Food brokers; Food brokers
Pr: Burhan Nasser
Pr: Bill Arink
CFO: Bruce Nye
Ch: Ken Darienzo
**Sec:* Mary Beth Nasser
VP: Nevart Majarian
VP: Dean Sandello
**VP Admn:* Becky Salazar
MIS Dir: Gregory Dapkus
Dir IT: Jan Hornstrom
IT Man: Frank Garcia

NASSER COMPANY OF ARIZONA
See NASSER CO INC

D-U-N-S 09-946-9488
NASSIRI INC
2035 Helm Dr, Las Vegas, NV 89119-3909
Tel (702) 837-7332 *Founded/Ownrshp* 1966
Sales 89.3MM^E *EMP* 45
Accts Grobstein Horwath & Company L
SIC 5136 5137 Sportswear, men's & boys'; Sportswear, women's & children's
Pr: Fred Nassiri

NASSP
See NATIONAL ASSOCIATION OF SECONDARY SCHOOL PRINCIPALS

D-U-N-S 80-737-5258 IMP
NASTASI & ASSOCIATES INC
500 Wheeler Rd, Hauppauge, NY 11788-2962
Tel (516) 746-1800 *Founded/Ownrshp* 1993
Sales 53.3MM^E *EMP* 400
SIC 1742 Drywall; Acoustical & ceiling work; Drywall; Acoustical & ceiling work
Pr: Anthony Nastasi

D-U-N-S 80-831-0007
NASTOS CONSTRUCTION INC
1421 Kenilworth Ave Ne, Washington, DC 20019-2712
Tel (202) 398-5500 *Founded/Ownrshp* 1993
Sales 26.3MM^E *EMP* 95
Accts Vardavas & Concannon Pa Ba
SIC 1542 1522 Commercial & office building contractors; Residential construction; Commercial & office building contractors; Residential construction
Pr: Manuel Santos
**VP:* Ray Amirian
IT Man: Amporn Oneil
Snr PM: Ray Smith

NASTRA AUTOMOTIVE
See NAS-TRA AUTOMOTIVE INDUSTRIES INC

D-U-N-S 02-703-5553 IMP/EXP
NASTY GAL INC
523 W 6th St Ste 330, Los Angeles, CA 90014-1233
Tel (213) 542-3436 *Founded/Ownrshp* 2008
Sales 65.7MM^E *EMP* 286
SIC 5621 5139 2389 Ready-to-wear apparel, women's; Shoes; Academic vestments (caps & gowns); Ready-to-wear apparel, women's; Shoes; Academic vestments (caps & gowns)
CEO: Sheree Waterson
**Ch Bd:* Sophia Amoruso
CFO: Bob Ross
Sr VP: Lonna Rimestad
VP: Grig Gheorghiu
VP: Jason Sirota
Genl Mgr: Erin Gray
Genl Mgr: Anne Murphy
Plng Mgr: Molly Tapp
Store Mgr: Gillian Goldstein
CTO: Thomas David

NAT
See NORTH AMERICAN TITLE CO INC

D-U-N-S 14-104-9101
NAT NETWORKS INC
NEW H TECH
1768 46th St, Brooklyn, NY 11204-1211
Tel (718) 564-4468 *Founded/Ownrshp* 2003
Sales 25.0MM *EMP* 78
SIC 7359 Business machine & electronic equipment rental services; Business machine & electronic equipment rental services
CEO: Joseph Lowenbein
**Pr:* Boruch Lowenbein
**VP:* Sholo Oveb

D-U-N-S 13-794-9715 IMP/EXP
NAT SHERMAN INC
2200 Fletcher Ave Ste Ul, Fort Lee, NJ 07024-5016
Tel (201) 735-9000 *Founded/Ownrshp* 1989
Sales 44.7MM^E *EMP* 105
SIC 5194 5993 5947 2111 2121 Cigarettes; Cigarette store; Novelties; Cigarettes; Cigars; Cigarettes; Cigarette store; Novelties; Cigarettes; Cigars
Pr: Joel J Sherman
**CFO:* Louis S Carbone
**CFO:* Brendon B Scott
**Treas:* Larry Sherman
Ex VP: William Sherman
VP: Herb Fincher
VP: Michael Herklots
**VP:* William M Sherman
Creative D: Stephen Silvestri
IT Man: Lionel Legry
Natl Sales: Greg Dillon

D-U-N-S 15-956-0072
NAT SOFT CORP
1075 Easton Ave Ste 3 4, Somerset, NJ 08873-1648
Tel (732) 726-0593 *Founded/Ownrshp* 2004
Sales 20.6MM *EMP* 190
SIC 7371 7361 Computer software development; Executive placement; Computer software development; Executive placement
Pr: Tirumala R Cheedala
Sftwr Eng: Suresh Vangapally

D-U-N-S 10-854-8053
NATAHALEY LLC
2902 South Island Rd, Georgetown, SC 29440-4420
Tel (843) 957-6593 *Founded/Ownrshp* 2002
Sales 60.0MM *EMP* 1
SIC 6719 Personal holding companies, except banks
Pr: Maxine McAlhnay

NATALIES ORCHID ISLAND JUICE
See ORCHID ISLAND JUICE CO

D-U-N-S 78-811-8961
NATASHA ACCESSORIES LTD
7 W 36th St Fl 2, New York, NY 10018-7169
Tel (212) 643-2525 *Founded/Ownrshp* 2006
Sales 25.8MM^E *EMP* 80
SIC 5137 Women's & children's accessories
Pr: Gokaran Singh

NATCA
See NATIONAL AIR TRAFFIC CONTROLLERS ASSOCIATION

D-U-N-S 09-206-8667
NATCHAUG HOSPITAL INC
189 Storrs Rd, Mansfield Center, CT 06250-1683
Tel (860) 456-1311 *Founded/Ownrshp* 1954
Sales 49.6MM *EMP* 415
Accts Ernst & Young Us Llp Philadel
SIC 8063 8069 Psychiatric hospitals; Substance abuse hospitals; Psychiatric hospitals; Substance abuse hospitals
CEO: Stephen W Larcen
VP: Robert Elson
Chf Nrs Of: Nancy Miner
Prgrm Mgr: Melissa Deasy
Genl Mgr: Sheila Koch
Off Mgr: Wendy Sullivan
QA Dir: Scott Crawford
Psych: Stacy Cruess
Nrsg Dir: Lakisha Hyatt
HC Dir: David Wheeler

D-U-N-S 13-923-9875
NATCHEZ FORD LINCOLN MERCURY INC
14 Sgt Prentiss Dr, Natchez, MS 39120-4726
Tel (601) 445-0076 *Founded/Ownrshp* 1991
Sales 26.2MM *EMP* 43
SIC 5511 Automobiles, new & used; Automobiles, new & used
Pr: Brad Yarbrough
Off Mgr: Jeff Morris

D-U-N-S 13-353-9895
NATCHEZ HARDWARE CENTER INC
HOME HARDWARE CENTER
187 Sgt Prentiss Dr, Natchez, MS 39120-4733
Tel (601) 445-5352 *Founded/Ownrshp* 1984
Sales 34.7MM^E *EMP* 200
SIC 5251 Hardware; Hardware
Pr: Jimmy R Smith

D-U-N-S 04-775-7687
■ NATCHEZ HOSPITAL CO LLC
NATCHEZ REGIONAL MEDICAL CTR
(*Suby of* COMMUNITY HEALTH SYSTEMS INC) ★
54 Sgt Prentiss Dr, Natchez, MS 39120-4726
Tel (601) 443-2100 *Founded/Ownrshp* 2014
Sales 55.4MM^E *EMP* 390
SIC 8062 General medical & surgical hospitals; General medical & surgical hospitals
CEO: Eric Robinson
Dir Recs: Tammie Dixey
**CFO:* Nicholas Renda
Ofcr: Bill Heburn
Dir Lab: Margo Maxwell
Dir Rx: Michelle Babb
CTO: Steed Scott
Dir IT: Ed Mohrman
Dir IT: Lesley Mukoro
Ansthgy: Jack Dunn

NATCHEZ REGIONAL MEDICAL CTR
See NATCHEZ HOSPITAL CO LLC

D-U-N-S 00-696-4217
NATCHEZ TRACE ELECTRIC POWER ASSOCIATION
555 E Madison St, Houston, MS 38851-2410
Tel (662) 456-3037 *Founded/Ownrshp* 1939
Sales 35.6MM *EMP* 58
Accts Watkins Ward And Stafford Pllc
SIC 4911 Electric services; Electric services
Genl Mgr: Norma F Kilgore
**Prin:* Gail Allen

D-U-N-S 10-820-1054
NATCHEZ-ADAMS SCHOOL DISTRICT
10 Homochitto St, Natchez, MS 39120-3996
Tel (601) 442-0212 *Founded/Ownrshp* 1952
Sales 39.3MM *EMP* 750
Accts The Gillon Group Pllc Natche
SIC 8211 Public vocational/technical school; Public vocational/technical school
Exec: Allison Jowers

D-U-N-S 88-360-0546
NATCHITOCHES PARISH HOSPITAL SERVICE DISTRICT
501 Keyser Ave, Natchitoches, LA 71457-6018
Tel (318) 356-5859 *Founded/Ownrshp* 1957
Sales 81.9M *EMP* 550
Accts Lester Miller & Wells Alexand
SIC 8062 General medical & surgical hospitals; General medical & surgical hospitals
CEO: Mark Marley
**CFO:* William Page
Ofcr: Kirk Soileau

D-U-N-S 10-002-8356
NATCHITOCHES PARISH SCHOOL DISTRICT
310 Royal St, Natchitoches, LA 71457-5709
Tel (318) 352-2358 *Founded/Ownrshp* 1890
Sales 19.6MM^E *EMP* 283
SIC 8211 Public elementary & secondary schools; School board; Public elementary & secondary schools; School board

Pr Dir: Tiffany Valentine
Instr Medi: Margaret Hall

NATCO
See NATIONAL MEAT & PROVISION CO INC

NATCO
See CAMERON SOLUTIONS INC

D-U-N-S 60-563-2884 IMP
■ NATCO GROUP INC
(*Suby of* CAMERON INTERNATIONAL CORP) ★
11210 Equity Dr Ste 100, Houston, TX 77041-8239
Tel (713) 849-7500 *Founded/Ownrshp* 2009
Sales 305.8MM^E *EMP* 2,100^E
SIC 3533 1389 Oil & gas field machinery; Gas field machinery & equipment; Oil field machinery & equipment; Oil field services; Gas field services; Oil & gas field machinery; Gas field machinery & equipment; Oil field machinery & equipment; Oil field services; Gas field services
Pr: Les Hiller
Sr VP: Byron J Eiermann
VP: Elizabeth Evans
VP: Scott Thompson
Sfty Mgr: Jim Leblanc
Opers Mgr: Philip Hamilton
Plnt Mgr: Charlie Gordon

D-U-N-S 87-718-4457 IMP
NATCO HOME FASHIONS INC
'BEST HOME FASHIONS
155 Brookside Ave, West Warwick, RI 02893-3800
Tel (401) 828-0300 *Founded/Ownrshp* 2006
Sales 54.4MM^E *EMP* 326
SIC 2391 2221 Curtains, window: made from purchased materials; Draperies, plastic & textile: from purchased materials; Bedspreads, silk & manmade fiber; Curtains, window: made from purchased materials; Draperies, plastic & textile: from purchased materials; Bedspreads, silk & manmade fiber
Ch Bd: Michael Litner
**Pr:* Robert T Galkin
**Treas:* Alan Ross

D-U-N-S 05-666-7231
NATCO INDUSTRIES INC DEL
150 Thorn Hill Rd, Warrendale, PA 15086-7528
Tel (724) 776-4857 *Founded/Ownrshp* 1991
Sales 97.1MM *EMP* 7
SIC 6799 Investors; Investors
Ch Bd: Jay Schottenstein
**Ex VP:* Joseph E Kerin
**Ex VP:* Thomas Kettler

D-U-N-S 00-119-8522 IMP
NATCO PRODUCTS CORP (RI)
155 Brookside Ave, West Warwick, RI 02893-3800
Tel (401) 828-0300 *Founded/Ownrshp* 1923
Sales 157.3MM^E *EMP* 580
SIC 3996 2273 5023 Asphalted-felt-base floor coverings: linoleum, carpet; Carpets, textile fiber; Mats & matting; Rugs; Asphalted-felt-base floor coverings: linoleum, carpet; Carpets, textile fiber; Mats & matting; Rugs
Ch Bd: Robert T Galkin
**Pr:* Michael Litner
**V Ch Bd:* Warren B Galkin
**Ex VP:* Alan Ross
VP Sls: Larry Hill
VP Sls: Marc Zukowski

D-U-N-S 04-875-0363
NATCOM BANCSHARES INC
1127 Tower Ave, Superior, WI 54880-1502
Tel (715) 394-5531 *Founded/Ownrshp* 1998
Sales NA *EMP* 115
SIC 6712 Bank holding companies; Bank holding companies
Pr: Larry Cappas

D-U-N-S 08-531-6396
NATE WADE INC
NATE WADE LEASING
1207 S Main St, Salt Lake City, UT 84111-4409
Tel (801) 355-7571 *Founded/Ownrshp* 1996
Sales 30.3MM^E *EMP* 80
SIC 5511 5012 7538 7515 5531 5521 Automobiles, new & used; Automobiles; General automotive repair shops; Passenger car leasing; Automotive & home supply stores; Used car dealers; Automobiles, new & used; Automobiles; General automotive repair shops; Passenger car leasing; Automotive & home supply stores; Used car dealers
Pr: Kirk Schneider
Off Admin: Bonnie Johnson
Sls Mgr: Ken Howe
Sls Mgr: Mario Tonel
Sales Asso: Rich Beeler
Sales Asso: Roger Bird
Sales Asso: Manny Flores
Sales Asso: Eric Lithgow
Sales Asso: Lamar Moody
Sales Asso: Craig Simpson
Sales Asso: Fred Southwick

NATE WADE LEASING
See NATE WADE INC

NATEL
See EPIC TECHNOLOGIES LLC

D-U-N-S 07-624-4789 IMP
NATEL ENGINEERING CO INC
NEOTECH
9340 Owensmouth Ave, Chatsworth, CA 91311-6915
Tel (818) 734-6500 *Founded/Ownrshp* 1975
Sales 915.6MM^E *EMP* 2,095
SIC 3674 3679 Hybrid integrated circuits; Modules, solid state; Printed circuit boards; Semiconductors & related devices; Antennas, receiving
Pr: Sudesh K Arora
**COO:* Kunal Sharma
CFO: John W Lorey
**CFO:* Laura Siegal
VP: Will Bolinger
VP: Varun Dhingra
VP: William Freitag
**VP:* Mike Goryl
**VP:* Zareen Mohta
VP: Martin Sosa
Prgrm Mgr: Tracy Hille

D-U-N-S 82-677-2188
NATELCO CORP
NATELCO ELECTRICAL CONTACTORS
140 W Hampton Ave, Capitol Heights, MD 20743-3516
Tel (301) 350-1325 *Founded/Ownrshp* 2004
Sales 82.8MM^E *EMP* 330
Accts Simonian Katz & Co Llp Yar
SIC 1731 General electrical contractor; General electrical contractor
CEO: Donna Lascola
**Pr:* Calvin Driskill
CFO: Leann Manginell
**Treas:* Daniel O'Connor
IT Man: Randy Sellner
IT Man: Johnson Steve

NATELCO ELECTRICAL CONTACTORS
See NATELCO CORP

D-U-N-S 01-896-2756
▲ NATERA INC
201 Industrial Rd Ste 410, San Carlos, CA 94070-2396
Tel (650) 249-9090 *Founded/Ownrshp* 2007
Sales 94.9MM^E *EMP* 270
Tkr Sym NTRA *Exch* NGS
SIC 8734 Testing laboratories; Testing laboratories
CEO: Matthew Rabinowitz
**COO:* Brad Roberts
CFO: Herm Rosenman
**Ofcr:* Susan Gross
VP: Darrin Crisitello
**VP:* Matthew Hill
**VP:* Asim Siddiqui
Dir Lab: Susan Zneimer
Assoc Dir: Robert Pelham
Dir Bus: John Fesko
Dir Bus: Marin Markov
Board of Directors: James Healy

D-U-N-S 87-905-6786 EXP
NATERRA INTERNATIONAL INC
1250 Freeport Pkwy, Coppell, TX 75019-4410
Tel (972) 616-6100 *Founded/Ownrshp* 1994
Sales 21.1MM^E *EMP* 60
SIC 2844 Toilet preparations
Pr: Jin K Song
**Ex VP:* Peter Song

D-U-N-S 13-063-1872
NATERRA LAND INC
43 Se Main St Ste 506, Minneapolis, MN 55414-1049
Tel (906) 892-8665 *Founded/Ownrshp* 1979
Sales 40.0MM *EMP* 120
SIC 6552 Subdividers & developers
Pr: Philip C Taylor
**Ex VP:* Steve Roman
**VP:* Paul Essler
VP: David Evans

D-U-N-S 01-923-6595
NATGUN CORP (MA)
(*Suby of* DN TANKS INC) ★
11 Teal Rd, Wakefield, MA 01880-1292
Tel (781) 246-1133 *Founded/Ownrshp* 1929, 2011
Sales 32.8MM^E *EMP* 200
SIC 3795 Tanks & tank components; Tanks & tank components
CEO: Charles E Crowley
**COO:* Bill Crowley
COO: Kevin Peacock
**Treas:* Donald Paula
VP: Chris Hodgson
VP: Wade Wells
Rgnl Mgr: Dan McVay
Tech Mgr: Joseph Pappo
Opers Mgr: Mike Clinton
Opers Mgr: Robert Walsh

D-U-N-S 96-923-0788
NATH COMPANIES INC
900 American Blvd E # 300, Minneapolis, MN 55420-1392
Tel (952) 853-1400 *Founded/Ownrshp* 1996
Sales 173.4MM^E *EMP* 900
SIC 5812 Fast-food restaurant, chain; Fast-food restaurant, chain
Pr: Mahendra Nath
Sec: Asha Nath
Dir IT: Russell Sweeney
Opers Mgr: Scott Henning
Mktg Dir: Jodi Schoenauer
Mktg Mgr: Sara Nath

D-U-N-S 82-593-3815
NATH FLORIDA FRANCHISE GROUP INC
(*Suby of* NATH COMPANIES INC) ★
900 American Blvd E # 300, Minneapolis, MN 55420-1392
Tel (952) 853-1400 *Founded/Ownrshp* 1993
Sales 8.6MM^E *EMP* 345
SIC 5812 Fast-food restaurant, chain; Fast-food restaurant, chain
Pr: Mahendra Nath
**Sec:* Asha Nath

D-U-N-S 55-694-4163
NATH MINNESOTA FRANCHISE GROUP INC
(*Suby of* NATH COMPANIES INC) ★
900 E 79th St Ste 300, Minneapolis, MN 55420-1393
Tel (952) 853-1400 *Founded/Ownrshp* 1991
Sales 160.0MM *EMP* 1,300
SIC 5812 8741 Fast-food restaurant, chain; Management services; Fast-food restaurant, chain; Management services
CEO: Mahendra Nath
**COO:* Ashok Mehta
**CFO:* Patti Porteous
**VP:* Asha Nath

D-U-N-S 80-956-1488
NATHALIE MONTREUIL CORP
600 Mmaroneck Ave Ste 400, Harrison, NY 10528
Tel (646) 434-1092 *Founded/Ownrshp* 2008
Sales 30.0MM *EMP* 150
SIC 8748 8741 8742 7389 Business consulting; Administrative management; Administrative services consultant; ; Business consulting; Administrative management; Administrative services consultant;
Pr: Nathalie Montreuil

D-U-N-S 18-763-7913
■ NATHAN & LEWIS SECURITIES INC
(*Suby of* NL HOLDING CORP (DEL)) ★
260 Madison Ave Ste 11, New York, NY 10016-2412
Tel (212) 413-4553 *Founded/Ownrshp* 1998
Sales 115.0MM *EMP* 130
Accts Ernst & Young Llp
SIC 6211 Brokers, security; Dealers, security; Brokers, security; Dealers, security
Pr: Jay L Lewis
CFO: Michael Caska
**VP:* Tom Wirtshafter
Netwrk Mgr: Mohammad Akbar

D-U-N-S 04-983-5408
NATHAN ADELSON HOSPICE
4141 Swenson St, Las Vegas, NV 89119-6718
Tel (702) 733-0320 *Founded/Ownrshp* 1978
Sales 31.0MM *EMP* 300
Accts Crowe Horwath Llp Chicago Il
SIC 8059 8082 Personal care home, with health care; Home health care services; Personal care home, with health care; Home health care services
Pr: Carole A Fisher
**Pr:* Karen Rubel
COO: Aisha Mitchell
COO: Julie Peasley
**CFO:* Dawn Metcalfe
Ofcr: Nathan Mowad
Ofcr: Lynn Stange
Dir Soc: Laura Norcia
Dir Rx: Veronica Walters
CTO: Michael Karagiozis
IT Man: Sally Johnson

D-U-N-S 07-932-7466
NATHAN AND MIRIAM BARNERT MEMORIAL HOSPITAL ASSOCIATION (NJ)
BARNERT HOSPITAL
680 Broadway, Paterson, NJ 07514-1524
Tel (973) 977-6600 *Founded/Ownrshp* 1908, 2002
Sales 32.9MM^E *EMP* 680
SIC 8062 8063 General medical & surgical hospitals; Psychiatric hospitals; General medical & surgical hospitals; Psychiatric hospitals
CEO: Joseph Orlando
**CFO:* Stuart May
CFO: Alfred Setter
Sr VP: Alfred Fetter
Dir IT: Farooq Ajmal
Pharmcst: Rita Fritz

D-U-N-S 07-483-7444
NATHAN ASSOCIATES INC
1777 N Kent St Ste 1400, Arlington, VA 22209-2133
Tel (703) 516-7700 *Founded/Ownrshp* 1946
Sales 25.4MM^E *EMP* 140
Accts Grant Thornton
SIC 8748 Economic consultant; Economic consultant
Ch Bd: John C Beyer
**CEO:* Susan Chodakewitz
**Sr VP:* Paul Kent
**Sr VP:* Russel Lamb
**Sr VP:* Russell Mangum
VP: Richard Blankfeld
**VP:* Paul Moore
**VP:* Jayleen Moroney
**Prin:* Usha Chaudhary
**Prin:* Wolfgang Tolle
IT Man: Chris White
Board of Directors: Richard Burtner, Richard Burtner, Katherine Clark, Valerie Perlowitz

D-U-N-S 78-308-8222
NATHAN CUMMINGS FOUNDATION INC
475 10th Ave Fl 14, New York, NY 10018-1193
Tel (646) 674-0751 *Founded/Ownrshp* 1949
Sales 23.9MM *EMP* 21
SIC 7389 Fund raising organizations; Fund raising organizations
CEO: Lance E Lindblom
**CFO:* Leisle Lin
VP: Henry Ng
Genl Mgr: Maria Rubio
Genl Mgr: Michael Ryan

D-U-N-S 06-054-1570
NATHAN LITTAUER HOSPITAL ASSOCIATION
NATHAN LTTAUER HOSP NURSING HM
99 E State St, Gloversville, NY 12078-1293
Tel (518) 725-8621 *Founded/Ownrshp* 1891
Sales 95.2MM *EMP* 918
SIC 8051 8062 8011

NATHAN LTTAUER HOSP NURSING HM
See NATHAN LITTAUER HOSPITAL ASSOCIATION

D-U-N-S 01-260-6737
▲ NATHANS FAMOUS INC
1 Jericho Plz, Jericho, NY 11753-1680
Tel (516) 338-8500 *Founded/Ownrshp* 1916
Sales 99.1MM *EMP* 228^E
Accts Grant Thornton Llp New York
Tkr Sym NATH *Exch* NGM
SIC 5812 6794 Fast-food restaurant, chain; Franchises, selling or licensing; Fast-food restaurant, chain; Franchises, selling or licensing
CEO: Eric Gatoff
**Ch Bd:* Howard Lorber
**Pr:* Wayne Norbitz
CFO: Ronald G Devos
**Ex VP:* Donald L Perlyn
Board of Directors: Robert J Eide, Brian S Genson, Barry Leistner, Attilio F Petrocelli, Charles Raich

D-U-N-S 01-230-8128 IMP/EXP
NATHEL & NATHEL INC
NATHEL INTERNATIONAL
357 Row C Nyc Trml Mkt, Bronx, NY 10474
Tel (718) 991-6050 *Founded/Ownrshp* 1971
Sales 126.5MM^E *EMP* 125^E
SIC 5148 Fresh fruits & vegetables; Fresh fruits & vegetables
Ch Bd: Ira Nathel
**Pr:* Sheldon Nathel
**CFO:* Richard Byllott
Ex Dir: Angel Helck

NATHEL INTERNATIONAL
See NATHEL & NATHEL INC

D-U-N-S 86-011-7907
NATICK AUTO SALES INC
MHQ MUNICIPAL VEHICLES
401 Elm St, Marlborough, MA 01752-4566
Tel (508) 485-2800 *Founded/Ownrshp* 1994
Sales 28.9MM^E *EMP* 97
SIC 5999 Police supply stores
CEO: Bill Kieckhafer
**Pr:* Charles Ribakoff
**COO:* Frank Chase
**CFO:* Diane C Mohieldin

D-U-N-S 07-979-9473
NATICK PUBLIC SCHOOLS
13 E Central St, Natick, MA 01760-4629
Tel (508) 647-6500 *Founded/Ownrshp* 2015
Sales 8.2MM^E *EMP* 559^E
SIC 8211 Public elementary & secondary schools
Teacher Pr: Maryanne Davis

NATIO COUN ON COMP INSU
See NCCI HOLDINGS INC

NATION FRESH
See PETER CONDAKES CO INC

D-U-N-S 62-513-2535
NATION PIZZA PRODUCTS LP
601 E Algonquin Rd, Schaumburg, IL 60173-3803
Tel (847) 397-3320 *Founded/Ownrshp* 1991
Sales 222.6MM^E *EMP* 700
SIC 2038 2045 2033 Pizza, frozen; Pizza doughs, prepared: from purchased flour; Pizza sauce: packaged in cans, jars, etc.; Pizza, frozen; Pizza doughs, prepared: from purchased flour; Pizza sauce: packaged in cans, jars, etc.
Co-CEO: Marshall Bauer
**Pr:* Richard Auskalnis
**COO:* Michael Alagna
**CFO:* Joe Giglio
**Co-CEO:* Jay Bauer
**VP:* Jack Campolo
**VP:* Keith Ohlsen
MIS Dir: Bruce Waid
**QA Dir:* Teresa Martinez
IT Man: Mark Comstock
Mtls Mgr: Aaron Brown

NATION WIDE SECURITY
See NATION WIDE SERVICES INC

D-U-N-S 04-569-0224
NATION WIDE SERVICES INC
NATION WIDE SECURITY
223 Sequoyah Rd, Loudon, TN 37774-2885
Tel (248) 355-0500 *Founded/Ownrshp* 1996
Sales 11.1MM^E *EMP* 1,200
SIC 7381 Security guard service; Detective services; Security guard service; Detective services
Pr: John Montville
VP: William M Foster
**VP:* Craig Michalski
Brnch Mgr: Robert Bradberry

D-U-N-S 05-055-7933 IMP
NATIONAL 4-H COUNCIL (OH)
7100 Connecticut Ave, Chevy Chase, MD 20815-4934
Tel (301) 961-2800 *Founded/Ownrshp* 1921
Sales 35.9MM *EMP* 253
Accts Bdo Usa Llp Bethesda Md
SIC 8641 8699 Youth organizations; Charitable organization; Youth organizations; Charitable organization
Pr: Jennifer Sirangelo
**Sr VP:* Christina Alford
Sr VP: Artis Stevens
Off Admin: Kathy Hartman
**CIO:* Mitch Head
Mktg Mgr: Leila Beltramo

D-U-N-S 00-895-1196
NATIONAL ACADEMY OF RECORDING ARTS & SCIENCES INC
RECORDING ACADEMY, THE
3030 Olympic Blvd, Santa Monica, CA 90404-5073
Tel (310) 392-3777 *Founded/Ownrshp* 1957
Sales 77.5MM *EMP* 110
Accts Deloitte Tax Llp Los Angeles
SIC 8621 Professional membership organizations
Pr: Neil Portnow
**CFO:* Wayne J Zahner
Chf Mktg O: Evan Greene
**Ofcr:* Gaetano Frizzi
**Ex VP:* David Grossman
VP: Peter Anton
**VP:* Barb Dehgan
VP: Ron W Roecker
**CIO:* Rick Engdahl
Mktg Dir: Mike Greene

D-U-N-S 04-196-4057
NATIONAL ACADEMY OF SCIENCES OF UNITED STATES OF AMERICA
N A S
2101 Constitution Ave Nw, Washington, DC 20418-0006
Tel (202) 334-2000 *Founded/Ownrshp* 1863
Sales 793.9MM *EMP* 1,175
SIC 8733 8999 8748

D-U-N-S 18-357-1462
NATIONAL ACCOUNT SERVICE CO LLC
NASCO
1200 Abernathy Rd # 1000, Atlanta, GA 30328-5662
Tel (678) 441-0061 *Founded/Ownrshp* 1987
Sales 22.7MM^E *EMP* 204
SIC 7374 Data processing service; Data processing service
CEO: Chet Burrell

Sr VP: Mike Malec
VP: Alan Bunn
VP: Lauret Howard
VP: Tim Waage
Telecom Ex: Sandy Holcomb
IT Man: Diana Alden

D-U-N-S 00-172-4129
NATIONAL ACOUSTICS INC (NY)
1306 43rd Ave, Long Island City, NY 11101-6833
Tel (212) 695-1252 *Founded/Ownrshp* 1970
Sales 36.9MM *EMP* 135
Accts Grassi & Co Cpas Pc New Yor
SIC 1742 5039 Plaster & drywall work; Acoustical & ceiling work; Architectural metalwork; Plaster & drywall work; Acoustical & ceiling work; Architectural metalwork
Pr: Timothy Malone
**CFO:* William Jessop
**Ex VP:* Wayne Burmaster
**VP:* James McQuade
**VP:* Stephan Togher
Board of Directors: Tim Malo

D-U-N-S 00-506-4257
NATIONAL ACTION FINANCIAL SERVICES INC
3102 West End Ave, Nashville, TN 37203-1301
Tel (615) 301-7226 *Founded/Ownrshp* 2003
Sales 21.6MM^E *EMP* 210^E
SIC 6282 Investment advice; Investment advice
Pr: Robert Camenzind
Ex Dir: Tim Maroney

D-U-N-S 00-325-9074
■ **NATIONAL AERONAUTICS AND SPACE ADMINISTRATION**
NASA
(*Suby of* EXECUTIVE OFFICE OF UNITED STATES GOVERNMENT) ★
300 E St Sw Ste 5r30, Washington, DC 20546-0002
Tel (202) 358-0000 *Founded/Ownrshp* 1958
Sales NA *EMP* 17,749
SIC 9661 Space flight operations, government; Space research & development, government; ; Space flight operations, government; Space research & development, government;
CFO: Alethea Mack
CFO: David Radzanowski
Bd of Dir: Bill Garner
Assoc Dir: David B King
Adv Bd Mbr: Margaret Pippin
Adm Dir: Laverne Randolph
Adm Dir: Jacquelyn Rubeck
Ex Dir: Mark V Glorioso
CIO: Valarie Burks
CIO: Linda Y Cureton
CIO: Larry N Sweet

NATIONAL AGENTS ALLIANCE
See SUPERIOR PERFORMERS INC

D-U-N-S 92-933-2310
■ **NATIONAL AGRICULTURAL STATISTICS SERVICE**
N A S S
(*Suby of* U S D A) ★
1400 Independence Ave Sw, Washington, DC 20250-0002
Tel (202) 720-2707 *Founded/Ownrshp* 1816
Sales NA *EMP* 1,100
SIC 9641 Regulation of agricultural marketing; ; Regulation of agricultural marketing;
Top Exec: Craig Flynn
Top Exec: Chris Mertz
MIS Dir: Phill Zellers

NATIONAL AIR AMBULANCE
See NATIONAL JETS INC

NATIONAL AIR AND ENERGY
See NATIONAL AIR INC

D-U-N-S 84-213-4988
NATIONAL AIR CARGO GROUP INC
NATIONAL AIRLINES
(*Suby of* NATIONAL AIR CARGO HOLDINGS INC) ★
5955 T G Lee Blvd Ste 500, Orlando, FL 32822-4457
Tel (716) 580-6961 *Founded/Ownrshp* 2006
Sales 70.0MM *EMP* 238^E
SIC 4581 Airports, flying fields & services; Airports, flying fields & services
Pr: Glen Joerger
Plng Mgr: Charles Decker
VP Sls: Bryan Perraud

D-U-N-S 78-373-0641
NATIONAL AIR CARGO HOLDINGS INC
5955 T G Lee Blvd Ste 200, Orlando, FL 32822-4423
Tel (716) 631-0011 *Founded/Ownrshp* 1990
Sales 95.3MM^E *EMP* 410
SIC 4731

D-U-N-S 80-873-6693
NATIONAL AIR CARGO INC
(*Suby of* NATIONAL AIR CARGO HOLDINGS INC) ★
350 Windward Dr, Orchard Park, NY 14127-1596
Tel (716) 631-0011 *Founded/Ownrshp* 1990
Sales 25.1MM^E *EMP* 83
SIC 4731 Freight forwarding; Freight forwarding
Ch Bd: Christopher J Alf
**Pr:* Preston Murry
CFO: Brian Conaway
Ex VP: Glen Joerger
Mng Dir: James Millora
Off Mgr: Tricia Klingensmith
Dir IT: Bryan Wherry
Opers Supe: Michael Gorney
Opers Mgr: William Lawless
S&M/VP: Lori Smistek
Sls Dir: Alex Munro

D-U-N-S 11-341-4189
NATIONAL AIR INC
NATIONAL AIR AND ENERGY
2053 Kurtz St, San Diego, CA 92110-2014
Tel (619) 299-2500 *Founded/Ownrshp* 1995
Sales 34.2MM^E *EMP* 110
SIC 1711 Warm air heating & air conditioning contractor; Warm air heating & air conditioning contractor
CEO: Jared M Wells

D-U-N-S 60-642-0024
NATIONAL AIR TRAFFIC CONTROLLERS ASSOCIATION
NATCA
1325 Massachusetts Ave Nw, Washington, DC 20005-4171
Tel (202) 628-5451 *Founded/Ownrshp* 1987
Sales 24.3MM *EMP* 65
SIC 8631 Employees' association; Employees' association
Pr: Patrick Forrey
**Pr:* Paul Rinaldi
**Ex VP:* Trish Gilbert
VP: Hamid Ghaffari
VP: Garth Koleszar
VP: Timothy Leonard
VP: Ruth Marlin
VP: Larry Melton
VP: Scot Morrison
VP: Tim Smith

NATIONAL AIRLINES
See NATIONAL AIR CARGO GROUP INC

D-U-N-S 18-378-5120
NATIONAL AMERICAN INSURANCE CO
NAICO
(*Suby of* CHANDLER (USA) INC) ★
1006 Manvel Ave, Chandler, OK 74834-3854
Tel (405) 236-1751 *Founded/Ownrshp* 1987
Sales NA *EMP* 167
SIC 6411 6351 Insurance agents, brokers & service; Liability insurance; Fidelity or surety bonding
CEO: W Brent Lagere
**Pr:* Lance A Lagere
**Pr:* Mark T Paden
**CFO:* Mark Hart
**Ex VP:* Malinda Laird
**VP:* M Steven Blain
VP: Rick Cooper-Evans
**VP:* Richard Evans
**VP:* R Patrick Gilmore
**VP:* Gary Lagere
VP: Tracie Lagere

NATIONAL AMERICAN UNIVERSITY
See DLORAH INC

D-U-N-S 82-937-0134
▲ **NATIONAL AMERICAN UNIVERSITY HOLDINGS INC**
5301 S Highway 16 Ste 200, Rapid City, SD 57701-8931
Tel (605) 721-5220 *Founded/Ownrshp* 1941
Sales 117.8MM *EMP* 740^E
Accts Deloitte & Touche Llp Minneap
Tkr Sym NAUH *Exch* NGM
SIC 8221 6531 1531 Colleges universities & professional schools; University; Rental agent, real estate; Condominium developers; Colleges universities & professional schools; University; Rental agent, real estate; Condominium developers
CEO: Ronald L Shape
**Ch Bd:* Robert D Buckingham
Pr: Michael Buckingham
Pr: Robert A Paxton
CFO: David K Heflin
**V Ch Bd:* Jerry L Gallentine
VP: Weston Neiffer
VP: Joseph K Sallustio
Board of Directors: Jeffrey B Berzina, Therese K Crane, Richard L Halbert, Thomas D Saban

NATIONAL AMMONIA DIV
See TANNER INDUSTRIES INC

D-U-N-S 04-942-2439 IMP/EXP
▲ **NATIONAL AMUSEMENTS INC**
C B S
846 University Ave, Norwood, MA 02062-2631
Tel (781) 461-1600 *Founded/Ownrshp* 1959
Sales 27.6MMM^E *EMP* 133,269
SIC 7832 7833 4832 4833 4841 Motion picture theaters, except drive-in; Drive-in motion picture theaters; Radio broadcasting stations; Television broadcasting stations; Cable & other pay television services; Motion picture theaters, except drive-in; Drive-in motion picture theaters; Radio broadcasting stations; Television broadcasting stations; Cable & other pay television services
Ch Bd: Sumner M Redstone
Pr: Shari E Redstone
Pr: John Shahbazian
CFO: Michael Kszystyniak
Treas: Jerome Magner
Ex VP: Tad Jankowski
Sr VP: Joe Mollo
VP: Scott Bernstein
VP: Rick Bruner
VP: Thaddeus P Jankowski
VP: William Leclair
VP: George Levitt
VP: William Moscarelli
VP: Elaine Purdy
VP: Amber Stepper
VP: Mark Walukevich
Exec: Michael Long
Dir Risk M: Roy Murphy

D-U-N-S 01-311-4231
NATIONAL ANIMAL DISEASE CENTER
GOVERNMENT RESEARCH OFFICE
1920 Dayton Ave, Ames, IA 50010-9602
Tel (515) 663-7200 *Founded/Ownrshp* 1961
Sales 24.3MM^E *EMP* 365
SIC 8732 Research services, except laboratory; Research services, except laboratory
Ex Dir: Kurt Zuelke

D-U-N-S 07-263-2995
NATIONAL APARTMENT ASSOCIATION
4300 Wilson Blvd Ste 400, Arlington, VA 22203-4168
Tel (703) 518-6141 *Founded/Ownrshp* 1939
Sales 20.2MM *EMP* 56^E
SIC 8611 Trade associations
Pr: Doug Culkin
**CFO:* Melissa Cecchine
Sr VP: Maureen Lambe

D-U-N-S 09-300-8183
NATIONAL AQUARIUM INC
501 E Pratt St, Baltimore, MD 21202-3194
Tel (410) 576-3800 *Founded/Ownrshp* 1976
Sales 44.1MM *EMP* 350^E
SIC 8422

D-U-N-S 09-734-8114
NATIONAL ARBOR DAY FOUNDATION
ARBOR DAY FOUNDATION, THE
211 N 12th St Ste 501, Lincoln, NE 68508-1497
Tel (402) 474-5655 *Founded/Ownrshp* 1971
Sales 44.0MM *EMP* 300^E
Accts Hbe Becker Meyer Love Llp Lin
SIC 8611 Business associations; Business associations
CEO: John Rosenow
**Pr:* Matt Harris
**Treas:* Gary Deemer
Board of Directors: Ed Jacnke, Richard H Beahrs, Bill Kruidemier, Doug Bereuter, Ed Meek, Helen Boosalis, Ken Munson, Preston Cole, James O'hanlon, Carolyn Crayton, Dan Patterson, Leticia R Fortany, Joy Grant, Gary Hergenrader, Jack Hill

D-U-N-S 10-467-1235
■ **NATIONAL ARCHIVES & RECORDS ADMINISTRATION**
(*Suby of* EXECUTIVE OFFICE OF UNITED STATES GOVERNMENT) ★
8601 Adelphi Rd Ste 4200, College Park, MD 20740-6001
Tel (301) 837-2000 *Founded/Ownrshp* 1934
Sales NA *EMP* 2,907
SIC 9199 General government administration; ; General government administration;
COO: William J Bosanko
Ofcr: Rick Morgan
Exec: Tony Clark
Adm Dir: Ann Baker
Adm Dir: Marie Carbone
Adm Dir: Vurniece Jackson
Adm Dir: Kelley Yackley
CIO: Martha Morphy
CTO: Vivek Navale
IT Man: Queenie Ogden
IT Man: Sam Watkins

NATIONAL ASB WKRS MED FUND
See CARDAY ASSOCIATES INC

D-U-N-S 78-759-5912
NATIONAL ASSET MANAGEMENT LLC
400 Rouser Rd Ste 105, Coraopolis, PA 15108-2749
Tel (412) 424-0250 *Founded/Ownrshp* 2007
Sales 16.7MM^E *EMP* 412
SIC 8741 Management consulting services; Financial management for business
Opers Mgr: Sara Peterson

D-U-N-S 07-280-5328
NATIONAL ASSOCIATION FOR ADVANCEMENT OF COLORED PEOPLE
NAACP
4805 Mount Hope Dr, Baltimore, MD 21215-3206
Tel (410) 358-8900 *Founded/Ownrshp* 1909
Sales 31.0MM *EMP* 2,300
Accts Bert Smith & Co Washington D
SIC 8641 Social associations; Social associations
Pr: Ben Jealous
Pt: Marvin Beatty
Pr: Rose Joshua
COO: Nelson B Rivers
COO: Claudia A Withers
CFO: Roger Vann
Ch: Roslyn M Brock
Treas: Jesse H Turner Jr
Bd of Dir: Bishop Graves
Bd of Dir: David L Lewis
Bd of Dir: Joe Madison
Ex VP: Virgil E Ecton
Ex VP: Peter M Williams
Sr VP: Hilary O Shelton
VP: Moneese Delara
VP: Stephen Jackson
VP: Tonya Jones
VP: Leila McDowell
VP: Jesse Milan
Comm Dir: Derek Turner

D-U-N-S 08-351-1329
NATIONAL ASSOCIATION FOR EDUCATION OF YOUNG CHILDREN
NAEYC
1313 L St Nw Ste 500, Washington, DC 20005-4110
Tel (202) 232-8777 *Founded/Ownrshp* 1926
Sales 21.6MM *EMP* 103^E
Accts Heimlantz Pc Alexandria Va
SIC 8322 2721 2731 Child guidance agency; Periodicals: publishing only; Books: publishing only; Child guidance agency; Periodicals: publishing only; Books: publishing only
Ex Dir: Rhian Evans Allvin
COO: Donna Wormley
**CFO:* Diny Sonkan
Bd of Dir: Francis Brockington
Bd of Dir: Harriet Egertson
Bd of Dir: Frank Gettridge
Bd of Dir: Jane Henderson
Bd of Dir: Gera Jacobs
Bd of Dir: Naomi Karp
Bd of Dir: Lori Longueville
Bd of Dir: Alison Lutton
Bd of Dir: Tammy Mann
Bd of Dir: Davida McDonald
Bd of Dir: Stephanie Olmore
Bd of Dir: Sue Russell
Bd of Dir: Jason Sachs
Bd of Dir: James Scott
Bd of Dir: Gwen Simmons
Bd of Dir: Michelle D Soltero
Bd of Dir: Ursula Thomas
Bd of Dir: Gail Weinstein

D-U-N-S 08-586-2282
NATIONAL ASSOCIATION FOR EXCHANGE OF INDUSTRIAL RESOURCES INC
NAEIR
560 Mcclure St, Galesburg, IL 61401-4286
Tel (309) 343-0704 *Founded/Ownrshp* 1977
Sales 78.3MM *EMP* 80
Accts Mcgladrey Llp Galesburg Illi
SIC 8611 Trade associations; Trade associations
Ch Bd: John Hettery
**Pr:* Gary C Smith
**CFO:* Robert B Gilstrap
**VP:* Paula R Dejaynes
VP: Cruz Ramos
Exec: Robert Clark

D-U-N-S 12-250-6785
NATIONAL ASSOCIATION FOR SPECIALTY FOOD TRADE INC
136 Madison Ave Fl 12, New York, NY 10016-6711
Tel (212) 482-6441 *Founded/Ownrshp* 2006
Sales 25.2MM *EMP* 50^E
SIC 8611 Trade associations
Pr: Ann Daw

D-U-N-S 96-449-8468
NATIONAL ASSOCIATION FOR SPECIALTY FOOD TRADE INC
120 Wall St Fl 27, New York, NY 10005-4011
Tel (212) 482-6440 *Founded/Ownrshp* 2010
Sales 22.9MM *EMP* 2
Accts Tate And Tryon Washington Dc
SIC 8699 Membership organizations; Membership organizations
Pr: John Roberts

D-U-N-S 07-758-8945
NATIONAL ASSOCIATION FOR STOCK CAR AUTO RACING INC
NASCAR
1 Daytona Blvd, Daytona Beach, FL 32114-1252
Tel (386) 310-5000 *Founded/Ownrshp* 1948
Sales 35.3MM^E *EMP* 100
SIC 8611 7948 Business associations; Motor vehicle racing & drivers
V Ch: Brian Z France
**CFO:* James C France
**CFO:* R Todd Wilson
**Treas:* Tom Bledsoe
**Chf Mktg O:* Steve Phelps
Sr VP: Kim Brink
**Sr VP:* Paul Brooks
Sr VP: Jim Cassidy
Sr VP: Bob Gfeller
Sr VP: Steven Herbst
**VP:* W Garrett Crotty
**VP:* William L France Jr
**VP:* Lesa F Kennedy

D-U-N-S 10-192-8760
NATIONAL ASSOCIATION OF ATTORNEYS GENERAL
NAAG
2030 M St Nw Ste 800, Washington, DC 20036-3379
Tel (202) 326-6000 *Founded/Ownrshp* 1907
Sales 25.7MM *EMP* 35
SIC 8621 Professional membership organizations; Professional membership organizations
Ex Dir: James McPherson
**CFO:* Theresia Heller

D-U-N-S 08-586-8651
NATIONAL ASSOCIATION OF BOARDS OF PHARMACY
NABP
1600 Feehanville Dr, Mount Prospect, IL 60056-6014
Tel (847) 391-4406 *Founded/Ownrshp* 1904
Sales 27.2MM *EMP* 105
SIC 8621 8611 Professional membership organizations; Professional standards review board; Business associations; Professional membership organizations; Professional standards review board; Business associations
Ex Dir: Carmen Catizone
COO: Robert Cowan
Ex Dir: Howard C Anderson Jr
Ex Dir: Jack W Campbell IV
Ex Dir: Barbara Wells
IT Man: Ernie Iwanski

D-U-N-S 07-480-0020
NATIONAL ASSOCIATION OF BROADCASTERS
N A B
1771 N St Nw, Washington, DC 20036-2800
Tel (202) 429-5300 *Founded/Ownrshp* 1927
Sales 57.8MM *EMP* 173^E
Accts Tate And Tryon Washington Dc
SIC 8611 Trade associations; Trade associations
Pr: Edward O Fritts
**CFO:* Ken Almgrem
Ex VP: Henry Baumann
Ex VP: Neil Berry
Ex VP: John Knebel
Sr VP: Marci Burdick
**Sr VP:* Mary Dickson
VP: So Vang
**Prin:* David Rehr

D-U-N-S 07-779-1200
NATIONAL ASSOCIATION OF CHAIN DRUG STORES INC
NACDS
1776 Wilson Blvd Ste 200, Arlington, VA 22209-2516
Tel (703) 549-3001 *Founded/Ownrshp* 1933
Sales 38.6MM *EMP* 72
SIC 8611 Trade associations; Trade associations
CEO: Anderson Steven C
Sr VP: Susan Guiterman
**Sr VP:* Kathleen Jaeger
**Sr VP:* Carol Kelly
Sr VP: Larry Kocot
**Sr VP:* Christopher Krese
**Sr VP:* James Whitman
VP: John Coster
VP: Sandra Guckian
VP: Chrissy Kopple

VP: James Link
VP: Phil Schneider
VP: John Shepherd
VP: William Sittmann

D-U-N-S 80-779-6255
NATIONAL ASSOCIATION OF CHILD CARE RESOURCE AND REFERRAL AGENCIES
NACCRRA
1515 N Courthouse Rd # 11, Arlington, VA 22201-2909
Tel (703) 341-4100 *Founded/Ownrshp* 1987
Sales 71.5MM *EMP* 150
Accts Tate And Tryon Washington Dc
SIC 8322 Child related social services; Child related social services
Ex Dir: Lynette Fraga
Prgrm Mgr: Michelle Warren
QA Dir: Gail Upton
Snr Mgr: Michelle McCready

D-U-N-S 11-439-2525
NATIONAL ASSOCIATION OF CHILDRENS HOSPITALS AND RELATED INSTITUTIONS INC
NACHRI
600 13th St Nw Ste 500, Washington, DC 20005-3026
Tel (202) 753-5500 *Founded/Ownrshp* 1970
Sales 21.2MM *EMP* 90
Accts Tate & Tryon Washington Dc
SIC 8621 Medical field-related associations; Medical field-related associations
CEO: Mark Wietecha
VP: Mary Gorman
Assoc Dir: Carrie Hoover

D-U-N-S 79-148-7296
NATIONAL ASSOCIATION OF COLLEG
500 E Lorain St, Oberlin, OH 44074-1238
Tel (440) 775-7777 *Founded/Ownrshp* 2007
Sales 31.9MM *EMP* 21^E
Accts Maloney Novotny Llc Cleveland
SIC 8699 Membership organizations; Membership organizations
Prin: Cynthia D'Angelo

D-U-N-S 04-409-6584
NATIONAL ASSOCIATION OF COLLEGE STORES INC
N A C S
500 E Lorain St, Oberlin, OH 44074-1238
Tel (207) 287-3531 *Founded/Ownrshp* 1923
Sales 34.1MM *EMP* 175
Accts Maloney Novotny Llc Cleveland
SIC 5942 College book stores
CEO: Brian Cartier
**Pr:* Curt Schoen
**CFO:* Jane Nizza
**VP:* Hugh Keogh
Prgrm Mgr: Pamela Hammond
Board of Directors: Richard Hershman

D-U-N-S 07-484-6601
NATIONAL ASSOCIATION OF COMMUNITY HEALTH CENTERS INC
7501 Wscnsin Ave Ste 1100, Bethesda, MD 20814
Tel (301) 347-0400 *Founded/Ownrshp* 1970
Sales 33.9MM *EMP* 75
Accts Gelman Rosenberg & Freedman B
SIC 8641 Civic associations; Civic associations
Pr: Tom Van Coverden
**VP:* Mary Hawbecker

D-U-N-S 07-778-8834
NATIONAL ASSOCIATION OF CONVENIENCE STORES (VA)
NACS
1600 Duke St Ste 700, Alexandria, VA 22314-3421
Tel (703) 684-3600 *Founded/Ownrshp* 1961
Sales 32.9MM *EMP* 58
Accts Tate & Tryon Washington Dc
SIC 8611 Trade associations; Trade associations
CEO: Henry Armour
**Ch Bd:* Jeffrey G Miller
**Ch:* Dave Carpenter
**Treas:* Brad Call
**Sr VP:* Lyle Beckwith
**VP:* Michael Davis
**VP:* John Eichberger
**VP:* Bob Hughes
VP: David Podeschi
CTO: John C Hervey

D-U-N-S 07-779-1168
NATIONAL ASSOCIATION OF COUNTIES
NACO
25 Madcachusetts Ave, Washington, DC 20001
Tel (202) 393-6226 *Founded/Ownrshp* 1946
Sales 20.0MM *EMP* 80^E
Accts Tate & Tryon Washington Dc
SIC 8743 Lobbyist
COO: Bryce Petersen
Ex Dir: Matt Chase
Prgrm Mgr: Emmanuelle Jean
Dir IT: Paul Keister
Netwrk Mgr: Patrick McNulty

D-U-N-S 87-715-5762
NATIONAL ASSOCIATION OF COUNTY AND CITY HEALTH OFFICIALS
1100 17th St Nw Fl 7, Washington, DC 20036-4601
Tel (202) 783-5550 *Founded/Ownrshp* 1985
Sales 25.6MM *EMP* 115
Accts Raffa Pc Washington Dc
SIC 8621 Professional membership organizations; Professional membership organizations
Ex Dir: Robert Pestronk
**CFO:* John Mericsko
Prgrm Mgr: Carolyn Leep

D-U-N-S 01-029-1490
NATIONAL ASSOCIATION OF EVANGELICALS
7 E Baltimore St, Baltimore, MD 21202-1602
Tel (443) 451-1900 *Founded/Ownrshp* 1942
Sales 56.8MM^E *EMP* 500
SIC 8661 Religious organizations; Religious organizations

Pr: Leeth Anderson

D-U-N-S 05-532-5575
NATIONAL ASSOCIATION OF GOVERNMENT EMPLOYEES INC
N.A.G.E.
159 Thomas Burgin Pkwy, Quincy, MA 02169-4213
Tel (617) 376-0220 *Founded/Ownrshp* 1947
Sales 22.2MM *EMP* 130
Accts Accounting Office Of Michael R
SIC 8631 6552 Employees' association; Collective bargaining unit; Subdividers & developers; Employees' association; Collective bargaining unit; Subdividers & developers
Pr: David J Holway
**Ex VP:* James G Farley
Ex VP: Paula Moura
**Ex VP:* Barbara A Osgood
VP: Patrick Beaulieu

D-U-N-S 04-672-4183
NATIONAL ASSOCIATION OF HOME BUILDERS
NAHB
1201 15th St Nw, Washington, DC 20005-2899
Tel (202) 822-0200 *Founded/Ownrshp* 1942
Sales 82.3MM^E *EMP* 752^E
SIC 8611 8742 8732 Contractors' association; Marketing consulting services; Market analysis or research; Contractors' association; Marketing consulting services; Market analysis or research
CEO: Gerald M Howard
Pr: Dennis Harrison
**CFO:* Eileen Ogrady Ramage
Treas: Elliot Eisenberg
Bd of Dir: Anne M Chapman
Bd of Dir: Pam Griswold
Bd of Dir: Joe Gumm
Bd of Dir: Bonnie Hoffman
Bd of Dir: Thomas Koror
**Sr VP:* Mary Dicrescenzo
**Sr VP:* Daniel Durden
Sr VP: Ed Sutton
VP: Joseph Burak
VP: Neila Cbo
VP: Paul Emrath
VP: Meghan Everngam
VP: Earl Gruber
VP: Melissa Voorhees

D-U-N-S 96-793-7413
NATIONAL ASSOCIATION OF HOME BUILDERS OF UNITED STATES
1201 15th St Nw, Washington, DC 20005-2899
Tel (202) 266-8200 *Founded/Ownrshp* 2011
Sales 51.8MM *EMP* 3^E
Accts Tate And Tryon Washington Dc
SIC 1521 New construction, single-family houses

D-U-N-S 06-514-1905
NATIONAL ASSOCIATION OF INDEPENDENT SCHOOLS INC
NAIS
1129 20th St Nw Ste 800, Washington, DC 20036-3425
Tel (202) 973-9700 *Founded/Ownrshp* 1980
Sales 21.8MM *EMP* 42
Accts Squire Lemkin Company Llp Roc
SIC 8621 Education & teacher association; Education & teacher association
Pr: John E Chubb
**Pr:* Patrick Bassett
**CFO:* Corey McYntire
Off Mgr: Janice Bryant
Snr Mgr: George Breeden

D-U-N-S 07-383-8377
NATIONAL ASSOCIATION OF INSURANCE COMMISSIONERS
NAIC
1100 Walnut St Ste 1500, Kansas City, MO 64106-2277
Tel (816) 842-3600 *Founded/Ownrshp* 1871
Sales 94.7MM *EMP* 469
Accts Mcgladrey Llp Kansas City Mi
SIC 8621 Professional membership organizations; Professional membership organizations
CEO: Ben Nelson
CFO: Richard Ford
CFO: Brady Kelley
Sr Cor Off: Catherine Weatherford
Off Mgr: Wanda Carlson
Mktg Mgr: Julie Fritz
Genl Couns: Ross S Myers
Counsel: Sarah Heidenreich
Counsel: Jennifer McAdam
Counsel: Matthew Todd

D-U-N-S 07-480-4501
NATIONAL ASSOCIATION OF LETTER CARRIERS
NALC
100 Indiana Ave Nw Ste 709, Washington, DC 20001
Tel (202) 393-4695 *Founded/Ownrshp* 1889
Sales 1.4MMM *EMP* 5,000
SIC 8631 Labor union; Labor union
Pr: Fredric V Rolando
**Treas:* Jane E Broendell
Off Mgr: Steven Harrell

D-U-N-S 04-227-6352
NATIONAL ASSOCIATION OF MANUFACTURERS OF UNITED STATES OF AMERICA INC
NAM
733 10th St Nw Ste 700, Washington, DC 20001-4888
Tel (202) 637-3000 *Founded/Ownrshp* 1895
Sales 39.1MM *EMP* 165
Accts Johnson Lambert Llp Raleigh
SIC 8611 Manufacturers' institute; Manufacturers' institute
Pr: Jay Timmons
Pr: John Engler
COO: Leanne Wilson
Sr VP: Ann E Heins
Sr VP: Linda E Kelly
Sr VP: Ned Monroe
Sr VP: Aric Newhouse
Sr VP: Richard I Klein

VP: Chrysovalantis P Kefalas
VP: Tim Rogers
Exec: Dan Akman
Board of Directors: Jeff Shuman, James F Stern, Michael S Williams

D-U-N-S 06-999-3061
NATIONAL ASSOCIATION OF MUSIC MERCHANTS INC
NAMM
5790 Armada Dr, Carlsbad, CA 92008-4608
Tel (760) 438-8001 *Founded/Ownrshp* 1901
Sales 21.5MM *EMP* 62
Accts Allan Rosenthal & Assoc Ac Ca
SIC 8611 Trade associations; Trade associations
Pr: Joe Lamond
**CFO:* Larry Manley
**Treas:* Larry Morton
Dir Soc: Lisha Baer
Dir IT: Dan Kessler
IT Man: Mark Baratti
Mktg Dir: Scott Robertson
Pr Dir: Lora Bodmer

D-U-N-S 07-264-7621
NATIONAL ASSOCIATION OF REAL ESTATE INVESTMENT TRUSTS INC (MA)
NAREIT
1875 I St Nw Ste 600, Washington, DC 20006-5413
Tel (202) 739-9400 *Founded/Ownrshp* 1960
Sales 25.9MM *EMP* 33
Accts Tate And Tryon Washington Dc
SIC 8611 Trade associations
Pr: Steven A Wechsler
Pt: Kenneth L Betts
Pt: James J Hanks
COO: John Maleckar
**CFO:* Sheldon M Groner
**Treas:* Bernard Winograd
**Sr VP:* Tony Edwards
Sr VP: Victoria Rostow

D-U-N-S 04-757-9214
NATIONAL ASSOCIATION OF REALTORS
REALTOR MAGAZINE
430 N Michigan Ave Lowr 2, Chicago, IL 60611-4088
Tel (800) 874-6500 *Founded/Ownrshp* 2005
Sales 190.1MM *EMP* 623
Accts Crowe Horwath Llp Chicago Il
SIC 8611 2721 8299 Trade associations; Periodicals: publishing & printing; Educational service, nondegree granting: continuing educ.; Trade associations; Periodicals: publishing & printing; Educational service, nondegree granting: continuing educ.
CEO: Dale Stinton
**Pr:* Steve Brown
**Pr:* Maurice Veissi
**Treas:* William J Armstrong III
Bd of Dir: Catherine Dickinson
Ex VP: Terrence M McDermott
VP: Scott Louser
VP: Dj Snapp
**Prin:* John Pierpoint
Mng Dir: Jason Beatty
Mng Dir: Chad Curry

D-U-N-S 07-482-0945
NATIONAL ASSOCIATION OF SECONDARY SCHOOL PRINCIPALS
NASSP
1904 Association Dr, Reston, VA 20191-1502
Tel (703) 860-0200 *Founded/Ownrshp* 1916
Sales 21.7MM *EMP* 97
Accts Cliftonlarsonallen Llp Arling
SIC 8621 Education & teacher association; Education & teacher association
Ex Dir: Joann Bartoletti
**CFO:* John N Dripps
Assoc Dir: Donna Clark
Assoc Dir: David Cordts
Assoc Dir: Elizabeth Goldsby
Assoc Dir: Patti Kinney
Assoc Dir: Mel Riddile
Assoc Dir: Tanya Seneff
Ex Dir: N Tirozzi
Prgrm Mgr: Anne Knudsen
Sls&Mrk Ex: Vicki Fernandez

D-U-N-S 07-481-0805
NATIONAL ASSOCIATION OF SOCIAL WORKERS
750 1st St Ne Ste 800, Washington, DC 20002-8011
Tel (202) 408-8600 *Founded/Ownrshp* 1955
Sales 25.4MM *EMP* 90^E
Accts Mcgladrey Llp Gaithersburg M
SIC 8621 Education & teacher association; Education & teacher association
CEO: Angelo McClain
**Pr:* Darrell Wheeler
Treas: Josefina Ahumada
Treas: Paul A D'Gostino
Act CFO: Lisa Kingsley
VP: Richard Brown
VP: Robert Candea
VP: Christine Ford
VP: Anthony Oladipo
Admn Mgr: Elaine Lowenstein
Mktg Mgr: Susan Rubin

D-U-N-S 03-959-4551
NATIONAL ASSOCIATION OF STATE BOARDS OF ACCOUNTANCY INC
CPA EXAMINATION SERVICES
150 4th Ave N Ste 700, Nashville, TN 37219-2496
Tel (615) 880-4200 *Founded/Ownrshp* 1908
Sales 29.6MM *EMP* 220
Accts Lattimore Black Morgan & Cain
SIC 8621 Professional membership organizations; Professional membership organizations
Pr: Ken Bishop
**CFO:* Michael Bryant
Bd of Dir: James Suh
Genl Mgr: Shawn Bell
Software D: Dee Wilcox
Mktg Mgr: Perri Dugard-Owens

D-U-N-S 09-777-8104
NATIONAL ASSOCIATION OF STATE DEPARTMENTS OF AGRICULTURE INC
NASDA
4350 Fairfax Dr Ste 910, Arlington, VA 22203-1619
Tel (202) 296-9680 *Founded/Ownrshp* 1996
Sales 34.8MM *EMP* 3,339
Accts Gelman Rosenberg & Freedman
SIC 8611 Trade associations; Trade associations
Ex Dir: Stephen Haterius

D-U-N-S 07-313-5808
NATIONAL AUDUBON SOCIETY INC
225 Varick St Fl 7, New York, NY 10014-4396
Tel (212) 979-3000 *Founded/Ownrshp* 1961
Sales 88.9MM *EMP* 600
Accts O Connor Davies Lp Harrison
SIC 8641 2721 Environmental protection organization; Magazines: publishing only, not printed on site; Environmental protection organization; Magazines: publishing only, not printed on site
Pr: David Yarnold
COO: Bob Perciasepe
CFO: Mary Beth Henson
Ch: David B Ford
VP: Diane Clifford
VP: Mike Daulton
VP: Mark Jannot
VP: Stephen Kress
VP: Glenn Olson
VP: Joe Ryan
VP: Chandra Taylor Smith
Assoc Dir: Sarah Porter
Board of Directors: Stephanie Little, Jane Alexander, Alexis Maybank, Jon Anda, Hector E Morales Jr, Susan Bell, David Roux, Michele Crist, Hugh Simmons, Joseph H Ellis, Jack Stewart, Jeffrey Goodby, Doug Varley, James C Greenwood, Maggie Walker, Constance Holsinger, Karim Al-Khafaji

D-U-N-S 15-020-5243
■ **NATIONAL AUTO DEALERS EXCHANGE (INC)**
N. A. D. E.
(*Suby of* MANHEIM INVESTMENTS INC) ★
730 State Route 68, Bordentown, NJ 08505-4412
Tel (609) 298-3400 *Founded/Ownrshp* 1985
Sales 35.1MM^E *EMP* 275^E
SIC 5012 Automobiles & other motor vehicles; Automobiles & other motor vehicles
Pr: James C Kennedy
Genl Mgr: Pete Sauber
IT Man: Jeff Geyer

D-U-N-S 05-216-4118 EXP
NATIONAL AUTO PARTS WAREHOUSE INC
NATIONAL PERFORMANCE WAREHOUSE
11150 Nw 32nd Ave, Miami, FL 33167-3301
Tel (305) 953-7270 *Founded/Ownrshp* 1991
Sales 51.2MM^E *EMP* 60^E
SIC 5013 Automotive supplies & parts
Pr: Laurence M Pacey
VP: Richard Ferguson
Exec: Monica Blandon
Sales Exec: George Petru
Manager: Sandy Oldham
Sls Mgr: Matt Bacalis
Sales Asso: Anthony Ciarrocchi

D-U-N-S 96-633-8881
NATIONAL AUTO PLAZA INC
10790 S State St, Sandy, UT 84070-4105
Tel (801) 545-9292 *Founded/Ownrshp* 1996
Sales 27.3MM^E *EMP* 70
SIC 5511 Automobiles, new & used
Pr: Kolby L Hansen
Genl Mgr: Erik Terry

NATIONAL AUTO STORES
See TIFORP INC

D-U-N-S 05-713-9776
NATIONAL AUTO STORES INC
(*Suby of* NATIONAL AUTO STORES) ★
2512 Quakertown Rd, Pennsburg, PA 18073-1010
Tel (215) 679-2300 *Founded/Ownrshp* 1969
Sales 51.6MM^E *EMP* 140
SIC 5531 Automotive parts; Automotive accessories; Automotive parts; Automotive accessories
CEO: David Stein
**Treas:* Richard Stein

D-U-N-S 17-518-8176
NATIONAL AUTOMATIC SPRINKLER INDUSTRY WELFARE FUND
(*Suby of* NATIONAL AUTOMATIC SPRINKLER INDUSTRY)
8000 Corporate Dr, Landover, MD 20785-2239
Tel (301) 577-1700 *Founded/Ownrshp* 1953
Sales 185.9MM *EMP* 50
SIC 8741 6371 Administrative management; Union welfare, benefit & health funds; Administrative management; Union welfare, benefit & health funds

D-U-N-S 00-325-8878 IMP
NATIONAL AUTOMOBILE DEALERS ASSOCIATION (DE)
NADA
8400 Westpark Dr Ste 1, Mc Lean, VA 22102-3522
Tel (703) 821-7000 *Founded/Ownrshp* 1917
Sales 83.9MM *EMP* 300
SIC 8611 2721 2741 Trade associations; Trade journals: publishing only, not printed on site; Newsletter publishing; Trade associations; Trade journals: publishing only, not printed on site; Newsletter publishing
Pr: Peter K Welch
**COO:* Joseph Cowden
**COO:* Carl Ragsdale
Ofcr: Colleen Kelly
Ex VP: Bruce M Kelleher
**Ex VP:* Andrew D Koblenz
Ex VP: David W Regan
VP: Jonathan Collegio
VP: David F Hyatt
VP: Richard E Malaise
Dir IT: William Fitzpatrick

D-U-N-S 07-556-5978
NATIONAL AUTOMOTIVE GROUP INC
NATIONAL SABURU
2223 N Marine Blvd, Jacksonville, NC 28546-6916
Tel (910) 347-3777 *Founded/Ownrshp* 1981
Sales 80.0MM *EMP* 120
SIC 5511 Automobiles, new & used; Automobiles, new & used
Pr: Harry Brown
**Sec:* John Edwards
Sls Mgr: Chris Hines

D-U-N-S 06-746-6235
■ NATIONAL AUTOMOTIVE PARTS ASSOCIATION INC
NAPA
(*Suby of* GENUINE PARTS CO) ★
2999 Circle 75 Pkwy Se, Atlanta, GA 30339-3050
Tel (770) 859-2818 *Founded/Ownrshp* 1984
Sales 45.2MM^E *EMP* 100
SIC 5531 Automotive & home supply stores
CFO: Carol B Yancey
**Pr:* Dan Askey
**Pr:* Steve Handschuh
Area Mgr: Bobby Leuschen
Dist Mgr: Ken Meadows
Manager: Jon Andrade
Sls Mgr: Lou Fattore
Sls Mgr: Thomas Pantani DC

D-U-N-S 55-625-3040
NATIONAL AVIATION SERVICES LLC
19810 W Catawba Ave Ste C, Cornelius, NC 28031-4057
Tel (704) 987-3336 *Founded/Ownrshp* 2005
Sales 50.6MM^E *EMP* 600
SIC 4581 Aircraft cleaning & janitorial service; Aircraft cleaning & janitorial service
Dir Bus: Dan Kasdorf
Ex Dir: Jack McCown

D-U-N-S 55-630-4491 IMP
NATIONAL AZON INC
NATIONAL COATINGS
1148 Rochester Rd, Troy, MI 48083-2832
Tel (248) 307-9308 *Founded/Ownrshp* 1989
Sales 57.8MM *EMP* 72
SIC 5113 2621 Industrial & personal service paper; Printing paper; Industrial & personal service paper; Printing paper
CEO: Robert Anderson
**Pr:* David L Dodge
CFO: Pat McKowsky
S&M/VP: Rich Gigl

D-U-N-S 03-632-2360
NATIONAL BANK
905 E Main St, Gatesville, TX 76528-1434
Tel (254) 865-2211 *Founded/Ownrshp* 1889
Sales NA *EMP* 152
SIC 6021 National commercial banks; National commercial banks
Ch Bd: F W Straw
**Pr:* Eugene Worthington
**CEO:* David S Barnard
COO: John Dedoncker
Ofcr: David Conner
Ex VP: Duane Hogg
Ex VP: Donald Pall
Ex VP: Richard Shook
Sr VP: Marcia Hagwood
Sr VP: Lloyd Harrison
**Sr VP:* Kenneth K Poston
VP: Pat Brazzil

D-U-N-S 00-693-6199
NATIONAL BANK & TRUST CO OF SYCAMORE (INC)
230 W State St, Sycamore, IL 60178-1489
Tel (815) 895-2125 *Founded/Ownrshp* 1867
Sales NA *EMP* 141
SIC 6021 6163 National commercial banks; Loan brokers; National commercial banks; Loan brokers
Ch Bd: Jim Dutton
**Pr:* Michael Cullen
COO: Jeffrey Yordon
CFO: David McCoy
Chf Cred: Brian Hawes
**Sr VP:* Howard Heidlauf
VP: Michael Quinn
Mktg Dir: Tami Armstrong

NATIONAL BANK AND TRUST
See CUMBERLAND VALLEY NATIONAL BANK & TRUST CO INC

NATIONAL BANK AND TRUST
See CUMBERLAND VALLEY FINANCIAL CORP

D-U-N-S 96-302-3408
▲ NATIONAL BANK HOLDINGS CORP
7800 E Orchard Rd Ste 300, Greenwood Village, CO 80111-2549
Tel (720) 529-3336 *Founded/Ownrshp* 2009
Sales NA *EMP* 1,056^E
Tkr Sym NBHC *Exch* NYS
SIC 6021 Bank holding companies; National commercial banks
Ch Bd: G Timothy Laney
CFO: Brian F Lilly
Ofcr: Zsolt K Bessko
Dir Risk M: Richard U Newfield Jr
Mng Dir: Eric Edwards

D-U-N-S 12-146-0430
■ NATIONAL BANK OF ARIZONA
(*Suby of* ZIONS BANCORPORATION) ★
6001 N 24th St, Phoenix, AZ 85016-2021
Tel (602) 235-6000 *Founded/Ownrshp* 1994
Sales NA *EMP* 900
SIC 6021 National commercial banks; National commercial banks
Ch Bd: John J Gisi
Pt: Julie Seguin
Pr: Peter Eberle
Pr: Peggy Maberry
**Pr:* Keith Maio
Pr: Lucinda Naegele
CFO: Curtis J Hansen
**CFO:* Zachary Price
Treas: Ben Allen
Treas: Pam Bayles
**V Ch Bd:* Jim S Lee
Ofcr: Patty Attebery
Ofcr: Catheryn Avalos
Ofcr: Ann Camuso
Ofcr: Elton Crowe
Ofcr: Gail Dike
Ofcr: Cole Lysons
Ofcr: Alison Townsend
Ofcr: Zak Wagner
Ofcr: Rich Watson
Ex VP: Jim Batdorf

D-U-N-S 00-895-5338
■ NATIONAL BANK OF BLACKSBURG
(*Suby of* NATIONAL BANKSHARES INC) ★
100 S Main St, Blacksburg, VA 24060-4859
Tel (540) 951-6246 *Founded/Ownrshp* 1986
Sales NA *EMP* 87
SIC 6021 National commercial banks; National commercial banks
Pr: James G Rakes
Ofcr: Shelby Evans
Ex VP: F Brad Denardo
**VP:* Phillip Baker
CIO: Lawrence Hayes
Opers Mgr: Don Buchanan

D-U-N-S 00-792-2081
■ NATIONAL BANK OF COMMERCE (TN)
(*Suby of* SUNTRUST BANKS INC) ★
1 Commerce Sq, Memphis, TN 38103-2514
Tel (901) 523-3434 *Founded/Ownrshp* 1873
Sales NA *EMP* 5,194
SIC 6021 6211 7374 6712 National commercial banks; Investment bankers; Data processing service; Bank holding companies; National commercial banks; Investment bankers; Data processing service; Bank holding companies
Ch Bd: Ernest C Roessler
**Ch Bd:* William Reed
**Pr:* William Minkel
**V Ch Bd:* Lewis Holland
Ofcr: Ken Milman
**Ex VP:* Gus B Denton
**Ex VP:* Dick Grantham
**Ex VP:* Ron Reddin
**Ex VP:* John Womble
VP: Trina McCoy
VP: John Mistretta
VP: Brian Sims

D-U-N-S 00-794-7773
NATIONAL BANK OF COMMERCE
(*Suby of* NATCOM BANCSHARES INC) ★
2822 Tower Ave, Superior, WI 54880-5321
Tel (715) 395-5555 *Founded/Ownrshp* 1934
Sales NA *EMP* 115
SIC 6021 National commercial banks; National commercial banks
Pr: Larry L Kappes
**Pr:* Joseph Konradt
**Pr:* Bruce Thompson
**Pr:* Bruce Webb
CFO: Rick A Mgnuson
**Ch:* James Jarocki
**Chf Cred:* Lonnie Swartz
Sr VP: Mamie Hughes
Sr VP: Jenn Ryan
VP: Tom Broughton
VP: Bobbie Dumonsau
VP: Dean Fries
VP: Connie Rislov
VP: Kelly Wilson

D-U-N-S 06-167-7582
NATIONAL BANK OF COMMERCE
813 Shades Creek Pkwy # 100, Birmingham, AL 35209-4459
Tel (205) 313-8100 *Founded/Ownrshp* 2010
Sales NA *EMP* 156
SIC 6029 6021 Commercial banks; National commercial banks; Commercial banks; National commercial banks
Sr VP: Kelly Parkinson
Ex VP: Davis Goodson
Sr VP: Todd Beard
Sr VP: Jim Godfrey
Sr VP: Wanda McCaghren
Brnch Mgr: Lauren Dobson

D-U-N-S 78-266-1672
NATIONAL BANK OF COMMERCE INC
5500 Saint Charles Rd, Berkeley, IL 60163-1216
Tel (708) 544-5500 *Founded/Ownrshp* 1999
Sales NA *EMP* 100
SIC 6021 National commercial banks; National commercial banks
Pr: Dominic Pantano
**Ex VP:* Jeff Teague

D-U-N-S 10-299-9872
NATIONAL BANK OF INDIANAPOLIS CORP
107 N Penn St Ste 700, Indianapolis, IN 46204-2423
Tel (317) 261-9000 *Founded/Ownrshp* 1993
Sales NA *EMP* 279
SIC 6021 National commercial banks; National commercial banks
Pr: Morris L Maurer
Pr: Charissa Ambrose
Pr: Carla Morris
Pr: Maureen Schoch
Pr: Timothy Wallace
Pr: Kim Wharton
COO: John Snyder
**CFO:* Debbie Ross
Chf Cred: Terry Scott
Ofcr: Della Dietz
Ofcr: Kimberly Jewell
Ofcr: Jeff O'Brien
Ofcr: Joanna Terhune
Trst Ofcr: Angela Berg
Trst Ofcr: Scott Bilyou
Trst Ofcr: Julie Lenahan
Trst Ofcr: J P Randall
Trst Ofcr: John E Thomason
Ex VP: Amy Begley
**Ex VP:* Mark E Bruin
VP: Linda Allen
Board of Directors: Kathryn G Betley, Nathan Feltman, David R Frick, Christie B Kelly, Michael S Maurer, William S Oesterle, John T Thompson

D-U-N-S 06-088-3589
NATIONAL BANK OF KANSAS CITY
(*Suby of* AMERI-NATIONAL CORPORATION)
10700 Nall Ave, Overland Park, KS 66211-1364
Tel (913) 498-2220 *Founded/Ownrshp* 1999
Sales NA *EMP* 220
SIC 6021 National commercial banks; National commercial banks
Pr: Brian Unruh
COO: Michael Bartkoski
**CFO:* Eric Garretson
Chf Mktg O: Julie Beets
Ofcr: Regina Brummett
Ofcr: Todd Bukaty
Ofcr: Trevor Campbell
Ofcr: David Devine
Ofcr: Andy Friscia
Ofcr: Kirby Hinton
Ofcr: Matthew Johnson
Ofcr: Nate Lahaih
Ofcr: Tim Lander
Ofcr: Mike Limback
Ofcr: Donna Lydon
Ofcr: Greg Mealman
Ofcr: Maggie Nguyen
Ofcr: Jason Payne
Ofcr: Greg Ramirez
Ofcr: Michael Thompson
Ofcr: C H Tinsman Jr

D-U-N-S 14-162-2253
NATIONAL BANKRUPTCY SERVICES LLC
NBS
14841 Dallas Pkwy Ste 300, Dallas, TX 75254-7883
Tel (972) 643-6600 *Founded/Ownrshp* 2012
Sales 102.3MM^E *EMP* 610
SIC 7389 Financial services; Financial services
CEO: Lawrence J Buckley
COO: Brad Cloud
Ex VP: Luke Madole
Sr VP: Betsy Hanson

D-U-N-S 15-650-4698
▲ NATIONAL BANKSHARES INC
101 Hubbard St, Blacksburg, VA 24060-5743
Tel (540) 951-6300 *Founded/Ownrshp* 1986
Sales NA *EMP* 226
Tkr Sym NKSH *Exch* NAS
SIC 6021 National commercial banks; National commercial banks
Ch Bd: James G Rakes
CFO: David K Skeens
Trst Ofcr: Deana Kelsey
Ex VP: F Brad Denardo
Ex VP: Curtis Hansen
Sr VP: Joe Beury
Sr VP: Doug Thompson
VP: Bryce McCall
VP: Joan Nelson
VP: Rick Reed
Brnch Mgr: Betty Johnson

D-U-N-S 00-733-9518 IMP/EXP
NATIONAL BANNER CO INC (TX)
WORLD DIVISION USA
11938 Harry Hines Blvd, Dallas, TX 75234-5999
Tel (972) 241-2131 *Founded/Ownrshp* 1952
Sales 34.4MM^E *EMP* 180
Accts Howard Llp Dallas Tx
SIC 2399 Banners, made from fabric; Banners, made from fabric
Pr: Marc Goldfarb
**Ch Bd:* Abraham Goldfarb
**Treas:* Don Girard
Sls Mgr: Brandon Westmoreland
Board of Directors: Carol Holcomb, Cindy Marten

D-U-N-S 07-525-5729 IMP
NATIONAL BASKETBALL ASSOCIATION INC
N B A
100 Plaza Dr Fl 3, Secaucus, NJ 07094-3766
Tel (212) 407-8000 *Founded/Ownrshp* 1969
Sales 110.3MM^E *EMP* 865
SIC 7941 Professional & semi-professional sports clubs; Basketball club; Professional & semi-professional sports clubs; Basketball club
Pr: Joel M Litvin
**COO:* Russell T Granik
CFO: Carol Sawdye
Chf Mktg O: Fred Nangione
Ex VP: Mitch Kupchak
Ex VP: Gregg Winik
**Sr VP:* Michael T Allen
Sr VP: Timothy P Andree
VP: Barbara Decristofaro
VP: Jene Elzie
VP: Todd Harris
VP: Phil Horn
VP: Rachel Jacobson
VP: Kurt Rambis
VP: Susan Tohyama
VP: Jim Tucker
VP: David Wang
Creative D: Ryan Flaherty
Creative D: Henry Moore
Creative D: Emilie Rainsberry

D-U-N-S 00-924-2964
NATIONAL BASKETBALL PLAYERS ASSOCIATION
310 Malcolm X Blvd Fl 3, New York, NY 10027-4515
Tel (212) 655-0880 *Founded/Ownrshp* 2000
Sales 32.6MM *EMP* 2
Accts Calibre Cpa Group Pllc Washin
SIC 7941 Basketball club
Pr: Derek Fisher
VP: Roger Mason
Exec: Dan Wasserman
Ex Dir: William Hunter

D-U-N-S 82-904-7997
NATIONAL BATH SYSTEMS LLC
BATH FITTER
472 Meadowland Dr Ste 3, South Burlington, VT 05403-4468
Tel (802) 860-2999 *Founded/Ownrshp* 1997
Sales 23.5MM^E *EMP* 172^E
SIC 1799 Bathtub refinishing; Bathtub refinishing
CFO: Raffi Apanian
IT Man: Melanie Boissonneault

D-U-N-S 60-302-5933 IMP
NATIONAL BEDDING CO LLC
SERTA MATTRESS COMPANY
(*Suby of* SERTA SIMMONS BEDDING LLC) ★
2600 Forbs Ave, Hoffman Estates, IL 60192-3723
Tel (847) 645-0200 *Founded/Ownrshp* 1989
Sales 565.7MM^E *EMP* 2,400
SIC 2515 Box springs, assembled; Box springs, assembled
Ch Bd: Norman Axelrod
Ch Bd: Richard E Yulman
CFO: Brian Callaham
Sr VP: Barbara Bradford
VP: Charissa Dillard
VP: Thomas Wenholz
VP Mfg: Jay Patel

D-U-N-S 82-988-8952 IMP
■ NATIONAL BEEF LEATHERS LLC
(*Suby of* NATIONAL BEEF PACKING CO LLC) ★
205 Florence Rd, Saint Joseph, MO 64504-1069
Tel (816) 236-1603 *Founded/Ownrshp* 2009
Sales 228.8MM^E *EMP* 1,113
SIC 3111 Leather tanning & finishing; Leather tanning & finishing

D-U-N-S 14-795-0794 IMP/EXP
■ NATIONAL BEEF PACKING CO LLC
(*Suby of* LEUCADIA NATIONAL CORP) ★
12200 N Ambassador Dr # 101, Kansas City, MO 64163-1201
Tel (800) 449-2333 *Founded/Ownrshp* 2011
Sales 1.4MMM^E *EMP* 8,900
SIC 2011 Meat packing plants; Beef products from beef slaughtered on site
CEO: Timothy M Klein
V Ch: Terry Ryan
**COO:* Terry L Wilkerson
**CFO:* Simon McGee
Ex VP: Russell Cross
**Ex VP:* David Grosenheider
**Ex VP:* Carey Hoskinson
**Ex VP:* Monte E Lowe
Ex VP: Steve Rhodes
VP: Robert Hein
VP: John Hopkins
VP: Bret G Wilson

D-U-N-S 61-971-4041
NATIONAL BENEFIT SERVICES LLC
8523 S Redwood Rd, West Jordan, UT 84088-9311
Tel (801) 532-4000 *Founded/Ownrshp* 1984
Sales 28.9MM^E *EMP* 200
SIC 8748 Business consulting; Business consulting
Sr VP: Scott Betts
VP: David Beal
VP: James Morrison
Sales Exec: Kim Stephens

D-U-N-S 06-854-8593
NATIONAL BENEVOLENT ASSOCIATION OF CHRISTIAN CHURCH
733 Union Blvd 300, Saint Louis, MO 63108-1037
Tel (314) 993-9000 *Founded/Ownrshp* 1887
Sales 30.1MM^E *EMP* 250
Accts Ernst & Young Us Llp Clayton
SIC 8361 6512 Children's home; Home for the mentally handicapped; Home for the aged; Nonresidential building operators; Children's home; Home for the mentally handicapped; Home for the aged; Nonresidential building operators
Pr: Mark D Anderson
**COO:* Sterling Ellis
**CFO:* Gary Zimmerman
**VP:* Rebecca L Hale
Netwrk Mgr: Sharon Clayton
Netwrk Mgr: Mindy M Lewis
Netwrk Mgr: Brad White
Sls&Mrk Ex: Pat Hunter

D-U-N-S 10-340-2343 EXP
■ NATIONAL BEVERAGE CORP
(*Suby of* IBS PARTNERS LTD) ★
8100 Sw 10th St Ste 4000, Plantation, FL 33324-3224
Tel (954) 581-0922 *Founded/Ownrshp* 1985
Sales 645.8MM *EMP* 1,200^E
Accts Mcgladrey Llp West Palm Beach
Tkr Sym FIZZ *Exch* NGS
SIC 2086 Bottled & canned soft drinks; Carbonated beverages, nonalcoholic: bottled & canned; Water, pasteurized: packaged in cans, bottles, etc.; Fruit drinks (less than 100% juice): packaged in cans, etc.; Bottled & canned soft drinks; Carbonated beverages, nonalcoholic: bottled & canned; Water, pasteurized: packaged in cans, bottles, etc.; Fruit drinks (less than 100% juice): packaged in cans, etc.
Ch Bd: Nick A Caporella
**Pr:* Joseph G Caporella
Ex VP: Michael Bahr
Ex VP: James Bolton
Ex VP: George R Bracken
Ex VP: Charles Maier
VP: Dennis Blair
VP: Gregory P Cook
VP: John Hlebica
VP: Worth Shuman
VP: Robert Spindler
Exec: Paul Barton
Dir Risk M: Richard Berkes
Board of Directors: Cecil D Conlee, Samuel C Hathorn Jr, Stanley M Sheridan

NATIONAL BEVPAK
See SHASTA BEVERAGES INC

D-U-N-S 82-556-9957 IMP
NATIONAL BIOCHEMICALS LLC
220 Lena Dr, Aurora, OH 44202-9244
Tel (330) 425-2522 Founded/Ownrshp 2015
Sales 23.3MM^E EMP 36
SIC 5169

D-U-N-S 18-566-0495
NATIONAL BOARD FOR PROFESSIONAL TEACHING STANDARDS INC
NBPTS
1525 Wilson Blvd Ste 700, Arlington, VA 22209-2444
Tel (703) 465-2700 Founded/Ownrshp 1987
Sales 37.6MM EMP 53^E
Accts Plante & Moran Pllc Southfiel
SIC 8621 Professional standards review board; Professional standards review board
Pr: Ronald Thorpe
CFO: Laura Lee
Ch: Robert Wise
Ex VP: Peggy Brookins
VP: Sally Mernissi

D-U-N-S 06-184-0328
NATIONAL BOARD OF MEDICAL EXAMINERS OF UNITED STATES OF AMERICA
3750 Market St, Philadelphia, PA 19104-3102
Tel (215) 590-9500 Founded/Ownrshp 1915
Sales 137.1MM EMP 300
Accts Mitchell & Titus Philadelphia
SIC 8748 Testing service, educational or personnel; Testing service, educational or personnel
Ch: Lewis R First
COO: Kathleen Kilkenny
*Treas: Suzanne T Anderson
Ofcr: Brent Pierce
Ofcr: Colleen Ward
Assoc VP: Elizabeth Azari
Assoc VP: Kenny Yu
Ex VP: Barbara Atkinson
Sr VP: Frank Bilotta
VP: Brownie Anderson
VP: John Bird
*VP: Lynn M Cleary
VP: Robert Galbraith
VP: Stephen Lopez
VP: Sumit Nair
VP: Dave Swanson
Exec: Barbara Davidson
Assoc Dir: DOT Horber
Dir Soc: Kate Vangraafeiland

D-U-N-S 07-069-0847
NATIONAL BOARD OF OSTEOPATHIC MEDICAL EXAMINERS INC
NBOME
8765 W Higgins Rd Ste 200, Chicago, IL 60631-4174
Tel (773) 714-0622 Founded/Ownrshp 1943
Sales 23.2MM EMP 11
Accts Cliftonlarsonallen Llp Oak Br
SIC 8621 Medical field-related associations
CEO: John R Gimpel
Mng Dir: Crystal Wilson

D-U-N-S 61-573-3839
NATIONAL BOILER SERVICE INC
176 N Industrial Blvd, Trenton, GA 30752-2208
Tel (423) 531-8326 Founded/Ownrshp 1989
Sales 22.4MM^E EMP 112
SIC 3443 1711 Boiler & boiler shop work; Boiler maintenance contractor; Boiler & boiler shop work; Boiler maintenance contractor
Pr: David Duplissey
*CFO: Kurt R Johnson
CFO: Kurt Johnson
*Sec: Jim A Woods
*VP: Robert Hunter
VP: Robert K Hunter
*VP: Robert E Perry
Area Mgr: Jim Minor
Div Mgr: Fred Pace
VP Opers: Steve Harville
Sfty Dirs: Craig Bellew

D-U-N-S 05-091-8663
NATIONAL BOOK CO INC (DE)
(Suby of W W NORTON & CO INC) ★
800 Keystone Indus Park, Dunmore, PA 18512-1531
Tel (570) 346-2029 Founded/Ownrshp 1960
Sales 28.3MM^E EMP 200
SIC 4226 Special warehousing & storage; Special warehousing & storage
Pr: Michael Charnuzorsky
*Pr: W Drake McFeely
*Sec: Victor D Schmalzer
*Ex VP: Mike Charnogorski
Ex VP: Michael Charnogursky

D-U-N-S 62-198-8732 IMP
NATIONAL BOOK NETWORK INC
(Suby of ROWMAN & LITTLEFIELD PUBLISHING GROUP INC) ★
4501 Forbes Blvd Ste 200, Lanham, MD 20706-4346
Tel (301) 459-8020 Founded/Ownrshp 1986
Sales 136.7MM^E EMP 450^E
SIC 5192 Books, periodicals & newspapers; Books, periodicals & newspapers
Ch: Stanley Plotnick
*Pr: James Lyons
VP: Marianne Bohr
VP: Ron Powers

D-U-N-S 10-584-2801 IMP/EXP
NATIONAL BRONZE AND METALS INC
NBM METALS
(Suby of METCHEM ANSTALT)
2929 W 12th St, Houston, TX 77008-6113
Tel (713) 869-9600 Founded/Ownrshp 1983
Sales 100.0MM EMP 186
Accts Snell Levin & Co Llp Houst
SIC 3366 Bronze foundry; Bronze foundry
Pr: Michael J Greathead
*Treas: Laurence Rosenberg
*Sr VP: Norman M Lazarus
VP: William Austerberry
Ql Cn Mgr: Jim Haase

NATIONAL BUILDERS SUPPLY
See HMWALLACE INC

D-U-N-S 09-036-4662
NATIONAL BUILDING MAINTENANCE CORP
(Suby of GCA SERVICES GROUP INC) ★
855 Ave Hostos, Ponce, PR 00716-1105
Tel (787) 290-7020 Founded/Ownrshp 2003
Sales 30.1MM^E EMP 2,189
SIC 7349 5169 Building maintenance, except repairs; Industrial chemicals; Building maintenance, except repairs; Industrial chemicals
Pr: Helcias Bermudez
*Treas: Provines Torres
*VP: Mildred Aviles De Bermudez

D-U-N-S 03-279-2251
NATIONAL BUILDING MAINTENANCE INC OF FLORIDA
JANUS SECURITY DIV
5005 N Hesperides St, Tampa, FL 33614-6434
Tel (813) 877-7467 Founded/Ownrshp 1962
Sales 1.5MM EMP 550
Accts Prida Guida & Company Pa T
SIC 7349 7381 Janitorial service, contract basis; Protective services, guard; Janitorial service, contract basis; Protective services, guard
Pr: Ursula E Page
*Treas: Robert L Page Jr

D-U-N-S 05-455-2435
NATIONAL BUREAU OF ECONOMIC RESEARCH INC (NY)
NBER
1050 Massachusetts Ave # 32, Cambridge, MA 02138-5398
Tel (617) 868-3900 Founded/Ownrshp 1920
Sales 39.7MM EMP 70
Accts Alexander Aronson Finning & Co
SIC 8733 Economic research, noncommercial; Economic research, noncommercial
Pr: James Poterba
Treas: Robert Mednick
Prgrm Mgr: Annice Correia
Dir IT: Dan Feenberg
Pgrm Dir: Jeffrey Frankel
Board of Directors: Bart Van Ark

D-U-N-S 07-031-8670
NATIONAL BUS SALES AND LEASING INC (GA)
800 Pickens Drive Ext, Marietta, GA 30062-3170
Tel (770) 422-8920 Founded/Ownrshp 1975
Sales 33.5MM^E EMP 80^E
SIC 5012 Buses; Vans, noncommercial; Buses; Vans, noncommercial
CEO: John T Smith
*CFO: John A Noyd
CFO: John Noyd
Dir IT: William Henderson
Opers Mgr: Brian Cooke
Opers Mgr: Bill Mayer
Sales Exec: Ken Bosland
VP Sls: Drew Hawkins
Sls Mgr: Ryan Frost

D-U-N-S 78-799-4037
NATIONAL BUS SALES INC
8649 S Regency Dr, Tulsa, OK 74131-3626
Tel (918) 224-1049 Founded/Ownrshp 2001
Sales 28.7MM^E EMP 40
SIC 5012 Buses
CEO: Shannon D Henshaw
*Pr: Steve Henshaw
VP: Steve A Henshw
*Prin: Debra Carter
*Prin: Mike Curtis
Mktg Dir: Michael Jankovic
Sls Dir: Markus Lazenby
Manager: James Lamb
Manager: Brandon Thomason
Manager: Paul Thompson
Sls Mgr: Daryl Tarver

D-U-N-S 00-740-6528
NATIONAL BUSINESS & ACCOUNTING CONSULTANTS CORP
NBAC
451 Hungerford Dr Ste 300, Rockville, MD 20850-4157
Tel (301) 977-0090 Founded/Ownrshp 1995
Sales 26.2MM^E EMP 400
SIC 8721 7389 6153 Certified public accountant; Financial services; Short-term business credit; Certified public accountant; Financial services; Short-term business credit
Pr: Boris Foxman
*VP: Natalie Berman
*VP: Jane Savchenko

D-U-N-S 80-680-9091
NATIONAL BUSINESS ASSOCIATION INC
16775 Addison Rd Ste 410, Addison, TX 75001-5122
Tel (800) 456-0440 Founded/Ownrshp 1982
Sales NA EMP 825
SIC 6411 Insurance agents; Insurance brokers; Insurance agents; Insurance brokers
Pr: Raj Nisankarao

D-U-N-S 07-781-3426
NATIONAL BUSINESS AVIATION ASSOCIATION INC
NBAA
1200 G St Nw Ste 1100, Washington, DC 20005-3830
Tel (202) 783-9000 Founded/Ownrshp 1947
Sales 36.0MM^E EMP 60
Accts Bdo Usa Llp Bethesda Md
SIC 8611 Trade associations; Trade associations
Ch Bd: Ken Emerick
*Pr: Ed Bolen
*Treas: Jeff Lee
Sr VP: Maureen Cameron
Sr VP: Chris Strong
VP: Paul Anderson
VP: Katrina Bradshaw
VP: Christa Fornarotto
Mktg Dir: Aimee Kaufman
Snr Mgr: Scott O'Brien

D-U-N-S 07-616-4771 IMP/EXP
NATIONAL BUSINESS FURNITURE LLC
(Suby of TAKKT AMERICA HOLDING INC) ★
735 N Water St Ste 400, Milwaukee, WI 53202-4103
Tel (414) 276-8511 Founded/Ownrshp 2005
Sales 114.1MM^E EMP 500
SIC 5021 Office furniture; Office furniture
Pr: Kent Anderson
CFO: Perry Amadon
CFO: Eileen Baus
Ch: Felix Zimmerman
VP: Dean Stier
MIS Dir: Steve Fry
IT Man: Laura Tomter
Software D: Susan Russell
Sls Mgr: Rusty Jenkins
Sls Mgr: Jacqueline Kelsey

D-U-N-S 19-228-0915
NATIONAL BUSINESS GROUP INC
NATIONAL TUBE & STEEL
15319 Chatsworth St, Mission Hills, CA 91345-2040
Tel (818) 221-6000 Founded/Ownrshp 1985
Sales 98.4MM^E EMP 1,000
SIC 7353 5039 7359 3496 7519 Earth moving equipment, rental or leasing; Wire fence, gates & accessories; Garage facility & tool rental; Fencing, made from purchased wire; Utility trailer rental; Earth moving equipment, rental or leasing; Wire fence, gates & accessories; Garage facility & tool rental; Fencing, made from purchased wire; Utility trailer rental
Pr: James Mooneyham

D-U-N-S 01-695-4467
NATIONAL BUSINESS INSTITUTE INC
1218 Mccann Dr, Altoona, WI 54720-2561
Tel (715) 835-8525 Founded/Ownrshp 1997
Sales 23.7MM EMP 7
SIC 8742 Marketing consulting services
VP: Tom Hayes
VP: Roger Amundson
VP: Matt Mickelson
Mng Dir: Jim Embke
Genl Mgr: Ary Luedtke
Dir IT: Scott Eslinger
IT Man: Kim Thomas
Web Dev: Nicole Best-Campbell

D-U-N-S 15-985-2219
NATIONAL BUSINESS RESEARCH INSTITUTE INC
2701 Dallas Pkwy Ste 650, Plano, TX 75093-8711
Tel (800) 756-6168 Founded/Ownrshp 1982
Sales 15.1MM^E EMP 309
SIC 8732 Business research service; Business research service
*Treas: Dr EC Frieze
VP: Dr Bill Glascock

D-U-N-S 01-725-7189
NATIONAL BUSINESS SUPPLY INC
NAVIGATING BUSINESS SPACE
2595 Bellingham Dr, Troy, MI 48083-2036
Tel (248) 823-5400 Founded/Ownrshp 1997
Sales 43.7MM^E EMP 120
Accts Plante & Moran Pllc Auburn H
SIC 5712 5021 Office furniture; Furniture; Office furniture; Furniture
Pr: Richard Schwabauer
CFO: Kristin Gula
Creative D: Jill Burton
VP Sls: Pam Smith
Sales Asso: Tim Henkel
Snr PM: Tom Elsey

D-U-N-S 10-717-9731
NATIONAL BUSINESS SUPPLY INC
5419 S Decatur Blvd Ste A, Las Vegas, NV 89118-6250
Tel (702) 257-7007 Founded/Ownrshp 1996
Sales 28.2MM^E EMP 95
SIC 5085 Ink, printers'; Ink, printers'
Pr: Mike Starr
Sls Mgr: Mark Woods

D-U-N-S 07-176-7420
NATIONAL BUSINESS SYSTEMS INC
2919 W Service Rd, Eagan, MN 55121-1224
Tel (651) 688-0202 Founded/Ownrshp 1972
Sales 61.9MM^E EMP 500
SIC 7374 7389 2741 5044 7334 2761 Data entry service; Data processing service; Microfilm recording & developing service; Micropublishing; Microfilm equipment; Photocopying & duplicating services; Manifold business forms; Data entry service; Data processing service; Microfilm recording & developing service; Micropublishing; Microfilm equipment; Photocopying & duplicating services; Manifold business forms
CEO: David Ihle
*Pr: Joe Tafs
*CFO: Lisa Gobin
Genl Mgr: Brad Buchanan
MIS Dir: Theodore Naegeli
IT Man: Duwayne Dixon
Mktg Dir: Doug Calhoon

D-U-N-S 07-482-0408
NATIONAL CABLE & TELECOMMUNICATIONS ASSOCIATION
N C T A
25 Massachusetts Ave Nw, Washington, DC 20001-1430
Tel (202) 222-2300 Founded/Ownrshp 1963
Sales 70.9MM EMP 86
Accts Watkins Meegan Llc Bethesda
SIC 8611 Trade associations
Pr: Michael Powell
*Ex VP: James M Assey
*Sr VP: Bruce Carnes
*Sr VP: William Check
*Sr VP: Jadz Janucik
VP: Mark Bell
Exec: Lon Goldstein
*Prin: K Dane Snowden

D-U-N-S 00-519-6704
■ **NATIONAL CABLE COMMUNICATIONS LLC**
NCA
(Suby of NATIONAL CABLE COMMUNICATIONS LLC) ★
400 Broadacres Dr Ste 3, Bloomfield, NJ 07003-3156
Tel (973) 780-1700 Founded/Ownrshp 1980
Sales 25.5MM^E EMP 389
SIC 7311 Advertising agencies; Advertising agencies
Genl Pt: Katz Media Corp
Ltd Pt: Cox Cablevision
Ltd Pt: Comcast Corporation
Tech Mgr: John Hoadley

D-U-N-S 12-973-8212
■ **NATIONAL CABLE COMMUNICATIONS LLC**
NCC MEDIA
(Suby of COMCAST CORP) ★
405 Lexington Ave Fl 6, New York, NY 10174-0699
Tel (212) 548-3300 Founded/Ownrshp 1999
Sales 223.1MM^E EMP 500
SIC 4841 Cable & other pay television services; Cable & other pay television services
CEO: Greg Schaefer
*Pt: Andrew Capone
*Pt: Dan Griffin
COO: Kenneth Little
*CFO: Bob Curcuruto
Sr VP: Chip Carmody
Sr VP: James Loughran
VP: Jeff Boehme
VP: Chuck Cowdrey
VP: Robin Miller
VP: Greg Veitch
VP: Karenann Weingartner

D-U-N-S 03-776-3653
NATIONAL CABLE SATELLITE CORP
C-SPAN
400 N Capitol St Nw # 650, Washington, DC 20001-1550
Tel (202) 737-3220 Founded/Ownrshp 1978
Sales 69.7MM EMP 260
Accts Watkins Meegan Llc Bethesda
SIC 4841 Subscription television services; Satellite master antenna systems services (SMATV); Subscription television services; Satellite master antenna systems services (SMATV)
CEO: Robert Kennedy
*Ch: Brian P Lamb
Treas: Jana Fay
VP: Barkley Kern
VP: Roxane Kerr
Admn Mgr: Donald Hirsch
Tech Mgr: Alan Cloutier
Web Dev: Yi-Pei Eastin
Software D: Pam McGorry
Opers Mgr: Teri Michel
Opers Mgr: Steve Strother

NATIONAL CAMERA EXCH & VIDEO
See NATIONAL CAMERA EXCHANGE INC

D-U-N-S 02-292-4278
NATIONAL CAMERA EXCHANGE INC
NATIONAL CAMERA EXCH & VIDEO
9300 Olson Memorial Hwy, Golden Valley, MN 55427-4789
Tel (763) 591-5168 Founded/Ownrshp 1914
Sales 24.4MM^E EMP 185
SIC 5946 5731 5999 7384

D-U-N-S 96-995-9899
NATIONAL CAMPAIGN TO PREVENT TEEN AND UNPLANNED PREGNANCY
1776 Mass Ave Nw Ste 200, Washington, DC 20036-1916
Tel (202) 293-1708 Founded/Ownrshp 1996
Sales 24.8MM EMP 30
SIC 8399 Social change association
Ex VP: Lauren Dolgen
Sr VP: Cynthia Pellegrini
Sr VP: Alfredo Richard
Sr VP: Kathleen King
VP: Mina Stanard
Comm Dir: Jessica Pika
IT Man: Alice Singdahlsen
VP Mktg: Carmen Ford
Snr Mgr: Austin Castillo-Leovan
Snr Mgr: Becky Griesse
Snr Mgr: Leslie Walker

D-U-N-S 92-675-3919
NATIONAL CANCER COALITION LLC
225 Hillsborough St # 280, Raleigh, NC 27603-1767
Tel (919) 821-2182 Founded/Ownrshp 2007
Sales 140.3MM EMP 2^E
SIC 8099 Medical services organization; Medical services organization
Pr: Robert Landry
CFO: Hall C Overall

NATIONAL CAR RENTAL
See RYDELL AUTO CENTER INC

NATIONAL CAR RENTAL
See AIRPORT EQUIPMENT RENTALS INC

NATIONAL CAR RENTAL
See CLERAC LLC

D-U-N-S 06-492-3808
NATIONAL CARGO BUREAU INC
17 Battery Pl Ste 1232, New York, NY 10004-1110
Tel (212) 785-8300 Founded/Ownrshp 1952
Sales 21.7MM EMP 160^E
Accts O Connor Davies & Co Cpa S
SIC 4785 Surveyors, marine cargo; Surveyors, marine cargo
Pr: James J McNamara
*Ch Bd: James Zeriebec
*Pr: James J Mc Namara
*Treas: Tom Pendergast
*VP: Ian Lennard

D-U-N-S 05-086-4909
■ **NATIONAL CARRIERS INC**
(*Suby of* NATIONAL BEEF PACKING CO LLC) ★
1501 E 8th St, Liberal, KS 67901-2879
Tel (620) 624-1621 *Founded/Ownrshp* 1969
Sales 48.7MM^E *EMP* 260
SIC 4213 Refrigerated products transport; Refrigerated products transport
Pr: Jim Frank
**CFO:* Jay Nielsen
**VP:* Loren Bridge
Sls Dir: James Resh

D-U-N-S 09-670-7989 IMP/EXP
NATIONAL CART CO INC (MO)
3125 Boschertown Rd, Saint Charles, MO 63301-3263
Tel (636) 947-3800 *Founded/Ownrshp* 1979
Sales 59.5MM^E *EMP* 130
SIC 3537 7699 Trucks, tractors, loaders, carriers & similar equipment; Shopping cart repair; Trucks, tractors, loaders, carriers & similar equipment; Shopping cart repair
CEO: Robert Unnerstall Sr
**Pr:* Rob Unnerstall
**Pr:* Robert Unnerstall Jr
Treas: Dolores Unnerstall
Top Exec: Mark Harsy
VP: John Tigges
**VP:* John Unnerstall
IT Man: Leann Snow
VP Opers: Bob Helmes
Plnt Mgr: Kurt Boyer
Manager: Mike Henke

D-U-N-S 05-910-4406
NATIONAL CARTON & COATING CO
1439 Lavelle Dr, Xenia, OH 45385-5679
Tel (937) 347-1042 *Founded/Ownrshp* 1987
Sales 20.3MM^E *EMP* 80
SIC 2631 Packaging board
Pr: James Yost
Exec: Gary Hansford
**Prin:* Charles S Goodwin
CIO: Karen Nolen
Sales Exec: Greg Swartz

D-U-N-S 61-511-3982
NATIONAL CATASTROPHE ADJUSTERS INC
NCA GROUP
9725 Windermere Blvd, Fishers, IN 46037-9015
Tel (317) 915-8888 *Founded/Ownrshp* 2012
Sales NA *EMP* 246
SIC 6411 Insurance adjusters; Insurance adjusters
Prin: James Pearl President
COO: Ken Averitt
CFO: Jeffrey Wawok
VP: Tim Gardner
**Prin:* David Ross
Mktg Mgr: Darby Day

D-U-N-S 15-410-0903
NATIONAL CATASTROPHE RESTORATION INC
NCRI
8447 E 35th St N, Wichita, KS 67226-1344
Tel (316) 636-5700 *Founded/Ownrshp* 1972
Sales 40.2MM^E *EMP* 75
SIC 1542 1541 1521 Commercial & office buildings, renovation & repair; Renovation, remodeling & repairs: industrial buildings; Repairing fire damage, single-family houses
CEO: Nicholas Easter
**Pr:* Patricia Easter
VP: Brenda Smith

D-U-N-S 07-576-7616
NATIONAL CATTLEMENS BEEF ASSOCIATION
NCBA
9110 E Nichols Ave # 300, Centennial, CO 80112-3425
Tel (303) 694-0305 *Founded/Ownrshp* 1896
Sales 59.7MM *EMP* 123
Accts Grant Thornton Llp Wichita K
SIC 8611 Trade associations; Trade associations
Pr: Scott George
**Pr:* Jim McAdams
**CEO:* Terry Stokes
COO: Rick Husted
Treas: Robert Fountain Jr
Treas: Dave True
VP: Kim Essex
VP: Marvin Kokes
VP: Bob McCan
**VP:* Don Pemberton
Exec: Karen Taylor
Assoc Dir: Barbara Wizniak
Creative D: Don Waite

D-U-N-S 02-031-6568
NATIONAL CAUCUS AND CENTER ON BLACK AGING INC
1220 L St Nw Ste 800, Washington, DC 20005-4023
Tel (202) 637-8400 *Founded/Ownrshp* 1974
Sales 21.7MM *EMP* 2,300
Accts Bert Smith & Co Washington
SIC 8322 8641 Geriatric social service; Civic social & fraternal associations; Geriatric social service; Civic social & fraternal associations
Pr: Karyne Jones
**Pr:* Karyne Conley
Comm Man: Colette Beyer

D-U-N-S 06-712-7068 IMP
NATIONAL CEMENT CO INC
(*Suby of* VICAT)
15821 Ventura Blvd # 475, Encino, CA 91436-2935
Tel (818) 788-4228 *Founded/Ownrshp* 1920, 1974
Sales 274.7MM^E *EMP* 1,100
SIC 3241 3273 Portland cement; Ready-mixed concrete; Portland cement; Ready-mixed concrete
Ch Bd: James E Rotch
**Pr:* D J Bidet
CFO: Daniel Yukelson
IT Man: Stuart Haddock
Trfc Mgr: David Ollis

D-U-N-S 62-239-3825 IMP
NATIONAL CEMENT CO OF ALABAMA INC
(*Suby of* NATIONAL CEMENT CO INC) ★
2000 Southbridge Pkwy, Birmingham, AL 35209-1303
Tel (205) 423-2600 *Founded/Ownrshp* 1990
Sales 27.9MM^E *EMP* 140
SIC 3241 Portland cement; Portland cement
Pr: Spencer Weitman
**CFO:* Dominique J Bidet
VP: Derek Alpert
VP Opers: Eric Verbrugghe
**VP Sls:* Steven Snipes
Sls Mgr: Rick Passey

D-U-N-S 18-873-9932
NATIONAL CEMENT CO OF CALIFORNIA INC
(*Suby of* NATIONAL CEMENT CO INC) ★
15821 Ventura Blvd # 475, Encino, CA 91436-2935
Tel (818) 788-4228 *Founded/Ownrshp* 1987
Sales 31.4MM^E *EMP* 126
SIC 3241 Portland cement; Portland cement
Pr: Don Unmacht
**Treas:* Dominique Bidet

D-U-N-S 92-725-8350
■ **NATIONAL CEMETERY ADMINISTRATION**
(*Suby of* UNITED STATES DEPT OF VETERANS AFFAIRS) ★
810 Vrmont Ave Nw Ste 427, Washington, DC 20420-0001
Tel (800) 827-1000 *Founded/Ownrshp* 1862
Sales 45.2MM^E *EMP* 1,400
SIC 6553 9451 Cemetery subdividers & developers;

D-U-N-S 14-187-2916
NATIONAL CENTER FOR AMERICAN REVOLUTION
AMERICAN REVOLUTION CENTER, TH
123 Chestnut St Ste 401, Philadelphia, PA 19106-3060
Tel (215) 253-6731 *Founded/Ownrshp* 2000
Sales 32.1MM *EMP* 8
Accts Eisneramper Llp Jenkintown P
SIC 8412 Museum
Pr: Michael C Quinn
Ofcr: Herman O Benninghoff II
**Sr VP:* Zeeann Mason

NATIONAL CENTER FOR ATMOSPHERI
See UNIVERSITY CORP FOR ATMOSPHERIC RESEARCH

D-U-N-S 16-892-1000
NATIONAL CENTER FOR ATMOSPHERIC RESEARCH
NCAR
(*Suby of* NATIONAL CENTER FOR ATMOSPHERI) ★
1850 Table Mesa Dr, Boulder, CO 80305-5602
Tel (303) 497-1000 *Founded/Ownrshp* 1997
Sales 47.7MM^E *EMP* 930^E
SIC 8731 Environmental research; Environmental research
Pr: Richard A Anthes
IT Man: Karl Werner
Web Dev: Jeff Alipit
Sftwr Eng: John Clyne
Sftwr Eng: Irfan Elahi
Sftwr Eng: Pamela Gillman
Sftwr Eng: Tim Scheitlin
Snr Mgr: Betty Singleton

D-U-N-S 07-485-0165
NATIONAL CENTER FOR CHILDREN AND FAMILIES INC
FUTUREBOUND IND LIVING PROGRAM
6301 Greentree Rd, Bethesda, MD 20817-3368
Tel (301) 365-4480 *Founded/Ownrshp* 1915
Sales 20.2MM *EMP* 189
Accts Bdo Usa Llp Bethesda Md
SIC 8322 8361 Individual & family services; Children's home; Individual & family services; Children's home
CEO: Cheryl B Chapman
Dir Vol: Dahlia Levin
**CFO:* Mohammad Doka
**Prin:* Ralph Belk
**Ex Dir:* Sheryl Chapman
Pgrm Dir: Myrna Moses

NATIONAL CENTER FOR CRISIS
See NC4 INC

NATIONAL CENTER FOR DEATH EDUC
See MOUNT IDA COLLEGE

D-U-N-S 07-998-1489
NATIONAL CENTER FOR DEFENSE MANUFACTURING AND MACHINING
486 Cornell Rd Ste 2, Blairsville, PA 15717-8007
Tel (724) 539-8811 *Founded/Ownrshp* 2015
Sales 50.0MM *EMP* 33^E
SIC 8711 2752 Engineering services; Promotional printing, lithographic
Pr: Ralph Resnick

D-U-N-S 18-003-5768
NATIONAL CENTER FOR MANUFACTURING SCIENCES INC
3025 Boardwalk St Ste 250, Ann Arbor, MI 48108-3260
Tel (734) 995-0300 *Founded/Ownrshp* 1987
Sales 48.7MM *EMP* 35
SIC 8731

D-U-N-S 12-231-4321
NATIONAL CENTER FOR MISSING & EXPLOITED CHILDREN INC
699 Prince St, Alexandria, VA 22314-3117
Tel (703) 224-2150 *Founded/Ownrshp* 1984
Sales 43.5MM *EMP* 350
Accts Grant Thornton Llp Mclean Va
SIC 8322 Child related social services; Child related social services
Pr: John F Clark
Ch Bd: Patty Wetterling
Pr: Ernest E Allen
CFO: Linda M Krieg
CFO: Michael Lynch
VP: Herb Jones
VP: Yiota G Souras
Prin: Michael T Geraghty
Board of Directors: Paula Kruger

D-U-N-S 07-644-3563
NATIONAL CENTER FOR STATE COURTS
NATIONAL CTR FOR STATE COURTS
300 Newport Ave, Williamsburg, VA 23185-4147
Tel (757) 253-2000 *Founded/Ownrshp* 1971
Sales 41.4MM *EMP* 400
Accts Raffa Pc Washington Dc
SIC 8733 Research institute; Research institute
Pr: Mary C McQueen
**CFO:* Gwen Williams
**Ex VP:* Robert Baldwin
Ex VP: Steven Bennett
**VP:* Jeffrey Apperson
VP: James Bender
**VP:* Thomas Clarke
**VP:* Daniel Hall
VP: John Meeks
Comm Dir: Lorri Montgomery
Admn Mgr: Toni Engle

D-U-N-S 06-768-1783
■ **NATIONAL CENTER FOR TOXICOLOGICAL RESEARCH**
OFFICE OF THE CENTER DIRECTOR
(*Suby of* FDA- OFM) ★
3900 Nctr Rd, Jefferson, AR 72079-9501
Tel (870) 543-7517 *Founded/Ownrshp* 2010
Sales NA *EMP* 600^E
SIC 9431 Administration of public health programs; ; Administration of public health programs;

D-U-N-S 09-410-9436
NATIONAL CENTER ON INSTITUTIONS AND ALTERNATIVES INC
NCIA
7222 Ambassador Rd, Baltimore, MD 21244-2724
Tel (410) 265-1490 *Founded/Ownrshp* 1977
Sales 23.7MM *EMP* 650
SIC 8641 Civic associations; Civic associations
CEO: Herbert J Hoelter
COO: George Dehority
**Sr VP:* Kirk Larter
Ex Dir: Larry Norris

D-U-N-S 96-497-0230
NATIONAL CENTER ON INSTITUTIONS AND ALTERNATIVES INC
NCIA/AUGUSTUS INSTITUTE
7222 Ambassador Rd, Windsor Mill, MD 21244-2724
Tel (410) 265-1490 *Founded/Ownrshp* 1984
Sales 24.0MM *EMP* 5
SIC 8049 Clinical psychologist; Clinical psychologist
Owner: Herbert J Hoelter
**Ex Dir:* Herb Hoelter

D-U-N-S 00-228-9619 IMP/EXP
NATIONAL CHEMICAL LABORATORIES OF PA INC (PA)
401 N 10th St, Philadelphia, PA 19123-3893
Tel (215) 922-1200 *Founded/Ownrshp* 1946
Sales 38.0MM^E *EMP* 108
SIC 2842 2899 2841 Specialty cleaning preparations; Floor waxes; Chemical preparations; Soap & other detergents; Specialty cleaning preparations; Floor waxes; Chemical preparations; Soap & other detergents
Pr: Harry Pollack
**Treas:* Samuel Pollack
VP: James Redwanowski
VP: Ed Turner
Genl Mgr: Joe Reinert
Dir IT: William Smith
Sls&Mrk Ex: Judy Stryjewski
Manager: Anthony Bransford
Manager: Richard Hall
Manager: Jeff Hart
Manager: Jonathan Palecko

D-U-N-S 07-779-2042
NATIONAL CHILDRENS CENTER INC
NCC
6200 2nd St Nw, Washington, DC 20011-1493
Tel (202) 722-2300 *Founded/Ownrshp* 1958
Sales 27.9MM *EMP* 400^E
Accts Johnson Lambert Llp Raleigh
SIC 8211 School for the retarded; School for the retarded
CEO: Scott R Filer
**CFO:* Jamal Malone
Bd of Dir: Carol Politi
**Ex Dir:* Scott Filer

NATIONAL CHOICE BAKERY
See TWIN CITY BAGEL INC

D-U-N-S 85-938-3130
NATIONAL CHRISTIAN CHARITABLE
11625 Rainwater Dr # 500, Alpharetta, GA 30009-8678
Tel (404) 252-0100 *Founded/Ownrshp* 2008
Sales 665.6MM *EMP* 2
SIC 8699 Charitable organization; Charitable organization
Prin: Terra Parker
**Treas:* David D Johnson
Ex VP: Mardi Mountford
VP: George Cox
VP: Roger Sandberg
VP: Marsha Walker
Ex Dir: Lyston Peebles
Mng Dir: Pam Chumley
CIO: Wesley Barlow
CIO: Amy Garrett

D-U-N-S 07-942-3323
NATIONAL CHURCH RESIDENCES
2333 N Bank Dr, Columbus, OH 43220
Tel (614) 451-2151 *Founded/Ownrshp* 1961
Sales 47.1MM *EMP* 1,500
SIC 6531 6513 8051 8059 Real estate agents & managers; Real estate managers; Apartment building operators; Apartment hotel operation; Retirement hotel operation; Skilled nursing care facilities; Convalescent home with continuous nursing care; Convalescent home; Nursing home, except skilled & intermediate care facility; Real estate agents & managers; Real estate managers; Apartment building operators; Apartment hotel operation; Retirement hotel operation; Skilled nursing care facilities; Convalescent home with continuous nursing care; Convalescent home; Nursing home, except skilled & intermediate care facility
Pr: Thomas W Slemmer
**COO:* Jerry B Kuyoth
**CFO:* Joseph R Kasberg
**Treas:* Doug Vesey
VP: Teresa D Allton
**VP:* David A Kayuha
VP: Sarah Ortlieb
MIS Mgr: Jeff Sanderson

D-U-N-S 60-241-8100
NATIONAL CHURCH RESIDENCES OF HARPER WOODS MI
PARK PLACE OF HARPER WOODS
(*Suby of* NATIONAL CHURCH RESIDENCES) ★
19460 Park Dr Ofc, Harper Woods, MI 48225-2373
Tel (313) 884-2122 *Founded/Ownrshp* 1983
Sales 22.0MM *EMP* 5
SIC 6531 Real estate managers; Real estate managers
Pr: Mark R Ricketts

D-U-N-S 00-433-0528
NATIONAL CHURCH SUPPLY CO (WV)
SOUTHERN CH ENVELOPE & SUP DIV
2670 Pyramus Rd, Chester, WV 26034-1766
Tel (304) 387-5200 *Founded/Ownrshp* 1916
Sales 36.3MM^E *EMP* 255
SIC 2677

D-U-N-S 79-649-4222
▲ **NATIONAL CINEMEDIA INC**
9110 E Nichols Ave # 200, Centennial, CO 80112-3450
Tel (303) 792-3600 *Founded/Ownrshp* 2007
Sales 394.0MM *EMP* 595^E
Tkr Sym NCMI *Exch* NGS
SIC 7311 7389 Advertising agencies; Advertising, promotional & trade show services; Advertising agencies; Advertising, promotional & trade show services
Pr: Kurt C Hall
**Ch Bd:* Scott N Schneider
COO: Alfonso P Rosabal Jr
Ex VP: Bennett Fogel
Ex VP: Ralph E Hardy
Ex VP: Tom Reilly
Sr VP: Jeff Cabot
Sr VP: David J Oddo
VP: Rich Faul
VP: Mike Fenne
VP: Jill Long
VP: Steve Ried
VP: Kristine Schiller
VP: Peter Wolke
Board of Directors: Peter B Brandow, Lawrence A Goodman, David R Haas, Stephen L Lanning, Thomas F Lesinski, Paula Williams Madison, Lee Roy Mitchell, Craig R Ramsey, Scott N Schneider

D-U-N-S 19-773-2162
■ **NATIONAL CINEMEDIA LLC**
(*Suby of* NATIONAL CINEMEDIA INC) ★
9110 E Nichols Ave # 200, Centennial, CO 80112-3450
Tel (303) 792-3600 *Founded/Ownrshp* 2005
Sales 394.0MM *EMP* 150
Accts Deloitte & Touche Llp Denver
SIC 7311 Advertising agencies; Advertising agencies
Pr: Kurt Hall
CFO: Gary Ferrera
Ex VP: Ralph Hardy
VP: Michael Eaton
CIO: Bob Paige
Natl Sales: Lucas Metz
VP Sls: Mike Schonbuger
S&M/VP: Doug Gellerman
S&M/VP: Bridget Zukas

NATIONAL CITY BANK
See PNC BANK NATIONAL ASSOCIATION

D-U-N-S 61-722-2518
■ **NATIONAL CITY COMMUNITY DEVELOPMENT CORP**
(*Suby of* PNC FINANCIAL SERVICES GROUP INC) ★
1900 E 9th St, Cleveland, OH 44114-3404
Tel (216) 575-2000 *Founded/Ownrshp* 2008
Sales 75.2MM^E *EMP* 250
SIC 8742 Planning consultant; Planning consultant
Pr: Danny Cameran
VP: Atwiine Bernard
VP: Jason Birky
VP: Cathy Graham
VP: Joe McCarthy
VP: Garry McCaul
VP: Danna McLeod
VP: Jill Peller
VP: Lee Rodgers

D-U-N-S 07-128-9128
■ **NATIONAL CITY MORTGAGE INC**
(*Suby of* PNC FINANCIAL SERVICES GROUP INC) ★
3232 Newmark Dr, Miamisburg, OH 45342-5433
Tel (937) 910-1200 *Founded/Ownrshp* 1955, 2008
Sales NA *EMP* 5,800
Accts Ernst & Youngs Llp Cleveland
SIC 6162 Mortgage bankers & correspondents; Mortgage bankers & correspondents
Ch Bd: Leo E Knight Jr
**Pr:* Rick A Smalldon
**Treas:* Steven M Scheid
Ex VP: James Bell
**Ex VP:* Jack Case
**Ex VP:* Phil Cunningham
**Ex VP:* Gregory A Davis
Ex VP: Jon Gorney
**Ex VP:* Todd A Householder

Sr VP: Steve Atwood
Sr VP: Edward R Metzger
Sr VP: Theodore W Tozer
VP: Brad Belcher
**VP:* John D Bollman
VP: Jeff Crothers
VP: Alex Laufersweiler
VP: Dave Menker
Exec: Jon McBride
Board of Directors: Bernadine Healy, Jeffrey D Kelly

NATIONAL CNSTR WORKFORCE
See NATIONAL LABOR CONTRACTORS INC

D-U-N-S 14-568-4184
NATIONAL COAL LLC
(*Suby of* RANGER ENERGY INVESTMENTS, LLC)
8915 George Williams Rd, Knoxville, TN 37923-5312
Tel (865) 690-6900 *Founded/Ownrshp* 2010
Sales 20.2MM^E *EMP* 273^E
SIC 1221 Bituminous coal & lignite-surface mining; Bituminous coal & lignite-surface mining
Pr: Daniel A Roling
**COO:* William Snodgrass
**CFO:* Michael R Castle

NATIONAL COATINGS
See NATIONAL AZON INC

D-U-N-S 83-173-8732
NATIONAL COATINGS & SUPPLIES
2635 Belknap Ave, Billings, MT 59101-4539
Tel (406) 245-5585 *Founded/Ownrshp* 2013
Sales 26.1MM^E *EMP* 99
SIC 5198 Paints, varnishes & supplies; Paints, varnishes & supplies
Prin: Tammy Gran
Genl Mgr: Craig Heying

D-U-N-S 96-776-7216 IMP
NATIONAL COATINGS & SUPPLIES INC
4900 Falls Of Neuse Rd # 150, Raleigh, NC 27609-5490
Tel (919) 573-2900 *Founded/Ownrshp* 2008
Sales 547.1MM^E *EMP* 766^E
SIC 5198 Paints
Pr: Wayne Lavrack
**CFO:* Curtis Beeson
VP: Craig Glazebrook
VP: Harry Hall
VP: Jay Sharp
Store Mgr: Craig Holschlag
Store Mgr: Tom Lanning
Store Mgr: Amanda Panchyshyn
Store Mgr: Wesley Russell
Store Mgr: Donna Snyder
Site Mgr: Sherri Wood

D-U-N-S 94-850-0848
NATIONAL COATINGS INC
3520 Rennie School Rd, Traverse City, MI 49685-9171
Tel (231) 943-2557 *Founded/Ownrshp* 1996
Sales 25.6MM^E *EMP* 120
SIC 1721 Commercial painting; Industrial painting
Pr: Patrick Burden
Exec: Rachel Bunner
Genl Mgr: Jeff Burtch

D-U-N-S 82-525-2575 IMP
NATIONAL COIL CO
SUPERIOR COILS
1998 Fm 2011, Longview, TX 75603-4204
Tel (903) 643-2261 *Founded/Ownrshp* 2007
Sales 26.5MM^E *EMP* 68^E
SIC 3585 Air conditioning equipment, complete; Heating equipment, complete
Pr: Keith N Leonard
Sales Asso: Alex Hernandez

NATIONAL COLLECTION
See NATIONAL GROUPS LLC

D-U-N-S 96-480-3535
NATIONAL COLLEGE OF NATURAL MEDICINE
049 Sw Porter St, Portland, OR 97201-4848
Tel (503) 449-4343 *Founded/Ownrshp* 2010
Sales 21.3MM *EMP* 99
Accts Hoffman Stewart & Schmidt Pc
SIC 8221 University; University
Pr: David Schleich PHD

D-U-N-S 07-625-3095
NATIONAL COLLEGIATE ATHLETIC ASSOCIATION
NCAA
700 W Washington St, Indianapolis, IN 46204-2710
Tel (317) 917-6222 *Founded/Ownrshp* 1906
Sales 906.1MM *EMP* 508
Accts Deloitte Tax Llp Indianapolis
SIC 8699 Athletic organizations; Athletic organizations
Pr: Mark A Emmert
CFO: Kathleen McNeely
Ex VP: Bernard Franklin
Ex VP: Donald Remy
VP: Jonathan Duncan
VP: Dan Gavitt
Assoc Dir: Michael Miranda
Mng Dir: Bob Williams
Netwrk Mgr: Kim Johnson
Board of Directors: Karl Eller

D-U-N-S 07-976-9708
NATIONAL COMMERCE CORP
813 Shades Creek Pkwy # 100, Birmingham, AL 35209-4459
Tel (205) 313-8100 *Founded/Ownrshp* 2006
Sales NA *EMP* 240^E
Accts Porter Keadle Moore Llc Atla
Tkr Sym NCOM *Exch* NGS
SIC 6021 National commercial banks
Ch Bd: John H Holcomb III
**Pr:* Richard Murray IV
Board of Directors: Bobby A Bradley, R Holman Head, Jerry D Kimbrough, C Phillip McWane, G Ruffner Page Jr, W Stancil Starnes, Temple W Tutwiler III, Russell H Vandevelde IV, Donald F Wright

D-U-N-S 10-793-9084
NATIONAL COMMITTE TO PRESERVE SOCIAL SECURITY AND MEDICARE
10 G St Ne Ste 600, Washington, DC 20002-4253
Tel (202) 216-0420 *Founded/Ownrshp* 1982
Sales 30.4MM *EMP* 40
Accts Argy Wiltse & Robinson Pc M
SIC 8399 Social service information exchange; Advocacy group; Social service information exchange; Advocacy group
Pr: Barbara Kennelly
COO: Mike Prucker
**CFO:* Christine Kim
**Ex VP:* Max Richtman
Info Man: Cheryl Bruce
Snr Mgr: John Glaser

D-U-N-S 61-135-4523
NATIONAL COMMITTEE FOR QUALITY ASSURANCE
NCQA
1100 13th St Nw Ste 1000, Washington, DC 20005-4285
Tel (202) 955-3500 *Founded/Ownrshp* 1979
Sales 58.3MM *EMP* 234
Accts Mcgladrey Llp Washington Dc
SIC 8611 Business associations; Business associations
Pr: Margaret E O'Kane
COO: Ester Emard
**CFO:* Scott Hartranft
CFO: Scott A Hartrant
VP: Mary Barton
VP: James Laflamme
VP: Sarah Thomas
**VP:* Phyllis Torda
Mktg Mgr: Denise Diggs
Genl Couns: Sharon Donohue
**Genl Couns:* Sharon King-Donahue
Board of Directors: Michael L Davis, George C Halvorson, Jeffrey L Kang, David Kendrick, Talmadge E King Jr

D-U-N-S 96-481-1553
NATIONAL COMMITTEE TO PRESERVE SOCIAL
10 G St Ne, Washington, DC 20002-4213
Tel (202) 216-0420 *Founded/Ownrshp* 2010
Sales 22.0MM *EMP* 22^E
Accts Bdo Usa Llp Mc Lean Va
SIC 8699 Charitable organization; Charitable organization
Pr: Barbara Kennelly

D-U-N-S 62-533-3497
NATIONAL COMMUNICATION SERVICE
1600 124th Ave Ne Ste A, Bellevue, WA 98005-2132
Tel (425) 378-8080 *Founded/Ownrshp* 1990
Sales 29.2MM^E *EMP* 115
SIC 5065 1731 Telephone equipment; Telephone & telephone equipment installation; Telephone equipment; Telephone & telephone equipment installation
Pr: Ben Hayes
**Sec:* Jody Tangney
**VP:* Ron Green

NATIONAL COMMUNITY DEVELOPMENT
See LIVING CITIES INC

D-U-N-S 06-950-5030
NATIONAL COMMUNITY PHARMACISTS ASSOCIATION
NCPA
100 Daingerfield Rd, Alexandria, VA 22314-6302
Tel (703) 683-8200 *Founded/Ownrshp* 1898
Sales 44.1MM *EMP* 60^E
Accts Watkins Meegan Llc Bethesda
SIC 8611 Trade associations; Trade associations
CFO: Stephen Albert
**Pr:* John Sherrer
**CEO:* B Douglas Hoey
Sr VP: Steve Pfister
Sr VP: Kurt Proctor
VP: Zachary L French
VP: William Popomaronis
VP: Peter Whitestone
Assoc Dir: Jennifer Bruckart
VP Opers: Terry Hall
Snr Mgr: Mac Ovenell

D-U-N-S 79-651-6748
NATIONAL COMMUNITY RENAISSANCE OF CALIFORNIA
9421 Haven Ave Ste 100, Rancho Cucamonga, CA 91730-5890
Tel (909) 483-2444 *Founded/Ownrshp* 1992
Sales 199.9MM^E *EMP* 350
Accts Cohnreznick Llp Sacramento C
SIC 6552 Subdividers & developers; Subdividers & developers
CEO: Steven J Pontell
**Pr:* Orlando Cabrera
**COO:* Tracy Thomas
**CFO:* Richard Whittingham
**Ch:* Sebastiano Sterpa
Bd of Dir: Sammi Reeves
VP: Kevin Chin
VP: Byron Ely
VP: Julie Mungai
VP: Alexa Washburn
Dir Risk M: Jim Bigler

D-U-N-S 06-418-0847
NATIONAL CONEY ISLAND INC
27947 Groesbeck Hwy, Roseville, MI 48066-5221
Tel (586) 772-1324 *Founded/Ownrshp* 1970
Sales 28.5MM^E *EMP* 600
SIC 5812 Fast food restaurants & stands; Fast food restaurants & stands
Pr: James Giftos
CFO: Dan Roma
**VP:* Tom Giftos
**VP:* Nick Psilopoulos
Dir Risk M: Bill Zanetti
Dir Bus: Bradford Egan
Dist Mgr: John Kilimas
Dir IT: Bryan Buck
Mktg Dir: Martyna Nowak

NATIONAL CONFERENCE CENTER
See WXIII/OXFORD DTC REAL ESTATE LLC

D-U-N-S 06-061-3346
NATIONAL CONFERENCE OF STATE LEGISLATURES
NCSL
7700 E 1st Pl, Denver, CO 80230-7143
Tel (303) 364-7700 *Founded/Ownrshp* 1975
Sales 27.5MM *EMP* 150
Accts Eks&H Lllp Denver Colorado
SIC 8231 8651 Government library; Political organizations; Government library; Political organizations
Ex Dir: William Pound
**CFO:* Mary Wild
VP: Michael Gronstal
IT Man: Paul Bary
Pgrm Dir: Steffanie Clothier
Pgrm Dir: Robyn Lipkowitz

D-U-N-S 18-325-4432
NATIONAL CONSTITUTION CENTER
525 Arch St, Philadelphia, PA 19106-1595
Tel (215) 409-6600 *Founded/Ownrshp* 1986
Sales 22.4MM *EMP* 160^E
Accts Mitchell & Titus Llp New York
SIC 8299 8412 Educational services; Museum
Pr: Jeffrey Rosen
COO: Joe Barber
Bd of Dir: David Boies
Bd of Dir: Madison E Bond
Bd of Dir: Daniel R Butler
Bd of Dir: Gilbert F Casellas
Bd of Dir: Richard Dreyfuss
Bd of Dir: W J Duckworth
Bd of Dir: Andre V Duggin
Bd of Dir: John A Miller
Bd of Dir: Sandra D O'Connor
Bd of Dir: Edward G Rendell
VP: Jane Eisner
VP: Alison Young

D-U-N-S 05-475-7612
NATIONAL CONSTRUCTION ENTERPRISES INC
5075 Carpenter Rd, Ypsilanti, MI 48197-9601
Tel (734) 434-1600 *Founded/Ownrshp* 1978
Sales 96.2MM^E *EMP* 1,000
Accts Crowe Horwath South Bend In
SIC 8741 Construction management; Construction management
CEO: Pino Mancina
**VP:* Don Quinn
Off Mgr: Cindy Ennis
Snr PM: Oleh Szekera
Board of Directors: James R Markiewicz, Robert C Walrich

D-U-N-S 06-666-9995
NATIONAL CONSTRUCTION RENTALS INC
(*Suby of* NATIONAL BUSINESS GROUP INC) ★
15319 Chatsworth St, Mission Hills, CA 91345-2040
Tel (818) 221-6000 *Founded/Ownrshp* 1991
Sales 98.4MM^E *EMP* 900
SIC 7353 Heavy construction equipment rental; Heavy construction equipment rental
Pr: James R Mooneyham
**Pr:* W Robert Mooneyham

D-U-N-S 09-777-8633
NATIONAL CONSUMER COOPERATIVE BANK
N C B
2001 Penn Ave Nw Ste 625, Washington, DC 20006-1878
Tel (202) 349-7444 *Founded/Ownrshp* 1982
Sales NA *EMP* 248
SIC 6021 National commercial banks; National commercial banks
Pr: Charles E Snyder
COO: Chris Goettke
**COO:* Kathleen H Luzik
COO: Kathleen Luzik
**CFO:* Richard L Reed
**Ofcr:* Mark W Hiltz
Sr VP: Shawn Brenneman
**Sr VP:* Patrick N Connealy
**Sr VP:* Casey Fannon
Sr VP: Kevin Haga
Sr VP: Robert Jenkens
Sr VP: Becky Marsh
Sr VP: Patricia Poznanski
Sr VP: Matt Wehland
Sr VP: Jeffrey Whitlatch
VP: Jim Bethea
VP: Earl Carson
VP: Darren Flavell
VP: Kevin Goldthwaite
VP: Isaac Holt
VP: Laura Johnson
Board of Directors: Stuart M Saft, Roger B Collins, Walden Swanson, Peter A Conrad, Nguyen Van Hanh Phd, Irma Cota, Judy Ziewacz, Steven F Cunningham, Jane Garcia, William F Hampel, Janis Herschkowitz, Alfred A Plamann, Kenneth Rivkin

D-U-N-S 18-741-6540 IMP/EXP
NATIONAL CONSUMER OUTDOORS CORP
BRINKMANN PET
(*Suby of* COOK N CAJUN) ★
4215 Mcewen Rd, Dallas, TX 75244-5202
Tel (972) 716-4200 *Founded/Ownrshp* 1994
Sales 107.1MM^E *EMP* 292
SIC 3999 2399 2394 3732 Pet supplies; Horse & pet accessories, textile; Pet collars, leashes, etc.: non-leather; Liners & covers, fabric: made from purchased materials; Boat building & repairing; Pet supplies; Horse & pet accessories, textile; Pet collars, leashes, etc.: non-leather; Liners & covers, fabric: made from purchased materials; Boat building & repairing
Pr: J B Brinkmann
VP: M Donoghue
VP: Milly McDonald
Telecom Ex: John Lacy
Info Man: Jason Limber

D-U-N-S 96-170-8745
NATIONAL CONSUMER PANEL LLC
NCP
6800 Jericho Tpke 102e, Syosset, NY 11791-4401
Tel (516) 682-6000 *Founded/Ownrshp* 2009
Sales 26.0MM *EMP* 90
SIC 7299 Consumer purchasing services; Consumer purchasing services

D-U-N-S 82-806-0983 IMP
NATIONAL CONTAINER GROUP LLC
NCG CHICAGO
(*Suby of* MAUSER CORPORATE GMBH)
3620 W 38th St, Chicago, IL 60632-3308
Tel (773) 847-7575 *Founded/Ownrshp* 1988
Sales 53.3MM^E *EMP* 100^E
SIC 5085 Commercial containers; Commercial containers
Sales Asso: Paul Ingram

D-U-N-S 02-135-7819
NATIONAL CONTRACTORS INC (KS)
621 N Birkdale Dr, Wichita, KS 67230-1528
Tel (316) 722-8484 *Founded/Ownrshp* 1980, 1996
Sales 30.0MM *EMP* 25
SIC 1542 Nonresidential construction; Nonresidential construction
Ch Bd: Clay Davis
**Sec:* Karen Rumford
**VP:* Steve Koegeboehn

D-U-N-S 02-663-0269
■ **NATIONAL CONVENIENCE STORES INC**
STOP N GO
(*Suby of* DIAMOND SHAMROCK REFINING AND MARKETING CO) ★
6000 N Loop 1604 W, San Antonio, TX 78249-1100
Tel (830) 995-4303 *Founded/Ownrshp* 2002
Sales 85.7MM^E *EMP* 1,000
SIC 5411 5812 Convenience stores, chain; Fast food restaurants & stands; Convenience stores, chain; Fast food restaurants & stands
Ch Bd: Jean Gaulin
CFO: H Pete Smith
Treas: Steven A Blank
Ex VP: Timothy J Fretthold
Ex VP: William R Klesse
Sr VP: W Paul Eisman
Sr VP: Christopher Havens

D-U-N-S 96-819-6100
NATIONAL CONVENTION SERVICES LLC
145 W 30th St Rm 200, New York, NY 10001-4039
Tel (212) 947-8255 *Founded/Ownrshp* 2002
Sales 17.3MM *EMP* 2,500
Accts Dominic Loguidice Cpa Yonker
SIC 7389 Exhibit construction by industrial contractors; Exhibit construction by industrial contractors
VP Sls: Frank Philips
S&M/VP: Salvatore Longhitano

NATIONAL COOPERATIVE BUSINESS
See COOPERATIVE LEAGUE OF UNITED STATES OF AMERICA

D-U-N-S 10-673-4510
NATIONAL COOPERATIVE SERVICES CORP
NCSC
20701 Cooperative Way, Dulles, VA 20166-6691
Tel (800) 424-2954 *Founded/Ownrshp* 1981
Sales NA *EMP* 180
SIC 6159 Small business investment companies; Small business investment companies
CEO: Sheldon Peterson
**Pr:* Jean Smith

NATIONAL COPPER AND SMELTING
See STANWOOD CORP

D-U-N-S 11-371-1795
NATIONAL CORPORATE HOUSING INC
365 Herndon Pkwy Ste 111, Herndon, VA 20170-6235
Tel (703) 464-5700 *Founded/Ownrshp* 1999
Sales 31.8MM^E *EMP* 136
SIC 6531 Real estate managers
CEO: Tom Atchison
Pr: Gary Ciabotti
**CFO:* Kregg Anderson
**VP:* Jim Foley
**VP:* Greg Ryan
Genl Mgr: Laura Isaacs
Genl Mgr: Kevin Jones
Genl Mgr: Tracy Roberts
QA Dir: Matt Bealer

D-U-N-S 02-128-8006
NATIONAL CORPORATE RESEARCH LTD (KS)
10 E 40th St Fl 10, New York, NY 10016-0201
Tel (212) 947-7200 *Founded/Ownrshp* 1980, 1984
Sales 20.8MM^E *EMP* 150
SIC 8111 Legal services; Legal services
Ch Bd: Bruce Jacobi
**Pr:* Howard Wagner
Ex VP: Bruce Gallo
VP: Andrew Lundgren
VP: Teri Mayor
VP: Despina Shields
IT Man: Tom Freeman
Opers Mgr: Mark Thomas
Genl Couns: Heather Jefferson
Snr Mgr: Eric Thompson

D-U-N-S 79-035-4831
NATIONAL CORVETTE MUSEUM FOUNDATION INC
350 Corvette Dr, Bowling Green, KY 42101-9134
Tel (270) 781-7973 *Founded/Ownrshp* 1988
Sales 21.9MM *EMP* 80
SIC 8412 5947 Museum; Gift shop
Ex Dir: Wendell Strode
Bd of Dir: Tom Ferrara
Plnt Mgr: Brian Schandel
Mktg Mgr: Bobbie J Lee

NATIONAL COTTON COUNCIL
See COTTON COUNCIL INTERNATIONAL

D-U-N-S 02-031-4472
NATIONAL COUNCIL FOR BEHAVIORAL HEALTH
1400 K St Nw Ste 400, Washington, DC 20005-2434
Tel (202) 684-7457 Founded/Ownrshp 2004
Sales 27.2MM EMP 49
Accts Rapfa Pc Washington Dc
SIC 8621 2741 2721 Medical field-related associations; Newsletter publishing; Trade journals: publishing only, not printed on site; Periodicals: publishing only; Medical field-related associations; Newsletter publishing; Trade journals: publishing only, not printed on site; Periodicals: publishing only
Pr: Linda Rosenberg
Sr VP: Alicia Aebersold
VP: Tom Willis

D-U-N-S 02-031-5677
NATIONAL COUNCIL OF ARCHITECTURAL REGISTRATION BOARDS (IA)
NCARB
1801 K St Nw Ste 700k, Washington, DC 20006-1301
Tel (202) 783-6500 Founded/Ownrshp 1918, 1920
Sales 23.8MM EMP 95E
Accts Tate And Tryon Washington Dc
SIC 8621 Architect association; Architect association
CEO: Michael Armstrong
VP: Mary Dsouza
*VP: Stephen Nutt
Sftwr Eng: Joseph Feinour

D-U-N-S 15-226-6607
NATIONAL COUNCIL OF ARCHTECTURAL REGISTRATION BOARD
1801 K St Nw Ste 1100, Washington, DC 20006-1305
Tel (202) 783-6500 Founded/Ownrshp 1999
Sales 21.4MM EMP 60
Accts Johnson Lambert & Co Llp Fal
SIC 8621 8111 Architect association; Corporate, partnership & business law; Architect association; Corporate, partnership & business law
Pr: Lenore Lucy

D-U-N-S 07-744-0824
NATIONAL COUNCIL OF EXAMINERS FOR ENGINEERING AND SURVEYING
NCEES
280 Seneca Creek Rd, Seneca, SC 29678-1405
Tel (864) 654-6824 Founded/Ownrshp 1920
Sales 22.4MM EMP 70
Accts Dixon Hughes Goodman Llp Gree
SIC 8748 Testing services; Testing services
CEO: Jerry Carter
*COO: Davy McDowell P
*CFO: Betsy Pearson
Ex Dir: Ashlie Bernavzoli

D-U-N-S 07-480-9369
NATIONAL COUNCIL OF LA RAZA
N C L R
1126 16th St Nw Ste 600, Washington, DC 20036-4845
Tel (202) 785-1670 Founded/Ownrshp 1968
Sales 44.3MM EMP 120
Accts Bdo Usa Llp Bethesda Md
SIC 8399 8641 Advocacy group; Civic associations; Advocacy group; Civic associations
Pr: Janet Murguia
*Ex VP: Charles Kamasaki
Sr VP: Cecilia Mu Oz
*Sr VP: Sonia M Perez
*Sr VP: Delia Pompa
Sr VP: Sonia M P Rez
VP: Lautaro D AZ
*VP: Ron Estrada
VP: Ruben Gonzales
VP: Rachel Griego
VP: Eric Rodr Guez
VP: Eric Rodriguez
VP: Maria Rosa
Assoc Dir: Lindsay Daniels
Comm Dir: Teixeira Julian
Board of Directors: Sergio M Gonzalez

D-U-N-S 03-850-2019
NATIONAL COUNCIL OF STATE BOARDS OF NURSING INC
NCSBN
111 E Wacker Dr Ste 2900, Chicago, IL 60601-4277
Tel (312) 525-3600 Founded/Ownrshp 1978
Sales 76.7MM EMP 70
Accts Plante & Moran Pllc Chicago
SIC 8748 8611 Testing service, educational or personnel; Business associations; Testing service, educational or personnel; Business associations
CEO: Kathy Apple
*Treas: Joe Baker Jr
VP: Robin Carretta
VP: Gloria Melton
Ex Dir: Rose Nunnery
Prgrm Mgr: Narender Saraswati
Admn Mgr: Melissa Franke
Dir IT: Nur Rajwany
IT Man: Steve Kaiser
IT Man: Strawbridge Wade
Software D: Albert Hincapie
Board of Directors: Julio Santiago

D-U-N-S 00-591-2589 IMP
NATIONAL COUNCIL OF YOUNG MENS CHRISTIAN ASSOCIATIONS OF UNITED STATES OF AMERICA
YMCA OF THE USA
101 N Wacker Dr Ste 1600, Chicago, IL 60606-7310
Tel (312) 977-0031 Founded/Ownrshp 1982
Sales 114.2MM EMP 350E
Accts Grant Thornton Llp Chicago I
SIC 7997 8399 8322 Membership sports & recreation clubs; Community action agency; Individual & family services; Membership sports & recreation clubs; Community action agency; Individual & family services
Pr: Neil J Nicoll
*Ch Bd: Sharon L Allen
COO: Gary Clarke
COO: Kent Johnson
CFO: Jim Mellor
CFO: Jody Shaffer
Bd of Dir: Jay Alexander
Bd of Dir: Eunice Azzani
Bd of Dir: Barbara M Barron
Bd of Dir: Andrew Boninti
Bd of Dir: James C Bourke
Bd of Dir: Henry E Brown
Bd of Dir: Mary C Carroll
Bd of Dir: Michael A Colling
Bd of Dir: Michael A Corfield
Bd of Dir: Barbara Dingfield
Bd of Dir: Cindy Doyle
Bd of Dir: Ron Edele
Bd of Dir: David Epperson
Bd of Dir: Anne M Fawcett
Bd of Dir: Lillian G Frank
Board of Directors: John G Conley, Curt Hazelbaker, Christopher A Padilla, Derrick Stewart, Janice Reals Ellig

D-U-N-S 07-483-8848
NATIONAL COUNCIL ON AGING INC
251 18th St S Ste 500, Arlington, VA 22202-3410
Tel (202) 479-1200 Founded/Ownrshp 1960
Sales 39.0MM EMP 80
Accts Mcgladrey Llp Gaithersburg M
SIC 8399 Advocacy group; Social service information exchange; Advocacy group; Social service information exchange
Pr: James Firman
CFO: Donna Whitt
Prgrm Mgr: Jo A Wolfe
Board of Directors: Robert Blancato, Richard Browdie, Josefina Carbonell, Heather Dupre, Mark McClellan, Maya Rockeymoore, David Sidwell, June Simmons, Cass Wheeler

D-U-N-S 13-219-9873
NATIONAL COUNCIL ON COMPENSATION INSURANCE INC
NATIONAL WORKERS COMPENSATION
(Suby of NATIO COUN ON COMP INSU) ★
901 Peninsula Corp Cir, Boca Raton, FL 33487-1339
Tel (561) 893-1000 Founded/Ownrshp 2000
Sales NA EMP 800
SIC 6331 Workers' compensation insurance; Workers' compensation insurance
CEO: Stephen Klingel
CFO: Guerra Alfedo
*CFO: Alfredo Guerra

D-U-N-S 07-870-6876
NATIONAL COUNCIL ON CRIME AND DELINQUENCY
N C C D
1970 Broadway Ste 500, Oakland, CA 94612-2217
Tel (800) 306-6223 Founded/Ownrshp 1907
Sales 20.6MM EMP 100
Accts Rina Accountancy Corporation
SIC 8732 Sociological research; Sociological research
Pr: Alex Busansky
Pr: Aaron Juchau
Bd of Dir: Marjorie Kelly
*VP: Chris Baird
Assoc Dir: Robert Williams
Prgrm Mgr: Peggy Ritchie
Prgrm Mgr: Aishatu Yusuf
Dir IT: Anna Boldon
IT Man: Markus Conell
IT Man: Deb Paulus

D-U-N-S 04-291-9084 IMP
NATIONAL COUPLING CO INC (TX)
HUNTING ENERGY SERVICES
(Suby of HUNTING ENERGY SERVICES INC) ★
1316 Staffordshire Rd, Stafford, TX 77477-6321
Tel (281) 499-2583 Founded/Ownrshp 1968, 2009
Sales 59.5MME EMP 162
SIC 3494 Couplings, except pressure & soil pipe; Couplings, except pressure & soil pipe
Pr: Dane Tipton
Pr: Dennis Proctor
Pr: Gary G Weathers
Sr VP: Jim Johnson
Prgrm Mgr: Lee Currier
S&M/VP: Larry Rogers

D-U-N-S 07-880-3387
NATIONAL CREDIT ADJUSTERS LLC (KS)
327 W 4th Ave, Hutchinson, KS 67501-4842
Tel (620) 665-7708 Founded/Ownrshp 2002
Sales 20.2MME EMP 200
SIC 7322 Adjustment & collection services; Adjustment & collection services
CFO: Mark Huston
Genl Couns: Mark Fletchall

D-U-N-S 09-539-9812
NATIONAL CREDIT CORP
7091 Orchard Lake Rd # 333, West Bloomfield, MI 48322-3654
Tel (734) 459-8100 Founded/Ownrshp 1962
Sales NA EMP 150E
SIC 6153 6512 3949 6111 Purchasers of accounts receivable & commercial paper; Commercial & industrial building operation; Exercise equipment; Federal & federally sponsored credit agencies; Purchasers of accounts receivable & commercial paper; Commercial & industrial building operation; Exercise equipment; Federal & federally sponsored credit agencies
Pr: William F Hubner
*VP: Glenn A Barth
*VP: James P Hoppin

D-U-N-S 08-636-3157
■ NATIONAL CREDIT UNION ADMINISTRATION
NCUA
(Suby of EXECUTIVE OFFICE OF UNITED STATES GOVERNMENT) ★
1775 Duke St Ste 4206, Alexandria, VA 22314-6115
Tel (703) 518-6300 Founded/Ownrshp 1970
Sales NA EMP 996
Accts Kpmg Llp Washington Dc
SIC 9199 General accounting office, government; ; General accounting office, government;
Ch Bd: Debbie Matz
Bd of Dir: Richard Metsger
Ofcr: Timothy Bankroff
Ofcr: Russ Barlow
Ofcr: Raelene Barr
Ofcr: Victoria Bennett
Ofcr: Steven Farrar
Ofcr: Gail Laster
Ofcr: Vincent Vieten
Ofcr: James Woodrich
Ex Dir: David Arquis

D-U-N-S 80-006-4727
NATIONAL CREDITORS CONNECTION INC
NCCI
14 Orchard Ste 200, Lake Forest, CA 92630-8313
Tel (949) 461-7540 Founded/Ownrshp 1992
Sales NA EMP 65
SIC 6411 Inspection & investigation services, insurance
CEO: Richard Rodriguez
CFO: Charles Ortiz
Sr VP: Jerry Rahon
VP: Richard Bellows
*VP: Jay Loeb
*VP: Lori Lynn
Exec: Todd Canfield
Dir Bus: Lance Perry
CTO: Bob Spittal
QA Dir: Patrick Ndukwe
Natl Sales: Anthony Hipp

NATIONAL CTR FOR STATE COURTS
See NATIONAL CENTER FOR STATE COURTS

D-U-N-S 03-209-3585 IMP
NATIONAL CUSTOMER ENGINEERING INC
NCE COMPUTER GROUP
1866 Friendship Dr Ste B, El Cajon, CA 92020-1156
Tel (619) 212-3000 Founded/Ownrshp 2004
Sales 24.1MME EMP 60
SIC 5045 7378 7376 7374 Computers, peripherals & software; Computer maintenance & repair; Computer facilities management; Data processing & preparation
CEO: James P Raven
*CFO: Keith Ranson
Prgrm Mgr: John Sheppard
Natl Sales: John Cummings

D-U-N-S 09-188-0393
NATIONAL CUTTING HORSE ASSOCIATION
NCHA
260 Bailey Ave, Fort Worth, TX 76107-1862
Tel (817) 244-6188 Founded/Ownrshp 1946
Sales 23.6MM EMP 33
Accts Whitley Penn Llp Dallas Tx
SIC 8641 Social associations; Social associations
Ex Dir: Jeff Hooper
Ex Dir: Jim Campbell
Advt Mgr: Nathan Smiley

D-U-N-S 00-545-4111 IMP
NATIONAL CYCLE INC (IL)
BARRY ELECTRIC DIV
2200 S Maywood Dr, Maywood, IL 60153-1783
Tel (708) 343-0400 Founded/Ownrshp 1937
Sales 32.0MME EMP 80
SIC 3714 3751 3451 3441 Motor vehicle parts & accessories; Motorcycle accessories; Screw machine products; Fabricated structural metal
Pr: Barry Willey
VP: Gordon B Willey

D-U-N-S 01-843-2612
NATIONAL DAIRY LLC
(Suby of BORDEN DAIRY CO) ★
8750 N Central Expy # 400, Dallas, TX 75231-6417
Tel (469) 587-0190 Founded/Ownrshp 2009
Sales 3.5MMME EMP 3,800E
SIC 5143 Milk; Milk & cream, fluid; Milk; Milk & cream, fluid
VP: Diego Rosenfledt

D-U-N-S 11-619-9142
NATIONAL DAIRY PROMOTION AND RESEARCH BOARD
10255 W Higgins Rd # 900, Rosemont, IL 60018-5638
Tel (847) 803-2000 Founded/Ownrshp 1984
Sales 85.7MM EMP 15
SIC 8611 Trade associations; Trade associations
Pr: Thomas Gallagher

D-U-N-S 78-215-7291
NATIONAL DATA SERVICES OF CHICAGO INC
DIAMOND MARKETING SOLUTIONS
(Suby of DIAMOND MARKETING SOLUTIONS GROUP INC) ★
900 Kimberly Dr, Carol Stream, IL 60188-1859
Tel (630) 845-7000 Founded/Ownrshp 2007
Sales 39.6MME EMP 127
SIC 7371 7331 2759 Custom computer programming services; Direct mail advertising services; Commercial printing; Custom computer programming services; Direct mail advertising services; Commercial printing
CEO: Bruce D'Angello
*Pr: Mark Peterson
Pr: William Pingel
CFO: Louis Sedivy
Ex VP: Michael Nevolo
Sr VP: James Bailey
Sr VP: Jim Renella
VP: Dave O'Malley
VP: John Puffer
VP: Jeff Ziegler
Snr Sftwr: Jeff Byttow

D-U-N-S 80-560-8762 EXP
NATIONAL DCP LLC
DUNKIN' DONUTS
3805 Crestwood Pkwy Nw, Duluth, GA 30096-7164
Tel (770) 369-8600 Founded/Ownrshp 2005
Sales 264.4MME EMP 1,100E
SIC 5461 Doughnuts; Doughnuts

D-U-N-S 19-955-2774
NATIONAL DEALERS WARRANTY INC
339 Mid Rivers Mall Dr, Saint Peters, MO 63376-1516
Tel (314) 960-6832 Founded/Ownrshp 2005
Sales NA EMP 146
SIC 6399 Warranty insurance, automobile
Pr: Rudge Gilman
*VP: Mark J Travis

D-U-N-S 15-087-2997
NATIONAL DEFAULT SERVICING LLC
(Suby of NATIONAL COLLECTION) ★
500 S Brd St Bldg Aste, Meriden, CT 06450
Tel (860) 368-3400 Founded/Ownrshp 2004
Sales 23.2MME EMP 138
SIC 6541 Title abstract offices

D-U-N-S 94-485-9065
NATIONAL DEFENSE UNIVERSITY
NDU
L J Mcnair 300 5th Ave Bl, Washington, DC 20319-0001
Tel (202) 685-4700 Founded/Ownrshp 1982
Sales NA EMP 650
SIC 9199 ;
Pr: Gregg Martin
COO: Thomas Hauser
Ofcr: Carolyn Kokko
VP: Hans Binnendijk
VP: John Deegan
VP: John Jy
VP: Donna Powers
Exec: Eugene Warshaw
Prgrm Mgr: Dale Cockman
Off Mgr: Alena Ho
Doctor: Thomas Blau

D-U-N-S 12-198-3852
NATIONAL DEFERRED COMPENSATION INC
(Suby of NATIONWIDE FINANCIAL SERVICES INC) ★
1 W Nationwide Blvd # 100, Columbus, OH 43215-2752
Tel (614) 451-4926 Founded/Ownrshp 1998
Sales NA EMP 130
SIC 6411 8742 Insurance information & consulting services; Management consulting services
Pr: Joseph M Mollmann
Treas: Frederick H Genel
*Ex VP: Herman H Mollmann Jr
Sr VP: Bernard J Austing
VP: Michael J Studebaker
Board of Directors: Janet Mollmann

D-U-N-S 02-635-6225 EXP
NATIONAL DELI LLC
7250 Nw 35th Ter, Miami, FL 33122-1356
Tel (305) 592-0300 Founded/Ownrshp 2001
Sales 117.3MME EMP 130
SIC 5147 Meats & meat products; Meats & meat products
Ex VP: Joey Bonomo
VP: Richie Fives
VP: Nestor Martinez
VP: Bert Patterson
VP Opers: Charlie Hart
S&M/VP: Chris Marriott
Sls Mgr: Tim Petrilak

D-U-N-S 11-030-9622
NATIONAL DEMOCRATIC INSTITUTE FOR INTERNATIONAL AFFAIRS
455 Mdcchstts Ave Nw Fl 8, Washington, DC 20001
Tel (202) 728-5500 Founded/Ownrshp 1983
Sales 135.3MM EMP 1,300
Accts Bdo Usa Llp Bethesda Md
SIC 8651 Political action committee; Political action committee
Pr: Kenneth Wollack
Ofcr: Hodan Ahmed
Ofcr: Mijack Aquain
Ofcr: Menna Baumann
Ofcr: Sarah Bedy
Ofcr: Sara Cady
Ofcr: Karol Caldera
Ofcr: John Cavanaugh
Ofcr: Katherine Conway
Ofcr: Jesper Frant
Ofcr: Teona Kupunia
Ofcr: Francis Madugu
Ofcr: Rebecca Mar
Ofcr: Maka Meshveliani
Ofcr: Layla Moughari
Ofcr: Katy Mudge
Ofcr: Kellen Nahumbya
Ofcr: Kyleigh Payne
Ofcr: Daniel Reilly
Ofcr: Michael Samras
Ofcr: Tamara Sartania

D-U-N-S 05-531-2342
NATIONAL DENTEX CORP
(Suby of GEODIGM CORP) ★
3910 Rca Blvd Ste 1015, Palm Beach Gardens, FL 33410-4284
Tel (877) 942-5871 Founded/Ownrshp 2010
Sales 86.9MME EMP 1,745
SIC 8072 Crown & bridge production; Denture production; Orthodontic appliance production; Crown & bridge production; Denture production; Orthodontic appliance production
CEO: Steven E Casper
*CFO: Mark Brockelman
CFO: Wayne M Coll
CFO: Micheal Schantz
VP: Lynn D Dine
VP: James F Dodd III
Manager: Danny Davis

D-U-N-S 60-192-4384
NATIONAL DESIGN & TRADE NETWORK INC
INTERIOR SOLUTIONS
522 S 400 W, Salt Lake City, UT 84101-2203
Tel (801) 531-7538 Founded/Ownrshp 2002
Sales 26.1MME EMP 100E
SIC 5712 7389 1799 Office furniture; Interior design services; Office furniture installation

CEO: Scot Wilcox
**CFO:* Brent Kartchner
**Sec:* J Brent Kartchner
**VP:* Karl Hanson
**VP:* Peter Harris
**VP:* Roland Walker
Admn Mgr: Robert Dasek
Sls Mgr: Les Reiners
Board of Directors: Scott Wilcox

D-U-N-S 00-432-2680
NATIONAL DESIGN BUILD SERVICES LLC
3843 Mcclay Rd, Saint Peters, MO 63376-7328
Tel (636) 229-8400 *Founded/Ownrshp* 2007
Sales 23.0MM *EMP* 14
Accts Uhy Llp Saint Louis Missouri
SIC 1711 Heating & air conditioning contractors
CEO: Ben Vacca
**Pt:* Jim Vineyard
Off Mgr: Pam Gamache

D-U-N-S 79-055-2509
NATIONAL DEVELOPMENT ASSOCIATES OF NEW ENGLAND INC
2310 Washington St # 200, Newton, MA 02462-1476
Tel (617) 965-7300 *Founded/Ownrshp* 1992
Sales 45.9MME *EMP* 119
SIC 1522 1542 Residential construction; Nonresidential construction; Residential construction; Nonresidential construction
Pr: Thomas Alperin
**CFO:* Stephen Kinsella
**Prin:* John J O'Neil III
Mng Dir: Theodore R Tye

D-U-N-S 96-478-7928
■ **NATIONAL DIGITAL TELEVISION CENTER LLC**
COMCAST MEDIA CENTER
(*Suby of* COMCAST CORP) ★
4100 E Dry Creek Rd, Centennial, CO 80122-3729
Tel (303) 486-3800 *Founded/Ownrshp* 1997
Sales 46.0MME *EMP* 700
SIC 4822 7812 Cable, telegram & telex services; Motion picture & video production; Cable, telegram & telex services; Motion picture & video production
VP: Richard Buchanan
VP: Bruce Davis
VP: Dave Higgins
VP: Leslie E Russell
Ex Dir: Mitch Weinraub

NATIONAL DISTRIBUTING CO
See KRONHEIM CO

D-U-N-S 00-884-7105 IMP
NATIONAL DISTRIBUTING CO INC (GA)
1 National Dr Sw, Atlanta, GA 30336-1631
Tel (404) 696-1681 *Founded/Ownrshp* 1935, 1946
Sales 552.3MME *EMP* 1,000
SIC 5182 5181 Liquor; Wine; Beer & other fermented malt liquors; Liquor; Wine; Beer & other fermented malt liquors
Ch Bd: Jay Davis
**Pr:* John A Carlos
**Ex VP:* Chris Carlos
Ex VP: Tom Donlevy
VP: Leon Cikota
VP: Stef Kirshenbaum
Area Mgr: Mike Crotty
Area Mgr: David Patzke
Dist Mgr: Jason Bothe
Dist Mgr: Chris Bowen
Dist Mgr: Darrin Carpenter

D-U-N-S 00-983-1413 EXP
NATIONAL DISTRIBUTION & CONTRACTING INC
N D C
402 Bna Dr Ste 500, Nashville, TN 37217-2551
Tel (615) 366-3230 *Founded/Ownrshp* 1953
Sales 29.4MME *EMP* 65E
SIC 5047

D-U-N-S 00-804-0338
NATIONAL DISTRIBUTION ALLIANCE LLC
NDA
3010 Review Ave, Long Island City, NY 11101-3240
Tel (718) 706-2300 *Founded/Ownrshp* 2006
Sales 25.9MME *EMP* 105
SIC 5192 Newspapers
CEO: Michael Presto
**Pr:* Michael Pouchie
**VP:* Eric Newman

D-U-N-S 09-077-1676 IMP
NATIONAL DISTRIBUTION CENTERS LP
NFI DISTRIBUTION
(*Suby of* NFI INDUSTRIES INC) ★
1515 Burnt Mill Rd, Cherry Hill, NJ 08003-3637
Tel (856) 691-7000 *Founded/Ownrshp* 1993
Sales 156.5MME *EMP* 805
SIC 4225 Warehousing, self-storage; Warehousing, self-storage
Pt: Sidney R Brown
Pt: Irwin Brown

D-U-N-S 01-795-1162
NATIONAL DISTRIBUTION SERVICES INC
340 N Grant Ave, Corona, CA 92882-1828
Tel (951) 739-2400 *Founded/Ownrshp* 2011
Sales 37.2MME *EMP* 64E
SIC 5099 Firearms & ammunition, except sporting
Pr: Gregor Gekghyan

D-U-N-S 01-905-3107 IMP
NATIONAL DISTRIBUTORS INC
116 Wallace Ave, South Portland, ME 04106-6198
Tel (207) 773-1719 *Founded/Ownrshp* 1959
Sales 48.0MME *EMP* 185
SIC 5181 5149 5182

D-U-N-S 60-354-4909
NATIONAL DISTRIBUTORS INC
1517 Avco Blvd, Sellersburg, IN 47172-1875
Tel (812) 246-6306 *Founded/Ownrshp* 1986
Sales 56.2MME *EMP* 416
SIC 4213 Trucking, except local; Trucking, except local
Pr: Keith Vaughn
**COO:* Eric Vaughn
**CFO:* Bruce Callam
**VP:* Jeff Kapps
CIO: Mike Ware
IT Man: Tom Miller

D-U-N-S 09-599-5809 IMP
NATIONAL DIVERSIFIED SALES INC
A D P
(*Suby of* NORMA GROUP SE)
21300 Victory Blvd # 215, Woodland Hills, CA 91367-2525
Tel (559) 562-9888 *Founded/Ownrshp* 2014
Sales 175.6MME *EMP* 500
SIC 3089 Plastic hardware & building products; Fittings for pipe, plastic; Plastic hardware & building products; Fittings for pipe, plastic
CEO: David Silver
**Pr:* Michael Gummeson
**CFO:* Randall Stott
Ofcr: Mark Peterson
VP: Michael Fallon
VP: Barry McHone
VP: Ron Sentman
Tech Mgr: Ryan Larsen
Sfty Mgr: Alex Rodriguez
Natl Sales: Dawn Hylen
Natl Sales: Dawn Lyons

NATIONAL DME
See NATIONAL DURABLE MEDICAL EQUIPMENT LLC

D-U-N-S 12-464-6105
NATIONAL DURABLE MEDICAL EQUIPMENT LLC
NATIONAL DME
310 E 4500 S Ste 280, Salt Lake City, UT 84107-4236
Tel (801) 262-3236 *Founded/Ownrshp* 1999
Sales 28.6MME *EMP* 200E
SIC 5999 Medical apparatus & supplies; Medical apparatus & supplies
Opers Mgr: Jon Hill

D-U-N-S 78-532-6286
NATIONAL ECOLOGICAL OBSERVATORY NETWORK INC
NEON
1685 38th St Ste 100, Boulder, CO 80301-2735
Tel (720) 746-4844 *Founded/Ownrshp* 2005
Sales 92.4MM *EMP* 40
Accts Eidebailly Llp Golden Colora
SIC 8733 Scientific research agency; Scientific research agency
CFO: Tom Sheldon
Sftwr Eng: Wilson Yang

D-U-N-S 07-280-1798
■ **NATIONAL ECONOMIC RESEARCH ASSOCIATES INC**
NERA ECONOMICS CONSULTING
(*Suby of* MERCER INC) ★
1166 Ave Of The Americas, New York, NY 10036-2708
Tel (212) 345-3000 *Founded/Ownrshp* 1991
Sales 40.7MME *EMP* 411
SIC 8732 Commercial nonphysical research; Business economic service; Commercial nonphysical research; Business economic service
CEO: Andrew Sharpe Carron
Pr: Lawrence Wu
COO: Phillip Beutel
Ex VP: Denise Martin
Ex VP: Thomas McCarthy
Ex VP: Steven Schwartz
Ex VP: Kent Van Liere
Sr VP: Patrick Conroy
Sr VP: Alex Grecu
Sr VP: Richard Hawkins
Sr VP: Christopher Laursen
Sr VP: Gregory K Leonard
Sr VP: Jeff Makholm
Sr VP: Tom Mc Carthy
Sr VP: Amparo Nieto
**Sr VP:* Chudozie Okongwu
Sr VP: Agustin Ros
Sr VP: Kent D Van Liere
Sr VP: Jon Wainwright
Sr VP: Paul Weiss
VP: Beth Becker

D-U-N-S 06-677-8044
NATIONAL EDUCATION ASSOCIATION OF UNITED STATES
N E A
1201 16th St Nw, Washington, DC 20036-3290
Tel (202) 833-4000 *Founded/Ownrshp* 1857
Sales 110.0MME *EMP* 735
SIC 8631 Labor union; Labor union
Pr: Reg Weaver
COO: Lisa Zimmerman
**CFO:* Mike McPherson
**Treas:* Lily Eskelsen
Treas: Rebecca Pringle
**VP:* Dennis Vanroekel
Ex Dir: John C Stocks
**Ex Dir:* John Wilson
Dist Mgr: Ruben Cedeno
Snr Ntwrk: Nicole Wexler
IT Man: Richard Costanzo

D-U-N-S 13-387-6037
NATIONAL EDUCATION SEMINARS INC
HONDROS COLLEGE
4140 Executive Pkwy, Westerville, OH 43081-3855
Tel (775) 246-8700 *Founded/Ownrshp* 1983
Sales 20.3MME *EMP* 270
SIC 8249 Real estate & insurance school; Real estate & insurance school
Ch Bd: John Hondros
**Pr:* Linda Schwan-Hondros
VP: Joe Schiska
Snr Sftwr: Romaine Smith
IT Man: Tammy Fancelli
Site Mgr: Denise Werlinich
Opers Mgr: Leanna Anderkin

D-U-N-S 87-723-2793 IMP
NATIONAL ELECTRIC COIL INC
N E C COLUMBUS
800 King Ave, Columbus, OH 43212-2644
Tel (614) 488-1151 *Founded/Ownrshp* 1994
Sales 70.6MME *EMP* 500
SIC 7694 Electric motor repair; Electric motor repair
CEO: Robert Barton
Pr: Beant Nindra
Sr VP: Robert Hodge
**VP:* Danial Bucklew
**VP:* Stephen I Jeney
**Prin:* Athena Amaxas
IT Man: Janice Kirts
Plnt Mgr: Rowland Hill
Ql Cn Mgr: Tatyana Vakhlamova
Sls Mgr: Chuck Drake

D-U-N-S 08-037-5447
NATIONAL ELECTRIC SUPPLY CO INC
2200 Midtown Pl Ne, Albuquerque, NM 87107-3217
Tel (505) 345-3577 *Founded/Ownrshp* 1976
Sales 32.1MME *EMP* 40
SIC 5063 3699 Electrical apparatus & equipment; Electrical equipment & supplies
Pr: Rocklan E Lawrence
Ex VP: Steve Holdman
VP: Aaron Ingram
Brnch Mgr: Joe Durbin
Sls Mgr: Creig Bann
Sales Asso: Matt Jaramillo
Snr Mgr: Cindy Flores

D-U-N-S 08-919-4211
NATIONAL ELECTRICAL BENEFIT FUND
NEBF
2400 Res Blvd Ste 500, Rockville, MD 20850
Tel (301) 556-4300 *Founded/Ownrshp* 1946
Sales NA *EMP* 160
SIC 6371 Pension funds; Pension funds
Ex Dir: Lawrence J Bradley
Exec: Crystal Davis
Ex Dir: Terry Moloznik
Dir IT: Chris Yeapanis

D-U-N-S 15-133-5742 IMP
NATIONAL ELECTRICAL CARBON PRODUCTS INC
(*Suby of* MORGANITE INDUSTRIES INC) ★
251 Forrester Dr, Greenville, SC 29607-5328
Tel (864) 458-7777 *Founded/Ownrshp* 1986
Sales 65.0MME *EMP* 500
SIC 3624 Carbon & graphite products; Carbon & graphite products
CEO: John Stang
**Pr:* Don Klas
CFO: Bill Chandler
Rgnl Mgr: Jerry Lipski
Rgnl Mgr: Deborah Moore
Rgnl Mgr: David Oswald
Genl Mgr: Gavin Tan
Mfg Mgr: Ashley Francain
Prd Mgr: Rickey Moore
Ql Cn Mgr: Randy Massey

D-U-N-S 06-928-5575
NATIONAL ELECTRICAL CONTRACTORS ASSOCIATION INC (DC)
NECA
3 Bethesda Metro Ctr # 1100, Bethesda, MD 20814-5330
Tel (301) 657-3110 *Founded/Ownrshp* 1901
Sales 26.5MM *EMP* 72
Accts Tate And Tryon Washington Dc
SIC 8611 Trade associations; Contractors' association
CEO: John M Grau
**COO:* Daniel Gwalter
CFO: Michael Thompson
**CFO:* Tracy Tickus
**Sec:* Traci Pickus
VP: John Colson
VP: John M Gueldner
**VP:* Geary Higgins
VP: Richard J Nogleberg
VP: Franklin D Russell
Ex Dir: Robert Colgan Jr

D-U-N-S 07-522-8304
NATIONAL ELECTRICAL MANUFACTURERS ASSOCIATION
NEMA
1300 17th St N Ste 900, Arlington, VA 22209-3801
Tel (703) 841-3200 *Founded/Ownrshp* 1926
Sales 25.7MM *EMP* 92E
Accts Dixon Hughes Goodman Rockvill
SIC 8611 Trade associations
Pr: Evanr Gaddis
Pt: Nick Paleologos
**Pr:* Kevin J Cosgriff
Bd of Dir: Williams J Sims
Sr VP: Frank Kitzantides
VP: Timothy Feldman
VP: Tom Hicks
VP: Don Leavens
VP: John Snow
Exec: Kyle Pitsor
Comm Dir: Ric Talley

D-U-N-S 06-605-1178 IMP
NATIONAL ELECTRO-COATINGS INC
NATIONAL OFFICE
15655 Brookpark Rd, Cleveland, OH 44142-1619
Tel (216) 898-0080 *Founded/Ownrshp* 1967
Sales 20.4MME *EMP* 90
SIC 2522 2521 1721 Office furniture, except wood; Wood office furniture; Painting & paper hanging
Ch: Robert W Schneider
**Pr:* Richard Corl
**CEO:* Gregory R Schneider
Sfty Dirs: Michael Schneider
Prd Mgr: Connie Moore
Mktg Dir: Don Harnegie

D-U-N-S 60-420-2184 IMP/EXP
NATIONAL ELECTRONICS INC
500 Smith St, Farmingdale, NY 11735-1115
Tel (631) 683-8000 *Founded/Ownrshp* 1989
Sales 155.7MM *EMP* 20E
SIC 5065 Electronic parts & equipment; Electronic parts & equipment
CEO: Abdulrahman S Khwaja
**Treas:* Nadia Khwaja

D-U-N-S 13-936-4426
NATIONAL ELECTRONICS WARRANTY LLC
22894 Pacific Blvd, Sterling, VA 20166-6722
Tel (703) 375-8100 *Founded/Ownrshp* 1983
Sales NA *EMP* 6,000
Accts Pricewaterhousecoopers Llp Fr
SIC 6411 Insurance agents, brokers & service; Insurance agents, brokers & service
CEO: Anthony P Nader
Ch Bd: Fredrick D Schaufeld
Sr VP: Christina Derosa
VP: Bill Hoke
Exec: Danny Hourigan
Exec: Kevin Porter

D-U-N-S 00-178-2226 IMP
NATIONAL ELECTROSTATICS CORP
7540 Graber Rd, Middleton, WI 53562-1002
Tel (608) 831-7600 *Founded/Ownrshp* 1999
Sales 23.3MM *EMP* 93
Accts Smith & Gesteland Llp Madiso
SIC 3699 Electrostatic particle accelerators; Electrostatic particle accelerators
Pr: James A Ferry PHD
**COO:* Robert Daniel
**Sr VP:* James B Schroeder
**Sr VP:* Mark Sundquist
**VP:* George Klody
**VP:* Greg Norton
**VP:* Scott Phillips
Board of Directors: Eric Apfelbach, Robert Daniel, James Ferry, George Klody, James Schroeder, Mark Sundquist

D-U-N-S 62-259-7003
NATIONAL ELEVATOR INDUSTRY (NEI) BENEFIT PLANS
19 Campus Blvd Ste 200, Newtown Square, PA 19073-3288
Tel (610) 325-9100 *Founded/Ownrshp* 1962
Sales NA *EMP* 80
SIC 6371 Union welfare, benefit & health funds; Union welfare, benefit & health funds
Ex Dir: Robert O Betts Jr
**Ch:* Kevin P Stringer
**Ch:* E James Walker

D-U-N-S 06-985-1962
NATIONAL ELEVATOR INDUSTRY EDUCATIONAL PROGRAM
NEIEP TRUST FUND
11 Larsen Way, Attleboro Falls, MA 02763-1068
Tel (508) 699-0747 *Founded/Ownrshp* 1968
Sales 27.4MM *EMP* 23
Accts Daniel A Winters & Company Cpa
SIC 8331 Job training services
**Prin:* James Higgins
IT Man: Michael Brockman
IT Man: Stan Steliga
IT Man: Jeffrey Waskiewicz
Sftwr Eng: Colby Lithyouvong

D-U-N-S 96-775-0030
NATIONAL ELEVATOR INDUSTRY HEALTH BENEFIT PLAN
19 Campus Blvd Ste 200, Newtown Square, PA 19073-3288
Tel (610) 325-9100 *Founded/Ownrshp* 2012
Sales NA *EMP* 2E
Accts Daniel A Winters & Company Cpa
SIC 6411 Pension & retirement plan consultants

D-U-N-S 06-666-4913
NATIONAL EMBLEM INC
3925 E Vernon St, Long Beach, CA 90815-1727
Tel (310) 515-5055 *Founded/Ownrshp* 1972
Sales 46.6MME *EMP* 275
SIC 2395 2396 Emblems, embroidered; Automotive & apparel trimmings; Emblems, embroidered; Automotive & apparel trimmings
Pr: Milton H Lubin Sr
VP: Milton Lubin
**VP:* Milton H Lubin Jr
Dir IT: William Wood
Sls Dir: Marvin Grimm

NATIONAL EMBLEM SALES DIV
See AMERICAN LEGION NATIONAL HEADQUARTERS

D-U-N-S 83-616-1315
NATIONAL EMPLOYERS SOLUTIONS INC
2575 Westside Pkwy # 100, Alpharetta, GA 30004-6410
Tel (770) 754-0054 *Founded/Ownrshp* 1999
Sales 76.0MM *EMP* 25
SIC 7363 Employee leasing service; Employee leasing service
CEO: Ronald K Cates
**Pr:* Lori Rives Kinney

D-U-N-S 13-227-9084
NATIONAL ENDOWMENT FOR DEMOCRACY INC
1025 F St Nw Ste 800, Washington, DC 20004-1432
Tel (202) 378-9700 *Founded/Ownrshp* 1983
Sales 134.0MM *EMP* 99E
Accts Mcgladrey Llp Vienna Va
SIC 8399 Social change association; Social change association
Pr: Carl Gershman
**Ch Bd:* Martin Frost
Bd of Dir: Igor Blazevic
Bd of Dir: Francesca Bomboko
Bd of Dir: Yuri Dzhibladze
Bd of Dir: Paul Graham
Bd of Dir: Jana Hybaskova
Bd of Dir: George Mathew
Bd of Dir: Inna Pidluska
Bd of Dir: Yevgeniy Zhovtis
Ofcr: Melissa Aten
Board of Directors: Barry Jackson, Jayne M Kurzman, Ellen O Tauscher, Robert B Zoellick

D-U-N-S 00-790-1028
NATIONAL ENGINEERING & CONTRACTING CO (OH)
NETCO
(*Suby of* BALFOUR BEATTY LLC) ★
50 Public Sq Ste 2175, Cleveland, OH 44113-2252
Tel (440) 238-3331 *Founded/Ownrshp* 1933, 2001
Sales 72.9MM^E *EMP* 700
SIC 1622 1623 Bridge construction; Highway construction, elevated; Sewer line construction; Pumping station construction; Bridge construction; Highway construction, elevated; Sewer line construction; Pumping station construction
CEO: Walter Gratz
**Treas:* Anthony Martin
Ex VP: Bob Mancuso
**VP:* Clarke Wilson

D-U-N-S 11-808-2395
NATIONAL ENGINEERING SERVICE CORP
72 Mirona Rd Ste 20, Portsmouth, NH 03801-5374
Tel (603) 427-0125 *Founded/Ownrshp* 1984
Sales 28.4MM^E *EMP* 666
SIC 7363 Temporary help service; Temporary help service
Pr: James A Klein
VP: Betty Lefferts
**VP:* L Leonard Tierney

D-U-N-S 00-663-5168
NATIONAL ENTERPRISE SYSTEMS INC (OH)
NES
29125 Solon Rd, Solon, OH 44139-3442
Tel (440) 542-1360 *Founded/Ownrshp* 1987
Sales 44.5MM^E *EMP* 500^E
SIC 7322 Collection agency, except real estate; Collection agency, except real estate
Pr: Ernest Pollak
VP: Kimberly Bonn
**VP:* Ellen Pollak
VP: Jeff Pollak
VP: Mary Shaw
VP: Jim Vahalik
Genl Mgr: Robbie Hudson
IT Man: Chris Taylor
Software D: Stephen Bielewicz
Software D: Syed Kazmi
S&M/VP: Jack Clark

D-U-N-S 00-230-9511 IMP
NATIONAL ENTERTAINMENT COLLECTIBLES ASSOCIATION INC
NECA
603 Sweetland Ave, Hillside, NJ 07205-1799
Tel (908) 686-3300 *Founded/Ownrshp* 1996
Sales 119.2MM^E *EMP* 200^E
SIC 5199 Gifts & novelties; Gifts & novelties
Ch: Joel Weinshanker
CFO: Michael Sosidka
Dir Bus: Russell Rafael

D-U-N-S 19-608-3869 IMP
NATIONAL ENTERTAINMENT NETWORK LLC
SUGARLOAF CREATIONS
(*Suby of* NEN HOLDINGS INC) ★
325 Intrlcken Pkwy Bldg B, Broomfield, CO 80021-8043
Tel (303) 444-2559 *Founded/Ownrshp* 2009
Sales 186.2MM^E *EMP* 750
SIC 5046 5962 Commercial equipment; Novelty vending machines; Commercial equipment; Novelty vending machines
CEO: Ed Flaherty
CFO: John Cash
CFO: Peter Jacobson
VP: John Bocker
VP: Dave Schwartz

D-U-N-S 19-480-3946
NATIONAL ENVIRONMENTAL SAFETY CO INC
1217 38th Ave, Long Island City, NY 11101-6032
Tel (718) 361-0044 *Founded/Ownrshp* 1988
Sales 20.2MM^E *EMP* 40
SIC 1542 1751 1799 Nonresidential construction; Window & door installation & erection; Asbestos removal & encapsulation
Pr: Dominick Fertitta
**VP:* Mark Canellos

D-U-N-S 16-003-9954
■ NATIONAL ENVIRONMENTAL SATELLITE DATA AND INFORMATION SERVICE
OCEAN RESEARCH
(*Suby of* NATIONAL OCEANIC AND ATMOSPHERIC ADMINISTRATION) ★
1315 E West Hwy Ste 3, Silver Spring, MD 20910-6233
Tel (301) 713-2458 *Founded/Ownrshp* 1970
Sales NA *EMP* 853
SIC 9511 Environmental quality & control agency, government; ; Environmental quality & control agency, government;
Prin: Braig McLean
VP: Kenneth Carey
Netwrk Eng: Coreen Hickey

D-U-N-S 02-524-2157 IMP/EXP
NATIONAL ENZYME CO INC
15366 Us Highway 160, Forsyth, MO 65653-8107
Tel (417) 546-8012 *Founded/Ownrshp* 1942
Sales 50.2MM^E *EMP* 115
SIC 2869 5499 Enzymes; Health foods; Enzymes; Health foods
CEO: Anthony W Collier
**Pr:* Terese Mansell
VP: Charles Amidon
VP: Victoria Ploshay
Dir Lab: Ken Paydon
Dir IT: Lexley Duffy
VP Opers: Roger Holvick
Mfg Dir: Kevin Hampton
Sfty Mgr: Carol Schwartckopf
Sfty Mgr: Mitch Sims
Mfg Mgr: Kevin King

D-U-N-S 00-753-8473
NATIONAL EQUIPMENT SERVICES INC
(*Suby of* DIAMOND CASTLE) ★
540 Lake Cook Rd Ste 100, Deerfield, IL 60015-5631
Tel (773) 695-3999 *Founded/Ownrshp* 1996
Sales 67.7MM^E *EMP* 1,100
SIC 7359 Equipment rental & leasing; Equipment rental & leasing
Pr: Andrew P Studdert
**CFO:* Michael D Milligan
Sr VP: Michael Milligan

D-U-N-S 19-500-7729
NATIONAL EQUITY FUND INC
NEF ASSIGNMENT
10 S Riverside Plz Lbby 1, Chicago, IL 60606-3709
Tel (312) 360-0400 *Founded/Ownrshp* 1987
Sales 35.7MM *EMP* 108
Accts Kpmg Llp Mc Lean Va
SIC 6531 Real estate agents & managers
CEO: Joe Hagan
CFO: Kevin Boes
Sr VP: Peter Harrison
Sr VP: Michael A Jacobs
Sr VP: Karen Przypyszny
Sr VP: Suanne Reed
Sr VP: Susan Weaver
VP: Jason Aldridge
VP: James Baugh
VP: Omar Chaudhry
VP: Carey Connolly
VP: Rose Eaton
VP: Monika Elgert
VP: Tom Flanagan
VP: Mark Leitson
VP: Susan Murray
VP: Laura Pishion
VP: Robert Poznanski
VP: Rachel Rhodes
VP: Timothy Schalk
VP: Judy Schneider
Board of Directors: Jane Graf, Patrick J Nash, Kris Switzer

D-U-N-S 95-913-2622
NATIONAL EQUITY TITLE AGENCY INC
NETCO
415 N La Salle Dr Ste 202, Chicago, IL 60654-2730
Tel (312) 782-4290 *Founded/Ownrshp* 1991
Sales NA *EMP* 500
SIC 6361 Real estate title insurance; Real estate title insurance
Pr: John Baumgart
**CFO:* Thomas Evans
**VP:* Edward Cook

D-U-N-S 61-586-5201
NATIONAL ERECTORS REBAR INC
2373 Kenric Rd, Lumberton, NC 28360-0348
Tel (910) 618-9200 *Founded/Ownrshp* 1987
Sales 27.1MM^E *EMP* 280
SIC 1771 Concrete work; Concrete work
Pr: Jeff Jones
**Treas:* Anita Jones

D-U-N-S 05-650-7037 IMP
NATIONAL EWP INC
500 Main St, Woodland, CA 95695-3434
Tel (530) 419-7300 *Founded/Ownrshp* 2010
Sales 91.1MM^E *EMP* 100
SIC 1081 Metal mining exploration & development services; Metal mining exploration & development services
Pr: Jeffrey D Morgan
**CFO:* Michael Paris

D-U-N-S 05-456-4793
NATIONAL EWP INC
580 W Silver St, Elko, NV 89801-3724
Tel (916) 825-6180 *Founded/Ownrshp* 2010
Sales 26.4MM^E *EMP* 273
Accts Perry Bunch Battaglia & John
SIC 1241 1381 Coal mining services; Service well drilling; Coal mining services; Service well drilling
Pr: Jeffrey Morgan
**CFO:* Ray Imbsen
Opers Mgr: Bill Eddy

NATIONAL EXCELSIOR COMPANY
See TEMP EXCEL PROPERTIES LLC

D-U-N-S 00-794-5926
NATIONAL EXCHANGE BANK & TRUST (INC)
(*Suby of* NEB CORP) ★
130 S Main St, Fond Du Lac, WI 54935-4248
Tel (920) 533-8386 *Founded/Ownrshp* 1933, 1986
Sales NA *EMP* 280
SIC 6021 National commercial banks; National commercial banks
Ch Bd: Peter E Stone
**Pr:* Michael L Burch
COO: Lisa Benike
**Sr VP:* David R Moody
VP: John Klotz
VP: Cindy Mueller
VP: Lori Ruch
VP: Gary Ryan
VP: Nicole Wiese
VP Opers: Trudi Marquardt
Board of Directors: Michael Wagner, John Ahern, David Weber, William Allen, Thomas Baker, Joseph Colwin, Donald Jones, Larry Lunda, Peter Mackey, Stephen Peterson, Gary Sadoff

D-U-N-S 10-759-0002
NATIONAL EXCHANGE CARRIER ASSOCIATION
NECA
80 S Jefferson Rd Ste 1, Whippany, NJ 07981-1049
Tel (973) 884-8000 *Founded/Ownrshp* 1983
Sales 91.1MM^E *EMP* 427
SIC 7389 8611 Telephone answering service; Regulatory associations; Telephone answering service; Regulatory associations
Pr: Bill Hegmann
**CFO:* Peter Dunbar
**VP:* James W Frame
**VP:* Regina McNeil Gc
VP: Peter Tyrrell
Netwrk Mgr: Laurie Debeer

D-U-N-S 12-215-4466
NATIONAL EXECUTIVE QUARTERS INC
5525 Louetta Rd Ste C, Spring, TX 77379-7881
Tel (713) 529-8222 *Founded/Ownrshp* 2002
Sales 22.5MM *EMP* 9
SIC 3131 Quarters; Quarters
Pr: Wendy McNatt
**Pr:* Wendy Kyle
**VP:* Wendy Janda
VP: Julie Sobon

D-U-N-S 82-706-0026
NATIONAL EXPRESS LLC
NEC
(*Suby of* NATIONAL EXPRESS GROUP PLC)
4300 Weaver Pkwy Ste 100, Warrenville, IL 60555-3920
Tel (800) 950-0485 *Founded/Ownrshp* 1998
Sales 644.1MM^E *EMP* 10,001^E
SIC 4119 Vanpool operation; Vanpool operation
Pr: Brian Stock
Pr: Andrew Ptak
Pr: Ron Sanborn
CFO: Judith Crawford
Sr VP: Cristen Kogl
Sr VP: Norman Nicholson
VP: Rick Klaus
VP: John Lebens
VP: Michael Settle
VP: Andrew Tarman
Dir Bus: Justin Grygiel
Dir Bus: Tim Hemans
Dir Bus: Reno Navarette

D-U-N-S 07-317-0748
NATIONAL FARM LIFE INSURANCE CO (INC)
6001 Bridge St, Fort Worth, TX 76112-2494
Tel (817) 451-9550 *Founded/Ownrshp* 1946
Sales NA *EMP* 23
SIC 6311 Life insurance carriers; Life insurance carriers
Pr: Ronald G Dg Downing
CFO: Chip Davis
Treas: J D Davis Jr
Ex VP: Cary Wright
Sr VP: Mark Bigsby
VP: Brad Coon
VP: Leslee Gerhardt
VP: Linda Huens
VP: Mark Williams
Mktg Mgr: Ron Downing

D-U-N-S 86-791-2511
NATIONAL FARMERS ORGANIZATION
(*Suby of* NFO, INC.)
528 Billy Sunday Rd # 100, Ames, IA 50010-8087
Tel (515) 292-2000 *Founded/Ownrshp* 1991
Sales 600.0MM *EMP* 90
SIC 8631 Collective bargaining unit
Pr: Paul Olson
CFO: Micheal Miller
VP: Paul Riniker
Board of Directors: Dale Depies, Bill Goettemoeller, Brian Harris, Ernest Muhlenkamp, Mark Rubin, Dan Sorenson, Ed Tvrdy, Leander Wagner

D-U-N-S 04-813-0728
NATIONAL FARMERS UNION PROPERTY & CASUALTY CO
(*Suby of* QBE INSURANCE GROUP LIMITED)
5619 Dtc Pkwy Ste 300, Greenwood Village, CO 80111-3136
Tel (303) 337-5500 *Founded/Ownrshp* 2005
Sales NA *EMP* 230
SIC 6331 Fire, marine & casualty insurance; Fire, marine & casualty insurance
Pr: Jerry Mackey
CFO: Craig Tuecke
VP: Ron Clark
VP: Darrell Moberg
VP: Steven Osguthorpe
VP: Ercella Stevenson
Dir IT: Don Giltz
Dir IT: Mark Rupp
Netwrk Mgr: Richard Dinge
Mktg Dir: Alan Seigfreid

D-U-N-S 06-962-7941
NATIONAL FEDERATION OF BLIND
NFB
1800 Johnson St, Baltimore, MD 21230-4914
Tel (410) 659-9314 *Founded/Ownrshp* 1940
Sales 20.0MM *EMP* 68
Accts Rosen Sapperstein & Friedlande
SIC 8399 8331 Health & welfare council; Job training services; Health & welfare council; Job training services
Pr: Mark A Riccobono
**Treas:* Pam Allen
**VP:* Ron Brown

D-U-N-S 00-923-8221
NATIONAL FEDERATION OF INDEPENDENT BUSINESS
N F I B
53 Century Blvd Ste 250, Nashville, TN 37214-4618
Tel (615) 872-5800 *Founded/Ownrshp* 1943
Sales 104.6MM *EMP* 825
Accts Kpmg Llp Nashville Tn
SIC 8611 Business associations; Business associations
Pr: Dan Danner
**CFO:* Tammy Boehms
CFO: Tammy S Boehms
**Sr VP:* Mary Blasinsky
Sr VP: Tammy Boehms
Sr VP: John Casella
Sr VP: Brad Close
**Sr VP:* John Lanier
**Sr VP:* David Silverman
**Sr VP:* Steve Woods
VP: Amanda Austin
**VP:* Jannet Connor
**VP:* Susan Eckerly
VP: Tim Franke
**VP:* Roger Geiger
**VP:* Lisa Goeas
**VP:* Jeff Koch
**VP:* Susan Ridge
VP: Beverly Shea
Exec: Janet Conner
Dir Soc: Lani Babin

NATIONAL FFA ORGANIZATION
See FUTURE FARMERS OF AMERICA INC

D-U-N-S 09-921-1005 EXP
NATIONAL FIBER SUPPLY LLC
303 W Madison St Ste 1650, Chicago, IL 60606-3328
Tel (312) 346-4800 *Founded/Ownrshp* 1995
Sales 34.0MM^E *EMP* 35
SIC 5113 5093 Industrial & personal service paper; Waste paper & cloth materials; Waste paper
Opers Mgr: John Rowe
Trfc Mgr: Yvette Jimenez

D-U-N-S 00-116-6511 IMP
NATIONAL FILTER MEDIA CORP (CT)
NFM
(*Suby of* ALSCO INC) ★
691 N 400 W, Salt Lake City, UT 84103-1313
Tel (801) 363-6736 *Founded/Ownrshp* 1906
Sales 54.4MM^E *EMP* 330
SIC 3569 Filters, general line: industrial; Filters, general line: industrial
Pr: John R Eugster
**VP:* Denis Charest

NATIONAL FINANCIAL NETWORK
See PARK AVE SECURITIES LLC

D-U-N-S 09-628-4047
NATIONAL FINANCIAL SERVICES LLC
(*Suby of* FIDELITY INVESTMENTS) ★
200 Seaport Blvd Ste 630, Boston, MA 02210-2031
Tel (800) 471-0382 *Founded/Ownrshp* 1978
Sales 2.5MMM^E *EMP* 36,000
SIC 6211 6411 6282 Security brokers & dealers; Brokers, security; Dealers, security; Investment firm, general brokerage; Insurance agents; Investment advisory service; Security brokers & dealers; Brokers, security; Dealers, security; Investment firm, general brokerage; Insurance agents; Investment advisory service
Ex VP: Peter Benzie
Sr VP: Andy Giddings
VP: Patrick H McEvoy
VP: Sean Walsh
VP: Todd Wiltshire
Dir IT: Naveed Deshmukh

NATIONAL FIRE FIGHTER WILDLAND
See EUGENE WELDERS SUPPLY CO

D-U-N-S 00-787-4191
■ NATIONAL FIRE INSURANCE CO OF HARTFORD (CT)
(*Suby of* CNA INSURANCE) ★
Cna Plz, Chicago, IL 60604
Tel (312) 822-5000 *Founded/Ownrshp* 1869, 2008
Sales NA *EMP* 2,000
SIC 6331 Fire, marine & casualty insurance; Fire, marine & casualty insurance
Prin: Brian Hartford

D-U-N-S 00-196-3206
NATIONAL FIRE PROTECTION ASSOCIATION INC
NFPA
1 Batterymarch Park Bsmt, Quincy, MA 02169-7484
Tel (617) 770-3000 *Founded/Ownrshp* 1896
Sales 82.4MM *EMP* 309
Accts Cbiz Tofias Boston Ma
SIC 8621 2721 8748 Professional membership organizations; Magazines: publishing only, not printed on site; Trade journals: publishing only, not printed on site; Safety training service; Professional membership organizations; Magazines: publishing only, not printed on site; Trade journals: publishing only, not printed on site; Safety training service
Pr: James Shannon
VP: Darryl Jewell
VP: Nancy Perkins
Sales Exec: Alma Manning
Board of Directors: Harold A Schaitberger

D-U-N-S 80-011-6100
NATIONAL FIRE PROTECTION LLC
KIRLIN
515 Dover Rd Ste 2600, Rockville, MD 20850-1235
Tel (301) 340-6500 *Founded/Ownrshp* 1987
Sales 45.4MM^E *EMP* 300^E
SIC 7389 7336 1799 Fire protection service other than forestry or public; Inspection & testing services; Commercial art & graphic design; Fire escape installation; Fire protection service other than forestry or public; Inspection & testing services; Commercial art & graphic design; Fire escape installation
VP: Darryl Jewell
**Pr:* F George Buell
**CEO:* Robert W Bacon
VP: Edward Schneider

NATIONAL FIRE SUPPRESSION
See WESTERN STATES FIRE PROTECTION CO INC

D-U-N-S 17-517-2527
NATIONAL FISH & WILDLIFE FOUNDATION
1133 15th St Nw Fl 11, Washington, DC 20005-2708
Tel (202) 857-0166 *Founded/Ownrshp* 1984
Sales 185.6MM *EMP* 85
Accts Grant Thornton Llp Mc Lean V
SIC 8641 Environmental protection organization; Environmental protection organization
Ch Bd: Don J McGrath
**CEO:* Jeff Trandahl
COO: William Torgerson
**CFO:* Robert Menzi
Ex VP: Jennifer C Simpson
VP: Eric Schwaab
Pgrm Dir: Michelle Pico
Pgrm Dir: Andrew Purkey

Board of Directors: Charles McCrary, R King Milling, Edwin R Rodriquez Jr, Thomas L Strickland

D-U-N-S 09-744-7403 IMP
NATIONAL FISH AND SEAFOOD INC
(*Suby of* PACIFIC ANDES INTERNATIONAL HOLDINGS LIMITED)
11 15 Parker St, Gloucester, MA 01930
Tel (978) 282-7880 *Founded/Ownrshp* 1997
Sales 175.7MM^E *EMP* 253
SIC 5146 2092 Fish, frozen, unpackaged; Fresh or frozen packaged fish; Fish, frozen, unpackaged; Fresh or frozen packaged fish
Pr: Jack A Ventola
Ex VP: Richard Pandolfo
VP: Tim Benevelli
VP: James Dimino
VP: Patrick Pandalfo
VP: Richard Reeder
VP: Rick Waltzer
Genl Mgr: Andrew Marenghi
Sfty Mgr: Jack Duarte
Plnt Mgr: Brian Lima
Trfc Mgr: Ernie Viens

D-U-N-S 09-869-9671
NATIONAL FLORAL SUPPLY OF MARYLAND INC
3825 Leonardtown Rd Ste 4, Waldorf, MD 20601-3694
Tel (301) 932-7600 *Founded/Ownrshp* 2003
Sales 24.6MM^E *EMP* 350
SIC 5992 Florists; Florists
Pr: Steve Seely
Treas: Kathryn B Obrien

D-U-N-S 13-826-6981 IMP/EXP
NATIONAL FOAM INC
350 E Union St, West Chester, PA 19382-3450
Tel (610) 363-1400 *Founded/Ownrshp* 1993
Sales 51.8MM^E *EMP* 197^E
SIC 5012 Fire trucks
Pr: Jack Hittson
Mktg Mgr: Chuck Labonty
Mktg Mgr: Ashley Price
Sales Asso: Renee Grasmuck
Sales Asso: Mike McCracken

D-U-N-S 02-745-8009 IMP/EXP
NATIONAL FOOD CORP
808 134th St Sw Ste 116, Everett, WA 98204-2300
Tel (425) 349-4257 *Founded/Ownrshp* 1956
Sales 168.6MM^E *EMP* 500
SIC 0252 Chicken eggs; Chicken eggs
Pr: Brian Bookkey
**Sec:* Dean Fox
**VP:* Roger Deffner

D-U-N-S 78-349-5005 IMP
NATIONAL FOOD GROUP INC
C S V SALES
46820 Magellan Dr Ste A, Novi, MI 48377-2454
Tel (734) 453-4544 *Founded/Ownrshp* 1990
Sales 96.4MM^E *EMP* 72^E
SIC 5142 Packaged frozen goods; Packaged frozen goods
Pr: Sean Zecman
**Sec:* Vaughn H Zecman
Off Admin: Nick Crivac

D-U-N-S 07-127-0888
NATIONAL FOOD LABORATORY LLC
(*Suby of* SAFE FOODS INTERNATIONAL HOLDINGS, LLC)
365 N Canyons Pkwy # 201, Livermore, CA 94551-7703
Tel (925) 828-1440 *Founded/Ownrshp* 1976
Sales 27.8MM^E *EMP* 150
SIC 8733 Scientific research agency; Scientific research agency
Pr: Austin Sharp
CFO: Bill Pappas
VP: Debbie Lohmeyer
VP: Wilfredo Ocasio
**VP:* Jena Roberts
Div Mgr: Grace Bandong
Div Mgr: Shaunti Luce
Cmptr Lab: Daljit Kaur
IT Man: Bonnie Chau
IT Man: Sonya Finley
Tech Mgr: Ken Amaral

D-U-N-S 07-828-6530
NATIONAL FOOTBALL LEAGUE INC
N F L
345 Park Ave Bsmt Lc1, New York, NY 10154-0017
Tel (212) 450-2000 *Founded/Ownrshp* 1920
Sales 294.4MM *EMP* 1,795
SIC 8699 Athletic organizations; Athletic organizations
Pr: Eric P Grubman
COO: Kim Williams
CFO: Adrian Bracy
**CFO:* Anthony Noto
CFO: Bill Prescott
**Chf Mktg O:* Dawn Hudson
Ex VP: Steve Bornstein
**Ex VP:* Jeff Pash
Ex VP: Troy Vincent
Exec: Sara Levinson
Creative D: Lan Campbell

D-U-N-S 07-483-9218
NATIONAL FOOTBALL LEAGUE PLAYERS ASSOCIATION (VA)
1133 20th St Nw Frnt 1, Washington, DC 20036-3449
Tel (202) 756-9100 *Founded/Ownrshp* 1969
Sales 65.9MM *EMP* 89
Accts Calibre Cpa Group Pllc Bethes
SIC 8631 Employees' association; Employees' association
Pr: Domonique Foxworth
**VP:* Drew Brees
**VP:* Brian Dawkins
**VP:* Scott Fujita
Genl Mgr: Mary Moran
Dir IT: Heather McPhee
Dir IT: Ahmad Nassar
Dir IT: Teri Patterson
Dir IT: Leslie Satchell
Dir IT: Mike Shehan
Genl Couns: Richard Berthelsen

D-U-N-S 92-629-8225 IMP
NATIONAL FORGE CO HOLDINGS INC
1 Front St, Irvine, PA 16329-1801
Tel (814) 563-7522 *Founded/Ownrshp* 1995
Sales NA *EMP* 793
SIC 3462 3544 3312 3489

D-U-N-S 04-089-0121
NATIONAL FORWARDING CO INC
(*Suby of* NATIONAL VAN LINES INC) ★
2800 W Roosevelt Rd, Broadview, IL 60155-3756
Tel (708) 345-0550 *Founded/Ownrshp* 1973
Sales 40.0MM *EMP* 10
SIC 4731 Freight forwarding; Freight forwarding
Pr: Patrick Johnson
**Treas:* Maureen Beal
VP: Kevin Spealman
Dir IT: Ronald McKee
VP Opers: Eileen Sherman
Opers Mgr: Len Bambach
Sales Exec: Mark Wagner

D-U-N-S 18-303-7779
NATIONAL FOUNDATION FOR CREDIT COUNSELING INC
2000 M St Nw Ste 505, Washington, DC 20036-3358
Tel (202) 677-4300 *Founded/Ownrshp* 1951
Sales 20.3MM *EMP* 15
Accts Tate & Tryon Washington Dc
SIC 7389 Financial services
Pr: Susan C Keating
**COO:* Robert Ensinger
CFO: Debra Adlis
**CFO:* Denis Russell
**Sr VP:* William Binzel

D-U-N-S 00-248-3659
NATIONAL FREIGHT INC (NJ)
NFI TRANSPORTATION
(*Suby of* NFI INDUSTRIES INC) ★
1515 Burnt Mill Rd, Cherry Hill, NJ 08003-3637
Tel (856) 691-7000 *Founded/Ownrshp* 1932, 2012
Sales 277.4MM^E *EMP* 1,526
SIC 7513 4213 Truck rental & leasing, no drivers; Trucking, except local; Truck rental & leasing, no drivers; Trucking, except local
Ch Bd: Bernard A Brown
**Pr:* Jeffrey Brown
Pr: Joe Cohill
**CEO:* Sidney Brown
COO: Josiah Knapp
CFO: Gary Nichols
VP: Jeffrey Kanterman
VP: Matt Thompson
VP: George Travassos
Dir Risk M: Ross Ennis
Dir Bus: Robert Madden

D-U-N-S 00-926-2064 IMP/EXP
NATIONAL FROZEN FOODS CORP
PAC/GRO AND ASSOCIATES
1600 Frview Ave E Ste 200, Seattle, WA 98102
Tel (206) 322-8900 *Founded/Ownrshp* 1912
Sales 202.5MM *EMP* 1,009
SIC 2037 Vegetables, quick frozen & cold pack, excl. potato products; Vegetables, quick frozen & cold pack, excl. potato products
Pr: Richard Grader
**Treas:* Celeste Gazarek
Chf Mktg O: Bob Ashmun
**VP:* Robert Ashmun
**VP:* Jonathan Bafus
**VP:* Edward Rosenbach
Admn Mgr: Judy Barron
Genl Mgr: Bill Obryan
CIO: Pete Larson
Dir IT: Peter Larsen
IT Man: Sunshine Sang

D-U-N-S 00-306-2684
NATIONAL FRUIT PRODUCT CO INC
550 Fairmont Ave, Winchester, VA 22601-3931
Tel (540) 662-3401 *Founded/Ownrshp* 1908
Sales 94.9MM^E *EMP* 550
SIC 2033 2099 2035 0723

D-U-N-S 00-698-8059
▲ **NATIONAL FUEL GAS CO** (NJ)
6363 Main St, Williamsville, NY 14221-5887
Tel (716) 857-7000 *Founded/Ownrshp* 1902
Sales 1.7MMM *EMP* 2,010^E
Accts Pricewaterhousecoopers Llp Bu
Tkr Sym NFG *Exch* NYS
SIC 4924 4922 1311 1382 Natural gas distribution; Pipelines, natural gas; Storage, natural gas; Natural gas production; Oil & gas exploration services; Natural gas distribution; Pipelines, natural gas; Storage, natural gas; Natural gas production; Oil & gas exploration services
Pr: Ronald J Tanski
**Ch Bd:* David F Smith
CFO: David P Bauer
VP: Jay Lesch
VP: Robert Sauer
VP: Ann Wegrzyn
Area Mgr: Scott Swartzfager
Genl Mgr: Ronald Grabowski
Dir IT: Joan Obrien
Plnt Mgr: Jeremy Young
Sls Dir: Kenneth Lawton
Board of Directors: Philip C Ackerman, David C Carroll, R Don Cash, Stephen E Ewing, Joseph N Jaggers, Ronald W Jibson, Craig G Matthews, Jeffrey W Shaw

D-U-N-S 00-697-6666
■ **NATIONAL FUEL GAS DISTRIBUTION CORP** (NY)
(*Suby of* NATIONAL FUEL GAS CO) ★
6363 Main St, Williamsville, NY 14221-5887
Tel (716) 857-7000 *Founded/Ownrshp* 1973
Sales 760.6MM^E *EMP* 1,267^E
SIC 4925 Gas production and/or distribution; Gas production and/or distribution
Pr: Anna M Cellino
**Ch Bd:* Rj Tanski
Genl Mgr: Patricia Galbo
Plnt Mgr: Jennifer Schaller
Snr Mgr: Ruth Friedrich-Alf

D-U-N-S 00-791-2959
■ **NATIONAL FUEL GAS SUPPLY CORP** (PA)
(*Suby of* NATIONAL FUEL GAS CO) ★
6363 Main St, Williamsville, NY 14221-5887
Tel (716) 857-7000 *Founded/Ownrshp* 1902, 1974
Sales 189.1MM *EMP* 312
SIC 4924 Natural gas distribution; Natural gas distribution
Pr: Ronald J Tanski
**Ch:* David F Smith
**VP:* Matthew D Cabell
**VP:* John R Pustulka
**VP:* James D Ramsdell
Genl Mgr: Patricia Galbo

D-U-N-S 79-489-8775
■ **NATIONAL FUEL RESOURCES INC**
(*Suby of* NATIONAL FUEL GAS CO) ★
165 Lawrence Bell Dr # 120, Buffalo, NY 14221-7900
Tel (716) 630-6786 *Founded/Ownrshp* 1990
Sales 22.8MM^E *EMP* 40
SIC 4924 Natural gas distribution
Ch Bd: Joseph N Del Vecchio

NATIONAL FULFILLMENT SERVICES
See KRUEGER ASSOCIATES INC

D-U-N-S 05-321-9924
NATIONAL FUNDING INC (CA)
9820 Towne Centre Dr # 200, San Diego, CA 92121-1944
Tel (888) 576-4685 *Founded/Ownrshp* 1999
Sales NA *EMP* 135
SIC 6153 6159 7389

D-U-N-S 79-180-3885
NATIONAL FURNITURE LIQUIDATORS I LLC
NFL OFFICEWORKS
2865 Log Cabin Dr Se, Atlanta, GA 30339-1568
Tel (404) 872-7280 *Founded/Ownrshp* 1992
Sales 152.8MM^E *EMP* 50
SIC 5021 5712 5932 Furniture; Office furniture; Furniture stores; Office furniture; Office furniture, secondhand
Pr: Rick Robillard
**CEO:* William Jones
**VP:* Tim Butler

D-U-N-S 05-239-4764
NATIONAL FUTURES ASSOCIATION (INC)
N F A
2600 Mccormick Dr, Clearwater, FL 33759-1001
Tel (312) 781-1300 *Founded/Ownrshp* 1982
Sales 67.1MM *EMP* 500
Accts Grant Thornton Llp Chicago I
SIC 8611 Regulatory associations; Regulatory associations
Pr: Daniel Roth
**COO:* Daniel Driscoll
**Ch:* Christopher Hehmeyer
**Treas:* David Hawrysz
Sr VP: Thomas W Sexton III
VP: Louis P Nazzaro
**Prin:* Rober Felkar
Dir IT: Kenneth Haase

D-U-N-S 02-187-0837 IMP
■ **NATIONAL GALLERY OF ART**
(*Suby of* EXECUTIVE OFFICE OF UNITED STATES GOVERNMENT) ★
6th And Cnsttution Ave Nw, Washington, DC 20565-0001
Tel (202) 737-4215 *Founded/Ownrshp* 1941
Sales 146.8MM *EMP* 1,000
Accts Kpmg Llp Washington Dc
SIC 5942 8412 Book stores; Art gallery, noncommercial; Book stores; Art gallery, noncommercial
Ch: John Wilmerding
**Pr:* Victoria P Sant
**Pr:* Robert H Smith
Treas: George-Ann Tobin
Ofcr: Naomi Remes
Off Mgr: Carol Koelemay
CIO: Greg Swift
IT Man: Chris Caldwell
IT Man: Kristhian Senzano
Web Dev: John Gordy
Netwrk Eng: Ward Meier

D-U-N-S 12-818-3725
NATIONAL GALVANIZING LP
1500 Telb St, Monroe, MI 48162-2572
Tel (734) 243-1882 *Founded/Ownrshp* 1983
Sales 180.4MM^E *EMP* 1,000
SIC 3312 3316 3471 3341 5051 Sheet or strip, steel, hot-rolled; Strip steel, cold-rolled: from purchased hot-rolled; Plating & polishing; Secondary nonferrous metals; Metals service centers & offices; Sheet or strip, steel, hot-rolled; Strip steel, cold-rolled: from purchased hot-rolled; Plating & polishing; Secondary nonferrous metals; Metals service centers & offices
Prin: Mike Robinson

D-U-N-S 01-693-6544
■ **NATIONAL GARAGES INC**
(*Suby of* CENTRAL PARKING CORP) ★
104 Lothrop Rd Ste A, Detroit, MI 48202-2712
Tel (313) 874-7019 *Founded/Ownrshp* 1926, 1999
Sales 16.8MM^E *EMP* 750
SIC 7521 Parking lots; Parking structure; Parking lots; Parking structure
Ch Bd: Monroe Carell Jr

NATIONAL GARDEN WHOLESALE
See SUNLIGHT SUPPLY INC

D-U-N-S 00-105-3560
NATIONAL GAS & OIL CO INC
1500 Granville Rd, Newark, OH 43055-1500
Tel (740) 344-2102 *Founded/Ownrshp* 1981
Sales 65.8MM^E *EMP* 146
SIC 4922 4924 1311 Natural gas transmission; Natural gas distribution; Natural gas production; Natural gas transmission; Natural gas distribution; Natural gas production
Ch Bd: William H Sullivan Jr
**Pr:* Patrick J Mc Gonagle
VP: Todd Ware

D-U-N-S 00-790-3784
NATIONAL GAS & OIL CORP
PERMIAN OIL & GAS DIVISION
(*Suby of* NATIONAL GAS & OIL CO INC) ★
1500 Granville Rd, Newark, OH 43055-1500
Tel (740) 344-2102 *Founded/Ownrshp* 1941
Sales 37.1MM *EMP* 96
SIC 4922 4924 4932 4911 2813 Natural gas transmission; Natural gas distribution; Gas & other services combined; Electric services; Industrial gases; Natural gas transmission; Natural gas distribution; Gas & other services combined; Electric services; Industrial gases
Ch Bd: William Sullivan Jr
Pr: Patrick J Mc Gonagle
VP: Gordon M King
VP: Todd P Ware

D-U-N-S 96-191-8468
▲ **NATIONAL GENERAL HOLDINGS CORP**
59 Maiden Ln Fl 38, New York, NY 10038-4502
Tel (212) 380-9500 *Founded/Ownrshp* 2009
Sales NA *EMP* 2,034^E
Tkr Sym NGHC *Exch* NGM
SIC 6331 Investment holding companies, except banks; Fire, marine & casualty insurance; Automobile insurance; Property damage insurance
Ch Bd: Michael Karfunkel
Pr: Peter Cassoli
CFO: Michael Weiner
Chf Mktg O: Barry Karfunkel
Ex VP: Robert Karfunkel
Ex VP: Michael Murphy
VP: Susan Eylward
Board of Directors: Ephraim Brecher, Donald Decarlo, Patrick Fallon, Barbara Paris, Howard Zuckerman, Barry Zyskind

D-U-N-S 07-942-0838
NATIONAL GENERAL INSURANCE
59 Maiden Ln Fl 38, New York, NY 10038-4502
Tel (212) 380-9477 *Founded/Ownrshp* 2014
Sales NA *EMP* 500
SIC 6411 Insurance agents, brokers & service; Insurance agents & brokers
Prin: Kevin Bailey
Prin: Matthew Milner
VP Sls: Brian Macias

D-U-N-S 08-163-2044
■ **NATIONAL GENERAL INSURANCE CO**
GMAC INSURANCE
(*Suby of* NAVCO CORP)
13736 Rverport Dr Ste 700, Maryland Heights, MO 63043
Tel (314) 493-8000 *Founded/Ownrshp* 1966
Sales NA *EMP* 700
SIC 6331 Property damage insurance; Fire, marine & casualty insurance & carriers; Automobile insurance; Property damage insurance; Fire, marine & casualty insurance & carriers; Automobile insurance
Pr: Gary Y Kusumi
**Treas:* Donald J Bolar
Chf Mktg O: Scott Eckman
Sr VP: Matthew Detwiler
VP: John J Dunn Jr
VP: Rick Pierce
**VP:* Verne Purvines
**VP:* Mitchell White
Mng Dir: John Davis
Brnch Mgr: Jonathan Eaby
Brnch Mgr: Teresa Mason

D-U-N-S 15-029-8131
■ **NATIONAL GENERAL MANAGEMENT CORP**
GMAC INSURANCE
(*Suby of* NATIONAL GENERAL HOLDINGS CORP) ★
5630 University Pkwy, Winston Salem, NC 27105-1312
Tel (336) 435-3164 *Founded/Ownrshp* 2010
Sales NA *EMP* 400
SIC 6411 Insurance agents, brokers & service; Insurance agents, brokers & service
Pr: Gary Kusumi
CFO: Michael Weiner
**VP:* Don Bolar
VP: Erinn Dutt-Bowser
**VP:* George Hall
VP: Renee Kero
Brnch Mgr: Natasha Hairston
Brnch Mgr: Sandra Mason
CIO: Leslie Leb
IT Man: Wayne Goede
IT Man: Don Hawes

NATIONAL GEOGRAPHIC CHANNEL
See NGC NETWORK US LLC

D-U-N-S 00-324-7756 IMP/EXP
NATIONAL GEOGRAPHIC SOCIETY (DC)
1145 17th St Nw, Washington, DC 20036-4707
Tel (202) 857-7000 *Founded/Ownrshp* 1888
Sales 410.4MM^E *EMP* 1,700
SIC 2721

D-U-N-S 61-480-8681
■ **NATIONAL GEOSPATIAL-INTELLIGENCE AGENCY**
N G A
(*Suby of* OFFICE OF THE SECRETARY OF DEFENSE) ★
4600 Sangamore Rd, Bethesda, MD 20816-5004
Tel (703) 262-4316 *Founded/Ownrshp* 1947
Sales NA *EMP* 8,500
SIC 9711 National security;
Exec: Robert Murrett
Ofcr: Carole Brooks
Ofcr: Billie Chavis
Dir IT: Joseph Dessau

IT Man: Frank Chamberlain
IT Man: James Stephens

NATIONAL GGRPHIC CHANNELS INTL
See NGC NETWORK INTERNATIONAL LLC

D-U-N-S 05-614-2169
NATIONAL GLASS & GATE SERVICE INC
NG&G FACILITY SERVICES INTL
263 Jenckes Hill Rd, Lincoln, RI 02865-4415
Tel (401) 333-4800 *Founded/Ownrshp* 1971
Sales 43.5MM^E *EMP* 100
SIC 8744 Facilities support services
Pr: Charles Vachon
**COO:* Alan P Riendeau
VP: Kit Filbey
Netwrk Mgr: R Boynes
Site Mgr: Rich Wentlejewski

D-U-N-S 80-201-4741 IMP/EXP
NATIONAL GOLDEN TISSUE INC
NGT
858 Willow Cir, Hagerstown, MD 21740-6827
Tel (301) 739-1001 *Founded/Ownrshp* 2006
Sales 21.6MM^E *EMP* 60
SIC 2679 Paper products, converted
CEO: Sam Shahrooz

D-U-N-S 80-844-5803
NATIONAL GOLF PROPERTIES LLC
2951 28th St Ste 3000, Santa Monica, CA 90405-2987
Tel (310) 664-4000 *Founded/Ownrshp* 2003
Sales 13.9MM^E *EMP* 1,040
SIC 6519 8111 Real property lessors; Legal services; Real property lessors; Legal services
Pr: Charles S Paul
CFO: Keith Brown

D-U-N-S 80-789-9653
■ NATIONAL GOVERNMENT SERVICES INC
(*Suby of* ANTHEM INSURANCE COMPANIES INC) ★
8115 Knue Rd, Indianapolis, IN 46250-1936
Tel (317) 841-4400 *Founded/Ownrshp* 1991
Sales 171.4MM^E *EMP* 2,200
SIC 8099 Medical services organization; Medical services organization
Ch Bd: Angela Braley
**Pr:* Michael Kapp
**CFO:* Jim Maguire
**Treas:* R David Kretschmer
**VP:* Jeff Hannah
**VP:* Mary Ludden
**VP:* Dave Marshall
**VP:* Tim Masheck
**VP:* Wendy Perkins
**CIO:* Frank Lasota

D-U-N-S 79-115-2312
NATIONAL GRANGE MUTUAL INSURANCE CO
MGM
(*Suby of* MAIN STREET AMERICA GROUP) ★
55 West St, Keene, NH 03431-3348
Tel (603) 358-6517 *Founded/Ownrshp* 2007
Sales NA *EMP* 227^E
SIC 6411 Insurance agents, brokers & service
CEO: Thomas M Van Berkel
VP: Ron James

D-U-N-S 00-194-0758 IMP/EXP
NATIONAL GRAPE CO-OPERATIVE ASSOCIATION INC (NY)
2 S Portage St, Westfield, NY 14787-1400
Tel (716) 326-5200 *Founded/Ownrshp* 1945
Sales 608.4MM *EMP* 1,325
Accts Kpmg Llp Boston Ma
SIC 2033 2037 Fruit juices: packaged in cans, jars, etc.; Fruit juices: concentrated, hot pack; Tomato juice: packaged in cans, jars, etc.; Jams, jellies & preserves: packaged in cans, jars, etc.; Frozen fruits & vegetables; Fruit juices, frozen; Fruit juice concentrates, frozen; Fruit juices: packaged in cans, jars, etc.; Fruit juices: concentrated, hot pack; Tomato juice: packaged in cans, jars, etc.; Jams, jellies & preserves: packaged in cans, jars, etc.; Frozen fruits & vegetables; Fruit juices, frozen; Fruit juice concentrates, frozen
Pr: Randolph Graham
Trst Ofcr: Craig Bardwell
**VP:* Joseph C Falcone
**VP:* Harold Smith

D-U-N-S 03-751-1177
NATIONAL GRAPHICS INC
248 Branford Rd, North Branford, CT 06471-1328
Tel (203) 481-2351 *Founded/Ownrshp* 1980
Sales 3.0MM^E *EMP* 359
SIC 2759

NATIONAL GRID
See MASSACHUSETTS ELECTRIC CO

NATIONAL GRID
See NIAGARA MOHAWK POWER CORP

NATIONAL GRID
See KEYSPAN GAS EAST CORP

D-U-N-S 93-786-9261
NATIONAL GRID
(*Suby of* NATIONAL GRID USA SERVICE CO INC) ★
1 Metrotech Ctr Fl 1, Brooklyn, NY 11201-3850
Tel (718) 643-4050 *Founded/Ownrshp* 1998
Sales 184.5MM^E *EMP* 189
SIC 4932 8748 Gas & other services combined; Energy conservation consultant; Gas & other services combined; Energy conservation consultant
CEO: Steve Holliday Freng
**Pr:* J Philip Frazier
**Pr:* Philip Van Horne
Treas: James Holodak
**Treas:* Richard Pluchino
Ex VP: John Caroselli
VP: Charles Derosa
VP: Anthony Dibrita
**VP:* Frank Duesel
VP: Joseph Newman
**VP:* Raymond Tasch

D-U-N-S 84-474-9010 IMP
NATIONAL GRID CORPORATE SERVICES LLC
KEYSPAN ENERGY
(*Suby of* KEYSPAN CORP) ★
175 E Old Country Rd, Hicksville, NY 11801-4257
Tel (718) 403-2000 *Founded/Ownrshp* 2007
Sales 6.1MMM^E *EMP* 9,594
SIC 4924 4911 1311 4922 Natural gas distribution; Distribution, electric power; Generation, electric power; Transmission, electric power; Crude petroleum & natural gas; Natural gas transmission; Pipelines, natural gas; Storage, natural gas; Natural gas distribution; Distribution, electric power; Generation, electric power; Transmission, electric power; Crude petroleum & natural gas; Natural gas transmission; Pipelines, natural gas; Storage, natural gas
Ch: Peter Gershon Cbe
CEO: Steve Holliday Freng
Ex VP: John A Caroselli
Ex VP: Joseph Giordano
Ex VP: Ellen Smith
Ex VP: Jim Stephenson
Sr VP: James Madej
Sr VP: Colin Owyang
VP: James Brennan
VP: Robert Demarinis
VP: Brian Noone
VP: Nereida Perez
VP: Martin Wheatcroft
Board of Directors: Colin Owyang

D-U-N-S 83-040-9947
NATIONAL GRID DEVELOPMENT HOLDINGS CORP
(*Suby of* NATIONAL GRID ENERGY CORP) ★
1 Metrotech Ctr Fl 1, Brooklyn, NY 11201-3850
Tel (718) 403-2000 *Founded/Ownrshp* 2009
Sales 41.8MM^E *EMP* 300
SIC 8748 Business consulting; Business consulting
Pr: John Gregory Cochrane
**Treas:* Lorraine Lynch

D-U-N-S 83-041-0150
NATIONAL GRID ENERGY CORP
(*Suby of* KEYSPAN CORP) ★
1 Metrotech Ctr Fl 1, Brooklyn, NY 11201-3850
Tel (718) 403-2000 *Founded/Ownrshp* 2009
Sales 549.6MM^E *EMP* 500
SIC 8748 Business consulting; Business consulting

D-U-N-S 83-040-9566
NATIONAL GRID ENERGY SERVICES LLC
(*Suby of* NATIONAL GRID SERVICES INC) ★
55 Bearfoot Rd, Northborough, MA 01532-1513
Tel (508) 393-2307 *Founded/Ownrshp* 2001
Sales 78.4MM^E *EMP* 250
SIC 4911 Distribution, electric power; Distribution, electric power
Pr: Martin Cook
COO: Charlie Connell
CFO: Cyndi Moore
Treas: Edward Carr
Ex VP: Ellen Smith
Sr VP: John Cochrane
VP: Dennis Elsenbeck
VP: Kwong Neuy
VP: Joseph Newman
VP: Kwong Nuey
VP: Sharon Partridge

D-U-N-S 08-617-3403 IMP
NATIONAL GRID GENERATION LLC
(*Suby of* KEYSPAN CORP) ★
175 E Old Country Rd, Hicksville, NY 11801-4257
Tel (631) 755-6650 *Founded/Ownrshp* 1998
Sales 79.3MM^E *EMP* 200
SIC 4924 Natural gas distribution; Natural gas distribution
Pr: John Gregory Cochrane
**Treas:* Malcolm Charles Cooper
**VP:* Robert Teetz
Board of Directors: Colin Owyang

D-U-N-S 82-538-2455 IMP
NATIONAL GRID HOLDINGS INC
(*Suby of* NATIONAL GRID PLC)
300 Erie Blvd W, Syracuse, NY 13202-4250
Tel (315) 474-1511 *Founded/Ownrshp* 2008
Sales 23.0MM^E *EMP* 73^E
SIC 4922 Natural gas transmission
Pr: Stephen C Burrard-Lucas
**Treas:* Malcolm Charles Cooper
**Sr VP:* Colin Owyang
**VP:* Martin Wheatcroft
Board of Directors: Colin Owyang, Linda Clair Ryan

D-U-N-S 83-040-9871
NATIONAL GRID NE HOLDINGS 2 LLC
(*Suby of* KEYSPAN CORP) ★
40 Sylvan Rd, Waltham, MA 02451-1120
Tel (508) 389-2000 *Founded/Ownrshp* 2009
Sales 16.7MM^E *EMP* 400
SIC 8748 Business consulting; Business consulting
**Treas:* David B Doxsee
**VP:* Martin Wheatcroft
Exec: David Thomas
Prgrm Mgr: Ann Callahan
IT Man: Beata Lutz
IT Man: Manuel Macedo
Tech Mgr: Don Woodruff
Genl Couns: Francis J Murphy
Genl Couns: Erik P Weingold

NATIONAL GRID NY
See BROOKLYN UNION GAS CO

D-U-N-S 09-004-7122
NATIONAL GRID SERVICES INC (NY)
(*Suby of* NATIONAL GRID ENERGY CORP) ★
1 Metrotech Ctr Fl 1, Brooklyn, NY 11201-3850
Tel (718) 403-2000 *Founded/Ownrshp* 1998
Sales 428.0MM^E *EMP* 450
SIC 4924 Natural gas distribution; Natural gas distribution
Ch Bd: John G Cochrane
**CEO:* Wallace P Parker Jr
VP: Elaine Weinstein

D-U-N-S 83-041-0176
NATIONAL GRID TECHNOLOGIES INC
(*Suby of* NATIONAL GRID ENERGY CORP) ★
1 Metrotech Ctr Fl 1, Brooklyn, NY 11201-3850
Tel (718) 403-2000 *Founded/Ownrshp* 2009
Sales 13.1MM^E *EMP* 300
SIC 8748 Business consulting; Business consulting

D-U-N-S 00-450-7930
NATIONAL GRID TRANSMISSION SERVICES CORP (MA)
(*Suby of* NATIONAL GRID USA) ★
25 Research Dr, Westborough, MA 01581-3680
Tel (315) 474-1511 *Founded/Ownrshp* 2000
Sales 79.6MM^E *EMP* 150
SIC 4911 Electric services
Pr: Marc Mahoney
COO: Jeff Scott
**Treas:* Patricia C Easterly
Ex VP: John Caroselli
**VP:* Peter G Flynn
VP: David Way
Dir Bus: Wob Gerretsen
CIO: Paul Schmiedel
IT Man: Edward Bonetti
IT Man: Richard Kent
IT Man: Ruth Medford

D-U-N-S 82-993-7965
NATIONAL GRID USA
(*Suby of* NATIONAL GRID PLC)
40 Sylvan Rd, Waltham, MA 02451-1120
Tel (508) 389-2000 *Founded/Ownrshp* 1999
Sales 17.9MMM^E *EMP* 18,100^E
SIC 4911 Transmission, electric power; Transmission, electric power
Pr: Thomas B King
Pr: Kenneth Daly
**CEO:* Steve Holliday
**COO:* Ellen Smith
**CFO:* Linda Claire Ryan
**Treas:* Malcolm Charles Cooper
**Chf Cred:* David Lodemore
**Ex VP:* John A Caroselli
Ex Dir: Nick Winser
Dir IT: Jeanne Campbell
Dir IT: Timothy Graham
Board of Directors: Lisa Crutchfield, Thomas King, Colin Owyang, Andrew Sloey, Ellen Smith, Nickolas Stavropoulos

D-U-N-S 00-695-2840 IMP
NATIONAL GRID USA SERVICE CO INC
(*Suby of* NATIONAL GRID USA) ★
40 Sylvan Rd, Waltham, MA 02451-1120
Tel (800) 260-0054 *Founded/Ownrshp* 1926
Sales 8.1MMM^E *EMP* 18,100
SIC 4911 1311 Generation, electric power; Transmission, electric power; Distribution, electric power; Crude petroleum production; Natural gas production; Generation, electric power; Transmission, electric power; Distribution, electric power; Crude petroleum production; Natural gas production
Pr: Thomas B King
Pr: Vivienne Bracken
Pr: Carmen Fields
CFO: Kenneth D Daly
Treas: Malcolm Charles Cooper
Treas: Lorraine Lynch
Ex VP: John A Caroselli
Sr VP: William J Akley
Sr VP: Colin Owyang
VP: Mallik Angalakudati
VP: Warren Bamford
VP: Mike Courtien
VP: Marie Jordan
VP: Sue Mais
VP: Brian McCabe
VP: Martin Wheatcroft
VP: Bradley White

NATIONAL GRINDING WHEEL
See RADIAC ABRASIVES INC

D-U-N-S 01-904-7751
NATIONAL GROUPS LLC
NATIONAL COLLECTION
500 S Broad St Ste 1, Meriden, CT 06450-6643
Tel (860) 368-3400 *Founded/Ownrshp* 2007
Sales 23.3MM^E *EMP* 150
SIC 6531 Real estate agents & managers
Pr: Wayne Arute

NATIONAL GUARD
See VIRGINIA DEPARTMENT OF MILITARY AFFAIRS

NATIONAL GUARD
See WEST VIRGINIA DEPARTMENT OF MILITARY AFFAIRS AND PUBLIC SAFETY

NATIONAL GUARD & ADJUTANT GEN
See NORTH DAKOTA DEPARTMENT OF MILITARY AFFAIRS

D-U-N-S 78-958-8191
NATIONAL GUARD DELAWARE
ARMY NATIONAL GUARD, DELAWARE
(*Suby of* EXECUTIVE OFFICE OF GOVERNOR OF DELAWARE) ★
250 Airport Rd, New Castle, DE 19720-1502
Tel (302) 326-7160 *Founded/Ownrshp* 1787
Sales NA *EMP* 2,000
SIC 9711 National Guard; ; National Guard;

D-U-N-S 09-748-2470
NATIONAL GUARD NORTH CAROLINA
(*Suby of* NORTH CAROLINA DEPARTMENT OF PUBLIC SAFETY) ★
1636 Gold Star Dr, Raleigh, NC 27607-3371
Tel (919) 664-6000 *Founded/Ownrshp* 1975
Sales NA *EMP* 11,500^E
SIC 9711 National Guard;

NATIONAL GUARD OF NEW MEXICO
See NEW MEXICO DEPT OF MILITARY AFFAIRS

D-U-N-S 00-702-2932
NATIONAL GUARD PRODUCTS INC
4985 E Raines Rd, Memphis, TN 38118-7024
Tel (901) 795-6900 *Founded/Ownrshp* 1936
Sales 33.0MM *EMP* 180
SIC 3053 3442 Gaskets, packing & sealing devices; Weather strip, metal; Gaskets, packing & sealing devices; Weather strip, metal
Pr: Chuck Smith
**COO:* Jeff Morrow
**CFO:* Cynthia Keough
**VP:* Neal Frazier
**VP:* Foster Smith

D-U-N-S 09-060-6872
NATIONAL GUARD PUERTO RICO
GUARDIA NACIONAL DE PR
(*Suby of* EXECUTIVE OFFICE OF COMMONWEALTH OF PUERTO RICO) ★
Parada 3 1/2 Prta De Trra, San Juan, PR 00901
Tel (787) 724-5605 *Founded/Ownrshp* 1969
Sales NA *EMP* 800
SIC 9711 National security; National security
Pr: Benjamin Guzman
**CEO:* Juan Colon

D-U-N-S 08-109-9710
NATIONAL GUARD UTAH
(*Suby of* EXECUTIVE OFFICE OF STATE OF UTAH) ★
12953 S Minuteman Dr, Draper, UT 84020-9286
Tel (801) 432-4439 *Founded/Ownrshp* 1763
Sales NA *EMP* 6,381
SIC 9711 National Guard; ; National Guard;
Prin: Todd Valline

D-U-N-S 00-794-6379
NATIONAL GUARDIAN LIFE INSURANCE CO (INC) (WI)
2 E Gilman St Stop 1, Madison, WI 53703-1480
Tel (608) 257-5611 *Founded/Ownrshp* 1909
Sales NA *EMP* 270^E
SIC 6311 Mutual association life insurance; Mutual association life insurance
Pr: John D Larson
Pr: Janet Fosdick
Pr: Tracy Fritz
Pr: Michelle Hartley
Pr: Brenda Larson
Pr: Mike Wiley
COO: Jessica Oehrlein
CFO: Brian Hogan
**Treas:* Robert A Mucci
Ofcr: John Egan
Ofcr: Jerie Olson
VP: Joseph Freitas
VP: Phil Grece
VP: Walter Lethem
VP: Jill Muenich
**VP:* Timothy J Nicholson
VP: Steve Phelps
**VP:* Mark Solverud
VP: Casey Wolfe
VP: Tom Zupko

D-U-N-S 04-655-3454
NATIONAL GYPSUM BALTO EMP
2301 S Newkirk St, Baltimore, MD 21224-6410
Tel (410) 631-4900 *Founded/Ownrshp* 1956
Sales NA *EMP* 120
SIC 6061 Federal credit unions; Federal credit unions
CEO: Thomas Nelson
Plnt Mgr: Rick Smith

NATIONAL GYPSUM COMPANY
See NEW NGC INC

NATIONAL GYPSUN COMP
See NGC INDUSTRIES INC

NATIONAL HEADQUARTERS
See CIVIL AIR PATROL INC

D-U-N-S 93-187-3004
NATIONAL HEALTH CARE AFFILIATES INC
(*Suby of* HAMISTER GROUP INC) ★
10 Lafayette Sq Ste 1900, Buffalo, NY 14203-1801
Tel (716) 839-4000 *Founded/Ownrshp* 1997
Sales 15.2MM^E *EMP* 2,500
SIC 8082 8052 Home health care services; Intermediate care facilities; Home health care services; Intermediate care facilities
Pr: Jack Turesky
Ch Bd: Mark Hamister
IT Man: Craig Adams
IT Man: Carl Yost

D-U-N-S 86-100-8035
NATIONAL HEALTH CARE ASSOCIATES INC
NHCA
46 Stauderman Ave, Lynbrook, NY 11563-2524
Tel (516) 705-4800 *Founded/Ownrshp* 1984
Sales 292.6MM^E *EMP* 5,500^E
SIC 8741 Hospital management; Nursing & personal care facility management; Hospital management; Nursing & personal care facility management
Pr: Marvin Ostreicher
VP: Barry Bokow
VP: Sue Pappadoulas
VP: Trish Thomas
Exec: Michael Biderman
Off Mgr: Andrew Wildman
IT Man: Uuan Grant
Mktg Dir: Jennifer Kennedy
Pr Dir: Elza Augustin
Nrsg Dir: Jennifer Donovan
HC Dir: Rebecca Simpson
Board of Directors: Susan Ostreicher

D-U-N-S 61-737-1760
NATIONAL HEALTH CORP
2221 E Lamar Blvd Ste 960, Arlington, TX 76006-7419
Tel (817) 312-1007 *Founded/Ownrshp* 1978
Sales NA *EMP* 327
SIC 6321 6311 7389 8741 Accident & health insurance carriers; Life insurance carriers; Telemarketing services; Business management
Ch Bd: Paul D Wood
**Pr:* G Scott Smith

VP: Ann Barnes
VP: Al Johnson

D-U-N-S 02-690-0068
■ NATIONAL HEALTH INDUSTRIES INC
(*Suby of* ALMOST FAMILY INC) ★
9510 Ormsby Station Rd # 300, Louisville, KY 40223-4081
Tel (502) 448-5862 *Founded/Ownrshp* 1991
Sales 38.1MM^E *EMP* 2,200
SIC 8082 Home health care services; Home health care services
Pr: William B Yarmuth
**CFO:* C Steven Guenthner
**Sr VP:* Todd Lyles
**Sr VP:* Rick Pritchard
**Sr VP:* Mary A Yarmuth

NATIONAL HEALTH INFO NETWRK
See PDX INC

D-U-N-S 05-311-8261
NATIONAL HEALTH INSURANCE CO (TX)
NHIC
(*Suby of* NATIONAL HEALTH CORP) ★
2221 E Lamar Blvd Ste 960, Arlington, TX 76006-7419
Tel (800) 237-1900 *Founded/Ownrshp* 1966, 1978
Sales NA *EMP* 103^E
SIC 6321 6311 Accident & health insurance carriers; Life insurance; Life insurance funds, savings bank
Pr: G Scott Smith
**Treas:* Riley Anderson
VP: Ann G Barnes
**VP:* Derrick Duke
VP: Eva A Green
**VP:* Charles W Harris
VP: Cindi J Holt
VP: Rene' C Salinas
**VP:* Bob Smith
VP: Jennifer G Tennison
VP: Dana L Weckherlin

D-U-N-S 78-813-4542
▲ NATIONAL HEALTH INVESTORS INC
222 Robert Rose Dr, Murfreesboro, TN 37129-6346
Tel (615) 890-9100 *Founded/Ownrshp* 1991
Sales 177.5MM *EMP* 4^E
Tkr Sym NHI *Exch* NYS
SIC 6798 Real estate investment trusts; Real estate investment trusts
Pr: Eric Mendelsohn
**Ch Bd:* W Andrew Adams
Chf Cred: Kristin S Gaines
Ex VP: Kevin Pascoe

D-U-N-S 19-045-3167
NATIONAL HEALTH MANAGEMENT INC
4415 5th Ave Ste B, Pittsburgh, PA 15213-2679
Tel (412) 578-7800 *Founded/Ownrshp* 1986
Sales 22.9MM^E *EMP* 600
SIC 8741 Nursing & personal care facility management; Nursing & personal care facility management
Ch Bd: Seymour Baskin
**Pr:* Martin Mason

D-U-N-S 06-910-0097 IMP/EXP
▲ NATIONAL HEALTHCARE CORP (DE)
100 E Vine St, Murfreesboro, TN 37130-3734
Tel (615) 890-2020 *Founded/Ownrshp* 1971
Sales 871.6MM *EMP* 13,050^E
Tkr Sym NHC *Exch* ASE
SIC 8051 8082 Skilled nursing care facilities; Home health care services; Skilled nursing care facilities; Home health care services
Ch Bd: Robert G Adams
Pr: Bruce Duncan
Pr: Stephen F Flatt
Pr: Dinsie Hale
Pr: Charles Wysocki
COO: Michael Ussery
CFO: Donald K Daniel
Treas: Charlotte A Swafford
Sr VP: Gerald Coggin
Sr VP: John K Lines
Genl Mgr: Melinda Vance

D-U-N-S 36-123-6847
■ NATIONAL HEALTHCARE OF CLEVELAND INC
SKYRIDGE MEDICAL CENTER
(*Suby of* COMMUNITY HEALTH SYSTEMS INC) ★
2800 Westside Dr Nw, Cleveland, TN 37312-3501
Tel (423) 339-4100 *Founded/Ownrshp* 1986
Sales 58.4MM^E *EMP* 1,000
SIC 8062 General medical & surgical hospitals; General medical & surgical hospitals
CFO: Coleman Foss
CFO: Bill Zeismer

D-U-N-S 07-545-6897
■ NATIONAL HEALTHCARE OF DECATUR INC
PARKWAY MEDICAL CENTER
(*Suby of* COMMUNITY HEALTH SYSTEMS INC) ★
2 N Jackson St Ste 605, Montgomery, AL 36104-3821
Tel (256) 350-2211 *Founded/Ownrshp* 1996
Sales 39.7MM^E *EMP* 250
SIC 8062 General medical & surgical hospitals; General medical & surgical hospitals
Dir OR: Becky Wheeler
Dir Lab: Tony REA
Dir IT: Doyle Haynes
HC Dir: Paula Mann

D-U-N-S 36-123-6698
■ NATIONAL HEALTHCARE OF LEESVILLE INC
BYRD REGIONAL HOSPITAL
(*Suby of* COMMUNITY HEALTH SYSTEMS INC) ★
1020 W Fertitta Blvd, Leesville, LA 71446-4645
Tel (337) 239-9041 *Founded/Ownrshp* 1995
Sales 68.7MM^E *EMP* 350
SIC 8062 General medical & surgical hospitals; General medical & surgical hospitals
CEO: Roger Leduex
Chf Rad: Joe Rankin
**Pr:* Martin G Schweinhart
**Treas:* James W Doucette
**Treas:* Barry Stewart
**VP:* T Mark Beauford
**VP:* Kevin J Hammons
Dir OR: David Wheeler
Dir Lab: Kary Wilson
Dir Rx: Joann Gibbs
Off Mgr: Cheryl Mayo

D-U-N-S 78-539-5526
■ NATIONAL HEALTHCARE OF MT VERNON INC
CROSSROADS COMMUNITY HOSPITAL
(*Suby of* COMMUNITY HEALTH SYSTEMS INC) ★
Doctors Park Rd Ste 8, Mount Vernon, IL 62864
Tel (618) 244-5500 *Founded/Ownrshp* 1994
Sales 41.3MM *EMP* 200
SIC 8062 General medical & surgical hospitals; General medical & surgical hospitals
Pr: Wayne Smith
**CFO:* Gay Huff
CFO: Mark Stover
Ofcr: Finny Mathew
Dir OR: Jeff Fischer
Dir Lab: Susan Smith
Ex Dir: Terri Wilson
Phys Thrpy: Andrea Hills
Snr Mgr: Sam White

D-U-N-S 12-732-3512
NATIONAL HEALTHCARE REVIEW LLC
ADREIMA, LLC
2651 Warrenville Rd # 500, Downers Grove, IL 60515-5544
Tel (630) 981-8300 *Founded/Ownrshp* 2013
Sales 48.6MM^E *EMP* 277^E
SIC 8721 Accounting services, except auditing; Accounting services, except auditing
Pr: Rob Wilhelm
Pr: Robb C Cass Jr
CEO: Mike Jacoutot
COO: Mary Ann McLaughlin
CFO: Eric Gordon
Sr VP: Kathy Turner-Motley
VP: Elaine Dunn
VP: Frank Mencini
VP: Gregory J Rassier
VP: Donna Allen Reddy
VP: Steve Warner
Dir Bus: Shirley Barton
Dir Bus: Victor Zediker

D-U-N-S 12-986-2954
NATIONAL HEALTHCARE STAFFING LLC
5901 Broken Sound Pkwy Nw, Boca Raton, FL 33487-2773
Tel (561) 420-4100 *Founded/Ownrshp* 2004
Sales 10.0MM^E *EMP* 425
SIC 7361 Employment agencies; Employment agencies
Pr: Peter E Kilissaniy
**CFO:* Aldo Rodriguez
Ex VP: Odalys Font
Ex VP: Robert Santana

D-U-N-S 02-524-2223
NATIONAL HEAT & POWER CORP (IL)
GOODMAN PLUMBING
6340 Oakton St, Morton Grove, IL 60053-2723
Tel (847) 965-3900 *Founded/Ownrshp* 1979
Sales 24.7MM^E *EMP* 110
SIC 1711 Plumbing contractors; Warm air heating & air conditioning contractor; Plumbing contractors; Warm air heating & air conditioning contractor
CEO: Harold Hurvitz
**Pr:* Bruce L Hurvitz
**Treas:* Michael L Russ
VP: Brad Borchers
**VP:* Michael S Hurvitz
Trfc Dir: Karen Monti

D-U-N-S 96-074-2484
NATIONAL HERITAGE ACADEMIES INC
N H A
3850 Broadmoor Ave Se # 201, Grand Rapids, MI 49512-3975
Tel (877) 223-6402 *Founded/Ownrshp* 1995
Sales 283.5MM^E *EMP* 4,500
SIC 8211 8741 Private elementary & secondary schools; Management services; Private elementary & secondary schools; Management services
Ch Bd: J C Huizenga
Pr: Robert J Bellafiore
**Pr:* Harry Hurlburt III
**CFO:* Stephen Conley
VP: Mark Dehaan
VP: Aric Dersham
VP: Nick Paradiso
Dir IT: Susan Mills
Dir IT: Jeff Reinke

D-U-N-S 92-842-0090
■ NATIONAL HIGHWAY TRAFFIC SAFETY ADMINISTRATION
NHTSA
(*Suby of* US DEPARTMENT OF TRANSPORTATION) ★
1200 New Jersey Ave Se # 5, Washington, DC 20590-0001
Tel (202) 366-9561 *Founded/Ownrshp* 1970
Sales NA *EMP* 665
SIC 9621 Regulation, administration of transportation; ; Regulation, administration of transportation;
Ofcr: Richard Compton
Prgrm Mgr: Dwight Lockwood
Rgnl Mgr: Shannon Purdy
Netwrk Mgr: Sandy Washington
Doctor: Steve Bloomfield
Pgrm Dir: Gina Beretta
Snr Mgr: John Brophy
Snr Mgr: Maria Vegega

D-U-N-S 79-915-6943
NATIONAL HME INC
7451 Airport Fwy, Richland Hills, TX 76118-6955
Tel (817) 332-4433 *Founded/Ownrshp* 2006
Sales 37.0MM^E *EMP* 357
SIC 8082 Home health care services; Home health care services
CEO: William Monast
**CEO:* George Robertson
COO: Michael McAdams
**CFO:* Michael Miller
Bd of Dir: Alan Dahl
**VP:* Clay Ingram
**VP:* Joshua T Robertson
Dir Bus: David Clapp
CTO: Raymond Kimbrell
Opers Mgr: Lisa Rojas
Opers Mgr: Anthony Ross

D-U-N-S 17-655-3402
▲ NATIONAL HOLDINGS CORP
410 Park Ave Fl 14, New York, NY 10022-9442
Tel (212) 417-8000 *Founded/Ownrshp* 1947
Sales 184.2MM *EMP* 352^E
Accts Eisneramper Llp New York New
Tkr Sym NHLD *Exch* NAS
SIC 6211 6282 Investment bankers; Brokers, security; Investment advisory service; Investment bankers; Brokers, security; Investment advisory service
Ch Bd: Robert B Fagenson
**Pr:* Mark Goldwasser
CFO: Alan B Levin
Ex VP: Glenn C Worman
VP: Andrei Amaritei
VP: David Cohen
Board of Directors: Richard Abbe, James Ciocia, Salvatore Giardina, William Lerner, Frank S Plimpton, Frederic B Powers III, Joshua Silverman, Frederick Wasserman

D-U-N-S 06-860-4545
NATIONAL HOME DELIVERY INC
USSPI
(*Suby of* USSPI MEDIA, INC.)
428 E State Pkwy Ste 226, Schaumburg, IL 60173-6408
Tel (847) 490-6000 *Founded/Ownrshp* 1996
Sales 27.0MM^E *EMP* 17
SIC 7311 Advertising consultant; Advertising consultant
CEO: Phillip Miller
**Pr:* Frank O' Connell

D-U-N-S 11-543-5935
NATIONAL HOME HEALTH CARE CORP
(*Suby of* A G HOME HEALTH LLC)
700 White Plains Rd Ste 2, Scarsdale, NY 10583-5013
Tel (914) 722-9000 *Founded/Ownrshp* 2007
Sales 79.7MM^E *EMP* 3,680
SIC 8082 7361 Home health care services; Employment agencies; Home health care services; Employment agencies
Pr: Steven Fialkow
**CFO:* Robert P Heller
Bd of Dir: Harold Shulman
CTO: Jason Pickman
Dir IT: Heather Massaro

NATIONAL HOSE & ACCESSORY
See NATIONAL HOSE AQUISITION CORP

D-U-N-S 07-857-3955 IMP
NATIONAL HOSE AQUISITION CORP
NATIONAL HOSE & ACCESSORY
(*Suby of* HAMPTON RUBBER CO) ★
1831 Richey St, Pasadena, TX 77502-1710
Tel (713) 920-2030 *Founded/Ownrshp* 1985
Sales 30.1MM^E *EMP* 66
SIC 3069 3541 3449 Reclaimed rubber (reworked by manufacturing processes); Machine tools, metal cutting: exotic (explosive, etc.); Miscellaneous metalwork
CEO: Don Fritzinger
Genl Mgr: Tom Degraffenried
Opers Mgr: David Sharp
Sales Asso: Susan Anderson
Sales Asso: David Morris

D-U-N-S 01-888-9062
NATIONAL HOSPICE HOLDINGS LLC
200 Dryden Rd E Ste 3300, Dresher, PA 19025-1052
Tel (267) 781-7276 *Founded/Ownrshp* 2009
Sales 8.3MM^E *EMP* 481^E
SIC 8051 Skilled nursing care facilities; Skilled nursing care facilities
CEO: David Glick
CFO: Marc Rose

D-U-N-S 07-412-2078
NATIONAL HOT ROD ASSOCIATION
NHRA
2035 E Financial Way, Glendora, CA 91741-4602
Tel (626) 914-4761 *Founded/Ownrshp* 1951
Sales 99.2MM *EMP* 220
Accts Moss Adams Llp Stockton Ca
SIC 7948 2711 2741 Automotive race track operation; Newspapers: publishing only, not printed on site; Miscellaneous publishing; Automotive race track operation; Newspapers: publishing only, not printed on site; Miscellaneous publishing
V Ch: Harvey Palash
Pr: Tom Compton
CFO: Peter Clifford
Treas: Kurt Wolfe
Ofcr: Craig Larson
Sr VP: Gary Darcy
Sr VP: Graham Light
VP: Glen Gray
VP: Wayne McMurtry
VP: Brian Tracy
Web Dev: Julieanne Gee

NATIONAL HOT WATER
See NATIONAL WHOLESALE SUPPLY INC

D-U-N-S 05-040-4128
NATIONAL HOUSING CORP
45 N 4th St Ste 200, Columbus, OH 43215-3602
Tel (614) 481-8106 *Founded/Ownrshp* 1963
Sales 74.0MM^E *EMP* 300
SIC 1522 1542 6513 Apartment building construction; Commercial & office building, new construction; Apartment building operators; Apartment building construction; Commercial & office building, new construction; Apartment building operators
Pr: H Burkley Showe
**Treas:* David M Showe
**VP:* Andrew Showe
**VP:* Hugh B Showe II
**VP:* Kevin M Showe
**Prin:* Showe Builders
**Prin:* Betty Hays

D-U-N-S 79-111-9142
NATIONAL HVAC SERVICE LTD
Stonewood Cms Ste 340, Wexford, PA 15090
Tel (724) 935-9390 *Founded/Ownrshp* 1991
Sales 33.3MM^E *EMP* 150
SIC 1711 Plumbing, heating, air-conditioning contractors; Ventilation & duct work contractor; Plumbing, heating, air-conditioning contractors; Ventilation & duct work contractor
Pt: Jay W Noel
Genl Mgr: John Harrison

D-U-N-S 14-367-8006
NATIONAL I A M BENEFIT TRUST FUND
1300 Conn Ave Nw Ste 300, Washington, DC 20036-1707
Tel (202) 785-8148 *Founded/Ownrshp* 2005
Sales NA *EMP* 11
Accts Salter & Company Llc Bethesda
SIC 6371 Pension, health & welfare funds; Pension, health & welfare funds
Admn Mgr: Steve Lostoski

D-U-N-S 93-221-0727
■ NATIONAL IMAGING ASSOCIATES INC
NIA MAGELLAN
(*Suby of* MAGELLAN HEALTH INC) ★
433 Hackensack Ave Fl 6, Hackensack, NJ 07601-6313
Tel (201) 530-3200 *Founded/Ownrshp* 2006
Sales 13.1MM^E *EMP* 400
Accts Deloitte Touche Ny Ny
SIC 8741 8099 Management services; Management services; Eye banks
Pr: John Donahue
**Pr:* Frank Apgar
**Pr:* Ray Pingle
**CFO:* Robert Lagalia
**Chf Mktg O:* Dr Thomas G Dehn
**Sr VP:* Jamie Burns

D-U-N-S 61-126-5984
■ NATIONAL IMPRINT CORP
(*Suby of* PRINTEGRA CORP) ★
William Ward Indus Park, Claysburg, PA 16625
Tel (814) 239-8141 *Founded/Ownrshp* 2005
Sales 73.9MM^E *EMP* 800
SIC 2677 2678 2679 Envelopes; Stationery: made from purchased materials; Memorandum books, except printed: purchased materials; Labels, paper: made from purchased material; Envelopes; Stationery: made from purchased materials; Memorandum books, except printed: purchased materials; Labels, paper: made from purchased material
Pr: Casey T Campbell

D-U-N-S 00-697-0354
■ NATIONAL INDEMNITY CO (INC) (NE)
(*Suby of* BERKSHIRE HATHAWAY INC) ★
1314 Douglas St Ste 1400, Omaha, NE 68102-1944
Tel (402) 916-3000 *Founded/Ownrshp* 1940, 1967
Sales NA *EMP* 650
SIC 6331 6411 6311 Fire, marine & casualty insurance: stock; Insurance agents, brokers & service; Property & casualty insurance agent; Insurance claim processing, except medical; Life insurance; Fire, marine & casualty insurance: stock; Insurance agents, brokers & service; Property & casualty insurance agent; Insurance claim processing, except medical; Life insurance
Ch Bd: Marc Hamberg
**Pr:* Donald F Wurster
**V Ch Bd:* Michael A Goldberg
Sr VP: Philip Wolf
VP: Les Baller
VP: Lori Cleary
VP: Tracy Gulden
VP: Timaree McKillip
VP: Ty Reil
VP: Tom Young
Exec: Rainwater Karen

D-U-N-S 03-203-9724 IMP
NATIONAL INDUSTRIAL CONCEPTS INC
NIC GLOBAL
23518 63rd Ave Se, Woodinville, WA 98072-8664
Tel (425) 483-6370 *Founded/Ownrshp* 2000
Sales 93.1MM^E *EMP* 350
SIC 3444 Sheet metalwork; Sheet metalwork
Pr: Bridget Brewer
**Treas:* William King
**VP:* Michael Ryan
**VP:* Troy Wood
Dir IT: Tom Bailey
Prd Mgr: Bob Liebhart

D-U-N-S 00-893-9902
NATIONAL INDUSTRIAL LUMBER CO
ERIE LUMBER CO DIVISION
1221 W Maple St, Hartville, OH 44632-8511
Tel (412) 384-3900 *Founded/Ownrshp* 1936
Sales 100.8MM^E *EMP* 134
SIC 5031 Lumber: rough, dressed & finished; Building materials, exterior; Lumber: rough, dressed & finished; Building materials, exterior
CEO: Michael Hoag
**Pr:* Jim Smith
**Ch:* William R Hoag
**VP:* Richard D Hoag
Sales Asso: David Daugherty
Sales Asso: Deb Heineman
Sales Asso: Chris Hogan

D-U-N-S 00-167-2120
NATIONAL INDUSTRIES FOR BLIND (NY)
ABILITYONE.COM
1310 Braddock Pl, Alexandria, VA 22314-1691
Tel (703) 310-0500 *Founded/Ownrshp* 1938
Sales 34.2MM *EMP* 160
Accts Gelman Rosenberg & Freedman B

SIC 8331 3991 2392 Vocational rehabilitation agency; Brooms & brushes; Household furnishings; Vocational rehabilitation agency; Brooms & brushes; Household furnishings
Pr: Kevin Lynch
*CFO: Steven Brice
Prgrm Mgr: Sally Didonato
Prgrm Mgr: Rhonda Woodbridge
Telecom Ex: Bernard Wawrzeniak
Dir IT: Jim Gallamo
Natl Sales: Ray Sullivan
Natl Sales: Edward Talbert
Genl Couns: Heather Lyons
Board of Directors: Reinhard Mabry

D-U-N-S 05-545-8350
NATIONAL INFORMATION SOLUTIONS COOPERATIVE INC
NISC
1 Innovation Cir, Lake Saint Louis, MO 63367-2649
Tel (636) 755-2300 Founded/Ownrshp 2000
Sales 150.0MM EMP 850
SIC 7374 Data processing service; Data processing service
Pr: Vern Dosch
*CFO: Tracy Porter
*VP: Todd Eisenhauer
VP: Kari Reichert
*VP: Doug Remboldt
*VP: Dan Wilbanks
*VP: Ed Wolff
Off Mgr: Jackie Rocha
Snr Sftwr: Frank Barnhart
Snr Sftwr: Robert Carey
Snr Sftwr: Debbie Havermann

D-U-N-S 60-993-5965
NATIONAL INSPECTION SERVICES LLC
110 Harold Gauthe Rd, Scott, LA 70583-5284
Tel (337) 233-2121 Founded/Ownrshp 2004
Sales 27.2MM EMP 206E
Accts Broussard Poche Lewis & Brea
SIC 8734 X-ray inspection service, industrial; X-ray inspection service, industrial
VP: Ed Manuel

D-U-N-S 11-405-4443
NATIONAL INSTITUTE OF AEROSPACE ASSOCIATES
100 Exploration Way # 210, Hampton, VA 23666-6266
Tel (757) 325-6700 Founded/Ownrshp 2002
Sales 27.3MM EMP 98
SIC 8249 8733 Aviation school; Physical research, noncommercial; Aviation school; Physical research, noncommercial
Pr: Robert E Lindberg
*CFO: Kerry Christian
*VP: Karl Drews
*VP: Bernard Grossman
*VP: Calvin Lowe
VP: Bo Walkley
Exec: Cathy Hopkins
Dir IT: Wendy Murray

D-U-N-S 92-933-2385
■ NATIONAL INSTITUTE OF FOOD AND AGRICULTURE
NIFA
(Suby of U S D A) ★
1400 Independence Ave Sw, Washington, DC 20250-0002
Tel (202) 720-4276 Founded/Ownrshp 1914
Sales NA EMP 5,839E
SIC 9641 Regulation of agricultural marketing;

D-U-N-S 80-163-0633
■ NATIONAL INSTITUTE OF MENTAL HEALTH
NIMH
(Suby of N I H) ★
6001 Executive Blvd, Bethesda, MD 20892-0001
Tel (301) 443-4513 Founded/Ownrshp 1992
Sales NA EMP 677E
SIC 9431 Administration of public health programs;
COO: Walter Jones Jr
Sftwr Eng: Walid Benmohamed
Snr Mgr: Kevin Conway
Snr Mgr: Eve Reider

D-U-N-S 92-995-6050
■ NATIONAL INSTITUTE OF STANDARDS & TECHNOLOGY
(Suby of UNITED STATES DEPARTMENT OF COMMERCE) ★
100 Bureau Dr Stop 1070, Gaithersburg, MD 20899-0003
Tel (301) 975-6478 Founded/Ownrshp 1901
Sales NA EMP 3,000
SIC 9611 Administration of general economic programs; ; Administration of general economic programs;
CFO: George Jenkins
Assoc Dir: Mary H Saunders
Assoc Dir: Phillip Singerman
Admn Mgr: Herb Jones
CIO: Daniel Benigni
CIO: Thomas Chung
CIO: Charles L Eater
CIO: Michele Montgomery
CIO: Simon Szykman
DP Exec: Larry Buck
Dir IT: Seymour Weiss

D-U-N-S 92-764-5168
■ NATIONAL INSTITUTES OF HEALTH
N I H
(Suby of UNITED STATES DEPARTMENT OF HEALTH & HUMAN SERVICES) ★
9000 Rockville Pike # 1, Bethesda, MD 20892-0001
Tel (301) 496-4000 Founded/Ownrshp 1954
Sales NA EMP 19,000
SIC 9431 Administration of public health programs; ; Administration of public health programs;
Pr: David Lisle
Ofcr: Marsha Hennings
Exec: Valery Gheen
Assoc Dir: Mark Chavez
Assoc Dir: Jason Paragas
Adm Dir: Virginia Betson
Adm Dir: Darlene Blocker
Adm Dir: Mitzi Diley
Adm Dir: Lisa Freeny
Adm Dir: Kathleen Grillo
Adm Dir: Penny Kisner

D-U-N-S 07-048-7657
▲ NATIONAL INSTRUMENTS CORP
11500 N Mopac Expy, Austin, TX 78759-3563
Tel (512) 338-9119 Founded/Ownrshp 1976
Sales 1.2MMM EMP 7,094
Accts Ernst & Young Llp Austin Tex
Tkr Sym NATI Exch NGS
SIC 7372 Prepackaged software; Application computer software; Prepackaged software; Application computer software
Ch Bd: James J Truchard
COO: Craig Claassen
COO: Alexander M Davern
CFO: Chris Mutschler
Treas: Alexander M Davem
Ex VP: Eric H Starkloff
Sr VP: Francis Griffiths
Sr VP: Scott A Rust
Exec: Scott Christman
Exec: Christie Kurtz
Area Mgr: C K Chung
Board of Directors: John M Berra, Donald M Carlton, Jeffrey L Kodosky, Michael E McGrath, Charles J Roesslein

D-U-N-S 62-615-1935
NATIONAL INSULATION CONTRACTORS EXCHANGE LLC
1890 S 14th St Ste 212, Fernandina Beach, FL 32034-4730
Tel (904) 491-3112 Founded/Ownrshp 2004
Sales 40.0MM EMP 3
SIC 8631 Employees' association; Employees' association

D-U-N-S 03-703-6340 IMP
NATIONAL INSURANCE CRIME BUREAU INC
NICB
1111 E Touhy Ave Ste 400, Des Plaines, IL 60018-5804
Tel (847) 544-7000 Founded/Ownrshp 1991
Sales 49.6MM EMP 349
Accts Grant Thornton Llp Chicago
SIC 8611 Business associations; Business associations
Pr: Joseph H Wehrle Jr
*COO: James K Schweitzer
*CFO: Robert Jachnicki
*Chf Cred: Roger Morris
Sr VP: Daniel Abbott
*Sr VP: Andrew Sosnowski
*VP: Daniel Abbot
*VP: Judith Fitzgerald
*VP: Barbarar Low
*VP: Brian Smidt
*VP: Tom Welsh

D-U-N-S 96-233-3071
NATIONAL INSURANCE PRODUCER REGISTRY
1100 Walnut St Ste 1500, Kansas City, MO 64106-2277
Tel (816) 783-8038 Founded/Ownrshp 2010
Sales 25.1MM EMP 3
Accts Mcgladrey Llp Kansas City Mo
SIC 7361 Registries; Registries
Prin: Amy Ward
Tech Mgr: Thomas Bergin

D-U-N-S 04-120-6863
NATIONAL INTEGRATED INDUSTRIES INC
AMERICAN ELECTRO PRODUCTS
322 Main St, Farmington, CT 06032-2961
Tel (860) 677-7995 Founded/Ownrshp 1950
Sales 49.6MME EMP 135
SIC 3471 3312 Electroplating & plating; Electroplating of metals or formed products; Plating of metals or formed products; Tool & die steel & alloys
Pr: Dennis M Burke

NATIONAL INTERAD
See COBALT GROUP INC

D-U-N-S 96-363-1853
■ NATIONAL INTEREST ADVANCED SOLUTIONS LLC
(Suby of IBM) ★
83 Upper Complex Rd, Keyser, WV 26726-6687
Tel (304) 726-4809 Founded/Ownrshp 2010
Sales 23.6MME EMP 975
SIC 7379 Computer related consulting services; Computer related consulting services

D-U-N-S 01-369-5486
NATIONAL INTEREST SECURITY CO LLC
83 Upper Complex Rd, Keyser, WV 26726-6687
Tel (304) 726-4809 Founded/Ownrshp 2010
Sales NA EMP 450
SIC 7375 7374

D-U-N-S 62-607-6707
■ NATIONAL INTERSTATE CORP
(Suby of GREAT AMERICAN INSURANCE CO) ★
3250 Interstate Dr, Richfield, OH 44286-9000
Tel (330) 659-8900 Founded/Ownrshp 1989
Sales NA EMP 641E
Tkr Sym NATL Exch NGS
SIC 6331 6411 Fire, marine & casualty insurance; Property & casualty insurance agent; Fire, marine & casualty insurance; Property & casualty insurance agent
Pr: David W Michelson
*Ch Bd: Joseph E Consolino
Pr: Anthony J Mercurio
CFO: Julie A McGraw
Sr VP: Arthur J Gonzales
Sr VP: Terry E Phillips
VP: Gary N Monda
VP: Brad Scofield
Prgrm Mgr: Tim Ley
Off Mgr: Daniel Keenan
Mktg Mgr: Mike Bissler
Board of Directors: Ronald J Brichler, I John Cholnoky, Patrick J Denzer, Gary J Gruber, Keith A Jensen, Donald D Larson, Donald W Schwegman, Alan R Spachman, Michael A Spachman

D-U-N-S 36-462-4205
■ NATIONAL INTERSTATE INSURANCE CO
(Suby of NATIONAL INTERSTATE CORP) ★
3250 Interstate Dr, Richfield, OH 44286-9000
Tel (330) 659-8900 Founded/Ownrshp 1989
Sales NA EMP 310
Accts Ernst & Young Llp Cleveland
SIC 6331 Fire, marine & casualty insurance; Fire, marine & casualty insurance
Ch: Alan R Spachman
*Pr: David W Michelson
*Treas: Arthur M Kraus
VP: Arthur Gonzales
Genl Mgr: Keith Boyle
Dir IT: Ron Steiger
Corp Couns: Thomas King
Snr Mgr: Lauren Fronczek

NATIONAL INVENTORS HALL OF FAM
See INVENT NOW INC

D-U-N-S 07-986-5663
NATIONAL JETS INC
NATIONAL AIR AMBULANCE
(Suby of CAROLINA AIRCRAFT CORP) ★
3495 Sw 9th Ave, Fort Lauderdale, FL 33315-3401
Tel (954) 359-9400 Founded/Ownrshp 2002
Sales 21.6MME EMP 98
SIC 4522 4581 5172 Flying charter service; Ambulance services, air; Aircraft servicing & repairing; Aircraft fueling services
Pr: Sam Robbin
CFO: Shiryl Schnieder
*Sec: Wendy Robbin
VP: Mark Binko
*VP: T Russell Boy
Opers Mgr: Russell Boy Jr

D-U-N-S 61-588-1448 IMP
NATIONAL JEWELRY & PAWN INC
FRIENDLY JEWELRY AND PAWN
2334 Guess Rd Ste 2, Durham, NC 27705-3582
Tel (919) 286-3333 Founded/Ownrshp 1987
Sales 23.8MME EMP 31
SIC 5932 5944 5094 Pawnshop; Jewelry stores; Jewelry & precious stones; Pawnshop; Jewelry stores; Jewelry & precious stones
Pr: Robert Moulton
*Sec: Teresa T Moulton

D-U-N-S 07-644-3019
NATIONAL JEWISH HEALTH
1400 Jackson St, Denver, CO 80206-2762
Tel (303) 388-4461 Founded/Ownrshp 2005
Sales 225.7MM EMP 1,500E
SIC 8069

NATIONAL JEWISH SPORTS HALL OF
See SUFFOLKY JEWISH COMMUNITY CENTER INC

D-U-N-S 07-265-1326
NATIONAL JOINT APPRENTICESHIP & TRAINING COMMITTEE FOR ELECTRICAL INDUSTRY (INC)
NJATC
5001 Howerton Way Ste A, Bowie, MD 20715-4459
Tel (301) 249-2042 Founded/Ownrshp 1941
Sales 22.7MM EMP 92E
Accts Calibre Cpa Group Pllc Bethes
SIC 8299 Educational services
Ex Dir: Michael Callanan

D-U-N-S 07-100-4980
NATIONAL KIDNEY FOUNDATION INC
30 E 33rd St Fl 3, New York, NY 10016-5337
Tel (212) 889-2210 Founded/Ownrshp 1950
Sales 39.6MM EMP 200
Accts Bdo Usa Llp New York Ny
SIC 8733 Medical research; Medical research
CEO: Richard Kevin Longino
*CFO: Petros Gregoriou
*Chf Mktg O: Joseph Vassalotti MD
Comm Man: Lindsey Kellman
Mng Dir: Mable Barringer
*Dir Sec: Kerry Willis
Prgrm Mgr: Sharai Gaillard
Prgrm Mgr: Karen Meyer
Mktg Dir: Bryan Williams

NATIONAL KNIFE AND SUPPLY
See NATIONAL KWIKMETAL SERVICE LP

D-U-N-S 62-026-1990 IMP
NATIONAL KWIKMETAL SERVICE LP
NATIONAL KNIFE AND SUPPLY
560 Santa Rosa Dr, Des Plaines, IL 60018-2602
Tel (847) 257-6570 Founded/Ownrshp 1989
Sales 38.5MME EMP 45
SIC 5051 Iron or steel flat products
Pt: Stephen Wolff
*CFO: Glenn Rolbiecki
*VP: Vincent Cmelo
*Genl Mgr: Todd Kennedy
Off Mgr: Lisa Graham
Sls Mgr: Vince Cmelo

D-U-N-S 00-228-3547 IMP
NATIONAL LABEL CO
2025 Joshua Rd, Lafayette Hill, PA 19444-2426
Tel (610) 825-3250 Founded/Ownrshp 1914
Sales 179.3MME EMP 285
SIC 2672 2679 2759 2671 Labels (unprinted), gummed: made from purchased materials; Tape, pressure sensitive: made from purchased materials; Paper products, converted; Commercial printing; Packaging paper & plastics film, coated & laminated; Labels (unprinted), gummed: made from purchased materials; Tape, pressure sensitive: made from purchased materials; Paper products, converted; Commercial printing; Packaging paper & plastics film, coated & laminated
CEO: James H Shacklett III
*COO: Dean R Shacklett

D-U-N-S 16-925-2520
NATIONAL LABOR CONTRACTORS INC
NATIONAL CNSTR WORKFORCE
2500 E 46th St, Indianapolis, IN 46205-2427
Tel (317) 334-1222 Founded/Ownrshp 1999
Sales 21.4MME EMP 225
SIC 7361 7363 Labor contractors (employment agency); Help supply services; Labor contractors (employment agency); Help supply services
Pr: Steve Wise
*VP: David Label
Dir Bus: Ashley Kutch

D-U-N-S 00-325-6633
■ NATIONAL LABOR RELATIONS BOARD
(Suby of EXECUTIVE OFFICE OF UNITED STATES GOVERNMENT) ★
1015 Half St Se, Washington, DC 20003-3320
Tel (202) 273-3884 Founded/Ownrshp 1935
Sales NA EMP 1,800
SIC 9651 Labor-management negotiations board, government; ; Labor-management negotiations board, government;
Ch: Mark Gaston Pierce
Ofcr: Jacqueline Jones
Ex VP: Ethan Ray
Admn Mgr: Annette Burrelaao
Sales Exec: Sydney Lee
Pr Dir: Gregory King
Counsel: David Schwartz

D-U-N-S 05-054-0538
NATIONAL LAND PARTNERS LLC
665 Simonds Rd, Williamstown, MA 01267-2105
Tel (413) 458-2172 Founded/Ownrshp 1999
Sales 25.2MME EMP 180
SIC 6552 Land subdividers & developers, residential
VP: Brian Patten

D-U-N-S 00-788-6572
NATIONAL LEISURE GROUP INC
(Suby of CRUISES ONLY) ★
100 Sylvan Rd Ste 750, Woburn, MA 01801-1839
Tel (617) 587-6000 Founded/Ownrshp 2010
Sales 45.0MME EMP 542E
SIC 4724 Travel agencies
Prin: Sobol Ethan
Sr VP: Jamie Cash
VP: Dave Crooks

D-U-N-S 05-783-0879
■ NATIONAL LIABILITY & FIRE INSURANCE CO
(Suby of BERKSHIRE HATHAWAY INC) ★
3024 Harney St, Omaha, NE 68131-3535
Tel (402) 536-3000 Founded/Ownrshp 1958
Sales NA EMP 30
SIC 6411 Insurance agents, brokers & service; Insurance agents, brokers & service
Pr: Donald F Wurster
*Treas: Dale Geistkemper
*VP: Leslie J Baller
*VP: J Michael Gottschalk
*VP: Forrest N Krutter
*VP: Philip M Wolf
Board of Directors: Warren E Buffett, Michael A Goldberg, Ajit Jain, Barry L Kroll, Forrest N Krutter, Charles B Montgomery, Robert D O'connell, Lloyd E Williams Jr, Donald F Wurster

NATIONAL LIBRARY OF MEDICINE
See NIH/NLM/LO/PSD/CAS

NATIONAL LIFE GROUP
See NATIONAL LIFE HOLDING CO

D-U-N-S 17-641-0939
NATIONAL LIFE HOLDING CO
NATIONAL LIFE GROUP
1 National Life Dr, Montpelier, VT 05604-1000
Tel (802) 229-3333 Founded/Ownrshp 1998
Sales NA EMP 850
SIC 6311 6321 Mutual association life insurance; Accident insurance carriers; Health insurance carriers; Mutual association life insurance; Accident insurance carriers; Health insurance carriers
CEO: Mehran Assadi
*Ch Bd: Thomas H Mac Leay
Pr: Chris Graff
Pr: Christina Johnson
CFO: Robert Cotton
*Treas: Donald P Messier
Chf Inves: Thomas Brownell
Ofcr: Russell Morgan
*Sr VP: Tom Anfuso
Sr VP: Pamela Blalock
Sr VP: Rich Pedersen
Sr VP: Ruth Smith
VP: Jed Brody
VP: Jim Carroll
VP: Graff Chris
VP: Mike Dellipriscoli
VP: Matthew Desantos
VP: Mike Duncan
VP: Stephen Farr
VP: David Gilmore
VP: Michelle Jones

D-U-N-S 00-793-9572
NATIONAL LIFE INSURANCE CO (VT)
NATIONAL LIFE OF VERMONT
(Suby of NATIONAL LIFE GROUP) ★
1 National Life Dr, Montpelier, VT 05604-0001
Tel (802) 229-3333 Founded/Ownrshp 1850, 1999
Sales NA EMP 850

SIC 6411 6321 Insurance agents, brokers & service; Health insurance carriers; Accident insurance carriers; Insurance agents, brokers & service; Health insurance carriers; Accident insurance carriers
Pr: Mehran Assadi
**Ch Bd:* Thomas H Macleay
**CFO:* Edward Bonach
**Treas:* Robert Cotton
**Treas:* Mary Eileen Vongal
Ofcr: Mary M Lee
**Ex VP:* Wade Mayo
**Ex VP:* Ruth B Smith
**Ex VP:* Christian Thwaites
**Sr VP:* Thomas H Brownell
**Sr VP:* Allen N Hanson
**Sr VP:* Richard Pederson
**Sr VP:* Gregory D Woodworth
VP: Jim Carroll
VP: Michael Crawford
VP: Maryann Ellis
**VP:* Frank A Hacker
VP: David Longfritz
VP: Heather Lyon
VP: Brian E McGonegal
VP: Robert Mullett

NATIONAL LIFE OF VERMONT
See NATIONAL LIFE INSURANCE CO

D-U-N-S 02-547-7837 IMP
NATIONAL LIFT TRUCK INC (IL)
NATIONAL SPECIALISED HAULING
3333 Mount Prospect Rd, Franklin Park, IL 60131-1337
Tel (630) 782-1000 *Founded/Ownrshp* 1977
Sales 24.6MM^E *EMP* 100^E
SIC 7359 5084 4731 Industrial truck rental; Lift trucks & parts; Brokers, shipping; Industrial truck rental; Lift trucks & parts; Brokers, shipping
Pr: Perry D Du Bose
**VP:* Jeffrey P Dubose
Genl Mgr: Jim Dietz
Genl Mgr: Tom Smith
IT Man: Christine Charbonneau
Sls Mgr: Bruce Deford
Sls Mgr: Carl Smith

D-U-N-S 82-944-4843 EXP
NATIONAL LIFT TRUCK SERVICE INC
2110 N Andrews Ave, Pompano Beach, FL 33069-1417
Tel (954) 462-6500 *Founded/Ownrshp* 1975
Sales 42.7MM^E *EMP* 100
SIC 5084 Trucks, industrial; Trucks, industrial
Pr: Robert Siano
Sls Mgr: Jorge Sanchez

D-U-N-S 00-503-8336
NATIONAL LIME AND STONE CO
551 Lake Cascade Pkwy, Findlay, OH 45840-1388
Tel (419) 422-4341 *Founded/Ownrshp* 1903
Sales 6.2MMM^E *EMP* 320
SIC 1422 1442 3273 1423 1499

NATIONAL LIQUID BLASTING
See NLB CORP

D-U-N-S 79-138-2836
■ **NATIONAL LLOYDS INSURANCE CO**
(*Suby of* HILLTOP HOLDINGS INC) ★
510 N Vly Mills Dr # 202, Waco, TX 76710-6075
Tel (254) 399-0626 *Founded/Ownrshp* 2007
Sales NA *EMP* 48^E
SIC 6331 Fire, marine & casualty insurance; Property damage insurance
CEO: Robert Otis
**Ch Bd:* C Clifton Robinson
**VP:* Paul Boswell
**VP:* Murali Chidurala
**VP:* Carl Kirk
Exec: Nancy Hollinger
**VP Mktg:* Mitchell Jawitz

D-U-N-S 07-761-6399
■ **NATIONAL LLOYDS INSURANCE CO INC**
(*Suby of* NATIONAL LLOYDS INSURANCE CO) ★
510 N Valley Mills Dr # 202, Waco, TX 76710-6075
Tel (254) 756-5531 *Founded/Ownrshp* 2000
Sales NA *EMP* 118
SIC 6331 Fire, marine & casualty insurance
Ch Bd: C Clifton Robinson
**Pr:* Gregory Duane Vanek
**CFO:* Bill Stanton
Treas: Darren Parmenter

D-U-N-S 06-848-8626
NATIONAL LOUIS UNIVERSITY
122 S Michigan Ave # 600, Chicago, IL 60603-6162
Tel (312) 261-3599 *Founded/Ownrshp* 1886
Sales 69.0MM *EMP* 2,300
SIC 8221 8211

D-U-N-S 62-521-4804 IMP/EXP
NATIONAL LUMBER AND HARDWARE CORP
Ave Campo Rico Edf Koda S, Carolina, PR 00982
Tel (787) 641-8200 *Founded/Ownrshp* 1991
Sales NA *EMP* 721
SIC 5211 5251

D-U-N-S 00-257-7732 IMP
NATIONAL LUMBER CO (MA)
DO IT BEST
245 Oakland St, Mansfield, MA 02048-1554
Tel (508) 337-8020 *Founded/Ownrshp* 1934, 1955
Sales 138.4MM^E *EMP* 400
SIC 5211 2431 Millwork & lumber; Insulation material, building; Siding; Roofing material; Millwork; Millwork & lumber; Insulation material, building; Siding; Roofing material; Millwork
CEO: Marjorie Kaitz
**CEO:* Steven Kaitz
**CFO:* Louis Kaitz
VP: Kaplan Elliot
**VP:* John Intravaia
**VP:* Michael McDole
**VP:* Marc Osborne Mr
VP: Mike Murphy
**VP:* David M Pelletier
Exec: Lynne Goodrich
CIO: Mark Osborn

D-U-N-S 07-780-2056
NATIONAL LUTHERAN HOME FOR AGED INC
9701 Veirs Dr, Rockville, MD 20850-3414
Tel (301) 424-9560 *Founded/Ownrshp* 1890
Sales 23.2MM *EMP* 280
SIC 8051

D-U-N-S 04-811-2213 IMP
NATIONAL MACHINE CO
NMG AEROSPACE
4880 Hudson Dr, Stow, OH 44224-1799
Tel (330) 688-6494 *Founded/Ownrshp* 1967
Sales NA *EMP* 400
Accts Bober Markey Fedorovich Co
SIC 3599 3492 Machine shop, jobbing & repair; Control valves, fluid power: hydraulic & pneumatic; Machine shop, jobbing & repair; Control valves, fluid power: hydraulic & pneumatic
Ch: Peter Piglia
**Pr:* Bill Anop
**CEO:* Michael Piglia
CFO: Jeff Bissell
**CFO:* Jeffrey Bissell
Dir Bus: Jeremy Earley
Dir IT: Darren Dunn
IT Man: Michael Binder
IT Man: Glen Pennington
Sfty Mgr: Jenni Ticer
Plnt Mgr: David Kubala

D-U-N-S 14-621-4692
NATIONAL MACHINERY & CONVEYOR INC
NMC
3225 S Torrence St, Marion, IN 46953-3930
Tel (765) 662-1934 *Founded/Ownrshp* 2003
Sales 24.6MM *EMP* 40
Accts Dulin Ward & Dewald Inc Ma
SIC 1791 1796 Structural steel erection; Millwright; Structural steel erection; Millwright
Pr: Joshua M Clifton
**VP:* Mike Spencer

D-U-N-S 04-103-5788 IMP/EXP
NATIONAL MACHINERY LLC
(*Suby of* NM GROUP GLOBAL LLC) ★
161 Greenfield St, Tiffin, OH 44883-2471
Tel (419) 447-5211 *Founded/Ownrshp* 2002
Sales 86.2MM^E *EMP* 386
SIC 3542 Headers; High energy rate metal forming machines; Mechanical (pneumatic or hydraulic) metal forming machines; Headers; High energy rate metal forming machines; Mechanical (pneumatic or hydraulic) metal forming machines
COO: John Bolte
Sr VP: Tom Hay
Dist Mgr: Brad Hawkins
Dist Mgr: Doug Schubert
IT Man: Glenn Burgderfer
QC Dir: Robert Loy
Prd Mgr: Dan Frank
Mktg Mgr: Jerry Bupp
Snr Mgr: Robert Foster

D-U-N-S 00-214-2560 IMP
NATIONAL MAGNETICS GROUP INC (PA)
MAGNETICSGROUP
1210 Win Dr, Bethlehem, PA 18017-7061
Tel (610) 867-7600 *Founded/Ownrshp* 1940, 1977
Sales 20.7MM^E *EMP* 110
SIC 3264 Ferrite & ferrite parts; Magnets, permanent: ceramic or ferrite
Pr: Paul B Oberbeck
**VP:* Abby Oberbeck
Dir IT: Chris Carson
Ql Cn Mgr: Raymond Zimmerman
VP Sls: Mark Northrup

D-U-N-S 18-647-1397 IMP
NATIONAL MAINTENANCE & REPAIR INC
(*Suby of* MCNATIONAL INC) ★
401 S Hawthorne St, Hartford, IL 62048-1052
Tel (618) 254-7451 *Founded/Ownrshp* 1988
Sales 61.7MM^E *EMP* 425
SIC 3731 7699 Shipbuilding & repairing; Engine repair & replacement, non-automotive; Shipbuilding & repairing; Engine repair & replacement, non-automotive
Pr: Bruce D McGinnis
**CFO:* Bill Jessie
VP: John Sticht
Genl Mgr: John Moren
Sfty Mgr: Steve Geist

D-U-N-S 05-548-4539
NATIONAL MANAGEMENT RESOURCES CORP
113 Corporate Park E Dr, Lagrange, GA 30241-3680
Tel (706) 884-7489 *Founded/Ownrshp* 1978, 1995
Sales 30.4MM^E *EMP* 814
SIC 7349

NATIONAL MANUFACTURING
See TMCO INC

D-U-N-S 00-526-3124 IMP/EXP
■ **NATIONAL MANUFACTURING CO**
STANLEY NATIONAL HARDWARE
(*Suby of* STANLEY BLACK & DECKER INC) ★
19701 Da Vinci, Foothill Ranch, CA 92610-2622
Tel (800) 346-9445 *Founded/Ownrshp* 1901, 2014
Sales 7.6MM^E *EMP* 1,660
SIC 3429

D-U-N-S 00-218-2335 IMP
NATIONAL MANUFACTURING CO INC
12 River Rd, Chatham, NJ 07928-1989
Tel (973) 635-8846 *Founded/Ownrshp* 1944, 1997
Sales 36.4MM^E *EMP* 150
SIC 3469 Metal stampings; Metal stampings
Pr: Robert Staudinger
**VP:* Patrick Burke
**VP:* Brian Kelly
VP: Prasad Mahadev
VP: Prasad Mahvade
VP: Matthew Minnick
VP: Mike Sabon
VP: Mulraj Ved
QA Dir: Courtney Chronley
IT Man: Oliver Ibrahim
IT Man: Kristina Sterni

D-U-N-S 92-996-2413
■ **NATIONAL MARINE FISHERIES SERVICE**
(*Suby of* NATIONAL OCEANIC AND ATMOSPHERIC ADMINISTRATION) ★
1315 E West Hwy, Silver Spring, MD 20910-6233
Tel (301) 713-2239 *Founded/Ownrshp* 1871
Sales NA *EMP* 1,223
SIC 9611 Administration of general economic programs; ; Administration of general economic programs;
Pr: Eric Schwaab
CIO: Larry Tymenski
Sftwr Eng: Tom Henderson
Sftwr Eng: Jacques Middlecoff

D-U-N-S 08-042-6315 IMP
NATIONAL MARINE MANUFACTURERS ASSOCIATION (INC)
NMMA
231 S La Salle St # 2050, Chicago, IL 60604-1440
Tel (312) 946-6251 *Founded/Ownrshp* 1979
Sales 47.2MM *EMP* 99
Accts Bdo Usa Llp Chicago Il
SIC 8611 7999 Trade associations; Exposition operation; Trade associations; Exposition operation
Pr: Thomas Dammrich
**Ex VP:* Nelson Wold
**VP:* Carl Blackwell
**VP:* Craig Boskey
Software D: Tomas Kirda
Pr Mgr: Colleen Kenny

D-U-N-S 79-694-8487 IMP/EXP
NATIONAL MARINE SUPPLIERS INC
2800 Sw 2nd Ave, Fort Lauderdale, FL 33315-3120
Tel (954) 462-3131 *Founded/Ownrshp* 1990
Sales 106.4MM^E *EMP* 95
SIC 5088 Marine supplies; Marine supplies
Pr: Dean Dutoit
Store Mgr: Ivan Caro
IT Man: Anthony Nickel
Mktg Dir: Tom Rowe
Sales Asso: Ana Averza
Sales Asso: Gordon Demary

D-U-N-S 62-322-5737
NATIONAL MARROW DONOR PROGRAM INC
500 N 5th St, Minneapolis, MN 55401-1206
Tel (612) 627-5800 *Founded/Ownrshp* 1987
Sales 383.2MM *EMP* 800^E
Accts Deloitte Tax Lp Minneapolis
SIC 8099 8742 Medical services organization; Management consulting services; Medical services organization; Management consulting services
CEO: Jeffrey W Chell
CFO: Amy Ronneberg
Ofcr: Michael Boo
VP: Molly McCormick
VP: John Miller
Snr Sftwr: Jon Erickson
QA Dir: Sallie Allman
QA Dir: Anthony Barber
Dir IT: Kyle Nelson
Dir IT: Ericka Wheeler
IT Man: John Dailey

D-U-N-S 82-915-3100
NATIONAL MATERIAL CO LLC
1965 Pratt Blvd, Elk Grove Village, IL 60007-5905
Tel (847) 806-7200 *Founded/Ownrshp* 1999
Sales 33.0MM^E *EMP* 300
SIC 3399 3315 3341 Aluminum atomized powder; Wire, ferrous/iron; Aluminum smelting & refining (secondary)

D-U-N-S 18-329-5195 IMP/EXP
NATIONAL MATERIAL LP
INTERSTATE STEEL
1965 Pratt Blvd, Elk Grove Village, IL 60007-5905
Tel (847) 806-7200 *Founded/Ownrshp* 1988
Sales 492.9MM^E *EMP* 2,500
SIC 5051 3469 3354 5093 4911 4924

D-U-N-S 03-442-3186 EXP
NATIONAL MEAT & PROVISION CO INC
NATCO
321 W 10th St, Reserve, LA 70084-6603
Tel (985) 479-4200 *Founded/Ownrshp* 1925
Sales 51.7MM *EMP* 66
SIC 5147 5143 5144 2013 Meats & meat products; Cheese; Poultry & poultry products; Sausages & other prepared meats; Meats & meat products; Cheese; Poultry & poultry products; Sausages & other prepared meats
Pr: Anne Lalla Babin
**VP:* Thomas Lalla
IT Man: Sam Najm
Sls&Mrk Ex: Joseph Swab

NATIONAL MEDICAL CARE ASSN
See PARK ASSOCIATES INC

D-U-N-S 83-157-5548
NATIONAL MEDICAL CARE INC
(*Suby of* FRESENIUS MEDICAL CARE HOLDINGS INC) ★
920 Winter St Ste A, Waltham, MA 02451-1519
Tel (781) 699-9000 *Founded/Ownrshp* 1984
Sales 283.7MM^E *EMP* 16,757^E
SIC 8092 Kidney dialysis centers
CEO: Ronald Kuerbitz
**Pr:* Simon Castellanos
**Pr:* William J Valle
**CFO:* Angelo Moesslang
**Treas:* Mark Fawcett
**VP:* Jolene Varney
IT Man: Mary Garber

D-U-N-S 06-434-1449
NATIONAL MEDICAL SERVICES INC
NMS LABS
3701 Welsh Rd, Willow Grove, PA 19090-2910
Tel (215) 657-4900 *Founded/Ownrshp* 1970
Sales 21.5MM^E *EMP* 200
SIC 8071 Testing laboratories; Testing laboratories
Ch Bd: Eric F Rieders
**CEO:* Pierre G Cassigneul
CFO: James G Murphy
Ch: Michael F Rieders
Ofcr: Shelly H Carolan
VP: Shelly Carolan
VP: Ron Fazio
VP: Marlow Hicks
VP: Wenzhe Li
VP: Robert A Middleberg
VP: Robert Middleberg
VP: James Murphy
VP: Jack Wright
Dir Lab: Paul Miller

D-U-N-S 80-565-0447
NATIONAL MENTOR HEALTHCARE LLC
(*Suby of* NATIONAL MENTOR INC) ★
313 Congress St Fl 5, Boston, MA 02210-1261
Tel (617) 790-4800 *Founded/Ownrshp* 1985
Sales 16.7MM^E *EMP* 852
SIC 8361 Home for the mentally handicapped; Home for the mentally handicapped
Pr: Gregory Torres
Sr VP: Elizabeth Hopper
VP: Paula Finley
VP: Chris T Holland
VP: Robert Longo
VP: Iovanna Lopez-Diaz
VP: Teri Mahoney
VP: Philip Massey
VP: Donald Monack
VP: Bruce Nardella
VP: Charlotte A Sanford
VP: Margie M Smith

D-U-N-S 13-624-6043
NATIONAL MENTOR HOLDINGS INC
313 Congress St Fl 5, Boston, MA 02210-1218
Tel (617) 790-4800 *Founded/Ownrshp* 1980
Sales 1.2MMM *EMP* 20,200^E
SIC 8082 8361 Home health care services; Home for the mentally handicapped; Home health care services; Home for the mentally handicapped
CEO: Edward M Murphy
**Ch Bd:* Gregory T Torres
Pr: Bruce F Nardella
CFO: Denis M Holler
Ex VP: Juliette Fay
VP: Dan Giurelo
CIO: Jeffrey M Cohen
Board of Directors: Chris A Durbin, James L Elrod Jr, Patrick M Gray, Pamela F Lenehan, Kevin A Mundt, Guy Sansone

D-U-N-S 15-779-2052
NATIONAL MENTOR INC
NEURORESTORATIVE
(*Suby of* NATIONAL MENTOR HOLDINGS INC) ★
313 Congress St Fl 5, Boston, MA 02210-1218
Tel (617) 790-4800 *Founded/Ownrshp* 2001
Sales 68.6MM^E *EMP* 1,655
SIC 8361 Residential care; Residential care
Pr: Gregory Torres
**Treas:* Donald Monack
Ex VP: Juliette Fay
**VP:* John Gillespie
VP: Victoria Harding

D-U-N-S 05-541-9048
NATIONAL MERIT SCHOLARSHIP CORP
1560 Sherman Ave Ste 200, Evanston, IL 60201-4816
Tel (847) 866-5100 *Founded/Ownrshp* 1955
Sales 57.3MM *EMP* 38
SIC 8299 Educational service, nondegree granting: continuing educ.; Educational service, nondegree granting: continuing educ.
Pr: Timothy E McGuire
VP: Jeffrey Little

NATIONAL METAL FINISHING
See FIGEAC AERO NORTH AMERICA INC

D-U-N-S 05-942-4598 IMP
NATIONAL METALWARES LP
900 N Russell Ave, Aurora, IL 60506-2852
Tel (630) 892-9000 *Founded/Ownrshp* 1995
Sales 50.0MM^E *EMP* 280
SIC 3317 3498 Steel pipe & tubes; Fabricated pipe & fittings; Steel pipe & tubes; Fabricated pipe & fittings
Pr: Gary C Hill
**Pt:* Steve La Fond
**Pt:* Jack L May Jr
**Pt:* Mike Sullivan
CFO: Mike Podjasek
IT Man: Bill Nic
VP Opers: Jerry Guthke
Plnt Mgr: Jim Kallembach
Trfc Mgr: Gary Harvala
VP Sls: Steve L Fond

D-U-N-S 18-723-6992
■ **NATIONAL METER & AUTOMATION INC**
(*Suby of* BADGER METER INC) ★
7220 S Fraser St, Englewood, CO 80112-4286
Tel (303) 339-9100 *Founded/Ownrshp* 2014
Sales 25.0MM^E *EMP* 52^E
SIC 5084 Meters, consumption registering; Meters, consumption registering
Pr: Noel Frakes
CFO: Frank Milliron
Opers Mgr: Hilary Richards
Opers Mgr: Steven Wheeler
Sls Mgr: Chuck Cummings
Sls Mgr: Jimmy Terry

D-U-N-S 10-822-6259
NATIONAL MICRO RENTALS INC
NMR STAGING AND EVENTS
28 Abeel Rd, Monroe Township, NJ 08831-2036
Tel (609) 395-0550 *Founded/Ownrshp* 1995
Sales 32.0MM *EMP* 150
Accts A J Santye & Co Somerville
SIC 7377 Computer rental & leasing; Computer rental & leasing
Pr: Michael J Meduri
**VP:* Anthony Meduri Jr

*Prin: Anthony Meduri
Rgnl Mgr: Pat Kennedy
Dir IT: Addai Williams
VP Sls: Mark Brown

D-U-N-S 07-485-3029
NATIONAL MILK PRODUCERS FEDERATION
2101 Wilson Blvd Ste 400, Arlington, VA 22201-3062
Tel (703) 243-6111 Founded/Ownrshp 1916
Sales 34.1MM EMP 20
SIC 8611 Trade associations; Trade associations
Pr: Jerry Kozak
*Ch: Charles Beckondorf
Comm Man: Rob Yunich

D-U-N-S 80-826-0665 IMP
■ **NATIONAL MOBILE COMMUNICATIONS CORP**
SOVERNET COMMUNICATIONS
(Suby of SOVERNET COMMUNICATIONS) ★
5 Canal St, Bellows Falls, VT 05101-1371
Tel (802) 463-2111 Founded/Ownrshp 2000
Sales 22.6MM^E EMP 80
SIC 4813 Telephone communication, except radio
Pr: Richard L Kendall

D-U-N-S 82-931-5568 IMP/EXP
NATIONAL MOLDING LLC
SECURITY PLASTICS
14427 Nw 60th Ave, Miami Lakes, FL 33014-2806
Tel (305) 823-5440 Founded/Ownrshp 2008
Sales 61.6MM^E EMP 175
SIC 3089 Injection molding of plastics; Injection molding of plastics
CEO: John Johnson
COO: Enibio Gomez
CFO: Steven Healy
*CFO: Stella Laurella
Mng Dir: Richard Baum

NATIONAL MORTGAGE & FINANCE CO
See ISLAND HOLDINGS INC

D-U-N-S 07-105-0462
NATIONAL MULTIPLE SCLEROSIS SOCIETY (NY)
M S
733 3rd Ave Fl 3, New York, NY 10017-3211
Tel (212) 463-9791 Founded/Ownrshp 1946
Sales 105.7MM EMP 1,200
Accts Grant Thornton Llp New York
SIC 8322 Association for the handicapped; Association for the handicapped
Ch Bd: Tom Kuhn
Dir Vol: Sandra Baldi
Pt: Patti Radzik
*Ch Bd: Neal S Grunstra
Pr: Jim Fussell
*Pr: Joyce Nelson
CFO: Jeff Gentry
CFO: Lisa Iris
CFO: James Nangle
*Treas: Earl K Chism
Ofcr: David Cotter
Assoc VP: Mark Allegretta
Assoc VP: David Sobel
Ex VP: Bruce Bebo
Ex VP: Jennifer Douglas
Ex VP: Kaye Gooch
Ex VP: Linda Guiod
Ex VP: Kay Julian
Ex VP: Jennifer Lee
Ex VP: Mark Neagli
Ex VP: Debbie Pope
Board of Directors: Lori Leidholm, Chuck Riley, Mindy B Alpert, Thomas P Leist, Loren A Rolak, Donald Barone, Clyde Markowitz, Barbara Travis, Michael Brady, Bernadine Munley, Timothy L Vollmer, Kim Coma, Beth Norviel, Bill Whitaker, Jim Coulson, Elizabeth Pelley, Jacquelyn Dezort, J T Phillips Jr, Pamela Gray, Katherine S Ploessel, John Hall, Cynthia Pritchard, David Jones, Elizabeth Reeves

D-U-N-S 77-997-2033
NATIONAL MUSIC RACK INC
311 E Park St, Moonachie, NJ 07074-1142
Tel (201) 641-8188 Founded/Ownrshp 1990
Sales 107.8MM^E EMP 1,000
SIC 5099 Phonograph records; Phonograph records
Pr: Jeffrey Bitensky

D-U-N-S 07-385-1313
NATIONAL MUTUAL BENEFIT CORPORATE AGENCY INC
6522 Grand Teton Plz, Madison, WI 53719-1008
Tel (608) 833-1936 Founded/Ownrshp 1916
Sales NA EMP 95^E
SIC 6311 6321 Fraternal life insurance organizations; Disability health insurance; Fraternal life insurance organizations; Disability health insurance
Pr: George Yanna
*CFO: Jenna Dunker
VP: Anne Rogers

D-U-N-S 05-176-6509 IMP
NATIONAL NAIL CORP
WEST MICHIGAN NAIL & WIRE CO
2964 Clydon Ave Sw, Wyoming, MI 49519-2497
Tel (616) 538-8000 Founded/Ownrshp 1962
Sales 66.0MM^E EMP 200
SIC 5051 3315 3442 Nails; Nails, steel: wire or cut; Storm doors or windows, metal; Nails; Nails, steel: wire or cut; Storm doors or windows, metal
Ch Bd: Roger C Bruins
*Pr: Scott Baker
*CFO: John Krugman
CFO: Forry Sattler
*Sec: John P Krugman
Chf Mktg O: Kris Anderson
VP: Chris Baker
VP: Dan Braun
*VP: Jack Deyoung
VP: Jim Winn
Exec: Zac Gray
Board of Directors: Janet Deyoung, Jon Tanis

D-U-N-S 61-441-5789
NATIONAL NETWORK OF DIGITAL SCHOOLS CORP
NNDS
294 Massachusetts Ave, Rochester, PA 15074
Tel (724) 764-7200 Founded/Ownrshp 2005
Sales 20.4MM^E EMP 325
SIC 8299 Educational services; Educational services
CEO: Elder Mark
*Pr: Bob Clements
*COO: George Pacinda
*CFO: Andrew Sutton
*VP: Tim Albanese
Comm Dir: Christina Zarek
*Prin: Bryan Bown

D-U-N-S 79-585-7494
NATIONAL NETWORK OF DIGITAL SCHOOLS MANAGEMENT FOUNDATION
1000 3rd St Midland Ave, Midland, PA 15059
Tel (724) 764-7200 Founded/Ownrshp 2005
Sales 37.3MM EMP 9
Accts Cottrill Arbutina & Associates
SIC 8211 Specialty education; Specialty education
Pr: Charles Cerjak
*VP: Nick Trombetta

D-U-N-S 00-100-1478 IMP/EXP
NATIONAL NONWOVENS INC
110 Pleasant St, Easthampton, MA 01027-1342
Tel (413) 527-3445 Founded/Ownrshp 1905
Sales 30.7MM^E EMP 150
SIC 2231 2297 Felts, woven: wool, mohair or similar fibers; Nonwoven fabrics; Felts, woven: wool, mohair or similar fibers; Nonwoven fabrics
Ch Bd: Anthony J Centofanti
IT Man: Rick Reddel

D-U-N-S 83-776-4729
NATIONAL NOTARY ASSOCIATION
NNA SERVICES
9350 De Soto Ave, Chatsworth, CA 91311-4926
Tel (818) 739-4071 Founded/Ownrshp 1984
Sales 43.9MM^E EMP 204
SIC 8621 Professional membership organizations; Professional membership organizations
Ch: Milton G Valera
*CEO: Thomas A Heymann
*CFO: Robert Clarke
*Ex VP: Deborah M Thaw
Prgrm Mgr: Ed Jacobs

D-U-N-S 15-550-5027
■ **NATIONAL NUCLEAR SECURITY ADMINISTRATION/SERVICE CENTER**
NNSA
(Suby of EXECUTIVE OFC OF UNITED STATES) ★
Pennsylvania & H St Se, Albuquerque, NM 87185
Tel (505) 845-5952 Founded/Ownrshp 2003
Sales NA EMP 470^E
SIC 9611 Energy development & conservation agency, government; Energy development & conservation agency, government;

D-U-N-S 19-900-3955
NATIONAL NURSES SERVICE INC
(Suby of MID-ATLANTIC HOME HEALTH NETWORK INC) ★
8630 Fenton St Ste 924, Silver Spring, MD 20910-3810
Tel (301) 565-7890 Founded/Ownrshp 1981
Sales 7.9MM^E EMP 500
SIC 7363 Medical help service; Medical help service
Ch Bd: Philip Warman

NATIONAL NURSES UNITED
See CALIFORNIA NURSES ASSOCIATION

NATIONAL O RINGS
See HUTCHINSON SEAL CORP

D-U-N-S 94-708-2095 EXP
NATIONAL OAK DISTRIBUTORS INC
6529 Southern Blvd Ste 6, West Palm Beach, FL 33413-1735
Tel (561) 478-2711 Founded/Ownrshp 2000
Sales 237.7MM^E EMP 290
SIC 5013 5198 Automotive supplies & parts; Automotive servicing equipment; Automotive supplies; Paints, varnishes & supplies; Automotive supplies & parts; Automotive servicing equipment; Automotive supplies; Paints, varnishes & supplies
Pr: Geoffrey S Peckham
Pr: Chuck Vanslaars
*CFO: Zachary Tapp
VP: Marc Noland
Rgnl Mgr: Edward Gross
Brnch Mgr: Sammy Pineda
Dir IT: Steve West
Opers Mgr: Brian Bronson
Opers Mgr: Sue Johnson
VP Mktg: Greg Laffey
Sls Dir: Tom Fogarty

D-U-N-S 16-003-6091
■ **NATIONAL OCEAN SERVICE**
(Suby of NATIONAL OCEANIC AND ATMOSPHERIC ADMINISTRATION) ★
1305 E West Hwy, Silver Spring, MD 20910-3278
Tel (301) 713-3074 Founded/Ownrshp 1970
Sales NA EMP 1,000^E
SIC 9511 Water control & quality agency, government; ; Water control & quality agency, government;
CFO: Peter Gibson
CIO: Hugh Johnson

D-U-N-S 78-476-9085
■ **NATIONAL OCEANIC AND ATMOSPHERIC ADMINISTRATION**
(Suby of UNITED STATES DEPARTMENT OF COMMERCE) ★
1305 Ew Hwy Fl 10, Silver Spring, MD 20910
Tel (301) 713-3155 Founded/Ownrshp 1970
Sales NA EMP 1,225^E
SIC 9611 ; ; ;
*CFO: Maureen Wylie
Ofcr: Renee Desrosiers
Ofcr: Ray Wolf
Ex Dir: Jawed Hameedi
Admn Mgr: Jesse Abdul
Admn Mgr: Pradeep Amberpet
Admn Mgr: Guy Angouma
Admn Mgr: Carol Austin
Admn Mgr: Kenneth Batty
Admn Mgr: Pam Bussey
Admn Mgr: Greg Byrd

NATIONAL OFFICE
See NATIONAL ELECTRO-COATINGS INC

D-U-N-S 13-913-7611
■ **NATIONAL OFFICE FURNITURE INC**
(Suby of ARTEC MANUFACTURING) ★
1610 Royal St, Jasper, IN 47549-0001
Tel (812) 482-1600 Founded/Ownrshp 2008
Sales 71.8MM^E EMP 1,200
SIC 5712 Office furniture; Office furniture
VP: Richard Fassar
*VP: Don Banwinkle
*VP: Kevin McCoy
VP: Kourtney Smith
Dist Mgr: Linda Barry
Dist Mgr: Carolyn Coughlin
Dist Mgr: Lisa Elson
Dist Mgr: Dana Flocco
Dist Mgr: Maria Gonzales
Dist Mgr: Genene Hayden
Dist Mgr: Holly Haynes

D-U-N-S 83-171-0475 IMP
■ **NATIONAL OILWELL DHT LP**
NATIONAL OILWELL VARCO DHT
(Suby of NATIONAL OILWELL VARCO INC) ★
7909 Parkwood Circle Dr, Houston, TX 77036-6565
Tel (713) 346-7500 Founded/Ownrshp 2001
Sales 22.7MM^E EMP 37^E
SIC 3533 Oil & gas field machinery
Prin: Richard Legocki

NATIONAL OILWELL VARCO DHT
See NATIONAL OILWELL DHT LP

D-U-N-S 16-168-1044 IMP
▲ **NATIONAL OILWELL VARCO INC**
NOV
7909 Parkwood Circle Dr, Houston, TX 77036-6757
Tel (713) 346-7500 Founded/Ownrshp 1987
Sales 21.4MMM EMP 63,642
Accts Ernst & Young Llp Houston Te
Tkr Sym NOV Exch NYS
SIC 3533 3594 5084 Oil & gas field machinery; Oil field machinery & equipment; Gas field machinery & equipment; Petroleum industry machinery; Oil & gas field machinery; Oil & gas drilling rigs & equipment; Gas field machinery & equipment; Oil field machinery & equipment; Pumps, hydraulic power transfer; Motors: hydraulic, fluid power or air; Petroleum industry machinery
Pr: Clay C Williams
Pr: Burk Ellison
Pr: Robert Workman
CFO: Jose A Bayardo
Ex VP: Craig L Weinstock
Dir Bus: Keith Casey
Area Mgr: Douglas Kidd
Area Mgr: Veronica Morgante
Admn Mgr: Christopher Lagana
CIO: Alex Philips
Dir IT: Ingo Zachert
Board of Directors: Greg L Armstrong, Ben A Guill, David D Harrison, Roger L Jarvis, Eric L Mattson, Jeffery A Smisek, William R Thomas

D-U-N-S 08-339-5843 IMP/EXP
■ **NATIONAL OILWELL VARCO LP**
(Suby of NATIONAL OILWELL VARCO INC) ★
7909 Parkwood Circle Dr, Houston, TX 77036-6757
Tel (713) 960-5100 Founded/Ownrshp 1996
Sales 217.8MM^E EMP 700
SIC 3533 5082 5084 Oil field machinery & equipment; Oil field equipment; Industrial machinery & equipment; Oil field machinery & equipment; Oil field equipment; Industrial machinery & equipment
Pt: Joel Staff
Pt: Merrill Miller
Pt: Dan Molinaro
Pt: Frederick Pheasey
Exec: Rudy Moreno
Dir Bus: Paul Conover
Area Mgr: Tullos Adkins
Brnch Mgr: Kjwaldo Waldo
CTO: Rice Moody
Dir IT: Bill Droke
Mfg Mgr: Rufus Mathews

D-U-N-S 17-188-5353
NATIONAL OLDER WORKER CAREER CENTER INC
3811 Fairfax Dr Ste 900, Arlington, VA 22203-1757
Tel (703) 558-4200 Founded/Ownrshp 1996
Sales 23.2MM EMP 27
SIC 8699 Personal interest organization; Personal interest organization
CEO: Greg Merrill
*CFO: Cito Vanegas
*Prin: Jack Everett

D-U-N-S 06-951-2291
NATIONAL OPINION RESEARCH CENTER
NORC
1155 E 60th St, Chicago, IL 60637-2799
Tel (773) 753-7500 Founded/Ownrshp 1941
Sales 187.8MM^E EMP 1,200
SIC 8732

D-U-N-S 03-392-6775
NATIONAL ORGANIZATION OF INDUSTRIAL TRADE UNIONS INSURANCE TRUST FUND
N O I T U INSURANCE TRUST FUND
14806 Hillside Ave, Jamaica, NY 11435-3331
Tel (718) 291-3434 Founded/Ownrshp 1954
Sales NA EMP 150
Accts Buchbinder Tunick & Co Llp Ne
SIC 6371 Union trust funds; Union welfare, benefit & health funds; Union trust funds; Union welfare, benefit & health funds
*Trst: Ed Berger
*Trst: Gerald Hustick
*Trst: Robert Rogoff
*Trst: Donald Saslow
*Trst: Irwin Seigel
*Trst: Phillip Siegel

D-U-N-S 07-834-1328
NATIONAL OUTDOOR LEADERSHIP SCHOOL
NOLS
284 Lincoln St, Lander, WY 82520-2848
Tel (800) 710-6657 Founded/Ownrshp 1965
Sales 40.6MM EMP 1,000
Accts Porter Muirhead Cornia & How
SIC 8299 5941 Survival school; Camping equipment; Survival school; Camping equipment
Ch: Katherine Gunness Williams
*CFO: Jeff Buchanan
*Treas: Jonathan Kleisner
Ofcr: Kit Mitchell
Ofcr: Greta Olafsen
Ofcr: Katie Price
Dir Risk M: Drew Leemon
*Ex Dir: John Gans
Ex Dir: Liz Tuohy
Off Mgr: Gabi Jackson
Snr Ntwrk: Bobby Johnston

D-U-N-S 14-458-2848
NATIONAL PACKAGING CO INC
101 Lenwood Rd Se, Decatur, AL 35603
Tel (256) 260-0178 Founded/Ownrshp 1984
Sales 38.2MM^E EMP 260
SIC 7389 2099 Packaging & labeling services; Food preparations; Packaging & labeling services; Food preparations
Pr: Ralph E Matthews
*Pr: Joel Matthews
QA Dir: Jane Lipham

D-U-N-S 09-575-8405 IMP
NATIONAL PACKAGING CORP
NPC GLOBAL SERVICES
100 Middlesex Ave Ste 2, Carteret, NJ 07008-3499
Tel (973) 344-0100 Founded/Ownrshp 1978
Sales 26.0MM EMP 30
SIC 5162 5113 Paper & products, wrapping or coarse; Boxes, paperboard & disposable plastic; Industrial supplies; Plastics materials & basic shapes; Plastics materials & basic shapes; Paper & products, wrapping or coarse
Pr: Martin Schlesinger
VP: Jay Schlesinger

D-U-N-S 96-160-2281 IMP/EXP
NATIONAL PACKAGING SERVICES CORP
SPILFYTER
3303 Spirit Way, Green Bay, WI 54304-5663
Tel (920) 983-9223 Founded/Ownrshp 1996
Sales 69.1MM^E EMP 170
SIC 2679 Paper products, converted; Paperboard products, converted; Paper products, converted; Paperboard products, converted
Pr: Andrew F Hetzel Jr
Sr VP: Mike Graverson

D-U-N-S 03-848-0091 EXP
NATIONAL PACKAGING SPECIALISTS INC
N P S
3708 International Blvd, Vienna, OH 44473-9796
Tel (800) 524-1618 Founded/Ownrshp 1980
Sales 25.0MM EMP 11
SIC 5199 Plastics foam; Plastics foam
Pr: William A Jackson
*Treas: Melvyn B Bunson

NATIONAL PACKING SUPPLY
See REAL REEL CORP

D-U-N-S 01-260-6968 IMP/EXP
NATIONAL PAINT INDUSTRIES INC
BLUE WATER MARINE PAINT
1999 Elizabeth St, North Brunswick, NJ 08902-4905
Tel (732) 821-3200 Founded/Ownrshp 1959
Sales 51.1MM^E EMP 51
SIC 5198 Paints
Ch Bd: Michael Schnurr
*VP: Donald Schnurr

NATIONAL PAPERBOX
See SIMKINS CORP

NATIONAL PARK COLLEGE
See NATIONAL PARK COMMUNITY COLLEGE

D-U-N-S 12-023-3267
NATIONAL PARK COMMUNITY COLLEGE
NATIONAL PARK COLLEGE
101 College Dr, Hot Springs, AR 71913-9173
Tel (501) 760-4222 Founded/Ownrshp 1973
Sales 9.5MM EMP 435^E
SIC 8222 Community college; Community college
Pr: John Hogan
V Ch: Les Warren
Pr: Luke Robins
Pr: Gordon Watts
VP: Janis Sawyer
Store Mgr: Todd Craig
Mktg Mgr: Charlie Mohamed
Psych: Audrey Smelser

D-U-N-S 09-410-6739
NATIONAL PARK FOUNDATION (INC)
1201 I St Nw Ste A, Washington, DC 20005-5920
Tel (202) 354-6460 Founded/Ownrshp 1967
Sales 46.7MM^E EMP 35
SIC 8641 Environmental protection organization; Environmental protection organization
Pr: Will Shafroth
Pt: Christy Hartsell
COO: Patricia Nicklin
CFO: Celeste Regan
Ex VP: Jill Nicoll
Sr VP: Valerie Dorian
Comm Dir: Dan Puskar

Comm Man: Alanna Sobel
Ex Dir: Midy Aponte
Dir IT: James Duncan
Mktg Mgr: Alex Ladeau
Board of Directors: Bryan S Traubert, Kathleen Lynn Brown, Susan M Gonzales, Tom Goss, Steve Hightower, Jeremy Jaech, Joseph Landy, Ellen R Malcolm, Roxanne Quimby, David Shaw

NATIONAL PARK MEDICAL CENTER
See HOT SPRINGS NATIONAL PARK HOSPITAL HOLDINGS LLC

D-U-N-S 87-724-5639
NATIONAL PARK MEDICAL CENTER INC
NPMC HOME TOUCH HEALTHCARE
(*Suby of* CAPELLA HEALTHCARE INC) ★
1910 Malvern Ave, Hot Springs, AR 71901-7752
Tel (501) 321-1000 *Founded/Ownrshp* 2008
Sales 97.5MM^E *EMP* 800
SIC 8062 General medical & surgical hospitals; General medical & surgical hospitals
Owner: Cathy A Sewell
**CFO:* Robbie Pettey
VP: Mandy Brown
Dir Lab: Paulette Johnson
Dir Rx: William Reeves
Mtls Mgr: Pat Herrin
Surgeon: James Campbell
Ansthlgy: Katherine Latimer
Doctor: Ferrell D Hass
Doctor: John R Pace
Doctor: Brenda Powell

D-U-N-S 92-618-0977 IMP/EXP
■ NATIONAL PARK SERVICE
(*Suby of* UNITED STATES DEPARTMENT OF INTERIOR) ★
1849 C St Nw, Washington, DC 20240-0001
Tel (202) 208-6843 *Founded/Ownrshp* 1916
Sales NA *EMP* 20,000^E
SIC 9512 Land, mineral & wildlife conservation; ; Land, mineral & wildlife conservation;
**Pr:* John L Nau III
Bd of Dir: Donald Stevens
Adm Dir: Rachel Acker
Adm Dir: Lorna Akima
Adm Dir: Anne Ashe
Adm Dir: Joe Aull
Adm Dir: Judy Bachler
Adm Dir: Marcus Banks
Adm Dir: Sue Benson
Adm Dir: Sherry Birney
Adm Dir: Mary Blevins

D-U-N-S 07-484-5157
NATIONAL PARKS & CONSERVATION ASSOCIATION
777 6th St Nw, Washington, DC 20001-3723
Tel (202) 223-6722 *Founded/Ownrshp* 1919
Sales 28.6MM *EMP* 102
SIC 8641 Environmental protection organization; Environmental protection organization
Pr: Thomas C Kiernan
CFO: Stephanie Murphy
Treas: Donald Murphy
VP: Amy Hagovsky
VP: Carla A Killam
VP: Tracy Lamondue
**VP:* Kate Marshall
VP: Phil Voorhees
Prgrm Mgr: Kevin Dahl
Prgrm Mgr: Patricia Dowd
Prgrm Mgr: Laine J Hendricks

NATIONAL PARTS DEPOT
See AUTO CRAFT INVESTMENTS INC

D-U-N-S 04-579-1746
NATIONAL PARTS SUPPLY CO INC
535 Milltown Rd, North Brunswick, NJ 08902-3347
Tel (732) 247-5171 *Founded/Ownrshp* 1968
Sales 33.3MM^E *EMP* 80
SIC 5531 Automotive parts; Automotive accessories
Pr: John Salasko
**Sec:* William Salasko
**VP:* Michael Povlick

D-U-N-S 11-977-7428
NATIONAL PASTEURIZED EGGS INC
2963 Bernice Rd Ste 1, Lansing, IL 60438-1285
Tel (708) 418-8500 *Founded/Ownrshp* 2001
Sales 104.1MM^E *EMP* 125
SIC 5144 Eggs; Eggs
Pr: Gregory M West
**CFO:* Michael Smith
**VP:* Joseph Berglind
**VP:* Hector Lara
**Prin:* Marvin Aardema
**Prin:* Brian Boomsma
QA Dir: Shalini Ravindran
Natl Sales: Chip Baxter
Mktg Mgr: Deborah Rayhab
Manager: Jim Schlindwein

NATIONAL PEN COMPANY
See NATIONAL PEN CO LLC

D-U-N-S 05-988-3975 IMP
NATIONAL PEN CO LLC
NATIONAL PEN COMPANY
12121 Scripps Summit Dr # 200, San Diego, CA 92131-4609
Tel (866) 907-7367 *Founded/Ownrshp* 2012
Sales 241.8MM^E *EMP* 1,250
SIC 3951 3993 Pens & mechanical pencils; Advertising novelties; Pens & mechanical pencils; Advertising novelties
CEO: David F Thompson
COO: Alison Bushan
CFO: Kathy McDermott
**CFO:* Richard N Obrigawitch
Sr Cor Off: Kathy McDermott
**Sr VP:* Ron Childs
**Sr VP:* Gregg Kornfeld
VP: Annette Williams
VP: Laurent Yung
Creative D: Christopher Coats
CIO: Allen Rist

D-U-N-S 80-708-1638 IMP
NATIONAL PEN CORP
12121 Scripps Summit Dr # 200, San Diego, CA 92131-4609
Tel (858) 675-3000 *Founded/Ownrshp* 1966
Sales 156.9MM^E *EMP* 1,929
SIC 5961 Educational supplies & equipment, mail order; Educational supplies & equipment, mail order
CEO: Dave Thompson
**CFO:* Rich Obrigawitch
**Sr VP:* Ron Childs
**Sr VP:* Gregg Kornfeld
**Sr VP:* Laurent Yung
VP: Bill Owen
IT Man: Sandra Gibson
IT Man: Deborah Jones
IT Man: Rico McDowell
Software D: Mark Nelson
Sales Exec: Mallary West

D-U-N-S 07-937-3247
▲ NATIONAL PENN BANCSHARES INC
645 Hamilton St Ste 1100, Allentown, PA 18101-2188
Tel (800) 822-3321 *Founded/Ownrshp* 1982
Sales NA *EMP* 3,505
Tkr Sym NPBC *Exch* NGS
SIC 6021 National commercial banks; National commercial banks
Pr: Scott V Fainor
CFO: Michael J Hughes
Ofcr: Bridget Keretz
Ex VP: Dawn Hamm
Ex VP: Tito L Lima
Sr VP: Thomas Braunsberg
Sr VP: Stephen C Lyons
VP: Todd Balthaser
VP: Robert Bem
VP: Marc Benner
VP: Mary Bossard
VP: Martin Braam
VP: Tony Cusatis
VP: Kyle Fitzpatrick
VP: Debra Hippensteel
VP: Doug Leonzi
VP: Terry Morris
VP: Debbie Nowak
VP: Michael Squires
VP: Carl Walbert
VP: Bruce Waugh
Board of Directors: Thomas A Beaver, Jeffrey P Feather, Donna D Holton, Thomas L Kennedy, Patricia L Langiotti, Christian F Martin IV, R Chadwick Paul Jr, C Robert Roth, Wayne R Weidner

D-U-N-S 00-790-9914
■ NATIONAL PENN BANK
(*Suby of* NATIONAL PENN BANCSHARES INC) ★
645 Hamilton St Ste 900, Allentown, PA 18101-2198
Tel (610) 705-9101 *Founded/Ownrshp* 1874
Sales NA *EMP* 1,768
SIC 6021 National trust companies with deposits, commercial; National trust companies with deposits, commercial
CEO: Glenn E Moyer
CEO: Pam Koeshartanto
**Ch:* Wayne Weidner
Ofcr: Mary Lorah
Ofcr: Thomas Miller
Ofcr: Lisa Shuryn
Ofcr: Tracy Smithnosky
Ex VP: Todd Alderfer
Ex VP: Deborah Goldsmith
Ex VP: Peter Gray
Ex VP: Tito Lima
Ex VP: Hugh Marshall
Ex VP: Donald Worthington
Sr VP: Karen Christman
Sr VP: Doug Denlinger
Sr VP: Jim Ferry
Sr VP: Anne Gannon
Sr VP: Tina Gibbons
Sr VP: Scott Herald
Sr VP: Sharon Kemmerer
Sr VP: Todd Kirk

D-U-N-S 79-223-7299
NATIONAL PERFORMANCE SOLUTIONS INC
SQUEAKY CLEAN
7106 13th Ave, Brooklyn, NY 11228-1606
Tel (718) 833-4767 *Founded/Ownrshp* 1987
Sales 20.1MM *EMP* 100
SIC 3993 Advertising artwork; Advertising artwork
Ch Bd: Lola Bizas
**Co-Ownr:* Greg Bowman
**Co-Ownr:* Michell Bowman
**Prin:* Jacob Kahle

NATIONAL PERFORMANCE WAREHOUSE
See NATIONAL AUTO PARTS WAREHOUSE INC

D-U-N-S 17-044-4371
NATIONAL PHILANTHROPIC TRUST
165 Township Line Rd # 150, Jenkintown, PA 19046-3594
Tel (215) 277-3010 *Founded/Ownrshp* 1996
Sales 670.3MM *EMP* 19
SIC 7389 Fund raising organizations
Pr: Eileen Heisman
CEO: John Canady
Comm Dir: Brian Case
Prin: Patricia Patrizi
CTO: Bobbie Chapman

D-U-N-S 96-670-6764 IMP/EXP
NATIONAL PIPE & PLASTICS INC
NPPI
3421 Vestal Rd, Vestal, NY 13850-2188
Tel (607) 729-9381 *Founded/Ownrshp* 2004
Sales 93.7MM^E *EMP* 280
SIC 3084 Plastics pipe; Plastics pipe
CEO: David J Culbertson
**Treas:* Michelle Suer
**VP:* Charles E Miller
CIO: Karen Krouse
MIS Dir: Bill Scott
Dir IT: Karen Krause
IT Man: Dave Kunkel
Plnt Mgr: Victor Rozeboom
Prd Mgr: Neil Rigby

Sales Exec: Mark Cuda
Natl Sales: Angela Cwynar

D-U-N-S 13-781-5127
NATIONAL PLANNING CORP
100 N Sepulveda Blvd # 1800, El Segundo, CA 90245-5612
Tel (800) 881-7174 *Founded/Ownrshp* 1998
Sales NA *EMP* 150
SIC 6141 Automobile & consumer finance companies; Automobile & consumer finance companies
Pr: John C Johnson
Mng Pt: Ethan Grodofsky
Mng Pt: Jeffrey Stern
CFO: Maura Collins
Treas: Patrick Carroll
**Chf Cred:* Patricia McCallop
Ofcr: Melina Degelsmith
Sr VP: Jim Miller
Sr VP: Scott Montgomery
VP: John Anderson
VP: Court Chynces
**VP:* Sarah Corce
**VP:* Jim Dafalco
VP: Frank Hayn
VP: Bryan K Jacobsen
VP: Randy Miller
VP: Keith Mistretta
VP: David Rae
Exec: Daniel Piro

D-U-N-S 19-987-4371 IMP/EXP
NATIONAL PLASTICS COLOR INC
100 W Industrial St, Valley Center, KS 67147-4912
Tel (316) 755-1273 *Founded/Ownrshp* 1989
Sales 54.0MM^E *EMP* 111
SIC 2821 Molding compounds, plastics; Molding compounds, plastics
Pr: Steven Sutherland
Ex VP: Michael Piontek

D-U-N-S 09-471-6560 IMP
■ NATIONAL POOL TILE GROUP INC
(*Suby of* POOL CORP) ★
2840 E Miraloma Ave, Anaheim, CA 92806-1803
Tel (714) 630-2216 *Founded/Ownrshp* 2008
Sales 60.7MM^E *EMP* 100
SIC 5032 Ceramic wall & floor tile; Ceramic wall & floor tile
Pr: Karl Frykman
**Treas:* Michael G Meyer
**VP:* Robert D Miller

D-U-N-S 09-031-2765
NATIONAL PORK BOARD
1776 Nw 114th St, Des Moines, IA 50325-7000
Tel (515) 223-2600 *Founded/Ownrshp* 1986
Sales 99.0MM *EMP* 75
Accts Mcgladrey & Pullen Llp Des M
SIC 5147 Meats, fresh; Meats, fresh
CEO: Chris Novak
**CFO:* Calvin Van Dekrol
**Ex VP:* Jim Meimann
VP: Paul Sundberg
Tech Mgr: Charles Cozad
Art Dir: Chris Oldt

D-U-N-S 07-122-5155
NATIONAL POSTAL MAIL HANDLERS UNION
1101 Conn Ave Nw Ste 500, Washington, DC 20036-4325
Tel (202) 223-2294 *Founded/Ownrshp* 1920
Sales 67.2MM^E *EMP* 1,100
SIC 8631 Labor union
Pr: John F Hegarty
**Sec:* Mark A Gardner
**VP:* Paul Hogrogian
Dir IT: Robin Daniels

D-U-N-S 00-350-2614 IMP
NATIONAL POSTERS INC
N P G
(*Suby of* ROCK-TENN CONVERTING CO) ★
1001 Latta St, Chattanooga, TN 37406-3742
Tel (423) 622-1106 *Founded/Ownrshp* 1978
Sales 39.9MM^E *EMP* 235
SIC 2752 2759 Posters, lithographed; Screen printing; Posters, including billboards: printing; Posters, lithographed; Screen printing; Posters, including billboards: printing
Ch Bd: George Diamantis
**Pr:* Joel Stuart
CFO: Phil Harris
**VP:* Linda N Matthews
**VP:* Kerry Reedy

D-U-N-S 62-560-1091
NATIONAL POWER CORP
4541 Preslyn Dr, Raleigh, NC 27616-3178
Tel (919) 790-1672 *Founded/Ownrshp* 1986
Sales 27.1MM^E *EMP* 61
SIC 5063 4931

D-U-N-S 02-524-2470
NATIONAL POWER RODDING CORP
(*Suby of* CARYLON CORP) ★
2500 W Arthington St, Chicago, IL 60612-4108
Tel (312) 624-9001 *Founded/Ownrshp* 1949, 1977
Sales 25.9MM^E *EMP* 85
SIC 4953
Pr: Harold Kasova
**VP:* Leslie Bortz
Prgrm Mgr: John Manijak

D-U-N-S 08-976-7842 IMP
NATIONAL PRESORT LP
14901 Trinity Blvd, Fort Worth, TX 76155-2611
Tel (214) 634-2288 *Founded/Ownrshp* 1978
Sales 68.3MM^E *EMP* 150
SIC 3579 7629 Mailing, letter handling & addressing machines; Business machine repair, electric; Mailing, letter handling & addressing machines; Business machine repair, electric
Pt: Henry Daboub
**Pt:* Catherine Daboub
COO: Nopei Butler
CFO: James Curgus

VP: Mike Anderson
VP: Brent Daboub
VP: Brent Debow
VP: Si Kelly
VP: Shohei Takatmatsu
Genl Mgr: David Harvey
Genl Mgr: David Vanderberg

D-U-N-S 18-292-3672
NATIONAL PRESORT SERVICES INC
14901 Trinity Blvd, Fort Worth, TX 76155-2611
Tel (214) 634-2288 *Founded/Ownrshp* 1987
Sales 26.6MM^E *EMP* 250
SIC 7389 Presorted mail service; Presorted mail service
Pr: Henry Daboub
**Treas:* Catherine Daboub
**Sec:* ARI Daboub
IT Man: Cathy Turner
Tech Mgr: Charlie Betau
Ql Cn Mgr: Patrick Reilly
Sls Dir: Everett Costa
Sls Mgr: Aaron McDaniel

D-U-N-S 00-619-6174 IMP/EXP
▲ NATIONAL PRESTO INDUSTRIES INC
3925 N Hastings Way, Eau Claire, WI 54703-3703
Tel (715) 839-2121 *Founded/Ownrshp* 1905
Sales 412.3MM *EMP* 889^E
Accts Bdo Usa Llp Milwaukee Wisco
Tkr Sym NPK *Exch* NYS
SIC 2211 3483 3634 Diaper fabrics; Ammunition components; Housewares, excluding cooking appliances & utensils; Diaper fabrics; Ammunition components; Housewares, excluding cooking appliances & utensils
Ch Bd: Maryjo Cohen
**CFO:* Randy F Lieble
VP: Spence W Ahneman
VP: Lawrence J Tienor
Ql Cn Mgr: Linda Honda
VP Sls: Spencer W Ahneman
Mktg Mgr: Todd Wekkin
Board of Directors: Richard N Cardozo, Patrick J Quinn, Joseph G Stienessen

D-U-N-S 61-045-6217 IMP/EXP
■ NATIONAL PRETZEL CO INC
(*Suby of* CONAGRA FOODS INC) ★
2060 Old Philadelphia Pike, Lancaster, PA 17602-3413
Tel (717) 299-2321 *Founded/Ownrshp* 2011
Sales 68.4MM^E *EMP* 600^E
SIC 2052 Pretzels; Pretzels
Pr: Richard Dwinell
**CFO:* David Hurd
**Ex VP:* David Digiacinto
**VP:* Norman Randall
IT Man: Mark Stambaugh
Plnt Mgr: Robert Bard
Plnt Mgr: Joseph Chrismer
**VP Sls:* Rick Bishop

D-U-N-S 00-527-1673
■ NATIONAL PROCESSING CO (NE)
(*Suby of* VANTIV INC) ★
5100 Interchange Way, Louisville, KY 40229-2160
Tel (502) 961-5200 *Founded/Ownrshp* 1993
Sales 27.8MM^E *EMP* 130^E
SIC 6719 Investment holding companies, except banks; Investment holding companies, except banks
Pr: Tom Wimsett
**Treas:* George Willett
Sr VP: Chris Lee

D-U-N-S 94-417-2816
NATIONAL PROCESSING CO
RETRIEVER PAYMENTS SYSTEMS
(*Suby of* FAIRMOUNT FOOD GROUP INC) ★
20405 State Highway 249 # 700, Houston, TX 77070-3815
Tel (281) 376-3399 *Founded/Ownrshp* 2007
Sales 221.8MM^E *EMP* 546
SIC 5065 Electronic parts & equipment; Electronic parts & equipment
Pr: Thomas A Wimsett
**Ch Bd:* William H Higgins
**Pr:* Adam Coyle
**CFO:* Steve Stevenson
Treas: Tim Cooper
**Ex VP:* James Oberman
VP: Thomas Smith

D-U-N-S 04-852-7451
NATIONAL PRODUCTS SALES INC
N P S
1600 S Empire Rd, Salt Lake City, UT 84104-3805
Tel (801) 973-4949 *Founded/Ownrshp* 1969
Sales 41.2MM^E *EMP* 300
SIC 5399 Surplus & salvage goods; Surplus & salvage goods
Pr: Kelly N Farmer
**Treas:* Kelly Lee Farmer
**Sec:* Julie Haltom
VP: Daniel Farmer
**VP:* Elaine Farmer
IT Man: Mike Anderson

D-U-N-S 15-427-6521
■ NATIONAL PROJECTS INC
(*Suby of* URS ENERGY & CONSTRUCTION INC) ★
720 E Park Blvd, Boise, ID 83712-7758
Tel (208) 386-5000 *Founded/Ownrshp* 1985
Sales 67.7MM^E *EMP* 1,162
SIC 1629 1542 1541 Dam construction; Commercial & office building, new construction; Industrial buildings & warehouses; Dam construction; Commercial & office building, new construction; Industrial buildings & warehouses
Pr: Stephen G Hanks
**Ch:* Dennis Washington
Sec: Jeanne C Baughman

D-U-N-S 05-338-7221
NATIONAL PUBLIC RADIO INC
N P R
1111 N Capitol St Ne, Washington, DC 20002-7502
Tel (202) 513-2000 *Founded/Ownrshp* 1970
Sales 204.2MM *EMP* 741

Accts Bdo Usa Llp Bethesda Md
SIC 8611 Business associations; Business associations
CEO: Jarl Mohn
COO: Loren Mayor
CFO: Deborah A Cowan
**CFO:* Debbie Cullen
**Chf Mktg O:* Emma Carrasco
Sr VP: Michael Oreskes
VP: Marty Garrison
VP: Robert Kempf
Dir Risk M: Kathleen Rocheska
Dir Soc: Terry Gross
Dir Soc: Peter Sagal

D-U-N-S 00-322-8546 IMP/EXP
NATIONAL PUBLIC SEATING CORP (NJ)
149 Entin Rd, Clifton, NJ 07014-1424
Tel (973) 594-1100 *Founded/Ownrshp* 1997
Sales 22.6MM^{E} *EMP* 30
SIC 5021 2514 Chairs; Chairs, household: metal
CEO: Benjamin Grunwald
**Pr:* Barry Stauber
Mng Dir: Joe Lefkowitz
Manager: Leo Drel
Sales Asso: David Hastings
Sales Asso: Rhonda Naidoff

D-U-N-S 00-229-1110 IMP
■ **NATIONAL PUBLISHING CO** (PA)
(*Suby of* RR DONNELLEY & SONS CO) ★
11311 Roosevelt Blvd, Philadelphia, PA 19154-2175
Tel (215) 676-1863 *Founded/Ownrshp* 1863, 2015
Sales 29.8MM^{E} *EMP* 315
SIC 2731 2732 2789 Book publishing; Books: printing & binding; Bookbinding & related work; Book publishing; Books: printing & binding; Bookbinding & related work
Pr: James F Conway III
Treas: Lee E Cochrane
Sr VP: Rajeev Balakrishna
Sr VP: Peter M Folger
VP: Joseph L Brennan
VP: Anthony F Caruso
VP: Robert Chilton
VP: Danny Grubert
VP: Mike Larusso
Trfc Mgr: Harry Fow

D-U-N-S 83-488-1179 IMP/EXP
■ **NATIONAL PUMP CO**
(*Suby of* GORMAN-RUPP CO) ★
7706 N 71st Ave, Glendale, AZ 85303-1703
Tel (623) 979-3560 *Founded/Ownrshp* 1998
Sales 31.9MM^{E} *EMP* 135
SIC 3561 Pumps & pumping equipment; Pumps & pumping equipment
Ch: Jeffrey S Gorman
**Pr:* Allan Hobratschk
**CFO:* Wayne L Knabel
Treas: Gene Hofkins
Genl Mgr: Ira Friedman

D-U-N-S 07-885-9701
NATIONAL RADIO ASTRONOMY OBSERVATORY
NRAO
520 Edgemont Rd, Charlottesville, VA 22903-2454
Tel (434) 296-0211 *Founded/Ownrshp* 2013
Sales 101.7MM^{E} *EMP* 577^{E}
SIC 8731 Commercial physical research
Prin: Andrea Gianopoulos
Ofcr: James Sullivan
Ofcr: Anthony Thompson
VP: Sue Heatherly
Exec: Charles Blue
Prgrm Mgr: Michael Shannon
CIO: David Halstead
Web Dev: Davis Murphy
Web Dev: John Shipman
Sftwr Eng: Rodrigo Amestica
Sftwr Eng: Jorge Avarias

D-U-N-S 05-442-7745 IMP
■ **NATIONAL RAILROAD PASSENGER CORP**
AMTRAK
(*Suby of* US DEPARTMENT OF TRANSPORTATION) ★
60 Massachusetts Ave Ne, Washington, DC 20002-4285
Tel (202) 906-3741 *Founded/Ownrshp* 1970
Sales 2.9MMM^{E} *EMP* 18,650
Accts Kpmg Llp Mclean Va
SIC 4011 4013 Interurban railways; Railroad terminals; Interurban railways; Railroad terminals
Pr: Joseph H Boardman
Ch Bd: Anthony R Coscia
COO: William Crosby
COO: William Cry
CFO: Deno Bokas
CFO: William H Campbell
Sr Cor Off: Wade Jones
Sr Cor Off: Dale Steine
V Ch Bd: Jeffrey R Moreland
Act CFO: Dale M Stein
Bd of Dir: Robert Hunter
Chf Mktg O: George Raed
Ofcr: Magdy El-Sibaie
Ofcr: James Rusbarsky
Assoc VP: Floyd L Kemerer
Ex VP: Karen Seibert
Sr VP: James T Lloyd
VP: Eleanor D Acheson
VP: Sandy J Brown
VP: Delando Cavanaugh
VP: Roy Deitchman
Board of Directors: Christopher R Beall, Joseph H Boardman, Yvonne Brathwaite Burke, Thomas C Carper, Anthony R Coscia, Albert Diclemente, Anthony Foxx, Jeffrey R Moreland

D-U-N-S 10-319-3751 IMP/EXP
NATIONAL RAILWAY EQUIPMENT CO
NREC
1100 Shawnee St, Mount Vernon, IL 62864-5454
Tel (618) 242-6590 *Founded/Ownrshp* 1980
Sales 206.2MM^{E} *EMP* 750
SIC 5088 3743

D-U-N-S 15-774-8914
NATIONAL RAILWAY EQUIPMENT CO
(*Suby of* NATIONAL RAILWAY EQUIPMENT CO) ★
1300 Kentucky Ave, Paducah, KY 42003-1961
Tel (270) 444-4555 *Founded/Ownrshp* 1994
Sales 100.6MM^{E} *EMP* 950
SIC 3743 Mining locomotives & parts, electric or nonelectric; Railroad locomotives & parts, electric or nonelectric; Mining locomotives & parts, electric or nonelectric; Railroad locomotives & parts, electric or nonelectric
Pr: Robert A Pedersen
**Sr VP:* Charles E Marshall
**VP:* Burton Lamont

NATIONAL RAISIN COMPANY
See SUNSHINE RAISIN CORP

NATIONAL RAZORBACK CLUB
See RAZORBACK FOUNDATION INC

D-U-N-S 61-326-0629
■ **NATIONAL RE CORP**
(*Suby of* GENERAL REINSURANCE CORP) ★
120 Long Ridge Rd, Stamford, CT 06902-1839
Tel (203) 328-5000 *Founded/Ownrshp* 1996
Sales NA *EMP* 800^{E}
SIC 6331 6321 6311 Fire, marine & casualty insurance; Accident & health insurance; Life insurance; Fire, marine & casualty insurance; Accident & health insurance; Life insurance
Prin: Joseph Brandon

NATIONAL RECOVERY AGENCY
See NRA GROUP LLC

D-U-N-S 10-143-9925 IMP/EXP
NATIONAL REFRIGERANTS INC
N R I
11401 Roosevelt Blvd, Philadelphia, PA 19154-2197
Tel (215) 698-6620 *Founded/Ownrshp* 1983
Sales 112.0MM^{E} *EMP* 100
SIC 5169 Chemicals & allied products; Chemicals & allied products
Pr: John H Reilly Jr
CFO: Nick Hope
**Treas:* Hope V Nicholas
VP: Maureen Beatty
VP: Carmen Carosella
**VP:* John H Reilly III
Dir Lab: Robert Yost
Prd Mgr: Seth Barringer
Sls Mgr: Jim Lavelle

D-U-N-S 19-558-2853 IMP
NATIONAL REFRIGERATION & AIR CONDITIONING PRODUCTS INC
NATIONAL REFRIGERATION PDTS
539 Dunksferry Rd, Bensalem, PA 19020-5908
Tel (215) 244-1400 *Founded/Ownrshp* 1988
Sales 106.2MM^{E} *EMP* 230
SIC 3585 5075 Refrigeration equipment, complete; Air conditioning equipment, complete; Warm air heating & air conditioning; Refrigeration equipment, complete; Air conditioning equipment, complete; Warm air heating & air conditioning
Pr: Michael Coyle
**Pr:* Brian Kelly
**CEO:* John H Reilly
**Treas:* Carmen Carosella
**Treas:* William Hawkins
**VP:* Nicholas V Hope
VP: John Morris
Sfty Dirs: Mike Coyle
Sls Mgr: Kevin Brown
Sls Mgr: Grant Price

NATIONAL REFRIGERATION PDTS
See NATIONAL REFRIGERATION & AIR CONDITIONING PRODUCTS INC

D-U-N-S 07-736-6664
NATIONAL REHABILITATION HOSPITAL INC
N R H
102 Irving St Nw, Washington, DC 20010-2921
Tel (202) 877-1000 *Founded/Ownrshp* 1983
Sales 118.0MM *EMP* 900
Accts Kpmg Llp Norfolk Va
SIC 8069 Specialty hospitals, except psychiatric; Specialty hospitals, except psychiatric
Ch: Jimmy V Reyes
Pr: Edward Eckenhoff
CFO: Michael Bammel
Treas: Robert B Ourisman
Exec: Casey Yazel
Mng Dir: Penny Wolfe
Dir Sec: Anthony Benson
CIO: Anjoo Marchant
HC Dir: Mona Calhoun
Dietician: Leslie Adams

D-U-N-S 08-872-6972
NATIONAL RELIEF CHARITIES
16415 Addison Rd Ste 200, Addison, TX 75001-3203
Tel (214) 217-2600 *Founded/Ownrshp* 2015
Sales 42.0MM *EMP* 3^{E}
SIC 8699 8322 Charitable organization; Individual & family services
Prin: Mario R Porro

D-U-N-S 80-134-1959
NATIONAL RELIEF CHARITIES
AMERICAN INDIAN RELIEF COUNCIL
10029 Sw Nimbus Ave # 200, Beaverton, OR 97008-7110
Tel (503) 641-4466 *Founded/Ownrshp* 1990
Sales 21.6MM *EMP* 49
SIC 8399 Fund raising organization, non-fee basis; Fund raising organization, non-fee basis
Pr: Brian J Brown

D-U-N-S 83-251-7879
NATIONAL RENEWABLE ENERGY CORP
NARENCO
227 Southside Dr Ste B, Charlotte, NC 28217-1727
Tel (704) 930-7700 *Founded/Ownrshp* 2009
Sales 50.0MM *EMP* 18

SIC 4931
CEO: Robert A Cox
CFO: Stanley Allen
**CFO:* Andrew Giraldo
Sr VP: Dennis Richter
VP: Keith Davis
**VP:* Jesse Montgomery
VP Opers: Ed Spooner

NATIONAL RENT A CAR
See NATIONAL RENTAL (US) INC

NATIONAL RENT TO OWN
See D L COLE & ASSOCIATES INC

D-U-N-S 80-700-1628
NATIONAL RENTAL (US) INC
NATIONAL RENT A CAR
(*Suby of* VANGUARD CAR RENTAL USA INC.)
6929 N Lakewood Ave # 100, Tulsa, OK 74117-1824
Tel (918) 401-6000 *Founded/Ownrshp* 2003
Sales 175.0MM^{E} *EMP* 4,965^{E}
SIC 7514 Rent-a-car service
Pr: Greg Stubblefield
Treas: Steve Busskohl
Treas: Brenda Miller
Ex VP: Thomas C Kennedy
Ex VP: Travis Tanner
Sr VP: Thomas Kennedy
VP: Dan Artone
VP: Jeff Coggin
VP: Gary Cunningham
VP: Wesley C Fredenburg
VP: Mark Friedman
VP: John Howell
VP: Thomas Klingler
VP: Bill Lazzarino
VP: Jim Maher
VP: John Valas
VP: Roger Van Horn
Dir Bus: Dick Hunt

NATIONAL RENTAL ANALYST
See RYDER SYSTEMS INC

D-U-N-S 01-216-0982
NATIONAL REPROGRAPHICS INC
NRI
44 W 18th St Fl 2, New York, NY 10011-4694
Tel (212) 366-7000 *Founded/Ownrshp* 1930
Sales 54.4MM^{E} *EMP* 300
SIC 7334 7374 Photocopying & duplicating services; Blueprinting service; Computer graphics service; Photocopying & duplicating services; Blueprinting service; Computer graphics service
Ch Bd: Ellen Feuer
**Ch Bd:* Nan Magid
**Pr:* Doug Magid
**CFO:* Alan Sussman
**VP:* Daniel Gabrich
**VP:* Russ Genest
VP: Ira Packer
Dept Mgr: Lillie Braxton
Dept Mgr: Branden Brillon
Dept Mgr: Alan Napiorski
Brnch Mgr: Peter Barbella

D-U-N-S 00-798-0857
NATIONAL REPUBLIC BANK (IL)
1201 W Harrison St Fl 1, Chicago, IL 60607-3329
Tel (312) 738-4900 *Founded/Ownrshp* 1893, 1984
Sales NA *EMP* 44
SIC 6021 National commercial banks; National commercial banks
Pr: Edward Fitzgerald
VP: Gloria Armendariz
VP: B Mehta
VP: John Rybicki
VP: Farrokh Siganporia

D-U-N-S 05-085-7788
▲ **NATIONAL RESEARCH CORP** (WI)
1245 Q St Ste 100, Lincoln, NE 68508-1454
Tel (402) 475-2525 *Founded/Ownrshp* 1981
Sales 98.8MM *EMP* 397^{E}
Tkr Sym NRCIA *Exch* NGS
SIC 8732 Market analysis or research; Market analysis or research
CEO: Michael D Hays
Pr: Steve Jackson
CFO: Kevin R Karas
Ofcr: Kimberle Hall
Ofcr: Jona Raasch
Sr VP: Helen Hrdy
VP: Mary Oakes
VP: Jon Zvolanek
IT Man: Dana Pet
Software D: Alex Gallichotte
Sftwr Eng: Lanny Boswell
Board of Directors: Donald Berwick, Joann M Martin, Barbara Mowry, John N Nunnelly, Gail L Warden

D-U-N-S 93-331-2886
NATIONAL RESORTS CORP
100 N Tucker Blvd, Saint Louis, MO 63101-1931
Tel (314) 558-6120 *Founded/Ownrshp* 1989
Sales 9.2MM^{E} *EMP* 300
SIC 7041 6531 Membership-basis organization hotels; Real estate agents & managers; Membership-basis organization hotels; Real estate agents & managers
Prin: Pat Hudson

D-U-N-S 79-738-4252 EXP
NATIONAL RESPONSE CORP
3500 Sunrise Hwy, Great River, NY 11739-1001
Tel (631) 224-9141 *Founded/Ownrshp* 2012
Sales 127.4MM *EMP* 700
SIC 4959 8999 Oil spill cleanup; Earth science services; Oil spill cleanup; Earth science services
Pr: Steve Candito
**CFO:* Sal Sacco
**Sr VP:* Neil Challis
**Sr VP:* Mike Reese
**Sr VP:* Todd Roloff
VP: Michael Reese
Genl Mgr: James Haeghaert

D-U-N-S 07-313-3969
NATIONAL RESTAURANT ASSOCIATION
2055 L St Nw Ste 700, Washington, DC 20036-4985
Tel (202) 973-3951 *Founded/Ownrshp* 1919
Sales 71.3MM *EMP* 250
SIC 8611 Trade associations; Trade associations
Pr: Dawn Sweeney
**CFO:* Marvin Irby
**Ch:* John G Crawford
**Treas:* Jeffrey W Davis
Sr VP: Katherine Schieffelin
Natl Sales: Louis Helms

D-U-N-S 11-124-5049
NATIONAL RESTAURANT DEVELOPMENT INC
KFC
4170 Ashford Dunwoody Rd, Brookhaven, GA 30319-1442
Tel (770) 674-0091 *Founded/Ownrshp* 1996
Sales 22.8MM^{E} *EMP* 700
SIC 5812 Fast-food restaurant, chain; Fast-food restaurant, chain
CEO: Aziz A Hashim
**CFO:* Andy Bhayani
VP: Wendy Harkness

D-U-N-S 02-638-1830 IMP
NATIONAL RESTAURANT SUPPLY INC (TX)
7125 Industrial Ave, El Paso, TX 79915-1215
Tel (915) 544-2121 *Founded/Ownrshp* 1960
Sales 30.5MM^{E} *EMP* 75
SIC 5046 Restaurant equipment & supplies; Restaurant equipment & supplies
Pr: Bruce Gulbas
**VP:* Brent Gulbas
**VP:* Jacqueline Gulbas
VP: Irma Juarez
Sales Asso: Wanda Modkins

D-U-N-S 01-216-1568
NATIONAL RESTAURANTS MANAGEMENT INC
RIESE ORGANIZATION
560 5th Ave Fl 3, New York, NY 10036-5005
Tel (212) 563-7440 *Founded/Ownrshp* 1955
Sales 75.3MM^{E} *EMP* 2,500
SIC 5812 6531 Eating places; Real estate agents & managers; Eating places; Real estate agents & managers
CEO: Dennis Riese
**Ex VP:* Larry Abrams
**VP:* Ann Martinez
VP: James Rosenzweig
VP: Mark Stempel
Dir Sec: Ronnie Lichtman
Dist Mgr: Lisa Dibello
Mktg Dir: Joe De Nardo

D-U-N-S 18-649-7644
NATIONAL RESTAURANTS MANAGEMENT INC
RIESE ORGANIZATION
(*Suby of* NATIONAL RESTAURANTS MANAGEMENT INC) ★
604 5th Ave Fl 5, New York, NY 10020-2304
Tel (212) 563-7440 *Founded/Ownrshp* 1981
Sales 50.4MM^{E} *EMP* 2,400
SIC 5812 Eating places; Eating places
Pr: Dennis Riese
**CFO:* John Dunne

D-U-N-S 84-790-8829
■ **NATIONAL RETAIL BRANDS INC**
(*Suby of* NEWBEVCO INC) ★
1165 Palmour Dr, Gainesville, GA 30501-6858
Tel (770) 535-2214 *Founded/Ownrshp* 1985
Sales 29.3MM^{E} *EMP* 600
SIC 2086 Bottled & canned soft drinks; Bottled & canned soft drinks
Pr: Nick A Caporella

D-U-N-S 00-591-3231
NATIONAL RETAIL FEDERATION INC
1101 New York Ave Nw, Washington, DC 20005-4269
Tel (202) 626-8155 *Founded/Ownrshp* 1994
Sales 56.2MM *EMP* 135
Accts Tate & Tryon Washington Dc
SIC 2721 8611 Magazines: publishing only, not printed on site; Trade associations; Magazines: publishing only, not printed on site; Trade associations
CEO: Matthew Shay
**Ch Bd:* Stephen I Sadove
V Ch: Larry Bergman
Pr: Kathy Grannis
**COO:* Carleen Kohut
Ch: Dennis Cohen
Bd of Dir: Jane T Elfers
Bd of Dir: Paul Franz
Bd of Dir: John McAteer
Bd of Dir: Paul Miller
Bd of Dir: Stephanie Miller
**Ex VP:* Vicki Cantrell
**Sr VP:* Ellen Davis
Sr VP: Tita Freeman
Sr VP: David Hogan
**Sr VP:* Susan Newman
VP: Erik Autor
VP: Rachelle Bernstein
VP: Denise Brass
VP: Jason Hoolsema
VP: Cathy Hotka
Board of Directors: Steve Knopik, Ravi Saligram

D-U-N-S 10-915-1175
▲ **NATIONAL RETAIL PROPERTIES INC**
450 S Orange Ave Ste 900, Orlando, FL 32801-3339
Tel (407) 265-7348 *Founded/Ownrshp* 1984
Sales 434.8MM *EMP* 64^{E}
Tkr Sym NNN *Exch* NYS
SIC 6798 Real estate investment trusts; Real estate investment trusts
Ch Bd: Craig Macnab
Pr: Julian E Whitehurst
CFO: Kevin B Habicht
Ex VP: Paul E Bayer
Ex VP: Stephen A Horn Jr
Ex VP: Christopher P Tessitore

Board of Directors: Don Defosset, David M Fick, Edward J Fritsch, Richard B Jennings, Ted B Lanier, Robert C Legler, Robert Martinez

D-U-N-S 13-047-6831
NATIONAL RETAIL SYSTEMS INC
N R S
2820 16th St, North Bergen, NJ 07047-1541
Tel (201) 330-1900 *Founded/Ownrshp* 1983
Sales 220.0MM^E *EMP* 1,500
SIC 7363 Country general stores; Truck driver services
Pr: Raymond Wisniewski
VP: Irene Kneeter
VP: Jim Olker
VP: Dan Orlandi
VP: John Tempesta
Dir Risk M: Jack Gavin
IT Man: Mark Semeraro
Opers Mgr: Brian Daniels

D-U-N-S 09-926-3725
NATIONAL RETAIL TRANSPORTATION INC
(*Suby of* N R S) ★
2820 16th St, North Bergen, NJ 07047-1541
Tel (201) 866-0462 *Founded/Ownrshp* 1979
Sales 138.8MM^E *EMP* 1,040
SIC 4213 Trucking, except local; Trucking, except local
Pr: Raymond Wisniewski
**CFO:* Paul K Hennessy
Dir IT: Gregory Cole

D-U-N-S 04-072-2287
NATIONAL RETIREMENT SERVICES INC
N R S
5832 Bolsa Ave Ste 100, Huntington Beach, CA 92649-1181
Tel (714) 622-3188 *Founded/Ownrshp* 2001
Sales NA *EMP* 76
SIC 6411 Pension & retirement plan consultants
CEO: John Sciarra
**CFO:* Marc Davis
**Ex VP:* James Houpt

D-U-N-S 00-325-6500
NATIONAL RIFLE ASSOCIATION OF AMERICA (NY)
INSTITUTE FOR LGSLATIVE ACTION
11250 Waples Mill Rd # 1, Fairfax, VA 22030-9400
Tel (703) 267-1000 *Founded/Ownrshp* 1997
Sales 347.9MM *EMP* 500
Accts Mcgladrey Llp Vienna Va
SIC 8699 Amateur sports promotion; Amateur sports promotion
Pr: Porter II James W
**Pr:* John C Sigler
**CFO:* Wilson H Phillips
**Treas:* Phillips Jr Wilson H
Treas: H P Wilson
Bd of Dir: Dolores R Gresham
**VP:* Cors Allan D
**VP:* David Keene
**VP:* Lapierre Jr Wayne
**VP:* Brownell Pete
VP: James W Porter II
**VP:* Ronald L Schmeits

D-U-N-S 04-673-4190
NATIONAL RIGHT TO WORK COMMITTEE INC (VA)
8001 Braddock Rd Ste 500, Springfield, VA 22160-0002
Tel (703) 321-9820 *Founded/Ownrshp* 1955
Sales 13.6MM *EMP* 386
Accts Dixon Hughes Goodman Llp Tyso
SIC 8641 Civic social & fraternal associations; Civic social & fraternal associations
Pr: Mark Mix
**Ch:* Charles R Serio
**Treas:* Stephen O Goodrick
**VP:* Steven Goodrick
**VP:* Matthew M Leen
Comm Dir: Jessica Appelberg

D-U-N-S 08-526-5379
NATIONAL ROOFING CO INC
3408 Columbia Dr Ne, Albuquerque, NM 87107-2004
Tel (505) 883-3000 *Founded/Ownrshp* 1976
Sales 27.5MM^E *EMP* 130
SIC 1761 Roofing contractor; Roofing contractor
CEO: Thomas F Johns
**Pr:* Todd Jackson
**Treas:* Jill Johns
**VP:* Ed McFarnane
**VP:* Teresa Serna
**VP:* Crish Smith

D-U-N-S 04-549-7427
NATIONAL RURAL ELECTRIC COOPERATIVE ASSOCIATION
NRECA
4301 Wilson Blvd Ste 1, Arlington, VA 22203-1867
Tel (703) 907-5500 *Founded/Ownrshp* 1942
Sales 230.4MM *EMP* 885
Accts Bdo Usa Llp Bethesda Md
SIC 8611 Trade associations; Trade associations
CEO: Glenn L English Jr
**CEO:* Joann Emerson
COO: Denise Aranoff-Brown
COO: Jeffrey Connor
COO: Tom Lovas
**Sec:* Curtis Wynn
Ofcr: Cathy Windfield-Jones
Ex VP: Martin Lowery
VP: Peter Baxter
VP: Abigail Bell
VP: Scott Spencer
VP: Jim Spiers
VP: Tom Stangroom

D-U-N-S 07-781-8904
NATIONAL RURAL LETTER CARRIERS ASSOCIATION
1630 Duke St Fl 4, Alexandria, VA 22314-3465
Tel (703) 684-5545 *Founded/Ownrshp* 1998
Sales 31.4MM *EMP* 58
SIC 8621 8111 Professional membership organizations; Legal services; Professional membership organizations; Legal services
Pr: Jeanette P Dwyer
Treas: Clifford Dalling

D-U-N-S 07-483-3401
NATIONAL RURAL UTILITIES COOPERATIVE FINANCE CORP
20701 Cooperative Way, Dulles, VA 20166-6691
Tel (703) 467-1800 *Founded/Ownrshp* 1969
Sales NA *EMP* 232^E
Accts Kpmg Llp Mclean Virginia
SIC 6141 Personal credit institutions; Personal credit institutions
CEO: Sheldon C Petersen
**Pr:* Ray Beavers
Pr: Eileen Iciek
COO: Roger Ball
COO: John T Evans
CFO: J Andrew Don
**Sec:* Mike Campbell
Sr VP: Joel Allen
Sr VP: Roberta B Aronson
Sr VP: Graceann Clendenen
Sr VP: Robin Reed
Sr VP: Gregory Starheim
VP: Mike Bunney
**VP:* R Grant Clawson
VP: Russell Laird
VP: Amy Luongo
Comm Man: Beth A Johnson
Board of Directors: Jimmy A Lafoy, Patrick L Bridges, Harry N Park, Phillip A Carson, Bradley J Schardin, Mel Coleman, Mark D Snowden, Kent D Farmer, Dean R Tesch, Roman E Gillen, Kirk A Thompson, Doyle Jay Hanson, Stephen C Vail, Thomas L Hayes, Robert M Hill, Lyle Korver

D-U-N-S 09-845-6585
NATIONAL RURAL WATER ASSOCIATION
2915 S 13th St, Duncan, OK 73533-9086
Tel (580) 252-0629 *Founded/Ownrshp* 1976
Sales 49.0MM^E *EMP* 28
SIC 8331 8611 Job training services; Job counseling; Business associations; Job training services; Job counseling; Business associations
CEO: Sam Wade
**CFO:* Claudette Atwood

NATIONAL SABURU
See NATIONAL AUTOMOTIVE GROUP INC

NATIONAL SAFE
See HENRY BROS ELECTRONICS INC

D-U-N-S 04-657-3085
NATIONAL SAFETY COUNCIL
NSC
1121 Spring Lake Dr, Itasca, IL 60143-3201
Tel (630) 285-1121 *Founded/Ownrshp* 1913
Sales 58.6MM *EMP* 350
Accts Mcgladrey Llp Chicago Illino
SIC 8399 2721 1731 5084 Health & welfare council; Periodicals: publishing only; Safety & security specialization; Safety equipment; Health & welfare council; Periodicals: publishing only; Safety & security specialization; Safety equipment
Pr: Deborah AP Hersman
**Ch Bd:* Kent McElhattan
**Ch Bd:* John Surma
**Pr:* Joseph Ucciferro
**CFO:* Patrick Phelam
CFO: Patrick Phelan
CFO: Ed Rylco
**V Ch Bd:* Mark P Vergnano
Chf Mktg O: Lyn Fitzgerald
Ex VP: Ted Borek Jr
Ex VP: Cathy Milley
**Ex VP:* Paulette Moulos
VP: Shay Gallagher
VP: John Kennedy
Board of Directors: Raymond T Betler, Brian J Cook, Michael Gambrell, Lynne Lachenmyer, Douglas C Pontsler

NATIONAL SALON RESOURCES DIV
See MIKARA CORP

D-U-N-S 19-739-5551
NATIONAL SALVAGE & SERVICE CORP
MID WEST RAILROAD TIE SALES
6755 S Old State Road 37, Bloomington, IN 47401-8918
Tel (812) 339-8437 *Founded/Ownrshp* 1988
Sales 77.8MM^E *EMP* 130^E
Accts Katz Sapper & Miller Indiana
SIC 5088 1629 1795 5099 5093 Railroad equipment & supplies; Railroad & railway roadbed construction; Wrecking & demolition work; Demolition, buildings & other structures; Timber products, rough; Scrap & waste materials; Railroad equipment & supplies; Railroad & railway roadbed construction; Wrecking & demolition work; Demolition, buildings & other structures; Timber products, rough; Scrap & waste materials
Pr: Curtis C Schopp
**Pr:* Victoria E Schopp
**Sec:* Catherine Ruf
IT Man: Keri Decker

D-U-N-S 07-873-0983
NATIONAL SCHOOL DISTRICT
1500 N Ave, National City, CA 91950-4827
Tel (619) 336-7500 *Founded/Ownrshp* 1871
Sales 182.9MM^E *EMP* 6,000
SIC 8211 School board; School board
Ofcr: Myrna Ramirez
Dir Sec: Meghann O'Connor
CTO: Karen White
Schl Brd P: Alma Sarmiento
Psych: Raz Gibson
Psych: Susie Rico

D-U-N-S 08-779-4525
NATIONAL SCHOOL OF TECHNOLOGY INC
(*Suby of* CORINTHIAN COLLEGES INC) ★
6 Hutton Cntre Dr Ste 400, Santa Ana, CA 92707
Tel (714) 893-0005 *Founded/Ownrshp* 2002
Sales 9.8MM^E *EMP* 523
SIC 8221 8222 Colleges universities & professional schools; Junior colleges & technical institutes
CEO: Jack D Massimino
**Pr:* Martin Knobel
**CFO:* Brandon Pope
**VP:* Rosa Iverson
**VP:* Art Ortiz

D-U-N-S 07-481-1803
■ **NATIONAL SCIENCE FOUNDATION**
NSF
(*Suby of* EXECUTIVE OFFICE OF UNITED STATES GOVERNMENT) ★
4201 Wilson Blvd Ste 1205, Arlington, VA 22230-0002
Tel (703) 292-5050 *Founded/Ownrshp* 1950
Sales NA *EMP* 1,300^E
SIC 9199 9111

D-U-N-S 07-265-5665
NATIONAL SCIENCE TEACHERS ASSOCIATION
1840 Wilson Blvd Ste 300, Arlington, VA 22201-3000
Tel (703) 243-7100 *Founded/Ownrshp* 1944
Sales 25.3MM *EMP* 110
Accts Gelman Rosenberg & Freedman B
SIC 8621 Professional membership organizations; Professional membership organizations
Pr: Patricia Simmons
**Ch Bd:* Alan McCormick
**Pr:* Page Keely
**COO:* Moira F Baker
**Treas:* Randy Johnson
VP Sls: Brian Short

D-U-N-S 79-350-9928
NATIONAL SCOUTING REPORT INC
128 Total Solutions Way, Alabaster, AL 35007-4839
Tel (205) 216-0080 *Founded/Ownrshp* 1992
Sales 9.7MM^E *EMP* 300
SIC 7999 Sports professionals; Sports professionals
Pr: Robert Rigney
Off Mgr: Peggy Adams
Pharmcst: Derek Burchett

D-U-N-S 78-847-7305
NATIONAL SEATING & MOBILITY INC
318 Seaboard Ln Ste 202, Franklin, TN 37067-8289
Tel (615) 595-1115 *Founded/Ownrshp* 2013
Sales 201.0MM^E *EMP* 750
SIC 5999 3842 8099 Convalescent equipment & supplies; Convalescent equipment & supplies; Wheelchairs; Eye banks
CEO: William Mixon
COO: Sandi Neiman
CFO: Laurie Dotson
CFO: Tim Maddox
Ch: Mike Ballard
Sr VP: Bill Noelting
VP: John Bertone
VP: Jim Campanell
VP: David Catoe
VP: Kevin Harmon
VP: Bill Rogers
VP: Charles Sargeant

D-U-N-S 04-937-3095 IMP
■ **NATIONAL SEATING CO**
COMMERCIAL VEHICLE GROUP
(*Suby of* COMMERCIAL VEHICLE GROUP INC) ★
200 National Dr, Vonore, TN 37885-2124
Tel (423) 884-6651 *Founded/Ownrshp* 1985
Sales 6.3MM^E *EMP* 800
SIC 2531

D-U-N-S 79-134-2194 IMP
■ **NATIONAL SEATING CO**
C V G
(*Suby of* COMMERCIAL VEHICLE GROUP INC) ★
7800 Walton Pkwy, New Albany, OH 43054-8233
Tel (219) 872-7295 *Founded/Ownrshp* 1976
Sales 110.3MM^E *EMP* 467^E
SIC 2392 Chair covers & pads: made from purchased materials
Pr: Mervin Dunn
VP: Ray Miller
VP: Logan Mullinix
CTO: Paul Bennett
Netwrk Mgr: Jeff Vanscyoc
Opers Mgr: Bill Stimel

D-U-N-S 04-620-7635
■ **NATIONAL SECURITIES CORP**
(*Suby of* NATIONAL HOLDINGS CORP) ★
1001 4th Ave Ste 3750, Seattle, WA 98154-1193
Tel (206) 622-7200 *Founded/Ownrshp* 1997
Sales 20.7MM^E *EMP* 70^E
SIC 6211 Stock brokers & dealers
Pr: Michael Bresner
**COO:* David McCoy
**CFO:* Allan Levin
**Ofcr:* Chris Drea
**VP:* Janice Green
Mng Dir: Peter Rettman

D-U-N-S 13-840-4111
NATIONAL SECURITY AGENCY INC
343 S Dearborn St # 1610, Chicago, IL 60604-4000
Tel (312) 322-0000 *Founded/Ownrshp* 2003
Sales 1.7MM *EMP* 400
SIC 7381 Security guard service; Security guard service
Pr: Ibriham Kiswani

D-U-N-S 08-763-8433
■ **NATIONAL SECURITY FIRE AND CASUALTY CO**
(*Suby of* NATIONAL SECURITY GROUP INC) ★
661 Davis St E, Elba, AL 36323-1621
Tel (334) 897-2273 *Founded/Ownrshp* 1990
Sales NA *EMP* 60
SIC 6331 Fire, marine & casualty insurance; Fire, marine & casualty insurance
Pr: Jack E Brunson
CFO: Brian Leod
**CFO:* Brian McLeod

D-U-N-S 55-606-9110
▲ **NATIONAL SECURITY GROUP INC**
661 Davis St E, Elba, AL 36323-1621
Tel (334) 897-2273 *Founded/Ownrshp* 1947
Sales NA *EMP* 1,591^E
Accts Warren Averett Llc Birmingha
Tkr Sym NSEC *Exch* NGM
SIC 6311 6331 Life insurance; Fire, marine & casualty insurance; Life insurance; Fire, marine & casualty insurance
Pr: William L Brunson Jr
**Ch Bd:* Winfield Baird
CFO: Brian R McLeod

D-U-N-S 94-284-9787
NATIONAL SECURITY INDUSTRIES
940 Park Ave Frnt Frnt, San Jose, CA 95126-3074
Tel (408) 371-6505 *Founded/Ownrshp* 1995
Sales 8.3MM^E *EMP* 300
SIC 7381 Security guard service; Security guard service
Pr: Micheal Gerami

D-U-N-S 96-821-1842
NATIONAL SECURITY PARTNERS INC
3150 Fairview Park Dr, Falls Church, VA 22042-4504
Tel (703) 610-2000 *Founded/Ownrshp* 2011
Sales 12.1MM^E *EMP* 286
SIC 8742 7373 Management consulting services; Computer systems analysis & design; Management consulting services; Computer systems analysis & design

NATIONAL SECURITY PARTNERS LLC
See NOBLIS NSP LLC

D-U-N-S 06-596-9966
NATIONAL SECURITY SYSTEMS INC (NY)
511 Manhasset Woods Rd, Manhasset, NY 11030-1663
Tel (516) 627-2222 *Founded/Ownrshp* 1958, 1975
Sales 34.6MM *EMP* 26
Accts M R Weiser
SIC 3699 Security control equipment & systems; Security control equipment & systems
Ch: John W Walter
**Pr:* Jay Baron
**VP:* William T Walter

D-U-N-S 19-519-4779
NATIONAL SECURITY TECHNOLOGIES LLC
NSTEC
2621 Losee Rd, North Las Vegas, NV 89030-4129
Tel (702) 295-1000 *Founded/Ownrshp* 2005
Sales 584.5MM^E *EMP* 2,543
SIC 8711 1629 Civil engineering; Industrial plant construction; Civil engineering; Industrial plant construction
Pr: Raymond Juzaicis
CFO: Jack Stumpf
VP: Terry Marotta
VP: Adam Riback
Mng Dir: Hany Awadalla
CTO: Robert Morrow
IT Man: Kevin Forcade
IT Man: Tim McCreary
IT Man: David Patterson
Web Dev: Bev Larson
Sftwr Eng: Ryan Bellow

NATIONAL SEMINARS TRAINING
See ROCKHURST UNIVERSITY CONTINUING EDUCATION CENTER INC

D-U-N-S 18-143-5236
NATIONAL SENIOR CARE INC
1 Ravinia Dr Ste 1500, Atlanta, GA 30346-2115
Tel (678) 443-7000 *Founded/Ownrshp* 2004
Sales 4.4MMM^E *EMP* 35,000
SIC 5912 8051 8093 8741 8062 3443 Drug stores & proprietary stores; Extended care facility; Mental retardation hospital; Rehabilitation center, outpatient treatment; Industrial management; General medical & surgical hospitals; Chambers & caissons; Drug stores & proprietary stores; Extended care facility; Mental retardation hospital; Rehabilitation center, outpatient treatment; Industrial management; General medical & surgical hospitals; Chambers & caissons
Pr: Harry Grunstein

D-U-N-S 02-187-5162
NATIONAL SEPTEMBER 11 MEMORIAL & MUSEUM AT WORLD TRADE CENTER
20 Vesey St Lbby C, New York, NY 10007-4214
Tel (212) 267-2047 *Founded/Ownrshp* 2009
Sales 82.8MM *EMP* 3
SIC 8412 Museum
Prin: Bob Halio

D-U-N-S 17-848-0146
NATIONAL SEPTEMBER 11 MEMORIAL AND MUSEUM AT WORLD TRADE CENTER FOUNDATION INC
200 Liberty St Fl 16, New York, NY 10281-2103
Tel (212) 266-5211 *Founded/Ownrshp* 2003
Sales 82.8MM *EMP* 15
Accts O Connor Davies Llp New York
SIC 8412 Museum; Museum
Ch: Michael R Bloomberg
**Pr:* George H W Bush
**Pr:* Jimmy Carter
**Pr:* William J Clinton
Creative D: Michael Shulan

D-U-N-S 15-263-2006
NATIONAL SERVICE SOURCE INC
UNITED SERVICE SOURCE
(*Suby of* KYADAX CORP) ★
9145 Ellis Rd, Melbourne, FL 32904-1019
Tel (321) 723-5395 *Founded/Ownrshp* 1985
Sales 42.9MM^E *EMP* 160
SIC 1799 7622 8742 Antenna installation; Antenna repair; Industrial consultant; Antenna installation; Antenna repair; Industrial consultant
Pr: David Christiano
**Sr VP:* Bob Dunbar
VP: Brian Dunfee

VP: Guy Klenke
VP: Michele B Tully
VP Admn: Michele Brylanski
Prgrm Mgr: Debbie Jacobini
Prgrm Mgr: Todd Matarazzo
Prgrm Mgr: Gayle Person
Prgrm Mgr: Paul Weinfurtner
CTO: Brian Clinton

NATIONAL SERVICES
See MEDCO HEALTH SOLUTIONS OF SPOKANE INC

D-U-N-S 88-399-3698
NATIONAL SERVICES GROUP INC
COLLEGE WORKS PAINTING
1682 Langley Ave, Irvine, CA 92614-5620
Tel (714) 564-7900 *Founded/Ownrshp* 1999
Sales 84.7MM[E] *EMP* 685
SIC 1721 Painting & paper hanging

NATIONAL SLEEP PRODUCTS
See PACIFIC COAST FEATHER CO

D-U-N-S 03-724-3987
NATIONAL SLOVAK SOCIETY OF USA INC
351 Valley Brook Rd, Mc Murray, PA 15317-3337
Tel (724) 731-0094 *Founded/Ownrshp* 1890
Sales NA *EMP* 11
SIC 6311 Fraternal life insurance organizations
Pr: David Blazek
**Treas:* Paul Payerchin
**VP:* Dean A Burns
**Prin:* Paul Good

NATIONAL SMALLWARES
See WASSERSTROM CO

NATIONAL SPECIALISED HAULING
See NATIONAL LIFTTRUCK INC

NATIONAL SPECIALITY ALLOYS
See NATIONAL SPECIALTY ALLOYS INC

D-U-N-S 14-873-3413 IMP/EXP
■ **NATIONAL SPECIALTY ALLOYS INC**
NATIONAL SPECIALITY ALLOYS
(*Suby of* RELIANCE STEEL & ALUMINUM CO) ★
18250 Kieth Harrow Blvd, Houston, TX 77084-5739
Tel (281) 345-2115 *Founded/Ownrshp* 2012
Sales 41.2MM[E] *EMP* 103
SIC 5051 3356 Steel; Nickel & nickel alloy pipe, plates, sheets, etc.; Steel; Nickel & nickel alloy pipe, plates, sheets, etc.
CEO: Mark J Russ
Pr: Anthony Kosler
Sr Cor Off: Mark Russ
VP: Eileen Casiraghi
VP: Jim Rauch
Genl Mgr: Ron Galvan
IT Man: Karen Falkenbury
VP Opers: Eileen Schulman
Ql Cn Mgr: Heather Thomas
Sales Exec: Brad Poole
VP Sls: Ron Haynie

NATIONAL SPINE AND PAIN CTRS
See CENTER FOR PAIN MANAGEMENT LLC

D-U-N-S 00-160-3570 IMP/EXP
NATIONAL SPINNING CO INC (NY)
1481 W 2nd St, Washington, NC 27889-4157
Tel (252) 975-7111 *Founded/Ownrshp* 1900, 1919
Sales 181.7MM[E] *EMP* 650
SIC 2281 Wool yarn, spun; Acrylic yarn, spun: made from purchased staple; Polyester yarn, spun: made from purchased staple; Wool yarn, spun; Acrylic yarn, spun: made from purchased staple; Polyester yarn, spun: made from purchased staple
Pr: James W Chesnutt
**Ch Bd:* Morgan Miller
**Pr:* Jim Booterbaugh
**CFO:* Linda Fanton
**Ch:* Joseph N Leff
Treas: Thomas Markey
**Ex VP:* Bob Millere
**VP:* Robert Miller
Admn Mgr: Chris Jarman
VP Sls: Robert Gordon

D-U-N-S 06-949-9325
NATIONAL SPIRITUAL ASSEMBLY OF BAHAIS OF UNITED STATES
BAHAI NATIONAL CENTER
1233 Central St, Evanston, IL 60201-1611
Tel (847) 869-9039 *Founded/Ownrshp* 1927
Sales 42.9MM *EMP* 275
Accts Mcgladrey Llp Chicago Illino
SIC 8661 Religious organizations; Religious organizations
Ex Dir: Jacqueline Bull
**Treas:* William Roberts
Off Mgr: Vicki Carl
Software D: Rolando Avila
Snr Mgr: Roger Dahl
Assoc Ed: Tom Mennillo

D-U-N-S 96-657-5735
NATIONAL STABILIZATION AGREEMENT OF SHEET METAL INDUSTRY TRUST FUND
601 N Fairfax St Apt 400, Alexandria, VA 22314-2079
Tel (703) 739-7250 *Founded/Ownrshp* 2011
Sales 90.7MM *EMP* 2[E]
Accts Novak Francella Llc Bala Cynw
SIC 1761 Sheet metalwork; Sheet metalwork
Prin: Gerald Olejniczak

D-U-N-S 62-697-5481
NATIONAL STAFFING SOLUTIONS INC
925 S Semoran Blvd, Winter Park, FL 32792-5313
Tel (407) 277-2067 *Founded/Ownrshp* 2006
Sales 21.5MM[E] *EMP* 220[E]
SIC 7363 Help supply services; Help supply services
Pr: Steve Trinklein
**CFO:* Bart Richert
VP: Steven Didier
VP: Chanin Griffin
VP: Larry Jones
VP: Heidi Sanchez
Dir Bus: Amy Costello
IT Man: Steven Anderson
Manager: Stephanie Villacreces
Phys Thrpy: Michelle Stringer
Board of Directors: Heidi Sanchez

NATIONAL STARCH AND CHEMICAL
See INDOPCO INC

D-U-N-S 15-428-8666 EXP
■ **NATIONAL STARCH AND CHEMICAL HOLDING CORP**
(*Suby of* INGREDION INC) ★
10 Finderne Ave, Bridgewater, NJ 08807-3365
Tel (908) 685-5000 *Founded/Ownrshp* 1978
Sales 219.8MM[E] *EMP* 6,000
Accts Coopers & Lybrand
SIC 2891 2046 2869 Adhesives & sealants; Wet corn milling; Industrial organic chemicals; Vinyl acetate; Adhesives & sealants; Wet corn milling; Industrial organic chemicals; Vinyl acetate
Pr: Ned W Bandler
CFO: Tim Brownly
VP: Herbert J Baumgarten
VP: Tony Delio
Board of Directors: Robert B Albert

NATIONAL STATES ELC SYSTEMS
See KNIGHT ELECTRICAL SERVICES CORP

D-U-N-S 07-199-2358
NATIONAL STATES INSURANCE CO INC
2388 Schuetz Rd Ste A10, Saint Louis, MO 63146-4128
Tel (314) 878-0101 *Founded/Ownrshp* 1964
Sales NA *EMP* 130
SIC 6321 Accident & health insurance carriers; Accident & health insurance carriers
Pr: Thomas R Green
Treas: Phil Buibee
Treas: Ginger Wall
**Sec:* Pat Stuarn
**VP:* William Morrison
Admn Mgr: Linda Warren
CTO: Ben Messina
Plnt Mgr: Michael Nugent

NATIONAL STEAK & POULTRY
See NATIONAL STEAK PROCESSORS INC

D-U-N-S 09-444-0328
NATIONAL STEAK PROCESSORS INC
NATIONAL STEAK & POULTRY
301 E 5th Ave, Owasso, OK 74055-3450
Tel (918) 274-8787 *Founded/Ownrshp* 1980
Sales 101.6MM[E] *EMP* 325
SIC 2013 2015 Prepared beef products from purchased beef; Poultry slaughtering & processing; Prepared beef products from purchased beef; Poultry slaughtering & processing
CEO: Dave Albright
**Pr:* Steven A Kormondy
VP: Chuck Rogers
Dir IT: Joe Johnson
IT Man: Rick Schultz
Opers Mgr: Tanta Ward
Natl Sales: Bob Olson
Sls Mgr: Becky Flesher

D-U-N-S 00-915-8932 IMP
■ **NATIONAL STEEL & SHIPBUILDING CO**
NASSCO
(*Suby of* NASSCO HOLDINGS INC) ★
2798 Harbor Dr, San Diego, CA 92113-3650
Tel (619) 544-3400 *Founded/Ownrshp* 1989
Sales 556.7MM[E] *EMP* 3,000[E]
SIC 3731 Military ships, building & repairing; Commercial cargo ships, building & repairing; Military ships, building & repairing; Commercial cargo ships, building & repairing
Pr: Frederick J Harris
**Ch Bd:* Michael Toner
Pr: Timothy P McCue
CFO: Eric Murray
**Treas:* D H Fogg
Ofcr: Joseph Pileggi
**Ex VP:* Phebe Novakoviz
VP: Steve Clarey
VP: Richard Danehy
VP: Steven Davison
VP: Janice Grace
VP: Matthew Luxton
VP: Lane McVey
Comm Dir: James Gill

D-U-N-S 05-243-8215 IMP
NATIONAL STEEL RULE CO
750 Commerce Rd, Linden, NJ 07036-2496
Tel (908) 862-3366 *Founded/Ownrshp* 1967
Sales 39.1MM[E] *EMP* 280
SIC 3423 3546 3425 Rules or rulers, metal; Power-driven handtools; Saw blades & handsaws; Rules or rulers, metal; Power-driven handtools; Saw blades & handsaws
Pr: Edmund Mucci Jr
Sr VP: Gregory Zimmer
VP: Joseph E Bialoglow
VP: Bethann Bialoglow-Masiello
VP: John White
Off Mgr: Elizabeth Ferreira
Plnt Mgr: William Pinkasavage
Sales Exec: David Bialoglow

NATIONAL STONEWORKS CABINETRY
See NATIONAL STONEWORKS LLC

D-U-N-S 84-861-6392 IMP
NATIONAL STONEWORKS LLC
NATIONAL STONEWORKS CABINETRY
3200 Meridian Pkwy # 101, Weston, FL 33331-3502
Tel (954) 349-1609 *Founded/Ownrshp* 2009
Sales 30.0MM[E] *EMP* 41
SIC 3281 2434 Table tops, marble; Wood kitchen cabinets; Table tops, marble; Wood kitchen cabinets
Off Mgr: Vilma Schwartz

D-U-N-S 07-980-8768
NATIONAL STORAGE AFFILIATES TRUST
5200 Dtc Pkwy Ste 200, Greenwood Village, CO 80111-2715
Tel (720) 630-2600 *Founded/Ownrshp* 2013
Sales 76.9MM *EMP* 13
Accts Kpmg Llp Denver Colorado
SIC 6798 Real estate investment trusts
Pr: Arlen D Nordhagen
CFO: Tamara D Fischer
Sr VP: Steven B Treadwell

NATIONAL STORES
See J&M SALES OF TEXAS LLC

D-U-N-S 04-222-9328 IMP
NATIONAL STORES INC (CA)
FALLAS-PAREDES
15001 S Figueroa St, Gardena, CA 90248-1721
Tel (310) 324-9962 *Founded/Ownrshp* 1961
Sales 935.7MM[E] *EMP* 4,000
SIC 5651 Family clothing stores; Family clothing stores
CEO: Michael Fallas
**Pr:* George Bellino
Sr VP: Dwane Huesers
VP: Chris Nichols
Dir Soc: Veasna Koy
Dist Mgr: Cheryl Gause
Dist Mgr: Robert Perez
Site Mgr: Bertha Mendoza

D-U-N-S 82-703-4414
NATIONAL STUDENT CLEARINGHOUSE INC
2300 Dulles Station Blvd # 300, Herndon, VA 20171-6350
Tel (703) 742-4200 *Founded/Ownrshp* 1993
Sales 40.8MM *EMP* 150
Accts Mcgladrey Llp Gaithersburg M
SIC 7374 Data verification service; Data verification service
Pr: Ricardo D Torres
Pr: Mark Jones
Assoc VP: Herb R Chereck
Assoc VP: Heather Smith
VP: Peter S Fong
VP: William R Haid
VP: James Kathman
VP: Christine Kerlin
VP: George Levathes
VP: W Pelham
Dir Bus: Jim Leahy

NATIONAL STUDENT LOAN PROGRAM
See NEBRASKA STUDENT LOAN PROGRAM INC

NATIONAL SUPER SERVICE CO
See NSS ENTERPRISES INC

D-U-N-S 09-049-7095
NATIONAL SUPPORT CENTER LLC
NSC
3600 Thayer Ct Ste 110, Aurora, IL 60504-6709
Tel (630) 778-4100 *Founded/Ownrshp* 1998
Sales 10.5MM[E] *EMP* 300
SIC 7378 Computer maintenance & repair; Computer maintenance & repair
Pr: Ron Janusz

D-U-N-S 00-691-2752
NATIONAL SURETY CORP
(*Suby of* FIREMANS FUND INSURANCE CO) ★
777 San Marin Dr, Novato, CA 94945-1345
Tel (415) 899-2000 *Founded/Ownrshp* 1933, 1954
Sales NA *EMP* 1,000
SIC 6351 Surety insurance; Surety insurance
CEO: Lori D Fouche
Board of Directors: Lauren R Bailey, Douglas E Franklin, John F Huddleston Jr, Jeffery F Johnson, Sally B Narey, Frank A Sapio, D Andrew Torrance, Kevin E Walker, David M Zona

D-U-N-S 13-125-8159
■ **NATIONAL SURGICAL CARE INC**
AMSURG
(*Suby of* AMSURG CORP) ★
20 Burton Hills Blvd # 500, Nashville, TN 37215-6176
Tel (615) 665-1283 *Founded/Ownrshp* 2002
Sales 20.0MM[E] *EMP* 530
SIC 8062 General medical & surgical hospitals; General medical & surgical hospitals
Ch Bd: Sami S Abbasi
**Pr:* Richard D Pence
COO: Brian Fisher
**Treas:* Letietia Bonthrm
Exec: John Garcia
Off Mgr: Holly Cruz
Dir IT: Shawn Clark
Mtls Mgr: Gloria Bessette
Mtls Mgr: Mike Taylor

D-U-N-S 17-356-5529
NATIONAL SURGICAL HOSPITALS INC
250 S Wacker Dr Ste 500, Chicago, IL 60606-5897
Tel (312) 627-8400 *Founded/Ownrshp* 1998
Sales 296.4MM[E] *EMP* 3,100
Accts E&Y Chicago Il
SIC 8062 8093 General medical & surgical hospitals; Specialty outpatient clinics; General medical & surgical hospitals; Specialty outpatient clinics
CEO: David Crane
Pr: Bryan Fisher
Pr: Donna Worsham
CFO: David N T Watson
Ofcr: Rob Guenthner
Ex VP: James T Grant
Sr VP: Scott B Clark
Sr VP: Dennis D Solheim
Sr VP: Christopher Suscha
VP: Carl Ericson
VP: Donna Giles
VP: Charlie Smith
VP: Doug Watkins
Dir Lab: Michelle Cornstubble
Dir Lab: Brenda Gutierrez
Dir Rad: Kevin Bassett

NATIONAL SWAGE
See CROSBY GROUP LLC

D-U-N-S 05-395-2201
NATIONAL SYSTEMS AMERICA LP
5945 Dallas Pkwy Ste 100, Plano, TX 75093-7878
Tel (972) 212-7433 *Founded/Ownrshp* 1996
Sales 20.6MM *EMP* 175
Accts Jp Plano Texas
SIC 7379 7361 7371 Computer related consulting services; Employment agencies; Computer software development & applications; Computer related consulting services; Employment agencies; Computer software development & applications
Pt: Hari Patro
Pt: Seelam Reddy
Pt: Mukesh Shah
S&M/VP: Daren Bitter

D-U-N-S 05-298-8306
NATIONAL TEACHERS ASSOCIATES LIFE INSURANCE CO
NTA LIFE
4949 Keller Springs Rd, Addison, TX 75001-5910
Tel (972) 532-2100 *Founded/Ownrshp* 2010
Sales NA *EMP* 200
SIC 6311 Life insurance; Life insurance
CEO: Raymond Martin Jr
Assoc VP: Chris Rogers
**Ex VP:* James T Langham Jr
CIO: Matt Ginette
Mktg Dir: Scott Calaway

D-U-N-S 06-381-8587 IMP
NATIONAL TECHNICAL SYSTEMS INC
NTS
(*Suby of* NEST PARENT, INC.)
24007 Ventura Blvd # 200, Calabasas, CA 91302-1430
Tel (818) 591-0776 *Founded/Ownrshp* 1996
Sales 518.1MM[E] *EMP* 1,162[E]
SIC 8711 Engineering services; Engineering services
Pr: William McGinnis
V Ch: Aaron Cohen
Pr: Bruce Irwin
Pr: Vicki Panhuise
COO: Derek Coppinger
CFO: Michael El-Hillow
Treas: John Buono
Chf Mktg O: Dwight Moore
Sr VP: Douglas Briskie
VP: Martha Andreani
VP: Loren Isley
VP: Walter Levonowich
VP: Barry Peter
VP: Jim Pinyan
VP: Austin Schaffter
Exec: Julio Arizaga

D-U-N-S 13-228-1031
NATIONAL TECHNOLOGIES ASSOCIATES INC
NTA
2800 S Shirlington Rd # 700, Arlington, VA 22206-3601
Tel (703) 941-3695 *Founded/Ownrshp* 1981
Sales 43.6MM[E] *EMP* 600
SIC 8741 8711 7374 Management services; Engineering services; Management services; Engineering services; Data processing & preparation
CEO: Michael Fraser
**CFO:* Alexander Abramidis
**CFO:* Robert Richards
VP: Paul Beaumont
VP: Ken Graeser

D-U-N-S 00-610-6512 EXP
NATIONAL TECHNOLOGIES INC (WI)
7641 S 10th St, Oak Creek, WI 53154-1911
Tel (414) 571-1000 *Founded/Ownrshp* 1959
Sales 27.0MM[E] *EMP* 162
SIC 3469 3599

D-U-N-S 03-069-0825
NATIONAL TECHNOLOGY LEASING CORP
11601 Blocker Dr Ste 110, Auburn, CA 95603-4650
Tel (530) 887-5486 *Founded/Ownrshp* 2000
Sales NA *EMP* 8
SIC 6159 Machinery & equipment finance leasing; Machinery & equipment finance leasing
Pr: Mike Coffelt

D-U-N-S 07-483-0720
NATIONAL TELECOMMUNICATIONS COOPERATIVE ASSOCIATION
NTCA RURAL BROADBAND ASSN
4121 Wilson Blvd Ste 1000, Arlington, VA 22203-4145
Tel (703) 351-2000 *Founded/Ownrshp* 1954
Sales 294.2MM[E] *EMP* 136
Accts Cliftonlarsonallen Llp Arling
SIC 8611 8741 Trade associations; Management services; Trade associations; Management services
CEO: Shirley Bloomfield
**Pr:* Force Terry
**Treas:* Ronald Laudner
VP: Shary Denes
**VP:* Lisa I Schweitzer
**VP:* Donald D Miller
**Prin:* Michael E Brunner
Counsel: Gregory Whiteaker

D-U-N-S 00-999-8626
NATIONAL TELECOMMUTING INSTITUTE INC
69 Canal St, Boston, MA 02114-2006
Tel (617) 787-4426 *Founded/Ownrshp* 1995
Sales 9.7MM *EMP* 350[E]
Accts Alexander Aronson Finning & Co
SIC 7363 Help supply services; Help supply services
CEO: Mary J Willard
**CFO:* Denise Horgan
Dir IT: Peter Oleary

D-U-N-S 02-794-9593
NATIONAL TELECONSULTANTS LLC
550 N Brand Blvd Fl 17, Glendale, CA 91203-1944
Tel (818) 265-4400 *Founded/Ownrshp* 1981
Sales 32.3MM[E] *EMP* 108
SIC 8711 Electrical or electronic engineering; Electrical or electronic engineering
Mng Pt: Elliot Gram
Ex VP: Charles C Phelan
Sr VP: John Aalto
Sr VP: Kevin Scott
VP: Andre Abed
VP: Peter Adamiak

VP: John Footen
VP: John Scandurra
Snr Sftwr: Tanmay Goel
Dir IT: Nadine Cohen
Sftwr Eng: Mansi Vora

D-U-N-S 00-843-3948 IMP
NATIONAL TERRAZZO TILE & MARBLE INC (TX)
(*Suby of* LONGO ENTERPRISES INC) ★
5728 Hood St, Houston, TX 77023-5998
Tel (713) 923-8600 *Founded/Ownrshp* 1920
Sales 21.8MM^E *EMP* 170
SIC 1743 5032 Terrazzo, tile, marble, mosaic work; Brick, stone & related material; Terrazzo, tile, marble, mosaic work; Brick, stone & related material
Pr: Victor Longo
**Sec:* Ann Longo
**VP:* Ronald Gonzales
CTO: Cheryl Falgoust

D-U-N-S 87-810-8497 IMP
NATIONAL TEXTILE AND APPAREL INC
1018 Industrial Dr, Hazlehurst, MS 39083-8800
Tel (601) 892-4356 *Founded/Ownrshp* 1994
Sales 44.9MM^E *EMP* 295
SIC 2326 5137 Men's & boys' work clothing; Women's & children's clothing; Men's & boys' work clothing; Women's & children's clothing
Pr: Frederic Lepoutre
**VP:* Teresa Lepoutres
Mktg Mgr: Jennifer King

NATIONAL THEATRE CONSERVATORY
See DENVER CENTER FOR PERFORMING ARTS

D-U-N-S 10-910-9207
NATIONAL THERAPEUTIC ASSOCIATES INC
REHAB VISIONS
11623 Arbor St Ste 200, Omaha, NE 68144-2996
Tel (402) 334-1919 *Founded/Ownrshp* 1983
Sales 17.4MM^E *EMP* 550
SIC 8049 Physical therapist; Physical therapist
Pr: Joel A Larmore
**CFO:* Darrell A Metcalf
CFO: Darrell Metcalf
**Sr VP:* Rick D Larmore
**VP:* Debbie Lacey

D-U-N-S 00-304-6968 EXP
NATIONAL TICKET CO (PA)
5562 Snydertown Rd, Paxinos, PA 17860-7536
Tel (570) 672-2900 *Founded/Ownrshp* 1905
Sales 33.9MM^E *EMP* 130
SIC 2752 2791 2789 2759 Tickets, lithographed; Coupons, lithographed; Tags, lithographed; Typesetting; Bookbinding & related work; Commercial printing; Tickets, lithographed; Coupons, lithographed; Tags, lithographed; Typesetting; Bookbinding & related work; Commercial printing
Ch Bd: Earl Foura
**Pr:* Earl D Foura
**CEO:* Robert J Yost
**Sec:* Margaret L Timco
**VP:* John J Conway
VP: Todd Hauck
**VP:* Edward A Ludes
Dir Bus: Mark Lacoste
Plnt Mgr: Melvin Helwig
Board of Directors: John J Conway Jr, Gerald Donohue, Thomas Strausser

D-U-N-S 01-520-4050 IMP
NATIONAL TISSUE CO LLC
(*Suby of* NATIONAL PACKAGING SERVICES CORP) ★
3326 E Layton Ave, Cudahy, WI 53110-1405
Tel (414) 239-7026 *Founded/Ownrshp* 2014
Sales 40.5MM^E *EMP* 110
SIC 2679 Paper products, converted; Paper products, converted
Pr: Mike Graverson
CFO: Doug Rued
VP: Jill Lambrecht
Prd Mgr: Orlando Santiago

NATIONAL TITLE SOURCE
See TITLE SOURCE INC

D-U-N-S 18-656-5255 IMP
NATIONAL TOBACCO CO LP
(*Suby of* NORTH ATLANTIC TRADING CO INC) ★
5201 Interchange Way, Louisville, KY 40229-2184
Tel (502) 961-7452 *Founded/Ownrshp* 1997
Sales 49.3MM^E *EMP* 246
SIC 2131 Chewing tobacco; Chewing tobacco
Ch Bd: Thomas Helms Jr
Mtls Mgr: David Goodin
Manager: Pak Tacbco
Snr Mgr: Todd Milligan

D-U-N-S 08-535-4421
NATIONAL TOOL & MANUFACTURING CO
NTM
581 Wheeling Rd, Wheeling, IL 60090-4743
Tel (847) 806-9800 *Founded/Ownrshp* 1933
Sales 21.9MM^E *EMP* 100
SIC 3599 Ties, form: metal
Pr: Jim Soderquist
**VP:* Mitch Predki
**Prd Mgr:* David Niedbalec
Mktg Mgr: John Chung
Manager: Eric Sandberg

D-U-N-S 06-914-7866 IMP/EXP
NATIONAL TOOL SUPPLY INC (FL)
5725 W Hllandale Bch Blvd, West Park, FL 33023-5277
Tel (954) 963-7222 *Founded/Ownrshp* 1978
Sales 22.0MM^E *EMP* 38
SIC 5072 Hand tools; Power handtools
Pr: Lawrence Weiner

NATIONAL TRAIL BANKING CENTER
See FIRST NATIONAL BANK OF DIETERICH

D-U-N-S 60-873-9363
NATIONAL TRAINING SYSTEMS ASSOCIATION INC
N D I A
2111 Wilson Blvd Ste 400, Arlington, VA 22201-3001
Tel (703) 522-1820 *Founded/Ownrshp* 1988
Sales 24.2MM *EMP* 3
Accts Cliftonlarsonallen Llp Arling
SIC 8742 Training & development consultant; Training & development consultant
Pr: Fred Lewis
V Ch: Joel Goldman
**CEO:* Lawrence Farrell
Bd of Dir: Cindy Adams
Bd of Dir: Michael S Allen
Bd of Dir: William P Carter
Bd of Dir: Diane Garcia
Bd of Dir: Arlo Gravseth
Bd of Dir: Doug Hartmann
Bd of Dir: Michael J Moniz
Bd of Dir: David C Rosenblum
Bd of Dir: Rachel Yates
VP: Tim Bagniefski
VP: Barry Bates
VP: Peters Edmond
VP: Tim French
VP: Mark S Gruenberg
VP: Jim Kumpost
VP: Eric Laurin
VP: Mark C Rohlena
VP: Patrick Ryan

D-U-N-S 04-054-8521
■ **NATIONAL TRANSPORTATION SAFETY BOARD**
NTSB
(*Suby of* EXECUTIVE OFFICE OF UNITED STATES GOVERNMENT) ★
490 L'enfant Plz East Sw, Washington, DC 20594-0001
Tel (202) 314-6000 *Founded/Ownrshp* 1975
Sales NA *EMP* 440
SIC 9229 Public safety bureau, government; ; Public safety bureau, government;
Ch Bd: Mark Rosenker
V Ch: Harkey Mayo
Ofcr: Christopher Blumberg
Adm Dir: Mary Jones
Adm Dir: Tawanna Terrell-Thomas
Mng Dir: Karen Bury
Genl Couns: Katie Inman
Genl Couns: David Tolchen
Counsel: Benjamin Allen
Snr Mgr: Michael Budinski
Snr Mgr: John Clark

NATIONAL TRCK PARTS OF MIDWEST
See CCC PARTS CO

D-U-N-S 14-491-3113 IMP
NATIONAL TRENCH SAFETY LLC
NTS
260 N Sam Houston Pkwy E # 200, Houston, TX 77060-2022
Tel (832) 200-0988 *Founded/Ownrshp* 2004
Sales 27.8MM^E *EMP* 40
SIC 7359 Equipment rental & leasing
CEO: Ronald W Chilton
**Pr:* Steve Barnhardt
**COO:* Shelly Bangerter
**Sr VP:* Thomas H Hartman
**Sr VP:* Wes Jones Jr
Area Mgr: Brant Frederick
Area Mgr: Pat Hewitt
Brnch Mgr: Chris Breed
Brnch Mgr: Steve Brinkley
Brnch Mgr: Rick Chavez
Brnch Mgr: Brad Copleston

D-U-N-S 19-550-3263
NATIONAL TRUCK PARTS OF MIDWEST INC
TRUCK PARTS SPECIALIST
(*Suby of* CCI CORP) ★
1901 N Sheridan Rd, Tulsa, OK 74115-3602
Tel (918) 836-0151 *Founded/Ownrshp* 1983
Sales 180.2MM^E *EMP* 1,150
SIC 5531 Truck equipment & parts; Truck equipment & parts
Pr: Joseph M Klein
**VP:* D M Hardin

D-U-N-S 07-482-0499 IMP
NATIONAL TRUST FOR HISTORIC PRESERVATION IN UNITED STATES
N T H P
2600 Virginia Ave Nw # 1000, Washington, DC 20037-1922
Tel (202) 588-6000 *Founded/Ownrshp* 1949
Sales 50.3MM *EMP* 469
SIC 8412 Historical society; Historical society
Pr: Stephanie K Meeks
COO: Randy Bartholomew
**CFO:* Michael L Forster
Trst: William W Grant
**Ex VP:* David J Brown
**VP:* Greg Coble
VP: Kristine M Dahlberg
VP: Henry Jordan

NATIONAL TUBE & STEEL
See NATIONAL BUSINESS GROUP INC

D-U-N-S 62-157-3773 EXP
NATIONAL TUBE HOLDING CO INC
290 21st St N, Birmingham, AL 35203-3323
Tel (205) 322-8816 *Founded/Ownrshp* 1990
Sales 76.2MM^E *EMP* 475
SIC 3351 3585 3498 Tubing, copper & copper alloy; Parts for heating, cooling & refrigerating equipment; Fabricated pipe & fittings; Tubing, copper & copper alloy; Parts for heating, cooling & refrigerating equipment; Fabricated pipe & fittings
Ch Bd: Thomas Fox

D-U-N-S 62-048-7637 IMP
NATIONAL TUBE SUPPLY CO
(*Suby of* SICAM SOCIETA' ITALIANA COMMERCIO ACCIAI E METALLI SPA)
925 Central Ave, University Park, IL 60484-3143
Tel (708) 534-2700 *Founded/Ownrshp* 1990
Sales 187.4MM^E *EMP* 170
SIC 5051 Tubing, metal; Tubing, metal
Pr: Gary Chess
COO: Brian Kluge
Dir Bus: Marc Biolchin
Area Mgr: Fred Boatman
Area Mgr: Tag Green
Area Mgr: Amy Jacobs
Area Mgr: Debbie Keppler-Stepp
Area Mgr: Carl Wyant
Dir IT: Sean Tomei
IT Man: Michele Markowski
Trfc Dir: Josh Peek

NATIONAL UNDERWRITER COMPANY
See SUMMIT PROFESSIONAL NETWORKS

D-U-N-S 04-361-4098
■ **NATIONAL UNION FIRE INSURANCE CO OF PITTSBURGH PA**
(*Suby of* CHARTIS US INC) ★
70 Pine St Fl 50, New York, NY 10270-0001
Tel (631) 692-4545 *Founded/Ownrshp* 1973
Sales NA *EMP* 1,000
SIC 6331 Property damage insurance; Fire, marine & casualty insurance: stock; Property damage insurance; Fire, marine & casualty insurance: stock
Pr: John Q Doyle
Pr: Tracy Johnson
CFO: Robert Jacobson
VP: Christopher Blum
VP: Michael Castelli
Dir IT: Peter McKenna

D-U-N-S 17-021-3078
NATIONAL UNITY INSURANCE CO
15303 Huebner Rd Ste 1, San Antonio, TX 78248-0982
Tel (210) 479-8886 *Founded/Ownrshp* 1993
Sales NA *EMP* 35
SIC 6411 Insurance agents & brokers; Insurance agents & brokers
Pr: Ramon Rodriguez
Treas: Harry Salinas
Treas: Santa Yeverino

D-U-N-S 07-334-7809
NATIONAL UNIVERSITY
11255 N Torrey Pines Rd, La Jolla, CA 92037-1011
Tel (858) 642-8000 *Founded/Ownrshp* 1971
Sales 247.4MM *EMP* 1,954
SIC 8221 University; University
Ofcr: Erhan Bozkurt
Ofcr: Caitlin Valdez
Assoc VP: Jonathon Chillas
Assoc VP: Vernon Taylor
Assoc Dir: Megan Hall
Prgrm Mgr: Kimberleigh Kopp
CIO: Scott Moss
MIS Dir: Mark Sotelo
Dir IT: Anthony Swope
Mktg Dir: Jason Bullock
Pr Dir: David Neville

D-U-N-S 07-156-9413
NATIONAL UNIVERSITY ACADEMY (CA)
11355 N Torrey Pines Rd, La Jolla, CA 92037-1013
Tel (858) 642-8000 *Founded/Ownrshp* 2011
Sales 5.9MM *EMP* 298
Accts Jgd & Associates Llp San Dieg
SIC 8211 Academy; Academy
Prin: Bernie Hanlon

D-U-N-S 06-860-7589
NATIONAL UNIVERSITY OF HEALTH SCIENCES
200 E Roosevelt Rd, Lombard, IL 60148-4539
Tel (630) 932-5623 *Founded/Ownrshp* 1906
Sales 22.8MM *EMP* 200
Accts Sikich Llp Naperville Il
SIC 8221 8733 Professional schools; Noncommercial research organizations; Professional schools; Noncommercial research organizations
Pr: James F Winterstein
VP: Hilary Kluczynski
CTO: Michelle Jourdan
Snr Mgr: Hyundo Kim
Snr Mgr: Victoria Sweeney

D-U-N-S 07-327-5547
NATIONAL URBAN LEAGUE INC
120 Wall St Fl 7, New York, NY 10005-3900
Tel (212) 558-5300 *Founded/Ownrshp* 1910
Sales 49.2MM *EMP* 100
Accts Mitchell & Titus Llp New York
SIC 8399 Advocacy group; Social change association
Ch: John D Hofmeister
**Pr:* Marc H Morial
**CFO:* Paul Wycisk
**Treas:* Willard Brittain
Trst: Ajay Banga
Sr VP: Cheryl F McCants
Sr VP: Michael Miller
Sr VP: Rhonda Spears-Bell
VP: Terry Clark
VP: Lynn Law
VP: Nicolaine Lazarre
VP: Harry Smith

D-U-N-S 06-823-1554
NATIONAL UTILITY SERVICE INC (NJ)
NUS CONSULTING GROUP
1 Maynard Dr Ste 2, Park Ridge, NJ 07656-1878
Tel (201) 391-4300 *Founded/Ownrshp* 1933, 1990
Sales 31.7MM^E *EMP* 74
SIC 8748 Energy conservation consultant
Pr: Gary J Soultanian
Pr: Richard D Soultanian
CFO: Paul Dugandzic
VP: Robert Heinrich
VP: Robert Macksoud
VP: Craig Thalmann
VP: Linda Vazquez

Netwrk Mgr: John Daniel
Sales Asso: Phil Magers

D-U-N-S 05-841-6488 IMP
NATIONAL VACUUM EQUIPMENT INC
2707 Aero Park Dr, Traverse City, MI 49686-9101
Tel (231) 941-0215 *Founded/Ownrshp* 1980
Sales 22.6MM^E *EMP* 50^E
SIC 5084 5085 Industrial machinery & equipment; Industrial supplies
Pr: Bruce Louma

D-U-N-S 00-543-7595
NATIONAL VAN LINES INC (IL)
2800 W Roosevelt Rd, Broadview, IL 60155-3771
Tel (708) 450-2900 *Founded/Ownrshp* 1930
Sales 71.9MM^E *EMP* 135
Accts Clifton Gunderson Llp Oak Bro
SIC 4213 4731 Household goods transport; Domestic freight forwarding; Foreign freight forwarding; Household goods transport; Domestic freight forwarding; Foreign freight forwarding
CEO: Maureen Beal
**Pr:* Tim Helenthal
CFO: Robert Buti
**Sr VP:* Ron McKee
**VP:* Jorja Coulter
**VP:* Mark Doyle
**VP:* Gerry Mundt
VP: Tom Philbin
MIS Dir: Sam Buonauro
Sls Dir: James Andersen
Sls Dir: Donna Martin

D-U-N-S 80-663-3285
NATIONAL VENDOR INC
1754 Bagdad Rd Ste D100, Cedar Park, TX 78613-6478
Tel (512) 628-8324 *Founded/Ownrshp* 1997
Sales NA *EMP* 70^E
SIC 6411 Insurance claim adjusters, not employed by insurance company
Pr: Randy Joshua Barnaby
COO: Alex Xiros
VP: Kenny Stefan
VP Mktg: Kelly Henry

D-U-N-S 15-782-6058
NATIONAL VETERINARY ASSOCIATES INC
29229 Canwood St Ste 100, Agoura Hills, CA 91301-1503
Tel (805) 777-7722 *Founded/Ownrshp* 1997
Sales 728.6MM^E *EMP* 1,900^E
SIC 0742 Nonresidential building operators; Veterinary services, specialties
CEO: Greg Hartmann
Pr: Nick Burda
**COO:* Thomas Sawicki
CFO: Jim Woloshyn
**CFO:* R James Woloshyn
Bd of Dir: Craig Frances
Chf Mktg O: Carol Henry
VP: Scott Norby
Prac Mgr: Amy Cole
Prac Mgr: Eric Young
Rgnl Mgr: Lisa Suever

D-U-N-S 61-874-5954 IMP
NATIONAL VISION INC
2435 Commerce Ave # 2200, Duluth, GA 30096-4980
Tel (770) 822-3600 *Founded/Ownrshp* 1990
Sales 898.4MM^E *EMP* 5,000
SIC 5995 8042 Optical goods stores; Eyeglasses, prescription; Contact lenses, prescription; Contact lense specialist optometrist; Optical goods stores; Eyeglasses, prescription; Contact lenses, prescription; Contact lense specialist optometrist
Pr: Reade Fahs
Pr: Michelle Berger
**Pr:* Bruce J Steffey
COO: Jay Bruce Steffey
**CFO:* Paul A Criscills Jr
Treas: Timothy W Renney
**Sr VP:* Chuck Criscillis
Sr VP: Nancy Evert
**Sr VP:* Mitchell Goodman
VP: Renee Himel
VP: Tim Ranney
VP: Robert E Schnelle
Dir Lab: Mike Gibson
Board of Directors: L Reade Fahs, D Randolph Peeler

D-U-N-S 10-209-8324 IMP
NATIONAL VITAMIN CO INC
NVC
1145 W Gila Bend Hwy, Casa Grande, AZ 85122-4308
Tel (520) 316-9104 *Founded/Ownrshp* 1974
Sales 54.9MM^E *EMP* 180^E
SIC 2834 Vitamin preparations; Vitamin preparations
Pr: Earl Wesley Courtney Jr
**Pt:* Earl Courtney III
CFO: Chantel Garcia
**VP:* Roger Mann
Off Mgr: Chachi Rodriguez
QC Dir: Kalani Kraus
Sls Mgr: Gregg Beason
Sls Mgr: Michael Kee

D-U-N-S 19-714-3548
NATIONAL WALLCOVERING INC
10020 Maumelle Blvd, North Little Rock, AR 72113-6612
Tel (501) 378-0039 *Founded/Ownrshp* 1983
Sales 27.1MM^E *EMP* 52
SIC 5198 Wallcoverings
Pr: Larry Bixler
CFO: Mark Moseley
**Sec:* Pat Bixler
**VP:* Michael Bixler
IT Man: Michael Currey
IT Man: Currey Michael
Sls Mgr: Kim M Clain
Sales Asso: Kate Kenwell
Sales Asso: Cristina Pena

D-U-N-S 01-498-9525
NATIONAL WARRANTY CORP
6120 Powers Ferry Rd, Atlanta, GA 30339-2996
Tel (678) 894-3500 *Founded/Ownrshp* 1992
Sales NA *EMP* 57

SIC 6399 Warranty insurance, automobile; Warranty insurance, automobile
CEO: Mark Mishler
COO: Cesar Soriano
CFO: Geoffrey Tirone

D-U-N-S 06-950-6236
■ NATIONAL WASTE SERVICE INC
ALLIED WASTE SERVICES
(Suby of ALLIED WASTE INDUSTRIES INC) ★
2608 S Damen Ave, Chicago, IL 60608-5209
Tel (773) 579-3600 Founded/Ownrshp 1992
Sales 83.7MM^E EMP 205
SIC 4953 Refuse systems; Refuse systems
Pr: Thomas Van Weelden
*VP: Richard Van Hattem

D-U-N-S 92-995-9153
■ NATIONAL WEATHER SERVICE
NATIONAL WEATHER SERVICE OHD1
(Suby of NATIONAL OCEANIC AND ATMOSPHERIC ADMINISTRATION) ★
1325 E West Hwy, Silver Spring, MD 20910-3280
Tel (609) 261-6600 Founded/Ownrshp 1870
Sales NA EMP 1,225
SIC 9611 Administration of general economic programs; ; Administration of general economic programs;
Ofcr: Kathleen Oleary

NATIONAL WEATHER SERVICE OHD1
See NATIONAL WEATHER SERVICE

D-U-N-S 00-787-5206
▲ NATIONAL WESTERN LIFE INSURANCE CO
850 E Anderson Ln, Austin, TX 78752-1602
Tel (512) 836-1010 Founded/Ownrshp 1956
Sales NA EMP 279^E
Accts Bkd Little Rock Arkansas
Tkr Sym NWLI Exch NGS
SIC 6311 Life insurance; Life insurance carriers; Life insurance; Life insurance carriers
Ch Bd: Robert L Moody
Pr: Fabiola Best
Pr: Daniel Calderon
*Pr: Ross R Moody
CFO: Brian M Pribyl
Chf Mktg O: S Christopher Johnson
Sr VP: Paul D Facey
Sr VP: James P Payne
Sr VP: Robert Sweeney
VP: John Bower
VP: Gary Fischer
VP: Chris Johnson
VP: Jo Morris
VP: Lawrence Scott
VP: Bruce E Wood
Board of Directors: Frances A Moody-Dahlberg, Stephen E Glasgow, E Douglas McLeod, Charles D Milos, Ann M Moody, Russell S Moody, Louis E Pauls Jr, E J Pederson

NATIONAL WHL LQUIDATORS STORES
See NSC WHOLESALE HOLDINGS LLC

D-U-N-S 02-467-6892 IMP
NATIONAL WHOLESALE CO INC
400 National Blvd, Lexington, NC 27294-0002
Tel (336) 248-5904 Founded/Ownrshp 1952
Sales 38.8MM EMP 200
Accts Terry Ng Cpa Pllc Greenvill
SIC 5961 5632 Women's apparel, mail order; Women's dancewear, hosiery & lingerie; Women's apparel, mail order; Women's dancewear, hosiery & lingerie
Pr: Lynda Smith Swann
*Pr: Edward C Smith Sr
VP: Betty McMahan
*VP: Edward C Smith Jr
IT Man: David Lyttle
Software D: Tanya Gunter
Mktg Dir: Julie Morrow
Mktg Mgr: Melinda Riddle

D-U-N-S 11-178-1279
NATIONAL WHOLESALE SUPPLY INC
NATIONAL HOT WATER
1972 Cal Crossing Rd, Dallas, TX 75220-7006
Tel (972) 432-8883 Founded/Ownrshp 2002
Sales 94.5MM^E EMP 130
SIC 5074 Plumbing fittings & supplies; Plumbing fittings & supplies
Pr: Charles Reynolds
Genl Mgr: M Huffman
Genl Mgr: Randy Meyer
Dir IT: Dario Meucci

D-U-N-S 07-744-0709
NATIONAL WILD TURKEY FEDERATION INC
NWTF
770 Augusta Rd, Edgefield, SC 29824-1573
Tel (803) 637-3106 Founded/Ownrshp 1973
Sales 8.5MM EMP 286
SIC 8699 Animal humane society; Animal humane society
Ch: Jim Hinkle
*Pr: Sam Mars III
*CEO: George C Thornton
*Treas: Laura Close
Treas: Steve McNeil
Sr VP: Tom Stuckey
VP: Mike Roach
*VP: Vern Ross
VP Opers: Bob Fountain

D-U-N-S 05-518-9070 IMP
NATIONAL WILDLIFE FEDERATION INC
11100 Wildlife Center Dr, Reston, VA 20190-5362
Tel (703) 438-6000 Founded/Ownrshp 1936
Sales 86.3MM EMP 350^E
Accts Bdo Usa Llp Bethesda Maryla
SIC 8641 Environmental protection organization; Environmental protection organization
CEO: Larry J Schweiger
V Ch: Stephen K Allinger
*Treas: Dulce Gomez-Zormelo
Treas: Liz Soper
Ofcr: Julie Koo

Ex VP: Maria Litman
Sr VP: Dan Chu
VP: Alene Archer
VP: Maia Becker
VP: Julie Blessyn
VP: Kevin Coyle
VP: Jennifer Jones

D-U-N-S 00-385-4189 IMP
NATIONAL WINE & SPIRITS INC
ALLEN PRODUCTS COMPANY
700 W Morris St, Indianapolis, IN 46225-1447
Tel (317) 636-6092 Founded/Ownrshp 1935
Sales 326.2MM^E EMP 1,600
SIC 5182 Wine & distilled beverages; Wine & distilled beverages
Ch Bd: James E Lacrosse
*COO: John J Baker
*Treas: Patrick A Trefun
*Ex VP: Gregory J Mauloff
*VP: Dwight Deming
Comm Man: Debra Boyer
Dir Sec: Chris Youngblood
Dist Mgr: Bill Brown
Dist Mgr: Eric Steinberg
*VP Sls: Catherine M Lacrosse
VP Sls: Brian Pizzuti
Board of Directors: James R Beck, Vaughn D Bryson, William M Cockrum, David W Goodrich, Norma M Johnston, Stephen E Lacrosse, Mitchell T Stoltz

NATIONAL WINE & SPIRITS MICH
See NWS MICHIGAN INC

D-U-N-S 92-704-8983 IMP/EXP
NATIONAL WIRE LLC
12262 Fm 3083 Rd, Conroe, TX 77301-6106
Tel (936) 760-2040 Founded/Ownrshp 1995
Sales 46.4MM^E EMP 43
SIC 5051 Steel; Reinforcement mesh, wire; Concrete reinforcing bars
Plnt Mgr: Rafael Sala
*VP: Alejandra Abbott
Prd Mgr: Jose Torres
Sls Mgr: Annet De Leon

NATIONAL WNS CNCER RES ALIANCE
See ENTERTAINMENT INDUSTRY FOUNDATION

D-U-N-S 12-121-7087 IMP
NATIONAL WOOD PRODUCTS INC
2705 S 600 W, Salt Lake City, UT 84115-2967
Tel (801) 977-1171 Founded/Ownrshp 1984
Sales 78.8MM^E EMP 160
SIC 5031 Lumber: rough, dressed & finished; Plywood; Lumber: rough, dressed & finished; Plywood
Pr: Donald L Meyer
*Sec: Donald A Eichler
Bd of Dir: Chad Bingham
VP: Kurt Mitek
*VP: Kurt Winn
Exec: Tanya Coy
Sales Asso: Gino Marallo

NATIONAL WORKERS COMPENSATION
See NATIONAL COUNCIL ON COMPENSATION INSURANCE INC

D-U-N-S 82-468-3635
NATIONAL WORLD WAR II MUSEUM INC
945 Magazine St, New Orleans, LA 70130-3813
Tel (504) 528-1944 Founded/Ownrshp 1991
Sales 49.9MM EMP 176
Accts Bourgeois Bennett Llc Metairi
SIC 8399 Fund raising organization, non-fee basis
CEO: Nick Muller
Dir Vol: Katie Alpert
*Ch Bd: Philip G Satre
Sr VP: Robert Farnsworth
VP: Peter Boese
VP: Michael Carroll
VP: Alan Franco
VP: Owen Glendening
VP: Clem Goldberger
VP: Rebecca Mackie
Exec: Kacey Hill
Exec: Cindi Mistrot
Comm Dir: Andy Myer

D-U-N-S 00-380-3210
NATIONAL WRECKING CO
2441 N Leavitt St, Chicago, IL 60647-2005
Tel (773) 489-4170 Founded/Ownrshp 1954
Sales 24.8MM^E EMP 130
SIC 1795 Demolition, buildings & other structures
Pr: Sheldon J Mandell
*VP: Arthur Mandell
Exec: Cheryl Campbell
Dir Teleco: Matt Hughs

D-U-N-S 96-974-9758
NATIONAL YMCA EMPLOYEE BENEFITS TRUST
101 N Wacker Dr Ste 1500, Chicago, IL 60606-7380
Tel (312) 977-0031 Founded/Ownrshp 2011
Sales 78.0MM EMP 3
Accts Grant Thornton Chicago Il
SIC 8641 Youth organizations; Youth organizations
Pr: Michael Bright

D-U-N-S 17-009-9923
NATIONAL YOUTH ADVOCATE PROGRAM INC
1801 Watermark Dr Ste 200, Columbus, OH 43215-7088
Tel (614) 487-8758 Founded/Ownrshp 1983
Sales 43.6MM EMP 386
Accts Clark Schaefer Hackett & Co S
SIC 8322 Individual & family services; Individual & family services
Ex Dir: Marvena Twigg
*CFO: Robert Clay
*CIO: Duane Phillips

D-U-N-S 00-506-9257 IMP
NATIONAL-STANDARD LLC
(Suby of HEICO COMPANIES L L C) ★
1631 Lake St, Niles, MI 49120-1270
Tel (269) 683-9902 Founded/Ownrshp 2008
Sales 94.4MM^E EMP 300^E
SIC 3315 3496 Wire & fabricated wire products; Wire, ferrous/iron; Wire products, ferrous/iron: made in wiredrawing plants; Miscellaneous fabricated wire products; Wire cloth & woven wire products; Wire & fabricated wire products; Wire, ferrous/iron; Wire products, ferrous/iron: made in wiredrawing plants; Miscellaneous fabricated wire products; Wire cloth & woven wire products
Dist Mgr: Vic Shorkey
Mktg Mgr: Heidi Valenzuela
Sls Mgr: Scott McCall
Sls Mgr: Justin Mercer

D-U-N-S 80-987-5602
NATIONALCARE MARKETING CORP
(Suby of US HEALTH GROUP INC) ★
801 Cherry St Unit 33, Fort Worth, TX 76102-6888
Tel (817) 878-3300 Founded/Ownrshp 2006
Sales NA EMP 123
SIC 6411 Insurance agents, brokers & service; Insurance agents, brokers & service
Pr: Patrick Mitchell
*Pr: James White
*Treas: Cynthia Koenig
*Ex VP: Patrick Oneill
VP: John Maurer

NATIONALEASE
See AMERIQUEST BUSINESS SERVICES INC

NATIONALEASE
See SALEM LEASING CORP

NATIONALEASE
See SCHOWS INC

NATIONALEASE
See BROWN TRUCK LEASING CORP

NATIONALEASE
See AIM LEASING CO

NATIONALEASE
See FREIGHTLINER OF MAINE INC

NATIONALEASE
See AIM INTEGRATED LOGISTICS INC

NATIONALS SPORT LIQUIDATORS
See SUMMIT SPORTS INC

D-U-N-S 92-692-2758
NATIONS BROADBAND INC
NATIONS TEL
15455 Dallas Pkwy Ste 600, Addison, TX 75001-6760
Tel (972) 851-7851 Founded/Ownrshp 1993
Sales 25.0MM EMP 2,500
SIC 4813 Telephone communication, except radio; Telephone communication, except radio
Pr: Eric Green
*VP: Robert Green

D-U-N-S 07-395-2533
NATIONS FOODSERVICE INC
NATION'S GIANT HAMBURGERS
11090 San Pablo Ave # 200, El Cerrito, CA 94530-2365
Tel (510) 237-1952 Founded/Ownrshp 1974
Sales 20.8MM^E EMP 450
SIC 5812 Hamburger stand; Hamburger stand
CEO: Dale J Power
*Pr: Dale Power
Dir IT: Jonathan Hagwood

NATION'S GIANT HAMBURGERS
See NATIONS FOODSERVICE INC

D-U-N-S 15-982-0588
NATIONS HOLDING CO
5370 W 95th St, Prairie Village, KS 66207-3204
Tel (913) 383-8185 Founded/Ownrshp 1995
Sales 56.2MM^E EMP 100
SIC 6719 Investment holding companies, except banks
Pr: Chris Likens
*COO: Charles Burton
*CFO: Michael Riley
*VP: David Link
VP: Greg Medley
IT Man: Karen Ye

D-U-N-S 13-732-0961
NATIONS LENDING CORP
N L C
4 Summit Park Dr Ste 200, Independence, OH 44131-2583
Tel (216) 503-8242 Founded/Ownrshp 2003
Sales NA EMP 100
SIC 6162 6163 Mortgage bankers; Mortgage brokers arranging for loans, using money of others
CEO: Jeremy E Sopko
Pr: George Chapin
*CFO: William Lee Osborne Jr
Chf Mktg O: Dave Scilabro
Ofcr: Martin Wilson
VP: Mark Fantozzi
Brnch Mgr: Stephen Anderson
Brnch Mgr: Jeremy McClure
Sls Mgr: Ruben Garcia
Sls Mgr: Alan Luber
Snr Mgr: Eric Roman

NATIONS LENDING SERVICES
See NATIONS TITLE AGENCY

D-U-N-S 79-653-7517
NATIONS RELIABLE LENDING LLC
NRL MORTGAGE
2506 W Main St, Houston, TX 77098-3223
Tel (713) 275-1300 Founded/Ownrshp 2006
Sales NA EMP 80^E
SIC 6162 Mortgage bankers & correspondents
Pr: Ron Zach

D-U-N-S 78-785-5001
NATIONS ROOF CENTRAL LLC
AFFILIATED WITH NATIONS ROOF
2914 Lawing Ln, Rowlett, TX 75088-7514
Tel (972) 278-9200 Founded/Ownrshp 2006
Sales 87.4MM EMP 600
SIC 1761 Roofing, siding & sheet metal work; Roofing, siding & sheet metal work

D-U-N-S 36-209-5775
NATIONS ROOF EAST LLC
AFFILIATE OF NATIONS ROOF
70 Saint Casimir Ave, Yonkers, NY 10701-3304
Tel (914) 423-6171 Founded/Ownrshp 2004
Sales 87.4MM EMP 600
SIC 1761 Roofing contractor; Siding contractor; Roofing contractor; Siding contractor

D-U-N-S 60-301-2373
NATIONS ROOF LLC
NATIONS ROOF NORTH
1633 Blairs Bridge Rd, Lithia Springs, GA 30122-3118
Tel (678) 567-1533 Founded/Ownrshp 2004
Sales 108.1MM EMP 600
SIC 1761 Roofing contractor; Roofing contractor
CEO: Richard Nugent
CFO: Sue Kimble
VP: James Nugen
VP Opers: Mark Duncan
Natl Sales: John Sedenquist

NATIONS ROOF NORTH
See NATIONS ROOF LLC

D-U-N-S 18-486-2204
NATIONS ROOF NORTH LLC
(Suby of NATIONS ROOF LLC) ★
901 Sentry Dr, Waukesha, WI 53186-5964
Tel (262) 542-0002 Founded/Ownrshp 2004
Sales 87.4MM EMP 600
SIC 1761 Roofing contractor; Siding contractor; Roofing contractor; Siding contractor
Pr: David Hinkley
Exec: Kevin Lux

D-U-N-S 15-687-8543
NATIONS ROOF OF CONNECTICUT LLC
NATIONS ROOF OF NEW ENGLAND
1400 Honeyspot Road Ext, Stratford, CT 06615-7142
Tel (203) 335-8109 Founded/Ownrshp 2004
Sales 87.4MM EMP 600
SIC 1761 Roofing contractor; Roofing contractor
CFO: Claude Carnahan
Sfty Dirs: Ismet Dalipi
VP Sls: Larry Morgan

D-U-N-S 55-721-8158
NATIONS ROOF OF FLORIDA LLC
(Suby of NATIONS ROOF LLC) ★
1313 E Landstreet Rd, Orlando, FL 32824-7926
Tel (407) 649-1333 Founded/Ownrshp 2005
Sales 87.4MM EMP 600
SIC 1761 Roofing contractor; Siding contractor; Roofing contractor; Siding contractor
Pr: Burt Logan
Off Mgr: Wendy Allman

D-U-N-S 79-365-4224
NATIONS ROOF OF ILLINOIS LLC
865 N Ellsworth Ave, Villa Park, IL 60181-1212
Tel (847) 870-1133 Founded/Ownrshp 2006
Sales 45.7MM^E EMP 600
SIC 1761 Roofing contractor; Roofing contractor
Pr: Doug Duncan

NATIONS ROOF OF NEW ENGLAND
See NATIONS ROOF OF CONNECTICUT LLC

D-U-N-S 16-855-9909
NATIONS ROOF OF NEW YORK LLC
AFFILIATES OF NATIONS ROOF
70 Saint Casimir Ave, Yonkers, NY 10701-3304
Tel (914) 509-7020 Founded/Ownrshp 2004
Sales 87.4MM EMP 600
SIC 1761 Roof repair; Roof repair
Sls&Mrk Ex: Michael Johannes

D-U-N-S 78-223-5415
NATIONS ROOF OF OHIO LLC
AFFILIATE OF NATIONS ROOF
275 S Pioneer Blvd, Springboro, OH 45066-1180
Tel (937) 439-4160 Founded/Ownrshp 2006
Sales 87.4MM EMP 50
SIC 1761 Roofing contractor; Siding contractor; Roofing contractor; Siding contractor
Pr: Chuck Painter
VP: Andrew Strauser
Off Mgr: Karen Wagner
Off Admin: Mindi Mescher
Manager: Alma Cochran
Manager: Dora Weis
Sls Mgr: Jennifer Dunaway

NATIONS ROOF WEST
See ROOF SYSTEMS INC

NATIONS TEL
See NATIONS BROADBAND INC

D-U-N-S 96-029-1409
NATIONS TITLE AGENCY
NATIONS LENDING SERVICES
(Suby of NATIONS HOLDING CO) ★
5370 W 95th St, Prairie Village, KS 66207-3204
Tel (913) 341-2705 Founded/Ownrshp 1994
Sales NA EMP 50^E
SIC 6411 6541 6531 ; Title & trust companies; Appraiser, real estate
Pr: Steve Likens
*Sec: Chris Likens
Ex VP: Kelly Kern
VP: Todd Lautzenheiser
VP: Brad Likens
*VP: Larry Likens
VP: Marcia Quackenbush
Exec: Cora Blew
IT Man: Bill Noel
Sls Mgr: Mark Fantozzi

D-U-N-S 06-677-3326
■ NATIONSBANK NA (INC)
(Suby of BANK OF AMERICA CORP) ★
100 S Charles St Ste 207, Baltimore, MD 21201-2735
Tel (410) 605-5000 Founded/Ownrshp 1993
Sales NA EMP 802

SIC 6021 6531 National commercial banks; Real estate managers; National commercial banks; Real estate managers
Pr: R Eugene Taylor
VP: Kevin J Kelley
VP: Lee Martinec
VP: Kathryn C Swain
VP: John B Wood II
VP: Regina M Zussman

D-U-N-S 13-890-0589
NATIONSBUILDERS INSURANCE SERVICES INC
800 Overlook Ter, Atlanta, GA 30349-6772
Tel (770) 257-1777 *Founded/Ownrshp* 2004
Sales NA *EMP* 100
Accts Bdo Seidman Llp Atlanta Geo
SIC 6411 Insurance agents, brokers & service; Insurance agents, brokers & service
CEO: Ned N Fleming III
**CFO:* Ron Smith
**CFO:* William Tepe
**Sr VP:* Kevin Cunningham
VP: Henry Butler
VP: Art Kirkner
Exec: Peter Foley

NATIONSCHOICE MORTGAGE
See FISHER FINANCIAL GROUP INC

D-U-N-S 02-814-1186
■ **NATIONSTAR CAPITAL CORP**
(*Suby of* NATIONSTAR MORTGAGE HOLDINGS INC) ★
350 Highland Dr, Lewisville, TX 75067-4177
Tel (469) 549-2000 *Founded/Ownrshp* 2010
Sales NA *EMP* 2,842ᴱ
SIC 6162 Mortgage bankers & correspondents; Bond & mortgage companies
Prin: Jay Bray

D-U-N-S 07-841-9794
▲ **NATIONSTAR MORTGAGE HOLDINGS INC**
8950 Cypress Waters Blvd, Coppell, TX 75019-4620
Tel (469) 549-2000 *Founded/Ownrshp* 1994
Sales NA *EMP* 5,500ᴱ
Tkr Sym NSM *Exch* NYS
SIC 6162 Mortgage bankers & correspondents; Bond & mortgage companies; Mortgage bankers & correspondents; Bond & mortgage companies
Pr: Jay Bray
**Ch Bd:* Wesley R Edens
CFO: Robert D Stiles
Ex VP: Tony Ebers
Ex VP: David C Hisey
Ex VP: Ramesh Lakshminarayanan
Ex VP: Chad T Patton
Ex VP: Anthony W Villani
CIO: Bob Orkis
Board of Directors: Robert H Gidel, Roy A Guthrie, Brett Hawkins, Michael D Malone

D-U-N-S 11-048-5328 IMP
■ **NATIONSTAR MORTGAGE LLC**
(*Suby of* NATIONSTAR MORTGAGE HOLDINGS INC) ★
8950 Cypress Waters Blvd, Coppell, TX 75019-4620
Tel (469) 549-2000 *Founded/Ownrshp* 2006
Sales NA *EMP* 2,599ᴱ
SIC 6162 Mortgage bankers & correspondents; Mortgage bankers & correspondents
CEO: Jay Bray
**Pr:* Harold Lewis
Pr: Jason McRonal
**CFO:* David C Hisey
Ex VP: Robert Appel
Ex VP: John Butler
Ex VP: Steve Mix
Ex VP: Shawn Stone
**Ex VP:* Anthony W Villani
VP: Jon Hodge
VP: Ingrid Jaschok
VP: Binni Skariah
VP: Sam Wilson
Board of Directors: Anthony H Barone, Peter Smith

NATIONWIDE
See SCOTTSDALE INSURANCE CO

D-U-N-S 06-249-6542
NATIONWIDE ACCEPTANCE LLC
3435 N Cicero Ave, Chicago, IL 60641-3794
Tel (773) 777-7600 *Founded/Ownrshp* 1954
Sales NA *EMP* 131
Accts Plante & Moran Pllc Chicago
SIC 6141 Consumer finance companies; Personal finance licensed loan companies, small; Financing: automobiles, furniture, etc., not a deposit bank; Installment sales finance, other than banks; Consumer finance companies; Personal finance licensed loan companies, small; Financing: automobiles, furniture, etc., not a deposit bank; Installment sales finance, other than banks
Pr: Martin Less
**Treas:* Peter Riofski
**Sr VP:* Beverly Carroll
**Sr VP:* Bonnie Herden
**VP:* Paul Schmidt
Manager: Glenn Wheeler

D-U-N-S 03-065-1533
NATIONWIDE AGRIBUSINESS INSURANCE CO
(*Suby of* NATIONWIDE MUTUAL INSURANCE CO) ★
1100 Locust St Dept 3000, Des Moines, IA 50391-3000
Tel (515) 237-3600 *Founded/Ownrshp* 1982
Sales NA *EMP* 362
SIC 6411 Insurance agents, brokers & service; Insurance agents, brokers & service
Pr: Brett Harmon
Pr: Eric Ryan
COO: Kevin Burns
Ofcr: Robert Ridnour
Ex VP: Patricia R Hatler
VP: Tom Jurgens
VP: Doug Pearson
Assoc Dir: Steve Schuster
Dir IT: Brent Hayes
IT Man: Anne Berg
IT Man: Chris Hanson

D-U-N-S 04-059-6434 IMP/EXP
NATIONWIDE ARGOSY SOLUTIONS LLC
NWAS
2764 Bingle Rd, Houston, TX 77055-1135
Tel (713) 961-4700 *Founded/Ownrshp* 1998
Sales 217.4MMᴱ *EMP* 469ᴱ
SIC 2759 Commercial printing; Commercial printing
CEO: Carl L Norton
**Pr:* Jerry L Hyde
VP: Todd Bone
VP Opers: John Rodriguez

D-U-N-S 14-561-4181
NATIONWIDE BANK
NATIONWIDE FINANCIAL
(*Suby of* NATIONWIDE FINANCIAL SERVICES INC) ★
3 Nationwide Plz 1323r1, Columbus, OH 43215-2410
Tel (614) 249-9619 *Founded/Ownrshp* 1998
Sales NA *EMP* 4
SIC 6035 Federal savings banks; Federal savings banks
Pr: Steven J Rose
Snr Mgr: Peter Moenickheim

D-U-N-S 79-912-8959
NATIONWIDE BETTER HEALTH INC
(*Suby of* NATIONWIDE MUTUAL INSURANCE CO) ★
1 Nationwide Plz, Columbus, OH 43215-2226
Tel (614) 249-7111 *Founded/Ownrshp* 2005
Sales NA *EMP* 350
SIC 6321 Accident & health insurance; Accident & health insurance
Prin: Paragtt Shah
VP: Bill Evans Jr

D-U-N-S 13-678-5685
NATIONWIDE BIWEEKLY ADMINISTRATION INC
NBA
855 Lower Bellbrook Rd, Xenia, OH 45385-7306
Tel (937) 376-5800 *Founded/Ownrshp* 2002
Sales NA *EMP* 105
Accts Balestra Harr & Scherer Cpas
SIC 6099 Clearinghouse associations, bank or check; Clearinghouse associations, bank or check
Pr: Daniel Lipsky
Sls Mgr: Brian Davis

D-U-N-S 04-165-4542
NATIONWIDE BOILER INC
42400 Christy St, Fremont, CA 94538-3141
Tel (510) 490-7100 *Founded/Ownrshp* 1967
Sales 29.9MM *EMP* 43
Accts Berger Lewis Accountancy Corpo
SIC 7359 Equipment rental & leasing; Equipment rental & leasing
Pr: Jeff Shallcross
**VP:* Larry Day
**VP:* James Hermerding

D-U-N-S 02-330-2966
NATIONWIDE BUILDING SERVICES INC
401 N Bowser Rd Ste 105, Richardson, TX 75081-2855
Tel (972) 671-3700 *Founded/Ownrshp* 2001
Sales 21.9MMᴱ *EMP* 140
SIC 1231 Anthracite mining; Anthracite mining
Pr: Joe Luna

D-U-N-S 04-643-0013 IMP
NATIONWIDE CHILDRENS HOSPITAL
700 Childrens Dr, Columbus, OH 43205-2639
Tel (614) 722-3040 *Founded/Ownrshp* 1892
Sales 1.6MMM *EMP* 6,000
SIC 8069 Children's hospital; Children's hospital
CEO: Steve Allen
**COO:* Rick Miller
**CFO:* Timothy Robinson
Trst: Theodore L Adams
Trst: Ann I Wolfe
Trst: Pamela T Farber
Trst: James H Gilmour
Trst: Lawrence A Hilsheimer
Trst: William G Jurgensen
Trst: James A Rutherford
Trst: Barbara C Trueman
Ofcr: Stephen A Koff
Exec: Carl Kappeler
Dir Lab: Adam Studebaker

NATIONWIDE CONSTRUCTION
See MEEHAN CONTRACTORS LTD

NATIONWIDE CONSTRUCTION GROUP
See RMD HOLDINGS LTD

D-U-N-S 00-790-2026 IMP/EXP
NATIONWIDE CORP (OH)
(*Suby of* NATIONWIDE MUTUAL INSURANCE CO) ★
1 Nationwide Plz, Columbus, OH 43215-2226
Tel (614) 249-7111 *Founded/Ownrshp* 1947
Sales NA *EMP* 6,523
SIC 6411 6321 Insurance agents, brokers & service; Accident insurance carriers; Health insurance carriers; Insurance agents, brokers & service; Accident insurance carriers; Health insurance carriers
Prin: Henry S Ballard
Pr: Cathy Ellwood
Pr: Damon R McFerson
CEO: Steve Rasmussen
CFO: Robert J Bobien
CFO: John Helmsdoerfer
CFO: Robert A Oakley
Treas: David Diamond
Chf Inves: Mark Bronzo
Chf Inves: Bharat B Nauriyal
Assoc VP: Brad Davis
Assoc VP: Marc Lincewicz
Assoc VP: Jerri Lybarger
Assoc VP: Gus Martinez
Assoc VP: Mike Morron
Assoc VP: Steve Pierce
Assoc VP: Betsy Radley
Assoc VP: John Reese
Assoc VP: Hollie Ringer
Ex VP: Donna A James
Ex VP: Robert Rusholt

D-U-N-S 10-199-0398
NATIONWIDE CREDIT INC
NCI
(*Suby of* ALTISOURCE SOLUTIONS INC) ★
1225 W Washington St # 300, Tempe, AZ 85281-1239
Tel (800) 456-4729 *Founded/Ownrshp* 1990
Sales 40.4MMᴱ *EMP* 2,000
Accts Deloitte & Touche Llp Atlanta
SIC 7322 Collection agency, except real estate; Collection agency, except real estate
CEO: Vivek Bhandari
**Pr:* Arindam Bose
**CFO:* John P Barrack
CFO: Jeff Estep
Treas: Tim Farmer
Treas: Alfred Norris
**VP:* David Albers
**VP:* Arindam Ghosh
VP: Kay Staggs

NATIONWIDE DISTRIBUTING
See HOMEDICS USA LLC

D-U-N-S 10-348-1219 IMP
NATIONWIDE DISTRIBUTORS INC
NATIONWIDE FURNITURE DISTR
1000 S Kostner Ave, Chicago, IL 60624-3833
Tel (773) 379-7690 *Founded/Ownrshp* 2001
Sales 24.3MMᴱ *EMP* 25
SIC 5021 Household furniture
Pr: Nidal Jarad
**Sec:* Jamal Jarad
**VP:* Abdul Hamad

D-U-N-S 13-979-1990
NATIONWIDE DOCUMENT SOLUTIONS INC
(*Suby of* ALLIED INSURANCE) ★
3820 109th St, Des Moines, IA 50391-9800
Tel (515) 508-8400 *Founded/Ownrshp* 1989
Sales NA *EMP* 230ᴱ
SIC 6411 Insurance agents, brokers & service; Insurance agents, brokers & service
Pr: Barry Paterson

NATIONWIDE EXPRESS
See ROMEO EXPEDITORS INC

D-U-N-S 05-589-2863
NATIONWIDE EXPRESS INC
1211 E Lane St, Shelbyville, TN 37160-3643
Tel (931) 680-2400 *Founded/Ownrshp* 1980
Sales 57.3MMᴱ *EMP* 320
SIC 4213 4225 Trucking, except local; General warehousing; Trucking, except local; General warehousing
CEO: Mike Coffey
**Pr:* David Coffey
CFO: Daniel Liddell
Dir Bus: Jerry Barber

NATIONWIDE FINANCIAL
See NATIONWIDE BANK

D-U-N-S 79-044-2230
NATIONWIDE FINANCIAL INSTITUTION DISTRIBUTORS AGENCY INC
(*Suby of* NATIONWIDE CORP) ★
1 W Nationwide Blvd 2-0501, Columbus, OH 43215-2752
Tel (614) 249-6825 *Founded/Ownrshp* 1990
Sales 127.3MMᴱ *EMP* 60ᴱ
SIC 6211 Mutual funds, selling by independent salesperson
Pr: David L Giertz
**Pr:* Richard Karas
**CEO:* Mark R Thresher
CIO: Carol Dimonda
CIO: James Korcykoski
CTO: Shekhar Mahajan
CTO: Guru Vasudeva

D-U-N-S 96-641-8220
NATIONWIDE FINANCIAL SERVICES INC
(*Suby of* NATIONWIDE CORP) ★
1 Nationwide Plz, Columbus, OH 43215-2226
Tel (614) 249-7111 *Founded/Ownrshp* 1996
Sales NA *EMP* 4,644ᴱ
SIC 6311 6411 8742 Life insurance; Pension & retirement plan consultants; Life insurance agents; Advisory services, insurance; Banking & finance consultant; Life insurance; Pension & retirement plan consultants; Life insurance agents; Advisory services, insurance; Banking & finance consultant
Pr: Mark R Thresher
Pr: Vince Antonucci
Pr: Jeff Hazel
Pr: Lisa Hughes
**CFO:* Timothy G Frommeyer
Treas: Harry H Hallowell
Bd of Dir: James Bachmann
Ofcr: Don Devlin
Ofcr: Elaine Duffus
Ofcr: Michael C Keller
Ofcr: James Rabenstine
Ofcr: Thomas Starr
Assoc VP: Bobbi Allan
Assoc VP: Claudia Comtois
Ex VP: Stephen S Rasmussen
Ex VP: Kathleen D Ricord
Sr VP: David A Diamond
Sr VP: Philip C Gath
Sr VP: Donna A James
VP: Michael Benson
VP: Vince Centineo

D-U-N-S 04-830-6294
NATIONWIDE FOODS INC
BROOKFIELD FARMS
700 E 107th St, Chicago, IL 60628-3806
Tel (773) 787-4900 *Founded/Ownrshp* 1969
Sales 125.0MM *EMP* 500
SIC 2013 5142 5147 Corned beef from purchased meat; Meat, frozen: packaged; Meats, fresh; Corned beef from purchased meat; Meat, frozen: packaged; Meats, fresh
Ch Bd: Frank Swan
Pr: Dennis Gleason
Exec: David Peterson
MIS Mgr: Patrick Keable

NATIONWIDE FURNITURE DISTR
See NATIONWIDE DISTRIBUTORS INC

D-U-N-S 11-262-6168 IMP
NATIONWIDE FURNITURE INC
NATIONWIDE MAT & FURN WHSE
(*Suby of* SUN CAPITAL PARTNERS INC) ★
170 Stiles Ave, Orange Park, FL 32073-4142
Tel (904) 278-8123 *Founded/Ownrshp* 2002
Sales 55.4MMᴱ *EMP* 450
SIC 5712 Furniture stores; Beds & accessories; Mattresses; Furniture stores; Beds & accessories; Mattresses
CEO: Rick Meiser
**Pr:* Steve Glucksman

D-U-N-S 08-443-0727
NATIONWIDE GENERAL INSURANCE CO
(*Suby of* NATIONWIDE MUTUAL INSURANCE CO) ★
1 W Nationwide Blvd # 100, Columbus, OH 43215-2752
Tel (614) 249-7111 *Founded/Ownrshp* 1958
Sales NA *EMP* 75
SIC 6411 Insurance agents, brokers & service
Pr: Dimon Richard Mc Frson
**Ch Bd:* Harold Weihl
**Pr:* Richard D Crabtree
Pr: Dimon Richard Mc Ferson
Pr: Brenda L Ross-Mathes
CFO: Michael Leach
CFO: Robert Oakley
Treas: Duane M Campbell
Ofcr: Mark Chamberlain
Ofcr: James Cleary
Ofcr: Laurel Elmore
Ofcr: Katherine Miller
Assoc VP: Kathy Koontz
Ex VP: Donald Seale
Ex VP: Robert Woodward Jr
Sr VP: W Sidney Druen
Sr VP: Deb Tedeschi
VP: Dennis W Click
VP: David A Diamond
VP: Gregory Gates
VP: Lynn Greenstein
Board of Directors: Arden L Shisler, Lewis L Alphin, Robert L Stewart, A I Bell, Nancy C Thomas, Willard J Engel, Fred C Finney, Charles L Fuellgraf Jr, David O Miller, Yvonne L Montgomery, C Ray Noecker, James F Patterson

D-U-N-S 14-830-5121
NATIONWIDE HOLDINGS INC
3425 N Cicero Ave Fl 2, Chicago, IL 60641-3798
Tel (773) 777-7600 *Founded/Ownrshp* 1982
Sales NA *EMP* 90
SIC 6311 6331 Life insurance; Property damage insurance
CEO: David Lathrop
**Pr:* Michael Lutz
**Treas:* Charles Koziol
**VP:* Marshall Lutz

D-U-N-S 05-464-0649
NATIONWIDE HOMES INC (AZ)
1100 London Bridge Rd G102, Lake Havasu City, AZ 86404-2495
Tel (928) 453-6600 *Founded/Ownrshp* 1993
Sales 100.0MM *EMP* 35
SIC 1521 6531 New construction, single-family houses; Real estate agents & managers; New construction, single-family houses; Real estate agents & managers
Pr: Maureen M Tate
CFO: Ema Broquin
**VP:* Arthur W Tate
Sales Asso: Lorelei Tuss

D-U-N-S 79-686-0273
NATIONWIDE HOUSING SYSTEMS LP
(*Suby of* AMERICAN HOMESTAR CORP) ★
2450 S Shore Blvd Ste 300, League City, TX 77573-2997
Tel (281) 334-9700 *Founded/Ownrshp* 2001
Sales 69.0MM *EMP* 150
SIC 2451 Mobile homes, personal or private use; Mobile homes, personal or private use
Pt: Charles Carney
Treas: Craig A Reynolds

D-U-N-S 60-740-8994
NATIONWIDE INDEMNITY CO
(*Suby of* NATIONWIDE MUTUAL INSURANCE CO) ★
1 W Nationwide Blvd # 100, Columbus, OH 43215-2752
Tel (614) 249-7111 *Founded/Ownrshp* 1994
Sales NA *EMP* 279ᴱ
SIC 6411 Insurance agents, brokers & service
Pr: David A Bano

D-U-N-S 16-198-2108
NATIONWIDE INSURANCE CO OF FLORIDA
(*Suby of* NATIONWIDE MUTUAL INSURANCE CO) ★
2 Nationwide Plz, Columbus, OH 43215-2534
Tel (614) 249-7111 *Founded/Ownrshp* 1998
Sales NA *EMP* 29ᴱ
SIC 6411 Insurance agents, brokers & service; Insurance information & consulting services; Insurance agents, brokers & service; Insurance information & consulting services
Prin: David Meyer

D-U-N-S 92-951-2341
NATIONWIDE LABORATORY SERVICES INC
1537 Nw 65th Ave, Plantation, FL 33313-4542
Tel (954) 633-3580 *Founded/Ownrshp* 1995
Sales 14.7MM *EMP* 567
Accts Ahearn Jasco & Company Pa P
SIC 8071 Blood analysis laboratory; Blood analysis laboratory
CEO: Mark I Delahunty
Pr: Shiv Purewal
Pr: Mark Wisniewski
COO: Bates Jason
CFO: Tom Mann

*VP: Sean Martin
VP: James Petruso
*VP: Mary T Petruso
*VP: Ricki Robinson
Dir Lab: Marvin Lessig
Dir Bus: Joseph Moscato

D-U-N-S 80-143-7307
NATIONWIDE LEGAL LLC
HEADQUARTERS
1609 James M Wood Blvd, Los Angeles, CA 90015-1005
Tel (213) 249-9999 Founded/Ownrshp 2007
Sales 31.5MM^E EMP 350^E
SIC 8111 Legal services; Legal services
CEO: Tony Davoodi
*COO: Joe Caamal
*Ex VP: Louis Nelson
*Sr VP: Michael Lazcano
VP: Joe Huber
Brnch Mgr: Hector Velazquez
IT Man: M J Naderi
IT Man: Chad Sandrini

D-U-N-S 00-790-2034
NATIONWIDE LIFE INSURANCE CO
(Suby of NATIONWIDE FINANCIAL SERVICES INC) ★
1 Nationwide Plz, Columbus, OH 43215-2226
Tel (877) 669-6877 Founded/Ownrshp 1929
Sales NA EMP 691^E
SIC 6411 Insurance agents, brokers & service; Pension & retirement plan consultants; Insurance agents, brokers & service; Pension & retirement plan consultants
Pr: Kirt A Walker
Pr: David Arango
Pr: Thomas Hickey
*CFO: Timothy G Frommeyer
Rgnl VP: Matthew Cowell
Rgnl VP: Melody Digman
*Ex VP: Mark Berven
*Ex VP: Matt Jauchius
Ex VP: Michael C Keller
*Ex VP: Gale V King
Ex VP: Melanie Kolp
Sr VP: Tammy Craig
VP: Kevin Fisher
VP: Andy Lucas
VP: Timothy Lyons
VP: Dan Mahlum
VP: Marlene O'Neil
VP: Stephen Sedlak
VP: Gary Sorrell
Board of Directors: Peter A Golato, Stephen S Rasmussen, Mark R Thresher

D-U-N-S 00-791-4641
NATIONWIDE LIFE INSURANCE CO OF AMERICA (PA)
(Suby of NATIONWIDE FINANCIAL SERVICES INC) ★
1000 Chesterbrook Blvd, Berwyn, PA 19312-1084
Tel (610) 407-1717 Founded/Ownrshp 1865, 2002
Sales NA EMP 1,500
SIC 6411 6211 6719 Insurance agents, brokers & service; Brokers, security; Investment holding companies, except banks; Insurance agents, brokers & service; Brokers, security; Investment holding companies, except banks
Pr: Gary D McMahan
*CFO: Mary Lynn Finelli
*Treas: Rosanne Gatta
*Ex VP: James G Potter Jr
*Ex VP: Joan Tucker
*Sr VP: Sarah Coxe Lange
*VP: Jim Benson
VP: Dana Brown
VP: Jeffrey Brusko
VP: Donald Hans
VP: Maureen Hobson
VP: Gary Kinn
VP: Rose Radcliff

D-U-N-S 04-603-3122 EXP
NATIONWIDE LIFT TRUCKS INC
TOYOTA
3900 N 28th Ter, Hollywood, FL 33020-1178
Tel (800) 327-4431 Founded/Ownrshp 1969
Sales 38.8MM^E EMP 86
SIC 5511 5531 7359 7538 5084 5013 Trucks, tractors & trailers: new & used; Truck equipment & parts; Industrial truck rental; General truck repair; Lift trucks & parts; Truck parts & accessories; Trucks, tractors & trailers: new & used; Truck equipment & parts; Industrial truck rental; General truck repair; Lift trucks & parts; Truck parts & accessories
Pr: Arthur R Conte
*VP: Joseph Conte
*VP: Thomas Conte
*VP: Frank Koneski
VP: Dale Tower

D-U-N-S 09-644-1761
NATIONWIDE MAGAZINE & BOOK DISTRIBUTORS INC
3000 E Grauwyler Rd, Irving, TX 75061-3499
Tel (972) 438-2123 Founded/Ownrshp 1979
Sales 34.7MM^E EMP 230
SIC 4213 Trucking, except local; Trucking, except local
Pr: Ben Madill
*Sr VP: Tim Sand
*VP: Kathy Madill

NATIONWIDE MAT & FURN WHSE
See NATIONWIDE FURNITURE INC

D-U-N-S 07-831-8671
NATIONWIDE MORTGAGE GROUP INC
21053 Devonshire St # 105, Chatsworth, CA 91311-8249
Tel (408) 644-6479 Founded/Ownrshp 2011
Sales NA EMP 7
SIC 6162 Mortgage bankers & correspondents
Pr: George Youhana

D-U-N-S 02-249-0858
NATIONWIDE MOTOR SALES CORP
NATIONWIDE NISSAN
2085 York Rd, Lutherville Timonium, MD 21093-4242
Tel (410) 252-8000 Founded/Ownrshp 1964
Sales 86.3MM^E EMP 225
SIC 5511 4812 Automobiles, new & used; Radio telephone communication; Automobiles, new & used; Radio telephone communication
Pr: Bill William Schaefer Jr
Sls Mgr: Christine Belt
Sls Mgr: Mike Williams
Board of Directors: Fatima McArthur, Steve Zimmerman

D-U-N-S 02-998-1540
NATIONWIDE MOVE MANAGEMENT LLC
2000 N State Road 7, Margate, FL 33063-5712
Tel (954) 580-8200 Founded/Ownrshp 1999
Sales 24.1MM^E EMP 257
SIC 7389 Relocation service; Loan brokers; Relocation service
Pr: Aldo Disorbo
*VP: Katherine Bach
DP Exec: Cory Coddington

D-U-N-S 00-790-2042
NATIONWIDE MUTUAL FIRE INSURANCE CO
(Suby of NATIONWIDE MUTUAL INSURANCE CO) ★
1 W Nationwide Blvd # 100, Columbus, OH 43215-2752
Tel (614) 249-7111 Founded/Ownrshp 1934
Sales NA EMP 46^E
SIC 6411 Insurance agents, brokers & service; Insurance agents, brokers & service
Ch Bd: Dimon R Mc Ferson
*Pr: Richard D Crabtree
CFO: Robert A Oakley
Treas: Harry H Hallowell
Ex VP: Gordon E Mc Cutchan
Ex VP: Robert J Woodward Jr
VP: Duane M Campbell

NATIONWIDE MUTUAL INSURANCE
See FARMLAND MUTUAL INSURANCE CO INC

D-U-N-S 00-790-2059 IMP/EXP
NATIONWIDE MUTUAL INSURANCE CO
1 Nationwide Plz, Columbus, OH 43215-2226
Tel (614) 249-7111 Founded/Ownrshp 1925
Sales NA EMP 34,417
SIC 6331 6311 6321 6531 Fire, marine & casualty insurance: mutual; Property damage insurance; Automobile insurance; Life insurance carriers; Accident insurance carriers; Health insurance carriers; Real estate agents & managers; Fire, marine & casualty insurance: mutual; Property damage insurance; Automobile insurance; Life insurance carriers; Accident insurance carriers; Health insurance carriers; Real estate agents & managers
CEO: Steve Rasmussen
Pr: Anne Arvia
Pr: Larry Hilsheimer
CFO: Robert A Rosholt
CFO: Mark R Thresher
Ofcr: Kirk Herath
Ofcr: Rich Laye
Ofcr: Michael W Mahaffey
Assoc VP: Lynn Carnes
Assoc VP: Oyauma Garrison
Assoc VP: Travis Hodges
Assoc VP: Lisa Hodkinson
Assoc VP: Lori Pierson
Ex VP: Patricia R Hatler
Ex VP: Michael C Keller
Ex VP: Gale V King
Ex VP: Syed Rizvi
Sr VP: Harry H Hallowell
VP: Joe Case
Board of Directors: M Diane Koken, Lewis J Alphin, Lydia M Marshall, James B Bachmann, Terry W McClure, Arthur I Bell, Barry J Nalebuff, Timothy J Corcoran, Ralph M Paige, Yvonne M Curl, Brent Porteus, Kenneth D Davis, Jeffrey W Zellers, Keith W Eckel, Fred C Finney, Daniel T Kelley

NATIONWIDE NISSAN
See NATIONWIDE MOTOR SALES CORP

D-U-N-S 04-531-0430 IMP
NATIONWIDE OF CHICAGO-FOOD BROKERS INC
915 Harger Rd Ste 110, Oak Brook, IL 60523-1400
Tel (630) 286-1500 Founded/Ownrshp 1963
Sales 194.0MM^E EMP 12^E
SIC 5142 Packaged frozen goods; Fruits, frozen; Fruit juices, frozen
Pr: Ian Rahal
*VP: Jordan D Rahal
Brnch Mgr: Markus Farnleitner
IT Man: Mark Smith

D-U-N-S 03-881-6393
NATIONWIDE PLASTICS INC
2001 Timberlake Dr, Arlington, TX 76010-5321
Tel (214) 239-3870 Founded/Ownrshp 1980
Sales 38.0MM^E EMP 65
SIC 5162 3081

D-U-N-S 00-246-2448 IMP
NATIONWIDE PRECISION PRODUCTS CORP (NY)
HN PRECISION-NY
200 Tech Park Dr, Rochester, NY 14623-2445
Tel (585) 272-7100 Founded/Ownrshp 1999, 2015
Sales 136.2MM^E EMP 425
SIC 3356 Nonferrous rolling & drawing; Machine shop, jobbing & repair; Nonferrous rolling & drawing
CEO: Dan Nash
*CFO: Paul Ainsworth
*VP: Dan Brooks
*VP: Rick Menaldino
*VP: Sharon Pierce
IT Man: Greg Gillete
Mfg Mgr: Tony Amadio
Mfg Mgr: Jim Merritt
Mfg Mgr: Mark Piccarreto
Ql Cn Mgr: Brian Borowiec
Ql Cn Mgr: Steve Rogers

D-U-N-S 06-077-5756
NATIONWIDE RETIREMENT SOLUTIONS
(Suby of NATIONWIDE CORP) ★
5900 Parkwood Pl, Dublin, OH 43016-1216
Tel (614) 854-8300 Founded/Ownrshp 1982
Sales NA EMP 205
Accts Kpmg Llp
SIC 6371 8748 8742 6411 Pension funds; Employee programs administration; Management consulting services; Insurance agents, brokers & service; Pension funds; Employee programs administration; Management consulting services; Insurance agents, brokers & service
Pr: Duane Meek
Pgrm Dir: Jennifer Brown

D-U-N-S 05-979-3935
NATIONWIDE SECURITY & BUILDING SERVICES INC
9045 Imperial Hwy, Downey, CA 90242-2711
Tel (562) 862-1782 Founded/Ownrshp 1983
Sales 24.3MM EMP 75
Accts Kusher Smith Joanon Gregson L
SIC 7699 7349 1793 Miscellaneous building item repair services; Building maintenance services; Glass & glazing work; Miscellaneous building item repair services; Building maintenance services; Glass & glazing work
CEO: Rhonda Blanchard
*VP: Gary Blanchard
*VP: Sheryl Bowman Cordero
VP: Marnie Cullen
IT Man: Bryan Sampson
Natl Sales: Liz Kreeger

D-U-N-S 05-133-8283
NATIONWIDE STUDIOS INC
TEDDY BEAR PORTRAITS
400 N Belvedere Dr, Gallatin, TN 37066-5405
Tel (615) 452-8353 Founded/Ownrshp 2008
Sales 24.8MM^E EMP 400
SIC 7221 Photographic studios, portrait; Photographic studios, portrait
CEO: Patricia Asp
Pr: Phillip B Rooney
VP: Lara Blackwell
VP: Micheal Bohannon
VP: Keith Dobbs
VP: Michelle Freeman
VP: Terrie Kahler
VP: Keith Tippitt
Dir IT: Daniel Heisel
IT Man: Daniel Hazel
Sls&Mrk Ex: Joey Newgarden

D-U-N-S 06-381-4255
NATIONWIDE THEATRES CORP
(Suby of DECURION CORP) ★
120 N Robertson Blvd Fl 3, Los Angeles, CA 90048-3115
Tel (310) 657-8420 Founded/Ownrshp 1966
Sales 41.3MM^E EMP 3,000
SIC 7833 7832 Drive-in motion picture theaters; Motion picture theaters, except drive-in; Drive-in motion picture theaters; Motion picture theaters, except drive-in
Pr: Christopher Forman
*COO: Nora Dashwood

D-U-N-S 79-109-8270
NATIONWIDE TITLE CLEARING INC
2100 Alt 19, Palm Harbor, FL 34683-2620
Tel (727) 771-4000 Founded/Ownrshp 1992
Sales NA EMP 150
SIC 6162 6541 Bond & mortgage companies; Title reconveyance companies; Bond & mortgage companies; Title reconveyance companies
Pr: Jim Stewart
*Sr VP: John Hillman
Sr VP: Arta Lavaie
Sr VP: Dave Pearson
*Sr VP: Alan Turbin
VP: Debbie Lastoria
*VP: Edward E Marsh
VP: Shawn Sorensen
VP: Michael Verneuille
Exec: Sean Hunt
Comm Dir: Donna Jones

D-U-N-S 10-229-1598
NATIONWIDE TRANSPORTATION INC
4601 S 70th Cir, Omaha, NE 68117-1039
Tel (402) 592-2924 Founded/Ownrshp 1982
Sales 30.1MM^E EMP 140
SIC 4213 Trucking, except local; Trucking, except local
Pr: Paul D Moore
*Treas: Paul M Moore
*VP: Justin Pretzer
CTO: Denise West
VP Opers: Kathie Rice
Sfty Dirs: Tim Becker
Sfty Dirs: Ben Rogers

D-U-N-S 07-256-7936
NATIONWIDE TRUCK BROKERS INC
N T B
4203 R B Chaffee Mem Dr, Wyoming, MI 49548
Tel (616) 878-5554 Founded/Ownrshp 1974
Sales 44.8MM EMP 400
Accts Vander Ploeg Bergakker & Asso
SIC 4213 4212 Trucking, except local; Refrigerated products transport; Local trucking, without storage; Trucking, except local; Refrigerated products transport; Local trucking, without storage
Pr: Henry Schwarz
Pr: Daniel Wood
*Treas: Kurt D Koster
*VP: Rick A Koster
VP: Kurt Morton
VP Opers: David Birge
VP Sls: Terry Blackburn

D-U-N-S 00-423-5081 IMP
■ **NATIONWIDE UNIFORM CORP** (KY)
FECHHEIMER BROTHERS
(Suby of FECHHEIMER BROTHERS CO) ★
235 Shephardsville Rd, Hodgenville, KY 42748-9468
Tel (270) 358-4173 Founded/Ownrshp 1961
Sales 36.6MM^E EMP 375
SIC 2311 2337 2339 2326 Men's & boys' uniforms; Uniforms, except athletic: women's, misses' & juniors'; Women's & misses' outerwear; Men's & boys' work clothing; Men's & boys' uniforms; Uniforms, except athletic: women's, misses' & juniors'; Women's & misses' outerwear; Men's & boys' work clothing
Pr: John Karnes
Treas: Barbara Barros
Plnt Mgr: Doline Ard
Board of Directors: Roger Heldman

D-U-N-S 15-127-8660
NATIONWIDE VISION CENTER INC
220 N Mckemy Ave, Chandler, AZ 85226-2651
Tel (480) 961-1865 Founded/Ownrshp 1986
Sales 79.0MM^E EMP 450
SIC 5995 8042 Optical goods stores; Offices & clinics of optometrists; Optical goods stores; Offices & clinics of optometrists
Pr: Dr Mark A Hechtman Do
*Pr: Al Bernstein
*CEO: Dr Neal A Weinstein Do
*CFO: Tom Hull
*VP: Vince Hayes

D-U-N-S 07-876-0501
NATIVE AMERICAN HEALTH CENTER INC (CA)
2950 International Blvd, Oakland, CA 94601-2228
Tel (510) 535-4400 Founded/Ownrshp 1971
Sales 22.3MM EMP 150
SIC 8011 8021 8093 Clinic, operated by physicians; Dentists' office; Mental health clinic, outpatient; Clinic, operated by physicians; Dentists' office; Mental health clinic, outpatient
CEO: Martin Waukazoo
COO: Ana O'Connor
Exec: Kevin Goff
Adm Dir: Lucy Nelson
Off Mgr: Amadene Castillo
Dir IT: Steven Stringham
IT Man: David Nobile
IT Man: Chirag Patel
IT Man: Sandra Tavel
IT Man: Brent Wiley
Sales Exec: Jerri Davis

D-U-N-S 80-562-1307
NATIVE AMERICAN HERITAGE ASSOCIATION
12085 Quaal Rd, Black Hawk, SD 57718-9862
Tel (540) 636-1020 Founded/Ownrshp 1988
Sales 31.8MM EMP 27
Accts Bullock & Associates Pc Le
SIC 7389 Fund raising organizations; Fund raising organizations
Pr: David G Myers

D-U-N-S 84-877-2237
NATIVE AMERICAN LOGISTICS WORLDWIDE LLC
(Suby of CHIEFTAIN CONTRACT SERVICES) ★
3039 Airpark Dr N, Flint, MI 48507-3471
Tel (810) 233-7331 Founded/Ownrshp 2010
Sales 23.5MM EMP 14^E
SIC 4212 4731 Local trucking, without storage; Truck transportation brokers; Local trucking, without storage; Truck transportation brokers
CEO: Steve Barr
*CFO: Jeff Berlin

D-U-N-S 04-853-0112
NATIVE AMERICAN SERVICES CORP
NASCO
53285 Silver Valley Rd, Kellogg, ID 83837-9708
Tel (208) 783-0361 Founded/Ownrshp 1997
Sales 59.7MM^E EMP 120
SIC 1611 General contractor, highway & street construction; General contractor, highway & street construction
Pr: Matthew James
*Ch Bd: Dennis Rusty Sheppard
*CFO: Rick Luna
IT Man: Scott Schelley
Ql Cn Mgr: Todd Sheppard
Snr PM: John Bloom

D-U-N-S 10-402-4208
NATIVE ANGELS HOME CARE AGENCY INC
201 Livermore Dr, Pembroke, NC 28372-7322
Tel (910) 735-1541 Founded/Ownrshp 2001
Sales 9.9MM^E EMP 283^E
Accts Griffin Maxwell & Frazelle P
SIC 8082 Home health care services; Home health care services
Pr: Bobbie Ghaffar
Exec: Steve Thomas

D-U-N-S 79-038-1425
NATIVE OILFIELD SERVICES LLC
7900 S Interstate 35 W, Alvarado, TX 76009-7297
Tel (817) 783-3636 Founded/Ownrshp 2006
Sales 96.3MM^E EMP 75^E
SIC 1389 Oil field services
Exec: Chris Levine

D-U-N-S 11-036-7927
NATIVE RESOURCE DEVELOPMENT CO INC
QUALITY HOME CARE
51 Jemez Dam Rd Ste 110, Bernalillo, NM 87004-5986
Tel (505) 867-5372 Founded/Ownrshp 1990
Sales 24.9MM^E EMP 300
SIC 8744 7349 Facilities support services; Janitorial service, contract basis; Hospital housekeeping; Facilities support services; Janitorial service, contract basis; Hospital housekeeping
Pr: Elvina D Emerson
*VP: Tom Teegarden
Genl Mgr: Gabreil Alonzo
Genl Mgr: Elvira Emerson
Genl Mgr: Challotte Mendosa
Snr Mgr: Penny Emerson

D-U-N-S 80-887-1776
NATIVE WHOLESALE INC
245 Dixie Blvd, Delray Beach, FL 33444-3849
Tel (561) 265-1201 Founded/Ownrshp 1992
Sales 27.3MM^E EMP 56
SIC 5193 Flowers, fresh
Pr: Paul Peterson
Off Mgr: Lisa Matchell

D-U-N-S 07-170-2745
NATIVIDAD HOSPITAL INC
OCCUPATIONAL MEDICINE
1441 Constitution Blvd, Salinas, CA 93906-3100
Tel (831) 515-8866 Founded/Ownrshp 1950
Sales 37.0MM^E EMP 659
SIC 8062 8011 8093 General medical & surgical hospitals; Offices & clinics of medical doctors; Specialty outpatient clinics; General medical & surgical hospitals; Offices & clinics of medical doctors; Specialty outpatient clinics
Pr: William Foley

D-U-N-S 13-166-5358
NATIXIS GLOBAL ASSET MANAGEMENT LP
(Suby of NATIXIS ASSET MANAGEMENT)
399 Boylston St, Boston, MA 02116-3305
Tel (617) 449-2100 Founded/Ownrshp 1997
Sales 503.2MM^E EMP 1,425
SIC 6282 8742 Investment advisory service; Investment counselors; Financial consultant; Investment advisory service; Investment counselors; Financial consultant
Pt: Pierre Servant
Pt: Beverly Bearden
Pt: Philip Bertram
Pt: Jeffrey D Plunkett
Pt: Neal Ryland
Pr: David Giunta
COO: Spiro Christopulos
Ex VP: Beverly Beardon
Ex VP: Mark Doyle
Ex VP: Beatriz Pinasmith
Sr VP: Ian Macduff
Sr VP: Duncan Wilkinson
VP: Paul C Anderson
VP: Richard R Davis
VP: Thomas Kartanowicz

NATIXIS GLOBAL ASSET MGT
See NATIXIS SECURITIES AMERICAS LLC

D-U-N-S 78-935-0535
NATIXIS NORTH AMERICA LLC
(Suby of NATIXIS)
9 W 57th St Fl 36, New York, NY 10019-2704
Tel (212) 891-6100 Founded/Ownrshp 1990
Sales 58.2MM^E EMP 260^E
SIC 8742 Management consulting services; Management consulting services
Pr: Luc De Clapiers
Pr: Jorome Jaroussie
Pr: Thomas Sharpe
COO: Natalie Ramos
VP: Julia Becerra
VP: Samuel Bouchot
VP: Doris Chiu
VP: Nick Mitra
VP: Brook Payner
VP: Melissa Saint-Amour
VP: Vishal Vanjani
Dir Risk M: Satyan Persaud
Assoc Dir: Jesse Sable

D-U-N-S 00-698-0288
NATIXIS SECURITIES AMERICAS LLC
NATIXIS GLOBAL ASSET MGT
(Suby of NATIXIS)
1251 Avenue Of The Americ, New York, NY 10020-1104
Tel (212) 891-6100 Founded/Ownrshp 2001
Sales 65.1MM^E EMP 300
SIC 6211 Security brokers & dealers; Security brokers & dealers
*CFO: Howard Green
Ofcr: Steve Cohen
Ex VP: Henri Chermont
Ex VP: Gregg Schoenberg
VP: Alan Barr
VP: Aline BEC
VP: Kevin Donovan
VP: Ralph Esposito
VP: Michael Kellen
VP: Kenny Lee
VP: Jamie Leiss
VP: Jocelyn Noel
VP: Joseph Piskorowski
VP: Mary Rail
VP: Tracy Saltwick
VP: Eric Seyffer
VP: Graeme Smith

D-U-N-S 07-939-1943
NATIXIS US FINANCE CO LLC
1251 Avenue Of The Americ, New York, NY 10020-1104
Tel (212) 872-5042 Founded/Ownrshp 2014
Sales 27.1MM^E EMP 221^E
SIC 8742 Banking & finance consultant
Pr: Perol Francois
*CFO: Debroux Laurence
*Ch: Cahn Thierry
Ofcr: Cristina Heurtevent
Ofcr: Jacques Sudre
Ex VP: Tatiana Issa
Sr VP: Kevin Finney
Sr VP: David Goodsell
Sr VP: Michael Magner
VP: William Chen
VP: Thomas Collins
VP: Steven Eberhardt
VP: Slava Kulik
VP: Benoit Maupome
VP: Vinh Nguyen
VP: Agata Polisiewicz
VP: Jon Scott
VP: Brian Staley
VP: Daniel Wall
VP: Fan Zhang

NAT'L ASSN FOR HISPANIC ELDERL
See LA ASOCIACION NACIONAL PRO PERSONAS MAYORES

D-U-N-S 96-489-6232
NATL ASSN OF CHILDRENS HOSPITALS INC
401 Wythe St, Alexandria, VA 22314-1915
Tel (703) 683-7961 Founded/Ownrshp 2007
Sales 21.5MM EMP 38^E
Accts Tate And Tryon Washington Dc
SIC 8062 General medical & surgical hospitals; General medical & surgical hospitals
Prin: Larry Mc Andrews
VP: Thomas Fache
Sls&Mrk Ex: Brian Winston

D-U-N-S 06-464-7688 IMP
NATOLI ENGINEERING CO INC
28 Research Park Cir, Saint Charles, MO 63304-5624
Tel (636) 926-8900 Founded/Ownrshp 1971
Sales 27.1MM^E EMP 150
SIC 3559 7629 3544 Pharmaceutical machinery; Electrical repair shops; Special dies, tools, jigs & fixtures; Pharmaceutical machinery; Electrical repair shops; Special dies, tools, jigs & fixtures
VP: Dale Natoli
Prd Mgr: Ryan Wohlers

D-U-N-S 10-000-7541
NATOMAS UNIFIED SCHOOL DISTRICT
1901 Arena Blvd, Sacramento, CA 95834-3721
Tel (916) 567-5400 Founded/Ownrshp 1952
Sales 61.8MM^E EMP 1,000
SIC 8211 Public elementary & secondary schools; High school, junior or senior; Public elementary & secondary schools; High school, junior or senior
Pr: Susan Heredia
*VP: Scott Dosick
Ex Dir: Javier Carrillo
Ex Dir: Joel Rabin
Off Mgr: Pat Hargreaves
Dir IT: Angela Herrera
Dir IT: Rosa Rijo
Dir IT: Karen Whitlock
Trfc Dir: Kandy Wolfe-Natomas
Schl Brd P: Susane Heredia
HC Dir: Brent Johnson

D-U-N-S 08-520-9526 IMP
NATORI CO INC
180 Madison Ave Fl 19, New York, NY 10016-5267
Tel (212) 532-7796 Founded/Ownrshp 1977
Sales 43.5MM^E EMP 200
SIC 2384 2341 Bathrobes, men's & women's: made from purchased materials; Women's & children's nightwear; Bathrobes, men's & women's: made from purchased materials; Women's & children's nightwear
Ch Bd: Josie Natori
*CFO: Eileen Montellese
VP: Jeanette Cantone
VP: Maryann Kraker
VP: Cheryl Nowak
VP: Elizabeth Yee
VP Prd: Helen Zinn
Prd Mgr: Blair Boyer
Merch Mgr: Linda Delgado
Sls Mgr: Danielle Zamudio

D-U-N-S 07-970-4682
NATROL LLC
(Suby of AUROBINDO PHARMA USA INC) ★
21411 Prairie St, Chatsworth, CA 91311-5829
Tel (818) 739-6000 Founded/Ownrshp 2015
Sales 110.0MM EMP 212^E
SIC 5122 2099 Drugs, proprietaries & sundries; Food preparations
CFO: Jeff Perea
Sr VP: Richard Hiraga
Rgnl Mgr: Shiju Joseph
CIO: Shankar Murty
Dir IT: Mirrella Jolicoeur
IT Man: Michael Berinde
Prd Mgr: German Miranda
Natl Sales: Tom Lane
Natl Sales: Joseph Mullan
S&M/VP: Brian Armstrong
Mktg Mgr: Stacy Dill

D-U-N-S 07-575-8540
NATRONA COUNTY SCHOOL DISTRICT
NATRONA COUNTY SCHOOL DST 1
970 N Glenn Rd, Casper, WY 82601-1635
Tel (307) 577-0200 Founded/Ownrshp 1900
Sales 106.6MM^E EMP 1,500
Accts Porter Muirhead Cornia & How
SIC 8211 Public elementary school; Public junior high school; Public senior high school; Public elementary school; Public junior high school; Public senior high school
Off Mgr: Deb Fields
Off Mgr: Paulette Moore
MIS Dir: Drew Walker
Teacher Pr: Mike Jenning
HC Dir: Andrea Nestor

NATRONA COUNTY SCHOOL DST 1
See NATRONA COUNTY SCHOOL DISTRICT

D-U-N-S 13-710-9336
NATT MCDOUGALL CO
20182 Sw 112th Ave, Tualatin, OR 97062-6886
Tel (503) 968-7552 Founded/Ownrshp 1988
Sales 27.0MM EMP 53^E
SIC 1542 Nonresidential construction; Nonresidential construction
CEO: Natt McDougall
*Pr: Michael S McDougall
*CFO: Maryanne Krumm
*VP: Richard Krumm
*VP: Jerry Martin

NATURA-VIGOR
See ARNET PHARMACEUTICAL CORP

D-U-N-S 05-479-3658 IMP
▲ **NATURAL ALTERNATIVES INTERNATIONAL INC**
1185 Linda Vista Dr Ste C, San Marcos, CA 92078-3877
Tel (760) 744-7340 Founded/Ownrshp 1980
Sales 79.5MM EMP 166
Accts Ernst & Young Llp San Diego
Tkr Sym NAII Exch NGM
SIC 2833 Vitamins, natural or synthetic: bulk, uncompounded; Vitamins, natural or synthetic: bulk, uncompounded
Ch Bd: Mark A Ledoux
Pr: Kenneth E Wolf
CFO: Michael E Fortin
Ex VP: John Dullea
VP: Robert A Kay
VP Mktg: Timothy E Belanger
VP Mktg: Theo N Niewenhuis
Board of Directors: Joe E Davis, Alan G Dunn, Alan J Lane, Lee G Weldon

D-U-N-S 07-924-5402
NATURAL AMERICAN FOODS INC
10464 Bryan Hwy, Onsted, MI 49265-9551
Tel (517) 467-2065 Founded/Ownrshp 2013
Sales 22.9MM^E EMP 75
SIC 2099 Honey, strained & bottled
CEO: Rolf Richter
*CFO: Jack Irvin
VP: Joyce Schlachter
VP: John Wolf
VP Opers: Chol Kim

D-U-N-S 86-762-0767 IMP
■ **NATURAL BALANCE PET FOODS INC**
(Suby of BIG HEART PET BRANDS) ★
100 N First St Ste 200, Burbank, CA 91502-1845
Tel (800) 829-4493 Founded/Ownrshp 1989
Sales 21.8MM^E EMP 140^E
SIC 2048 5199 Prepared feeds; Pet supplies; Prepared feeds; Pet supplies
Pr: Joseph Herrick
*CEO: David J West
*Sec: Lynnda Herrick
Genl Mgr: Heather Govea
VP Opers: Stuart Kowarsky
QC Dir: Steve Lunetta
Prd Mgr: Cliff Grimes
*VP Sls: Frank Koch
Mktg Dir: Alice Ahn
Mktg Dir: Alice Kim
Mktg Mgr: Kathy Sun

NATURAL BEAUTY GROWERS
See FLORAL PLANT GROWERS LLC

NATURAL CHOICE
See NUTRO CO

D-U-N-S 04-111-8100 IMP
NATURAL COUNTRY FARMS INC
(Suby of COUNTRY PURE FOODS INC) ★
681 W Waterloo Rd, Akron, OH 44314-1547
Tel (330) 753-2293 Founded/Ownrshp 1995
Sales 229.0MM EMP 180
SIC 2033 2037 2086 Fruit juices: fresh; Fruit juice concentrates, frozen; Pasteurized & mineral waters, bottled & canned; Fruit juices: fresh; Fruit juice concentrates, frozen; Pasteurized & mineral waters, bottled & canned
CEO: Raymond Lee
Sr VP: Tom Kolb
Sr VP: Paul E Sukalich

D-U-N-S 94-438-3660
NATURAL DATA INC
7418 E Helm Dr, Scottsdale, AZ 85260-2418
Tel (480) 648-2607 Founded/Ownrshp 1995
Sales 13.1MM^E EMP 325
SIC 7361 Employment agencies; Employment agencies
Pr: Pat Smith

NATURAL FOOD MILL
See FOOD FOR LIFE BAKING CO INC

D-U-N-S 00-693-1794
■ **NATURAL GAS PIPELINE CO OF AMERICA LLC**
(Suby of KINDER MORGAN INC) ★
1001 Louisiana St, Houston, TX 77002-5089
Tel (713) 369-9000 Founded/Ownrshp 1950, 2012
Sales 504.8MM^E EMP 1,747
SIC 4922 1311 8741 Pipelines, natural gas; Storage, natural gas; Natural gas production; Management services; Pipelines, natural gas; Storage, natural gas; Natural gas production; Management services
Pr: David Devine
*CFO: Jim Saunders
*Ex VP: Steve Kean
Plnt Mgr: William Allison

D-U-N-S 07-140-5690
NATURAL GAS PROCESSING CO
WYOMING GAS COMPANY DIVISION
101 Division, Worland, WY 82401-8702
Tel (307) 347-2416 Founded/Ownrshp 1974
Sales 36.5MM^E EMP 83
SIC 4924 1311 Natural gas distribution; Crude petroleum & natural gas
Pr: David L Hamilton
*Sec: Kathy Loveland
*VP: Janeen Capshaw

D-U-N-S 06-455-5232
■ **NATURAL GAS REPOWERING LLC**
(Suby of NRG YIELD OPERATING LLC) ★
211 Carnegie Ctr, Princeton, NJ 08540-6213
Tel (609) 524-4500 Founded/Ownrshp 2011
Sales 114.8M^E EMP 912^E
SIC 1321 Butane (natural) production

D-U-N-S 06-851-7171
▲ **NATURAL GAS SERVICES GROUP INC**
508 W Wall St Ste 550, Midland, TX 79701-5079
Tel (432) 262-2700 Founded/Ownrshp 1998
Sales 96.9MM EMP 353^E
Tkr Sym NGS Exch NYS
SIC 7353 3563 Oil field equipment, rental or leasing; Air & gas compressors; Oil field equipment, rental or leasing; Air & gas compressors
Ch Bd: Stephen C Taylor
CFO: G Larry Lawrence
VP: Ronald D Bingham
VP: James R Hazlett
VP: S Craig Rogers
Pr Dir: Jim Drewitz
Board of Directors: David L Bradshaw, John W Chisholm, Charles G Curtis, William F Hughes

D-U-N-S 07-854-0211
▲ **NATURAL GROCERS BY VITAMIN COTTAGE INC**
12612 W Alameda Pkwy, Lakewood, CO 80228-2824
Tel (303) 986-4600 Founded/Ownrshp 1955
Sales 624.6MM EMP 2,830^E
Accts Kpmg Llp Denver Colorado
Tkr Sym NGVC Exch NYS
SIC 5411 5499 Grocery stores; Grocery stores, chain; Health & dietetic food stores; Grocery stores; Grocery stores, chain; Health & dietetic food stores
Ch Bd: Kemper Isely
Pr: Zephyr Isely
CFO: Sandra Buffa
Treas: Mario Pasquale
Ex VP: Elizabeth Isely
Ex VP: Heather Isely
Sls Dir: Nancy Flynn
Board of Directors: Michael T Campbell, Edward Cerkovnik, Richard Halle

D-U-N-S 61-301-3580
▲ **NATURAL HEALTH TRENDS CORP**
4514 Cole Ave Ste 1400, Dallas, TX 75205-4181
Tel (972) 241-4080 Founded/Ownrshp 1988
Sales 124.5MM EMP 99
Tkr Sym NHTC Exch NAS
SIC 5122 5961 Cosmetics, perfumes & hair products; Vitamins & minerals; Pharmaceuticals, mail order; Cosmetics & perfumes, mail order; Cosmetics, perfumes & hair products; Vitamins & minerals; Pharmaceuticals, mail order; Cosmetics & perfumes, mail order
Pr: Chris T Sharng
*Ch Bd: Randall A Mason
Pr: Curtis Broome
Pr: Richard S Johnson
Pr: Paul Rogers
CFO: Timothy S Davidson
CFO: Timothy Davidson
VP: Flora Berry
VP: Paolo Giuliani
IT Man: Damon Tomlinson

D-U-N-S 07-962-2991
NATURAL HISTORY MUSEUM OF LOS ANGELES COUNTY
900 Exposition Blvd, Los Angeles, CA 90007-4057
Tel (213) 763-3442 Founded/Ownrshp 2014
Sales 54.0MM EMP 300
SIC 8412 Museum

D-U-N-S 07-917-6973
NATURAL MARKETS FOOD GROUP
PLANET ORGANIC MARKET
1 Bridge St Ste 2, Irvington, NY 10533-1552
Tel (914) 472-7900 Founded/Ownrshp 1992
Sales 132.8MM^E EMP 1,200
SIC 5499 Health foods; Health foods
CEO: Pat Brown
CEO: Pallavi Moorthy
*CFO: Brian Shelton
*Sr VP: Sherry Nolan-Schultz
Off Mgr: Curt Avallone
Store Mgr: Pat McAvoy
Mktg Mgr: Kristine Drier
Counsel: Lexis Termini

D-U-N-S 94-150-3799
■ **NATURAL NUTRITION GROUP INC**
(Suby of HAIN CELESTIAL GROUP INC) ★
58 S Svc Rd Ste 250, Melville, NY 11747
Tel (631) 730-2200 Founded/Ownrshp 1999
Sales 70.0MM EMP 410
SIC 5149 2043 2052 Health foods; Natural & organic foods; Cereal breakfast foods; Cookies & crackers; Health foods; Cereal breakfast foods; Cookies & crackers
Pr: Irwin Simon
*Treas: Gary Jacobs
*VP: Benjamin Brecher

D-U-N-S 07-727-9206 IMP
NATURAL ORGANICS INC
NATURE'S PLUS
548 Broadhollow Rd, Melville, NY 11747-3708
Tel (631) 293-0030 Founded/Ownrshp 1972
Sales 0.2 EMP 400
SIC 2833 Vitamins, natural or synthetic: bulk, uncompounded; Vitamins, natural or synthetic: bulk, uncompounded
Ch Bd: Gerald Kessler
*Pr: James Gibbons
Rgnl Mgr: Tom Grein
QA Dir: Bonnie Miller
QA Dir: Greg Polkowski
Dir IT: Christopher Pendergast
IT Man: Niemit Trivedi
Opers Supe: John Esposito
Opers Mgr: Scott Devoti
VP Mktg: Susan Dorsey
Mktg Mgr: Des Dugquem

D-U-N-S 61-344-0684
NATURAL ORGANICS LABORATORIES
UNIVERSAL PROTEINS
9500 New Horizons Blvd, Amityville, NY 11701-1155
Tel (631) 957-5600 Founded/Ownrshp 1989
Sales 75.4MM^E EMP 500
SIC 2834 2087 Vitamin preparations; Flavoring extracts & syrups; Vitamin preparations; Flavoring extracts & syrups
Pr: Gerald Kessler
Plnt Mgr: Mike Augello

QI Cn Mgr: Heather Fairman
QI Cn Mgr: Philip George

D-U-N-S 96-211-8071 IMP
NATURAL POLYMER INTERNATIONAL CORP
NPIC
3601 E Plano Pkwy Ste 150, Plano, TX 75074-1802
Tel (972) 509-0449 *Founded/Ownrshp* 1996
Sales 26.5MM^E *EMP* 139
SIC 3999 Pet supplies; Pet supplies
CEO: Andrew Kang
**Pr:* James Chang
**VP:* Dan Cauffman

D-U-N-S 80-857-2965
NATURAL PRODUCTS GROUP LLC
9200 Mason Ave, Chatsworth, CA 91311-6005
Tel (818) 882-2951 *Founded/Ownrshp* 2004
Sales 119.9MM^E *EMP* 220^E
SIC 6799 Investors; Investors

D-U-N-S 03-408-4968
NATURAL PROPERTIES LLC (TX)
RACE RUNNER
1801 E Southeast Loop 323, Tyler, TX 75701-8325
Tel (903) 592-2970 *Founded/Ownrshp* 2010
Sales 38.0MM *EMP* 200
SIC 5172 Fuel oil; Fuel oil

D-U-N-S 78-027-2824
NATURAL RESOURCE GOVERNANCE INSTITUTE
REVENUE WATCH INSTITUTE
80 Broad St Ste 1801, New York, NY 10004-3326
Tel (646) 929-9750 *Founded/Ownrshp* 2006
Sales 21.5MM *EMP* 6
Accts Lutz And Carr Cpas Llp New
SIC 7389 Fund raising organizations
Ch Bd: Karin Lissakers
**Ch Bd:* Ernesto Zedillo
**Treas:* Alan Detheridge
Ofcr: George Lugalambi
Ofcr: Varsha Venugopal
Comm Dir: Lee Bailey

D-U-N-S 79-928-4294
NATURAL RESOURCE GROUP LLC
(*Suby of* ERM-DELAWARE, INC.)
80 S 8th St Ste 1000, Minneapolis, MN 55402-2162
Tel (612) 347-6789 *Founded/Ownrshp* 2014
Sales 27.3MM^E *EMP* 146
SIC 8748 Environmental consultant; Energy conservation consultant; Environmental consultant; Energy conservation consultant
Pr: Mark B Larson
**CFO:* Scott W Poellinger
Treas: Sari Ebert
VP: Elizabeth Dolezal
**VP:* Douglas J Lake
VP: Tom Umenhofer
Exec: Beth Saufley
Dir IT: Keith Kendall

D-U-N-S 06-080-1813
▲ NATURAL RESOURCE PARTNERS LP
601 Jefferson St Ste 3600, Houston, TX 77002-7906
Tel (713) 751-7507 *Founded/Ownrshp* 2002
Sales 399.7MM *EMP* 269^E
Tkr Sym NRP *Exch* NYS
SIC 1221 Bituminous coal & lignite-surface mining; Bituminous coal & lignite-surface mining
Ch Bd: Corbin J Robertson Jr
Genl Pt: Nrp LP
Pr: Wyatt L Hogan
Bd of Dir: Matthew Fifield
VP: George Angus
VP: Dennis F Coker
VP: Kevin J Craig
VP: Kathy E Hagr
VP: David Hensley
VP: Paul Sebastian
VP: Gregory Wooten

D-U-N-S 80-792-7579
NATURAL RESOURCE TECHNOLOGY INC
234 W Florida St Ste 500, Milwaukee, WI 53204-1659
Tel (414) 837-3607 *Founded/Ownrshp* 1993
Sales 29.0MM *EMP* 71^E
SIC 8748 Environmental consultant
Pr: Laurie J Parsons
**VP:* Clark Crosby
**VP:* Richard Fax
**VP:* Bruce Hensel
**VP:* Richard Webber
**VP:* Roy Wittenburg
Admn Mgr: Jenni Plamann

D-U-N-S 19-603-5430
■ NATURAL RESOURCES CONSERVATION SERVICE
USDA NRCS
(*Suby of* U S D A) ★
1400 Independence Ave Sw, Washington, DC 20250-0002
Tel (202) 720-4525 *Founded/Ownrshp* 1935
Sales NA *EMP* 12,000
SIC 9512 Soil conservation services, government; ; Soil conservation services, government;
CFO: Joseph D O'Leska Jr
Snr Mgr: Walter Douglas

D-U-N-S 07-861-5580
NATURAL RESOURCES DEFENSE COUNCIL INC
NRDC
40 W 20th St, New York, NY 10011-4211
Tel (212) 727-2700 *Founded/Ownrshp* 1970
Sales 115.9MM *EMP* 500
Accts Grant Thornton Lp New York N
SIC 8641 Environmental protection organization; Environmental protection organization
CEO: Daniel R Tishman
**Pr:* Frances G Beinecke
COO: Tianya Coachman
CFO: Lawrence Levine
**Treas:* Joy Covey
Bd of Dir: Robin Marx
Ex VP: Hamilton Candee
Ex VP: Richard Schrader
Sr VP: Roseann Rock
VP: Sonah Allie
VP: Evelyn Arevalo
VP: Sevi Armstrong
VP: George Black
VP: Lisa Goffredi
VP: Albert Huang
VP: Desrene Walton
Exec: Brian James
Creative D: Bob Comire
Comm Dir: Matt Howes

D-U-N-S 80-938-8713
NATURAL RESOURCES VIRGINIA
(*Suby of* EXECUTIVE OFFICE OF VIRGINIA)
1111 E Broad St, Richmond, VA 23219-1934
Tel (804) 786-0044 *Founded/Ownrshp* 1986
Sales NA *EMP* 1,680
SIC 9511 9512 Air, water & solid waste management; ; Land, mineral & wildlife conservation; ; Air, water & solid waste management; ; Land, mineral & wildlife conservation;
Bd of Dir: Mac McArthur-Fox
Bd of Dir: Sandy Hermann

D-U-N-S 80-913-5676 IMP
■ NATURAL RETAIL GROUP INC
EARTH ORIGINS MARKET
(*Suby of* UNITED NATURAL FOODS INC) ★
30555 Us Highway 19 N, Palm Harbor, FL 34684-4415
Tel (727) 785-7951 *Founded/Ownrshp* 1993
Sales 48.7MM^E *EMP* 354
SIC 5499 Health foods; Health foods
Genl Mgr: Crystal Noble
**Pr:* Marvin O Jeffers
**CFO:* Mark Shamber
**VP:* Daniel Atwood

D-U-N-S 85-855-6517 IMP
NATURAL SELECTION FOODS LLC
EARTHBOUND FARM
1721 San Juan Hwy, San Juan Bautista, CA 95045-9780
Tel (831) 623-7880 *Founded/Ownrshp* 2014
Sales NA *EMP* 1,025
SIC 0723 2037 2099 Vegetable packing services; Fruit crops market preparation services; Frozen fruits & vegetables; Food preparations

D-U-N-S 11-127-7062
■ NATURAL SELECTION FOODS MANUFACTURING LLC
(*Suby of* EARTHBOUND HOLDINGS III LLC) ★
3701 S Avenue 3 1/2 E, Yuma, AZ 85365-6510
Tel (831) 623-7880 *Founded/Ownrshp* 2013
Sales 41.1MM^E *EMP* 539^E
SIC 5148 Fresh fruits & vegetables
Prin: Drew Goodman

D-U-N-S 80-692-3699
NATURAL STONE MFG CO INC
4902 W Superior Ave, Phoenix, AZ 85043-6101
Tel (602) 484-0827 *Founded/Ownrshp* 1998
Sales 21.6MM^E *EMP* 150
SIC 4214 Local trucking with storage; Local trucking with storage
Ch: Carl E Hess
**Pr:* Richard K Krause
**CFO:* Howard Scheurner
Genl Mgr: Kelly Davis

D-U-N-S 62-755-1955
■ NATURAL SUPPLEMENT ASSOCIATION INC
EXPERIMENTAL APPLIED SCIENCES
(*Suby of* ABBOTT LABORATORIES) ★
3300 Stelzer Rd, Columbus, OH 43219-3034
Tel (614) 624-7677 *Founded/Ownrshp* 2004
Sales 34.1MM^E *EMP* 220^E
SIC 5122 5961 Vitamins & minerals; Mail order house; Vitamins & minerals; Mail order house
Pr: David Lumley
**COO:* Peter Noverr
**CFO:* Nancy Maston
VP: Rick Anderson

NATURAL SYSTEMS UTILITIES
See APPLIED WATER MANAGEMENT INC

D-U-N-S 07-838-7984
NATURAL SYSTEMS UTILITIES LLC
2 Clerico Ln Ste 210, Hillsborough, NJ 08844-1620
Tel (908) 359-5501 *Founded/Ownrshp* 2007
Sales 30.0MM^E *EMP* 109
SIC 8741 Industrial management
CEO: Robert D Dixon
Pt: Jeff Speck
**Pr:* Ed Clerico
**CEO:* Charles R Gordon
**CFO:* Hamsa Shadaksharappa
Ex VP: Ryan C Brandt
Ex VP: Richard H Cisterna
Ex VP: Axel Hester
**Ex VP:* Jonathan C Kaledin
VP: Zachary F Gallagher
VP: Sharon Pellicane

D-U-N-S 08-109-8881 IMP
NATURALIFE ECO VITE LABORATORIES INC
PARAGON LABORATORIES
20433 Earl St, Torrance, CA 90503-2414
Tel (310) 370-1563 *Founded/Ownrshp* 1971
Sales 26.9MM^E *EMP* 100
SIC 2023 2844 2834 5122 Dietary supplements, dairy & non-dairy based; Toilet preparations; Suppositories; Vitamins & minerals; Dietary supplements, dairy & non-dairy based; Toilet preparations; Suppositories; Vitamins & minerals
CEO: Jay Kaufman
**CFO:* Steven Billis
**Ex VP:* Richard Kaufman
Prd Mgr: Gustavo Feder

D-U-N-S 04-210-1360 IMP
■ NATURALLY FRESH INC (GA)
(*Suby of* TREEHOUSE FOODS INC) ★
1000 Naturally Fresh Blvd, Atlanta, GA 30349-2909
Tel (404) 765-9000 *Founded/Ownrshp* 1966
Sales 87.1MM^E *EMP* 340
SIC 2035 2099 Dressings, salad: raw & cooked (except dry mixes); Maple syrup; Dips, except cheese & sour cream based; Sauces: dry mixes; Dressings, salad: raw & cooked (except dry mixes); Maple syrup; Dips, except cheese & sour cream based; Sauces: dry mixes
CEO: Edward J Greene
**Ch Bd:* Coby G Brooks
**Pr:* Jerry Greene
COO: Boyd Stevens
**CFO:* Pete Rostad
**VP:* Patricia B Frederick
Dir IT: Ted Young
Sls Mgr: Rick Brownlee

NATURALLY VITAMIN SUPPLEMENTS
See MARLYN NUTRACEUTICALS INC

D-U-N-S 60-255-3828
NATURCHEM INC
270 Bruner Rd, Lexington, SC 29072-3767
Tel (803) 957-8989 *Founded/Ownrshp* 1987
Sales 32.0MM *EMP* 240^E
Accts Randall L Raber Cpa Pa Col
SIC 0721 Weed control services after planting; Weed control services after planting
Pr: Rom D Kellis III
Ofcr: Dana Dubose
Sr VP: Johnny Staples
**VP:* Lance Daniel
**VP:* Mark Davis
**VP:* Rom Kellis IV
Genl Mgr: Ricky Blevins
Genl Mgr: Daniel Bolton
Genl Mgr: Garrett Burnett
Genl Mgr: Benji Hook
Genl Mgr: Wes Jackson

D-U-N-S 08-690-0578 EXP
NATURE AMERICA INC
NATURE PUBLISHING GROUP
(*Suby of* MACMILLAN MAGAZINES LIMITED)
1 New York Plz Ste 4500, New York, NY 10004-1562
Tel (212) 726-9200 *Founded/Ownrshp* 1979
Sales 300.0MM *EMP* 440
SIC 2721 Magazines: publishing only, not printed on site; Magazines: publishing only, not printed on site
Pr: Steven Inchcoombe
COO: John Carroll
Ex VP: Peter Honig
Sr VP: Nick Kemp
Sr VP: Deborah Parker
VP: John Elduff
VP: Wendy Elman
VP: Michael Florek
VP: Richard Lalonde
Assoc Dir: Pankaj Jay
Mng Dir: Christian Dorbandt

NATURE BAKE
See AVB INC

D-U-N-S 07-265-6630
NATURE CONSERVANCY
4245 Fairfax Dr Ste 100, Arlington, VA 22203-1650
Tel (703) 841-5300 *Founded/Ownrshp* 1951
Sales 949.9MM *EMP* 3,400
SIC 8641 Environmental protection organization; Environmental protection organization
Ch: Teresa Beck
**Pr:* Mark Trecek
COO: Brian McPeek
COO: Lois E Quam
**Treas:* Muneer Satter
Chf Mktg O: Geof Rochester
Ofcr: Claudia Sherman
Ex VP: Mark Burget
VP: Russell Hoeflich
**VP:* Stephen Howell
VP: Francis Quitazol
Exec: Stephanie McNamara
Exec: Tara Zadeh
Assoc Dir: C J Hudlow
Assoc Dir: Jon Schwedler
Assoc Dir: Daniel Wendell
Assoc Dir: Constance Wolfe
Comm Dir: Kara Jackson
Comm Dir: Connie Prickett

NATURE PUBLISHING GROUP
See NATURE AMERICA INC

NATURE SWEET TOMATOES
See NATURESWEET LTD

D-U-N-S 06-280-8196 IMP
NATUREPLEX LLC (TN)
11085 Airport Rd, Olive Branch, MS 38654-4001
Tel (662) 874-1370 *Founded/Ownrshp* 2001
Sales 24.4MM^E *EMP* 51^E
SIC 5122 5999 Pharmaceuticals; Cosmetics
CFO: Steve Alm

NATURE'S BAKERY
See BELLA FOUR BAKERY INC

D-U-N-S 06-382-1722
NATURES BEST
6 Pointe Dr Ste 300, Brea, CA 92821-6323
Tel (714) 255-4600 *Founded/Ownrshp* 1969
Sales NA *EMP* 360
SIC 5149

D-U-N-S 07-952-5954
NATURES BEST DISTRIBUTION LLC
(*Suby of* KEHE DISTRIBUTORS LLC) ★
6 Pointe Dr Ste 300, Brea, CA 92821-6323
Tel (714) 255-4600 *Founded/Ownrshp* 2014
Sales 179.7MM^E *EMP* 1^E
SIC 5149 Health foods
CEO: James Beck
VP: Jim Lajeunesse
VP Sls: Amy Kirtland
Mktg Mgr: Charis Neves

D-U-N-S 11-925-7814 EXP
NATURES BEST INC
195 Engineers Rd, Hauppauge, NY 11788-4020
Tel (631) 232-3355 *Founded/Ownrshp* 1984
Sales 20.6MM^E *EMP* 40
SIC 5122 2833 8049 Vitamins & minerals; Vitamins, natural or synthetic: bulk, uncompounded; Nutrition specialist
Pr: Hal Katz

NATURE'S BOUNTY
See NBTY MANUFACTURING LLC

D-U-N-S 36-150-7622 IMP
■ NATURES BOUNTY INC
(*Suby of* ARCO PHARMACEUTICAL) ★
2100 Smithtown Ave, Ronkonkoma, NY 11779-7347
Tel (631) 580-6137 *Founded/Ownrshp* 1995
Sales 558.8MM^E *EMP* 6,000
SIC 2834 Vitamin preparations; Vitamin preparations
Ch Bd: Scott Rudolph
**Ch Bd:* Michael Collins
**Pr:* Harvey Kamil
VP: John Altenberg
VP: Kristine Urea
Web Dev: Yulia Fedotov

D-U-N-S 80-208-8682
NATURES CHOICE CORP
482 Houses Corner Rd, Sparta, NJ 07871-3404
Tel (908) 687-0178 *Founded/Ownrshp* 2003
Sales 40.2MM^E *EMP* 85
SIC 4953 Recycling, waste materials
CEO: James Schafle
**Pr:* James Panzini

NATURES EAT
See TEXAS STAR NUT AND FOOD CO INC

D-U-N-S 03-167-3549
NATURES FINEST FOODS LTD
1505 Paramount Pkwy, Batavia, IL 60510-1469
Tel (630) 879-5200 *Founded/Ownrshp* 2000
Sales 25.0MM *EMP* 3
SIC 5141 Food brokers; Food brokers
Pr: Dan Zedan
**Prin:* Rosa Alvarado

NATURE'S FLOWERS
See DIRECT FLOWERS DISTRIBUTORS INC

NATURE'S PLUS
See NATURAL ORGANICS INC

D-U-N-S 78-167-4296 IMP
NATURES PRODUCE CO
2622 S Alameda St, Vernon, CA 90058-1331
Tel (323) 235-4343 *Founded/Ownrshp* 2000
Sales 55.6MM^E *EMP* 80
SIC 5148 Fresh fruits & vegetables; Fresh fruits & vegetables
CEO: Rick Polisky
Off Mgr: Irene Perez

D-U-N-S 18-328-2862 IMP/EXP
NATURES PRODUCTS INC
1301 Sawgrs Corp Pkwy, Sunrise, FL 33323-2813
Tel (954) 233-3300 *Founded/Ownrshp* 1986
Sales 184.9MM^E *EMP* 244
SIC 5122 5499 Vitamins & minerals; Health & dietetic food stores; Vitamins & minerals; Health & dietetic food stores
Pr: Jose Minski
CFO: Mary Sanchez
**Sr Cor Off:* Meyer Minski
**VP:* Ruben Minski
VP Opers: Randy Clark
Plnt Mgr: Felipe Garay

D-U-N-S 08-183-2388 IMP/EXP
▲ NATURES SUNSHINE PRODUCTS INC
2500 W Executive Pkwy # 100, Lehi, UT 84043-3857
Tel (801) 341-7900 *Founded/Ownrshp* 1972
Sales 366.3MM *EMP* 1,010^E
Tkr Sym NATR *Exch* NAS
SIC 2834 Pharmaceutical preparations; Vitamin, nutrient & hematinic preparations for human use; Vitamin preparations; Pharmaceutical preparations; Vitamin, nutrient & hematinic preparations for human use; Vitamin preparations
Ch Bd: Gregory L Probert
Pr: Paul Noack
COO: Susan M Armstrong
CFO: Stephen M Bunker
CFO: Sohil Mansuri
**V Ch Bd:* Kristine F Hughes
Chf Cred: Richard D Strulson
Bd of Dir: Rebecca Steinfort
Ex VP: Greg Huff
Ex VP: Jamon A Jrvis
Ex VP: Matthew L Tripp
VP: Stacy Glovsky
Dir Soc: Gayle Warren
Board of Directors: Albert R Dowden, Robert B Mercer, Willem Mesdag, Mary Beth Springer, Rebecca L Steinfort, Jeffrey D Watkins

D-U-N-S 13-180-5707
NATURES TREES INC
SAVE A TREE
(*Suby of* GLENWOOD TREE EXPERTS) ★
550 Bedford Rd, Bedford Hills, NY 10507-1605
Tel (914) 241-4999 *Founded/Ownrshp* 2013
Sales 99.3MM^E *EMP* 310
SIC 0783 0782 0781 1629 Ornamental shrub & tree services; Arborist services; Lawn & garden services; Landscape counseling & planning; Irrigation system construction; Ornamental shrub & tree services; Arborist services; Lawn & garden services; Landscape counseling & planning; Irrigation system construction
Pr: Daniel Van Starrenburg
CFO: Jon Cervoni
Sec: Irving Eskenazi
VP: Rich Anda
VP: Ralph J Robbins
VP: Ralph Robbins
Exec: Ryan Moore
Exec: Ronald Sieracki

Brnch Mgr: Matt Donahoo
Brnch Mgr: Kevin Kraft
Off Mgr: Cecilia Cardell

D-U-N-S 79-031-8406 IMP
NATURES VALUE INC
468 Mill Rd, Coram, NY 11727-4108
Tel (631) 846-2500 *Founded/Ownrshp* 1992
Sales 82.3MM^E *EMP* 300^E
Accts Capraro Centofranchi Tidona
SIC 2834 Vitamin preparations; Vitamin preparations
CEO: Oscar Ramjeet
COO: Carl Ramjeet
**CFO:* Joe Kramer
VP: Manny Jimenez

D-U-N-S 60-123-4875
NATURES WAY FARMS INC
7795 Suttontown Rd, Faison, NC 28341-7267
Tel (910) 594-0096 *Founded/Ownrshp* 1984
Sales 32.6MM *EMP* 80
Accts Bobby F Herring Pa Cpas Mo
SIC 0723 7389 Vegetable packing services; Packaging & labeling services; Brokers' services; Vegetable packing services; Packaging & labeling services; Brokers' services
Pr: Debbie G Crawford
**Sec:* Ann M Crawford
**VP:* Mark Crawford
VP Sls: Parker Cooper

NATURE'S WAY PRODUCTS
See SCHWABE NORTH AMERICA INC

D-U-N-S 78-812-0137
NATURESCAPE
12601 W Janesville Rd, Muskego, WI 53150-3005
Tel (414) 425-4331 *Founded/Ownrshp* 1985
Sales 23.1MM^E *EMP* 100
SIC 0782 Lawn services
Owner: Todd Furry

D-U-N-S 78-320-9281 IMP
NATURESWEET LTD
NATURE SWEET TOMATOES
2338 N Loop 1604 W, San Antonio, TX 78248-4521
Tel (210) 408-8500 *Founded/Ownrshp* 1999
Sales 249.9MM^E *EMP* 830^E
SIC 0161 Tomato farm; Tomato farm
Pr: Bryant Ambelang
CFO: Armando C Lanes
VP: Adrian Almeida
VP: Kathryn Ault
VP: Dave Shaver
Mktg Mgr: Christina Winkler

D-U-N-S 07-887-0715 IMP
NATURESWEET USA LLC
EUROFRESH FARMS
26050 S Eurofresh Ave, Willcox, AZ 85643-3754
Tel (520) 384-4621 *Founded/Ownrshp* 2013
Sales 221.8MM^E *EMP* 800
SIC 5148 Fresh fruits & vegetables; Fresh fruits & vegetables
Dir Bus: J C Myers
Sls Dir: Robert Hartmann

D-U-N-S 02-267-1478 IMP/EXP
NATUREWORKS LLC
(*Suby of* CARGILL INC) ★
15305 Minnetonka Blvd, Minnetonka, MN 55345-1512
Tel (952) 742-0400 *Founded/Ownrshp* 2012
Sales 30.1MM^E *EMP* 120
SIC 3089 Plastic processing; Plastic processing
CEO: Marc Verbruggen
CFO: Pat Brunner
Snr Mgr: Peter Clydesdale

D-U-N-S 09-249-3501 IMP/EXP
NATUREX INC
(*Suby of* NATUREX)
375 Huyler St, South Hackensack, NJ 07606-1532
Tel (201) 440-5000 *Founded/Ownrshp* 2005
Sales 175.8MM *EMP* 185
Accts Prager Metis Cpas Llc Baskin
SIC 2833 Botanical products, medicinal: ground, graded or milled; Botanical products, medicinal: ground, graded or milled
CEO: Olivier Rigaud
**Ch Bd:* Thierry Lambert
**COO:* Maxime Angeluccim
**CFO:* Thierr Bertrand Lambert
**CFO:* Gaetan Sourceau
Ex VP: Qun Zheng
**VP:* Stephane Ducroux
Plng Mgr: S Rymarczuk
IT Man: Cornetin Huart
IT Man: Alex Martin
Opers Mgr: Clement Faye

D-U-N-S 00-923-1655
NATURIPE BERRY GROWERS INC
1611 Bunker Hill Way # 200, Salinas, CA 93906-6007
Tel (831) 722-2430 *Founded/Ownrshp* 1917
Sales 26.0MM^E *EMP* 25
SIC 0723 Fruit crops market preparation services; Vegetable crops market preparation services
CEO: Richard Amirsehhi
CFO: Jeff Mink
VP Opers: Tom Amrhein
VP Opers: Walt Motoza
Snr Mgr: Thomas Welch

D-U-N-S 01-376-1981 IMP
NATURIPE FARMS LLC
(*Suby of* HORTIFRUT IMPORTS INC) ★
9450 Corkscrew Palms Cir # 202, Estero, FL 33928-6422
Tel (239) 591-1664 *Founded/Ownrshp* 2000
Sales 51.7MM^E *EMP* 35
SIC 5148 Fresh fruits & vegetables
VP: David Fanaroff
Dir IT: John Conner
Opers Mgr: Kevin O'Brein
VP Mktg: Robert Verloop
**S&M/VP:* Brian Bocock
Snr Mgr: Gonzalo Canessa

D-U-N-S 82-822-5974 IMP
NATURIPE FOODS LLC
04726 County Road 215, Grand Junction, MI 49056-9218
Tel (269) 434-6791 *Founded/Ownrshp* 2008
Sales 29.6MM *EMP* 12
Accts Cliftonlarsonallen Llp Steve
SIC 0171 Berry crops; Berry crops
VP Mktg: Maurice Moragne

D-U-N-S 02-904-1274 IMP
NATURWOOD HOME FURNISHINGS INC
2711 Mercantile Dr, Rancho Cordova, CA 95742-6520
Tel (916) 638-2424 *Founded/Ownrshp* 1948
Sales 20.0MM^E *EMP* 90
SIC 5712 Furniture stores; Beds & accessories; Unfinished furniture
CEO: Lisa Keyes Chord
**COO:* Don Lemieux
**CFO:* Virginia Keyes
Advt Dir: Michelle Howard-Jones

D-U-N-S 11-292-5144 IMP
▲ **NATUS MEDICAL INC**
6701 Koll Center Pkwy # 150, Pleasanton, CA 94566-8060
Tel (925) 223-6700 *Founded/Ownrshp* 1987
Sales 355.8MM *EMP* 943^E
Tkr Sym BABY *Exch* NGS
SIC 3845 Electromedical equipment; Electromedical equipment
CEO: James B Hawkins
**Ch Bd:* Robert A Gunst
CFO: Jonathan Kennedy
Bd of Dir: Franco Avolio
Ofcr: Julie McDonough
VP: Ajay A Bhave
VP: D Christopher Chung
VP: Austin F Noll III
VP: Kenneth M Traverso
Exec: Gnanika Wijayaratne
Mng Dir: Eddie Pang
Board of Directors: Doris E Engibous, Kenneth E Ludlum, William M Moore

D-U-N-S 87-425-7488 IMP/EXP
■ **NATUS NEUROLOGY INC**
(*Suby of* NATUS MEDICAL INC) ★
3150 Pleasant View Rd, Middleton, WI 53562-4800
Tel (608) 829-8500 *Founded/Ownrshp* 2012
Sales 73.9MM^E *EMP* 300
SIC 3845 Ultrasonic scanning devices, medical; Ultrasonic scanning devices, medical
CEO: James Hawkins
**CFO:* Jonathan Kennedy
IT Man: Elliott Smith
Software D: Terry Henning
Mtls Mgr: Ben Schmidt
Mktg Mgr: John La Breche
Mktg Mgr: Amy Racki
Mktg Mgr: Marijean Trew

D-U-N-S 14-463-0597 IMP
NATUZZI AMERICAS INC
(*Suby of* NATUZZI SPA)
130 W Commerce Ave, High Point, NC 27260-4906
Tel (336) 887-8300 *Founded/Ownrshp* 1985
Sales 116.7MM *EMP* 65
SIC 5021 Furniture; Furniture
Pr: Joseph Mussallem
COO: David Jacobstein
CFO: Ian Mocori
**Treas:* Karen Skinner
**Ex VP:* Gaetano De Cataldo
Sr VP: Christian Schwab
Off Mgr: Cheryllel Deal

D-U-N-S 79-696-2868
NAU COUNTRY INSURANCE CO
(*Suby of* QBE AMERICAS) ★
7333 Sunwood Dr Nw, Ramsey, MN 55303-5119
Tel (763) 323-0175 *Founded/Ownrshp* 2010
Sales NA *EMP* 25^E
SIC 6331 Fire, marine & casualty insurance & carriers; Property damage insurance
CFO: James R Korin
Sr VP: Jim Christianson
Sr VP: Doug Jakway
VP: Jay Domer
VP: Hope Floberg
VP: Randy Hinders
VP: Dennis Keifer
VP: Elliot Konschak
VP: Mark Mossman
VP: John Wienstroer
**Prin:* James D Deal

NAU GROUP
See NAU HOLDING CO LLC

D-U-N-S 87-999-2493
NAU HOLDING CO LLC
NAU GROUP
(*Suby of* QBE AMERICAS) ★
7333 Sunwood Dr Nw, Anoka, MN 55303-5119
Tel (763) 433-2061 *Founded/Ownrshp* 2010
Sales NA *EMP* 108
SIC 6331 Fire, marine & casualty insurance & carriers
Pr: James Deal
**COO:* Gregory J Deal
VP: Bill Wilson

D-U-N-S 83-327-4991
NAUGATUCK VALLEY FINANCIAL CORP
333 Church St, Naugatuck, CT 06770-2806
Tel (203) 720-5000 *Founded/Ownrshp* 2004
Sales NA *EMP* 169^E
Accts Mcgladrey Llp New Haven Con
Tkr Sym NVSL *Exch* NGM
SIC 6035 Federal savings banks; Federal savings banks
Pr: William C Calderara
**Ch Bd:* Carlos S Batista
COO: James E Cotter
CFO: James Hastings
Ex VP: Mark C Foley
VP: Tyson Blackburn
VP: Bill Partington
Board of Directors: Orville G Aarons, Robert M Bolton, Frederick A Dlugokecki, Richard M Famiglietti, Kevin A Kennedy, James A Mengacci, Lawrence B Seidman

D-U-N-S 07-212-5628
NAUGATUCK VALLEY SAVINGS AND LOAN ASSOCIATION INC
NAUGATUCK VLY SAV & LN ASSOCI
333 Church St, Naugatuck, CT 06770-2806
Tel (203) 720-5000 *Founded/Ownrshp* 1922
Sales NA *EMP* 160
SIC 6035 6163 Federal savings & loan associations; Loan brokers; Federal savings & loan associations; Loan brokers
Pr: William C Calderara
**Treas:* Lee R Schlesinger
Ofcr: Robert Stabile
**Ex VP:* James Cotter
**Ex VP:* Mark C Foley
**Ex VP:* James Hastings
**Sr VP:* Sharon A Blanchette
**Sr VP:* Ann M Marino
**Sr VP:* Rita Myers
**Sr VP:* Charlene A Straznitskas
VP: Tyson Blackburn
VP: Ann Marino
VP: Ann M Marino
VP: Hunter Merrill
VP: Michael Milo
VP: Marcia Narciso
VP: Matthew Obrien
VP: Bill Partington
VP: Charlene Straznitskas
VP: Annette Strumolo
VP: Michael Yao
Board of Directors: Orville G Aarons, Frederick Hennick, J Allen Kosowsky, Dr Gerald Labriola, Michael J Magas, Lawrence Mambrino, James A Mengacci, Frank Rodrigues, Robert Ruccio

NAUGATUCK VLY SAV & LN ASSOCI
See NAUGATUCK VALLEY SAVINGS AND LOAN ASSOCIATION INC

D-U-N-S 05-163-7932
NAUGHTON ENERGY CORP
1898 Route 940, Pocono Pines, PA 18350-7744
Tel (570) 646-0422 *Founded/Ownrshp* 1976
Sales 21.3MM^E *EMP* 12
SIC 5172 5052 Gasoline; Lubricating oils & greases; Fuel oil; Coal
Pr: Mariette Naughton
**Sec:* Sean Naughton

NAUGHTY MONKEY
See BRAND HEADQUARTERS LLC

D-U-N-S 08-339-6861
NAULT ENTERPRISES INC (NH)
NAULT'S HONDA POWERHOUSE
420 2nd St, Manchester, NH 03102-4822
Tel (603) 669-7220 *Founded/Ownrshp* 1968
Sales 21.7MM^E *EMP* 60
Accts Howe Riley & Howe
SIC 5511 Automobiles, new & used; Automobiles, new & used
Pr: Richard M Nault
Genl Mgr: Mike Difonzo

D-U-N-S 17-705-9896 IMP/EXP
NAULT HOLDINGS INC
SUMMIT PET PRODUCTS
(*Suby of* ANIMAL SUPPLY CO LLC) ★
420 N Chimney Rock Rd, Greensboro, NC 27410-6249
Tel (336) 294-3200 *Founded/Ownrshp* 1987
Sales 49.0MM^E *EMP* 200^E
SIC 5999 5199 Pet supplies; Pet supplies; Pet supplies; Pet supplies
Pr: Richard Nault
**Pr:* Jay Joyce
**VP:* James Joyce
IT Man: Tammy Holyfield
Manager: Lauren Patterson

NAULT'S HONDA POWERHOUSE
See NAULT ENTERPRISES INC

D-U-N-S 00-901-0562
NAUMANN/HOBBS MATERIAL HANDLING CORP II INC (AZ)
4335 E Wood St, Phoenix, AZ 85040-2045
Tel (602) 437-1331 *Founded/Ownrshp* 1949, 1968
Sales 80.1MM^E *EMP* 412
SIC 7539 7359 7699 7629 5046 Electrical services; Equipment rental & leasing; Industrial machinery & equipment repair; Electrical repair shops; Commercial equipment; Electrical services; Equipment rental & leasing; Industrial machinery & equipment repair; Electrical repair shops; Commercial equipment
Pr: Bryan Armstrong
**CFO:* Keith Sawottke
**Ex VP:* Tom Hobbs
VP: Karen A Hobbs
Genl Mgr: Kimberly McMahon
CTO: Pete Kingsley
IT Man: Nathan Sherwood
IT Man: Robin Smith
IT Man: Ryan Sullivan
IT Man: Luke Thomas
VP Sls: John Schellinger

D-U-N-S 02-768-1485
NAUMES INC
2 W Barnett St, Medford, OR 97501-3666
Tel (541) 772-6268 *Founded/Ownrshp* 1946
Sales 167.8MM^E *EMP* 700
SIC 0175 0723 4222 Deciduous tree fruits; Fruit crops market preparation services; Warehousing, cold storage or refrigerated; Deciduous tree fruits; Fruit crops market preparation services; Warehousing, cold storage or refrigerated
Pr: Michael D Naumes
**VP:* Laura F Naumes
Genl Mgr: Dave Bridge
IT Man: Jessie Sanchez
Snr Mgr: Rita Eadie

NAUSET DISTRIBUTING CO
See NAUSET MARINE INC

D-U-N-S 01-955-6307
NAUSET MARINE INC
NAUSET DISTRIBUTING CO
45 Rt 6a, Orleans, MA 02653-2451
Tel (508) 255-0781 *Founded/Ownrshp* 1961
Sales 22.8MM^E *EMP* 56
SIC 5551 3732 Boat dealers; Marine supplies; Boat building & repairing
Pr: Philip A Deschamps
**Sec:* Peter D Walker
**VP:* David Deschamps
**VP:* Ronald Deschamps
**VP:* Dawson L Farber III
**VP:* Todd Walker
Board of Directors: Barbara Deschamps, Carol E Walker

D-U-N-S 07-172-5691
NAUSET REGIONAL SCHOOL DISTRICT (INC)
78 Eldridge Park Way, Orleans, MA 02653-3326
Tel (508) 255-8800 *Founded/Ownrshp* 1967
Sales 35.8MM^E *EMP* 763
SIC 8211 8748 Public combined elementary & secondary school; Business consulting; Public combined elementary & secondary school; Business consulting
Plnt Mgr: Bob Lewis

D-U-N-S 09-773-4388 EXP
NAUTEL MAINE INC
(*Suby of* NAUTEL LIMITED)
201 Target Industrial Cir, Bangor, ME 04401-5799
Tel (207) 947-8200 *Founded/Ownrshp* 1975
Sales 34.6MM^E *EMP* 175
SIC 3663 Radio & TV communications equipment; Transmitting apparatus, radio or television; Radio & TV communications equipment; Transmitting apparatus, radio or television
Ch Bd: Peter Conlon
**Pr:* Darlene Fowlow
**Treas:* Doreen Commeau
Exec: Hilary Chisholm
Exec: Hal Kneller
CTO: Gary Warner
Plnt Mgr: Charles Drillen
Mktg Mgr: John Whyte
Sls Mgr: John Macdonald

D-U-N-S 87-283-4080
NAUTIC PARTNERS LLC
100 Westminster St # 1220, Providence, RI 02903-2395
Tel (401) 278-6770 *Founded/Ownrshp* 2000
Sales 480.8MM^E *EMP* 1,797
SIC 6799 7629 Real estate investors, except property operators; Electrical equipment repair services; Telecommunication equipment repair (except telephones); Real estate investors, except property operators; Electrical equipment repair services; Telecommunication equipment repair (except telephones)
VP: Chris Pierce
Mng Dir: Douglas Hill

NAUTIC STAR BOATS
See NAUTIC STAR LLC

D-U-N-S 12-236-2416
NAUTIC STAR LLC
NAUTIC STAR BOATS
500 Waterway Dr, Amory, MS 38821-8207
Tel (662) 256-5636 *Founded/Ownrshp* 2002
Sales 36.4MM^E *EMP* 120
SIC 3732 Boat building & repairing; Boat building & repairing
**VP:* Robert Booser
Sls Mgr: Bryan Faulkner

D-U-N-S 11-850-3135
■ **NAUTICA INTERNATIONAL INC**
(*Suby of* NAUTICA VF) ★
40 W 57th St Fl 3, New York, NY 10019-4005
Tel (212) 541-5757 *Founded/Ownrshp* 1984
Sales 22.7MM^E *EMP* 218
SIC 2329 Men's & boys' sportswear & athletic clothing; Men's & boys' leather, wool & down-filled outerwear; Men's & boys' sportswear & athletic clothing; Men's & boys' leather, wool & down-filled outerwear
Pr: Karen Murray
Pr: Sarah A Deckey
**CFO:* Matt Puckett
Ofcr: Anders Richardm
**Ex VP:* Harvey Sanders
VP: Christopher Fuentes

D-U-N-S 87-737-4140
■ **NAUTICA RETAIL USA INC**
(*Suby of* NAUTICA VF) ★
40 W 57th St Fl 3, New York, NY 10019-4005
Tel (212) 541-5990 *Founded/Ownrshp* 1992
Sales 101.1MM^E *EMP* 1,250
SIC 5611 Clothing, sportswear, men's & boys'; Clothing, sportswear, men's & boys'
CEO: David Lawner
**Pr:* Karen Murray
VP: Bosha Stone
Rgnl Mgr: John Mosier
Off Mgr: Tracy Lier
Mktg Mgr: Alexandra List

NAUTICA VF
See VF SPORTSWEAR INC

NAUTICON IMAGING SYSTEMS
See EMILY STREET ENTERPRISES LLC

D-U-N-S 02-059-5299
NAUTILUS GROUP
NEW YORK LIFE
15305 Dallas Pkwy Ste 950, Addison, TX 75001-6755
Tel (972) 720-6600 *Founded/Ownrshp* 1993
Sales NA *EMP* 38
SIC 6411 Insurance agents & brokers; Insurance agents & brokers
CEO: Walter Ridlon

VP: Todd Beaird
VP: Gerald Gaeta
VP: Jeanmarie Holm
VP: Joseph Kuo
VP: Geoffrey Pfeiffer
VP: Gilbert Resendez
VP: Robert Stern

D-U-N-S 15-766-1877 IMP/EXP
▲ NAUTILUS INC
17750 Se 6th Way, Vancouver, WA 98683-7565
Tel (360) 859-2900 *Founded/Ownrshp* 1986
Sales 274.4MM *EMP* 340
Tkr Sym NLS *Exch* NYS
SIC 3949 Sporting & athletic goods; Gymnasium equipment; Sporting & athletic goods; Gymnasium equipment
CEO: Bruce M Cazenave
Pr: Tom Moran
COO: Bill McMahon
COO: William B McMahon
CFO: Sid Nayar
CFO: Sidharth Nayar
Bd of Dir: Craig L McKibben
Chf Mktg O: Randal Potter
Ofcr: Jinsun Kang
Ofcr: Dyana Mardon
Sr VP: Ronald D Arp
Sr VP: Wayne M Bolio
Sr VP: Mark Meussner
VP: Aaron Atkinson
VP: Wayne Bollio
VP: Jeff Collins
VP: Jeffery L Collins
VP: Robert O Murdock
Exec: Timothy Hawkins
Exec: Corey Stringfellow
Comm Dir: Karine Larose
Board of Directors: Ronald P Badie, Richard A Horn, M Carl Johnson III, Anne G Saunders, Marvin G Siegert

D-U-N-S 17-365-2330
■ NAUTILUS INSURANCE CO INC
NAUTILUS INSURANCE GROUP
(*Suby of* W R BERKLEY CORP) ★
7233 E Butherus Dr, Scottsdale, AZ 85260-2410
Tel (480) 951-0905 *Founded/Ownrshp* 1985
Sales NA *EMP* 200[E]
SIC 6331 6411 Property damage insurance; Insurance agents, brokers & service; Property damage insurance; Insurance agents, brokers & service
Pr: Thomas M Kuzma
**Treas:* John Runberg
**Ex VP:* Richard P Shemitis
Sr VP: Mick Kallo
**Sr VP:* Miklos F Kallo
**Sr VP:* Wendy Markham
VP: Ellen Hageman
VP: Thomas Joyce
VP: Michael J Kilgas
VP: Janeth Shemanske
Dir IT: Eddie Robinson

NAUTILUS INSURANCE GROUP
See NAUTILUS INSURANCE CO INC

NAUTILUS INSURANCE GROUP
See GREAT DIVIDE INSURANCE CO

D-U-N-S 00-405-7816 EXP
NAUTIQUE BOAT CO INC (FL)
NAUTIQUES
14700 Aerospace Pkwy, Orlando, FL 32832-7100
Tel (407) 855-4141 *Founded/Ownrshp* 1925
Sales 125.0MM *EMP* 360[E]
SIC 3799 3732 Boat trailers; Boats, fiberglass: building & repairing; Boat trailers; Boats, fiberglass: building & repairing
CEO: Bill Yeargin
**CFO:* Sean Marrero
Treas: Gilbert Paul
VP: Greg Meloon
**VP:* Angela R Pilkington
Exec: Matt Tierney
**Prin:* Yeargin William E
**Prin:* Marrero Sean
Prgrm Mgr: Kimberly Sweetman
CIO: Thomas Bates
Dir IT: Walter Melloon

NAUTIQUES
See NAUTIQUE BOAT CO INC

D-U-N-S 07-576-0850
NAVAJO AGRICULTURAL PRODUCTS INDUSTRY
NAPI
10086 Nm Hwy 371, Farmington, NM 87499
Tel (505) 326-2730 *Founded/Ownrshp* 1976
Sales 57.6MM[E] *EMP* 1,200
SIC 0191 General farms, primarily crop; General farms, primarily crop
CEO: Tsosie Lewis
COO: Leonard Scott
CFO: Pierre Dotson
**CFO:* Darryl Multine
Sr Cor Off: Lewis Tsosie
Genl Mgr: Lorenzo Baten
Genl Mgr: T Sosie Lewis

NAVAJO COUNTY
See COUNTY OF NAVAJO

D-U-N-S 06-842-1650
NAVAJO COUNTY COMMUNITY COLLEGE DISTRICT
NORTHLAND PIONEER COLLEGE
2251 Navajo Blvd, Holbrook, AZ 86025-1824
Tel (800) 266-7845 *Founded/Ownrshp* 1973
Sales 21.0MM[E] *EMP* 500
SIC 8222 Community college; Community college
Pr: Jeanne Swarthout
Pr: John Valet
COO: Curtis Casey
**VP:* Blaine Hatch
DP Exec: Mindy Neff

D-U-N-S 02-682-5757
NAVAJO ENGINEERING & CONSTRUCTION AUTHORITY
1 Uranium Blvd, Shiprock, NM 87420
Tel (505) 368-5151 *Founded/Ownrshp* 1973
Sales 106.8MM[E] *EMP* 490
SIC 1611 1623 Highway & street construction; Water, sewer & utility lines; Highway & street construction; Water, sewer & utility lines
Genl Mgr: William C Brouthton
IT Man: James Henry
Mtls Mgr: Shoni Shorthair

NAVAJO EXPRESS
See NAVAJO SHIPPERS INC

D-U-N-S 03-098-3712
NAVAJO EXPRESS INC
(*Suby of* NAVAJO EXPRESS) ★
1400 W 64th Ave, Denver, CO 80221-2430
Tel (303) 287-3800 *Founded/Ownrshp* 1990
Sales 96.7MM[E] *EMP* 527
SIC 4213 Refrigerated products transport; Refrigerated products transport
Pr: Don Digby
**Pr:* Don Digby Jr
**CFO:* Chris Kelly
**Ex VP:* Becky Mackintosh
VP: Chris Parson
**VP:* Jim Schram
**VP:* George Snyder
Dir Bus: Scott Guymon
Dir Bus: Douglas Webberley
VP Opers: Steve Lusty
Mktg Dir: Collin Varner

D-U-N-S 07-753-1697
NAVAJO HEALTH FOUNDATION - SAGE MEMORIAL HOSPITAL INC
Hwy 264 & Junction 191, Ganado, AZ 86505
Tel (928) 755-3411 *Founded/Ownrshp* 1973
Sales 37.1MM *EMP* 235
Accts Bradshaw Smith And Co Llp Las
SIC 8011 Medical centers; Medical centers
CEO: Ahmad R Razaghi
**Pr:* Stenson Wauneka
Cmptr Lab: Shirlene Bigwater

D-U-N-S 06-842-1718
NAVAJO HOUSING AUTHORITY
1 Morgan Blvd, Window Rock, AZ 86515
Tel (928) 871-2600 *Founded/Ownrshp* 1963
Sales NA *EMP* 350
SIC 9531 Housing programs; ; Housing programs;
CEO: Aneva J Yazzie
**CFO:* Marlene Lynch
**Prin:* Asa Begaye
**Prin:* Ervin Chavez
**Prin:* Kenneth Chester
**Prin:* Wayne Claw
**Prin:* Lula Jackson
**Prin:* Ben Johnson
**Prin:* Christina Lewis
**Prin:* Marvin Murphy
CIO: Jason Attakai

D-U-N-S 09-191-7799 IMP
NAVAJO MANUFACTURING CO
HANDY SOLUTIONS CELL TECH
5330 Fox St, Denver, CO 80216-1630
Tel (303) 292-3090 *Founded/Ownrshp* 1978
Sales 50.9MM *EMP* 200
SIC 5122 5099 5013

D-U-N-S 02-776-5099
NAVAJO NATION GAMING ENTERPRISE
249 E Nm State Hwy 118, Church Rock, NM 87311
Tel (505) 905-7100 *Founded/Ownrshp* 2006
Sales 152.5MM[E] *EMP* 1,400[E]
SIC 8748 Business consulting; Business consulting
CEO: Derrick Watchman
CFO: Kurt Schmidt

D-U-N-S 83-760-0519
NAVAJO NATION OIL AND GAS CO INC
NAVAJO PETROLEUM
50 Narbono Cir W, Saint Michaels, AZ 86511
Tel (928) 871-4880 *Founded/Ownrshp* 2006
Sales 72.0MM[E] *EMP* 89
SIC 5172 Petroleum products; Petroleum products
CEO: Louis Denetsosie
**Pr:* Wilson Groen
**Ch:* Manuel Morgan
**VP:* David Rubenking
**Prin:* Merv Lynch
Dir IT: Mark Littman
IT Man: Lional Dodge
Opers Mgr: Deborah Klein

D-U-N-S 00-900-1702
NAVAJO NATION TRIBAL GOVERNMENT
2 Miles N Of Hwy 264, Window Rock, AZ 86515
Tel (928) 871-6352 *Founded/Ownrshp* 1923
Sales NA *EMP* 5,000
SIC 9131 Indian reservation; ; Indian reservation;
Pr: Ben Shelly
Comm Dir: George Hardeen
**Prin:* Joe Shirley Jr
IT Man: Cordell Shortey

NAVAJO PETROLEUM
See NAVAJO NATION OIL AND GAS CO INC

D-U-N-S 04-891-8817
■ NAVAJO REFINING CO LLC
(*Suby of* HOLLYFRONTIER CORP) ★
501 E Main St, Artesia, NM 88210-9606
Tel (575) 748-3311 *Founded/Ownrshp* 1969
Sales 138.8MM[E] *EMP* 500
SIC 2911 2951 Light distillates; Gasoline blending plants; Jet fuels; Diesel fuels; Asphalt paving mixtures & blocks; Light distillates; Gasoline blending plants; Jet fuels; Diesel fuels; Asphalt paving mixtures & blocks
Ch Bd: Matthew P Clifton
**Pr:* Dave Lamp
**CFO:* Bruce Shaw
**Sr VP:* W John Glancy
VP: Mike McKee
Sfty Mgr: Steve Hollis

D-U-N-S 02-026-4248
NAVAJO SHIPPERS INC
NAVAJO EXPRESS
1400 W 64th Ave, Denver, CO 80221-2430
Tel (303) 287-3800 *Founded/Ownrshp* 1980
Sales 125.8MM[E] *EMP* 700
SIC 4213 Refrigerated products transport; Less-than-truckload (LTL) transport; Contract haulers; Refrigerated products transport; Less-than-truckload (LTL) transport; Contract haulers
Pr: Don Digby
**VP:* George Synder
Dir Bus: C Morgan
Off Mgr: Rebeca Mackintosh
MIS Dir: Ackbar Mirmortazavi
Opers Mgr: Paul Harris
Sls Mgr: Wally Cremeans

D-U-N-S 08-064-8561
NAVAJO TECHNICAL COLLEGE
Lower Point Rd Hwy 371, Crownpoint, NM 87313
Tel (505) 786-4100 *Founded/Ownrshp* 1982
Sales 27.0MM *EMP* 130
SIC 8221

D-U-N-S 80-002-1990
NAVAJO TRIBAL UTILITY AUTHORITY
NTUA
(*Suby of* NAVAJO NATION TRIBAL GOVERNMENT) ★
Hwy 12 N, Fort Defiance, AZ 86504
Tel (928) 729-5721 *Founded/Ownrshp* 1959
Sales 110.0MM *EMP* 619[E]
SIC 4939 4924 4911 Combination utilities; Natural gas distribution; Electric services; Combination utilities; Natural gas distribution; Electric services
Genl Mgr: Sidney Dietz II
CFO: Dennis Carter
**CFO:* Thomas Nelson
Bd of Dir: Sonny Clark
Ofcr: Jackson Yazzie
VP: Sherwin Curley
Prgrm Mgr: Larry Ahasteen
Dist Mgr: Rubianne Dugi
Dist Mgr: Ntua KY
Dist Mgr: Justin Paul
Div Mgr: Paul Bemore

D-U-N-S 07-828-7448
■ NAVAL ACADEMY BUSINESS SERVICES DIVISION
(*Suby of* UNITED STATES DEPARTMENT OF THE NAVY) ★
101 Wilson Rd, Annapolis, MD 21402-5011
Tel (410) 293-5270 *Founded/Ownrshp* 2001
Sales 42.0MM *EMP* 258
SIC 5942 7215 7251 7241 5962 0241

D-U-N-S 60-658-3961
NAVAL CONTINUING CARE RETIREMENT FOUNDATION INC
FLEET LANDING RETIREMENT COMMU
1 Fleet Landing Blvd, Atlantic Beach, FL 32233-4599
Tel (904) 246-9900 *Founded/Ownrshp* 1985
Sales 32.1MM *EMP* 330
Accts Moore Stephens Lovelace Pa
SIC 8059 8052 Rest home, with health care; Intermediate care facilities; Rest home, with health care; Intermediate care facilities
Ex Dir: John Meserve
**CFO:* Roger Palmer

D-U-N-S 00-435-6832 IMP
NAVAL FOUNDRY PROPELLER CENTER
1701 Kitty Hawk Ave 20a, Philadelphia, PA 19112-1805
Tel (215) 897-3537 *Founded/Ownrshp* 2011
Sales 25.0MM[E] *EMP* 150
SIC 3366 Propellers
Prd Mgr: Dennis Luketina

D-U-N-S 07-976-8934
NAVAL OCEANGRAPHIC OFFICE
1002 Balch Blvd, Stennis Space Center, MS 39522-5001
Tel (228) 689-8387 *Founded/Ownrshp* 2015
Sales 325.0M[E] *EMP* 800
SIC 7336 Commercial art & graphic design

D-U-N-S 19-017-1467
■ NAVAL POSTGRADUATE SCHOOL
(*Suby of* UNITED STATES DEPARTMENT OF THE NAVY) ★
1 University Cir Rm M10, Monterey, CA 93943-5019
Tel (831) 656-7893 *Founded/Ownrshp* 1970
Sales 156.5MM[E] *EMP* 1,100
SIC 8221 9711 University; Navy; ; University; Navy;
**Pr:* Ronald Route
Prgrm Mgr: Rudy Darken
Prgrm Mgr: Jennifer Duncan
Dir IT: Joe Lopiccolo
Tech Mgr: Maxine Reneker
Opers Mgr: Jean Ferreira
HC Dir: Susan Dooley

D-U-N-S 02-006-0658
■ NAVAL RESEARCH LABORATORY
NRL
(*Suby of* UNITED STATES DEPARTMENT OF THE NAVY) ★
4555 Overlook Ave Sw, Washington, DC 20375-0001
Tel (202) 767-2370 *Founded/Ownrshp* 1999
Sales NA *EMP* 3,300[E]
SIC 9661 ;
Ofcr: Paul Stewart
Top Exec: David Abe
Top Exec: Michael Mook
Top Exec: Ken Sarkady
VP: Matthew Carey
VP: Olle G Heinonen
VP: Robert Morris
Adm Dir: Kim Best
Adm Dir: John Tomlinson
IT Man: Amey Peltzer
Tech Mgr: Kiera Vincent

D-U-N-S 96-421-5979
NAVAPACHE REGIONAL MEDICAL CENTER
2200 E Show Low Lake Rd, Show Low, AZ 85901-7800
Tel (928) 537-4375 *Founded/Ownrshp* 2010
Sales 134.1MM *EMP* 20[E]
SIC 8011 Offices & clinics of medical doctors; Offices & clinics of medical doctors
CEO: Leigh Cox
CFO: Brian Hoefle
CFO: Kurk Loveless
Chf Mktg O: Terrence J Cavanaugh
Dir Rad: Grant Berges
Dir Rad: Kenneth A Giles
Dir Rad: Linda Michel
Dir Rx: James Parkinson
Mktg Dir: Kim Mayfield
Pr Dir: Kim Mayfeild
Opthamlgy: Daryl Pfister

D-U-N-S 02-597-0872
NAVARRE CHEVROLET INC
1310 E College St, Lake Charles, LA 70607-1948
Tel (337) 474-1999 *Founded/Ownrshp* 1982
Sales 61.3MM[E] *EMP* 140[E]
SIC 5511 5531 7538 Automobiles, new & used; Pickups, new & used; Vans, new & used; Automotive parts; Engine repair; Automobiles, new & used; Pickups, new & used; Vans, new & used; Automotive parts; Engine repair
Pr: William John Navarre

NAVARRE DISTRIBUTION SERVICES
See NAVARRE LOGISTICAL SERVICES INC

D-U-N-S 07-847-2116 IMP
NAVARRE DISTRIBUTION SERVICES INC
9700 W 76th St Ste 116, Eden Prairie, MN 55344-4202
Tel (763) 535-8333 *Founded/Ownrshp* 2006
Sales 59.0MM[E] *EMP* 95[E]
SIC 5045

D-U-N-S 79-405-8599
■ NAVARRE LOGISTICAL SERVICES INC
NAVARRE DISTRIBUTION SERVICES
(*Suby of* SPEED COMMERCE INC) ★
9700 W 76th St Ste 116, Eden Prairie, MN 55344-4202
Tel (763) 535-8333 *Founded/Ownrshp* 2006
Sales 31.3MM[E] *EMP* 80
SIC 4731 Freight transportation arrangement
CEO: Richard Willis
Sr VP: Lina Shurslep
Sr VP: Ward Thomas
VP: Mike Janousek
VP: J C Lindquist
VP: Margot McManus
Exec: Sheila Anderson
Dir IT: Brian Bakken
Tech Mgr: Paul Ablen
Manager: Roger Vanhoven
Natl Sales: Kathy Burton

D-U-N-S 07-487-2680
NAVARRO COLLEGE
3200 W 7th Ave, Corsicana, TX 75110-4899
Tel (903) 874-6501 *Founded/Ownrshp* 1946
Sales 22.4MM *EMP* 851
Accts Whitley Penn Llp Houston Tex
SIC 8221 8222 Colleges universities & professional schools; Junior college; Colleges universities & professional schools; Junior college
Pr: Richard Sanchez
**Ch:* Lloyd D Huffman
**Sec:* Phil Judson
**Ex VP:* Kenneth Martin
Ex VP: Gertrud Moreno
Ex VP: Larry Reed
VP: Robin Dorety
**VP:* Harold Housley
VP: Alex J Kajstura
VP: Tommy Stringer
Off Admin: Karen Lenamond

D-U-N-S 00-677-0101
NAVARRO COUNTY ELECTRIC COOPERATIVE INC (TX)
3800 W State Highway 22, Corsicana, TX 75110-2464
Tel (903) 874-7411 *Founded/Ownrshp* 1937
Sales 55.5MM *EMP* 35
SIC 4911 Distribution, electric power
CEO: Billy P Jones
Genl Mgr: Mark Rash
Sfty Dirs: Mark Dixon
Sales Exec: Lindy Shaw

D-U-N-S 09-493-0963 IMP/EXP
■ NAVARRO DISCOUNT PHARMACIES LLC (FL)
NAVARRO DISCOUNT PHARMACY
(*Suby of* CVS HEALTH CORP) ★
9400 Nw 104th St, Medley, FL 33178-1333
Tel (305) 805-1076 *Founded/Ownrshp* 2006, 2014
Sales 294.9MM[E] *EMP* 1,300
SIC 5912 Drug stores; Drug stores
**CEO:* Juan Ortiz
**Chf Mktg O:* Cristina Leon-Rivero
**Ex VP:* Albert Garcia
**VP:* Manuel Leon
**VP:* Vicente A Urrutia
**CIO:* Sergio Campos
Opers Mgr: Daniel Sotes
Sls&Mrk Ex: Christina Rivero
Advt Mgr: Jorge Barrios
Pharmcst: Ivan Page
Cert Phar: Kevin Torres

NAVARRO DISCOUNT PHARMACY
See NAVARRO DISCOUNT PHARMACIES LLC

D-U-N-S 80-525-0842 IMP
■ NAVARRO DISTRIBUTION CENTER LLC
(*Suby of* NAVARRO DISCOUNT PHARMACIES LLC) ★
9400 Nw 104th St, Medley, FL 33178-1333
Tel (305) 633-3000 *Founded/Ownrshp* 1940
Sales 54.9MM[E] *EMP* 60
SIC 5122 Drugs, proprietaries & sundries

D-U-N-S 80-132-2843
NAVARRO GROUP LTD INC
NAVARRO TECHNICAL SERVICES
4100 S Hospital Dr # 100, Plantation, FL 33317-2831
Tel (754) 200-6835 *Founded/Ownrshp* 1993
Sales 16.8MM^E *EMP* 508
SIC 7381 Detective & armored car services; Detective & armored car services
Pr: Nicholas Navarro
**VP:* Sharron Navarro
MIS Dir: Vern Reynolds

D-U-N-S 78-595-4751
■ **NAVARRO HOSPITAL LP**
NAVARRO REGIONAL HOSPITAL
(*Suby of* COMMUNITY HEALTH SYSTEMS INC) ★
3201 W State Highway 22, Corsicana, TX 75110-2450
Tel (903) 654-6800 *Founded/Ownrshp* 2007
Sales 68.6MM^E *EMP* 400
SIC 8062 General medical & surgical hospitals; General medical & surgical hospitals
CEO: Michael Stewart
Chf Rad: Leslie Kennedy
Pt: Nancy Byrnes
Pt: Xavier Villarreal
Exec: Larry Stevener
Dir OR: Emily Fortson
Dir Risk M: Keira Maynard
Dir Lab: Ivan Webb
Dir Lab: Alan Wells
Dir Rad: Jack Wepler
Mktg Dir: Frank Martinez

D-U-N-S 07-986-0350
NAVARRO MIDSTREAM SERVICES LLC
(*Suby of* LEWIS ENERGY GROUP LP) ★
10101 Reunion Pl Ste 1000, San Antonio, TX 78216-4157
Tel (956) 728-6000 *Founded/Ownrshp* 1983
Sales 16.2MM^E *EMP* 1,500
SIC 1382 Oil & gas exploration services
Pr: Craig Rosenstein

D-U-N-S 08-515-6024 IMP/EXP
NAVARRO PECAN CO INC
2131 E Highway 31, Corsicana, TX 75109-9077
Tel (903) 872-5641 *Founded/Ownrshp* 1991
Sales 50.0MM *EMP* 230^E
SIC 0723 2068

NAVARRO REGIONAL HOSPITAL
See NAVARRO HOSPITAL LP

D-U-N-S 00-592-9810
NAVARRO RESEARCH AND ENGINEERING INC
669 Emory Valley Rd, Oak Ridge, TN 37830-7758
Tel (865) 220-9650 *Founded/Ownrshp* 1993
Sales 100.8MM^E *EMP* 327
SIC 8711 8744 Engineering services; ; Engineering services;
CEO: Susana Navarro-Valenti PHD
**Ex VP:* Mark Valenti
VP: Beverly Cook
Prgrm Mgr: Tony Lachance
Prgrm Mgr: Cissy Perkins
Prgrm Mgr: Mike West
Mktg Mgr: Joellen Kuszmaul
Snr PM: Thomas McCrory

NAVARRO TECHNICAL SERVICES
See NAVARRO GROUP LTD INC

D-U-N-S 02-081-8779
NAVASOTA INDEPENDENT SCHOOL DISTRICT (INC)
NAVASOTA ISD
705 E Washington Ave, Navasota, TX 77868-3005
Tel (936) 825-4200 *Founded/Ownrshp* 1900
Sales 31.7MM *EMP* 415
SIC 8211 Public elementary school; Public junior high school; Public senior high school; Public elementary school; Public junior high school; Public senior high school
Dir IT: Krista Dyer
Schl Brd P: John Price
Teacher Pr: Babs Blair
Instr Medi: Carol Woehler
Psych: Flora Mason
Snr Mgr: Benjamin Mendez

D-U-N-S 13-112-5585
NAVASOTA INDUSTRIAL SUPPLY LTD
NIS
9527 Fm 379, Navasota, TX 77868-7234
Tel (936) 825-7368 *Founded/Ownrshp* 1986
Sales 31.7MM^E *EMP* 27
SIC 5084 Machine tools & accessories
Genl Pt: Robert Nathan Wilson
Genl Mgr: Philip Stapp
Opers Mgr: Scott Stapp
Sls Mgr: Brad Defoy
Sales Asso: Barry Byers
Sales Asso: Brett Donnahoe
Sales Asso: Jeffrey Noto
Sales Asso: Chad Shead

NAVASOTA ISD
See NAVASOTA INDEPENDENT SCHOOL DISTRICT (INC)

D-U-N-S 82-849-6310
NAVASOTA OILFIELD SERVICES INC
5808 Fm 3455 Rd, Navasota, TX 77868-6816
Tel (936) 825-9403 *Founded/Ownrshp* 2008
Sales 21.7MM^E *EMP* 59^E
SIC 3533 1389 Oil field machinery & equipment; Oil field services
Pr: Wesley E Goodson
**VP:* Ray A Seidl

D-U-N-S 04-629-9913
NAVASOTA VALLEY ELECTRIC COOPERATIVE INC
2281 E Us Highway 79, Franklin, TX 77856-4383
Tel (979) 828-3232 *Founded/Ownrshp* 1941
Sales 38.0MM *EMP* 50
SIC 4911 Distribution, electric power; Distribution, electric power
Prin: Fred Elliott
Genl Mgr: James Calhoun
Board of Directors: Wayland Oakes, Harlan Zill

NAVCO SECURITY SYSTEMS
See NORTH AMERICAN VIDEO CORP

D-U-N-S 78-547-4339
NAVELLIER & ASSOCIATES INC
1 E Liberty St Ste 504, Reno, NV 89501-2107
Tel (775) 785-2300 *Founded/Ownrshp* 1987
Sales 22.3MM *EMP* 52
SIC 6282 Investment advisory service; Investment advisory service
CEO: Louis Navellier
**Pr:* Arjen Kuyper
CFO: David Machen
Sr VP: John Ranft
VP: Seth Lee
Mng Dir: John Coyle
MIS Dir: Clayton Tippinger
Manager: Brent Farber

D-U-N-S 13-518-5606
NAVEX GLOBAL INC
6000 Meadows Rd Ste 200, Lake Oswego, OR 97035-3177
Tel (971) 250-4100 *Founded/Ownrshp* 2014
Sales 119.2MM^E *EMP* 450
SIC 8748 Business consulting; Business consulting
Pr: Bob Conlin
COO: Luis Ramos
CFO: Todd Henne
CFO: Craig Stoehr
Chf Cred: Carrie Penman
Ofcr: Amanda Gratchner
Ex VP: Doug Coblens
Sr VP: Roger Akers
Sr VP: Stephen Chapman
Sr VP: Tom McNamara
Sr VP: Chris Morton
Sr VP: Jennifer Sherman
VP: Jeff Angtuaco
VP: Ian Carswell
VP: Steve Chapman
VP: Nick Ciancio
VP: Edward Petry

D-U-N-S 07-247-9710
NAVICENT HEALTH INC (GA)
HOSPICE OF CENTRAL GEORGIA
(*Suby of* CENTRAL GEORGIA HEALTH SYSTEMS INC) ★
777 Hemlock St, Macon, GA 31201-2102
Tel (478) 633-1000 *Founded/Ownrshp* 1895, 1994
Sales 683.3MM *EMP* 3,750
Accts Dixon Hughes Pllc Atlanta Ge
SIC 8062 Hospital, medical school affiliated with residency; Hospital, medical school affiliated with residency
CEO: Ninfa M Saunders
**COO:* Mike Gilstrap
**CFO:* Virgil E Cooper Jr
**CFO:* Rhonda S Perry
Ofcr: King Dave
VP: Susan Lowery
Dir Risk M: Kathy Bowen
Dir Lab: Lee Chapman
Dir Rad: Ericha Benshoff
Dir Rad: Paul W Chandler
Dir Sec: Quinton Jude
Board of Directors: Oscar Battles, Kathy Bowen, Seth Bush, James Cunningham, Jim Doyle, Kay Lucia, Bernard Meyer Von Breme

D-U-N-S 00-713-9199 IMP
NAVICO INC
EAGLE ELECTRONICS
(*Suby of* NAVICO HOLDING AS)
4500 S 129th East Ave # 200, Tulsa, OK 74134-5885
Tel (918) 437-6881 *Founded/Ownrshp* 2006
Sales 472.1MM^E *EMP* 1,500
SIC 3812 Navigational systems & instruments; Navigational systems & instruments
Pr: Leif Ottosson
**CFO:* Marcel Crince
CFO: Rodney Hyde
**CFO:* Paul C Murphy
**Ex VP:* Lucinda Abood
**Ex VP:* Jim Brailey
**Ex VP:* Louis Chemi
**Ex VP:* Tom Edvardsen
**Ex VP:* Jose Herrero
**Ex VP:* Greg Konig
**Ex VP:* John Scott
**Ex VP:* Ronald G Weber
Sr VP: Robert Earnest
Sr VP: Kent Jopling
**Sr VP:* Larry B Toering
VP: John Bay
**VP:* Jane M Kaiser

D-U-N-S 00-180-5857
NAVICURE INC
2055 Sugarloaf Cir # 600, Duluth, GA 30097-4131
Tel (770) 342-0200 *Founded/Ownrshp* 2000
Sales 33.2MM^E *EMP* 160
Accts Ha&W Atlanta Ga
SIC 7371 Custom computer programming services; Custom computer programming services
Pr: James M Denny Sr
**COO:* Craig Bridge
**CFO:* James McDevitt
**Treas:* Phil Dolan
**VP:* Ken Bradley
**VP:* Laura Bridge
VP: Leigh A Gerlach
**VP:* Matthew Halkos
Snr Sftwr: Alan Carlyle
CTO: Kernie Brashier
QA Dir: Dallas Heath

D-U-N-S 01-624-2890
▲ **NAVIENT CORP**
123 S Justison St Ste 300, Wilmington, DE 19801-5363
Tel (302) 283-8000 *Founded/Ownrshp* 2013
Sales 5.6MMM *EMP* 6,200^E
Tkr Sym NAVI *Exch* NGS
SIC 6211 Security brokers & dealers; Security brokers & dealers
Pr: Jack Remondi
COO: John Kane
CFO: Somsak Chivavibul
Dir Risk M: Tim Hynes
CIO: Pat Lawicki
Board of Directors: Jane J Thompson, John K Adams Jr, Laura S Unger, Ann Torre Bates, Barry L Williams, Anna Escobedo Cabral, William M Diefenderfer III, Diane Suitt Gilleland, Katherine A Lehman, Linda A Mills, Barry A Munitz, Steven L Shapiro

D-U-N-S 07-264-6094
■ **NAVIENT SOLUTIONS INC** (DC)
(*Suby of* NAVIENT CORP) ★
2001 Edmund Halley Dr, Reston, VA 20191-3436
Tel (703) 810-3000 *Founded/Ownrshp* 1972, 1997
Sales NA *EMP* 6,000
SIC 6111 Student Loan Marketing Association; Student Loan Marketing Association
CEO: John F Remondi
Pr: Thomas Fitzpatrick
COO: Jon Mello
CFO: Chivavibul Somsak
Trst Ofcr: Letitia Reyna
Sr VP: Charlie Colligan
Sr VP: John Kane
Sr VP: Steve Kirkpatrick
VP: Debby Bragg
VP: Ameri Christian
VP: Doug Maurer
VP: Mark Perrault
VP: Patrick Ryan
Exec: Patricia McCarthy

D-U-N-S 02-258-2428
▲ **NAVIGANT CONSULTING INC**
30 S Wacker Dr Ste 3550, Chicago, IL 60606-7481
Tel (312) 573-5600 *Founded/Ownrshp* 1996
Sales 859.6MM *EMP* 3,559
Accts Kpmg Llp Chicago Illinois
Tkr Sym NCI *Exch* NYS
SIC 8742 Management consulting services; Management consulting services
CEO: Julie M Howard
COO: Stephan A James
CFO: Cindy Baier
CFO: Lucinda M Baier
Ex VP: Thomas A Gildehaus
Ex VP: Lee A Spirer
Ex VP: Lee Spirer
Ex VP: Monica M Weed
VP: J Donald Fancher
VP: Jeff Green
VP: Russell Hoke
Assoc Dir: Jennifer Barnes
Assoc Dir: Scott Beisler
Assoc Dir: Bill Beven
Assoc Dir: Dave Foshage
Assoc Dir: Mahima Gupta
Assoc Dir: Phil Karbo
Assoc Dir: Peter King
Assoc Dir: Colette Lamontagne
Assoc Dir: Amy Lawless
Assoc Dir: Eric Potter

D-U-N-S 36-290-3853
NAVIGANT CREDIT UNION
1005 Douglas Pike, Smithfield, RI 02917-1206
Tel (401) 233-4300 *Founded/Ownrshp* 1915
Sales NA *EMP* 210
SIC 6062 State credit unions; State credit unions
Pr: Gary Furtado
Pr: Chris Harkness
Pr: Bruce Lavine
VP: Karen Balch
VP: Joanne Baz
VP: Daniel J O Brien
VP: Melissa Carlton
VP: Jeffrey P Cascione
VP: Gidget Grivers
VP: Cidalia Rocha
Brnch Mgr: Martha Correia
Board of Directors:

NAVIGATING BUSINESS SPACE
See NATIONAL BUSINESS SUPPLY INC

D-U-N-S 79-902-1279
NAVIGATION CAPITAL PARTNERS INC
3060 Peachtree Rd Nw, Atlanta, GA 30305-2234
Tel (404) 504-4070 *Founded/Ownrshp* 2006
Sales 103.4MM^E *EMP* 716
SIC 6726 Investment offices; Investment offices
CEO: Lawrence E Mock
CFO: Darlene Clott
CFO: Jennifer White
**Sec:* John Richardson
VP: Zuri Briscoe
**VP:* David Panton
**Prin:* Mark Downs
**Prin:* Eerik Giles

D-U-N-S 07-585-0029 IMP
■ **NAVIGATION SOLUTIONS LLC**
(*Suby of* HERTZ CORP) ★
1700 Capital Ave Ste 100, Plano, TX 75074-1209
Tel (972) 461-4528 *Founded/Ownrshp* 2004
Sales 39.5MM^E *EMP* 230
SIC 1731 Voice, data & video wiring contractor; Voice, data & video wiring contractor
CEO: Roger Stevens
CFO: Ray Mathis
Sr VP: Dave Logan
Sr VP: Dewayne Nelon
VP: Margie Diskin
VP: Pat Ray

D-U-N-S 15-001-6918
NAVIGATOR MANAGEMENT PARTNERS LIMITED LIABILITY CO
1400 Goodale Blvd Ste 100, Columbus, OH 43212-3777
Tel (614) 796-0090 *Founded/Ownrshp* 2001
Sales 35.5MM *EMP* 43
Accts Rea & Associates Inc Dublin
SIC 7379 8742 Computer related consulting services; Management consulting services
Sr Pt: David K Schoettmer
Genl Mgr: Arturo Sanabria
Board of Directors: Rich Helmreich, Angelo Mazzocco, Wil Schroter

D-U-N-S 05-493-3502 IMP
NAVIGATORS
GLEN EYRIE CHRSTN CNFRENCE CTR
3820 N 30th St, Colorado Springs, CO 80904-5000
Tel (719) 598-1212 *Founded/Ownrshp* 1933
Sales 115.8MM *EMP* 1,750
SIC 8661 7032 5942

D-U-N-S 14-463-8251
▲ **NAVIGATORS GROUP INC**
400 Atlantic St Fl 8, Stamford, CT 06901-3512
Tel (203) 905-6090 *Founded/Ownrshp* 1982
Sales NA *EMP* 567^E
Accts Kpmg Llp New York New York
Tkr Sym NAVG *Exch* NGS
SIC 6331 6351 Fire, marine & casualty insurance; Liability insurance; Fire, marine & casualty insurance; Liability insurance
Pr: Stanley A Galanski
**Ch Bd:* Robert V Mendelsohn
Pr: Timothy D Ryan
Pr: Brett Schoech
COO: Michael L Civisca
CFO: Ciro M Defalco
Chf Mktg O: Alastair Burns
Chf Mktg O: Loriann Lowery-Biggers
Ofcr: Bruce J Byrnes
Ofcr: Ciro Defalco
Ofcr: R Scott Eisdorfer
Ofcr: Denise M Lowsley
Ofcr: Jennifer Yang
Ex VP: Noel Higgitt
Sr VP: Thomas A Konopka
VP: Ellen Dion
VP: Scott Eisdorfer
VP: Robert Hatcher
VP: George Iacono
VP: Stuart Kohn
VP: Steven Kuuskvere
Board of Directors: Saul L Basch, H J Mervyn Blakeney, Terence N Deeks, Geoffrey E Johnson, David M Platter, Patricia Roberts, Janice C Tomlinson, Marc M Tract

D-U-N-S 13-679-0305
■ **NAVIGATORS MANAGEMENT CO INC**
(*Suby of* NAVIGATORS GROUP INC) ★
6 International Dr # 100, Port Chester, NY 10573-1099
Tel (914) 934-8999 *Founded/Ownrshp* 1974
Sales 20.2MM^E *EMP* 400^E
SIC 8741 Management services; Management services
Ch Bd: Stanley A Galanski
Pr: Christopher Duca
COO: Michael Civisca
CFO: Frank McDonnell
Ofcr: Christopher F Finneran
Rgnl VP: Steven R Kuuskvere
Sr VP: H Clay Bassett Jr
Sr VP: Bruce J Byrnes
Sr VP: Susan Fontaine
Sr VP: James E Hutchinson
Sr VP: Duane Ludden
Sr VP: Jerry Wosleger
Sr VP: Mark A Yunque
VP: Celeste Cook
VP: Gregory Donnal
VP: Michael Dunn
VP: Allan Jann
VP: Paul Kluga
VP: Sherry Little
VP: Henry Lopez
VP: Sandra Renda

D-U-N-S 07-836-1401
NAVIHEALTH INC
210 Westwood Pl Ste 400, Brentwood, TN 37027-7554
Tel (615) 577-1900 *Founded/Ownrshp* 2011
Sales 33.8MM^E *EMP* 400
SIC 8099 Medical services organization; Medical services organization
Pr: Clay Richards
COO: David Azzolina
Ex VP: Rick Glanz
Ex VP: Karey Witty
Sr VP: Patricia Bradford
Sr VP: Joel Hasenwinkel
Sr VP: Erik Kraemer
Sr VP: Sanjoy Musunuri
Sr VP: Carter Paine
VP: Patrick Bork
VP: Charlie Bryan
VP: Jennifer Coffman
VP: Kelsey Gowin
VP: Beth Lance
VP: Keith Thompson
VP: Reg Warren
VP: Chris Wright

NAVILLUS CONTRACTING
See NAVILLUS TILE INC

D-U-N-S 19-853-6898
NAVILLUS TILE INC
NAVILLUS CONTRACTING
575 5th Ave Fl 29, New York, NY 10017-2467
Tel (718) 784-0500 *Founded/Ownrshp* 1987
Sales 162.0MM^E *EMP* 400
Accts Grassi & Co Cpas Pc Jerich
SIC 1741 1771 1743 Masonry & other stonework; Concrete work; Tile installation, ceramic; Masonry & other stonework; Concrete work; Tile installation, ceramic
Pr: Donald Sullivan
IT Man: Mina Asaad

D-U-N-S 80-969-9023 IMP
■ **NAVILYST MEDICAL INC**
(*Suby of* ANGIODYNAMICS INC) ★
10 Glens Fls Technical Pa, Glens Falls, NY 12801
Tel (518) 792-4112 *Founded/Ownrshp* 2012
Sales 179.2MM^E *EMP* 670

SIC 3841 Surgical & medical instruments; Surgical & medical instruments
Pr: Joseph M Devivo

D-U-N-S 07-183-3896
NAVINET INC
179 Lincoln St Ste 100, Boston, MA 02111-2425
Tel (617) 715-6000 *Founded/Ownrshp* 1997
Sales 89.1MM^E *EMP* 220^E
SIC 7371 Computer software development; Computer software development
CEO: Frank Ingari
**CFO:* Sean W Bridgeo
**Treas:* William Romeo
**Ex VP:* Thomas Moreson
Sr VP: Mark Dudman
Sr VP: David Kates
VP: Kim Francour
VP: Paul Johnson
VP: Jason White
VP: Shari L Zedeck
**CIO:* John Kelly

D-U-N-S 13-100-6798
NAVIS CORP
55 Harrison St, Oakland, CA 94607-3790
Tel (510) 267-5000 *Founded/Ownrshp* 1988
Sales 31.5MM^E *EMP* 300
SIC 4491 Marine cargo handling; Marine cargo handling
CEO: Rob Dillon
VP: Leif Chastaine
VP: Lou Chauvin
VP: Michael Cho
VP: Philip Gerskovich
VP: Samuel Levy
VP: Jeff Romano
VP: Joanne Townsend
Genl Mgr: Ashley Ford

D-U-N-S 79-453-7035
NAVIS LLC
(*Suby of* CARGOTEC UK LIMITED)
55 Harrison St Ste 600, Oakland, CA 94607-3776
Tel (510) 267-5000 *Founded/Ownrshp* 1998
Sales 26.5MM^E *EMP* 139^E
SIC 7372

D-U-N-S 96-994-1806
■ NAVISITE INC
NAVISITE INTERNET SERVICES
(*Suby of* TIME WARNER CABLE INC) ★
400 Minuteman Rd, Andover, MA 01810-1093
Tel (978) 682-8300 *Founded/Ownrshp* 2011
Sales 130.5MM^E *EMP* 83
SIC 4813 ;
Sr VP: Chris Cordom
Pr: Kenneth Drake
CFO: John Gavin
CFO: James W Pluntze
CFO: Jim Pluntze
Treas: David Flynn
Treas: Kenneth Hale
Bd of Dir: James Dennedy
Chf Mktg O: Claudine Bianchi
Ofcr: Allen Allison
Ex VP: John Muleta
Sr VP: Mark Clayman
Sr VP: Christopher Cordom
Sr VP: Michael Poole
Sr VP: Sumeet Sabharwal
Sr VP: Roger Schwanhausser
VP: Jim Ciampaglio
VP: Paul Cioni
VP: Katie Hamler
VP: Bernd Leger
VP: Staci Lyons

NAVISITE INTERNET SERVICES
See NAVISITE INC

D-U-N-S 79-809-3931 IMP/EXP
■ NAVISTAR DIESEL OF ALABAMA LLC
(*Suby of* NAVISTAR INC) ★
646 James Record Rd Sw, Huntsville, AL 35824-1520
Tel (256) 772-1200 *Founded/Ownrshp* 1999
Sales 58.0MM^E *EMP* 340
SIC 3519 Engines, diesel & semi-diesel or dual-fuel; Engines, diesel & semi-diesel or dual-fuel
Brnch Mgr: Shirley Smith

D-U-N-S 02-516-7669
■ NAVISTAR FINANCIAL CORP
(*Suby of* NAVISTAR INC) ★
2701 Navistar Dr, Lisle, IL 60532-3637
Tel (630) 753-4000 *Founded/Ownrshp* 1949
Sales NA *EMP* 311
SIC 6153 6159 Financing of dealers by motor vehicle manufacturers organ.; Truck finance leasing; Financing of dealers by motor vehicle manufacturers organ.; Truck finance leasing
Pr: David J Johanneson
**CFO:* William V McMenamin
VP: David L Derfelt
Board of Directors: Jack J Allen, Andrew J Cederoth, John V Mulvaney Sr, Alice M Peterson, Richard C Tarapchak

D-U-N-S 00-521-4200 IMP/EXP
■ NAVISTAR INC
(*Suby of* NAVISTAR INTERNATIONAL CORP) ★
2701 Navistar Dr, Lisle, IL 60532-3637
Tel (331) 332-5000 *Founded/Ownrshp* 1965
Sales 761.1MM^E *EMP* 1,696
Accts Miller Cooper & Co Ltd Deerfi
SIC 3711 3714 3519 6153 6159 6331 Truck & tractor truck assembly; Chassis, motor vehicle; Motor vehicle parts & accessories; Engines, diesel & semi-diesel or dual-fuel; Financing of dealers by motor vehicle manufacturers organ.; Purchasers of accounts receivable & commercial paper; Buying of installment notes; Truck finance leasing; Finance leasing, vehicles: except automobiles & trucks; Property damage insurance; Fire, marine & casualty insurance: stock; Motor vehicles & car bodies; Chassis, motor vehicle; Motor vehicle parts & accessories; Engines, diesel & semi-diesel or dual-fuel; Financing of dealers by motor vehicle manufacturers organ.; Purchasers of accounts receivable & commercial paper; Buying of installment notes; Truck finance leasing; Finance leasing, vehicles: except automobiles & trucks; Property damage insurance; Fire, marine & casualty insurance: stock
CEO: Troy Clarke
Pr: Bill Kozek
**Pr:* Persio V Lisboa
Pr: Persio Lisboa
Pr: Rudi Von Meister
**CEO:* Troy A Clarke
**COO:* Jack Allen
**CFO:* Walter G Borst
**CFO:* Andrew J Cederoth
Treas: Stephen Gilligan
Treas: Karen Kalejs
Treas: Jim Moran
Chf Cred: James K Spangler
Chf Mktg O: Al Saltiel
**Sr VP:* Steven K Covey
**Sr VP:* Greg W Elliott
Sr VP: Pamela J Hamilton
**Sr VP:* James M Moran
**Sr VP:* Richard C Tarapchak
Sr VP: Pamela J Turbeville
VP: Annette Freund

D-U-N-S 07-927-0694 IMP
NAVISTAR INC
Caller Service 59010, Knoxville, TN 37950
Tel (865) 558-1904 *Founded/Ownrshp* 1965
Sales 94.1MM^E *EMP* 68^E
SIC 5085 Industrial supplies
Pr: Troy A Clarke

D-U-N-S 16-198-4646 IMP/EXP
▲ NAVISTAR INTERNATIONAL CORP
2701 Navistar Dr, Lisle, IL 60532-3637
Tel (331) 332-5000 *Founded/Ownrshp* 1993
Sales 10.1MMM *EMP* 15,400
Accts Kpmg Llp Chicago Illinois
Tkr Sym NAV *Exch* NYS
SIC 3711 3714 3713 3519 6159 Truck & tractor truck assembly; Chassis, motor vehicle; Motor homes, self-contained, assembly of; Motor vehicle parts & accessories; Truck & bus bodies; Engines, diesel & semi-diesel or dual-fuel; Automobile finance leasing; Truck & tractor truck assembly; Chassis, motor vehicle; Motor homes, self-contained, assembly of; Motor vehicle parts & accessories; Truck & bus bodies; Engines, diesel & semi-diesel or dual-fuel; Automobile finance leasing
Pr: Troy A Clarke
Pt: Bill Kozek
Pr: Kathy Henehan
Pr: Eric Tech
CFO: Walter G Borst
Treas: James M Moran
Assoc VP: Bart Torres
Sr VP: Steven K Covey
Sr VP: Pamela J Hamilton
Sr VP: Jeff Sass
Sr VP: Samara A Strycker
VP: Jon F Harmon
VP: John Lamoureux
VP: John P Waldron
Assoc Dir: Doug Elston
Assoc Dir: Sheri Seibert
Board of Directors: John D Correnti, Michael N Hammes, Vincent J Intrieri, James H Keyes, Stanley A McChrystal, Samuel J Merksamer, Mark H Rachesky, Michael Sirignano, Dennis D Williams

NAVISTAR MEXICO SA DE CV
See GONZALEZ DE CASTILLA INC

D-U-N-S 01-677-4304
NAVITAIRE LLC (DE)
(*Suby of* ACCENTURE LLP) ★
333 S 7th St Ste 1800, Minneapolis, MN 55402-2414
Tel (612) 317-7000 *Founded/Ownrshp* 1997
Sales 120.6MM^E *EMP* 800
SIC 7373 Computer integrated systems design; Computer integrated systems design
Pr: John Dabkowski
Chf Cred: Curt Blumberg
Dir Bus: Tim Vaughan
Prgrm Mgr: Jim Wedge
Rgnl Mgr: Carina Klasse
Dir IT: David Rooke
Sales Exec: Jennifer Meyer
Sales Asso: Soumitra Panda

D-U-N-S 03-964-2017
NAVITAS INC
TAKE
502 Carnegie Ctr Ste 100, Princeton, NJ 08540-6289
Tel (609) 720-1002 *Founded/Ownrshp* 2000
Sales 146.5MM^E *EMP* 1,100
SIC 7379 Computer related maintenance services; Computer related maintenance services
CEO: Ram Yeleswarapu
CFO: D V Rai
Ex VP: Bala Latupalli
Ex VP: Mike Lewis
Sr VP: Vijay Gnanaraj
VP: Anil Kodali
Ex Dir: Mohamed Ibrahim
Prgrm Mgr: Manikanda Poopathy
Genl Mgr: Reji Nair
Snr Sftwr: Mark Araas
Dir IT: Dayasan Swaminathan

D-U-N-S 62-717-0546
NAVITOR INC
COSCO INDUSTRIES
(*Suby of* TAYLOR CORP) ★
1725 Roe Crest Dr, North Mankato, MN 56003-1807
Tel (507) 625-2828 *Founded/Ownrshp* 2005
Sales 274.9MM^E *EMP* 1,657
SIC 2759 Commercial printing; Commercial printing
CEO: Thomas C Ninneman
**Treas:* Thomas Johnson
**VP:* Suzanne Spellacy
Dir Bus: Victoria Hailey
Dept Mgr: Dan Kunst
Genl Mgr: Linda Cox
Off Mgr: Wendy Trandahl
Dir IT: Greg Taylor
Software D: Jim Blare
Software D: Bobby Fahnestock
Software D: Dale Looft

D-U-N-S 13-878-4827
NAVITUS HEALTH SOLUTIONS LLC
(*Suby of* DEAN HEALTH PLAN INC) ★
2601 W Beltline Hwy # 600, Madison, WI 53713-2316
Tel (608) 729-1500 *Founded/Ownrshp* 2008
Sales 25.2MM^E *EMP* 310^E
SIC 8099 Medical services organization; Medical services organization
Pr: Tammy Miller
Mng Dir: Ebbie Nakhjavani

D-U-N-S 80-920-0533
NAVL LLC
(*Suby of* SIRVA INC) ★
700 Oakmont Ln, Westmont, IL 60559-5551
Tel (630) 570-3009 *Founded/Ownrshp* 2005
Sales 14.8MM^E *EMP* 400
SIC 4212 Moving services; Moving services
Prin: Steve Smetko

D-U-N-S 96-243-7963 IMP
■ NAVMAN WIRELESS HOLDINGS LP
(*Suby of* DANAHER CORP) ★
2701 Patriot Blvd Ste 150, Glenview, IL 60026-8039
Tel (847) 832-2367 *Founded/Ownrshp* 2013
Sales 203.9MM^E *EMP* 350
SIC 3812 Search & navigation equipment
Genl Pt: Tzau J Chung
VP: Chris Bradley
VP: Renaat Eecke

D-U-N-S 09-527-5343
NAVMAR APPLIED SCIENCES CORP
NASC
65 W Street Rd Ste C, Warminster, PA 18974-3225
Tel (215) 675-4900 *Founded/Ownrshp* 1977
Sales 210.1MM *EMP* 460
SIC 8731 8711 Commercial physical research; Engineering services; Commercial physical research; Engineering services
Pr: Thomas Fenerty
CFO: Dave Lewbery
Ex VP: Harold Cody
**VP:* Robert Bauder
VP: Carl Engelbert
Prgrm Mgr: Butch Snead
CTO: Jack Hirsh
Sfty Mgr: Mike Kelley
Mktg Dir: Daniel Fenerty

NAVMEDEAST
See NAVY MEDICINE EAST

D-U-N-S 00-378-8403
NAVOPACHE ELECTRIC COOPERATIVE INC (AZ)
NECO
1878 W White Mtn Blvd, Lakeside, AZ 85929-6348
Tel (928) 368-5118 *Founded/Ownrshp* 1946
Sales 52.9MM *EMP* 107
SIC 4911 Distribution, electric power; Distribution, electric power
CEO: David Plum
**Pr:* Bradley L Baker
**COO:* Dennis Hughes
**CFO:* Paul O'Dair
Treas: Callie Menges
**VP:* Fred S Harper
VP: Ann Menges
IT Man: Tillman McDaniel
Sfty Mgr: Ron Jones
Opers Mgr: Kevin Streett

D-U-N-S 07-185-2099
NAVOS MENTAL HEALTH SOLUTIONS
2600 Sw Holden St, Seattle, WA 98126-3505
Tel (206) 933-7000 *Founded/Ownrshp* 1966
Sales 53.6MM *EMP* 250
Accts Moss Adams Llp Everett Wa
SIC 8093 8063 Mental health clinic, outpatient; Hospital for the mentally ill; Mental health clinic, outpatient; Hospital for the mentally ill
Pr: David M Johnson
Pr: Jim Rudnick
**COO:* Jerry Scott
**CFO:* Lisa Yamilkoski
Bd of Dir: Clark Daffern
Ofcr: Cassie Undlin
Exec: Judi Mitchell
Dir Rx: Paul Thompson
Off Mgr: Stacy Konsack
Dir QC: Diane Browning
Opers Supe: Wyatt Helin

D-U-N-S 03-730-7469
NAVY ARMY COMMUNITY CREDIT UNION
5725 Spohn Dr, Corpus Christi, TX 78414-4117
Tel (361) 986-4500 *Founded/Ownrshp* 1976
Sales NA *EMP* 330
SIC 6061 Federal credit unions; Federal credit unions
Pr: Wayne Vann
CFO: Dana Sisk
**Treas:* Oran Chapman
Treas: Vicki Gonzales
Ex VP: Sarah Brien
Ex VP: Louise Foreman
Ex VP: Sarah O'Brien
Sr VP: Georgeann Joo
Sr VP: Georgeann Reeve
**VP:* Sarah O Brien
VP: Helen Gibbs
VP: Alissa Villegas

D-U-N-S 00-170-7694 EXP
■ NAVY EXCHANGE SERVICE COMMAND
NEXCOM
(*Suby of* UNITED STATES DEPARTMENT OF DEFENSE) ★
3280 Virginia Beach Blvd, Virginia Beach, VA 23452-5799
Tel (800) 448-3996 *Founded/Ownrshp* 1946
Sales 2.8MMM *EMP* 14,000
Accts Kpmg Llp Norfolk Va
SIC 5399 Duty-free goods; Department stores, discount; ; Navy; Duty-free goods
CEO: Robert Bianchi
**COO:* Michael P Good
**CFO:* Laurie P Hasten
**Treas:* Thomas McDonald
Treas: Stephen P Rodgers
VP: Kevin Comer
Dept Mgr: Anthony Eugeni
Dist Mgr: Sante Campanile
Genl Mgr: Jackie Hanson
Genl Mgr: Jamie Menne
Genl Mgr: Marcelina Smith

D-U-N-S 06-926-9975
NAVY FEDERAL CREDIT UNION
820 Follin Ln Se, Vienna, VA 22180-4907
Tel (703) 255-8000 *Founded/Ownrshp* 1933
Sales NA *EMP* 6,037
SIC 6061 Federal credit unions; Federal credit unions
Pr: Cutler Dawson
Pr: Dave Ledwell
CFO: Brady Cole
Treas: Brian McDonnell
Ofcr: April Blevins
Ofcr: Ivah Buzon
Ofcr: Russell Kinser
Ofcr: Stephen Newlin
Ofcr: Lisa Pyritz
Ofcr: Maureen Sweeney
Assoc VP: Kim Engman
Ex VP: Steve Romano
VP: Bob Berger
VP: Debby Carter
VP: Nancy Dedona
VP: John Giaquinto
VP: Donalda Gibson
VP: Julie Griffin
VP: Ed Guckenberger
VP: Joseph Jucha
VP: Richard Longhurst

D-U-N-S 07-481-3072
NAVY LEAGUE OF UNITED STATES
2300 Wilson Blvd Ste 200, Arlington, VA 22201-5435
Tel (703) 528-1775 *Founded/Ownrshp* 1902
Sales 7.1MM *EMP* 900
Accts Cliftonlarsonallen Llp Arling
SIC 8621 2741 Education & teacher association; Miscellaneous publishing; Education & teacher association; Miscellaneous publishing
Pr: James Offutt
Treas: Yvonne Cantu
Bd of Dir: Alan Guggenheim
**Sr VP:* Amy Wittman
VP: Gwen Hinton
VP: Sherre Lovick
VP: Stacy McFarland
VP: Bradley Nemeth
VP: David Todd
VP: Seymour Ulansey
Exec: Michael Poles

D-U-N-S 82-864-2202
NAVY MEDICINE EAST
NAVMEDEAST
620 John Paul Jones Cir, Portsmouth, VA 23708-2111
Tel (757) 953-0431 *Founded/Ownrshp* 2008
Sales NA *EMP* 99
SIC 6324 Hospital & medical service plans
Prin: William Kiser

NAVY MUSIC PROGRAM
See US NAVY FLEET BAND ACTIVITIES

D-U-N-S 07-264-6888
NAVY MUTUAL AID ASSOCIATION
Henderson Hall, 29, Arlington, VA 22212-0001
Tel (703) 945-1440 *Founded/Ownrshp* 1879
Sales 253.1MM *EMP* 75
SIC 8641 6411 Veterans' organization; Insurance agents, brokers & service
Pr: Philip Coady
COO: Stephen Pietropaoli
Assoc VP: Tom Edwareds
VP: John McVeigh

D-U-N-S 00-713-9952
NAVY PIER INC (IL)
600 E Grand Ave Ste 134, Chicago, IL 60611-6335
Tel (312) 595-5333 *Founded/Ownrshp* 2011
Sales 57.2MM *EMP* 84^E
Accts Bdo Usa Llp Chicago Il
SIC 6519 7999 Real property lessors; Sub-lessors of real estate; Exhibition operation; Carnival operation
Ch: William J Brodsky
**Pr:* Andrea Zopp
**CEO:* James R Reilly
COO: Brian Murphy
CFO: Ralph Leslie
Ex VP: Steve Haemmerle
VP: Gail Mahaffey
Dir Risk M: Gina Kirchner
Dir Soc: Timothy Dillon
Dir Soc: Joseph Giannelli
Dir Soc: Danielle Pratl
Dir Soc: Jared Rush
Dir Soc: Lyndsey Van
Dir Soc: Lyndsey Van Wyk

D-U-N-S 96-486-2739
NAVY PLUM LLC
47 Plum Rd, Monsey, NY 10952-1525
Tel (845) 641-7441 *Founded/Ownrshp* 2009
Sales 40.0MM *EMP* 3

SIC 2299 5199 Fabrics: linen, jute, hemp, ramie; Yarn: flax, jute, hemp & ramie; Fabrics, yarns & knit goods; Fabrics: linen, jute, hemp, ramie; Yarn: flax, jute, hemp & ramie; Fabrics, yarns & knit goods

D-U-N-S 07-480-3909
NAVY-MARINE CORPS RELIEF SOCIETY
875 N Randolph St Ste 225, Arlington, VA 22203-1767
Tel (703) 696-4901 *Founded/Ownrshp* 1904
Sales NA *EMP* 255
SIC 6141 8742 8322 Personal credit institutions; Remedial loan societies; Financial consultant; Individual & family services; Family service agency; Personal credit institutions; Remedial loan societies; Financial consultant; Individual & family services; Family service agency
Pr: Steve Abbot
**CFO:* George F Warren
Ofcr: Susan Humann
**Ex VP:* Jan Gaudio
VP: Janyce Hansen
**VP:* Wes Schmidt
CIO: Willie Williams
Software D: William Mellen

D-U-N-S 12-274-5185
NAYLOR & BREEN BUILDERS INC
191 Alta Woods, Brandon, VT 05733-9705
Tel (802) 247-6527 *Founded/Ownrshp* 1978
Sales 29.3MM *EMP* 60
SIC 1542 1522 Commercial & office building, new construction; Commercial & office buildings, renovation & repair; Multi-family dwelling construction; Multi-family dwellings, new construction; Commercial & office building, new construction; Commercial & office buildings, renovation & repair; Multi-family dwelling construction; Multi-family dwellings, new construction
Pr: Robert Naylor
**VP:* Tanner Romano
VP: Richard Stirde
IT Man: Mary Kirby
Snr Mgr: Doug Gorton

D-U-N-S 14-711-3286
NAYLOR COMMERCIAL INTERIORS INC
2765 W Kingsley Rd, Garland, TX 75041-2406
Tel (972) 278-2620 *Founded/Ownrshp* 1985
Sales 30.0MM^E *EMP* 100
SIC 1542 1721 Commercial & office buildings, renovation & repair; Painting & paper hanging; Commercial & office buildings, renovation & repair; Painting & paper hanging
CEO: Paula Naylor
**Pr:* Joshua Naylor
**Sr VP:* Greg Naylor

D-U-N-S 84-549-2701
NAYLOR LLC
5950 Nw 1st Pl, Gainesville, FL 32607-6060
Tel (800) 369-6220 *Founded/Ownrshp* 2013
Sales 111.1MM^E *EMP* 420
SIC 2759 7374 Publication printing; Computer graphics service; Publication printing; Computer graphics service
Pr: Alex Debarr
CFO: Tim Hedke
Ex VP: Chris Caldwell
Ex VP: Robert S Ingraham
VP: Tara Ericson
VP: Jon Meurlott
VP: Charles Popper
VP: William Sharkey
VP: Camille Stern
Exec: Douglas Pratt
Dir Soc: Dan Gardner
Dir Soc: Jake Gregory

D-U-N-S 00-514-5180
NAYLOR PIPE CO (IL)
1230 E 92nd St, Chicago, IL 60619-7997
Tel (773) 721-9400 *Founded/Ownrshp* 1925
Sales 24.5MM^E *EMP* 181
SIC 3317 Pipes, seamless steel; Tubes, seamless steel; Pipes, seamless steel; Tubes, seamless steel
Pr: John J Czulno
**Ch Bd:* William B Skeates
**Ex VP:* Michael T O'Rourke
**VP:* Russell A Blais
VP: Kevin Joyce

D-U-N-S 00-713-8217 IMP
NAZARENE PUBLISHING HOUSE
BEACON HILL PRESS KANSAS CITY
2923 Troost Ave, Kansas City, MO 64109-1593
Tel (816) 931-1900 *Founded/Ownrshp* 1898
Sales 29.6MM^E *EMP* 198
Accts Keller & Owens Llc
SIC 2731 2741 Pamphlets: publishing & printing; Textbooks: publishing & printing; Book music: publishing & printing; Music, sheet: publishing & printing; Pamphlets: publishing & printing; Textbooks: publishing & printing; Book music: publishing & printing; Music, sheet: publishing & printing
Pr: C Hardy Weathers
**VP:* Mark D Brown
Exec: M Gaikwad
Opers Mgr: Ray Davis
Mktg Dir: Tim Curtis
Sls Dir: Eric Bryant
Mktg Mgr: Kelly Gallegher

D-U-N-S 03-141-6381
NAZARETH AREA SCHOOL DISTRICT
1 Education Plz, Nazareth, PA 18064-2332
Tel (610) 759-1170 *Founded/Ownrshp* 1950
Sales 68.2MM *EMP* 426
Accts Gorman & Associates Pc Nor
SIC 8211 9411 Public elementary & secondary schools; High school, junior or senior; School board; Administration of educational programs; Public elementary & secondary schools; High school, junior or senior; School board; Administration of educational programs
Dir IT: Michael Uelses
IT Man: Tracy Smith
Schl Brd P: Lorin Bradley
HC Dir: Pamela Vlasaty

D-U-N-S 07-839-5325
NAZARETH COLLEGE OF ROCHESTER
4245 East Ave, Rochester, NY 14618-3790
Tel (585) 381-7190 *Founded/Ownrshp* 2012
Sales 108.4MM *EMP* 8^E
SIC 8221 Colleges universities & professional schools
Pr: Daan Braveman

D-U-N-S 07-367-0143
NAZARETH COLLEGE OF ROCHESTER INC
4245 East Ave, Rochester, NY 14618-3790
Tel (585) 389-2525 *Founded/Ownrshp* 1925
Sales 74.7MM *EMP* 401^E
Accts Kpmg Llp Albany Ny
SIC 8221 College, except junior; College, except junior
Pr: Daan Brazeman
COO: Stephen Beecher
Ofcr: David Bagley
Ofcr: Sydney Bell
Ofcr: Lisa Gerst
Ofcr: Varna Nyanforh
Ofcr: Devin Thomas
Ofcr: Matthew Whitney
Ex VP: Michael Lawrence
VP: Joseph Arcarese
VP: Stephen Lasalle
VP: Karen Rohr
Exec: Greg Dec
Dir: Marguerite Martin

D-U-N-S 06-987-3958
NAZARETH HOSPITAL
MERCY HEALTH SYSTEM
(*Suby of* MERCY HEALTH FOUNDATION OF SOUTHEASTERN PENNSYLVANIA) ★
2601 Holme Ave, Philadelphia, PA 19152-2096
Tel (215) 335-6000 *Founded/Ownrshp* 1995
Sales 146.6MM *EMP* 1,230
SIC 8062 General medical & surgical hospitals; General medical & surgical hospitals
Pr: Susan Croushore
CEO: Lynn Odonneoo
COO: Thomas Campione
**CFO:* Dave Wajda
VP: Mary Ellen Cockerham
Dir Inf Cn: Jim Hunter
Dir Lab: Geralyn Fattore
Dir Soc: Elaine March' McDonald
Dir Rx: Richard Centafonte
Dir Env Sv: Kelly Brennan
**Prin:* Cristina Fitzpatrick
Board of Directors: Mike Murphy

D-U-N-S 05-250-1756
NAZARETH LITERARY & BENEVOLENT INSTITUTION INC
SISTERS OF CHARITY OF NAZARETH
200 Nazareth Rd, Nazareth, KY 40048-9905
Tel (502) 348-1555 *Founded/Ownrshp* 1812
Sales 18.8MM^E *EMP* 700
SIC 8211 8059

D-U-N-S 00-523-3960 IMP
NAZDAR CO
NAZDAR SOURCE ONE
(*Suby of* THRALL ENTERPRISES INC) ★
8501 Hedge Lane Ter, Shawnee, KS 66227-3289
Tel (913) 422-1888 *Founded/Ownrshp* 1977
Sales 105.6MM^E *EMP* 470
SIC 2893 Screen process ink; Screen process ink
CEO: J Jeffrey Thrall
**Pr:* Mike Fox
CFO: Tom Muldan
**Ch:* Stanley D Christianson
**Treas:* Nancy G Haller
**VP:* Richard Bowles
VP: Randy Thrall
QA Dir: Bill Rayburn
Software D: Sean Lange
Plnt Mgr: Tony Goodson
Sls Dir: Patrick Wong
Board of Directors: Jerome A Thrall

NAZDAR SOURCE ONE
See NAZDAR CO

NAZTECH
See HYPERCEL CORP

D-U-N-S 00-522-9448 IMP
NB COATINGS INC (IL)
(*Suby of* NIPPON PAINT (USA) INC) ★
2701 E 170th St, Lansing, IL 60438-1107
Tel (708) 474-7000 *Founded/Ownrshp* 1945, 2006
Sales 89.7MM^E *EMP* 400
SIC 2851 2865 2816 Plastics base paints & varnishes; Coating, air curing; Color pigments, organic; Inorganic pigments; Plastics base paints & varnishes; Coating, air curing; Color pigments, organic; Inorganic pigments
Sec: Hidefumi Morita
**CEO:* Kristina Nelson
COO: Kenji Mitsushio
**Ch:* Mitsuo Yamada
**Ex VP:* Takashi Tohi
VP: Jerry McInerney
Exec: Sam Giarraputo
Genl Mgr: Luis Medelln
Dir IT: Hector Centeno
Tech Mgr: Yutaro Kawasaki
VP Mfg: Jack Wickham

D-U-N-S 08-465-3526
NB KENNEY CO INC
68 Barnum Rd, Devens, MA 01434-3508
Tel (978) 849-5200 *Founded/Ownrshp* 1970
Sales 39.7MM^E *EMP* 150
SIC 1711 Mechanical contractor; Mechanical contractor
Pr: Steven P Kenney
**CEO:* Norman B Kenney
**CFO:* Harold McQuestion
**Treas:* Lynda Kenney
**Ex VP:* Robert Nims
**VP:* Brian Curran
VP: Robert Dejadon
**VP:* Aidan G Maguire Jr
**VP:* Robert B Nims
**VP:* Kenneth Reid
VP Opers: Bob Nims

D-U-N-S 13-489-8071 EXP
NB MOTORS INC
BRAMAN MANAGEMENT ASSOCIATION
2060 Biscayne Blvd, Miami, FL 33137-5024
Tel (305) 576-1889 *Founded/Ownrshp* 1982
Sales 55.0MM^E *EMP* 106
SIC 5511 Automobiles, new & used; Automobiles, new & used
Pr: Leibowitz Ed
**Pr:* Norman Braman
**CFO:* Bob Burnstein
**Sec:* Stanley Kreiger
Sales Exec: Carlos Ayure
Sls Mgr: Michael Chestnut
Sls Mgr: Juan Hinestrosa
Sls Mgr: Sergio Rivera
Sales Asso: Paulo Roi
Sales Asso: F A Steve

D-U-N-S 13-850-6162
NB VENTURES INC
GEP
100 Walnut Ave Ste 304, Clark, NJ 07066-1247
Tel (732) 382-6565 *Founded/Ownrshp* 2000
Sales 60.0MM *EMP* 1,200
SIC 8742 Management consulting services; Management consulting services
Pr: Roopa Makhija
CEO: Subhash Makhija
COO: Jagadish Turimella
VP: Tunir Chatterjee
VP: Joel Goldhammer
VP: Joshua House
VP: David Medvedeff
VP: Neha Shah
Dir Bus: Chris Davis
Snr Sftwr: Akbar Ansari
Snr Sftwr: Dhiraj Gosavi

D-U-N-S 96-697-6417
NB WHOLESALE INC
SILVER STAR
11220 Harry Hines Blvd, Dallas, TX 75229-4605
Tel (972) 241-4181 *Founded/Ownrshp* 2009
Sales 35.0MM^E *EMP* 24
SIC 5199 5194 5145 General merchandise, non-durable; Tobacco & tobacco products; Candy; General merchandise, non-durable; Tobacco & tobacco products; Candy
Pr: Nizar Ali
**Pr:* Akbarali Bana

D-U-N-S 10-150-1716
NB&T FINANCIAL GROUP INC
48 N South St, Wilmington, OH 45177-2212
Tel (937) 382-1441 *Founded/Ownrshp* 1980
Sales NA *EMP* 392
SIC 6021 National commercial banks

NBA
See NATIONWIDE BIWEEKLY ADMINISTRATION INC

NBAA
See NATIONAL BUSINESS AVIATION ASSOCIATION INC

NBAC
See NATIONAL BUSINESS & ACCOUNTING CONSULTANTS CORP

NBBJ CONSTRUCTION SERVICES
See NBBJ LLC

D-U-N-S 06-175-4859
NBBJ LLC
NBBJ CONSTRUCTION SERVICES
250 S High St Ste 300, Columbus, OH 43215-4504
Tel (206) 223-5026 *Founded/Ownrshp* 1992
Sales 36.8MM *EMP* 700
Accts Moss-Adams Llp Seattle Washi
SIC 8712 Architectural services; Architectural services
CIO: Scott Carmichael

D-U-N-S 04-302-5915
NBBJ LP
223 Yale Ave N, Seattle, WA 98109-5430
Tel (206) 223-5555 *Founded/Ownrshp* 1961
Sales 107.4MM *EMP* 700
Accts Moss-Adams Llp Seattle Washi
SIC 8712 Architectural services; Architectural services
Pt: William J Bain Jr
Pt: Mackenzie L Skene AIA
Pt: Richard F Dallam
Pt: Helen Dimoff
Pt: John J F Halleran
Pt: Timothy J Johnson
Pt: David Lewis
Pt: Robert C Mankin
Pt: Aj Montero
Pt: Ryan Mullenix
Pt: William J Nichols
Pt: R Douglas Parris
Pt: Joan L Saba
Pt: Thomas Sieniewicz
Pt: Jonathan R Ward
Pt: Scott W Wyatt
Pt: David Yuan
Mng Pt: Steven R McConnell
CEO: R Steven McConnell
COO: Juli Cook
Dir Bus: Fred Coons

NBC
See NASHVILLE BUN CO LLC

D-U-N-S 83-817-5081
NBC ACQUISITION CORP
(*Suby of* NBC HOLDINGS CORP) ★
4700 S 19th St, Lincoln, NE 68512-1216
Tel (402) 421-7300 *Founded/Ownrshp* 2004
Sales 171.1MM^E *EMP* 2,700
SIC 5192 5942 Books; Book stores; Books; Book stores
CEO: Mark W Oppegard
Pr: Barry S Major
CFO: Alan G Siemek
Board of Directors: Mark L Bono

D-U-N-S 82-933-2548
NBC HOLDINGS CORP
(*Suby of* WESTON PRESIDIO CAPITAL MANAGEMENT II LP) ★
4700 S 19th St, Lincoln, NE 68512-1216
Tel (402) 421-7300 *Founded/Ownrshp* 1990
Sales 248.9MM^E *EMP* 3,000^E
SIC 5192 6719 Books; Investment holding companies, except banks; Books; Investment holding companies, except banks
CEO: Mark W Oppegard
**Pr:* Barry Major
**CFO:* Alan Siemeck
Dir IT: Ramon Bescansa

D-U-N-S 62-006-2281
■ **NBC INTERNATIONAL LTD**
(*Suby of* NBC SUBSIDIARY 18 INC)
30 Rockefeller Plz Fl 2, New York, NY 10112-0037
Tel (212) 664-4444 *Founded/Ownrshp* 1970
Sales 11.0MM^E *EMP* 2,022^E
SIC 7822 Motion picture & tape distribution
CEO: Robert C Wright
**Ch Bd:* Gerard Petry
**Pr:* Fedrick Huntsberry
VP: Richard Westcott
Dir Soc: Rachel Maddow
Snr Mgr: Nancy Snyderman

D-U-N-S 11-311-9700
■ **NBC INTERNET INC**
NBCI.COM
(*Suby of* NBC UNIVERSAL INC) ★
30 Rockefeller Plz Fl 2, New York, NY 10112-0037
Tel (212) 315-9016 *Founded/Ownrshp* 1999
Sales 596.2M^E *EMP* 500
SIC 7372 7375 Business oriented computer software; Information retrieval services; Business oriented computer software; Information retrieval services
CEO: William J Lansing
**Ch Bd:* Robert C Wright
CFO: Anthony E Altig
**V Ch Bd:* Chris Kitze
CTO: Leo Chang

D-U-N-S 01-086-7726
NBC OKLAHOMA
13401 N Pennsylvania Ave, Oklahoma City, OK 73120-9008
Tel (405) 748-9100 *Founded/Ownrshp* 2010
Sales NA *EMP* 45^E
SIC 6022 State commercial banks; State commercial banks
Prin: H Hatcher

D-U-N-S 04-507-4357 IMP
NBC RADIO NETWORK SALES
3000 W Alameda Ave, Burbank, CA 91523-0002
Tel (818) 840-3051 *Founded/Ownrshp* 2011
Sales 22.2MM^E *EMP* 416^E
SIC 4832 Radio broadcasting stations
Pr: Mark Fuhrman
Chf Mktg O: John Miller
Ofcr: Karen Carranza
Ex VP: Hilary Hoffman
Ex VP: Jim Hoffman
VP: Alexa Wilson
Exec: Barbara Lackman
Assoc Dir: Erica Enfinger
Creative D: Douglas Parker
Comm Dir: Chloe Ellers
Comm Man: Kristen Hynes

D-U-N-S 07-298-6149 IMP
■ **NBC SPORTS NETWORK LP**
(*Suby of* COMCAST CORP) ★
1 Blachley Rd Ste 1, Stamford, CT 06902-0003
Tel (203) 276-7000 *Founded/Ownrshp* 2007
Sales 52.3MM^E *EMP* 130
SIC 4841 Cable & other pay television services
Pt: Gavin Harvey
VP: Neal Scarbrough
Dir IT: Becker Anthony
Dir IT: Bill Kunz
Counsel: Suzana Carlos

D-U-N-S 60-713-0762
■ **NBC STUDIOS INC**
(*Suby of* NBC UNIVERSAL INC) ★
100 Universal City Plz, Universal City, CA 91608-1002
Tel (818) 840-4444 *Founded/Ownrshp* 1961
Sales 1.1MM^E *EMP* 1,000
SIC 7922 Television program, including commercial producers; Television program, including commercial producers
CEO: Richard Cotton
Sr VP: Dave Dore
VP: Bruce Levinson
VP: Amy Randall
VP: Alicen Schneider
VP: Doug Vaughan
VP Sls: Patrick Notley
Snr Mgr: Kim Anderson

D-U-N-S 00-698-8034 IMP
■ **NBC UNIVERSAL INC**
(*Suby of* NBCUNIVERSAL MEDIA LLC) ★
1221 Avenue Of The Americ, New York, NY 10020-1001
Tel (212) 664-4444 *Founded/Ownrshp* 1987
Sales 7.3MM^E *EMP* 6,152
SIC 4833 8111 Television broadcasting stations; Legal services; Television broadcasting stations; Legal services
Pr: Andrew R Lack
Pr: Christopher Baker
Pr: Adriane Berman
Pr: Neil Braun
**Pr:* Steve Capus
**Pr:* Scott M Sassa
**Pr:* Pamela Thomas-Graham
**CEO:* William Bolster

*CEO: Stephen B Burke
COO: Beth Roberts
*CFO: Stuart J Epstein
Ch: Mark Lazarus
*Ex VP: Mark W Begor
*Ex VP: Richard Cotton
*Ex VP: Edward L Scanlon
Sr VP: Scot Chastain
Sr VP: Macelon D'Sa
*Sr VP: Stephen Doerr
VP: Christina M Bailey
*VP: Krishan Bhatia
*VP: Cameron Blanchard
Board of Directors: Barbara Scott Preiskel, D W Calloway, Frank Rhodes, Silas S Cathcart, Keith Sherrin, Dennis D Dammerman, Andrew C Sigler, Claudio X Gonzalez, Douglas A Warner III, Robert E Mercer, Gertrude G Michelson, Sam Nunn, John D Opie, Roger Penske

D-U-N-S 01-694-1234 IMP/EXP
■ NBC UNIVERSAL INC
(Suby of COMCAST CORP) ★
100 Universal City Plz, Universal City, CA 91608-1002
Tel (818) 777-1000 Founded/Ownrshp 1987
Sales 122.1MM^E EMP 532
SIC 7812 Motion picture production & distribution; Motion picture production & distribution, television; Non-theatrical motion picture production; Non-theatrical motion picture production, television; Motion picture production & distribution; Motion picture production & distribution, television; Non-theatrical motion picture production; Non-theatrical motion picture production, television
Pr: Katherine Pope
Pr: Michelle Hagen
*CEO: Jeffrey Zucker
CFO: Sunil Chadda
CFO: Douglas Keith
CFO: Salil Mehta
*Treas: Melissa Leffler
*Sr VP: Neil Strum
*VP: David Karnes
VP: Richard Rothstein
VP: Vernon Sanders
Assoc Dir: Ben Cowling
Assoc Dir: John Gillispie
Assoc Dir: Erica Levens
Creative D: Renate Radford

D-U-N-S 96-770-1769
■ NBC UNIVERSAL LLC
NBCUNIVERSAL
(Suby of COMCAST CORP) ★
30 Rockefeller Plz Fl 51, New York, NY 10112-0015
Tel (212) 664-4444 Founded/Ownrshp 2011
Sales NA EMP 30,000
SIC 4832 4833 4841 6021 6531 7383 Radio broadcasting stations; Television broadcasting stations; Cable television services; National commercial banks; Real estate brokers & agents; News syndicates; Radio broadcasting stations; Television broadcasting stations; Cable television services; National commercial banks; Real estate brokers & agents; News syndicates
CEO: Stephen B Burke
Pr: Linda Yaccarino
CFO: Stuart Epstein
CFO: Anand Kini
CFO: Earl Marshall
Ofcr: Eric Baculinao
Ofcr: Craig Robinson
Ex VP: Henry Ahn
Ex VP: Krishan Bhatia
Ex VP: Matt Bond
Ex VP: Cesar Conde
Ex VP: Darren Feher
Ex VP: Patricia Fili-Krushel
Ex VP: Lisa Hsia
Ex VP: John Shea
Ex VP: Laura Tankenson
Sr VP: Catherine Balsam-Schwaber
Sr VP: Phil Cara
Sr VP: James Kreckler
Sr VP: Tom Stevens
Sr VP: Maggie McLean Suniewick

D-U-N-S 78-248-7151
■ NBC-NTOP HOLDING INC
(Suby of NBC UNIVERSAL INC) ★
1221 Ave Of The Americas, New York, NY 10020-1001
Tel (212) 664-4444 Founded/Ownrshp 1986
Sales 561.6M^E EMP 471^E
SIC 7383 News syndicates; News syndicates
Pr: Therese Byrne
VP: Anne Grotefeld
VP: Randy Raddatz
Opers Mgr: Craig Schneider

D-U-N-S 55-544-4520
NBCCAT CORP
XMGM COMPANY
7431 W 90th St, Bridgeview, IL 60455-2121
Tel (708) 793-5191 Founded/Ownrshp 1999
Sales 6.3MM^E EMP 290
SIC 7539 Trailer repair; Trailer repair
Pr: Randy Schwoeble
*VP: Chuck Genoar
*Exec: J Thomas Williams

NBCI.COM
See NBC INTERNET INC

NBCUNIVERSAL
See NBC UNIVERSAL LLC

D-U-N-S 60-713-0036 IMP
■ NBCUNIVERSAL MEDIA LLC
(Suby of NBC UNIVERSAL LLC) ★
30 Rockefeller Plz Fl 2, New York, NY 10112-0037
Tel (212) 664-4444 Founded/Ownrshp 2011
Sales 25.4MMM EMP 30,000
SIC 4841 4833 7812 7996 Cable television services; Television broadcasting stations; Motion picture production & distribution; Amusement parks; Cable television services; Television broadcasting stations; Motion picture production & distribution; Amusement parks
CEO: Stephen B Burke
V Ch: Ronald Meyer
Pr: Bridget Baker
Pr: Mark Lund
Pr: Jean-Briac Perrette
Pr: Peter Smith
Pr: Lauren Zalaznick
COO: Salil Mehta
CFO: Megan Canavan
CFO: Jeff Fleeher
CFO: Anand Kini
Chf Mktg O: John Miller
Ofcr: George Kliavkoff
Ofcr: Vivian Schiller
Ex VP: Henry Ahn
Ex VP: Meredith Ahr
Ex VP: Cameron Blanchard
Ex VP: Jay Bockhaus
Ex VP: Marianne Gambelli
Ex VP: Kimberley D Harris
Ex VP: Robert Hayes

D-U-N-S 07-313-1377
■ NBD SERVICE CORP
(Suby of JPMORGAN CHASE & CO) ★
1235 E Big Beaver Rd, Troy, MI 48083-1905
Tel (248) 680-2600 Founded/Ownrshp 1998
Sales 19.6MM^E EMP 1,000
SIC 7389 Credit card service; Credit card service
Pr: Leonard E Ciokajlo
*Treas: Robert E Allison
Board of Directors: Fred M Adams Jr, James E Barlett, Gerald K Hanson, Richard J McCullen

D-U-N-S 84-513-8106
NBDI INC
3300 W Esplanade Ave S # 21, Metairie, LA 70002-7406
Tel (504) 486-4570 Founded/Ownrshp 1991
Sales 12.8MM^E EMP 652
Accts Kpmg
SIC 5812 Italian restaurant; Italian restaurant
Pr: John Paisant
CFO: Linda Brewster Meffert

NBER
See NATIONAL BUREAU OF ECONOMIC RESEARCH INC

NBGHOME
See HOME DECOR HOLDING CO

D-U-N-S 00-890-7461
■ NBH BANK NATIONAL ASSOCIATION
BANK MIDWEST
(Suby of NATIONAL BANK HOLDINGS CORP) ★
1111 Main St Ste 100, Kansas City, MO 64105-2114
Tel (816) 471-9800 Founded/Ownrshp 2010
Sales NA EMP 986
SIC 6021 National commercial banks; National commercial banks
Pr: Thomas M Metzger
*CEO: G Timothy Laney
*CFO: Dennis P Ambroske
*CFO: Brian Lilly
Ofcr: Amy Prater
Ex VP: Bob Hall
Ex VP: Kevin Kramer
Ex VP: Marvin Schutte
Sr VP: Cynthia Aaron
Sr VP: Whitney Bartelli
Sr VP: John Baxter
*Sr VP: Margaret Bosley
Sr VP: Bobbie McCauley
Sr VP: John Minnis
Sr VP: Jeffrey Schutte
Sr VP: Steve Sturm
*Sr VP: Eugene J Twellman
VP: Charlie Argard
VP: Sharon Bock
VP: Brian Bower
VP: Rick Brucker

NBHCC'S
See NORTHEAST BEHAVIORAL HEALTH CARE CONSORTIUM

D-U-N-S 60-686-2878 IMP
NBHX TRIM USA CORP
(Suby of NBHX TRIM GMBH)
1020 7 Mile Rd Nw, Comstock Park, MI 49321-9542
Tel (616) 785-9400 Founded/Ownrshp 2011
Sales 64.7MM EMP 425^E
Accts Cliftonlarsonallen Llp Oak Br
SIC 3714 Motor vehicle parts & accessories; Motor vehicle parts & accessories
Pr: Stefan Clemens
*VP: Michael Homrich
Prgrm Mgr: Frank Vorst
Prd Mgr: Joel Clark
Ql Cn Mgr: Troy Caswell
Ql Cn Mgr: Shawn Helms

D-U-N-S 10-228-9220
NBI INC
1218 Mccann Dr, Altoona, WI 54720-2561
Tel (715) 835-8525 Founded/Ownrshp 1998
Sales 23.7MM EMP 85
SIC 8299 8111

D-U-N-S 07-986-5084
■ NBL TEXAS LLC
(Suby of NOBLE ENERGY INC) ★
1001 Noble Energy Way, Houston, TX 77070-1435
Tel (281) 872-3100 Founded/Ownrshp 2015
Sales 493.3MM^E EMP 253^E
SIC 1311 Crude petroleum production
CEO: Charles J Rimer

NBM METALS
See NATIONAL BRONZE AND METALS INC

D-U-N-S 78-306-5345
NBN INFUSIONS INC
2 Pin Oak Ln Ste 250, Cherry Hill, NJ 08003-1630
Tel (856) 235-9111 Founded/Ownrshp 1991
Sales 20.1MM^E EMP 49
SIC 5047 Medical equipment & supplies
Pr: Linda Begley
*COO: Joseph Borettcher

NBOME
See NATIONAL BOARD OF OSTEOPATHIC MEDICAL EXAMINERS INC

NBPTS
See NATIONAL BOARD FOR PROFESSIONAL TEACHING STANDARDS INC

NBRC
See APPLIED MEASUREMENT PROFESSIONALS INC

NBS
See NATIONAL BANKRUPTCY SERVICES LLC

D-U-N-S 36-225-0391
▲ NBT BANCORP INC
52 S Broad St, Norwich, NY 13815-1646
Tel (607) 337-2265 Founded/Ownrshp 1986
Sales NA EMP 1,742
Tkr Sym NBTB Exch NGS
SIC 6021 National commercial banks; National commercial banks
Pr: Martin A Dietrich
*Ch Bd: Daryl R Forsythe
Pr: Heidi Fisher
Pr: Linda Kelsey
Pr: Jennifer Olds
Pr: Arlene Somer
CFO: Michael J Chewens
Ex VP: Ronald Bently
Ex VP: Timothy L Brenner
Ex VP: Thomas Delduchetto
Ex VP: Stephen Green
Ex VP: Jeffrey M Levy
Ex VP: Christine Pollard
Ex VP: F Sheldon Prentice
Ex VP: David E Raven
Ex VP: John D Roberts
Ex VP: Catherine M Scarlett
Ex VP: Mary H Serwatka
Ex VP: Joseph R Stagliano
Sr VP: William Aitken
Sr VP: David Theleman

D-U-N-S 00-699-3364
■ NBT BANK NA
N B T BANK
(Suby of NBT BANCORP INC) ★
52 S Broad St, Norwich, NY 13815-1699
Tel (607) 337-2265 Founded/Ownrshp 1986
Sales NA EMP 1,472
SIC 6021 National commercial banks; National commercial banks
CEO: Martin A Dietrich
Pr: Jeffrey Lake
Pr: Richard Shirtz
Chf Inves: John Cook
Ofcr: Kathy Black
Ofcr: Bradley Eaton II
Ofcr: Paul J Ward
*Trst Ofcr: Timothy Handy
Ex VP: Timothy L Brenner
Ex VP: Lance Mattingly
Ex VP: Catherine Scarlett
Sr VP: John Buffa
Sr VP: Richard Callahan
Sr VP: James Campone
Sr VP: John Carpenter
*Sr VP: Michael J Chewens
Sr VP: Jeffrey Delepine
Sr VP: George Doherty
Sr VP: Elizabeth Reynolds
Sr VP: Patrick Ward
VP: Bradford Adams

NBTC
See NORTHERN BANK & TRUST CO

D-U-N-S 05-279-0318 IMP/EXP
■ NBTY INC
ARCO PHARMACEUTICAL
(Suby of ALPHABET HOLDING CO INC) ★
2100 Smithtown Ave, Ronkonkoma, NY 11779-7347
Tel (631) 200-2000 Founded/Ownrshp 1971, 2010
Sales 3.2MMM EMP 14,650
Accts Pricewaterhousecoopers Llp Ne
SIC 2833 5122 5499 5961 Vitamins, natural or synthetic: bulk, uncompounded; Vitamins & minerals; Health & dietetic food stores; Vitamin food stores; Health foods; Dietetic foods; Pharmaceuticals, mail order; Vitamins, natural or synthetic: bulk, uncompounded; Vitamins & minerals; Health & dietetic food stores; Vitamin food stores; Health foods; Dietetic foods; Pharmaceuticals, mail order
CEO: Jeffrey A Nagel
*Pr: Glenn Schneider
Pr: Kevin Warren
*CFO: Dipak Golechha
*V Ch Bd: Harvey Kamil
*Ofcr: Andrew Archambault
Sr VP: Barry Drucker
*Sr VP: James P Flaherty
VP: Christopher S Brennan
VP: Glenn Davis
VP: William Doherty
VP: William Dougherty
VP: Irene Fisher
VP: Curt Morgan
VP: Kathy Tobiasen
Comm Man: Ronnie Brucato

D-U-N-S 02-365-3095
■ NBTY MANUFACTURING LLC
NATURE'S BOUNTY
(Suby of ARCO PHARMACEUTICAL) ★
5115 E La Palma Ave, Anaheim, CA 92807-2018
Tel (714) 765-8323 Founded/Ownrshp 1978
Sales 52.6MM^E EMP 224
SIC 2834 Vitamin preparations; Vitamin preparations
CEO: Steve Cahillane
Prgrm Mgr: Rajani Rallapalli
Plnt Mgr: Alan Srutowski
Ql Cn Mgr: Sunil Ratnayake

D-U-N-S 96-568-4199 IMP
■ NBTY MANUFACTURING LLC
(Suby of ARCO PHARMACEUTICAL) ★
2100 Smithtown Ave, Ronkonkoma, NY 11779-7347
Tel (631) 567-9500 Founded/Ownrshp 2001
Sales 57.5MM^E EMP 550^E
SIC 2833 5122 Vitamins, natural or synthetic: bulk, uncompounded; Vitamins & minerals; Vitamins, natural or synthetic: bulk, uncompounded; Vitamins & minerals
VP: Joe Looney

D-U-N-S 02-147-1646
NC & SONS INC
NICHOLSON
201 Chambers Brook Rd, Branchburg, NJ 08876-3592
Tel (908) 575-0055 Founded/Ownrshp 1997
Sales 47.3MM EMP 65
Accts Wiss & Company Llp Livingston
SIC 1542 Commercial & office building, new construction; Commercial & office building, new construction
CEO: Cynthia Nicholson
*VP: Brandon Nicholson

NC BLUMENTHAL PERFORMING ARTS
See NORTHCAROLINA PERFORMING ARTS CENTER AT CHARLOTTE FOUNDATION

NC DEPARMENT OF INSURANCE
See NORTH CAROLINA DEPARTMENT OF INSURANCE

D-U-N-S 09-900-4061 IMP
NC DYNAMICS INC
NCDI
(Suby of AEROSPACE HOLDINGS INC) ★
3401 E 69th St, Long Beach, CA 90805-1872
Tel (562) 634-7394 Founded/Ownrshp 2012
Sales 52.7MM^E EMP 151
SIC 3728 Aircraft parts & equipment; Aircraft parts & equipment
CEO: Kevin Minter
*Pr: Randall L Bazz
VP: Ron Scott
VP: Chris Thompson
Prgrm Mgr: Mike Perrin
Prd Mgr: Mikael Norrbom
Ql Cn Mgr: Juan Recalde

D-U-N-S 07-973-0653
NC ENERGY SERVICES US INC
(Suby of NCSG CRANE & HEAVY HAUL CORPORATION)
1200 Westlake Ave N # 310, Seattle, WA 98109-3543
Tel (206) 689-5686 Founded/Ownrshp 2008
Sales 38.4MM^E EMP 140
SIC 4213 Heavy hauling
Pr: Ted Redmond

D-U-N-S 02-405-8192
NC GAMES & ARCADES OF AMERICA INC
2105 Nw 115th Ave, Doral, FL 33172-4920
Tel (305) 470-4622 Founded/Ownrshp 2006
Sales 56.1MM EMP 5
SIC 5092 Video games; Video games
Pr: Claudio C Macedo

D-U-N-S 07-979-9010
NC HEALTH AND HUMAN SERVICES
3006 Mail Service Ctr, Raleigh, NC 27699-3000
Tel (919) 855-4430 Founded/Ownrshp 2015
Sales 16.1MM^E EMP 1,741^E
SIC 8211 Public elementary & secondary schools

D-U-N-S 01-666-8188
NC INC
WHOLESALE BUILDING MATERIALS C
1422 E Elkhorn Rd, Vincennes, IN 47591-7093
Tel (812) 886-4412 Founded/Ownrshp 1933
Sales 83.0MM^E EMP 180
SIC 5031 5211 Lumber: rough, dressed & finished; Home centers; Lumber: rough, dressed & finished; Home centers
CEO: Bernard G Niehaus
Pr: Bernard F Niehaus
VP: David Niehaus
Opers Mgr: Eric Feagley
Sls Mgr: Todd Donovan

D-U-N-S 61-250-1221
NC INDUSTRIES INC
NIAGARA CUTTER
200 John James Audubon, Buffalo, NY 14228-1120
Tel (248) 528-5200 Founded/Ownrshp 1954
Sales 48.5MM^E EMP 465
SIC 3545 3479 5084 Cutting tools for machine tools; Coating of metals & formed products; Machine tools & accessories; Cutting tools for machine tools; Coating of metals & formed products; Machine tools & accessories
Ch Bd: Roger D Bollier
*Treas: William C Szabo
*VP: Sherwood L Bollier
Off Mgr: William Rees

NC INTERACTIVE.
See NC INTERACTIVE LLC

D-U-N-S 12-483-0030
NC INTERACTIVE LLC
NC INTERACTIVE.
(Suby of NCSOFT)
3180 139th Ave Se Ste 500, Bellevue, WA 98005-4095
Tel (206) 588-7200 Founded/Ownrshp 2002
Sales 42.6MM^E EMP 300
SIC 7379
*CEO: Taekjin Kim
*CFO: Mike S Grajeda
*CFO: Hong Heo
Sr VP: Jae-SOO Yoon
VP: Lisa Larry
Prgrm Mgr: Gary Beebe
Off Mgr: Theresa Bottenhorn
Secur Mgr: Paul Freund
VP Mktg: David Reid
VP Sls: Lisa Bell-Cabrera
Sls Mgr: Julius Ekeroma
Board of Directors: Robert Garriott, Young K Hahn

NC MEDASSIST
See MEDASSIST OF MECKLENBURG

D-U-N-S 13-985-7549
NC MEDICAL SOCIETY HEALTH
700 Spring Forest Rd # 400, Raleigh, NC 27609-9124
Tel (919) 878-7513 *Founded/Ownrshp* 2003
Sales 104.7MM *EMP* 2
SIC 8621 Health association; Health association

NC MUTUAL
See NORTH CAROLINA MUTUAL LIFE INSURANCE CO INC

D-U-N-S 96-965-2531
NC STATE INVESTMENT FUND INC
Ncsu, Raleigh, NC 27695-0001
Tel (919) 513-7149 *Founded/Ownrshp* 2011
Sales 59.9MM *EMP* 2
Accts Williams Overman Pierce Llp R
SIC 6722 Management investment, open-end; Management investment, open-end
Genl Mgr: Libby George

NC STATE UNI VETRINRY HLTH COM
See NC STATE VETERINARY HOS

D-U-N-S 96-904-2311
NC STATE VETERINARY HOS
NC STATE UNI VETRINRY HLTH COM
1052 William Moore Dr, Raleigh, NC 27607-4065
Tel (919) 513-6821 *Founded/Ownrshp* 2011
Sales 14.5MM^E *EMP* 500
SIC 0742 Veterinary services, specialties; Veterinary services, specialties
Snr Mgr: Jon Brann

D-U-N-S 96-622-1421
NC TEACHERS AND STATE EMPLOYEES BENEFIT TRUST
325 N Salisbury St, Raleigh, NC 27603-1388
Tel (919) 807-4991 *Founded/Ownrshp* 2011
Sales 75.8MM *EMP* 2^E
SIC 6733 Trusts; Trusts
Prin: Mark Massey

D-U-N-S 80-924-6648
NC-CNH INC
COLISEUM NORTHSIDE HOSPITAL
400 Charter Blvd, Macon, GA 31210-4831
Tel (478) 757-8200 *Founded/Ownrshp* 2007
Sales 26.0MM^E *EMP* 350
SIC 8062 8093 8071 8049 8011 General medical & surgical hospitals; Rehabilitation center, outpatient treatment; X-ray laboratory, including dental; Physical therapist; Freestanding emergency medical center; General medical & surgical hospitals; Rehabilitation center, outpatient treatment; X-ray laboratory, including dental; Physical therapist; Freestanding emergency medical center
CEO: Bud Costelo
Chf Rad: Arthur McCain
COO: Sandy Taylor
CFO: Curtis Herrin
Dir Lab: Danny Manville
Dir Rx: Richard Penn
QA Dir: Jan Rogers
Dir IT: Lonna Peacock
Sfty Dirs: Randy Willis
Mktg Dir: Robin Parker
Pr Mgr: Christie Amerson

D-U-N-S 14-363-0502
NC4 INC
NATIONAL CENTER FOR CRISIS
100 N Sepulveda Blvd, El Segundo, CA 90245-4359
Tel (310) 606-4444 *Founded/Ownrshp* 2004
Sales 46.5MM^E *EMP* 127
SIC 7371 Computer software development
Pr: Aubrey Chernick
**Pr:* Jim Montagnino
Pr: Thanh Nguyen
VP: Chris Gundel
VP: Karie Wohlgemuth
Prgrm Mgr: Jennifer Owen
Off Mgr: Kathy Condellire
Off Mgr: Lois Hubbs
Snr Sftwr: Jason Renschler
Software D: Manuel Garcia
Software D: Michael Holloway

NCA
See NATIONAL CABLE COMMUNICATIONS LLC

NCA
See NETWORK COMPUTING ARCHITECTS INC

NCA GROUP
See NATIONAL CATASTROPHE ADJUSTERS INC

NCAA
See NATIONAL COLLEGIATE ATHLETIC ASSOCIATION

D-U-N-S 01-475-3680
NCAL BANCORP (CA)
145 S Fairfax Ave, Los Angeles, CA 90036-2166
Tel (323) 655-6001 *Founded/Ownrshp* 2001
Sales NA *EMP* 46
SIC 6021 National commercial banks; National commercial banks
Pr: Barry W Uzel
**CFO:* Richard P Ritter
**Chf Cred:* G Scott Peterson
**Ex VP:* Timothy J Herles
Ex VP: Jon Matalon
VP: John JG Batiste
VP: Adrienne Caldwell
VP: Normand F Leduc
Dir IT: William Bowman
IT Man: David Ward

NCAR
See NATIONAL CENTER FOR ATMOSPHERIC RESEARCH

NCARB
See NATIONAL COUNCIL OF ARCHITECTURAL REGISTRATION BOARDS

D-U-N-S 77-998-6277
NCB ASSET MANAGEMENT LLC
20 N Michigan Ave Ste 400, Chicago, IL 60602-4828
Tel (312) 456-7000 *Founded/Ownrshp* 1988
Sales 12.5MM^E *EMP* 350^E
SIC 6531 Real estate agent, commercial; Real estate agent, commercial
Ch: Robert A Wislow
**V Ch:* Camille Julmy
**CFO:* Michael Brim
**Sr VP:* Dean Johnson
**Sr VP:* Cindy O'Drobinak
**Sr VP:* John Simon
**Sr VP:* William Vail

D-U-N-S 11-938-8937
NCB FSB
N C B
(*Suby of* N C B) ★
2011 Crystal Dr Ste 800, Arlington, VA 22202-3734
Tel (703) 302-8000 *Founded/Ownrshp* 2011
Sales NA *EMP* 248
SIC 6035 Savings institutions, federally chartered; Savings institutions, federally chartered
Pr: Charles Snyder
Treas: Mary Blanton
**VP:* Gloria Exum

D-U-N-S 96-726-3443
NCB MANAGEMENT SERVICES INC
1 Allied Dr Ste 1, Trevose, PA 19053-6945
Tel (215) 633-9900 *Founded/Ownrshp* 1994
Sales NA *EMP* 350^E
SIC 6162 8741 Mortgage bankers & correspondents; Management services; Mortgage bankers & correspondents; Management services
Ch Bd: Brett Silver
**CEO:* Marcelo A Aita
**CFO:* James Lasala
Ofcr: Daniel Venditti
**Ex VP:* Greg Paulo
**Sr VP:* Joe Kimsal
**Sr VP:* Paul Paleo
Sr VP: Paul Paleologus
Off Mgr: Hank McGarrigle
IT Man: Frank Rich
Sales Exec: Susan Richards

NCBA
See NATIONAL CATTLEMENS BEEF ASSOCIATION

NCC
See NATIONAL CHILDRENS CENTER INC

NCC
See NORTH COAST CONTAINER CORP

NCC
See NASSAU COMMUNITY COLLEGE

D-U-N-S 18-695-4244 IMP
NCC AUTOMATED SYSTEMS INC
255 Schoolhouse Rd Ste 2, Souderton, PA 18964-2430
Tel (215) 721-1900 *Founded/Ownrshp* 1986
Sales 41.3MM^E *EMP* 44
SIC 5084 3535 Industrial machinery & equipment; Conveyors & conveying equipment
Pr: Kevin J Mauger
VP: Les Patkos
Mtls Mgr: Robert Berry
Opers Mgr: Jason Link
Opers Mgr: Bob Winterer
Mktg Dir: Chris Round

D-U-N-S 82-816-9453
NCC GROUP INC
(*Suby of* NCC GROUP PLC)
123 Mission St Ste 1020, San Francisco, CA 94105-5126
Tel (415) 268-9300 *Founded/Ownrshp* 2005
Sales 35.6MM^E *EMP* 250
SIC 7379 Computer data escrow service
Pr: Rob Cotton
**Pr:* Craig Motta
**CFO:* Craig Foster
Dir IT: Tony Sanders
Mktg Mgr: Sangeeta Sastry

NCC MEDIA
See NATIONAL CABLE COMMUNICATIONS LLC

NCCI
See NATIONAL CREDITORS CONNECTION INC

D-U-N-S 06-023-0794
NCCI HOLDINGS INC
NATIO COUN ON COMP INSU
901 Peninsula Corp Cir, Boca Raton, FL 33487-1362
Tel (561) 893-1000 *Founded/Ownrshp* 1919
Sales NA *EMP* 950
SIC 6331 Workers' compensation insurance; Workers' compensation insurance
Pr: Stephen J Klingel
**CFO:* Alfredo Guerra
CFO: Alfredo Tguerra
**Treas:* Craig Ehrnst
Ofcr: Cheryl Budd
Ofcr: Michael B Spears
VP: Joanne Barbour
VP: Laura B Hall
CIO: Jimmy McMullan
CIO: Michael S Orourke
CIO: Ali A Subaihin
Board of Directors: David H Long, Susan Rivera

NCCRC
See NORTHERN CALIFORNIA CARPENTERS REGIONAL COUNCIL

NCDEQ
See NORTH CAROLINA DEPARTMENT OF ENVIRONMENTAL QUALITY

NCDI
See NC DYNAMICS INC

NCDOT
See NORTH CAROLINA DIVISION OF HIGHWAYS

NCE
See NORTH COAST ELECTRIC CO

NCE COMPUTER GROUP
See NATIONAL CUSTOMER ENGINEERING INC

NCEES
See NATIONAL COUNCIL OF EXAMINERS FOR ENGINEERING AND SURVEYING

NCEMC
See NORTH CAROLINA ELECTRIC MEMBERSHIP CORP

NCFE
See NORTH CENTRAL FARMERS ELEVATOR

NCFI
See BARNHARDT MANUFACTURING CO

D-U-N-S 00-346-8998 IMP/EXP
NCFI POLYURETHANES (NC)
(*Suby of* BARNHARDT MANUFACTURING CO) ★
1515 Carter St, Mount Airy, NC 27030-5721
Tel (336) 789-9161 *Founded/Ownrshp* 1964
Sales 85.0MM^E *EMP* 200
SIC 3086 Insulation or cushioning material, foamed plastic; Padding, foamed plastic; Insulation or cushioning material, foamed plastic; Padding, foamed plastic
Pr: Steve Riddle
Pr: Jeff Wilmoth
Dir Bus: Mitch Clifton
Mfg Dir: Tim Martin
Sls Mgr: Alan Blackmon
Sls Mgr: Doug Boyles

NCG CHICAGO
See NATIONAL CONTAINER GROUP LLC

NCH
See NEMOURS CHILDRENS HOSPITAL

D-U-N-S 00-896-3910 IMP/EXP
NCH CORP
CHEMSEARCH DIVISION
2727 Chemsearch Blvd, Irving, TX 75062-6454
Tel (972) 438-0211 *Founded/Ownrshp* 1919
Sales 1.1MMM^E *EMP* 8,500
Accts Deloitte & Touche Llp Dallas
SIC 2842 2899 3432 3548 3429 Specialty cleaning preparations; Sanitation preparations, disinfectants & deodorants; Water treating compounds; Fluxes: brazing, soldering, galvanizing & welding; Plumbing fixture fittings & trim; Welding & cutting apparatus & accessories; Electrodes, electric welding; Soldering equipment, except hand soldering irons; Metal fasteners; Specialty cleaning preparations; Sanitation preparations, disinfectants & deodorants; Water treating compounds; Fluxes: brazing, soldering, galvanizing & welding; Plumbing fixture fittings & trim; Welding & cutting apparatus & accessories; Electrodes, electric welding; Soldering equipment, except hand soldering irons; Metal fasteners
Pr: Irvin Levy
CFO: Iris Ho
**CFO:* Christopher T Sortwell
CFO: Jim Warnker
**Treas:* Irena Ki
Treas: Susan Sullivan
Bd of Dir: Marga Tubb
Ex VP: Don Carafiol
Ex VP: James R Fiedbeg
**Ex VP:* Levy John
Ex VP: John I Levy
Ex VP: Lester A Levy
Ex VP: Robert M Levy
VP: Garland Edgell
VP: Joe Farrier
**VP:* Donald L Jones
VP: Kevin Jones
VP: James Marshall
Exec: Lynda Aguayo
Dir Bus: Jason Edwards
Board of Directors: Mike Benton

D-U-N-S 36-240-7058
NCH CORP
2850 E Skyline Dr Ste 200, Tucson, AZ 85718-8014
Tel (520) 544-4000 *Founded/Ownrshp* 1988
Sales 22.5MM^E *EMP* 800
SIC 7231 Beauty shops; Beauty shops
Pr: Michael J Hanson
CFO: Cynthia Zezuto
**VP:* Randal G Dix

NCH DOWNTOWN NAPLES HOSPITAL
See NCH HEALTHCARE SYSTEM INC

NCH HEALTHCARE SYSTEM
See NAPLES COMMUNITY HOSPITAL INC

D-U-N-S 15-130-6057
NCH HEALTHCARE SYSTEM INC
NCH DOWNTOWN NAPLES HOSPITAL
350 7th St N, Naples, FL 34102-5754
Tel (239) 624-5000 *Founded/Ownrshp* 1983
Sales 381.1MM^E *EMP* 3,500^E
Accts Pricewaterhousecoopers Llp Fo
SIC 8062 General medical & surgical hospitals; General medical & surgical hospitals
Pr: Allan Weiss
V Ch: Mariann T Macdonald
COO: Gail Dolan
COO: Gail A Doln
Trst: Linda Flewelling
Trst: Melody Kappauf
Trst: Robert D Landon
Trst: Raymond F Pettit
Trst: Raymond E Rilly
Trst: Barbara Tellinghuisen
Trst: Howard Willner
Ofcr: Zachary Bostock
Ofcr: Kelly Daly
Exec: John McGirl
Dir Rad: Jim Bates

D-U-N-S 92-988-3036
NCH MANAGEMENT SYSTEMS INC
675 Placentia Ave Ste 300, Brea, CA 92821-6167
Tel (714) 680-4987 *Founded/Ownrshp* 2002
Sales 50.0MM *EMP* 75
SIC 8741 Management services; Management services
Pr: Joseph Perez
VP: Steven S Fichtelberg

D-U-N-S 93-321-0734
NCH MARKETING SERVICES INC
(*Suby of* VALASSIS COMMUNICATIONS INC) ★
155 N Pfingsten Rd # 200, Deerfield, IL 60015-4961
Tel (847) 317-9039 *Founded/Ownrshp* 2003
Sales 118.7MM^E *EMP* 3,300
SIC 7389 Coupon redemption service; Coupon redemption service
Pr: Brian Husselbee
COO: Wan Ling
**CFO:* Maria Rosselli
Ofcr: Pearl Fields
Sr VP: David G Johnson
**VP:* Javier Acosta
VP: Laura Czekala
**VP:* Maureen Greene
VP: Timothy Halfmann
**VP:* Michelle Carey Jones
VP: Neil McManus

NCHA
See NATIONAL CUTTING HORSE ASSOCIATION

NCHC
See NORTH CENTRAL HEALTH CARE

D-U-N-S 96-650-4594
NCHMD INC DBA SOUTHWEST FLORIDA HEMATOLOGY AND ONCOLOGY
681 4th Ave N, Naples, FL 34102-5729
Tel (239) 513-7630 *Founded/Ownrshp* 2011
Sales NA *EMP* 7^E
SIC 6035 Savings institutions, federally chartered; Savings institutions, federally chartered
Prin: Lori Smith
VP: Mary Felix

NCI
See NETWORK CABLING INFRASTRUCTURES INC

NCI
See NATIONWIDE CREDIT INC

D-U-N-S 13-023-4529 IMP
▲ NCI BUILDING SYSTEMS INC
10943 N Sam Huston Pkwy W, Houston, TX 77064-5758
Tel (281) 897-7788 *Founded/Ownrshp* 1984
Sales 1.5MMM *EMP* 4,556
Tkr Sym NCS *Exch* NYS
SIC 3448 3444 3442 1542 1541 7389 Prefabricated metal buildings; Prefabricated metal components; Metal roofing & roof drainage equipment; Rolling doors for industrial buildings or warehouses, metal; Nonresidential construction; Steel building construction; Drafting service, except temporary help; Prefabricated metal buildings; Prefabricated metal components; Metal roofing & roof drainage equipment; Rolling doors for industrial buildings or warehouses, metal; Nonresidential construction; Steel building construction; Drafting service, except temporary help
Ch Bd: Norman C Chambers
Pr: Don Riley
Pr: Bradley D Robeson
COO: William M Young
CFO: Mark E Johnson
Ex VP: Eric J Brown
Ex VP: Todd R Moore
VP: Anthony Bilow
VP: Charles W Dickinson
VP: Jeff Feaster
VP: Jime Garza
VP: Mark T Golladay
VP: Mark Golladay
VP: Dan Happel
VP: Todd Harbour
VP: Jerome Kelleher
VP: Chris Pettis
VP: Quintin Prior
VP: Dan Ronchetto
VP: Laura Santiago
VP: Fred Schubert
Board of Directors: Jonathan L Zrebiec, Kathleen J Affeldt, George L Ball, James G Berges, Matthew J Espe, Gary L Forbes, John J Holland, Lawrence J Kremer, George Martinez, Nathan K Sleeper

D-U-N-S 06-071-3047 EXP
■ NCI GROUP INC
M B C I
(*Suby of* NCI BUILDING SYSTEMS INC) ★
10943 N Sam Huston Pkwy W, Houston, TX 77064-5758
Tel (281) 897-7500 *Founded/Ownrshp* 1998
Sales 452.8MM^E *EMP* 2,364
SIC 3448 3446 Prefabricated metal buildings; Prefabricated metal components; Architectural metalwork; Prefabricated metal buildings; Prefabricated metal components; Architectural metalwork
CEO: Norman Chambers
**Ex VP:* Eric J Brown
**Ex VP:* Mark E Johnson
Ex VP: Todd R Moore
VP: Jason Dansby
VP: Quintin Prior
Exec: Renae Timmons
Dir Risk M: Chad Wieberg
Assoc Dir: Chris Brehm
Rgnl Mgr: Johnny Johnson
Rgnl Mgr: Robert Pawelek

D-U-N-S 19-531-3866
▲ NCI INC
11730 Plaza America Dr # 700, Reston, VA 20190-4764
Tel (703) 707-6900 *Founded/Ownrshp* 1989
Sales 317.0MM *EMP* 1,800^E
Accts Deloitte & Touche Llp Mclean
Tkr Sym NCIT *Exch* NGS
SIC 7373 8711 Computer integrated systems design; Engineering services; Computer integrated systems design; Engineering services
Ch Bd: Charles K Narang
**Pr:* Brian J Clark
Pr: Martin Mullican
COO: Marco F De Vito

CFO: Lucas J Narel
Ofcr: Mitzi Wilson
Sr VP: Christopher M Bishop
Sr VP: Michele R Cappello
Sr VP: Thomas Decot
Sr VP: J Greg Hanson
Sr VP: W Greg Henson
Sr VP: William Howard
Sr VP: John C Woloski
VP: Sean Bauer
VP: Joseph Dominguez
VP: Curt Geiger
VP: Dave Goodman
VP: Tim Henderson
VP: Margaret Jarrett
VP: Scott Royse
VP: Neil Sommerfield
Board of Directors: James P Allen, John E Lawler, Paul V Lombardi, Cindy Moran, Philip O Nolan, Austin J Yerks, Daniel R Young

D-U-N-S 62-086-4504
■ NCI INFORMATION SYSTEMS INC
(*Suby of* NCI INC) ★
11730 Plaza America Dr # 700, Reston, VA 20190-4764
Tel (703) 707-6900 *Founded/Ownrshp* 1989
Sales 242.0MM^E *EMP* 1,374^E
Accts Ernst & Young Llp Mclean Va
SIC 7373 Computer integrated systems design; Computer integrated systems design
CEO: Brian J Clark
**Ch Bd:* Charles K Narang
**Pr:* Terry W Glasgow
**CFO:* Judith L Bjornaas
CFO: Gerard Parker
Ofcr: Cody Smith
Ex VP: Amorette Jones
Sr VP: Tom McDermott
VP: Maureen Boyette
VP: Krista Castillo
VP: David Gardner
VP: Tim Henderson
VP: Carol Miller
VP: Sharyn Pensmith
Board of Directors: Stephen L Waechter

D-U-N-S 96-220-8450 IMP
NCI MFG INC
N C I
209 Lnnie E Crawford Blvd, Scottsboro, AL 35769-7408
Tel (256) 259-2105 *Founded/Ownrshp* 1996
Sales 41.5MM *EMP* 90
SIC 5531 3053 Automotive parts; Gaskets, packing & sealing devices; Plumbing, heating, air-conditioning contractors; Automotive parts; Gaskets, packing & sealing devices
Pr: Hitoshi Saito
Ql Cn Mgr: Theresa Brown

NCIA
See NATIONAL CENTER ON INSTITUTIONS AND ALTERNATIVES INC

NCIA/AUGUSTUS INSTITUTE
See NATIONAL CENTER ON INSTITUTIONS AND ALTERNATIVES INC

NCIC INMATE TELEPHONE SERVICES
See NETWORK COMMUNICATIONS INTERNATIONAL CORP

NCIRE
See NORTHERN CALIFORNIA INSTITUTE FOR RESEARCH AND EDUCATION INC

D-U-N-S 82-824-9073
■ NCL (BAHAMAS) LTD A BERMUDA CO
NORWEGIAN CRUISE LINE
(*Suby of* NCL CORP LTD) ★
7665 Corporate Center Dr, Miami, FL 33126-1201
Tel (305) 436-4000 *Founded/Ownrshp* 2004
Sales 91.1MM^E *EMP* 1,800
SIC 4729 Transportation ticket offices; Transportation ticket offices
CEO: Frank J Del Rio
**CFO:* Wendy Beck
**VP:* Daniel Farkas

D-U-N-S 17-539-2547
■ NCL CORP LTD
NORWEGIAN CRUISE LINES
(*Suby of* NORWEGIAN CRUISE LINE HOLDINGS LTD) ★
7665 Nw 19th St, Miami, FL 33126-1201
Tel (305) 436-4000 *Founded/Ownrshp* 2000
Sales 3.1MMM *EMP* 16,900
SIC 4481 Deep sea passenger transportation, except ferry; Deep sea passenger transportation, except ferry
Pr: Frank J Del Rio
Pr: Robert J Binder
Pr: Jason M Montague
Pr: Andrew Stuart
CFO: Wendy A Beck
Ex VP: Wendy Beck
Sr VP: Daniel S Farkas
Exec: Diana Hartman
Dir IT: Rudy Rosa
IT Man: Ric Farias
IT Man: Mark Keliher
Board of Directors: David M Abrams, Adam M Aron, John Chidsey, Kevin Crowe, Steve Martinez, Karl Peterson, Walter L Revell, F Robert Salerno, Robert Seminara

D-U-N-S 00-177-9560
NCL GRAPHIC SPECIALTIES INC (WI)
N29w22960 Marjean Ln, Waukesha, WI 53186-1016
Tel (262) 832-6120 *Founded/Ownrshp* 1965
Sales 30.0MM^E *EMP* 200
SIC 2759 Promotional printing; Promotional printing
Pr: Steven F Klopp
**Ch Bd:* Richard Mueller
VP: Russell Volmar
Ql Cn Mgr: Bill Vetter

D-U-N-S 07-628-4728
NCM ASSOCIATES INC
TRAVEL SOLUTIONS
4717 Grand Ave Ste 500, Kansas City, MO 64112-2210
Tel (913) 649-7830 *Founded/Ownrshp* 1988
Sales 40.8MM^E *EMP* 85
SIC 8748 Business consulting
Ch: Scott Norman
**CEO:* Paul Faletti
COO: Robert E Lee
Bd of Dir: Brian Faulkenberry
**VP:* Jill Hobbie
**VP:* Gerald Kuehl
**VP:* Fredrick O'Dwyer
Dir Bus: Kevin Cunningham
Mktg Dir: Skye Nguyen
Sls Dir: Veronica Guzman
Mktg Mgr: Alex Ball

D-U-N-S 01-298-5635
NCM GROUP HOLDINGS LLC
1700 7th Ave Ste 2300, Seattle, WA 98101-1387
Tel (714) 672-3500 *Founded/Ownrshp* 2006
Sales NA *EMP* 917^E
SIC 1795

D-U-N-S 80-741-7584
NCMC INC
1801 16th St, Greeley, CO 80631-5154
Tel (970) 350-6052 *Founded/Ownrshp* 1984
Sales 53.0MM *EMP* 1
Accts Eide Bailly Llp Fargo Nd
SIC 6519 8062 Real property lessors; General medical & surgical hospitals
CEO: Ken Schultz

NCMF
See AULTMAN NORTH CANTON MEDICAL GROUP

D-U-N-S 02-751-1406
NCMIC GROUP INC
14001 University Ave, Clive, IA 50325-8258
Tel (515) 313-4500 *Founded/Ownrshp* 1946
Sales 30.8MM^E *EMP* 186
SIC 7389 6321 Financial services; Accident & health insurance; Accident & health insurance carriers; Financial services; Accident & health insurance; Accident & health insurance carriers
Pr: Louis Sportelli
CFO: Gary Hoffman
**Treas:* Roger Schlueter
Chf Inves: David Baccile
**Ex VP:* Larry Rister
VP: Bruce Baeal
VP: Bruce Beal
VP: Barb Clark

NCO FINANCIAL SYSTEMS, INC.
See EGS FINANCIAL CARE INC

NCOMPASS INTERNATIONAL
See N COMPASS INTERNATIONAL INC

D-U-N-S 78-967-4574 IMP
NCOMPUTING INC
1100 La Avenida St Ste A, Mountain View, CA 94043-1453
Tel (408) 380-8400 *Founded/Ownrshp* 2005
Sales 23.3MM^E *EMP* 130
SIC 5734 Computer software & accessories
CEO: Young Song
**CEO:* Raj Dhingra
**CFO:* Bill Herrick
**Ofcr:* Raj Shah
Sr VP: Kim Niederman
Sr VP: Simon Pearce
VP: Jay Mellman
Dir IT: Vanderburg Susan
Sls Mgr: Ahmad Zia

NCP
See NATIONAL CONSUMER PANEL LLC

D-U-N-S 82-699-3011
NCP 2 LP
3060 Peachtree Rd Nw # 780, Atlanta, GA 30305-2234
Tel (404) 504-4080 *Founded/Ownrshp* 1997
Sales 107.7MM^E *EMP* 570
SIC 6211 Investment firm, general brokerage; Investment firm, general brokerage
Pt: John Richardson
Pt: Lawrence E Mock
Pt: David Panton

D-U-N-S 01-910-8872
NCP SOLUTIONS LLC
(*Suby of* HARLAND CLARKE CORP) ★
5200 E Lake Blvd, Birmingham, AL 35217-3546
Tel (205) 849-5200 *Founded/Ownrshp* 2013
Sales 97.2MM^E *EMP* 400
SIC 7374 Data processing service; Data verification service; Data processing service; Data verification service
Pr: Steven D Greenwalt
**CFO:* Russell McEwen
Treas: Ivanka Zovko
**Sr VP:* Tim Cooper
**Sr VP:* Dave Erwin
**Sr VP:* Kris Ness
**VP:* Jeff Booker
VP: Laura Cain
**VP:* Forrest Cook
**VP:* Mark Frechette
VP: Gerard Johnson
VP: Laura Wix

NCPA
See NATIONAL COMMUNITY PHARMACISTS ASSOCIATION

NCPA
See NORTHERN CALIFORNIA POWER AGENCY

NCQA
See NATIONAL COMMITTEE FOR QUALITY ASSURANCE

D-U-N-S 00-131-6090 IMP
▲ NCR CORP
3097 Satellite Blvd # 100, Duluth, GA 30096-1293
Tel (937) 445-5000 *Founded/Ownrshp* 1884
Sales 6.5MMM *EMP* 30,200
Accts Pricewaterhousecoopers Llp A
Tkr Sym NCR *Exch* NYS
SIC 3575 3578 7379 7374 7371 Computer terminals; Point-of-sale devices; Computer related maintenance services; Data processing & preparation; Custom computer programming services; Software programming applications; Computer terminals; Point-of-sale devices; Computer related maintenance services; Data processing & preparation; Custom computer programming services; Software programming applications
Ch Bd: William R Nuti
Pr: Michael Bayer
CFO: Robert P Fishman
Chf Mktg O: Ken Partyka
Ofcr: Laur Nyquist
Ex VP: John G Bruno
Ex VP: Rick Marquardt
Sr VP: Michael B Bayer
Sr VP: Malcolm Collins
Sr VP: Patrick G Cronin
Sr VP: Sean Fernandez
Sr VP: A Gagliardi
Sr VP: Scott Kingsfield
Sr VP: Mike Koehler
Sr VP: Andrea L Ledford
Sr VP: Michael Olaughlin
Sr VP: Lee Schram
Sr VP: Mohsen Sohi
Exec: Chris Armitage
Exec: Jeffrey Lovett
Exec: Renato Manongdo
Board of Directors: Edward P Boykin, Richard L Clemmer, Gary Daichendt, Robert P Derodes, Kurt P Kuehn, Linda Fayne Levinson, Deanna W Oppenheimer

D-U-N-S 96-629-6527
■ NCR GOVERNMENT SYSTEMS LLC
(*Suby of* NCR CORP) ★
20370 Seneca Meadows Pkwy, Germantown, MD 20876-7004
Tel (301) 820-6500 *Founded/Ownrshp* 1996
Sales 42.1MM^E *EMP* 250
SIC 8748 7371 7372 Business consulting; Custom computer programming services; Prepackaged software; Business consulting; Custom computer programming services; Prepackaged software
COO: Carl Galloway
Treas: Quinn Coburn
Ofcr: Julie Saylor
VP: Bob Ciminera
VP: Ruth Fornell
VP: Nelson Gomez
VP: Mark Oswald
Exec: Jeff Ball
Exec: Rick Bigler
Exec: Janis Blauel
Exec: Lou Desantes
Exec: Terry Eberhardt
Exec: Neill Harris
Exec: Keith Hunter
Exec: James Hutchins
Exec: Mario Mosesso
Exec: Stephen Murphy
Exec: Jaivinder Singh

NCREN
See MCNC

NCRI
See NATIONAL CATASTROPHE RESTORATION INC

D-U-N-S 09-262-9427
NCS HEALTHCARE INC
3201 Entp Pkwy Ste 220, Cleveland, OH 44122
Tel (216) 514-3350 *Founded/Ownrshp* 2003
Sales NA *EMP* 2,640
SIC 5122 8093 8049 8082 8742 5912

D-U-N-S 05-005-2943
■ NCS HEALTHCARE OF KENTUCKY INC (OH)
VANGARD LABS
(*Suby of* OMNICARE INC) ★
120 Carroll Knicely Dr, Glasgow, KY 42141-7224
Tel (270) 651-6188 *Founded/Ownrshp* 1966, 1997
Sales 21.0MM^E *EMP* 100
SIC 5912 Drug stores & proprietary stores
Pr: Kathy Jones
**Treas:* Donna M Lecky
**Prin:* James Cialdini

D-U-N-S 84-160-1565
■ NCS HEALTHCARE OF OHIO LLC
(*Suby of* NEIGHBORCARE PHARMACY SERVICES INC) ★
201 E 4th St Ste 900, Cincinnati, OH 45202-4160
Tel (513) 719-2600 *Founded/Ownrshp* 2005
Sales 29.0MM^E *EMP* 239^E
SIC 5122 Drugs, proprietaries & sundries

D-U-N-S 11-505-1877
NCS MULTISTAGE LLC
19450 State Highway 249 # 200, Houston, TX 77070-1553
Tel (281) 453-2222 *Founded/Ownrshp* 2014
Sales 200.0MM *EMP* 200
SIC 5084 Industrial supplies; Machine tools & metalworking machinery; Machine tools & metalworking machinery
CEO: Robert Nipper
COO: Marty Stromquist
**COO:* Tim Willems
**CFO:* Wade Bitter
VP: Joe Degeare
**VP:* John Ravensberger
**VP:* Wes Stephens
Dist Mgr: Eric Duckett
Dist Mgr: Anthony Rosten
**CTO:* Don Getzlaf
Mktg Mgr: Don Francis

D-U-N-S 04-385-6723 IMP/EXP
NCS PEARSON INC
(*Suby of* PEARSON EDUCATION INC) ★
5601 Green Valley Dr # 220, Minneapolis, MN 55437-1187
Tel (952) 681-3000 *Founded/Ownrshp* 2000
Sales 1.1MMM^E *EMP* 6,981
SIC 3577 7372 7374 8748 7379 Optical scanning devices; Application computer software; Tabulating service; Optical scanning data service; Testing service, educational or personnel; Computer related maintenance services; Optical scanning devices; Application computer software; Tabulating service; Optical scanning data service; Testing service, educational or personnel; Computer related maintenance services
CEO: John Fallon
**COO:* Eileen Youds
**CFO:* Robin Freestone
**Ch:* Glen Moreno
VP: Clive Hay-Smith
VP: Charles Johnston
Counsel: Mary Lany

D-U-N-S 96-100-3720 IMP
NCS TECHNOLOGIES INC
N C S
7669 Limestone Dr Ste 130, Gainesville, VA 20155-4038
Tel (703) 743-8500 *Founded/Ownrshp* 1996
Sales 49.8MM^E *EMP* 108^E
SIC 3571 7373 Electronic computers; Computer integrated systems design; Electronic computers; Computer integrated systems design
Pr: An Van Nguyen
Ex VP: Mark Christopher
VP: Dewayne Adams
**VP:* John Eldred
VP: Joe Guest
VP: Mike Maggio
Dir IT: Sunitha Gardella
Mfg Dir: Dale Cross
Sales Asso: Chad Norris
Board of Directors: Mark Christopher, an Nguyen

NCSBN
See NATIONAL COUNCIL OF STATE BOARDS OF NURSING INC

NCSC
See NATIONAL COOPERATIVE SERVICES CORP

NCSD
See NOVI COMMUNITY SCHOOL DISTRICT

NCSH
See NORTH CAROLINA SPECIALTY HOSPITAL LLC

NCSL
See NATIONAL CONFERENCE OF STATE LEGISLATURES

NCSRCC
See NORTH CENTRAL STATE REGIONAL COUNCIL

NCSU FOUNDATION
See NORTH CAROLINA STATE UNIVERSITY FOUNDATION

NCTC
See NORTH CENTRAL TELEPHONE COOPERATIVE CORP

NCTCOG
See NORTH CENTRAL TEXAS COUNCIL OF GOVERNMENTS FOUNDATION INC

NCTI
See JX NIPPON CHEMICAL TEXAS INC

NCTI
See CORPORATE TRAINING HOLDINGS INC

NCUA
See NATIONAL CREDIT UNION ADMINISTRATION

D-U-N-S 07-839-5803
ND INDUSTRIES INC
ND TECHNOLOGIES
1000 N Crooks Rd, Clawson, MI 48017-1003
Tel (248) 288-0000 *Founded/Ownrshp* 1992
Sales 98.5MM^E *EMP* 400
SIC 3452 5072 3479 2891 2851 Bolts, nuts, rivets & washers; Coating of metals & formed products; Paints & allied products; Adhesives & sealants; Miscellaneous fasteners; Bolts, nuts, rivets & washers; Miscellaneous fasteners; Coating of metals & formed products; Adhesives & sealants; Paints & allied products
Pr: Richard Wallace
COO: Sean Costin
**CFO:* Bonnie M Spanke
**VP:* Michael Garofalo
**Prin:* Tracy Haase
Dir IT: Joe Gutowstk
Dir IT: Chad Nordstrom
QC Dir: James Barr
Ql Cn Mgr: Michael Fanfair
Ql Cn Mgr: Samuel Milo
Ql Cn Mgr: Donna Timms

D-U-N-S 15-242-8103
ND PROPERTIES INC
(*Suby of* TEACHERS INSURANCE AND ANNUITY ASSOCIATION OF AMERICA) ★
730 3rd Ave Ste 15485, New York, NY 10017-3206
Tel (800) 842-2252 *Founded/Ownrshp* 1990
Sales 427.5MM *EMP* 1
Accts Agh Llc Atlanta Georgia
SIC 6512 Commercial & industrial building operation; Commercial & industrial building operation
Prin: Mark L Serlen
Dir Surg: Robert Redican

ND TECHNOLOGIES
See ND INDUSTRIES INC

NDA
See NATIONAL DISTRIBUTION ALLIANCE LLC

D-U-N-S 10-582-0484
NDA SERVICES CORP
ADRIEL AUTO
Carr 2 Km 23 Hm 0 St Ca, Dorado, PR 00646
Tel (787) 626-3838 *Founded/Ownrshp* 1993
Sales 27.4MM^E *EMP* 100
SIC 5511 Automobiles, new & used; Automobiles, new & used
Pr: Nicolas Amaro

D-U-N-S 12-122-4570
■ **NDC HEALTH INFORMATION SERVICES**
(*Suby of* N D C) ★
7120 S Lewis Ave Ste 200, Tulsa, OK 74136-5413
Tel (918) 496-2451 *Founded/Ownrshp* 1996
Sales 11.1MM^E *EMP* 333
SIC 8741 Financial management for business; Office management; Administrative management; Financial management for business; Office management; Administrative management
Sr VP: Chuck Miller
**VP:* Paul Hoyt
**VP:* Jeff Jansen
Dir Surg: Jay H Burgess
Dir IT: Ron Catlin

D-U-N-S 04-553-2934 IMP
NDC INFRARED ENGINEERING INC
NDC TECHNOLOGIES
(*Suby of* SPECTRIS INC) ★
5314 Irwindale Ave, Irwindale, CA 91706-2086
Tel (626) 960-3300 *Founded/Ownrshp* 1997
Sales 55.7MM^E *EMP* 300
SIC 3823

NDC MEDICAL CENTER
See SENTARA MEDICAL GROUP

NDC TECHNOLOGIES
See NDC INFRARED ENGINEERING INC

D-U-N-S 04-297-8528
■ **NDCHEALTH CORP**
N D C
(*Suby of* MCKESSON TECHNOLOGIES INC) ★
1564 Northeast Expy Ne, Brookhaven, GA 30329-2071
Tel (404) 728-2000 *Founded/Ownrshp* 1967, 2006
Sales 68.1MM^E *EMP* 1,100
SIC 7374 8742 Data processing service; Data verification service; Industry specialist consultants; Data processing service; Data verification service; Industry specialist consultants
Pr: Philip M Pead
COO: Thomas M Dunn
CFO: Gordon Campbell
**CFO:* Chris E Perkins
**Sr VP:* Philip J Jordan
**Sr VP:* Paul J Quiner
VP: Art Keegan
VP: David Shenk
Dir: Natasha Brathwaite
Genl Mgr: William C McCahan
Snr Ntwrk: Scott Lokey

NDCS
See NEBRASKA DEPARTMENT OF CORRECTIONAL SERVICES

NDF
See NEWPARK DRILLING FLUIDS LLC

NDGA
See BANDAI NAMCO ENTERTAINMENT AMERICA INC

D-U-N-S 13-108-5896
NDI ENGINEERING CO
100 Grove Rd, West Deptford, NJ 08086-2259
Tel (856) 848-0033 *Founded/Ownrshp* 1990
Sales 28.1MM^E *EMP* 100
SIC 8711 Engineering services; Engineering services
CEO: Francis M Walton
**Prin:* F Clark Walton
Prgrm Mgr: William Buonaccorsi
Prgrm Mgr: Carl Eith
Prgrm Mgr: Arlene Korn
Prgrm Mgr: Harry Maul

D-U-N-S 01-666-3544 IMP
NDIANA BEVERAGE INC
2850 Barley Rd, Valparaiso, IN 46383-8024
Tel (219) 464-2337 *Founded/Ownrshp* 1939, 1963
Sales 41.9MM^E *EMP* 145
SIC 5181 5149 Beer & other fermented malt liquors; Soft drinks; Mineral or spring water bottling; Beer & other fermented malt liquors; Soft drinks; Mineral or spring water bottling
Pr: Bruce Leetz
**VP:* Judy Leetz

NDOT
See NEVADA DEPARTMENT OF TRANSPORTATION

D-U-N-S 79-739-1034
■ **NDS AMERICAS INC**
(*Suby of* NDS GROUP LTD)
3500 Hyland Ave, Costa Mesa, CA 92626-1469
Tel (714) 434-2100 *Founded/Ownrshp* 1997
Sales 47.2MM^E *EMP* 190
SIC 4841 Cable & other pay television services; Cable & other pay television services
Pr: Abe Peled
VP: Steve Hastie
VP: Michael Ick
VP: Edward Landsberg
VP: Peter Lynskey
**VP:* Dov Rubin
Dir IT: Mary Bishop
Dir IT: Konstantin Wil
IT Man: Chad Stevenson
Prd Mgr: T L Horton

D-U-N-S 82-748-3814
NDS HOLDINGS LP
3811 West Chester Pike, Newtown Square, PA 19073-2323
Tel (610) 408-0500 *Founded/Ownrshp* 2000
Sales 28.6MM^E *EMP* 501
SIC 3089 Plastic hardware & building products; Plastic hardware & building products; Fittings for pipe, plastic
CFO: Mike Bradey

D-U-N-S 95-969-1940 IMP/EXP
■ **NDS SURGICAL IMAGING LLC**
(*Suby of* GSI GROUP INC) ★
5750 Hellyer Ave, San Jose, CA 95138-1000
Tel (408) 776-0085 *Founded/Ownrshp* 2013
Sales 55.3MM^E *EMP* 215^E
Accts Deloitte & Touche Llp San Jos
SIC 5047 Patient monitoring equipment; Patient monitoring equipment
COO: Jeff Zhou
Pr: Rok Sribar
**CFO:* Sam Brown
CFO: Deborah Young
Bd of Dir: Katia Bejan
Sr VP: Karim Khadr
VP: Rajesh Bhakta
VP: Kees Poot
VP: Daniel Webster
Dir: Ken Compton
Snr Sftwr: Gary Duggan

NDSCS
See NORTH DAKOTA STATE COLLEGE OF SCIENCE

NDSU DEVELOPMENT FOUNDATION
See NORTH DAKOTA STATE UNIVERSITY ALUMNI ASSOCIATION INC

NDTC
See NORTH DAKOTA TELEPHONE CO

NDTI
See NEW DIRECTIONS TECHNOLOGIES INC

NDU
See NATIONAL DEFENSE UNIVERSITY

D-U-N-S 07-392-1897
NE COLORADO CELLULAR INC
VIAERO WIRELESS
1224 W Platte Ave, Fort Morgan, CO 80701-2949
Tel (970) 768-0000 *Founded/Ownrshp* 1991
Sales 313.9MM^E *EMP* 370^E
SIC 4812 Cellular telephone services; Cellular telephone services
Pr: Frank Dirico
VP: Jeff Brown
VP: Stephen Hatfield
Dist Mgr: Jorge Carrasco
Store Mgr: Kristy Beegle
Store Mgr: Reuben Heikkinen
Store Mgr: Niki Songer
Opers Mgr: Dan Meininger
Sls Dir: Oliver Lei
Genl Couns: Eric Preston

D-U-N-S 62-343-1376
NE CONSTRUCTION LLP
420 Southfork Dr, Lewisville, TX 75057-3081
Tel (972) 219-5900 *Founded/Ownrshp* 1980
Sales 24.4MM^E *EMP* 39
SIC 1522 1542 Residential construction; Nonresidential construction
Pr: Charlie M Nicholas
VP: Andre Nicholas
Software D: Ken Lokey

D-U-N-S 15-980-6079
NE FOODS INC
1640 Freeport Rd, North East, PA 16428-1963
Tel (814) 725-4835 *Founded/Ownrshp* 2003
Sales 150.8MM^E *EMP* 570^E
SIC 2038 Frozen specialties; Pizza, frozen
Pr: Christopher R Miller
Sr VP: Richard Steele

NE KIDS
See NEW ENERGY INC

D-U-N-S 79-933-3489
NE LIQUIDATING INC
(*Suby of* CHAMPION ENTERPRISES HOLDINGS LLC) ★
451 Southern Ave, Strattanville, PA 16258
Tel (814) 764-5581 *Founded/Ownrshp* 2010
Sales 22.1MM^E *EMP* 280
SIC 2452 Modular homes, prefabricated, wood; Modular homes, prefabricated, wood
Pr: Elliot J Fabri
**Sec:* Larry L Kifer

D-U-N-S 00-103-2358
NE MEDIA GROUP INC (MA)
135 Wlliam T Mrrssey Blvd, Boston, MA 02125-3310
Tel (617) 929-2000 *Founded/Ownrshp* 1989, 2013
Sales 668.7MM^E *EMP* 2,300
SIC 2711 Newspapers, publishing & printing; Newspapers, publishing & printing
CEO: Michael J Sheehan
**Pr:* Christopher Mayer
**Pr:* Kenneth Arichieri
**Treas:* Laurena L Emhoff
**Treas:* Christopher Pircio
**VP:* R Anthony Benten
Exec: J P Giuggio
Div Mgr: Kathryn Colafemina
Dir IT: Dan Bunker
Netwrk Eng: Ron Briggs
Opers Mgr: Frank Foley

D-U-N-S 85-854-7714
■ **NE MOVES MORTGAGE LLC**
(*Suby of* PHH HOME LOANS ETRAFFICERS) ★
52 2nd Ave Ste 3, Waltham, MA 02451-1129
Tel (781) 863-8585 *Founded/Ownrshp* 2007
Sales NA *EMP* 140^E
SIC 6162 Mortgage bankers & correspondents; Mortgage bankers & correspondents
Pr: Gary Teixeira
CFO: Cindy Vitale
Ofcr: Daniel Mullin
Sr VP: Steve Messeck
VP: Clark Andrews
VP: Scott Dana
VP: Rick Harrington
VP: Adam Moore
VP: Rick Renna

NEA
See NEW ENTERPRISE ASSOCIATES INC

D-U-N-S 96-487-1730
NEA - ALASKA HEALTH PLAN TRUST FUND
4003 Iowa Dr, Anchorage, AK 99517-2539
Tel (907) 274-7526 *Founded/Ownrshp* 2010
Sales 117.5MM *EMP* 2^E
Accts Hemming Morse San Frandisco
SIC 8099 Health & allied services; Health & allied services
Prin: Teri Burke

D-U-N-S 02-754-0607
NEA BAPTIST CLINIC
3024 Red Wolf Blvd, Jonesboro, AR 72401-7415
Tel (870) 972-7000 *Founded/Ownrshp* 2009
Sales 102.9MM *EMP* 91^E
SIC 8011 Medical centers; Medical centers
CEO: Brad Parsons
COO: Kara Cooper
**CFO:* Kyle Sanders
Doctor: Gregory Lewis

NEA CLINIC
See NORTHEAST ARKANSAS MANAGEMENT CO LLC

D-U-N-S 79-503-9098
NEACE & ASSOCIATES INSURANCE AGENCY OF OHIO INC
NEACE LUKENS
4000 Smith Rd Ste 400, Cincinnati, OH 45209-1967
Tel (513) 333-0700 *Founded/Ownrshp* 1991
Sales NA *EMP* 57
SIC 6411 Insurance agents
Pr: Joe Lukens
**CEO:* John Neace
Ex VP: Herb Kuppin
Sr VP: Mark Hamilton
VP: Teresa Faulkner
VP: Janice Freytag
**VP:* Steve Wilken
Mng Dir: Wayne Willis
Pr Mgr: Larry Lynn

NEACE LUKENS
See ASSURED NL INSURANCE AGENCY INC

NEACE LUKENS
See NEACE & ASSOCIATES INSURANCE AGENCY OF OHIO INC

NEACE, MUSSELMAN & MAYFIELD
See NL OF KY INC

NEAD ELECTRIC
See NEAD ORGANIZATION INC

D-U-N-S 36-230-6151
NEAD ELECTRIC INC
(*Suby of* NEAD ELECTRIC) ★
187 E Union Ave, East Rutherford, NJ 07073-2123
Tel (201) 460-5200 *Founded/Ownrshp* 1987
Sales 56.7MM *EMP* 200
Accts Saxbst Llp Clifton New Jerse
SIC 1731 General electrical contractor; General electrical contractor
CEO: Robert Marziotto
**COO:* Robert J Marziotto
**CFO:* Joseph Gusera
VP: Ted Tzoulis
Snr Mgr: Maria Cucalon

D-U-N-S 85-841-2497
NEAD ORGANIZATION INC
NEAD ELECTRIC
187 E Union Ave, East Rutherford, NJ 07073-2123
Tel (201) 460-5200 *Founded/Ownrshp* 1993
Sales 59.9MM^E *EMP* 550
Accts Grassi & Co
SIC 1731 Electrical work; Communications specialization; Electrical work; Communications specialization
Co-Pr: Robert Marziotto
**Co-Pr:* Dorothy Marziotto
Snr PM: Marco Totaro

D-U-N-S 11-858-8649
NEAL ELECTRIC CORP
(*Suby of* MERUELO ENTERPRISES INC) ★
13250 Kirkham Way, Poway, CA 92064-7115
Tel (858) 513-2525 *Founded/Ownrshp* 2008
Sales 55.4MM^E *EMP* 300
SIC 1731 General electrical contractor; General electrical contractor
Pr: Daniel Zupp
Pr: Terry Johnson
**Treas:* Alex Meruelo
**VP:* Luis Armona
**VP:* Lance Neal
**VP:* Dennis Ramsey
**VP:* Jeremy Roos
**VP:* Casimier Wesolowski
**VP:* Scott Williams
IT Man: Paula Menard
Sfty Dirs: Todd Zalkan

D-U-N-S 15-453-3814
NEAL GERBER & EISENBERG LLP
2 N La Salle St Ste 1700, Chicago, IL 60602-4000
Tel (312) 269-8000 *Founded/Ownrshp* 1986
Sales 83.8MM^E *EMP* 400
SIC 8111 General practice law office; General practice law office
Pt: Jerry Biederman
Pt: Marshall E Eisenberg
Pt: Phil C Neal
Pr: Ruth Adams
Pr: Anita Cuvala
Pr: Sharon Hensley
Pr: Teresa Kirby
Pr: Lily Martinez
COO: Sonia Menon
Chf Mktg O: Angela Elbert
Chf Mktg O: Lee J Eulgen
Exec: Kader Gacem

D-U-N-S 02-704-7463
NEAL INC
ONE-STOP FOOD STORES
1330 Gembler Rd, San Antonio, TX 78219-3245
Tel (210) 337-8490 *Founded/Ownrshp* 1967
Sales 22.1MM^E *EMP* 65
SIC 5541 5411 Filling stations, gasoline; Convenience stores
Ch Bd: H Doak Neal Sr
**Pr:* H D Neal Jr
**VP:* Loretta Neal

NEAL MAST & SONS GREENHOUSE
See NEAL MAST AND SON INC

D-U-N-S 08-887-1181 IMP
NEAL MAST AND SON INC
NEAL MAST & SONS GREENHOUSE
1780 4 Mile Rd Nw, Grand Rapids, MI 49544-9702
Tel (616) 784-3323 *Founded/Ownrshp* 1985
Sales 101.1MM^E *EMP* 165
SIC 5193 Flowers & nursery stock; Flowers & nursery stock
Owner: James Mast
**Owner:* James Raterink

D-U-N-S 79-547-0079
NEAL MERCHANT ENTERPRISES INC
BATTLEFIELD FORD MERCURY
10463 James Monroe Hwy, Culpeper, VA 22701-8028
Tel (540) 547-3673 *Founded/Ownrshp* 2000
Sales 20.9MM^E *EMP* 50
SIC 5511 Automobiles, new & used; Trucks, tractors & trailers: new & used
Pr: Steve Fay

NEAL TIRE & AUTO SERVICE
See BEN TIRE DISTRIBUTORS LTD

D-U-N-S 02-563-5483
NEALEYS FOODS INC
90018 W Fulton St, Chicago, IL 60607
Tel (312) 243-2141 *Founded/Ownrshp* 1989
Sales 32.1MM^E *EMP* 35
SIC 5147 5144 Meats, fresh; Poultry: live, dressed or frozen (unpackaged)
Pr: Douglas A Nealey

D-U-N-S 17-932-8117
NEANY INC
44010 Commerce Ave Ste A, Hollywood, MD 20636-3117
Tel (301) 373-3017 *Founded/Ownrshp* 1994
Sales 36.6MM^E *EMP* 250
SIC 3812 Electronic field detection apparatus (aeronautical); Electronic field detection apparatus (aeronautical)
CEO: Steven Steptoe
**COO:* Johnnie D Taylor Jr
VP: Darcella Lowe

D-U-N-S 08-879-5091 IMP
NEAPCO COMPONENTS LLC
(*Suby of* NEAPCO HOLDINGS LLC) ★
740 Queen St, Pottstown, PA 19464-6008
Tel (610) 323-6000 *Founded/Ownrshp* 2006
Sales 420.9MM^E *EMP* 2,200
SIC 3714 3568 Transmission housings or parts, motor vehicle; Motor vehicle transmissions, drive assemblies & parts; Power transmission equipment; Transmission housings or parts, motor vehicle; Motor vehicle transmissions, drive assemblies & parts; Power transmission equipment
CEO: Kenneth L Hopkins
Pr: Keith Sanford
COO: Gerald Coster
VP: Chris Espinoza

D-U-N-S 80-961-3990 IMP
NEAPCO DRIVELINES LLC
(*Suby of* NEAPCO HOLDINGS LLC) ★
6735 Haggerty Rd, Belleville, MI 48111-5271
Tel (734) 447-1300 *Founded/Ownrshp* 2007
Sales 135.7MM^E *EMP* 350
SIC 3714 Transmission housings or parts, motor vehicle; Motor vehicle transmissions, drive assemblies & parts; Transmission housings or parts, motor vehicle; Motor vehicle transmissions, drive assemblies & parts
CEO: Kenneth L Hopkins
Pr: Robert W Hawkey
COO: J Robert Mangini
CFO: Patrick W Flanagan

D-U-N-S 96-832-9347
NEAPCO HOLDINGS LLC
6735 Haggerty Rd, Belleville, MI 48111-5271
Tel (734) 447-1380 *Founded/Ownrshp* 2010
Sales 556.6MM^E *EMP* 2,530
SIC 3714 3568 Transmission housings or parts, motor vehicle; Power transmission equipment; Transmission housings or parts, motor vehicle; Power transmission equipment; Investment holding companies, except banks
CEO: Kenneth Hopkins
COO: Gerald Coster
CFO: Gregory Anderson
VP: Arvind Srinivasan
Genl Mgr: Darwish Alami

NEAR NORTH INSURANCE BROKERAGE
See NEAR NORTH NATIONAL GROUP INC

D-U-N-S 01-842-2670
NEAR NORTH NATIONAL GROUP INC
NEAR NORTH INSURANCE BROKERAGE
875 N Michigan Ave # 3100, Chicago, IL 60611-1962
Tel (312) 867-0064 *Founded/Ownrshp* 1991
Sales NA *EMP* 739^E
SIC 6411 Insurance agents; Insurance agents
Pr: William Bartholomay
**COO:* John Harney
**CFO:* Maggie Mastensen
**Ch:* Fred Foreman
VP: Ingrid Naudzius
**VP:* Elizabeth O Simer
Mng Dir: Duncan Ashurst
Mktg Dir: Renee Formell

D-U-N-S 00-496-7717
NEAR-CAL CORP
512 Chaney St, Lake Elsinore, CA 92530-2747
Tel (951) 245-5400 *Founded/Ownrshp* 1964
Sales 23.0MM[E] *EMP* 23
Accts Anthony & Associates Brea Ca
SIC 1542 1541 Commercial & office building, new construction; Factory construction
Ch Bd: Carl J Johnson
**Treas:* Harold R Johnson
**VP:* Dwight Johnson

NEARBY EGGS
See HILLANDALE FARMS EAST INC

D-U-N-S 05-435-4839
NEARPOD INC
1062 Nw 1st Ct, Hallandale Beach, FL 33009-3905
Tel (305) 677-5030 *Founded/Ownrshp* 2012
Sales 22.2MM[E] *EMP* 530
SIC 7371 7372 Computer software development & applications; Educational computer software; Computer software development & applications; Educational computer software
CEO: Felipe Sommer
Sls Dir: Ella Sherman
Manager: Laura Gallagher

D-U-N-S 60-207-0810 IMP
NEASE CO LLC
(*Suby of* WP MANNHEIM GMBH)
4480 Lake Forest Dr # 312, Blue Ash, OH 45242-3753
Tel (513) 587-2800 *Founded/Ownrshp* 2005
Sales 20.8MM[E] *EMP* 70
SIC 2843 Surface active agents
Pr: Dave Iden
COO: Frank Canepa

D-U-N-S 14-797-6919 IMP/EXP
NEAT CO INC
NEATRECEIPTS
1601 Market St Fl 35, Philadelphia, PA 19103-2342
Tel (215) 382-4283 *Founded/Ownrshp* 2002
Sales 34.2MM[E] *EMP* 150
SIC 7371 7372 Computer software development; Prepackaged software; Computer software development; Prepackaged software
CEO: Jim Foster
Ch Bd: Les Spero
COO: Rafi Spero
CFO: Brian Doran
CFO: Dan Doyle
Chf Mktg O: Kevin Garton
Ex VP: Lindsay Hurst
VP: Chris Barbier
VP: Michael Crincoli
QA Dir: Thomas Goodman
Mktg Mgr: Melissa Benedetto

NEATLYSMART
See UNITED STATES PLASTIC CORP

D-U-N-S 11-623-6597 IMP
NEATON AUTO PRODUCTS MANUFACTURING INC
(*Suby of* NIHON PLAST CO.,LTD.)
975 S Franklin St, Eaton, OH 45320-9400
Tel (937) 456-7103 *Founded/Ownrshp* 1984
Sales 94.5MM[E] *EMP* 427[E]
SIC 3714 Motor vehicle parts & accessories; Steering mechanisms, motor vehicle
Pr: Naoki Horikawa
**Ex VP:* David Gulling
VP: Tetsuji-Terry Endo
VP: Waturo Suto
**VP:* Kazuhiro Watanabe
VP: Wade Wataru
Dir Lab: William Schommer
Dir IT: Rodney Reynolds
Dir IT: Tim Taulbee
IT Man: John Norton
Info Man: Kay Volpe

D-U-N-S 12-599-9354 IMP
NEATON ROME INC
(*Suby of* NEATON AUTO PRODUCTS MANUFACTURING INC) ★
1634 Technology Pkwy Nw, Rome, GA 30165-1268
Tel (706) 368-9901 *Founded/Ownrshp* 2000
Sales 64.3MM[E] *EMP* 150
SIC 5531 Automotive parts; Automotive parts
CEO: Masanori Toyotake
**CFO:* Toshihiro Hayashida
Ql Cn Mgr: Mike Cole
Ql Cn Mgr: Yoshimasa Pakahashi

NEATRECEIPTS
See NEAT CO INC

D-U-N-S 78-657-5147
NEB CORP
130 S Main St, Fond Du Lac, WI 54935-4210
Tel (920) 921-7700 *Founded/Ownrshp* 1974
Sales NA *EMP* 315[E]
SIC 6029 Commercial banks; Commercial banks
Pr: Peter E Stone

NEBCO
See AMWINS GROUP BENEFITS INC

D-U-N-S 00-725-9179
NEBCO INC (NE)
REIMERS-KAUFMAN CONCRETE PDTS
1815 Y St, Lincoln, NE 68508-1233
Tel (402) 434-1212 *Founded/Ownrshp* 1922, 1949
Sales 150.0MM[E] *EMP* 1,000
SIC 5999 3273 3272 3271 1442 4013 Concrete products, pre-cast; Ready-mixed concrete; Concrete products, precast; Concrete block & brick; Construction sand & gravel; Railroad switching; Concrete products, pre-cast; Ready-mixed concrete; Concrete products, precast; Concrete block & brick; Construction sand & gravel; Railroad switching
Pr: James P Abel
Pr: Robert Nordquist
Treas: Charles D Meyer
VP: Dale Kisling
VP: J Ross Mc Cown
VP: Bob Miller
VP: Robert E Miller
IT Man: Trent Heiser
Sfty Mgr: Dan Brock
Opers Mgr: Terry Landen
Plnt Mgr: Mike Mueller

NEBF
See NATIONAL ELECTRICAL BENEFIT FUND

D-U-N-S 07-300-3360
NEBO SCHOOL DISTRICT
350 S Main St, Spanish Fork, UT 84660-2408
Tel (801) 354-7400 *Founded/Ownrshp* 1915
Sales 236.7MM *EMP* 2,000
Accts Gilbert & Stewart Cpa Pc Pr
SIC 8211 Public elementary school; Public junior high school; Public senior high school; Public elementary school; Public junior high school; Public senior high school
Bd of Dir: Randy Boothe
Bd of Dir: Amber Rees
Bd of Dir: Christine Riley
**VP:* Kristen Betts
**VP:* Rod Oldroyd
Dir Risk M: Dave Gneiting
IT Man: Chris Loveless
HC Dir: John Allen
Counsel: Reed Park

D-U-N-S 87-713-4908 EXP
NEBRASKA BEEF LTD
4501 S 36th St, Omaha, NE 68107-1330
Tel (402) 734-6823 *Founded/Ownrshp* 1994
Sales 219.6MM[E] *EMP* 900
SIC 2011 Meat packing plants; Meat packing plants
Pt: William Hughes
Pt: Marvin Schrack
Pt: Mike Thatcher
COO: Katie Dornhoff
CFO: Fred Fromi
VP: Emile Randazzo
Exec: Misty Mattox
Mktg Dir: Adam Wegner

D-U-N-S 06-864-0457 IMP/EXP
NEBRASKA BOOK CO INC
(*Suby of* NEBRASKA BOOK INTERMEDIATE HOLDINGS INC) ★
4700 S 19th St, Lincoln, NE 68512-1216
Tel (402) 421-7300 *Founded/Ownrshp* 2012
Sales 472.8MM[E] *EMP* 2,600[E]
SIC 5942 5192 5961 College book stores; Books; Educational supplies & equipment, mail order; College book stores; Books; Educational supplies & equipment, mail order
Pr: Benjamin Riggsby
Mng Pt: Rick Reeble
CFO: John Macieo
CFO: Alan Siemk
Sr Cor Off: Noreen Manfield
Chf Mktg O: Barry Major
Sr VP: Michael Kelly
Sr VP: Nathan D Rempe
Sr VP: Alan G Siemek
VP: Bill Allen
VP: John A Callahan
VP: Bill Edmonds
VP: Justin Fry
VP: Kenneth Jirovsky
VP: Sue Riedman
VP: Kevin Wright
VP: Bill Zeuch
Assoc Dir: Doug Farley
Assoc Dir: Scott Hoover

D-U-N-S 07-925-5689
NEBRASKA BOOK HOLDINGS INC
4700 S 19th St, Lincoln, NE 68512-1216
Tel (402) 421-0500 *Founded/Ownrshp* 2012
Sales 688.1MM[E] *EMP* 2,600[E]
SIC 6719 5942 5192 5961 Investment holding companies, except banks; Investment holding companies, except banks; College book stores; Books; Educational supplies & equipment, mail order
Pr: Benjamin Riggsby
CFO: John Macieo
VP: John Callahan
VP: Nathan Rempe
Rgnl Mgr: Garrett Barton
Rgnl Mgr: Scott Mehr
Rgnl Mgr: Aubrey Williamson
Genl Mgr: Ruby Fowler
Genl Mgr: Michael Jaynes
Store Mgr: Jeff Fawcett

D-U-N-S 02-461-9149
NEBRASKA BOOK INTERMEDIATE HOLDINGS INC
NEEBO HOLDING COMPANY
(*Suby of* NEBRASKA BOOK HOLDINGS INC) ★
4701 S 19th St, Lincoln, NE 68512
Tel (402) 421-7300 *Founded/Ownrshp* 2012
Sales 191.3MM[E] *EMP* 2,600[E]
SIC 6719 5942 5192 5961 Investment holding companies, except banks; Investment holding companies, except banks; College book stores; Books; Educational supplies & equipment, mail order
Pr: Benjamin Riggsby
CFO: John Macieo
VP: Nathan Rempe

NEBRASKA CITY READY MIX
See CONCRETE INDUSTRIES INC

D-U-N-S 12-983-4420
NEBRASKA COMMUNITY FOUNDATION
3833 S 14th St, Lincoln, NE 68502-5340
Tel (402) 323-7330 *Founded/Ownrshp* 1993
Sales 28.7MM *EMP* 17
Accts Hbe Becker Meyer Love Llp Lin
SIC 8611 8733 Community affairs & services; Noncommercial research organizations; Community affairs & services; Noncommercial research organizations
Pr: Jeff Yost
**CFO:* Diane Wilson
Off Admin: Angie Parrish

D-U-N-S 80-882-0054
NEBRASKA DEPARTMENT OF ADMINISTRATIVE SERVICES
(*Suby of* EXECUTIVE OFFICE OF STATE OF NEBRASKA) ★
State Capitol Ste 1315, Lincoln, NE 68509
Tel (402) 471-2331 *Founded/Ownrshp* 1965
Sales NA *EMP* 1,262[E]
SIC 9199 General government administration;

D-U-N-S 80-882-0021
NEBRASKA DEPARTMENT OF CORRECTIONAL SERVICES
NDCS
(*Suby of* EXECUTIVE OFFICE OF STATE OF NEBRASKA) ★
Folsom W Prspector Bldg 1, Lincoln, NE 68509
Tel (402) 471-2654 *Founded/Ownrshp* 1973
Sales NA *EMP* 495
SIC 9223 Prison, government; ; Prison, government;
IT Man: Mikki Kirkpatrick

D-U-N-S 80-881-9882
NEBRASKA DEPARTMENT OF EDUCATION
(*Suby of* EXECUTIVE OFFICE OF STATE OF NEBRASKA) ★
301 Centennial Mall S, Lincoln, NE 68508-2529
Tel (402) 471-2295 *Founded/Ownrshp* 1875
Sales NA *EMP* 500[E]
SIC 9411 Administration of educational programs; ; Administration of educational programs;
Adm Dir: Janice Eret
MIS Dir: Bev Newton
Info Man: Pam Kasl

D-U-N-S 80-882-0260
NEBRASKA DEPARTMENT OF ENVIRONMENTAL QUALITY
(*Suby of* EXECUTIVE OFFICE OF STATE OF NEBRASKA) ★
1200 N St Ste 400, Lincoln, NE 68508-2024
Tel (402) 471-2186 *Founded/Ownrshp* 1977
Sales NA *EMP* 330
SIC 9511 Environmental agencies; ; Environmental agencies;

D-U-N-S 80-881-9957
NEBRASKA DEPARTMENT OF HEALTH & HUMAN SERVICES
NEBRASKA FOOD DIST PROGRAM
(*Suby of* EXECUTIVE OFFICE OF STATE OF NEBRASKA) ★
301 Centennial Mall S, Lincoln, NE 68508-2529
Tel (402) 471-3121 *Founded/Ownrshp* 1933
Sales NA *EMP* 500
SIC 9431 9441 Administration of public health programs; ; Administration of social & human resources; ; Administration of public health programs; ; Administration of social & human resources;
CEO: Courtney Phillips
Prgrm Mgr: Tom Christopherson

D-U-N-S 87-807-2446
NEBRASKA DEPARTMENT OF LABOR
(*Suby of* EXECUTIVE OFFICE OF STATE OF NEBRASKA) ★
550 S 16th St, Lincoln, NE 68508-2601
Tel (402) 471-9000 *Founded/Ownrshp* 1996
Sales 210.8M *EMP* 475
SIC 8748 9441 Employee programs administration; Systems engineering consultant, ex. computer or professional; ; Employee programs administration; Systems engineering consultant, ex. computer or professional;

D-U-N-S 80-888-1429
NEBRASKA DEPARTMENT OF MILITARY
NEBRASKA NATIONAL GUARD
(*Suby of* EXECUTIVE OFFICE OF STATE OF NEBRASKA) ★
2433 Nw 24th St, Lincoln, NE 68524-1801
Tel (402) 309-7210 *Founded/Ownrshp* 1880
Sales NA *EMP* 500[E]
SIC 9711 National security; ; National security;
Prin: Timothy Kadavy
IT Man: Shawn Fitzgerald

D-U-N-S 80-888-1411
NEBRASKA DEPARTMENT OF REVENUE
(*Suby of* EXECUTIVE OFFICE OF STATE OF NEBRASKA) ★
301 Centennial Mall S, Lincoln, NE 68508-2529
Tel (402) 471-2971 *Founded/Ownrshp* 1969
Sales NA *EMP* 500
SIC 9311 Finance, taxation & monetary policy; ; Finance, taxation & monetary policy;
VP: Len Sloup

D-U-N-S 80-888-1403
NEBRASKA DEPARTMENT OF ROADS
(*Suby of* EXECUTIVE OFFICE OF STATE OF NEBRASKA) ★
1500 Highway 2, Lincoln, NE 68502-5480
Tel (402) 471-4567 *Founded/Ownrshp* 1895
Sales NA *EMP* 500[E]
SIC 9621 ; Bureau of public roads; ; Bureau of public roads
Ofcr: Greg Weinertat
Genl Mgr: Craig Harrington

D-U-N-S 04-410-1467 IMP
NEBRASKA DISTRIBUTING CO INC
PREMIED WIDWEST BEVERAGE
(*Suby of* AMCON CORP) ★
10367 S 134th St, Omaha, NE 68138-3737
Tel (402) 891-1212 *Founded/Ownrshp* 1976
Sales 32.0MM[E] *EMP* 58
SIC 5181 2086 Beer & other fermented malt liquors; Carbonated beverages, nonalcoholic: bottled & canned; Beer & other fermented malt liquors; Carbonated beverages, nonalcoholic: bottled & canned
Pr: Brad Genners
**Pr:* Scott Brannon
**Treas:* Rob Knaak
Sls&Mrk Ex: Paul Neelans
Sls&Mrk Ex: Mark Wright

D-U-N-S 07-935-8911
NEBRASKA EARLY CHILDHOOD COLLABORATIVE LLC
1612 N 24th St, Omaha, NE 68110-2308
Tel (402) 341-0933 *Founded/Ownrshp* 2013
Sales 20.0MM *EMP* 1
SIC 8351 Child day care services; Child day care services
CFO: Kevin Cloonan
VP: Jessie Rasmussen
Ex Dir: Dan Pedersen
Pgrm Dir: Michael Burke

D-U-N-S 04-557-6279
NEBRASKA ELECTRIC GENERATION & TRANSMISSION COOPERATIVE INC
2472 18th Ave, Columbus, NE 68601-2604
Tel (402) 564-8142 *Founded/Ownrshp* 1956
Sales 274.9MM *EMP* 4
SIC 4911 Generation, electric power; Transmission, electric power; Generation, electric power; Transmission, electric power
Pr: Mike Siefken
Genl Mgr: Bruce Pontow

D-U-N-S 14-501-1511
NEBRASKA ENGINEERING CO
NECO
(*Suby of* GLOBAL INDUSTRIES INC) ★
9364 N 45th St, Omaha, NE 68152-1328
Tel (402) 453-6912 *Founded/Ownrshp* 2001
Sales 22.0MM[E] *EMP* 110
SIC 3462 Iron & steel forgings; Iron & steel forgings
CEO: Virgil Eihusen
**Pr:* Doug Fargo
Sls Mgr: Pat McCarthy

D-U-N-S 01-136-7579
NEBRASKA FAMILIES COLLABORATIVE INC
2110 Ppllion Pkwy Ste 110, Omaha, NE 68164
Tel (402) 492-2500 *Founded/Ownrshp* 2009
Sales 54.0MM *EMP* 282
SIC 8621 Professional membership organizations; Professional membership organizations
CEO: Dave Newell
**COO:* Donna Rozell Msw
COO: Donna Rozell
IT Man: Jaimie Anderson-Hoyt
Counsel: Monika Anderson

NEBRASKA FOOD BANK
See FOODBANK FOR HEARTLAND

NEBRASKA FOOD DIST PROGRAM
See NEBRASKA DEPARTMENT OF HEALTH & HUMAN SERVICES

D-U-N-S 00-787-5040 IMP
■ **NEBRASKA FURNITURE MART INC**
(*Suby of* BERKSHIRE HATHAWAY INC) ★
700 S 72nd St, Omaha, NE 68114-4697
Tel (402) 397-6100 *Founded/Ownrshp* 1937
Sales 896.2MM[E] *EMP* 2,614
SIC 5712 5713 5722 5731 5734 5946 Furniture stores; Floor covering stores; Household appliance stores; Radio, television & electronic stores; Television sets; Video recorders, players, disc players & accessories; Video cameras & accessories; Computer & software stores; Camera & photographic supply stores; Furniture stores; Floor covering stores; Household appliance stores; Radio, television & electronic stores; Television sets; Video recorders, players, disc players & accessories; Video cameras & accessories; Computer & software stores; Camera & photographic supply stores
Pr: Ronald Blumkin
CEO: Irvin Blumkin
CFO: Doug Hamlin
CFO: Brian Koenig
VP: Ryan Blumkin
VP: Brady Garren
VP: Brian Hoppe
Store Dir: Jeff Lind
CIO: David Bash
IT Man: Fred Fritz
IT Man: Dana Haynes

D-U-N-S 03-823-4467
NEBRASKA HARVEST CENTER INC
925 280th, Seward, NE 68434-7567
Tel (402) 643-4399 *Founded/Ownrshp* 2012
Sales 50.0MM *EMP* 25[E]
SIC 5083 Farm equipment parts & supplies; Farm equipment parts & supplies
Prin: Craig Gile

D-U-N-S 13-168-1640
NEBRASKA HEART HOSPITAL LLC
7500 S 91st St, Lincoln, NE 68526-9772
Tel (402) 327-2700 *Founded/Ownrshp* 2001
Sales 31.2MM[E] *EMP* 325[E]
SIC 8062 General medical & surgical hospitals; General medical & surgical hospitals
CEO: Andrea Jung
CFO: Dan Chonlau
Ofcr: Trish Wilmes
Exec: Joseph Petty
Dir Lab: Ryan Storz
Dir Rx: Emily Mannschreck
Genl Mgr: Janet Huenink
Telecom Ex: Deb Jicha
Dir QC: Becca Eckert
Dir IT: Mike Rose
Dir IT: Cindy Smith

D-U-N-S 19-717-1234
NEBRASKA HEART INSTITUTE P C
7440 S 91st St, Lincoln, NE 68526-9797
Tel (402) 328-3999 *Founded/Ownrshp* 1987
Sales NA *EMP* 300
SIC 8011

D-U-N-S 17-195-6568
NEBRASKA INDUSTRAIL COMPETITIVENESS SERVICE
SENIOR INDEPENDENCE ADULT DAY
(*Suby of* STATE OF NEBRASKA) ★
8800 O St, Lincoln, NE 68520-1227
Tel (402) 437-2535 *Founded/Ownrshp* 1997
Sales NA *EMP* 5,004E
SIC 9199 General government administration;

NEBRASKA LUTHERAN DISTRICT OFF
See LUTHERAN CHURCH-MISSOURI SYNOD

D-U-N-S 04-353-1607
NEBRASKA MEDICAL CENTER
NEBRASKA MEDICINE
987400 Nebraska Med Ctr, Omaha, NE 68198-0001
Tel (402) 552-2000 *Founded/Ownrshp* 1997
Sales 1.0MMME *EMP* 9,100
Accts Kpmg Llp Omaha Ne
SIC 8062 Hospital, professional nursing school with AMA residency; Hospital, professional nursing school with AMA residency
CEO: William S Dinsmoor
Chf Rad: Craig Walker
**Ch Bd:* Harlan J Noddle
CFO: William Dinsmoor
**Treas:* Bruce E Grewcock
**Treas:* Bruce R Lauritsen
**V Ch Bd:* Kenneth E Stinson
Ofcr: Leslie Spethman
Sr VP: Tadd Pullin
VP: Jennifer Graber
Exec: Nedra Marion
Dir Risk M: Dave Poppert

NEBRASKA MEDICINE
See NEBRASKA MEDICAL CENTER

D-U-N-S 11-507-2787
NEBRASKA METHODIST HEALTH SYSTEM INC
8511 W Dodge Rd, Omaha, NE 68114-3403
Tel (402) 354-2176 *Founded/Ownrshp* 1981
Sales 42.3MM *EMP* 5,200
SIC 8062

D-U-N-S 18-475-8498
NEBRASKA METHODIST HOSPITAL FOUNDATION
8401 W Dodge Rd Ste 225, Omaha, NE 68114-3447
Tel (402) 354-4825 *Founded/Ownrshp* 1977
Sales 29.0MM *EMP* 8
Accts Kpmg Llp Omaha Ne
SIC 7389 Fund raising organizations; Fund raising organizations
Pr: Cynthia S Peacock
Chf Nrs Of: Rose Leavitt
Off Mgr: Rhonda Rowley
CIO: Roger Hertz
Netwrk Mgr: Brandon Eaves
Doctor: Lanette Guthmann
Doctor: Joseph McAslin
Pgrm Dir: Kevin Borcher
Snr Mgr: Anton Piskac

D-U-N-S 06-152-9418 IMP
NEBRASKA METHODIST HOSPITAL INC
METHODIST HOSP PAIN MGT CLINIC
(*Suby of* NEBRASKA METHODIST HEALTH SYSTEM INC) ★
8303 Dodge St, Omaha, NE 68114-4108
Tel (402) 354-4540 *Founded/Ownrshp* 1981
Sales 449.4MM *EMP* 2,635
Accts Kpmg Llp Omaha Ne
SIC 8062 General medical & surgical hospitals; General medical & surgical hospitals
Pr: John M Fraser
**CFO:* Linda K Burt
Chf Mktg O: William Shiffermiller
Ofcr: Jacquie Kluck
Ofcr: J C Moore
**VP:* Mark A Burmester
VP: Amy Freeman
Dir Rad: Jennifer Brase
Dir Rad: Jim Luchtel
**Prin:* Steven Zuber
QA Dir: Bev Johnson

NEBRASKA NATIONAL GUARD
See NEBRASKA DEPARTMENT OF MILITARY

D-U-N-S 14-729-7126
NEBRASKA ORTHOPAEDIC HOSPITAL LLC
2808 S 143rd Plz, Omaha, NE 68144-5611
Tel (402) 637-0600 *Founded/Ownrshp* 2004
Sales 48.7MME *EMP* 240
SIC 8011 Orthopedic physician; Orthopedic physician
CEO: Thomas C Macy
**COO:* Mark Longacre
**CFO:* Anna E McCaslin
CIO: Chris Cornett
IT Man: Tim Pugsley
Mktg Dir: Brad Pfeiffer

D-U-N-S 96-628-6283
NEBRASKA PEDIATRIC PRACTICE INC
8200 Dodge St, Omaha, NE 68114-4113
Tel (402) 955-4116 *Founded/Ownrshp* 2011
Sales 46.9MM *EMP* 4E
Accts Kpmg Llp Omaha Ne
SIC 8011 General & family practice, physician/surgeon; General & family practice, physician/surgeon
Prin: Robert Joseph Glow

D-U-N-S 00-725-9153 EXP
NEBRASKA PLASTICS INC (NE)
700 W Highway 30, Cozad, NE 69130-1367
Tel (308) 784-3224 *Founded/Ownrshp* 1945
Sales 56.3MME *EMP* 130
SIC 3084 Plastics pipe; Plastics pipe
Pr: Rex German
**VP:* Lois German
Comm Dir: Stephanie Aden
Sales Exec: Rod Wood
Manager: Brad Spencer

D-U-N-S 00-729-5272
NEBRASKA PUBLIC POWER DISTRICT
NUCLEAR FACILITY
1414 15th St, Columbus, NE 68601-5226
Tel (402) 564-8561 *Founded/Ownrshp* 1939
Sales 1.1MMM *EMP* 2,010
Accts Pricewaterhousecoopers Llp St
SIC 4911 Generation, electric power; Transmission, electric power; Distribution, electric power; Generation, electric power; Transmission, electric power; Distribution, electric power
Pr: Patrick Pope
V Ch: Gary Thompson
**COO:* Tom Kent
**CFO:* Traci Bender
Treas: Christine Pillen
Bd of Dir: Jerry Cholopek
VP: Beth Boesch
VP: Michael Culjat
**VP:* Ken Curry
VP: Brian Grady
**VP:* Oscar Limpias
**VP:* John McClure
VP: William Merrill
VP: Dave Rich
**VP:* Roy Steiner
Exec: Brenda Recek
Board of Directors: Ed Schrock, Jerry Chlopek, Gary Thompson, Fred Christensen, Barry Dekay, Virgil Froehlich, Mary Harding, Thomas Hoff, Ken Kunze, Ron Larsen, Larry Linstrom

D-U-N-S 07-013-0265
NEBRASKA SALT & GRAIN CO
115 W 16th St, Gothenburg, NE 69138-1302
Tel (308) 537-7191 *Founded/Ownrshp* 1975
Sales 20.8MME *EMP* 49
SIC 5153 4213 5191 Grains; Trucking, except local; Farm supplies; Grains; Trucking, except local; Farm supplies
Pr: Norman Geiken
**VP:* Colleen Geiken

D-U-N-S 96-493-1914
NEBRASKA SPINE HOSPITAL LLC
(*Suby of* CHI) ★
6901 N 72nd St Ste 20300, Omaha, NE 68122-1755
Tel (402) 572-3000 *Founded/Ownrshp* 2009
Sales 50.0MM *EMP* 120
SIC 8011 Surgeon
CEO: Troy P Stockman
Chf Nrs Of: Teresa Hawlik

D-U-N-S 19-132-0233
NEBRASKA STATE COLLEGES
BOARD OF TRUSTEES
1115 K St Ste 102, Lincoln, NE 68508-2879
Tel (402) 471-2505 *Founded/Ownrshp* 2001
Sales 61.5MM *EMP* 747
Accts Don Dunlap Cpa Lincoln Nebr
SIC 8221 Colleges universities & professional schools; Colleges universities & professional schools
**CFO:* Carolyn Murphy
IT Man: Dennis Linster
Pr Dir: Kovine Tande

D-U-N-S 17-555-6067
NEBRASKA STUDENT LOAN PROGRAM INC
NATIONAL STUDENT LOAN PROGRAM
1300 O St, Lincoln, NE 68508-1511
Tel (402) 475-8686 *Founded/Ownrshp* 1986
Sales NA *EMP* 100
Accts Kpmg Llp Omaha Ne
SIC 6111 Federal & federally sponsored credit agencies; Federal & federally sponsored credit agencies
CEO: Randy Heesacker
CFO: Jill Hicks
VP: Bill Kohl
VP: Mike Lubben
VP: David Macoubrie
VP: Sue Riedman
VP: Kathryn Trombitas
VP: Mark Willet
Ex Dir: Helga Kirst
Sls&Mrk Ex: Robyn Langel
Board of Directors: Gene Crump, Brett Lief, Doug Seipelt, Thomas Smith, Richard Vierk

D-U-N-S 06-864-8674
NEBRASKA TRANSPORT CO INC
N T C
1225 Country Club Rd, Gering, NE 69341-1738
Tel (308) 635-1214 *Founded/Ownrshp* 1987
Sales 79.3MME *EMP* 225
SIC 4213

D-U-N-S 04-164-9849
NEBRASKA TRUCK CENTER INC
4747 Juergen Rd, Grand Island, NE 68801-9680
Tel (308) 384-0130 *Founded/Ownrshp* 1969
Sales 38.1MME *EMP* 85
SIC 5511 5012 Trucks, tractors & trailers: new & used; Trucks, commercial; Trucks, noncommercial; Trucks, tractors & trailers: new & used; Trucks, commercial; Trucks, noncommercial
Ch Bd: Lloyd Brown
**Pr:* L Kent Coen
**Treas:* Kent Brown
Store Mgr: Tim Zigler
Sls Mgr: Lonnie Persinger

D-U-N-S 82-959-6993
NEBRASKA UTILITY CORP
1040 O St, Lincoln, NE 68508-3609
Tel (402) 473-3300 *Founded/Ownrshp* 2001
Sales 27.5MM *EMP* 5E
Accts Virchow Krause & Company Llp
SIC 4911 Electric services; Electric services
Pr: Shelley Sahling-Zart
CFO: Keith Brown
**Sec:* Christine Jackson
**VP:* Ted Weidner

D-U-N-S 06-866-9134
NEBRASKA WESLEYAN UNIVERSITY INC
N W U
5000 Saint Paul Ave, Lincoln, NE 68504-2760
Tel (402) 466-2371 *Founded/Ownrshp* 1886
Sales 43.5MM *EMP* 303
Accts Dana F Cole & Company Llp Lin
SIC 8221 University; University
Pr: Frederik Ohles
COO: Terri Anania
Ofcr: Anthony Dworak
**VP:* Sara Boatman
VP: Clark Chendoer
VP: John Greving
VP: Kim Johnson
VP: Erin Kautz
VP: Bill Motzer
Area Supr: Elizabeth Cox
Dir IT: Steven Dow

D-U-N-S 03-499-0374
NEBRASKA-IOWA SUPPLY CO INC
CONWAY OIL COMPANY
1160 Lincoln St, Blair, NE 68008-2163
Tel (402) 426-2171 *Founded/Ownrshp* 1985
Sales 183.7MM *EMP* 95
Accts Masimore Magnuson & Associate
SIC 5172 Gasoline; Crude oil; Lubricating oils & greases; Gasoline; Crude oil; Lubricating oils & greases
**Pr:* Mark T Lippincott
CFO: John Borchardt
**Treas:* John P Borchardt
Treas: Celeste Lux
**VP:* Janice Lippincott
Genl Mgr: Luke Wiese

D-U-N-S 61-484-1625 IMP
NEBRASKALAND INC
355 Food Center Dr Ste G4, Bronx, NY 10474-7580
Tel (718) 842-0700 *Founded/Ownrshp* 1989
Sales 203.6MME *EMP* 200E
SIC 5147 Meats & meat products; Meats & meat products
Pr: Richard Romanoff
COO: Stanley Marvel
Snr Mgr: Mark Bruscella

D-U-N-S 09-432-0418
NEBRASKALAND NATIONAL BANK
121 N Dewey St, North Platte, NE 69101-3942
Tel (308) 534-7552 *Founded/Ownrshp* 1998
Sales NA *EMP* 50E
SIC 6021 National commercial banks; National commercial banks
Pr: Mike Jacobson
Ofcr: Bobbi Sweet
Ex VP: Krista Heiss
Sr VP: Barbara Barr
Sr VP: Mary Hanson
Sr VP: Gary Ott
Sr VP: Justin Schwartz
VP: Josh Harm
VP: Dan Paradis
VP: Sandy Roose
VP: Sandy Ross

NEBRASKALAND TIRE CO OF NORTH
See NEBRASKALAND TIRE INC

D-U-N-S 07-012-0985
NEBRASKALAND TIRE INC
NEBRASKALAND TIRE CO OF NORTH
Hwy 283 & Hwy I 80, Lexington, NE 68850
Tel (308) 324-2338 *Founded/Ownrshp* 1974
Sales 92.4MM *EMP* 340
Accts Bkd Llp Wichita Ks
SIC 5531 5541 5411 Automotive tires; Truck stops; Convenience stores, independent; Automotive tires; Truck stops; Convenience stores, independent
Pr: Gary K Wright
**Treas:* Scott Samway
**Sec:* Nancy Wright
Genl Mgr: Nick Phillippi

NEBS
See NEW ENGLAND BUSINESS SERVICE INC

NEC
See NATIONAL EXPRESS LLC

D-U-N-S 14-725-5405 IMP
NEC CORP OF AMERICA
(*Suby of* NEC CORPORATION)
6535 State Highway 161, Irving, TX 75039-2402
Tel (214) 262-6000 *Founded/Ownrshp* 2004
Sales 1.6MMME *EMP* 3,000
SIC 5045 5065 Computers, peripherals & software; Electronic parts & equipment; Computers, peripherals & software; Electronic parts & equipment
CEO: Shinsuke Takahashi
**Pr:* Nobuhiro Endo
COO: Pierre Richer
CFO: Yoshio Kakishita
CFO: Hiroyuki Matsukura
CFO: Glenn Means
Treas: Yoshihiro Mori
**Treas:* Ed Welch
Ex VP: Gordon Chapple
**Ex VP:* Harumi Ikeda
**Ex VP:* Toshiyuki Mineno
Sr VP: Brian Archer
Sr VP: Iwao Fuchigami
Sr VP: Kazumasa Fujie
Sr VP: Kevin Hooper
**Sr VP:* Kenichi Kanazu
Sr VP: Gerald P Kenney
Sr VP: Kazuhiko Kobayashi
**Sr VP:* Takashi Niino
**Sr VP:* Kuniaki Okada
Sr VP: Phil Scarfo

D-U-N-S 79-976-0165 IMP/EXP
NEC DISPLAY SOLUTIONS OF AMERICA INC
(*Suby of* NEC DISPLAY SOLUTIONS, LTD.)
500 Park Blvd Ste 1100, Itasca, IL 60143-2602
Tel (630) 467-3000 *Founded/Ownrshp* 2007
Sales 47.2MME *EMP* 160
SIC 3575 Computer terminals, monitors & components; Computer terminals, monitors & components
Pr: Pierre Richer
Pr: Todd Bouman
Sr VP: Jean Dubois
VP: Douglas Albert
VP: Clark Brown
Dir Bus: Michael Zmuda
Genl Mgr: Mick Koike
DP Exec: Mark Wenigar
Natl Sales: Carolina Mahecha
VP Mktg: Jennifer Cheh
VP Sls: Douglas D Albert

D-U-N-S 07-943-4293
NEC ENERGY SOLUTIONS INC
N E C
(*Suby of* NEC CORPORATION)
155 Flanders Rd, Westborough, MA 01581-1032
Tel (508) 497-7319 *Founded/Ownrshp* 2014
Sales 66.4MME *EMP* 151
SIC 5999 3691 Batteries, non-automotive; Batteries, rechargeable
CEO: Bud Collins
**VP:* Steve Debruyn
**VP:* C Michael Hoff
**VP:* Jim Prueitt
**Genl Couns:* Deborah Collum

D-U-N-S 18-907-6532
NEC LABORATORIES AMERICA INC
(*Suby of* NEC CORP OF AMERICA) ★
4 Independence Way # 200, Princeton, NJ 08540-6685
Tel (609) 520-1555 *Founded/Ownrshp* 2002
Sales 38.4MM *EMP* 119
SIC 8731 Computer (hardware) development; Electronic research; Computer (hardware) development; Electronic research
Pr: Roger Tran
COO: Shirley Bowles
COO: Surendra Byna
COO: Hans Graf
COO: Yoshi Hara
COO: Paul Vincent
Ex VP: Nick Satomi
Sr VP: Masao Fukuma
Sr VP: Yukio Yamazaki
**VP:* Barbara J Connor
Exec: Sarah Arnesen
Exec: David Pennock
Exec: Debbie Thomas
Exec: Earl Withers
Dir Bus: Manuel Gallo

NEC LOGISTICS AMERICA
See NIPPON EXPRESS LOGISTICS AMERICA INC

D-U-N-S 07-879-2306 IMP
NEC TOKIN AMERICA INC (CA)
(*Suby of* NECTOKIN CORPORATION)
2460 N 1st St Ste 220, San Jose, CA 95131-1024
Tel (408) 570-9136 *Founded/Ownrshp* 1967, 2006
Sales 28.8MM *EMP* 17
Accts Kpmg Llp Santa Clara Ca
SIC 5065 Electronic parts; Electronic parts
CEO: Yoshio Ito
**CFO:* Takao Takahashi

NECA
See NATIONAL ENTERTAINMENT COLLECTIBLES ASSOCIATION INC

NECA
See NATIONAL ELECTRICAL CONTRACTORS ASSOCIATION INC

NECA
See NATIONAL EXCHANGE CARRIER ASSOCIATION

D-U-N-S 01-230-2230
NECA IBEW FAMILY MEDICAL CARE PLAN
5837 Highway 41, Ringgold, GA 30736-2632
Tel (706) 937-9600 *Founded/Ownrshp* 2005
Sales NA *EMP* 3E
Accts Calibre Cpa Group Pllc Bethes
SIC 6371 Union trust funds; Union trust funds
Ex Dir: Lawrence J Bradley

D-U-N-S 11-477-0654
NECA IBEW WELFARE TRUST FUND
2120 Hubbard Ave, Decatur, IL 62526-2871
Tel (800) 765-4239 *Founded/Ownrshp* 1955
Sales 125.1MM *EMP* 40
SIC 8631 Labor unions & similar labor organizations; Labor unions & similar labor organizations

D-U-N-S 96-485-2912
NECA LOCAL 145 WELFARE FUND
1700 52nd Ave, Moline, IL 61265-6378
Tel (309) 764-8080 *Founded/Ownrshp* 2010
Sales NA *EMP* 3
Accts Moorhead & Company Pc Davenpo
SIC 6371 Pension, health & welfare funds; Pension, health & welfare funds
Prin: John Bosso

NECAC
See NORTH EAST COMMUNITY ACTION CORP

NECC
See NEW ENGLAND CENTER FOR CHILDREN INC

D-U-N-S 96-007-4193
NECC CORP
10 State St Ste 2c, Woburn, MA 01801-6820
Tel (781) 994-1260 *Founded/Ownrshp* 1995
Sales 14.4MM *EMP* 695
SIC 7349 4959 0782 Cleaning service, industrial or commercial; Sanitary services; Lawn & garden services; Cleaning service, industrial or commercial; Sanitary services; Lawn & garden services
Pr: Patrick J Leyne
**CEO:* Jeff Smith
**CFO:* Matthew Cummings
**Treas:* Joel Smith
Exec: Dyanne Morin

NECCO
See NEW ENGLAND CONFECTIONERY CO INC

NECCO
See ENA INC

NECO
See NAVOPACHE ELECTRIC COOPERATIVE INC

NECO
See NEBRASKA ENGINEERING CO

NECS
See NEW ENGLAND COPY SPECIALISTS INC

D-U-N-S 60-424-5170
NECTAR ACQUISITION CORP
(*Suby of* T N S GROUP HOLDINGS LTD)
410 Horsham Rd Frnt, Horsham, PA 19044-2041
Tel (215) 442-9000 *Founded/Ownrshp* 2003
Sales 24.3MM^E *EMP* 1,301
SIC 8732 Market analysis or research; Market analysis or research
Pr: Kenneth M Freeman
Treas: Brian Haveson
VP: Thomas C Mattick

NECU
See NORTHEAST CREDIT UNION

NED DAVIS RESEARCH
See DAVIS MENDEL & REGENSTEIN INC

D-U-N-S 16-196-3236
NEDCO ELECTRONICS INC
12110 Prichard Farm Rd, Maryland Heights, MO 63043-4201
Tel (314) 344-0344 *Founded/Ownrshp* 1975
Sales 29.2MM^E *EMP* 42
SIC 5065 Electronic parts & equipment
Pr: Louis D Dinkel
Off Mgr: Kevin Dahlke
Sales Asso: Terry Mitchell-Klaus

NEDCO SUPPLY
See PHILCOR TV & ELECTRONIC LEASING INC

D-U-N-S 00-728-9121 IMP
NEDEC AMERICA CORP
2251 Nicholas Blvd, Elk Grove Village, IL 60007-5927
Tel (847) 290-1398 *Founded/Ownrshp* 2005
Sales 35.0MM *EMP* 5
SIC 5013 Automotive supplies & parts; Automotive supplies & parts
Pr: SE Joon Hwang
**VP:* Alex Hwang

D-U-N-S 10-229-1309
NEDELCO INC
HAMILTON TELECOMMUNICATIONS
1001 12th St, Aurora, NE 68818-2004
Tel (402) 694-5101 *Founded/Ownrshp* 1963
Sales 136.4MM^E *EMP* 800^E
SIC 4813 Local telephone communications; Long distance telephone communications; ;Telemarketing services; Local telephone communications; Long distance telephone communications;
Pr: Phillip C Nelson
CFO: Phil Fendt
**Sec:* Betty A Van Luchene
**VP:* John Nelson
Mng Dir: Douglas Salmon
Genl Mgr: Pat Shaw
Off Mgr: Ronni Harvey
Snr Sftwr: Ross Norder
Dir IT: Wayne Hinnerman
Sftwr Eng: Keo Sabell
Mktg Mgr: Gary Lewien

D-U-N-S 07-392-1249
NEDERLAND INDEPENDENT SCHOOL DISTRICT
NISD
220 N 17th St, Nederland, TX 77627-5029
Tel (409) 724-2391 *Founded/Ownrshp* 1920
Sales 45.7MM *EMP* 660
Accts West Davis & Company Llp Au
SIC 8211 Public elementary school; Public junior high school; Public senior high school; Public elementary school; Public junior high school; Public senior high school

D-U-N-S 04-728-8949
NEEB KEARNEY & CO LLC
JACKSON KEARNEY GROUP, THE
1555 Poydras St Ste 1600, New Orleans, LA 70112-3769
Tel (504) 587-1100 *Founded/Ownrshp* 1946
Sales 73.2MM^E *EMP* 575
SIC 4491 4222 4225 Stevedoring; Waterfront terminal operation; Storage, frozen or refrigerated goods; General warehousing; Stevedoring; Waterfront terminal operation; Storage, frozen or refrigerated goods; General warehousing
Pr: Daniel L Haeuser
**COO:* David G Mannella
**Sec:* Elisa Azze
VP: David Mannella
Genl Mgr: David Harrington
Genl Mgr: Wojciech Rutkowski
Genl Mgr: Don Zemo
VP Opers: Wallace Binford
Sfty Mgr: Dave Kelly
Opers Mgr: Greg Davis
Sales Exec: Elizabeth Jackson

NEEBO HOLDING COMPANY
See NEBRASKA BOOK INTERMEDIATE HOLDINGS INC

D-U-N-S 13-191-1307
NEEDHAM & CO LLC
(*Suby of* NEEDHAM GROUP INC) ★
445 Park Ave Fl 3, New York, NY 10022-8639
Tel (212) 371-8300 *Founded/Ownrshp* 1985
Sales 53.0MM^E *EMP* 150
Accts Ernst & Young Llp New York N
SIC 6211 Investment bankers; Investment bankers
CEO: John J Prior Jr
CFO: Robert Fiordaliso
CFO: Robert Fiordalizo
CFO: James Giangrasso
Ofcr: Mike Lamb
Ex VP: Mark Whalen
VP: Dan Fulop
VP: Thena Levine
VP: Donald McGannon
VP: Shawn Rassouli
VP: Clay Wilson

D-U-N-S 08-465-4706
NEEDHAM BANK
1063 Great Plain Ave, Needham, MA 02492-2302
Tel (781) 449-4724 *Founded/Ownrshp* 1892
Sales NA *EMP* 166
SIC 6022 State commercial banks; State commercial banks
Pr: Robert F Day
Ex VP: Barry Whittaker
Sr VP: Richard Buttermore
Sr VP: Laura Dorfman
Sr VP: Gene Graham
Sr VP: Stephanie Maiona
Sr VP: William Paish
Sr VP: Charlie Steele
**Sr VP:* Mark Whalen
VP: Doug Ashworth
**VP:* Evelyn B Bowles
VP: Michael Browne
**VP:* William R Day
VP: Mark Drew
VP: Frank Driscoll
VP: James Gordon
VP: Nancy Harrison
**VP:* Jack McGeorge
VP: Eric Morse
VP: John Shea
VP: Danielle Walsh

D-U-N-S 01-950-5056
■ **NEEDHAM ELECTRIC SUPPLY CORP** (MA)
NESCO
(*Suby of* WESCO DISTRIBUTION INC) ★
5 Shawmut Rd, Canton, MA 02021-1408
Tel (781) 828-9494 *Founded/Ownrshp* 1958, 2015
Sales 99.8MM^E *EMP* 250
SIC 5063 3648

D-U-N-S 77-999-4123
NEEDHAM GROUP INC
445 Park Ave Fl 3, New York, NY 10022-8639
Tel (212) 371-8300 *Founded/Ownrshp* 2006
Sales 53.0MM^E *EMP* 177
SIC 6211 Investment firm, general brokerage; Investment firm, general brokerage
CEO: George A Needham
**Ofcr:* Robert Fiordaliso
Mng Dir: William Dailey
Mng Dir: Jack Iacovone

D-U-N-S 02-545-6844
NEEDHAM PUBLIC SCHOOLS
NEWMAN ELEMENTARY SCHOOL
1330 Highland Ave, Needham, MA 02492-2613
Tel (781) 455-0400 *Founded/Ownrshp* 1711
Sales 32.6MM^E *EMP* 619
SIC 8211 Public elementary & secondary schools; Public elementary & secondary schools
MIS Dir: Debra Gammerman
**Opers Mgr:* Ann Gullaty
Teacher Pr: Thomas Campbell
HC Dir: Kathy Pinkham
Snr Mgr: Mary Rizzuto

D-U-N-S 00-561-1137
NEEDHAM ROOFING INC
6160 S Syracuse Way # 315, Greenwood Village, CO 80111-4781
Tel (303) 333-7663 *Founded/Ownrshp* 1995
Sales 20.8MM^E *EMP* 250
SIC 1761 Roofing contractor; Roofing contractor
Pr: Danny Needham
**VP:* Steve Needham

D-U-N-S 96-809-1202
NEEDLE HOLDINGS INC
5555 Darrow Rd, Hudson, OH 44236-4011
Tel (330) 656-2600 *Founded/Ownrshp* 2010
Sales 577.8MM^E *EMP* 22,000^E
SIC 5945 Arts & crafts supplies; Arts & crafts supplies
Pr: Darrell Webb

D-U-N-S 17-411-1849
NEEDLECRAFT SHOP LLC
ANNIE'S ATTIC
111 Corporate Dr, Big Sandy, TX 75755-2446
Tel (903) 636-2233 *Founded/Ownrshp* 1994
Sales 34.3MM^E *EMP* 240^E
SIC 7389 5961 2741 5131 Subscription fulfillment services: magazine, newspaper, etc.; Catalog sales; Mail order house; Miscellaneous publishing; Piece goods & notions; Subscription fulfillment services: magazine, newspaper, etc.; Catalog sales; Mail order house; Miscellaneous publishing; Piece goods & notions
CEO: David McKee
**Pr:* Anthony Pytlak
**Pr:* Tony Pytlak
**CFO:* Mike Klansek
VP: Stephen Martin
**VP:* Steve Martin
Exec: Kimberly Mabry
**Exec:* John Trotter
Dir Bus: Sally Allen
Dir IT: Marc Merit
Dir IT: Mark Merritt

D-U-N-S 94-606-6396
NEEDLER ENTERPRISES INC
FRESH ENCOUNTER
317 W Main Cross St, Findlay, OH 45840-3314
Tel (419) 422-8090 *Founded/Ownrshp* 1985
Sales 165.4MM^E *EMP* 1,371
SIC 5411 Grocery stores; Grocery stores
Ch Bd: Michael S Needler
**COO:* Mark Gephart
CFO: Dale Hoffman
**CFO:* Ken Williams
Ofcr: Eric Anderson
MIS Dir: Chris Groman
Dir IT: Bob Hanson

D-U-N-S 03-816-6054
NEEDVILLE INDEPENDENT SCHOOL DISTRICT
16227 Highway 36, Needville, TX 77461-9320
Tel (979) 793-4308 *Founded/Ownrshp* 1946
Sales 30.6MM *EMP* 300
Accts Belt Harris Pechacek Lllp Be
SIC 8211 Public elementary & secondary schools; Public elementary & secondary schools

D-U-N-S 14-772-1229
NEEL-SCHAFFER INC
125 S Congress St # 1100, Jackson, MS 39201-3395
Tel (601) 948-3071 *Founded/Ownrshp* 1983
Sales 68.7MM^E *EMP* 350
SIC 8711

D-U-N-S 06-986-6028 IMP/EXP
NEELTRAN INC
71 Pickett District Rd, New Milford, CT 06776-4412
Tel (860) 350-5964 *Founded/Ownrshp* 1983
Sales 44.7MM^E *EMP* 117
SIC 3612 3677 3679 Line voltage regulators; Electronic transformers; Static power supply converters for electronic applications; Line voltage regulators; Electronic transformers; Static power supply converters for electronic applications
Pr: Antonio Capanna Jr
Owner: Dave Franco
CFO: David Falco
VP Opers: Marco Cignarale

D-U-N-S 09-313-9947
NEELY COBLE CO
(*Suby of* NEELY COBLE CO INC) ★
319 Fesslers Ln, Nashville, TN 37210-2905
Tel (615) 244-8900 *Founded/Ownrshp* 1977
Sales NA *EMP* 172
SIC 6159 Truck finance leasing; Truck finance leasing
Ch Bd: Neely B Coble Jr
**Pr:* Neely Coble III
**Ex VP:* William R Foster
**VP:* G William Coble

D-U-N-S 00-405-2734
NEELY COBLE CO INC (TN)
319 Fesslers Ln, Nashville, TN 37210-2905
Tel (615) 244-8900 *Founded/Ownrshp* 1951
Sales 88.0MM^E *EMP* 172
SIC 5012 5013 Trucks, commercial; Automotive supplies & parts; Trucks, commercial; Automotive supplies & parts
Pr: Neely B Coble III
**Ch Bd:* Neely B Coble Jr
CFO: John Carroll
**CFO:* William R Foster
**VP:* G W Coble III
Exec: Pam Kittrell
Manager: Kirk Scott
Sls Mgr: Dudley Smith
Sales Asso: Myles Baldwin
Sales Asso: Edward Coble

D-U-N-S 00-598-6799 IMP/EXP
NEEMA CLOTHING LTD (NY)
BENORA CLOTHING
74 Gould St 76, Bayonne, NJ 07002-5016
Tel (212) 765-2802 *Founded/Ownrshp* 1936
Sales 25.1MM^E *EMP* 100
SIC 5136 Suits, men's & boys'; Trousers, men's & boys'
Pr: James Ammeen
CFO: Neil Goldberg

D-U-N-S 02-387-6381
▲ **NEENAH ENTERPRISES INC**
2121 Brooks Ave, Neenah, WI 54956-4756
Tel (920) 725-7000 *Founded/Ownrshp* 2010
Sales 365.5MM^E *EMP* 1,650^E
Tkr Sym NNHE *Exch* OTO
SIC 3272 3312 Cast stone, concrete; Axles, rolled or forged: made in steel mills; Cast stone, concrete; Axles, rolled or forged: made in steel mills
Pr: Thomas J Riordan
**CFO:* Thomas Adrians
VP: Bob Spence
VP: Mark Steine
QA Dir: Mike Thomack
Netwrk Eng: Michael Hoeppner

NEENAH FOUNDERY
See NFC CASTINGS INC

D-U-N-S 19-471-8961 IMP/EXP
■ **NEENAH FOUNDRY CO**
(*Suby of* NEENAH FOUNDERY) ★
2121 Brooks Ave, Neenah, WI 54956-4700
Tel (920) 725-7000 *Founded/Ownrshp* 2006
Sales 365.5MM^E *EMP* 1,650
Accts Ernst & Young Llp Milwaukee
SIC 3321 3315 Ductile iron castings; Gray iron castings; Steel wire & related products; Ductile iron castings; Gray iron castings; Steel wire & related products
CEO: Thomas J Riordan
**CFO:* Thomas Adrians
VP: Craig Fisher
VP: Louis Fratarcangeli
VP: Frank Headington
VP: Scott Hoffman
VP: Karl Jerde
VP: Heidi Mitchell
**VP:* Robert Spence
VP: Joseph Varkoly
Ex Dir: Scott Harper
Board of Directors: Tim Bernlohr, James Chapman, John Forsgren, Walter Jones, Ted Lodge, Mark Richards, Thomas Riordan

D-U-N-S 10-067-5479
NEENAH JOINT SCHOOL DISTRICT
410 S Commercial St, Neenah, WI 54956-2593
Tel (920) 751-6800 *Founded/Ownrshp* 1875
Sales 55.1MM^E *EMP* 689
SIC 8211 Public elementary & secondary schools; Elementary school; Secondary school; Public elementary & secondary schools; Elementary school; Secondary school
Pr Dir: James Strick

D-U-N-S 79-293-6353 IMP/EXP
■ **NEENAH PAPER FR LLC**
(*Suby of* NEENAH PAPER INC) ★
1376 Kimberly Dr, Neenah, WI 54956-1641
Tel (800) 558-8327 *Founded/Ownrshp* 2010
Sales 227.9MM^E *EMP* 775
SIC 2679 2621 Paper products, converted; Paper mills; Paper products, converted; Paper mills
Ch: Robert C Buchanan
VP: Robert M McDonald
VP: Lyle H Richter
Dir IT: Lynn Asten
Board of Directors: Richard W Gygi

D-U-N-S 17-598-4137 EXP
▲ **NEENAH PAPER INC**
3460 Preston Ridge Rd # 150, Alpharetta, GA 30005-2064
Tel (678) 566-6500 *Founded/Ownrshp* 2004
Sales 902.7MM *EMP* 1,875
Tkr Sym NP *Exch* NYS
SIC 2621 2741 Paper mills; Specialty or chemically treated papers; Book, bond & printing papers; Stationery, envelope & tablet papers; Technical manual & paper publishing; Paper mills; Specialty or chemically treated papers; Book, bond & printing papers; Stationery, envelope & tablet papers; Technical manual & paper publishing
Pr: John P O'Donnell
**Ch Bd:* Sean T Erwin
CFO: Bonnie C Lind
Bd of Dir: O Everbach
Sr VP: Steven S Heinrichs
Sr VP: Bonnie Lind
Sr VP: James R Piedmonte
VP: Kyle Anderson
VP: Cindy Hanson
VP: Mary Palmer
Exec: Larry Brownlee
Exec: Sharon Eucce
Board of Directors: Margaret S Dano, Edward Grzedzinski, Mary Ann Leeper, Timothy S Lucas, John F McGovern, Philip C Moore, Stephen M Wood

D-U-N-S 00-718-5432
NEENAN CO (MO)
NEENAN CO. EAST
5701 Blue Pkwy, Kansas City, MO 64130-2314
Tel (316) 942-9524 *Founded/Ownrshp* 1951, 1975
Sales 35.5MM^E *EMP* 48
Accts Donnelly Meiners Jordan Kline
SIC 5074 5085 Plumbing & hydronic heating supplies; Industrial supplies; Valves & fittings
Pr: Michael Neenan
**VP:* David Lorenz
**VP:* Joseph Neenan
Brnch Mgr: Bruce Neill
**Genl Mgr:* Bob Kuhnlein
Sls Mgr: Andrew Neenan
Sales Asso: Dan Orpin

NEENAN CO. EAST
See NEENAN CO

D-U-N-S 04-071-5013
NEENAN CO LLLP
2607 Midpoint Dr, Fort Collins, CO 80525-4427
Tel (970) 493-8747 *Founded/Ownrshp* 1973
Sales 84.5MM^E *EMP* 140
SIC 1542 Commercial & office building, new construction; Commercial & office buildings, renovation & repair; Commercial & office building, new construction; Commercial & office buildings, renovation & repair
Ch Bd: David G Neenan
Pr: Randolph Myers
Treas: Ryan Dellos
Ex Dir: Dave Spencer
IT Man: Russell Anderson

D-U-N-S 03-425-3344 IMP
NEESE INDUSTRIES INC
10646 Airline Hwy, Gonzales, LA 70737-7913
Tel (225) 647-6553 *Founded/Ownrshp* 1961
Sales 20.0MM^E *EMP* 83^E
SIC 2385 2326 Raincoats, except vulcanized rubber: purchased materials; Men's & boys' work clothing
Pr: Timothy Sands
**Ex VP:* Robert Riches
**VP:* Bob Riches
Manager: Tim Hoffpauir

D-U-N-S 08-994-1496
NEESER CONSTRUCTION INC
2501 Blueberry Rd Ste 100, Anchorage, AK 99503-2656
Tel (907) 276-1058 *Founded/Ownrshp* 1970
Sales 116.3MM^E *EMP* 250
Accts Bernston Porter & Co Pllc B
SIC 1542 Commercial & office building, new construction; Commercial & office buildings, renovation & repair; Commercial & office building, new construction; Commercial & office buildings, renovation & repair
Pr: Gerald Neeser
**CEO:* Jerry Neeser
VP: Natalie Neeser
Dir Bus: Denise Tousignant
IT Man: Rusty Myrick
Sfty Dirs: John Stallone
Prd Mgr: Neil Bhargava

NEESO JEANS
See EK DENIM GROUP INC

NEF ASSIGNMENT
See NATIONAL EQUITY FUND INC

D-U-N-S 96-715-1205
NEF COMMUNITY INVESTMENTS INC
120 S Riverside Plz Fl 15, Chicago, IL 60606-3913
Tel (312) 360-0400 *Founded/Ownrshp* 2011
Sales 26.2MM *EMP* 2
Accts Kpmg Llp Mc Lean Va
SIC 6799 Investors; Investors
Pr: Sidney Katz

NEFAB COMPANIES
See NEFAB PACKAGING INC

D-U-N-S 07-838-4841 IMP
NEFAB COMPANIES INC
(*Suby of* NEFAB AB)
204 Airline Dr Ste 600, Coppell, TX 75019-4676
Tel (469) 444-5330 *Founded/Ownrshp* 1870, 2010
Sales 112.3MM[E] *EMP* 550
SIC 2448 2449 2441 Pallets, wood & wood with metal; Skids, wood & wood with metal; Rectangular boxes & crates, wood; Nailed wood boxes & shook; Pallets, wood & wood with metal; Skids, wood & wood with metal; Rectangular boxes & crates, wood; Nailed wood boxes & shook
Pr: Brian Bulatao
**Pr:* Kenneth Wilson

D-U-N-S 15-088-1852 IMP
NEFAB PACKAGING INC
NEFAB COMPANIES
(*Suby of* NEFAB COMPANIES INC) ★
204 Airline Dr Ste 100, Coppell, TX 75019-4602
Tel (469) 444-5264 *Founded/Ownrshp* 2011
Sales 112.3MM[E] *EMP* 550
SIC 2448 2449 2441 Pallets, wood & wood with metal; Skids, wood & wood with metal; Rectangular boxes & crates, wood; Nailed wood boxes & shook; Pallets, wood & wood with metal; Skids, wood & wood with metal; Rectangular boxes & crates, wood; Nailed wood boxes & shook
CEO: Wade Mullis
**CFO:* Frank Slovacek
**Ex VP:* Eric Howe
DP Exec: Carlos Miranda

D-U-N-S 04-823-4074 EXP
NEFCO CORP (CT)
NORTHEASTERN FASTENERS
411 Burnham St, East Hartford, CT 06108-1157
Tel (860) 290-9044 *Founded/Ownrshp* 1981
Sales 97.5MM[E] *EMP* 106
SIC 5085 5072 Industrial supplies; Fasteners & fastening equipment; Fasteners, industrial: nuts, bolts, screws, etc.; Hardware; Industrial supplies; Fasteners & fastening equipment; Fasteners, industrial: nuts, bolts, screws, etc.; Hardware
Pr: David Gelles
**CFO:* Tom Drennen
**VP:* Ronald L Cipriano
VP: Skip Maxfield
Dir Bus: George Johnson
Rgnl Mgr: Lou Goodman
Sales Asso: Dick Linscott
Sales Asso: Christine Silver
Sales Asso: Troy Taschereau
Sales Asso: Bob Woerle

NEFCU
See NASSAU EDUCATORS FEDERAL CREDIT UNION

D-U-N-S 15-985-3576
NEFESH BNEFESH JEWISH SOULS UNITED INC
50 Eisenhower Dr, Paramus, NJ 07652-1429
Tel (201) 291-1060 *Founded/Ownrshp* 2004
Sales 22.8MM *EMP* 5
Accts Caspy & Caspy Cpa Jerusalem
SIC 8399 8621 Community development groups; Professional membership organizations; Community development groups; Professional membership organizations
Prin: David Suskauer
Bd of Dir: Tani Kramer
Bd of Dir: Adam Stopek

D-U-N-S 83-717-9167
NEFF BNP/COOPER INC
(*Suby of* BNP PARIBAS)
555 Croton Rd Fl 4, King of Prussia, PA 19406-3176
Tel (610) 491-1400 *Founded/Ownrshp* 1994
Sales 21.0MM[E] *EMP* 129[E]
SIC 6211 Investment bankers; Investment bankers
Ch Bd: Andrew Sterge
**COO:* Thomas Mahoney
**CFO:* Cathy Beckett
Sr Cor Off: Michel Laversanne
Sr VP: Ronald Gawel

D-U-N-S 07-962-6838
▲ NEFF CORP
3750 Nw 87th Ave Ste 400, Doral, FL 33178-2433
Tel (305) 513-3350 *Founded/Ownrshp* 2014
Sales 371.9MM *EMP* 1,064[E]
Tkr Sym NEFF *Exch* NYS
SIC 7359 Equipment rental & leasing; Equipment rental & leasing
CEO: Graham Hood
Ch Bd: James Continenza
Pr: Steve Michaels
COO: Westley Parks
COO: Jorge Vargas
CFO: Mark Irion
VP: John Anderson
Exec: Kevin Landgraver
Brnch Mgr: Graham Glasgow
CTO: Tim Shaw
Dir IT: Bill Carrillo
Board of Directors: Joseph Deignan, Gerard Holthaus, Robert Singer

NEFF ENGINEERING CO.
See NEFF GROUP DISTRIBUTORS INC

D-U-N-S 18-577-6150
NEFF GROUP DISTRIBUTORS INC
NEFF ENGINEERING CO.
7114 Innovation Blvd, Fort Wayne, IN 46818-1373
Tel (260) 489-6007 *Founded/Ownrshp* 1987
Sales 62.5MM[E] *EMP* 138
SIC 5084 Hydraulic systems equipment & supplies; Hydraulic systems equipment & supplies
Pr: John J Neff
**Treas:* Harry M Neff
VP: Patrick Madden
**VP:* Daniel W Neff
Exec: Bruce Miller
Brnch Mgr: Kurt Quine
Brnch Mgr: Kevin Smith
Dir IT: Patrick Scherrer
Sls Mgr: Chris Arvin
Sales Asso: Billy Davenport

D-U-N-S 96-253-9040
NEFF HOLDING LLC
3750 Nw 87th Ave Ste 400, Doral, FL 33178-2433
Tel (305) 513-3350 *Founded/Ownrshp* 2012
Sales 53.3MM[E] *EMP* 64[E]
SIC 6719 7359 Personal holding companies, except banks; Equipment rental & leasing
**CEO:* Graham Hood
**CFO:* Mark H Irion

D-U-N-S 00-790-3016 IMP/EXP
NEFF MOTIVATION INC
(*Suby of* VISANT CORP) ★
645 Pine St, Greenville, OH 45331-1624
Tel (937) 548-3194 *Founded/Ownrshp* 2007
Sales NA *EMP* 750
SIC 2399 3999 2329 2395 2759

D-U-N-S 00-427-8446
NEFF PACKAGING SOLUTIONS INC (OH)
10 Kingbrook Pkwy, Simpsonville, KY 40067-5625
Tel (502) 722-5020 *Founded/Ownrshp* 1959
Sales 90.2MM[E] *EMP* 346
SIC 2657 Folding paperboard boxes; Folding paperboard boxes
Ch Bd: Robert D Neff
**VP:* James M Younkin
Sfty Mgr: John Rulander

D-U-N-S 04-350-1956
NEFF POWER INC
13750 Shoreline Dr, Earth City, MO 63045-1221
Tel (314) 298-2300 *Founded/Ownrshp* 1965
Sales 33.3MM[E] *EMP* 24
SIC 5084 Instruments & control equipment
Pr: Kent Wemhoener
**VP:* Harry Heitmeier

D-U-N-S 83-276-7680
NEFF RENTAL LLC
(*Suby of* NEFF HOLDING LLC) ★
3750 Nw 87th Ave Ste 400, Doral, FL 33178-2433
Tel (305) 513-3350 *Founded/Ownrshp* 2010
Sales 45.0MM[E] *EMP* 64[E]
SIC 7359 Equipment rental & leasing; Equipment rental & leasing
Pr: Graham Hood
**CFO:* Mark Irion
Brnch Mgr: Wain Reed
Genl Mgr: Tim Bradshaw
CTO: Tim Shaw
IT Man: Edwin Rivera
Mktg Dir: Mark King

D-U-N-S 00-452-3205 IMP
NEFF-PERKINS CO (OH)
16080 Industrial Pkwy, Middlefield, OH 44062-9382
Tel (440) 632-1658 *Founded/Ownrshp* 1979
Sales 33.1MM[E] *EMP* 290
SIC 3069 3089

NEFTIN WESTLAKE CAR COMPANY
See CONEJO AUTO IMPORTS INC

D-U-N-S 07-920-1404
NEGAWATT BUSINESS SOLUTIONS
(*Suby of* GLACIAL ENERGY HOLDINGS) ★
24 Route 6a, Sandwich, MA 02563-1862
Tel (508) 833-3500 *Founded/Ownrshp* 2013
Sales 7.2MM[E] *EMP* 293[E]
SIC 8748 Energy conservation consultant
Pr: Gary Mole

D-U-N-S 00-633-4478
NEGWER MATERIALS INC (MO)
49 Airport Rd, Saint Louis, MO 63135-1998
Tel (314) 522-0579 *Founded/Ownrshp* 1928
Sales 67.5MM[E] *EMP* 195
SIC 5031

D-U-N-S 11-118-2189 IMP/EXP
NEH INC
Airport Ofc Pk Bl 2 400 R, Coraopolis, PA 15108
Tel (412) 299-7200 *Founded/Ownrshp* 2000
Sales 91.0MM[E] *EMP* 359
SIC 3313 6719 Electrometallurgical products; Investment holding companies, except banks; Electrometallurgical products; Investment holding companies, except banks
Pr: Geir I Kvernmo
**CFO:* Al Woodrich

D-U-N-S 83-170-1466 IMP
NEHEMIAH MANUFACTURING CO LLC
1130 Findlay St, Cincinnati, OH 45214-2052
Tel (513) 351-5700 *Founded/Ownrshp* 2009
Sales 30.0MM[E] *EMP* 50
SIC 5122 2844 Toiletries; Toilet preparations
CEO: Daniel Meyer
Pr: Richard T Palmer
COO: Mike Pachko
VP: Richard Halsey
VP: Dan Wall
Plnt Mgr: Randy Miller

D-U-N-S 00-521-2337 IMP
NEHRING ELECTRICAL WORKS CO (IL)
1005 E Locust St, Dekalb, IL 60115-3967
Tel (815) 756-2741 *Founded/Ownrshp* 1912, 1995
Sales 72.9MM[E] *EMP* 130
SIC 3351 3355 7692 Wire, copper & copper alloy; Aluminum wire & cable; Welding repair
Pr: Raymond C Hott
**Prin:* David Kozin
Sls Mgr: Nick Johnson

NEI
See NAMCO ENTERTAINMENT INC

NEI
See UNICOM ENGINEERING INC

NEI ADVANCED COMPOSITE TECH
See NORTHERN ELASTOMERIC INC

D-U-N-S 12-211-1081
NEI GLOBAL RELOCATION CO
(*Suby of* N P DODGE CO) ★
2707 N 118th St, Omaha, NE 68164-9672
Tel (402) 397-8486 *Founded/Ownrshp* 1979
Sales 71.8MM[E] *EMP* 400
SIC 8741 Management services; Management services
Pr: Kathleen C Dodge
Pr: Kate Chretien
**CEO:* Randy L Wilson
**Sec:* Michelle M Moore
**Sr VP:* Marti Briney
Sr VP: Kathy Hedley
Opers Mgr: Janell Anderson
Opers Mgr: Patricia Bond
Opers Mgr: Connie Smith
Plnt Mgr: Mitch Ulrich
VP Sls: Larry Brouder

NEI SYSTEMS
See NEW ENGLAND INTERCONNECT SYSTEMS INC

NEIEP TRUST FUND
See NATIONAL ELEVATOR INDUSTRY EDUCATIONAL PROGRAM

D-U-N-S 84-743-0543
NEIGHBOR INSURANCE AGENCY INC
FARMERS STATE BANK
1240 8th Ave, Marion, IA 52302-3504
Tel (319) 373-4307 *Founded/Ownrshp* 1968
Sales NA *EMP* 160
SIC 6022 State commercial banks; State commercial banks
Pr: Doug Neighbor
VP: Gene Neighbor
VP: Kent Neighbor
Dir IT: Lisa Beck

D-U-N-S 17-841-5469
NEIGHBORCARE HEALTH
1200 12th Ave S, Seattle, WA 98144-2712
Tel (206) 461-6935 *Founded/Ownrshp* 1972
Sales 53.7MM *EMP* 450
Accts Cliftonlarsonallen Llp Bellev
SIC 8011 8021 8741 Clinic, operated by physicians; Dental clinics & offices; Management services; Clinic, operated by physicians; Dental clinics & offices; Management services
Ex Dir: Mark Secord
Dir IT: Farhad Hyder
IT Man: Bob Austin
Doctor: Jinna Kim
Doctor: Lois Thetford

D-U-N-S 07-939-1435
■ NEIGHBORCARE HOLDINGS INC
(*Suby of* NEIGHBORCARE INC) ★
201 E 4th St Ste 900, Cincinnati, OH 45202-4160
Tel (513) 719-2600 *Founded/Ownrshp* 2014
Sales 388.0MM[E] *EMP* 3,533[E]
SIC 8741 Nursing & personal care facility management

D-U-N-S 13-108-8833
■ NEIGHBORCARE INC
(*Suby of* OMNICARE HOLDING COMPANY)
201 E 4th St Ste 900, Cincinnati, OH 45202-4160
Tel (513) 719-2600 *Founded/Ownrshp* 2005
Sales 388.0MM[E] *EMP* 3,000
SIC 5122 5912 5047 7389 Pharmaceuticals; Drug stores & proprietary stores; Medical equipment & supplies; Purchasing service; Pharmaceuticals; Drug stores & proprietary stores; Medical equipment & supplies; Purchasing service
Pr: Elizabeth A Haley
**COO:* Robert A Smith
**CFO:* Richard W Hunt
**Ex VP:* John L Kordash
**Sr VP:* John F Gaither Jr
Sr VP: Kirk Popeo
VP: Laurence F Lane
VP: James W Tabak
Exec: Tracey Crandell

D-U-N-S 07-942-3656
■ NEIGHBORCARE OF VIRGINIA LLC
(*Suby of* OMNICARE OF NEW YORK LLC) ★
201 E 4th St Ste 900, Cincinnati, OH 45202-4160
Tel (513) 719-2600 *Founded/Ownrshp* 2014
Sales 7.9MM[E] *EMP* 283[E]
SIC 5912 Drug stores & proprietary stores

D-U-N-S 07-942-6652
■ NEIGHBORCARE PHARMACY OF VIRGINIA LLC
(*Suby of* NEIGHBORCARE OF VIRGINIA LLC) ★
201 E 4th St Ste 900, Cincinnati, OH 45202-4160
Tel (513) 719-2600 *Founded/Ownrshp* 2001
Sales 7.9MM[E] *EMP* 280[E]
SIC 5912 Drug stores & proprietary stores

D-U-N-S 78-938-1873
■ NEIGHBORCARE PHARMACY SERVICES INC
(*Suby of* NEIGHBORCARE SERVICES CORP) ★
201 E 4th St Ste 1500, Cincinnati, OH 45202-4121
Tel (513) 719-2600 *Founded/Ownrshp* 1998
Sales 387.1MM[E] *EMP* 3,525[E]
SIC 5912 Drug stores
Pr: Elizabeth A Haley
**Treas:* Regis T Robbins

D-U-N-S 07-862-6571
■ NEIGHBORCARE SERVICES CORP
(*Suby of* NEIGHBORCARE HOLDINGS INC) ★
201 E 4th St Ste 900, Cincinnati, OH 45202-4160
Tel (513) 719-2600 *Founded/Ownrshp* 1989
Sales 387.1MM[E] *EMP* 3,528[E]
SIC 5122 Pharmaceuticals
CEO: John L Workman

D-U-N-S 01-607-8552
NEIGHBORGALL CONSTRUCTION CO
1216 7th Ave, Huntington, WV 25701-2320
Tel (304) 525-5181 *Founded/Ownrshp* 1926
Sales 20.0MM[E] *EMP* 75
SIC 1542 1541 Commercial & office building contractors; Institutional building construction; Industrial buildings & warehouses
Ch: Charles R Neighborgall III
**Pr:* C R Neighborgall IV
**VP:* Chad Johnson

D-U-N-S 94-751-5615
NEIGHBORHOOD ASSISTANCE CORP OF AMERICA
225 Centre St, Roxbury, MA 02119-1288
Tel (617) 250-6222 *Founded/Ownrshp* 1994
Sales 51.4MM *EMP* 100
Accts Gonzalez And Associates Pc St
SIC 8322 Individual & family services; Individual & family services
**Pr:* Bruce Marks
**Treas:* Glynn Lloyd

D-U-N-S 07-303-2765
NEIGHBORHOOD CENTERS INC
WORK SOURCE
4500 Bissonnet St Ste 200, Bellaire, TX 77401-3113
Tel (713) 667-9400 *Founded/Ownrshp* 1907
Sales 246.1MM *EMP* 1,000
Accts Blazek & Vetterling Houston
SIC 8351 8322 Child day care services; Neighborhood center; Child day care services; Neighborhood center
Pr: Angela Blanchard
Dir Vol: Lauren Duplessis
Treas: Nancy Mitchell
**Sr VP:* Ray Chung
**Sr VP:* Emelda Douglas
Sr VP: Samuel Palacios
**Sr VP:* Claudia Vasquez
VP: Karim Ellsworth
VP: Ann Hilbig
VP: Karim Kafray
VP: Katherine Lebla
VP: Joe Rubio

D-U-N-S 88-309-6299
■ NEIGHBORHOOD HEALTH PARTNERSHIP INC
(*Suby of* UNITED HEALTHCARE OF FLORIDA INC) ★
7600 Nw 19th St Ste 100, Miami, FL 33126-1219
Tel (305) 715-2200 *Founded/Ownrshp* 2005
Sales NA *EMP* 421
SIC 6324 6321 Health maintenance organization (HMO), insurance only; Accident & health insurance; Health maintenance organization (HMO), insurance only; Accident & health insurance
CEO: Joseph Papa
CFO: Mercy C Kirk
**CFO:* Mercy Kirkpatrick
**Ex VP:* John Fries
**Sr VP:* Charles Ricevuto
CIO: Thomas Packert
Dir IT: Gary Kalin

D-U-N-S 18-117-4434
NEIGHBORHOOD HEALTH PLAN
NHP
(*Suby of* PARTNERS HEALTHCARE SYSTEM INC) ★
253 Summer St Fl 5, Boston, MA 02210-1120
Tel (617) 772-5500 *Founded/Ownrshp* 2012
Sales 1.3MMM *EMP* 340[E]
SIC 8011 Health maintenance organization; Health maintenance organization
Pr: Deborah Enos
COO: Shantha Diaz
**CFO:* Garrett Parker
CFO: Doug Thompson
**VP:* Jill D Arbeloff
VP: Jill Arbeloff
**VP:* Carla Bettano
VP: Deb Bonin
**VP:* Katie Catlender
VP Bus Dev: Jill D'Arbeloff
Genl Mgr: Kathy Foley

D-U-N-S 87-450-3998
NEIGHBORHOOD HEALTH PLAN OF RHODE ISLAND
299 Promenade St, Providence, RI 02908-5720
Tel (401) 459-6000 *Founded/Ownrshp* 1995
Sales NA *EMP* 150
Accts Ernst & Young Llp Boston Ma
SIC 6411 Insurance agents; Insurance agents
Ch: Merrill Thomas
**CEO:* James A Hooley
COO: Shantha Diaz
COO: Raymond M Sessler
CFO: Debbie Greve
CFO: Scott F Ogorman
**CFO:* T Clark Phillip Jr
CFO: Thomas Clark Phillip Jr
CFO: Gregory J Young
**Treas:* Peter Walsh
Dir Rx: Vargas Peter
Dir Rx: Peter Vargas
Comm Man: Tom Boucher

D-U-N-S 01-566-9193
NEIGHBORHOOD HEALTH PROVIDERS INC
521 5th Ave Fl 3, New York, NY 10175-0399
Tel (212) 883-0883 *Founded/Ownrshp* 2010
Sales 415.3MM *EMP* 5
SIC 8099 Health & allied services
CEO: Steven J Bory

D-U-N-S 09-824-4783
NEIGHBORHOOD HEALTHCARE
425 N Date St Ste 203, Escondido, CA 92025-3413
Tel (760) 746-0395 *Founded/Ownrshp* 1971
Sales 43.1MM *EMP* 490
Accts Tca Partners Llp Fresno Cal
SIC 8011 Clinic, operated by physicians; Clinic, operated by physicians
CEO: Tracy Ream
**Pr:* Johnny Watson
**COO:* Amparo Mahler

*CFO: Lisa Daigle
*Treas: Stephen P Yerxa
*VP: Richard Marino
Dir Lab: Claudia Olague
Dir IT: Marina Lomeli
Site Mgr: Lourdes Acevedo
Doctor: Rakesh Patel

D-U-N-S 07-333-7461
NEIGHBORHOOD HOUSE ASSOCIATION
N H A
5660 Copley Dr, San Diego, CA 92111-7902
Tel (858) 715-2642 Founded/Ownrshp 1914
Sales 40.9MM^E EMP 1,000
SIC 8322 Neighborhood center; Neighborhood center
CEO: Rudolph A Johnson III
COO: Michael Kemp
CFO: Kim Peck
Treas: Derek Brown
VP: Norma Johnson

D-U-N-S 09-636-3700
NEIGHBORHOOD REINVESTMENT CORP
NEIGHBORWORKS OF AMERICA
999 N Capitol St Ne # 900, Washington, DC 20002-4684
Tel (202) 760-4000 Founded/Ownrshp 1978
Sales 261.2MM EMP 260
Accts Bdo Usa Llp Bethesda Md
SIC 8611 Community affairs & services; Community affairs & services
Pr: Chuck Wehrwein
*Ch Bd: Sarah Bloom Raskin
V Ch: Rodney E Hood
V Ch: Rodney Hood
*CEO: Paul Weech
COO: Eileen Fitzgerald
COO: Margo Kelly
*CFO: Leonard Williams
Treas: Jeff Marshall
*V Ch Bd: Debbie Matz
Bd of Dir: Terry Cunningham
Bd of Dir: Stacey Epperson
Bd of Dir: Randall S Kroszner
Bd of Dir: Paul Lopez
Bd of Dir: Vickie McGinnis
Bd of Dir: Jon Murakami
Sr VP: Christina McHenry
Sr VP: Zewdneh Shiferaw
Sr VP: Steve Slepian
VP: Richard Berliner
VP: Damodar Konda
Board of Directors: Craig Gilmore, Bonnie Gilovich, Connie Lindsey, Brian Montgomery, Frank Pagura, Andre Payten

D-U-N-S 86-945-9180 IMP
NEIGHBORHOOD RESTAURANTS INC
601 Main St Ste 102, Hazard, KY 41701-1382
Tel (606) 436-0736 Founded/Ownrshp 1991
Sales 66.6MM^E EMP 2,000
SIC 5812 Fast-food restaurant, chain; Fast-food restaurant, chain
Pr: Theresa Johnson
*Treas: Marty Johnson

D-U-N-S 04-341-9399
NEIGHBORHOOD SERVICE ORGANIZATION INC (MI)
882 Oakman Blvd Ste C, Detroit, MI 48238-4019
Tel (313) 961-4890 Founded/Ownrshp 1955
Sales 26.6MM EMP 310
Accts George Johnson & Company Detr
SIC 8399 Antipoverty board; Antipoverty board
Pr: Sheliah Clay
*COO: William Weld-Wallis
*CFO: Allyson S Farquhar Boyle
Treas: Reginald Pelzer
*VP: Joe Heaphy
*VP: Laneice Jones
Dir IT: Brad Bishop
Mktg Mgr: Denise Figurski
Pgrm Dir: Staci Hirsch
Pgrm Dir: Reginald Williams

NEIGHBORS CARE HOME HEALTH
See CHESTER HMA LLC

D-U-N-S 03-122-6434
NEIGHBORS CONSTRUCTION CO INC
9800 Legler Rd, Lenexa, KS 66219-1263
Tel (913) 422-5555 Founded/Ownrshp 1951
Sales 76.9MM EMP 70
SIC 1522 5031 Residential construction; Lumber, plywood & millwork; Residential construction; Lumber, plywood & millwork
Pr: Roger H Neighbors
VP: Steve Buche
*VP: Aaron Neighbors
*VP: Nancy L Neighbors

D-U-N-S 01-783-9637
NEIGHBORS EMERGENCY CENTER LLC
(Suby of NEIGHBORS HEALTH SYSTEM INC) ★
11200 Broadway St # 2320, Pearland, TX 77584-9785
Tel (713) 436-5200 Founded/Ownrshp 2013
Sales 30.8MM^E EMP 250^E
SIC 8011 Freestanding emergency medical center; Freestanding emergency medical center
CEO: Setul Patel
COO: Bruce McVeigh
CFO: John Decker
Chf Nrs Of: Lauren Cotton

D-U-N-S 08-555-6348
NEIGHBORS FEDERAL CREDIT UNION
12529 Perkins Rd, Baton Rouge, LA 70810-1907
Tel (225) 819-2178 Founded/Ownrshp 1954
Sales NA EMP 150
SIC 6061 Federal credit unions; Federal credit unions
Ch Bd: Melody Brunson
V Ch: Bill Robins
CEO: Norman Thompson
Treas: Andrew Redmond
Ofcr: Deidre Harbor
Ofcr: Patrice Kelly
Ofcr: Randy Pastuszek
Ex VP: Kathy Gill
Ex VP: Lee Gound
Sr VP: Dan Robichaux
VP: Christy Jewell
VP: Jody Lee
VP: Stephen Mathews
VP: Leah Tate
VP: Christina Viso

D-U-N-S 07-933-9756
NEIGHBORS HEALTH SYSTEM INC
11200 Broadway St # 2320, Pearland, TX 77584-9786
Tel (713) 436-5200 Founded/Ownrshp 2008
Sales 32.2MM^E EMP 211^E
SIC 8011 Freestanding emergency medical center
Pr: Setul G Patel MD

D-U-N-S 78-977-6168
NEIGHBORS IN NEED OF SERVICES INC
NINOS
402 W Robertson St, San Benito, TX 78586-3778
Tel (956) 399-9944 Founded/Ownrshp 1990
Sales 24.2MM^E EMP 550
Accts Schriver Carmona & Carrera Pll
SIC 8351 Head start center, except in conjunction with school; Head start center, except in conjunction with school
Pr: Alberto Garcia
*Treas: Mary F Sosa
*VP: Roque Rodriguez

D-U-N-S 02-257-7506
NEIGHBORS STORES INC
ACTION OUTDOOR ADVERTISING
1314 Old Highway 601, Mount Airy, NC 27030-7211
Tel (336) 789-5561 Founded/Ownrshp 1982
Sales 102.3MM EMP 130
SIC 5541 5411 Filling stations, gasoline; Grocery stores, independent; Filling stations, gasoline; Grocery stores, independent
Pr: Gary York
*CFO: Donna Draughn

NEIGHBORWORKS OF AMERICA
See NEIGHBORHOOD REINVESTMENT CORP

NEIL
See NUCLEAR ELECTRIC INSURANCE LIMITED

D-U-N-S 82-882-2929
NEIL COLLIN
YORK PHOTO LABS
10501 Rhode Island Ave, Beltsville, MD 20705-2317
Tel (301) 937-5300 Founded/Ownrshp 2008
Sales 13.1MM^E EMP 650
SIC 7221 Photographic studios, portrait; Photographic studios, portrait
Owner: Neil Collin

D-U-N-S 00-389-7139
NEIL F LAMPSON INC
607 E Columbia Dr, Kennewick, WA 99336-3778
Tel (509) 586-0411 Founded/Ownrshp 1971
Sales 31.9MM^E EMP 200
SIC 7353 3531 1799 4213 3537 Heavy construction equipment rental; Cranes & aerial lift equipment, rental or leasing; Backhoes, tractors, cranes, plows & similar equipment; Rigging & scaffolding; Heavy machinery transport; Industrial trucks & tractors; Heavy construction equipment rental; Backhoes, tractors, cranes, plows & similar equipment; Rigging & scaffolding; Heavy machinery transport; Industrial trucks & tractors
Ch Bd: William N Lampson
*Treas: Mary Lampson
*VP: Jenny Lampson

D-U-N-S 04-491-1311
NEIL HUFFMAN VOLKSWAGEN INC
NEIL HUFFMAN VOLKSWGN SUBRU MA
4926 Dixie Hwy, Louisville, KY 40216-2598
Tel (502) 448-6666 Founded/Ownrshp 1968
Sales 37.1MM^E EMP 75
SIC 5511 7538 7532 7515 5531 5521 Automobiles, new & used; Pickups, new & used; Vans, new & used; General automotive repair shops; Top & body repair & paint shops; Passenger car leasing; Automotive & home supply stores; Used car dealers; Automobiles, new & used; Pickups, new & used; Vans, new & used; General automotive repair shops; Top & body repair & paint shops; Passenger car leasing; Automotive & home supply stores; Used car dealers
CEO: Dow Huffman
*VP: Ethel Huffman
Genl Mgr: Kent Foushee
Sls Mgr: Steve Al-Jabiri
Sls Mgr: Arthur Galitsky
Sls Mgr: Chuck Norton
Sales Asso: Christopher Stewart

NEIL HUFFMAN VOLKSWGN SUBRU MA
See NEIL HUFFMAN VOLKSWAGEN INC

D-U-N-S 05-222-3401 IMP/EXP
NEIL JONES FOOD CO
NORTHWEST PACKING CO.
1701 W 16th St, Vancouver, WA 98660-1067
Tel (360) 696-4356 Founded/Ownrshp 1980
Sales 21.9MM^E EMP 125
SIC 2033

D-U-N-S 02-773-3369
NEIL KELLY CO INC
NEIL KLLY DESIGNERS/REMODELERS
804 N Alberta St, Portland, OR 97217-2693
Tel (503) 288-7461 Founded/Ownrshp 1990
Sales 73.8MM^E EMP 205
SIC 1521 1542

NEIL KLLY DESIGNERS/REMODELERS
See NEIL KELLY CO INC

NEIL MEDICAL GROUP
See PHARM-SAVE INC

D-U-N-S 00-827-8525
NEILL AIRCRAFT CO (CA)
1260 W 15th St, Long Beach, CA 90813-1390
Tel (562) 435-4574 Founded/Ownrshp 1956
Sales 51.4MM^E EMP 174
SIC 3728 Aircraft body & wing assemblies & parts; Aircraft body & wing assemblies & parts
Pr: Judith L Carpenter
COO: Don Tole
*CFO: Sydney T Wakeling
Dir Bus: Brad Barnette
Genl Mgr: Brad Barnett
Genl Mgr: Sue Christiansen
Genl Mgr: Gonzalo Riya
IT Man: Gonzalo Rivas

D-U-N-S 04-973-3777 IMP
NEILL CORP
SALONBIZ
303 S Pine St, Hammond, LA 70403-4133
Tel (985) 345-1085 Founded/Ownrshp 1968
Sales 135.9MM^E EMP 550
SIC 5087 5999 Barber shop equipment & supplies; Hair care products; Barber shop equipment & supplies; Hair care products
CEO: Edwin H Neill III
*Ch Bd: Debra Neill
VP: Donna Dixon
*VP: Roger Doody
VP: Kim Mason
Rgnl Mgr: Richelle Richardson
Area Mgr: Kim Poole
Area Mgr: Lauren Roy
MIS Dir: Keith Stokes
Dir IT: Bill Curry
Genl Couns: Jennifer Lee

D-U-N-S 00-694-5596 IMP
NEILL-LAVIELLE SUPPLY CO LLC (KY)
1711 S Floyd St, Louisville, KY 40208-2741
Tel (502) 637-5401 Founded/Ownrshp 1908, 1916
Sales 61.4MM^E EMP 127
SIC 5085

NEILLO AUDI
See NIELLO IMPORTS II INC

D-U-N-S 79-929-5915 IMP
NEILMED PHARMACEUTICALS INC
601 Aviation Blvd, Santa Rosa, CA 95403-1025
Tel (707) 525-3784 Founded/Ownrshp 2000
Sales 71.8MM^E EMP 300
SIC 5999 Medical apparatus & supplies; Medical apparatus & supplies
CEO: Kaetan Mehta MD
*Pr: Nina K Mehta
VP: Dinesh Patel
Mng Dir: Poonam Prabhu
QA Dir: Evelinda Ruiz
IT Man: Judy Brewer
IT Man: Ken Di Lillo
IT Man: Bharat Mehta

NEIL'S FINANCE PLAZA
See FINANCE PLAZA INC

D-U-N-S 10-915-9405
NEIMAN ENTERPRISES INC
RUSHMORE FOREST PRODUCTS
51 State Highway 112, Hulett, WY 82720-9657
Tel (307) 467-5252 Founded/Ownrshp 1958
Sales 98.2MM^E EMP 400
SIC 2421 Lumber: rough, sawed or planed; Kiln drying of lumber; Planing mills; Lumber: rough, sawed or planed; Kiln drying of lumber; Planing mills
Pr: James S Neiman
*COO: Tom Shaffer
*CFO: Chad Voyles
*VP: Jim D Neiman

D-U-N-S 07-918-1478
NEIMAN MARCUS GROUP INC
1618 Main St, Dallas, TX 75201-4748
Tel (214) 743-7600 Founded/Ownrshp 2013
Sales 5.1MMM^E EMP 16,500^E
SIC 5311 5961 Department stores; Catalog & mail-order houses; Department stores; Catalog & mail-order houses
Pr: Karen Katz

D-U-N-S 17-909-7431 IMP/EXP
NEIMAN MARCUS GROUP LLC
(Suby of NEIMAN MARCUS GROUP LTD LLC) ★
1618 Main St, Dallas, TX 75201-4748
Tel (214) 741-6911 Founded/Ownrshp 2005
Sales 2.0MMM^E EMP 14,400
SIC 5311 Department stores, non-discount; Department stores, non-discount
CFO: James E Skinner
COO: James Skinner
CFO: Michael Wirkkala
Ex VP: Karen Katz
Ex VP: Dale Stapleton
Ex VP: Connie Wald
Sr VP: Nelson A Bangs
Sr VP: Steven Dennis
Sr VP: Marita O'Dea
VP: Gail Mann
VP: Cynthia Marcus
Creative D: Georgia Christensen
Board of Directors: David A Barr, Ron Beegle, Jonathan Coslet, James Coulter, John G Danhakl, Sidney Lapidus, Carrie Wheeler

D-U-N-S 60-731-5137 IMP/EXP
NEIMAN MARCUS GROUP LTD LLC
(Suby of MARIPOSA INTERMEDIATE HOLDINGS LLC) ★
1618 Main St, Dallas, TX 75201-4748
Tel (214) 743-7600 Founded/Ownrshp 2013
Sales 5.1MMM EMP 15,100^E
Accts Ernst & Young Llp Dallas Tex
SIC 5311 5961 Department stores; Catalog & mail-order houses; Department stores; Catalog & mail-order houses
Pr: Karen W Katz
Pr: Bob Devlin
Pr: James J Gold
Pr: John E Koryl
Pr: Joshua G Schulman
Pr: Ariela Shani
COO: Donald T Grimes
Treas: Stacie R Shirley
Chf Mktg O: Wanda M Gierhart
Ofcr: Joseph N Weber
Sr VP: Wanda Gierhar
Sr VP: Wayne Hussey
Sr VP: Michael R Kingston
Sr VP: Thomas J Lind
Sr VP: Martia O'Dea
Sr VP: Tracy M Preston
Sr VP: T Dale Stapleton
Creative D: Trey Hoffmann

D-U-N-S 04-853-9472
NEIMAN SAWMILLS INC
RUSHMORE FOREST PRODUCTS
(Suby of NEIMAN ENTERPRISES INC) ★
51 State Highway 112, Hulett, WY 82720-9657
Tel (307) 467-5252 Founded/Ownrshp 1958
Sales 24.2MM^E EMP 190
SIC 2421 Lumber: rough, sawed or planed; Kiln drying of lumber; Lumber: rough, sawed or planed; Kiln drying of lumber
Pr: James Samuel Neiman
*Sec: Sally Ann Neiman
VP: Jerry Wood
Plnt Mgr: Tom Shaffer

NEIMAN-REED LUMBER CO
See LUMBER CITY CORP

NEIMAN'S FAMILY MARKET
See ALPENAS SUPERMARKET INC

D-U-N-S 10-237-0426
NEISEWANDER ENTERPRISES INC
RAYNOR GARAGE DOOR
1101 E River Rd, Dixon, IL 61021-3252
Tel (815) 288-1431 Founded/Ownrshp 1944
Sales 223.1MM^E EMP 1,800
SIC 3442 2431 3429 Garage doors, overhead: metal; Garage doors, overhead: wood; Manufactured hardware (general); Garage doors, overhead: metal; Garage doors, overhead: wood; Manufactured hardware (general)
Pr: Ray H Neisewander III

NEIU 19
See NORTHEASTERN EDUCATIONAL INTERMEDIATE UNIT 19

D-U-N-S 78-203-1272 IMP
NEJ INC
NORTHEAST JOBBERS
170 Pines Bridge Rd, Beacon Falls, CT 06403-1018
Tel (203) 759-0016 Founded/Ownrshp 1990
Sales 78.5MM^E EMP 80
SIC 5136 5137 Men's & boys' clothing; Women's & children's clothing; Men's & boys' clothing; Women's & children's clothing
Pr: Ed Mascolo
*CFO: Linda Trudel
*VP: Irene Mascolo

D-U-N-S 60-424-1120 IMP/EXP
NEKOOSA COATED PRODUCTS LLC
(Suby of WINGATE PARTNERS LP) ★
841 Market St, Nekoosa, WI 54457-1134
Tel (715) 886-4700 Founded/Ownrshp 2005
Sales 45.4MM^E EMP 160
SIC 2671 Packaging paper & plastics film, coated & laminated; Packaging paper & plastics film, coated & laminated
CEO: Paul Charapata
CFO: Walter Weigel
Opers Mgr: Mike Bluell
Opers Mgr: Abe Gildenzoph
Sls Mgr: Aaron Bares

D-U-N-S 00-613-7202
NEKOOSA PAPERS INC
GEORGIA PACIFIC
(Suby of GEORGIA-PACIFIC LLC) ★
133 Peachtree St Ne # 1, Atlanta, GA 30303-1804
Tel (404) 652-4000 Founded/Ownrshp 1908
Sales 33.4MM^E EMP 100
SIC 2621 Fine paper; Fine paper
Ch Bd: A D Correll
Treas: Jerry Shark
Chf Mktg O: Michael Dunn
Ex VP: Keith Parker
VP: Bob Clark
VP: Diana Knigge
Off Mgr: Joyce Mitchell
QA Dir: Tobi Tommasini
Dir IT: Russ Durham
Info Man: Deb Edler
Sfty Mgr: Ray Fararo

D-U-N-S 78-329-6023
▲ NEKTAR THERAPEUTICS
455 Mission Bay Blvd S, San Francisco, CA 94158-2158
Tel (415) 482-5300 Founded/Ownrshp 1990
Sales 200.7MM EMP 438
Tkr Sym NKTR Exch NGS
SIC 2834 Pharmaceutical preparations; Pharmaceutical preparations
Pr: Howard W Robin
*Ch Bd: Robert B Chess
CFO: John Nicholson
Chf Mktg O: Ivan P Gergel
Sr VP: Stephen K Doberstein
Sr VP: Ivan Gergel
Sr VP: Gil M Labrucherie
Sr VP: Timothy A Riley
Sr VP: Jillian B Thomsen
VP: Deirdre Bevard
VP: Frank Curtis
VP: Dorian Hirth
VP: Chulani Karunatilake
VP: Gil Labrucherie
VP Bus Dev: James Hattersley
Exec: Michael Weickert
Assoc Dir: Neel Anand
Assoc Dir: Yen Chia
Assoc Dir: Michael Lungrin
Assoc Dir: Theodore Maylath
Assoc Dir: Chanthaly Phonthibsvads
Board of Directors: R Scott Greer, Joseph J Krivulka, Christopher A Kuebler, Lutz Lingnau, Susan Wang, Roy A Whitfield, Dennis L Winger

D-U-N-S 07-853-8991
NEKTOVA GROUP LIMITED LIABILITY CO
534 Whitesville Rd, Jackson, NJ 08527-5044
Tel (732) 835-2303 *Founded/Ownrshp* 2012
Sales 55.0MM *EMP* 28
SIC 5065 Electronic parts
Mng Pt: Yakov Anisfeld

NELA
See NORTHWEST EDUCATION LOAN ASSOCIATION

NELCO
See NEW ENGLAND LEAD BURNING CO INC

NELCO
See GREATLAND CORP

D-U-N-S 03-804-7601 IMP
■ **NELCO PRODUCTS INC**
(*Suby of* PARK ELECTROCHEMICAL CORP) ★
1411 E Orangethorpe Ave, Fullerton, CA 92831-5297
Tel (714) 879-4293 *Founded/Ownrshp* 1975
Sales 21.3MM[E] *EMP* 135
SIC 3083 Laminated plastics plate & sheet; Laminated plastics plate & sheet
CEO: Margaret M Kendrick
VP: Jim Stewart
Sfty Mgr: Mick Walker
Opers Mgr: Timothy Slipp
Mktg Dir: Amy Greenberg
Sls Mgr: Emily Groehl

D-U-N-S 08-669-8404
NELCON INC
304 Jellison Rd, Kalispell, MT 59901-6503
Tel (406) 756-8560 *Founded/Ownrshp* 1994
Sales 22.2MM[E] *EMP* 80
SIC 1623 1611 Underground utilities contractor; General contractor, highway & street construction
Pr: Mike P White
**Sec:* George Schultz
Ofcr: Lorna Smith
**VP:* Val B White

D-U-N-S 00-167-6030 IMP
NELIPAK CORP
21 Amflex Dr, Cranston, RI 02921-2028
Tel (401) 946-2699 *Founded/Ownrshp* 1965, 2013
Sales 34.4MM[E] *EMP* 174[E]
SIC 3081 3083 2671 Packing materials, plastic sheet; Laminated plastics plate & sheet; Packaging paper & plastics film, coated & laminated
Ch Bd: Gregory Myers
**Pr:* Michael Kelly
**Treas:* Paul Hogan
IT Man: Chris Sowdon
QI Cn Mgr: Juanita Evans

D-U-N-S 80-696-8991
NELL LITTLE HOTEL
(*Suby of* ASPEN SKIING CO LLC) ★
675 E Durant Ave, Aspen, CO 81611-2001
Tel (970) 920-4600 *Founded/Ownrshp* 1995
Sales 19.9MM[E] *EMP* 350
SIC 7011 Hotels; Hotels
Dir Soc: Jennifer Carlson
Dir Soc: Casarae Clark
Dir Soc: Mark Elias
Dir Soc: Lindsay McConnell
Dir Soc: Lindsay Potts
Genl Mgr: Efren Vargas
Pr Mgr: Sally Spaulding

D-U-N-S 05-465-2201 IMP
■ **NELLCOR PURITAN BENNETT INC**
COVIDIEN
(*Suby of* COVIDIEN LP) ★
15 Hampshire St, Mansfield, MA 02048-1113
Tel (508) 261-8000 *Founded/Ownrshp* 2012
Sales 305.2MM[E] *EMP* 4,000
SIC 3845 3841 Patient monitoring apparatus; Automated blood & body fluid analyzers, except laboratory; Respiratory analysis equipment, electromedical; Electromedical apparatus; Surgical & medical instruments; Patient monitoring apparatus; Automated blood & body fluid analyzers, except laboratory; Respiratory analysis equipment, electromedical; Electromedical apparatus; Surgical & medical instruments
VP: William Stone
Sys Eng: Hoa Nguy

D-U-N-S 09-309-9943
NELLIS MANAGEMENT CO LLC (IA)
LONG JOHN SILVER'S
2940 104th St, Urbandale, IA 50322-3815
Tel (515) 252-1742 *Founded/Ownrshp* 1964
Sales 20.1MM[E] *EMP* 520
SIC 5812 Fast-food restaurant, chain; Fast-food restaurant, chain
COO: Jon L Harmsen
**Pr:* Mark A Levitt
**VP:* Ken Waltman
Dir IT: John Wilson
Site Mgr: Michelle Engelman
Site Mgr: Michelle Manders

D-U-N-S 11-825-1649
NELLO CAPITAL INC
105 E Jefferson Blvd, South Bend, IN 46601-1922
Tel (574) 288-3632 *Founded/Ownrshp* 2002
Sales 30.7MM[E] *EMP* 136
SIC 3663 Airborne radio communications equipment; Airborne radio communications equipment
Pr: Daniel Ianello
**CFO:* Kevin Brisson
**VP:* Robert Rumpler

NELLO CONSTRUCTION
See GITO INC

D-U-N-S 11-829-2841 IMP/EXP
NELLO INC
(*Suby of* NELLO CAPITAL INC) ★
105 E Jefferson Blvd # 525, South Bend, IN 46601-1992
Tel (574) 288-3632 *Founded/Ownrshp* 2001
Sales 31.5MM[E] *EMP* 120
SIC 3441 Fabricated structural metal; Fabricated structural metal
Pr: Dan Ianello
**CFO:* Kevin Brisson
**VP:* Bob Rumpler
Sales Exec: Jason Lambert

NELL'S FAMILY MARKET
See NK LIQUIDATION INC

D-U-N-S 04-741-9627 IMP
NELLSON NUTRACEUTICAL LLC
5801 Ayala Ave, Irwindale, CA 91706-6216
Tel (626) 812-6522 *Founded/Ownrshp* 2002
Sales 62.5MM[E] *EMP* 297
SIC 2064 Candy bars, including chocolate covered bars; Candy bars, including chocolate covered bars
CEO: Scott Greenwood
**Pr:* Ben Muhlenkamp
**CEO:* Jeff Moran
**CFO:* Ted Schouten
**Sr VP:* Paul Hanson
QA Dir: Evelyn Reher

D-U-N-S 80-957-7716
NELLSON NUTRACEUTICAL LLC
5801 Ayala Ave, Irwindale, CA 91706-6216
Tel (626) 815-3312 *Founded/Ownrshp* 2013
Sales 127.0MM[E] *EMP* 400[E]
SIC 5499 Health foods; Health foods
Pr: Scott Greenwood
CFO: Manuel Martinez
Ex VP: Andrew Rodgers
VP: Bart Child
VP: Raymond Collins
VP: Paul Hanson
VP: Jeremy Ivie
IT Man: Ken Tran
VP Mfg: Tom Jagiela
VP Opers: Frank Lingenfelter
Mfg Dir: Jim Terry

D-U-N-S 13-496-0447
▲ **NELNET INC**
121 S 13th St Ste 201, Lincoln, NE 68508-1922
Tel (402) 458-2370 *Founded/Ownrshp* 1977
Sales NA *EMP* 3,100[E]
Tkr Sym NNI *Exch* NYS
SIC 6141 7389 Personal credit institutions; Financial services; Personal credit institutions; Financial services
CEO: Jeffrey R Noordhoek
**Ch Bd:* Michael S Dunlap
Pr: Timothy A Tewes
COO: Terry J Heimes
CFO: James D Kruger
**V Ch Bd:* Stephen F Butterfield
Board of Directors: James P Abel, William R Cintani, Kathleen A Farrell, David S Graff, Thomas E Henning, Kimberly K Rath, Michael D Reardon

D-U-N-S 06-809-6275
■ **NELNET STUDENT LOAN CORP-1**
UNION FINANCIAL SERVICES
(*Suby of* NELNET INC) ★
121 S 13th St Ste 301, Lincoln, NE 68508-1904
Tel (402) 458-2370 *Founded/Ownrshp* 1996
Sales NA *EMP* 1
SIC 6111 Student Loan Marketing Association; Student Loan Marketing Association
CEO: Steven Butterfield

D-U-N-S 03-999-7200 IMP
NELSEN CORP
3250 Barber Rd, Norton, OH 44203-1012
Tel (330) 745-6000 *Founded/Ownrshp* 1954
Sales 32.0MM[E] *EMP* 50[E]
SIC 5074 Water heaters & purification equipment; Water purification equipment
CEO: Ronald E Nelsen
**Pr:* David Nelsen
**Sec:* Jeanette Nelsen
**VP:* Kim Bell
Off Mgr: Christine Villalobos
Sales Asso: Calvin Washechek

NELSEN RV WORLD
See A C NELSEN ENTERPRISES INC

D-U-N-S 00-507-5528 IMP
NELSEN STEEL AND WIRE LP
NELSEN STEEL COMPANY
9415 King St, Franklin Park, IL 60131
Tel (847) 671-9700 *Founded/Ownrshp* 1939
Sales 62.2MM[E] *EMP* 80
SIC 3316 Bars, steel, cold finished, from purchased hot-rolled; Bars, steel, cold finished, from purchased hot-rolled
CEO: C Davis Nelsen II
VP: John R Mc Vicker
Sls Mgr: Tony Eyck
Snr Mgr: Davis Nelsen

NELSEN STEEL COMPANY
See NELSEN STEEL AND WIRE LP

NELSON & ASSOCIATES
See NELSON WORLDWIDE INC

D-U-N-S 03-818-3224
NELSON & ASSOCIATES INC
12816 Leffingwell Ave, Santa Fe Springs, CA 90670-6343
Tel (562) 921-4423 *Founded/Ownrshp* 1977
Sales 33.0MM[E] *EMP* 75
SIC 5063 Electrical supplies; Telephone & telegraph wire & cable
CEO: Todd James Nelson
**Ex VP:* Brian Haupt
**Prin:* Kurt Nelson
VP Sls: Jim Lewis
Sls Mgr: Jimmy Boyd
Sales Asso: Kathy Arnold
Sales Asso: Theresa Coppock
Sales Asso: Brett Murphy
Sales Asso: Steve Vasquez

D-U-N-S 00-909-3410 IMP/EXP
NELSON & SONS INC
SKRETTING USA
(*Subsy of* NUTRECO N.V.)
712 E 2400 N, Tooele, UT 84074-3476
Tel (435) 277-2100 *Founded/Ownrshp* 2012
Sales 27.0MM *EMP* 50[E]
SIC 2048

NELSON A TAYLOR CO
See TAYLOR MADE GROUP HOLDINGS INC

NELSON AGRI CENTER
See NELSON MILL & AGRI-CENTER INC

D-U-N-S 00-155-8642
NELSON AIR DEVICE CORP (NY)
C W SHEET METAL
4628 54th Ave, Maspeth, NY 11378-1012
Tel (718) 729-3801 *Founded/Ownrshp* 1938, 1965
Sales 89.4MM[E] *EMP* 200
SIC 3444 1711 Ducts, sheet metal; Heating & air conditioning contractors; Ducts, sheet metal; Heating & air conditioning contractors
Pr: Nelson Blitz Jr
**VP:* Michael Doff
**VP:* Peter Unrath
Opers Mgr: Mike Fry
Snr PM: Charles Arcuri
Snr PM: Gordon Mund
Snr PM: Scott Niemann
Snr Mgr: Brian Flynn

D-U-N-S 02-279-3624
NELSON AUTO CENTER INC
2228 College Way, Fergus Falls, MN 56537-1062
Tel (218) 998-8818 *Founded/Ownrshp* 1992
Sales 31.0MM[E] *EMP* 80
SIC 5511 Automobiles, new & used; Pickups, new & used; Automobiles, new & used; Pickups, new & used
Pr: Brent Nelson
**VP:* Laurel Nelson
Mktg Mgr: Janell Yutrzenka
Sls Mgr: Tom Moll
Sales Asso: Dean Anderson
Sales Asso: Tanner Drewelow
Sales Asso: Trevor Funkhouser
Sales Asso: Travis Hopkins
Sales Asso: Chad Swenson

D-U-N-S 06-367-1234 IMP
NELSON BROTHERS INC
820 Shades Creek Pkwy # 2000, Birmingham, AL 35209-4528
Tel (205) 414-2900 *Founded/Ownrshp* 1980
Sales 138.8MM[E] *EMP* 300
SIC 2892 5169 Amatols (explosive); Nitromannitol (explosive); Explosives; Amatols (explosive); Nitromannitol (explosive); Explosives
CEO: William H Nelson III
**Pr:* Charles A Nelson
**CFO:* Ralph M Hymer
**VP:* Gary L Self

D-U-N-S 82-907-1906
NELSON BROTHERS LLC
ORICA
820 Shades Creek Pkwy # 2000, Birmingham, AL 35209-4528
Tel (205) 414-2900 *Founded/Ownrshp* 2000
Sales 96.4MM[E] *EMP* 400[E]
SIC 2892 Explosives; Explosives
CEO: William Nelson
**Ex VP:* Ralph Hymer
Dir Risk M: Skylar Everette
Dir IT: Larry Sparks
Sales Exec: Tab Hudson
Snr Mgr: Terry Brown

D-U-N-S 07-663-4179
NELSON CAMPBELL VOLKSWAGEN
CAMPBELL/NELSON VOLKSWAGEN
24329 Highway 99, Edmonds, WA 98026-9138
Tel (425) 774-2174 *Founded/Ownrshp* 1955
Sales 54.8MM[E] *EMP* 150
SIC 5511 5093 Automobiles, new & used; Automotive wrecking for scrap; Automobiles, new & used; Automotive wrecking for scrap
Pr: Robert Campbell
**Sec:* Arne Nelson
Ex VP: Mike Cardenas
**VP:* Erna Nelson
**Genl Mgr:* Kurt Campbell
IT Man: Greg Nelson
Sales Exec: Travis Meyers
Sales Asso: Matty Clough
Sales Asso: Alan Kemper
Sales Asso: Adam Low
Sales Asso: John Obrien

D-U-N-S 00-342-7234 IMP
NELSON CO (MD)
4517 North Point Blvd, Baltimore, MD 21219-1798
Tel (410) 477-3000 *Founded/Ownrshp* 1921
Sales 23.9MM[E] *EMP* 95
SIC 2448 5031 2441 3089 Pallets, wood; Skids, wood; Pallets, wood; Nailed wood boxes & shook; Pallets, plastic
Pr: David C Caltrider
**CFO:* John G Williams
Rgnl Mgr: Janice Schiefer
Plnt Mgr: John Martin

NELSON COUNTY PUBLIC SCHOOLS
See NELSON COUNTY SCHOOL DISTRICT

NELSON COUNTY SCHOOL DISTRICT
See COUNTY OF NELSON

D-U-N-S 01-363-6501
NELSON COUNTY SCHOOL DISTRICT
NELSON COUNTY PUBLIC SCHOOLS
84 Courthouse Sq, Lovingston, VA 22949-2359
Tel (434) 260-7646 *Founded/Ownrshp* 1807
Sales 19.9MM[E] *EMP* 425
SIC 8211 Public elementary & secondary schools; Public elementary & secondary schools
Schl Brd P: David Parr
HC Dir: Kelly Hughes

D-U-N-S 04-042-2693
NELSON COUNTY SCHOOL DISTRICT
288 Wildcat Ln, Bardstown, KY 40004-9075
Tel (502) 349-7000 *Founded/Ownrshp* 1875
Sales 30.3MM[E] *EMP* 551
Accts Brown & Company Cpa S Bardsto
SIC 8211 Elementary school; High school, junior or senior; Elementary school; High school, junior or senior
Pr: Frank Hall
**Treas:* Wanda Parker
**VP:* Nicky Rapier
Pr Dir: Tom Dekle

D-U-N-S 05-566-6325
NELSON DISTRIBUTING INC
NELSON PETROLEUM
1125 80th St Sw, Everett, WA 98203-6280
Tel (425) 353-9701 *Founded/Ownrshp* 1982
Sales 57.7MM[E] *EMP* 55
SIC 5171 5984 Petroleum bulk stations; Liquefied petroleum gas dealers; Petroleum bulk stations; Liquefied petroleum gas dealers
Pr: Mark Nelson
COO: Jeff Wilson
**VP:* Erla Rae Nelson
IT Man: Dustin Nelson

D-U-N-S 06-782-4847
NELSON ELECTRIC CO INC (NV)
1410 Freeport Blvd, Sparks, NV 89431-5942
Tel (775) 358-0643 *Founded/Ownrshp* 1978
Sales 62.9MM[E] *EMP* 250
SIC 1731 General electrical contractor; General electrical contractor
Pr: Lisa Marie Teglia
**Sec:* Patricia A Nelson
Snr Mgr: Robbie Nelson

D-U-N-S 00-643-3759 EXP
NELSON ELECTRIC SUPPLY CO INC (WI)
926 State St, Racine, WI 53404-3346
Tel (262) 635-5050 *Founded/Ownrshp* 1949, 1965
Sales 33.6MM[E] *EMP* 50
SIC 5063 Electrical apparatus & equipment
Pr: Thomas Leuenberger
**VP:* Chris Fiorentino
**VP:* David Heide
**VP:* Steve Shuman
Dir IT: Linda Laake
Sales Exec: Chris Smith
Sales Asso: Bill Colby
Sales Asso: Scott Meyers

D-U-N-S 18-347-3685
NELSON ENGINEERING CONSTRUCTION INC
2610 Dakota Ave, South Sioux City, NE 68776-3232
Tel (402) 494-6927 *Founded/Ownrshp* 1985
Sales 44.4MM[E] *EMP* 100
SIC 1542 1541 Nonresidential construction; Industrial buildings & warehouses; Nonresidential construction; Industrial buildings & warehouses
Pr: James L Nelson

D-U-N-S 96-568-3050
NELSON FAMILY FOUNDATION
211 N Broadway Ste 1000, Saint Louis, MO 63102-2748
Tel (314) 244-5812 *Founded/Ownrshp* 2010
Sales 46.3MM *EMP* 2[E]
Accts Ernst & Young Llp
SIC 8699 Charitable organization
COO: Karen L Christiansen

D-U-N-S 02-365-4361
NELSON FORD INC
AUTO SALVAGE
201 Commonwealth Blvd W, Martinsville, VA 24112-1820
Tel (276) 638-2331 *Founded/Ownrshp* 1975
Sales 58.2MM[E] *EMP* 160
SIC 5511 Automobiles, new & used; Automobiles, new & used
Pr: G R Nelson
**Sec:* Jo Ann Nelson
**VP:* Barry Nelson
Opers Mgr: Gary Bryd

D-U-N-S 96-802-1886 IMP
NELSON GLOBAL PRODUCTS INC
1560 Williams Dr, Stoughton, WI 53589-3336
Tel (608) 719-1800 *Founded/Ownrshp* 2010
Sales 954.7MM[E] *EMP* 3,000
SIC 3714 3317 Mufflers (exhaust), motor vehicle; Steel pipe & tubes; Mufflers (exhaust), motor vehicle; Steel pipe & tubes
Pr: Sergio L Carvalho
**CFO:* Kris Radhakrishnan
VP: Robert Bass
VP: Joseph Freeman
Dir Bus: Susan Ullman
IT Man: Linda Swangstu
QC Dir: Tim Rusch
Snr Mgr: Jason Drost
Snr Mgr: Jill Hauk
Snr Mgr: Jon Kille
Snr Mgr: Scott Lubenow

NELSON HONDA
See EL MONTE AUTOMOTIVE GROUP LLC

NELSON INDUSTRIES DIVISION
See NELSON INDUSTRIES INC

D-U-N-S 00-610-5944
■ **NELSON INDUSTRIES INC**
NELSON INDUSTRIES DIVISION
(*Suby of* CUMMINS INC) ★
1801 Us Highway 51 & 138, Stoughton, WI 53589-1909
Tel (608) 873-4200 *Founded/Ownrshp* 1939
Sales 228.8MM[E] *EMP* 2,200

SIC 3714 3519 3569 Mufflers (exhaust), motor vehicle; Motor vehicle electrical equipment; Exhaust systems & parts, motor vehicle; Filters: oil, fuel & air, motor vehicle; Parts & accessories, internal combustion engines; Filters; Mufflers (exhaust), motor vehicle; Motor vehicle electrical equipment; Exhaust systems & parts, motor vehicle; Filters: oil, fuel & air, motor vehicle; Parts & accessories, internal combustion engines; Filters
Pr: Trevor Passmore
Bd of Dir: Greg Anderson
VP: Douglas Benham
Exec: Ashley Everson
IT Man: Andrew Westphal
Sls Dir: Paulette Carter
Snr Mgr: Tim Kraus

D-U-N-S 05-994-9362 IMP/EXP
NELSON IRRIGATION CORP
WALLA WALLA SPRINKLER COMP
848 Airport Rd, Walla Walla, WA 99362-2271
Tel (509) 525-7660 *Founded/Ownrshp* 1972
Sales 51.0MM^E *EMP* 160
SIC 3494 5085 3523 Sprinkler systems, field; Valves, pistons & fittings; Farm machinery & equipment; Sprinkler systems, field; Valves, pistons & fittings; Farm machinery & equipment
Pr: Craig Nelson
COO: Bryan Zessin
**Ch:* Barton Nelson
VP: Bob Rupar
**VP:* Robert Rupar
Dist Mgr: Jason Hester
Dist Mgr: Don Zimmerman
Telecom Ex: Jeff Lyford
CIO: Jerry Humphreys
IT Man: Lynnette Brown
VP Mfg: Charles Harrold
Board of Directors: Dirk R Nelson, Reid A Nelson, John F Reno, Kendra Wenzel

NELSON J.I.T.
See NELSON JIT PACKAGING SUPPLIES INC

D-U-N-S 82-646-4299 IMP
NELSON JIT PACKAGING SUPPLIES INC
NELSON J.I.T.
4022 W Turney Ave Ste 3, Phoenix, AZ 85019-3329
Tel (623) 939-3365 *Founded/Ownrshp* 1994
Sales 22.7MM^E *EMP* 28^E
SIC 5199 Packaging materials
Pr: Greg Nelson
**Sec:* Gloria Nelson
**VP:* Bob Nelson

D-U-N-S 02-541-0853
NELSON KEN AUTO PLAZA INC
1000 N Galena Ave, Dixon, IL 61021-1523
Tel (815) 288-4455 *Founded/Ownrshp* 2010
Sales 27.5MM^E *EMP* 90
SIC 5511 5521 Automobiles, new & used; Pickups, new & used; Used car dealers; Automobiles, new & used; Pickups, new & used; Used car dealers
Pr: Richard Curia
Sales Asso: Clayton Bonnell
Sales Asso: Donielle Freytag
Sales Asso: Alex Riley

D-U-N-S 15-166-3234
NELSON LABORATORIES INC
6280 S Redwood Rd, Salt Lake City, UT 84123-6600
Tel (801) 955-3056 *Founded/Ownrshp* 1985
Sales 81.4MM^E *EMP* 415
SIC 8734 Testing laboratories; Testing laboratories
Pr: Jeff Nelson
CFO: Todd Orullian
**Ch:* Lynda Nelson
**Sec:* Jerry R Nelson
VP: Jeff Hills
Exec: Pamela Lyman-Kasper
Dept Mgr: Dania Cortes
Dept Mgr: Kelsey Pearson
Dir IT: Liz McGuire
Ql Cn Mgr: Sherri Robbins
S&M/VP: Lane Jensen

D-U-N-S 00-504-0407 EXP
NELSON MANUFACTURING CO (DE)
6448 State Route 224, Ottawa, OH 45875-9789
Tel (419) 523-5321 *Founded/Ownrshp* 1947
Sales 20.0MM *EMP* 83
SIC 3715 7539 Semitrailers for truck tractors; Trailer repair; Semitrailers for truck tractors; Trailer repair
Pr: George F Rellinger
**Pr:* Anthony Niese
**Treas:* Patricia Taylor

D-U-N-S 05-156-2049
NELSON MIDWEST OPERATING CO
30 W Monroe St Ste 200, Chicago, IL 60603-2411
Tel (312) 263-3967 *Founded/Ownrshp* 1955
Sales 18.5MM^E *EMP* 500
SIC 8712 7389 Architectural services; Interior design services; Architectural services; Interior design services
Prin: Mitch Cohen
**CEO:* Ozzie Nelson
**CFO:* Steven Malter
**Prin:* Frank Torchia

D-U-N-S 02-358-4089
NELSON MILL & AGRI-CENTER INC
NELSON AGRI CENTER
217 N Center Ave, Viroqua, WI 54665-1496
Tel (608) 637-2192 *Founded/Ownrshp* 1989
Sales 68.6MM^E *EMP* 89
SIC 5191 5251 Feed; Seeds: field, garden & flower; Fertilizer & fertilizer materials; Hardware; Feed; Seeds: field, garden & flower; Fertilizer & fertilizer materials; Hardware
Pr: Dan Kanis
**Treas:* Roy G Kanis
**VP:* Mark Brueggen
Sls&Mrk Ex: Cheryl Day

D-U-N-S 08-471-1993
NELSON MULLINS RILEY & SCARBOROUGH LLP
1320 Main St Ste 1700, Columbia, SC 29201-3268
Tel (803) 799-2000 *Founded/Ownrshp* 1898
Sales 146.4MM^E *EMP* 1,000
SIC 8111 General practice attorney, lawyer; General practice attorney, lawyer
Mng Pt: James C Gray Jr
**Pt:* Bianca Brazell
**Pt:* Valorie M Songer
**Pt:* David N Worth
Mng Pt: David E Duks
Mng Pt: Peter Haley
Mng Pt: William T Hogan III
Mng Pt: Michael E Hollingsworth
Mng Pt: Noah Huffstetler
Mng Pt: Amy Mandragouras
Mng Pt: Kenneth L Millwood
Mng Pt: Marvin Quattlebaum
Mng Pt: Jonathan H Talcott
Mng Pt: George B Wolfe
V Ch: Ron Thomas
**CFO:* Douglas M Webb
Bd of Dir: S Hutto
Ofcr: Valorie Songer
VP: Amy Starzynski
Dir Bus: Jonathan Gardner

D-U-N-S 00-832-9963 IMP
NELSON NAME PLATE CO
NELSON-MILLER
2800 Casitas Ave, Los Angeles, CA 90039-2942
Tel (323) 663-3971 *Founded/Ownrshp* 2011
Sales 62.1MM^E *EMP* 205
SIC 2759 3479 3993 2796 Screen printing; Name plates: engraved, etched, etc.; Signs & advertising specialties; Platemaking services; Screen printing; Name plates: engraved, etched, etc.; Signs & advertising specialties; Platemaking services
CEO: Hosmel Galan
**Pr:* Jim Kaldem
**CFO:* David Balce
**Co-Pr:* Thomas Cassutt
**Co-Pr:* David Lazier
**VP:* Patrick Hee
**VP:* Eric Shumway
Netwrk Mgr: David Bunds
VP Mfg: Bill Gallis
Natl Sales: John Beilfuss
Sls Mgr: Bob Menelly

NELSON PETROLEUM
See NELSON DISTRIBUTING INC

D-U-N-S 08-528-3448
NELSON PIPELINE CONSTRUCTORS INC
10741 Highway 52, Fort Lupton, CO 80621-8427
Tel (303) 857-1580 *Founded/Ownrshp* 2005
Sales 25.4MM^E *EMP* 200
SIC 1623 Underground utilities contractor; Underground utilities contractor
CEO: Phil Scott
**CFO:* Chris Goodwin
**Ch:* Jon Andrews
**VP:* David Nelson

D-U-N-S 02-580-0426
NELSON PIPING CO (IL)
MASTER SHEET METAL CONTRS DIV
1417 22nd St, Rockford, IL 61108-3546
Tel (815) 398-1910 *Founded/Ownrshp* 1919
Sales 28.7MM^E *EMP* 100
SIC 1711 1761 Plumbing, heating, air-conditioning contractors; Process piping contractor; Warm air heating & air conditioning contractor; Ventilation & duct work contractor; Sheet metalwork
Pr: David A Nelson
**COO:* Lenny Hill
VP Opers: Greg Hill

NELSON PLANT SERVICES CO.
See CARL A NELSON & CO

NELSON STAFFING SOLUTIONS
See GARY D NELSON ASSOCIATES INC

D-U-N-S 02-995-0438
NELSON STARK CO
7685 Fields Ertel Rd # 3, Cincinnati, OH 45241-6084
Tel (513) 489-0866 *Founded/Ownrshp* 1993
Sales 36.2MM *EMP* 170
Accts Vonlehman & Company Inc Cinc
SIC 1711 1623 1794 Plumbing contractors; Water, sewer & utility lines; Underground utilities contractor; Excavation work; Plumbing contractors; Water, sewer & utility lines; Underground utilities contractor; Excavation work
Pr: Jeff Read
**Pr:* Mark Stark
**CFO:* Edward T Bulach
CFO: Edward Bulach
**Sr VP:* Charles Nelson
**VP:* H Joseph Iori
Exec: Todd Elliott
Admn Mgr: Amy Wilson
CTO: Tom Kattelman

D-U-N-S 00-446-6199 IMP/EXP
NELSON STUD WELDING INC
(*Suby of* DONCASTERS 456 LIMITED)
7900 W Ridge Rd, Elyria, OH 44035-1952
Tel (440) 329-0400 *Founded/Ownrshp* 2000, 2007
Sales 167.6MM^E *EMP* 351^E
SIC 3452 3548 Bolts, nuts, rivets & washers; Welding apparatus; Bolts, nuts, rivets & washers; Welding apparatus
Pr: Ken Caratelli
**CFO:* David Bubar
**VP:* Debbie Hunnel
VP: Jim King
Dir Bus: Bob Rak
Telecom Ex: Nick Hellums
IT Man: Nick Hullums
Opers Mgr: John Garmon
Opers Mgr: Doug Shantz
Plnt Mgr: Cornel Irimies
Ql Cn Mgr: David Ballou

NELSON WESTERBERG
See NEWESCO INC

D-U-N-S 04-101-5173
NELSON WHITE SYSTEMS INC
8725 Loch Raven Blvd A, Towson, MD 21286-2207
Tel (410) 668-9628 *Founded/Ownrshp* 1994
Sales 27.0MM^E *EMP* 80
SIC 5999 7629 7819 Audio-visual equipment & supplies; Electrical repair shops; Equipment rental, motion picture
CEO: Arlene Wilder
**Pr:* Thomas Wilder
VP: Wes Hull
Genl Mgr: Ted Mysczkowski
Sales Asso: Kristen Cooley

D-U-N-S 09-683-8701
NELSON WORLDWIDE INC (PA)
NELSON & ASSOCIATES
222-230 Walnut St, Philadelphia, PA 19106
Tel (215) 925-6562 *Founded/Ownrshp* 1978
Sales 114.1MM^E *EMP* 425
SIC 7389 Interior decorating; Interior decorating
CEO: John Nelson Jr
**CFO:* Tony Manuelli
**Ex VP:* Jill Hackenmueller
VP: Daniel Nelson
Genl Mgr: Cherryl Wardwell

D-U-N-S 07-627-3341 IMP
NELSON-ATKINS MUSEUM OF ART
4525 Oak St, Kansas City, MO 64111-1818
Tel (816) 561-4000 *Founded/Ownrshp* 1933
Sales 27.6MM *EMP* 250
Accts Ernst & Young Us Llp Indianap
SIC 8412 8231 5947 5812 Art gallery, noncommercial; Libraries; Gift, novelty & souvenir shop; Eating places; Art gallery, noncommercial; Libraries; Gift, novelty & souvenir shop; Eating places
**COO:* Karen Christiansen
COO: Linda Haney
Pr Mgr: Toni Straws

D-U-N-S 02-734-6600 EXP
NELSON-BALL PAPER PRODUCTS INC
NEWARK PAPERBOARD PRODUCTS
620 11th Ave, Longview, WA 98632-1619
Tel (360) 423-3420 *Founded/Ownrshp* 1984
Sales 20.3MM^E *EMP* 167
SIC 2655 2679 Tubes, fiber or paper: made from purchased material; Cores, fiber: made from purchased material; Paper products, converted
CEO: Fred P Thompson Jr
**Pr:* Andy M Stewart III
**VP:* Juan Del Valle
**VP:* Eugene C Thomas

D-U-N-S 02-334-1597 IMP
NELSON-JAMESON INC
2400 E 5th St, Marshfield, WI 54449-4661
Tel (715) 387-1151 *Founded/Ownrshp* 1947
Sales 145.0MM *EMP* 175
SIC 5084 Food industry machinery; Dairy products manufacturing machinery; Food industry machinery; Dairy products manufacturing machinery
Ch Bd: John E Nelson
**Pr:* Jerry Lippert
CFO: Brian Lautenschlag
Dir IT: Kay Leicht
IT Man: Fritz Buss
Info Man: Bruce Lautenchlager
Sales Exec: Sharon Copet
Mktg Dir: Murray Smith
Pr Dir: Donald Koch
Manager: Amanda Sasse

NELSON-MILLER
See NELSON NAME PLATE CO

D-U-N-S 78-840-9415 IMP
■ **NELTEC INC**
(*Suby of* PARK ELECTROCHEMICAL CORP) ★
1420 W 12th Pl, Tempe, AZ 85281-5214
Tel (480) 449-2345 *Founded/Ownrshp* 1999
Sales 26.8MM^E *EMP* 75
SIC 3612 Transformers, except electric
Pr: Brian E Shore
Ex VP: Stephen E Gilhuley
Ex VP: Christopher T Mastrogiacomo
VP: Stephen M Banker
VP: P Matthew Farabaugh
VP: Thomas B Steele
VP: Gregory B Westphal
VP Admn: Heather Rafter

NEMA
See NATIONAL ELECTRICAL MANUFACTURERS ASSOCIATION

D-U-N-S 16-075-5476
NEMA ENCLOSURE MFG CORP
1118 Pleasantville Dr, Houston, TX 77029-3232
Tel (713) 921-2233 *Founded/Ownrshp* 2000
Sales 23.4MM^E *EMP* 83
SIC 3444 Sheet metalwork
Pr: James R Bohn Jr
Ex VP: Luis Luarca
Mtls Mgr: Robert Guadiana
Opers Mgr: Erik Palacios
Plnt Mgr: Oscar Diaz
Prd Mgr: Arturo Salazar
Ql Cn Mgr: Rene Garces

D-U-N-S 18-190-5662
NEMACOLIN WOODLANDS INC
NEMACOLIN WOODLANDS RESORT
1001 Lafayette Dr, Farmington, PA 15437-9757
Tel (724) 329-8555 *Founded/Ownrshp* 2001
Sales 73.2MM^E *EMP* 700
SIC 7011 7991 Resort hotel; Ski lodge; Spas; Resort hotel; Ski lodge; Spas
Pr: Maggie H Magerko
VP: Ron Howard
VP: Jeff Nobers
Off Admin: Kaitlyn Wrona
CIO: Davonne Leber
Dir IT: Ron Kimmel
Opers Mgr: Don Moser
Natl Sales: Phil Lucostic
Natl Sales: J Wagner
Mktg Dir: Jennifer Jubin
Mktg Dir: Zelma Kassimer

NEMACOLIN WOODLANDS RESORT
See NEMACOLIN WOODLANDS INC

D-U-N-S 00-386-7710
NEMAHA COUNTY COOPERATIVE ASSOCIATION
223 E Main St, Seneca, KS 66538
Tel (785) 336-6153 *Founded/Ownrshp* 1936
Sales 108.6MM^E *EMP* 88
SIC 5153 5191 5541 Grains; Grain elevators; Feed; Fertilizer & fertilizer materials; Chemicals, agricultural; Filling stations, gasoline; Grains; Grain elevators; Feed; Fertilizer & fertilizer materials; Chemicals, agricultural; Filling stations, gasoline
CEO: Bobby Martin
**V Ch Bd:* Kent Heinen

NEMAK
See JL FRENCH AUTOMOTIVE CASTINGS INC

D-U-N-S 07-954-6922
NEMAK KENTUCKY
20 Prestwick Dr, Glasgow, KY 42141-8254
Tel (270) 651-8334 *Founded/Ownrshp* 1994
Sales 11.9MM^E *EMP* 300
SIC 7389 ;

D-U-N-S 04-726-0591 EXP
NEMAK USA INC
(*Suby of* NEMAK, S.A.B. DE C.V.)
3101 S Taylor Dr, Sheboygan, WI 53081-8424
Tel (920) 458-7724 *Founded/Ownrshp* 2007
Sales 514.6MM^E *EMP* 3,000
SIC 3363 Aluminum die-castings; Aluminum die-castings
CEO: Leon E Cueto
VP: Steve Schrader

D-U-N-S 17-433-0365 IMP
NEMAK USA INC
(*Suby of* NEMAK, S.A.B. DE C.V.)
1635 Old Columbia Rd, Dickson, TN 37055-7705
Tel (615) 446-8110 *Founded/Ownrshp* 2007
Sales 11.0MM^E *EMP* 1,097
SIC 3363 3714 Cylinder heads, motor vehicle; Aluminum die-castings; Cylinder heads, motor vehicle
Pr: Armando Tamez
Sfty Dirs: Matthew Driscoll

D-U-N-S 06-366-5616
NEMANCO INC
(*Suby of* YATES COMPANIES INC) ★
1028 Rd 553, Philadelphia, MS 39350
Tel (601) 656-7361 *Founded/Ownrshp* 1973
Sales 33.5MM^E *EMP* 130
SIC 1542 Commercial & office building, new construction; Commercial & office building, new construction
Pr: Don Fulton
**Sec:* Marvin Blanks
**VP:* W G Yates Jr

D-U-N-S 08-617-0156
NEMCO ELECTRONICS CORP
675 Mariners Island Blvd # 101, San Mateo, CA 94404-1040
Tel (650) 571-1234 *Founded/Ownrshp* 1976
Sales 25.5MM^E *EMP* 150
SIC 3675 Electronic capacitors; Electronic capacitors
Ch: Eugene J Porto
**Pr:* John Nolan
**Ex VP:* James Rapoport
VP: Phil Kansky
Manager: Joe Distefano

D-U-N-S 78-002-5995 IMP/EXP
NEMCO FOOD TRADING INC
NORTHEAST MARKETING COMPANY
207 Bedford St, Lakeville, MA 02347-1525
Tel (508) 923-0066 *Founded/Ownrshp* 1975
Sales 35.0MM *EMP* 5
SIC 3993 8742

NEMER CHRYSLER PLYMOUTH DODGE
See NEMER TRANSPORTATION CORP

D-U-N-S 01-267-9627
NEMER TRANSPORTATION CORP
NEMER CHRYSLER PLYMOUTH DODGE
728 Quaker Rd, Queensbury, NY 12804-3960
Tel (518) 793-2571 *Founded/Ownrshp* 1889
Sales 20.9MM^E *EMP* 40
SIC 5511 Automobiles, new & used
Pr: Peter Nemer
**VP:* Robert Nemer
Sls Mgr: Jason Rushia
Sls Mgr: Ed Schuster
Sales Asso: Greg Pratt
Sales Asso: Jim Sears

D-U-N-S 07-940-9914
NEMERA BUFFALO GROVE LLC
(*Suby of* NEMERA US HOLDING INC) ★
600 Deerfield Pkwy, Buffalo Grove, IL 60089-7050
Tel (847) 541-7900 *Founded/Ownrshp* 2014
Sales 93.3MM^E *EMP* 300
SIC 3841 Surgical & medical instruments; Surgical & medical instruments

D-U-N-S 07-989-7056
NEMERA US HOLDING INC
(*Suby of* NEMERA LA VERPILLIERE)
600 Deerfield Pkwy, Buffalo Grove, IL 60089-7050
Tel (847) 325-3620 *Founded/Ownrshp* 2015
Sales 93.3MM^E *EMP* 318^E
SIC 3841 Surgical & medical instruments

D-U-N-S 01-240-8373 IMP
NEMET MOTORS LLC
VOLVO
15312 Hillside Ave, Jamaica, NY 11432-3322
Tel (718) 523-5858 *Founded/Ownrshp* 1946
Sales 37.3MM^E *EMP* 90

SIC 5511 Automobiles, new & used; Automobiles, new & used
Mktg Mgr: Lasable Goode
Sls Mgr: Douglas Jones
Sls Mgr: Sharen McAvoy

NEMETSCHEK NORTH AMERICA
See NEMETSCHEK VECTORWORKS INC

D-U-N-S 15-459-6803
NEMETSCHEK VECTORWORKS INC
NEMETSCHEK NORTH AMERICA
(*Suby of* NEMETSCHEK AG)
7150 Riverwood Dr, Columbia, MD 21046-1295
Tel (410) 290-5114 *Founded/Ownrshp* 2000
Sales 20.7MM^E *EMP* 106
SIC 7371 Computer software development
Ch: Richard B Diehl
**CEO:* Sean Flaherty
CFO: Joe Schmelcee
**CFO:* Joseph Schmelzle
**Chf Mktg O:* Stewart Rom
VP: Robert Anderson
Creative D: Justin Malbrough
Mng Dir: Daniel Monaghan
Snr Sftwr: Rick Berge
Snr Sftwr: Joshua Loy
Snr Sftwr: Hernan Stamati

NEMF
See NEW ENGLAND MOTOR FREIGHT INC

D-U-N-S 01-281-8613
NEMITH MOTOR CORP
VOLVO
962 New Loudon Rd, Latham, NY 12110-2107
Tel (518) 785-8531 *Founded/Ownrshp* 1947
Sales 33.7MM^E *EMP* 75
SIC 5511 7538 Automobiles, new & used; General automotive repair shops; Automobiles, new & used; General automotive repair shops
CEO: Mark L Nemith
**Pr:* Walter S Riddell
**Treas:* Stanley Goldbaum
**VP:* Catherine Nemith
Off Mgr: Moe Szlamowicz

NEMONT
See SAGEBRUSH CELLULAR INC

D-U-N-S 02-199-7184
NEMONT COMMUNICATIONS INC
(*Suby of* PROJECT TELEPHONE COMPANY)
Hwy Ste 13s, Scobey, MT 59263
Tel (800) 636-6680 *Founded/Ownrshp* 1979
Sales 41.5MM *EMP* 22
Accts Chms Pc Sidney Montana
SIC 4841 4813 7377 4812 Cable television services; Direct broadcast satellite services (DBS); ; Computer rental & leasing; Cellular telephone services
Pr: Mike Mitchell
**CFO:* Remi Sun
**Treas:* Scott Mvgowan
**VP:* Linda Nelson
**Genl Mgr:* Mike Kilgore
Opers Mgr: Dennis Dunn
Opers Mgr: Richard Hood

D-U-N-S 00-682-9337
NEMONT TELEPHONE CO-OPERATIVE INC
61 Hwy 13 S, Scobey, MT 59263
Tel (406) 783-2200 *Founded/Ownrshp* 1950
Sales 63.7MM *EMP* 200
Accts Chms Pc Sidney Montana
SIC 4813 Local telephone communications; Long distance telephone communications; Local telephone communications; Long distance telephone communications
Pr: Ben Boreson
**CFO:* Remi Sun
**Treas:* Linda Nelson
Trst: Brenda Schye
**VP:* Roy Neufeld
**Genl Mgr:* Mike Kilgore
IT Man: Kevin McConnell

D-U-N-S 08-757-6336 IMP
NEMOS BAKERY INC
(*Suby of* HORIZON HOLDINGS LLC) ★
416 N Hale Ave, Escondido, CA 92029-1496
Tel (760) 741-5725 *Founded/Ownrshp* 1975
Sales 55.7MM *EMP* 3
SIC 2053 Cakes, bakery: frozen; Croissants, frozen; Pastries (danish): frozen
CEO: Phillip S Estes
**Sr VP:* Sam Delucca Jr
Sr VP: Pete Petersen
**VP:* Bob Yurick
Dir IT: Roger L Beard
Dir IT: Roger Beard
Sfty Mgr: Jose Pelayo
Sfty Mgr: Steve Senese
Plnt Mgr: Mike Morales

NEMOURS
See LANKENAU MEDICAL CENTER FOUNDATION

D-U-N-S 03-692-7204
NEMOURS CHILDRENS HOSPITAL
NCH
13535 Nemours Pkwy, Orlando, FL 32827-7402
Tel (407) 567-4000 *Founded/Ownrshp* 2010
Sales 115.6MM *EMP* 87^E
SIC 8069 Children's hospital
Pr: David J Bailey
CFO: Randy Hartley
**Ex VP:* Roy Proujansky
**Sr VP:* Steven Sparks
**VP:* Gina Altieri
Doctor: Adalberto Torres
Snr Mgr: Robert Burns

D-U-N-S 03-729-3792
NEMOURS FOUNDATION
ALFRED I DUPONT HOSPITAL FOR
10140 Centurion Pkwy N, Jacksonville, FL 32256-0532
Tel (904) 697-4100 *Founded/Ownrshp* 1974
Sales 1.7MM *EMP* 4,400
Accts Kpmg Llp Jacksonville Fl
SIC 8069 8093 Children's hospital; Specialty outpatient clinics; Children's hospital; Specialty outpatient clinics
Ch Bd: John S Lord
**Ch Bd:* Brian P Anderson
**Pr:* David J Bailey
CFO: Kimberly Englert
Treas: Bill Higginbotham
Sec: Stacie Lynne Pack
**V Ch Bd:* Richard T Christopher
Chf Mktg O: David West
Ofcr: Kevin Haynes
VP: Robert Bridges
VP: Jay Cummings
Exec: Linda Favorite
Exec: Debra Hunting
Dir Risk M: Mary Cariseo
Board of Directors: John S Lord

D-U-N-S 07-924-3752
NEMOURS FOUNDATION PENSION PLAN
10140 Centurion Pkwy N, Jacksonville, FL 32256-0532
Tel (904) 697-4100 *Founded/Ownrshp* 2014
Sales NA *EMP* 88^E
SIC 6371 Pensions
COO: Michelle Arnold
Sr VP: Roger Oxendale
Exec: Wanda Heavner
Assoc Dir: Suzanne Murphy
Prgrm Mgr: Susan Yeager
Nurse Mgr: Amber Degrenier
Nurse Mgr: Lisa Sayo
Web Dev: Gerald Murray
Mktg Mgr: Karen Kent
Psych: Lisa Schilling
Pharmcst: Thao Dinh

D-U-N-S 00-607-1104 IMP/EXP
■ **NEMSCHOFF CHAIRS INC** (WI)
(*Suby of* HERMAN MILLER INC) ★
909 N 8th St Stop 1, Sheboygan, WI 53081-4056
Tel (920) 457-7726 *Founded/Ownrshp* 1950, 2009
Sales 58.9MM^E *EMP* 400
SIC 2531 Public building & related furniture; Public building & related furniture
CEO: Mark Nemschoff
**COO:* C Kent Gawart
**CFO:* Matt Loan
Mng Dir: Randy Miller
Area Mgr: Vicki Kibler
IT Man: Dan Kelley
MIS Mgr: Daniel Kelly
VP Mfg: Sue Neerhof
Opers Mgr: Mike Scheele
Sales Exec: David Simon
VP Sls: John Rademacher

D-U-N-S 83-192-1692 IMP
NEN HOLDINGS INC
397 S Taylor Ave, Louisville, CO 80027-3027
Tel (303) 444-2559 *Founded/Ownrshp* 2009
Sales 186.2MM^E *EMP* 750^E
Accts Brock And Company Cpas Pc
SIC 5962 Merchandising machine operators; Merchandising machine operators
Pr: Kevin J Wall

D-U-N-S 07-975-5202
NEO INDUSTRIES LLC
(*Suby of* HEICO COMPANIES L L C) ★
1775 Willowcreek Rd, Portage, IN 46368-1324
Tel (219) 762-6075 *Founded/Ownrshp* 1998
Sales 34.5MM^E *EMP* 250^E
SIC 3471 Plating & polishing
Pr: Michael Quig

D-U-N-S 61-438-0421
NEO PHILANTHROPY INC
45 W 36th St Fl 6, New York, NY 10018-7635
Tel (212) 378-2800 *Founded/Ownrshp* 1983
Sales 41.6MM *EMP* 31
Accts Owen J Flanagan & Co New York
SIC 8399 Fund raising organization, non-fee basis
Pr: John Gilroy
**CFO:* Selvin Osbourne
**Co-Pr:* Berta Colon
Ofcr: Ly Nguyen
Comm Dir: Robert Bray

NEO RAY LIGHTING PRODUCTS
See COOPER LIGHTING LLC

D-U-N-S 94-945-8632
NEOFORMA INC
(*Suby of* GLOBAL HEALTHCARE EXCHANGE LLC) ★
1315 W Century Dr, Louisville, CO 80027-9560
Tel (720) 887-7140 *Founded/Ownrshp* 2006
Sales 8.3MM^E *EMP* 300
SIC 7371 Custom computer programming services; Custom computer programming services
Pr: Michael Mahoney
CFO: Andrew L Guggenhime
Treas: Greg Nash

NEOGARD DIVISION
See JONES-BLAIR CO LLC

D-U-N-S 06-955-0929 IMP
▲ **NEOGEN CORP**
620 Lesher Pl, Lansing, MI 48912-1509
Tel (517) 372-9200 *Founded/Ownrshp* 1982
Sales 283.0MM *EMP* 1,062^E
Accts Bdo Usa Llp Grand Rapids Mi
Tkr Sym NEOG *Exch* NGS
SIC 2835 3841 2836 In vitro & in vivo diagnostic substances; Veterinary diagnostic substances; Veterinarians' instruments & apparatus; Veterinary biological products; In vitro & in vivo diagnostic substances; Veterinary diagnostic substances; Veterinarians' instruments & apparatus; Veterinary biological products
Ch Bd: James L Herbert
Pr: Richard Calk Jr
CFO: Steven J Quinlan
Bd of Dir: William Boehm
Ofcr: Lesher Rice
VP: Edward L Bradley
VP: Jason W Lilly
VP: Joseph Madden
VP: Dave Melton
VP: David A Wall
Exec: Richard Lang
Exec: Anthony Lupo
Exec: Don Pielack
Exec: Roger Ray
Dir Lab: Rod Poland
Board of Directors: William T Boehm, Richard T Crowder, A Charles Fischer, Ronald D Green, G Bruce Papesh, Jack C Parnell, Thomas H Reed, Clayton K Yeutter

D-U-N-S 11-300-7301
▲ **NEOGENOMICS INC**
12701 Commwl Dr Ste 9, Fort Myers, FL 33913
Tel (239) 768-0600 *Founded/Ownrshp* 2001
Sales 87.0MM *EMP* 440
Tkr Sym NEO *Exch* NAS
SIC 8734 8071 Testing laboratories; Testing laboratories; Testing laboratories; Testing laboratories
Ch Bd: Douglas M Vanoort
COO: Robert J Shovlin
CFO: George A Cardoza
**Chf Cred:* Steven C Jones
VP: Jennifer Balliet
VP: Matthew Moore
VP: Jack G Spitz
Dir Lab: Donna Ulmschneider
Snr Sftwr: Trisha Yost
CIO: Steven A Ross
CIO: Steven Ross
Board of Directors: Bruce K Crowther, Alison L Hannah, Raymond R Hipp, Kevin C Johnson, William J Robison, Lynn A Tetrault

D-U-N-S 07-870-9787
NEOLPHARMA INC
99 Calle Jardines, Caguas, PR 00725-3382
Tel (787) 286-4000 *Founded/Ownrshp* 2013
Sales 162.8MM^E *EMP* 240
SIC 5122 Pharmaceuticals; Pharmaceuticals
Pr: Efren Ocampo
**CFO:* Marco A Monrouzeau Bonilla

NEOMED
See NORTHEAST OHIO MEDICAL UNIVERSITY

D-U-N-S 79-832-3721
NEOMED CENTER INC
CENTRO DE MEDICINA FAMILIAR
Salida Bo Haguas Rr 941, Gurabo, PR 00778
Tel (787) 737-5207 *Founded/Ownrshp* 1992
Sales 22.7MM *EMP* 150
SIC 8052 Intermediate care facilities; Intermediate care facilities
Ex Dir: Luisa Rivera
Ex Dir: Rosa Castro

D-U-N-S 19-525-1595 EXP
■ **NEOMEND INC**
(*Suby of* C R BARD INC) ★
60 Technology Dr, Irvine, CA 92618-2301
Tel (949) 783-3300 *Founded/Ownrshp* 2012
Sales 24.2MM^E *EMP* 90
SIC 3841 Surgical & medical instruments
Pr: David Renzi
**CFO:* Kevin Cousins
VP: Jeff Anderson
**VP:* Pete Davis
**VP:* David Hanson
VP: Ken Watson
IT Man: John Rees
IT Man: Hugo Renteria

D-U-N-S 02-794-5786
NEOMETRICS INC
2605 Fernbrook Ln N Ste J, Plymouth, MN 55447-4756
Tel (763) 559-4440 *Founded/Ownrshp* 2001
Sales 20.0MM^E *EMP* 105
SIC 3841 Surgical instruments & apparatus; Surgical instruments & apparatus
CEO: Eugene Champeau
IT Man: Mike Faul
Ql Cn Mgr: Dave Douglas
S&M/VP: Craig Weber

NEON
See NATIONAL ECOLOGICAL OBSERVATORY NETWORK INC

D-U-N-S 80-835-0867 IMP
NEOPART LLC
5051 Horseshoe Pike # 300, Honey Brook, PA 19344-1365
Tel (610) 273-3744 *Founded/Ownrshp* 1986
Sales 42.2MM^E *EMP* 50
SIC 5013 Garage service equipment
CEO: Harold R Boade
Pr: Phil Gendall
COO: Paul Hoppe
CFO: Bill Armstrong
Manager: Grant Miller

D-U-N-S 96-825-0977 IMP
▲ **NEOPHOTONICS CORP**
2911 Zanker Rd, San Jose, CA 95134-2125
Tel (408) 232-9200 *Founded/Ownrshp* 2002
Sales 306.1MM *EMP* 2,541
Tkr Sym NPTN *Exch* NYS
SIC 3674 Semiconductors & related devices; Semiconductors & related devices
Ch Bd: Timothy S Jenks
COO: CHI Yue Cheung
CFO: Clyde Raymond Wallin
CFO: Ray Wallin
Sr VP: Benjamin L Sitler
Sr VP: Wupen Yuen
VP: Raymond Cheung
Exec: Ezmina Mohammed
Plng Mgr: Motohiro Imai
Snr Sftwr: Igor Gopp
IT Man: Ikram Lakhani
Board of Directors: Charles J Abbe, Michael J Sophie, Lee Sen Ting

D-U-N-S 08-070-8241 IMP
NEOPOST USA INC
(*Suby of* NEOPOST SA)
478 Wheelers Farms Rd, Milford, CT 06461-9105
Tel (203) 301-3400 *Founded/Ownrshp* 1992
Sales 210.8MM^E *EMP* 1,017
SIC 3579 7359 7629 Postage meters; Business machine & electronic equipment rental services; Business machine repair, electric; Postage meters; Business machine & electronic equipment rental services; Business machine repair, electric
Pr: Dennis P Lestrange
COO: Bill Quinn
CFO: Kenneth Kocher
Sr VP: Tara Whitmore
**VP:* Christopher M Obrien
Dept Mgr: Chris Harry
Brnch Mgr: Robert Szehner
CTO: Keith Robertson
QA Dir: Christina Fekany
Dir IT: Bastien S Cantos
Dir IT: Sam Lavanaway

D-U-N-S 79-942-6064 IMP
NEOPTX LLC
3201 Commerce Pkwy, Miramar, FL 33025-3908
Tel (954) 441-9611 *Founded/Ownrshp* 2005
Sales 34.1MM^E *EMP* 100
SIC 5048 Contact lenses
VP: Jason Orlinsky

D-U-N-S 01-065-3751
NEORIS USA INC
(*Suby of* CEMEX, S.A.B. DE C.V.)
703 Nw 62nd Ave Ste 700, Miami, FL 33126-4689
Tel (305) 728-6000 *Founded/Ownrshp* 2000
Sales 281.0MM^E *EMP* 1,200
SIC 4813 Telephone communication, except radio; Telephone communication, except radio
CEO: Claudio Muruzabal
Pr: Sam Elfawal
CFO: Rubio Guillermo
Ofcr: Rafael Alfonso
Ofcr: Jairo Fern Ndez
VP: Alejandro Garcia
VP: Stephen Hitchings
VP: Greg Reynolds
VP: Raymond Russ
Exec: Paula Amador
Mng Dir: Roberto Arias

NEOS GEOSOLUTIONS
See NEOS INC

D-U-N-S 03-446-7745
NEOS GEOSOLUTIONS INC
(*Suby of* NEOS GEOSOLUTIONS) ★
10350 Richmond Ave # 550, Houston, TX 77042-4129
Tel (713) 425-0505 *Founded/Ownrshp* 2004
Sales 4.3MM^E *EMP* 339^E
SIC 1382 Geological exploration, oil & gas field; Geophysical exploration, oil & gas field
Pr: Jim Hollis
Chf Mktg O: Chris M Friedemann
VP: Larry Scott

D-U-N-S 14-163-5883 IMP
NEOS INC
NEOS GEOSOLUTIONS
10350 Richmond Ave # 550, Houston, TX 77042-4129
Tel (713) 977-3410 *Founded/Ownrshp* 2003
Sales 17.9MM^E *EMP* 369
SIC 1382 Oil & gas exploration services; Oil & gas exploration services
Pr: Jim Hollis
**CFO:* Steve Bach
Treas: Alexander Nickolatos
**Chf Mktg O:* Chris Friedemann
**VP:* Dr Craig Beasly
VP: Trevor Hicks
VP: David Jones
**VP:* Dr Tom Speeter
Snr Ntwrk: Jeff Macres
IT Man: Sean Sultani

D-U-N-S 83-612-6052
NEOS THERAPEUTICS LP
2940 N State Highway 360, Grand Prairie, TX 75050-6425
Tel (972) 408-1300 *Founded/Ownrshp* 1999
Sales 21.1MM^E *EMP* 70
SIC 2834 Vitamin, nutrient & hematinic preparations for human use
Pr: Mark Tengler
COO: Ellen Hoffing
CFO: Richard I Eisenstadt
VP: Margaret Cabano
VP: Dorothy Engelking
VP: Bryan Hill
VP: Russ McMahen
VP: Asif Mughal

D-U-N-S 07-831-6933
NEOSHO MEMORIAL REGIONAL MEDICAL CENTER
629 S Plummer Ave, Chanute, KS 66720-1928
Tel (620) 431-4000 *Founded/Ownrshp* 2014
Sales 47.7MM *EMP* 35^E
SIC 8062 General medical & surgical hospitals
CEO: Murray L Brown
HC Dir: Billy Browne
Snr Mgr: Brett Olson

D-U-N-S 08-410-1013
NEOSHO R-5 SCHOOL DISTRICT
418 Fairground Rd, Neosho, MO 64850-1626
Tel (417) 451-8600 *Founded/Ownrshp* 1866
Sales 45.1MM^E *EMP* 700
SIC 8211 Public elementary & secondary schools; Public elementary & secondary schools
Dir IT: Scott Harris
IT Man: Judy Manhatton
Schl Brd P: Brett Day
HC Dir: Cindy Sanders

NEOSTRATA
See TRISTRATA INC

D-U-N-S 60-575-4829 IMP
NEOSTRATA CO INC
(*Suby of* NEOSTRATA) ★
307 College Rd E, Princeton, NJ 08540-6608
Tel (609) 520-0715 *Founded/Ownrshp* 1993
Sales 106.9MM^E *EMP* 85^E
SIC 5122 Cosmetics; Cosmetics
CEO: Mark D Steele
Opers Mgr: Tom Demattia
Mktg Mgr: Amy Bernhard
Mktg Mgr: Meaghan McCarthy

D-U-N-S 12-665-9676
NEOSYSTEMS CORP
1861 Intl Dr Ste 200, Tysons Corner, VA 22102
Tel (571) 234-4940 *Founded/Ownrshp* 2000
Sales 33.4MM^E *EMP* 100
SIC 8742 Management consulting services
Pr: Michael Tinsley
Pr: Jeff Dale
**Pr:* Jerry Falvey
Pr: Kevin Hite
**COO:* Rob Wilson
Chf Mktg O: Laurie Powers
**Sr VP:* Richard Kirby
**Sr VP:* Robin Prausa
**Sr VP:* Jeff Woerner
VP: Carlos Alvarado
VP: Shawn Chen
VP: Randy Cole
VP: Sandy Fox
VP: James Henriksen
VP: Andy Hoskins
VP: Jay Kester
VP: Terri Light
VP: David Myer
VP: Pamela Potts
VP: Dexter Tucker
VP: Mark Vieno

NEOTECH
See NATEL ENGINEERING CO INC

D-U-N-S 96-455-5341
NEOVIA LOGISTICS DISTRIBUTION LLC
(*Suby of* NEOVIA LOGISTICS SERVICES LLC) ★
6363 N State Highway # 700, Irving, TX 75038-2262
Tel (469) 513-7000 *Founded/Ownrshp* 2013
Sales 52.0MM^E *EMP* 555^E
SIC 4225 General warehousing & storage
CEO: Jos Opdeweegh

D-U-N-S 05-703-1854
NEOVIA LOGISTICS SERVICES LLC
6363 N State Highway 161 # 700, Irving, TX 75038-2262
Tel (469) 513-7000 *Founded/Ownrshp* 1999
Sales 191.0MM^E *EMP* 75^E
SIC 4789 Cargo loading & unloading services
CEO: Jos Opdeweegh
CFO: Joe Tomczak
Chf Cred: Carey Falcone
CTO: Tim Oglesby

D-U-N-S 07-908-7702
NEOVIA LOGISTICS SERVICES LLC
(*Suby of* PLATINUM EQUITY LLC) ★
2001 Bttrfeld Rd Ste 1400, Downers Grove, IL 60515
Tel (630) 743-4101 *Founded/Ownrshp* 2012
Sales 280.6MM^E *EMP* 341^E
SIC 6719 Investment holding companies, except banks
CEO: Jozef J Opdeweegh
COO: Dan Spellman
CFO: Joe Tomczak
VP: Craig Braun
Plnt Mgr: Douglas Francois
Snr Mgr: Carey Falcone

NEP
See NOBLE ENVIRONMENTAL POWER LLC

D-U-N-S 07-077-5056
NEP BROADCASTING LLC
2 Beta Dr, Pittsburgh, PA 15238-2916
Tel (412) 826-1414 *Founded/Ownrshp* 2012
Sales 23.2MM^E *EMP* 52
SIC 4832 Radio broadcasting stations
CEO: Kevin Rabbitt
Pr: Michael Fernander
Pr: Bill Humphrey
Ex VP: Daniel P Wilhelm
VP: Terence Brady
IT Man: Justin Reinard

D-U-N-S 08-690-4570 IMP
NEP ELECTRONICS INC
805 Mittel Dr, Wood Dale, IL 60191-1118
Tel (630) 595-8500 *Founded/Ownrshp* 1977
Sales 59.3MM^E *EMP* 125
SIC 5065 3679 Electronic parts; Harness assemblies for electronic use: wire or cable; Electronic parts; Harness assemblies for electronic use: wire or cable
Pr: Thomas Lotus
**VP:* William Federighi
IT Man: John Hazucha
MIS Mgr: Dave Molter
Sfty Mgr: Sean Fisher
Prd Mgr: James Neff
Sls Mgr: Stacey Pollard
Sls Mgr: Melissa Zankowski
Sales Asso: Mike Babler
Sales Asso: Samantha Barczak
Sales Asso: Fred Brickman

NEP ENTERTAINMENT GROUP
See NEP SUPERSHOOTERS LP

D-U-N-S 02-219-5908
NEP GROUP INC
NEP SUPERSHOOTERS
2 Beta Dr, Pittsburgh, PA 15238-2916
Tel (412) 826-1414 *Founded/Ownrshp* 1995, 2004
Sales 82.8MM^E *EMP* 590
SIC 7812 Television film production; Television film production
Pr: Kevin Rabbitt
**Pr:* Nancy Oman
**VP:* Terence Brady
**VP:* George Hoover
VP: Thomas P Shelburne III
VP Opers: Glenn Levine

NEP SUPERSHOOTERS
See NEP GROUP INC

D-U-N-S 18-566-4364 EXP
NEP SUPERSHOOTERS LP
NEP ENTERTAINMENT GROUP
(*Suby of* NEP GROUP INC) ★
2 Beta Dr, Pittsburgh, PA 15238-2916
Tel (412) 826-1414 *Founded/Ownrshp* 2000
Sales 52.9MM^E *EMP* 262^E
SIC 7812 Television film production; Television film production
CEO: Kevin Rabbitt
Ch Bd: Debra Honkus
Pr: Mike Fernander
Pr: Mike Zlaket
CFO: Gerry Delon
CFO: George Hoover
Tech Mgr: Sal Morreale
Tech Mgr: Jim Weaver
Software D: Chris Seewald

D-U-N-S 19-478-4096
NEPC LLC
255 State St, Boston, MA 02109-2617
Tel (617) 314-3176 *Founded/Ownrshp* 1986
Sales NA *EMP* 218
Accts Kpmg Peat Marwick
SIC 6411 6282 Pension & retirement plan consultants; Investment advice; Pension & retirement plan consultants; Investment advice
Pr: Richard Charlton
Sr Pt: William Bogle
Mng Pt: Joseph Breitfelder
Mng Pt: Catherine Konicki
**Prin:* Mike Manning
Off Mgr: Terri Sacramone
CIO: Donna Szeto
IT Man: Kevin Leonard
IT Man: James Reichert
IT Man: John Shanklin
MIS Mgr: Eric Hill

NEPCO
See MATRIX METALS HOLDINGS INC

NEPERA
See RUTHERFORD CHEMICAL LLC

NEPHI MEDICAL CLINIC
See CENTRAL VALLEY MEDICAL CENTER INC

D-U-N-S 14-845-1305 IMP/EXP
NEPHI RUBBER PRODUCTS CORP
NRP-JONES
255 W 1100 N, Nephi, UT 84648-2502
Tel (435) 623-1740 *Founded/Ownrshp* 1985
Sales 25.4MM^E *EMP* 90^E
SIC 3052 Rubber & plastics hose & beltings; Rubber hose; Rubber & plastics hose & beltings; Rubber hose
Pr: Mark Trast
CFO: Mike Lapczynski
**Sec:* Keith H Jones
**VP:* K Brian Jones
**Prin:* Terry H Jones
Off Mgr: Shauna Winter
CTO: Kyle Kay
Sfty Mgr: Charlie Castellano
Plnt Mgr: Glade Nielson
Ql Cn Mgr: Daniel Nelson
Sls Mgr: Bob Hansen

D-U-N-S 11-012-0102
NEPHROLOGY INC
NEPHROLOGY PHYSICIANS
710 Park Pl, Mishawaka, IN 46545-3519
Tel (574) 273-6767 *Founded/Ownrshp* 1994
Sales 22.6MM^E *EMP* 250
SIC 8092 5812 Kidney dialysis centers; Eating places; Kidney dialysis centers; Eating places
Pr: Samuel Milligan
**VP:* Dr Paul Herman
**VP:* Amy Lashbrook
Dir IT: Kelly Klink
Doctor: Margaret Operacz MD

NEPHROLOGY PHYSICIANS
See NEPHROLOGY INC

NEPHRON PHARMACEUTICALS
See NEPHRON SC INC

D-U-N-S 78-390-5201 IMP
NEPHRON PHARMACEUTICALS CORP
4121 Sw 34th St, Orlando, FL 32811-6475
Tel (407) 999-2225 *Founded/Ownrshp* 1991
Sales 110.3MM^E *EMP* 560^E
Accts Robert Kimelman
SIC 2834 Pharmaceutical preparations; Pharmaceutical preparations
Pr: Lou W Kennedy
COO: Ritchie Monteith
**COO:* John Petta
Ex VP: William Dudley
VP: Denise Sullivan
**Dir Sec:* Jerry Webb
Rgnl Mgr: Gregg Polacek
QA Dir: Ryan Lamsee
Prd Mgr: Nermin Cehajic
Ql Cn Mgr: Edward Burt
Natl Sales: Christine Neeld

D-U-N-S 07-916-0190
NEPHRON SC INC
NEPHRON PHARMACEUTICALS
4500 12th Street Ext, West Columbia, SC 29172-3025
Tel (803) 727-5881 *Founded/Ownrshp* 2011
Sales 37.9MM^E *EMP* 43^E
SIC 5122 Pharmaceuticals

D-U-N-S 00-120-0781 IMP/EXP
■ **NEPTCO INC** (RI)
(*Suby of* CHASE CORP) ★
30 Hamlet St, Pawtucket, RI 02861-2827
Tel (401) 722-5500 *Founded/Ownrshp* 1953, 2012
Sales 94.3MM^E *EMP* 500
SIC 3496 3083 2672 3827 Woven wire products; Laminated plastic sheets; Coated & laminated paper; Optical instruments & lenses; Woven wire products; Laminated plastic sheets; Coated & laminated paper; Optical instruments & lenses
CEO: Guy Marini
**VP:* Frank Conti
**VP:* Ken Feroldi
VP: Charles Glue
**VP:* Joel Gruhn
**VP:* Lois Kilsey
Prgrm Mgr: George Shanahan
IT Man: Stephen Wan
Mfg Mgr: Anthony Ketchel
Plnt Mgr: Ashok Gordhandas
Ql Cn Mgr: Dave Gaugler

D-U-N-S 80-795-4177 IMP
NEPTUNE AVIATION SERVICES INC
1 Corporate Way, Missoula, MT 59808-8674
Tel (406) 542-0606 *Founded/Ownrshp* 1993
Sales 26.2MM^E *EMP* 100
SIC 0851 Fire prevention services, forest
CEO: Ronald Hooper
**Pr:* Kristen Schloemer
**COO:* Daniel Snyder
**Ch:* Marta Amelia Timmons
**VP:* Kristen Nicolarsen
IT Man: Jennifer Draughon
IT Man: Suzie Kendall

D-U-N-S 02-661-8947 IMP
■ **NEPTUNE CHEMICAL PUMP CO**
NEPTUNE MIXER
(*Suby of* DOVER FLUID MANAGEMENT INC) ★
295 Dekalb Pike, North Wales, PA 19454-1806
Tel (215) 699-8700 *Founded/Ownrshp* 2008
Sales 32.7MM^E *EMP* 130
SIC 3561 3586 Pumps & pumping equipment; Measuring & dispensing pumps; Pumps & pumping equipment; Measuring & dispensing pumps
CEO: Michael Dowse
**Pr:* Sivasankaran Somasundaram
**Sec:* William Barton
**VP:* John Allen
Mktg Mgr: Alan Dickel
Mktg Mgr: Thomas O Dnnell

NEPTUNE FOODS
See FISHERMANS PRIDE PROCESSORS INC

NEPTUNE LIFETIME SINKS
See ELKAY MANUFACTURING CO INC

NEPTUNE MIXER
See NEPTUNE CHEMICAL PUMP CO

D-U-N-S 00-909-9537 IMP/EXP
■ **NEPTUNE TECHNOLOGY GROUP INC**
(*Suby of* ROPER TECHNOLOGIES INC) ★
1600 Al Highway 229 S, Tallassee, AL 36078-1714
Tel (334) 283-6555 *Founded/Ownrshp* 2001
Sales 112.5MM^E *EMP* 500^E
SIC 3824 Water meters; Water meters
Pr: Charles C Dilaura
Pr: Thierry Swinson
VP: Mike Berg
**VP:* Lawrence Russo
Dir Bus: Brad Dreier
Area Mgr: David Wyble
Dist Mgr: Tony Glassier
QA Dir: David Hyde
Dir IT: Margie West
Telecom Mg: Charlie Cauthen
IT Man: Bob Brown

D-U-N-S 08-198-1276
NEPTUNE TOWNSHIP BOARD OF EDUCATION
60 Neptune Blvd, Neptune, NJ 07753-4852
Tel (732) 776-2000 *Founded/Ownrshp* 1891
Sales 39.0MM^E *EMP* 910
Accts Ernst & Young Llp
SIC 8211 Public elementary & secondary schools; Public elementary & secondary schools
Ofcr: Elena Gonzalez
HC Dir: Giuseppina Diamante

D-U-N-S 07-980-7077
NEPTUNE TOWNSHIP SCHOOL DISTRICT
60 Neptune Blvd, Neptune, NJ 07753-4852
Tel (732) 776-2200 *Founded/Ownrshp* 2015
Sales 6.7MM^E *EMP* 606^E
SIC 8211 Public elementary & secondary schools
Ofcr: Nora Freeman
Adm Dir: Denise Casper
IT Man: Patrick Keith
Schl Brd P: Jason Jones

D-U-N-S 06-391-7140 IMP/EXP
NEPTUNE-BENSON LLC
6 Jefferson Dr, Coventry, RI 02816-6219
Tel (401) 821-2200 *Founded/Ownrshp* 1957
Sales 25.0MM^E *EMP* 74^E
SIC 3589 Swimming pool filter & water conditioning systems
Ch: Barry Gertz
**Pr:* Jon McClea
**CEO:* Kenneth Rodi
**CFO:* Michael Burns
**CFO:* Timothy Jeakins
Sr VP: Paul Nehlen
VP: Bob Laduke
VP: David Richout
IT Man: William Grady
Prd Mgr: John Okeefe
VP Sls: Robert Hawkin

D-U-N-S 17-482-6255
NER CONSTRUCTION MANAGEMENT CORP
867 Woburn St, Wilmington, MA 01887-3490
Tel (978) 988-1111 *Founded/Ownrshp* 1980
Sales 46.0MM^E *EMP* 260
SIC 1741 Masonry & other stonework; Tuckpointing or restoration; Masonry & other stonework; Tuckpointing or restoration
CEO: Frank Loconte
VP: Christopher Hilgert
**Prin:* Richard W Sylvester Jr
Sfty Dirs: Mark Brown

D-U-N-S 62-758-0665
NER DATA CORP
307 Delsea Dr S, Glassboro, NJ 08028-2647
Tel (856) 881-5524 *Founded/Ownrshp* 1985
Sales 77.5MM^E *EMP* 530
SIC 7374 Data processing service; Data processing service
Ch Bd: Francis C Oatway
**Pr:* Stephen F Oatway
**CFO:* Chris Oatway
**Ex VP:* James Coffey
**Sr VP:* Greg Stover
**VP:* Eric Austin
Dir IT: Christian Banfer
Sftwr Eng: David Wieting

D-U-N-S 05-326-9049 IMP
NER DATA PRODUCTS INC
(*Suby of* NER DATA CORP) ★
307 Delsea Dr S, Glassboro, NJ 08028-2647
Tel (856) 881-2569 *Founded/Ownrshp* 1971
Sales 47.3MM^E *EMP* 250
Accts Pricewaterhousecoopers Llp
SIC 3577 3955 3861 3572 2542 Computer peripheral equipment; Carbon paper & inked ribbons; Photographic equipment & supplies; Computer storage devices; Partitions & fixtures, except wood; Computer peripheral equipment; Carbon paper & inked ribbons; Photographic equipment & supplies; Computer storage devices; Partitions & fixtures, except wood
Ch Bd: Francis C Oatway
**Pr:* Stephen F Oatway
CFO: Daniel C Checchia
**CFO:* Christopher Oatway
Treas: H Y Hoppes
Ex VP: Dudley Devore
**Ex VP:* Scott Steele
VP: Thomas Brosseau
Genl Mgr: Robert Huttemann
Plng Mgr: Devon Rojas
Dir IT: Christian Banfer

NERA ECONOMICS CONSULTING
See NATIONAL ECONOMIC RESEARCH ASSOCIATES INC

D-U-N-S 05-889-9725
NERANGIS ENTERPRISES INC
MCDONALD'S
621 W Jubal Early Dr D, Winchester, VA 22601-6510
Tel (540) 667-1322 *Founded/Ownrshp* 1970
Sales 14.3MM^E *EMP* 400
SIC 5812 Fast-food restaurant, chain; Fast-food restaurant, chain
Pr: Nicholas J Nerangis
**Treas:* Kathy Nerangis

D-U-N-S 08-050-6397
NERCON ENG & MFG INC
600 S Commercial St, Neenah, WI 54956-3312
Tel (844) 293-2814 *Founded/Ownrshp* 1976
Sales 25.5MM^E *EMP* 125
Accts Schenck Sc Oshkosh Wisconsin
SIC 3565 5084 Packaging machinery; Industrial machinery & equipment; Packaging machinery; Industrial machinery & equipment
Pr: James L Nerenhausen Jr
**Pr:* James Nerenhausen Sr
**VP:* Joseph Roesler
VP: Joseph E Roesler
Plnt Mgr: Tom Apts
Sls Dir: Tom Luft
Sls Dir: Tim Reder
Manager: Tim Lacroix
Manager: Ryan Neabling
Manager: Mike Webb
Manager: Steve Zehner

D-U-N-S 85-849-5443
NERIS BAKERY PRODUCTS INC
31 Pearl St 37, Port Chester, NY 10573-4610
Tel (914) 937-3235 *Founded/Ownrshp* 1990
Sales 96.5MM^E *EMP* 200
SIC 5149 5461 2051 Bakery products; Bakeries; Bread, cake & related products; Bakery products; Bakeries; Bread, cake & related products
Pr: Dominick Neri
**VP:* Paul Neri

D-U-N-S 85-942-0916
NERIUM BIOTECHNOLOGY INC
NERIUM SKINCARE
11467 Huebner Rd Ste 175, San Antonio, TX 78230-1074
Tel (210) 822-7908 *Founded/Ownrshp* 2007
Sales 32.0MM *EMP* 7^E
SIC 2819 8731 Industrial inorganic chemicals; Commercial physical research
Pr: Dennis Knocke
**CFO:* Joseph Nester

NERIUM SKINCARE
See NERIUM BIOTECHNOLOGY INC

D-U-N-S 16-878-8912
NEROBE LLC
3157 E 14th Fairway Dr, Washington, UT 84780
Tel (801) 597-2327 *Founded/Ownrshp* 2004
Sales 10.0MM *EMP* 287
SIC 8741 Restaurant management; Restaurant management
Pr: Neil Roberts

NERSCM
See NEW ENGLAND REHABILITATION SERVICES OF CENTRAL MASSACHUSETTS INC

NES
See NATIONAL ENTERPRISE SYSTEMS INC

D-U-N-S 62-501-3409
NES ASSOCIATES LLC
6400 Beulah St Ste 300, Alexandria, VA 22310-2628
Tel (703) 224-2600 *Founded/Ownrshp* 2006
Sales 78.3MM *EMP* 365^E

Accts Matthews Carter & Boyce Fair
SIC 7373 Local area network (LAN) systems integrator; Local area network (LAN) systems integrator
CEO: Andrew Gomer
COO: Tim Murray
CFO: Dan Rice

NES COSTUME
See NES JEWELRY INC

D-U-N-S 10-421-3785
NES GLOBAL LLC
(*Suby of* NES GLOBAL LIMITED)
800 Gessner Rd Ste 310, Houston, TX 77024-4599
Tel (713) 551-4444 *Founded/Ownrshp* 2000
Sales 183.9MM *EMP* 35
SIC 1799 Athletic & recreation facilities construction
CEO: Neil Tregarthen
Ofcr: Ufuoma Idoghor
Opers Mgr: Cheryl Peavoy

D-U-N-S 83-862-2256
NES HOLDINGS INC
39 Main St, Belvedere Tiburon, CA 94920-2507
Tel (415) 435-4591 *Founded/Ownrshp* 1994
Sales 100.0MM *EMP* 196
SIC 7363 Medical help service; Medical help service
Ch Bd: Allan H Rappaport MD
CFO: Dave Ulrich
**VP:* Thomas Botts
**Prin:* William H Warren
Counsel: Sanford Pomerantz

D-U-N-S 05-270-8745
■ **NES INVESTMENT CO**
(*Suby of* JOY GLOBAL INC) ★
6140 Parkland Blvd, Cleveland, OH 44124-6142
Tel (440) 461-6000 *Founded/Ownrshp* 2000, 2008
Sales 92.2MM^E *EMP* 1,431
SIC 5065 5085 5169 5013 Security control equipment & systems; Fasteners, industrial: nuts, bolts, screws, etc.; Industrial chemicals; Automotive supplies & parts; Security control equipment & systems; Fasteners, industrial: nuts, bolts, screws, etc.; Industrial chemicals; Automotive supplies & parts
Pr: Robert J Tomsich
VP: Patrick Brainard
Counsel: David Sweeny

D-U-N-S 93-158-9340 IMP
NES JEWELRY INC
NES COSTUME
20 W 33rd St Fl 6, New York, NY 10001-3305
Tel (212) 502-0025 *Founded/Ownrshp* 2000
Sales 42.7MM *EMP* 115
Accts Mayer Rispler & Company Pc B
SIC 3961 Silverware or plated ware; Costume jewelry
Pr: Nemo Gindi
CFO: Jay Gassar
CFO: Paul Kopyt
Chf Mktg O: Eddy Chacoury
**VP:* Jack Yedid
IT Man: Yosi Arish
IT Man: Aaron Klein
VP Sls: Ralph Hanan

D-U-N-S 15-077-1959
NES RENTALS HOLDINGS INC
DIAMOND CASTLE
(*Suby of* DIAMOND CASTLE HOLDINGS LLC) ★
8420 W Bryn Mawr Ave # 310, Chicago, IL 60631-3479
Tel (773) 695-3999 *Founded/Ownrshp* 2006
Sales 347.0MM *EMP* 1,100
Accts Kpmg Llp Chicago Il
SIC 7359 7699 5082 Equipment rental & leasing; Industrial machinery & equipment repair; Construction & mining machinery; Equipment rental & leasing; Industrial machinery & equipment repair; Construction & mining machinery
Pr: Andrew P Studdert
Pr: Andrew Cho
**CFO:* Michael D Milligan
**Sr VP:* Christopher Bowers
VP: John Christiansen
VP: Dave Meirick
**VP:* Ananda Rakhit
Brnch Mgr: Jim Anderson
Off Mgr: Don Lonard
VP Opers: Brent Mumford
VP Mktg: Mike Disser

D-U-N-S 06-895-3676
NES RENTALS INC
540 Lake Cook Rd Ste 100, Deerfield, IL 60015-5631
Tel (773) 695-3999 *Founded/Ownrshp* 2011
Sales 20.3MM^E *EMP* 140^E
SIC 7359 Equipment rental & leasing
CEO: Andrew P Studdert
Brnch Mgr: Zack Ballard
Brnch Mgr: Reid Clark
Brnch Mgr: David Coley
Brnch Mgr: Chad Feenstra
Brnch Mgr: Jim Herdon
Brnch Mgr: Matt Pequignot
Brnch Mgr: Trey Sharp
Brnch Mgr: Michael Werden
Genl Mgr: Charles Edde
Opers Mgr: Leighton Alston

D-U-N-S 60-258-0771
NESBITT BURNS SECURITIES INC
(*Suby of* BMO FINANCIAL CORP) ★
115 S La Salle St Ste 20w, Chicago, IL 60603-3801
Tel (312) 461-6220 *Founded/Ownrshp* 1993
Sales 256.0MM^E *EMP* 7,000
SIC 6211 Security brokers & dealers; Security brokers & dealers
CEO: Jeff Orr
**Ch Bd:* James K Beqaj
**Pr:* Aubrey W Baillie
VP: Don King
VP: Dean Starke
Mng Dir: James Walsh

D-U-N-S 04-145-8308
NESBITT CONTRACTING CO INC
(*Suby of* NESBITT INVESTMENT CO)
100 S Price Rd, Tempe, AZ 85281-3118
Tel (480) 894-2831 *Founded/Ownrshp* 1955
Sales 28.9MM^E *EMP* 140
SIC 1611

NESCO
See METAL WARE CORP

NESCO
See NEEDHAM ELECTRIC SUPPLY CORP

NESCO ELECTRICAL DISTRIBUTORS
See NESCO LLC

D-U-N-S 05-551-5076 IMP/EXP
NESCO INC
NESCO RESOURCE
6140 Parkland Blvd # 110, Cleveland, OH 44124-6106
Tel (440) 461-6000 *Founded/Ownrshp* 1988
Sales 760.3MM^E *EMP* 5,000
SIC 3535 3541 3544 8711 6531 Conveyors & conveying equipment; Machine tools, metal cutting type; Special dies, tools, jigs & fixtures; Engineering services; Real estate managers; Conveyors & conveying equipment; Machine tools, metal cutting type; Special dies, tools, jigs & fixtures; Engineering services; Real estate managers
Pr: Robert Tomsich
**CFO:* Frank Rzicznek
Ex VP: James Parker
VP: Michael Gallagher
Area Mgr: Michael Schneider
Area Mgr: Tom Villhard
Brnch Mgr: Jerry Arena
Brnch Mgr: Justin Brake
Brnch Mgr: Kori Carlson
Brnch Mgr: Maggie Carter
Brnch Mgr: Christy Fee

D-U-N-S 00-705-0255
NESCO LLC (MS)
NESCO ELECTRICAL DISTRIBUTORS
2344 S Green St, Tupelo, MS 38801-6569
Tel (662) 840-4750 *Founded/Ownrshp* 1965
Sales 26.1MM^E *EMP* 50
SIC 5063

D-U-N-S 15-513-1477 IMP/EXP
NESCO LLC
6714 Pointe Inverness Way # 220, Fort Wayne, IN 46804-7935
Tel (260) 824-6340 *Founded/Ownrshp* 2014
Sales 65.5MM^E *EMP* 65^E
SIC 5012 7513 Trucks, commercial; Truck leasing, without drivers
Area Mgr: Jerry Whiteland

NESCO RESOURCE
See NESCO SERVICE CO

NESCO RESOURCE
See NESCO INC

D-U-N-S 03-809-2706
NESCO SERVICE CO
NESCO RESOURCE
12708 Dupont Cir, Tampa, FL 33626-3041
Tel (813) 855-9136 *Founded/Ownrshp* 1989
Sales 53.1MM^E *EMP* 175
SIC 8711 7363 7361 Engineering services; Help supply services; Engineering help service; Employment agencies; Engineering services; Help supply services; Engineering help service; Employment agencies
Pr: Timothy McPherson
Pr: Frank Rzicznek
IT Man: Scott Gammon

NESCOM
See HUSSON UNIVERSITY

D-U-N-S 11-411-9969
NESCONSET ACQUISITION LLC
NESCONSET CENTER
100 Southern Blvd, Nesconset, NY 11767-1749
Tel (631) 361-8800 *Founded/Ownrshp* 2006
Sales 35.9MM *EMP* 400
SIC 8051 Skilled nursing care facilities; Skilled nursing care facilities
CFO: Colleen Spitzner
CFO: Louis Viteritti
Ofcr: Suzy Douyon
IT Man: Denise Chavez

NESCONSET CENTER
See NESCONSET ACQUISITION LLC

D-U-N-S 06-988-8741
NESHAMINY ELECTRICAL CONTRACTORS INC (PA)
1700 Byberry Rd, Bensalem, PA 19020-4532
Tel (215) 638-2900 *Founded/Ownrshp* 1972
Sales 30.9MM^E *EMP* 103
Accts Lopez Teodosio & Larkinllp
SIC 1731 1541 Electrical work; Industrial buildings & warehouses
Pr: John W Lyons
**VP:* Daniel Morrin
Sys Mgr: Brian Walters
Snr Mgr: Dan Dorr

D-U-N-S 07-710-7696
NESHAMINY SCHOOL DISTRICT
2001 Old Lincoln Hwy, Langhorne, PA 19047-3240
Tel (215) 809-6562 *Founded/Ownrshp* 1925
Sales 80.9MM^E *EMP* 1,200
Accts Maillie Falconiero & Company
SIC 8211 Public combined elementary & secondary school; Public combined elementary & secondary school
**Pr:* Ritchie Webb
**Treas:* Barbara Markowitz
**VP:* Scott E Congdon
Admn Mgr: Alexander Menio
Psych: Helen Szodfridt
HC Dir: Anthony Devlin

D-U-N-S 96-902-8351
NESHER PHARMACEUTICALS (USA) LLC
(*Suby of* CADILA HEALTHCARE LIMITED)
13910 St Charles Rock Rd, Bridgeton, MO 63044-3826
Tel (314) 209-4700 *Founded/Ownrshp* 2011
Sales 315.2MM *EMP* 120^E
SIC 2834 Pharmaceutical preparations; Pharmaceutical preparations
Pr: Vince Kaiman

D-U-N-S 15-941-3897
NESHOBA CO SCHOOL DISTRICT
401 E Beacon St Ste 102, Philadelphia, MS 39350-2954
Tel (601) 656-3752 *Founded/Ownrshp* 1920
Sales 10.5MM^E *EMP* 381
SIC 8211 Public elementary & secondary schools; School board; Public elementary & secondary schools; School board
VP: Cyndi Weldy

D-U-N-S 06-735-5547
NESHOBA COUNTY GENERAL HOSPITA
NESHOBA PEDIATRIC MEDICAL CLIN
10140 Road 571, Philadelphia, MS 39350-7210
Tel (601) 656-3628 *Founded/Ownrshp* 2011
Sales 46.9MM *EMP* 5
SIC 8099 Health & allied services
Prin: Vicky L Rivers

D-U-N-S 07-764-1983
NESHOBA COUNTY GENERAL HOSPITAL - NURSING HOME
1001 Holland Ave, Philadelphia, MS 39350-2161
Tel (601) 663-1200 *Founded/Ownrshp* 1948
Sales 43.9MM *EMP* 500
Accts Watkins Ward And Stafford Pl
SIC 8051 8062 Convalescent home with continuous nursing care; General medical & surgical hospitals; Convalescent home with continuous nursing care; General medical & surgical hospitals
CEO: Lee McCall
Pr: Annette Watkins
**CFO:* Scott McNair
Ofcr: Roger Cole
Dir Rad: Kerry Smith
IT Man: Chris Stokes
Pharmcst: Tony Fieber
HC Dir: Beth Boatner

NESHOBA PEDIATRIC MEDICAL CLIN
See NESHOBA COUNTY GENERAL HOSPITA

NESI
See NON PUBLIC EDUCATIONAL SERVICES INC

D-U-N-S 06-450-7387
NESMITH CHEVROLET OF HINESVILLE INC
NESMITH OLDSMOBILE
Hwy 280 W, Claxton, GA 30417
Tel (912) 739-1744 *Founded/Ownrshp* 1974
Sales 24.7MM^E *EMP* 80^E
SIC 5511 Automobiles, new & used; Automobiles, new & used
Pr: Martin W Nesmith
**Sec:* Suzette P Nesmith
Opers Mgr: Star Harris
Sls Mgr: John McKinnon

NESMITH OLDSMOBILE
See NESMITH CHEVROLET OF HINESVILLE INC

NESN
See NEW ENGLAND SPORTS NETWORK LIMITED PARTNERSHIP

D-U-N-S 79-466-1801 IMP/EXP
NESPRESSO USA INC
(*Suby of* NESTLE HOLDINGS INC) ★
100 Park Ave Fl 8, New York, NY 10017-5559
Tel (800) 562-1465 *Founded/Ownrshp* 1990
Sales 177.1MM^E *EMP* 400
SIC 5149 5046 5499 Coffee, green or roasted; Coffee brewing equipment & supplies; Coffee; Coffee, green or roasted; Coffee brewing equipment & supplies; Coffee
Pr: Fredrick Levy
VP: Alexis Giguere
Off Mgr: Danielle Diaz
IT Man: Yezid Acosta
IT Man: Thierry Aiello
Manager: Mary Lang
Sls Mgr: Ricky Samaroo
Sales Asso: Gordon Dutfield
Snr Mgr: Farrukh Madaminov
Snr Mgr: Brandon Sosa

D-U-N-S 04-577-6853
NESS & CAMPBELL CRANE INC
NESS & CAMPBELL RIGGING SVC
5730 Ne 138th Ave, Portland, OR 97230-3410
Tel (503) 283-3111 *Founded/Ownrshp* 2008
Sales 28.2MM^E *EMP* 150
SIC 7353 Cranes & aerial lift equipment, rental or leasing; Cranes & aerial lift equipment, rental or leasing
Pr: Tony Steelman
Genl Mgr: Shelley Brown
Genl Mgr: Kurt Klette
IT Man: Valarie Owens
Sales Asso: Ole Pedersen

D-U-N-S 04-748-1973
NESS & CAMPBELL CRANE INC
8612 S 218th St, Kent, WA 98031-1949
Tel (206) 784-1054 *Founded/Ownrshp* 2005
Sales 29.8MM^E *EMP* 190
SIC 7353 Heavy construction equipment rental; Cranes & aerial lift equipment, rental or leasing; Heavy construction equipment rental; Cranes & aerial lift equipment, rental or leasing
Pr: Tony Steelman
**VP:* Ralph Esary
**VP:* Kurt Kleppe
**VP:* Ricky Moultrie
**VP:* Daniel Pollard
VP: Michael Teeter
Off Mgr: Cheryl Osborne
Off Admin: Cherie Johanson
VP Opers: Kurt Wilson
Sales Asso: John Mitcham
Sales Asso: Rick Wolff

NESS & CAMPBELL RIGGING SVC
See NESS & CAMPBELL CRANE INC

D-U-N-S 02-292-5051 IMP
NESS ELECTRONICS INC
1800 E 121st St, Burnsville, MN 55337-6801
Tel (651) 251-5700 *Founded/Ownrshp* 1999
Sales 450.0MM *EMP* 28
SIC 5065 Electronic parts
Pr: Michael Ness
**VP:* Arlene Ness

D-U-N-S 02-774-2758
NESS HOLDING CO
KOOL PAK
4550 Kruse Way Ste 350, Lake Oswego, OR 97035-3588
Tel (503) 240-0400 *Founded/Ownrshp* 1968
Sales 88.7MM^E *EMP* 345
SIC 5141 Groceries, general line; Food brokers; Groceries, general line; Food brokers
Pr: Steven A Ness
**CFO:* Wade J Palmer
VP: Bill Knechtel
Board of Directors: Brian Hart

D-U-N-S 13-472-0544
■ **NESS TECHNOLOGIES INC**
(*Suby of* JERSEY HOLDING CORPORATION)
300 Frank W Burr Blvd, Teaneck, NJ 07666-6704
Tel (201) 488-7222 *Founded/Ownrshp* 2011
Sales 478.0MM^E *EMP* 7,710^E
SIC 7379 7373 Computer related consulting services; Computer integrated systems design; Computer related consulting services; Computer integrated systems design
CEO: Ofer Segev
**Ch Bd:* Sachi Gerlitz
**Pr:* Issachar Gerlitz
CFO: Irene Math
**Ofcr:* Holly Ripley-Boyd
Top Exec: Rohit Jayaswal
Top Exec: Narayan Parameswaran
Assoc VP: Kelly S Cook
**Ex VP:* Atzmon Lifshitz
VP: Ness Israel
VP: Shakthi Kumar
VP: Matthew Lee
VP: Shannon Shirk
VP: Drew Wright
VP: Roi Zohar
Assoc Dir: Jaxa Unadkat
Dir Bus: Parvez Kadbal

D-U-N-S 79-947-3871
■ **NESS USA INC**
(*Suby of* NESS TECHNOLOGIES INC) ★
1000 Town Center Way # 210, Canonsburg, PA 15317-5834
Tel (201) 488-7222 *Founded/Ownrshp* 1997
Sales 69.3MM^E *EMP* 388
SIC 7371 7373 Computer software systems analysis & design, custom; Computer systems analysis & design; Computer software systems analysis & design, custom; Computer systems analysis & design
CEO: Ofer Segev
Pr: Jose Delaossa
Pr: Venkatesh Ganapathy
**Pr:* Rajeev Srivastava
**Treas:* Mitesh Ashar
VP: Krishna Bayya
**VP:* Robert Mason
Mng Dir: Clement Chua
Snr Sftwr: Sheela Choudhari
Sls Mgr: Christy Decola
Sls Mgr: Howard Goodkind

D-U-N-S 79-119-1505
NEST ENTERTAINMENT INC
1461 S Belt Line Rd # 300, Coppell, TX 75019-4937
Tel (972) 402-7100 *Founded/Ownrshp* 1988
Sales 13.3MM^E *EMP* 500
SIC 7812 Video tape production; Video tape production
Ch Bd: Seldon Young
**Pr:* Doug Martin
CFO: Ernie Frausto
VP: Barbara Beasley
VP: Mark Dixon
Dir IT: Rodney Starcher

D-U-N-S 96-817-5377 IMP/EXP
■ **NEST LABS INC**
(*Suby of* GOOGLE INC) ★
3400 Hillview Ave, Palo Alto, CA 94304-1346
Tel (650) 331-1127 *Founded/Ownrshp* 2014
Sales 30.1MM^E *EMP* 35^E
SIC 5065 Electronic parts & equipment
CEO: Tony Fadell
**Owner:* Matthew Rogers
CFO: Ton Vonreichbauer
VP: Bryan James
VP: Lee Mighdoll
Creative D: Matteo Vianello
Comm Dir: Kate Brinks
Prgrm Mgr: David Cassano
Sftwr Eng: Gints Klimanis
Sftwr Eng: Jiakang Lu
Sftwr Eng: Jared Luxenberg

D-U-N-S 13-659-3980
NEST SEEKERS LLC
415 Madison Ave Fl 20, New York, NY 10017-7939
Tel (212) 252-8772 *Founded/Ownrshp* 2000
Sales 21.5MM^E *EMP* 80^E
SIC 6531 Real estate agents & managers
Ex VP: Joseph Decristofaro
Sr VP: Regis Roumila
Creative D: Ben Zeitlin
Mng Dir: Barbara Feldman
Mng Dir: Marisa Zanuck
Rgnl Mgr: Geoff Gifkins
IT Man: Tom Ruane
Opers Mgr: Pauline Trinh
Sales Asso: Nazan Aykent

Sales Asso: Damon Carpentier
Sales Asso: Genoveva Ciornei

D-U-N-S 60-409-0316
NESTER HOSIERY INC
1546 Carter St, Mount Airy, NC 27030-5720
Tel (336) 789-0026 *Founded/Ownrshp* 1993
Sales 38.1MM^E *EMP* 190^E
SIC 2252 Socks; Socks
CEO: Martin W Nester
**Pr:* Kelly S Nester

D-U-N-S 06-656-3859 IMP/EXP
NESTLE DREYERS ICE CREAM CO
HAAGEN-DAZS
(*Suby of* DREYERS GRAND ICE CREAM HOLDINGS INC) ★
5929 College Ave, Oakland, CA 94618-1325
Tel (510) 594-9466 *Founded/Ownrshp* 2003
Sales 288.0MM^E *EMP* 5,000
SIC 5812 2024 Ice cream stands or dairy bars; Ice cream & frozen desserts; Ice cream stands or dairy bars; Ice cream & frozen desserts
CEO: Michael Mitchell
**CFO:* Steven P Barbour
CFO: Doug Holdt
Ex VP: William Rolden
VP: Jeffrey Vogt
Sfty Mgr: Chris Duffield
Plnt Mgr: Dan Braswell
Plnt Mgr: Nicholas Tsiolas
Plnt Mgr: Mike Vernear
VP Mktg: Mary Gold
Mktg Dir: Craig Whitney

D-U-N-S 07-911-5380
NESTLE HEALTH SCIENCE - PAMLAB INC
(*Suby of* NESTLE HEALTH SCIENCE SA)
4099 Hwy 190, Covington, LA 70433
Tel (985) 893-4097 *Founded/Ownrshp* 2013
Sales 82.8MM^E *EMP* 99^E
SIC 5122 Drugs & drug proprietaries
CEO: Eric Wingerter
CFO: Matthew Hutton
Sls Mgr: Matt Guilfoyle

D-U-N-S 00-624-7332 IMP/EXP
NESTLE HEALTHCARE NUTRITION INC
(*Suby of* NESTLE S.A.)
12 Vreeland Rd Fl 2, Florham Park, NJ 07932-1521
Tel (952) 848-6000 *Founded/Ownrshp* 2007
Sales 102.6MM^E *EMP* 488^E
SIC 2099 2032 Food preparations; Canned specialties; Food preparations; Canned specialties
CEO: Greg Behar
**Pr:* David Yates
COO: Mark Sponsler
VP: Diana Bryan
VP: Steve Drozda
Corp Couns: Mary Prentnieks

D-U-N-S 13-148-1657 IMP/EXP
NESTLE HOLDINGS INC
(*Suby of* NESTLE S.A.)
800 N Brand Blvd, Glendale, CA 91203-1245
Tel (818) 549-6000 *Founded/Ownrshp* 1983
Sales 8.0MMM^E *EMP* 25,000
Accts Kpmg Llp Los Angeles Ca
SIC 2023 2032 2038 2033 2064 2026 Dry, condensed, evaporated dairy products; Canned specialties; Soups & broths: canned, jarred, etc.; Beans & bean sprouts, canned, jarred, etc.; Italian foods: packaged in cans, jars, etc.; Frozen specialties; Fruits & fruit products in cans, jars, etc.; Vegetables & vegetable products in cans, jars, etc.; Jams, jellies & preserves: packaged in cans, jars, etc.; Tomato products: packaged in cans, jars, etc.; Candy & other confectionery products; Fluid milk; Dry, condensed, evaporated dairy products; Canned specialties; Soups & broths: canned, jarred, etc.; Beans & bean sprouts, canned, jarred, etc.; Italian foods: packaged in cans, jars, etc.; Frozen specialties; Fruits & fruit products in cans, jars, etc.; Vegetables & vegetable products in cans, jars, etc.; Jams, jellies & preserves: packaged in cans, jars, etc.; Tomato products: packaged in cans, jars, etc.; Candy & other confectionery products; Fluid milk
Ch Bd: Brad Alford
CFO: Mario Corti
CFO: Dana Sherman
**Treas:* Don Gosline
**Sr VP:* John Gatlin

D-U-N-S 12-731-2358 IMP
NESTLE ICE CREAM CO
(*Suby of* DREYERS GRAND ICE CREAM HOLDINGS INC) ★
7301 District Blvd, Bakersfield, CA 93313-2042
Tel (661) 398-3500 *Founded/Ownrshp* 1993
Sales 221.8MM^E *EMP* 1,920
SIC 5143 5451 Ice cream & ices; Ice cream (packaged); Ice cream & ices; Ice cream (packaged)
CEO: James L Dintaman
Brnch Mgr: Paul Stanberry

NESTLE INFANT NUTRITION
See GERBER PRODUCTS CO

NESTLE PREPARED FOODS - DENVER
See NESTLE PREPARED FOODS CO

D-U-N-S 07-113-0868 IMP
NESTLE PREPARED FOODS CO
(*Suby of* STOUFFER CORP) ★
5750 Harper Rd, Solon, OH 44139-1831
Tel (440) 248-3600 *Founded/Ownrshp* 1969
Sales 1.4MMM^E *EMP* 8,610
SIC 2038 5411 2037 Dinners, frozen & packaged; Soups, frozen; Pizza, frozen; Grocery stores; Vegetables, quick frozen & cold pack, excl. potato products; Dinners, frozen & packaged; Soups, frozen; Pizza, frozen; Grocery stores; Vegetables, quick frozen & cold pack, excl. potato products
Pr: C Wayne Partin
**Ch Bd:* David H Jennings
**VP:* James M Biggar
**VP:* Charles Werner

D-U-N-S 18-918-5903
NESTLE PREPARED FOODS CO
NESTLE PREPARED FOODS - DENVER
(*Suby of* NESTLE USA INC) ★
345 Invrneco Dr S Ste 200, Englewood, CO 80112
Tel (303) 790-0303 *Founded/Ownrshp* 1979
Sales 31.1MM^E *EMP* 100
SIC 2038 Frozen specialties; Frozen specialties
Pr: Anthony Iantosco

NESTLE PRODUCT TECHNOLOGY CTR
See R & D NESTLE CENTER INC

NESTLE PROFESSIONAL VITALITY
See VITALITY FOODSERVICE INC

D-U-N-S 09-014-5707 IMP/EXP
NESTLE PUERTO RICO INC
(*Suby of* NESTEC S.A.)
Cond Park Ln, San Juan, PR 00907-1868
Tel (787) 788-4300 *Founded/Ownrshp* 1954
Sales 46.6MM^E *EMP* 225
SIC 5149 Groceries & related products
Ql Cn Mgr: Magba Garcia

NESTLE PURINA FACTORY
See NESTLE PURINA PETCARE CO

D-U-N-S 00-626-6811 IMP
NESTLE PURINA PETCARE CO (MO)
NESTLE PURINA FACTORY
(*Suby of* NESTLE HOLDINGS INC) ★
901 Chouteau Ave, Saint Louis, MO 63102-1009
Tel (314) 982-1000 *Founded/Ownrshp* 1894, 2001
Sales 1.5MMM^E *EMP* 8,000
SIC 2047 Dog & cat food; Dog & cat food
Pr: W Patrick McGinnis
Pr: Thomas Blair
**CFO:* Rock Foster
Ex VP: Bill Kumke
Opers Mgr: Tiffany Alexander
Plnt Mgr: Terence E Block

D-U-N-S 12-125-8110 IMP/EXP
NESTLE PURINA PETCARE GLOBAL RESOURCES INC
(*Suby of* NESTEC S.A.)
1 Checkerboard Sq, Saint Louis, MO 63164-0001
Tel (513) 223-7715 *Founded/Ownrshp* 2002
Sales 58.8MM^E *EMP* 200
SIC 2048 5999 Canned pet food (except dog & cat); Canned pet food (except dog & cat); Pet food
VP: Robert Clarke
V Ch: Stephen Demeritt
**Treas:* Dixie Boatman
VP: Jorje Quinn
**VP:* Daniel Smith
Telecom Ex: Rene Martinez
CIO: Michael J Morgan
Dir IT: John Dossenbach
IT Man: Julie Siess
Info Man: John Williams
Mktg Dir: Margaret Gurgol

D-U-N-S 18-921-6476
NESTLE REFRIGERATED FOOD CO
(*Suby of* NESTLE USA INC) ★
800 N Brand Blvd Fl 5, Glendale, CA 91203-4281
Tel (818) 549-6000 *Founded/Ownrshp* 2006
Sales 63.7MM^E *EMP* 500
SIC 2098 2033 Macaroni products (e.g. alphabets, rings & shells), dry; Tomato paste: packaged in cans, jars, etc.

D-U-N-S 06-203-8351 IMP/EXP
NESTLE TRANSPORTATION CO
(*Suby of* NESTLE USA INC) ★
800 Nestle Ct, Dekalb, IL 60115-8676
Tel (815) 754-2600 *Founded/Ownrshp* 1985
Sales 40.0MM^E *EMP* 250
SIC 4213

D-U-N-S 00-825-6224 IMP/EXP
NESTLE USA INC
WONKA BAMBOOZLE
(*Suby of* NESTLE HOLDINGS INC) ★
800 N Brand Blvd, Glendale, CA 91203-3213
Tel (818) 549-6000 *Founded/Ownrshp* 1985
Sales 1.5MMM^E *EMP* 25,000
SIC 2023 2033 2064 2047 2099 2032

D-U-N-S 10-133-6568 IMP/EXP
NESTLE WATERS NORTH AMERICA HOLDINGS INC
(*Suby of* NESTLE WATERS)
900 Long Ridge Rd Bldg 2, Stamford, CT 06902-1140
Tel (203) 531-4100 *Founded/Ownrshp* 1992
Sales 4.6MMM^E *EMP* 8,500
SIC 5149 Mineral or spring water bottling; Mineral or spring water bottling
CEO: Tim Brown
**CFO:* William J Pearson
**Treas:* Don W Gosline
**Ex VP:* Dave Muscato
**Ex VP:* Heidi Paul
**Ex VP:* Bill Pearson
Sr VP: Dennis Crumbine
**VP:* Charles D Broll

D-U-N-S 84-744-9121 IMP/EXP
NESTLE WATERS NORTH AMERICA INC
PERRIER WATER
(*Suby of* NESTLE WATERS NORTH AMERICA HOLDINGS INC) ★
900 Long Ridge Rd Bldg 2, Stamford, CT 06902-1140
Tel (203) 531-4100 *Founded/Ownrshp* 2009
Sales 4.6MMM *EMP* 4,817
SIC 5149 Mineral or spring water bottling; Mineral or spring water bottling
CEO: Tim Brown
CFO: Rick Croarken
**CFO:* Rick Croarkin
**CFO:* Bill Pearson
**Ex VP:* Dave Muscato
Ex VP: Mike Pengue
**VP:* Charlie Broll
**VP:* David Colville
VP: Chon Searfoss

**Prin:* Thomas Muttitt
Genl Mgr: Guy Ferri

D-U-N-S 06-469-5190 IMP
■ **NESTOR SALES LLC**
AIM SUPPLY CO
(*Suby of* ESSENDANT CO) ★
7337 Bryan Dairy Rd, Largo, FL 33777-1507
Tel (727) 544-6114 *Founded/Ownrshp* 2015
Sales 139.8MM^E *EMP* 270
SIC 5013 5085 Tools & equipment, automotive; Industrial supplies; Tools & equipment, automotive; Industrial supplies
Pr: Peter Hofbauer
CFO: Barry Katz
Dist Mgr: Jeff Hoch
Dir IT: Monica Evenstad
IT Man: Michael Huling
Mktg Dir: Kevin Amico
Mktg Dir: Karen Bowser
Mktg Mgr: Trice Edwards
Sls Mgr: John Darovich
Sls Mgr: Dick Dickman

D-U-N-S 07-867-0407
■ **NESTWISE LLC**
(*Suby of* LPL FINANCIAL HOLDINGS INC) ★
444 Spear St Ste 210, San Francisco, CA 94105-1693
Tel (855) 444-6378 *Founded/Ownrshp* 2012
Sales 16.3MM^E *EMP* 610^E
SIC 7389 Financial services
CEO: Esther Stearns
Chf Mktg O: Beth Stelluto
Chf Inves: Burt White
Ofcr: Kandis Bates
Ofcr: Rudy Bethea
Ofcr: Paul Middlemiss
CTO: Jennifer Dutton

D-U-N-S 60-689-8856
NET 100 LTD
3675 Concorde Pkwy # 800, Chantilly, VA 20151-1159
Tel (703) 995-5200 *Founded/Ownrshp* 1989
Sales 35.6MM^E *EMP* 188
SIC 1731 Communications specialization; Communications specialization
Pr: Rodney W Cannon
**CFO:* John Clinton
**VP:* William Paris

D-U-N-S 17-752-6423 IMP
NET ACCESS LLC
NAC.NET
(*Suby of* COLOGIX INC) ★
9 Wing Dr, Cedar Knolls, NJ 07927-1006
Tel (973) 590-5000 *Founded/Ownrshp* 2015
Sales 38.4MM^E *EMP* 50
SIC 4813
Pr: Blake Ellman
CFO: Aaron L Pullin
Sr VP: Jason Vanderploog
VP: Dan Collier
VP: Sam Machiz
VP: Gene Rogers
VP: Alex Rubenstein
CTO: Dan J Cech
Opers Mgr: Aaron Endly
VP Sls: George Vaughan
Sls Mgr: Alex Weiss

D-U-N-S 07-865-5050
▲ **NET ELEMENT INC**
3363 Ne 163rd St Ste 705, North Miami Beach, FL 33160-4436
Tel (305) 507-8808 *Founded/Ownrshp* 2012
Sales 21.1MM *EMP* 65^E
Tkr Sym NETE *Exch* NAS
SIC 7374 Data processing & preparation; Data processing & preparation
CEO: Oleg Firer
**Ch Bd:* Kenges Rakishev
CFO: Jonathan New
Off Admin: Sinead Crosthwaite
CTO: Andrey Krotov
Snr Mgr: Irina Bukhanova
Board of Directors: James Caan, Drew J Freeman, William Healy, David P Kelley

D-U-N-S 12-178-3690
NET GAIN TECHNOLOGIES INC
2031 Georgetown Rd # 100, Lexington, KY 40511-2019
Tel (859) 255-0155 *Founded/Ownrshp* 1995
Sales 65.7MM^E *EMP* 185
SIC 5045 Computers, peripherals & software; Computers, peripherals & software
CEO: Mark Jacobson
VP: Bret Anderson
**Prin:* Jim Jacobson
Netwrk Eng: Brent Poynter
VP Sls: Tim Hutton

D-U-N-S 00-365-1056
NET HEALTH SYSTEMS INC
40 24th St Fl 5, Pittsburgh, PA 15222-4657
Tel (412) 261-1366 *Founded/Ownrshp* 1993
Sales 28.3MM^E *EMP* 80^E
SIC 7371 Computer software systems analysis & design, custom
CEO: Anthony Sanzo
Ch Bd: Jim Quagliaroli
Pr: Jason Baim
Pr: Patrick Colletti
CFO: Patrick Rooney
Sec: John T Bender
VP: Cathy Hess
VP: Mary Mieure
VP: Kelley J Shudy
Admn Mgr: Cathy Strobridge
CTO: Chris Hayes

D-U-N-S 00-564-4663
NET HOLDINGS MANAGEMENT LLC
5847 San Felipe St # 1910, Houston, TX 77057-3000
Tel (713) 800-1970 *Founded/Ownrshp* 2007
Sales 23.0MM^E *EMP* 60^E
SIC 6719 Personal holding companies, except banks; Pipelines, natural gas
Treas: Judy Barton

D-U-N-S 17-509-1495
NET SHAPES INC
1336 E Francis St Ste B, Ontario, CA 91761-5723
Tel (909) 947-3231 *Founded/Ownrshp* 1986
Sales 24.7MM^E *EMP* 120
SIC 3324 Steel investment foundries
Pr: Joseph S Cannone
CFO: Patricia Schwent
QA Dir: Cordy Champan

D-U-N-S 19-734-5093
NET TREATMENT SERVICES INC
NORTHEAST TREATMENT CENTERS
499 N 5th St Ste A, Philadelphia, PA 19123-4005
Tel (215) 451-7000 *Founded/Ownrshp* 1986
Sales 38.5MM *EMP* 375
Accts Larsonallen Llp Blue Bell Pe
SIC 8093 8069 8322 Alcohol clinic, outpatient; Drug clinic, outpatient; Mental health clinic, outpatient; Alcoholism rehabilitation hospital; Drug addiction rehabilitation hospital; Child related social services; Alcohol clinic, outpatient; Drug clinic, outpatient; Mental health clinic, outpatient; Alcoholism rehabilitation hospital; Drug addiction rehabilitation hospital; Child related social services
Pr: Regan Kelly
**CFO:* Kevin Noel

NET WEST
See WESTERN PAPER DISTRIBUTORS INC

NET WORK
See NETWORK INC

NET.COM
See NETWORK EQUIPMENT TECHNOLOGIES INC

D-U-N-S 17-510-0309
■ **NET2PHONE GLOBAL SERVICES LLC**
(*Suby of* IDT CORP) ★
520 Broad St Fl 5, Newark, NJ 07102-3111
Tel (973) 438-3111 *Founded/Ownrshp* 2006
Sales 76.3MM *EMP* 50
SIC 4813 Data telephone communications; Data telephone communications
CEO: Jonathan Reich
Mng Dir: John Stowe

D-U-N-S 06-953-8093 IMP/EXP
■ **NET2PHONE INC**
(*Suby of* IDT CORP) ★
520 Broad St Fl 5, Newark, NJ 07102-3195
Tel (973) 438-3111 *Founded/Ownrshp* 2002
Sales 45.9MM^E *EMP* 274
SIC 4813 4841 Data telephone communications; Voice telephone communications; Local telephone communications; Long distance telephone communications; Cable & other pay television services; Cable television services; Data telephone communications; Voice telephone communications; Local telephone communications; Long distance telephone communications; Cable & other pay television services; Cable television services
CEO: Loire Alroy
Ch Bd: Stephen Greenberg
V Ch: Howard S Jona
Pr: Yonah Lloyd
Treas: Jonathan Rand
Sr VP: Sarah Hofstetter
VP: Jonah Fink
VP: Jordan Katz
VP: Joe Kelly
VP Bus Dev: Natasha Stone
Dir Bus: Gerald Pearce

D-U-N-S 16-500-8199
NETA SCIENTIFIC INC
4206 Sylon Blvd, Hainesport, NJ 08036-3736
Tel (609) 265-8210 *Founded/Ownrshp* 1999
Sales 28.5MM *EMP* 28
SIC 5049 5047 Scientific instruments; Medical laboratory equipment; Scientific instruments; Medical laboratory equipment
CEO: Garnetta Sanders
**Pr:* Winfred Sanders
IT Man: Varun Singh
Sls Mgr: Rejean Morissette

D-U-N-S 02-478-7483 IMP
NETAFIM IRRIGATION INC (NY)
(*Suby of* NETAFIM LTD)
5470 E Home Ave, Fresno, CA 93727-2107
Tel (559) 453-6800 *Founded/Ownrshp* 1965, 1981
Sales 67.2MM^E *EMP* 150
SIC 5083 3523 Irrigation equipment; Irrigation equipment, self-propelled; Irrigation equipment; Irrigation equipment, self-propelled
Pr: Igal Aisenberg
**CFO:* Lauri Hanover
VP: Eli Bensimon
VP: Yossi Ingber
VP: Shuli Ishai
VP: Udi Levit
VP: Gabriel Miodownik
VP: Hezi Shifroni
Exec: Eduardo Currea
Exec: Cori Winn
Mng Dir: Ziv Kremer

D-U-N-S 80-205-4742
▲ **NETAPP INC**
495 E Java Dr, Sunnyvale, CA 94089-1125
Tel (408) 822-6000 *Founded/Ownrshp* 1992
Sales 6.1MMM *EMP* 12,810
Accts Deloitte & Touche Llp San Jos
Tkr Sym NTAP *Exch* NGS
SIC 3572 7373 7372 Computer storage devices; Computer integrated systems design; Systems software development services; Computer system selling services; Prepackaged software; Computer storage devices; Computer integrated systems design; Systems software development services; Computer system selling services; Prepackaged software
CEO: George Kurian
**Ch Bd:* T Michael Nevens
Pr: Robert E Salmon
CFO: Nicholas R Noviello
Sr VP: Matthew K Fawcett

Exec: Kelly Gillespie
Exec: Joan Levine
Exec: Jackie Parr
Exec: Karen Townsend
Admn Mgr: Anna Manzano
CTO: Mark Bregman
Board of Directors: Jeffry R Allen, Tor R Braham, Alan L Earhart, Gerald Held, Kathryn M Hill, George T Shaheen, Robert T Wall, Richard P Wallace

D-U-N-S 83-057-2983
NETCARRIER INC
4000 N Cannon Ave, Lansdale, PA 19446-1880
Tel (215) 257-4917 *Founded/Ownrshp* 2000
Sales 38.1MM^E *EMP* 100
SIC 4813
Pr: Brook J Lenfest
COO: Gail Snyder
CFO: Dave Wilson
**Treas:* Chris Peltier
**Ex VP:* Barry J Bella
Ex VP: Ray Shannann
Sr VP: Barry Bella
VP: Michael L Waerman
**VP:* Michael L Wasserman
Snr Sftwr: David Carroll
Dir IT: Bob Bonfanti

D-U-N-S 94-113-0619
NETCENTRICS CORP
(*Suby of* HAYSTAX TECHNOLOGY INC) ★
205 Van Buren St Ste 420, Herndon, VA 20170-5344
Tel (703) 714-7345 *Founded/Ownrshp* 2014
Sales 24.3MM^E *EMP* 200
SIC 7379 Computer related consulting services
Pr: Cynthia Barreda
Pr: Robert J Dougherty
COO: Cyndi Barreda
VP: John Robert Dixon
VP: Dean H Hering
VP: Steven Walker
Exec: Lewis Bean
Prgrm Mgr: Kelsey Bishop
Prgrm Mgr: Jill Czelusniak
Prgrm Mgr: Mike Fullerton
Prgrm Mgr: Ramona Gomez

NETCO
See NATIONAL ENGINEERING & CONTRACTING CO

NETCO
See NATIONAL EQUITY TITLE AGENCY INC

D-U-N-S 18-645-7552
NETCO INC (IL)
EQUITY TITLE COMPANY AMERICA
7501 Lemont Rd 305, Woodridge, IL 60517-2653
Tel (312) 782-4290 *Founded/Ownrshp* 1994
Sales NA *EMP* 370
SIC 6361 Title insurance; Title insurance
CEO: John Baumgart
**Pr:* Mark Schlueter
**CFO:* Thomas Evans
**Ex VP:* Edward Cook

D-U-N-S 08-307-9780 IMP
NETCOM INC (IL)
599 Wheeling Rd, Wheeling, IL 60090-4743
Tel (847) 537-6300 *Founded/Ownrshp* 1977, 1999
Sales 43.1MM^E *EMP* 149^E
SIC 3679 3677 Electronic crystals; Oscillators; Power supplies, all types: static; Filtration devices, electronic
Ch Bd: Evangelos Argoudelis
**Pr:* Soren Pihlman
**CEO:* Bob Cantarutti
**VP:* Wayne Roeder
**Prin:* John Victor
QA Dir: Ethel Bartelt

D-U-N-S 88-352-9042
NETCOM SOLUTIONS INTERNATIONAL INC
673 Potomac Station Dr Ne, Leesburg, VA 20176-1819
Tel (757) 961-9475 *Founded/Ownrshp* 1995
Sales 76.6MM *EMP* 215
SIC 4225 7373 4813 8711 7378 4899 General warehousing & storage; Local area network (LAN) systems integrator; Telephone communication, except radio; Engineering services; Computer maintenance & repair; Data communication services; General warehousing & storage; Local area network (LAN) systems integrator; Telephone communication, except radio; Engineering services; Computer maintenance & repair; Data communication services
CEO: Emmit McHenry
**Pr:* Samuel D Wyman III
**COO:* Kurt M McHenry
CFO: Bob Waldron
**CFO:* C R Waldron
VP: Julian Wigman
**VP:* M C Wingate
**CTO:* Russell Gilbertson
CTO: Will McDuffie
IT Man: Andy Todd

D-U-N-S 84-907-0701
NETCRACKER TECHNOLOGY CORP
(*Suby of* NEC CORPORATION)
95 Sawyer Rd, Waltham, MA 02453-3464
Tel (781) 419-3300 *Founded/Ownrshp* 2008
Sales 181.6MM^E *EMP* 1,000^E
SIC 7372 Prepackaged software; Prepackaged software
Pr: Andrew Feinberg
VP: Rick Frizalone
VP: Uzi Murad
VP: Sanjeev Patel
VP: Angela Pinette
Dir IT: Victor Krivulets
Dir IT: Doug Witsken
IT Man: Scott Coffman
IT Man: SAI Ravula
Sftwr Eng: Alexey Savin
Mktg Mgr: Erin Oreilly

D-U-N-S 00-125-6663
NETCUBE SYSTEMS INC
1275 Arbor Ave, Los Altos, CA 94024-5330
Tel (650) 862-7858 *Founded/Ownrshp* 1999
Sales 35.0MM *EMP* 75
SIC 7372 7379 7371 7361 Application computer software; Computer related consulting services; Custom computer programming services; Employment agencies; Application computer software; Computer related consulting services; Custom computer programming services; Employment agencies
Pr: Mallikarjuna Reddy

NETDEPOT
See GLOBAL NET ACCESS LLC

NETDOCUMENTS
See NETVOYAGE CORP

D-U-N-S 96-562-8746
NETECH CORP
6355 E Paris Ave Se, Caledonia, MI 49316-9139
Tel (616) 871-1500 *Founded/Ownrshp* 1996
Sales 162.9MM^E *EMP* 275
SIC 5065 Electronic parts & equipment; Electronic parts & equipment
Pr: James Engen
Ex VP: Sheri Springvloed
**VP:* Mark Wierenga

D-U-N-S 83-687-7142
NETEFFECTS INC
500 Chstrfeld Ctr Ste 350, Chesterfield, MO 63017
Tel (636) 237-1000 *Founded/Ownrshp* 1995
Sales 37.1MM^E *EMP* 160^E
SIC 7371 4813 7361 Custom computer programming services; ; Employment agencies
Pr: Jack Bader
**CFO:* Claire Nottingham
**VP:* Stephanie Schroeder
VP: Laurie Wilson
CTO: Kevin Gregory

D-U-N-S 10-676-6496
■ **NETEGRITY INC**
(*Suby of* CA INC) ★
1 Ca Plz, Central Islip, NY 11749-5305
Tel (631) 342-6000 *Founded/Ownrshp* 2004
Sales 20.2MM^E *EMP* 400
SIC 7372 Prepackaged software; Prepackaged software
Pr: Barry N Bycoff
**CFO:* Regina O Sommer
**VP:* William C Bartow
VP: Steve McLaughlin
VP: James Rosen
VP: Deepak Taneja
Genl Mgr: Erik Hansen
**CTO:* Vadim Lander

D-U-N-S 14-844-5260
NETELLIGENT CORP
16401 Swingley Ridge Rd # 500, Chesterfield, MO 63017-0742
Tel (314) 392-6900 *Founded/Ownrshp* 2003
Sales 29.4MM^E *EMP* 96
SIC 7373 Computer integrated systems design
Pr: Aaron Stone
**VP:* Richard Chapman
VP: Bob Hollander
**VP:* Luke Johnson
**VP:* Susan Overby
Off Admin: Michelle Huber
IT Man: Todd Mazurkiewicz
IT Man: Nicholle Rosson
IT Man: Mark Thomas
Sftwr Eng: Jason Shiffler
Opers Mgr: Jim McDonnell

D-U-N-S 01-730-0718
NETENRICH INC
226 Airport Pkwy Ste 550, San Jose, CA 95110-1028
Tel (408) 436-5900 *Founded/Ownrshp* 2003
Sales 31.1MM^E *EMP* 170^E
SIC 5734 Computer & software stores; Computer & software stores
Pr: Raju Chekuri
**Sr VP:* Justin Crotty
**Sr VP:* Varma Kunaparaju
VP: Jennifer Anaya
**VP:* Nick Blozan
**VP:* Mitchell Cipriano
VP: Dan Dempsey
VP: Bob Fasano
VP: Chris Joseph
VP: Raghu Kamath
VP: Sanjeev Motwani

D-U-N-S 01-545-0617
■ **NETEZZA CORP**
(*Suby of* IBM) ★
26 Forest St Ste 300, Marlborough, MA 01752-3068
Tel (508) 382-8200 *Founded/Ownrshp* 2000, 2010
Sales 42.0MM^E *EMP* 469
SIC 7371 Computer software development; Software programming applications; Computer software development; Software programming applications
CFO: Patrick J Scannell Jr
Bd of Dir: William Oglesby
Ofcr: Cory McQueen
Ofcr: Jitendra Saxena
**Sr VP:* Patricia Cotter
**Sr VP:* David R Flaxman
**Sr VP:* Prat Moghe
**Sr VP:* Raymond Tacoma
**VP:* Phil Francisco
**VP:* John Metzger
**VP:* Jon Niess
VP: Dennis O'Leary
**VP:* Marty Woodford
**VP:* Tim Young

D-U-N-S 18-163-0299
NETFABRIC TECHNOLOGIES INC
UCA SERVICES
(*Suby of* FORTIFY INFRASTRUCTURE SERVICES INC) ★
117 Randolph Ave, Jersey City, NJ 07305-4418
Tel (973) 537-0077 *Founded/Ownrshp* 2009
Sales 14.2MM^E *EMP* 300
SIC 7371 Custom computer programming services
CEO: Fahad Syed
**CFO:* Vasan Thatham

D-U-N-S 79-964-6716 IMP
▲ **NETFLIX INC**
100 Winchester Cir, Los Gatos, CA 95032-1815
Tel (408) 540-3700 *Founded/Ownrshp* 1997
Sales 5.5MMM *EMP* 2,450
Accts Ernst & Young Llp San Jose C
Tkr Sym NFLX *Exch* NGS
SIC 2741 7841 Miscellaneous publishing; Video tape rental; Video disk/tape rental to the general public; Miscellaneous publishing; Video tape rental; Video disk/tape rental to the general public
Ch Bd: Reed Hastings
CFO: David Wells
Bd of Dir: Rich Barton
Chf Mktg O: Kelly Bennett
Ofcr: Ted Sarandos
Exec: Liz Coddington
Exec: Lilly Guadarrama
Dir Bus: Masato Shimoi
Snr Sftwr: Daniel Wong
CTO: Coriell Wright
Corp Couns: Reg Thompson
Board of Directors: Richard N Barton, A George Battle, Timothy M Haley, Jay C Hoag, Leslie Kilgore, Ann Mather, Brad Smith

NETFORTRIS
See TELECOMMUNICATIONS COMMUNICATIONS SERVICES INC

D-U-N-S 12-519-4592
NETGAIN TECHNOLOGY INC
720 W Saint Germain St # 200, Saint Cloud, MN 56301-3501
Tel (320) 251-4700 *Founded/Ownrshp* 1999
Sales 21.4MM^E *EMP* 100
SIC 7371 Custom computer programming services
Pr: Scott Warzecha
**Pr:* Scott Baynes
Off Mgr: Lora Schuster
CIO: Tim Amundson
Dir IT: David O'Keefe
Netwrk Eng: Andrew Plas
Opers Mgr: Glenn Hankosky
Mktg Dir: Kayla Welle
Snr Mgr: Matt Riley

D-U-N-S 94-576-6863 IMP/EXP
▲ **NETGEAR INC**
350 E Plumeria Dr, San Jose, CA 95134-1911
Tel (408) 907-8000 *Founded/Ownrshp* 1996
Sales 1.3MMM *EMP* 1,038
Tkr Sym NTGR *Exch* NGS
SIC 3661 3577 Modems; Carrier equipment, telephone or telegraph; Computer peripheral equipment; Modems; Carrier equipment, telephone or telegraph; Computer peripheral equipment
Ch Bd: Patrick C S Lo
CFO: Christine M Gorjanc
Bd of Dir: Timothy A Godwin
Sr VP: Michael F Falcon
Sr VP: Andrew W Kim
Sr VP: Charles T Olson
Sr VP: Tamesa T Rogers
VP: Vivek Pathela
VP: Tamesa Rogers
Exec: Jamie Hansen
Mng Dir: Antoinette Switzer
Board of Directors: Ralph E Faison, A Timothy Godwin, Jef Graham, Jocelyn Carter-Miller, Gregory J Rossmann, Barbara V Scherer, Julie A Shimer, Thomas H Waechter

D-U-N-S 07-054-6812
NETHERLAND PLAZA ASSOCIATES LIMITED
35 W 5th St, Cincinnati, OH 45202-2801
Tel (513) 421-9100 *Founded/Ownrshp* 1983
Sales 11.1MM^E *EMP* 350
SIC 7011 Hotels; Hotels
Pt: Jim Bastin
Pt: Michel Sheer

D-U-N-S 07-508-6371
NETHERLAND SEWELL & ASSOCINC
2100 Ross Ave Ste 2200, Dallas, TX 75201-2737
Tel (214) 969-5401 *Founded/Ownrshp* 1961
Sales 29.7MM^E *EMP* 100
SIC 8711 Consulting engineer; Consulting engineer
CEO: Clifford H Rees III
**Pr:* Danny D Simmons
**CFO:* Philip S Frost
CFO: Scott P Frost
Bd of Dir: Jane Dooley
**Ex VP:* G Lance Binder
**Sr VP:* Robert C Barg
Sr VP: Dan Smith
**Sr VP:* Thomas J Tella II
VP: David Adams
VP: Michael Begland
VP: Joseph Coleman
VP: Randolph Green
VP: Margaret Hill
VP: William Knights
VP: Richard F Krenek II
VP: Philip Longacre
VP: David Miller
VP: Derek Newton
VP: David Nice
VP: Thomas Souers

D-U-N-S 17-558-8826
NETHERLANDS INSURANCE CO
(*Suby of* LIBERTY MUTUAL GROUP INC) ★
62 Maple Ave, Keene, NH 03431-1625
Tel (603) 352-3221 *Founded/Ownrshp* 2005
Sales NA *EMP* 8^E
SIC 6411 Insurance agents, brokers & service; Insurance agents, brokers & service
Pr: Gary R Gregg

D-U-N-S 82-912-7674 IMP
NETIG LLC
21229 72nd Ave S, Kent, WA 98032-1916
Tel (425) 291-4200 *Founded/Ownrshp* 2008
Sales 57.1MM^E *EMP* 70
SIC 5065 Electronic parts

D-U-N-S 94-130-1624
NETIQ CORP
(*Suby of* ATTACHMATE CORP) ★
515 Post Oak Blvd # 1000, Houston, TX 77027-9435
Tel (713) 548-1700 *Founded/Ownrshp* 2006
Sales 132.2MM^E *EMP* 857
SIC 7372 7371 Prepackaged software; Computer software development & applications; Prepackaged software; Computer software development & applications
Ch: Jeff Hawn
**Pr:* Jay Gardner
**COO:* Marc B Andrews
Sr VP: Flint Brenton
Sr VP: Daniel J Meub
Sr VP: Richard J Pleczko
VP: James Barth
**VP:* Edwin Bowman
**VP:* John Delk
**VP:* Ron Hardy
**VP:* Boris Ivancic
**VP:* Luann Johnson
**VP:* Bill Koehl
**VP:* Ron Milton
VP: Sergio Toshio Mituiwa
VP: Ton Musters
**VP:* Somesh Singh
VP: Will Smith
Dir: Steve Latham

D-U-N-S 05-993-4919
■ **NETJETS AVIATION INC**
(*Suby of* NETJETS INC) ★
4111 Bridgeway Ave, Columbus, OH 43219-1882
Tel (614) 239-5500 *Founded/Ownrshp* 1998
Sales 151.9MM^E *EMP* 2,500
SIC 4522

D-U-N-S 60-622-2552
■ **NETJETS INC**
(*Suby of* BERKSHIRE HATHAWAY INC) ★
4111 Bridgeway Ave, Columbus, OH 43219-1882
Tel (614) 239-5500 *Founded/Ownrshp* 1998
Sales 3.8MMM *EMP* 6,157
SIC 4522 5088 7359 Flying charter service; Aircraft & parts; Aircraft rental; Flying charter service; Aircraft & parts; Aircraft rental
CEO: Adam Johnson
**Pr:* Bill Noe
**COO:* Robert Molsbergen
**CFO:* Brent Smith
Bd of Dir: Lindsey Brammer
Ofcr: Pierre Doyon
**Sr VP:* Colleen Nissl
VP: Deron Brown
**CIO:* Ken Green
Opers Mgr: Allan Ball
Snr Mgr: Andrew Mossman

D-U-N-S 00-367-1062
■ **NETJETS INTERNATIONAL INC**
(*Suby of* NETJETS INC) ★
4111 Bridgeway Ave, Columbus, OH 43219-1882
Tel (614) 239-5500 *Founded/Ownrshp* 1995
Sales 25.6MM^E *EMP* 700
SIC 4522 Air transportation, nonscheduled; Air transportation, nonscheduled
Treas: Lesha Thorpe
Board of Directors: Marc Hamburg, Jordan Hansell, Robert Molsbergen, Brent Smith

D-U-N-S 06-358-3397
■ **NETJETS SALES INC**
(*Suby of* NETJETS INC) ★
4111 Bridgeway Ave, Columbus, OH 43219-1882
Tel (614) 239-5500 *Founded/Ownrshp* 1998
Sales 97.8MM^E *EMP* 200
SIC 5088 4522 Aircraft & parts; Air transportation, nonscheduled; Aircraft & parts; Air transportation, nonscheduled
Pr: Bill Noe
**Treas:* Lesha Thorpe
Sr VP: David Macghee
Exec: Greg Rapp
Board of Directors: Marc Hamburg, Jordan Hansell, Bill Noe, Brent Smith

D-U-N-S 93-298-7266
NETLINE CORP
750 University Ave # 200, Los Gatos, CA 95032-7697
Tel (408) 374-4200 *Founded/Ownrshp* 1994
Sales 20.9MM^E *EMP* 53^E
SIC 4813
CEO: Robert S Alvin
Pr: Werner Mansfeld
Ex VP: Richard Schaefer
VP: David Fortino
VP: Jayaram Kalpathy
VP: Mitchell Wright
Dir Bus: Elizabeth Jarvis
Off Mgr: Michelle McKeon
Off Admin: Neetu Rai
Snr Sftwr: Andrew Abel
Snr Sftwr: Bing Banayat

D-U-N-S 00-958-5113
NETLINK SOFTWARE GROUP AMERICA INC (MI)
999 Tech Row, Madison Heights, MI 48071-4680
Tel (248) 204-8803 *Founded/Ownrshp* 1999
Sales 119.3MM^E *EMP* 300
SIC 7379 7371 Computer related consulting services; Computer software development; Computer related consulting services; Computer software development
CEO: Dilip Dubey
**V Ch:* Anurag Shrivastava
Pr: Frank Tsiang
CFO: Sharma Ajoy
**CFO:* Ajoy Sharma
Ex VP: Derrick Green

Ex VP: Russ Miller
Sr VP: Neil Lal
VP: Jim Cnossen
VP: Sam George
**VP:* Greg Hacias
VP: Ashutosh Kale
VP: Anil Lal
VP: Nikhil Mehrotra
VP: Amit Soni

D-U-N-S 92-918-3630
■ NETLOGIC MICROSYSTEMS LLC
BROADCOM
(*Suby of* BROADCOM CORP) ★
3975 Freedom Cir Ste 900, Santa Clara, CA 95054-1255
Tel (408) 454-3000 *Founded/Ownrshp* 2011
Sales 103.1MM^E *EMP* 645
Accts Pricewaterhousecoopers Llp Sa
SIC 3674 Integrated circuits, semiconductor networks, etc.; Integrated circuits, semiconductor networks, etc.
CEO: Ronald S Jankov
Pr: Scott A McGregor
CFO: Michael Tate
Ex VP: Behrooz Abdi
Ex VP: Eric K Brandt
Ex VP: Arthur Chong
Sr VP: Ibrahim Korgav
VP: Roland Cortes
VP: Surendra Mandava
Prin: Norman Godinho
Snr Sftwr: Parineeth Reddy

D-U-N-S 01-644-5715
NETMOTION WIRELESS INC (WA)
(*Suby of* CLEARLAKE CAPITAL GROUP LP) ★
701 N 34th St Ste 250, Seattle, WA 98103-3414
Tel (206) 691-5500 *Founded/Ownrshp* 2001, 2012
Sales 42.2MM^E *EMP* 152
SIC 7373 Systems software development services; Systems software development services
CEO: Erik Prusch
**Ch Bd:* Chris Gibbons
**Pr:* Jim Ryder
**CFO:* Cary Baker
Chf Mktg O: Eric Aarrestad
Sr VP: Andrew Willett
**Sr VP:* Andy Willett
**VP:* Brian Rice
Prgrm Mgr: Aruna Balasubramanian
Snr Sftwr: Reyes Canales
Snr Sftwr: Louis Giliberto

D-U-N-S 83-966-5635
NETNOW
41 Heritage Village Ln, Campbell, CA 95008-2036
Tel (408) 370-0425 *Founded/Ownrshp* 1989
Sales 15.0MM *EMP* 300
SIC 4813 ;
Owner: Daniel Bryant
**VP:* Peggy Patwardhan

D-U-N-S 19-712-3755
NETPLANNER SYSTEMS INC
3145 Northwoods Pkwy # 800, Peachtree Corners, GA 30071-4794
Tel (770) 662-5482 *Founded/Ownrshp* 1987
Sales 37.0MM *EMP* 210
Accts Agl Ascent Llc Duluth Ga
SIC 1731 Communications specialization; Fiber optic cable installation; Communications specialization; Fiber optic cable installation
CEO: J Clinton Bridges
**Pr:* John E Potts
**CFO:* Clint Bridges
Off Mgr: Ted Santaguida
Dir IT: David Williams
IT Man: Tony Roberts
MIS Mgr: William Bridges
Opers Mgr: Brian Little
Sales Asso: Steven Nisbet
Sales Asso: John Sartain
Sales Asso: Kenneth Wolf

D-U-N-S 15-805-1560
NETPOLARITY INC
900 E Campbell Ave, Campbell, CA 95008-2362
Tel (408) 971-1100 *Founded/Ownrshp* 2000
Sales 54.6MM^E *EMP* 500
SIC 7361 Employment agencies; Employment agencies
CEO: Haixia Zhang
**Pr:* David Chuang
Exec: Orlando Azueta
Genl Mgr: Cathleen Lariviere
IT Man: Pamela Cummins
Mktg Mgr: Lisa Amorao

D-U-N-S 83-982-1951
■ NETQOS INC
CA
(*Suby of* CA INC) ★
2291 Wood Oak Dr Ste 140, Herndon, VA 20171-6008
Tel (703) 708-3699 *Founded/Ownrshp* 2009
Sales 38.4MM^E *EMP* 500
SIC 7372 Prepackaged software; Prepackaged software
Pr: Joel Trammell
Pt: Alex Newton
**CFO:* Brett Panter
**Sr VP:* Joseph Page
VP: Jim Duster
**VP:* Robert Machnacki
VP: Matt Sherrod
**VP:* Gene Trmmell
Exec: Keith Bendy
Exec: Erick Faul
Exec: Ernie Fontes
Exec: Chuck Hartman
Exec: James Philpott
Exec: Jim Tranquill
Dir Surg: Steve Fulton
Dir Surg: Mark Gully
Dir Surg: Rob Osterhouse

D-U-N-S 08-902-7127
NETRIX LLC
(*Suby of* FGMK HOLDINGS LLC) ★
2801 Lakeside Dr Ste 125, Bannockburn, IL 60015-1253
Tel (847) 283-7300 *Founded/Ownrshp* 2001
Sales 55.8MM^E *EMP* 100
SIC 7379 5045 Computer related consulting services; Computers
Pr: Rob Dang
Exec: Julian Pretto
Prac Mgr: Patrick Adlam
Prac Mgr: Ryan Williams
Rgnl Mgr: Brian Dale
CTO: Jeff Wampler
IT Man: Brian Axford
**IT Man:* Anthony Donato
Sftwr Eng: Paul Jensen
Netwrk Eng: Kevin Hoy
Netwrk Eng: James Kennedy

D-U-N-S 79-909-7246
NETRONIX INTEGRATION INC
2170 Paragon Dr, San Jose, CA 95131-1305
Tel (408) 573-1444 *Founded/Ownrshp* 2007
Sales 30.4MM^E *EMP* 138
SIC 1731 General electrical contractor
Pr: Craig E Jarrett
**CFO:* Steve Piechota
VP: Kimberly Jarrett
Off Admin: Kris Miles
Snr PM: Luis Valle

D-U-N-S 14-795-1230
▲ NETSCOUT SYSTEMS INC
310 Littleton Rd, Westford, MA 01886-4105
Tel (978) 614-4000 *Founded/Ownrshp* 1984
Sales 453.6MM *EMP* 72,069
Accts Pricewaterhousecoopers Llp Bo
Tkr Sym NTCT *Exch* NGS
SIC 7373 3577 Computer integrated systems design; Computer peripheral equipment; Computer integrated systems design; Computer peripheral equipment
Pr: Anil K Singhal
COO: Michael Szabados
CFO: Jean Bua
Sr VP: John W Downing
Sr VP: Ashwani Singhal
VP: Lesley Blume
VP: Lisa Fiorentino
VP: Michelle Flaherty
VP: Brian P McCann
Prgrm Mgr: Harsha Sachdev
Genl Mgr: Chittaranjan Narayana
Board of Directors: Victor A Demarines, Robert E Donahue, John R Egan, Joseph G Hadzima Jr, Vincent J Mullarkey, Christopher Perretta

D-U-N-S 05-650-7455
NETSERTIVE
2400 Perimeter Park Dr # 100, Morrisville, NC 27560-5405
Tel (800) 940-4351 *Founded/Ownrshp* 2010
Sales 23.4MM^E *EMP* 140
SIC 7373 Computer system selling services; Computer system selling services
Prin: Sandy K Dockter
Dir Bus: Ken Kovasala
Snr Sftwr: Michael Caldwell
Snr Sftwr: Ramin Shahriari
CTO: Paul Bock
IT Man: Arshad Ahmadi
VP Sls: Bob Bradley
Mktg Dir: Loren Shumate
Sls Dir: Laura Nadler
Sls Dir: Tim O'Rourke
Mktg Mgr: Tim McLain

D-U-N-S 10-516-2312 IMP
NETSHAPE TECHNOLOGIES INC
(*Suby of* SAW MILL CAPITAL LLC) ★
3620 Paoli Pike Ste 8, Floyds Knobs, IN 47119-9787
Tel (812) 248-9273 *Founded/Ownrshp* 2007
Sales 96.5MM^E *EMP* 500
SIC 3399 3399 Friction material, made from powdered metal; Metal powders, pastes & flakes; Friction material, made from powdered metal; Metal powders, pastes & flakes
CEO: Lance Harris
Pr: Paul Gangopadhyay
CFO: Patricia Burkland
**CFO:* Dax Whitehouse
Dir Bus: Ron Arble
Dir IT: William Edwards
IT Man: David Dorgan
Tech Mgr: Robert Doyle
Ql Cn Mgr: Todd Ross
Sales Exec: Don Leonard

D-U-N-S 07-871-7254
NETSKOPE INC
270 3rd St, Los Altos, CA 94022-3617
Tel (650) 281-9636 *Founded/Ownrshp* 2012
Sales 22.9MM^E *EMP* 100
SIC 7371 Computer software development
CEO: Sanjay Beri
Sr VP: Chris Andrews
VP: Rajneesh Chopra
VP: Rick Holden
VP: Abhay Kulkarni
VP: Bobby Shoker
VP Mktg: Jamie Barnett
Sls Dir: Billy Bond
Sls Dir: Tony Burnside
Mktg Mgr: Kimberly Lessard
Manager: Brian Pinfold
Board of Directors: Enrique Salem

D-U-N-S 07-104-4556
NETSMART NEW YORK INC
(*Suby of* NETSMART TECHNOLOGIES INC) ★
3500 Sunrise Hwy, Great River, NY 11739-1001
Tel (631) 968-2011 *Founded/Ownrshp* 1994
Sales 80.0MM *EMP* 349
SIC 7371 7372 Computer software development; Prepackaged software; Computer software development; Prepackaged software
CEO: Jerry Koop
**Ch Bd:* James L Conway
**Pr:* John Phillips
**CFO:* Anthony Grisanti
VP: Nancy Brill
Sls Dir: Chris Newman

D-U-N-S 80-791-8628
NETSMART TECHNOLOGIES INC
4950 College Blvd, Overland Park, KS 66211-1612
Tel (913) 327-7444 *Founded/Ownrshp* 1992
Sales 282.1MM^E *EMP* 790
SIC 7371 7372 Custom computer programming services; Prepackaged software; Custom computer programming services; Prepackaged software
CEO: Michael Valentine
CFO: Anthony F Grisanti
CFO: Tony Ritz
**Ex VP:* Kevin Scalia
**Ex VP:* Alan B Tillinghast
Sr VP: Ian Chuang
VP: Jim Bartunek
VP: Kevin Davidson
VP: Timothy Donovan
VP: Liz Vasti
Dir Rx: Michael Littman
Dir Bus: Steve Kang
Board of Directors: Paul Black, Francis J Calcagno, Joseph G Sicinski, John S T Gallagher

D-U-N-S 13-029-9568
▲ NETSOL TECHNOLOGIES INC
24025 Park Sorrento # 410, Calabasas, CA 91302-4036
Tel (818) 222-9195 *Founded/Ownrshp* 1997
Sales 51.0MM *EMP* 1,590^E
Accts Kabani & Company Inc Los An
Tkr Sym NTWK *Exch* NAS
SIC 7372 7373 7299 Prepackaged software; Computer integrated systems design; Personal document & information services; Prepackaged software; Computer integrated systems design; Personal document & information services
Ch Bd: Najeeb Ghauri
CFO: Roger Almond
Sr VP: Patti L W McGlasson
Sftwr Eng: Neelam Dawood
Sftwr Eng: Naseem Jafar
Sales Exec: Joe Stankowich
Mktg Mgr: Ali Aurangzeb
Snr Mgr: Naeem Aftab
Board of Directors: Eugen Beckert, Jeffrey Bilbrey, Mark Caton

D-U-N-S 06-981-1862
■ NETSPEND CORP
(*Suby of* NETSPEND HOLDINGS INC) ★
701 Brazos St, Austin, TX 78701-3258
Tel (512) 532-8200 *Founded/Ownrshp* 1999
Sales NA *EMP* 300^E
SIC 6091 Nondeposit trust facilities; Nondeposit trust facilities
CEO: Daniel R Henry
Pt: Lisa Henken
Pr: Chuck Harris
COO: Frank Cotroneo
CFO: Adam Chibib
CFO: George W Gresham
CFO: Jim Sargent
Ex VP: Steven Coleman
Ex VP: Anh Vazquez
Sr VP: James De Voglaer
Sr VP: Roger Kidwell
VP: James Devoglaer
VP: Paige Ellis
VP: Scott Gardner
VP: Joe Silva
VP: Trent Sorbe

D-U-N-S 96-225-7395
■ NETSPEND HOLDINGS INC
(*Suby of* TOTAL SYSTEM SERVICES INC) ★
701 Brazos St Ste 1300, Austin, TX 78701-2674
Tel (512) 532-8200 *Founded/Ownrshp* 2013
Sales NA *EMP* 484^E
SIC 6153 Credit card services, central agency collection; Credit card services, central agency collection
CEO: Daniel R Henry
Pr: Charles J Harris
CFO: George W Gresham
Ex VP: Steven F Coleman
Ex VP: James Devoglaer
Ex VP: Anh Hatzopoulos

D-U-N-S 11-639-3195
▲ NETSUITE INC
2955 Campus Dr Ste 100, San Mateo, CA 94403-2539
Tel (650) 627-1000 *Founded/Ownrshp* 1998
Sales 556.2MM *EMP* 3,357^E
Tkr Sym N *Exch* NYS
SIC 7372 Prepackaged software; Prepackaged software
CEO: Zachary Nelson
**Ch Bd:* Evan M Goldberg
Pr: Peter Daffern
Pr: James McGeever
CFO: Ronald Gill
Chf Mktg O: David Downing
Ofcr: Kathy Zwickert
Ex VP: Jason Maynard
Sr VP: Mike Arntz
Sr VP: Frank Iannotti
Sr VP: Harvey North
Sr VP: Douglas P Solomon
Sr VP: Lee Thompson
VP: Doug Kennedy
Board of Directors: Deborah A Farrington, Steve Gomo, Catherine R Kinney, Kevin Thompson, Edward J Zander

D-U-N-S 07-980-2333
NETTLETON SCHOOL DISTRICT
3300 One Pl, Jonesboro, AR 72404-9318
Tel (870) 910-7800 *Founded/Ownrshp* 2015
Sales 4.0MM^E *EMP* 460
SIC 8299 8211 Arts & crafts schools; High school, junior or senior
HC Dir: Lori Ellis

D-U-N-S 00-355-2341 IMP/EXP
NETUNO USA INC (FL)
P & P SEA FOOD
18501 Pines Blvd Ste 206, Pembroke Pines, FL 33029-1420
Tel (305) 513-0904 *Founded/Ownrshp* 2000
Sales 49.5MM^E *EMP* 15
SIC 5146 Seafoods; Seafoods
Pr: Luciano Bonaldo
**VP:* Guilherme Colaferri

D-U-N-S 82-989-8910
NETVERSANT SOLUTIONS II LLC
(*Suby of* NETVERSANT SOLUTIONS LLC) ★
9750 W Sm Hstn Pkwy N 1, Houston, TX 77064
Tel (832) 487-1900 *Founded/Ownrshp* 2008
Sales 25.8MM^E *EMP* 173
SIC 7373 8999 7381 Local area network (LAN) systems integrator; Communication services; Security guard service; Local area network (LAN) systems integrator; Communication services; Security guard service
Prin: Paul Alexander Zwickey
Genl Pt: Robert E Macchi
Mng Pt: Robin-Jan Delange
Sr VP: Sabra Manchac
VP: Kenneth G Watler
IT Man: Blain Williams
Opers Mgr: Robert Carter
Opers Mgr: Sean Condon
Opers Mgr: Dave Stevenson
Sales Exec: Dana Fisher
Sls Dir: Marv Williams

D-U-N-S 82-989-6666
NETVERSANT SOLUTIONS LLC
(*Suby of* PATRIARCH PARTNERS LLC) ★
9750 W Sam Houston Pkwy N # 100, Houston, TX 77064-5552
Tel (800) 540-2739 *Founded/Ownrshp* 2009
Sales 109.4MM^E *EMP* 541
SIC 7373 8999 7381 Local area network (LAN) systems integrator; Communication services; Security guard service; Local area network (LAN) systems integrator; Communication services; Security guard service
CEO: Charles Sweet
**CFO:* Ronald E Hale Jr
**Ex VP:* Reagan S Busbee
**Ex VP:* Robert N Feldman
Brnch Mgr: Kenneth Kana
Off Mgr: Terri Nixon
Netwrk Eng: Nicholas Howland

D-U-N-S 00-843-6201
NETVIEW INC (NC)
221 S Tryon St Ste 200, Charlotte, NC 28202-3227
Tel (704) 748-1445 *Founded/Ownrshp* 1996
Sales 38.9MM^E *EMP* 350
SIC 7379 Computer related consulting services; Computer related consulting services
Pr: Carson Burns
**VP:* Geoffrey I Goff
Dir Bus: Alan Brown
Mng Dir: Laura Kesler

D-U-N-S 94-142-7007
NETVOYAGE CORP
NETDOCUMENTS
2500 W Executive Pkwy, Lehi, UT 84043-3856
Tel (801) 226-6882 *Founded/Ownrshp* 1995
Sales 23.6MM^E *EMP* 45^E
SIC 7373 4226 Systems software development services; Special warehousing & storage
CEO: Matt Duncan
**Pr:* Kenneth W Duncan
**Treas:* Lee A Duncan
Sr VP: Wayne Harris
**VP:* Alvin S Tedjamulia
CIO: David Worth
DP Dir: Lowell Nelson
Sftwr Eng: Steve Goodrich

NETWORK 180
See KENT COUNTY OF (INC)

NETWORK 180
See KENT COUNTY CMH AUTHORITY

D-U-N-S 02-038-0747
NETWORK ASSOCIATES INC
CLEANWISE
1100 E Wdfield Rd Ste 200, Schaumburg, IL 60173
Tel (847) 803-4888 *Founded/Ownrshp* 1976
Sales 1.0MMM *EMP* 140^E
SIC 8611 5113 Trade associations; Industrial & personal service paper; Trade associations; Industrial & personal service paper
Pr: Tracy Evatt
**CFO:* Bob Mtchum
**Sr VP:* Walter Dethlefsen
**VP:* Cheryl Gilbert
Board of Directors: Paul Weyand, David Brown, Leonard Green, James Jackson, Fred Kfoury Jr, Brooks Lammey, John Miller, Matthew Moore, Steve Morris, Herb Sedler

D-U-N-S 02-395-6266
■ NETWORK BILLING SYSTEMS LLC
INTER CONNECT SVCS GROUP II
(*Suby of* FUSION TELECOMMUNICATIONS INTERNATIONAL INC) ★
155 Willowbrook Blvd, Wayne, NJ 07470-7032
Tel (973) 638-2100 *Founded/Ownrshp* 2012
Sales 27.8MM^E *EMP* 100
SIC 4813 4812 Telephone communication, except radio; Radio telephone communication
Pr: Jon Kaufman
Ex VP: Anthony Hidalgo
Ex VP: Russell P Markman
Assoc Dir: Judy S Fox
IT Man: Peter Zimmerli
Info Man: Doug Gillespe
Mktg Dir: Michael Salerno

D-U-N-S 01-990-7901 IMP
NETWORK CABLING INFRASTRUCTURES INC
NCI
4825 River Green Pkwy, Duluth, GA 30096-2569
Tel (770) 495-0798 *Founded/Ownrshp* 2001
Sales 31.3MM *EMP* 150
Accts Hlb Gross Collins Pc Atlan
SIC 1731 Fiber optic cable installation; Fiber optic cable installation
Pr: William F Valentine
**CFO:* Steve Holcombe
Treas: Monty Bostwick
**VP:* Wayne Gibson
**VP:* Donnie Richards
VP Sls: Steve Holcomb

D-U-N-S 03-184-0346
NETWORK CABLING SERVICES INC
12626 Fuqua St, Houston, TX 77034-4629
Tel (281) 484-1777 *Founded/Ownrshp* 2001
Sales 27.4MM *EMP* 220
SIC 1731 4813 7389 7373 Computerized controls installation; Wire telephone; Drafting service, except temporary help; Computer integrated systems design; Computerized controls installation; Wire telephone; Drafting service, except temporary help; Computer integrated systems design
CEO: Robert Apgar
**Pr:* Lori Veltri
**COO:* Mark Veltri

D-U-N-S 13-417-0807
NETWORK CAPITAL FUNDING CORP
5 Park Plz Ste 800, Irvine, CA 92614-8501
Tel (949) 442-0060 *Founded/Ownrshp* 2002
Sales NA *EMP* 363
Accts Val J Benincosa Hunting Beac
SIC 6162 Mortgage bankers; Mortgage bankers
Pr: Tri Nguyen
CFO: Val Benincasa
Sls Dir: Sean Wilson

D-U-N-S 01-014-9230 IMP/EXP
NETWORK COMMUNICATIONS INC (GA)
(*Suby of* COURT SQUARE CAPITAL PARTNERS LP) ★
2 Sun Ct Ste 300, Norcross, GA 30092-2865
Tel (678) 346-9300 *Founded/Ownrshp* 1980, 2005
Sales 177.6MM^E^ *EMP* 800
SIC 2731 2721 Book publishing; Periodicals; Book publishing; Periodicals
CEO: Fulton Collins
**Pr:* Gerard Parker
Sr VP: Ed Barnes
Sr VP: Desse Susan
Sr VP: Kelly Vincent
VP: Audrey Beharie
VP: Charles Brucaro
**VP:* Charles J Brucato
VP: Michelle Childers
VP: David Coleman
**VP:* Peggy Koenig
**VP:* Robert Macinnis
VP: Stuart Richens
VP: Brian Whitehurst
Board of Directors: Daniel McCarthy

D-U-N-S 96-018-7730
NETWORK COMMUNICATIONS INTERNATIONAL CORP
NCIC INMATE TELEPHONE SERVICES
606 Magrill St, Longview, TX 75601-6538
Tel (903) 757-4455 *Founded/Ownrshp* 1996
Sales 21.0MM *EMP* 60
SIC 4813 Long distance telephone communications; Voice telephone communications; Telephone/video communications; Long distance telephone communications; Voice telephone communications; Telephone/video communications
Pr: William Pope
**VP:* Jay Walters
Dir IT: Randy Rosenthal
Opers Mgr: Randy Bilbay
Sales Exec: Teena Sessions
Sls Dir: Frances Schultz

D-U-N-S 79-543-6179
NETWORK COMPUTING ARCHITECTS INC
NCA
330 120th Ave Ne Ste 210, Bellevue, WA 98005-3035
Tel (425) 451-8995 *Founded/Ownrshp* 1992
Sales 20.8MM^E^ *EMP* 55
SIC 7373 Value-added resellers, computer systems
Pr: Tom Gobeille
VP: Greg Brown
**VP:* Craig M Suhadolnik
Sales Exec: Clint Bogard
VP Sls: Walter Boos
Snr PM: Tina Jochumsen

D-U-N-S 83-076-8987
NETWORK CRAZE TECHNOLOGIES INC
7037 Fly Rd, East Syracuse, NY 13057-9659
Tel (800) 505-2078 *Founded/Ownrshp* 2009
Sales 25.0MM *EMP* 40^E^
SIC 5045 Computer peripheral equipment; Computer peripheral equipment
Pr: Matthew Goncalves

D-U-N-S 17-662-7610
NETWORK DATA SYSTEMS INC
50 Commerce Dr Ste 120, Schaumburg, IL 60173-5316
Tel (847) 385-6700 *Founded/Ownrshp* 1997
Sales 35.0MM *EMP* 175
SIC 7373 8748 Value-added resellers, computer systems; Business consulting; Value-added resellers, computer systems; Business consulting
CEO: Allan L Siders
**Pr:* Mike Doyle
VP: Patrick Sweeney
Admn Mgr: Diane Moutvic
Telecom Ex: Wayne Dumas
Snr Ntwrk: Bob Bucciarelli
Netwrk Eng: Lonnie Brown
Sales Exec: Jim Pullano
VP Sls: Karl Marterstock

D-U-N-S 95-744-9812
NETWORK DESIGNS INC
1651 Old Madow Rd Ste 105, Mclean, VA 22102
Tel (703) 255-2206 *Founded/Ownrshp* 1995
Sales 24.4MM *EMP* 65^E^
Accts Dalal & Company Alexandria V
SIC 7373 4813 7371 7372 7376 7378 Computer integrated systems design; Telephone communication, except radio; Custom computer programming services; Prepackaged software; Computer facilities management; Computer maintenance & repair; Computer integrated systems design; Telephone communication, except radio; Custom computer programming services; Prepackaged software; Computer facilities management; Computer maintenance & repair
COO: Martin Schweitzer
Ofcr: Nancy Pierce
**Sr VP:* Sylvia F McGreevy
**Exec:* Gregory Conran
**Exec:* Kevin McGreevy
QA Dir: David Hopkins
IT Man: Chris Conran

D-U-N-S 80-852-1074
NETWORK ENGINEERING TECHNOLOGIES INC
3140 Deming Way, Middleton, WI 53562-1461
Tel (608) 827-6700 *Founded/Ownrshp* 1993
Sales 73.8MM^E^ *EMP* 375
SIC 1731 Electronic controls installation; Communications specialization; Electronic controls installation; Communications specialization
CFO: Gregory B Williams
**Treas:* Rob Hammacher
VP: Chris Coley
Prgrm Mgr: Todd Kuehl
Opers Mgr: Summer Johnson
Snr PM: Jon Fritz
Snr PM: David Yang

D-U-N-S 10-277-6481 IMP/EXP
■ **NETWORK EQUIPMENT TECHNOLOGIES INC**
NET.COM
(*Suby of* SONUS NETWORKS INC) ★
6900 Paseo Padre Pkwy, Fremont, CA 94555-3641
Tel (510) 713-7300 *Founded/Ownrshp* 2012
Sales 24.1MM^E^ *EMP* 177^E^
SIC 3577 Computer peripheral equipment; Computer peripheral equipment
Pr: David Wagenseller
**CFO:* Karen C Carte
CFO: John F McGrath
**Ofcr:* Kevin N Isacks
Sr VP: James Fitzpatrick
VP: Thaison Chu
VP: Matthew Krueger
**VP:* Francois P Le
VP: David Owen
**VP:* Pete Patel
VP: Micheal Shapard
**VP:* Frank Slattery
Board of Directors: Frederick D D'alessio, C Nicholas Keating Jr, David R Laube

NETWORK FOB
See NETWORK FOB INC

D-U-N-S 62-709-1184
NETWORK FOB INC
NETWORK FOB
6622 Sthpint Dr S Ste 210, Jacksonville, FL 32216
Tel (651) 256-1000 *Founded/Ownrshp* 1987
Sales 105.0MM *EMP* 150
SIC 4731 Freight forwarding; Freight forwarding
Ch Bd: Timothy Taylor
Pr: Jim Handoush
CFO: Alan Unger
Ofcr: Bill Sandberg
Off Mgr: Edeline Davis

D-U-N-S 12-996-9809
NETWORK FOR GOOD INC
GROUNDSPRING
1140 Conn Ave Nw Ste 700, Washington, DC 20036-4011
Tel (202) 627-1600 *Founded/Ownrshp* 2001
Sales 195.9MM *EMP* 20^E^
SIC 4813
CEO: Bill Strathmann
Pr: Jing Gu
COO: Susan Kearney
Ch: Meredith Maples
Bd of Dir: Ted Cahall Jr
Sr VP: Sean Zito
VP: Louise Felton
VP: Stacie Mann
VP: Caryn Stein
Sls Dir: Mark Gaswirth
Cust Svc D: Annie Olmsted

D-U-N-S 01-679-9947
NETWORK FUNDING LP
9700 Richmond Ave Ste 320, Houston, TX 77042-6600
Tel (713) 334-1100 *Founded/Ownrshp* 1998
Sales NA *EMP* 550
SIC 6163 Mortgage brokers arranging for loans, using money of others; Mortgage brokers arranging for loans, using money of others
Pt: Rex Chamberlain
**Pt:* Buzz Baker
**CFO:* Greg N Baker
Brnch Mgr: Jody Jordan
Brnch Mgr: Kuleen Lala
Brnch Mgr: Kevin Reid
Brnch Mgr: Apurva Sanghavi
Brnch Mgr: James Spice
Brnch Mgr: Joe Stiles
Opers Mgr: Laura Clark

D-U-N-S 07-190-3819
NETWORK GLOBAL LOGISTICS LLC
N G L
320 Interlocken Pkwy # 100, Broomfield, CO 80021-3475
Tel (866) 938-1870 *Founded/Ownrshp* 2005
Sales 203.6MM^E^ *EMP* 610
SIC 4731 Freight transportation arrangement; Freight transportation arrangement
CEO: Scott Riddle
**Ch Bd:* Raymond J Garcia
**CFO:* Forrest Kragten
Sr VP: Paul Gettings
VP: Bill Hale

D-U-N-S 78-684-7640
NETWORK HARDWARE RESALE INC
6500 Hollister Ave # 210, Santa Barbara, CA 93117-3011
Tel (800) 230-6638 *Founded/Ownrshp* 1986
Sales 337.7MM^E^ *EMP* 525
SIC 5045 Computers; Computers
CEO: Mike Sheldon
**Pr:* Michael Lodato
**COO:* Sachi Thompson
CFO: Andrea Greene
CFO: Stephen Haley
**CFO:* Thomas Pickett
Ofcr: Laetitia Kunst
**VP:* Mark Kelly
**VP:* Jeff Zanardi
Exec: Shaleen Goh
Dir Bus: Jayne Tan

D-U-N-S 83-273-7642
NETWORK HEALTH INC
(*Suby of* TUFTS ASSOCIATED HEALTH PLANS INC) ★
101 Sttion Lndg Fl 4, Medford, MA 02155
Tel (888) 257-1985 *Founded/Ownrshp* 2011
Sales 41.6MM^E^ *EMP* 350
Accts Pricewaterhousecoopers Llp Bo
SIC 8011 Health maintenance organization; Health maintenance organization
CEO: Dennis Keefe
**Pr:* Christina Severin
**CFO:* Jeffrey Hulburt
**Chf Mktg O:* Deborah Gordon
**Chf Mktg O:* Pano Yeracaris MD
**Sr VP:* George Moran
**VP:* Leanne Berge
**VP:* Peter Bristol
**VP:* Paul Burke
VP: Kathleen Connolly
VP: Helene Forte
**VP:* Mary McKendry

D-U-N-S 96-408-1603
NETWORK HEALTH INSURANCE CORP
1570 Midway Pl, Menasha, WI 54952-1165
Tel (800) 983-7587 *Founded/Ownrshp* 2010
Sales 69.0MM *EMP* 111^E^
SIC 8082 Home health care services; Home health care services

D-U-N-S 07-831-1197
NETWORK HEALTH LLC
101 Station Lndg Fl 4, Medford, MA 02155-5134
Tel (781) 393-3526 *Founded/Ownrshp* 2011
Sales NA *EMP* 99
SIC 6321 Accident & health insurance

NETWORK HEALTH PLAN
See NETWORK PLAN OF WISCONSIN INC

D-U-N-S 08-281-7073
NETWORK HEALTH SYSTEM INC
(*Suby of* AFFINITY HEALTH SYSTEM) ★
1165 Appleton Rd, Menasha, WI 54952-1905
Tel (920) 831-8920 *Founded/Ownrshp* 1998
Sales 266.1MM^E^ *EMP* 1,020
SIC 8011 Offices & clinics of medical doctors; Offices & clinics of medical doctors
CEO: Kevin Nolan
**COO:* Sheila Jenkins

NETWORK HEALTHCARE
See NUTRITIONAL SUPPORT SERVICES LP

D-U-N-S 92-688-3844
NETWORK IMAGING SOLUTIONS INC
NIS
242 E 90th St, Davenport, IA 52806-7341
Tel (563) 285-6123 *Founded/Ownrshp* 1995
Sales 90.7MM *EMP* 220
Accts Reiser Jennings & Co Pc Da
SIC 4225 General warehousing & storage; General warehousing & storage
Pr: Michael R Strajack
**Pr:* Randall J McDonald
IT Man: Apollinaire Kayembe
QI Cn Mgr: Bill Hopkins

D-U-N-S 15-349-4000
NETWORK IN AGING OF WNY INC
3435 Main St, Buffalo, NY 14214-3001
Tel (716) 829-3712 *Founded/Ownrshp* 1981
Sales 40.2M *EMP* 450
SIC 8322 Old age assistance; Old age assistance
Pr: DOT Swift
**Treas:* Kristin Surdej
Assoc VP: Sharon Plant
**VP:* Charles Battaglia Jr
**VP:* Dana Dee
Ex Dir: Lisa Wheeler
Netwrk Mgr: Kelly Vollmer

D-U-N-S 96-643-0639
NETWORK INC
NET WORK
575 8th Ave Fl 10, New York, NY 10018-3525
Tel (212) 997-5200 *Founded/Ownrshp* 1996
Sales 48.0MM^E^ *EMP* 149^E^
SIC 7371 7373 7378 7372 Custom computer programming services; Computer integrated systems design; Computer maintenance & repair; Prepackaged software; Custom computer programming services; Computer integrated systems design; Computer maintenance & repair; Prepackaged software
Pr: Alexander Solomon
**VP:* Edward Solomon
Creative D: Edgar Payamps
Off Mgr: Sue Halstead
Off Mgr: Jasmine Rinaldo
Telecom Ex: Rick Hollahan
CTO: Uri Mentzel
Web Dev: Joe Murray
Software D: Rod Quenneville
Software D: Edward Soloman
Software D: Peter Tolchin

D-U-N-S 00-974-7390
NETWORK INFRASTRUCTURE INC
94 Taft Ave 96, Hempstead, NY 11550-4819
Tel (516) 385-3030 *Founded/Ownrshp* 1999
Sales 35.7MM^E^ *EMP* 100
SIC 1623 Water, sewer & utility lines
Pr: Patrick Clarke
**VP:* Kenneth Walsh

D-U-N-S 13-640-6621
NETWORK INNOVATIONS INC
NITEL
1101 W Lake St Fl 6, Chicago, IL 60607-1647
Tel (773) 529-6300 *Founded/Ownrshp* 2001
Sales 46.6MM^E^ *EMP* 108
SIC 4813 Local & long distance telephone communications
Pr: Rick Stern
**COO:* Ron Grason
**CFO:* Milan Saric
VP: Lawrence Edmond
Mng Dir: Jim Hessmer
Snr Ntwrk: Erik Sundberg
CTO: Maria Arteaga
Software D: James Arhelger
Netwrk Eng: Phil Lukacek
VP Opers: Jim McCabe
VP Sls: Kevin Weber

D-U-N-S 88-435-6288
■ **NETWORK INSTRUMENTS LLC**
(*Suby of* VIAVI SOLUTIONS INC) ★
10260 Viking Dr Ste 1, Eden Prairie, MN 55344-4560
Tel (952) 358-3800 *Founded/Ownrshp* 2014
Sales 25.7MM^E^ *EMP* 153^E^
SIC 7372 Prepackaged software; Prepackaged software
Pr: Douglas Smith
**CFO:* Jenny Kray
VP: Dwight Benson
Snr Sftwr: Paul Allex
Snr Sftwr: Eric Wegscheid
IT Man: Bruce Clark
IT Man: Walt Flanagan
Sftwr Eng: Steven Cohen
Sftwr Eng: Matt Galligan
VP Sls: Ian Cummins
Sls Mgr: Jeff Jolicoeur

D-U-N-S 01-389-3636
NETWORK MANAGEMENT RESOURCES INC
NMR CONSULTING
15000 Conference Cen Dr, Chantilly, VA 20151-3819
Tel (703) 229-1055 *Founded/Ownrshp* 1996
Sales 26.4MM *EMP* 131^E^
Accts Hildebrand Limparis & Associa
SIC 7379 ;
Pr: David A Garcia

D-U-N-S 01-142-1367
NETWORK MULTI-FAMILY SECURITY CORP
(*Suby of* PROTECTION ONE ALARM MONITORING INC) ★
1035 N 3rd St Ste 101, Lawrence, KS 66044-1491
Tel (785) 856-5500 *Founded/Ownrshp* 1986
Sales 3.1MM^E^ *EMP* 502^E^
SIC 7381 Guard services

D-U-N-S 19-692-6836
NETWORK OPERATOR SERVICES INC
CENTRIS INFORMATION SERVICES
119 W Tyler St Ste 260, Longview, TX 75601-6327
Tel (903) 323-4500 *Founded/Ownrshp* 1988
Sales 29.6MM^E^ *EMP* 180
SIC 4813 Telephone communication, except radio; Long distance telephone communications; Telephone communication, except radio; Long distance telephone communications
Pr: Tim Martin
**CFO:* Ron Hutchison
**Sr VP:* Ron Martin
**VP:* Linda Martin
Dir IT: John Andrews
Dir IT: Carol Sarno
Snr Mgr: Linda Platt

D-U-N-S 08-188-1617
NETWORK PLAN OF WISCONSIN INC
NETWORK HEALTH PLAN
(*Suby of* NETWORK HEALTH SYSTEM INC) ★
1570 Midway Pl, Menasha, WI 54952-1165
Tel (920) 720-1200 *Founded/Ownrshp* 1982
Sales NA *EMP* 300
SIC 6324 Health maintenance organization (HMO), insurance only; Health maintenance organization (HMO), insurance only
Pr: Sheila Jenkins
Pt: Orlando Ayala
VP: Tom Laabs

NETWORK SERVICES
See TALKAMERICA INC

D-U-N-S 08-294-1204 IMP
NETWORK SERVICES CO
(*Suby of* CLEANWISE) ★
1100 E Wdfield Rd Ste 200, Schaumburg, IL 60173
Tel (847) 803-4888 *Founded/Ownrshp* 1975
Sales 1.0MMM *EMP* 140
SIC 5113

D-U-N-S 19-471-5934
■ **NETWORK SERVICES PLUS INC**
NSPI
(*Suby of* SARCOM INC) ★
5080 Old Ellis Pt, Roswell, GA 30076-3885
Tel (678) 710-8517 *Founded/Ownrshp* 2010
Sales 20.9MM^E^ *EMP* 75
SIC 7373 Systems integration services
Pr: Stephen Moss
Tech Mgr: Tom Reilly
Mktg Dir: Tim Roe

Sls Mgr: Patrick Lohmeyer
Sales Asso: Larry Chesser
Pgrm Dir: Todd Wood

D-U-N-S 09-636-1225
■ NETWORK SOLUTIONS LLC
(*Suby of* WEB.COM GROUP INC) ★
13861 Sunrise Valley Dr # 300, Herndon, VA 20171-6124
Tel (703) 668-4600 *Founded/Ownrshp* 2011
Sales 116.7MM^E *EMP* 900
SIC 7375 7389 4813 7374 Information retrieval services; Credit card service; ; Computer graphics service; Information retrieval services; Credit card service; ; Computer graphics service
CEO: David L Brown
Sr VP: Kurt Gastrock
Sr VP: Steve Olson
Sr VP: George Rau
Sr VP: Donald N Telage
VP: Joanne Del Toro
VP Bus: Harry Lalor
Exec: Ana Rossi
Prgrm Mgr: Jeff Cooke
Snr Sftwr: Jigar Parikh
CIO: Rick Walsh

D-U-N-S 61-209-2916
NETWORK SYNERGY INC
4631 Wdlnd Crprate Blvd Ste 310, Tampa, FL 33614
Tel (813) 207-0727 *Founded/Ownrshp* 1997
Sales 25.0MM *EMP* 94
SIC 8099 Medical services organization; Medical services organization
Ch: Ronald Araujo
**Pr:* John Hanselman
**Treas:* Tracy Bell
**Ex VP:* James W Harris
Sr VP: Brian Bell
Sr VP: Patrick Chavanu
VP: Ray Lepage
VP: Kim Lough

D-U-N-S 03-197-7478
NETWORK TELEPHONE CORP
1720 W Frfield Dr Ste 100, Pensacola, FL 32501
Tel (850) 432-4855 *Founded/Ownrshp* 1998
Sales 37.0MM^E *EMP* 360
SIC 4813 7375 Telephone communication, except radio; ; Information retrieval services; Telephone communication, except radio; ; Information retrieval services
Pr: Meyer Cord
**VP:* Charles Emling
**VP:* Mark Miller
S&M/VP: Caron Sjoberg
Mktg Mgr: Christian Whipps

D-U-N-S 18-744-3395
NETWORK TELEPHONE SERVICES INC
N T S
21135 Erwin St, Woodland Hills, CA 91367-3713
Tel (619) 938-9999 *Founded/Ownrshp* 1988
Sales 69.7MM^E *EMP* 500
SIC 2541 4813 Telephone booths, wood; ;Telephone booths, wood;
Ch Bd: Joseph Preston
**Pr:* Gary Passon
**VP:* Dan Coleman
VP: John Maddox
**VP:* Marlene Tanner
VP: David Wood
Mktg Mgr: Steve Woodruff

D-U-N-S 80-852-4375
NETWORKED INSURANCE AGENTS LLC
(*Suby of* NETWORKED HOLDINGS, LLC)
443 Crown Point Cir Ste A, Grass Valley, CA 95945-9557
Tel (800) 682-8476 *Founded/Ownrshp* 2013
Sales NA *EMP* 150
SIC 6411 Insurance agents, brokers & service
Pr: George Biancardi
Pr: Tammy Magliola
COO: Melissa Masles
CFO: Kelly McRae
Ex VP: Larry Oslie

D-U-N-S 85-842-6260
■ NETWORKFLEET INC
VERIZON NETWORKFLEET
(*Suby of* VERIZON TELEMATICS INC) ★
6363 Greenwich Dr Ste 200, San Diego, CA 92122-5987
Tel (858) 450-3245 *Founded/Ownrshp* 2006
Sales 30.4MM^E *EMP* 95
SIC 7371 Computer software development & applications
Pr: Keith Schneider
Pr: Craig Kirkpatrick
VP: Alan Lewin
Dist Mgr: Jose Batlle
Dist Mgr: Bob Laabs
Snr Sftwr: Chris Schulz
Snr Sftwr: Chaz Watson
Dir IT: Larkin Lowry
Dir IT: Eric Simon
IT Man: Jason Davis
Web Dev: Rich Pontillo

D-U-N-S 96-719-4051
NETWORKING TECHNOLOGIES AND SUPPORT INC
N T S
14421 Justice Rd, Midlothian, VA 23113-6875
Tel (804) 379-1800 *Founded/Ownrshp* 1997
Sales 57.3MM^E *EMP* 152
SIC 7373 7378 5734 Systems integration services; Computer peripheral equipment repair & maintenance; Modems, monitors, terminals & disk drives: computers; Systems integration services; Computer peripheral equipment repair & maintenance; Modems, monitors, terminals & disk drives: computers
Pr: Bernard E Robinson
COO: Mark Brandon
**Sr VP:* Mark Roberts
VP: Jack Akers
**VP:* Star Neill
Dir IT: Sam Kemnitz
Dir IT: Sam Panicker
VP Mktg: Robert Schnell
Sls Dir: Dwayne Tharp
Mktg Mgr: Carol Nitz

D-U-N-S 01-689-0993
NETXPERTS INC
1777 Botelho Dr Ste 102, Walnut Creek, CA 94596-8522
Tel (925) 806-0800 *Founded/Ownrshp* 1996
Sales 51.0MM *EMP* 20
Accts Armanino Llp San Ramon Calif
SIC 7373 Computer integrated systems design; Computer integrated systems design
Pr: Gary Nordine
Area Mgr: Alexis Nordine
Off Mgr: Michelle Pardoca
Dir IT: Carol Nordine
Netwrk Eng: Robert Rulon

D-U-N-S 04-354-4142
■ NETZERO INC
(*Suby of* UNITED ONLINE INC) ★
21301 Burbank Blvd Fl 3, Woodland Hills, CA 91367-6697
Tel (805) 418-2000 *Founded/Ownrshp* 2001
Sales 25.5MM^E *EMP* 363
SIC 7371 Computer software systems analysis & design, custom; Computer software systems analysis & design, custom
Ch Bd: Mark R Goldston
**CFO:* Charles S Hilliard
**CTO:* Gerald Popek
Dir IT: Byron Darrah

D-U-N-S 83-199-2859
NETZSCH USA HOLDINGS INC
37 North Ave, Burlington, MA 01803-3305
Tel (781) 272-5353 *Founded/Ownrshp* 2009
Sales 22.1MM^E *EMP* 150^E
SIC 3561 Industrial pumps & parts; Industrial pumps & parts
Mng Dir: Dr Otto Max Schaefer
**Pr:* Thomas Streubel
**Treas:* Mark Drazen
VP: Randy Smith
Natl Sales: Frank Warburg
Sls Mgr: Holger Spranger

D-U-N-S 02-341-8965
NEU TOOL & SUPPLY CORP
16333 W Rogers Dr, New Berlin, WI 53151-2248
Tel (414) 543-4450 *Founded/Ownrshp* 1953
Sales 23.9MM^E *EMP* 40
SIC 5072 5084 Hand tools; Pneumatic tools & equipment
Pr: Robert Neu
**VP:* Paul Neu
Genl Mgr: Robert McInturff
Sls Mgr: Tim Neu
Sls Mgr: David Schmid

D-U-N-S 09-095-6129
NEUBERGER & BERMAN PARTNERS FUND INC
605 3rd Ave Fl 21, New York, NY 10158-2199
Tel (212) 476-8800 *Founded/Ownrshp* 1967
Sales 44.0MM^E *EMP* 1,000
SIC 6722 Management investment, open-end; Management investment, open-end
Pr: Lawrence Zicklin
Sr VP: Philip Ambrosio
VP: Alex Easton

D-U-N-S 83-176-6113
NEUBERGER BERMAN GROUP LLC
605 3rd Ave Fl 21, New York, NY 10158-2199
Tel (212) 476-9000 *Founded/Ownrshp* 2009
Sales 709.5MM^E *EMP* 1,649^E
SIC 6282 6211 6722 Investment advice; Security brokers & dealers; Management investment, open-end; Investment advice; Security brokers & dealers; Management investment, open-end
Ch Bd: George H Walker IV
**Pr:* Joseph V Amato
**COO:* Andrew Komaroff
**Chf Inves:* Erik Knutzen
Assoc VP: Il Decaro
**Ex VP:* Heather Zuckerman
Sr VP: Jolie Cornelius
VP: Peter Andjelkovich
Mktg Dir: Barbara Bresnahan
Board of Directors: Steven A Kandarian

D-U-N-S 08-464-3803
NEUBERGER BERMAN LLC
(*Suby of* NEUBERGER BERMAN GROUP LLC) ★
605 3rd Ave Fl 21, New York, NY 10158-2199
Tel (212) 476-9000 *Founded/Ownrshp* 2003
Sales 665.5MM^E *EMP* 1,200
SIC 6282 6211 6722 Investment advice; Security brokers & dealers; Management investment, open-end; Investment advice; Security brokers & dealers; Management investment, open-end
Pr: Joseph V Amato
Pr: Peter Janczewski
Pr: Bala Muthuswamy
COO: Bob Matza
COO: Amir Nooriala
COO: Matthew S Stadler
CFO: Philip Ambrosio
CFO: Matthew S Tadler
Ofcr: Andrew Allard
Ofcr: Yonah Feder
Ofcr: Jason Hauptman
Ofcr: Erik L Knutzen
Ex VP: Steve Kwong
Ex VP: Richard Pustorino
Ex VP: Peter E Sundman
Sr VP: Jonathan Cohen
Sr VP: Patrick Heffernan
Sr VP: Ilich Martinez
Sr VP: Ralph D Sinsheimer
VP: John Geer
VP: Andrea Trachtenberg

D-U-N-S 07-102-4574
NEUBERGER BERMAN MANAGEMENT LLC
(*Suby of* NEUBERGER BERMAN LLC) ★
605 3rd Ave Frnt 2, New York, NY 10158-0180
Tel (212) 476-8800 *Founded/Ownrshp* 2008
Sales 64.9MM^E *EMP* 986^E
SIC 6722 Management investment, open-end
Pr: Joseph V Amato
CFO: Edward Grieb
Treas: Irene Ashkenazy
Sr VP: William Hunter
Sr VP: Henry Rosenberg
Sr VP: Brenden Smith
Sr VP: Gregory Spiegel
VP: Catherine Zieman
Mng Dir: Tom Sontag
Software D: David Lopez

NEUBURGER, KAREN
See VAN MAR INC

D-U-N-S 02-524-4161
NEUCO INC (IL)
5101 Thatcher Rd, Downers Grove, IL 60515-4072
Tel (630) 960-3800 *Founded/Ownrshp* 1963
Sales 110.3MM^E *EMP* 85
SIC 5075 Air conditioning & ventilation equipment & supplies; Air conditioning & ventilation equipment & supplies
Pr: Paul J Neustadt
**CEO:* William Neustadt
**VP:* Brian Neustadt
VP: Tim Stelzer
Sls Mgr: Ed Benway
Sales Asso: Godek Chris
Sales Asso: Michael Emory
Sales Asso: Lucas Kozlowski
Sales Asso: Brian Pepiot
Sales Asso: Ken Pikus

D-U-N-S 12-239-6356
NEUDESIC LLC
100 Spectrum Center Dr # 1200, Irvine, CA 92618-4962
Tel (949) 754-4500 *Founded/Ownrshp* 2002
Sales 114.7MM^E *EMP* 300
SIC 7379 Computer related consulting services; Computer related consulting services
CEO: Parsa Rohani
VP: Shantanu Sarkar
Exec: Steve Oprian
Genl Mgr: Jason Noble
Genl Mgr: Marty Wasznicky
Off Admin: Jennifer Leader
Snr Sftwr: Matt Declercq
IT Man: Austin Bailey
Sftwr Eng: Michael Martin
VP Opers: Mike Collins
Sls&Mrk Ex: Bekah Bowman

D-U-N-S 00-813-5923
NEUHAUS & CO INC
JOHN DEERE
2000 E Expressway 83, Weslaco, TX 78599-5057
Tel (956) 968-7502 *Founded/Ownrshp* 1996
Sales 75.0MM^E *EMP* 96
SIC 5083 5251 Tractors, agricultural; Farm implements; Farm equipment parts & supplies; Hardware; Tractors, agricultural; Farm implements; Farm equipment parts & supplies; Hardware
Pr: Lance Neuhaus
**Prin:* Earl Neuhaus
Store Mgr: Tate Helmer
IT Man: Renay Martinez
VP Sls: Eddie Sada
Sls Mgr: Gary McWhorter

D-U-N-S 15-212-8729
■ NEULEVEL INC
(*Suby of* NEUSTAR INC) ★
46000 Center Oak Plz, Sterling, VA 20166-6579
Tel (571) 434-5400 *Founded/Ownrshp* 2000
Sales 15.5MM^E *EMP* 500
SIC 4813 ;
VP: Richard Tindal

D-U-N-S 14-874-9497 IMP
▲ NEULION INC
1600 Old Country Rd, Plainview, NY 11803-5013
Tel (516) 622-8300 *Founded/Ownrshp* 2003
Sales 55.5MM *EMP* 453^E
Tkr Sym NEUL *Exch* OTO
SIC 4841 7372 Cable & other pay television services; Prepackaged software; Cable & other pay television services; Prepackaged software
Pr: Kanaan Jemili
**Ch Bd:* Charles B Wang
CFO: Arthur J McCarthy
**V Ch Bd:* G Scott Paterson
QA Dir: Xiaoqing Jia
Web Dev: Schmar James
Web Dev: Joji Langston
Software D: Ryan Lauer
Software D: Jordan Montpetit
Software D: Matthew Pawluk
Sftwr Eng: Matthew Lemar
Board of Directors: John R Anderson, Gabriel A Battista, Robert E Bostrom, John A Coelho, James R Hale, Shirley Strum Kenny, David Kronfeld

D-U-N-S 94-371-9195
NEUMAN & ESSER INVESTMENTS INC
(*Suby of* NEUMAN & ESSER VERWALTUNGS- UND BETEILIGUNGSGES. MBH)
802 N West St, Wilmington, DE 19801-1526
Tel (281) 497-5113 *Founded/Ownrshp* 1992
Sales 76.3MM *EMP* 29
Accts Melton & Melton Llp Houst
SIC 3563 Air & gas compressors
Mng Dir: Scott De Baldo
CFO: Henning Von Haefen

D-U-N-S 80-131-1432 IMP
NEUMAN & ESSER USA INC
(*Suby of* NEUMAN & ESSER GMBH & CO. KG)
1502 E Summitry Cir, Katy, TX 77449-5350
Tel (281) 497-5113 *Founded/Ownrshp* 2006
Sales 36.8MM *EMP* 45
SIC 3585 Refrigeration & heating equipment
Pr: Scott Debaldo
VP: Henning Haefen
VP: Fred Trackwell
Board of Directors: Scot Jenkins, Alexander Peters

D-U-N-S 96-999-6677 IMP
NEUMAN ALUMINIUM IMPACT EXTRUSION INC
1418 Genicom Dr, Waynesboro, VA 22980-1956
Tel (540) 248-2703 *Founded/Ownrshp* 1997
Sales 39.6MM^E *EMP* 85
SIC 5051 Metals service centers & offices; Metals service centers & offices
CFO: Stan Platek
Genl Pt: Harvey Ellinger
**Pr:* Patrick Carroll
**VP:* David Armentrout

NEUMAN GROUP
See NEUMAN POOLS INC

D-U-N-S 04-079-1758
NEUMAN POOLS INC
NEUMAN GROUP
W9684 Beaverland Pkwy, Beaver Dam, WI 53916-9217
Tel (920) 885-3366 *Founded/Ownrshp* 1975
Sales 33.0MM^E *EMP* 100
Accts Baker Tilly Virchow Krause
SIC 1799 Swimming pool construction
Pr: Randal S Neuman
**CFO:* Cinda S Keegan
CFO: Cinda Keegan
VP Mfg: Troy Melhoff
Oper/Mgr: Mike Nelson

D-U-N-S 07-543-3102
NEUMAN SARAH R NURSING HOME
845 Palmer Ave, Mamaroneck, NY 10543-2499
Tel (914) 698-6005 *Founded/Ownrshp* 1969
Sales 10.7MM^E *EMP* 400
SIC 8051 Skilled nursing care facilities; Skilled nursing care facilities
Telecom Ex: Peter Bloom
QC Dir: Yvette Allen
Pr Dir: Harriet Rosenberg
HC Dir: Melanie Dorn

D-U-N-S 00-798-8363
NEUMANN BROTHERS INC (IA)
1435 Ohio St, Des Moines, IA 50314-3423
Tel (515) 243-0156 *Founded/Ownrshp* 1912
Sales 69.1MM^E *EMP* 200
SIC 1542 Commercial & office building, new construction; Commercial & office buildings, renovation & repair; Commercial & office building, new construction; Commercial & office buildings, renovation & repair
CEO: Michael Simpson
VP: John Neumann

NEUMANN FAMILY SERVICES
See VICTOR C NEUMANN ASSOCIATION INC

D-U-N-S 01-619-4875
NEUMANN SYSTEMS GROUP INC
DIRECTED ENERGY SOLUTIONS
890 Elkton Dr Ste 101, Colorado Springs, CO 80907-3554
Tel (719) 593-7848 *Founded/Ownrshp* 1997
Sales 22.6MM *EMP* 60^E
Accts Stockman Kast Ryan & Co Llp
SIC 8731 7371 Commercial physical research; Computer software development; Commercial physical research; Computer software development
CEO: Todd Tiahrt
**Ch Bd:* David Neumann
**COO:* Jay Brasseur
COO: Richard Durham
Brnch Mgr: Nicole Myers
**CTO:* Eric Klein
Sls Mgr: Michael Neumann

D-U-N-S 07-548-2208
NEUMANN UNIVERSITY
1 Neumann Dr, Aston, PA 19014-1277
Tel (610) 558-5505 *Founded/Ownrshp* 1965
Sales 53.9MM *EMP* 332
Accts Baker Tilly Virchow Krause Ll
SIC 8221 College, except junior; College, except junior
Pr: Rosalie M Mirenda Dnsc
CFO: Douglas Young
**VP:* Henry Sumner
Exec: Paul Reid
Dir IT: Lisa Cadorette

D-U-N-S 03-107-4818
NEUMAYER EQUIPMENT CO
5060 Arsenal St, Saint Louis, MO 63139-1012
Tel (314) 772-4501 *Founded/Ownrshp* 1989
Sales 34.3MM^E *EMP* 100
SIC 5013 Automobile service station equipment
Pr: Susan Burkhart
**CFO:* Kraig Spisack
**Sec:* Sharon Hurt

NEURO DRINKS
See NEUROBRANDS LLC

D-U-N-S 78-515-0350
NEURO INSTITUTE OF AUSTIN L P
TEXAS NEUROREHAB CENTER
1106 W Dittmar Rd, Austin, TX 78745-6328
Tel (512) 444-4835 *Founded/Ownrshp* 2001
Sales 43.9MM^E *EMP* 322
SIC 8063 Psychiatric hospitals; Psychiatric hospitals
CFO: Omar Correa
**Pt:* PSI Hospitals LLC
Pr: Juan Alonzo
Nurse Mgr: Juliet Weldin

D-U-N-S 07-857-9207
NEURO INTERNATIONAL LLC
4004 Fruitville Rd, Sarasota, FL 34232-1617
Tel (941) 371-7147 *Founded/Ownrshp* 2009
Sales 3.4MM^E *EMP* 300
SIC 8082 Home health care services; Home health care services

NEURO MEDICAL HOSPITAL
See NMC OPERATING CO LLC

NEURO REHABILATATION
See LAKEVIEW MANAGEMENT INC

NEURO REHABILITATION SERVICES
See WORTH HOME CARE INC

D-U-N-S 78-808-1073
NEURO-REHAB ASSOCIATES INC
NORTHEAST REHABILITATION HOSP
70 Butler St, Salem, NH 03079-3925
Tel (603) 893-2900 *Founded/Ownrshp* 1983
Sales 35.1MME *EMP* 500
SIC 8049 8011 8361 Physical therapist; Offices & clinics of medical doctors; Rehabilitation center, residential: health care incidental; Physical therapist; Offices & clinics of medical doctors; Rehabilitation center, residential: health care incidental
CEO: John F Prochilo
**Pr:* Howard M Gardner
VP: Sudhir Tawalare
Psych: Robert Moverman
Doctor: Shihab Ahmed MD

D-U-N-S 83-107-4690 IMP
NEUROBRANDS LLC
NEURO DRINKS
2550 N Hollywood Way # 100, Burbank, CA 91505-5015
Tel (310) 393-6444 *Founded/Ownrshp* 2009
Sales 97.6MME *EMP* 125
SIC 5149 Soft drinks; Soft drinks
CEO: Diana Jenkins
**CFO:* Greg Buscher
Area Mgr: Chad Bell
Area Mgr: Lindsey Bertelsen
Area Mgr: Jake Bolton
Area Mgr: Jeff Quitasol
Area Mgr: Kyle Ransom
Area Mgr: Jason Sloma
Area Mgr: Kelley Vallette
Area Mgr: Marshall Whitaker
Natl Sales: Michael Goodz

D-U-N-S 80-098-1276
NEUROCRINE BIOSCIENCES INC
12780 El Camino Real # 100, San Diego, CA 92130-2042
Tel (858) 617-7600 *Founded/Ownrshp* 1992
Sales 30.2MME *EMP* 81
Accts Ernst & Young Llp San Diego
Tkr Sym NBIX *Exch* NGS
SIC 2834 2833 Pituitary gland pharmaceutical preparations; Drugs acting on the central nervous system & sense organs; Endocrine products
Pr: Kevin C Gorman
**Ch Bd:* William H Rastetter
CFO: Timothy P Coughlin
Chf Cred: Eric Benevich
Chf Mktg O: Henry Y Pan MD PHD
Ofcr: Haig P Bozigian
Ofcr: Kyle Gano
Ofcr: Dimitri E Grigoriadis
Ofcr: Christopher F O'Brien
Sr VP: Richard Ranieri
VP: Bill Aurora
Assoc Dir: T A Chen
Board of Directors: Gary A Lyons, W Thomas Mitchell, Joseph A Mollica, George J Morrow, Corinne H Nevinny, Richard F Pops, Alfred W Sandrock Jr, Stephen A Sherwin

NEUROENDOCRINE-UNIT
See MGH INSTITUTE OF HEALTH PROFESSIONS INC

D-U-N-S 14-500-8178 IMP
NEUROLOGICA CORP
(*Suby of* SAMSUNG ENGINEERING AMERICA INC) ★
14 Electronics Ave, Danvers, MA 01923-1011
Tel (978) 564-8500 *Founded/Ownrshp* 2013
Sales 29.8MME *EMP* 80
SIC 3841 Surgical & medical instruments
Pr: In Ryu
**Treas:* Jungtae Ahn
VP: Philip Sullivan
VP: Andrew Tybinkowski
Ql Cn Mgr: William Caputo
Snr Mgr: Richard Desalvo

D-U-N-S 08-764-4852
NEUROMEDICAL CENTER (A PROFESSIONAL MEDICAL CORP)
10101 Park Rowe Ave # 200, Baton Rouge, LA 70810-1686
Tel (225) 906-3820 *Founded/Ownrshp* 1977
Sales 30.0MME *EMP* 120
SIC 8011 Clinic, operated by physicians; Neurologist
Pr: Kelly J Scrantz
**VP:* Gerald J Calegan
**VP:* Kevin J Callerame
**VP:* Luke A Corsten

D-U-N-S 13-496-0348 IMP
NEURONETICS INC
3222 Phoenixville Pike # 300, Malvern, PA 19355-9610
Tel (610) 640-4202 *Founded/Ownrshp* 2003
Sales 26.3MME *EMP* 110
SIC 3841 Surgical & medical instruments; Surgical & medical instruments
Pr: Christopher Thatcher
Pr: Rajiv Sawhney
CFO: Mark R Bausinger
Treas: Jill Bond-Sawhney
VP: Peter Anastasiou
VP: Stanford W Miller
VP: Mark E Riehl
VP: Aj Sawhney
VP: Judy P Ways
Assoc Dir: Eric Mandelbaum
Assoc Dir: Cindy Prybelski
Assoc Dir: Angela Waltman

NEURORESTORATIVE
See NATIONAL MENTOR INC

NEURORESTORATIVE CARBONDALE
See CENTER FOR COMPREHENSIVE SERVICES INC

D-U-N-S 80-815-7283 IMP
NEUS BUILDING CENTER INC
NEUS HARDWARE GALLERY
N95w16915 Falls Pkwy, Menomonee Falls, WI 53051-1436
Tel (262) 251-6005 *Founded/Ownrshp* 1952
Sales 25.1MME *EMP* 50
SIC 5072 Builders' hardware; Power tools & accessories
Pr: Harvey Neu
**CFO:* Robert E Gross
**VP:* Cindy Neu
Genl Mgr: Michael Karch
IT Man: David Bolthouse
Sales Asso: Scott Plopper

NEUS HARDWARE GALLERY
See NEUS BUILDING CENTER INC

D-U-N-S 11-240-3295 EXP
▲ NEUSTAR INC
21575 Ridgetop Cir, Sterling, VA 20166-6505
Tel (571) 434-5400 *Founded/Ownrshp* 1996
Sales 963.5MM *EMP* 1,576E
Accts Ernst & Young Llp Mclean Vir
Tkr Sym NSR *Exch* NYS
SIC 7375 Information retrieval services; Data base information retrieval; Remote data base information retrieval; On-line data base information retrieval; Information retrieval services; Data base information retrieval; Remote data base information retrieval; On-line data base information retrieval
Pr: Lisa A Hook
CFO: Paul S Lalljie
Sr VP: Alex L Berry
Sr VP: Alexander L Berry
Sr VP: Christine C Brennan
Sr VP: Peter Burke
Sr VP: Steven J Edwards
Sr VP: Brian Foster
Sr VP: Rob Gatto
Sr VP: Leonard J Kennedy
Sr VP: Guenter H Krauss
Sr VP: Julian Lighton
Sr VP: Edward M Prince Jr
Sr VP: Steve Sharp
Sr VP: Hank Skorny
Sr VP: Alex Tulchinsky
VP: Mohan Atreya
VP: Steven Johnson
VP: Chris McArdle
VP: Paul McLenaghan
VP: Carl Steffens
Board of Directors: Paul Ballew, Gareth C C Chang, James G Cullen, Joel P Friedman, Mark N Green, Ross K Ireland, Paul A Lacouture, Deborah Rieman, Michael J Rowny

D-U-N-S 93-139-0975
■ NEUSTAR INFORMATION SERVICES INC
(*Suby of* NEUSTAR INC) ★
1861 Intl Dr Fl 6, Mclean, VA 22102
Tel (703) 272-6200 *Founded/Ownrshp* 2011
Sales 29.1MME *EMP* 120
SIC 7375 Information retrieval services; Information retrieval services
CEO: Lisa A Hook
**Pr:* Dennis Ainge
Pr: Tom McNeal
Ex VP: Jim Bruning
Ex VP: Jim Mollica
Ex VP: Stephen Smith
**Sr VP:* Mark F Bregman
**Sr VP:* Steve J Edwards
Sr VP: Daniel Gallagher
**Sr VP:* Len Kennedy
**Sr VP:* Paul S Lalljie
Sr VP: Ioe Nicnulty
VP: Dennis Brouwer
VP: Greg Schibler
VP: Tyler E Williams

D-U-N-S 92-640-2611 EXP
NEUTRON INC
220 Reese Rd Ste 1, State College, PA 16801-7568
Tel (814) 237-0902 *Founded/Ownrshp* 1995
Sales 20.1MME *EMP* 16
SIC 5072 Hardware
Pr: Horng Huei Kuo
**VP:* Yvonne Juan
Sales Exec: Shirley Xu
Mktg Mgr: Michael Lin

D-U-N-S 96-860-8609
NEUTRONA NETWORKS INTERNATIONAL LLC
IFX INTERNATIONAL CARRIER SVCS
(*Suby of* NNI VENTURES LLC) ★
1111 Brickell Ave Fl 11, Miami, FL 33131-3122
Tel (305) 728-8501 *Founded/Ownrshp* 2010
Sales 7.0MME *EMP* 317
SIC 4899 Data communication services; Data communication services
COO: Luciano Salata

D-U-N-S 04-887-2352
NEUVILLE MOTORS INC
NEVCO LEASING DIVISION
721 W Fulton St, Waupaca, WI 54981-1403
Tel (715) 256-2900 *Founded/Ownrshp* 1976
Sales 31.3MM *EMP* 49
SIC 5521 7515 Used car dealers; Passenger car leasing; Used car dealers; Passenger car leasing
Pr: Timothy Neuville
**Sec:* Morris Neuville
**VP:* Joy Neuville
IT Man: Mary Adamczak

D-U-N-S 02-486-9307
NEUWIRTH MOTORS INC (NC)
219 S College Rd, Wilmington, NC 28403-1609
Tel (910) 799-1815 *Founded/Ownrshp* 1958
Sales 60.3MME *EMP* 115
SIC 5511 Automobiles, new & used; Automobiles, new & used
Pr: John Gillilan
Sls Mgr: Alan Thomas

D-U-N-S 96-504-3388
NEV HOLDINGS LLC
3211 Internet Blvd # 200, Frisco, TX 75034-1948
Tel (972) 731-1100 *Founded/Ownrshp* 2010
Sales 218.3MME *EMP* 3,401
SIC 2677 Envelopes; Envelopes
CFO: Shelby Marlowe

D-U-N-S 04-981-7144
NEVADA AFFORDABLE HOUSING ASSI
760 Margrave Dr Ste 100, Reno, NV 89502-3566
Tel (775) 284-0302 *Founded/Ownrshp* 2010
Sales 81.8MM *EMP* 2E
Accts Grant Thornton Llp Reno Nv
SIC 6531 Real estate agent, residential; Real estate agent, residential

NEVADA AUTOMOTIVE TEST CENTER
See HODGES TRANSPORTATION INC

D-U-N-S 00-697-0925
■ NEVADA BELL TELEPHONE CO (NV)
AT&T NEVADA
(*Suby of* AT&T INC) ★
645 E Plumb Ln B128, Reno, NV 89502-3595
Tel (775) 333-3124 *Founded/Ownrshp* 1913, 2006
Sales 16.0MMM *EMP* 860
SIC 4813 Local telephone communications; Long distance telephone communications; Local telephone communications; Long distance telephone communications
Prin: Marsha Lindsey
**Pr:* Sivia Samano
**Treas:* R W Wohlert

D-U-N-S 00-968-8599
NEVADA BEVERAGE CO (NV)
ALTERNATIVE BEVERAGE
3940 W Tropicana Ave, Las Vegas, NV 89103-5516
Tel (702) 739-9998 *Founded/Ownrshp* 1943
Sales 134.0MME *EMP* 280
SIC 5181 Beer & other fermented malt liquors; Beer & other fermented malt liquors
Pr: Pat Clark
Dir IT: Derick Hufstader
Sales Exec: Phillip Carrillo
Mktg Mgr: Ken Wrathall
Sls Mgr: Harry Moses
Snr Mgr: Wade Bruhn
Snr Mgr: Art Garland

NEVADA CANCER INSTITUTE
See REGENTS OF UNIVERSITY OF CALIFORNIA

D-U-N-S 93-985-4709
NEVADA CHECKER CAB CORP
5225 W Post Rd, Las Vegas, NV 89118-4331
Tel (702) 873-8012 *Founded/Ownrshp* 1981
Sales 15.0MME *EMP* 450
SIC 4121 Taxicabs; Taxicabs
Pr: Milton I Schwartz
**Sec:* Harry Eliades
VP: Maritha Burton
**VP:* Howard Dudley
**VP:* Peter Eliades
VP: Schwartz Milton
**VP:* David Willden

D-U-N-S 03-064-4579
NEVADA CITY HOSPITAL (INC)
NEVADA REGIONAL MEDICAL CENTER
800 S Ash St, Nevada, MO 64772-3223
Tel (417) 667-3355 *Founded/Ownrshp* 1945
Sales 47.0M *EMP* 450
Accts Bkd Llp Springfield Mo
SIC 8062 8051 General medical & surgical hospitals; Extended care facility; General medical & surgical hospitals; Extended care facility
Pr: Robert Ohlen
**CFO:* Cindy Buck
VP: Denise Sloniler
Nrsg Dir: Carol Girven
Diag Rad: M T Moore

D-U-N-S 02-531-2567
NEVADA COMMUNITY FOUNDATION INC (NV)
1635 Vlg Ctr Cir Ste 160, Las Vegas, NV 89134-6375
Tel (702) 892-2326 *Founded/Ownrshp* 1988
Sales 103.0MM *EMP* 3
Accts Houldsworth Russo & Company Pc
SIC 8699 Charitable organization
Pr: Gian Brosco
**Pr:* Bret Bicoy
Bd of Dir: Pamela M Goldberg
Bd of Dir: Dara Goldsmith
Bd of Dir: Patricia A Markos
Ofcr: Seth Wongsavit

NEVADA COUNTY PUBLISHING CO
See SWIFT COMMUNICATIONS INC

D-U-N-S 02-551-9349 EXP
NEVADA COUNTY PUBLISHING CO
UNION, THE
(*Suby of* NEVADA COUNTY PUBLISHING CO) ★
464 Sutton Way, Grass Valley, CA 95945-4102
Tel (530) 273-9561 *Founded/Ownrshp* 1967
Sales 27.6MME *EMP* 650
SIC 2711 Newspapers, publishing & printing; Newspapers, publishing & printing
COO: Jeff Ackerman
CFO: Becky Dirk
Dir Soc: Mary Davis
Advt Dir: Carole Bukovich
Advt Dir: Patrick Connolly
Advt Mgr: Courtney Walker
Snr Mgr: Ross Maak

D-U-N-S 80-988-7656
NEVADA DEPARTMENT OF ADMINISTRATION
OFFICE OF GRANT PROCUREMENT
(*Suby of* EXECUTIVE OFFICE OF STATE OF NEVADA) ★
209 E Musser St Ste 200, Carson City, NV 89701-4298
Tel (775) 684-0222 *Founded/Ownrshp* 1973
Sales NA *EMP* 325
SIC 9199 General government administration; ; General government administration;

D-U-N-S 80-988-7680
NEVADA DEPARTMENT OF BUSINESS AND INDUSTRY
(*Suby of* EXECUTIVE OFFICE OF STATE OF NEVADA) ★
555 E Washington Ave # 4900, Las Vegas, NV 89101-1076
Tel (702) 486-2750 *Founded/Ownrshp* 1993
Sales NA *EMP* 650
SIC 9651 Regulation, miscellaneous commercial sectors; ; Regulation, miscellaneous commercial sectors;

D-U-N-S 80-988-7706
NEVADA DEPARTMENT OF CONSERVATION AND NATURAL RESOURCES
(*Suby of* EXECUTIVE OFFICE OF STATE OF NEVADA) ★
901 S Stewart St Ste 5001, Carson City, NV 89701-5244
Tel (775) 684-2710 *Founded/Ownrshp* 1957
Sales NA *EMP* 450
SIC 9511 9512 Air, water & solid waste management; Land, mineral & wildlife conservation; ; Land, mineral & wildlife conservation
Ex Dir: Allen Biaggi
Ofcr: Jason Dietrich
IT Man: Adele Basham
IT Man: Shannon Webb

D-U-N-S 03-289-4342
NEVADA DEPARTMENT OF CORRECTIONS
(*Suby of* EXECUTIVE OFFICE OF STATE OF NEVADA) ★
5500 Snyder Ave Bldg 89, Carson City, NV 89701-6752
Tel (775) 887-3285 *Founded/Ownrshp* 1977
Sales NA *EMP* 2,600E
SIC 9223 Prison, government; ; Prison, government;
**CFO:* Lorraine Pagwell
**Prin:* Darell Wreck
Snr Mgr: Betty Farris

D-U-N-S 80-988-8241
NEVADA DEPARTMENT OF EMPLOYMENT TRAINING AND REHABILITATION
REHABLTTION EMPLOYMENT SEC DIV
(*Suby of* EXECUTIVE OFFICE OF STATE OF NEVADA) ★
500 E 3rd St Ste 200, Carson City, NV 89713-0001
Tel (775) 684-3909 *Founded/Ownrshp* 1993
Sales NA *EMP* 850
SIC 9441 Administration of social & manpower programs; ; Administration of social & manpower programs;
CFO: Martin Ramirez
IT Man: Lani Smith

D-U-N-S 80-988-8266
NEVADA DEPARTMENT OF HEALTH AND HUMAN SERVICES
DIRECTOR'S OFFICE
(*Suby of* EXECUTIVE OFFICE OF STATE OF NEVADA) ★
4126 Tech Way Ste 100, Carson City, NV 89706
Tel (775) 684-4000 *Founded/Ownrshp* 1963
Sales NA *EMP* 5,374
SIC 9431 Administration of public health programs; ; Administration of public health programs;
Ofcr: Michael Torvinen

D-U-N-S 80-988-8399
NEVADA DEPARTMENT OF MOTOR VEHICLES
(*Suby of* EXECUTIVE OFFICE OF STATE OF NEVADA) ★
555 Wright Way, Carson City, NV 89711-0001
Tel (775) 684-4549 *Founded/Ownrshp* 1957
Sales NA *EMP* 1,030
SIC 9621 Motor vehicle licensing & inspection office, government; ; Motor vehicle licensing & inspection office, government;

D-U-N-S 14-786-0105
NEVADA DEPARTMENT OF PUBLIC SAFETY
(*Suby of* EXECUTIVE OFFICE OF STATE OF NEVADA) ★
555 Wright Way, Carson City, NV 89701-5229
Tel (775) 684-4556 *Founded/Ownrshp* 2001
Sales NA *EMP* 1,600
SIC 9229 Public safety bureau, government; ; Public safety bureau, government;
Ex Ofcr: Kathalie Koche

D-U-N-S 82-469-5555
NEVADA DEPARTMENT OF TAXATION
(*Suby of* EXECUTIVE OFFICE OF STATE OF NEVADA) ★
1550 College Pkwy Ste 115, Carson City, NV 89706-7937
Tel (775) 684-2096 *Founded/Ownrshp* 1975
Sales NA *EMP* 321
SIC 9311 Taxation department, government; ; Taxation department, government;
Prin: Charles Chinnock
Ex Dir: Dave Pursell
Snr Mgr: Terry Rubald

D-U-N-S 82-469-5720
NEVADA DEPARTMENT OF TRANSPORTATION
NDOT
(*Suby of* EXECUTIVE OFFICE OF STATE OF NEVADA) ★
1263 S Stewart St, Carson City, NV 89712-0001
Tel (775) 888-7440 *Founded/Ownrshp* 1982
Sales NA *EMP* 1,604
SIC 9621 Regulation, administration of transportation; ; Regulation, administration of transportation;
Comm Dir: Sean Sever
Snr Mgr: Mark Elicegui

D-U-N-S 04-810-1831
NEVADA DIVISION OF FORESTRY
(*Suby of* NEVADA DEPARTMENT OF CONSERVATION AND NATURAL RESOURCES) ★
2478 Fairview Dr Ste A, Carson City, NV 89701-6871
Tel (775) 684-2500 *Founded/Ownrshp* 1924
Sales NA *EMP* 300
SIC 9512 Land, mineral & wildlife conservation; ; Land, mineral & wildlife conservation;
IT Man: Lauri Dunn

D-U-N-S 09-901-2221
▲ NEVADA GOLD & CASINOS INC
133 E Warm Springs Rd # 102, Las Vegas, NV 89119-4122
Tel (702) 685-1000 *Founded/Ownrshp* 1994
Sales 64.3MM *EMP* 1,315ᴱ
Accts Ernst & Young Llp Las Vegas
Tkr Sym UWN *Exch* ASE
SIC 7011 Casino hotel; Casino hotel
CEO: Michael P Shaunnessy
**Ch Bd:* William J Sherlock
CFO: Christopher C Domijan
CFO: James J Kohn
Ex VP: Lan Bentsen
Sr VP: Jay Dodds
Sr VP: Alan J Greenstein
Sr VP: Eric H Persson
VP: Ernest E East
VP: Victor H Mena
Ex Dir: Kandace Blanchard
Board of Directors: Frank Catania, William G Jayroe, Francis M Ricci, Wayne H White

D-U-N-S 95-941-1984
NEVADA HAND INC
NEVADA HSING NEIGHBORHOOD DEV
295 E Warm Springs Rd # 101, Las Vegas, NV 89119-4212
Tel (702) 739-3345 *Founded/Ownrshp* 1993
Sales 50.9MMᴱ *EMP* 135ᴱ
Accts Novogradac & Company Llp San
SIC 1531 Operative builders; Operative builders
Pr: Michael Mullin
CFO: Peg Freman
**Treas:* Bruce McAnnany
Ex VP: Robert Feibleman
VP: Deborah Kamprath
Dist Mgr: Mark Lytle
Off Admin: Ana Zelaya
Snr Mgr: Sandra Lewis

D-U-N-S 13-976-7255
NEVADA HEALTH CENTERS INC
3325 Research Way, Carson City, NV 89706-7913
Tel (775) 888-6600 *Founded/Ownrshp* 1978
Sales 29.3MM *EMP* 330
Accts Tca Partners Llp Fresno Ca
SIC 8011 Clinic, operated by physicians; Clinic, operated by physicians
CEO: Steven C Hansen
**Pr:* Steve Comer
Pr: Art Rempp
COO: Monica Taylor
**COO:* Mitchell Wilson
**CFO:* Linda Costa
**Treas:* Jared Carter
**Chf Mktg O:* Carl Heard
VP: Lisa Dettling
IT Man: Elizabeth Duffrin
Snr Mgr: Jassmin Martell

NEVADA HSING NEIGHBORHOOD DEV
See NEVADA HAND INC

D-U-N-S 04-788-3061 IMP
NEVADA IRRIGATION DISTRICT
N I D
1036 W Main St, Grass Valley, CA 95945-5424
Tel (530) 273-6185 *Founded/Ownrshp* 1921
Sales 43.2MM *EMP* 198
Accts Richardson & Company Llp Sac
SIC 4971 4911 Irrigation systems; Generation, electric power; Irrigation systems; Generation, electric power
Genl Mgr: Remleh Scherzinger
**Pr:* John H Drew
**CEO:* Keane Sommers
**Treas:* Marie Owens
Bd of Dir: David Hernandez
VP: Doug Roderick
**Prin:* Scott Miller
CTO: Tonia Herrera
Sls Mgr: Adrian Schneider

NEVADA LEGISLATURE
See LEGISLATIVE OFFICE OF STATE OF NEVADA

D-U-N-S 96-294-9983
NEVADA MEZZ 1 LLC
60 Wall St, New York, NY 10005-2836
Tel (702) 314-3265 *Founded/Ownrshp* 2008
Sales 13.1MMᴱ *EMP* 4,187
SIC 7011 Resort hotel; Casino hotel; Resort hotel; Casino hotel
CEO: John Unwin

NEVADA NATIONAL GUARD
See MILITARY NEVADA OFFICE OF

D-U-N-S 00-697-0891 IMP
■ NEVADA POWER CO
NV ENERGY
(*Suby of* NV ENERGY INC) ★
6226 W Sahara Ave, Las Vegas, NV 89146-3060
Tel (702) 402-5000 *Founded/Ownrshp* 1999
Sales 2.3MMM *EMP* 1,524
Accts Deloitte & Touche Llp Las Veg
SIC 4911 Electric services; Distribution, electric power; Generation, electric power; Transmission, electric power; Electric services; Distribution, electric power; Generation, electric power; Transmission, electric power
Pr: Paul J Caudill
**Ch Bd:* Philip G Satre
Pr: Paul J Kaleta
COO: Dilek L Samil
CFO: Jonathan S Halkyard
Treas: Mohammed N Mughal
Ofcr: Eskil Elmer
VP: E Kevin Bethel
Exec: James Doubek
Exec: Linda Garver
Exec: Johanna Melaragno
Exec: Debra Steinberg
Board of Directors: Joseph B Anderson Jr, Glenn C Christenson, Susan F Clark, Stephen E Frank, Brian J Kennedy, Maureen T Mullarkey, John F O'reilly, Donald D Snyder

D-U-N-S 82-894-7601
NEVADA PROPERTY 1 LLC
COSMOPOLITAN OF LAS VEGAS, THE
(*Suby of* BRE SPADE VOTECO LLC) ★
3708 Las Vegas Blvd S, Las Vegas, NV 89109-4309
Tel (702) 698-7000 *Founded/Ownrshp* 2014
Sales 528.5MMᴱ *EMP* 4,400ᴱ
SIC 7011 Resort hotel; Casino hotel; Resort hotel; Casino hotel
CEO: John Unwin
**Ch Bd:* Enrico Sanna
COO: Thomas McCartney
**CFO:* Ronald G Eidell
Chf Mktg O: Lisa Marchese
Ofcr: Anthony Pearl
VP: Robert Davies
VP: Daniel Espino
Exec: Jeff Walter
Dir Sec: Billy Huddy
Genl Mgr: Arthur Keith

D-U-N-S 05-190-8994
NEVADA R-V SCHOOL DISTRICT
SUPERINTENDENTS OFFICE
811 W Hickory St, Nevada, MO 64772-2000
Tel (417) 448-2000 *Founded/Ownrshp* 1850
Sales 19.0MMᴱ *EMP* 400
SIC 8211 Public elementary & secondary schools; School board; Public elementary & secondary schools; School board
Treas: Rhonda Rowland
**Ofcr:* Tina Williams
Schl Brd P: Amanda Fisher

D-U-N-S 80-754-0364
NEVADA RAILROAD MATERIALS INC
N R M
917 Country Hills Dr # 3, Ogden, UT 84403-2536
Tel (801) 621-5544 *Founded/Ownrshp* 1993
Sales 45.7MMᴱ *EMP* 103
SIC 5088 3312 5211 2421 Railroad equipment & supplies; Rails, steel or iron; Lumber products; Sawmills & planing mills, general; Railroad equipment & supplies; Rails, steel or iron; Lumber products; Sawmills & planing mills, general
Pr: Robert Ollendick
**VP:* Thomas Ollendick
**Prin:* Bob Ollendick
Off Mgr: Shelle Kautzman

NEVADA REGIONAL MEDICAL CENTER
See NEVADA CITY HOSPITAL (INC)

D-U-N-S 02-474-1949
NEVADA REPUBLIC ELECTRIC NORTH INC
11855 White Rock Rd, Rancho Cordova, CA 95742-6603
Tel (916) 294-0140 *Founded/Ownrshp* 1999
Sales 22.0MMᴱ *EMP* 140
SIC 1731 Electrical work; Electrical work
Pr: Eric Stafford
**Treas:* Jeff Stafford

D-U-N-S 11-039-7411
NEVADA RESTAURANT SERVICES INC
DOTTY'S
3645 Losee Rd, North Las Vegas, NV 89030-3324
Tel (702) 531-7161 *Founded/Ownrshp* 1994
Sales 29.9MMᴱ *EMP* 116ᴱ
SIC 8742 7011 Restaurant & food services consultants; Casino hotel
Pr: Paula Graziano
**Sec:* Kathrine Estey
**Sec:* Richard Craig Estey
Ofcr: Josh Trudell

D-U-N-S 08-007-0040
■ NEVADA SITE SCIENCE SUPPORT AND TECHNOLOGIES CORP
ASEC INTERNATIONAL INC
(*Suby of* LOCKHEED MARTIN INTEGRATED TECHNOLOGY LLC) ★
700 N Frederick Ave, Gaithersburg, MD 20879-3328
Tel (301) 240-4000 *Founded/Ownrshp* 1981
Sales 10.6MMᴱ *EMP* 1,325ᴱ
SIC 8711 Engineering services

D-U-N-S 93-203-4788
■ NEVADA SPEEDWAY LLC
LAS VEGAS MOTOR SPEEDWAY
(*Suby of* SPEEDWAY MOTORSPORTS INC) ★
7000 Las Vegas Blvd N, Las Vegas, NV 89115-1708
Tel (702) 644-4444 *Founded/Ownrshp* 1994
Sales 8.8MMᴱ *EMP* 600
SIC 7948 Racing, including track operation; Racing, including track operation
Ch Bd: O Bruton Smith
**Genl Mgr:* Chris Powell

D-U-N-S 00-357-4790
NEVADA STAR CAB CORP
5225 W Post Rd, Las Vegas, NV 89118-4331
Tel (702) 873-8012 *Founded/Ownrshp* 1986
Sales 7.3MMᴱ *EMP* 300
SIC 4121 Taxicabs; Taxicabs
Pr: Peter Eliades
**VP:* Maritha Burton
**VP:* Howard Dudley
**VP:* Harry Eliades
**VP:* Milton Schwartz
**VP:* David Willden

D-U-N-S 00-697-0909
■ NEVADA STATE BANK
(*Suby of* ZIONS BANCORPORATION) ★
230 Las Vegas Blvd S # 100, Las Vegas, NV 89101-5712
Tel (702) 382-1803 *Founded/Ownrshp* 1985
Sales NA *EMP* 922
SIC 6022 State commercial banks; State commercial banks
Pr: Dallas Haun
Pr: Kathy Asetta
Pr: Kelly Hahn
Pr: Sally Lanzalaco
Pr: Becky Petring
Pr: Katherine Powell
Pr: Kent Rose
Pr: Donna Sebastian
Pr: Ruth Worsley
**CFO:* Jacquelyn A Williams
Treas: Brianna McCullough
**Treas:* Terry Shirey
Bd of Dir: John Gisi
Ofcr: Miyone Ennis
Ofcr: Angela Nelson
Ofcr: Raymond Vallejos
Ex VP: Thomas Elmer
Ex VP: Bruce Hillier
Ex VP: Robert Hillier
Ex VP: Craig Kirkland
**Ex VP:* Jerry Martin

D-U-N-S 04-165-4195 IMP
NEVADA SYSTEM OF HIGHER EDUCATION
(*Suby of* EXECUTIVE OFFICE OF STATE OF NEVADA) ★
2601 Enterprise Rd, Reno, NV 89512-1666
Tel (775) 784-4901 *Founded/Ownrshp* 1864
Sales 628.0MMᴱ *EMP* 8,000
SIC 8221 9411 University; Community college; Administration of educational programs; ; University; Administration of educational programs;
CEO: Daniel Klaich
Pr: Rene Cantu
Ofcr: Sean Thompson
VP: Lois Becker
VP: Marylin Delamont
VP: Jim Labuda
Board of Directors: Howard Rosenberg, Mark Alden, Steve Sisolak, Dr Stavros Anthony Phd, Bret Whipple, Michael Wixom Chair, Cedric Crear, Thalia M Dondero, Dorothy S Gallagher, Jason Geddes, Ron Knecht, James Dean Leavitt

D-U-N-S 07-622-9871
NEVADA TITLE CO
2500 N Buffalo Dr Ste 150, Las Vegas, NV 89128-7854
Tel (702) 251-5000 *Founded/Ownrshp* 1979
Sales 87.0MMᴱ *EMP* 220
SIC 6541 Title abstract offices; Title abstract offices
Ch Bd: Terrence L Wright
**Pr:* Jeffrey T Harris
CFO: Liz Vandenberg
**Sec:* Lisbet Vandenburg
Ofcr: Shannon Ambur
Ofcr: Judy Armstrong
Ofcr: Mary Boland
Ofcr: Michele Dobar
Ofcr: Michele Eaton
Ofcr: Debbie Milton
Ofcr: Karen Patton
Ofcr: Michelle Robbins
VP: Eileen Bechtol
VP: Dawn Massaro
VP: Travis Nelson
VP: Robert Ray
VP: Andre Williams
Board of Directors: Tom Mangione, Nikki Wilcox

D-U-N-S 96-859-9852
NEVADA TRIO INC
PETRO STOPPING CENTERS
24601 Center Ridge Rd # 200, Westlake, OH 44145-5634
Tel (440) 808-9100 *Founded/Ownrshp* 1994
Sales 52.7MMᴱ *EMP* 136
SIC 5172 Petroleum products; Petroleum products
CEO: James A Cardwell Sr

D-U-N-S 04-622-9720
NEVADA YELLOW CAB CORP
5225 W Post Rd, Las Vegas, NV 89118-4331
Tel (702) 873-8012 *Founded/Ownrshp* 1980
Sales 75.8MMᴱ *EMP* 1,500
SIC 4121 Taxicabs; Taxicabs
Pr: David Willden
CFO: Gene Auffert
**Sec:* Harry Eliades
**VP:* Milton I Schwartz
Genl Couns: Marc Gordon

D-U-N-S 00-743-4615 IMP
NEVAMAR CO LLC
NEVAMAR DISTRIBUTORS
(*Suby of* PANOLAM INDUSTRIES INTERNATIONAL INC) ★
20 Progress Dr, Shelton, CT 06484-6216
Tel (203) 925-1556 *Founded/Ownrshp* 2002
Sales 126.7MMᴱ *EMP* 1,000
SIC 3089 5162 Panels, building: plastic; Plastics materials & basic shapes; Panels, building: plastic; Plastics materials & basic shapes

NEVAMAR DISTRIBUTORS
See NEVAMAR CO LLC

D-U-N-S 00-631-2920 IMP
NEVCO INC
301 E Harris Ave, Greenville, IL 62246-2193
Tel (618) 664-0360 *Founded/Ownrshp* 1934
Sales 28.4MMᴱ *EMP* 92ᴱ
SIC 3993 Scoreboards, electric
Pr: Gayla Moore
**CFO:* Dan Phalen
Ex VP: Michael Lane
QA Dir: Eric Haugland
Manager: Scott Butler
Sales Asso: Michael Spiezio

NEVCO LEASING DIVISION
See NEUVILLE MOTORS INC

NEVELE GRAND HOTEL
See NEVELE HOTEL LLC

D-U-N-S 00-697-7102
NEVELE HOTEL LLC
NEVELE GRAND HOTEL
1 Nevele Rd, Ellenville, NY 12428-2101
Tel (845) 647-6000 *Founded/Ownrshp* 1997
Sales 8.0MMᴱ *EMP* 350ᴱ
SIC 7011 Resort hotel; Resort hotel

D-U-N-S 12-978-0537
NEVELL GROUP INC
N G I
3001 Entp St Ste 200, Brea, CA 92821
Tel (714) 579-7501 *Founded/Ownrshp* 2002
Sales 102.6MMᴱ *EMP* 350
Accts Jlk Partners Llp Tustin Cali
SIC 1542 Commercial & office building, new construction; Commercial & office building, new construction
Pr: Michael J Nevell
**CFO:* Bryan Bodine
**Ex VP:* Therese Belisle
**Sr VP:* Bruce Pasqua
**VP:* Greg Thomas
Exec: Carl Fernald
Exec: Rich Holloway
Exec: David Kaiser
Exec: R J Knutson
Netwrk Mgr: Heather Charest

D-U-N-S 03-015-1583
NEVILL DOCUMENT SOLUTIONS LLC (TX)
2825 Story Rd W, Irving, TX 75038-5268
Tel (469) 574-0041 *Founded/Ownrshp* 1975, 2012
Sales 31.7MMᴱ *EMP* 100
SIC 5044 Office equipment
Pr: Reed Melnick
VP: Yong Sharpe
IT Man: Jay Kondorss
VP Sls: Karen Enriquez
Sls Mgr: Roberto Arteaga
Sales Asso: Matthew Garnett
Sales Asso: Lea Webb

D-U-N-S 00-433-4157 IMP
NEVILLE CHEMICAL CO (PA)
2800 Neville Rd, Pittsburgh, PA 15225-1496
Tel (412) 331-4200 *Founded/Ownrshp* 1925
Sales 35.5MMᴱ *EMP* 240ᴱ
SIC 2821 2869

NEVIN LABS
See DENTALEZ ALABAMA INC

D-U-N-S 84-744-2860
NEVINS LEWBEL PROPERTY MANAGEMENT INC
920 Garden St Ste A, Santa Barbara, CA 93101-7465
Tel (805) 963-2884 *Founded/Ownrshp* 1994
Sales 6.7MMᴱ *EMP* 350
SIC 6531 Real estate managers; Real estate managers
Pr: Michael S Lewbel
**VP:* Henry Nevins
Dist Mgr: Chad Barron
Sales Exec: David Bore

D-U-N-S 92-659-9155
NEVRO CORP
1800 Bridge Pkwy, Redwood City, CA 94065-1164
Tel (650) 251-0005 *Founded/Ownrshp* 2006
Sales 32.5MM *EMP* 132
Accts Pricewaterhousecoopers Llp S
Tkr Sym NVRO *Exch* NYS
SIC 3841 Surgical & medical instruments
Ch Bd: Michael Demane
Pr: Rami Elghandour
CFO: Andrew H Galligan
Chf Mktg O: David Caraway
Sr VP: Andre Walker
VP: Balakrishnan Shankar
Assoc Dir: Frances Rubenstein
Assoc Dir: Denise Taylor
Dir Bus: Katherine Bock
Dir IT: Jeff Wilson
QI Cn Mgr: Wye Chok
Board of Directors: Ali Behbahani, Lisa Earnhardt, Frank Fischer, Wilfred E Jaeger, Shawn T McCormick, Nathan B Pliam, Brad Vale

D-U-N-S 17-124-5280
NEW AA HOLDINGS INC
AMERICAN ACCESS CASUALTY
2211 Butterfield Rd # 200, Downers Grove, IL 60515-1493
Tel (773) 527-6621 *Founded/Ownrshp* 1999
Sales NA *EMP* 100
SIC 6331 Fire, marine & casualty insurance
Pr: Daniel C Cummings
CFO: Steve Szubert
Sr VP: Sandra Hayes
**VP:* David Blum
VP: Sam Cardullo
Prgrm Mgr: Steve Harlow
CIO: Kevin Rooney
QA Dir: Lakshmi Abbaraju
Dir IT: Emily Winters
Netwrk Mgr: Chris Vanallman
Mktg Dir: Michelle Thibault

D-U-N-S 13-838-2960
NEW ACTON MOBILE INDUSTRIES LLC
809 Glen Eagles Ct # 300, Baltimore, MD 21286-2202
Tel (410) 931-9100 *Founded/Ownrshp* 2014
Sales 39.7MM^E EMP 165
SIC 7519 Trailer rental; Trailer rental
Pr: Ingrid West
**COO:* Rodney Shrader
Ex VP: Collier Beall
VP Admn: Marietta Adamo
**CIO:* Eddie Jenkins
DP Exec: Katy Giannelli
Sales Asso: Karen Grondin

NEW ADVISORY GP L.L.C.
See PJT PARTNERS HOLDINGS LP

D-U-N-S 62-387-5114
NEW AFFIRMATIVE LLC
4450 Sojourn Dr Ste 500, Addison, TX 75001-5094
Tel (972) 728-6300 *Founded/Ownrshp* 2005
Sales NA EMP 1,269
SIC 6331 Automobile insurance; Automobile insurance
Ch Bd: Kevin R Callahan

D-U-N-S 13-542-2207 IMP
NEW AGE BEVERAGES LLC
NEWAGE BEVERAGE
1700 E 68th Ave, Denver, CO 80229-7303
Tel (303) 289-8655 *Founded/Ownrshp* 2003
Sales 36.4MM^E EMP 76
SIC 5182 Wine & distilled beverages; Wine & distilled beverages
CFO: Charles Ence

D-U-N-S 04-286-0478 IMP
NEW AGE INDUSTRIAL CORP INC (KS)
16788 Us Highway 36, Norton, KS 67654-5488
Tel (785) 877-5121 *Founded/Ownrshp* 1966
Sales 54.2MM^E EMP 155
SIC 3441 3444 3556 2542 Fabricated structural metal; Sheet metalwork; Food products machinery; Partitions & fixtures, except wood; Fabricated structural metal; Sheet metalwork; Food products machinery; Partitions & fixtures, except wood
Pr: Larry Nelson
**VP:* Thomas Sharp
VP: Tom Vajcovec
Sls Dir: Shari Kaplan

D-U-N-S 10-313-3211
NEW AGE INVESTMENTS INC
METRO NISSAN OF MONTCLAIR
9440 Autoplex St, Montclair, CA 91763-2300
Tel (909) 625-8990 *Founded/Ownrshp* 1970
Sales 125.5MM^E EMP 366
SIC 5511 Automobiles, new & used; Automobiles, new & used
CEO: David A Marvin
CFO: Michelle Lowe
**Sec:* Susie Mc Nutt
Genl Mgr: Cordy Cerami
Genl Mgr: Alvarez Katalina
Dir IT: Naveen Kathuria
Dir IT: Shane Powell
Sls Mgr: Jodie Caccavale
Sls Mgr: Carlos Carillo
Sls Mgr: Joe Rodriguez

NEW AGE LA MIRADA INN
See KAM SANG CO INC

D-U-N-S 09-826-1068
NEW AGE METAL FABRICATING CO INC
NAMF
26 Daniel Rd, Fairfield, NJ 07004-2522
Tel (973) 227-9107 *Founded/Ownrshp* 1979
Sales 20.1MM^E EMP 70
SIC 3444 Sheet metalwork
Pr: Mario Costa
**VP:* Jeff Lechowicz

D-U-N-S 78-277-3170
NEW AGE TRANSPORTATION DISTRIBUTION AND WAREHOUSING INC
1881 Rose Rd, Lake Zurich, IL 60047-1552
Tel (847) 545-1894 *Founded/Ownrshp* 1989
Sales 43.9MM^E EMP 50
SIC 4731 Truck transportation brokers
Pr: Carolyn Gable
Pr: Chris Shelhamer
**VP:* Pam Troy
IT Man: Robin Rock

D-U-N-S 07-965-1675
NEW ALBANY CITY OF (INC)
NEW ALBNY-FLOYD CNTY DPRTMNT
311 Hauss Sq Ste 235, New Albany, IN 47150-3570
Tel (812) 948-5333 *Founded/Ownrshp* 1839
Sales NA EMP 350
SIC 9111 Mayors' offices; ; Mayors' offices;
Ex Dir: Scott Wood
Plnt Mgr: Randy Sikes

D-U-N-S 07-406-5061
NEW ALBANY FLOYD COUNTY CONSOLIDATED SCHOOL CORP
2813 Grant Line Rd, New Albany, IN 47150-2457
Tel (812) 949-4200 *Founded/Ownrshp* 1956
Sales 68.7MM^E EMP 1,800
SIC 8211

D-U-N-S 01-655-2101
NEW ALBANY MOTOR CO INC
COYLE CHEVROLET, GEO & DODGE
1801 Broadway St, Clarksville, IN 47129-7761
Tel (812) 948-7711 *Founded/Ownrshp* 1937
Sales 26.6MM^E EMP 65^E
SIC 5511 Automobiles, new & used; Pickups, new & used; Vans, new & used; Automobiles, new & used; Pickups, new & used; Vans, new & used
Pr: Michael Coyle
IT Man: Rhonda Straughn

D-U-N-S 55-726-2664
NEW ALBANY SCHOOL DISTRICT
203 State Highway 15 N, New Albany, MS 38652-5414
Tel (662) 534-1800 *Founded/Ownrshp* 2001
Sales 24.1MM EMP 325
SIC 8211 Private combined elementary & secondary school; Private combined elementary & secondary school
**Prin:* Jackie Ford
Pr Dir: Melanie Shannon

D-U-N-S 13-732-1126
NEW ALBANY SURGERY CENTER LLC
(*Suby of* MOUNT CARMEL HEALTH) ★
5040 Forest Dr Ste 100, New Albany, OH 43054-9187
Tel (614) 775-1616 *Founded/Ownrshp* 2001
Sales 23.4MM^E EMP 175
SIC 8062 General medical & surgical hospitals
Prin: Jacqueline A Primeau

D-U-N-S 17-423-1746 EXP
NEW ALBERTSONS INC
JEWEL-OSCO
(*Suby of* ALBERTSONS) ★
150 E Pierce Rd Ste 200, Itasca, IL 60143-1224
Tel (630) 948-6000 *Founded/Ownrshp* 2013
Sales 1.4MMM^E EMP 18,021^E
SIC 5411 5912 5331 Grocery stores; Supermarkets; Drug stores; Variety stores
CEO: Robert Miller

D-U-N-S 78-014-8537 IMP
NEW ALBERTSONS INC
ACME
(*Suby of* ALBERTSONS) ★
11840 Valley View Rd, Eden Prairie, MN 55344-3643
Tel (952) 828-4000 *Founded/Ownrshp* 2008
Sales 4.7MMM^E EMP 36,822
SIC 5411 Supermarkets, chain; Supermarkets, chain
Pr: Michael L Jackson
**CFO:* Pamela K Knous
**Ex VP:* David L Boehnen
VP: Yolanda Scharton

NEW ALBNY-FLOYD CNTY DPRTMNT
See NEW ALBANY CITY OF (INC)

D-U-N-S 12-170-8747
NEW ALTERNATIVES INC
3589 4th Ave, San Diego, CA 92103-4912
Tel (619) 543-0293 *Founded/Ownrshp* 1978
Sales 50.4MM EMP 1,000
SIC 8322 Child related social services; Child related social services
Ex Dir: Michael Bruich

NEW AMEREN ENERGY RESOURCES
See ILLINOIS POWER GENERATING CO

NEW AMEREN ENERGY RESOURCES
See ILLINOIS POWER RESOURCES LLC

NEW AMERICAN FUNDING
See BROKER SOLUTIONS INC

D-U-N-S 13-518-1993
NEW APPLE INC
APPLEBEE'S
170 Wind Chime Ct, Raleigh, NC 27615-6433
Tel (919) 870-0513 *Founded/Ownrshp* 2000
Sales 33.6MM^E EMP 1,500
SIC 5812 Restaurant, family: chain; Restaurant, family: chain
Pr: Michael Olander

D-U-N-S 02-619-2968
NEW AQUA LLC
AQUA SYSTEMS
7785 E Us Highway 36, Avon, IN 46123-7973
Tel (614) 265-9000 *Founded/Ownrshp* 1997
Sales 22.2MM^E EMP 130
SIC 3589 7389 5074 5149 5499 5999 Water filters & softeners, household type; Water purification equipment, household type; Water treatment equipment, industrial; Water softener service; Water purification equipment; Water softeners; Water, distilled; Water: distilled mineral or spring; Water purification equipment; Water filters & softeners, household type; Water purification equipment, household type; Water treatment equipment, industrial; Water softener service; Water purification equipment; Water softeners; Water, distilled; Water: distilled mineral or spring; Water purification equipment
CFO: Don Line
CFO: Thomas O'Leary
CTO: Kent Wilson
IT Man: Renee Byrd
IT Man: Erik Junker
Opers Mgr: Chris Utterback
Opers Mgr: Wayne Waterman
Sales Exec: Shawn Massie

D-U-N-S 07-929-3442
NEW ASURION CORP
648 Grassmere Park, Nashville, TN 37211-3663
Tel (615) 459-7460 *Founded/Ownrshp* 2008
Sales NA EMP 11,011^E
SIC 6331 Property damage insurance
CEO: Bret Comolli

D-U-N-S 16-963-3943 IMP
NEW ATHENS GENERATING CO LLC
ATHENS GENERATING PLANT
9300 Us Hwy 9w, Athens, NY 12015
Tel (518) 945-3750 *Founded/Ownrshp* 2003
Sales 43.6MM^E EMP 29
SIC 4911 Generation, electric power
Pr: Paul A Farr
IT Man: Matt Whalen
Opers Mgr: Timothy Pearson
Plnt Mgr: Daniel Devinney
Plnt Mgr: Dan D Nney

D-U-N-S 79-022-2145 EXP
NEW ATICO INTERNATIONAL LIMITED CORP
501 S Andrews Ave, Fort Lauderdale, FL 33301-2831
Tel (954) 779-2500 *Founded/Ownrshp* 1987
Sales 46.7MM^E EMP 150
SIC 5199 General merchandise, non-durable; General merchandise, non-durable
Pr: Kenneth P Ross

D-U-N-S 11-055-5260
NEW ATLANTIC CONTRACTING INC
2635 Reynolda Rd, Winston Salem, NC 27106-3834
Tel (336) 759-7440 *Founded/Ownrshp* 2002
Sales 22.5MM^E EMP 36
SIC 1542 Commercial & office building contractors; Institutional building construction
Pr: John R Adkins
COO: Angela Hutchins
**Ch:* David O Walters
VP: Beth Binkley
**VP:* Charles Bruns
VP: Chip Bruns
**VP:* Jay Morgan
**VP:* John Morrison
Snr PM: Jesse Walters
Board of Directors: Jesse Walters

D-U-N-S 01-083-2384
NEW AVENUES TO INDEPENDENCE INC
17608 Euclid Ave, Cleveland, OH 44112-1216
Tel (216) 481-1907 *Founded/Ownrshp* 1956
Sales 14.2MM EMP 350
Accts Howard Wershbale & Co Clevela
SIC 8361 Home for the mentally retarded; Home for the physically handicapped; Home for the mentally retarded; Home for the physically handicapped
Pr: Tom Lewins
CIO: David Carr
Sales Asso: Carmen Siciliano
Pgrm Dir: Gail Remeika

D-U-N-S 07-974-5045
NEW BAKERY OF ZANESVILLE LLC
(*Suby of* EAST BALT OHIO LLC) ★
1 Dave Thomas Blvd, Dublin, OH 43017-5452
Tel (614) 764-3100 *Founded/Ownrshp* 2015
Sales 10.2MM^E EMP 345^E
SIC 2051 Bread, cake & related products

NEW BALANCE ATHLETIC SHOE INC
See NEW BALANCE ATHLETICS INC

D-U-N-S 05-888-5963 IMP/EXP
NEW BALANCE ATHLETICS INC
NEW BALANCE ATHLETIC SHOE INC
(*Suby of* NEW BALANCE INC) ★
100 Guest St Fl 5, Boston, MA 02135-2028
Tel (617) 783-4000 *Founded/Ownrshp* 1972
Sales 1.6MMM^E EMP 2,200
SIC 5139 Athletic shoes, except rubber or plastic; Women's footwear, except athletic; Men's footwear, except athletic; Footwear, athletic
Pr: Rob Demartini
Pr: Barry Gutwillig
**CFO:* John Withee
**Ch:* James S Davis
**Treas:* Kevin Doyle
Ex VP: Christopher Ladd
Ex VP: Joe Preston
Ex VP: John Wilson
VP: Ken Benser
VP: Kevin Holian
VP: Martin Walter

D-U-N-S 01-795-3639 IMP
NEW BALANCE INC
20 Guest St Ste 1000, Boston, MA 02135-2088
Tel (617) 783-4000 *Founded/Ownrshp* 1972
Sales 2.2MMM^E EMP 4,000
SIC 5139 Footwear, athletic; Footwear, athletic
CEO: Robert T Demartini
**CEO:* James S Davis
**CFO:* Bill Hayden
Ofcr: Brian Kay
Ex VP: Fran Allen
Ex VP: Laura Bonfitto
**Ex VP:* Anne Davis
Ex VP: Paul Heffernan
Ex VP: Chris Ladd
**Ex VP:* John Withee
VP: Christine Madigan

D-U-N-S 07-571-9187
NEW BEDFORD CITY OF (INC)
133 William St Unit 208, New Bedford, MA 02740-6113
Tel (508) 979-1400 *Founded/Ownrshp* 1787
Sales NA EMP 3,657
Accts Hague Sahady & Co Pc
SIC 9111 Mayors' offices; ; Mayors' offices;
**Treas:* Renee Fernandes-Abbott
Ofcr: Christopher Cotter
Exec: Elizabeth Treadup
Dir IT: Robert Tetreault
Snr Mgr: Christina Connelly

D-U-N-S 96-166-4708
NEW BEDFORD PUBLIC SCHOOLS
455 County St, New Bedford, MA 02740-5194
Tel (508) 997-4511 *Founded/Ownrshp* 2010
Sales 21.7MM^E EMP 200^E
SIC 8211 Elementary & secondary schools; Public elementary & secondary schools
Dir Sec: Peter Cabral
Teacher Pr: Heather Emsley

D-U-N-S 14-279-6551
NEW BEDFORD REHABILITATION HOSPITAL LLC
(*Suby of* VIBRA HEALTHCARE LLC) ★
4499 Acushnet Ave, New Bedford, MA 02745-4707
Tel (508) 985-9083 *Founded/Ownrshp* 2004
Sales 30.9MM EMP 240
SIC 8069 Alcoholism rehabilitation hospital; Alcoholism rehabilitation hospital
CEO: Edward Leary
Dir Rx: Jeff Newberg
Dir Bus: Gay Martin
Off Mgr: Jen Amaral
Mktg Dir: Joan Thomas
Surgeon: Muiz Khir
Phys Thrpy: Pam Gouveia
HC Dir: Lisa Carvara

D-U-N-S 12-569-8782 EXP
NEW BEDFORD TECHNOLOGY LLC
2424 Armour Rd, Worthington, MN 56187-2661
Tel (507) 372-5558 *Founded/Ownrshp* 1998
Sales 50.7MM^E EMP 90
SIC 5211 Lumber products
CEO: Brian Larsen
**Pr:* Jeff Breitzman
Exec: Patty Grimmius
Opers Mgr: Bernie Platt
Sls Mgr: Jesse Hooge
Sls Mgr: Doug Johnson

D-U-N-S 00-485-4040
NEW BEGINNINGS SCHOOLS FOUNDATION (LA)
2045 Lakeshore Dr, New Orleans, LA 70122-3534
Tel (504) 280-2311 *Founded/Ownrshp* 2004
Sales 22.9MM EMP 99^E
SIC 8641 Civic social & fraternal associations; Civic social & fraternal associations
CFO: Karen Craig
**Prin:* Fitzpatrick S Nedd

NEW BEGINNINGS WEIGHT LOSS PRO
See VIRTUA HEALTH INC

NEW BEGINNINGS WEIGHT LOSS PRO
See VIRTUA MEDICAL GROUP PA

D-U-N-S 78-220-5611 IMP
NEW BELGIUM BREWING CO INC
500 Linden St, Fort Collins, CO 80524-2457
Tel (970) 221-0524 *Founded/Ownrshp* 1990
Sales 77.9MM^E EMP 210^E
Accts Ehrhardt Keefe Steiner & Hottm
SIC 2082 Beer (alcoholic beverage); Beer (alcoholic beverage)
Pr: Kimberly Jordan
CFO: David McMahon
**CFO:* Jennifer Vervier-Orgolini
Creative D: Melyssa Glassman
Creative D: Melyssa Mead
Mng Dir: Dick Knight
Area Mgr: Brian Corrie
Genl Mgr: Nate Turner
CIO: Phil Tew
QA Dir: Christian Holbrook
QA Dir: Mandy Miller
Board of Directors: Peter Bouckaert, Floris Delee, Jeff Lebesch, Greg Owsley, Nate Turner

D-U-N-S 07-894-8288 IMP
NEW BERLIN PLASTICS INC
5725 S Westridge Dr, New Berlin, WI 53151-7952
Tel (262) 784-3120 *Founded/Ownrshp* 2001
Sales 42.6MM^E EMP 125
SIC 3089 Injection molding of plastics; Injection molding of plastics
Pr: Jeffery P Held
**CFO:* Joy Hertlein
**VP:* Mark Siewert

D-U-N-S 07-894-8544
NEW BERLIN PUBLIC SCHOOLS INC
SCHOOL DISTRICT OF NEW BERLIN
4333 S Sunnyslope Rd, New Berlin, WI 53151-6844
Tel (262) 789-6200 *Founded/Ownrshp* 1961
Sales 44.4MM^E EMP 535
SIC 8211 Public junior high school; Public senior high school; Public elementary school; Public junior high school; Public senior high school; Public elementary school
Dir IT: Brandon Kostolni
Prd Mgr: Barbara Schemmel
Schl Brd P: Dave Maxey

D-U-N-S 00-431-9992
NEW BERRY INC
2408 Evans City Rd, Harmony, PA 16037-7724
Tel (724) 452-8040 *Founded/Ownrshp* 1983
Sales 20.0MM^E EMP 100
SIC 3548

NEW BERRY TRADING
See WIN WOO TRADING LLC

D-U-N-S 14-476-2002
NEW BOSTON FUND IV INC
NEW BOSTON REAL ESTATE
75 State St Ste 1410, Boston, MA 02109-1943
Tel (617) 723-7760 *Founded/Ownrshp* 1993
Sales 32.6MM^E EMP 135
SIC 6552 6799 Land subdividers & developers, residential; Real estate investors, except property operators
Pr: Jerome L Rappaport Jr
COO: Kenneth A Munkacy
CFO: Michael J Doherty
CFO: Timmothy Medlock
**Treas:* James W Rappaport
Chf Inves: James P Kelleher
Chf Inves: William McAvoy
Sr VP: Michael J Buckley
Sr VP: Pryse R Elam
Sr VP: Gary J Hofstetter
Sr VP: Timothy Shine
Sr VP: Eric Vandusen
VP: Mark Runde
VP: Paul Stuart

D-U-N-S 01-836-0912
NEW BOSTON MANAGEMENT SERVICES INC
NEW BOSTON REAL ESTATE
75 State St Lbby 2, Boston, MA 02109-1948
Tel (617) 723-7760 *Founded/Ownrshp* 1995
Sales 24.2MM^E EMP 100
SIC 6552 6531 Land subdividers & developers, residential; Real estate agents & managers
Pr: Jerome L Rappaport Jr
COO: John W Gomez
**CFO:* Joseph Harris
**Treas:* James W Rappaport
VP: Dana C Rowan
VP: Paul Stuart
Off Mgr: Mike Norris

NEW BOSTON REAL ESTATE
See NEW BOSTON MANAGEMENT SERVICES INC

NEW BOSTON REAL ESTATE
See NEW BOSTON FUND IV INC

D-U-N-S 07-048-0074
NEW BRAUNFELS INDEPENDENT SCHOOL DISTRICT
430 W Mill St, New Braunfels, TX 78130-7915
Tel (830) 643-5700 Founded/Ownrshp 1900
Sales 48.6MM^E EMP 812
SIC 8211 Public elementary & secondary schools; Public junior high school; Public senior high school; Public elementary & secondary schools; Public junior high school; Public senior high school
Pr: Rigo Montero
VP: Sherry Harrison
Pr Dir: Rebecca Villarriel
Schl Brd P: James Bettersworth
HC Dir: Karen Schwind

D-U-N-S 02-687-7050
NEW BRAUNFELS SMOKEHOUSE INC
146 S State Highway 46, New Braunfels, TX 78130-3216
Tel (830) 625-7316 Founded/Ownrshp 1928
Sales 21.8MM^E EMP 119
SIC 5421 5812 Meat markets, including freezer provisioners; Restaurant, family: independent
Ch Bd: Dudley Snyder
*Pr: John Dudley Snyder
*Treas: Susan Snyder
*Sec: Susan D Snyder
*VP: Michael Dietert
Exec: Barbara Henk
Plnt Mgr: Clint Skarovsky
Plnt Mgr: Rocky Tays
Mktg Dir: Hale Snyder

D-U-N-S 03-834-6169
NEW BRAUNFELS UTILITIES (TX)
263 Main Plz, New Braunfels, TX 78130-5135
Tel (830) 608-8867 Founded/Ownrshp 1942
Sales 140.9MM^E EMP 210^E
Accts Holtman Wagner & Company Llp
SIC 4911 4941 4952 Distribution, electric power; Water supply; Sewerage systems; Distribution, electric power; Water supply; Sewerage systems
CEO: Paula J Difonzo
Trst: John Harrell
Dir Soc: Gretchen Reuwer
*Prin: Rick Tobias
*Ex Dir: Al Kaufmann
Dir IT: Kurt Knettel

D-U-N-S 03-992-6746
NEW BRIGHTON AREA SCHOOL DISTRICT
3225 43rd St, New Brighton, PA 15066-2655
Tel (724) 843-1795 Founded/Ownrshp 1940
Sales 16.9MM^E EMP 290
SIC 8211 Public elementary & secondary schools; Public elementary & secondary schools
Prin: Joe Guarino
Board of Directors: Joanne Brown, Linda Emert, Sharon Kovach, Dennis Pasquale

D-U-N-S 02-077-6910
NEW BRUNSWICK PUBLIC SCHOOLS
268 Baldwin St, New Brunswick, NJ 08901-2947
Tel (732) 246-6344 Founded/Ownrshp 1900
Sales 87.4MM^E EMP 1,352
SIC 8211 Public elementary & secondary schools; High school, junior or senior; Public elementary & secondary schools; High school, junior or senior
Dir IT: Del Kunert
Instr Medi: Nicole Sette

D-U-N-S 00-215-7782 IMP
NEW BRUNSWICK SCIENTIFIC CO INC (NJ)
(Suby of EPPENDORF HOLDING INC) ★
175 Freshwater Blvd, Enfield, CT 06082-4444
Tel (732) 287-1200 Founded/Ownrshp 1946, 2007
Sales 51.5MM^E EMP 437
SIC 3821 Laboratory apparatus & furniture; Shakers & stirrers; Sterilizers; Chemical laboratory apparatus; Laboratory apparatus & furniture; Shakers & stirrers; Sterilizers; Chemical laboratory apparatus
Pr: James T Orcutt
*CFO: Thomas Bocchino
*CFO: Christian Jaaks
*VP: William Dunne
*VP: Dr Lee Eppstein
MIS Dir: Derderian Kiko
Ql Cn Mgr: Luis Velez

D-U-N-S 06-317-5871
NEW BRUNSWICK-EDISON RECREATIONAL VEHICLES INC
OPEN ROAD HONDA/ISUZU/MAZDA
50 Us Highway 1, Edison, NJ 08817-5030
Tel (732) 985-0290 Founded/Ownrshp 1972
Sales 21.6MM^E EMP 75
SIC 5511 Automobiles, new & used; Automobiles, new & used
Pr: W Rodman Ryan
*Sec: Dianne Ryan

D-U-N-S 05-739-3464
NEW BUFFALO CONCRETE PRODUCTS
OZINGA READY MIX
825 S Whittaker St, New Buffalo, MI 49117-1771
Tel (269) 469-2515 Founded/Ownrshp 1971
Sales 22.8MM^E EMP 350
SIC 3273 3271 Ready-mixed concrete; Blocks, concrete or cinder: standard; Ready-mixed concrete; Blocks, concrete or cinder: standard
Pt: Richard Wittenberg
Genl Mgr: Mike Vasta
Off Mgr: David Lowe
Plnt Mgr: Timve Stephenson

NEW BURGH ENLARGED CY SCHL DST
See NEWBURGH CITY SCHOOL DISTRICT

D-U-N-S 80-375-0439 IMP
NEW C F & I INC
ROCKEY MOUNTAIN STEEL MILLS
(Suby of EVRAZ INC NA) ★
200 E Randolph St # 7800, Chicago, IL 60601-6436
Tel (312) 533-3555 Founded/Ownrshp 1993
Sales 78.0MM^E EMP 750
SIC 3312 Blast furnaces & steel mills; Blast furnaces & steel mills
VP: Rob Simon
*Ch: William Swindels
Treas: Jeff Stewart
*VP: Jennifer Murray
VP: Steven Rowan
VP Opers: David Cranston
Trfc Mgr: Brad Trumbull

D-U-N-S 07-538-9999
NEW CANAAN COUNTRY SCHOOL INC
545 Ponus Rdg, New Canaan, CT 06840-3406
Tel (203) 972-0771 Founded/Ownrshp 1919
Sales 26.2MM EMP 110
Accts Capossela Cohen Llc Southport
SIC 8211 Private elementary school; Private junior high school; Private elementary school; Private junior high school
Prin: Timothy Bazemore

D-U-N-S 07-219-7676
NEW CANEY INDEPENDENT SCHOOL DISTRICT
21580 Loop 494, New Caney, TX 77357-8239
Tel (281) 577-8600 Founded/Ownrshp 1937
Sales 62.6MM^E EMP 1,250
SIC 8211 Public elementary school; Public elementary school; Public junior high school; Public senior high school; Public special education school
*CFO: Clisty Vaden
Admn Mgr: Janet Adare
MIS Dir: Dan Reed
Netwrk Mgr: Doug Crosby
Pr Dir: Melecio Franco
Pr Dir: Cindy Reynolds
Instr Medi: Leslie Bell
HC Dir: Chiristina Nunez
Pgrm Dir: Sheri Lowe
Snr Mgr: Deanie Murry

D-U-N-S 17-951-5168 EXP
NEW CARBON CO LLC
CARBON'S GOLDEN MALTED
4101 Wlliam Richardson Dr, South Bend, IN 46628-9485
Tel (574) 247-2270 Founded/Ownrshp 2014
Sales 50.0MM EMP 240
SIC 2045 2041 5149 Pancake mixes, prepared: from purchased flour; Flour & other grain mill products; Flour
Sr VP: Rich Cleaver
Treas: Joseph Crowley

D-U-N-S 02-734-6956
NEW CASTLE AREA SCHOOL DISTRICT
420 Fern St, New Castle, PA 16101-2684
Tel (724) 656-4757 Founded/Ownrshp 1911
Sales 38.7MM^E EMP 500
Accts Philip Weiner And Company Ltd
SIC 8211 Public elementary & secondary schools; Public elementary & secondary schools
Schl Brd P: David Digiammarino
Schl Brd P: Stacey Fleo

NEW CASTLE BUILDING PRODUCTS
See S & K DISTRIBUTION LLC

D-U-N-S 07-206-5287
NEW CASTLE COMMUNITY SCHOOL BUILDING CORP
322 Elliott Ave, New Castle, IN 47362-4899
Tel (765) 521-7201 Founded/Ownrshp 1910
Sales 40.1MM^E EMP 620
SIC 8211 Public elementary & secondary schools; Public elementary school; Public junior high school; Public senior high school; Public elementary & secondary schools; Public elementary school; Public junior high school; Public senior high school
Pr: Richard W Myers
Treas: Jane Kellam-Tolllett
Dir IT: Dustin Chew

D-U-N-S 60-908-8059 IMP
■ **NEW CASTLE CORP**
EXCALIBUR HOTEL & CASINO
(Suby of MANDALAY BAY RESORT AND CASINO) ★
3850 Las Vegas Blvd S, Las Vegas, NV 89109-4324
Tel (702) 597-7777 Founded/Ownrshp 2005
Sales 71.8MM^E EMP 4,200
SIC 5812 7011 Eating places; Casino hotel; Eating places; Casino hotel
Ch Bd: Jim Murran
*Pr: Rene West
VP: Michelle Borgel
Mng Dir: Lorenzo Herrera
Sls Mgr: Linda Lang

D-U-N-S 96-850-7442
NEW CASTLE COUNTY VOCATIONAL SCHOOL DISTRICT
1417 Newport Rd, Wilmington, DE 19804-3425
Tel (302) 995-8000 Founded/Ownrshp 1978
Sales 26.1MM^E EMP 990
SIC 8249 Vocational schools; Vocational schools

D-U-N-S 05-349-1812
NEW CASTLE GOLF LLC
GOLF CLUB AT NEW CASTLE
15500 6 Penny Ln, Newcastle, WA 98059-3086
Tel (425) 793-4653 Founded/Ownrshp 1994
Sales 20.4MM^E EMP 185
SIC 1629 Golf course construction; Golf course construction
Pr: Scott Oki
CFO: Mark Chriest
VP: Nancy Carlstrom
Exec: Jesse Olsen
Sls Mgr: Brooke Byrne
Sls Mgr: Keith Williams

D-U-N-S 95-915-7652
NEW CASTLE HOTELS LLC
2 Corporate Dr Ste 154, Shelton, CT 06484-6253
Tel (203) 925-8370 Founded/Ownrshp 1994
Sales 139.8MM^E EMP 4,200
SIC 7011 8741 8742 Hotel, franchised; Hotel or motel management; Industry specialist consultants; Hotel, franchised; Hotel or motel management; Industry specialist consultants
*COO: Gerry Chase
Treas: Judith Scofield
Ofcr: Robin Kramme
VP: Lisa Blank
VP: Vince Varrett
VP: Alan Zaccario
VP: Caitlin Zaccario
Exec: Mariam Barieri
Dir Bus: Charles Snyder
Admn Mgr: Lisa Besescheck
Genl Mgr: Vince Barrett

D-U-N-S 01-046-6688
■ **NEW CASTLE INDUSTRIES INC**
(Suby of NORDSON XALOY INC) ★
1399 County Line Rd, New Castle, PA 16101-2955
Tel (724) 654-2603 Founded/Ownrshp 2003
Sales 20.6MM^E EMP 321
SIC 3451 3471 Screw machine products; Chromium plating of metals or formed products; Screw machine products; Chromium plating of metals or formed products
Pr: Walter Cox
VP: Keith Young
VP Sls: Fred Scocchera

D-U-N-S 01-728-3750 IMP
NEW CASTLE MEGASTORE CORP (AZ)
2202 E University Dr # 1, Phoenix, AZ 85034-6810
Tel (480) 921-1005 Founded/Ownrshp 1987
Sales 29.8MM^E EMP 225
SIC 5632 5735 Women's dancewear, hosiery & lingerie; Lingerie & corsets (underwear); Video tapes, prerecorded; Women's dancewear, hosiery & lingerie; Lingerie & corsets (underwear); Video tapes, prerecorded
*Pr: Mark Franks
CFO: Brett Fredericks
*CFO: Brett Fredrick
*Ch: Vern Schweigert
VP Opers: Brandy Jefferson
Mktg Mgr: Roderick Nez
Mktg Mgr: Dean St Louis

D-U-N-S 79-115-2713
■ **NEW CASTLE TELEPHONE CO**
TDS
(Suby of TDS TELECOMMUNICATIONS CORP) ★
320 Salem Ave, New Castle, VA 24127
Tel (608) 831-1000 Founded/Ownrshp 1990
Sales 853.0MM^E EMP 99
SIC 4813 Telephone communication, except radio; Telephone communication, except radio
Pr: David Wittwer
*Treas: Paul Abraham
*VP: G Ronnie Barnes
*VP: Jerry Harms

D-U-N-S 07-213-3689
NEW CEDAR LANE NURSING HOME INC
(Suby of CONNECTICUT SUBACUTE LLC) ★
128 Cedar Ave, Waterbury, CT 06705-2700
Tel (203) 757-9271 Founded/Ownrshp 1992
Sales 4.0MM^E EMP 300
SIC 8051 Skilled nursing care facilities; Skilled nursing care facilities
Sr VP: Stuart Lindeman

D-U-N-S 82-957-8132
NEW CENTAUR LLC
CENTAUR GAMING
(Suby of CENTAUR HOLDINGS LLC) ★
10 W Market St Ste 2700, Indianapolis, IN 46204-2982
Tel (317) 656-8787 Founded/Ownrshp 2011
Sales 28.5MM^E EMP 1,010
SIC 8741 Administrative management; Administrative management
CEO: Roderick J Ratcliff
*CFO: Kurt E Wilson
Ex VP: Kurt Wilson

D-U-N-S 79-180-5633
NEW CENTER STAMPING INC
950 E Milwaukee St, Detroit, MI 48211-2008
Tel (313) 872-3500 Founded/Ownrshp 1992
Sales 38.2MM^E EMP 110
SIC 3465 Body parts, automobile: stamped metal; Body parts, automobile: stamped metal
CEO: Ronald Hall
*Pr: Ric Monkaba
*COO: Greg Smith
*CFO: Chris Garvey
*VP: Don Stein
Opers Mgr: Rick Barron
Prd Mgr: Perry Wilson

D-U-N-S 03-182-4154
NEW CENTURY AG
100 N Main St, Fortuna, ND 58844-9998
Tel (701) 834-2311 Founded/Ownrshp 1913
Sales 21.8MM EMP 90
SIC 5999 5989 Farm machinery; Farm equipment & supplies; Coal; Farm machinery; Farm equipment & supplies; Coal
Prin: Richard Larsen
Genl Mgr: Richard N Larsen

D-U-N-S 88-360-4787
NEW CENTURY AUTOS INC
NEW CENTURY VOLKSWAGEN
1220 S Brand Blvd, Glendale, CA 91204-2615
Tel (818) 552-6263 Founded/Ownrshp 1994
Sales 23.7MM^E EMP 60
SIC 5511 5521 Automobiles, new & used; Used car dealers; Automobiles, new & used; Used car dealers
Pr: Dennis Lin
Genl Mgr: Rene Williamson
Sls Mgr: Ronnie Soares

D-U-N-S 78-968-3034
NEW CENTURY BMW INC
1139 W Main St, Alhambra, CA 91801-3328
Tel (323) 283-3781 Founded/Ownrshp 1991
Sales 40.4MM^E EMP 85
SIC 5511 Automobiles, new & used; Automobiles, new & used
Pr: Frank Lin
*VP: Dennis Lin
Sls Mgr: Devon Hsieh
Sls Mgr: Stephen Pan

D-U-N-S 60-846-1021
NEW CENTURY FINANCIAL SERVICES INC
110 S Jefferson Rd # 104, Whippany, NJ 07981-1038
Tel (973) 753-9400 Founded/Ownrshp 1996
Sales 26.5MM EMP 15
Accts Warner Lott Duritza & Lowe
SIC 7389 Financial services; Financial services
CEO: Eric Sombers
*Pr: Lee Pressler
*Treas: Lauri Herman

NEW CENTURY FOOTWEAR
See SCHWARTZ & BENJAMIN INC

D-U-N-S 10-999-9636
NEW CENTURY TRANSPORTATION INC
45 E Park Dr, Mount Holly, NJ 08060-5123
Tel (609) 265-1110 Founded/Ownrshp 2000
Sales NA EMP 1,713
SIC 4213

NEW CENTURY VOLKSWAGEN
See NEW CENTURY AUTOS INC

D-U-N-S 17-359-1595
■ **NEW CHAPTER INC**
NEW CHARTER DISTRIBUTION
(Suby of PROCTER & GAMBLE CO) ★
90 Technology Dr, Brattleboro, VT 05301-9180
Tel (802) 257-0018 Founded/Ownrshp 2012
Sales 42.7MM^E EMP 220^E
SIC 2834 Vitamin preparations; Vitamin preparations
CEO: Larry Allgaier
*Pr: Mark Gavin
*Ch: Tom Newmark
Ex VP: Myron Lyskanycz
*VP: Ruth B Austin

D-U-N-S 96-962-0827
NEW CHARLOTTE CORP
600 E 4th St Fl 10, Charlotte, NC 28202-2816
Tel (704) 336-3992 Founded/Ownrshp 2011
Sales 38.0MM^E EMP 1
Accts Cherry Bekaert Llp Charlotte
SIC 7389 Financial services; Financial services
Pr: Greg Gaskins

NEW CHARTER DISTRIBUTION
See NEW CHAPTER INC

D-U-N-S 17-375-8269 IMP
NEW CHEMIC (US) INC
50 Chestnut Ridge Rd # 117, Montvale, NJ 07645-1814
Tel (201) 573-9220 Founded/Ownrshp 1995
Sales 27.9MM EMP 10
Accts Weisberg Mole Krantz & Goldf
SIC 5169 5122 Pharmaceuticals; Chemicals & allied products; Industrial chemicals; Chemicals & allied products; Pharmaceuticals
CEO: Gregory J Rummo

D-U-N-S 13-059-8238 IMP
■ **NEW CINGULAR WIRELESS SERVICES INC**
AT&T MOBILITY
(Suby of AT&T MOBILITY LLC) ★
7277 164th Ave Ne, Redmond, WA 98052-7823
Tel (425) 580-7764 Founded/Ownrshp 1987
Sales 7.1MMM^E EMP 31,000
SIC 4812 Cellular telephone services; Paging services; Cellular telephone services; Paging services
Pr: Michael G Keith
*CFO: Joseph McCabe Jr
CFO: Peter Ritcher
*Ex VP: William Hague
*Ex VP: Brian Shay
Sr VP: Steven L Elfman
Sr VP: Kendra Vandermeulen
*VP: Sean P Foley
Prin: Tina Hart
Ex Dir: Todd Wilson
Dir Sec: Linda Jensen

NEW CITY NISSAN
See HAWAII NISSAN INC

D-U-N-S 10-037-3534 IMP/EXP
NEW CLASSIC HOME FURNISHING INC
7351 Mcguire Ave, Fontana, CA 92336-1668
Tel (909) 484-7676 Founded/Ownrshp 2001
Sales 83.9MM EMP 80^E
SIC 5712 Furniture stores; Furniture stores
Pr: Jean Tong
CEO: Vicky Wang
VP: Michele McPherson

D-U-N-S 13-858-3161
NEW CO-OPERATIVE INC
MAPS
(Suby of NEW COOPERATIVE INC) ★
2626 1st Ave S, Fort Dodge, IA 50501-4381
Tel (515) 955-2040 Founded/Ownrshp 1924
Sales 611.2MM^E EMP 225
SIC 5153 Grains; Grains
Prin: Dennis Knight
COO: Mary Peterson
VP: Jon Larson
Dir IT: Jordan Mundie
IT Man: Terry Panbecker
IT Man: Craig Schultz
IT Man: Greg Sheltz
Opers Mgr: Lance Peed

D-U-N-S 14-125-4685
NEW COLLEGE OF FLORIDA PROPERTY CORP
BOARD OF GVRNRS STATE
(*Suby of* BOARD GOVERNORS GENERAL OFFICE) ★
5800 Bay Shore Rd, Sarasota, FL 34243-2109
Tel (941) 487-5000 *Founded/Ownrshp* 2001
Sales 40.7MM^E *EMP* 375^E
SIC 8221 Colleges & universities; Colleges & universities
Pr: Dr Donal O'Shea
**CFO:* John U Martin
Treas: Patrick Hennigan
Ofcr: Adam Desantis
Ofcr: Kelley Fisher
Ex VP: Carly Grimm
VP: Barbara Brosius
VP: Shannon Duvall
Assoc Dir: Alan Dawson
Comm Dir: Jessica Rood
Off Mgr: Lisa Croy

D-U-N-S 87-652-5932
NEW COLT HOLDING CORP
(*Suby of* COLT DEFENSE LLC) ★
545 New Park Ave, West Hartford, CT 06110-1336
Tel (860) 236-6311 *Founded/Ownrshp* 2013
Sales 49.4MM^E *EMP* 171^E
SIC 3484

D-U-N-S 12-214-4645
NEW COMMUNITY CORP
N C C
233 W Market St, Newark, NJ 07103-2713
Tel (973) 623-2800 *Founded/Ownrshp* 1968
Sales 53.0M *EMP* 1,200^E
Accts Withumsmithbrown Pc New Bruns
SIC 8399 Community development groups; Community development groups
Pr: Arthur L Wilson
**CEO:* Richard Rohrman
**CFO:* Elizabeth Mbakaya
**Treas:* Edgar Nemorin
Assoc Ed: Angela Stewart
Board of Directors: Maida Avellanet, Barry Baker, Elma Bateman, Patrick Duff, Edgar Nemorin, Desmond O'connell, Felix Roig, Madge Wilson

D-U-N-S 14-518-4482
NEW CONCEPT MANUFACTURING LLC
320 Busser Rd, Emigsville, PA 17318
Tel (717) 741-0840 *Founded/Ownrshp* 2004
Sales 30.7MM^E *EMP* 160
SIC 3089 Bands, plastic; Bands, plastic
Pr: Thomas Baughman
Mtls Mgr: Andrew Flaim
Ql Cn Mgr: Holly Sowers

D-U-N-S 82-899-7056 IMP
NEW CONCEPTS DEVELOPMENT CORP
8 Galaxy Way, Woodstock, IL 60098-5900
Tel (815) 338-8685 *Founded/Ownrshp* 1988
Sales 44.0MM^E *EMP* 113
SIC 5734 5045 4813

D-U-N-S 02-235-4377
NEW COOPERATIVE INC
2626 1st Ave S, Fort Dodge, IA 50501-4381
Tel (515) 955-2040 *Founded/Ownrshp* 1973
Sales 611.2MM^E *EMP* 226
SIC 5153 5191 Grain elevators; Grains; Feed; Seeds: field, garden & flower; Fertilizer & fertilizer materials; Chemicals, agricultural; Grain elevators; Feed
Opers Mgr: Robert Koestern
Sls Mgr: Dennis Habben
Sls Mgr: Tony Hilbert

D-U-N-S 05-433-3534
NEW COUNTRY AUDI OF GREENWICH
(*Suby of* NEW COUNTRY MOTOR CAR GROUP INC) ★
181 W Putnam Ave, Greenwich, CT 06830-5203
Tel (203) 661-1800 *Founded/Ownrshp* 2000
Sales 34.3MM^E *EMP* 200
SIC 5511 Automobiles, new & used; Automobiles, new & used
Owner: Michael Cantanucci
VP: Mark Edens
Genl Mgr: John Vitro

NEW COUNTRY BMW
See NEW COUNTRY MOTOR CARS INC

D-U-N-S 00-901-0245
NEW COUNTRY CHRYSLER INC
NEW COUNTRY KIA
1200 Carbon Jct, Durango, CO 81301-3454
Tel (970) 247-1212 *Founded/Ownrshp* 1983
Sales 23.3MM^E *EMP* 110
SIC 5511 Automobiles, new & used; Automobiles, new & used
Pr: Nancy Sellers
**VP:* Robert Ariano

NEW COUNTRY KIA
See NEW COUNTRY CHRYSLER INC

D-U-N-S 18-175-7659
NEW COUNTRY MOTOR CAR GROUP INC
358 Broadway Ste 403, Saratoga Springs, NY 12866-3190
Tel (518) 583-4896 *Founded/Ownrshp* 1983
Sales 186.3MM^E *EMP* 234
SIC 8741 5511 Business management; Automobiles, new & used; Business management; Automobiles, new & used
Ch Bd: Michael Cantanucci
CFO: Carl Leuchten
**VP:* Chris Mackey
IT Man: Michael Armbruster

D-U-N-S 93-830-2783
NEW COUNTRY MOTOR CARS INC
NEW COUNTRY BMW
(*Suby of* NEW COUNTRY MOTOR CAR GROUP INC) ★
1 Weston Park Rd, Hartford, CT 06120-1588
Tel (860) 522-6134 *Founded/Ownrshp* 1995
Sales 35.6MM^E *EMP* 100
SIC 5511 Automobiles, new & used; Automobiles, new & used
Pr: Michael J Cantanucci
VP: Lester Li
**Prin:* Anthony Ianniello
IT Man: Tom Girard
Sls Mgr: Donald Salierno
Sales Asso: Jackson Felix
Snr PM: Jeff Hessert

D-U-N-S 01-866-6495 IMP
NEW COUNTRY MOTORCARS
NEW COUNTRY VOLKSWAGEN
(*Suby of* NEW COUNTRY MOTOR CAR GROUP INC) ★
200 W Putnam Ave, Greenwich, CT 06830-5241
Tel (203) 869-4600 *Founded/Ownrshp* 1988
Sales 53.4MM^E *EMP* 220
SIC 5511 7538 7515 5521 Automobiles, new & used; General automotive repair shops; Passenger car leasing; Used car dealers; Automobiles, new & used; General automotive repair shops; Passenger car leasing; Used car dealers
Pr: Michael Cantanucci
Genl Mgr: John Penna
Off Mgr: Erin McGee
Sales Exec: Anthony Corbett

NEW COUNTRY VOLKSWAGEN
See NEW COUNTRY MOTORCARS

NEW COURTESY FORD, THE
See FORD COURTESY

NEW CRYSTAL PARK HT & CASINO
See CALIFORNIA CASINO MANAGEMENT INC

D-U-N-S 03-018-5656
NEW CURATIVE REHABILITATION INC
2900 Curry Ln, Green Bay, WI 54311-5857
Tel (920) 468-1161 *Founded/Ownrshp* 1948
Sales 6.6MM *EMP* 300
Accts Wipfli Llp Madison Wi
SIC 8322 Rehabilitation services; Rehabilitation services
Pr: John L Bloor
**Ch Bd:* Thomas Gauthier
**V Ch:* Mark Deprey
**Treas:* Mark Olsen
Bd of Dir: Denise Misovec
Mktg Dir: Dian Massart

D-U-N-S 03-693-1215
NEW CUSTOMER SERVICE COMPANIES INC
(*Suby of* NEW ASURION CORP) ★
22894 Pacific Blvd, Sterling, VA 20166-6722
Tel (703) 318-7700 *Founded/Ownrshp* 2015
Sales 95.7MM^E *EMP* 1,200^E
SIC 8748 Business consulting; Business consulting
Ch Bd: Fredrick Schaufeld
**Pr:* Tony Nader
**COO:* David Bosserman
CFO: David Basserman
**Sr VP:* Ray Zukowski
VP: Glenn Gibney
VP: Mark Malnati
VP: Joe Romano
VP: Louis Rose
VP: Rich Schneider
CTO: Bill Keating

D-U-N-S 04-300-3672 EXP
NEW DAY CHRISTIAN DISTRIBUTORS INC
126 Shivel Dr, Hendersonville, TN 37075-3517
Tel (615) 822-3633 *Founded/Ownrshp* 1982
Sales 33.9MM^E *EMP* 52
SIC 5065 5192 Cassettes, recording; Books
Pr: Dottie Leonard
**Sec:* Edward Leonard
Genl Mgr: Vince Wehby

D-U-N-S 62-705-6364
NEW DAY FINANCIAL LLC
NEWDAY USA
8160 Maple Lawn Blvd # 300, Fulton, MD 20759-2623
Tel (877) 423-1400 *Founded/Ownrshp* 2006
Sales 66.7MM^E *EMP* 68^E
SIC 6282 Investment advice
CEO: Rob Posner
**Ch Bd:* Thomas C Lynch
Pr: Ken Harthausen
Pr: Julie McMillin Lee
**Pr:* Joseph J Murin
COO: Gavin Brady
**CFO:* Paul Thompson III
Bd of Dir: Doug Friedrich
**Sr VP:* Bob Shanklin
VP: Eric Armstrong
VP: Amy Coyne
VP: Jennifer Davis
VP: Mike Howett
VP: Michael Oursler
VP: Roberta Pek
VP: Sean Reynolds
VP: Matt Russell
VP: Larry Silver
VP: Rich Tibbetts
Board of Directors: R James Nicholson

D-U-N-S 15-448-5031 IMP
NEW DAY OFFICE PRODUCTS & FURNISHINGS INC
7025 Harbour View Blvd # 108, Suffolk, VA 23435-2761
Tel (757) 398-0718 *Founded/Ownrshp* 1986
Sales 20.3MM^E *EMP* 26
Accts Mcphillips Roberts & Deans P
SIC 5021 Office furniture
Pr: Matthew Brady
**VP:* Lynn Medlin
**VP:* Kevin Smith

NEW DEAL FURNITURE
See NEW DEAL MERCANTILE INC

D-U-N-S 93-191-0483
NEW DEAL LLC
AGAINST ALL ODDS
222 Bridge Plz S Ste 6, Fort Lee, NJ 07024-5730
Tel (201) 944-1286 *Founded/Ownrshp* 2009
Sales 42.0MM^E *EMP* 415
Accts Friedman Llp NewYork Ny
SIC 5611 Men's & boys' clothing stores; Men's & boys' clothing stores
Exec: Mintu Alam
IT Man: Tom Kim

D-U-N-S 06-237-7742 IMP
NEW DEAL MERCANTILE INC (TX)
NEW DEAL FURNITURE
7130 Gateway Blvd E, El Paso, TX 79915-1201
Tel (915) 778-9230 *Founded/Ownrshp* 1949
Sales 25.1MM^E *EMP* 130
SIC 5712 Furniture stores; Furniture stores
Pr: Robert Falvey
Genl Mgr: John Falvey

D-U-N-S 62-384-3419
NEW DESSERTS INC
JUST DESSERTS
5000 Fulton Dr, Fairfield, CA 94534-1677
Tel (415) 780-6860 *Founded/Ownrshp* 2003
Sales 61.5MM^E *EMP* 93
SIC 5149 2024 Bakery products; Bakery products; Ice cream & frozen desserts
CEO: Michael Mendes
CFO: Leilani Muller
Bd of Dir: Frank Gerber
VP: Terry Watson
**VP Opers:* John Wohlgemuth
VP Mktg: Larry Tsai

D-U-N-S 18-956-4461 IMP
NEW DIMENSION METALS CORP
(*Suby of* GRAY AMERICA CORP) ★
3050 Dryden Rd, Moraine, OH 45439-1620
Tel (937) 299-2233 *Founded/Ownrshp* 1986
Sales 23.7MM^E *EMP* 40
SIC 3316 Bars, steel, cold finished, from purchased hot-rolled
Pr: John Gray
**CFO:* Jeff Schroder
Ex VP: Randall Fox
Mtls Mgr: Phil Huston
Sales Asso: Kerry Quatman

D-U-N-S 17-571-1746
NEW DIMENSIONS PRECISION MACHINING INC
6614 S Union Rd, Union, IL 60180-9514
Tel (815) 923-8300 *Founded/Ownrshp* 1987
Sales 30.6MM^E *EMP* 98
SIC 3594 Fluid power pumps & motors
Pr: Nancy Ann Halwix
**CEO:* Martin Halwix III
DP Exec: Bill Jones
Plnt Mgr: Marco Alejandre

D-U-N-S 00-206-2131 IMP
NEW DIMENSIONS RESEARCH CORP (NY)
260 Spagnoli Rd, Melville, NY 11747-3593
Tel (631) 694-1356 *Founded/Ownrshp* 1957
Sales 33.1MM^E *EMP* 125
SIC 3993 7389 Signs & advertising specialties; Design, commercial & industrial; Signs & advertising specialties; Design, commercial & industrial
Ch Bd: Timothy L Mason
**Pr:* Jeffrey Mason
VP: Kenneth Dasrath
Opers Mgr: Ranga Kanadam
Opers Mgr: Patricia Vendryes

D-U-N-S 00-254-7214
NEW DIRECTION YOUTH & FAMILY SERVICES INC
RANDOLPH CHILDRENS HOME
356 Main Street Er, Randolph, NY 14772-9696
Tel (716) 358-3636 *Founded/Ownrshp* 1878
Sales 22.5MM^E *EMP* 109
Accts John S Trussalo Cpa Pc Jamest
SIC 8361 Children's home; Children's home
Ex Dir: James Coder
IT Man: Michael Angelucci
IT Man: Sheila Searle

D-U-N-S 96-334-6056
NEW DIRECTIONS B & S LLC
(*Suby of* ALLEGIANCE HEALTH MANAGEMENT INC) ★
504 Texas St Ste 200, Shreveport, LA 71101-3526
Tel (318) 226-8202 *Founded/Ownrshp* 2007
Sales 11.1MM^E *EMP* 451^E
SIC 8741 Hospital management

D-U-N-S 00-605-3057
NEW DIRECTIONS BEHAVIORAL HEALTH LLC (MO)
8140 Ward Pkwy Ste 500, Kansas City, MO 64114-2036
Tel (913) 982-8200 *Founded/Ownrshp* 1994
Sales NA *EMP* 87
SIC 6371 Pension, health & welfare funds
CEO: John Quick
Pt: Elizabeth Decarlis
Ch Bd: Jim Bailey
Pr: Paul Krippenstapel
CFO: Roger Crane
V Ch Bd: Ron Simmons
Sr VP: Peggy Decarlis
Sr VP: Griff Docking
Sr VP: John P Emerick
Sr VP: Deborah Happ
VP: Miki Antonelli
VP: Michelle Hills
VP: Bob Moore
VP: Sesha Mudunuri
VP: Adam Powell

D-U-N-S 96-010-3620
NEW DIRECTIONS TECHNOLOGIES INC
NDTI
137 Drummond Ave Ste A, Ridgecrest, CA 93555-3583
Tel (760) 384-2444 *Founded/Ownrshp* 1992
Sales 27.9MM^E *EMP* 166
SIC 7373 7374 8711 7371 7376 Systems software development services; Data processing & preparation; Engineering services; Computer software development & applications; Computer facilities management; Systems software development services; Data processing & preparation; Engineering services; Computer software development & applications; Computer facilities management
Pr: Cedric Knight
Ex VP: Michele Hoopes
Dir Bus: John Dermatas
Opers Mgr: Shant Tossounian
Snr Mgr: Bert Belisch
Snr Mgr: Brandon Dooley

D-U-N-S 03-020-9860
NEW DIRECTIONS YOUTH AND FAMILY SERVICES INC
RANDOLPH CHILDRENS HOME
6395 Old Niagara Rd, Lockport, NY 14094-1421
Tel (716) 433-4487 *Founded/Ownrshp* 1999
Sales 23.0MM *EMP* 420
Accts Wittlin Cain & Dry Llp Buffal
SIC 8361 Home for the emotionally disturbed; Home for the emotionally disturbed
CEO: James W Coder
**CFO:* Michael C Angelucci
Off Mgr: Patricia McMahon

D-U-N-S 03-092-8543
NEW DISTRIBUTING CO INC
FUEL EXPRESS
4102 Us Highway 59 N, Victoria, TX 77905-5592
Tel (361) 575-1981 *Founded/Ownrshp* 1959
Sales 158.0MM *EMP* 25^E
SIC 5171 Petroleum bulk stations; Petroleum bulk stations
Pr: Jon R New
Genl Mgr: Mike Ross
Sls Mgr: Larry Surratt
Sales Asso: Larry McDowell
Sales Asso: Diane Stone
Sales Asso: Tiffany Williams

D-U-N-S 02-476-8194
NEW DIXIE OIL CORP (NC)
1501 Marshall St, Roanoke Rapids, NC 27870-4415
Tel (252) 537-4118 *Founded/Ownrshp* 1962
Sales 121.8MM *EMP* 195
Accts Mcgladrey & Pullen Llp Rocky
SIC 5983 Fuel oil dealers; Fuel oil dealers
Pr: Timothy Scott Aman
**Sec:* Renee L Aman
Sales Exec: John Elam
Board of Directors: Barbara Aman, Carey Wallace Aman Charim

D-U-N-S 13-244-0236
NEW DOMINION LLC
1307 S Boulder Ave # 400, Tulsa, OK 74119-3220
Tel (918) 587-6242 *Founded/Ownrshp* 2002
Sales 24.1MM^E *EMP* 25
SIC 1311 Crude petroleum production; Natural gas production
**Pr:* Kevin A Easley
**CFO:* Susan Keary
Ex VP: Janet McGehee
VP: Jean Antonides
**VP:* Virginia Albert Bullock
**VP:* Fred M Buxton
**VP:* Richard Hart
VP: William Kulkin
Dir IT: Corey McCormick
Dir IT: Corey Montanaro
Counsel: Fred Buxton

D-U-N-S 61-484-3964 IMP
NEW DONGHAI TEXTILE USA INC
939 S Atl Blvd Ste 217, Monterey Park, CA 91754
Tel (626) 576-4390 *Founded/Ownrshp* 2005
Sales 33.2MM^E *EMP* 500
SIC 5131 Textile converters; Textile converters
Pr: Xu Cong
**VP:* Frank Jin

D-U-N-S 16-220-7729
NEW DREAM NETWORK LLC
DREAMHOST.COM
135 S State College Blvd, Brea, CA 92821-5823
Tel (626) 644-9466 *Founded/Ownrshp* 1997
Sales 58.1MM^E *EMP* 140
SIC 4813
VP: Patrick Lane
Snr Mgr: Dallas Kashuba

NEW EGYPT MIDDLE SCHOOL
See PLUMSTEAD TOWNSHIP SCHOOL DISTRICT

NEW ENERGIZER
See ENERGIZER HOLDINGS INC

NEW ENERGY
See CONSTELLATION NEWENERGY INC

D-U-N-S 10-576-7008
NEW ENERGY CO OF INDIANA LTD
3201 W Calvert St, South Bend, IN 46613-1010
Tel (574) 280-2700 *Founded/Ownrshp* 1980
Sales 21.0MM^E *EMP* 132
SIC 2869 Ethyl alcohol, ethanol; Ethyl alcohol, ethanol
Pr: Naphan Kimpel
Opers Mgr: Randall Chrobot
Plnt Mgr: Nathan P Kimpel
Mktg Mgr: Bruce Heine

D-U-N-S 01-305-7500 IMP
NEW ENERGY INC (VA)
NE KIDS
2300 Prospect Dr, Christiansburg, VA 24073-2561
Tel (540) 382-7377 *Founded/Ownrshp* 1979
Sales 140.0MM *EMP* 26
SIC 5021

D-U-N-S 94-799-5213
■ **NEW ENGLAND ACCEPTANCE CORP**
(*Suby of* CITIZENS BANK) ★
875 Elm St, Manchester, NH 03101-2104
Tel (603) 634-7000 *Founded/Ownrshp* 2000
Sales NA *EMP* 626[E]
SIC 6022 State commercial banks
Prin: Fred Manning

D-U-N-S 96-160-7152
NEW ENGLAND AIR SYSTEMS LLC
43 Krupp Dr, Williston, VT 05495-8911
Tel (802) 264-1214 *Founded/Ownrshp* 2009
Sales 26.7MM[E] *EMP* 99
SIC 1711 Plumbing, heating, air-conditioning contractors
Genl Mgr: Richard Brooks
IT Man: Sandra Rexford
Mktg Mgr: Cindy Benenta
Snr PM: Randy Chicoine

D-U-N-S 96-337-3530
NEW ENGLAND ALLIANCE FOR HEALTH LLC
(*Suby of* DARTMOUTH-HITCHCOCK) ★
1 Medical Center Dr, Lebanon, NH 03756-1000
Tel (603) 653-1223 *Founded/Ownrshp* 2008
Sales 69.6MM[E] *EMP* 2,828[E]
SIC 8742 Hospital & health services consultant
Prin: Stephen Leblanc
Doctor: Julia Burdick
Doctor: Heather Gray
Doctor: Christian Hallowell
Doctor: Jeffrey Harnsberger
Doctor: Douglas Marks
Doctor: Christine Rosenwasser
Doctor: Eric Shulman

D-U-N-S 04-942-9111 IMP
NEW ENGLAND APPLIANCE & ELECTRONICS GROUP INC
126 Grove St, Franklin, MA 02038-3159
Tel (508) 528-4500 *Founded/Ownrshp* 1963
Sales 40.4MM[E] *EMP* 45
SIC 5064 Electrical appliances, major; Electric household appliances
Pr: Stephen Moran
**CFO:* Albert Souza
**Treas:* Arthur Redding
**VP:* Robert Crane

D-U-N-S 07-382-7859 EXP
NEW ENGLAND AQUARIUM CORP
1 Central Wharf, Boston, MA 02110-3309
Tel (617) 973-5200 *Founded/Ownrshp* 1957
Sales 38.1MM *EMP* 350[E]
Accts Cbiz Tofias Boston Ma
SIC 8422 Aquarium; Aquarium
Pr: Howard Bud Ris Jr
**Pr:* Edmund C Toomey
**CFO:* Joseph A Zani
**Ch:* Bill Burgess
**Treas:* Walter J Flaherty
**Sec:* Michael J Bohnen
Bd of Dir: Deborah Bobek
Bd of Dir: Tricia Wong
Exec: William Bradley
Comm Dir: Tony Lacasse
Dir IT: Robert Loyot

D-U-N-S 00-103-7951
NEW ENGLAND ART PUBLISHERS INC (MA)
BIRCHCRAFT STUDIOS
10 Railroad St, Abington, MA 02351-1705
Tel (781) 878-5151 *Founded/Ownrshp* 1926
Sales 38.1MM[E] *EMP* 250
SIC 2771 2759 Greeting cards; Thermography; Greeting cards; Thermography
Pr: Richard L Evans
**Ex VP:* Kenneth L Evans
VP: Doris Evans
Genl Mgr: Jason Evans
Dir IT: Norm Dobransky

D-U-N-S 07-957-9376
NEW ENGLAND ASSOCIATION FOR COLLEGE ADMISSION COUNSELING INC
258 Harvard St, Brookline, MA 02446-2904
Tel (603) 367-3292 *Founded/Ownrshp* 1966
Sales 25.2MM *EMP* 1
SIC 8699 Athletic organizations
Pr: John Westover

D-U-N-S 02-100-5657
■ **NEW ENGLAND AUTO AUCTION INC**
AMERICAN AUTO AUCTION
(*Suby of* MANHEIM INVESTMENTS INC) ★
123 Williams St, North Dighton, MA 02764-1201
Tel (508) 823-6600 *Founded/Ownrshp* 1983
Sales 33.1MM[E] *EMP* 460
SIC 5012 Automobile auction; Automobile auction
Pr: Darryl Ceccoli
**CFO:* Robert Gartin
**Treas:* James Hatcher
MIS Mgr: Michael Yung

D-U-N-S 82-506-8950
NEW ENGLAND AUTO MAX INC
1199 Worcester Rd, Framingham, MA 01701-5214
Tel (508) 370-9600 *Founded/Ownrshp* 1996
Sales 40.2MM *EMP* 30
SIC 5521 Automobiles, used cars only; Automobiles, used cars only
Pr: Howard J Wilner
**VP:* Michael Wilner

D-U-N-S 11-413-2256
NEW ENGLAND BANCSHARES INC
UNITED BANK
855 Enfield St, Enfield, CT 06082-2927
Tel (860) 253-5200 *Founded/Ownrshp* 2005
Sales NA *EMP* 142[E]
SIC 6035 Federal savings banks; Federal savings banks
Pr: David J O'Connor
CFO: Jeffrey J Levitsky
Ex VP: Charles J Desimone Jr
Ex VP: Peter W McClintock
VP: Tony Ciccomascolo

D-U-N-S 07-661-8883 EXP
NEW ENGLAND BAPTIST HOSPITAL INC
125 Parker Hill Ave Ste 2, Boston, MA 02120-2865
Tel (617) 754-5000 *Founded/Ownrshp* 1996
Sales 220.3MM *EMP* 1,200
SIC 8062 General medical & surgical hospitals; General medical & surgical hospitals
CEO: Joe Dioniso
**Pr:* Raymond C McAfoose
COO: Arnold Scheller
**CFO:* Tom Gerangalli
CFO: Robert Kelly
CFO: John Szum
**Treas:* Edward Fraioli
Ofcr: Sandra Gaston
Ofcr: Maureen Tringale
Assoc VP: Scott W Anderson
Assoc VP: Valerie J Giordano
VP: Debra Coleman
**VP:* Thomas J Gheringhelli
VP: Mary Smith
VP: Linda Thompson
Dir Lab: Christine Paolillo

D-U-N-S 06-660-5403
NEW ENGLAND BIOLABS INC
240 County Rd, Ipswich, MA 01938-2723
Tel (978) 927-5054 *Founded/Ownrshp* 1971
Sales 55.1MM[E] *EMP* 300
SIC 2869

D-U-N-S 19-574-8298 IMP
NEW ENGLAND BOATWORKS INC
EAST PASSAGE YACHTING CENTER
1 Lagoon Rd Ste 4, Portsmouth, RI 02871-6142
Tel (401) 683-4000 *Founded/Ownrshp* 1988
Sales 28.2MM[E] *EMP* 100
SIC 3732 4493 4213 3429 Boat building & repairing; Marinas; Heavy hauling; Marine hardware
Pr: Steve Casella
**Treas:* Thomas Rich

D-U-N-S 00-109-6239
NEW ENGLAND BUILDING MATERIALS LLC (ME)
TRUE VALUE
563 New Dam Rd, Sanford, ME 04073-5703
Tel (207) 324-3350 *Founded/Ownrshp* 1943, 1999
Sales 28.6MM[E] *EMP* 253
SIC 5211 2421 Millwork & lumber; Lumber: rough, sawed or planed; Millwork & lumber; Lumber: rough, sawed or planed
Sls Mgr: Steve Johnson

NEW ENGLAND BUILDING SUPPLY
See HH DISTRIBUTION INC

D-U-N-S 00-142-0686 EXP
■ **NEW ENGLAND BUSINESS SERVICE INC** (DE)
NEBS
(*Suby of* DELUXE CORP) ★
500 Main St, Groton, MA 01471-0001
Tel (978) 448-6111 *Founded/Ownrshp* 1952, 2004
Sales 344.5MM[E] *EMP* 3,611[E]
SIC 2759 2771 5045 2653 3089 3069 Commercial printing; Business forms: printing; Stationery: printing; Labels & seals: printing; Greeting cards; Computer software; Corrugated & solid fiber boxes; Boxes, corrugated: made from purchased materials; Boxes, solid fiber: made from purchased materials; Plastic containers, except foam; Tape, pressure sensitive: rubber; Commercial printing; Business forms: printing; Stationery: printing; Labels & seals: printing; Greeting cards; Computer software; Corrugated & solid fiber boxes; Boxes, corrugated: made from purchased materials; Boxes, solid fiber: made from purchased materials; Plastic containers, except foam; Tape, pressure sensitive: rubber
Pr: Richard H Rhoads
**Sec:* Paul F Robinson
Sr VP: Joel Hughes
Sr VP: Philip Peters
Sr VP: Robert D Warren
VP: Tim Althof
VP: Timothy Althof
**VP:* Barbara Baklund
VP: David Foster
VP: Robert H Glaudel
Counsel: Ellen Grant

D-U-N-S 14-411-8692
NEW ENGLAND CENTER FOR CHILDREN INC
NECC
33 Turnpike Rd, Southborough, MA 01772-2108
Tel (508) 481-1015 *Founded/Ownrshp* 1980
Sales 72.4MM *EMP* 700
Accts Alexander Aronson Finning & Co
SIC 8361 8211 Home for the mentally retarded; School for the retarded; Home for the mentally retarded; School for the retarded
CEO: L Vincent Strully Jr
**COO:* Katherine E Foster
COO: Katherine Foster
**CFO:* Michael Downey
Dir Soc: Bethany McCann
Psych: Julie Likas
Pgrm Dir: Stacie Bancroft
Pgrm Dir: Jason Bourret
Pgrm Dir: Erin Carmody
Pgrm Dir: Richard Graff
Pgrm Dir: Heather Morrison

NEW ENGLAND COFFEE COMPANY
See NEW ENGLAND PARTNERSHIP INC

D-U-N-S 07-397-9171
NEW ENGLAND COLLEGE
98 Bridge St, Henniker, NH 03242-3292
Tel (603) 428-2000 *Founded/Ownrshp* 1947
Sales 29.1MM *EMP* 250
Accts Berry Dunn Mcneil & Parker Ll
SIC 8221 College, except junior; College, except junior
Pr: Michelle Perkins
**CFO:* Paula Amato
**CFO:* Kevin Corimir
VP: Hilton Hallock
Exec: Lionel Tandy
Assoc Dir: Keith Hrasky
DP Exec: Darin Ninness
MIS Dir: Don Dennis
HC Dir: Yasin Alsaidi

D-U-N-S 07-661-4874
NEW ENGLAND COLLEGE OF OPTOMETRY
424 Beacon St, Boston, MA 02115-1129
Tel (617) 266-2030 *Founded/Ownrshp* 1894
Sales 24.8MM *EMP* 150
SIC 8221 8042 Professional schools; Offices & clinics of optometrists; Professional schools; Offices & clinics of optometrists
Pr: Clifford Scott
Pr: Jo Gershaw
**CFO:* Bruce Bernier
Chf Mktg O: Clem Trempe
VP: Dan Bastian
VP: Stephanie Britton
VP: Gary Chu
**VP:* Robert Gordon
VP: Brittney Mazza
VP: Aynsley Tinkham
VP: Alina Wheeler
Comm Dir: Ingrid Hoogendoorn

D-U-N-S 00-101-3812 IMP/EXP
NEW ENGLAND CONFECTIONERY CO INC
NECCO
135 American Legion Hwy, Revere, MA 02151-2405
Tel (781) 485-4500 *Founded/Ownrshp* 2007
Sales 28.8MM[E] *EMP* 135
SIC 2064 2066

D-U-N-S 07-658-0752
NEW ENGLAND CONSERVATORY OF MUSIC
290 Gainesborough St, Boston, MA 02115
Tel (617) 585-1100 *Founded/Ownrshp* 1867
Sales 38.7MM *EMP* 782[E]
Accts Mcgladrey Llp Boston Massach
SIC 7929 8221 8299 Colleges universities & professional schools; Music school; Entertainers & entertainment groups; Entertainers & entertainment groups; Colleges universities & professional schools; Music school
Pr: Tony Woodcock
Treas: Robert B Fraser
Top Exec: Patrick Maxfield
Top Exec: Richard Vallone
**Sr VP:* Edward R Lesser
VP: Susan Davy
VP: John C Kennedy
VP: John Kennedy
**VP:* Carol Phelan
Adm Dir: Greta Digiorgio
Adm Dir: Alison Garner

D-U-N-S 06-933-7186
NEW ENGLAND CONTROLS INC
9 Oxford Rd, Mansfield, MA 02048-1126
Tel (508) 339-5522 *Founded/Ownrshp* 1966
Sales 107.7MM[E] *EMP* 115
SIC 5085 Industrial supplies; Industrial supplies
Pr: Thomas A Ramundo
Ofcr: Jacob Yany
**VP:* Tim Alosi
**VP:* Jenn Azar
**VP:* Ed Browne
**VP:* Mike Stajduhar
Sales Asso: Cindy Maga
Sales Asso: Pete Plucinski

D-U-N-S 07-170-8937
NEW ENGLAND COPY SPECIALISTS INC (MA)
NECS
39 6th Rd, Woburn, MA 01801-1757
Tel (781) 935-4340 *Founded/Ownrshp* 1965
Sales 34.6MM[E] *EMP* 150[E]
SIC 5044 7378 7629 7359 Office equipment; Computer maintenance & repair; Business machine repair, electric; Business machine & electronic equipment rental services; Office equipment; Computer maintenance & repair; Business machine repair, electric; Business machine & electronic equipment rental services
Pr: Charles A Tiernan
Pr: Vince McHugh
VP: Mike McLaughlin
**VP:* Robert V Tiernan
**VP:* Robert Witbeck
Brnch Mgr: Robert Kenney
IT Man: Frank Costa
Netwrk Eng: James Grigg
Sales Exec: Cindy Albano
Natl Sales: Craig Maguire
Mktg Dir: Frank Nones

NEW ENGLAND CRANE SERVICE
See MACMILLIN CO INC

D-U-N-S 07-658-9423
NEW ENGLAND DEACONESS ASSOCIATION
RIVERCREST
80 Deaconess Rd Ofc, Concord, MA 01742-4165
Tel (978) 369-5151 *Founded/Ownrshp* 1889
Sales 29.7MM *EMP* 280
Accts Parentebeard Llc Philadelphia
SIC 8051 8059 6513 Convalescent home with continuous nursing care; Rest home, with health care; Apartment building operators; Convalescent home with continuous nursing care; Rest home, with health care; Apartment building operators
CEO: Rev Herbert B Taylor
**CFO:* Susan Shakoor
**Ch:* Earl Hutt
**Treas:* Robert S Cummings
Ofcr: Willis Brucker
**VP:* Sharon Buehrle

D-U-N-S 15-518-5903
NEW ENGLAND DEACONESS HOSPITAL CORP
1 Deaconess Rd, Boston, MA 02215-5321
Tel (814) 777-4805 *Founded/Ownrshp* 1984
Sales 17.0MM *EMP* 2,521
Accts Deloitte & Touche Llp Boston
SIC 8062 General medical & surgical hospitals; General medical & surgical hospitals
Pr: Robert Norton
**CFO:* Cheryl A Hoffman
Doctor: Benjamin W White MD

D-U-N-S 00-176-8092
NEW ENGLAND DETROIT DIESEL-ALLISON INC
POWER PRODUCT SYSTEMS
90 Bay State Rd, Wakefield, MA 01880-1047
Tel (781) 246-1810 *Founded/Ownrshp* 1974
Sales 27.2MM[E] *EMP* 93
SIC 5084

D-U-N-S 95-604-9571
NEW ENGLAND DEVELOPMENT INC
75 Park Plz Ste 3, Boston, MA 02116-3934
Tel (617) 965-8700 *Founded/Ownrshp* 1985
Sales 184.9MM[E] *EMP* 140[E]
SIC 6552 Subdividers & developers
Pr: Stephen R Karp
**CEO:* Steven S Fischman
**Ex VP:* Armen D Aftandilian
Ex VP: Carol Carbonaro
**Ex VP:* Bruce Herman
Ex VP: Douglass Karp
Sr VP: Bill Cronin
**VP:* Douglass E Karp
**VP:* Greg Murphy
VP: Paul Query
VP: Issie Shait
Dir Risk M: Kathy Doukas

D-U-N-S 17-602-2502
NEW ENGLAND ELECTRICAL WORKERS BENEFITS
60 N Main St, Wallingford, CT 06492-3720
Tel (203) 284-3000 *Founded/Ownrshp* 2005
Sales NA *EMP* 2
SIC 6399 Insurance carriers
Prin: H Lawrence Bourland

D-U-N-S 18-350-0024 EXP
NEW ENGLAND EXTRUSION INC
(*Suby of* NEX PERFORMANCE FILMS INC) ★
18 Industrial Blvd, Turners Falls, MA 01376-1608
Tel (413) 863-3171 *Founded/Ownrshp* 2010
Sales 37.2MM[E] *EMP* 180
SIC 3081 Polyethylene film; Polyethylene film
Pr: Cathy Bolhous

D-U-N-S 06-697-8107
NEW ENGLAND FARM WORKERS COUNCIL INC
11 Hampden St Ste 4, Springfield, MA 01103-1269
Tel (413) 272-2200 *Founded/Ownrshp* 1971
Sales 69.5MM *EMP* 60
Accts Maletta & Company Bristol Ct
SIC 8322 8351 8331 Social service center; Child day care services; Job training & vocational rehabilitation services; Social service center; Child day care services; Job training & vocational rehabilitation services
Ex Dir: Heriberto Flores
Bd of Dir: John Motto
VP: Eric Thomas
VP: Luis Valderrama
Pgrm Dir: Bill Scruggs

D-U-N-S 08-047-1071
NEW ENGLAND FEDERAL CREDIT UNION CO
141 Harvest Ln, Williston, VT 05495-7331
Tel (802) 879-8790 *Founded/Ownrshp* 1968
Sales NA *EMP* 165
SIC 6061 Federal credit unions; Federal credit unions
Ch: Geoff Akiki
**Ch Bd:* Charles Deslauries
**Pr:* John Dwyer Jr
**CEO:* David Bard
**CFO:* Susan E Leonard
**Treas:* Michael Nix
Ofcr: Jeanne Boucher
Ofcr: Vickie Larocque
IT Man: Jackie Flynn

NEW ENGLAND FINANCIAL
See NEW ENGLAND LIFE INSURANCE CO

D-U-N-S 19-861-2657
NEW ENGLAND FINISH SYSTEMS LLC
1 Delaware Dr, Salem, NH 03079-4034
Tel (603) 893-5083 *Founded/Ownrshp* 1988
Sales 52.8MM[E] *EMP* 250[E]
SIC 1742 Drywall; Drywall
Pr: Jon Marquis
**VP:* Ray Houle

D-U-N-S 14-412-6240
NEW ENGLAND FOUNDATION CO INC
1 Westinghouse Plz Ste 27, Hyde Park, MA 02136-2078
Tel (617) 361-9750 *Founded/Ownrshp* 1985
Sales 20.3MM[E] *EMP* 150
SIC 1771 3448 1794 1781 1381 Foundation & footing contractor; Prefabricated metal buildings; Excavation work; Water well drilling; Drilling oil & gas wells; Foundation & footing contractor; Prefabricated metal buildings; Excavation work; Water well drilling; Drilling oil & gas wells
Pr: Patrick A O'Neill
Pr: Diedra Oneill
VP: Diedra O'Neill

D-U-N-S 10-800-6180
NEW ENGLAND GUARANTY INSURANCE CO INC (ACT 244)
(*Suby of* UNION MUTUAL FIRE INSURANCE CO) ★
139 State St, Montpelier, VT 05602-2973
Tel (802) 223-5261 *Founded/Ownrshp* 1960
Sales NA *EMP* 67

SIC 6331 6411 Property damage insurance; Insurance agents, brokers & service; Property damage insurance; Insurance agents, brokers & service
Ch Bd: Lawrence Riley
**Pr:* Douglas J Wacek
**Treas:* Michael Nobles
**Sec:* Eileen Corti
**VP:* Robert J Shuttle
**VP:* Robert S Tulley

D-U-N-S 96-782-3738
NEW ENGLAND HEALTH CARE EMPLOYEES WELFARE FUND
77 Huyshope Ave, Hartford, CT 06106-7000
Tel (860) 728-1100 *Founded/Ownrshp* 2011
Sales NA *EMP* 3^E
Accts Buckley Frame Boudreau & Co Pc
SIC 6371 Pension, health & welfare funds; Pension, health & welfare funds
Ex Dir: Robert Tessier

D-U-N-S 96-702-8028
NEW ENGLAND HOME CARE
STAFFING WORKS
(*Suby of* NEW ENGLAND HOME CARE INC) ★
136 Berlin Rd Ste 203, Cromwell, CT 06416-2622
Tel (860) 632-4000 *Founded/Ownrshp* 1994
Sales 8.3MM^E *EMP* 483
SIC 8082 Home health care services; Home health care services
Pr: Kimberly Nystrom
VP: Bill Sullivan
**VP:* William Sullivan

D-U-N-S 19-919-6437
NEW ENGLAND HOME CARE INC
(*Suby of* NATIONAL HOME HEALTH CARE CORP) ★
136 Berlin Rd Ste 203, Cromwell, CT 06416-2622
Tel (800) 286-6300 *Founded/Ownrshp* 1996
Sales 35.0MM *EMP* 623
SIC 8049 8082 Nurses, registered & practical; Home health care services; Nurses, registered & practical; Home health care services
Pr: Kimberly Nystorm
VP: Bill Sullivan

D-U-N-S 06-004-3812
NEW ENGLAND ICE CREAM CORP
555 Constitution Dr, Taunton, MA 02780-7365
Tel (508) 824-0500 *Founded/Ownrshp* 1988
Sales 65.9MM^E *EMP* 70
SIC 5084 Food industry machinery; Food industry machinery
CEO: Bruce C Ginsberg
**Pr:* Stephen W Beck
**COO:* Robert Frotten
**Treas:* Jamey Lagor
Dir Surg: Mike Dinatale
VP Sls: Jon Klenk
Manager: Brian Garcia

D-U-N-S 01-946-6473 IMP
NEW ENGLAND INDUSTRIAL TRUCK INC
(*Suby of* NISSAN FORKLIFT) ★
195 Wildwood Ave, Woburn, MA 01801-2024
Tel (781) 935-9105 *Founded/Ownrshp* 2014
Sales 29.7MM^E *EMP* 80
SIC 5084 Materials handling machinery; Materials handling machinery
Pr: Richard P Rossi
Sls Mgr: William Leavitt

D-U-N-S 07-950-4601
■ **NEW ENGLAND INSTITUTE OF ART INC** (MA)
(*Suby of* EDUCATION MANAGEMENT CORP) ★
10 Brookline Pl Ste W, Brookline, MA 02445-7226
Tel (800) 903-4425 *Founded/Ownrshp* 1952, 2007
Sales 30.0MM *EMP* 34^E
SIC 8222 Junior colleges & technical institutes; Junior colleges & technical institutes
Pr: Dr Susan Lane
Treas: Daniel K Day
**Treas:* Dorinda Pannozzo
Ex Dir: Erica Keaney
IT Man: Jeannett Aufiero
HC Dir: David Leech

D-U-N-S 07-571-1051
NEW ENGLAND INSTITUTE OF TECHNOLOGY
NEW ENGLAND TECH
1 New England Tech Blvd, East Greenwich, RI 02818-1258
Tel (401) 467-7744 *Founded/Ownrshp* 1940
Sales 20.8MM^E *EMP* 445^E
Accts Disanto Priest & Co Warwick
SIC 8222 Technical institute; Technical institute
Pr: Richard I Gouse
Ofcr: Dawn Tanzi
**Ex VP:* Seth Kurn
Dir Lab: Ryan Campos
Off Mgr: Rhonda Foley
CIO: Jacques Laflamme
Software D: Robert Marcotte
HC Dir: Mark Blondin

D-U-N-S 19-112-2691
NEW ENGLAND INTERCONNECT SYSTEMS INC
NEI SYSTEMS
(*Suby of* NEW ENGLAND WIRE TECHNOLOGIES CORP) ★
180 Emerald St Ste 204, Keene, NH 03431-3616
Tel (603) 355-3515 *Founded/Ownrshp* 2000
Sales 31.7MM^E *EMP* 300
SIC 3357 3643 Nonferrous wiredrawing & insulating; Current-carrying wiring devices; Nonferrous wiredrawing & insulating; Current-carrying wiring devices
Genl Mgr: Harry Avonti

NEW ENGLAND JOURNAL OF MEDICIN
See MASSACHUSETTS MEDICAL SOCIETY INC

NEW ENGLAND LAW
See NEW ENGLAND SCHOOL OF LAW

D-U-N-S 00-140-3203 IMP/EXP
NEW ENGLAND LEAD BURNING CO INC (MA)
NELCO
2 Burlington Woods Dr # 300, Burlington, MA 01803-4543
Tel (781) 933-1940 *Founded/Ownrshp* 1930
Sales 40.7MM^E *EMP* 115
SIC 1799 Corrosion control installation; Airwave shielding installation
CEO: Richard J Leblanc
**Ex VP:* Gary J Miller
**Sr VP:* Audrey Fredrich
Exec: Beth Monroe
Off Mgr: Tracie Doyal
Snr PM: Steve Robinson

D-U-N-S 78-950-6367
NEW ENGLAND LIFE CARE INC
600 Sthborough Dr Ste 200, South Portland, ME 04106
Tel (207) 321-6352 *Founded/Ownrshp* 1992
Sales 37.0MM *EMP* 110
SIC 8082 Home health care services; Home health care services
CEO: Michael G Souza
**CFO:* Thomas Sahrmann
Pharmcst: Tim Horton

D-U-N-S 10-800-6438
NEW ENGLAND LIFE FLIGHT INC
BOSTON MEDFLIGHT
Robins St Hngr 1727 Hangar, Bedford, MA 01730
Tel (781) 863-2213 *Founded/Ownrshp* 1980
Sales 21.6MM *EMP* 85
Accts Alexander Aronson Finning & Co
SIC 4522 Ambulance services, air
CEO: Suzanne Wedel MD
**Pr:* Alasdair K Conn MD
**Pr:* Ann Prestipino
**Treas:* John Fernandez
Exec: Maria Taylor
Comm Dir: Kenneth Panciocco

D-U-N-S 18-809-0732
■ **NEW ENGLAND LIFE INSURANCE CO**
NEW ENGLAND FINANCIAL
(*Suby of* METLIFE) ★
501 Boylston St Ste 1, Boston, MA 02116-3738
Tel (617) 578-2000 *Founded/Ownrshp* 1980
Sales NA *EMP* 2,400
SIC 6411 Life insurance agents; Life insurance agents
Pr: Robert A Shafto
Pr: Tony Gandito
**Pr:* Rob Henrickson
CFO: Philippe Bertrand
CFO: Bill Lampley
Treas: Frank Nesvet
Ofcr: Jack Boland
Ofcr: Donna Degennaro
Ofcr: Ross Leonard
Ofcr: Lisa Mulvaney
Sr VP: Breneman Brian
Sr VP: Gordon Mackay
Sr VP: Donald R Shephed
VP: Terri Eilers
VP: James Medeiros
VP: Joseph Naselli
VP: Douglas D Ramos
VP: Nathan R Wentworth
Exec: Ingrid Wood

D-U-N-S 05-132-0679
■ **NEW ENGLAND MECHANICAL SERVICES INC**
EMCOR SERVICES
(*Suby of* EMCOR GROUP INC) ★
166 Tunnel Rd, Vernon, CT 06066-5505
Tel (860) 871-1111 *Founded/Ownrshp* 2002
Sales 61.6MM^E *EMP* 365
SIC 1711

NEW ENGLAND METAL RECYCLING
See PROLERIZED NEW ENGLAND CO LLC

D-U-N-S 01-952-9007
NEW ENGLAND MOBILE BOOK FAIR INC
JESSICA'S BISCUIT
82 Needham St Ste 84, Newton, MA 02461-1621
Tel (617) 527-5817 *Founded/Ownrshp* 1958
Sales 21.4MM^E *EMP* 60^E
SIC 5192

D-U-N-S 06-134-2879
NEW ENGLAND MOTOR FREIGHT INC
NEMF
1-71 North Ave E, Elizabeth, NJ 07201-2958
Tel (908) 965-0100 *Founded/Ownrshp* 1972
Sales 717.1MM^E *EMP* 3,200
SIC 4213 Less-than-truckload (LTL) transport; Less-than-truckload (LTL) transport
Ch Bd: Myron P Shevell
COO: Rich Cabral
**CFO:* Craig Eisenberg
**VP:* Nancy Shevell Blakeman
**VP:* Ernest Hardy
Off Mgr: Daisy Santiago
IT Man: Jim Pileggi
Opers Supe: Alexander Millan
Opers Supe: Deshawn White
Opers Mgr: John McAdams
Sales Exec: Rose Cirne

D-U-N-S 93-221-9124
■ **NEW ENGLAND NEWSPAPERS INC**
TOWN CRIER, THE
(*Suby of* MEDIANEWS GROUP INC) ★
75 S Church St Ste L1, Pittsfield, MA 01201-6140
Tel (413) 447-7311 *Founded/Ownrshp* 2002
Sales 42.6MM^E *EMP* 400
SIC 2711 Newspapers; Newspapers
CEO: W Dean Singleton
**Pr:* Kevin Corrado
**Treas:* James McDougald
VP: Warren C Dews Jr
**VP:* Joseph James Lodovic IV
VP: Edward Woods
Advt Dir: Bob Chatman

D-U-N-S 01-929-2721
NEW ENGLAND OFFICE SUPPLY INC
59 Centre St, Brockton, MA 02301-4014
Tel (781) 794-8800 *Founded/Ownrshp* 1993
Sales 74.2MM^E *EMP* 75
SIC 5112 5044 Stationery & office supplies; Office equipment; Stationery & office supplies; Office equipment
Pr: Indira Patel
VP: Harry Gorban
**VP:* Dennis McCarthy
Sls Mgr: Joe Shaw
Snr Mgr: Krystle Herring

D-U-N-S 10-790-0722
NEW ENGLAND ORGAN BANK INC
60 1st Ave, Waltham, MA 02451-1106
Tel (800) 446-6362 *Founded/Ownrshp* 1968
Sales 46.5MM *EMP* 170
Accts Feeley & Driscoll Pc Boston
SIC 8099 Organ bank; Organ bank
Pr: Richard S Luskin
**Ch Bd:* Jane Holtz
CFO: Dara Washburn
VP: Diana Buck
CIO: Mathew Moss
**Med Dir:* Francis Delmonico

NEW ENGLAND ORGANICS
See NEW ENGLAND WASTE SERVICES INC

D-U-N-S 01-946-6481
NEW ENGLAND PARTNERSHIP INC
NEW ENGLAND COFFEE COMPANY
(*Suby of* LUZIANNE) ★
100 Charles St, Malden, MA 02148-6704
Tel (800) 225-3537 *Founded/Ownrshp* 1916, 2013
Sales 57.6MM^E *EMP* 200
SIC 2095 5149 Coffee roasting (except by wholesale grocers); Coffee & tea; Coffee roasting (except by wholesale grocers); Coffee & tea
Pr: James M Kaloyanides
**Pr:* Chuck Kozubal
**Treas:* James P Dostou
**Treas:* Scott Simpson Mr
**VP:* James Kaloyanides Jr
**VP:* John C Kaloyanides
VP: Robert Milliken
**VP:* Michael Poore Mr
Dir IT: Larry Bisal
IT Man: Larry Brousseau
Opers Mgr: James Barker

D-U-N-S 07-658-4408
NEW ENGLAND PATRIOTS LIMITED PARTNERSHIP
1 Patriot Pl, Foxboro, MA 02035-1374
Tel (508) 543-8200 *Founded/Ownrshp* 1988
Sales 26.3MM^E *EMP* 150
SIC 7389 Credit card service; Credit card service
CEO: Myra Kraft
Pt: Robin Boudreau
Pt: Mark Briggs
Pt: Pat Curely
Pr: Jonathan A Kraft
Top Exec: Erik Scalavino
VP: Jennifer Ferron
VP: Jessica Gelman
VP: Stacey James
VP: Jim Nolan
Adm Dir: Ted Fire

D-U-N-S 96-676-3443 IMP
NEW ENGLAND PETROLEUM LIMITED PARTNERSHIP
6 Kimball Ln Ste 400, Lynnfield, MA 01940-2685
Tel (617) 660-7400 *Founded/Ownrshp* 1994
Sales 1.0MMM *EMP* 25
Accts Pricewaterhousecoopers Llp B
SIC 5172 Petroleum products; Petroleum products
Pt: Gary Kaneb

D-U-N-S 03-082-9337 IMP
■ **NEW ENGLAND POTTERY LLC**
(*Suby of* BREEDERS CHOICE) ★
800 John Quincy Adams Rd, Taunton, MA 02780-7316
Tel (508) 543-7700 *Founded/Ownrshp* 2004
Sales 23.7MM^E *EMP* 170
SIC 5999 5023

D-U-N-S 00-695-2881
NEW ENGLAND POWER CO
(*Suby of* NATIONAL GRID USA) ★
25 Research Dr, Westborough, MA 01581-3680
Tel (315) 460-3981 *Founded/Ownrshp* 1916
Sales 393.7MM^E *EMP* 842
SIC 4911 Electric services
Pr: Rudolph L Wynter

D-U-N-S 80-788-9415
NEW ENGLAND PRECISION INC
281 Beanville Rd, Randolph, VT 05060-9300
Tel (800) 293-4112 *Founded/Ownrshp* 1999
Sales 39.0MM *EMP* 68
SIC 3469 3364 3366 Metal stampings; Nonferrous die-castings except aluminum; Copper foundries
Pr: Bruce Uryase
**CFO:* Joseph Holland
QC Dir: Doreen Rokusek
Ql Cn Mgr: Ed Merrill

NEW ENGLAND PRTG & GRAPHICS
See MERCURY PRINT & MAIL CO INC

D-U-N-S 09-628-3510
▲ **NEW ENGLAND REALTY ASSOCIATES LIMITED PARTNERSHIP** (MA)
39 Brighton Ave, Allston, MA 02134-2301
Tel (617) 783-0039 *Founded/Ownrshp* 1977
Sales 42.6MM *EMP* 2^E
Tkr Sym NEN *Exch* ASE
SIC 6513 Apartment building operators; Apartment building operators
Pr: Ronald Brown
Genl Pt: New Real
CFO: Andrew Bloch
Treas: Harold Brown

D-U-N-S 79-027-3114
NEW ENGLAND REHABILITATION SERVICES OF CENTRAL MASSACHUSETTS INC
NERSCM
189 May St, Worcester, MA 01602-4339
Tel (508) 791-6351 *Founded/Ownrshp* 1986
Sales 11.0MM^E *EMP* 350
SIC 8062 General medical & surgical hospitals; General medical & surgical hospitals
CEO: Peter M Mantegazza
**Ex VP:* William Johnson

D-U-N-S 03-709-7938
NEW ENGLAND RESIDENTIAL SERVICE INC
81 Hope Ave, Worcester, MA 01603-2212
Tel (508) 755-2340 *Founded/Ownrshp* 1979
Sales 14.1MM *EMP* 360
SIC 8361 8322 Home for the mentally retarded; Individual & family services; Home for the mentally retarded; Individual & family services
Pr: David Jordan
COO: Joseph Tosches

NEW ENGLAND RHABILITATION HOSP
See RELIANT REHABILITATION HOSPITAL NEW ENGLAND LLC

D-U-N-S 07-657-4268
NEW ENGLAND SCHOOL OF LAW
NEW ENGLAND LAW
154 Stuart St, Boston, MA 02116-5616
Tel (617) 451-0010 *Founded/Ownrshp* 1908
Sales 40.2MM *EMP* 180^E
Accts Obrien Riley & Ryan Pc Braint
SIC 8221 Colleges universities & professional schools; Colleges universities & professional schools
CEO: John F O'Brien
**Pr:* John R Simpson
**CFO:* Frank A Scioli
**Ch:* Martin C Foster
**Treas:* Darrell L Outlaw
VP: Brian Vandenbosch
Comm Dir: Patrick Collins
Netwrk Eng: Gareth Flangen

D-U-N-S 96-811-2672
NEW ENGLAND SEAFARER MISSION INC
1 Black Falcon Ave Ste 1, Boston, MA 02210-2469
Tel (617) 443-0282 *Founded/Ownrshp* 1880
Sales 300.0M *EMP* 300
SIC 8011 Health maintenance organization; Health maintenance organization
Ex Dir: Stephen Cushing
**Pr:* Lawrence Andrews

D-U-N-S 00-913-9437
NEW ENGLAND SHEET METAL WORKS INC
2731 S Cherry Ave, Fresno, CA 93706-5423
Tel (559) 268-7375 *Founded/Ownrshp* 1920
Sales 34.2MM^E *EMP* 150
SIC 8711 8741 1542 Warm air heating & air conditioning contractor; Ventilation & duct work contractor; Engineering services; Construction management; Commercial & office building, new construction; Commercial & office buildings, renovation & repair; Hospital construction; School building construction
CEO: Michael Hensley
VP: Bill Sharp
Comm Dir: Robert Bell
Sfty Dirs: Benjamin Sohr
Snr PM: Bill Simonson
Snr Mgr: Joelon Chinn
Snr Mgr: Paul Kapigian
Board of Directors: Robert Bell, James Boone, Gail Perry-Henricksen, Michael Hensley, Paul Kapigian

D-U-N-S 07-661-3983 IMP
NEW ENGLAND SINAI HOSPITAL A STEWARD FAMILY HOSPITAL INC
CARITAS CHRISTI HEALTH CARE
(*Suby of* CARITAS CHRISTI HEALTH CARE) ★
150 York St, Stoughton, MA 02072-1881
Tel (781) 297-1299 *Founded/Ownrshp* 2012
Sales 43.7MM *EMP* 800
SIC 8069 8062 Specialty hospitals, except psychiatric; Chronic disease hospital; Hospital, medical school affiliated with residency; Specialty hospitals, except psychiatric; Chronic disease hospital; Hospital, medical school affiliated with residency
Ch Bd: Richard Blanstein
Pr: Judith Waterston
CEO: Lester Schinele
VP: Janet Madigan
Dir Case M: Kathy Girard
Netwrk Mgr: Luke Bessey
Nrsg Dir: Ellen Klund
Pharmcst: Peter Cardoza
Snr Mgr: Kevin Leonard

D-U-N-S 94-745-6419
NEW ENGLAND SPORTS ENTERPRISES LLC
FENWAY SPORTS GROUP
82 Brookline Ave, Boston, MA 02215-3905
Tel (617) 226-6300 *Founded/Ownrshp* 2004
Sales 58.2MM^E *EMP* 231^E
SIC 7313 Electronic media advertising representatives
Sr VP: Greg Morris
Site Mgr: Jason Davis

D-U-N-S 10-790-2504
NEW ENGLAND SPORTS NETWORK LIMITED PARTNERSHIP
NESN
480 Arsenal St Bldg 1, Watertown, MA 02472-2896
Tel (617) 536-9233 *Founded/Ownrshp* 1982
Sales 28.8MM^E *EMP* 200
SIC 7812 Motion picture & video production; Motion picture & video production
Pr: Sean McGreil
CFO: Raymond Guilbault
VP: Paul Bermel
VP: Joseph Maar
VP: Peter Plaehn

Creative D: Tony Saia
IT Man: Rick Rosa
Opers Mgr: Nancy Rose
Mktg Dir: Andy Brickley
Assoc Ed: Alison Smith

NEW ENGLAND TECH
See NEW ENGLAND INSTITUTE OF TECHNOLOGY

D-U-N-S 01-860-0379
NEW ENGLAND TRUCK SALES & SERVICES INC (CT)
SOUTHERN CONN FREIGHTLINER
15 E Industrial Rd, Branford, CT 06405-6508
Tel (203) 481-0373 *Founded/Ownrshp* 1963
Sales 31.4MM^{E} *EMP* 58
SIC 5012 5511 Trucks, commercial; Truck tractors; Trailers for trucks, new & used; Trucks, tractors & trailers: new & used
Pr: Gerald R Beauton
**VP:* Micheal Beauton
Sales Asso: Marc Toni

D-U-N-S 84-892-9907
■ **NEW ENGLAND WASTE SERVICES INC**
NEW ENGLAND ORGANICS
(*Suby of* CASELLA WASTE SYSTEMS INC) ★
25 Green Hill Ln, Rutland, VT 05701-3804
Tel (802) 775-0325 *Founded/Ownrshp* 1974
Sales 22.9MM^{E} *EMP* 83
SIC 4212 4953 Local trucking, without storage; Rubbish collection & disposal
Pr: John W Casella
**VP:* Edmond Coletta

D-U-N-S 10-116-8656
NEW ENGLAND WIRE PRODUCTS INC
307 Airport Rd, Fitchburg, MA 01420-8170
Tel (978) 343-7725 *Founded/Ownrshp* 1980
Sales 39.9MM^{E} *EMP* 152^{E}
SIC 3496 3993 2542 Wire cloth & woven wire products; Signs & advertising specialties; Partitions & fixtures, except wood; Wire cloth & woven wire products; Signs & advertising specialties; Partitions & fixtures, except wood
Pr: Charles Peters Jr
**Treas:* Karen Peters
Mktg Dir: Samuel Sunderland

D-U-N-S 00-108-5836 IMP
NEW ENGLAND WIRE TECHNOLOGIES CORP (NH)
(*Suby of* MJM HOLDINGS INC) ★
130 N Main St, Lisbon, NH 03585-6603
Tel (603) 838-6624 *Founded/Ownrshp* 1898, 1985
Sales 63.0MM *EMP* 576
SIC 3357 Nonferrous wiredrawing & insulating; Nonferrous wiredrawing & insulating
Pr: Richard Johns
CFO: Rick Tellez
**Ch:* Wendell W Jesseman
Genl Mgr: Terry O Brien
Dir IT: Kimberly Conover
Mtls Mgr: Melissa Poore
Opers Mgr: Bruce Mason
Natl Sales: Leo Dickinson
Mktg Dir: Rick Jesseman
Sls Dir: Kelly Mackay
Sls Dir: Terry Obrien

D-U-N-S 04-565-0587 IMP/EXP
NEW ENGLAND WOODCRAFT INC
481 North St, Brandon, VT 05733
Tel (802) 247-8211 *Founded/Ownrshp* 1977
Sales 35.0MM *EMP* 100
Accts Gallagaher Flynn & Company L
SIC 2512 2511 2531 2521 Upholstered household furniture; Wood household furniture; Public building & related furniture; Wood office furniture; Upholstered household furniture; Wood household furniture; Public building & related furniture; Wood office furniture
Pr: Harmon Thurston
CFO: Gary Marini
**VP:* Maxine Thurston
Dir IT: Patrick Ross
IT Man: Rachel Chartrand
Plnt Mgr: Lee J Thurston

D-U-N-S 00-112-6200
NEW ENGLAND WOODEN WARE CORP
205 School St Ste 201, Gardner, MA 01440-2781
Tel (978) 632-3600 *Founded/Ownrshp* 1834
Sales 35.5MM *EMP* 148
Accts Griffin And Company Pc Hudso
SIC 3993 2653 Signs & advertising specialties; Boxes, corrugated: made from purchased materials; Signs & advertising specialties; Boxes, corrugated: made from purchased materials
Pr: David L Urquhart
**Treas:* Alexander Urquhart
**VP:* Mark S Salisbury
MIS Dir: Don Geoffroy
Dir IT: Cheryl Menard
Plnt Mgr: Victor Donofrio
Prd Mgr: Todd Darling
Mktg Dir: Raymond Goguen

D-U-N-S 09-301-0353
NEW ENTERPRISE ASSOCIATES INC
NEA
1954 Greenspring Dr # 600, Lutherville Timonium, MD 21093-4135
Tel (410) 842-4000 *Founded/Ownrshp* 1977
Sales 24.2MM^{E} *EMP* 60
Accts Pricewater House Coopers Llp
SIC 6726 8741 Management investment funds, closed-end; Management services
Mng Pt: Peter Barris
Genl Pt: James M Barrett
**Genl Pt:* M James Barrett
Genl Pt: Patrick Kearns
Genl Pt: Patrick Kerins
**Genl Pt:* David M Mott
Genl Pt: Harry Weller
Pt: Patrick Chung
Pt: Robert Garland
Pt: Joshua Makower
Pt: Arno Penzias
Pt: Jimmy Treybig
**Ch Bd:* C Richard Kramlich
**CFO:* Tim Schaller
VP: Qiang Fu

D-U-N-S 00-194-3869
NEW ENTERPRISE STONE & LIME CO INC
BUFFALO CRUSHED STONE
3912 Brumbaugh Rd, New Enterprise, PA 16664-9137
Tel (814) 224-6883 *Founded/Ownrshp* 1924
Sales 661.8MM *EMP* 3,500
SIC 1422 1611 Crushed & broken limestone; Highway & street paving contractor; Crushed & broken limestone; Highway & street paving contractor
Ch Bd: Paul I Detwiler Jr
Pr: Paul Detwiler III
COO: Tim Servello
COO: James Van Buren
CFO: Paul Detwiller
CFO: Albert L Stone
Treas: Thomas G Frye
**V Ch Bd:* Donald L Detwiler
Sr VP: Steven B Detwiler
VP: Read Bachman
VP: Garry Horner
VP: Ransom Roberts
VP: Randal Van Scyoc
Board of Directors: Steven B Detwiler, James W Van Buren

D-U-N-S 00-602-5225
NEW ERA CANNING CO
4856 1st St, New ERA, MI 49446-9677
Tel (231) 861-2151 *Founded/Ownrshp* 1910, 1987
Sales 33.3MM^{E} *EMP* 250
SIC 2033 Canned fruits & specialties; Fruits: packaged in cans, jars, etc.; Vegetables: packaged in cans, jars, etc.; Apple sauce: packaged in cans, jars, etc.; Canned fruits & specialties; Fruits: packaged in cans, jars, etc.; Vegetables: packaged in cans, jars, etc.; Apple sauce: packaged in cans, jars, etc.
Pr: Rick Ray
VP Mktg: Michael Busscher
Sls Mgr: Kim Klotz

D-U-N-S 05-661-2773 IMP
NEW ERA CAP CO INC
160 Delaware Ave, Buffalo, NY 14202-2404
Tel (716) 604-9000 *Founded/Ownrshp* 1920
Sales 423.6MM^{E} *EMP* 1,388
SIC 2353 Uniform hats & caps; Baseball caps; Uniform hats & caps; Baseball caps
Ch Bd: Christopher Koch
**Pr:* Peter M Augustine
COO: Jim Patterson
CFO: Kevin Wilson
**Sec:* Valerie Koch
Sr VP: Gerry Matos
VP: Kevin Boleware
VP: Paul Gils
VP: Paul McAdam
VP: Matthew Reeves
VP: Howard Smith

D-U-N-S 61-291-9852
NEW ERA LIFE INSURANCE CO
11720 Katy Fwy, Houston, TX 77079-1242
Tel (800) 713-4680 *Founded/Ownrshp* 1989
Sales NA *EMP* 250^{E}
SIC 6321 6411 6311 Health insurance carriers; Life insurance agents; Life insurance; Health insurance carriers; Life insurance agents; Life insurance
Pr: Bill S Chen
Pr: Lyle Ross
Sr VP: Mike Rambo
**VP:* Mary D Frazier
VP: Brian Hull
IT Man: Mike Wiegman
IT Man: Kevin Zhao
Mktg Dir: Keith Barton

D-U-N-S 06-947-5853 IMP
NEW ERA OPTICAL CO
E-DR. NETWORK.
5575 N Lynch Ave, Chicago, IL 60630-1481
Tel (773) 286-2001 *Founded/Ownrshp* 1973
Sales 67.3MM^{E} *EMP* 150
SIC 3851 Eyeglasses, lenses & frames; Eyeglasses, lenses & frames
Pr: Herbert Natkin
Ofcr: Doris Miltenberger
Dept Mgr: Benjamin Becker

D-U-N-S 07-844-2601
NEW ERA PRODUCE LLC
23150 Fashion Dr Ste 233, Estero, FL 33928-2568
Tel (239) 495-5002 *Founded/Ownrshp* 2002
Sales 39.0MM *EMP* 3
SIC 5431 Fruit & vegetable markets

D-U-N-S 03-250-4553
NEW ERA REALTY INC
2563 15th St Ste 101, Denver, CO 80211-3944
Tel (303) 248-3519 *Founded/Ownrshp* 2005
Sales 100.0MM *EMP* 3
SIC 6531 Real estate agent, residential; Real estate agent, residential
Pr: John Stegner
**Pr:* Brian Leahnerz
Off Mgr: Laura Apodaca

D-U-N-S 86-923-9269
NEW FASHION PORK INC
164 Industrial Park, Jackson, MN 56143-9588
Tel (507) 847-4610 *Founded/Ownrshp* 1994
Sales 31.6MM^{E} *EMP* 180
SIC 0213 Hogs; Hogs
Pr: Brad Freking
**Treas:* Gary Dial

D-U-N-S 07-914-1634
NEW FLYER OF AMERICA INC
6200 Glenn Carlson Dr, Saint Cloud, MN 56301-8852
Tel (320) 203-0576 *Founded/Ownrshp* 1995
Sales 32.3MM^{E} *EMP* 191^{E}
SIC 3711 Buses, all types, assembly of
Pr: Paul Soubry
CFO: Glenn Asham
VP: Joe Gibson
VP: Ian Smart
VP: Chris Stoddart
Exec: Martin Cloutier
Brnch Mgr: David Ben
Prd Mgr: Geff Magsam
Ql Cn Mgr: Alan Husby

D-U-N-S 62-188-7959
NEW FLYER OF AMERICA INC
(*Suby of* NEW FLYER INDUSTRIES CANADA ULC)
214 5th Ave Sw, Crookston, MN 56716-2118
Tel (218) 277-7100 *Founded/Ownrshp* 1990
Sales 228.8MM^{E} *EMP* 990
SIC 3713 3711 Truck & bus bodies; Buses, all types, assembly of; Truck & bus bodies; Buses, all types, assembly of
Pr: Paul Soubry
**CFO:* Glenn Asham
**Ex VP:* Wayne Joseph
**Ex VP:* Ian Smart
**Ex VP:* Paul Smith
**Ex VP:* David White
**Prin:* John Marinucci
MIS Dir: Greg Gowryluk
IT Man: Darrin Smith
Sfty Mgr: Dan Chaney

D-U-N-S 01-601-7102
NEW FRENCH BAKERY INC
2325 Pine St, San Francisco, CA 94115-2714
Tel (415) 440-0356 *Founded/Ownrshp* 1996
Sales 24.6MM^{E} *EMP* 1,200
SIC 5461 Bakeries; Bakeries
CEO: Clifford Burrows

D-U-N-S 83-802-8710 IMP
NEW FRENCH BAKERY INC
(*Suby of* ARBOR INVESTMENTS) ★
828 Kasota Ave Se, Minneapolis, MN 55414-2814
Tel (612) 728-0193 *Founded/Ownrshp* 2013
Sales 47.0MM *EMP* 350
SIC 5149 5461 Bakery products; Bakeries; Bread, cake & related products; Bakery products; Bakeries
CEO: Brian Owens
**CEO:* Peter Kelsey
**CFO:* Eric Ahlgren
**VP:* Jeff Getzkin
QA Dir: Matthew Dickman

D-U-N-S 93-973-0321
NEW FRONTIER MEDIA INC
(*Suby of* LFP BROADCASTING LLC) ★
6000 Spine Rd Ste 100, Boulder, CO 80301-3323
Tel (303) 444-0900 *Founded/Ownrshp* 2012
Sales 55.4MM^{E} *EMP* 192^{E}
SIC 4841 7812 Cable & other pay television services; Cable television services; Direct broadcast satellite services (DBS); Subscription television services; Motion picture production & distribution; Audio-visual program production; Cable & other pay television services; Cable television services; Direct broadcast satellite services (DBS); Subscription television services; Motion picture production & distribution; Audio-visual program production
CFO: Grant Williams
Bd of Dir: Michael Weiner
**Ofcr:* Marc Callipari
VP: Ira Bahr
**CTO:* Scott A Piper
CTO: Jason Sokoloski
IT Man: Howard Kennedy
Web Dev: Brent Fox
VP Sls: Jeff Kreger
Sls Mgr: Amy Rowcliffe

NEW FRONTIERS NATURAL MKT PL
See NORTHERN HOLDINGS INC

D-U-N-S 55-719-6958
NEW FULTON FISH MARKET COOPERATIVE AT HUNTS POINT INC
800 Food Center Dr 65b, Bronx, NY 10474-0015
Tel (718) 378-2356 *Founded/Ownrshp* 2001
Sales 17.0MM^{E} *EMP* 300
SIC 5421 Fish & seafood markets; Fish & seafood markets
Pr: Frank Minio
VP: Henry Parente

D-U-N-S 55-710-5608
■ **NEW GALVESTON CO**
(*Suby of* CULLEN/FROST BANKERS INC) ★
100 W Houston St, San Antonio, TX 78205-1414
Tel (210) 220-4011 *Founded/Ownrshp* 1981
Sales NA *EMP* 3,132
SIC 6712 Bank holding companies; Bank holding companies
Ch Bd: T C Frost
**Treas:* Phillip D Green
Dir IT: Susan Murr

D-U-N-S 92-930-4822
NEW GENERATION HOMES INC
3 Widefield Blvd, Colorado Springs, CO 80911-2126
Tel (719) 392-0194 *Founded/Ownrshp* 1994
Sales 25.4MM *EMP* 40
SIC 1521 Single-family housing construction; Single-family housing construction
Pr: Mark Watson
**Treas:* Frank Watson
**VP:* Roger Dekloe

NEW GENERATIONS INTERNATIONAL
See CITYTEAM MINISTRIES

D-U-N-S 96-999-1764
NEW GULF RESOURCES LLC
10441 S Regal Blvd # 210, Tulsa, OK 74133-7234
Tel (918) 728-3020 *Founded/Ownrshp* 2011
Sales 52.2MM^{E} *EMP* 55
SIC 1311 1382 Natural gas production; Geological exploration, oil & gas field
CEO: Ralph Hill
**CFO:* Danni Morris
Sr VP: Michael Brown
Sr VP: Rob Moore
VP: Craig Young

NEW H TECH
See NAT NETWORKS INC

D-U-N-S 00-108-6321 IMP
NEW HAMPSHIRE BALL BEARINGS INC (NH)
NHBB
(*Suby of* NMB (USA) INC) ★
175 Jaffrey Rd, Peterborough, NH 03458-1767
Tel (603) 924-3311 *Founded/Ownrshp* 1946, 1985
Sales 264.0MM *EMP* 1,250
SIC 3562 Ball bearings & parts; Ball bearings & parts
Pr: Gary Yomantas
Treas: Yasunari Kuwano
VP: Rich Bargellini
VP: Jim Geary
VP: Dan Lemieux
VP: James Petersen
QA Dir: Andrew Fischer
IT Man: Sue Broderick
IT Man: Mike Hanley
IT Man: Tammy Kirouac
Mtls Mgr: Mike Selby

D-U-N-S 09-936-9308
NEW HAMPSHIRE CATHOLIC CHARITIES INC
CATHOLIC CHARITIES NEW HAMPSHI
215 Myrtle St, Manchester, NH 03104-4354
Tel (603) 669-3030 *Founded/Ownrshp* 1945
Sales 74.4MM *EMP* 1,000
Accts Howe Riley & Howe Pllc Manche
SIC 8322 8059 8331 8661 8361 Individual & family services; Social service center; General counseling services; Adoption services; Nursing home, except skilled & intermediate care facility; Community service employment training program; Religious organizations; Children's home; Individual & family services; Social service center; General counseling services; Adoption services; Nursing home, except skilled & intermediate care facility; Community service employment training program; Religious organizations; Children's home
Pr: Thomas E Blonski
COO: Dominique Russt
**COO:* Dominique Rust
CFO: Joanne Hollen
VP: Lisa Merrill-Burzak
Snr Mgr: Lexie Kwiek

D-U-N-S 02-773-3179
NEW HAMPSHIRE CHARITABLE FOUNDATION
37 Pleasant St, Concord, NH 03301-4005
Tel (603) 225-6641 *Founded/Ownrshp* 1962
Sales 70.2MM *EMP* 36^{E}
Accts Ernst & Young Llp Manchester
SIC 6732 Charitable trust management; Educational trust management; Charitable trust management; Educational trust management
Pr: Lewis M Feldstein
CFO: Michael Wilson
Bd of Dir: Roberta Barrett
Bd of Dir: Maureen A Beauregard
Bd of Dir: David L Brassard
Bd of Dir: Mary L Caffrey
Bd of Dir: John J Colony
Bd of Dir: James G Cook
Bd of Dir: Jeffrey R Crocker
Bd of Dir: Jonathan Edwards
Bd of Dir: Lisa M Foley
Bd of Dir: Charles S Goodwin
Bd of Dir: Morton E Goulder
Bd of Dir: David W Hess
Bd of Dir: Marilyn F Hoffman
Bd of Dir: Anne L Jamieson
Bd of Dir: Peter G Kachavos
Bd of Dir: Jane S Keough
Bd of Dir: John Kieley
Bd of Dir: Stephen H Krause
Bd of Dir: Michael M Krueger

D-U-N-S 80-859-0178
NEW HAMPSHIRE DEPARTMENT OF CULTURAL RESOURCES
(*Suby of* EXECUTIVE OFFICE OF STATE OF NEW HAMPSHIRE) ★
20 Park St, Concord, NH 03301-6316
Tel (603) 271-2540 *Founded/Ownrshp* 1985
Sales NA *EMP* 716
SIC 9199 General government administration; ; General government administration;

D-U-N-S 80-859-0756
NEW HAMPSHIRE DEPARTMENT OF EMPLOYMENT SECURITY
(*Suby of* EXECUTIVE OFFICE OF STATE OF NEW HAMPSHIRE) ★
45 S Fruit St, Concord, NH 03301-4857
Tel (603) 229-4353 *Founded/Ownrshp* 1957
Sales NA *EMP* 450
SIC 9441 Unemployment insurance office, government; ; Unemployment insurance office, government;
Ofcr: Paula Degen III
Dir IT: William Laycock
Counsel: Richard Lavers

D-U-N-S 80-859-0814
NEW HAMPSHIRE DEPARTMENT OF ENVIRONMENTAL SERVICES
(*Suby of* EXECUTIVE OFFICE OF STATE OF NEW HAMPSHIRE) ★
29 Hazen Dr, Concord, NH 03301-6509
Tel (603) 271-3503 *Founded/Ownrshp* 1986
Sales NA *EMP* 580^{E}
SIC 9511 Air, water & solid waste management; ; Air, water & solid waste management;
IT Man: Chris Simmers

D-U-N-S 80-859-1127
NEW HAMPSHIRE DEPARTMENT OF JUSTICE
(*Suby of* EXECUTIVE OFFICE OF STATE OF NEW HAMPSHIRE) ★
33 Capitol St, Concord, NH 03301-6310
Tel (603) 271-3658 *Founded/Ownrshp* 1985

Sales NA *EMP* 292
Accts Kpmg Llp Boston Ma
SIC 9222 Attorney General's office; ; Attorney General's office;
Prin: Philip T Mc Laughlin
IT Man: Timothy Brackett
IT Man: Susan Dearborn

D-U-N-S 80-859-1523
NEW HAMPSHIRE DEPARTMENT OF REVENUE ADMINISTRATION
(*Suby of* EXECUTIVE OFFICE OF STATE OF NEW HAMPSHIRE) ★
45 Chenell Dr, Concord, NH 03301-8541
Tel (603) 230-5000 *Founded/Ownrshp* 1973
Sales NA *EMP* 340
SIC 9311 Finance, taxation & monetary policy; ; Finance, taxation & monetary policy;

D-U-N-S 80-859-1697
NEW HAMPSHIRE DEPARTMENT OF TRANSPORTATION
(*Suby of* EXECUTIVE OFFICE OF STATE OF NEW HAMPSHIRE) ★
7 Hazen Dr, Concord, NH 03301-6502
Tel (603) 271-3734 *Founded/Ownrshp* 1985
Sales NA *EMP* 6,463ᴱ
SIC 9621 Regulation, administration of transportation;
IT Man: Dennis Fowler

D-U-N-S 80-858-9923
NEW HAMPSHIRE DEPT OF ADMINISTRATIVE SERVICES
(*Suby of* EXECUTIVE OFFICE OF STATE OF NEW HAMPSHIRE) ★
25 Capitol St Rm 120, Concord, NH 03301-6312
Tel (603) 271-3201 *Founded/Ownrshp* 1983
Sales NA *EMP* 400
SIC 9199 General government administration; ; General government administration;
IT Man: Beth Sirrine
Sls&Mrk Ex: Susan Belliveau
Sls&Mrk Ex: James Young

D-U-N-S 87-798-5119
NEW HAMPSHIRE DEPT OF CORRECTIONS
(*Suby of* EXECUTIVE OFFICE OF STATE OF NEW HAMPSHIRE) ★
105 Pleasant St Fl 4, Concord, NH 03301-3852
Tel (603) 271-4053 *Founded/Ownrshp* 1995
Sales NA *EMP* 1,000
SIC 9223 Prison, government; ; Prison, government;

D-U-N-S 80-859-0954
NEW HAMPSHIRE DEPT OF HEALTH AND HUMAN SERVICES
DHHS
(*Suby of* EXECUTIVE OFFICE OF STATE OF NEW HAMPSHIRE) ★
129 Pleasant St, Concord, NH 03301-3857
Tel (603) 271-4688 *Founded/Ownrshp* 1983
Sales NA *EMP* 3,000
SIC 9431 9441 Administration of public health programs; ; Administration of social & manpower programs; ; Administration of public health programs; ; Administration of social & manpower programs;
Ofcr: Irvin Heth
Ofcr: Brady Serafin
Ofcr: Nicola Whitley
Snr Mgr: Peter Hastings

D-U-N-S 01-890-1843 IMP
NEW HAMPSHIRE DISTRIBUTORS LLC (NH)
65 Regional Dr, Concord, NH 03301-8542
Tel (603) 224-9991 *Founded/Ownrshp* 1946
Sales 58.7MMᴱ *EMP* 150
SIC 5181 5142 Beer & ale; Fruit juices, frozen; Beer & ale; Fruit juices, frozen
**Ch Bd:* Thomas Brown
Snr Mgr: Bill Hancock
Snr Mgr: Keith Watts

D-U-N-S 00-881-9492
NEW HAMPSHIRE ELECTRIC COOPERATIVE INC
579 Tenney Mountain Hwy, Plymouth, NH 03264-3147
Tel (603) 536-8824 *Founded/Ownrshp* 1939
Sales 135.4MM *EMP* 199
SIC 4911 Distribution, electric power; Distribution, electric power
Pr: Steven Camerino
Ex VP: William R Gosney
VP: Dina Deluca
VP: Judy Gove
IT Man: Dave Lague
IT Man: Lynne Uhlman
Ql Cn Mgr: Guy Ford

NEW HAMPSHIRE INDUSTRIES
See CASCADED PURCHASE HOLDINGS INC

D-U-N-S 00-697-1345
■ **NEW HAMPSHIRE INSURANCE CO** (PA)
(*Suby of* CHARTIS US INC) ★
70 Pine St Fl 23, New York, NY 10270-0001
Tel (212) 770-7000 *Founded/Ownrshp* 1869
Sales NA *EMP* 1,279
SIC 6331 Fire, marine & casualty insurance & carriers; Fire, marine & casualty insurance & carriers
Treas: Robert S Schimek
**Sr VP:* Robert P Jacobson
VP: Charles H Dangelo
VP: Gary Whitehead

D-U-N-S 87-807-2016
NEW HAMPSHIRE LIQUOR COMMISSION
NH LIQUOR COMMISSION
50 Storrs St, Concord, NH 03301-4837
Tel (603) 230-7015 *Founded/Ownrshp* 1970
Sales NA *EMP* 336
SIC 9651 Alcoholic beverage control board, government; ; Alcoholic beverage control board, government;
Ch: Joseph W Mollica
CFO: Craig Bulkley
IT Man: Julie Mento

D-U-N-S 07-915-2959
NEW HAMPSHIRE MUTUAL BANCORP
111 Amherst St, Manchester, NH 03101-1809
Tel (603) 279-7986 *Founded/Ownrshp* 2013
Sales NA *EMP* 328
SIC 6712 Bank holding companies; Bank holding companies
CEO: Samual Laverack
CEO: Paul Rizzi
Treas: Jason Hicks

D-U-N-S 05-633-5334
NEW HAMPSHIRE PLASTICS LLC
1 Bouchard St, Manchester, NH 03103-3313
Tel (603) 669-8523 *Founded/Ownrshp* 1971
Sales 38.5MMᴱ *EMP* 75
SIC 2821 Thermoplastic materials
Pr: Michael Desmarais
**CFO:* Richard Desmarais
**VP:* Gertrude Desmarais
Dir Lab: Bob McMaster
Opers Mgr: Robert Turgon
Sls Mgr: Kevin Dale

D-U-N-S 15-088-5176
NEW HAMPSHIRE PUBLIC DEFENDER
NHPD
10 Ferry St Ste 434, Concord, NH 03301-5019
Tel (603) 224-1236 *Founded/Ownrshp* 2001
Sales 38.4MM *EMP* 160
Accts Dugdale Livolsi And Wood Pc M
SIC 8111 Legal services; Legal services
Ex Dir: Randy Hawkes
Ex Dir: Michael Skibbie
IT Man: Jeffrey Cousino

D-U-N-S 19-969-5214
NEW HAMPSHIRE PUBLIC RISK MANAGEMENT EXCHANGE
PRIMEX3
46 Donovan St Ste 1, Concord, NH 03301-2619
Tel (603) 225-2841 *Founded/Ownrshp* 1979
Sales NA *EMP* 50
Accts Peter C Brankman & Company P
SIC 6331 6733 8742 Workers' compensation insurance; Trusts, except educational, religious, charity: management; Business consultant
CEO: Paul Genovese
**CFO:* Rodney Tenney
Ch: M Katherine Fuller
**Prin:* Kimberly Decosta
Dir IT: Chris Caley
Dir IT: Kerry Goode
Dir IT: Ken Levis
Sys/Mgr: Steve Lavoie
Sls Mgr: James Dennis
Sls Mgr: Lori Pearson

D-U-N-S 80-859-1572
NEW HAMPSHIRE STATE POLICE
(*Suby of* EXECUTIVE OFFICE OF STATE OF NEW HAMPSHIRE) ★
33 Hazen Dr, Concord, NH 03305-0011
Tel (603) 223-8500 *Founded/Ownrshp* 1961
Sales NA *EMP* 1,175
SIC 9221 9229 State police; ; Public order & safety statistics centers; ; State police; ; Public order & safety statistics centers;
Prgrm Mgr: Joe Nadeau
IT Man: Peter Croteau

NEW HAMPSHIRE UNION LEADER
See UNION LEADER CORP

D-U-N-S 08-340-2990
NEW HAMPSHIRE-VERMONT HEALTH SERVICE
ANTHEM
1155 Elm St Ste 200, Manchester, NH 03101-1508
Tel (603) 541-2000 *Founded/Ownrshp* 1977
Sales NA *EMP* 32ᴱ
SIC 6321 8011 Health insurance carriers; Health maintenance organization
Pr: Daniel P Corcoran
**CFO:* Mike Smith
**Prin:* David Jensen

NEW HAMPTON GROUP HOME
See COMPREHENSIVE SYSTEMS INC

D-U-N-S 14-437-2299
NEW HANOVER COUNTY ABC BOARD
6009 Market St, Wilmington, NC 28405-3617
Tel (910) 762-7611 *Founded/Ownrshp* 1991
Sales 28.2MM *EMP* 36
SIC 5921 Liquor stores; Liquor stores
CEO: Dan Sykes

D-U-N-S 10-066-4572
NEW HANOVER COUNTY BLACK LEADERSHIP CONFERENCE
6410 Carolina Beach Rd, Wilmington, NC 28412-2908
Tel (910) 763-5431 *Founded/Ownrshp* 1937
Sales 80.7MMᴱ *EMP* 3,600ᴱ
SIC 8211 School board; School board

D-U-N-S 82-633-8506
NEW HANOVER COUNTY SCHOOLS
NHCS
6410 Carolina Beach Rd, Wilmington, NC 28412-2908
Tel (910) 254-4206 *Founded/Ownrshp* 2008
Sales 223.7MM *EMP* 3,500ᴱ
Accts Cherry Bekaert Llp Raleigh N
SIC 8211 Public elementary & secondary schools; Public elementary & secondary schools
V Ch: Beth Dawson
CFO: Donna Rossers
**CFO:* Mary Hazel Small
Treas: Holley Evans
Bd of Dir: Tammy Covil
Bd of Dir: Lisa Estep
**Prin:* Jeannette S Nichols
Dir IT: Jonathan Allen
Dir IT: Rhonda Welmers
IT Man: Bev Haley
Info Man: Lori Bradberry

NEW HANOVER REGIONAL MED CTR
See COASTAL REHABILITATION HOSPITAL

D-U-N-S 07-202-9143 IMP
NEW HANOVER REGIONAL MEDICAL CENTER INC
2131 S 17th St, Wilmington, NC 28401-7407
Tel (910) 343-7001 *Founded/Ownrshp* 1967
Sales 601.5MM *EMP* 3,692
SIC 8062 General medical & surgical hospitals; General medical & surgical hospitals
CEO: Jack Barto
Chf Rad: Fred Scialabba
CEO: Kathy Batchelor
COO: John Gizdic
COO: Matthew Haewood
COO: Sharon Timmons
CFO: Ed Ollie
Trst: Carl D Brown
Trst: Robert G Greer
Trst: David B Sims
Ofcr: Stephania Bloodworth
Sr VP: Susan Phillips
VP: Donna B Fache
VP: Alice Reynolds
Dir Rad: Steven T Crawford
Dir Rad: Nguyen Evans
Comm Man: Iris Baker

D-U-N-S 10-005-6415
NEW HARTFORD CENTRAL SCHOOL DISTRICT
33 Oxford Rd, New Hartford, NY 13413-2699
Tel (315) 624-1000 *Founded/Ownrshp* 1899
Sales 19.0MMᴱ *EMP* 400
Accts Dermody Burke & Brown Cpa S
SIC 8211 Public elementary school; Public junior high school; Public senior high school; Public elementary school; Public junior high school; Public senior high school
MIS Dir: C J Amarosa
Schl Brd P: John Jadmon
HC Dir: Donna Jordan

D-U-N-S 79-347-8293
NEW HARVEST PARTNERS LP
280 Park Ave Fl 25, New York, NY 10017-1264
Tel (212) 599-6300 *Founded/Ownrshp* 2009
Sales 1.3MMMᴱ *EMP* 12,924ᴱ
SIC 6799 7349 Real estate investors, except property operators; Cleaning service, industrial or commercial; Real estate investors, except property operators; Cleaning service, industrial or commercial
Mng Pt: Trevor Nelson
CFO: Debra R Kravetz
Mng Dir: Jay Wilkins

D-U-N-S 62-259-9777 IMP
NEW HAVEN COMPANIES INC
NEW HAVEN MOVING EQUIPMENT
4820 Suthpoint Dr Ste 102, Fredericksburg, VA 22407
Tel (540) 898-2354 *Founded/Ownrshp* 1989
Sales 30.3MMᴱ *EMP* 96ᴱ
SIC 5046 Commercial equipment
Pr: Dana Hearn

NEW HAVEN MOVING EQUIPMENT
See NEW HAVEN COMPANIES INC

D-U-N-S 00-551-7814
NEW HAVEN PUBLIC SCHOOLS
54 Meadow St Fl 1, New Haven, CT 06519-1719
Tel (203) 946-8501 *Founded/Ownrshp* 2007
Sales 88.2MMᴱ *EMP* 3,396ᴱ
SIC 8211 Public elementary & secondary schools
CEO: Reginald Mayo
**COO:* William F Clark
**CFO:* Victor De La Paz
**Prin:* Glen Worthy
Dir Sec: Dwight Ware
MIS Dir: Kevin Moriarty
Pr Dir: Abbe Smith
Instr Medi: Stephanie Shteirman
HC Dir: Susan Peters
Snr Mgr: Carl Carangelo

D-U-N-S 00-145-1145 IMP
NEW HAVEN REGISTER LLC
(*Suby of* JOURNAL REGISTER CO) ★
100 Gando Dr, New Haven, CT 06513-1014
Tel (203) 789-5200 *Founded/Ownrshp* 1915, 1997
Sales 38.5MMᴱ *EMP* 590
SIC 2711 2752 Newspapers, publishing & printing; Commercial printing, lithographic; Newspapers, publishing & printing; Commercial printing, lithographic
Pr: Kevin F Walsh
**CFO:* John Collins
CFO: Terry Spak
**Sr VP:* Thomas Rice
VP: Robert Lee
Ex Dir: Vern Williams
Dir IT: Hope Hogetree
Prd Dir: Rick Bolognese

D-U-N-S 08-184-7113
NEW HAVEN UNIFIED SCHOOL DISTRICT
34200 Alvarado Niles Rd, Union City, CA 94587-4402
Tel (510) 471-1100 *Founded/Ownrshp* 1954
Sales 59.3MMᴱ *EMP* 1,201
Accts Vavrinek Trine Day & Company
SIC 8211 Public elementary & secondary schools; Public elementary school; Public junior high school; Public senior high school; Public elementary & secondary schools; Public elementary school; Public junior high school; Public senior high school
Pr: Michelle Matthews
Exec: Nancy George
Exec: Rick Laplante
Adm Dir: Jill Ahnen
Dir IT: Raymond Mar
Teacher Pr: Derek McNamara
HC Dir: Sara Kappler

D-U-N-S 02-477-8891
NEW HEALTH SERVICES INC (WI)
2020 W Wells St, Milwaukee, WI 53233-2720
Tel (414) 937-2033 *Founded/Ownrshp* 2001
Sales 20.2MM *EMP* 2
Accts Wegner Llp Madison Wi
SIC 8093 Rehabilitation center, outpatient treatment; Rehabilitation center, outpatient treatment

D-U-N-S 06-486-2934
NEW HERITAGE CAPITAL LLC
800 Boylston St Ste 1535, Boston, MA 02199-8036
Tel (617) 428-3616 *Founded/Ownrshp* 2007, 2013
Sales 493.4Mᴱ *EMP* 357
SIC 6799 Investors
Prin: Mark Jrolf
Genl Pt: Nickie Norris
Prin: Charles K Gifford Jr

NEW HMPSHIRE LCAL GVRNMENT CTR
See LOCAL GOVERNMENT CENTER INC

D-U-N-S 17-993-2785 IMP
NEW HOLLAND BREWING CO LLC
66 E 8th St, Holland, MI 49423-3504
Tel (616) 355-2941 *Founded/Ownrshp* 1996
Sales 47.1MMᴱ *EMP* 200
SIC 2082 5813 5812 Malt beverages; Drinking places; Eating places; Malt beverages; Drinking places; Eating places
CFO: Dave White
Ex Dir: Isaac Hartman
Sls Mgr: Rich Blair

D-U-N-S 80-938-4076
NEW HOLLAND CREDIT CO LLC
(*Suby of* CNH CAPITAL LLC) ★
700 State St, Racine, WI 53404-3343
Tel (262) 636-6011 *Founded/Ownrshp* 1991
Sales NA *EMP* 330
SIC 6159 Machinery & equipment finance leasing; Machinery & equipment finance leasing
Pr: Paolo Monferino
**COO:* Mario Ferla
**CFO:* Michel Lecomte

NEW HOLLAND FORD ISUZU
See BEANS-CLASS FORD MERCURY INC

D-U-N-S 15-136-2431 EXP
NEW HOLLAND NORTH AMERICA INC
(*Suby of* FIAT ALLIS NORTH AMERICA INC)
300 Diller Ave, New Holland, PA 17557-1631
Tel (717) 355-1121 *Founded/Ownrshp* 1991
Sales 589.3MMᴱ *EMP* 3,840
SIC 3523 Farm machinery & equipment; Farm machinery & equipment
Pr: A R Rider
**CFO:* W T Kennedy
**VP:* M D Jack
**VP:* Gary L Tessitore
Area Mgr: Magee Brian
Netwrk Mgr: Michael McElravy
Natl Sales: Ron Shaffer
S&M/VP: Abe Hughes
Mktg Dir: Franco Invernizzi
Mktg Mgr: Bob Bledsoe
Mktg Mgr: Frederik Klein
Board of Directors: Richard E Cook, Bruno Doria, Horace G McCarty, Mario Rosso, Bert Urrunaga

D-U-N-S 18-214-1002
NEW HOLLAND ROCHESTER INC
1260 E 100 S, Rochester, IN 46975-8036
Tel (574) 223-2714 *Founded/Ownrshp* 1989
Sales 23.7MMᴱ *EMP* 35
SIC 5083 5261 Agricultural machinery & equipment; Agricultural machinery; Farm implements; Lawn & garden equipment
Pr: James E Straeter
**Treas:* Melinda Straetor

D-U-N-S 07-887-6973
▲ **NEW HOME CO INC**
85 Enterprise Ste 450, Aliso Viejo, CA 92656-2680
Tel (949) 382-7800 *Founded/Ownrshp* 2009
Sales 149.6MM *EMP* 234ᴱ
Tkr Sym NWHM *Exch* NYS
SIC 1531 Operative builders; Operative builders
Ch Bd: H Lawrence Webb
COO: Tom Redwitz
**CFO:* Wayne Stelmar
VP: Mike Cunningham
VP: Ashley Feeney
VP: Kim Forbes
VP: Mark Kawanami
VP: Robin Koenemann
VP: John Sherwood
VP: Douglas Woodward
CIO: Joseph D Davis
Board of Directors: Sam Bakhshandehpour, Michael J Berchtold, David Berman, Paul Heeschen, Gregory P Lindstrom, Cathey S Lowe, Douglas C Neff, Nadine Watt, William A Witte

NEW HOME LENDING
See FM LENDING SERVICES INC

D-U-N-S 79-079-0059
NEW HOME MEDIA
9408 Gunston Cove Rd E, Lorton, VA 22079-2302
Tel (703) 550-2233 *Founded/Ownrshp* 1987
Sales 23.1MMᴱ *EMP* 178
SIC 3993 1799 Signs, not made in custom sign painting shops; Sign installation & maintenance; Signs, not made in custom sign painting shops; Sign installation & maintenance
Pr: Charles B Smith Jr

D-U-N-S 08-846-4581 IMP
NEW HOP INC (NY)
(*Suby of* HERMES HOLDING U S INC) ★
55 E 59th St Frnt 2, New York, NY 10022-1197
Tel (800) 441-4488 *Founded/Ownrshp* 1930, 1990
Sales 72.2MMᴱ *EMP* 350
SIC 5611 5621 5932 5136 5137 Clothing accessories: men's & boys'; Ready-to-wear apparel, women's; Building materials, secondhand; Men's & boys' clothing; Women's & children's clothing; Clothing accessories: men's & boys'; Ready-to-wear apparel, women's; Building materials, secondhand; Men's & boys' clothing; Women's & children's clothing
Ch Bd: Robert B Chavez
**Ch Bd:* Jean Louis Dumas

CFO: Gael Duchemin
Sr VP: Peter Malachi
VP: Corinna Berthold
VP: Anthony Fuccillo
VP: Priya Narang
VP: Carole Silverman
Dir Soc: Lisa Krupnick
Comm Dir: Fiona Rushton
Mng Dir: Diana D'Amato

D-U-N-S 16-091-7241
NEW HOPE CAROLINAS INC
NEW HOPE TREATMENT
101 Sedgewood Dr, Rock Hill, SC 29732-2315
Tel (803) 328-9300 *Founded/Ownrshp* 1993
Sales 9.1MM *EMP* 400
Accts Gamble Givens & Moody Pa
SIC 8063 8361 Psychiatric hospitals; Residential care; Psychiatric hospitals; Residential care
Ex Dir: Sam Phifer
IT Man: Mike Bisceglia

D-U-N-S 02-067-1343
NEW HOPE COMMUNITY INC
5 New Hope Community Dr, Loch Sheldrake, NY 12759
Tel (845) 434-8300 *Founded/Ownrshp* 1975
Sales 34.2MM *EMP* 200
Accts Marks Paneth Llp New York Ny
SIC 8361 Rehabilitation center, residential: health care incidental; Rehabilitation center, residential: health care incidental
CFO: Tariq Iqbal
Ex Dir: Dan Berkowicz
**Ex Dir:* Art Moretti

D-U-N-S 07-595-3125
NEW HOPE OF INDIANA INC
8450 N Payne Rd Ste 300, Indianapolis, IN 46268-6621
Tel (317) 338-9600 *Founded/Ownrshp* 1988
Sales 22.6MM *EMP* 530
Accts Deloitte Tax Llp Indianapolis
SIC 8361 Home for the mentally handicapped; Home for the physically handicapped; Home for the mentally handicapped; Home for the physically handicapped
CEO: Allison Wharry
CFO: Laura Tomlin

D-U-N-S 15-180-9423
NEW HOPE SOLE BURY SCHOOL DISTRICT
180 W Bridge St, New Hope, PA 18938-1392
Tel (215) 862-2552 *Founded/Ownrshp* 1930
Sales 37.1MM *EMP* 189^E^
Accts Mayer Hoffman Mccann Pc Plym
SIC 8211 Public elementary & secondary schools; School board; Public elementary & secondary schools; School board
**Ch:* Stephen Fiala
**VP:* Christine Flynn
Prin: Sherry Kondrosky
Prin: Joy F Kurtz
Prin: Stephen Young
Dir IT: Scott Radaszkiewicz
Schl Brd P: Joseph Harraka

NEW HOPE TREATMENT
See NEW HOPE CAROLINAS INC

NEW HOPE TREATMENT CENTERS
See SAFARI CORP

D-U-N-S 07-807-5504
NEW HOPE VILLAGE INC (IA)
CARROLL ENTERPRISE SYSTEMS
1211 E 18th St, Carroll, IA 51401-1893
Tel (712) 792-5500 *Founded/Ownrshp* 1975
Sales 14.8MM *EMP* 380
Accts Ryun Givens & Company Plc Ur
SIC 8361 8331 Rehabilitation center, residential: health care incidental; Job training & vocational rehabilitation services; Rehabilitation center, residential: health care incidental; Job training & vocational rehabilitation services
Ex Dir: Frank Hermsen
Treas: Vicky Robinson
VP: Sandy Rohe
Assoc Dir: Rhonda Mart
IT Man: Gary Engelen
Nrsg Dir: Linda Kruthoff
Board of Directors: Don Derner, Angie Schoeppner, Tom Twit, Lou Walsh

NEW HORIZON CHILD CARE
See NEW HORIZON ENTERPRISES INC

D-U-N-S 09-391-3408
NEW HORIZON CHILD CARE INC (ID)
(*Suby of* NEW HORIZON CHILD CARE) ★
3405 Annapolis Ln N # 100, Minneapolis, MN 55447-5342
Tel (763) 383-6275 *Founded/Ownrshp* 1972, 1992
Sales 17.9MM^E^ *EMP* 600
SIC 8351 Preschool center; Preschool center
Ch: William M Dunkley
**Pr:* Susan Dunkley
**CFO:* Penny L Allen
**Sec:* Lorraine Dunkley

D-U-N-S 78-267-1648
NEW HORIZON ENTERPRISES INC
NEW HORIZON CHILD CARE
3405 Annapolis Ln N # 100, Minneapolis, MN 55447-5342
Tel (763) 557-1111 *Founded/Ownrshp* 1976
Sales 40.2MM^E^ *EMP* 2,300
SIC 8351 Child day care services; Child day care services
Ch Bd: William M Dunkley
**Sec:* Lorraine Dunkley
**VP:* Susan Dunkley
IT Man: Jill Dunkley
Mktg Dir: Mary Terrass

D-U-N-S 83-696-0971
NEW HORIZON KIDS QUEST INC
3405 Annapolis Ln N # 100, Minneapolis, MN 55447-5343
Tel (763) 383-6201 *Founded/Ownrshp* 1992
Sales 24.4MM^E^ *EMP* 600
Accts Silverman Olson Thorvilson & K
SIC 8351 Preschool center; Preschool center
CEO: William M Dunkley
Pr: Susan K Dunkley
COO: Troy Dunkley
CFO: Patrick R Cruzen
CFO: David Grzan
IT Man: Matt Evans
Opers Mgr: Traci Peterson
Sales Exec: Aimee Maidi

D-U-N-S 36-213-2602
NEW HORIZON SECURITY SERVICES INC
7820 Sudley Rd Ste 201, Manassas, VA 20109-2896
Tel (571) 248-6944 *Founded/Ownrshp* 1998
Sales 19.8MM^E^ *EMP* 550^E^
SIC 7381 Guard services; Guard services
Pr: John M Frazer

D-U-N-S 96-484-7417
NEW HORIZONS AREA MH-MR SA PROGRAM
2401 Buena Vista Rd, Columbus, GA 31906-3142
Tel (706) 596-5757 *Founded/Ownrshp* 2010
Sales 24.2MM *EMP* 1
SIC 7389 ;
Prin: Alfred Green

D-U-N-S 15-126-4512
NEW HORIZONS BAKING CO INC
211 Woodlawn Ave, Norwalk, OH 44857-2276
Tel (419) 668-8226 *Founded/Ownrshp* 1995
Sales 94.0MM *EMP* 350
SIC 2051 Buns, bread type: fresh or frozen; Breads, rolls & buns; Buns, bread type: fresh or frozen; Breads, rolls & buns
CEO: Tilmon F Brownm
**Ex VP:* Trina Bediako
**Ex VP:* John Widman
**VP:* Robert Creighton
**VP:* Mark Duke
**VP:* Mike Porter
Opers Mgr: Jim McFadden

NEW HORIZONS CLC
See NEW HORIZONS COMPUTER LEARNING CENTERS INC

D-U-N-S 14-982-0131
NEW HORIZONS COMMUNICATIONS CORP
420 Bedford St Ste 250, Lexington, MA 02420-1506
Tel (781) 290-4600 *Founded/Ownrshp* 2002
Sales 20.3MM^E^ *EMP* 50
SIC 4813 Telephone communication, except radio
CEO: Robert Fabbricatore
**Pr:* Steven Gibbs
**Sec:* Glen E Nelson

D-U-N-S 05-603-4721
NEW HORIZONS COMMUNITY MENTAL HEALTH
1469 Nw 36th St, Miami, FL 33142-5557
Tel (305) 635-0366 *Founded/Ownrshp* 1981
Sales 10.5MM *EMP* 322
Accts Thomas & Company Cpa Pa Coope
SIC 8093 Mental health clinic, outpatient; Mental health clinic, outpatient
CEO: Luvermice Croskey
**Pr:* Israel Milton
COO: Ana Benitez-Wiggins
COO: Ana B Wiggins
**Treas:* Labib Baltagi
**Sec:* Leslie Holland
**VP:* James Kelly
MIS Dir: Debra Kooray

D-U-N-S 94-293-2609
NEW HORIZONS COMMUNITY SERVICE BOARD
2100 Comer Ave, Columbus, GA 31904-8725
Tel (706) 596-5583 *Founded/Ownrshp* 1969
Sales NA *EMP* 700
SIC 9431 Mental health agency administration, government; Mental health agency administration, government
Pr: Perry Alexander
Exec: Shannon Robertson
Mktg Dir: Jenn Green

D-U-N-S 83-567-1306
NEW HORIZONS COMPUTER LEARNING CENTER LTD
NEW HORIZONS COMPUTER LRNG
1 Infinity Corp Ctr Dr, Cleveland, OH 44125-5369
Tel (216) 332-7960 *Founded/Ownrshp* 2007
Sales 62.8MM^E^ *EMP* 690
SIC 7379 Computer related consulting services; Computer related consulting services
CEO: Thomas J Bresnan
**CEO:* Mark McManus Jr
**Genl Mgr:* Karl Hoenecke

D-U-N-S 79-299-7074
NEW HORIZONS COMPUTER LEARNING CENTERS INC
NEW HORIZONS CLC
(*Suby of* NEW HORIZONS WORLDWIDE INC) ★
1900 S State College Blvd, Anaheim, CA 92806-0101
Tel (714) 940-8062 *Founded/Ownrshp* 2001
Sales 45.0MM^E^ *EMP* 120
SIC 6794 8243 Franchises, selling or licensing; Software training, computer
CEO: Earle Pratt
Pr: Ryan Landry
**CEO:* Mark Miller
Sr Cor Off: Terry Alexander
Sr Cor Off: Jim Jonas
Sr Cor Off: Robert Maher
Bd of Dir: Martin Bean
Ex VP: Shane Plank
**VP:* Joseph Diplacido
VP: John Golden

VP: Jack Routh
VP: Jeff Solberg
VP: Cindy Sutherland
Exec: Bob Handy
Exec: Bhairavi Nagonde
Exec: Greg Weddle

NEW HORIZONS COMPUTER LRNG
See NEW HORIZONS COMPUTER LEARNING CENTER LTD

D-U-N-S 05-083-6637
NEW HORIZONS OF TREASURE
404 Ixoria Ave, Fort Pierce, FL 34982-6250
Tel (772) 468-3910 *Founded/Ownrshp* 2010
Sales 23.0MM *EMP* 1
SIC 5947 Gift, novelty & souvenir shop; Gift, novelty & souvenir shop
Prin: Bob Quam

D-U-N-S 07-601-8829
NEW HORIZONS OF TREASURE COAST INC
4500 W Midway Rd, Fort Pierce, FL 34981-4823
Tel (772) 468-5600 *Founded/Ownrshp* 2005
Sales 22.3MM *EMP* 322
Accts Kmetz Nuttall Elwell Graham
SIC 8093 8063 Mental health clinic, outpatient; Drug clinic, outpatient; Psychiatric hospitals; Mental health clinic, outpatient; Drug clinic, outpatient; Psychiatric hospitals
CEO: John Romano
Treas: Robert Zomok
VP: Joanne Knight
Dir Rx: Amanda Chaucey
Dir Rx: Amanda Chauncey
Dir Sec: Ellis Poindexter
Prgrm Mgr: Ann Posey
Off Mgr: Venus Bubel
Off Mgr: Olivia Garcia
Off Mgr: Liz Woods
CIO: Robin Curby

D-U-N-S 01-004-6258
NEW HORIZONS REGIONAL EDUCATION CENTER
520 Butler Farm Rd, Hampton, VA 23666-1500
Tel (757) 766-1100 *Founded/Ownrshp* 1965
Sales 11.6MM^E^ *EMP* 300
SIC 8249 Vocational schools; Vocational schools
Prin: J Joseph Johnson
**Prin:* Edward W Carr
Prgrm Mgr: Valencia Huggins
DP Exec: Ken Throupe
Plnt Mgr: Richard Carter

D-U-N-S 01-889-3123
NEW HORIZONS TELECOM INC
901 Cope Industrial Way, Palmer, AK 99645-6739
Tel (907) 761-6000 *Founded/Ownrshp* 1977
Sales 23.3MM^E^ *EMP* 88^E^
SIC 1623 1731 8711 Transmitting tower (telecommunication) construction; Electrical work; Engineering services
CEO: John S Lee
**Pr:* Jon E Shepherd
**COO:* Nate Morton
**Sr VP:* Dean A Mudd
VP: Stephen Kieser
Prgrm Mgr: Emily Bentti
Prgrm Mgr: Kristina Buckley
Prgrm Mgr: Juhree Psenak
Sls&Mrk Ex: Donna Morigeau

D-U-N-S 06-314-1063
NEW HORIZONS WORLDWIDE INC
100 4 Falls Corporate Ctr # 408, Conshohocken, PA 19428-2950
Tel (888) 236-3625 *Founded/Ownrshp* 1988
Sales 795.8MM^E^ *EMP* 3,500
SIC 6794 8243 Franchises, selling or licensing; Software training, computer
Pr: Mark A Miller
Mng Pt: Robert J Hussey
V Ch: Mark Miller
Pr: Earl Pratt
VP: Mark Villareal
Genl Mgr: Dave Butterfield
Genl Mgr: Kristin Catlett
CIO: Howard Mark
Dir IT: Adam Goodman
VP Mktg: Hilary Olsen
Board of Directors: William H Heller, Donald W Hughes, Robert Orleyand Curtis Lee, David L Warnock, Arnold M Jacob,mark Miller

D-U-N-S 00-820-5411
NEW HOTEL MONTELEONE LLC
214 Royal St, New Orleans, LA 70130-2227
Tel (504) 523-3341 *Founded/Ownrshp* 1886
Sales 31.9MM^E^ *EMP* 390
SIC 7011 Hotels; Hotels
CFO: Charles Lacinak
Off Admin: Katie Roques
Sls Dir: Chme Fisher
Mktg Mgr: Carly Plotkin
Mktg Mgr: Tiffany Scott
Sls Mgr: Kristen Barbera
Sls Mgr: Jessica Cassioppi

D-U-N-S 07-506-7975
NEW IBERIA HEALTHCARE CORP
(*Suby of* PROGRESSIVE ACUTE CARE LLC) ★
600 N Lewis St, New Iberia, LA 70563-2043
Tel (337) 365-7311 *Founded/Ownrshp* 2013
Sales 40.8MM^E^ *EMP* 500
SIC 8099 8062 Medical services organization; General medical & surgical hospitals; Medical services organization; General medical & surgical hospitals
CEO: Alan Fabian
**Pr:* Samuel N Hazen
COO: Rachael Martinez
**CFO:* Laura Allen
Ofcr: Ryan Turner
**VP:* David G Anderson
**VP:* Dora A Blackwood
**VP:* Natalie H Cline
**VP:* John M Franck II
**VP:* Donald W Stinnett
Anesthlgy: Stephen Collins

D-U-N-S 14-256-0593 IMP
NEW IEM LLC
INDUSTRIAL ELECTRIC MFG
(*Suby of* ABD EL & LARSON HOLDINGS LLC) ★
48205 Warm Springs Blvd, Fremont, CA 94539-7654
Tel (510) 656-1600 *Founded/Ownrshp* 2003
Sales 33.3MM^E^ *EMP* 90^E^
SIC 3613 Switchboards & parts, power; Switchboard apparatus, except instruments; Control panels, electric; Switchgear & switchgear accessories; Switchboards & parts, power; Switchboard apparatus, except instruments; Control panels, electric; Switchgear & switchgear accessories
Pr: Edward Rossi
CFO: Cindy Goodsell
CFO: John Hulme
Ex VP: Doug Kristensen
Mfg Mgr: Frank Cavezza
Plnt Mgr: Tony Perreira
Ql Cn Mgr: Bob Walter Jr
S&M/VP: Clayton Such
Pdt Mgr: Jerry Gierke
Sales Asso: Andrew Davidson
Sales Asso: Joyce Gotschall

D-U-N-S 96-870-3467
NEW ILC DOVER INC
1 Moonwalker Rd, Frederica, DE 19946-2080
Tel (302) 335-3911 *Founded/Ownrshp* 2008
Sales 74.9MM^E^ *EMP* 475^E^
SIC 3842 Personal safety equipment; Personal safety equipment
Pr: William Wallach

D-U-N-S 61-642-8645
NEW IMAGE BUILDING SERVICES INC
NEW IMAGE BUILDING SUPPLIES
1405 Combermere Dr, Troy, MI 48083-2745
Tel (586) 465-4420 *Founded/Ownrshp* 1988
Sales 19.2MM^E^ *EMP* 500
SIC 7349 5999 5169 Building maintenance services; Maid services, contract or fee basis; Cleaning equipment & supplies; Chemicals & allied products; Building maintenance services; Maid services, contract or fee basis; Cleaning equipment & supplies; Chemicals & allied products
Pr: John Ezzo
Chf Mktg O: Joe Cobb
**VP:* Earl Ezzo
Opers Mgr: Scott Greenleaf

NEW IMAGE BUILDING SUPPLIES
See NEW IMAGE BUILDING SERVICES INC

N.E.W. INDIANA CO.,
See NAGAKURA ENGINEERING WORKS CO INC

D-U-N-S 10-663-8653
NEW INDUSTRIES INC
905 S Neenah Ave, Sturgeon Bay, WI 54235-1907
Tel (920) 743-8575 *Founded/Ownrshp* 1983
Sales 45.0MM *EMP* 200
SIC 3599 2396 Machine shop, jobbing & repair; Automotive & apparel trimmings; Machine shop, jobbing & repair; Automotive & apparel trimmings
Pr: Chris Moore
**VP:* Dan Moore
VP: Don Warnke
Ql Cn Mgr: Mark Stephenson

D-U-N-S 84-190-0124
■ **NEW INSPIRATION BROADCASTING CO INC**
(*Suby of* SALEM MEDIA GROUP INC) ★
4880 Santa Rosa Rd, Camarillo, CA 93012-5190
Tel (805) 987-0400 *Founded/Ownrshp* 1982
Sales 39.4MM^E^ *EMP* 1,457
SIC 4832 2731 Radio broadcasting stations; Book publishing; Radio broadcasting stations; Book publishing
CEO: Edward G Atsinger III
**Ch Bd:* Stuart Epperson
**Pr:* David Evans
**CFO:* Evan Masyr
**VP:* Christopher Henderson

D-U-N-S 03-421-2548
NEW ISRAEL FUND INC (CA)
2100 M St Nw Ste 619, Washington, DC 20037-1269
Tel (202) 842-0900 *Founded/Ownrshp* 1979
Sales 28.2MM *EMP* 35
Accts Gelman Rosenberg & Freedman B
SIC 8699 Charitable organization
Ex Dir: Larry Garber
Off Mgr: Fathiyya Hussein

D-U-N-S 60-407-0198
NEW JERNBERG SALES INC
(*Suby of* KPS CAPITAL PARTNERS LP) ★
39475 W 13 Mile Rd # 105, Novi, MI 48377-2359
Tel (248) 479-2699 *Founded/Ownrshp* 2005
Sales 170.0MM *EMP* 8
SIC 5051 Steel; Steel
Pr: George Phanopoulos

D-U-N-S 17-724-7145
NEW JERS ORGA & TISS SHAR NETW
NJ SHARING NETWORK
691 Central Ave, New Providence, NJ 07974-1560
Tel (908) 516-5400 *Founded/Ownrshp* 1983
Sales 33.6MM *EMP* 180
Accts Withum Smith Brown Pc Morrist
SIC 8099 Organ bank; Organ bank
Pr: Joseph S Roth
**COO:* Prakash RAO
**CFO:* Barry Newman
**VP:* William Reitsma
VP: Alida Sandoval
Exec: Beverly Hunt
Ex Dir: William G Dressel Jr
Ex Dir: Elisse Glennon
CIO: Jorge Kalil
Pr Mgr: Lernard Freeman

D-U-N-S 18-481-4317
■ NEW JERSEY AMERICAN WATER CO
(*Suby of* AMERICAN WATER WORKS CO INC) ★
131 Woodcrest Rd, Cherry Hill, NJ 08003-3620
Tel (856) 310-2206 *Founded/Ownrshp* 1988
Sales 195.7MM^E *EMP* 565
SIC 4941 Water supply; Water supply
CEO: Jeffry Sterba
**Pr:* John R Bigelow
**Sr VP:* Susan N Story
**Sr VP:* Mark Strauss
VP: Karl Kyriss
VP: William Pearce
**VP:* Edward D Vallejo
VP: Bill Walsh
VP: Howard Woods

D-U-N-S 96-380-7219
NEW JERSEY ANESTHESIA ASSOCIATES PC
200 S Orange Ave Ste 201, Livingston, NJ 07039-5817
Tel (888) 287-3652 *Founded/Ownrshp* 1996
Sales 39.0MM *EMP* 100
SIC 8011 Anesthesiologist; Anesthesiologist
Pr: Hang R Pak
Treas: Mark Hausdorss
Ansthlgy: Miro N Bergam
Ansthlgy: Jonathan D Blank
Ansthlgy: Joel M Braverman
Ansthlgy: Ronald J Cardoso
Ansthlgy: Dae S Chung
Ansthlgy: Eric N Fein
Ansthlgy: Joseph R Gaudio
Ansthlgy: Mark A Hausdorff
Ansthlgy: Kevin E Klebba

D-U-N-S 04-840-8033 IMP
NEW JERSEY BUSINESS FORMS MANUFACTURING CORP
JBF
55 W Sheffield Ave, Englewood, NJ 07631-4804
Tel (201) 569-4500 *Founded/Ownrshp* 1952, 1977
Sales 34.0MM^E *EMP* 115
SIC 2761 2679 7331

NEW JERSEY CARPENTERS FUNDS
See NEW JERSEY CARPENTERS PENSION FUND

D-U-N-S 08-920-4788
NEW JERSEY CARPENTERS PENSION FUND
NEW JERSEY CARPENTERS FUNDS
91 Fieldcrest Ave, Edison, NJ 08837-3627
Tel (732) 417-3900 *Founded/Ownrshp* 1958
Sales NA *EMP* 72
SIC 6371 Pension funds; Pension funds
Admn Mgr: George R Laufenberg
VP: Phillip Cooney

D-U-N-S 08-675-4566
NEW JERSEY CASUALTY INSURANCE CO
(*Suby of* NEW JERSEY MANUFACTURERS INSURANCE CO) ★
301 Sullivan Way, Ewing, NJ 08628-3406
Tel (609) 883-1300 *Founded/Ownrshp* 1999
Sales NA *EMP* 56^E
SIC 6331 Fire, marine & casualty insurance
Ch Bd: Anthony G Dickson
**CFO:* Thomas Meyers
Treas: Steven Kerner
Dir IT: Ed Buker
IT Man: Johanna Cordisco
IT Man: Stephen Knorr
IT Man: Robert Ventriglia

D-U-N-S 08-728-1531
NEW JERSEY CITY UNIVERSITY
NJCU
2039 Kennedy Blvd, Jersey City, NJ 07305
Tel (201) 200-2000 *Founded/Ownrshp* 1927
Sales 98.7MM^E *EMP* 900^E
SIC 8221 College, except junior; College, except junior
Pr: Sue Henderson
**Ch Bd:* Rafael Perez
Pr: Daniel P Elwell
COO: Mauro Altamura
Treas: Deatra Ashley
Ex VP: Joanne Bruno
VP: Adele Bey
VP: William Fellenberg
VP: Daniel Julius
VP: John Melendez
VP: K Osseiran-Hanna
VP: Tiana Sweeney
VP: John Zuzo
Exec: Harris Hordon
Exec: Robert Piaskowsky
Dir Lab: Aylen Wargniez
Assoc Dir: Nancy Bookbinder
Assoc Dir: Devan Salem

D-U-N-S 80-665-6682
NEW JERSEY COMMISSION ON HIGHER EDUCATION
(*Suby of* EXECUTIVE OFFICE OF STATE OF NEW JERSEY) ★
20 W State St Fl 7, Trenton, NJ 08608-1206
Tel (609) 292-4310 *Founded/Ownrshp* 1967
Sales NA *EMP* 16,641
SIC 9411 Administration of educational programs; ; Administration of educational programs;

D-U-N-S 80-719-8023
NEW JERSEY DEPARTMENT OF BANKING AND INSURANCE
(*Suby of* EXECUTIVE OFFICE OF STATE OF NEW JERSEY) ★
20 W State St, Trenton, NJ 08608-1206
Tel (609) 292-5360 *Founded/Ownrshp* 1891
Sales NA *EMP* 774
SIC 9651 Insurance commission, government; ; Insurance commission, government;
Dir Teleco: Donna Jackson
MIS Dir: Joseph Mingo
IT Man: Paul Penna
Snr Mgr: Reginald Young

D-U-N-S 80-641-6798
NEW JERSEY DEPARTMENT OF COMMERCE AND ECONOMIC DEVELOPMENT
(*Suby of* EXECUTIVE OFFICE OF STATE OF NEW JERSEY) ★
20 W State St, Trenton, NJ 08608-1206
Tel (609) 633-3606 *Founded/Ownrshp* 1981
Sales NA *EMP* 775
SIC 9611 Administration of general economic programs; Economic development agency, government; ; Administration of general economic programs; Economic development agency, government;

D-U-N-S 80-632-7268
NEW JERSEY DEPARTMENT OF ENVIRONMENTAL PROTECTION
(*Suby of* EXECUTIVE OFFICE OF STATE OF NEW JERSEY) ★
401 E State St, Trenton, NJ 08608-1501
Tel (609) 292-2885 *Founded/Ownrshp* 1970
Sales NA *EMP* 2,800
SIC 9512 9511 Land, mineral & wildlife conservation; Air, water & solid waste management; ; Land, mineral & wildlife conservation; Air, water & solid waste management;
Ofcr: John Burke
Ofcr: Robin Stancampiano
Ofcr: Diane Zalaskus
Snr Mgr: Rick Reilly

D-U-N-S 80-641-8075
NEW JERSEY DEPARTMENT OF HEALTH
(*Suby of* EXECUTIVE OFFICE OF STATE OF NEW JERSEY) ★
369 S Warren St, Trenton, NJ 08608-2308
Tel (609) 292-6915 *Founded/Ownrshp* 1948
Sales NA *EMP* 1,508
SIC 9431 Administration of public health programs; ; Administration of public health programs;
Snr Mgr: Floyd Genicola

D-U-N-S 80-641-8257
NEW JERSEY DEPARTMENT OF HUMAN SERVICES
(*Suby of* EXECUTIVE OFFICE OF STATE OF NEW JERSEY) ★
222 S Warren St, Trenton, NJ 08608-2306
Tel (609) 292-3717 *Founded/Ownrshp* 1976
Sales NA *EMP* 19,000
SIC 9441 Public welfare administration: non-operating, government; Public welfare administration: non-operating, government
Ofcr: Ellen Lovejoy
Off Mgr: Julie Culliton
**CIO:* Douglas Mc Grugher
IT Man: Lou Marino

D-U-N-S 80-641-8430
NEW JERSEY DEPARTMENT OF LABOR AND WORKFORCE DEVELOPMENT
(*Suby of* EXECUTIVE OFFICE OF STATE OF NEW JERSEY) ★
1 John Fitch Plz Fl 13, Trenton, NJ 08611-1760
Tel (609) 292-2323 *Founded/Ownrshp* 1948
Sales NA *EMP* 4,214
SIC 9651 Labor regulatory agency; ; Labor regulatory agency;
**Prin:* Marilyn Davis
Dir IT: Sriram Vilayanur
IT Man: Bob Schisler
Art Dir: Mar Wadiak

D-U-N-S 80-665-6856
NEW JERSEY DEPARTMENT OF PERSONNEL
(*Suby of* EXECUTIVE OFFICE OF STATE OF NEW JERSEY) ★
44 S Clinton Ave, Trenton, NJ 08609-1241
Tel (609) 984-1064 *Founded/Ownrshp* 1908
Sales NA *EMP* 622
SIC 9199 Personnel agency, government; Civil service commission, government; ; Personnel agency, government; Civil service commission, government;
Prin: Janice Mitchell-Mintz
Dir IT: Joseph Gambino

D-U-N-S 80-665-6963
NEW JERSEY DEPARTMENT OF STATE
OFFICE OF SECRETARY OF STATE
(*Suby of* EXECUTIVE OFFICE OF STATE OF NEW JERSEY) ★
225 W State St, Trenton, NJ 08608-1001
Tel (609) 292-9292 *Founded/Ownrshp* 1948
Sales NA *EMP* 276
SIC 9199 General government administration; ; General government administration;
Exec: Lynne Richmond
Comm Dir: Allison Tratner
Snr Mgr: Joseph Klett

D-U-N-S 80-747-7898
NEW JERSEY DEPARTMENT OF TREASURY
(*Suby of* EXECUTIVE OFFICE OF STATE OF NEW JERSEY) ★
125 W State St, Trenton, NJ 08608-1101
Tel (609) 292-6748 *Founded/Ownrshp* 1948
Sales NA *EMP* 3,500
SIC 9311 Treasurers' office, government; ; Treasurers' office, government;
Treas: Andrew P Sidamon-Eristoff
Treas: Bradley Abelow
Treas: Andrew Alessi
Treas: Andrew Eristoff
CTO: George Kelly
Dir IT: David Eater

D-U-N-S 80-641-7143
NEW JERSEY DEPT OF COMMUNITY AFFAIRS
(*Suby of* EXECUTIVE OFFICE OF STATE OF NEW JERSEY) ★
101 S Broad St, Trenton, NJ 08608-2401
Tel (609) 292-6420 *Founded/Ownrshp* 1966
Sales NA *EMP* 1,100
SIC 9441 Administration of social & manpower programs; ; Administration of social & manpower programs;

D-U-N-S 80-665-6781
NEW JERSEY DEPT OF LAW & PUBLIC SAFETY
OFFICE OF THE ATTORNEY GENERAL
(*Suby of* EXECUTIVE OFFICE OF STATE OF NEW JERSEY) ★
25 Market St Fl 8, Trenton, NJ 08611-2148
Tel (609) 292-4925 *Founded/Ownrshp* 1948
Sales NA *EMP* 7,500^E
SIC 9222 9221 Attorney General's office; ; Police protection; Attorney General's office; ; Police protection
Prin: John Jay Hoffman
Comm Dir: David Wald
IT Man: Fred Gmitter
Snr Mgr: Patrick Callahan

D-U-N-S 80-665-7177
NEW JERSEY DEPT OF TRANSPORTATION
(*Suby of* EXECUTIVE OFFICE OF STATE OF NEW JERSEY) ★
1035 Parkway Ave Fl 2, Ewing, NJ 08618-2309
Tel (609) 530-3855 *Founded/Ownrshp* 1966
Sales NA *EMP* 3,400
SIC 9621 Regulation, administration of transportation; ; Regulation, administration of transportation;
**CFO:* Gary Brune
Ofcr: Andrew Feller
VP: Eileen Sheehy
Ex Dir: William S Beetle
Plng Mgr: Joseph Powell
IT Man: Jim Vari
Snr Mgr: Marylou Mycoff
Snr Mgr: John Semler

NEW JERSEY DIVISION
See ELIZABETHTOWN GAS CO

D-U-N-S 07-146-4515
NEW JERSEY EDUCATION ASSOCIATION INC
NJEA
180 W State St, Trenton, NJ 08608-1104
Tel (609) 599-4561 *Founded/Ownrshp* 1853
Sales 129.6MM *EMP* 257
SIC 8621 Professional membership organizations; Professional membership organizations
Ex Dir: Vince Giordan
Treas: Anne Simon
**Sec:* Marie Blistan
**VP:* Barbara Keshishian
VP: Joyce Powell
**VP:* Wendell Steinhauer
Assoc Dir: Howard Bookin
Assoc Dir: Beth Buonsante
Assoc Dir: Kim Cowing
Assoc Dir: Wayne Dibofsky
Assoc Dir: Christina Farrell
Assoc Dir: Janet Morrison
Assoc Dir: Julie Plotkin
Assoc Dir: Pete Vala
Comm Dir: Lynn Maher

D-U-N-S 78-697-6308
NEW JERSEY ENVIRONMENTAL INFRASTRUCTURE TRUST
3131 Princeton Pike, Lawrenceville, NJ 08648-2201
Tel (609) 219-8600 *Founded/Ownrshp* 1986
Sales 49.8MM *EMP* 14
Accts Bowman & Company Llpl Voorhee
SIC 6211 Bond dealers & brokers; Bond dealers & brokers
V Ch: Briant Robert
**COO:* Mary Pearsall
**Treas:* Warren Victor

D-U-N-S 04-735-5839
NEW JERSEY HERALD
(*Suby of* QUINCY NEWSPAPERS INC) ★
2 Spring St, Newton, NJ 07860-2077
Tel (973) 383-1500 *Founded/Ownrshp* 1991
Sales 39.1MM^E *EMP* 1,000
SIC 2711 Newspapers, publishing & printing; Newspapers, publishing & printing
Pr: Thomas Oakley
CFO: David Oakley
VP: Tony Rose
Dist Mgr: Leland Bonelli
Genl Mgr: James Collins

D-U-N-S 07-376-3724
NEW JERSEY HOSPITAL ASSOCIATION
760 Alexander Rd, Princeton, NJ 08540-6305
Tel (609) 275-4000 *Founded/Ownrshp* 1918
Sales 10.1MM *EMP* 402
Accts Eisneramper Llp Iselin Nj
SIC 8062 General medical & surgical hospitals; General medical & surgical hospitals
Pr: Gary S Carter
**Ch Bd:* Leslie D Hirsch
**CFO:* David P Lavins
Bd of Dir: Kathi Sengin
Sr VP: Sheryl Slonim
VP: Neal Eicher
VP: Peter Lillo
VP: Marc Lory
IT Man: Jennifer Hass
**Genl Couns:* Sarah Lechner
Counsel: Karen Ali
Board of Directors: Joanne Carrocino, John Lloyd, Michael Maron

D-U-N-S 09-925-4682
NEW JERSEY HOUSING MORTGAGE FINANCE AGENCY
(*Suby of* EXECUTIVE OFFICE OF STATE OF NEW JERSEY) ★
637 S Clinton Ave, Trenton, NJ 08611-1811
Tel (609) 278-7400 *Founded/Ownrshp* 1984
Sales NA *EMP* 250
Accts Cliftonlarsonallen Llp Baltim
SIC 6162 9199 Mortgage bankers & correspondents; ; Mortgage bankers & correspondents;
Ex Dir: Marge D Vecchia
**CFO:* David Bonomo
Ofcr: Kevin Ambrose
Prin: Dawn Parreott
**Ex Dir:* Anthony L Marchetta
Snr Mgr: Annie Bowser
Snr Mgr: James Robertson

D-U-N-S 08-199-2695
NEW JERSEY INSTITUTE FOR DISABILITIES INC
10a Oak Dr, Edison, NJ 08837-2313
Tel (732) 549-6187 *Founded/Ownrshp* 1948
Sales 30.0MM *EMP* 377
Accts Sobel & Co Llc Livingston
SIC 8322 Social service center; Social service center
Ex Dir: Robert Ferrara
IT Man: Anton Weck

D-U-N-S 07-516-2990
NEW JERSEY INSTITUTE OF TECHNOLOGY (INC)
NJIT
323 Dr Martin Luth, Newark, NJ 07102
Tel (973) 596-3000 *Founded/Ownrshp* 1928
Sales 220.5MM *EMP* 1,047
Accts Grant Thornton Llp Edison N
SIC 8221 University; University
Pr: Joel S Bloom
CFO: Anthony Tomandel
Treas: Tworischuk Assistant
Ex VP: Jerry Paris
Sr VP: Henry A Mauermeyer
VP: Andrew P Christ
VP: Charles Dees
VP: Matthew Golden
VP: Kathryn Kelly
VP: Victor Reynaga
VP: Shakera Rodgers
VP: Gale Spak
Exec: Angela Vega
Assoc Dir: Rosa Cano
Assoc Dir: Bernadette Longo
Assoc Dir: James McHugh
Assoc Dir: Alexis Schug
Adv Bd Mbr: Eseosa Eriamiato

D-U-N-S 05-499-9100
NEW JERSEY LIFE AND HEALTH INSURANCE GUARANTY ASSOCIATION
11 Wharf Ave Apt 1, Red Bank, NJ 07701-6617
Tel (732) 345-5200 *Founded/Ownrshp* 2010
Sales NA *EMP* 2^E
SIC 6311 Life insurance; Life insurance
Prin: Roger Leach

D-U-N-S 00-697-4851
NEW JERSEY MANUFACTURERS INSURANCE CO
NJM INSURANCE GROUP
301 Sullivan Way, Ewing, NJ 08628-3406
Tel (609) 883-1300 *Founded/Ownrshp* 1913
Sales NA *EMP* 2,500
SIC 6331 Workers' compensation insurance; Fire, marine & casualty insurance: mutual; Automobile insurance; Workers' compensation insurance; Fire, marine & casualty insurance: mutual; Automobile insurance
Pr: Bernard M Flynn
Pr: Mitchell Livingston
**CFO:* Charles A Prall
**Ex VP:* Robert H Vetterstrom
Ex VP: Robert H Zetterstrom
**VP:* Neil Delaney
Genl Mgr: Tanya Spirk
DP Dir: Tracy Trinian
Dir IT: Ed Buker
IT Man: Michael Dillon
IT Man: Stephen Knorr

D-U-N-S 06-184-3553
■ NEW JERSEY NATURAL GAS CO
(*Suby of* NEW JERSEY RESOURCES CORP) ★
1415 Wyckoff Rd, Wall Township, NJ 07727-3940
Tel (732) 938-1000 *Founded/Ownrshp* 1982
Sales 501.9MM^E *EMP* 750
SIC 4924 Natural gas distribution; Natural gas distribution
Ch Bd: Lawrence M Downes
**COO:* Kathleen T Ellis
Treas: Laurie McGraw
**Sr VP:* Oleta J Harden
**Sr VP:* Thomas J Kononowitz
**VP:* Francis X Colford
VP: Keith Hartman
VP: Joseph Marazzo
VP: Thomas J Massaro
VP: Thomas Massaro
VP: Deborah Zilai
Board of Directors: Bruce Coe, Warren R Haas, Lester Johnson, Dorothy Light

D-U-N-S 62-236-8470
NEW JERSEY PERFORMING ARTS CENTER CORP
1 Center St, Newark, NJ 07102-4501
Tel (973) 642-8989 *Founded/Ownrshp* 1989
Sales 30.3MM *EMP* 340
SIC 7922 Performing arts center production; Performing arts center production
Pr: John Schreiber
Pr: Gayle Allen
CFO: Warren Tranquada
**Ch:* Arthur F Ryan
VP: Donna Kuhne
VP: David Rodriguez
VP: Alison Scott-Williams
Assoc Dir: Stephanie Miller
Dir Soc: Roslyn Brown
Prgrm Mgr: Evan White
CIO: Ernie Dirocco

D-U-N-S 15-377-1662
NEW JERSEY PROPERTY LIABILITY INSURANCE GUARANTY ASSOCIATION
222 Mount Airy Rd, Basking Ridge, NJ 07920-2335
Tel (908) 953-9533 *Founded/Ownrshp* 1975
Sales NA *EMP* 22
Accts Eisneramper Llp Bridgewater

SIC 6411 Insurance agents
Ex Dir: Holly C Bakke

D-U-N-S 16-719-8840
NEW JERSEY PUBLIC EMPLOYMENT RELATIONS COMMISSION
(*Suby of* EXECUTIVE OFFICE OF STATE OF NEW JERSEY) ★
495 W State St, Trenton, NJ 08618-5625
Tel (609) 984-7372 *Founded/Ownrshp* 2004
Sales 2.4MM^E *EMP* 706^E
SIC 8322 Helping hand service (Big Brother, etc.); Offender self-help agency
Prin: Lawrence Henderson

D-U-N-S 06-004-0953
NEW JERSEY RE-INSURANCE CO
(*Suby of* NEW JERSEY MANUFACTURERS INSURANCE CO) ★
301 Sullivan Way, Ewing, NJ 08628-3406
Tel (609) 883-1300 *Founded/Ownrshp* 1977
Sales NA *EMP* 9
SIC 6311 6331 Life reinsurance; Automobile insurance; Property damage insurance; Workers' compensation insurance; Life reinsurance; Automobile insurance; Property damage insurance; Workers' compensation insurance
CEO: Anthony G Dickson
**CFO:* Thomas A Meyers
Treas: Steven P Kerner Jr

D-U-N-S 00-697-1592
▲ NEW JERSEY RESOURCES CORP
1415 Wyckoff Rd, Wall Township, NJ 07727-3940
Tel (732) 938-1480 *Founded/Ownrshp* 1981
Sales 2.7MMM *EMP* 968^E
Tkr Sym NJR *Exch* NYS
SIC 4924 Natural gas distribution; Natural gas distribution
Ch Bd: Laurence M Downes
CFO: Glenn C Lockwood
Treas: Timothy C Hearne
Sr VP: Mariellen Dugan
Sr VP: Kathleen T Ellis
Sr VP: Thomas J Kononowitz
Sr VP: Kevin A Moss
Sr VP: Wayne K Tarney
Sr VP: Stephen D Westhoven
Sr VP: Debbie Zilai
Mktg Dir: Robert Gallo
Board of Directors: George R Zoffinger, Lawrence R Codey, Donald L Correll, Robert B Evans, M William Howard Jr, Jane M Kenny, Alfred C Koeppe, J Terry Strange, Sharon C Taylor, David A Trice

NEW JERSEY SCHOOL CONSTRUCTION
See NEW JERSEY SCHOOLS DEVELOPMENT AUTHORITY

D-U-N-S 13-389-1650
NEW JERSEY SCHOOLS DEVELOPMENT AUTHORITY
NEW JERSEY SCHOOL CONSTRUCTION
32 E Front St, Trenton, NJ 08608-2106
Tel (609) 943-5955 *Founded/Ownrshp* 2007
Sales 96.9MM^E *EMP* 256^E
SIC 1542 School building construction; School building construction
CEO: Charles McKenna
Ofcr: Thomas Ahern
Ofcr: Jorge Alfonso
Ofcr: Hugo Horcada
Ofcr: Kevin Niemeyer
VP: Donald R Guarriello Jr
VP: Donald Guarriello
VP: Andrew Yosha
Comm Dir: Kristen Maclean
Mng Dir: John Rivera
CTO: Joseph Vanstory

D-U-N-S 06-427-5316
NEW JERSEY SPORTS & EXPOSITION AUTHORITY
MONMOUTH PARK RACETRACK
1 Dekorte Park Plz, Lyndhurst, NJ 07071
Tel (201) 460-1700 *Founded/Ownrshp* 1971
Sales 80.1MM^E *EMP* 3,500
SIC 8641 7941 6512

D-U-N-S 00-697-3200
NEW JERSEY TRANSIT BUS OPERATIONS INC
(*Suby of* NEW JERSEY TRANSIT CORP) ★
1 Penn Plz E, Newark, NJ 07105-2245
Tel (973) 491-7000 *Founded/Ownrshp* 1928
Sales 194.0MM^E *EMP* 10,000
SIC 4131 4111 Intercity bus line; Subway operation; Intercity bus line; Subway operation
CFO: Charlie Wedel
Ex Dir: George D Warrington
IT Man: Daryl Gibson

D-U-N-S 03-848-5140 IMP
NEW JERSEY TRANSIT CORP
NJ TRANSIT
1 Penn Plz E, Newark, NJ 07105-2245
Tel (973) 491-7000 *Founded/Ownrshp* 1979
Sales 738.8MM^E *EMP* 10,000
Accts Ernst & Young Llp Iselin New
SIC 4111 4131 Commuter rail passenger operation; Intercity bus line; Commuter rail passenger operation; Intercity bus line
**Ch Bd:* Stephen Dilts
CFO: H Charles Wedel
Ofcr: Elaine Donnadio
Ofcr: Inez Linton
Ofcr: Anthony Vetrano
Dir Risk M: Lisa Caudullo
Ex Dir: Nancy Bassett
Ex Dir: Shirley A Delibero
Ex Dir: James Weinstein
Prgrm Mgr: John Clark
Prgrm Mgr: Keith Davis

D-U-N-S 95-791-5986
NEW JERSEY TRANSPORTATION TRUST FUND AUTHORITY
(*Suby of* STATE OF NEW JERSEY) ★
1035 Parkway Ave, Ewing, NJ 08618-2309
Tel (609) 530-2035 *Founded/Ownrshp* 1920
Sales 934.3MM *EMP* 46^E
Accts Mercadien Pc Princeton Nj
SIC 8611 Business associations; Business associations

D-U-N-S 00-177-4736
NEW JERSEY TURNPIKE AUTHORITY INC
581 Mack Cali Bldg Main, Woodbridge, NJ 07095
Tel (732) 750-5300 *Founded/Ownrshp* 1948
Sales 1.5MMM *EMP* 2,400
SIC 4785 Toll road operation; Toll road operation
Ch Bd: Jamie Fox
**CEO:* Ronald Gravino
**COO:* John F O Hern
CFO: Catherine Coryat
**Treas:* Michael R Dupont
Treas: Gary Lewis
VP: John Lewis
Exec: John O'Hern
**Ex Dir:* Veronique Hakim
IT Man: Dawn Iacobelli
Sfty Mgr: Edward Marsh

D-U-N-S 18-377-5394
NEW JERSEY WATER SUPPLY AUTHORITY INC
1851 State Route 31, Clinton, NJ 08809-2018
Tel (908) 638-6121 *Founded/Ownrshp* 1981
Sales 25.8MM *EMP* 130
Accts Meercadien Pc Cpas Princeto
SIC 4941 Water supply; Water supply
Ex Dir: Henry S Patterson III
**CFO:* Michael R Citarelli
**Ex Dir:* Michael Catania
Opers Mgr: Stephen Hardick
Snr Mgr: Jerald Hoagland

D-U-N-S 78-673-5506
NEW JERUSALEM PRAISE & WORSHIP INC
NEW JRSALEM PRAISE WORSHIP CTR
62340 Highway 1090, Pearl River, LA 70452-4118
Tel (985) 863-9444 *Founded/Ownrshp* 1987
Sales 3.3MM^E *EMP* 300
SIC 8661 Non-denominational church; Non-denominational church

NEW JRSALEM PRAISE WORSHIP CTR
See NEW JERUSALEM PRAISE & WORSHIP INC

D-U-N-S 01-317-8231
NEW KENSINGTON-ARNOLD SCHOOL DISTRICT (PA)
707 Stevenson Blvd, New Kensington, PA 15068-5372
Tel (724) 335-4401 *Founded/Ownrshp* 1952
Sales 20.9MM^E *EMP* 308
SIC 8211 Public elementary & secondary schools; Public elementary & secondary schools
Off Mgr: Debbei Vellre
Schl Brd P: Robert Pallone

D-U-N-S 07-979-9042
NEW KENT COUNTY PUBLIC SCHOOLS
12003 New Kent Hwy, New Kent, VA 23124
Tel (804) 966-9650 *Founded/Ownrshp* 2015
Sales 15.3MM^E *EMP* 285^E
SIC 8211 Public elementary & secondary schools
Teacher Pr: Cynthia Pitts

D-U-N-S 79-170-0800
NEW KENT COUNTY SCHOOL BOARD
11920 New Kent Hwy, New Kent, VA 23124-2005
Tel (804) 966-9650 *Founded/Ownrshp* 2004
Sales 14.4MM^E *EMP* 300
SIC 8211 School board; School board
Dir IT: Phyllis Geron
IT Man: Valerie Bivans

D-U-N-S 06-599-8411
NEW KENT COUNTY SCHOOL DISTRICT (VA)
Rr 249, New Kent, VA 23124
Tel (804) 966-9861 *Founded/Ownrshp* 1654
Sales 286.0M *EMP* 400
SIC 8211 Public elementary & secondary schools; Public elementary & secondary schools

D-U-N-S 11-836-5022
NEW KING INC
BURGER KING
874 Silas Deane Hwy, Wethersfield, CT 06109-3412
Tel (860) 257-9000 *Founded/Ownrshp* 1980
Sales 9.1MM^E *EMP* 320
SIC 5812 Fast-food restaurant, chain; Fast-food restaurant, chain
Pr: Jack Muirhead

NEW LEADER
See HIGHWAY EQUIPMENT CO

NEW LEADERS FOR NEW SCHOOLS
See NEW LEADERS INC

D-U-N-S 03-010-5659
NEW LEADERS INC
NEW LEADERS FOR NEW SCHOOLS
30 W 26th St Fl 9, New York, NY 10010-2089
Tel (646) 792-1070 *Founded/Ownrshp* 2000
Sales 34.0MM *EMP* 286^E
Accts Weisermazars Llp New York Ny
SIC 8299 Educational service, nondegree granting: continuing educ.; Educational service, nondegree granting: continuing educ.
CEO: Jean Desravines
CFO: Angela Vanderploeg
VP: Charles Richardson
Ex Dir: Millard House
Ex Dir: Terrence Kneisel
Mng Dir: Karen Bryan
Mng Dir: Tomeka Carwell
Mng Dir: Verta Maloney
Mng Dir: Michele Mason
Off Admin: Dena Kessler
Dir IT: David Clodomir
Board of Directors: Janice Crawford, Sandra Licon, Frances McLaughlin, Lory Pilchik

D-U-N-S 15-345-2834
NEW LEAF COMMUNITY MARKETS INC
(*Suby of* NEW SEASONS MARKET LLC) ★
1101 Pacific Ave Ste 333, Santa Cruz, CA 95060-7510
Tel (831) 466-9060 *Founded/Ownrshp* 2013
Sales 54.4MM^E *EMP* 335
SIC 5411

NEW LEAF DISTRIBUTING
See AL-WALI CORP

NEW LEAF LAB
See NEW LEAF MANAGEMENT LLC

D-U-N-S 07-971-0362
NEW LEAF MANAGEMENT LLC (AZ)
NEW LEAF LAB
8000 S Kolb Rd, Tucson, AZ 85756-9272
Tel (928) 263-6300 *Founded/Ownrshp* 2014
Sales 33.0MM *EMP* 200
SIC 8711 Chemical engineering; Consulting engineer

D-U-N-S 78-341-1759
NEW LEGEND INC
LEGEND TRANSPOTATION
1235 Oswald Rd, Yuba City, CA 95991-9719
Tel (530) 674-3100 *Founded/Ownrshp* 2006
Sales 77.7MM^E *EMP* 200
SIC 4213 4212 Trucking, except local; Local trucking, without storage; Trucking, except local; Local trucking, without storage
Pr: Sunny Samara
**CFO:* Bobby Samara
Sfty Mgr: Simran Singh
**Sls Mgr:* Robert Moffitt
Sales Asso: David Paintner

D-U-N-S 10-001-8829
NEW LENOX SCHOOL DISTRICT 122
102 S Cedar Rd, New Lenox, IL 60451-1702
Tel (815) 485-2169 *Founded/Ownrshp* 2001
Sales 36.7MM^E *EMP* 600
SIC 8211 Public elementary school; Public junior high school; Public elementary school; Public junior high school
Bd of Dir: Amanda Novotny
VP: Kathy Miller
IT Man: Melissa Chojnacki
Pr Dir: Carolyn Zimba

D-U-N-S 09-754-6519
NEW LEXINGTON CITY SCHOOLS
2549 Panther Dr Ne, New Lexington, OH 43764-1396
Tel (740) 342-4133 *Founded/Ownrshp* 1966
Sales 22.0MM *EMP* 232
Accts Dave Yost Athens Ohio
SIC 8211 Public elementary & secondary schools; Public elementary & secondary schools
MIS Dir: Michael Stilwell
HC Dir: Molly Dupler

D-U-N-S 93-250-3394
NEW LEXINGTON CLINIC PSC
1221 S Broadway, Lexington, KY 40504-2701
Tel (859) 258-4950 *Founded/Ownrshp* 1994
Sales 125.5MM^E *EMP* 1,075
SIC 8011 Medical centers; Primary care medical clinic; Medical centers; Primary care medical clinic
CEO: Andrew Henderson MD
**CFO:* Randall K Lemay
Dir Rx: Carol Erwin
Dept Mgr: Cale Jacobs
Off Mgr: Sharon Baker
Off Mgr: Brenda Hay
CIO: Brent Baldwin
Dir IT: Audra Wray
Orthpdst: David Burandt
Orthpdst: David Dome
Pathlgst: Mary O'Daniel-Pierce
Board of Directors: Dr John Collins, John Dineen, Michael Eden, Dr David Gammon, Andrew Henderson, Michael McKinney, Dr Henry Tutt, Dr Pell Wardrop, Dr Paul Warfield

D-U-N-S 07-302-2683
NEW LIBERTY HOSPITAL DISTRICT OF CLAY COUNTY MISSOURI
2525 Glenn Hendren Dr, Liberty, MO 64068-9625
Tel (816) 781-7200 *Founded/Ownrshp* 1974
Sales 233.5MM^E *EMP* 1,700^E
Accts Paige Cooper
SIC 8062 8051 General medical & surgical hospitals; Skilled nursing care facilities; General medical & surgical hospitals; Skilled nursing care facilities
Pr: David Feess
Dir Vol: Carmella Kovach
CFO: Erin Parde
Chf Mktg O: Kent Haggard
Dir Lab: Damon Cluts
Dir Rx: Janice Hennings
**Prin:* Richard Boswell
**Prin:* Dennis L Carter
**Prin:* William Christian Sizemore
**Prin:* Jim Streu
Ex Dir: Mark Bertrand

NEW LIFE PUBLICATIONS
See CAMPUS CRUSADE FOR CHRIST INC

NEW LIFE PUBLICATIONS
See GAIN INTERNATIONAL

NEW LIFE TRANSPORT PARTS CTR
See JOMAR INVESTMENTS INC

D-U-N-S 06-407-0197
NEW LIFECARE HOSPITALS OF DAYTON LLC
(*Suby of* LIFECARE FAMILY OF HOSPITALS) ★
4000 Mmsburg Cntrville Rd, Miamisburg, OH 45342
Tel (937) 384-8300 *Founded/Ownrshp* 2013
Sales 32.9MM^E *EMP* 654^E
SIC 8062 General medical & surgical hospitals
Ch Bd: Phillip B Douglas
Mtls Mgr: Kristen Myers
Phys Thrpy: Colleen Andrews
Dir Health: Sheila Simons

D-U-N-S 80-776-4340
NEW LIFECARE HOSPITALS OF MILWAUKEE LLC
LIFECARE HOSPITALS WISCONSIN
(*Suby of* LIFECARE FAMILY OF HOSPITALS) ★
2400 Golf Rd, Pewaukee, WI 53072-5590
Tel (262) 524-2600 *Founded/Ownrshp* 2008
Sales 83.7MM^E *EMP* 1,156^E
SIC 8062 General medical & surgical hospitals
CEO: Phillip B Douglas
CFO: Lynette Carini
**VP:* Maegan Bowman
**VP:* Stephanie Carpenter
Dir Rx: Lori Breckheimer
QA Dir: Diane Batten
Phys Thrpy: Lisa Crogan
HC Dir: Christine Hendricks

D-U-N-S 60-438-4511
NEW LIGHT CHURCH WORLD OUTREACH AND WORSHIP CENTERS INC
LIGHT MINISTRIES
11233 Crown Park Dr, Houston, TX 77067-4008
Tel (281) 257-6554 *Founded/Ownrshp* 1989
Sales 14.6MM^E *EMP* 292
SIC 8661 Non-denominational church; Non-denominational church

D-U-N-S 04-312-2407 IMP/EXP
NEW LIMECO LLC (FL)
25251 Sw 139th Ave, Princeton, FL 33032-5505
Tel (305) 258-1611 *Founded/Ownrshp* 1966, 2001
Sales 36.1MM^E *EMP* 50
SIC 5148 Fruits, fresh; Vegetables, fresh
Genl Mgr: Eddie Caram
Plnt Mgr: Charlie Caves

NEW LINE MORTGAGE
See REPUBLIC MORTGAGE HOME LOANS LLC

D-U-N-S 07-844-0132
NEW LINE TRANSPORT LLC
(*Suby of* CEMEX INC) ★
1501 Belvedere Rd, West Palm Beach, FL 33406-1501
Tel (561) 833-5555 *Founded/Ownrshp* 2012
Sales 27.3MM^E *EMP* 330^E
SIC 4789 Transportation services
Prin: Juan C Herrera

D-U-N-S 10-426-4499 IMP/EXP
NEW LOGIC RESEARCH INC
1295 67th St, Emeryville, CA 94608-1120
Tel (510) 655-7305 *Founded/Ownrshp* 2002
Sales 22.8MM^E *EMP* 90
SIC 3559 Chemical machinery & equipment; Chemical machinery & equipment
CEO: Gregory Johnson
**Pr:* Dr J Brad Culkin
**CFO:* Julie Vukovojac
Dir Lab: Landon Graham
VP Opers: Chip Johnson
Mktg Mgr: Monty Burns
Sls Mgr: Peter Corboy

D-U-N-S 07-478-8464
NEW LONDON FAMILY MEDICAL CENTER INC
NEW LONDON FAMILY MEDICAL CTR
(*Suby of* MEDICARE) ★
1405 Mill St, New London, WI 54961-2155
Tel (920) 531-2044 *Founded/Ownrshp* 1930
Sales 35.0MM *EMP* 260
SIC 8062 General medical & surgical hospitals; General medical & surgical hospitals
Pr: William Schmidt
Phys Thrpy: Michael Radtke

NEW LONDON FAMILY MEDICAL CTR
See NEW LONDON FAMILY MEDICAL CENTER INC

D-U-N-S 07-398-8792
NEW LONDON HOSPITAL ASSOCIATION INC
273 County Rd, New London, NH 03257-7700
Tel (603) 526-2911 *Founded/Ownrshp* 2013
Sales NA *EMP* 510
SIC 8062 General medical & surgical hospitals; Extended care facility; General medical & surgical hospitals
Pr: Bruce T King
Ch: Susan A Reeves Edd
Treas: David Marshall
Admn Mgr: Coua Earley

D-U-N-S 10-001-1873
NEW LONDON PUBLIC SCHOOL DISTRICT
134 Williams St, New London, CT 06320-5231
Tel (860) 447-6000 *Founded/Ownrshp* 1950
Sales 24.8MM^E *EMP* 293
SIC 8211 School board; School board
VP: Elaine Maynard-Adams
Comm Man: Julianne Hanckel
Netwrk Mgr: Kathy Slufik
Snr Mgr: Marie Smith

D-U-N-S 10-008-3641
NEW LONDON SCHOOL DISTRICT
901 W Washington St, New London, WI 54961-1653
Tel (920) 982-8530 *Founded/Ownrshp* 1963
Sales 30.0MM *EMP* 325
Accts Erickson & Associates Sc A
SIC 8211 Public elementary & secondary schools; Public elementary & secondary schools
Dir IT: Julie Haase
IT Man: Terry Wetzel
HC Dir: Susan Resch

NEW LONDON TAPE DISTRIBUTORS
See CONSUMERS INTERSTATE CORP

D-U-N-S 62-536-2777
NEW LOOK CONTRACTING INC
14045 Northdale Blvd # 1, Rogers, MN 55374-4628
Tel (763) 241-1596 *Founded/Ownrshp* 1988

Sales 31.9MM^E *EMP* 80
SIC 1389 1611 1623 Construction, repair & dismantling services; Highway & street construction; Water & sewer line construction
Pr: Bevin Mitchell
**Treas:* Diane Mitchell
**VP:* Jonathan Mitchell

D-U-N-S 02-553-9719
NEW MADRID CO SCHOOL DIST R1
NEW MADRID COUNTY CENTRAL
310 Us Highway 61, New Madrid, MO 63869-9753
Tel (573) 688-2165 *Founded/Ownrshp* 1968
Sales 13.0MM^E *EMP* 300^E
SIC 8211 Public elementary & secondary schools; Public elementary & secondary schools

NEW MADRID COUNTY CENTRAL
See NEW MADRID CO SCHOOL DIST R1

D-U-N-S 78-972-9019
■ NEW MANHEIM AUTO AUCTIONS LIMITED (INC)
COX MEDIA GROUP
(*Suby of* MANHEIM INVESTMENTS INC) ★
6205 Pachtree Dunwoody Rd, Atlanta, GA 30328-4524
Tel (678) 645-0000 *Founded/Ownrshp* 1993
Sales 193.0MM^E *EMP* 1,000
SIC 5012 Automobiles & other motor vehicles; Automobiles & other motor vehicles
Pr: Dean H Eisner
Sr VP: Ralph M Liniado
VP: Mark Brunn
VP: Patty Dontje
**VP:* Jamie D Porter

D-U-N-S 01-454-0848 IMP
NEW MAVERICK DESK INC
(*Suby of* HAMILTON SORTER) ★
15100 S Figueroa St, Gardena, CA 90248-1724
Tel (310) 217-1554 *Founded/Ownrshp* 1998
Sales 20.6MM^E *EMP* 150
SIC 2521 Wood office furniture; Wood office furniture
CEO: John Long
**Pr:* Rich Mealey
**CEO:* Ted Jaroszewicz
Exec: KOA Toon
Board of Directors: Jeffrey Pfeffer

D-U-N-S 07-920-5441
▲ NEW MEDIA INVESTMENT GROUP INC
1345 Avenue Of The Americ, New York, NY 10105-0014
Tel (212) 479-3160 *Founded/Ownrshp* 2013
Sales 652.3MM *EMP* 8,322
Accts Ernst & Young Llp New York N
Tkr Sym NEWM *Exch* NYS
SIC 2711 7373 Newspapers, publishing & printing; Systems integration services
CEO: Michael E Reed
Ch Bd: Wesley R Edens
COO: Kirk Davis
CFO: Gregory W Freiberg
Board of Directors: Theodore P Janulis, Kevin M Sheehan, Laurence Tarica

NEW MERIDIAN
See EDEN FOODS INC

D-U-N-S 01-655-1223
■ NEW MEXICO BANK & TRUST
(*Suby of* HEARTLAND FINANCIAL USA INC) ★
320 Gold Ave Sw Ste 100, Albuquerque, NM 87102-3240
Tel (505) 830-8100 *Founded/Ownrshp* 1998, 1999
Sales NA *EMP* 125
SIC 6021 National commercial banks; National commercial banks
Pr: R Greg Leyendecker
Sr VP: Christopher Gibbon
Sr VP: Brad Marsh
Sr VP: Patrick Schaefer
VP: Robert Gallegos
VP: Mari Goodner

D-U-N-S 94-903-9036
NEW MEXICO BANQUEST CORP
(*Suby of* STRATEGIC GROWTH BANCORP INC) ★
62 Lincoln Ave, Santa Fe, NM 87501-2004
Tel (505) 984-7400 *Founded/Ownrshp* 2013
Sales NA *EMP* 500
SIC 6021 National trust companies with deposits, commercial; National trust companies with deposits, commercial
Pr: Greg Ellena

NEW MEXICO CANCER CENTER
See NEW MEXICO ONCOLOGY HEMATOLOGY CONSULTANTS LTD

NEW MEXICO COFFEE COMPANY
See TRILLIANT FOOD AND NUTRITION LLC

D-U-N-S 80-856-1823
NEW MEXICO DEPARTMENT OF CHILDREN YOUTH AND FAMILIES
(*Suby of* OFFICE OF SECRETARY) ★
1120 Paseo De Peralta, Santa Fe, NM 87501-2747
Tel (505) 827-7602 *Founded/Ownrshp* 1992
Sales NA *EMP* 2,161
SIC 9441 Administration of social & manpower programs; ; Administration of social & manpower programs;
Exec: Dorothy Montoya
CIO: Crawford Spooner

D-U-N-S 80-856-1567
NEW MEXICO DEPARTMENT OF FINANCE & ADMINISTRATION
(*Suby of* OFFICE OF SECRETARY) ★
Bataan Memorial Bldg 180, Santa Fe, NM 87501
Tel (505) 827-4985 *Founded/Ownrshp* 1957
Sales NA *EMP* 1,000
SIC 9311 Finance, taxation & monetary policy; ; Finance, taxation & monetary policy;
Prin: Tom Clifford

D-U-N-S 80-838-9662
NEW MEXICO DEPARTMENT OF GENERAL SERVICES
(*Suby of* OFFICE OF SECRETARY) ★
715 Alta Vista St, Santa Fe, NM 87505-4108
Tel (505) 827-2000 *Founded/Ownrshp* 1983
Sales NA *EMP* 303
SIC 9199 General government administration; ; General government administration;
Dir IT: Kevin Baltvey
Dir IT: David McCutcheon
IT Man: Ronald Pack
Genl Couns: Maria Sanchez

D-U-N-S 80-838-9274
NEW MEXICO DEPARTMENT OF HEALTH
(*Suby of* OFFICE OF SECRETARY) ★
1190 S Saint Francis Dr, Santa Fe, NM 87505-4173
Tel (505) 827-2613 *Founded/Ownrshp* 1991
Sales NA *EMP* 4,000
SIC 9431 Administration of public health programs; ; Administration of public health programs;
Prin: Retta Ward SEC
Off Mgr: Jeanne Alano
CIO: Mike Mier
CIO: Elisa Storie
Snr Mgr: Lawrence White

D-U-N-S 83-771-0722
NEW MEXICO DEPARTMENT OF HUMAN SERVICES
(*Suby of* OFFICE OF SECRETARY) ★
2009 S Pacheco St, Santa Fe, NM 87505-5473
Tel (505) 827-7750 *Founded/Ownrshp* 2001
Sales NA *EMP* 1,535
SIC 9441 Administration of social & human resources; ; Administration of social & human resources;
Doctor: Jeanne Cournoyer

D-U-N-S 80-838-9357
NEW MEXICO DEPARTMENT OF PUBLIC SAFETY
(*Suby of* OFFICE OF SECRETARY) ★
4491 Cerrillos Rd, Santa Fe, NM 87507-9721
Tel (505) 827-9000 *Founded/Ownrshp* 1987
Sales NA *EMP* 1,200
SIC 9229 Public order & safety statistics centers; ; Public order & safety statistics centers;
Ofcr: Jeffrey Lara
Ofcr: Denise Lazzari
Ofcr: Jeanelle Lerouge
Ofcr: Leslie Torrez
Comm Dir: Kim Clark
Ex Dir: Micheal Vinyard
Admn Mgr: Marla Rivera
Brnch Mgr: Stephen Libicer
CIO: Ron Burton
Dir IT: David Keys
Dir IT: Mark Molina

D-U-N-S 80-838-9233
NEW MEXICO DEPARTMENT OF TAXATION AND REVENUE
(*Suby of* OFFICE OF SECRETARY) ★
1100 S Saint Francis Dr, Santa Fe, NM 87505-4147
Tel (505) 827-0700 *Founded/Ownrshp* 1978
Sales NA *EMP* 1,304
SIC 9311 Taxation department, government; ; Taxation department, government;
Treas: Jim Burleson
S&M/VP: Grace Haggerty
Doctor: Rand Tilton

D-U-N-S 80-838-9407
NEW MEXICO DEPARTMENT OF TRANSPORTATION
(*Suby of* OFFICE OF SECRETARY) ★
1120 Cerrillos Rd, Santa Fe, NM 87505-1842
Tel (505) 827-5100 *Founded/Ownrshp* 1903
Sales NA *EMP* 2,600
Accts Meyners & Company Llc Albaqu
SIC 9621 Regulation, administration of transportation; ; Regulation, administration of transportation;
Ofcr: Erik Gomez
Exec: Don Graham
Exec: Chris Liebson
Exec: Maxine Lopez
Exec: Jackie Padilla
Exec: Mary Segura
Genl Mgr: Greg Clarke
Tech Mgr: Robert Brown
Site Mgr: Chris Hanson
Ql Cn Mgr: Rosanne Rodriguez
Counsel: Michal Hayes

D-U-N-S 80-838-9290
NEW MEXICO DEPARTMENT OF WORKFORCE SOLUTIONS
(*Suby of* OFFICE OF SECRETARY) ★
401 Broadway Blvd Ne, Albuquerque, NM 87102-2330
Tel (505) 841-8405 *Founded/Ownrshp* 1936
Sales NA *EMP* 600
SIC 9441 Administration of social & manpower programs; ; Administration of social & manpower programs;
**CFO:* Richard Montes
Dir IT: Aaron Hindes
IT Man: Aaron Hids
IT Man: Jose Lucero
Pgrm Dir: Bill Range

D-U-N-S 86-740-6639
NEW MEXICO DEPT OF MILITARY AFFAIRS
NATIONAL GUARD OF NEW MEXICO
(*Suby of* OFFICE OF SECRETARY) ★
47 Bataan Blvd, Santa Fe, NM 87508-4695
Tel (505) 474-1200 *Founded/Ownrshp* 1996
Sales NA *EMP* 4,000
SIC 9711 National Guard; ; National Guard;
Ofcr: Darryl Dellarossa
Ofcr: Sheila Stewart
Adm Dir: Trina Littlejohn
Genl Mgr: Lawrence Montano
IT Man: Lorenzo Gurule
Opers Mgr: Leslie REA
Doctor: Mark Goldberg
Doctor: Amy Shurtleff
HC Dir: Jennifer Kuntz
Snr Mgr: Roberto Alvarez
Snr Mgr: Julie Anderson

D-U-N-S 00-222-4731
NEW MEXICO EDUCATIONAL ASSISTANCE FOUNDATION (NM)
NEW MEXICO STUDENT LOANS
7400 Tiburon St Ne, Albuquerque, NM 87109-5910
Tel (505) 345-3371 *Founded/Ownrshp* 1982
Sales NA *EMP* 190
Accts Urbielewicz Murphee Cpas Pc
SIC 6111 6163 6141 Student Loan Marketing Association; Loan brokers; Personal credit institutions; Student Loan Marketing Association; Loan brokers; Personal credit institutions
Ch: Ben Haines
**Pr:* Elwood G Woody Farber
**CFO:* Brad Allpass
**VP:* Sarah Branch
**VP:* Paul Padilla
Dir IT: Covington Lucas
Snr Mgr: Lucas Covington

D-U-N-S 06-969-1350
NEW MEXICO EDUCATORS FEDERAL CREDIT UNION (INC)
NAFCU
4100 Pan American Fwy Ne, Albuquerque, NM 87107-4752
Tel (505) 872-5427 *Founded/Ownrshp* 1935
Sales NA *EMP* 335
SIC 6061 Federal credit unions; Federal credit unions
Pr: Terry Laudick
Ofcr: Stephanie Graham
Ofcr: Babar Khawaja
Ofcr: Paul Long
**Ex VP:* Carl Benanty
Ex VP: Susan Verbeck
**Sr VP:* Larry Erickson
Sr VP: Tom Hagan
VP: Robin Brulaa
**VP:* Joseph Christian
Dir Bus: Sharla Reinhart

D-U-N-S 80-856-1658
NEW MEXICO ENVIRONMENT DEPARTMENT
(*Suby of* OFFICE OF SECRETARY) ★
1190 S Saint Francis Dr, Santa Fe, NM 87505-4173
Tel (505) 827-2919 *Founded/Ownrshp* 1992
Sales NA *EMP* 720
SIC 9511 Environmental agencies; ; Environmental agencies;
Prgrm Mgr: Erika Martinez
Prgrm Mgr: Jennifer Prada
Prgrm Mgr: Curt Vollbrecht

D-U-N-S 82-524-4697
■ NEW MEXICO GAS CO INC
(*Suby of* NEW MEXICO GAS INTERMEDIATE INC) ★
7120 Wyoming Blvd Ne # 20, Albuquerque, NM 87109-4887
Tel (505) 697-3803 *Founded/Ownrshp* 2008
Sales 375.8MM *EMP* 729^E
SIC 4924 4922 Natural gas distribution; Pipelines, natural gas; Natural gas distribution; Pipelines, natural gas
Pr: Ryan Shell
**Pr:* Annette Gardiner
**Ch:* William Real
**VP:* Douglas Arney
**VP:* Thomas Domme
**VP:* Kenneth Oostman Jr
**VP:* Aaron Roberson
**VP:* Tommy Sanders
Dir IT: Barbara Lopez

D-U-N-S 07-954-8183
■ NEW MEXICO GAS INTERMEDIATE INC
(*Suby of* TECO ENERGY INC) ★
7201 Wyoming Blvd Ne, Albuquerque, NM 87109-4814
Tel (505) 697-3827 *Founded/Ownrshp* 2014
Sales 375.8MM^E *EMP* 740^E
SIC 4924 Natural gas distribution; Natural gas distribution
VP: Thomas M Domme

D-U-N-S 87-855-9004
NEW MEXICO HEART INSTITUTE PA
502 Elm St Ne, Albuquerque, NM 87102-2512
Tel (505) 841-1000 *Founded/Ownrshp* 1994
Sales 28.9MM^E *EMP* 218
SIC 8011 Clinic, operated by physicians; Clinic, operated by physicians
Pr: Sean Mazer
Mng Dir: Michaela B Bujoi
IT Man: Martha Burnham
Doctor: Paul Armstrong
Doctor: Steve Henao
Doctor: John Mackenzie
Board of Directors: Geoffrey Kunz, Mark Zolnick

D-U-N-S 04-713-4101
NEW MEXICO HIGHLANDS UNIVERSITY
800 National Ave, Las Vegas, NM 87701-4002
Tel (505) 425-7511 *Founded/Ownrshp* 1893
Sales 33.6MM *EMP* 915
Accts Moss Adams Llp Albuquerque N
SIC 8221 5942 8351 University; College book stores; Child day care services; University; College book stores; Child day care services
Pr: James Fries
V Ch: Walter Adams
Bd of Dir: Paul Martinez
VP: Ana Fredlund
VP: Gilbert Rivera
VP: Steve Wilson
Exec: Raymond Chavez
Exec: Carol Linder
Exec: Emily Montoya
Exec: Ben Nelson
Exec: Kent Reid
Exec: Prescilla Salazar

D-U-N-S 04-135-8904
NEW MEXICO INSTITUTE OF MINING AND TECHNOLOGY
NEW MEXICO TECH
801 Leroy Pl, Socorro, NM 87801-4750
Tel (575) 835-5312 *Founded/Ownrshp* 1981
Sales 120.0MM *EMP* 1,000
Accts Atkinson & Co Ltd Albuquer
SIC 8221 University; University
Pr: Daniel H Lopez
CFO: Chris Armstrong
Assoc VP: Daniel Walsh
VP: Brian Borchers
**VP:* Melissa Jaramillo-Fleming
VP: John Juarez
VP: Ricardo Maestas
**VP:* Lonnie Marquez
VP: Warren Ostergren
VP: Van Romero
VP: Leyla Sedillo
VP: Stewart Youngblood
Assoc Dir: David Collis

D-U-N-S 07-760-0724
NEW MEXICO JUNIOR COLLEGE
5317 N Lovington Hwy, Hobbs, NM 88240-9123
Tel (575) 392-4510 *Founded/Ownrshp* 1965
Sales 52.9MM^E *EMP* 310
SIC 8222 8221 Junior college; Colleges universities & professional schools; Junior college; Colleges universities & professional schools
Pr: Steve McCleery
V Ch: Guy Kesner
CFO: Dan Hardin
VP: Dennis Atherton
VP: Roybal Phillip
VP: Robert Rhodes
Ex Dir: Darrell Beauchamp
Store Mgr: Robert Adams
IT Man: Beth Hancock
Psych: Larae Ellison
Psych: Kelly Rueda

D-U-N-S 07-673-7899
NEW MEXICO MILITARY INSTITUTE INC
NMMI
101 W College Blvd, Roswell, NM 88201-5173
Tel (575) 622-6250 *Founded/Ownrshp* 1898
Sales 50.4MM^E *EMP* 300
SIC 8222 8211 Junior college; Military academy; Junior college; Military academy
CEO: Maj Gen Jerry Grizzle
**Pr:* Dr C Robert Campbell
**Pr:* BR Gen Rick Geraci
**Pr:* Jerry W Grizzle
**CFO:* Col Judy Scharmer
Ofcr: Michael Oneil
Ofcr: Dyanna Treat
VP: Carmen Bell
CIO: Duane Elms
Opers Mgr: Cindy Gomez
**HC Dir:* Ltc Pete Nacy

D-U-N-S 08-321-4742
NEW MEXICO MORTGAGE FINANCE AUTHORITY
NMMFA
344 4th St Sw, Albuquerque, NM 87102-3206
Tel (505) 843-6880 *Founded/Ownrshp* 1975
Sales NA *EMP* 67
Accts Kpmg Llp Albuquerque Nm
SIC 6163 Mortgage brokers arranging for loans, using money of others; Mortgage brokers arranging for loans, using money of others
Ex Dir: Jay Czar
Comm Man: Leann Kemp
Ex Dir: John Monforte
Prgrm Mgr: Karen Anderson
Off Admin: Stacy Huggins

D-U-N-S 55-628-5120
NEW MEXICO MUTUAL CASUALTY CO
3900 Singer Blvd Ne, Albuquerque, NM 87109-5817
Tel (800) 788-8851 *Founded/Ownrshp* 1991
Sales NA *EMP* 145
SIC 6331 Workers' compensation insurance; Workers' compensation insurance
CEO: Chris Krahling
**Ch Bd:* Evangeline Tinajero
**Pr:* Warren D Smalley
Pr: Tim Thackaberry
CFO: Louis Volk
VP: John Franchini
VP: Nick Franklin
VP: Deborah Hartz
**VP:* Beverly Jornigan
VP: Quinn Lopez
**VP:* Patricia McCarthy
VP: Dwight Ward

D-U-N-S 06-491-5861 IMP
NEW MEXICO OFFICE FURNITURE INC
BUSINESS ENVIRONMENTS
5351 Wilshire Ave Ne, Albuquerque, NM 87113-1934
Tel (505) 888-4400 *Founded/Ownrshp* 1973
Sales 51.4MM^E *EMP* 80^E
SIC 5021 5023 7389 Office furniture; Carpets; Interior designer
CEO: Bruce Hoover
**Pr:* Scott Hoover
**VP:* Michael Franklin
**VP:* Dan Lewis
Opers Mgr: Anita Dodson

D-U-N-S 10-940-1976
NEW MEXICO ONCOLOGY HEMATOLOGY CONSULTANTS LTD
NEW MEXICO CANCER CENTER
4901 Lang Ave Ne, Albuquerque, NM 87109-4495
Tel (505) 828-3788 *Founded/Ownrshp* 1982
Sales 24.8MM^E *EMP* 185
SIC 8011 Oncologist; Hematologist; Oncologist; Hematologist
Pr: Barbara McAneny MD
**Treas:* Richard O Guidice
**VP:* Clark E Haskins
Pr Dir: Paul Sanchez
Doctor: Brian Goss

Doctor: Jan Merin
Diag Rad: Linda Casey

D-U-N-S 36-218-2698
NEW MEXICO ORTHOPAEDICS SURGERY CENTER LP
201 Cedar St Se Ste 7650, Albuquerque, NM 87106-4911
Tel (505) 724-4395 *Founded/Ownrshp* 2000
Sales 21.3MM^E *EMP* 82
SIC 8011 Ambulatory surgical center
Prin: Barbara Montano
Treas: Dwight Burney
Treas: Dwight W Burney III
VP: Richard E Whit Jr
VP: Richard White
Exec: James Carabajal
Mtls Mgr: Matt Atkinson
Doctor: Chris Patton

D-U-N-S 80-856-1690
NEW MEXICO PUBLIC EDUCATION DEPARTMENT
(*Suby of* OFFICE OF SECRETARY) ★
300 Don Gaspar Ave, Santa Fe, NM 87501-2744
Tel (505) 827-5800 *Founded/Ownrshp* 1912
Sales NA *EMP* 452
SIC 9411 Administration of educational programs; ; Administration of educational programs;
VP: Stan Valdez
MIS Dir: Michael Archibeque
IT Man: Michele Lewis
Pr Dir: Jennifer Chavez
Pr Dir: Beverly Friedman
Pr Dir: Robert McEntyre
Teacher Pr: Marian K Rael
HC Dir: Dean Hopper

D-U-N-S 80-838-9175
NEW MEXICO REGULATION & LICENSING DEPARTMENT
(*Suby of* OFFICE OF SECRETARY) ★
2550 Cerrillos Rd, Santa Fe, NM 87505-3260
Tel (505) 827-7000 *Founded/Ownrshp* 1980
Sales NA *EMP* 328^E
SIC 9651 Regulation, miscellaneous commercial sectors; ; Regulation, miscellaneous commercial sectors;
CFO: Cynthia Marietta
Exec: Kate Dauber
Comm Dir: Betina McCracken
IT Man: Julia Gil
Opers Mgr: Ken Giles
Snr Mgr: Auralie Ashley-Marx

D-U-N-S 86-136-7373
NEW MEXICO STATE UNIVERSITY
NMSU
2850 Weddell St Rm 210, Las Cruces, NM 88003-1245
Tel (575) 646-0111 *Founded/Ownrshp* 1888
Sales 324.9MM *EMP* 5,000
Accts Moss Adams Llp Albuquerque N
SIC 8221 University; University
Pr: Garrey Carruther
Pr: Glen Haubold
Pr: Ken Ramsey
CEO: Andy Burke
Bd of Dir: James Duffey
Ofcr: Eva Hernandez
VP: Kevin Boberg
VP: Robert Franklin
VP: Maureen Howard
Assoc Dir: Bruce Hinrichs
Assoc Dir: Kathleen Huttlinger
Assoc Dir: Angela Velasco
Dir Rx: John Landrum

D-U-N-S 19-260-3566
NEW MEXICO STATE UNIVERSITY FOUNDATION INC
1305 N Horseshoe Dr Dove, Las Cruces, NM 88003
Tel (575) 646-6125 *Founded/Ownrshp* 1959
Sales 30.2MM *EMP* 54^E
Accts Moss-Adams Llp Albuquerque
SIC 8299 Educational services; Educational services
Pr: Jose Uranga
**Treas:* John Papen
**Sec:* Terry Johnson
**VP:* Mike Johnson

D-U-N-S 96-353-0436
NEW MEXICO STATE VETERANS HOME
922 S Broadway St, T or C, NM 87901-3198
Tel (575) 894-4200 *Founded/Ownrshp* 2009
Sales 281.2MM *EMP* 41^E
SIC 8051 Skilled nursing care facilities; Skilled nursing care facilities

NEW MEXICO STUDENT LOANS
See NEW MEXICO EDUCATIONAL ASSISTANCE FOUNDATION

NEW MEXICO TECH
See NEW MEXICO INSTITUTE OF MINING AND TECHNOLOGY

D-U-N-S 86-834-1371
NEW MIDWEST CO LLC
209 N Main St, Renville, MN 56284
Tel (320) 329-3363 *Founded/Ownrshp* 2004
Sales 55.2MM^E *EMP* 509^E
SIC 5144 Poultry & poultry products; Eggs; Poultry & poultry products; Eggs
Pr: Dana Persson
COO: Robert A Harrington
CFO: Thomas A Powell
Sec: Paul Wilson

D-U-N-S 80-077-4127
NEW MILFORD HOSPITAL HOLDING CORP
21 Elm St, New Milford, CT 06776-2915
Tel (860) 355-2611 *Founded/Ownrshp* 1984
Sales 13.9MM^E *EMP* 550
SIC 8741 Hospital management; Hospital management
Pr: Richard E Pugh
**Ch Bd:* Terry Pellegrini
COO: Leila Dragger
**Treas:* Lawrence Greenhaus

D-U-N-S 06-000-7481
NEW MILFORD HOSPITAL INC (CT)
WESTERN CONN HLTH NETWRK
21 Elm St, New Milford, CT 06776-2993
Tel (860) 355-2611 *Founded/Ownrshp* 1922
Sales 61.8MM *EMP* 400
SIC 8062 8011 General medical & surgical hospitals; Offices & clinics of medical doctors; General medical & surgical hospitals; Offices & clinics of medical doctors
CEO: John M Murphy
Chf Rad: Andrea Crowley
Dir Risk M: Suzanne Furia
Dir Risk M: Monica Sousa
Mng Ofcr: Peter Wilson
**Ex Dir:* Deborah Weymouth
Dir IT: Michael Hendrick
IT Man: Kevin Meade
Ansthlgy: Peter Fine
Pharmcst: Sharon Morrison

D-U-N-S 10-001-1881
NEW MILFORD PUBLIC SCHOOLS
50 East St, New Milford, CT 06776-3030
Tel (860) 355-8406 *Founded/Ownrshp* 1890
Sales 34.8MM^E *EMP* 600
SIC 8211 Public elementary & secondary schools; Public elementary & secondary schools
Dir IT: David Elmore
Schl Brd P: Danielle Shook

D-U-N-S 07-270-8639
NEW MILFORD SCHOOL DISTRICT
145 Madison Ave, New Milford, NJ 07646-2707
Tel (201) 261-2952 *Founded/Ownrshp* 1899
Sales 24.2MM^E *EMP* 540
SIC 8211 Public elementary school; Public junior high school; Public senior high school; Public elementary school; Public junior high school; Public senior high school
Bd of Dir: Fran Eagleson
Trst: Joseph Steele
Prin: Phillip A Haramia
Dir IT: Ron Wilson

D-U-N-S 10-546-7133
■ **NEW MILLENNIUM BUILDING SYSTEMS LLC**
(*Suby of* STEEL DYNAMICS INC) ★
7575 W Jefferson Blvd, Fort Wayne, IN 46804-4131
Tel (260) 969-3500 *Founded/Ownrshp* 1999
Sales 43.3MM^E *EMP* 210
SIC 3441 Joists, open web steel: long-span series; Joists, open web steel: long-span series
Pr: Gary Heasley
**Prin:* Bert Hollman
Genl Mgr: Doug Lang
Genl Mgr: Art Ullom
Natl Sales: Doug Robbins

D-U-N-S 01-504-5362
NEW MONROEVILLE CHRYSLER-PLYMOUTH INC
3651 William Penn Hwy, Monroeville, PA 15146-2123
Tel (412) 856-1422 *Founded/Ownrshp* 1967
Sales 27.2MM^E *EMP* 83
SIC 5511 Automobiles, new & used; Automobiles, new & used
Pr: Edward J Little
**Treas:* Robert T Crothers
**VP:* Debbie Little

D-U-N-S 82-619-6743
NEW MONROEVILLE DODGE INC
MONROEVILLE DODGE THE
3633 William Penn Hwy, Monroeville, PA 15146-2123
Tel (412) 856-1700 *Founded/Ownrshp* 1994
Sales 28.4MM^E *EMP* 65
SIC 5511 Automobiles, new & used; Automobiles, new & used
Pr: Francis Affenberg Jr

D-U-N-S 01-419-6125
NEW MOTORS INC
8670 Peach St, Erie, PA 16509-4789
Tel (814) 868-4805 *Founded/Ownrshp* 1976
Sales 41.4MM^E *EMP* 95
SIC 5511 Automobiles, new & used; Automobiles, new & used
Pr: Lawrence New
CFO: Steve Dillon
**VP:* Gary V New
Sls Mgr: Gabriel Pulvino
Sales Asso: Kyle McLntyre

D-U-N-S 05-237-1981
NEW MOUNTAIN CAPITAL I LLC
787 7th Ave Fl 49, New York, NY 10019-6018
Tel (212) 720-0300 *Founded/Ownrshp* 1999
Sales 1.8MMM^E *EMP* 6,823
SIC 6726 Management investment funds, closed-end; Management investment funds, closed-end
COO: John R Kline
CFO: David M Cordova
VP: Trish Belfiore
VP: Linda Chiu
VP: Josh Hirschhorn
VP: Matthew S Holt
Mng Dir: Michael Ajouz
Mng Dir: Mathew Lori
Mng Dir: Peter Masucci
Mng Dir: Sunil Mishra
Mng Dir: James W Stone III

D-U-N-S 07-878-0198
NEW MOUNTAIN FINANCE CORP
787 7th Ave Fl 48, New York, NY 10019-6018
Tel (212) 720-0300 *Founded/Ownrshp* 2010
Sales 135.6MM *EMP* 6
Tkr Sym NMFC *Exch* NYS
SIC 6726 Management investment funds, closed-end; Management investment funds, closed-end
Pr: Robert A Hamwee
**Ch Bd:* Steven B Klinsky
COO: John R Kline
CFO: David Cordova
Chf Cred: Paula A Bosco
**Ofcr:* Adam B Weinstein

D-U-N-S 80-856-7940
NEW MOUNTAIN LAKE HOLDINGS LLC
4080 Jenkins Rd, Chattanooga, TN 37421-1174
Tel (423) 510-3000 *Founded/Ownrshp* 2007
Sales 1.1MMM^E *EMP* 10,885
SIC 4213 4731 Trucking, except local; Freight transportation arrangement; Trucking, except local; Freight transportation arrangement
CEO: Max L Fuller
Pr: Lisa M Pate

D-U-N-S 19-802-5863
NEW MOUNTAIN LEARNING LLC
(*Suby of* WICKS COMMUNICATIONS & MEDIA PARTNERS III LP) ★
875 Montreal Way, Saint Paul, MN 55102-4245
Tel (651) 290-2800 *Founded/Ownrshp* 2005
Sales 39.2MM *EMP* 121^E
Accts Kpmg Llp Mclean Va
SIC 2731 Textbooks: publishing only, not printed on site; Textbooks: publishing only, not printed on site
CEO: Steve Vanthornout

D-U-N-S 80-883-6894 IMP/EXP
NEW NGC INC
NATIONAL GYPSUM COMPANY
(*Suby of* DELCOR INC) ★
2001 Rexford Rd, Charlotte, NC 28211-3415
Tel (704) 365-7300 *Founded/Ownrshp* 1993
Sales 422.6MM^E *EMP* 2,100
SIC 2679 Wallboard, decorated: made from purchased material; Wallboard, decorated: made from purchased material
Ch Bd: Thomas C Nelson
CFO: George Beckwith
CFO: Richard Parkhurst
Ofcr: Jo Winn
Sr VP: Craig Weisbruch
VP: John C Corsi
VP: Craig Robertson
VP: Craig C Robertson
VP: Samuel A Schiffman
Rgnl Mgr: Frank Stola
Dept Mgr: Brian Wood

D-U-N-S 05-828-4790
NEW NORTHWEST BROADCASTERS LLC
315 5th Ave S Ste 700, Seattle, WA 98104-4603
Tel (206) 204-0213 *Founded/Ownrshp* 1998
Sales 20.3MM^E *EMP* 175
SIC 4832 Radio broadcasting stations; Radio broadcasting stations
Pr: Peter Benedetti
**CFO:* Trila Bumstead

D-U-N-S 80-558-3353
NEW OMAHA HOLDINGS LP
9 W 57th St Ste 4200, New York, NY 10019-2707
Tel (212) 750-8300 *Founded/Ownrshp* 2007
Sales NA *EMP* 29,010
SIC 6712 Bank holding companies; Bank holding companies

D-U-N-S 01-015-4367
NEW OPPORTUNITIES INC (CT)
232 N Elm St Ste 1, Waterbury, CT 06702-1516
Tel (203) 575-9799 *Founded/Ownrshp* 1964
Sales 42.7MM *EMP* 250
Accts Blum Shapiro & Company Pc Cpa
SIC 8322 Individual & family services; Individual & family services
Pr: James H Gatling
CFO: Michael Riso
Pr Dir: Etta Royster

D-U-N-S 00-272-0660
NEW ORLEAN JAZZ HERITAGE FESTIVAL
336 Camp St Ste 250, New Orleans, LA 70130-2818
Tel (504) 410-4100 *Founded/Ownrshp* 2007
Sales 33.2MM *EMP* 2
SIC 7999 Festival operation; Festival operation

NEW ORLEANS AIRPORT
See ARMSTRONG AIRPORT CONCESSIONS

D-U-N-S 06-083-3761
NEW ORLEANS BAPTIST THEOLOGICAL SEMINARY
NOBTS
3939 Gentilly Blvd, New Orleans, LA 70126-4858
Tel (504) 816-8007 *Founded/Ownrshp* 1917
Sales 35.8MM^E *EMP* 450
SIC 8221 Theological seminary; Theological seminary
Pr: Charles S Kelley Jr
Pr: Charles Harvey
**CFO:* L Clay Corvin
Treas: Jim Davison Jr
VP: Clay Corvin
VP: Lisa Paulson
Genl Mgr: Denise Wrye
Dir IT: Kyara St Amant
Dir IT: Bill Turco
IT Man: Dennis Cole
IT Man: Adam Corvin

NEW ORLEANS BEVERAGE AGENCY
See GLAZERS DISTRIBUTORS OF LOUISIANA INC

D-U-N-S 00-816-2380
NEW ORLEANS COLD STORAGE AND WAREHOUSE CO LTD
NOCS TRANSPORT
3411 Jourdan Rd, New Orleans, LA 70126-5049
Tel (504) 944-4400 *Founded/Ownrshp* 1947
Sales 54.4MM^E *EMP* 160
SIC 4222 4731

D-U-N-S 11-897-5457
NEW ORLEANS EXHIBITION HALL AUTHORITY (INC)
900 Convention Ctr Blvd, New Orleans, LA 70130-1714
Tel (504) 582-3082 *Founded/Ownrshp* 1978
Sales 27.9MM *EMP* 350
Accts Postlethwaite & Netterville N
SIC 6512 Auditorium & hall operation; Auditorium & hall operation
Pr: Robert Johnson

Treas: Frederick Sawyers
**VP:* Alita Caparotta
IT Man: Mary Jones

D-U-N-S 55-755-6045
NEW ORLEANS FISH HOUSE LLC
921 S Dupre St, New Orleans, LA 70125-1343
Tel (504) 821-9700 *Founded/Ownrshp* 2001
Sales 33.1MM *EMP* 68
SIC 3556 Meat, poultry & seafood processing machinery; Meat, poultry & seafood processing machinery
Sales Exec: Michael Ketchum

D-U-N-S 17-562-7769 IMP
NEW ORLEANS JAZZ & HERITAGE FESTIVAL AND FOUNDATION INC
1205 N Rampart St, New Orleans, LA 70116-2436
Tel (504) 522-4786 *Founded/Ownrshp* 1970
Sales 35.9MM *EMP* 4
SIC 7999 Festival operation; Festival operation
Treas: Beverly Andry
VP: Demetric Mercadel
IT Man: Jarrod Remetich
Site Mgr: Tague Richardson

NEW ORLEANS LAMP
See MEMPHIS LAMP INC

D-U-N-S 07-791-8258
NEW ORLEANS LOUISIANA SAINTS LLC
NEW ORLEANS SAINTS
5800 Airline Dr, Metairie, LA 70003-3876
Tel (504) 731-1700 *Founded/Ownrshp* 1985
Sales 20.9MM^E *EMP* 120
SIC 7941 Football club
Pr: Dennis Lauscha
**CFO:* Ed Lang
**Ex VP:* Mickey Loomis
**VP:* Greg Bensel
VP: Jean-Paul Dardenne
**VP:* Ben Hales
**VP:* Vicky Neumeyer
Mktg Mgr: Connie Kowal

D-U-N-S 07-507-4526
NEW ORLEANS PRIVATE PATROL SERVICE INC
GURVICH DETECTIVE AGENCY
1620 Martin Luther, New Orleans, LA 70130
Tel (504) 525-7116 *Founded/Ownrshp* 1930
Sales 13.0MM^E *EMP* 400
SIC 7381 Security guard service; Detective services; Security guard service; Detective services
Pr: Louis S Gurvich Jr

NEW ORLEANS PUBLIC BELT RR
See PUBLIC BELT RAILROAD COMMISSION

D-U-N-S 55-694-7646
NEW ORLEANS PUBLIC FACILITY MANAGEMENT INC
ERNEST N MORIAL CONVENTION CTR
900 Convention Ctr Blvd, New Orleans, LA 70130-1714
Tel (504) 582-3000 *Founded/Ownrshp* 1984
Sales 51.7MM^E *EMP* 338
SIC 8741 Management services; Management services
Pr: Robert Johnson
Exec: Tim Tumminello
Dir Soc: Jill Alexander
Dir Soc: Cliff Glaviano
Dir Soc: Garrett Lemoine
Dir Soc: Shawn Torrey
Comm Man: Rosalie Mortillaro
VP Opers: Bryan Hayden
Sls Mgr: Gina Ellis
Sls Mgr: Kelly Johnson
Sls Mgr: Mae Johnson

D-U-N-S 92-987-2505
NEW ORLEANS REGIONAL PHYSICIAN HOSPITAL ORGANIZATION INC
PEOPLES HEALTH NETWORK
3838 N Causeway Blvd # 100, Metairie, LA 70002-8194
Tel (504) 849-4500 *Founded/Ownrshp* 1994
Sales 69.5MM^E *EMP* 950^E
SIC 8099 Medical services organization; Medical services organization
CEO: Carol Solomon
**COO:* Warren Murrell
COO: Gerald Parton
**CFO:* Kim Eller
Bd of Dir: Michelle Petty
Ofcr: Stephen Long
VP: Jeffrey Friedman
VP: Macon Moore
**VP:* Janice Ortego
**Exec:* Michael Robert
Dir Rx: Sean Kennedy

NEW ORLEANS SAINTS
See NEW ORLEANS LOUISIANA SAINTS LLC

D-U-N-S 80-933-0041
■ **NEW OXFORD FOODS LLC**
(*Suby of* HAIN PURE PROTEIN CORP) ★
304 S Water St, New Oxford, PA 17350-9688
Tel (717) 624-2191 *Founded/Ownrshp* 2009
Sales 20.1MM^E *EMP* 1^E
SIC 5149 Natural & organic foods
Pr: Jay L Lieberman

D-U-N-S 04-301-5400
NEW PACIFIC NORTHWEST GENERATING COOPERA
711 Ne Halsey St Ste 200, Portland, OR 97232-1268
Tel (503) 288-1234 *Founded/Ownrshp* 2010
Sales 170.8MM *EMP* 3
Accts Moss Adams Llp Portland Or
SIC 8399 Social services; Social services
Prin: R P Reiten
Sr VP: John Prescott
VP: Scott Corwin
VP: Aleka Scott
IT Man: Dragan Dokic

IT Man: Dan James
Genl Couns: Chris Hill

D-U-N-S 96-730-8628
NEW PALACE CASINO LLC
PALACE CASINO RESORT
231 5th St, Biloxi, MS 39530-4526
Tel (228) 432-8888 *Founded/Ownrshp* 1996
Sales 24.8MM^E *EMP* 589
SIC 7011 Casino hotel; Casino hotel
CFO: George Conwill
CFO: Renee Dellenger
IT Man: Keith Crosby

D-U-N-S 06-052-6274
NEW PALTZ CENTRAL SCHOOL DISTRICT
196 Main St, New Paltz, NY 12561-1298
Tel (845) 256-4100 *Founded/Ownrshp* 1956
Sales 16.7MM^E *EMP* 300
Accts Cooper Niemann & Co Llp Mo
SIC 8211 Public senior high school; Public junior high school; Public elementary school; Public senior high school; Public junior high school; Public elementary school
Treas: Michelle Diana
VP: Donald Kerr
VP: Ruth Quinn
Schl Brd P: Brian Cournoyer
Psych: Mary K Fiore

D-U-N-S 11-122-0729
NEW PARADIGM PRODUCTIONS INC
EDELMAN PRODUCTIONS
39 Mesa St Ste 212, San Francisco, CA 94129-1019
Tel (415) 924-8000 *Founded/Ownrshp* 1981
Sales 24.3MM^E *EMP* 150
SIC 7812 Video production; Video production
Pr: Steve Edelman
Off Mgr: Natalie Acevedo

D-U-N-S 11-299-0452
NEW PARTNERS INC
PARTNERS IN CARE
(*Suby of* VISITING NURSE SERVICE OF NEW YORK) ★
1250 Broadway Fl 10, New York, NY 10001-3746
Tel (212) 609-7700 *Founded/Ownrshp* 1983
Sales 213.0MM *EMP* 4,400
Accts Kpmg Llp Albany Ny
SIC 8082 Home health care services; Home health care services
Ch Bd: Richard Flender
Exec: Jacci Obrien

NEW PASSAGES
See ALTERNATIVE COMMUNITY LIVING INC

D-U-N-S 80-699-4153
NEW PENN FINANCIAL LLC
(*Suby of* SHELLPOINT PARTNERS LLC) ★
4000 Chemical Rd Ste 200, Plymouth Meeting, PA 19462-1708
Tel (484) 594-1000 *Founded/Ownrshp* 2015
Sales NA *EMP* 346
Accts St Clair Cpa S Pc Coshohocke
SIC 6162 Mortgage bankers & correspondents; Mortgage bankers & correspondents
Pr: Jerry Schiano
Pr: Patrica Peirce
COO: Brian Simon
CFO: Daniel Egan
VP: Vicki Bannon
VP: Nelson Daluz
VP: Mercedes Dotter
VP: Tony Hale
VP: Mark Lebrett
VP: Todd Stiverson
Sls Mgr: Michael Boyle

D-U-N-S 00-893-6759
■ **NEW PENN MOTOR EXPRESS INC**
(*Suby of* ROADWAY LLC) ★
625 S 5th Ave, Lebanon, PA 17042-7715
Tel (800) 285-5000 *Founded/Ownrshp* 1982, 2002
Sales 270.0MM *EMP* 1,800
SIC 4213 4231 Less-than-truckload (LTL) transport; Trucking terminal facilities; Less-than-truckload (LTL) transport; Trucking terminal facilities
Pr: Steven D Gast
Treas: Cornelius J Keim
VP: Terry L Gerrond
VP: Anthony Nicosia
VP: Daniel Schmidt
Telecom Mg: Brian Smith
IT Man: Randy Croce
Opers Mgr: Sean McKittrick
Opers Mgr: Delia Oyola
Manager: John Barry
Sls Mgr: Jaimi Huber

D-U-N-S 11-009-7081
■ **NEW PEOPLES BANK INC**
(*Suby of* NEW PEOPLES BANKSHARES INC) ★
2 Gents Dr, Honaker, VA 24260-7011
Tel (276) 873-6288 *Founded/Ownrshp* 1997
Sales NA *EMP* 367
SIC 6081 Branches & agencies of foreign banks; Branches & agencies of foreign banks
Pr: Jonathan Mullins
**COO:* Frank Sexton
**CFO:* Todd Asberry
Chf Cred: Charlie Paschall
Bd of Dir: Virginia Council
Ex VP: Todd Asbury
VP: Glenn Hill
VP: Doug Horne
VP: Larry Mullins
VP: Brenda Pritt
VP: Linda Rasnick
VP: Vicki Shortt
VP: Lynn Street
VP: Shelia Street
VP: Robbie Sturgill
VP: Ruby Yost

D-U-N-S 11-269-8951
▲ **NEW PEOPLES BANKSHARES INC**
67 Commerce Dr, Honaker, VA 24260
Tel (276) 873-7000 *Founded/Ownrshp* 2001
Sales NA *EMP* 277^E
Tkr Sym NWPP *Exch* OTO
SIC 6022 State commercial banks; State commercial banks
Pr: C Todd Asbury
**Ch Bd:* Harold Lynn Keene
COO: Frank Sexton Jr
CFO: Joseph D Pennington
**V Ch Bd:* Charles H Gent Jr
Site Mgr: Sharon Duckett

NEW PHASE TECHNOLOGIES
See BAKER PETROLITE LLC

NEW PHILADELPHIA BOARD EDUCATN
See NEW PHILADELPHIA CITY SCHOOL DISTRICT

D-U-N-S 03-729-0335
NEW PHILADELPHIA CITY SCHOOL DISTRICT
NEW PHILADELPHIA BOARD EDUCATN
248 Front Ave Sw Fl 2, New Philadelphia, OH 44663-2150
Tel (330) 364-0613 *Founded/Ownrshp* 1833
Sales 29.1MM *EMP* 672
SIC 8211 9411 Public elementary & secondary schools; Administration of educational programs; Public elementary & secondary schools; Administration of educational programs
**Pr:* Don Kemp
Treas: Michelle Keitz
**Treas:* Steven Sherer
**Prin:* G R Gibbs
MIS Dir: Mike Emery
Schl Brd P: Chris Weaver

NEW PHOENIX
See DRAGONSLAYER INC

NEW PHOENIX, THE
See GEORGE TEENY

D-U-N-S 14-817-3784 IMP/EXP
NEW PIG CORP
1 Pork Ave, Tipton, PA 16684-9001
Tel (814) 684-0101 *Founded/Ownrshp* 1985
Sales 72.9MM^E *EMP* 330
SIC 2842

D-U-N-S 06-521-2771
NEW PIONEERS COOPERATIVE SOCIETY
22 S Van Buren St, Iowa City, IA 52240-1821
Tel (319) 338-9441 *Founded/Ownrshp* 1971
Sales 21.0MM *EMP* 150
SIC 5411 Grocery stores; Grocery stores
Pr: Janet Razbadouski
COO: Theresa Carbrey
**VP:* Jon Fogarty
Genl Mgr: Matt Hartz
Plnt Mgr: Jason Thrasher

D-U-N-S 04-314-6604
NEW PLASTICS CORP
112 4th St, Luxemburg, WI 54217-8396
Tel (920) 845-2326 *Founded/Ownrshp* 1968
Sales 28.9MM^E *EMP* 200
SIC 3083 3085

NEW PORT MANSIONS
See PRESERVATION SOCIETY OF NEWPORT COUNTY

D-U-N-S 96-260-4104
■ **NEW PORT RICHEY HOSPITAL INC**
COMMUNITY HOSPITAL
(*Suby of* HCA INC) ★
1 Park Plz, Nashville, TN 37203-6527
Tel (727) 848-1733 *Founded/Ownrshp* 1978
Sales 37.8MM^E *EMP* 1,007
SIC 8062 General medical & surgical hospitals; General medical & surgical hospitals
CFO: Glenn Romig
Dir Rx: Matthew Mc Neill
Doctor: Joel Frazier
Doctor: James Rosacker
Doctor: Houshang Seradge
Doctor: Glenn Smith
Doctor: Cheng SOO
Pharmcst: George Bopp
Pharmcst: Louis Passannante
Pharmcst: Phillip Yeh

D-U-N-S 96-879-2940
NEW PRAGUE PUBLIC SCHOOL
410 Central Ave N, New Prague, MN 56071-1807
Tel (952) 758-1700 *Founded/Ownrshp* 2011
Sales 12.7MM^E *EMP* 318^E
SIC 8211 Public elementary & secondary schools
Prin: Larry Kauzlarich
Dir IT: Greg Pint
Schl Brd P: Tammy Pexa

D-U-N-S 15-218-2473
NEW PRIME INC
2740 N Mayfair Ave, Springfield, MO 65803-5084
Tel (417) 866-0001 *Founded/Ownrshp* 1986
Sales 1.1MMM *EMP* 5,000
Accts Abacus Cpas Llc Springfield
SIC 4213 Refrigerated products transport; Refrigerated products transport
Pr: Robert E Low
**CFO:* Dean Hoedl
**Treas:* Lawana L Low
VP: Jim Owen
IT Man: William Kozerski
Opers Mgr: Troy Rich
Genl Couns: Steve Crawford

D-U-N-S 62-358-0466
NEW PRIMECARE LLC
(*Suby of* DOSHI DIAGNOSTIC IMAGING SERVICES PC) ★
560 S Broadway Ste 201, Hicksville, NY 11801-5013
Tel (516) 933-2800 *Founded/Ownrshp* 2005
Sales 25.6MM^E *EMP* 340
SIC 8011 Radiologist; Radiologist
CFO: Fred Tylutki

NEW PRINTING
See DIGITAL ROOM INC

D-U-N-S 06-803-1376
NEW PROCESS STEEL HOLDING CO INC
5800 Westview Dr, Houston, TX 77055-5495
Tel (713) 686-9631 *Founded/Ownrshp* 1977
Sales 88.5MM^E *EMP* 500
SIC 5051 Steel; Steel
Pr: Richard E Fant
**Sec:* Phil O Kelley

D-U-N-S 05-826-5513 IMP/EXP
NEW PROCESS STEEL LP
1322 N Post Oak Rd, Houston, TX 77055-5406
Tel (713) 686-9631 *Founded/Ownrshp* 1999
Sales 249.5MM^E *EMP* 375
SIC 5051 3469 Sheets, metal; Steel; Sheets, galvanized or other coated; Stamping metal for the trade; Sheets, metal; Steel; Sheets, galvanized or other coated; Stamping metal for the trade
CEO: Richard E Fant
**Pr:* Robert L Proch
**CFO:* Francis Hawes
Div Mgr: David Bowman
Genl Mgr: Bill Remik
Dir IT: Jim Wilson
Sales Exec: Tammy Rasmussen

D-U-N-S 01-529-2654
NEW PROFIT INC
200 Clarendon St Ste 2902, Boston, MA 02116-5369
Tel (617) 912-8800 *Founded/Ownrshp* 1998
Sales 42.1MM *EMP* 16
Accts Leonard Mulherin & Greene P
SIC 8742 Management consulting services; Management consulting services
Pr: Vanessa Kirsch
Comm Dir: Jennifer Anderson
Comm Dir: Sam Hiersteiner
Ex Dir: Deborah Smolover
Off Mgr: Karstin Barde
Opers Mgr: Jessica Kirby

D-U-N-S 07-981-5496
NEW PROSYS CORP
6575 The Corners Pkwy # 300, Norcross, GA 30092-3312
Tel (678) 268-1300 *Founded/Ownrshp* 2010
Sales 7.1MM^E *EMP* 300
SIC 8731 Computer (hardware) development
CEO: Shaun Maine

D-U-N-S 07-849-4284
NEW PUBLISHING HOLDINGS LLC
10151 Carver Rd Ste 200, Blue Ash, OH 45242-4760
Tel (513) 531-2690 *Founded/Ownrshp* 2005
Sales 220.0MM^E *EMP* 651
SIC 2731 2721 Books: publishing only; Magazines: publishing only, not printed on site; Trade journals: publishing only, not printed on site; Books: publishing only; Magazines: publishing only, not printed on site; Trade journals: publishing only, not printed on site
CEO: David Nussbaum

D-U-N-S 83-518-4813 IMP
NEW RAVENNA MOSAICS INC
3268 Broad St, Exmore, VA 23350
Tel (757) 442-3379 *Founded/Ownrshp* 1991
Sales 21.7MM^E *EMP* 100
SIC 5032 Tile, clay or other ceramic, excluding refractory
Pr: Wes Lablanc
**CFO:* Daniel Brown
**Founder:* Sara Baldwin
Genl Mgr: Jodie Sokel
Mktg Dir: Christine Campbell
Corp Couns: John Hopkins

NEW REAL VEAL
See NRV INC

D-U-N-S 96-348-2737
NEW REGIONAL MEDICAL CENTER INC
5501 Old York Rd, Philadelphia, PA 19141-3018
Tel (800) 346-7834 *Founded/Ownrshp* 2006
Sales 68.2MM *EMP* 4^E
Accts Pricewaterhousecoopers Llp Ph
SIC 8011 Offices & clinics of medical doctors; Offices & clinics of medical doctors
Prin: Brian Derrick

D-U-N-S 82-589-7833
▲ **NEW RELIC INC**
188 Spear St Ste 1200, San Francisco, CA 94105-1750
Tel (650) 777-7600 *Founded/Ownrshp* 2008
Sales 110.3MM *EMP* 534^E
Tkr Sym NEWR *Exch* NYS
SIC 7372 Prepackaged software; Application computer software
CEO: Lewis Cirne
Pr: Hilarie Koplow-Mcadams
CFO: Mark Sachleben
Chf Mktg O: Patrick Moran
Ex VP: Erica Schultz
Sr VP: John Gray
VP: Robin J Schulman
Dir Bus: Cooper Marcus
Dir Bus: Steven Sheinfield
CIO: Yvonne Wassenaar
IT Man: Rodrigo Lois
Board of Directors: Peter L S Currie, Peter Fenton, Sarah Friar, Adam Messinger, Dan Scholnick

D-U-N-S 07-874-2068
NEW RESIDENTIAL INVESTMENT CORP
1345 Ave Of The Americas, New York, NY 10105-0302
Tel (212) 479-3150 *Founded/Ownrshp* 2011, 2013
Sales 346.8MM *EMP* 2
Tkr Sym NRZ *Exch* NYS
SIC 6798 Real estate investment trusts; Real estate investment trusts
Pr: Kenneth Riis
CFO: Susan Givens
CFO: Robert Williams
Ofcr: Jonathan Brown

D-U-N-S 07-473-3585
NEW RICHMOND EXEMPTED VILLAGE SCHOOL DISTRICT
212 Market St Fl 3, New Richmond, OH 45157-1373
Tel (513) 553-2017 *Founded/Ownrshp* 1837
Sales 29.4MM *EMP* 350
Accts Clark Schaefer Hackett & Co
SIC 8211 Public elementary school; Public junior high school; Public senior high school; School board; Public elementary school; Public junior high school; Public senior high school; School board
**Treas:* Teresa Napier
Schl Brd P: Kim Hayden

D-U-N-S 00-307-8532
NEW RIDGE ASSOCIATES INC (MD)
HIGH'S
2700 Loch Raven Rd, Baltimore, MD 21218-4729
Tel (410) 859-3636 *Founded/Ownrshp* 1929, 2015
Sales 132.0MM^E *EMP* 968
SIC 5411 Convenience stores, chain; Convenience stores, chain
Pr: Brian Darnell
CFO: David Shade
**VP:* Briana Darnell
**VP:* Ben Jatlow

D-U-N-S 09-736-9367
NEW RIVER AREA BOARD OF MENTAL HEALTH DEVELOPMENTAL DISABILITIES & SUBSTANCE ABUSE
NEW RIVER BEHAVIORAL HLTH CARE
895 State Farm Rd Ste 508, Boone, NC 28607-4917
Tel (828) 264-9007 *Founded/Ownrshp* 1963
Sales 7.3MM^E *EMP* 300
SIC 8093 8063 Mental health clinic, outpatient; Psychiatric hospitals; Mental health clinic, outpatient; Psychiatric hospitals
Ex Dir: Pam Andrews

NEW RIVER BEHAVIORAL HLTH CARE
See NEW RIVER AREA BOARD OF MENTAL HEALTH DEVELOPMENTAL DISABILITIES & SUBSTANCE ABUSE

D-U-N-S 00-979-7416 IMP/EXP
NEW RIVER ELECTRICAL CORP
15 Cloverdale Pl, Cloverdale, VA 24077-3124
Tel (540) 966-1650 *Founded/Ownrshp* 1984
Sales 242.4MM *EMP* 900
Accts Kennett & Kennett Pc Roanoke
SIC 1731 1623 Electrical work; Electric power systems contractors; Fire detection & burglar alarm systems specialization; General electrical contractor; Electric power line construction; Electrical work; Electric power systems contractors; Fire detection & burglar alarm systems specialization; General electrical contractor; Electric power line construction
Pr: Thomas M Wolden
**Ex VP:* Richard C Furr II
**Sr VP:* Robert B Arritt Jr
**Sr VP:* John E Swim
VP: R C Furr II
**VP:* Terry M Garrett
**VP:* John E Lanning
VP: Frank R Mille
**VP:* Frank R Miller
VP: Jake Miller
**VP:* Barry S Murray
**VP:* John F Ney
VP: Christopher J Whitely
VP: Larry Worrell
Board of Directors: Robert Arritt Jr, Terry Garrett, John Lanning, Jeffrey Leinard, Barry Murray, John Ney, Thomas Wolden

D-U-N-S 03-000-5040
NEW ROADS SCHOOL (CA)
3131 Olympic Blvd, Santa Monica, CA 90404-5002
Tel (310) 828-5582 *Founded/Ownrshp* 2000
Sales 23.2MM *EMP* 90^E
Accts Green Hasson & Janks Llp Los
SIC 8211 Private junior high school; Private junior high school
Pr: David Brian

NEW ROCHELLE TOYOTA
See NR AUTOMOTIVE INC

D-U-N-S 87-434-5705
NEW ROGERS PONTIAC INC
ROGERS AUTO GROUP
2720 S Michigan Ave, Chicago, IL 60616-2819
Tel (312) 225-4300 *Founded/Ownrshp* 1992
Sales 55.9MM^E *EMP* 120
SIC 5511 Automobiles, new & used; Automobiles, new & used
Pr: Monty Sher
Telecom Ex: John Scher
Sls Mgr: William G Beale

D-U-N-S 17-559-7137 IMP
NEW SABINA INDUSTRIES INC
(*Suby of* NIPPON SEIKI CO.,LTD.)
12555 Us Highway 22 And 3, Sabina, OH 45169-9463
Tel (937) 584-2433 *Founded/Ownrshp* 1986
Sales 119.3MM^E *EMP* 500
SIC 3714 Instrument board assemblies, motor vehicle; Instrument board assemblies, motor vehicle
Pr: Kazu Kishi
VP: Carol Engle
VP: Ryan Higgins
Exec: Pat McGreevy
CTO: Steve Clark
Plnt Mgr: Stuart Lohrum

NEW SAMARITAN HOUSING
See ELDERLY HOUSING MANAGEMENT INC

D-U-N-S 07-888-9449
NEW SBARRO INTERMEDIATE HOLDINGS INC
1328 Dublin Rd, Columbus, OH 43215-1054
Tel (614) 769-9911 *Founded/Ownrshp* 2013
Sales 266.5MM^E *EMP* 1,723^E
SIC 6719 Investment holding companies, except banks

Pr: David Karam
Pr: Tony Missano
**CFO:* Carolyn Spatafora
**Treas:* Stuart Steinberg

D-U-N-S 07-103-0969
NEW SCHOOL (NY)
66 W 12th St, New York, NY 10011-8871
Tel (212) 229-5600 *Founded/Ownrshp* 1919
Sales 354.1MM *EMP* 855
Accts Kpmg Llp New York Ny
SIC 8221 Colleges universities & professional schools; Colleges universities & professional schools
Pr: David Van Zandt
COO: Melanie Hiner
**COO:* Tim Marshall-Provost
Treas: Mary Dixon
Bd of Dir: Baillie Aaron
Bd of Dir: Apryl A Alexander
Bd of Dir: Timothy Allen
Bd of Dir: Zhanna Bagdasarov
Bd of Dir: Marcelle Bartolo-Abela
Bd of Dir: Stacie Bigelow
Bd of Dir: Todd Bishop
Bd of Dir: Rebecca Blais
Bd of Dir: Chloe G Bland
Bd of Dir: Stefanie Boswell
Bd of Dir: Markus Burrell
Bd of Dir: Jason Cantone
Bd of Dir: Jennifer Carusone
Bd of Dir: Sungkun Cho
Bd of Dir: Alin Coman
Bd of Dir: Guyla Davis
Bd of Dir: John Denboer

D-U-N-S 05-688-0495
NEW SCHOOL FOR CHILD DEVELOPMENT A NON PROFIT ORGANIZATION INC
13130 Burbank Blvd, Sherman Oaks, CA 91401-6037
Tel (818) 779-5262 *Founded/Ownrshp* 1977
Sales 29.0MM *EMP* 400
Accts Singerlewak Llp Los Angeles
SIC 8211 Specialty education; School for physically handicapped; School for the retarded; Specialty education; School for physically handicapped; School for the retarded
Pr: Barbara Firestone
**Ex VP:* Susan Berman
**Sr VP:* Tom Komp

D-U-N-S 11-441-2468 IMP
NEW SEASONS MARKET LLC
1300 Se Stark St Ste 401, Portland, OR 97214-2473
Tel (503) 292-1987 *Founded/Ownrshp* 1999
Sales 143.0MM^E *EMP* 620
SIC 5411 Grocery stores; Grocery stores
Pt: Lisa Sedlar
**Pt:* Joanne Morrissey
**Pt:* Brian Rohter
CFO: Jeremy Fogle
IT Man: Ezra Hunt

NEW SKAGIT
See SKAGIT GARDENS INC

NEW SKIN
See MEDTECH PRODUCTS INC

NEW SMYRNA DAILY JOURNAL
See NEWS-JOURNAL CORP

D-U-N-S 07-872-3658
▲ NEW SOURCE ENERGY PARTNERS LP
914 N Broadway Ave # 230, Oklahoma City, OK 73102-5850
Tel (405) 272-3028 *Founded/Ownrshp* 2012
Sales 165.6MM *EMP* 136^E
Tkr Sym NSLP *Exch* NYS
SIC 1311 1389 Crude petroleum & natural gas; Gas field services; Crude petroleum & natural gas; Gas field services
Ch Bd: Kristian B Kos
Genl Pt: New Source Energy GP LLC
Pr: Dikran Tourian

D-U-N-S 00-480-3821
NEW SOUTH COMMUNICATIONS INC (MS)
RADIO STATION WOKK-FM
3436 Highway 45 N, Meridian, MS 39301-1509
Tel (601) 703-0215 *Founded/Ownrshp* 1960
Sales 22.9MM^E *EMP* 150
SIC 4832 Radio broadcasting stations; Radio broadcasting stations
Pr: Frank E Holladay
**Sec:* Ann S Holladay
Genl Mgr: Paul Bucurel
Trfc Dir: Dee Williams
Sls Mgr: Diane Horton
Pgrm Dir: Scott Stevens

D-U-N-S 05-528-4368 EXP
NEW SOUTH COMPANIES INC
(*Suby of* CANFOR (1988) LTEE)
3700 Claypond Rd Ste 6, Myrtle Beach, SC 29579-7330
Tel (843) 236-9399 *Founded/Ownrshp* 2006
Sales 266.0MM^E *EMP* 700
SIC 2421 2491 2431 Lumber: rough, sawed or planed; Wood chips, produced at mill; Sawdust & shavings; Piles, foundation & marine construction: treated wood; Structural lumber & timber, treated wood; Millwork; Lumber: rough, sawed or planed; Wood chips, produced at mill; Sawdust & shavings; Piles, foundation & marine construction: treated wood; Structural lumber & timber, treated wood; Millwork
Pr: Douglas J Warstler

D-U-N-S 62-101-4000
NEW SOUTH CONSTRUCTION CO INC
1132 W Peachtree St Nw, Atlanta, GA 30309-3610
Tel (404) 443-4000 *Founded/Ownrshp* 1993
Sales 147.7MM^E *EMP* 185
SIC 1541 8741 Industrial buildings & warehouses; Construction management; Industrial buildings & warehouses; Construction management
Pr: Douglas C Davidson
**CFO:* Dan Smith
**Ex VP:* Huntly Gordon
**Ex VP:* Tom Troutman
VP: Rob Dunn
Dir Risk M: Gregory Schlich
Mng Dir: Dan Hobson
Mng Dir: Klay Simpson
Off Mgr: Kelley Thomas
IT Man: Robert Schulten
Sfty Mgr: Bryan Fowler

D-U-N-S 05-513-9547 EXP
NEW SOUTH CONSTRUCTION SUPPLY LLC
9 N Kings Rd, Greenville, SC 29605-1324
Tel (864) 263-4376 *Founded/Ownrshp* 2001
Sales 23.2MM^E *EMP* 59
SIC 5032 Concrete building products; Masons' materials; Plastering materials
CEO: James Sobeck
VP: David Hodgin
VP: Jimmy Sobeck
Off Mgr: Suzanne Godwin
IT Man: Martin Carruth
Opers Mgr: Andrew Black
Opers Mgr: Frank Crouse
Opers Mgr: Andrew Myers
Sls Mgr: Peter Bemisderfer

D-U-N-S 02-206-3456
NEW SOUTH EQUIPMENT MATS LLC
281 Old Jackson Rd, Madison, MS 39110-9485
Tel (601) 859-7472 *Founded/Ownrshp* 2007
Sales 20.9MM^E *EMP* 34
SIC 5084 Industrial machinery & equipment
CFO: Elaine Saxton
VP: Scott Jones
Sls Dir: John McClendon
Manager: Lawrence John

D-U-N-S 03-459-2654
NEW SOUTH EXPRESS LLC
(*Suby of* MIDWEST EXPRESS INC) ★
200 Homer Dr, Talladega, AL 35160-6378
Tel (256) 480-5919 *Founded/Ownrshp* 2000
Sales 75.5MM^E *EMP* 600
SIC 4225 General warehousing & storage; General warehousing & storage
Dir IT: Stefanie Player
Snr Mgr: Todd Beck

D-U-N-S 03-339-6029
NEW SOUTH FORD NISSAN INC
1200 N Frontage Rd, Meridian, MS 39301-6149
Tel (601) 693-6821 *Founded/Ownrshp* 1977
Sales 27.1MM^E *EMP* 68
SIC 5511 Automobiles, new & used; Pickups, new & used; Vans, new & used; Automobiles, new & used; Pickups, new & used; Vans, new & used
Pr: Milburn Vanveckhoven

D-U-N-S 05-205-0585 EXP
NEW SOUTH LUMBER CO INC
(*Suby of* NEW SOUTH COMPANIES INC) ★
3700 Claypond Rd Ste 6, Myrtle Beach, SC 29579-7330
Tel (843) 347-4288 *Founded/Ownrshp* 2006
Sales 260.0MM^E *EMP* 600
SIC 2421 Lumber: rough, sawed or planed; Lumber: rough, sawed or planed
Pr: Douglas Warstler
**CFO:* Ken Thomas
**Treas:* Doug J Warstler

D-U-N-S 96-954-5698
NEW SOUTH PIZZA INC
BRIXX WOOD FIRE PIZZA
100 N Main St, Belmont, NC 28012-3104
Tel (704) 825-4349 *Founded/Ownrshp* 2011
Sales 10.7MM^E *EMP* 600
SIC 5812 Buffet (eating places)
Pr: Stowe D Harding
**VP:* Van Dyke
**VP:* Morgan Barbara J

NEW SOUTHWEST BAKING CO
See BRYAN BAKING CO LLC

D-U-N-S 00-300-2060 IMP
NEW STANDARD CORP (PA)
74 Commerce Way, York, PA 17406-8038
Tel (717) 757-9450 *Founded/Ownrshp* 1909, 1940
Sales 130.7MM^E *EMP* 450
SIC 3469 3465 Metal stampings; Automotive stampings; Metal stampings; Automotive stampings
Pr: Morton F Zifferer Jr
CFO: Mark Wheeler
Treas: Tom McEvoy
Prgrm Mgr: Greg Eisenbach
Ql Cn Mgr: Cliff Warner
Ql Cn Mgr: Gus Ziesman
Sls Mgr: Bill Schenck

D-U-N-S 80-907-1470
■ NEW STAR HOLDINGS INTERNATIONAL INC
(*Suby of* MARSHALL MIDDLEBY INC) ★
10 Sunnen Dr, Saint Louis, MO 63143-3800
Tel (800) 264-7827 *Founded/Ownrshp* 2008
Sales 93.0MM^E *EMP* 614
SIC 3589 Commercial cooking & foodwarming equipment; Commercial cooking & foodwarming equipment
Pr: Frank Ricchio

D-U-N-S 96-995-5769
NEW START INTERNATIONAL LLC
611 Pa Ave Se 299, Washington, DC 20003-4303
Tel (301) 499-7821 *Founded/Ownrshp* 2011
Sales 25.0MM *EMP* 10
SIC 6798 Real estate investment trusts; Real estate investment trusts
Genl Mgr: Ywuana Peden

D-U-N-S 86-723-0559
NEW STUFF CO INC
STUFF MAGAZINE
150 Chestnut St, Providence, RI 02903-4645
Tel (617) 536-5390 *Founded/Ownrshp* 1990
Sales 25.2MM^E *EMP* 325
SIC 2721 Magazines: publishing only, not printed on site; Magazines: publishing only, not printed on site
Pr: H Barry Morris
**CEO:* Stephen Mindich
Sr VP: Bill Risteen
**VP:* Bradley Mindich
Creative D: Michael Diskin
Opers Mgr: David Scharfenberg
Prd Mgr: Travis Ritch
Trfc Mgr: Kevin Lawrence
Mktg Dir: Brian Appel
Art Dir: Kevin Banks
Snr Mgr: Everett Finkelstein

D-U-N-S 78-951-9472
NEW SUNSHINE LLC
6270 Corporate Dr, Indianapolis, IN 46278-2921
Tel (800) 633-0069 *Founded/Ownrshp* 2006
Sales 69.0MM^E *EMP* 343^E
SIC 7299 Tanning salon; Tanning salon

D-U-N-S 82-919-2017
NEW TEACHER CENTER
110 Cooper St Fl 5, Santa Cruz, CA 95060-4576
Tel (831) 600-2200 *Founded/Ownrshp* 2008
Sales 41.4MM *EMP* 99^E
Accts Armanino Llp San Ramon Calif
SIC 8299 Educational services; Educational services
Pr: Ellen Moir
**COO:* Scott Ellis
**CFO:* Garfield Byrd
**Prin:* Jory Post

D-U-N-S 80-059-0452
NEW TEACHER PROJECT INC
186 Joralemon St Fl 3, Brooklyn, NY 11201-4326
Tel (718) 233-2800 *Founded/Ownrshp* 1995
Sales 57.8MM *EMP* 30^E
Accts O Connor Davies Llp New York
SIC 8748 Educational consultant; Educational consultant
CEO: Michelle Rhee
**CEO:* Ariela Rozman
**CFO:* Wendy Chang
IT Man: Courtney Atwood
IT Man: Lara Oerter
Site Mgr: Emily Appel
Site Mgr: Elena Kennedy

D-U-N-S 03-183-3688
NEW TEAM LLC
TEAM ENTERPRISES
110 E Broward Blvd, Fort Lauderdale, FL 33301-3503
Tel (954) 862-2400 *Founded/Ownrshp* 1989
Sales 60.0MM *EMP* 400
SIC 8742 Marketing consulting services; Marketing consulting services
CEO: Daniel Gregory
Prgrm Mgr: William Domico
Area Mgr: Heather Johnston
Off Mgr: Shannon Deveza
Web Dev: John Chirila
Sls&Mrk Ex: Frank Fanelli
Sls&Mrk Ex: Greg Goldhaber

D-U-N-S 19-142-1598
NEW TECH ENGINEERING LIMITED PARTNERSHIP
1030 Regional Park Dr, Houston, TX 77060-1117
Tel (281) 951-4330 *Founded/Ownrshp* 1998
Sales 25.0MM^E *EMP* 82
SIC 8711 Engineering services
CEO: Larry Cress
Pt: Scott Johnson
Pt: T Dean Wood
Pr: Dusty Kinchen
Pr: Dick Polk
Sr VP: Regan Wood
VP: Dan Breeding
VP: Jeff Cummins
VP: Daniel Lockwood
VP: Richard Polk
Area Mgr: Craig Gary

D-U-N-S 79-401-4902
NEW TECH MACHINERY CORP
N T M
(*Suby of* MAZELLA COMPANIES) ★
1300 40th St Ste A, Denver, CO 80205-3315
Tel (303) 294-0538 *Founded/Ownrshp* 2015
Sales 20.9MM^E *EMP* 45
SIC 3531 5033 3547 Roofing equipment; Roofing, asphalt & sheet metal; Rolling mill machinery
Pr: Lawrence F Coben
**COO:* Roger Geer
Plnt Mgr: Raul Leyva
Mktg Mgr: Kristin Peregoy
Sls Mgr: Tom Laird

D-U-N-S 03-749-9910
NEW TECH PLASTICS INC
1300 Mote Dr, Covington, OH 45318-1218
Tel (937) 473-3011 *Founded/Ownrshp* 1980
Sales 30.0MM *EMP* 87
SIC 3081

D-U-N-S 02-014-9303
NEW TECH SOLUTIONS INC (CA)
4179 Business Center Dr, Fremont, CA 94538-6355
Tel (510) 353-4070 *Founded/Ownrshp* 1997
Sales 70.0MM *EMP* 32
SIC 5734 5045 7373 3571 7371 Computer & software stores; Computers, peripherals & software; Computer integrated systems design; Electronic computers; Custom computer programming services; Computer & software stores; Computers, peripherals & software; Computer integrated systems design; Electronic computers; Custom computer programming services
CEO: Vijay Kumar
**Pr:* Rajesh Patel
Prgrm Mgr: Anita New
Netwrk Eng: Himanshu Parikh
Mktg Dir: Vijay Singh
Sls Dir: Bob Udermann
Sales Asso: Priyanka Kapil

D-U-N-S 07-845-4154
NEW TESTAMENT BAPTIST CHURCH INC OF MIAMI
6601 Nw 167th St, Hialeah, FL 33015-4206
Tel (305) 822-7690 *Founded/Ownrshp* 1963
Sales 16.7MM^E *EMP* 300
SIC 8661 8211 Baptist Church; Private combined elementary & secondary school; Baptist Church; Private combined elementary & secondary school
VP: Dan Burrell
**Prin:* Mrs Marjorie Decarion
**Prin:* Mrs Elisa Froehling
Pr Dir: Rhonda McNeal

D-U-N-S 11-438-5409
NEW TEXAS AUTO AUCTION SERVICES LP
TEXAS HOBBY AUTO AUCTION
8215 Kopman Dr, Houston, TX 77061-5050
Tel (713) 649-8233 *Founded/Ownrshp* 1988
Sales 27.4MM^E *EMP* 350
SIC 5012 Automobile auction; Automobile auction
Genl Mgr: Jerry Branam
Exec: Freda Cunningham
Exec: Jack Robertson
Exec: Vali Runnels

D-U-N-S 02-602-3478 IMP
NEW THERMO-SERV LTD
THERMOSERV
3901 Pipestone Rd, Dallas, TX 75212-6017
Tel (214) 631-0307 *Founded/Ownrshp* 2000
Sales 46.9MM^E *EMP* 200
SIC 3089 Cups, plastic, except foam; Cups, plastic, except foam
CEO: Jack Rigby
CFO: Dwayne Warren
CFO: Lance Wimmer

NEW TIMES WEEKLY
See VILLAGE VOICE MEDIA HOLDINGS LLC

D-U-N-S 05-410-1944
NEW TRIBES MISSION INC (FL)
NEW TRIBES MISSION INSTITUTE
1000 E 1st St, Sanford, FL 32771-1487
Tel (407) 323-3430 *Founded/Ownrshp* 1942
Sales 38.9MM^E *EMP* 1,055
Accts Batts Morrison Wales And Lee
SIC 8661 Religious organizations; Religious organizations
Ch Bd: Larry Brown
**COO:* Dan Kreider
COO: Kirk Rogers
**Treas:* Tim Meisel
Chf Mktg O: Dan Stokes
**Ex Dir:* Paul Wyma
Off Mgr: Terresa Hiebert
Nurse Mgr: Susan Russell
Dir IT: Alan Foster
IT Man: Arnie Sutton
IT Man: Sterling Tucker

NEW TRIBES MISSION INSTITUTE
See NEW TRIBES MISSION INC

D-U-N-S 06-847-7017
NEW TRIER TOWNSHIP HIGH SCHOOL DISTRICT 203
7 Happ Rd, Northfield, IL 60093-3411
Tel (847) 446-7000 *Founded/Ownrshp* 1897
Sales 53.7MM^E *EMP* 838
SIC 8211 8741 Public senior high school; School board; Management services; Public senior high school; School board; Management services
Trst Ofcr: Susan O Kim
Prin: Jan Borja
Prin: Timothy Dohrer
Sfty Dirs: Jerry Hatp

D-U-N-S 17-271-9155
NEW ULM INDEPENDENT SCHOOL DISTRICT 88
NEW ULM PUBLIC SCHOOL
15 N State St, New Ulm, MN 56073-1854
Tel (507) 359-8401 *Founded/Ownrshp* 1900
Sales 39.3MM^E *EMP* 330
Accts Abdo Eick & Meyers Llp Mankat
SIC 8211 Public combined elementary & secondary school; School board; Public combined elementary & secondary school; School board
Psych: Gretchen Lilly
Psych: Kayla Sandersfeld

NEW ULM PUBLIC SCHOOL
See NEW ULM INDEPENDENT SCHOOL DISTRICT 88

D-U-N-S 00-890-4641
▲ NEW ULM TELECOM INC
NU-TELECOM
27 N Minnesota St, New Ulm, MN 56073-1727
Tel (507) 354-4111 *Founded/Ownrshp* 1905
Sales 39.9MM *EMP* 141^E
Accts Olsen Thielen & Co Ltd St
Tkr Sym NULM *Exch* OTO
SIC 4813 5999 Local telephone communications; ; Telephone/video communications; Mobile telephones & equipment; Local telephone communications; ; Telephone/video communications; Mobile telephones & equipment
Pr: Bill D Otis
**Ch Bd:* James P Jensen
COO: Barbara A J Bornhoft
CFO: Curtis O Kawlewski
Dir IT: Scott Steinhaus
Board of Directors: Duane Lambrecht, Perry Meyer, Dennis Miller, Wesley E Schultz, Colleen R Skillings, Suzanne M Spellacy

D-U-N-S 10-297-0571 IMP/EXP
NEW UNITED MOTOR MANUFACTURING INC
NUMMI
45500 Fremont Blvd, Fremont, CA 94538-6326
Tel (510) 498-5500 *Founded/Ownrshp* 1983
Sales NA *EMP* 5,000^E
SIC 3714 3711

D-U-N-S 15-952-2718
NEW URBAN LEARNING
14669 Curtis St Fl 2, Detroit, MI 48235
Tel (313) 270-2532 *Founded/Ownrshp* 1999
Sales 21.3MM *EMP* 12
SIC 8299 Educational services; Educational services
Pr: Doug Ross

D-U-N-S 12-336-5244 IMP
NEW VAD LLC
VADDIO
131 Cheshire Ln Ste 500, Minnetonka, MN 55305-1068
Tel (763) 971-4400 *Founded/Ownrshp* 2007
Sales 60.0MM^E *EMP* 45
SIC 3861 Cameras & related equipment
Pr: Bill Fischer
CFO: Steve Vanhandel
**VP:* Thomas Mingo
DP Dir: Jon Reiss
Web Dev: Aaron Sheriff
Sftwr Eng: Eliza Hudson
Prd Mgr: John Pham
Sls Mgr: Paul Cords
Sls Mgr: Kevin Olson
Sls Mgr: Erik Soderlund
Sls Mgr: Doug Waldoch

D-U-N-S 00-699-2242
■ **NEW VALLEY LLC**
(*Suby of* VECTOR GROUP LTD) ★
4400 Biscayne Blvd, Miami, FL 33137-3212
Tel (305) 579-8000 *Founded/Ownrshp* 1851
Sales 30.5MM^E *EMP* 123
SIC 6512 Nonresidential building operators
Ch Bd: Bennett S Lebow
**Pr:* Howard M Lorber
CFO: Bryant Kirkland III
**CFO:* J Bryant Kirkland III
**Ex VP:* Richard J Lampen
**VP:* Marc N Bell

D-U-N-S 02-152-6132
NEW VANDERBILT REHABILITATION AND CARE CENTER INC
135 Vanderbilt Ave, Staten Island, NY 10304-2604
Tel (718) 447-0701 *Founded/Ownrshp* 1988
Sales 20.2MM^E *EMP* 285
SIC 8051 Skilled nursing care facilities; Skilled nursing care facilities
Ch Bd: Clara Heisler
**Pr:* Henry Schon
**VP:* Baron Schon
Med Dir: Seth Brum
Med Dir: Shye Wortman

NEW VENTURE FOUNDRY
See PARAGON METALS INC

D-U-N-S 96-212-6541
NEW VENTURE FUND
1201 Conn Ave Nw Ste 300, Washington, DC 20036-2656
Tel (202) 595-1061 *Founded/Ownrshp* 2010
Sales 112.9MM *EMP* 3
Accts Cliftonlarsonallen Llp Arling
SIC 7389 Services; Fund raising organizations
Pr: Eric Kessler

D-U-N-S 11-325-9878 IMP
NEW VENTURE HOLDINGS LLC
DUMP, THE
5324 Virginia Beach Blvd, Virginia Beach, VA 23462-1828
Tel (757) 497-5833 *Founded/Ownrshp* 2002
Sales 21.3MM^E *EMP* 250
SIC 5712 Furniture stores; Furniture stores

D-U-N-S 13-104-9756
NEW VENTURE PARTNERS LLC
430 Mountain Ave, New Providence, NJ 07974-2761
Tel (908) 464-8131 *Founded/Ownrshp* 2001
Sales 29.8MM^E *EMP* 600
SIC 7372 Prepackaged software; Prepackaged software; Business oriented computer software
Mng Pt: Stephen Socolof
**CFO:* Anthony Abrahams

D-U-N-S 12-539-1396
NEW VISA HEALTH SERVICES INC
3414 Preakness Ct, Fallbrook, CA 92028-9096
Tel (760) 723-0053 *Founded/Ownrshp* 2000
Sales 4.7MM^E *EMP* 500
SIC 8059 Nursing home, except skilled & intermediate care facility; Nursing home, except skilled & intermediate care facility
Pr: Robert Craig

D-U-N-S 03-905-2704
NEW VISION CO-OP
38438 210th St, Brewster, MN 56119-2017
Tel (507) 842-2001 *Founded/Ownrshp* 1998
Sales 140.5MM^E *EMP* 73
SIC 5153 Grain elevators; Grain elevators
CEO: Frank McDowell

D-U-N-S 04-854-7946 IMP
NEW VISION DISPLAY INC
1430 Blue Oaks Blvd # 100, Roseville, CA 95747-5156
Tel (916) 786-8111 *Founded/Ownrshp* 2012
Sales 113.0MM *EMP* 3,000
SIC 3679 Liquid crystal displays (LCD); Liquid crystal displays (LCD)
CEO: Jeff Olyniec
**Ch Bd:* Owen Chen
**CFO:* Alan M Lefko
CTO: Farouk Zabel
VP Sls: Steve Gerisch

D-U-N-S 12-367-0551
NEW VISION GROUP LLC
3525 Piedmont Rd Ne, Atlanta, GA 30305-1578
Tel (404) 995-4711 *Founded/Ownrshp* 2002
Sales 59.6MM^E *EMP* 365
SIC 4833 Television broadcasting stations; Television broadcasting stations
**CFO:* Eric Simontis
Snr Mgr: David Bird

NEW VISIONS
See CANAPE CONNECTION

D-U-N-S 62-501-4691
NEW VISIONS FOR PUBLIC SCHOOLS INC
320 W 13th St Ste 600, New York, NY 10014-1265
Tel (212) 645-5110 *Founded/Ownrshp* 1989
Sales 22.9MM *EMP* 97
Accts Cbiz Mhm Llc New York Ny
SIC 8699 Personal interest organization; Personal interest organization
Pr: Robert L Hughes
**COO:* Stacy Martin
**CFO:* Stacy J Martin
CFO: David J Perlman
Ofcr: Lindsay Elliman
Ofcr: Raymond Johnson
Ofcr: Marci Maguire
Ofcr: Jessica Sasko
Ofcr: Danielle Scaramellino
**VP:* Ronald Chaluisan
**VP:* Beverly Donohue
**VP:* Mark Dunetz
Assoc Dir: Deborah Kiskis

NEW VISTA
See 300 BROADWAY HEALTHCARE LLC

D-U-N-S 15-909-5546
NEW VISTA HEALTH SERVICES INC
1987 Vartikian Ave, Clovis, CA 93611-0634
Tel (559) 298-3236 *Founded/Ownrshp* 1996
Sales 17.2MM^E *EMP* 450
SIC 8059 8361 8051 Nursing home, except skilled & intermediate care facility; Rehabilitation center, residential: health care incidental; Skilled nursing care facilities; Nursing home, except skilled & intermediate care facility; Rehabilitation center, residential: health care incidental; Skilled nursing care facilities
Pr: Robert Craig
**CFO:* Steve Saunders

NEW VITALITY
See NAC MARKETING CO LLC

D-U-N-S 84-890-1062
NEW WATER STREET CORP
55 Water St Ste Conc6, New York, NY 10041-0033
Tel (212) 422-1320 *Founded/Ownrshp* 1993
Sales 134.9MM *EMP* 10
SIC 6531 Real estate agent, commercial

NEW WAVE COMMUNICATION
See TELECOMMUNICATIONS MANAGEMENT LLC

D-U-N-S 02-512-3063
NEW WAVE PEOPLE INC
66 Witherspoon St, Princeton, NJ 08542-3239
Tel (732) 786-9070 *Founded/Ownrshp* 2000
Sales 9.4MM^E *EMP* 325
SIC 7363 Temporary help service; Engineering help service; Office help supply service; Temporary help service; Engineering help service; Office help supply service
Pr: Kathryn Amenerios

D-U-N-S 78-850-2573
NEW WAVE TECHNOLOGIES INC
4635 Wedgewood Blvd # 107, Frederick, MD 21703-3300
Tel (301) 624-5300 *Founded/Ownrshp* 1992
Sales 94.3MM^E *EMP* 64
SIC 5045 Computers, peripherals & software
Pr: William Cordell
**Pt:* Frank Lee
Pr: Thomas Boyle
**VP:* Lenny Martin
IT Man: Dale Andrews
IT Man: Stacey Hutt
IT Man: Jay Stobie
Software D: Carol Dorsey
Mfg Dir: Bobbi Stackman
Opers Mgr: Tim Voigt
Natl Sales: Matt Cornell

D-U-N-S 07-888-9812
NEW WAVE USA INC
(*Suby of* NEW WAVE GROUP AB)
101 Elliott Ave W Ste 100, Seattle, WA 98119-4293
Tel (206) 622-4191 *Founded/Ownrshp* 2008
Sales 29.8MM^E *EMP* 280
SIC 6719 Investment holding companies, except banks; Investment holding companies, except banks
Pr: Ernest Johnson

D-U-N-S 12-643-6919
NEW WAVERLY VENTURES LTD CO
LANDSCAPERS PRIDE
146 Fm 2793, New Waverly, TX 77358
Tel (936) 295-2870 *Founded/Ownrshp* 2002
Sales 21.0MM^E *EMP* 43
SIC 5191 Farm supplies
Plnt Mgr: Brad Volker
Pt: Lawrence Dobraski

NEW WAY
See SCRANTON MANUFACTURING CO INC

D-U-N-S 15-183-9131
NEW WAY LANDSCAPE & TREE SERVICES
7485 Ronson Rd, San Diego, CA 92111-1507
Tel (858) 505-8300 *Founded/Ownrshp* 1980
Sales 20.0MM^E *EMP* 175
SIC 0782 Landscape contractors
CEO: Randy Newhard
**Pr:* Kathryn Dejong
COO: Monty Bell
**CFO:* Dan Suhovecky
VP: Bob Rogers
Brnch Mgr: Dave Howell
Brnch Mgr: Robert Nutter
Brnch Mgr: Paul Smith
Brnch Mgr: Mike Wengeler
Genl Mgr: Daniel Fatheree
Genl Mgr: Alex Llerenas

D-U-N-S 07-839-8281 IMP
NEW WEATHERVANE RETAIL CORP
300 John Downey Dr, New Britain, CT 06051-2925
Tel (860) 224-6027 *Founded/Ownrshp* 1999
Sales 24.1MM^E *EMP* 400
Accts Tonya Dibella Corporate Accou
SIC 5621 Ready-to-wear apparel, women's; Ready-to-wear apparel, women's
Pr: Lawrence J Davidson Jr
**Ch:* Michael G Frieze
Treas: Edwin Davison
**Sr VP:* Edwin W Davidson
**Sr VP:* Thomas H Davidson
**VP:* Matthew R Kahn

D-U-N-S 80-558-2892
NEW WERNER HOLDING CO INC
93 Werner Rd, Greenville, PA 16125-9434
Tel (724) 588-2000 *Founded/Ownrshp* 2007
Sales 486.5MM^E *EMP* 1,804
SIC 3499 3355 3089 3446 2499 6512 Ladders, portable: metal; Extrusion ingot, aluminum: made in rolling mills; Synthetic resin finished products; Scaffolds, mobile or stationary: metal; Stepladders, wood; Nonresidential building operators; Ladders, portable: metal; Extrusion ingot, aluminum: made in rolling mills; Synthetic resin finished products; Scaffolds, mobile or stationary: metal; Stepladders, wood; Nonresidential building operators
Pr: William T Allen
**CFO:* Larry Friend
CFO: Marc L Werner
**VP:* Edward Gericke
MIS Dir: Lee Easton
Dir IT: Howard Solot

D-U-N-S 87-714-0269
NEW WEST
1707 Coal Blvd Ste 250, Golden, CO 80401
Tel (303) 763-4900 *Founded/Ownrshp* 1994
Sales 12.1MM^E *EMP* 300
SIC 8741 Office management; Office management
Pr: Thomas Jeffers

D-U-N-S 03-495-9486 IMP
NEW WEST DISTRIBUTING INC
COORS-NEW WEST DISTRIBUTORS
325 E Nugget Ave Ste 101, Sparks, NV 89431-5856
Tel (775) 355-5500 *Founded/Ownrshp* 1982
Sales 27.0MM^E *EMP* 60
SIC 5181 5149 Beer & other fermented malt liquors; Soft drinks
CEO: John Beal
**Treas:* Madonna Beal

D-U-N-S 17-719-9940
NEW WEST HEALTH SERVICES
130 Neill Ave, Helena, MT 59601-3329
Tel (406) 457-2200 *Founded/Ownrshp* 1997
Sales NA *EMP* 89^E
SIC 6324 Health maintenance organization (HMO), insurance only; Health maintenance organization (HMO), insurance only
CEO: Angela Huschak
**Pr:* David Henry
**CEO:* David Kidde
CFO: Rick Gorenflo
Dir IT: D J Howell
Doctor: Cory Hartman

D-U-N-S 18-519-3612
NEW WEST PHYSICIANS PC
1707 Cole Blvd Ste 100, Golden, CO 80401-3219
Tel (303) 763-4900 *Founded/Ownrshp* 1999
Sales 28.6MM^E *EMP* 300
SIC 8011 8721 Physicians' office, including specialists; Accounting, auditing & bookkeeping; Physicians' office, including specialists; Accounting, auditing & bookkeeping
CEO: Ruth Benton
VP: Mary Murphy
Prac Mgr: Gina Hart
Dir IT: Kou Vang
IT Man: Kurt Waschak
VP Opers: Lucie Owens
Doctor: Dawn Baker
Doctor: Dana Benner
Doctor: Amanda Doetsch MD
Doctor: Nicole Dorotik MD
Doctor: Lisa Gidday MD

D-U-N-S 80-102-5789
NEW WEST REALTY DEVELOPMENT CORP
1440 W Taylor St, Chicago, IL 60607-4623
Tel (312) 829-2100 *Founded/Ownrshp* 2005
Sales 40.0MM *EMP* 12^E
SIC 6552 Land subdividers & developers, commercial; Land subdividers & developers, residential; Land subdividers & developers, commercial; Land subdividers & developers, residential
Pr: Theodore Mazola
COO: Carolyn Godman

D-U-N-S 01-498-3246
NEW WEST TECHNOLOGIES LLC (CA)
10333 E Dry Creek Rd # 200, Englewood, CO 80112-1590
Tel (202) 470-6435 *Founded/Ownrshp* 1996
Sales 27.9MM^E *EMP* 160
SIC 8748 Energy conservation consultant; Energy conservation consultant
**Ex VP:* Mark Owen
Sftwr Eng: Reid Phillips

D-U-N-S 15-097-9230 IMP
NEW WINCUP HOLDINGS INC
(*Suby of* WINCUP INC) ★
4640 Lewis Rd, Stone Mountain, GA 30083-1004
Tel (770) 938-5281 *Founded/Ownrshp* 1962
Sales 259.4MM^E *EMP* 1,000^E
SIC 3086 Cups & plates, foamed plastic; Cups & plates, foamed plastic
CEO: Jack Brucker
**Pr:* Glenn Wredenhagen
**Pr:* George W Wurtz III
**CFO:* Scott Haftmann
**CFO:* Mark Thomas
**Treas:* Evan Hardin
**Sr VP:* Mike Revier
**Sr VP:* Michael Winters
Sls Mgr: Henry Bowen

D-U-N-S 02-099-1407 IMP
NEW WORLD AUTO IMPORTS OF CONROE INC (TX)
SOUTHWEST KIA
39650 Lyndon B Jhnson Fwy, Dallas, TX 75237-3901
Tel (972) 283-9797 *Founded/Ownrshp* 2001
Sales 38.3MM^E *EMP* 66^E
SIC 5511 Automobiles, new & used; Automobiles, new & used
Pr: Shahab Salehoun
Ofcr: Rudy Samboruk
Mktg Mgr: Kelsy Allen
Mktg Mgr: Russell Paulov
Sls Mgr: Keith Amason
Sls Mgr: Cecil Cain
Sls Mgr: Bill Dickerson
Sls Mgr: Amer Husseini

D-U-N-S 93-750-7176
NEW WORLD CAR NISSAN INC
12908 N Interstate 35, Live Oak, TX 78233-2613
Tel (210) 599-5959 *Founded/Ownrshp* 1993
Sales 27.9MM^E *EMP* 75
SIC 5511 Automobiles, new & used; Automobiles, new & used
Prin: Ahmad Zabihian
VP: Tim Cliver
Genl Mgr: Jimmy Willis
IT Man: Chuck Guilhas
IT Man: Scott Kreuser

D-U-N-S 86-717-0789
■ **NEW WORLD COMMUNICATIONS OF ATLANTA INC**
FOX FIVE
(*Suby of* FOX TELEVISION STATIONS INC) ★
1551 Briarcliff Rd Ne, Atlanta, GA 30306-2217
Tel (404) 875-5555 *Founded/Ownrshp* 1997
Sales 27.1MM^E *EMP* 190
SIC 4833

D-U-N-S 04-118-8814
■ **NEW WORLD COMMUNICATIONS OF MILWAUKEE INC**
WITI-TV
(*Suby of* LOCAL TV LLC) ★
9001 N Green Bay Rd, Milwaukee, WI 53209-1204
Tel (414) 586-2166 *Founded/Ownrshp* 2012
Sales 21.6MM^E *EMP* 210
SIC 4833 Television broadcasting stations; Television broadcasting stations
Genl Mgr: Chuck Steinmetz
Sls Mgr: Mike Neale

D-U-N-S 03-053-9808
NEW WORLD ENERGY RESOURCES INC
1500 Granville Rd, Newark, OH 43055-1536
Tel (740) 344-4087 *Founded/Ownrshp* 2001
Sales 42.0MM^E *EMP* 488
SIC 1382 Geological exploration, oil & gas field; Geological exploration, oil & gas field
CEO: John Manczak

D-U-N-S 16-144-8964 IMP
NEW WORLD INTERNATIONAL INC
(*Suby of* NAPA AUTO PARTS) ★
1720 E State Highway 356, Irving, TX 75060-3214
Tel (214) 352-1191 *Founded/Ownrshp* 1986
Sales 37.8MM^E *EMP* 150
SIC 5531 5013 Automotive parts; Automotive supplies & parts
Pr: Yao H Tsai
**VP:* Steve Culver

D-U-N-S 96-205-6383
NEW WORLD LTD LP
5875 N Rogers Ave, Chicago, IL 60646-5953
Tel (773) 685-3399 *Founded/Ownrshp* 1995
Sales 66.0MM *EMP* 69
SIC 4212 4226 Moving services; Special warehousing & storage; Moving services; Special warehousing & storage
Pt: David Marx
Pt: Edward M Marx Jr
Pt: Janet Marx
Pt: Jerome K Marx
Pt: Richard J Wilkus

D-U-N-S 04-874-5165 IMP
NEW WORLD PASTA CO
(*Suby of* EBRO FOODS, SA)
85 Shannon Rd, Harrisburg, PA 17112-2787
Tel (717) 526-2200 *Founded/Ownrshp* 1996
Sales 175.2MM^E *EMP* 800
SIC 2098 Macaroni & spaghetti; Macaroni & spaghetti
CEO: Bastiaan De Zeeuw
**COO:* Peter E Cotter
**CFO:* Edward J Lyons
**CFO:* Horst O Sieben
**Sr VP:* Brett Beckfield
**Sr VP:* Douglas W Ehrenkranz
**Sr VP:* Gerard Ferguson
**Sr VP:* Lawrence C Kleinman
**Sr VP:* Gregory Richardson
VP: Angelo Fraggos
VP: Laurent Huynh
**VP:* Joseph Marelli Jr
VP: Cary Metz

NEW WORLD SALES
See STEVE SELVIN ASSOCIATES INC

D-U-N-S 05-240-3391 IMP
NEW WORLD SYSTEMS CORP
888 W Big Beavr Rd # 600, Troy, MI 48084-4749
Tel (248) 269-1000 *Founded/Ownrshp* 1981
Sales 49.9MM^E *EMP* 201
SIC 7371 5045 Computer software systems analysis & design, custom; Computer software development; Computers

D-U-N-S 05-354-0746
NEW WORLD TRAVEL INC
LIZARD INCENT EVENTS COMPANY
(*Suby of* DER TOURISTIK FRANKFURT GMBH & CO. KG)
1040 Ave Of America Fl 7, New York, NY 10018
Tel (212) 754-9100 *Founded/Ownrshp* 1979
Sales 21.7MM^E *EMP* 80
SIC 4725 Tours, conducted
Ch Bd: Peter Dorner
Sls Mgr: Katharina Doerr

NEW WORLD VAN LINES CALIFORNIA
See NEW WORLD VAN LINES INC

D-U-N-S 05-775-9276 IMP/EXP
NEW WORLD VAN LINES INC
NEW WORLD VAN LINES CALIFORNIA
5875 N Rogers Ave, Chicago, IL 60646-5966
Tel (773) 685-3399 *Founded/Ownrshp* 1982
Sales 91.4MM^E *EMP* 500
SIC 4213

D-U-N-S 14-918-6442 IMP/EXP
▲ **NEW YORK & CO INC**
330 W 34th St Fl 9, New York, NY 10001-2406
Tel (212) 884-2000 *Founded/Ownrshp* 1918
Sales 923.3MM *EMP* 6,400
Tkr Sym NWY *Exch* NYS
SIC 5621 Women's clothing stores; Women's clothing stores
CEO: Gregory J Scott
Pr: John M Worthington
CFO: Sheamus Toal
Ofcr: Cheryl Callan
Ofcr: Wallace Tiffany
Ex VP: Faeth Bradley
Ex VP: John D Dewolf
Ex VP: Sarah Elsom Eustis
Ex VP: Kevin L Finnegan
Ex VP: Christine Munnelly
Ex VP: David Witkewicz
VP: Adam Ratner
Assoc Dir: Charisse Taylor
Creative D: Darryl Powlus
Board of Directors: David H Edwab, James O Egan, Lori H Greeley, John D Howard, Grace Nichols, Michelle Pearlman, Richard L Perkal, Arthur E Reiner

D-U-N-S 92-957-4168
■ **NEW YORK - NEW YORK HOTEL & CASINO LLC**
(*Suby of* MGM RESORTS INTERNATIONAL) ★
3790 Las Vegas Blvd S, Las Vegas, NV 89109-4338
Tel (702) 740-6969 *Founded/Ownrshp* 1997
Sales 103.9MM^E *EMP* 2,300
SIC 7011 7996 Casino hotel; Theme park, amusement; Casino hotel; Theme park, amusement
Pr: Cynthia Kiser Murphey
COO: David Cacci
**CFO:* William Basborg
VP: Michael Dejong
VP: Thomas Reich
VP: Cathryn Schmit
Dir Sec: Greg Goll
Secur Mgr: Glenn Nulle

NEW YORK AIR BRAKE
See KNORR BRAKE TRUCK SYSTEMS CO

D-U-N-S 05-868-2740
NEW YORK AIR BRAKE LLC
(*Suby of* NEW YORK AIR BRAKE LLC) ★
5201 Regent Blvd Ste 130, Irving, TX 75063-2428
Tel (972) 893-2401 *Founded/Ownrshp* 1990
Sales 1.8MM^E *EMP* 557^E
SIC 7539 Brake repair, automotive
Ch: Dieter Wilhelm
Pr: Michael J Hawthorne
Sr VP: Jason T Connell
VP: Marshall G Beck
VP: John M Chatterton
Genl Mgr: William Sturtz
Software D: Steven Deans

D-U-N-S 82-614-0519
NEW YORK AIR BRAKE LLC
(*Suby of* KNORR BRAKE HOLDING CORP) ★
748 Starbuck Ave, Watertown, NY 13601-1620
Tel (315) 786-5219 *Founded/Ownrshp* 1990
Sales 22.5MM *EMP* 750^E
SIC 3743 Brakes, air & vacuum: railway; Brakes, air & vacuum: railway
Ch Bd: Heinz Thiele
Pr: Frank Henderson
Pr: J Paul Morgan
Sr VP: Marshall G Beck
Sr VP: Gerald Hettick
Prgrm Mgr: Luann Lalone
Snr Sftwr: Walter Valkema
IT Man: Ozgurmine Ismail
Sftwr Eng: Dan James
VP Opers: John Chatterton
QI Cn Mgr: Gregory Dana

D-U-N-S 00-697-8092
■ **NEW YORK AMERICAN WATER CO INC** (NY)
LI WATER
(*Suby of* AMERICAN WATER WORKS CO INC) ★
60 Brooklyn Ave, Merrick, NY 11566-3402
Tel (516) 596-4800 *Founded/Ownrshp* 1925
Sales 38.1MM^E *EMP* 110^E
SIC 4941 Water supply; Water supply
Pr: Robert Gallo
VP Bus Dev: Edmund Deveaux
Exec: Chuck Johnston
Comm Dir: Maureen Duffy
Rgnl Mgr: Donald Shields
Rgnl Mgr: Andre Zinkevich
Off Mgr: Thomas Huber

D-U-N-S 01-272-9476 IMP
NEW YORK AND PRESBYTERIAN HOSPITAL
NEW YORK-PRESBYTERIAN HOSPITAL
525 E 68th St, New York, NY 10065-4870
Tel (212) 746-5454 *Founded/Ownrshp* 1998
Sales 4.2MMM *EMP* 15,078
SIC 8062 8011 General medical & surgical hospitals; Offices & clinics of medical doctors; General medical & surgical hospitals; Offices & clinics of medical doctors
Ch Bd: John J Mack
**Pr:* Herbert Pardes
COO: Andria Castellanos
**COO:* Steven J Corwin MD
**CFO:* Phyllis R Lantos
CFO: Mark E Larmore
Bd of Dir: Mathew Eapen
Bd of Dir: Wendy Goldstein
Bd of Dir: Judy Graham
Bd of Dir: Roger Greene
Trst: Roger C Altman
Trst: Raymond J McGuire
Trst: Daniel S Och
Trst: Sanford I Weill
Trst: Ivan G Seidenberg
**Ofcr:* Maxine Fass
Ofcr: William Greene
Ofcr: Carol Silk
Sr VP: Gloria D Reeg
Sr VP: Lauren Yedvab
VP: Jos Nu EZ

D-U-N-S 02-066-4884
NEW YORK ASSOCIATION FOR RETARDED CHILDREN INC (NY)
ARC OF RENSSELAER COUNTY, THE
(*Suby of* NYSARC INC) ★
79 102nd St, Troy, NY 12180-1125
Tel (518) 274-3110 *Founded/Ownrshp* 1949
Sales 54.3M *EMP* 385
Accts Doyle & Golden Cpas Pc Troy
SIC 8331 8361 Vocational training agency; Home for the mentally retarded; Vocational training agency; Home for the mentally retarded
CEO: Hanns Meissner
**CFO:* Donald J Mullin
Genl Mgr: Tammy McIsaac
Sls Mgr: Joe Starzyk

D-U-N-S 06-820-6143
NEW YORK ATHLETIC CLUB OF CITY OF NEW YORK (NY)
180 Central Park S, New York, NY 10019-1562
Tel (212) 247-5100 *Founded/Ownrshp* 1868
Sales 24.8MM^E *EMP* 360
SIC 7041 7991 Lodging house, organization; Physical fitness facilities; Athletic club & gymnasiums, membership; Lodging house, organization; Physical fitness facilities; Athletic club & gymnasiums, membership
Pr: Valentine J Taubner Jr
**Treas:* Christopher O Cassell
**VP:* Robert S Geary
**VP:* S Colin Neill
**Genl Mgr:* Len Terradista

D-U-N-S 78-434-9839
■ **NEW YORK AUTO AUCTION SERVICES INC**
NORTHWAY EXCHANGE
(*Suby of* MANHEIM INVESTMENTS INC) ★
Rr 146, Clifton Park, NY 12065
Tel (518) 371-7500 *Founded/Ownrshp* 1991
Sales 27.1MM^E *EMP* 300
SIC 5012 Automobile auction; Automobile auction
Pr: G Dennis Berry
**Treas:* Robert Gartin
**VP:* Darryl Ceccoli

D-U-N-S 05-405-9407
NEW YORK BITUMINOUS PRODUCTS CORP
1297 Craigville Rd, Chester, NY 10918-4524
Tel (845) 782-7231 *Founded/Ownrshp* 2007
Sales 21.0MM^E *EMP* 40
SIC 5085 Industrial supplies
Pr: Robert H Maggard

D-U-N-S 07-327-1827
NEW YORK BLOOD CENTER INC
LONG ISLAND BLOOD SERVICES
310 E 67th St, New York, NY 10065-6273
Tel (212) 570-3010 *Founded/Ownrshp* 1959
Sales 320.2MM *EMP* 1,600
Accts Kpmg Llp New York Ny
SIC 8099 2836 Blood bank; Blood donor station; Blood derivatives; Blood bank; Blood donor station; Blood derivatives
CEO: Christopher D Hillyer
**CFO:* Elizabeth C Gibson
**CFO:* Lawrence Hannigan
Treas: Christine Foran
Top Exec: Sara Lustigman
Sr VP: Ollie Cheatham
**Sr VP:* Elizabeth J McQuail
**Sr VP:* Michael J Monahan
VP: Doriane Gloria
VP: Frederick Hill
VP: Donald Kender
VP: John Mullen
VP: Pablo Purvis
VP: Eva Quinley
VP: David Silverman
VP: Edward Travaglianti
Exec: Michele Shenfeld
Dir Soc: Rolf Kovenetsky

D-U-N-S 00-506-9414 IMP/EXP
NEW YORK BLOWER CO
NY B
7660 S Quincy St, Willowbrook, IL 60527-5596
Tel (630) 794-5700 *Founded/Ownrshp* 1889
Sales 67.0MM^E *EMP* 350
SIC 3564

D-U-N-S 00-216-1051 IMP
NEW YORK BOTANICAL GARDEN
412 Bedford Park Blvd, Bronx, NY 10458-2410
Tel (718) 817-8680 *Founded/Ownrshp* 2007
Sales 89.0MM *EMP* 36^E
SIC 7999 8211 8299 Instruction schools, camps & services; Elementary & secondary schools; Floral arrangement instruction
VP: Dennis Stevenson

D-U-N-S 07-325-0946 IMP
NEW YORK BOTANICAL GARDEN
2900 Southern Blvd, Bronx, NY 10458-5153
Tel (718) 817-8700 *Founded/Ownrshp* 1891
Sales 101.6MM *EMP* 500
Accts Deloitte & Touche Llp Jericho
SIC 8422 8299 Botanical garden; Educational services; Botanical garden; Educational services
Pr: Gregory R Long
Dir Vol: Jackie Martinez
CFO: David Kleiser
Assoc VP: Margaret Falk
**Sr VP:* J V Cossaboom
VP: Michael Balick
VP: Sophia Black
VP: Annemarie Blancato
VP: Dale Brooks
VP: Robert Carotenuto
VP: Francisca Coelho
VP: Karl Lauby
VP: Cynthia Mooney
**VP:* Dennis Stevenson
VP: Brian Sullivan
VP: Karen Yesnick

D-U-N-S 14-406-6599
NEW YORK BUS SALES LLC
7765 Lakeport Rd, Chittenango, NY 13037-9545
Tel (315) 687-9543 *Founded/Ownrshp* 2003
Sales 45.8MM^E *EMP* 100
SIC 5012 Buses
Sr VP: Marlene Costanzo

D-U-N-S 00-243-0072
NEW YORK CENTRAL MUTUAL FIRE INSURANCE CO
NYCM INSURANCE
1899 Central Plz E, Edmeston, NY 13335-1828
Tel (607) 965-8321 *Founded/Ownrshp* 1899
Sales NA *EMP* 850
SIC 6331 Fire, marine & casualty insurance: mutual; Life insurance funds, savings bank; Fire, marine & casualty insurance
Ch Bd: Vanness D Robinson
Pr: Kevin Plows
**Pr:* D Daniel Robinson II
Pr: Robert Snyder
**CFO:* Albert Pylinski Jr
Treas: Jeremy Robinson
Sr VP: Stephen M Cembrinski
Sr VP: Doughlas Franklin
Sr VP: John E Holdorf
Sr VP: James R Slosek
Sr VP: Timothy Trueworth
VP: William Couperthwait
VP: Mike Sweet

D-U-N-S 07-860-6324
NEW YORK CHIROPRACTIC COLLEGE
DEPEW HEALTH CENTER
2360 State Route 89, Seneca Falls, NY 13148-9460
Tel (315) 568-3000 *Founded/Ownrshp* 1919
Sales 29.9MM *EMP* 400
Accts Cliftonlarsonallen Llp Plymou
SIC 8221 Colleges universities & professional schools; Colleges universities & professional schools
Pr: Frank J Nicchi
**CFO:* Sean Anglim
CFO: Victoria Barody
Ex VP: Angela Ferragamo
VP: Magdalen Kellogg
VP: Christopher McQueeney
**VP:* Dr Michael Mestan
Ex Dir: Judy Silvestrone
Off Mgr: Patricia Kaska-Caver
Off Mgr: Anne Smith
Store Mgr: Helen Stuck

D-U-N-S 07-816-3383 IMP
NEW YORK CITY BOARD OF EDUCATION
DEPARTMENT OF EDUCATION
52 Chambers St Ste 320, New York, NY 10007-1222
Tel (212) 374-5141 *Founded/Ownrshp* 1900
Sales 0.0 *EMP* 135,000
SIC 8211

D-U-N-S 08-040-3512
NEW YORK CITY CENTER INC
CITY CENTER THEATER
42 E Main St 204, Freehold, NJ 07728-2295
Tel (212) 581-1212 *Founded/Ownrshp* 1976
Sales 23.0MM *EMP* 50
Accts Lutz & Carr Llp New York Ne
SIC 7922 Performing arts center production; Performing arts center production
Pr: Arlene Shuler
Ch: Ray Lamontagne
VP: Hawley Abelow
VP: Mark Litvin
VP: Will Maitland Weiss
VP: Vanessa Wise
Genl Mgr: Stephenie Overton
CIO: Robert Palm
Mktg Mgr: Karla Salguero
Mktg Mgr: Michelle Vallucci

D-U-N-S 09-612-1546
NEW YORK CITY CRIMINAL JUSTICE AGENCY INC
52 Duane St Fl 3, New York, NY 10007-1231
Tel (646) 213-2500 *Founded/Ownrshp* 1977
Sales 18.1MM *EMP* 320
SIC 8111 Legal services; Legal services
Ex Dir: Jerome E Mc Elroy
**Ch:* Lowell Johnston
**Treas:* Mario Nieves

D-U-N-S 02-313-7024
NEW YORK CITY DEPARTMENT OF DESIGN & CONSTRUCTION
DDC
3030 Thomson Ave, Long Island City, NY 11101-3019
Tel (718) 391-1951 *Founded/Ownrshp* 1995
Sales 33.5MM^E *EMP* 140
SIC 1542 School building construction
Mng Ofcr: Magalie Austin
Pgrm Dir: Bruce Rudolph
Pgrm Dir: Barbara Spandorf
Snr PM: Moses Ros
Snr PM: John Ziedonis
Snr Mgr: Chris Gallo

D-U-N-S 80-046-9715
NEW YORK CITY DEPT OF EDUCATION
NYC EMPOWERMENT SCHOOLS
Tweed Cthose 52 Chmbrs St Tweed Courthouse, New York, NY 10007
Tel (212) 374-6000 *Founded/Ownrshp* 2007
Sales 118.1MM^E *EMP* 908^E
SIC 8732 Educational research
**COO:* Veronica Conforme
**Prin:* Kemi Akinsanya-Rose
Phys Thrpy: Carlo Vialu

D-U-N-S 07-324-6910
NEW YORK CITY ECONOMIC DEVELOPMENT CORP
NYCEDC
110 William St Fl 4, New York, NY 10038-3950
Tel (212) 619-5000 *Founded/Ownrshp* 1966
Sales NA *EMP* 438
Accts Ernst & Young Llp New York N
SIC 9611 Economic consultant; Administration of general economic programs
Pr: Maria Torres-Springer
**COO:* Euan Robertson
COO: Josh Wallack
**CFO:* Kim Vaccari
**Treas:* Spencer Hobson
**Ex VP:* Seth Myers
Sr VP: Joe Coletti
Sr VP: Matthew Kwatinetz
Sr VP: Michael Moynihan
Sr VP: Peyton Sise
VP: Lydia Downing
VP: John McGlynn
VP: Kate Van Tassel
VP: Elizabeth Verostek
VP: Jiin Wen
VP: Lauren Wolf

D-U-N-S 03-240-5222
NEW YORK CITY FINANCIAL INFORMATION SERVICES AGENCY
450 W 33rd St Fl 4, New York, NY 10001-2633
Tel (212) 857-1533 *Founded/Ownrshp* 2001
Sales 55.2MM^E *EMP* 350
SIC 6289 Financial reporting; Financial reporting
Ex Dir: Robert Townsend
Sr VP: George Thomas
VP: Don Pascali

D-U-N-S 07-995-4994
NEW YORK CITY GEOGRAPHIC DISTRICT 1
166 Essex St, New York, NY 10002-1502
Tel (212) 353-2948 *Founded/Ownrshp* 2015
Sales 13.5MM^E *EMP* 1,630^E
SIC 8211 Public elementary & secondary schools

D-U-N-S 07-980-6893
NEW YORK CITY GEOGRAPHIC DISTRICT 10
1 Fordham Plz Rm 805, Bronx, NY 10458-5871
Tel (718) 741-5852 *Founded/Ownrshp* 2015
Sales 27.1MM^E *EMP* 6,586^E
SIC 8211 Public elementary & secondary schools

D-U-N-S 07-991-6345
NEW YORK CITY GEOGRAPHIC DISTRICT 12
1970 W Farms Rd, Bronx, NY 10460-6024
Tel (718) 328-2310 *Founded/Ownrshp* 2015
Sales 19.8MM^E *EMP* 22,219
SIC 8211 Public elementary & secondary schools

D-U-N-S 07-995-5108
NEW YORK CITY GEOGRAPHIC DISTRICT 12
1434 Longfellow Ave, Bronx, NY 10459-1604
Tel (718) 328-2310 *Founded/Ownrshp* 2015
Sales 64.8MM^E *EMP* 2,540^E
SIC 8211 Public elementary & secondary schools

D-U-N-S 07-980-6891
NEW YORK CITY GEOGRAPHIC DISTRICT 13
355 Park Pl, Brooklyn, NY 11238-4001
Tel (718) 636-3204 *Founded/Ownrshp* 2015
Sales 13.7MM^E *EMP* 2,546^E
SIC 8211 Public elementary & secondary schools

D-U-N-S 95-643-1373
NEW YORK CITY GEOGRAPHIC DISTRICT 14
215 Heyward St, Brooklyn, NY 11206-2966
Tel (718) 302-7600 *Founded/Ownrshp* 1999
Sales 23.0MM^E *EMP* 2,889^E
SIC 8211 Public elementary & secondary schools

D-U-N-S 07-995-5120
NEW YORK CITY GEOGRAPHIC DISTRICT 15
131 Livingston St Rm 301, Brooklyn, NY 11201-5105
Tel (718) 935-4317 *Founded/Ownrshp* 2015
Sales 16.2MM^E *EMP* 2,881^E
SIC 8211 Public elementary & secondary schools

D-U-N-S 15-955-5457
NEW YORK CITY GEOGRAPHIC DISTRICT 16
1010 Lafayette Ave, Brooklyn, NY 11221-2303
Tel (718) 574-2800 *Founded/Ownrshp* 1999
Sales 9.7MM^E *EMP* 570
SIC 8211 Public elementary & secondary schools; School board; Administration of educational programs; Public elementary & secondary schools; School board
Prin: Marshall Lyles
IT Man: Darnley Moore

D-U-N-S 07-976-7516
NEW YORK CITY GEOGRAPHIC DISTRICT 17
1224 Park Pl, Brooklyn, NY 11213-2703
Tel (718) 221-4372 Founded/Ownrshp 1900
Sales 23.3MM^E EMP 4,141^E
SIC 8211 Public elementary & secondary schools

D-U-N-S 07-980-6898
NEW YORK CITY GEOGRAPHIC DISTRICT 19
557 Pennsylvania Ave, Brooklyn, NY 11207-5727
Tel (718) 342-3625 Founded/Ownrshp 2015
Sales 17.2MM^E EMP 2,894^E
SIC 8211 Public elementary & secondary schools

D-U-N-S 07-980-6914
NEW YORK CITY GEOGRAPHIC DISTRICT 2
333 7th Ave Fl 7, New York, NY 10001-5119
Tel (212) 356-3815 Founded/Ownrshp 2015
Sales 22.6MM^E EMP 5,070^E
SIC 8211 Public elementary & secondary schools

D-U-N-S 04-530-3065
NEW YORK CITY GEOGRAPHIC DISTRICT 20
415 89th St, Brooklyn, NY 11209-5905
Tel (718) 759-3942 Founded/Ownrshp 2010
Sales 24.2MM^E EMP 3,852^E
SIC 8211 Public elementary & secondary schools

D-U-N-S 07-980-6916
NEW YORK CITY GEOGRAPHIC DISTRICT 21
501 West Ave, Brooklyn, NY 11224-4220
Tel (718) 714-2502 Founded/Ownrshp 2015
Sales 438.6M^E EMP 3,784^E
SIC 8211 Public elementary & secondary schools

D-U-N-S 07-859-9455
NEW YORK CITY GEOGRAPHIC DISTRICT 22
5619 Flatlands Ave, Brooklyn, NY 11234-2501
Tel (718) 968-6117 Founded/Ownrshp 2012
Sales 1.2MM^E EMP 3,788^E
SIC 8211 Elementary & secondary schools
Prin: Mary Bosco

D-U-N-S 06-107-5229
NEW YORK CITY GEOGRAPHIC DISTRICT 23
1665 Saint Marks Ave, Brooklyn, NY 11233-4813
Tel (718) 922-4794 Founded/Ownrshp 2011
Sales 11.7MM^E EMP 1,993^E
SIC 8211 Public elementary & secondary schools

D-U-N-S 03-271-4159
NEW YORK CITY GEOGRAPHIC DISTRICT 24
9850 50th Ave, Corona, NY 11368-2757
Tel (718) 592-3357 Founded/Ownrshp 2011
Sales 141.4MM^E EMP 5,410^E
SIC 7336 Commercial art & graphic design

D-U-N-S 07-980-6903
NEW YORK CITY GEOGRAPHIC DISTRICT 26
6115 Oceania St, Bayside, NY 11364-2139
Tel (718) 631-6982 Founded/Ownrshp 2015
Sales 17.4MM^E EMP 2,540^E
SIC 8211 Public elementary & secondary schools

D-U-N-S 04-530-3461
NEW YORK CITY GEOGRAPHIC DISTRICT 28
9027 Sutphin Blvd Rm 24, Jamaica, NY 11435-3647
Tel (718) 557-2618 Founded/Ownrshp 2010
Sales 20.2MM^E EMP 3,288^E
SIC 8211 Public elementary & secondary schools
Prin: Beverly Ffolkes-Bryant

D-U-N-S 04-530-3416
NEW YORK CITY GEOGRAPHIC DISTRICT 29
22214 Jamaica Ave, Queens Village, NY 11428-2018
Tel (718) 264-3146 Founded/Ownrshp 2010
Sales 19.0MM^E EMP 2,927^E
SIC 8211 Public elementary & secondary schools
Prin: Lenon Murray

D-U-N-S 07-995-5013
NEW YORK CITY GEOGRAPHIC DISTRICT 3
501 W 165th St, New York, NY 10032-4206
Tel (212) 678-5857 Founded/Ownrshp 2015
Sales 13.1MM^E EMP 2,325^E
SIC 8211 Public elementary & secondary schools

D-U-N-S 04-812-4719
NEW YORK CITY GEOGRAPHIC DISTRICT 30
2811 Queens Plz N, Long Island City, NY 11101-4008
Tel (718) 391-8323 Founded/Ownrshp 1900
Sales 75.9MM^E EMP 3,536^E
SIC 8211 Public elementary & secondary schools

D-U-N-S 07-995-5135
NEW YORK CITY GEOGRAPHIC DISTRICT 31
715 Ocean Ter Rm 129, Staten Island, NY 10301-4542
Tel (718) 420-5667 Founded/Ownrshp 2015
Sales 110.7MM^E EMP 5,817^E
SIC 8211 Public elementary & secondary schools

D-U-N-S 07-980-6920
NEW YORK CITY GEOGRAPHIC DISTRICT 4
319 E 117th St, New York, NY 10035-4902
Tel (212) 831-4981 Founded/Ownrshp 2015
Sales 12.8MM^E EMP 1,653^E
SIC 8211 Public elementary & secondary schools

D-U-N-S 07-980-6901
NEW YORK CITY GEOGRAPHIC DISTRICT 5
425 W 123rd St, New York, NY 10027-5002
Tel (212) 769-7500 Founded/Ownrshp 2015
Sales 12.9MM^E EMP 1,999^E
SIC 8211 Public elementary & secondary schools

D-U-N-S 07-980-6904
NEW YORK CITY GEOGRAPHIC DISTRICT 6
4360 Broadway Rm 527, New York, NY 10033-2409
Tel (212) 521-3757 Founded/Ownrshp 2015
Sales 16.8MM^E EMP 2,760^E
SIC 8211 Public elementary & secondary schools

D-U-N-S 07-995-5036
NEW YORK CITY GEOGRAPHIC DISTRICT 7
501 Courtland Ave, Bronx, NY 10451
Tel (718) 742-6500 Founded/Ownrshp 2015
Sales 57.9MM^E EMP 2,476^E
SIC 8211 Public elementary & secondary schools

D-U-N-S 07-995-5080
NEW YORK CITY GEOGRAPHIC DISTRICT 8
601 Stickball Blvd, Bronx, NY 10473-2624
Tel (718) 828-6653 Founded/Ownrshp 2015
Sales 64.8MM^E EMP 3,281^E
SIC 8211 Public elementary & secondary schools

D-U-N-S 04-945-8580
NEW YORK CITY GEOGRAPHIC DISTRICT 9
1377 Jerome Ave, Bronx, NY 10452-3337
Tel (718) 842-0138 Founded/Ownrshp 2010
Sales 1.0MM^E EMP 3,714^E
SIC 8211 School board
Prin: Calvin Diaz

NEW YORK CITY HEALTH AND HOSPI
See METROPLUS HEALTH PLAN INC

D-U-N-S 06-496-1261 IMP
NEW YORK CITY HEALTH AND HOSPITALS CORP
NEW YORK CITY HLTH & HOSPITALS
125 Worth St Rm 514, New York, NY 10013-4006
Tel (212) 788-3321 Founded/Ownrshp 1970
Sales 4.0MMM^E EMP 35,700
SIC 8062 8069 8093 General medical & surgical hospitals; Chronic disease hospital; Specialty outpatient clinics; General medical & surgical hospitals; Chronic disease hospital; Specialty outpatient clinics
Pr: Ramanathan Raju
Pr: Robert Kee
COO: Antonio Martin
CFO: Marlene Zurack
Ch: Ross Wilson
Ofcr: Joanne Lischin
Ex VP: Ramanathan Raju MD
Sr VP: Laray Brown
Sr VP: Lynda D Curtis
Sr VP: Caroline M Jacobs
Sr VP: Tony Martin
Sr VP: Cynthia Murray
Sr VP: Joanna OMI
Sr VP: Carlos Perez
Sr VP: Norberto Robles
Sr VP: Anne Marie Sullivan
Sr VP: William P Walsh
VP: Ken Powell
Dir Risk M: Jane Carlson
Dir Lab: Wilfredo Santos
Assoc Dir: Charlene Bailey-Ayers
Board of Directors: Edwin Mendez-Santiago, Ruth Bloom, Edwin Mendez-Santiago, Josephine Bolus, Lloyd I Sederer MD, Marcia R Brown MD, Marc V Shaw, Verna Eggleston, Bruce J Teitelbaum, Thomas R Frieden, Rev Diane E Lacey Winley, John R Maese MD, Cecilia E Norat, Daniel D Ricciardi, Bernard Rosen

NEW YORK CITY HLTH & HOSPITALS
See NEW YORK CITY HEALTH AND HOSPITALS CORP

D-U-N-S 00-167-2062
NEW YORK CITY HOUSING AUTHORITY
250 Broadway, New York, NY 10007-2516
Tel (212) 306-3000 Founded/Ownrshp 1934
Sales NA EMP 11,605
SIC 9531 Housing authority, non-operating: government; Housing authority, non-operating: government
Ch Bd: Shola Olatoye
CFO: Richard Couch
Ofcr: Victor Martinez
Ofcr: Jean Weinberg
Ex VP: David Farber
Ex VP: Melanie Hart
Ex VP: Bob Marano
Ex VP: Cathy Pennington
Ex VP: Raymond A Ribeiro
Ex VP: Natalie Y Rivers
Ex VP: Andreas Spitzer
Sr VP: Brian Clarke
Sr VP: Luis Ponce
Sr VP: Colette Rodgers
VP: Bill Crawley
VP: Anne-Marie Flatley
VP: Richard French
VP: Deidra Gilliard
VP: Rudolph Kurkjian
VP: Celeste Morgan
VP: Michael Rosen

D-U-N-S 11-850-2426
NEW YORK CITY HOUSING DEVELOPMENT CORP
110 William St Fl 10, New York, NY 10038-3946
Tel (212) 227-5500 Founded/Ownrshp 1971
Sales 35.0MM^E EMP 130
SIC 6799 9111 8322 Investors; Mayors' offices; Individual & family services; Investors; Mayors' offices; Individual & family services
Pr: Emily Yussuf
Pr: Catherine Marshall
VP: Simon Bacchus
*VP: John Crotty
VP: Anthony Richardson
VP: Karen Santiago
VP: James Tafuro
VP: Catherine Townsend
Prgrm Mgr: Elana Berenson
Software D: Michelle Antao
Genl Couns: Susannah Lipsyte

NEW YORK CITY MARATHON
See NEW YORK ROAD RUNNERS INC

D-U-N-S 09-949-3090 IMP/EXP
NEW YORK CITY OPERA INC
75 Broad St Rm 510, New York, NY 10004-3222
Tel (212) 870-5600 Founded/Ownrshp 1943
Sales 13.3MM EMP 1,000
Accts Lutz And Carr Cpas Llp New Yo
SIC 7922 Opera company; Opera company
Ch Bd: Susan L Baker
*CFO: Derek Davis
*VP: Roy Furman

D-U-N-S 13-975-4332
NEW YORK CITY SCHOOL CONSTRUCTION AUTHORITY
3030 Thomson Ave Fl 3, Long Island City, NY 11101-3045
Tel (718) 472-8000 Founded/Ownrshp 1988
Sales 2.1MMM EMP 600
Accts Pricewaterhousecooper Llp Ne
SIC 1542 School building construction; School building construction
Pr: Loraine Grillo
CFO: Juanita Rosillo
Ofcr: Bassam Abdu
Ofcr: Jimmy Ahn
Ofcr: Gabriela Arevalo II
Ofcr: Juan Aviles II
Ofcr: Adolfo Bautista
Ofcr: Dwight Clarke
Ofcr: Glen Crandall
Ofcr: Bruno Genari
Ofcr: Cornel Heghes
Ofcr: Marios Karageorgiades
Ofcr: Kiwesa King-Yara
Ofcr: Gregory Koelbel
Ofcr: Lissa Pauld
Ofcr: Ingrid Robaina
Ofcr: Henry Rogan
Ofcr: Boris Rubin
Ofcr: Abdul Shaheen
Ofcr: Arthur Umebuani
Ofcr: Narendra Vora

NEW YORK CITY SCOOP
See SCOOP MANAGEMENT LLC

D-U-N-S 00-970-2853
NEW YORK CITY TRANSIT AUTHORITY
PUBLIC TRANSPORTATION
(Suby of M T A) ★
2 Broadway, New York, NY 10004-3357
Tel (718) 330-1234 Founded/Ownrshp 1968
Sales 1.6MMM^E EMP 47,956
Accts Pricewaterhousecoopers Llp St
SIC 4111 Subway operation; Bus transportation; Subway operation; Bus transportation
Pr: Lawrence G Reuter
CFO: Timothy Slauson
*Ex VP: Barbara Spencer
Sr VP: Gerald Provenzano
Sr VP: Thomas Savage
Counsel: Paul Twarog
Snr Mgr: Ann Feldman
Snr Mgr: Dyanne Sampson
Snr Mgr: John Santamaria

D-U-N-S 96-723-4670
NEW YORK CITY TRUCKING INDUSTRY WELFARE TRUST FUND LOCAL 282
2500 Marcus Ave, New Hyde Park, NY 11042-1097
Tel (516) 488-2822 Founded/Ownrshp 2011
Sales 59.7MM EMP 1
Accts Gould Kobrick & Schlapp Pc Ne
SIC 4212 Local trucking, without storage; Local trucking, without storage
Prin: Richard Genatt

D-U-N-S 60-698-7808
■ **NEW YORK COMMERCIAL BANK**
ATLANTIC BANK DIVISION
(Suby of NEW YORK COMMUNITY BANCORP INC) ★
1601 Veterans Hwy Ste 100, Ronkonkoma, NY 11749-1543
Tel (631) 348-0888 Founded/Ownrshp 2005
Sales NA EMP 509
SIC 6022 State commercial banks; State commercial banks
Ch Bd: Joseph Ficalora
*CFO: Thomas Buonaiuto
*V Ch Bd: Frank J Esposito
*V Ch Bd: John C Tsunis
*Ofcr: James T Burns
*Ofcr: Kevin Hennessy
*Ofcr: Scott Swain
*Ofcr: Mel Vizzini
*Ex VP: Kenneth M Scheriff
*Sr VP: James Jsperanza
VP: Charles Baker
VP: Judith Guarino
VP: Mike Pesce
VP: Kevin Wolfe
Board of Directors: Lawrence Rosano Jr, Lawrence J Savares

D-U-N-S 36-443-8036
NEW YORK COMMERCIAL LUBRICANTS INC
METROLUBE
229 Arlington Ave, Staten Island, NY 10303-1605
Tel (718) 720-3434 Founded/Ownrshp 1988
Sales 55.7MM^E EMP 34
SIC 5172 Engine fuels & oils
Pr: Joseph Ioia
CFO: Gary Stetz

D-U-N-S 80-914-3217
▲ **NEW YORK COMMUNITY BANCORP INC**
615 Merrick Ave, Westbury, NY 11590-6607
Tel (516) 683-4100 Founded/Ownrshp 1993
Sales NA EMP 3,381^E
Tkr Sym NYCB Exch NYS
SIC 6036 State savings banks, not federally chartered; State savings banks, not federally chartered
Pr: Joseph R Ficalora
*Ch Bd: Dominick Ciampa
*COO: Robert Wann
CFO: Thomas R Cangemi
Ofcr: Elizabeth Veliz
Ex VP: John J Pinto
Ex VP: R Quinn
Sr VP: Jo-Anne Camacho
Sr VP: Mark Mazmanian
Sr VP: James Speranza
VP: John Adams
VP: Alicia Geiser
VP: Thomas Graziano
VP: John Langton
VP: Sharon Michitsch
VP: Linda Orth
VP: Donna Redman
VP: Georgiana Reese
VP: Lou Riccio
VP: Elizabeth Stratico
VP: Joanne Strucker
Board of Directors: Maureen E Clancy, Leslie Dolin, Michael J Levine, James J O'donovan, Lawrence Rosano Jr, Ronald A Rosenfeld, Lawrence J Savarese, John M Tsimbinos

D-U-N-S 00-699-3018
■ **NEW YORK COMMUNITY BANK**
(Suby of NEW YORK COMMUNITY BANCORP INC) ★
615 Merrick Ave, Westbury, NY 11590-6607
Tel (516) 203-0010 Founded/Ownrshp 1859, 1993
Sales NA EMP 2,550
SIC 6036 State savings banks, not federally chartered; State savings banks, not federally chartered
Ch Bd: Joseph R Ficalora
*CFO: Thomas R Cangemi
*Ex VP: Michael J Lincks
*Ex VP: John J Pinto
*Sr VP: Russ Dibenedetto
*Sr VP: James J O'Donovan
*Sr VP: Robert Wann
VP: Robert Brown
Dir IT: Dwayne Pringle

D-U-N-S 05-935-0421
NEW YORK COMMUNITY HOSPITAL
2525 Kings Hwy, Brooklyn, NY 11229-1705
Tel (718) 692-5300 Founded/Ownrshp 1945
Sales 99.7MM^E EMP 400
SIC 8062 General medical & surgical hospitals; General medical & surgical hospitals
Ch Bd: George Weinberger
*Pr: Lin H MO
*V Ch Bd: Richard Goldberg
Sr VP: Una Morrissey
VP: Vincent Desantis
MIS Dir: Alex Litvinov

NEW YORK COMMUNITY TRUST
See COMMUNITY FUNDS INC

D-U-N-S 06-823-6686
NEW YORK COMMUNITY TRUST AND COMMUNITY FUNDS INC
LONG ISLAND COMMUNITY FOUNDATI
909 3rd Ave Fl 22, New York, NY 10022-4752
Tel (212) 686-0010 Founded/Ownrshp 1924, 1923
Sales 304.5MM EMP 65
Accts Kpmg Llp New York Ny
SIC 6732 Trusts: educational, religious, etc.; Trusts: educational, religious, etc.
Pr: Lorie A Slutsky
Ofcr: Amy Wolf
*Sr VP: Joyce Bove
*VP: Robert V Edgar
*VP: Mercedes M Leon

D-U-N-S 02-056-9588
NEW YORK CONGREGATIONAL NURSING CENTER
135 Linden Blvd, Brooklyn, NY 11226-3302
Tel (718) 462-1137 Founded/Ownrshp 1908
Sales 28.0MM EMP 5
Accts Loeb & Troper Llp New York N
SIC 8051 Skilled nursing care facilities
Pr: Celia Zuckerman
*Pr: Celia Zuckerman
Off Mgr: Jean Huang
HC Dir: Brenda Williams

D-U-N-S 80-887-4234 IMP
NEW YORK CONTAINER TERMINAL INC
GCT NEW YORK
300 Western Ave Ste 101, Staten Island, NY 10303-1123
Tel (718) 568-1700 Founded/Ownrshp 2007
Sales NA EMP 450
SIC 4491 Marine terminals

D-U-N-S 05-456-7326 IMP
NEW YORK CONVENTION CENTER OPERATING CORP
JACOB K JAVITS CONVENTION CENT
655 W 34th St, New York, NY 10001-1114
Tel (212) 216-2000 Founded/Ownrshp 1980
Sales 169.9MM EMP 350^E
Accts Uhy Llp New York New York
SIC 7389 Convention & show services; Tourist information bureau; Convention & show services; Tourist information bureau
Ch Bd: Henry Silverman
*Pr: Gerald T McQueen
*CEO: Edward B Macdonald
*CEO: Alan E Steel
*Sr VP: Elizabeth Bradford
*Sr VP: Doreen Guerin
*VP: Kenneth Sanchez
*VP: Mark Sims
Opers Mgr: Thomas Lauro
Opers Mgr: Emmanuel Offin
Sls Mgr: Heidi Rega

D-U-N-S 13-191-8708 IMP
NEW YORK CRUISE LINES INC
1030 Clay Ave, New York, NY 10001
Tel (212) 563-3200 Founded/Ownrshp 1994
Sales 33.7MM EMP 250
SIC 7389 4489 Yacht brokers; Excursion boat operators; Yacht brokers; Excursion boat operators
Ch: Robert E Maher
*Pr: Gus Markou
*CEO: Daniel Boockvar
*CFO: David Bodnar
CFO: Len Sinisgalli

*Ch: Samuel A Cooperman
Sec: Joseph Pannetta

NEW YORK DAILY NEWS
See DAILY NEWS LP

D-U-N-S 80-678-0565
NEW YORK DEPARTMENT OF AGRICULTURE & MARKETS
(Suby of EXECUTIVE OFFICE OF STATE OF NEW YORK) ★
10b Airline Dr B, Albany, NY 12235-1000
Tel (518) 457-2080 Founded/Ownrshp 1884
Sales NA EMP 489
SIC 9641 Regulation of agricultural marketing; ; Regulation of agricultural marketing;
Counsel: John Rusnica

D-U-N-S 80-678-1886
NEW YORK DEPARTMENT OF CIVIL SERVICE
(Suby of EXECUTIVE OFFICE OF STATE OF NEW YORK) ★
80 S Swan St Ste 1147, Albany, NY 12210-8001
Tel (518) 457-9375 Founded/Ownrshp 1788
Sales NA EMP 700
SIC 9441 Administration of social & human resources; ; Administration of social & human resources;
Pr: Nancy G Groenwegen

D-U-N-S 80-678-0573
NEW YORK DEPARTMENT OF CORRECTIONS AND COMMUNITY SUPERVISION
NYS DPRTMENT CORRECTIONAL SVCS
(Suby of EXECUTIVE OFFICE OF STATE OF NEW YORK) ★
1220 Washngtn Ave Bldg 2, Albany, NY 12226-1799
Tel (518) 457-8126 Founded/Ownrshp 1788
Sales 1.2MMM^E EMP 30,000
SIC 8322 9223 Prison, government; ; Offender rehabilitation agency; Offender rehabilitation agency; Prison, government;
IT Man: Darlene Horner

D-U-N-S 36-366-1802
NEW YORK DEPARTMENT OF ECONOMIC DEVELOPMENT
(Suby of EXECUTIVE OFFICE OF STATE OF NEW YORK) ★
625 Broadway Fl 8, Albany, NY 12207-2942
Tel (518) 292-5155 Founded/Ownrshp 1987
Sales NA EMP 400
SIC 9611 Economic development agency, government; ; Economic development agency, government;

D-U-N-S 80-678-0912
NEW YORK DEPARTMENT OF ENVIRONMENTAL CONSERVATION
(Suby of EXECUTIVE OFFICE OF STATE OF NEW YORK) ★
625 Broadway, Albany, NY 12207-2942
Tel (518) 402-8545 Founded/Ownrshp 1970
Sales NA EMP 3,400
SIC 9512 Land, mineral & wildlife conservation; ; Land, mineral & wildlife conservation;
Ofcr: Scott Atwood
Ex VP: Michael Herlihy
Genl Couns: Jodi Aubin
Genl Couns: Edward McTiernan

D-U-N-S 80-678-1100
NEW YORK DEPARTMENT OF INSURANCE
(Suby of EXECUTIVE OFFICE OF STATE OF NEW YORK) ★
1 Commerce Plz, Albany, NY 12260-1000
Tel (518) 474-6600 Founded/Ownrshp 1788
Sales NA EMP 890
SIC 9651 Insurance commission, government; ; Insurance commission, government;

D-U-N-S 80-678-0607
NEW YORK DEPARTMENT OF LABOR
(Suby of EXECUTIVE OFFICE OF STATE OF NEW YORK) ★
State Ofc Campus, Albany, NY 12240-0001
Tel (518) 457-2741 Founded/Ownrshp 1901
Sales NA EMP 800^E
SIC 9651 Labor regulatory agency; ; Labor regulatory agency;
Comm Dir: Chris White

NEW YORK DEPARTMENT OF LAW
See ATTORNEY GENERAL NEW YORK STATE

D-U-N-S 80-678-2041
NEW YORK DEPARTMENT OF STATE
(Suby of EXECUTIVE OFFICE OF STATE OF NEW YORK) ★
99 Washington Ave Ste 110, Albany, NY 12210-2822
Tel (518) 474-2754 Founded/Ownrshp 1778
Sales NA EMP 508
SIC 9199 General government administration; ; General government administration;
Dir IT: Jeff Evans
Genl Couns: Susan L Watson

D-U-N-S 83-542-2064
NEW YORK DEPARTMENT OF TRANSPORTATION
NYS DEPARTMENT TRANSPORTATION
(Suby of EXECUTIVE OFFICE OF STATE OF NEW YORK) ★
50 Wolf Rd Ste 5, Albany, NY 12205-2645
Tel (518) 457-4445 Founded/Ownrshp 1960
Sales NA EMP 2,600
SIC 9621 Transportation department: government, non-operating; ; Transportation department: government, non-operating;
Prin: Joan McDonald
MIS Dir: Don Wells

D-U-N-S 78-603-9396
NEW YORK DIALYSIS MANAGEMENT INC
207 E 94th St Ste 301, New York, NY 10128-3705
Tel (212) 360-4900 Founded/Ownrshp 1990
Sales 24.0MM EMP 140
SIC 8092 Kidney dialysis centers; Kidney dialysis centers
Ch Bd: Craig Moore

D-U-N-S 13-472-1856
NEW YORK DIVISION OF HOMELAND SECURITY AND EMERGENCY SERVICES
DHSES
(Suby of EXECUTIVE OFFICE OF STATE OF NEW YORK) ★
1220 Washington Ave, Albany, NY 12226-1800
Tel (518) 242-5000 Founded/Ownrshp 2002
Sales NA EMP 700^E
SIC 9111 Executive offices; ; Executive offices;
Counsel: Kristine Hoffman
Snr Mgr: Lou Valenti

D-U-N-S 04-477-6024
NEW YORK DIVISION OF MILITARY AND NAVAL AFFAIRS
(Suby of EXECUTIVE OFFICE OF STATE OF NEW YORK) ★
330 Old Niskayuna Rd, Latham, NY 12110-3514
Tel (518) 786-4500 Founded/Ownrshp 1985
Sales NA EMP 3,538^E
SIC 9711 National security; ; National security;
Prin: Patrick A Murphy
IT Man: Thomas Halabuda
IT Man: Jane Sherwood
IT Man: Roger Townsend

D-U-N-S 07-886-9807
NEW YORK DOWNTOWN HOSPITAL
170 William St, New York, NY 10038-2649
Tel (212) 312-5000 Founded/Ownrshp 1979
Sales NA EMP 1,400
SIC 8062

NEW YORK DST CNL CPTRS BFT FD
See CARPENTERS WELFARE BENEFIT FUND OF NEW YORK CITY (INC)

D-U-N-S 80-260-1596
NEW YORK EHEALTH COLLABORATIVE INC
40 Worth St, New York, NY 10013-2904
Tel (646) 619-6403 Founded/Ownrshp 2006
Sales 64.7MM EMP 36
Accts Schall & Ashenfarb Cpas New Y
SIC 8732 Research services, except laboratory
CEO: David H Klein
*COO: Inez Sieden
*Sr VP: Pedro Villalba
*VP: James C Gunver
Dir Bus: Anuj Desai
*Ex Dir: David Whitlinger
Prgrm Mgr: Ralph Figueroa
Pgrm Dir: Sudipto Srivastava
Board of Directors: Paul Francis, Michael Golden

D-U-N-S 14-883-2046
NEW YORK ENERGY INC
(Suby of BLUEROCK ENERGY HOLDINGS INC) ★
432 N Franklin St Ste 20, Syracuse, NY 13204-1560
Tel (315) 701-1549 Founded/Ownrshp 2007
Sales 25.0MM EMP 45
SIC 4939 Combination utilities; Combination utilities
Pr: Philip Van Horne
*CFO: Jason Klaben
Off Mgr: Tammy Maule
Board of Directors: John O'shea, David Ramm, Philip Vanhorne

NEW YORK EYE
See HART SPECIALTIES INC

NEW YORK EYE & EAR INFIRMARY
See NEW YORK EYE AND EAR INFIRMARY IPA INC

D-U-N-S 07-102-4277
NEW YORK EYE AND EAR INFIRMARY IPA INC (NY)
NEW YORK EYE & EAR INFIRMARY
310 E 14th St, New York, NY 10003-4201
Tel (212) 979-4000 Founded/Ownrshp 1822
Sales 156.8MM EMP 850
Accts Ernst & Young Us Llp Indianap
SIC 8069 Eye, ear, nose & throat hospital; Eye, ear, nose & throat hospital
CEO: D McWilliams Kessler
Chf Path: Steven Mc Cormick
Pr: Carol Bohdan
*Pr: James Itsai MD
*CFO: Charles Figliozzi
Trst: Jay Wisnicki
VP: Edgar Enriquez
Dir Soc: Geraldine Capanong
Dir Rx: William Stratis
Mng Dir: Michael Samson
Prac Mgr: Sabrina Munoz

NEW YORK FAIR PLAN
See NEW YORK PROPERTY INSURANCE UNDERWRITING ASSOCIATION

D-U-N-S 80-014-5823
NEW YORK FOUNDATION FOR SENIOR CITIZENS
11 Park Pl Rm 1416, New York, NY 10007-2817
Tel (212) 962-7653 Founded/Ownrshp 1968
Sales 32.0MM EMP 200
Accts O Connor Davies Munns & Dobbin
SIC 8322 Individual & family services; Senior citizens' center or association; Individual & family services; Senior citizens' center or association
Pr: Linda Hoffman

D-U-N-S 05-729-3656
NEW YORK FOUNDATION FOR SENIOR CITIZENS HOME ATTENDANT SERVICES INC
11 Park Pl Rm 1416, New York, NY 10007-2817
Tel (212) 374-9169 Founded/Ownrshp 1968
Sales 33.0MM EMP 9
Accts O Connor Davies Munns & Dobbin
SIC 8322 Senior citizens' center or association; Senior citizens' center or association
Pr: Linda Hoffman

D-U-N-S 96-947-1825
NEW YORK FOUNDLING CHARITABLE CORP
590 Ave Of The Americas, New York, NY 10011-2022
Tel (212) 886-3246 Founded/Ownrshp 2011
Sales 45.6MM EMP 47^E
Accts Bdo Usa Llp New York Ny
SIC 8062 General medical & surgical hospitals; General medical & surgical hospitals
CFO: Michael Kurtz
Ofcr: Shanna Gumaer
Off Mgr: Ana Adorno
IT Man: Eric Alter
Opers Mgr: Jena Dropela
Genl Couns: Joe Moliterno

D-U-N-S 07-100-8221
NEW YORK FOUNDLING HOSPITAL
590 Ave Of The Americas, New York, NY 10011-2022
Tel (212) 633-9300 Founded/Ownrshp 1869
Sales 120.8MM EMP 1,500
Accts Bdo Usa Llp New York Ny
SIC 8361 8399 Group foster home; Community development groups; Group foster home; Community development groups
Ch Bd: Kenneth R Horner
Pr: Beth Stellato
*CEO: Bill Baccaglini
*COO: Bethany Lampland
*CFO: Kenneth Klum
*Treas: Carol A Barnes
Treas: Rita Meaney
*Sec: Sister Rita Meaney
*V Ch Bd: Robert J Farrell
VP: Jennifer Apple
VP: Stephanie Kearns
Assoc Dir: Carmen Rivera

D-U-N-S 36-386-0529
NEW YORK FRANKFURTER CO OF CALIFORNIA INC
17 Shemran Ct, Fairfax, CA 94930-1321
Tel (415) 861-0778 Founded/Ownrshp 1983
Sales 75.0MM EMP 8
SIC 5812 Food bars; Food bars
Pr: Catherine Schoop

NEW YORK FREIGHTLINER
See DIEHL & SONS INC

D-U-N-S 04-620-2305
■ **NEW YORK FROZEN FOODS INC**
(Suby of INN MAID PRODUCTS) ★
25900 Fargo Ave, Cleveland, OH 44146-1302
Tel (216) 292-5655 Founded/Ownrshp 1978
Sales 52.6MM^E EMP 320
SIC 2051 Bread, all types (white, wheat, rye, etc): fresh or frozen; Bread, all types (white, wheat, rye, etc): fresh or frozen
Pr: Bruce Rosa
Ex Dir: Mike Mahon
*VP Mfg: Donald Penn
Sfty Mgr: Bob Hanel
Sfty Mgr: Brad McWithey

D-U-N-S 07-847-3711
NEW YORK GENOME CENTER INC
NYGC
101 Ave Of The Americas, New York, NY 10013-1941
Tel (888) 415-6942 Founded/Ownrshp 2010
Sales 26.9MM^E EMP 99
SIC 8733 Research institute
Pr: Robert B Darnell
VP: Andrea Armstrong
VP: William Fair
*VP: Matt Pelo
Prgrm Mgr: Soren Germer
Genl Couns: Paula Leca
Board of Directors: Robert B Darnell

D-U-N-S 07-995-5102
NEW YORK GEOGRAPHIC DISTRICT 11
2750 Throop Ave, Bronx, NY 10469-5327
Tel (718) 519-2620 Founded/Ownrshp 2015
Sales 71.1MM^E EMP 4,684^E
SIC 8211 Public elementary & secondary schools

D-U-N-S 07-995-5127
NEW YORK GEOGRAPHIC DISTRICT 18
1106 E 95th St, Brooklyn, NY 11236-3735
Tel (718) 566-6008 Founded/Ownrshp 2015
Sales 45.1MM^E EMP 2,300^E
SIC 8211 Public elementary & secondary schools

D-U-N-S 07-103-3344
NEW YORK GRACIE SQUARE HOSPITAL INC
420 E 76th St, New York, NY 10021-3396
Tel (212) 988-4400 Founded/Ownrshp 1958
Sales 42.0MM EMP 345
SIC 8063 Psychiatric hospitals; Psychiatric hospitals
CEO: Frank Bruno
*CFO: David Wiecks
Off Mgr: David Trupp
Snr Mgr: Jerry Vogl

D-U-N-S 13-131-5046 IMP
NEW YORK HALL OF SCIENCE
4701 111th St, Corona, NY 11368-2950
Tel (718) 271-5150 Founded/Ownrshp 1964
Sales 24.9MM EMP 150
Accts Kpmg Peat Marwick Llp
SIC 8412 Arts or science center; Arts or science center
*Ch Bd: Ivan G Seidenberg
Pr: Steve Uzzo
CFO: Patricia Huie
*Ch: Joel Moser
*Treas: Alan Sinsheimer
*Ex VP: Jane Dunne
VP: Jennifer Brunjes
VP: Martin Duus
VP: Kiryn Hoffman
VP: Dmitry Lopatukhin
VP: Doug Moore
VP: Marcia Rudy
Comm Dir: Mary Record

NEW YORK HEALTH & RACQUET CLUB
See NEW YORK HEALTH CLUB INC

D-U-N-S 10-367-0485 IMP
▲ **NEW YORK HEALTH CARE INC**
20 E Sunrise Hwy Ste 201, Valley Stream, NY 11581-1257
Tel (718) 375-6700 Founded/Ownrshp 1983
Sales 145.9MM^E EMP 1,462
Tkr Sym BBAL Exch OTO
SIC 2834 8082 Drugs acting on the gastrointestinal or genitourinary system; Home health care services

D-U-N-S 07-524-5068
NEW YORK HEALTH CLUB INC (NY)
NEW YORK HEALTH & RACQUET CLUB
18 E 50th St Fl 4, New York, NY 10022-9116
Tel (212) 737-6666 Founded/Ownrshp 1972
Sales 24.6MM^E EMP 500
SIC 7991 7997 Athletic club & gymnasiums, membership; Racquetball club, membership; Tennis club, membership; Athletic club & gymnasiums, membership; Racquetball club, membership; Tennis club, membership
Ch Bd: Fraydun Manocherian
COO: Jeff Bodner
Genl Mgr: John Buzzerio
Genl Mgr: Debbie Newell-Antler

D-U-N-S 10-681-4148
NEW YORK HOLDINGS LLC
CINGULAR WIRELESS
2875 Union Rd Ste 356, Cheektowaga, NY 14227-1466
Tel (716) 833-1926 Founded/Ownrshp 1983
Sales 67.2MM^E EMP 559
SIC 4812 Cellular telephone services; Cellular telephone services

NEW YORK HOSPITAL QUEENS
See NEW YORK-PRESBYTERIAN/QUEENS

D-U-N-S 07-888-4103
NEW YORK HOTEL & MOTEL TRADES COUNCIL AFL-CIO (NY)
707 8th Ave Fl 4, New York, NY 10036-7102
Tel (212) 245-8100 Founded/Ownrshp 1938
Sales 22.7MM EMP 120
Accts Armao Costa & Ricciardi Cpa S
SIC 8631 Labor union; Labor union
Pr: Peter Ward
VP: Rich Maroko
VP: George Padilla
Counsel: Alyssa Tramposch
Counsel: Amy Tremonti

D-U-N-S 60-531-2412
NEW YORK HOTEL TRADES COUNCIL & HOTEL ASSOC OF NEW YORK
305 W 44th St, New York, NY 10036-5402
Tel (212) 586-6400 Founded/Ownrshp 1949
Sales 112.6MM EMP 825
Accts Armao Llp Garden City Ny
SIC 8011 Medical centers; Medical centers
Ch Bd: Joseph E Spinnato
*Pr: Peter Ward
*CEO: Robert Greenstan
COO: John Driscoe
COO: Glenn Hirsch
*CFO: Harry Veras
Chf Mktg O: Vincent Jarvis

D-U-N-S 96-630-5356
NEW YORK HOTEL TRADES COUNCIL AND HOTEL ASSOC OF NYC INC HEALTH BENEFITS FUND
305 W 44th St, New York, NY 10036-5498
Tel (212) 586-6400 Founded/Ownrshp 2011
Sales 355.0MM EMP 23^E
Accts Armao Costa & Ricciardi Cpa S
SIC 8631 Labor unions & similar labor organizations; Labor unions & similar labor organizations
Prin: Marisol Suarez

D-U-N-S 08-227-3269
NEW YORK INDEPENDENT SYSTEM OPERATOR INC
NYISO
10 Krey Blvd, Rensselaer, NY 12144-9681
Tel (518) 356-6000 Founded/Ownrshp 1997
Sales 159.8MM EMP 500
SIC 4911 Electric services; Electric services
Pr: Stephen G Whitley
Pr: Karen Antion
Pr: James V Mahoney
COO: Richard Gonzales
COO: Rick Gonzales
COO: Jr Thomas F Ryan
CFO: Cheryl Hussey
CFO: Kevin Jones
CFO: Mary McGarvey
CFO: Christopher Russell
Ofcr: Jean Dergurahian
Ofcr: Susan Disco
VP: Douglas L Chapman
VP: Rana Mukerji
VP: Emilie Nelson
*Int Pr: Robert A Hiney
Board of Directors: Alfred F Boschulte, Richard J Grossi, Erland E Kailbourne, Thomas F Ryan, Harold N Scherer, Richard E Schuler

D-U-N-S 06-811-4743
NEW YORK INSTITUTE FOR SPECIAL EDUCATION
999 Pelham Pkwy N, Bronx, NY 10469-4905
Tel (718) 708-6580 Founded/Ownrshp 1831
Sales 30.7MM EMP 360
Accts Condon O Meara Mcginty & Donne
SIC 8211 School for physically handicapped; School for physically handicapped
Ex Dir: Bernadette Kappen
Netwrk Mgr: Steve Thomas
Psych: Chris Velez

D-U-N-S 05-059-4019
NEW YORK INSTITUTE OF TECHNOLOGY INC
NYIT
Northern Blvd, Old Westbury, NY 11568
Tel (516) 686-7530 *Founded/Ownrshp* 1950
Sales 276.9MM *EMP* 2,000
SIC 8221 Professional schools; Professional schools
Pr: Edward Guiliano PHD
CFO: Leonard Aubrey
CFO: Charlene Smith
VP: Nancy Donner
VP: Patrick Love
Exec: Jong Lee
Assoc Dir: Nadia Agarrat
Dir Sec: Anthony Repalone
Off Admin: June Bukovinsky
Off Admin: Timothy Gang
Off Admin: Josephine Spinelli

D-U-N-S 14-247-1494
■ **NEW YORK INTERCONNECT LLC**
(*Suby of* CABLEVISION) ★
530 5th Ave Fl 6, New York, NY 10036-5119
Tel (212) 382-5300 *Founded/Ownrshp* 2004
Sales 28.5MM^E *EMP* 548^E
SIC 7311 Advertising agencies
VP: William Chambers
Mktg Dir: Amy Friedland
Sls Mgr: Dora Rivas

D-U-N-S 10-893-7582
NEW YORK INTERNATIONAL BREAD CO
1500 W Church St, Orlando, FL 32805-2408
Tel (407) 843-9744 *Founded/Ownrshp* 1985
Sales 21.2MM^E *EMP* 90
SIC 2051 Bakery: wholesale or wholesale/retail combined; Bread, all types (white, wheat, rye, etc): fresh or frozen; Rolls, bread type: fresh or frozen
Pr: Vincent Masella Jr
* *VP:* Laura Masella
IT Man: Lisa Joseph

D-U-N-S 07-327-4995
NEW YORK JETS LLC
NY JETS
50 W 57th St, New York, NY 10019-3914
Tel (212) 757-0724 *Founded/Ownrshp* 2001
Sales 20.6MM^E *EMP* 250^E
SIC 7941 Football club; Football club
VP: Jay L Cross
VP: Matt Higgins
VP Sls: Jason Gonella

D-U-N-S 19-728-5299
NEW YORK JUNIOR TENNIS LEAGUE INC
5812 Queens Blvd Ste 1, Woodside, NY 11377-7764
Tel (718) 786-7110 *Founded/Ownrshp* 1974
Sales 12.1MM *EMP* 367
Accts Loeb & Troper Llp New York N
SIC 7999 Tennis club, non-membership; Tennis club, non-membership
Pr: Gary L Davis
CFO: Chris Ramdhani
Bd of Dir: Summer Gala
Site Mgr: Daisy Rivera

NEW YORK LAW JOURNAL
See ALM MEDIA LLC

D-U-N-S 07-520-0949
NEW YORK LAW SCHOOL (NY)
185 W Broadway, New York, NY 10013-2921
Tel (212) 431-2100 *Founded/Ownrshp* 1891
Sales 72.8MM *EMP* 208^E
Accts Nawrocki Smith Llp Melville
SIC 8221 8111 Professional schools; Legal services; Professional schools; Legal services
Pr: Anthony W Crowell
* *Treas:* Fred De John
VP: Travis Fraser
* *VP:* Nancy Guida
* *VP:* Stuart A Klein
Assoc Dir: Howard Meyers
Ex Dir: Lenni Benson
Off Admin: Lillian Santiago
CIO: John Southard
Mktg Dir: Darcee Espelien
Snr Mgr: Donald Blanchard

D-U-N-S 02-692-5529
NEW YORK LEAGUE FOR EARLY LEARNING INC
WILLIAM O'CONNEL SCHOOL
460 W 34th St Fl 11, New York, NY 10001-2320
Tel (212) 563-7474 *Founded/Ownrshp* 1978
Sales 55.6MM *EMP* 400
Accts Loeb & Troper Llp New York N
SIC 8211 Specialty education; Specialty education
Ex Dir: Ronald Lenkowsky
* *CFO:* Karen Wegmann

D-U-N-S 61-617-6384
NEW YORK LEGAL ASSISTANCE GROUP INC
BETTZEDEK LEGAL SERVICES OF N
7 Hanover Sq Fl 18, New York, NY 10004-4027
Tel (212) 613-5000 *Founded/Ownrshp* 1990
Sales 20.0MM *EMP* 3
Accts Loeb & Troper Llp New York N
SIC 8111 Legal services; Legal services
Ex Dir: Yisroel Schulman
Ofcr: Lyudmila Rabkina
Assoc Dir: Elvira Pinkhasova
Assoc Dir: Lisa Rivera
Ex Dir: Isaak Melamud

NEW YORK LIFE
See NAUTILUS GROUP

D-U-N-S 62-189-9798
NEW YORK LIFE FOUNDATION
NEW YORK LIFE INSURANCE CO
51 Madison Ave Bsmt 1b, New York, NY 10010-1612
Tel (212) 576-7000 *Founded/Ownrshp* 1979
Sales NA *EMP* 2
SIC 6411 Insurance agents & brokers; Insurance agents & brokers
Pr: Peter Bushyeager
Dir IT: Patrick Fennessey
Dir IT: Michael Razzino
IT Man: Toba Seide

NEW YORK LIFE INSURANCE CO
See NEW YORK LIFE FOUNDATION

D-U-N-S 00-698-8307
NEW YORK LIFE INSURANCE CO
51 Madison Ave Bsmt 1b, New York, NY 10010-1655
Tel (212) 576-7000 *Founded/Ownrshp* 1845
Sales NA *EMP* 12,150
SIC 6311 6321 6282 Life insurance carriers; Health insurance carriers; Investment advice; Life insurance carriers; Health insurance carriers; Investment advice
Ch Bd: Ted Mathas
V Ch: Phillip Hluebrand
Pr: Galina Ksendzov
COO: Christopher O Blunt
COO: Paul T Pasteris
COO: Paul Pasteris
CFO: Chris Ashe
CFO: David G Bedard
CFO: Stephen Devito
CFO: John Fleurant
CFO: Mark Grass
CFO: Michael E Sproule
Treas: Jay S Calhoun
Treas: Richard J Witterschein
V Ch Bd: Gary Wendlandt
Bd of Dir: Stephen Carrillo
Bd of Dir: Osbert Hood
Ofcr: David J Castellani
Ofcr: Joel Steinberg
Assoc VP: Robert Tabick
Assoc VP: Aaron Zachko
Board of Directors: Ronald Pressman, Edward D Shirley

D-U-N-S 62-189-9624
NEW YORK LIFE INTERNATIONAL INC
(*Suby of* NEW YORK LIFE INSURANCE CO) ★
51 Madison Ave Bsmt 1b, New York, NY 10010-1612
Tel (212) 576-7000 *Founded/Ownrshp* 2001
Sales NA *EMP* 50^E
SIC 6411 Insurance agents & brokers
Ch Bd: Richard L Mucci
* *Ch Bd:* Gary Benanav
Pr: Anthony Mak
* *COO:* Russell Bundschuh
COO: George Nichols III
* *Sr VP:* John D Fleming

NEW YORK LIFE INV MGT GROUP
See NEW YORK LIFE INVESTMENT MANAGEMENT LLC

D-U-N-S 83-565-7966
NEW YORK LIFE INVESTMENT MANAGEMENT LLC
NEW YORK LIFE INV MGT GROUP
(*Suby of* NEW YORK LIFE INSURANCE CO) ★
169 Lackawanna Ave, Parsippany, NJ 07054-1007
Tel (973) 394-3000 *Founded/Ownrshp* 2000
Sales 237.0MM^E *EMP* 1,500^E
SIC 6799 Real estate investors, except property operators; Real estate investors, except property operators
Pr: John Kim
* *CFO:* David G Bedard
CFO: William Gibson
* *Ch:* Gary Wendlandt
Bd of Dir: Patrick Boyle
Chf Mktg O: John Abbott
Chf Invest: Jerrold Senser
Ofcr: Alison Micucci
* *Ofcr:* Don Salama
Rgnl VP: Nancy Lavin
Rgnl VP: Cheryl Potter
Rgnl VP: Frances Rogell
Rgnl VP: Matthew Silver
Ex VP: Pamela Conroy
Ex VP: Gary Maurer
Ex VP: Paula Rogers
Sr VP: Matthew Swanson
VP: William Anglyn
VP: Robert W Baker
VP: Bart Battista
VP: Justin Bentley

D-U-N-S 01-938-1685
NEW YORK LIGHT SOURCE CORP
494 8th Ave Ste 900, New York, NY 10001-2519
Tel (212) 947-7410 *Founded/Ownrshp* 1998
Sales 24.0MM^E *EMP* 13
SIC 5063 Lighting fixtures; Lighting fixtures
Pr: Gary Bornstein
* *CFO:* Paula Lavery

D-U-N-S 14-200-9575
NEW YORK MEDIA LLC
75 Varick St, New York, NY 10013-1917
Tel (212) 508-0700 *Founded/Ownrshp* 2004
Sales 89.5MM^E *EMP* 250
SIC 2721 Periodicals; Periodicals
* *COO:* Katharine Taylor
Ex Dir: Marisa Woocher
Sftwr Eng: Victor Alvarez
Sftwr Eng: Colin Flanagan
VP Mfg: Lisa Goren
Prd Dir: Ann Amrhein
Prd Mgr: Kaitlin Butz
Prd Mgr: Manny Gomes
Prd Mgr: Ruth Monsanto
Doctor: Zerona York
Art Dir: Randy Minor

D-U-N-S 04-190-7486
NEW YORK MEDICAL COLLEGE
(*Suby of* TOURO COLLEGE AND UNIVERSITY SYSTEM) ★
40 Sunshine Cottage Rd, Valhalla, NY 10595-1524
Tel (914) 594-4100 *Founded/Ownrshp* 2011
Sales 145.4MM *EMP* 1,100
Accts Kpmg Llp New York Ny
SIC 8221 Professional schools; Professional schools
CEO: Edward C Halperin
* *Pr:* Allan Kadish
* *Pr:* George Nestler
* *CFO:* Stephen Piccolo Jr
* *VP:* Robert W Amler MD
CIO: Sandra Shivers
Sftwr Eng: Philip Chen
Pathlgst: Michael Balazy
Ansthlgy: Brooke Albright
Ansthlgy: Abraham Lehman
Doctor: Joy Calo

D-U-N-S 04-525-5478
■ **NEW YORK MERCANTILE EXCHANGE INC**
NYMEX
(*Suby of* CME GROUP INC) ★
1 N End Ave Frnt, New York, NY 10282-1101
Tel (212) 299-2000 *Founded/Ownrshp* 2008
Sales 105.7MM^E *EMP* 635
SIC 6221 Commodity traders, contracts; Commodity traders, contracts
Ch Bd: Terrence Duffy
* *CEO:* Frank Donnahill
Treas: Bruce Rubin
Sr VP: Madeline Boyd
Sr VP: Allen Fergus
Sr VP: Thomas Lasala
Sr VP: Robert Levin
VP: Richard Daniele
VP: John Higgins
VP: Carla Seales-Penn
Dir Sec: Charles McSweeney

D-U-N-S 05-281-0801
NEW YORK METHODIST HOSPITAL (NY)
506 6th St, Brooklyn, NY 11215-3609
Tel (718) 780-3000 *Founded/Ownrshp* 1881
Sales 687.7MM *EMP* 3,185
Accts Ernst & Young Llp New York N
SIC 8062 General medical & surgical hospitals; General medical & surgical hospitals
Ch Bd: John E Carrington
* *Pr:* Mark J Mundy
* *CFO:* Edward Zaidberg
* *Treas:* Robert Rodgers Jr
Sr VP: Lauren Yedvab
VP: Lyn Hill
VP: Steven Silber
Dir Teleco: Laura Maturano
Chf Nrs Of: Lamarcia Parkin
Mtls Dir: Jennele Sinckler
Pharmcst: Jack Rapp

NEW YORK METS
See STERLING METS LP

D-U-N-S 16-368-3498
NEW YORK MORTGAGE TRUST INC
275 Madison Ave Fl 32, New York, NY 10016-1116
Tel (212) 792-0107 *Founded/Ownrshp* 2004
Sales 484.0MM *EMP* 7^E
SIC 6798 6163 Real estate investment trusts; Mortgage investment trusts; Mortgage brokers arranging for loans, using money of others; Real estate investment trusts; Mortgage investment trusts; Mortgage brokers arranging for loans, using money of others
Ch Bd: Steven R Mumma
CFO: Kristine R Nario
VP: Nathan R Reese

D-U-N-S 02-302-2432
NEW YORK MUNICIPAL POWER AGENCY
6652 Hammersmith Dr, East Syracuse, NY 13057-9650
Tel (315) 453-1761 *Founded/Ownrshp* 1998
Sales 61.5MM *EMP* 2
Accts Evans And Benneth Llp Syracu
SIC 4911 Distribution, electric power; Distribution, electric power
Genl Mgr: Anthony Modafferi

D-U-N-S 80-226-3137 IMP/EXP
NEW YORK MUTUAL TRADING INC
(*Suby of* MT C) ★
77 Metro Way Ste 1, Secaucus, NJ 07094-1918
Tel (201) 933-9555 *Founded/Ownrshp* 1974
Sales 24.3MM^E *EMP* 50
SIC 5149 5181 5182 Groceries & related products; Beer & ale; Wine & distilled beverages
Pr: Noritoshi Kanai
COO: Kentaro Tsurushima
* *VP:* Yasuo Katsumata
Sls Mgr: Terutada Kohmae

D-U-N-S 04-238-0167
NEW YORK OFFICE OF ALCOHOLISM & SUBSTANCE ABUSE SERVICES
(*Suby of* EXECUTIVE OFFICE OF STATE OF NEW YORK) ★
1450 Western Ave, Albany, NY 12203-3539
Tel (518) 457-2061 *Founded/Ownrshp* 1999
Sales NA *EMP* 1,000
SIC 9431 Administration of public health programs; ; Administration of public health programs;
CEO: Arlene Gonzlez Snchez
* *Prin:* Jackie Reider

D-U-N-S 04-238-7717
NEW YORK OFFICE OF CHILDREN & FAMILY SERVICES
(*Suby of* EXECUTIVE OFFICE OF STATE OF NEW YORK) ★
52 Washington St, Rensselaer, NY 12144-2834
Tel (518) 473-7793 *Founded/Ownrshp* 1998
Sales NA *EMP* 740
SIC 9441 Administration of social & manpower programs; ; Administration of social & manpower programs;
Prin: Roberto Velez
Dist Mgr: Craig Walton
Psych: Colleen Degraff
Counsel: Elana Marton
Pgrm Dir: Alissa Deakin
Snr Mgr: Patricia Chabla
Snr Mgr: Melinda Scofield

D-U-N-S 09-815-9275
NEW YORK OFFICE OF GENERAL SERVICES
O G S
(*Suby of* EXECUTIVE OFFICE OF STATE OF NEW YORK) ★
41st Fl Of Corning Tower, Albany, NY 12242-0001
Tel (518) 474-5991 *Founded/Ownrshp* 1999
Sales NA *EMP* 700
SIC 9199 General government administration; ; General government administration;
* *CFO:* Brian Matthews

D-U-N-S 80-678-1860
NEW YORK OFFICE OF TEMPORARY & DISABILITY ASSISTANCE
(*Suby of* EXECUTIVE OFFICE OF STATE OF NEW YORK) ★
40 N Pearl St Ste 100, Albany, NY 12207-2729
Tel (518) 426-2950 *Founded/Ownrshp* 1922
Sales NA *EMP* 2,500
SIC 9441 Administration of social & human resources; ; Administration of social & human resources;

D-U-N-S 09-266-2865
NEW YORK ORGAN DONOR NETWORK INC (NY)
132 W 31st St Fl 11, New York, NY 10001-3406
Tel (212) 244-0114 *Founded/Ownrshp* 1978
Sales 30.3MM *EMP* 200
SIC 8099 Organ bank; Organ bank
Pr: Helen Irving
* *CFO:* Jim Aranda

D-U-N-S 78-999-4217 IMP
NEW YORK PACKAGING CORP
REDI-BAG USA
135 Fulton Ave, New Hyde Park, NY 11040-5305
Tel (516) 746-0600 *Founded/Ownrshp* 1991
Sales 25.0MM^E *EMP* 90
SIC 2673 Plastic bags: made from purchased materials; Plastic bags: made from purchased materials
Pr: Jeffrey Rabiea

D-U-N-S 78-230-5986 IMP
NEW YORK PACKAGING II LLC
REDI BAG BRAND
135 Fulton Ave, Garden City, NY 11530
Tel (516) 746-0600 *Founded/Ownrshp* 2005
Sales 33.1MM^E *EMP* 249
SIC 2673 Plastic bags: made from purchased materials; Plastic bags: made from purchased materials
Pr: Jeffrey Rabiea

NEW YORK PALACE HOTEL, THE
See NWPH INC

D-U-N-S 09-883-1530
NEW YORK PAVING INC
3718 Railroad Ave, Long Island City, NY 11101-2033
Tel (718) 482-0780 *Founded/Ownrshp* 1976
Sales 83.2MM^E *EMP* 308^E
SIC 1611 Surfacing & paving; Surfacing & paving
Pr: Anthony Bartone
* *Treas:* Mike Bartone

NEW YORK PHILHARMONIC
See PHILHARMONIC-SYMPHONY SOCIETY OF NEW YORK INC

NEW YORK POST
See NYP HOLDINGS INC

D-U-N-S 07-525-2098 IMP/EXP
NEW YORK POWER AUTHORITY
POWER AUTH OF THE STATE NY
123 Main St Mail Stp 16p Mail Stop, White Plains, NY 10601
Tel (914) 681-6200 *Founded/Ownrshp* 1931
Sales 3.1MMM *EMP* 4,450
Accts Kpmg Llp New York New York
SIC 4911 Generation, electric power; Transmission, electric power; Generation, electric power; Transmission, electric power
CEO: Gil C Quiniones
Pr: Roger B Kelley
COO: Edward A Welz
CFO: Joseph M Del Sindaco
CFO: Stephen Dowd
CFO: Robert F Lurie
Treas: Michael Brodey
Treas: Brian McElroy
Treas: Ben Murtagh
Trst: Eugene Nicandri
Ofcr: Sharon Green
Ex VP: Justin E Driscoll
Ex VP: Thomas J Kelly
Ex VP: Vincent C Vesce
Sr VP: Steven J Decarlo
Sr VP: Angelo S Esposito
Sr VP: Louise M Morman
Sr VP: James Pasquale
Sr VP: Dennis E Rigr
Sr VP: Brian Vattimo
VP: Arnold M Bellis

D-U-N-S 93-267-4484
NEW YORK PRESBYTERIAN & COLUMBIA MEDICAL CENTER
COLUMBIA UNIV MED RES CTR PHRM
622 W 168th St Ph 14-105, New York, NY 10032-3720
Tel (212) 305-2500 *Founded/Ownrshp* 1992
Sales 21.5MM^E *EMP* 60
SIC 8748 Testing services
CEO: Steven Corwin
Sr VP: Maxine Frank
Obsttrcn: Silvana Ribaudo

D-U-N-S 15-085-5203 IMP
NEW YORK PRODUCE INC
125 Seaview Dr, Secaucus, NJ 07094-1811
Tel (201) 223-0909 *Founded/Ownrshp* 1984
Sales 60.8MM *EMP* 80
SIC 5148 5149

D-U-N-S 07-772-0589
NEW YORK PROPERTY INSURANCE UNDERWRITING ASSOCIATION
NEW YORK FAIR PLAN
100 William St Fl 4, New York, NY 10038-4599
Tel (212) 208-9700 *Founded/Ownrshp* 1968
Sales NA *EMP* 45
SIC 6331 Fire, marine & casualty insurance & carriers
Pr: Joseph A Calvo
**VP:* John Rusnak

D-U-N-S 07-852-3453 EXP
NEW YORK PSYCHOTHERAPY AND COUNSELING CENTER (NY)
17620 148th Ave, Jamaica, NY 11434-5518
Tel (718) 553-1100 *Founded/Ownrshp* 1974
Sales 32.0MM *EMP* 37E
SIC 8049 Psychologist, psychotherapist & hypnotist; Psychologist, psychotherapist & hypnotist
Genl Pt: Elliott Klein
**Treas:* Bernice Rubin
**Ex Dir:* Isadore Klein
Board of Directors: Dr Milton Aisenson, Morton Kleichman

D-U-N-S 04-543-3919 IMP
NEW YORK PUBLIC LIBRARY
5th Ave & 42nd St, New York, NY 10018
Tel (212) 592-7400 *Founded/Ownrshp* 1895
Sales 115.3MME *EMP* 3,645
SIC 8231 Libraries; Libraries
CEO: Anthony Marx
Treas: Ralph E Hansmann
VP: Jeffrey Roth
**Prin:* Davi Offensent
Prin: Kathleen Riegelhaupt
CTO: David M Stur
Pr Dir: Joan Harris
Counsel: Daniel Dex

D-U-N-S 96-958-8149
NEW YORK PUBLIC LIBRARY ASTOR LENOX AND TILDEN FOUNDATIONS
188 Madison Ave, New York, NY 10016-4314
Tel (212) 592-7403 *Founded/Ownrshp* 2011
Sales 305.0MM *EMP* 71E
Accts Kpmg Llp New York Ny
SIC 8231 General public libraries
COO: Iris Weinshall
Top Exec: Denise Hibay
Opers Mgr: Anne Lehmann
Secur Mgr: Thomas Sinclair
Merch Mgr: Elana Sinsabaugh
Counsel: Bridget Langer
Counsel: Bridget Smith
Snr PM: Hassan Kholdi
Snr Mgr: Evelyn Frangakis
Snr Mgr: Carrie Welch

D-U-N-S 10-512-9779
NEW YORK PUBLIC RADIO
WNYC RADIO
160 Varick St Fl 7, New York, NY 10013-1270
Tel (646) 829-4400 *Founded/Ownrshp* 1979
Sales 68.7MM *EMP* 120E
Accts Kpmg Llp New York Ny
SIC 4832 Radio broadcasting stations; Radio broadcasting stations
CEO: Laura R Walker
V Ch: Jean B Angell
V Ch: Frank D Yeary
**Treas:* Howard Stein
Bd of Dir: Peter H Darrow
Bd of Dir: Anne Klepper
Bd of Dir: Thomas B Morgan
Bd of Dir: Joann Rodriguez
Bd of Dir: Grantley N Thornhill
Bd of Dir: Estelle Ubell
Ofcr: Patrick Daughtry
Ofcr: Tralana Gamadia
Ofcr: Ashley Milian
Assoc VP: Rob Christiansen
Assoc VP: Myiesha Gordon
Ex VP: Thomas Hjelm
Sr VP: Amy Fitzpatrick
VP: Tom Bartunek
VP: Dean Cappello
VP: Rachna Karrol
VP: Noreen O'Loughlin

D-U-N-S 01-998-4908
NEW YORK RACING ASSOCIATION INC
11000 Rockaway Blvd Ste 1, South Ozone Park, NY 11420-1004
Tel (718) 641-4700 *Founded/Ownrshp* 1955
Sales 41.0MME *EMP* 1,400
SIC 7948 Horse race track operation; Horse race track operation
CFO: Michael Lagamma
**Pr:* Charles E Hayward

D-U-N-S 96-269-4787
NEW YORK REIT INC
NYRT
405 Park Ave Fl 14, New York, NY 10022-9406
Tel (212) 415-6500 *Founded/Ownrshp* 2011
Sales 155.5MM *EMP* 3
SIC 6531 Selling agent, real estate; Selling agent, real estate
Pr: Michael A Happel
**Ch Bd:* William M Kahane
COO: Gregory W Sullivan
Sr VP: Michael Ead

D-U-N-S 08-740-7193
NEW YORK REPLACEMENT PARTS CORP (NY)
19 School St, Yonkers, NY 10701-4104
Tel (914) 965-0122 *Founded/Ownrshp* 1978
Sales 30.2MME *EMP* 51
SIC 5074 5999 Plumbing fittings & supplies; Plumbing & heating supplies
Pr: John Green
**Sec:* George Green
**VP:* Richard Green

D-U-N-S 09-432-1064
NEW YORK ROAD RUNNERS INC (NY)
NEW YORK CITY MARATHON
156 W 56th St Fl 3, New York, NY 10019-3877
Tel (212) 860-4455 *Founded/Ownrshp* 1979
Sales 72.7MM *EMP* 300
SIC 8699 2721 2741 5699 Athletic organizations; Magazines: publishing only, not printed on site; Newsletter publishing; T-shirts, custom printed; Sports apparel; Athletic organizations; Magazines: publishing only, not printed on site; Newsletter publishing; T-shirts, custom printed; Sports apparel
Ch Bd: Elfie Chang
**Ch Bd:* George A Hirsch
**Pr:* Peter Ciaccia
**Pr:* Mary Wittenberg
**CEO:* Michael Capiraso
**CFO:* Allan Steinfeld
Ex VP: Jake Lasala
VP: Jeffery Carnevale
VP: John Gassner
VP: Jim Heim
**VP:* Michael Rodgers
**VP:* Cliff Sperber
**VP:* Ronnie Tucker
**VP:* Chris Weiller

D-U-N-S 79-473-3121
NEW YORK SCHOOLS INSURANCE RECIPROCAL
NYSIR
333 Earle Ovington Blvd # 505, Uniondale, NY 11553-3610
Tel (516) 227-2300 *Founded/Ownrshp* 1989
Sales NA *EMP* 130
SIC 6411 Insurance agents, brokers & service
Pr: Robert Lulley
VP: Robert Libby

D-U-N-S 07-101-1944 IMP
NEW YORK SHAKESPEARE FESTIVAL
PUBLIC THEATER, THE
425 Lafayette St, New York, NY 10003-7021
Tel (212) 539-8500 *Founded/Ownrshp* 1954
Sales 35.1MM *EMP* 100
Accts Lutz And Carr Cpas Llp New Yo
SIC 7922 Theatrical production services; Theatrical production services
Genl Mgr: Steven Showalter
Mng Pt: Kevin Abbott
CFO: Rachel Pivnick
Treas: Warren Spector
**Ex Dir:* Patrick Willingham
Mng Dir: Susan Adam
CTO: Jenn Baldwin
Dir IT: David Blasinsky
Dir IT: Arthur Pinori
IT Man: Rob Cohn
Prd Mgr: Peggy Carey

D-U-N-S 07-101-2413
NEW YORK SHIPPING ASSOCIATION INC
333 Thornall St Ste 3a, Edison, NJ 08837-2220
Tel (732) 452-7800 *Founded/Ownrshp* 1939
Sales 242.2MM *EMP* 40E
SIC 8611 Shipping & steamship company association; Shipping & steamship company association
Pr: John Nardi
COO: Beverly Fedorko
CFO: Daniel Massaro
Ex VP: Charles Darrell
Off Mgr: Nancy Olsen
Board of Directors: O A Sweedlund, James A Capo, William A Trok, V Carreras, C De Zego, J Gebhardt, R F Gronda, S Y Kuo, M B Maher, J W Millard, J F Reardon

D-U-N-S 00-393-7364 IMP
NEW YORK SOCIETY RELIEF RUPT CRIPPLD
HOSPITAL FOR SPECIAL SURGERY
535 E 70th St, New York, NY 10021-4823
Tel (212) 606-1000 *Founded/Ownrshp* 1863, 1987
Sales 204.6MME *EMP* 1,238
Accts Ernst & Young Llp New York
SIC 8069 Specialty hospitals, except psychiatric; Orthopedic hospital; Specialty hospitals, except psychiatric; Orthopedic hospital
CEO: Louis Shapiro
V Ch: Emil Mosbacher
Trst: Charles P Coleman
Trst: Henry U Harris
Trst: Charlton Reynders
Trst: Henry A Wilmerding
Trst: Kendrick R Wilson
**Ex VP:* Lisa A Goldstein
**Ex VP:* Stacey L Malakof
**Ex VP:* Constance B Margolin
**Ex VP:* Deborah M Sale

NEW YORK SPORTS CLUB
See TOWN SPORTS INTERNATIONAL INC

NEW YORK SPORTS CLUB
See TSI EAST 59 INC

NEW YORK SPORTS CLUB
See TSI EAST 23 INC

NEW YORK SPORTS CLUB
See TSI FAIRFAX LLC

NEW YORK STATE ASSEMBLY
See LEGISLATIVE OFFICE STATE OF NY

D-U-N-S 82-964-8315
NEW YORK STATE ASSOCIATION FOR NYSARC INC
10 St Patrick Pl, Port Henry, NY 12974-1200
Tel (518) 546-3051 *Founded/Ownrshp* 2009
Sales 42.3MM *EMP* 2
Accts Martindale Keysor & Co Pllc P
SIC 8611 Business associations; Business associations

D-U-N-S 00-967-8103
NEW YORK STATE ASSOCIATION FOR RETARDED CHILDREN INC
OPPORTNITIES UNLIMITED NIAGARA
(*Suby of* NYSARC INC NIAGARA COUNTY CHAPTER) ★
1555 Fashion Outlet Blvd, Niagara Falls, NY 14304-1798
Tel (716) 297-2350 *Founded/Ownrshp* 1978
Sales 10.0MME *EMP* 480
SIC 8399 Health & welfare council; Health & welfare council
CEO: Connie Brown
COO: Peter Drew
**CFO:* Charlene McDonald
Dir IT: Monty Bartholomew

D-U-N-S 04-566-9173
NEW YORK STATE ASSOCIATION FOR RETARDED CHILDREN INC
WESTCHESTER COUNTY CHAPTER
(*Suby of* NYSARC INC) ★
393 Delaware Ave, Delmar, NY 12054-3004
Tel (518) 439-8311 *Founded/Ownrshp* 1950
Sales 54.1MM *EMP* 683
SIC 8211 8331 8361 School for the retarded; Sheltered workshop; Home for the mentally retarded; School for the retarded; Sheltered workshop; Home for the mentally retarded
Ex Dir: Marc Brandt
**CFO:* Norman Szymanski

D-U-N-S 07-312-8704
NEW YORK STATE BAR ASSOCIATION (NY)
1 Elk St, Albany, NY 12207-1002
Tel (518) 463-3200 *Founded/Ownrshp* 1877
Sales 27.0MM *EMP* 120
Accts Uhy Advisors Ny Inc Albany N
SIC 8621 2731 Bar association; Book publishing; Bar association; Book publishing
Ex Dir: Patricia Bucklin
Mng Pt: Carrie Cohen
VP: Susan Lindenauer
Prgrm Mgr: Cheryl Wallingford
Web Dev: Christopher Frederick
Mktg Mgr: Connie Schin

D-U-N-S 17-580-1216
NEW YORK STATE BRIDGE AUTHORITY
Mid Hdson Bridge Toll Plz, Highland, NY 12528
Tel (845) 691-7245 *Founded/Ownrshp* 1932
Sales 56.2MM *EMP* 200E
Accts Toski & Co Cpas Pc Willi
SIC 4785 Toll bridge operation; Toll bridge operation
Ex Dir: Joseph Ruggiero
**Ch:* Francis Vecellio
**Treas:* Bryan Bushek
**Treas:* John Sewell
Bd of Dir: Thomas J Madison
Dir Sec: Brad Moritt
Dir IT: Gregory Helton

D-U-N-S 80-789-5537
NEW YORK STATE CANAL CORP
(*Suby of* THRUWAY AUTHORITY OF NEW YORK STATE) ★
200 Southern Blvd, Albany, NY 12209-2018
Tel (518) 436-2700 *Founded/Ownrshp* 1992
Sales 31.4MME *EMP* 537
SIC 4499 8711 Canal operation; Engineering services; Canal operation; Engineering services
Ch: John Buono
VP: Dave Boshart
Opers Mgr: William Rinaldi
Pr Dir: Sharon Leighton

D-U-N-S 87-923-0431
NEW YORK STATE CATHOLIC HEALTH PLAN INC
FIDELIS CARE NEW YORK
9525 Queens Blvd Ste 8, Rego Park, NY 11374-4510
Tel (888) 343-3547 *Founded/Ownrshp* 1993
Sales 5.3MMM *EMP* 1,625
Accts Deloitte Tax Llp Jericho Ny
SIC 8011 Health maintenance organization; Health maintenance organization
Pr: Mark Lane
**Pr:* Rev Patrick J Frawley
Pr: Maryjean Valigorsky
**COO:* Father Patrick Frawley
**COO:* David P Thomas
**CFO:* Thomas Halloran
CFO: Ronald Weingartner
VP: Pamela Hassen
CIO: Martin Krebs
Dir IT: Don Martia
Dir IT: Don Martin

D-U-N-S 94-791-2531
NEW YORK STATE COURT OFFICERS ASSOCIATION SECURITY BENEFIT FUND
321 Broadway Ste 600, New York, NY 10007-3636
Tel (212) 608-1124 *Founded/Ownrshp* 1994
Sales NA *EMP* 1,600
Accts Gould Kobrick & Schlapp Pc Ne
SIC 6371 Union funds; Union funds
Pr: Dennis Quirk

D-U-N-S 80-678-1340
NEW YORK STATE DEPARTMENT OF HEALTH
(*Suby of* EXECUTIVE OFFICE OF STATE OF NEW YORK) ★
Empire State Plz, Albany, NY 12237-0001
Tel (518) 474-2011 *Founded/Ownrshp* 1901
Sales NA *EMP* 17,226
SIC 9431 Administration of public health programs; ; Administration of public health programs;
**Ch:* Larita R Boren
Ex Dir: Bob Reed

D-U-N-S 80-678-0730
NEW YORK STATE DEPARTMENT OF MOTOR VEHICLES
(*Suby of* EXECUTIVE OFFICE OF STATE OF NEW YORK) ★
6 Empire State Plz Rm 321, Albany, NY 12223
Tel (518) 474-0835 *Founded/Ownrshp* 1960
Sales NA *EMP* 3,482
SIC 9621 Regulation, administration of transportation; ; Regulation, administration of transportation;

D-U-N-S 78-087-5423
NEW YORK STATE DIVISION OF CRIMINAL JUSTICE SERVICES
(*Suby of* EXECUTIVE OFFICE OF STATE OF NEW YORK) ★
80 S Swan St, Albany, NY 12210-8001
Tel (518) 457-9896 *Founded/Ownrshp* 2013
Sales NA *EMP* 1,985E
SIC 9211

D-U-N-S 12-412-2123
NEW YORK STATE DIVISION OF HOUSING AND COMMUNITY RENEWAL
(*Suby of* EXECUTIVE OFFICE OF STATE OF NEW YORK) ★
38-40 State St, Albany, NY 12207-2837
Tel (518) 473-2517 *Founded/Ownrshp* 2002
Sales NA *EMP* 1,178E
SIC 9531 Housing programs;
Ofcr: Paul Fuller
Sr VP: Bret Garwood
VP: Wanda Graham
VP Admn: Edwin Bonilla

D-U-N-S 04-186-6497
NEW YORK STATE ELECTRIC & GAS CORP
18 Link Dr, Binghamton, NY 13904-3222
Tel (607) 762-7200 *Founded/Ownrshp* 2015
Sales 1.2MMME *EMP* 2,648
SIC 4911 4924 4923

D-U-N-S 07-328-9634
NEW YORK STATE ENVIRONMENTAL FACILITIES CORP
625 Broadway, Albany, NY 12207-2942
Tel (518) 486-9267 *Founded/Ownrshp* 2005
Sales 528.7MM *EMP* 13E
Accts Uhp Llp Albany New York
SIC 8742 Compensation & benefits planning consultant; Compensation & benefits planning consultant
Pr: David Sterman

D-U-N-S 09-989-1558
NEW YORK STATE FEDERATION OF GROWERS & PROCESSORS ASSOCIATIONS INC
AGRI-BUSINESS CHILD DEV
847 Union St, Schenectady, NY 12308-2705
Tel (518) 346-6447 *Founded/Ownrshp* 1946
Sales 16.7MM *EMP* 350
Accts Wojeski & Company Cpas Pc
SIC 8351 8741 Preschool center; Management services; Preschool center; Management services
Ex Dir: Maggie Evans
**CFO:* Rona Heaton
IT Man: Rona Lee
Sls&Mrk Ex: Susan Dingee

D-U-N-S 15-086-6374
NEW YORK STATE INDUSTRIES FOR DISABLED INC
NYSID
11 Columbia Cir, Albany, NY 12203-5156
Tel (518) 463-9706 *Founded/Ownrshp* 1975
Sales 214.8MM *EMP* 50
Accts Uhy Advisors Ny Inc Albany
SIC 8322 Association for the handicapped; Association for the handicapped
CEO: Ronald P Romano
**Pr:* Larry Barker
**Ch:* James Flannagan
**Ch:* Edward Lokomski
Treas: Henry Cohen
**Treas:* Jack Manganello
**V Ch Bd:* Tim Gieselsman
VP: Tim Mott
IT Man: Frank Heuer
Board of Directors: Frank Coco, Kevin Crosley, Mary Jo Thorn, Carolina Cordero Dyer, Donaldrsiegel

D-U-N-S 07-110-0572
NEW YORK STATE NURSES ASSOCIATION
NYSNA
131 W 33rd St Fl 4, New York, NY 10001-2966
Tel (518) 782-9400 *Founded/Ownrshp* 1902
Sales 39.6MM *EMP* 170
Accts Bst Advisors Llc Albany Ny
SIC 8621 Professional membership organizations; Professional membership organizations
Ex Dir: Lola Fehr
**CFO:* John Daley
Chf Nrs Of: Tina Gerardi
Ex Dir: Jill Furillo
MIS Dir: John Harder

D-U-N-S 04-441-5979
NEW YORK STATE OFFICE FOR PEOPLE WITH DEVELOPMENTAL DISABILITIES
OPWDD
(*Suby of* EXECUTIVE OFFICE OF STATE OF NEW YORK) ★
44 Holland Ave, Albany, NY 12208-3411
Tel (518) 473-1341 *Founded/Ownrshp* 1978
Sales NA *EMP* 2,200
SIC 9431 Administration of public health programs; Administration of public health programs;
Ofcr: Selina Hughes
Snr Mgr: Larry Domenech

D-U-N-S 80-678-0623
NEW YORK STATE OFFICE OF MENTAL HEALTH
(*Suby of* EXECUTIVE OFFICE OF STATE OF NEW YORK) ★
44 Holland Ave, Albany, NY 12208-3411
Tel (518) 474-4403 *Founded/Ownrshp* 1978
Sales NA *EMP* 17,000
SIC 9431 Mental health agency administration, government; ; Mental health agency administration, government;
CFO: Martha Schaefer
**CFO:* Martha Schefer
Exec: Roberto Cerda
Dir: Jeremy Darman
Dir Rx: Gerald M Engel
Admn Mgr: Rose Celestin
IT Man: Tim Shaer
Doctor: Khadija Faridi
Doctor: Robert Lowinger
Doctor: Nicole Reid
Doctor: Arona Sheth

D-U-N-S 01-400-0249
NEW YORK STATE OLYMPIC REGIONAL DEVELOPMENT AUTHORITY
OLYMPIC CENTER, THE
2634 Main St, Lake Placid, NY 12946-3648
Tel (518) 523-4436 *Founded/Ownrshp* 1982
Sales 50.5MM^E *EMP* 600
SIC 7032 7941 7999 Sporting & recreational camps; Sports field or stadium operator, promoting sports events; Aerial tramway or ski lift, amusement or scenic; Skating instruction, ice or roller; Sporting & recreational camps; Sports field or stadium operator, promoting sports events; Aerial tramway or ski lift, amusement or scenic; Skating instruction, ice or roller
Pr: Ted Blazer
**VP:* Jeffery Byrne
Comm Man: Stephanie Ryan

D-U-N-S 04-928-4151
NEW YORK STATE PUBLIC EMPLOYEE FEDERATION
NYSPEF
1168 Troy Schenectady Rd # 70, Latham, NY 12110-1014
Tel (800) 342-4306 *Founded/Ownrshp* 1979
Sales 36.3MM *EMP* 130
Accts Marvin And Company Pc Latham
SIC 8631 Labor union; Labor union
Pr: Ken Brynien
Treas: Kim Patridge
**VP:* Patricia Baker
**VP:* Joe Fox
Dir IT: Alan Schulkin

D-U-N-S 12-495-5332
NEW YORK STATE TEAMSTERS BENEFIT FUNDS
3 Northern Concourse, Syracuse, NY 13212-4047
Tel (315) 455-9790 *Founded/Ownrshp* 1999
Sales NA *EMP* 50
SIC 6371 Union welfare, benefit & health funds
Dir IT: Joseph Salerno

NEW YORK STATE THEATRE, THE
See CITY CENTER OF MUSIC & DRAMA INC

D-U-N-S 13-818-7539
NEW YORK STATE UNITED TEACHERS
N E A
(*Suby of* N E A) ★
800 Troy Schenectady Rd, Latham, NY 12110-2424
Tel (518) 213-6000 *Founded/Ownrshp* 1972
Sales 137.3MM *EMP* 550
Accts Buchbinder Tunick & Company Ll
SIC 8631 Labor unions & similar labor organizations; Labor unions & similar labor organizations
Pr: Richard C Iannuzzi
CFO: Dan Frasca
**Sec:* Lee Cutler
Bd of Dir: Mary Schneider
Ex VP: John Costello
**Ex VP:* Andrew Pallotta
**VP:* Kathleen M Donahue
**VP:* Maria Neira
Web Dev: Michael Prinzo
Netwrk Eng: Anthony Kovel
Mktg Dir: Sheryl Allen

D-U-N-S 79-119-5311
■ **NEW YORK STOCK EXCHANGE LLC**
(*Suby of* NYSE GROUP INC) ★
11 Wall St Fl 6, New York, NY 10005-1905
Tel (212) 656-3000 *Founded/Ownrshp* 2005
Sales 577.6MM^E *EMP* 1,503^E
SIC 6231 Security & commodity exchanges
CEO: Duncan L Niederauer

D-U-N-S 92-682-3535 IMP
NEW YORK STONE CO INC
10 Harbor Park Dr, Port Washington, NY 11050-4648
Tel (516) 299-5252 *Founded/Ownrshp* 1992
Sales 24.2MM *EMP* 5
Accts Greene & Company Llp Melvill
SIC 1741 Masonry & other stonework; Masonry & other stonework
Pr: Despo Cougentakis
**VP:* Photios Cougentakis

NEW YORK, SUSQUEHANNA
See DELAWARE OTSEGO CORP

D-U-N-S 14-861-2922
NEW YORK SUSQUEHANNA AND WESTERN RAILWAY CORP
(*Suby of* DELAWARE OTSEGO CORP) ★
1 Railroad Ave, Cooperstown, NY 13326-1110
Tel (607) 547-2555 *Founded/Ownrshp* 1997
Sales 31.0MM *EMP* 130
SIC 4011 Interurban railways; Interurban railways
CEO: Nathan R Fenno
**VP:* Richard Hansel
**VP:* Tabetha Rathbon

VP Admn: Joseph Senchyshyn
Pr Dir: Melanie Boyer

D-U-N-S 10-926-3751
NEW YORK TECHNOLOGY PARTNERS INC
NYTP
111 Town Square Pl # 1205, Jersey City, NJ 07310-2783
Tel (201) 521-0300 *Founded/Ownrshp* 1999
Sales 25.0MM *EMP* 200^E
SIC 7379 Computer related consulting services; Computer related consulting services
CEO: Blake Bhatia
**Pr:* Nick Bhatia
Ofcr: Christie Lopez
Sales Exec: Seema Kapur

D-U-N-S 00-131-5613 IMP
▲ **NEW YORK TIMES CO** (NY)
620 8th Ave, New York, NY 10018-1618
Tel (212) 556-1234 *Founded/Ownrshp* 1896
Sales 1.5MMM *EMP* 3,529^E
Accts Ernst & Young Llp New York N
Tkr Sym NYT *Exch* NYS
SIC 2711 4832 4833 7383 7375 Newspapers, publishing & printing; Radio broadcasting stations; Television broadcasting stations; News feature syndicate; Information retrieval services; Newspapers, publishing & printing; Radio broadcasting stations; Television broadcasting stations; News feature syndicate; Information retrieval services
Pr: Mark Thompson
**Ch Bd:* Arthur Sulzberger Jr
Pr: Tom Bartunek
Pr: Scott Heekin-Canedy
Pr: Mary Jacobus
CFO: James M Follo
CFO: Suzanne Yvern S
Ch: Arthur O Sulzberger
**V Ch Bd:* Michael Golden
Bd of Dir: Rupert Murdoch
Chf Mktg O: Alyse Myers
Ex VP: Kenneth A Richieri
Grp VP: Virginia French
Sr VP: R Anthony Benten
Sr VP: Robert H Christie
Sr VP: Catherine J Mathis
Sr VP: Jeff Moriarty
Sr VP: Yasmin Namini
Sr VP: Martin A Nisenholtz
Sr VP: David K Norton
Sr VP: Tracy Raiser
Board of Directors: Raul E Cesan, Robert E Denham, Steven B Green, Carolyn D Greenspon, James A Kohlberg, David E Liddle, Ellen R Marram, Brian P McAndrews, Doreen A Toben

D-U-N-S 00-110-7176
■ **NEW YORK TIMES REGIONAL NEWSPAPER GROUP** (DE)
(*Suby of* NEW YORK TIMES CO) ★
2339 Beville Rd, Daytona Beach, FL 32119-8720
Tel (212) 556-4673 *Founded/Ownrshp* 1878, 2011
Sales 89.1MM^E *EMP* 2,900
SIC 2711 Newspapers; Newspapers
Pr: Lynn Matthews
**CFO:* Stephen Dewitt
**Ex VP:* P Steven Ainsley

D-U-N-S 12-052-0978
■ **NEW YORK TIMES SYNDICATION SALES CORP**
(*Suby of* NEW YORK TIMES CO) ★
620 8th Ave Frnt 5, New York, NY 10018-1618
Tel (212) 556-4063 *Founded/Ownrshp* 1976
Sales 26.0MM *EMP* 25
SIC 7383 News feature syndicate; News feature syndicate
Pr: Gloria Brown Anderson
**Pr:* Carl Horwitz
Ex VP: Cristian Edwards

NEW YORK TOWER
See PAN-AM EQUITIES INC

NEW YORK UNAGI HOUSE
See OCEAN PACIFIC SEAFOOD GROUP INC

D-U-N-S 04-196-8306 IMP
NEW YORK UNIVERSITY
N Y U
70 Washington Sq S, New York, NY 10012-1019
Tel (212) 998-1212 *Founded/Ownrshp* 1831
Sales 8.1MMM^E *EMP* 21,000^E
Accts Pricewaterhousecoopers Llp Ne
SIC 8221 University; University
Pr: John Sexton
**Ch Bd:* Richard Foley
V Ch: William R Bekley
V Ch: Kenneth G Lanone
Trst: Eric J Gleacher
Trst: Norman Goodman
Trst: Charles Kushner
Trst: Henry R Silveman
Trst: John L Vogestein
Trst: Martin J Wygod
Trst: Mariuccia Zerilli-Marim
Trst: Mortimer B Zuckerman
Top Exec: Paula De Stefano
**Ex VP:* Bob Berne
**Ex VP:* Martin S Dorph
Ex VP: Carolyn Keller
**Ex VP:* Alison Leary
Ex VP: Jacob J Lew
Ex VP: Reginald Odom
Sr VP: Bonnie S Brier
VP: Ashlee Ford

D-U-N-S 82-999-9213
NEW YORK UNIVERSITY
NYU COLLEGE OF NURSING
(*Suby of* N Y U) ★
726 Broadway Fl 10, New York, NY 10003-9502
Tel (212) 998-5152 *Founded/Ownrshp* 2009
Sales 5.9MMM *EMP* 30
Accts Pricewaterhousecoopers Llp Ne
SIC 8621 Nursing association; Nursing association
Pr: John Sexton

Dir Opers: Barbara Bricoli
Doctor: Jacqueline E Friedman MD

D-U-N-S 17-282-1936
NEW YORK UNIVERSITY MEDICAL CENTER
NYU LANGONE MEDICAL CENTER
560 1st Ave, New York, NY 10016-6402
Tel (212) 263-7000 *Founded/Ownrshp* 1980
Sales 206.1MM^E *EMP* 30,000
SIC 8011 General & family practice, physician/surgeon
CEO: Robert I Grossman
V Ch: Melissa Olivero
Dir Rad: Andrew Litt
Dir Rad: John Loh
**Prin:* Itzhak Kronzon
Off Mgr: Linda Hood
MIS Mgr: Michael Cannizzo
Ansthlgy: Wanda A Chin
Doctor: Christopher Marshall
Doctor: Leonid Yatskar
Pharmcst: Manny Horvitz

D-U-N-S 95-809-7164
NEW YORK UNIVERSITY OF LAW FOUNDATION INC
(*Suby of* NEW YORK UNIVERSITY SCHOOL OF LAW)
40 Washngton Sq S Ste 406, New York, NY 10012
Tel (212) 998-6000 *Founded/Ownrshp* 1970
Sales 28.2MM *EMP* 79
SIC 8221 University; University
Prin: Richard Revesz
Treas: Daniel Evans
Bd of Dir: Norm Fruchter

D-U-N-S 07-953-2618
NEW YORK UNIVERSITY SCHOOL OF ENGINEERING
6 Metrotech Ctr, Brooklyn, NY 11201-3840
Tel (718) 260-3600 *Founded/Ownrshp* 2014
Sales 20.1MM^E *EMP* 552^E
SIC 8221 Colleges universities & professional schools; Colleges universities & professional schools
Pr: Katepalli R Sreenivasan
Sr VP: Dennis D Dintino
VP: Richard Thorsen
Adm Dir: Bohdan Hoshovsky
Mng Dir: Kathleen Hamilton
Prgrm Mgr: Mgavi Brathwaite
CIO: Tom Schmidt

D-U-N-S 94-723-8929 IMP
NEW YORK VALUE CLUB LTD
BELCO DISTRIBUTORS
100 Adams Blvd, Farmingdale, NY 11735-6633
Tel (631) 501-2020 *Founded/Ownrshp* 1995
Sales 48.2MM^E *EMP* 125
SIC 5122 Hair preparations; Hair preparations
Pr: Jerry Sabella

NEW YORK WATERWAY
See PORT IMPERIAL FERRY CORP

D-U-N-S 07-326-3436
NEW YORK WESTCHESTER SQUARE MEDICAL CENTER INC
2475 Saint Raymonds Ave, Bronx, NY 10461-3124
Tel (718) 430-7300 *Founded/Ownrshp* 1969
Sales 18.0MM *EMP* 700^E
SIC 8062
Pr: Alan Kopman
Dir Inf Cn: Jean M Battissta
Dir Lab: Lynn Lippo
Opers Mgr: Ivan Santiago
Pharmcst: Arnie Dosanvil
Pharmcst: Mudassir Khan
Pharmcst: Theodora Kitcher

NEW YORK WIRE
See WIRE CO HOLDINGS INC

D-U-N-S 00-301-0428 IMP/EXP
NEW YORK WIRE CO
500 E Middle St, Hanover, PA 17331-2027
Tel (717) 854-9571 *Founded/Ownrshp* 1928, 2000
Sales 106.5MM^E *EMP* 400^E
SIC 2221 3496 3357 Fiberglass fabrics; Woven wire products; Aluminum wire & cable; Fiberglass fabrics; Woven wire products; Aluminum wire & cable
Pr: Guy Fritz
VP: Frank R Giateri Jr
VP: Greg Steger

D-U-N-S 02-155-7824
NEW YORK WOMENS FOUNDATION
39 Broadway Fl 23, New York, NY 10006-3059
Tel (212) 514-6993 *Founded/Ownrshp* 1987
Sales 21.0MM *EMP* 18
SIC 8641 Civic social & fraternal associations; Civic social & fraternal associations
Pr: Ana Olivera
Ofcr: Jennifer Agmi
Ofcr: Camille Emeagwali

D-U-N-S 07-851-2209 EXP
NEW YORK YANKEES PARTNERSHIP
1 E 161st St, Bronx, NY 10451-2100
Tel (718) 293-4300 *Founded/Ownrshp* 1903, 1973
Sales 3.3MM *EMP* 300
Accts Pricewaterhousecoopers Llp Ta
SIC 7941 Baseball club, professional & semi-professional; Baseball club, professional & semi-professional
Genl Pt: Joseph A Molloy
Pt: Robert Nederlander
Pt: George M Steinbrenner III
COO: Lonn Trost
Sr VP: Felix Lopez
VP: Marty Greenspoon
VP: Scott Krug
VP: Mike Lane
VP: Richard Smith
VP: Michael Tusiani
VP Bus Dev: Jim Ross

NEW YORK ZOOLOGICAL SOCIETY
See WILDLIFE CONSERVATION SOCIETY

D-U-N-S 96-452-8231
NEW YORK-PRESBYTERIAN FUND INC
525 E 68th St, New York, NY 10065-4870
Tel (212) 297-4356 *Founded/Ownrshp* 2010
Sales 385.5MM *EMP* 4^E
Accts Ernst & Young Us Llp New Yo
SIC 8011 Medical centers; Medical centers
CEO: Phyllis Lantos

D-U-N-S 07-274-4592
NEW YORK-PRESBYTERIAN/QUEENS
NEW YORK HOSPITAL QUEENS
5645 Main St, Flushing, NY 11355-5045
Tel (718) 670-2000 *Founded/Ownrshp* 1992
Sales 439.3MM^E *EMP* 2,380
Accts Ernst & Young Llp Indianapol
SIC 8062 General medical & surgical hospitals; General medical & surgical hospitals
Pr: Stephen S Mills
**CFO:* Kevin Ward
Assoc VP: Adam Weinstein
**Ex VP:* Stephen Rimar
**Ex VP:* John E Sciortino
Sr VP: Louis Reuter
**Sr VP:* Kevin J Ward
**Sr VP:* Michaelle Williams
VP: William Wissemann
Dir Lab: Grace Consiglio
Adm Dir: Maria Durso

D-U-N-S 03-642-5437
■ **NEW YORK/VIRGINIA DDESS SCHOOLS**
(*Suby of* DEPARTMENT OF DEFENSE EDUCATION ACTIVITY) ★
3308 John Quick Rd # 201, Quantico, VA 22134-1752
Tel (703) 784-2319 *Founded/Ownrshp* 1940
Sales NA *EMP* 346^E
SIC 9411 9711 Administration of educational programs; National security;
Prin: Micheal Gould

D-U-N-S 86-816-2249
NEW YORKER HOTEL MANAGEMENT CO INC
WYNDHAM NEW YORKER HOTEL
481 8th Ave, New York, NY 10001-1809
Tel (212) 244-0719 *Founded/Ownrshp* 1993
Sales 37.9MM^E *EMP* 450
SIC 7011 Hotels; Hotels
Pr: Chang Shik Yang
**Ch Bd:* Sylvia Lima
**Pr:* Kevin H Smith
Exec: Paul Valin
Rgnl Mgr: Barry Mann
Genl Mgr: Rowen Beckford
Off Mgr: Glenn Merone
CTO: Katherine Johnston
Mktg Mgr: Tony Appia

NEW YORK'S HOTEL PENNSYLVANIA
See 401 HOTEL TRS INC

D-U-N-S 96-729-0680
■ **NEW YOUNG BROADCASTING HOLDING CO INC**
(*Suby of* MGOC INC) ★
599 Lexington Ave, New York, NY 10022-6030
Tel (212) 754-7010 *Founded/Ownrshp* 2013
Sales 2.5MM^E *EMP* 311^E
SIC 4832 Radio broadcasting stations
CEO: Deborah McDermott

D-U-N-S 82-564-0097 IMP
NEW YUNG WAH TRADING LLC
311 Richardson St, Brooklyn, NY 11222-5709
Tel (718) 388-3322 *Founded/Ownrshp* 1993
Sales 104.9MM *EMP* 25^E
Accts Anita Siew Cpa Brooklyn
SIC 5141 Groceries, general line; Groceries, general line
Genl Mgr: Jessi Zheng
Sls Mgr: Wayne Fan

D-U-N-S 13-700-3711
NEW-ALBANY PLAIN LOCAL SCHOOL DISTRICT
55 N High St, New Albany, OH 43054-7099
Tel (614) 855-2040 *Founded/Ownrshp* 1900
Sales 36.6MM^E *EMP* 400
SIC 8211 Public elementary & secondary schools; School board; Public elementary & secondary schools; School board
**Treas:* Brian Ramsey
IT Man: Andy Moore
Pr Dir: Patrick Gallaway
Teacher Pr: Marlyn Troyer
Snr Mgr: Lori Cheney

D-U-N-S 60-426-2311
NEW-CELL LLC
CELLCOM
(*Suby of* NORTHEAST COMMUNICATIONS OF WISCONSIN INC) ★
1580 Mid Valley Dr, De Pere, WI 54115-8193
Tel (920) 617-7800 *Founded/Ownrshp* 1986
Sales 93.7MM^E *EMP* 370
SIC 4812 Cellular telephone services; Cellular telephone services
Pr: Patrick Riordan
**Ex VP:* Robert H Riordan
VP: Dan Fabry
Exec: Susan Powers
Comm Man: Jodi Delahaut
IT Man: Bubb Lidke
Mtls Mgr: Debbie Verheyen
Mktg Dir: Al Dummer
Sls Dir: Judy Maki
Snr Mgr: Corey O'Connell

D-U-N-S 14-416-1841
NEW-COM INC
6600 Amelia Earhart Ct B, Las Vegas, NV 89119-3535
Tel (702) 642-3331 *Founded/Ownrshp* 1984
Sales 96.6MM^E *EMP* 340
SIC 7353 Heavy construction equipment rental; Heavy construction equipment rental
Pr: Greg Jpaulk
CFO: Janell Cassell

CFO: Michael Threet
**Sec:* Brady Stevens

NEW-INDY CONTAINERBOARD
See NEW-INDY ONTARIO LLC

NEW-INDY CONTAINERBOARD
See NEW-INDY OXNARD LLC

D-U-N-S 61-405-5619 IMP
NEW-INDY CONTAINERBOARD HOLD CO LLC
5100 Jurupa St, Ontario, CA 91761-3618
Tel (909) 390-1055 *Founded/Ownrshp* 2012
Sales 430.6MM[E] *EMP* 329
SIC 2631 Container, packaging & boxboard; Container board; Container, packaging & boxboard; Container board

D-U-N-S 07-852-6056 IMP
NEW-INDY CONTAINERBOARD LLC
INTERNATIONAL PAPER
(*Suby of* NEW-INDY CONTAINERBOARD HOLD CO LLC) ★
3500 Porsche Way Ste 150, Ontario, CA 91764-4969
Tel (909) 296-3400 *Founded/Ownrshp* 2012
Sales 430.6MM[E] *EMP* 310
SIC 2621 Paper mills; Paper mills
CEO: Richard Hartman
**VP:* Mike Conkey

D-U-N-S 07-852-4909
NEW-INDY ONTARIO LLC
NEW-INDY CONTAINERBOARD
(*Suby of* INTERNATIONAL PAPER) ★
5100 Jurupa St, Ontario, CA 91761-3618
Tel (909) 390-1055 *Founded/Ownrshp* 2012
Sales 345.0MM *EMP* 110
SIC 2621 Paper mills; Paper mills
CEO: Richard Hartman
VP: Mike Conkey
Genl Mgr: Scott Conant

D-U-N-S 07-852-4922 IMP
NEW-INDY OXNARD LLC
NEW-INDY CONTAINERBOARD
(*Suby of* INTERNATIONAL PAPER) ★
5936 Perkins Rd, Oxnard, CA 93033-9044
Tel (805) 986-3881 *Founded/Ownrshp* 2012
Sales 38.1MM[E] *EMP* 107
SIC 2621 Paper mills; Paper mills
CEO: Richard Hartman
VP: Mike Conkey

D-U-N-S 06-668-2469
NEW-JACK INDUSTRIES INC
2613 Manhattan Beach Blvd # 100, Redondo Beach, CA 90278-1604
Tel (310) 297-3605 *Founded/Ownrshp* 1972
Sales 4.0MM[E] *EMP* 400
SIC 7381 Security guard service; Security guard service
Pr: W Tom Bragg
**VP:* Ramon Rodriguez

D-U-N-S 00-784-8617
NEW-MAC ELECTRIC COOPERATIVE INC
12105 E Highway 86, Neosho, MO 64850-7063
Tel (417) 451-1515 *Founded/Ownrshp* 1939
Sales 39.9MM *EMP* 54
SIC 4911 Distribution, electric power; Distribution, electric power
Pr: Mitch Mc Cumber
Ofcr: Tom Bower
VP: Billie White
VP: Martin Youngblood
Sfty Dirs: Mark Stuart
Opers Mgr: Josh King

D-U-N-S 11-528-1644 IMP
NEW-TECH PACKAGING INC
2718 Pershing Ave, Memphis, TN 38112-1954
Tel (901) 324-5553 *Founded/Ownrshp* 1984
Sales 47.7MM[E] *EMP* 116[E]
SIC 2653 3086 7389 Boxes, corrugated: made from purchased materials; Packaging & shipping materials, foamed plastic; Packaging & labeling services
Pr: J C Heotis
QA Dir: Marie French

D-U-N-S 07-772-2254
NEW-YORK HISTORICAL SOCIETY
170 Central Park W, New York, NY 10024-5152
Tel (212) 873-3400 *Founded/Ownrshp* 1809
Sales 45.1MM *EMP* 150
Accts Kpmg Llp New York Ny
SIC 8231 8412 Libraries; Museum; Libraries; Museum
CFO: Richard A Shein
Pr: Matthew Bregman
**Pr:* Louise Mirrer
CFO: Richard Schein
VP: Sean Lally
VP: Valerie Paley
IT Man: Cheryl Morgan
Info Man: Albert Min
Web Dev: Ryan McCarthy

NEWAGE BEVERAGE
See NEW AGE BEVERAGES LLC

D-U-N-S 00-251-5229 IMP
NEWAGE INDUSTRIES INC
ADVANTAPURE DIVISION
145 James Way, Southampton, PA 18966-3817
Tel (215) 526-2151 *Founded/Ownrshp* 1948, 1954
Sales 34.7MM[E] *EMP* 116
Accts Kreischer Miller Horsham Pa
SIC 3052 Rubber & plastics hose & beltings; Rubber & plastics hose & beltings
Pr: Kenneth Baker
**Treas:* Steve Midgette
**Treas:* Mary Vander Neut
Rgnl Mgr: Gregg Donovan
Genl Mgr: Don Malizia
QA Dir: Evan Frye
Mfg Dir: Mike Needling
Mfg Dir: Robert Volk
QC Dir: Chris Boytim
Mfg Mgr: Audrey Burke
Natl Sales: Stephen Kuhns

D-U-N-S 07-513-3926
NEWARK ACADEMY
91 S Orange Ave, Livingston, NJ 07039-4989
Tel (973) 992-7000 *Founded/Ownrshp* 1774
Sales 26.0MM[E] *EMP* 99
Accts Eisneramper Llp Iselin Nj
SIC 8211 Private junior high school; Private senior high school
Assoc Dir: Alexandra Holzman

D-U-N-S 07-118-3214
NEWARK BETH ISRAEL MEDICAL CENTER INC
CHILDREN'S HOSPITAL NEW JERSEY
201 Lyons Ave, Newark, NJ 07112-2027
Tel (973) 926-7000 *Founded/Ownrshp* 1996
Sales 563.8MM *EMP* 3,000[E]
Accts Withumsmithbrown Pc Morristown
SIC 8062 General medical & surgical hospitals; General medical & surgical hospitals
Pr: Paul Mertz
Chf Rad: Steven Parmett
Dir Vol: Kim Cook
**COO:* Kenneth Tyson
**CFO:* Veronica Zichner
Ofcr: John Brennan
Ofcr: Sunitha Ramamurthy
VP: Bruce Brener
Dir Rad: Michael Abiri
Dir Rad: Michael Connely
Dir Rx: Craig Dolan

D-U-N-S 06-907-4334
NEWARK BOARD OF EDUCATION
NEWARK CITY SCHOOLS
621 Mount Vernon Rd, Newark, OH 43055-4615
Tel (740) 670-7000 *Founded/Ownrshp* 1812
Sales 80.7MM *EMP* 1,046
Accts Kennedy Cottrell Richards Llc
SIC 8211 Public senior high school; Public junior high school; Public elementary school; Public senior high school; Public junior high school; Public elementary school
Pr: Beverly Niccum
**Treas:* Jeffery Anderson
**VP:* Dan Bybee
VP: Tim Carr
DP Exec: Eric Smith
Schl Brd P: Tom Blind
Board of Directors: Dan Bybee, Mark Christenberry

D-U-N-S 11-657-9041
NEWARK CHARTER SCHOOL INC
2001 Patriot Way, Newark, DE 19711-1809
Tel (302) 369-2001 *Founded/Ownrshp* 2001
Sales 20.7MM *EMP* 200[E]
Accts Barbacane Thornton & Company
SIC 8211 Private elementary & secondary schools; Private elementary & secondary schools
Ch: Stephen Dressel

NEWARK CITY SCHOOLS
See NEWARK BOARD OF EDUCATION

D-U-N-S 07-982-7306
NEWARK CITY SCHOOLS
621 Mount Vernon Rd, Newark, OH 43055-4615
Tel (740) 670-7000 *Founded/Ownrshp* 2015
Sales 20.1MM[E] *EMP* 608[E]
SIC 8211 Public elementary & secondary schools
Pr Dir: Seth Roy
Teacher Pr: Barbara Quackenbush

D-U-N-S 11-471-2842 IMP/EXP
NEWARK CORP
NEWARK ELEMENT14
(*Suby of* NEWARK ELECTRONICS CORP) ★
300 S Riverside Plz # 2200, Chicago, IL 60606-6765
Tel (773) 784-5100 *Founded/Ownrshp* 1970
Sales 543.9MM *EMP* 597
SIC 5065 Electronic parts & equipment; Electronic parts & equipment
Pr: Patrick Milbourne
CFO: Mark Whiteling
**Treas:* Paul M Barlak
Chf Mktg O: Dianne Kibbey
**Sr VP:* Tamara Jurgenson
Sr VP: Barry Litwin
**Sr VP:* Jim Seifert
**Sr VP:* Benjamin Topercer
**VP:* Chris Binion
VP: Colin Campbell
VP: Greg Clopton
**VP:* Joseph R Daprile
**VP:* Steven Webb
**VP:* Mark Whitelling

D-U-N-S 01-924-1129 IMP
NEWARK ELECTRONICS CORP
(*Suby of* PREMIER FARNELL CORP) ★
300 S Riverside Plz, Chicago, IL 60606-6613
Tel (773) 784-5100 *Founded/Ownrshp* 1995
Sales 543.9MM *EMP* 964
SIC 5065 5063 5961 Electronic parts & equipment; Electrical apparatus & equipment; Catalog & mail-order houses; Electronic parts & equipment; Electrical apparatus & equipment; Catalog & mail-order houses
CEO: Patrick Milbourne
Treas: Paul M Barlak
Ofcr: Larisa Miles
Sr VP: Susan Fischer
Sr VP: Tamara Jurgenson
Sr VP: Paula Manley
Sr VP: Jimmy Seifert
VP: Chris Binion
**VP:* Jospeh R Daprile
VP: Benjamin Topercer
**VP:* Steven Webb
VP: Mark Whiteling

NEWARK ELEMENT14
See NEWARK CORP

D-U-N-S 03-025-1243
NEWARK EXTENDED CARE FACILITY INC
NEWARK MEDICAL DAY CARE CTR
65 Jay St, Newark, NJ 07103-3235
Tel (973) 483-6800 *Founded/Ownrshp* 1974
Sales 29.8MM *EMP* 500
SIC 5947 8051 Extended care facility; Gift, novelty & souvenir shop; Gift, novelty & souvenir shop; Extended care facility
Pr: Samuel Paneth
Exec: Miriam Nachfolger

D-U-N-S 08-565-3186 IMP
NEWARK GROUP INC
NEWARK RCYCLED PPRBD SOLUTIONS
(*Suby of* CARAUSTAR INDUSTRIES INC) ★
20 Jackson Dr, Cranford, NJ 07016-3609
Tel (908) 276-4000 *Founded/Ownrshp* 2015
Sales 563.6MM[E] *EMP* 1,700
SIC 2679 2631 Paperboard products, converted; Paperboard mills; Paperboard products, converted; Paperboard mills
CEO: Frank Papa
Sr VP: James Carbine
Sr VP: Johnny Gold
Sr VP: Philip B Jones
Sr VP: Mark Klein
Sr VP: Dick Poppe
Sr VP: Manny Silva
VP: Joseph Byrne
VP: Gregg Kam
VP: Eddie Tolentino
Genl Mgr: Scott Brissette

NEWARK MEDICAL DAY CARE CTR
See NEWARK EXTENDED CARE FACILITY INC

D-U-N-S 00-218-7342
NEWARK MORNING LEDGER CO
SUNDAY STAR LEDGER
(*Suby of* ADVANCE PUBLICATIONS INC) ★
1 Gateway Ctr Ste 1100, Newark, NJ 07102-5323
Tel (973) 392-4141 *Founded/Ownrshp* 1916
Sales 184.1MM[E] *EMP* 1,200
SIC 2711 Newspapers, publishing & printing; Newspapers, publishing & printing
Pr: Donald E Newhouse
Pr: Steve Alessi
Treas: William Perlman
VP: Brad Young
Exec: James Loughlin
Genl Mgr: John Dennan
Genl Mgr: Mark Newhouse
Dir IT: Gene Rizzo
IT Man: Keith Marchese
Netwrk Eng: Michael Montenegro
Opers Mgr: Joe Maeker
Board of Directors: Samuel I Newhouse Jr

NEWARK PAPERBOARD PRODUCTS
See NELSON-BALL PAPER PRODUCTS INC

D-U-N-S 79-620-3305
NEWARK PRE-SCHOOL COUNCIL INC
570 Broad St Ste 1000, Newark, NJ 07102-4496
Tel (973) 848-5000 *Founded/Ownrshp* 1965
Sales 30.9MM *EMP* 650
Accts Maligu Associates Llc Jersey
SIC 8211 8351 Private elementary & secondary schools; Child day care services; Private elementary & secondary schools; Child day care services
Prin: Karen Highsmith
CFO: Sunil Varshneya
Ex Dir: Jacqueline Crawford

D-U-N-S 04-074-0334
NEWARK PUBLIC SCHOOLS
2 Cedar St Ste 1, Newark, NJ 07102-3015
Tel (973) 733-7360 *Founded/Ownrshp* 1995
Sales 415.1MM[E] *EMP* 8,061
SIC 8211 Public elementary & secondary schools; Public elementary & secondary schools
Bd of Dir: Sonn Sam
Ex Dir: Rita Salley
CIO: Alejandro Echevarria
Genl Couns: Arsen Zartarian

NEWARK RCYCLED PPRBD SOLUTIONS
See NEWARK GROUP INC

D-U-N-S 06-791-3749
NEWARK SCHOOL DISTRICT
100 E Miller St Ste 6, Newark, NY 14513-1525
Tel (315) 332-3230 *Founded/Ownrshp* 1955
Sales 40.3MM *EMP* 500
Accts Raymond F Wager Cpa Pc R
SIC 8211 Public elementary school; Public junior high school; Public senior high school; Public elementary school; Public junior high school; Public senior high school
**Pr:* Roberta Colacino
VP: Andy Correia
Exec: Joann Swick
IT Man: Robert Speciale
Schl Brd P: Roberta Colaciaino

NEWARK TOYOTA WORLD
See ROYAL IMPORTS INC

D-U-N-S 07-015-9645
NEWARK UNIFIED SCHOOL DISTRICT
5715 Musick Ave, Newark, CA 94560-2554
Tel (510) 818-4103 *Founded/Ownrshp* 1954, 1961
Sales 59.0MM *EMP* 620
SIC 8211 Public elementary school; School board; Public elementary school; School board
Bd of Dir: Ray Rodriguez
VP: Charlie Mensinger
Snr Mgr: Steven Shields

D-U-N-S 07-367-0689
NEWARK-WAYNE COMMUNITY HOSPITAL
(*Suby of* ROCHESTER GENERAL HEALTH SYSTEM) ★
1200 Driving Park Ave, Newark, NY 14513-1090
Tel (315) 332-2022 *Founded/Ownrshp* 2005
Sales 102.4MM *EMP* 800
Accts Fust Charles Chambers Llp Syr
SIC 8062 General medical & surgical hospitals; General medical & surgical hospitals
Pr: Annette Leahy
Ofcr: Mark Klyczek
Dir Lab: William Fricke
Dir Rad: Yvonne Mactaggart
Dir Pat Ac: John Midolo
Phys Thrpy: Tom Jackson

D-U-N-S 96-149-6049
NEWARK-WAYNE COMMUNITY HOSPITAL FOUNDATION
DE MAY LIVING CENTER AT NEWARK WAYNE HOSPITAL
(*Suby of* ROCHESTER GENERAL HEALTH SYSTEM) ★
1200 Driving Park Ave, Newark, NY 14513-1090
Tel (315) 332-2700 *Founded/Ownrshp* 1965
Sales 1.3MM *EMP* 600[E]
Accts Ernst & Young Us Llp Buffalo
SIC 6733 7389 Trusts; Fund raising organizations; Trusts; Fund raising organizations
COO: Brad Smith

D-U-N-S 08-469-1781 IMP
NEWAY PACKAGING CORP
1973 E Via Arado, Rancho Dominguez, CA 90220-6102
Tel (602) 454-9000 *Founded/Ownrshp* 1977
Sales 77.7MM[E] *EMP* 89
SIC 5113 5084 Shipping supplies; Packaging machinery & equipment; Shipping supplies; Packaging machinery & equipment
Pr: Russell E Freebury
**VP:* Sarah D Giles-Bell
Brnch Mgr: Susan Freebury
Off Mgr: April Boling
VP Sls: Chuck Soper
Sales Asso: Sonia Hayes

D-U-N-S 05-581-8249
NEWAY STAMPING & MANUFACTURING INC
4820 E 345th St, Willoughby, OH 44094-4607
Tel (440) 951-8500 *Founded/Ownrshp* 2011
Sales 23.0MM[E] *EMP* 85
SIC 3469 3544 Stamping metal for the trade; Special dies, tools, jigs & fixtures
Pr: Adam Bowden
Pr: Davis Briggs
**VP:* Jason H Bowden

D-U-N-S 07-257-5848
NEWAYGO COUNTY GENERAL HOSPITAL ASSOCIATION
SPECTRUM HEALTH GERBER MEM
(*Suby of* SPECTRUM HEALTH SYSTEM) ★
212 S Sullivan Ave, Fremont, MI 49412-1548
Tel (231) 924-3300 *Founded/Ownrshp* 2010
Sales 72.2MM *EMP* 600
Accts Crowe Horwath Llp Chicago Il
SIC 8082 8062 Home health care services; General medical & surgical hospitals; Home health care services; General medical & surgical hospitals
Pr: Randal J Stasik
**CFO:* John Sella
Dir Rad: Debra Dillon
Dir Rx: Heather Christianson
Sfty Mgr: Debbie Beassler
Mktg Mgr: Stephanie Zinn
Pharmcst: Dawn Patterson
Phys Thrpy: Jenny Babcock
HC Dir: Mary Huss

D-U-N-S 12-815-9183
NEWAYGO PUBLIC SCHOOLS
360 Mill St, Newaygo, MI 49337-8545
Tel (231) 652-6984 *Founded/Ownrshp* 1967
Sales 15.0MM[E] *EMP* 330
SIC 8211 Public elementary & secondary schools; Public elementary & secondary schools

NEWAYS INTERNATIONAL
See MAPLE MOUNTAIN GROUP INC

D-U-N-S 00-667-9633 IMP/EXP
NEWBASIS WEST LLC
(*Suby of* ECHO ROCK VENTURES INC) ★
2626 Kansas Ave, Riverside, CA 92507-2600
Tel (951) 787-0600 *Founded/Ownrshp* 1989
Sales 47.5MM[E] *EMP* 115
SIC 3272 Manhole covers or frames, concrete; Tanks, concrete; Meter boxes, concrete; Concrete products, precast; Manhole covers or frames, concrete; Tanks, concrete; Meter boxes, concrete; Concrete products, precast
CEO: Karl Stockbridge
CFO: Richard Bengtson
**CFO:* Jennifer Ewing
VP: Christopher Larkins
VP Mfg: Tom Griffin
VP Mfg: Eddie Ruiz
Manager: Bill Isaacson

D-U-N-S 15-349-1329
NEWBAY MEDIA LLC
(*Suby of* WICKS GROUP OF COMPANIES LLC (DE CORP)) ★
28 E 28th St Fl 12, New York, NY 10016-7959
Tel (212) 378-0400 *Founded/Ownrshp* 2006
Sales 80.9MM[E] *EMP* 165
SIC 4833 Television broadcasting stations; Television broadcasting stations
CEO: Steve Palm
**CFO:* Paul Mastronardi
**Ex VP:* Adam Goldstein
**Ex VP:* Carmel King
VP: Robert Ames
VP: Ed Hecht
VP: John Morr
**VP:* Eric Trabb
Mng Dir: Mark Burton
IT Man: Ileana Vega
Prd Dir: Davis White

NEWBERG FORD MERCURY
See CEW INC

D-U-N-S 10-006-8394
NEWBERG SCHOOL DISTRICT 29 JT
714 E 6th St, Newberg, OR 97132-3406
Tel (503) 554-5000 *Founded/Ownrshp* 1950
Sales 35.5MM^E *EMP* 587
SIC 8211 Public elementary & secondary schools; Public elementary & secondary schools

D-U-N-S 06-932-9159
NEWBERRY COLLEGE (SC)
2100 College St, Newberry, SC 29108-2197
Tel (803) 276-5010 *Founded/Ownrshp* 1856
Sales 39.0MM *EMP* 154
Accts Derrick Stubbs & Stith Llp Co
SIC 8221 College, except junior; College, except junior
Pr: Mitchell Zais
**CFO:* Steven Feld
**VP:* Wayne Kannaday
**VP:* John Robertson
Dir IT: Terry Sabol

D-U-N-S 07-372-3314
NEWBERRY COUNTY MEMORIAL HOSPITAL (INC)
2669 Kinard St, Newberry, SC 29108-2911
Tel (803) 276-7570 *Founded/Ownrshp* 1925
Sales 40.7MM^E *EMP* 302^E
SIC 8062 General medical & surgical hospitals; General medical & surgical hospitals
CEO: Bruce Baldwin
**CEO:* Lynn Beasley
**Ch:* Willie Morris
**Treas:* Lou Oxner
VP: Fred Taylor
Dir Risk M: Rob Torres
Dir Lab: Randy Litzenberger
Dir Rx: Stephanie Haltiwanger
Ex Dir: Brenda Williams
IT Man: Joseph Bigham
Obsttrcn: Stephen F Dyke

D-U-N-S 01-256-7822
NEWBERRY COUNTY SCHOOL DISTRICT
3419 Main St, Newberry, SC 29108-4145
Tel (803) 321-2600 *Founded/Ownrshp* 1889
Sales 66.8MM *EMP* 1,000
Accts Greene Finney & Horton Llp
SIC 8211 Public elementary & secondary schools; Vocational high school; Public elementary & secondary schools; Vocational high school
Dir Sec: Wesley Palmore

D-U-N-S 00-792-0119
NEWBERRY ELECTRIC COOPERATIVE INC (SC)
882 Wilson Rd, Newberry, SC 29108-4618
Tel (803) 276-1121 *Founded/Ownrshp* 1940
Sales 31.3MM *EMP* 35
Accts K Eve Mccoy Cpa Llc Columbia
SIC 4911 Distribution, electric power
Pr: George Keith Avery
Ch Bd: William D Kibler Jr
Sec: Johnnie L Dickert
VP: Charles J Bishop
VP: Scott Bryant
Board of Directors: Virginia M Boland, William B Lominick Sr, J Wayne Nichols, Harold L Pitts, Richard Henry Ruff, Tobie R Shealy

D-U-N-S 10-715-2886
NEWBERRY GROUP INC
5650 Mexico Rd Ste 1, Saint Peters, MO 63376-1696
Tel (636) 928-9944 *Founded/Ownrshp* 1996
Sales 20.0MM^E *EMP* 100^E
SIC 8742 Management information systems consultant
Ch Bd: Christopher J Steinbach
**CFO:* Chris Pugh
**VP:* R Steven Cadogan
VP: Steven Cadogan
Ex Dir: Phillip G Justice Jr
Dir IT: Fay Aubuchon
IT Man: John Saxbury
IT Man: Sandra Schleicher
Netwrk Mgr: Nick Prifiletti
Netwrk Eng: Tammy Davidson

D-U-N-S 00-703-3707 IMP
NEWBERRY TANKS & EQUIPMENT LLC (AR)
FAITH TANK & MANUFACTURING
205 N Walker Ave, West Memphis, AR 72301-3695
Tel (870) 735-4473 *Founded/Ownrshp* 1927, 1987
Sales 20.8MM^E *EMP* 40
SIC 5085 5084 3441 3443 5088 Industrial supplies; Industrial machinery & equipment; Fabricated structural metal; Fabricated plate work (boiler shop); Tanks, standard or custom fabricated: metal plate; Tanks & tank components
Pr: Chris Long
Pr: Brian Brinkley
**Treas:* Ellen Rogers
VP: Thomas Kemp
IT Man: Rebecca Long
Manager: Charlie Redford

NEWBERRY TECHNICAL SERVICES
See NTS INC

D-U-N-S 79-119-3428
■ **NEWBEVCO INC**
(*Suby of* NATIONAL BEVERAGE CORP) ★
1 N University Dr, Plantation, FL 33324-2038
Tel (954) 581-0922 *Founded/Ownrshp* 1996
Sales 841.4MM^E *EMP* 1,200
SIC 2086 Bottled & canned soft drinks; Bottled & canned soft drinks
Pr: Nick A Caporella
**Pr:* Joseph G Caporella

D-U-N-S 82-968-0008 IMP/EXP
NEWBOLD CORP
DIGIPOS
450 Weaver St, Rocky Mount, VA 24151-2207
Tel (540) 489-4400 *Founded/Ownrshp* 1994
Sales 21.9MM^E *EMP* 165^E
SIC 3579 3578 Mailing, letter handling & addressing machines; Cash registers; Mailing, letter handling & addressing machines; Cash registers
Pr: Robert Scott
Ex VP: Donna Austin
**Ex VP:* Frank Canestari
**VP:* Dan Harrison
VP: Gary Spellman
VP: John Wilson
IT Man: Patrick Climer
IT Man: Todd Lowe
IT Man: Greg Williams
Natl Sales: Mike Kelley

D-U-N-S 07-480-1937 IMP
NEWBORN BROS CO INC
8221 Preston Ct Ste D, Jessup, MD 20794-9368
Tel (301) 604-1500 *Founded/Ownrshp* 1974
Sales 34.3MM^E *EMP* 178
SIC 5072 Hardware; Hand tools
Pr: Peter J Chang

D-U-N-S 04-529-3123
NEWBORN ENTERPRISES INC
ALTOONA NEWS AGENCY
808 Green Ave, Altoona, PA 16601-4724
Tel (814) 944-3593 *Founded/Ownrshp* 1968
Sales 63.8MM^E *EMP* 142
SIC 5192 7841 Magazines; Newspapers; Books; Video tape rental; Magazines; Newspapers; Books; Video tape rental
Pr: Barry Newborn
**Treas:* Jay Bakale
**VP:* Barbara Newborn

D-U-N-S 10-348-6486
▲ **NEWBRIDGE BANCORP**
1501 Highwoods Blvd # 400, Greensboro, NC 27410-2050
Tel (336) 369-0900 *Founded/Ownrshp* 1982
Sales NA *EMP* 449^E
Tkr Sym NBBC *Exch* NGS
SIC 6022 State commercial banks; State commercial banks
Pr: Pressley A Ridgill
CFO: Ramsey K Hamadi
Ofcr: David P Barksdale
Ofcr: William W Budd Jr
Ofcr: Brenda M Houser
Ex VP: Robin S Hager
Sr VP: Coretta J Bigelow
Sr VP: Craig L Call
Sr VP: Ronald E Coleman
Sr VP: Nicholas A Daves
Sr VP: Philip G Gibson
Sr VP: Donna G Hench
Sr VP: Andrew G McDowell
Sr VP: Charles N Reynolds
Sr VP: Kathy V Richardson
Sr VP: Ronald W Sink
Sr VP: Edward C Sopp
Sr VP: Pamela J Varela
Sr VP: Joseph T Wallace
VP: Marcus Smith
Exec: Linda Maynard
Board of Directors: E Reid Teague, Michael S Albert, Richard A Urquhart III, Robert A Boyette, G Alfred Webster, C Arnold Britt, Julius S Young Jr, Robert C Clark, J David Branch, Alex A Diffey Jr, Donald P Johnson, Joseph H Kinnaney, Michael S Patterson, Mary E Rittling

D-U-N-S 07-158-0971
■ **NEWBRIDGE BANK**
(*Suby of* NEWBRIDGE BANCORP) ★
1501 Highwoods Blvd, Greensboro, NC 27410-2050
Tel (336) 248-6500 *Founded/Ownrshp* 1949, 1983
Sales NA *EMP* 385
SIC 6022 State trust companies accepting deposits, commercial; State trust companies accepting deposits, commercial
Pr: H Franklin Sherron Jr
Bd of Dir: Walter A Hill
Bd of Dir: Julius S Young
Chf Inves: Ken Banner
Ofcr: David Barksdale
**Ofcr:* Spence H Broadhurst
Ofcr: Joe Wallace
Assoc VP: Jeri Hand
Ex VP: Wes Budd
Ex VP: Mike McMahan
**Ex VP:* Monty J Oliver
Sr VP: Laura Bailey
Sr VP: Coretta Bigelow
Sr VP: Edwin Bland
Sr VP: Ginny Carter
Sr VP: Gill Cooper
Sr VP: Richard Hendricks
Sr VP: Bryan Lunsford
Sr VP: Albert May
Sr VP: Brantley Moody
Sr VP: Melany Pierman

D-U-N-S 14-853-9489 IMP
NEWBURG EGG CORP
17 Novogrodsky Rd, Woodridge, NY 12789-5517
Tel (845) 434-8115 *Founded/Ownrshp* 1994
Sales 28.7MM^E *EMP* 120
SIC 0252 Chicken eggs; Chicken eggs
Pr: Emile Moses Goldstein
**Ex VP:* Moses Neustadt
Off Mgr: Connie Hillson
IT Man: Moses Goldstein
IT Man: Nicole Zotta

D-U-N-S 09-948-6847
NEWBURGH CITY SCHOOL DISTRICT
NEW BURGH ENLARGED CY SCHL DST
124 Grand St, Newburgh, NY 12550-7301
Tel (845) 563-3400 *Founded/Ownrshp* 1825
Sales 111.4MM^E *EMP* 3,356^E
SIC 8211 Public elementary & secondary schools; Public elementary school; Public junior high school; Public senior high school; Public elementary & secondary schools; Public elementary school; Public junior high school; Public senior high school
Pr: Dawn M Fucheck
Bd of Dir: Thomas Woodhull
**VP:* Pamela R Freeman-Resc
Off Mgr: Dale Salisbury
MIS Dir: Anne Lytle

D-U-N-S 10-132-6759 IMP
NEWBURGH DISTRIBUTION CORP
463 Temple Hill Rd, New Windsor, NY 12553-5527
Tel (845) 561-6330 *Founded/Ownrshp* 1982
Sales 58.7MM^E *EMP* 634
SIC 2844 Cosmetic preparations; Cosmetic preparations
Pr: Donald Harkness
**VP:* Sharon Harkness

D-U-N-S 96-050-0341
NEWBURGH METALS INC
N H
75 Pierces Rd, Newburgh, NY 12550-3263
Tel (845) 565-7222 *Founded/Ownrshp* 2006
Sales 20.8MM^E *EMP* 38^E
SIC 5051 Metals service centers & offices
Ch Bd: Angel Rivera
**Ch Bd:* Ann Marie Rivera

NEWBURGH TOYOTA
See HOMETOWN NEWBURGH INC

D-U-N-S 07-950-4783
NEWBURY COLLEGE INC
129 Fisher Ave, Brookline, MA 02445-5750
Tel (617) 730-7000 *Founded/Ownrshp* 1968
Sales 20.2MM *EMP* 225
Accts O Connor & Drew Pc Braintre
SIC 8221 College, except junior; College, except junior
Pr: Hanna McCarthy
Pr: Clare McCully
VP: Doug Flor
VP: Joyce Hanlon
VP: Salvadore Liberto
Assoc Dir: Dameka Halfkenny
CTO: Les Vaughan
Opers Mgr: Lilly Jan
Snr Mgr: Kaitlyn Berkowitz

D-U-N-S 06-778-2235 IMP
NEWBURY COMICS INC
5 Guest St, Brighton, MA 02135-2016
Tel (617) 254-1666 *Founded/Ownrshp* 1978
Sales 83.6MM *EMP* 440
Accts Kpmg Llp Boston Ma
SIC 5735 5947 5942 5994 Compact discs; Records; Audio tapes, prerecorded; Gift shop; Comic books; Magazine stand; Compact discs; Records; Audio tapes, prerecorded; Gift shop; Comic books; Magazine stand
Pr: John W Brusger
Pr: Natalie Waleik
**Treas:* Michael W Dreese
VP: Alison Dewolfe
Brnch Mgr: Sean Obrien
Genl Mgr: Sean Carroll
Genl Mgr: Brian Izzi
Store Mgr: Chris Foley
Store Mgr: Nick Kirlis
Dir IT: Tom Scott
VP Mktg: Amy Dorfman

NEWBURY-ROWLEY-SALISBURY
See TRITON REGIONAL SCHOOL DISTRICT

NEWBURYPORT BANK
See NEWBURYPORT FIVE CENTS SAVINGS BANK INC

D-U-N-S 00-695-5330
NEWBURYPORT FIVE CENTS SAVINGS BANK INC
NEWBURYPORT BANK
63 State St, Newburyport, MA 01950-6615
Tel (978) 462-3136 *Founded/Ownrshp* 1854
Sales NA *EMP* 90
SIC 6036 State savings banks, not federally chartered; State savings banks, not federally chartered
Pr: Janice C Morse
Pr: Keri Sullivan
CFO: Timothy Felter
Ofcr: Catherine Batchelder
Ofcr: Terry Martin
Sr VP: Scott Eaton
VP: Susan Ballard
VP: Jerry Bazata
**VP:* Kellie Wood
Brnch Mgr: Allison Hunt
Brnch Mgr: Donna Leary

D-U-N-S 07-979-9389
NEWBURYPORT PUBLIC SCHOOLS
70 Low St, Newburyport, MA 01950-4049
Tel (978) 465-4457 *Founded/Ownrshp* 2015
Sales 5.4MM^E *EMP* 339^E
SIC 8211 Public elementary & secondary schools

D-U-N-S 03-534-6592
NEWBY BUICK GMC INC
NEWBY OLDSMOBILE
1629 S Convention Ctr Dr, St George, UT 84790-6753
Tel (435) 673-1100 *Founded/Ownrshp* 1962
Sales 27.7MM^E *EMP* 90
SIC 5511 Automobiles, new & used; Automobiles, new & used
Pr: Kenneth B Newby
**Sec:* Russell J Newby
Exec: Bruce Prisbrey
Sales Exec: Steve Smith
Sls Mgr: Eric Todd

NEWBY OLDSMOBILE
See NEWBY BUICK GMC INC

D-U-N-S 09-414-7266
▲ **NEWCASTLE CAPITAL MANAGEMENT LP**
200 Crescent Ct Ste 1400, Dallas, TX 75201-7826
Tel (317) 704-6000 *Founded/Ownrshp* 1999
Sales 108.0MM^E *EMP* 700^E
SIC 6799 Investors
Ch Bd: Mark E Schwarz

D-U-N-S 78-426-1401
▲ **NEWCASTLE INVESTMENT CORP**
1345 Avenue Of America, New York, NY 10105
Tel (212) 798-6100 *Founded/Ownrshp* 1998
Sales 493.6MM *EMP* 4,600^E
Tkr Sym NCT *Exch* NYS
SIC 6798 Real estate investment trusts; Real estate investment trusts
Pr: Kenneth M Riis
**Ch Bd:* Wesley R Edens
COO: Justine Cheng

D-U-N-S 10-168-8856 IMP
NEWCASTLE SHIPYARDS LLC
195 Comfort Rd, Palatka, FL 32177-8637
Tel (386) 312-0000 *Founded/Ownrshp* 2002
Sales 20.4MM^E *EMP* 105
SIC 3732 Yachts, building & repairing

D-U-N-S 79-296-0999
NEWCEN COMMUNITIES INC
CENTURY VILLAGE PEMBROKE PINES
13460 Sw 10th St, Pembroke Pines, FL 33027-1833
Tel (954) 435-6000 *Founded/Ownrshp* 1992
Sales 31.0MM^E *EMP* 160^E
SIC 1531 6552 Condominium developers; Land subdividers & developers, residential
Pr: Tony Gliteson
**Pr:* Michael S Rubin
**VP:* Harold Cohen
**VP:* James A Geddes
**VP:* Antoinette Gleeson
**VP:* Jack Jaiven
**VP:* Michael A Rich

D-U-N-S 06-447-3325
NEWCO DISTRIBUTORS INC
10700 7th St, Rancho Cucamonga, CA 91730-5404
Tel (909) 291-2240 *Founded/Ownrshp* 1973
Sales 64.1MM^E *EMP* 60
SIC 5191 5149 Animal feeds; Pet foods; Animal feeds; Pet foods
CEO: Randall Barb
COO: Rob Chell
CFO: Kellie Clark
VP: Sarah Watkins
IT Man: Todd Noe

D-U-N-S 07-714-6595 IMP
NEWCO ENTERPRISES INC
3650 New Town Blvd, Saint Charles, MO 63301-4357
Tel (636) 946-1330 *Founded/Ownrshp* 1974
Sales 53.2MM^E *EMP* 160
SIC 3589 3634 Coffee brewing equipment; Electric housewares & fans; Coffee brewing equipment; Electric housewares & fans
CEO: Joseph P Webster
Pr: Jody Jacobson
CFO: Karen McEnke
**VP:* Jason College
**VP:* Karen Enke
**VP:* Pat McGuire
VP: Patrick McGuire
IT Man: Steve Reed
Info Man: Dave Beard
Plnt Mgr: Bruce Edler
Prd Mgr: Mark Meyer

D-U-N-S 02-741-7807 IMP/EXP
NEWCO INC
CASCADE COLUMBIA DIST CO
6900 Fox Ave S, Seattle, WA 98108-3419
Tel (206) 282-6334 *Founded/Ownrshp* 1972
Sales 53.0MM^E *EMP* 80
SIC 5169 Industrial chemicals; Acids; Industrial chemicals; Acids
Pr: Robert B Code
**VP:* James Code
Exec: Shari Digerness
IT Man: Gary Miller
Opers Mgr: Bob Sollesvik
Sales Exec: Bob Code

D-U-N-S 60-222-4938
NEWCO INDUSTRIES LLC
NEX SOLUTIONS
900 Anderson Rd, Litchfield, MI 49252-9776
Tel (517) 542-0105 *Founded/Ownrshp* 2004
Sales 22.9MM^E *EMP* 45
SIC 3441 Fabricated structural metal
Off Mgr: Turkey Minton

D-U-N-S 16-802-0795 IMP
NEWCO INTERNATIONAL INC
HARMONY KIDS
13600 Vaughn St, San Fernando, CA 91340-3017
Tel (818) 834-7100 *Founded/Ownrshp* 2004
Sales 44.7MM^E *EMP* 350
SIC 2511 Children's wood furniture; Children's wood furniture
Pr: Howard Napolske
**VP:* Ernest Johnston
VP: Ellie Yamini
VP: Kristen Zimmer

D-U-N-S 07-945-2719
■ **NEWCO LIGHTING INC**
(*Suby of* HUBBELL INC) ★
40 Waterview Dr, Shelton, CT 06484-4300
Tel (475) 882-4000 *Founded/Ownrshp* 2014
Sales 45.7MM^E *EMP* 209^E
SIC 3646 Fluorescent lighting fixtures, commercial; Ceiling systems, luminous
Pr: David G Nord

D-U-N-S 00-893-3442 IMP
■ **NEWCO VALVES LLC**
NEWMANS
(*Suby of* CAMERON INTERNATIONAL CORP) ★
13127 Trinity Dr, Stafford, TX 77477-4297
Tel (281) 325-0041 *Founded/Ownrshp* 2010
Sales 73.2MM^E *EMP* 185
Accts Weikel Johnson Parris Rouse
SIC 5085 3494 Industrial supplies; Valves & fittings; Valves & pipe fittings; Industrial supplies; Valves & fittings; Valves & pipe fittings
Brnch Mgr: Vicki Greer
Opers Mgr: Jack Rosin

D-U-N-S 02-475-4152
NEWCOMB AND CO
3000 Comfort Ct, Raleigh, NC 27604-1388
Tel (919) 862-3000 *Founded/Ownrshp* 1954
Sales 48.4MM^E *EMP* 180
SIC 1711 5074 Warm air heating & air conditioning contractor; Plumbing & hydronic heating supplies; Warm air heating & air conditioning contractor; Plumbing & hydronic heating supplies
Pr: Robert Newcomb
* *CFO:* Paul Thomas
* *VP:* Alan Davis
* *VP:* Chris Evans
* *VP:* Michael S Penick
VP Opers: Wesley Jones

D-U-N-S 36-447-0294
NEWCOMB ENTERPRISES INC JOHN
BURGER KING
910 Triangle St, Blacksburg, VA 24060-7716
Tel (540) 552-7718 *Founded/Ownrshp* 1989
Sales 28.1MM^E *EMP* 1,000
SIC 5812 Fast-food restaurant, chain; Fast-food restaurant, chain
Pr: John W Newcomb

D-U-N-S 07-709-0819
NEWCOMB MEDICAL CENTER
65 S State St, Vineland, NJ 08360-4849
Tel (201) 891-3777 *Founded/Ownrshp* 1921
Sales 10.8MM^E *EMP* 730
SIC 8062 General medical & surgical hospitals; General medical & surgical hospitals
Pr: Joseph Ierardi

D-U-N-S 05-000-6196
NEWCOMB OIL CO LLC
FIVE STAR FOOD MART
1360 E John Rowan Blvd, Bardstown, KY 40004-2049
Tel (502) 348-3961 *Founded/Ownrshp* 1924
Sales 141.4MM^E *EMP* 850
SIC 5411 5171 Convenience stores, chain; Petroleum bulk stations; Convenience stores, chain; Petroleum bulk stations
Prin: William D Newcomb
Mktg Mgr: Ruth Seward
Sls Mgr: Kenny Fletcher

D-U-N-S 03-141-2570
NEWCOMER FUNERAL SERVICE GROUP INC
WEB & RODRICK FUNERAL HOME
520 Sw 27th St, Topeka, KS 66611-1228
Tel (785) 233-6655 *Founded/Ownrshp* 1978
Sales 25.8MM^E *EMP* 500
SIC 7261 6531 6351 Funeral home; Cemetery management service; Surety insurance; Funeral home; Cemetery management service; Surety insurance
Pr: Warren J Newcomer Jr
* *Sec:* Mike Land
* *Ex VP:* Edward Tuggle
Sr VP: Perry Hasselbeck
VP: Jed Dunnichay
VP: Suzette Yost
Software D: Dennis Guilbault

NEWCOR, DECO DIVISION
See DECO ENGINEERING INC

D-U-N-S 00-535-7769
NEWCOR INC
BAY CITY DIVISION
(*Suby of* EXX INC) ★
715 South Blvd E Ste 101, Rochester Hills, MI 48307-5362
Tel (248) 537-0014 *Founded/Ownrshp* 2003
Sales 71.2MM^E *EMP* 750
SIC 3714 Motor vehicle transmissions, drive assemblies & parts; Motor vehicle transmissions, drive assemblies & parts; Gears, motor vehicle; Drive shafts, motor vehicle; Transmission housings or parts, motor vehicle
CEO: David Segal

D-U-N-S 94-608-9807
NEWCOURTLAND LIFE PROGRAM
(*Suby of* THE PRESBYTERIAN FOUNDATION FOR PHILADELPHIA)
5457 Wayne Ave, Philadelphia, PA 19144-3433
Tel (215) 951-4289 *Founded/Ownrshp* 2006
Sales 21.1MM *EMP* 71
SIC 8322 Individual & family services; Individual & family services
Prin: David Auten

NEWDAY USA
See NEW DAY FINANCIAL LLC

D-U-N-S 78-277-1898
NEWEDGE ALTERNATIVE STRATEGIES INC
(*Suby of* NEWEDGE GROUP)
45 Rockefeller Plz # 600, New York, NY 10111-0100
Tel (646) 557-9000 *Founded/Ownrshp* 2001
Sales 16.1MM^E *EMP* 300
SIC 7389 Commodities sampling; Commodities sampling
Pr: Cynthia Zeltwanger
COO: Jeanluc Savignac
* *Treas:* Thomas Locurto
Sr VP: Mark Blumberg
Sr VP: Reginald Browne
Sr VP: Raymond Denney
Sr VP: Michael McDougall
Sr VP: Chris Shepard
Sr VP: Scott Skyrm
VP: Darwyn Broker
VP: Sam Bushrui
VP: Yolanda Chez
VP: Anne Kelly-Banks
VP: Wayne Richard
Exec: Susan Lesniak
Assoc Dir: Yukiko Roberts

D-U-N-S 36-447-0583 IMP
NEWEDGE USA LLC
45 Rockefeller Plz # 600, New York, NY 10111-0100
Tel (646) 557-2720 *Founded/Ownrshp* 2011
Sales NA *EMP* 353
SIC 6221 Futures brokers & dealers, commodity

D-U-N-S 16-966-9616 IMP/EXP
NEWEGG INC
NEWEGG.COM
17560 Rowland St, City of Industry, CA 91748-1114
Tel (626) 271-9700 *Founded/Ownrshp* 2005
Sales 2.5MMM *EMP* 1,072
SIC 5734 Computer & software stores; Computer peripheral equipment; Computer & software stores; Computer peripheral equipment
CEO: Danny Lee
V Ch: Fred Chang
Pr: Bob Bellack
COO: Edison Chih
COO: James Wu
CFO: Robert Chang
CFO: David King
Bd of Dir: Thomas Chia
Ofcr: Soren A Mills
Ex VP: Craig Hayes
Ex VP: Shih C Lee
VP: Ron L Bester
VP: Chung Patrick
VP: Howard Tong
Exec: Nion Cao
Exec: Rick Quiroga

NEWEGG.COM
See NEWEGG INC

NEWELL EQUIPMENT
See COLUMBIA TRAILER CO INC

D-U-N-S 11-672-1668
■ **NEWELL INVESTMENTS INC**
(*Suby of* NEWELL RUBBERMAID INC) ★
29 E Stephenson St, Freeport, IL 61032-4235
Tel (815) 235-4171 *Founded/Ownrshp* 1991
Sales 33.4MM^E *EMP* 62^E
SIC 6719 Personal holding companies, except banks
Pr: Joseph Galli Jr

D-U-N-S 10-735-7485 EXP
NEWELL MACHINERY CO INC
NMC
1405 Mitchell Dr, Hiawatha, IA 52233-2102
Tel (319) 393-1610 *Founded/Ownrshp* 1986
Sales 30.9MM^E *EMP* 100
SIC 1796 3535 Millwright; Conveyors & conveying equipment; Millwright; Conveyors & conveying equipment
Pr: Timothy K Grissel
* *Exec:* Greg Mulherin
VP Opers: Jason Walker
Sfty Mgr: Cheryl Wise

D-U-N-S 00-523-8183 IMP/EXP
■ **NEWELL OPERATING CO**
(*Suby of* NEWELL RUBBERMAID INC) ★
29 E Stephenson St, Freeport, IL 61032-4235
Tel (815) 235-4171 *Founded/Ownrshp* 1903
Sales 743.6MM^E *EMP* 9,800
SIC 3365 3991 3089 2591 3965 3596 Cooking/kitchen utensils, cast aluminum; Paint rollers; Paint brushes; Trays, plastic; Shade, curtain & drapery hardware; Shade pulls, window; Window shade rollers & fittings; Needles, hand or machine; Hooks, crochet; Bathroom scales; Cooking/kitchen utensils, cast aluminum; Paint rollers; Paint brushes; Trays, plastic; Shade, curtain & drapery hardware; Shade pulls, window; Window shade rollers & fittings; Needles, hand or machine; Hooks, crochet; Bathroom scales
Pr: Mark D Ketchum
* *Pr:* William A Burke III
CFO: Danniel Connel
* *VP:* Dale L Matschullat
Sls Mgr: Jesus Cital

NEWELL PAPER CO OF COLUMBUS
See JACKSON PAPER CO

D-U-N-S 82-927-3650
NEWELL RECYCLING LLC
1359 Central Ave, East Point, GA 30344-4946
Tel (404) 766-1621 *Founded/Ownrshp* 2014
Sales 69.3MM^E *EMP* 367^E
SIC 7389 Scrap steel cutting
* *VP:* Bobby Triesch
VP: Andy Wahl
Sfty Mgr: Diana Maldonado

D-U-N-S 96-921-4782 EXP
NEWELL RECYCLING OF ATLANTA LLC
1359 Central Ave, Atlanta, GA 30344-4946
Tel (404) 766-1621 *Founded/Ownrshp* 2014
Sales 129.2MM^E *EMP* 240
SIC 4953

D-U-N-S 07-953-0231
NEWELL RECYCLING OF GEORGIA LLC (GA)
1359 Central Ave, East Point, GA 30344-4946
Tel (404) 766-1621 *Founded/Ownrshp* 2014
Sales 84.1MM^E *EMP* 163^E
SIC 4953 Recycling, waste materials
CEO: Sharon Newell Shirley
Pr: Chip Shirley
CFO: Bob Ward
VP: Joe Carrico
VP: Michael Neuser
VP: Andy Wahl
VP Opers: Bobby Triesch
VP Mktg: Frank Goulding

D-U-N-S 07-953-0219
NEWELL RECYCLING SOUTHEAST LLC
(*Suby of* NEWELL RECYCLING OF GEORGIA LLC) ★
1359 Central Ave, East Point, GA 30344-4946
Tel (404) 766-1621 *Founded/Ownrshp* 2014
Sales 84.1MM^E *EMP* 154^E
SIC 4953 Recycling, waste materials
CEO: Sharon Newell Shirley
Pr: Chip Shirley
CFO: Bob Ward
VP: Joe Carrico
VP: Michael Neuser
VP: Andy Wahl
VP Opers: Bobby Triesch
VP Mktg: Frank Goulding

D-U-N-S 00-585-6299
NEWELL ROAD BUILDERS INC (AL)
13266 Us Highway 31, Hope Hull, AL 36043-5027
Tel (334) 288-2702 *Founded/Ownrshp* 1956
Sales 21.5MM^E *EMP* 150
SIC 1611 General contractor, highway & street construction; General contractor, highway & street construction
Pr: Lee Newell
* *Pr:* Lee Newel

D-U-N-S 00-506-7574 EXP
■ **NEWELL RUBBERMAID INC**
SANFORD NORTH AMERICA
(*Suby of* NEWELL RUBBERMAID INC) ★
2707 Butterfield Rd # 100, Oak Brook, IL 60523-1267
Tel (770) 418-7000 *Founded/Ownrshp* 1992
Sales 387.8MM^E *EMP* 2,425
SIC 2891 3951 3952 Adhesives; Pens & mechanical pencils; Lead pencils & art goods; Embossing seals & hand stamps; Adhesives; Pens & mechanical pencils; Lead pencils & art goods
Pt: Ben Gadbois
VP: Rusty Snow
Prgrm Mgr: David Dylkiewicz
Genl Mgr: Debra Svennizik
VP Sls: Maureen Wolthuis
Mktg Mgr: Michael Larmon
Sales Asso: Leslie Hoalt

D-U-N-S 16-140-3852 IMP
▲ **NEWELL RUBBERMAID INC**
3 Glenlake Pkwy, Atlanta, GA 30328-3447
Tel (770) 418-7000 *Founded/Ownrshp* 1903
Sales 5.7MMM *EMP* 17,400
Accts Ernst & Young Llp Atlanta Ge
Tkr Sym NWL *Exch* NYS
SIC 3089 3469 2591 3951 3999 3546 Plastic kitchenware, tableware & houseware; Household cooking & kitchen utensils, porcelain enameled; Household cooking & kitchen utensils, metal; Drapery hardware & blinds & shades; Pens & mechanical pencils; Markers, soft tip (felt, fabric, plastic, etc.); Hair & hair-based products; Combs, except hard rubber; Power-driven handtools; Plastic kitchenware, tableware & houseware; Household cooking & kitchen utensils, porcelain enameled; Household cooking & kitchen utensils, metal; Drapery hardware & blinds & shades; Pens & mechanical pencils; Markers, soft tip (felt, fabric, plastic, etc.); Hair & hair-based products; Power-driven handtools
Pr: Michael B Polk
Ch Bd: Michael T Cowhig
Pr: Jeffrey E Cooley
Pr: Shaun Holliday
Pr: Timothy J Jahnke
Pr: Ray Johnson
Pr: David A Klatt
Pr: David L Lumley
Pr: Magnus Nicolin
Pr: Robert S Parker
Pr: David Walsh
COO: William A Burke
CFO: John K Stipancich
Ofcr: Paula S Larson
Ex VP: Mark S Tarchetti
Sr VP: Hiroko Koide
VP: Mike Mangiaracina
VP: Michael Peterson
Board of Directors: Raymond G Viault, Thomas E Clarke, Kevin C Conroy, Scott S Cowen, Domenico De Sole, Jose Ignacio Perez-Lizaur, Cynthia A Montgomery, Christopher D O'leary, Steven J Strobel, Michael A Todman

D-U-N-S 79-286-9687 IMP
NEWELL SOUTH LLC
BLAZE RECYCLING & METALS
(*Suby of* NEWELL RECYCLING SOUTHEAST LLC) ★
1359 Central Ave, Atlanta, GA 30344-4946
Tel (770) 447-0175 *Founded/Ownrshp* 2014
Sales 84.1MM^E *EMP* 198^E
SIC 5093 Metal scrap & waste materials; Metal scrap & waste materials
CEO: Cary Grossman
* *Prin:* Nicholas Rueter

D-U-N-S 88-315-1037 IMP
■ **NEWELL WINDOW FURNISHINGS INC**
(*Suby of* NEWELL RUBBERMAID INC) ★
3 Glenlake Pkwy, Atlanta, GA 30328-3447
Tel (770) 418-7000 *Founded/Ownrshp* 1994
Sales 52.8MM^E *EMP* 390
SIC 2591 Window blinds; Blinds vertical; Window blinds; Blinds vertical
CEO: Michael B Polk
* *Pr:* Jeff Heoler
* *COO:* William A Burke III
* *CFO:* Douglas L Martin
VP: Mark Carroll
VP: Jim Morando
VP: Craig York
Area Mgr: Stefani Goosic

D-U-N-S 00-777-4664 IMP/EXP
NEWESCO INC (GA)
NELSON WESTERBERG
1500 Arthur Ave Ste 200, Elk Grove Village, IL 60007-5744
Tel (847) 437-7050 *Founded/Ownrshp* 1904
Sales 67.1MM^E *EMP* 400
Accts Rockoff Harlan Rasof Ltd
SIC 4213 4214 Household goods transport; Household goods moving & storage, local; Household goods transport; Household goods moving & storage, local
Ch Bd: John R Westerberg
* *Pr:* Edward J Pionke
* *CFO:* Lawrence Cap
Sr VP: Natalie Nisivaco
VP: James Kanik
Exec: Lou REO
Genl Mgr: Jay Shawron
Genl Mgr: Nelson Westerberg
IT Man: Jeff Beaumont
Sales Exec: Tom Philbin
* *VP Sls:* Greg Koehlinger

D-U-N-S 87-933-5883
NEWFIELD BANCORP INC
NEWFIELD NATIONAL BANK
18 S West Blvd, Newfield, NJ 08344-9558
Tel (856) 692-3440 *Founded/Ownrshp* 1934
Sales NA *EMP* 150
SIC 6712 Bank holding companies; Bank holding companies
Pr: John Borelli Jr
* *Ch Bd:* Ronald Cunningham
* *Ex VP:* Joseph J Biegaliski Jr
* *Sr VP:* Martin Mastro

D-U-N-S 06-066-8837
NEWFIELD CONSTRUCTION INC (CT)
225 Newfield Ave, Hartford, CT 06106-3635
Tel (860) 953-1477 *Founded/Ownrshp* 1976
Sales 83.9MM *EMP* 50
Accts Whittlesey & Hadley Pc Har
SIC 1541 1542 Industrial buildings, new construction; Renovation, remodeling & repairs: industrial buildings; Commercial & office building, new construction; Commercial & office buildings, renovation & repair; Industrial buildings, new construction; Renovation, remodeling & repairs: industrial buildings; Commercial & office building, new construction; Commercial & office buildings, renovation & repair
Pr: Damien T Davis
* *VP:* Paul W Davis

D-U-N-S 19-706-7267 IMP
▲ **NEWFIELD EXPLORATION CO**
4 Waterway Square Pl # 100, The Woodlands, TX 77380-2764
Tel (281) 210-5100 *Founded/Ownrshp* 1988
Sales 2.2MMM *EMP* 1,331
Tkr Sym NFX *Exch* NYS
SIC 1311 Crude petroleum production; Natural gas production; Crude petroleum production; Natural gas production
Ch Bd: Lee K Boothby
COO: Gary D Packer
CFO: Lawrence S Massaro
Treas: Vilma Segove
Sr VP: George T Dunn
Exec: Shareena Yunus
CTO: John Carroll
Dir IT: Sherrell Berstein
Dir IT: Sean Stevens
IT Man: MO Taing
Prd Mgr: Chua Kuan
Board of Directors: Pamela J Gardner, John Randolph Kemp III, Steven W Nance, Roger B Plank, Thomas G Ricks, Juanita F Romans, John W Schanck, J Terry Strange, James Kent Wells

D-U-N-S 12-237-5892
■ **NEWFIELD EXPLORATION GULF COAST INC**
(*Suby of* NEWFIELD EXPLORATION CO) ★
363 N Sam Houston Pkwy E # 2020, Houston, TX 77060-2421
Tel (713) 243-3100 *Founded/Ownrshp* 2002
Sales 47.9MM^E *EMP* 1,500
SIC 1311 Crude petroleum production; Natural gas production
Ch Bd: Thomas M Hamilton
* *Pr:* Lee K Boothby
* *COO:* David R Henderson
* *CFO:* Richard S Langdon
* *Treas:* Susan G Riggs
* *Ex VP:* Larry S Massaro
* *Ex VP:* Gary D Packer
* *Sr VP:* George T Dunn
VP: Tracey E Coats

D-U-N-S 02-080-2802
■ **NEWFIELD EXPLORATION MID-CONTINENT INC**
(*Suby of* NEWFIELD EXPLORATION CO) ★
101 E 2nd St, Tulsa, OK 74103
Tel (918) 582-2690 *Founded/Ownrshp* 2001
Sales 190.9MM^E *EMP* 327
SIC 1311 Crude petroleum production; Natural gas production; Crude petroleum production; Natural gas production
CEO: Lee K Boothby
* *Ex VP:* Larry S Massaro
* *Ex VP:* Gary D Packer
* *Ex VP:* Terry W Rathert
* *Sr VP:* George T Dunn
VP: Steve Campbell
Sfty Mgr: Jason Nace
Board of Directors: Lee K Boothby

NEWFIELD NATIONAL BANK
See NEWFIELD BANCORP INC

D-U-N-S 01-409-8792
NEWFIELD NATIONAL BANK
(*Suby of* NEWFIELD BANCORP INC) ★
18 S West Blvd, Newfield, NJ 08344-9558
Tel (856) 692-3440 *Founded/Ownrshp* 1934
Sales NA *EMP* 100
SIC 6021 National commercial banks; National commercial banks
Pr: John Borelli Jr
COO: Kathleen Valla
CFO: Joanne Barsuglia
Ex VP: Biegalski Joseph
Sr VP: Peter Capizola
Sr VP: Mark Mastro
VP: Tracy Asselta
VP: James Bilderback
VP: Michael Flem
Brnch Mgr: Patricia Sample
Sls&Mrk Ex: Michelle Sterchelle

D-U-N-S 08-836-2330
■ **NEWFIELD PRODUCTION CO**
(*Suby of* NEWFIELD EXPLORATION CO) ★
1001 17th St Ste 2000, Denver, CO 80202-2035
Tel (303) 893-0102 *Founded/Ownrshp* 2004
Sales 171.5MM^E *EMP* 486^E

SIC 1311 Crude petroleum & natural gas; Crude petroleum & natural gas
CEO: Lee K Boothby
**Pr:* Stephen C Campbell
**Pr:* Daryll T Howard
**COO:* Gary D Packer
**CFO:* Larry S Massaro
**Ex VP:* Terry W Rathert
**Sr VP:* George T Dunn
VP: William War
Counsel: Andrew Bremner
Board of Directors: Lee K Boothby

D-U-N-S 00-894-8085
NEWFIRST NATIONAL BANK
202 E Jackson St, El Campo, TX 77437-4414
Tel (979) 543-3349 *Founded/Ownrshp* 1902
Sales NA *EMP* 95
SIC 6021 National commercial banks; National commercial banks
Pr: Guy Stovall
**CFO:* Wayne Crawford
CFO: Chris Garza
**Ex VP:* Jane Blaha
**Sr VP:* Charles R Collins
**VP:* Kathy Bartosh
VP: Ann Hopkins
VP: Jane Priesmeyer
VP: Ross Russell
**VP:* Brenda Steelman
VP: Linda Stovall

D-U-N-S 02-296-8317
NEWFOLDEN CO OP ELEVATOR ASSOCIATION
243 Railroad St, Newfolden, MN 56738
Tel (218) 874-7465 *Founded/Ownrshp* 1912
Sales 32.9MM *EMP* 10
Accts Erickson & Associates Ltd F
SIC 5153 Grain elevators; Grain elevators
Genl Mgr: Clyde Fering

D-U-N-S 17-275-7382
NEWFORMA INC
1750 Elm St Fl 10, Manchester, NH 03104-2907
Tel (603) 625-6212 *Founded/Ownrshp* 2003
Sales 22.9MM[E] *EMP* 100
SIC 7371 Computer software development & applications
CEO: Ian Howell
CFO: Raymond Dezenzo
CFO: Barbara Labonte
Ofcr: Alan C Facey
Ofcr: Allen Preger
Ex VP: Bob Batcheler
Ex VP: David Plunkett
VP: Chad Ames
VP: Dan Conery
VP: Marni Hoyle
VP: Allen Patrick
VP: Alexandre Tartas
VP: Shari Zedeck
VP Bus Dev: Francois Tanguay
Board of Directors: Jim Baum, Joseph E Esposito, Norbert W Young Jr

D-U-N-S 09-552-0896
NEWFOUND AREA SCHOOL DISTRICT
20 N Main St, Bristol, NH 03222-3512
Tel (603) 744-5555 *Founded/Ownrshp* 1964
Sales 23.0MM *EMP* 300
Accts Ron L Beaulieu & Company Por
SIC 8211 Public elementary & secondary schools; Public elementary & secondary schools
Dir IT: Kristin Paterson
Schl Brd P: Ruby Hill

D-U-N-S 96-343-7418
■ NEWGISTICS INC
(*Suby of* LITTLEJOHN & CO LLC) ★
2700 Via Fortuna Ste 300, Austin, TX 78746-7996
Tel (512) 225-6000 *Founded/Ownrshp* 2013
Sales 137.5MM[E] *EMP* 479
SIC 4731 Freight transportation arrangement; Freight transportation arrangement
CEO: William Razzouk
Pr: Brandie Clevenger
COO: Trent Brown
COO: Todd Everett
CFO: Michael Twomey
Ofcr: Sabina Szymura
Sr VP: Ken Johnson
Sr VP: Benoit Robinot
Sr VP: Edward Stashluk
VP: Elizabeth Hunter
VP: Mike Stevens
Exec: Richard Baun
Exec: Paul Gates
Board of Directors: Robert Rosenblatt, Andrea Weiss

D-U-N-S 61-950-2784
NEWGROUND RESOURCES INC
BANK BUILDING
15450 South Outer 40 Rd # 300, Chesterfield, MO 63017-2066
Tel (314) 821-2265 *Founded/Ownrshp* 1976
Sales 78.0MM[E] *EMP* 115
SIC 1542 8712 Bank building construction; Architectural services; Bank building construction; Architectural services
CEO: Kevin Blair
**Ch Bd:* John T Golitz
**Ch Bd:* Ted Golitz
**CFO:* Skip Zaegel
**Treas:* Charles J Zaegel
Ex VP: James Kueneke
**Sr VP:* Tom Auer
Sr VP: Gordon Baker
**Sr VP:* Steve Clark
**Sr VP:* Robert E Mannion
VP: Rob Reis
VP: Barry Theobald
VP: Bruce Wolferding

D-U-N-S 00-470-0620
NEWHALL HOLDING CO LLC
25124 Springfield Ct, Valencia, CA 91355-1085
Tel (661) 255-4000 *Founded/Ownrshp* 2009
Sales 34.5MM[E] *EMP* 55
SIC 6719 Personal holding companies, except banks
Pr: Greg H McWilliams
**Ex VP:* Donald L Kimball
**Sr VP:* James C Bizzelle

D-U-N-S 09-641-9627
NEWHALL SCHOOL DISTRICT (CA)
25375 Orchard Village Rd # 200, Valencia, CA 91355-3000
Tel (661) 291-4000 *Founded/Ownrshp* 1878
Sales 30.1MM[E] *EMP* 516
Accts Vavrinek Trine Day & Co Ll
SIC 8211 Elementary school; Elementary school

D-U-N-S 95-942-5240
NEWICKS HOSPITALITY GROUP INC
431 Dover Point Rd, Dover, NH 03820-9123
Tel (603) 742-3235 *Founded/Ownrshp* 1987
Sales 11.8MM[E] *EMP* 350
SIC 5812 Seafood restaurants; Seafood restaurants
Pr: John F Newick
Board of Directors: Marie Ann

D-U-N-S 01-365-6251
NEWINS BAY SHORE FORD INC
219 W Main St, Bay Shore, NY 11706-8380
Tel (631) 665-1300 *Founded/Ownrshp* 1959
Sales 41.0MM *EMP* 75
SIC 5511 Automobiles, new & used; Pickups, new & used; Vans, new & used; Automobiles, new & used; Pickups, new & used; Vans, new & used
Pr: Charles J Stickney
**VP:* Christopher Stickney
Off Mgr: Sue Sandvik
Sls Mgr: Bryan Blanco
Sls Mgr: Phil Calabretta
Sales Asso: Chris Belesi

D-U-N-S 60-943-3255
NEWJAC INC
415 S Grant St, Lebanon, IN 46052-3605
Tel (765) 483-2190 *Founded/Ownrshp* 1990
Sales 31.9MM[E] *EMP* 100
SIC 3399 Iron ore recovery from open hearth slag; Iron ore recovery from open hearth slag
Pr: Loren Gard
**Treas:* Derrick Hutson
VP: Tony Haag
**VP:* Barry Newton
Sales Exec: R A McIntosh

D-U-N-S 01-727-1313 IMP
NEWKIRK ELECTRIC ASSOCIATES INC
1875 Roberts St, Muskegon, MI 49442-6094
Tel (231) 722-1691 *Founded/Ownrshp* 1972
Sales 88.3MM *EMP* 400
Accts Rehman Robson Llc Muskegon M
SIC 1731 1629 8711 Electrical work; Power plant construction; Engineering services; Electrical work; Power plant construction; Engineering services
Pr: Theodore Anton
**VP:* Jim Anton
Exec: Pam Porter
Sfty Dirs: Curt Cusack
Sfty Dirs: Melissa Dunham
Sfty Mgr: Randy Milam

D-U-N-S 02-436-3517
NEWKIRK HOLDING CO INC (SD)
ACE HARDWARE
320 West Blvd, Rapid City, SD 57701-2671
Tel (605) 342-4840 *Founded/Ownrshp* 1928, 1978
Sales 83.4MM[E] *EMP* 500
SIC 5211 5251 Lumber & other building materials; Hardware; Lumber & other building materials; Hardware
Ch Bd: Robert Mead
**Pr:* Craig Bradshaw
Genl Mgr: Wallace Bork
Genl Mgr: Bryan Rice

D-U-N-S 06-519-5471
■ NEWKIRK PRODUCTS INC
(*Suby of* DST SYSTEMS INC) ★
15 Corporate Cir, Albany, NY 12203-5177
Tel (518) 862-3200 *Founded/Ownrshp* 2011
Sales 27.4MM[E] *EMP* 270
SIC 2731 Pamphlets: publishing & printing; Pamphlets: publishing & printing
CEO: Raymond Newkirk
**Pr:* Peter Newkirk
**CFO:* John J Graham
VP: Louise Foote
VP: James B Salada
**CIO:* Dennis Donohue

D-U-N-S 12-874-9855
NEWLAND MANAGEMENT LLC
MCDONALD'S
5741 Cleveland St Ste 180, Virginia Beach, VA 23462-1777
Tel (757) 468-6300 *Founded/Ownrshp* 2002
Sales 8.2MM[E] *EMP* 300
SIC 5812 Fast-food restaurant, chain; Fast-food restaurant, chain

D-U-N-S 83-877-4396
NEWLAND REAL ESTATE GROUP LLC
(*Suby of* AMERICAN NEWLAND COMMUNITIES LP) ★
4790 Eastgate Mall 150, San Diego, CA 92121-1970
Tel (858) 455-7503 *Founded/Ownrshp* 2000
Sales 68.7MM[E] *EMP* 270[E]
SIC 6282 6552 Investment advice; Subdividers & developers; Investment advice; Subdividers & developers
Pr: Robert B McLeod
Treas: Darlynn Burke
Chf Mktg O: Teri Slavik-Tsuyuki
VP: James Delhamer
**VP:* Douglas L Hageman
**VP:* Vicki R Mullins
**VP:* Daniel C Van Epp
**VP:* Noel C Webb
Off Mgr: Gaye McCalip
CIO: Zachary Britton

D-U-N-S 01-066-4329
▲ NEWLINK GENETICS CORP
2503 S Loop Dr Ste 5100, Ames, IA 50010-8641
Tel (515) 296-5555 *Founded/Ownrshp* 1999
Sales 172.5MM *EMP* 104[E]
Accts Kpmg Llp Des Moines Iowa
Tkr Sym NLNK *Exch* NGM
SIC 2834 8731 Pharmaceutical preparations; Biological research
Ch Bd: Charles J Link Jr
COO: Thomas P Monath
CFO: John B Henneman III
Chf Mktg O: Nicholas N Vahanian
VP: Eugene P Kennedy
VP: Brian Wiley
Board of Directors: Paul R Edick, Paolo Pucci, Thomas A Raffin, Joseph Saluri, Ernest J Talarico III, Nicholas Vahanian

D-U-N-S 04-623-8325
NEWLONBRO LLC
CONNECTICUT'S OWN VOLVO
915 Boston Post Rd, Milford, CT 06460-3500
Tel (203) 877-0311 *Founded/Ownrshp* 1997
Sales 34.4MM[E] *EMP* 65
SIC 5511 Automobiles, new & used; Pickups, new & used; Automobiles, new & used; Pickups, new & used
Sls Mgr: Liza Herringshaw
Sales Asso: Julian Gangemi

D-U-N-S 00-514-3987 IMP/EXP
NEWLY WEDS FOODS INC
4140 W Fullerton Ave, Chicago, IL 60639-2198
Tel (773) 489-7000 *Founded/Ownrshp* 1932
Sales 2.0MM *EMP* 3,100
SIC 2099 Bread crumbs, not made in bakeries; Sugar powdered from purchased ingredients; Seasonings & spices; Bread crumbs, not made in bakeries; Sugar powdered from purchased ingredients; Seasonings & spices
CFO: Brian Johnson
**Pr:* Charles T Angell
**Sr VP:* John J Seely
**VP:* Sharon Angell
VP: Leo Culligan
VP: Donald Harr
VP: Mike Hopp
VP: Bruce Leshinski
VP: Helen Mendoza
Genl Mgr: Jack Conway
Off Admin: Jessica Martinez

D-U-N-S 00-228-0626 IMP/EXP
NEWMAN & CO INC
6101 Tacony St, Philadelphia, PA 19135-2998
Tel (215) 333-8700 *Founded/Ownrshp* 1919
Sales 59.4MM[E] *EMP* 150
SIC 2631 Paperboard mills; Paperboard mills
Ch Bd: Bernard Newman
Pr: Fred Herman
CFO: Lee D Cohen
Genl Mgr: David Newman
MIS Dir: Robert Bennet
Sfty Mgr: Steve Whitney
Prd Mgr: Joseph Partito
Snr Mgr: Chuck Ott
Board of Directors: Lynne Ferman

D-U-N-S 04-705-9191
NEWMAN ASSOCIATES INC
80 Hudson Rd Ste 200, Canton, MA 02021-1416
Tel (781) 329-4000 *Founded/Ownrshp* 1959
Sales 24.9MM[E] *EMP* 32
SIC 5074 Plumbing fittings & supplies
Pr: Henry D Newman III
**CFO:* Al Bourre
**VP:* Brian G Ray
**VP:* Richard Tamulionis
Sales Asso: Brian Brown

D-U-N-S 01-864-9038
NEWMAN CHEVROLET INC
460 Connecticut Blvd, East Hartford, CT 06108-3077
Tel (860) 528-1554 *Founded/Ownrshp* 1990
Sales 30.0MM *EMP* 53
SIC 5511 Automobiles, new & used; Automobiles, new & used
Pr: Robert Newman
**Sec:* Bill Newman

D-U-N-S 02-317-9864
NEWMAN CHEVROLET OLDSMOBILE GEO INC
NEWMAN OLDSMOBILE
1181 Wauwatosa Rd, Cedarburg, WI 53012-8902
Tel (262) 377-3020 *Founded/Ownrshp* 1978
Sales 21.6MM[E] *EMP* 52
SIC 5511 Automobiles, new & used
Pr: Gary Newman
**Sec:* Rebecca J Freitag
Exec: Dan Drinkwine
Sales Exec: Rich Warner
Mktg Mgr: Adam Buettner
Sales Asso: Matt Ratkowski
Sales Asso: James Spors
Sales Asso: Donald Wright

D-U-N-S 07-308-7058
NEWMAN CONSTRUCTION INC
13331 S Redwood Rd, Riverton, UT 84065-6109
Tel (801) 254-3524 *Founded/Ownrshp* 1953
Sales 23.9MM[E] *EMP* 70
SIC 1794 1629 Excavation & grading, building construction; Earthmoving contractor
Pr: William Mark Newman
**Treas:* Jeff Newman
**VP:* John Davis

NEWMAN ELEMENTARY SCHOOL
See NEEDHAM PUBLIC SCHOOLS

NEWMAN EQUIPMENT REPAIR
See DEKALB MECHANICAL INC

D-U-N-S 94-422-5333 IMP
NEWMAN INTERNATIONAL INC
NEWMAN SANITARY GASKET
964 W Main St, Lebanon, OH 45036-9173
Tel (513) 932-7379 *Founded/Ownrshp* 1988
Sales 22.7MM[E] *EMP* 52[E]
SIC 5085 Gaskets
Pr: Thomas C Moore
**VP:* David Wj Newman

D-U-N-S 03-331-7785 IMP
NEWMAN LUMBER CO
11367 Reichold Rd, Gulfport, MS 39503-6022
Tel (228) 604-2178 *Founded/Ownrshp* 1947
Sales 108.8MM[E] *EMP* 800
SIC 5031 Lumber: rough, dressed & finished; Lumber: rough, dressed & finished
Pr: Dug Newman
**CEO:* Cynthia N Bergin
**CFO:* Roianne Gutierrez
Treas: N Gutierrez
**VP:* Douglas Newman

D-U-N-S 07-302-3939
NEWMAN MEMORIAL HOSPITAL FOUNDATION
NEWMAN REGIONAL HEALTH
1201 W 12th Ave, Emporia, KS 66801-2504
Tel (620) 343-6800 *Founded/Ownrshp* 1955
Sales 81.1MM[E] *EMP* 575
Accts Wendling Noe Nelson Johnson Ll
SIC 8062 5047 8011 Hospital, medical school affiliated with nursing & residency; Medical & hospital equipment; Hospital equipment & supplies; Clinic, operated by physicians; Hospital, medical school affiliated with nursing & residency; Medical & hospital equipment; Hospital equipment & supplies; Clinic, operated by physicians
CEO: John Rossfeld
Dir Vol: Kristi Nichols
Ch Bd: Deanne Korsak
**CFO:* Holly French
**Treas:* William O Barnes
Bd of Dir: Jodi Heermann
Dir OR: Heather Arndt
Dir Inf Cn: Linda Crook
Dir Lab: Barb Haag
Dir Rad: Jim Crump
Chf Nrs Of: Denisa Ketterman

NEWMAN OLDSMOBILE
See NEWMAN CHEVROLET OLDSMOBILE GEO INC

NEWMAN REGIONAL HEALTH
See NEWMAN MEMORIAL HOSPITAL FOUNDATION

NEWMAN SANITARY GASKET
See NEWMAN INTERNATIONAL INC

D-U-N-S 61-426-4752 IMP
NEWMAN TECHNOLOGY INC
(*Suby of* SANKEI GIKEN CO.,LTD.)
100 Cairns Rd, Mansfield, OH 44903-8990
Tel (419) 525-1856 *Founded/Ownrshp* 1987
Sales 228.8MM[E] *EMP* 1,200
SIC 3714 3751 Motor vehicle parts & accessories; Mufflers (exhaust), motor vehicle; Motorcycle accessories; Motor vehicle parts & accessories; Mufflers (exhaust), motor vehicle; Motorcycle accessories
Pr: Shigeyuki Handa
**Ex VP:* Yukihisa Murata
**Sr VP:* Dick Pacelli
**Sr VP:* Stephen Rourke
CIO: Luke Abrams
Prd Mgr: Rusty Gilbert
Ql Cn Mgr: Thomas Bader
Ql Cn Mgr: Mike Blevins
Ql Cn Mgr: Paul Harper
Ql Cn Mgr: Clay Smith
Snr Mgr: Tim Berry

D-U-N-S 00-697-1787 IMP
NEWMAN TECHNOLOGY SOUTH CAROLINA INC
(*Suby of* SANKEI GIKEN CO.,LTD.)
450 Ab Miles Dr, Aiken, SC 29805-8012
Tel (803) 502-1250 *Founded/Ownrshp* 1999
Sales 37.0MM[E] *EMP* 140
SIC 3714 3751 Motor vehicle parts & accessories; Mufflers (exhaust), motor vehicle; Motorcycle accessories; Motor vehicle parts & accessories; Mufflers (exhaust), motor vehicle; Motorcycle accessories
Pr: Nobuo Tanifuji
**Sec:* Noriyoshi Asami
IT Man: Jason Johnson

D-U-N-S 04-360-0535
NEWMAN UNIVERSITY INC
3100 W Mccormick St, Wichita, KS 67213-2008
Tel (316) 942-4291 *Founded/Ownrshp* 1952
Sales 44.6MM *EMP* 310
SIC 8221 College, except junior; College, except junior
Pr: Dr Noreen Karochi
Bd of Dir: J Johnston
VP: Michael Austin
VP: Mark Dresselhaus
VP: Harry Pape
CTO: Billy Bledsoe
Dir IT: Linda Unrein
IT Man: Shelly Small
Mktg Dir: David Shubert
Nrsg Dir: Ron Shipley

NEWMANS
See NEWCO VALVES LLC

D-U-N-S 01-139-1345
NEWMANS OWN FOUNDATION
790 Farmington Ave Ste 1, Farmington, CT 06032-2318
Tel (860) 284-4200 *Founded/Ownrshp* 2007
Sales 38.3MM *EMP* 3
SIC 8641 Civic social & fraternal associations; Civic social & fraternal associations
Prin: Thomas Witherspoon

D-U-N-S 10-235-6888
NEWMAR CORP
355 Delaware St, Nappanee, IN 46550-9453
Tel (574) 773-7791 Founded/Ownrshp 1968
Sales 290.7MM^E EMP 1,840
SIC 3716 3792 Motor homes; Travel trailers & campers; Motor homes; Travel trailers & campers
Pr: Mahlon Miller
*VP: Mahlon A Miller
VP: Michael O'Connell
VP: Phil Stilley
Exec: Barbara Barnett
*Prin: Richard Parks
Dir IT: Kevin Bogan
IT Man: Todd Martin
Sfty Dirs: Dennis Ramer
Plnt Mgr: Todd Beachy
Plnt Mgr: Chris Gray

D-U-N-S 07-684-9009
■ NEWMARK & CO REAL ESTATE INC
NEWMARK GRUBB KNIGHT FRANK
(Suby of BGC PARTNERS INC) ★
125 Park Ave, New York, NY 10017-5529
Tel (212) 372-2000 Founded/Ownrshp 2011
Sales 421.0MM^E EMP 2,250
SIC 6531 Real estate brokers & agents; Real estate brokers & agents
CEO: Barry M Gosin
Pr: David A Falk
*Pr: James D Kuhn
Pr: Carol Miles
*COO: Joseph I Rader
COO: Joseph Rader
*CFO: Michael J Rispoli
*Ch: Jeffrey R Gural
Bd of Dir: Tom McChesney
Assoc VP: Mark Gleason
Ex VP: Michael Sheinkop
Assoc Dir: Amir Araghi
Assoc Dir: Keith W Cade
Assoc Dir: Kate Cohen
Assoc Dir: Evan T Djikas
Assoc Dir: Kurt Gottschling
Assoc Dir: David Lipp
Assoc Dir: Karen Mankowski
Assoc Dir: Dan Marcus
Assoc Dir: Carolyn Martinez
Assoc Dir: Patrick McCoy

NEWMARK AND COMPANY RE
See 53RD STREET ASSOCIATION INC

NEWMARK CORNISH & CAREY
See CORNISH & CAREY COMMERCIAL INC

NEWMARK GRUBB KNIGHT FRANK
See NEWMARK & CO REAL ESTATE INC

D-U-N-S 13-001-1336 EXP
NEWMARK HOMES LP
1470 First Colony Blvd, Sugar Land, TX 77479-4084
Tel (713) 346-0200 Founded/Ownrshp 1996
Sales 41.2MM^E EMP 500^E
SIC 1522 Condominium construction; Condominium construction
CEO: Antonio B Mon

NEWMARK KNIGHT FRA
See ROSS REAL ESTATE LIMITED

D-U-N-S 15-222-7067 IMP/EXP
▲ NEWMARKET CORP
330 S 4th St, Richmond, VA 23219-4350
Tel (804) 788-5000 Founded/Ownrshp 2004
Sales 2.3MMM EMP 1,789^E
Accts Pricewaterhousecoopers Llp Ri
Tkr Sym NEU Exch NYS
SIC 2869 2899 2841 2865 Industrial organic chemicals; Chemicals & allied products; Corrosion preventive lubricant; Oil treating compounds; Soap & other detergents; Cyclic crudes & intermediates; Industrial organic chemicals; Corrosion preventive lubricant; Oil treating compounds; Soap & other detergents; Cyclic crudes & intermediates
Ch Bd: Thomas E Gottwald
CFO: Brian D Paliotti
Ofcr: Bruce R Hazelgrove III
Sr VP: Newton Perry
VP: Hazelgrove Bruce
VP: Steven M Edmonds
VP: David Fiorenza
VP: Ron Kollman
VP: Jim Leary
VP: Barbara Little
Exec: Steven Mayer
Board of Directors: Phyllis L Cothran, Mark M Gambill, Bruce C Gottwald, Patrick D Hanley, H Hiter Harris III, James E Rogers, Charles B Walker

D-U-N-S 18-198-8064
NEWMARKET INTERNATIONAL INC
(Suby of NMTI HOLDINGS INC) ★
75 Nh Ave, Portsmouth, NH 03801-2864
Tel (603) 436-7500 Founded/Ownrshp 2007
Sales 76.6MM^E EMP 380
SIC 7371 Computer software development; Computer software development
Pr: Jeff Hiscox
COO: Shawn McGowan
CFO: Gene Reardon
Ex VP: Lee Horgan
VP: Paul Barron
VP: Tim Beaulieu
VP: Alberto Santana
VP: Joanne Tiereny
Sftwr Eng: Mellissa Field
Manager: Adam Bermingham

D-U-N-S 07-159-2831
▲ NEWMARKET TECHNOLOGY INC
14860 Montfort Dr Ste 210, Dallas, TX 75254-6772
Tel (972) 386-3372 Founded/Ownrshp 1997
Sales 30.9MM^E EMP 500^E
Tkr Sym NWMT Exch OTO
SIC 7372 Prepackaged software; Prepackaged software
CEO: Bruce Noller
Pr: Aubrey Brown
Pr: Henryk Dabrowski
*CFO: Philip J Rauch
Dir Bus: John Verges

D-U-N-S 60-619-0742
NEWMEYER & DILLION LLP
895 Dove St Fl 5, Newport Beach, CA 92660-2999
Tel (949) 854-7000 Founded/Ownrshp 1984
Sales 35.7MM EMP 120
Accts Warnick Maestas & Maroney Ir
SIC 8111 General practice law office; General practice law office
Pt: Gregory L Dillion
Pt: Michael S Cucchissi
Pt: Joseph A Ferrentino
Pt: John A O Hara
Pt: Jon J Janecek
Pt: Thomas F Newmeyer
Pr: Joanne Kenney
Pr: Sue Peterson
Pr: Nakia Plummer
VP: Andi Hughes
Ex Dir: Paul Manhart

D-U-N-S 04-278-6921
■ NEWMONT GOLD CO
(Suby of NEWMONT MINING CORP) ★
6363 S Fiddlers Green Cir, Greenwood Village, CO 80111-5011
Tel (303) 863-7414 Founded/Ownrshp 2001
Sales NA EMP 3,600
SIC 1041 Gold ores mining; Gold ore milling; Gold ores mining; Gold ore milling
CEO: Gary J Goldberg
*Ch Bd: Ronald C Cambre

NEWMONT MINING
See NEWMONT USA LIMITED

D-U-N-S 00-698-8414 IMP
▲ NEWMONT MINING CORP
6363 S Fiddlers Green Cir, Greenwood Village, CO 80111-5011
Tel (303) 863-7414 Founded/Ownrshp 1921
Sales 7.2MMM EMP 13,700
Tkr Sym NEM Exch NYS
SIC 1041 1021 Gold ores mining; Gold ores processing; Copper ore milling & preparation; Gold ores mining; Gold ores processing; Copper ore milling & preparation
Pr: Gary Goldberg
Pr: Nick Cotts
COO: Dave Kerbaugh
COO: Chris Robison
CFO: Laurie Brlas
CFO: Richard Obriea
Ex VP: Russell D Ball
Ex VP: Elaine Dorward-King
Ex VP: John A S Dow
Ex VP: Randy Engel
Ex VP: Stephen P Gottesfeld
Ex VP: Guy Lansdown
Ex VP: Bill Macgowan
Sr VP: David A Baker
Sr VP: Ramzi R Fawaz
Sr VP: Jeffrey R Huspeni
Sr VP: Lawrence T Kurlander
Sr VP: Grigore Simon
VP: David V Gutierrez
VP: Christopher S Howson
VP: Christopher Howson
Board of Directors: Greg Boyce, Bruce R Brook, J Kofi Bucknor, Vincent A Calarco, Joseph A Carrabba, Noreen Doyle, Veronica M Hagen, Jane Nelson, Julio Quintana

D-U-N-S 79-146-2245
■ NEWMONT PERU LLP
(Suby of NEWMONT MINING CORP) ★
6363 S Fiddlers Green Cir, Denver, CO 80203
Tel (303) 837-5804 Founded/Ownrshp 1993
Sales 9.1MM^E EMP 500
SIC 1041 Gold ores mining; Gold ore milling; Gold ores mining; Gold ore milling
Pt: Ron Cambre

D-U-N-S 12-250-2870
■ NEWMONT USA LIMITED
NEWMONT MINING
(Suby of NEWMONT MINING CORP) ★
6363 Sout Fidd Gree Cir, Greenwood Village, CO 80111
Tel (303) 863-7414 Founded/Ownrshp 2000
Sales 57.6MM^E EMP 1,000
SIC 1041 1021 Gold ores mining; Copper ore mining & preparation; Gold ores mining; Copper ore mining & preparation
Treas: Thomas Mahoney
*CFO: Russell D Ball
Ofcr: Debbie Robinson
VP: Thomas Enos
Exec: David Grander
Dir Surg: John Gundersen
Comm Dir: Michie Ogura-Huerta
Prgrm Mgr: Alex Young
Genl Mgr: Scott Santti
CIO: John Huber

D-U-N-S 79-728-6411
NEWNAN IMPORTS INC
TOYOTA OF NEWNAN
2 Herring Rd, Newnan, GA 30265-1006
Tel (770) 502-1333 Founded/Ownrshp 2007
Sales 23.9MM^E EMP 54
SIC 5511 Automobiles, new & used
CEO: Walt Gutierrez
*CFO: Joseph D Obrien Jr
CFO: Joseph Obrien Jr
Sls Mgr: Mark Feldman

D-U-N-S 79-121-8097
NEWNAN UTILITIES
70 Sewell Rd, Newnan, GA 30263-2638
Tel (770) 683-0292 Founded/Ownrshp 1904
Sales 24.2MM^E EMP 110
SIC 4941 Water supply; Water supply
Ch: Robert L Lee
Dir IT: Troy Patterson
Prd Mgr: Randy Gilbert
Snr Mgr: Matt Anderson
Snr Mgr: Terry Brown
Snr Mgr: Jerry Crider
Snr Mgr: Rex Dunson
Snr Mgr: Kenny Gilbert
Snr Mgr: Danny Smith
Snr Mgr: Scott Wade
Snr Mgr: Chris Wheelus

D-U-N-S 01-122-6373
NEWNET COMMUNICATION TECHNOLOGIES LLC
700 E Butterfield Rd # 350, Lombard, IL 60148-6006
Tel (224) 795-5200 Founded/Ownrshp 2007
Sales 25.2MM^E EMP 58^E
SIC 7371 4813 Computer software development & applications;
CFO: Darren F Loos
*CEO: Jonathan Huberman
*Ex VP: Chris Aye
*Ex VP: Jim Hall
*Sr VP: Matt Thompson
VP: Angie Batterson
VP: Art Matteotti
VP: Sal Morlando
*VP: Carrie Murphy
Snr Sftwr: Kris Novak
S&M/VP: Rick Landry

D-U-N-S 83-692-7541 IMP
NEWONICS INC
1883 S 5070 W, Salt Lake City, UT 84104-4731
Tel (801) 886-9424 Founded/Ownrshp 2005
Sales 22.4MM^E EMP 75
SIC 3672 Printed circuit boards
Pr: Steve Sorensen

NEWPAGE
See LUKE PAPER CO

D-U-N-S 79-892-9514
NEWPAGE ENERGY SERVICES LLC
8540 Gander Creek Dr, Miamisburg, OH 45342-5439
Tel (877) 855-7243 Founded/Ownrshp 2004
Sales 228.8MM^E EMP 6,000
SIC 2672 2621 2611 Coated & laminated paper; Paper mills; Uncoated paper; Pulp mills; Coated & laminated paper; Paper mills; Uncoated paper; Pulp mills

D-U-N-S 82-619-3612
■ NEWPAGE GROUP INC
(Suby of CERBERUS CAPITAL MANAGEMENT LP) ★
8540 Gander Creek Dr, Miamisburg, OH 45342-5439
Tel (937) 242-9500 Founded/Ownrshp 2007
Sales 3.5MMM^E EMP 6,000^E
SIC 2671 Packaging paper & plastics film, coated & laminated; Packaging paper & plastics film, coated & laminated
Pr: George F Martin
*Ch: Chan W Galbato
Treas: Tim Nusbaum
Treas: Randal Spence
*Ex VP: James C Tyrone
*Sr VP: Daniel A Clark
*Sr VP: Douglas K Cooper
*Sr VP: Jay A Epstein
Exec: Randal Romberio

D-U-N-S 60-273-9877
■ NEWPAGE HOLDING CORP
(Suby of NEWPAGE GROUP INC) ★
8540 Gander Creek Dr, Miamisburg, OH 45342-5439
Tel (877) 855-7243 Founded/Ownrshp 2011
Sales 756.0MM^E EMP 6,000
SIC 2621 2672 2611 Fine paper; Coated & laminated paper; Pulp mills; Fine paper; Coated & laminated paper; Pulp mills
Pr: George F Martin
CFO: Matthew L Jesch
*CFO: David J Prystash
*Ex VP: James C Tyrone
*Sr VP: Daniel A Clark
*Sr VP: Laszlo M Lukacs
*VP: Douglas K Cooper
*VP: Jay A Epstein
*VP: David L Santez
CIO: Christine Walroth
IT Man: Jon Lafreniere
Board of Directors: Robert M Armstrong, Chan W Galbato, Ronald C Kesselman, Julian Markby, Robert L Nardelli, Lenard B Tessler, Raymond H Wechsler, Alexander M Wolf, George J Zahringer III

D-U-N-S 07-872-2065
■ NEWPAGE HOLDINGS INC
(Suby of VERSO PAPER HOLDINGS LLC) ★
8540 Gander Creek Dr, Miamisburg, OH 45342-5439
Tel (877) 855-7243 Founded/Ownrshp 2015
Sales 263.0MM^E EMP 2,000^E
SIC 2621 Paper mills; Paper mills
Pr: George F Martin
CFO: Jay A Epstein
Ofcr: Daniel A Clark
Sr VP: David L Santez
Ql Cn Mgr: Barb Bennett

D-U-N-S 07-949-1249
■ NEWPAGE INVESTMENT CO LLC
(Suby of NEWPAGE HOLDINGS INC) ★
8540 Gander Creek Dr, Miamisburg, OH 45342-5439
Tel (877) 855-7243 Founded/Ownrshp 2012
Sales 228.8MM^E EMP 6,000
SIC 2621 Fine paper; Uncoated paper; Fine paper; Uncoated paper

D-U-N-S 94-554-3770 IMP
NEWPAGE WISCONSIN SYSTEM INC
111 W Jackson St, Wisconsin Rapids, WI 54495
Tel (715) 422-3111 Founded/Ownrshp 2000
Sales NA EMP 1,200
SIC 2621 2611 2653 7011 Paper mills; Pulp mills; Corrugated & solid fiber boxes; Hotels & motels

NEWPAK PACKAGING
See CORK SUPPLY USA INC

D-U-N-S 78-436-7372
NEWPAPER LLC
PARTY CITY
422 Minnesota Ave, Breckenridge, MN 56520-1929
Tel (218) 643-8354 Founded/Ownrshp 2003
Sales 16.5MM^E EMP 300
SIC 5947 7299 Gifts & novelties; Party planning service; Gifts & novelties; Party planning service

D-U-N-S 60-660-2175 IMP
■ NEWPARK DRILLING FLUIDS LLC
NDF
(Suby of NEWPARK RESOURCES INC) ★
21920 Merchants Way, Katy, TX 77449-6834
Tel (281) 754-8600 Founded/Ownrshp 2007
Sales NA EMP 860
SIC 5169 5172 4953 Drilling mud; Petroleum products; Refuse systems; Drilling mud; Petroleum products; Refuse systems
Pr: Bruce Smith
*Sr VP: Steve Daniel
VP: Tim Armand
*VP: Joseph L Gocke
Dir IT: Larry Douglas
Software D: Siva Yenneti
Sfty Dirs: Marcus Overstreet
Opers Mgr: Gary Brown
Board of Directors: James D Cole

NEWPARK ENVIRONMENTAL MGT
See NEWPARK ENVIRONMENTAL SERVICES LLC

D-U-N-S 10-244-3363
■ NEWPARK ENVIRONMENTAL SERVICES LLC
NEWPARK ENVIRONMENTAL MGT
(Suby of NEWPARK RESOURCES INC) ★
207 Towncenter Pkwy Fl 2, Lafayette, LA 70506-7524
Tel (337) 984-4445 Founded/Ownrshp 1996
Sales 78.0MM^E EMP 173
SIC 4953 Refuse collection & disposal services; Refuse collection & disposal services
Pr: Jeffery L Juergens
*Pr: Sammi Cooper
Treas: John Dardenne
*Treas: Brian Feldott
*VP: Mike Breaux
*VP: Gregg Piontek

D-U-N-S 00-287-6977
■ NEWPARK MATS & INTEGRATED SERVICES LLC (TX)
(Suby of NEWPARK RESOURCES INC) ★
9320 Lkeside Blvd Ste 100, The Woodlands, TX 77381
Tel (281) 362-6800 Founded/Ownrshp 2007
Sales 135.4MM^E EMP 300
SIC 1389 Construction, repair & dismantling services; Excavating slush pits & cellars; Oil field services; Construction, repair & dismantling services; Excavating slush pits & cellars; Oil field services
CEO: Paul L Howes
Pr: Jeff L Juergens
CFO: Gregg Piontek
Ex VP: Bruce C Smith
Sr VP: Mark J Airola
VP: WT Ballantine
VP: Eric Wingerter
Tech Mgr: David Spencer
Opers Mgr: Brent Barnard

D-U-N-S 00-697-0982 IMP
▲ NEWPARK RESOURCES INC
9320 Lkeside Blvd Ste 100, The Woodlands, TX 77381
Tel (281) 362-6800 Founded/Ownrshp 1932
Sales 1.1MMM EMP 2,478
Accts Deloitte & Touche Llp Housto
Tkr Sym NR Exch NYS
SIC 1389 4959 4953 2273 Construction, repair & dismantling services; Excavating slush pits & cellars; Testing, measuring, surveying & analysis services; Cleaning wells; Environmental cleanup services; Non-hazardous waste disposal sites; Recycling, waste materials; Mats & matting; Construction, repair & dismantling services; Excavating slush pits & cellars; Testing, measuring, surveying & analysis services; Cleaning wells; Environmental cleanup services; Non-hazardous waste disposal sites; Recycling, waste materials; Mats & matting
Pr: Paul L Howes
Pr: William D Moss
CFO: Gregg S Piontek
Ex VP: Bruce C Smith
Sr VP: Mark J Airola
VP: Joseph Gocke
VP: Roger Hayes
VP: Frank Lyon
IT Man: Chris Hale
IT Man: Nanda Kumar
VP Sls: Steve Pierson
Board of Directors: David C Anderson, Anthony J Best, G Stephen Finley, Roderick A Larson, James W McFarland, Gary L Warren

NEWPOINT ENERGY SOLUTIONS
See STANDARD RENEWABLE ENERGY LP

D-U-N-S 07-853-8876
NEWPOINT MEDIA GROUP LLC
2305 Newpoint Pkwy, Lawrenceville, GA 30043-5530
Tel (770) 962-7220 Founded/Ownrshp 2012
Sales 35.0MM^E EMP 160
SIC 2752 Commercial printing, lithographic; Commercial printing, lithographic
VP: Jamie Correll
VP: Patrick McGroder
VP: David Vining
Prd Mgr: Andrea Fitzpatrick
Prd Mgr: Alisa Hudson
Sls Mgr: Dave Osgood

D-U-N-S 19-411-8196 IMP
NEWPORT APPAREL CORP
I N G
1215 W Walnut St, Compton, CA 90220-5009
Tel (310) 605-1900 Founded/Ownrshp 1988
Sales 34.9MM^E EMP 65
SIC 5137 Sportswear, women's & children's
Pr: James Kim

*Treas: Kimberly Kim
Genl Mgr: Susie Ahn
Genl Mgr: Yong Chung
IT Man: Esther Kim
Opers Mgr: Tony Yoo

NEWPORT AUTO CENTER
See NEWPORT BEACH CARS LLC

D-U-N-S 15-369-4534
■ NEWPORT BEACH CARS LLC
NEWPORT AUTO CENTER
(Suby of AUTONATION INC) ★
445 E Coast Hwy, Newport Beach, CA 92660-6133
Tel (949) 478-0590 Founded/Ownrshp 2006
Sales 29.5MM[E] EMP 100
SIC 5511 New & used car dealers; New & used car dealers
Div Mgr: Tim Tauber
VP: Leif Alexandersson
VP: Michael Araluce
VP: Manjit Daniel
Sls Mgr: Dan Comouche

NEWPORT BEACH SIDE RESORT
See NEWPORT HOSPITALITY LLC

D-U-N-S 92-720-1058
NEWPORT BIODIESEL INC
312 Connell Hwy, Newport, RI 02840-6005
Tel (401) 846-1117 Founded/Ownrshp 2006
Sales 22.9MM[E] EMP 20
SIC 5172 Diesel fuel
Pr: Blake Banky
Mng Pt: Chris Benzak
Mng Pt: Ed Booth
Treas: Delia Pendleton
*Prin: Nathaniel G Harris

NEWPORT BOATS
See RENIX CORP

NEWPORT BRASS
See BRASSTECH INC

D-U-N-S 13-580-1467 IMP/EXP
NEWPORT CH INTERNATIONAL LLC
1100 W Town And Country R, Orange, CA 92868-4662
Tel (714) 572-8881 Founded/Ownrshp 2003
Sales 257.3MM EMP 50
Accts Jkl Rosenberger Llp Irvine
SIC 5093 Waste paper; Waste paper
CFO: Mike Milby

D-U-N-S 00-914-5814 IMP/EXP
▲ NEWPORT CORP
1791 Deere Ave, Irvine, CA 92606-4814
Tel (949) 863-3144 Founded/Ownrshp 1938
Sales 605.1MM EMP 2,570[E]
Accts Deloitte & Touche Llp Costa M
Tkr Sym NEWP Exch NGS
SIC 3821 3699 3827 3826 Worktables, laboratory; Laser systems & equipment; Optical instruments & lenses; Mirrors, optical; Prisms, optical; Analytical optical instruments; Laser scientific & engineering instruments; Worktables, laboratory; Laser systems & equipment; Optical instruments & lenses; Mirrors, optical; Prisms, optical; Analytical optical instruments; Laser scientific & engineering instruments
Pr: Robert J Phillippy
*Ch Bd: Kenneth F Potashner
CFO: Charles F Cargile
Ex VP: Eric McPhee
Ex VP: Andrew Powell
Sr VP: David J Allen
Sr VP: Jeffrey B Coyne
Sr VP: Laurence D Parson
Sr VP: Dennis L Werth
Dir Lab: Jackson Sapudar
Prgrm Mgr: Robert Nguyen
Board of Directors: Christopher Cox, Oleg Khaykin, Cherry A Murray, Peter J Simone

D-U-N-S 08-081-4999
NEWPORT COUNTY CHAPTER R I A R C INC (RI)
JAMES L MAHER CENTER
120 Hillside Ave, Newport, RI 02840-1461
Tel (401) 846-0340 Founded/Ownrshp 1968
Sales 13.1MM EMP 400
Accts Mayer Hoffman Mccann Pc Prov
SIC 8331 Sheltered workshop; Community service employment training program; Sheltered workshop; Community service employment training program
Ex Dir: John Maher
Ex Dir: Angelo Tartaglione

D-U-N-S 11-226-9464
NEWPORT CREAMERY LLC
35 Sockanosset Cross Rd, Cranston, RI 02920-5535
Tel (401) 946-4000 Founded/Ownrshp 2001
Sales 27.1MM[E] EMP 350
SIC 2024 2013 5451 5421 Ice cream & frozen desserts; Prepared beef products from purchased beef; Ice cream (packaged); Meat markets, including freezer provisioners; Ice cream & frozen desserts; Prepared beef products from purchased beef; Ice cream (packaged); Meat markets, including freezer provisioners
Pr: Nicholas Janikies

D-U-N-S 09-620-3604
NEWPORT DISTRIBUTION INC
748 Bethlehem Pike, Spring House, PA 19477-1005
Tel (267) 419-8086 Founded/Ownrshp 1999
Sales 30.0MM EMP 2
SIC 5047 5122 Medical & hospital equipment; Drugs, proprietaries & sundries; Medical & hospital equipment; Drugs, proprietaries & sundries
Pr: Melissa Kraras

D-U-N-S 14-479-1993
NEWPORT DIVERSIFIED INC
PARKWAY BOWL
2301 Dupont Dr Ste 500, Irvine, CA 92612-7504
Tel (949) 851-1355 Founded/Ownrshp 1984
Sales 1.2MM EMP 445
SIC 7389 5962 7993 7933 Flea market; Food vending machines; Amusement arcade; Video game arcade; Bowling centers; Flea market; Food vending machines; Amusement arcade; Video game arcade; Bowling centers
Pr: Tad Danz
Mng Dir: William Foote
Genl Mgr: Olegario Garcia

D-U-N-S 03-559-2351
NEWPORT EQUIPMENT CO (AR)
(Suby of CONMAC INVESTMENTS INC) ★
S Hwy 49, Weiner, AR 72479
Tel (870) 684-7720 Founded/Ownrshp 1954, 1989
Sales 22.3MM[E] EMP 135
SIC 5083 Tractors, agricultural; Agricultural machinery & equipment; Tractors, agricultural; Agricultural machinery & equipment
CEO: John Conner

D-U-N-S 13-057-0476
NEWPORT GROUP INC
300 International Pkwy, Heathrow, FL 32746-5035
Tel (407) 333-2905 Founded/Ownrshp 1984
Sales NA EMP 80
SIC 6411 8742 Insurance brokers; Financial consultant
CEO: Peter S Cahall
*Pr: James M Campisi
*COO: Bryant W Kirk
Chf Mktg O: Tom Pittman
Ofcr: Hope Newsome
*Sr VP: Eric Brickman
*Sr VP: Dennis Sain
Sr VP: Jeff Wirth
*VP: Neil Chaffee
*VP: Anthony Laudato
*VP: James Robinson
VP: Rob Schaffernoth
VP: George Whit

D-U-N-S 93-891-8950
NEWPORT GROUP SECURITIES INC
300 International Pkwy, Lake Mary, FL 32746-5035
Tel (407) 333-2905 Founded/Ownrshp 1991
Sales 25.5MM[E] EMP 100
Accts Mc Gladrey & Pullen
SIC 6211 Security brokers & dealers; Security brokers & dealers
Pr: James Campisi
Pr: David Burkart
*Pr: Charles R Mc Grew
Pr: Geraldine O'Brien
Pr: George White
*Sec: Teresa J Sherrard
Ofcr: Chad Robson
Sr VP: Samuel Brkich
VP: Kevin Bachler
VP: Eric Brickman
VP: Andrew Eldredge
VP: Rob Schaffernoth
*VP: Thomas R Yeaser

D-U-N-S 11-834-4936
NEWPORT HARBOR CORP
366 Thames St Fl 3, Newport, RI 02840-6626
Tel (401) 848-7010 Founded/Ownrshp 1925
Sales 42.3MM[E] EMP 900
SIC 5812 7011 7999 4493

NEWPORT HARBOR HIGH SCHOOL
See NEWPORT MESA UNIFIED SCHOOL DISTRICT

D-U-N-S 79-180-3158
NEWPORT HEALTH CARE CORP
NEWPORT HOSPITAL
11 Friendship St, Newport, RI 02840-2209
Tel (401) 253-4063 Founded/Ownrshp 1983
Sales 94.3MM[E] EMP 700[E]
Accts Kpmg Llp Providence Rhode Is
SIC 8062 6531 6732 General medical & surgical hospitals; Real estate agents & managers; Charitable trust management; General medical & surgical hospitals; Real estate agents & managers; Charitable trust management
CEO: Timothy J Babineau
*Pr: Arthur Sampson
CFO: Frank Burn
CFO: Frank Byrne
Ofcr: Edward Silva
*Ex VP: Cathy Duquette
*Sr VP: Kenneth E Arnold
*Sr VP: Carole M Cotter
*Sr VP: Richard J Goldberg
VP: Lynn Francis
VP: M Francis
Dir Rx: Paul Parchesky

NEWPORT HOSPITAL
See NEWPORT HEALTH CARE CORP

D-U-N-S 07-567-8177
NEWPORT HOSPITAL
11 Friendship St Ste 1, Newport, RI 02840-2299
Tel (401) 846-6400 Founded/Ownrshp 2004
Sales 98.0MM[E] EMP 700
Accts Kpmg Llp Boston Ma
SIC 8062 General medical & surgical hospitals; General medical & surgical hospitals
Pr: Arthur Sampson

NEWPORT HOSPITAL LTC
See PUBLIC HOSPITAL DISTRICT 1 OF PEND OREILLE COUNTY

D-U-N-S 15-686-6444
NEWPORT HOSPITALITY LLC
NEWPORT BEACH SIDE RESORT
16701 Collins Ave, Sunny Isles Beach, FL 33160-4201
Tel (305) 949-1300 Founded/Ownrshp 1985
Sales 23.0MM[E] EMP 160
SIC 7011 5812 5813 Hotels & motels; Restaurant, family: independent; Bar (drinking places)
Pr: Robert M Cornfeld DMD
*VP: Jeffery Cornfeld
Creative D: Tierney Winick
Mktg Dir: Saul Rodriguez

D-U-N-S 06-091-9560
NEWPORT INDEPENDENT SCHOOLS
30 E 8th St, Newport, KY 41071-1824
Tel (859) 292-3001 Founded/Ownrshp 1870
Sales 21.8MM[E] EMP 350
SIC 8211 Public elementary school; Public junior high school; Public senior high school; Public elementary school; Public junior high school; Public senior high school

D-U-N-S 06-848-9413
NEWPORT LABORATORIES INC
(Suby of MERIAL)
1520 Prairie Dr, Worthington, MN 56187-5184
Tel (507) 372-7779 Founded/Ownrshp 2012
Sales 35.0MM[E] EMP 115
SIC 2836 Biological products, except diagnostic; Biological products, except diagnostic
CEO: Wayne R Freese
*COO: Randy Simonson
*CFO: Daniel Greve
*Ex VP: Craig Pfeifer
Off Mgr: Donna Roadshaeffer
Mfg Mgr: Cindy Becker
Ql Cn Mgr: Brian Bosma
Ql Cn Mgr: Brenda Wehking

NEWPORT MEAT
See ECONOMY FOODS INC

D-U-N-S 07-488-6953
■ NEWPORT MEDICAL CENTER
HMA
(Suby of HEALTH MANAGEMENT ASSOCIATES INC) ★
435 2nd St, Newport, TN 37821-3703
Tel (423) 625-2200 Founded/Ownrshp 2011
Sales 38.7MM EMP 231
SIC 8062 8052 General medical & surgical hospitals; Intermediate care facilities; General medical & surgical hospitals; Intermediate care facilities
CEO: Spencer Thomas
CFO: Phillip Childree
Dir OR: Diana McGaha
Dir Lab: Gabriel Long
Pgrm Dir: Mathew Nunnelley

D-U-N-S 05-033-4275 IMP/EXP
■ NEWPORT MEDICAL INSTRUMENTS INC
COVIDIEN
(Suby of COVIDIEN LIMITED)
1620 Sunflower Ave, Costa Mesa, CA 92626-1513
Tel (949) 642-3910 Founded/Ownrshp 2012
Sales 20.2MM[E] EMP 95
SIC 3841 3842 3845 Surgical & medical instruments; Respirators; Electromedical equipment
Pr: Philippe Negre
CFO: Robert Gerger
IT Man: Patti Gunter
Sftwr Eng: Victor Rosero
VP Prd: Elliot Blank
Mktg Dir: Jay Nash

D-U-N-S 08-117-3080
NEWPORT MESA UNIFIED SCHOOL DISTRICT
NEWPORT HARBOR HIGH SCHOOL
2985 Bear St Ste A, Costa Mesa, CA 92626-4300
Tel (714) 424-5000 Founded/Ownrshp 1966
Sales 93.2M EMP 3,000
Accts E Wayne Lytle Dba Pay Oll
SIC 8211 Public combined elementary & secondary school; Public combined elementary & secondary school
Pr: Dana Black
Bd of Dir: Dave Brooks
Bd of Dir: Walt Davenport
Bd of Dir: Judy A Franco
Bd of Dir: Maggie Tool
Exec: Brenda Quinn
Off Mgr: Erik Pannizzo
Off Mgr: Denise Potterton
Off Admin: Veronica Cisneros
Off Admin: Christine Holguin
Cmptr Lab: Tim Covert

D-U-N-S 07-362-3209
NEWPORT NEWS BAPTIST RETIREMENT COMMUNITY INC (VA)
CHESEAPEAKE
(Suby of VIRGINIA BAPTIST HOMES, INCORPORATED)
955 Harpersville Rd, Newport News, VA 23601-1085
Tel (757) 223-1641 Founded/Ownrshp 1985
Sales 20.0MM EMP 110
Accts Larsonallen Llp Charlotte Nc
SIC 8051 Skilled nursing care facilities; Skilled nursing care facilities
Pr: Randall Robinson
*COO: Stephen McElmurray
*Ex VP: Kevin W Quinn

D-U-N-S 15-072-2028 IMP/EXP
NEWPORT NEWS HOLDINGS CORP
711 3rd Ave Fl 4, New York, NY 10017-9213
Tel (212) 986-2585 Founded/Ownrshp 2004
Sales 47.2MM[E] EMP 500
SIC 5961 Women's apparel, mail order; Furniture & furnishings, mail order; Women's apparel, mail order; Furniture & furnishings, mail order
Ch Bd: Geralynn Madonna
*COO: Jim Brewster

D-U-N-S 19-307-5876
NEWPORT NEWS PUBLIC SCHOOL DISTRICT
NNPS
12465 Warwick Blvd, Newport News, VA 23606-3041
Tel (757) 591-4500 Founded/Ownrshp 1898
Sales 315.7MM EMP 1,500
Accts Cherry Bekaert Llp Richmond
SIC 8211 Public elementary & secondary schools; Public elementary & secondary schools
Ch: Jeff Stodghill
*Ch: Carlton Ashby
*Ex Dir: Ashby C Kilgore
Dir Sec: Jeff Nelson

D-U-N-S 08-512-5227
NEWPORT NEWS SHIPBUILDING EMPLOYEES CREDIT UNION INC
NNSECU
3711 Huntington Ave, Newport News, VA 23607-2710
Tel (757) 928-8800 Founded/Ownrshp 1928
Sales NA EMP 250
SIC 6062 State credit unions, not federally chartered; State credit unions, not federally chartered
Pr: George R Dudley Jr
V Ch: Suzanne Beckstoffer
COO: James B Mears Sr
Treas: Lori Gay
VP: Jennifer Coyne
VP: James Mears
VP: Harry E Wikle
VP: Craig Zuidema
Brnch Mgr: Brenda Shonyo
CIO: Denise McRoberts
Dir IT: Monte Crowl

NEWPORT NWS-WLLSBRG INTL ARPT
See PENINSULA AIRPORT COMMISSION

NEWPORT OFFICE EQUIPMENT
See NEWPORT STATIONERS INC

D-U-N-S 62-175-8440
NEWPORT PUBLIC SCHOOLS
AQUIDNECK ISLAND LEARNING CTR
15 Wickham Rd, Newport, RI 02840-4232
Tel (401) 847-2100 Founded/Ownrshp 1867
Sales 16.2MM[E] EMP 350
SIC 8211 Public elementary school; Public junior high school; Public senior high school; Public elementary school; Public junior high school; Public senior high school
Schl Brd P: Patrick Kelley

D-U-N-S 80-042-9420
NEWPORT RETIREMENT SERVICES INC
300 International Pkwy P, Lake Mary, FL 32746-5035
Tel (407) 333-2905 Founded/Ownrshp 2001
Sales NA EMP 200
SIC 6411 Pension & retirement plan consultants; Pension & retirement plan consultants
CEO: Peter S Cahall
*Pr: James M Campisi
*VP: Stephen Fehr

D-U-N-S 00-212-3871
NEWPORT RICHEY HOSPITAL INC (FL)
MEDICAL CENTER OF TRINITY
9330 State Road 54, Trinity, FL 34655-1808
Tel (727) 834-4000 Founded/Ownrshp 1972, 2002
Sales 32.2MM[E] EMP 123[E]
SIC 8011 Medical centers
CEO: Leigh Massenpill
*CFO: Alex Romanchik

D-U-N-S 06-674-9391
NEWPORT SAND & GRAVEL CO INC
CARROLL CONCRETE
8 Reeds Mill Rd, Newport, NH 03773-1249
Tel (603) 298-0199 Founded/Ownrshp 1973
Sales 39.2MM[E] EMP 200
SIC 3273 3297 Ready-mixed concrete; Nonclay refractories; Ready-mixed concrete; Nonclay refractories
Pr: Shaun P Carroll Sr
Exec: Lawrence Janowski
Genl Mgr: Bob Carroll

NEWPORT SPECIALTY HOSPITAL
See TUSTIN HOSPITAL AND MEDICAL CENTER

D-U-N-S 02-874-2237
NEWPORT STATIONERS INC
NEWPORT OFFICE EQUIPMENT
17681 Mitchell N Ste 120, Irvine, CA 92614-6090
Tel (949) 863-1200 Founded/Ownrshp 1964
Sales 25.7MM[E] EMP 53
SIC 5112 5943 Stationers, commercial; Office supplies; Office forms & supplies
CEO: Colin C West
*VP: Barry T West
Opers Mgr: John Packman

D-U-N-S 94-745-8295
NEWPORT TANK CONTAINERS (USA) LLC
1340 Depot St Ste 202, Cleveland, OH 44116-1741
Tel (440) 356-8866 Founded/Ownrshp 1995
Sales 66.5MM[E] EMP 275[E]
SIC 4783 Containerization of goods for shipping
CEO: Michael Derijk
*Pr: Frederick M Hunger
*Treas: John Hunger
VP: David Hertvik
Opers Mgr: Tom Starck
Sales Exec: Rob Thomas
Sls Mgr: Alina Butugea
Sales Asso: Mary Joyce

D-U-N-S 01-418-5499
NEWPORT TELEVISION LLC
460 Nichols Rd Ste 250, Kansas City, MO 64112-2047
Tel (816) 751-0200 Founded/Ownrshp 2007
Sales 51.9MM[E] EMP 2,000[E]
SIC 7922 Television program, including commercial producers; Television program, including commercial producers

D-U-N-S 62-389-2411
NEWPORT TIMBER CORP
(Suby of INTERSTATE RESOURCES INC) ★
1300 Wilson Blvd Ste 1075, Arlington, VA 22209-2330
Tel (703) 243-3355 Founded/Ownrshp 1997
Sales 53.3MM[E] EMP 500
SIC 2621 Bond paper; Bond paper
Ch: Antoine Frem
*Genl Mgr: Tom Norris

D-U-N-S 03-068-1415
NEWPORT UTILITIES BOARD
170 Cope Blvd, Newport, TN 37821-2870
Tel (423) 625-2800 Founded/Ownrshp 1939
Sales 51.3MM[E] EMP 91

SIC 4911 4941 4952 8741 Electric services; Water supply; Sewerage systems; Management services; Electric services; Water supply; Sewerage systems; Management services
Admn Mgr: Gary Lynn Lowe
**Prin:* Ron Fugate
Plnt Mgr: Topper Allen

D-U-N-S 80-104-0171 EXP
NEWPORT WHOLESALERS INC
8751 W Broward Blvd # 306, Plantation, FL 33324-2632
Tel (954) 927-0003 *Founded/Ownrshp* 1992
Sales 35.0MM *EMP* 20^E
SIC 5141 Groceries, general line; Groceries, general line
Pr: Howard J Lewis
Sr VP: Ira Schwartz
Off Mgr: Laura Mancuso

D-U-N-S 01-922-8535
NEWPRO OPERATING LLC
NEWPRO REPLACEMENT WIN PEOPLE
26 Cedar St, Woburn, MA 01801-2100
Tel (781) 933-4100 *Founded/Ownrshp* 2005
Sales 27.8MM^E *EMP* 100
SIC 1751 5211 Window & door (prefabricated) installation; Windows, storm: wood or metal
Pr: Nick Cogliani
CFO: Kevin Felton
Rgnl Mgr: Rob Donadio
Sales Asso: Joey Vasil

NEWPRO REPLACEMENT WIN PEOPLE
See NEWPRO OPERATING LLC

D-U-N-S 02-450-8000
■ **NEWQUEST LLC**
(*Suby of* HEALTHSPRING INC) ★
44 Vantage Way Ste 300, Nashville, TN 37228-1550
Tel (615) 291-7000 *Founded/Ownrshp* 2000
Sales NA *EMP* 1,567^E
SIC 6321 Health insurance carriers
CEO: Herbert Fritch

D-U-N-S 93-983-2689
NEWS & RECORD COMMERCIAL PRINTING
200 E Market St, Greensboro, NC 27401-2910
Tel (336) 373-7300 *Founded/Ownrshp* 1965
Sales 24.3MM^E *EMP* 500
SIC 2759 2711 Commercial printing; Newspapers; Commercial printing; Newspapers
Mktg Dir: Diane Rice

D-U-N-S 93-888-5035
■ **NEWS 12 NEW JERSEY INC**
(*Suby of* AMC NETWORKS INC) ★
450 Rritan Ctr Pkwy Ste H, Edison, NJ 08837
Tel (732) 346-3200 *Founded/Ownrshp* 1996
Sales 23.6MM^E *EMP* 150
SIC 4833 Television broadcasting stations
Dir Soc: Brian Voynick
Ex Dir: Jonathan Knopf
CTO: James Fisher
Sls&Mrk Ex: Patrick Young
Mktg Mgr: Deborah Feeney

D-U-N-S 06-196-3567
■ **NEWS AMERICA MARKETING IN-STORE SERVICES LLC** (ID)
SMART SOURCE
(*Suby of* NEWS CORP) ★
20 Westport Rd Ste 320, Wilton, CT 06897-4550
Tel (203) 563-6600 *Founded/Ownrshp* 1971, 2013
Sales 191.7MM^E *EMP* 20,000
SIC 7319 Display advertising service; Display advertising service
COO: Gene Klein
Ex VP: Steve Ross
VP: Christopher Blanco
VP: Kathy McNamara
Natl Sales: Patrick Reynolds
Sls Mgr: Kayleigh Walls

D-U-N-S 00-319-4875 IMP
■ **NEWS AND OBSERVER PUBLISHING CO** (NC)
GOLD LEAF PUBLISHERS
(*Suby of* MCCLATCHY NEWSPAPERS INC) ★
215 S Mcdowell St, Raleigh, NC 27601-2929
Tel (919) 829-4500 *Founded/Ownrshp* 1894, 1995
Sales 115.3MM^E *EMP* 1,000
SIC 2711 2741 2721 2752 Newspapers, publishing & printing; Commercial printing & newspaper publishing combined; Job printing & newspaper publishing combined; Shopping news: publishing & printing; Magazines: publishing & printing; Commercial printing, lithographic; Newspapers, publishing & printing; Commercial printing & newspaper publishing combined; Job printing & newspaper publishing combined; Shopping news: publishing & printing; Magazines: publishing & printing; Commercial printing, lithographic
Pr: Orage Quarles III
Sr VP: Richard Rinehart
VP: John Drescher
**VP:* George McCanless
IT Man: Mark Williams
Opers Mgr: Deborah Jackson
Prd Mgr: Matt Long
Sales Exec: Pam Corey

D-U-N-S 07-882-6673
▲ **NEWS CORP**
1211 Ave Of The Americas, New York, NY 10036-8701
Tel (212) 416-3400 *Founded/Ownrshp* 2012
Sales 8.6MMM *EMP* 25,000^E
Accts Ernst & Young Llp New York N
Tkr Sym NWS *Exch* NGS
SIC 2711 2731 7375 Newspapers; Newspapers, publishing & printing; Book publishing; On-line data base information retrieval; Newspapers; Newspapers, publishing & printing; Book publishing; On-line data base information retrieval
Ch Bd: K Rupert Murdoch
Ch Bd: Lachlan K Murdoch
Pr: Gianluca Daniello
CEO: Robert J Thomson
CFO: Bedi Ajay Singh
Chf Cred: David B Pitofsky
Ex VP: Ian Moore
Ex VP: John P Nallen
Ex VP: Jeremy Phillips
Sr VP: Neil Aaron
Sr VP: Marc Heller
Sr VP: Janet Nova
Sr VP: William Sorenson
VP: Karen Bartholow
VP: Aashish Chandarana
VP: Bill Defazio
VP: Robert Ennis
VP: Lou Ermilio
VP: David Fares
VP: Michael Florin
VP: Stacy Grossman

D-U-N-S 82-861-3518
NEWS DISTRIBUTION NETWORK INC
3445 Peachtree Rd Ne # 1000, Atlanta, GA 30326-1256
Tel (404) 962-7400 *Founded/Ownrshp* 2007
Sales 29.6MM^E *EMP* 110
SIC 7379
Pr: Gregory A Peters
VP: Charlie Chance
VP: Michael Gay
**VP:* Joe Martin
Off Mgr: Toni Beauchamp
Sls Dir: Chad Hickey

NEWS GAZETTE
See LUMBER SPECIALISTS INC

NEWS GROUP
See COWLEY DISTRIBUTING INC

D-U-N-S 07-299-0448
NEWS GROUP
901 Avenue S, Grand Prairie, TX 75050-1134
Tel (253) 896-2370 *Founded/Ownrshp* 1999
Sales 31.6MM^E *EMP* 200
SIC 5192 Books; Magazines; Newspapers; Books; Magazines; Newspapers
Pr: David Perry

NEWS GROUP BISMARCK
See SAKS NEWS INC

D-U-N-S 94-238-2433
NEWS GROUP INC
LONE STAR PERIODICALS
5130 Comm Pkwy, San Antonio, TX 78218
Tel (210) 226-9333 *Founded/Ownrshp* 2005
Sales 90.8MM^E *EMP* 140
SIC 5192 5994 Books, periodicals & newspapers; Magazine stand; Books, periodicals & newspapers; Magazine stand
CEO: Michael Korenberg
**Pr:* John Seebach
Sr VP: Scott Shepherd
**VP:* Rod Bergen
VP: Mike Cullingham
VP: Ingrid Jakabcsin
Off Mgr: Joy Neimer
CTO: Mike Manero
Natl Sales: Monica Duplantis

NEWS GROUP-SOUTHEAST, THE
See GREAT ATLANTIC NEWS LLC

NEWS MARKETER
See MIDWEST SUBURBAN PUBLISHING INC

D-U-N-S 85-903-0512
NEWS MEDIA CORP
211 E Il Route 38, Rochelle, IL 61068-2303
Tel (815) 562-2061 *Founded/Ownrshp* 1979
Sales 82.8MM^E *EMP* 570
SIC 2711 Newspapers; Newspapers
Pr: John C Tompkins
**Treas:* R Michael Tompkins
**VP:* Bret Yager
Div Mgr: Keith Cerny
Genl Mgr: Matt Koyak
Sls&Mrk Ex: Pat Duffy

NEWS PRESS MEDIA GROUP, THE
See NEWS PRESS PUBLISHING CO (INC)

D-U-N-S 06-278-2925 IMP
■ **NEWS PRESS PUBLISHING CO (INC)**
NEWS PRESS MEDIA GROUP, THE
(*Suby of* TEGNA INC) ★
2442 Dr M Luther Kng Jr Martin, Fort Myers, FL 33901
Tel (239) 335-0200 *Founded/Ownrshp* 1884
Sales 40.4MM^E *EMP* 310
SIC 2711 Newspapers, publishing & printing; Newspapers, publishing & printing
Pr: MEI-Nei Chan
VP: Cindy Burgess
VP: Greg Helton
VP: Matt Petro
VP: Wendy Powell
Ex Dir: Janet Entler
Assoc Ed: Brian Hubbard

D-U-N-S 00-332-2856
NEWS PUBLISHING CO (GA)
WALKER COUNTY MESSENGER
305 E 6th Ave, Rome, GA 30161-6007
Tel (706) 291-6397 *Founded/Ownrshp* 1919, 1946
Sales 51.5MM^E *EMP* 275
SIC 2711 Newspapers, publishing & printing; Newspapers, publishing & printing
CEO: B H Mooney
**Pr:* Burgett H Mooney III
**Sec:* Joseph Morgan
**Prin:* Raymond Kennedy
Off Mgr: Linda Forsyth
Opers Mgr: Mark White
Mktg Mgr: Jamie Bennett

D-U-N-S 00-522-4126
■ **NEWS PUBLISHING CO INC**
(*Suby of* MCCLATCHY CO) ★
600 W Main St, Fort Wayne, IN 46802-1408
Tel (260) 461-8444 *Founded/Ownrshp* 1917, 2006
Sales 111.1MM^E *EMP* 601
SIC 2711 Newspapers; Newspapers
Pr: Scott Mc Gehee
CFO: John Kovatch

D-U-N-S 08-167-4830 IMP
NEWS WORLD COMMUNICATIONS INC
WASHINGTON TIMES NEWSPAPER
(*Suby of* ONE UP ENTERPRISES INC) ★
3600 New York Ave Ne, Washington, DC 20002-1947
Tel (202) 636-3000 *Founded/Ownrshp* 1977
Sales 88.3MM^E *EMP* 1,000
SIC 2711 Newspapers, publishing & printing; Newspapers, publishing & printing
Pr: Thomas McDevitt
**Treas:* Keith Cooperrider
Mktg Dir: Tom McDevitt

D-U-N-S 00-406-6585 IMP
NEWS-JOURNAL CORP
NEW SMYRNA DAILY JOURNAL
901 6th St, Daytona Beach, FL 32117-8099
Tel (386) 252-1511 *Founded/Ownrshp* 1927
Sales 103.7MM^E *EMP* 875
SIC 2711 Newspapers; Newspapers
Pr: Herbert M Davidson Jr
**Treas:* Marc L Davidson
Sr VP: Leween Jones
**VP:* Georgia M Kaney
**VP:* David R Kendall
Off Mgr: Patricia Winston
CIO: Karen M Coy
Advt Dir: Kathy Coughlin

D-U-N-S 00-713-4190
NEWS-PRESS & GAZETTE CO INC (MO)
NPG NEWSPAPERS
825 Edmond St, Saint Joseph, MO 64501-2737
Tel (816) 271-8500 *Founded/Ownrshp* 1951
Sales 163.0MM^E *EMP* 1,025
SIC 2711

NEWS-SENTINEL
See FORT WAYNE NEWSPAPERS INC

D-U-N-S 06-339-7442
NEWSBANK INC
READEX
5801 Pelican Bay Blvd, Naples, FL 34108-2755
Tel (239) 263-6004 *Founded/Ownrshp* 1985
Sales 84.2MM^E *EMP* 250
SIC 5192 2741 Newspapers; Miscellaneous publishing; Newspapers; Miscellaneous publishing
Pr: Daniel S Jones
Ofcr: Brian Murphy
Sr VP: Susan Bokern
VP: Phil Chimbolo
VP: Deborah Harmer
**VP:* August A Imholtz
**VP:* Susan Jones
VP: John A McDowell
**VP:* Remmel Nunn
VP: Michael G Walker
Dir Bus: Linda Paschal

D-U-N-S 83-733-2258
NEWSCHOOLS VENTURE FUND
1970 Broadway Ste 350, Oakland, CA 94612-2238
Tel (415) 615-6860 *Founded/Ownrshp* 1998
Sales 30.8MM *EMP* 18
Accts Hood & Strong Llp Cpas San Fr
SIC 7389 8742 Fund raising organizations; Management consulting services; Fund raising organizations; Management consulting services
CEO: Stacey Childress

D-U-N-S 07-925-2140
NEWSCYCLE SOLUTIONS INC
7900 Intl Dr Ste 800, Minneapolis, MN 55425
Tel (651) 639-0662 *Founded/Ownrshp* 2013
Sales 145.2MM^E *EMP* 555^E
SIC 7371 Computer software development & applications; Computer software development & applications
CEO: Preston McKenzie
**COO:* Scott Roessler
**CFO:* Lynn Danko
**Dir Risk M:* Dan Paulus

D-U-N-S 05-278-2497
■ **NEWSDAY LLC**
NEWSDAY MEDIA GROUP
(*Suby of* CABLEVISION) ★
235 Pinelawn Rd, Melville, NY 11747-4250
Tel (631) 843-4050 *Founded/Ownrshp* 2008
Sales 222.6MM^E *EMP* 1,228
SIC 2711 Newspapers, publishing & printing; Newspapers, publishing & printing
CFO: Terry Jimenez
**Pr:* Fred Groser
Treas: Richard Jones
Sr VP: Larry Dunn
VP: Denise Fulham
VP: David Kniffin
**VP:* Timothy Martin
**VP:* Robert Rosenthal
Brnch Mgr: Patricia Burne
IT Man: Andrew R McCaffey
Opers Mgr: Ed Bushey

NEWSDAY MEDIA GROUP
See NEWSDAY LLC

D-U-N-S 78-497-1728 IMP
NEWSEUM INC
555 Pennsylvania Ave Nw, Washington, DC 20001-2114
Tel (202) 292-6100 *Founded/Ownrshp* 2005
Sales 62.5MM *EMP* 2
Accts Grant Thornton Llp Philadelph
SIC 8412 Museums & art galleries
Pr: James C Duff
**Ch:* Peter S Prichard
**Sr VP:* Mary Kay Blake
**Sr VP:* Nicole F Mandeville
Sr VP: Courtney L Surls
**Sr VP:* Pam Galloway Tabb
**Sr VP:* Jim Updike
Sr VP: Joe Urschel
Sr VP: Chris Wells
VP: Pam Galloway-Tabb
VP: Paul Sparrow
Dir Soc: Ashlie Hampton

D-U-N-S 80-885-2284
NEWSLINK OF JFK LLC
6910 Nw 12th St, Miami, FL 33126-1336
Tel (305) 594-5754 *Founded/Ownrshp* 2004
Sales 24.9MM^E *EMP* 450
SIC 5942 5441 5994 5947 Book stores; Candy, nut & confectionery stores; News dealers & newsstands; Gift, novelty & souvenir shop; Book stores; Candy, nut & confectionery stores; News dealers & newsstands; Gift, novelty & souvenir shop
CEO: Raymond Kayal Jr
**Ch:* Christopher G Korge
**VP:* Stan Synkoski

D-U-N-S 05-020-6288 IMP
NEWSMAX MEDIA INC
750 Park Of Commerce Dr # 100, Boca Raton, FL 33487-3650
Tel (561) 686-1165 *Founded/Ownrshp* 1998
Sales 103.5MM *EMP* 275
Accts Daszkal Bolton Llp Sunrise F
SIC 2721 2741 Periodicals; Miscellaneous publishing; Periodicals; Miscellaneous publishing
Pr: Christopher Ruddy
**COO:* Brian Todd
VP: Kevin Byrnes

D-U-N-S 00-482-2826 IMP/EXP
NEWSOM DESIGNS LLC (TX)
WISTERIA
13780 Benchmark Dr, Farmers Branch, TX 75234-9011
Tel (972) 919-3638 *Founded/Ownrshp* 2000
Sales 25.9MM^E *EMP* 100^E
SIC 5719 5261 5932 Housewares; Garden supplies & tools; Antiques
Pr: Andrew Newsom
CFO: Peter Yan
VP: Shannon Newsom
Dir IT: Michael Beacom
IT Man: Asad Saleem

NEWSOME CHEVROLET WORLD
See CAPITOL CHEVROLET

NEWSOME SAND & GRAVEL
See COMMERCIAL READY MIX PRODUCTS INC

NEWSOUND HEARING AID CENTERS
See MCCRAE MANAGEMENT & INVESTMENTS LTD

NEWSOUTH COMMUNICATIONS
See NUVOX INC

D-U-N-S 00-434-1434
NEWSPAPER HOLDING INC
JOHNSTOWN TRIBUNE DEMOCRAT
(*Suby of* COMMUNITY NEWSPAPER HOLDINGS INC) ★
425 Locust St, Johnstown, PA 15901-1817
Tel (814) 532-5102 *Founded/Ownrshp* 1902, 1999
Sales 238.5MM^E *EMP* 2,150
SIC 2711 Newspapers, publishing & printing; Newspapers, publishing & printing
Pr: Donna Barrett
**Treas:* Mike Reed
**VP:* Keith Blevins

D-U-N-S 13-196-5725 EXP
NEWSPAPER PRINTING CO
N P C
5210 S Lois Ave, Tampa, FL 33611-3445
Tel (813) 839-0035 *Founded/Ownrshp* 1984
Sales 52.8MM^E *EMP* 200
SIC 2752 Commercial printing, offset; Commercial printing, offset
Pr: John L Tevlin
Exec: Kim Marshall

D-U-N-S 96-252-0987
NEWSPAPERS OF MASSACHUSETTS INC
THE RECORDER
(*Suby of* NEWSPAPERS OF NEW ENGLAND INC) ★
14 Hope St, Greenfield, MA 01301-3308
Tel (978) 544-2118 *Founded/Ownrshp* 1792
Sales 19.3MM^E *EMP* 412
SIC 2711 2791 2752 Newspapers: publishing only, not printed on site; Typesetting; Commercial printing, lithographic; Newspapers: publishing only, not printed on site; Typesetting; Commercial printing, lithographic
Pr: Kay Derenson
Div Mgr: George Wilson

D-U-N-S 00-108-9051 IMP
NEWSPAPERS OF NEW ENGLAND INC
VALLEY NEWS
1 Monitor Dr, Concord, NH 03301-1834
Tel (603) 224-5301 *Founded/Ownrshp* 1923, 1979
Sales 76.5MM^E *EMP* 413
SIC 2711 Newspapers, publishing & printing; Newspapers, publishing & printing
Pr: George W Wilson
**Pr:* Aaron Julien
**CFO:* Scott Graff
**Treas:* Daniel McClory
Dist Mgr: Holly Field
Dir IT: Tundra Slosek
Sls Dir: Barbara Schmelzer

D-U-N-S 18-623-8317
NEWSPAPERS OF NEW HAMPSHIRE INC
MONADNOCK LEDGER
(*Suby of* NEWSPAPERS OF NEW ENGLAND INC) ★
1 Monitor Dr, Concord, NH 03301-1834
Tel (603) 224-5301 *Founded/Ownrshp* 1986
Sales 25.8MM^E *EMP* 302
SIC 2711 Newspapers: publishing only, not printed on site; Newspapers: publishing only, not printed on site
Pr: George W Wilson
**Pr:* Geoidi Wilson
CFO: Scott Graff
IT Man: Ben Allen
Tech Mgr: Gerard Wallace

D-U-N-S 08-560-4077
NEWSPRING CHURCH INC
2940 Concord Rd, Anderson, SC 29621-3619
Tel (864) 226-6585 *Founded/Ownrshp* 1999
Sales 48.0MM *EMP* 421
SIC 8661 Community church

D-U-N-S 16-891-7552
▲ NEWSTAR FINANCIAL INC
500 Boylston St Ste 1200, Boston, MA 02116-3891
Tel (617) 848-2500 *Founded/Ownrshp* 2004
Sales NA *EMP* 98E
Tkr Sym NEWS *Exch* NGS
SIC 6162 Mortgage bankers & correspondents; Loan correspondents; Mortgage bankers; Mortgage bankers & correspondents; Loan correspondents; Mortgage bankers
Ch Bd: Timothy J Conway
Pr: Seth Frink
CFO: John K Bray
Chf Cred: Daniel D McCready
Chf Inves: Peter A Schmidt-Fellner
Ex VP: Joseph Kinkenon
Sr VP: Nina Fairchild
VP: Derek Dubois
VP: Jenifer Mulbroom
VP: Kevin Mulcahy
VP: Tristan Pierce
Board of Directors: Charles N Bralver, Bradley E Cooper, Brian L P Fallon, Frank R Noonan, Maureen P O'hara, Richard E Thornburgh

D-U-N-S 62-141-7914 EXP
NEWSTAR FRESH FOODS LLC
900 Work St, Salinas, CA 93901-4386
Tel (831) 758-7800 *Founded/Ownrshp* 1996
Sales 83.8MME *EMP* 250
SIC 0723 Vegetable crops market preparation services; Vegetable crops market preparation services
CEO: Mark Drever
VP: Susan Ajeska
VP: Tom Browning
VP: Mitch Secondo
VP: Lewis Watson
**Exec:* Ken Schoenthal
Prgrm Mgr: Alejandro Fimbres
Dir IT: Stan Kline
IT Man: Scott Komar
IT Man: Robert McCown
Plnt Mgr: Hemanshu Goda

NEWSTART LOAN ,THE
See 722 REDEMPTION FUNDING INC

D-U-N-S 61-905-3069
NEWSTREAM ENTERPRISES LLC
1925 E Chestnut Expy, Springfield, MO 65802-2279
Tel (417) 831-3112 *Founded/Ownrshp* 1990
Sales 44.2MME *EMP* 160E
SIC 7389 Packaging & labeling services; Packaging & labeling services
Genl Mgr: Gary Goetz
Opers Mgr: Paul Wilkerson
Prd Mgr: Doug Mooneyham
Mktg Mgr: Sara Kaderly

NEWSWAYS DISTRIBUTORS
See NEWSWAYS SERVICES INC

D-U-N-S 80-606-1750 IMP
NEWSWAYS SERVICES INC
NEWSWAYS DISTRIBUTORS
1324 Cypress Ave, Los Angeles, CA 90065-1220
Tel (323) 258-6000 *Founded/Ownrshp* 1993
Sales 57.3MME *EMP* 135
SIC 5192 Magazines; Magazines
Pr: John Dorman

NEWSWEEK/DAILY BEAST CO LLC
See DAILY BEAST CO LLC

D-U-N-S 07-990-9897
NEWTEK BUSINESS SERVICES CORP
5901 Broken Sound Pkwy, Boca Raton, FL 33487-2773
Tel (212) 356-9500 *Founded/Ownrshp* 1998
Sales 200.0MM *EMP* 350
SIC 7389 Personal service agents, brokers & bureaus
Pr: Barry Sloane

D-U-N-S 01-473-3005
▲ NEWTEK BUSINESS SERVICES INC
SMALL BUSINESS AUTHORITY, THE
212 W 35th St Fl 2, New York, NY 10001-2508
Tel (212) 356-9500 *Founded/Ownrshp* 1998
Sales 143.5MM *EMP* 335E
Tkr Sym NEWT *Exch* NAS
SIC 7389 7374 4813 Financial services; Data processing service; ; Financial services; Data processing service;
Ch Bd: Barry Sloane
Pr: William Bayer
Pr: Harold Gartner
Pr: Bruce Hopkins
Pr: Becky Mulch
Pr: Richard Rebetti
Pr: Jordan Stein
Pr: Gary T Taylor
Pr: Mike Valerio
Pr: Chris Wells
CFO: Michael Holden
Treas: Dean Choksi
Chf Cred: Matthew G Ash
Ofcr: Peter Downs
Ofcr: Michael A Schwartz
Ex VP: Craig J Brunet
Ex VP: Jennifer Eddelson
Sr VP: Dian F Gamble
VP: Ryan Bishop
VP: Seth Cohen
VP: Ericka Davis
Board of Directors: Sam Kirschner, Salvatore Mulia, Richard J Salute

D-U-N-S 17-348-1136
NEWTEK INC
NEWTEK PARTNERS
5131 Beckwith Blvd, San Antonio, TX 78249-2256
Tel (210) 370-8000 *Founded/Ownrshp* 1985
Sales 26.2MME *EMP* 50E
SIC 5045 Computer software
Pr: Jim Plant
**Ch Bd:* Timothy P Jenison
**Pr:* Andrew Cross
Pr: Michael Kornet
**COO:* Chuck Silber
**CFO:* Stephen J Doubleday
Ex VP: Donetta Colboch
**Sr VP:* Pat Grogan
Sr VP: Charles Silber
VP: Jim Ball
VP: Scott Gentry
VP: Rob Powers
VP: Kevin Rouviere
VP: Ruben Ruiz
Dir Soc: Steve Paulsen
Creative D: Marion Dewall

NEWTEK PARTNERS
See NEWTEK INC

D-U-N-S 03-537-7010
NEWTERRA INC
(*Suby of* NEWTERRA GROUP LTD)
2248 Meridian Blvd Ste H, Minden, NV 89423-8620
Tel (800) 420-4056 *Founded/Ownrshp* 2004
Sales 30.2MME *EMP* 160E
SIC 3589 Water treatment equipment, industrial
Pr: Robert Kennedy
**Treas:* Domenic Crudo

D-U-N-S 95-737-0323 IMP
■ NEWTON BUYING CORP
MARMAXX GROUP, THE
(*Suby of* TJ MAXX) ★
770 Cochituate Rd, Framingham, MA 01701-4666
Tel (508) 390-1000 *Founded/Ownrshp* 1987
Sales 41.1MME *EMP* 97
SIC 5311 Department stores, discount
Pr: Richard Sherr
Pr: Jim Hannon
**Pr:* Ernie Herrman
**Ch:* Bernard Cammarata
**Treas:* Mary Reynolds
Ex VP: Arnold Barron
**Ex VP:* Carol Meyrowitz
Ex VP: David J Weiner
Sr VP: Doug Benjamin
Sr VP: Douglas Benjamin
Sr VP: R Churchill
Sr VP: Scott Goldenberg
Sr VP: L Julian
Sr VP: Richard Lesser
Sr VP: Robertd Maclea
Sr VP: Paul Metcalf
Sr VP: Alan Porte
Sr VP: Michael Tilley
VP: L Atwood
VP: Jim Cutone
VP: Sue Flynn

D-U-N-S 07-807-2907
NEWTON COMMUNITY SCHOOL DISTRICT (IA)
700 N 4th Ave E Ste 300, Newton, IA 50208-3362
Tel (641) 792-5809 *Founded/Ownrshp* 1875
Sales 13.6MM *EMP* 450
Accts Nolte Cornman & Johnson Pc N
SIC 8211 9411 Public junior high school; Public senior high school; School board; Administration of educational programs; Public junior high school; Public senior high school; School board; Administration of educational programs
Exec: Lorraine Kalkhoff
Teacher Pr: Carol Coon

D-U-N-S 07-593-7110
NEWTON COUNTY BOARD OF EDUCATION
NEWTON COUNTY SCHOOLS
2109 Newton Dr Ne, Covington, GA 30014-2459
Tel (770) 787-1330 *Founded/Ownrshp* 1972
Sales 125.8MME *EMP* 2,500
Accts Russell W Hinton Cpa Cgfm
SIC 8211 Public elementary & secondary schools; Public elementary & secondary schools
Dir IT: Gary Shattuck
Psych: Marge Paz

NEWTON COUNTY SCHOOLS
See NEWTON COUNTY BOARD OF EDUCATION

D-U-N-S 07-989-3881
NEWTON COUNTY SCHOOLS
2109 Newton Dr Ne, Covington, GA 30014-2459
Tel (770) 787-1330 *Founded/Ownrshp* 2015
Sales 74.5MME *EMP* 2,675E
SIC 8211 Public elementary & secondary schools

D-U-N-S 80-057-7954
NEWTON FALLS FINE PAPER CO LLC
875 County Rte 60, Newton Falls, NY 13666
Tel (315) 848-3321 *Founded/Ownrshp* 2007
Sales 22.4MME *EMP* 114
SIC 2621

D-U-N-S 07-342-8302
NEWTON HEALTH SYSTEM INC
NEWTON MEDICAL CENTER
5126 Hospital Dr Ne, Covington, GA 30014-2566
Tel (770) 786-7053 *Founded/Ownrshp* 1996
Sales 81.5MM *EMP* 840
Accts Draffin & Tucker Llp Albany
SIC 8011 8062 Offices & clinics of medical doctors; General medical & surgical hospitals; Offices & clinics of medical doctors; General medical & surgical hospitals
CEO: James F Weadick
**CFO:* Troy Brooks
Dir OR: Karen McAfee
Dir Lab: Debbie Tuten
Off Mgr: Cindy Norwood
Off Mgr: Lisa Williams
Snr Ntwrk: Erric Grandy
QA Dir: Kate Smith
Dir IT: Becky Thomas
Mktg Dir: Linda Moseley
Sls Mgr: Becky Needham

D-U-N-S 18-388-1994
NEWTON HEALTHCARE CORP
NEWTON MEDICAL CENTER
600 Medical Center Dr, Newton, KS 67114-8780
Tel (316) 283-2700 *Founded/Ownrshp* 1903
Sales 73.2MM *EMP* 539
Accts Knudsen Monroe & Company Llc
SIC 8062 8011 2411 General medical & surgical hospitals; Offices & clinics of medical doctors; Wooden logs; General medical & surgical hospitals; Offices & clinics of medical doctors; Wooden logs
Ch: Nancy Craig
**CEO:* Steven G Kelly
**CFO:* Todd Kasitz
**Treas:* Jim Heinicke
**VP:* Jeff Barton
Dir OR: Cindy Knoeppel
Dir Rad: Tom Wells
Dir Rx: Allen Graber
Ex Dir: Kendra Tinsley
CIO: Micheal Cottle
MIS Dir: Mike Cottle
Board of Directors:

D-U-N-S 00-694-1983 IMP
NEWTON MANUFACTURING CO
1123 1st Ave E, Newton, IA 50208-3912
Tel (641) 792-4121 *Founded/Ownrshp* 1909
Sales 53.7MME *EMP* 160
SIC 5199

NEWTON MEDICAL CENTER
See NEWTON HEALTH SYSTEM INC

NEWTON MEDICAL CENTER
See NEWTON HEALTHCARE CORP

D-U-N-S 06-857-2544 EXP
NEWTON MEMORIAL HOSPITAL INC
(*Suby of* AHS HOSPITAL CORP) ★
175 High St, Newton, NJ 07860-1099
Tel (973) 383-2121 *Founded/Ownrshp* 1985
Sales 88.1MME *EMP* 805E
Accts Parentebeard Llc Wilkesbarre
SIC 8062 General medical & surgical hospitals; General medical & surgical hospitals
Pr: Tom Senker
Pr: Catherine Enright
**COO:* Sean O'Rourke
CFO: Robert Ragona
Treas: Robert E McCrackn
Ofcr: Maryanne Fox
Exec: Sean Mulch
Dir OR: Sharon Sefcik
Dir Risk M: Stephanie Dubanowicz
Dir Risk M: Stephanie Dubanowitz
Dir Lab: Susan Wetze

D-U-N-S 09-456-2717
NEWTON NORTH SCHOOL CORP (IN)
310 S Lincoln St, Morocco, IN 47963-8293
Tel (219) 285-2228 *Founded/Ownrshp* 1969, 2004
Sales 22.5MM *EMP* 225
SIC 8211 Public elementary & secondary schools; Public elementary & secondary schools
IT Man: Mary Sheldon

D-U-N-S 04-029-9299
NEWTON OIL CO INC
WGGENTRY
3150 S 460 E, Lafayette, IN 47905-7725
Tel (765) 742-4001 *Founded/Ownrshp* 1976
Sales 29.4MME *EMP* 27
SIC 5171 Petroleum bulk stations
Owner: Chuck Newton
**Sec:* Joyce Newton
**VP:* James Newton
IT Man: Ashley Wright

D-U-N-S 09-219-1428
NEWTON PUBLIC SCHOOL DISTRICT
100 Walnut St, Newton, MA 02460-1314
Tel (617) 559-6000 *Founded/Ownrshp* 1858
Sales 86.3MME *EMP* 1,900E
SIC 8211 Public elementary & secondary schools; Public elementary school; Public junior high school; Public senior high school; Public elementary & secondary schools; Public elementary school; Public junior high school; Public senior high school
MIS Dir: Leo Brim
IT Man: Susan Dzikowski
Schl Brd P: Matt Hills

D-U-N-S 04-389-2660
NEWTON PUBLIC SCHOOLS
57 Trinity St, Newton, NJ 07860-1824
Tel (973) 383-1900 *Founded/Ownrshp* 1870
Sales 17.0MME *EMP* 315
SIC 8211 Public elementary & secondary schools; Public elementary & secondary schools

D-U-N-S 07-330-6607
NEWTON PUBLIC SCHOOLS
308 E 1st St, Newton, KS 67114-3846
Tel (316) 284-6200 *Founded/Ownrshp* 1962
Sales 35.9MME *EMP* 700
SIC 8211 Public elementary & secondary schools; Public elementary & secondary schools

NEWTON REGIONAL HOSPITAL
See PIONEER COMMUNITY HOSPITAL OF NEWTON

D-U-N-S 03-309-3287
NEWTON WALL CO
WALLS BARGAIN CENTERS
1600 N Harrison St, Shawnee, OK 74804-4023
Tel (405) 275-1582 *Founded/Ownrshp* 1951
Sales 30.0MM *EMP* 500
SIC 5331 5199 Variety stores; General merchandise, non-durable; Variety stores; General merchandise, non-durable
Ch: Mary E Wall
**Pr:* Elizabeth Wall
**COO:* Rosanne Conley
**VP:* Michael G Hughes
Dir IT: Dennis Jackson
IT Man: Brian Frost
Snr Mgr: Jeff Cassidy

D-U-N-S 07-658-1768
NEWTON WELLESLEY HOSPITAL CORP
(*Suby of* PARTNERS HEALTHCARE SYSTEM INC) ★
2014 Washington St, Newton, MA 02462-1607
Tel (617) 243-6000 *Founded/Ownrshp* 1981
Sales 405.1MM *EMP* 2,500E
SIC 8062 General medical & surgical hospitals; General medical & surgical hospitals
Pr: Kerry Russell Watson
Chf Path: Dennis J Feen
**Pr:* Patrick Jordan
CFO: Dan Gross
CFO: Marlene Ward
Sr VP: Edward D Mueller
VP: Gerard Hadley
VP: Brian Odea
Dir OR: Susan Duffy-Smith
Dir Risk M: Barbara Lightizer
Dir Risk M: Lynn Nuti
Dir Rad: Mary Drinkwater

D-U-N-S 18-740-3142
NEWTON WILLIAM MEMORIAL HOSPITAL
W N H
1300 E 5th Ave, Winfield, KS 67156-2407
Tel (620) 221-2300 *Founded/Ownrshp* 1927
Sales 27.3MM *EMP* 350
Accts Wendling Noe & Nelson Johnson
SIC 8062 General medical & surgical hospitals; General medical & surgical hospitals
COO: Christopher Morrissey
CFO: Debbie Hockenbury
Dir OR: Tonya Gibson
Dir Inf Cn: Connie Schaefer
Dir Lab: Dave Van Allen
Dir Rx: Kelle Thompson
Dir IT: Charles Tatro
IT Man: Randy Mayo
Mktg Mgr: Tom Embers
Obsttrcn: Daniel Miller
Phys Thrpy: Linda Lange

D-U-N-S 10-005-8874
NEWTON-CONOVER CITY SCHOOL DISTRICT
605 N Ashe Ave, Newton, NC 28658-3120
Tel (828) 464-3191 *Founded/Ownrshp* 1933
Sales 27.0MM *EMP* 450
SIC 8211 School board; School board
V Ch: Jeanne Jarrett

D-U-N-S 12-101-4658
NEWTON-WELLESLEY HEALTH CARE SYSTEM INC
2014 Washington St, Newton, MA 02462-1607
Tel (617) 243-6000 *Founded/Ownrshp* 1983
Sales 173.5MM *EMP* 31
SIC 8741 7374 6512 Hospital management; Data processing & preparation; Commercial & industrial building operation; Hospital management; Data processing & preparation; Commercial & industrial building operation
Pr: John P Bihldorff
COO: Patrick Jordan
**Treas:* Ronald E Bartlett
Assoc Dir: Ashot Ionesian
Assoc Dir: Francis Luscinskas
Admn Mgr: Ivy Babbitt
Admn Mgr: Brenda Hudd
Off Mgr: Patricia Barylick
Nurse Mgr: Deborah Phillips
Off Admin: Georgeana McKenzie
Off Admin: Dorothy Voutiritsa

D-U-N-S 06-042-8943 IMP
NEWTOWN NINE INC
OHIO MATERIALS HANDLING
8155 Roll And Hold Pkwy, Macedonia, OH 44056-2146
Tel (440) 871-0623 *Founded/Ownrshp* 1976
Sales 44.9MME *EMP* 131
SIC 5084 Lift trucks & parts; Materials handling machinery; Lift trucks & parts; Materials handling machinery
Pr: James P Orenga
COO: Eric Eide

D-U-N-S 96-391-6031
NEWTOWN PUBLIC SCHOOL DISTRICT
3 Primrose St, Newtown, CT 06470-5307
Tel (203) 426-7621 *Founded/Ownrshp* 2010
Sales 32.5MME *EMP* 600
SIC 8211 Public combined elementary & secondary school; Public combined elementary & secondary school
Teacher Pr: David Abby

D-U-N-S 96-883-7737
NEWTOWN SAVINGS BANK
39 Main St, Newtown, CT 06470-2134
Tel (203) 426-2563 *Founded/Ownrshp* 2011
Sales NA *EMP* 68E
SIC 6022 State commercial banks; State commercial banks
CEO: John Martocci
CFO: William McCarthy
Ofcr: Shawn Gregory
Sr VP: Jim Cotter
Sr VP: Kenneth Weinstein
VP: Lyndell Bartulis
VP: Michael Dimech
VP: Dave Loftus
VP: Dan Long
VP: Tom Lutz
VP: David McNamara
VP: Tanya Truax
VP: Marlene Warren
VP: Pauta Woodhouse

D-U-N-S 02-992-5488
NEWTRON BEAUMONT LLC
(*Suby of* NEWTRON HOLDINGS LLC) ★
1905 Industrial Park Rd, Nederland, TX 77627-3125
Tel (409) 727-6344 *Founded/Ownrshp* 2011
Sales 109.3MM *EMP* 600
SIC 1731 Electrical work; Electrical work
Pr: Mike Defee

D-U-N-S 10-719-2858
NEWTRON GROUP L L C
8183 W El Cajon Dr, Baton Rouge, LA 70815-8093
Tel (225) 927-8921 *Founded/Ownrshp* 1982
Sales 430.3MM *EMP* 2,000[E]
Accts Hannis T Bourgeois Llp Baton
SIC 1731 Professional instrument repair services; Electrical work; Electrical work
CEO: Newton B Thomas
Pr: Bruce A Beard
Pr: John Schempf
CFO: Tami H Misuraca
VP: Duff Schempf
Rgnl Mgr: Mark Richardson
Genl Mgr: Phillip Morgan
Site Mgr: Steve Aaser
Site Mgr: Phillip Darbonne
Site Mgr: Kevin Ganucheau
Site Mgr: Richard Riddle

D-U-N-S 07-920-0732
NEWTRON HOLDINGS LLC
(*Suby of* NEWTRON GROUP L L C) ★
8183 W El Cajon Dr, Baton Rouge, LA 70815-8093
Tel (225) 927-8921 *Founded/Ownrshp* 2013
Sales 138.4MM *EMP* 800[E]
Accts Hannis T Bourgeois Llp Baton
SIC 1731 Professional instrument repair services; Electrical work; Industrial buildings, new construction; Electrical work
CFO: Tami H Misuraca

D-U-N-S 13-357-0601
NEWWAVE TELECOM AND TECHNOLOGIES INC
6518 Meadowridge Rd # 100, Elkridge, MD 21075-6458
Tel (410) 782-0476 *Founded/Ownrshp* 2004
Sales 30.0MM *EMP* 115
SIC 7371 Computer software development
CEO: Patrick Munis
**CFO:* Richard Marksberry
CIO: John Booth
Pgrm Dir: Timothy Breland

NEWYORK-PRESBYTERIAN HOSPITAL
See NEW YORK AND PRESBYTERIAN HOSPITAL

D-U-N-S 13-336-4179
NEWZOOM INC
ZOOM-SYSTEMS
22 4th St Fl 16, San Francisco, CA 94103-3148
Tel (415) 400-8000 *Founded/Ownrshp* 2001
Sales 37.1MM[E] *EMP* 110
SIC 5963 Direct selling establishments
CEO: John Jack Lawrence
**Ch:* Gower Smith
Ex VP: Bob Bear
**Sr VP:* David Popler
**Sr VP:* Jen Stephan
Sr VP: Jennifer Stephan
**Sr VP:* Russ Yoshinaka
VP: Kalon Guiterrex
Mktg Mgr: Peggy Chiu
Board of Directors: John Anderson, Christopher Dawe, John Dyson, John Jack Lawrence, Tom Naughton, Dave Schwab, Gower Smith, Steve Williams

D-U-N-S 96-351-3648
NEX PERFORMANCE FILMS INC
(*Suby of* MASON WELLS INC) ★
1264 E High St, Milton, WI 53563-8682
Tel (608) 531-1405 *Founded/Ownrshp* 2010
Sales 53.0MM[E] *EMP* 180
SIC 3081 Polyethylene film; Polyethylene film
Pr: Kathy Bolhous
Dir IT: Eric Tuttle

NEX SOLUTIONS
See NEWCO INDUSTRIES LLC

D-U-N-S 60-623-4052
NEXTRANSPORT INC
(*Suby of* NIPPON EXPRESS USA INC) ★
13900 State Route 287, East Liberty, OH 43319-9466
Tel (937) 645-3761 *Founded/Ownrshp* 1989
Sales 34.9MM *EMP* 220
Accts Gbq Partners Llc Columbus Oh
SIC 4226 Special warehousing & storage; Special warehousing & storage
Pr: Tosaki Watanabe
**Pr:* Fumio Moriyama
**Pr:* Toshiaki Watanabe
**Ex VP:* Tomie Mori
**VP:* Teizo Kanda
Snr Mgr: Charlene Jacobs

NEX-TECH
See RURAL TELEPHONE SERVICE CO INC

D-U-N-S 96-118-2037 IMP
NEX-TECH INC
(*Suby of* NEX-TECH) ★
2418 Vine St, Hays, KS 67601-2456
Tel (785) 625-7070 *Founded/Ownrshp* 1989
Sales 51.6MM *EMP* 300
SIC 5999 Telephone & communication equipment; Telephone & communication equipment
CEO: Jimmy Todd
COO: Eric Helm
**COO:* Michael Pollock
**CFO:* Rhonda Goddard
Treas: Marcie Williams
Exec: Thomas Green
CIO: Mike Pollack
IT Man: Justin Dempsey
IT Man: Bobby Wagoner
Site Mgr: Diana Staab
VP Mktg: Todd Tortoretti

D-U-N-S 17-220-1845
NEX-TECH WIRELESS LLC
(*Suby of* NEX-TECH INC) ★
3001 New Way, Hays, KS 67601-3262
Tel (785) 567-4281 *Founded/Ownrshp* 2004
Sales 27.0MM[E] *EMP* 100
SIC 4812 Cellular telephone services
CEO: Jon Lightle
Opers Supe: Roy Inlow

D-U-N-S 94-316-9482 IMP/EXP
NEXAIR LLC
1385 Corporate Ave, Memphis, TN 38132-1723
Tel (901) 396-5050 *Founded/Ownrshp* 1940
Sales 236.0MM[E] *EMP* 307[E]
Accts Thompson Dunavant Plc Memphis
SIC 5169 5084 7699 7359 Industrial gases; Industrial machinery & equipment; Welding equipment repair; Equipment rental & leasing; Industrial gases; Industrial machinery & equipment; Welding equipment repair; Equipment rental & leasing
CEO: M Kevin McEniry
**Treas:* John Coker
**Bd of Dir:* Mike Dlugach
Ex VP: Steve Atkins
VP: Terry Federline
VP: Michael McFerrin
VP: Becky Reed
**VP:* Ben Wingfield
Area Mgr: Merrel Pennington
Brnch Mgr: Cameron Donahoe
IT Man: Jeff Corkran

D-U-N-S 00-318-3548 IMP
NEXANS AEROSPACE USA LLC
(*Suby of* NEXANS USA INC) ★
600 S Parker Street Ext, Elm City, NC 27822-8304
Tel (252) 236-4311 *Founded/Ownrshp* 2000
Sales 24.3MM[E] *EMP* 125
SIC 3357 Nonferrous wiredrawing & insulating
Pr: Stephen Hall
Dir IT: Bob Travitz

D-U-N-S 62-365-2427 IMP/EXP
NEXANS ENERGY USA INC
INDUSTRIAL CABLES
(*Suby of* NEXANS CANADA INC)
25 Oakland Ave, Chester, NY 10918-1011
Tel (845) 469-2141 *Founded/Ownrshp* 2002
Sales 63.6MM[E] *EMP* 160
SIC 3496 Cable, uninsulated wire: made from purchased wire; Cable, uninsulated wire: made from purchased wire
Ch Bd: Steve Hall
**Pr:* Gordon Thursfield
**CFO:* Julie Land
**VP:* Sande Aivaliotis
Sfty Dirs: Frank Onofrio
Plnt Mgr: David Hawker

D-U-N-S 01-072-7712 IMP/EXP
NEXANS USA INC
(*Suby of* NEXANS PARTICIPATIONS)
39 2nd St Nw, Hickory, NC 28601-6104
Tel (828) 323-2660 *Founded/Ownrshp* 2000
Sales 215.8MM[E] *EMP* 850
SIC 3357 3661 3678 Communication wire; Telephones & telephone apparatus; Electronic connectors; Communication wire; Telephones & telephone apparatus; Electronic connectors
Pr: Stephen Hall
**Pr:* Yvon Raak
**Treas:* Kevin Stinson
Genl Mgr: Carlos Sanchez

D-U-N-S 11-956-0824
NEXANT INC
101 2nd St Ste 1000, San Francisco, CA 94105-3651
Tel (415) 369-1000 *Founded/Ownrshp* 1999
Sales 174.9MM[E] *EMP* 610
SIC 8748 Energy conservation consultant; Energy conservation consultant
Pr: Basam Sarandah
CFO: Michael Alvarez
CFO: Jonathan Foster
Bd of Dir: Richard Balzhiser
Sr VP: Bruce Burke
VP: Michael Alexander
VP: Marcos Cesar
VP: Gerald Choi
VP: Richard Edwards
VP: Clive Gibson
VP: Oton Iskarpatyoti
VP: Sarah Yarger Kienzle
VP: Peter Noland
VP: Virgil Rose
VP: Bob Streich
Exec: Bill O'Riordan

D-U-N-S 61-450-4707
NEXBANK SSB
2515 Mckinney Ave # 1100, Dallas, TX 75201-1945
Tel (972) 934-4700 *Founded/Ownrshp* 2005
Sales NA *EMP* 85[E]
SIC 6021 National commercial banks; National commercial banks
Pr: John Holt
V Ch: Matt Beshears
**COO:* S Matt Siekiels
**CFO:* Kenneth R Hanks
CFO: Mike Rossi
**Ex VP:* Joshua B Bock
Sr VP: Tamara Hambright
Sr VP: Mary Pirrello
**Sr VP:* Grant Smith
VP: Tish Ashley
VP: Jeffrey Kocher
VP: Mike Mendelow
VP: Joe Synatschk

D-U-N-S 12-890-3288
NEXCARE HEALTH SYSTEMS LLC
10503 Citation Dr Ste 100, Brighton, MI 48116-6551
Tel (810) 534-0150 *Founded/Ownrshp* 2004
Sales 32.6MM[E] *EMP* 245
SIC 8741 Nursing & personal care facility management
COO: Henry Boutros
Snr Mgr: Carolyn Merucci

D-U-N-S 02-760-1061 IMP/EXP
NEXCEL SYNTHETICS LLC
799 Industrial Blvd, Chatsworth, GA 30705-2021
Tel (706) 695-8230 *Founded/Ownrshp* 1997
Sales 21.7MM[E] *EMP* 200
SIC 2281 2824 Manmade & synthetic fiber yarns, spun; Organic fibers, noncellulosic; Manmade & synthetic fiber yarns, spun; Organic fibers, noncellulosic
**CFO:* Christopher R Martin

NEXCOM
See NAVY EXCHANGE SERVICE COMMAND

D-U-N-S 94-779-7650
NEXCYCLE INC
5221 N O Connor Blvd # 850, Irving, TX 75039-3714
Tel (972) 506-7200 *Founded/Ownrshp* 1994
Sales 130.8MM[E] *EMP* 570
SIC 4953 Recycling, waste materials; Recycling, waste materials
CEO: Alex Rankin

NEXEN ENERGY HOLDINGS
See NEXEN PETROLEUM HOLDINGS USA INC

D-U-N-S 17-675-5437
NEXEN PETROLEUM HOLDINGS USA INC
NEXEN ENERGY HOLDINGS
(*Suby of* NEXEN HOLDINGS (USA) INC)
945 Bunker Hill Rd # 1400, Houston, TX 77024-1358
Tel (832) 714-5000 *Founded/Ownrshp* 1989
Sales 62.9MM[E] *EMP* 145
SIC 1382 1311 Oil & gas exploration services; Crude petroleum production; Oil & gas exploration services; Crude petroleum production
Pr: Brian C Reinsborough
**Pr:* Douglas B Otten
**Treas:* George Harvey
**VP:* Grant W Dreger
**VP:* Gregg E Radetsky
**VP:* Edward L Ramirez Jr

D-U-N-S 06-413-7938
NEXEN PETROLEUM USA INC
(*Suby of* NEXEN ENERGY HOLDINGS) ★
945 Bunker Hill Rd # 1400, Houston, TX 77024-1358
Tel (972) 450-4600 *Founded/Ownrshp* 1988
Sales 62.9MM[E] *EMP* 145
SIC 1311 1382 Crude petroleum production; Natural gas production; Oil & gas exploration services
Pr: Peter D Addy
**Pr:* Douglas B Otten
**Treas:* George E Harvey
**VP:* Grant W Dreger
**VP:* Ian W Macleod
**VP:* Amit K Mehra
**VP:* Gregg E Radetsky
**VP:* Edward L Ramirez Jr
Exec: Abu Elfaki
Genl Mgr: Dan Murray

D-U-N-S 83-043-5637
NEXENTA SYSTEMS INC
451 El Cmino Real Ste 201, Santa Clara, CA 95050
Tel (408) 791-3341 *Founded/Ownrshp* 2004
Sales 42.9MM[E] *EMP* 230
SIC 7372 Operating systems computer software; Operating systems computer software
Ch Bd: Tarkan Maner
Pr: Fitzgerald Jim
COO: Phil Underwood
**CFO:* Rick Martig
Bd of Dir: Toshiya Otani
**Ofcr:* Evan Powell
VP: Ricardo Antuna
**VP:* Jon Ash
VP: Chris Farnum
**VP:* Rick Hayes
**VP:* Brad Stone
VP: Jason Yoho
Adv Bd Mbr: Mark Lockareff

D-U-N-S 07-834-6156
NEXEO SOLUTIONS HOLDINGS LLC
3 Waterway Square Pl # 1000, The Woodlands, TX 77380-3488
Tel (281) 297-0700 *Founded/Ownrshp* 2011
Sales 3.9MMM *EMP* 2,450[E]
Accts Pricewaterhousecoopers Llp Ho
SIC 5169 5162 Industrial chemicals; Plastics materials & basic shapes; Industrial chemicals; Plastics materials & basic shapes
Pr: David A Bradley
**Ch Bd:* Dan F Smith
CFO: Ross J Crane
Treas: Michael Everett
Ofcr: Lisa P Britt
Ofcr: David L Chapman
Ofcr: Michael B Farnell Jr
Sr VP: Henry E Harrell III
Sr VP: Alberto J Machado
Sr VP: Shawn D Williams
VP: Philip S Krichilsky
VP: Steven Seelig
Board of Directors: Kenneth M Burke, Steven J Schneider, Steven B Schwarzwaelder, Walter L Sharp, John H Williford, Nathan H Wright, Christopher J Yip

D-U-N-S 07-013-9068 IMP/EXP
NEXEO SOLUTIONS LLC
CHEMICAL SPECIALISTS & DEV CSD
(*Suby of* NEXEO SOLUTIONS LLC) ★
9733 Meador Rd, Conroe, TX 77303-2335
Tel (800) 292-3336 *Founded/Ownrshp* 2013
Sales 23.9MM[E] *EMP* 65
SIC 2851 7389 5198 2842 5172 Paints & allied products; Paints & paint additives; Lacquer: bases, dopes, thinner; Packaging & labeling services; Paints; Specialty cleaning, polishes & sanitation goods; Fuel oil
Pr: David Bradley
**CFO:* Michael J Farnell Jr
**Ex VP:* Ross Crane
VP: Sheila Rooker
VP: Tom Waltermier
Sls Mgr: Joe Kimball

D-U-N-S 96-641-0859 IMP/EXP
NEXEO SOLUTIONS LLC
(*Suby of* NEXEO SOLUTIONS HOLDINGS LLC) ★
3 Waterway Square Pl # 1000, The Woodlands, TX 77380-3487
Tel (281) 297-0700 *Founded/Ownrshp* 2010
Sales 3.3MMM *EMP* 2,584[E]
Accts Pricewaterhousecoopers Llp
SIC 5169 5162 2821 Industrial chemicals; Plastics materials & basic shapes; Plastics materials & resins; Industrial chemicals; Plastics materials & basic shapes; Plastics materials & resins
Pr: David A Bradley
**Pr:* Michael B Farnell Jr
**Treas:* Michael Everett
**Ex VP:* Lisa Britt
**Ex VP:* David Chapman
**Sr VP:* Alberto Machado
VP: Jim Harris
Dir Lab: Melissa Lettow
Dist Mgr: Greg Bermosk
Dist Mgr: Michael Dvorak
Dist Mgr: John Frattini

D-U-N-S 00-193-0502 IMP
NEXERGY INC (OH)
ICCNEXERGY
(*Suby of* ICC NEXERGY) ★
5115 Prkcnter Ave Ste 275, Dublin, OH 43017
Tel (614) 351-2191 *Founded/Ownrshp* 1951, 1991
Sales 31.3MM[E] *EMP* 300
Accts Gbq Partners Llc Columbus Oh
SIC 3679 Harness assemblies for electronic use: wire or cable; Harness assemblies for electronic use: wire or cable
CEO: Phil Glandon
**COO:* Joe Dougherty
**CFO:* John Stanton
**Ex VP:* John Costa
**Ex VP:* Joseph A Dougherty
**VP:* Randy Ibrahim
**Prin:* Geo McConnaughey
**Prin:* Earl Sala
**Prin:* Jr Robert Whitesell
CIO: Bill Ford
IT Man: Bill Foard
Board of Directors: Lynn S Glandon, Penny S Rothrock, Sammy P Rothrock

D-U-N-S 05-564-9319
NEXERGY TAUBER LLC
(*Suby of* ICC NEXERGY)
4 Westbrook Corp Ctr 90, Westchester, IL 60154-5752
Tel (708) 316-4407 *Founded/Ownrshp* 2010
Sales 35.5MM[E] *EMP* 345[E]
SIC 3629 Battery chargers, rectifying or nonrotating
Pr: Stephen McClure
CFO: Joseph Italiano

D-U-N-S 18-538-4328 EXP
NEXFOR (USA) INC
FRASER PAPERS
(*Suby of* NORBORD INC)
82 Bridge Ave, Madawaska, ME 04756-1229
Tel (207) 728-3321 *Founded/Ownrshp* 1987
Sales 147.9MM[E] *EMP* 1,000
SIC 2621 2493 Paper mills; Fiberboard, other vegetable pulp; Waferboard; Paper mills; Fiberboard, other vegetable pulp; Waferboard
Pr: Bert Martin
QC Dir: Roger Bergeron
Opers Mgr: Richard Arnold

NEXGEN BUILDING SUPPLY
See NEXGEN ENTERPRISES INC

NEXGEN BUILDING SUPPLY
See HWZ DISTRIBUTION GROUP LLC

D-U-N-S 16-967-0366
■ **NEXGEN COMMUNICATIONS LLC**
(*Suby of* EDO CORP) ★
44965 Aviation Dr Ste 400, Dulles, VA 20166-7540
Tel (703) 996-2900 *Founded/Ownrshp* 2005
Sales 33.1MM[E] *EMP* 117
SIC 8748 Telecommunications consultant
Pr: Charles Gumas
**CEO:* Mark D Adams
**Prin:* Jonathan R Stehn
IT Man: Catherine Lewine
Opers Mgr: Bill Clouse

D-U-N-S 00-184-8203
NEXGEN ENTERPRISES INC (OH)
NEXGEN BUILDING SUPPLY
3274 Spring Grove Ave, Cincinnati, OH 45225-1338
Tel (513) 618-0300 *Founded/Ownrshp* 1920
Sales 144.2MM[E] *EMP* 320
Accts Barnes Dennig & Company Ltd C
SIC 5032 Brick, stone & related material; Brick, stone & related material
CEO: Robert Hoge
**Pr:* Richard C Wolgemuth
**CFO:* Bruce J Fahey
**Sr VP:* Bruce Kirchhofer
**VP:* Richard J Hoge

D-U-N-S 82-726-7746 EXP
NEXGEN MOLD & TOOL INC
4300 Security Pkwy, New Albany, IN 47150-9374
Tel (812) 945-3375 *Founded/Ownrshp* 2009
Sales 20.4MM[E] *EMP* 40
SIC 3089 3544 Injection molded finished plastic products; Special dies, tools, jigs & fixtures
Pr: John Lukes
CFO: Kevin Rose
VP: Nichole Lukes

D-U-N-S 78-362-2330 IMP/EXP
NEXGEN PACKAGING LLC
1130 Windham Pkwy, Romeoville, IL 60446-1692
Tel (805) 848-4004 *Founded/Ownrshp* 2006
Sales 24.8MM[E] *EMP* 60[E]
SIC 5199 Packaging materials

D-U-N-S 04-848-8621
NEXGEN PHARMA INC
46 Corporate Park Ste 100, Irvine, CA 92606-3121
Tel (949) 261-2928 *Founded/Ownrshp* 1959
Sales 73.4MM[E] *EMP* 210
SIC 2834 Pharmaceutical preparations; Pharmaceutical preparations
CEO: Steven Brown
Sr VP: Connie Taylor
VP: Jane Drinkwater
VP: Robert Van Osdel

Prgrm Mgr: Cory Brown
IT Man: Robert Verdugo
Info Man: Joel Garry
Prd Mgr: Glendaa Finn
VP Sls: Jane Drinkwalter

D-U-N-S 60-800-8280
NEXGENIX INC
2 Peters Canyon Rd # 200, Irvine, CA 92606-1798
Tel (714) 665-6240 *Founded/Ownrshp* 1990
Sales 25.1MM^E *EMP* 441
SIC 7371 8748 4813 Computer software development; Systems analysis or design; ; Computer software development; Systems analysis or design;
CEO: Rick Dutta
Ch Bd: Don Ganguly
COO: Mark Iwanowski
VP: Dave R Andrade
VP: Carol Munroe
VP: Scott Raskin
VP: Ravi Renduchintala

D-U-N-S 13-170-3688 IMP
NEXGRILL INDUSTRIES INC
14050 Laurelwood Pl, Chino, CA 91710-5454
Tel (909) 598-8799 *Founded/Ownrshp* 1993
Sales 39.2MM^E *EMP* 100
SIC 5023 3631 Grills, barbecue; Barbecues, grills & braziers (outdoor cooking); Grills, barbecue; Barbecues, grills & braziers (outdoor cooking)
Pr: Sherman Lin
Exec: Shirley Chan

NEXICOR
See SENCO BRANDS INC

D-U-N-S 00-320-7714
NEXIDIA INC
FAST-TALK COMMUNICATIONS
3565 Piedmont Rd Ne 2-400, Atlanta, GA 30305-8203
Tel (404) 495-7220 *Founded/Ownrshp* 2000
Sales 40.4MM^E *EMP* 100
SIC 7371 Computer software development
Ex VP: David Bridges
**CFO:* Thomas Allgood
Ch: Trevor Chamberlain
**Sr VP:* Drew Lanham
**Sr VP:* Ryan Pellet
**Sr VP:* Mark Reich
**Sr VP:* Howard Smith
**VP:* Byron Arnold
**VP:* James Delmerico
**VP:* Jon W Ezrine
**VP:* Marsal Gavalda
VP: Jon Harmer
VP: Mike Hutchison
VP: Newton Quantz
VP: Chad Rounsavall
VP: Jeff Schlueter
**VP:* Larry Skowronek
VP: Jeff Strnad
VP: Daniel Turnell
VP: Jonathan Wax
VP: Mike Whitehouse

D-U-N-S 00-209-0979
NEXIENT LLC
7707 Gateway Blvd Ste 100, Newark, CA 94560-1160
Tel (415) 992-7277 *Founded/Ownrshp* 2009
Sales 32.4MM^E *EMP* 250^E
SIC 7379 Computer related consulting services; Computer related consulting services
CEO: Mark Orttung
**Ch Bd:* Neeraj Gupta
**Chf Mktg O:* Debashish Sinha
**Ofcr:* Stephanie Moore

D-U-N-S 00-645-8350
NEXION HEALTH AT CHERRY CREEK INC
CHERRY CREEK NURSING CENTER
14699 E Hampden Ave, Aurora, CO 80014-3903
Tel (303) 693-0111 *Founded/Ownrshp* 1995
Sales 17.0MM *EMP* 304
SIC 8051 8093 Skilled nursing care facilities; Rehabilitation center, outpatient treatment; Skilled nursing care facilities; Rehabilitation center, outpatient treatment
CEO: Gary Walker
Mktg Dir: Brian Troccoli

D-U-N-S 00-306-5252
NEXION HEALTH AT ROCKFORD INC
ROCKFORD HEALTH CARE CENTER
6937 Warfield Ave, Sykesville, MD 21784-7454
Tel (410) 552-9860 *Founded/Ownrshp* 2000
Sales 7.4MM^E *EMP* 309
SIC 8051 Skilled nursing care facilities; Skilled nursing care facilities
Pr: Fran Kirley

D-U-N-S 01-268-2295
NEXION HEALTH INC
6937 Warfield Ave, Sykesville, MD 21784-7454
Tel (410) 552-4800 *Founded/Ownrshp* 2000
Sales 182.0MM^E *EMP* 5,000
SIC 8051 Skilled nursing care facilities; Skilled nursing care facilities
Pr: Fran Kirley
**CFO:* Bretton Bolt
**Treas:* Keith Mutschler
VP: Merra Riner
VP: Ayanna Tasby
IT Man: Ryan Langlan
Mktg Dir: Kimberly Howard
Mktg Dir: Melissa Louviere
Mktg Dir: Ronda Marsh
Genl Couns: Brian Lee

D-U-N-S 05-691-8980 IMP/EXP
NEXIRA INC
(Suby of NEXIRA)
15 Somerset St, Somerville, NJ 08876-2828
Tel (908) 704-7480 *Founded/Ownrshp* 1981
Sales 22.5MM *EMP* 10
Accts Constantin Associates Llp Ne
SIC 2051 5145 2099 Bakery: wholesale or wholesale/retail combined; Confectionery; Emulsifiers, food

Pr: Stephane Dondain
COO: Barbara Thiello

D-U-N-S 55-758-3296
NEXITY BANK
3680 Grandview Pkwy, Birmingham, AL 35243-3326
Tel (205) 972-1378 *Founded/Ownrshp* 2011
Sales NA *EMP* 37^E
SIC 6022 State commercial banks; State commercial banks
Ch Bd: Greg L Lee
Sr VP: Cheryl Ervi
Sr VP: Gibilterra Jennifer
Sr VP: S Lokey
Sr VP: Cindy Russo
Sr VP: Frank Wagnon
VP: Michael Bridges
VP: Marc Gall

D-U-N-S 07-876-3974
NEXIUS SOLUTIONS INC
1301 Central Expy S # 200, Allen, TX 75013-8090
Tel (703) 650-7777 *Founded/Ownrshp* 2010
Sales 197.8MM *EMP* 464
SIC 5045 Computers, peripherals & software; Computers, peripherals & software
Pr: Mark Baysinger
VP: Richard Statler
VP Mktg: Schanen Mickolas
VP Mktg: Julia Pitlik
VP Sls: John Harris
Sls Mgr: Minnie Walker

NEXIUS WIRELESS
See CSWS INC

D-U-N-S 16-730-1675 IMP/EXP
NEXLINK COMMUNICATIONS LLC
3355 Bald Mountain Rd # 10, Auburn Hills, MI 48326-4312
Tel (248) 409-2511 *Founded/Ownrshp* 2004
Sales 124.0MM^E *EMP* 200^E
SIC 5065 Communication equipment; Communication equipment
Pr: Jeffrey Messano
**VP:* Steve Cosgrove
VP: Rick Johnson
Mktg Dir: Scott Conner
Sls Mgr: Andy Griglio

D-U-N-S 06-724-8711
NEXONE INC
1725 E 1450 S Ste 330, Clearfield, UT 84015-2289
Tel (801) 926-1060 *Founded/Ownrshp* 2003
Sales 21.1MM^E *EMP* 180
SIC 7389 Telemarketing services
Pr: Stan Nakamura
Dir Bus: Kent Carson
Secur Mgr: Sheri Butler

D-U-N-S 10-257-4139
NEXREV LLC
601 Development Dr # 300, Plano, TX 75074-8358
Tel (972) 578-0505 *Founded/Ownrshp* 1994
Sales 42.1MM^E *EMP* 150
SIC 1731 Energy management controls
CEO: Kenneth R Smith
Opers Mgr: William Wright
Mktg Dir: Kenny Robinson

D-U-N-S 06-415-5755
■ **NEXSAN CORP**
(Suby of IMATION CORP) ★
1445 Lawrence Dr, Thousand Oaks, CA 91320-1311
Tel (866) 463-9726 *Founded/Ownrshp* 2012
Sales 80.7MM^E *EMP* 200
SIC 5084 Tanks, storage; Tanks, storage
CEO: Philip Black
**CFO:* Gene Spies
Ex VP: Jim Molenda
Ex VP: Walter X Palhetas
Sr VP: Robert Woolery
VP: Jim Melenda
Natl Sales: Raymond Cabana
Sls Dir: Dave Stoner

D-U-N-S 01-762-1454 IMP
NEXSAN TECHNOLOGIES INC
1445 Lawrence Dr, Thousand Oaks, CA 91320-1311
Tel (805) 418-2700 *Founded/Ownrshp* 2001
Sales 54.4MM^E *EMP* 189
SIC 3572 Computer storage devices; Computer storage devices
CEO: Philip Black
**CFO:* Gene Spies
**Ofcr:* George Symons
Ex VP: Andy Hill
Sr VP: Victoria Grey
Sr VP: Kevin Herrington
VP: Frank Patterson
Dir IT: Bob Hayes
IT Man: Catherine Christian
Opers Mgr: Daniel Thom
Manager: Ross Distefano

D-U-N-S 15-441-1524
NEXSEN PRUET LLC
1230 Main St Ste 700, Columbia, SC 29201-6220
Tel (803) 771-8900 *Founded/Ownrshp* 1945
Sales 40.7MM^E *EMP* 225
SIC 8111

D-U-N-S 05-816-8001
▲ **NEXSTAR BROADCASTING GROUP INC**
545 E John Carpenter Fwy # 700, Irving, TX 75062-3932
Tel (972) 373-8800 *Founded/Ownrshp* 1997
Sales 631.3MM *EMP* 3,464
Tkr Sym NXST *Exch* NGM
SIC 4833 Television broadcasting stations; Television broadcasting stations
Ch Bd: Perry A Sook
Pr: Rich Engberg
COO: Brian Jones
CFO: Thomas E Carter
Ex VP: Timothy C Busch
Sr VP: Todd A Porch
Sr VP: Todd Porch
Sr VP: Julie Pruett

Sr VP: Rick Rogala
Sr VP: Elizabeth Ryder
Sr VP: William Sally
VP: Patrick Cusick
VP: Craig Marrs
VP: Dione Rigsby
VP: Jon Skorburg
VP: Richard Stolpe
VP: Randy Stone
VP: Stephen Ventura
VP: Arika Zink
Exec: Ethan Miller
Exec: Scott Price
Board of Directors: Geoff Armstrong, Jay M Grossman, C Thomas McMillen, Lisbeth McNabb, Dennis A Miller, I Martin Pompadur

NEXT
See NILPETER USA INC

D-U-N-S 96-500-7052 IMP
NEXT CREATIONS HOLDINGS LLC
(Suby of ALOK INTERNATIONAL INC) ★
105 Madison Ave Rm 502, New York, NY 10016-7547
Tel (212) 447-8700 *Founded/Ownrshp* 2010
Sales 45.0MM *EMP* 10^E
SIC 5023 Decorative home furnishings & supplies
CEO: Arun Agarwal
Pr: Michael Vidra
CFO: Gary Adelman
VP Sls: Francine Lauri

D-U-N-S 86-109-6816 IMP
NEXT DAY BLINDS CORP
8251 Preston Ct Ste B, Jessup, MD 20794-9369
Tel (240) 568-8800 *Founded/Ownrshp* 1993
Sales 78.7MM^E *EMP* 400
SIC 5023 2591 5719 1799 Window furnishings; Drapery hardware & blinds & shades; Window furnishings; Window treatment installation; Window furnishings; Drapery hardware & blinds & shades; Window furnishings; Window treatment installation
Pr: Steve Freishtat
Ofcr: Allison Siegel
**Ex VP:* Fred Alladin
VP: Meghan Hodge
Dist Mgr: Meredith Bell
Dist Mgr: Evan Roberts
Store Mgr: Justin Moran
CIO: Mike Schmitt
IT Man: Jamie Patel
Web Dev: Stephen Blades
Mtls Mgr: Adam Steinbock

D-U-N-S 02-045-3320
NEXT DOOR FOUNDATION INC
FAMILY LITERACY
2545 N 29th St, Milwaukee, WI 53210-3155
Tel (414) 562-2929 *Founded/Ownrshp* 1971
Sales 18.8MM *EMP* 280
Accts Wipfli Llp Madison Wi
SIC 8211 Kindergarten; Kindergarten
Pr: Thomas E Arenberg
Dir Vol: Martina Stevens
Bd of Dir: Marcia Y Lucas
Prgrm Mgr: Sharon Marks
Mktg Dir: Beverly Watkins

D-U-N-S 84-345-7669
NEXT FINANCIAL GROUP INC
2500 Wilcrest Dr Ste 620, Houston, TX 77042-2757
Tel (713) 789-7122 *Founded/Ownrshp* 1998
Sales 30.0MM^E *EMP* 130
SIC 8742 Financial consultant
Pr: Barry Knight
COO: Robert Levitt
CFO: Mark Brooks
Ch: Gordon D Angelo
Ofcr: Leslie Jallans
VP: Heather Barker
VP: Karen Eyster
VP: Glen McRary
VP: Mike Muluihill
VP: Michael Spriggs
Dist Mgr: Solomon Howard

NEXT GENERATION BAG
See NEXT GENERATION FILMS INC

D-U-N-S 14-317-4873
NEXT GENERATION BAG INC
230 Industrial Dr, Mansfield, OH 44904-1346
Tel (419) 884-1327 *Founded/Ownrshp* 2001
Sales 23.2MM^E *EMP* 350
SIC 2673 Plastic & pliofilm bags; Plastic & pliofilm bags
CEO: John D Frecka

D-U-N-S 80-916-7190
NEXT GENERATION CHILDRENS CENTER INC
201 Cedar Hill St, Marlborough, MA 01752-3004
Tel (508) 480-9222 *Founded/Ownrshp* 1993
Sales 6.4MM^E *EMP* 300
SIC 8351 Child day care services; Child day care services
Pr: Donna Kelleher
**Pr:* Walter Kelleher

D-U-N-S 96-223-5375 IMP
NEXT GENERATION FILMS INC
NEXT GENERATION BAG
230 Industrial Dr, Mansfield, OH 44904-1346
Tel (419) 884-8150 *Founded/Ownrshp* 2007
Sales 38.1MM^E *EMP* 128
SIC 2671 2673 Plastic film, coated or laminated for packaging; Plastic & pliofilm bags; Plastic film, coated or laminated for packaging; Plastic & pliofilm bags
CEO: David A Frecka
**Pr:* Dan Niss
**CFO:* David J Rehfeldt
IT Man: Jason Poth
Sls Mgr: Michael Helinski

D-U-N-S 80-806-2504
NEXT GENERATION VENDING AND FOOD SERVICE INC
5 Campanelli Cir Ste 200, Canton, MA 02021-2480
Tel (781) 828-2345 *Founded/Ownrshp* 2011
Sales NA *EMP* 850^E
SIC 5046

D-U-N-S 06-017-8073
NEXT GENERATION VENDING LLC
800 Technology Center Dr 1a, Stoughton, MA 02072-4721
Tel (781) 828-2345 *Founded/Ownrshp* 2011
Sales NA *EMP* 505
SIC 3581

D-U-N-S 08-903-1780
NEXT GENERATION WIRELESS INC
215 1/2 Main St, Cedar Falls, IA 50613-2735
Tel (319) 266-5070 *Founded/Ownrshp* 2001
Sales 23.0MM *EMP* 97
SIC 4812 Cellular telephone services
Pr: Bill Bradford
CFO: James Rozendaal

D-U-N-S 10-545-7746
NEXT PHASE INC
COMFORT KEEPERS
1410 S Main St, Roswell, NM 88203-5568
Tel (575) 624-9999 *Founded/Ownrshp* 2001
Sales 3.7MM *EMP* 2,400
SIC 8082 Home health care services; Home health care services
Pr: Cindy Lewis

D-U-N-S 83-138-9387
NEXT STEP LIVING INC
21 Drydock Ave Ste 142, Boston, MA 02210-2397
Tel (866) 867-8729 *Founded/Ownrshp* 2008
Sales 177.6MM^E *EMP* 400^E
SIC 1521 General remodeling, single-family houses; General remodeling, single-family houses
CEO: Chris Catalano
**Ch Bd:* Geoff Chapin
**CFO:* Brian Greenfield
Exec: Megan Raye
Dir IT: Jim Simon
VP Opers: Dave Boettcher
VP Opers: Peter Dellamonica
Sfty Mgr: Mel Cheeks
Opers Mgr: Shawn Boilard
Sls Dir: Jeff Caron
Sales Asso: Michael Leelman

D-U-N-S 04-281-5709
NEXT TIER CONCEPTS INC
NT CONCEPTS
1945 Old Gallows Rd # 400, Vienna, VA 22182-3931
Tel (703) 288-0010 *Founded/Ownrshp* 1998
Sales 34.0MM *EMP* 115
Accts Stitely & Karstetter Chantill
SIC 7379 Computer related consulting services; Computer related consulting services
CEO: Michele Bolos
**Ex VP:* Chris Cusano
VP: Mark Cosgrove
VP: Mac Oxford
Creative D: Paige Harley
Dir Bus: Lisa Newell
CTO: Christopher Powell
IT Man: Philip Chase
IT Man: Champ Weeraphao
VP Sls: John Treires

NEXT2NEW U CAR TRCK AUTO MALL
See SHAMALEY BUICK-GMC LP

D-U-N-S 07-155-4971
NEXTAG INC
800 Bridge Pkwy 200, Redwood City, CA 94065-1156
Tel (650) 645-4700 *Founded/Ownrshp* 1999
Sales 46.5MM^E *EMP* 200^E
SIC 2741 Shopping news: publishing & printing; Shopping news: publishing & printing
CEO: Jeff Katz
**CFO:* Brian Regan
Snr Sftwr: Almir Grbic
Snr Sftwr: Amir Gur
Snr Sftwr: Natalie Hill
CTO: Bahman Koohestani
Sls&Mrk Ex: Garth Chouteau

D-U-N-S 08-409-8042
NEXTCARE HOLDINGS INC
1138 N Alma School Rd, Mesa, AZ 85201-3000
Tel (480) 924-8382 *Founded/Ownrshp* 2008
Sales 62.1MM^E *EMP* 1,000
SIC 8093 8741 8011 Specialty outpatient clinics; Management services; Medical centers
Pr: John Julian
COO: Larry Crist Jr
CFO: Rex T Clevenger
Ofcr: Laura Becker
Ofcr: Ken Walsh
Sr VP: Jeffrey R Gerlach
Sr VP: Keith Marple
VP: Joleen Haxton

D-U-N-S 94-735-0922
NEXTCARE INC
NEXTCARE URGENT CARE
(Suby of NEXTCARE HOLDINGS INC) ★
1138 N Alma School Rd, Mesa, AZ 85201-3000
Tel (480) 924-8382 *Founded/Ownrshp* 1993
Sales 61.5MM^E *EMP* 1,000
SIC 8093 8741 Specialty outpatient clinics; Management services; Specialty outpatient clinics; Management services
Pr: John Julian
Ch Bd: John J Shufeldt
CFO: Ken Walsh
Ex VP: Kellyann Kimble
VP: Keith Marple
Off Mgr: Bernie Gunia
Off Mgr: Edy Taylor
Off Mgr: Barbara Williams
Dir IT: Chris Ulrey
Opers Mgr: Stephanie Boling
Opers Mgr: Michael Marino

NEXTCARE URGENT CARE
See NEXTCARE INC

D-U-N-S 80-962-2322 IMP
NEXTEER AUTOMOTIVE CORP
(*Suby of* PACIFIC CENTURY MOTORS INC.)
3900 E Holland Rd, Saginaw, MI 48601-9494
Tel (989) 757-5000 *Founded/Ownrshp* 2012
Sales 2.1MMM^E *EMP* 4,647
SIC 3714 Motor vehicle parts & accessories; Motor vehicle parts & accessories
Ch: Guibin Zhao
**Pr:* Joseph Perkins
**Sr VP:* Joe Perkins
**Sr VP:* Mike Richardson
IT Man: Keshav Hegde

D-U-N-S 00-868-9437 IMP
NEXTEK INC
201 Next Technology Dr, Madison, AL 35758-9117
Tel (256) 772-1995 *Founded/Ownrshp* 1995
Sales 68.6MM^E *EMP* 130
SIC 3812 3672 Search & navigation equipment; Printed circuit boards; Search & navigation equipment; Printed circuit boards
Pr: John C Roberts
**CFO:* Scott Nicol
VP: Tom Abernathy
VP: Danny Draffen
VP: Rick Gunn
VP: Jim Harris
VP: Al Reichert
Dir Surg: Peter Robert
Prgrm Mgr: Barry Cline
Prgrm Mgr: John Gould
Prgrm Mgr: David Hester

D-U-N-S 17-821-9796
■ **NEXTEL COMMUNICATIONS INC**
(*Suby of* SPRINT COMMUNICATIONS INC) ★
12502 Sunrise Valley Dr, Reston, VA 20191-3438
Tel (703) 433-4000 *Founded/Ownrshp* 2005
Sales 4.1MMM^E *EMP* 19,000
SIC 4812 Radio telephone communication; Radio telephone communication
CEO: Paul Saleh
**COO:* Thomas N Kelly Jr
VP: Kevin Gleason
Genl Couns: Len Kennedy
Board of Directors: James Hance Jr Chb

D-U-N-S 13-804-8462
■ **NEXTEL INTERNATIONAL (SERVICES) LTD**
(*Suby of* NEXTEL COMMUNICATIONS INC) ★
1875 Explorer St Ste 1000, Reston, VA 20190-6279
Tel (703) 433-4000 *Founded/Ownrshp* 1991
Sales 27.2MM^E *EMP* 150^E
SIC 4812 Radio telephone communication; Radio telephone communication
Pr: Steve Shindler
**VP:* Catherine Neel

D-U-N-S 79-064-5188
■ **NEXTEL OF CALIFORNIA INC**
SPRINT
(*Suby of* NEXTEL FINANCE COMPANY)
12502 Sunrise Valley Dr, Reston, VA 20191-3438
Tel (703) 390-9764 *Founded/Ownrshp* 1991
Sales 769.4MM^E *EMP* 966
SIC 4812 Cellular telephone services; Cellular telephone services
Sr Cor Off: Mike Egan
Exec: David Kellogg
VP Opers: Dennis Lombardi
VP Opers: Randy Shaneyfelt
Sls&Mrk Ex: Gary Godbout

D-U-N-S 80-940-8545
■ **NEXTEL OF NEW YORK INC**
(*Suby of* NEXTEL FINANCE COMPANY)
565 Taxter Rd Ste 450, Elmsford, NY 10523-2341
Tel (914) 421-2800 *Founded/Ownrshp* 1991
Sales 72.9MM^E *EMP* 1,200
SIC 4812 Radio telephone communication; Radio telephone communication
Pr: Jerry Reynolds

D-U-N-S 05-187-3040
■ **NEXTEL OF TEXAS INC** (TX)
(*Suby of* NEXTEL FINANCE COMPANY)
8911 N Capital Of Texas, Austin, TX 78759-7247
Tel (512) 342-3800 *Founded/Ownrshp* 1987
Sales 100.0MM^E *EMP* 1,700
SIC 4812 Radio telephone communication; Radio telephone communication
Pr: Tim Donahue

D-U-N-S 05-850-0716
■ **NEXTEL PARTNERS OPERATING CORP**
(*Suby of* SPRINT COMMUNICATIONS INC) ★
6200 Sprint Pkwy, Overland Park, KS 66251-6117
Tel (800) 829-0965 *Founded/Ownrshp* 1998
Sales 680.8MM^E *EMP* 6,125^E
SIC 4812 Cellular telephone services
Pr: John Chapple
**Treas:* John D Thompson

D-U-N-S 82-484-2520
■ **NEXTEL SOUTH CORP**
(*Suby of* NEXTEL FINANCE COMPANY)
6575 The Corners Pkwy, Norcross, GA 30092-3312
Tel (703) 592-7422 *Founded/Ownrshp* 1996
Sales 199.1MM^E *EMP* 1,555
SIC 4812 Radio telephone communication; Radio telephone communication
Pr: Dan Hesse
Sftwr Eng: David Pragel

D-U-N-S 60-886-2546
■ **NEXTEL WEST CORP**
(*Suby of* NEXTEL FINANCE COMPANY)
10545 Willows Rd Ne # 100, Redmond, WA 98052-2505
Tel (253) 924-8545 *Founded/Ownrshp* 1995
Sales 193.2MM^E *EMP* 2,616
SIC 4812 Radio telephone communication; Radio telephone communication
CEO: Tim Donahue

D-U-N-S 03-979-2689 IMP
NEXTEP INC
BRAWNY PLASTICS
9484 Double R Blvd Ste B, Reno, NV 89521-2993
Tel (775) 827-4447 *Founded/Ownrshp* 2001
Sales 39.2MM^E *EMP* 70
SIC 5199 General merchandise, non-durable
Pr: Brian Davis
**CFO:* Phil Neff
VP: Tom Cross
**VP:* Charles L Farinella

NEXTERA ENERGY
See FLORIDA POWER & LIGHT CO INC

D-U-N-S 14-980-7000
■ **NEXTERA ENERGY CAPITAL HOLDINGS INC**
(*Suby of* NEXTERA ENERGY INC) ★
700 Universe Blvd, Juno Beach, FL 33408-2657
Tel (561) 694-6311 *Founded/Ownrshp* 1985
Sales 4.7MMM^E *EMP* 1,297^E
SIC 6799 Investors
Pr: James Robo

D-U-N-S 12-272-3174 IMP/EXP
▲ **NEXTERA ENERGY INC**
700 Universe Blvd, Juno Beach, FL 33408-2657
Tel (561) 694-4000 *Founded/Ownrshp* 1984
Sales 17.0MMM *EMP* 13,400
Accts Deloitte & Touche Llp Boca Ra
Tkr Sym NEE *Exch* NYS
SIC 4911 Electric services; Distribution, electric power; Generation, electric power; Transmission, electric power; Electric services; Distribution, electric power; Generation, electric power; Transmission, electric power
Ch Bd: James L Robo
CFO: Moray P Dewhurst
Treas: Paul I Cutler
Ex VP: Chris Bennett
Ex VP: Joseph T Kelliher
Ex VP: Charles E Sieving
VP: Chris N Froggatt
Snr Mgr: David Balog
Snr Mgr: Matthew Ukestad

D-U-N-S 05-908-6145 IMP
■ **NEXTERA ENERGY OPERATING SERVICES LLC**
(*Suby of* NEXTERA ENERGY INC) ★
700 Universe Blvd, West Palm Beach, FL 33408-2657
Tel (561) 691-7171 *Founded/Ownrshp* 1998
Sales 140.0MM^E *EMP* 335
SIC 4911 Distribution, electric power; Generation, electric power; Transmission, electric power; Distribution, electric power; Generation, electric power; Transmission, electric power
Pr: C O Woody
**Treas:* Peter D Boylan
**VP:* John W Stanton

D-U-N-S 07-941-1676
▲ **NEXTERA ENERGY PARTNERS LP**
700 Universe Blvd, Juno Beach, FL 33408-2657
Tel (561) 694-4000 *Founded/Ownrshp* 1989
Sales 301.0MM *EMP* 67^E
Tkr Sym NEP *Exch* NYS
SIC 4911 Electric services; Generation, electric power
Ch Bd: James L Robo
Genl Pt: Nextera E GP
Pr: Armando Pimentel Jr

D-U-N-S 08-003-1390
■ **NEXTERA ENERGY PARTNERS VENTURES LLC**
(*Suby of* NEXTERA ENERGY PARTNERS LP) ★
700 Universe Blvd, Juno Beach, FL 33408-2657
Tel (561) 694-4000 *Founded/Ownrshp* 2015
Sales 23.1MM^E *EMP* 60^E
SIC 1711 Solar energy contractor
Ch Bd: James L Robo

D-U-N-S 80-800-7962
■ **NEXTERA ENERGY POINT BEACH LLC**
POINT BEACH NUCLEAR PLANT
(*Suby of* NEXTERA ENERGY INC) ★
6610 Nuclear Rd, Two Rivers, WI 54241-9516
Tel (920) 755-7705 *Founded/Ownrshp* 2006
Sales 508.1MM^E *EMP* 1,216^E
SIC 4911 ; Generation, electric power
CEO: Eric Silagy

D-U-N-S 05-448-1341 IMP
■ **NEXTERA ENERGY POWER MARKETING LLC**
(*Suby of* NEXTERA ENERGY INC) ★
700 Universe Blvd, North Palm Beach, FL 33408-2657
Tel (561) 691-7171 *Founded/Ownrshp* 1998
Sales 257.0MM^E *EMP* 615^E
SIC 4911 Distribution, electric power
Pr: Thomas Sutton
**CEO:* James L Robo
**CFO:* Moray P Dewhurst
**Ex VP:* Maria V Fogarty
**Ex VP:* Joseph T Kelliher
**Ex VP:* Charles E Sieving

D-U-N-S 05-900-6937 IMP/EXP
■ **NEXTERA ENERGY RESOURCES LLC**
(*Suby of* NEXTERA ENERGY CAPITAL HOLDINGS INC) ★
700 Universe Blvd, Juno Beach, FL 33408-2657
Tel (561) 691-7171 *Founded/Ownrshp* 1997
Sales 4.7MMM^E *EMP* 4,700
SIC 4911 Generation, electric power; Generation, electric power
Pr: Armando Pimentel

D-U-N-S 13-517-1630 IMP
■ **NEXTERA ENERGY SEABROOK LLC**
(*Suby of* NEXTERA ENERGY RESOURCES LLC) ★
626 Lafayette Rd, Seabrook, NH 03874
Tel (603) 474-3808 *Founded/Ownrshp* 2002
Sales 3.7MMM^E *EMP* 750
SIC 4911 ; Generation, electric power; ; Generation, electric power

D-U-N-S 60-216-9265
NEXTERA ENERGY SERVICES HOLDINGS LLC
(*Suby of* ESI ENERGY LLC) ★
700 Universe Blvd, North Palm Beach, FL 33408-2657
Tel (561) 691-7171 *Founded/Ownrshp* 2005
Sales 88.3MM^E *EMP* 100^E
SIC 4911 Electric services
Pr: Michael L Leighton
**Treas:* Mark R Sorensen
**Sec:* Charles S Schultz
**VP:* Bryan J Fennell
**VP:* Michael O'Sullivan

D-U-N-S 60-217-7193
NEXTERA ENERGY SERVICES LLC
(*Suby of* NEXTERA ENERGY SERVICES HOLDINGS LLC) ★
700 Universe Blvd, North Palm Beach, FL 33408-2657
Tel (561) 691-7171 *Founded/Ownrshp* 2005
Sales 88.3MM^E *EMP* 92^E
SIC 4911 Electric services
CEO: Armando Pimentel
**Pr:* Michael Leighton
**Treas:* Mark R Sorensen
**VP:* S Mitchell Davidson
**VP:* Charles J Muoio
**VP:* Michael O'Sullivan
**VP:* Ronald L Scheirer

D-U-N-S 01-452-5401 IMP
■ **NEXTEST SYSTEMS CORP**
NEXTEST SYSTEMS TERADYNE CO
(*Suby of* TERADYNE INC) ★
875 Embedded Way, San Jose, CA 95138-1030
Tel (408) 960-2400 *Founded/Ownrshp* 1997, 2008
Sales 54.7MM^E *EMP* 125
SIC 3825 Instruments to measure electricity; Instruments to measure electricity
CEO: Mark Jadiela
**Pr:* Tim F Moriarty
**CFO:* James P Moniz
**VP:* Paul Barics
**VP:* Howard D Marshall
Snr Sftwr: Eric Wampler
CTO: Jack Ip
IT Man: William Valella
Opers Mgr: Mike Falco
Sales Exec: Richard Simtob
VP Mktg: Young Kim

NEXTEST SYSTEMS TERADYNE CO
See NEXTEST SYSTEMS CORP

D-U-N-S 61-193-0590
■ **NEXTGEAR CAPITAL INC**
(*Suby of* COX AUTOMOTIVE INC) ★
11799 N College Ave, Carmel, IN 46032-5605
Tel (317) 571-3721 *Founded/Ownrshp* 2005
Sales NA *EMP* 215
SIC 6159 Automobile finance leasing; Automobile finance leasing
Pr: Brian Geitner
Pr: Todd Gunderson
**Pr:* Marty McFarland
**COO:* Shane Odell
**CFO:* David Horan
**VP:* Rich Coutu
Dir Bus: Susan Moritz
Genl Mgr: Peter Grupposo
Sales Exec: Jarrod Baer
Sales Exec: Stacy Burton
Sales Exec: Lynetta Harwood

D-U-N-S 09-791-2096
NEXTGEN ALLIANCE INC
3750 Gunn Hwy Ste 103, Tampa, FL 33618-8911
Tel (813) 471-0747 *Founded/Ownrshp* 1999
Sales 69.3MM *EMP* 100^E
Accts Rivero Gordimer & Company Pa
SIC 8361 8322 Group foster home; Aid to families with dependent children (AFDC); Group foster home; Aid to families with dependent children (AFDC)
Ch: Mindy Murphy
**Pr:* Jeff Rainey
**COO:* Sunny Hall
**CFO:* Karen Maziarz
**Treas:* Constance Trojanowsk

D-U-N-S 83-209-0935
NEXTGEN GLOBAL RESOURCES LLC
300 S Wacker Dr Ste 300, Chicago, IL 60606-6757
Tel (312) 450-8717 *Founded/Ownrshp* 2009
Sales 26.5MM *EMP* 250
SIC 8748 Telecommunications consultant; Telecommunications consultant

D-U-N-S 83-546-8075
■ **NEXTGEN HEALTHCARE INFORMATION SYSTEMS LLC**
(*Suby of* QUALITY SYSTEMS INC) ★
795 Horsham Rd, Horsham, PA 19044-1208
Tel (215) 657-7010 *Founded/Ownrshp* 1996
Sales 81.3MM^E *EMP* 612
SIC 7371 Computer software systems analysis & design, custom; Computer software systems analysis & design, custom
Pr: John Frantz
Pr: Gene Gallogly
**COO:* Daniel J Morefield
**CFO:* Paul Holt
**CFO:* John Stumpf
Ex VP: Kimberly Cline
Ex VP: Tim Eggena
**Ex VP:* Donn Neufeld
Ex VP: Gary Voydanoff
**Sr VP:* Michael Lovett
VP: Chris Button
VP: Charles W Jarvis
VP: Lancer Seaman
VP Bus: Ike Ellison

D-U-N-S 03-959-8714
NEXTGEN INFORMATION SERVICES INC
906 Olive St Ste 600, Saint Louis, MO 63101-1431
Tel (314) 588-1212 *Founded/Ownrshp* 1997
Sales 53.3MM^E *EMP* 375
SIC 7379 Computer related consulting services; Computer related consulting services
Pr: Carmen Jacob
**COO:* Michael Barton
CFO: Linda Jacob
Brnch Mgr: Richard Zenner
IT Man: Kit Payne
Mktg Dir: Ashley Fowler

D-U-N-S 94-705-6149
■ **NEXTGEN RCM SERVICES LLC**
HEALTHCARE STRGC INITIATIVES
(*Suby of* QUALITY SYSTEMS INC) ★
1836 Lackland Hill Pkwy, Saint Louis, MO 63146-3572
Tel (314) 989-0300 *Founded/Ownrshp* 1995
Sales 31.3MM^E *EMP* 575
SIC 8721 Billing & bookkeeping service; Billing & bookkeeping service
Ex VP: Monte Sandler
Sr VP: Mike A Noble
Sr VP: Ben Tischler
VP: Adam Steinberg
Exec: Deb Whetts
Dir Rx: Mike Gehrling
IT Man: Selehud Din
VP Mktg: Lois Durbin
VP Mktg: Sandy Morgan

D-U-N-S 15-198-3921
NEXTHERMAL CORP
(*Suby of* NEXTHERMAL MANUFACTURING INDIA PRIVATE LIMITED)
1045 Harts Lake Rd, Battle Creek, MI 49037-7357
Tel (269) 964-0271 *Founded/Ownrshp* 1989
Sales 23.9MM^E *EMP* 95
Accts Plante Moran Battle Creek Mi
SIC 3567 Heating units & devices, industrial: electric; Heating units & devices, industrial: electric
Pr: Srekumar Bandyopadhyay
**VP:* Ken Sunden

D-U-N-S 00-893-5827
NEXTIER BANK NATIONAL ASSOCIATION
(*Suby of* CITIZENS NATIONAL BANK OF EVANS CITY)
245 Pittsburgh Rd Ste 200, Butler, PA 16001-3883
Tel (724) 538-9808 *Founded/Ownrshp* 1893
Sales NA *EMP* 149^E
SIC 6021 National trust companies with deposits, commercial; National trust companies with deposits, commercial
CEO: Donald S Shamey
**Pr:* Margaret L Irvine
**COO:* Jennifer A Roxbury
**CFO:* Mark De Biasio
**Ch:* S J Irvine III
**Sr VP:* Linda Batykefer
Sr VP: Susan Duker
**Sr VP:* James Mc Ginnis
Sr VP: Paul Tomko
VP: Dennis Alworth
VP: Mark Biasio
VP: Ronald Dambaugh
VP: Peggy Eddens
VP: William Elliott
VP: Ronald Germani
VP: Mark Kappeler
VP: Hans Kuring
**VP:* Brenda Lemmon
VP: Joe Messner
VP: Ronald Pasic
VP: Patty Perhacs

D-U-N-S 78-645-7689
■ **NEXTIRAONE FEDERAL LLC**
BLACK BOX NETWORK SERVICES
(*Suby of* BLACK BOX CORP) ★
510 Spring St Ste 200, Herndon, VA 20170-5148
Tel (703) 885-7900 *Founded/Ownrshp* 2006
Sales 114.5MM^E *EMP* 450
SIC 5065

D-U-N-S 06-867-2153
■ **NEXTIRAONE LLC**
(*Suby of* BLACK BOX CORP) ★
5050 Lincoln Dr Ste 300, Minneapolis, MN 55436-1179
Tel (952) 352-4410 *Founded/Ownrshp* 1997
Sales NA *EMP* 3,464
SIC 5065 7629 1731 5999 4813 4841 Telephone equipment; Communication equipment; Telecommunication equipment repair (except telephones); Telephone & telephone equipment installation; Telephone equipment & systems; Telephone communication, except radio; Long distance telephone communications; Cable television services; Telephone equipment; Communication equipment; Telecommunication equipment repair (except telephones); Telephone & telephone equipment installation; Telephone equipment & systems; Telephone communication, except radio; Long distance telephone communications; Cable television services
Pr: Dale Booth
**CFO:* Bob Buhay
CFO: J R ME An
VP: Jean-Jacques Berthelon
Mng Dir: Foucault De La Roch RE
Prgrm Mgr: Christine Howard
Genl Mgr: Larry Underwood

D-U-N-S 96-145-7186
NEXTIVA INC
8800 E Chaparral Rd # 300, Scottsdale, AZ 85250-2609
Tel (480) 648-0833 *Founded/Ownrshp* 2007
Sales 60.0MM^E *EMP* 100
SIC 4813
CEO: Thomas Gorny
**Pr:* Tracy Conrad
**CFO:* Colleen Fritz

VP: Jen Fritz
*VP: Lukas Gorny
VP: James Murphy
*CIO: Josh Lesavoy
CIO: Joshua Lesavoy
IT Man: Eric Andrews
Sftwr Eng: Aleksandar Todorovic
Mktg Dir: Mary Miller

D-U-N-S 78-885-5174 IMP
NEXTIVITY INC
12230 World Trade Dr # 250, San Diego, CA 92128-3799
Tel (858) 485-9442 Founded/Ownrshp 2007
Sales 57.9MM^E EMP 70
SIC 5065 Communication equipment
Pr: Werner R Sievers
VP: Jim Berridge
VP: Tom Bilotta
VP: Tom Cooper
VP: George Lamb
*VP: Michiel Lotter
VP: Matthew McFee
Exec: Laurent Gil
Snr Mgr: Deb Onge

NEXTLINK MANAGEMENT SERVICE
See XO UTAH INC

D-U-N-S 03-230-9028
NEXTMED HOLDINGS LLC
6339 E Speedway Blvd, Tucson, AZ 85710-1147
Tel (520) 323-8732 Founded/Ownrshp 1999
Sales NA EMP 150^E
SIC 6324 Hospital & medical service plans; Hospital & medical service plans
Pr: Chris Gleason
CFO: Jeff Gerwin
VP: Matt Gleason
VP: Todd Pierce

D-U-N-S 00-257-7927
NEXTMEDIA OPERATING INC
6312 S Fiddlers Green Cir # 2, Greenwood Village, CO 80111-4943
Tel (303) 694-9118 Founded/Ownrshp 2000
Sales 109.4MM^E EMP 1,020
SIC 4832 Radio broadcasting stations; Radio broadcasting stations
Pr: Jim Donahoe
*CFO: Sean Stover
VP: Eric Neumann
Genl Mgr: John Leathers

D-U-N-S 79-573-5856
NEXTPOINT INC
BREAK MEDIA
8750 Wilshire Blvd 300e, Beverly Hills, CA 90211-2700
Tel (310) 360-5904 Founded/Ownrshp 2005
Sales 33.7MM^E EMP 100
SIC 4813
Pr: Keith Richman
*CFO: Andrew Doyle
Sr VP: Mitch Rotte
Sr VP: Brian Tu
VP: Nancy Argent
*CTO: David Subar
Dir IT: Josh Elcik
IT Man: Jerimiah Schirle
Sls Dir: Justin Traina
Manager: Steven Mikalis

D-U-N-S 80-393-3725
NEXTRA REALTY INC
RE/MAX NEXTRA
2790 State Rt 23, Stockholm, NJ 07460-1327
Tel (973) 697-7778 Founded/Ownrshp 2007
Sales 23.5MM EMP 27
SIC 6531 Real estate brokers & agents; Real estate brokers & agents
Pr: Gary Anderson
*VP: Aurora Corrente

D-U-N-S 07-926-0273
NEXTRACKER INC
6200 Paseo Padre Pkwy, Fremont, CA 94555-3601
Tel (510) 279-3292 Founded/Ownrshp 2013
Sales 22.7MM^E EMP 17
SIC 5074 Heating equipment & panels, solar
CEO: Daniel Shugar
*COO: Tyroan Hardy
*CFO: Robert Zapotosky
*VP: Mike Mehawich
CTO: Alexander Au

D-U-N-S 07-919-3017 EXP
NEXTRAN CORP
NEXTRAN TRCK CNTR-JACKSONVILLE
1986 W Beaver St, Jacksonville, FL 32209-7540
Tel (904) 354-3721 Founded/Ownrshp 1992
Sales 248.4MM^E EMP 480
SIC 5511 5531 7538 Trucks, tractors & trailers: new & used; Truck equipment & parts; General truck repair; Trucks, tractors & trailers: new & used; Truck equipment & parts; General truck repair
Ch Bd: Marvin H Pritchett
*CEO: Jon W Pritchett
*CFO: Steve F Perez
Brnch Mgr: Vicki Coy
Store Mgr: Milo Williams
Mktg Dir: Denis Abromavage
Sls Mgr: Cesar Esquivel
Sls Mgr: Eric Schmidt

NEXTRAN TRCK CNTR-JACKSONVILLE
See NEXTRAN CORP

D-U-N-S 78-595-1781
NEXTRIDGE INC
12 Elmwood Rd, Albany, NY 12204-2422
Tel (518) 292-6505 Founded/Ownrshp 1990
Sales 37.0MM^E EMP 175
Accts Wojeski & Co Cpas Pc East
SIC 1731 7629 8742 Telephone & telephone equipment installation; Telecommunication equipment repair (except telephones); Industry specialist consultants; Telephone & telephone equipment installation; Telecommunication equipment repair (except telephones); Industry specialist consultants

CEO: Shaun P Mahoney
Ch Bd: Shaun Mahoney
*Ch Bd: Patrick T Maney Jr
Prin: Sarah R Cozzolino
VP Admn: Bob Hebert

D-U-N-S 13-414-2988
NEXTSOURCE INC
1040 Avenue Of The Americ, New York, NY 10018-3726
Tel (212) 736-5870 Founded/Ownrshp 2009
Sales 164.8MM^E EMP 3,500
SIC 7363 8741 Labor resource services; Management services; Labor resource services; Management services
Ch Bd: Joseph Musacchio
COO: Joanne Bocci
COO: Janet Cross
*CFO: Fern Swiss
Dir IT: Melissa Alexander
IT Man: David Amatuly
Web Dev: Richard Couzzi

D-U-N-S 80-230-9419
NEXTSTUDENT INC
1801 W Knudsen Dr Ste 11, Phoenix, AZ 85027-1399
Tel (623) 879-5000 Founded/Ownrshp 1992
Sales 16.8MM^E EMP 300
Accts Clifton Gunderson Llp Phoenix
SIC 8742 8748 Administrative services consultant; Educational consultant; Administrative services consultant; Educational consultant
Pr: Donald Fenstermaker
*Pr: SOO Zembala

D-U-N-S 61-694-7219
NEXTWORTH SOLUTIONS INC
900 Technology Park Dr # 200, Billerica, MA 01821-4167
Tel (978) 374-6398 Founded/Ownrshp 2006
Sales 40.0MM EMP 30
SIC 5932 Used merchandise stores; Used merchandise stores
CEO: Dave Chen
Pr: Lars Noreng
*Pr: Jeff Stone
*CFO: Mark Pover
Chf Mktg O: Jeff Trachsel
Opers Mgr: Robert Joseph
Mktg Dir: Elisabeth Branham
Sls Mgr: Brendan McCue

D-U-N-S 11-087-3101
NEXUM INC
190 S La Salle St # 1450, Chicago, IL 60603-3489
Tel (312) 726-6900 Founded/Ownrshp 2002
Sales 28.4MM^E EMP 65
SIC 7379 Computer related maintenance services; Computer related consulting services; Computer hardware requirements analysis
Pr: David Lesser
*VP: JD B Utt
Dir Bus: Che Bhatia
Mng Dir: Tom Lifvendahl
IT Man: Michael Fatigati
Sales Exec: Doug Nordhaus
Sales Exec: Dirk Nowka
Sales Exec: Edward Shuman
Mktg Mgr: Jennifer Keenan
Mktg Mgr: Amanda Parsley
Mktg Mgr: Eric Rodriguez

D-U-N-S 07-026-8545
NEXUS (MN)
505 Highway 169 N Ste 500, Plymouth, MN 55441-6447
Tel (763) 551-8640 Founded/Ownrshp 1974, 1981
Sales 42.2MM EMP 1,000
Accts Messerli & Schadow Pllp Minne
SIC 8322 8361 Individual & family services; Group foster home; Individual & family services; Group foster home
Pr: David Hutchinson
*COO: Brock Wolff
*CFO: Alan K Nordby
VP: Jack Ewing
Exec: Patricia Nott
Ex Dir: Jan Talbot
IT Man: Tyson Schumacher

D-U-N-S 07-940-1791
NEXUS BIOENERGY INC
3026 Castle Peak Ave, Superior, CO 80027-6067
Tel (720) 318-2339 Founded/Ownrshp 2015
Sales 316.4MM^E EMP 4,939
SIC 4939 7389 8731 Combination utilities; ; Combination utilities; ; Energy research
Pr: Syed Reza

D-U-N-S 03-851-0129
NEXUS DISTRIBUTION CORP
6220 W 73rd St, Chicago, IL 60638-6117
Tel (847) 590-6200 Founded/Ownrshp 1980
Sales 36.2MM^E EMP 80
SIC 4213 4225 Trucking, except local; General warehousing
Ch: Dean W Hansen
CFO: Brian King
Mktg Dir: Jennifer Nix

D-U-N-S 83-269-7093 EXP
NEXUS DX INC
(Suby of SAMSUNG ELECTRONICS CO., LTD.)
6759 Mesa Ridge Rd, San Diego, CA 92121-4902
Tel (858) 410-4600 Founded/Ownrshp 2009
Sales 92.6MM^E EMP 480
SIC 3841 Surgical & medical instruments; Surgical & medical instruments
CEO: Nam Shin
Pr: Joseph M Nemmers Jr
VP: Jim P McMenamy
VP: Gordon Sangster
Opers Supe: Spencer Baker
Mfg Mgr: Greg Hamilton

NEXUS HEALTH
See FORT WASHINGTON MEDICAL CENTER INC

D-U-N-S 01-148-3059 IMP
NEXUS HEALTH SYSTEMS INC
1 Riverway Ste 600, Houston, TX 77056-1993
Tel (713) 355-6111 Founded/Ownrshp 1997
Sales 72.2MM^E EMP 500
SIC 8011 Psychiatrist; Psychiatrist
CEO: John W Cassidy
*COO: Guido Cubellis
*CFO: Julia Hatton
CFO: Julia Perry
*CFO: Mike Rzendzian
*Ex VP: Kathy Roberts
VP: Deepak Chaudhry
*VP: Guy Murdock
Sfty Dirs: Cris Acosta
Mktg Dir: Ann Larosa
HC Dir: Angel Bonaventure

D-U-N-S 14-240-6334
NEXUS IS INC
(Suby of DIMENSION DATA NORTH AMERICA INC) ★
27202 Turnberry Ln # 100, Valencia, CA 91355-1022
Tel (661) 257-1500 Founded/Ownrshp 2014
Sales 234.3MM^E EMP 340
SIC 4899 Data communication services; Data communication services
CEO: Deron Pearson
*Pr: Waheed Choudhry
*CFO: Dan Dougherty
*VP: Sabrina Anderson
*VP: Dale Hardy
*VP: Mike Heiman
*VP: Tom Lyon
Exec: Todd Caporal
Genl Mgr: Rhonda Eiffe
IT Man: Brad Clink
IT Man: Craig Hadix

D-U-N-S 10-139-4658 EXP
NEXUS PLASTICS INC
1 Loretto Ave, Hawthorne, NJ 07506-1300
Tel (973) 427-3311 Founded/Ownrshp 1982
Sales 28.8MM^E EMP 90
Accts Shalhoub & Shalhoub Cpas
SIC 3081 2673 Plastic film & sheet; Plastic bags: made from purchased materials; Plastic film & sheet; Plastic bags: made from purchased materials
Pr: Marwan Sholakh
Genl Mgr: Tamer Sholakh
MIS Dir: Rick Walsh
Sls Mgr: Joe Esak

D-U-N-S 14-805-3119
NEXUS PROPERTIES INC
1333 Brunswick Ave # 200, Lawrenceville, NJ 08648-4502
Tel (609) 396-6800 Founded/Ownrshp 1986
Sales 33.7MM^E EMP 60^E
SIC 6552 Subdividers & developers
Pr: Sydney Sussman
Ex VP: Andrea Sussman
*VP: Jeff Sussman

D-U-N-S 88-437-9363 IMP
NEXUS VALVE INC
9982 E 121st St, Fishers, IN 46037-9727
Tel (317) 257-6050 Founded/Ownrshp 1995
Sales 24.7MM^E EMP 40
SIC 5074 Plumbing & heating valves
Pr: Kurt Fazekas
VP: Sean Kalman
Sales Asso: Dale Lyons

D-U-N-S 14-718-4969
NEXXAR GROUP INC
580 Sylvan Ave Ste Ma, Englewood Cliffs, NJ 07632-3105
Tel (201) 477-6045 Founded/Ownrshp 2004
Sales NA EMP 900
SIC 6099 Check clearing services; Check clearing services
Pr: Frank J Petrilli
*CFO: Eric Eaton
Board of Directors: Colin Vickerie

D-U-N-S 02-257-6560
NEXXLINX CORP INC
3565 Piedmont Rd Ne 2-100, Atlanta, GA 30305-8210
Tel (877) 747-0658 Founded/Ownrshp 1998
Sales 135.3MM^E EMP 1,200
Accts Rc Financials Services Decatu
SIC 7389 8742 Telemarketing services; Management consulting services; Telemarketing services; Management consulting services
CEO: Craig Mento
*COO: William I Coffeen II
*CFO: Neil Quarterman
*Ex VP: William J Hadel
VP: Stephen Smith
*CIO: Robert Hornbuckle
Opers Mgr: Mel Warner

D-U-N-S 01-556-2494
NEXXLINX OF MAINE INC
(Suby of NEXXLINX CORP INC) ★
3 Godfrey Dr, Orono, ME 04473-3607
Tel (207) 866-6017 Founded/Ownrshp 1998, 2011
Sales 20.2MM^E EMP 300
SIC 7378 Computer maintenance & repair; Computer maintenance & repair
CEO: Craig Mento
*CFO: Neil Quaterman
Genl Mgr: Susan Chute

NEXXT
See ALOK INTERNATIONAL INC

NEY METAL & ALLOYS
See BELMONT METALS INC

D-U-N-S 01-823-1480
NEY OIL CO INC
145 S Water St, Ney, OH 43549-9624
Tel (419) 658-2324 Founded/Ownrshp 1927
Sales 84.8MM EMP 100
Accts Donald A Hohenbrink Ottawa
SIC 5171 Petroleum bulk stations; Petroleum bulk stations
Pr: Lynn Bergman

*Treas: Barbara Vance
*Sec: Tom Vance
*VP: Jerry Bergman

NEZ FOODS
See NORTHWESTERN SELECTA INC

D-U-N-S 07-820-8303
NEZ PERCE TRIBE
120 Bever Grade, Lapwai, ID 83540
Tel (208) 843-2253 Founded/Ownrshp 1855
Sales NA EMP 557
SIC 9131 ;
Ex Dir: Rebecca Miles
*Ch Bd: McCoy Oatman
CFO: Kelly Wasson
VP: Jessica Moser
Exec: Kermit Mankiller
Ex Dir: Laurie Smith
Brnch Mgr: Jack Bell
IT Man: Phyllis Nash

D-U-N-S 07-910-7209
NF REINSURANCE LTD
(Suby of NATIONWIDE FINANCIAL SERVICES INC) ★
1 Nationwide Plz, Columbus, OH 43215-2226
Tel (614) 249-7111 Founded/Ownrshp 2013
Sales NA EMP 1,132^E
SIC 6311 Life insurance
Prin: Raymond Blake

D-U-N-S 05-068-6633 IMP
NFA CORP
HOPE GLOBAL DIV
50 Martin St, Cumberland, RI 02864-5335
Tel (617) 232-6060 Founded/Ownrshp 1982
Sales 326.2MM^E EMP 1,000
SIC 5012 2241 Automobiles; Narrow fabric mills; Automobiles; Narrow fabric mills
CEO: Ronald G Casty
CFO: Michael Pawlitschek
*Ex VP: Emil Bernsten
VP: Jewel Buben
VP: Chris Deignan
VP: Tom Ferruci
VP: Jim Hanahan
VP: John Luca
VP: Leslie Taito
MIS Dir: Thomas Ferrucci
Mfg Mgr: John Martin

NFB
See NATIONAL FEDERATION OF BLIND

D-U-N-S 00-924-3887
■ **NFC CASTINGS INC**
NEENAH FOUNDERY
(Suby of NEENAH ENTERPRISES INC) ★
2121 Brooks Ave, Neenah, WI 54956-4756
Tel (920) 725-7000 Founded/Ownrshp 2010
Sales 365.5MM^E EMP 1,650^E
SIC 3325 3321 Gray & ductile iron foundries; Steel foundries; Steel foundries; Gray & ductile iron foundries
CEO: Thomas Riordan
*CFO: Thomas Arians

D-U-N-S 00-741-6332
NFCG LLC
SUNSHINE FOODS
600 W 41st St, Sioux Falls, SD 57105-6404
Tel (605) 331-7967 Founded/Ownrshp 1996
Sales 30.5MM^E EMP 500
SIC 5411 Grocery stores; Grocery stores

NFI DISTRIBUTION
See NATIONAL DISTRIBUTION CENTERS LP

D-U-N-S 15-092-4439
NFI INDUSTRIES INC
1515 Burnt Mill Rd, Cherry Hill, NJ 08003-3637
Tel (856) 691-7000 Founded/Ownrshp 1985
Sales 924.8MM^E EMP 2,100
SIC 4213 4212 8741 4225 4214 Trucking, except local; Local trucking, without storage; Management services; General warehousing & storage; Local trucking with storage; Trucking, except local; Local trucking, without storage; Management services; General warehousing & storage; Local trucking with storage
CEO: Sidney Brown
*Pr: Jeffrey Brown
COO: Joe Roeder
CFO: Steve Grabell
Sr VP: Rob Barron
Sr VP: Susanne Batchelor
Sr VP: Bill Bliem
VP: Jeff Berger
VP: Scott Brucker
VP: Brian Gillmore
VP: John Krauser

D-U-N-S 87-911-2063
NFI INTERACTIVE LOGISTICS LLC
NFI LOGISTICS
1515 Burnt Mill Rd, Cherry Hill, NJ 08003-3637
Tel (856) 857-1324 Founded/Ownrshp 2005
Sales 88.0MM^E EMP 123
SIC 4731 8742 Transportation agents & brokers; Materials mgmt. (purchasing, handling, inventory) consultant; Transportation agents & brokers; Materials mgmt. (purchasing, handling, inventory) consultant
CEO: Sidney Brown
COO: Josiah Knapp
CFO: Frank Raschilla
*Treas: Jeffrey Brown

NFI LOGISTICS
See NFI INTERACTIVE LOGISTICS LLC

D-U-N-S 07-660-2002
NFI MASSACHUSETTS INC
NORTHEASTERN FAMILY INSTITUTE
26 Howley St Ste 2, Peabody, MA 01960-8634
Tel (978) 538-0286 Founded/Ownrshp 1974
Sales 20.3MM EMP 333
Accts Kpmg Llp Boston Ma
SIC 8322 Individual & family services; Individual & family services

CEO: Steven Hahn
**Pr:* James Zafris
COO: Hildy Paris
**CFO:* Pamela Bruce
**Treas:* Dan Nakamoto
Dir IT: Louisa Look
Doctor: Yitzhak Bakal

D-U-N-S 04-160-7966
NFI NORTH INC
10 Harbor St Ste 2, Danvers, MA 01923-3390
Tel (978) 774-0774 *Founded/Ownrshp* 1992
Sales 15.8MM *EMP* 352
Accts Kpmg Llp Boston Ma
SIC 8322 Individual & family services; Individual & family services
Pr: Yitzhak Bakal
**CFO:* Pamela Bruce
**Treas:* Suanne Nader

NFI TRANSPORTATION
See NATIONAL FREIGHT INC

NFISD
See NORTH FOREST INDEPENDENT SCHOOL DISTRICT

NFK INTERNATIONAL
See SLAVA INDUSTRIES INC

NFL OFFICEWORKS
See NATIONAL FURNITURE LIQUIDATORS I LLC

D-U-N-S 96-487-5509
NFL PLAYER SUPPLEMENTAL DISABILITY PLAN TRUST
200 Saint Paul St # 2420, Baltimore, MD 21202-2008
Tel (410) 685-5069 *Founded/Ownrshp* 2010
Sales 32.9MM *EMP* 2E
Accts Abrams Foster Nole & Williams
SIC 5099 Durable goods
Prin: Sarah Gaunt

D-U-N-S 08-166-4849
NFL PROPERTIES LLC
345 Park Ave Bsmt Lc1, New York, NY 10154-0017
Tel (212) 450-2000 *Founded/Ownrshp* 1963, 2001
Sales 58.6MME *EMP* 414
SIC 7941 6794 8743 2731 Sports clubs, managers & promoters; Copyright buying & licensing; Sales promotion; Books: publishing only; Sports clubs, managers & promoters; Copyright buying & licensing; Sales promotion; Books: publishing only
Sr VP: Dennis Lewin
VP: Douglas P Aoletti
VP: Wallace Bennett
VP: Anastasia Danias
VP: Tammy Fruits
VP: Jennifer Manzo
VP: Mary Oliveti
Ex Dir: Jim Steeg
Mng Dir: Jim Connelly
Dir Sec: Rusty Guy
Dir IT: David Port

NFM
See NATIONAL FILTER MEDIA CORP

D-U-N-S 04-540-7942
NFM INC
N F M
505 Progress Dr Ste 100, Linthicum, MD 21090-2249
Tel (410) 347-9988 *Founded/Ownrshp* 1998
Sales NA *EMP* 150E
SIC 6163 Loan brokers; Loan brokers
CEO: David Silverman
**Pr:* Jan Ozga
**COO:* Robert N Tyson III
**CFO:* Matthew Glyder
VP: Gregory Sher
Dir IT: Chris Folsom
**Genl Couns:* Latasha Rowe

D-U-N-S 06-768-4782 IMP
■ **NFM OF KANSAS INC**
(*Suby of* NEBRASKA FURNITURE MART INC) ★
1601 Village West Pkwy, Kansas City, KS 66111-1878
Tel (913) 288-6327 *Founded/Ownrshp* 2003
Sales 58.5MME *EMP* 199E
SIC 5712 Furniture stores

D-U-N-S 13-046-8150 IMP
NFM/WELDING ENGINEERS INC
N F M
577 Oberlin Ave Sw, Massillon, OH 44647-7820
Tel (330) 837-3868 *Founded/Ownrshp* 1985
Sales 39.2MME *EMP* 160
SIC 3599 Machine shop, jobbing & repair; Machine shop, jobbing & repair
Pr: Philip A Roberson
**Sr VP:* Ronald Pribich
**VP:* John Roberson
**VP:* Scott Swallen
Dir Lab: Timothy Moles

NFP ADVISORS
See NFP SECURITIES INC

NFP ADVISORS
See NFP CORP

D-U-N-S 08-207-0892
NFP CORP
NFP ADVISORS
(*Suby of* PATRIOT INTERMEDIATE HOLDINGS B CORP) ★
340 Madison Ave Fl 21, New York, NY 10173-0401
Tel (212) 301-4000 *Founded/Ownrshp* 2013
Sales NA *EMP* 2,835E
SIC 6411 7389 6282 Insurance agents, brokers & service; Financial services; Investment advice; Insurance agents, brokers & service; Financial services; Investment advice
CEO: Douglas Hammond
COO: Michael Goldman
Ex VP: Tim Robb
Ex VP: Terrence Scali
Sr VP: Kim Davis
Sr VP: John Orth
VP: Eric Boester
VP: Kristin Bulat
VP: Levi Friedbauer
VP: Alan Littman
VP: Dan Schwamb
VP: Jason Sickle
VP: Amanda Zukowski
VP Bus Dev: Bill Marsden
Dir Soc: Nickie Morgan

D-U-N-S 60-692-9677
NFP INSURANCE SERVICES INC
N F P SECURITIES
1250 S Capital Of Texas, West Lake Hills, TX 78746-6446
Tel (512) 329-5761 *Founded/Ownrshp* 1987
Sales NA *EMP* 50
SIC 6331

D-U-N-S 08-401-5676
NFP PROPERTY & CASUALTY SERVICES INC
(*Suby of* NFP ADVISORS) ★
707 Westchester Ave # 201, White Plains, NY 10604-3102
Tel (914) 683-3990 *Founded/Ownrshp* 1999
Sales NA *EMP* 63E
SIC 6411 Insurance agents, brokers & service; Insurance agents
CEO: Terry Scali
CFO: Dennis Via
Sr VP: George Knotts
Sr VP: David J Maxham
Sr VP: Harris Tsangaris
VP: Miles Neivert
VP: Lisa Levin Stegall
VP: Scott Stegall
Snr Mgr: Irv Baum

D-U-N-S 01-645-1747
NFP SECURITIES INC
NFP ADVISORS
(*Suby of* NFP ADVISORS) ★
1250 S Capital Of Texas H, West Lake Hills, TX 78746-6395
Tel (512) 697-6000 *Founded/Ownrshp* 1996
Sales 84.1MME *EMP* 268
SIC 6211 Security brokers & dealers; Security brokers & dealers
CEO: Jeff Montgomery
Pr: James L Poer
Treas: Michael Forsythe
Ex VP: Brian Propes
Sr VP: Dodd McGough
Sr VP: John P Vanderheyden
Sr VP: Kristen Whisnant
VP: Lori M Lieser
Sls Mgr: Sterling Broadbent

NFPA
See NATIONAL FIRE PROTECTION ASSOCIATION INC

NG&G FACILITY SERVICES INTL
See NATIONAL GLASS & GATE SERVICE INC

NGC
See NUMISMATIC GUARANTY CORP OF AMERICA

D-U-N-S 09-941-8600 IMP/EXP
NGC INC
TOWN DOCK, THE
45 State St, Narragansett, RI 02882-5712
Tel (401) 789-2200 *Founded/Ownrshp* 1980
Sales 21.5MME *EMP* 45E
SIC 5146 2092 Seafoods; Fresh or frozen packaged fish
Pr: Noah C Clark
**VP:* Ryan Clark
Off Mgr: Heather Ford
Natl Sales: Brian Dorman
Natl Sales: Stuart Walker
Sls Mgr: Mark Fratiello

D-U-N-S 94-198-4312
NGC INDUSTRIES INC
NATIONAL GYPSUN COMP
(*Suby of* NATIONAL GYPSUM CO) ★
2001 Rexford Rd, Charlotte, NC 28211-3415
Tel (704) 365-7300 *Founded/Ownrshp* 1996
Sales 124.2MME *EMP* 2,100
SIC 2679 Wallboard, decorated: made from purchased material; Wallboard, decorated: made from purchased material
CEO: Thomas C Nelson
**CFO:* George Beckwith
**Treas:* Richard G Parkhurst
**VP:* Gerald P Carroll
**VP:* John Mixson
**VP:* Samuel A Schiffman
**VP Mfg:* John Corsi
**VP Sls:* Craig Weisbruch
Snr Mgr: John Lewis

D-U-N-S 15-869-4617
■ **NGC NETWORK INTERNATIONAL LLC**
NATIONAL GGRPHIC CHANNELS INTL
(*Suby of* FOX INTERNATIONAL CHANNELS (US) INC) ★
1145 17th St Nw, Washington, DC 20036-4707
Tel (202) 857-7000 *Founded/Ownrshp* 2015
Sales 50.4MME *EMP* 148E
SIC 4841 Cable television services; Cable television services
CEO: David Haslingden
VP: J-T Ladt
VP: Michelle Upton
Sls Dir: Joanna Rowley

D-U-N-S 18-294-1117
NGC NETWORK US LLC
NATIONAL GEOGRAPHIC CHANNEL
1145 17th St Nw, Washington, DC 20036-4707
Tel (202) 912-6500 *Founded/Ownrshp* 2003
Sales 20.8MME *EMP* 140
SIC 7319 Media buying service
Pr: Ann Blakey
CFO: James Bond
Ex VP: Sydney Suissa
Sr VP: Heather Moran
Sr VP: Janet Vissering
VP: Lisa Clark
VP: Brad Dancer
VP: Rupert Fei
VP: Mary Jacobson
VP: Joyce Romano
VP: Germaine Sweet
Assoc Dir: Stephanie Montgomery

D-U-N-S 00-704-6053
NGHS
(*Suby of* NORTHEAST GEORGIA HEALTH SYSTEM INC) ★
4889 Golden Pkwy Ste 100, Buford, GA 30518-5878
Tel (678) 714-3178 *Founded/Ownrshp* 2007
Sales 107.4ME *EMP* 1,097E
SIC 8011 Medical centers
Prin: John Alsobrook

NGI CONSTRUCTION
See NOVA GROUP INC

NGK BERYLCO
See NGK METALS CORP

D-U-N-S 60-241-2835 IMP/EXP
NGK CERAMICS USA INC
(*Suby of* NGK INSULATORS, LTD.)
119 Mazeppa Rd, Mooresville, NC 28115-7927
Tel (704) 664-7000 *Founded/Ownrshp* 1988
Sales 4.7MME *EMP* 475
SIC 3261 3253 5211

D-U-N-S 15-214-2394 IMP
NGK METALS CORP
NGK BERYLCO
(*Suby of* NGK NORTH AMERICA INC) ★
917 Highway 11 S, Sweetwater, TN 37874-5730
Tel (423) 351-0394 *Founded/Ownrshp* 1986
Sales 21.5MME *EMP* 70E
SIC 3341 3339 3351 5051 Secondary nonferrous metals; Primary nonferrous metals; Copper rolling & drawing; Copper products
Pr: Glade F Nelson
**Treas:* Satoshi Yoshida
Exec: Roy Heape
Genl Mgr: Doug Harrod
Dir IT: Heath Harrison
Manager: Bob Cupchak
Manager: David St Amour

D-U-N-S 19-475-5534 IMP/EXP
NGK NORTH AMERICA INC
(*Suby of* NGK INSULATORS, LTD.)
1105 N Market St Ste 1300, Wilmington, DE 19801-1241
Tel (302) 654-1344 *Founded/Ownrshp* 2005
Sales 132.8MME *EMP* 820
SIC 3714 5013 3264 5063 Motor vehicle parts & accessories; Automotive supplies & parts; Insulators, electrical: porcelain; Insulators, electrical; Motor vehicle parts & accessories; Automotive supplies & parts; Insulators, electrical: porcelain; Insulators, electrical
Pr: Susumu Sakabe
**Treas:* Tomokazu Asai
VP: Josh Niwa
**Genl Mgr:* Yutaka Yonekura

D-U-N-S 60-382-1062 IMP/EXP
NGK SPARK PLUGS (USA) HOLDING INC
(*Suby of* NGK SPARK PLUG CO., LTD.)
1011 Centre Rd, Wilmington, DE 19805-1267
Tel (302) 288-0131 *Founded/Ownrshp* 1995
Sales 172.7MME *EMP* 763E
SIC 3643 3264 Current-carrying wiring devices; Porcelain parts for electrical devices, molded; Spark plugs, porcelain
Pr: Shin Odo
IT Man: John Morici

D-U-N-S 04-522-2874 IMP
NGK SPARK PLUGS (USA) INC
NGK SPARK PLUGS USA
(*Suby of* NGK SPARK PLUGS (USA) HOLDING INC) ★
46929 Magellan, Wixom, MI 48393-3699
Tel (248) 926-6900 *Founded/Ownrshp* 1995
Sales 154.3MME *EMP* 600
SIC 3643 3264 Current-carrying wiring devices; Porcelain parts for electrical devices, molded; Current-carrying wiring devices; Porcelain parts for electrical devices, molded
CEO: Goro Ogawa
**Pr:* Shin Odo
Ex VP: Ken Furusaki
Ex VP: Kazuhiro Tsuzuki
VP: Ken Minoha
VP: Michael Schwab
VP: Yoel Tovi
VP: Mike Vanca
VP: Amy Zivic
Exec: Steven Burgett
Exec: Chris Hillestad

D-U-N-S 87-851-6160 IMP
NGK SPARK PLUGS (USA) INC
(*Suby of* NGK SPARK PLUGS (USA) INC) ★
1 Ngk Dr, Sissonville, WV 25320-9546
Tel (304) 988-0060 *Founded/Ownrshp* 1994
Sales 154.3MME *EMP* 450
SIC 5013 3694 Automotive engines & engine parts; Ignition apparatus & distributors; Automotive engines & engine parts; Ignition apparatus & distributors
CEO: Norihiko Adachi
CFO: Yosnitaka Nakita
Ofcr: Hiraoki Hiraoka
Ex VP: Larry Magee
**VP:* Richard Sullivan
VP: Thomas Wetzel
Exec: Rosanna Gahran
Exec: Yoshiyuk Takayanagi
Brnch Mgr: Greg Phillips
IT Man: Mark Kennell
IT Man: Davey Perdue

NGK SPARK PLUGS USA
See NGK SPARK PLUGS (USA) INC

D-U-N-S 93-385-2188 IMP/EXP
NGK-LOCKE POLYMER INSULATORS INC
(*Suby of* NGK NORTH AMERICA INC) ★
1609 Diamond Springs Rd, Virginia Beach, VA 23455-3009
Tel (757) 460-3649 *Founded/Ownrshp* 2003
Sales 36.4MM *EMP* 100
SIC 3264 Insulators, electrical: porcelain; Insulators, electrical: porcelain
Pr: Rit Sato
**Sec:* Yuya Hagiwara
**Sec:* Naoto Saito
**Ex VP:* Kimihiko Matsuzaki
**VP:* Scott Yoshita
**Prin:* Kenny Nakano
**Prin:* Koichi Nakano
Ql Cn Mgr: April De Campo
Ql Cn Mgr: Olaf Kampschmidt

D-U-N-S 96-885-1126
NGL CROSSTEX MARKETING L P
2501 Cedar Springs Rd, Dallas, TX 75201-1409
Tel (214) 754-4752 *Founded/Ownrshp* 2005
Sales 216.4MME *EMP* 560
SIC 5172 Petroleum products; Petroleum products
Pt: William W Davis
Pt: Crosstex Energy Services GP

D-U-N-S 82-747-6230
■ **NGL CRUDE LOGISTICS LLC**
(*Suby of* NGL ENERGY PARTNERS LP) ★
1299 Farnam St Ste 120, Omaha, NE 68102-1127
Tel (402) 889-4000 *Founded/Ownrshp* 2013
Sales 544.2MME *EMP* 600
SIC 6221 5153 Commodity contracts brokers, dealers; Grain & field beans; Commodity contracts brokers, dealers; Grain & field beans
Pr: Greg Heckman
**COO:* Jim Anderson
**COO:* Greg Piper
**CFO:* John Neppl
**Ofcr:* Robert Jones
**VP:* Dana Wright
**CIO:* Gary Acromite
VP Opers: Dennis Stieren

D-U-N-S 96-546-5086
▲ **NGL ENERGY PARTNERS LP**
6120 S Yale Ave Ste 805, Tulsa, OK 74136-4233
Tel (918) 481-1119 *Founded/Ownrshp* 2010
Sales 16.8MMM *EMP* 3,227
Tkr Sym NGL *Exch* NYS
SIC 5172 5984 Petroleum products; Gases, liquefied petroleum (propane); Propane gas, bottled; Petroleum products; Gases, liquefied petroleum (propane); Propane gas, bottled
CEO: H Michael Krimbill
CFO: Atanas H Atanasov
Ex VP: David Eastin
Ex VP: Gregory J Pound
Sr VP: Donald Jensen
VP: Patrice Armbruster
VP: Stan Bugh
VP: Mark McGinty
VP: Aaron Reece
VP: Sharra L Straight
VP Bus Dev: Bob Foster

D-U-N-S 15-352-4541
■ **NGL SUPPLY LLC**
(*Suby of* NGL ENERGY PARTNERS LP) ★
6120 S Yale Ave Ste 805, Tulsa, OK 74136-4233
Tel (918) 481-1119 *Founded/Ownrshp* 2010
Sales 90.7MME *EMP* 119
SIC 5172 Gases, liquefied petroleum (propane); Gases, liquefied petroleum (propane)
CEO: Stephen D Tuttle
**Pr:* Brian K Pauling
**CFO:* Craig S Jones
Sr VP: Stan Perry
VP: Stan A Bugh
VP: Mark McGinty

D-U-N-S 36-273-0710
■ **NGL SUPPLY WHOLESALE LLC**
(*Suby of* NGL SUPPLY LLC) ★
6120 S Yale Ave Ste 805, Tulsa, OK 74136-4233
Tel (918) 481-1119 *Founded/Ownrshp* 2003
Sales 48.6MME *EMP* 33
SIC 5172 Gases, liquefied petroleum (propane)
CEO: Michael Krimbill
**Pr:* Shawn W Coady
**CFO:* Atanas H Atanasov
**Treas:* Scott Daniel

D-U-N-S 05-303-8537
NGL WATER SOLUTIONS DJ LLC
3773 E Cherry Creek N Dr, Denver, CO 80209-3804
Tel (720) 287-5335 *Founded/Ownrshp* 2011
Sales 27.6MME *EMP* 100E
SIC 7389 Water softener service
Pr: James Burke
**Ex VP:* David Kehoe
Sr VP: Greg Blais
**Sr VP:* Jack Eberhardt
**Sr VP:* Bill Laughlin
**Sr VP:* James Winter

D-U-N-S 00-697-1170
NGM INSURANCE CO
MAIN STREET AMERICA GROUP, THE
4601 Touchton Rd E # 3400, Jacksonville, FL 32246-4486
Tel (904) 380-7282 *Founded/Ownrshp* 1923
Sales NA *EMP* 1,000
Accts Ernst & Young Llp Boston Ma
SIC 6331 Fire, marine & casualty insurance; Fire, marine & casualty insurance
CEO: Tom Van Berkel
**Pr:* William Mc Kenna
**Ex VP:* Ed Kuhl
**Sr VP:* Doug Eden
**Sr VP:* Susan E Mack

D-U-N-S 92-887-1185
NGP ENERGY CAPITAL MANAGEMENT LLC
5221 N O Connor Blvd, Irving, TX 75039-3714
Tel (972) 432-1440 *Founded/Ownrshp* 1988
Sales 24.2MM^E *EMP* 75
SIC 1731 Energy management controls
Mng Pt: Kenneth A Hersh
**Mng Pt:* David Albin
**Mng Pt:* William J Quinn
**COO:* Tony R Weber
CFO: Scott Lakey
**CFO:* Jill W Lampert
**Ex VP:* Richard L Covington
**Ex VP:* Robert A Edwards
Ex VP: Preston Windham
Mng Dir: Tomas Ackerman
Snr Mgr: J B Hayes

D-U-N-S 02-109-8538
NGS AMERICAN INC
(*Suby of* CORESOURCE INC) ★
27575 Harper Ave, Saint Clair Shores, MI 48081-1923
Tel (586) 552-4656 *Founded/Ownrshp* 2006
Sales NA *EMP* 380
SIC 6411 8741 Medical insurance claim processing, contract or fee basis; Administrative management; Medical insurance claim processing, contract or fee basis; Administrative management
Pr: Kimberly A Gunter
VP: Susan Darga

NGT
See NATIONAL GOLDENTISSUE INC

D-U-N-S 07-950-6990
NH LEARNING SOLUTIONS CORP
14115 Farmington Rd, Livonia, MI 48154-5457
Tel (734) 525-1501 *Founded/Ownrshp* 2014
Sales 10.2MM^E *EMP* 300^E
SIC 8243 Software training, computer; Software training, computer
CEO: Mark McManus
**CFO:* John Morgan
**VP:* Scott McLean

D-U-N-S 07-216-2464
■ **NH LEGACY INC**
(*Suby of* CONEMAUGH HEALTH SYSTEM INC) ★
105 Nason Dr, Roaring Spring, PA 16673-1202
Tel (877) 224-2141 *Founded/Ownrshp* 2015
Sales 32.5MM *EMP* 275
SIC 8062 General medical & surgical hospitals; General medical & surgical hospitals
CEO: Richard Grogan
VP: Debra McGraw
Dir Soc: Lee Lightner
Dir Rad: Patricia Aungst
Dir Sec: Craig Hattler
MIS Dir: George Berger
QA Dir: Deborah Miller
HC Dir: Debbie Ginter

NH LIQUOR COMMISSION
See NEW HAMPSHIRE LIQUOR COMMISSION

N.H. SUPERVISORY ADMIN UNIT 5
See OYSTER RIVER COOPERATIVE SCHOOL DISTRICT

D-U-N-S 82-848-8200 EXP
NH-HAY INC
(*Suby of* NONGHYUP FEED INC.)
33757 Columbus St Se, Albany, OR 97322-7246
Tel (541) 791-8454 *Founded/Ownrshp* 2008
Sales 23.2MM *EMP* 13
SIC 5191 Hay; Hay
Pr: Youngil Lee

D-U-N-S 02-906-5935
NH3 SERVICE CO LLC
945 Johnson Ave, Salinas, CA 93901-4327
Tel (831) 424-5716 *Founded/Ownrshp* 1941
Sales 38.9MM^E *EMP* 68
SIC 5191

D-U-N-S 95-798-7654
NHB INDUSTRIES INC
(*Suby of* BEAM SUNTORY INC) ★
101 E Parkway, Talladega, AL 35160-3285
Tel (256) 362-5530 *Founded/Ownrshp* 1999
Sales 51.8MM^E *EMP* 740
SIC 2434 Wood kitchen cabinets; Wood kitchen cabinets
CEO: Rich Forbes
**Ex VP:* Gary Lautzenhiser

NHBB
See NEW HAMPSHIRE BALL BEARINGS INC

NHCA
See NATIONAL HEALTH CARE ASSOCIATES INC

D-U-N-S 36-123-9478
■ **NHCI OF HILLSBORO INC**
HILL REGIONAL HOSPITAL
(*Suby of* COMMUNITY HEALTH SYSTEMS INC) ★
101 Circle Dr, Hillsboro, TX 76645-2670
Tel (254) 580-8500 *Founded/Ownrshp* 1994
Sales 38.0MM^E *EMP* 200
SIC 8062 General medical & surgical hospitals; General medical & surgical hospitals
Pr: Martin G Schweinhart
**Pr:* Jan Mc Clure
**CFO:* Bill Beachamp
**CFO:* Larry W Cash
**VP:* T Mark Buford
**VP:* James W Doucette
Dir Lab: Angela Belew
Dir Rx: Ryan Gadi
QA Dir: Gay Templeton
Opers Mgr: Mary Taylor
Mktg Dir: Rosemary Smith

NHCS
See NEW HANOVER COUNTY SCHOOLS

D-U-N-S 07-554-9139
NHCS INC
NASH GENERAL HOSPITAL
2416 Professional Dr, Rocky Mount, NC 27804-2253
Tel (252) 962-8585 *Founded/Ownrshp* 1966
Sales 172.3MM^E *EMP* 1,653
Accts Deloitte & Touche Llp Charlot
SIC 8062 8093 8063 General medical & surgical hospitals; Substance abuse clinics (outpatient); Psychiatric hospitals; General medical & surgical hospitals; Substance abuse clinics (outpatient); Psychiatric hospitals
Pr: Larry Chewning
Chf Rad: Jerald Capps
V Ch: Wilmer Brantley
COO: Bradford Weiner
CFO: Al Hooks
**CFO:* Claude Allen Hooks
Dir OR: Patricia Boone
Dir OR: Julie Lawler
Dir Inf Cn: Wanda Lamm
Dir Lab: Arnette Davis
Dir Lab: Rachel Sutton
Dir Rad: Jay Streater

NHIC
See NATIONAL HEALTH INSURANCE CO

D-U-N-S 00-997-4817
■ **NHIC CORP**
(*Suby of* ELECTRONIC DATA SYSTEMS) ★
402 Otterson Dr, Chico, CA 95928-8248
Tel (530) 332-1168 *Founded/Ownrshp* 2006
Sales NA *EMP* 304
SIC 6411 6321 Medical insurance claim processing, contract or fee basis; Accident & health insurance; Medical insurance claim processing, contract or fee basis; Accident & health insurance
Exec: Jeff Brooks
**VP:* Anne Bockhoff-Dalton

D-U-N-S 83-821-7701
NHK INTERNATIONAL CORP
(*Suby of* NHK SPRING CO., LTD.)
50706 Varsity Ct, Wixom, MI 48393-2072
Tel (248) 926-0111 *Founded/Ownrshp* 1976
Sales 842.8MM *EMP* 200
Accts Ernst & Young Llp Louisville
SIC 8711 Engineering services; Engineering services
Pr: Yosei Morioka
Treas: Masakazu Toyoda
Sales Asso: Mark Sakata

D-U-N-S 60-246-5825 IMP
NHK LABORATORIES INC
12230 Florence Ave, Santa Fe Springs, CA 90670-3806
Tel (562) 903-5835 *Founded/Ownrshp* 1987
Sales 25.6MM^E *EMP* 95^E
SIC 2834 5122 Vitamin preparations; Vitamins & minerals; Vitamin preparations; Vitamins & minerals
CEO: M Amirul Karim
**CFO:* Shafiel Ahmed
**VP:* Nasima A Karim
Dir Lab: Jun Lin
Cmptr Lab: Waffae Taha
Site Mgr: Emdadul Haque
Plnt Mgr: Ghulam Yazdan
Ql Cn Mgr: Mohammad Zaman
Sls&Mrk Ex: Shabbir Akand
Sls&Mrk Ex: Shabbir Akane
Sls Mgr: Aaron Rovenger

D-U-N-S 62-714-9045 IMP
NHK SPRING PRECISION OF AMERICA INC
(*Suby of* NHK INTERNATIONAL CORP) ★
10600 Freeport Dr, Louisville, KY 40258-1883
Tel (502) 935-5556 *Founded/Ownrshp* 2012
Sales 35.0MM^E *EMP* 200
SIC 3495 Wire springs; Wire springs
Pr: Tomoyuki Chino

D-U-N-S 07-329-7509
NHL ENTERPRISES LP
1185 Ave Of The, New York, NY 10036
Tel (212) 789-2000 *Founded/Ownrshp* 1996
Sales 36.4MM^E *EMP* 148
SIC 6794 7941 8743 Copyright buying & licensing; Sports clubs, managers & promoters; Public relations services; Copyright buying & licensing; Sports clubs, managers & promoters; Public relations services
Pt: Richard L Dudley
Pt: Craig C Harnett
Sr VP: Robert Pulford
Sr VP: Richard H Zand

D-U-N-S 78-128-8688
NHM COMMUNITY COLLEGE DISTRICT
5000 Research Forest Dr, Spring, TX 77381-4356
Tel (832) 813-6500 *Founded/Ownrshp* 1972
Sales 11.0MM^E *EMP* 1,400
SIC 8222 Community college; Community college
Prin: John Pickleman

NHP
See NEIGHBORHOOD HEALTH PLAN

D-U-N-S 87-906-2719
NHP FOUNDATION
122 E 42nd St Rm 3500, New York, NY 10168-3599
Tel (646) 336-4936 *Founded/Ownrshp* 1989
Sales 22.8MM^E *EMP* 21
SIC 6552 Subdividers & developers
CEO: Richard F Burns
**CFO:* Glenn F Hopps
**CFO:* Gary Parkinson
Chf Inves: Stephen Green
**Sr VP:* Joseph P Wiedorfer
VP: Mecky Adnani
**VP:* Frank Cerbini
**VP:* Neal Dorbenare
**VP:* Patrick J Fry
**VP:* Fred Mitchell
**VP:* Jamie A Smarr

NHPD
See NEW HAMPSHIRE PUBLIC DEFENDER

NHRA
See NATIONAL HOT ROD ASSOCIATION

D-U-N-S 05-719-1876
NHS HUMAN SERVICES INC
620 Germantown Pike, Lafayette Hill, PA 19444-1810
Tel (610) 260-4600 *Founded/Ownrshp* 1981
Sales 44.3MM *EMP* 6,500
SIC 8093 8059 8082 Mental health clinic, outpatient; Alcohol clinic, outpatient; Drug clinic, outpatient; Rehabilitation center, outpatient treatment; Home for the mentally retarded, exc. skilled or intermediate; Visiting nurse service; Mental health clinic, outpatient; Alcohol clinic, outpatient; Drug clinic, outpatient; Rehabilitation center, outpatient treatment; Home for the mentally retarded, exc. skilled or intermediate; Visiting nurse service
CEO: M Joseph Rocks
COO: Michael J Breslin
**CFO:* Kevin W McClure
Ofcr: Stephanie Ziegler
Ex VP: Michael A Barton
VP: Terri Close
VP: Cathy Murphy
VP: Lean Pason
Prac Mgr: Dana Schaffer
Telecom Ex: John Grosso
CIO: Christopher Rieder

D-U-N-S 05-563-5130 IMP
NHS INC
SANTA CRUZ SKATEBOARDS
104 Bronson St Ste 9, Santa Cruz, CA 95062-3487
Tel (831) 459-7800 *Founded/Ownrshp* 1972
Sales 26.0MM^E *EMP* 92
SIC 3949 2329 Skateboards; Winter sports equipment; Athletic (warmup, sweat & jogging) suits: men's & boys'; Skateboards; Winter sports equipment; Athletic (warmup, sweat & jogging) suits: men's & boys'
CEO: Robert A Denike
**Pr:* Bob Denike
**Ch:* Richard H Novak
**VP:* Jeff Kendall
Board of Directors: Richard Novak, Tim Piumarta

D-U-N-S 04-972-7332
NHS MANAGEMENT LLC
931 Fairfax Park, Tuscaloosa, AL 35406-2805
Tel (205) 391-3600 *Founded/Ownrshp* 1981
Sales 215.6MM^E *EMP* 5,000
SIC 8082 8059 Home health care services; Nursing home, except skilled & intermediate care facility; Home health care services; Nursing home, except skilled & intermediate care facility
Pr: J Norman Estes
CFO: Claude Lee
Exec: Norman Estes
Nrsg Dir: Marian Peeples

D-U-N-S 96-939-2146
NHS PENNYLVANIA
620 Germantown Pike, Lafayette Hill, PA 19444-1810
Tel (610) 238-4403 *Founded/Ownrshp* 2011
Sales 149.6MM *EMP* 2^B
SIC 8699 8299 Charitable organization; Educational services; Charitable organization; Educational services

D-U-N-S 07-983-2851
NHS WOODHAVEN
620 Germantown Pike, Lafayette Hill, PA 19444-1810
Tel (610) 260-4681 *Founded/Ownrshp* 1994
Sales 25.8MM *EMP* 99
SIC 8093 Mental health clinic, outpatient
CFO: Derrick Yacovelli

NHTSA
See NATIONAL HIGHWAY TRAFFIC SAFETY ADMINISTRATION

D-U-N-S 07-837-1667
NHVS INTERNATIONAL INC
7600 Tyler Blvd, Mentor, OH 44060-4853
Tel (440) 527-8610 *Founded/Ownrshp* 2010
Sales 29.5MM^E *EMP* 325
SIC 3812 Acceleration indicators & systems components, aerospace; Acceleration indicators & systems components, aerospace
CEO: Sherry Richcreek

NI STEEL
See NORTHERN ILLINOIS STEEL SUPPLY CO

D-U-N-S 17-955-8697
NI WELDING SUPPLY LLC
TNT WELDING SUPPLY
1315 Highway 90 E, New Iberia, LA 70560-8763
Tel (337) 837-7311 *Founded/Ownrshp* 1999
Sales 38.4MM^E *EMP* 40
SIC 5085 Welding supplies
Pr: Ray Romero
VP: Ken McGrew
Sls Mgr: Jerry Gondron
Sales Asso: Roland Fruge
Sales Asso: Sanford Landry
Sales Asso: Brandon Segura
Sales Asso: Keith Vincent

D-U-N-S 01-097-1331
■ **NIA GROUP LLC**
NIA-GROUP ASSOCIATES
(*Suby of* MARSH & MCLENNAN AGENCY LLC) ★
66 N State Rt 17 Ste 200, Paramus, NJ 07652-2776
Tel (914) 397-1600 *Founded/Ownrshp* 2009
Sales NA *EMP* 400
SIC 6411 Insurance agents, brokers & service; Insurance brokers; Insurance agents, brokers & service; Insurance brokers
CEO: Kevin W Conboy
V Ch: John Voorhees
COO: Roger Gross
Ex VP: Gregg Coffey
Ex VP: Bob Feldman
Ex VP: Robert Feldman
Ex VP: Peter A Hutton
Ex VP: Rob Peason
Sr VP: Denise Angleman
VP: Bob Cottone
VP: Bill Diana
VP: Patti Smith
Comm Dir: Kim Keating

NIA MAGELLAN
See NATIONAL IMAGING ASSOCIATES INC

NIA-GROUP ASSOCIATES
See NIA GROUP LLC

NIACC
See NORTH IOWA AREA COMMUNITY COLLEGE

D-U-N-S 00-211-2423 EXP
NIAGARA BLOWER CO (NY)
(*Suby of* ALFA LAVAL US HOLDING INC) ★
91 Sawyer Ave, Tonawanda, NY 14150-7716
Tel (800) 426-5169 *Founded/Ownrshp* 1904, 2013
Sales 34.9MM^E *EMP* 120^E
SIC 3585 Refrigeration & heating equipment; Air conditioning units, complete: domestic or industrial; Humidifying equipment, except portable; Refrigeration & heating equipment; Air conditioning units, complete: domestic or industrial; Humidifying equipment, except portable
Pr: Peter G Demakos
**VP:* Craig D Boyce
IT Man: John Russo
Ql Cn Mgr: Brad Wildey
Sls Mgr: Mark Vogel

D-U-N-S 11-837-0142 IMP/EXP
NIAGARA BOTTLING LLC
2560 E Philadelphia St, Ontario, CA 91761-7768
Tel (909) 980-9493 *Founded/Ownrshp* 1998
Sales 342.0MM^E *EMP* 445
SIC 2086 Water, pasteurized: packaged in cans, bottles, etc.; Water, pasteurized: packaged in cans, bottles, etc.
Ex VP: Bill Hall
Ex VP: Rali Sanderson
Ex VP: Stella Shabo
**VP:* Brian Hess
Plng Mgr: Sun Kwok
Snr Ntwrk: Kevin Crocker
QA Dir: Octavia Ferrell
Dir IT: Sreesha RAO
IT Man: Anna Horner
Netwrk Eng: Wilson Shiao
VP Mfg: Paul Johnson

NIAGARA CHOCOLATES
See SWEETWORKS INC

D-U-N-S 06-365-4271
NIAGARA COUNTY COMMUNITY COLLEGE
(*Suby of* STATE UNIVERSITY OF NEW YORK) ★
3111 Saunders Settlement, Sanborn, NY 14132-9506
Tel (716) 614-6222 *Founded/Ownrshp* 1962
Sales 23.4MM^E *EMP* 600
SIC 8222 9411 Community college; Administration of educational programs; ; Community college; Administration of educational programs;
Pr: James P Klyczek
Pr: Walter Lukhaup
CFO: Bill Schickling
**CFO:* William Schickling
VP: Randy Bowen
VP: Kathleen Saunders

NIAGARA CUTTER
See NC INDUSTRIES INC

D-U-N-S 04-746-8863 IMP/EXP
NIAGARA DISTRIBUTORS INC
3701 N 29th Ave, Hollywood, FL 33020-1005
Tel (954) 925-6775 *Founded/Ownrshp* 1979
Sales 49.2MM^E *EMP* 40
SIC 5141 5149 7389 Groceries, general line; Bakery products;
Pr: Pat Lucci
**Pr:* Janet S Lucci
**VP:* Vincent Lucci

NIAGARA FALLS BOARD OF EDUCATI
See CITY SCHOOL DISTRICT OF CITY OF NIAGARA FALLS

D-U-N-S 07-849-0389
NIAGARA FALLS BRIDGE COMMISSION
5365 Military Rd, Lewiston, NY 14092-2122
Tel (716) 297-7513 *Founded/Ownrshp* 1938
Sales 39.6MM *EMP* 95
SIC 4785 Transportation inspection services
CFO: Victor Montalbo
Genl Mgr: Lew Holloway
IT Man: Michelle Rheinheimer

D-U-N-S 07-993-4667
NIAGARA FALLS MEMORIAL MEDICAL CENTER INC (NY)
621 10th St, Niagara Falls, NY 14301-1813
Tel (716) 278-4000 *Founded/Ownrshp* 1895
Sales 82.6MM *EMP* 1,105
SIC 8062 General medical & surgical hospitals; General medical & surgical hospitals
CEO: Joseph Ruffalo
CFO: Chris D Frauenhofer
CFO: Phillip Johnson
CFO: Raj Mehta
Treas: Charles Rader
Ex VP: Maryanne Wooley
VP: Vijay Bojedla
VP: Marnie Lavigne
Dir Rad: Les Mackenzie
Dir Rad: Peter Sanders
Dir Rx: Mary Ibegbu
Dir Rx: Jack Koford

NIAGARA FALLS PUBLIC WTR AUTH
See NIAGARA FALLS WATER BOARD

D-U-N-S 09-395-2807
NIAGARA FALLS WATER BOARD
NIAGARA FALLS PUBLIC WTR AUTH
5815 Buffalo Ave, Niagara Falls, NY 14304-3832
Tel (716) 283-9770 *Founded/Ownrshp* 2002
Sales 25.9MM *EMP* 90

SIC 7389 Water softener service; Water softener service
Ex Dir: Paul Drof
**Ch Bd:* Ted Janese III
Ex Dir: Robert Game
**Ex Dir:* Gerald Grose
Snr Mgr: Joe Lagamba

D-U-N-S 03-022-3663
NIAGARA FRONTIER HOCKEY LP
BUFFALO SABRES
111 Eight Ave, Buffalo, NY 14203
Tel (716) 855-4160 *Founded/Ownrshp* 2000
Sales 51.5MM^{E} *EMP* 1,587
SIC 7941 Ice hockey club; Ice hockey club
Genl Mgr: Darcy Regier
MIS Dir: Ken Bass

D-U-N-S 07-400-3708
NIAGARA FRONTIER TRANSIT METRO SYSTEM INC
(*Suby of* BUFFALO NIAGARA INTL ARPRT) ★
181 Ellicott St, Buffalo, NY 14203-2221
Tel (716) 855-7300 *Founded/Ownrshp* 1974
Sales 24.9MM^{E} *EMP* 800
Accts Price Waterhouse
SIC 4111 Bus line operations; Local railway passenger operation; Bus line operations; Local railway passenger operation
Ex Dir: Lawrence Meckler

D-U-N-S 05-661-5677
NIAGARA FRONTIER TRANSPORTATION AUTHORITY
BUFFALO NIAGARA INTL ARPRT
181 Ellicott St Ste 1, Buffalo, NY 14203-2298
Tel (716) 855-7300 *Founded/Ownrshp* 1967
Sales 137.9MM^{E} *EMP* 1,500
Accts Kpmg Llp Buffalo Ny
SIC 4111 4581 Bus line operations; Subway operation; Airport; Bus line operations; Subway operation; Airport
Ex Dir: Kimberly Minkel
COO: Peter Deglopper
**CFO:* John Cox
**Ch:* Howard Zemsky
IT Man: Darren Kempner
Mktg Mgr: Dominick Bordonaro
Mktg Mgr: James Lynch
**Genl Couns:* David Spate

D-U-N-S 62-055-7355
NIAGARA HEALTH CORP
(*Suby of* CATHOLIC HEALTH EAST) ★
6150 E Broad St, Columbus, OH 43213-1574
Tel (614) 898-4000 *Founded/Ownrshp* 1988
Sales 454.0MM^{E} *EMP* 8,000
SIC 8741 8062 Hospital management; General medical & surgical hospitals; Hospital management; General medical & surgical hospitals
Prin: Randall E Moore
Mktg Mgr: Jessica Amendolare
Mktg Mgr: Brandi Pennington

D-U-N-S 78-788-4381
■ **NIAGARA HOLDINGS INC**
(*Suby of* CARLYLE GROUP L P) ★
300 Lindenwood Dr, Malvern, PA 19355-1740
Tel (610) 651-4200 *Founded/Ownrshp* 2007
Sales 367.3MM^{E} *EMP* 1,300
SIC 2819 3231 Sodium & potassium compounds, exc. bleaches, alkalies, alum.; Sodium hyposulfite, sodium hydrosulfite; Potassium compounds or salts, except hydroxide or carbonate; Products of purchased glass; Sodium & potassium compounds, exc. bleaches, alkalies, alum.; Sodium hyposulfite, sodium hydrosulfite; Potassium compounds or salts, except hydroxide or carbonate; Products of purchased glass
Pr: Michael R Boyce
Pr: Michael R Imbriani
Pr: Scott Randolph
CFO: James P Cox
Ofcr: William Sichko

D-U-N-S 15-478-1579 IMP
NIAGARA LASALLE CORP
(*Suby of* OPTIMA SPECIALTY STEEL INC) ★
1412 150th St, Hammond, IN 46327-1743
Tel (219) 853-6000 *Founded/Ownrshp* 2011
Sales 312.0MM^{E} *EMP* 1,000
SIC 3316 Bars, steel, cold finished, from purchased hot-rolled; Bars, steel, cold finished, from purchased hot-rolled
Pr: Michael Salamon
**CEO:* Mordechai Korf
Exec: Mike Flood
Genl Mgr: Michael Burchwell
Mtls Mgr: Thomas Gozdecki
Opers Mgr: Kip Ingmanson
Ql Cn Mgr: Joel Gomez

D-U-N-S 03-176-5530
NIAGARA LUTHERAN HEALTH SYSTEM INC (NY)
64 Hager St, Buffalo, NY 14208-1327
Tel (716) 886-4377 *Founded/Ownrshp* 1996
Sales 25.3MM *EMP* 748
SIC 8051 Skilled nursing care facilities; Skilled nursing care facilities
CEO: Jurgen Arndt
CFO: Laurie Jankowski
Doctor: Jennifer Grzebinski
Nrsg Dir: Judith Kelly

D-U-N-S 03-021-7350
NIAGARA LUTHERAN HOME & REHABILITATION CENTER INC
(*Suby of* NIAGARA LUTHERAN HEALTH SYSTEM INC) ★
64 Hager St, Buffalo, NY 14208-1399
Tel (716) 886-4377 *Founded/Ownrshp* 1956
Sales 9.9MM *EMP* 280
Accts Freed Maxick & Battaglia Cpas
SIC 8051 Skilled nursing care facilities; Skilled nursing care facilities
CEO: Jurgen Arndt

NIAGARA MACHINE
See CNB INTERNATIONAL INC

D-U-N-S 05-454-2779
NIAGARA MOHAWK HOLDINGS INC (NY)
(*Suby of* NATIONAL GRID USA) ★
300 Erie Blvd W, Syracuse, NY 13202-4201
Tel (315) 474-1511 *Founded/Ownrshp* 1998, 2002
Sales 2.7MM *EMP* 3,950
SIC 4911 4924 Generation, electric power; Transmission, electric power; Distribution, electric power; Natural gas distribution; Generation, electric power; Transmission, electric power; Distribution, electric power; Natural gas distribution
CEO: Thomas B King
Pr: Albert J Budney Jr
CFO: William F Edwards
Treas: Arthur Roos
Sr VP: David J Arrington
VP: Theresa Flaim
VP: William Flynn
VP: Nabil Hitti
VP: Michael Kelleher
VP: Steven W Tasker
VP: David Walsh

D-U-N-S 00-699-4735
NIAGARA MOHAWK POWER CORP
NATIONAL GRID
(*Suby of* NIAGARA MOHAWK HOLDINGS INC) ★
300 Erie Blvd W, Syracuse, NY 13202-4250
Tel (315) 474-1511 *Founded/Ownrshp* 1937, 2002
Sales 3.2MM^{E} *EMP* 3,950
SIC 4911 4924 Generation, electric power; Transmission, electric power; Distribution, electric power; Natural gas distribution; Generation, electric power; Transmission, electric power; Distribution, electric power; Natural gas distribution
CEO: Kenneth Daly
**Pr:* Thomas B King
**Treas:* Malcolm Charles Cooper
**Sr VP:* James B Howe
**VP:* Susan M Crossett
VP: T Flaim
**VP:* Martin Wheatcroft
Prin: Greg Hunter
Prin: Doug Newton
Prgrm Mgr: Chris Murphy
Prgrm Mgr: Janet Roods

NIAGARA SCREEN PRODUCTS
See PUROLATOR EFP LLC

D-U-N-S 02-076-3331 IMP
NIAGARA SHEETS LLC
(*Suby of* JAMESTOWN CONTAINER CORP) ★
7393 Shawnee Rd, North Tonawanda, NY 14120-1325
Tel (716) 692-1129 *Founded/Ownrshp* 2007
Sales 28.0MM^{E} *EMP* 75
SIC 2653 Corrugated boxes, partitions, display items, sheets & pad
Pr: John Bolender
**VP:* Skip Polowy
Prd Mgr: Jeff Gebauer

D-U-N-S 13-550-7023 IMP
NIAGARA THERMAL PRODUCTS LLC
3315 Haseley Dr, Niagara Falls, NY 14304-1460
Tel (716) 297-0652 *Founded/Ownrshp* 1998
Sales 20.7MM^{E} *EMP* 120^{E}
SIC 3443 Heat exchangers, condensers & components; Heat exchangers, condensers & components
CEO: Barry Heckman
CFO: Lida Grimaldi-Sykes
**VP:* Scott Mowry
IT Man: Tana Laskowski
Plnt Mgr: Donald Hall

D-U-N-S 00-210-6177 IMP
NIAGARA TRANSFORMER CORP (NY)
1747 Dale Rd, Buffalo, NY 14225-4964
Tel (716) 896-6500 *Founded/Ownrshp* 1928
Sales 27.7MM^{E} *EMP* 75
SIC 3612 Power transformers, electric
Pr: John F Darby
**VP:* Robert Fishlock
VP: Sheldon Kennedy
Mfg Mgr: Stan Hatch
Ql Cn Mgr: Bob Murphy

D-U-N-S 03-022-5734
NIAGARA UNIVERSITY
5795 Lewiston Rd, Niagara University, NY 14109-9809
Tel (716) 285-1212 *Founded/Ownrshp* 1856
Sales 117.3MM *EMP* 500^{E}
Accts Bonadio & Co Llp Buffalo Ny
SIC 8221 University; University
Pr: Rev Joseph Levesque
Ofcr: John Gangloff
Ofcr: Paul Gorski
Ofcr: Wade Hart
Ofcr: Frederick Titman
Ofcr: Ward Wilmot
Assoc VP: Mary Borgognoni
Ex VP: Marisa Barile
Ex VP: Michele Celeste
Ex VP: Linda Coram
Ex VP: Michele Gansworth
**Ex VP:* Bonnie Rose
VP: Kevin Hearn
**VP:* Michael S Jaszka

D-U-N-S 07-993-8544
NIAGARA WHEATFIELD CENTRAL SCHOOL DISTRICT INC
6700 Schultz St, Niagara Falls, NY 14304-4531
Tel (716) 215-3000 *Founded/Ownrshp* 1950
Sales 39.9MM^{E} *EMP* 800
SIC 8211 Public elementary school; Public junior high school; Public senior high school; Public elementary school; Public junior high school; Public senior high school
Prin: Lynn Marie Fusco PHD
COO: Julie Winden
**Prin:* Timothy Carter
**Prin:* Elizabeth Corieri
**Prin:* Theron Mong
**Prin:* Nora O'Bryan
**Prin:* Laura Palka

**Prin:* Charles Smillrich
Dir IT: Mary Buch
Psych: Elizabeth Antonelli
Psych: Jennifer Ertel

D-U-N-S 04-009-6740 EXP
NIAGRA THERMAL PRODUCTS (NY)
3315 Haseley Dr, Niagara Falls, NY 14304-1460
Tel (716) 297-0652 *Founded/Ownrshp* 1996
Sales 21.7MM^{E} *EMP* 125
SIC 5084 Heat exchange equipment, industrial
CEO: Barry Heckman
Sls Mgr: David Patrick

D-U-N-S 00-506-7616 IMP/EXP
NIBCO INC
1516 Middlebury St, Elkhart, IN 46516-4740
Tel (574) 295-3000 *Founded/Ownrshp* 1909
Sales 500.0MM *EMP* 2,420
Accts Bdo Usa Llp Grand Rapids Mi
SIC 3494 3491 3089 Valves & pipe fittings; Pipe fittings; Plumbing & heating valves; Industrial valves; Plastic hardware & building products; Fittings for pipe, plastic; Valves & pipe fittings; Pipe fittings; Plumbing & heating valves; Industrial valves; Plastic hardware & building products; Fittings for pipe, plastic
Ch Bd: Rex Martin
Pr: Steven E Malm
VP: Kenneth J Eme Jr
VP: David Goodling
VP: Todd A Nowicki
Genl Mgr: Randy Doering
Mktg Mgr: Rebecca Foletta
Board of Directors: Howard L Clark Jr, Arthur J Decio, William C Kunkler, Richard E Newsted

NIBR
See NOVARTIS INSTITUTES FOR BIOMEDICAL RESEARCH INC

D-U-N-S 88-323-3363 IMP
NIC & ZOE CO
323 Speen St Ste 2, Natick, MA 01760-1500
Tel (508) 651-0000 *Founded/Ownrshp* 1992
Sales 20.6MM^{E} *EMP* 60
SIC 5137 Women's & children's clothing
Pr: Kent T Spellman
**Treas:* James E Buckley
VP: Dorian Lightbown
VP Sls: Taal McLean

NIC GLOBAL
See NATIONAL INDUSTRIAL CONCEPTS INC

D-U-N-S 08-922-8477 IMP
NIC HOLDING CORP
25 Melville Park Rd # 202, Melville, NY 11747-3156
Tel (631) 753-4200 *Founded/Ownrshp* 2000
Sales 299.7MM^{E} *EMP* 60
SIC 5171 Petroleum bulk stations; Petroleum bulk stations
Ch Bd: Jay H Bernstein
**CFO:* Peter Ripp

D-U-N-S 07-081-6710
▲ **NIC INC**
25501 W Valley Pkwy # 300, Olathe, KS 66061-8474
Tel (877) 234-3468 *Founded/Ownrshp* 1997
Sales 272.1MM *EMP* 818^{E}
Tkr Sym EGOV *Exch* NGS
SIC 7371 Custom computer programming services; Computer software development & applications; Custom computer programming services; Computer software development & applications
Ch Bd: Harry H Herington
Pr: James Dodd
COO: Robert W Knapp Jr
CFO: Stephen M Kovzan
Ofcr: William F Bradley Jr
Ofcr: J D Sherry
Ex VP: Kevin C Childress
Ex VP: Samuel Somerhalder
Sr VP: Ron E Thornburgh
VP: Tom Platis
VP: Jeff Shaw
Comm Dir: Angela Skinner
Dir Bus: Phil Billingsley
Dir Bus: Erica Stuckey
Comm Man: Chris Neff
Board of Directors: Art N Burtscher, Karen S Evans, Ross C Hartley, C Brad Henry, Alexander C Kemper, William M Lyons, Pete Wilson

D-U-N-S 13-794-4992
NICA INC
1451 E Lincoln Ave, Madison Heights, MI 48071-4136
Tel (248) 586-3300 *Founded/Ownrshp* 1998
Sales 273.8MM^{E} *EMP* 1,300^{E}
SIC 2396 Automotive trimmings, fabric; Automotive trimmings, fabric
Ch Bd: Jorge Morales
Dir IT: Steven Capraro

D-U-N-S 11-623-7488
NICAR MANAGEMENT INC
GREAT STEAK & FRY
188 N Brookwood Ave # 100, Hamilton, OH 45013-1304
Tel (513) 896-9695 *Founded/Ownrshp* 1984
Sales 9.0MM^{E} *EMP* 300
SIC 5812 6794 Steak restaurant; Franchises, selling or licensing; Steak restaurant; Franchises, selling or licensing
Pr: Nicola J Lanni
**VP:* Pat Lanni

NICB
See NATIONAL INSURANCE CRIME BUREAU INC

D-U-N-S 10-824-7255
NICE BUILDERS INC DAVID A
4571 Ware Creek Rd, Williamsburg, VA 23188-1125
Tel (757) 566-3032 *Founded/Ownrshp* 1975
Sales 49.1MM *EMP* 75
Accts Pbmares Llp Williamsburg Vi
SIC 1542 Commercial & office building contractors; Commercial & office building contractors
Pr: David A Nice

**CFO:* Linda L Butler
**Treas:* Kimberly N Woodroffe
Ofcr: Danielle Creekmore
**VP:* Brandon A Nice
**VP:* Deborah L Nice
VP: Kimberly Nice

D-U-N-S 09-990-0136
NICE N EASY GROCERY SHOPPES INC
7840 Oxbow Rd, Canastota, NY 13032-4665
Tel (315) 397-2802 *Founded/Ownrshp* 1980
Sales 179.0MM^{E} *EMP* 650
Accts Bowers & Company Cpas Pllc Sy
SIC 5411 5541 Convenience stores; Filling stations, gasoline; Convenience stores; Filling stations, gasoline
CEO: John Macdougall
VP: Patrick Callahan
VP: Matt Paduano
Exec: Andrew Franco
Store Mgr: Christopher Leclair
CTO: Edward Bliss
IT Man: Michael Levrigaz
IT Man: Jean McKeever
Site Mgr: Penny Chenoweth
Site Mgr: Michelle Fobare
Sales Asso: Samantha Bradford

D-U-N-S 01-452-1947
NICE SYSTEMS INC
(*Suby of* NICE-SYSTEMS LTD)
461 From Rd Ste 103, Paramus, NJ 07652-3526
Tel (201) 964-2600 *Founded/Ownrshp* 1989
Sales NA *EMP* 537
SIC 8742

D-U-N-S 00-377-8198 IMP/EXP
NICE-PAK PRODUCTS INC (NY)
2 Nice Pak Park, Orangeburg, NY 10962-1376
Tel (845) 365-2772 *Founded/Ownrshp* 1955
Sales 440.6MM^{E} *EMP* 1,000
SIC 2621 7389 2676 Towels, tissues & napkins: paper & stock; Sanitary tissue paper; Packaging & labeling services; Sanitary paper products; Towels, tissues & napkins: paper & stock; Sanitary tissue paper; Packaging & labeling services; Sanitary paper products
Pr: Robert Julius
Pr: John Culligan
Pr: Jon Kupperman
CFO: Ron Cerasuolo
Ex VP: Wallis Brooks
Ex VP: Zachary Julius
**Sr VP:* William E Dwan
VP: Paul Davies
VP: William Dawn
VP: Scott Manske
VP: Matt Marshhouser
VP: Keith McQuaid
Creative D: Lisa Meyers

D-U-N-S 19-762-9637 IMP
NICHIA AMERICA CORP
(*Suby of* NICHIA CORPORATION)
48561 Alpha Dr Ste 100, Wixom, MI 48393-3456
Tel (248) 349-9800 *Founded/Ownrshp* 1988
Sales 21.0MM^{E} *EMP* 52
SIC 5063 Transformers & transmission equipment
Pr: Susumu Wako
**Pr:* Shigeo Kuboniwa
**Ex VP:* Kazuhisa Miyata
Sales Asso: Ryoko Sharpe

D-U-N-S 05-440-9201 IMP
NICHIHA USA INC
(*Suby of* NICHIHA CORPORATION)
6465 E Johns Xing, Johns Creek, GA 30097-1580
Tel (770) 805-9466 *Founded/Ownrshp* 1998
Sales 49.9MM^{E} *EMP* 275^{E}
SIC 3241 3299 3272 Masonry cement; Mica products; Dry mixture concrete; Masonry cement; Mica products; Dry mixture concrete
Ch: Yoichi Ikeda
**CFO:* Michihide Yamamoto
Sr VP: Darrin Haugan
IT Man: Eric Daugherty
Tech Mgr: Carolina Albano
VP Sls: Michael Cobb
Mktg Mgr: Melba Garris
Manager: Thomas Balduf
Manager: Bill Cooke
Manager: Jeff Locke
Manager: Mike McCraw

D-U-N-S 86-944-5614 IMP
NICHIHA USA INC
3150 Avondale Mill Rd, Macon, GA 31216-7716
Tel (478) 238-9070 *Founded/Ownrshp* 1998
Sales 58.7MM^{E} *EMP* 212
SIC 3241 Masonry cement; Masonry cement
Pr: Yoichi Ikeda
**Pr:* Michide Yamamoto
COO: Jim Wueste
Treas: Fumiaki Ikai
Chf Mktg O: Darrin Haugan
**VP:* Michael Cob
Opers Mgr: Julie Calcutt
Opers Mgr: Clifford Danzy
VP Sls: Michael Cobb
Sls Dir: Thomas Wingard
Sls Mgr: John Burgess

NICHIRIN COUPLER
See NICHIRIN-FLEX USA INC

D-U-N-S 04-363-8985 IMP
NICHIRIN-FLEX USA INC
NICHIRIN COUPLER
(*Suby of* NICHIRIN CO., LTD.)
9600 Plaza Cir, El Paso, TX 79927-2105
Tel (915) 859-1199 *Founded/Ownrshp* 1997
Sales 60.6MM^{E} *EMP* 350
SIC 3498 3714 3585 Fabricated pipe & fittings; Motor vehicle parts & accessories; Refrigeration & heating equipment; Fabricated pipe & fittings; Motor vehicle parts & accessories; Refrigeration & heating equipment
Pr: Yoshiaki Takashima

D-U-N-S 04-891-8353
NICHO PRODUCE CO INC
925 N 10th Ave, Edinburg, TX 78541-3129
Tel (956) 383-5633 Founded/Ownrshp 1969
Sales 31.3MM^E EMP 55
Accts Luis Gustavo Castilleja Cpa
SIC 5148 Fresh fruits & vegetables; Fresh fruits & vegetables
Pr: Tommy Villarreal
*VP: Mirtala Villarreal
QA Dir: Paul Ludden

D-U-N-S 03-537-5757 IMP
NICHOLAS & CO INC
5520 W Harold Gatty Dr, Salt Lake City, UT 84116-3725
Tel (801) 531-1100 Founded/Ownrshp 1939
Sales 508.0MM EMP 555
SIC 5046 5141 5142 Restaurant equipment & supplies; Groceries, general line; Packaged frozen goods; Restaurant equipment & supplies; Groceries, general line; Packaged frozen goods
Ch Bd: William N Mouskondis
Sr Pt: Walter E Rogers Jr
*Pr: Peter Mouskondis
CFO: Jeffrey May
*Treas: Bill Athens
Ex VP: Dave Robbins
VP: Ken Adams
VP: Paul Lyon
CIO: George Adondakis
Dir IT: Michael Kattelman
Dir IT: Tony Sansone

D-U-N-S 00-982-0531
NICHOLAS ACOUSTICS AND SPECIALTY CO INC
120 Comm Pk Dr, Jackson, MS 39213
Tel (601) 981-1531 Founded/Ownrshp 1957
Sales 21.4MM^E EMP 80
SIC 1542 Commercial & office building, new construction
Ch Bd: Donald E Nicholas
*Pr: David Nicholas
*VP: Gary Coker
Exec: Bonnie McMillian

D-U-N-S 13-114-5153
NICHOLAS CONSOLIDATED INC
CANYON PIPE & SUPPLY
10779 N Solar Canyon Way, Surprise, AZ 85379-2303
Tel (602) 353-4146 Founded/Ownrshp 1983
Sales 45.8MM^E EMP 100
SIC 5075 5074 Air conditioning equipment, except room units; Warm air heating equipment & supplies; Plumbing & hydronic heating supplies; Air conditioning equipment, except room units; Warm air heating equipment & supplies; Plumbing & hydronic heating supplies
Pr: Nicholas Formento
*VP: Charles Menard
IT Man: Stephanie Jurgens
IT Man: Bob Leo

D-U-N-S 08-224-4757
NICHOLAS COUNTY BOARD OF EDUCATION
NICHOLAS COUNTY SCHOOL
400 Old Main Dr, Summersville, WV 26651-1360
Tel (304) 872-3611 Founded/Ownrshp 1933
Sales 36.7MM EMP 650
SIC 8211 Public elementary & secondary schools; School board; Public elementary & secondary schools; School board
*Pr: Lloyd Adkins
Teacher Pr: Ernie Jarvis

NICHOLAS COUNTY SCHOOL
See NICHOLAS COUNTY BOARD OF EDUCATION

D-U-N-S 79-071-7292
▲ NICHOLAS FINANCIAL INC
2454 N Mcmullen Booth Rd, Clearwater, FL 33759-1353
Tel (727) 726-0763 Founded/Ownrshp 2008
Sales NA EMP 280
Accts Dixon Hughes Goodman Llp Atla
Tkr Sym NICK Exch NGS
SIC 6141 Financing: automobiles, furniture, etc., not a deposit bank; Financing: automobiles, furniture, etc., not a deposit bank
Ch Bd: Ralph T Finkenbrink
CFO: Katie Macgillivary
Board of Directors: Kevin D Bates

D-U-N-S 06-791-4648
NICHOLAS H NOYES MEMORIAL HOSPITAL INC (NY)
NOYES HEALTH
111 Clara Barton St, Dansville, NY 14437-9503
Tel (585) 335-6001 Founded/Ownrshp 1927, 1998
Sales 46.9MM EMP 493
Accts Efp Rotenberg Llp Rochester
SIC 8062 General medical & surgical hospitals; General medical & surgical hospitals
Pr: James Wissler
Pr: Helen Hurlburt
*CFO: Jay Maslyn
*VP: Amy Pollard
Obsttrcn: Robert Bonvino
Doctor: Deb Dupont
Doctor: Jennifer Graham
Doctor: Asad Majid
Doctor: Steven Posnick
Doctor: Ahsen Sheikh
Nrsg Dir: Lynette Green

NICHOLAS HOMES
See MNI ENTERPRISES INC

D-U-N-S 02-931-6759
NICHOLAS K CORP
FORD STORE SAN LEANDRO
1111 Marina Blvd, San Leandro, CA 94577-3364
Tel (510) 352-2000 Founded/Ownrshp 2008
Sales 70.5MM EMP 109
SIC 5511 7515 Automobiles, new & used; Pickups, new & used; Passenger car leasing; Automobiles, new & used; Pickups, new & used; Passenger car leasing
Pr: Robert Knezevich
Genl Mgr: Phil Baltazar
Sls Mgr: Ching Chou
Sls Mgr: Julio Coronado
Sls Mgr: Gus Knezevich

D-U-N-S 19-665-2978
NICHOLAS LANE CONTRACTORS INC
1157 N Red Gum St, Anaheim, CA 92806-2515
Tel (714) 630-7630 Founded/Ownrshp 1984
Sales 26.0MM EMP 400
SIC 1521 1542 New construction, single-family houses; Commercial & office buildings, renovation & repair; New construction, single-family houses; Commercial & office buildings, renovation & repair
Pr: Scott N Shaddix
*Sec: Jo Ann Shaddix

D-U-N-S 05-273-6535
NICHOLAS MARKETS INC
NORTH HALEDON FOODTOWN
195 Browertown Rd, Woodland Park, NJ 07424-2609
Tel (973) 595-5080 Founded/Ownrshp 1943
Sales 62.6MM^E EMP 425
SIC 5411 Supermarkets, chain; Supermarkets, chain
CEO: David Maniaci
*Ch Bd: Ann Maniaci
*Co-Ch Bd: Ray Maniaci
*VP: Chris Nigro
Off Mgr: Bob Greenway

D-U-N-S 80-740-4244 IMP
NICHOLAS MICHAEL DESIGNS INC
2330 Raymer Ave, Fullerton, CA 92833-2515
Tel (714) 562-8101 Founded/Ownrshp 2003
Sales 22.9MM^E EMP 120
SIC 2519 Household furniture, except wood or metal: upholstered
CEO: Michael A Cimarueti
Off Mgr: Gloria Licano

D-U-N-S 11-859-3169
NICHOLAS-APPLEGATE CAPITAL MANAGEMENT LLC
(Suby of ALLIANZ SE)
600 W Broadway Ste 2900, San Diego, CA 92101-3398
Tel (619) 687-8000 Founded/Ownrshp 2004
Sales 101.5MM^E EMP 661
SIC 6282 Investment advisory service; Investment advisory service
Pt: Andy Gallagher
VP: Lawrence Spiedell
CTO: George Kenney
Sales Asso: Michael Powell

D-U-N-S 06-547-9529
NICHOLLS STATE UNIVERSITY
N S U
906 E 1st St, Thibodaux, LA 70301-6701
Tel (985) 446-8111 Founded/Ownrshp 1948
Sales 1.2MM^E EMP 600
SIC 8221 9411 University; Administration of educational programs; ; University; Administration of educational programs;
Pr: Dr Bruce Murphy
VP: Todd Keller
*VP: Lionel O Naquin
VP: Mike Naquin
Dir Teleco: Slade Besson
*Prin: Stephen T Hulbert
Adm Dir: Tona C Savoie
CTO: Deborah Moorhead
Netwrk Mgr: Nik Dronet
Software D: Chris Usey
Psych: David Ford

D-U-N-S 05-100-3077
NICHOLS AGRISERVICE LLC
SWEETLAND AG TECH
1783 Davis Ave, Nichols, IA 52766-9700
Tel (319) 723-4221 Founded/Ownrshp 1997
Sales 22.9MM EMP 32
Accts Td&T Financial Group Pc Musc
SIC 5153 5191 Grains; Fertilizer & fertilizer materials; Grains; Fertilizer & fertilizer materials
Off Mgr: Kim Chamberlain
Sls Mgr: Jerry Gerot

D-U-N-S 82-500-3494
NICHOLS ALUMINUM LLC
DAVENPORT ROLLING MILL
(Suby of ALERIS ROLLED PRODUCTS LLC) ★
1725 Rockingham Rd, Davenport, IA 52802-1825
Tel (563) 324-2121 Founded/Ownrshp 2014
Sales 90.3MM^E EMP 542
SIC 3354 3355

D-U-N-S 83-127-5891
■ NICHOLS ALUMINUM-ALABAMA LLC
(Suby of QUANEX BUILDING PRODUCTS CORP) ★
2001 Hwy 20, Decatur, AL 35601-7509
Tel (256) 353-1550 Founded/Ownrshp 1993
Sales 25.9MM^E EMP 130
SIC 3353 Aluminum sheet, plate & foil; Aluminum sheet, plate & foil

NICHOLS BROTHERS BOAT BUILDERS
See ICE FLOE LLC

D-U-N-S 07-534-8714
NICHOLS COLLEGE
124 Center Rd, Dudley, MA 01571-6310
Tel (508) 213-1560 Founded/Ownrshp 1815
Sales 24.4MM^E EMP 160
Accts Bollus Lynch Llp Worcester M
SIC 8221 College, except junior; College, except junior
Pr: Susan W Engelkemeyer
*Treas: Kurt R Harrington
VP: Bill Boffi
VP: Jared Hamilton
VP: Patricia Hertzfeld
Comm Dir: DOT Millhofer

D-U-N-S 85-845-4135 IMP
■ NICHOLS CONSTRUCTION LLC
(Suby of DYCOM INDUSTRIES INC) ★
1098 Clear Creek Rd, Vansant, VA 24656-8590
Tel (276) 597-7441 Founded/Ownrshp 2001
Sales 26.0MM^E EMP 160
SIC 1623 Telephone & communication line construction; Electric power line construction; Telephone & communication line construction; Electric power line construction
Pr: Jack Nichols
*Treas: H Andrew Deferrari
VP: Aaron Morrison
*VP: Brandon Nichols

D-U-N-S 09-377-8314
NICHOLS DODGE INC
988 Plantation Dr, Burlington, NC 27215-6713
Tel (336) 229-6901 Founded/Ownrshp 1979
Sales 30.1MM^E EMP 50
SIC 5511 Automobiles, new & used; Automobiles, new & used
Pr: Larry W Nichols
Genl Mgr: Perry Nichols

NICHOLS DOLLAR SAVER
See G L N OF CHECOTAH INC

NICHOLS FARMS
See NICHOLS PISTACHIO

D-U-N-S 19-758-1853
■ NICHOLS INSTITUTE REFERENCE LABORATORIES
(Suby of QUEST DIAGNOSTICS NICHOLS INSTITUTE) ★
33608 Ortega Hwy, San Juan Capistrano, CA 92675-2042
Tel (949) 728-4000 Founded/Ownrshp 1971
Sales 14.8MM^E EMP 1,000
SIC 8071 Testing laboratories; Testing laboratories
Pr: Douglas Harrington
*CFO: Charles Olson
*Treas: Jolene Kahn
*VP: Michael O'Gorman
*VP: Murugan R Pandian
*VP Sls: Chuck Miller
S&M/Mgr: Robert Menna

D-U-N-S 02-788-9039
NICHOLS LUMBER & HARDWARE CO
13470 Dalewood St, Baldwin Park, CA 91706-5883
Tel (626) 960-4802 Founded/Ownrshp 1958
Sales 42.3MM^E EMP 75
SIC 5031 5251 2421 Lumber: rough, dressed & finished; Hardware; Sawmills & planing mills, general; Lumber: rough, dressed & finished; Hardware; Sawmills & planing mills, general
Pr: Judith A Nichols
VP: Rick Dean
Exec: Valarie Deen
Sales Asso: Derek Chang
Sales Asso: Jose Jimenez

D-U-N-S 01-727-1339
NICHOLS PAPER & SUPPLY CO
1391 Judson Rd, Norton Shores, MI 49456-9691
Tel (231) 799-2120 Founded/Ownrshp 1976
Sales 101.9MM^E EMP 90
SIC 5113 5087 Industrial & personal service paper; Shipping supplies; Cleaning & maintenance equipment & supplies; Carpet & rug cleaning equipment & supplies, commercial; Industrial & personal service paper; Shipping supplies; Cleaning & maintenance equipment & supplies; Carpet & rug cleaning equipment & supplies, commercial
CEO: Michael K Olthoff
*COO: Kevin Rahrig
CFO: Will Kelderhouse
VP: Richard Billadeau
Mktg Mgr: Marcie Palmer

D-U-N-S 12-407-2724 IMP/EXP
NICHOLS PISTACHIO
NICHOLS FARMS
13762 1st Ave, Hanford, CA 93230-9316
Tel (559) 584-6811 Founded/Ownrshp 1990
Sales 54.8MM^E EMP 200
SIC 2068 Salted & roasted nuts & seeds; Salted & roasted nuts & seeds
Pr: Charles C Nichols
*Treas: Susan Nichols
Opers Mgr: Dennis Santos

NICHOLS SUPER THRIFT
See G L N INC

D-U-N-S 00-708-1243 IMP
NICHOLS TILLAGE TOOLS INC
312 Hereford St, Sterling, CO 80751-8472
Tel (970) 522-8676 Founded/Ownrshp 1957
Sales 30.6MM^E EMP 125
SIC 3523 3469 Farm machinery & equipment; Metal stampings; Farm machinery & equipment; Metal stampings
Pr: R Joseph Nichols
*VP: Rob Nichols
CTO: Emily Hollingshead
Opers Mgr: Robert Ogle

NICHOLSON
See NC & SONS INC

NICHOLSON
See APEX TOOL GROUP LLC

D-U-N-S 79-556-6769
NICHOLSON & GALLOWAY INC
261 Glen Head Rd, Glen Head, NY 11545-1997
Tel (212) 685-6677 Founded/Ownrshp 1990
Sales 21.3MM^E EMP 75
SIC 1542 1761 Specialized public building contractors; Hospital construction; Religious building construction; Roofing contractor
CEO: Andrew Wilson
*Sr VP: Edward Caban Jr
*Sr VP: Thomas Cusa
IT Man: Mark Haynes

D-U-N-S 00-450-4684 IMP/EXP
NICHOLSON CONSTRUCTION CO (PA)
(Suby of BACHY SOLETANCHE LIMITED)
12 Mcclane St, Cuddy, PA 15031-9754
Tel (412) 221-4500 Founded/Ownrshp 1955, 1969
Sales 142.0MM EMP 250
Accts Schneider Downs & Co Inc P
SIC 1629 1771 1799 Pile driving contractor; Foundation & footing contractor; Grouting work; Shoring & underpinning work; Pile driving contractor; Foundation & footing contractor; Grouting work; Shoring & underpinning work
CFO: Jeffrey Lewis
Ex VP: Christopher Hynes
VP: Roger Baldwin
*VP: Richard Deschamps
*VP: Laurent Lefebvre
VP: Fred Tarquinio
*VP: John D Wise
Dir Bus: Brian O'Gara
Rgnl Mgr: Richard Crockford
Rgnl Mgr: Matt Johnson
Dist Mgr: Ron Hall

NICHOLSON MANUFACTURING
See NORTHERN INDUSTRIAL INC

NICHOLSON STEAM TRAP
See SPENCE ENGINEERING CO INC

D-U-N-S 00-695-8664
NICHOLSON TERMINAL & DOCK CO
380 E Great Lakes St, River Rouge, MI 48218-2606
Tel (313) 842-4300 Founded/Ownrshp 1928
Sales 20.4MM^E EMP 150
Accts Ernst & Young Llp Detroit Mi
SIC 4491 3731 4225 7692 3444 3443 Marine terminals; Shipbuilding & repairing; General warehousing; Welding repair; Sheet metalwork; Fabricated plate work (boiler shop); Marine terminals; Shipbuilding & repairing; General warehousing; Welding repair; Sheet metalwork; Fabricated plate work (boiler shop)
Pr: Daniel Deane
*Treas: Patrick Sutka
*VP: Thomas Deane
VP: Rod Scott
*Genl Mgr: Brendan Deane
Board of Directors: Thomas A Deane, Roderick J Scott

D-U-N-S 09-643-7215
NICK ALEXANDER IMPORTS
6333 S Alameda St, Los Angeles, CA 90001-1812
Tel (323) 582-3709 Founded/Ownrshp 1978
Sales 47.7MM^E EMP 110
SIC 5511 7549 Automobiles, new & used; Automotive maintenance services; Automobiles, new & used; Automotive maintenance services
CEO: Elizabeth Alexander
*VP: Mary Alexander
Sls Mgr: Alex Guyenne
Sls Mgr: Mark La Rambelje
Sls Mgr: Shep Nelson
Sls Mgr: Andy Park
Sls Mgr: Jason Serot

D-U-N-S 01-461-8128
NICK CHEVROLET INC (PA)
22 W 7th Ave, Tarentum, PA 15084-1499
Tel (724) 224-2700 Founded/Ownrshp 1955
Sales 22.5MM^E EMP 51
SIC 5511 5521 Automobiles, new & used; Used car dealers; Automobiles, new & used; Used car dealers
Pr: John Petrishen
*Sec: Mary Petrishen
*VP: Nick J Petrishen
Sls Mgr: Mark Koprivnikar

D-U-N-S 00-196-7207
NICK CORSELLO CHEVROLET INC (PA)
CLASSIC CHEVROLET
500 Lincoln Ave 2, Bellevue, PA 15202-3508
Tel (412) 734-5000 Founded/Ownrshp 1950
Sales 23.1MM^E EMP 65
SIC 5511 Automobiles, new & used; Trucks, tractors & trailers: new & used; Automobiles, new & used; Trucks, tractors & trailers: new & used
Pr: Lee V Corsello

D-U-N-S 03-211-4753
NICK DAVIDSON INC
DAVIDSON CHVRLET BUICK PONTIAC
3880 Test Dr, Loveland, CO 80538-7103
Tel (303) 571-5372 Founded/Ownrshp 1960
Sales 22.8MM^E EMP 58^E
SIC 5511 5531 7538 Automobiles, new & used; Automotive parts; General automotive repair shops; Automobiles, new & used; Automotive parts; General automotive repair shops
Pr: Joseph Gebhardt
*Treas: Jackie Gebhardt
*VP: Archie Davidson

D-U-N-S 02-123-3739
NICK GRIEGO & SONS CONSTRUCTION INC (NM)
1155 Kimberly Ln, Clovis, NM 88101-1132
Tel (575) 935-5400 Founded/Ownrshp 1972
Sales 33.8MM^E EMP 100
Accts Red With & Ahrendsen Santa F
SIC 1542 1522 1611 1622 Nonresidential construction; Residential construction; Highway & street construction; Bridge, tunnel & elevated highway; Nonresidential construction; Residential construction; Highway & street construction; Bridge, tunnel & elevated highway
Pr: Nick Griego Sr
*Treas: David Griego
*VP: Gerald Greigo
*VP: Nick Griego Jr
IT Man: Gerald Griego

D-U-N-S 03-236-2162
NICK NICHOLAS FORD INC
2901 Highway 44 W, Inverness, FL 34453-3799
Tel (352) 489-0661 Founded/Ownrshp 1981
Sales 39.8MM EMP 73

SIC 5511 7538 5521 Automobiles, new & used; Pickups, new & used; Vans, new & used; General automotive repair shops; Used car dealers; Automobiles, new & used; Pickups, new & used; Vans, new & used; General automotive repair shops; Used car dealers
Pr: Nick Nicholas
**CFO:* Dora Hunt
**Sec:* Lynda Nicholas
**VP:* Shane Bryant
Sales Asso: Kimberly Williams
Sales Asso: Matthew Wilson

D-U-N-S 00-283-4703
NICK STRIMBU INC
3500 Parkway Dr, Brookfield, OH 44403-9755
Tel (330) 448-4046 *Founded/Ownrshp* 1926
Sales 23.6MM^E *EMP* 148^E
SIC 4213 Trucking, except local
Pr: William Strimbu
Treas: Nick Strimbu III
**Ex VP:* Nicholas Strimbu III
Sr VP: Elizabeth Murray
**VP:* Tom Nesbit
VP Opers: Mark Lorenz

D-U-N-S 01-690-6299
NICKELL MOULDING CO INC
3015 Mobile Dr, Elkhart, IN 46514-5525
Tel (574) 264-3129 *Founded/Ownrshp* 1981
Sales 33.6MM^E *EMP* 150
SIC 2431 Moldings, wood: unfinished & prefinished; Moldings, wood: unfinished & prefinished
Pr: George Nickell
**VP:* Scott McAfoos
Genl Mgr: Kevin Coffman
Off Admin: Linda Doering
IT Man: Ben Leazenby
Sfty Mgr: Ben Sweever

D-U-N-S 07-671-2231 IMP
NICKELS AND DIMES INC
GOLD MINE
4534 Old Denton Rd, Carrollton, TX 75010-2399
Tel (972) 939-4200 *Founded/Ownrshp* 2005
Sales 48.7MM^E *EMP* 650
SIC 7993 Video game arcade; Video game arcade
Pr: Ron Kostelny
**CEO:* Craig B Singer
**CFO:* Chris Watt
**VP:* Carol G Singer
Prgrm Mgr: Mary Yap
Dir IT: David Polasek
VP Opers: Kevin Jordan
Merch Mgr: Elizabeth Aptilon

D-U-N-S 04-424-9191
NICKELSON INDUSTRIAL SERVICE INC
8501 S Baltimore Ave, Chicago, IL 60617-2636
Tel (773) 375-0874 *Founded/Ownrshp* 1969
Sales 32.0MM^E *EMP* 60
SIC 5093 1795 Scrap & waste materials; Demolition, buildings & other structures
Pr: Jeffrey A Lev

D-U-N-S 00-882-3783
NICKERSON & ODAY INC (ME)
35 Airport Rd, Brewer, ME 04412-1770
Tel (207) 989-7400 *Founded/Ownrshp* 1953, 2006
Sales 21.5MM *EMP* 39
SIC 1542 1522 Commercial & office building, new construction; School building construction; Multi-family dwellings, new construction
Pr: Karl Ward
**VP:* Kevin Gresser
**VP:* Randall L Poulton

D-U-N-S 03-537-5781
NICKERSON CO INC
2301 W Indiana Ave, Salt Lake City, UT 84104-3614
Tel (801) 895-4235 *Founded/Ownrshp* 1924
Sales 20.9MM^E *EMP* 26
SIC 5084 Water pumps (industrial)
Pr: R C Nickerson
**Sec:* Scott D Roberts
**VP:* Richard C Nickerson

D-U-N-S 00-144-9701
NICKERSON CORP (NY)
11 Moffitt Blvd, Bay Shore, NY 11706-7006
Tel (732) 264-0770 *Founded/Ownrshp* 1952, 1970
Sales 38.3MM *EMP* 44
Accts Jones Little & Co Cpas Llp
SIC 5021 Office & public building furniture; School desks; Office & public building furniture; School desks
Ch Bd: Robert Keller
Treas: Lisa Gentila
**VP:* Stephanie Keller
VP: Dana Lundin
**VP:* Bruce Paci
Brnch Mgr: Mark Cowie
Mktg Mgr: Kayla Metherell
Mktg Mgr: Jonathan Nugent

D-U-N-S 00-141-3913
NICKERSON LUMBER CO (MA)
MID-CAPE HOME CENTERS
465 Route 134, South Dennis, MA 02660-3401
Tel (508) 398-6071 *Founded/Ownrshp* 1895
Sales 32.5MM^E *EMP* 180
SIC 5211

D-U-N-S 13-115-3798
NICKEY GREGORY CO LLC
16 Forest Pkwy Bldg N1, Forest Park, GA 30297-2085
Tel (404) 366-7410 *Founded/Ownrshp* 2000
Sales 48.7MM^E *EMP* 50
SIC 5148 Fresh fruits & vegetables
Pr: Nickey Gregory
Pr: Matt Houmes
**VP:* Scott Chapman
**VP:* Vicki Gilbert
VP: Vicky Gilbert
**VP:* Cheryl Gregory
**VP:* Johnny Gregory
VP: Johny Gregory
VP Sls: Andrew Moste

NICKLAUS CHILDREN'S HOSPITAL
See VARIETY CHILDRENS HOSPITAL

D-U-N-S 17-552-8991
NICKLE ELECTRICAL COMPANIES INC
14 Mill Park Ct Ste E, Newark, DE 19713-1986
Tel (302) 453-4000 *Founded/Ownrshp* 1986
Sales 35.0MM *EMP* 195
Accts Santora Cpa Group Newark Del
SIC 1731 General electrical contractor; General electrical contractor
Pr: Steven Dignan
**CFO:* Neal Donaldson
VP: Steve Cummins
VP: John Dematteis
VP: Dave Spittle
VP Opers: Jeromy Newton
Sfty Dirs: Mike Anderson
Sfty Dirs: Annita Grandel
Snr PM: Stan Twardus
Snr Mgr: Mark Benson

D-U-N-S 08-273-8196
NICKOLAS M SAVKO & SONS INC (OH)
4636 Shuster Rd, Columbus, OH 43214-1934
Tel (614) 451-2242 *Founded/Ownrshp* 1977
Sales 44.3MM^E *EMP* 150
SIC 1611 1623 1794

NICK'S FASTERNER AND INDUS SUP
See J & B FASTENERS LP

NICL LABORATORIES
See NORTHERN ILLINOIS CLINICAL LABORATORY LTD

D-U-N-S 04-681-6294 EXP
NICOLAS VILLALBA WHOLESALERS INC
NORTH & SOUTH DISTRIBUTORS
20600 Nw 47th Ave, Miami Gardens, FL 33055-1257
Tel (305) 638-4450 *Founded/Ownrshp* 1962
Sales 22.5MM^E *EMP* 59
SIC 5122 Drugs, proprietaries & sundries
Pr: Nicolas Villalba Jr
**Sec:* Nereida Villalba

D-U-N-S 07-831-4636
NICOLE CRAFTS LLC
14 Sbar Blvd, Moorestown, NJ 08057-1057
Tel (856) 234-8220 *Founded/Ownrshp* 2011
Sales 546.1MM^E *EMP* 4,400^E
SIC 5092 Arts & crafts equipment & supplies; Arts & crafts equipment & supplies
Prin: Nicole McGuigan

D-U-N-S 12-369-2175
▲ **NICOLET BANKSHARES INC**
111 N Washington St, Green Bay, WI 54301-4255
Tel (920) 430-1400 *Founded/Ownrshp* 2002
Sales NA *EMP* 280
Tkr Sym NCBS *Exch* OTC
SIC 6021 National commercial banks; National commercial banks
Ch Bd: Robert B Atwell
CFO: Ann K Lawson

D-U-N-S 83-987-5700
■ **NICOLET NATIONAL BANK**
(*Suby of* NICOLET BANKSHARES INC) ★
111 N Washington St # 100, Green Bay, WI 54301-4256
Tel (920) 430-1400 *Founded/Ownrshp* 2000
Sales NA *EMP* 310
SIC 6021 National commercial banks; National commercial banks
CEO: Robert Atwell
**Pr:* Mike Daniels
**Pr:* Eric Witczak
**CFO:* Ann Lawson
Chf Inves: Mike Steppe
Ofcr: Kathy Maronek
Ofcr: Cheryl Parker
Ofcr: Taylor Reetz
Ofcr: Kirk Uslabar
Trst Ofcr: Pete Hoeft
Sr VP: Wayne Bouchonville
Sr VP: Jason Buenger
Sr VP: Rick Leatherbarrow
Sr VP: Margaret Merlino
Sr VP: Peter Morimoto
**Sr VP:* Gerald Mortell
Sr VP: Stevan Paton
Sr VP: Mitchell Pindus
Sr VP: Andrew Siegel
Sr VP: Patrick Vance
Sr VP: Mike Waters

D-U-N-S 09-858-2505 EXP
NICOLON CORP
TENCATE NICOLON
(*Suby of* ROYAL TEN CATE (USA) INC) ★
365 S Holland Dr, Pendergrass, GA 30567-4625
Tel (706) 693-2226 *Founded/Ownrshp* 1979
Sales 159.3MM *EMP* 648^E
SIC 2221 5949 Polypropylene broadwoven fabrics; Polyester broadwoven fabrics; Sewing, needlework & piece goods; Polypropylene broadwoven fabrics; Polyester broadwoven fabrics; Sewing, needlework & piece goods
Pr: Lee Bryan
COO: Joseph Morris
CFO: Joseph Averette
VP: Todd M Anderson
VP: Mike Stanhope
Exec: Julie Patty
Prgrm Mgr: Caroline Enright
Prgrm Mgr: Eric Howard
Genl Mgr: Doug Demasie
CIO: Scott Gleeson
QA Dir: Darrell Scoggins

D-U-N-S 18-770-0237
NICOLOSI AND FITCH INC
5501 N Swan Rd Ste 100, Tucson, AZ 85718-5445
Tel (520) 577-9700 *Founded/Ownrshp* 2005
Sales 30.6MM^E *EMP* 214^E
SIC 1522 Remodeling, multi-family dwellings; Remodeling, multi-family dwellings
Pr: Nancy Nicolosi
**VP:* Kimberly Fitch

NICOR ENERGY SERVICES COMPANY
See NICOR SERVICES

D-U-N-S 88-378-4597
■ **NICOR ENERGY VENTURES CO**
(*Suby of* OTTAWA ACQUISITION LLC) ★
1844 W Ferry Rd, Naperville, IL 60563-9600
Tel (630) 435-6400 *Founded/Ownrshp* 2011
Sales 21.0MM^E *EMP* 60
SIC 4924 Natural gas distribution
Pr: Thomas L Fisher
VP: Terry Redman

NICOR GAS COMPANY
See NORTHERN ILLINOIS GAS CO

D-U-N-S 83-944-0096 IMP
NICOR INC
NICOR LIGHTING & FANS
2200 Midtown Pl Ne Ste A, Albuquerque, NM 87107-3217
Tel (505) 343-5390 *Founded/Ownrshp* 1998
Sales 34.7MM^E *EMP* 38
SIC 5063 3648 3634 Electrical apparatus & equipment; Lighting equipment; Electric housewares & fans
Pr: R E Lawrence
Ex VP: Lyle McDaniels
VP: Robert Cochran
Natl Sales: Joe Taubman

NICOR LIGHTING & FANS
See NICOR INC

D-U-N-S 62-366-1019
■ **NICOR SERVICES**
NICOR ENERGY SERVICES COMPANY
(*Suby of* OTTAWA ACQUISITION LLC) ★
2019 Corporate Ln Ste 159, Naperville, IL 60563-9748
Tel (630) 718-2707 *Founded/Ownrshp* 2011
Sales 36.0MM^E *EMP* 1,452^E
SIC 4924 Natural gas distribution
Pr: Daniel Dodge
VP: Gerald O'Connor

D-U-N-S 96-524-8714
NICOR WELFARE BENEFIT TRUST CASH 22
1611 Ada Ln, Naperville, IL 60540-0360
Tel (630) 983-8676 *Founded/Ownrshp* 2010
Sales 21.5MM *EMP* 2^E
SIC 6733 Trusts; Trusts

D-U-N-S 00-531-7156
NICOTRA HOTEL I LLC
HILTON
1110 South Ave Ste 401, Staten Island, NY 10314-3411
Tel (718) 477-2400 *Founded/Ownrshp* 2000
Sales 22.0MM^E *EMP* 500
SIC 7011 Hotels & motels; Hotels & motels
CEO: Lois Nicotra
Sr VP: Sam B Stein
Sr VP: Carroll Tavella
Dir Soc: Susan Anderson

NICRAFT
See DELTACRAFT PAPER CO LLC

D-U-N-S 17-705-2156
NICS PIC KWIK INC
17341 Aberdeen Rd, Laurinburg, NC 28352-0003
Tel (910) 277-0050 *Founded/Ownrshp* 1987
Sales 20.7MM^E *EMP* 140
SIC 5411 5541 5812 Convenience stores; Filling stations, gasoline; Delicatessen (eating places)
Pr: Charles Nichols
**VP:* Ken Nichols

D-U-N-S 78-598-4662
■ **NICUSA INC**
N I C
(*Suby of* NIC INC) ★
25501 W Valley Pkwy # 300, Olathe, KS 66061-8474
Tel (913) 498-3468 *Founded/Ownrshp* 1992
Sales 57.2MM^E *EMP* 714
SIC 7371 7373 7375 Computer software development & applications; Computer integrated systems design; Information retrieval services; Computer software development & applications; Computer integrated systems design; Information retrieval services
CEO: Harry H Herington
CFO: Eric Bur
**CFO:* Stephen M Kovzan
Bd of Dir: Brad Henry
**Ex VP:* William F Bradley Jr
Sr VP: Ron Thornburgh

D-U-N-S 00-893-1537
NID CORP
15436 N Florida Ave # 200, Tampa, FL 33613-1248
Tel (813) 908-8400 *Founded/Ownrshp* 1944
Sales 13.1MM^E *EMP* 390
SIC 7011 6512 6531

D-U-N-S 10-395-5381 IMP
NIDEC AMERICA CORP
(*Suby of* NIDEC CORPORATION)
50 Braintree Hill Park # 110, Braintree, MA 02184-8735
Tel (781) 769-0619 *Founded/Ownrshp* 1983
Sales 25.2MM^E *EMP* 70
SIC 5075 5063 Fans, heating & ventilation equipment; Motors, electric
Ch Bd: Kenji Sawamura
**Pr:* Michael F Kulik
**CFO:* Thomas A Keenan
**VP:* Masaaki Yamata

D-U-N-S 07-864-5628
NIDEC AMERICAS HOLDING CORP
(*Suby of* NIDEC CORPORATION)
8050 W Florissant Ave, Saint Louis, MO 63136-1414
Tel (314) 595-8000 *Founded/Ownrshp* 2012
Sales 801.8MM^E *EMP* 2,849^E
SIC 3621 6719 Electric motor & generator parts; Investment holding companies, except banks; Electric motor & generator parts; Investment holding companies, except banks
Pr: Shigenobu Nagamori
**Pr:* Patrick Murphy
**CFO:* Masuo Yoshimatsu
**VP:* Motoyoshi Hanaoka

D-U-N-S 00-887-4096
NIDEC AVTRON AUTOMATION CORP
AVTRON INDUSTRIAL AUTOMATION
(*Suby of* NIDEC AMERICAS HOLDING CORP) ★
7555 E Pleasant Valley Rd, Independence, OH 44131-5562
Tel (216) 642-1230 *Founded/Ownrshp* 2007, 2012
Sales 33.7MM^E *EMP* 150^E
SIC 3823 3829 Industrial instrmnts msrmnt display/control process variable; Aircraft & motor vehicle measurement equipment; Industrial instrmnts msrmnt display/control process variable; Aircraft & motor vehicle measurement equipment
Pr: Dennis Anderson

D-U-N-S 11-987-9786 IMP
NIDEC ELESYS AMERICAS CORP
(*Suby of* NIDEC ELESYS CORPORATION)
70 Crestridge Dr Ste 150, Suwanee, GA 30024-7263
Tel (770) 904-3400 *Founded/Ownrshp* 2002
Sales 53.7MM^E *EMP* 250
SIC 3699 Automotive driving simulators (training aids), electronic; Automotive driving simulators (training aids), electronic
Pr: Toshihiko Kono
VP: Phil Rittmueller
Ql Cn Mgr: Ray Byrd
Ql Cn Mgr: Toua Thao
Ql Cn Mgr: Tyrone Walker

D-U-N-S 00-503-5969 IMP/EXP
NIDEC MINSTER CORP (OH)
(*Suby of* NIDEC-SHIMPO CORPORATION)
240 W 5th St, Minster, OH 45865-1065
Tel (419) 628-2331 *Founded/Ownrshp* 1901, 2012
Sales 139.7MM *EMP* 517^E
SIC 3542 3568

D-U-N-S 96-500-4240 IMP/EXP
NIDEC MOTOR CORP
HURST MANUFACTURING DIVISION
(*Suby of* NIDEC AMERICAS HOLDING CORP) ★
8050 W Florissant Ave, Saint Louis, MO 63136-1414
Tel (314) 595-8000 *Founded/Ownrshp* 2010
Sales 541.7MM^E *EMP* 1,250
SIC 3621 Motors, electric; Motors, electric
Pr: Kei Pang
**Pr:* Sidney J Ambort
**Pr:* Richard A Heppe
**Pr:* Kevin Kissling
**CFO:* Elizabeth Miller
CFO: Darryl Weinrich
**Ex VP:* Mark D Becker
Ex VP: Greg Levine
Exec: Maggie Sun
Dir Bus: Tom Aloor
Snr Sftwr: Prakash Shahi

D-U-N-S 06-652-4612 IMP
NIDEK INC
(*Suby of* NIDEK CO.,LTD.)
47651 Westinghouse Dr, Fremont, CA 94539-7474
Tel (510) 226-5700 *Founded/Ownrshp* 1982
Sales 21.5MM^E *EMP* 50
SIC 5048 8011 3845 3841 3699 Optometric equipment & supplies; Offices & clinics of medical doctors; Electromedical equipment; Surgical & medical instruments; Electrical equipment & supplies
CEO: Motoki Ozawa
**Ch Bd:* Hideo Ozawa
COO: Jun Iwata
Chf Mktg O: Sheryl Nicholls
VP: Kato Ken
Sls&Mrk Ex: Hiro Matsuzaki
Manager: Christopher Blasi
Manager: Leesa Chelminiak
Manager: Randy Honeywell
Manager: Hugo Hur
Doctor: Ron Kaiser

NIDERA NORTH AMERICA
See NIDERA US LLC

D-U-N-S 83-007-1101
NIDERA NORTH AMERICA LLC
(*Suby of* NIDERA B.V.)
195 Danbury Rd Ste 240, Wilton, CT 06897-4075
Tel (203) 834-5700 *Founded/Ownrshp* 2008
Sales 35.7MM *EMP* 0^E
Accts Ernst & Young Llp New York
SIC 6719 Investment holding companies, except banks; Investment holding companies, except banks

D-U-N-S 13-180-8081 EXP
NIDERA US LLC
NIDERA NORTH AMERICA
(*Suby of* NIDERA B.V.)
195 Danbury Rd Ste 240, Wilton, CT 06897-4075
Tel (203) 834-5700 *Founded/Ownrshp* 1984
Sales 1.0MMM^E *EMP* 50
Accts Dbh & Associates Llc Normal
SIC 5153 Grain elevators; Grains; Grain elevators; Grains
Pr: Hugh Niven

D-U-N-S 83-194-9789 IMP
NIEBAUM-COPPOLA ESTE WINERY LP
1991 St Helena Hwy, Rutherford, CA 94573
Tel (707) 968-1100 *Founded/Ownrshp* 1992
Sales 24.9MM^E *EMP* 200
SIC 2084 Wines; Wines
CFO: Gordon Wang
**Genl Pt:* Niebaum-Coppola Estate Winery
**Ltd Pt:* The Coppola Family Trust
**Ltd Pt:* American Zoetrope
**Pr:* Earl Martin

D-U-N-S 79-015-8612 IMP/EXP
■ **NIECO CORP**
(*Suby of* MIDDLEBY CORP) ★
7950 Cameron Dr, Windsor, CA 95492-8594
Tel (707) 838-3226 *Founded/Ownrshp* 2012
Sales 21.3MM^E *EMP* 70
SIC 3589 Commercial cooking & foodwarming equipment

Pr: Edward D Baker Sr
COO: Korey Kohl
**VP:* Edward Baker Jr
**VP:* Matthew Baker
VP: Tom Holmes
Rgnl Mgr: Ted Schaefer
Sls Mgr: Roxie Iversen

D-U-N-S 15-653-3742
NIEDERST MANAGEMENT LTD
NM RESIDENTIAL
21400 Lorain Rd, Cleveland, OH 44126-2125
Tel (440) 331-8800 *Founded/Ownrshp* 2005
Sales 32.2MM *EMP* 201^E
SIC 8741 Management services; Management services

NIELLO ACURA PORSCHE
See NIELLO IMPORTS

NIELLO ACURA PORSCHE
See NIELLO MOTOR CAR CO

NIELLO BMW
See NIELLO VOLKSWAGEN

D-U-N-S 05-020-9964
NIELLO IMPORTS (CA)
NIELLO ACURA PORSCHE
150 Automall Dr, Roseville, CA 95661-3031
Tel (916) 334-6300 *Founded/Ownrshp* 1969, 1981
Sales 37.3MM^E *EMP* 100
SIC 5511 7515 Automobiles, new & used; Passenger car leasing; Automobiles, new & used; Passenger car leasing
Pr: Richard L Niello Jr
**Ch Bd:* Richard L Niello Sr
**VP:* Roger L Niello
Sls Mgr: Geoffrey Vaio
Sales Asso: Kaberly Doerr
Sales Asso: Michael Havard
Sales Asso: Nathan Holland
Sales Asso: A J Howard
Sales Asso: Demetrius Walls
Sales Asso: Jake Womack

D-U-N-S 78-883-9269
NIELLO IMPORTS II INC
NEILLO AUDI
2350 Auburn Blvd, Sacramento, CA 95821-1756
Tel (916) 480-2800 *Founded/Ownrshp* 2005
Sales 42.8MM^E *EMP* 150
SIC 5511 7538 Automobiles, new & used; General automotive repair shops; Automobiles, new & used; General automotive repair shops
Pr: Richard L Neillo Jr
Genl Mgr: Michael Austin

D-U-N-S 86-143-7705
NIELLO IMPORTS OF CONCORD INC
NIELLO INFINITI
(*Suby of* NIELLO BMW) ★
1001 Burnett Ave, Concord, CA 94520-5711
Tel (925) 676-0200 *Founded/Ownrshp* 1981
Sales 20.6MM^E *EMP* 50
SIC 5511 Automobiles, new & used; Automobiles, new & used
Pr: David Niello

NIELLO INFINITI
See NIELLO IMPORTS OF CONCORD INC

D-U-N-S 15-355-3169
NIELLO MOTOR CAR CO
NIELLO ACURA PORSCHE
150 Automall Dr, Roseville, CA 95661-3031
Tel (916) 334-6300 *Founded/Ownrshp* 1990
Sales 31.5MM^E *EMP* 100
SIC 5511 Automobiles, new & used; Automobiles, new & used
Pr: Richard Niello Jr
**Ch Bd:* Richard L Niello Sr
**VP:* Roger L Niello

D-U-N-S 02-904-1761
NIELLO VOLKSWAGEN
NIELLO BMW
2701 Arden Way, Sacramento, CA 95825-1366
Tel (916) 481-9735 *Founded/Ownrshp* 1963
Sales 63.6MM^E *EMP* 180
SIC 5511 Automobiles, new & used; Automobiles, new & used
Ch Bd: Richard L Niello Sr
**Pr:* Richard L Niello Jr
**Pr:* Roger Niello
**VP:* David Niello

D-U-N-S 00-942-8681
■ **NIELS FUGAL SONS CO LLC**
(*Suby of* DYCOM INDUSTRIES INC) ★
1005 S Main St, Pleasant Grove, UT 84062-3509
Tel (801) 785-3152 *Founded/Ownrshp* 1924
Sales 52.8MM^E *EMP* 325
SIC 1623 Underground utilities contractor; Underground utilities contractor
Pr: Gary McQueen
**VP:* Ray Fugal
**VP:* Boyd J Holdaway
Area Mgr: Hank Nielsen
Div Mgr: Brad Mills
IT Man: Kaystan Drew
Sfty Dirs: Kevin Lebaron
Opers Mgr: David McDonald
Sls Mgr: Erik Sundstrom
Sls Mgr: Erik Sundstron

D-U-N-S 08-940-5539 IMP/EXP
NIELSEN & BAINBRIDGE LLC
PINNACLE FRAMES & ACCENTS
12303 Tech Blvd Ste 950, Austin, TX 78727
Tel (512) 506-3900 *Founded/Ownrshp* 1999
Sales 317.8MM^E *EMP* 1,155
SIC 2499 5023 Picture & mirror frames, wood; Frames & framing, picture & mirror; Picture & mirror frames, wood; Frames & framing, picture & mirror
Pr: Scott Slater
Mng Pt: Dave Gereau
Mng Pt: Mort Madison
COO: Terry Cole
CFO: Gary Golden
VP: Randy Faltesek
VP: Peter Tamuzza
IT Man: Mike Latimer
Natl Sales: John Rabushka
VP Sls: Tim Charon
Mktg Mgr: Gretchen Faltesek

D-U-N-S 06-677-8036
NIELSEN AUDIO INC
(*Suby of* N V NIELSEN) ★
9705 Patuxent Woods Dr, Columbia, MD 21046-1565
Tel (410) 312-8000 *Founded/Ownrshp* 2013
Sales 143.8MM^E *EMP* 1,443
SIC 8732 7372 Market analysis or research; Survey service: marketing, location, etc.; Application computer software; Market analysis or research; Survey service: marketing, location, etc.; Application computer software
CEO: David Calhoun
Pr: Pierre Bouvard
Pr: Owen Charlebois
COO: Mitchell Habib
Ofcr: Delores L Cody
Ofcr: Debra Delman
Ex VP: Taher G Behbehani
Ex VP: Manish Bhatia
Ex VP: Katie Burke
Ex VP: Paul Donato
Ex VP: Itzhak Fisher
Ex VP: Robert F Henrick
Ex VP: Vaughan S Henry
Ex VP: Gregg Lindner
Ex VP: Steven M Smith
Sr VP: Carol Hanley
Sr VP: William J McKenna
VP: Joseph Alisa
VP: Gary Marince
VP: John Poche
VP: Osullivan Tom

D-U-N-S 00-684-8907
NIELSEN BUILDERS INC
3588 Early Rd, Harrisonburg, VA 22801-9724
Tel (540) 434-7376 *Founded/Ownrshp* 1951
Sales 32.1MM *EMP* 115
Accts Yount Hyde & Barbour Pc Winch
SIC 1542 1541 Hospital construction; School building construction; Religious building construction; Institutional building construction; Industrial buildings, new construction; Warehouse construction; Hospital construction; School building construction; Religious building construction; Institutional building construction; Industrial buildings, new construction; Warehouse construction
Ch Bd: John N Neff
**Pr:* Tony E Biller
**COO:* Thomas Moomaw
**CFO:* John W Morsch
**VP:* James D Delucas Jr
VP: James N Lucas
**VP:* Gary McBride
**VP:* Joseph R Miller
VP Admn: Monty Cox
CTO: David Hall
IT Man: Kim Smith

D-U-N-S 78-714-8410
NIELSEN CLARITAS INC
9444 Waples St Ste 280, San Diego, CA 92121-2985
Tel (858) 622-0800 *Founded/Ownrshp* 2008
Sales 16.4MM^E *EMP* 455
SIC 7371 8742 Computer software development; Marketing consulting services; Computer software development; Marketing consulting services
VP Sls: Michael Schorr
VP Sls: Michael Youmans

D-U-N-S 80-045-7801
NIELSEN CO
85 Broad St Bsmt, New York, NY 10004-2781
Tel (646) 654-5000 *Founded/Ownrshp* 1924
Sales 5.5MMM^E *EMP* 30,000
SIC 7389

D-U-N-S 95-973-8261
NIELSEN CO US LLC
NIELSEN MEDIA RESERCH
(*Suby of* TNC (US) HOLDINGS INC) ★
85 Broad St, New York, NY 10004-2434
Tel (646) 654-5000 *Founded/Ownrshp* 2002
Sales 1.7MMM^E *EMP* 34,730
SIC 8732

D-U-N-S 08-075-8170
NIELSEN CONSUMER INSIGHTS INC
HARRIS INTERACTIVE
(*Suby of* VALCON ACQUISITION B.V.)
60 Corporate Woods, Rochester, NY 14623-1457
Tel (585) 272-8400 *Founded/Ownrshp* 1997
Sales 87.5MM^E *EMP* 564^E
SIC 8732 Market analysis or research; Business research service; Market analysis or research; Business research service
CEO: Dwight M Barns
Pr: Frank Forkin
Pr: William Miller
Pr: Stefan Schmelcher
CEO: Nathalie Perrio-Combeaux
CEO: Patrick Van Bloeme
COO: Marc Levin
CFO: Bob Cox
CFO: Brian J West
Chf Mktg O: Robert Fonk
Assoc VP: Kara Wagner
Ex VP: Jeni Lee Chapman
Ex VP: Jeni Chapman
Ex VP: Michael M Dabadie
Ex VP: Patti Hoffman
Ex VP: Enzo Micali
Sr VP: Jon Harding
Sr VP: Matt Knoeck
Sr VP: Eric Narowsk
Sr VP: Jeff Neiheisel
Sr VP: Berkeley Scott

NIELSEN MEDIA RESERCH
See NIELSEN CO US LLC

D-U-N-S 09-013-6123
NIELSEN MOBILE LLC
(*Suby of* NIELSEN CO US LLC) ★
101 Green St, San Francisco, CA 94111-1300
Tel (917) 435-9301 *Founded/Ownrshp* 2007
Sales 20.0MM^E *EMP* 260
SIC 7389 Inspection & testing services; Inspection & testing services
Pr: Sid Gorham
COO: Tom Stahl
Treas: Jim Wandrey
VP: Lotte Vester
VP: Stuart Zussman

D-U-N-S 06-460-2329
NIELSEN NATIONAL RESEARCH GROUP INC
(*Suby of* NIELSEN CO US LLC) ★
6255 W Sunset Blvd Fl 19, Los Angeles, CA 90028-7420
Tel (323) 817-2000 *Founded/Ownrshp* 1999
Sales 18.8MM^E *EMP* 400
SIC 8732 Market analysis or research; Market analysis or research
CEO: Andrew Wing

NIELSEN SCARBOROUGH
See SCARBOROUGH RESEARCH CORP

D-U-N-S 00-910-0348
NIELSON CONSTRUCTION
825 N Loop Rd, Huntington, UT 84528
Tel (435) 687-2494 *Founded/Ownrshp* 1946
Sales 102.5MM^E *EMP* 280
SIC 1611 Highway & street construction; Highway & street construction
Ch: Wayne L Nielson
**Pr:* John Wayne Nielson
**COO:* Steve Ogden
**CFO:* Gary Miyasaki
Ex VP: Mark Greenhalgh
Genl Mgr: Timothy Frame
Mtls Mgr: Shawn Ward

D-U-N-S 04-053-2186
NIEMAN PRINTING INC
10615 Newkirk St Ste 100, Dallas, TX 75220-2333
Tel (972) 506-7911 *Founded/Ownrshp* 1979
Sales 53.3MM^E *EMP* 185^E
SIC 2752 2791 2796 Commercial printing, offset; Typesetting; Platemaking services; Commercial printing, offset; Typesetting; Platemaking services
CEO: Joan Nieman
**Pr:* Mike Nieman
**COO:* Matt Nieman
**VP:* Gary Goodman
**VP:* Craig Owens
Dir IT: Brian Wheeler
Mktg Dir: Joe Costa

D-U-N-S 02-577-1635
NIEMANN FOODS FOUNDATION
CUB FOODS
923 N 12th St, Quincy, IL 62301-2129
Tel (217) 221-5600 *Founded/Ownrshp* 1917
Sales 156.4M *EMP* 5,000^E
SIC 5411 5541 Supermarkets, chain; Grocery stores; Supermarkets; Gasoline service stations
CEO: Richard H Niemann
**Pr:* Richard H Niemann II
**CFO:* Christopher Niemann
VP: Ron Cook
**VP:* James Cox
Dir Risk M: Casey Robertson
**Prin:* Connie Roberts
Genl Mgr: Scott Mounce
Store Mgr: Steve Hoffman

D-U-N-S 01-284-8847
■ **NIES ARTCRAFT COMPANIES INC**
(*Suby of* CONSOLIDATED GRAPHICS INC) ★
3049 Chouteau Ave, Saint Louis, MO 63103-2900
Tel (314) 951-0400 *Founded/Ownrshp* 2006
Sales 68.7MM^E *EMP* 364
SIC 2752 Commercial printing, offset; Commercial printing, offset
CEO: James W Finger II
Treas: Ken Ulrich
**VP:* Tom Hedrick
VP: John Kruszka
Exec: Carol Schallert
Dept Mgr: John Geisler
Sales Exec: Catherine McGavin
Sales Exec: Larry Stoneman
Mktg Dir: Chris Hebron
Snr Mgr: Brendan Delong

D-U-N-S 80-838-7158
NIF GROUP INC
30 Park Ave, Manhasset, NY 11030-2444
Tel (516) 365-7440 *Founded/Ownrshp* 1998
Sales NA *EMP* 34^E
SIC 6399 Deposit insurance
Ch Bd: Michael A Orlando
**Pr:* Mark P Maher
COO: Michael Brooker
**CFO:* Michael Orlando Jr
**Ex VP:* Daniel M Mogelnicki
**Ex VP:* David L Vicari
Ex VP: David Vicari
Sr VP: Michael Defeo
VP: Daphne Alvarado
VP: Tony Mancini
VP: John Orlando
VP: Joanne Parrotta
VP: Barbara Sheehan
VP: Leslie Wilson

NIFA
See NATIONAL INSTITUTE OF FOOD AND AGRICULTURE

D-U-N-S 18-298-1514 IMP
NIFAST CORP
(*Suby of* METAL ONE HOLDINGS AMERICA INC) ★
815 Carol Ct, Carol Stream, IL 60188-9408
Tel (630) 539-0097 *Founded/Ownrshp* 2004
Sales 43.8MM^E *EMP* 95
SIC 5085 5051 Fasteners, industrial: nuts, bolts, screws, etc.; Wire; Fasteners, industrial: nuts, bolts, screws, etc.; Wire
Pr: Kiyohide Takagi
**VP:* Nancy P Bryers
**VP:* David Groh
Exec: Bob Meifert
Genl Mgr: Masaru Anzai
Ql Cn Mgr: Michael King
Ql Cn Mgr: Alex Polowinkin
S&M/VP: Rebecca Goins

D-U-N-S 00-742-1712 IMP
NIFCO AMERICA CORP
(*Suby of* NIFCO INC.)
8015 Dove Pkwy, Canal Winchester, OH 43110-9697
Tel (614) 836-3808 *Founded/Ownrshp* 1996
Sales 174.1MM^E *EMP* 650
SIC 3089 Automotive parts, plastic; Automotive parts, plastic
Pr: Toshiyuki Yamamoto
**CFO:* John Kosik
**VP:* Tom Day

D-U-N-S 07-282-4485
NIGHTINGALE BAMFORD SCHOOL INC
20 E 92nd St, New York, NY 10128-0660
Tel (212) 289-5020 *Founded/Ownrshp* 1922
Sales 33.9MM *EMP* 125
Accts Eisneramper Llp New York Ny
SIC 8211 Private combined elementary & secondary school; Private combined elementary & secondary school
Pr: Nina Joukowsky Kprl
**Treas:* James D Forbes
**VP:* Lisa Grunwald Adler
**Prin:* Dorothy Hutcheson

D-U-N-S 10-211-1890
NIGHTINGALE HOLDINGS LLC
PEBBLE CREEK
670 Jarvis Rd, Akron, OH 44319-2538
Tel (330) 645-0200 *Founded/Ownrshp* 1998
Sales 9.9MM^E *EMP* 441
SIC 8051 Skilled nursing care facilities; Skilled nursing care facilities

D-U-N-S 14-586-5304
NIGHTINGALE HOLDINGS LLC
4700 Ashwood Dr Ste 200, Blue Ash, OH 45241-2424
Tel (513) 489-7100 *Founded/Ownrshp* 2000
Sales 8.6MM^E *EMP* 1,000^E
SIC 8051 Skilled nursing care facilities; Skilled nursing care facilities
Pr: Steve Rosedale
IT Man: Ann Trimble

D-U-N-S 94-563-1133
NIGHTINGALE HOME HEALTHCARE INC
1036 S Rangeline Rd, Carmel, IN 46032-2544
Tel (317) 334-7777 *Founded/Ownrshp* 1996
Sales 25.1MM^E *EMP* 394^E
SIC 8082 Home health care services; Home health care services
Pr: Dev A Brar
Exec: Tamara Croy
Dir IT: Wolf Rubio
IT Man: Anju Bathla
IT Man: Claire Sequeira
HC Dir: Michele Bulger
Genl Couns: Pamela Kissel

D-U-N-S 95-889-6706
NIGHTINGALE NURSES INC
2411 W Rose Garden Ln # 110, Phoenix, AZ 85027-2583
Tel (602) 504-1555 *Founded/Ownrshp* 1994
Sales 15.3MM^E *EMP* 350
SIC 7363 8082 Temporary help service; Home health care services; Temporary help service; Home health care services
Pr: Mary Glatt
**VP:* Tom Glatt
Sls Mgr: Jean Gonynor

D-U-N-S 10-626-5668
NIGHTINGALE NURSING SERVICE INC
CONSUMER DIRECT SERVICES
3301 Great Northrn Ave203 Ste 203, Missoula, MT 59808
Tel (406) 541-1700 *Founded/Ownrshp* 1996
Sales 22.6MM^E *EMP* 1,000^E
SIC 8082 Home health care services; Home health care services
Pr: William F Woody
IT Man: Ron Dunbar

D-U-N-S 01-694-5045
NIGRO KARLIN SEGAL FELDSTEIN & BOLNO LLC
10960 Wilshire Blvd Fl 5, Los Angeles, CA 90024-3708
Tel (310) 277-4657 *Founded/Ownrshp* 1981
Sales 68.6MM^E *EMP* 300
Accts Nksfb Llc Los Angeles Ca
SIC 8721 Certified public accountant; Certified public accountant
Pt: Mickie Segal
Mng Dir: Andra R Bacon
Off Mgr: Tina Mardula
Snr Mgr: Melissa Earnhart

D-U-N-S 01-533-3032
■ **NIH/NLM/LO/PSD/CAS**
NATIONAL LIBRARY OF MEDICINE
(*Suby of* N I H) ★
8600 Rockville Pike, Bethesda, MD 20894-0001
Tel (301) 496-3497 *Founded/Ownrshp* 1995
Sales 16.0MM^E *EMP* 360
SIC 8231 Government library; Government library
Top Exec: Deirdre Clarkin
Snr Mgr: Kim Pruitt

D-U-N-S 02-106-3219 IMP
NIHON KOHDEN AMERICA INC
(*Suby of* NIHON KOHDEN CORPORATION)
15353 Barranca Pkwy, Irvine, CA 92618-2216
Tel (949) 580-1555 *Founded/Ownrshp* 1979
Sales 57.8MM^E *EMP* 105

SIC 5047 Electro-medical equipment; Electro-medical equipment
CEO: Fumio Izumida
**Pr:* Eiichi Tanaka
**COO:* Wilson Constantine
Sr VP: Michael Stone
Sales Exec: Bill Brickell
Mktg Dir: Gregg McClure
Manager: Michael Bittner

D-U-N-S 83-756-8609 IMP
▲ NII HOLDINGS INC
1875 Explorer St Ste 1000, Reston, VA 20190-6279
Tel (703) 390-5100 *Founded/Ownrshp* 1995
Sales 3.6MMM *EMP* 9,800
Tkr Sym NIHD *Exch* NGS
SIC 4812 Cellular telephone services; Cellular telephone services
CEO: Steven M Shindler
Pr: Salvador Alvarez
Pr: Francisco Tosta Valim Filho
CFO: Juan R Figuereo
Ex VP: Gary D Begeman
Ex VP: Raul Ramirez
Ex VP: Raul R Ramirez
Ex VP: David Truzinski
VP: Enrique Barraza
VP: Jeffrey Chandler
VP: Mat Eshpeter
VP: Mary McGuiness
VP: Tim Mulieri
VP: Michel Perussault
VP: Kevin Polchow
VP: Peter Taft
Exec: Margaret Stewart
Dir Risk M: Rebecca Cardwell
Board of Directors: Kevin L Beebe, Donald Guthrie, Charles M Herington, Carolyn F Katz, Ricardo Knoepfelmacher, Rosendo G Parra, John W Risner

D-U-N-S 79-997-5438
NIIT (USA) INC
(*Suby of* NIIT LIMITED)
1050 Crown Pointe Pkwy, Atlanta, GA 30338-7707
Tel (770) 551-9494 *Founded/Ownrshp* 1991
Sales 43.4MM *EMP* 180
SIC 5045 Computer software; Computer software
Ch: Vijay Kumar Thadani
**CEO:* Sapnesh Lalla
**CFO:* P R Subramanian
Mktg Dir: Kimberley Kelly

D-U-N-S 14-945-7454
NIIT TECHNOLOGIES INC
(*Suby of* NIIT TECHNOLOGIES LIMITED)
1050 Crown Pinte Pkwy 5th # 5, Atlanta, GA 30338
Tel (770) 551-9494 *Founded/Ownrshp* 2004
Sales 140.0MM *EMP* 55
SIC 7379 7371 Computer related consulting services; Software programming applications; Computer related consulting services; Software programming applications
Pr: Lalit Kumardhingra
**Pr:* C N Madhusudan
Sr VP: Milind Gurjar
VP: Georgy Mathews
Exec: Antara Das
Exec: Sumit Dhingra
Exec: Pia N Gaurav
Exec: Ashit Madhok
Dir Bus: Gaurav Bhatia
Dir Bus: Sarvesh Bhatnagar
Prgrm Mgr: Arvind Kanaujia

NIITEK
See NON-INTRUSIVE INSPECTION TECHNOLOGY INC

NIJIYA MARKET
See JINON CORP

NIKA ARCHITECTS ENGINEERS
See NIKA TECHNOLOGIES INC

D-U-N-S 02-201-6658
NIKA TECHNOLOGIES INC
NIKA ARCHITECTS ENGINEERS
451 Hungerford Dr Ste 400, Rockville, MD 20850-4196
Tel (301) 770-3520 *Founded/Ownrshp* 1998
Sales 28.4MM^E *EMP* 135
SIC 8711 8712 8744 8742 7371 1542 Engineering services; Building construction consultant; Architectural services; Facilities support services; Management consulting services; Custom computer programming services; Custom computer programming services; Institutional building construction
CEO: Kabir Chaudhary
**Pr:* Jawahar Chaudhary
**CFO:* Usman Shakir
**Chf Mktg O:* Stephen White
Ex VP: Chip Denman
VP: Marvin Denson

D-U-N-S 96-705-5356
NIKE FOUNDATION
1 Sw Bowerman Dr, Beaverton, OR 97005-0979
Tel (503) 671-6453 *Founded/Ownrshp* 1994
Sales 56.4MM *EMP* 3
Accts Clark Nuber Ps Bellevue Wa
SIC 8699 Charitable organization; Charitable organization
Pr: Maria S Eitel

D-U-N-S 00-632-2655
■ NIKE IHM INC (MO)
(*Suby of* NIKE INC) ★
8 Research Park Dr, Saint Charles, MO 63304-5685
Tel (636) 939-1387 *Founded/Ownrshp* 1964, 1991
Sales 61.4MM^E *EMP* 331^E
SIC 3081 3082 Unsupported plastics film & sheet; Unsupported plastics profile shapes; Tubes, unsupported plastic
Pr: Richard E Millar
**VP:* Jim Hurley
VP: Mark Parker
**VP:* Ron Weiss
Area Mgr: Caryn Jones
Brnch Mgr: Tim Thompson
Dir IT: Jason Babicky
Dir IT: Johan Geuens
Dir IT: Ron Paanakker
Dir IT: Nancy Papan
IT Man: Anne Edwards

D-U-N-S 05-095-7364 IMP/EXP
▲ NIKE INC
1 Sw Bowerman Dr, Beaverton, OR 97005-0979
Tel (503) 671-6453 *Founded/Ownrshp* 1964
Sales 30.6MMM *EMP* 62,600
Accts Pricewaterhousecoopers Llp Po
Tkr Sym NKE *Exch* NYS
SIC 3021 2329 2339 5139 5661 5136 Rubber & plastics footwear; Athletic (warmup, sweat & jogging) suits: men's & boys'; Athletic clothing: women's, misses' & juniors'; Footwear, athletic; Shoes; Footwear, athletic; Men's & boys' sportswear & work clothing; Rubber & plastics footwear; Athletic (warmup, sweat & jogging) suits: men's & boys'; Athletic clothing: women's, misses' & juniors'; Footwear, athletic; Shoes; Footwear, athletic; Men's & boys' sportswear & work clothing
Pr: Mark G Parker
**Ch Bd:* Philip H Knight
Pr: Daric Ashford
COO: Eric D Sprunk
CFO: Donald W Blair
Ofcr: Hilary K Krane
Top Exec: Ed Elworthy
Top Exec: Kris Van Assche
Ex VP: Henry Richbourg
Ex VP: John F Slusher
Sr VP: Nick Stowe
VP: Reenie Benziger
VP: Amy Montagne
VP: Heidi Oneill
Dir Bus: Francois Halfen
Comm Man: Djnusha Gooneratne
Comm Man: Cassi Wika
Adv Bd Mbr: Mario Lafortune
Board of Directors: John R Thompson Jr, Elizabeth J Comstock, Phyllis M Wise, John G Connors, Timothy D Cook, John J Donahoe II, Alan B Graf Jr, Travis A Knight, John C Lechleiter, Michelle A Peluso, Johnathan A Rodgers

D-U-N-S 05-432-4207 EXP
■ NIKE INTERNATIONAL LTD
(*Suby of* NIKE INC) ★
1 Sw Bowerman Dr, Beaverton, OR 97005-0979
Tel (503) 671-6750 *Founded/Ownrshp* 1981
Sales 155.6MM^E *EMP* 291
SIC 5139 5136 5137 Shoes; Sportswear, men's & boys'; Sportswear, women's & children's; Shoes; Sportswear, men's & boys'; Sportswear, women's & children's
CEO: Philip H Knight
**Pr:* Thomas E Clarke
**VP:* David Kottkamp
Brnch Mgr: Ron Quering

D-U-N-S 62-069-1147 EXP
■ NIKE RETAIL SERVICES INC
(*Suby of* NIKE INC) ★
1 Sw Bowerman Dr, Beaverton, OR 97005-0979
Tel (503) 671-6453 *Founded/Ownrshp* 1985
Sales 101.6MM^E *EMP* 1,100
SIC 5661 5699 Footwear, athletic; Sports apparel; Footwear, athletic; Sports apparel
Pr: Mark G Parker
VP: Charles Denson
Mktg Mgr: Erin Caldwell

D-U-N-S 62-387-3473 IMP/EXP
■ NIKE USA INC
(*Suby of* NIKE INC) ★
1 Sw Bowerman Dr, Beaverton, OR 97005-0979
Tel (503) 671-6453 *Founded/Ownrshp* 1998
Sales 169.3MM^E *EMP* 10,000^E
SIC 7941 Sports clubs, managers & promoters; Sports clubs, managers & promoters
Pr: Mark G Parker

D-U-N-S 00-715-4818 EXP
NIKING CORP
235 Kellog St, Wahiawa, HI 96786-2210
Tel (808) 622-0443 *Founded/Ownrshp* 1982
Sales 22.1MM *EMP* 30
SIC 1542 Nonresidential construction; Nonresidential construction
Pr: Robert L King
**Treas:* Penny King
Sfty Mgr: Greg Mescan
Sfty Mgr: Ke-ARI Sumpter
Ql Cn Mgr: Mario Bol

D-U-N-S 61-984-3790
NIKISKI MIDDLE HIGH SCHOOL
52275 Education Dr, Levelock, AK 99625
Tel (907) 776-3456 *Founded/Ownrshp* 1988
Sales 4.3MM^E *EMP* 297
SIC 8211 Public senior high school; Public senior high school
Prin: John O'Brien
**Prin:* Dan Crestens

D-U-N-S 60-620-4931 IMP
NIKKEI MC ALUMINUM AMERICA INC
MCA
(*Suby of* NIKKEI MC ALUMINIUM CO.,LTD.)
6875 Inwood Dr, Columbus, IN 47201-4946
Tel (812) 342-1141 *Founded/Ownrshp* 1989
Sales 22.5MM^E *EMP* 74
Accts Larry E Nunn & Associates Co
SIC 3339 Primary nonferrous metals
Pr: Akhiro Mori
**Pr:* Tatsuo Nakamura
**Pr:* Shigeru Suzuki
**VP:* Van Anthony
**VP:* Satoru Kobayashi
Genl Mgr: Scott Fields
Genl Mgr: Dean Trapp

D-U-N-S 17-195-3805 IMP
NIKKEN GLOBAL INC
(*Suby of* NIKKEN INTERNATIONAL INC) ★
2 Corporate Park Ste 100, Irvine, CA 92606-5103
Tel (949) 789-2000 *Founded/Ownrshp* 2001
Sales 43.3MM^E *EMP* 350
SIC 5087 5023 5013 5122 4813 Stress reducing equipment, electric; Bedspreads; Seat covers; Vitamins & minerals; Long distance telephone communications
Ch Bd: Tom Toshizo Watanabe
**Pr:* Kendall Cho
VP: David Balzer
Dir IT: Bill Noyes
Snr Mgr: Kurt Fulle

D-U-N-S 60-280-1870 IMP/EXP
NIKKEN INTERNATIONAL INC
2 Corporate Park Ste 100, Irvine, CA 92606-5103
Tel (949) 789-2000 *Founded/Ownrshp* 2001
Sales 99.9MM *EMP* 480^E
Accts Bdo Usa Llp Costa Mesa Ca
SIC 5199 General merchandise, non-durable; General merchandise, non-durable
Ch Bd: Toshizo Watanabe
**Pr:* Doug Beaun
**CEO:* Kurt H Fulle
**VP:* Larry Proffitm

D-U-N-S 92-923-2478 IMP
NIKON AMERICAS INC
(*Suby of* NIKON CORPORATION)
1300 Walt Whitman Rd Fl 2, Melville, NY 11747-3064
Tel (631) 547-4200 *Founded/Ownrshp* 1981
Sales 400.8MM^E *EMP* 750
SIC 5043 5084 Photographic equipment & supplies; Industrial machinery & equipment; Photographic equipment & supplies; Industrial machinery & equipment
Ch Bd: Notio Hashizume
**Pr:* Atsuo Nakada
Sr VP: Peter J Moleski
Snr Mgr: Nick Beharry

D-U-N-S 00-196-2976 IMP/EXP
NIKON INC (NY)
(*Suby of* NIKON AMERICAS INC) ★
1300 Walt Whitman Rd Fl 2, Melville, NY 11747-3064
Tel (631) 547-4200 *Founded/Ownrshp* 1960, 1981
Sales 171.2MM^E *EMP* 335
SIC 5043 5049 Photographic equipment & supplies; Optical goods; Photographic equipment & supplies; Optical goods
Pr: Nobuyoshi Gokyu
**Treas:* Peter Moleski
**Sr VP:* David C Lee
VP: John P Browne
VP: Joseph J Carfora
Assoc Dir: Mike Boyle
Comm Man: Anna Marie Bakker
Comm Man: Jillian Cutrone
Genl Mgr: Ed Fasano
Genl Mgr: Steven Heiner
Genl Mgr: Douglas E Howe

D-U-N-S 03-874-0051 IMP
NIKON INSTRUMENTS INC
(*Suby of* NIKON AMERICAS INC) ★
1300 Walt Whitman Rd Fl 2, Melville, NY 11747-3064
Tel (631) 547-4200 *Founded/Ownrshp* 2000
Sales 40.8MM^E *EMP* 190^E
SIC 3827 Optical instruments & lenses; Optical instruments & lenses
Ch Bd: Yoshinobu Ishikawa
**Pr:* Toshiaki Nagano
**Treas:* Peter Moleski
**VP:* James Hamlin
Area Mgr: Dinillo Rosado-Sanchez
IT Man: Sukir Kumaresan
Sftwr Eng: Ilya Burda
Sftwr Eng: Dustin Tilley
Mktg Mgr: Mark Soares

D-U-N-S 07-770-3457 IMP
NIKON METROLOGY INC
(*Suby of* NIKON METROLOGY NV)
12701 Grand River Rd, Brighton, MI 48116-8506
Tel (810) 220-4360 *Founded/Ownrshp* 1998
Sales 26.9MM^E *EMP* 170
SIC 3829 Meteorological instruments; Meteorological instruments
CEO: Kenji Yoshikawa
Ofcr: Wayne Jaggernauth
VP: Jim Clark
VP: Peter Higgins
VP: Brian Samson
**Mng Dir:* Hideaki Okamoto
CTO: Filip Geuens
Dir IT: Duncan Mackenzie
IT Man: Andrea Davidson
IT Man: Tony Rodriguez
Sftwr Eng: Nigel Martin

D-U-N-S 11-508-1903 IMP
NIKON PRECISION INC
(*Suby of* NIKON AMERICAS INC) ★
1399 Shoreway Rd, Belmont, CA 94002-4107
Tel (650) 508-4674 *Founded/Ownrshp* 1982
Sales 176.3MM^E *EMP* 600
SIC 5084 5065 Industrial machinery & equipment; Electronic parts & equipment; Industrial machinery & equipment; Electronic parts & equipment
CEO: Toyohiro Takamine
**Pr:* Takao Naito
Ex VP: Hamid Zarringhalam
Sr VP: Tom Novak
Sr VP: Mitsuaki Yonekawa
CTO: Sue Gradek
Cmptr Lab: David Mahan
Sftwr Eng: Mark Wu

D-U-N-S 00-894-0186
NIKSUN INC
100 Nassau Park Blvd # 300, Princeton, NJ 08540-5932
Tel (609) 936-9999 *Founded/Ownrshp* 1997
Sales 64.3MM^E *EMP* 200
SIC 7373 3571 Computer integrated systems design; Electronic computers; Computer integrated systems design; Electronic computers
CEO: Parag Pruthi
Pr: Bill Pilkington
**Pr:* Satish C Pruthi
VP: Ted Galletta
VP: Bryan Kerl
VP: Robert King
VP: T K Srinivas
VP: Edward Talpade
VP: Craig Wentzel
Ex Dir: Rajesh Talpade
Snr Sftwr: Michael Huang

D-U-N-S 01-077-0998
NILAND BUILDING SERVICES INC
MATRIX INTEGRATED FACILITY MGT
401 Ashdale Dr, Syracuse, NY 13206-1659
Tel (315) 437-0061 *Founded/Ownrshp* 2009
Sales 4.0MM^E *EMP* 300
SIC 7349 Janitorial service, contract basis; Janitorial service, contract basis
Ex VP: Thomas J Niland III
**VP:* Pat Niland

D-U-N-S 01-526-8279
NILCO ENTERPRISES INC
1839 Ryan Rd, Dallas, TX 75220-7019
Tel (972) 501-0266 *Founded/Ownrshp* 1996
Sales 28.8MM^E *EMP* 17
SIC 4212 Local trucking, without storage
Pr: Bruce Nilsson
**VP:* Millie Nilsson

THE NILE HEALTH CARE CENTER
See HEALTH CARE CENTER

D-U-N-S 92-673-0276 IMP
NILES AMERICA WINTECH
1175 Enterprise Dr, Winchester, KY 40391-9668
Tel (859) 745-9933 *Founded/Ownrshp* 1994
Sales NA *EMP* 460
SIC 3751

D-U-N-S 01-940-9036
NILES BOLTON ASSOCIATES INC
3060 Peachtree Rd Nw # 600, Atlanta, GA 30305-2240
Tel (404) 365-7600 *Founded/Ownrshp* 1975
Sales 20.8MM^E *EMP* 195
SIC 0781 7389 Landscape architects; Interior design services; Landscape architects; Interior design services
CEO: G Niles Bolton
**Pr:* Edwin R Kimsey
**VP:* Rebecca J Bradshaw
**VP:* William V Hedeman
VP: Daniel R Meacham
VP: Bill Vonhedemann
IT Man: Chuck Purcell

D-U-N-S 07-430-5483
NILES COMMUNITY SCHOOL DISTRICT 60
111 Spruce St, Niles, MI 49120-2963
Tel (269) 683-0734 *Founded/Ownrshp* 1850
Sales 26.3MM^E *EMP* 625
SIC 8211 Public combined elementary & secondary school; Public junior high school; Public special education school; Public adult education school; Public combined elementary & secondary school; Public junior high school; Public special education school; Public adult education school

D-U-N-S 07-982-7321
NILES COMMUNITY SCHOOLS
111 Spruce St, Niles, MI 49120-2963
Tel (269) 683-0734 *Founded/Ownrshp* 2015
Sales 13.7MM^E *EMP* 403^E
SIC 8211 Public elementary & secondary schools

D-U-N-S 83-043-6049
NILES GRAND LLC
FRESH FARMS INTERNATIONAL MKT
5740 W Touhy Ave, Niles, IL 60714-4628
Tel (847) 779-7343 *Founded/Ownrshp* 2007
Sales 32.5MM^E *EMP* 150
SIC 5411 Supermarkets

D-U-N-S 07-866-6735
NILES INDUSTRIAL SERVICES LLC
(*Suby of* SMS ASSIST LLC) ★
284 W 1050 N, Chesterton, IN 46304-8806
Tel (219) 764-9800 *Founded/Ownrshp* 2009
Sales 20.1MM^E *EMP* 85^E
SIC 1799 Exterior cleaning, including sandblasting
CEO: Chris Kaminski
Opers Mgr: Frank Colon

D-U-N-S 01-823-2983
NILES IRON & METAL CO LLC
NILES SCRAP IRON & METAL CO
700 S Main St, Niles, OH 44446-1372
Tel (330) 652-2262 *Founded/Ownrshp* 1917
Sales 25.5MM^E *EMP* 50
SIC 5093 Scrap & waste materials
VP: Joel Clayman

D-U-N-S 15-133-1501
NILES MANUFACTURING & FINISHING INC
465 Walnut St, Niles, OH 44446-2374
Tel (330) 544-0402 *Founded/Ownrshp* 1984
Sales 21.7MM^E *EMP* 110
SIC 3469 3479 3471 3444 Metal stampings; Coating of metals & formed products; Plating & polishing; Sheet metalwork
Pr: Robert Hendricks
CFO: Beth Hall
Opers Mgr: Richard Handricks

D-U-N-S 05-286-7405
NILES PRECISION CO
1308 Fort St, Niles, MI 49120-3898
Tel (269) 683-0585 *Founded/Ownrshp* 1970
Sales 36.1MM^E *EMP* 168
SIC 3724 3728 3812 Aircraft engines & engine parts; Aircraft parts & equipment; Search & navigation equipment; Aircraft engines & engine parts; Aircraft parts & equipment; Search & navigation equipment
Ch Bd: James F Skalla
**Pr:* Jay C Skalla

NILES SCRAP IRON & METAL CO
See NILES IRON & METAL CO LLC

D-U-N-S 02-479-5317 IMP
NILES TC CORP
THERMAL CARE
(*Suby of* CONAIR) ★
7720 N Lehigh Ave, Niles, IL 60714-3416
Tel (847) 966-2260 *Founded/Ownrshp* 1965, 2013
Sales 34.9MM^E *EMP* 112
SIC 3585 Refrigeration & heating equipment; Refrigeration & heating equipment
Pr: Stephen C Buck
* *VP:* Thomas A Benson
Sls Dir: Lee Sobocinski
Mktg Mgr: Audrey Guidarelli
Board of Directors: Bob Smith

D-U-N-S 02-094-9939
NILES TOWNSHIP HIGH SCHOOL DISTRICT 219
7700 Gross Point Rd, Skokie, IL 60077-2614
Tel (847) 626-3000 *Founded/Ownrshp* 1938
Sales 49.8M *EMP* 638
SIC 8211 Public senior high school; Specialty education; Public senior high school; Specialty education
Dir Sec: Jim Dijohn
MIS Dir: Guy Ballard
Dir IT: Ben Grais
Web Dev: Chris Veneris
Pr Dir: Jim Szczepaniak
Schl Brd P: Robert Silverman
Psych: Drew Johnson
Psych: Venesa Ocasio
Snr Mgr: John Heintz

D-U-N-S 00-624-9338 IMP/EXP
NILFISK-ADVANCE INC (MN)
EURO CLEAN
(*Suby of* NILFISK A/S)
9435 Winnetka Ave N, Brooklyn Park, MN 55445-1618
Tel (763) 745-3500 *Founded/Ownrshp* 1910, 1994
Sales 188.8MM^E *EMP* 598
SIC 3589 5087 Floor washing & polishing machines, commercial; Service establishment equipment; Floor washing & polishing machines, commercial; Service establishment equipment
CEO: Christian C Knudsen
* *CFO:* Scott Lunger
Mng Dir: Don Galley
Prac Mgr: Andy Chicks
Rgnl Mgr: Drew Dean
Rgnl Mgr: Anders Morup
Area Mgr: Agne Valentin
Brnch Mgr: Todd Emery
Genl Mgr: Anton Soerensen
Genl Mgr: Olaf Tafur
Plng Mgr: Donna Dyslin

D-U-N-S 61-426-5221 IMP
NILIT AMERICA CORP
(*Suby of* NILIT LTD)
202 Centreport Dr, Greensboro, NC 27409-9705
Tel (336) 605-1962 *Founded/Ownrshp* 1987
Sales 50.0MM *EMP* 10
SIC 2282 Nylon yarn: throwing, twisting, winding or spooling; Nylon yarn: throwing, twisting, winding or spooling
Pr: Karen Johnson
CFO: Zvika Jakobovitz
Genl Mgr: Boaz Rubel
IT Man: Michael Petro
Mktg Mgr: Molly Kremidas
Sls Mgr: Roberto Feuer
Sls Mgr: Gabriele Zanni

D-U-N-S 94-144-9142 IMP/EXP
NILIT AMERICA INC
(*Suby of* NILIT B.V.)
420 Industrial Park Rd, Ridgeway, VA 24148-4439
Tel (276) 638-2434 *Founded/Ownrshp* 1974
Sales 129.7MM^E *EMP* 210
SIC 5199 Industrial yarns; Industrial yarns
Ch Bd: Michael P Levi
* *CEO:* Basil B Walker Jr
* *CFO:* Zvika Jakobovitz
* *Genl Mgr:* Zion Ginat
Plnt Mgr: Paul McKnight

D-U-N-S 10-203-2786
NILOY INC
DCT SYSTEMS GROUP
6050 Peachtree Indus Blvd, Norcross, GA 30071-1311
Tel (770) 734-4311 *Founded/Ownrshp* 1989
Sales 44.3MM^E *EMP* 140
SIC 5045 7378 Computers; Computer software; Computer maintenance & repair; Computers; Computer software; Computer maintenance & repair
CEO: Chuck Thakkar
* *Pr:* Saloni Thakkar
Sls Mgr: Barb Elyea

D-U-N-S 07-677-2169 IMP/EXP
NILPETER USA INC
NEXT
(*Suby of* NILPETER-FONDEN)
11550 Goldcoast Dr, Cincinnati, OH 45249-1640
Tel (513) 489-4400 *Founded/Ownrshp* 2012
Sales 39.6MM^E *EMP* 110
SIC 3555 3554 3565 2759 2672 2671 Printing trades machinery; Die cutting & stamping machinery, paper converting; Packaging machinery; Commercial printing; Coated & laminated paper; Packaging paper & plastics film, coated & laminated; Printing trades machinery; Die cutting & stamping machinery, paper converting; Packaging machinery; Commercial printing; Coated & laminated paper; Packaging paper & plastics film, coated & laminated
Pr: Lenny Degirolmo
* *VP:* Timothy Taggart
* *VP:* Eric Vandenburg
MIS Dir: Andrew Colletta
IT Man: Rick Roberts
VP Mfg: Norris Smith
VP Sls: Lenny De Girolmo
VP Sls: Michael Scmidt
Manager: Chris Baldwin

D-U-N-S 01-993-7709
▲ **NIMBLE STORAGE INC**
211 River Oaks Pkwy, San Jose, CA 95134-1913
Tel (408) 432-9600 *Founded/Ownrshp* 2007
Sales 227.6MM *EMP* 592^E
Accts Ernst & Young Llp San Jose C
Tkr Sym NMBL *Exch* NYS
SIC 3572 Computer storage devices; Computer storage devices
Ch Bd: Suresh Vasudevan
CFO: Anup Singh
CFO: Anup V Singh
Ofcr: Janet Matsuda
VP: Carolyn Crandall
VP: Leonard Iventosch
VP: Dan Leary
VP: Eric Mann
VP: Denis Murphy
VP: John Sapone
VP: Mike Wallerstedt
Board of Directors: Frank Calderoni, James J Goetz, William D Jenkins Jr, Jerry M Kennelly, Ping Li, William J Schroeder

D-U-N-S 06-101-5889
NIMED CORP
(*Suby of* CENTEGRA HEALTH SYSTEM) ★
4201 W Medical Center Dr, McHenry, IL 60050-8409
Tel (815) 344-5555 *Founded/Ownrshp* 1982
Sales 590.5M *EMP* 1,500
SIC 8062 General medical & surgical hospitals; General medical & surgical hospitals
Pr: Paul Laudick
* *Ch Bd:* Ernest Rich
* *Sec:* James F Frasor
* *V Ch Bd:* Ronald Bykowski

NIMH
See NATIONAL INSTITUTE OF MENTAL HEALTH

D-U-N-S 07-768-8273
NIMITZ PARTNERS
BEST WESTERN PLAZA HOTEL
3253 N Nimitz Hwy 400, Honolulu, HI 96819-1907
Tel (808) 836-8889 *Founded/Ownrshp* 1971
Sales 12.6MM^E *EMP* 300
SIC 7011 5812 5813 Hotels & motels; Eating places; Cocktail lounge; Hotels & motels; Eating places; Cocktail lounge
Prin: David G Elmore
Pt: 120 Hotel Corporation

D-U-N-S 03-549-1166
NIMOCKS OIL CO INC (AR)
EXXON DISTRIBUTOR
322 N Izard St Fl 2, Forrest City, AR 72335-3360
Tel (870) 633-3666 *Founded/Ownrshp* 1954
Sales 60.7MM *EMP* 75
SIC 5541 5411 5172 Filling stations, gasoline; Convenience stores; Petroleum products; Filling stations, gasoline; Convenience stores; Petroleum products
Pr: J Mallory Nimocks
* *Treas:* Carla Nimock
* *VP:* David Baldwin

NIMPA
See NORTHERN ILLINOIS MUNICIPAL POWER AGENCY

D-U-N-S 18-000-2250
■ **NIMSOFT INC**
(*Suby of* CA INC) ★
1919 S Bascom Ave Ste 600, Campbell, CA 95008-2220
Tel (408) 796-3400 *Founded/Ownrshp* 2010
Sales 25.4MM^E *EMP* 132
SIC 5045 Computer software; Computer software
CEO: Chris O'Malley
COO: Gordon Daugherty
* *CFO:* Mark Harris
* *Sr VP:* Lokesh Jindal
Sys Mgr: Steve Danseglio
Mktg Dir: Phil Sheridan

D-U-N-S 00-186-7290 IMP
NINA FOOTWEAR CORP
SEVEN STAR SHOES
200 Park Ave S Fl 3, New York, NY 10003-1529
Tel (212) 399-2323 *Founded/Ownrshp* 1955
Sales 52.1MM^E *EMP* 100
SIC 5139 Shoes; Shoes
CEO: Ezra Dabah
CFO: Bill Taylor
* *CFO:* Seth Udasin
Sr VP: Patti Cohen
VP: Dennis Okeefe
VP: Jane Taintor
CTO: Jeana Ferdon
IT Man: John Bewely
Snr Mgr: Jason Yagoda

D-U-N-S 01-238-0154
NINA HALE CONSULTING INC
100 S 5th St Ste 2000, Minneapolis, MN 55402-1220
Tel (612) 392-2427 *Founded/Ownrshp* 2012
Sales 24.3MM^E *EMP* 310
SIC 8748 Business consulting; Business consulting
CEO: Donna Robinson
* *CEO:* Nina Hale
Sr VP: Katie Pennell
Off Mgr: Mary Kay Delaney

D-U-N-S 02-617-3281
NINA MASON PULLIAM CHARITABLE TRUST
135 N Penn St Ste 1200, Indianapolis, IN 46204-1956
Tel (317) 231-6075 *Founded/Ownrshp* 1998
Sales 42.0MM^E *EMP* 17
SIC 6732 Charitable trust management; Charitable trust management
Pr: Gene Dadamo
* *Pr:* Hariett M Ivey
* *CFO:* Robert Lowry
Trst: Kent Agness
* *Trst:* Carol Peden-Schatt
* *Trst:* Frank E Russell
* *Trst:* Nancy Russell

NINE ENERGY SERVICE
See CDK PERFORATING LLC

D-U-N-S 01-978-5303
NINE ENERGY SERVICE INC
16945 Northchase Dr, Houston, TX 77060-2135
Tel (281) 730-5100 *Founded/Ownrshp* 2013
Sales 280.7MM^E *EMP* 300^E
SIC 5211 Energy conservation products
CEO: Paul Butero
CFO: Ann G Fox
Sr VP: Rocky Seale

NINE GROUP
See N-M VENTURES LLC

D-U-N-S 82-482-2522 IMP
NINE WEST DISTRIBUTION CORP
1250 Forest Pkwy, Paulsboro, NJ 08066-1763
Tel (856) 224-1890 *Founded/Ownrshp* 2010
Sales 54.4MM^E *EMP* 500
SIC 5139 Footwear; Footwear
Prin: Jerome Fisher
Exec: Mark Roark

D-U-N-S 14-493-0922 IMP
NINE WEST FOOTWEAR CORP
1411 Broadway Fl 20, New York, NY 10018-3496
Tel (800) 999-1877 *Founded/Ownrshp* 1933
Sales 33.4MM^E *EMP* 6,000
SIC 3144 3171 5661 5632 5139 Women's footwear, except athletic; Boots, canvas or leather: women's; Dress shoes, women's; Sandals, women's; Women's handbags & purses; Handbags, women's; Purses, women's; Shoe stores; Women's shoes; Women's boots; Apparel accessories; Handbags; Footwear; Women's footwear, except athletic; Boots, canvas or leather: women's; Dress shoes, women's; Sandals, women's; Women's handbags & purses; Handbags, women's; Purses, women's; Shoe stores; Women's shoes; Women's boots; Apparel accessories; Handbags; Footwear
Pr: Rick Paterno
CFO: John T McClain
Ofcr: Whitney Alan
VP: Ira Dansky
VP: Stacy Lastina
VP: Dora Thagouras
Creative D: Fred Allard
Creative D: Mark Kucharski
Brnch Mgr: Beth Romanelli
Dir IT: Thomas Murray
IT Man: Peter Caracciolo

D-U-N-S 78-471-0423
NINE WEST GROUP INC
(*Suby of* JONES NEWYORK) ★
1129 Westchester Ave, White Plains, NY 10604-3505
Tel (800) 999-1877 *Founded/Ownrshp* 2014
Sales 74.0MM^E *EMP* 1^E
SIC 3144 Boots, canvas or leather: women's
CEO: Kathy Nedorostek
Sr VP: Ron Dente
VP: Rosa Genovesi
VP: Patricia Lind
VP: Patrick McLaughlin
VP: Helene Whitney
Plng Mgr: Glenn Arshansky
Mktg Dir: M J Murphy
Mktg Mgr: Nessa Tallo
Genl Couns: Joel Bedol

D-U-N-S 00-586-1955 IMP/EXP
NINE WEST HOLDINGS INC
JONES NEWYORK
1411 Broadway Fl 15, New York, NY 10018-3410
Tel (212) 642-3860 *Founded/Ownrshp* 1997, 2015
Sales 1.8MMM^E *EMP* 13,056^E
SIC 2337 Women's & misses' suits & coats; Women's & misses' suits & coats
Pr: Wesley R Card
Ofcr: Christopher R Cade
Ex VP: Ira M Dansky
Ex VP: Joseph T Donnalley
VP: Frances Colon
VP: Mark De Zao
* *VP:* Jay Friedman
VP: Mike Havardansky
VP: Jamie Jorgensen
VP: Josh Podell
VP: Denitza Skorcheva
VP: Lynn Stubofsky
VP: Lori Yoos

NINETY EIGHT PACKING
See SDJ TRADING INC

NINETY PLUS CELLARS
See LATITUDE BEVERAGE CO

D-U-N-S 03-376-8552
NINFAS HOLDINGS LP
MAMA NINFA'S
3004 Philfall St, Houston, TX 77098-1101
Tel (713) 228-1175 *Founded/Ownrshp* 1998
Sales 14.7MM^E *EMP* 900
SIC 5812 Mexican restaurant; Mexican restaurant
Pt: Niel Morgan
Pt: Adam Gonzales
Pt: Jorge Guitierrez
Pt: Santiago Moreno
Pt: David Quintanilla
Pt: Arthur Rayos

D-U-N-S 16-495-4716
NINO SALVAGGIO FRUIT & VEGETABLE MARKET OF CLINTON TOWNSHIP INC
6835 Rochester Rd, Troy, MI 48085-1242
Tel (248) 879-9222 *Founded/Ownrshp* 2003
Sales 22.2MM^E *EMP* 210
SIC 5411 Grocery stores
Pr: Kirk Taylor

NINOS
See NEIGHBORS IN NEED OF SERVICES INC

D-U-N-S 06-769-5015 IMP
NINTENDO OF AMERICA INC (WA)
(*Suby of* NINTENDO CO., LTD.)
4600 150th Ave Ne, Redmond, WA 98052-5115
Tel (425) 882-2040 *Founded/Ownrshp* 1980
Sales 697.3MM^E *EMP* 955
SIC 5092 Video games; Video games
Pr: Reggie Fils-Aime
Pr: Carrie Bergstrom
CFO: Shirley Hornstein
Chf Mktg O: Reginald Aime
Top Exec: Sudha Sudharsanan
* *Ex VP:* John Bauer
Ex VP: Cammie Dunaway
Ex VP: Manabu Fukuda
* *Ex VP:* Mike Fukuda
Ex VP: Don James
Ex VP: Matt Kasson
* *Ex VP:* Peter Main
* *Ex VP:* Phillip Rogers
* *Ex VP:* Jacqualee Story
* *Sr VP:* Rick Flamm
* *Sr VP:* George Harrison
* *Sr VP:* Flip Morse
Sr VP: Duncan Orrell-Jones
Sr VP: Sara Rades
* *Sr VP:* Rob Thompson
VP: Doug Bowser

D-U-N-S 82-879-4193
NINTEX USA LLC
(*Suby of* NINTEX GROUP PTY LTD)
10900 Ne 8th St Ste 230, Bellevue, WA 98004-4453
Tel (425) 324-2455 *Founded/Ownrshp* 2006
Sales 20.0MMM *EMP* 68^E
SIC 5734 Computer software & accessories; Computer software & accessories
CEO: John Burton
* *CFO:* Eric Johnson
CFO: Garry Salter
* *Founder:* Brett Campbell
* *Ofcr:* Russ Mann
Sr VP: Christian Smith
VP: Kim Albrecht
VP: Mike Constantelo
VP: Justin Donato
* *VP:* Ryan Duguid
VP: Mike Fitzmaurice
* *VP:* Steve Heaney
* *VP:* Alberto Sutton
VP: Josh Waldo
Board of Directors: Steve Largent, Brian V Turner, Mark Woodward

D-U-N-S 07-032-2342
NINTH DISTRICT OPPORTUNITY INC
308 Spring St Sw, Gainesville, GA 30501-3748
Tel (770) 532-3191 *Founded/Ownrshp* 1967
Sales 35.1MM *EMP* 515
Accts Alexander Almand & Bangs Llp
SIC 8399 Community action agency; Community action agency
Ex Dir: Janice Riley
IT Man: Brenda Dalin

D-U-N-S 15-410-4079
NINYO & MOORE GEOTECHNICAL & ENVIRONMENTAL SCIENCES CONSULTANTS
5710 Ruffin Rd, San Diego, CA 92123-1013
Tel (858) 576-1000 *Founded/Ownrshp* 1986
Sales 50.9MM *EMP* 350
Accts Silberman Langner Associates
SIC 8748 Business consulting; Environmental consultant; Business consulting; Environmental consultant
CEO: Avram Ninyo
CFO: David Binns
Admn Mgr: Ellen Roe
Admn Mgr: Pat Zaby
CTO: Tim Timmerman
Opers Mgr: Michael Price

D-U-N-S 06-579-2590
NIP GROUP INC
NIP PROGRAMS
900 Us Highway 9 N # 503, Woodbridge, NJ 07095-1003
Tel (800) 446-7647 *Founded/Ownrshp* 2015
Sales NA *EMP* 132
SIC 6411 Insurance agents, brokers & service
CEO: Richard Augustyn
* *COO:* David Springer
* *CFO:* Lawrence J Dunn III
Chf Mktg O: Tracy Wehringer
VP: Anthony Amadeo
VP: Brian Erlandsen
VP: Robert Lieberman
VP: Susan Lieberman
VP: Robert Persico
VP: Howard Rosenbaum
VP: Steven Strauss

NIP PROGRAMS
See NIP GROUP INC

NIPCO
See NORTHWEST IOWA POWER COOPERATIVE

D-U-N-S 96-750-2779
NIPPON CARGO AIRLINES CO LTD
(*Suby of* NIPPON CARGO AIRLINES CO.,LTD.)
663 N Access Rd, Chicago, IL 60666-5052
Tel (773) 894-8411 *Founded/Ownrshp* 1985
Sales 19.3MM^E *EMP* 315^E
SIC 4512 Air transportation, scheduled
Pr: Shawn McWhorter
Sls Mgr: F McInerney

D-U-N-S 62-260-4317 IMP
NIPPON EXPRESS LOGISTICS AMERICA INC
NEC LOGISTICS AMERICA
(*Suby of* NEC CORP OF AMERICA) ★
18615 S Ferris Pl, Rancho Dominguez, CA 90220-6452
Tel (310) 604-6100 *Founded/Ownrshp* 1990
Sales 26.5MM^E *EMP* 75

SIC 4212 4213 4225 Local trucking, without storage; Trucking, except local; General warehousing & storage
CEO: Kazuhiko Takahashi
**CEO:* Hidehito Tachikawa
VP: Hideo Tsujioka
Dir IT: Brian Driesse

D-U-N-S 13-972-1252
NIPPON EXPRESS USA (ILLINOIS) INC
(*Suby of* NIPPON EXPRESS USA INC) ★
401 E Touhy Ave, Des Plaines, IL 60018-2607
Tel (630) 350-0202 *Founded/Ownrshp* 1987
Sales 30.1MM[E] *EMP* 200
SIC 4213 Trucking, except local; Trucking, except local
Pr: Kemryo Senda
**VP:* Tetsuaki Masuda

D-U-N-S 04-682-4090
NIPPON EXPRESS USA INC
(*Suby of* NIPPON EXPRESS CO., LTD.)
2401 44th Rd Fl 14, Long Island City, NY 11101
Tel (212) 758-6100 *Founded/Ownrshp* 1962
Sales 534.3MM[E] *EMP* 1,500
SIC 4731 4225 Foreign freight forwarding; Domestic freight forwarding; Customhouse brokers; General warehousing & storage; Foreign freight forwarding; Domestic freight forwarding; Customhouse brokers; General warehousing & storage
CEO: Kenji Fujii
VP: Joanne Ferrell
VP: Tadaaki Hashimoto
VP: Osamu Murasawa
VP: Norman Sawanobori
Admn Mgr: Dianne Palmar
Genl Mgr: Rich Davidson
Genl Mgr: Toshikzu Kitai
Genl Mgr: Kunihiko Shimizu
Genl Mgr: Hideki Takami
IT Man: Ken Hirano

D-U-N-S 80-749-5668
NIPPON LIFE INSURANCE CO OF AMERICA
TRADE STYLE NIPPON LF INSUR CO
(*Suby of* NIPPON LIFE INSURANCE COMPANY)
655 3rd Ave Fl 16, New York, NY 10017-9113
Tel (212) 682-3000 *Founded/Ownrshp* 1992
Sales NA *EMP* 100
SIC 6311 6321 Life insurance; Health insurance carriers
Pr: Kip Headeley
**Pr:* Takayuki Murai
COO: Toshihiro Nakashima
Treas: Junichi Kumagai
VP: Aimee Averill
VP: James Brone
VP: Kelly Peters

D-U-N-S 78-761-2795 IMP
NIPPON PAINT (USA) INC
NIPPON PAINT AMERICA
(*Suby of* NIPPON PAINT HOLDINGS CO., LTD.)
300 Frank W Burr Blvd # 10, Teaneck, NJ 07666-6726
Tel (201) 692-1111 *Founded/Ownrshp* 1990
Sales 90.5MM[E] *EMP* 560
SIC 2851 Paints & allied products; Paints & allied products
CEO: Hiroaki Ueno
**Pr:* Hidefumi Morita
COO: Jeffrey M Yordon
CFO: Joan P Daniels
Genl Mgr: Toshio Harada

NIPPON PAINT AMERICA
See NIPPON PAINT (USA) INC

D-U-N-S 06-337-5919 IMP/EXP
NIPPON PAPER INDUSTRIES USA CO LTD
(*Suby of* DAISHOWA NORTH AMERICA CORPORATION)
1815 Marine Dr, Port Angeles, WA 98363-1836
Tel (360) 457-4474 *Founded/Ownrshp* 2007
Sales 75.7MM[E] *EMP* 299
SIC 2621 2421 Paper mills; Wood chips, produced at mill; Paper mills; Wood chips, produced at mill
Pr: Yoshifumi Nagaura
CFO: Marysue French
CFO: Masayuki Yamamoto
**Treas:* Yoichiro Nakada
**Treas:* Minori Yabu
**VP:* Steve Johnson
Mng Dir: Bruce Zavon
Tech Mgr: Steven Johnson

D-U-N-S 03-389-1463 IMP
NIPPON SHOKKEN USA
2970 Ramco St, West Sacramento, CA 95691-5841
Tel (916) 371-1621 *Founded/Ownrshp* 2012
Sales 23.7MM[E] *EMP* 67
SIC 5141 Food brokers
Genl Mgr: Chiaara Kuroski

D-U-N-S 00-959-6289 IMP/EXP
NIPPON STEEL & SUMIKIN BUSSAN AMERICAS INC
SB MACHINE TOOLS
(*Suby of* NIPPON STEEL & SUMIKIN BUSSAN CORPORATION)
200 N Martingale Rd # 801, Schaumburg, IL 60173-2040
Tel (847) 882-6700 *Founded/Ownrshp* 2012
Sales 33.5MM[E] *EMP* 50
SIC 5051 Structural shapes, iron or steel
Pr: Yoshiharu Shimizu
VP: Tatsushi Tajima
Off Mgr: Chris Warrick

D-U-N-S 00-170-9302 IMP
NIPPON STEEL & SUMITOMO METAL USA INC (NY)
(*Suby of* NIPPON STEEL & SUMITOMO METAL CORPORATION)
1251 Ave Of The Ave Fl 23, New York, NY 10020
Tel (212) 486-7150 *Founded/Ownrshp* 1972
Sales 132.2MM[E] *EMP* 757
SIC 5051 5084 Steel; Pipe & tubing, steel; Printing trades machinery, equipment & supplies; Steel; Pipe & tubing, steel; Printing trades machinery, equipment & supplies
Pr: Nobuhiko Ikura
**Treas:* Takeshi Uchida
VP: Scott Davidson
**Exec:* Yuki Ishii
Genl Mgr: Akira Usami

D-U-N-S 07-662-7934 IMP/EXP
NIPPON SUISAN (USA) INC
(*Suby of* NIPPON SUISAN KAISHA,LTD.)
15400 Ne 90th St 100, Redmond, WA 98052-3507
Tel (425) 869-1703 *Founded/Ownrshp* 1974
Sales 251.0MM[E] *EMP* 1,003
SIC 5146 Seafoods; Seafoods
Pr: Volker Kuntzsch
Treas: Shinya Yamamoto
**Sec:* Kazuo Kozakai
**VP:* Hiroyuki Hamano

D-U-N-S 06-625-9441
NIPPON TRAVEL AGENCY PACIFIC INC
NTA PACIFIC
(*Suby of* NIPPON TRAVEL AGENCY CO.,LTD.)
1025 W 190th St Ste 300, Gardena, CA 90248-4332
Tel (310) 630-0898 *Founded/Ownrshp* 1973
Sales 27.9MM[E] *EMP* 311
SIC 4724 Travel agencies; Travel agencies
Pr: Tadashi Wakayama
**CFO:* Akio Tsuna

NIPPON YUSEN KABUSHIKI
See NYK LINE (NORTH AMERICA) INC

D-U-N-S 15-181-0868 IMP/EXP
NIPRO DIAGNOSTICS INC
(*Suby of* NIPRO CORPORATION)
2400 Nw 55th Ct, Fort Lauderdale, FL 33309-2672
Tel (954) 677-9201 *Founded/Ownrshp* 2010
Sales 336.4MM[E] *EMP* 571[E]
SIC 5047 3826 Diagnostic equipment, medical; Blood testing apparatus; Diagnostic equipment, medical; Blood testing apparatus
Ch: George H Holley
**Pr:* Scott I Verner
**CFO:* Dean Sorrentino
Sr VP: Mario Benedetti
VP: Daniel Falter
**VP:* George S Godfrey
**VP:* Jason Mondek
VP: Gary Neel
Snr Sftwr: Ed Cardello
CIO: Mark Rousseau
QA Dir: Nickey Williams

D-U-N-S 96-937-0464 IMP/EXP
NIPRO GLASS AMERICAS CORP
(*Suby of* NIPRO CORPORATION)
1200 N 10th St, Millville, NJ 08332-2032
Tel (856) 825-1400 *Founded/Ownrshp* 2011
Sales 169.4MM[E] *EMP* 750[E]
SIC 3221 Vials, glass; Vials, glass
Pr: Kurt Van Dal
Prd Mgr: John Birdsall
Ql Cn Mgr: Howard Loveless
Mktg Dir: Tom Alexander

D-U-N-S 79-737-2554 IMP/EXP
NIPRO MEDICAL CORP
(*Suby of* NIPRO CORPORATION)
3150 Nw 107th Ave, Doral, FL 33172-2135
Tel (305) 599-7174 *Founded/Ownrshp* 1992
Sales 299.3MM *EMP* 24[E]
SIC 5047 Medical equipment & supplies; Medical equipment & supplies
Pr: Goichi Miyazumi
**Pr:* Luis Candelario
CFO: Silvia Delafe
**Treas:* Seiyi Ishida
**VP:* Minuro Sano
Rgnl Mgr: Joseph Marrero
IT Man: Nelson Flores
VP Sls: Mike Rothe
VP Sls: Omar Valenzuela
Mktg Dir: Mauro Arguello

NIRAV
See INDIAN GROCERIES & SPICES INC

D-U-N-S 07-831-0292
NIRK MAGNATE HOLDING CORP
201 S Biscayne Blvd Fl 28, Miami, FL 33131-4309
Tel (786) 238-1045 *Founded/Ownrshp* 2010
Sales 32.0MM *EMP* 15
SIC 5983 Fuel oil dealers; Fuel oil dealers
Pr: George Mesa Sr
**VP:* George Mesa Jr

D-U-N-S 13-060-5582
NIRU (NY) LTD
535 5th Ave Fl 27, New York, NY 10017-3675
Tel (212) 972-3007 *Founded/Ownrshp* 2002
Sales 92.9MM *EMP* 15
Accts Fohn Kanne & Co Tel-Aviv Is
SIC 5094 Diamonds (gems); Diamonds (gems)
CEO: Rakesh Barmecha

D-U-N-S 02-394-0567 IMP
NIRVANA INC
1 Nirvana Plz, Forestport, NY 13338
Tel (315) 942-4900 *Founded/Ownrshp* 1998
Sales 86.4MM[E] *EMP* 160
Accts Gruver Zweifel & Scott Llp
SIC 2086 Mineral water, carbonated: packaged in cans, bottles, etc.; Water, pasteurized: packaged in cans, bottles, etc.; Mineral water, carbonated: packaged in cans, bottles, etc.; Water, pasteurized: packaged in cans, bottles, etc.
Pr: Mozafar Rafizadeh
**VP:* Mansur Rafizadeh
**VP:* MO Rafizadeh
**VP:* Edward Wiehl
Sls Mgr: Darya Rafizadeh

NIS
See NAVASOTA INDUSTRIAL SUPPLY LTD

NIS
See NETWORK IMAGING SOLUTIONS INC

D-U-N-S 86-723-6358
NISA INVESTMENT ADVISORS INC
101 S Hanley Rd Ste 1700, Saint Louis, MO 63105-3487
Tel (314) 721-1900 *Founded/Ownrshp* 1994
Sales 88.5MM[E] *EMP* 210
SIC 6722 6282 Management investment, open-end; Investment advice; Management investment, open-end; Investment advice
Prin: Jess Yawitz
CFO: Mark Folkins
Ofcr: Marianne O'Doherty
Ofcr: Alex Shipp
VP: Tom Merritt
**Prin:* William Marshall
Mng Dir: Ken Lester
IT Man: Richard Benduski
IT Man: Stephan Guilford
IT Man: Suhel Shah
MIS Mgr: Davé Dew

NISBET BROWER
See NISBET INC

D-U-N-S 00-893-0034 IMP
NISBET INC
NISBET BROWER
(*Suby of* DO IT BEST) ★
11575 Reading Rd, Cincinnati, OH 45241-2240
Tel (513) 563-1111 *Founded/Ownrshp* 1870
Sales 58.4MM[E] *EMP* 210
SIC 5211 5251 Lumber & other building materials; Hardware; Lumber & other building materials; Hardware
Pr: Mark Rippe
CFO: Tom Knabb
CFO: Jeff Miller
**Sec:* Irvin T Scharfenberger
Ex VP: Bob Chamberlain
**Ex VP:* Joseph F Rippe
**Sr VP:* Brian Critchell
VP: Dave Hadden
IT Man: Dan Cavanaugh
Mfg Dir: Charles Harrell
Mktg Dir: Mary Fairfield

D-U-N-S 88-495-6277
NISBET INVESTMENT CORP
DO IT BEST
11575 Reading Rd, Cincinnati, OH 45241-2240
Tel (513) 563-1111 *Founded/Ownrshp* 1995
Sales 58.4MM[E] *EMP* 210[E]
SIC 5211 5251 Lumber & other building materials; Hardware; Lumber & other building materials; Hardware
Pr: Mark A Rippe
**VP:* Mark Ferericks
CIO: Keith Wallace

D-U-N-S 00-685-2503
NISBET OIL CO (NC)
RHODES AND BEAL OIL COMPANY
1818 Baxter St, Charlotte, NC 28204-3118
Tel (704) 688-7105 *Founded/Ownrshp* 1927
Sales 27.9MM[E] *EMP* 40
SIC 5172 5983 Diesel fuel; Fuel oil dealers
Pr: James White IV
**Sec:* William S Johns Jr

NISC
See NATIONAL INFORMATION SOLUTIONS COOPERATIVE INC

D-U-N-S 06-536-9365
■ **NISCAYAH INC**
HAMILTON PACIFIC
(*Suby of* STANLEY BLACK & DECKER INC) ★
2400 Commerce Ave Ste 500, Duluth, GA 30096-8920
Tel (678) 474-1720 *Founded/Ownrshp* 2011
Sales 80.9MM[E] *EMP* 605
SIC 5065 Security control equipment & systems; Security control equipment & systems
Pr: Martin Schnurr
CFO: Kevin M Lobdell
VP: Thomas Benson
VP: Marty Guay
Brnch Mgr: Dagostin Tina
Brnch Mgr: Joe Zulli
Opers Mgr: Kyle Harris
Manager: Marshall Pinnix

NISCO
See NISHIKAWA COOPER LLC

NISD
See NEDERLAND INDEPENDENT SCHOOL DISTRICT

D-U-N-S 95-701-6934
NISEC
2150 W 97th Pl, Crown Point, IN 46307-2346
Tel (219) 663-6500 *Founded/Ownrshp* 1973
Sales 5.6MM[E] *EMP* 500
SIC 8211 Specialty education; Specialty education

D-U-N-S 18-198-9807 IMP
NISHIBA INDUSTRIES CORP
(*Suby of* NISHIBA INDUSTRY CO.,LTD.)
2360 Marconi Ct, San Diego, CA 92154-7241
Tel (619) 661-8866 *Founded/Ownrshp* 1987
Sales 134.4MM[E] *EMP* 650
SIC 3089 3544 5162 Plastic hardware & building products; Special dies, tools, jigs & fixtures; Plastics materials & basic shapes; Plastic hardware & building products; Special dies, tools, jigs & fixtures; Plastics materials & basic shapes
Pr: Yoshiaki Nishiba
Opers Mgr: Daniel Bosco

D-U-N-S 14-707-9123 IMP
NISHIKAWA COOPER LLC
NISCO
(*Suby of* NISHIKAWA OF AMERICA INC) ★
324 Morrow St, Topeka, IN 46571-9076
Tel (260) 593-2156 *Founded/Ownrshp* 1987
Sales 207.9MM[E] *EMP* 923
Accts Ernst & Young Llp Indianapoli
SIC 3069 Weather strip, sponge rubber; Weather strip, sponge rubber
Pr: Futoshi Higashida
VP: Chad Klopfenstein
**VP:* Michael Talaga
Prgrm Mgr: Matt Ensign
Prgrm Mgr: Robert Rhinesmith
Prgrm Mgr: Tim Vogeler
Opers Mgr: Steve Folden
Snr Mgr: Linda Herendeen

D-U-N-S 60-535-3267
NISHIKAWA OF AMERICA INC
(*Suby of* NISHIKAWA RUBBER CO.,LTD.)
324 Morrow St, Topeka, IN 46571-9076
Tel (260) 593-2156 *Founded/Ownrshp* 1989
Sales 207.9MM[E] *EMP* 923
SIC 3069 Weather strip, sponge rubber; Weather strip, sponge rubber
Pr: Bunji Yamamoti
Pt: Jol Vanatti
**VP:* Bill Burga

D-U-N-S 02-856-6933 IMP/EXP
NISHIMOTO TRADING CO LTD
WISMETTAC FRESH FISH
(*Suby of* NISHIMOTO COMPANY LIMITED.)
13409 Orden Dr, Santa Fe Springs, CA 90670-6336
Tel (562) 802-1900 *Founded/Ownrshp* 2002
Sales 520.6MM[E] *EMP* 1,200
SIC 5149 Groceries, general line; Groceries & related products
CEO: Takayuki Kanai
**CEO:* Seiichiro Isoda
**CFO:* Tom Kawaguchi
**VP:* Toshiyoki Nishikawa
Brnch Mgr: Shoichi Kaku
Brnch Mgr: Hiroshi Kikumori
Brnch Mgr: Ichiro Sasaki
MIS Dir: Takeo Shibata
IT Man: Masanori Tabata
Opers Mgr: Jay Yamamoto
Sls Dir: Daryl Asato

D-U-N-S 96-210-5792
▲ **NISKA GAS STORAGE PARTNERS LLC**
170 N Radnor Chester Rd, Radnor, PA 19087-5280
Tel (484) 367-7462 *Founded/Ownrshp* 2006
Sales 98.3MM *EMP* 128[E]
Tkr Sym NKA *Exch* NYS
SIC 4922 Storage, natural gas; Storage, natural gas
Ch Bd: William H Shea Jr
COO: Mark D Casaday
CFO: Vance E Powers
Chf Cred: Rick J Staples
Ofcr: Bruce D Davis Jr
VP: Jason A Dubchak

D-U-N-S 07-109-1748
NISKAYUNA CENTRAL SCHOOL DISTRICT
1239 Van Antwerp Rd, Schenectady, NY 12309-5317
Tel (518) 377-4666 *Founded/Ownrshp* 1953
Sales 45.6MM[E] *EMP* 800
SIC 8211 Public combined elementary & secondary school; Public combined elementary & secondary school
**Treas:* John Tamburello
Bd of Dir: Patricia Lanotte
IT Man: Carrie Chevrier
Pr Dir: Matt Leon
Teacher Pr: Lynn L Macan
Psych: Ann Joyce

D-U-N-S 07-840-6884
NISKAYUNA OPERATING CO LLC
PATHWAYS NURSING & REHABILITAT
1805 Providence Ave, Niskayuna, NY 12309-3923
Tel (518) 374-2212 *Founded/Ownrshp* 2008
Sales 21.0MM[E] *EMP* 175
SIC 8051 Skilled nursing care facilities
Ex Dir: Eli Grinspan
**Ex Dir:* Mathew Varghese
IT Man: AVI Kagan

NISKY HILL CEMETERY
See BETHLEHEM AREA MORAVIANS INC

D-U-N-S 01-988-4712
■ **NISOURCE CORPORATE SERVICES CO**
(*Suby of* NISOURCE INC) ★
801 E 86th Ave, Merrillville, IN 46410-6272
Tel (219) 647-4222 *Founded/Ownrshp* 2000
Sales 98.4MM[E] *EMP* 1,700
SIC 8741 Business management; Business management
Pr: Robert C Skaggs Jr
**CFO:* Stephen Smith
**VP:* Gary Pottorff
IT Man: Christine Butcher
Counsel: Christine Morace
Snr Mgr: Michael Sojka

D-U-N-S 18-565-4076
▲ **NISOURCE INC**
801 E 86th Ave, Merrillville, IN 46410-6272
Tel (219) 647-5990 *Founded/Ownrshp* 1987
Sales 6.4MMM *EMP* 8,982[E]
Accts Deloitte & Touche Llp Chicago
Tkr Sym NI *Exch* NYS
SIC 4939 4922 Gas & other services combined; Electric & other services combined; Pipelines, natural gas; Combination utilities; Pipelines, natural gas
Pr: Robert C Skaggs Jr
CEO: Eileen O'Neill Odum
CFO: Donald Brown
CFO: Stephen P Smith
Chf Cred: Scott Wilkerson
Ex VP: Carrie J Hightman
Ex VP: Eileen O'Neill
Sr VP: Karl Brack
Sr VP: Robert D Campbell
VP: Joseph W Mulpas
Dir Risk M: James Clarke
Comm Dir: Bob Innes
Board of Directors: Richard A Abdoo, Aristides S Candris, Teresa A Taylor Carolyn Y, Sigmund L Cornelius, Michael E Jesanis, Kevin T Kabat, Marty R Kittrell, W Lee Nutter, Deborah S Parker

D-U-N-S 08-148-9676
NISQUALLY INDIAN TRIBE
4820 She Nah Num Dr Se, Olympia, WA 98513-9105
Tel (360) 456-5221 Founded/Ownrshp 1946
Sales NA EMP 600E
SIC 9131 Indian reservation; ; Indian reservation;
Prin: Pauline Simmons
CFO: Eletta Tiam

D-U-N-S 00-952-2728
NISQUALLY RED WIND CASINO CORP
12819 Yelm Hwy Se, Olympia, WA 98513-9111
Tel (360) 412-5000 Founded/Ownrshp 1997
Sales 32.7MME EMP 600
SIC 7999 Gambling & lottery services; Gambling & lottery services
Genl Mgr: Quinton Boshoff
*CFO: Douglas Morrison
CFO: Bill Quinn
Dir Risk M: Cindy Bonzer
MIS Mgr: Tim Pak
Secur Mgr: Chris Dawson
Mktg Mgr: Daniel White

D-U-N-S 05-262-8187
NISSAN
KNIGHT'S GARAGE NISSAN
225 Cowesett Ave, West Warwick, RI 02893-2236
Tel (401) 822-9000 Founded/Ownrshp 1960
Sales 40.9MME EMP 300
SIC 5511 Automobiles, new & used; Automobiles, new & used
Pr: Michael Brown
*COO: Marcel Valois
*CFO: Christina Eolbashian
CIO: Steve Younan
S&M/VP: Richard Gray

D-U-N-S 06-596-8208
NISSAN 112 SALES CORP
730 Medford Ave, Patchogue, NY 11772-1342
Tel (631) 289-9100 Founded/Ownrshp 1984
Sales 30.0MME EMP 51
SIC 5511 Automobiles, new & used; Automobiles, new & used
Pr: Tony Tantillo

NISSAN 46
See AUTO MALL 46 INC

D-U-N-S 09-920-2459
NISSAN AL PIEMONTE INC
1600 W North Ave, Melrose Park, IL 60160-1318
Tel (708) 343-3800 Founded/Ownrshp 1977
Sales 22.2MME EMP 49
SIC 5511 Automobiles, new & used; Pickups, new & used
Pr: Alex A Piemonte Jr
Off Mgr: Bernadette Michaels
Sls Mgr: Vince Moreno

D-U-N-S 05-000-3334
NISSAN ANDERSON
ANDERSON LINCOLN-MERCURY
629 Brevard Rd, Asheville, NC 28806-2229
Tel (828) 348-6850 Founded/Ownrshp 1972
Sales 21.9MME EMP 65
SIC 5511 7538 5521 Automobiles, new & used; General automotive repair shops; Automobiles, used cars only; Automobiles, new & used; General automotive repair shops; Automobiles, used cars only
Pr: Frederick H Anderson
Sales Asso: Bob Miles
Sales Asso: Nathan Ray

NISSAN AUTHORIZED SALES & SVC
See NISSAN SANSONE INC

D-U-N-S 09-146-0154
NISSAN AUTO-MALL INC
ATLANTIC NISSAN
193 Sunrise Hwy Ste 205, West Islip, NY 11795-2015
Tel (631) 587-0700 Founded/Ownrshp 1997
Sales 34.9MME EMP 80E
SIC 5511 5012 7538 7515 7513 5521 Automobiles, new & used; Automobiles; General automotive repair shops; Passenger car leasing; Truck rental & leasing, no drivers; Used car dealers; Automobiles, new & used; Automobiles; General automotive repair shops; Passenger car leasing; Truck rental & leasing, no drivers; Used car dealers
Ch Bd: John Staluppi Sr
Sls Mgr: Jesus Ramirez

D-U-N-S 09-005-7808
NISSAN AUTOCENTERS INC (IL)
AUTO CENTERS NISSAN
1825 E Edwardsville Rd, Wood River, IL 62095-2275
Tel (618) 251-2094 Founded/Ownrshp 1998, 2010
Sales 24.1MME EMP 60
SIC 5511 Automobiles, new & used; Automobiles, new & used
Pr: William Haegele
*VP: Craig Schmitz
Opers Mgr: Wil Lickenbrock

D-U-N-S 79-976-9716
NISSAN BAKER SOUTH LP
BAKER JACKSON NISSAN
2901 S Loop W, Houston, TX 77054-1307
Tel (713) 661-9955 Founded/Ownrshp 1997
Sales 30.0MME EMP 85
SIC 5511 5521 Automobiles, new & used; Used car dealers; Automobiles, new & used; Used car dealers
CFO: Janie Davila
Genl Mgr: Steve Dean
Dir IT: Alex Valdez

D-U-N-S 87-730-8924
NISSAN BENSON INC
INGRAM PARK AUTO CENTER
(Suby of BENSON ENTERPRISES INC) ★
6990 Nw Loop 410, San Antonio, TX 78238-4198
Tel (210) 681-6300 Founded/Ownrshp 1997
Sales 26.7MME EMP 90
SIC 5511 Automobiles, new & used; Automobiles, new & used
CEO: Baker Shaw
*Prin: Ed Devane

D-U-N-S 01-972-7304
NISSAN BERTERA INC (MA)
569 Oxford St S, Auburn, MA 01501-1809
Tel (508) 832-9611 Founded/Ownrshp 1922, 2007
Sales 32.6MME EMP 90
SIC 5511 Automobiles, new & used; Automobiles, new & used
Pr: Aldo M Bertera
*VP: Razmik Ghazarian
Genl Mgr: Anthony Latorre
IT Man: Anthony Morabito
Sls Mgr: Joseph Colitti
Sls Mgr: Jereme Erlandson

D-U-N-S 05-962-6242
NISSAN BOMMARITO INC
661 Dunn Rd, Hazelwood, MO 63042-1725
Tel (314) 731-2228 Founded/Ownrshp 1981
Sales 31.1MME EMP 64E
SIC 5511 Automobiles, new & used
Pr: Frank Bommarito
VP: Tom Bommarito
Exec: Janet Hutchinson
Exec: Dan King
Sls Mgr: Jerry Eickel
Sales Asso: Chris Colesworthy

D-U-N-S 11-276-5961
NISSAN BONDESEN-HARDY INC
NISSAN ISUZU OF DAYTONA
950 Tomoka Rd, Daytona Beach, FL 32117-4729
Tel (386) 274-6800 Founded/Ownrshp 1969
Sales 20.1MME EMP 45
SIC 5511 Automobiles, new & used
Pr: Terry Taylor
VP: Gary Yeomans
Genl Mgr: Kendall Garrison
Sls Mgr: Sam Brutus
Sls Mgr: Dustin Ketchum
Sls Mgr: Glen Knoch
Sls Mgr: Fred Smith
Sls Mgr: Brian Tokarczyk
Sales Asso: Don Albright
Sales Asso: David Glassburn
Sales Asso: John Notaras

D-U-N-S 12-235-2057
NISSAN CASA INC
5855 Montana Ave, El Paso, TX 79925-3388
Tel (915) 772-1488 Founded/Ownrshp 1984
Sales 32.3MME EMP 75
SIC 5511 Automobiles, new & used; Automobiles, new & used
Prin: Justin Lowenfield
*Pr: William Horn
*CEO: Wallace Lowenfield
*Treas: Louis Cortez
VP: Ken Johnson
*VP: Luke Lowenfield

D-U-N-S 79-041-6903 IMP/EXP
NISSAN CHEMICAL AMERICA CORP
(Suby of NISSAN CHEMICAL INDUSTRIES, LTD.)
10375 Richmond Ave # 1000, Houston, TX 77042-4156
Tel (713) 532-4745 Founded/Ownrshp 1989
Sales 20.4MME EMP 29
Accts Kpmg Llp Atlanta Ga
SIC 5169 Chemicals & allied products
Ch Bd: Suketoshi Tsukamoto
Sec: Yasuyuki Baba
VP: Robert Griffith
VP: Masayuki Harada
VP: William Smith
Prin: Michael Berg
Prin: Orasio Mendoza
Admn Mgr: Kerry Maglitto

D-U-N-S 96-796-1632
■ **NISSAN CONYERS INC**
(Suby of PENSKE AUTOMOTIVE GROUP INC) ★
1420 Iris Dr, Morrow, GA 30260
Tel (770) 922-7600 Founded/Ownrshp 2005
Sales 64.6MME EMP 35E
SIC 5511 New & used car dealers
Pr: Terry Tayllor
Genl Mgr: Pat Zill
Sls Mgr: Eddie Card
Sls Mgr: Darrell Crowder
Sls Mgr: Ryan Martin
Sls Mgr: Jake Meissner
Sls Mgr: Carl Whipple
Sales Asso: Corey Lewis

D-U-N-S 09-350-9453 EXP
■ **NISSAN COURTESY INC**
(Suby of GROUP 1 AUTOMOTIVE INC) ★
1777 N Central Expy, Richardson, TX 75080-3599
Tel (972) 231-2600 Founded/Ownrshp 1978
Sales 33.7MME EMP 80
SIC 5511 5013 Automobiles, new & used; Automotive supplies & parts; Automobiles, new & used; Automotive supplies & parts
Pr: Charles M Smith
*COO: Ronald Kutz
*Treas: Ronald J Kutz
*VP: Scott L Thompson
Exec: Scott Valdez
Sls&Mrk Ex: Trapper Collova
Sales Asso: Damien Bernal

D-U-N-S 36-116-6655
NISSAN COURTESY INC
COURTESY CAR CITY
2301 39th Ave, Moline, IL 61265-7257
Tel (309) 764-6700 Founded/Ownrshp 1989
Sales 28.0MME EMP 90
SIC 5511 7538 Automobiles, new & used; General automotive repair shops; Automobiles, new & used; General automotive repair shops
Pr: Dale D Zude
*Treas: Dan Kehoe
*VP: Dave Kehoe
Sls Mgr: Doug Bahls
Sls Mgr: Jason Murley
Sls Mgr: Martin Rothschild
Sls Mgr: Eric Warren
Sls Mgr: Mike Wolf
Sales Asso: Clay Allen
Sales Asso: Missy Day
Sales Asso: Jeff Vinar

D-U-N-S 01-509-2497
NISSAN EISENHAUER INC
6210 W Penn Ave, Wernersville, PA 19565-1657
Tel (610) 678-8071 Founded/Ownrshp 2000
Sales 20.7MME EMP 42
SIC 5511 5013 Automobiles, new & used; Automotive supplies & parts
Pr: Peter T Eisenhauer

D-U-N-S 05-856-2679 EXP
NISSAN ESSERMAN LTD
ESSERMAN VOLKSWAGEN
16725 Nw 57th Ave, Miami Gardens, FL 33055-3919
Tel (305) 626-2600 Founded/Ownrshp 1989
Sales 35.4MME EMP 145
SIC 5511 5013 7538 7532 5531 Automobiles, new & used; Pickups, new & used; Vans, new & used; Automotive supplies & parts; General automotive repair shops; Top & body repair & paint shops; Automotive & home supply stores; Automobiles, new & used; Pickups, new & used; Vans, new & used; Automotive supplies & parts; General automotive repair shops; Top & body repair & paint shops; Automotive & home supply stores
Ltd Pt: Ronald Esserman
Ltd Pt: Richard Assmar

D-U-N-S 07-885-7489
NISSAN EVERHART INC
WILMINGTON NISSAN
5406 Market St, Wilmington, NC 28405-3508
Tel (910) 392-4300 Founded/Ownrshp 1977
Sales 24.6MME EMP 80
SIC 5511 5521 7538 7515 5531 Automobiles, new & used; Pickups, new & used; Used car dealers; General automotive repair shops; Passenger car leasing; Automotive & home supply stores; Automobiles, new & used; Pickups, new & used; Used car dealers; General automotive repair shops; Passenger car leasing; Automotive & home supply stores
Pr: Wayne Stamey

D-U-N-S 09-986-3953
NISSAN FALHABER INC
8680 Colerain Ave, Cincinnati, OH 45251-2930
Tel (513) 385-1400 Founded/Ownrshp 1980
Sales 20.0MME EMP 43
SIC 5511 5521 Automobiles, new & used; Used car dealers
CEO: Wilbur H Falhaber
*Sec: Marlene Falhaber
*VP: Kenneth W Falhaber
Exec: Gary Darpel

NISSAN FORKLIFT
See UNICARRIERS AMERICAS CORP

D-U-N-S 09-424-7269
NISSAN FREEHOLD INC (NJ)
D C H FREEHOLD NISSAN
(Suby of DCH NORTH AMERICA INC.)
4041 Us Highway 9, Freehold, NJ 07728-2534
Tel (732) 780-3123 Founded/Ownrshp 1978, 1982
Sales 23.7MME EMP 62
SIC 5511 Automobiles, new & used; Automobiles, new & used
Pr: Shau Wai Lam

D-U-N-S 07-070-6060
NISSAN FUCCILLO INC
3893 State Route 31, Liverpool, NY 13090-1309
Tel (315) 944-3200 Founded/Ownrshp 2012
Sales 30.0MM EMP 100
SIC 5511 Automobiles, new & used; Automobiles, new & used
Pr: William B Fuccillo Jr

D-U-N-S 05-340-5411
NISSAN FUTURE INC
FUTURE NISSAN OF ROSEVILLE
600 Automall Dr, Roseville, CA 95661-3022
Tel (916) 786-7878 Founded/Ownrshp 1988
Sales 31.0MME EMP 80
SIC 5511

NISSAN GARDEN GROVE
See QUALITY NISSAN

D-U-N-S 05-080-0242
NISSAN GARDENA INC
1670 W Redondo Beach Blvd, Gardena, CA 90247-3286
Tel (310) 532-1600 Founded/Ownrshp 1969
Sales 22.9MME EMP 60E
SIC 5511

D-U-N-S 11-837-4904
NISSAN GETTEL INC
GETTEL NISSAN
3530 Bee Ridge Rd, Sarasota, FL 34239-7233
Tel (941) 921-2655 Founded/Ownrshp 1997
Sales 33.8MME EMP 100
SIC 5511 Automobiles, new & used; Automobiles, new & used
Pr: James C Gettel
*Pr: James Gettel
*Sec: Robert E Bisplinghoff
*Genl Mgr: Larry Narroney
Genl Mgr: Craig Spurling
Sls Mgr: Jim Lebeau

D-U-N-S 08-206-8735
NISSAN GLENDALE INC
484 E North Ave, Glendale Heights, IL 60139-3497
Tel (630) 469-6100 Founded/Ownrshp 1990
Sales 39.0MME EMP 100
SIC 5511 5521 Automobiles, new & used; Used car dealers; Automobiles, new & used; Used car dealers
Pr: William A Slevin

D-U-N-S 17-136-3765
NISSAN GLENN INC
3360 Richmond Rd, Lexington, KY 40509-1835
Tel (859) 263-5020 Founded/Ownrshp 1984
Sales 32.9MME EMP 75
SIC 5511 Automobiles, new & used; Automobiles, new & used
Pr: Bruce Glenn
*Sec: Cyrus Dicken
Sales Asso: David Burnside
Sales Asso: Sarah Mahmoud
Sales Asso: Brian Thompson
Sales Asso: Jimmy Williams
Sales Asso: Greg Woods

D-U-N-S 79-551-8398
NISSAN GRUBBS MID-CITIES LTD
BEDFORD RENT A CAR
310 Airport Fwy, Bedford, TX 76022-6404
Tel (817) 268-1000 Founded/Ownrshp 2000
Sales 58.7MME EMP 85
SIC 5511

D-U-N-S 09-291-0991
NISSAN GUNN INC
(Suby of CURTIS C GUNN INC) ★
750 Ne Loop 410 Unit 1, San Antonio, TX 78209-1200
Tel (210) 496-0806 Founded/Ownrshp 1980
Sales 20.3MME EMP 45
SIC 5511 Automobiles, new & used; Pickups, new & used
Ch Bd: Curtis C Gunn Jr
Pr: Wes Burke
VP: Paul Young
Genl Mgr: Rob Sabom
Sls Mgr: Jim Bressman
Sls Mgr: John Jimenez

D-U-N-S 17-670-2892
NISSAN HABBERSTAD INC
850 E Jericho Tpke, Huntington Station, NY 11746-7505
Tel (631) 439-7000 Founded/Ownrshp 1996
Sales 24.0MME EMP 88
SIC 5511 Automobiles, new & used; Automobiles, new & used
Pr: Howard Habberstad Jr

D-U-N-S 02-260-5885
NISSAN HAMILTON INC
1929 Dual Hwy, Hagerstown, MD 21740-6603
Tel (301) 733-7222 Founded/Ownrshp 1961
Sales 35.1MME EMP 85E
SIC 5511 Automobiles, new & used; Automobiles, new & used
Pr: Derreck Hamilton
*Prin: Richard J Hamilton
Store Mgr: Mark Wolfe
Sls Mgr: Sean Lewis

D-U-N-S 84-052-3141
NISSAN HARRELSON INC
550 Galleria Blvd, Rock Hill, SC 29730-6500
Tel (803) 366-8171 Founded/Ownrshp 1998
Sales 31.2MME EMP 75
SIC 5511 Automobiles, new & used; Automobiles, new & used

D-U-N-S 62-162-7207
NISSAN HAYS INC
NISSAN OF RIVER GATE
(Suby of HAYS AUTOMOTIVE SUPERVISION INC) ★
1550 Gallatin Pike N, Madison, TN 37115-2117
Tel (615) 239-0492 Founded/Ownrshp 1992
Sales 24.4MME EMP 80
SIC 5511 7538 5521 7515 7513 Automobiles, new & used; General automotive repair shops; Used car dealers; Passenger car leasing; Truck rental & leasing, no drivers; Automobiles, new & used; General automotive repair shops; Used car dealers; Passenger car leasing; Truck rental & leasing, no drivers
Pr: William E Hays Sr
*Owner: Hilly Hays
*Treas: J Dan Bouchillon
*VP: William Hays Jr
*Ex Dir: Bob McCracken
*Genl Mgr: Ted Williams

D-U-N-S 08-599-9175
NISSAN HOSELTON INC
HOSELTON NISSAN
50 Marsh Rd, East Rochester, NY 14445-1975
Tel (585) 586-2960 Founded/Ownrshp 1976
Sales 22.9MME EMP 60E
SIC 5511 Automobiles, new & used; Pickups, new & used; Automobiles, new & used; Pickups, new & used
Ch Bd: David C Hoselton
*Pr: Drew Hoselton
Ex VP: Rob Clark
Exec: Diane Fico

D-U-N-S 19-947-1368
NISSAN HUBLER INC
HUBLER MAZDA WEST
8435 Us 31 S, Indianapolis, IN 46227-6277
Tel (317) 882-4389 Founded/Ownrshp 1989
Sales 20.7MME EMP 70
SIC 5511 Automobiles, new & used; Trucks, tractors & trailers: new & used; Automobiles, new & used; Trucks, tractors & trailers: new & used
Pr: John Hubler
*Sec: Ann Vaughn
Sls Mgr: Erik Perez

D-U-N-S 09-614-4282
NISSAN HUDIBURG INC
HUDIBURG COLLISION CENTER S
200 E I 240 Service Rd, Oklahoma City, OK 73149-1614
Tel (405) 631-7771 Founded/Ownrshp 1977
Sales 49.1MME EMP 140
SIC 5511 Automobiles, new & used; Pickups, new & used; Vans, new & used; Automobiles, new & used; Pickups, new & used; Vans, new & used
Pr: David Hudiburg
*Sec: Steve Clairy

*VP: Paul Hudiburg
Genl Mgr: Brad Smicklas

NISSAN ISUZU OF DAYTONA
See NISSAN BONDESEN-HARDY INC

D-U-N-S 03-480-8444
NISSAN JIM KERAS INC
JIM KERAS AUTOMOTIVE
2080 Covington Pike, Memphis, TN 38128-6982
Tel (901) 373-2800 Founded/Ownrshp 1981
Sales 54.7MM^E EMP 150
SIC 5511 5013 Automobiles, new & used; Pickups, new & used; Vans, new & used; Automotive supplies & parts; Automobiles, new & used; Pickups, new & used; Vans, new & used; Automotive supplies & parts
Pr: James J Keras
Sls Mgr: Maurice Walker

D-U-N-S 15-123-1156
NISSAN KOEPPEL INC
7415 Northern Blvd, Jackson Heights, NY 11372-1146
Tel (718) 898-7800 Founded/Ownrshp 1983
Sales 51.0MM^E EMP 102
SIC 5511 7538

NISSAN LAKE CHARLES
See PARAMOUNT NISSAN LLC

D-U-N-S 04-543-3104
NISSAN LAMB INC
LAMB NISSAN
400 Prescott Lakes Pkwy, Prescott, AZ 86301-6532
Tel (928) 717-2289 Founded/Ownrshp 1987
Sales 22.6MM^E EMP 76
SIC 5511 Automobiles, new & used; Automobiles, new & used
Pr: Theo F Lamb
Genl Mgr: Ed Walsh

D-U-N-S 11-924-9340
NISSAN LOKEY INC
27758 Us Highway 19 N, Clearwater, FL 33761-4901
Tel (727) 789-8100 Founded/Ownrshp 1991
Sales 59.3MM^E EMP 300
SIC 5511 Automobiles, new & used; Automobiles, new & used
Pr: Paul Lokey
*COO: T C Staton

D-U-N-S 83-983-3407
NISSAN LYNCHBURG INC
18588 Forest Rd, Forest, VA 24551-4051
Tel (434) 385-7733 Founded/Ownrshp 1997
Sales 24.8MM^E EMP 58
SIC 5511 Automobiles, new & used; Automobiles, new & used
Pr: Chris Mabry
*Ch: Larry Nichols
*Treas: Jimmy C Stout
*VP: C J Franzelas
VP: Chris Franzelas
VP: Kyle Kimball
Sls Mgr: Andrew Kappler
Sales Asso: Mark Travis

D-U-N-S 02-544-6998
NISSAN MC GRATH INC
MC GRATH NISSAN
945 E Chicago St, Elgin, IL 60120-6820
Tel (847) 695-6700 Founded/Ownrshp 1964
Sales 28.7MM^E EMP 100
SIC 5511 Automobiles, new & used; Automobiles, new & used
Pr: Leo Mc Grath
*VP: Scott Mc Grath
Sls Mgr: Joe Parks

D-U-N-S 03-226-4368
NISSAN MOSSY INC
MOSSY NISSAN KEARNY MESA
(Suby of MOSSY HOLDING CO INC) ★
4625 Brinnell St, San Diego, CA 92111-2301
Tel (619) 474-7011 Founded/Ownrshp 1982
Sales 342.5MM^E EMP 1,000
SIC 5511 Automobiles, new & used; Automobiles, new & used
Pr: Philip Mossy
*CFO: John Epps
*VP: Peter Mossy
Genl Mgr: Gary Webb
Sls Mgr: Ali Arshad
Sls Mgr: Bill Dorrel
Sls Mgr: Alfred Parker
Sales Asso: David Sapp

D-U-N-S 06-138-0739
NISSAN MOTOR ACCEPTANCE CORP
INFINITI FINANCIAL SERVICE
(Suby of NISSAN NORTH AMERICA INC) ★
1 Nissan Way, Franklin, TN 37067-6367
Tel (615) 725-1000 Founded/Ownrshp 1982
Sales NA EMP 700
SIC 6141 Financing: automobiles, furniture, etc., not a deposit bank; Financing: automobiles, furniture, etc., not a deposit bank
Pr: Mark Kaczynski
VP: Brian Carolin
VP: William J Krueger
VP: Motohiro Matsumura
VP: Mark McNabb
VP: Mark Stout
VP: Tsuyoshi Yamaguchi
Area Mgr: Jeffrey Thompson
Mktg Dir: Nat Mason
Mktg Mgr: Erin Buhrmaster
Sls Mgr: Henry Pareja

D-U-N-S 07-197-7664
NISSAN NELSON INC
800 W Queens St, Broken Arrow, OK 74012-1799
Tel (918) 258-6581 Founded/Ownrshp 1989
Sales 23.5MM^E EMP 47
SIC 5511 Automobiles, new & used; Pickups, new & used
Pr: Robert Nelson
COO: Brandon Murphy
*Sec: James Edward Nelson
Chf Mktg O: Tom Penland

Dir Bus: Lindsey Toscano
VP Sls: Rodney Gist
Sales Asso: Sean Elliott
Sales Asso: Anthony Ezell
Sales Asso: Jared Hannah
Sales Asso: Randy Hatchett
Sales Asso: Robert Markham

D-U-N-S 00-960-2533 IMP/EXP
NISSAN NORTH AMERICA INC
(Suby of NISSAN MOTOR CO.,LTD.)
1 Nissan Way, Franklin, TN 37067-6367
Tel (615) 725-1000 Founded/Ownrshp 2014
Sales 9.0MMM^E EMP 13,000
SIC 5012 8711 8734 6141 8741 3711 Commercial vehicles; Designing: ship, boat, machine & product; Product testing laboratories; Automobile proving & testing ground; Financing: automobiles, furniture, etc., not a deposit bank; Financial management for business; Automobile assembly, including specialty automobiles; Trucks, pickup, assembly of; Commercial vehicles; Designing: ship, boat, machine & product; Product testing laboratories; Automobile proving & testing ground; Financing: automobiles, furniture, etc., not a deposit bank; Financial management for business; Automobile assembly, including specialty automobiles; Trucks, pickup, assembly of
Pr: Carlos Ghosn
V Ch: Jim Morton Jr
Pr: Jack Wilkerson
CFO: Matt Loader
Chf Mktg O: Tom F Smith
Ofcr: Alfred Glodleck
Ex VP: Hidetoshi Imazu
Ex VP: Bill Krueger
Ex VP: Hiroto Saikawa
*Sr VP: Doug Betts
Sr VP: John Martin
*Sr VP: Dominique Thormann
Sr VP: Mitsuhiko Yamashita
VP: Eric Anderson
*VP: Scott E Becker
VP: Alan J Buddendeck
VP: Thomas Eastwood
VP: Shoukei Kimura
VP: Randy Knight
VP: Ronald N Petty
VP: Jason Potter

D-U-N-S 08-240-6059
NISSAN OCALA INC
OCALA NISSAN-MITSUBISHI
(Suby of PEARSON COMPANIES INC) ★
2200 Sw College Rd, Ocala, FL 34471-1616
Tel (352) 622-4111 Founded/Ownrshp 1984
Sales 22.5MM^E EMP 55
SIC 5511 5531 Automobiles, new & used; Automotive parts; Automotive accessories; Automobiles, new & used; Automotive parts; Automotive accessories
Pr: Max H Pearson
Exec: Bill Berry
*Genl Mgr: Steve Lightbody

D-U-N-S 60-247-5923 EXP
■ **NISSAN OF BRANDON INC**
AUTOWAY NISSAN OF BRANDON
(Suby of AUTONATION INC) ★
9920 E Adamo Dr, Tampa, FL 33619-2618
Tel (813) 623-1148 Founded/Ownrshp 1990
Sales 30.4MM^E EMP 90
SIC 5511 5521 Automobiles, new & used; Used car dealers; Automobiles, new & used; Used car dealers
Pr: Jim Venderos
*Pr: Ron Salhany
Genl Mgr: Bill Atchinson
Genl Mgr: Mark Perryman

NISSAN OF BUENA PARK
See INDUSTRIOUS MOTORS LLC

D-U-N-S 06-172-7322
NISSAN OF DOWNTOWN LA
DOWNTOWN L.A. NISSAN
714 W Olympic Blvd # 1131, Los Angeles, CA 90015-1425
Tel (888) 419-0743 Founded/Ownrshp 2001
Sales 28.1MM^E EMP 98
SIC 5511 Automobiles, new & used; Automobiles, new & used

D-U-N-S 18-922-4194
NISSAN OF EASTSIDE INC
BELLEVUE NISSAN
14762 Se E Gtwy, Bellevue, WA 98007
Tel (425) 289-1200 Founded/Ownrshp 2005
Sales 23.1MM^E EMP 42^E
SIC 5511 Automobiles, new & used
Pr: Gregory Brackett
*VP: Richard Snyder
*Prin: Nasiruddin Lalani
Genl Mgr: Greg Brackett
Sls Mgr: Dennis Smoot

NISSAN OF ELK GROVE
See SACRAMENTO MOTORCARS LLC

D-U-N-S 15-374-2176
NISSAN OF FONTANA INC
METRO NISSAN OF REDLANDS
(Suby of METRO NISSAN OF MONTCLAIR) ★
9440 Autoplex St, Montclair, CA 91763-2300
Tel (909) 625-5575 Founded/Ownrshp 1985
Sales 24.9MM^E EMP 110
SIC 5511 Automobiles, new & used; Automobiles, new & used
Ch Bd: James Lukens
*Pr: David A Marvin

D-U-N-S 60-475-4841
NISSAN OF MCKINNEY INC
3800 S Central Expy, McKinney, TX 75070-5509
Tel (214) 491-6400 Founded/Ownrshp 2002
Sales 28.9MM^E EMP 62^E
SIC 5511 Automobiles, new & used
Owner: Williams Adakins
Off Mgr: Amy Keenan
Off Mgr: Amy Kenan
Sls Mgr: Rick Butler

Sls Mgr: Todd Wright
Sales Asso: Danyail Brown

NISSAN OF OPELOUSAS
See GILES AUTOMOTIVE INC

NISSAN OF QUEENS
See J & R IMPORTS LTD

NISSAN OF RIVER GATE
See NISSAN HAYS INC

NISSAN OF ROANOKE RAPIDS
See NRR INC

D-U-N-S 19-858-4914
NISSAN OF SAN LEANDRO
1066 Marina Blvd, San Leandro, CA 94577-3437
Tel (510) 347-4000 Founded/Ownrshp 1975
Sales 29.5MM EMP 95
SIC 5511 Automobiles new & used; Automobiles, new & used
Sec: Lisa Biggers
*Pr: George Assoun

D-U-N-S 03-725-7037
NISSAN OF SLIDELL
400 E Howze Beach Rd, Slidell, LA 70461-4638
Tel (985) 643-7600 Founded/Ownrshp 2001
Sales 32.5MM^E EMP 100
SIC 5511 7539 7532 5531 5521 Automobiles, new & used; Automotive repair shops; Top & body repair & paint shops; Automotive & home supply stores; Used car dealers; Automobiles, new & used; Automotive repair shops; Top & body repair & paint shops; Automotive & home supply stores; Used car dealers
Pr: Allen Krake
*VP: Chuck Morris

D-U-N-S 05-422-6972
NISSAN OF SOUTH ATLANTA LLC
NISSAN SOUTH
6889 Jonesboro Rd, Morrow, GA 30260-2902
Tel (770) 968-1360 Founded/Ownrshp 2005
Sales 32.3MM^E EMP 75
SIC 5511 Automobiles, new & used; Automobiles, new & used
Sales Asso: Winifred Copeland

NISSAN OF SOUTH UNION CITY
See UNION CITY NISSAN INC

NISSAN OF THOUSAND OAKS
See WESTLAKE MOTORS INC

D-U-N-S 05-822-2373
NISSAN PAT PECK GROUP
9480 Highway 49, Gulfport, MS 39503-4213
Tel (228) 864-6411 Founded/Ownrshp 1972
Sales 23.3MM^E EMP 74
SIC 5511 Automobiles, new & used; Automobiles, new & used
Pr: Pat Peck
*Sec: Edward Switzer
*VP: Betty Peck
Genl Mgr: Scott Sanders

D-U-N-S 06-907-1004
NISSAN PEORIA CO
TNBT MOTORS
9151 W Bell Rd, Peoria, AZ 85382-4712
Tel (623) 815-5600 Founded/Ownrshp 1999
Sales 61.4MM^E EMP 180
SIC 5511 Automobiles, new & used; Automobiles, new & used
Pr: Cecil V Tuyl
Genl Mgr: John Vance
Sls Mgr: Shawn Cottrell

D-U-N-S 94-919-2611
NISSAN PINNACLE INC
PINNACLE NISSAN
7601 E Frank Lloyd Wright, Scottsdale, AZ 85260-1000
Tel (480) 998-9800 Founded/Ownrshp 1995
Sales 71.8MM^E EMP 240
SIC 5511 Automobiles, new & used; Automobiles, new & used
*Sec: Allan M Cady
VP: Martin Peters
VP: Patricia Tuyl
Genl Mgr: Shalee Bleeker
Genl Mgr: Christine Cady
Sales Exec: Dustin Donner
Sls&Mrk Ex: John Cleaves
Sales Asso: Cory Baldwin
Sales Asso: Huy Nguyen
Sales Asso: Tony Toth

D-U-N-S 05-817-9854
NISSAN POUGHKEEPSIE INC
KEEPSIE NISSAN
1445 Route 9, Wappingers Falls, NY 12590-4422
Tel (845) 297-4314 Founded/Ownrshp 1970
Sales 25.3MM^E EMP 60
SIC 5511 Automobiles, new & used; Automobiles, new & used
Pr: Farn Pomarico
Genl Mgr: Eric Hartmann
Off Mgr: Bobbie Sarrica

D-U-N-S 08-335-8002
NISSAN PUYALLUP INC
NISSAN SUZUKI
101 Valley Ave Nw, Puyallup, WA 98371-3301
Tel (253) 845-0471 Founded/Ownrshp 1976
Sales 24.5MM^E EMP 51
SIC 5511 5521 Automobiles, new & used; Used car dealers; Automobiles, new & used; Used car dealers
Pr: William K Korum
Sls Mgr: Brent Winter

D-U-N-S 96-981-2510
NISSAN QUIRK INC
600 Southern Artery, Quincy, MA 02169-4612
Tel (617) 472-6700 Founded/Ownrshp 1996
Sales 21.2MM^E EMP 70
SIC 5511 Automobiles, new & used; Automobiles, new & used
Pr: Daniel J Quirk

D-U-N-S 04-097-4490
NISSAN REIDSVILLE INC
1123 Freeway Dr, Reidsville, NC 27320-7102
Tel (336) 342-5741 Founded/Ownrshp 1999
Sales 22.9MM^E EMP 44
SIC 5511 Automobiles, new & used
Pr: Will Hedgecock
Sales Asso: Ron Handy

D-U-N-S 02-487-4014
NISSAN RISER INC (AR)
4111 Central Ave, Hot Springs, AR 71913-7294
Tel (501) 525-4511 Founded/Ownrshp 2006
Sales 20.8MM^E EMP 48^E
SIC 5511 Automobiles, new & used
Pr: Paul G Riser

D-U-N-S 61-056-0971
NISSAN ROBBINS INC
ROBBINS NISSAN-OLDS
18711 Highway 59 N, Humble, TX 77338-4223
Tel (281) 446-3181 Founded/Ownrshp 1989
Sales 74.2MM EMP 80
SIC 5511 Automobiles, new & used; Pickups, new & used; Vans, new & used; Automobiles, new & used; Pickups, new & used; Vans, new & used
Pr: William Robbins

D-U-N-S 08-094-8391
NISSAN SANSONE INC (NJ)
NISSAN AUTHORIZED SALES & SVC
100 Us Highway 1, Avenel, NJ 07001-1630
Tel (732) 815-0500 Founded/Ownrshp 1976
Sales 46.0MM EMP 47
SIC 5511 Automobiles, new & used; Automobiles, new & used
Pr: Paul Sansone Jr
*Pr: Paul J Sansone Sr

D-U-N-S 15-772-3578
NISSAN SMITHTOWN INC
535 Middle Country Rd, Saint James, NY 11780-3203
Tel (631) 361-9696 Founded/Ownrshp 1988
Sales 29.2MM^E EMP 76^E
SIC 5511 New & used car dealers; New & used car dealers
Ch Bd: Joseph Oscar Rubio
*Pr: Thomas Rubio

NISSAN SOUTH
See NISSAN OF SOUTH ATLANTA LLC

NISSAN SUZUKI
See NISSAN PUYALLUP INC

D-U-N-S 62-199-7097
NISSAN TEAM INC
70 Keller St, Manchester, NH 03103-3201
Tel (603) 644-8326 Founded/Ownrshp 1992
Sales 23.7MM^E EMP 45
SIC 5511 5012 7538 7515 5531 5521 Automobiles, new & used; Automobiles; General automotive repair shops; Passenger car leasing; Automotive & home supply stores; Used car dealers
Pr: Victoria J Marcinkevich
*Treas: Daniel Enxing
Sr Cor Off: Vicki Marcinkevich
*VP: Samuel Verge III
IT Man: John Marcinkevich
Mktg Dir: Ralph Fast
Mktg Dir: Francis Leone
Sls Mgr: Rob Miller

D-U-N-S 60-280-6676
NISSAN TONKIN WILSONVILLE
(Suby of RON TONKIN CHEVROLET CO) ★
26700 Sw 95th Ave, Wilsonville, OR 97070-9206
Tel (503) 222-2277 Founded/Ownrshp 2005
Sales 27.9MM^E EMP 100
SIC 5511 Automobiles, new & used; Automobiles, new & used
Pr: Brad Tonkin
*CFO: John Cady
*VP: Ed Tonkin
Sls Mgr: Sean Alderman
Sales Asso: Wally James
Sales Asso: Greg Nee
Sales Asso: David Ross

D-U-N-S 15-136-1854 IMP/EXP
NISSAN TRADING CORP AMERICAS
NISSAN TRADING CORP U.S.A.
(Suby of NISSAN TRADING CO.,LTD.)
1974 Midway Ln, Smyrna, TN 37167-5872
Tel (615) 220-7100 Founded/Ownrshp 1984
Sales 165.0MM^E EMP 150
SIC 5013 5012 5051 5084 Automotive supplies & parts; Automobiles; Aluminum bars, rods, ingots, sheets, pipes, plates, etc.; Machine tools & metalworking machinery; Automotive supplies & parts; Automobiles; Aluminum bars, rods, ingots, sheets, pipes, plates, etc.; Machine tools & metalworking machinery
Pr: Mamoru Kawahara
*Pr: Taichi Matsuda

NISSAN TRADING CORP U.S.A.
See NISSAN TRADING CORP AMERICAS

D-U-N-S 08-882-2598
NISSAN TRI-CITIES INC
EAST TENNESSEE NISSAN
5496 W Andrew Johnson Hwy, Morristown, TN 37814-1029
Tel (423) 587-2506 Founded/Ownrshp 1978
Sales 35.5MM^E EMP 87
SIC 5511 7538 7515 7513 7359 5531 Automobiles, new & used; General automotive repair shops; Passenger car leasing; Truck rental & leasing, no drivers; Equipment rental & leasing; Automotive & home supply stores; Automobiles, new & used; General automotive repair shops; Passenger car leasing; Truck rental & leasing, no drivers; Equipment rental & leasing; Automotive & home supply stores
Pr: Jeffrey E Cappo
*Sec: Scott Schaeffer
Exec: Larry McGowan
Genl Mgr: Cory Bugdorg

Off Mgr: Diane Hicks
CTO: Gene Turley
Sls Mgr: Travis Frazier
Sales Asso: Charles Fitzgerald
Sales Asso: Mitchell Holden
Sales Asso: Andrew Wiedman
Sales Asso: Walter Zunda

D-U-N-S 03-368-5512
■ **NISSAN TRONCALLI INC**
NALLEY INFINITI
(*Suby of* ASBURY AUTOMOTIVE GROUP INC) ★
1625 Church St, Decatur, GA 30033-5999
Tel (404) 292-3853 *Founded/Ownrshp* 2007
Sales 57.6MM^E *EMP* 244
SIC 5511 5531 7538 Automobiles, new & used; Automotive parts; General automotive repair shops; Automobiles, new & used; Automotive parts; General automotive repair shops
Pr: Charles D Troncalli
**Sec:* Wayne Brown
**VP:* Catherine Brown
IT Man: Stephen Lee

D-U-N-S 06-763-6720
NISSAN TUSTIN (CA)
TUSTIN NISSAN
30 Auto Center Dr, Tustin, CA 92782-8401
Tel (714) 669-8282 *Founded/Ownrshp* 1972
Sales 59.2MM^E *EMP* 149
SIC 5511 6159 Automobiles, new & used; Automobile finance leasing; Automobiles, new & used; Automobile finance leasing
Pr: James H Parkinson
**VP:* Mark Parkinson
Sls Mgr: Steve Cardenas
Sls Mgr: Anthony Jackson
Sales Asso: Christopher Johnson
Sales Asso: Kal Latif

D-U-N-S 05-123-0324
NISSAN TYNANS INC
TYNANS VOLKSWAGEN
780 S Havana St, Aurora, CO 80012-3014
Tel (303) 341-7330 *Founded/Ownrshp* 1970
Sales 54.0MM^E *EMP* 140
SIC 5511 Automobiles, new & used; Automobiles, new & used
Pr: Sean Tynan
**Sec:* Ralph Germeroth
**VP:* Mike Tynan
Genl Mgr: Michael Tynan
Sls Mgr: Tim Hardin
Sales Asso: Chris Patrick

D-U-N-S 87-738-3273
NISSAN TYSINGER INC
TYSINGER DODGE MERCEDES
2712 Magruder Blvd, Hampton, VA 23666-1565
Tel (757) 827-5042 *Founded/Ownrshp* 1994
Sales 25.0MM *EMP* 45
SIC 5511 Automobiles, new & used; Automobiles, new & used
Pr: Mark L Tysinger

NISSAN VILLAGE NORTH ATTLEBORO
See VILLAGE IMPORTS INC

D-U-N-S 03-309-4021
■ **NISSAN WEST WARWICK**
(*Suby of* PENSKE AUTOMOTIVE GROUP INC) ★
885 Quaker Ln, West Warwick, RI 02893-2146
Tel (401) 824-2259 *Founded/Ownrshp* 2011
Sales 23.7MM^E *EMP* 12^E
SIC 5511 Automobiles, new & used
Prin: Marilyn Letchworth

D-U-N-S 09-656-1279
NISSAN WOODBRIDGE CORP (VA)
WOODBRIDGE CHRYSLER-PLYMOUTH
14777 Jefferson Davis Hwy, Woodbridge, VA 22191-3416
Tel (703) 497-3000 *Founded/Ownrshp* 1978
Sales 22.9MM^E *EMP* 68
SIC 5511 Automobiles, new & used; Automobiles, new & used
Pr: Frank L Cowles Jr
**Treas:* Pamela S Payne
**VP:* Monte Cowles

D-U-N-S 80-990-4634
NISSAN WOODFIELD INC
700 W Higgins Rd, Hoffman Estates, IL 60169-4804
Tel (847) 310-1900 *Founded/Ownrshp* 1993
Sales 39.3MM^E *EMP* 100
SIC 5511 Automobiles, new & used; Automobiles, new & used
Pr: William A Slevin
Sls Mgr: Chris Moran

D-U-N-S 01-175-4835
NISSAN WORLD LLC
NISSAN WORLD OF SPRINGFIELD
146 Us Highway 22, Springfield, NJ 07081-3190
Tel (973) 376-8821 *Founded/Ownrshp* 1999
Sales 23.2MM^E *EMP* 50
SIC 5511 7538 5521 Automobiles, new & used; General automotive repair shops; Used car dealers; Automobiles, new & used; General automotive repair shops; Used car dealers
Pr: Chris Preziosi
Sls Mgr: Anthony Cerillo
Sales Asso: Adeyemi Akande
Sales Asso: Hector Gomez

NISSAN WORLD OF SPRINGFIELD
See NISSAN WORLD LLC

D-U-N-S 09-332-2790
NISSAN WRIGHT INC
WRIGHT AUTOMOTIVE GROUP
10520 Perry Hwy, Wexford, PA 15090-9719
Tel (724) 935-4646 *Founded/Ownrshp* 1975
Sales 26.6MM^E *EMP* 70
SIC 5511 Automobiles, new & used; Automobiles, new & used
Pr: Robert Wright
**VP:* Kenneth E Wright

NISSAN-HONDA-CADILLAC
See NOURSE FMLY OF DLRSHP-CHILLI

NISSAN-SUBARU
See ROYAL MOORE BUICK-GMC INC

D-U-N-S 01-791-5463
NISSAN/NORTH INC
8645 N High St, Columbus, OH 43235-1003
Tel (614) 846-8100 *Founded/Ownrshp* 1983
Sales 24.2MM^E *EMP* 55
SIC 5511 Automobiles, new & used; Automobiles, new & used
Pr: Thomas Carpenter
**Ex VP:* William L Denney
**Ex VP:* Robert W Vance
Genl Mgr: Scott Bean
Ql Cn Mgr: Jean-Yves Berard
Sls Mgr: Mike Dunlap
Sales Asso: Dave Dillon

D-U-N-S 08-651-9873 IMP
NISSEI AMERICA INC
(*Suby of* NISSEI PLASTIC INDUSTRIAL CO., LTD.)
1480 N Hancock St, Anaheim, CA 92807-1920
Tel (714) 693-3000 *Founded/Ownrshp* 1977
Sales 25.5MM^E *EMP* 56
SIC 5084 7699 3544 Plastic products machinery; Industrial machinery & equipment repair; Special dies, tools, jigs & fixtures
CEO: Takanori Taresawa
**Pr:* Hozumi Yoda
Ofcr: Carlos Ortega
**Prin:* Isamu Kato
Rgnl Mgr: Elena Fukuda
Rgnl Mgr: Ted Maruyama

D-U-N-S 19-580-4372 IMP
NISSEN CHEMITEC AMERICA INC
(*Suby of* NISSEN CHEMITEC CORPORATION)
350 E High St, London, OH 43140-9773
Tel (740) 852-3200 *Founded/Ownrshp* 1998
Sales 50.8MM^E *EMP* 230
SIC 3089 Injection molding of plastics; Injection molding of plastics
Pr: Shinya Kawakami
**Sr VP:* Richard Hendrix
**VP:* Kunihiko Nagura
Sfty Mgr: Scott Ford
Sfty Mgr: Dave Ludwick
Plnt Mgr: Damion Manns
Natl Sales: Doug Reynolds
Snr Mgr: Toru Ichimiya

D-U-N-S 12-889-5773 IMP
NISSHA USA INC
(*Suby of* NISSHA PRINTING CO.,LTD.)
1051 Perimeter Dr Ste 525, Schaumburg, IL 60173-5089
Tel (847) 413-2665 *Founded/Ownrshp* 1993
Sales 30.5MM^E *EMP* 217
SIC 2759 2752 Commercial printing; Commercial printing, lithographic; Commercial printing; Commercial printing, lithographic
Pr: Junya Suzuki
**CFO:* Rocky Tsuruta
Genl Mgr: Wataru Watanabe
Sls Mgr: Ryan Penty
Sls Mgr: Hiro Uenishi

D-U-N-S 96-859-9626
NISSHIN HOLDING INC
(*Suby of* NISSHIN STEEL CO., LTD.)
1701 Golf Rd, Rolling Meadows, IL 60008-4227
Tel (847) 290-5100 *Founded/Ownrshp* 2011
Sales 483.1MM^E *EMP* 192^E
SIC 8742 Management consulting services

D-U-N-S 01-239-5856 IMP
NISSHINBO AUTOMOTIVE MANUFACTURING INC
(*Suby of* NISSHINBO HOLDINGS INC.)
14187 Nisshinbo Dr, Covington, GA 30014-6435
Tel (770) 787-2002 *Founded/Ownrshp* 1997
Sales 59.1MM^E *EMP* 301
SIC 3714 Motor vehicle brake systems & parts; Motor vehicle brake systems & parts
Pr: Tatsuya Shigemasa

D-U-N-S 15-538-4274
NISSHO OF CALIFORNIA INC
1902 S Santa Fe Ave, Vista, CA 92083-7721
Tel (760) 727-9719 *Founded/Ownrshp* 1989
Sales 73.0MM^E *EMP* 420^E
SIC 0781 0782 Landscape services; Turf installation services, except artificial; Landscape contractors; Landscape services; Turf installation services, except artificial; Landscape contractors
CEO: Nobu J Kato
**Pr:* Ed Trotter
VP: Tony Angelo
VP: Cecilia Dolleton
Dir Bus: George Goodrich
IT Man: Tom Baird
Snr Mgr: Kathryn Stanford

D-U-N-S 82-949-0551 IMP
NISSIN BRAKE GEORGIA INC
(*Suby of* NISSIN KOGYO CO., LTD.)
216 Thacker Dr, Rock Spring, GA 30739-7200
Tel (706) 764-1239 *Founded/Ownrshp* 2000
Sales 28.5MM^E *EMP* 350
SIC 3714 Motor vehicle brake systems & parts
CEO: Junichi Beppu
**CFO:* Masashi Kobayashi
Admn Mgr: Masayuki Doi
Dept Mgr: David McGee
Ql Cn Mgr: Denny Clark

D-U-N-S 19-840-1259 IMP
NISSIN BRAKE OHIO INC
(*Suby of* NISSIN KOGYO CO., LTD.)
1901 Industrial Dr, Findlay, OH 45840-5442
Tel (419) 420-3800 *Founded/Ownrshp* 1988
Sales 130.8MM^E *EMP* 677
SIC 3714 Motor vehicle brake systems & parts; Motor vehicle brake systems & parts
Pr: Itsuo Miyake
**Treas:* Hiro Sato
Sr VP: Jim Owen
VP: Ronald Hall
VP: Ken Lee
VP: Larry Robinson
**VP:* Wilson J Schroeder
VP: Hiroshi Shimizu
QA Dir: Kossi Ayivi
Dir IT: Deiter Jennifer
Opers Supe: Jim Gove

D-U-N-S 05-924-5753 IMP
NISSIN FOODS (USA) CO INC
(*Suby of* NISSIN FOODS HOLDINGS CO.,LTD.)
2001 W Rosecrans Ave, Gardena, CA 90249-2994
Tel (310) 327-8478 *Founded/Ownrshp* 1970
Sales 106.1MM^E *EMP* 350
SIC 2098 2038 Noodles (e.g. egg, plain & water), dry; Ethnic foods, frozen; Noodles (e.g. egg, plain & water), dry; Ethnic foods, frozen
CEO: Hiroyuki Yoshida
Pr: Evelyn Jareno
CFO: Toshio Shigeta
CFO: Toshio Shigete
**VP:* Takahiro Enomoto
VP: Eiichi Yamakawa
Rgnl Mgr: Cathy Yochem
Genl Mgr: Susumu Nakagawa
CIO: Henry Fukuoka
Dir IT: Ruben Haritoonian
IT Man: David Lee

D-U-N-S 07-292-4640 IMP/EXP
NISSIN INTERNATIONAL TRANSPORT USA INC
(*Suby of* NISSIN CORPORATION)
1540 W 190th St, Torrance, CA 90501-1121
Tel (310) 222-8500 *Founded/Ownrshp* 1973
Sales 153.3MM^E *EMP* 540
SIC 4731 Domestic freight forwarding; Domestic freight forwarding
CEO: Yasushi Ihara
**CFO:* Mitsugu Matsusaka
VP: Masahiro Ugai
Brnch Mgr: Hiro Kawano
Brnch Mgr: Tak Kono
Brnch Mgr: Tetsuya Taga
Brnch Mgr: Kazuhiko Usami
Div Mgr: Toshiharu Sakai
Genl Mgr: David Hartnett
Genl Mgr: Linda Kwok
Genl Mgr: Anita Ng

D-U-N-S 61-895-1644
NISSIN TRAVEL SERVICE (USA) INC
(*Suby of* NISSIN TRAVEL SERVICE CO.,LTD.)
1540 W 190th St, Torrance, CA 90501-1121
Tel (310) 782-1151 *Founded/Ownrshp* 1987
Sales 40.0MM *EMP* 45
SIC 4724 Travel agencies; Travel agencies
Pr: Yoshihiko Otsuka
Adm Dir: Melodee King
Brnch Mgr: Lisa Erter
Brnch Mgr: Hiroshi Tanno
Dir IT: Long Trinh
Sls Mgr: Jim Morrow

D-U-N-S 61-871-4653 IMP
NISUS CORP
100 Nisus Dr, Rockford, TN 37853-3069
Tel (865) 577-6119 *Founded/Ownrshp* 1990
Sales 23.9MM^E *EMP* 25
SIC 5191 2879 Insecticides; Pesticides, agricultural or household
CEO: Allan H Dietrich
Pr: Lee Barrett
**Pr:* Kevin Kirkland
**CFO:* Jerry Ditz
CFO: Diana Lacy
**Sec:* Pat Dietrich
VP: Jeff Lloyd
Area Mgr: Scott Lafave
Area Mgr: Charlene Mertz
Area Mgr: Ed Szymanski
VP Opers: Tracy Malone

NITCO
See NORTHWESTERN INDIANA TELEPHONE CO INC

NITCO
See NORTHLAND INDUSTRIAL TRUCK CO INC

NITEL
See NETWORK INNOVATIONS INC

D-U-N-S 07-981-9568
NITEO PRODUCTS LLC
(*Suby of* HIGHLANDER PARTNERS LP) ★
300 Crescent Ct Ste 550, Dallas, TX 75201-1817
Tel (214) 245-5000 *Founded/Ownrshp* 2015
Sales 38.3MM^E *EMP* 143
SIC 2899 Chemical preparations
Pr: Allen Schaar
**CFO:* David Boylan

D-U-N-S 96-192-6073 IMP/EXP
NITINOL DEVELOPMENT CORPORATIO
N D C
47533 Westinghouse Dr, Fremont, CA 94539-7463
Tel (510) 683-2000 *Founded/Ownrshp* 2007
Sales 85.9MM^E *EMP* 525
SIC 3841 5047 Surgical & medical instruments; Medical & hospital equipment; Surgical & medical instruments; Medical & hospital equipment
CEO: Dean Schauer
Pr: Tom Duerig
CFO: Gordon Sangster
CFO: Chun Tam
VP: Craig Bonsignore
VP: John Dicello
VP: Chuck Faris
VP: David Johnston
VP: Steve Kleshinski
VP: Tim Tigner
Mng Dir: Kaiya Duerig
Board of Directors: Dan Lemaitre

D-U-N-S 06-424-5015 IMP
NITORI USA INC
AKI-HOME
(*Suby of* NITORI CO.,LTD.)
20 Centerpointe Dr # 130, La Palma, CA 90623-2562
Tel (714) 323-2099 *Founded/Ownrshp* 2012
Sales 49.5MM^E *EMP* 130
SIC 5712 Unfinished furniture
CEO: Shoshin Komiaya
**CFO:* Tetsuo Kumun

D-U-N-S 95-844-1362
■ **NITRO ELECTRIC CO INC**
(*Suby of* ENERGY SERVICES OF AMERICA CORP) ★
4300 1st Ave Ste 2, Nitro, WV 25143-1001
Tel (304) 204-1500 *Founded/Ownrshp* 2007
Sales 33.2MM^E *EMP* 166
SIC 1731 1796 1711 Electronic controls installation; Millwright; Mechanical contractor; Electronic controls installation; Millwright; Mechanical contractor
Pr: Lowell L Ferguson
Treas: Larry Blount
Ex VP: Bruce Ward
VP: Daniel S Belinski
VP: Gabe Holstein
**VP:* Jerry B Ward
Dir IT: Chris White
S&M/VP: Clark Lamp

D-U-N-S 07-882-6409
NITRO FLUIDS LLC
117 Broadway, Nordheim, TX 78141-3111
Tel (361) 938-5300 *Founded/Ownrshp* 2010
Sales 21.0MM^E *EMP* 58^E
SIC 1389 Oil field services

NITRO GROUP
See NITRO USA INC

D-U-N-S 36-365-6963
NITRO LIFT TECHNOLOGIES LLC
8980 Highway 1 S, Mill Creek, OK 74856-5563
Tel (580) 371-3700 *Founded/Ownrshp* 2005
Sales 30.3MM^E *EMP* 100^E
SIC 2813 Nitrogen; Nitrogen
Pr: Vernon Daniels
Opers Mgr: Chase Daniels

D-U-N-S 14-596-5229 EXP
NITRO SOFTWARE INC
(*Suby of* NITRO SOFTWARE PTY LTD)
225 Bush St Ste 700, San Francisco, CA 94104-4221
Tel (415) 369-9296 *Founded/Ownrshp* 2007
Sales 30.7MM^E *EMP* 125
SIC 5734 7371 Computer software & accessories; Computer software development
Pr: Sam Chandler
COO: Gina O Reilly
CFO: Peter Bardwick
VP: Tiho Bajic
VP: Mike Leyden
VP: John O'Keeffe
Ex Dir: Richard Crocker
Ex Dir: Kurt Johnson
QA Dir: Harrison McClymont
IT Man: Richard Ingram
Sftwr Eng: Raghuram Ashok
Board of Directors: Anthony Glenning

NITRO STEEL
See GERDAU MACSTEEL INC

D-U-N-S 15-505-7388
NITRO USA INC
NITRO GROUP
(*Suby of* SAPIENT CORP) ★
215 Park Ave S Fl 2, New York, NY 10003-1625
Tel (212) 206-1005 *Founded/Ownrshp* 2009
Sales 36.5MM^E *EMP* 500
SIC 5199 Advertising specialties; Advertising specialties
Pr: Christopher Clarke
**COO:* Stan Schwarz
**CFO:* Larri Sherman
Dir IT: Joe Calabria

D-U-N-S 07-493-2658 IMP/EXP
NITRON INTERNATIONAL CORP
35 Mason St Ste 3a, Greenwich, CT 06830-5436
Tel (203) 622-6620 *Founded/Ownrshp* 1982
Sales 42.6MM^E *EMP* 40
SIC 5191 Fertilizers & agricultural chemicals; Fertilizers & agricultural chemicals
Ch: Toros Mangassarian
**Ex VP:* Tomas Novak
Ex VP: Javier Urrutia
VP: Alejandro Flores
**VP:* Enzo Formato
Genl Mgr: Enzil Formato

D-U-N-S 05-412-2403 IMP
NITTA CASINGS INC
(*Suby of* NITTA GELATIN INC.)
141 Southside Ave, Bridgewater, NJ 08807-3256
Tel (908) 218-4400 *Founded/Ownrshp* 1996
Sales 66.1MM^E *EMP* 200
SIC 2013 5149 Sausage casings, natural; Sausage casings; Sausage casings, natural; Sausage casings
CEO: Ronald J Frump
COO: Francisco Sousa
CFO: Marcia Casas
Genl Mgr: Vernon Lee
QA Dir: Tony Linhares
Manager: Jeff Holmes
Sls Mgr: Wendy Wexler

D-U-N-S 04-672-0199 IMP
NITTA CORP OF AMERICA
(*Suby of* NITTA CORPORATION)
7605 Nitta Dr, Suwanee, GA 30024-6666
Tel (770) 497-0212 *Founded/Ownrshp* 1980
Sales 48.6MM^E *EMP* 82
SIC 5085 3052 Power transmission equipment & apparatus; Rubber belting
Pr: Kin Millsaps
**CFO:* Tracy McSoley
**VP:* Seiichi Kitamura
CIO: Michael Wallace
Ql Cn Mgr: Rex Gallups

Sls Mgr: Bill Barbee
Sls Mgr: Margie Howell
Sales Asso: Peggy Mann

D-U-N-S 93-346-3556
NITTANY OIL CO INC
1540 Martin St, State College, PA 16803-3058
Tel (814) 237-4859 *Founded/Ownrshp* 1994
Sales 90.5MM^E *EMP* 250
SIC 5171 1711 Petroleum bulk stations; Plumbing, heating, air-conditioning contractors; Petroleum bulk stations; Plumbing, heating, air-conditioning contractors
Pr: Jart V Martin
**Sec:* John Martin
**Sec:* James W Scott
**VP:* Sharon S Martin
**Prin:* James O Martin
Off Admin: Tara Tressler

D-U-N-S 62-163-2822 IMP
NITTANY PAPER MILLS INC
NP
6395 State Route 103 N 5b, Lewistown, PA 17044-7899
Tel (888) 288-7907 *Founded/Ownrshp* 2005
Sales 26.8MM^E *EMP* 63
SIC 2676 Towels, napkins & tissue paper products
**CFO:* Patrick Stewart
Plnt Mgr: Dave Fowler
Mktg Dir: Emily Royer

D-U-N-S 00-301-4479 IMP
NITTERHOUSE CONCRETE PRODUCTS INC
2655 Molly Pitcher Hwy, Chambersburg, PA 17202-7220
Tel (717) 264-6154 *Founded/Ownrshp* 1923
Sales 42.5MM^E *EMP* 165
SIC 3272 5999 Prestressed concrete products; Concrete products, precast; Concrete products, pre-cast; Prestressed concrete products; Concrete products, precast; Concrete products, pre-cast
Pr: Mark T Taylor
**Sec:* Lindsey S Lemaster
**VP:* John H Gorrell Jr
**VP:* John M Jones
**VP:* Clifford Miles
Ql Cn Mgr: Ed Luke
Sls Mgr: Daryl Wenger

D-U-N-S 00-466-6330 IMP/EXP
NITTO AMERICAS INC (NY)
PERMACEL-AUTOMOTIVE
(*Suby of* NITTO DENKO CORPORATION)
48500 Fremont Blvd, Fremont, CA 94538-6579
Tel (510) 445-5400 *Founded/Ownrshp* 1968
Sales 406.4MM^E *EMP* 1,050
SIC 2672 3589 5162 5065 Tape, pressure sensitive: made from purchased materials; Water treatment equipment, industrial; Plastics products; Electronic parts; Tape, pressure sensitive: made from purchased materials; Water treatment equipment, industrial; Plastics products; Electronic parts
Ch Bd: Toru Takeuchi
**Pr:* Yoichiro Sakuma
**CFO:* Steve Evans

D-U-N-S 05-497-9661 IMP
NITTO DENKO AMERICA INC
(*Suby of* NITTO AMERICAS INC) ★
48500 Fremont Blvd, Fremont, CA 94538-6579
Tel (510) 445-5400 *Founded/Ownrshp* 1968
Sales 23.2MM^E *EMP* 60^E
SIC 5065 5162 Electronic parts; Plastics products; Plastics resins
CEO: Brian Brace
**Pr:* Youichirou Sakuma
**CEO:* Yukio Nagiram
COO: Yukio Nagira
**COO:* Yoji Raita
Bd of Dir: Takashi Awazu
Bd of Dir: Masashi Teranishi
**VP:* AG Hayashi
VP: Steve Suzuki
Exec: Matt Alteiri
Sales Asso: Julie Pacheco

D-U-N-S 03-148-1166 IMP
NITTO DENKO AUTOMOTIVE KENTUCKY INC
(*Suby of* NITTO DENKO CORPORATION)
2284 Danforth Dr Ste 600, Lexington, KY 40511-2505
Tel (859) 231-9854 *Founded/Ownrshp* 1997
Sales 23.9MM^E *EMP* 60
SIC 5012 Automobiles & other motor vehicles
Pr: Seiji Natsuo
**CEO:* Hideo Takasaki
VP: Stephanie Adams
VP: Masaru Kawai
**VP:* Makoto Sakuraeda
Admn Mgr: Miho Stepka

D-U-N-S 12-422-5215 IMP
NITTO DENKO AUTOMOTIVE MISSOURI INC
(*Suby of* NITTO AMERICAS INC) ★
8485 Prospect Ave, Kansas City, MO 64132-2376
Tel (816) 444-3611 *Founded/Ownrshp* 2002
Sales 97.2MM^E *EMP* 340
SIC 2891 3543 Adhesives & sealants; Industrial patterns; Adhesives & sealants; Industrial patterns
CEO: Hideo Takasaki
Treas: Kent Cooper
**VP:* William J Leonard
Genl Mgr: Bryan Brayes

D-U-N-S 02-325-6705 IMP/EXP
NITTO DENKO AUTOMOTIVE NEW JERSEY INC
(*Suby of* NITTO DENKO CORPORATION)
1990 Rutgers Blvd, Lakewood, NJ 08701-4537
Tel (732) 901-7905 *Founded/Ownrshp* 2009
Sales 33.0MM^E *EMP* 150^E
SIC 3714 2295 Motor vehicle parts & accessories; Resin or plastic coated fabrics; Tape, varnished: plastic & other coated (except magnetic); Sealing or insulating tape for pipe: coated fiberglass; Motor vehicle parts & accessories; Resin or plastic coated fabrics; Tape, varnished: plastic & other coated (except magnetic); Sealing or insulating tape for pipe: coated fiberglass
Pr: Takei Nishioka
**Pr:* Yoichiro Sakuma
**Pr:* Hideo Takasaki
**CFO:* Steve Evans
**Ch:* Yukio Nagira
**Ex VP:* Toshihiko Omote
**Sr VP:* Toru Takeuchi
**VP:* Eric Pike
Dir IT: Bob Vath
Plnt Mgr: Glen Betler
Ql Cn Mgr: Maggie Bargeron

D-U-N-S 60-275-9714 IMP
NITTO DENKO AUTOMOTIVE OHIO INC
(*Suby of* NITTO DENKO CORPORATION)
1620 S Main St, Piqua, OH 45356-8320
Tel (937) 773-4820 *Founded/Ownrshp* 2009
Sales 61.3MM^E *EMP* 200
SIC 3053 3296 Gaskets & sealing devices; Mineral wool; Gaskets & sealing devices; Mineral wool
Ch: Yukio Nagira
**CEO:* Hideo Takasaki
**Sr VP:* Toru Takeuchi
**VP:* Toshihiko Omote
**VP:* Yoichiro Sakuma
Ql Cn Mgr: David Brown
Sls Mgr: Darrin Bigony

NITTO TYRES
See TOYO TIRE USA CORP

D-U-N-S 78-401-1566
NITYO INFOTECH CORP
666 Plainsboro Rd Ste 210, Plainsboro, NJ 08536-3004
Tel (609) 799-5959 *Founded/Ownrshp* 2005
Sales 66.9MM^E *EMP* 1,000
SIC 7379 Computer related consulting services; Computer related consulting services
Pr: Naveen Kumar
**CFO:* Baskar Nathan
Exec: Charmaine Lo
Sales Exec: Peter Schwoerer

D-U-N-S 92-965-7497
NITYO INFOTECH CORP
2652 Hidden Valley Rd # 103, Pittsburgh, PA 15241-3915
Tel (412) 894-9054 *Founded/Ownrshp* 2005
Sales 55.1MM^E *EMP* 1,000
SIC 7379 Computer related consulting services; Computer related consulting services
Pr: Naveen Kumar
**CFO:* Bhaskar Nathan

D-U-N-S 80-838-2159 IMP
NIVEL HOLDINGS LLC
NIVEL PARTS MANUFACTURING
3510 Pt Jacksonville Park Ste 5, Jacksonville, FL 32226
Tel (904) 741-6161 *Founded/Ownrshp* 2012
Sales 72.5MM^E *EMP* 450
SIC 3799 5088 Golf carts, powered; Golf carts; Golf carts, powered; Golf carts

NIVEL PARTS MANUFACTURING
See NIVEL HOLDINGS LLC

D-U-N-S 00-341-0271
NIVERT METAL SUPPLY INC (PA)
1100 Marshwood Rd, Throop, PA 18512-1426
Tel (570) 222-4487 *Founded/Ownrshp* 1966
Sales 22.0MM *EMP* 58
Accts Mcgrail Merkel Quinn & Associa
SIC 5051 Steel; Aluminum bars, rods, ingots, sheets, pipes, plates, etc.; Nonferrous metal sheets, bars, rods, etc.; Steel; Aluminum bars, rods, ingots, sheets, pipes, plates, etc.; Nonferrous metal sheets, bars, rods, etc.
Pr: Louis Nivert
**Sec:* James M Griffiths
**Genl Mgr:* Bill Burns

D-U-N-S 07-431-7012 IMP
NIVIS LLC
6300 Powers Ferry Rd, Atlanta, GA 30339-2919
Tel (678) 576-5235 *Founded/Ownrshp* 1999
Sales 21.8MM^E *EMP* 139
SIC 7373 7371

D-U-N-S 08-255-7612
NIX AUTO CENTER INC
700 S George Nigh Expy, McAlester, OK 74501-6714
Tel (918) 423-6200 *Founded/Ownrshp* 1999
Sales 21.4MM^E *EMP* 60
SIC 5511 Automobiles, new & used; Automobiles, new & used
Pr: Johnny Nix
Genl Mgr: Tommy Nix

NIX CHECK CASHING SERVICE
See KINECTA ALTERNATIVE FINANCIAL SOLUTIONS INC

NIX HEALTH CARE SYSTEM
See ACCORD MEDICAL MANAGEMENT LP

NIX HEALTHCARE SYSTEM
See NIX HOSPITALS SYSTEM LLC

D-U-N-S 07-868-0042
NIX HOSPITALS SYSTEM LLC (TX)
NIX HEALTHCARE SYSTEM
414 Navarro St Ste 600, San Antonio, TX 78205-2541
Tel (210) 271-1800 *Founded/Ownrshp* 2011
Sales 62.4MM^E *EMP* 950
SIC 8062 General medical & surgical hospitals; General medical & surgical hospitals
Pr: John F Strieby
**CFO:* Lester E Surrock
Tech Mgr: John Maddison

D-U-N-S 15-099-0018
NIX-FOWLER CONSTRUCTORS INC
N F C
1875 Mitchell Rd Se Ste B, Mableton, GA 30126-2935
Tel (404) 691-2414 *Founded/Ownrshp* 1986
Sales 36.3MM *EMP* 22
Accts Jerry Davis Cpa Pc Roswell
SIC 1542 Nonresidential construction; School building construction; Hospital construction
Pr: Clarence M Nix
**Treas:* Carey A Fowler

NIXA HARDWARE AND SEED
See NIXA HARDWARE CO

D-U-N-S 02-993-2845
NIXA HARDWARE CO
NIXA HARDWARE AND SEED
510 W Mount Vernon St, Nixa, MO 65714-9329
Tel (417) 725-3512 *Founded/Ownrshp* 1967
Sales 28.3MM^E *EMP* 65^E
SIC 5191 5251

D-U-N-S 10-004-1862
NIXA R-II SCHOOL DISTRICT
CHRISTIAN COUNTY R-2 SCHL DST
205 North St 8751400, Nixa, MO 65714-8663
Tel (417) 875-5400 *Founded/Ownrshp* 1921
Sales 24.3MM^E *EMP* 640
SIC 8211 Public elementary school; Public junior high school; Public senior high school; Public elementary school; Public junior high school; Public senior high school

D-U-N-S 15-076-8109
NIXON & VANDERHYE PC
901 N Glebe Rd Ste 1100, Arlington, VA 22203-4184
Tel (703) 816-4000 *Founded/Ownrshp* 1985
Sales 50.0MM *EMP* 106
SIC 8111 Patent, trademark & copyright law; Patent, trademark & copyright law
Pr: Larry S Nixon
**Treas:* John Lastova
**VP:* Robert Faris

D-U-N-S 09-299-2940
NIXON AND CO (MO)
13205 Manchester Rd # 100, Saint Louis, MO 63131-1733
Tel (314) 821-4888 *Founded/Ownrshp* 1976
Sales NA *EMP* 46
SIC 6411 Insurance adjusters
Pr: Terence E Nixon
**VP:* Ken Pini

D-U-N-S 12-386-2455 IMP
NIXON INC
NIXON WATCHES
701 S Coast Highway 101, Encinitas, CA 92024-4441
Tel (760) 944-0900 *Founded/Ownrshp* 2012
Sales 72.1MM^E *EMP* 175
SIC 5094 5611 5136 Watches & parts; Clothing accessories: men's & boys'; Leather & sheep lined clothing, men's & boys'; Watches & parts; Clothing accessories: men's & boys'; Leather & sheep lined clothing, men's & boys'
CEO: Nicholas Stowe
**Pr:* Andrus Laats
COO: David Laverty
VP: Mike Hoefer
Exec: Megan Brunner
Exec: Sandra Fichter
Exec: Christina Madrid
Software D: Heather Denis
Mktg Dir: Michel Murciano
Mktg Mgr: Scott Carrington
Manager: Sandi Townsend

D-U-N-S 07-969-5508
NIXON PEABODY LLP
1300 Clinton Sq, Rochester, NY 14604-1707
Tel (585) 263-1000 *Founded/Ownrshp* 1875
Sales 193.2MM^E *EMP* 1,300
SIC 8111 General practice law office; General practice law office
Genl Pt: Richard F Langan Jr
Pt: Bruce J Baker
**Pt:* James Curley
**Pt:* Karen Greenbaum
**Pt:* Carolyn S Kaplan
Pt: Jennifer Kuenster
**Pt:* Nestor M Nicholas
Pt: Philip B Taub
**Pt:* Harry P Trueheart III
Pt: Stephen D Zubiago
Mng Pt: Arnaud De Senilhes
Mng Pt: Kevin M Fitzgerald
Mng Pt: Richard Jones
Mng Pt: Cheng Lam
Mng Pt: Jeffrey S Lesk
Mng Pt: Neal J McNamara
Mng Pt: Carolyn Nussbaum
Mng Pt: Denise D Pursley
Mng Pt: Susan C Roney
Mng Pt: Andrew C Rose
Mng Pt: Arthur J Rosner

NIXON POWER SERVICES COMPANY
See NIXON POWER SERVICES LLC

D-U-N-S 96-748-4325 IMP
NIXON POWER SERVICES LLC
NIXON POWER SERVICES COMPANY
5038 Thoroughbred Ln, Brentwood, TN 37027-4225
Tel (615) 309-5823 *Founded/Ownrshp* 2003
Sales 176.8MM^E *EMP* 200
SIC 5063 4911 Generators; Generation, electric power; Generators; Generation, electric power
CEO: Ronald M Stanley Jr
Pr: Bryant Phillips
CFO: Kevin W Mann

NIXON UNIFORM SERVICE & MED WR
See NIXON UNIFORM SERVICE INC

D-U-N-S 07-554-6671
NIXON UNIFORM SERVICE INC
NIXON UNIFORM SERVICE & MED WR
500 Centerpoint Blvd, New Castle, DE 19720-8106
Tel (302) 325-2875 *Founded/Ownrshp* 2007
Sales 31.1MM^E *EMP* 418
SIC 7218 Industrial equipment launderers; Industrial equipment launderers
Pr: Jason Berstein
Genl Mgr: Barry Clements
DP Dir: Paul Capuano
VP Sls: Mike Peele
Mktg Mgr: Arthur Hand
Manager: Mike O'Neal
Manager: Michael Small
Manager: Lisa Timko

NIXON WATCHES
See NIXON INC

D-U-N-S 05-645-2741 IMP
NIXON-EGLI EQUIPMENT CO OF SOUTHERN CALIFORNIA INC
2044 S Vineyard Ave, Ontario, CA 91761-7748
Tel (909) 930-1822 *Founded/Ownrshp* 1971
Sales 30.8MM^E *EMP* 67
SIC 5082 General construction machinery & equipment; General construction machinery & equipment
Pr: Steve Nixon
**VP:* Carl Bahnsen
**VP:* Dana Randall
Mtls Mgr: David Cucinelli
Sls Mgr: James Nixon

D-U-N-S 79-483-7075 IMP
NIZI INTERNATIONAL (US) INC
4040 Embassy Pkwy Ste 140, Akron, OH 44333-8391
Tel (330) 665-0610 *Founded/Ownrshp* 2007
Sales 57.0MM^E *EMP* 124
SIC 5051 Steel
Pr: Matt Wood
Ex VP: John Way

D-U-N-S 07-838-3409
NJ ADVANCE MEDIA LLC
(*Suby of* ADVANCE PUBLICATIONS INC) ★
485 Route 1, Iselin, NJ 08830-3009
Tel (732) 902-4300 *Founded/Ownrshp* 2014
Sales 13.7MM^E *EMP* 350^E
SIC 7311 7313 Advertising agencies; Advertising consultant; Electronic media advertising representatives; Advertising agencies; Advertising consultant; Electronic media advertising representatives
Pr: Matt Kraner
VP: Steve Alesai
VP Mktg: David Martel

D-U-N-S 96-912-0398
NJ CARPENTERS CATASTROPHIC HEALTH FUND
P.O. Box 7818 (08818-7818)
Tel (732) 417-3900 *Founded/Ownrshp* 2011
Sales 133.9MM *EMP* 4^E
SIC 8631 Trade union

D-U-N-S 80-641-7549
NJ DEPARTMENT OF CORRECTIONS
(*Suby of* EXECUTIVE OFFICE OF STATE OF NEW JERSEY) ★
Stuyvsant Av Whttlesey Rd Whittlesey, Trenton, NJ 08618
Tel (609) 292-2162 *Founded/Ownrshp* 1976
Sales NA *EMP* 10,000^E
SIC 9223 ;

D-U-N-S 10-258-9082
NJ MALIN & ASSOCIATES LLC
(*Suby of* RAYMOND CORP) ★
15870 Midway Rd, Addison, TX 75001-4279
Tel (972) 458-2680 *Founded/Ownrshp* 2011
Sales 123.6MM^E *EMP* 400
SIC 5046 5084

NJ SHARING NETWORK
See NEW JERS ORGA & TISS SHAR NETW

NJ TRANSIT
See NEW JERSEY TRANSIT CORP

NJATC
See NATIONAL JOINT APPRENTICESHIP & TRAINING COMMITTEE FOR ELECTRICAL INDUSTRY (INC)

D-U-N-S 96-653-3726
NJBLS WELFARE FUND
3218 John F Kennedy Blvd, Jersey City, NJ 07306-3416
Tel (201) 963-0633 *Founded/Ownrshp* 2011
Sales NA *EMP* 3
Accts Schultheis & Panettieri Llp H
SIC 6371 Pension, health & welfare funds

NJCU
See NEW JERSEY CITY UNIVERSITY

NJDWSC
See NORTH JERSEY DISTRICT WATER SUPPLY COMMISSION

NJEA
See NEW JERSEY EDUCATION ASSOCIATION INC

NJIT
See NEW JERSEY INSTITUTE OF TECHNOLOGY (INC)

D-U-N-S 62-311-2349
NJK HOLDING CORP
8500 Normandale Lake Blvd, Minneapolis, MN 55437-3813
Tel (952) 831-7777 *Founded/Ownrshp* 1988
Sales 21.8MM^E *EMP* 153
SIC 5045 Computer software; Computer integrated systems design; Computers, peripherals & software
CEO: Nasser J Kazeminy

NJM INSURANCE GROUP
See NEW JERSEY MANUFACTURERS INSURANCE CO

D-U-N-S 93-024-9888 IMP
NJOY INC
15211 N Kierland Blvd # 200, Scottsdale, AZ 85254-8164
Tel (480) 397-2271 *Founded/Ownrshp* 2006
Sales 22.5MM^E *EMP* 80
SIC 5993 Cigarette store; Cigarette store
Pr: Paul Sturman
**CFO:* John Bax
Sr VP: David Graham
Sr VP: Vito Maurici
**VP:* Roy Anise
VP: Tom Siebenaler
Exec: Warren Dickey
Opers Mgr: Bob Raymond
Mktg Mgr: Erin Dullea
Manager: Jimmie Gaukler
Manager: Justin Kelly
Board of Directors: Michael Farello, Doug Teitelbaum, Jeff Weiss, Elie Wurtman

D-U-N-S 02-571-5165
■ **NJR ENERGY SERVICES CO**
(*Suby of* NEW JERSEY RESOURCES CORP) ★
1415 Wyckoff Rd, Belmar, NJ 07719
Tel (732) 938-1000 *Founded/Ownrshp* 1996
Sales 73.1MM^E *EMP* 100
SIC 4924 Natural gas distribution; ; Natural gas distribution;
Pr: Laurence M Downes
**COO:* Kathleen T Ellis
**COO:* Joseph P Shields
**Sr VP:* Stephen Westhoven
**VP:* Maryellen Dugan
VP: Rick Gardner
**VP:* Ginger Richman
Off Mgr: Kathy Cassey
Mktg Dir: Jeff Wolfe

NJT ENTERPRISES LLC
See MAYCO INTERNATIONAL LLC

D-U-N-S 00-838-5903
NJVC LLC
(*Suby of* CHENEGA CORP) ★
14295 Park Meadow Dr, Chantilly, VA 20151-2220
Tel (703) 429-9000 *Founded/Ownrshp* 2001
Sales 443.8MM *EMP* 1,300
Accts Mcgladrey Llp Frederick Mary
SIC 7379 ;
Pr: Chris Andersen
COO: Andrew Gallegos
Sr VP: Patrick Gayhardt
VP: Umit Basoglu
VP: John Darocha
VP: Jennifer IAMS
VP: Charles McGaugh
VP: Fredrick Turman
Prgrm Mgr: Denise Droneburg
Snr Sftwr: Daniel Gilbert
Snr Sftwr: Melissa Hendricksen

D-U-N-S 01-404-2147
NK LIQUIDATION INC
NELL'S FAMILY MARKET
(*Suby of* C&S WHOLESALE GROCERS INC) ★
600 Arsenal Rd, York, PA 17402-2127
Tel (717) 854-1505 *Founded/Ownrshp* 1983
Sales 118.2MM^E *EMP* 1,000
SIC 5411 Supermarkets; Supermarkets
VP: J Warren Weaver
**Sec:* Thomas Teeter

D-U-N-S 61-274-3997 IMP/EXP
NK PARTS INDUSTRIES INC
(*Suby of* NIKKON HOLDINGS CO., LTD.)
777 S Kuther Rd, Sidney, OH 45365-8861
Tel (937) 498-4651 *Founded/Ownrshp* 1987
Sales 179.8MM^E *EMP* 1,060
SIC 5013 1796 4731

D-U-N-S 82-888-0075
NK STEEL LLC
31731 Northwstrn Hwy 15 Ste 157 W, Farmington Hills, MI 48334
Tel (248) 865-9000 *Founded/Ownrshp* 2008
Sales 100.0MM *EMP* 12
SIC 5051 Steel; Steel

D-U-N-S 03-940-6301 IMP
NKC OF AMERICA INC (TN)
(*Suby of* NAKANISHI METAL WORKS CO.,LTD.)
1584 E Brooks Rd, Memphis, TN 38116-1988
Tel (901) 396-6334 *Founded/Ownrshp* 1980
Sales 44.8MM^E *EMP* 200
SIC 3535 5084 1796 Conveyors & conveying equipment; Conveyor systems; Machinery installation; Conveyors & conveying equipment; Conveyor systems; Machinery installation
Pr: Yoshitaka Tanaka
Pr: Kiichiro Yamamoto
VP: John Gorris
Genl Mgr: S Chb-Pres
Genl Mgr: Paul Hayashida
Snr Mgr: Bob Turcotte

D-U-N-S 96-738-1653
NKOTB LLC
REVERE HOTEL BOSTON COMMON
200 Stuart St, Boston, MA 02116-5442
Tel (617) 482-1800 *Founded/Ownrshp* 2010
Sales 17.3MM^E *EMP* 300
SIC 7011 Hotels; Hotels
Pr Dir: Bryan Barbieri
Sls Dir: Susan Cullen

D-U-N-S 01-104-2892 IMP
NKS DISTRIBUTORS INC
399 Churchmans Rd, New Castle, DE 19720-3111
Tel (302) 322-1811 *Founded/Ownrshp* 1946, 1950
Sales 34.7MM^E *EMP* 105^E
SIC 5181 5182 Beer & other fermented malt liquors; Wine; Beer & other fermented malt liquors; Wine
Ch Bd: James V Tigani Sr
**Pr:* Robert Tigani
VP: Joanne Lee
Mng Dir: Bob Tigani
Area Mgr: Blair Hickman
Trfc Dir: Joanne Peake
Sales Exec: Alan Mc Bride
VP Mktg: Chris Tigani
Mktg Dir: Alan McBride
Sls Mgr: Mike Lashomb

D-U-N-S 61-783-5244
■ **NL HOLDING CORP (DEL)**
(*Suby of* NEW ENGLAND FINANCIAL) ★
260 Madison Ave Ste 11, New York, NY 10016-2412
Tel (212) 354-8800 *Founded/Ownrshp* 1998
Sales 115.0MM^E *EMP* 170^E
SIC 6211 6411 Brokers, security; Dealers, security; Insurance agents; Insurance brokers; Brokers, security; Dealers, security; Insurance agents; Insurance brokers
Ch: James Benson
**Pr:* Jay L Lewis
**Exec:* Thomas Wirtshafter

D-U-N-S 00-131-7577
■ **NL INDUSTRIES INC** (NJ)
(*Suby of* VALHI INC) ★
5430 Lbj Fwy Ste 1700, Dallas, TX 75240-2620
Tel (972) 233-1700 *Founded/Ownrshp* 1891
Sales 103.8MM *EMP* 2,956^E
Accts Pricewaterhousecoopers Llp Da
Tkr Sym NL *Exch* NYS
SIC 2819 3572 3699 Industrial inorganic chemicals; Computer storage devices; Security devices; Industrial inorganic chemicals; Computer storage devices; Security devices
Pr: Robert D Graham
**Ch Bd:* Steven L Watson
CFO: Gregory M Swalwell
Treas: John A St Wrba
Ex VP: Kelly D Luttmer
VP: Tim C Hafer
Board of Directors: Loretta J Feehan, Cecil H Moore Jr, Thomas P Stafford, Terry N Worrell

D-U-N-S 78-723-7668
NL OF KY INC
NEACE, MUSSELMAN & MAYFIELD
(*Suby of* ASSUREDPARTNERS INC) ★
2305 River Rd, Louisville, KY 40206-1010
Tel (502) 894-2100 *Founded/Ownrshp* 2013
Sales NA *EMP* 434
SIC 6411 Insurance agents & brokers; Insurance agents & brokers
Pr: John F Neace
Pr: Louis M Berman
Pr: Scott R Heiser
Pr: Alan J Jones
Pr: Joseph T Lukens
Pr: Douglas A Stough
Sr VP: Daniel Rossen
VP: Gerald B Budde

D-U-N-S 05-469-5333 IMP/EXP
NLB CORP (MI)
NATIONAL LIQUID BLASTING
29830 Beck Rd, Wixom, MI 48393-2824
Tel (248) 624-5555 *Founded/Ownrshp* 1971
Sales 26.6MM^E *EMP* 163
SIC 3569 7359 3561

D-U-N-S 00-772-4095
NLFH ACCT PAYABLE BILL CH
541 N Fairbanks Ct Fl 16, Chicago, IL 60611-3319
Tel (312) 926-2094 *Founded/Ownrshp* 2011
Sales 606.2M^E *EMP* 7,000
SIC 8721 Accounting, auditing & bookkeeping
Off Mgr: Sue Davis-Bilbo

D-U-N-S 79-981-1646 IMP
NLIGHT PHOTONICS CORP
5408 Ne 88th St Ste E, Vancouver, WA 98665-0990
Tel (360) 566-4460 *Founded/Ownrshp* 2000
Sales 132.1MM^E *EMP* 549
SIC 3674 3699 Semiconductors & related devices; Laser systems & equipment; Semiconductors & related devices; Laser systems & equipment
CEO: Scott Keeney
**CFO:* David Schaezler
**VP:* Jake Bell
**VP:* Mike Boston
**VP:* Joe Debartolo
**VP:* Mark Devito
**VP:* Rob Martinsen
VP: Joseph Sauvageau
Dir IT: Todd Brainard
Dir IT: Sandra Garcia
Dir IT: David Greer
Board of Directors: Doug Carlisle, Bill Ericson, Jeff Grant, Scott Keeney, Ray Link, Dave Osborne

D-U-N-S 60-973-2979 IMP
NLMK INDIANA LLC
(*Suby of* NLMK, OAO)
6500 S Boundary Rd, Portage, IN 46368-1334
Tel (219) 787-8200 *Founded/Ownrshp* 2008
Sales 181.3MM^E *EMP* 380
SIC 3312 Hot-rolled iron & steel products; Hot-rolled iron & steel products
Pr: Robert Miller
**CFO:* Corinn Grossetti
**VP:* Alexander Tseitline
Genl Mgr: Ken Crain
Mktg Mgr: Bob Coppiellie

D-U-N-S 04-679-8059 IMP
NLMK PENNSYLVANIA LLC
15 Roemer Blvd, Farrell, PA 16121-2201
Tel (724) 983-6464 *Founded/Ownrshp* 2011
Sales 228.8MM^E *EMP* 500
SIC 3316 3356 3312 Blast furnaces & steel mills; Cold finishing of steel shapes; Nonferrous rolling & drawing; Cold finishing of steel shapes; Nonferrous rolling & drawing; Blast furnaces & steel mills
Pr: Robert Miller
**CEO:* Benedict Sciortino
**Ex VP:* James Banker
**VP:* Jason Adams
VP: Corinn Grossetti
VP: Al Robertson
Mng Dir: Christian Morgan
Area Supr: Kevin Szolek
Tech Mgr: Carter Johnston
Ql Cn Mgr: Paul Harpst
Sls Dir: Frank Fonner

NLS
See NUTRACEUTICAL LIFE SCIENCES INC

D-U-N-S 08-795-0056
NLV FINANCIAL CORP
(*Suby of* NATIONAL LIFE INSURANCE CO) ★
1 National Life Dr, Montpelier, VT 05604-1000
Tel (802) 229-3333 *Founded/Ownrshp* 2006
Sales NA *EMP* 850
Accts Pricewaterhousecoopers Llp B
SIC 6311 6321 Mutual association life insurance; Accident insurance carriers; Health insurance carriers; Mutual association life insurance; Accident insurance carriers; Health insurance carriers
Pr: Mehran Assadi
CFO: Bob Cotton
**Treas:* Robert E Cotton
Chf Inves: Thomas H Brownell
Sr VP: Tom Anfuso

D-U-N-S 09-532-3213
NM GROUP GLOBAL LLC
161 Greenfield St, Tiffin, OH 44883-2499
Tel (419) 447-5211 *Founded/Ownrshp* 2002
Sales 109.6MM^E *EMP* 490
SIC 3542 3599 6799 Forging machinery & hammers; Custom machinery; Investors; Forging machinery & hammers; Custom machinery; Investors

D-U-N-S 04-623-4407
NM HOLDINGS INC
OHLHEISER CORPORATION
(*Suby of* OHIO TRANSMISSION CORP) ★
831 N Mountain Rd, Newington, CT 06111-1414
Tel (860) 953-7632 *Founded/Ownrshp* 2014
Sales 29.1MM^E *EMP* 23
SIC 5084 Pneumatic tools & equipment
Pr: Robert B Pellettier
Sales Exec: Debbie Thompson
Manager: Steve Muise

NM RESIDENTIAL
See NIEDERST MANAGEMENT LTD

D-U-N-S 07-989-8886
▲ **NM Z PARENT INC**
787 7th Ave Fl 49, New York, NY 10019-6018
Tel (212) 720-0300 *Founded/Ownrshp* 2015
Sales 696.4MM^E *EMP* 2,300^E
SIC 6726 2841 2879 2842 Investment offices; Soap & other detergents; Pesticides, agricultural or household; Degreasing solvent
CEO: Steven B Klinsky

D-U-N-S 11-749-5838 IMP/EXP
NMB (USA) INC
NMB TECH
(*Suby of* MINEBEA CO., LTD.)
9730 Independence Ave, Chatsworth, CA 91311-4323
Tel (818) 709-1770 *Founded/Ownrshp* 1983
Sales 313.4MM^E *EMP* 2,800
SIC 3562 5063 5084 3728 5065

NMB TECH
See NMB (USA) INC

D-U-N-S 04-646-8195 IMP
NMB TECHNOLOGIES CORP
(*Suby of* NMB (USA) INC) ★
9730 Independence Ave, Chatsworth, CA 91311-4323
Tel (818) 341-0820 *Founded/Ownrshp* 1968
Sales 49.4MM^E *EMP* 174
SIC 5085

NMC
See NEWELL MACHINERY CO INC

N.M.C
See NUCLEAR MANAGEMENT CO LLC

NMC
See NATIONAL MACHINERY & CONVEYOR INC

D-U-N-S 00-696-9919 IMP
NMC GROUP INC (NE)
NMC POWER SYSTEMS
11002 Sapp Brothers Dr, Omaha, NE 68138-4812
Tel (402) 346-6500 *Founded/Ownrshp* 1938
Sales 112.9MM^E *EMP* 150^E
SIC 5082 5084 Construction & mining machinery; Road construction equipment; Graders, motor; Pavers; Lift trucks & parts; Construction & mining machinery; Road construction equipment; Graders, motor; Pavers; Lift trucks & parts
Ch: Jerry L Swanson
**Ch Bd:* J Duane Swanson
**Pr:* Richard Swanson
**CFO:* John Swanson
**Treas:* Jay M Samuelson
VP: Curtis Akey
VP: Lmccormick Amup
VP: Rich Kolkman
VP: Nicholas Mizaur
Ex Dir: Brad Foster
Brnch Mgr: Aaron Rubesh

D-U-N-S 06-512-2459 IMP
■ **NMC GROUP INC**
NYLON MOLDING CORPORATION
(*Suby of* KIRKHILL-TA CO) ★
2755 Thompson Creek Rd, Pomona, CA 91767-1861
Tel (909) 451-2290 *Founded/Ownrshp* 1972
Sales 42.0MM^E *EMP* 64
SIC 5085 3089 Fasteners & fastening equipment; Injection molding of plastics; Fasteners & fastening equipment; Injection molding of plastics
CEO: Douglas P Stephen
Pr: Mitch Iverson
**Pr:* Jim Sweeney
**CEO:* Ichard Brad Lawrence
**Sec:* Barbara Stephen
VP: Frank Houston
IT Man: Gail Russell
IT Man: Jamie Wearp

D-U-N-S 15-527-2664
NMC OPERATING CO LLC
NEURO MEDICAL HOSPITAL
10105 Park Rowe Cir Fl 2, Baton Rouge, LA 70810
Tel (225) 763-9900 *Founded/Ownrshp* 2002
Sales 32.6MM *EMP* 192
SIC 8062 General medical & surgical hospitals
Dir Recs: Jennifer Ericson
CEO: Robert D Blair
CEO: Thomas Flynn
Chf Nrs Of: Monica Nijoka
CIO: Brice Hamilton

NMC POWER SYSTEMS
See NMC GROUP INC

D-U-N-S 18-586-9146 IMP
NMC/WOLLARD INC
2021 Truax Blvd, Eau Claire, WI 54703-9693
Tel (715) 835-3151 *Founded/Ownrshp* 1948
Sales 20.9MM^E *EMP* 55
SIC 3537 Aircraft loading hoists
CEO: Kevin C Steingart
**VP:* Bruce A Steingart
IT Man: Mark Brown

NMCOV
See ORO VALLEY HOSPITAL LLC

NMCS
See NORTH METRO COMMUNITY SERVICES INC

D-U-N-S 80-622-4205 IMP
NMF INC
ADDISON SHOE COMPANY
1421 Falls Blvd N, Wynne, AR 72396-1623
Tel (870) 238-2331 *Founded/Ownrshp* 2007
Sales 45.2MM^E *EMP* 140
SIC 5139 Footwear
Plnt Mgr: Robert Godfrey

NMG AEROSPACE
See NATIONAL MACHINE CO

D-U-N-S 83-304-0657
NMH INVESTMENT LLC
313 Congress St Fl 5, Boston, MA 02210-1218
Tel (617) 790-4800 *Founded/Ownrshp* 2006
Sales 70.1MM^E *EMP* 19,000
SIC 8361 Residential care; Residential care

D-U-N-S 17-254-7015
NMHG FINANCIAL SERVICES INC
10 Riverview Dr, Danbury, CT 06810-6268
Tel (888) 338-2487 *Founded/Ownrshp* 1985
Sales 111.1MM^E *EMP* 133^E
SIC 6282 Investment advice
CEO: Diane Cooper
**Pr:* Daniel Henson
**Treas:* Paul Costas
VP: James Donoghue
**VP:* Jonathan Kipp
**VP:* Matt Lesage
VP: Christina McCaughey
VP: Robert Sattler
VP: Linda Velez

D-U-N-S 13-859-3913
■ **NMHG HOLDING CO**
HYSTER AND YALE
(*Suby of* NACCO INDUSTRIES INC) ★
650 Ne Holladay St # 1600, Portland, OR 97232-2045
Tel (503) 721-6000 *Founded/Ownrshp* 1999
Sales 2.8MMM^E *EMP* 7,800
SIC 3537 5084 Lift trucks, industrial: fork, platform, straddle, etc.;Trucks, tractors, loaders, carriers & similar equipment; Lift trucks & parts; Lift trucks, industrial: fork, platform, straddle, etc.; Trucks, tractors, loaders, carriers & similar equipment; Lift trucks & parts
Pr: Reginald R Eklund
**CFO:* Michael K Smith

D-U-N-S 12-316-1650
■ **NMHG OREGON LLC**
(*Suby of* HYSTER) ★
4000 Ne Blue Lake Rd, Fairview, OR 97024-8710
Tel (503) 721-6010 *Founded/Ownrshp* 2001
Sales 60.8MM^E *EMP* 400
SIC 5084 Industrial machinery & equipment; Industrial machinery & equipment
Pr: Reginald R Eklund
Treas: Jeff Mattern

D-U-N-S 06-895-5062
NMI HOLDINGS INC
2100 Powell St Fl 12th, Emeryville, CA 94608-1894
Tel (855) 530-6642 *Founded/Ownrshp* 2011
Sales NA *EMP* 141^E
Tkr Sym NMIH *Exch* NGM
SIC 6351 Mortgage guarantee insurance
Ch Bd: Bradley M Shuster
Pr: John M Sherwood Jr
CFO: Glenn Farrell
Ex VP: Patrick L Mathis
Ex VP: Claudia J Merkle
Board of Directors: Michael Embler, James G Jones, Michael Montgomery, John Brandon Osmon, James H Ozanne, Steven L Scheid

NMMA
See NATIONAL MARINE MANUFACTURERS ASSOCIATION (INC)

NMMFA
See NEW MEXICO MORTGAGE FINANCE AUTHORITY

D-U-N-S 10-279-6976 EXP
■ **NMMFP INC**
(*Suby of* DXP ENTERPRISES INC) ★
910 E Osborn Rd Ste C, Phoenix, AZ 85014-5220
Tel (602) 956-9200 *Founded/Ownrshp* 1976
Sales 35.8MM^E *EMP* 75

SIC 5084 5085 Pumps & pumping equipment; Industrial supplies; Pumps & pumping equipment; Industrial supplies
CEO: J Russell Perlich
**Pr:* Jeff Wright
**CFO:* Al Priem
IT Man: Tiffany Johnson

NMMI
See NEW MEXICO MILITARY INSTITUTE INC

NMR CONSULTING
See NETWORK MANAGEMENT RESOURCES INC

D-U-N-S 11-032-8288
NMR PIPELINE LLC
300 S Main St Loop 207, Eunice, NM 88231
Tel (575) 394-0144 *Founded/Ownrshp* 2001
Sales 71.0MM *EMP* 320
SIC 1623 Oil & gas pipeline construction

NMR STAGING AND EVENTS
See NATIONAL MICRO RENTALS INC

NMS LABS
See NATIONAL MEDICAL SERVICES INC

D-U-N-S 82-695-2041
NMS SECURITY SERVICES LLC
(*Suby of* NANA CORPORATE SERVICES) ★
5600 B St, Anchorage, AK 99518-1641
Tel (907) 273-2424 *Founded/Ownrshp* 2008
Sales 13.0MM^E *EMP* 717^E
SIC 7381 Security guard service
Prin: Ron Otte
Secur Mgr: Don Savage

D-U-N-S 01-807-1261
■ NMSA INC
UNILIN FLOORING
(*Suby of* UNILIN FLOORING NC LLC) ★
100 Maxine Rd, Danville, VA 24541-6412
Tel (434) 793-4647 *Founded/Ownrshp* 1996, 2011
Sales 60.7MM^E *EMP* 620
SIC 2435 Hardwood veneer & plywood; Hardwood veneer & plywood
Pr: David Wootten
**Pr:* Bradley L Thompson
**Treas:* Ron Mullenburg
Sls Dir: Steve Bunch

NMSU
See NEW MEXICO STATE UNIVERSITY

D-U-N-S 00-599-1098
NMTAP
435 Sint Mchaels Dr Ste D, Santa Fe, NM 87505
Tel (505) 954-8521 *Founded/Ownrshp* 2009
Sales 24.0MM *EMP* 400
SIC 8331 Vocational rehabilitation agency; Vocational rehabilitation agency
Prin: Andrew Winnegar

D-U-N-S 82-945-0634 IMP
■ NMTC INC
MATCO TOOLS
(*Suby of* DH HOLDINGS CORP) ★
4403 Allen Rd, Stow, OH 44224-1033
Tel (330) 929-4949 *Founded/Ownrshp* 1953
Sales 350.0MM *EMP* 500
SIC 5251 5072 3469 3423 5013 Hardware; Hardware; Metal stampings; Hand & edge tools; Tools & equipment, automotive; Hardware; Hardware; Metal stampings; Hand & edge tools; Tools & equipment, automotive
Ch: Thomas N Willis
**Pr:* Timothy J Gilmore
**Treas:* Raymond Michaud
**VP:* John C Green
**VP:* Eric Hagen
**VP:* Thomas M Hill
**VP:* Jeffrey J Peterson
**VP:* Jill Willis
Brnch Mgr: Omar Al-Dosari
Dist Mgr: David Miller
IT Man: Janet Coghan

D-U-N-S 83-035-0372
NMTI HOLDINGS INC
75 Nh Ave, Portsmouth, NH 03801-2864
Tel (603) 427-5794 *Founded/Ownrshp* 2007
Sales 76.6MM *EMP* 380
SIC 7371 Computer software development; Computer software development
CEO: Sean O'Neill
**Pr:* Jeff Hiscox
**CFO:* Kenneth Smaha

NMWD
See NORTH MARIN WATER DISTRICT

NN
See NANDANSONS INTERNATIONAL INC

D-U-N-S 03-790-5247 IMP
▲ NN INC
207 Mockingbird Ln Ste 10, Johnson City, TN 37604-3137
Tel (423) 743-9151 *Founded/Ownrshp* 1980
Sales 488.6MM *EMP* 1,721
Accts Pricewaterhousecoopers Llp Ch
Tkr Sym NNBR *Exch* NGS
SIC 3562 Ball bearings & parts; Roller bearings & parts; Ball bearings & parts; Roller bearings & parts
Pr: Richard D Holder
Ofcr: William C Kelly Jr
Sr VP: James H Dorton
Sr VP: Matthew Heiter
Sr VP: Warren Veltman
Sr VP: Jr Widders
VP: Thomas C Burwell
VP: Jeff Hodge
CIO: Scott Weinstein

NNA INSURANCE SERVICES
See NNA SERVICES LLC

NNA SERVICES
See NATIONAL NOTARY ASSOCIATION

D-U-N-S 07-798-3690
NNA SERVICES LLC
NNA INSURANCE SERVICES
9350 De Soto Ave, Chatsworth, CA 91311-4926
Tel (818) 739-4071 *Founded/Ownrshp* 2012
Sales NA *EMP* 204
SIC 6411 Insurance agents, brokers & service
Ch Bd: Milton G Valera
**CEO:* Thomas A Heymann
**CFO:* Robert A Clarke
**Ex VP:* Deborah M Thaw
VP: Deborah Valera
Exec: Kelly Rush
Dir IT: Bob Byers
Board of Directors: Deborah M Thaw, Milton G Valera

NNDS
See NATIONAL NETWORK OF DIGITAL SCHOOLS CORP

D-U-N-S 36-218-9388
NNE PHARMAPLAN INC
NNE PHARMERPAN
(*Suby of* NNE PHARMAPLAN A/S)
3005 Carrington Mill Blvd, Morrisville, NC 27560-8885
Tel (919) 481-3765 *Founded/Ownrshp* 1967
Sales 175.3MM^E *EMP* 1,700
SIC 8711 Consulting engineer; Consulting engineer
CEO: Morten Nielsen
**Pr:* Bob Brown Petersen
**CFO:* Soren Jelert
Ql Cn Mgr: Emily Nelson

NNE PHARMERPAN
See NNE PHARMAPLAN INC

D-U-N-S 07-864-2181
NNI VENTURES LLC
160 Greentree Dr Ste 101, Dover, DE 19904-7620
Tel (305) 728-8501 *Founded/Ownrshp* 2010
Sales 40.9MM^E *EMP* 323^E
SIC 6799 4899 Venture capital companies; Data communication services

NNPS
See NEWPORT NEWS PUBLIC SCHOOL DISTRICT

NNR
See CLYDE/WEST INC

D-U-N-S 06-247-1537
NNR GLOBAL LOGISTICS USA INC
(*Suby of* NISHI-NIPPON RAILROAD CO.,LTD.)
450 E Devon Ave Ste 260, Itasca, IL 60143-1262
Tel (630) 773-1490 *Founded/Ownrshp* 1971
Sales 252.3MM *EMP* 340
Accts Ernst & Young Llp Chicago I
SIC 4731 Foreign freight forwarding; Foreign freight forwarding
Pr: Kenji Oki
Opers Supe: Brad Jordan
Opers Mgr: Don Hutzenbuehler
Board of Directors: John Beggin, John Beggin, Andrew Hadley, Akira Nokuo

NNRH
See NORTHEASTERN NEVADA REGIONAL HOSPITAL AUXILARY/VOLUNTEERS INC

NNSA
See NATIONAL NUCLEAR SECURITY ADMINISTRATION/SERVICE CENTER

NNSECU
See NEWPORT NEWS SHIPBUILDING EMPLOYEES CREDIT UNION INC

D-U-N-S 17-598-3670
NO COOTIES INC
4416 Falcon Ave, Long Beach, CA 90807-2505
Tel (562) 856-1168 *Founded/Ownrshp* 2005
Sales 50.0MM *EMP* 4
SIC 2899 Essential oils; Essential oils
Pr: Hope Vaughan
**VP:* Jonathan Vaughan

D-U-N-S 11-869-4629
NO FRILLS SUPERMARKETS INC OF OMAHA
11163 Mill Valley Rd, Omaha, NE 68154-3933
Tel (402) 399-9244 *Founded/Ownrshp* 1955
Sales NA *EMP* 1,300
SIC 5411

NO KIDDING
See HIS INTERNATIONAL CORP

NO LIMITS
See WRIGHT & FILIPPIS INC

D-U-N-S 02-718-9542
NO MAGIC INC
700 Central Expy S # 110, Allen, TX 75013-8098
Tel (214) 291-9100 *Founded/Ownrshp* 1995
Sales 36.7MM^E *EMP* 175
SIC 7371 8243 7373 8748 Computer software development; Operator training, computer; Systems engineering, computer related; Office computer automation systems integration; Systems analysis & engineering consulting services; Systems engineering consultant, ex. computer or professional; Computer software development; Operator training, computer; Systems engineering, computer related; Office computer automation systems integration; Systems analysis & engineering consulting services; Systems engineering consultant, ex. computer or professional
Ch: Paul T Duncanson Jr
**Ch Bd:* Paul Duncanson
**Pr:* Gary Duncanson
**COO:* Roger Klotz
Chf Mktg O: Raymond Hertz
VP: Pete Ianace
**Dir Risk M:* Clarence Moreland
Mng Dir: Gitana Akliene
CTO: Kent Laursen
IT Man: Tadas Jarockas
Sftwr Eng: Aleczander Jackson

D-U-N-S 02-817-6061
NO MASS TEL WKRS C U
87 Hale St, Lowell, MA 01851-3340
Tel (978) 454-5342 *Founded/Ownrshp* 2009
Sales 21.8MM *EMP* 3^E
SIC 8631 Labor unions & similar labor organizations; Labor unions & similar labor organizations
Prin: Kenneth M Del Rossi

NO NONSENSE
See KAYSER-ROTH CORP

D-U-N-S 19-636-4558 IMP/EXP
NO-FADE COATINGS INC
ALLEGRO INDUSTRIES
1360 Shiloh Church Rd, Piedmont, SC 29673-9067
Tel (800) 622-3530 *Founded/Ownrshp* 1984
Sales 21.1MM^E *EMP* 100
SIC 3842 Personal safety equipment
Pr: Thomas Johnston
**VP:* Ben Matranga
QA Dir: Todd McGee

D-U-N-S 62-512-1660
NO/AIDS TASK FORCE
2601 Tulane Ave Ste 500, New Orleans, LA 70119-7400
Tel (504) 821-2601 *Founded/Ownrshp* 1983
Sales 26.7MM *EMP* 211
Accts Postlethwaite & Netterville M
SIC 8322 8011 General counseling services; General counseling services; Primary care medical clinic; Specialized medical practitioners, except internal
CEO: Noel Twilbeck
**Ch:* Sergio Farfan
**Ch:* Helen Siegel
**Treas:* Barry Schlaile
Prin: Dorian-Gray Alexander
Prin: Rosa Bustamante-Forest
Prin: Wayne Christenberry
Prin: Maureen Clary
**Prin:* Cara Harrison Daniels
Prin: Otis Fennell
Prin: Raymond Jasper

D-U-N-S 96-996-2799
NOAH BANK
7301 Old York Rd Ste 1, Elkins Park, PA 19027-3004
Tel (215) 424-5100 *Founded/Ownrshp* 2005
Sales NA *EMP* 50^E
SIC 6022 State commercial banks; State commercial banks
CEO: Edward Shin
Ofcr: Gloria Ahn
Ofcr: Abraham Chung
Ofcr: Sam Leigh
Ex VP: Kwang Chang
Ex VP: Kenny Hong
Ex VP: David Suh
Sr VP: Bhavesh Sheth
VP: Ted Kim
VP: Julie Ko
Brnch Mgr: Yoomi Choi

D-U-N-S 96-261-8125
NOAH MEB JV2
1112 Jensen Dr, Virginia Beach, VA 23451-5881
Tel (757) 487-5858 *Founded/Ownrshp* 2010
Sales 9.6MM^E *EMP* 290
SIC 1542 Commercial & office building contractors; Commercial & office building contractors

D-U-N-S 96-261-8158
NOAH MEB JV3
1112 Jensen Dr, Virginia Beach, VA 23451-5881
Tel (757) 487-5858 *Founded/Ownrshp* 2010
Sales 9.4MM^E *EMP* 290
SIC 1542 Commercial & office building contractors; Commercial & office building contractors

NOANET
See NORTHWEST OPEN ACCESS NETWORK

D-U-N-S 07-533-6719
NOARUS INVESTMENTS INC
AIRPORT HONDA
5850 W Centinela Ave, Los Angeles, CA 90045-1504
Tel (310) 649-2440 *Founded/Ownrshp* 1998
Sales 26.2MM^E *EMP* 65
SIC 5511 5521 5531 7514 7538 Automobiles, new & used; Automobiles, used cars only; Automotive parts; Passenger car rental; General automotive repair shops; Automobiles, new & used; Automobiles, used cars only; Automotive parts; Passenger car rental; General automotive repair shops
Pr: Norris J Bishton
Store Mgr: Alvin Benjamin
Sls Mgr: Bob Garcia

D-U-N-S 05-095-8321
NOARUS TGG
TOYOTA SCION PLACE
9444 Trask Ave, Garden Grove, CA 92844-2824
Tel (714) 895-5595 *Founded/Ownrshp* 1987
Sales 41.1MM^E *EMP* 97
SIC 5511 5531 7538 Automobiles, new & used; Automotive parts; General automotive repair shops; Automobiles, new & used; Automotive parts; General automotive repair shops
Pr: Norris J Bishton
**CFO:* Gary Alwood
**VP:* William Hurst
Sls Mgr: Jose Cendejas
Sls Mgr: Elio Chemaly
Sls Mgr: Andy Doan
Sls Mgr: Ly Duong
Sls Mgr: Jeff Locastro
Sls Mgr: Gabriela Lopez
Sls Mgr: Jennie Lu
Sls Mgr: Hung Ngo

D-U-N-S 02-823-9689
NOB HILL GENERAL STORE INC
SUPPORT CENTER
(*Suby of* BEL AIR MARKETS) ★
500 W Capitol Ave, West Sacramento, CA 95605-2624
Tel (916) 373-3333 *Founded/Ownrshp* 1998
Sales 400.4MM *EMP* 1,645
SIC 5411 5961 Supermarkets, chain; Pharmaceuticals, mail order; Supermarkets, chain; Pharmaceuticals, mail order
CEO: Michael Teel

D-U-N-S 04-486-2894
NOB HILL PROPERTIES INC
BIG FOUR RESTAURANT
1075 California St, San Francisco, CA 94108-2281
Tel (415) 474-5400 *Founded/Ownrshp* 1976
Sales 18.9MM^E *EMP* 280
SIC 7011 5812 Hotels; Eating places; Hotels; Eating places
Pr: John Cope
**Ch Bd:* Newton Cope Sr
**CEO:* Charles S Swanson
**VP:* Newton Cope Jr
Sls Mgr: Martina Milnar

D-U-N-S 00-623-4266
NOBE-NASH INC
727 N Shepherd Dr, Houston, TX 77007-1320
Tel (713) 452-1500 *Founded/Ownrshp* 2012
Sales 33.7MM^E *EMP* 80^E
SIC 5074 1542 8744 8711 Heating equipment & panels, solar; Nonresidential construction; Commercial & office building, new construction; ; Building construction consultant
CEO: Robin Nash
**Pr:* Vance Nobe
Dir Opers: Tim Parker

NOBEL AUTOMOTIVE
See ORHAN NORTH AMERICA INC

D-U-N-S 80-565-6498
NOBEL AUTOMOTIVE OHIO LLC
(*Suby of* NOBEL AUTOMOTIVE) ★
190 County Home Rd, Paris, TN 38242-6625
Tel (731) 641-6700 *Founded/Ownrshp* 2007
Sales 35.0MM *EMP* 200
SIC 5013 Automotive supplies; Automotive supplies
Plnt Mgr: Chris Cobb

D-U-N-S 60-945-7494
■ NOBEL BIOCARE USA LLC
(*Suby of* NOBEL BIOCARE AB)
22715 Savi Ranch Pkwy, Yorba Linda, CA 92887-4609
Tel (714) 282-4800 *Founded/Ownrshp* 2004
Sales 290.0MM *EMP* 500
SIC 3843 Dental equipment & supplies; Dental equipment & supplies
Pr: Thomas Olsen
Ch: Ken Darienzo
Treas: Frederick Walther
Sr VP: Mike Thompson
VP: Dan Hinkle
Dist Mgr: Michaela Ganzer
QA Dir: Promise Lumati
Dir IT: Tim Cronin
Sftwr Eng: Vanessa Simon
Ql Cn Mgr: Mir Khan
Natl Sales: Bryan Moeslein

D-U-N-S 11-261-9762
NOBEL LEARNING COMMUNITIES INC
(*Suby of* ACADEMIC ACQUISITION CORP) ★
1615 W Chester Pike # 200, West Chester, PA 19382-6223
Tel (484) 947-2000 *Founded/Ownrshp* 2011
Sales 272.2MM^E *EMP* 4,700^E
SIC 8211 8299 Private elementary & secondary schools; Specialty education; Educational services; Private elementary & secondary schools; Specialty education; Educational services
Pr: George H Bernstein
COO: Patricia B Miller
CFO: Thomas Frank
Sr VP: G Lee Bohs
Sr VP: Jeanne Marie Welsko
Ex Dir: Susanne Bernard
CIO: Jada Hightower
CIO: Folake Odunlami

D-U-N-S 07-915-3423
▲ NOBILIS HEALTH CORP
11700 Katy Fwy Ste 300, Houston, TX 77079-1218
Tel (713) 355-8614 *Founded/Ownrshp* 2007
Sales 84.0MM *EMP* 452^E
Accts Calvettiferguson Houston Tex
Tkr Sym HLTH *Exch* ASE
SIC 8011 Offices & clinics of medical doctors; Clinic, operated by physicians
CEO: Chris Lloyd
**Ch Bd:* Harry Fleming
CFO: Kenny Klein
Ex VP: Andy Chen
Board of Directors: Richard Ganley, Jennifer Pfahler

D-U-N-S 04-239-2761
▲ NOBILITY HOMES INC
3741 Sw 7th St, Ocala, FL 34474-1945
Tel (352) 732-5157 *Founded/Ownrshp* 1967
Sales 21.1MM *EMP* 110^E
Accts Averett Warmus Durkee Pa Orl
Tkr Sym NOBH *Exch* OTO
SIC 2451 Mobile homes; Mobile homes
Ch Bd: Terry E Trexler
**CFO:* Thomas W Trexler
Treas: Lynn J Cramer Jr
Treas: U Cramer
VP: Edward C Sims
Genl Mgr: Bill Henke
S&M/VP: Todd Frobrish
Board of Directors: Richard C Barberie, Robert P Holliday, Robert P Saltsman

NOBLE & ASSOCIATES
See NOBLE COMMUNICATIONS CO

D-U-N-S 96-788-8330
NOBLE AMERICAS CORP
(*Suby of* NOBLE GROUP LIMITED)
4 Stamford Plz, Stamford, CT 06902-3834
Tel (203) 324-8555 *Founded/Ownrshp* 2008
Sales 2.1MMM^E *EMP* 630
SIC 5052 1311 Coal & coke; Natural gas production; Coal & coke; Natural gas production
Ch Bd: Richard Samuel Elman

*Pr: Richard Didonna
CFO: Judy Fung
*Ch: Edward Rubin
Treas: Connie Grossman
*Treas: Christina Reynolds
*Treas: Eric B Twombly
Ofcr: Salvatore Penna
*Ex VP: Williams Coonin
*Ex VP: Theodore W Robinson
*Ex VP: Robert Jan Van Der Zalm
Sr VP: Donald England
Sr VP: Thomas Silva
VP: Michael Davis
VP: Steven Frost
*VP: Ram Patel
*VP: Thomas F Reich
VP: James Scholes

D-U-N-S 96-825-4276
NOBLE AMERICAS ENERGY SOLUTIONS LLC
NOBLE AMERICAS ENRGY SOLUTIONS
(Suby of NOBLE GROUP LIMITED)
401 W A St Ste 500, San Diego, CA 92101-7991
Tel (877) 273-6772 Founded/Ownrshp 2010
Sales 306.5MM^E EMP 400^E
SIC 4931 4932 Electric & other services combined; Gas & other services combined; Electric & other services combined; Gas & other services combined
Pr: James Wood
VP: Dee Chambless
VP: Alex Fazekas-Paul
VP: Gayle McCutchan
VP: Drake Welch
*Prin: Neil Bresnan
Mng Dir: Michael Mann
Mktg Dir: Robbie Hale
Sls Mgr: Teresa Acosta
Sls Mgr: Scott Puckett
Sales Asso: Angela Ghormley

NOBLE AMERICAS ENRGY SOLUTIONS
See NOBLE AMERICAS ENERGY SOLUTIONS LLC

D-U-N-S 96-882-3034
NOBLE AMERICAS RESOURCES CORP
NARC
4 Stamford Plz, Stamford, CT 06902-3834
Tel (203) 324-8555 Founded/Ownrshp 2011
Sales 108.8MM^E EMP 280
SIC 6221 5153 5149 2099 Commodity dealers, contracts; Grain & field beans; Cocoa; Sugar; Commodity dealers, contracts; Grain & field beans; Cocoa; Sugar
Pr: William J Cronin
*CEO: Ernesto Leon-Gambetta
*Treas: Christina Reynolds
*Treas: Eric Twombly
*Ex VP: David E Behrends

D-U-N-S 07-382-5432
NOBLE AND GREENOUGH SCHOOL
NOBLES
10 Campus Dr, Dedham, MA 02026-4099
Tel (781) 326-3700 Founded/Ownrshp 1866
Sales 48.8MM EMP 160
Accts Mcgladrey Llp Charlestown Ma
SIC 8211 Secondary school; Secondary school
*Treas: Robert Stanky
Ofcr: Peter Hamilton
Dir: Jeffrey Berndt
Comm Dir: Heather Sullivan
Off Mgr: Karen Ortendahl
CIO: Dan Weir

D-U-N-S 78-123-2702 IMP
NOBLE BIOMATERIALS INC
300 Palm St, Scranton, PA 18505-1618
Tel (570) 955-1800 Founded/Ownrshp 2005
Sales 26.4MM^E EMP 100^E
SIC 2299 Broadwoven fabrics: linen, jute, hemp & ramie
CEO: Jeff B Keane
*Pr: Joel Furey
*Pr: Guy Grubel
*CFO: James F Walsh
VP: Satish Chandra
VP: Brad Selman
Mng Dir: Alison Tsui
CIO: Mauricio Somekh
*VP Opers: Gregory Gianforcaro
Sfty Mgr: Ken Walker
Opers Mgr: Ed Trowbridge

D-U-N-S 01-896-1042
NOBLE CASING INC
2020 Caribou Dr Ste 201, Fort Collins, CO 80525-4352
Tel (970) 631-8428 Founded/Ownrshp 2009
Sales 22.1MM^E EMP 30
SIC 1389 Cementing oil & gas well casings
CEO: Chance Innis
Pr: Tobi Wold
CFO: J J Hannah
VP Opers: Shane Craig

D-U-N-S 05-070-2695
NOBLE COMMUNICATIONS CO (MO)
NOBLE & ASSOCIATES
2215 W Chesterfield Blvd, Springfield, MO 65807-8683
Tel (417) 875-5000 Founded/Ownrshp 1969
Sales 35.0MM EMP 534
SIC 7311 Advertising agencies; Advertising agencies
V Ch: Keith Acuff
Pr: David Nehmer
Pr: Dick Sanderson
CEO: Robert B Noble
Sr VP: Nancy Banasik
Sr VP: Leslie Hutter
Art Dir: Jim Knapp

D-U-N-S 78-628-2756 IMP
NOBLE DRILLING (US) INC
(Suby of NOBLE DRILLING CORP) ★
13135 Dry Ashfd 800, Sugar Land, TX 77478
Tel (281) 276-6100 Founded/Ownrshp 1990
Sales 191.3MM^E EMP 400
SIC 1381 Drilling oil & gas wells; Drilling oil & gas wells
Pr: James C Day
*Treas: Michael Lamb
*VP: William C Hofman

D-U-N-S 00-790-7785 IMP/EXP
NOBLE DRILLING CORP
(Suby of NOBLE HOLDING (US) CORP) ★
13135 S Dairy Ste 800, Sugar Land, TX 77478
Tel (281) 276-6100 Founded/Ownrshp 1921
Sales 844.1MM^E EMP 500
SIC 1381 8711 Drilling oil & gas wells; Petroleum engineering; Drilling oil & gas wells; Petroleum engineering
Ch Bd: James C Day
*Pr: Mark A Jackson
*CFO: Tom Mitchell
*Treas: Mike Lamb
*Sr VP: Robert D Campbell
*Sr VP: Julie J Robertson
*Sr VP: David Williams
VP: Kevin D Roche

D-U-N-S 83-169-8779
NOBLE DRILLING HOLDING LLC
(Suby of NOBLE CORPORATION PLC)
13135 Dairy Ashford Rd # 700, Sugar Land, TX 77478-3685
Tel (281) 276-6100 Founded/Ownrshp 2002
Sales 102.6MM^E EMP 216^E
SIC 1381 Drilling oil & gas wells
Ch: David W Williams
COO: Mark Jackson

D-U-N-S 78-388-1956 IMP/EXP
NOBLE DRILLING SERVICES INC
(Suby of NOBLE DRILLING CORP) ★
13135 Dairy Ashford Rd # 800, Sugar Land, TX 77478-3698
Tel (281) 276-6100 Founded/Ownrshp 1990
Sales 226.2MM^E EMP 500
SIC 3541 Drilling & boring machines; Drilling & boring machines
Pr: David W Williams
*Pr: James C Day
*Pr: Dennis J Lubojacky
*VP: Bob Campbell
VP: Jeffrey Chastain
VP: James Darnell
VP: Bob Newhouse
VP Mktg: Andrew W Tietz
S&M/VP: Dan Donaldson
Counsel: Kirk Moore

NOBLE ENERGY
See SAMEDAN OIL CORP

D-U-N-S 05-287-7586 IMP/EXP
▲ **NOBLE ENERGY INC**
1001 Noble Energy Way, Houston, TX 77070-1435
Tel (281) 872-3100 Founded/Ownrshp 1932
Sales 5.1MMM EMP 2,987^E
Tkr Sym NBL Exch NYS
SIC 1311 Crude petroleum production; Natural gas production; Crude petroleum production; Natural gas production
Pr: David L Stover
CFO: Kenneth M Fisher
Ex VP: Susan M Cunningham
Sr VP: J K Elliott
Sr VP: Arnold J Johnson
Sr VP: Charles J Rimer
Sr VP: A Lee Robison
Sr VP: Gary W Willingham
Prgrm Mgr: Carrie Lezama
Prgrm Mgr: Cathy Molitoriss
CTO: Ismael Carbajal
Board of Directors: Jeffrey L Berenson, Michael A Cawley, Edward F Cox, Thomas J Edelman, Eric P Grubman, Kirby L Hedrick, Scott D Urban, William T Van Kleef, Molly K Williamson

D-U-N-S 19-286-9142
NOBLE ENVIRONMENTAL POWER LLC
NEP
8 Railroad Ave Ste 8, Essex, CT 06426-1535
Tel (860) 581-5010 Founded/Ownrshp 2008
Sales 111.8MM^E EMP 120
SIC 4911 Generation, electric power; Generation, electric power
Sr VP: Daniel Mandli
Sr VP: Kay C Mann
VP: Dick Augustine
VP: Richard Augustine
VP: Peter Capitelli
*VP: Robert Depalermo
VP: Neil Dyment
VP: Sandra L Dykstra Sayyeau
VP: Francis R Stone
VP: Pamela Sutton-Hall
Mng Dir: Thomas Swank
Board of Directors: Christopher C Behrens, Stephen P Murray, John M Warner

D-U-N-S 11-510-2121
NOBLE FINANCE CORP
25331 W Interstate 10 # 101, San Antonio, TX 78257-9506
Tel (210) 698-0448 Founded/Ownrshp 1980
Sales NA EMP 55
Accts Fisher Herbst & Kembele Pc
SIC 6141 Consumer finance companies; Consumer finance companies
Pr: A P Gentry
CFO: J D Gonzalez
*Sec: Rebecca Hudson
*VP: D L Belcher
*Genl Mgr: M L Belcher

D-U-N-S 02-219-8998
NOBLE FORD-MERCURY INC
2406 N Jefferson Way, Indianola, IA 50125-9483
Tel (515) 961-8151 Founded/Ownrshp 1985
Sales 24.8MM^E EMP 62
SIC 5511 Automobiles, new & used; Pickups, new & used; Automobiles, new & used; Pickups, new & used
Pr: Dimaggio Nichols
*Sec: Terry Beedle
*VP: Lizzie S Nichols

Off Mgr: Jone Hembry
Sls Mgr: Rick Pattison
Sales Asso: Dan Fox
Sales Asso: Purmon Greene
Sales Asso: Dave Kritenbrink
Sales Asso: Chris Lashier
Sales Asso: Shane Memhen
Sales Asso: Doug Thomson

D-U-N-S 82-524-1391
NOBLE HEALTH SYSTEMS INC
115 W Silver St, Westfield, MA 01085-3678
Tel (413) 568-6259 Founded/Ownrshp 1986
Sales 28.8MM^E EMP 600
SIC 8741 Hospital management; Hospital management
Pr: Ronald Bryant

D-U-N-S 11-916-6556 IMP/EXP
NOBLE HOLDING (US) CORP
(Suby of NOBLE CORPORATION)
3135 S Dairy Ashford, Sugar Land, TX 77478
Tel (281) 276-6100 Founded/Ownrshp 2003
Sales 3.2MMM EMP 3,744
Accts Pricewaterhousecoopers Llp Ho
SIC 1381 Drilling oil & gas wells; Drilling oil & gas wells
Pr: Mark A Jackson
*Treas: Michael N Lamb
VP: Ross W Gallup
VP: Mike Lowther
*VP: Julie J Robertson
VP: John T Rynd

D-U-N-S 93-906-6296
NOBLE HOSPITALITY INC
1641 Anderson Ave, Manhattan, KS 66502-4031
Tel (785) 539-3800 Founded/Ownrshp 1991
Sales 23.9MM^E EMP 750
SIC 8741 Hotel or motel management; Hotel or motel management
Pr: Colin Noble
VP: Bridget McCombe
VP: Bridget McCome

NOBLE HOUSE
See FLOORCO ENTERPRISES LLC

D-U-N-S 92-814-9659
NOBLE HOUSE HOTELS & RESORTS LTD
600 6th St S, Kirkland, WA 98033-6716
Tel (425) 827-8737 Founded/Ownrshp 1984
Sales 110.5MM^E EMP 2,000
SIC 7011 Resort hotel; Resort hotel
CEO: John M Donoghue
Pr: Michael Benecke
Pr: Sean Mullen
Pr: Steve Sanborn
COO: Chris Gautier
CFO: Patricia Handjaja
Ch: Patrick R Colee
VP: Darrell Stark

NOBLE HOUSE OF ASHLAND
See CENTRAL ARKANSAS NURSING CENTERS INC

D-U-N-S 93-339-8075
NOBLE INTERNATIONAL LTD
840 W Long Lake Rd # 601, Troy, MI 48098-6356
Tel (248) 519-0700 Founded/Ownrshp 1993
Sales 146.7MM^E EMP 2,700
SIC 3714 Motor vehicle body components & frame; Motor vehicle body components & frame
CEO: Andrew J Tav
Ch Bd: Richard P McCracken
CEO: Andrew J Tavi
COO: David J Fallon
CFO: Jay J Hansen
V Ch Bd: Jean-Francois Crancee
VP: Craig S Parsons
VP: Thomas D Talboys
VP Opers: Larry W Garretson
Board of Directors: Philippe Landron, Gerard Picard, James R Thomas

D-U-N-S 55-724-1945
NOBLE INVESTMENT GROUP LLC
3424 Peachtree Rd Ne, Atlanta, GA 30326-1118
Tel (404) 262-9660 Founded/Ownrshp 2003
Sales 93.6MM^E EMP 195
SIC 6726 Investment offices
*CFO: Jim Conley
Treas: David Brown
*Sr VP: Roy Croop
Sr VP: Robert Mruz
VP: Michael Quinlan
Genl Mgr: Brian Cole
Genl Mgr: Tanveer Dogar
Genl Mgr: Marcel Girard
Genl Mgr: Sharon Priester
Genl Mgr: Don Singletary
Sls Dir: Kevin Fraser

D-U-N-S 16-864-1871
NOBLE LOGISTICS INC
8844 N Sam Houston Pkwy W # 240, Houston, TX 77064-2307
Tel (713) 690-0200 Founded/Ownrshp 2006
Sales 46.1MM^E EMP 200^E
SIC 4225 4731 General warehousing; Domestic freight forwarding; General warehousing; Domestic freight forwarding
CEO: Doak Medchill
*CFO: Stan Mason
*VP: Christoph Brunner
VP: Chris Delahoyssaye
VP: John Paiva
Genl Mgr: Brandon Games
Genl Mgr: Leo Gilliam
Genl Mgr: Michelle Green
Genl Mgr: Tanner Hamilton
Genl Mgr: Scott Kafora
Dir IT: Bryan Barton

D-U-N-S 19-892-6060
NOBLE NETWORK OF CHARTER SCHOOLS
NOBLE STREET CHARTER SCHOOL
1 N State St Fl 7, Chicago, IL 60602-3311
Tel (773) 278-6895 Founded/Ownrshp 1998

Sales 134.9MM EMP 85^E
Accts Ostrow Reisin Berk & Abrams Lt
SIC 8211 Elementary & secondary schools; Elementary & secondary schools
CEO: Michael Milky
*Pt: John Harris
*Ch Bd: Allan Muchin
IT Man: Sima David
IT Man: Mike Deliberto
Snr PM: Elliott Mitiu
Snr Mgr: Matt Niksch

D-U-N-S 15-394-4442
NOBLE OIL SERVICES INC
5617 Clyde Rhyne Dr, Sanford, NC 27330-9562
Tel (919) 774-8180 Founded/Ownrshp 1984
Sales 44.4MM^E EMP 120
SIC 1799 4953 7699 1795 4959 2992 Decontamination services; Recycling, waste materials; Tank repair & cleaning services; Dismantling steel oil tanks; Oil spill cleanup; Lubricating oils & greases
Pr: James Noble
*VP: Richard Kalin
VP: William E Noble
Dir Bus: Vince Martin
Dir Bus: Stephanie Zorn
CIO: Larry Humes
IT Man: Jim Jolliff
IT Man: James Keith
Plnt Mgr: Mark Giaquinto
Sls Mgr: Gary McNeely

D-U-N-S 15-424-2502
NOBLE RESOURCES CORP
7102 N 30th St, Tampa, FL 33610-1106
Tel (813) 241-6968 Founded/Ownrshp 2002
Sales 23.0MM EMP 125
SIC 1623 Fiber optic cable installation; Telephone & communication line construction; Telephone & communication line construction
Pr: Michael L Wallace

D-U-N-S 96-261-0218
NOBLE RESTAURANT GROUP INC
REUBEN'S STEAKHOUSE & FRESH
3176 Pullman St Ste 120, Costa Mesa, CA 92626-3317
Tel (949) 887-1901 Founded/Ownrshp 1996
Sales 5.7MM^E EMP 300
Accts Fleishmann Wada
SIC 5812 American restaurant; American restaurant
Pr: Gregg Diganci
*VP: Denise Quinn

D-U-N-S 10-791-0259
NOBLE SALES CO INC
NOBLE SUPPLY AND LOGISTICS
302 Weymouth St Ste 202, Rockland, MA 02370-1172
Tel (781) 871-1911 Founded/Ownrshp 1982
Sales 70.0MM EMP 78
SIC 5085

D-U-N-S 12-733-6519
NOBLE SCHOOL DIST 40
111 S 4th St, Noble, OK 73068-9379
Tel (405) 872-3452 Founded/Ownrshp 1912
Sales 19.7MM EMP 340
SIC 8211 School board; School board

NOBLE STREET CHARTER SCHOOL
See NOBLE NETWORK OF CHARTER SCHOOLS

NOBLE SUPPLY AND LOGISTICS
See NOBLE SALES CO INC

D-U-N-S 62-214-1299
NOBLE SYSTEMS CORP
1200 Ashwood Pkwy Ste 300, Atlanta, GA 30338-4747
Tel (404) 851-1331 Founded/Ownrshp 2006
Sales 114.2MM^E EMP 400
SIC 3661 Telephone dialing devices, automatic; Telephone dialing devices, automatic
CEO: James K Noble Jr
*CFO: Martin D Kidder
CFO: Bruce Reese
CFO: Michael Sturdivan
Sr VP: Kevin Ball
Sr VP: Craig Isaacs
Sr VP: Ellwood Neuer
VP: Ruben Maury
VP: Patrick McDaniel
VP: Michaele Rose
Exec: Patrick Taylor
Dir Bus: Steve Spratt

D-U-N-S 07-430-9220
NOBLE WEST SCHOOL BUILDING CORP
WEST NOBLE HIGH SCHOOL
5050 N Us Highway 33, Ligonier, IN 46767-9606
Tel (260) 894-3191 Founded/Ownrshp 1960
Sales 16.9MM^E EMP 373
Accts State Of Indiana Indianapolis
SIC 8211 Public combined elementary & secondary school; Public combined elementary & secondary school
*Treas: Barbara Fought
Cmptr Lab: Amy Groff
Schl Brd P: Geana Leamon
HC Dir: Denise Hershman

D-U-N-S 18-617-5709 IMP
NOBLE WINES LTD
(Suby of WINEBOW GROUP LLC) ★
9860 40th Ave S, Seattle, WA 98118-5603
Tel (206) 326-5274 Founded/Ownrshp 2015
Sales 41.2MM^E EMP 80
SIC 5182 Wine; Wine
Pr: Charles E Marush
VP: Molly Andrews
VP: Greg Nelson
VP: Molly Smith
Exec: Mary Rhodes
Exec: Paul Webster
CIO: Molly A Smith
Sales Exec: Scott Cornelius

NOBLE WORLDWIDE FLA CITRUS SLS
See G ROE WM & SONS INC

D-U-N-S 78-480-7229
NOBLE-AEW COLONY SQUARE LLC
W ATLANTA MIDTOWN HOTEL
188 14th St Ne, Atlanta, GA 30361-2003
Tel (404) 892-6000 *Founded/Ownrshp* 2006
Sales 25.0MM *EMP* 250
SIC 7011 Hotels & motels; Hotels & motels
Exec: Mauro Gomez

D-U-N-S 60-225-3569
■ NOBLE-MET LLC
(*Suby of* ACCELLENT LLC) ★
200 S Yorkshire St, Salem, VA 24153-6902
Tel (540) 389-7860 *Founded/Ownrshp* 2000
Sales 24.0MM^E *EMP* 185
SIC 3317 3671 Steel pipe & tubes; Electron tubes; Steel pipe & tubes; Electron tubes
MIS Mgr: Jeff Bijwaard
Prd Mgr: Jeff Conley

NOBLES
See NOBLE AND GREENOUGH SCHOOL

D-U-N-S 17-323-0426
NOBLESSE OBLIGE INC
EIGHT STAR EQUIPMENT
2015 Silsbee Rd, El Centro, CA 92243-9671
Tel (760) 353-3336 *Founded/Ownrshp* 1985
Sales 21.2MM^E *EMP* 1,200
SIC 0722 Combining services; Cotton, machine harvesting services; Hay, machine harvesting services; Vegetables & melons, machine harvesting services; Combining services; Cotton, machine harvesting services; Hay, machine harvesting services; Vegetables & melons, machine harvesting services
Pr: Alex Abatti Jr
CFO: Tim Castelli
**CFO:* David Wells

D-U-N-S 03-823-9430
NOBLESVILLE SCHOOLS
18025 River Rd Ste 101, Noblesville, IN 46062-8302
Tel (317) 773-3171 *Founded/Ownrshp* 1879
Sales 83.2M *EMP* 703
Accts Shipley & Wall An Association
SIC 8211 Public elementary & secondary schools; Public elementary & secondary schools
Treas: Bethany Robinson
Dir IT: Frances Marcum
Dir IT: Andrew Swickheimer
Pr Dir: Marine Cooke

D-U-N-S 93-290-2364
NOBLIS INC
3150 Fairview Park Dr, Falls Church, VA 22042-4504
Tel (703) 610-2000 *Founded/Ownrshp* 1995
Sales 252.0MM *EMP* 804
Accts Grant Thornton Llp Mclean Vi
SIC 8733 8748 Noncommercial research organizations; Business consulting; Noncommercial research organizations; Business consulting
Pr: AMR A Elsawy
**CFO:* Mark A Simione
Bd of Dir: Jean Cain
VP: Ernie Giuffriday
Prin: Luis Rose
Ex Dir: Alan F Dowling
Ex Dir: Steven Pomerantz
Prgrm Mgr: Walter Berger
Prgrm Mgr: Matt Salter
Snr Sftwr: Mark Korenkiewicz
Snr Ntwrk: Lorena Marsans

D-U-N-S 07-837-7575
NOBLIS NSP LLC
NATIONAL SECURITY PARTNERS LLC
(*Suby of* NOBLIS INC) ★
2721 Tech Dr Ste 400, Annapolis Junction, MD 20701
Tel (410) 934-4900 *Founded/Ownrshp* 2011, 2014
Sales 31.4MM^E *EMP* 90^E
SIC 8742 7379 7374 Business consultant; ; Computer graphics service
Pr: Leslee Belluchie
COO: David J Lee
CFO: David Karish
Ex VP: William Ard
Ex VP: Matthew McKnight
Ex VP: Wajeeha A Naeem

NOBTS
See NEW ORLEANS BAPTIST THEOLOGICAL SEMINARY

D-U-N-S 00-417-3753 IMP
NOCK AND SON CO
27320 W Oviatt Rd, Cleveland, OH 44140-2195
Tel (440) 871-5525 *Founded/Ownrshp* 1961
Sales 37.0MM^E *EMP* 19
SIC 3255 3297 Clay refractories; Nonclay refractories
Pr: Charles J Nock
**Treas:* Michael C Nock
**VP:* Stephen Nock

D-U-N-S 01-329-3519 IMP
NOCO ENERGY CORP (NY)
NOCO LUBRICANTS
(*Suby of* NOCO INC) ★
2440 Sheridan Dr Ste 202, Tonawanda, NY 14150-9493
Tel (716) 614-6626 *Founded/Ownrshp* 1933
Sales 165.5M *EMP* 900
Accts Bonadio & Co Llp Pittsford
SIC 2992 5172 4924 Petroleum products; Lubricating oils & greases; Natural gas distribution; Lubricating oils & greases; Petroleum products; Natural gas distribution
CEO: James D Newma
**CFO:* Michael L Bradley
**Ex VP:* Michael Newman
Exec: Jimmy Lee
Dir Bus: Jim Defilippis
Genl Mgr: Jack Catanzaro
Genl Mgr: Dave Krueger
Dir IT: Jim Cochran
IT Man: Irving Isenberg
IT Man: Jim Korczykowski
IT Man: Todd Robinson

Board of Directors: Robert Spampata

D-U-N-S 83-124-3857
NOCO INC
2440 Sheridan Dr Ste 202, Tonawanda, NY 14150-9416
Tel (716) 833-6626 *Founded/Ownrshp* 1999
Sales 393.0MM^E *EMP* 900
Accts Bonadio & Co Llp Pittsford
SIC 2992 6719 5172 4924 Lubricating oils & greases; Investment holding companies, except banks; Petroleum products; Natural gas distribution; Lubricating oils & greases; Investment holding companies, except banks; Petroleum products; Natural gas distribution
Ch Bd: James D Newman
**Ch Bd:* R J Stapell
**CFO:* Michael L Bradley
**Ex VP:* Michael Newman
Genl Mgr: Laurence Sentiff
Manager: Chuck Rapelje

NOCO LUBRICANTS
See NOCO ENERGY CORP

D-U-N-S 80-675-0449
NOCO NATURAL GAS LLC
2440 Sheridan Dr, Tonawanda, NY 14150-9416
Tel (716) 614-1152 *Founded/Ownrshp* 2006
Sales 104.6MM^E *EMP* 620
SIC 5171 Petroleum bulk stations; Petroleum bulk stations

NOCONA GEN HOSP HM HLTH CARE
See NOCONA GENERAL HOSPITAL

D-U-N-S 07-512-7308
NOCONA GENERAL HOSPITAL
NOCONA GEN HOSP HM HLTH CARE
100 Park Rd, Nocona, TX 76255-3616
Tel (940) 825-3235 *Founded/Ownrshp* 1974
Sales 20.7MM^E *EMP* 125
SIC 8062 8082 General medical & surgical hospitals; Home health care services
Prin: Michale Graham
**CEO:* Lance Meekins
CFO: Lance McCann
Doctor: Danny Samples
Dir Health: Robin Bowles
HC Dir: Bonnie Robertson

NOCROP
See NORTH ORANGE COUNTY REGIONAL OCCUPATIONAL PROGRAM

NOCS TRANSPORT
See NEW ORLEANS COLD STORAGE AND WAREHOUSE CO LTD

D-U-N-S 00-892-6081
NODAK ELECTRIC COOPERATIVE INC
4000 32nd Ave S, Grand Forks, ND 58201-5944
Tel (701) 746-4461 *Founded/Ownrshp* 1939
Sales 94.3MM *EMP* 64
SIC 4911 Distribution, electric power; Distribution, electric power
Pr: George Berg
**Prin:* Mylo Einarson

D-U-N-S 00-699-8017
NODAK MUTUAL INSURANCE CO (ND)
1101 1st Ave N, Fargo, ND 58102-4651
Tel (701) 298-4200 *Founded/Ownrshp* 1946
Sales NA *EMP* 95
SIC 6331 Fire, marine & casualty insurance: mutual; Fire, marine & casualty insurance: mutual
CEO: Michael Alexander
**Pr:* Eric Aasmundstad
**CFO:* Brian Doom

D-U-N-S 83-181-9540
NODAL EXCHANGE LLC
1921 Gallows Rd Ste 300, Vienna, VA 22182-3900
Tel (703) 962-9800 *Founded/Ownrshp* 2007
Sales 23.3MM^E *EMP* 45^E
SIC 4911 Electric services
CEO: Paul Cusenza
Ofcr: Anita Herrera
Sftwr Eng: Xiao Ren
Snr Mgr: Michael Julian

D-U-N-S 00-718-5283
NODAWAY VALLEY BANK
304 N Main St, Maryville, MO 64468-1644
Tel (816) 324-6813 *Founded/Ownrshp* 1868
Sales NA *EMP* 160
SIC 6022 State commercial banks; State commercial banks
Ch Bd: Theodore Robinson
Ex VP: David Lewis
**Sr VP:* Cheryl Bilby
Sr VP: Cheryl Hale
Sr VP: Bob Hall
Sr VP: Jerry Ingle
Sr VP: Randy Luke
VP: Ben Byrd
VP: Beth Jameson
VP: Judy Rogers
VP: Donna Wilmes

D-U-N-S 18-542-5022
NOEL CO INC
5214 2nd St Nw, Albuquerque, NM 87107-4010
Tel (505) 344-2226 *Founded/Ownrshp* 1987
Sales 32.2MM^E *EMP* 200
SIC 1611 1521 1542 Concrete construction: roads, highways, sidewalks, etc.; New construction, single-family houses; Commercial & office building, new construction; Concrete construction: roads, highways, sidewalks, etc.; New construction, single-family houses; Commercial & office building, new construction
Pr: Phil B Noel
**VP:* Randall Voff
**VP:* Randall Voss

D-U-N-S 04-302-5212
NOEL CORP
PEPSICO
1001 S 1st St, Yakima, WA 98901-3403
Tel (509) 248-4545 *Founded/Ownrshp* 1956
Sales 107.3MM^E *EMP* 255
SIC 2086 7389 4212 6512 4225 5962 Soft drinks: packaged in cans, bottles, etc.; Interior designer; Local trucking, without storage; Nonresidential building operators; General warehousing & storage; Merchandising machine operators; Soft drinks: packaged in cans, bottles, etc.; Interior designer; Local trucking, without storage; Nonresidential building operators; General warehousing & storage; Merchandising machine operators
Pr: Roger Noel
**Treas:* Cindy Zimmerman
**VP:* Justin Noel
Exec: Tamara Kline
Plnt Mgr: Sam Brackney
Sls&Mrk Ex: Mike Sutton

D-U-N-S 05-799-0017
NOEL GROUP LLC
501 Nmc Dr, Zebulon, NC 27597-2762
Tel (919) 269-6500 *Founded/Ownrshp* 1996
Sales 88.9MM^E *EMP* 442
SIC 3086 Plastics foam products; Plastics foam products

D-U-N-S 19-288-1337
NOEL GROUP LLC
1145 Clark St, Stevens Point, WI 54481-2933
Tel (608) 294-9400 *Founded/Ownrshp* 2002
Sales NA *EMP* 73
SIC 6351 Surety insurance
CFO: John Cowden
Sr VP: James Flavell
VP: Josh Jandrain
Software D: Joshua Werra
Sftwr Eng: Corey Kruzicki

D-U-N-S 04-781-2560
NOETIX CORP
(*Suby of* MAGNITUDE SOFTWARE INC) ★
5010 148th Ave Ne Ste 100, Redmond, WA 98052-5127
Tel (425) 372-2699 *Founded/Ownrshp* 2013
Sales 36.9MM^E *EMP* 116
SIC 7371 5734 Computer software development; Computer software & accessories; Computer software development; Computer software & accessories
Pr: Doug Moore
Mng Pt: Jon Flint
**Pr:* Morris Beton
**COO:* Cris Ney
**Ex VP:* Pat Roche
VP: Jan Gomez
Snr Sftwr: Alex Chin
Snr Sftwr: Mohan Nalam
IT Man: Helene Hall
IT Man: Sally Hicks
IT Man: Richard Singer

D-U-N-S 19-732-9931 IMP
NOF AMERICA CORP
(*Suby of* NOF CORPORATION)
1 N Broadway Ste 912, White Plains, NY 10601-2322
Tel (914) 681-9790 *Founded/Ownrshp* 1989
Sales 45.0MM *EMP* 14
SIC 5169 Industrial chemicals
Pr: Toru Tsujimoto
**Ch Bd:* Norihiro Kaiya
Mng Dir: Motohiro Mitani

D-U-N-S 13-046-9406 IMP
NOF METAL COATINGS NORTH AMERICA INC
275 Industrial Pkwy, Chardon, OH 44024-1052
Tel (440) 285-2231 *Founded/Ownrshp* 2011
Sales 36.1MM^E *EMP* 54
SIC 2899 Chemical preparations; Chemical preparations
CFO: Norman Gertz
**Pr:* Shin Masuda
VP: Frederic Gheno
VP: Adam Stals
Genl Mgr: John Dutton
Opers Mgr: David Katila
Sls Dir: Jose Guzman
Mktg Mgr: Lori Kumsman

D-U-N-S 00-707-5179 IMP
NOFFSINGER MANUFACTURING CO INC
500 6th Ave, Greeley, CO 80631-2419
Tel (970) 352-0463 *Founded/Ownrshp* 1924
Sales 28.2MM^E *EMP* 128
SIC 3523 0212 0115 0119 3312 2296 Soil sampling machines; Tractors, farm; Trailers & wagons, farm; Windmills for pumping water, agricultural; Beef cattle except feedlots; Corn; Bean (dry field & seed) farm; Blast furnaces & steel mills; Tire cord & fabrics; Soil sampling machines; Tractors, farm; Trailers & wagons, farm; Windmills for pumping water, agricultural; Beef cattle except feedlots; Corn; Bean (dry field & seed) farm; Blast furnaces & steel mills; Tire cord & fabrics
Pr: Robert W Noffsinger Jr
**VP:* Jacky Lynn Miller
**VP:* James L Noffsinger
**Genl Mgr:* Matt Napier

D-U-N-S 04-524-6535
NOFZIGER DOOR SALES INC
HAAS DOORS
320 Sycamore St, Wauseon, OH 43567-1100
Tel (419) 337-9900 *Founded/Ownrshp* 1971
Sales 29.6MM^E *EMP* 198
SIC 3442 5211 1751 Metal doors; Garage doors, overhead: metal; Garage door, installation or erection; Doors, wood or metal, except storm; Metal doors; Garage doors, overhead: metal; Doors, wood or metal, except storm; Garage door, installation or erection
Pr: Edward L Nofziger
**Sec:* Carol Nofziger
VP: Dawn Haas

D-U-N-S 14-508-9939
NOG INC
3240 E Van Norman Ave, Cudahy, WI 53110-1048
Tel (414) 294-3000 *Founded/Ownrshp* 1999
Sales 22.9MM^E *EMP* 125
SIC 3462 3494 Iron & steel forgings; Valves & pipe fittings; Iron & steel forgings; Valves & pipe fittings
CEO: James Mitchell
Dir IT: Paul Pingel

D-U-N-S 80-865-2239
NOGALES INVESTORS MANAGEMENT LLC
9229 W Sunset Blvd # 900, Los Angeles, CA 90069-3410
Tel (310) 276-7439 *Founded/Ownrshp* 2001
Sales 25.9MM^E *EMP* 300^E
SIC 6722 Management investment, open-end; Management investment, open-end

D-U-N-S 62-129-4412 IMP
NOGALES PRODUCE INC
8220 Forney Rd, Dallas, TX 75227-4212
Tel (214) 275-3500 *Founded/Ownrshp* 1990
Sales 84.8MM^E *EMP* 240
SIC 5148

D-U-N-S 10-000-1759
NOGALES UNIFIED SCHOOL DISTRICT 1
310 W Plum St, Nogales, AZ 85621-2613
Tel (520) 287-0800 *Founded/Ownrshp* 1912
Sales 31.3MM^E *EMP* 630
SIC 8211 Public elementary & secondary schools; School board; Public elementary & secondary schools; School board
HC Dir: Judith Jimenenz

D-U-N-S 09-003-4091
NOGAMA CONSTRUCTION CORP
8 Calle 1 Metro Office St, Guaynabo, PR 00968
Tel (787) 273-7633 *Founded/Ownrshp* 1948
Sales 27.9MM *EMP* 175
SIC 1623 1542 Water, sewer & utility lines; Commercial & office building, new construction; Water, sewer & utility lines; Commercial & office building, new construction
Ch Bd: Luis M Nolla
**Pr:* Jose Gonzalez Nolla
**Treas:* Warren Gonzalez
**VP:* Jose Nolla Vila

D-U-N-S 07-854-0854
NOKIA INC
(*Suby of* NOKIA OYJ)
6363 N State Highway 161 # 800, Irving, TX 75038-2262
Tel (214) 496-0329 *Founded/Ownrshp* 2012
Sales 100.0MM^E *EMP* 179^E
SIC 3663

D-U-N-S 10-664-8322 IMP
NOKIA INC
200 S Mathilda Ave, Sunnyvale, CA 94086-6135
Tel (408) 530-7600 *Founded/Ownrshp* 1992
Sales NA *EMP* 2,500
SIC 3663 5065 3661 3577 Cellular radio telephone; Television broadcasting & communications equipment; Mobile telephone equipment; Telephone & telegraph apparatus; Computer peripheral equipment

D-U-N-S 61-163-9035
NOKIA LOCATION & COMMERCE
(*Suby of* HERE HOLDING CORP) ★
425 W Randolph St, Chicago, IL 60606-1530
Tel (312) 894-7000 *Founded/Ownrshp* 2005
Sales 58.3MM^E *EMP* 900^E
SIC 7371 Custom computer programming services; Custom computer programming services
Prin: Bob Burns
Snr Sftwr: Narayanan Alwar
Web Dev: Ivan Lalic
Web Dev: Susan Stephens
Secur Mgr: Jeffrey L Mize

D-U-N-S 79-406-4571 IMP
NOKIA SOLUTIONS AND NETWORKS US LLC
(*Suby of* NOKIA SOLUTIONS AND NETWORKS BRANCH OPERATIONS OY)
6000 Connection Dr, Irving, TX 75039-2600
Tel (972) 374-3000 *Founded/Ownrshp* 2008
Sales 1.2MMM^E *EMP* 4,000
SIC 3663 5999 4813 Telephone communication, except radio; Radio broadcasting & communications equipment; Telephone & communication equipment; Radio broadcasting & communications equipment; Telephone & communication equipment; Telephone communication, except radio
COO: Samih Elhage
CFO: Natalie Koopman
Sr Cor Off: Bodhisattwa Gangopadhyay
Comm Dir: Sangita Sanju
Dir Bus: Senthil Sengodan
Div Mgr: WEI Xiong
CIO: Nivedita Sethupathy
IT Man: Asa Kadane
Sftwr Eng: Brian Zulawinski
VP Sls: Reggie Perry
Mktg Mgr: Paul Norkus

D-U-N-S 02-347-0896
NOKIAN TYRES INC
(*Suby of* NOKIAN RENKAAT OYJ)
1945 Main St, Colchester, VT 05446-7652
Tel (802) 655-8030 *Founded/Ownrshp* 1997
Sales 126.8MM^E *EMP* 120
SIC 5014 Tires & tubes; Tires & tubes
Pr: Bernie Del Duca
**Pr:* Bernie Delduca
VP: Bob Hepp
VP: Sirkka Thangavelu

D-U-N-S 11-287-2411
NOL-TEC SYSTEMS INC
(*Suby of* KC GREEN HOLDINGS CO., LTD.)
425 Apollo Dr, Lino Lakes, MN 55014-1093
Tel (651) 780-8600 *Founded/Ownrshp* 2010

Sales 26.4MM[E] *EMP* 70
SIC 3535 8711 Conveyors & conveying equipment; Designing: ship, boat, machine & product; Conveyors & conveying equipment; Designing: ship, boat, machine & product
CEO: Wayne Johnson
**Pr:* Vernon Hudalla
**VP:* Dean Kriskovich
**VP:* Roger Schmitz
VP Sls: Erik Johnson
Manager: Jerry Vanderwerff
Sls Mgr: Michael Thiel
Sls Mgr: Mike Weyandt

D-U-N-S 78-945-1114
NOLAN ASSOCIATES LLC
BOSTON HARBOR CRUISES
1 Long Wharf, Boston, MA 02110-3602
Tel (617) 720-9200 *Founded/Ownrshp* 2006
Sales 26.8MM[E] *EMP* 150
SIC 4489 Sightseeing boats; Sightseeing boats
IT Man: Juanaita Richardson

D-U-N-S 07-318-1588
NOLAN COUNTY HOSPITAL DISTRICT
ROLLING PLAINS MEMORIAL HOSPIT
200 E Arizona Ave, Sweetwater, TX 79556-7120
Tel (325) 235-2030 *Founded/Ownrshp* 1935
Sales 20.9MM *EMP* 300
Accts Durbin & Company Llp Lubb
SIC 8062 General medical & surgical hospitals; General medical & surgical hospitals
CEO: Don Boatright
**CFO:* Rhonda Guelker
Dir OR: Bonnie Garcia
Dir Lab: Walter Best
Dir Rx: Lynn Staggs
**Chf Nrs Of:* Rosa Best
Surgeon: Mark Seibel
Obsttrcn: Saundra Lane
Snr Mgr: Judy Clayton

D-U-N-S 79-534-6212
NOLAN INSURANCE CORP
INSURANCE OUTLET
903 E Chestnut St, Louisville, KY 40204-1016
Tel (502) 589-4746 *Founded/Ownrshp* 1970
Sales NA *EMP* 10
SIC 6411 6331 Insurance agents, brokers & service; Automobile insurance; Insurance agents, brokers & service; Automobile insurance
CEO: Thomas Nolan

D-U-N-S 09-963-9171 IMP/EXP
NOLAN POWER GROUP LLC
21448 Marion Ln, Mandeville, LA 70471-7756
Tel (985) 801-5000 *Founded/Ownrshp* 2001
Sales 25.3MM[E] *EMP* 55
SIC 5063 7699

D-U-N-S 03-070-6519
NOLAN REAL ESTATE SERVICES INC
2020 W 89th St Ste 320, Leawood, KS 66206-1961
Tel (816) 753-8380 *Founded/Ownrshp* 1974
Sales 25.9MM[E] *EMP* 250
SIC 6531 Real estate managers; Real estate managers
CEO: Ronald C Nolan
**Owner:* Ron Nolan
**Pt:* Paul Fingersh
**Pr:* Kyle Scott
**CFO:* Lynn Wright
**VP:* Cheryl Ducote
**VP:* Kelly Kinnaman
**VP:* Susan Pohl
Rgnl Mgr: Bill Burk
Rgnl Mgr: Missy Singer
Sales Asso: Lauren Turner

D-U-N-S 60-690-7603
NOLAN TRANSPORTATION GROUP INC
N T G
85 Mill St Ste 214, Roswell, GA 30075-4955
Tel (770) 509-9611 *Founded/Ownrshp* 2005
Sales 114.9MM *EMP* 135
SIC 4731 Freight transportation arrangement; Freight transportation arrangement
CEO: Kevin Nolan
**COO:* Blake Malone
**CFO:* Fritz Owens
**Sr VP:* Harold Baron
Manager: Hamilton Schuler

D-U-N-S 00-794-0604 IMP/EXP
NOLAND CO (VA)
GREENVILLE NOLAND
(*Suby of* WINSUPPLY INC) ★
3110 Kettering Blvd, Moraine, OH 45439-1924
Tel (937) 396-7980 *Founded/Ownrshp* 1915, 2005
Sales 216.4MM[E] *EMP* 600
SIC 5074 5075 5063 5085 Plumbing & hydronic heating supplies; Air conditioning equipment, except room units; Electrical supplies; Industrial supplies; Plumbing & hydronic heating supplies; Air conditioning equipment, except room units; Electrical supplies; Industrial supplies
Pr: Arjay Hoggard
**COO:* James H Adcox
COO: John W Simmons
**Treas:* David E Metzger
Treas: James E Sykes
VP: Ron K Binger
VP: Paul H Donarum
VP: Steven B Edwards
VP: Roger E Gibbs
VP: Robert C Guiney
VP: Arthur P Henderson
**VP:* Jack W Johnston
**VP:* Monte L Salsman
VP: Aaron Stanley

NOLAND FACILITIES SERVICES
See NOLAND SALES INDUSTRIES INC

D-U-N-S 19-820-5622
NOLAND HEALTH SERVICES INC
600 Corporate Pkwy # 100, Birmingham, AL 35242-5451
Tel (205) 321-5373 *Founded/Ownrshp* 2001
Sales 130.8MM *EMP* 1,100[E]
Accts Warren Averett Llc Birmingham
SIC 8051 Skilled nursing care facilities; Skilled nursing care facilities
Pr: Gary M Glasscock
**Ch:* Leon C Hamrick Sr
**Ex VP:* R Gary Goff
VP: John Heffner
VP: Pam Nichols
Dir Rx: John Barnwell
CIO: Joey Sestili
Sys Mgr: Jason Rosolowski
Nutrtnst: Christina Turner
Nrsg Dir: Janet Langford

D-U-N-S 01-060-0427 IMP
NOLAND SALES CORP
815 Mittel Dr, Wood Dale, IL 60191-1118
Tel (630) 787-9500 *Founded/Ownrshp* 1975
Sales 21.8MM[E] *EMP* 75[E]
Accts Cray Kaiser Ltd Oakbrook Ter
SIC 5713 Floor covering stores
Pr: Jeffrey D Chassee
**VP:* Brian H Butler
**VP:* Michael J Ryan
Sls Dir: Tom Lober

D-U-N-S 62-279-6373
NOLAND SALES INDUSTRIES INC
NOLAND FACILITIES SERVICES
(*Suby of* NOLAND SALES CORP) ★
815 Mittel Dr, Wood Dale, IL 60191-1118
Tel (630) 787-9500 *Founded/Ownrshp* 1990
Sales 20.0MM[E] *EMP* 69
SIC 5023 Resilient floor coverings: tile or sheet; Resilient floor coverings: tile or sheet
Pr: Jeffrey Chassee
**VP:* Brian H Butler
**VP:* Donna McCaleb
**VP:* Michael J Ryan

D-U-N-S 62-531-2012 IMP
NOLATO CONTOUR INC
(*Suby of* NOLATO AB)
660 Vandeberg St, Baldwin, WI 54002-3251
Tel (715) 684-4614 *Founded/Ownrshp* 2010
Sales 54.6MM[E] *EMP* 180
SIC 3089 Injection molding of plastics; Injection molding of plastics
Pr: Barry Grant
VP: Monica Adams
VP: Gus Myran
Exec: Johan Arvidsson
Dir Bus: Mattias Persson
Ex Dir: Christer Wahlquist
Prgrm Mgr: Gary Freiberg
Prgrm Mgr: Paul Weidling
Sls Mgr: Steve Roth

NOLI INDIAN SCHOOL
See SOBOBA BAND OF LUISENO INDIANS

D-U-N-S 08-939-4006
■ NOLIJ CORP
(*Suby of* LEXMARK ENTERPRISE SOFTWARE LLC) ★
138 Conant St Ste 6, Beverly, MA 01915-1666
Tel (888) 818-6654 *Founded/Ownrshp* 2012
Sales 24.8MM[E] *EMP* 426[E]
SIC 7373 Systems software development services
Pr: Scott Coons
**CFO:* John Dording
VP: Gern Carl
**VP:* John J Collins
**VP:* Jay Lacroix
**VP:* Maureen McCarthy
**VP:* Ron Wellman
**Prin:* Jack Collins
Snr Sftwr: Jeff Seaman

NOLIN RECC
See NOLIN RURAL ELECTRIC COOPERATIVE CORP

D-U-N-S 00-799-1987
NOLIN RURAL ELECTRIC COOPERATIVE CORP (KY)
NOLIN RECC
411 Ring Rd, Elizabethtown, KY 42701-8701
Tel (270) 765-6153 *Founded/Ownrshp* 1938
Sales 87.3MM *EMP* 97[E]
Accts Alan Zumst Lexington Ky
SIC 4911 Distribution, electric power; Distribution, electric power
Pr: Michael L Miller
Bd of Dir: Gene Straney
Bd of Dir: Robert Wade
**VP:* O Sparks
Exec: Dawna Dalton
IT Man: Gregory Harrington
IT Man: Mechonda O'Brien
Mktg Dir: Billy Pait
Pgrm Dir: Michelle Rogers

D-U-N-S 79-695-5370
■ NOLL/NORWESCO LLC
(*Suby of* GIBRALTAR INDUSTRIES INC) ★
1320 Performance Dr, Stockton, CA 95206-4925
Tel (209) 234-1600 *Founded/Ownrshp* 2007
Sales 24.1MM[E] *EMP* 130
SIC 3444 Sheet metalwork; Sheet metalwork
Plnt Mgr: Ralph Fruguglietti

NOLS
See NATIONAL OUTDOOR LEADERSHIP SCHOOL

NOLTE ASSOCIATES, INC.
See NV5 INC

D-U-N-S 09-522-5983 EXP
NOMACO INC
(*Suby of* NOEL GROUP LLC) ★
501 Nmc Dr, Zebulon, NC 27597-2762
Tel (919) 269-6500 *Founded/Ownrshp* 2008
Sales 70.3MM[E] *EMP* 408
SIC 3089 Extruded finished plastic products; Extruded finished plastic products
CFO: Steven Thompson
CFO: Vince Clark
VP: Ed Lauer
VP: James Teagle
VP: Christophe Theunissen
Brnch Mgr: Nadav Sharir
QA Dir: Greg Merrill
Opers Mgr: Steve Dixon
Opers Mgr: Chuck Marckwardt
Opers Mgr: Joann Tanner
Opers Mgr: Dona Updegraff

D-U-N-S 80-982-1510
NOMACO INSULATION INC
(*Suby of* NOMACO INC) ★
3006 Anaconda Rd, Tarboro, NC 27886-8836
Tel (866) 876-2684 *Founded/Ownrshp* 2003
Sales 36.3MM[E] *EMP* 1[E]
SIC 3086 Plastics foam products
CEO: Mick Dannin
**Pr:* Scott Edwards
Tech Mgr: Antonio CUNA
Opers Mgr: Mike Sellers
Opers Mgr: Douglas Stolpe
Sales Asso: Lisa Groover

D-U-N-S 00-693-5345 IMP/EXP
NOMACORC LLC (NC)
400 Vintage Park Dr, Zebulon, NC 27597-3803
Tel (919) 269-0190 *Founded/Ownrshp* 1998
Sales 126.4MM[E] *EMP* 400
SIC 3089 Caps, plastic; Caps, plastic
VP: Malcolm Thompson
Genl Mgr: Eric Dunkelberg
Cmptr Lab: Sallie Grimes
Mfg Mgr: Christopher Reinhardt
Prd Mgr: Don Ellis
Prd Mgr: Todd Lee
Ql Cn Mgr: Alton Nowell
Ql Cn Mgr: Christophe Robert
Mktg Dir: Jeff Slater
Sls Mgr: Mark Coleman
Board of Directors: Jason Glass, Kevin Mohan, Mark Noel

D-U-N-S 02-509-5774
NOMI CORP
2 Sun Ct Ste 400, Norcross, GA 30092-2865
Tel (770) 447-0911 *Founded/Ownrshp* 2000
Sales 39.6MM[E] *EMP* 120[E]
SIC 7371 Computer software development
CEO: Stephen P Jeffery
Pr: Ralph Crabtree
**CFO:* Jeff Babka
**CFO:* John E Kahn
CFO: Paul Williams
VP: Kevin Ashworth
**VP:* Iain Currie
**VP:* Steven M Hornyak
Dir Bus: Lori Mabunga
Opers Mgr: Lee Rainwater
Mktg Dir: David Rubini

D-U-N-S 13-658-1852
NOMINUM INC
800 Bridge Pkwy 100, Redwood City, CA 94065-1156
Tel (650) 381-6000 *Founded/Ownrshp* 1999
Sales 59.8MM[E] *EMP* 126
SIC 7371 Computer software development; Computer software development
CEO: Garry Messiana
**Ch Bd:* Paul Mockapetris
COO: Gopala Tumuluri
**CFO:* Kenton Chow
**CFO:* Bob Verheecke
CFO: Robert Verheecke
**Ex VP:* Pete Wisowaty
**Sr VP:* Srini Avirneni
VP: Bob Beaulieu
VP: Daniel Blasingame
VP: Brian McElroy
**VP:* Vivian Neou
VP: Simon Rowell
VP: Geoffrey Stilley
VP: Tom Tovar
**VP:* Sandy Wilbourn
Exec: Venkata West
Dir Surg: Alan Slater
Dir Bus: Jill Walton
Board of Directors: David Cowan, Gary Morgenthaler, Chris Risley

D-U-N-S 61-293-6385
NOMURA HOLDING AMERICA INC
(*Suby of* NOMURA HOLDINGS, INC.)
309 W 49th St, New York, NY 10019-9102
Tel (212) 667-9300 *Founded/Ownrshp* 1989
Sales 541.2MM[E] *EMP* 1,600
SIC 6211 Dealers, security; Dealers, security
Ch Bd: David Findlay
**CEO:* Hideyuki Takahashi
CFO: Jonathan Lewis
**Treas:* Ray Carli
Sr VP: Kenneth Munt
VP: Deepesh Bhandari
VP: Michael Bohan
VP: Noel Carrero
VP: Raja Chris
VP: Richard Daquesian
VP: Michael Kirshenbaum
VP: Frances Llano
VP: Elizabeth Nicklas
VP: Igor Reznikovsky
VP: Ryan Scaffe
Comm Dir: Thomas Salatte

D-U-N-S 07-985-0807
NOMURA RESEARCH INSTITUTE HOLDINGS AMERICA INC
(*Suby of* NOMURA RESEARCH INSTITUTE, LTD.)
810 7th Ave Ste 1100c, New York, NY 10019-7597
Tel (212) 636-0500 *Founded/Ownrshp* 2014
Sales 23.4MM[E] *EMP* 250[E]
SIC 6719 Investment holding companies, except banks
Pr: Satoru Nakagawa

D-U-N-S 04-361-3520
NOMURA SECURITIES INTERNATIONAL INC
(*Suby of* NOMURA HOLDING AMERICA INC) ★
Worldwide Plaza 309 W 49t, New York, NY 10019
Tel (212) 667-9000 *Founded/Ownrshp* 1989
Sales 501.9MM[E] *EMP* 1,581
SIC 6211 Dealers, security; Dealers, security
Ch Bd: Hideyuki Takahashi
**Ch Bd:* David Findlay
Pr: Maryana Kushnir
**Pr:* Joseph R Schmuckler
**CFO:* Larry Wagner
Chf Mktg O: Jonathan Hodgkinson
VP: Christopher Becker
VP: George Chernenko
VP: John McCallum
VP: Anurag Poddar
VP: Carlos Rosso
VP: Judy Wong

D-U-N-S 60-245-6738 IMP/EXP
NOMURA TRADING CO LTD
(*Suby of* NOMURA TRADING CO.,LTD.)
10940 Ne 33rd Pl Ste 111, Bellevue, WA 98004-1432
Tel (425) 284-3338 *Founded/Ownrshp* 2002
Sales 60.0MM *EMP* 5
SIC 5147 Meats & meat products; Meats & meat products
Pr: Katsushige Miyashita
Genl Mgr: Kapsumi Osawa
Genl Mgr: Makoto Takahashi
Sls Mgr: Jason Kumai

NON PROFIT CENTER, THE
See THIRD SECTOR NEW ENGLAND INC

NON PROFIT ECONOMIC DEVELOPMEN
See UNIVERSITY CITY SCIENCE CENTER

D-U-N-S 05-625-1168
NON PUBLIC EDUCATIONAL SERVICES INC
NESI
3460 Comm Ct Ste 200, Woodbridge, VA 22192
Tel (703) 494-7882 *Founded/Ownrshp* 1978
Sales 15.6MM[E] *EMP* 600
SIC 8211 8299 Secondary school; Educational services; Secondary school; Educational services
Pr: Robert H Crosby
**CFO:* David Morrissette
**Sr VP:* Rochelle Schneickert
**VP:* Donna Eldridge
VP: Donald M Geraghty
**VP:* Edla Hodgeson
**VP:* Dr Kenneth Underwood

NON-DESTRUCTIVE TESTING SVCS
See TUV RHEINLAND INDUSTRIAL SOLUTIONS INC

D-U-N-S 84-126-9199
NON-INTRUSIVE INSPECTION TECHNOLOGY INC
NIITEK
(*Suby of* CHG GROUP INC) ★
23031 Ladbrook Dr Ste 100, Dulles, VA 20166-2067
Tel (703) 661-0283 *Founded/Ownrshp* 2008
Sales 21.1MM[E] *EMP* 91
SIC 3812 Infrared object detection equipment; Infrared object detection equipment
Pr: Thomas H Thebes Jr
Pr: Terrence Marsh
**CFO:* Joshua Golden
CFO: Thomas Thebes
VP: John Domitrovits
VP: Yang Lin
Snr Sftwr: Roderick Simons
CTO: Mark Hibbard
CTO: Jeff Okamitsu
Sftwr Eng: Shaun Grant
Sftwr Eng: John McLaughlin

NONDESTRUCTIVE & VISUAL INSPTN
See NVI LLC

NONE
See PLYMOUTH TUBE CO

NONE
See BLEVINS INC

D-U-N-S 12-720-2187 IMP/EXP
NONGSHIM AMERICA INC
(*Suby of* NONGSHIM CO., LTD.)
12155 6th St, Rancho Cucamonga, CA 91730-6115
Tel (909) 481-3698 *Founded/Ownrshp* 1994
Sales 245.4MM[E] *EMP* 300
SIC 5141 2098 Groceries, general line; Noodles (e.g. egg, plain & water), dry; Groceries, general line; Noodles (e.g. egg, plain & water), dry
CEO: Dong Y Shin
**Prin:* Chris Gepford
Genl Mgr: Krith Roth
IT Man: John Seo
Prd Mgr: Martin Lizarraga
Ql Cn Mgr: Abel Escalante
Sls Mgr: Daniel Morales

D-U-N-S 60-992-7905 EXP
NONI TAHITIAN INTERNATIONAL INC
333 River Park Dr, Provo, UT 84604-5787
Tel (801) 234-1000 *Founded/Ownrshp* 2003
Sales 48.4MM[E] *EMP* 200
SIC 5149 Diet foods; Health foods; Diet foods; Health foods
CEO: Kerry Asay
CFO: Randy Smith
VP: Stephen Story
Mng Dir: Brandon Groves
Mng Dir: Howard Silverman
Rgnl Mgr: Shane Greer
Genl Mgr: Diane Nelson
Dir IT: Jon Williams
Web Dev: Trent Pehrson
VP Opers: Charlie Smith
Mktg Mgr: Laura Kimball

D-U-N-S 17-495-9692 IMP
NONIN MEDICAL INC
13700 1st Ave N, Plymouth, MN 55441-4594
Tel (763) 476-5083 *Founded/Ownrshp* 1986
Sales 47.9MM[E] *EMP* 180
SIC 3841 3845 Surgical & medical instruments; Electromedical equipment; Surgical & medical instruments; Electromedical equipment
CEO: Philip Isaacson
Pr: Chris Holland

*COO: Steve Bucholz
*Ofcr: Christopher Holland
Ex VP: Greg Marx
VP: Jim Russell
VP: Mark Vanderwerf
Exec: Lydia Denogean
Prgrm Mgr: Hugh Ferguson
Snr Sftwr: Doug Ehrreich
Snr Sftwr: Dirk Helgemo

D-U-N-S 13-019-2776
NONNS FLOORING INC
MIRAGE IMPORT
7550 Graber Rd, Middleton, WI 53562-1002
Tel (608) 824-1017 Founded/Ownrshp 1985
Sales 44.4MM^E EMP 150
SIC 1752 5713 5023 Floor laying & floor work; Carpets; Floor tile; Linoleum; Floor coverings; Floor laying & floor work; Carpets; Floor tile; Linoleum; Floor coverings
Pr: Ken Nonn
*Pr: Adam Nonn
*Treas: Alan Breunig
*VP: Steve Ballweg
*VP: Jeff Nehmer

D-U-N-S 13-937-7436
NONOTUCK RESOURCE ASSOCIATES INC
425 Prospect St, Northampton, MA 01060-2046
Tel (413) 586-5256 Founded/Ownrshp 1972
Sales 21.4MM EMP 100
SIC 8361 Home for the mentally retarded
Pgrm Dir: Denise Dumais
Pgrm Dir: Jill Gallagher

D-U-N-S 06-797-6340
NONPAREIL CORP (ID)
40 N 400 W, Blackfoot, ID 83221-5632
Tel (208) 785-5880 Founded/Ownrshp 1945
Sales 103.9MM^E EMP 485^E
SIC 2099 Packaged combination products: pasta, rice & potato; Packaged combination products: pasta, rice & potato
Pr: Chris Abend
*CFO: John Fullmer
*Sec: Tracy Fullmer
*VP: Walter Gay
*VP: Howard Phillips
VP: Charles H Ulrich
Opers Mgr: Patti Callison
Trfc Mgr: Rulon Robinson
S&M/VP: Scott Phillips
Snr Mgr: Fran Taylor

D-U-N-S 14-785-1935
NONPROFIT FINANCE FUND
70 W 36th St Fl 11, New York, NY 10018-1249
Tel (212) 868-6710 Founded/Ownrshp 1984
Sales 35.1MM EMP 76^E
SIC 8399 Community development groups; Community development groups
CEO: Janet Thompson
*Ch Bd: Elizabeth Sullivan
*COO: Elizabeth Ortiz
*CFO: Bruce Skyer
VP: Rodney Christopher
VP: Anne Dyjak
VP: Kristin Giantris
VP: David Greco
VP: Jennifer Talansky
Assoc Dir: Emily Guthman
Ex Dir: William Pinakiewicz

D-U-N-S 61-814-2889
■ **NONPROFIT HOSPITAL CORP**
(Suby of TENET HEALTHCARE CORPORATION)
7 Medical Pkwy, Dallas, TX 75234-7829
Tel (972) 247-1000 Founded/Ownrshp 2001
Sales 8.2MM^E EMP 475
SIC 8062 General medical & surgical hospitals; General medical & surgical hospitals
CEO: Joe D Thomason

D-U-N-S 62-351-6770
NONPROFITS INSURANCE ALLIANCE OF CALIFORNIA
333 Front St Ste 200, Santa Cruz, CA 95060-4533
Tel (831) 459-0980 Founded/Ownrshp 1988
Sales NA EMP 45
Accts Johnson Lambert & Co Llp Rale
SIC 6351 Liability insurance; Liability insurance
Pr: Pamela E Davis
Board of Directors: Audrey Alvarado, R Lawrence Bacon, John Christenson, Meredith Clark

D-U-N-S 19-569-3333 IMP
NOODLE WORLD INC
3024 N Powers Dr Apt 96, Orlando, FL 32818-3273
Tel (877) 815-9081 Founded/Ownrshp 2005
Sales 35.4MM EMP 8
SIC 2098 Noodles (e.g. egg, plain & water), dry; Noodles (e.g. egg, plain & water), dry
Pr: Viroon Charoenmitr

NOODLES & COMPANY
See PER PASTATRIO INC

D-U-N-S 95-621-2542
▲ **NOODLES & CO**
520 Zang St Ste D, Broomfield, CO 80021-8239
Tel (720) 214-1900 Founded/Ownrshp 1995
Sales 403.7MM EMP 9,500
Tkr Sym NDLS Exch NGS
SIC 5812 Eating places; Eating places
Ch Bd: Kevin Reddy
COO: Keith Kinsey
*CFO: Dave Boennighausen
Ofcr: Dawn Voss
Ex VP: Jason Gallelli
Ex VP: Mark Mears
Ex VP: Mark A Mears
Ex VP: Phil Petrilli
Ex VP: Paul Strasen
VP: Gia Borado
VP: Jeff Harrison
VP: David Lane
VP: David Lehn
VP: Kathy Lockhart
VP: Bill Long
VP: Alison Meadows
VP: Tim Mosbacher
VP: Michael Ulm
Exec: Kara Mann
Exec: Mary Orlando
Board of Directors: Scott Dahnke, Stuart Frenkiel, Jeffrey Jones, Johanna Murphy, James Rand, Andrew Taub

D-U-N-S 03-720-2772 IMP/EXP
■ **NOOK DIGITAL LLC**
BARNES & NOBLE
(Suby of BARNES & NOBLE INC) ★
1166 Ave Of The Americas, New York, NY 10036-2708
Tel (212) 414-6000 Founded/Ownrshp 2003
Sales 52.9MM^E EMP 500
SIC 5942 5932 5735 Book stores; Book stores, secondhand; Record & prerecorded tape stores; Records, audio discs & tapes; Book stores; Book stores, secondhand; Record & prerecorded tape stores; Records, audio discs & tapes
Ex VP: Tom Burke
*CFO: Kevin M Frain
*V Ch Bd: Stephen Riggio
*Chf Mktg O: David Gitow
VP: John Kristie
Dist Mgr: Joe Labedz
Dist Mgr: Leslie Poitier
Dist Mgr: Colette Stewart
Dist Mgr: Rodney Toft
Off Mgr: Bryan Stewart
QA Dir: Antonio Burgos

D-U-N-S 05-726-0721 IMP
NOOK INDUSTRIES INC
4950 E 49th St, Cleveland, OH 44125-1016
Tel (216) 271-7900 Founded/Ownrshp 1969
Sales 38.6MM^E EMP 160^E
SIC 3451 3699 3593 3568 3545 Screw machine products; Electrical equipment & supplies; Fluid power cylinders & actuators; Power transmission equipment; Machine tool accessories; Screw machine products; Electrical equipment & supplies; Fluid power cylinders & actuators; Power transmission equipment; Machine tool accessories
Ch: Joseph H Nook Jr
*Pr: Ronald Domeck
*CEO: Chirstopher Nook
*COO: Joseph H Nook III
VP: Mike Cook
Genl Mgr: James Ellacott

D-U-N-S 80-627-0000
NOOKSACK BUSINESS CORP
NOOKSACK RIVER CASINO
(Suby of NOOKSACK BUSINESS CORP 1) ★
5048 Mt Baker Hwy, Deming, WA 98244
Tel (360) 592-5864 Founded/Ownrshp 2007
Sales 6.5MM^E EMP 300
SIC 7011 Casino hotel; Casino hotel
Ch Bd: Narcisco Cunanan
CFO: Scott Cannady
Genl Mgr: Gary Kentner

NOOKSACK BUSINESS CORP 1
See NOOKSACK INDIAN TRIBE

D-U-N-S 03-951-5234
NOOKSACK INDIAN TRIBE
NOOKSACK BUSINESS CORP 1
5016 Deming Rd, Deming, WA 98244-9903
Tel (360) 592-5176 Founded/Ownrshp 1973
Sales NA EMP 848
SIC 9131 Indian reservation; Indian reservation
Ch: Robert Kelly
*V Ch: Richard D George
*Treas: Agripina Smith
*Ex Dir: Katherine Canete
IT Man: Raynell Wurtz

NOOKSACK RIVER CASINO
See NOOKSACK BUSINESS CORP

D-U-N-S 88-375-9565
NOONAN BROTHERS PETROLEUM PRODUCTS INC
415 West St, West Bridgewater, MA 02379-1030
Tel (508) 588-8026 Founded/Ownrshp 1994
Sales 142.9MM EMP 14
Accts Nicholas P Dinatale Cpa Sto
SIC 5172 Petroleum products; Petroleum products
Pr: J Peter Noonan Sr
*Treas: J Timothy Noonan
*Sec: Laurence Noonan Jr
Off Mgr: Bill Vieno

D-U-N-S 95-807-3624 IMP
NOORDA ARCHITECTURAL METALS INC
2160 W 1700 S, Salt Lake City, UT 84104-4236
Tel (801) 282-8400 Founded/Ownrshp 1997
Sales 27.1MM^E EMP 95
SIC 1761 Sheet metalwork
Pr: Chris Noorda
Ofcr: Jeremy Daniel Estrada

D-U-N-S 02-277-4147
NOOSA YOGHURT LLC
(Suby of ADVENT INTERNATIONAL CORP) ★
4120 N County Road 25 E, Bellvue, CO 80512-5900
Tel (970) 493-0949 Founded/Ownrshp 2014
Sales 35.6MM^E EMP 95
SIC 2026 Yogurt; Yogurt
Pr: Wade Groetsch
CFO: David Bacek
Genl Mgr: Koel Thomae
Opers Mgr: Dustin Braeger

D-U-N-S 62-199-2288
NOOTER CONSTRUCTION CO
(Suby of NOOTER CORP) ★
1500 S 2nd St, Saint Louis, MO 63104-4513
Tel (314) 621-6000 Founded/Ownrshp 1981
Sales 152.3MM^E EMP 300
SIC 1541 Industrial buildings & warehouses; Industrial buildings & warehouses
Pr: Bernard C Wicklein
VP: Chris Cimarolli
VP: John Walling
VP: Jim Woodward
*VP: David Zach
Ql Cn Mgr: Thomas Moslander

D-U-N-S 00-627-4385 IMP
NOOTER CORP (MO)
(Suby of CIC GROUP INC) ★
1500 S 2nd St, Saint Louis, MO 63104-4513
Tel (314) 421-7200 Founded/Ownrshp 1896
Sales 326.1MM^E EMP 811
SIC 3443 3479 1796 8711 7699 1542 Tanks, standard or custom fabricated: metal plate; Pressurizers or auxiliary equipment, nuclear: metal plate; Columns (fractioning, etc.): metal plate; Towers (bubble, cooling, fractionating, etc.): metal plate; Coating of metals & formed products; Hot dip coating of metals or formed products; Machinery installation; Pollution control equipment installation; Energy conservation engineering; Heating & ventilation engineering; Tank repair; Tank truck cleaning service; Nonresidential construction; Tanks, standard or custom fabricated: metal plate; Pressurizers or auxiliary equipment, nuclear: metal plate; Columns (fractioning, etc.): metal plate; Towers (bubble, cooling, fractionating, etc.): metal plate; Coating of metals & formed products; Hot dip coating of metals or formed products; Machinery installation; Pollution control equipment installation; Energy conservation engineering; Heating & ventilation engineering; Tank repair; Tank truck cleaning service; Nonresidential construction
Pr: Michael W Bytnar
*Ch Bd: Ross G Osiek
*Pr: John A Drehor
*Pr: Vernon L Eriksen
Pr: Don Majchrowski
Sec: Derek Falb
*Sr VP: Ronald C Zinzer
VP Admn: David Zach
IT Man: William Robinson
VP Opers: Bernard Wicklein
Sfty Mgr: Tony Templet

D-U-N-S 16-152-0994 IMP
NOOTER/ERIKSEN INC
(Suby of CIC GROUP INC) ★
1509 Ocello Dr, Fenton, MO 63026-2406
Tel (636) 651-1000 Founded/Ownrshp 1987
Sales 258.4MM^E EMP 280^E
SIC 5075 Warm air heating equipment & supplies; Warm air heating equipment & supplies
Pr: Tim Peterson
Pr: Joe Schroeder
Sec: Derek Falb
Ex VP: Phillip J Hanks
Sr VP: Steven Moss
VP: Yuri Rechtman
Off Mgr: Marlene Gentile
VP Opers: Bill Peskorse
Opers Mgr: Andy Febus
Opers Mgr: Dave Wright
Mktg Mgr: Kevin Graven

D-U-N-S 00-911-3374 EXP
NOR-CAL BEVERAGE CO INC
2150 Stone Blvd, West Sacramento, CA 95691-4049
Tel (916) 372-0600 Founded/Ownrshp 1937
Sales 245.3MM^E EMP 574
SIC 5181 2086 Beer & ale; Soft drinks: packaged in cans, bottles, etc.; Fruit drinks (less than 100% juice): packaged in cans, etc.; Beer & ale; Soft drinks: packaged in cans, bottles, etc.; Fruit drinks (less than 100% juice): packaged in cans, etc.
Pr: Shannon Deary-Bell
*Ch Bd: Donald Deary
*Pr: Grant Deary
*CFO: Mike Montroni
*CFO: Michael Motroni
*VP: Roy Grant Deary III
*VP: Timothy Deary
VP: Paul Orebaugh
VP: Tracy Tucker
Exec: Shannon Bell
Dist Mgr: Ryan Fiksdal

D-U-N-S 05-894-0404
NOR-CAL PRODUCE INC
2995 Oates St, West Sacramento, CA 95691-5902
Tel (916) 373-0830 Founded/Ownrshp 1972
Sales 83.2MM^E EMP 130
SIC 5148 Fruits, fresh; Fruits, fresh
Pr: Todd D Achondo
*Pr: Daniel L Achondo Sr
*Pr: Todd Achondo
*VP: Linda Achondo
Opers Mgr: Stephen Achondo

D-U-N-S 00-947-6755 IMP
NOR-CAL PRODUCTS INC (CA)
1967 S Oregon St, Yreka, CA 96097-3462
Tel (530) 842-4457 Founded/Ownrshp 1946
Sales 32.1MM^E EMP 150
SIC 3494 Valves & pipe fittings; Valves & pipe fittings
Pr: Tom Deany
Pr: George Landreth
*CFO: David Stone
*VP: Sean Mallory
*VP: Tim Nilsson
*VP: Mitchell Taylor

D-U-N-S 09-625-8587
NOR-CAR FEDERAL CREDIT UNION INC
2804 William Penn Hwy, Easton, PA 18045-5245
Tel (610) 258-0629 Founded/Ownrshp 1938
Sales NA EMP 25
SIC 6062 6061 State credit unions; Federal credit unions
Pr: Michael J Symons
*Treas: Bruce E Dotts
*VP: Lucinda Sterling

D-U-N-S 00-616-9189 IMP
■ **NOR-LAKE INC**
NOR-LAKE SCIENTIFIC
(Suby of STANDEX INTERNATIONAL CORP) ★
727 2nd St, Hudson, WI 54016-2514
Tel (715) 386-2323 Founded/Ownrshp 2003
Sales 74.6MM^E EMP 300
SIC 3585 Refrigeration equipment, complete; Counters & counter display cases, refrigerated; Ice boxes, industrial; Lockers, refrigerated; Refrigeration equipment, complete; Counters & counter display cases, refrigerated; Ice boxes, industrial; Lockers, refrigerated
Pr: Chuck Dullea
VP: Robert Bakken
Ql Cn Mgr: Joanne Woloskie

NOR-LAKE SCIENTIFIC
See NOR-LAKE INC

D-U-N-S 03-831-0199
NOR-LEA HOSPITAL DISTRICT
1600 N Main Ave, Lovington, NM 88260-2830
Tel (575) 396-6611 Founded/Ownrshp 1980
Sales 53.5MM^E EMP 400
SIC 8062 General medical & surgical hospitals; General medical & surgical hospitals
CEO: David Shaw
VP: Amanda Graham
Dir Lab: Amy Molinar
Dir Rad: Nick Rodriguez
CIO: Brent Kelley
IT Man: Tim Lee
IT Man: Helen Moore
Pr Dir: John McCulloch
Nrsg Dir: Cyndie Cribbs
HC Dir: Lynda Davis

D-U-N-S 04-472-1926
NOR-MAR INC
BURGER KING
6550 Gunpark Dr Ste 100, Boulder, CO 80301-3597
Tel (303) 581-0300 Founded/Ownrshp 1968
Sales 19.6MM^E EMP 600
SIC 5812 Fast-food restaurant, chain; Fast-food restaurant, chain
Pr: Joe Lukas
VP: Nancy Pingel

D-U-N-S 08-947-6410
NOR-SON INC
7900 Hastings Rd, Baxter, MN 56425-8465
Tel (218) 828-1722 Founded/Ownrshp 1978
Sales 81.1MM^E EMP 190
SIC 1521 1542 1541 New construction, single-family houses; Commercial & office building, new construction; Commercial & office buildings, renovation & repair; Industrial buildings, new construction; Renovation, remodeling & repairs: industrial buildings; New construction, single-family houses; Commercial & office building, new construction; Commercial & office buildings, renovation & repair; Industrial buildings, new construction; Renovation, remodeling & repairs: industrial buildings
CEO: Robert Sweeney
*Pr: Brooke Silvernail
*CEO: Scott D Kuehl
CFO: Jeff Fox
Exec: Mark Korte
IT Man: Lila Eastvold
Sfty Mgr: Ron Myrvold
Opers Mgr: Shirley Gronholm
Opers Mgr: Paul Maki
Sales Exec: Jim Larson
Snr PM: Kevin Littman

NOR-TECH
See NORTHERN COMPUTER TECHNOLOGIES INC

D-U-N-S 62-794-3301 IMP
NORA LIGHTING INC
6505 Gayhart St, Commerce, CA 90040-2507
Tel (800) 686-6672 Founded/Ownrshp 1989
Sales 62.1MM^E EMP 72
SIC 5063 3648 5719 Lighting fixtures; Lighting fixtures, except electric: residential; Lighting fixtures; Lighting fixtures; Lighting fixtures, except electric: residential; Lighting fixtures
CEO: Fred Farzan
*Ex VP: Jill Farzan
IT Man: Nelson Brown

D-U-N-S 18-796-3988 IMP/EXP
NORA SYSTEMS INC
(Suby of NORA SYSTEMS GMBH)
9 Northeastern Blvd, Salem, NH 03079-1996
Tel (603) 894-1021 Founded/Ownrshp 1986
Sales 26.9MM^E EMP 150
SIC 3069 Flooring, rubber: tile or sheet; Flooring, rubber: tile or sheet
Pr: Andreas Mueller
Rgnl Mgr: Mark Jones
S&M/VP: Susanna Loecher
Sls Dir: Michael Sage

D-U-N-S 00-835-2957 EXP
NORAC INC
405 S Motor Ave, Azusa, CA 91702-3232
Tel (626) 334-2908 Founded/Ownrshp 1953
Sales 62.0MM^E EMP 258
SIC 2869 Industrial organic chemicals; Industrial organic chemicals
Pr: Wallace McCloskey
COO: Ahsan Ahmed
VP: Richard Carlson
VP: Jim Puse
Dir Lab: Brian Sanchez
*Prin: Olive J Mc Closkey
*Prin: Lee Miller
*Prin: Jim Scholler
CTO: Wally McCloskey
QA Dir: Rosalinda Raquiza
*QA Dir: Randall Wong

NORAD
See NORTH ATLANTIC DISTRIBUTION INC

D-U-N-S 92-650-2720
NORAM DRILLING CO
8400 N Sam Houston Pkwy W # 120, Houston, TX 77064-3462
Tel (281) 598-9200 Founded/Ownrshp 2006
Sales 20.1MM^E EMP 50
SIC 1381 Drilling oil & gas wells
CEO: Herman E McInnis

**Pr:* Bruce Seeley
CFO: Dale Wilhelm

D-U-N-S 16-097-4064 IMP
NORAM INTERNATIONAL PARTNERS INC
1 Tara Blvd Ste 200, Nashua, NH 03062-2809
Tel (603) 881-3151 *Founded/Ownrshp* 2004
Sales 22.9MME *EMP* 160E
SIC 5399 Surplus & salvage goods
CEO: Michael Dugally
**Pr:* Kelly Dugally
Bd of Dir: Arthur Maxwell

NORAMCO
See NORTH AMERICAN PLASTICS CHEMICALS INC

NORAMCO
See NORTH AMERICAN TRADE CORP

D-U-N-S 05-723-4486 IMP
■ NORAMCO INC
(*Suby of* JOHNSON & JOHNSON) ★
1440 Olympic Dr, Athens, GA 30601-1645
Tel (706) 353-4400 *Founded/Ownrshp* 1980
Sales 26.0MME *EMP* 150
SIC 2834 2833 Pharmaceutical preparations; Medicinals & botanicals; Pharmaceutical preparations; Medicinals & botanicals
CEO: Courtney L Billington
CFO: Cunningham Js
**CFO:* David Smith
VP: Tim Raher
Comm Dir: Charles Martin
Prgrm Mgr: Ross Denisco
Opers Mgr: Peter Goodridge
Mktg Dir: Mathew Minardi

D-U-N-S 16-650-6142
■ NORAMCO INC
(*Suby of* JOHNSON & JOHNSON) ★
500 Swedes Landing Rd, Wilmington, DE 19801-4596
Tel (302) 652-3840 *Founded/Ownrshp* 2000
Sales 26.7MME *EMP* 100
SIC 2834 Pharmaceutical preparations; Pharmaceutical preparations
Pr: Arthur Nemitz
Mng Dir: Raymond Plourde
Mtls Mgr: Charles Martin

D-U-N-S 18-115-7769 IMP
NORAMPAC INDUSTRIES INC
(*Suby of* CASCADES CANADA ULC)
4001 Packard Rd, Niagara Falls, NY 14303-2297
Tel (716) 284-9214 *Founded/Ownrshp* 1987
Sales 845.4MME *EMP* 4,900E
SIC 2631 2653 Container board; Corrugated & solid fiber boxes; Container board; Corrugated & solid fiber boxes
VP: Charles Malo
**Treas:* Sal Sciarrino
Bd of Dir: Eric Laflamme
**VP:* Robert Lanthier
**VP:* Jean Parent
**VP:* Maurice Plante
Genl Mgr: Jean Goulet
Genl Mgr: Mario Lacharit
Genl Mgr: Luc Langevin
Dir IT: John Keller
Genl Couns: Lucie Lalonde

D-U-N-S 00-128-1468
NORAMPAC NEW YORK CITY INC (NY)
5515 Grand Ave, Maspeth, NY 11378-3113
Tel (718) 386-3200 *Founded/Ownrshp* 1906, 2001
Sales 47.5MME *EMP* 160
SIC 2653 3993 2675 Boxes, corrugated: made from purchased materials; Display items, corrugated: made from purchased materials; Signs & advertising specialties; Die-cut paper & board; Boxes, corrugated: made from purchased materials; Display items, corrugated: made from purchased materials; Signs & advertising specialties; Die-cut paper & board
Ch Bd: Marc Andre Depin

D-U-N-S 16-729-7899
NORAMPAC SCHENECTADY INC
(*Suby of* NORAMPAC INC)
801 Corporation Park, Schenectady, NY 12302-1097
Tel (518) 346-6151 *Founded/Ownrshp* 2013
Sales 55.0MM *EMP* 150
SIC 2653 Corrugated & solid fiber boxes; Corrugated & solid fiber boxes
Pr: Marc Andre Depin
**Pr:* Charles Smith
**Genl Mgr:* Craig Griffith
Genl Mgr: Scott Russell
Plnt Mgr: Jay Toland

D-U-N-S 07-651-2383
NORAN NEUROLOGICAL CLINIC PA
2828 Chicago Ave Ste 300, Minneapolis, MN 55407-1573
Tel (612) 879-1000 *Founded/Ownrshp* 1972
Sales 20.7MME *EMP* 180
SIC 8011 Neurologist; Neurologist
**Pr:* Soren Ryberg MD
CFO: Mark Franklin
**Treas:* Gerald K Morley MD
**VP:* George Adam MD
**VP:* Lawrence Burstein MD
**VP:* Mary J Chiasson Do
**VP:* David Dorn MD
**VP:* Susan Evans
**VP:* Richard Golden MD
**VP:* Franciso Gomez MD
**VP:* Steven Jannousek MD
**VP:* Steven S Lebow MD
**VP:* Fred Lux MD
**VP:* Debra Peven Do
**VP:* Michael Sethna MD
**VP:* Shelly Svoboda MD
**VP:* Ronald Tarrel Do

NORANCO DEER VALLEY DIVISION
See NORANCO MANUFACTURING USA LTD

D-U-N-S 96-986-7501
NORANCO MANUFACTURING USA LTD
NORANCO DEER VALLEY DIVISION
(*Suby of* NORANCO INC)
1620 W Knudsen Dr, Phoenix, AZ 85027-1317
Tel (623) 582-2261 *Founded/Ownrshp* 1999
Sales 50.5MME *EMP* 190
SIC 3728 Aircraft parts & equipment; Aircraft parts & equipment
CFO: Kelly Clinton

D-U-N-S 16-831-6557 IMP/EXP
■ NORANDA ALUMINA LLC
(*Suby of* NORANDA ALUMINUM HOLDING CORP) ★
1111 E Airline Hwy Us61, Gramercy, LA 70052-6302
Tel (225) 869-2100 *Founded/Ownrshp* 2009
Sales 228.8MME *EMP* 500
SIC 3334 Primary aluminum; Primary aluminum
**CFO:* Dale Boyles
**VP:* Mike Fox
**VP:* John Habisreitinger
Opers Mgr: Eddie Bowden

D-U-N-S 80-137-2686
▲ NORANDA ALUMINUM HOLDING CORP
801 Crescent Cntre Dr 6 Ste 600, Franklin, TN 37067
Tel (615) 771-5700 *Founded/Ownrshp* 2007
Sales 1.3MMM *EMP* 7,621
Tkr Sym NOR *Exch* NYS
SIC 3334 2819 3353 Primary aluminum; Ingots (primary), aluminum; Bauxite, refined; Flat rolled shapes, aluminum; Primary aluminum; Ingots (primary), aluminum; Bauxite, refined; Flat rolled shapes, aluminum
Pr: Layle K Smith
**Ch Bd:* William H Brooks
Pr: Scott M Croft
CFO: Dale W Boyles
Ofcr: Gail E Lehman
VP: Cara Feeney
Board of Directors: Richard B Evans, Thomas R Miklich, Carl J Rickertsen, Ronald S Rolfe, Elliot G Sagor, Alan H Schumacher

D-U-N-S 07-198-4652 IMP
■ NORANDA ALUMINUM INC
(*Suby of* NORANDA ALUMINUM HOLDING CORP) ★
801 Crescent Centre Dr # 600, Franklin, TN 37067-6224
Tel (615) 771-5700 *Founded/Ownrshp* 2007
Sales 531.5MME *EMP* 2,350
SIC 3353 3354 3334 3714 Flat rolled shapes, aluminum; Aluminum extruded products; Primary aluminum; Wheels, motor vehicle; Flat rolled shapes, aluminum; Aluminum extruded products; Primary aluminum; Wheels, motor vehicle
Pr: Scott M Croft
**Pr:* William H Brooks
**Pr:* Wayne Hale
**CFO:* Robert B Mahoney
CFO: Robert Mahoney
**Treas:* Mark J Walker
**VP:* Richard J Anderson
**VP:* Devonne Canady
**VP:* Ronald Rowe

D-U-N-S 80-943-0023
NORANDA FINANCE HOLDINGS INC
(*Suby of* GLENCORE CANADA CORPORATION)
6000 Lombardo Ctr Ste 650, Seven Hills, OH 44131-6916
Tel (216) 642-7342 *Founded/Ownrshp* 2007
Sales 203.3MME *EMP* 162
SIC 2819 Industrial inorganic chemicals; Industrial inorganic chemicals
Pr: Paul Shaw

D-U-N-S 80-139-8079
■ NORANDA INTERMEDIATE HOLDING CORP
(*Suby of* NORANDA ALUMINUM HOLDING CORP) ★
801 Crescent Centre Dr, Franklin, TN 37067-6224
Tel (615) 771-5700 *Founded/Ownrshp* 2008
Sales 228.8MME *EMP* 2,350
SIC 3353 3334 3714 3354 Flat rolled shapes, aluminum; Primary aluminum; Wheels, motor vehicle; Aluminum extruded products; Flat rolled shapes, aluminum; Primary aluminum; Wheels, motor vehicle; Aluminum extruded products
CEO: Layle K Smith
VP: Thomas Harris

D-U-N-S 09-379-0277 IMP
■ NORANDAL USA INC
(*Suby of* NORANDA ALUMINUM HOLDING CORP) ★
801 Crescent Centre Dr # 600, Franklin, TN 37067-7202
Tel (615) 778-2000 *Founded/Ownrshp* 1978
Sales 210.5MME *EMP* 820
SIC 3353 Coils, sheet aluminum; Foil, aluminum; Tubes, welded, aluminum; Coils, sheet aluminum; Foil, aluminum; Tubes, welded, aluminum
CEO: Layle K Smith
**Pr:* Scott Croft
**Pr:* S H Sutherland
CFO: Steven Douglas
**CFO:* Robert B Mahoney
**Sec:* Rick Anderson
**VP:* Stephen Robuck
Rgnl Mgr: Vern Arseneau
Rgnl Mgr: Gary Woods
Prd Mgr: Chad Pinson

D-U-N-S 04-571-4342 IMP
NORANDEX BUILDING MATERIALS DISTRIBUTION INC
NORANDEX BUILDING MTLS DIST
300 Executive Park Ste 100, Hudson, OH 44236
Tel (330) 656-8924 *Founded/Ownrshp* 1997
Sales 647.8MME *EMP* 1,000
SIC 5033 5031 Siding, except wood; Doors & windows

NORANDEX BUILDING MTLS DIST
See NORANDEX BUILDING MATERIALS DISTRIBUTION INC

D-U-N-S 01-863-8940 IMP
NORBERT E MITCHELL CO INC (CT)
MITCHELL OIL
7 Federal Rd, Danbury, CT 06810-6195
Tel (203) 744-0600 *Founded/Ownrshp* 1945
Sales 32.7MME *EMP* 140
SIC 5983 5541 5984 Fuel oil dealers; Gasoline service stations; Propane gas, bottled; Fuel oil dealers; Gasoline service stations; Propane gas, bottled
VP: Norbert Mitchell Jr
**Sec:* Janet Mitchell Hoyt
**VP:* Donald Mitchell
**Prin:* Mat Mitchelle

D-U-N-S 07-996-9385
NORBEST LLC
15 E 1900 S Feed Mill Rd, Moroni, UT 84646
Tel (435) 436-8211 *Founded/Ownrshp* 2015
Sales 5.8MME *EMP* 600
SIC 0253 2015 Turkey farm; Turkey, processed: fresh
CEO: Matt Cook
Sr VP: Robert Wangerien
VP: Colby Mellor
VP: Scott Whitman

D-U-N-S 11-262-2167 IMP
NORBORD GEORGIA LLC
(*Suby of* NORBORD INC)
964 Us Highway 280 W, Cordele, GA 31015-5465
Tel (229) 276-2827 *Founded/Ownrshp* 2002
Sales 34.2MME *EMP* 160
SIC 2493 Reconstituted wood products; Reconstituted wood products
CEO: Peter Wijnbergen
**CFO:* Jim Black
**Prin:* Yuvonne McKinlay

D-U-N-S 02-158-5989
NORBORD MINNESOTA INC
(*Suby of* NORBORD INC)
4409 Northwood Rd Nw, Solway, MN 56678-4322
Tel (218) 751-2023 *Founded/Ownrshp* 1979
Sales 29.8MME *EMP* 140
SIC 2493 Waferboard
CEO: Peter C Wijnbergen
**Sr VP:* Nigel Banks
**Sr VP:* Robin E Lampard
**Sr VP:* Karl R Morris
**VP:* Michael J Dawson
**Genl Mgr:* Jack Wallingford

D-U-N-S 84-706-8954
NORBORD MISSISSIPPI INC
(*Suby of* NORBORD INDUSTRIES INC)
1194 Highway 145, Guntown, MS 38849-7919
Tel (662) 348-2800 *Founded/Ownrshp* 1993
Sales 30.5MME *EMP* 125
SIC 2493 Strandboard, oriented
Pr: John C Tremayne
**Sr VP:* Bruce Grebe
**VP:* Jim Black
**VP:* Jeff Johnson

D-U-N-S 11-132-8857 IMP/EXP
NORBORD SOUTH CAROLINA INC
(*Suby of* NORBORD INC)
564 Woodyard Rd, Kinards, SC 29355-9077
Tel (864) 697-5437 *Founded/Ownrshp* 2000
Sales 41.4MME *EMP* 131
SIC 2436 2493 Softwood veneer & plywood; Reconstituted wood products
CEO: J Barrie Shineton
Mktg Mgr: Luke Smith

D-U-N-S 79-687-3839
NORBORD TEXAS (NACOGDOCHES) INC
(*Suby of* NORBORD INC)
2301 Se Stallings Dr, Nacogdoches, TX 75961-6873
Tel (936) 568-8000 *Founded/Ownrshp* 2007
Sales 25.2MME *EMP* 121
SIC 2493 Reconstituted wood products
Pr: Peter C Wijnbergen
Top Exec: Cheryl Hardin
Genl Mgr: Jim E Ward

D-U-N-S 09-191-9022
NORBORD TEXAS LIMITED PARTNERSHIP
(*Suby of* NORBORD INC)
500 Nexfor Blvd, Jefferson, TX 75657-1055
Tel (936) 568-8009 *Founded/Ownrshp* 2002
Sales 140.2MME *EMP* 1,000
SIC 2493 Reconstituted wood products; Reconstituted wood products
Genl Pt: Norbord Georgia
CEO: Peter C Wijnbergen
Exec: Michael Weekes

D-U-N-S 16-192-5375 IMP
NORBY DISTRIBUTING CO
NORBY FARM FLEET
5700 Saratoga Rd, Asbury, IA 52002-2118
Tel (563) 556-8972 *Founded/Ownrshp* 1986
Sales 38.9MME *EMP* 100
SIC 5072 5699 5531 Hardware; Power handtools; Work clothing; Automotive parts; Automotive accessories; Hardware; Power handtools; Work clothing; Automotive parts; Automotive accessories
Pr: Gregory Norby
**VP:* Constance Norby

NORBY FARM FLEET
See NORBY DISTRIBUTING CO

NORC
See NATIONAL OPINION RESEARCH CENTER

NORCAL CEMENT MASONS
See CEMENT MASONS HEALTH AND WELFARE TRUST FUND FOR NORTHERN CALIFORNIA

D-U-N-S 61-596-6504
NORCAL GOLD INC
RE/MAX
5200 Sunrise Blvd Ste 5, Fair Oaks, CA 95628-3500
Tel (916) 218-6700 *Founded/Ownrshp* 1994
Sales 29.2MME *EMP* 100
SIC 6531 Real estate agent, residential
CEO: James Obrian

D-U-N-S 94-284-7294
NORCAL HARVESTING LLC
27 Quail Run Cir, Salinas, CA 93907-2345
Tel (831) 422-5230 *Founded/Ownrshp* 1996
Sales 29.2MME *EMP* 300E
SIC 0171 Strawberry farm; Strawberry farm
Genl Mgr: John Ramirez

D-U-N-S 09-255-8741
NORCAL MUTUAL INSURANCE CO INC
560 Davis St Fl 2, San Francisco, CA 94111-1974
Tel (415) 397-9703 *Founded/Ownrshp* 1975
Sales NA *EMP* 310
SIC 6351 6411 6331 Liability insurance; Insurance agents, brokers & service; Fire, marine & casualty insurance; Liability insurance; Insurance agents, brokers & service; Fire, marine & casualty insurance
CEO: Theodore Scott Diener
Pr: Jim Sunsari
Assoc VP: Christoph Dugre
Assoc VP: Bradley Ignasiak
Assoc VP: Michael Osborne
Assoc VP: Lucy Sam
Ex VP: Scott Diener
Sr VP: Mark Johnson
Sr VP: Ronald Rumin
VP: Joy Corso
VP: Mark Gire
VP: Doug Hall
VP: Keith Hui
VP: John McClain
VP: Michael Roque
VP: Neil Simons
VP: Kevin Smith
VP: Bruce Williams

D-U-N-S 17-807-7012
NORCAL RENTAL GROUP LLC
CRESCO EQUIPMENT RENTALS
318 Stealth Ct, Livermore, CA 94551-9303
Tel (925) 961-0130 *Founded/Ownrshp* 1997
Sales 45.5MME *EMP* 210
SIC 7353 Heavy construction equipment rental; Cranes & aerial lift equipment, rental or leasing; Earth moving equipment, rental or leasing; Heavy construction equipment rental; Cranes & aerial lift equipment, rental or leasing; Earth moving equipment, rental or leasing
Rgnl Mgr: Alan Beales
Genl Mgr: Clark Welch

D-U-N-S 80-088-5964
NORCAR INC
PAPA JOHN'S
12201 Plantside Dr, Louisville, KY 40299-6347
Tel (502) 261-7272 *Founded/Ownrshp* 1992
Sales 30.5MME *EMP* 700
SIC 5812 Pizzeria, chain; Pizzeria, chain
CEO: John H Schnatter
**CFO:* Dave Flanery
**Prin:* Charles W Schnatter
Sales Exec: Phillip Clark

D-U-N-S 17-368-4713
NORCARE ENTERPRISES INC
NORTH CENTER, THE
6140 S Broadway, Lorain, OH 44053-3821
Tel (440) 233-7232 *Founded/Ownrshp* 1985
Sales 361.8M *EMP* 289
Accts Howard Wershbale & Co
SIC 8093 Mental health clinic, outpatient; Mental health clinic, outpatient
CEO: Amy Denger
**CFO:* Bernadek Stchick

D-U-N-S 94-836-5382 EXP
NORCATEC LLC
100 Garden Cy Plz Ste 530, Garden City, NY 11530
Tel (516) 222-7070 *Founded/Ownrshp* 1995
Sales 23.2MME *EMP* 90
SIC 3714 Motor vehicle parts & accessories
Pr: Eytan Erez
Off Mgr: Patricia Waters
Mktg Dir: Allen Rosen

D-U-N-S 04-875-2091
NORCO DELIVERY SERVICE INC
851 E Cerritos Ave, Anaheim, CA 92805-6328
Tel (714) 520-8600 *Founded/Ownrshp* 1965
Sales 40.8MME *EMP* 258
SIC 4214 7389 Local trucking with storage; Local trucking with storage; Courier or messenger service
CEO: Tom Hoskins
VP: Mark Nakaihara

D-U-N-S 79-633-8791
NORCO FIRE DEPARTMENT
3902 Hillside Ave, Norco, CA 92860-1515
Tel (951) 737-8097 *Founded/Ownrshp* 2007
Sales NA *EMP* 700
SIC 6371 Union funds
Pr: Ron Larson

D-U-N-S 03-914-8457
NORCO INC
811 Edwards St, Gillette, WY 82718-6401
Tel (307) 682-8250 *Founded/Ownrshp* 1989
Sales 22.4MME *EMP* 147
SIC 5084 5169 5087 7359 Welding machinery & equipment; Industrial gases; Cleaning & maintenance equipment & supplies; Janitors' supplies; Equipment rental & leasing; Welding machinery & equipment; Industrial gases; Cleaning & maintenance equipment & supplies; Janitors' supplies; Equipment rental & leasing
IT Man: Brenda Holzer
Prd Mgr: James Ross
Sales Asso: Amy Harvey
Sales Asso: Scot White

D-U-N-S 04-369-4645
NORCO INC
1125 W Amity Rd, Boise, ID 83705-5412
Tel (208) 336-1643 *Founded/Ownrshp* 1989
Sales 469.8MME *EMP* 1,070

SIC 5084 5169 7352 5999 3548 2813 Welding machinery & equipment; Safety equipment; Industrial gases; Medical equipment rental; Medical apparatus & supplies; Welding apparatus; Industrial gases; Welding machinery & equipment; Safety equipment; Industrial gases; Medical equipment rental; Medical apparatus & supplies; Welding apparatus; Industrial gases
Pr: Ned Pontious
**CFO:* Mike Sabin
**Ch:* James Kissler
Ex VP: Robert Gerry
VP: Brent Seward
VP: Greg Stanley
Exec: Toni Ayers
Brnch Mgr: Mandie Day
Store Mgr: Rick Lundgren
IT Man: Chris Dominiak
IT Man: Cassandra Nixion

D-U-N-S 07-920-8258
NORCO INC
3030 Hoyt Ave, Everett, WA 98201-4005
Tel (425) 205-4200 *Founded/Ownrshp* 2000
Sales 39.0MM^E *EMP* 1,150
SIC 7352 Medical equipment rental; Medical equipment rental
CEO: James Ross

D-U-N-S 07-920-8277
NORCO INC
101 E Stuart Rd, Bellingham, WA 98226-8196
Tel (360) 746-0826 *Founded/Ownrshp* 2013
Sales 39.3MM^E *EMP* 1,150
SIC 7352 Medical equipment rental; Medical equipment rental
CEO: James Ross

D-U-N-S 00-960-6906 IMP/EXP
NORCO INDUSTRIES INC
FLO DYNAMICS
365 W Victoria St, Compton, CA 90220-6029
Tel (310) 639-4000 *Founded/Ownrshp* 1964
Sales 48.3MM^E *EMP* 350
SIC 3569 2531 5085 3537

D-U-N-S 00-986-8480
NORCO RANCH INC
(*Suby of* MOARK LLC) ★
12005 Cabernet Dr, Fontana, CA 92337-7703
Tel (951) 737-6735 *Founded/Ownrshp* 2001
Sales 37.6MM^E *EMP* 369
SIC 0252 Chicken eggs; Chicken eggs
Pr: Creig Williardson
Board of Directors: Howard Eisen

D-U-N-S 96-811-9974 IMP
NORCOLD INC
(*Suby of* THETFORD CORP) ★
600 S Kuther Rd, Sidney, OH 45365-8840
Tel (937) 497-3080 *Founded/Ownrshp* 1997
Sales 100.5MM^E *EMP* 380
SIC 3632 Refrigerators, mechanical & absorption: household; Refrigerators, mechanical & absorption: household
CEO: Michael Harris
COO: Michael Larime
VP: Dave Roberts
Info Man: Dale Bertke
Mtls Mgr: John Jones
Site Mgr: Ronald Morosky
Plnt Mgr: Ernest Hinegardner
Ql Cn Mgr: Maria Kowalski
Ql Cn Mgr: Aliana Mabelitini

D-U-N-S 08-744-3909 IMP
NORCOM INC
200 Wilson Rd, Griffin, GA 30223-4537
Tel (770) 412-7690 *Founded/Ownrshp* 1978, 1987
Sales 43.6MM^E *EMP* 225
SIC 2678

D-U-N-S 08-090-2661
NORCON INC
(*Suby of* CH2M HILL COMPANIES LTD) ★
949 E 36th Ave Ste 500, Anchorage, AK 99508-4370
Tel (907) 275-6320 *Founded/Ownrshp* 2007
Sales 28.8MM^E *EMP* 400
SIC 1711 1731 Mechanical contractor; Electrical work; Mechanical contractor; Electrical work
Pr: Tom Arnold
**Treas:* Chow Allan KY
**VP:* Jeff Doyle
**VP:* Steven Larson
**VP:* Davinia J Lyon

D-U-N-S 12-618-8718
NORCON INC
661 W Ohio St, Chicago, IL 60654-5516
Tel (312) 243-4006 *Founded/Ownrshp* 1999
Sales 20.0MM^E *EMP* 47
SIC 1542 1522 Commercial & office building, new construction; Commercial & office buildings, renovation & repair; Residential construction
Pr: Charles Norwesh
**Sec:* Jeff Jozwiak

NORCRAFT CABINETARY
See NORCRAFT HOLDINGS LP

D-U-N-S 05-191-6638
■ **NORCRAFT COMPANIES INC**
(*Suby of* FORTUNE BRANDS HOME & SECURITY INC) ★
950 Blue Gentian Rd # 200, Saint Paul, MN 55121-3486
Tel (800) 297-0661 *Founded/Ownrshp* 2015
Sales 338.4MM^E *EMP* 2,234
SIC 2434 Wood kitchen cabinets; Vanities, bathroom: wood; Wood kitchen cabinets; Vanities, bathroom: wood
CEO: Mark Buller
Pr: John Swedeen
Pr: Kurt Wanninger
CFO: Leigh Ginter
Sls Mgr: Chad Larson
Sls Mgr: Bob Snedeker

D-U-N-S 07-762-7594 IMP/EXP
■ **NORCRAFT COMPANIES LP**
MID CONTINENT CABINETRY
(*Suby of* FORTUNE BRANDS HOME & SECURITY INC) ★
950 Blue Gentian Rd # 200, Saint Paul, MN 55121-3486
Tel (651) 234-3300 *Founded/Ownrshp* 2015
Sales NA *EMP* 1,892
SIC 2434 Wood kitchen cabinets; Vanities, bathroom: wood; Wood kitchen cabinets; Vanities, bathroom: wood
Pr: Mark Buller
**CFO:* Leigh Ginter
VP: John Loucks
Dir Bus: Will Darragh
Genl Mgr: Scott Raschke
Off Mgr: Julie Oftedahl
IT Man: Rod Brewer
Sfty Mgr: Joey Lecy
Plnt Mgr: Kevin Andersen
Plnt Mgr: Monte Young
Ql Cn Mgr: Daudi Eck

D-U-N-S 16-845-4135
NORCRAFT HOLDINGS LP
NORCRAFT CABINETARY
950 Blue Gentian Rd, Eagan, MN 55121-1576
Tel (800) 297-0661 *Founded/Ownrshp* 2003
Sales 35.0MMM *EMP* 2,500^E
SIC 2434 Wood kitchen cabinets; Vanities, bathroom: wood; Wood kitchen cabinets; Vanities, bathroom: wood
CEO: Mark Buller
CFO: Leigh Ginter
Sfty Mgr: Joey Lecy

D-U-N-S 04-140-8584
NORCROSS CO
PRESTON FEATHER BUILDING CTRS
900 Spring St, Petoskey, MI 49770-2855
Tel (231) 347-2501 *Founded/Ownrshp* 1979
Sales 21.9MM^E *EMP* 98
SIC 5211 Lumber & other building materials; Cabinets, kitchen; Door & window products
CEO: William N Norcross
**Pr:* Tim Lancaster
**Treas:* Judy Vanavery
**Prin:* William H Norcross

D-U-N-S 60-760-1267
NORCROSS ELECTRIC SUPPLY CO
4190 Capital View Dr, Suwanee, GA 30024-3979
Tel (770) 623-4350 *Founded/Ownrshp* 1989
Sales 36.5MM^E *EMP* 33^E
SIC 5063 Electrical fittings & construction materials
CEO: Danny C Mathis
**CFO:* Janis D Mathis
Off Mgr: Tomy Rinaldi

D-U-N-S 88-488-0998 IMP
NORCROSS SAFETY PRODUCTS LLC
HONEYWELL SAFETY PRODUCTS
900 Douglas Pike Ste 100, Smithfield, RI 02917-1879
Tel (800) 430-5490 *Founded/Ownrshp* 2008
Sales NA *EMP* 2,700
SIC 3842 3021 3469 Respiratory protection equipment, personal; Gloves, safety; Shoes, rubber or plastic molded to fabric; Helmets, steel

D-U-N-S 09-854-6567 IMP
NORD GEAR CORP
(*Suby of* GTNI GETRIEBETECHNIK-NORD INTERNATIONAL GMBH)
800 Nord Dr, Waunakee, WI 53597-9598
Tel (608) 849-2901 *Founded/Ownrshp* 1979
Sales 29.8MM^E *EMP* 180
SIC 3566 Reduction gears & gear units for turbines, except automotive; Reduction gears & gear units for turbines, except automotive
Pr: Terry Schadeberg
Mng Pt: Jutta Humbert
Pr: Mark Jones
**CFO:* Brian S Baumgart
CFO: Shawn Liverseed
VP: Eric Haugen
Dir Bus: Kevin Zwar
Mng Dir: Christine Behnke
Mng Dir: Mauricio Callejas
Mng Dir: Tony Isaksson
Mng Dir: Dong-Wook Kim

D-U-N-S 11-912-7074 IMP
NORD-LOCK INC/SUPERBOLT INC
1000 Gregg St, Carnegie, PA 15106
Tel (412) 279-1149 *Founded/Ownrshp* 2011
Sales 27.5MM^E *EMP* 85
SIC 3452 Nuts, metal; Nuts, metal
Pr: Robert Steinbock
Sec: Allan Steinbock

D-U-N-S 08-595-7876 IMP
NORDAM GROUP INC (CA)
NORDAM REPAIR DIVISION
6911 Whirlpool Dr, Tulsa, OK 74117-1306
Tel (918) 878-4000 *Founded/Ownrshp* 1969
Sales 831.2MM^E *EMP* 2,413
SIC 3728 3724 Aircraft parts & equipment; Bodies, aircraft; Aircraft engines & engine parts; Aircraft parts & equipment; Bodies, aircraft; Aircraft engines & engine parts
Ch: Paul Kenneth Lackey Jr
**Ch Bd:* Ken Lackey
Pr: Jim Thompson
**CEO:* Meredith Siegfried
CFO: William Peacher
VP: Mark Ferrari
VP: Terry Gray
VP: Daryl Hartzell
VP: Parker James
VP: James Parker
VP: Alain Poupin
VP: Raymond H Siegfried
Board of Directors: Bill Peacher, Mike Shonka

NORDAM REPAIR DIVISION
See NORDAM GROUP INC

D-U-N-S 17-755-4573 IMP
NORDCO INC
(*Suby of* GREENBRIAR EQUITY GROUP LLC) ★
245 W Forest Hill Ave, Oak Creek, WI 53154-2903
Tel (414) 766-2180 *Founded/Ownrshp* 1987
Sales 48.6MM^E *EMP* 171
SIC 3531 7353 3743 Railroad related equipment; Heavy construction equipment rental; Railroad equipment; Railroad related equipment; Heavy construction equipment rental; Railroad equipment
Pr: Bruce Boczkiewicz
**Pr:* Bill Straub
**CFO:* Dan Griesbach
VP: Thomas Bal
**VP:* Rich Carollo
**VP:* Jan Furst
**VP:* Howard Kietzke
Mtls Mgr: Kathy Bifford
Natl Sales: Greg Spilker
Manager: Jennifer Kincaid
Snr Mgr: Ken Krupski

D-U-N-S 17-224-8804 IMP/EXP
NORDEX USA INC
(*Suby of* NORDEX ENERGY GMBH)
300 S Wacker Dr Ste 1500, Chicago, IL 60606-6762
Tel (208) 383-6500 *Founded/Ownrshp* 1999
Sales 66.7MM^E *EMP* 250
SIC 3511 7389 Turbines & turbine generator sets; Industrial & commercial equipment inspection service; Turbines & turbine generator sets; Industrial & commercial equipment inspection service
CEO: Jrgen Zeschky
Pr: Edward Gareis
**Pr:* Ralf Sigrist
**CFO:* Bernard Schferbarthold
Ofcr: Jeff Andrews
Ofcr: Michael Magajne
VP: Joseph Fonio
VP: William Lutz
VP: Dan McDevitt
VP: Dan Morrison
Site Mgr: Brian Dobbins

D-U-N-S 07-860-4521
NORDFAB LLC
(*Suby of* NEDERMAN HOLDING AB)
150 Transit Ave, Thomasville, NC 27360-8927
Tel (336) 821-0829 *Founded/Ownrshp* 2011
Sales 400.0MM *EMP* 200
SIC 3443 Ducting, metal plate; Ducting, metal plate
Pr: Pear Erickson
Sls Mgr: Deane Adams
Sales Asso: Melanie Brown

D-U-N-S 02-010-7546
NORDHAUS RESEARCH INC
450 Enterprise Ct, Bloomfield Hills, MI 48302-0386
Tel (248) 836-5845 *Founded/Ownrshp* 1970
Sales 9.8MM^E *EMP* 350
Accts Follmer Rudzewicz & Co Southf
SIC 8732 Market analysis or research; Market analysis or research
Ch Bd: Robert L Van Dam
**Pr:* John King
**Treas:* Gayle P Van Dam
Ex VP: Alan Benedict
VP: Michael Alloto
**VP:* Allan L Benedict
CTO: John Gordon
MIS Dir: Tim Quainance

NORDIC
See PHYSICIANS INSURANCE A MUTUAL CO

D-U-N-S 96-177-5637
NORDIC CONSULTING PARTNERS INC
(*Suby of* NCT HOLDING COMPANY)
740 Regent St Ste 400, Madison, WI 53715-2650
Tel (608) 268-6900 *Founded/Ownrshp* 2010
Sales 37.8MM^E *EMP* 425
Accts Mcgladrey Llp Madison Wiscon
SIC 7379 Computer related consulting services; Computer related consulting services
Pr: Drew Madden
**COO:* Eric Sampson
**CFO:* Glenn Cole
Off Mgr: Teri Sandiford

D-U-N-S 82-940-2379
NORDIC CONTRACTING CO INC
111 Howard Blvd, Ledgewood, NJ 07852-9504
Tel (973) 584-5213 *Founded/Ownrshp* 1993
Sales 41.5MM^E *EMP* 100
Accts Gilbert & Calabrese Llc Flan
SIC 1542 Commercial & office building contractors; Commercial & office building contractors
Pr: John D Jacobsen
CFO: Bob Tiefenbacher
**Sec:* Ken Jacobsen
**VP:* Ted Vitcusky

D-U-N-S 05-020-8045
NORDIC CORP
TACO BELL
11019 Mccormick Rd # 320, Hunt Valley, MD 21031-8670
Tel (410) 771-1880 *Founded/Ownrshp* 1997
Sales 19.9MM^E *EMP* 1,000
SIC 5812 Fast-food restaurant, chain; Fast-food restaurant, chain
Pr: Kurt Aarsand
**Sec:* Krista Bedford

D-U-N-S 62-220-9179
NORDIC GROUP OF COMPANIES LTD
715 Lynn Ave Ste 100, Baraboo, WI 53913-2744
Tel (608) 356-7303 *Founded/Ownrshp* 1988
Sales 315.6MM *EMP* 2,500
SIC 8742 8111 5561 Management consulting services; Legal services; Recreational vehicle parts & accessories; Management consulting services; Legal services; Recreational vehicle parts & accessories
Ch: William R Sauey
**CFO:* Bill Hans
**Treas:* Todd L Sauey
IT Man: Allan Freuller
Mktg Mgr: Sonja Stauffacher

D-U-N-S 60-895-8823
NORDIC IMPORTS II LTD
PORSCHE CENTER
1326 Ne Loop 410, San Antonio, TX 78209-1512
Tel (210) 824-3214 *Founded/Ownrshp* 1990
Sales 25.0MM^E *EMP* 75
SIC 5511 Automobiles, new & used; Automobiles, new & used
Genl Pt: John Bruns
Off Mgr: Debbie Sutherland

D-U-N-S 06-695-3696
NORDIC INTERIOR INC
5601 Maspeth Ave Gf, Maspeth, NY 11378-2222
Tel (718) 456-7000 *Founded/Ownrshp* 1973
Sales 26.6MM^E *EMP* 150
SIC 2431 1742 Woodwork, interior & ornamental; Drywall; Carpentry work; Woodwork, interior & ornamental; Drywall
Ch Bd: Helge Halvorsen
**Sec:* Lloyd Jacobsen
**VP:* Harald Haegeland
VP: David Kleinworth
Snr PM: Eric Haegeland

D-U-N-S 00-462-3695
NORDIC LOGISTICS AND WAREHOUSING LLC
4300 Pleasantdale Rd, Atlanta, GA 30340-3526
Tel (770) 871-2600 *Founded/Ownrshp* 2000
Sales 99.5MM^E *EMP* 500
SIC 4222 Warehousing, cold storage or refrigerated; Warehousing, cold storage or refrigerated
Pr: Don Schoenl
Off Mgr: Rita Hamilton

D-U-N-S 93-271-3308 IMP
NORDIC NATURALS INC
WESTPORT SCANDINAVIA
111 Jennings Way, Watsonville, CA 95076-2054
Tel (831) 724-6200 *Founded/Ownrshp* 1995
Sales 29.2MM^E *EMP* 150
SIC 2077 Fish oil
CEO: Joar A Opheim
**VP:* Michele Opheim
IT Man: Mark Timares
Natl Sales: Max Poritzky
Sls Mgr: Jean Burke
Sales Asso: Kelly Enix
Sales Asso: Jason Kiser
Sales Asso: Zack Micheals
Sales Asso: Amelia Palermo
Sales Asso: Mari Ponza
Sales Asso: Melinda Powers

D-U-N-S 00-797-7903
NORDIC PCL CONSTRUCTION INC (HI)
(*Suby of* PCL CONSTRUCTION SERVICES INC) ★
1099 Alakea St Ste 1600, Honolulu, HI 96813-4500
Tel (808) 541-9101 *Founded/Ownrshp* 1950, 2008
Sales 61.6MM^E *EMP* 150
SIC 1541 1542 Industrial buildings & warehouses; Commercial & office building contractors; Industrial buildings & warehouses; Commercial & office building contractors
Pr: Glen Kaneshige
**Pr:* Wayne Melnyk
**Treas:* Ken Spence
**VP:* Aaron Wiehe
Opers Mgr: Marlon Garces
Snr Mgr: Steve Galicinao

D-U-N-S 06-335-9806 IMP
NORDIC PRODUCTS INC
NORPRO
2215 Merrill Creek Pkwy, Everett, WA 98203-5853
Tel (425) 261-1000 *Founded/Ownrshp* 1976
Sales 28.2MM^E *EMP* 70
SIC 5023 Kitchen tools & utensils; Kitchenware
CEO: Gunnar Lie
**Pr:* Kirsten Miller
IT Man: Damion Harlan
Natl Sales: Jennifer Anderson

NORDIC WARE
See NORTHLAND ALUMINUM PRODUCTS INC

D-U-N-S 01-693-8839
NORDLIE INC
NORDLIE WARREN
25300 Guenther, Warren, MI 48091-3759
Tel (586) 755-4200 *Founded/Ownrshp* 1928
Sales 50.7MM^E *EMP* 160
SIC 5193 Florists' supplies; Florists' supplies
Ch Bd: James O Nordlie
**Treas:* Thomas G Addison
**VP:* Kevin F Smith

NORDLIE WARREN
See NORDLIE INC

D-U-N-S 06-790-9127 IMP/EXP
NORDON INC
691 Exchange St, Rochester, NY 14608-2714
Tel (585) 546-6200 *Founded/Ownrshp* 1999
Sales 30.0MM^E *EMP* 118
SIC 3089 3544 Injection molding of plastics; Industrial molds; Injection molding of plastics; Industrial molds
CEO: Terry J Donovan
CIO: Theresa Sutton
Sls Dir: Paul Reed

D-U-N-S 05-720-2541 IMP
NORDON LLC
COOLER SOLUTIONS
1 Cabot Blvd E, Langhorne, PA 19047-1801
Tel (215) 504-4700 *Founded/Ownrshp* 2006
Sales 25.0MM^E *EMP* 55
SIC 5046 Restaurant equipment & supplies
Pr: Niki Arakelian
CFO: David S Stauffer
CFO: Scott Stauffer
Sales Exec: David Rourke

D-U-N-S 03-809-2508
NORDONIA HILLS SCHOOL DISTRICT
9370 Olde 8 Rd, Northfield, OH 44067-2046
Tel (330) 467-0580 *Founded/Ownrshp* 1817

Sales 44.5MM *EMP* 500
SIC 8211 Public elementary & secondary schools; Public elementary & secondary schools
Exec: Lynne Jones

NORDSON
See MICROMEDICS INC

NORDSON ASYMTEK
See NORDSON CALIFORNIA INC

D-U-N-S 10-627-0218 IMP
■ NORDSON ASYMTEK INC
(*Suby of* NORDSON CORP) ★
2747 Loker Ave W, Carlsbad, CA 92010-6601
Tel (760) 431-1919 *Founded/Ownrshp* 1996
Sales 46.6MM^E *EMP* 250
SIC 3823 Industrial flow & liquid measuring instruments; Industrial flow & liquid measuring instruments
CEO: Peter Bierhuis
VP: Alec Babiarz
VP: Alec Babiraz
VP: Ian Nagano
VP: Tom Ratledge
VP: Martin Stone
VP: Gregory Thaxton
Comm Dir: Roberta Johnson
Area Mgr: Paul Gallo
Genl Mgr: Rosie Truesdell
Dir IT: Nikki Cozakos

D-U-N-S 05-319-9100 IMP
■ NORDSON CALIFORNIA INC
NORDSON ASYMTEK
(*Suby of* NORDSON CORP) ★
2747 Loker Ave W, Carlsbad, CA 92010-6601
Tel (760) 918-8490 *Founded/Ownrshp* 1996
Sales 73.8MM^E *EMP* 128^E
SIC 3695 3561 3586 Computer software tape & disks: blank, rigid & floppy; Pump jacks & other pumping equipment; Measuring & dispensing pumps
CEO: Michael F Hilton
**Sr VP:* Gregory A Thaxton
**VP:* Robert E Veillette
Opers Mgr: Kathleen Clausen
Natl Sales: Jim Cordova
VP Sls: Dave Ellis
Sls Dir: Debbie Bernath
Sls Dir: Jerry Frost
Mktg Mgr: Roberta Foster-Smith

D-U-N-S 00-416-6005 IMP/EXP
▲ NORDSON CORP (OH)
28601 Clemens Rd, Westlake, OH 44145-1119
Tel (440) 892-1580 *Founded/Ownrshp* 1935
Sales 1.6MMM *EMP* 5,966
Accts Ernst & Young Llp Cleveland
Tkr Sym NDSN *Exch* NGS
SIC 3563 Spraying outfits: metals, paints & chemicals (compressor); Robots for industrial spraying, painting, etc.; Spraying outfits: metals, paints & chemicals (compressor); Robots for industrial spraying, painting, etc.
Pr: Michael F Hilton
**Ch Bd:* Joseph P Keithley
CFO: Gregory A Thaxton
Sr VP: Robert A Dunn
Sr VP: John J Keane
Sr VP: Gregory P Merk
VP: James E Devries
VP: Jim Devries
VP: Jim Landreth
VP: James W Messerly
VP: Robert E Veillette
VP: Axel Wenz
Board of Directors: Lee C Banks, Randolph W Carson, Arthur L George Jr, Frank M Jaehnert, Michael J Merriman Jr, Mary G Puma, Victor L Richey Jr

NORDSON DAWSONVILLE
See J AND M LABORATORIES INC

D-U-N-S 04-661-2776 IMP
■ NORDSON EFD LLC
E F D
(*Suby of* NORDSON CORP) ★
40 Catamore Blvd, East Providence, RI 02914-1206
Tel (401) 434-1680 *Founded/Ownrshp* 2000
Sales 91.4MM^E *EMP* 350
SIC 3548 3586 3699 Welding apparatus; Measuring & dispensing pumps; Electrical equipment & supplies; Welding apparatus; Measuring & dispensing pumps; Electrical equipment & supplies
Pr: Jeff Pembroke
**Sr VP:* Gregory A Thaxton
**VP:* David Guiot
VP: Virginia Lacy
VP: Steve Lord
VP: Francis Moreau
VP: Roman Skonieczny
Exec: Wil Boogaard
Exec: William Lema
Dir Lab: Kevin Gaugler
Ex Dir: Wil Vandenboogaard

D-U-N-S 00-246-1812 IMP
■ NORDSON XALOY INC
(*Suby of* NORDSON CORP) ★
1399 County Line Rd, New Castle, PA 16101-2955
Tel (724) 656-5600 *Founded/Ownrshp* 1929, 2012
Sales 184.6MM^E *EMP* 580
SIC 3544 Forms (molds), for foundry & plastics working machinery; Forms (molds), for foundry & plastics working machinery
CEO: Michael F Hilton
Treas: Keith E Young
VP: Myron Marsh
Telecom Ex: Tom Woolaway
CTO: Timothy W Womer
Manager: Shannon Abts
Manager: Brad Casale
Manager: Steve Jackson
Manager: Roland Kim
Manager: Scott Linn
Manager: Pat O'Connor

D-U-N-S 83-016-2611
■ NORDSON YESTECH INC
(*Suby of* NORDSON CORP) ★
2370 Oak Ridge Way Ste B, Vista, CA 92081-8345
Tel (949) 361-2714 *Founded/Ownrshp* 2002
Sales 25.0MM *EMP* 32
SIC 3827 Optical test & inspection equipment
Pr: Don Miller
**CFO:* Christine Schwarzmann
Manager: David Upton
Sls Mgr: Joshua Petras
Board of Directors: John J Keane, Gregory A Thaxton, Robert E Veillette

D-U-N-S 00-794-2915 IMP
▲ NORDSTROM INC (WA)
1617 6th Ave, Seattle, WA 98101-1707
Tel (206) 628-2111 *Founded/Ownrshp* 1901
Sales 13.5MMM *EMP* 67,000^E
Accts Deloitte & Touche Llp Seattle
Tkr Sym JWN *Exch* NYS
SIC 5651 5661 5632 5611 5641 5961 Family clothing stores; Shoe stores; Women's accessory & specialty stores; Men's & boys' clothing stores; Children's & infants' wear stores; Children's wear; Catalog sales; Family clothing stores; Shoe stores; Women's accessory & specialty stores; Men's & boys' clothing stores; Children's & infants' wear stores; Children's wear; Catalog sales
Pr: Blake W Nordstrom
Pr: Kevin Knight
**Pr:* Erik B Nordstrom
Pr: Jamie Nordstrom
**Pr:* Peter E Nordstrom
CFO: Michael G Koppel
Co-Pr: Blake Nordstrom
Chf Mktg O: Brian K Dennehy
Ex VP: Jammie A Baugh
Ex VP: Kirk Beardsley
Ex VP: Linda Finn
Ex VP: Daniel F Little
Ex VP: Robert B Sari
Ex VP: Loretta Soffe
Ex VP: Susan A Wilson Tabor
Board of Directors: Alison A Winter, Phyllis J Campbell, Michelle M Ebanks, Enrique Hernandez Jr, Robert G Miller, Philip G Satre, Brad D Smith, Gordon Smith, B Kevin Turner, Robert D Walter

D-U-N-S 02-205-3722
NORDSTROM OIL CO
HANDIMART FOOD STORES
1400 6th St Sw, Cedar Rapids, IA 52404-5841
Tel (319) 365-7594 *Founded/Ownrshp* 1973
Sales 59.0MM^E *EMP* 350
SIC 5541 5411 5172 5983 Filling stations, gasoline; Convenience stores; Service station supplies, petroleum; Fuel oil dealers; Filling stations, gasoline; Convenience stores; Service station supplies, petroleum; Fuel oil dealers
Pr: David Nordstrom
**CFO:* David Fry

D-U-N-S 07-953-4374
■ NORDSTROM PUERTO RICO LLC
(*Suby of* NORDSTROM INC) ★
4000 Mall Of San Juan Blv, San Juan, PR 00924-4007
Tel (787) 274-6300 *Founded/Ownrshp* 2014
Sales 14.5MM^E *EMP* 400
SIC 5621 5651 5661 5632 5611 5641 Women's clothing stores; Family clothing stores; Shoe stores; Women's accessory & specialty stores; Men's & boys' clothing stores; Children's & infants' wear stores; Children's wear
Store Mgr: Manolo Gonzalez

D-U-N-S 00-220-0749
NORDT CO INC JOHN C (VA)
GUERTIN BROS
1420 Coulter Dr Nw, Roanoke, VA 24012-1132
Tel (540) 362-4164 *Founded/Ownrshp* 1872
Sales 22.0MM^E *EMP* 130
SIC 3911 3915 Rings, finger: precious metal; Jewelers' castings; Rings, finger: precious metal; Jewelers' castings
Ch Bd: Paul W Nordt III
**Pr:* Nordt III Paul W
**CFO:* Gary Leatherman
**Ex VP:* Robert O Nordt Sr
**Ex VP:* Nordt Robert O
**VP:* Nordt William F
**VP:* William F Nordt
Dir IT: Tom Burns
VP Mfg: James Fletchall

D-U-N-S 01-119-5109
NORDX
(*Suby of* MAINEHEALTH) ★
301 Us Route 1 Ste A, Scarborough, ME 04074-4401
Tel (800) 773-5814 *Founded/Ownrshp* 1996
Sales 62.4MM *EMP* 13^E
SIC 8071 Medical laboratories
Pr: Stan Schofield
**COO:* J Joseph Fiore
**CFO:* James McAvoy
Comm Man: Matt Driscoll

D-U-N-S 07-866-0127
■ NORESCO INC
(*Suby of* CARRIER CORP) ★
1 Research Dr Ste 400c, Westborough, MA 01581-3963
Tel (508) 614-1000 *Founded/Ownrshp* 2001
Sales 98.4MM^E *EMP* 350^E
SIC 8711 8741 8748 4911 4924 Energy conservation engineering; Construction management; Energy conservation consultant; ; Natural gas distribution
Pr: Neil Petchers
Pr: Britta Macintosh
VP: Wade Carleton
VP: Jerry Reilley
VP: Gopal Shiddapur
Rgnl Mgr: Leonard Bernard
Brnch Mgr: David Mowrey
Off Admin: Lindsay Turner
IT Man: Chris Johnston
IT Man: Rick Matz
IT Man: Patricia Palanzo

D-U-N-S 60-672-7402
■ NORESCO LLC
(*Suby of* NORESCO INC) ★
1 Research Dr Ste 400c, Westborough, MA 01581-3963
Tel (508) 614-1000 *Founded/Ownrshp* 2008
Sales 98.4MM^E *EMP* 340
SIC 8711 8741 8744 8748 4911 4924 Energy conservation engineering; Construction management; Facilities support services; Energy conservation consultant; ; ; Energy conservation engineering; Construction management; Facilities support services; Energy conservation consultant; ;
Pr: Neil Petchers
Pr: Michael Beccaria
Pr: Randall Clark
Pr: Britta Macintosh
**CFO:* David G Mannherz
CFO: Jack Martin
**VP:* Paul Pimentel
Brnch Mgr: Paul Ravenelle
Dir IT: Christopher Johnston
Sfty Dirs: Kimberly Payson
Sls Mgr: Chuck Coyne

D-U-N-S 03-325-1401 IMP/EXP
NORFALCO LLC
(*Suby of* NORANDA FINANCE HOLDINGS INC) ★
6000 Lombardo Ctr Ste 650, Seven Hills, OH 44131-6916
Tel (216) 642-7342 *Founded/Ownrshp* 2001
Sales 202.8MM *EMP* 35^E
SIC 2819 Sulfuric acid, oleum; Sulfuric acid, oleum
Pr: Paul Shaw
Mktg Mgr: Christina Lundblad

D-U-N-S 04-165-0011
NORFIELD INDUSTRIES
725 Entler Ave, Chico, CA 95928-7411
Tel (530) 891-4214 *Founded/Ownrshp* 1959
Sales 23.0MM^E *EMP* 166
SIC 3553 5085

D-U-N-S 01-006-6959
NORFOLK ACADEMY (VA)
1585 Wesleyan Dr, Norfolk, VA 23502-5591
Tel (757) 461-6236 *Founded/Ownrshp* 1728
Sales 45.1MM *EMP* 175
Accts Mcphillips Roberts & Deans P
SIC 8211 Private combined elementary & secondary school; Private combined elementary & secondary school
Prin: Dennis G Manning
Ofcr: Kate Wilson
VP: Erin Cummings
Assoc Dir: Trent Blythe
Comm Dir: Vincent Delalla
Dir Bus: Betsy Guzik
HC Dir: Jay Lasley
HC Dir: Patricia McLaughlin

D-U-N-S 00-794-1644
■ NORFOLK AND WESTERN RAILWAY CO (INC)
(*Suby of* NORFOLK SOUTHERN RAILWAY CO) ★
3 Commercial Pl, Norfolk, VA 23510-2108
Tel (757) 629-2600 *Founded/Ownrshp* 1896, 1982
Sales 2.0MMM *EMP* 9
SIC 4011 Railroads, line-haul operating; Railroads, line-haul operating
Ch Bd: David R Goode
Treas: Ronald E Sink
**VP:* James C Bishop Jr
**VP:* L I Prillaman
**VP:* Stephen C Tobias

D-U-N-S 05-098-5969
NORFOLK BANANA DISTRIBUTORS INC
1104 Ingleside Rd, Norfolk, VA 23502-5609
Tel (757) 853-0694 *Founded/Ownrshp* 1970
Sales 65.0MM^E *EMP* 115
SIC 5148 Banana ripening; Fruits; Banana ripening; Fruits
IT Man: Cynthia Berney

D-U-N-S 05-098-9532 IMP
NORFOLK DREDGING CO
110 Centerville Tpke N, Chesapeake, VA 23320-3004
Tel (757) 547-9391 *Founded/Ownrshp* 1999
Sales 87.3MM^E *EMP* 180
SIC 1629 Dredging contractor; Dredging contractor
Pr: G Dudley Ware
**Sec:* James M Brady
**Sec:* Judith C Stultz
**Ex VP:* Mike B Haverty
**Ex VP:* F Graham Payne
**VP:* Paul C Knowles
VP: Paul Knowles
**VP:* Stephen M Newton
VP Mktg: Mike Haverty

D-U-N-S 00-749-7514
NORFOLK IRON & METAL CO
3001 N Victory Rd, Norfolk, NE 68701-0833
Tel (402) 371-1810 *Founded/Ownrshp* 1908
Sales 1.5M *EMP* 575^E
SIC 5051 3469 3356 Steel; Metal stampings; Nonferrous rolling & drawing; Steel; Metal stampings; Nonferrous rolling & drawing
Pr: Richard A Robinson
**CFO:* Steve C Ball
VP: Mike Fluent
Sfty Mgr: Skip Schleicher
Opers Mgr: Milt Wedgewood
Sales Asso: Thomas Smith

D-U-N-S 13-661-8506
NORFOLK IRON & METAL CO
1701 E South Ave, Emporia, KS 66801-9788
Tel (620) 342-9202 *Founded/Ownrshp* 2001
Sales 55.0MM^E *EMP* 200
SIC 5051 Steel; Steel
Pr: Jeff Beckmer
Sales Asso: Kevin Bikus
Sales Asso: Teresa Rozzell

NORFOLK PUBLIC SCHOOLS
See SCHOOL BOARD OF CITY OF NORFOLK

D-U-N-S 09-734-4675
NORFOLK PUBLIC SCHOOLS
512 W Phillip Ave, Norfolk, NE 68701-5208
Tel (402) 644-2500 *Founded/Ownrshp* 1900
Sales 34.1MM^E *EMP* 750
Accts Morrow Davies & Toelle Pc C
SIC 8211 Public combined elementary & secondary school; School board; Public combined elementary & secondary school; School board
**Treas:* Mary Meyer
Bd of Dir: Brad Krivohlavek

D-U-N-S 80-076-6136
NORFOLK PUBLIC SCHOOLS
800 E City Hall Ave # 1201, Norfolk, VA 23510-2723
Tel (757) 628-3830 *Founded/Ownrshp* 2007
Sales 107.4MM^E *EMP* 7,332^E
SIC 8211 Public elementary & secondary schools
Pr Dir: Elizabeth Mathers
Instr Medi: Elaine Marrion

D-U-N-S 87-933-0314
NORFOLK REDEVELOPMENT HOUSING AUTHORITY
NRHA
201 Granby St, Norfolk, VA 23510-1820
Tel (757) 623-1111 *Founded/Ownrshp* 1940
Sales 44.9MM^E *EMP* 400
SIC 8111 6531 Administrative & government law; Administrative & government law; Housing authority operator
CEO: Shurl R Montgomery
**CFO:* Clara W Graves
Netwrk Eng: Mike Diaz

D-U-N-S 04-918-4690 IMP
▲ NORFOLK SOUTHERN CORP
3 Commercial Pl Ste 1a, Norfolk, VA 23510-2108
Tel (757) 629-2680 *Founded/Ownrshp* 1980
Sales 11.6MMM *EMP* 29,482
Accts Kpmg Llp Norfolk Virginia
Tkr Sym NSC *Exch* NYS
SIC 4011 Railroads, line-haul operating; Railroads, line-haul operating
Ch Bd: Charles W Moorman
Pr: James Bolander
Pr: Robert C Fort
**Pr:* James A Squires
COO: Mark D Manion
CFO: Mike Monroe
CFO: Marta R Stewart
Chf Mktg O: Alan H Shaw
Ofcr: Adam Lively
Ofcr: Randy Rowan
Ofcr: Simon Scott
Ex VP: Deborah H Butler
Ex VP: Kitty Vollbrecht
VP: Joseph C Dimino
VP: Timothy J Drake
VP: Fred Ehlers
VP: Bob Fort
VP: Donald D Graab
VP: Jeffrey Heller
VP: Thomas E Hurlbut
VP: David F Julian
Board of Directors: Martin H Nesbitt, Thomas D Bell Jr, John R Thompson, Erskine B Bowles, Robert A Bradway, Wesley G Bush, Daniel A Carp, Karen N Horn, Steven F Leer, Michael D Lockhart, Amy E Miles

D-U-N-S 00-692-0417
■ NORFOLK SOUTHERN RAILWAY CO
(*Suby of* NORFOLK SOUTHERN CORP) ★
3 Commercial Pl Ste 1a, Norfolk, VA 23510-2108
Tel (757) 629-2680 *Founded/Ownrshp* 1894
Sales 2.3MMM^E *EMP* 28,057
SIC 4011 Railroads, line-haul operating; Railroads, line-haul operating
CEO: Charles W Moorman
COO: Mark D Manion
Treas: Judith K Sublett
Ex VP: James A Hixon
VP: Fredric M Ehlers
VP: Tim Heilig
VP: Michael R McClellan
VP: John P Rathbone
VP: James A Squires
VP: Marta R Stewarte
QA Dir: Stephen Skelley
Board of Directors: L I Prillaman, Stephen C Tobias

D-U-N-S 07-475-4805
NORFOLK STATE UNIVERSITY
700 Park Ave, Norfolk, VA 23504-8090
Tel (757) 823-8600 *Founded/Ownrshp* 1935
Sales 96.9MM^E *EMP* 1,095
SIC 8221 9411 University; Administration of educational programs; ; University; Administration of educational programs;
CEO: Eddie N Moore Jr
COO: Kim Luckes
COO: Patricia Mead
CFO: Marry Weaver
VP: Philip Adams
VP: Alvin Schexnider
Exec: Clarence Coleman
Exec: Charles Ford
Exec: Antwanne Marable
Exec: Samuel Ray
Exec: Pamela Riddick
Assoc Dir: Gail Levine

NORFOLK WIRE & ELECTRONICS
See NORFOLK WIRE - RICHMOND INC

D-U-N-S 13-140-1424
NORFOLK WIRE & ELECTRONICS INC
5301 Cleveland St, Virginia Beach, VA 23462-6524
Tel (757) 499-1100 *Founded/Ownrshp* 1985
Sales 26.4MM^E *EMP* 100
Accts Coopers & Lybrand Virginia Be

SIC 5063 Electrical apparatus & equipment; Electronic wire & cable; Wiring devices; Switches, except electronic; Electrical apparatus & equipment; Electronic wire & cable; Wiring devices; Switches, except electronic
Pr: Ronald A Hurley
Brnch Mgr: Clint Andrews
Brnch Mgr: Mike Egeland
Brnch Mgr: Ron Joye
Brnch Mgr: Brian Tucei
Brnch Mgr: T Watson
Brnch Mgr: Bernie Winn
Genl Mgr: Jamie Brookover
Off Mgr: Karen Aldridge
Sales Asso: Taylor Haycox
Sales Asso: Kim Joye

D-U-N-S 03-346-2388
NORFOLK WIRE - RICHMOND INC
NORFOLK WIRE & ELECTRONICS
5901 W Broad St, Richmond, VA 23230-2219
Tel (804) 521-6737 *Founded/Ownrshp* 2001
Sales 20.2MM^E *EMP* 12
SIC 5063 Electronic wire & cable
CEO: Ronald A Hurley
**Pr:* David Jarrett
**CFO:* Deryl Zalewski
Brnch Mgr: Mike Davis
Sales Asso: Lance Armstrong

D-U-N-S 00-257-4366
NORGLEN CORP
EMPIRE WAREHOUSE
629 Broadway, Long Branch, NJ 07740-5443
Tel (732) 222-3833 *Founded/Ownrshp* 1916, 1986
Sales 25.2MM^E *EMP* 135
SIC 5013 5531

D-U-N-S 00-538-9770 IMP
NORGREN AUTOMATION SOLUTIONS LLC
I.S.I. AUTOMATION PRODUCTS
(*Suby of* IMI PRECISION ENGINEERING) ★
1325 Woodland Dr, Saline, MI 48176-1626
Tel (734) 429-4989 *Founded/Ownrshp* 2012, 1996
Sales 44.0MM^E *EMP* 250
SIC 3549 Assembly machines, including robotic; Assembly machines, including robotic
Pr: Tim Key
**CFO:* Frank Alex
Manager: Ken Geromette
Sls Mgr: Todd Hoeft
Snr Mgr: Joseph Kania

D-U-N-S 00-705-9439 IMP
NORGREN INC
IMI PRECISION ENGINEERING
(*Suby of* IMI AMERICAS INC) ★
5400 S Delaware St, Littleton, CO 80120-1698
Tel (303) 794-5000 *Founded/Ownrshp* 1972
Sales 145.4MM^E *EMP* 673
SIC 3492 Control valves, fluid power: hydraulic & pneumatic; Control valves, fluid power: hydraulic & pneumatic
Pr: Robert Guerra
**CFO:* Matt Drosendahl
CFO: Liamy Kelly
VP: Richard Fish
VP: Donald McMahan
VP: Robin Papadimitrio
Area Mgr: Tom O'Donnell
Dir IT: Jim Wilson
Tech Mgr: Michael Suman
Sls&Mrk Ex: O'Dell Byron
Mktg Mgr: Rob Howard

D-U-N-S 07-120-3466 IMP
NORIBACHI CORP
1515 240th St, Harbor City, CA 90710-1308
Tel (855) 283-1100 *Founded/Ownrshp* 2011
Sales 22.0MM *EMP* 75
SIC 3646 3674 Commercial indusl & institutional electric lighting fixtures; Light emitting diodes
CEO: Farzad Dibachi
Pr: Troy Hesselgesser
**CFO:* Rhonda Dibachi
Board of Directors: Rhonda Dibachi

D-U-N-S 13-001-2599
NORIDIAN HEALTHCARE SOLUTIONS LLC
(*Suby of* BLUE CROSS BLUE SHIELD ND) ★
900 42nd St S, Fargo, ND 58103-2119
Tel (701) 277-6500 *Founded/Ownrshp* 2002
Sales NA *EMP* 1,909
SIC 6324 Hospital & medical service plans; Hospital & medical service plans
Pr: Tom McGraw
**CFO:* Richard Haugen
**Sr VP:* Kevin Erickson
**Sr VP:* Paul O'Donnell
**Sr VP:* Emy Stenerson
VP: Jeanne Narum
VP: Mark Tschider
IT Man: Karla Isley
Doctor: Monique Eva

D-U-N-S 07-313-0601
NORIDIAN MUTUAL INSURANCE CO
BLUE CROSS BLUE SHIELD ND
4510 13th Ave S, Fargo, ND 58121-0002
Tel (701) 282-1100 *Founded/Ownrshp* 1940
Sales NA *EMP* 16,000
SIC 6324 Group hospitalization plans; Group hospitalization plans
Pr: Tim Huckle
Pr: Jack Easton
Pr: Steven Rodvold
Pr: James Wynstra
COO: Tim Huckle
Ofcr: Rebecca Nichol
**Sr VP:* Dane Breuer
VP: Craig Campbell
VP: Dan Conrad
VP: Daniel Schwandt
**VP:* Judd Wagner
VP: Jacquelyn Walsh
Exec: Pat Bellmore

D-U-N-S 00-197-1142 IMP/EXP
NORITAKE CO INC
(*Suby of* NORITAKE CO., LIMITED)
15-22 Fair Lawn Ave, Fair Lawn, NJ 07410-2322
Tel (201) 796-2222 *Founded/Ownrshp* 1947, 1999
Sales 38.4MM^E *EMP* 150
SIC 5023 5085 5065 China; Abrasives; Electronic parts; China; Abrasives; Electronic parts
Ch: Hitoshi Tanemura
**Pr:* Tadashi Ogura
VP: Gereld Vollmer
Mktg Mgr: Peter Goldberger

D-U-N-S 09-642-3819 IMP
NORITSU AMERICA CORP (CA)
(*Suby of* NORITSU KOKI CO., LTD.)
6900 Noritsu Ave, Buena Park, CA 90620-1372
Tel (714) 521-9040 *Founded/Ownrshp* 1978
Sales 100.0MM^E *EMP* 310
SIC 5043 Photographic processing equipment; Photographic processing equipment
CEO: Michiro Niikura
**Ch Bd:* Kanichi Nishimoto
VP: Patrick Todd
VP: David Warburton
VP: Mehrdad Zolfaghari
**Prin:* Akihiko Kuwabara
IT Man: Sid Suraya
S&M/VP: Ron Kubara
Mktg Mgr: Raul Alvarez
Mktg Mgr: Gregory Joe
Manager: John Moore

D-U-N-S 11-378-7084 IMP
NORITZ AMERICA CORP
(*Suby of* NORITZ CORPORATION)
11160 Grace Ave, Fountain Valley, CA 92708-5436
Tel (714) 433-2905 *Founded/Ownrshp* 2001
Sales 37.0MM^E *EMP* 80
SIC 5075 Warm air heating equipment & supplies
CEO: Hisashi Uryu
**CEO:* Toshiyuki Otaki
VP Sls: Carlos Morales
Manager: Mike Gray
Manager: Kevin Tague
Sls Mgr: Fernando Castro
Sls Mgr: Ryan Simmerman

D-U-N-S 10-692-0028 IMP/EXP
NORIX GROUP INC
1800 W Hawthorne Ln Ste N, West Chicago, IL 60185-1863
Tel (630) 231-1331 *Founded/Ownrshp* 1983
Sales 22.5MM^E *EMP* 25
SIC 5021 2599 Furniture; Office & public building furniture; Cafeteria furniture
CEO: Richard B Karl
**Pr:* Scott C Karl
**Sr VP:* Heather L Karl
Exec: Ron Schram
IT Man: John Zheng
Prd Mgr: David Carlson
Mktg Dir: Brent Mayer
Sls Mgr: Jim Cook
Sls Mgr: Randy Duffer
Sls Mgr: Erich Massat

D-U-N-S 04-658-8422 IMP/EXP
NORKOL CONVERTING CORP
11650 W Grand Ave, Melrose Park, IL 60164-1300
Tel (708) 531-1000 *Founded/Ownrshp* 1968
Sales 79.2MM^E *EMP* 250
SIC 2621 Printing paper; Printing paper
Pr: Lawrence Kolinski
**Pr:* Michael Maloy
CFO: Dominick Fafhoda
**CFO:* Dominic Fashoda
**Sec:* Mary Ellen Kolinski
**Sr VP:* Ellen Rehm
VP: Michael Doherty
VP: Richard Harris
Genl Mgr: James Anderson
Prd Mgr: Michael Schippers
Prd Mgr: Kevin Westerman

D-U-N-S 04-530-8830
NORKOL INC
11650 W Grand Ave, Northlake, IL 60164-1300
Tel (708) 531-1000 *Founded/Ownrshp* 1985
Sales 127.1MM^E *EMP* 175
SIC 2679 Book covers, paper; Book covers, paper
Pr: Denise M Callahan
Ch Bd: Lawrence Kolinski
CFO: Dominick Fashoda
Sec: Mary E Kolinski
VP: Michael Doherty
VP: James Lindquist
Exec: Ellen Rehm
Genl Mgr: Eric Holzer

D-U-N-S 01-127-5468
NORKUS ENTERPRISES INC
FOODTOWN
505 Richmond Ave, Point Pleasant Beach, NJ 08742-2552
Tel (732) 899-8485 *Founded/Ownrshp* 1935
Sales 129.7MM^E *EMP* 1,000
SIC 5411 Supermarkets, independent; Supermarkets, independent
Pr: Gerard K Norkus
**VP:* Mark F Norkus

D-U-N-S 17-443-7962 IMP
NORLAINE INC
PATINA V
1449 W Industrial Park St, Covina, CA 91722-3414
Tel (626) 961-2471 *Founded/Ownrshp* 1991
Sales 27.5MM^E *EMP* 200
SIC 3999 Mannequins; Mannequins
CEO: Norman Glazer
**CFO:* Stan Chen

D-U-N-S 00-445-4690 EXP
NORLAKE MANUFACTURING CO (OH)
39301 Taylor Pkwy, Elyria, OH 44035-6272
Tel (440) 353-3200 *Founded/Ownrshp* 1963
Sales 41.8MM^E *EMP* 90
SIC 3677 3714 3612 Transformers power supply, electronic type; Motor vehicle parts & accessories; Transformers, except electric
Pr: James Markus
CFO: Bruce Pastermak
**VP:* Daryl Jackson
IT Man: Mary Strandburg
Prd Mgr: Kenneth Sroka

D-U-N-S 82-506-2318 IMP/EXP
NORLAND INTERNATIONAL INC
2001 Sw 6th St, Lincoln, NE 68522-1732
Tel (402) 441-3737 *Founded/Ownrshp* 1993
Sales 20.0MM^E *EMP* 27
SIC 5074 Water purification equipment
Pr: Mike McFarland
**CEO:* Don Liu
**Treas:* Sam Noordhoff
**VP:* Bruce Kucera
Sls Mgr: Daren Waters
Sales Asso: Jon Marco
Sales Asso: Chris McCormack

D-U-N-S 18-194-3531
NORLARCO CREDIT UNION
2545 Research Blvd, Fort Collins, CO 80526-8108
Tel (970) 416-5000 *Founded/Ownrshp* 1959
Sales NA *EMP* 130
SIC 6062 State credit unions, not federally chartered; State credit unions, not federally chartered
Pr: Ray Swanson
**CEO:* Bob Hamer
**CEO:* Dave Maus

D-U-N-S 00-614-3341
NORLEN INC
900 Grossman Dr, Schofield, WI 54476-1845
Tel (715) 355-7538 *Founded/Ownrshp* 1964
Sales 32.5MM *EMP* 115
Accts Wipfli Llp Wausau Wisconsin
SIC 3469 3599 3443 Stamping metal for the trade; Machine shop, jobbing & repair; Fabricated plate work (boiler shop); Stamping metal for the trade; Machine shop, jobbing & repair; Fabricated plate work (boiler shop)
Pr: Thomas A Suthers
**VP:* Darlene S Suthers
IT Man: Gary Gebert
Mfg Mgr: Allen Larsen
Sls Dir: Rod Dash
Sales Asso: Todd Marciniak

D-U-N-S 15-403-0183
NORLIFT OF OREGON INC
7373 Se Milwaukie Expy, Portland, OR 97222-1243
Tel (503) 659-5438 *Founded/Ownrshp* 1985
Sales 40.0MM^E *EMP* 55
SIC 5084 7699 3537 Materials handling machinery; Industrial machinery & equipment repair; Forklift trucks
Pr: Thomas Leslie
Exec: Maureen Davis
CTO: Jan Davis
Sales Asso: Peter Kresse

D-U-N-S 06-991-9934
NORLITE CORP
(*Suby of* TRADEBE ENVIRONMENTAL SERVICES LLC) ★
628 Saratoga St, Cohoes, NY 12047-4697
Tel (518) 235-0030 *Founded/Ownrshp* 1973
Sales 44.5MM^E *EMP* 325
SIC 3295 Shale, expanded; Shale, expanded
Pr: Robert O'Brien
**Sec:* Michael Ferraro
VP: Brian Abely
Dir IT: Mark Hewitt

D-U-N-S 02-769-8356
NORM POOLE OIL INC
87 Se 7th Ave, Ontario, OR 97914-3654
Tel (541) 889-3128 *Founded/Ownrshp* 1961
Sales 43.3MM^E *EMP* 11
Accts Stephen D Long Cpa Ontario
SIC 5172 Diesel fuel; Gasoline; Lubricating oils & greases; Service station supplies, petroleum; Diesel fuel; Gasoline; Lubricating oils & greases; Service station supplies, petroleum
Pr: Ralph E Poole

NORM REEVES HONDA
See COASTAL AUTO SALES INC

NORM REEVES HONDA SUPERSTORE
See NORM REEVES INC

NORM REEVES HONDA SUPERSTORE
See WEST COVINA AUTO RETAIL INC

D-U-N-S 09-786-9218
NORM REEVES INC
NORM REEVES HONDA SUPERSTORE
18500 Studebaker Rd, Cerritos, CA 90703-5337
Tel (562) 402-3844 *Founded/Ownrshp* 1995
Sales 129.7MM^E *EMP* 325
SIC 5511 5521 Automobiles, new & used; Used car dealers; Automobiles, new & used; Used car dealers
CEO: David M Conant
**Sec:* Marlene Lewis
**VP:* Lee Stacey
Genl Mgr: John Dalpe

D-U-N-S 06-344-3949 IMP
■ **NORM THOMPSON OUTFITTERS INC**
SAHALIE
(*Suby of* BEDFORD FAIR APPAREL) ★
3188 Nw Aloclek Dr, Hillsboro, OR 97124-7134
Tel (503) 690-8462 *Founded/Ownrshp* 1981
Sales 122.5MM^E *EMP* 500
SIC 5961 5947 5611 5621 Catalog sales; Gift items, mail order; Clothing, mail order (except women's); Women's apparel, mail order; Gift shop; Men's & boys' clothing stores; Women's clothing stores; Catalog sales; Gift items, mail order; Clothing, mail order (except women's); Women's apparel, mail order; Gift shop; Men's & boys' clothing stores; Women's clothing stores
Pr: Martin McClanan
V Ch: Rebecca Jewitt
Pr: Kristin Fisch
CFO: Bill Stanners
**V Ch Bd:* Rebecca L Jewett
**Sr VP:* William J Stanner Jr
VP: Adrienne Cote
VP: David Lamb
VP: Louisa Van Eepoel
Creative D: Elaine Olson
Ex Dir: John Snyder
Board of Directors: Patrick J Connolly, Al W Emrick Jr, Larry B Gordon

D-U-N-S 06-981-9431 IMP
NORMA MICHIGAN INC
NORMA PRODUCTS US
(*Suby of* NORMA GROUP SE)
2430 E Walton Blvd, Auburn Hills, MI 48326-1956
Tel (248) 373-4300 *Founded/Ownrshp* 1974
Sales 41.8MM^E *EMP* 200^E
SIC 3498 3714 3713 3429 Couplings, pipe: fabricated from purchased pipe; Motor vehicle parts & accessories; Truck & bus bodies; Manufactured hardware (general); Couplings, pipe: fabricated from purchased pipe; Motor vehicle parts & accessories; Truck & bus bodies; Manufactured hardware (general)
CEO: Werner Deggim
Pr: Timothy Jones
COO: John Stephenson
CFO: Othmar Belker
CFO: Ron Laboda
VP: Ron Loboda
VP: Aaron Lopas
VP Opers: Tony Tibbitts
Opers Mgr: Tina Turlescu
Sls Mgr: Greg Nibling
Sls Mgr: Mike Slavin

D-U-N-S 03-185-3240 IMP
NORMA PENNSYLVANIA INC
BREEZE INDUSTRIAL PRODUCTS
(*Suby of* NORMA GROUP HOLDING GMBH)
3582 Tunnelton Rd, Saltsburg, PA 15681-3305
Tel (724) 639-3571 *Founded/Ownrshp* 2007
Sales 137.1MM^E *EMP* 465
SIC 3429 Clamps & couplings, hose; Clamps & couplings, hose
CEO: Werner Deggim
**Pr:* Tim Jones
**Pr:* Mike Russel
**COO:* John Stephenson
**CFO:* Othmar Belker
**Sec:* Durg Kumar
Sales Exec: Lynnette Kinter
Sls Mgr: John Seifert

NORMA PRODUCTS US
See NORMA MICHIGAN INC

NORMACK
See N C HOLDINGS

D-U-N-S 07-919-7293
NORMAL EARS INC
150 W 22nd St Frnt 1, New York, NY 10011-2421
Tel (617) 448-2744 *Founded/Ownrshp* 2013
Sales 30.0MM *EMP* 22
SIC 7371 Computer software development & applications; Computer software development & applications
CEO: Nikki Kaufman

NORMAL LIFE OF SHERIDAN
See TRANSITIONAL HEALTH PARTNERS

NORMAN BOARD OF EDUCATION
See INDEPENDENT SCHOOL DISTRICT I-29

NORMAN CHARTER
See NORMAN INTERNATIONAL INC

NORMAN CHRYSLER JEEP DODGE
See NORMAN CHRYSLER-JEEP INC

D-U-N-S 10-240-2716
NORMAN CHRYSLER-JEEP INC
NORMAN CHRYSLER JEEP DODGE
481 N Interstate Dr, Norman, OK 73069-6304
Tel (405) 321-8228 *Founded/Ownrshp* 1983
Sales 27.1MM^E *EMP* 75
SIC 5511 Automobiles, new & used; Automobiles, new & used
Pr: Bob Nouri
**VP:* Doug Travis

D-U-N-S 00-826-4691
NORMAN DISTRIBUTION INC
940 Greenleaf Ave, Elk Grove Village, IL 60007-5011
Tel (847) 228-2887 *Founded/Ownrshp* 2009
Sales 20.4MM^E *EMP* 25
SIC 5141 Food brokers
Pr: Norman Ryan Meczyk
Pr: Jeff Lozinski
VP: Zachary C Damato
VP: Zachary Nudeolman

D-U-N-S 00-175-1171
NORMAN EQUIPMENT CO
9850 Industrial Dr, Bridgeview, IL 60455-2319
Tel (708) 430-4000 *Founded/Ownrshp* 1946, 1986
Sales 36.6MM^E *EMP* 110
SIC 5084 3569

D-U-N-S 06-456-6961 IMP
NORMAN FOX & CO
14970 Don Julian Rd, City of Industry, CA 91746-3111
Tel (626) 581-5600 *Founded/Ownrshp* 1971
Sales 63.4MM^E *EMP* 42
SIC 5169 2841 Chemicals & allied products; Soap: granulated, liquid, cake, flaked or chip; Detergents, synthetic organic or inorganic alkaline
Pr: Stephen Halpin
VP: Patrick Morris

D-U-N-S 04-630-4317
NORMAN FREDE CHEVROLET CO
16801 Feather Craft Ln, Houston, TX 77058-2693
Tel (281) 486-2200 *Founded/Ownrshp* 1968
Sales 64.1MM^E *EMP* 126

SIC 5511 Automobiles, new & used; Trucks, tractors & trailers: new & used; Automobiles, new & used; Trucks, tractors & trailers: new & used
Pr: Norman Frede
Genl Mgr: Joan McKinney
IT Exec: Laura Grabach
Sales Exec: Mark Brown
Sls Dir: Nick Norris
Sls Mgr: Tony Marino
Sales Asso: Nathan Cook

D-U-N-S 04-316-5703 IMP/EXP
NORMAN G JENSEN INC (MN)
(*Suby of* LIVINGSTON INTERNATIONAL INC) ★
3050 Metro Dr Ste 300, Minneapolis, MN 55425-1545
Tel (952) 854-7363 *Founded/Ownrshp* 1937, 2012
Sales 50.3MM^E *EMP* 400
SIC 4731

D-U-N-S 11-922-3543 IMP
NORMAN GROUP INC
NORMANS HALLMARK
126 Terry Dr, Newtown, PA 18940-1851
Tel (215) 579-2600 *Founded/Ownrshp* 1963
Sales 77.3MM^E *EMP* 900
SIC 5947 Gift shop; Greeting cards; Gift shop; Greeting cards
Pr: Howard Henschel
Treas: Joan Henschel
**Treas:* Harold Norman
VP: Vince Navitsky

D-U-N-S 02-795-7695 IMP/EXP
NORMAN INDUSTRIAL MATERIALS INC
INDUSTRIAL METAL SUPPLY CO
8300 San Fernando Rd, Sun Valley, CA 91352-3222
Tel (818) 729-3333 *Founded/Ownrshp* 1945
Sales 162.8MM^E *EMP* 300
SIC 5051 3441 3449 Metals service centers & offices; Fabricated structural metal; Miscellaneous metalwork; Metals service centers & offices; Fabricated structural metal; Miscellaneous metalwork
CEO: Eric Steinhauer
**COO:* David Pace
CFO: Cleve Adams
**CFO:* David Berkey
Genl Mgr: Dan Seigel
Sfty Mgr: Julio Galvez
Ql Cn Mgr: Diana Rising
Sls Mgr: Aaron Brown
Sales Asso: Gary Barbour
Sales Asso: Mark Hernandez
Sales Asso: Stephanie Soriano

D-U-N-S 02-081-0540 IMP/EXP
NORMAN INTERNATIONAL INC
NORMAN CHARTER
12301 Hawkins St, Santa Fe Springs, CA 90670-3366
Tel (562) 946-0420 *Founded/Ownrshp* 2001
Sales 60.1MM^E *EMP* 70
SIC 5023 Home furnishings
CEO: Ranjan Mada
Dir IT: Ricky Wang
IT Man: James Wang
Sales Exec: Chris Warner
Manager: Dan Ogilvie
Manager: Carreen Toland
Manager: Janine Tuttle
Sls Mgr: Lynne Huang
Sls Mgr: Chuck Riegel

D-U-N-S 04-981-6978
NORMAN MECHANICAL INC
HARD CORE CORING & CON CUTNG
3850 Industrial Ave, Rolling Meadows, IL 60008-1022
Tel (847) 253-2238 *Founded/Ownrshp* 1976
Sales 25.6MM^E *EMP* 150
SIC 1711 Plumbing contractors; Plumbing contractors
Pr: Martin Nixon

D-U-N-S 11-973-7088
NORMAN MOORE TECHNOLOGY CENTER
4701 12th Ave Nw, Norman, OK 73069-8308
Tel (405) 364-5763 *Founded/Ownrshp* 1972
Sales 16.6MM^E *EMP* 500
SIC 8249 8211 Vocational schools; Elementary & secondary schools; Vocational schools; Elementary & secondary schools

D-U-N-S 00-417-5147
NORMAN NOBLE INC (OH)
5507 Avion Park Dr, Highland Heights, OH 44143-1921
Tel (216) 761-5387 *Founded/Ownrshp* 1962
Sales 85.7MM^E *EMP* 400
SIC 3599 Machine shop, jobbing & repair; Machine shop, jobbing & repair
Pr: Lawrence Noble
**VP:* Chris Noble
**VP:* Dan Stefano
Genl Mgr: Rick Link
Dir IT: Rebecca Noble
Opers Mgr: Rob Ellins
Natl Sales: Brian Hrouda

D-U-N-S 07-427-8896 IMP
NORMAN REGIONAL HOSPITAL AUTHORITY
901 N Porter Ave, Norman, OK 73071-6482
Tel (405) 307-1000 *Founded/Ownrshp* 1927
Sales 347.1MM *EMP* 2,900
Accts Bkd Llp Tulsa Oklahoma
SIC 8062 General medical & surgical hospitals; General medical & surgical hospitals
Pr: David Whitaker
Chf Rad: Merl Kardokus
COO: Greg Terrel
Bd of Dir: Carol Anderson
Ofcr: Janice Carr
**Sr VP:* Greg Terrell
**VP:* Melvin Alexander
**VP:* Nancy A Brown
VP: Nancy Brown
**VP:* Meegan Carter
VP: Kathey Drummond
**VP:* Ken Hopkins
**VP:* Richie Splitt
Dir Inf Cn: Sam McAdams
Dir Rx: James Hughes
Dir Rx: Darin Smith
Board of Directors: Robin Wiens Campbell, Terry J Garrett

D-U-N-S 02-926-5063
NORMAN S WRIGHT CO MANUFACTURERS REPRESENTATIVE
2121 E Magnolia St, Phoenix, AZ 85034-6814
Tel (602) 275-4467 *Founded/Ownrshp* 1951
Sales 30.0MM *EMP* 50
SIC 5075 Air conditioning equipment, except room units
Treas: Beatrice Langmade
**Pr:* Dianne Langmade
**CEO:* Robert H Langmade
**Treas:* Timothy J Murphy
**VP:* David Gallegos
**VP:* Dale Langmade
**VP:* Thomas P Watters

D-U-N-S 10-283-8588
NORMAN S WRIGHT MECHANICAL EQUIPMENT CORP
99 S Hill Dr Ste A, Brisbane, CA 94005-1282
Tel (415) 467-7600 *Founded/Ownrshp* 1906
Sales 153.6MM^E *EMP* 115
SIC 5075 Warm air heating equipment & supplies; Air conditioning & ventilation equipment & supplies; Warm air heating equipment & supplies; Air conditioning & ventilation equipment & supplies
Pr: Richard F Leao
**Ex VP:* Robert L Beyer
**Ex VP:* Salvatore M Giglio

D-U-N-S 80-278-8836
NORMAN S WRIGHT/AIRELINK MECHANICAL EQUIPMENT LLC
AIRLINKS PRODUCTS
13031 Bradley Ave, Sylmar, CA 91342-3832
Tel (818) 367-6100 *Founded/Ownrshp* 2002
Sales 33.8MM^E *EMP* 43
SIC 5075 Air conditioning & ventilation equipment & supplies

D-U-N-S 14-005-9549 EXP
NORMAN W FRIES INC
CLAXTON POULTRY FARMS
8816 Us Highway 301, Claxton, GA 30417-5428
Tel (912) 739-1158 *Founded/Ownrshp* 1958
Sales 228.8MM^E *EMP* 1,700
SIC 2015 Chicken slaughtering & processing; Chicken slaughtering & processing
CEO: Doris Fries
**Pr:* Jerry Lane
CFO: Greg Finch
Sfty Dirs: David Moore

D-U-N-S 00-348-1348 IMP
NORMAN W PASCHALL CO INC (GA)
1 Paschall Rd, Peachtree City, GA 30269-1692
Tel (770) 487-7945 *Founded/Ownrshp* 1946
Sales 63.5MM^E *EMP* 120^E
SIC 5159 4953 Cotton merchants & products; Refuse systems; Cotton merchants & products; Refuse systems
Pr: Norman W Paschall
**VP:* Charles P Stephens
VP Sls: Michael Carroll

D-U-N-S 07-933-1007
NORMAN YORK INTERNATIONAL
JCI
5005 York Dr, Norman, OK 73069-9504
Tel (405) 364-4040 *Founded/Ownrshp* 2005
Sales 330.0MM *EMP* 600
SIC 5075 Warm air heating & air conditioning; Warm air heating & air conditioning

D-U-N-S 19-966-4798
NORMAN-SPENCER AGENCY INC
MIAMI VALLEY INSURANCE ASSOC
8075 Washington Vlg Dr, Dayton, OH 45458-1847
Tel (937) 432-1600 *Founded/Ownrshp* 1988
Sales 29.1MM^E *EMP* 37
SIC 5088 Marine supplies
Ch Bd: Paul J Norman
**Pr:* Brian Norman
CFO: Pat Malone
Bd of Dir: Brian Harrold
Bd of Dir: Greg Rose
Sr VP: Debbie George
VP: Phil Keeter
**VP:* Sandy Welker
Sales Exec: Lynn Dorton
Mktg Dir: Chris Hoffer
Sls Dir: Joe Drozda

D-U-N-S 07-832-5744
NORMANDALE COMMUNITY COLLEGE
9700 France Ave S, Bloomington, MN 55431-4399
Tel (952) 358-8200 *Founded/Ownrshp* 1977
Sales 25.8MM^E *EMP* 191^E
SIC 8221 Colleges & universities
VP: Tom Peterson
Exec: Dionne Doering
Off Mgr: Amanda Ryan
**CIO:* Stephen Winckelman
Mktg Dir: Geoffrey Jones
Psych: Kristen Cooper
Nrsg Dir: Katherine Andersen
Pgrm Dir: Amanda Gustafson
Snr Mgr: Sanu Patel-Zellinger

D-U-N-S 82-487-0786
NORMANDEAU ASSOCIATES INC
25 Nashua Rd, Bedford, NH 03110-5500
Tel (508) 548-0700 *Founded/Ownrshp* 2000
Sales 47.9MM^E *EMP* 285
Accts Feeley & Driscoll Pc Bosto
SIC 8748 Environmental consultant; Environmental consultant
Pr: Pamela S Hall
**CFO:* Susan Sanborn
Ex VP: Robert Varney
**Sr VP:* Peter C Kinner
VP: Robert Bibbo
**VP:* Paul Harmon
**VP:* Dilip Mathur
**VP:* Mark T Mattson
VP: Christian Newman
**VP:* Mike Scherer
Off Admin: Alexis Hampton

NORMANDIE CASINO & SHOWROOM
See NORMANDIE CLUB LP

D-U-N-S 02-822-6306 IMP
NORMANDIE CLUB LP
NORMANDIE CASINO & SHOWROOM
1045 W Rosecrans Ave, Gardena, CA 90247-2601
Tel (310) 352-3486 *Founded/Ownrshp* 1961
Sales 31.7MM^E *EMP* 600
SIC 7999 5812 Card & game services; Eating places; Card & game services; Eating places
Mng Pt: Lawrence F Miller
Genl Pt: Russel Miller Jr
Pt: Greg Miller
Info Man: Bill Curd
Mktg Dir: Marco Casillas
Mktg Mgr: Sandra Holtzmann

D-U-N-S 07-938-3867
NORMANDIE/WILSHIRE RETIREMENT HOTEL INC
CALIFORNIA HEALTHCARE AND REHA
6700 Sepulveda Blvd, Van Nuys, CA 91411-1248
Tel (818) 373-5429 *Founded/Ownrshp* 2014
Sales 21.5MM *EMP* 99
SIC 6513 8059 Retirement hotel operation; Convalescent home

NORMANDIN CHRYSLER JEEP
See NORMANDINS

D-U-N-S 02-929-9757
NORMANDINS
NORMANDIN CHRYSLER JEEP
900 Cptl Expy Aut Mall, San Jose, CA 95136-1102
Tel (408) 266-9500 *Founded/Ownrshp* 1980
Sales 20.3MM^E *EMP* 119
SIC 7538 5511 General automotive repair shops; New & used car dealers; General automotive repair shops; New & used car dealers
CEO: Mark Normandin
**Ex VP:* Paul Normandin
**VP:* Margaret Normandin
Store Mgr: Doug Kasch
Sls Mgr: Ronnie Cho

D-U-N-S 15-299-4369
NORMANDY REAL ESTATE MANAGEMENT LLC
NORMANDY REAL ESTATE PARTNERS
53 Maple Ave, Morristown, NJ 07960-5219
Tel (973) 898-1160 *Founded/Ownrshp* 2004
Sales 27.3MM^E *EMP* 100^E
SIC 6726 Investment offices; Investment offices
Sr VP: Melissa Donohoe
Sr VP: Stephen Trapp
VP: Jamie Nicholson
Dir Sec: John Cappetta
Genl Mgr: Javier Lezamiz
Genl Mgr: Ken Negri
Off Mgr: Susan Kloss

NORMANDY REAL ESTATE PARTNERS
See NORMANDY REAL ESTATE MANAGEMENT LLC

D-U-N-S 61-939-8022
NORMANDY REAL ESTATE PARTNERS LLC
53 Maple Ave, Morristown, NJ 07960-5219
Tel (973) 898-1160 *Founded/Ownrshp* 2003
Sales 40.0MM^E *EMP* 100
SIC 6799 Real estate investors, except property operators
VP: David Galdi

D-U-N-S 07-589-5193
NORMANDY SCHOOLS COLLABORATIVE
3855 Lcas Hunt Rd Ste 100, Saint Louis, MO 63121
Tel (314) 493-0446 *Founded/Ownrshp* 1894
Sales 52.4MM^E *EMP* 99
SIC 8211 Public combined elementary & secondary school; Public combined elementary & secondary school
Ofcr: Charles Carter-Oliver
**Ofcr:* Candice Carter-Oliver
**Ofcr:* Mick Willis
Dir Sec: Fred Abernathy
Teacher Pr: Brenda Harris

NORMANDY TERRACE NURSING REHAB
See SENIOR MANAGEMENT SERVICES OF NORMANDY AT SAN ANTONIO INC

D-U-N-S 01-178-7603
NORMANS GIFT SHOPS III INC
NORMAN'S HALLMARK
(*Suby of* NORMAN GROUP INC) ★
126 Terry Dr, Newtown, PA 18940-1851
Tel (215) 579-2600 *Founded/Ownrshp* 1965
Sales 52.4MM^E *EMP* 600
SIC 5947 Greeting cards; Greeting cards
Pr: Howard Henschel

NORMAN'S HALLMARK
See NORMANS GIFT SHOPS III INC

NORMANS HALLMARK
See NORMAN GROUP INC

D-U-N-S 02-889-9748 EXP
NORMANS NURSERY INC
8665 Duarte Rd, San Gabriel, CA 91775-1139
Tel (626) 285-9795 *Founded/Ownrshp* 1949
Sales 219.5MM^E *EMP* 620
SIC 5193 0181 Nursery stock; Nursery stock, growing of; Nursery stock; Nursery stock, growing of
Pr: Charles Norman
**Treas:* Caroline Norman

D-U-N-S 00-620-0315 IMP
NORMARK CORP (MN)
RAPALA
(*Suby of* N C HOLDINGS) ★
10395 Yellow Circle Dr, Hopkins, MN 55343-9133
Tel (952) 939-4391 *Founded/Ownrshp* 1962, 1998
Sales 41.6MM^E *EMP* 60^E
SIC 5091 3949 Sporting & recreation goods; Fishing tackle; Hunting equipment & supplies; Bait, artificial: fishing
Pr: Tom Mackin
**VP:* Nancy Adelmann
VP: Naomi Dwyer
VP: Gregg Wollner
CIO: Brian Behrens
Dir IT: Bob Miller
VP Opers: Rick Billings
Trfc Mgr: Mark Suttle
VP Sls: George Large
Manager: Matt Jensen
Sales Asso: John Holterhaus

D-U-N-S 18-278-9412
NORMENT SECURITY GROUP INC
AIRTEQ
(*Suby of* CORNERSTONE DETENTION PRODUCTS INC) ★
2511 Midpark Rd, Montgomery, AL 36109-1407
Tel (334) 281-8440 *Founded/Ownrshp* 2014
Sales 25.6MM^E *EMP* 148
Accts Mcgladrey & Pullen Llp Denve
SIC 7382 Confinement surveillance systems maintenance & monitoring
Pr: Charles Veniez
CFO: Richard Covington
CFO: David Watts
VP: David Beeler
VP: Thomas J Hammer
VP: Jack Johnson
VP: Chad Lucynski
VP: Jim Mann
VP: Adam Yapkowitz
Off Mgr: Sheila Gross
Dir IT: Greg Cain

NORMS
See NORMS RESTAURANTS

D-U-N-S 05-240-2450
NORMS RESTAURANTS
NORMS
17844 Lakewood Blvd, Bellflower, CA 90706-6414
Tel (562) 867-4511 *Founded/Ownrshp* 1949
Sales 43.9MM^E *EMP* 1,100
SIC 5812 American restaurant; American restaurant
CEO: Philip H Singerman
**Pr:* Sterling Bogart
**VP:* Janice Derowen

NORO PARKING
See BCD PARKING INC

D-U-N-S 00-122-7131 IMP/EXP
NOROC ENTERPRISES INC
415 Concord Ave, Bronx, NY 10455-4801
Tel (718) 585-3230 *Founded/Ownrshp* 1987
Sales 21.0MM^E *EMP* 150
SIC 3251 3053 Fireproofing tile, clay; Gasket materials; Fireproofing tile, clay; Gasket materials
CEO: Elias Wexler
**VP:* Jerry Heid

NORPAC
See NORTH PACIFIC PAPER CORP

D-U-N-S 00-905-8561 IMP
NORPAC FOODS INC (OR)
3225 25th St Se, Salem, OR 97302
Tel (503) 480-2100 *Founded/Ownrshp* 1924
Sales 1.1MMM^E *EMP* 4,000
SIC 2037 2033 2038 Fruits, quick frozen & cold pack (frozen); Vegetables, quick frozen & cold pack, excl. potato products; Fruits: packaged in cans, jars, etc.; Vegetables: packaged in cans, jars, etc.; Soups, frozen; Fruits, quick frozen & cold pack (frozen); Vegetables, quick frozen & cold pack, excl. potato products; Fruits: packaged in cans, jars, etc.; Vegetables: packaged in cans, jars, etc.; Soups, frozen
Pr: George Smith
**CFO:* Jon Greeley
VP: Steve Cerri
VP: Al Lave
VP: Tom Lelmini
VP: Manuel Silveira
Dir IT: Barry Brown
Dir IT: Joe Vondrachek
IT Man: Dave Early
**VP Opers:* Bill Burich
Sfty Mgr: Ray Noble

NORPAK
See NORTON PACKAGING INC

D-U-N-S 01-210-7459 IMP
NORPLAS INDUSTRIES INC
MAGNA
(*Suby of* DECOMA ADMARK) ★
7825 Caple Blvd, Northwood, OH 43619-1070
Tel (419) 662-3317 *Founded/Ownrshp* 1997
Sales 348.4MM^E *EMP* 1,000^E
SIC 3469 Metal stampings; Metal stampings
CEO: Donald J Walker
**VP:* Graham Burrow
Prgrm Mgr: Doug Leader
IT Man: Russ Keckler
Mfg Mgr: Chad Suntken
Opers Mgr: Andrew Watson
Snr Mgr: Tim Croll

NORPRO
See NORDIC PRODUCTS INC

D-U-N-S 05-750-4599
NORQUIST SALVAGE CORP INC
THRIFT TOWN
2151 Prof Dr Ste 200, Roseville, CA 95661
Tel (916) 787-1070 *Founded/Ownrshp* 1972
Sales 109.6MM^E *EMP* 700
SIC 5932

D-U-N-S 06-436-0878
NORRED & ASSOCIATES INC
1003 Virginia Ave Ste 200, Atlanta, GA 30354-1387
Tel (404) 761-5058 *Founded/Ownrshp* 1981
Sales 36.7MM^E *EMP* 650
SIC 8742 7381 Industry specialist consultants; Private investigator; Security guard service; Protective services, guard; Industry specialist consultants; Private investigator; Security guard service; Protective services, guard
CEO: Greg D Norred
**Pr:* Jeff Bohling
**Pr:* Charles R Simmons
CFO: Jeff Bowling
**VP:* Danielle Getman
Opers Mgr: John Wilkins

D-U-N-S 06-243-4329
NORRENBERNS FOODS INC
TOM'S SUPERMARKETS
205 E Harnett St, Mascoutah, IL 62258-1405
Tel (618) 566-7010 *Founded/Ownrshp* 1978
Sales 59.1MM^E *EMP* 400
SIC 5411 Grocery stores; Grocery stores
Pr: Donald T Norrenberns
**COO:* Thomas J Schmutz
Plnt Mgr: Bob Butz

NORRENBERNS TRUCK SERVICE
See TKT INC

D-U-N-S 82-559-3114
NORRIS BEGGS & SIMPSON NORTHWEST LIMITED PARTNERSHIP
N A I
121 Sw Morrison St # 200, Portland, OR 97204-3117
Tel (503) 223-7181 *Founded/Ownrshp* 1993
Sales 21.7MM *EMP* 170
Accts Perkins & Co Pc Portland
SIC 6531 Real estate managers; Real estate managers
Pt: L Jan Robertson
Pt: Kenneth J Griggs
Pt: J Clayton Hering
Pt: Chris Johnson
Pt: H Roger Qualman
Pt: Jan Robertson
Pr: Blake Hering
Ofcr: Mick Stapleton
Assoc VP: Scott Maclean
Assoc VP: Mary Mitch
Assoc VP: Maija Mueller
Ex VP: Jenifer McWade
Ex VP: Michael Wood
VP: Tamara Fuller
VP: Todd Harding
VP: Melody Martinez
VP: Joy Thayer

D-U-N-S 00-445-5663
NORRIS BROTHERS CO INC (OH)
2138 Davenport Ave, Cleveland, OH 44114-3724
Tel (216) 771-2233 *Founded/Ownrshp* 1867
Sales 20.8MM^E *EMP* 120
SIC 1796 1541 7699 1771 Machinery installation; Industrial buildings, new construction; Boiler repair shop; Concrete work; Machinery installation; Industrial buildings, new construction; Boiler repair shop; Concrete work
Pr: Bernard E Weir Jr
**Pr:* Kenneth McBride
**Sec:* Catherine McBride
VP: Richard S Thomas

D-U-N-S 86-133-6493 IMP/EXP
■ **NORRIS CYLINDER CO**
(*Suby of* TRIMAS CORP) ★
4818 W Loop 281 S, Longview, TX 75603-8405
Tel (903) 757-7633 *Founded/Ownrshp* 1988
Sales 49.9MM^E *EMP* 250^E
SIC 3443 Cylinders, pressure: metal plate; Cylinders, pressure: metal plate
Pr: Jerry Van Auken
Pr: Brian McGuire
Treas: Robert J Zalupski
VP: A Mark Zeffiro
Genl Mgr: Jerry Banauken
Opers Mgr: Cindy Porter

D-U-N-S 00-686-5414
NORRIS ELECTRIC CO-OP (IL)
8543 N State Highway 130, Newton, IL 62448-9914
Tel (618) 783-8765 *Founded/Ownrshp* 1938
Sales 34.0MM *EMP* 69
SIC 4931 1711 4911 Electric & other services combined; Plumbing, heating, air-conditioning contractors; Electric services; Electric & other services combined; Plumbing, heating, air-conditioning contractors; Electric services
**Pr:* Kent Hetzer
Board of Directors: Larry Buser, Dean Deitrich, Wilbert Deters, Walter Hart, Kent Hetzer, Norbert Nix, Russell Scherer, Keith Sherwood

D-U-N-S 96-942-6092
NORRIS ELECTRIC COOPERATIVE
8543 N State Highway 130, Newton, IL 62448-9914
Tel (618) 783-8765 *Founded/Ownrshp* 2011
Sales 34.0MM *EMP* 60
Accts London Witte Group Llc India
SIC 3613 Distribution boards, electric; Distribution boards, electric
Genl Mgr: Keith McKinney

NORRIS FOOD SERVICES
See CONSTANCE FOOD GROUP INC

NORRIS FORD
See NORRIS-MJ LLC

NORRIS FORD
See GEORGE R NORRIS INC

D-U-N-S 17-022-8238 IMP
NORRIS INTERNATIONAL SERVICES LLC
3011 W Admiral Doyle Dr, New Iberia, LA 70560-9127
Tel (337) 367-2844 *Founded/Ownrshp* 2004
Sales 24.5MM^E *EMP* 100
SIC 3533 Oil field machinery & equipment
Owner: Patrick Norris

D-U-N-S 08-761-7700
NORRIS MCLAUGHLIN & MARCUS PA
721 Us Highway 202/206 # 200, Bridgewater, NJ 08807-1784
Tel (908) 722-0700 *Founded/Ownrshp* 1953
Sales 47.0MM^E *EMP* 240
SIC 8111 General practice attorney, lawyer; General practice attorney, lawyer
Pr: G Robert Marcus
Pr: Donna Spector
**Treas:* John J Eagen
Sr VP: Robert Medina
**VP:* Joel Jacobson
**VP:* Richard Norris
Dir IT: Dhruv Desai
Mktg Dir: Edward Miller
Counsel: Melinda Bramwit
Counsel: Jill Lebowitz

D-U-N-S 09-458-9751
NORRIS PRECISION MFG INC
4680 110th Ave N, Clearwater, FL 33762-4951
Tel (727) 572-6330 *Founded/Ownrshp* 1978
Sales 23.1MM^E *EMP* 75
SIC 3724 Aircraft engines & engine parts
Pr: Arthur Norris III
**Sec:* Nancy L Norris
CTO: Joe Norris
IT Man: John Just
Ql Cn Mgr: Richard Nash

NORRIS PRODUCTION SOLUTIONS
See DOVER ARTIFICIAL LIFT INTERNATIONAL LLC

D-U-N-S 00-696-9448
NORRIS PUBLIC POWER DISTRICT INC (NE)
606 Irving St, Beatrice, NE 68310-2052
Tel (402) 223-4038 *Founded/Ownrshp* 1933
Sales 69.4MM *EMP* 80
Accts Dana F Cole & Company Llp Gr
SIC 4911 Transmission, electric power; Distribution, electric power; Transmission, electric power; Distribution, electric power
CEO: Bruce Vitosh
**CFO:* Michelle Junker

D-U-N-S 01-488-4019
NORRIS SALES CO INC
1010 Conshohocken Rd, Conshohocken, PA 19428-1002
Tel (610) 279-5777 *Founded/Ownrshp* 2000
Sales 50.4MM^E *EMP* 53
SIC 5082 7353 General construction machinery & equipment; Heavy construction equipment rental
Pr: Don Zajick
**Sec:* Rachel Zajick
**VP:* Karen Zajick

D-U-N-S 02-249-2607
NORRIS-MJ LLC
NORRIS FORD
8559 Baltimore Nat Pike, Ellicott City, MD 21043-4202
Tel (410) 313-8361 *Founded/Ownrshp* 2001
Sales 69.3MM^E *EMP* 231^E
Accts American Express Tax & Busines
SIC 5511 Automobiles, new & used
Pr: G Norris Cook
Treas: David Norris Cook
Treas: Gerald Maizlish
Genl Mgr: Warren Paugh
Sls Mgr: Andrew Ortiz
Sls Mgr: Bill Vowles
Sales Asso: Gene Coxson
Sales Asso: Victor Hong
Sales Asso: Dennis Kleppin
Sales Asso: Pat Nash
Sales Asso: Demi Sentino

NORRISEAL CONTROLS
See NORRISEAL INC

D-U-N-S 82-511-3629 IMP
■ **NORRISEAL INC**
NORRISEAL CONTROLS
(*Suby of* DOVER ARTIFICIAL LIFT INTERNATIONAL LLC) ★
11122 W Little York Rd, Houston, TX 77041-5016
Tel (713) 466-3552 *Founded/Ownrshp* 1955
Sales 22.0MM^E *EMP* 110^E
SIC 3559 Automotive related machinery; Automotive related machinery
Pr: Robert E Funk
VP: Vince Cipresso
VP: Larry Williams
Dir IT: Michael Bankard
Sftwr Eng: Didi Hu
Plnt Mgr: Floyd Weeks
Mktg Dir: Chris Giles
Sls Mgr: Biju Narayanan

D-U-N-S 01-893-0339 IMP
■ **NORRISEAL-WELLMARK INC**
(*Suby of* DOVER CORP) ★
1903 Se 29th St, Oklahoma City, OK 73129-7625
Tel (405) 672-6660 *Founded/Ownrshp* 2014
Sales 39.5MM^E *EMP* 100
SIC 3533 Oil field machinery & equipment; Gas field machinery & equipment; Oil field machinery & equipment; Gas field machinery & equipment
CEO: Luis Gomez
**CFO:* John Miller
**VP:* Vince Cipresso
Exec: Jeanette Palmer
Area Mgr: Julie Banks
Area Mgr: Kim McDonough
Area Mgr: Adam Raprich
Genl Mgr: Mac Swindell
IT Man: Bernadette Jacobsmeier
Info Man: Todd Canedy
Prd Mgr: John Claborn

D-U-N-S 07-058-2390
NORRISTOWN AREA SCHOOL DISTRICT
401 N Whitehall Rd, Norristown, PA 19403-2745
Tel (610) 630-5000 *Founded/Ownrshp* 1836
Sales 89.6MM^E *EMP* 950
Accts Maillie Falconiero & Company
SIC 8211 Public elementary & secondary schools; Public elementary & secondary schools
MIS Dir: Mark Long
Cmptr Lab: Samuel Stansbery
IT Man: Karen Ovington
Secur Mgr: Gary Stahl
Schl Brd P: Pamela Assenmacher

D-U-N-S 85-849-7688
NORSAN MEATS LLC
PRIME MEATS
2150 Boggs Rd Ste 500, Duluth, GA 30096-5893
Tel (770) 414-5331 *Founded/Ownrshp* 1992
Sales 68.2MM^E *EMP* 80
SIC 5147 Meats & meat products; Meats & meat products
Pr: Norberto Sanchez
**COO:* Alfonso Villareal
Sales Asso: Ebert Toribio
Board of Directors: Norberto Sanchez

NORSE DAIRY SYSTEMS
See INTERBAKE FOODS LLC

D-U-N-S 92-949-0126 EXP
NORSE DAIRY SYSTEMS LP
(*Suby of* INTERBAKE FOODS LLC) ★
1740 Joyce Ave, Columbus, OH 43219-1026
Tel (614) 421-5297 *Founded/Ownrshp* 1995
Sales 79.0MM^E *EMP* 340
SIC 3556 2052 2656 Ice cream manufacturing machinery; Cones, ice cream; Ice cream containers: made from purchased material; Ice cream manufacturing machinery; Cones, ice cream; Ice cream containers: made from purchased material
Pt: Scott Fullbright
VP: Cindy Linkiewicz
VP: Harry Seniea
VP: Daniel Tillwick
Plnt Mgr: Jack Frysztak
Plnt Mgr: Steven Krotz

D-U-N-S 09-360-9022 IMP/EXP
NORSELAND INC
3 Parklands Dr Ste 203, Darien, CT 06820-3652
Tel (203) 324-5620 *Founded/Ownrshp* 1978
Sales 20.1MM^E *EMP* 27
Accts Arthur Allen & Co Llc Cpas
SIC 5143 Dairy products, except dried or canned; Cheese
Pr: John J Sullivan
**Ch Bd:* Hanne Refsholt
CFO: Gareth Harris
Treas: Mark Bishop
Genl Mgr: Ann Freeburg
Sls Dir: Steve Watson
Mktg Mgr: Jose Carranza
Mktg Mgr: Deanna Finegan
Mktg Mgr: Ruth Flore
Snr Mgr: David Schroeder

NORSEMAN DEFENSE TECHNOLOGIES
See NORSEMAN INC

D-U-N-S 79-880-6766
NORSEMAN INC
NORSEMAN DEFENSE TECHNOLOGIES
8172 Lark Brown Rd, Elkridge, MD 21075-6423
Tel (410) 579-8600 *Founded/Ownrshp* 1992
Sales 72.6MM *EMP* 58
Accts Bdo Usa Llp Mclean Va
SIC 5045 Computers
Pr: Eileen Cave
**CFO:* Chris Geros
Opers Mgr: George Kapnolas
Sales Asso: Kelly Oneill

D-U-N-S 96-163-2929
NORSHEILD HOLDINGS LLC
3232 Mobile Hwy, Montgomery, AL 36108-4454
Tel (334) 551-0650 *Founded/Ownrshp* 2009
Sales 21.0MM^E *EMP* 57^E
SIC 3699 Security devices
Pr: Barry White

D-U-N-S 96-644-6403
NORSHIELD SECURITY PRODUCTS LLC
(*Suby of* NORSHEILD HOLDINGS LLC) ★
3232 Mobile Hwy, Montgomery, AL 36108-4454
Tel (334) 551-0650 *Founded/Ownrshp* 2009
Sales 21.0MM *EMP* 47
SIC 3446 3442 Architectural metalwork; Metal doors, sash & trim
Pr: Barry White
CFO: Richard Covington
Prgrm Mgr: J T Rose
Mktg Mgr: John Wood
Sls Mgr: Roy Igou

NORSHIPCO
See BAE SYSTEMS NORFOLK SHIP REPAIR INC

D-U-N-S 18-907-4990
NORSOUTH CORP
10 Chatham Ctr S Ste 300, Savannah, GA 31405-7494
Tel (912) 354-6096 *Founded/Ownrshp* 1985
Sales 58.9MM^E *EMP* 120
SIC 1522 6552 Apartment building construction; Subdividers & developers; Apartment building construction; Subdividers & developers
Pr: William E Johnston
**Sec:* Faith M Williams

D-U-N-S 06-819-6054
■ **NORSTAN COMMUNICATIONS INC** (MN)
BLACK BOX NETWORK SERVICES
(*Suby of* NORSTAN INC) ★
5050 Lincoln Dr Ste 300, Minneapolis, MN 55436-1179
Tel (952) 935-9002 *Founded/Ownrshp* 1974, 1975
Sales 230.8MM^E *EMP* 1,090
SIC 5065 1731 7629 Telephone equipment; Telephone & telephone equipment installation; Telecommunication equipment repair (except telephones); Telephone equipment; Telephone & telephone equipment installation; Telecommunication equipment repair (except telephones)
Ch Bd: Paul Baszucki
**Pr:* Scott Christian
**Treas:* Alice Vazquez

D-U-N-S 05-341-7945
■ **NORSTAN INC**
(*Suby of* BLACK BOX CORP) ★
5050 Lincoln Dr Ste 300, Minneapolis, MN 55436-1179
Tel (952) 352-4000 *Founded/Ownrshp* 2005
Sales 277.4MM^E *EMP* 1,090
SIC 7389 3661 8748 7379 Telephone services; Teleconferencing services; Telephone answering service; Telephones & telephone apparatus; Electronic secretary; Message concentrators; Telecommunications consultant; Computer related consulting services; Telephone services; Teleconferencing services; Telephone answering service; Telephones & telephone apparatus; Electronic secretary; Message concentrators; Telecommunications consultant; Computer related consulting services
Pr: Scott G Christian
Pr: Jeffery Lusenhop
Ex VP: Peter Stilson
**Sr VP:* Steven D Anderson
**Sr VP:* Roger D Van Beusekom
**Sr VP:* Donna M Warner
VP: Richard A Camuso
VP: Kenneth R Croken
VP: Kim Keller
VP: Kenneth Larson
VP: Jeffery Mattson
VP: Larry Schmidt
VP: Jack White

D-U-N-S 79-469-4166 IMP/EXP
NORSTAR OFFICE PRODUCTS INC
BOSS
5353 Jillson St, Commerce, CA 90040-2115
Tel (323) 262-1919 *Founded/Ownrshp* 1999
Sales 262.2MM^E *EMP* 2,367
SIC 2521 2522 Chairs, office: padded, upholstered or plain: wood; Chairs, office: padded or plain, except wood; Chairs, office: padded, upholstered or plain: wood; Chairs, office: padded or plain, except wood
Pr: William W Huang
Chf Mktg O: Kari Brown

D-U-N-S 19-516-3600
NORSTAR PIPELINE CO INC
ENSTAR NATURAL GAS
(*Suby of* SEMCO ENERGY INC) ★
3000 Spenard Rd, Anchorage, AK 99503-3606
Tel (907) 277-5551 *Founded/Ownrshp* 2001
Sales 99.9MM^E *EMP* 166^E
SIC 4922 Natural gas transmission
Pr: George A Schreiber Jr
Pr: Moira Smith
**Pr:* M Colleen Starring
**VP:* Peter F Clark
**VP:* Michael V Palmeri
**VP:* Mark T Prendeville
**VP:* Steven W Warsinske
Exec: Kelsie Anderson
IT Man: Ray Anderson

NORSUN
See DICKINSON FROZEN FOODS INC

D-U-N-S 96-247-5398
NORSWISS FARMS INC
1563 19th Ave, Rice Lake, WI 54868-9571
Tel (715) 234-7169 *Founded/Ownrshp* 1991
Sales 40.0MM *EMP* 18
SIC 0241 Dairy farms; Dairy farms
Pr: Andreas Heer
**Treas:* Freida Lee
**VP:* Alfred Lee

D-U-N-S 07-799-6598
NORTAP ENTERPRISES INC
SONIC DRIVE-IN
4825 Polk Ln, Olive Branch, MS 38654-8358
Tel (662) 895-4342 *Founded/Ownrshp* 1993
Sales 8.7MM^E *EMP* 596^E
SIC 5812 Drive-in restaurant
Pr: Ronald A Solberg

D-U-N-S 55-710-1433 IMP
NORTEC HUMIDITY INC
(*Suby of* WALTER MEIER HOLDINGS CORP) ★
835 Commerce Park Dr, Ogdensburg, NY 13669-2209
Tel (315) 425-1255 *Founded/Ownrshp* 1993
Sales 24.9MM^E *EMP* 79
SIC 5075 3585 Air conditioning & ventilation equipment & supplies; Humidifiers & dehumidifiers
Pr: URS Schenk

D-U-N-S 01-042-9728 IMP
▲ **NORTECH SYSTEMS INC**
7550 Meridian Cir N # 150, Maple Grove, MN 55369-4932
Tel (952) 345-2244 *Founded/Ownrshp* 1981
Sales 112.0MM *EMP* 717
Accts Mcgladrey Llp Minneapolis Mi
Tkr Sym NSYS *Exch* NAS
SIC 3674 3679 Computer terminals, monitors & components; Computer maintenance & repair; Semiconductors & related devices; Integrated circuits, semiconductor networks, etc.; Electronic circuits
CEO: Richard G Wasielewski
**Ch Bd:* Michael J Degen
CFO: Paula M Graff
CFO: Richard Wasielewski
Ofcr: Curtis J Steichen
Ex VP: Gregory Tweed
VP: Keith Pieper
Prgrm Mgr: Steve Trnka
IT Man: Charlie Mockenhaupt
Sftwr Eng: Tim Gack
Sfty Dirs: Louis Fournier
Board of Directors: Kathleen Iverson, Michael Kennedy, David B Kunin, Kenneth Larson, Richard W Perkins

D-U-N-S 88-486-6781
NORTECH WASTE LLC
3033 Fiddyment Rd, Roseville, CA 95747-9705
Tel (916) 645-5230 *Founded/Ownrshp* 1996

Sales 32.6MM^E *EMP* 120
SIC 4953 3341 3312 3231 2611 Refuse systems; Secondary nonferrous metals; Blast furnaces & steel mills; Products of purchased glass; Pulp mills; Refuse systems; Secondary nonferrous metals; Blast furnaces & steel mills; Products of purchased glass; Pulp mills
Genl Mgr: Paul Scura

D-U-N-S 08-909-0534 IMP
■ NORTEK AIR SOLUTIONS LLC
(*Suby of* NORTEK INC) ★
13200 Pioneer Trl Ste 150, Eden Prairie, MN 55347-4125
Tel (952) 358-6600 *Founded/Ownrshp* 2015
Sales 611.0MM^E *EMP* 2,100
SIC 3585 Air conditioning equipment, complete; Heating equipment, complete; Air conditioning equipment, complete; Heating equipment, complete
Pr: Eric Roberts
**CFO:* Brian Smith
VP: Mike Murphy
VP: Mike Smith
Ex Dir: Izuh Obinelo
IT Man: John Clayton
Mktg Dir: Chris Sackrison

D-U-N-S 00-632-3034 IMP
■ NORTEK GLOBAL HVAC LLC
INTERTHERM
(*Suby of* NORTEK INC) ★
8000 Phoenix Pkwy, O Fallon, MO 63368-3827
Tel (800) 422-4328 *Founded/Ownrshp* 1919, 1985
Sales 886.5MM^E *EMP* 2,300
SIC 3585 3567 3433 Heating & air conditioning combination units; Water heaters, electric; Heaters, space electric; Industrial furnaces & ovens; Heating equipment, except electric; Heating & air conditioning combination units; Industrial furnaces & ovens; Heating equipment, except electric
Pr: David J Legrand
Pr: Alan Reisel
CFO: Almon C Hall
VP: Jeff Antonelli
VP: Carolyn Baker
VP: Jim Fox
VP: Bill Kormeier
VP: Michael Nix
VP: Richard Ruth
VP: Mike Seaubaugh
VP: Philip Windham
VP: Tammy Yackey
Board of Directors: Richard L Bready, Richard J Harris

D-U-N-S 61-533-2900 IMP/EXP
▲ NORTEK INC
500 Exchange St, Providence, RI 02903-2630
Tel (401) 751-1600 *Founded/Ownrshp* 1967
Sales 2.5MMM *EMP* 11,200
Tkr Sym NTK *Exch* NGS
SIC 3585 3444 3634 3699 2434 Refrigeration & heating equipment; Heating equipment, complete; Air conditioning equipment, complete; Air conditioning units, complete: domestic or industrial; Metal ventilating equipment; Hoods, range: sheet metal; Electric housewares & fans; Fans, exhaust & ventilating, electric: household; Electrical equipment & supplies; Security control equipment & systems; Door opening & closing devices, electrical; Chimes, electric; Wood kitchen cabinets; Vanities, bathroom: wood; Refrigeration & heating equipment; Heating equipment, complete; Air conditioning equipment, complete; Air conditioning units, complete: domestic or industrial; Metal ventilating equipment; Hoods, range: sheet metal; Electric housewares & fans; Fans, exhaust & ventilating, electric: household; Electrical equipment & supplies; Security control equipment & systems; Door opening & closing devices, electrical; Chimes, electric; Wood kitchen cabinets; Vanities, bathroom: wood
Pr: Michael J Clarke
**Ch Bd:* J David Smith
Pr: Andrew Bonham
Pr: Mark Devincent
Pr: Jeffrey L Mueller
Pr: Peter R Segar
CFO: Almon C Hall
Treas: Matt Hughes
Ofcr: Kris Holla
Sr VP: Timothy J Burling
Sr VP: Kevin W Donnelly
VP: Ben Durley
VP: Donald Moseley
Board of Directors: Jeffrey C Bloomberg, John T Coleman, James B Hirshorn, Thomas A Keenan, Daniel C Lukas, Chris A McWilton, Bennett Rosenthal

D-U-N-S 80-808-2585
NORTEX MIDSTREAM PARTNERS LLC
(*Suby of* FALCON OIL & GAS CORP) ★
1201 Louisiana St Ste 700, Houston, TX 77002-5603
Tel (713) 961-3204 *Founded/Ownrshp* 2006
Sales 40.6MM^E *EMP* 50
SIC 4922 Storage, natural gas
Pr: Ben Moore
**Pr:* Gary Jones
CFO: Steve Toon
**VP:* Andrew Barbe
**VP:* John H Holcomb
Mng Dir: Jeffery Fawcett

D-U-N-S 04-228-7102 IMP
NORTEX WHOLESALE NURSERY INC
NORTH HAVEN GARDENS
7700 Northaven Rd, Dallas, TX 75230-3224
Tel (214) 363-5316 *Founded/Ownrshp* 1967
Sales 25.7MM^E *EMP* 120
SIC 5261 Nurseries & garden centers
Pr: Jon Pinkus
**VP:* Aaron Pinkus
**VP:* Lillian Pinkus
Mktg Dir: Mark Black

NORTH & SOUTH DISTRIBUTORS
See NICOLAS VILLALBA WHOLESALERS INC

NORTH 40 OUTFITTERS
See CSWW INC

D-U-N-S 08-874-4172
NORTH ADAMS COMMUNITY SCHOOL CORP
625 Stadium Dr, Decatur, IN 46733-2721
Tel (260) 724-7146 *Founded/Ownrshp* 1920
Sales 20.7MM^E *EMP* 345
SIC 8211 Public elementary school; Public junior high school; Public senior high school; Public elementary school; Public junior high school; Public senior high school
**Treas:* Kathy Brown
Schl Brd P: Ben Farot
Schl Brd P: Kurt Rash
Teacher Pr: Arnida Holely

NORTH ADAMS REGIONAL HOSPITAL
See NORTHERN BERKSHIRE HEALTHCARE INC

D-U-N-S 03-010-4025
NORTH ADVOCATE SIDE HEALTH NETWORK
(*Suby of* ADVOCATE HEALTH CARE NETWORK) ★
836 W Wellington Ave, Chicago, IL 60657-5147
Tel (773) 296-5699 *Founded/Ownrshp* 1981
Sales 471.4MM *EMP* 1,600
SIC 8741 8721 Hospital management; Accounting, auditing & bookkeeping; Hospital management; Accounting, auditing & bookkeeping
CEO: Kenneth J Rojek
Opers Mgr: Paul Mangura

D-U-N-S 03-411-2425
NORTH ALABAMA ELECTRIC COOPERATIVE
NAEC
41103 Us Highway 72, Stevenson, AL 35772-4560
Tel (256) 437-2281 *Founded/Ownrshp* 1940
Sales 37.6MM *EMP* 39
Accts Mda Professional Group Pc Alb
SIC 4911 Distribution, electric power; Transmission, electric power; Distribution, electric power; Transmission, electric power
Pr: Willard Townson
**CFO:* Carolyn Wooden
**Treas:* Martin Anderson
**Treas:* Parks Tubbs
**VP:* Bryan Hicks
Genl Mgr: Bruce Purdy
Off Mgr: William Selby

D-U-N-S 03-406-2737
NORTH ALABAMA FABRICATING CO INC (AL)
4632 Richard Blvd, Birmingham, AL 35212-1304
Tel (205) 591-5554 *Founded/Ownrshp* 1967, 1996
Sales 55.9MM^E *EMP* 180^E
SIC 1791 Structural steel erection; Structural steel erection
Pr: John R Parrish
Treas: Margaret Parrish
Ex VP: Jim Smothers
**VP:* Kathy Parrish
VP: Harry Walght
Board of Directors: Wesley P Zeahah

D-U-N-S 05-511-5505
NORTH ALAMO WATER SUPPLY CORP
420 S Doolittle Rd, Edinburg, TX 78542-9707
Tel (956) 383-1618 *Founded/Ownrshp* 1966
Sales 22.3MM *EMP* 60^E
Accts Long Chilton Llp Mcallen Tx
SIC 4941 Water supply
Pr: Dennis Goldsberry
**VP:* Steve Krenek
Genl Mgr: Charles Browning
Genl Mgr: Nikki Reyes
IT Man: Irma Tamez

D-U-N-S 07-215-9288
NORTH ALLEGHENY SCHOOL DISTRICT
200 Hillvue Ln Ste 1, Pittsburgh, PA 15237-5391
Tel (412) 369-5484 *Founded/Ownrshp* 1948
Sales 131.7MM *EMP* 1,019
Accts Maher Duessel Pittsburgh Pen
SIC 8211 Public elementary & secondary schools; Public elementary & secondary schools
Recvr: Brian Austin
Bd of Dir: Karen Boujoukos
Bd of Dir: Thomas Schwartzmier
VP: Linda Bishop
VP: Diane Feliciani
IT Man: Thomas Stabryla
Sales Exec: Lynn Reaghard
VP Sls: Beth Ludwig
Pr Mgr: Joy Ed
Teacher Pr: Jo Jowelter
Psych: Terry Valentino

NORTH AMERCN MEMBERSHIP GROUP
See NORTH AMERICAN MEMBERSHIP GROUP HOLDINGS INC

NORTH AMERCN MEMBERSHIP GROUP
See NORTH AMERICAN AFFINITY CLUBS INC

D-U-N-S 17-048-1352
NORTH AMERICA ADMINISTRATORS LP
(*Suby of* LUCENT HEALTH SOLUTIONS INC) ★
1826 Elm Hill Pike, Nashville, TN 37210-3710
Tel (615) 256-3561 *Founded/Ownrshp* 2014
Sales NA *EMP* 75
SIC 6321 Accident & health insurance
Pr: Daniel J Dugan
COO: Patricia C Grooms
Dir IT: Michael Sledge
VP Sls: Jim Snyder
Mktg Dir: Karen Dugan
Mktg Mgr: Debbie Franklin

D-U-N-S 18-141-4715
NORTH AMERICA DUTY FREE INC
5320 N 37th St, Hollywood, FL 33021-2201
Tel (954) 962-3432 *Founded/Ownrshp* 1982
Sales 46.6MM^E *EMP* 65
SIC 5141 5182 Groceries, general line; Liquor
CEO: Steven Fortgang
**Pr:* Janet Fortgang
**VP:* Jess Fortgang
Site Mgr: Dara Fortgang

D-U-N-S 05-098-3451 IMP/EXP
NORTH AMERICA FIRE EQUIPMENT CO INC
NAFECO
1515 Moulton St W, Decatur, AL 35601-2100
Tel (256) 353-7100 *Founded/Ownrshp* 1968
Sales 30.5MM *EMP* 90
SIC 5087 7699

D-U-N-S 04-687-1716
NORTH AMERICA FUEL SYSTEMS REMANUFACTURING LLC
(*Suby of* DETROIT DIESEL CORP) ★
4232 Brockton Dr Se, Grand Rapids, MI 49512-4048
Tel (616) 541-1100 *Founded/Ownrshp* 1998
Sales 49.4MM^E *EMP* 140
SIC 3561 Pumps & pumping equipment; Pumps & pumping equipment
VP: Adam Knobeloch

D-U-N-S 18-283-8516 EXP
NORTH AMERICA PACKAGING CORP
NAMPAC
(*Suby of* BWAY CORP) ★
1515 W 22nd St Ste 550, Oak Brook, IL 60523-8742
Tel (630) 203-4100 *Founded/Ownrshp* 2004
Sales 157.4MM^E *EMP* 1,200
SIC 3089 Plastic containers, except foam; Plastic containers, except foam
Pr: Tom Linton
**VP:* Danny Byrne

D-U-N-S 06-625-6842
NORTH AMERICA SEKISUI HOUSE LLC
(*Suby of* SEKISUI HOUSE, LTD.)
2101 Wilson Blvd Ste 1004, Arlington, VA 22201-3048
Tel (703) 740-0229 *Founded/Ownrshp* 2010
Sales 200.0MM *EMP* 1
SIC 6719 Investment holding companies, except banks; Investment holding companies, except banks
COO: Satoshi Yoshimura

D-U-N-S 62-341-1886
NORTH AMERICA SPORTS MEDIA INC
PREMIERE GLOBAL SPORTS
(*Suby of* PRIMESPORT INC) ★
3575 Piedmon Rd Ne Ste 1, Atlanta, GA 30305-1623
Tel (800) 591-9198 *Founded/Ownrshp* 2013
Sales 45.0MM *EMP* 24^E
SIC 4725 Arrangement of travel tour packages, wholesale
Pr: Joseph Bennet

D-U-N-S 61-934-6047
NORTH AMERICA STEVEDORING CO LLC
9301 S Kreiter Ave, Chicago, IL 60617-4645
Tel (773) 734-4885 *Founded/Ownrshp* 2005
Sales 32.5MM^E *EMP* 50
SIC 5051 Steel
Genl Mgr: Steve Mosher
Off Mgr: Page Mosher

D-U-N-S 92-878-1269 IMP
NORTH AMERICAN ACQUISITION CORP
AMTEC PRECISION PRODUCTS
(*Suby of* AMTEC PRECISION PRODUCTS INC) ★
1875 Holmes Rd, Elgin, IL 60123-1298
Tel (847) 695-8030 *Founded/Ownrshp* 2005
Sales 41.1MM^E *EMP* 190
SIC 3714 3089 3469 Transmission housings or parts, motor vehicle; Fuel systems & parts, motor vehicle; Motor vehicle transmissions, drive assemblies & parts; Injection molding of plastics; Machine parts, stamped or pressed metal; Transmission housings or parts, motor vehicle; Fuel systems & parts, motor vehicle; Motor vehicle transmissions, drive assemblies & parts; Injection molding of plastics; Machine parts, stamped or pressed metal
Ch Bd: Jaykar Krishnamurthy
**Pr:* Ganesh Subramanian
**VP:* Kenneth Formanski
Opers Mgr: Shawn Mock

D-U-N-S 01-126-2789
NORTH AMERICAN AERODYNAMICS INC (NJ)
1803 N Main St, Roxboro, NC 27573-4047
Tel (336) 599-9266 *Founded/Ownrshp* 1964
Sales 23.6MM^E *EMP* 200^E
SIC 2399 Parachutes; Parachutes
Pr: John P Higgins
**Genl Mgr:* Jim Barker

D-U-N-S 62-790-4969 IMP
NORTH AMERICAN AFFINITY CLUBS INC
NORTH AMERCN MEMBERSHIP GROUP
915 Mainstreet 2, Hopkins, MN 55343-7515
Tel (952) 936-9333 *Founded/Ownrshp* 1978
Sales 16.7MM^E *EMP* 415
SIC 7997 Membership sports & recreation clubs; Membership sports & recreation clubs
CEO: James C Heckman
**VP:* Leaha Wirth
**Prin:* Nancy Ezensen

D-U-N-S 60-408-9995
NORTH AMERICAN AIRLINE INC
101 World Dr, Peachtree City, GA 30269-6965
Tel (770) 632-8000 *Founded/Ownrshp* 2007
Sales NA *EMP* 550
SIC 4522

D-U-N-S 62-309-5718
■ NORTH AMERICAN ASSET DEVELOPMENT CORP
(*Suby of* NORTH AMERICAN TITLE GROUP INC) ★
1855 Gateway Blvd Ste 650, Concord, CA 94520-8454
Tel (925) 935-5599 *Founded/Ownrshp* 1998
Sales NA *EMP* 1,001^E
SIC 6361 6531 Title insurance; Escrow agent, real estate; Title insurance; Escrow agent, real estate
Pr: Dan R Wentzel
**CFO:* Jeff Wright

D-U-N-S 04-595-5465 IMP
■ NORTH AMERICAN ATK CORP
ATK NORTH AMERICA
(*Suby of* LKQ CORP) ★
1102 W N Carrier, Grand Prairie, TX 75050
Tel (972) 647-1400 *Founded/Ownrshp* 2011
Sales 24.8MM^E *EMP* 90
SIC 3714 Motor vehicle parts & accessories
Pr: Peter Butterfield
**CFO:* Mark Spaulding
VP: Juan Luis Bernal Blanco
VP: Steve Gamble
VP: Orjan Kers
**VP:* Scott Miller
VP: Bill Steffancin
**Exec:* Shannon Empting
IT Man: Christopher Rogers
Sftwr Eng: Thomas Moore
Opers Mgr: Jimmy Godsey

D-U-N-S 87-651-5172
NORTH AMERICAN BANCARD LLC
ADVANCED PAYMENT SOLUTIONS
250 Stephenson Hwy, Troy, MI 48083-1117
Tel (800) 226-2273 *Founded/Ownrshp* 1991
Sales 199.6MM^E *EMP* 600^E
Accts Doeren Mayhew Troy Michigan
SIC 7389 Credit card service; Credit card service
Pr: Marc Gardner
**COO:* Terri Harwood
COO: Gary Rutledge
**CFO:* Kirk Haggarty
CFO: Howard Morof
Bd of Dir: Sarah Becker
Sr VP: Jason Dennis
VP: Scott Addyman
VP: Dan Buckner
VP: Rita Feldman
VP: Scott Fessler
VP: Richard Parrott
VP: Jon Pielak
VP: Robert Seward
VP: David Tepoorten
VP: Scott Webb
Exec: Calvin Reed
Dir Risk M: Randy Lobban

D-U-N-S 80-307-5266
NORTH AMERICAN BANCSHARES INC
2011 Texoma Pkwy, Sherman, TX 75090-2688
Tel (903) 893-7555 *Founded/Ownrshp* 1984
Sales NA *EMP* 330
SIC 6712 Bank holding companies; Bank holding companies
Ch Bd: Steve Smith
**Pr:* James F Parker
Board of Directors: W D Bayless Sr, Dr Emmett Essin, Dean Gilbert, Lacy J Harber, Dr Darius Maggi

D-U-N-S 07-868-0538
NORTH AMERICAN BREWERIES HOLDINGS LLC
445 Saint Paul St, Rochester, NY 14605-1726
Tel (585) 546-1030 *Founded/Ownrshp* 2009
Sales 73.2MM^E *EMP* 850^E
SIC 2082 Beer (alcoholic beverage); Beer (alcoholic beverage)
CEO: Rich Lozyniak

D-U-N-S 82-978-2445 EXP
NORTH AMERICAN BREWERIES INC
NORTHAMERICAN BREWERIES
(*Suby of* FLORIDA BEBIDAS SA)
445 Saint Paul St, Rochester, NY 14605-1726
Tel (585) 546-1030 *Founded/Ownrshp* 2012
Sales 287.0MM^E *EMP* 1,043
SIC 2082 Beer (alcoholic beverage); Beer (alcoholic beverage)
Ch Bd: Richard Lozyniak
**Pr:* Raquel Vargas
**CEO:* Kris Sirchio
Area Mgr: Lisa Godbey
Dist Mgr: Thomas Mitchell
CIO: Paul Yarnot
QA Dir: Frank Barbero
IT Man: Ali Wilkes

D-U-N-S 61-860-9122
■ NORTH AMERICAN CASUALTY CO
(*Suby of* APPLIED UNDERWRITERS INC) ★
10805 Old Mill Rd, Omaha, NE 68154-2607
Tel (402) 342-4900 *Founded/Ownrshp* 2005
Sales NA *EMP* 509^E
SIC 6411 Insurance agents, brokers & service
Pr: Steven Menzies
**VP:* Sidney Ferenc

D-U-N-S 03-007-8927 IMP
NORTH AMERICAN CERUTTI CORP
(*Suby of* OFFICINE MECCANICHE GIOVANNI CERUTTI SPA)
15800 W Overland Dr, New Berlin, WI 53151-2815
Tel (262) 827-3800 *Founded/Ownrshp* 1977
Sales 30.6MM^E *EMP* 75
SIC 3555 5084 Printing presses; Printing trades machinery, equipment & supplies
Pr: Giancarlo Cerutti
**Sec:* Francesca Lungo
**Ex VP:* Paul Cappa
Manager: Michael Huc

D-U-N-S 94-788-8525 IMP
NORTH AMERICAN CINEMAS INC
917 College Ave, Santa Rosa, CA 95404-4110
Tel (707) 523-1586 *Founded/Ownrshp* 1995
Sales 16.2MM^E *EMP* 400
SIC 7832 Motion picture theaters, except drive-in; Motion picture theaters, except drive-in
Pr: Daniel F Tocchini
**Treas:* Amy Tocchini

D-U-N-S 06-949-6867
NORTH AMERICAN CO FOR LIFE & HEALTH INSURANCE
(*Subsy of* SAMMONS FINANCIAL GROUP INC) ★
525 W Van Buren St # 1200, Chicago, IL 60607-3820
Tel (312) 648-7600 *Founded/Ownrshp* 1986
Sales NA *EMP* 350
SIC 6311 6321 Life insurance carriers; Accident insurance carriers; Health insurance carriers; Life insurance carriers; Accident insurance carriers; Health insurance carriers
Pr: Steven C Palmitier
Sr Pt: Steppe Gregory
Sr Pt: Beucler Lykens
Pr: Jeremy Bill
**Treas:* John J Craig
Ofcr: Brent Mardis
Ofcr: Anna Sherony
**Ex VP:* Edward Turner
VP: Norma Davis
VP: Curtis Foody
VP: C Haley
VP: Gary Helder
VP: William Keffer
VP: Barbara Murray
VP: Mary Nolan
VP: Julia Roper
VP: Robert Tekolste
VP: Heath Williams
Board of Directors: Gary Gaspar, Steve Horvat, Brian Rohr

D-U-N-S 00-790-1085 IMP
■ **NORTH AMERICAN COAL CORP**
(*Subsy of* NACCO INDUSTRIES INC) ★
5340 Legacy Dr Ste 300, Plano, TX 75024-3141
Tel (972) 448-5400 *Founded/Ownrshp* 1986
Sales 193.6MM *EMP* 1,500
Accts Ernst & Young Llp Richmond V
SIC 1221 Bituminous coal & lignite-surface mining; Bituminous coal & lignite-surface mining
Ch: Alfred M Rankin
**Pr:* Bob Benson
**CEO:* Robert L Benson
**CFO:* Bob D Carlton
**Treas:* Donald Grischow
**VP:* Thomas Andrew Koza
VP: Wilma Mayo
Genl Mgr: Phil Berry
IT Exec: Bruce Daves
IT Man: Zacharia Vinduska
Opers Mgr: Travis Horning

D-U-N-S 17-078-1848
NORTH AMERICAN COATINGS LLC
SEI COATINGS
8450 W 191st St Ste 19, Mokena, IL 60448-8868
Tel (815) 464-3053 *Founded/Ownrshp* 2004
Sales 59.0MM^E^ *EMP* 280
Accts Callero & Callero Llp Niles
SIC 1721 Industrial painting; Industrial painting
**CFO:* Christoper Murphy
IT Man: Andrea Archambeault

D-U-N-S 06-763-0582
NORTH AMERICAN COMMUNICATIONS INC
N A C
7 Edgemont Rd, Katonah, NY 10536-1503
Tel (914) 273-8620 *Founded/Ownrshp* 1982
Sales 64.5MM^E^ *EMP* 1,000
SIC 7331 Direct mail advertising services; Direct mail advertising services
CEO: Nicholas D Robinson
**Pr:* Robert Herman
**Ch:* Michael Herman
Genl Mgr: Pamela Leach
VP Prd: Stephen Roberts

D-U-N-S 82-541-0319
NORTH AMERICAN COMMUNICATIONS RESOURCE INC
NACR
(*Subsy of* CONVERGEONE HOLDINGS CORP) ★
3344 Highway 149, Eagan, MN 55121-2316
Tel (651) 994-6800 *Founded/Ownrshp* 2005
Sales 235.0MM^E^ *EMP* 710
SIC 4813 5999 1731 Telephone communication, except radio; Telephone equipment & systems; Telephone & telephone equipment installation; Telephone communication, except radio; Telephone equipment & systems; Telephone & telephone equipment installation
Pr: John Lyons
CFO: Robert Barbieri
Ex VP: John F Lyons
Sr VP: Paul Maier
VP: Pete Anderson
VP: Dick Bourdow
VP: Joseph Fabrizio
VP: Richard Scott Ford
VP: Seth Frank
VP: David Garlich
VP: Dan Gorski
VP: E Bruce Johnson
VP: Gerry Pearce
VP: Lisa Tonn
Exec: Steve Sanderson

D-U-N-S 14-915-4614 IMP
NORTH AMERICAN COMPOSITES CO
(*Subsy of* INTERPLASTIC CORP) ★
300 Apollo Dr, Circle Pines, MN 55014-3018
Tel (651) 766-6892 *Founded/Ownrshp* 1999
Sales 114.4MM^E^ *EMP* 150^E^
SIC 5162 Plastics materials; Plastics materials
Pr: James D Wallenfelsz
VP: David Engelsgaard
**VP:* Richard Rodriguez
Rgnl Mgr: Douglas Kennedy
Dist Mgr: Paul Congelosi
Opers Supe: Teresa Bergamin
Opers Supe: Mike Roe
Opers Mgr: Tina Anderson
Opers Mgr: Floyd Lynch

D-U-N-S 04-295-3810
NORTH AMERICAN CONTAINER CORP (GA)
1811 W Oak Pkwy Ste D, Marietta, GA 30062-2279
Tel (770) 431-4858 *Founded/Ownrshp* 1967
Sales 174.5MM^E^ *EMP* 600
SIC 3443 Nailed wood boxes & shook; Cargo containers, wood; Corrugated & solid fiber boxes; Wood containers; Sawmills & planing mills, general; Steel pipe & tubes; Containers, shipping (bombs, etc.): metal plate
CEO: John Grigsby Jr
**CFO:* Michael Grigsby
VP: Charles Grigsby
Opers Mgr: Harold Briner
Plnt Mgr: Paul Burkart
Plnt Mgr: Ken Wilson
Sls Mgr: Steve Rollins

D-U-N-S 02-524-7354
NORTH AMERICAN CORP OF ILLINOIS (IL)
2101 Claire Ct, Glenview, IL 60025-7634
Tel (847) 832-4000 *Founded/Ownrshp* 1919
Sales 273.2MM^E^ *EMP* 330
SIC 5113 5169 Industrial & personal service paper; Chemicals & allied products; Industrial & personal service paper; Chemicals & allied products
Pr: John A Miller
**CFO:* Rosemarie Egan
**CFO:* Matt Zimmermann

D-U-N-S 12-152-7063
NORTH AMERICAN DISMANTLING CORP
384 Lake Nepessing Rd, Lapeer, MI 48446-2996
Tel (810) 664-2888 *Founded/Ownrshp* 1984
Sales 38.0MM *EMP* 131
Accts Fenner Melstrom & Dooling Pl
SIC 1795 Demolition, buildings & other structures; Demolition, buildings & other structures
Pr: Rick Marcicki
CFO: Ivan Bain
IT Man: Nichole Rodabaugh
Sls Mgr: Victor Chappel

NORTH AMERICAN DRAGER
See DRAEGER MEDICAL INC

D-U-N-S 11-274-3588 IMP
NORTH AMERICAN DRILLERS LLC
SHAFTER DRILLERS INTERNATIONAL
(*Subsy of* SHAFT DRILLERS INTERNATIONAL LLC) ★
70 Gum Springs Rd, Morgantown, WV 26508-3534
Tel (304) 291-0175 *Founded/Ownrshp* 2006
Sales 73.3MM^E^ *EMP* 600
SIC 1781 1481 Water well servicing; Shaft sinking, nonmetallic minerals; Water well servicing; Shaft sinking, nonmetallic minerals
Pr: Scott Kiger
Opers Mgr: John Mayfield

D-U-N-S 80-883-2729 IMP
NORTH AMERICAN ELECTRIC INC
350 Vaiden Dr, Hernando, MS 38632-2328
Tel (662) 429-8049 *Founded/Ownrshp* 1993
Sales 27.4MM^E^ *EMP* 30
SIC 3621 Motors, electric; Motors, electric
Pr: David Hackman
Treas: Gillian Cunningham
Natl Sales: John Richardson
Mktg Mgr: Brent Lewis
Sls Mgr: Sandy Chadwick
Sls Mgr: Sandy Covington

D-U-N-S 08-477-8901
NORTH AMERICAN ELECTRIC RELIABILITY CORP
N E R C
3353 Peachtree Rd Ne # 600, Atlanta, GA 30326-1063
Tel (404) 446-2560 *Founded/Ownrshp* 1968
Sales 58.7MM *EMP* 175^E^
SIC 8611 Business associations; Business associations
CEO: Gerald W Cauley
**CFO:* Michael Walker
**VP:* David N Cook
Off Admin: Alicia Wade
CTO: Stan Hoptroff
Web Dev: Conrado Caunan
Counsel: Thomas Devita
Counsel: Lauren Perotti
Counsel: Teresina Stasko

D-U-N-S 00-204-9252 IMP
NORTH AMERICAN ENCLOSURES INC (NY)
NAE
85 Jetson Ln Ste B, Central Islip, NY 11722-1202
Tel (631) 234-9500 *Founded/Ownrshp* 1962
Sales 64.9MM^E^ *EMP* 550
Accts Schultz & Sage Great Neck Ny
SIC 2499 3827 Picture & mirror frames, wood; Mirrors, optical; Picture & mirror frames, wood; Mirrors, optical
Ch Bd: Richard Schwartz
**Pr:* Norman S Grafstein
**Sec:* Marie Neubert

D-U-N-S 06-092-8251
NORTH AMERICAN EQUIPMENT UPFITTERS INC (NH)
6 Sutton Cir, Hooksett, NH 03106-2039
Tel (603) 624-6288 *Founded/Ownrshp* 1999
Sales 31.5MM^E^ *EMP* 50
SIC 5084 Lift trucks & parts
Pr: Janet A Dunican
**Pr:* Mike Dunican

D-U-N-S 96-319-3404 IMP/EXP
NORTH AMERICAN FABRICATORS LLC
LASHIP
367 Dickson Rd, Houma, LA 70363-7310
Tel (985) 917-2000 *Founded/Ownrshp* 1996
Sales 99.8MM^E^ *EMP* 300
SIC 3731 Offshore supply boats, building & repairing; Cargo vessels, building & repairing; Crew boats, building & repairing; Offshore supply boats, building & repairing; Cargo vessels, building & repairing; Crew boats, building & repairing

D-U-N-S 19-645-6917
NORTH AMERICAN FAMILY INSTITUTE INC
NAFI
26 Howley St Ste 2, Peabody, MA 01960-8634
Tel (978) 538-0286 *Founded/Ownrshp* 1986
Sales 21.6MM *EMP* 1,600
Accts Kpmg Llp Boston Ma
SIC 8322 Child related social services; Family counseling services; Child related social services; Family counseling services
Pr: Yitzhak Bakal
CFO: Pamela Bruce
**Treas:* Hildegarde Paris
CTO: Karley Root
Dir IT: Christian Tirella
Opers Supe: Martha Adams
Pgrm Dir: Carlos Agudelo
Pgrm Dir: Jill Dichiara
Pgrm Dir: Ted Holmes

NORTH AMERICAN FOAM & PACKG
See GOLD VENTURE INC

D-U-N-S 04-027-8889 IMP
■ **NORTH AMERICAN FOREST PRODUCTS LIQUIDATION INC**
(*Subsy of* PATRICK INDUSTRIES INC) ★
27263 May St, Edwardsburg, MI 49112-8680
Tel (269) 663-8500 *Founded/Ownrshp* 2015
Sales 100.0MM^E^ *EMP* 220
SIC 2421 5031 Resawing lumber into smaller dimensions; Lumber: rough, sawed or planed; Building & structural materials, wood; Lumber: rough, dressed & finished; Resawing lumber into smaller dimensions; Lumber: rough, sawed or planed; Building & structural materials, wood; Lumber: rough, dressed & finished
Pr: Jonh Robert Wiley II
COO: Andrew Clark
VP: Brett Lamont
Sls Mgr: Tim Bontrager

D-U-N-S 60-936-8550 IMP
NORTH AMERICAN FUND III LP
135 S La Salle St # 3225, Chicago, IL 60603-4169
Tel (312) 332-4950 *Founded/Ownrshp* 1989
Sales 50.8MM^E^ *EMP* 900
SIC 3089 5162 Injection molding of plastics; Plastics resins; Injection molding of plastics; Plastics resins
Mng Pt: Charles L Palmer

D-U-N-S 00-884-1058
NORTH AMERICAN GALVANIZING & COATINGS INC
AZZ GALVANIZING SERVICES
3100 W 7th St Ste 500, Fort Worth, TX 76107-8701
Tel (817) 810-0095 *Founded/Ownrshp* 2010
Sales NA *EMP* 1,156
SIC 7539 3312 Electrical services; Iron & steel: galvanized, pipes, plates, sheets, etc.

NORTH AMERICAN GEAR AND FORGE
See AMERICAN GEAR PRODUCTS LLC

NORTH AMERICAN GROUP
See NORTH AMERICAN INSURANCE AGENCY INC

D-U-N-S 60-687-4782
NORTH AMERICAN HEALTH CARE INC
32836 Pacific Coast Hwy, Dana Point, CA 92629-3472
Tel (949) 240-2423 *Founded/Ownrshp* 1989
Sales 87.9MM^E^ *EMP* 299
SIC 8741 Nursing & personal care facility management; Nursing & personal care facility management
Pr: John L Sorensen
**CFO:* Tim Paulson
**Ch:* Donald G Laws
**Ex VP:* Timothy J Paulsen
Sr VP: Meg Gelvezon
VP: Darian Dahl
Dir Bus: Roxanne Bernier
Prd Mgr: Joelean Beddingfield
Counsel: Catherine Stroutin-House
Board of Directors: Sandra Cornett- Davis

D-U-N-S 05-003-8595
NORTH AMERICAN HERITAGE SERVICES INC
(*Subsy of* PKDM HOLDINGS INC) ★
1407 N Dixie Ave Ste 101, Elizabethtown, KY 42701-2999
Tel (270) 765-5216 *Founded/Ownrshp* 2008
Sales 23.1MM^E^ *EMP* 177
SIC 5999 Monuments, finished to custom order; Tombstones; Monuments, finished to custom order; Tombstones
Pr: Rich Urbach
**Treas:* Jim Barnes

D-U-N-S 36-266-5353 IMP/EXP
NORTH AMERICAN HOGANAS HIGH ALLOYS LLC
(*Subsy of* NORTH AMERICAN HOGANAS HOLDINGS INC) ★
101 Bridge St, Johnstown, PA 15902-2904
Tel (814) 361-6800 *Founded/Ownrshp* 2005
Sales 83.4MM *EMP* 100
SIC 3399 Powder, metal; Powder, metal
VP: Nasser Ahmad
VP: David Johnson
Plnt Mgr: Gary Flick

D-U-N-S 09-016-0008 EXP
NORTH AMERICAN HOGANAS HOLDINGS INC
(*Subsy of* HOGANAS AB)
111 Hoganas Way, Hollsopple, PA 15935-6416
Tel (814) 479-2551 *Founded/Ownrshp* 1999
Sales 348.4MM^E^ *EMP* 360
SIC 3462 Ornamental metal forgings, ferrous; Ornamental metal forgings, ferrous
Pr: Avinash Gore
VP: Perry Heinrich
**VP:* Dean Howard
VP: Sydney Luk
**VP:* Sydney Luke
VP: Nagarjuna Nandivada
VP: Ronald Soloman
**VP:* Ronald Solomon
Plnt Mgr: Donald Bowman
Sls Mgr: Jack Troxell

D-U-N-S 19-667-1416 IMP
NORTH AMERICAN HOGANAS INC
(*Subsy of* NORTH AMERICAN HOGANAS HOLDINGS INC) ★
111 Hoganas Way, Hollsopple, PA 15935-6416
Tel (814) 479-2551 *Founded/Ownrshp* 2001
Sales 249.8MM *EMP* 355^E^
SIC 3399 Metal powders, pastes & flakes; Metal powders, pastes & flakes
Pr: Avinash Gore
Pr: Sydney Luk
Pr: Sydney Tomlinson
**VP:* Terry Henrich
**VP:* Ronald Solomon
Ex Dir: Judy Mason
IT Man: Debra Gindlesperger
Opers Mgr: Matthew Smith
Plnt Mgr: Donald Bowman
Plnt Mgr: Milligan David
Plnt Mgr: Terry Hunsicker

NORTH AMERICAN HYDRO
See EAGLE CREEK RENEWABLE ENERGY HOLDINGS LLC

D-U-N-S 84-988-3392
NORTH AMERICAN INDUSTRIAL SERVICES INC
1240 Saratoga Rd, Ballston Spa, NY 12020-3500
Tel (518) 885-1820 *Founded/Ownrshp* 1994
Sales 98.1MM^E^ *EMP* 400
SIC 7349 Cleaning service, industrial or commercial; Cleaning service, industrial or commercial
Pr: Frank Zilka
CFO: Chris Scaringe
**VP:* Kurt Prouty
**VP:* Timothy Zilka
Genl Mgr: Chris Spain
Dir IT: Michael Kelly
Opers Mgr: James Lehrke
Sales Exec: Gary Horinka
Sls Dir: Chris Tinnell
Sls Mgr: Tiffany Collins

D-U-N-S 07-732-7013
NORTH AMERICAN INSURANCE AGENCY INC
NORTH AMERICAN GROUP
5101 Classen Cir, Oklahoma City, OK 73118-4424
Tel (405) 523-2100 *Founded/Ownrshp* 1959
Sales NA *EMP* 369
SIC 6411 Insurance agents, brokers & service; Insurance agents; Insurance agents, brokers & service; Insurance agents
Ch Bd: Bill Durrett
**Pr:* Mike Ross
VP: John Hester
**VP:* Gary Jarmon
IT Man: Todd West

D-U-N-S 36-255-7589
■ **NORTH AMERICAN INSURANCE CO (INC)**
(*Subsy of* OXFORD FINANCIAL INC) ★
575 Donofrio Dr Ste 100, Madison, WI 53719-2832
Tel (608) 662-1232 *Founded/Ownrshp* 1997
Sales NA *EMP* 60
SIC 6311 6321 6324 Life insurance carriers; Disability health insurance; Health insurance carriers; Hospital & medical service plans
Pr: Mark Haydukovich
CFO: Jason A Berg
Dir IT: Charles Miller

D-U-N-S 12-507-3432 IMP
NORTH AMERICAN INTERCONNECT LLC
(*Subsy of* NAI GROUP LLC) ★
7975 N Hayden Rd Ste D105, Scottsdale, AZ 85258-3247
Tel (480) 556-6066 *Founded/Ownrshp* 2002
Sales 271.3MM^E^ *EMP* 1,100
SIC 2298 Cable, fiber; Cable, fiber
CEO: Preston Spears
Prgrm Mgr: Olga Reyes
Snr Sftwr: Harjinder Kaur
Ql Cn Mgr: Carlos Tellez
Snr Mgr: John Oberdank
Snr Mgr: Ruben Orduno

D-U-N-S 62-123-5477
NORTH AMERICAN INTERNATIONAL HOLDINGS INC
(*Subsy of* NORTH AMERICAN VAN LINES INC) ★
5001 Us Highway 30 W, Fort Wayne, IN 46818-9701
Tel (260) 429-2511 *Founded/Ownrshp* 1994
Sales 24.2MM^E^ *EMP* 599
SIC 4213 4731 6719 Trucking, except local; Freight transportation arrangement; Investment holding companies, except banks; Trucking, except local; Freight transportation arrangement; Investment holding companies, except banks
Pr: Michael T Wolfe
**Treas:* Douglas V Gathany

NORTH AMERICAN INVESTMENT
See AMERICAN AGENCIES INC

D-U-N-S 01-846-8756
NORTH AMERICAN KIOSK LLC
AKM
3930 Howard Hughes Pkwy # 500, Las Vegas, NV 89169-0948
Tel (702) 691-2948 *Founded/Ownrshp* 1998
Sales 91.6MM^E^ *EMP* 1,350
SIC 8741 Business management; Business management
CEO: Linda Johansen-James
**Pr:* Linda Johensen
**COO:* Scott Jackson
**CFO:* Kenneth E Jones
**VP:* Patricia Adame
**VP:* Joe Lecak
**VP:* Nicole Lloyd
Dir IT: Victoria Sanders

D-U-N-S 61-493-0717
NORTH AMERICAN LAWN & LANDSCAPE LLC
4200 Performance Rd, Charlotte, NC 28214-7000
Tel (704) 394-3300 Founded/Ownrshp 1986
Sales 49.3MM^E EMP 275
SIC 0782 Landscape contractors; Garden maintenance services; Landscape contractors; Garden maintenance services
CFO: Elizabeth Winchester
Genl Mgr: Brandon Gurley
Opers Mgr: Scott Wildrick

D-U-N-S 11-580-5228 IMP
NORTH AMERICAN LIGHTING INC
(Suby of KOITO MANUFACTURING CO., LTD.)
2275 S Main St, Paris, IL 61944-2963
Tel (217) 465-6600 Founded/Ownrshp 1998
Sales 606.1MM^E EMP 2,200
SIC 3647 Automotive lighting fixtures; Automotive lighting fixtures
CEO: Takashi Ohtake
Pr: Jun Toyota
COO: Bobbi Meyer
Sec: Kirk Gadberry
VP: Kishore Ahuja
VP: Kem Cooley
VP: Naoshi Misawa
VP: Kazuhiro Yamazaki
Prgrm Mgr: Keith Blain
Prgrm Mgr: Cindy Bunkelman
Prgrm Mgr: Niles Dufrenne

D-U-N-S 03-049-4475
NORTH AMERICAN LUBRICANTS CO
7337 E Doubletree Ranch R, Scottsdale, AZ 85258-2172
Tel (480) 624-5800 Founded/Ownrshp 2001
Sales 53.1MM^E EMP 40
SIC 5172 Petroleum products
CEO: Larry Read
*Pr: Andrew Bornstein
*CFO: Charlie Pass
*VP: Kyle Read
VP Sls: Brian Davis
VP Sls: Aaron Read
Sls Mgr: Dave Brown
Sls Mgr: John Combs
Sls Mgr: Mark Wolf

D-U-N-S 01-869-1303 IMP
NORTH AMERICAN MARKETING CORP (CT)
NAMCO
100 Sanrico Dr, Manchester, CT 06042-9010
Tel (860) 649-3666 Founded/Ownrshp 1962
Sales 243.3MM^E EMP 1,024^E
SIC 5999 Swimming pools, hot tubs & sauna equipment & supplies; Swimming pool chemicals, equipment & supplies
Pr: Stephen Radocchia
*CFO: Stephen Park
Ex VP: Robert Albrecht
VP: Barry Ruth
Dir IT: Bill Cooney
Netwrk Mgr: Domingo Serrano

D-U-N-S 09-179-2242
■ **NORTH AMERICAN MECHANICAL INC**
(Suby of COMFORT SYSTEMS USA INC) ★
4401 State Road 19, Windsor, WI 53598-9621
Tel (608) 241-2665 Founded/Ownrshp 1998
Sales 37.8MM^E EMP 190^E
SIC 1711 Mechanical contractor; Mechanical contractor
Pr: Steve Ross

D-U-N-S 09-279-1003 IMP
NORTH AMERICAN MEMBERSHIP GROUP HOLDINGS INC
NORTH AMERCN MEMBERSHIP GROUP
(Suby of PILOT GROUP LP) ★
915 Mainstreet 2, Hopkins, MN 55343-7515
Tel (952) 936-9333 Founded/Ownrshp 2007
Sales 23.9MM^E EMP 160
SIC 7997 2721 5961 Membership sports & recreation clubs; Hunting club, membership; Magazines: publishing & printing; Fishing, hunting & camping equipment & supplies: mail order; Membership sports & recreation clubs; Hunting club, membership; Magazines: publishing & printing; Fishing, hunting & camping equipment & supplies: mail order
CEO: James Heckman
*Ch Bd: Robert Pittman
*Pr: Nancy Evensen
*CEO: Bryan Ellis
*CEO: Michael Graves
*VP: Anthony Defrance

D-U-N-S 19-782-0314 IMP
NORTH AMERICAN MIDWAY ENTERTAINMENT LLC
109 S Main St, Farmland, IN 47340
Tel (601) 898-5533 Founded/Ownrshp 2004
Sales 12.8MM^E EMP 400
SIC 7929 Entertainment group; Entertainment group
CEO: James M Williams

D-U-N-S 07-344-1727
NORTH AMERICAN MISSION BOARD OF SOUTHERN BAPTIST CONVENTION INC
4200 N Point Pkwy, Alpharetta, GA 30022-4176
Tel (770) 410-6000 Founded/Ownrshp 1883
Sales 19.1MM^E EMP 340
SIC 8661 7922 Religious organizations; Theatrical producers & services; Religious organizations; Theatrical producers & services
CEO: Michael Kevin Ezell
*Pr: Geoff Hammond
*CFO: Carlos A Ferrer
Mktg Mgr: Rebbecca Cozart

D-U-N-S 01-053-8051
NORTH AMERICAN OFFICE SOLUTIONS INC
6314 Kingspointe Pkwy # 7, Orlando, FL 32819-6531
Tel (407) 248-8329 Founded/Ownrshp 2001
Sales 20.1MM^E EMP 35
SIC 5112 Computer & photocopying supplies
CEO: Steve W Clapp
*Pr: Kyle Muehlestein
Sr VP: Rich Johnson
VP: Robert Cowan
Opers Mgr: Pat Waters
VP Sls: Anthony Arritt
Sls Mgr: Andrew Gross

D-U-N-S 17-392-7620
NORTH AMERICAN PACKAGING LLC
ECONO PAK
535 Route 6 And 209 Ste A, Milford, PA 18337-7847
Tel (570) 296-4200 Founded/Ownrshp 2004
Sales 38.9MM^E EMP 100
SIC 2043 Cereal breakfast foods; Cereal breakfast foods
Prin: Bob Szyani
Brnch Mgr: Paul Wiebel

D-U-N-S 06-472-4370
NORTH AMERICAN PARTNERS IN ANESTHESIA LLP
NAPA
68 S Service Rd Ste 350, Melville, NY 11747-2358
Tel (516) 945-3000 Founded/Ownrshp 1982
Sales 53.3MM^E EMP 420
SIC 8011 Anesthesiologist; Anesthesiologist
CEO: John Di Capua MD
Mng Pt: Dale Anderson
Mng Pt: Timothy Dowd
Pr: Lloyd Straus
CEO: Vincent Vilasi
Bd of Dir: Gregory Adkisson
Sr VP: Thomas Delaney
Sr VP: Ronald Mullahey
VP: Leslie Russo
IT Man: Kevin McEvoy
Ansthlgy: Michael Houston

NORTH AMERICAN PET PRODUCTS
See PET PARTNERS INC

D-U-N-S 79-181-4387 IMP/EXP
■ **NORTH AMERICAN PIPE CORP**
(Suby of WESTLAKE CHEMICAL CORP) ★
2801 Post Oak Blvd # 600, Houston, TX 77056-6110
Tel (713) 840-7473 Founded/Ownrshp 1992
Sales 1.1MMM^E EMP 889
SIC 3084 Plastics pipe; Plastics pipe
Pr: Mike Powell
Treas: M S Bender Sr
*Treas: Steve Bender
Sr VP: Steven Bender
VP: Jennifer House
*VP: Michael Mattina
Prd Mgr: Bill Yee
Sls Mgr: Shawn Owhadi
Board of Directors: Albert Chao

D-U-N-S 07-674-4721
NORTH AMERICAN PLASTICS CHEMICALS INC
NORAMCO
1400 E 222nd St, Euclid, OH 44117-1108
Tel (216) 531-3400 Founded/Ownrshp 1974
Sales 20.3MM^E EMP 80
SIC 2673 2671 Plastic & pliofilm bags; Packaging paper & plastics film, coated & laminated; Plastic & pliofilm bags; Packaging paper & plastics film, coated & laminated
Pr: James Popela
CFO: James Keaton
*Sec: Hana Popela
*VP: Tom Nichols
Plnt Mgr: Mike Voit
Plnt Mgr: Doral Wilkes
Prd Mgr: Rhyan Christian

D-U-N-S 83-246-1086
NORTH AMERICAN POWER AND GAS LLC
20 Glover Ave Ste 1, Norwalk, CT 06850-1234
Tel (203) 893-4196 Founded/Ownrshp 2009
Sales 350.0MM EMP 96
SIC 4931 Electric & other services combined
Ch: Kerry Breitbart
Pr: Bill Kinneary
Pr: Laurence Wright
CEO: Deryl Brown
COO: Taff Tschamlar
CFO: Keith Schwartz
Chf Mktg O: Gregory Breitbart
Sr VP: Jim Mannion
Sr VP: Taff Tschamler
VP: Dana Coates
VP: Paul Rossi

D-U-N-S 79-501-2061
NORTH AMERICAN POWER GROUP LTD
8480 E Orchard Rd # 4000, Greenwood Village, CO 80111-5014
Tel (303) 796-8600 Founded/Ownrshp 1992
Sales 66.3MM EMP 11
Accts Kushner Smith Joanou And Gre
SIC 4911 Electric services; Electric services
Pr: Michael J Ruffatto

D-U-N-S 83-570-3075
NORTH AMERICAN PRECAST CO INC
6949 Low Bid Ln, San Antonio, TX 78250-4632
Tel (210) 509-9100 Founded/Ownrshp 1994
Sales 41.5MM^E EMP 200
SIC 3272 1791 Concrete products; Precast concrete structural framing or panels, placing of; Concrete products; Precast concrete structural framing or panels, placing of
Pr: Jaime Iragorri
VP: Jorge Londono
Sfty Dirs: Matt Herschell
Sls Mgr: Ricardo Tapicha
Snr Mgr: Alfredo Virrueta

D-U-N-S 78-900-3774
NORTH AMERICAN PROPANE INC
100 Myles Standish Blvd, Taunton, MA 02780-7340
Tel (800) 822-1300 Founded/Ownrshp 2001
Sales 67.2MM^E EMP 432
SIC 5172 5984 Gases, liquefied petroleum (propane); Liquefied petroleum gas dealers; Propane gas, bottled; Gases, liquefied petroleum (propane); Liquefied petroleum gas dealers; Propane gas, bottled
Pr: Mark A Cleaves
*CFO: Edward Burke

D-U-N-S 09-390-2542
NORTH AMERICAN REFRACTORIES CO
(Suby of AP GREEN REFRACTORIES) ★
1305 Cherrington Pkwy # 100, Coraopolis, PA 15108-4355
Tel (412) 375-6600 Founded/Ownrshp 2013
Sales 118.6MM^E EMP 835^E
SIC 3297 3255 Nonclay refractories; Clay refractories
CEO: Steven M Delo
*CFO: Frances Winfield
*Sr VP: Douglas Hall
*Sr VP: Carol Jackson
VP: Carl Todaro

D-U-N-S 82-516-8235
NORTH AMERICAN RISK SERVICES INC
NARS
240 E Central Pkwy # 1060, Altamonte Springs, FL 32701-7848
Tel (407) 875-1700 Founded/Ownrshp 2008
Sales NA EMP 168
SIC 6411 Insurance agents, brokers & service
CEO: Robert Ruryk
*Treas: John M McCully
Dir Bus: O L Anderson
Dir Bus: Jamie Bernardo
CIO: Richard Lemons
QA Dir: Elaina Denhardt

D-U-N-S 80-720-0902 EXP
NORTH AMERICAN ROOFING SERVICES INC
41 Dogwood Rd, Asheville, NC 28806-2208
Tel (828) 687-7767 Founded/Ownrshp 1979
Sales 130.0MM^E EMP 500
SIC 1761 Roofing contractor; Roofing contractor
Pr: Brian Verble
*CFO: Timothy Sparrow
*Ex VP: Kelly Wade
VP: Sam Phillips
Dir IT: Deforest Hipps
Opers Mgr: Grant Hower
Natl Sales: Michael Fain
Natl Sales: Tim Stokes
Natl Sales: Curt Thomas
Natl Sales: Robin Wilkie
Sls Mgr: Jeff Brummett

D-U-N-S 07-304-9827
NORTH AMERICAN SAFETY VALVE INDUSTRIES INC
KUNKLE VALVE
1500 Iron St, North Kansas City, MO 64116-3809
Tel (816) 421-7042 Founded/Ownrshp 1975
Sales 28.0MM^E EMP 32
SIC 5085 7699 Valves, pistons & fittings; Valve repair, industrial
Pr: Allen Tannis

D-U-N-S 06-271-5214
■ **NORTH AMERICAN SAVINGS BANK FSB**
(Suby of NASB FINANCIAL INC) ★
12498 S Us Highway 71, Grandview, MO 64030-1782
Tel (816) 765-2200 Founded/Ownrshp 1923, 1997
Sales NA EMP 314
SIC 6035 Federal savings & loan associations; Federal savings & loan associations
CEO: Paul L Thomas
*Ch Bd: David H Hancock
Pr: Keith B Cox
Pr: Christine Todd
Ofcr: Jeff Baldner
Ofcr: Tom Wagers
Sr VP: Brad Lee
Sr VP: John Nesselrode
Sr VP: Bruce Thielen
VP: Mark Bitteker
VP: Michael Braman
VP: Sherrie Eimer
VP: Jesseka Endecott
VP: Cathleen Gwin
VP: Scott Haase
VP: Jennie Harris
VP: Lisa M Reynolds
VP: Rick Speciale
VP: Ron Stafford
VP: Drake Vidrine

D-U-N-S 06-372-2102
NORTH AMERICAN SCIENCE ASSOCIATES INC
NAMSA
6750 Wales Rd, Northwood, OH 43619-1012
Tel (419) 666-9455 Founded/Ownrshp 1967
Sales 121.9MM^E EMP 533
SIC 8731 8734 Commercial physical research; Testing laboratories; Commercial physical research; Testing laboratories
Pr: John J Gorski
*CFO: Scott Sellick
*VP: Jane A Kervin
*VP: Dennis Nevins
*VP: Gina Skolmowski
Dir Bus: Sheri Bibins

D-U-N-S 07-912-3633
NORTH AMERICAN SECURITY AND INVESTIGATIONS INC
550 E Carson Plaza Dr, Carson, CA 90746-3229
Tel (323) 634-1911 Founded/Ownrshp 2004
Sales 5.0MM^E EMP 500
SIC 7381 Private investigator; Private investigator
CEO: Arthur Lopez

D-U-N-S 93-908-0248
NORTH AMERICAN SECURITY INC
550 E Carson St P, Carson, CA 90745-2714
Tel (310) 630-4840 Founded/Ownrshp 1994
Sales 12.8MM EMP 420
Accts Teresa Crivello Cpa San Pedr
SIC 7381 Security guard service; Security guard service
Pr: Arthur L Lopez
*VP: Kenneth Hillman
Off Mgr: Atzi Camarena

D-U-N-S 06-951-8868 IMP
NORTH AMERICAN SHIPBUILDING LLC
800 Industrial Park Rd, Larose, LA 70373-5147
Tel (985) 693-4072 Founded/Ownrshp 1974
Sales 119.7MM^E EMP 550
SIC 3731 Offshore supply boats, building & repairing; Cargo vessels, building & repairing; Crew boats, building & repairing; Offshore supply boats, building & repairing; Cargo vessels, building & repairing; Crew boats, building & repairing
Prin: Gary J Chouest
*CFO: Charles Comeaux
*Prin: Dino Chouest
Sfty Dirs: Rene Stewart

D-U-N-S 62-081-9318
NORTH AMERICAN STAINLESS
N A S
(Suby of ACERINOX, SA)
6870 Us Highway 42 E, Ghent, KY 41045-8451
Tel (502) 347-6000 Founded/Ownrshp 2005
Sales 364.1MM^E EMP 1,375^E
SIC 3316 3312 Cold finishing of steel shapes; Blast furnaces & steel mills; Cold finishing of steel shapes; Blast furnaces & steel mills
CEO: Cristobal Fuentes
Snr Mgr: Chris Burch
Snr Mgr: Bruce Trapp

NORTH AMERICAN STAMPING GROUP
See NASG TENNESSEE NORTH 1 LLC

D-U-N-S 13-211-7636
NORTH AMERICAN STAMPING GROUP LLC
TENNESSEE STAMPINGS PORTLAND
119 Kirby Dr, Portland, TN 37148-2004
Tel (615) 323-0500 Founded/Ownrshp 1998
Sales 284.0MM^E EMP 555^E
SIC 3469 6719 Metal stampings; Investment holding companies, except banks
Opers Mgr: Mike Rigsby

D-U-N-S 82-476-9694
NORTH AMERICAN SUBSTATION SERVICES LLC
NASS
190 N Westmonte Dr, Altamonte Springs, FL 32714-3342
Tel (407) 788-3717 Founded/Ownrshp 2015
Sales 31.1MM^E EMP 92
SIC 1731 Electrical work
Pr: Mark Roberts
Pr: Pierre Feghali
VP: Ken Harrison

D-U-N-S 84-863-0042
NORTH AMERICAN SYSTEMS INTERNATIONAL INC
2975 Lone Oak Dr Ste 140, Saint Paul, MN 55121-1784
Tel (952) 374-6700 Founded/Ownrshp 1993
Sales 50.4MM^E EMP 55
SIC 5045 Computers, peripherals & software
Pr: Phil Bettenburg
CFO: Gregory J Springer
VP: John Bettenburg
*VP: David Bogie

D-U-N-S 80-483-3093
NORTH AMERICAN TECHNOLOGIES GROUP INC
429 S Memory Ln, Marshall, TX 75670-8405
Tel (972) 996-5750 Founded/Ownrshp 1986
Sales 32.7MM^E EMP 131^E
SIC 2491 Railroad cross-ties, treated wood; Railroad cross-ties, treated wood
Ch Bd: D Patrick Long
VP: Rod Wallace
Genl Couns: Joe B Dorman

D-U-N-S 08-696-6744
NORTH AMERICAN THEATRICAL PHOTOGRAPHERS INC (MI)
5385 Five Frks Trickum Rd, Stone Mountain, GA 30087-3018
Tel (770) 925-3355 Founded/Ownrshp 1973
Sales 11.1MM^E EMP 945
SIC 7221 Photographer, still or video; Photographer, still or video
Pr: Roland Thornton
*Treas: Lila Thornton

D-U-N-S 14-873-3053
NORTH AMERICAN TIE & TIMBER LLC
6406 N Santa Fe Ave Ste B, Oklahoma City, OK 73116-9117
Tel (405) 848-1800 Founded/Ownrshp 2003
Sales 480.0MM EMP 43
SIC 5099 Timber products, rough; Timber products, rough

D-U-N-S 14-411-3685
■ **NORTH AMERICAN TITLE CO**
(Suby of NORTH AMERICAN TITLE GROUP INC) ★
760 Nw 107th Ave Ste 100, Miami, FL 33172-3155
Tel (305) 552-1102 Founded/Ownrshp 1986
Sales NA EMP 125
SIC 6361 Title insurance
Pr: Beverly McReynolds
*CFO: Nancy Kamimsky
*CFO: Cloty Keller
*Treas: Donnis Benso
*Treas: Janis Munoz
Ex VP: Valerie Grandin
*Ex VP: Linda Reed
Creative D: Robin Wester
Brnch Mgr: Krishna Almond
Brnch Mgr: Nancy Smith
Brnch Mgr: Lesley Williams

D-U-N-S 10-341-1757
■ **NORTH AMERICAN TITLE CO INC**
NAT
(*Suby of* NORTH AMERICAN ASSET DEVELOPMENT CORP) ★
1855 Gateway Blvd Ste 600, Concord, CA 94520-8474
Tel (925) 935-5599 *Founded/Ownrshp* 1983
Sales NA *EMP* 1,000
SIC 6361 6531 Title insurance; Escrow agent, real estate; Title insurance; Escrow agent, real estate
Pr: Linda L Reed
**CEO:* Anita Demmon
**CFO:* Jeffrey Wright
Ex VP: John Fries
Sr VP: Richard Lundbeck

D-U-N-S 80-935-2271
■ **NORTH AMERICAN TITLE CO OF COLORADO**
(*Suby of* NORTH AMERICAN ASSET DEVELOPMENT CORP) ★
101 University Blvd # 310, Denver, CO 80206-4621
Tel (303) 316-3400 *Founded/Ownrshp* 1993
Sales NA *EMP* 222
SIC 6361 Real estate title insurance; Real estate title insurance
Pr: Dick Kelly

D-U-N-S 02-818-2074
■ **NORTH AMERICAN TITLE GROUP INC** (FL)
(*Suby of* LENNAR FINANCIAL SERVICES LLC) ★
700 Nw 107th Ave Ste 300, Miami, FL 33172-3139
Tel (305) 552-1102 *Founded/Ownrshp* 1984
Sales NA *EMP* 1,050
SIC 6361 Title insurance; Title insurance
Pr: Linda L Reed
**CFO:* Clotilde C Keller
**Treas:* Donnis Benson
**Ex VP:* Emilio Fernandez
Ex VP: Nancy A Kminsky
**Sr VP:* Richard K Kasunick
**VP:* Carol Burgin
**VP:* Alex Kidd
Dir Bus: Loni Andal

D-U-N-S 08-697-5497 EXP
NORTH AMERICAN TRADE CORP
NORAMCO
18948 Freeport Dr, Montgomery, TX 77356-4445
Tel (936) 588-1010 *Founded/Ownrshp* 1984
Sales 26.3MM^E *EMP* 16
Accts Cook Johnston & Co Houston
SIC 5082 3949 5085 Oil field equipment; Treadmills; Industrial supplies
Pr: Jorge Guiloff
**VP:* Jacqueline Guiloff
**VP:* George Hoepner
IT Man: Mike Connery

D-U-N-S 96-796-1418
NORTH AMERICAN TRAILER LLC
2896 W 2100 S, Salt Lake City, UT 84119-1206
Tel (801) 973-4407 *Founded/Ownrshp* 1996
Sales 24.7MM^E *EMP* 58
SIC 5012 Trailers for trucks, new & used
Pr: Del Keffer
CFO: Randy Olsen
CFO: Mark J Wright
Opers Mgr: John Solario

D-U-N-S 15-065-2923
NORTH AMERICAN TRUCK & TRAILER INC
4500 N Cliff Ave, Sioux Falls, SD 57104-0553
Tel (605) 332-7112 *Founded/Ownrshp* 1989
Sales 91.0MM^E *EMP* 240
SIC 5012 7538

NORTH AMERICAN VAN LINES
See AIR VAN LINES INC

NORTH AMERICAN VAN LINES
See A-1 FREEMAN MOVING & STORAGE LLC

NORTH AMERICAN VAN LINES
See MOVING SOLUTIONS INC

NORTH AMERICAN VAN LINES
See ANTONIO ROGER WARD-SAN INC

D-U-N-S 00-693-7197
NORTH AMERICAN VAN LINES INC (TX)
(*Suby of* SIRVA WORLDWIDE INC) ★
5001 Us Highway 30 W, Fort Wayne, IN 46818-9799
Tel (260) 429-1682 *Founded/Ownrshp* 1933
Sales 215.9MM^E *EMP* 1,382
SIC 4213 4731 4214 6331 7389 4212 Trucking, except local; Household goods transport; Freight forwarding; Furniture moving & storage, local; Assessment associations: fire, marine & casualty insurance; Property damage insurance; Relocation service; Local trucking, without storage; Trucking, except local; Household goods transport; Freight forwarding; Furniture moving & storage, local; Assessment associations: fire, marine & casualty insurance; Property damage insurance; Relocation service; Local trucking, without storage
CEO: Michael T Wolfe
**Sr VP:* John M Dupuy
**Sr VP:* Eryk J Spytek
VP: Dennis Koziol
VP: Richard Omlor
Exec: Joe Steen
Genl Mgr: O Neil
Sales Exec: Tammy Smith
Board of Directors: Robert W Tieken, Kathleen Affeldt, Frederick Brace, Robert J Dellinger, Laban P Jackson Jr, Gen Sir Jeremy Mackenzie, James Roger, Richard Schnall, Joseph A Smialowski, Carl Stocker

NORTH AMERICAN VIDEO
See HALIFAX SECURITY INC

D-U-N-S 07-659-2187 IMP/EXP
NORTH AMERICAN VIDEO CORP
NAVCO SECURITY SYSTEMS
1041 N Pacificenter Dr, Anaheim, CA 92806-2126
Tel (714) 779-7499 *Founded/Ownrshp* 1979
Sales 104.0MM^E *EMP* 115
SIC 5065 3812 Video equipment, electronic; Security control equipment & systems; Acceleration indicators & systems components, aerospace; Video equipment, electronic; Security control equipment & systems; Acceleration indicators & systems components, aerospace
CEO: Jason Oakley
**Ch Bd:* Margaret Groves
**Pr:* William Groves
COO: Paul Spruiell
**Treas:* Debra Laberge
**Prin:* William Augustus Groves
Natl Sales: Casey Knapp
Natl Sales: Rob Weisberg
Sls Mgr: Ali Nik

NORTH AMERICAN WOOD PRODUCTS
See NORTH AMERICAN WORLD TRADE GROUP INC

D-U-N-S 78-766-5074 IMP/EXP
NORTH AMERICAN WORLD TRADE GROUP INC
NORTH AMERICAN WOOD PRODUCTS
7007 Sw Cardinal Ln # 135, Portland, OR 97224-7248
Tel (503) 620-6655 *Founded/Ownrshp* 1992
Sales 20.3MM *EMP* 19^E
Accts Mack Roberts & Company Llc
SIC 5031 Lumber, plywood & millwork; Structural assemblies, prefabricated: wood; Lumber, plywood & millwork; Structural assemblies, prefabricated: wood
Pr: Cliff Chulos
CFO: Ann Pham
VP: Vern Aden
VP: Steve Allison
Trfc Mgr: Matt Loutzenhiser

NORTH AMERICAS BREWERIES
See HIGH FALLS BREWING CO LLC

NORTH ANDOVER PUBLIC SCHL DST
See NORTH ANDOVER PUBLIC SCHOOLS

D-U-N-S 10-028-6814
NORTH ANDOVER PUBLIC SCHOOLS
NORTH ANDOVER PUBLIC SCHL DST
566 Main St, North Andover, MA 01845-4011
Tel (978) 794-1503 *Founded/Ownrshp* 1985
Sales 23.7MM^E *EMP* 450^E
SIC 8211 Public elementary & secondary schools; Public elementary school; Public elementary & secondary schools; Public elementary school
Pr: Paul McCabe
**Prin:* Marybeth Keane
Teacher Pr: Debra Vartinian

NORTH ANDOVER RESCO
See WHEELABRATOR NORTH ANDOVER INC

D-U-N-S 05-974-0378
NORTH ARKANSAS COLLEGE
1515 Pioneer Dr, Harrison, AR 72601-5508
Tel (870) 743-3000 *Founded/Ownrshp* 1966
Sales 795.1M *EMP* 500
Accts Holt & Hudson Cpas Pa Harriso
SIC 8222 Junior college; Junior college
Pr: Dr Jeff Olson
Bd of Dir: Marcus Jones
Bd of Dir: Matt Miller
Bd of Dir: Jim Milum
Bd of Dir: Wayne Thompson
Ofcr: Robert Wheatley
Ex VP: Michael Wiggins
VP: Rodney Arnold
VP: Mindy Maddux
Exec: Paula Melton
Store Mgr: Kevin Middleton

D-U-N-S 00-780-7266
NORTH ARKANSAS ELECTRIC COOPERATIVE INC
225 S Main St, Salem, AR 72576-9419
Tel (870) 895-3221 *Founded/Ownrshp* 1939
Sales 67.2MM *EMP* 142
SIC 4911 Electric services; Electric services
CEO: Mel Coleman
VP: Sherry Jackson
CTO: Dustin Denton

D-U-N-S 04-733-5815
NORTH ARKANSAS LIVESTOCK AUCTION INC
304 W Main St, Green Forest, AR 72638-3005
Tel (870) 438-6915 *Founded/Ownrshp* 1982
Sales 41.5MM *EMP* 35
SIC 5154 Auctioning livestock; Auctioning livestock
Pr: Kirk Powell

D-U-N-S 83-230-2322
NORTH ARKANSAS REGIONAL MEDICA
620 N Main St, Harrison, AR 72601-2911
Tel (870) 365-2000 *Founded/Ownrshp* 2009
Sales 95.7MM *EMP* 35^E
Accts Bkd Llp Little Rock Ar
SIC 8011 Medical centers; Medical centers
Owner: Timothy A Gannon
CFO: Debbie Henry
Off Mgr: Lucia Gonzalez
DP Exec: Kent Kimes
Doctor: Tarik Sidani

D-U-N-S 14-473-5198
NORTH ARKANSAS REGIONAL MEDICAL CENTER
620 N Main St, Harrison, AR 72601-2911
Tel (870) 414-4000 *Founded/Ownrshp* 1996
Sales 93.5MM *EMP* 700
Accts Bkd Llp Little Rock Ar
SIC 8062 General medical & surgical hospitals; General medical & surgical hospitals
CEO: Vincent Leist
COO: Richard McBride
**COO:* Richard McBryde
COO: Chris Whybrew
**CFO:* Bebbie Henry
**CFO:* Debbie Henry
VP: Sammie Cribbs
VP: Ronnie McAlister
Dir Risk M: Jeanette Milligan
Dir Lab: Vincent List
Dir Lab: Jane Van Boskirk
Dir Lab: Jane Vanboskirk
Dir Rx: Jean Senn

D-U-N-S 01-419-7474
NORTH ARKANSAS REGIONAL MEDICAL CENTER INC
AMBULANCE SERVICE NORTH ARK
620 N Main St, Harrison, AR 72601-2911
Tel (870) 414-4000 *Founded/Ownrshp* 1950
Sales 79.5MM *EMP* 4
SIC 4119 Ambulance service; Ambulance service
CEO: Tim Hill
**CFO:* Debbie Henry
Ofcr: Molly Mc Cammon
Dir Risk M: Jeanette Milligan
Diag Rad: Robert L Brand

D-U-N-S 13-818-7133
NORTH ARLINGTON SCHOOL DISTRICT
222 Ridge Rd, North Arlington, NJ 07031-6036
Tel (201) 991-6800 *Founded/Ownrshp* 1900
Sales 28.0MM *EMP* 300
SIC 8211 Public combined elementary & secondary school; Kindergarten; Public combined elementary & secondary school; Kindergarten
Prin: Robert Kinloch
Brnch Mgr: Clair Greene
Instr Medi: Ellen Bratowitz

D-U-N-S 80-342-1296 IMP
NORTH ATLANTIC CORP
NAMCO
1255 Grand Army Hwy, Somerset, MA 02726-1203
Tel (508) 324-7700 *Founded/Ownrshp* 1992
Sales 98.3MM^E *EMP* 180
SIC 5031 Doors; Door frames, all materials; Doors; Door frames, all materials
Pr: Peter Humphrey
**Treas:* Irving D Humphrey
**VP:* I Gary Fox

D-U-N-S 17-433-4706
NORTH ATLANTIC DISTRIBUTION INC
NORAD
100 Tidal Dr Unit 2, North Kingstown, RI 02852-8040
Tel (401) 667-7000 *Founded/Ownrshp* 1986
Sales 26.1MM^E *EMP* 300
SIC 7549 3711 5599 Automotive customizing services, non-factory basis; High performance auto repair & service; Automobile bodies, passenger car, not including engine, etc.; Dunebuggies
Pr: Michael Miranda
CFO: Aldo Caputo
Dir IT: Steve Andreozzi

D-U-N-S 94-507-2676
■ **NORTH ATLANTIC ENERGY CORP**
(*Suby of* FLORIDA POWER & LIGHT CO INC) ★
626 Lafayette Rd, Seabrook, NH 03874-4213
Tel (603) 474-9521 *Founded/Ownrshp* 2002
Sales 836.8MM^E *EMP* 1,000
SIC 4911 Electric services; Electric services
Pr: Bruce D Kenyon
**Treas:* David McHale
**Ofcr:* Ted C Feigenbaum
**VP:* John J Roman
VP Opers: Leighton Bicknell

D-U-N-S 14-426-3340
■ **NORTH ATLANTIC ENERGY SERVICE CORP**
SEABROOK NUCLEAR POWER PROJECT
(*Suby of* EVERSOURCE ENERGY) ★
626 Lafayette Rd, Seabrook, NH 03874-4213
Tel (603) 474-9521 *Founded/Ownrshp* 1992
Sales 330.8MM^E *EMP* 800
SIC 4924 Natural gas distribution; Natural gas distribution
Ch Bd: Michael Morris
**Pr:* Bruce Kenyonn
**CFO:* John Forsgren
**Ofcr:* Ted C Feigenbaum

D-U-N-S 79-346-0940
NORTH ATLANTIC INDUSTRIES INC
110 Wilbur Pl, Bohemia, NY 11716-2402
Tel (631) 567-1100 *Founded/Ownrshp* 1992
Sales 43.9MM *EMP* 115^E
SIC 3825 Instruments to measure electricity; Instruments to measure electricity
Pr: William Forman
Pr: Paul Feldman
Ofcr: Kathy Schwartz
VP: Shawn Lannerd
**VP:* Lino Massafra
Genl Mgr: Larry Rubin
Snr Sftwr: Obimma Okafor
Software D: Jonathan Soldo
Sftwr Eng: Richard Varone
Mfg Mgr: Joe Tuccio
Plnt Mgr: Edward Doepp

NORTH ATLANTIC MEDICAL
See REGIONAL HOME CARE INC

D-U-N-S 96-228-9398
NORTH ATLANTIC SECURITY CO
4072 Highway 45 N, Columbus, MS 39705-3352
Tel (662) 327-3555 *Founded/Ownrshp* 2006
Sales 6.4MM^E *EMP* 300
SIC 7381 7382 Security guard service; Confinement surveillance systems maintenance & monitoring; Security guard service; Confinement surveillance systems maintenance & monitoring
Pr: Jim Bell
**VP:* Cassandra Boyd
Rgnl Mgr: Jeanette Rich

D-U-N-S 00-289-8182 IMP
NORTH ATLANTIC TRADING CO INC
(*Suby of* NORTH ATLANTIC HOLDING COMPANY, INC)
5201 Interchange Way, Louisville, KY 40229-2184
Tel (502) 778-4421 *Founded/Ownrshp* 1997
Sales 180.2MM *EMP* 299^E
Accts Mcgladrey Llp Greensboro No
SIC 2131 Chewing & smoking tobacco; Chewing & smoking tobacco
Pr: Lawrence S Wexler
**Ch Bd:* Thomas F Helms Jr
**CFO:* Brian C Harris
**V Ch Bd:* Jack Africk
**Sr VP:* James W Dobbins
**Sr VP:* James M Murray
Board of Directors: Gregory H A Baxter, Geoffrey J F Gorman

D-U-N-S 10-371-6478
NORTH ATTLEBORO PUBLIC SCHOOL DISTRICT
6 Morse St, North Attleboro, MA 02760-1604
Tel (508) 643-2100 *Founded/Ownrshp* 1887
Sales 33.3MM^E *EMP* 700
SIC 8211 Public elementary & secondary schools; Public elementary & secondary schools

D-U-N-S 07-982-3233
NORTH BABYLON UNION FREE SCHOOL DISTRICT
5 Jardine Pl, Babylon, NY 11703-4203
Tel (631) 321-3209 *Founded/Ownrshp* 1932
Sales 48.8MM^E *EMP* 1,000
SIC 8211 8741 Public combined elementary & secondary school; Management services; Public combined elementary & secondary school; Management services

D-U-N-S 08-988-1114
NORTH BAY DEVELOPMENTAL DISABILITIES SERVICES INC (CA)
NORTH BAY REGIONAL CENTER
10 Executive Ct Ste A, NAPA, CA 94558-6267
Tel (707) 256-1224 *Founded/Ownrshp* 1972
Sales 149.4MM *EMP* 160
Accts Thompson Noble Company Llp Sa
SIC 8331 8322 Job training services; Individual & family services; Job training services; Individual & family services
Ex Dir: Nancy Gardner
CFO: Bob Hamilton
CFO: David Johnson
VP: Matt Bloom
Ex Dir: Robert Hamilton

D-U-N-S 11-991-3119 IMP
NORTH BAY DISTRIBUTION INC
NORTH BAY WAREHOUSE EQUIPMENT
2050 Cessna Dr, Vacaville, CA 95688-8712
Tel (707) 450-1219 *Founded/Ownrshp* 1997
Sales 172.7MM^E *EMP* 170
SIC 5136 Men's & boys' clothing; Men's & boys' clothing
Pr: Lee Perry
Ex VP: Riza Suma

D-U-N-S 02-939-4525
NORTH BAY FORD LINCOLN
1999 Soquel Ave, Santa Cruz, CA 95062-1389
Tel (831) 457-5858 *Founded/Ownrshp* 1982
Sales 34.8MM^E *EMP* 92
SIC 5511 Automobiles, new & used; Automobiles, new & used
Pr: W R Winterhalder
**Pr:* William R Winterhalder

D-U-N-S 07-838-5322
NORTH BAY GENERAL HOSPITAL INC (TX)
CARE REGIONAL MEDICAL CENTER
1711 W Wheeler Ave, Aransas Pass, TX 78336-4536
Tel (361) 758-8585 *Founded/Ownrshp* 2000
Sales 27.7MM^E *EMP* 210
SIC 8062 General medical & surgical hospitals; General medical & surgical hospitals
CEO: Sunil Reddy
CFO: Mark Wishard
CIO: Greg Palmer
Nrsg Dir: Christal Burns
Occ Thrpy: Chris Taylor

D-U-N-S 78-423-9485 IMP/EXP
NORTH BAY PRODUCE INC
1771 N Us Highway 31 S, Traverse City, MI 49685-8748
Tel (231) 946-1941 *Founded/Ownrshp* 1991
Sales 153.3MM *EMP* 25
Accts Dennis Gartland & Niergarth
SIC 5148 Fruits; Vegetables; Fruits; Vegetables
Ch Bd: George Wright
**Pr:* Mark Girardin
**Sec:* Ken Schwallier
**V Ch Bd:* Tom Gee
**VP:* Richard L Bogard
Sls Mgr: Eric Olshove

NORTH BAY REGIONAL CENTER
See NORTH BAY DEVELOPMENTAL DISABILITIES SERVICES INC

D-U-N-S 79-549-3394
NORTH BAY SATURN GROUP INC
3001 Corby Ave, Santa Rosa, CA 95407-7884
Tel (707) 525-1800 *Founded/Ownrshp* 1992
Sales 33.1MM^E *EMP* 100
SIC 5511 Automobiles, new & used; Automobiles, new & used
CEO: Robert C Benson
**Pr:* Todd Barnes
VP Mktg: Jennifer Persall
Sls Mgr: Mark Hobbins

NORTH BAY WAREHOUSE EQUIPMENT
See NORTH BAY DISTRIBUTION INC

D-U-N-S 06-195-8104
NORTH BELLMORE PUBLIC LIBRARY
1551 Newbridge Rd, North Bellmore, NY 11710-1696
Tel (516) 785-6260 *Founded/Ownrshp* 1948
Sales 22.5MM *EMP* 49
SIC 8231 Public library; Public library
Pr: Edward Diller
**Trst:* Lawrence Lupo

NORTH BELLMORE PUBLIC SCHOOLS
See NORTH BELLMORE UNION FREE SCHOOL DISTRICT

D-U-N-S 01-000-2913
NORTH BELLMORE UNION FREE SCHOOL DISTRICT
NORTH BELLMORE PUBLIC SCHOOLS
2616 Martin Ave, Bellmore, NY 11710-3131
Tel (516) 992-3000 *Founded/Ownrshp* 1904
Sales 50.6MM *EMP* 400
Accts Nawrocki Smith Llp Melville
SIC 8211 Public elementary school; Public elementary school
Pr: Neena Lanci
Bd of Dir: Grace Cramsie
Bd of Dir: Joseph Perrone

D-U-N-S 06-058-0743
NORTH BEND MEDICAL CENTER INC
MACLEAN, HEATHER CNM NP
1900 Woodland Dr, Coos Bay, OR 97420-2099
Tel (541) 267-5151 *Founded/Ownrshp* 1974
Sales 24.0MM^E *EMP* 130
SIC 8011 Physicians' office, including specialists
Ch Bd: Oded Shulsinger
**Ch Bd:* Oded Z Shulsinger MD
**Pr:* Philip C Lagesse
**Pr:* Kent Sharman
**CEO:* John Burles
**Prin:* Pete Johnson
CIO: Robert Schmidt
CTO: Doug McLeod
Obsttrcn: Brigitte Fink
Plas Surg: Garrett Vangelisti
Doctor: Sasha Jackson

D-U-N-S 84-708-3151
NORTH BERGEN MUNICIPAL UTILITIES AUTHORITY
NORTH BERGEN MUNICIPAL UTILITY
6200 Tonnelle Ave, North Bergen, NJ 07047-3312
Tel (201) 422-0100 *Founded/Ownrshp* 1982
Sales 31.8MM^E *EMP* 90
SIC 4953 ; Refuse collection & disposal services
Ex Dir: Frank Pestama
CFO: Patricia Bartoli
Ch: John Odell
V Ch Bd: Salvatore Desantis
Ex Dir: Frank Pestana
Counsel: John Napolitano

NORTH BERGEN MUNICIPAL UTILITY
See NORTH BERGEN MUNICIPAL UTILITIES AUTHORITY

D-U-N-S 02-467-1091
NORTH BERGEN TOWNSHIP OF INC (NJ)
4233 Kennedy Blvd Ste 4, North Bergen, NJ 07047-2779
Tel (201) 392-2000 *Founded/Ownrshp* 1850
Sales NA *EMP* 545
Accts Mcenerney Brady & Company Ll
SIC 9111 City & town managers' offices; ; City & town managers' offices;
**CFO:* Robert Pittfield

D-U-N-S 01-040-6635
NORTH BRANCH AREA PUBLIC SCHOOLS (MN)
6644 Main St, North Branch, MN 55056-7069
Tel (651) 674-1000 *Founded/Ownrshp* 1875, 1998
Sales 38.2MM *EMP* 291
Accts Larsonallen Llp Minneapolis
SIC 8211 Public elementary school; Public junior high school; Public senior high school; Public elementary school; Public junior high school; Public senior high school

D-U-N-S 10-003-6003
NORTH BRANCH AREA SCHOOL DISTRICT
6655 Jefferson Rd, North Branch, MI 48461-9735
Tel (810) 688-3660 *Founded/Ownrshp* 1950
Sales 24.0MM *EMP* 300
Accts Anderson Tuckey Bernhardt &
SIC 8211 Public combined elementary & secondary school; Public elementary school; Public junior high school; Public senior high school; Public combined elementary & secondary school; Public elementary school; Public junior high school; Public senior high school

D-U-N-S 01-897-1549
NORTH BRANCH CONSTRUCTION INC (NH)
76 Old Turnpike Rd, Concord, NH 03301-5242
Tel (603) 224-3233 *Founded/Ownrshp* 1958, 1978
Sales 22.2MM^E *EMP* 55
SIC 1542 1521 1522 Commercial & office building, new construction; Commercial & office buildings, renovation & repair; New construction, single-family houses; General remodeling, single-family houses; Multi-family dwellings, new construction; Remodeling, multi-family dwellings
CEO: Robert G Smith
Pr: Kenneth F Holmes
Treas: Robert C Terry
VP: Bruce Blazon
VP: James J Schwartzkopf
Sfty Dirs: Kevin Temple

NORTH BRANFORD LITTLE LEAGUE
See TOWN OF NORTH BRANFORD

D-U-N-S 78-057-2058
NORTH BRANFORD SCHOOL DISTRICT
1388 Middletown Ave, Northford, CT 06472-1344
Tel (203) 484-1440 *Founded/Ownrshp* 2006
Sales 13.3MM^E *EMP* 676^E
SIC 8211 Public elementary & secondary schools
Bd of Dir: Lauren Barry
CTO: Barbara Girard
Psych: Allison Tetreault
Psych: Joan Williams

NORTH BROOKLYN HEALTH NETWORK
See WOODHULL MEDICAL & MENTAL HEALTH CENTER AUXILIARY INC

D-U-N-S 80-965-7997
NORTH BROTHERS FORD INC
33300 Ford Rd, Westland, MI 48185-3088
Tel (734) 421-1300 *Founded/Ownrshp* 2008
Sales 40.9MM^E *EMP* 100
SIC 5511 Automobiles, new & used; Automobiles, new & used
Ch: James E Northm
**Pr:* Douglas North
Treas: Dorothy Hovestreydt
Sls Mgr: Mark Vizachero

D-U-N-S 07-225-2703
NORTH BROWARD HOSPITAL DISTRICT
BROWARD HEALTH MEDICAL CENTER
1800 Nw 49th St, Fort Lauderdale, FL 33309-3092
Tel (954) 473-7010 *Founded/Ownrshp* 1951
Sales 855.0MM^E *EMP* 7,000
SIC 8062 General medical & surgical hospitals; General medical & surgical hospitals
CEO: Nabil El Sanadi
**COO:* Paul Echelard
**CFO:* Robert Martin
Sr VP: Georges Boutin
Sr VP: Doris Peek
Sr VP: Joseph S Rogers
VP: Sara Howley Callari
VP: Laura Hunter
Dir Risk M: Steve Bard
Rgnl Mgr: Tony Gagliano
Rgnl Mgr: Amos Linton
Board of Directors: Paul Echelard, Robert Martin, Nabil El Sanadi

D-U-N-S 80-181-2801
NORTH BROWARD HOSPITAL DISTRICT FEDERAL CREDIT UNION
303 Se 17th St Ste 106, Fort Lauderdale, FL 33316-2523
Tel (954) 355-4400 *Founded/Ownrshp* 1994
Sales NA *EMP* 11
SIC 6061 Federal credit unions; Federal credit unions
Ex Dir: Kevin Hall
CFO: Kathy Cameron
Sec: Linda Lazouna
Off Mgr: Suzen Smith
CIO: Steve Benson
QA Dir: Beverly Beyerlein
QA Dir: Deborah Williams

D-U-N-S 05-612-1098
NORTH BROWARD MEDICAL CENTER INC
CORAL GIFT TREE BROWARD HOSP
201 E Sample Rd, Pompano Beach, FL 33064-3596
Tel (954) 786-6400 *Founded/Ownrshp* 1971
Sales 22.3M *EMP* 457^E
SIC 8011 Medical centers; Medical centers
Pr: Gloria Pucci
Dir Lab: Donna Valerioti
Dir Rx: Winn Castro
Opthamlgy: Arthur Fishman
HC Dir: Kimberly Brown

D-U-N-S 10-380-5370
NORTH BRUNSWICK TOWNSHIP BOARD OF EDUCATION
NORTH BRUNSWICK TWP SCHL DST
300 Old Georges Rd, North Brunswick, NJ 08902-4800
Tel (732) 289-3000 *Founded/Ownrshp* 1917
Sales 31.9MM^E *EMP* 800
SIC 8211 Public elementary school; Public junior high school; Public senior high school; Public elementary school; Public junior high school; Public senior high school
Pr Dir: Vincent Delucia

D-U-N-S 05-649-4560
NORTH BRUNSWICK TOWNSHIP OF (INC)
710 Hermann Rd, North Brunswick, NJ 08902-2850
Tel (732) 247-0922 *Founded/Ownrshp* 1779
Sales NA *EMP* 300^E
Accts Hoduluk And Morrison Pa
SIC 9111 Executive offices; ; Executive offices;
IT Man: Judith Delanoy
IT Man: Troy Gorski
Mktg Dir: Tom Vigna
Schl Brd P: Richard Liguori

D-U-N-S 07-980-6918
NORTH BRUNSWICK TOWNSHIP PUBLIC SCHOOLS
300 Old Georges Rd, North Brunswick, NJ 08902-4800
Tel (732) 289-3000 *Founded/Ownrshp* 2015
Sales 530.3M^E *EMP* 589^E
SIC 8211 Public elementary & secondary schools
MIS Dir: Martin Schneider
Pr Dir: Jennifer Divler

NORTH BRUNSWICK TWP SCHL DST
See NORTH BRUNSWICK TOWNSHIP BOARD OF EDUCATION

D-U-N-S 06-973-3517
NORTH CADDO HOSPITAL SERVICE DISTRICT (LA)
NORTH CADDO MEDICAL CENTER
1000 S Spruce St, Vivian, LA 71082-3232
Tel (318) 375-3235 *Founded/Ownrshp* 1965
Sales 29.1MM^E *EMP* 143
SIC 8062 General medical & surgical hospitals
CEO: David C Jones
**CFO:* Allyson Allums
Dir Lab: Greg Guest
Dir Rx: Judith Blalock
Dir IT: Ross Hansen
Sfty Dirs: Amy Mouser
Mtls Mgr: Lula Laduke
Mktg Dir: Mary Murdock-Coil
Nrsg Dir: Stacy Alexander

NORTH CADDO MEDICAL CENTER
See NORTH CADDO HOSPITAL SERVICE DISTRICT

NORTH CAMPUS
See LUCY LEE HOSPITAL INC

D-U-N-S 08-016-4478
NORTH CANTON CITY SCHOOL DISTRICT
NORTH CANTON CITY SCHOOLS
525 7th St Ne, Canton, OH 44720-2012
Tel (330) 497-5600 *Founded/Ownrshp* 1903
Sales 57.4MM^E *EMP* 925
SIC 8211 Public elementary & secondary schools; Public elementary & secondary schools
**Treas:* Todd Tolson

NORTH CANTON CITY SCHOOLS
See NORTH CANTON CITY SCHOOL DISTRICT

NORTH CAROLINA A&T STATE UNIV
See NORTH CAROLINA AGRICULTURAL AND TECHNICAL STATE UNIVERSITY

D-U-N-S 07-157-6482
NORTH CAROLINA AGRICULTURAL AND TECHNICAL STATE UNIVERSITY
NORTH CAROLINA A&T STATE UNIV
(*Suby of* UNIVERSITY OF NORTH CAROLINA) ★
1601 E Marke St Dowdy Bld, Greensboro, NC 27411-0001
Tel (336) 334-7684 *Founded/Ownrshp* 1891
Sales 250.0MM^E *EMP* 3,600
SIC 8221 University; University
CFO: Willie Ellis
Brnch Mgr: Linda Wilson
Info Man: Wilsonia Carter
Pgrm Dir: Nichole Florence
Pgrm Dir: D C Lofton

D-U-N-S 96-383-6874
NORTH CAROLINA ASSOCIATION OF REGIONAL COUNCILS OF GOVERNMENT
115 W Jones St Fl 3, Raleigh, NC 27603
Tel (828) 273-0276 *Founded/Ownrshp* 1966
Sales 54.0MM^E *EMP* 455
SIC 8611 Business associations; Business associations
Ex Dir: Betty Huskins

D-U-N-S 07-202-6321
NORTH CAROLINA CENTRAL UNIVERSITY
(*Suby of* UNIVERSITY OF NORTH CAROLINA) ★
1801 Fayetteville St, Durham, NC 27707-3129
Tel (919) 530-6100 *Founded/Ownrshp* 1923
Sales 122.1MM^E *EMP* 1,100
SIC 8221 Colleges universities & professional schools; Colleges universities & professional schools

D-U-N-S 80-978-4648
NORTH CAROLINA COMMUNITY COLLEGE SYSTEM
(*Suby of* EXECUTIVE OFFICE OF STATE OF NORTH CAROLINA) ★
200 W Jones St, Raleigh, NC 27603-1378
Tel (919) 807-7100 *Founded/Ownrshp* 1963
Sales 855.5MM^E *EMP* 1,000
SIC 8222 9411 Community college; Administration of educational programs; ; Community college; Administration of educational programs;
Pr: Scott Ralls

D-U-N-S 08-914-6799
NORTH CAROLINA COUNTY OF CLEVELAND
CLEVELAND COUNTY GOVERNMENT
311 E Marion St, Shelby, NC 28150-4611
Tel (704) 484-4800 *Founded/Ownrshp* 1841
Sales NA *EMP* 800
Accts Martin Starnes & Associates C
SIC 9111 Executive offices; Executive offices
Ex Dir: Debbie Clapper
Mktg Dir: Chris Cronin
Pr Dir: Donna Carpenter

D-U-N-S 80-978-4580
NORTH CAROLINA DEPARTMENT OF AGRICULTURE & CONSUMER SERVICES
(*Suby of* STATE OF NORTH CAROLINA) ★
2 W Edenton St, Raleigh, NC 27601-1020
Tel (919) 707-3000 *Founded/Ownrshp* 1877
Sales NA *EMP* 1,400^E
SIC 9641 Regulation of agricultural marketing; ; Regulation of agricultural marketing;
V Ch: Craig Frazier
Ofcr: Terri Butler
Ofcr: Karen Hunt
Ofcr: Charles Walls
Exec: Jen Nixon
Adm Dir: Cheri Toner
Off Admin: Torrey Vest
Mktg Mgr: Myrtle Earley

D-U-N-S 80-978-4606
NORTH CAROLINA DEPARTMENT OF COMMERCE
(*Suby of* EXECUTIVE OFFICE OF STATE OF NORTH CAROLINA) ★
301 N Wilmington St, Raleigh, NC 27601-1058
Tel (919) 733-4151 *Founded/Ownrshp* 1993
Sales NA *EMP* 800
SIC 9611 Administration of general economic programs; ; Administration of general economic programs;
**CFO:* Shanon Hobby
Ofcr: Julie Snee
Ofcr: Dan Spuller
Rgnl Mgr: Bill Shore
IT Man: Kenneth Barbour
Opers Mgr: Lisa Law
Mktg Dir: David Rhoades

D-U-N-S 80-978-4762
NORTH CAROLINA DEPARTMENT OF CRIME CONTROL AND PUBLIC SAFETY
(*Suby of* EXECUTIVE OFFICE OF STATE OF NORTH CAROLINA) ★
512 N Salisbury St, Raleigh, NC 27604-1170
Tel (919) 825-2720 *Founded/Ownrshp* 1977
Sales NA *EMP* 2,800
SIC 9221 Police protection; Police protection
Ofcr: Lisa Roberts
Sls&Mrk Ex: Danyel Davis
Board of Directors: Doug Phillips

D-U-N-S 80-978-4895
NORTH CAROLINA DEPARTMENT OF CULTURAL RESOURCES
DIVISION OF STATE LIBRARY
(*Suby of* EXECUTIVE OFFICE OF STATE OF NORTH CAROLINA) ★
109 E Jones St, Raleigh, NC 27601-1023
Tel (252) 473-2655 *Founded/Ownrshp* 1971
Sales 52.4MM^E *EMP* 750
SIC 8999 9441 Natural resource preservation service; ; Natural resource preservation service;
Ofcr: Kimberly Hinton
Top Exec: Carolyn Chesarino
Snr Mgr: Marlene Minshew

D-U-N-S 80-978-5280
NORTH CAROLINA DEPARTMENT OF ENVIRONMENTAL QUALITY
NCDEQ
(*Suby of* EXECUTIVE OFFICE OF STATE OF NORTH CAROLINA) ★
217 W Jones St Ste 5103, Raleigh, NC 27603-6100
Tel (919) 707-8318 *Founded/Ownrshp* 1784
Sales NA *EMP* 5,344
SIC 9512 Land, mineral & wildlife conservation; ; Land, mineral & wildlife conservation;
Sfty Dirs: Chuck Stanfill
Board of Directors: Donald Van Der Vaart

D-U-N-S 80-978-5363
NORTH CAROLINA DEPARTMENT OF HEALTH & HUMAN SERVICES
(*Suby of* EXECUTIVE OFFICE OF STATE OF NORTH CAROLINA) ★
2025 Mail Service Ctr, Raleigh, NC 27699-2000
Tel (919) 733-4534 *Founded/Ownrshp* 1972
Sales NA *EMP* 17,697
SIC 9441 Administration of social & manpower programs; ; Administration of social & manpower programs;

D-U-N-S 80-978-5421
NORTH CAROLINA DEPARTMENT OF INSURANCE
NC DEPARMENT OF INSURANCE
(*Suby of* EXECUTIVE OFFICE OF STATE OF NORTH CAROLINA) ★
430 N Salisbury St, Raleigh, NC 27603-5926
Tel (919) 807-6750 *Founded/Ownrshp* 2007
Sales NA *EMP* 400^E
SIC 9651 Insurance commission, government; ; Insurance commission, government;
Ofcr: Wendy Holland
Off Admin: Avis Alston
Opers Mgr: Josephine Paul
Snr Mgr: Louis Belo

D-U-N-S 80-978-5934
NORTH CAROLINA DEPARTMENT OF JUSTICE
DOJ
(*Suby of* EXECUTIVE OFFICE OF STATE OF NORTH CAROLINA) ★
114 W Edenton St, Raleigh, NC 27603-1712
Tel (919) 733-5760 *Founded/Ownrshp* 1789
Sales NA *EMP* 1,140
SIC 9222 Attorney General's office; ; Attorney General's office;
**CFO:* Nels Roseland
VP: Bill Hart
Exec: Noelle Talley
Adm Dir: Cynthia Vinson
Dir IT: Gelinda Richardson
IT Man: Ronnie Blake
IT Man: Loretta Wynder
Snr Mgr: Michael Denning
Snr Mgr: Nels Roselend

D-U-N-S 80-978-6189
NORTH CAROLINA DEPARTMENT OF LABOR
(*Suby of* EXECUTIVE OFFICE OF STATE OF NORTH CAROLINA) ★
4 W Edenton St, Raleigh, NC 27601-1020
Tel (919) 733-7166 *Founded/Ownrshp* 1887
Sales NA *EMP* 430
SIC 9651 Labor regulatory agency; ; Labor regulatory agency;
CFO: Jack Brinson
Ofcr: Kathryn Castelloes
CIO: Van Preslar

D-U-N-S 80-958-1762
NORTH CAROLINA DEPARTMENT OF PUBLIC INSTRUCTION
(*Suby of* EXECUTIVE OFFICE OF STATE OF NORTH CAROLINA) ★
301 N Wilmington St, Raleigh, NC 27601-1058
Tel (919) 807-3304 *Founded/Ownrshp* 1852
Sales NA *EMP* 498^E
SIC 9411 Administration of educational programs; ; Administration of educational programs;
Ofcr: Shannon Hobby
CIO: Douglas Phillips

D-U-N-S 80-978-4721
NORTH CAROLINA DEPARTMENT OF PUBLIC SAFETY
(*Suby of* EXECUTIVE OFFICE OF STATE OF NORTH CAROLINA) ★
512 N Salisbury St, Raleigh, NC 27604-1170
Tel (919) 733-2126 *Founded/Ownrshp* 1975
Sales NA *EMP* 18,000
SIC 9223 Prison, government; ; Prison, government;

D-U-N-S 80-958-1879
NORTH CAROLINA DEPARTMENT OF REVENUE
(*Suby of* EXECUTIVE OFFICE OF STATE OF NORTH CAROLINA) ★
501 N Wilmington St, Raleigh, NC 27604-8002
Tel (877) 252-3052 *Founded/Ownrshp* 1921
Sales NA *EMP* 1,400
SIC 9311 Finance, taxation & monetary policy; ; Finance, taxation & monetary policy;

Ofcr: Lucinda Goodwine
Ofcr: Justin Hunter
Ofcr: Joshua King
Ofcr: Jacqueline McDonald
Dir IT: Patrick Blalock
Dir IT: Joe Tetro
IT Man: Richard Costello
IT Man: Barbara Watson
Pr Mgr: Thomas Beam
Snr Mgr: Raj Desai
Snr Mgr: Tracy Doaks

D-U-N-S 80-958-1937
NORTH CAROLINA DEPARTMENT OF TRANSPORTATION
(*Suby of* EXECUTIVE OFFICE OF STATE OF NORTH CAROLINA) ★
1 S Wilmington St, Raleigh, NC 27601-1494
Tel (919) 707-2500 *Founded/Ownrshp* 1971
Sales NA *EMP* 14,000
SIC 9621 Regulation, administration of transportation; ; Regulation, administration of transportation;
Ofcr: Randy Garris
Comm Dir: Mike Charbonneau
Off Mgr: Tracey Creech
Opers Mgr: Kirk Pistel

D-U-N-S 80-978-4507
NORTH CAROLINA DEPT OF ADMINISTRATION
(*Suby of* EXECUTIVE OFFICE OF STATE OF NORTH CAROLINA) ★
116 W Jones St Ste 5106, Raleigh, NC 27603-1300
Tel (919) 807-2425 *Founded/Ownrshp* 1957
Sales NA *EMP* 900
SIC 9199 General government administration; ; General government administration;
MIS Dir: Smitty Locklear

D-U-N-S 94-913-6527
NORTH CAROLINA DIVISION OF ADULT PROBATION AND PAROLE
(*Suby of* NORTH CAROLINA DEPARTMENT OF PUBLIC SAFETY) ★
4000 Wake Forest Rd, Raleigh, NC 27609-6879
Tel (919) 850-2900 *Founded/Ownrshp* 1996
Sales NA *EMP* 2,188
SIC 9223 Prison, government; ; Prison, government;

D-U-N-S 00-273-5517
NORTH CAROLINA DIVISION OF HIGHWAYS
NCDOT
(*Suby of* NORTH CAROLINA DEPARTMENT OF TRANSPORTATION) ★
1 S Wilmington St, Raleigh, NC 27601-1453
Tel (919) 733-7384 *Founded/Ownrshp* 2000
Sales NA *EMP* 2,293^{E}
SIC 9621 Regulation, administration of transportation; ; Regulation, administration of transportation;

D-U-N-S 00-273-5582
NORTH CAROLINA DIVISION OF MOTOR VEHICLES
N C D M V
(*Suby of* NORTH CAROLINA DEPARTMENT OF TRANSPORTATION) ★
3101 Mail Service Ctr, Raleigh, NC 27697-0001
Tel (919) 861-3015 *Founded/Ownrshp* 1909
Sales NA *EMP* 800
SIC 9621 Motor vehicle licensing & inspection office, government; ; Motor vehicle licensing & inspection office, government;

D-U-N-S 94-901-1902
NORTH CAROLINA DIVISION OF PRISONS
(*Suby of* NORTH CAROLINA DEPARTMENT OF PUBLIC SAFETY) ★
831 W Morgan St, Raleigh, NC 27603-1658
Tel (919) 838-4000 *Founded/Ownrshp* 1974
Sales NA *EMP* 10,000
SIC 9223 Prison, government; ; Prison, government;

D-U-N-S 10-587-2147
NORTH CAROLINA EASTERN MUNICIPAL POWER AGENCY
1427 Meadow Wood Blvd, Raleigh, NC 27604-1532
Tel (919) 760-6000 *Founded/Ownrshp* 1976
Sales 696.5MM *EMP* 100^{E}
Accts Cherry Bekaert Llp Raleigh
SIC 4911 Distribution, electric power; Distribution, electric power
CEO: Jesse C Tilton III
COO: Art Hubert
COO: Roy Jones
**CFO:* Al Conyers
Dir IT: Don Gillett
IT Man: Caroline Casey
Secur Mgr: Matt Schull
Mktg Mgr: Robert Tugwell

D-U-N-S 07-555-0962
NORTH CAROLINA ELECTRIC MEMBERSHIP CORP
NCEMC
3400 Sumner Blvd, Raleigh, NC 27616-2950
Tel (919) 872-0800 *Founded/Ownrshp* 1949
Sales 1.1MMM *EMP* 150
Accts Deloitte Tax Llp Atlanta Ga
SIC 4911 Electric services; Electric services
CEO: Richard K Thomas
CFO: Lark James
Sr VP: David Beam
Sr VP: Lewis Hovson
VP: Tim Bennett
VP: Tim Eisel
VP: Bob Goodson
VP: Joy Hart
Plnt Mgr: Shawn Fowler
Pr Dir: Rich Kenner
Pr Dir: Eddie Miller

D-U-N-S 04-895-8995
NORTH CAROLINA FARM BUREAU INSURANCE AGENCY INC
N C FARM BUREAU MUTUAL INSUR
5301 Glenwood Ave, Raleigh, NC 27612-3244
Tel (919) 782-1705 *Founded/Ownrshp* 1953
Sales NA *EMP* 750
Accts A T Allen & Company Llp Cpas
SIC 6331 6411 6311 Property damage insurance; Fire, marine & casualty insurance & carriers; Insurance agents, brokers & service; Life insurance; Property damage insurance; Fire, marine & casualty insurance & carriers; Insurance agents, brokers & service; Life insurance
Pr: Larry Wooten
Pr: Misty Smith
**CFO:* Ronald Medeiros
**Treas:* Perry Crutchfield
**Ex VP:* Steve Carrol
**VP:* J M Wright Jr
Exec: Steve Brinn
Exec: Bryan Crook
CTO: Phillips Ian
Dir IT: Louis Hodnett
Dir IT: Lawrence B Wooten

D-U-N-S 83-069-0306
NORTH CAROLINA HEALTH INSURANCE RISK POOL INC
INCLUSIVE HEALTH
3739 National Dr Ste 228, Raleigh, NC 27612-4063
Tel (919) 783-5766 *Founded/Ownrshp* 2009
Sales NA *EMP* 2
Accts Cherry Bekaert & Holland Ll
SIC 6321 Health insurance carriers; Health insurance carriers
Ex Dir: Michael Keough
Genl Couns: Shannon Frankel
Genl Couns: Thomas Stroud
Genl Couns: Nathan Taylor

D-U-N-S 15-393-2066
NORTH CAROLINA INSURANCE UNDERWRITING ASSOCIATION
5651 Dillard Dr, Cary, NC 27518-9226
Tel (919) 821-1299 *Founded/Ownrshp* 1969
Sales NA *EMP* 65
Accts Ncjua-Nciua Cary Nc
SIC 6331 Fire, marine & casualty insurance; Fire, marine & casualty insurance
Genl Mgr: Dewey Meshaw

D-U-N-S 14-818-9632
NORTH CAROLINA JOINT UNDERWRITING ASSOCIATION
5520 Dillard Dr Ste 180, Cary, NC 27518-9280
Tel (919) 821-1299 *Founded/Ownrshp* 1969
Sales NA *EMP* 100
SIC 6331 Property damage insurance; Fire, marine & casualty insurance & carriers; Property damage insurance; Fire, marine & casualty insurance & carriers
Ch Bd: Drew Klasing
Genl Mgr: Gina Schwitzgebel

D-U-N-S 80-172-6951
NORTH CAROLINA LIFE AND HEALTH INSURANCE GUARANTY ASSOCIATION
505 Oberlin Rd Ste 203, Raleigh, NC 27605-1345
Tel (919) 833-6838 *Founded/Ownrshp* 1974
Sales NA *EMP* 1
SIC 6361 8611 Guarantee of titles; Trade associations; Guarantee of titles; Trade associations
Ex Dir: Lowell Miller

D-U-N-S 78-808-0364
NORTH CAROLINA MUSEUM OF ART FOUNDATION INC
2110 Blue Ridge Rd, Raleigh, NC 27607-6433
Tel (919) 839-6262 *Founded/Ownrshp* 1969
Sales 20.6MM *EMP* 106
Accts Vatchelor Tillery And Roberts
SIC 7389 Fund raising organizations; Fund raising organizations
Pr: Joeseph Kluttz
**Treas:* Paxton Badham
**VP:* Peter M Scott
Mktg Dir: Jennifer Bahus

D-U-N-S 00-699-6466
NORTH CAROLINA MUTUAL LIFE INSURANCE CO INC
NC MUTUAL
411 W Chapel Hill St, Durham, NC 27701-3272
Tel (919) 682-9201 *Founded/Ownrshp* 1899
Sales NA *EMP* 93
SIC 6311 Life insurance carriers; Life insurance carriers
Pr: James H Speed Jr
**COO:* Michael L Lawrence
**CFO:* Gracie Johnson-Lopez
Chf Mktg O: Willie T Closs
Sr VP: Charles Watts
VP: David Baylock
VP: Edward LL Bowser
VP: Stafford L Thompson
Dir IT: Debra Taylor
IT Man: Dennis Daniel
Sftwr Eng: Larry Porter

D-U-N-S 00-687-1743
NORTH CAROLINA MUTUAL WHOLESALE DRUG CO
MUTUAL DRUG
816 Ellis Rd, Durham, NC 27703-6019
Tel (919) 596-2151 *Founded/Ownrshp* 1952
Sales 221.8MM^{E} *EMP* 160
Accts Thomas Knight Trent King An
SIC 5122 Drugs & drug proprietaries; Druggists' sundries; Drugs & drug proprietaries; Druggists' sundries
CEO: David S Moody
**Pr:* Thomas P Davis
**VP:* Hal Harrison
Board of Directors: Dave Marley

D-U-N-S 00-892-4409
■ **NORTH CAROLINA NATURAL GAS CORP**
(*Suby of* PIEDMONT NATURAL GAS CO INC) ★
410 S Wilmington St, Raleigh, NC 27601-1849
Tel (800) 275-6264 *Founded/Ownrshp* 2003
Sales 85.5MM^{E} *EMP* 390
SIC 4923 5984 1382 6282 Gas transmission & distribution; Liquefied petroleum gas dealers; Oil & gas exploration services; Investment research; Gas transmission & distribution; Liquefied petroleum gas dealers; Oil & gas exploration services; Investment research
CEO: Donald K Davis
**Treas:* Mark F Mulhern
**Sr VP:* Terrence D Davis
**VP:* George M Baldwin

D-U-N-S 95-678-3849
NORTH CAROLINA PARTNERSHIP FOR CHILDREN INC
N C PARTNERSHIP FOR CHILDREN
1100 Wake Forest Rd, Raleigh, NC 27604-1354
Tel (919) 821-7999 *Founded/Ownrshp* 1993
Sales 99.0MM *EMP* 48
Accts Blackman & Sloop Cpas Pa Chap
SIC 8399 Social change association; Social change association
Pr: Stephanie Fanjul
**Treas:* Leslie Karlsson
Comm Dir: Heather Strickland

D-U-N-S 01-322-8858
NORTH CAROLINA SPECIALTY HOSPITAL LLC
NCSH
(*Suby of* NATIONAL SURGICAL HOSPITALS INC) ★
3916 Ben Franklin Blvd, Durham, NC 27704-2383
Tel (919) 489-1279 *Founded/Ownrshp* 1998
Sales 49.9MM *EMP* 200
SIC 8062 General medical & surgical hospitals; General medical & surgical hospitals
CEO: Randi Shults
**CFO:* Bill Wilson
Dir Lab: Michelle Cornstubble
Dir Rad: Kim Lyon
Dir Rx: Chris Meiferdt
Dir Sec: Sheree Barak
Pharmcst: June Croft
HC Dir: Nakija Jones

NORTH CAROLINA STATE PARKS
See DIVISION OF PARKS AND RECREATION NORTH CAROLINA

D-U-N-S 14-436-1839
NORTH CAROLINA STATE PORTS AUTHORITY FOUNDATION INC
2202 Burnett Blvd, Wilmington, NC 28401-7002
Tel (910) 763-1621 *Founded/Ownrshp* 1945
Sales 39.5MM *EMP* 281
SIC 4491 Marine cargo handling; Marine cargo handling
Ch: Michael V Lee
**COO:* Jeff Miles
**CFO:* Jeffrey L Strader
Bd of Dir: Jesse Capel
**VP:* Glenn A Carlson
Exec: Lance Kenworthy
Comm Man: Susan Clizbe
Ex Dir: Rex Edwards
CIO: Terry Gibson
Dir IT: Brad Lewis
Snr Mgr: Carey Gibson

NORTH CAROLINA STATE STUDENT A
See WOLFPACK CLUB

D-U-N-S 04-209-2122
NORTH CAROLINA STATE UNIVERSITY
(*Suby of* UNIVERSITY OF NORTH CAROLINA) ★
2701 Sullivan Dr Ste 240, Raleigh, NC 27695-0001
Tel (919) 515-2011 *Founded/Ownrshp* 1887, 1987
Sales 750.0MM *EMP* 2,560^{E}
SIC 8221 University; University
Pr: Randy Woodsen
V Ch: Robert B Jordan
Trst: Bob L Mattocks
Trst: Burley B Mitchell Jr
Ofcr: Harvey Charlton
Ofcr: Erin Folk
Ofcr: Darren Treml
Dir Lab: Roberto Garcia
Adm Dir: Gwen Bell
Adm Dir: Helen Crane
Adm Dir: Susan Davis

D-U-N-S 15-393-7800
NORTH CAROLINA STATE UNIVERSITY FOUNDATION
NCSU FOUNDATION
12 Holladay Hall, Raleigh, NC 27695-0001
Tel (919) 515-2143 *Founded/Ownrshp* 1942
Sales 73.0MM *EMP* 5
SIC 6732 Educational trust management; Educational trust management
Treas: Tapitha Groelle
**Pr:* Nevin Kessler
**VP:* Ken Sigmon

D-U-N-S 96-967-9187
NORTH CAROLINA STATE UNIVERSITY FOUNDATION INC
1210 Varsity Dr, Raleigh, NC 27606-2084
Tel (919) 513-7149 *Founded/Ownrshp* 2011
Sales 29.5MM^{E} *EMP* 3^{E}
Accts Williams Overman Pierce Llp R
SIC 8641 Civic social & fraternal associations; Civic social & fraternal associations

D-U-N-S 07-555-8361
NORTH CAROLINA WESLEYAN COLLEGE INC
3400 N Wesleyan Blvd, Rocky Mount, NC 27804-8699
Tel (252) 985-5100 *Founded/Ownrshp* 1959
Sales 32.8MM *EMP* 175
Accts Brown Edwards & Company Llp B
SIC 8221 College, except junior; College, except junior
Pr: Jim Gray
CFO: Belinda Faulkner
**Treas:* Loren Loomishubbell
VP: James Traer
MIS Dir: Andy Castillo

D-U-N-S 08-002-2659
NORTH CAROLINA WILDLIFE RESOURCES COMMISSION
1751 Varsity Dr, Raleigh, NC 27606-2576
Tel (919) 707-0010
Sales NA *EMP* 500
SIC 9512

D-U-N-S 13-082-9844
NORTH CAROLINA WILDLIFE RESOURCES COMMISSION
1751 Varsity Dr, Raleigh, NC 27606-2576
Tel (919) 707-0010 *Founded/Ownrshp* 2015
Sales NA *EMP* 500
SIC 9512 Wildlife conservation agencies
Ex Dir: Gordon Myers
Trfc Dir: Shawnna Smith

D-U-N-S 06-965-0179
NORTH CASTLE PARTNERS LLC
183 E Putnam Ave, Greenwich, CT 06830-5613
Tel (203) 485-0216 *Founded/Ownrshp* 1997
Sales 499.7MM^{E} *EMP* 3,510
SIC 6211 7299 6794 5149 5499 Investment bankers; Investment bankers; Diet center, without medical staff; Franchises, selling or licensing; Diet foods; Dietetic foods
Mng Dir: Lou Marinaccio
Mng Dir: Alison Minter
IT Man: Chip Baird
Opers Mgr: John Young

NORTH CENTER, THE
See NORCARE ENTERPRISES INC

D-U-N-S 96-677-2055
■ **NORTH CENTRAL BANCSHARES INC**
GREAT WESTERN BANK
(*Suby of* GREAT WESTERN BANCORPORATION INC) ★
825 Central Ave, Fort Dodge, IA 50501-3901
Tel (515) 576-7531 *Founded/Ownrshp* 2012
Sales NA *EMP* 137^{E}
SIC 6035 Federal savings banks; Federal savings banks
Pr: David M Bradley
CFO: Jane M Funk
Ex VP: C Thomas Chalstrom
VP: Russell Ruhland
Opers Mgr: Dave Mitchell

D-U-N-S 06-857-7667
NORTH CENTRAL COLLEGE
NAPERVILLE COLLEGE
30 N Brainard St, Naperville, IL 60540-4690
Tel (630) 637-5100 *Founded/Ownrshp* 1861
Sales 79.2MM *EMP* 699
Accts Grant Thornton Llp Chicago
SIC 8221 College, except junior; College, except junior
Pr: Troy D Hammond
VP: Laurie Hamen
**VP:* Paul H Loscheider
**VP:* R Devadoss Pandian
**VP:* Martin Sauer
**VP:* Kimberly Sluis
VP: Rick Spencer
**Prin:* Harold R Wilde
Netwrk Eng: Chad Sutton
Mktg Dir: Valla Aguilar
Psych: Alina Keegan

D-U-N-S 10-866-4681 IMP
NORTH CENTRAL COMPANIES INC
601 Carlson Pkwy Ste 400, Minnetonka, MN 55305-5226
Tel (952) 449-0885 *Founded/Ownrshp* 1984
Sales 71.0MM^{E} *EMP* 60
SIC 5159 Fibers, vegetable
Pr: Larry Zilverberg

D-U-N-S 00-798-8009
NORTH CENTRAL COOPERATIVE
221 4th Ave Nw, Clarion, IA 50525-1035
Tel (515) 532-2881 *Founded/Ownrshp* 1907
Sales 227.7MM *EMP* 96
SIC 5153 5191 5172 Grain elevators; Feed; Seeds: field, garden & flower; Fertilizer & fertilizer materials; Petroleum products; Grain elevators; Feed; Seeds: field, garden & flower; Fertilizer & fertilizer materials; Petroleum products
Genl Mgr: Mike Nail

D-U-N-S 00-694-0209
NORTH CENTRAL COOPERATIVE INC
2025 S Wabash St, Wabash, IN 46992-4124
Tel (260) 563-9541 *Founded/Ownrshp* 1927
Sales 331.8MM *EMP* 280
Accts Blue & Co Llc Seymour In
SIC 5172 5153 5191 Petroleum products; Diesel fuel; Gasoline; Lubricating oils & greases; Grain elevators; Farm supplies; Fertilizer & fertilizer materials; Chemicals, agricultural; Seeds: field, garden & flower; Petroleum products; Diesel fuel; Gasoline; Lubricating oils & greases; Grain elevators; Farm supplies; Fertilizer & fertilizer materials; Chemicals, agricultural; Seeds: field, garden & flower
Pr: J Mark Tullis
**CFO:* Doug Bible
Plnt Mgr: Ronald Holcomb
Sales Exec: Ron Pettet
VP Sls: John Scicluna

D-U-N-S 00-386-8346
NORTH CENTRAL ELECTRIC COOPERATIVE INC (ND)
538 11th St W Ste 1, Bottineau, ND 58318-1913
Tel (701) 228-2202 *Founded/Ownrshp* 1941
Sales 23.6MM *EMP* 31

SIC 4911 Distribution, electric power
Pr: Jean Brandt
**Genl Mgr:* Wayne Martian

D-U-N-S 00-699-8587
NORTH CENTRAL ELECTRIC COOPERATIVE INC (OH)
350 Stump Pike Rd, Attica, OH 44807-9571
Tel (800) 426-3072 *Founded/Ownrshp* 1936
Sales 26.1MM *EMP* 44
SIC 4911 Distribution, electric power; Distribution, electric power
Pr: Richard Reichert
Treas: Duane E Frankard
Treas: Richard Lease
Bd of Dir: Jean Brandt
VP: Denny Schendler
VP: Dennis Schindler
Genl Mgr: Markus I Bryant

D-U-N-S 07-888-3487
■ **NORTH CENTRAL EMERGENCY ASSOCIATES LLC**
(*Suby of* TEAM HEALTH HOLDINGS INC) ★
3090 W Market St, Fairlawn, OH 44333-3608
Tel (330) 563-0603 *Founded/Ownrshp* 2013
Sales 36.8M *EMP* 338^E
SIC 8062 Hospital, professional nursing school
Pr: John Parente

D-U-N-S 16-236-2995
NORTH CENTRAL EQUITY LLC
60 S 6th St Ste 2535, Minneapolis, MN 55402-4406
Tel (612) 465-0260 *Founded/Ownrshp* 2004
Sales 99.8MM^E *EMP* 262
SIC 6799 4813 Venture capital companies; Long distance telephone communications; Venture capital companies; Long distance telephone communications
CEO: Elam Baer
**VP:* Laura Carlson
**VP:* Bernie Coyle
**VP:* Daniel Hogan
**VP:* Peter Jacobson
**VP:* Ron Jost
**VP:* Greg Wilmes
Off Mgr: Elizabeth Husman

D-U-N-S 02-433-4674
NORTH CENTRAL FARMERS ELEVATOR (SD)
NCFE
12 5th Ave, Ipswich, SD 57451
Tel (605) 447-5803 *Founded/Ownrshp* 1915
Sales 644.2MM^E *EMP* 200
Accts Eide Bailly Llp Aberdeen Sou
SIC 5153 5191 5171 5541 Grain elevators; Farm supplies; Chemicals, agricultural; Fertilizer & fertilizer materials; Petroleum bulk stations; Gasoline service stations; Grain elevators; Farm supplies; Chemicals, agricultural; Fertilizer & fertilizer materials; Petroleum bulk stations; Gasoline service stations
Pr: Rick Osterday
**Sec:* Quentin Larson
**VP:* Mike Clements
**VP:* Larry Vetch
IT Man: Richal Wambach
Sfty Dirs: Andy Clemen

NORTH CENTRAL FORD
See SONIC - RICHARDSON F LP

D-U-N-S 12-120-2840
NORTH CENTRAL GRAIN COOPERATIVE
5954 Highway 66, Bisbee, ND 58317
Tel (701) 656-3263 *Founded/Ownrshp* 1984
Sales 39.5MM^E *EMP* 25
SIC 5153 Grain elevators
Pr: Jeff Teubner
**CFO:* Lynnette Berg
**VP:* Randy Benson

NORTH CENTRAL GROUP
See NORTH CENTRAL MANAGEMENT INC

D-U-N-S 03-018-1754 IMP
NORTH CENTRAL HEALTH CARE
NCHC
1100 Lake View Dr, Wausau, WI 54403-6799
Tel (715) 848-4600 *Founded/Ownrshp* 1972
Sales 39.7MM^E *EMP* 900
SIC 8063 8051 Psychiatric hospitals; Skilled nursing care facilities; Psychiatric hospitals; Skilled nursing care facilities
CEO: Gary Bezucha
**CFO:* Brenda Glodowski
Ofcr: Lori Koeppel
VP: Jill Eckert
Dir Risk M: Bo Johnson
Dir QC: Becky Schultz
Dir IT: Theresa Szews
QC Dir: Dana Decker
Nrsg Dir: Lisa Henkelman

D-U-N-S 14-734-7491
NORTH CENTRAL HEALTH CARE FACILITIES
1100 Lake View Dr, Wausau, WI 54403-6799
Tel (715) 848-4600 *Founded/Ownrshp* 2004
Sales 17.1MM^E *EMP* 900
SIC 8082 Home health care services; Home health care services
CEO: Gary Bezucha
**CFO:* Brenda Glodowski

D-U-N-S 01-413-8232
NORTH CENTRAL HEALTH SERVICES INC
2900 N River Rd, West Lafayette, IN 47906-3744
Tel (765) 423-1604 *Founded/Ownrshp* 2009
Sales 32.5MM *EMP* 1
Accts Blue & Co Llc Indianapolis I
SIC 8099 Services; Health & allied services
Pr: John Walling
VP: Jeff Nagy

D-U-N-S 07-943-2103
NORTH CENTRAL ILLINOIS LABORERS HEALTH & WELFARE FUND
4208 W Patridgeway Unit N, Peoria, IL 61615
Tel (309) 692-0860 *Founded/Ownrshp* 2013
Sales NA *EMP* 3^E
Accts Romolo & Associates Peoria I
SIC 6371 Pension, health & welfare funds; Pension, health & welfare funds
Prin: Lynn A Marks

D-U-N-S 08-041-6340
NORTH CENTRAL INSULATION INC
7539 State Route 13, Bellville, OH 44813-8943
Tel (419) 886-2030 *Founded/Ownrshp* 1980
Sales 25.6MM^E *EMP* 150
SIC 1741 1742 3231 Foundation building; Insulation, buildings; Products of purchased glass; Foundation building; Insulation, buildings; Products of purchased glass
Pr: D Brent Dudgeon
**VP:* John Dudgeon
**VP:* Andrew Dungeon

D-U-N-S 80-959-1449
NORTH CENTRAL KANSAS COOPERATIVE ASSOCIATION
508 N Main St, Hope, KS 67451-9421
Tel (785) 366-7213 *Founded/Ownrshp* 1994
Sales 62.3MM *EMP* 30
Accts Lindburg Vogel Pierce Faris M
SIC 5153 5191 5541 Grain elevators; Fertilizer & fertilizer materials; Chemicals, agricultural; Feed; Filling stations, gasoline; Grain elevators; Fertilizer & fertilizer materials; Chemicals, agricultural; Feed; Filling stations, gasoline
Pr: Darel Anderson
**Sec:* Gregg Beemer

D-U-N-S 07-337-9778
NORTH CENTRAL MANAGEMENT INC
NORTH CENTRAL GROUP
1600 Aspen Cmns Ste 200, Middleton, WI 53562-4770
Tel (608) 836-6060 *Founded/Ownrshp* 1981
Sales 48.5MM^E *EMP* 810
SIC 7011 Hotels & motels; Hotels & motels
Ch Bd: David A Lenz
**Pr:* Jeff Lenz
**CEO:* Jonathan Bogatay
**COO:* Keith Osborne
**VP:* Jane F Braatz
**VP:* Cathy Gillman
**VP:* Laura Jaggi
**VP:* Mark Lenerz
Genl Mgr: Stephanie Bracken
Genl Mgr: Charles Elam
Genl Mgr: Peter Johnson

D-U-N-S 02-092-1630
NORTH CENTRAL STATE REGIONAL COUNCIL
NCSRCC
700 Olive St, Saint Paul, MN 55130-4405
Tel (651) 646-7207 *Founded/Ownrshp* 2008, 2011
Sales 30.0MM *EMP* 118
SIC 8631 Labor unions & similar labor organizations
Ex Dir: John G Raines
Ex Dir: Patrick Nilsen

D-U-N-S 60-862-4552
NORTH CENTRAL SURGERY CENTER
9301 N Central Expy # 100, Dallas, TX 75231-0806
Tel (214) 265-2810 *Founded/Ownrshp* 2005
Sales 23.5MM^E *EMP* 158^E
SIC 8062 General medical & surgical hospitals
Nrsg Dir: Jeina Getter

D-U-N-S 00-783-9368
NORTH CENTRAL TELEPHONE COOPERATIVE CORP (TN)
NCTC
872 Highway 52 Byp E, Lafayette, TN 37083-1023
Tel (270) 622-7500 *Founded/Ownrshp* 1951
Sales 25.7MM *EMP* 106
SIC 4813 Local telephone communications; Local telephone communications
CEO: Nancy J White
**Sec:* Shelvy Linville
**Int Pr:* Johnny McClanahan

D-U-N-S 15-051-7944
NORTH CENTRAL TEXAS BANCSHARES INC
104 W Park Ave, Iowa Park, TX 76367-2805
Tel (940) 592-4131 *Founded/Ownrshp* 1979
Sales NA *EMP* 90
SIC 6022 State commercial banks
Pr: Stanley Williamson
**Sec:* Bert Williamson
**VP:* Jack E Hallis

D-U-N-S 05-637-4051
NORTH CENTRAL TEXAS COLLEGE
1525 W California St, Gainesville, TX 76240-4678
Tel (940) 668-7731 *Founded/Ownrshp* 1924
Sales 20.2MM *EMP* 611
Accts Schalk & Smith Pc Gainesville
SIC 8222 8221 Junior college; Colleges universities & professional schools; Junior college; Colleges universities & professional schools
Ch: Bill Ledbetter
Bd of Dir: Lisa Bellows
VP: Heidi Ellis
VP: Lee Nutt
VP: Debbie Pounds
VP: Maurice Robeson
VP: Bill Winans
Store Mgr: Sharon Williams
MIS Dir: George Bradley
Psych: Magen Bunyard
Psych: Tracey Fleniken

D-U-N-S 10-246-2256
NORTH CENTRAL TEXAS COUNCIL OF GOVERNMENTS FOUNDATION INC
NCTCOG
616 Six Flags Dr Ste 200, Arlington, TX 76011-6317
Tel (817) 640-3300 *Founded/Ownrshp* 1966
Sales 0.0 *EMP* 331^E
Accts Weaver And Tidwell Llp Dalla
SIC 8651 Political organizations; Political organizations
Ex Dir: R Michael Eastland
**Pr:* John Murphy
**Prin:* Mike Eastland
**Ex Dir:* Monty Mercer
Ex Dir: David Setzer

D-U-N-S 04-012-6502
NORTH CENTRAL TEXAS SERVICES D/B/A C
3110 S Great Sw Pkwy, Grand Prairie, TX 75052-7238
Tel (214) 288-4559 *Founded/Ownrshp* 2010
Sales 68.3MM *EMP* 3
SIC 8999 Services
Prin: Stephen Beeson

NORTH CENTRAL TRUCK EQUIPMENT
See ST CLOUD INDUSTRIAL PRODUCTS INC

D-U-N-S 06-817-0208
NORTH CENTRAL UNIVERSITY
910 Elliot Ave, Minneapolis, MN 55404-1391
Tel (612) 343-4400 *Founded/Ownrshp* 1930
Sales 31.8MM *EMP* 332
Accts Clifton Larson Allen Llp Minn
SIC 8221 College, except junior; Theological seminary; College, except junior; Theological seminary
Pr: Gordon Anderson
**VP:* Cheryl Book
**VP:* Thomas Burkman
**VP:* Paul Freitag
**VP:* Mike Nosser
VP: Nate Ruch
Dir Sec: Mike Cappelli
IT Man: Nix Gray
IT Man: Bruce Jensen
IT Man: Dan Messerli
Mktg Dir: Ryan Decker

D-U-N-S 10-890-0317
NORTH CENTRAL WEST VIRGINIA COMMUNITY ACTION ASSOCIATION
AREA SCHOOLS
1304 Goose Run Rd, Fairmont, WV 26554-1345
Tel (304) 363-6869 *Founded/Ownrshp* 1966
Sales 11.6MM *EMP* 300
SIC 8399 Community action agency; Community action agency
Pr: Jeremiah Jasper
**VP:* Alcinda Shockey
Ex Dir: Kenneth Dean
**Ex Dir:* Vickie Geary
Dir IT: Don Reed
IT Man: Jow Masturzo

D-U-N-S 16-951-9589 IMP
NORTH CHARLESTON AUTOMOTIVE CO
RICK HENDRICK JEEP CHRYSLER
8333 Rivers Ave, North Charleston, SC 29406-9204
Tel (843) 569-2700 *Founded/Ownrshp* 1996
Sales 31.6MM^E *EMP* 70
SIC 5511 Automobiles, new & used; Automobiles, new & used
Genl Mgr: Jeremy Jimenez
Prin: Rick Hendrick

D-U-N-S 07-373-2083
NORTH CHARLESTON SEWER DISTRICT
7225 Stall Rd, North Charleston, SC 29406-4422
Tel (843) 764-3072 *Founded/Ownrshp* 1972
Sales 26.2MM *EMP* 125
Accts Reiser Mclaurin & Gibbons L
SIC 4952 Sewerage systems; Sewerage systems
Ch Bd: Gary C McJunkin
**Treas:* Mary M Trussell
**Dist Mgr:* Jimmy L Green

D-U-N-S 11-943-3985
NORTH CHICAGO SCHOOL DISTRICT 187
BOARD OF EDUCATION
2000 Lewis Ave, North Chicago, IL 60064-2543
Tel (847) 689-8150 *Founded/Ownrshp* 1890
Sales 31.9MM^E *EMP* 471
SIC 8211 8741 Public elementary & secondary schools; Management services; Public elementary & secondary schools; Management services
**CEO:* Ben Martindale
**Ex Dir:* Martha Gutierrez
**Ex Dir:* Jim Weise

NORTH CLACKAMAS, COUNTY OF
See NORTH CLACKAMAS SCHOOLS

D-U-N-S 05-596-3722
NORTH CLACKAMAS SCHOOLS
NORTH CLACKAMAS, COUNTY OF
4444 Se Lake Rd, Milwaukie, OR 97222-4740
Tel (503) 353-6001 *Founded/Ownrshp* 1971
Sales 202.9MM *EMP* 1,857
Accts Pauly Rogers And Co PcTig
SIC 8211 Public elementary school; Public junior high school; Public senior high school; Vocational high school; Public elementary school; Public junior high school; Public senior high school; Vocational high school
**V Ch:* Rein Vaga
CFO: Mary Knigge
Schl Brd P: Kyle Locker

NORTH CLAD
See NORTHSHORE SHEET METAL INC

D-U-N-S 11-490-6779 IMP
NORTH COAST BEARINGS LLC
AFTER MARKET PRODUCTS
1050 Jaycox Rd, Avon, OH 44011-1312
Tel (440) 930-7600 *Founded/Ownrshp* 1983
Sales 32.6MM^E *EMP* 50
SIC 5085 Bearings

Pr: William Hagy
Sales Asso: Joni Sichau

NORTH COAST CO-OP
See NORTH COAST COOPERATIVE INC

D-U-N-S 10-785-7856
NORTH COAST CONTAINER CORP
NCC
8806 Crane Ave, Cleveland, OH 44105-1622
Tel (216) 441-6214 *Founded/Ownrshp* 1983
Sales 27.5MM^E *EMP* 90
SIC 3412 Drums, shipping: metal; Drums, shipping: metal
CEO: Jim Beardsley
Pr: James Drozdowski
**Pr:* Randall D Reed
**CEO:* Earnest C Beardsley
Exec: William Syvuk
IT Man: Richard Micko
Sfty Mgr: Ray Dido
Plnt Mgr: Ken Konczos

D-U-N-S 06-885-5808
NORTH COAST COOPERATIVE INC
NORTH COAST CO-OP
811 I St, Arcata, CA 95521-6123
Tel (707) 822-5947 *Founded/Ownrshp* 1973
Sales 25.9MM^E *EMP* 180
SIC 5411 Co-operative food stores
CEO: Steve Suttell
**CEO:* Fred Moore
Exec: Wayne Hawkins
Genl Mgr: Kelli Reese
CIO: Pamella Olson
IT Man: Howard Julien

D-U-N-S 06-878-9833 EXP
NORTH COAST ELECTRIC CO
NCE
2450 8th Ave S Ste 200, Seattle, WA 98134-2005
Tel (206) 206-9898 *Founded/Ownrshp* 1974
Sales 664.2MM^E *EMP* 650
SIC 5063 Electrical construction materials; Lighting fixtures; Electrical construction materials; Lighting fixtures
Ch: Peter Lemman
Pr: Robert L Lemman
Pr: Michael Miller
Ex VP: Dean Lemman
VP: Rick Bumpus
VP: Alexander Hickethier
VP: Patrick Moore
VP: Ann Webb
Brnch Mgr: Dave Evans
MIS Mgr: Lester J Johnson
Opers Supe: Rebekah Peoples
Board of Directors: Barbara Carver, Marilyn Lemman

D-U-N-S 84-976-6571
■ **NORTH COAST FISHERIES INC**
ALCA TRAX SEA FOODS
(*Suby of* TONYS FINE FOODS) ★
3230 Sebastopol Rd, Santa Rosa, CA 95407-6739
Tel (707) 579-0679 *Founded/Ownrshp* 1993
Sales 24.1MM^E *EMP* 35
SIC 5146 2091 Seafoods; Fish, cured; Fish, fresh; Fish, frozen, unpackaged; Canned & cured fish & seafoods
CEO: Michael Schuyler
Sfty Mgr: Jeff Lucchesi
S&M/VP: Bill Timko

D-U-N-S 06-012-1928 IMP
NORTH COAST MEDICAL INC
8100 Camino Arroyo, Gilroy, CA 95020-7304
Tel (408) 776-5000 *Founded/Ownrshp* 1983
Sales 39.2MM^E *EMP* 145^E
SIC 5047

D-U-N-S 12-943-3913 IMP
NORTH COAST MEDICAL SUPPLY
ADVANCED DIABETES SUPPLY
2544 Campbell Pl Ste 150, Carlsbad, CA 92009-1768
Tel (760) 434-9887 *Founded/Ownrshp* 2002
Sales 22.1MM^E *EMP* 140
SIC 5999 5912 Medical apparatus & supplies; Drug stores; Medical apparatus & supplies; Drug stores
CEO: Mark M Howard
**Pr:* Tim Cady
CFO: Thomas Metzler
IT Man: Hunter Aune
IT Man: Michelle Bowman
Web Dev: James Lawrence
Software D: Daniel Prieto
Cert Phar: Ray Couch

D-U-N-S 92-771-1911
NORTH COAST MORTGAGE CO
80 E Sir Francis Drake Bl, Larkspur, CA 94939-1709
Tel (415) 461-2070 *Founded/Ownrshp* 1994
Sales NA *EMP* 20
SIC 6162 Mortgage bankers & correspondents; Mortgage bankers & correspondents
Pr: Christopher Solle

D-U-N-S 84-148-2867
NORTH COAST PROFESSIONAL CO LLC
FIRELANDS PHYSICIANS GROUP
1031 Pierce St, Sandusky, OH 44870-4669
Tel (419) 557-5541 *Founded/Ownrshp* 1989
Sales 20.1MM^E *EMP* 191
SIC 8011 Medical centers; Medical centers
CEO: Martin Tursky

D-U-N-S 60-449-6687 IMP
NORTH COAST SEA-FOODS CORP
5 Drydock Ave, Boston, MA 02210-2303
Tel (617) 345-4400 *Founded/Ownrshp* 1988
Sales 76.4MM^E *EMP* 200^E
SIC 2092 5146 Seafoods, fresh: prepared; Seafoods, frozen: prepared; Seafoods; Seafoods, fresh: prepared; Seafoods, frozen: prepared; Seafoods
Pr: Norman A Stavis
**Treas:* James M Stavis
Sls Mgr: Ken Parlo

D-U-N-S 04-858-4817
NORTH COLONIE CENTRAL SCHOOL DISTRICT (NY)
91 Fiddlers Ln, Latham, NY 12110-5343
Tel (518) 785-8591 *Founded/Ownrshp* 1950
Sales 102.5MM *EMP* 1,200
Accts West & Company Cpas Pc Glove
SIC 8211 Public elementary school; Public junior high school; Public senior high school; Public elementary school; Public junior high school; Public senior high school
Treas: Steve Zautner
**Treas:* Kathleen Caulfield
Bd of Dir: Nancy Hooley
Bd of Dir: Marie Oppedisano
Exec: Djoseph Corr
Pr Dir: Taryn Kane
Pr Dir: Stephen King
Schl Brd P: Linda Harrison
Schl Brd P: Mary Nordolillo
Psych: Kelly Armstrong
Snr Mgr: Shannon Delaney

D-U-N-S 60-877-6824
NORTH COLORADO MEDICAL CENTER
(*Suby of* BKRY PHYSICIAN GROUP INC) ★
1801 16th St, Greeley, CO 80631-5199
Tel (970) 352-4121 *Founded/Ownrshp* 2006
Sales 353.6MM *EMP* 12
SIC 8011 Offices & clinics of medical doctors
CEO: Gene O'Hara
Dir Rx: Richard Einhellig
QA Dir: Elaine Obleness
Sfty Dirs: Paul Reimer
Sls&Mrk Ex: John Smith
Doctor: Gary Bauerle

D-U-N-S 07-341-0839
NORTH COLORADO MEDICAL CENTER FOUNDATION INC
BANNER HEALTH
1801 16th St, Greeley, CO 80631-5154
Tel (970) 356-9020 *Founded/Ownrshp* 1975
Sales 3.2MM *EMP* 1,902
Accts Eks&H Lllp Denver Co
SIC 8062 Hospital, affiliated with AMA residency; Hospital, affiliated with AMA residency
CEO: Gene O'Hara
Dir Recs: Tami Figal
**Pr:* Chris Kiser
CFO: Mike Lewis
Ofcr: Trina Bogart
VP: Gene Haffner
Dir Rx: Don McNemar
Dir Rx: John Placko
Off Mgr: Tarena Engel
Off Mgr: Michelle Walling
Dir IT: Steve Rains

D-U-N-S 88-308-9492
NORTH COUNTRY ASSOCIATES INC
HALL-DALE MANOR
179 Lisbon St Ste 3, Lewiston, ME 04240-7248
Tel (207) 786-3554 *Founded/Ownrshp* 1986
Sales 54.1MM^E *EMP* 1,500
SIC 8361 Residential care; Residential care
Pr: John Orestis

D-U-N-S 02-271-9678
NORTH COUNTRY BUSINESS PRODUCTS INC
1112 Railroad St Se, Bemidji, MN 56601-4871
Tel (218) 751-4140 *Founded/Ownrshp* 1968
Sales 34.4MM *EMP* 205
SIC 5021 5112 5044 7629 Office furniture; Stationery & office supplies; Office equipment; Business machine repair, electric; Office furniture; Stationery & office supplies; Office equipment; Business machine repair, electric
Pr: Dean Crotty
**CEO:* Kris Rydberg
**Ex VP:* Darlene Geller
**VP:* Curt Crotty
Dir IT: Matthew Swanson
Manager: Jake Bomba

D-U-N-S 17-052-1314
NORTH COUNTRY COMMUNITY MENTAL HEALTH
1420 Paso Dr, Petoskey, MI 49770
Tel (231) 347-6701 *Founded/Ownrshp* 1973
Sales NA *EMP* 280
SIC 9431 Mental health agency administration, government; Mental health agency administration, government
Treas: William Denemy
Ex VP: Donna Wheeler
Off Mgr: Mary Macnaughton
MIS Dir: Dianne Forster
Child Psyc: Marit Bogel

NORTH COUNTRY FORD
See ANOKA MOTORS LLC

D-U-N-S 19-522-6147
NORTH COUNTRY HEALTH SYSTEMS INC
NORTH COUNTRY HOSPITAL
189 Prouty Dr, Newport, VT 05855-9326
Tel (802) 334-7331 *Founded/Ownrshp* 1984
Sales 90.8M *EMP* 400
SIC 8741 Hospital management; Nursing & personal care facility management; Hospital management; Nursing & personal care facility management
Pr: Robert Fotter
**Treas:* Kathryn Austin
VP: Joseph Falworth
VP: Thomas Frank
Dir Lab: Oren Martin
Dir IT: Ervin Goodwin
Dir IT: Carla Raboin

D-U-N-S 04-132-4992
NORTH COUNTRY HEALTHCARE INC
2920 N 4th St, Flagstaff, AZ 86004-1816
Tel (928) 522-9400 *Founded/Ownrshp* 1991
Sales 40.9MM *EMP* 330
Accts Fester & Champman Pc Phoeni
SIC 8099 Medical services organization; Medical services organization
CEO: Ann Roggenbuck
**CFO:* Ben Locklear
Dir Rx: Mary Brubaker
Prgrm Mgr: Elizabeth Markona
Mktg Dir: Tammy Howell
Obsttrcn: Linda Nassif
Doctor: E Claxton

D-U-N-S 13-085-3708
NORTH COUNTRY HOME SERVICES INC
25 Church St, Saranac Lake, NY 12983-1816
Tel (518) 891-1175 *Founded/Ownrshp* 1982
Sales 8.6MM *EMP* 300
SIC 8082 Home health care services; Home health care services
Ex Dir: Rebecca Lehey
**Pr:* Gladys Chatney
Ex Dir: Rebecca Leahy

NORTH COUNTRY HOSPITAL
See NORTH COUNTRY HEALTH SYSTEMS INC

D-U-N-S 07-648-8873
NORTH COUNTRY HOSPITAL
NORTH COUNTRY REGIONAL HOSP
1300 Anne St Nw, Bemidji, MN 56601-5117
Tel (218) 751-5430 *Founded/Ownrshp* 1930
Sales 36.6MM^E *EMP* 850
Accts Eide Bailly Llp Bemidji Minn
SIC 8062 8051 General medical & surgical hospitals; Extended care facility; General medical & surgical hospitals; Extended care facility
Pr: Paul Hanson
VP: Bob Verchota
Dir IT: Robin Galuxin
Doctor: William Muller

D-U-N-S 06-991-2731
NORTH COUNTRY HOSPITAL AND HEALTH CENTER INC
189 Prouty Dr, Newport, VT 05855-9326
Tel (802) 334-7331 *Founded/Ownrshp* 1919
Sales 77.9MM^E *EMP* 450^E
SIC 8062 General medical & surgical hospitals; General medical & surgical hospitals
Pr: Claudio D Fort
**CFO:* Andre Bissonnette
VP: Kim Campbell
VP: William Perket
Dir Lab: Oren Martin
Dir Rx: Michael Omar
Mng Ofcr: Larry Sisson
Mtls Dir: Michael Sanville
Doctor: Jennifer Ladd
Pharmcst: Larry Labor
HC Dir: Carmen Nolte

NORTH COUNTRY REGIONAL HOSP
See NORTH COUNTRY HOSPITAL

D-U-N-S 14-851-5661
NORTH COUNTRY REGIONAL HOSPITAL INC
(*Suby of* NORTH COUNTRY HOSPITAL) ★
1300 Anne St Nw, Bemidji, MN 56601-5103
Tel (218) 751-5430 *Founded/Ownrshp* 1980
Sales 740.3M *EMP* 560
SIC 8062 General medical & surgical hospitals; General medical & surgical hospitals
Pr: James Hanko
COO: Paul Hanson
VP: Sylvia Wildgen
Exec: Christine Kuzel
IT Man: Dan Moffin
Mktg Dir: Penny Echternach
Pathlgst: Mark Robia
Nutrtnst: Sondra Gudmundson
Pharmcst: Karla P Eischens
Phys Thrpy: John J Stender

D-U-N-S 19-355-6271
NORTH COUNTRY SUPERVISORY UNION
121 Duchess Ave, Newport, VT 05855-5517
Tel (802) 334-5704 *Founded/Ownrshp* 1999
Sales 9.5MM *EMP* 450
SIC 8211 Public elementary & secondary schools; Public elementary & secondary schools
Dir IT: John Peters
Schl Brd P: Jason Brueck
Schl Brd P: Frank Carbonneau
Schl Brd P: Jennifer Daigle
Schl Brd P: Bryan Davis
Schl Brd P: Corinna Lancaster
Schl Brd P: Steven Mason
Schl Brd P: Sally Rivard
Schl Brd P: Wilma Therrien

D-U-N-S 93-025-3732
NORTH COUNTRY UNION HIGH SCHOOL
209 Veterans Ave, Newport, VT 05855-5534
Tel (802) 334-7921 *Founded/Ownrshp* 2002
Sales 14.7MM^E *EMP* 290
SIC 8211 Vocational high school; Vocational high school
Prin: William Rivard
**Treas:* Nancy Griffith

D-U-N-S 07-874-3820
NORTH COUNTY HEALTH PROJECT INC (CA)
NORTH COUNTY SERVICES
150 Valpreda Rd Frnt, San Marcos, CA 92069-2944
Tel (760) 736-6755 *Founded/Ownrshp* 1973
Sales 57.0MM *EMP* 550
Accts Tca Partners Llp Fresno Ca
SIC 8011 Clinic, operated by physicians; Clinic, operated by physicians
CEO: Irma Cota
CFO: Phil Lenowski
CFO: Kathy Martinez
VP: Anwar Abbas
VP: Diane Slosar
Exec: Priscilla Meyette
Dir Lab: Frankie Seelenbinder
Sls&Mrk Ex: Mike De Leon
Doctor: Aaron Lehman
Doctor: Kenneth Morris

NORTH COUNTY JEEP GMC KIA
See EJE INC

D-U-N-S 60-890-5758
NORTH COUNTY PIZZA INC
DOMINO'S PIZZA
120 E Lincoln Ave, Escondido, CA 92026-3038
Tel (760) 480-0800 *Founded/Ownrshp* 1988
Sales 7.8MM^E *EMP* 284
SIC 5812 Pizzeria, chain; Pizzeria, chain
Pr: Richard Midlick
**CFO:* Paul Davis

NORTH COUNTY SERVICES
See NORTH COUNTY HEALTH PROJECT INC

D-U-N-S 01-728-7715
NORTH COUNTY TOYOTA & SCION
1331 N Euclid St, Anaheim, CA 92801-1956
Tel (714) 879-6300 *Founded/Ownrshp* 1996
Sales 25.9MM^E *EMP* 117
SIC 5511 Automobiles, new & used; Automobiles, new & used
Pr: Fritz Hitchcock
**VP:* Gregg Moss

NORTH CRLINA OFFICE OF GVERNOR
See EXECUTIVE OFFICE OF STATE OF NORTH CAROLINA

D-U-N-S 19-159-9971
NORTH CYPRESS MEDICAL CENTER OPERATING CO GP LLC
21208 Northwest Fwy, Cypress, TX 77429-5975
Tel (281) 949-5999 *Founded/Ownrshp* 2004
Sales 119.1MM^E *EMP* 423^E
SIC 8741 Hospital management
CEO: Robert A Behar
COO: Jimmy W C Lee
CFO: Robert Martel
VP: Elizabeth Dunphy
VP: Walter Pannone
Dir Rx: Joseph Ghebremichael
Mtls Mgr: Edward Root
Mktg Dir: Stacy Thornton

D-U-N-S 80-274-4052
NORTH DAKOTA DEPARTMENT OF CORRECTIONS AND REHABILITATION
D O C R
(*Suby of* EXECUTIVE OFFICE OF STATE OF NORTH DAKOTA) ★
3100 Railroad Ave, Bismarck, ND 58501-5011
Tel (701) 328-6390 *Founded/Ownrshp* 1989
Sales NA *EMP* 710
SIC 9223 Prison, government; ; Prison, government;
Ex Dir: Leann Bertsch
COO: John Halvorson
Ex Dir: Kent Bullinger
DP Dir: Warren Emmer
IT Man: David Krabbenhoft
Mktg Dir: Justin Swanson

D-U-N-S 80-274-8996
NORTH DAKOTA DEPARTMENT OF HEALTH
HEALTH DEPARTMENT
(*Suby of* EXECUTIVE OFFICE OF STATE OF NORTH DAKOTA) ★
600 E Boulevard Ave # 301, Bismarck, ND 58505-0601
Tel (701) 328-2372 *Founded/Ownrshp* 1885
Sales NA *EMP* 320
SIC 9431 Administration of public health programs; ; Administration of public health programs;
Prin: Terry L Dwelle
**Prin:* Darleen Bartz
**Prin:* Dave Glatt
**Prin:* Kirby Kruger
**Prin:* Arvy Smith
Dir IT: Jennifer Witham

D-U-N-S 80-274-3534
NORTH DAKOTA DEPARTMENT OF HUMAN SERVICES
(*Suby of* EXECUTIVE OFFICE OF STATE OF NORTH DAKOTA) ★
600 E Boulevard Ave # 325, Bismarck, ND 58505-0250
Tel (701) 872-2081 *Founded/Ownrshp* 1982
Sales NA *EMP* 2,100
SIC 9441 Administration of social & manpower programs; ; Administration of social & manpower programs;
Ex Dir: Maggie D Anderson
IT Man: Debra McDermott

D-U-N-S 80-274-9242
NORTH DAKOTA DEPARTMENT OF MILITARY AFFAIRS
NATIONAL GUARD & ADJUTANT GEN
(*Suby of* EXECUTIVE OFFICE OF STATE OF NORTH DAKOTA) ★
30 Fraine Barracks Ln, Bismarck, ND 58504-5222
Tel (701) 333-2079 *Founded/Ownrshp* 1891
Sales NA *EMP* 1,000
SIC 9711 National security;
Prin: Keith D Bjerke

D-U-N-S 80-375-5057
NORTH DAKOTA DEPARTMENT OF PUBLIC INSTRUCTION
(*Suby of* EXECUTIVE OFFICE OF STATE OF NORTH DAKOTA) ★
600 E Boulevard Ave # 201, Bismarck, ND 58505-0440
Tel (701) 328-2260 *Founded/Ownrshp* 1889
Sales NA *EMP* 307
SIC 9411 Administration of educational programs; ; Administration of educational programs;
Dir Sec: Valerie Fischer
MIS Dir: Steve Snow
Pr Dir: Dale Wetzel
Teacher Pr: Lisa Lee
Teacher Pr: Adeline Schmaltz

D-U-N-S 80-274-2742
NORTH DAKOTA DEPT OF TRANSPORTATION
(*Suby of* EXECUTIVE OFFICE OF STATE OF NORTH DAKOTA) ★
608 E Boulevard Ave, Bismarck, ND 58505-0606
Tel (701) 328-2500 *Founded/Ownrshp* 1989
Sales NA *EMP* 1,015
SIC 9621 Regulation, administration of transportation; ; Regulation, administration of transportation;
Ql Cn Mgr: Sonia Bar

NORTH DAKOTA EASTER SEAL SOC
See EASTER SEALS GOODWILL ND INC

D-U-N-S 00-616-1665 IMP/EXP
NORTH DAKOTA MILL & ELEVATOR ASSOCIATION INC
1823 Mill Rd, Grand Forks, ND 58203-1535
Tel (701) 795-7000 *Founded/Ownrshp* 1922
Sales 247.9MM *EMP* 120
Accts Robert R Peterson Fargo Nor
SIC 2052 2041 Bakery products, dry; Wheat flour; Bakery products, dry; Wheat flour
Pr: Vance Taylor
Brnch Mgr: Kevin Anderson
Plnt Mgr: Dan Korynta

NORTH DAKOTA MUSTARD & SPICE
See FUCHS NORTH AMERICA INC

D-U-N-S 80-388-2034
NORTH DAKOTA STATE COLLEGE OF SCIENCE
NDSCS
800 6th St N, Wahpeton, ND 58076-0001
Tel (701) 671-2401 *Founded/Ownrshp* 1903
Sales 19.0MM *EMP* 600
Accts Robert R Peterson State Audi
SIC 8222 Junior colleges & technical institutes; Junior colleges & technical institutes
Pr: John Richmond
Ofcr: Melissa Neitzke
Assoc VP: Gloria Dohman
Assoc VP: Philip Parnell
Ex Dir: Ann Hiedeman
Off Mgr: Sue Braun
CIO: Cly Tobola
CTO: Melissa Naslund
IT Man: John Kroshus
Pgrm Dir: Carol Meehan

D-U-N-S 80-388-2299
NORTH DAKOTA STATE UNIVERSITY
1919 University Dr N # 102, Fargo, ND 58102-1843
Tel (701) 231-7015 *Founded/Ownrshp* 1890
Sales 400.3MM^E *EMP* 4,500
SIC 8221 5191 Colleges universities & professional schools; Animal feeds; Colleges universities & professional schools; Animal feeds
Pr: Dean Bresciani
Ofcr: Alison Kavanaugh
Ex VP: Corey McIntire
VP: Philip Boudjouk
VP: Evie Myers
VP: Marc Wallman
CIO: Thomas Moberg
CIO: Randall Thursby
Software D: Eric Christeson
Manager: Bob Mecklenburg
Nutrtnst: Laura Penovich

D-U-N-S 04-739-2634
NORTH DAKOTA STATE UNIVERSITY ALUMNI ASSOCIATION INC
NDSU DEVELOPMENT FOUNDATION
1241 University Dr N, Fargo, ND 58102-2524
Tel (701) 231-6800 *Founded/Ownrshp* 1971
Sales 39.1MM *EMP* 32
Accts Eide Bailly Llp Fargo North
SIC 8399 Fund raising organization, non-fee basis; Fund raising organization, non-fee basis
Ex Dir: James A Meier
Bd of Dir: Robert C Montgomery
Ofcr: Randy Schmeling
Assoc Dir: Sherri Schmidt
Assoc Dir: Jason Wohlman
**Ex Dir:* James C Miller

D-U-N-S 80-442-2137
NORTH DAKOTA STATE WATER COMMISSION
(*Suby of* EXECUTIVE OFFICE OF STATE OF NORTH DAKOTA) ★
900 E Boulevard Ave # 770, Bismarck, ND 58505-0607
Tel (701) 328-2750 *Founded/Ownrshp* 1937
Sales 33.4MM^E *EMP* 84^E
SIC 4941 9511 Water supply; Air, water & solid waste management;
CFO: David Laschkewitsch

D-U-N-S 36-070-4761
NORTH DAKOTA SUPREME COURT
(*Suby of* STATE OF NORTH DAKOTA) ★
600 E Boulevard Ave # 406, Bismarck, ND 58505-0601
Tel (701) 328-2221 *Founded/Ownrshp* 1889
Sales NA *EMP* 447
SIC 9211 State courts; ; State courts;

D-U-N-S 80-897-2442
NORTH DAKOTA TELEPHONE CO
NDTC
211 22nd St Nw, Devils Lake, ND 58301-1534
Tel (701) 662-1100 *Founded/Ownrshp* 1993
Sales 22.0MM *EMP* 73
Accts Eide Bailly Llp Sioux Falls
SIC 4813 Local telephone communications; Local telephone communications
Pr: Norman Schommer
**Pr:* Ron Steinke
Treas: Todd Thompson
**Sec:* Rodney Suko
Bd of Dir: Gerald Eissinger
Bd of Dir: Mike Hallof
**VP:* Tom Eagan
Ex Dir: Tim Loen
Ex Dir: Tony Martin

*Genl Mgr: David Dircks
IT Man: Jennifer Brossart
Board of Directors: Harold Estenson, Harold Estenson, Amber Meyer, Doug Wede

D-U-N-S 80-450-1732
NORTH DAKOTA UNIVERSITY SYSTEM FOUNDATION
600 E Boulevard Ave # 215, Bismarck, ND 58505-0601
Tel (701) 328-2960 Founded/Ownrshp 1939
Sales 653.9MM EMP 26
Accts Robert R Peterson Fargo Nor
SIC 8221 Colleges universities & professional schools; Colleges universities & professional schools
Prin: Hamid Augustine Shirvani
V Ch: Dennis Cooley
*Pr: Kirsten Diederich
Ofcr: Kirsten Franzen
*VP: Terry Hjelmstad
Off Mgr: Janine Trowbridge
Off Mgr: Stephanie Wegner
Sftwr Eng: Andrew Jocobson
Sls&Mrk Ex: Cynthia Kozojed
Pgrm Dir: Berch Henry

D-U-N-S 00-894-7145 IMP
NORTH DALLAS BANK & TRUST CO INC
12900 Preston Rd, Dallas, TX 75230-1329
Tel (972) 387-1300 Founded/Ownrshp 1960
Sales NA EMP 152
SIC 6022 State commercial banks; State commercial banks
CEO: Mike Shipman
V Ch: Larry Nobles
Pr: Larry Miller
COO: Kelly Green
CFO: Sam Renshaw
Ofcr: Will Alexander
Ofcr: Julia McGarry
Ofcr: Judy Rambo
Trst Ofcr: Kathleen Martin
Ex VP: Pam Burdine
Ex VP: Greg Niemeyer
Sr VP: Glenn Henry
VP: Daniel Cahill
VP: Kim Cheshier
VP: Jeff Crow
VP: Kirk Dixon
VP: Julie Gates
VP: Toni McReynolds
VP: Margie Myers
VP: Teri Nahoolewa
VP: Shawna O'Dell
Board of Directors: Michael P Haggerty, Jay S Turner

D-U-N-S 02-151-3494
NORTH EAST COMMUNITY ACTION CORP
NECAC
16 N Court St, Bowling Green, MO 63334-1534
Tel (573) 324-2231 Founded/Ownrshp 1965
Sales 12.5MM EMP 300
Accts Botz Deal & Company Pc Saint
SIC 8399 Community action agency; Community action agency
Pr: Donald Patrick
Ofcr: Dan Page
Dir IT: Kevin Stumbaugh
IT Man: Sherry Windland

NORTH EAST HOUSE
See LTC EDDY INC

D-U-N-S 07-692-3283
NORTH EAST INDEPENDENT SCHOOL DISTRICT
8961 Tesoro Dr, San Antonio, TX 78217-6226
Tel (210) 407-0359 Founded/Ownrshp 1950
Sales 712.8MM EMP 10,000ᴱ
Accts Abip Pc San Antonio Texas
SIC 8211 Public combined elementary & secondary school; Public combined elementary & secondary school
*Pr: Beth Plummer
Ofcr: Wilson An
Ofcr: Powell Booker
Ofcr: Langley Charles
Ofcr: Andres De Leon
Ofcr: Sandoval Javier
Ofcr: Bieszk Kenneth
Ofcr: Alonzo Mario
Ofcr: Gauthier Raymond
Ofcr: Anderson Stephen
*VP: Susan Galindo

D-U-N-S 09-255-8063
NORTH EAST MEDICAL SERVICES
1520 Stockton St, San Francisco, CA 94133-3354
Tel (415) 391-9686 Founded/Ownrshp 1968
Sales 94.2MM EMP 120
SIC 8011

NORTH EAST POWER
See NORTHEAST MISSOURI ELECTRIC POWER COOPERATIVE

D-U-N-S 03-006-3499
NORTH EAST SCHOOL DISTRICT
E. C. DAVIS ELEMENTARY
50 E Division St, North East, PA 16428-1351
Tel (814) 725-8671 Founded/Ownrshp 1966
Sales 23.1MM EMP 230
Accts Gorzynski Uglow & Farrell Pc
SIC 8211 Public elementary & secondary schools; Public elementary & secondary schools
*Pr: Richard Winschel
Bd of Dir: Robert Boyd
Bd of Dir: Thomas Kelley
Bd of Dir: George Sucha
Bd of Dir: Kathleen Weinheimer
Cmptr Lab: Karen Lewis
Schl Brd P: Kerry Corbin

D-U-N-S 87-723-9319
NORTH EAST TRADING INC
38 S 21st St, Kenilworth, NJ 07033-1626
Tel (908) 709-0030 Founded/Ownrshp 1994
Sales 52.4MM EMP 10
SIC 7389 Brokers' services; Brokers' services

Pr: Pete Silverstein
*VP: Alan Pollack

D-U-N-S 84-826-7951
NORTH ELECTRIC INC
2438 W Robin Rd, Scottsburg, IN 47170-6860
Tel (812) 752-4804 Founded/Ownrshp 1990
Sales 83.9MM EMP 8
SIC 1731 General electrical contractor; General electrical contractor
Pr: Jerry North

D-U-N-S 01-973-9593
NORTH ESSEX COMMUNITY COLLEGE LAWRENCE
(Suby of NORTHERN ESSEX COMMUNITY COLLEGE) ★
45 Franklin St, Lawrence, MA 01840-1121
Tel (978) 738-7000 Founded/Ownrshp 1999
Sales 7.3MMᴱ EMP 800
SIC 8222 9199 Community college; ; Community college;
Pr: David Hartleb

D-U-N-S 13-358-2262
NORTH FLORIDA HOLSTEINS LC
2740 W County Road 232, Bell, FL 32619-1350
Tel (352) 463-7174 Founded/Ownrshp 1980
Sales 35.0MM EMP 110
Accts Beauchamp & Edwards Chiefland
SIC 0241 Dairy farms; Dairy farms
CEO: Donald T Bennink

D-U-N-S 03-238-7797
NORTH FLORIDA LINCOLN CO
NORTH FLORIDA LINCOLN MERCURY
4620 Southside Blvd, Jacksonville, FL 32216-6358
Tel (904) 642-4100 Founded/Ownrshp 1968
Sales 43.7MMᴱ EMP 150
SIC 5511 Automobiles, new & used; Automobiles, new & used
Pr: Hal Lynch Jr
*Sec: Larry Lynch
*VP: William B Lynch

NORTH FLORIDA LINCOLN MERCURY
See NORTH FLORIDA LINCOLN CO

NORTH FLORIDA REGIONAL HOSP
See NORTH FLORIDA REGIONAL MEDICAL CENTER INC

D-U-N-S 92-857-7410
■ **NORTH FLORIDA REGIONAL MEDICAL CENTER INC**
NORTH FLORIDA REGIONAL HOSP
(Suby of HCA INC) ★
6500 W Newberry Rd, Gainesville, FL 32605-4309
Tel (352) 333-4100 Founded/Ownrshp 1994
Sales 358.0MMᴱ EMP 2,000
SIC 8062 8093 8011 8082 8069 General medical & surgical hospitals; Rehabilitation center, outpatient treatment; Offices & clinics of medical doctors; Home health care services; Specialty hospitals, except psychiatric; General medical & surgical hospitals; Rehabilitation center, outpatient treatment; Offices & clinics of medical doctors; Home health care services; Specialty hospitals, except psychiatric
Pr: Samuel N Hazen
*COO: Matt Davis
*VP: John M Franck
*VP: Keith M Giger
*VP: Ronald L Grubbs
*VP: Donald W Stinnett
Dir Rad: Donald E Jackson
Doctor: Greg Imperi MD

D-U-N-S 13-056-5393
NORTH FLORIDA RETIREMENT VILLAGE INC
VILLAGE, THE
8000 Nw 27th Blvd, Gainesville, FL 32606-8633
Tel (352) 373-4032 Founded/Ownrshp 1979
Sales 26.3MM EMP 211
Accts Deloitte Tax Llp Tampa Fl
SIC 8052 Personal care facility; Personal care facility
CEO: Michael P Gallagher
*Treas: Carol Villemaire

D-U-N-S 92-821-3776
NORTH FLORIDA SALES CO INC
3601 Regent Blvd, Jacksonville, FL 32224-6500
Tel (904) 645-0283 Founded/Ownrshp 1995
Sales 66.4MMᴱ EMP 200
SIC 5181 Beer & other fermented malt liquors; Beer & other fermented malt liquors
Pr: Jefferies George A
*Pr: Virgil G Pelham
CFO: Carol Jackson
CFO: Tim Roberts
*VP: Thos H Jefferies
Genl Mgr: Greg Flowers
Manager: Cindy Heath
Sls Mgr: Keith Bush

D-U-N-S 09-359-8548 IMP
NORTH FLORIDA SHIPYARDS INC
2060 E Adams St, Jacksonville, FL 32202-1212
Tel (904) 354-3278 Founded/Ownrshp 1970
Sales 40.4MMᴱ EMP 253
SIC 7699 3731 Boiler repair shop; Tank & boiler cleaning service; Ship scaling, contractors; Shipbuilding & repairing; Boiler repair shop; Tank & boiler cleaning service; Ship scaling, contractors; Shipbuilding & repairing
Ch Bd: Joseph B Shiffert
*Pr: Matthew J Self
VP: Holly Shiffert-Self
*VP: Robert Wilson
Genl Mgr: Don Nickle
Snr Mgr: Eugene Alley
Snr Mgr: Gene Alley

D-U-N-S 05-554-3672 IMP
NORTH FOOD GROUP INC (TX)
EVERSPRING ENTERPRISES
1245 W Royal Ln, Dallas, TX 75261
Tel (972) 445-3322 Founded/Ownrshp 1981, 2006

Sales 91.0MM EMP 120
SIC 5146 5147 5149 5113 Fish & seafoods; Meats & meat products; Groceries & related products; Industrial & personal service paper; Disposable plates, cups, napkins & eating utensils; Fish & seafoods; Meats & meat products; Groceries & related products; Industrial & personal service paper; Disposable plates, cups, napkins & eating utensils
Pr: Hanhue Wang
*VP: Patrick Pang
*VP: Hong Xue

D-U-N-S 07-843-9528
NORTH FOREST INDEPENDENT SCHOOL DISTRICT
NFISD
6010 Little York Rd, Houston, TX 77016-2544
Tel (713) 633-1600 Founded/Ownrshp 1936
Sales 84.3MM EMP 1,091
Accts Walter D Davis Cpa Houston
SIC 8211 Public elementary & secondary schools; Finishing school, secondary; High school, junior or senior; Public elementary & secondary schools; Finishing school, secondary; High school, junior or senior
Prin: William Jones

D-U-N-S 61-797-0777
NORTH FOREST ISD
6010 Little York Rd, Houston, TX 77016-2544
Tel (713) 633-1600 Founded/Ownrshp 2008
Sales 84.3MM EMP 1,420
SIC 8211 Public elementary & secondary schools; Public elementary & secondary schools
Treas: Billy Hall
VP: Samuel Julian

NORTH FORK EQUIPMENT LEASING
See ALL POINTS CAPITAL CORP

D-U-N-S 01-127-0246
NORTH FRANKLIN SCHOOL DISTRICT 51 162
1100 W Clark Rd, Connell, WA 99326-9700
Tel (509) 234-2021 Founded/Ownrshp 1930, 1932
Sales 20.0MMᴱ EMP 350
SIC 8211 Public elementary & secondary schools; Public elementary & secondary schools
IT Man: Ryan Peterson
HC Dir: Julie Yager

NORTH FREEWAY HYUNDAI
See KINGWOOD HYUNDAI LLC

NORTH FRESNO FOODS
See MEAT MARKET INC

D-U-N-S 13-231-0160 IMP
■ **NORTH FULTON MEDICAL CENTER VOLUNTEER SERVICES ORGANIZATION INC**
NORTH FULTON REGIONAL HOSPITAL
(Suby of TENET HEALTHCARE CORPORATION)
3000 Hospital Blvd, Roswell, GA 30076-4915
Tel (770) 751-2500 Founded/Ownrshp 1995
Sales 156.6MM EMP 985ᴱ
SIC 8062 Hospital, affiliated with AMA residency; Hospital, affiliated with AMA residency
CEO: Debbie Keel
Chf Rad: David Rallis
Dir Rad: Tracy Wilkinson
Dir Rx: Misty Boachie
Sls&Mrk Ex: June Meltzer
Mktg Dir: Lindsey Harber
Surgeon: Mark Gravlee
Doctor: Cynthia Griggs
Phys Thrpy: Ann Clawson

D-U-N-S 79-547-9526
■ **NORTH FULTON REGIONAL CANCER CENTER INC**
(Suby of NORTH FULTON MEDICAL CENTER VOLUNTEER SERVICES ORGANIZATION INC) ★
11585 Alpharetta Hwy, Roswell, GA 30076-3865
Tel (770) 442-0068 Founded/Ownrshp 1991
Sales 4.0MMᴱ EMP 929ᴱ
SIC 8069 Cancer hospital
CEO: Frederick Bailey

NORTH FULTON REGIONAL HOSPITAL
See NORTH FULTON MEDICAL CENTER VOLUNTEER SERVICES ORGANIZATION INC

NORTH GA ELECTRIC MEMB
See NORTH GEORGIA ELECTRIC MEMBERSHIP FOUNDATION INC

D-U-N-S 08-436-2896
NORTH GEORGIA CONFERENCE OF METHODIST CHURCH INC
159 Ralph Mcgill Blvd Ne, Atlanta, GA 30308-3343
Tel (706) 548-6616 Founded/Ownrshp 1866
Sales NA EMP 1,400
SIC 8661

D-U-N-S 00-692-5978
NORTH GEORGIA ELECTRIC MEMBERSHIP FOUNDATION INC
NORTH GA ELECTRIC MEMB
1850 Cleveland Hwy, Dalton, GA 30721-8315
Tel (706) 259-9441 Founded/Ownrshp 1936
Sales 245.4MM EMP 192
Accts Henderson Hutcherson & Mccullo
SIC 4911 Distribution, electric power; Distribution, electric power
CEO: Bill Scott
CFO: Kathryn West
*CFO: Mary Whittington
VP: Brian Childers
*Genl Mgr: Ron Hutchins
Opers Mgr: Keith Queen
Sls Mgr: Allison Crossen

NORTH GEORGIA MEDICAL CENTER
See SOUTHERN HEALTH CORP ELLIJAY INC

D-U-N-S 04-650-6499
NORTH GREENVILLE UNIVERSITY
7801 N Tigerville Rd, Tigerville, SC 29688-9700
Tel (864) 977-7000 Founded/Ownrshp 1892
Sales 60.6MM EMP 403ᴱ
Accts Capin Crouse Llp Lawrencevill
SIC 8221 University; University
Pr: James B Epting
Ex VP: Don Dowless
VP: Keli Sewell
Mktg Dir: Burl Walker

NORTH HALEDON FOODTOWN
See NICHOLAS MARKETS INC

D-U-N-S 07-145-4581
NORTH HANOVER TOWNSHIP BOARD OF EDUCATION
331 Monmouth Rd, Wrightstown, NJ 08562-2127
Tel (609) 758-5280 Founded/Ownrshp 1916
Sales 23.2MM EMP 280ᴱ
Accts Holman Frenia Pc Medford Nj
SIC 8211 Public elementary & secondary schools; School board
Prin: Charles Bednarik
Board of Directors: Patricia Adragna, Janet Bruder, Edward Drechel, Michael Grant, Charles Schroeder

D-U-N-S 19-322-1116
NORTH HARRISON COMMUNITY SCHOOL CORP
1260 Highway 64 Nw, Ramsey, IN 47166-8542
Tel (812) 347-2407 Founded/Ownrshp 1969
Sales 19.4MMᴱ EMP 296
SIC 8211 Public combined elementary & secondary school; Public elementary school; Public junior high school; Public senior high school; Public combined elementary & secondary school; Public elementary school; Public junior high school; Public senior high school
*Prin: Joann Burson

NORTH HAVEN GARDENS
See NORTEX WHOLESALE NURSERY INC

D-U-N-S 60-647-1340
NORTH HAVEN SCHOOL DISTRICT
5 Linsley St, North Haven, CT 06473-2518
Tel (203) 239-2581 Founded/Ownrshp 1994
Sales 23.3MMᴱ EMP 500
SIC 8211 Public elementary & secondary schools; Public elementary & secondary schools
HC Dir: Annette Sauerbrunn

D-U-N-S 83-588-5377
NORTH HAWAII COMMUNITY HOSPITAL INC
67-1125 Mamalaho Hwy, Kamuela, HI 96743-8496
Tel (808) 885-4444 Founded/Ownrshp 1995
Sales 52.1MM EMP 300
Accts Ernst & Young Us Llp Denver
SIC 8062 General medical & surgical hospitals; General medical & surgical hospitals
Ch Bd: Robert Momsen
*Pr: Kenneth D Graham
*Pr: Lowell Johnson
*Pr: Ken Wood
CFO: Lexi Fields
*VP: Bill Brown
VP: William Brown
*VP: Marilynn Hata
*VP: Wayne Higaki
*VP: Lorrie Mortensen
*VP: Jason Paret
VP: Bill Park
Dir Rad: Ruthanne Rennert
Dir Rx: Cherrie Carse

NORTH HEALTH CARE SERVICES
See WOODBRIAR OF WILMINGTON

D-U-N-S 80-719-7090
NORTH HENNEPIN COMMUNITY COLLEGE
(Suby of BEMIDJI STATE UNIVERSITY) ★
7411 85th Ave N, Brooklyn Park, MN 55445-2231
Tel (763) 424-0702 Founded/Ownrshp 1962
Sales 53.2MMᴱ EMP 350
SIC 8222 9411 8221 Community college; Administration of educational programs; ; Colleges universities & professional schools; Community college; Administration of educational programs; ; Colleges universities & professional schools
Pr: Dr Lisa Larson
Ofcr: Susan Appelquist
Ofcr: Carolyn Boganey
Ofcr: Paula Henneberg
*VP: Jan Reinky
Netwrk Mgr: Ann Wynia
Mktg Dir: Cheryl McAlpine
Mktg Dir: Carmen Shoquist

D-U-N-S 14-224-3265
NORTH HIGHLAND CO
(Suby of NORTH HIGHLAND CO) ★
200 S Tryon St Ste 1100, Charlotte, NC 28202-0016
Tel (704) 840-1900 Founded/Ownrshp 2004
Sales 334.3Mᴱ EMP 708ᴱ
SIC 8748 Business consulting
Pr: Michael Lee

D-U-N-S 80-466-5990
NORTH HIGHLAND CO
3333 Piedmont Rd Ne, Atlanta, GA 30305-1811
Tel (404) 233-1015 Founded/Ownrshp 1992
Sales 370.0MM EMP 2,300
SIC 8742 7379 Management consulting services; Computer related consulting services; Management consulting services; Computer related consulting services
CEO: Dan Reardon
*Ch Bd: Marsha Evans
CFO: David D Cathcart
*CFO: Kirk Hancock
*Chf Mktg O: Matthew Klein
*Chf Mktg O: Ricardo Martinez
*VP: Greg Bradley
VP: Scott Demorest
VP: Tina Ehrig

VP: Steve Frenz
VP: Roger Hardgrove
VP: Jill Jacques
VP: David Kelleher
VP: Bill Lenihan
VP: Peter Lizotte
VP: Teri Mendelovitz
VP: Andy Moose
VP: Paul Patterson
VP: Dwight Specht
VP: Michael Winner
Dir Bus: Reid Graeber

D-U-N-S 07-832-7457
NORTH HIGHLAND HOLDING CO INC
3333 Piedmont Rd Ne, Atlanta, GA 30305-1811
Tel (404) 233-1015 *Founded/Ownrshp* 2009
Sales 327.8MM *EMP* 1E
Accts GrantThornton Llp Atlanta G
SIC 8742 Management consulting services; Management consulting services
CEO: Daniel D Reardon
**CFO:* J Kirk Hancock
**Sec:* Richard Dobb
**Prin:* Loretta Penn

D-U-N-S 03-625-1262 IMP
NORTH HILL NEEDHAM INC
865 Central Ave Apt A502, Needham, MA 02492-1365
Tel (781) 444-9910 *Founded/Ownrshp* 1979
Sales 25.0MM *EMP* 300
Accts Ernst & Young Us Llp Chicago
SIC 8051 Skilled nursing care facilities; Convalescent home with continuous nursing care; Extended care facility; Skilled nursing care facilities; Convalescent home with continuous nursing care; Extended care facility
Pr: Kevin Burke
VP Mktg: Paul Duffy
Sales Asso: Harriet Voyt

D-U-N-S 07-580-1878
NORTH HILLS OFFICE SERVICES INC
CEILING SAVERS
244 Crossways Park Dr W, Woodbury, NY 11797-2031
Tel (516) 364-2800 *Founded/Ownrshp* 1972
Sales 13.4MME *EMP* 500
Accts Paritz & Company Pa Hackensa
SIC 7349 Cleaning service, industrial or commercial; Cleaning service, industrial or commercial
Pr: Paul Kaplan
VP Opers: Mary Santos

D-U-N-S 03-008-7563
NORTH HILLS SCHOOL DISTRICT (INC)
135 6th Ave, Pittsburgh, PA 15229-1299
Tel (412) 318-1000 *Founded/Ownrshp* 1948
Sales 40.8MME *EMP* 600
SIC 8211 Public elementary & secondary schools; Public elementary school; Public junior high school; Public senior high school; Public elementary & secondary schools; Public elementary school; Public junior high school; Public senior high school
Dir IT: Jason King
Psych: Lynn Zalnasky

NORTH HILLS TOYOTA
See CONDOR LLC

D-U-N-S 10-066-3012
NORTH HUNTERDON-VOORHEES REGIONAL HIGH SCHOOL DISTRICT
1445 State Route 31 S, Annandale, NJ 08801-3117
Tel (908) 713-4199 *Founded/Ownrshp* 1950
Sales 23.3MME *EMP* 450
SIC 8211 Public senior high school; School board; Public senior high school; School board
Off Mgr: Lynn Baumeister
Psych: Allison Cassidy
Snr Mgr: Mary Meo

D-U-N-S 02-023-2484
NORTH IDAHO COLLEGE (ID)
1000 W Garden Ave, Coeur D Alene, ID 83814-2199
Tel (208) 769-3300 *Founded/Ownrshp* 1933, 1939
Sales 19.9MM *EMP* 421
Accts Magnuson Mchugh & Company P
SIC 8221 8222 Colleges universities & professional schools; Community college; Colleges universities & professional schools; Community college
Pr: Joe Dunlap
V Ch: Josh Misner

D-U-N-S 87-932-4960
NORTH IOWA AREA COMMUNITY COLLEGE
NIACC
500 College Dr, Mason City, IA 50401-7213
Tel (641) 423-1264 *Founded/Ownrshp* 1966
Sales 16.1MM *EMP* 501
Accts Hogan - Hansen Mason City Io
SIC 8221 8222 Colleges universities & professional schools; Community college; Colleges universities & professional schools; Community college
Pr: Steven Schulz
**Ex VP:* Mark Johnson
VP: Lyn Brobersen
**VP:* Karen Pierson
**Prin:* Debra Derr
**VP Admn:* Katherine Grove
Off Mgr: Donna Petersen
CIO: Tom Hausmann
Dir IT: Donna Orton
Pr Mgr: Tammy Hove
Snr Mgr: Diane Frank

D-U-N-S 02-234-8353
NORTH IOWA COOPERATIVE CO
105 S 1st St, Thornton, IA 50479-6044
Tel (641) 998-2711 *Founded/Ownrshp* 1982
Sales 56.9MME *EMP* 32
SIC 5153 5191 5171 Grains; Farm supplies; Feed; Petroleum bulk stations; Grains; Farm supplies; Feed; Petroleum bulk stations
**Pr:* Dallas Pals
**VP:* Doug Caffrey

NORTH ISLAND CREDIT UNION
See NORTH ISLAND FINANCIAL CREDIT UNION

NORTH ISLAND EXCESS & SURPLUS
See NORTH ISLAND GROUP INC

D-U-N-S 08-092-3816
NORTH ISLAND FINANCIAL CREDIT UNION
NORTH ISLAND CREDIT UNION
5898 Copley Dr Ste 100, San Diego, CA 92111-7917
Tel (619) 656-6525 *Founded/Ownrshp* 1940
Sales NA *EMP* 353
SIC 6062 State credit unions; State credit unions
CEO: Steve Oconnell
**Ch Bd:* Rebecca Collier
Pr: Michael Scogin
CFO: Hudson Lee
Treas: Dennis Doucette
**Ex VP:* Bill Vidano
Sr VP: Jerry Hicks
Sr VP: Roger McTighe
VP: Allen Ambort
VP: Deb Blackson
VP: Johnson Bret
VP: Pam Carlson
VP: Dante Chavez
VP: Ruth Duncan
VP: Brian Earley
VP: Richard Hubeny
VP: Carlton Roark
VP: Mark Russell
VP: Tom Tanida
VP: Curt Yasuhara

D-U-N-S 08-065-9956
NORTH ISLAND GROUP INC
NORTH ISLAND EXCESS & SURPLUS
30 Park Ave, Manhasset, NY 11030-2444
Tel (516) 365-7440 *Founded/Ownrshp* 2008
Sales NA *EMP* 75
Accts Ross & Ross
SIC 6411 Insurance brokers
Pr: Michael A Orlando
**VP:* William Battistini
**VP:* Dennis Loggie
**VP:* John G Orlando

D-U-N-S 07-932-5874
NORTH JERSEY DISTRICT WATER SUPPLY COMMISSION
NJDWSC
1 F A Orechio Dr, Wanaque, NJ 07465-1517
Tel (973) 831-6212 *Founded/Ownrshp* 1928
Sales 97.4MME *EMP* 174
Accts Mcenerney Brady & Company Ll
SIC 4971 4941 Irrigation systems; Water supply; Irrigation systems; Water supply
Ch: Charles P Shotmeyer
**CFO:* John Blonski
CFO: Danielle Holobinko
Exec: Colleen Desfano
**Prin:* Carmen A Orechio
**Ex Dir:* Todd R Caliguire
**Ex Dir:* Colleen Destefano
Ex Dir: Michael Restaino
Dir Sec: Bill Mullanaphy

D-U-N-S 78-850-4512
NORTH JERSEY HEALTH CARE CORP
175 High St, Newton, NJ 07860-1004
Tel (973) 383-2121 *Founded/Ownrshp* 1985
Sales 2.0MM *EMP* 1,350
SIC 8741 Hospital management; Nursing & personal care facility management; Hospital management; Nursing & personal care facility management
Pr: Dennis Collette
**Ch Bd:* Tom Digby MD
**Ch Bd:* H Alden Welch
**Pr:* Thomas J Senker
**COO:* Sean O'Rourke
CFO: David Richolas
IT Man: Ivy Gray

D-U-N-S 00-215-5869 IMP
NORTH JERSEY MEDIA GROUP INC
NORTH JRSEY MDIA GROUP FNDTION
(*Suby of* MACROMEDIA INC) ★
1 Garret Mountain Plz # 201, Woodland Park, NJ 07424-3318
Tel (201) 646-4000 *Founded/Ownrshp* 1964
Sales 236.3MME *EMP* 1,431
SIC 2711 4813 Newspapers, publishing & printing; ; Newspapers, publishing & printing;
Ch Bd: Malcolm A Borg
**Pr:* Stephen A Borg
Pr: Richard Nadeau
CFO: Charles Gibney
**CFO:* Thomas G Heffernan
**VP:* Susan Beard
VP: Glenn Garvie
VP: Martin Gottlieb
VP: Kathleen Hivish
VP: Greg Hoffman
VP: Bob Konig
**VP:* Robert Konig
VP: Richard A Ndeu

D-U-N-S 01-171-8095
NORTH JERSEY TRUCK CENTER INC
236 Us Highway 46, Saddle Brook, NJ 07663-6230
Tel (973) 478-8802 *Founded/Ownrshp* 1970
Sales 24.8MME *EMP* 50
SIC 5511 Trucks, tractors & trailers: new & used; Trucks, tractors & trailers: new & used
Pr: John Muchmore
**CFO:* Gary Strifer

NORTH JRSEY MDIA GROUP FNDTION
See NORTH JERSEY MEDIA GROUP INC

NORTH KANSAS CITY
See HENRY WURST INC

D-U-N-S 02-993-5251
NORTH KANSAS CITY BEVERAGE CO INC
203 E 11th Ave, Kansas City, MO 64116-4136
Tel (816) 471-4895 *Founded/Ownrshp* 1951
Sales 22.6MME *EMP* 60
SIC 5181 Beer & other fermented malt liquors
Owner: Curt Borland
**Sec:* Jane Johnson Borland
**Ex VP:* Lars Langhus
Sls Dir: Chad Curtis

D-U-N-S 00-315-9519
NORTH KANSAS CITY ELECTRIC CO INC (MO)
200 E 15th Ave, Kansas City, MO 64116-3913
Tel (816) 421-2352 *Founded/Ownrshp* 2000
Sales 21.6MME *EMP* 30
SIC 4911 Electric services
Pr: Michael W Quarles
**Sec:* William E Quarles
Off Mgr: Melissa Miller
Off Admin: Lindsay Elling
Sls Mgr: Mark McMichael

D-U-N-S 19-799-6163
NORTH KANSAS CITY HOSPITAL
BOARD TRUSTEE N KANS CY HOSP
2800 Clay Edwards Dr, North Kansas City, MO 64116-3220
Tel (816) 691-2000 *Founded/Ownrshp* 2005
Sales 206.1MME *EMP* 3,100
SIC 8062 General medical & surgical hospitals; General medical & surgical hospitals
CEO: Peggy Schmitt
**COO:* Jody Abbott
COO: Donna Cash
**CFO:* Jim McNey
Exec: Tara Turvey
Dir OR: April Patten
Dir OR: Gay Wiggs
Dir Inf Cn: Becky Smith
Dir Rad: Joe Strano
Dir Sec: Tom Morgan
Off Mgr: Sherri Tholl

D-U-N-S 01-065-4168
NORTH KANSAS CITY SCHOOL DISTRICT NO 74
2000 Ne 46th St, Kansas City, MO 64116-2042
Tel (816) 413-5000 *Founded/Ownrshp* 1913
Sales 245.6MM *EMP* 3,100
Accts Marr And Company Pc Kansas
SIC 8211 Public elementary school; Public junior high school; Public senior high school; Public elementary school; Public junior high school; Public senior high school
**CFO:* Paul Harrell
Dir Sec: Jon Brady
Off Mgr: Vickie Freese
IT Man: Joann Pearson
Netwrk Eng: Joel Brooks
Pr Dir: Michelle Cronk
Schl Brd P: Joe Jacobs
Instr Medi: Susan Anderson
Psych: Jean Laubach
Snr Mgr: Tammy Henderson

NORTH KENWOOD OAKLAND
See UNIVERSITY OF CHICAGO CHARTER SCHOOL CORP

D-U-N-S 10-008-0886
NORTH KITSAP SCHOOL DISTRICT
18360 Caldart Ave Ne, Poulsbo, WA 98370-8775
Tel (360) 779-8704 *Founded/Ownrshp* 1941
Sales 43.2MME *EMP* 879
SIC 8211 Public combined elementary & secondary school; School board; Public combined elementary & secondary school; School board

D-U-N-S 61-004-9157
NORTH LA COUNTY REGIONAL CENTER INC
15400 Sherman Way Ste 170, Van Nuys, CA 91406-4272
Tel (818) 778-1900 *Founded/Ownrshp* 1974
Sales 318.5MM *EMP* 350
Accts Lautze & Lautze San Francisco
SIC 8748 Test development & evaluation service; Test development & evaluation service
Bd of Dir: K Jennifr
Ex Dir: Thompson Kelly
Prgrm Mgr: Kimberly Benjamin
Prgrm Mgr: Shanna Munoz

D-U-N-S 07-944-7819
NORTH LAKE SUPPORT AND SERVICES CENTER
(*Suby of* LOUISIANA DEPARTMENT OF HEALTH AND HOSPITALS) ★
45439 Live Oak Dr, Hammond, LA 70401-4526
Tel (225) 567-3111 *Founded/Ownrshp* 1964
Sales 11.2MME *EMP* 795
SIC 8361 8051 Residential care; Skilled nursing care facilities; Residential care; Skilled nursing care facilities

D-U-N-S 10-067-2229
NORTH LAMAR INDEPENDENT SCHOOL DISTRICT
3201 Lewis Ln, Paris, TX 75460-9338
Tel (903) 737-2000 *Founded/Ownrshp* 1970
Sales 30.6MM *EMP* 500
Accts Malnory Mcneal & Company Pc
SIC 8211 Public elementary & secondary schools; School board; Public elementary & secondary schools; School board
IT Man: Nora Sullivan

D-U-N-S 60-854-1926 IMP
NORTH LANDING LIMITED LLC
610 Brighton Rd, Clifton, NJ 07012-1026
Tel (973) 249-5300 *Founded/Ownrshp* 2008
Sales 30.9MME *EMP* 55
SIC 5146 Fish & seafoods
IT Man: Bragi Henningsson
Sls Mgr: Dorvenir Amaral

NORTH LANES
See MCKNIGHT DEVELOPMENT CORP

NORTH LAUDERDALE
See ANSWER GROUP INC

NORTH LIBERTY ELEM SCHOOL
See JOHN GLENN SCHOOL CORP

D-U-N-S 83-217-4978
NORTH LIGHT COLOR INC
5008 Hillsboro Ave N, Minneapolis, MN 55428-4029
Tel (763) 531-8222 *Founded/Ownrshp* 1999
Sales 36.1MME *EMP* 30
SIC 5084 5734 Printing trades machinery, equipment & supplies; Printers & plotters: computers
CEO: Thomas Mittelstadt
**Treas:* William Duma
IT Man: Jeff Duma
Sls Mgr: Steve Shafer

D-U-N-S 83-272-0879
NORTH LIME HOLDINGS CORP
120 N Lime St, Lancaster, PA 17602-2923
Tel (717) 397-3633 *Founded/Ownrshp* 2006
Sales 246.7MM *EMP* 1,736
Accts Baker Tilly Wyomissing Pa
SIC 1799 Coating, caulking & weather, water & fireproofing; Insulation of pipes & boilers; Fireproofing buildings; Coating, caulking & weather, water & fireproofing; Insulation of pipes & boilers; Fireproofing buildings
Pr: W K Liddell
**Sec:* Lori A Pickell
VP: Gale Blefko
Ex Dir: Phyllis Burkholder

D-U-N-S 03-679-2823
NORTH LINCOLN COUNTY HOSPITAL DISTRICT
STAR VALLEY MEDICAL CENTER
110 Hospital Ln, Afton, WY 83110-9409
Tel (307) 885-5800 *Founded/Ownrshp* 1972
Sales 36.9MME *EMP* 150
SIC 8062 General medical & surgical hospitals
Prin: Ken Brough
CFO: Chad Turner
Surgeon: Brian Tallerico

D-U-N-S 14-400-2230
NORTH LITTLE ROCK ELECTRIC DEPARTMENT
120 Main St, North Little Rock, AR 72114-5631
Tel (501) 975-8888 *Founded/Ownrshp* 2004
Sales 22.2MME *EMP* 99
SIC 4911 Generation, electric power; Generation, electric power
IT Man: Suzanne Fletcher

D-U-N-S 00-122-0685
NORTH LITTLE ROCK PONTIAC -BUICK-GMC INC
GWATNEY BUICK GMC
5700 Landers Rd, North Little Rock, AR 72117-1922
Tel (501) 945-4444 *Founded/Ownrshp* 2005
Sales 29.8MME *EMP* 72
SIC 5511 7538 7532 Automobiles, new & used; General automotive repair shops; Body shop, automotive; Automobiles, new & used; General automotive repair shops; Body shop, automotive
CEO: Jamie Cobb
**Genl Mgr:* Lance Brown
Sales Asso: Willie Chester

D-U-N-S 62-102-9693
NORTH LITTLE ROCK SCHOOL DISTRICT
2700 N Poplar St, North Little Rock, AR 72114-2332
Tel (501) 771-8000 *Founded/Ownrshp* 1913
Sales 79.2MME *EMP* 1,532
SIC 8211 Public elementary & secondary schools; Public elementary & secondary schools
**CFO:* Denise Drennan

NORTH LOOP IMPORTS
See N A TEADIT INC

D-U-N-S 04-738-6859
NORTH MARIN WATER DISTRICT
NMWD
999 Rush Creek Pl, Novato, CA 94945-7716
Tel (415) 897-4133 *Founded/Ownrshp* 1948
Sales 20.3MM *EMP* 50
Accts Charles Z Fedak & Company Cy
SIC 4941 Water supply; Water supply
Prin: Chris Degabriele
Sls Mgr: Drew McIntyre

D-U-N-S 11-057-2187
NORTH MED FMLY PHYSICIANS PC
NORTH MEDICAL
5100 W Taft Rd Ste 1d, Liverpool, NY 13088-3808
Tel (315) 637-7878 *Founded/Ownrshp* 2008
Sales 5.1MME *EMP* 331E
SIC 8011 Offices & clinics of medical doctors
Prin: Geeta Roy
MIS Dir: Ira Lee
IT Man: Olga Stanton

NORTH MEDICAL
See NORTH MED FMLY PHYSICIANS PC

D-U-N-S 07-136-3634 IMP
NORTH MEMORIAL HEALTH CARE (MN)
NORTH MEMORIAL MEDICAL CENTER
3300 Oakdale Ave N, Minneapolis, MN 55422-2900
Tel (763) 520-5200 *Founded/Ownrshp* 1940
Sales 777.6MM *EMP* 5,180
Accts Deloitte & Touche Llp Minneap
SIC 8062 8011 General medical & surgical hospitals; Medical centers; General medical & surgical hospitals; Medical centers
Pr: Loren Taylor
Chf OB: Sherry Paulson
**COO:* David W Cress
**CFO:* Patrick Boran
CFO: Todd Ostendorf
VP: Laramie Anderson
**VP:* M Kaye Foley
VP: Lisa H Job
VP: Tracy Kirby
VP: Mike Parrish
VP: Melissa Smith
VP: Thomas E Timmons
Dir Inf Cn: Joanne Ferguson

Dir Rx: Tony Kausenberg
Dir Rx: Paul Krogh

NORTH MEMORIAL MEDICAL CENTER
See NORTH MEMORIAL HEALTH CARE

D-U-N-S 08-834-4106
NORTH METRO COMMUNITY SERVICES INC
NMCS
1001 W 124th Ave, Westminster, CO 80234-1705
Tel (303) 457-1001 *Founded/Ownrshp* 1964
Sales 28.1MM *EMP* 250
SIC 8322 Community center; Community center
Ex Dir: Roxanne Pinneo
Ex Dir: Gene Vanblaricom
Pgrm Dir: Shari Swinton
Snr Mgr: Geoff Davis

D-U-N-S 14-428-3293
NORTH METRO HARNESS INITIATIVE LLC
RUNNING ACES HARNESS PARK
15201 Running Aces Blvd, Forest Lake, MN 55025-9467
Tel (651) 925-4600 *Founded/Ownrshp* 2003
Sales 25.0MM^E *EMP* 450
SIC 7948 7011 Horse race track operation; Casino hotel; Horse race track operation; Casino hotel
**CFO:* Tracie Wilson
Mktg Dir: Margaret Murphy

NORTH METRO MEDICAL CENTER
See REBSAMEN MEDICAL CENTER INC

D-U-N-S 19-322-1546
NORTH MIAMI COMMUNITY SCHOOL DISTRICT
394 E 900 N, Denver, IN 46926-9308
Tel (765) 985-3891 *Founded/Ownrshp* 1961
Sales 14.0MM^E *EMP* 290
SIC 8211 9411 Public elementary & secondary schools; Administration of educational programs; Public elementary & secondary schools; Administration of educational programs

D-U-N-S 11-526-9813
NORTH MISSISSIPPI HEALTH SERVICES INC
HOSPITAL-NORTH MISS MED CTR
830 S Gloster St, Tupelo, MS 38801-4934
Tel (662) 377-3000 *Founded/Ownrshp* 1981
Sales 779.4MM *EMP* 6,000
SIC 8741 Hospital management; Nursing & personal care facility management; Hospital management; Nursing & personal care facility management
Ch Bd: Jim Kelley
Pr: John Heer
CEO: Shane Spees
CFO: Joe Reppert
Ofcr: Ormella Cummings
VP: Wally Davis
VP: Tim Moore
VP Inf Sys: Tommy Bozeman
IT Man: Dale Parker
Netwrk Mgr: Rachel Hill
Mtls Dir: Mike Switzer
Board of Directors: A E Bland, Henry Brevard, Dr James Cooper, Dr Roger Lowrey, Aubrey Patterson, John Smith, Travis Staub, Billy Wheeler

D-U-N-S 62-087-4698
■ **NORTH MISSISSIPPI HOSPICE OF OXFORD LLC**
(*Suby of* GENTIVA HEALTH SERVICES INC) ★
411 Cherokee Dr, Oxford, MS 38655-2701
Tel (662) 234-0140 *Founded/Ownrshp* 2012
Sales 4.3MM^E *EMP* 516^E
SIC 8052 Personal care facility
Pr: Gary Cooper

D-U-N-S 07-350-6487
NORTH MISSISSIPPI MEDICAL CENTER INC
HOSPITAL-NORTH MISSISSIPPI MED
(*Suby of* HOSPITAL-NORTH MISS MED CTR) ★
830 S Gloster St, Tupelo, MS 38801-4934
Tel (662) 377-3000 *Founded/Ownrshp* 1935
Sales 633.8MM *EMP* 6,000
SIC 8062 8051 8082 General medical & surgical hospitals; Skilled nursing care facilities; Home health care services; General medical & surgical hospitals; Skilled nursing care facilities; Home health care services
Pr: Steve Altmiller
Chf Path: Mark Huffman
Chf Rad: Doug Clark
Dir Recs: Sarah Beckham
Pr: Penny Brown
CFO: Joe Reppert
VP: Daniel Cotton
**VP:* Bruce Toppin
Exec: Linda Butler
Exec: Carla Enis
Exec: Cathy Waldrop
Exec: Angie Wilson
Dir Inf Cn: Rosaland Bush
Dir Risk M: Bridgette Wilson
Dir Rad: James Boyd
Dir Rad: Marshall Edmondson
Dir Rad: Bill Spitler
Dir Rx: William Calhoon
Dir Rx: Bill Calhoun

D-U-N-S 87-835-2228
NORTH MISSISSIPPI MEDICAL CLINICS INC
115o S Green St Ste A, Tupelo, MS 38804
Tel (662) 377-5009 *Founded/Ownrshp* 1997
Sales 75.8MM *EMP* 621
Accts Bkd Llp Jackson Ms
SIC 8011 Offices & clinics of medical doctors; Offices & clinics of medical doctors
Pr: Jeff Barber
**CFO:* Tony Palazzo
**Treas:* Gerald Wages
Bd of Dir: Stephen Shirley
**VP:* Jane George
Nutrtnst: April Hancock

D-U-N-S 09-599-0636
NORTH MONTEREY COUNTY UNIFIED SCHOOL DISTRICT
8142 Moss Landing Rd, Moss Landing, CA 95039-9617
Tel (831) 633-3343 *Founded/Ownrshp* 2000
Sales 28.5MM^E *EMP* 450
Accts Patel & Associates Oakland C
SIC 8211 Public elementary & secondary schools; High school, junior or senior; Vocational high school; Public elementary & secondary schools; High school, junior or senior; Vocational high school
Bd of Dir: Manuel Osorio
Schl Brd P: Sam Laaee
Teacher Pr: Craig Chavez
Teacher Pr: Don Pedroni
Psych: Arianna Hall

NORTH MOUNTAIN MEDICAL & REHAB
See RADIANT HILLS HEALTH ASSOC LLC

D-U-N-S 03-042-0129
NORTH OAK REGIONAL HOSPITAL INC
(PARENT COMPANY IS: ASSOCIATES CAPITAL GROUP INC, BIRMINGHAM, AL)
401 Getwell Dr, Senatobia, MS 38668-2213
Tel (662) 562-3100 *Founded/Ownrshp* 1999
Sales 23.5MM^E *EMP* 140
SIC 8062 General medical & surgical hospitals
Pr: Leonard P Bryant
**CEO:* Sonja Graham
CFO: Scott Turner
Dir Lab: Leslie Ryals
Dir Rad: Vicki Wright
Chf Nrs Of: Alisa Dye
Off Mgr: Donna Smith
CIO: Ollie Battle

NORTH OAKLAND MEDICAL CENTERS
See AUXILIARY TO NORTH OAKLAND MEDICAL CENTER INC

NORTH OAKS HEALTH SYSTEM
See HOSPITAL SERVICE DISTRICT NO 1 OF TANGIPAHOA PARISH

D-U-N-S 62-382-4013
NORTH OAKS HEALTH SYSTEM FOUNDATION
15790 Paul Vega Md Dr, Hammond, LA 70403-1434
Tel (985) 345-2700 *Founded/Ownrshp* 2003
Sales 141.2MM^E *EMP* 1,000
SIC 6733 Trusts; Trusts
CFO: Shirley Hsing
Chf Rad: Michael Doner
Pathlgst: Joan T Hoffpauir
Pharmcst: Heather Montz

NORTH OKALOOSA MEDICAL CENTER
See CRESTVIEW HOSPITAL CORP

D-U-N-S 19-732-2704
NORTH OKLAHOMA COUNTY MENTAL HEALTH CENTER
4336 Nw 50th St, Oklahoma City, OK 73112
Tel (405) 858-2700 *Founded/Ownrshp* 1981
Sales 18.0MM *EMP* 410
Accts Bkd Llp Tulsa Oklahoma
SIC 8093 Mental health clinic, outpatient; Mental health clinic, outpatient
CEO: Randy Tate
**CFO:* Butch Rice

D-U-N-S 04-664-4449
NORTH OLMSTED CITY SCHOOL DISTRICT
BOARD OF EDUCATION OFFICE
27425 Butternut Ridge Rd, North Olmsted, OH 44070-3154
Tel (440) 779-3549 *Founded/Ownrshp* 1945
Sales 31.3MM^E *EMP* 670
Accts Dave Yost-Auditor Of State Cl
SIC 8211 Public elementary school; Public junior high school; Public senior high school; Public elementary school; Public junior high school; Public senior high school
**Treas:* Robert Matson

D-U-N-S 02-821-7743
NORTH ORANGE COUNTY COMMUNITY COLLEGE DISTRICT
CYPRESS COLLEGE
1830 W Romneya Dr, Anaheim, CA 92801-1819
Tel (714) 808-4500 *Founded/Ownrshp* 1964
Sales 94.7MM^E *EMP* 2,567
Accts Vavrinek Trine Day & Co Llp
SIC 8222 Community college; Community college
Bd of Dir: Michael Matsuda
Trst: Donna Miller
VP: Molly McClanahan
Exec: Jennifer Perez
Dist Mgr: Fred Rocha
Off Admin: Santiago Galvis
IT Man: Rodrigo Garcia
IT Man: Kashu Vyas

D-U-N-S 07-606-1076
NORTH ORANGE COUNTY REGIONAL OCCUPATIONAL PROGRAM
NOCROP
385 N Muller St, Anaheim, CA 92801-5445
Tel (714) 502-5800 *Founded/Ownrshp* 1971
Sales 18.4MM^E *EMP* 400
SIC 8331 Vocational training agency; Vocational training agency
Sys Mgr: Julie Dentler
Pr Dir: Pat Hansmeyer

NORTH OTTAWA COMMUNITY HEALTH
See NORTH OTTAWA COMMUNITY HOSPITAL

D-U-N-S 02-090-2235
NORTH OTTAWA COMMUNITY HOSPITAL (MI)
NORTH OTTAWA COMMUNITY HEALTH
1309 Sheldon Rd, Grand Haven, MI 49417-2488
Tel (616) 842-3600 *Founded/Ownrshp* 1960
Sales 67.9MM *EMP* 540
Accts Cliftonlarsonallen Llp Minnea

SIC 8062 General medical & surgical hospitals; General medical & surgical hospitals
Pr: Shelley Yaklin
COO: Cheryl Foster
**CFO:* Donald Longpre
CFO: Donald Longtree
Treas: Richard Yount
VP: Frederic Bemmelen
VP: Mark Bitz
VP: Jevne Conover
Dir Rx: Darcy Tussing
CIO: Joe Abbott
CIO: John Bosco

D-U-N-S 05-497-0769
NORTH PACIFIC INSURANCE CO
(*Suby of* LIBERTY NORTHWEST INSURANCE CORP) ★
1 Liberty Ctr, Portland, OR 97232-2030
Tel (503) 239-5800 *Founded/Ownrshp* 2002
Sales NA *EMP* 350
SIC 6331 Automobile insurance; Fire, marine & casualty insurance & carriers; Burglary & theft insurance; Automobile insurance; Fire, marine & casualty insurance & carriers; Burglary & theft insurance
Pr: Larry Becker
**CFO:* Jim McKittrick
**VP:* Mark Backstrom
**VP:* Tom Becker
**VP:* John Shaw
**VP:* Jim Vavrek

D-U-N-S 04-195-6012 EXP
NORTH PACIFIC PAPER CORP
NORPAC
3001 Indl Way, Longview, WA 98632
Tel (360) 636-6400 *Founded/Ownrshp* 2003
Sales 530.0MM^E *EMP* 410
SIC 2621 Newsprint paper; Newsprint paper
Pr: Paul R Whyatt
**Prin:* Tim Haynes

D-U-N-S 05-835-3525 IMP
NORTH PACIFIC SEAFOODS INC
ALASKA PACIFIC SEAFOOD
(*Suby of* MARUBENI CORPORATION)
4 Nickerson St Ste 400, Seattle, WA 98109-1699
Tel (206) 726-9900 *Founded/Ownrshp* 1979
Sales 202.4MM^E *EMP* 1,200
SIC 2091 Canned & cured fish & seafoods; Canned & cured fish & seafoods
CEO: Masayuki Yano
**Pr:* Tomonobu Miki
**VP:* Jeff Backlund
VP: Luz Ignacio

D-U-N-S 78-672-2673
NORTH PALM HYUNDAI LLC
3703 Northlake Blvd, Palm Beach Gardens, FL 33403-1629
Tel (561) 721-3800 *Founded/Ownrshp* 2006
Sales 22.7MM^E *EMP* 100
SIC 5511 Automobiles, new & used; Automobiles, new & used

D-U-N-S 03-760-4857
NORTH PALOS SCHOOL DISTRICT 117
NORTH PALOS SCHOOL DST 117
7825 W 103rd St Ste 2, Palos Hills, IL 60465-1677
Tel (708) 233-8200 *Founded/Ownrshp* 1958
Sales 43.7MM *EMP* 350
Accts Knutte & Associates Pc Dar
SIC 8211 Public elementary school; Public elementary school
Prin: Jeannie Stathowiak

NORTH PALOS SCHOOL DST 117
See NORTH PALOS SCHOOL DISTRICT 117

NORTH PARK
See PARK NORTH LINCOLN-MERCURY INC

NORTH PARK LEXUS
See KAHLIG MOTOR CO

NORTH PARK TOYOTA SAN ANTONIO
See PARK NORTH SOUTH TEXAS INC

D-U-N-S 03-200-8005
NORTH PARK TRANSPORTATION CO INC
5150 Columbine St, Denver, CO 80216-2305
Tel (303) 295-0300 *Founded/Ownrshp* 1944
Sales 71.1MM^E *EMP* 350^E
SIC 4213 Trucking, except local; Contract haulers; Trucking, except local; Contract haulers
Pr: Peter Kooi
**Ch:* Blaine Burt

D-U-N-S 06-996-3312
NORTH PARK UNIVERSITY
2543 W Cullom Ave, Chicago, IL 60618-1501
Tel (773) 244-6200 *Founded/Ownrshp* 1891
Sales 94.3MM *EMP* 375
SIC 8221 College, except junior; Theological seminary; College, except junior; Theological seminary
Pr: David G Horner
**Pr:* David Parkyn
Ofcr: Frederick Brehmer
Ofcr: Tracy Byerly
Ofcr: Thomas Crowley
Ofcr: Charisma Eaglin
Ofcr: Michael Flynn
Ofcr: William Greene
Ofcr: Kevin Haas
Ofcr: Randall Hiller
Ofcr: Latrice Jones
Ofcr: Edward Kane
Ofcr: Frank Keller
Ofcr: Matthew Kennedy
Ofcr: Jimmy Krklus
Ofcr: Jeesu Lee
Ofcr: Gerald Murphy
Ofcr: Candace Nicholas
Ofcr: Joseph Pedersen
Ofcr: Brian Richards
Ofcr: Dina Rosellini
Board of Directors: Alfred Johnson

NORTH PENN BANK
See WAYNE BANK

NORTH PENN MAZDA-VOLKSWAGEN
See PENN NORTH IMPORTS INC

D-U-N-S 08-079-8762
NORTH PENN YOUNG MENS CHRISTIAN ASSOCIATION
YMCA
2506 N Broad St Ste 208, Colmar, PA 18915-9439
Tel (215) 368-1601 *Founded/Ownrshp* 1987
Sales 11.8MM^E *EMP* 300
SIC 8641 7991 8351 7032 8322 Youth organizations; Physical fitness facilities; Child day care services; Youth camps; Individual & family services; Youth organizations; Physical fitness facilities; Child day care services; Youth camps; Individual & family services
CEO: Robert Gallagher
CFO: Mary Luxton
Dir IT: Dan Keene
Pgrm Dir: Dan Silverman

D-U-N-S 05-051-8315
NORTH PIERCEY INC (CA)
PIERCEY TOYOTA
950 Thompson St, Milpitas, CA 95035-6296
Tel (408) 436-8890 *Founded/Ownrshp* 1969, 1988
Sales 26.0MM^E *EMP* 110
SIC 5511 5531 5521 5013 Automobiles, new & used; Automotive & home supply stores; Used car dealers; Motor vehicle supplies & new parts; Automobiles, new & used; Automotive & home supply stores; Used car dealers; Motor vehicle supplies & new parts
CEO: William R Piercey
**Pr:* Artus V Whicker
**Sec:* Tom A Chadwell
VP: William R Piecey

D-U-N-S 19-301-1459
NORTH PIKE SCHOOL DISTRICT
1036 Jaguar Trl, Summit, MS 39666-8188
Tel (601) 276-2216 *Founded/Ownrshp* 1962
Sales 16.4MM^E *EMP* 316
Accts Patrick E Lowery And Associate
SIC 8211 Public elementary & secondary schools; School board; Public elementary & secondary schools; School board
Schl Brd P: Freddie Deer

D-U-N-S 00-791-0953
■ **NORTH PITTSBURG TELEPHONE CO** (PA)
(*Suby of* NORTH PITTSBURGH SYSTEMS INC) ★
4008 Gibsonia Rd, Gibsonia, PA 15044-9311
Tel (724) 443-9600 *Founded/Ownrshp* 1906, 1985
Sales 25.2MM^E *EMP* 204^E
SIC 4813 Local telephone communications; Local telephone communications
Pr: Bob Udell
Pr: John Brungo
Pr: Christine Olson
Pr: Vicki Preston
Pr: Karen Terzich
**Ch:* Charles E Thoma Sr
VP: Mary Lewis
VP: Mark Lipsius
VP: Mike Rovnak
Adm Dir: Konrad Kammerer

D-U-N-S 14-818-6844
■ **NORTH PITTSBURGH SYSTEMS INC**
(*Suby of* CONSOLIDATED COMMUNICATIONS HOLDINGS INC) ★
4008 Gibsonia Rd, Gibsonia, PA 15044-9311
Tel (724) 443-9600 *Founded/Ownrshp* 2007
Sales 115.8MM^E *EMP* 357
SIC 4813 5065 Telephone communication, except radio; ; Telephone equipment; Telephone communication, except radio; ; Telephone equipment
Pr: Harry R Brown
CFO: Allen P Kimble
Treas: David Doedtman
Treas: Matthew D Poleski
VP: N William Barthlow
VP: Frank A McEfe
VP: Mark Steward
IT Man: Albert W Weigand
VP Opers: Harry Bown
VP Sls: Frank A Macefe

D-U-N-S 03-716-9810
NORTH PLAINFIELD BOARD OF EDUCATION INC
33 Mountain Ave, North Plainfield, NJ 07060-4101
Tel (908) 769-6060 *Founded/Ownrshp* 1885
Sales 21.3MM^E *EMP* 402
SIC 8211 Public elementary & secondary schools; Public elementary & secondary schools
Dir Sec: Stuart Buckman
MIS Dir: Ronald Fisher

NORTH PLAINFIELD NISSAN
See JERSEY NISSAN LLC

D-U-N-S 07-980-6919
NORTH PLAINFIELD SCHOOL DISTRICT
33 Mountain Ave, North Plainfield, NJ 07060-4101
Tel (908) 769-6000 *Founded/Ownrshp* 2015
Sales 5.7MM^E *EMP* 432^E
SIC 8211 Public elementary & secondary schools

D-U-N-S 00-585-5267
NORTH PLAINS ELECTRIC COOPERATIVE INC (TX)
14585 Us Hwy 83, Perryton, TX 79070
Tel (806) 435-5482 *Founded/Ownrshp* 1944
Sales 42.5MM *EMP* 38
SIC 4911 Distribution, electric power; Distribution, electric power
Pr: James F Greene
Bd of Dir: Steve Waide
IT Man: Jaime Pugh
IT Man: Cynthia Turner

D-U-N-S 01-029-3184
NORTH PLAINS ENERGY LLC
1888 N Sherman St Ste 375, Denver, CO 80203-1158
Tel (303) 800-5100 *Founded/Ownrshp* 2007

Sales 22.7MM^E *EMP* 14
SIC 1382 Oil & gas exploration services
Pr: Clif Simonson
COO: Clayton Miller

D-U-N-S 02-017-3340
NORTH PLATTE NEBRASKA HOSPITAL CORP
GREAT PLAINS HEALTH
601 W Leota St, North Platte, NE 69101-6525
Tel (308) 534-9310 *Founded/Ownrshp* 1975
Sales 151.7MM *EMP* 900^E
Accts Seim Johnson Llp Omaha Ne
SIC 8062 8082 General medical & surgical hospitals; Home health care services; General medical & surgical hospitals; Home health care services
CEO: Melvin McNea
Pr: Lance Arterburn
COO: Brian Bielicki
CFO: Lana Webster
VP: Pamela Sweeney
Dir Surg: Michael Feagler
Snr Mgr: Ryan Rathjen

D-U-N-S 03-923-3374
NORTH PLATTE PUBLIC SCHOOLS
301 W F St, North Platte, NE 69101-5201
Tel (308) 535-7100 *Founded/Ownrshp* 1873
Sales 23.2MM^E *EMP* 569
SIC 8211 Public senior high school; Public combined elementary & secondary school; Public elementary school; School board; Public senior high school; Public combined elementary & secondary school; Public elementary school; School board
Prin: James Ayres
VP: Darrel Smith

D-U-N-S 02-604-2713
NORTH POCONO SCHOOL DISTRICT
701 Church St, Moscow, PA 18444-9391
Tel (570) 842-7659 *Founded/Ownrshp* 1959
Sales 29.3MM^E *EMP* 400
Accts Murphy Dougherty & Company Sc
SIC 8211 Public elementary & secondary schools; School board; Public elementary & secondary schools; School board
COO: Michelle Koelsch
Exec: Robert Deremer
Exec: Terrence Gallagher
Exec: Michael Lafave
Exec: Rose Warner
IT Man: John Brundage
Sls&Mrk Ex: Judith Fritz
Schl Brd P: Ralph Colo
Schl Brd P: Howard Muntosh
Board of Directors: Michael Milewski, Gary Reigal, Maureen Richards, Jacob Wentland Meetings A

D-U-N-S 04-492-0499
NORTH POINT BANCSHARES INC
3333 Deposit Dr Ne # 310, Grand Rapids, MI 49546-1470
Tel (616) 656-9924 *Founded/Ownrshp* 1998
Sales NA *EMP* 167
SIC 6712 Bank holding companies; Bank holding companies
Pr: Charles Williams
**VP:* Randy Ferris

D-U-N-S 10-788-9909
NORTH POINT CHRYSLER JEEP INC
7726 N Point Blvd, Winston Salem, NC 27106-3310
Tel (336) 759-0599 *Founded/Ownrshp* 1993
Sales 35.3MM^E *EMP* 90
SIC 5511 Automobiles, new & used; Automobiles, new & used
Pr: Jeffrey Michael
**Sec:* David T Neill
**VP:* Chester A Michael III
**VP:* Junie Michael
Sls Mgr: Gene Lashley
Sales Asso: Charles Walker

NORTH POINT COMMUNITY CHURCH
See NORTH POINT MINISTRIES INC

D-U-N-S 62-533-0642
■ **NORTH POINT FORD INC**
LINCOLN MERCURY
(*Suby of* ASBURY AUTOMOTIVE ARKANSAS DEALERSHIP HOLDINGS LLC) ★
4400 Landers Rd, North Little Rock, AR 72117-2526
Tel (501) 945-8240 *Founded/Ownrshp* 1991
Sales 42.1MM^E *EMP* 175
SIC 5511 7532 Automobiles, new & used; Body shop, automotive; Automobiles, new & used; Body shop, automotive
Pr: Gerry A Riser
**Ch Bd:* Thomas Mc Larty
**VP:* Jack Caldwell
Genl Mgr: Jeff Boyce
Dir IT: Mark Fink
Sls Mgr: David Manos

D-U-N-S 84-032-7860
NORTH POINT LINCOLN-MERCURY INC
4336 Landers Rd, North Little Rock, AR 72117-2525
Tel (501) 945-3200 *Founded/Ownrshp* 1991
Sales 23.0MM *EMP* 20
SIC 5511 5521 7532 Automobiles, new & used; Automobiles, used cars only; Body shop, automotive; Automobiles, new & used; Automobiles, used cars only; Body shop, automotive
Pr: David Surguine
Sls Mgr: Larry Parks
Sales Asso: Josh Alexander
Sales Asso: Nabil Asma
Sales Asso: Ronald Brown
Sales Asso: Bruce Davis
Sales Asso: Carolyn Denney
Sales Asso: Gary Ford
Sales Asso: Bill Fortson
Sales Asso: Basel Khalil
Sales Asso: Kylee Malkmus

NORTH POINT MAZDA
See NP MZD LLC

D-U-N-S 96-673-3602
NORTH POINT MINISTRIES INC
NORTH POINT COMMUNITY CHURCH
4350 N Point Pkwy, Alpharetta, GA 30022-4101
Tel (678) 892-5000 *Founded/Ownrshp* 1995
Sales 30.5MM^E *EMP* 300
SIC 8661 Community church; Community church
CEO: Robert P Bryant
COO: Jason Gray
**CFO:* Gary A Delaney
Web Dev: Chris Ames

D-U-N-S 18-475-4948
NORTH POINTE HOLDINGS CORP
(*Suby of* QBE AMERICAS) ★
1 General Dr, Sun Prairie, WI 53596-0001
Tel (248) 358-1171 *Founded/Ownrshp* 2008
Sales NA *EMP* 268
SIC 6411 6331 Property & casualty insurance agent; Fire, marine & casualty insurance; Fire, marine & casualty insurance: stock; Property damage insurance; Automobile insurance; Property & casualty insurance agent; Fire, marine & casualty insurance; Fire, marine & casualty insurance: stock; Property damage insurance; Automobile insurance
Ch Bd: James G Petcoff
**COO:* B Matthew Petcoff
CFO: Brian J Roney
Treas: John H Berry
Ex VP: Matt Pettcoff
Sr VP: Bradford T Lyons

D-U-N-S 07-865-8030
NORTH POINTE INSURANCE CO
116 Pine St, Harrisburg, PA 17101-1244
Tel (248) 358-1171 *Founded/Ownrshp* 2012
Sales NA *EMP* 2^E
SIC 6411 Insurance agents, brokers & service; Insurance agents, brokers & service

D-U-N-S 17-832-3457
NORTH POINTE INSURANCE CO
(*Suby of* NORTH POINTE FINANCIAL SERVICES INC)
28819 Franklin Rd Ste 300, Southfield, MI 48034-1656
Tel (248) 358-1171 *Founded/Ownrshp* 1991
Sales NA *EMP* 110
SIC 6411 Property & casualty insurance agent
Ch Bd: Jim Petcoff
**CFO:* John N Barry
CFO: Brian Roney
Ex VP: B Petcoff

NORTH POLE PHOTO
See GREG HASYN

NORTH PONTOTOC
See PONTOTOC COUNTY SCHOOL DISTRICT

D-U-N-S 10-007-1075
NORTH PROVIDENCE SCHOOL DEPARTMENT
2240 Mineral Spring Ave, North Providence, RI 02911-1729
Tel (401) 233-1100 *Founded/Ownrshp* 1800
Sales 0.6 *EMP* 480
SIC 8211 9411 Public elementary & secondary schools; Administration of educational programs; Public elementary & secondary schools; Administration of educational programs
MIS Dir: Ralph Nahigian

D-U-N-S 62-387-8035
NORTH PUGET SOUND CENTER FOR SLEEP DISORDERS LLC
ASSOCIATE EVERETT CLINIC PS
1728 W Marine View Dr, Everett, WA 98201-2094
Tel (425) 339-5460 *Founded/Ownrshp* 2004
Sales 17.0MM^E *EMP* 2,500^E
SIC 8011 Oncologist
COO: Jeff Bissey

NORTH QUINCY
See LIVERMORE VALLEY JOINT UNIFIED SCHOOL DISTRICT

D-U-N-S 07-833-7938
NORTH RANGE BEHAVIORAL HEALTH
1300 N 17th Ave, Greeley, CO 80631-9584
Tel (970) 347-2120 *Founded/Ownrshp* 1971
Sales 23.9MM *EMP* 280
Accts Anderson & Whitney Pc Greeley
SIC 8093 Mental health clinic, outpatient; Mental health clinic, outpatient
Pr: Josh Noonan
**Treas:* David Owen
Bd of Dir: Rebecca K Conway
**VP:* Keith Abbott
**Ex Dir:* Larry D Pottorff
Snr Mgr: Jason Dobson
Snr Mgr: Jayne Hayes

D-U-N-S 13-066-1148
NORTH REACH HEALTH CARE
3120 Riverside Ave, Marinette, WI 54143-1123
Tel (715) 732-2075 *Founded/Ownrshp* 2001
Sales 20.2MM *EMP* 65
SIC 8011 Fertility specialist, physician; Fertility specialist, physician
CEO: John M Blackburn
Dir Rx: Carol Hipke

D-U-N-S 10-003-2606
NORTH READING PUBLIC SCHOOL DISTRICT
191 Park St, North Reading, MA 01864-2324
Tel (978) 664-7810 *Founded/Ownrshp* 1996
Sales 30.0MM *EMP* 300
SIC 8211 Public elementary & secondary schools; Public elementary & secondary schools

NORTH READING TRANSPORTATION
See NRT BUS INC

NORTH RIDGE HEALTH AND REHAB
See NORTH RIDGE SKILLED LLC

D-U-N-S 01-033-1726
NORTH RIDGE SKILLED LLC
NORTH RIDGE HEALTH AND REHAB
5430 Boone Ave N, Minneapolis, MN 55428-3615
Tel (763) 592-3000 *Founded/Ownrshp* 1966
Sales 85.2MM^E *EMP* 1,000^E
SIC 6513 8051 Retirement hotel operation; Skilled nursing care facilities; Retirement hotel operation; Skilled nursing care facilities
Sr VP: Tina Thomas
**CEO:* Eric Neetenbeek
Off Mgr: Lisa Padgett
Dir IT: Debbie Deutsch
HC Dir: Pam Haase

D-U-N-S 08-014-1930
NORTH RIDGEVILLE CITY SCHOOL DISTRICT
5490 Mills Creek Ln, North Ridgeville, OH 44039-2339
Tel (440) 327-4444 *Founded/Ownrshp* 1900
Sales 24.8MM^E *EMP* 400
SIC 8211 Public senior high school; Public junior high school; Public elementary school; Kindergarten; Public senior high school; Public junior high school; Public elementary school; Kindergarten
Ofcr: Calvin Cross
MIS Dir: David Pritt
IT Man: Jack Henry

NORTH RIVER BOATS
See NW BEND BOATS LLC

D-U-N-S 07-930-9233
NORTH RIVER INSURANCE CO (NJ)
(*Suby of* CRUM & FORSTER INC) ★
305 Madison Ave, Morristown, NJ 07960-6117
Tel (973) 490-6600 *Founded/Ownrshp* 1822, 1993
Sales NA *EMP* 400
SIC 6331 Property damage insurance; Property damage insurance
Pr: Nikolas Antonopoulos
Bd of Dir: Diana Cossetti
Sr VP: Robert Himmer
Sr VP: Martha Van Hise
CIO: Nicole Bennett
Mktg Mgr: Pam Gaddy
Snr Mgr: Martin Horsman

NORTH ROCKLAND CENTL SCHL DST
See HAVERSTRAW STONY POINT CENTRAL SCHOOL DISTRICT INC

D-U-N-S 08-074-8619
NORTH ROSE-WOLCOTT CENTRAL SCHOOL DISTRICT (NY)
11669 Salter Colvin Rd, Wolcott, NY 14590-9376
Tel (315) 594-3141 *Founded/Ownrshp* 1967
Sales 16.2MM *EMP* 450
SIC 8211 Public elementary school; Public junior high school; Public senior high school; Public elementary school; Public junior high school; Public senior high school
Prin: Mary A Boogaard
IT Man: Kaaren Thompson
Netwrk Mgr: Kevin Coons
Schl Brd P: Kari Durham
Schl Brd P: Edward Megan
Psych: Emily D Meisch

D-U-N-S 02-560-5288
NORTH ROYALTON CITY SCHOOL DISTRICT
6579 Royalton Rd, Cleveland, OH 44133-4925
Tel (440) 237-8800 *Founded/Ownrshp* 1821
Sales 51.8MM *EMP* 500
Accts Grant Thornton Llp Cleveland
SIC 8211 Public elementary & secondary schools; Public elementary & secondary schools
Adm Dir: Edward Jaykel
MIS Dir: Bruce Bradley
IT Man: Kathleen Spirakus
Teacher Pr: Gary Puntel
HC Dir: Carolyn Baetjer

D-U-N-S 01-366-6649
NORTH SACRAMENTO SCHOOL DISTRICT
(*Suby of* TWIN RIVERS UNIFIED SCHOOL DISTRICT) ★
670 Dixieanne Ave, Sacramento, CA 95815-3023
Tel (916) 263-8300 *Founded/Ownrshp* 2007
Sales 16.4MM^E *EMP* 700
SIC 8211 Public elementary & secondary schools; Public elementary & secondary schools
Bd of Dir: Vern Coleman
Bd of Dir: Carol Wheeler
Prin: Richard Draeger
Prin: Tl Anne W Rios

D-U-N-S 05-998-0441 IMP/EXP
NORTH SAFETY PRODUCTS LLC
2000 Plainfield Pike, Cranston, RI 02921-2012
Tel (401) 943-4400 *Founded/Ownrshp* 2008
Sales NA *EMP* 1,050^E
SIC 3842

D-U-N-S 06-204-5984 IMP
NORTH SAILS GROUP LLC
NORTH TECHNOLOGY GROUP
(*Suby of* WINDWAY CAPITAL CORP) ★
125 Old Gate Ln Ste 7, Milford, CT 06460-3611
Tel (203) 874-7548 *Founded/Ownrshp* 2000
Sales 63.1MM^E *EMP* 300
SIC 2394 2211 Sails: made from purchased materials; Sail cloth; Sails: made from purchased materials; Sail cloth
CEO: Thomas A Whidden
**CFO:* Jay Kiraly
Treas: Thomas Nuzzaci
VP: Bruno Dubois
VP: Dan Neri
Genl Mgr: Robin Morgan
Off Mgr: Catalina Cuenca
Software D: George Sheehy
Mfg Dir: Rodrigo Meireles
Prd Mgr: Glen Ford
Prd Mgr: Bacci Sgarbossa

D-U-N-S 06-937-7468
NORTH SAINT PAUL MAPLEWOOD & OAKDALE SCHOOL DISTRICT 622
2520 12th Ave E, Saint Paul, MN 55109-2420
Tel (651) 748-7420 *Founded/Ownrshp* 2002
Sales 145.0MM *EMP* 69
Accts Malloy Montague Karnowski R
SIC 8211 Public elementary & secondary schools; Public elementary & secondary schools
Teacher Pr: Keith Gray
Psych: Debra Biddick

D-U-N-S 08-400-6675
NORTH SALEM CENTRAL SCHOOL DISTRICT
230 June Rd, North Salem, NY 10560-1211
Tel (914) 669-5414 *Founded/Ownrshp* 1925
Sales 38.0MM *EMP* 240
SIC 8211 Public combined elementary & secondary school; Public combined elementary & secondary school

D-U-N-S 07-310-5678
NORTH SANPETE SCHOOL DISTRICT (INC)
220 E 700 S, Mount Pleasant, UT 84647-2013
Tel (435) 462-2485 *Founded/Ownrshp* 1890
Sales 17.8MM *EMP* 350
Accts Gilbert & Stewart Cpa S Prov
SIC 8211 Public elementary & secondary schools; Public elementary & secondary schools
Bd of Dir: Rickie Stewart
HC Dir: Alice Sperry

D-U-N-S 01-025-4282
NORTH SCOTT COMMUNITY SCHOOL DISTRICT INC (IA)
251 E Iowa St, Eldridge, IA 52748-1917
Tel (563) 285-3104 *Founded/Ownrshp* 1958
Sales 32.0MM *EMP* 653
SIC 8211 Public combined elementary & secondary school; Public senior high school; Public combined elementary & secondary school; Public senior high school

D-U-N-S 79-317-7465
NORTH SEA ASSOCIATES LLC
HAMPTONS CENTER FOR
64 County Road 39, Southampton, NY 11968-5215
Tel (631) 702-1000 *Founded/Ownrshp* 2005
Sales 37.0MM *EMP* 1
SIC 8051 Skilled nursing care facilities
Prin: Robert T Kolman
Dietician: Christine Merrihew

D-U-N-S 12-270-2392
NORTH SECOND STREET STEEL SUPPLY INC
2212 N 2nd St, Minneapolis, MN 55411-2207
Tel (612) 522-6626 *Founded/Ownrshp* 1984
Sales 30.9MM^E *EMP* 27
SIC 5051 Steel
CEO: Larry R Rosen

D-U-N-S 80-792-0368
NORTH SHORE - LONG ISLAND JEWISH HEALTH SYSTEM INC
NSLIJ
145 Community Dr, Great Neck, NY 11021-5502
Tel (516) 465-8000 *Founded/Ownrshp* 1997
Sales 4.8MMM^E *EMP* 5,700
SIC 8082 8062 Hospital, medical school affiliation; Home health care services; Home health care services; Hospital, medical school affiliation
Ch Bd: Richard D Goldstein
Pr: Michael J Dowling
COO: Mark J Solazzo
CFO: Robert Shapiro
CFO: Robert S Shapiro
Trst: Aim E Merszei
Ofcr: David L Battinelli MD
Ex VP: Lawrence G Smith
Sr VP: Joseph Cabral
Sr VP: Kevin Dwyer
Sr VP: Howard Gold
Sr VP: Arthur Klein MD
Sr VP: Jeff Kraut
Sr VP: Karen Nelson
Sr VP: Gene Tangney
Sr VP: Keith Thompson
VP: Donna Armellino
VP: Jeremy Boal
VP: John Bosco
VP: John Kane
VP: Jeffrey A Kraut

D-U-N-S 00-705-2125
NORTH SHORE ANIMAL LEAGUE
17 Lewyt St, Port Washington, NY 11050-3756
Tel (516) 944-5148 *Founded/Ownrshp* 2009
Sales 35.6MM *EMP* 4^E
SIC 0742 Veterinary services, specialties

NORTH SHORE ARC
See NORTHEAST ARC INC

D-U-N-S 96-785-2612
NORTH SHORE BANCORP
248 Andover St, Peabody, MA 01960-1502
Tel (978) 532-4200 *Founded/Ownrshp* 2011
Sales NA *EMP* 158^E
SIC 6022 6163 6712 State commercial banks; Loan brokers; Bank holding companies
CEO: David Laflamme
**Pr:* Kevin M Tierney Sr
Sr VP: Salerno Jerome
Sr VP: James Muse

D-U-N-S 09-743-5606
NORTH SHORE BANK A CO-OPERATIVE BANK
(*Suby of* NORTH SHORE BANCORP) ★
248 Andover St, Peabody, MA 01960-1502
Tel (978) 532-4200 *Founded/Ownrshp* 1888
Sales NA *EMP* 100
SIC 6022 6163 State trust companies accepting deposits, commercial; Loan brokers; State trust companies accepting deposits, commercial; Loan brokers

CEO: David J Laflamme
**Pr:* Kevin M Tierney Sr
**Treas:* George J Sophinos
Sr VP: James Muse

D-U-N-S 06-044-4254
NORTH SHORE BANK F S B
15700 W Bluemound Rd # 1, Brookfield, WI 53005-6073
Tel (262) 785-1600 *Founded/Ownrshp* 1923
Sales NA *EMP* 500
SIC 6035 Federal savings banks; Federal savings banks
Pr: James F Mc Kenna
Pr: Gina Bontempo
Pr: Margie Brusa
Pr: Jerry Harmann
Pr: Michael Krause
Pr: Ron Olson
Pr: Barb Wisneski
CFO: Drew Wallach
Chf Cred: Larry Wickter
Ofcr: Mary Blazer
VP: Chris Boland
VP: Margaret Capper
VP: Lyneen Fischer
VP: Eric Freeman
VP: Murray Friedman
VP: Tom Hughes
VP: James Krcmarik
VP: Dorothy Krupa
VP: Laurie Maduscha
VP: Erika Milosevich
VP: Richard Nadolski

NORTH SHORE BANK OF COMMERCE
See NORTH SHORE FINANCIAL CORP

D-U-N-S 01-240-9900 IMP
NORTH SHORE BOTTLING CO INC
VITARROZ
1900 Linden Blvd, Brooklyn, NY 11207-6806
Tel (718) 272-8900 *Founded/Ownrshp* 1991
Sales 42.5MM^E *EMP* 95^E
SIC 5181 5149 2086 Beer & other fermented malt liquors; Soft drinks; Juices; Coffee & tea; Bottled & canned soft drinks; Beer & other fermented malt liquors; Soft drinks; Juices; Coffee & tea; Bottled & canned soft drinks
Ch: Eric Miller
**Pr:* Marilyn Miller
**CFO:* William Schneible
Sls Mgr: Michael Harford

D-U-N-S 06-031-9183
NORTH SHORE CENTRAL SCHOOL DISTRICT
112 Franklin Ave, Sea Cliff, NY 11579-1764
Tel (516) 277-7800 *Founded/Ownrshp* 1967
Sales 27.1MM^E *EMP* 425
SIC 8211 Public elementary school; Public junior high school; Public senior high school; Public elementary school; Public junior high school; Public senior high school
Pr Dir: Shelly Newman
Schl Brd P: Herman Berliner
Board of Directors: Nancy Benchimol, Brian Boehm, Katherine Grande, Nancy Hall, Robert McMahon President, Barbara Palermo, Amy Tabor

NORTH SHORE COMMUNITY BANK & TRUST
See WINTRUST BANK

D-U-N-S 15-994-9411
NORTH SHORE COMMUNITY COLLEGE
1 Ferncroft Rd, Danvers, MA 01923-4017
Tel (978) 762-4000 *Founded/Ownrshp* 1983
Sales 39.1MM *EMP* 600
SIC 8222 Community college; Community college
Pr: Patricia Jentile
Ofcr: Mike Monagle
Sr VP: Joseph Riley
VP: Mark Reimer
CIO: Gary Ham
HC Dir: Jennifer Kirk
Snr Mgr: Douglas Puska

D-U-N-S 80-318-8572
NORTH SHORE COMMUNITY SERVICES INC
300 Community Dr, Manhasset, NY 11030-3816
Tel (516) 562-0100 *Founded/Ownrshp* 1972
Sales 30.8MM *EMP* 14^E
SIC 6512 Commercial & industrial building operation; Commercial & industrial building operation
Pr: Michael Dowling
**Pr:* John S T Gallagher
**CFO:* Bob Shapiro

D-U-N-S 19-722-0718
NORTH SHORE FINANCIAL CORP
NORTH SHORE BANK OF COMMERCE
131 W Superior St, Duluth, MN 55802-3026
Tel (218) 722-4784 *Founded/Ownrshp* 1985
Sales NA *EMP* 277
SIC 6022 State commercial banks; State commercial banks
Ch: Douglas H Lewis
**Pr:* Larry D Johnson

D-U-N-S 00-693-6306
■ **NORTH SHORE GAS CO** (IL)
(*Suby of* PEOPLES ENERGY LLC) ★
200 E Randolph St # 2200, Chicago, IL 60601-6433
Tel (312) 240-4000 *Founded/Ownrshp* 1963
Sales 156.8MM^E *EMP* 335
SIC 4924 Natural gas distribution; Natural gas distribution
CEO: Lawrence T Borgard
**Pr:* Willard S Evans Jr
**CFO:* Joseph P O Leary
CFO: Joseph Oleary
Treas: Douglas M Ruschau
**VP:* Diane L Ford
VP: Dave Harpole
VP: Thomas Nardi
**VP:* James F Schott
Genl Couns: Theodore R Tetzlaff

Board of Directors: Thomas P Meinz, Phillip M Mikulsky, Charles A Schrock

NORTH SHORE LIJ
See FRANKLIN HOSPITAL

D-U-N-S 10-787-5007
NORTH SHORE LIJ HEALTH SYSTEM FEDERAL CREDIT UNION
NSLIJHSFCU
350 Jericho Tpke Ste 103, Jericho, NY 11753-1317
Tel (516) 301-3040 *Founded/Ownrshp* 1972
Sales NA *EMP* 23
SIC 6061 Federal credit unions
CEO: Joann Doyle
**Ch:* Gary Leonard
VP: Brian McKenna
VP: Deborah Schiff
Prgrm Mgr: Stacey Conklin
Doctor: Eran Bornstein
Doctor: Robert Dring
Doctor: Edward Hill

D-U-N-S 07-846-2611 EXP
■ **NORTH SHORE MEDICAL CENTER INC**
(*Suby of* TENET HEALTHCARE CORPORATION)
1100 Nw 95th St, Miami, FL 33150-2038
Tel (305) 835-6000 *Founded/Ownrshp* 1952
Sales 111.0MM^E *EMP* 1,100^E
SIC 8062 General medical & surgical hospitals; General medical & surgical hospitals
CEO: Manny Linares
Chf OB: Carlos Szajnert
V Ch: Alan Silbert
COO: Leonard Freehauf
COO: Patricia Sechia
**COO:* Joshua Tetillio
**CFO:* Alex Fernandes
Dir OR: Maria Ruiz
Dir Inf Cn: Veronica Torres
Opers Mgr: Judi Rankin
Nurse Mgr: Ruth Figueroa

D-U-N-S 62-065-5746
NORTH SHORE MEDICAL CENTER INC
(*Suby of* PARTNERS HEALTHCARE SYSTEM INC) ★
81 Highland Ave, Salem, MA 01970-2768
Tel (978) 741-1200 *Founded/Ownrshp* 1997
Sales 395.2MM *EMP* 5,000^E
SIC 8062 General medical & surgical hospitals; General medical & surgical hospitals
Ch: Terence McGinnis
**Pr:* Robert G Norton
**Treas:* John V Gandolfo
**V Ch Bd:* Richard Osgood
Sr VP: Mary J Gagnon
VP: Bea Thibedeau
CTO: Christopher Maccarini
MIS Dir: Patricia Spongberg
QA Dir: Karen Conti
QA Dir: Virginia Dolan-Horgan
Sfty Mgr: Paul Raucci

NORTH SHORE MEDICAL CLINIC
See DOOR COUNTY MEMORIAL HOSPITAL FOUNDATION INC

D-U-N-S 04-158-9490
NORTH SHORE OIL CO INC
2634 State Route 49, West Monroe, NY 13167-3287
Tel (315) 676-4431 *Founded/Ownrshp* 1999
Sales 33.7MM^E *EMP* 100
Accts Viera & Associates Cpas Pc
SIC 5541 5983 5411 5013 Gasoline service stations; Fuel oil dealers; Convenience stores; Motor vehicle supplies & new parts; Gasoline service stations; Fuel oil dealers; Convenience stores; Motor vehicle supplies & new parts
Pr: Harold D Pratt
**VP:* Bill Webb

D-U-N-S 96-661-0854
NORTH SHORE PHYSICIANS GROUP INC
81 Highland Ave, Salem, MA 01970-2714
Tel (617) 724-9841 *Founded/Ownrshp* 2011
Sales 96.0MM *EMP* 4
SIC 8011 Primary care medical clinic; Primary care medical clinic
Prin: Steven E Kapfhammer

NORTH SHORE STEEL
See NORTH SHORE SUPPLY CO INC

D-U-N-S 02-663-1770 IMP
NORTH SHORE SUPPLY CO INC
NORTH SHORE STEEL
1566 Miles St, Houston, TX 77015-6319
Tel (713) 453-3533 *Founded/Ownrshp* 1955
Sales 141.9MM^E *EMP* 217
SIC 5051 5085 3441 Pipe & tubing, steel; Steel; Valves & fittings; Fabricated structural metal; Pipe & tubing, steel; Steel; Valves & fittings; Fabricated structural metal
Pr: Buzzy Bluestone
**Pr:* Burton L Bluestone
Sr VP: Curtis Parnell
VP: Tim Dodson
VP: Cindy Howard
**VP:* Stanley D Katz
Dir IT: George Wynne
IT Man: Mack Deeann
Sls Mgr: Scott Shane
Sales Asso: Shawn Martin
Sales Asso: Jay Muscovalley
Board of Directors: Lou Beth Nemzin

D-U-N-S 06-241-5290
NORTH SHORE UNIVERSITY HEALTH SYSTEM
2650 Ridge Ave, Evanston, IL 60201-1718
Tel (847) 570-2640 *Founded/Ownrshp* 2011
Sales 1.4MM *EMP* 3
SIC 8011 Offices & clinics of medical doctors
Prin: Steven Swiryn
Chf Rad: Robert Edleman
Sr VP: Harry Jones
VP: Sharon Lawrence
Dir Teleco: Bill Allroth
Dir Inf Cn: Marc-Oliver Wright

Dir Rx: Colin Boyle
Dir Bus: Mariam Zrike
Adm Dir: Holly Hawes
Adm Dir: Rhea Trbojevic
Admn Mgr: Ruth Mandel

D-U-N-S 07-236-4490
NORTH SHORE UNIVERSITY HOSPITAL (NY)
(*Suby of* NORTH SHORE - LONG ISLAND JEWISH HEALTH SYSTEM INC) ★
300 Community Dr, Manhasset, NY 11030-3876
Tel (516) 562-0100 *Founded/Ownrshp* 1946
Sales 532.2MM^E *EMP* 5,000
SIC 8062 8011 General medical & surgical hospitals; Medical centers; General medical & surgical hospitals; Medical centers
Pr: Michael J Dowling
Mng Pt: Scott Christensen
Sr VP: David L Battinelli
Dir Lab: Leonard Kahn
Assoc Dir: Shifra Atik
Assoc Dir: Riza Cioku
Assoc Dir: Anne Ferguson
Assoc Dir: Nympha Meindel
Dir Rad: Edward Wind
Dir Rx: Len Langino
Dir Rx: Sanjai Singh
Comm Man: Denise Hall

D-U-N-S 96-777-5094
NORTH SHORE-LONG ISLAND JEWISH HEALTH CARE
972 Brush Hollow Rd 5th, Westbury, NY 11590-1740
Tel (516) 876-6611 *Founded/Ownrshp* 2011
Sales 351.5MM *EMP* 2
SIC 8099 Health & allied services; Health & allied services
Prin: Filippo Petti
Doctor: Sheldong Newman MD

D-U-N-S 83-041-4798
NORTH SHORE-LONG ISLAND JEWISH HEALTH SYSTEM LABORATORIES
10 Nevada Dr, New Hyde Park, NY 11042-1114
Tel (516) 719-1000 *Founded/Ownrshp* 1997
Sales 247.2MM *EMP* 99
SIC 8734 Testing laboratories; Testing laboratories
Pr: Richard Tesoriero
Manager: Marianne Howitt

D-U-N-S 11-943-3100 IMP
NORTH SIDE IMPORTS INC
3650 W Pratt Ave, Lincolnwood, IL 60712-3724
Tel (847) 674-5550 *Founded/Ownrshp* 1986
Sales 62.0MM^E *EMP* 115
Accts Porte Brown Llc Elk Grove Vil
SIC 5013 Automotive supplies & parts; Automotive supplies & parts
Pr: Tahsinulah Jalili
Sls Mgr: Tom Frawley
Sales Asso: Rolando Morales

NORTH SKY COMMUNICATIONS, INC.
See NORTH SKY COMMUNICATIONS LLC

D-U-N-S 62-195-4361
■ **NORTH SKY COMMUNICATIONS LLC**
NORTH SKY COMMUNICATIONS, INC.
(*Suby of* DYCOM INDUSTRIES INC) ★
11818 Se Mil Pl Blvd 41, Vancouver, WA 98684
Tel (360) 254-6920 *Founded/Ownrshp* 2012
Sales 30.8MM^E *EMP* 190
SIC 1731

D-U-N-S 07-924-8290
NORTH SLOPE BOROUGH (AK)
1274 Agvik St, Barrow, AK 99723
Tel (907) 852-2611 *Founded/Ownrshp* 1972
Sales NA *EMP* 1,027
Accts Kpmg Llp Achorage Ak
SIC 9111 City & town managers' offices; ; City & town managers' offices;
Pr: Grace Rosa
Pr: Caroline Uluave
Bd of Dir: Jess McCoy
Exec: Kristine Hilderbrand
Div Mgr: Max Ahgeak
Div Mgr: Matt Dunn
Div Mgr: Maria Esparza
Div Mgr: Sarah Nicely
Div Mgr: Roberta Oviok
Div Mgr: Charlie Sakeagak
Div Mgr: Richard Ungarook

D-U-N-S 00-238-1580
NORTH SLOPE BOROUGH SCHOOL DISTRICT (AK)
NSBSD
829 Aivik St, Barrow, AK 99723
Tel (907) 852-5311 *Founded/Ownrshp* 1971
Sales 80.7MM *EMP* 625
Accts Bdo Usa Llp Anchorage Ak
SIC 8211 Public elementary & secondary schools; Public senior high school; Public junior high school; Public elementary school; Public elementary & secondary schools; Public senior high school; Public junior high school; Public elementary school
Bd of Dir: Charlotte Brower
Prin: Brad Allen
Prin: Larry Bradley
Prin: Patricia Groholski
Prin: Scott Iverson
Prin: Dorothy Jordan
Prin: Glenn Olson
Prin: Rob Picou
Prin: Stephen Pile
Prin: Phil Reese
Prin: David Sharstrom

D-U-N-S 18-417-5784
NORTH SMITHFIELD SCH DISTRICT
83 Green St, Slatersville, RI 02876
Tel (401) 769-5492 *Founded/Ownrshp* 1850
Sales 11.3MM *EMP* 403
SIC 8211 Public elementary & secondary schools; Public elementary & secondary schools
Pr: Christine Charest
IT Man: Denis Belleville

D-U-N-S 02-419-9312
NORTH SONOMA COUNTY HEALTH CARE DISTRICT
SONOMA COUNTY LAB LINK
1375 University St, Healdsburg, CA 95448-3382
Tel (707) 431-6500 *Founded/Ownrshp* 2002
Sales 40.0MM *EMP* 21
SIC 8071 Testing laboratories
CEO: Nancy Schmid
**CEO:* Dale Iversen
Off Mgr: Vivian Beaulieu

D-U-N-S 09-138-9796
NORTH SONOMA COUNTY HOSPITAL DISTRICT
HEALDSBURG DISTRICT HOSPITAL
1375 University St, Healdsburg, CA 95448-3382
Tel (707) 431-6500 *Founded/Ownrshp* 2001
Sales 31.0MM^E *EMP* 171
SIC 8062 General medical & surgical hospitals; General medical & surgical hospitals
CEO: Evan J Rayner
COO: Regina Novello
**CFO:* Dan Hull
Dir Lab: Charlie Vela
Chf Nrs Of: Susan Spoelma
Ex Dir: Lynda Guthrie
Mtls Mgr: Jean Killian
Mtls Dir: Johnny Hargrove
Ql Cn Mgr: Andre Gerard
Doctor: Jose Ballesteros
Doctor: John Hunter

D-U-N-S 60-601-9750 IMP/EXP
NORTH SOUTH FOODS GROUP INC
3373 Sterling Ridge Ct, Longwood, FL 32779-3183
Tel (407) 805-9075 *Founded/Ownrshp* 1981
Sales 204.6MM^E *EMP* 7
Accts Kittell Branagan & Sargent St
SIC 5144 5147 5146 Poultry & poultry products; Meats & meat products; Meat brokers; Fish & seafoods; Poultry & poultry products; Meats & meat products; Meat brokers; Fish & seafoods
Pr: Ron Bateman
**Treas:* Brad Bateman
**VP:* Karen Bateman

D-U-N-S 01-161-7917
NORTH ST FRANCIS COUNTY SCHOOL DISTRICT R-1
300 Berry Rd, Bonne Terre, MO 63628-3580
Tel (573) 358-2247 *Founded/Ownrshp* 1967
Sales 25.4MM^E *EMP* 450
SIC 8211 Public elementary school; Public junior high school; Public senior high school; Public vocational/technical school; Public elementary school; Public junior high school; Public senior high school; Public vocational/technical school

D-U-N-S 80-641-7911
NORTH STAR ACADEMY CHARTER SCHOOL OF NEWARK
(*Suby of* EXECUTIVE OFFICE OF STATE OF NEW JERSEY) ★
100 River View Plz, Trenton, NJ 08611-3418
Tel (609) 984-4900 *Founded/Ownrshp* 1967
Sales NA *EMP* 800
SIC 9411 Administration of educational programs; Administration of educational programs;
**Prin:* Arthur Levinowitz
Adm Dir: Stephen R Blaustein
Genl Mgr: Chris Christie

D-U-N-S 83-675-0588 IMP
NORTH STAR BLUESCOPE STEEL LLC
(*Suby of* BLUESCOPE STEEL LIMITED)
6767 County Road 9, Delta, OH 43515-9449
Tel (419) 822-2399 *Founded/Ownrshp* 2015
Sales NA *EMP* 345
SIC 3312 Hot-rolled iron & steel products; Hot-rolled iron & steel products
Pr: Miguel Alvarez
VP: Joe Budion
VP: Michael Hanson
VP: Rich Menzel
VP: Hanson Michael
Dir IT: Malcolm Edge
IT Man: Steve Markward
Opers Supe: Ron Jurski
Plnt Mgr: Dave Rintoul
Ql Cn Mgr: Timothy Mitchell
Sales Asso: Bill Braithwaite

NORTH STAR BUMPER
See KEYSTONE AUTOMOTIVE INDUSTRIES MN INC

D-U-N-S 03-180-5385
NORTH STAR COOP (ND)
1304 Hwy 5 W, Cavalier, ND 58220
Tel (701) 284-7161 *Founded/Ownrshp* 1934
Sales 36.1MM^E *EMP* 36
SIC 5191 5171 Chemicals, agricultural; Petroleum bulk stations
Pr: Harvey Puppe
**Sec:* Randy Wagner
**VP:* James Brown
Genl Mgr: Jim Wiznick

NORTH STAR DISTRIBUTING
See ICE CREAM SPECIALTIES INC

NORTH STAR DODGE CHRYSLER JEEP
See BROADWAY LONE STAR LTD

D-U-N-S 80-376-7870
NORTH STAR ENERGY & CONSTRUCTION LLC
THREE WAY
135 Pine St, Buffalo, WY 82834-2332
Tel (307) 684-5933 *Founded/Ownrshp* 1983
Sales 87.8MM^E *EMP* 300
SIC 1623 Pipeline construction; Pipeline construction
Pr: Alex Mantle

D-U-N-S 00-331-1797 IMP
NORTH STAR EXCHANGE INC
510 N Main St, Walton, IN 46994-4137
Tel (574) 626-0326 *Founded/Ownrshp* 1996
Sales 31.1MM^E *EMP* 55
SIC 5172 Gases, liquefied petroleum (propane)
Pr: Jay Winters

D-U-N-S 93-752-5236
NORTH STAR GENERAL INSURANCE CO
(*Suby of* NORTH STAR MUTUAL INSURANCE CO INC) ★
269 Barstad Rd S, Cottonwood, MN 56229
Tel (507) 423-6262 *Founded/Ownrshp* 1991
Sales NA *EMP* 55
SIC 6411 Insurance agents, brokers & service; Insurance agents, brokers & service
Pr: Jeff Mauland
**VP:* Joe Hoff
VP: Melinda Smith

D-U-N-S 62-708-6101 EXP
■ **NORTH STAR IMAGING INC**
(*Suby of* ILLINOIS TOOL WORKS INC) ★
19875 S Dmnd Lk Rd Ste 10, Rogers, MN 55374
Tel (763) 463-5650 *Founded/Ownrshp* 2010
Sales 42.0MM^E *EMP* 68
SIC 5084 Measuring & testing equipment, electrical; Measuring & testing equipment, electrical
CEO: Steve Martindale
IT Man: Russ Kurtti
IT Man: Brett Muehlhauser
Manager: Peter Davis
Sls Mgr: Seth Taylor
Sls Mgr: Wes Wren

NORTH STAR INDUSTRIES
See CITIZEN ADVOCATES INC

D-U-N-S 10-671-0700
NORTH STAR INTERNATIONAL TRUCKS INC
ASTLEFORD INTERNATIONAL TRUCKS
3000 Broadway St Ne, Minneapolis, MN 55413-1794
Tel (612) 378-1660 *Founded/Ownrshp* 2003
Sales 51.2MM^E *EMP* 84
SIC 5012 7538 Trucks, commercial; Truck engine repair, except industrial; Trucks, commercial; Truck engine repair, except industrial
Pr: Scott Dowson
Genl Mgr: James Primmer
VP Mktg: Don Williams

D-U-N-S 00-644-7775
NORTH STAR MUTUAL INSURANCE CO INC
269 Barstad Rd S, Cottonwood, MN 56229
Tel (507) 423-6262 *Founded/Ownrshp* 1920
Sales NA *EMP* 197
SIC 6331 Fire, marine & casualty insurance; Fire, marine & casualty insurance
Pr: Jeffrey L Mauland
COO: Carol Myhre
**Sec:* Joe E Hoff
**Sr VP:* Terry Timm
VP: Melinda Smith
IT Man: Marvin Mohn

NORTH STAR NECO SERVICE CENTER
See KEYSTONE AUTOMOTIVE INDUSTRIES FL INC

NORTH STAR PUBLISHING
See RED WING PUBLISHING CO

D-U-N-S 60-626-1923
NORTH STAR RANCH INC
3575 W Grand River Ave, Howell, MI 48855-7604
Tel (517) 546-3900 *Founded/Ownrshp* 1986
Sales 21.9MM^E *EMP* 90
SIC 4213 Trucking, except local; Building materials transport
Pr: Donald Doty
**VP:* Brian Davis

D-U-N-S 07-971-7740
NORTH STAR RESOURCE GROUP
2701 University Ave Se # 300, Minneapolis, MN 55414-3236
Tel (612) 617-6000 *Founded/Ownrshp* 2009
Sales NA *EMP* 275
SIC 6411 Insurance agents, brokers & service; Insurance agents, brokers & service
Pr: Phillip C Richards
Sr Pt: Joseph Fox
Sr Pt: Marshall Gifford
Sr Pt: Eric Seybert
Mng Pt: Whitney Keane
**Pr:* Edward G Deutschlander
**Pr:* David Vasos
Ofcr: Parker Babbe
Ofcr: Brad Benjamin
Ofcr: Amy Bertle
Ofcr: Todd Bowditch
Ofcr: Christopher Hairston
Ofcr: Patrick Kenny
Ofcr: John Locke
Ofcr: Brendan McDermott
Ofcr: Emily Nelson
Ofcr: Josh Opatka
Ofcr: David Velez
Ofcr: Luke Walker
Sr VP: Mark Bonnett
Sr VP: Gary Schwartz

D-U-N-S 01-966-5954
NORTH STAR RESTAURANTS INC
MCDONALD'S
5900 Ne 112th Ave, Vancouver, WA 98662-5761
Tel (360) 253-8264 *Founded/Ownrshp* 1995
Sales 16.0MM^E *EMP* 450^E
SIC 5812 Fast-food restaurant, chain; Fast-food restaurant, chain
Pr: Matthew Hadwin

D-U-N-S 92-663-3983 IMP/EXP
NORTH STAR SEAFOOD LLC
2213 Nw 30th Pl Ste 7a, Pompano Beach, FL 33069-1026
Tel (954) 984-0006 *Founded/Ownrshp* 2011
Sales 59.8MM^E *EMP* 94^E
Accts Mayer Hoffman Mccann Pc Boca
SIC 5146 Seafoods; Seafoods
Pr: Eric Burman
Sls Dir: Batel Einhorn

NORTH STAR SERVICES
See REGION IV OFFICE OF DEVELOPMENTAL DISABILITIES

NORTH STAR SERVICES AUTO
See CHRISTS HOUSEHOLD OF FAITH INC

D-U-N-S 04-177-5008 IMP
NORTH STAR STEEL CO
3000 E Front St, Monroe, MI 48161-1991
Tel (734) 243-2446 *Founded/Ownrshp* 1985
Sales NA *EMP* 550
SIC 3312 3498 5051 Blast furnaces & steel mills; Bars, iron: made in steel mills; Pipes & tubes; Structural shapes & pilings, steel; Fabricated pipe & fittings; Iron & steel (ferrous) products

D-U-N-S 05-144-8611
NORTH STAR TRANSPORT INC
NORTH STAR TRANSPORTATION SVCS
112 2nd St Sw, Roseau, MN 56751-1402
Tel (218) 463-1711 *Founded/Ownrshp* 1969
Sales 69.9MM *EMP* 4
SIC 4213 Contract haulers; Contract haulers
Sec: Wayne L Czeh
**Pr:* Michael Kandris
**VP:* William Hagen
**VP:* Jon Miller

NORTH STAR TRANSPORTATION SVCS
See NORTH STAR TRANSPORT INC

D-U-N-S 84-070-5847
NORTH STAR UTILITIES GROUP INC
(*Suby of* SALTCHUK RESOURCES INC) ★
420 L St Ste 101, Anchorage, AK 99501-1976
Tel (206) 792-0077 *Founded/Ownrshp* 2008
Sales 122.7MM^E *EMP* 5^E
SIC 5172 Petroleum products
Prin: Brian Bogen

D-U-N-S 12-974-8252
NORTH STAR WASTE LLC
ALL COUNTY RESOURCE MANAGEMENT
4717 S Cobb Dr Se, Smyrna, GA 30080-6986
Tel (770) 433-2484 *Founded/Ownrshp* 2002
Sales 20.6MM^E *EMP* 135
SIC 4952 Sewerage systems; Sewerage systems

D-U-N-S 14-038-9607
▲ **NORTH STATE BANCORP**
6204 Fls Of The Neuse Rd, Raleigh, NC 27609
Tel (919) 719-9400 *Founded/Ownrshp* 2002
Sales NA *EMP* 119^E
Tkr Sym NSBC *Exch* OTC
SIC 6022 State commercial banks; State commercial banks
Ch: Fred J Smith Jr
Pr: Larry D Barbour
CFO: Kirk A Whorf

D-U-N-S 01-917-2308
■ **NORTH STATE BANK**
(*Suby of* NORTH STATE BANCORP) ★
6204 Falls Of Neuse Rd # 100, Raleigh, NC 27609-3506
Tel (919) 855-9925 *Founded/Ownrshp* 2000, 2002
Sales NA *EMP* 40^E
SIC 6022 6282 State commercial banks; Investment advice; State commercial banks; Investment advice
Pr: Larry Barbour
Treas: Diane Klietsch
Ex VP: Judy Stephenson
Ex VP: Andrew Wheeler
Ex VP: Kirk Whorf
Ex VP: Bill Wiley
Sr VP: Greg Asbelle
Sr VP: Christopher Bruffey
Sr VP: Jonathan Krieps
Sr VP: John Norwood
Sr VP: Laura Prim
Sr VP: Sandra Steadman
VP: Elaine Crabtree
VP: Lu Herring
VP: Gary Woodlief

D-U-N-S 00-478-9645
NORTH STATE COMMUNICATIONS LLC (NC)
111 Hayden Pl, High Point, NC 27260-4928
Tel (336) 886-3600 *Founded/Ownrshp* 1895, 2004
Sales 147.4MM^E *EMP* 400^E
SIC 4813 Telephone communication, except radio; Telephone communication, except radio
CEO: J Patrick Harman
Pr: Royster Tucker III
IT Man: Herbert Lyle
IT Man: Dan Nicholson
S&M/VP: Jim Cortes

NORTH STATE FLEXIBLES
See NS FLEXIBLES LLC

D-U-N-S 60-344-8770
NORTH STATE GROCERY INC
HOLIDAY QUALITY FOODS
20803 Front St, Cottonwood, CA 96022
Tel (530) 347-4621 *Founded/Ownrshp* 1988
Sales 187.3MM^E *EMP* 1,070
SIC 5411 Supermarkets, independent; Supermarkets, independent
Pr: Richard E Morgan Jr
VP: Brad Askeland
VP: Mike Bible
Store Mgr: Jason Van Note
Dir IT: Steve Kasper
Snr Mgr: Michel Leclerc

NORTH STATE PACKAGING
See NS PACKAGING LLC

NORTH STATE PYROPHYLLITE
See RESCO PRODUCTS INC

D-U-N-S 03-323-1916
NORTH STATE TELECOMMUNICATIONS CORP
111 N Main St, High Point, NC 27260-5007
Tel (336) 886-3600 *Founded/Ownrshp* 1895
Sales 114.4MM^E *EMP* 400
SIC 4813 Local telephone communications; Long distance telephone communications; Local telephone communications; Long distance telephone communications
Ch Bd: J Patrick Harman
**Pr:* Jonathan M Cage
**Pr:* Royster M Tucker III
Sr VP: Hayden C Mkenzie
**VP:* James D Mc Carson

D-U-N-S 00-699-6912
NORTH STATE TELEPHONE CO (NC)
(*Suby of* NORTH STATE TELECOMMUNICATIONS CORP) ★
111 N Main St, High Point, NC 27260-5007
Tel (336) 886-3660 *Founded/Ownrshp* 1905, 1997
Sales 93.1MM^E *EMP* 400
SIC 4813 Local telephone communications; Long distance telephone communications; Local telephone communications; Long distance telephone communications
Ch: J Patrick Harman
**CEO:* Hayden McKenzie
**CEO:* Royster M Tucker III
**CFO:* Jonathan Cage
**VP:* Jonathan M Cage
**VP:* Mark Dula
**VP:* James D McCarson
VP: Jim McCarson
**VP:* Richard Worden
Board of Directors: David L Harman, Lizbeth W Privette

D-U-N-S 00-624-9965 IMP
NORTH STATES INDUSTRIES INC
1507 92nd Ln Ne, Blaine, MN 55449-4334
Tel (763) 486-1754 *Founded/Ownrshp* 2000
Sales 21.2MM^E *EMP* 137
SIC 3089

D-U-N-S 04-866-7752
NORTH SUFFOLK MENTAL HEALTH ASSOCIATION INC
301 Broadway, Chelsea, MA 02150-2807
Tel (617) 889-3300 *Founded/Ownrshp* 1959
Sales 46.2MM *EMP* 850
SIC 8322 8093 Individual & family services; Substance abuse clinics (outpatient); Mental health clinic, outpatient; Individual & family services; Substance abuse clinics (outpatient); Mental health clinic, outpatient
CEO: Jackie K Moore
**Pr:* Deborah Wayne
**COO:* Judith Lemoine
**CFO:* Rita McDonough Ingersoll
Bd of Dir: Armando Alfano
Bd of Dir: Liz Gruber
VP: Phillip Todisco
**VP:* Tony Vaughn
Prgrm Mgr: Deanna Nieto
Doctor: Renee Sorrentino
Snr Mgr: Cheryl Audi

D-U-N-S 07-076-9740
NORTH SUNFLOWER MEDICAL CENTER
840 N Oak Ave, Ruleville, MS 38771-3227
Tel (662) 756-2711 *Founded/Ownrshp* 1950
Sales 48.0MM^E *EMP* 303^E
SIC 8062 8051 8052 8082 General medical & surgical hospitals; Skilled nursing care facilities; Intermediate care facilities; Home health care services; General medical & surgical hospitals; Skilled nursing care facilities; Intermediate care facilities; Home health care services
CEO: Billy Marlow
Chf Path: Andrew R Martin
Ofcr: Wayne Walters
Dir OR: Geletha McCool
Dir Inf Cn: Susan Burnside
Dir Lab: Vaqua Ervin
Dir Lab: Andrew Martin
Dir Rad: Kim Runnels
Dir Rx: Rhyan Ferguson
Dir Rx: Melissa Garrett
Dir Rx: Michael Gilbow

D-U-N-S 07-612-0286
NORTH SUTTER MEDICAL FOUNDATION
MULTI SPECIALTY GROUP PRACTICE
969 Plumas St, Yuba City, CA 95991-4011
Tel (530) 741-1300 *Founded/Ownrshp* 1947
Sales 29.7MM^E *EMP* 330
SIC 8011 Offices & clinics of medical doctors; Clinic, operated by physicians; Offices & clinics of medical doctors; Clinic, operated by physicians
CEO: Bruce Tigner
**COO:* Tom Walther
**CFO:* Kelly Danna
Exec: Lisa Osburn
Doctor: Nindya Burhan
Doctor: Barbara Renwick

D-U-N-S 07-160-2254
NORTH SYRACUSE CENTRAL SCHOOL DISTRICT
5355 W Taft Rd, North Syracuse, NY 13212-2796
Tel (315) 218-2123 *Founded/Ownrshp* 1930
Sales 155.1MM *EMP* 1,400
Accts Grossman St Amour Cpas Syra
SIC 8211 Public elementary & secondary schools; Public elementary & secondary schools
**Pr:* Pat V Carbone
**VP:* Robert Crabtree
Ex Dir: Donna Norton
Schl Brd P: Patrick Svoboda
Psych: Sean Kesselring

NORTH TECHNOLOGY GROUP
See NORTH SAILS GROUP LLC

D-U-N-S 79-703-9039
NORTH TEXAS CONTRACTING INC
4999 Keller Haslet Rd, Fort Worth, TX 76244-8106
Tel (817) 430-9500 *Founded/Ownrshp* 1990
Sales 68.1MM^E *EMP* 150
SIC 1623 1771

D-U-N-S 87-894-7886
■ **NORTH TEXAS DIVISION INC**
MCKINNEY HEALTHCARE ASSOC
(*Suby of* HCA INC) ★
4500 Medical Center Dr, McKinney, TX 75069-1650
Tel (972) 547-8000 *Founded/Ownrshp* 1999
Sales 27.1MM^E *EMP* 900
SIC 8062 General medical & surgical hospitals; General medical & surgical hospitals
CEO: Ernest Lynch
**CFO:* Dwayne Ray
Diag Rad: Nam T Nguyen

NORTH TEXAS FINANCIAL NETWORK
See PARK CITIES ELITE LTD

D-U-N-S 07-259-7966
NORTH TEXAS FOOD BANK
4500 S Cockrell Hill Rd, Dallas, TX 75236-2028
Tel (214) 330-1396 *Founded/Ownrshp* 1981
Sales 88.4MM *EMP* 150
Accts Bkd Llp Dallas Tx
SIC 8322 Meal delivery program; Meal delivery program
CEO: Jan Pruitt
Dir Vol: Meredith Landry
**COO:* Colleen Hager
CFO: Bill Alorn
Chf Mktg O: Brett Gray
Dir IT: Joel Clawson
Dir IT: Philip Virga
IT Man: Lori Kachner
Opers Mgr: Geoff Slaymaker
Snr Mgr: Simon Powell

D-U-N-S 07-934-3687
NORTH TEXAS HCL LP
LIFECARE HOSPITALS OF DALLAS
(*Suby of* LIFECARE FAMILY OF HOSPITALS) ★
1950 Record Crossing Rd, Dallas, TX 75235-6223
Tel (214) 640-9600 *Founded/Ownrshp* 2001
Sales 34.0MM^E *EMP* 241
SIC 8062 General medical & surgical hospitals; General medical & surgical hospitals
Pt: David Leblanc
Pt: John George
Pt: Leroy Thompson
Dir Rx: Yvette Pierre
Mtls Dir: Sandy Love
Nrsg Dir: Patricia Klause
Pharmcst: Vernon Burton
Pharmcst: Fredrena Daniels
Pharmcst: Rodney Harrison
Pharmcst: Win-Yu Lee
Pharmcst: Sailaja Paladugu

D-U-N-S 18-155-5616
NORTH TEXAS HIGHER EDUCATION AUTHORITY INC
4381 W Green Oaks Blvd # 200, Arlington, TX 76016-4477
Tel (800) 366-4372 *Founded/Ownrshp* 1979
Sales NA *EMP* 30
Accts Weaver And Tidwell Llp Fort
SIC 6111 Student Loan Marketing Association; Student Loan Marketing Association
CFO: Donna Swarb
Sr Cor Off: Barbara Heptig
Sr Cor Off: Christopher Mendez
Bd of Dir: K Tonn
Bd of Dir: Ruby Woolridge
Ex VP: Elzie Odom
Admn Mgr: Travis Andrews

NORTH TEXAS MEDICAL CENTER
See GAINESVILLE HOSPITAL DISTRICT

D-U-N-S 07-760-8933 IMP
NORTH TEXAS MUNICIPAL WATER DISTRICT
NTMWD
505 E Brown St, Wylie, TX 75098-4406
Tel (972) 442-5405 *Founded/Ownrshp* 1951
Sales 310.5MM *EMP* 670
Accts Weaver And Tidwell Llp Dalla
SIC 4953 4941 Refuse collection & disposal services; Water supply; Refuse collection & disposal services; Water supply
Ex Dir: James M Parks
Ofcr: Russell Moody
VP: Lynn Shuyler
IT Man: Ronnie Rowell
Sfty Dirs: Dan Dalton
Opers Mgr: Bobby J Reeves
Snr Mgr: Roger Farmer
Snr Mgr: Larry Hall

D-U-N-S 96-852-1349
NORTH TEXAS PUBLIC BROADCASTING INC
KERA
3000 Harry Hines Blvd, Dallas, TX 75201-1012
Tel (214) 871-9010 *Founded/Ownrshp* 1985
Sales 21.2MM *EMP* 70
Accts Rsm Mcgladrey Inc Dallas Tx
SIC 4833 Television broadcasting stations; Television broadcasting stations
CEO: Mary Anne Alhadeff
**CFO:* Bill Leftwich
**Chf Cred:* Sylvia Komatsu
VP: Millie Adan-Garza
VP: Jeff Luchsinger
Exec: Kimberly Campbell
Exec: Edward Fishman
IT Man: John Allison

D-U-N-S 11-479-3719
NORTH TEXAS SPECIALTY PHYSICIANS INC
NTSP
(Suby of SILVERBACK LLC) ★
1701 River Run Ste 210, Fort Worth, TX 76107-6547
Tel (817) 332-8847 Founded/Ownrshp 1995
Sales 22.5MM^E EMP 123
SIC 8011 Health maintenance organization
Pr: Dwayne Roberts
*Pr: Ira N Hollander
*Treas: Raymond Faires
*Sec: Kenneth A Mair
Chf Mktg O: Nancy Lecroy
*VP: Antonio Castaneda
*VP: Mark Collins
*Assoc Dir: Fowad Choudr
Ex Dir: Fowad Choudhry
Ex Dir: Jo Patton
*Ex Dir: Karen Vanwagner

D-U-N-S 00-803-2567
NORTH TEXAS TOLLWAY AUTHORITY
NTTA
(Suby of EXECUTIVE OFFICE OF STATE OF TEXAS) ★
5900 W Plano Pkwy Ste 100, Plano, TX 75093-4695
Tel (214) 461-2000 Founded/Ownrshp 1953
Sales NA EMP 733
Accts Crowe Horwath Llp Dallas Tex
SIC 9111 Executive offices; ; Executive offices;
Ch: Kenneth Barr
Bd of Dir: Ruby Franklin
Bd of Dir: Bill Moore
Ofcr: Carlos Sosa
VP Bus Dev: Mike Johnson
Comm Dir: Kimberly Jackson
*Ex Dir: Gerry Carrigan
Prgrm Mgr: Clarence Daugherty
Prgrm Mgr: Clif Davis
Snr Ntwrk: Steve Cowles
Snr Ntwrk: Rico Quintana
Board of Directors: David D Blair Jr, Jack Miller, Kay Walls

D-U-N-S 18-719-9513
NORTH TOLEDO GRAPHICS LLC
NT
5225 Telegraph Rd, Toledo, OH 43612-3570
Tel (419) 476-8808 Founded/Ownrshp 2004
Sales 25.7MM^E EMP 95
SIC 2752 Commercial printing, lithographic
VP: Mark Leese
Genl Mgr: Greg Tremonti
IT Man: Bill Garl
Plnt Mgr: Dan Priest
Sales Exec: Dale Hampshire

D-U-N-S 13-561-2083
NORTH TONAWANDA CITY SCHOOL DISTRICT
175 Humphrey St, North Tonawanda, NY 14120-4009
Tel (716) 807-3599 Founded/Ownrshp 1900
Sales 51.3MM EMP 850
Accts R A Mercer & Co Pc
SIC 8211 Public elementary school; Public junior high school; Public senior high school; Public elementary school; Public junior high school; Public senior high school
Ch: Arthur Pappas

NORTH TRAIL R V CENTER
See LEE COUNTY RV SALES CO

D-U-N-S 06-525-0607
NORTH VALLEY BANCORP
300 Park Marina Cir, Redding, CA 96001-0964
Tel (530) 226-2900 Founded/Ownrshp 1980
Sales NA EMP 319^E
SIC 6022

D-U-N-S 06-525-0318
NORTH VALLEY BANK
N V B
1327 South St, Redding, CA 96001-1979
Tel (530) 226-2920 Founded/Ownrshp 1981
Sales NA EMP 177
SIC 6022

NORTH VALLEY HOSPITAL
See OKANOGAN COUNTY PUBLIC HOSPITAL DISTRICT 4

D-U-N-S 01-036-4156
NORTH VALLEY HOSPITAL
1600 Hospital Way, Whitefish, MT 59937-2990
Tel (406) 863-2501 Founded/Ownrshp 1969
Sales 48.3MM EMP 400
Accts Dingus Zarecor & Associates S
SIC 8062 General medical & surgical hospitals; General medical & surgical hospitals
CEO: Jason Spring
*Ch Bd: Mark Johnson
*Ch Bd: Hank Ricklefx
V Ch: Cindy Walp
CFO: Wesley White
Dir Lab: Terry Benedict
Dir Rad: Sheri Yeager
Dir Rx: Harley Brotherton
Ex Dir: Carol Blake
Off Mgr: Rhonda Tallman
CIO: Michael Barnes

D-U-N-S 10-006-8840
NORTH WASCO COUNTY SCHOOL DISTRICT 21
3632 W 10th St, The Dalles, OR 97058-4365
Tel (541) 506-3420 Founded/Ownrshp 1854
Sales 82.4M EMP 400
SIC 8211 Public elementary & secondary schools; Public elementary & secondary schools
*CFO: Randal Anderson
Ex Dir: Carol Roderick
Instr Medi: Jim Tindall

D-U-N-S 01-976-5619
■ **NORTH WAY BANK**
(Suby of NORTHWAY FINANCIAL INC) ★
9 Main St, Berlin, NH 03570-2414
Tel (603) 752-1171 Founded/Ownrshp 1974
Sales NA EMP 230
SIC 6022 State commercial banks; State commercial banks
Pr: William J Woodward
COO: Mark Bechtold
Ofcr: Amy Osetek
Sr VP: Paula Caughey
Sr VP: George Fredette
Sr VP: John Gobel
VP: Diane Pelchat
VP: Dave Peterson
VP: John Stratton
VP: Evelyn Whelton
Exec: Paulette Gale
Dir Bus: Kathy Sanderson

D-U-N-S 05-549-2565 IMP
NORTH WEST HANDLING SYSTEMS INC
1100 Sw 7th St, Renton, WA 98057-2939
Tel (425) 255-0500 Founded/Ownrshp 1971
Sales 103.6MM^E EMP 240
SIC 5084 7699 Materials handling machinery; Industrial machinery & equipment repair; Materials handling machinery; Industrial machinery & equipment repair
Pr: James Franck
Exec: Joan Ebbeson
Exec: Erik Gordon
Sales Asso: Danny Saxe

D-U-N-S 00-585-3148
NORTH WEST RURAL ELECTRIC COOPERATIVE
1505 Albany Pl Se, Orange City, IA 51041-9678
Tel (712) 707-4935 Founded/Ownrshp 1938
Sales 47.7MM EMP 47
SIC 4911 Electric services; Electric services
Ex VP: Lyle D Korver
*CFO: Verdell Buss
Opers Mgr: Douglas Alons

D-U-N-S 80-040-1064
NORTH WESTERN ENERGY
40 E Broadway St, Butte, MT 59701-9350
Tel (406) 497-3000 Founded/Ownrshp 2002
Sales 425.4MM^E EMP 170^E
SIC 4911 Electric services
CFO: Brian Bird
CFO: Kipp Orme
Ofcr: Michael Cashell
Ofcr: John Hines
VP: Patrick Corcoran
VP: Miggie Cramblit
VP: David Gates
VP: Kendall Kliewer
VP: Michelle Lavallee
VP: Curtis Pohl
VP: Jana Quam
VP: Bobbi Schroeppel
VP: Bart Thielbar

NORTH WESTERN MUTAL INSURANCE
See NORTHWESTERN MUTUAL FINANCIAL NETWORK

NORTH WESTERN MUTUAL
See ATLANTIC BENEFIT GROUP INC

NORTH WIND GROUP
See CIRI DEVELOPMENT CORP

D-U-N-S 60-310-9161
NORTH WIND SERVICES LLC
(Suby of CIRI DEVELOPMENT CORP) ★
1425 Higham St Rm 220, Idaho Falls, ID 83402-1513
Tel (208) 528-8718 Founded/Ownrshp 2005
Sales 27.6MM^E EMP 50
Accts Kpmg Llp Anchorage Ak
SIC 1611 General contractor, highway & street construction; General contractor, highway & street construction
Pr: James Furr
CFO: Carsen Dye

D-U-N-S 09-130-8601 EXP
NORTH-SOUTH SUPPLY INC
686 3rd Pl, Vero Beach, FL 32962-3634
Tel (772) 569-3810 Founded/Ownrshp 1978
Sales 26.1MM^E EMP 56
SIC 5074 5083 5169 Plumbing & hydronic heating supplies; Irrigation equipment; Swimming pool & spa chemicals
Pr: Bobby J Hiers
*VP: Shelly Gianotti
VP: William Stephenson

NORTHAMERICAN BREWERIES
See NORTH AMERICAN BREWERIES INC

D-U-N-S 10-006-9939
NORTHAMPTON AREA SCHOOL DISTRICT
2014 Laubach Ave, Northampton, PA 18067-1351
Tel (610) 262-7811 Founded/Ownrshp 1964
Sales 42.2MM^E EMP 544
SIC 8211 Public senior high school; Public junior high school; Public elementary school; Public senior high school; Public junior high school; Public elementary school
Prin: Michael Munaghan
Dir Sec: Robert Peloquin
Instr Medi: Patti Gaetaniello

D-U-N-S 06-856-9870
NORTHAMPTON COMMUNITY COLLEGE
NORTHAMPTON COUNTY AREA
3835 Green Pond Rd, Bethlehem, PA 18020-7599
Tel (610) 861-5300 Founded/Ownrshp 1967
Sales 43.2MM^E EMP 1,582
Accts Kreischer Miller Horsham Pen
SIC 8222 Community college; Community college
Pr: Arthur Scott
V Ch: Loretta Leeson
*Pr: Mark H Erickson
Treas: Marilyn Kraemer
Trst: Nicholas Politi
Ofcr: Kate Helm
Ofcr: John Odonnell
Ofcr: Coleen Seng
VP: Carolyn Bortz
*VP: James Dunleavy
VP: Krista Freeh
*VP: Susan Kubik
VP: Michael Mc Govern
VP: Susan M Salvador
VP: A Smith

NORTHAMPTON COUNTY AREA
See NORTHAMPTON COMMUNITY COLLEGE

D-U-N-S 10-007-9433
NORTHAMPTON COUNTY PUBLIC SCHOOLS
7207 Young St, Machipongo, VA 23405-1725
Tel (804) 678-5151 Founded/Ownrshp 1907
Sales 17.8MM^E EMP 380
Accts Didawick & Phibbs Staunton V
SIC 8211 Public elementary & secondary schools; Public elementary & secondary schools
Dir IT: Dan Harris

D-U-N-S 79-467-4366
NORTHAMPTON COUNTY SCHOOL DISTRICT
701 N Church St, Jackson, NC 27845-9773
Tel (252) 534-1371 Founded/Ownrshp 1900
Sales 28.3MM^E EMP 674
SIC 8211 8741 Public elementary & secondary schools; Management services; Public elementary & secondary schools; Management services
Dir IT: Melchizedek Cherry

D-U-N-S 07-365-4121
■ **NORTHAMPTON HOSPITAL CORP**
EASTON HOSPITAL
(Suby of COMMUNITY HEALTH SYSTEMS INC) ★
250 S 21st St, Easton, PA 18042-3851
Tel (610) 250-4000 Founded/Ownrshp 1890, 2001
Sales 1.2MM^E EMP 1,425
SIC 8062 General medical & surgical hospitals; General medical & surgical hospitals
CEO: Brian Finestein
*CFO: Steven Murassky
Ofcr: Henriette Frey
VP: Lorry Ofner
VP: Om Sharma
Dir Risk M: Georgiann Gerlach
Dir Lab: Norine Schenck
Dir IT: Don Lutz
IT Man: Wayne Bruch
Netwrk Mgr: Cornelio Catena
QC Dir: Cristine Biege

NORTHAST MICH CMNTY MNTAL HLTH
See NORTHEAST MICHIGAN MENTAL HEALTH CENTERS INC

D-U-N-S 18-387-6887
NORTHBAY HEALTHCARE CORP
NORTHBAY HEALTHCARE SYSTEM
1200 B Gale Wilson Blvd, Fairfield, CA 94533-3552
Tel (707) 646-5000 Founded/Ownrshp 1987
Sales 47.7MM^E EMP 228
SIC 8062 8011 General medical & surgical hospitals; Offices & clinics of medical doctors; General medical & surgical hospitals; Offices & clinics of medical doctors
Pr: Gary J Passama
Dir Vol: Jane Schilling
CFO: Denio Art
VP: Paul Foley
VP: Mitesh Patel
Dir Lab: Jerry Simmers
Dir Rx: Ryan Seo
Ex Dir: Daralynn Phillips
Dir Sec: Rich Cinflo
Nurse Mgr: Kathleen Smith
CIO: Christopher Timbers

D-U-N-S 07-654-6829
NORTHBAY HEALTHCARE GROUP
NORTHBAY MEDICAL CENTER
1200 B Gale Wilson Blvd, Fairfield, CA 94533-3552
Tel (707) 646-5000 Founded/Ownrshp 1995
Sales 398.7MM EMP 1,200
Accts Moss Adams Llp San Francisco
SIC 8062 General medical & surgical hospitals; General medical & surgical hospitals
CEO: Deborah Sugiyama
Chf Rad: James Bronk
CFO: Gallen Gorman
CFO: George Stock
Dir OR: Susan Gornall
Ansthlgy: James Jaber
Ansthlgy: Ronald Stafford
Doctor: David A Ehrenfeld
Doctor: Craig L Gillespie
Doctor: Alina Hongsakaphadana
Doctor: Robert R Klingman

NORTHBAY HEALTHCARE SYSTEM
See NORTHBAY HEALTHCARE CORP

NORTHBAY MEDICAL CENTER
See NORTHBAY HEALTHCARE GROUP

D-U-N-S 17-929-1653
NORTHBOROUGH-SOUTHBOROUGH REGIONAL SCHOOL DISTRICT
ALGONQUIN REGIONAL HIGH SCHOOL
53 Parkerville Rd, Southborough, MA 01772-1516
Tel (508) 486-5115 Founded/Ownrshp 1960
Sales 25.5MM EMP 700
Accts Braver Pc Providence Rhode I
SIC 8211 Public elementary school; Public junior high school; Public senior high school; Public elementary school; Public junior high school; Public senior high school
Ofcr: Christopher Hoey
Dir IT: Jean Tower
Snr Mgr: Tom Maedler

D-U-N-S 07-979-9216
NORTHBRIDGE PUBLIC SCHOOLS
87 Linwood Ave, Whitinsville, MA 01588-2309
Tel (508) 234-8156 Founded/Ownrshp 2015
Sales 4.8MM^E EMP 342^E
SIC 8211 Public elementary & secondary schools
MIS Dir: Julianne Fields
Teacher Pr: Amy Allen-Magnan

D-U-N-S 96-119-4714
■ **NORTHBROOK BANK AND TRUST CO**
(Suby of WINTRUST FINANCIAL CORP) ★
1100 Waukegan Rd, Northbrook, IL 60062-4663
Tel (847) 418-2800 Founded/Ownrshp 2000
Sales NA EMP 184
SIC 6022 National commercial banks; State commercial banks
CEO: Douglas Boersma
*Pr: Richard Hushkewicz
Ofcr: Mary Hilbert
Ofcr: Brandon Karpeles
Ex VP: Tom Littau
*Ex VP: Dave Masters
Sr VP: Edward Bettenhausen
Sr VP: Joseph Frenzel
Sr VP: Kathleen Gallagher
Sr VP: James King
Sr VP: Babicz Mark
Sr VP: Gregory Pinter
VP: Sheila Allen
VP: Michael Brown
VP: Miriam Campbell
VP: Glen Couchman
VP: Corinne Dania
VP: John Durning
VP: Kevin Faley
VP: Cynthia Norton
VP: Jeff Persin

D-U-N-S 10-001-8969
NORTHBROOK SCHOOL DISTRICT 28
1475 Maple Ave, Northbrook, IL 60062-5497
Tel (847) 498-1918 Founded/Ownrshp 1910
Sales 12.8M EMP 400
Accts Cheryl Rohlfs & Sociate Ltd
SIC 8211 Public elementary & secondary schools; Public elementary & secondary schools
Pr: Joshua Prober
*VP: Anthony Forchetti
*Prin: Scott Warren
Dir IT: Debbie Segiet
Schl Brd P: Liz Hall
Psych: Erin Kerber

D-U-N-S 13-153-1324
■ **NORTHBROOK SERVICES INC**
(Suby of ALLSTATE NON INSURANCE HOLDINGS INC) ★
1600 S Wolf Rd, Wheeling, IL 60090-6516
Tel (847) 667-5100 Founded/Ownrshp 1998
Sales 10.0MM EMP 300
SIC 7389 Printers' services: folding, collating; Printers' services: folding, collating
Pr: Edward M Liddy

NORTHBROOK TOYOTA
See AUTOHAUS AUTOMOTIVE INC

D-U-N-S 12-694-1434
NORTHCAROLINA PERFORMING ARTS CENTER AT CHARLOTTE FOUNDATION
NC BLUMENTHAL PERFORMING ARTS
130 N Tryon St, Charlotte, NC 28202-2100
Tel (704) 333-1598 Founded/Ownrshp 1987
Sales 27.7MM EMP 119
Accts Dixon Hughes Pllc Asheville
SIC 7922 Community theater production; Performing arts center production; Community theater production; Performing arts center production
Pr: Thomas Gabbard
*CFO: Larry Adams
Treas: David Hauser
*Ex VP: Joyce Ford
IT Man: Rick Reynolds

D-U-N-S 06-185-3552
NORTHCENTER FOODSERVICE LLC
Dalton Rd, Augusta, ME 04330
Tel (207) 623-8451 Founded/Ownrshp 1999
Sales NA EMP 352^E
SIC 5147 5141 5142 5148 5143 5113

D-U-N-S 00-380-1800
NORTHCENTRAL MISSISSIPPI ELECTRIC POWER ASSOCIATION (INC)
4600 Northcentral Way, Olive Branch, MS 38654-5097
Tel (662) 838-2151 Founded/Ownrshp 1950
Sales 92.9MM EMP 61
Accts Williams Pitts & Beard Pllc H
SIC 4911 Distribution, electric power; Distribution, electric power
Pr: Pat Woods
*Sec: Jimmy Neal Andrews
VP: Kevin Doddridge
*VP: Robert F Williams

D-U-N-S 07-997-3178
NORTHCENTRAL TECHNICAL COLLEGE FOUNDATION INC
(Suby of WISCONSIN TECHNICAL COLLEGE SYSTEM BOARD) ★
1000 W Campus Dr, Wausau, WI 54401-1880
Tel (715) 675-3331 Founded/Ownrshp 1934
Sales 28.6MM EMP 500
Accts Wipfli Llp Rhinelander Wisco
SIC 8222 Technical institute; Technical institute
Pr: Lori A Weyers
COO: Tim Dunbar
*CFO: Jane Kittel
Treas: Jeff Musson
*VP: Laurie Borowicz
*VP: Jeannie Worden
Dir Sec: Dan Jacobson
Off Admin: Rosemarie Casar
CTO: Janet Sann
IT Man: Loren Beyersdorff
IT Man: Richard Chartier

D-U-N-S 01-626-9370
NORTHCENTRAL UNIVERSITY INC
(Suby of NCU HOLDINGS, LLC)
10000 E University Dr, Prescott Valley, AZ 86314-2336
Tel (928) 541-7777 Founded/Ownrshp 2009
Sales 20.0MM^E EMP 92
SIC 8221 University
Pr: Clinton Gardiner
CEO: George A Burnett
COO: Richard Kimbell
CFO: Christopher Lynne
Chf Mktg O: Ron Hendricks
Brnch Mgr: Karen Rizk
Snr Sftwr: Andrew Gorman
CIO: Patrick Pendleton
CTO: Wayne Perry
Dir IT: Richard Wirth
IT Man: Meredith Hughes

D-U-N-S 84-856-9989
NORTHCOAST WASHINGTON LLC
WESTCOAST GATEWAY HOTEL
2003 Western Ave Ste 500, Seattle, WA 98121-2106
Tel (206) 826-2700 Founded/Ownrshp 1998
Sales 26.4MM^E EMP 220
SIC 6719 Investment holding companies, except banks; Investment holding companies, except banks
Sls Dir: Jackie Collins

D-U-N-S 84-850-6580
NORTHCOTT HOSPITALITY INTERNATIONAL LLC
PERKINS FAMILY RESTAURANT
250 Lake Dr E, Chanhassen, MN 55317-9364
Tel (952) 294-5100 Founded/Ownrshp 2000
Sales 96.0MM^E EMP 1,900^E
SIC 7011 5812 Hotels & motels; Restaurant, family: chain; Hotels & motels; Restaurant, family: chain
*CFO: Joe Martin
*CFO: Brian Schwen
*Sr VP: Nasir H Raja
*VP: Howard Anderson
VP: Mark Clarey
VP: Jeannine Momchilovich
*VP: Mark S Nicpon
*VP: Robin L Oneill
*VP: Julie R Roettger
VP: Ron Shimek
Dist Mgr: Paul McHenry

D-U-N-S 08-351-7607
NORTHCREST MEDICAL CENTER
100 Northcrest Dr, Springfield, TN 37172-3961
Tel (615) 384-2411 Founded/Ownrshp 1954
Sales 74.8MM EMP 750
Accts Kraftcpas Pllc Nashville Tn
SIC 8062 General medical & surgical hospitals; General medical & surgical hospitals
Ch: Ted Stubblefield
*CEO: Randy Davis
COO: Randy Mills
*VP: Angie Beard
Dir Inf Cn: Rachel Goodman
Dir Lab: Ferdinand Pampolina
Dir Lab: Ron Trubilowicz
Dir Rx: Keith Kuboske
*Prin: Scott Raynes
Ex Dir: Adele Watts
Off Mgr: Sharon Vanderpool

NORTHCUTT BUICK
See NORTHCUTT CHEVROLET-BUICK CO INC

D-U-N-S 03-293-5009
NORTHCUTT CHEVROLET-BUICK CO INC
NORTHCUTT BUICK
3201 W Owen K Garriott Rd, Enid, OK 73703-4904
Tel (580) 234-5171 Founded/Ownrshp 1966
Sales 33.1MM^E EMP 85
SIC 5511 Automobiles, new & used; Automobiles, new & used
Prin: Leonard Northcutt
*Treas: Roxanne Northcutt
*VP: David H Eck
Exec: Youlonda Doffer
Genl Mgr: Scott Northcutt
Genl Mgr: Jeff Turnbow
Store Mgr: Tom Moody
Sales Asso: Ashley Allen
Sales Asso: Willi Kiryakakis
Sales Asso: Ryan Martin
Sales Asso: Jake Peterson

D-U-N-S 04-082-5473
NORTHDALE OIL INC
448 Main Ave, Neche, ND 58265-4005
Tel (218) 773-4345 Founded/Ownrshp 1966
Sales 110.8MM EMP 130
Accts Drees Riskey & Vallager Ltd
SIC 5171 Petroleum bulk stations; Petroleum bulk stations
Pr: Scott Reck
*Sec: Missy Reck

D-U-N-S 79-577-7973 IMP/EXP
NORTHDOWN INDUSTRIES INC
(Suby of NORMERICA INC)
2005 Sylvan Rd, Dyersburg, TN 38024-1723
Tel (731) 286-6999 Founded/Ownrshp 2000
Sales 27.5MM^E EMP 69
SIC 5199 Pets & pet supplies
CEO: John Kimmel

NORTHEAST ACURA
See NORTHEAST MOTORS INC

D-U-N-S 10-396-7246 IMP
NORTHEAST AGRI SYSTEMS INC
139a W Airport Rd, Lititz, PA 17543
Tel (717) 569-2702 Founded/Ownrshp 1982
Sales 21.8MM^E EMP 30
SIC 5083 Agricultural machinery
Pr: David Newman
*VP: Joseph Fortin

D-U-N-S 05-657-2092
NORTHEAST AIR
1011 Westbrook St, Portland, ME 04102-1914
Tel (207) 774-6318 Founded/Ownrshp 1970
Sales 73.9MM^E EMP 65
SIC 5172 Aircraft fueling services; Aircraft fueling services
Pr: Henry Laughlin
*VP: Mark Goodwin
VP: Marlyne Patch
Off Mgr: Linda Christensen
Plnt Mgr: Dan Gray

NORTHEAST ALA REGIONAL MED CTR
See REGIONAL MEDICAL CENTER BOARD

D-U-N-S 08-205-6763
NORTHEAST ALABAMA COMMUNITY COLLEGE
(Suby of ALABAMA COMMUNITY COLLEGE SYSTEM) ★
138 Alabama Hwy 35, Rainsville, AL 35986
Tel (256) 638-4418 Founded/Ownrshp 1965
Sales 13.2MM^E EMP 315^E
SIC 8222 9199 Community college; ; Community college;
Pr: David Campbell
Ofcr: Van McAlpin
VP: Alicia Bearden
VP: Joe Burke
VP: John Clements
VP: Scott Ivey
VP: Dusty Trotman
Off Mgr: Jada Freeman
Store Mgr: Gail Gross
CTO: Denise Patterson
Pgrm Dir: Sheila Barnes

D-U-N-S 00-409-8407
NORTHEAST ARC INC
NORTHEAST CLINICAL SERVICES
89 Newbury St Ste 202, Danvers, MA 01923-1075
Tel (978) 646-5200 Founded/Ownrshp 1956
Sales 9.3MM^E EMP 300
SIC 8082 8361 Home health care services; Visiting nurse service; Residential care for the handicapped; Rest home, with health care incidental; Home health care services; Visiting nurse service; Residential care for the handicapped; Rest home, with health care incidental
CEO: Diane Carrabine

D-U-N-S 07-658-0760
NORTHEAST ARC INC
NORTH SHORE ARC
64 Holten St, Danvers, MA 01923-1973
Tel (978) 762-4878 Founded/Ownrshp 1956
Sales 129.5MM EMP 1,000
Accts Cbiz Tofias Boston Ma
SIC 8361 8322 8331 Home for the mentally retarded; Family counseling services; General counseling services; Vocational training agency; Home for the mentally retarded; Family counseling services; General counseling services; Vocational training agency
CEO: Gerard L McCarthy
*Pr: Tim Brenton
*Pr: Jeffrey Musnan
*COO: Joanne Plourde
*CFO: Gary Penninam
*Treas: Stephen Johnson
Treas: Rob Rainer
*VP: Julie Cunnings
MIS Dir: Peter Cabral

D-U-N-S 01-191-1232
NORTHEAST ARKANSAS COMMUNITY MENTAL HEALTH CENTER INC
MID-SOUTH HEALTH SYSTEMS
2707 Browns Ln, Jonesboro, AR 72401-7213
Tel (870) 972-4000 Founded/Ownrshp 1993
Sales 38.7MM EMP 359^E
Accts Bkd Llp Little Rock Ar
SIC 8063 Hospital for the mentally ill; Hospital for the mentally ill
CEO: Bonnie White
*CFO: Jack Keathley
VP: Matt Knight
IT Man: Andy Davis
IT Man: Phillip Stewart
Sales Exec: Karla Cherry
Psych: David Blaske
Psych: Muhammad Khan
Psych: Vye Watson

D-U-N-S 12-161-4390
NORTHEAST ARKANSAS MANAGEMENT CO LLC
NEA CLINIC
4802 E Johnson Ave, Jonesboro, AR 72401-8413
Tel (870) 936-8000 Founded/Ownrshp 2000
Sales 56.8MM^E EMP 500
SIC 8011 Clinic, operated by physicians; Clinic, operated by physicians
*CFO: Scott Davis
Doctor: Michael Hightower
Doctor: Ben Naidoo
Doctor: David Nichols

D-U-N-S 18-113-3224
NORTHEAST AUTO OUTLET INC
754 Baltimore Pike, Springfield, PA 19064-3052
Tel (215) 824-0800 Founded/Ownrshp 1986
Sales 27.4MM^E EMP 120
SIC 5511 Automobiles, new & used; Automobiles, new & used
Ch Bd: Robert Potamkin
*Pr: Arthur Micchelli
*Treas: Alan Potamkin

D-U-N-S 19-150-4950
▲ NORTHEAST BANCORP
500 Canal St, Lewiston, ME 04240-6594
Tel (207) 786-3245 Founded/Ownrshp 1987
Sales NA EMP 195^E
Accts Ernst & Young Llp Boston Ma
Tkr Sym NBN Exch NGM
SIC 6022 State commercial banks; State commercial banks
Pr: Richard Wayne
*Ch Bd: Robert R Glauber
COO: Claire Bean
CFO: Brian W Shaughnessy

D-U-N-S 01-975-8127
■ NORTHEAST BANK FSB
(Suby of NORTHEAST BANCORP) ★
500 Canal St, Lewiston, ME 04240-6577
Tel (207) 786-3245 Founded/Ownrshp 1872
Sales NA EMP 142
SIC 6035 Federal savings banks; Federal savings banks
Pr: Richard Wayne
*CEO: Claire Bean
Ofcr: Robert Staab
Ofcr: Linda Thibault
VP: Steven Brown
Mng Dir: Patrick Dignan
Mng Dir: David Ellingrud
Mng Dir: Christopher Hickey
Mng Dir: James Krumsiek
Mng Dir: Justin Wahls
Netwrk Eng: Todd Henry

D-U-N-S 80-802-1885 IMP
NORTHEAST BATTERY & ALTERNATOR INC
STATE-NORTHEAST BATTERY
240 Washington St, Auburn, MA 01501-3225
Tel (508) 832-2700 Founded/Ownrshp 1985
Sales 22.4MM^E EMP 47
SIC 5013 Automotive batteries
Pr: Thomas Scarduzio

D-U-N-S 84-881-1142
NORTHEAST BEHAVIORAL HEALTH CARE CONSORTIUM
NBHCC'S
72 Glenmaura Nat Blvd, Moosic, PA 18507-2133
Tel (570) 344-9618 Founded/Ownrshp 2002
Sales 117.4MM EMP 4
SIC 8082 Home health care services; Home health care services
Prin: Steve Arnone
Snr Mgr: Ellen Walsh

D-U-N-S 04-906-7479
NORTHEAST BEHAVIORAL HEALTH CORP
199 Rosewood Dr Ste 250, Danvers, MA 01923-1388
Tel (978) 524-7100 Founded/Ownrshp 1982
Sales 71.3MM EMP 58^E
SIC 8093 Mental health clinic, outpatient; Mental health clinic, outpatient
CEO: Kevin Norton
COO: Mona Bastide
VP: Cynthia Dodick-Seyffert
Off Mgr: Cathy Marcos
Site Mgr: Pam Ryan
Opers Mgr: Tim Riel
Pgrm Dir: Colleen McKenna

D-U-N-S 86-768-4078 IMP
NORTHEAST BEVERAGE CORP
119 Hopkins Hill Rd, West Greenwich, RI 02817-1709
Tel (401) 822-6400 Founded/Ownrshp 1993
Sales 40.6MM^E EMP 45
SIC 5149 Beverages, except coffee & tea
Pr: Kenneth Mancini
*CFO: Gerald Freeman
*VP: Raymond Mancini

D-U-N-S 05-015-8625
NORTHEAST BROADCASTING CO INC (MA)
288 S River Rd Bldg B, Bedford, NH 03110-6815
Tel (603) 668-9999 Founded/Ownrshp 1979
Sales 22.1MM^E EMP 150
SIC 4832 Radio broadcasting stations; Radio broadcasting stations
Pr: Stephan Silberberg
*CFO: Eric Leuteritz
*Treas: Lisa Burgess
*Ex VP: Ed Flanagan

D-U-N-S 01-873-5076
NORTHEAST BUILDERS SUPPLY & HOME CENTERS LLC
1460 Barnum Ave, Bridgeport, CT 06610-3201
Tel (203) 366-4757 Founded/Ownrshp 1988
Sales 29.8MM EMP 58^E
Accts Dworken Hillman Lamorte & St
SIC 5211 5251 Lumber & other building materials; Home centers; Hardware; Lumber & other building materials; Home centers; Hardware

D-U-N-S 02-007-9679
NORTHEAST BUILDING PRODUCTS CORP
4280 Aramingo Ave, Philadelphia, PA 19124-5007
Tel (215) 535-7110 Founded/Ownrshp 1975
Sales 38.4MM^E EMP 200
SIC 3442 Storm doors or windows, metal; Storm doors or windows, metal
Pr: Alan M Levin
*CFO: John Seiner
*Sec: Fran Levin
*VP: Jeffrey M Witkin

NORTHEAST CAREER PLANNING
See WORKSHOP INC

D-U-N-S 13-091-3077
NORTHEAST CENTER FOR SPECIAL CARE
300 Grant Ave, Lake Katrine, NY 12449-5340
Tel (845) 336-3500 Founded/Ownrshp 1999
Sales 41.1MM^E EMP 500
SIC 8062 General medical & surgical hospitals; General medical & surgical hospitals

D-U-N-S 02-172-5247
NORTHEAST CENTER FOR YOUTH AND FAMILIES INC
TRI-COUNTY HIGH SCHOOL
203 East St, Easthampton, MA 01027-1234
Tel (413) 529-7777 Founded/Ownrshp 1976
Sales 17.1MM EMP 290
Accts Meyers Brothers Kalicka Pc Ho
SIC 8211 8742 Private elementary & secondary schools; Human resource consulting services; Private elementary & secondary schools; Human resource consulting services
Pr: Kevin Day
*CFO: Philip Pohlmeyer
*Prin: Steven Dion
Ex Dir: Rilla Paul
*Ex Dir: Paul Rilla
Pgrm Dir: Shawn Banks
*Pgrm Dir: Louis Giramma
*Pgrm Dir: Maria Rodriguez

NORTHEAST CENTRAL HIGH SCHOOL
See WEBUTUCK CENTRAL SCHOOL DISTRICT

D-U-N-S 01-074-1358 IMP
NORTHEAST CHEMICALS INC
110 Tices Ln, East Brunswick, NJ 08816-2048
Tel (732) 238-9980 Founded/Ownrshp 1999
Sales 20.4MM EMP 29
SIC 2869 2819 5169 Industrial organic chemicals; Industrial inorganic chemicals; Industrial chemicals
Pr: Frederick Borelli
*Co-Pr: Jimmy Hsu
*VP: Joe Busch

NORTHEAST CLINICAL SERVICES
See NORTHEAST ARC INC

D-U-N-S 10-234-4355
NORTHEAST COMMUNICATIONS OF WISCONSIN INC
NSIGHT TELESERVICES
450 Security Blvd, Green Bay, WI 54313-9705
Tel (920) 617-7000 Founded/Ownrshp 1982
Sales 209.8MM^E EMP 400
SIC 4812 4813 Cellular telephone services; Local telephone communications; Cellular telephone services; Local telephone communications
Pr: Patrick Riordan
COO: Roger Hermsen
CFO: Mark Naze
Ex VP: Robert H Riordan
VP: Amy Demeny
VP: Dan Fabry
VP: Robert Riordan
VP: Bob Webb
VP: Lloyd Wielgus
Snr Sftwr: Brian Hess
Dir IT: Bruce Lenoble

D-U-N-S 78-497-8061
■ NORTHEAST COMMUNITY BANCORP INC
(Suby of NORTHEAST COMMUNITY BANCORP MHC) ★
325 Hamilton Ave, White Plains, NY 10601-1803
Tel (914) 684-2500 Founded/Ownrshp 2006
Sales NA EMP 96^E
Tkr Sym NECB Exch NGM
SIC 6035 Savings institutions, federally chartered; Savings institutions, federally chartered
Ch Bd: Kenneth A Martinek
*Pr: Jose M Collazo
CFO: Donald S Hom
Ex VP: Salvatore Randazzo
VP: George Gaudet

D-U-N-S 96-976-0615
▲ NORTHEAST COMMUNITY BANCORP MHC
325 Hamilton Ave, White Plains, NY 10601-1803
Tel (914) 684-2500 Founded/Ownrshp 2006
Sales NA EMP 193^E
SIC 6035 Savings institutions, federally chartered; Savings institutions, federally chartered
Pr: Kenneth A Martinek
*COO: Salvatore Randazzo

D-U-N-S 07-328-1529
■ NORTHEAST COMMUNITY BANK
(Suby of NORTHEAST COMMUNITY BANCORP INC) ★
325 Hamilton Ave, White Plains, NY 10601-1886
Tel (914) 684-2500 Founded/Ownrshp 2007
Sales NA EMP 71
SIC 6035 Federal savings banks; Federal savings banks
Ch Bd: Kenneth Martinek
Pr: Jose M Collazo
CFO: Salvatore Randazzo
Treas: Donald S Hom
Chf Cred: Michael N Gallina
VP: Terrence J McArdle
VP: Francis McCauley
VP: Paul Simms
Brnch Mgr: James McGowan
Sls Dir: Anne Deblasi

D-U-N-S 11-811-6081
NORTHEAST COMMUNITY CLINIC
2550 W Main St Ste 301, Alhambra, CA 91801-7003
Tel (626) 457-6900 Founded/Ownrshp 1971
Sales 27.5MM EMP 250
Accts Kieckhafer Schiffer & Company
SIC 8011 Clinic, operated by physicians; Clinic, operated by physicians
CEO: Robert Nakahiro
*CEO: Christopher Lau

D-U-N-S 96-359-2543
NORTHEAST COMMUNITY COLLEGE
801 E Benjamin Ave, Norfolk, NE 68701-0469
Tel (402) 844-7051 Founded/Ownrshp 1973
Sales 25.6MM^E EMP 631^E
SIC 8222 Junior colleges & technical institutes; Junior colleges & technical institutes
CFO: Lynne Koski
Ofcr: Sarah Brown
Exec: Miller Timothy
Store Mgr: Michael Anson
IT Man: Kris Coan
Sls&Mrk Ex: Anna Meis
Mktg Dir: Meis Anna
Mktg Dir: Jennifer Greve
Pr Dir: Gerharter Janelle
Psych: Brundieck Stephanie

D-U-N-S 06-053-6018
NORTHEAST CONTROLS INC
3 Enterprise Ave, Halfmoon, NY 12065-3423
Tel (518) 664-6600 Founded/Ownrshp 1967
Sales 49.6MM^E EMP 49

SIC 5084 Controlling instruments & accessories
Ch Bd: David Rizzo
**CFO:* Susan Johnson
VP: Dan Shea
Sales Asso: Jayne Architzel
Sales Asso: Patricia Fisher
Sales Asso: Bill McClure
Sales Asso: Conor Murphy
Sales Asso: Eric Sanborn

D-U-N-S 08-340-6314
NORTHEAST CREDIT UNION
NECU
100 Borthwick Ave, Portsmouth, NH 03801-7117
Tel (603) 436-1847 *Founded/Ownrshp* 1936
Sales NA *EMP* 165
SIC 6062 State credit unions, not federally chartered; State credit unions, not federally chartered
Pr: Peter J Kavalauskas
**CFO:* Richard D Parks
Ofcr: David Maloney
Ofcr: Judy Pelletier
Ofcr: Dottie Richards
Ex VP: Tim Collia
**Sr VP:* Mike Chisholm
Sr VP: Thomas Weaver
**VP:* Ramona Dow
VP: June Gouldsbrough
VP: Jonathan Otterson
VP: Dave Wolf

NORTHEAST DELTA DENTAL
See DELTA DENTAL PLAN OF NEW HAMPSHIRE INC

D-U-N-S 03-709-7565
NORTHEAST DISTRIBUTORS INC
700 East Ave, Warwick, RI 02886-0736
Tel (401) 828-7145 *Founded/Ownrshp* 1981
Sales 25.9MM^E^ *EMP* 40
SIC 5031 Building materials, exterior; Building materials, interior; Lumber: rough, dressed & finished
Pr: Kenneth Caito
**VP:* Anthony Lisi

D-U-N-S 36-171-4962
NORTHEAST ELECTRIC LLC
7004 Green Mountain Rd, Woodland, WA 98674-8283
Tel (360) 225-7004 *Founded/Ownrshp* 2005
Sales 39.4MM^E^ *EMP* 40
SIC 4911 Electric services

D-U-N-S 08-291-6052 IMP
NORTHEAST ELECTRICAL DISTRIBUTORS
(*Suby of* SONEPAR MANAGEMENT US INC) ★
560 Oak St, Brockton, MA 02301-1346
Tel (781) 401-8500 *Founded/Ownrshp* 1994
Sales 377.6MM^E^ *EMP* 390
SIC 5063 Electrical apparatus & equipment; Electrical apparatus & equipment
Pr: Donald M Block
VP: Carl Svendsen
Brnch Mgr: Paul Deangelis
Brnch Mgr: Darrell Ferguson
Brnch Mgr: James Hall
Brnch Mgr: Scott Terceiro
Manager: Joel Flaherty
Sls Mgr: Steve Gilmartin
Sales Asso: Daniel Moriarty
Sales Asso: Tim Savastano
Sales Asso: David Young

NORTHEAST ELECTRICAL DISTRS
See SONEPAR DISTRIBUTION NEW ENGLAND INC

D-U-N-S 00-117-6486 IMP
NORTHEAST ELECTRONICS CORP (CT)
455 Bic Dr, Milford, CT 06461-1735
Tel (203) 878-3511 *Founded/Ownrshp* 1961
Sales 20.9MM^E^ *EMP* 100
SIC 3679 Hermetic seals for electronic equipment
Pr: Armand J Cantafio
**VP:* Timothy A Cantafio
**VP:* Frank Gaudiano
**VP:* John Short

D-U-N-S 02-364-6586
NORTHEAST ENERGY MANAGEMENT INC
2018 S 6th St, Indiana, PA 15701-6012
Tel (724) 465-7958 *Founded/Ownrshp* 1986
Sales 51.9MM^E^ *EMP* 120
SIC 1381 Drilling oil & gas wells; Drilling oil & gas wells
Pr: Michael Melnick
**Pr:* William Gregg
**Treas:* Paul G Ruddy

D-U-N-S 07-963-5211
NORTHEAST ENERGY SYSTEMS
8330 State Rd, Philadelphia, PA 19136-2915
Tel (215) 335-0500 *Founded/Ownrshp* 2004
Sales 12.8MM^E^ *EMP* 500
SIC 1711 5719 5211 Solar energy contractor; Wood burning stoves; Energy conservation products; Solar energy contractor; Wood burning stoves; Energy conservation products
CEO: Rick Roger
**Pr:* Al Clark
**CFO:* Phil Field

D-U-N-S 00-772-2028
NORTHEAST FABRICATORS LLC (WI)
30-35 William St, Walton, NY 13856-1497
Tel (607) 865-4031 *Founded/Ownrshp* 1997
Sales 20.6MM^E^ *EMP* 70
SIC 3444 3441 Sheet metalwork; Fabricated structural metal
Off Mgr: Kathy Cole

D-U-N-S 08-056-3745
NORTHEAST FOODS INC
AUTOMATIC ROLLS OF NEW YORK
601 S Caroline St, Baltimore, MD 21231-2814
Tel (410) 276-7254 *Founded/Ownrshp* 1976
Sales 356.3MM^E^ *EMP* 850
SIC 2051 5149 Bread, cake & related products; Bread, all types (white, wheat, rye, etc): fresh or frozen; Rolls, bread type: fresh or frozen; Bakery products; Bread, cake & related products; Bread, all types (white, wheat, rye, etc): fresh or frozen; Rolls, bread type: fresh or frozen; Bakery products
Ch Bd: John Paterakis
**Pr:* Steven Paterakis
COO: Larry Rollins
**VP:* William Paterakis
Genl Mgr: John Lyons
Opers Mgr: Richard Tommy

D-U-N-S 12-099-2149
NORTHEAST FREIGHTWAYS INC
179 Davis St, East Douglas, MA 01516-2313
Tel (508) 476-2066 *Founded/Ownrshp* 2000
Sales 23.0MM *EMP* 20
SIC 4213 Trucking, except local; Trucking, except local
Pr: Gerson Gurwitz

NORTHEAST GA INPATIENT SVCS
See LONGSTREET CLINIC P C

D-U-N-S 11-720-6677
■ **NORTHEAST GENERATION SERVICES CO**
(*Suby of* NU ENTERPRISES INC) ★
301 Hammer Mill Rd, Rocky Hill, CT 06067-3784
Tel (860) 810-1700 *Founded/Ownrshp* 1999
Sales 118.7MM^E^ *EMP* 300
SIC 4911 Electric services; Electric services
Pr: Bruce Kenyon
**VP:* Bill Nadeau
VP: Erick Pelletier
VP Opers: Dennis Brown

D-U-N-S 06-921-0425
NORTHEAST GEORGIA DIAGNOSTIC CLINIC LLC
1240 Jesse Jewell Pkwy Se # 500, Gainesville, GA 30501-3862
Tel (770) 536-9864 *Founded/Ownrshp* 1953
Sales 45.0MM^E^ *EMP* 200
SIC 8011 Internal medicine, physician/surgeon; Oncologist; Nephrologist; Pulmonary specialist, physician/surgeon; Internal medicine, physician/surgeon; Oncologist; Nephrologist; Pulmonary specialist, physician/surgeon
CEO: Bill Beyer
Mng Dir: Roberto Villanueva MD
Dir IT: Pam Helton
Nutrtnst: Amy Roark
Doctor: Mark Clark
Doctor: Meghan Cook
Doctor: Carol Hector
Doctor: Sean Sumner

D-U-N-S 06-450-2057
NORTHEAST GEORGIA HEALTH SYSTEM INC
743 Spring St Ne, Gainesville, GA 30501-3715
Tel (770) 219-9000 *Founded/Ownrshp* 1986
Sales 33.4MM *EMP* 7,000
Accts Pershing Yoakley & Associates
SIC 8062 General medical & surgical hospitals; General medical & surgical hospitals
Pr: James E Gardner
**COO:* Carol Burrell
CFO: Shawn Buffaloe
**CFO:* Tony Herdener
Ofcr: Kenneth McMillan
Top Exec: Alicia Harrison
VP: Karen Watts
Adm Dir: Bryan Jones
Nurse Mgr: Cheris Skelton
Nurse Mgr: Claire Washburn
CIO: Allana Cummings

D-U-N-S 62-088-3603
NORTHEAST GEORGIA MEDICAL CENTER INC
(*Suby of* NORTHEAST GEORGIA HEALTH SYSTEM INC) ★
743 Spring St Ne, Gainesville, GA 30501-3715
Tel (770) 219-9000 *Founded/Ownrshp* 1951
Sales 819.6MM *EMP* 3,053
SIC 8062 General medical & surgical hospitals; General medical & surgical hospitals
CEO: Carol Burrell
**CFO:* Anthony M Herdener
**VP:* Tracy Vardeman
**VP:* Paul Vervalin
**VP:* Anthony Williamson
Dir OR: Nydia Gonzalez
Dir Risk M: Jerry McConnell
Dir Case M: Janice Sanning
Dir Rad: Brett C Baudin
Dir Rad: Steven E Black
Dir Rad: Colby T Chasain
Dir Rad: Richard C Ory
Dir Rx: Steve Carlson
Dir Rx: Joanne Harden

D-U-N-S 01-816-9966
NORTHEAST GEORGIA PHYSICIANS GROUP INC
601 S Enota Dr Ne Ste P, Gainesville, GA 30501-2400
Tel (770) 219-8400 *Founded/Ownrshp* 1997
Sales 61.0MM^E^ *EMP* 316
Accts Pershing Yoakley & Associates
SIC 8011 Primary care medical clinic; Primary care medical clinic
CEO: Paul Vervalin
**CEO:* James E Gardner
**CFO:* Anthony M Herdener
Sls Mgr: Tammy Hulsey

NORTHEAST GREAT DANE
See LEUNER INC

D-U-N-S 94-669-8008
NORTHEAST HEALTH
NORTHEAST HEALTH REHABILITATIO
600 Northern Blvd, Albany, NY 12204-1004
Tel (518) 471-3229 *Founded/Ownrshp* 1867
Sales 396.9MM *EMP* 2,000
SIC 8741 Hospital management; Nursing & personal care facility management; Hospital management; Nursing & personal care facility management
CFO: Lori Santos
**CEO:* Norman Dascher
**COO:* Karen Passey
CFO: Santos Lon
Exec: Joe Brodzinski
CIO: Daniel Collins
CIO: Jay Wilcox
Dir IT: Robert Duth
Doctor: Gregory Bishop
Doctor: Ramon Fabregas
Doctor: John Filippone

D-U-N-S 96-853-1686
NORTHEAST HEALTH GROUP INC
GOVERNORS CENTER
200 Kendall St, Springfield, MA 01104-2532
Tel (561) 801-7585 *Founded/Ownrshp* 1995
Sales 35.6MM *EMP* 700
SIC 8051 Skilled nursing care facilities; Skilled nursing care facilities
Pr: Harry D Madonna
Board of Directors: John Corman, Linda Dale, Ann Jabro, Howard Jaffe

D-U-N-S 96-587-3763
NORTHEAST HEALTH INC
315 S Manning Blvd, Albany, NY 12208-1707
Tel (518) 292-6200 *Founded/Ownrshp* 1995
Sales 1.1MM *EMP* 4,000
Accts Deloitte Tax Llp Philadelphia
SIC 8059 8322 Personal care home, with health care; Senior citizens' center or association; Personal care home, with health care; Senior citizens' center or association
Pr: James Reed
COO: Tom Schuhley
CFO: Lynette Turo
VP: Davie Caesar
**VP:* Robert Ducey
VP: Richard Petterson
VP: Daniel Silverman
Exec: Susan Moran
Dir Risk M: Robert Allen
Comm Dir: Kimberly Tomlinson
Ex Dir: Donnamarie Martocci

NORTHEAST HEALTH REHABILITATIO
See NORTHEAST HEALTH

D-U-N-S 10-118-3184
NORTHEAST HEALTH SYSTEMS INC
BEVERLY HOSPITAL
85 Herrick St, Beverly, MA 01915-1777
Tel (978) 922-3000 *Founded/Ownrshp* 1994
Sales 10.8MM *EMP* 5,100
Accts Pricewaterhousecoopers Llp Bo
SIC 8741 Hospital management; Nursing & personal care facility management; Hospital management; Nursing & personal care facility management
CEO: Dennis S Conroy
**Ch Bd:* Henry Rameni
**Pr:* Steven Defossez
COO: Wendy Beesley
**COO:* Philip Cormier
COO: Philip M Cormier
CFO: Katharine Irvine
CFO: Michael Stefanowicz
Treas: Frederick Kauders
Treas: Peter Simonds
Trst: Joseph Haley
Sr VP: Jody Fleit
Sr VP: Michael Valentine
**VP:* Greg Bird
VP: Elliot Cohen
**VP:* William E Donaldson
VP: Dennis Gallagher
VP: Barbara McCarthy
VP: Lisa Nevling
VP: Paul Oshea
VP: Charles J Payson

NORTHEAST HOSPICE SERVICE
See NORTHEAST MEDICAL CENTER HOSPITAL

D-U-N-S 07-380-9121
NORTHEAST HOSPITAL CORP
BEVERLY HOSPITAL
(*Suby of* BEVERLY HOSPITAL) ★
85 Herrick St, Beverly, MA 01915-1790
Tel (978) 922-3000 *Founded/Ownrshp* 1893
Sales 346.5MM *EMP* 2,800
Accts Pricewaterhousecoopers Llp Bo
SIC 8062 Hospital, AMA approved residency; Hospital, AMA approved residency
CEO: Philip M Cormier
**Pr:* Robert Tufts
COO: Linda Cancellieri
**CFO:* Gary P Marlow
**VP:* Cynthia Cafasso Donaldson
**VP:* Althea Lyons
**VP:* Lisa Neveling
Dir OR: Mary Jenkins
Nurse Mgr: Candace Sklarz
Doctor: Elise Campagnolo
Doctor: Saul Cohen

D-U-N-S 08-348-1168
NORTHEAST HOSPITAL FOUNDATION
MEMORIAL HERMANN
18951 N Memorial Dr, Humble, TX 77338-4217
Tel (281) 540-7861 *Founded/Ownrshp* 1977
Sales 80.4MM^E^ *EMP* 900
SIC 8062 Hospital, affiliated with AMA residency; Hospital, affiliated with AMA residency
Pr: Norman Funderburk
Chf Rad: Scott Allison
COO: Sean Henderson
CFO: David Glassburn
**Sec:* Mary Lea Layton
Ofcr: Dan Peterson
**VP:* Barbara Reischmann MD
Dir OR: Ken Adams
Dir OR: Phyllis Austin
Dir Lab: Rita Glass
CIO: Louis Smith

D-U-N-S 05-227-2150
NORTHEAST ILLINOIS REGIONAL COMMUTER RAILROAD CORP
METRA METROPOLITAN RAIL
547 W Jackson Blvd Ste 1, Chicago, IL 60661-5768
Tel (312) 322-6900 *Founded/Ownrshp* 1981
Sales 381.8MM^E^ *EMP* 2,800
Accts Crowe Chizek And Company Llc
SIC 4111 4011 Commuter rail passenger operation; Railroads, line-haul operating; Commuter rail passenger operation; Railroads, line-haul operating
Ch: Jeffrey R Ladd
COO: Vaughn L Stoner
CFO: Frank Racibozynski
Ofcr: Deeanne Kroner
Ofcr: Sam Smith
Ex Dir: Philip A Pagano
Genl Couns: Michael Noland
Snr Mgr: Marty Ryan
Board of Directors: Lowell A Anderson, Larry A Huggins, Jeffrey R Ladd, W Warren Nugent, Gerald L Porter, Joseph A Tecson, Donald A Udsten

D-U-N-S 96-593-5666
NORTHEAST INDIANA WORKFORCE INVESTMENT BOARD INC
200 E Main St Ste 910, Fort Wayne, IN 46802-1915
Tel (260) 459-1400 *Founded/Ownrshp* 2010
Sales 26.6MM *EMP* 97
Accts Dunton & Co Pc Indianapolis
SIC 6799 Investors; Investors
Pr: Kathleen Randolph

D-U-N-S 82-703-2830 IMP
NORTHEAST INDUSTRIAL TECHNOLOGIES INC
7620 Evergreen St, Lima, NY 14485-9727
Tel (585) 768-8912 *Founded/Ownrshp* 1994
Sales 47.6MM^E^ *EMP* 89^E^
SIC 5013 Automotive supplies & parts
Ch Bd: Michael Shaffer
**Treas:* Beth Bartz
**VP:* Guy Bianchi
Sales Asso: Derek Bowman
Sales Asso: Sam Cruzado

D-U-N-S 07-952-3085
NORTHEAST INTERIORS INC
27 Pacella Park Dr, Randolph, MA 02368-1755
Tel (781) 356-7666 *Founded/Ownrshp* 1998
Sales 79.2MM *EMP* 71
Accts Cullen Murphy & Co Pc No
SIC 1542 Commercial & office buildings, renovation & repair; Interior designer; Interior decorating
Pr: Kevin B Fish
**Treas:* Josef Rettman
Exec: Marc Marcelli
Dir IT: Aaron D'Anna
Board of Directors: Kevin Fish, Andy Koines, Josef Rettman

D-U-N-S 88-425-9383
■ **NORTHEAST INVESTORS TITLE INSURANCE CO**
(*Suby of* INVESTORS TITLE CO) ★
121 N Columbia St Ste 103, Chapel Hill, NC 27514-3502
Tel (919) 968-2200 *Founded/Ownrshp* 1973
Sales NA *EMP* 140
SIC 6361 Title insurance
Pr: James Allen Fine Jr
**VP:* Elizabeth Patricia Bryan
**VP:* William Morris Fine
VP: Teresa Frost
**VP:* Andrew Mercaldo
**VP:* Carl Edison Wallace Jr
Board of Directors: Charles John Antonucci Sr, Gerald Michael Calvario, Julie Helen Dewitt

D-U-N-S 05-180-7121
NORTHEAST INVESTORS TRUST
125 High St Ste 1801, Boston, MA 02110-2749
Tel (857) 263-8100 *Founded/Ownrshp* 1950
Sales 133.0MM *EMP* 18
SIC 6722 Mutual fund sales, on own account; Mutual fund sales, on own account
Pr: William A Oates Jr
**Ch Bd:* Ernest E Monrad
**Treas:* Gordon Barrett
**Trst:* Robert B Minturn Jr
**Trst:* Bruce Monrad

D-U-N-S 87-814-3692
NORTHEAST IOWA COMMUNITY COLLEGE FOUNDATION
1625 Highway 150, Calmar, IA 52132-7606
Tel (563) 562-3263 *Founded/Ownrshp* 1967
Sales 40.6MM *EMP* 1,514
Accts Hacker Nelson & Co Pc Deco
SIC 8222 Junior college; Junior college
Pr: Mark Downhowe
**Sec:* John Noel
Ofcr: Kim Baumler
**VP:* Jim Anderson
VP: Linda Peterson
**Prin:* Dr Liang Chee Wee
Ex Dir: Wendy Knight
Prgrm Mgr: Edward Berry
Prgrm Mgr: Terry Jenkins
Prgrm Mgr: Peggy Johannsen
Prgrm Mgr: Michelle Langenberg

D-U-N-S 08-028-9242
NORTHEAST IOWA COOPERATIVE
806 Mill St, Clermont, IA 52135-4406
Tel (563) 423-5293 *Founded/Ownrshp* 1976
Sales 29.8MM^E^ *EMP* 90
SIC 5191 Feed; Seeds: field, garden & flower; Fertilizer & fertilizer materials; Chemicals, agricultural; Feed; Seeds: field, garden & flower; Fertilizer & fertilizer materials; Chemicals, agricultural
Pr: Kent Appler

NORTHEAST JOBBERS
See NEJ INC

D-U-N-S 04-023-1912
NORTHEAST KINGDOM HUMAN SERVICES INC
N K H S
181 Crawford Rd, Derby, VT 05829
Tel (802) 334-6744 *Founded/Ownrshp* 1960
Sales 30.9MM *EMP* 526
Accts Kittell Branagan & Sargent St
SIC 8093 Mental health clinic, outpatient; Substance abuse clinics (outpatient); Mental health clinic, outpatient; Substance abuse clinics (outpatient)
Pr: Nancy Warner
CFO: Linda Nygaard
**Treas:* Thad Richardson
**VP:* Bob Fitts
Exec: Mark Beattie
Dir IT: Tim Gould
IT Man: Timothy Gould
Psych: Karen Hack
Psych: Judy Young

D-U-N-S 00-799-5301
NORTHEAST LOUISIANA POWER COOPERATIVE INC (LA)
1411 Landis St, Winnsboro, LA 71295-2644
Tel (318) 435-4523 *Founded/Ownrshp* 1938
Sales 25.8MM *EMP* 57
SIC 4911 Distribution, electric power; Distribution, electric power
Pr: Thad Waters
VP: Alton Walch
IT Man: Jeff Churchwell
Board of Directors: Rudolph M Elkins, Roy M McIntyre, Alton Welch

D-U-N-S 06-675-3133
NORTHEAST LUBRICANTS LTD
4500 Renaissance Pkwy, Cleveland, OH 44128-5702
Tel (216) 478-0507 *Founded/Ownrshp* 1997
Sales 54.9MM^E *EMP* 143
SIC 5172 Petroleum products; Petroleum products
Off Admin: Andrea Montowski

D-U-N-S 10-618-6919
NORTHEAST MANAGEMENT INC
BLOCKBUSTER
42 Albro St, Providence, RI 02903
Tel (401) 273-2343 *Founded/Ownrshp* 1983
Sales 8.3MM^E *EMP* 350
SIC 7841 5735 5731 Video disk/tape rental to the general public; Video tapes, prerecorded; Video recorders, players, disc players & accessories; Video disk/tape rental to the general public; Video tapes, prerecorded; Video recorders, players, disc players & accessories
Pr: Mark Feinstein
Pt: David Guyer
CFO: Richard N Small
Ofcr: Weng Tao
VP: Al Reaves
VP Opers: William E Tente

NORTHEAST MARKETING COMPANY
See NEMCO FOOD TRADING INC

NORTHEAST MEDICAL CENTER
See CAROLINA MEDICAL CENTER NORTHEAST

D-U-N-S 94-205-8439
NORTHEAST MEDICAL CENTER HOSPITAL
NORTHEAST HOSPICE SERVICE
(*Suby of* MEMORIAL HERMANN HEALTHCARE SYSTEM) ★
9813 Memorial Blvd Ste H, Humble, TX 77338-4253
Tel (281) 540-7167 *Founded/Ownrshp* 2007
Sales 1.0MM^E *EMP* 1,000
SIC 8062 General medical & surgical hospitals
CEO: Hiath Rushing

D-U-N-S 93-869-9444
NORTHEAST MEDICAL GROUP INC
226 Mill Hill Ave Ste 3, Bridgeport, CT 06610-2826
Tel (203) 339-6499 *Founded/Ownrshp* 1991
Sales 143.3MM^E *EMP* 30^E
Accts Ernst & Young Us Llp Indianap
SIC 8011 Offices & clinics of medical doctors; Offices & clinics of medical doctors
CEO: Robert Nordgren
COO: Amit Rastogi

D-U-N-S 82-638-9967
NORTHEAST METAL TRADERS INC
7345 Milnor St Ste 1, Philadelphia, PA 19136-4222
Tel (215) 624-1153 *Founded/Ownrshp* 1994
Sales 36.7MM^E *EMP* 50
SIC 5093 Scrap & waste materials
Pr: Ronald W Greller
Bd of Dir: Ronald Hammond
**VP:* Elliott Goldberg
Opers Mgr: Gerry Tobin

NORTHEAST METRO 916
See NORTHEAST METROPOLITAN INTERMEDIATE SCHOOL DISTRICT 916

D-U-N-S 06-815-8880
NORTHEAST METROPOLITAN INTERMEDIATE SCHOOL DISTRICT 916
NORTHEAST METRO 916
2540 County Road F E, Saint Paul, MN 55110-3935
Tel (651) 415-5500 *Founded/Ownrshp* 1969
Sales 58.6MM *EMP* 650
SIC 8211 Public elementary & secondary schools; Public elementary & secondary schools
IT Man: Mike Smoczyk

D-U-N-S 07-953-2131
NORTHEAST METROPOLITAN REGIONAL VOCATIONAL TECHNICAL SCHOOL DISTRICT (MA)
100 Hemlock Rd, Wakefield, MA 01880-3568
Tel (781) 246-0810 *Founded/Ownrshp* 1970
Sales 24.7MM^E *EMP* 300
SIC 8211 Public elementary & secondary schools; Public elementary & secondary schools
Treas: Peter A Rossetti Jr
Exec: Marion Wedge

**Prin:* John X Crowley
Sls&Mrk Ex: Joseph Frimpong

D-U-N-S 02-090-5642
NORTHEAST MICHIGAN COMMUNITY SERVICE AGENCY INC (MI)
2375 Gordon Rd, Alpena, MI 49707-4627
Tel (989) 356-3474 *Founded/Ownrshp* 1968
Sales 42.0MM *EMP* 600
Accts Curt A Peppuhn Cpa Pllc Gayl
SIC 8322 Individual & family services; Individual & family services
Pr: Dale Huggler
CEO: John Swise
COO: John Briggs
Off Admin: Wanda Gougeon

D-U-N-S 09-780-7143
NORTHEAST MICHIGAN MENTAL HEALTH CENTERS INC
NORTHAST MICH CMNTY MNTAL HLTH
400 Johnson St, Alpena, MI 49707-1434
Tel (989) 356-2161 *Founded/Ownrshp* 1970
Sales 15.0MM^E *EMP* 406
SIC 8322 8361 8093 Social service center; Home for the mentally retarded; Home for the emotionally disturbed; Specialty outpatient clinics; Social service center; Home for the mentally retarded; Home for the emotionally disturbed; Specialty outpatient clinics
Ex Dir: Ed Laframboise

D-U-N-S 13-938-5595
NORTHEAST MILITARY SALES INC
17 Sherwood Dr, Sterling, MA 01564-2453
Tel (978) 422-7808 *Founded/Ownrshp* 1984
Sales 38.0MM *EMP* 475
SIC 5812 5461 Eating places; Bakeries; Eating places; Bakeries
Pr: Edwin J Fedeli II

D-U-N-S 00-378-8536 IMP
NORTHEAST MISSOURI ELECTRIC POWER COOPERATIVE
NORTH EAST POWER
3705 N Business 61, Palmyra, MO 63461-2641
Tel (573) 769-2107 *Founded/Ownrshp* 1986
Sales 75.3MM *EMP* 58
Accts Dennis G Koch Cpa Quincy Il
SIC 4911 Transmission, electric power; Transmission, electric power
CEO: Douglas H Aeilts
**Pr:* Emery Geisendorfer Jr
**Treas:* Jackie Serbin
**Sec:* Donnie White
**VP:* John Eggteston
**VP:* David Wright

D-U-N-S 06-892-0800
NORTHEAST MONTANA HEALTH SERVICES INC (MT)
POPLAR COMMUNITY HOSPITAL & NU
315 Knapp St, Wolf Point, MT 59201-1826
Tel (406) 653-6500 *Founded/Ownrshp* 1948
Sales 25.7MM *EMP* 280
Accts Green Health Group Pc Glasgow
SIC 8062 8051 General medical & surgical hospitals; Skilled nursing care facilities; General medical & surgical hospitals; Skilled nursing care facilities
Pr: Tom Ault
Pr: Jim Simons
**Treas:* Shane Gibson
**VP:* Dallas Oconnor
Exec: Elaine Long
Dir Lab: Myrna Kampen
Dir Rx: Larae Davis
Dir Rx: Rosanne Erickson
Dir IT: Scott Nefzger
Sfty Dirs: Terry Cody

D-U-N-S 17-721-6785
NORTHEAST MOTORS INC
NORTHEAST ACURA
942 New Loudon Rd, Latham, NY 12110-2107
Tel (518) 785-4105 *Founded/Ownrshp* 1987
Sales 37.0MM^E *EMP* 48
SIC 5511 Automobiles, new & used; Automobiles, new & used
Pr: Timothy Higgins
**Ch Bd:* James Higgins
**VP:* Dave Ellis
Off Mgr: Brenda Matoske
Off Mgr: Brenda Metoski
Sales Asso: Andy Middleton

D-U-N-S 05-253-7933
■ **NORTHEAST NUCLEAR ENERGY CO**
(*Suby of* EVERSOURCE ENERGY) ★
107 Selden St, Berlin, CT 06037-1616
Tel (860) 665-5000 *Founded/Ownrshp* 1950
Sales 82.7MM^E *EMP* 200
SIC 4911 Generation, electric power; Generation, electric power
Pr: Bruce D Kenyon
**Ch Bd:* Michael G Morris
**Treas:* John B Keane
**Ex VP:* John H Forsgen
**VP:* John Stack

D-U-N-S 04-023-1714
NORTHEAST NURSERY INC
234 Newbury St, Peabody, MA 01960-7466
Tel (978) 535-6550 *Founded/Ownrshp* 1982
Sales 20.3MM^E *EMP* 20^E
SIC 5193 5261 Nursery stock; Nurseries
Pr: Andrew F Cotreau
IT Man: Diane McIsaac
Mktg Dir: Gerianne Caruso

D-U-N-S 07-056-8980 EXP
NORTHEAST OHIO ELECTRIC LLC
DOAN PYRAMID ELECTRIC
5069 Corbin Dr, Cleveland, OH 44128-5413
Tel (216) 587-9510 *Founded/Ownrshp* 2000
Sales 55.6MM^E *EMP* 450
SIC 1731 General electrical contractor; General electrical contractor
CFO: Lenny Heiser

Genl Mgr: Douglas Fortney
Genl Mgr: Karen Zamlen
Off Mgr: Michael Forlani
VP Opers: David Lupica
Opers Mgr: Matt Fussner
Snr PM: Mike Schatz

D-U-N-S 07-777-9882
NORTHEAST OHIO MEDICAL UNIVERSITY
NEOMED
4209 State Route 44, Rootstown, OH 44272-9698
Tel (330) 325-2511 *Founded/Ownrshp* 1973
Sales 42.8MM *EMP* 330
Accts Plante & Moran Pllc Toledo
SIC 8221 College, except junior; College, except junior
Pr: Jay A Gershen
Pr: Michelle Mulhern
Ofcr: Michael Bussinger
Ofcr: Kelly Dibona
Ofcr: Christopher Hartlaub
Ofcr: Allan Jones
**VP:* Daniel Blain
VP: Kathleen Ruff
Exec: Ruth Schlabach
Exec: Jeanine Szczesny
Assoc Dir: Michael Kerrigan
Board of Directors: Ronald McGrady

D-U-N-S 07-452-8043
NORTHEAST OHIO NEIGHBORHOOD HEALTH SERVICES INC
8300 Hough Ave, Cleveland, OH 44103-4247
Tel (216) 231-2323 *Founded/Ownrshp* 1967
Sales 23.2MM *EMP* 280
SIC 8099 8071 8011 5912 Medical services organization; Medical laboratories; Offices & clinics of medical doctors; Drug stores & proprietary stores; Medical services organization; Medical laboratories; Offices & clinics of medical doctors; Drug stores & proprietary stores
Pr: Willie S Austin
CFO: James Odonnell
Exec: Shirley Carey
Dir IT: Al Barker

D-U-N-S 07-455-4098
NORTHEAST OHIO REGIONAL SEWER DISTRICT
3900 Euclid Ave, Cleveland, OH 44115-2506
Tel (216) 881-6600 *Founded/Ownrshp* 1972
Sales 239.1MM *EMP* 623
Accts Ciuni & Panichi Cleveland Oh
SIC 4959 Sanitary services; Sanitary services
Pr: Darnell Brown
Ofcr: Diana Djones
Ofcr: Mark Sullivan
VP: Nichole Pinson
**VP:* Ronald D Sulik
Exec: Allan Velez
Comm Man: Kim Jones
**Ex Dir:* Julius Ciaccia
Ex Dir: Julius Ciaecia
Plng Mgr: Devona Marshall
Dir IT: Humberto Sanchez

D-U-N-S 00-781-9725
NORTHEAST OKLAHOMA ELECTRIC COOPERATIVE INC
443857 E Highway 60, Vinita, OK 74301
Tel (918) 256-6405 *Founded/Ownrshp* 1938
Sales 87.0MM *EMP* 184
Accts Briscoe Burke & Grigsby Llp
SIC 4911 Distribution, electric power; Distribution, electric power
Genl Mgr: Robert Echenrode
IT Man: Rick Cagle

D-U-N-S 08-911-3047
NORTHEAST PARENT AND CHILD SOCIETY INC
530 Franklin St Ste 200, Schenectady, NY 12305-2011
Tel (518) 346-1284 *Founded/Ownrshp* 1888
Sales 40.1MM *EMP* 600
SIC 8361 8322

D-U-N-S 11-234-8425
NORTHEAST PENNSYLVANIA AUTO AUCTION INC
860 N Keyser Ave, Scranton, PA 18504-9723
Tel (570) 207-2277 *Founded/Ownrshp* 1999
Sales 27.7MM^E *EMP* 128
SIC 5012 Recreational vehicles, motor homes & trailers; Recreational vehicles, motor homes & trailers
CEO: James J Gaughan
IT Man: Nicole Henderson
IT Man: Kim Maconeghy

NORTHEAST POLY BAG
See LADDAWN INC

D-U-N-S 83-174-4615 IMP
NORTHEAST PRESTRESSED PRODUCTS LLC
N E PRESTRESSED PRODUCTS
121 River St, Cressona, PA 17929-1108
Tel (570) 385-2352 *Founded/Ownrshp* 2008
Sales 28.4MM^E *EMP* 139
SIC 3272 Concrete products; Concrete products
COO: Thomas Koons
CFO: Robert Barrett
VP: Dennis Fink
Plnt Mgr: Gary Lehman
Sls Mgr: Joseph Palko
Sls Mgr: Mark Pishock

D-U-N-S 80-423-7477
■ **NORTHEAST RECYCLING CORP**
WASTE MANAGEMENT
(*Suby of* WASTE MANAGEMENT INC) ★
1198 Prospect Ave, Westbury, NY 11590-2723
Tel (516) 937-0900 *Founded/Ownrshp* 1991
Sales 14.3MM^E *EMP* 300
SIC 4953 4212 Refuse systems; Local trucking, without storage; Refuse systems; Local trucking, without storage
Dist Mgr: Rich Geisser

D-U-N-S 00-141-1391
NORTHEAST REGIONAL MEDICAL CENTER
315 S Osteopathy Ave, Kirksville, MO 63501-6401
Tel (660) 785-1160 *Founded/Ownrshp* 2000
Sales 72.8MM *EMP* 75
SIC 8062 General medical & surgical hospitals; General medical & surgical hospitals
Pr: Hank Walkley

D-U-N-S 07-930-5396
NORTHEAST REGIONAL MEDICAL CENTER
315 S Osteopathy Ave, Kirksville, MO 63501-6401
Tel (660) 785-1000 *Founded/Ownrshp* 2013
Sales 13.5MM^E *EMP* 500
SIC 8011 Medical centers; Medical centers
Prin: Ranee C Brayton

NORTHEAST REGIONAL MEDICAL CTR
See NRMC INC

NORTHEAST REHABILITATION HOSP
See NEURO-REHAB ASSOCIATES INC

D-U-N-S 79-689-4392
NORTHEAST REMSCO CONSTRUCTION INC
(*Suby of* JAG COMPANIES INC) ★
1433 State Route 34, Wall Township, NJ 07727-1603
Tel (732) 557-6100 *Founded/Ownrshp* 2011
Sales 178.5MM^E *EMP* 450
SIC 1623 1622 1629 1611 Water, sewer & utility lines; Bridge construction; Land clearing contractor; General contractor, highway & street construction; Water, sewer & utility lines; Bridge construction; Land clearing contractor; General contractor, highway & street construction
Ch: Juan Gutierrez
**Pr:* Rolando E Acosta
**CFO:* Marcelo Afonso
Sr VP: A Solana
VP: Patrick O'Connor
Genl Mgr: Corinne Robbins
IT Man: Dan Alvarado

D-U-N-S 80-828-6496
NORTHEAST RESIDENCE INC
410 Little Canada Rd E, Saint Paul, MN 55117-1629
Tel (651) 766-1002 *Founded/Ownrshp* 1995
Sales 8.8MM *EMP* 300
Accts Olsen Thielen & Co Ltd St
SIC 8361 8322 Residential care; Self-help group home; Individual & family services; Residential care; Self-help group home; Individual & family services
Ex Dir: Heidi Holste

D-U-N-S 03-349-9336 IMP
NORTHEAST SALES DISTRIBUTING INC
840 Ronald Wood Rd, Winder, GA 30680-4130
Tel (678) 963-7700 *Founded/Ownrshp* 1957
Sales 65.8MM^E *EMP* 285
SIC 5181 5182 Beer & other fermented malt liquors; Ale; Wine; Beer & other fermented malt liquors; Ale; Wine
CEO: David Black
**Pr:* Frank F Sinkwich Jr
**CFO:* Deborah Q Tiller
Exec: Bobby Morris
Genl Mgr: Alan Gilmer
Sls Mgr: Chris Hunt
Sls Mgr: Craig Kingston

D-U-N-S 00-300-4777
NORTHEAST SEAFOOD PRODUCTS INC
4555 Kingston St, Denver, CO 80239-3016
Tel (303) 373-2226 *Founded/Ownrshp* 1980
Sales 29.0MM^E *EMP* 70
SIC 5146 Seafoods
Pr: Paul Packer
**Sec:* Scott Packer
**VP:* Blair Joyce

D-U-N-S 07-660-4354
NORTHEAST SECURITY INC
265 Washington St Ste 1, Westwood, MA 02090-1339
Tel (617) 739-1500 *Founded/Ownrshp* 1967
Sales 23.9MM^E *EMP* 820
SIC 7381 Security guard service; Detective agency; Security guard service; Detective agency
CEO: Brian J Kickham
**Pr:* John A Hennesey
**CFO:* Steven A Barner
**Sr VP:* C Crandlemire
VP: John Hennessey
**VP:* James O'Neil
**VP:* Sheila Quinlan
MIS Dir: Pitt Crandelmier
Secur Mgr: Jack Lasser
Board of Directors: George Simard, Ken Venti

D-U-N-S 96-519-0825
NORTHEAST SHIP REPAIR INC
32a Drydock Ave, Boston, MA 02210-2308
Tel (617) 330-5045 *Founded/Ownrshp* 2006
Sales 40.0MM *EMP* 173
SIC 3731 Shipbuilding & repairing; Shipbuilding & repairing
Pr: Edward Snyder
**CFO:* Bruce Zaniol
**VP:* Donna Connors
Dir Risk M: Bill Rowan

D-U-N-S 87-886-5591
NORTHEAST STATE COMMUNITY COLLEGE
2425 Highway 75, Blountville, TN 37617-6350
Tel (423) 323-3191 *Founded/Ownrshp* 1966
Sales 12.2MM *EMP* 300
SIC 8249 9411 8221 Vocational apprentice training; Administration of educational programs; ; Colleges universities & professional schools; Vocational apprentice training; Administration of educational programs; ; Colleges universities & professional schools
Pr: William Locke
**Pr:* Dr Janice Gilliam
Pr: Charles Hurley
**CFO:* Dr Steven Campbell
**VP:* Allana Hamilton Academic Affai
VP: Cynthia Lawson

**VP:* Fred Lewis
VP: Carole Shaw
Exec: Robert Carpenter
Mktg Dir: Amanda Adams

D-U-N-S 14-502-3529
NORTHEAST TEXAS ELECTRIC COOPERATIVE INC
2221 H G Mosley Pkwy # 100, Longview, TX 75604-3670
Tel (903) 757-3282 *Founded/Ownrshp* 1972
Sales 250.0MM *EMP* 3
SIC 4911 Generation, electric power; Generation, electric power
Pr: John Dugen
Genl Mgr: Rick Tyler

D-U-N-S 00-787-5180 IMP
NORTHEAST TEXAS FARMERS CO-OP (TX)
SABINE VALLEY FEEDS
428 Jackson St N, Sulphur Springs, TX 75482-2651
Tel (903) 885-4681 *Founded/Ownrshp* 1939
Sales 53.8MM^E *EMP* 70^E
SIC 5191 5153 Farm supplies; Feed; Pesticides; Fertilizer & fertilizer materials; Grains; Grain elevators; Corn; Wheat
Genl Mgr: Brad Johnson
Dir Lab: Charlotte Macinnes

D-U-N-S 18-343-8746 IMP
NORTHEAST TEXTILES INC
348 Huntington Rd, Gaffney, SC 29341-2183
Tel (864) 489-6099 *Founded/Ownrshp* 1985
Sales 22.3MM^E *EMP* 60
SIC 5131 Textile converters
Pr: Charles Cox
VP Opers: Ken Dollar

NORTHEAST TREATMENT CENTERS
See NET TREATMENT SERVICES INC

D-U-N-S 07-145-1652
NORTHEAST TREATMENT CENTERS INC (PA)
499 N 5th St Ste A, Philadelphia, PA 19123-4005
Tel (215) 451-7000 *Founded/Ownrshp* 1969, 1970
Sales 40.8MM *EMP* 815
Accts Cliftonlarsonallen Llp Plymou
SIC 8093 Specialty outpatient clinics; Specialty outpatient clinics
Pr: Terence Mc Sherry
**CFO:* Jonathan Solomons

D-U-N-S 13-164-0153
NORTHEAST UNITED CORP
3101 Shippers Rd, Vestal, NY 13850-2003
Tel (607) 770-1010 *Founded/Ownrshp* 1983
Sales 23.4MM^E *EMP* 100
SIC 1542 1541 Commercial & office building, new construction; Industrial buildings, new construction; Commercial & office building, new construction; Industrial buildings, new construction
CEO: Barry Newman
**Pr:* Marc Newman
Genl Mgr: Dennis Garges

D-U-N-S 05-254-3980 IMP
■ **NORTHEAST UTILITIES SERVICE CO INC**
(*Suby of* EVERSOURCE ENERGY) ★
107 Selden St, Berlin, CT 06037-1651
Tel (860) 665-5000 *Founded/Ownrshp* 1965
Sales 1.8MMM^E *EMP* 4,550
SIC 1623 Underground utilities contractor; Underground utilities contractor
CEO: Thomas J May
V Ch: Guy Carpenter
**CFO:* James Judge
**Sr VP:* Gregory B Butler
Sr VP: James A Muntz
VP: David H Boguslawski
VP: Mary J Keating
VP: Johnny D Magwood
VP: Dennis Welch
Comm Man: Russ Kelly
Dir IT: Elizabeth Hoisl

D-U-N-S 07-412-0866
NORTHEAST VALLEY HEALTH CORP
1172 N Maclay Ave, San Fernando, CA 91340-1328
Tel (818) 898-1388 *Founded/Ownrshp* 1971
Sales 75.4MM *EMP* 770
Accts Moss Adams Llp Los Angeles C
SIC 8322 Community center; Community center
CEO: Kimberly Wyard
COO: Missy Nitescu
**CFO:* Patricia Moraga
**Ch:* Nelson Wong
**Treas:* Antonio Lugo
Ofcr: Sherri Lewitz
Ex Dir: Nicholas Rocca
Dir Pat Ac: Leticia Bibian
Prgrm Mgr: Maria Guerrero
Prgrm Mgr: Jessica King
Doctor: Jesse Sanders

D-U-N-S 62-100-1635 IMP
NORTHEAST WHOLESALE NAIL & FASTENER SUPPLY CO INC
980 Turnpike St, Canton, MA 02021-2807
Tel (781) 767-1019 *Founded/Ownrshp* 1990
Sales 62.9MM^E *EMP* 50
SIC 5051 Nails; Nails
CEO: Rosalind Hurwitz
**Pr:* Richard Hurwitz
**Treas:* John Hurwitz
Genl Mgr: Jim Stewart

D-U-N-S 07-479-7739
NORTHEAST WISCONSIN TECHNICAL COLLEGE DISTRICT
NWTC
(*Suby of* WISCONSIN TECHNICAL COLLEGE SYSTEM BOARD) ★
2740 W Mason St, Green Bay, WI 54303-4966
Tel (920) 498-5400 *Founded/Ownrshp* 1911
Sales 131.5MM^E *EMP* 2,200
Accts Wipfli Llp Rhinelander Wisco
SIC 8221 8222 Colleges universities & professional schools; Technical institute; Colleges universities & professional schools; Technical institute
Pr: Dr Jeffrey Rafin
Pt: Kellian Collins
CFO: Jim Blumreich
VP: Karen Smith
Mktg Dir: Erica Plaza

NORTHEASTERN BUILDING SUPPLY
See NORTHEASTERN LUMBER & BUILDING SUPPLY CO INC

D-U-N-S 06-051-8511
NORTHEASTERN EDUCATIONAL INTERMEDIATE UNIT 19
NEIU 19
1200 Line St, Archbald, PA 18403-1918
Tel (570) 282-2694 *Founded/Ownrshp* 1963
Sales NA *EMP* 320
SIC 9411 State education department; ; State education department;
Ex Dir: Clarence Lamanna
**Treas:* Louise Brzuchalski
**VP:* Joseph Muracco

D-U-N-S 09-536-0269
NORTHEASTERN EYE INSTITUTE A PROFFESSIONAL CORP
200 Mifflin Ave, Scranton, PA 18503-1982
Tel (570) 253-1720 *Founded/Ownrshp* 1974
Sales 25.0MM *EMP* 250
SIC 8011 Ophthalmologist; Ophthalmologist
Pr: William Jordan MD
**Pr:* Jerome Jordan MD
CFO: Joe Carroll
Ofcr: Patty Cobb
**VP:* W Kehrli MD
**VP:* Arthur Jordan Od
**VP:* Stephen Pascucci MD
CIO: Natalie Dixon
IT Man: Dave Stesney

NORTHEASTERN FAMILY INSTITUTE
See NFI MASSACHUSETTS INC

NORTHEASTERN FASTENERS
See NEFCO CORP

NORTHEASTERN HEALTH SYSTEM
See TAHLEQUAH HOSPITAL AUTHORITY

D-U-N-S 87-933-1445
NORTHEASTERN ILLINOIS UNIVERSITY
RONALD WILLIAMS LIBRARY
5500 N Saint Louis Ave, Chicago, IL 60625-4699
Tel (773) 442-4000 *Founded/Ownrshp* 1961
Sales 84.5MM *EMP* 1,500
SIC 8221

D-U-N-S 10-006-2355
NORTHEASTERN LOCAL SCHOOL DISTRICT
1414 Bowman Rd, Springfield, OH 45502-8826
Tel (937) 325-7615 *Founded/Ownrshp* 1952
Sales 32.2MM *EMP* 500
SIC 8211 Public elementary & secondary schools; Public elementary & secondary schools
Pr: Leonard Kadel
**Treas:* Denise D Schneider
VP: Jeff Caivano
VP: Kelly Dobyns
**VP:* John McKinnon
Prgrm Mgr: Jeannie Anders

D-U-N-S 01-134-4249
NORTHEASTERN LUMBER & BUILDING SUPPLY CO INC
NORTHEASTERN BUILDING SUPPLY
255 Gatzmer Ave, Jamesburg, NJ 08831-1105
Tel (732) 605-0870 *Founded/Ownrshp* 1982
Sales 23.5MM^E *EMP* 50
SIC 5211 Lumber & other building materials; Lumber & other building materials
Pr: Guy Leonard
VP: Susan Leonard
Genl Mgr: Doug Swanner
Sales Asso: David Bloodgood

D-U-N-S 07-054-2584
■ **NORTHEASTERN NEVADA REGIONAL HOSPITAL AUXILARY/VOLUNTEERS INC** (NV)
NNRH
(*Suby of* LIFEPOINT HEALTH INC) ★
2001 Errecart Blvd, Elko, NV 89801-8333
Tel (775) 738-5151 *Founded/Ownrshp* 1921, 2006
Sales 30.8MM^E *EMP* 260^E
SIC 8062 General medical & surgical hospitals; General medical & surgical hospitals
Pr: Diane Longyear
Chf OB: Gary Wright
Chf Rad: Ross Golding
Chf Rad: Bobby Shah
**CEO:* Gene Miller
**COO:* Ann Cariker
**CFO:* Grant Trollope
**Treas:* Clarice Gamboa
Dir OR: Cathe Broeker
Dir Lab: Marla Asson
Dir Lab: Michelle Dack
Dir Rad: Bruce Jonas
Dir Rx: Andre Gouws
Dir Rx: Grace Lawrence

D-U-N-S 10-109-3847
NORTHEASTERN PENNSYLVANIA CENTER FOR INDEPENDENT LIVING INC
1142 Sanderson Ave, Scranton, PA 18509-2623
Tel (570) 344-7211 *Founded/Ownrshp* 1987
Sales 100.3MM *EMP* 84
Accts Joneskohanski & Co Pc Moosi
SIC 8322 Individual & family services; Individual & family services
Ex Dir: Timothy Moran
CIO: Mike Masters

D-U-N-S 15-213-9887
NORTHEASTERN PENNSYLVANIA HEALTH CORP
LEHIGH VLY HOSPITAL-HAZLETON
(*Suby of* LEHIGH VALLEY HEALTH NETWORK INC) ★
700 E Broad St, Hazleton, PA 18201-6835
Tel (570) 501-4000 *Founded/Ownrshp* 2013
Sales 108.2MM *EMP* 1,000^E
SIC 8062 General medical & surgical hospitals; General medical & surgical hospitals
Pr: John Fletcher
Chf Rad: Donald Patten
**CFO:* William C Bauer
Dir OR: Maryann Kolcun
Dir Risk M: James Nelson
Dir Rad: Tim Gutsie
Dir Rad: William Reppy
Dir Rx: Ray Bernardi
Nrsg Dir: Sally Bolesta

D-U-N-S 60-324-5499
NORTHEASTERN POWER CO
(*Suby of* GDF SUEZ ENERGY INTERNATIONAL) ★
90 Plant Rd, McAdoo, PA 18237-3133
Tel (570) 929-3111 *Founded/Ownrshp* 1996
Sales 26.5MM^E *EMP* 32
SIC 4911 Generation, electric power
Pr: Herman Schopman
**CFO:* Claudia Brace
**VP:* Michael Fields
**VP:* Rachel W Kilpatrick
Sfty Mgr: Peter Homnick

D-U-N-S 79-751-4379
NORTHEASTERN PROFESSIONAL NURSES REGISTRY INC
NORTHSTERN PROF NURSES REGISTR
134 Evergreen Pl Ste 504, East Orange, NJ 07018-2010
Tel (973) 673-6336 *Founded/Ownrshp* 1986
Sales 6.7MM^E *EMP* 351
SIC 7361 8082 Nurses' registry; Home health care services; Nurses' registry; Home health care services
Pr: Carlotta Hall

NORTHEASTERN REMC
See NORTHEASTERN RURAL ELECTRIC MEMBERSHIP CORP

D-U-N-S 80-893-1138
NORTHEASTERN REMC
4901 E Park Dr Fl 30, Columbia City, IN 46725
Tel (260) 625-3700 *Founded/Ownrshp* 2007
Sales 89.3MM *EMP* 2
SIC 4911 Electric services; Electric services
CEO: Gregg Kiess
VP Mktg: Michael Defreeuw

D-U-N-S 00-693-6587
NORTHEASTERN RURAL ELECTRIC MEMBERSHIP CORP
NORTHEASTERN REMC
4901 E Park 30 Dr, Columbia City, IN 46725-8885
Tel (260) 625-3700 *Founded/Ownrshp* 1936
Sales 110.8MM *EMP* 35
SIC 4911 Distribution, electric power; Distribution, electric power
Pr: Gregg L Kiess
**Treas:* Doug Schrader
**VP:* Gene Donaghy
VP: Jim Eitsert
**VP:* Curt Irven
VP: Rhonda Irven
**VP:* Marjorie Kennedy
**VP:* Richard R Smith
IT Man: Wayne O'Brien
Sfty Mgr: Lynn Sauders

D-U-N-S 03-407-9566
NORTHEASTERN SCHOOL DISTRICT OF YORK COUNTY
41 Harding St, Manchester, PA 17345-1119
Tel (717) 266-3667 *Founded/Ownrshp* 1984
Sales 27.9MM^E *EMP* 500
Accts Sager Swisher And Company Ll
SIC 8211 Public elementary & secondary schools; Public elementary & secondary schools
Treas: Vanessa Snell
IT Man: Antia Truax
Sls&Mrk Ex: Leah Pritchett
Schl Brd P: Margaret Walker

D-U-N-S 07-240-0500
NORTHEASTERN STATE UNIVERSITY
NSU
600 N Grand Ave, Tahlequah, OK 74464-2301
Tel (918) 456-5511 *Founded/Ownrshp* 2008
Sales 45.5MM *EMP* 1,031
Accts Arledge & Associates Pc Ed
SIC 8221 University; University
Pr: Steve Turner
**Pr:* Dr Steve Turner
Bd of Dir: Wyman Kirk
Ofcr: Brian Jordan
**VP:* Dr Laura Boren
**VP:* Dr Pam Fly
**VP:* Tim Foutch
**VP:* David Koehn
VP: James Pate
**VP:* William Rugg
Assoc Dir: Sandra Ranney
Dir: Peggy Summitt
Board of Directors: Dr Steve Turner

D-U-N-S 02-249-2987 EXP
NORTHEASTERN SUPPLY INC
8323 Pulaski Hwy, Baltimore, MD 21237-2941
Tel (410) 574-0010 *Founded/Ownrshp* 1971
Sales 111.3MM^E *EMP* 285
Accts Ellin & Tucker Chartered Bal
SIC 5074 Plumbing & hydronic heating supplies; Plumbing & hydronic heating supplies
Pr: Stephen D Cook
**Sec:* Cheryl Cook-Boyle
**VP:* Mike Cornbrooks
VP: Russ Everson
Brnch Mgr: Laura Caviness
Brnch Mgr: Rick Foxwell
Brnch Mgr: Dwayne Graham
Brnch Mgr: Vic Hart
Brnch Mgr: Keith Schwartz
Sales Asso: Allen Brown
Sales Asso: Dave Gibas

D-U-N-S 00-142-3631
NORTHEASTERN UNIVERSITY
360 Huntington Ave, Boston, MA 02115-5000
Tel (617) 373-2000 *Founded/Ownrshp* 1916
Sales 1.0MMM *EMP* 4,175
Accts Pricewaterhousecoopers Llp B
SIC 8221 University; University
Prin: Aoun
Exr: Stephen Zoloth
**Ch Bd:* Sy Sternberg
CFO: Thomas E Nedell
CFO: Jennifer Tonneson
Treas: Rodelio Mandawe
**Treas:* Sam Soloman
Sr VP: Ahmed T Abdelal
Sr VP: Philomena V Mantella
**Sr VP:* John McCarthy
Sr VP: Laurence F Mucciolo
Sr VP: Mark Putnam
Sr VP: Carol Scheman
Sr VP: George Triantaris
VP: Amelia Brizicky
VP: William J Cotter
VP: Robert Gittens
VP: Christopher E Hopey
**VP:* Steven Kadish
VP: Rehan Khan
VP: Edward Klotzbier

D-U-N-S 04-024-2232
NORTHEASTERN VERMONT REGIONAL HOSPITAL INC
CHERRY WHEEL HOSPITAL GIFTS
1315 Hospital Dr, Saint Johnsbury, VT 05819-9210
Tel (802) 748-8141 *Founded/Ownrshp* 1967
Sales 64.7MM *EMP* 500^E
SIC 8062 General medical & surgical hospitals; General medical & surgical hospitals
Pr: Charles Bucknam
**Treas:* Richard Lyon
Bd of Dir: Vivi Begin
Bd of Dir: Megan Haygood
Bd of Dir: Anea Lelong
Bd of Dir: Gregory McDonald
Trst: Richard Bennum
Trst: Candice Ortiz
VP: Colleen Sinon
CIO: Andrea Dinneen
Mktg Mgr: Hilary Carlo

NORTHEN A1 SERVICES
See AMERICAN WASTE INC

D-U-N-S 00-384-5526
NORTHERN AIR CARGO INC
(*Suby of* SALTCHUK RESOURCES INC) ★
3900 Old Intl Airport Rd, Anchorage, AK 99502-1097
Tel (907) 243-3331 *Founded/Ownrshp* 1956, 2006
Sales 52.6MM^E *EMP* 547
SIC 4512 4522 Air cargo carrier, scheduled; Air cargo carriers, nonscheduled; Air cargo carrier, scheduled; Air cargo carriers, nonscheduled
Pr: David Karp
**Ch Bd:* Rita Sholton
**Pr:* Bill Fowler
**CFO:* Eric Van Andel
**Treas:* Philip A Okeson
Sr VP: David W Karp
**VP:* Jeff Landrum
**VP:* Timo A Saarinen
**VP:* David E Squier
VP: David Squire
IT Man: Aurora Campbell

D-U-N-S 02-595-7098
NORTHERN AIR CARGO INC
N A C
(*Suby of* NORTHERN AIR CARGO INC) ★
3900 Old Intl Airport Rd, Anchorage, AK 99502-1097
Tel (907) 243-3331 *Founded/Ownrshp* 1956, 2006
Sales 22.9MM^E *EMP* 270
SIC 4512 Air transportation, scheduled; Air transportation, scheduled
Pr: William D Fowler
**CFO:* Eric Van Andel
**Sr VP:* David W Karp

D-U-N-S 13-072-9189
NORTHERN AIR CORP
NAC MECHANICAL & ELEC SVCS
1001 Labore Industrial Ct B, Saint Paul, MN 55110-5168
Tel (651) 490-9868 *Founded/Ownrshp* 1985
Sales 148.2MM^E *EMP* 320
SIC 1711 Warm air heating & air conditioning contractor; Ventilation & duct work contractor; Refrigeration contractor; Warm air heating & air conditioning contractor; Ventilation & duct work contractor; Refrigeration contractor
Pr: Lynn Bishop
**VP:* Steve Anderson
VP: Bill Zellmer
Sfty Dirs: Mike Heinze

D-U-N-S 60-708-8791
NORTHERN ARAPAHOE TRIBE
WIND RIVER CASINO
10369 State Highway 789, Riverton, WY 82501-9108
Tel (307) 856-9940 *Founded/Ownrshp* 2005
Sales 34.3MM^E *EMP* 300
SIC 7999 Bingo hall; Bingo hall
Prin: Jim Conrad
Dir IT: Brian Duran
Sls&Mrk Ex: Sherry Delorme

D-U-N-S 00-139-7488 IMP
NORTHERN ARCHITECTURAL SYSTEMS INC
111 Central Ave, Teterboro, NJ 07608-1123
Tel (201) 943-6400 *Founded/Ownrshp* 1956, 1978
Sales 22.3MM^E *EMP* 95^E
SIC 3442 Window & door frames
Pr: Robert Pecorella

CFO: Gregory Libertiny
S&M/VP: Michael Richard

D-U-N-S 08-371-6167
NORTHERN ARIZONA COUNCIL OF GOVERNMENTS (AZ)
NACOG
119 E Aspen Ave, Flagstaff, AZ 86001-5222
Tel (928) 774-1895 *Founded/Ownrshp* 1975
Sales NA *EMP* 550
SIC 9199 General government administration; General government administration
Pr: Kenneth Sweet
**Ch Bd:* Matt Ryan
Prgrm Mgr: Annick Desmeules
IT Man: Susan Joy
Snr Mgr: Andrew Dell

D-U-N-S 15-366-5070
NORTHERN ARIZONA HEALTHCARE CORP
1200 N Beaver St, Flagstaff, AZ 86001-3118
Tel (928) 779-3366 *Founded/Ownrshp* 1985
Sales 61.4MM *EMP* 2,500
Accts Ernst & Young Us Llp Phoenix
SIC 8741 8062 8399 4119 Hospital management; Nursing & personal care facility management; General medical & surgical hospitals; Fund raising organization, non-fee basis; Ambulance service; Hospital management; Nursing & personal care facility management; General medical & surgical hospitals; Fund raising organization, non-fee basis; Ambulance service
CEO: Chris Bavasi
Chf Path: Darlene Lee
Dir Recs: Jill Pennala
Dir Vol: Diane Hunt
Pr: Bill Bradeo
Pr: Roger Dewalt
CFO: Gregory D Kuzma
CFO: Tim Topell
Bd of Dir: Jackie Arseneau
Ofcr: Jack Dempsey
Ex VP: Gundrun Moll
VP: Marilynn Black
VP: R N Crofford
VP: Ginamarie Harris
VP: Tammy Lester
VP: Darlene Lewis
VP: Kathleen Macnamara
VP: Kai McSwain
VP: Thomas Ziffer
Exec: Dave Harrell
Exec: Greg Kouzma

D-U-N-S 80-634-5542
NORTHERN ARIZONA UNIVERSITY
523 S Knoles Dr Rm 106, Flagstaff, AZ 86011-7016
Tel (928) 523-9011 *Founded/Ownrshp* 1899
Sales 308.8MM *EMP* 3,863[E]
Accts Debra K Davenport Cpa Phoen
SIC 8221 Colleges universities & professional schools; Colleges universities & professional schools
Pr: John Haeger
**Pr:* Dr Rita Cheng
COO: David Richardson
Ofcr: Charlie Just
Assoc VP: Betsy Mennell
Sr VP: Mary Ellen C Williams
VP: Mason Gerety
VP: Laura Huenneke
Dir Lab: Janelle Bauerle
Genl Mgr: Shelly Watkins
IT Man: Dina Barnese

D-U-N-S 62-780-7100
NORTHERN AUTOMOTIVE INC
SATURN-WEST
8600 N High St, Columbus, OH 43235-1004
Tel (614) 436-2001 *Founded/Ownrshp* 1990
Sales 34.1MM[E] *EMP* 100
SIC 5511 7538 5521 Automobiles, new & used; General automotive repair shops; Used car dealers; Automobiles, new & used; General automotive repair shops; Used car dealers
Pr: Thomas Carpenter
**Ex VP:* William L Denney
**Ex VP:* Robert Vance

D-U-N-S 00-176-5650
NORTHERN BANK & TRUST CO
NBTC
275 Mishawum Rd Ste 100, Woburn, MA 01801-8804
Tel (781) 937-5400 *Founded/Ownrshp* 1960
Sales NA *EMP* 95
SIC 6022 State trust companies accepting deposits, commercial; State trust companies accepting deposits, commercial
Pr: James J Mawn
CFO: Francis Kenney
**Treas:* Donald P Queenin
**VP:* Edward J Cantillon Jr
VP: Raymond Clark
VP: Thomas Fratto
VP: Katie Gatcomb
VP: J L Mawn
VP: Joanne McNamara
VP: Claire Pappas
**VP:* John B Zocchi Jr

NORTHERN BATTERY
See JIM DONSKEY CORP

D-U-N-S 88-494-8985 IMP/EXP
NORTHERN BEEF INDUSTRIES INC
719 S Shoreline Blvd # 204, Corpus Christi, TX 78401-3548
Tel (361) 654-6180 *Founded/Ownrshp* 1995
Sales 90.0MM *EMP* 9
SIC 5147 Meats & meat products
Pr: David Hausman
**VP:* Laura Hausman

D-U-N-S 07-719-8232
NORTHERN BERKSHIRE HEALTHCARE INC
NORTH ADAMS REGIONAL HOSPITAL
71 Hospital Ave, North Adams, MA 01247-2504
Tel (413) 664-5000 *Founded/Ownrshp* 1984
Sales NA *EMP* 500[E]
SIC 8062 8063

D-U-N-S 83-300-1642
NORTHERN BERKSHIRE HEALTHCARE INC
NARH
1 Beacon St Fl 21, Boston, MA 02108-3196
Tel (413) 664-5000 *Founded/Ownrshp* 1984
Sales 56.4MM *EMP* 457[E]
SIC 8069 8063 Drug addiction rehabilitation hospital; Psychiatric hospitals; Drug addiction rehabilitation hospital; Psychiatric hospitals
Pr: William F Frado Jr
**Pr:* Richard T Palmisano
**CFO:* Christopher Hickey
VP: Jon Pfeil
VP: Eric Schrumpf
Dir Rx: Jeffrey Ddandurand
Mng Dir: John Bottomley
Prgrm Mgr: Suzette Naylor

D-U-N-S 84-707-0984
NORTHERN BERKSHIRE HEALTHCARE SYSTEMS INC
2 Park St Ste 201, Adams, MA 01220-2088
Tel (413) 664-4343 *Founded/Ownrshp* 1984
Sales 6.2MM *EMP* 495
SIC 8741 Hospital management; Hospital management
Pr: John C J Cronin
COO: Patricia Hanrahan
**Treas:* John C Craig
Sls Mgr: Ellen J Bernstein

D-U-N-S 02-163-2583
NORTHERN BORDER PIPELINE CO
TRANSCANADA KEYSTONE PIPELINE
700 Louisiana St Ste 700, Houston, TX 77002-2873
Tel (832) 320-5000 *Founded/Ownrshp* 1978
Sales 102.9MM[E] *EMP* 135[E]
Accts Kpmg Llp
SIC 4922 Pipelines, natural gas; Pipelines, natural gas
VP: Dean Ferguson
Pr: Jeff Rush
Treas: Rhonda Amundson
VP: Donna Friesen
VP: Rick Gateman
Genl Couns: Elizabeth Swanson
Counsel: Brenda Rawcliffe

D-U-N-S 07-875-2125 IMP/EXP
NORTHERN BREWER LLC
2221 Highway 36 W, Saint Paul, MN 55113-3856
Tel (651) 291-8849 *Founded/Ownrshp* 2011
Sales 21.8MM[E] *EMP* 104
SIC 2082 Brewers' grain; Brewers' grain
CEO: Chris Farley

NORTHERN BURLINGTON COUNTY HS
See NORTHERN BURLINGTON COUNTY SCHOOL DISTRICT

D-U-N-S 06-904-5771
NORTHERN BURLINGTON COUNTY SCHOOL DISTRICT
NORTHERN BURLINGTON COUNTY HS
160 Mansfield Rd E, Columbus, NJ 08022-2113
Tel (609) 298-7090 *Founded/Ownrshp* 1959
Sales 31.4MM[E] *EMP* 490
SIC 8211 Public elementary & secondary schools; Public elementary & secondary schools

D-U-N-S 14-702-9722
NORTHERN BUSINESS MACHINES INC
24 Terry Ave, Burlington, MA 01803-2516
Tel (781) 272-2034 *Founded/Ownrshp* 1985
Sales 21.2MM[E] *EMP* 90
SIC 5999 7359 Business machines & equipment; Office machine rental, except computers
Pr: William Tracia
VP: Vern Hydorn
IT Man: Michael Archambault
Sales Asso: Drew Ansara
Sales Asso: Alexandra Daniells

D-U-N-S 05-171-4202 IMP
NORTHERN BUSINESS PRODUCTS INC
2326 W Superior St, Duluth, MN 55806-1932
Tel (218) 726-0167 *Founded/Ownrshp* 1998
Sales 57.6MM[E] *EMP* 98
SIC 5021 Furniture; Furniture
CEO: James Farrell
**VP:* Michael Farrell
Off Mgr: Ann Honer
Dir IT: Bob Malkovich
Sls Mgr: William Norman
Sales Asso: Gary Massey
Sales Asso: Galen Sundeen

D-U-N-S 96-488-7520
NORTHERN CALIFORNIA BAKERY & CONFECTI
221 Main St Fl 2, San Francisco, CA 94105-1909
Tel (415) 546-7800 *Founded/Ownrshp* 2010
Sales 27.0MM *EMP* 3[E]
Accts Miller Kaplan Arase Llp San F
SIC 5461 Bakeries; Bakeries

D-U-N-S 96-231-8841
NORTHERN CALIFORNIA BAKERY DRIVERS SECURITY FUND
221 Main St Fl 2, San Francisco, CA 94105-1909
Tel (415) 546-7800 *Founded/Ownrshp* 2010
Sales 25.6MM *EMP* 1
Accts Lindquist Llp San Ramon Ca
SIC 7389 Personal service agents, brokers & bureaus; Personal service agents, brokers & bureaus
Prin: Mary Jane Bennett

D-U-N-S 01-635-6736
NORTHERN CALIFORNIA CARPENTERS REGIONAL COUNCIL
NCCRC
265 Hegenberger Rd, Oakland, CA 94621-1443
Tel (510) 568-4788 *Founded/Ownrshp* 2008
Sales 36.9MM *EMP* 50[E]
SIC 8631 Labor union; Labor union

D-U-N-S 05-163-6017
NORTHERN CALIFORNIA CONFERENCE OF SEVENTH-DAY ADVENTISTS
401 Taylor Blvd, Pleasant Hill, CA 94523-2146
Tel (925) 685-4300 *Founded/Ownrshp* 1911
Sales 67.5MM[E] *EMP* 1,150
SIC 8211 8661 Elementary school; Seventh Day Adventist Church; Elementary school; Seventh Day Adventist Church
CEO: James E Pedersen
**CFO:* John Rasmussen

D-U-N-S 07-154-7400
NORTHERN CALIFORNIA INALLIANCE
6950 21st Ave, Sacramento, CA 95820-5948
Tel (916) 381-1300 *Founded/Ownrshp* 1968
Sales 13.4MM *EMP* 340
Accts Propp Christensen Caniglia Ll
SIC 8331 Vocational rehabilitation agency; Vocational rehabilitation agency
Ex Dir: Richard Royse
Bd of Dir: Vanessa Simonich
Dir Bus: Jennifer Reuther

D-U-N-S 61-333-8789
NORTHERN CALIFORNIA INSTITUTE FOR RESEARCH AND EDUCATION INC
NCIRE
4150 Clement St, San Francisco, CA 94121-1545
Tel (415) 750-6954 *Founded/Ownrshp* 1988
Sales 44.3MM *EMP* 300
Accts Deloitte Tax Llp San Jose Ca
SIC 8399 8741 Fund raising organization, non-fee basis; Management services; Fund raising organization, non-fee basis; Management services
Ex Dir: Robert Obana
Chf Rad: Judy Yee
CFO: Stephen Morange
Bd of Dir: Renee Binder
Bd of Dir: Lilly Bourguignon
Bd of Dir: Sheila M Cullen
Bd of Dir: Charles Marmar
Bd of Dir: Diana Nicoll
Bd of Dir: Steve Peary
Bd of Dir: Alan Stanford
Bd of Dir: Paul M Sullam
Bd of Dir: Paul Volberding
Bd of Dir: Mary A Whooley
Comm Dir: Gerard Choucroun

D-U-N-S 08-384-8341
NORTHERN CALIFORNIA MEDICAL ASSOCIATES INC
3536 Mendocino Ave # 200, Santa Rosa, CA 95403-3634
Tel (707) 573-6925 *Founded/Ownrshp* 1975
Sales 28.9MM[E] *EMP* 175
SIC 8011 Cardiologist & cardio-vascular specialist; Cardiologist & cardio-vascular specialist
Pr: Thomas Dunlap
**Pr:* George L Smith
**Treas:* Greg Hopkins MD
IT Man: Susan Haseltine

D-U-N-S 08-290-0564
NORTHERN CALIFORNIA POWER AGENCY
NCPA
651 Commerce Dr, Roseville, CA 95678-6411
Tel (916) 781-3636 *Founded/Ownrshp* 1968
Sales 127.3MM[E] *EMP* 166
Accts Moss-Adams Llp Portland Oreg
SIC 4911 Transmission, electric power; Generation, electric power; Transmission, electric power; Generation, electric power
Prin: James H Pope
Treas: Ute Woodall
Bd of Dir: Karen England
Bd of Dir: Diane Morgan
Bd of Dir: Shelby Tyson
Dir Risk M: Rui Dai
Genl Mgr: Vicki Cichocki
Opers Mgr: Peter Hill

D-U-N-S 07-737-1961 IMP
NORTHERN CALIFORNIA PRESBYTERIAN HOMES AND SERVICES INC
1525 Post St, San Francisco, CA 94109-6567
Tel (415) 922-0200 *Founded/Ownrshp* 1958
Sales 65.0MM *EMP* 600
Accts Pricewaterhousecoopers Llp Sa
SIC 8051 8059 8361 Skilled nursing care facilities; Convalescent home with continuous nursing care; Convalescent home; Home for the aged; Skilled nursing care facilities; Convalescent home with continuous nursing care; Convalescent home; Home for the aged
CEO: Barbara Hood
VP: Mel Matsumoto
VP: Don Meninga
IT Man: Chulssang Ham
VP Opers: David Berg
Nrsg Dir: Linda Blando

D-U-N-S 96-854-6023
NORTHERN CALIFORNIA REHABILITATION HOSPITAL LLC
(*Suby of* VIBRA HEALTHCARE LLC) ★
2801 Eureka Way, Redding, CA 96001-0222
Tel (530) 246-9000 *Founded/Ownrshp* 2005
Sales 39.2MM *EMP* 250
SIC 8062 General medical & surgical hospitals; General medical & surgical hospitals
Dir Rx: George Lopez
Dir Bus: Chris Jones
Telecom Ex: Debbie Mclvor
Nrsg Dir: Chuck Owens
Snr Mgr: Lisa Stevens

D-U-N-S 18-045-3227
NORTHERN CALIFORNIA RETIRED OFFICERS COMMUNITY INC
PARADISE VALLEY ESTATES
2600 Estates Dr, Fairfield, CA 94533-9711
Tel (707) 432-1200 *Founded/Ownrshp* 1992
Sales 33.0MM *EMP* 225
Accts Hansen Hunter & Co Pc Beavert
SIC 8361 Residential care; Residential care

CEO: James G Mertz
**CFO:* Debra Murphy
VP: Janet Olson
Nrsg Dir: Jennifer Marlette

D-U-N-S 13-066-6642
NORTHERN CALIFORNIA TPG INC
PERFORMANCE GROUP
6673 Owens Dr, Pleasanton, CA 94588-3335
Tel (925) 556-0512 *Founded/Ownrshp* 2002
Sales 135.0MM *EMP* 25
SIC 5141 Food brokers
Pr: Phil Costello
Genl Mgr: Jerry Jenson
Sls Mgr: Tony Metz

D-U-N-S 05-791-5175
NORTHERN CHEMICAL CO
NORTHERN COMPANIES
6110 Nw Grand Ave, Glendale, AZ 85301-1896
Tel (623) 247-5553 *Founded/Ownrshp* 1977
Sales 25.5MM[E] *EMP* 44
SIC 5087 5169 Janitors' supplies; Chemicals & allied products
Pr: Charles P Hayes
**Treas:* Vickie Hayes
VP Opers: Clyde Hayes
Sales Asso: Kirk Kaiser

D-U-N-S 07-074-4123
NORTHERN CHEYENNE TRIBE
600 Cheyenne Ave S, Lame Deer, MT 59043
Tel (406) 477-8459 *Founded/Ownrshp* 1934
Sales 61.2MM[E] *EMP* 400
SIC 4119 Ambulance service; Ambulance service
Pr: John Robinson
**Pr:* Eugene Littlecoyte
Treas: Adam Spang
Ofcr: Krystal Hill
**VP:* Winfield Russell

D-U-N-S 02-314-2755
NORTHERN CLEARING INC
1805 Main St W, Ashland, WI 54806-1109
Tel (715) 682-6646 *Founded/Ownrshp* 1966
Sales 99.1MM *EMP* 350
SIC 1629

D-U-N-S 07-025-5260
NORTHERN COCHISE COMMUNITY HOSPITAL INC (AZ)
901 W Rex Allen Dr, Willcox, AZ 85643-1009
Tel (520) 384-3541 *Founded/Ownrshp* 1968
Sales 20.3MM *EMP* 110
Accts Regier Carr & Monroe Llp Tucs
SIC 8062 8051 General medical & surgical hospitals; Skilled nursing care facilities; General medical & surgical hospitals; Skilled nursing care facilities
CEO: Roland Knox
CFO: Carl Flanagan
Exec: Jeff Morrow
Dir Lab: Fili Escalante
Dir Rad: Tina Kelley
Dir Rx: Dianna Jones
Dir Rx: Leana Mahmoud
Dir Rx: Frank Smith
Chf Nrs Of: Lynette Svingen
CTO: Peach Unrast
QA Dir: Dena Petrequin

D-U-N-S 07-647-3727
NORTHERN COLORADO WATER CONSERVANCY DISTRICT
220 Water Ave, Berthoud, CO 80513-9245
Tel (970) 532-7700 *Founded/Ownrshp* 1937
Sales 67.9MM[E] *EMP* 115
SIC 4941

NORTHERN COMPANIES
See NORTHERN CHEMICAL CO

D-U-N-S 01-324-7809
NORTHERN COMPUTER TECHNOLOGIES INC
NOR-TECH
901 Cliff Rd E, Burnsville, MN 55337-1512
Tel (952) 808-1000 *Founded/Ownrshp* 1998
Sales 25.2MM[E] *EMP* 40
SIC 5045 Computers, peripherals & software
Pr: David Bollig
**Treas:* David Chang
**VP:* Todd Swank

D-U-N-S 94-987-2253
NORTHERN CONCRETE CONSTRUCTION INC
6601 County Road R, Denmark, WI 54208-9731
Tel (920) 863-3043 *Founded/Ownrshp* 1996
Sales 21.4MM[E] *EMP* 50
SIC 1771 Concrete work
Pr: Rob Larsen
CFO: Ron Likas
**VP:* Chad Kane

D-U-N-S 05-334-4149
NORTHERN CONCRETE PIPE INC (MI)
401 Kelton St, Bay City, MI 48706-5395
Tel (989) 892-3545 *Founded/Ownrshp* 1958
Sales 20.0MM[E] *EMP* 90
SIC 3272 3441 Pipe, concrete or lined with concrete; Fabricated structural metal
Pr: William Washabaugh Jr
VP: Robert Washabaugh
Off Mgr: Jim Horen
Snr Mgr: Dan Pletzke

D-U-N-S 94-887-1017
NORTHERN CONSTRUCTION SERVICE LLC
(*Suby of* NORTHERN GENERAL CONTRACTORS INC) ★
775 Pleasant St Ste 11, Weymouth, MA 02189-2373
Tel (781) 340-9440 *Founded/Ownrshp* 1993
Sales 20.6MM[E] *EMP* 80
SIC 1611 Highway & street construction

D-U-N-S 79-703-2190 IMP/EXP
NORTHERN CONTOURS INC
1355 Mendota Heights Rd # 100, Saint Paul, MN 55120-1112
Tel (651) 695-1698 Founded/Ownrshp 1992
Sales 119.3MM^E EMP 500
SIC 3083 1751 2435 Plastic finished products, laminated; Cabinet & finish carpentry; Hardwood veneer & plywood; Plastic finished products, laminated; Cabinet & finish carpentry; Hardwood veneer & plywood
CEO: John A Goebe
*CFO: James Moe
*VP: Duaine Miranowski
VP: Mike More
VP Sls: Larry Skow
Mktg Dir: David Estilow
Mktg Mgr: Melissa Sjerben
Mktg Mgr: Missy Sjerven
Manager: Nathan Klomp
Sls Mgr: Jason Kirchgatter

D-U-N-S 14-235-5796
NORTHERN CROSSING LLC
581 N 43rd Rd, Mendota, IL 61342
Tel (815) 539-3040 Founded/Ownrshp 2004
Sales 40.0MM EMP 5
SIC 5153 Grain elevators; Grain elevators
Prin: Jeff Mauck
Bd of Dir: Curt Zimmerman

NORTHERN DAUPHIN CNTY BRYMCA
See HARRISBURG AREA YMCA

NORTHERN DIVISION
See TRIUMPH TWIST DRILL CO INC

D-U-N-S 02-066-1757
NORTHERN DUTCHESS HOSPITAL
(Suby of HEALTH QUEST SYSTEMS INC) ★
6511 Spring Brook Ave, Rhinebeck, NY 12572-3709
Tel (845) 876-3001 Founded/Ownrshp 1924
Sales 85.9MM EMP 320
Accts Pricewaterhousecoopers Llp N
SIC 8062 General medical & surgical hospitals; General medical & surgical hospitals
Pr: Dennis George
Chf Rad: Judy Zaho
*CFO: Alan Mossoff
Dir OR: Gail Richardson
Ex Dir: Deborah Breen
Mktg Dir: Gina Mullen
Pathlgst: Uma Medapati

D-U-N-S 80-344-0536 IMP
NORTHERN EAGLE BEVERAGE INC
600 16th St, Carlstadt, NJ 07072-1922
Tel (201) 531-7100 Founded/Ownrshp 1993
Sales 27.1MM^E EMP 70
SIC 5181 Beer & other fermented malt liquors; Beer & other fermented malt liquors
Pr: Steve Reale
Info Man: Gerard Torsiello
Sales Exec: Terry O'Leary
Sls Mgr: Bryan Birdsall
Sls Mgr: Mike Reale

D-U-N-S 60-323-8320
■ **NORTHERN ELASTOMERIC INC**
NEI ADVANCED COMPOSITE TECH
(Suby of OWENS CORNING) ★
61 Pine Rd, Brentwood, NH 03833-6510
Tel (800) 998-4634 Founded/Ownrshp 2012
Sales 25.2MM^E EMP 94
SIC 1761 2952 Roofing materials; Roofing, siding & sheet metal work; Roofing, siding & sheet metal work; Roofing materials
Genl Mgr: Todd Tufto
*VP: Edmund Mangini

D-U-N-S 02-429-8168
NORTHERN ELECTRIC COOPERATIVE (INC)
39456 133rd St, Bath, SD 57427-5918
Tel (605) 225-0310 Founded/Ownrshp 1941
Sales 22.0MM EMP 34
SIC 4911 4841 Distribution, electric power; Cable television services; Distribution, electric power; Cable television services
Pr: Randy Knecht
*Treas: Ted Pazour
*Ex VP: Dennis Hagny
*VP: Larry Braun
Comm Dir: Erica Sperry
Genl Mgr: Char Hager
Off Mgr: Cyrece Kono
IT Man: Mark Fischer
IT Man: Cathi Podoll

D-U-N-S 10-252-9166
NORTHERN ELECTRIC INC
12789 Emerson St, Thornton, CO 80241-3396
Tel (303) 428-6969 Founded/Ownrshp 2001
Sales 158.5MM^E EMP 275
SIC 1731 Electrical work; Electrical work
Pr: Orville J Fleming
CFO: Tyler Fleming
*Treas: Joseph Dopler
Ex VP: Kurt Byrne
*VP: Albert Fisher
VP: Tom Keating
Dir Bus: George Haufler
IT Man: Jim Vercauteren
Sfty Dirs: Kurt Fisher
Snr PM: Steven Haney
Snr PM: Brian Pallissard

D-U-N-S 03-613-9681
NORTHERN EMPIRE PIZZA INC
DOMINO'S PIZZA
4141 38th St S Ste E1, Fargo, ND 58104-6919
Tel (701) 282-3484 Founded/Ownrshp 1981
Sales 7.9MM^E EMP 350
SIC 5812 Pizzeria, chain; Pizzeria, chain
Pr: Terry Nordenstrom
*VP: Jay Titus

D-U-N-S 02-276-9970 EXP
NORTHERN ENGINE & SUPPLY CO (MN)
9355 Westgate Blvd, Duluth, MN 55810-2127
Tel (218) 624-1443 Founded/Ownrshp 1953
Sales 21.5MM^E EMP 47
SIC 5082 5084 General construction machinery & equipment; Mining machinery & equipment, except petroleum; Industrial machinery & equipment
CEO: Gordon W Seitz
*Treas: Nancy Dodd
*VP: Thomas Seitz

D-U-N-S 09-709-2266 IMP
NORTHERN ENGRAVING CORP (WI)
(Suby of LAWRENCE HOLDING INC) ★
803 S Black River St, Sparta, WI 54656-2221
Tel (608) 269-6911 Founded/Ownrshp 2012
Sales 258.8MM^E EMP 1,200
SIC 3469 3544 3089 Stamping metal for the trade; Special dies, tools, jigs & fixtures; Automotive parts, plastic; Stamping metal for the trade; Special dies, tools, jigs & fixtures; Automotive parts, plastic
Pr: Bruce Dinger
*COO: Dan Schmitz
*CFO: Tom Kelbel
Treas: Clarence Hughes
VP: Rich Bahr
*VP: Aurel Mailath
*VP: Mike Mulvaney
Prgrm Mgr: Seth Jacobson
MIS Dir: Martin Passe
IT Man: Nathan Miller
QI Cn Mgr: Ken Schmidt

D-U-N-S 79-954-2170
NORTHERN ESSEX COMMUNITY COLLEGE
(Suby of MASSACHUSETTS BOARD OF HIGHER EDUCATION SYSTEM) ★
100 Elliott St, Haverhill, MA 01830-2399
Tel (978) 556-3000 Founded/Ownrshp 1972
Sales 35.7MM^E EMP 900^E
SIC 8222 9199 Community college; ; Community college;
Pr: Lane Glenn
*CFO: David Gingerella
*VP: Jean Poth

NORTHERN EXPLORATION SERVICES
See SAEXPLORATION INC

D-U-N-S 05-760-5669 IMP
NORTHERN FACTORY SALES INC
NORTHERN RADIATOR
2701 4th Ave Sw, Willmar, MN 56201-2778
Tel (320) 235-2288 Founded/Ownrshp 1971
Sales 40.7MM EMP 65
Accts Conway Deuth & Schmiesing Pl
SIC 5013 Automotive supplies & parts; Radiators; Heaters, motor vehicle; Tools & equipment, automotive; Automotive supplies & parts; Radiators; Heaters, motor vehicle; Tools & equipment, automotive
CEO: Roger Gauquie
*CFO: Tricia Payne
VP: Paul Freed
Prd Mgr: Kari Thompson
Mktg Mgr: Hope Thompson
Sls Mgr: Denny Engelmann

NORTHERN FISH - OLD TOWN
See NORTHERN FISH PRODUCTS INC

D-U-N-S 02-754-6399
NORTHERN FISH PRODUCTS INC
NORTHERN FISH - OLD TOWN
3911 S 56th St, Tacoma, WA 98409-2607
Tel (253) 475-3858 Founded/Ownrshp 1912
Sales 34.5MM^E EMP 75^E
SIC 5146 2092 Fish, fresh; Fish, cured; Fresh or frozen packaged fish; Fish, fresh; Fish, cured; Fresh or frozen packaged fish
Pr: John Swanes
*Sec: Pam Swanes
*VP: Ross Swanes

D-U-N-S 83-278-4834
NORTHERN FOUNDRY LLC
METAL TCHNLGIES-NORTHERN FNDRY
(Suby of KEY 3 CASTING LLC) ★
555 W 25th St, Hibbing, MN 55746-8347
Tel (218) 263-8871 Founded/Ownrshp 2009
Sales 27.9MM^E EMP 113
SIC 3321 3365 Gray iron castings; Aluminum & aluminum-based alloy castings
QI Cn Mgr: Bob Hedblom

D-U-N-S 01-780-8684
NORTHERN FROZEN FOODS INC
NORTHERN HASEROT
21500 Alexander Rd, Cleveland, OH 44146-5511
Tel (440) 439-0600 Founded/Ownrshp 1966
Sales 221.8MM^E EMP 200
SIC 5142 5149 5147 Packaged frozen goods; Canned goods: fruit, vegetables, seafood, meats, etc.; Meats, fresh; Packaged frozen goods; Canned goods: fruit, vegetables, seafood, meats, etc.; Meats, fresh
Pr: Douglas Kern
*Sec: Bruce Kern
*VP: Richard C Speicher
Comm Dir: Stefanie Reid
IT Man: Bruce Schaelffer
IT Man: Bruce Shaffner
Natl Sales: John Yachanin
VP Sls: Robert McKechnie
Sls Dir: Chuck Foerstner
Sls Mgr: Corrie Edwards
Sls Mgr: Travis Miller

D-U-N-S 00-490-4686 EXP
NORTHERN FRUIT CO (WA)
220 2nd St Ne, East Wenatchee, WA 98802-4851
Tel (509) 884-6651 Founded/Ownrshp 1924, 2006
Sales 85.9MM EMP 30
Accts Homchick Smith & Associates
SIC 0723 Fruit (fresh) packing services; Fruit (fresh) packing services
Pr: Doug Pauly
Opers Mgr: Jorge Sanchez

QI Cn Mgr: Tim Witter
Snr Mgr: Veronica Canchola

NORTHERN FUEL PARTNERS
See FARMERS UNION OIL CO OF WESTHOPE

D-U-N-S 09-822-7072
NORTHERN GC LLC
GOLDEN CORRAL
1515 N Academy Blvd # 400, Colorado Springs, CO 80909-2753
Tel (719) 573-8557 Founded/Ownrshp 1999
Sales 9.4MM^E EMP 400
SIC 5812 Restaurant, family: chain; Restaurant, family: chain
Genl Mgr: Amelia Defroy

D-U-N-S 05-762-8120
NORTHERN GENERAL CONTRACTORS INC
1516 Park St, Palmer, MA 01069-1644
Tel (413) 289-1230 Founded/Ownrshp 1995
Sales 20.6MM^E EMP 80
SIC 1622 Bridge construction
Prin: John Rahkonen
*Pr: John Divito
Off Mgr: Marianne Barrett

D-U-N-S 04-395-4192
NORTHERN GROWERS LLC
48416 144 St, Big Stone City, SD 57216
Tel (605) 862-7902 Founded/Ownrshp 2002
Sales 142.0MM EMP 51
SIC 6719 Investment holding companies, except banks; Investment holding companies, except banks
Pdt Mgr: Gail Street
Board of Directors: Ronald Anderson, Dennis Flemming, Robert Metz, Robert Narem, Brent Olson, Greg Toben, Bill Whipple, Robert Wittnebel

NORTHERN HASEROT
See NORTHERN FROZEN FOODS INC

D-U-N-S 60-547-3560
NORTHERN HOLDINGS INC
NEW FRONTIERS NATURAL MKT PL
1984 Old Mssion Dr Ste A7, Solvang, CA 93463
Tel (805) 693-1746 Founded/Ownrshp 2002
Sales 53.1MM^E EMP 600
SIC 5411 1795 1794 0161 Grocery stores, chain; Demolition, buildings & other structures; Excavation & grading, building construction; Vegetables & melons; Grocery stores, chain; Demolition, buildings & other structures; Excavation & grading, building construction; Vegetables & melons
Pr: Jonathan King
*Sec: Valerie King
*VP: David Adolphsen
*VP: Jacob Collier

D-U-N-S 07-782-9216
NORTHERN HOSPITAL DISTRICT OF SURRY COUNTY
NORTHERN HOSPITAL OF SURRY COU
830 Rockford St, Mount Airy, NC 27030-5322
Tel (336) 719-7000 Founded/Ownrshp 1953
Sales 76.6MM EMP 610
SIC 8062 8082 General medical & surgical hospitals; Home health care services; General medical & surgical hospitals; Home health care services
CEO: E Timothy Cook
Chf Path: Cullen Taylor
Dir Vol: Kaye Puckett
CFO: Bob Hetrick
Dir OR: Ann Riggs
Sfty Dirs: Greg Casstevens
Mktg Mgr: Amy Whitaker
Doctor: Lisa Snody

NORTHERN HOSPITAL OF SURRY COU
See NORTHERN HOSPITAL DISTRICT OF SURRY COUNTY

NORTHERN HOSPITILITY
See SAULT SAINTE MARIE TRIBE OF CHIPPEWA INDIANS

D-U-N-S 04-703-9888
NORTHERN ILLINOIS CLINICAL LABORATORY LTD
NICL LABORATORIES
306 Era Dr, Northbrook, IL 60062-1834
Tel (847) 509-9779 Founded/Ownrshp 1977
Sales 14.8MM^E EMP 300
SIC 8071 Medical laboratories; Medical laboratories
Pr: Paul Kent
VP: Joe Welder
*Dir Lab: Gradimir Vuckovic MD
Genl Mgr: Anna Welder
S&M/VP: J D Kirchberg

D-U-N-S 10-871-6408
NORTHERN ILLINOIS FOOD BANK
273 Dearborn Ct, Geneva, IL 60134-3587
Tel (630) 443-6910 Founded/Ownrshp 1982
Sales 131.9MM EMP 97
Accts Plante & Moran Pllc Chicago
SIC 8322 Individual & family services; Individual & family services
Pr: Pete Schaefer
Ofcr: Tiffany King
Dir: Julie Yurko
Comm Dir: Donna Lake
Software D: Corinne Boyd
Sls Mgr: Tom Netcher

D-U-N-S 00-692-7792
■ **NORTHERN ILLINOIS GAS CO**
NICOR GAS COMPANY
(Suby of OTTAWA ACQUISITION LLC) ★
1844 W Ferry Rd, Naperville, IL 60563-9600
Tel (630) 983-8676 Founded/Ownrshp 1954, 2011
Sales 1.2MMM^E EMP 2,050^E
SIC 4924 4922 Natural gas distribution; Natural gas transmission; Storage, natural gas; Natural gas distribution; Natural gas transmission; Storage, natural gas
Ch Bd: Henry P Linginfelter
Pr: Melvin D Williams

CFO: Andrew W Evans
Ex VP: Paul R Shlanta
Ex VP: Peter Tumminello
Sr VP: Bryan E Seas
VP: Gary Bartlett
VP: Kevin W Kirby
Dir Bus: David Haynes
Genl Mgr: Paul Delacey
Genl Mgr: Patrick Whiteside
Board of Directors: John Somerhalder II

D-U-N-S 14-478-2570
NORTHERN ILLINOIS HEALTH PLAN
1045 W Stephenson St, Freeport, IL 61032-4864
Tel (815) 599-6361 Founded/Ownrshp 1984
Sales 31.0MM^E EMP 1,200
SIC 8741 8721 Hospital management; Nursing & personal care facility management; Accounting, auditing & bookkeeping; Hospital management; Nursing & personal care facility management; Accounting, auditing & bookkeeping
Pr: Dennis L Hamilton
*Ch Bd: Woodruff A Burt
*Sec: Richard Zimmerman
Genl Mgr: Jeff Martin
Nurse Mgr: Deb Kent
Nutrtnst: Sarah Todd
Board of Directors: Harold Fenton

D-U-N-S 07-456-1432
NORTHERN ILLINOIS MEDICAL CENTER
4201 W Medical Center Dr, McHenry, IL 60050-8499
Tel (815) 344-5000 Founded/Ownrshp 1956
Sales 232.4MM EMP 1,200
Accts Kpmg Llp Columbus Oh
SIC 8062 General medical & surgical hospitals; General medical & surgical hospitals
Pr: Michael S Eesley
*Pr: Jason Sciarro
*CFO: David L Tomlinson
*Treas: Eric Zornow
*Sr VP: Aaron Shepley
Dir Lab: Judy Bjurstorm
Pharmcst: Heather Salinger
Snr Mgr: Abas Aimry
Snr Mgr: Sandy McCabe
Snr Mgr: Basudeb Saha

D-U-N-S 80-675-5505
NORTHERN ILLINOIS MUNICIPAL POWER AGENCY
NIMPA
333 Lincoln Hwy, Rochelle, IL 61068-1641
Tel (317) 575-3370 Founded/Ownrshp 2004
Sales 58.6MM EMP 4
SIC 8611 Public utility association; Public utility association
Pr: Dan Westin
VP: Gary Holm

D-U-N-S 02-555-7554
■ **NORTHERN ILLINOIS STEEL SUPPLY CO** (IL)
NI STEEL
(Suby of RELIANCE STEEL & ALUMINUM CO) ★
24005 S Northern Ill Dr, Channahon, IL 60410-5182
Tel (815) 467-9000 Founded/Ownrshp 1961, 2014
Sales 59.1MM^E EMP 45
SIC 5051 Steel
Pr: Michael Ruth
*VP: Timothy Ruth

D-U-N-S 00-174-5512
NORTHERN ILLINOIS UNIVERSITY ALUMNI ASSOCIATION (IL)
1425 W Lincoln Hwy, Dekalb, IL 60115-2828
Tel (815) 753-9500 Founded/Ownrshp 1895
Sales 587.7MM^E EMP 8,500
Accts Ec Ortiz & Co Llp Chicago
SIC 8221 University; University
Pr: Douglas Baker
COO: Deanna Sexton
Bd of Dir: Moonja Jeong
Ofcr: Devon Buckle
Assoc VP: Joseph Matty
VP: Jerry Blakemore
VP: Kathy Buettner
VP: Anne C Kaplan
Assoc Dir: Tracy Ash
Assoc Dir: Carolyn Bershad
Assoc Dir: Bobbie Cole
Assoc Dir: Joyce Keller
Assoc Dir: Ellen King
Assoc Dir: Mark Pietrowski
Assoc Dir: Mary Pritchard
Assoc Dir: Paul Wrezinski
Comm Man: Elizabeth Denius

D-U-N-S 03-181-8289
NORTHERN IMPROVEMENT CO
(Suby of MCCORMICK INC) ★
4000 12th Ave N, Fargo, ND 58102-2910
Tel (701) 277-1225 Founded/Ownrshp 1959
Sales 211.5MM EMP 125
Accts Eide Bailly Llp Fargo North
SIC 1611 1629 Highway & street paving contractor; Airport runway construction; Power plant construction; Highway & street paving contractor; Airport runway construction; Power plant construction
Pr: Thomas McCormick
*CFO: Jay Kjos
*Ex VP: Steve McCormick
*VP: Brad Ballweber
Off Mgr: Teri Marquart

D-U-N-S 04-935-1778
NORTHERN INDIANA COMMUTER TRANSPORTATION DISTRICT
N I C T D
33 Highway St 12, Chesterton, IN 46304
Tel (219) 926-5744 Founded/Ownrshp 1977
Sales 32.0MM^E EMP 339
SIC 4111 Passenger rail transportation; Passenger rail transportation
Pr: Gerald Hanas
*COO: Joe Black
*CFO: Keith Casey

**CIO:* Boris Matakovic
Mktg Dir: John N Parsons

NORTHERN INDIANA MED LAB SVCS
See ALVERNO CLINICAL LABORATORIES INC

D-U-N-S 00-693-7585 IMP
■ NORTHERN INDIANA PUBLIC SERVICE CO
(*Suby of* NISOURCE INC) ★
801 E 86th Ave, Merrillville, IN 46410-6271
Tel (877) 647-5990 *Founded/Ownrshp* 1988
Sales 1.8MMM^E *EMP* 3,096
SIC 4924 4911 Natural gas distribution; Generation, electric power; Natural gas distribution; Generation, electric power
Pr: Kathleen O'Leary
**CFO:* Pete Disser
Sr VP: Guy Ausmus
**Sr VP:* Timothy A Dehring
**VP:* Gary W Pottorff
**VP:* Jon D Veurink
Ex Dir: Karl Stanley

D-U-N-S 15-752-0362
NORTHERN INDUSTRIAL ERECTORS INC
2500 Glenwood Dr, Grand Rapids, MN 55744-3347
Tel (218) 326-8466 *Founded/Ownrshp* 2008
Sales 44.0MM *EMP* 100
Accts Charles R Ziegler Company Lt
SIC 1791 1796 Structural steel erection; Machinery installation; Structural steel erection; Machinery installation
Pr: Stan Bostyancic

D-U-N-S 15-147-4053 EXP
NORTHERN INDUSTRIAL INC
NICHOLSON MANUFACTURING
200 S Orcas St, Seattle, WA 98108-2441
Tel (206) 682-2752 *Founded/Ownrshp* 1986
Sales 45.9MM^E *EMP* 250
SIC 2421 3553 Sawmills & planing mills, general; Sawmill machines; Sawmills & planing mills, general; Sawmill machines
CEO: Scott Howell
Pr: Scott Nicholson
CFO: Paul Nishimura

D-U-N-S 07-960-6331
NORTHERN INYO COUNTY LOCAL HOSPITAL DISTRICT
NORTHERN INYO HOSPITAL
150 Pioneer Ln, Bishop, CA 93514-2556
Tel (760) 873-5811 *Founded/Ownrshp* 1946
Sales 72.9MM *EMP* 402
Accts Wipfli Llp Spokane Wa
SIC 8062 General medical & surgical hospitals; General medical & surgical hospitals
CEO: Victoria Alexander-Lane
Dir Recs: Kelli Huntsinger
Dir Recs: Ann Rusk
V Ch: Marie Boyd
**Pr:* M C Hubbard
**Treas:* Peter Watercott
**VP:* Denise Hayden
Comm Dir: Georgan Stottlmyre
Dir Rx: Jillene Freis
Mng Ofcr: Kathryn Erickson
Ex Dir: Greg Bissonette

NORTHERN INYO HOSPITAL
See NORTHERN INYO COUNTY LOCAL HOSPITAL DISTRICT

D-U-N-S 00-727-4715 IMP
NORTHERN IOWA DIE CASTING INC
702 E Railroad St, Lake Park, IA 51347-1012
Tel (712) 832-3661 *Founded/Ownrshp* 1984
Sales 25.5MM^E *EMP* 120
SIC 3363 3364 3369 Aluminum die-castings; Zinc & zinc-base alloy die-castings; Nonferrous foundries
Pr: Joanne Stockdale
IT Man: Mike Schweitzer
QC Dir: Jeannie Hawn
Sfty Mgr: Dana Klontz
Sfty Mgr: Luis Reece

NORTHERN IRON AND MACHINE
See NORTHERN IRON OF ST PAUL LLC

D-U-N-S 10-671-4793
NORTHERN IRON OF ST PAUL LLC
NORTHERN IRON AND MACHINE
867 Forest St, Saint Paul, MN 55106-3866
Tel (651) 778-3300 *Founded/Ownrshp* 1982
Sales 23.1MM^E *EMP* 100
SIC 3321 3322 3363 3679 Gray & ductile iron foundries; Ductile iron castings; Gray iron castings; Malleable iron foundries; Aluminum die-castings; Harness assemblies for electronic use: wire or cable
**CFO:* Gregory Leier
VP Opers: Ken Damewood
Plnt Mgr: Ray Van Allen
Sls Mgr: Mark Amland

D-U-N-S 07-971-0612
NORTHERN ITASCA HOSPITAL DISTRICT
BIGFORK VALLEY
258 Pine Tree Dr, Bigfork, MN 56628
Tel (218) 743-3177 *Founded/Ownrshp* 1938
Sales 22.2MM *EMP* 225
SIC 8062 8051 6513 General medical & surgical hospitals; Skilled nursing care facilities; Apartment building operators; General medical & surgical hospitals; Skilled nursing care facilities; Apartment building operators
CEO: H D Odegaard
V Ch: Tom Evenson
Brnch Mgr: Ken Westman
CIO: Rob Anderson
QA Dir: Meryl Ostendorf
Plnt Mgr: William Loosbrock
Mktg Dir: Sally Sedgwick
Phys Thrpy: Randy Herme

D-U-N-S 07-742-7854
NORTHERN KENTUCKY MENTAL HEALTH - MENTAL RETARDATION REGIONAL BOARD INC
NORTHKEY COMMUNITY CARE
503 Farrell Dr, Covington, KY 41011-3775
Tel (859) 578-3252 *Founded/Ownrshp* 1966
Sales 27.4MM *EMP* 450
Accts Vonlehman & Company Inc Fort
SIC 8093 8069 Mental health clinic, outpatient; Children's hospital; Mental health clinic, outpatient; Children's hospital
Ex Dir: Owen Nichols
**CFO:* Art Jones
**Ch:* James Thelen
VP: Gary Goetz
VP: Charles Kapp
Orthpdst: Jennie Hahn

D-U-N-S 07-287-9760
NORTHERN KENTUCKY UNIVERSITY
Nunn Dr, Newport, KY 41099-0001
Tel (859) 572-5100 *Founded/Ownrshp* 1970
Sales 143.7MM *EMP* 1,600
Accts Dean Dorton Allen Ford Pllc
SIC 8221 University; University
Pr: Geoffrey S Mearns
COO: Larry Terrell
Ofcr: Justin Aromas-Janosik
Ofcr: Becky Roberts
Ofcr: Pam Wagar
VP: Peter Gitau
VP: Kimberly Scranage
Dir Rx: Andy Meeks
CIO: Tim Ferguson
IT Man: Kim Baker
Opers Mgr: Ward Wenstrup

D-U-N-S 96-395-1983
NORTHERN KENTUCKY WATER DISTRICT
2835 Crescent Springs Pik, Erlanger, KY 41018-1326
Tel (859) 441-0482 *Founded/Ownrshp* 1997
Sales 50.8MM *EMP* 150
Accts Rankin Rankin & Company Ft
SIC 4941 Water supply; Water supply
CEO: C Ronald Lovan
**CFO:* Jack Bragg

D-U-N-S 05-529-6479 IMP/EXP
NORTHERN LABS INC
5800 West Dr, Manitowoc, WI 54220-8367
Tel (920) 684-7137 *Founded/Ownrshp* 1986
Sales 124.3MM^E *EMP* 250
SIC 2842 2841 Automobile polish; Toilet preparations; Hair preparations, including shampoos; Automobile polish; Detergents, synthetic organic or inorganic alkaline
Pr: James D Culea
CFO: Chermaine Meissner
CFO: N Weigarth
CFO: N Weingarth
Sls Mgr: Sven Richter

D-U-N-S 10-675-1530
NORTHERN LAKES COMMUNITY MENTAL HEALTH
105 Hall St Unit A, Traverse City, MI 49684-2288
Tel (231) 922-4850 *Founded/Ownrshp* 1974
Sales NA *EMP* 277
Accts Rehmann Robson Grand Rapids
SIC 9431 Mental health agency administration, government; Mental health agency administration, government
CEO: Greg Paffhouse
CFO: Bruce Bridges
Ofcr: Tom Benton
CIO: Keith Huggett

D-U-N-S 02-326-2397
NORTHERN LAKES COOPERATIVE
15877 W Us Highway 63, Hayward, WI 54843-7177
Tel (715) 634-3211 *Founded/Ownrshp* 1932
Sales 22.6MM^E *EMP* 100
SIC 5251 5411

D-U-N-S 14-754-6076
NORTHERN LAKES SEAFOOD & MEATS LLC
12301 Conant St, Detroit, MI 48212-2341
Tel (313) 368-2500 *Founded/Ownrshp* 2004
Sales 20.3MM^E *EMP* 45
SIC 5146 Seafoods

D-U-N-S 79-055-2574
NORTHERN LEASING SYSTEMS INC
419 E Main St Ste 102, Middletown, NY 10940-2552
Tel (800) 683-5433 *Founded/Ownrshp* 1991
Sales NA *EMP* 210
SIC 6159 Machinery & equipment finance leasing; Machinery & equipment finance leasing
Pr: Jay Cohen
**Ch Bd:* Len Mezei
CFO: Dan O'Connell
CFO: Beth Pascua
VP: Sam Bruno
CIO: Steve Bernardone
Dir IT: John Fragos
Dir IT: Randy Swain
Info Man: Michael Rodriguez

NORTHERN LEBANON HIGH SCHOOL
See NORTHERN LEBANON SCHOOL DISTRICT

D-U-N-S 02-741-4721
NORTHERN LEBANON SCHOOL DISTRICT
NORTHERN LEBANON HIGH SCHOOL
School Dr Rr 22, Fredericksburg, PA 17026
Tel (717) 432-8655 *Founded/Ownrshp* 1957
Sales 19.8MM^E *EMP* 520
Accts Wootton Reed & Associates Pc
SIC 8211 Public elementary & secondary schools; Public elementary & secondary schools
HC Dir: Michelle Fure

D-U-N-S 02-216-5690
NORTHERN LIGHTS DISTRIBUTING INC
2949 8th Ave S, Fort Dodge, IA 50501-5513
Tel (515) 576-0751 *Founded/Ownrshp* 1998
Sales 26.8MM^E *EMP* 50
SIC 5141 5142 5113 5148 5087 5149 Groceries, general line; Packaged frozen goods; Towels, paper; Napkins, paper; Fresh fruits & vegetables; Janitors' supplies; Beverages, except coffee & tea
Pr: Nicholas A Garst
**Treas:* Barbara Garst
IT Man: Joe McBride
Sls Mgr: Roger Colin

D-U-N-S 04-789-2393
NORTHERN LOCAL SCHOOL DISTRICT
8700 Sheridan Dr, Thornville, OH 43076-9757
Tel (740) 743-1303 *Founded/Ownrshp* 1959
Sales 20.6MM^E *EMP* 240
Accts Dave Yost Athens Ohio
SIC 8211 Public elementary school; Public junior high school; Public senior high school; School board; Public elementary school; Public junior high school; Public senior high school; School board
**Treas:* Elizabeth Arnold

D-U-N-S 80-752-1430
NORTHERN LOGISTICS INC
4915 E Colonville Rd, Clare, MI 48617-8920
Tel (989) 386-7556 *Founded/Ownrshp* 1977
Sales 20.4MM^E *EMP* 70
SIC 4213 Contract haulers
Pr: Steve Schunk

D-U-N-S 07-746-4444
NORTHERN MAINE MEDICAL CENTER INC
194 E Main St, Fort Kent, ME 04743-1428
Tel (207) 834-3155 *Founded/Ownrshp* 1952
Sales 43.4MM *EMP* 476
Accts Berry Dunn Mcneil & Parker Ll
SIC 8062 8011 General medical & surgical hospitals; Offices & clinics of medical doctors; General medical & surgical hospitals; Offices & clinics of medical doctors
Ofcr: Peter Sirois
CFO: Cindy Dagle
**CFO:* Cindy Daigle
Mng Ofcr: Joel Dye
Genl Mgr: Cindy St Jarre
Mktg Dir: Don Theriault
Psych: Joanne Fortin
Orthpdst: John Naranja
Obsttrcn: Joyce Hebert
Doctor: Irfan Asghar
Doctor: Jonathan Herland

D-U-N-S 78-117-5112
NORTHERN MANAGEMENT SERVICES INC
607 Church St, Sandpoint, ID 83864-1636
Tel (208) 263-1363 *Founded/Ownrshp* 1991
Sales 49.1MM^E *EMP* 120
SIC 1542 7349 Specialized public building contractors; Building maintenance, except repairs; Specialized public building contractors; Building maintenance, except repairs
Pr: John Deshon
**VP:* Kent Malone

D-U-N-S 93-363-5351
NORTHERN MANHATTAN NURSING HOME INC
NORTHERN MANHATTAN REHABILITA
116 E 125th St, New York, NY 10035-1612
Tel (212) 369-1300 *Founded/Ownrshp* 1993
Sales 34.6MM *EMP* 300
SIC 8051 Skilled nursing care facilities; Skilled nursing care facilities
CEO: AVI Klein

NORTHERN MANHATTAN REHABILITA
See NORTHERN MANHATTAN NURSING HOME INC

D-U-N-S 07-271-2169
NORTHERN MANOR MULTICARE CENTER INC (NY)
199 N Middletown Rd, Nanuet, NY 10954-1317
Tel (845) 623-3904 *Founded/Ownrshp* 1959, 1991
Sales 35.2MM *EMP* 320^E
SIC 8051 Skilled nursing care facilities; Skilled nursing care facilities
Pr: Morris Klein
MIS Dir: Oscar Abraham
Nrsg Dir: Marilyn Pitcher
HC Dir: Christine Dloughy

D-U-N-S 00-504-3070 IMP
NORTHERN MANUFACTURING CO INC (OH)
132 N Railroad St, Oak Harbor, OH 43449-1000
Tel (419) 898-2821 *Founded/Ownrshp* 1951
Sales 74.8MM^E *EMP* 145
SIC 3441 Fabricated structural metal; Fabricated structural metal
Pr: Quintin R Smith
**Prin:* Harry Bethel
**Prin:* Joe Bodner
**Prin:* Paul Schmitt
CTO: Jim Smith
Mtls Mgr: Chris Crump
Plnt Mgr: Chuck Rodenhauser
Prd Mgr: Roger Norenberg
Ql Cn Mgr: Karen Daniels
Snr Mgr: Tim Louk

NORTHERN METAL RECYCLING
See NORTHERN METALS LLC

D-U-N-S 01-999-4167
NORTHERN METALS LLC
NORTHERN METAL RECYCLING
(*Suby of* EMR (USA HOLDINGS) INC) ★
2800 Pacific St, Minneapolis, MN 55411-1624
Tel (612) 529-9221 *Founded/Ownrshp* 2007
Sales 45.7MM^E *EMP* 200
SIC 3341 Recovery & refining of nonferrous metals; Recovery & refining of nonferrous metals
Pr: Stephen Ettinger
**COO:* Scott Helberg
**VP:* Jerrold Bader
**VP:* Melinda House
**VP:* Jeff Popovich
**VP:* Tom Rutenberg
Sfty Mgr: Jack Bisbey
Opers Mgr: Bryan Plonski

NORTHERN METALS RECYCLING
See AMERICAN IRON & STEEL CO INC

NORTHERN MICHIGAN REGIONAL HOSPITAL
See MCLAREN NORTHERN MICHIGAN

D-U-N-S 07-313-5634
NORTHERN MICHIGAN UNIVERSITY
1401 Presque Isle Ave, Marquette, MI 49855-2818
Tel (906) 227-1000 *Founded/Ownrshp* 1899
Sales 101.3MM *EMP* 981
Accts Rehmann Robson Llc Traverse C
SIC 8221 College, except junior; College, except junior
Pr: Dr Fritz Erickson
**Pr:* David S Haynes
**Ch:* Brian D Cloyd
Treas: Patrick Lakenen
Bd of Dir: Dan Truckey
Ofcr: Julie Genore
Ex VP: Alfred Joyal
VP: Fred Joyal
VP: Ken Reindel
Assoc Dir: Bridget Berube
Prgrm Mgr: Tricia Bush
Board of Directors: Deanna Hemmila, Carol Carr, Amy Hubinger, Alison Crowley, Gina Lombardini, Gerri Daniels, Cindy L Paavola, Allison Erickson, Kathy Richards, Kristi Evans, Robyn Stille, Kathy Frazier, Jane Surrell, Sheri Giordana, Scott Thum, Brad Hamel, Dan Truckey, Martha Haynes

D-U-N-S 00-644-1257 IMP
NORTHERN MICHIGAN VENEERS INC
(*Suby of* FOREST BESSE PRODUCTS INC) ★
710 Rains Dr, Gladstone, MI 49837-1129
Tel (906) 428-1082 *Founded/Ownrshp* 1967
Sales 25.0MM *EMP* 65
SIC 2435 Veneer stock, hardwood; Veneer stock, hardwood
Pr: John D Besse
**Treas:* Melissa Besse
VP: Jim Moberg

D-U-N-S 83-285-8166
NORTHERN MONTANA HEALTH CARE INC
30 13th St, Havre, MT 59501-5222
Tel (406) 265-2211 *Founded/Ownrshp* 1985
Sales NA *EMP* 600
SIC 6324 Hospital & medical service plans; Hospital & medical service plans
CEO: David Henry

D-U-N-S 07-868-8421
NORTHERN MONTANA HOSPITAL
30 13th St, Havre, MT 59501-5222
Tel (406) 262-1107 *Founded/Ownrshp* 1920
Sales 62.0MM *EMP* 700
Accts Eide Badly Lp Minneapolis Mn
SIC 8062 General medical & surgical hospitals; General medical & surgical hospitals
Pr: David C Henry
Chf Rad: Steven Liston
V Ch: Ann Kuhr
COO: Julie Mariani
VP: Bonnie Neill
VP: Bonnie O'Neill
Dir Inf Cn: Ginny Heberly
Dir Rad: John Rosenbaum
Dir Rx: Elaine Morse
IT Man: Terri Earl
Sls Dir: Jeanna Parker

D-U-N-S 05-257-5768
NORTHERN MUNICIPAL POWER AGENCY (MN)
123 2nd St W, Thief River Falls, MN 56701-1912
Tel (218) 681-0962 *Founded/Ownrshp* 1976
Sales 45.5MM *EMP* 3
SIC 8399 Community action agency; Community action agency
Pr: Mylo Einarson
**Sec:* Dalene Monsebroten
VP: Darrel Anderson
Genl Mgr: Darryl Pveitbakk

D-U-N-S 78-415-8214
■ NORTHERN NATURAL GAS CO
(*Suby of* BERKSHIRE HATHAWAY ENERGY CO) ★
1111 S 103rd St, Omaha, NE 68124-1072
Tel (402) 398-7000 *Founded/Ownrshp* 2002
Sales 203.7MM^E *EMP* 1,055
SIC 4226 4922 4923 4925 Special warehousing & storage; Oil & gasoline storage caverns for hire; Natural gas transmission; Pipelines, natural gas; Gas transmission & distribution; Gas production and/or distribution; Special warehousing & storage; Oil & gasoline storage caverns for hire; Natural gas transmission; Pipelines, natural gas; Gas transmission & distribution; Gas production and/or distribution
CEO: Greg Abel
**Pr:* Mark A Hewett
Treas: Leanne Meyer
VP: Joe Lillo
VP: Joseph M Lillo
VP: Mary Miller
VP: Gregory Porter
Area Mgr: Terry Janzen
QA Dir: Jyothi Dodda
IT Man: Joanne Bisbee
Sfty Dirs: Russell Stewart

D-U-N-S 00-982-0036
NORTHERN NECK ELECTRIC COOPERATIVE INC
85 St Johns St, Warsaw, VA 22572-3571
Tel (804) 333-3621 *Founded/Ownrshp* 1937
Sales 34.0MM *EMP* 57
SIC 4911 Distribution, electric power; Distribution, electric power
Pr: Greg White
**Ch Bd:* J Steve Thomas Sr
V Ch: Hunter R Greenlaw Jr
Pr: Patrick Henry

COO: Jim Moss
**CFO:* Martin Mothershead
**Sec:* Elnora F Tompkins
VP: Richard McLendon
Board of Directors: John Allen, Russel Brown, Hunter Greenlaw, A Saunders, Ralph Sutton, Steve Thomas, Elnora Tompkins

D-U-N-S 00-794-0315
NORTHERN NECK INSURANCE CO (VA)
4981 Irvington Rd, Irvington, VA 22480-2127
Tel (804) 438-6611 *Founded/Ownrshp* 1896
Sales NA *EMP* 45
SIC 6331 Fire, marine & casualty insurance: mutual
Pr: Thomas A Gosse
CFO: Peter Cammarata
Treas: Donna Tibbs
VP: C Randall Conner
VP: Diane Starbuck
VP: Jerry Wacter
VP: Pam Walker
Board of Directors: Clarence Wyatt Alston, Ammon Gresham Dunton Jr, William Brockenbrough Grah, Lloyd Benjamin Hubbard, Melvin Carter Moss, Marion Davis Shannon, Robert Lee Stephens

D-U-N-S 79-161-8499
■ **NORTHERN NEVADA MEDICAL CENTER LP**
(*Suby of* UNIVERSAL HEALTH SERVICES INC) ★
2375 E Prater Way, Sparks, NV 89434-9665
Tel (775) 331-7000 *Founded/Ownrshp* 2000
Sales 85.5MM *EMP* 505
SIC 8062 8093 8071 8049 8011 General medical & surgical hospitals; Rehabilitation center, outpatient treatment; X-ray laboratory, including dental; Speech pathologist; Freestanding emergency medical center; General medical & surgical hospitals; Rehabilitation center, outpatient treatment; X-ray laboratory, including dental; Speech pathologist; Freestanding emergency medical center
CEO: Alan Olive
Pt: Wayne Allen
Pt: Gina Anderson
Pt: Meg Cleary
Pt: James R Pagels
COO: Tiffany Meert
CFO: Ryan Heit
Chf Mktg O: Ira Pauly
Dir OR: Kristi Eash
Dir Inf Cn: Beth Wilmer
Dir Risk M: Myrna Cpha
Dir Lab: Cheryl Snook

NORTHERN NEW ENGL CARPENTERS
See NORTHERN NEW ENGLAND DISTRICT COUNCIL OF CARPENTERS INC

D-U-N-S 07-397-1608
NORTHERN NEW ENGLAND BENEFIT TRUST
51 Goffstown Rd Ste 2, Manchester, NH 03102-2746
Tel (603) 669-4771 *Founded/Ownrshp* 1965
Sales NA *EMP* 8
Accts Howe Riley & Howe Pllc Manche
SIC 6371 Pension, health & welfare funds; Pension, health & welfare funds
Ex Dir: Robert Gibbons
**Trst:* William Clifford
**Trst:* Gerard Cole
**Trst:* Bob Gibbons
**Trst:* Robert Homes

D-U-N-S 06-098-6858
NORTHERN NEW ENGLAND DISTRICT COUNCIL OF CARPENTERS INC
NORTHERN NEW ENGL CARPENTERS
350 Fordham Rd, Wilmington, MA 01887-2174
Tel (800) 383-2759 *Founded/Ownrshp* 1974
Sales 123.1MM *EMP* 3
Accts Daniel A Winters & Company Cpa
SIC 8631 Labor unions & similar labor organizations; Labor unions & similar labor organizations
Pr: Bruce King

D-U-N-S 82-477-6749
NORTHERN NEW ENGLAND ENERGY CORP
(*Suby of* GAZ METRO INC)
85 Swift St, South Burlington, VT 05403-7306
Tel (802) 658-6555 *Founded/Ownrshp* 2008
Sales 717.6MM^E *EMP* 192^E
SIC 4911 Electric services; Electric services
Pr: Sophie Brochu

D-U-N-S 14-118-1391
NORTHERN NEW JERSEY TEAMSTERS BENEFIT PLAN
810 Belmont Ave, North Haledon, NJ 07508-2357
Tel (973) 423-4565 *Founded/Ownrshp* 2000
Sales 28.3MM *EMP* 3
Accts Lynch & Murray Cpas Bloomfiel
SIC 8631 Labor unions & similar labor organizations; Labor unions & similar labor organizations

D-U-N-S 06-941-8598
NORTHERN NEW MEXICO COLLEGE FOUNDATION
921 N Paseo De Onate, Espanola, NM 87532-2649
Tel (505) 747-2100 *Founded/Ownrshp* 1909
Sales 165.8M *EMP* 350
Accts Moss Adams Llp Albuquerque N
SIC 8221 8222 Colleges universities & professional schools; Community college; Colleges universities & professional schools; Community college
Pr: Henry Eda Trujillo
**Pr:* Nancy Barcelo
**Treas:* Danielle Duran
**Ex VP:* Thomas Garcia
**VP:* Loretto Garcia
**VP:* Ron Lovato

NORTHERN NM EMERGENCY MED
See ST VINCENT HOSPITAL

D-U-N-S 09-524-2301
NORTHERN NURSERIES OF NEWYORK INC
1695 King St, Enfield, CT 06082-6036
Tel (802) 295-2117 *Founded/Ownrshp* 1978
Sales 30.6MM^E *EMP* 60
SIC 5193 Nursery stock
Pr: Donald G Baker
Treas: Robert C Hunt
**VP:* Dale Baker
**Prin:* Robert Baker Jr
Opers Mgr: Floyd Appleby
Sales Asso: Bill Burden

D-U-N-S 60-365-9244 IMP/EXP
NORTHERN OCEAN MARINE INC
7 Parker St, Gloucester, MA 01930-3025
Tel (978) 283-0222 *Founded/Ownrshp* 1989
Sales 24.3MM^E *EMP* 4
SIC 5146 Seafoods; Seafoods
Pr: H James Leboeuf Jr
Mktg Mgr: Deke Fyrberg

D-U-N-S 82-536-0659 IMP/EXP
NORTHERN OFFSHORE LTD
(*Suby of* NORTHERN OFFSHORE LTD)
575 N Dairy Ashford Rd # 200, Houston, TX 77079-1117
Tel (281) 649-2600 *Founded/Ownrshp* 1988
Sales 25.6MM^E *EMP* 450
SIC 1381 Drilling oil & gas wells; Drilling oil & gas wells
CEO: Gary Casswell
Sr VP: Paul Ravesies III
Mng Dir: Richard Borghese

D-U-N-S 01-503-1904
NORTHERN OHIO MEDICAL SPECIALISTS LLC
2500 W Strub Rd, Sandusky, OH 44870-5390
Tel (419) 626-6161 *Founded/Ownrshp* 2000
Sales 27.0MM^E *EMP* 203
SIC 8011 Offices & clinics of medical doctors; Offices & clinics of medical doctors
Pr: Louis Ralofsky
CFO: Joshua Frederick
Off Mgr: Shelly Lindecamp
Dir IT: John Baus
Psych: Shealynne Baus
Podiatrist: Dr John Liebenthal

D-U-N-S 05-996-8883
NORTHERN OHIO PIZZA CO INC
PIZZA HUT
8100 E 22nd St N Bldg 200, Wichita, KS 67226-2302
Tel (316) 685-7090 *Founded/Ownrshp* 1972
Sales 7.4MM^E *EMP* 300
SIC 5812 Pizzeria, chain
Pr: Jack L Shelton
**Treas:* Douglas C O'Oconnor

D-U-N-S 82-985-9615
NORTHERN OIL AND GAS INC
315 Manitoba Ave Ste 200, Wayzata, MN 55391-1660
Tel (952) 476-9800 *Founded/Ownrshp* 2007
Sales 595.0MM *EMP* 23^E
Tkr Sym NOG *Exch* ASE
SIC 1311 Crude petroleum & natural gas; Crude petroleum & natural gas
Ch Bd: Michael L Reger
CFO: Thomas W Stoelk
Ex VP: Brandon R Elliott
Ex VP: Darrell R Finneman
Ex VP: Erik J Romslo

D-U-N-S 15-696-2524
NORTHERN OZAUKEE SCHOOL DISTRICT
OZAUKEE HIGH SCHOOL
401 Highland Dr, Fredonia, WI 53021-9499
Tel (262) 692-2401 *Founded/Ownrshp* 1964
Sales 46.1M *EMP* 301
SIC 8211 Public elementary & secondary schools; Public elementary & secondary schools
Prin: Blake A Peuse
Bd of Dir: Tom Hoffmann
Instr Medi: Linda Wavrunek

D-U-N-S 05-718-0283
NORTHERN PALM BEACH COUNTY IMPROVEMENT DISTRICT
359 Hiatt Dr, Palm Beach Gardens, FL 33418-7106
Tel (561) 799-2012 *Founded/Ownrshp* 1959
Sales 26.3MM *EMP* 17
Accts Marcum Llp West Palm Beach F
SIC 1629 Drainage system construction; Drainage system construction
Ex Dir: O'Neal Bardin Jr
COO: Eric Vincent
CFO: Tanya Quickel
Opers Supe: Rick Musgrove
Opers Mgr: Jon Iles

D-U-N-S 82-991-0848
NORTHERN PARTNERS COOPERATIVE
1000 6th Ave, Mendota, IL 61342-1736
Tel (815) 539-6772 *Founded/Ownrshp* 1915
Sales 114.9MM *EMP* 70
SIC 5153 Grain & field beans; Grain & field beans
CEO: Eric Anderson
**CFO:* Alan Zehr
Off Mgr: Sarah Cook
Off Mgr: Kim Higgins
Opers Mgr: James Meyer

D-U-N-S 04-337-9320
NORTHERN PHARMACY AND MEDICAL EQUIPMENT INC (MD)
GOOD NEIGHBOR PHARMACY
6701 Harford Rd, Baltimore, MD 21234-7721
Tel (410) 254-2055 *Founded/Ownrshp* 1984
Sales 46.4MM^E *EMP* 100
SIC 5912 5999 5047

D-U-N-S 08-251-5198
NORTHERN PINES MENTAL HEALTH CENTER INC (MN)
1906 5th Ave Se, Little Falls, MN 56345-3317
Tel (320) 632-6647 *Founded/Ownrshp* 1961
Sales 11.9MM^E *EMP* 285^E
Accts Wipfli Llp Duluth Mn
SIC 8011 8322 Psychiatric clinic; General counseling services
Ex Dir: Glenn Anderson
Board of Directors: Glenn Anderson

D-U-N-S 00-892-5869
NORTHERN PLAINS ELECTRIC COOPERATIVE (ND)
1515 Main St, Carrington, ND 58421
Tel (701) 652-3156 *Founded/Ownrshp* 1937
Sales 39.1MM^E *EMP* 50
SIC 4911 Distribution, electric power; Distribution, electric power
Prin: Jay Jacobson
**Genl Mgr:* Lowell Stave
Mktg Mgr: Connie Krapp

D-U-N-S 11-426-6091
NORTHERN PLAINS EQUIPMENT CO INC
KUBOTA
(*Suby of* KRIDER EQUIPMENT CO., INC.)
2933 Twin City Dr, Mandan, ND 58554-3800
Tel (701) 663-9864 *Founded/Ownrshp* 1984
Sales 30.0MM^E *EMP* 31
SIC 5083 7699 5082

D-U-N-S 07-938-7766
NORTHERN POWER SYSTEMS CORP
29 Pitman Rd, Barre, VT 05641-8920
Tel (802) 461-2903 *Founded/Ownrshp* 2014
Sales 29.1MM^E *EMP* 135^E
SIC 3511 Turbines & turbine generator sets
Pr: Troy C Patton
CFO: Ciel R Caldwell
Ch: William F Leimkuhler
VP: Elliot J Mark
CTO: Jonathan A Lynch
Board of Directors: Gregory C Wolf

D-U-N-S 82-837-3642 IMP/EXP
NORTHERN POWER SYSTEMS INC
29 Pitman Rd, Barre, VT 05641-8920
Tel (802) 461-2955 *Founded/Ownrshp* 2003
Sales 53.2MM^E *EMP* 135^E
SIC 3511 Turbines & turbine generator sets; Turbines & turbine generator sets
CEO: Troy Patton
**Pr:* John Danner
**COO:* Ciel Caldwell
**COO:* Lawrence Willey
**CFO:* Douglas Prince
**VP:* Parthiv Amin
**VP:* Elliot Mark
**VP:* Reinout G Oussoren
**CTO:* Jonathan Lynch
VP Mfg: Craig Gles
Board of Directors: David W Cornhill

D-U-N-S 00-608-2788
NORTHERN PRECISION CASTING CO INC (WI)
300 Interchange N, Lake Geneva, WI 53147-8916
Tel (262) 248-4461 *Founded/Ownrshp* 1948, 1962
Sales 38.5MM^E *EMP* 170
SIC 3324 3369 Steel investment foundries; Castings, except die-castings, precision; Steel investment foundries; Castings, except die-castings, precision
Ch Bd: Gary A Giovannetti
**Pr:* Jeffrey Giovannetti
**VP:* Lorna O'Rourke

D-U-N-S 36-188-8761
NORTHERN PRIDE INC
401 Conley Ave S, Thief River Falls, MN 56701-3117
Tel (218) 681-1201 *Founded/Ownrshp* 1989
Sales 37.1MM^E *EMP* 210
Accts Kays Benton Safranski & Co
SIC 2015 Turkey processing & slaughtering; Turkey processing & slaughtering
CEO: Troy Stauffenecker
**Treas:* Dennis Olson
**VP:* Doug Headland
**Prin:* Glen Jaenicke
Genl Mgr: Russ Christianson
Sfty Mgr: Sharon Wold

NORTHERN PRODUCE COMPANY
See NORTHERN PRODUCE/MUSHROOMS INC

D-U-N-S 02-856-7592
NORTHERN PRODUCE/MUSHROOMS INC
NORTHERN PRODUCE COMPANY
5354 E Slauson Ave, Los Angeles, CA 90040-2917
Tel (323) 724-6969 *Founded/Ownrshp* 1981
Sales 25.2MM^E *EMP* 50
SIC 5148 Fresh fruits & vegetables
CEO: Joey Weiss
**Sec:* Marcia Weiss
**VP:* Barry Weiss

NORTHERN RADIATOR
See NORTHERN FACTORY SALES INC

D-U-N-S 05-826-6669
NORTHERN REFRIGERATED TRANSPORTATION INC
2700 W Main St, Turlock, CA 95380-9537
Tel (209) 664-3800 *Founded/Ownrshp* 1947
Sales 41.5MM^E *EMP* 245
SIC 4213 Refrigerated products transport; Refrigerated products transport
CEO: Richard Mello
**Treas:* Judi Mello
**VP:* John Doidge

D-U-N-S 02-300-9996
NORTHERN RESOURCES COOPERATIVE
1504 Center St W, Roseau, MN 56751-1915
Tel (218) 463-1805 *Founded/Ownrshp* 1934
Sales 76.1MM^E *EMP* 70
SIC 5191 5172 5251 5541 Fertilizer & fertilizer materials; Chemicals, agricultural; Petroleum products; Gases, liquefied petroleum (propane); Hardware; Gasoline service stations; Fertilizer & fertilizer materials; Chemicals, agricultural; Petroleum products; Gases, liquefied petroleum (propane); Hardware; Gasoline service stations
Pr: Steve Dahl
**Sec:* Roger Falk
Genl Mgr: Kelly Christiansen

D-U-N-S 96-318-7653
NORTHERN RIVERVIEW HEALTHCARE CENTER INC
87 S Route 9w, Haverstraw, NY 10927-1700
Tel (845) 429-5381 *Founded/Ownrshp* 1995
Sales 19.6MM *EMP* 280
SIC 8051 Skilled nursing care facilities; Skilled nursing care facilities
Ex Dir: Morris Klein
**Pr:* Benjamin Klein
CFO: Oscar Abraham
CFO: Sonny Kaplan
**Treas:* George Margaretten
Treas: George Ohring
Psych: Eric Neblung

D-U-N-S 10-774-1878 IMP/EXP
NORTHERN SAFETY CO INC
232 Industrial Park Dr, Frankfort, NY 13340-4748
Tel (315) 793-4900 *Founded/Ownrshp* 1983
Sales 181.3MM^E *EMP* 400
SIC 5099

D-U-N-S 03-541-8987 IMP
NORTHERN SALES CO INC
KETCHIKAN NORTHERN SALES
15022 Puyallup St E # 101, Sumner, WA 98390-2401
Tel (253) 299-0500 *Founded/Ownrshp* 2006
Sales 79.9MM^E *EMP* 270
SIC 5145 5149 5194 5141 Snack foods; Potato chips; Soft drinks; Tobacco & tobacco products; Groceries, general line; Snack foods; Potato chips; Soft drinks; Tobacco & tobacco products; Groceries, general line
Pr: Lance Crosby
**CFO:* Rose Treutel
**VP:* Darrin Erdahl
Dir IT: Andrew Greco

NORTHERN SEA PRODUCTS
See GREAT NORTHERN PRODUCTS LTD

NORTHERN SECURITY INSURANCE CO
See VERMONT MUTUAL INSURANCE CO

D-U-N-S 08-964-3501
NORTHERN SERVICES GROUP INC
2000 Fountainview Dr, Monsey, NY 10952-2875
Tel (845) 356-9880 *Founded/Ownrshp* 2000
Sales 17.2MM *EMP* 1,100
Accts Abbate Demarinis Llp Garden C
SIC 8059 Nursing home, except skilled & intermediate care facility; Nursing home, except skilled & intermediate care facility
CEO: Morris Klein
CFO: Sonny Kaplan
Ofcr: Joseph Grunwald
Ofcr: Michael Nowicki

D-U-N-S 36-157-7687 IMP/EXP
NORTHERN STAMPING CO
6600 Chapek Pkwy, Cleveland, OH 44125-1049
Tel (216) 883-8888 *Founded/Ownrshp* 2009
Sales 352.2MM^E *EMP* 1,700
SIC 3465 3469 Automotive stampings; Metal stampings; Automotive stampings; Metal stampings
Ch Bd: Matthew S Friedman
**CFO:* Ian Hessel
**VP:* Scott Sheffield
Dir IT: Tom Benedict
IT Man: Jack Abbott
Mtls Mgr: Ed Packer
Plnt Mgr: Tina Sallamon
Ql Cn Mgr: Joe Harant
Board of Directors: Mady Friedman, Matthew S Friedman, Ian B Hessel

D-U-N-S 00-614-7516
■ **NORTHERN STAR CO** (MN)
NORTHERN STAR POTATOES
(*Suby of* MICHAEL FOODS OF DELAWARE INC) ★
101 W 82nd St, Chaska, MN 55318-9663
Tel (952) 368-6500 *Founded/Ownrshp* 1953
Sales 70.2MM^E *EMP* 240
SIC 2033 5148 2099 Vegetables: packaged in cans, jars, etc.; Fresh fruits & vegetables; Food preparations; Vegetables: packaged in cans, jars, etc.; Fresh fruits & vegetables; Food preparations
CEO: James Dwyer
VP: John D Reedy

D-U-N-S 07-972-1189
NORTHERN STAR COUNCIL BOY SCOUTS OF AMERICA (MN)
393 Marshall Ave, Saint Paul, MN 55102-1717
Tel (651) 224-1891 *Founded/Ownrshp* 1910
Sales 20.0MM *EMP* 200
Accts Wilkerson Guthmann & Johnson L
SIC 8641 Boy Scout organization; Boy Scout organization
Ex Dir: John Andrews
V Ch: Barbara Schmidt
**Pr:* Richard Neuner
**Pr:* Greg Page
CFO: Paula Miller

D-U-N-S 96-835-0715
NORTHERN STAR GENERATION LLC
2929 Allen Pkwy Ste 2200, Houston, TX 77019-7112
Tel (713) 580-6300 *Founded/Ownrshp* 2004
Sales 206.4MM^E *EMP* 250^E
SIC 4911 Generation, electric power; Generation, electric power
Pr: Jack F Browder
**CFO:* Vincent Schager
**Ofcr:* David A Kellermeyer
**VP:* Joe M Evans Jr
**VP:* David R Roth
Mng Dir: Shawn Simmers
Off Mgr: Ellen Roeth
Opers Mgr: Kristopher Calloway
Opers Mgr: Donald Day
Plnt Mgr: Allen Czerkiewicz
Plnt Mgr: Jim Murray

D-U-N-S 14-862-9848
NORTHERN STAR GENERATION SERVICES LLC
(*Suby of* NORTHERN STAR GENERATION LLC) ★
2929 Allen Pkwy Ste 2200, Houston, TX 77019-7112
Tel (713) 580-6300 *Founded/Ownrshp* 2007
Sales 122.2MM^E *EMP* 220^E
SIC 4911 Generation, electric power; Generation, electric power
CEO: Jack Browder
CFO: Wincent Scager
**VP:* Scott M Churbock
**VP:* David R Roth
**VP:* Robert W Schima
**VP:* David M Sims

D-U-N-S 00-614-4158
NORTHERN STAR INDUSTRIES INC (MI)
130 N Industrial Dr, Iron Mountain, MI 49801-1470
Tel (906) 776-3480 *Founded/Ownrshp* 1959
Sales 73.4MM^E *EMP* 475
SIC 3613

NORTHERN STAR POTATOES
See NORTHERN STAR CO

D-U-N-S 02-372-5617
NORTHERN STAR VENTURES LLC
WORLDS BEST CHEESECAKE
10440 Leadbetter Rd, Ashland, VA 23005-3415
Tel (804) 368-0747 *Founded/Ownrshp* 2004
Sales 106.6MM^E *EMP* 90
SIC 5149 5461 Bakery products; Bakeries; Bakery products; Bakeries
CEO: John D Fernandez
VP: Woody Vickery
Prd Mgr: Kim Gray
S&M/VP: John Josko

D-U-N-S 11-610-9398
NORTHERN STATE UNIVERSITY
UNIVERSITY BOOK STORE
(*Suby of* BOARD OF REGENTS SOUTH DAKOTA) ★
1200 S Jay St, Aberdeen, SD 57401-7198
Tel (605) 626-3011 *Founded/Ownrshp* 1901
Sales 57.9MM^E *EMP* 830
SIC 8221 University; University
Pr: Patrick Schloss
VP: Tom Hawley
IT Man: Lindsey Meester
Snr Mgr: Larry Brunmaier
Snr Mgr: Rodney Hall

D-U-N-S 60-313-2486
NORTHERN STATE UNIVERSITY FOUNDATION
620 15th Ave Se, Aberdeen, SD 57401-7610
Tel (605) 626-2550 *Founded/Ownrshp* 2005
Sales 20.5MM *EMP* 11
Accts Eide Bailly Llp Aberdeen Sd
SIC 8699 Charitable organization; Charitable organization
Ex Dir: Todd Jordre

D-U-N-S 00-696-2419 IMP
■ **NORTHERN STATES POWER CO**
(*Suby of* XCEL ENERGY INC) ★
414 Nicollet Mall, Minneapolis, MN 55401-1927
Tel (612) 330-5500 *Founded/Ownrshp* 2000
Sales 4.9MMM *EMP* 3,793
SIC 4931 Electric & other services combined; ; Electric & other services combined;
Ch Bd: Ben Fowke
**Pr:* Christopher B Clark
**CFO:* Teresa S Madden
Sr VP: Jeffrey S Savage

D-U-N-S 00-794-5868
■ **NORTHERN STATES POWER CO**
XCEL ENERGY
(*Suby of* XCEL ENERGY INC) ★
1414 W Hamilton Ave, Eau Claire, WI 54701-7252
Tel (715) 839-2625 *Founded/Ownrshp* 2000
Sales 1.0MMM *EMP* 570
Accts Deloitte & Touche Llp Minneap
SIC 4931 Electric & other services combined; ; Electric & other services combined;
Pr: Mark E Stoering
**Ch Bd:* Benjamin G S Fowke III
**CFO:* Teresa S Madden
Sr VP: Jeffrey S Savage
Netwrk Eng: Mark Larsen
Board of Directors: Marvin E McDaniel Jr

D-U-N-S 02-311-2634
NORTHERN STATES SUPPLY INC (MN)
KATO TOOL
600 Industrial Dr Sw, Willmar, MN 56201-2717
Tel (320) 235-0555 *Founded/Ownrshp* 1960, 1987
Sales 48.0MM^E *EMP* 109
SIC 5085 Industrial supplies; Fasteners, industrial: nuts, bolts, screws, etc.; Tools; Industrial supplies; Fasteners, industrial: nuts, bolts, screws, etc.; Tools
CEO: Robert J Dols
**VP:* Doug Gilbertson
VP: Tim Minter
**VP:* Don Nelson
Sales Exec: Jesse Stegeman
Sls&Mrk Ex: Tina Erpenbach
Sales Asso: Jason Bedel
Sales Asso: Mitch Kolrud
Sales Asso: Chris Wharton

D-U-N-S 05-492-4519
NORTHERN STEEL CASTINGS INC
80 Oliver St, Wisconsin Rapids, WI 54494-2957
Tel (715) 423-8040 *Founded/Ownrshp* 2000
Sales 26.4MM^E *EMP* 100^E
SIC 5051 Castings, rough: iron or steel; Castings, rough: iron or steel
Pr: Tom Nowak
**Prin:* Glenn Gregg

D-U-N-S 11-935-6186
NORTHERN SUBURBAN SPECIAL EDUCATION DISTRICT 804
NSSED
760 Red Oak Ln, Highland Park, IL 60035-3816
Tel (847) 831-5100 *Founded/Ownrshp* 1976
Sales 28.0MM^E *EMP* 600
Accts Bark Associates Ltd Arlingto
SIC 8211 Public special education school; Public special education school

D-U-N-S 05-448-4001 IMP/EXP
▲ **NORTHERN TECHNOLOGIES INTERNATIONAL CORP**
4201 Woodland Rd, Circle Pines, MN 55014-1794
Tel (763) 225-6600 *Founded/Ownrshp* 1970
Sales 30.3MM *EMP* 91^E
Tkr Sym NTIC *Exch* NGM
SIC 2631 2899 2821 Packaging board; Corrosion preventive lubricant; Rust resisting compounds; Plastics materials & resins; Packaging board; Corrosion preventive lubricant; Rust resisting compounds; Plastics materials & resins
Pr: G Patrick Lynch
CFO: Matthew C Wolsfeld
Ofcr: Alex Pepin
Ofcr: Jody Rieck
VP: Vineet R Dalal
VP: Efim Ya Lyublinski
VP: Gautam Ramdas
VP: Wade Rohland
Opers Mgr: Barb Keeler
Prd Mgr: Mia Thomton
Ql Cn Mgr: Liming Dong
Board of Directors: Barbara D Colwell, Richard J Nigon

D-U-N-S 03-015-7355
NORTHERN TIER BSA
(*Suby of* BOY SCOUTS OF AMERICA) ★
747 Kawishiwi Trl, Ely, MN 55731-8269
Tel (218) 365-4811 *Founded/Ownrshp* 2010
Sales 16.0MM^E *EMP* 1,185^E
SIC 7032 Recreational camps

D-U-N-S 96-535-5766
■ **NORTHERN TIER ENERGY LLC**
(*Suby of* NORTHERN TIER ENERGY LP) ★
38c Grove St Ste 5, Ridgefield, CT 06877-4667
Tel (203) 244-6550 *Founded/Ownrshp* 2010
Sales 4.6MMM *EMP* 10^E
Accts Pricewaterhousecoopers Llp Ho
Tkr Sym NTI *Exch* NYS
SIC 1311 Crude petroleum & natural gas production; Crude petroleum & natural gas production
CEO: David Lamp
COO: Hank Kuchta
Treas: Oscar Rodriguez
VP: Peter T Gelfman
VP: Chester J Kuchta
Genl Mgr: Peter Gelfman
Store Mgr: Brian Goodwin
CIO: Rick Locke
Dir IT: Michelle Gutwein

D-U-N-S 07-844-6962
▲ **NORTHERN TIER ENERGY LP**
1250 W Washington St # 101, Tempe, AZ 85281-1794
Tel (602) 302-5450 *Founded/Ownrshp* 2011
Sales 5.5MMM *EMP* 2,896^E
SIC 2911 Petroleum refining; Petroleum refining
Pr: Dave Lamp
Genl Pt: Northern Tier Energy GP LLC
CFO: David Bonczek
CFO: Karen Davis
Ex VP: Melissa M Buhrig
Sr VP: Scott L Stevens
VP: Jason Akey
VP: Rick Hastings
VP: Jack A Helmick

D-U-N-S 96-353-7860
NORTHERN TIER INS CONSORTIUM
33 Springbrook Dr, Canton, PA 17724-9356
Tel (570) 673-6001 *Founded/Ownrshp* 2010
Sales NA *EMP* 2
Accts Allen Rogers & Osgood Cpa S T
SIC 6411 Insurance agents, brokers & service; Insurance agents, brokers & service
Prin: Iu Blast

D-U-N-S 07-830-0765
■ **NORTHERN TIER RETAIL LLC**
SUPERAMERICA
(*Suby of* NORTHERN TIER ENERGY LLC) ★
576 Bielenberg Dr Ste 200, Woodbury, MN 55125-1735
Tel (651) 769-2099 *Founded/Ownrshp* 2010
Sales 21.2MM^E *EMP* 144^E
SIC 5411 5541 Convenience stores; Filling stations, gasoline
CEO: Mario Rodriguez
Sls Mgr: Shelley Branson

D-U-N-S 11-851-8000
NORTHERN TIER SOLID WASTE AUTHORITY
NTSWA
Us Rt 6, Burlington, PA 18814
Tel (570) 638-2107 *Founded/Ownrshp* 1974
Sales 22.0MM^E *EMP* 69
SIC 4953 Sanitary landfill operation; Rubbish collection & disposal; Recycling, waste materials
Ex Dir: David Terrill
**Ch Bd:* Robert Woodhead
**V Ch Bd:* Ken Palmer

D-U-N-S 09-422-6347
NORTHERN TIOGA SCHOOL DISTRICT
110 Ellison Rd, Elkland, PA 16920-1207
Tel (814) 258-5642 *Founded/Ownrshp* 1953
Sales 29.7MM *EMP* 328
SIC 8211 Public junior high school; Public senior high school; Public elementary school; Public junior high school; Public senior high school; Public elementary school

VP: Teressa Sasserson
IT Man: Jeremy Loveland

D-U-N-S 82-521-0263
NORTHERN TOOL & EQUIPMENT CATALOG CO INC
NORTHERN TOOL EQUIPMENT
(*Suby of* NORTHERN TOOL & EQUIPMENT CO INC) ★
2800 Southcross Dr W, Burnsville, MN 55306-6936
Tel (952) 894-9510 *Founded/Ownrshp* 1994
Sales 234.6MM^E *EMP* 1,600
SIC 5961 Tools & hardware, mail order; Tools & hardware, mail order
CEO: Donald L Kotula
**Pr:* Charles Albrecht

D-U-N-S 09-979-1493 IMP/EXP
NORTHERN TOOL & EQUIPMENT CO INC
2800 Southcross Dr W, Burnsville, MN 55306-6936
Tel (952) 894-9510 *Founded/Ownrshp* 1980
Sales 651.2MM^E *EMP* 2,000
SIC 5961 5251 Tools & hardware, mail order; General merchandise, mail order; Hardware; Tools & hardware, mail order; General merchandise, mail order; Hardware
CEO: Donald L Kotula
Ch Bd: Julie Gathern
**Pr:* Charles Albrecht
COO: Todd Gulbranson
**CFO:* Tom Ericson
Sr VP: Mark Kauffman
VP: John Bakke
VP: Jay Berlin
VP: Scott Carlson
VP: Al Kotula
VP: Bill Perizzo
VP: John Rose
VP: Dennis Shockro
Exec: Chris Erath
Exec: Nathan Miller
Dir Soc: Eric Randa

NORTHERN TOOL EQUIPMENT
See NORTHERN TOOL & EQUIPMENT CATALOG CO INC

D-U-N-S 08-360-5261 IMP
NORTHERN TRUST BANK OF FLORIDA NATIONAL ASSOCIATION
700 Brickell Ave, Miami, FL 33131-2810
Tel (305) 372-1000 *Founded/Ownrshp* 1974
Sales NA *EMP* 893
SIC 6022

D-U-N-S 00-693-1968
■ **NORTHERN TRUST CO** (DE)
(*Suby of* NORTHERN TRUST CORP) ★
50 S La Salle St, Chicago, IL 60603-1003
Tel (312) 630-6000 *Founded/Ownrshp* 1984
Sales NA *EMP* 8,000
SIC 6021 National commercial banks; National commercial banks
Pr: J C Goodall Jr
Pr: Robert Baillie
Pr: Frederick H Waddell
CFO: Steven L Fradkin
Treas: William R Dodds Jr
Trst Ofcr: Frank E Loomis
Ex VP: Sherry S Barrat
Ex VP: David C Blowers
Ex VP: S Biff Bowman
Ex VP: Penelope J Briggs
Ex VP: Jeffrey D Cohodes
Ex VP: Marianne G Doan
Ex VP: James Draths
Ex VP: John Jeffrey Kauffman
Ex VP: Wilson Leech
Ex VP: Connie L Lindsey
Ex VP: Lyle L Logan
Ex VP: Hugh R Magill
Ex VP: R Hugh Magill
Ex VP: William L Morrison
Ex VP: William A Osborn
Board of Directors: William D Smithburg, Linda Walker Bynoe, Enrique J Sosa, Nicholas D Chabraja, Charles A Tribbett III, Susan Crown, Frederick H Waddell, Arthur L Kelly, Robert C McCormack, Edward J Mooney, William A Osborn, John W Rowe, Harold B Smith

D-U-N-S 05-943-9083
▲ **NORTHERN TRUST CORP**
50 S La Salle St, Chicago, IL 60603-1003
Tel (312) 630-6000 *Founded/Ownrshp* 1971
Sales NA *EMP* 15,400
Tkr Sym NTRS *Exch* NGS
SIC 6022 State commercial banks; State commercial banks
Ch Bd: Frederick H Waddell
Pr: Jonathan Hershman
Pr: Lori Lewis
Pr: Vivek Menon
Pr: William L Morrison
Pr: Dee Plavsic
COO: Jana R Schreuder
CFO: S Biff Bowman
Chf Cred: Debra Mairs
Bd of Dir: Mike Mayer
Chf Mktg O: Maureen Bromwell
Chf Inves: James Grinney
Chf Inves: Richard Pell
Ofcr: Jeffery D Cohodes
Ofcr: Sara Davidson
Ofcr: Robert Groves
Trst Ofcr: Lloyd Sebastian
Ex VP: James Brand
Ex VP: Danny Carpenter
Ex VP: Orie L Dudley
Ex VP: John Fitzgerald
Board of Directors: Charles A Tribbett III, Linda Walker Bynoe, Susan Crown, Dean M Harrison, Jose Luis Prado, Thomas E Richards, John W Rowe, Martin P Slark, David H B Smith Jr, Donald Thompson

D-U-N-S 09-645-9334
■ **NORTHERN TRUST SECURITIES INC**
(*Suby of* NORTHERN TRUST CORP) ★
50 S La Salle St Ste 1, Chicago, IL 60603-1008
Tel (312) 557-2000 *Founded/Ownrshp* 1983

Sales 28.4MM^E *EMP* 122
SIC 6211 Brokers, security; Brokers, security
Pr: Lloyd Wennlund
**COO:* Sheila Dorman
**CFO:* Tim Salata
Ofcr: Jennifer Jeffries
Sr VP: Charles Hawkins
Sr VP: Steve Schneider
Sr VP: Eric Schweitzer
Sr VP: Chelsea Smith
Sr VP: Kay Vicino
VP: Ernesto Arteta
VP: Michael Binder
VP: Oscar Chavez
VP: Anne Gulotta
VP: Bonita Hoefler
VP: Steve Mille
VP: Patrick O'Connell
VP: Tracy Pawlak
**VP:* Wes Ringo
VP: Bob Schwarz
VP: Barry Stark

D-U-N-S 07-299-8032
■ **NORTHERN UTAH HEALTHCARE CORP**
ST MARK'S HOSPITAL
(*Suby of* HCA INC) ★
1200 E 3900 S, Salt Lake City, UT 84124-1300
Tel (801) 268-7111 *Founded/Ownrshp* 1994
Sales 102.9MM^E *EMP* 1,600
SIC 8082 8011 Home health care services; Neurologist; Home health care services; Neurologist
CEO: John Hanshaw
Chf Rad: Ronald Miller
**Pr:* Samuel N Hazen
Pr: Kathy Watt
**CFO:* Brian McKenley
Bd of Dir: Dan Chichester
Ofcr: Mary Hostetler
Dir Risk M: Pauline Parker
Dir Lab: Susan Wade
Dir Lab: Gloria Zuroff
Chf Nrs Of: Maryjoe Jones

D-U-N-S 04-928-6305
■ **NORTHERN UTILITIES INC**
(*Suby of* UNITIL CORP) ★
100 International Dr # 175, Portsmouth, NH 03801-6881
Tel (603) 436-0310 *Founded/Ownrshp* 2008
Sales 62.9MM^E *EMP* 276
SIC 4924 Natural gas distribution; Natural gas distribution
Pr: Stephen H Bryant
**VP:* Dan Cote

D-U-N-S 09-698-0693
NORTHERN VALLEY REGIONAL SCHOOL DISTRICT
162 Knickerbocker Rd, Demarest, NJ 07627-1033
Tel (201) 768-2262 *Founded/Ownrshp* 1950
Sales 25.6MM^E *EMP* 400
SIC 8211 Public senior high school; School board; Public senior high school; School board
VP: Maria Kim
MIS Dir: Patricia Deriso
Dir IT: William Timme
Schl Brd P: Alice Comer
Teacher Pr: Nancy Valentino
Psych: Tara Boyle

D-U-N-S 15-368-0277 IMP
NORTHERN VIDEO SYSTEMS INC
TRI-ED/NORTHERN VIDEO
(*Suby of* TRI-ED/NORTHERN VIDEO) ★
135 Cronyways Park Dr Ste 101, Woodbury, NY 11797
Tel (516) 941-2800 *Founded/Ownrshp* 2010
Sales 103.7MM^E *EMP* 260
SIC 5065 Closed circuit television; Video equipment, electronic; Security control equipment & systems; Radio receiving & transmitting tubes; Closed circuit television; Video equipment, electronic; Security control equipment & systems; Radio receiving & transmitting tubes
CEO: Steven Roth
**Pr:* Mark Haney
**CFO:* Paul Haney
**Ex VP:* James Rothstein

D-U-N-S 00-794-0356
NORTHERN VIRGINIA ELECTRIC COOPERATIVE (VA)
N O V E C
10323 Lomond Dr, Manassas, VA 20109-3113
Tel (703) 335-0500 *Founded/Ownrshp* 1976, 1983
Sales 433.0MM *EMP* 275
SIC 4911 8611 8741 4939 Distribution, electric power; Business associations; Management services; Combination utilities; Distribution, electric power; Business associations; Management services; Combination utilities
Pr: Stanley C Feuerberg
**Ch Bd:* Manley Garber
Sr VP: Wilber Rollin
VP: Patti Neal
VP: Wilber Rollins
VP: Patrick Toulme
Exec: Marlane Parsons
Dir IT: Howard Spinner
Info Man: Mark Gayda
Mtls Mgr: Kent R Cassell
Opers Mgr: Larry Shaffer

D-U-N-S 16-281-8561
NORTHERN VIRGINIA FAMILY SERVICE INC
10455 White Granite Dr # 100, Oakton, VA 22124-2764
Tel (571) 748-2500 *Founded/Ownrshp* 1924
Sales 28.8MM^E *EMP* 290
Accts Mcgladrey & Pullen Llp Vienna
SIC 8322 8399 General counseling services; Community center; Community development groups; General counseling services; Community center; Community development groups
Pr: Mary Agee
Dir Vol: Navara Jordan
COO: Larry Shaw
CFO: Anna Brent
Treas: Dory Halati

VP: Stephanie Berkowitz
Exec: Jim Byrnes
Ex Dir: Maria Gomez
Ex Dir: Nadia Moritz
Prgrm Mgr: Ondrea McLntyre-Hall
Prgrm Mgr: Nancy Pedulla

D-U-N-S 78-369-5406
NORTHERN VIRGINIA HEALTH CARE CENTER INC
BIRMINGHAM GREEN NRSING FCILTY
8605 Centreville Rd, Manassas, VA 20110-5265
Tel (703) 257-0935 *Founded/Ownrshp* 1991
Sales 10.7MM *EMP* 300
SIC 8052 Intermediate care facilities; Intermediate care facilities
CEO: David Rumford
CFO: Kelly Oliff
CFO: John Rickard
Top Exec: Corinne Hogan
Nrsg Dir: Sibyl Goodwin
HC Dir: Jeanie Carver

D-U-N-S 08-105-4066
NORTHERN VIRGINIA REGIONAL PARK AUTHORITY
FAIRFAX PARK AUTHORITY
5400 Ox Rd, Fairfax Station, VA 22039-1022
Tel (703) 352-5900 *Founded/Ownrshp* 1959
Sales NA *EMP* 625
Accts Pbgh Llp Harrisonburg Virgi
SIC 9512 Land, mineral & wildlife conservation; Land, mineral & wildlife conservation
Ex Dir: Paul Gilbert
VP: Laurie Short
VP: Keith Tomlinson

D-U-N-S 96-162-0643
NORTHERN VIRGINIA SURGERY CENTER II LLC
(*Suby of* INOVA FAIRFAX HOSPITAL) ★
3620 Joseph Siewick Dr # 406, Fairfax, VA 22033-1761
Tel (703) 766-6960 *Founded/Ownrshp* 2002
Sales 71.7MM^E *EMP* 2,218^E
SIC 8011 Ambulatory surgical center
Ofcr: Mary Lindsay
Off Mgr: Carol Viens

D-U-N-S 08-933-1370
NORTHERN VIRGINIA SURGERY CENTER LLC
(*Suby of* INOVA FAIRFAX HOSPITAL) ★
8110 Gatehouse Rd Ste 200, Falls Church, VA 22042-1252
Tel (703) 280-2700 *Founded/Ownrshp* 2001
Sales 2.7MM^E *EMP* 411^E
SIC 8011 Surgeon
Prin: John Knox Singleton

D-U-N-S 07-780-8087
NORTHERN VIRGINIA TRANSPORTATION COMMISSION
2300 Wilson Blvd Ste 620, Arlington, VA 22201-5426
Tel (703) 524-3322 *Founded/Ownrshp* 1964
Sales 178.6MM *EMP* 9
Accts Pbgh Llp Hrrisonburg Va
SIC 4111 Bus line operations; Bus line operations
Pr: Richard K Taube

D-U-N-S 00-986-1717
NORTHERN WASCO COUNTY PEOPLES UTILITY DISTRICT
NORTHERN WASCO COUNTY PUD
2345 River Rd, The Dalles, OR 97058-3551
Tel (541) 296-2226 *Founded/Ownrshp* 1939
Sales 45.7MM^E *EMP* 58
SIC 4911 Distribution, electric power
CFO: Jim Johnson
Genl Mgr: Dwight Langer
Opers Supe: Steve Horzynek

NORTHERN WASCO COUNTY PUD
See NORTHERN WASCO COUNTY PEOPLES UTILITY DISTRICT

D-U-N-S 10-002-1674
NORTHERN WELLS COMMUNITY SCHOOL DISTRICT
312 N Jefferson St, Ossian, IN 46777-9704
Tel (260) 543-2213 *Founded/Ownrshp* 1985
Sales 14.9MM^E *EMP* 283
SIC 8211 Public elementary school; Public junior high school; Public senior high school; Public elementary school; Public junior high school; Public senior high school
Schl Brd P: Peter Confer

D-U-N-S 07-871-6123 IMP
NORTHERN WESTCHESTER HOSPITAL ASSOCIATION (NY)
400 E Main St, Mount Kisco, NY 10549-3477
Tel (914) 666-1200 *Founded/Ownrshp* 1916
Sales 253.7MM *EMP* 1,000^E
Accts Deloitte Tax Llp Jericho Ny
SIC 8062 General medical & surgical hospitals; General medical & surgical hospitals
Pr: Joel Seligman
Dir Recs: Debbie Pirchio
Ofcr: Brian Blaufeux
Ofcr: Cathy Hartmann
**Ofcr:* John Partenza
**Sr VP:* Marla Koroly
**Sr VP:* Lauraine Szekely
**VP:* Michael Caruso
VP: Mike Caruso
VP: Mark Vincent
VP Bus: Sue Etkin
Exec: Carlos Forcade
Dir OR: Amy Chapman
Dir OR: Stephanie Vogel-Rosenthal
Dir Inf Cn: Kristine Goldstein
Dir Risk M: Kathryn Griffin
Dir Rx: Anthony Luppino

D-U-N-S 04-539-6538 IMP
NORTHERN WHOLESALE SUPPLY INC
6800 Otter Lake Rd Ste 2, Hugo, MN 55038-4428
Tel (651) 429-1515 *Founded/Ownrshp* 1984
Sales 48.6MM^E *EMP* 63
SIC 5091 5013 5012 5074 Boats, canoes, watercrafts & equipment; Motor vehicle supplies & new parts; Snowmobiles; Heating equipment (hydronic)
CEO: Nick Gargaro
**Sec:* Lee N Johnson
**VP:* Deborah Gargaro
Sls Mgr: John Perron
Sls Mgr: Dan Staples

D-U-N-S 19-699-0048 IMP/EXP
NORTHERN WIND INC
16 Hassey St, New Bedford, MA 02740-7209
Tel (508) 997-0727 *Founded/Ownrshp* 1987
Sales 64.2MM^E *EMP* 80
SIC 5146 2092 Seafoods; Fresh or frozen packaged fish; Seafoods; Fresh or frozen packaged fish
CEO: Kenneth Melanson
**Pr:* Michael Fernandes
Sfty Mgr: Gerald Chadwick
QI Cn Mgr: Eric Napoleoni

D-U-N-S 08-671-1256
NORTHERN WYOMING COMMUNITY COLLEGE
SHERIDAN COLLEGE
3059 Coffeen Ave, Sheridan, WY 82801-9133
Tel (307) 674-6446 *Founded/Ownrshp* 1948
Sales 36.5MM^E *EMP* 360
Accts Lenhart Mason & Associates L
SIC 8221 8222 Colleges universities & professional schools; Community college; Colleges universities & professional schools; Community college
Pr: Paul Young
**CFO:* Cheryl Heath
Ofcr: Chad Trebby
Ofcr: Jason Vela
VP: Doug Parrott
Exec: David Fisher
Exec: Stephen Maier
Ex Dir: Tim Stransky
Store Mgr: Brad Heins
CTO: Tobie Alsup
Nrsg Dir: Louise Posten
Board of Directors: Susan Bigelow

D-U-N-S 02-292-6869
NORTHERN X-RAY CO (MN)
NXC IMAGING
2118 4th Ave S, Minneapolis, MN 55404-2642
Tel (612) 870-1561 *Founded/Ownrshp* 1964
Sales 56.0MM *EMP* 92
SIC 5047 X-ray machines & tubes; X-ray film & supplies; X-ray machines & tubes; X-ray film & supplies
CEO: Bruce Veilinger
**Pr:* Steven Miller
**Treas:* Dan Koehnen
VP: Tom Zdon
VP: Bruce Zeilinger
Sls Mgr: Paul Carlson
Sls Mgr: Kevin Mattson

D-U-N-S 03-505-9179
NORTHERN YORK COUNTY SCHOOL DISTRICT
149 S Baltimore St, Dillsburg, PA 17019-1035
Tel (717) 432-8691 *Founded/Ownrshp* 1950
Sales 17.3MM^E *EMP* 295
SIC 8211 Public elementary school; Public junior high school; Public senior high school; Public elementary school; Public junior high school; Public senior high school
Bd of Dir: Natalie Slothower
HC Dir: Molly Sebright

D-U-N-S 80-040-7178
▲ NORTHFIELD BANCORP INC
581 Main St, Woodbridge, NJ 07095-1148
Tel (732) 499-7200 *Founded/Ownrshp* 2010
Sales NA *EMP* 326^E
Tkr Sym NFBK *Exch* NGS
SIC 6035 Bank holding companies; Savings institutions, federally chartered; Federal savings & loan associations; Federal savings banks
Ch Bd: John W Alexander
**Pr:* Steven M Klein
CFO: William R Jacobs
Ofcr: Kenneth J Doherty
Ex VP: Michael J Widmer
Sr VP: Judith Calabrese
Sr VP: Kathleen Owsiany
VP: Catherine Ruta

D-U-N-S 06-427-3915
NORTHFIELD BANK
(*Suby of* LIBERTY BANCORP INC) ★
1410 Saint Georges Ave, Avenel, NJ 07001-1158
Tel (732) 587-2222 *Founded/Ownrshp* 1927
Sales NA *EMP* 70
Accts Federal Deposit Insurance Corp
SIC 6035 Federal savings banks; Federal savings banks
Pr: Steven M Klein
**Ch Bd:* John R Bowen
CFO: William R Jacobs
Treas: Joseph F Coccaro
Sr VP: Judy Calabrese
Sr VP: Daniel Greene
VP: Dan Bennett
VP: Lucille Capece
VP: Michael Cozza
VP: Michael Malloy
VP: John Regina
VP: Michael J Widmer

D-U-N-S 00-507-5098 EXP
NORTHFIELD BLOCK CO
(*Suby of* OLD CASTLE APG INC) ★
1 Hunt Ct, Mundelein, IL 60060-4487
Tel (847) 816-9000 *Founded/Ownrshp* 2003
Sales 40.6MM^E *EMP* 406^E
SIC 3271 Blocks, concrete or cinder: standard
Pr: Craig M Belasco
CFO: Mike Chiappetta
CFO: Jerry Kniery
VP: Weign Wright
VP: Doug Yound

D-U-N-S 07-829-6861
NORTHFIELD CENTER 2006 LDHA LP
2444 Cranewood Dr, Fenton, MI 48430-1049
Tel (810) 750-7000 *Founded/Ownrshp* 2011
Sales 10.9MM^E *EMP* 334
SIC 1522 Multi-family dwellings, new construction; Multi-family dwellings, new construction
Pt: Frank Carswell

D-U-N-S 14-057-8548
NORTHFIELD HOSPITAL & SKILLED NURSING
2000 North Ave, Northfield, MN 55057-1498
Tel (507) 646-1000 *Founded/Ownrshp* 1910
Sales 87.6MM *EMP* 500^E
SIC 8062 General medical & surgical hospitals; General medical & surgical hospitals
Pr: Mary Crow
CFO: Michele Erickson
Nutrtnst: Kristi Winkels
Doctor: Monty Seper MD
Pharmcst: Beth Alexander

D-U-N-S 79-370-1314
NORTHFIELD IND SCHOOL DIST 659
ALTERNATIVE LEARNING CENTER
201 Orchard St S, Northfield, MN 55057-1663
Tel (507) 663-0629 *Founded/Ownrshp* 2007
Sales 10.1MM^E *EMP* 541^E
Accts Larsonallen Llp Austin Minn
SIC 8211 Elementary & secondary schools
Prin: Gary Lewis
VP: Danielle Amundson
VP: Angela Blewett
VP: Theresa Brake
VP: Kathryn Budig
VP: Patrick Bullard
VP: Monika Burkhead
VP: Ryan Driscoll
VP: Cheryl Dueffert
VP: Kelle Edwards
VP: Robert Garcia
VP: Sofia Garcia
VP: Cecelia Green
VP: Donna Hall
VP: Jackie Harding
VP: William Howard
VP: Sonia Johnson
VP: Linda Kovach
VP: Anne Larson
VP: Stephanie Mahal
VP: Mary McGovern

D-U-N-S 19-543-0103
■ NORTHFIELD INSURANCE CO
(*Suby of* NORTHLAND INSURANCE CO) ★
385 Washington St, Saint Paul, MN 55102-1309
Tel (651) 310-4100 *Founded/Ownrshp* 2007
Sales NA *EMP* 25
SIC 6331 Property damage insurance; Property damage insurance
Pr: Randall Dean Jones
VP: Robert Northrop Billings
VP: Kenneth Lee Brendle
VP: David Joseph Brick
VP: David Edward Byrne
VP: Larry Burton Colburn
VP: Weston Stanley Day
VP: Gregory Kevin Erickson
VP: Cheryl Olga Peters
VP: David Lee Pickard
VP: Dennis Merton Sager
VP: Robert Bruce Spanfelner
VP: Allen Jon Stendahl
VP: Barbara Lou Sutherland
VP: Daniel John Zaborsky

D-U-N-S 00-695-4143
NORTHFIELD MOUNT HERMON SCHOOL INC
N M H
1 Lamplighter Way, Mount Hermon, MA 01354-9637
Tel (413) 498-3000 *Founded/Ownrshp* 1879
Sales 60.8MM *EMP* 525^E
Accts Blum Shapiro & Company Pc Cpa
SIC 8211 Preparatory school; Preparatory school
CFO: Richard T Wood
V Ch: Mariah Calagione
Trst: Stephen Gauster
**Prin:* Joanna Schoen
**Ex Dir:* Sumita Ambasta
Prgrm Mgr: Sheila Loveland
IT Man: Dena Fletcher
Web Dev: Craig Hefner

NORTHFIELD PARK RACETRACK
See PARK NORTHFIELD ASSOCIATES LLC

D-U-N-S 10-003-8355
NORTHFIELD PUBLIC SCHOOLS FOUNDATION INC
1400 Division St S, Northfield, MN 55057-2799
Tel (507) 663-0610 *Founded/Ownrshp* 1876
Sales 36.9MM *EMP* 550
Accts Larson Allen Llp Austin Minn
SIC 8211 School board; School board
Netwrk Mgr: Cheryl Schmitz

D-U-N-S 02-057-2459
NORTHFIELD SAVINGS BANK
(*Suby of* NSB HOLDING CORP)
1731 Victory Blvd, Staten Island, NY 10314-3511
Tel (718) 448-1000 *Founded/Ownrshp* 1887
Sales NA *EMP* 127
SIC 6036 State savings banks, not federally chartered; State savings banks, not federally chartered
Ch Bd: John Alexander
**CFO:* Stephen Klein
**Ex VP:* Kenneth Doherty
Sr VP: William Jacobs
**Sr VP:* Robin Lefkowitz
Sr VP: Kevin McCloskey
**Sr VP:* Jeffrey Schnorbus
VP: Irene Greenman
VP: Denny John
VP: Richard Maida
Brnch Mgr: Maureen Deangelo

D-U-N-S 15-271-1388
NORTHFIELD SAVINGS BANK
33 S Main St, Northfield, VT 05663-6703
Tel (802) 485-5871 *Founded/Ownrshp* 1867
Sales NA *EMP* 129
SIC 6022 State commercial banks; State commercial banks
CEO: Thomas N Pelletier
Treas: Cory Richardson
**Sr VP:* Everett C Bell
**Sr VP:* Keith Clark
**Sr VP:* James Poulan
**Sr VP:* Gordon White
**VP:* William Pope
**VP:* Cindy Willis
Brnch Mgr: Chuck Abare
Brnch Mgr: Kelly Andrews
Brnch Mgr: Donna Bohonnon

D-U-N-S 06-238-6610
NORTHFIELD TOWNSHIP HIGH SCHOOL DISTRICT 225 (INC)
GLENBROOK NORTH HIGH SCHOOL
2550 Waukegan Rd Ste 100, Glenview, IL 60025-1777
Tel (847) 998-6100 *Founded/Ownrshp* 1950
Sales 52.8MM^E *EMP* 823
SIC 8211 Public elementary & secondary schools; Public elementary & secondary schools
HC Dir: Julie Haenisch
HC Dir: Barbara Marzillo

D-U-N-S 14-000-8934
NORTHFIELD TRUCKING CO INC
25086 Brest B, Taylor, MI 48180-4042
Tel (734) 231-8150 *Founded/Ownrshp* 2002
Sales 90.0MM^E *EMP* 90
SIC 4731 4212 Truck transportation brokers; Local trucking, without storage
Pr: Leighann Vallimont

D-U-N-S 00-782-2794
NORTHFORK ELECTRIC COOPERATIVE INC (OK)
301 E Main St, Sayre, OK 73662-2936
Tel (580) 928-3366 *Founded/Ownrshp* 1938
Sales 26.2MM *EMP* 38
Accts Briscoe Burke & Grigsby Llp
SIC 4911 Distribution, electric power; Distribution, electric power
Prin: Jimmy Taylor
**Prin:* Scott Copeland
**Prin:* Charles L Hickey
**Prin:* Ransom Snowden

NORTHGATE
See SECURITY PACKAGING INC

D-U-N-S 04-160-2012
NORTHGATE CHRYSLER JEEP INC
8536 Colerain Ave, Cincinnati, OH 45251-2914
Tel (513) 385-3900 *Founded/Ownrshp* 1992
Sales 24.3MM^E *EMP* 60
SIC 5511 7538 7515 5531 Automobiles, new & used; General automotive repair shops; Passenger car leasing; Automotive & home supply stores; Automobiles, new & used; General automotive repair shops; Passenger car leasing; Automotive & home supply stores
Pr: Peter Pannier
**Treas:* Kathy Hettesheimer

D-U-N-S 04-447-3692
NORTHGATE ELECTRIC CORP
63 Depot Rd, Huntington Station, NY 11746-1780
Tel (631) 271-2242 *Founded/Ownrshp* 1967
Sales 23.6MM^E *EMP* 200
SIC 1731 Electrical work; Electrical work
Ch Bd: Dina Dunn
**Sec:* Martin Bass
**VP:* Al Greco

D-U-N-S 04-873-6425 IMP
NORTHGATE GONZALEZ INC
CORPORATE OFFICE
1201 N Magnolia Ave, Anaheim, CA 92801-2609
Tel (714) 778-3784 *Founded/Ownrshp* 1980
Sales 242.4MM^E *EMP* 900
SIC 5411 Grocery stores, independent; Grocery stores, independent
Pr: Miguel Gonzalez Jr
Sr VP: Carl Middleton
**VP:* Jose Gonzalez
Dir Risk M: Teresa Jimenez
Store Dir: Robert Ascencio
Store Dir: Albert Ayala
Store Dir: Alex Diaz
Store Dir: Luis Flores
Store Dir: Frank Gonzalez
Store Dir: Luis Langle
Store Dir: Irma Salcido

D-U-N-S 79-649-7456 IMP
NORTHGATE GONZALEZ LLC
NORTHGATE MARKET
1201 N Magnolia Ave, Anaheim, CA 92801-2609
Tel (714) 778-3784 *Founded/Ownrshp* 2006
Sales 71.8MM^E *EMP* 4,000
SIC 5411 Grocery stores; Grocery stores

NORTHGATE MARKET
See NORTHGATE GONZALEZ LLC

D-U-N-S 80-730-9906
NORTHGATE RV CENTER INC
442 Candy Ln, Ringgold, GA 30736-3063
Tel (706) 935-8883 *Founded/Ownrshp* 2007
Sales 23.0MM^E *EMP* 12
SIC 5561 Recreational vehicle dealers; Recreational vehicle dealers
CEO: Billy Yates

NORTHGATE VOLKSWAGEN
See BALLWIN MOTORS INC

D-U-N-S 85-999-5966
NORTHGATEARINSO INC
ARINSO INTERNATIONAL
(*Suby of* NORTHGATE PUBLIC SERVICES (UK) LIMITED)
8880 Freedom Crossing Trl, Jacksonville, FL 32256-1215
Tel (678) 259-0500 *Founded/Ownrshp* 2003
Sales 34.7MM^E *EMP* 99^E
SIC 8742 Human resource consulting services
CEO: Adel Al-Saleh
Pr: Samuel V Campbell
Pr: Trey Campbell
CFO: Stuart Ross
CFO: John Steir
Ofcr: Pavan Sharma
VP: Hank Johnson
VP: Gary Melling
Prin: Katja Hertel
Ex Dir: Dan Maddux
Mng Dir: Rob Van Bavel

NORTHHAMPTON CROSSING
See RREF REGENCY PARK LLC

NORTHKEY COMMUNITY CARE
See NORTHERN KENTUCKY MENTAL HEALTH - MENTAL RETARDATION REGIONAL BOARD INC

D-U-N-S 11-798-5341
NORTHLAKE ENGINEERING INC
8320 193rd Ave, Bristol, WI 53104-9549
Tel (262) 857-6431 *Founded/Ownrshp* 1984
Sales 21.7MM^E *EMP* 80
SIC 3612 3677 3679 Harness assemblies for electronic use: wire or cable; Inductors, electronic; Transformers, except electric
Pr: William Hardt
CEO: David Dunbar
VP Sls: Debbie Hardt

D-U-N-S 09-762-5255 IMP/EXP
NORTHLAKE STEEL CORP
5455 Wegman Dr, Valley City, OH 44280-9707
Tel (330) 220-7717 *Founded/Ownrshp* 1977
Sales 25.7MM^E *EMP* 80
SIC 3398 3312 Annealing of metal; Bar, rod & wire products; Bars & bar shapes, steel, cold-finished: own hot-rolled; Rods, iron & steel: made in steel mills
CEO: William K Bissett
**Pr:* Craig O Curie
Plnt Mgr: Bill Bissett
Prd Mgr: Brad Mackenzie

D-U-N-S 00-624-8868 IMP
NORTHLAND ALUMINUM PRODUCTS INC
NORDIC WARE
5005 Hwy 25, Minneapolis, MN 55416
Tel (952) 924-8505 *Founded/Ownrshp* 1946
Sales 178.0MM^E *EMP* 350
SIC 3089 3479 Kitchenware, plastic; Coating of metals & formed products; Kitchenware, plastic; Coating of metals & formed products
CEO: David Dalquist
**CFO:* Dave Hopkins
**Ch:* Dorothy Dalquist
Sr VP: Kathy Severson
VP: Gene Karlson
CTO: Jamie Aker
Dir IT: Linda Olson
IT Man: Dennis Behm
IT Man: Dana Norsten
Plnt Mgr: Tracey Callahan
Plnt Mgr: Ron Jansen

D-U-N-S 05-891-7048
NORTHLAND ASSOCIATES INC
4701 Buckley Rd, Liverpool, NY 13088-3678
Tel (315) 451-3722 *Founded/Ownrshp* 1982
Sales 23.0MM^E *EMP* 62
SIC 1542 Commercial & office building, new construction; Commercial & office buildings, renovation & repair
Pr: James M Tyler
**CFO:* Ken Richardson
Genl Mgr: Diane Smith
Off Mgr: Gail Snyder
IT Man: Joshua Parsons

D-U-N-S 19-536-3767
NORTHLAND CABLE TELEVISION INC
(*Suby of* NORTHLAND TELECOMMUNICATIONS CORP) ★
101 Stewart St Ste 700, Seattle, WA 98101-2449
Tel (206) 621-1351 *Founded/Ownrshp* 1985
Sales 33.0MM^E *EMP* 140
SIC 4841 Cable television services; Cable television services
Pr: Gary Jones
**Treas:* Richard Clark
**VP:* R Ferrer
Dir IT: Matthew Cryan

D-U-N-S 80-123-2633
■ **NORTHLAND CASUALTY CO**
(*Suby of* NORTHLAND INSURANCE CO) ★
385 Washington St, Saint Paul, MN 55102-1309
Tel (651) 310-4326 *Founded/Ownrshp* 2007
Sales NA *EMP* 22^E
SIC 6411 Property & casualty insurance agent
Prin: Brian W Maclean
VP: Kim Jonas
Dir IT: John Tyler

NORTHLAND CHRYSLER-PLYMOUTH
See MCINERNEY INC

D-U-N-S 00-194-6482
■ **NORTHLAND CO**
NORTHLAND INSURANCE
(*Suby of* TRAVELERS INDEMNITY CO) ★
385 Washington St, Saint Paul, MN 55102-1309
Tel (800) 328-5972 *Founded/Ownrshp* 1937, 2000
Sales NA *EMP* 15,000
SIC 6331 6162 6531 Fire, marine & casualty insurance & carriers; Mortgage bankers; Real estate managers
Ch Bd: Edward H Hamm
**Pr:* Gene G Gopon
**Treas:* William C Peterson
Board of Directors: Norman Berg, Clarence G Frame, Robert E Grant

D-U-N-S 07-176-4674
NORTHLAND COLLEGE (WI)
1411 Ellis Ave, Ashland, WI 54806-3999
Tel (715) 682-1699 *Founded/Ownrshp* 1891
Sales 27.0MM *EMP* 170^E
SIC 8221

D-U-N-S 02-971-9614
NORTHLAND COMMUNICATIONS CORP
(*Suby of* NORTHLAND TELECOMMUNICATIONS CORP) ★
101 Stewart St Ste 700, Seattle, WA 98101-2449
Tel (206) 621-1351 *Founded/Ownrshp* 1985
Sales 52.0MM^E *EMP* 250
SIC 4841 Cable television services; Cable television services
Ch: John S Whetzell
**Pr:* Gary Jones
**VP:* Richard Clark
**VP:* Richard Dyste
**VP:* R G Ferrer
VP: Rick McElwee
Dir IT: Eric Gudgel

D-U-N-S 10-343-3769
NORTHLAND CONTROL SYSTEMS INC
44150 S Grimmer Blvd, Fremont, CA 94538-6310
Tel (510) 403-7600 *Founded/Ownrshp* 1982
Sales 38.0MM *EMP* 142^E
SIC 1731 7389 Fire detection & burglar alarm systems specialization; Automobile recovery service
CEO: Pierre Trapanese
**CFO:* Jim Conley
Ofcr: Liz Sherriff
Prgrm Mgr: Vic Demarzo
IT Man: James Barron
Opers Mgr: Dean Speer
Opers Mgr: Kim Tran

D-U-N-S 02-407-6531 IMP/EXP
NORTHLAND CORP (KY)
NORTHLAND TRADING
2600 E Highway 146, La Grange, KY 40031-9161
Tel (502) 222-2518 *Founded/Ownrshp* 1933
Sales 34.9MM^E *EMP* 55
SIC 5031 7389 Lumber: rough, dressed & finished; Veneer; Plywood; Molding, all materials; Log & lumber broker
CEO: Orn E Gudmundsson Jr
CFO: Donna Jackson
**Ch:* Orn E Gudmundsson Sr
Ex VP: Marlene Hughes
Opers Mgr: Joseph Earley
Sales Exec: Paul Vance

D-U-N-S 09-294-6508 IMP
■ **NORTHLAND CORP** (MI)
NORTHLAND REFRIGERATION
(*Suby of* AGA RANGEMASTER GROUP PLC)
1260 E Van Deinse St, Greenville, MI 48838-1400
Tel (616) 754-5601 *Founded/Ownrshp* 1892, 2003
Sales 40.3MM^E *EMP* 175^E
SIC 3632 3444 Freezers, home & farm; Sheet metalwork; Freezers, home & farm; Sheet metalwork
CEO: William McGrath
Sr VP: Bradley S Stauffer
VP: Tom Curtis
Ql Cn Mgr: Jim Nielsen
Ql Cn Mgr: Rick Waldorf
Trfc Mgr: Frank Wood
Sls Mgr: Larry Ferguson

NORTHLAND EXPRESS TRANSPORT
See SPECTRAL ENTERPRISES INC

NORTHLAND FISHING TACKLE
See BIG FISH AMERICA LLC

D-U-N-S 14-850-5670
NORTHLAND GROUP INC
7831 Glenroy Rd Ste 250, Minneapolis, MN 55439-3117
Tel (952) 831-4005 *Founded/Ownrshp* 1985
Sales 46.4MM^E *EMP* 350^E
SIC 7322 Collection agency, except real estate; Collection agency, except real estate
Pr: Lance Black
Pr: Greg Ferrall
**CEO:* John M Johnson
CFO: Kevin Swanson
**Ex VP:* Joe Burch
Ex VP: Fred Lundquist
Ex VP: Bob Schofield
VP: Nancy Lundeen
VP: Todd Sobiech
VP: Jodi Swenson
Dir Sec: Ryan Bruzek

D-U-N-S 10-584-9798 IMP
NORTHLAND INDUSTRIAL TRUCK CO INC
NITCO
6 Jonspin Rd, Wilmington, MA 01887-4408
Tel (978) 658-5900 *Founded/Ownrshp* 1983
Sales 98.6MM^E *EMP* 265
SIC 5084 7699 7359

NORTHLAND INSURANCE
See NORTHLAND CO

D-U-N-S 00-787-3409
■ **NORTHLAND INSURANCE CO**
(*Suby of* JUPITER HOLDINGS INC) ★
385 Washington St, Saint Paul, MN 55102-1309
Tel (651) 310-4100 *Founded/Ownrshp* 2000
Sales NA *EMP* 247
SIC 6331 Property damage insurance; Property damage insurance
Pr: Brian Maclean
**CFO:* Jay Benet
**Treas:* Mario Olivo
Mng Dir: Christopher Edwardson
Mng Dir: Steve Perovich
Genl Mgr: Carmela Garlow
Snr Mgr: Teri Greenwood

D-U-N-S 06-661-8125
NORTHLAND INVESTMENT CORP
2150 Washington St # 300, Newton, MA 02462-1443
Tel (617) 965-7100 *Founded/Ownrshp* 1970
Sales 322.1MM^E *EMP* 425
Accts Metis Group Cpas Llc New Yor
SIC 6799 6411 6531 Real estate investors, except property operators; Advisory services, insurance; Real estate managers; Real estate investors, except property operators; Advisory services, insurance; Real estate managers
Ch: Lawrence Gottesdiener
Pr: Robert Gatof
CEO: Steven P Rosenthal
CFO: AMI Fatula
CFO: Terence McNally
Sr VP: Kevin Bell
Sr VP: Suzanne M Bonito
VP: Bruce Noland
VP: Brad Swinnerton
Rgnl Mgr: James Anastos
CTO: Willman Miller

D-U-N-S 05-760-7087
NORTHLAND MECHANICAL CONTRACTORS INC
9001 Science Center Dr, Minneapolis, MN 55428-4561
Tel (763) 544-5100 *Founded/Ownrshp* 1971
Sales 28.3MM^E *EMP* 110
SIC 1711 Plumbing contractors; Heating & air conditioning contractors; Plumbing contractors; Heating & air conditioning contractors
CEO: Richard Tieva
**Pr:* Mike Tieva
VP: John Finley
Off Mgr: Joy Lemke
Snr PM: Howard Jokinen
Snr PM: Jim Parson

D-U-N-S 62-718-0433
NORTHLAND MORTGAGE CO INC
28 Copley Dr, Methuen, MA 01844-1745
Tel (978) 685-0070 *Founded/Ownrshp* 1988
Sales NA *EMP* 9
SIC 6163 Mortgage brokers arranging for loans, using money of others; Mortgage brokers arranging for loans, using money of others
Pr: Ronald Simoes
Ex Dir: Chad Simoes

D-U-N-S 08-329-7770
NORTHLAND PINES SCHOOL DISTRICT (WI)
1800 Pleasure Island Rd, Eagle River, WI 54521-8980
Tel (715) 479-4473 *Founded/Ownrshp* 1973
Sales 21.1MM *EMP* 240
Accts Schenck Sc Stevens Point Wi
SIC 8211 Public elementary school; Public junior high school; Public senior high school; School board; Public elementary school; Public junior high school; Public senior high school; School board
Instr Medi: Jone Davis
HC Dir: Caryn Jacob

NORTHLAND PIONEER COLLEGE
See NAVAJO COUNTY COMMUNITY COLLEGE DISTRICT

D-U-N-S 61-320-8628
NORTHLAND PROCESS PIPING INC
1662 320th Ave, Isle, MN 56342-4303
Tel (320) 679-2119 *Founded/Ownrshp* 1989
Sales 26.9MM^E *EMP* 100
SIC 3312 Stainless steel; Stainless steel
CEO: Danny L Tramm
**Sec:* Kathy Tramm
Sls Mgr: Cal Bredek

NORTHLAND PRODUCTS
See FRONTIER PRECISION INC

D-U-N-S 02-236-5480
NORTHLAND PRODUCTS CO
1000 Rainbow Dr, Waterloo, IA 50701-1198
Tel (319) 234-5585 *Founded/Ownrshp* 1944
Sales 28.2MM^E *EMP* 54
SIC 2992 5169 Re-refining lubricating oils & greases; Anti-freeze compounds; Re-refining lubricating oils & greases; Anti-freeze compounds
Pr: Robert W Petersen
**VP:* Eric P Petersen
Sfty Mgr: Brian Motzko
Prd Mgr: Michael Notermann

NORTHLAND REFRIGERATION
See NORTHLAND CORP

D-U-N-S 96-671-2275 IMP
NORTHLAND SYSTEMS INC
17200 Medina Rd Ste 800, Plymouth, MN 55447-5605
Tel (952) 525-0700 *Founded/Ownrshp* 1997
Sales 27.2MM^E *EMP* 40
SIC 5045 Computers, peripherals & software
CEO: Robert Bernu
**CFO:* Kathy Bernu
Prin: Dan Herbeck
CTO: Rod Lucero
Opers Mgr: Dana McMaster

D-U-N-S 15-147-0317
NORTHLAND TELECOMMUNICATIONS CORP
101 Stewart St Ste 700, Seattle, WA 98101-2449
Tel (206) 621-1351 *Founded/Ownrshp* 1985
Sales 87.2MM^E *EMP* 450
SIC 4841 7371 Cable television services; Computer software development; Cable television services; Computer software development
Ch Bd: John S Whetzell
**Treas:* Richard I Clark

NORTHLAND TRADING
See NORTHLAND CORP

D-U-N-S 00-683-0256
NORTHLAND TRANSPORTATION CO
(*Suby of* LYNDEN INC) ★
4025 Delridge Way Sw, Seattle, WA 98106-1249
Tel (206) 763-4244 *Founded/Ownrshp* 2013
Sales 42.6MM^E *EMP* 450
SIC 4424 Deep sea domestic transportation of freight; Deep sea domestic transportation of freight
Pr: Jonathan R Burdick
Treas: Brad McKeown
VP: Alexander S McKallor
Board of Directors: Jonathan Burdick, Jim Jansen, Richard A Korpela, Tom Martin

D-U-N-S 78-045-9124
NORTHLINE UTILITIES LLC
15 School Ln, Au Sable Forks, NY 12912
Tel (518) 647-8198 *Founded/Ownrshp* 2005
Sales 38.4MM^E *EMP* 92
SIC 1731 Electric power systems contractors
Pr: James C Atkins
IT Man: James Atkins
Sfty Mgr: Bill Martin

D-U-N-S 16-196-3426
NORTHMARQ CAPITAL LLC
(*Suby of* MARQUETTE REAL ESTATE HOLDINGS LLC) ★
3500 Amrcn Blvd W Ste 500, Minneapolis, MN 55431
Tel (952) 356-0100 *Founded/Ownrshp* 1998
Sales NA *EMP* 328^E
SIC 6162 Mortgage bankers
CEO: Edward Padilla
Pr: Barbara Gfroerer
Pr: Nancy Vaniseghem
Ex VP: Lisa Dongoske
VP: Elliot Auerbacher
VP: Brent Blake
VP: Steve Brown
VP: Paul Cairns
VP: Eric Carter
VP: Larry Curry
VP: Joe Derosa
VP: Sonja Dusil
VP: Jan Ehresman
VP: Joe Giordani
VP: Dan Gleason
VP: Beth Holmgren
VP: John Kinser
VP: William Libercci
VP: Matt Marshall
VP: Gary Rifkin
VP: Michael Surprenant

D-U-N-S 04-600-7543
NORTHMONT CITY SCHOOL DISTRICT
ELEMENTARY/SECONDARY SCHOOL
4001 Old Salem Rd, Englewood, OH 45322-2681
Tel (937) 832-5000 *Founded/Ownrshp* 1999
Sales 30.0MM^E *EMP* 393
Accts Clark Schaefer Hackett Spring
SIC 8211 Public elementary & secondary schools; Public elementary & secondary schools
Pr: Linda A Blum
IT Man: Sandy Harris
IT Man: Debbie Rutan
Psych: Beth Kessler
Psych: Kent McIntire
Psych: Marsha Reinhardt

NORTHON DISPOSAL CALLECIA
See WASTE CONNECTIONS OF KANSAS INC

NORTHPARK CENTER
See NORTHPARK MANAGEMENT

D-U-N-S 06-897-1472
NORTHPARK MANAGEMENT
NORTHPARK CENTER
8687 N Central Expy # 1030, Dallas, TX 75225-4434
Tel (214) 369-1234 *Founded/Ownrshp* 1955
Sales 26.3MM^E *EMP* 134
SIC 6512 Commercial & industrial building operation; Shopping center, property operation only
Pr: David Haemisegger
**VP:* Nancy Nasher
Dir Risk M: Liz Meyer
Mktg Dir: Victoria Snee
Mktg Mgr: Whitney Terrell

D-U-N-S 61-669-7905
NORTHPOINT COMMERCIAL CREDIT LLC
FLAGSHIP BANKS EQUIPMENT FIN
6465 Wayzata Blvd Ste 760, St Louis Park, MN 55426-1740
Tel (800) 552-8694 *Founded/Ownrshp* 2005
Sales 35.0MM^E *EMP* 12
SIC 7389 Financial services; Financial services
Off Mgr: Lori Becker

NORTHPOINT DAY TREATMENT SCH
See CHILD AND FAMILY GUIDANCE CENTER

D-U-N-S 07-841-0262
NORTHPOINT DEVELOPMENT LLC
5015 Nw Canal St Ste 200, Riverside, MO 64150-7203
Tel (816) 888-7380 *Founded/Ownrshp* 2004
Sales 100.0MM^E *EMP* 50^E
SIC 6552 6531 Land subdividers & developers, commercial; Real estate agent, commercial
CEO: Nathaniel Hagedorn
COO: Chad Meyer
CFO: Brett Grady
Off Mgr: Rene Halterman

NORTHPOINT FORD
See ASBURY AUTOMOTIVE ARKANSAS DEALERSHIP HOLDINGS LLC

D-U-N-S 61-429-9993
NORTHPOINT MORTGAGE CORP
10002 101st Ave, Ozone Park, NY 11416-2609
Tel (718) 641-7000 *Founded/Ownrshp* 2000
Sales NA *EMP* 3
SIC 6162 Mortgage brokers, using own money; Mortgage brokers, using own money
Pr: Attique Rehman
Off Mgr: Stephania Renz

D-U-N-S 01-033-0969
NORTHPOINT PROPERTY MANAGEMENT LLC
55 Lake St Ste 4, Nashua, NH 03060-4516
Tel (603) 594-2300 *Founded/Ownrshp* 2008
Sales 128.0MM *EMP* 23

SIC 8641 6531 Condominium association; Condominium manager

D-U-N-S 16-514-5785
NORTHPOINT SOLUTIONS LLC
130 W 42nd St Ste 550, New York, NY 10036-7804
Tel (212) 819-1700 Founded/Ownrshp 2003
Sales 22.2MM^E EMP 98^E
SIC 7379
Mng Pt: Joseph Amarante
Mng Pt: Kevin Goldstein
Mng Pt: Michael Molaro
Sr VP: Matthew Dorman
VP: Troy Layton
Exec: Edwin Pacheco
Prac Mgr: Apurva Patel
Tech Mgr: Meeky Hwang
Software D: Chenlin Wu
Ql Cn Mgr: Silvia Mendez
*VP Sls: Jeff Penner

D-U-N-S 14-094-8774 IMP
NORTHPOINT TRADING INC
347 5th Ave, New York, NY 10016-5010
Tel (212) 481-8001 Founded/Ownrshp 2003
Sales 39.2MM EMP 35
SIC 2273 2211 2392 6512 Carpets & rugs; Handkerchief fabrics, cotton; Blankets, comforters & beddings; Shopping center, property operation only
Pr: Abe Kassin
CFO: Jack Ezon
Ex VP: Danny Srour
*VP: Isaac Kassin
Sls Mgr: Joshua Kassin
Sls Mgr: Amit Krupkin

D-U-N-S 10-943-7181
NORTHPOINTE BANK
(Suby of NORTH POINT BANCSHARES INC) ★
3333 Deposit Dr Ne, Grand Rapids, MI 49546-1467
Tel (616) 940-9400 Founded/Ownrshp 1999
Sales NA EMP 167
SIC 6022 State trust companies accepting deposits, commercial; State trust companies accepting deposits, commercial
Pr: Charles A Williams
*COO: Leo Ditchcreek
*CFO: Steven L Germond
*Ex VP: Michael Winks
Sr VP: Mike Geib
*Sr VP: Mike Gibe
VP: Sara Amy
VP: Susan Andrews
VP: Dan Cooper
CIO: Jeff Tatreau
CTO: Jeff Tatro

D-U-N-S 60-615-1173
NORTHPORT HEALTH SERVICES OF MISSOURI LLC
WARSAW HLTH REHABILITATION CTR
1609 Sunchase Dr, Warsaw, MO 65355-3059
Tel (660) 438-2970 Founded/Ownrshp 1993
Sales 10.3MM^E EMP 355
SIC 8051 Skilled nursing care facilities; Skilled nursing care facilities
Pr: Norman Estes

D-U-N-S 10-005-6480
NORTHPORT-EAST NORTHPORT UNION FREE SCHOOL DISTRICT
158 Laurel Ave, Northport, NY 11768-3167
Tel (631) 262-6600 Founded/Ownrshp 1925
Sales 63.2MM^E EMP 900
SIC 8211 Public elementary & secondary schools; Public elementary & secondary schools
*Pr: Stephen V Waldenburg
Treas: Denise Lovaglio
VP: Terry Bouton
VP: Matthew Nelson
*VP: Jennifer Thompson
Exec: Tom Boylan

D-U-N-S 01-385-3616
NORTHRIDGE MEDICAL CENTER
BJC MEDICAL CTR
70 Medical Center Dr, Commerce, GA 30529-1078
Tel (706) 335-1000 Founded/Ownrshp 2011
Sales 30.8MM^E EMP 143^E
SIC 8011 Medical centers
CFO: Larry Ebert
Ofcr: Tabitha Evans
Dir Lab: Lanny Pope
Dir Bus: Ashley Riddle
Chf Nrs Of: Maura Cobb
Doctor: Paul Sergent
Snr Mgr: Richard Clark

D-U-N-S 06-624-4872
NORTHRIDGE TOYOTA
19550 Nordhoff St, Northridge, CA 91324-2419
Tel (818) 734-5600 Founded/Ownrshp 1967, 1997
Sales 55.7MM^E EMP 150
SIC 5511 Automobiles, new & used; Automobiles, new & used
Pr: Frederick Hitchcock
CFO: Brian Pardue
Dept Mgr: Jorge Cruz
Dept Mgr: Mirna Garcia
Dept Mgr: Jorge Martinez
Dept Mgr: Andrey Tolentino

D-U-N-S 62-250-5659
▲ NORTHRIM BANCORP INC
3111 C St, Anchorage, AK 99503-3901
Tel (907) 562-0062 Founded/Ownrshp 1990
Sales NA EMP 297^E
Tkr Sym NRIM Exch NGS
SIC 6022 6282 State commercial banks; Investment advisory service; State commercial banks; Investment advisory service
Pr: Joseph M Beedle
*Ch Bd: R Marc Langland
COO: Joseph M Schierhorn
CFO: Latosha M Frye
CFO: Latosha Frye
Ofcr: Steven L Hartung
Ex VP: Chris Knudson
Sr VP: Ramona Evers
Sr VP: Camilla Forstner
Sr VP: Leonard Horst
Sr VP: Debra Shannon
Sr VP: Suzanne Whittle
VP: Jay Blury
Board of Directors: Larry S Cash, Mark G Copeland, Anthony Drabek, Karl L Hanneman, David W Karp, David J McCambridge, John C Swalling, Linda C Thomas, David G Wight

D-U-N-S 96-206-8347
■ NORTHRIM BANK
(Suby of NORTHRIM BANCORP INC) ★
3111 C St Ste 400, Anchorage, AK 99503-3925
Tel (907) 562-0062 Founded/Ownrshp 2007
Sales NA EMP 269
SIC 6022 State commercial banks; State commercial banks
Prin: Edward J La Fleur
COO: Chris Knudson
Ofcr: Katie Bender
Ex VP: Steve Hartung
Sr VP: Carolyn Jennings
Sr VP: Jim Miller
Sr VP: Bob Shake
Sr VP: Suzanne Whittle
Sr VP: Lynn Wolfe
VP: Jason Criqui
VP: Barb Ervin
VP: Angela Freeman
VP: Sheri Gower
VP: Allen Hippler
VP: Michael Hook
VP: Brian Hove
VP: Josh King
VP: Paul Kirschner
VP: Jeanine Lillo
VP: Michael Martin
VP: Heidi Moes
Board of Directors: David McCambridge

D-U-N-S 07-966-6930
■ NORTHRIM CAPITAL INVESTMENTS CO
(Suby of NORTHRIM BANK) ★
3111 C St Ste 200, Anchorage, AK 99503-3925
Tel (907) 562-0062 Founded/Ownrshp 1998
Sales 38.8MM^E EMP 150^E
SIC 7389 Financial services
Pr: R Marc Langland
Pr: Joseph M Schierhorn
VP: Joseph M Beedle
VP: Steven L Hartung

NORTHROP GRMMAN TECHNICAL SVCS
See JOHN S CONNOR INC

NORTHROP GRUMMA
See REMOTEC INC

D-U-N-S 96-735-6127
▲ NORTHROP GRUMMAN CORP
2980 Fairview Park Dr, Falls Church, VA 22042-4511
Tel (703) 280-2900 Founded/Ownrshp 1939
Sales 23.9MMM EMP 64,300^E
Accts Deloitte & Touche Llp Mclean
Tkr Sym NOC Exch NYS
SIC 3812 Search & navigation equipment; Search & navigation equipment
Ch Bd: Wesley G Bush
CEO: Jack Dorsett
CFO: Kenneth L Bedingfield
Ofcr: Denise M Peppard
Sr VP: Bobby Lentz
VP: Patrick M Antkowiak
VP: Jane Bishop
VP: Jaime Bohnke
VP: Sheila C Cheston
VP: Sonal B Deshpande
VP: Robert J Fleming
VP: Ron Foudray
VP: Michael Hardesty
VP: Chris Hernandez
VP: Mick Jaggers
VP: Thomas H Jones
VP: Dana Z Keefer
VP: Douglas A Lawton
VP: Todd Leavitt
VP: Stuart Linsky
VP: Steve Lunny
Board of Directors: Thomas M Schoewe, Marianne C Brown, James S Turley, Victor H Fazio, Donald E Felsinger, Bruce S Gordon, William H Hernandez, Madeleine A Kleiner, Karl J Krapek, Richard B Myers, Gary Roughead

D-U-N-S 00-690-3900
■ NORTHROP GRUMMAN ENTERPRISE MANAGEMENT SERVICES CORP (DE)
(Suby of NORTHROP GRUMMAN TECHNICAL SERVICES INC) ★
2340 Dulles Corner Blvd, Herndon, VA 20171-3400
Tel (703) 713-4000 Founded/Ownrshp 2011
Sales 42.1MM^E EMP 3,000
SIC 8741 8744 4731 8331 7349 Business management; Facilities support services; Foreign freight forwarding; Skill training center; Building cleaning service; Business management; Facilities support services; Foreign freight forwarding; Skill training center; Building cleaning service
Pr: George R Petteys
*Pr: Patricia Parrish
*Treas: Edward L Bennardo
*Treas: James L Sanford
*VP: Alan R Cocks
*VP: Marsha A Klontz
*VP: Gary W McKenzie
*VP: Edward Shedlick
*VP: William A Warren
*VP: Kathleen A Weigand
Sftwr Eng: Bob Clark

D-U-N-S 04-038-1683
NORTHROP GRUMMAN FEDERAL CREDIT UNION
879 W 190th St Ste 800, Gardena, CA 90248-4205
Tel (310) 808-4000 Founded/Ownrshp 1946
Sales NA EMP 120
SIC 6061 Federal credit unions; Federal credit unions
Pr: Stanley R Swenson Jr
*Ch: Kathi Harper
Ofcr: Rochelle Hazzard
*VP: Georgetta A Wolff

D-U-N-S 02-232-8996 IMP
■ NORTHROP GRUMMAN FIELD SUPPORT SERVICES INC
(Suby of NORTHROP GRUMMAN SYSTEMS CORP) ★
5000 Us Highway 1 N B02-60, Saint Augustine, FL 32095-6200
Tel (904) 810-4665 Founded/Ownrshp 1996
Sales 22.5MM^E EMP 386
SIC 3721 3761 Aircraft; Guided missiles & space vehicles; Aircraft; Guided missiles & space vehicles
CEO: Ed Faye
VP: Steve Timmerman

D-U-N-S 82-782-0494 IMP/EXP
■ NORTHROP GRUMMAN GUIDANCE AND ELECTRONICS CO INC
(Suby of NORTHROP GRUMMAN SYSTEMS CORP) ★
2980 Fairview Park Dr, Falls Church, VA 22042-4511
Tel (703) 280-2900 Founded/Ownrshp 1960
Sales 48.3MM^E EMP 322^E
SIC 3812 3761 Search & navigation equipment; Guided missiles & space vehicles
Pr: Mark Rabinowitz
*CEO: Wes Bush

NORTHROP GRUMMAN INFO SYSTEMS
See NORTHROP GRUMMAN INFORMATION TECHNOLOGY INC

D-U-N-S 05-227-2044
■ NORTHROP GRUMMAN INFORMATION TECHNOLOGY INC
NORTHROP GRUMMAN INFO SYSTEMS
(Suby of NORTHROP GRUMMAN SYSTEMS CORP) ★
7575 Colshire Dr, Mc Lean, VA 22102-7508
Tel (703) 556-1000 Founded/Ownrshp 1978
Sales 884.1MM^E EMP 24,000
SIC 7373 7372 8733 Computer integrated systems design; Prepackaged software; Scientific research agency
Pr: Linda Amills
*Pr: Herb W Anderson
Pr: Mike Roberts
*CFO: Steve Movius
*VP: Nils Ericson
VP: John Huff
VP: Catherine Kuenzel
*VP: James Mmyers
*VP: David Lryan
*VP: Michael Rtwyman
*VP: Kathy Warden
*VP: Karen Awilliams
Dir Risk M: Andrew Harasim
Dir Risk M: Ray Hayes

D-U-N-S 07-961-2927
NORTHROP GRUMMAN INTERNATIONAL TRADING INC
21240 Burbank Blvd, Woodland Hills, CA 91367-6680
Tel (818) 715-3607 Founded/Ownrshp 2014
Sales 82.2MM^E EMP 958
SIC 3812 Search & navigation equipment; Search & navigation equipment
Sfty Mgr: Steven Bauer

D-U-N-S 60-229-5933 IMP
■ NORTHROP GRUMMAN MARITIME SYSTEMS
(Suby of TITAN II INC) ★
1070 Seminole Trl, Charlottesville, VA 22901-2827
Tel (434) 974-2000 Founded/Ownrshp 2002
Sales 108.8MM^E EMP 500^E
SIC 5088 Marine propulsion machinery & equipment; Marine propulsion machinery & equipment
VP: Michael S Dunn
COO: Dhanvant Goradia
*Treas: Steven D Spiegel
*VP: Rudolph L Linde
VP: Matthew Mulherin
Exec: Carl Miller
Sys Mgr: David Blevins
Mktg Mgr: Allan Adell

D-U-N-S 00-417-9453 IMP/EXP
■ NORTHROP GRUMMAN SPACE & MISSION SYSTEMS CORP
(Suby of NORTHROP GRUMMAN CORP) ★
6377 San Ignacio Ave, San Jose, CA 95119-1200
Tel (818) 947-3296 Founded/Ownrshp 1901, 2011
Sales 1.1MMM^E EMP 12,000
SIC 7373 3663 3661 3812 3761 Computer integrated systems design; Radio & TV communications equipment; Telephone & telegraph apparatus; Defense systems & equipment; Guided missiles & space vehicles; Computer integrated systems design; Radio & TV communications equipment; Telephone & telegraph apparatus; Defense systems & equipment; Guided missiles & space vehicles
Pr: Robert M Hamje
COO: Peter Thielen
Bd of Dir: Paul Duarte
Bd of Dir: Ernesto Galvan
Bd of Dir: Berta Hom
Bd of Dir: Richard Hunter
Bd of Dir: Paul Kendall
Bd of Dir: John Saxelby
Bd of Dir: Peter Sicardi
Bd of Dir: Bernard Wilson
Ex VP: William K Maciven
Sr VP: Nick Barnes
VP: S Lunn
VP: George R Petteys
VP: G C Roman
VP: Joe G Taylor
VP: Ginger Wierzbanowski
Exec: Mary Joseph
Dir Bus: Ryan Kunkle
Dir Bus: Marc Lindsley

D-U-N-S 00-825-5408 IMP/EXP
■ NORTHROP GRUMMAN SYSTEMS CORP
(Suby of NORTHROP GRUMMAN CORP) ★
2980 Fairview Park Dr, Falls Church, VA 22042-4511
Tel (703) 280-1220 Founded/Ownrshp 1985
Sales 7.7MMM^E EMP 40,000^E
SIC 3721 3761 3728 3812 3825 4581 Airplanes, fixed or rotary wing; Research & development on aircraft by the manufacturer; Guided missiles, complete; Guided missiles & space vehicles, research & development; Fuselage assembly, aircraft; Wing assemblies & parts, aircraft; Research & dev by manuf., aircraft parts & auxiliary equip; Inertial guidance systems; Gyroscopes; Warfare counter-measure equipment; Search & detection systems & instruments; Test equipment for electronic & electrical circuits; Aircraft servicing & repairing; Airplanes, fixed or rotary wing; Research & development on aircraft by the manufacturer; Guided missiles, complete; Guided missiles & space vehicles, research & development; Fuselage assembly, aircraft; Wing assemblies & parts, aircraft; Research & dev by manuf., aircraft parts & auxiliary equip; Inertial guidance systems; Gyroscopes; Warfare counter-measure equipment; Search & detection systems & instruments; Test equipment for electronic & electrical circuits; Aircraft servicing & repairing
CEO: Wesley G Bush
*Pr: Mark Rabinowitz
CFO: James L Sanford
Treas: Albert F Myers
Treas: Ronald P Vargo
Ofcr: Marty Kirwan
VP: Robert Brammer
VP: Rosanne Brien
VP: James L Cameron
VP: Gary W Ervin
VP: T A Gasparini
VP: Ed Halibozek
VP: CT Harvie
*VP: Gary W McKenzie
VP: Linda A Mills
VP: C Michael Peters
VP: James F Pitts
VP: Mary Simmerman
VP: W A Warren
VP: Kathleen A Weigand
VP: Carol Zierhoffer

D-U-N-S 05-906-9211
■ NORTHROP GRUMMAN TECHNICAL SERVICES INC
(Suby of NORTHROP GRUMMAN CORP) ★
2411 Dulles Corner Park # 140, Herndon, VA 20171-3430
Tel (703) 713-4163 Founded/Ownrshp 1973
Sales 395.6MM^E EMP 4,745
SIC 4581 Aircraft maintenance & repair services; Aircraft servicing & repairing; Aircraft maintenance & repair services; Aircraft servicing & repairing
CEO: Wes Bush
Pr: Gregory J Donley
Pr: Thomas E Vice
Treas: Mark Rabinowitz
VP: Sid Ashworth
VP: Mark Caylor
VP: Sheila C Cheston
VP: Martin Clark
VP: Nimish Doshi
VP: Gloria A Flach
VP: Catherine Gridley
VP: David Harvey
VP: Robert Hosozawa
VP: Stephen Movius
VP: Edgar Smith
VP: Louise Ussery

NORTHROP TEEN CENTER
See ROLLING MEADOWS PARK DISTRICT

NORTHRUP SUPPLY
See IRR SUPPLY CENTERS INC

D-U-N-S 17-388-2387
NORTHSHORE HEALTH CENTERS INC
STACY MCKAY HEALTH CENTER
6450 Us Highway 6, Portage, IN 46368-5110
Tel (219) 763-8112 Founded/Ownrshp 1997
Sales 23.0MM EMP 300
Accts Bradley Associates Indianapol
SIC 8011 8021 Offices & clinics of medical doctors; Offices & clinics of medical doctors; Dentists' office
Pr: Scott V Cherry
*CEO: Janice Wilson
COO: Rhonda Mendoza
CFO: Cristy Lovings
CFO: Joseph Winterhaler
*VP: Scott Fritz
Dir Rx: Robert Furto
Dir IT: Frank Brown
IT Man: Eric Serrano
Site Mgr: David Hall
Obsttrcn: Kim Hess

D-U-N-S 60-355-7687 EXP
■ NORTHSHORE MINING CO
CLIFFS
(Suby of CLIFFS NATURAL RESOURCES INC) ★
1100 Superior Ave E # 1500, Cleveland, OH 44114-2544
Tel (216) 694-5700 Founded/Ownrshp 1994
Sales 351.6MM^E EMP 500
SIC 1011 4931 Iron ore mining; Iron ore preparation; Electric & other services combined; Iron ore mining; Iron ore preparation; Electric & other services combined
VP: Donald R Prahl

D-U-N-S 08-148-0964
NORTHSHORE SCHOOL DISTRICT
3330 Monte Villa Pkwy, Bothell, WA 98021-8972
Tel (425) 408-6000 Founded/Ownrshp 1958
Sales 244.9MM EMP 2,312
SIC 8211 Public elementary & secondary schools; Public senior high school; Public junior high school; Public elementary school; Public elementary & secondary schools; Public senior high school; Public junior high school; Public elementary school

Bd of Dir: Sheila Guard
Ofcr: John Schmied
Ex Dir: Carmin Dalziel
Dir Sec: Robert Noll
Off Mgr: Stacia Miller
Off Mgr: Judy Mitchell
Off Mgr: Carlyn Rorke
IT Man: Rose Hertzog
Opers Mgr: Jon Wiederspan
Psych: Kjerstin N Lee
Nrsg Dir: Judy Harkess

D-U-N-S 80-702-8451
NORTHSHORE SCHOOL DST 112
1936 Green Bay Rd, Highland Park, IL 60035-3112
Tel (224) 765-3000 *Founded/Ownrshp* 1993
Sales 87.5MM *EMP* 618
Accts Baker Tilly Virchow Krause Ll
SIC 8211 Public elementary school; Public junior high school; Public elementary school; Public junior high school
**CFO:* Mohsin Dada

D-U-N-S 17-328-0413 IMP
NORTHSHORE SHEET METAL INC
NORTH CLAD
11831 Beverly Park Rd C, Everett, WA 98204-3526
Tel (425) 487-1111 *Founded/Ownrshp* 2005
Sales 21.0MM *EMP* 60
SIC 1761 3444 3442

D-U-N-S 07-194-3757
NORTHSHORE TECHNICAL COMMUNITY COLLEGE
SULLIVAN CAMPUS
1710 Sullivan Dr, Bogalusa, LA 70427-5866
Tel (985) 732-6640 *Founded/Ownrshp* 1940
Sales 46.5MM^E *EMP* 598
SIC 8221 Colleges universities & professional schools; Colleges universities & professional schools
CEO: William Wainwright
**Prin:* Mindy Chauvin
Board of Directors: Marc Chauvin

D-U-N-S 96-643-7233
NORTHSHORE UNIV HLTHSYS HOME AND HOSP
1301 Central St, Evanston, IL 60201-1613
Tel (847) 570-2000 *Founded/Ownrshp* 2011
Sales 15.2MM *EMP* 351^E
Accts Deloitte Tax Llp Chicago Il
SIC 8699 Charitable organization; Charitable organization
Prin: Alexis A Washa
Dir Bus: Mariam Zrike
Adm Dir: Georgas Patricia
Nurse Mgr: Mary Sankovich
IT Man: Linda Rosin
Psych: Alison Reynard
Pathlgst: Agatha Bogard
Pathlgst: Tiffany Thurow
Pathlgst: Thomas Victor
Surgeon: Tricia Moo-Young
Surgeon: David Winchester

D-U-N-S 06-949-0621
NORTHSHORE UNIVERSITY HEALTHSYSTEM
EVANSTON HOSPITAL
1301 Central St, Evanston, IL 60201-1613
Tel (847) 570-5295 *Founded/Ownrshp* 1891
Sales 764.1MM^E *EMP* 9,000
SIC 8399 Health systems agency; Health systems agency
Pr: Mark R Neaman
Dir Vol: Pat Feldheim
V Ch: Gregory K Jones
**Pr:* Raymond Grady
COO: J P Gallagher
**COO:* Jeffrey Hillebrand
CFO: Sue Allan
Ch: Julian E Bailes
**Chf Cred:* Harry Jones Sr
Ofcr: Michael S Caplan
Ex VP: Marsha Fache
VP: Tom Barnett
VP: Gina Cialoni
VP: Steve Foley

D-U-N-S 07-044-4633
NORTHSIDE BEHAVIORAL HEALTH CENTER INC
12512 Bruce B Downs Blvd, Tampa, FL 33612-9209
Tel (813) 977-8700 *Founded/Ownrshp* 1976
Sales 11.1MM *EMP* 304
Accts B Rivero Gord Imer & Company
SIC 8093 8063 Mental health clinic, outpatient; Psychiatric hospitals; Mental health clinic, outpatient; Psychiatric hospitals
Pr: Frances Sykes
**Pr:* Estelle Ross
COO: Joe Rutherford
**CFO:* Glen Blonquist
**Treas:* William Johnson
**VP:* Kelly Williams
Ex Dir: Marsha Brown
Brnch Mgr: Lisa Heredia
Dir QC: Elaine Churton
IT Man: Maria Stan
Sfty Mgr: Cecil Woodside

D-U-N-S 96-948-1720
NORTHSIDE CARTING INC
210 Holt Rd, North Andover, MA 01845-1029
Tel (978) 686-2020 *Founded/Ownrshp* 1996
Sales 34.7MM^E *EMP* 65^E
SIC 4953 Refuse systems
Pr: William Thomson
**Treas:* Brian J Thompson
**Prin:* Robert George
Sls Mgr: Lisa Donlon

D-U-N-S 02-331-1376
NORTHSIDE ELEVATOR INC
210 E Spring St, Loyal, WI 54446-9439
Tel (715) 255-8507 *Founded/Ownrshp* 1977
Sales 80.8MM *EMP* 45
SIC 5191 0723 Feed; Seeds: field, garden & flower; Fertilizer & fertilizer materials; Feed milling custom services; Feed; Seeds: field, garden & flower; Fertilizer & fertilizer materials; Feed milling custom services
VP: Tim Brussow
**Sec:* Rick Brussow
**Genl Mgr:* Ted Brussow

NORTHSIDE FORD
See FORD BRASADA LTD

D-U-N-S 06-148-3046
NORTHSIDE FORD TRUCK SALES INC
NORTHSIDE TRUCKS AND EQUIPMENT
6221 Nrthast Clumbia Blvd, Portland, OR 97218
Tel (503) 282-7773 *Founded/Ownrshp* 1997
Sales 38.2MM *EMP* 70
SIC 5511 Automobiles, new & used; Pickups, new & used; Trucks, tractors & trailers: new & used; Automobiles, new & used; Pickups, new & used; Trucks, tractors & trailers: new & used
Pr: Jim McDonough
Sls Mgr: Rod Bergquist
Sls Mgr: Sharon Tucker
Sales Asso: Pete Barnhouse
Sales Asso: Bruce Johnson

D-U-N-S 79-074-3140
■ **NORTHSIDE HOSPITAL**
COLUMBIA HCA
(*Suby of* HCA INC) ★
6000 49th St N, Saint Petersburg, FL 33709-2145
Tel (727) 521-4411 *Founded/Ownrshp* 1992
Sales 140.6MM *EMP* 340
SIC 8031 8011 8069 8062 Offices & clinics of osteopathic physicians; Offices & clinics of medical doctors; Specialty hospitals, except psychiatric; General medical & surgical hospitals; Offices & clinics of osteopathic physicians; Offices & clinics of medical doctors; Specialty hospitals, except psychiatric; General medical & surgical hospitals
CEO: Dia Nichols
**CEO:* Stephen J Daugherty
**COO:* Jayme Chancellor
**CFO:* Gary Searls
Dir Rad: Stephen Greenberg
Dir Rad: Gagandeep Mangat
Dir IT: Anne Reed
IT Man: Kirk Hendricks
Opers Supe: Linda Robert
Mktg Dir: Aimee Bennett
Mktg Dir: Russ Davis

D-U-N-S 06-918-9801
NORTHSIDE HOSPITAL - CHEROKEE INC (GA)
N H
(*Suby of* NORTHSIDE HOSPITAL INC) ★
201 Hospital Rd, Canton, GA 30114-2408
Tel (770) 720-5100 *Founded/Ownrshp* 1997
Sales 154.1MM *EMP* 575
SIC 8062 General medical & surgical hospitals; General medical & surgical hospitals
CEO: William M Hayes
Chf Path: Richard E Fingerle
Pr: Leah Allen
**CFO:* Steve Hudson
CFO: Brian Jennette
Dir Inf Cn: Sybil Gayton
Dir Case M: Jodi Ochler
Dir Lab: Sue Tidwell
CIO: Bill Dunford
Pharmcst: Robert Allen

D-U-N-S 08-969-7395
NORTHSIDE HOSPITAL INC
NORTHSIDE HOSPITAL-ATLANTA
1000 Johnson Ferry Rd, Atlanta, GA 30342-1611
Tel (404) 851-8000 *Founded/Ownrshp* 1970
Sales 1.2MMM *EMP* 8,000
SIC 8062 General medical & surgical hospitals; General medical & surgical hospitals
CEO: Robert T Quattrocchi
**CFO:* Debbie Mitcham
CFO: Debbie Mitchum
CFO: Gary Searls
Snr Ntwrk: Mario Eury
Dir IT: Kirk Hendrick
IT Man: Sarah Brown
IT Man: Nick Gubbins
Netwrk Eng: Wolfgang Walker
Sfty Dirs: Pete Shworles
Opers Supe: Lynne Hayway

NORTHSIDE HOSPITAL-ATLANTA
See NORTHSIDE HOSPITAL INC

D-U-N-S 06-945-0716
NORTHSIDE INDEPENDENT SCHOOL DISTRICT
5900 Evers Rd, San Antonio, TX 78238-1606
Tel (210) 397-8770 *Founded/Ownrshp* 1949
Sales 1.0MMM *EMP* 13,698
Accts Weaver And Tidwell Llp Ho
SIC 8211 Public elementary & secondary schools; Public elementary school; Public junior high school; Public senior high school; Public elementary & secondary schools; Public elementary school; Public junior high school; Public senior high school
**Pr:* Robert Blount Jr
CFO: Alisa Thienpont
Bd of Dir: Randall H Fields
Ofcr: Jennifer Moriarty
**VP:* Katie N Reed
Prin: Ellen Sutton
Dir Sec: Charlie Carnes
MIS Dir: Erika Foester
Dir IT: Paul Brusewitz
IT Man: John King
Plnt Mgr: Nick Valdez

D-U-N-S 03-924-7390
NORTHSIDE PLUMBING SUPPLY INC
9605 Kirkton Dr, Houston, TX 77095-5037
Tel (713) 699-5499 *Founded/Ownrshp* 1980
Sales 43.3MM^E *EMP* 34
SIC 5074 5999 Plumbing fittings & supplies; Plumbing & heating supplies
Pr: John G Huettel Jr
**Ch Bd:* John G Huettel Sr
**VP:* Kyle Huettel

D-U-N-S 00-331-4036
NORTHSIDE TOOL RENTAL INC (GA)
NTR
35 Irby Ave Nw, Atlanta, GA 30305-1881
Tel (404) 237-9515 *Founded/Ownrshp* 1953
Sales 72.6MM^E *EMP* 33
SIC 0781 5082

NORTHSIDE TRUCKS AND EQUIPMENT
See NORTHSIDE FORD TRUCK SALES INC

NORTHSTAR AEROSPACE CHICAGO
See HELIGEAR ACQUISITION CO

NORTHSTAR AEROSPACE PHOENIX
See HELIGEAR ACQUISITION CO

D-U-N-S 07-942-0909
▲ **NORTHSTAR ASSET MANAGEMENT GROUP INC**
399 Park Ave Fl 18, New York, NY 10022-4968
Tel (212) 547-2600 *Founded/Ownrshp* 2014
Sales 209.2MM^E *EMP* 202^E
Tkr Sym NSAM *Exch* NYS
SIC 6798 Real estate investment trusts; Mortgage investment trusts
Pr: Al Tylis
**Ch Bd:* David T Hamamoto
COO: Daniel R Gilbert
CFO: Debra A Hess
Ofcr: Kristen Whealon
Ex VP: Ronald J Lieberman
VP: Laura Nsam
Mng Dir: Jonathan Lang

D-U-N-S 80-569-9340
NORTHSTAR BANK
(*Suby of* NORTHSTAR FINANCIAL GROUP INC)
833 S Van Dyke Rd, Bad Axe, MI 48413-9604
Tel (989) 269-8077 *Founded/Ownrshp* 2007
Sales NA *EMP* 125^E
SIC 6029 Commercial banks; Commercial banks
CEO: Kevin Nelson
**Pr:* Debbie Cummingham
**COO:* Renae Eckland
**CFO:* Mary Cummingham
CFO: Rebecca Talaski
Ex VP: Edward Walker
VP: Ernest Paulick
Mktg Mgr: Melissa Stein

D-U-N-S 03-744-9964
NORTHSTAR BANK OF COLORADO
(*Suby of* CARLILE BANCSHARES INC) ★
155 Lake Ave, Colorado Springs, CO 80906-3706
Tel (303) 693-7009 *Founded/Ownrshp* 2013
Sales NA *EMP* 20
SIC 6022 State commercial banks; State commercial banks
CEO: Stuart Pattison
**Pr:* D Edward Sauer
Ofcr: Melea Weirauch
Sr VP: Patrick Sullivan
**VP:* John Webster
IT Man: Daniel Morin

D-U-N-S 06-636-5263
NORTHSTAR BANK OF TEXAS
(*Suby of* CARLILE BANCSHARES INC) ★
400 N Carroll Blvd, Denton, TX 76201-9011
Tel (940) 591-1200 *Founded/Ownrshp* 2011
Sales NA *EMP* 320
SIC 6022 State commercial banks; State commercial banks
Ch Bd: Robert Gentry
**Pr:* Tony Clark
**COO:* Judy Leveridge
COO: Greg Studer
CFO: Randy Fahm
CFO: Randy Sahmy
Chf Cred: Louis Williamson
Ofcr: Lupe Ramirez
Ofcr: Mark Stuart
Ex VP: Terry Almon
Ex VP: Ted Leveridge
**Sr VP:* Rita Bennett
Sr VP: Angela Duwe
Sr VP: Trenna Ezzell
Sr VP: Jim Garrison
Sr VP: Robert Humphreys
Sr VP: Stanley Koniecki
Sr VP: Ralph Ramsey
Sr VP: Jay Ross
Sr VP: Joye Williams
VP: Linda Alexander

D-U-N-S 01-033-6530 IMP/EXP
NORTHSTAR BATTERY CO LLC (MO)
4000 E Continental Way, Springfield, MO 65803-8801
Tel (417) 575-8200 *Founded/Ownrshp* 2000
Sales 170.0MM *EMP* 458
SIC 3692 Primary batteries, dry & wet; Primary batteries, dry & wet
Pr: Jerry Hoffman
**COO:* Joel Gibson
**CFO:* Hans AF Silln
VP: Thomas Bjarnemark
VP: David Leclaire
VP: John Semeniuk
**VP:* Thierry Tardivent
Exec: Amy Nelson
Dir IT: Jason Neeley
Tech Mgr: Russell Newnham
Sfty Dirs: Tom Price

D-U-N-S 05-707-6975
NORTHSTAR BUILDERS GROUP LLC
270 N Denton Tap Rd, Coppell, TX 75019-2144
Tel (972) 745-6900 *Founded/Ownrshp* 2012
Sales 61.0MM *EMP* 27
SIC 1541 8742 Industrial buildings, new construction; Construction project management consultant
Pr: Bruce D Helm
**COO:* Aaron Scates

NORTHSTAR CERAMIC TRADING
See STYLEACCESS LLC

D-U-N-S 17-381-8519
NORTHSTAR CG LP
(*Suby of* NORTHSTAR GROUP SERVICES INC) ★
8160 304th Ave Se, Issaquah, WA 98027-8889
Tel (425) 881-0623 *Founded/Ownrshp* 2008
Sales 40.9MM^E *EMP* 416
SIC 1795

D-U-N-S 94-919-2181 IMP
NORTHSTAR CHEMICAL INC
SPECIFIC STAR CHEMICAL, LLC
14200 Sw Tltn Shrwd Rd, Sherwood, OR 97140-9624
Tel (503) 625-3770 *Founded/Ownrshp* 1996
Sales 31.0MM^E *EMP* 30
SIC 5169 Chemicals & allied products
Pr: Sun-Ding Chang
VP: Robert Code
Sls Mgr: Clare Walker

NORTHSTAR COATINGS
See LUSID TECHNOLOGIES INC

NORTHSTAR COMPANIES, THE
See NORTHSTAR LOCATION SERVICES LLC

D-U-N-S 00-625-7950
■ **NORTHSTAR COMPUTER FORMS INC** (MN)
NORTHSTAR FINANCIAL FORMS
(*Suby of* ENNIS INC) ★
7130 Northland Cir N, Minneapolis, MN 55428-1530
Tel (763) 531-7340 *Founded/Ownrshp* 1962
Sales 24.1MM^E *EMP* 250
SIC 2761 Manifold business forms; Computer forms, manifold or continuous; Continuous forms, office & business; Strip forms (manifold business forms); Manifold business forms; Computer forms, manifold or continuous; Continuous forms, office & business; Strip forms (manifold business forms)
Genl Mgr: Tony Orsello
**CFO:* Mary Ann Morin
Genl Mgr: John Christenson
Off Mgr: Vicki Deringer
MIS Dir: Chad Rob
Natl Sales: Ken Riles

D-U-N-S 60-922-6873
NORTHSTAR CONTRACTING GROUP INC
LVI FACILITY SERVICES
(*Suby of* NORTHSTAR GROUP SERVICES INC) ★
31500 Hayman St, Hayward, CA 94544-7120
Tel (510) 491-1300 *Founded/Ownrshp* 2006
Sales 56.3MM *EMP* 200^E
Accts Grant Thornton Llp New York
SIC 1799 Asbestos removal & encapsulation; Asbestos removal & encapsulation
Co-Pr: Michael Kinelski
Co-Pr: Joe Catania
Co-Pr: Michael Moore
VP: Paul S Cutrone
VP: James Fredrickson
VP: Jack Hesotian
VP: John Leonard
VP: Kamal Sookram
HC Dir: Gary Thibodeaux
Board of Directors: Paul S Cutrone, Scott E State

D-U-N-S 80-548-7944
NORTHSTAR CONTRACTING GROUP INC
(*Suby of* NORTHSTAR GROUP SERVICES INC) ★
32 Williams Pkwy, East Hanover, NJ 07936-2105
Tel (973) 884-8682 *Founded/Ownrshp* 2007
Sales 57.0MM^E *EMP* 99
Accts Grant Thornton Llp New York
SIC 1795 Wrecking & demolition work; Wrecking & demolition work
Pr: Edward King
Treas: Paul S Cutrone
VP: Frank Aiello
VP: Peter Demeropoulos
VP: Gregory G Dicarlo
VP: Paul Mast
VP: Kamal Sookram
Board of Directors: Paul S Cutrone, Scott E State

D-U-N-S 18-683-8579
NORTHSTAR DEMOLITION AND REMEDIATION INC
(*Suby of* NORTHSTAR GROUP SERVICES INC) ★
12 Oak Dr, Shawnee, OK 74804-9251
Tel (405) 273-4800 *Founded/Ownrshp* 2006
Sales 22.3MM *EMP* 50^E
Accts Grant Thornton Llp New York
SIC 1795 Decontamination services; Asbestos removal & encapsulation; Environmental consultant; Demolition, buildings & other structures
Pr: Alfred C Draper III
VP: Mark Buescher
VP: Paul S Cutrone
VP: Gregory G Dicarlo
VP: Thomas W Gilmore
VP: Donald B McGlamery Jr
VP: Ward Phillips
VP: Kamal Sookram
VP: Edmund Vernier
Board of Directors: Paul S Cutrone, Scott E State

D-U-N-S 02-470-5667
NORTHSTAR DEMOLITION AND REMEDIATION LP
LVI ENVIRONMENTAL SERVICES
(*Suby of* NORTHSTAR GROUP SERVICES INC) ★
120 Elmgrove Park, Rochester, NY 14624-1359
Tel (585) 458-3570 *Founded/Ownrshp* 1987
Sales 24.0MM *EMP* 85
Accts Grant Thornton Llp New York
SIC 1795 1799 Demolition, buildings & other structures; Asbestos removal & encapsulation; Demolition, buildings & other structures; Asbestos removal & encapsulation
Pr: Peter Demeropoulos
**VP:* Frank Aiello
**VP:* Jeffrey Beckingham
**VP:* James Berry
**VP:* Paul S Cutrone
**VP:* Gregory G Dicarlo
**VP:* Scott R Maranto
**VP:* Paul Mast

*VP: Richard Meahan
*VP: Kamal Sookram

D-U-N-S 19-855-6276
NORTHSTAR DEMOLITION AND REMEDIATION LP
(*Suby of* NORTHSTAR GROUP SERVICES INC) ★
404 N Berry St, Brea, CA 92821-3104
Tel (714) 672-3500 Founded/Ownrshp 2014
Sales 310.4MM^E EMP 917
SIC 1795 1799 8744 Wrecking & demolition work; Decontamination services; ; Wrecking & demolition work; Decontamination services;
Pr: Subhas Khara
CFO: Duane Kerr
VP: Joseph Delahunty
VP: Chris Hertdel
VP: Trent Michaels
VP: Charles J Myers
VP: Philip Truedinger
Brnch Mgr: Donald B McGlamery
IT Man: Tiffany Bull
IT Man: Sharon Katsiroumbas

D-U-N-S 02-336-7498
NORTHSTAR EMS INC
2106 17th Ave, Tuscaloosa, AL 35401-5770
Tel (205) 752-5866 Founded/Ownrshp 1992
Sales 12.1MM^E EMP 300^E
SIC 8049 Paramedic; Paramedic
CEO: Jimmie Smelley Sr
Opers Mgr: Zack Drake

D-U-N-S 00-678-0688
■ **NORTHSTAR ENERGY SERVICES INC** (NC)
(*Suby of* QUANTA SERVICES INC) ★
920 Mmrial Cy Way Ste 650, Houston, TX 77024
Tel (704) 875-1341 Founded/Ownrshp 1949, 2001
Sales 63.8MM^E EMP 200
SIC 1623 4613 4612 8741 Oil & gas pipeline construction; Refined petroleum pipelines; Crude petroleum pipelines; Construction management; Oil & gas pipeline construction; Refined petroleum pipelines; Crude petroleum pipelines; Construction management
Pr: Daren E Austin
CFO: Matthew Hall
*Treas: Nicholas M Grindstaff
*VP: Cecil D Bradford III
*VP: Peter B Obrien
*VP: Leslie D Sackett
*VP: Thomas C Tise
Off Mgr: Susan Nelson

D-U-N-S 06-386-4623
NORTHSTAR FEDERAL SERVICES INC
(*Suby of* NORTHSTAR GROUP SERVICES INC) ★
1992 Saint St Ste B, Richland, WA 99354-5314
Tel (509) 545-5404 Founded/Ownrshp 2012
Sales 49.5MM EMP 22
Accts Grant Thornton Llp New York
SIC 1799 Commercial & office building contractors; Industrial buildings & warehouses; Asbestos removal & encapsulation
Pr: John Beyer
*VP: Paul Cutrone
*VP: Gregory Dicarlo
*VP: Raoul Mebane
*VP: Kamal Sookram
Genl Mgr: Khris Judy

NORTHSTAR FINANCIAL FORMS
See NORTHSTAR COMPUTER FORMS INC

D-U-N-S 02-898-4800
NORTHSTAR FIRE PROTECTION INC
10800 Lynda Ave S Ste 275, Bloomington, MN 55420
Tel (651) 456-9111 Founded/Ownrshp 1997
Sales 26.4MM^E EMP 300
SIC 8711 1731 Fire protection engineering; Fire detection & burglar alarm systems specialization; Fire protection engineering; Fire detection & burglar alarm systems specialization
CEO: R Colin Barnett

NORTHSTAR FIRE PROTECTION TX
See SOUTHSTAR FIRE PROTECTION CO

NORTHSTAR FORD
See DULUTH FORD LLC

NORTHSTAR FOREST MATERIALS
See FOREST WEEKES PRODUCTS INC

D-U-N-S 07-959-5753
NORTHSTAR GROUP HOLDINGS LLC
370 7th Ave Ste 1803, New York, NY 10001-3969
Tel (212) 951-3660 Founded/Ownrshp 2014
Sales 564.6MM^E EMP 3,500
SIC 1795 Demolition, buildings & other structures; Demolition, buildings & other structures
CEO: Scott E State
*Pr: Gregory G Dicarlo
*Pr: Subhas Kahara
*CFO: Paul S Cutrone
Board of Directors: Tim Bernardez, Richard Ferrucci, Gerald Girardi, Robert Hogan, Michael Nibarger, Jason Scheir, Brian Simmons, Irene Wang

D-U-N-S 18-140-5994 IMP
NORTHSTAR GROUP SERVICES INC
(*Suby of* LVI PARENT CORP) ★
370 7th Ave Ste 1803, New York, NY 10001-3969
Tel (212) 951-3660 Founded/Ownrshp 1986
Sales 760.2MM^E EMP 3,500
Accts Grant Thornton Llp New York
SIC 1795 1799 Demolition, buildings & other structures; Asbestos removal & encapsulation; Demolition, buildings & other structures; Asbestos removal & encapsulation
Pr: Scott E State
*CFO: Paul S Cutrone
*VP: Gregory G Dicarlo
*VP: John Leonard
*VP: Kamal Sookram
*VP: Gary Thibodeaux
VP Sls: Teresa Felder
Board of Directors: Scott State, Tim Bernardez, Richard Ferrucci, Gerald Girardi, Robert Hogan, T J McGill, Michael Nibarger, Jason Scheir, Brian Simmons, Irene Wang

D-U-N-S 93-244-8038
NORTHSTAR HEALTH SYSTEM
1400 W Ice Lake Rd, Iron River, MI 49935-9526
Tel (906) 265-6121 Founded/Ownrshp 1995
Sales 37.5MM EMP 298
Accts Wipfli Llp Green Bay Wi
SIC 8062 General medical & surgical hospitals; General medical & surgical hospitals
CEO: Connie Koutouzos
*CFO: Glen Dobson
VP: Ronald Dalton
Cmptr Lab: Kerri Weecks

D-U-N-S 07-861-3674
NORTHSTAR HEALTHCARE INCOME INC
399 Park Ave Fl 18, New York, NY 10022-4968
Tel (212) 547-2600 Founded/Ownrshp 2012
Sales 30.0MM EMP 2
Accts Grant Thornton Llp New York
SIC 6798 Real estate investment trusts
CEO: Ronald J Jeanneault
Ch Bd: Daniel R Gilbert
V Ch Bd: James F Flaherty III

D-U-N-S 17-357-0602
NORTHSTAR LOCATION SERVICES LLC
NORTHSTAR COMPANIES, THE
4285 Genesee St, Cheektowaga, NY 14225-1943
Tel (877) 630-6700 Founded/Ownrshp 2001
Sales 60.3MM^E EMP 743
SIC 7322 8741 Collection agency, except real estate; Management services; Collection agency, except real estate; Management services
*COO: Aaron Castle

D-U-N-S 62-322-6354
■ **NORTHSTAR MATERIALS INC**
KNIFE RIVER MATERIALS
(*Suby of* KNIFE RIVER COAL MINING) ★
4101 Bemidji Ave N, Bemidji, MN 56601-4348
Tel (218) 751-5413 Founded/Ownrshp 2002
Sales 39.2MM^E EMP 200
SIC 1611 Highway & street construction; Highway & street construction
Pr: Doug Muyres
*VP: Thomas Stockert

D-U-N-S 80-360-1165
NORTHSTAR MEMORIAL GROUP LLC
N S M G
1900 Saint James Pl # 300, Houston, TX 77056-4128
Tel (713) 979-9690 Founded/Ownrshp 2007
Sales 135.0MM^E EMP 550^E
SIC 8748 Business consulting; Business consulting
Sr VP: Detlef Taylor
Sr VP: Donna Wagner
VP: Chris Dickerson
VP: David Jenkins
Genl Mgr: John Bokas
Genl Mgr: Dennis Hamilton
Genl Mgr: John Roemmelt
Genl Mgr: Donnell Sullivan
Off Mgr: Tessa Armbrister
Off Mgr: Cindy Gruber
CIO: Michael Zislis

D-U-N-S 07-888-0284 IMP
NORTHSTAR POWER LLC
JOHN DEERE
7301 Northstar St, Ankeny, IA 50021-2501
Tel (515) 964-6100 Founded/Ownrshp 2013
Sales 56.0MM EMP 28
SIC 3519 Internal combustion engines; Internal combustion engines
Genl Mgr: Frank Christencen
Manager: Troy Kaney
Manager: Steve Korum

D-U-N-S 83-609-5588
NORTHSTAR POWER LLC
7301 Northstar St, Ankeny, IA 50021-2501
Tel (515) 964-6100 Founded/Ownrshp 1992
Sales 24.0MM EMP 24
SIC 5084 Engines & parts, diesel; Engines & parts, diesel
Pr: Ace Brandt
*Treas: Michael Vannett

D-U-N-S 18-689-1227 IMP
NORTHSTAR PULP & PAPER CO INC
89 Guion St, Springfield, MA 01104-3070
Tel (888) 394-1300 Founded/Ownrshp 2003
Sales 36.7MM^E EMP 51^E
SIC 4953 2679 Recycling, waste materials; Paperboard products, converted
Pr: Lori Goodman-Novak
*COO: Noah Goodman
CFO: Despina Costa
*Sec: Aaron E Goodman
Ex VP: Wes Wisniowski
*Prin: Seth Goodman
*Prin: Jeffrey Simpson

D-U-N-S 17-122-0192
NORTHSTAR REALTY FINANCE CORP
399 Park Ave Fl 18, New York, NY 10022-4968
Tel (212) 319-8801 Founded/Ownrshp 2004
Sales 634.7MM EMP 12^E
SIC 6798

D-U-N-S 78-450-8223
▲ **NORTHSTAR REALTY FINANCE CORP**
399 Park Ave Fl 18, New York, NY 10022-4968
Tel (212) 547-2600 Founded/Ownrshp 2003
Sales 991.2MM EMP 24^E
Tkr Sym NRF Exch NYS
SIC 6798 Real estate investment trusts
Ch Bd: David T Hamamoto
Pr: Matthew Sperrazza
Pr: Albert Tylis
CFO: Debra A Hess
Chf Inves: Daniel Gilbert
Ex VP: Ronald J Lieberman
VP: Jim Chance
VP: Marcin Orlowski
VP: Zachary Shull
VP: Brendan Thorpe
Mng Dir: Bill Bowman

D-U-N-S 60-611-6619
NORTHSTAR SOURCING GROUP LLC
10235 Main St, Bellevue, WA 98004-6121
Tel (425) 709-3005 Founded/Ownrshp 2003
Sales 27.4MM^E EMP 231
SIC 8748 Advertising agencies; Advertising consultant; Business consulting

D-U-N-S 05-201-8835 IMP
NORTHSTAR STEEL & ALUMINUM INC
205 Bouchard St, Manchester, NH 03103-3313
Tel (603) 668-3600 Founded/Ownrshp 1970
Sales 41.5MM^E EMP 54
SIC 5051 Steel; Aluminum bars, rods, ingots, sheets, pipes, plates, etc.; Steel; Aluminum bars, rods, ingots, sheets, pipes, plates, etc.
Pr: James Macvane
*CFO: Chet Mills
*Genl Mgr: Scott Lovely

NORTHSTAR TEACHERS RESOURCES
See GILSON GRAPHICS INC

D-U-N-S 14-509-0796
NORTHSTAR TECHNOLOGY CORP
32 Mauchly Ste C, Irvine, CA 92618-2336
Tel (949) 788-0738 Founded/Ownrshp 2003
Sales 26.7MM^E EMP 250
Accts Daniel Hernandez Cpa Fullert
SIC 7371 Custom computer programming services; Custom computer programming services
CEO: Frances Chiang
*COO: Warren Matthews

D-U-N-S 06-726-3181
NORTHSTAR TRAVEL MEDIA LLC
100 Lighting Way Ste 200, Secaucus, NJ 07094-3681
Tel (201) 902-2000 Founded/Ownrshp 2001
Sales 245.2MM^E EMP 1,012
SIC 2721 Periodicals; Periodicals
Ch Bd: Tom Kemp
Pr: Sheila Rice
Treas: Nadine Godwin
VP: Danielle Cirami-Gillis
VP: Megan Sheekey
VP: Robert Sullivan
Dir Soc: Susan Brooks
Dir Soc: Debbie Cortese
Prgrm Mgr: Lori Walton
Snr Sftwr: Jijie Song
IT Man: Timothy Ricablanca

NORTHSTAR-AT-TAHOE
See TRIMONT LAND CO

NORTHSTERN PROF NURSES REGISTR
See NORTHEASTERN PROFESSIONAL NURSES REGISTRY INC

D-U-N-S 04-983-3163
NORTHTOWN AUTOMOTIVE COMPANIES INC
NORTHTOWN WORLD AUTO CENTER
1135 Millersport Hwy, Amherst, NY 14226-1722
Tel (716) 836-4600 Founded/Ownrshp 1969
Sales 122.9MM^E EMP 336
SIC 5511 Automobiles, new & used; Automobiles, new & used
Pr: Norman Schreiber
CFO: Harold Erbacher
*VP: Joseph Calabrese
VP: Larry Schreiber
*VP: Craig Schreiber
Sls Mgr: Rick Shahin
Sales Asso: Paul Alfieri
Sales Asso: Joshua Lange

NORTHTOWN COMPANY, THE
See NORTHTOWN PRODUCTS INC

D-U-N-S 09-445-4006 IMP
NORTHTOWN PRODUCTS INC
NORTHTOWN COMPANY, THE
5202 Argosy Ave, Huntington Beach, CA 92649-1016
Tel (714) 375-4000 Founded/Ownrshp 1973
Sales 39.5MM^E EMP 100
SIC 5162 3081 Plastics products; Polypropylene film & sheet; Plastics products; Polypropylene film & sheet
Pr: Carryl Deck
Opers Mgr: Janette Reynolds
Mktg Dir: Maureen Sharp
Sls Dir: Travis Blair

NORTHTOWN WORLD AUTO CENTER
See NORTHTOWN AUTOMOTIVE COMPANIES INC

D-U-N-S 01-228-6365
NORTHTOWNE LINCOLN-MERCURY INC
21 Ne Vivion Rd, Kansas City, MO 64118-4504
Tel (816) 453-2710 Founded/Ownrshp 1982
Sales 45.6MM^E EMP 150
SIC 5511 Automobiles, new & used; Automobiles, new & used
Pr: K Lawrence Le Fever
*VP: Scott L Lefever

D-U-N-S 08-060-8461
NORTHUMBERLAND BANK CORP
245 Front St, Northumberland, PA 17857-1611
Tel (570) 473-3531 Founded/Ownrshp 1997
Sales NA EMP 55^E
Accts Sr Snodgrass Ac Wexford P
SIC 6712 6162 Bank holding companies; Mortgage bankers & correspondents; Bank holding companies; Mortgage bankers & correspondents
Pr: J Donald Steele Jr

NORTHVALE APARTMENTS
See PORTER STARKE SERVICES INC

D-U-N-S 06-587-4463
NORTHVIEW PUBLIC SCHOOL DIST
4451 Hunsberger Ave Ne, Grand Rapids, MI 49525-6126
Tel (616) 363-6861 Founded/Ownrshp 1960
Sales 20.4MM^E EMP 400^E
Accts Hungerford Aldrin Nichols &
SIC 8211 9411 Public elementary & secondary schools; School board; Administration of educational programs; Public elementary & secondary schools; School board; Administration of educational programs
Off Admin: Sheryl Purwin

D-U-N-S 00-697-6104 IMP
NORTHVILLE INDUSTRIES CORP
(*Suby of* NIC HOLDING CORP) ★
225 Broadhollow Rd, Melville, NY 11747-4822
Tel (631) 293-4700 Founded/Ownrshp 1954
Sales 30.9MM^E EMP 60
SIC 5171 Petroleum bulk stations & terminals; Petroleum bulk stations; Petroleum terminals; Petroleum bulk stations & terminals; Petroleum bulk stations; Petroleum terminals
Ch Bd: Gene M Bernstein
*Pr: H Brant Brown
*CEO: Jay H Bernstein
*CFO: Peter Ripp
Sr VP: Elizabeth McConaghy

D-U-N-S 07-634-2203
NORTHVILLE PUBLIC SCHOOL DISTRICT
501 W Main St, Northville, MI 48167-1576
Tel (248) 349-3400 Founded/Ownrshp 1867
Sales 97.2MM EMP 850
Accts Plante & Moran Pllc Auburnvi
SIC 8211 Public elementary school; Public junior high school; Public senior high school; Public special education school; Public elementary school; Public junior high school; Public senior high school; Public special education school
VP: Heather Bauer
Schl Brd P: James Mazurek
HC Dir: Nadine Harris

NORTHWAY EXCHANGE
See NEW YORK AUTO AUCTION SERVICES INC

D-U-N-S 02-364-9879
▲ **NORTHWAY FINANCIAL INC**
9 Main St, Berlin, NH 03570-2414
Tel (603) 752-1171 Founded/Ownrshp 1997
Sales NA EMP 249
Tkr Sym NWYF Exch OTO
SIC 6021 National commercial banks; National commercial banks
Ch Bd: William J Woodward
CFO: Richard P Orsillo
V Ch Bd: Fletcher W Adams
Bd of Dir: Robert Howe
Sr VP: Mark C Bechtold
Sr VP: Jeffrey D Smith
VP: David Cronin
VP: Marc Poyant
Dir Sec: David Doucette

D-U-N-S 00-498-1023
NORTHWAY MOTOR CAR CORP
727 New Loudon Rd, Latham, NY 12110-4017
Tel (518) 783-1951 Founded/Ownrshp 1966
Sales 28.8MM^E EMP 100
SIC 5511 Automobiles, new & used; Automobiles, new & used
Pr: Kevin Langan
Exec: Silvia Holton

D-U-N-S 07-665-2262
NORTHWEST ADMINISTRATORS INC
2323 Eastlake Ave E, Seattle, WA 98102-3305
Tel (206) 329-4900 Founded/Ownrshp 1958
Sales NA EMP 400
SIC 6371 Pension, health & welfare funds; Pension, health & welfare funds
Pr: Christopher R Hughes
*Ofcr: Gayle Bushnell
*Sr VP: Robert H Gies
*VP: James Baker
VP: Mark Coles
VP: Don Ditter
VP: Arlyn Escalona
VP: Bob Gies
VP: Aleksandra Gluhcheva
*VP: John Hughes Jr
VP: Jeannine Madrigal
VP: Thomas Wagner

NORTHWEST AEA
See NORTHWEST AREA EDUCATION AGENCY

D-U-N-S 01-223-7454
NORTHWEST AEROSPACE TECHNOLOGIES INC
2210 Hewitt Ave Ste 300, Everett, WA 98201-3767
Tel (425) 257-2044 Founded/Ownrshp 1997
Sales 27.1MM^E EMP 60^E
SIC 8711 3728 Aviation &/or aeronautical engineering; Aircraft parts & equipment
Pr: Paul Sobotta
*VP: Jeff McShane
Prgrm Mgr: Yoosin Park
Prgrm Mgr: Lindsay Stedford
Sys Mgr: Seth Moffit
Mtls Mgr: Steven Prussel
Ql Cn Mgr: Tom Dowler

D-U-N-S 00-696-3508
■ **NORTHWEST AIRLINES INC** (MN)
(*Suby of* DELTA AIR LINES INC) ★
7500 Airline Dr, Minneapolis, MN 55450-1101
Tel (404) 715-2600 Founded/Ownrshp 1926, 2008
Sales 706.5MM^E EMP 26,000
SIC 4512 4513 4522 Air passenger carrier, scheduled; Air cargo carrier, scheduled; Air courier services; Air transportation, nonscheduled; Air passenger carrier, scheduled; Air cargo carrier, scheduled; Air courier services; Air transportation, nonscheduled
CEO: Edward H Bastian
*Ch Bd: Richard Anderson
Pr: Mark Powers
CEO: Neal Cohen
*CFO: Dave Davis
*CFO: Bernard Han
Ch: Jun Mokudai
Treas: Joseph E Francht Jr

Treas: Robert Nazarian
Ofcr: Rolf Andresen
**Ex VP:* Philip C Haan
Sr VP: Doug Birdsall
Sr VP: Jim Friedel
Sr VP: J Timothy Griffin
Sr VP: Richard B Hirst
Sr VP: Thomas C Kennedy
Sr VP: Dirk McMahon
Sr VP: Timothy J Rainey
Sr VP: Andrew Roberts
**Sr VP:* Theresa Wise
Sr VP: Bernhardt Wruble

D-U-N-S 04-889-4711
NORTHWEST ALABAMA GAS DISTRICT INC
310 2nd St Sw, Hamilton, AL 35570-9700
Tel (205) 921-3106 *Founded/Ownrshp* 1952
Sales 27.2MM *EMP* 48
Accts Guin & Parish Llc Winfield
SIC 4923 Gas transmission & distribution; Gas transmission & distribution
Genl Mgr: Kelly Kinnett

D-U-N-S 09-317-8325
NORTHWEST ALABAMA MENTAL HEALTH CENTER
NWAMHC
1100 7th Ave, Jasper, AL 35501-4377
Tel (205) 302-9000 *Founded/Ownrshp* 1970
Sales NA *EMP* 600
Accts Phillip Morgan & Company Pc
SIC 9431 Mental health agency administration, government; ; Mental health agency administration, government;
Top Exec: Jenny Elliott
Ex Dir: Tony Jerrolds
Sls Mgr: Mary Key
Doctor: Kaycia Vansickle MD

D-U-N-S 08-677-2571
NORTHWEST ALLEN COUNTY SCHOOLS (IN)
13119 Coldwater Rd, Fort Wayne, IN 46845-9631
Tel (260) 637-3155 *Founded/Ownrshp* 1966
Sales 22.1MM^E *EMP* 370
SIC 8211 Public elementary & secondary schools; Public elementary & secondary schools
HC Dir: Sandy Kelty
HC Dir: Cynthia McAlister

D-U-N-S 78-782-3277
NORTHWEST ARCTIC BOROUGH SCHOOL DISTRICT
744 3rd Ave, Kotzebue, AK 99752
Tel (907) 442-3472 *Founded/Ownrshp* 1976
Sales 24.6MM^E *EMP* 450
SIC 8211 Public elementary & secondary schools; Public elementary & secondary schools
CEO: Charles F Mason
Exec: Y Valgren

D-U-N-S 10-371-7625
NORTHWEST AREA EDUCATION AGENCY
NORTHWEST AEA
1520 Morningside Ave, Sioux City, IA 51106-1716
Tel (712) 222-6000 *Founded/Ownrshp* 2006
Sales 12.8MM^E *EMP* 363
SIC 8299 8211 Educational services; Elementary & secondary schools; Educational services; Elementary & secondary schools
**CFO:* Wayne Hess
Bd of Dir: Nancy Brommer
Bd of Dir: Stephanie Robinson
Bd of Dir: Diane Schwartz
Bd of Dir: Judy Sweetman
Ofcr: Mary Groen
Teacher Pr: Jerome Schaefer

D-U-N-S 07-651-0866
NORTHWEST AREA FOUNDATION
60 Plato Blvd E Ste 400, Saint Paul, MN 55107-1832
Tel (651) 224-9635 *Founded/Ownrshp* 1934
Sales 28.3MM *EMP* 41
SIC 7389 Fund raising organizations; Fund raising organizations
Pr: Kevin Walker
Ch: Dorothy Bridges
Bd of Dir: John Taft
Ofcr: Nikki Foster
VP: Gary Cunningham
Comm Dir: Paul Bachleitner
Off Mgr: Marie Podratz
Board of Directors: James R Scott, Nina M Archabal, Sarah Vogel, W E Barsness, Steven L Belton, W John Driscoll, David F Hickok, Richard S Levitt, Natalie Camacho-Mendoza, Hazel R O'Leary, Sally Pederson

D-U-N-S 61-982-1077
NORTHWEST ARKANSAS COMMUNITY COLLEGE
1 College Dr, Bentonville, AR 72712-5091
Tel (479) 636-9222 *Founded/Ownrshp* 1989
Sales 74.0MM^E *EMP* 450
SIC 8222 Community college; Community college
Pr: Becky Paneitz
**Pr:* Evelyn Jorgerson
**Pr:* Dennis Smiley
**CFO:* Steve Pelphrey
**Treas:* M Kent Burger
Ofcr: Robert Coleman
Assoc VP: M S Brown Ed
VP: Ashley Bradley
**VP:* Michael Luttrell
CIO: Jason Degn
Nrsg Dir: Mary Keel

D-U-N-S 08-948-4034
NORTHWEST ASPHALT INC
1451 Stagecoach Rd, Shakopee, MN 55379-8045
Tel (952) 445-1003 *Founded/Ownrshp* 1978
Sales 31.9MM^E *EMP* 175
SIC 1771 1623 1794 Driveway, parking lot & blacktop contractors; Blacktop (asphalt) work; Parking lot construction; Excavation work; Driveway, parking lot & blacktop contractors; Blacktop (asphalt) work; Parking lot construction; Water & sewer line construction; Excavation work
CEO: Michael B Pfeiffer
**CFO:* Michael H Sand
**VP:* Debra Hendrickson
Snr Mgr: Girard Christopher

D-U-N-S 05-117-8684
NORTHWEST ASPHALT PRODUCTS INC
STARK ASPHALT
11710 W Hampton Ave, Brookfield, WI 53005
Tel (414) 466-7624 *Founded/Ownrshp* 1965
Sales 21.1MM^E *EMP* 80
SIC 1771 Blacktop (asphalt) work
CEO: Don Stark
**Pr:* Kirt Haggard
**VP:* Chuck Gassert
**VP:* Ron Kozlowski
**VP:* Thomas Skelton

D-U-N-S 11-521-9029
NORTHWEST ATLANTA AUTOMOTIVE GROUP LLC
TOWN CENTER NISSAN
2310 Brett Lakes Blvd Nw, Kennesaw, GA 30144-4907
Tel (770) 423-9691 *Founded/Ownrshp* 2002
Sales 24.3MM^E *EMP* 70
SIC 5511 Automobiles, new & used; Automobiles, new & used
VP: Ken Grant
Sls Dir: Percy Sledge

NORTHWEST AUTOMATION & CONTRLS
See NORTHWEST MECHANICAL INC

D-U-N-S 82-745-7586
NORTHWEST BANCORP MHC
100 Liberty St, Warren, PA 16365-2411
Tel (814) 728-7260 *Founded/Ownrshp* 2001
Sales NA *EMP* 1,967^E
SIC 6036 Savings institutions, not federally chartered; Savings institutions, not federally chartered
Ch Bd: William J Wagner

D-U-N-S 88-346-0958
NORTHWEST BANCORP INC
(*Suby of* NORTHWEST BANCORP MHC) ★
100 Liberty St, Warren, PA 16365-2411
Tel (814) 726-2140 *Founded/Ownrshp* 2001
Sales NA *EMP* 1,964^E
SIC 6036 Savings institutions, not federally chartered; Savings institutions, not federally chartered
Ch Bd: William J Wagner
Pr: Chip Pfohl
CFO: William W Harvey Jr
Chf Cred: Myra Sletson
Ofcr: Gina Schultz
Ofcr: Tracey Shultz
Ex VP: Beth Harman
Ex VP: Gregory C Larocca
Sr VP: Robert Bablak
Sr VP: Ben Jamieson
Sr VP: Roger Mosby
Sr VP: Robert A Ordiwy
Sr VP: Thomas Ziacik
VP: Kurt Bevan
VP: Jack Blank
VP: Steve Carman
VP: Drew Ecklund
VP: Norman Ewing
VP: Ken Faulconbridge
VP: Barry Francis
VP: Mark Gdog

D-U-N-S 78-816-1958
▲ NORTHWEST BANCORPORATION INC
421 W Riverside Ave, Spokane, WA 99201-0405
Tel (509) 456-8888 *Founded/Ownrshp* 1991
Sales NA *EMP* 120
Tkr Sym NBCT *Exch* OTO
SIC 6021 National commercial banks; National commercial banks
Pr: Randall L Fewel
Ch Bd: Anthony D Bonanzino
CFO: Holly A Poquette
Exec: Janelle Parenteau
Brnch Mgr: Janet Dibler
Board of Directors: Dwight B Aden Jr, Katie Brodie, Harlan D Douglass, Freeman B Duncan, Clark H Gemmill, Bryan S Norby, William E Shelby, Jennifer P West

D-U-N-S 83-228-2375
▲ NORTHWEST BANCSHARES INC
100 Liberty St, Warren, PA 16365-2411
Tel (814) 726-2140 *Founded/Ownrshp* 2009
Sales NA *EMP* 2,231^E
Tkr Sym NWBI *Exch* NGS
SIC 6021 National commercial banks; National commercial banks
Ch Bd: William J Wagner
CFO: William W Harvey Jr

D-U-N-S 02-019-0880
NORTHWEST BANK (IA)
(*Suby of* NORTHWEST FINANCIAL CORP) ★
101 W 5th St, Spencer, IA 51301-3821
Tel (712) 262-2202 *Founded/Ownrshp* 1988
Sales NA *EMP* 100
SIC 6035 Federal savings & loan associations; Federal savings & loan associations
CEO: Neil Stanley
**Pr:* Dean Jacobsen
**Pr:* William Orrison
**Ch:* C B Conover
**Ex VP:* Gregory Post
Ex VP: Larry Shaffer
Ex VP: Michael Williams
Sr VP: Cindy Dunaway
Sr VP: Autumn Hickman
Sr VP: Dean Schantz
VP: Brenda Bucklew
VP: Brenda Gibson
VP: Keith Heitritter
VP: Matt Hurd
VP: Brent Linn
VP: Sharon Lisac
VP: Brent Plantage
VP: Michael Scacci
VP: Yvonne Townsend

D-U-N-S 93-298-4511
NORTHWEST BROADCASTING INC
MOUNTAIN BROADCASTING
2111 University Park Dr # 650, Okemos, MI 48864-5938
Tel (517) 347-4141 *Founded/Ownrshp* 1995
Sales 39.9MM^E *EMP* 200
SIC 4833 Television broadcasting stations; Television broadcasting stations
Pr: Brian Brady
**CFO:* Bill Quarles

NORTHWEST BUILDING MATERIALS
See NORTHWEST BUILDING SUPPLY INC

D-U-N-S 13-106-2473
NORTHWEST BUILDING SUPPLY INC
NORTHWEST BUILDING MATERIALS
5535 Nw 5th St, Oklahoma City, OK 73127-5811
Tel (405) 946-0500 *Founded/Ownrshp* 1985
Sales 116.2MM^E *EMP* 100^E
SIC 5033 5031 5211 Roofing & siding materials; Building materials, interior; Building materials, exterior; Doors & windows; Millwork; Lumber & other building materials; Roofing material; Lumber products; Millwork & lumber
Pr: Cliff Stockton

D-U-N-S 10-942-2840
NORTHWEST CANCER SPECIALIST INC
COMPASS ONCOLOGY
1498 Se Tech Center Pl # 240, Vancouver, WA 98683-5508
Tel (503) 297-7403 *Founded/Ownrshp* 1976
Sales 1.0MM^E *EMP* 372^E
SIC 8011 Oncologist; Gynecologist
Pr: Brad Perrido

D-U-N-S 80-565-0058
NORTHWEST CAPITAL APPRECIATION INC
1200 Westlake Ave N # 310, Seattle, WA 98109-3543
Tel (206) 689-5615 *Founded/Ownrshp* 1992
Sales 83.2MM^E *EMP* 1,871
SIC 2611 Pulp produced from wood base; Pulp produced from wood base
Co-Pr: Brad Creswell
**Co-Pr:* E Perot Bissell

D-U-N-S 02-969-5053
NORTHWEST CASCADE INC
HONEYBUCKETS
10412 John Bananola Way E, Puyallup, WA 98374-9333
Tel (253) 848-2371 *Founded/Ownrshp* 1985
Sales 181.4MM^E *EMP* 300
Accts Sutor Krystad & Rosenfeld Pl
SIC 1623 7359 7699 3272 1711 Underground utilities contractor; Portable toilet rental; Septic tank cleaning service; Septic tanks, concrete; Septic system construction; Underground utilities contractor; Portable toilet rental; Septic tank cleaning service; Septic tanks, concrete; Septic system construction
Pr: Carl Liliequest
COO: Ron Inman
**CFO:* Greg Potts
**Ch:* Mark Perry
VP: Bob Howard
VP: Tom Rogers
Genl Mgr: Craig Goodwin
IT Man: Michael Sanford
Natl Sales: Paul McLaughlin
Mktg Mgr: Tom Ramsay

D-U-N-S 01-020-8312 IMP
NORTHWEST CENTER
7272 W Marginal Way S, Seattle, WA 98108-4140
Tel (206) 285-9140 *Founded/Ownrshp* 1965
Sales 39.4MM *EMP* 200^E
SIC 8331 8322 3599 7211 7389 Vocational training agency; Sheltered workshop; Child related social services; Social services for the handicapped; Machine & other job shop work; Power laundries, family & commercial; Packaging & labeling services; Vocational training agency; Sheltered workshop; Child related social services; Social services for the handicapped; Machine & other job shop work; Power laundries, family & commercial; Packaging & labeling services
CEO: Tom Everill
CFO: Robin Krueger
CFO: Jim Wood
Treas: David McRae
Bd of Dir: August Monday
Ex VP: Cameron Fellows
VP: Pat Butler
VP: Jean Kantu
**VP:* Mike Quinn
Dir Rx: Lavina McClam
Ex Dir: Jim McClurg

NORTHWEST CLINIC
See HURLEY SERVICES CORP

D-U-N-S 07-209-3172 IMP
NORTHWEST CO LLC
WILMINGTON PRODUCTS USA
49 Bryant Ave, Roslyn, NY 11576-1123
Tel (516) 484-6996 *Founded/Ownrshp* 2007
Sales 158.0MM *EMP* 140
Accts Mayer Hoffman Mccann Cpas
SIC 2211 Blankets, comforters & beddings; Bedding, manmade or silk fabric; Bathmats, cotton; Bathrobes, knit; Batting, wadding, padding & fillings; Sportswear, women's; Blankets & blanketings, cotton
Pr: Ross Auerbach
**COO:* Marc Friedman
**CFO:* Robert Jolson
Ex VP: Glenn Auerbach
Ex VP: Stan Mieszkowski
Sr VP: Kara Langer
VP: Karyn Benoit
VP: Kim Rizzardi
Creative D: Elizabeth Gilmore
Dir IT: Keith Stevens
VP Opers: Beau Chamale

NORTHWEST COLLEGE
See NORTHWEST COMMUNITY COLLEGE

D-U-N-S 07-762-1449
NORTHWEST COMMUNITY COLLEGE
NORTHWEST COLLEGE
231 W 6th St Bldg 3, Powell, WY 82435-1898
Tel (307) 754-6000 *Founded/Ownrshp* 1946
Sales 13.5MM^E *EMP* 461^E
Accts Mcgee Hearne & Paiz Llp Che
SIC 8222 8249 8221 Junior college; Vocational schools; Colleges universities & professional schools; Junior college; Vocational schools; Colleges universities & professional schools
Pr: Fran Feinerman
Treas: Martha Coe
VP: Sean Fox
VP: Gerald Giraud
VP: Nada Larsen
Ex Dir: Shelby Wetzel
Off Mgr: Jo Ann Heimer
IT Man: Joann Heimer
Web Dev: Carey Miller
Psych: Roena Halbur
Nrsg Dir: Marnee Crawford

D-U-N-S 03-707-8136
NORTHWEST COMMUNITY CREDIT UNION
545 E 8th Ave, Eugene, OR 97401-3189
Tel (541) 747-4231 *Founded/Ownrshp* 1949
Sales NA *EMP* 250
SIC 6062 State credit unions, not federally chartered; State credit unions, not federally chartered
CEO: John Iglesias
**CFO:* Patrick Force
CFO: Dennis Hren
**Ch:* Barb Blackmore
**Sec:* Dennis Powell
Ofcr: Boaz Wolpe
VP: Brent Gifford
VP: Otto Radke
VP: Vicki Roessler
Brnch Mgr: Dorinda Dawes
Brnch Mgr: Kim Luckman

NORTHWEST COMMUNITY HEALTH SER
See NORTHWEST COMMUNITY HOSPITAL INC

D-U-N-S 96-171-2465
NORTHWEST COMMUNITY HEALTHCARE PHO LLC
1614 W Central Rd Ste 202, Arlington Heights, IL 60005-2453
Tel (847) 618-1000 *Founded/Ownrshp* 2010
Sales 44.8MM^E *EMP* 319^E
Accts Ernst & Young Us Llp Chicago
SIC 8062 General medical & surgical hospitals; General medical & surgical hospitals
Pr: Bruce Crowther
QA Dir: Cynthia Dougherty
Mktg Dir: Melissa Gross

D-U-N-S 12-148-1832
NORTHWEST COMMUNITY HOSPITAL FOUNDATION
N C H
800 W Central Rd, Arlington Heights, IL 60005-2349
Tel (847) 618-1000 *Founded/Ownrshp* 1981
Sales 132.6MM^E *EMP* 4,000
SIC 8062 General medical & surgical hospitals; General medical & surgical hospitals
CEO: Stephen O Scogna
**Pr:* Bruce K Crowther
**VP:* Marsha Liu
VP: Dawn Walden

D-U-N-S 04-232-9615
NORTHWEST COMMUNITY HOSPITAL INC
NORTHWEST COMMUNITY HEALTH SER
800 W Central Rd, Arlington Heights, IL 60005-2349
Tel (847) 618-1000 *Founded/Ownrshp* 1953
Sales 422.4MM *EMP* 2,800
SIC 8062 Hospital, AMA approved residency; Hospital, AMA approved residency
CEO: Stephen Scogna
Chf OB: Kristen Stone-Mulhern
Dir Recs: Ron Tapnio
CFO: Marsha Liu
**CFO:* John Skeans
**CFO:* Michael Zenn
Ofcr: Jack King
VP: Jane D Mass
Dir Risk M: Mary Mulcrone
Dir Lab: Demetra Calas
Dir Lab: Demi Callias
Dir Rad: Daniel B Crane
Dir Rad: Carl L Kabhen
Dir Rx: Paul Zega
Comm Man: Laurice Knox

NORTHWEST COMMUNITY SCHOOLS
See NORTHWEST SCHOOL DISTRICT

D-U-N-S 82-504-6295 IMP
NORTHWEST COMPOSITES INC
12810 State Ave, Marysville, WA 98271-7849
Tel (360) 653-2211 *Founded/Ownrshp* 1993
Sales 33.5MM^E *EMP* 400^E
SIC 3089 Plastic processing; Plastic processing
Ch Bd: James Downey
**Pr:* Joseph Moran
VP: Brad Young

D-U-N-S 61-889-5486
NORTHWEST CONCRETE PRODUCTS INC
NORTHWEST LOGISTICS
1125 40th St Ste B, Woodward, OK 73801-1700
Tel (580) 254-8070 *Founded/Ownrshp* 1968
Sales 52.5MM *EMP* 95
SIC 4212 Local trucking, without storage; Local trucking, without storage
Pr: Robert A Hodges
**Prin:* Jim Bush
**Prin:* John W Dunn

D-U-N-S 62-807-6614
NORTHWEST CONSTRUCTION INC
2353 130th Ave Ne Ste 100, Bellevue, WA 98005-1759
Tel (425) 453-8380 *Founded/Ownrshp* 1990
Sales 28.6MM^E *EMP* 80
SIC 1611 General contractor, highway & street construction
Pr: Gregg Ferullo
**VP:* Brett Ferullo
VP: Mitch Harris
Opers Mgr: Jeff Nelson

D-U-N-S 12-118-9864
NORTHWEST CONTRACTING INC
3420 E Century Ave, Bismarck, ND 58503-0737
Tel (701) 255-7727 *Founded/Ownrshp* 1983
Sales 53.6MM^E *EMP* 108^E
SIC 1541 1771 Industrial buildings & warehouses; Concrete work; Industrial buildings & warehouses; Concrete work
Pr: Mike Todd
**Sec:* Jerry Splonskowski
VP: Jim Federico
Genl Mgr: Jennifer Krause

D-U-N-S 18-936-2655
NORTHWEST CONTRACTING SERVICES INC
3770 Cherry Rd, Memphis, TN 38118-6304
Tel (901) 365-6252 *Founded/Ownrshp* 2005
Sales 30.0MM *EMP* 20
SIC 1611 General contractor, highway & street construction; General contractor, highway & street construction
CEO: Jim Federico
**Pr:* Tony Federico

D-U-N-S 11-820-3918
NORTHWEST CONTRACTORS INC
200 Industrial Dr Unit A, Hampshire, IL 60140-7909
Tel (847) 695-5100 *Founded/Ownrshp* 1994
Sales 25.5MM *EMP* 50
Accts Gualandri & Company Pc
SIC 1541 1542 Industrial buildings, new construction; Commercial & office building, new construction; Industrial buildings, new construction; Commercial & office building, new construction
Pr: Daniel L Robinson
**VP:* Miles T Ackmann

D-U-N-S 92-957-2014 IMP
NORTHWEST COSMETIC LABORATORIES LLC
NORTHWEST COSMETICS
200 Technology Dr, Idaho Falls, ID 83401-1500
Tel (208) 522-6723 *Founded/Ownrshp* 2014
Sales 44.5MM^E *EMP* 100
SIC 2844 5999 Toilet preparations; Toiletries, cosmetics & perfumes; Toilet preparations; Toiletries, cosmetics & perfumes
CEO: Matt Bryant
CIO: Dennis Coffy
Manager: Leola Hansen

NORTHWEST COSMETICS
See NORTHWEST COSMETIC LABORATORIES LLC

D-U-N-S 80-793-7354
NORTHWEST COUNTRY PLACE INC
LIBERTY COUNTRY PLACE
9223 Amber Wood Dr, Willoughby, OH 44094-9350
Tel (440) 975-1749 *Founded/Ownrshp* 1993
Sales 11.2MM^E *EMP* 326
SIC 8742 Hospital & health services consultant; Hospital & health services consultant
CEO: Tom Armagno
Treas: Lorie Armango

D-U-N-S 04-043-1335
NORTHWEST CRANE SERVICE LLC
1125 40th St Ste B, Woodward, OK 73801-1700
Tel (406) 373-2979 *Founded/Ownrshp* 2001
Sales 70.0MM *EMP* 70
Accts Bledsoe & Assoc Pllc Edmond
SIC 7389 Crane & aerial lift service; Crane & aerial lift service
CFO: Charys Maher
CFO: Rebecca Nosler

D-U-N-S 11-850-0649 IMP/EXP
NORTHWEST DAIRY ASSOCIATION
1130 Rainier Ave S, Seattle, WA 98144-2842
Tel (206) 284-7220 *Founded/Ownrshp* 1916
Sales 1.4MMM^E *EMP* 1,300
SIC 2026 Fluid milk; Fluid milk
CEO: Jim Werkhoven
Pr: James Wegner
Treas: Sherman Polinder
Sec: Randy Lindley
VP: Tim McMillan
VP: Steve Rowe

D-U-N-S 80-481-2261
NORTHWEST EARTHMOVERS INC
N E I
13600 Sw Galbreath Dr, Sherwood, OR 97140-9247
Tel (503) 625-3100 *Founded/Ownrshp* 1984
Sales 25.0MM *EMP* 62
SIC 7353 Heavy construction equipment rental; Earth moving equipment, rental or leasing; Heavy construction equipment rental; Earth moving equipment, rental or leasing
Pr: Donnie L Martin
**Pr:* Jeff Hargens
**VP:* Craig Smelter
Off Mgr: Jackie Flores

D-U-N-S 01-944-8117
NORTHWEST EDUCATION LOAN ASSOCIATION
NELA
190 Queen Anne Ave N # 300, Seattle, WA 98109-4968
Tel (206) 461-5300 *Founded/Ownrshp* 1978
Sales NA *EMP* 70^E
SIC 6163 Loan brokers; Loan brokers
Prin: Denisefeser
**Ch Bd:* Carl Dalstrom
**Pr:* Denise Feser
**Ex Dir:* Karen Devilla

D-U-N-S 13-160-6829
NORTHWEST ENERGY EFFICIENCY ALLIANCE INC
421 Sw 6th Ave Ste 600, Portland, OR 97204-1619
Tel (503) 827-8416 *Founded/Ownrshp* 1996
Sales 40.1MM *EMP* 23
Accts Moss Adams Llp Portland Or
SIC 8699 Personal interest organization; Personal interest organization
Ex Dir: Margie Gardner
**Ch Bd:* Mike Weedall
**Pr:* Anita Decker
**Treas:* Jeff Bumgarner
Ofcr: John Harrison
Comm Man: Virginia Mersereau
Ex Dir: Steve Crow
Store Dir: Susan Stratton
Snr Mgr: Ken Baker
Snr Mgr: Sepideh Rezania
Snr Mgr: Stephanie Rider

D-U-N-S 10-839-9338
NORTHWEST EQUIPMENT SALES INC
2405 S Janeen St, Boise, ID 83709-3217
Tel (208) 362-3400 *Founded/Ownrshp* 1982
Sales 35.0MM *EMP* 64
SIC 5012 Trailers for trucks, new & used; Trailers for trucks, new & used
Pr: James Hibler
**Sec:* Judy Hibler
**VP:* Travis Hibler
**Prin:* Paul Brunstad
IT Man: Larry Coppinger

D-U-N-S 60-653-5177
NORTHWEST EVALUATION ASSOCIATION
NWEA
121 Nw Everett St, Portland, OR 97209-4049
Tel (503) 624-1951 *Founded/Ownrshp* 1977
Sales 108.7MM *EMP* 600
Accts Moss Adams Llp Portland Ore
SIC 8299 8748 Educational services; Educational consultant; Educational services; Educational consultant
Pr: Matt Chapman
**CFO:* Geri Cohen
**Ex VP:* Jeff Strickler
**VP:* Jill Hedrick
**VP:* Donna Schultz
**VP:* Dr Anne J Udall
Software D: Harry Pendergrass
Opers Mgr: Jedediah Gilchrist

D-U-N-S 03-354-8173
NORTHWEST EXTERMINATING CO INC
830 Kennesaw Ave Nw, Marietta, GA 30060-1006
Tel (770) 436-2020 *Founded/Ownrshp* 1953
Sales 36.0MM *EMP* 390
SIC 7342 Exterminating & fumigating; Termite control; Exterminating & fumigating; Termite control
Pr: Steve M Phillips
**CFO:* Dave Brown
**CFO:* Stephen Phillips
**Sec:* Stanford Phillips

D-U-N-S 06-958-5933
NORTHWEST FARM CREDIT SERVICES
1700 S Assembly St # 102, Spokane, WA 99224-2116
Tel (509) 838-2429 *Founded/Ownrshp* 1985
Sales NA *EMP* 500
Accts Pricewaterhousecoopers Llp Sa
SIC 6111 Federal & federally sponsored credit agencies; Federal & federally sponsored credit agencies
CEO: Phil Dipofi
Pr: Jessi Dressen
Pr: Matt Koch
Pr: Lance Zollinger
COO: Ben Showalter
Ofcr: Michael Babenko
Ofcr: Jeffrey Elston
Ofcr: Eric Gray
Ofcr: Stephanie Rennie
Ofcr: Dennis Schaefer
Ex VP: Roger Calhoun
Ex VP: Bill Johnson
Ex VP: Daniel Stainbrook
VP: Don Bellamy
VP: Candy Boswell
VP: Rich Fehringer
VP: Larry Gilpin
VP: Karen Goens
VP: Richard Harris
VP: Gary Hutchens
VP: Amy Kraft

D-U-N-S 08-635-2036
NORTHWEST FEDERAL CREDIT UNION FOUNDATION
NWFCU
200 Spring St, Herndon, VA 20170-5241
Tel (703) 709-8900 *Founded/Ownrshp* 1947
Sales NA *EMP* 350
SIC 6111

D-U-N-S 62-061-8918
NORTHWEST FINANCIAL CORP
101 W 5th St, Spencer, IA 51301-3821
Tel (712) 262-4100 *Founded/Ownrshp* 1988
Sales NA *EMP* 100
SIC 6712 Bank holding companies; Bank holding companies
Pr: C B Conover
**Ch Bd:* Dwight Conover
Chf Cred: Ron Adams
Sr VP: Steve Crittenden
Sr VP: Bill Orrison
Sr VP: Lee Schoenewe
CIO: Joseph Conover

D-U-N-S 08-524-8474
■ **NORTHWEST FINANCIAL GROUP INC**
BMW OF BELLEVUE
(*Suby of* AUTONATION INC) ★
13617 Ne 20th St, Bellevue, WA 98005-2031
Tel (425) 243-5201 *Founded/Ownrshp* 1995
Sales 27.7MM^E *EMP* 85
SIC 5511 Automobiles, new & used; Automobiles, new & used
Genl Mgr: Sean Zabihi

D-U-N-S 07-885-5502
NORTHWEST FISH CO
4317 S 188th St, Seatac, WA 98188-5027
Tel (206) 571-2900 *Founded/Ownrshp* 1998
Sales 40.0MM *EMP* 6^E
SIC 5146 Seafoods
Pr: Rodger May

NORTHWEST FLORIDA DAILY NEWS
See FLORIDA FREEDOM NEWSPAPERS INC

D-U-N-S 01-040-7930
NORTHWEST FLORIDA STATE COLLEGE
NWFSC
100 College Blvd E, Niceville, FL 32578-1347
Tel (850) 729-5361 *Founded/Ownrshp* 1963
Sales 8.6MM *EMP* 930
Accts Mauldin & Jenkins Llc Bradent
SIC 8222 Colleges universities & professional schools; Community college; Community college
Pr: Ty Handy
**CFO:* Randy White

NORTHWEST FORD & STERLING
See PATSON INC

NORTHWEST GEORGIA BANK
See NORTHWEST SERVICES CORP

D-U-N-S 08-448-0230
NORTHWEST GEORGIA HOSPITAL
1305 Redmond Rd Nw, Rome, GA 30165-9655
Tel (706) 295-6295 *Founded/Ownrshp* 1972
Sales 9.5MM^E *EMP* 500
SIC 8051 Mental retardation hospital; Mental retardation hospital
Prin: Dr Thomas Muller

D-U-N-S 96-217-7155
NORTHWEST GRAINS INTERNATIONAL LLC
308 1 Corp Plz 74, Minneapolis, MN 55439
Tel (952) 746-2888 *Founded/Ownrshp* 2010
Sales 68.8MM *EMP* 23^E
Accts Smith Schafer & Associates Lt
SIC 6221 Commodity traders, contracts; Commodity traders, contracts

NORTHWEST HAIRLINES DIVISION
See ED WYSE & CO INC

D-U-N-S 96-857-3399 IMP/EXP
NORTHWEST HARDWOODS INC
820 A St Ste 500, Tacoma, WA 98402-5297
Tel (253) 568-6800 *Founded/Ownrshp* 2014
Sales 753.7MM^E *EMP* 1,771
SIC 2426 5031 Lumber, hardwood dimension; Lumber, plywood & millwork; Lumber: rough, dressed & finished; Lumber, hardwood dimension; Lumber, plywood & millwork; Lumber: rough, dressed & finished
Pr: Tj Rosengarth
**CFO:* Jeffrey Gornev Steed
**VP:* Stan Edme
Exec: Mark Hayes
Mktg Mgr: Stephanie Happer

D-U-N-S 07-567-0463
■ **NORTHWEST HEALTH SYSTEM INC**
NORTHWEST MED CTR WASH CNTY
(*Suby of* COMMUNITY HEALTH SYSTEMS INC) ★
609 W Maple Ave, Springdale, AR 72764-5335
Tel (479) 751-5711 *Founded/Ownrshp* 2001
Sales 350.8MM^E *EMP* 1,400
SIC 8062 General medical & surgical hospitals; General medical & surgical hospitals
CEO: Dan McKay
Chf Rad: James Cherry
Dir Vol: Lesa Tucker
COO: Mark Bethell
**COO:* Donnie Frederick
**CFO:* Sean Barnett
Dir OR: Angela Cox
Dir OR: Bryon Taylor
Dir Lab: Peggy White
CIO: Holly Hamilton-Haynie
**CIO:* Shannon Williams

D-U-N-S 01-590-5081
■ **NORTHWEST HEALTHCARE ALLIANCE INC**
ASSURED HM HLTH HSPICE HM CARE
(*Suby of* LHC GROUP INC) ★
2120 Northpark St Ste A, Centralia, WA 98531-9098
Tel (360) 330-2640 *Founded/Ownrshp* 2009
Sales 13.3MM^E *EMP* 350
SIC 8082 Home health care services; Home health care services
CEO: Keith Myers
**Pr:* Richard D Block
VP: Florene Tomei
Sales Exec: Les England

NORTHWEST HERALD
See NORTHWEST NEWSPAPERS INC

D-U-N-S 07-748-0999 IMP
NORTHWEST HORTICULTURE LLC
NWH
14113 River Bend Rd, Mount Vernon, WA 98273-7288
Tel (360) 395-3305 *Founded/Ownrshp* 2001
Sales 72.3MM^E *EMP* 77^E
SIC 5193 Flowers & nursery stock
Genl Mgr: Bruce Gibson

NORTHWEST HOSPITAL & MED CTR
See NORTHWEST HOSPITAL & MEDICAL CENTER

NORTHWEST HOSPITAL & MEDICAL C
See UW MEDICINE/NORTHWEST

D-U-N-S 11-896-8684
NORTHWEST HOSPITAL & MEDICAL CENTER
NORTHWEST HOSPITAL & MED CTR
1550 N 115th St, Seattle, WA 98133-8498
Tel (206) 364-0500 *Founded/Ownrshp* 1981
Sales 310.6MM^E *EMP* 1,600^E
Accts Clark Nuber Ps Bellevue Wa
SIC 8741 8062 Hospital management; Nursing & personal care facility management; General medical & surgical hospitals; Hospital management; Nursing & personal care facility management; General medical & surgical hospitals
CEO: Cynthia Hecker
**Pr:* Bill Schneider
CFO: Bob Steigmeyer
Netwrk Mgr: Michael Dipietro
Ansthlgy: Jorg Dziersk
Ansthlgy: Rajninder Jutla
Ansthlgy: Richard Nguyen
Podiatrist: Kelly Hall
Doctor: Keiko Aikawa
Doctor: Gerald Bernstein
Doctor: Eugene Cha

D-U-N-S 06-936-9791 IMP
NORTHWEST HOSPITAL CENTER INC (MD)
5401 Old Court Rd, Randallstown, MD 21133-5103
Tel (410) 521-2200 *Founded/Ownrshp* 1984
Sales 231.6MM *EMP* 981
Accts Kpmg Llp Mc Lean Va
SIC 8062 General medical & surgical hospitals; General medical & surgical hospitals
Ch: Harold Weiss
Chf Path: Michael S Ballo
Dir Recs: Jennifer Marrujo
**Pr:* Erik Wexler
**Pr:* Brian White
**Sr VP:* David Krajewski
**VP:* Brian Cawley
VP: Julie Cox
VP: Christine Deangelis
**VP:* Ron Ginsberg
VP: Ronald L Ginsberg
**VP:* Candy Hamner
**VP:* Sue Jalbert
Dir OR: Sepi Gharanfoli
Dir Inf Cn: Betsy Addis
Dir Inf Cn: Mary Wallace
Dir Lab: Paul Griffey
Dir Rad: Rodney Hopkins
Dir Rad: Karen Steinhist
Dir Rx: Ken Mercer

D-U-N-S 07-821-6165
NORTHWEST HOSPITAL INC
(*Suby of* NORTHWEST HOSPITAL & MED CTR) ★
1550 N 115th St, Seattle, WA 98133-8498
Tel (206) 364-0500 *Founded/Ownrshp* 1949
Sales 310.4MM *EMP* 1,380
SIC 8062

D-U-N-S 96-718-9267
NORTHWEST HOSPITALITY GROUP
575 E Parkcenter Blvd # 500, Boise, ID 83706-6682
Tel (208) 343-3439 *Founded/Ownrshp* 1988
Sales 1.1MMM *EMP* 700
SIC 7011 Hotels & motels; Hotels & motels
Pt: Robert Suits
Pt: Jeff Eberle

D-U-N-S 10-007-6025
NORTHWEST INDEPENDENT SCHOOL DISTRICT
2001 Texan Dr, Justin, TX 76247-8791
Tel (817) 215-0000 *Founded/Ownrshp* 1952
Sales 202.4MM *EMP* 1,284
Accts Haynes And Associates Pc Roa
SIC 8211 Public elementary & secondary schools; School board; Public elementary & secondary schools; School board
Bd of Dir: Jennifer Wigant
VP: Jeannette Leong
VP: Mark Schluter
Prin: Ron Andres
MIS Dir: Carl Shawn
Dir IT: Linda Denning
Netwrk Eng: Bob Shatford
Pr Dir: Rob Ludwig
Teacher Pr: Kim Caley

D-U-N-S 01-412-7539
NORTHWEST INDIAN COLLEGE
2522 Kwina Rd, Bellingham, WA 98226-9278
Tel (360) 392-4326 *Founded/Ownrshp* 1983
Sales 20.4MM *EMP* 150
Accts Stauffer & Associates Pllc Li
SIC 8221 Colleges universities & professional schools; Colleges universities & professional schools
Pr: Justin Guillory
VP: Carole Rave

D-U-N-S 87-867-3797
▲ **NORTHWEST INDIANA BANCORP**
9204 Columbia Ave Ste 1, Munster, IN 46321-3571
Tel (219) 836-4400 *Founded/Ownrshp* 1994
Sales NA *EMP* 196
Tkr Sym NWIN *Exch* OTO
SIC 6035 State commercial banks; Savings institutions, federally chartered; Federal savings & loan associations
Ch Bd: David A Bochnowski
**Pr:* Benjamin J Bochnowski
CFO: Robert T Lowry
CFO: Robert Lowry
Ofcr: Christine Friel
Ex VP: Leane E Cerven
Ex VP: John J Diederich
VP: Jill Knight
Sales Exec: Carla Houck

D-U-N-S 94-156-1966
NORTHWEST INDIANA COMMUNITY ACTION CORP
5240 Fountain Dr, Crown Point, IN 46307-5301
Tel (219) 769-0210 *Founded/Ownrshp* 2007
Sales 23.0MM *EMP* 30^E
Accts Wipfli Llp Madison Wi

SIC 8322 Individual & family services
CEO: Gary Olund
**COO:* Ms Jennifer Malone
Comm Man: Melissa Bohacek
IT Man: Robyn Freel
QI Cn Mgr: John Hamlin

D-U-N-S 12-126-3982
NORTHWEST INDIANA SPECIAL EDUCATION COOPERATIVE
PARTNERSHIP FOR ASSISTED
2150 W 97th Pl, Crown Point, IN 46307-2346
Tel (219) 663-6500 *Founded/Ownrshp* 1971
Sales 9.2MM^E *EMP* 485^E
SIC 8299 8211 Educational service, nondegree granting: continuing educ.; Elementary & secondary schools; Educational service, nondegree granting: continuing educ.; Elementary & secondary schools

D-U-N-S 05-686-3202
NORTHWEST INSULATION CO INC
204 E Wilson St, Borger, TX 79007-6018
Tel (806) 274-7324 *Founded/Ownrshp* 1972
Sales 29.5MM^E *EMP* 200
SIC 1799

D-U-N-S 06-013-6017
NORTHWEST INSURANCE AGENCY INC (CA)
175 W College Ave, Santa Rosa, CA 95401-6503
Tel (707) 573-1300 *Founded/Ownrshp* 1976, 1978
Sales NA *EMP* 120
SIC 6411 Insurance agents; Insurance brokers; Property & casualty insurance agent
CEO: Charles L Bussman
**Pr:* Mary Fairow
**Ch:* Michael R Sullivan
**Sec:* Manny Mello
**VP:* Dennis Stanley

D-U-N-S 94-269-6451
NORTHWEST INSURANCE NETWORK INC
330 S Wells St Ste 1600, Chicago, IL 60606-7161
Tel (312) 427-1777 *Founded/Ownrshp* 1995
Sales NA *EMP* 122
SIC 6411 Insurance agents, brokers & service
Pr: Martin Joseph
Brnch Mgr: Amelia Siddiqui

NORTHWEST IOWA HOSPITAL
See ST LUKE HEALTH SYSTEM INC

D-U-N-S 07-698-3055
NORTHWEST IOWA HOSPITAL CORP
ST. LKES RGNAL MED CTR SOUX CY
2800 Pierce St Ste 410, Sioux City, IA 51104-3759
Tel (712) 279-3500 *Founded/Ownrshp* 1996
Sales 141.6MM *EMP* 1,200^E
SIC 8062 8051 General medical & surgical hospitals; Skilled nursing care facilities; General medical & surgical hospitals; Skilled nursing care facilities
Pr: Peter Thoreen
Chf Rad: Eric Luebbert
**CFO:* Mark Johnson
**VP:* Jim Gobell
**VP:* Richard Hildebrand
**VP:* Chad Markham
VP: Mike Schmidt
**VP:* Lynn Wold
Dir Rx: Janet Harcum
Pathlgst: Thomas J Carroll Jr
Doctor: Roger Heath

D-U-N-S 00-986-2053
NORTHWEST IOWA POWER COOPERATIVE
NIPCO
31002 C38, Le Mars, IA 51031-8197
Tel (712) 546-4141 *Founded/Ownrshp* 1949
Sales 90.6MM *EMP* 50
Accts Eide Bailly Llp Sioux Falls
SIC 4911 Transmission, electric power; Transmission, electric power
Genl Mgr: Kent Pauling
**CFO:* Matt Washburn
**Treas:* Louis Reed
VP: Chuck Soderberg

D-U-N-S 02-760-3232
NORTHWEST JEEP INC
10600 Sw Canyon Rd, Beaverton, OR 97005-1823
Tel (503) 646-5111 *Founded/Ownrshp* 1984
Sales 30.7MM^E *EMP* 78
SIC 5511 Automobiles, new & used; Automobiles, new & used
Pr: Robert McGrain

D-U-N-S 96-231-6279
NORTHWEST JUSTICE PROJECT
401 2nd Ave S Ste 407, Seattle, WA 98104-3811
Tel (206) 464-1519 *Founded/Ownrshp* 1995
Sales 22.5MM *EMP* 350
Accts Moss Adams Llp Seattle Wa
SIC 8111 Legal aid service; Legal aid service
Ex Dir: Patrick Henrymcintyre

D-U-N-S 08-246-4694
NORTHWEST KANSAS EDUCATIONAL SERVICE CENTER (KS)
703 W 2nd St, Oakley, KS 67748-1258
Tel (785) 672-3125 *Founded/Ownrshp* 1973
Sales 8.2MM^E *EMP* 300
SIC 8299 Educational services; Educational services
Ex Dir: Dan Thornton
Treas: Gerri Geist
Ex VP: Carinda McConnell
VP: Shirley Sheridan
DP Exec: Scott Gee

D-U-N-S 04-302-1880
NORTHWEST KIDNEY CENTERS
700 Broadway, Seattle, WA 98122-4302
Tel (206) 292-2771 *Founded/Ownrshp* 1961
Sales 93.6MM *EMP* 550
Accts Clark Nuber Ps Bellevue Wa
SIC 8092 Kidney dialysis centers; Kidney dialysis centers
Pr: Joyce Jackson
**CFO:* Scott Strandgord
Trst: Jean Rolfe
Chf Mktg O: John Stivelman
Ofcr: Bill Peckham
VP: Jane Pryor
VP: Austin Ross
Ex Dir: Gerry Morrison
Nurse Mgr: Cindy Black
Nurse Mgr: Ed Stauffer
Opers Mgr: Randy Thompson

D-U-N-S 96-485-4363
NORTHWEST LABORERS - EMPLOYERS TRAINING TRUST
201 Queen Anne Ave N, Seattle, WA 98109-4835
Tel (206) 282-4100 *Founded/Ownrshp* 2010
Sales 77.8MM *EMP* 3
Accts Anastasi & Moore Pllc Spokane
SIC 8631 Labor unions & similar labor organizations; Labor unions & similar labor organizations

NORTHWEST LANDSCAPE SERVICES
See VAUGHN WEEDMAN INC

D-U-N-S 07-662-6464 IMP
NORTHWEST LININGS AND GEOTEXTILE PRODUCTS INC
21000 77th Ave S, Kent, WA 98032-1360
Tel (253) 872-0244 *Founded/Ownrshp* 1973
Sales 29.7MM^E *EMP* 25
SIC 5131 3443 Textiles, woven; Water tanks, metal plate
Pr: Rod Newton
**Pr:* Scott Newton
**VP:* Kirk Lilleskare
VP: Scott Newman
Dir IT: Brian Preuss

NORTHWEST LIONS FOUNDATION FR
See SIGHTLIFE

D-U-N-S 36-427-4670
NORTHWEST LOCAL SCHOOL DISTRICT
3240 Banning Rd, Cincinnati, OH 45239-5207
Tel (513) 923-1000 *Founded/Ownrshp* 1924
Sales 65.2MM^E *EMP* 1,300
SIC 8211 Public elementary & secondary schools; Public elementary & secondary schools
**Pr:* David Denny
COO: Ken Broxterman
Bd of Dir: Jim Detzel
**VP:* Pam Detzel
CIO: David Plotts
IT Man: Scott Fortkamp
Pr Dir: Matt Fisher
Teacher Pr: Steffaniy Kessling
Instr Medi: Chris Rabold
Psych: Julie Martini
Psych: Kerri Randol

NORTHWEST LOGISTICS
See NORTHWEST CONCRETE PRODUCTS INC

D-U-N-S 08-331-6976
NORTHWEST LOUISIANA TECHNICAL COLLEGE
SHREVEPORT CAMPUS
2010 N Market St, Shreveport, LA 71107-5216
Tel (318) 371-3035 *Founded/Ownrshp* 1951
Sales 31.4MM^E *EMP* 497
SIC 8221 Colleges universities & professional schools; Colleges universities & professional schools
**Prin:* Annette Chanler
**Prin:* Gwen Nixon

D-U-N-S 01-025-6782
NORTHWEST MECHANICAL INC (IA)
NORTHWEST AUTOMATION & CONTRLS
5885 Tremont Ave, Davenport, IA 52807-2650
Tel (563) 391-1344 *Founded/Ownrshp* 1923, 1983
Sales 50.0MM^E *EMP* 230^E
Accts Anderson Lower Whitlow Pc B
SIC 1711 Mechanical contractor; Mechanical contractor
Pr: Hester Gregory J
**CEO:* Gregory J Hester
**CFO:* Barry Huber
**Treas:* Denise L Hester
Opers Mgr: Paul Krogman
Opers Mgr: Josh Younkin

NORTHWEST MED CTR WASH CNTY
See NORTHWEST HEALTH SYSTEM INC

D-U-N-S 00-905-0832
NORTHWEST MEDIA WASHINGTON LP
PENINSULA DAILY NEWS
500 108th Ave Ne, Bellevue, WA 98004-5580
Tel (425) 274-4782 *Founded/Ownrshp* 1937, 1994
Sales 22.2MM^E *EMP* 200
SIC 2711 Newspapers: publishing only, not printed on site; Newspapers: publishing only, not printed on site
Genl Pt: Peter Horvitz
VP: Howard Mullenary
VP: Ray Wolk

D-U-N-S 18-791-9907
■ **NORTHWEST MEDICAL CENTER**
CHS
(*Suby of* COMMUNITY HEALTH SYSTEMS INC) ★
6200 N La Cholla Blvd, Tucson, AZ 85741-3529
Tel (520) 742-9000 *Founded/Ownrshp* 1997
Sales 15.1MM *EMP* 1,100
SIC 8062 General medical & surgical hospitals; General medical & surgical hospitals
CEO: Kevin Stockton
Chf Path: Matthew A Baptista
Chf Path: Michael Lynch
Chf Rad: Mark Yoshino
COO: David Schultz
**CFO:* Ronald Patrick
Dir Case M: Rebecca Grisson
Dir Rad: James Block
Dir Rx: Ferena Salek
Dir Sec: Joe Carrasco
CTO: Dana Carreras

D-U-N-S 96-257-8266
■ **NORTHWEST MEDICAL CENTER MEDICAL STAFF INC**
(*Suby of* HCA INC) ★
2801 N State Road 7, Margate, FL 33063-5727
Tel (954) 974-0400 *Founded/Ownrshp* 1994
Sales 102.2M *EMP* 800
Accts Welzien Bowers Cpas Fort Laud
SIC 8062 General medical & surgical hospitals; General medical & surgical hospitals
CEO: Erica Gulrich
Dir Recs: Patricia Irorere
**Pr:* Peter Gach M D
COO: Michael Bass
CFO: Lynn Dick
**CFO:* Gary Mervak
Ofcr: Mark Rader
**VP:* Douglas Weiner M D
VP: Coral Modasseri
VP: Andrea Pinion
VP: Donna Walter
Dir Risk M: Renee Fletcher
Dir Lab: Linda Smith
Dir Lab: Todd Tiddmore
Dir Rad: Sandra Bourne

D-U-N-S 05-097-4906
NORTHWEST MEDICAL FOUNDATION OF TILLAMOOK (OR)
TILLAMOOK COUNTY GENERAL HOSP
1000 3rd St, Tillamook, OR 97141-3430
Tel (503) 842-4444 *Founded/Ownrshp* 1973
Sales 55.7MM *EMP* 420
SIC 8062 General medical & surgical hospitals; General medical & surgical hospitals
CEO: David Butler
**Pr:* Larry Davy
**CFO:* Walt Larson
**VP:* Karen Kellar
Genl Mgr: Kirk Ayers
Mktg Dir: Gina Seufert
Surgeon: Lyle Mohr
Diag Rad: Michael Veverka

D-U-N-S 80-574-2827
NORTHWEST MEDSTAR
6315 E Rutter Ave, Spokane, WA 99212-1445
Tel (800) 572-3210 *Founded/Ownrshp* 2007
Sales 25.5MM *EMP* 11^E
SIC 4119 Ambulance service
Prin: Robert Kerr
VP: Dustin Duncan

NORTHWEST MISS RGIONAL MED CTR
See CLARKSDALE HMA LLC

D-U-N-S 07-352-2492
NORTHWEST MISSISSIPPI COMMUNITY COLLEGE
4975 Highway 51 N, Senatobia, MS 38668-1714
Tel (662) 562-3200 *Founded/Ownrshp* 1927
Sales 871.9M *EMP* 450
Accts Ellis & Hirsberg Cpa Pllc C
SIC 8222 Community college; Community college
Pr: Gary Spears
**CFO:* Gary Mosley
VP: Chuck Strong
Exec: Mike Dottorey
Off Mgr: Hayley Hayes
DP Exec: Amy Latham
IT Man: Matt Sellers
Psych: Tonyalle Rush
Nrsg Dir: Victoria P Hale

D-U-N-S 07-625-3319
NORTHWEST MISSOURI STATE UNIVERSITY
800 University Dr, Maryville, MO 64468-6001
Tel (660) 562-1124 *Founded/Ownrshp* 1905
Sales 43.5MM^E *EMP* 700
SIC 8221

D-U-N-S 11-865-1533
NORTHWEST MOTORSPORT INC
400 River Rd, Puyallup, WA 98371-4155
Tel (253) 256-4600 *Founded/Ownrshp* 1996
Sales 31.1MM^E *EMP* 150
SIC 5521 Used car dealers
CEO: Don Fleming

D-U-N-S 03-402-2986
NORTHWEST MUTUAL FINANCIAL
12713 Wolf Rd, Geneseo, IL 61254-9295
Tel (309) 944-6186 *Founded/Ownrshp* 2014
Sales NA *EMP* 346^E
SIC 6411 Insurance agents, brokers & service
Prin: Nick Simon

D-U-N-S 60-600-5515
NORTHWEST MUTUAL FINANCIAL TRUST LLC
NORTHWESTERN MUTUAL
731 N Jackson St, Milwaukee, WI 53202-4697
Tel (414) 224-5000 *Founded/Ownrshp* 2005
Sales NA *EMP* 118^E
SIC 6411 6282 Insurance agents, brokers & service; Investment advisory service
Ofcr: Bob Chmielewski
Ofcr: David Franczyk
Ofcr: Joann Murtha
Sls Dir: Jerod Spaeth

D-U-N-S 00-790-8916
▲ **NORTHWEST NATURAL GAS CO** (OR)
NW NATURAL
220 Nw 2nd Ave, Portland, OR 97209-3991
Tel (503) 226-4211 *Founded/Ownrshp* 1859
Sales 754.0MM *EMP* 1,100^E
Accts Pricewaterhousecoopers Llp Po
Tkr Sym NWN *Exch* NYS
SIC 4924 Natural gas distribution; Natural gas distribution
Pr: Gregg S Kantor
COO: David H Anderson
CFO: Stephen P Feltz
Treas: C Alex Miller
Sr VP: Mardilyn Saathoff
VP: Sergio Ghirardelli
VP: Kimberly A Heiting
VP: Michael McCoy
VP: Grant M Yoshihara
Exec: Dave Otteman
Snr Sftwr: Vincent Kulandai-Samy
Board of Directors: Timothy P Boyle, Martha L Byorum, John D Carter, Mark S Dodson, C Scott Gibson, Tod R Hamachek, Jane L Peverett, Kenneth Thrasher, Malia H Wasson

D-U-N-S 03-119-1880 IMP/EXP
■ **NORTHWEST NATURAL PRODUCTS INC**
(*Suby of* AVID HEALTH INC) ★
10 S 56th Pl, Ridgefield, WA 98642-3428
Tel (360) 737-6800 *Founded/Ownrshp* 2003
Sales 43.5MM^E *EMP* 140
SIC 5122 2834 Vitamins & minerals; Vitamin, nutrient & hematinic preparations for human use; Vitamins & minerals; Vitamin, nutrient & hematinic preparations for human use
Pr: Kathryn Jones
**CFO:* Rick Falconer
**VP:* Martin Rifkin
Natl Sales: Randy McClinton
Mktg Mgr: Debbie Defreece

D-U-N-S 07-298-2507
NORTHWEST NAZARENE UNIVERSITY INC
623 S University Blvd, Nampa, ID 83686-5897
Tel (208) 467-8011 *Founded/Ownrshp* 1913, 1915
Sales 49.4MM *EMP* 184^E
Accts Cliftonlarsonallen Llp Boise
SIC 8221 University; University
Pr: Dr David Alexander
**Pr:* Joel Pearsall
Ofcr: Sally Heckathorn
Ofcr: Wes Maggard
Ofcr: Jessica Piper
**VP:* Dr Carey Cook
VP: Sam Dunn
**VP:* Dr Eric Forseth
VP: David Peterson
**VP:* Dr Mark Pitts
**VP:* Gary Skaggs
VP: Burton Webb
Exec: Gaymon Bennett

D-U-N-S 06-080-8219
NORTHWEST NEW JERSEY COMMUNITY ACTION PROGRAM INC
NORWESCAP
350 Marshall St, Phillipsburg, NJ 08865-3273
Tel (908) 454-5936 *Founded/Ownrshp* 1965
Sales 19.9MM *EMP* 300
SIC 8399 8351 8322 Community action agency; Head start center, except in conjunction with school; Alcoholism counseling, nontreatment; Community action agency; Head start center, except in conjunction with school; Alcoholism counseling, nontreatment
Ch: Allison Conley
**CEO:* Terry Newhard
**CFO:* Lynn Snyder
**Treas:* Marty Miller
Bd of Dir: Helene Meissner
**Prin:* Kay Reiss

D-U-N-S 05-429-7247
NORTHWEST NEWS CO INC (MT)
BENJAMIN NEWS GROUP
1701 Rankin St, Missoula, MT 59808-1629
Tel (406) 721-7801 *Founded/Ownrshp* 1971, 1996
Sales 266.3MM^E *EMP* 300
SIC 5192 Magazines; Books; Periodicals; Magazines; Books; Periodicals
Pr: Paul Benjamin
**Treas:* John Benjamin
**Genl Mgr:* Ray Anderson

D-U-N-S 10-693-1074
NORTHWEST NEWSPAPERS INC
NORTHWEST HERALD
(*Suby of* THE B F SHAW PRINTING COMPANY)
7717 S State Route 31, Crystal Lake, IL 60014-8150
Tel (815) 459-4040 *Founded/Ownrshp* 1983
Sales 21.0MM^E *EMP* 200
SIC 2711

D-U-N-S 12-797-3282
NORTHWEST OPEN ACCESS NETWORK
NOANET
5802 Overlook Ave Ne, Tacoma, WA 98422-1435
Tel (206) 219-3640 *Founded/Ownrshp* 1999
Sales 31.2MM *EMP* 48
Accts Moss Adams Llp Spokane Washi
SIC 4899 Communication signal enhancement network system; Data communication services; Communication signal enhancement network system; Data communication services
CEO: Greg L Marney
**COO:* David H Spencer
CTO: Rob Kopp

NORTHWEST PACKING CO.
See NEIL JONES FOOD CO

D-U-N-S 19-051-0503 IMP
NORTHWEST PALLET SUPPLY CO
3648 Morreim Dr, Belvidere, IL 61008-6346
Tel (815) 544-6001 *Founded/Ownrshp* 1983
Sales 47.2MM^E *EMP* 210
SIC 2448 Wood pallets & skids; Wood pallets & skids
Pr: Walter W Pollack
CFO: Mike Meersman
**Genl Couns:* Joe Keenan

D-U-N-S 00-902-3367
NORTHWEST PAPER BOX MFRS INC (OR)
5617 N Basin Ave, Portland, OR 97217-3901
Tel (503) 240-2800 *Founded/Ownrshp* 1953
Sales 31.2MM^E *EMP* 80
SIC 2653 5113 2652 Boxes, corrugated: made from purchased materials; Shipping supplies; Setup paperboard boxes; Boxes, corrugated: made from purchased materials; Shipping supplies; Setup paperboard boxes
Pr: Betty Van Allen
**Pr:* John Van Allen

*Sec: Debbie Guzie
*Ex VP: Rod V Allen
*VP: Brad Van Allen
Exec: Mike Reeves
VP Prd: Rod Allen

NORTHWEST PEA & BEAN COMPANY
See COOPERATIVE AGRICULTURAL PRODUCERS INC

D-U-N-S 78-278-6909 EXP
NORTHWEST PET PRODUCTS INC
WESTERN ANIMAL NUTRITION
(Suby of AMERICAN NUTRITION INC) ★
350 S Pekin Rd, Woodland, WA 98674-9534
Tel (360) 225-8855 Founded/Ownrshp 1986
Sales 71.0MM^E EMP 45
SIC 2047 Dog food; Cat food; Dog food; Cat food
CEO: William Behnken
*CFO: Ron Haws
*Sec: Ray Bialick
*VP: Sandi Behnken

D-U-N-S 94-464-7841
NORTHWEST PHYSICIANS ASSOCIATES PC
1012 Water St Ste 2, Meadville, PA 16335-3468
Tel (814) 333-2001 Founded/Ownrshp 1995
Sales 20.7MM^E EMP 160
SIC 8011 Offices & clinics of medical doctors
Ch Bd: Bruce Dratler
Dir Lab: Milly Keeler
Off Mgr: Deanna Nichols
Dir IT: Desiree Shorey
Doctor: Gerald Rochelle MD

D-U-N-S 13-147-4983 IMP
NORTHWEST PIONEER INC
PIONEER PACKAGING
6006 S 228th St, Kent, WA 98032-1806
Tel (253) 872-9693 Founded/Ownrshp 1984
Sales 31.0MM^E EMP 45
SIC 5113 7319 2679 Industrial & personal service paper; Industrial & personal service paper; Distribution of advertising material or sample services; Paper products, converted
Pr: Robert M Steele
Off Mgr: Cindy Paulson

D-U-N-S 00-399-3060 IMP
▲ NORTHWEST PIPE CO
5721 Se Columbia Way # 200, Vancouver, WA 98661-5991
Tel (360) 397-6250 Founded/Ownrshp 1966
Sales 403.3MM EMP 1,050
Accts Pricewaterhousecoopers Llp Po
Tkr Sym NWPX Exch NGS
SIC 3317 3443 Steel pipe & tubes; Welded pipe & tubes; Pipes, wrought: welded, lock joint or heavy riveted; Tubes, wrought: welded or lock joint; Industrial vessels, tanks & containers; Tanks, standard or custom fabricated: metal plate; Vessels, process or storage (from boiler shops): metal plate; Steel pipe & tubes; Welded pipe & tubes; Pipes, wrought: welded, lock joint or heavy riveted; Tubes, wrought: welded or lock joint; Industrial vessels, tanks & containers; Tanks, standard or custom fabricated: metal plate; Vessels, process or storage (from boiler shops): metal plate
Pr: Scott J Montross
*Ch Bd: Richard A Roman
CFO: Robin Gantt
CFO: Barbara Pittman
Ex VP: Martin Dana
Ex VP: William Smith
Ex VP: William M Smith
Sr VP: Richard Baum
Sr VP: Robert L Mahoney
VP: Greg Goad
VP: Gregory Goad
VP: Charles G King
Board of Directors: Michelle Galanter Applebau, James E Declusin, Harry L Demorest, Wayne B Kingsley, Keith R Larson

D-U-N-S 00-624-2481
NORTHWEST PIPE FITTINGS INC (MT)
(Suby of NORTHWEST PIPE FITTINGS INC) ★
33 S 8th St W, Billings, MT 59102-5840
Tel (406) 252-0142 Founded/Ownrshp 1957
Sales 71.0MM^E EMP 100
SIC 5074 5085 5051 5084 Plumbing & hydronic heating supplies; Industrial supplies; Valves & fittings; Pipe & tubing, steel; Copper sheets, plates, bars, rods, pipes, etc.; Drilling equipment, excluding bits; Plumbing & hydronic heating supplies; Industrial supplies; Valves & fittings; Pipe & tubing, steel; Copper sheets, plates, bars, rods, pipes, etc.; Drilling equipment, excluding bits
Pr: Jerry Evenson
*Ch Bd: W Robert Barbour
*Pr: Randy Bentley
*CFO: Greg Peterson
*Treas: Hank Meligren
*VP: Scott Barbour
*VP: Dick L Dede
Brnch Mgr: Dan Allen
Brnch Mgr: Dan Goodnature
Sales Asso: Mike Berst
Sales Asso: Ross Strending

D-U-N-S 00-749-9718
NORTHWEST PIPE FITTINGS INC
2309 W Omaha St, Rapid City, SD 57702-2462
Tel (605) 342-5587 Founded/Ownrshp 1955
Sales 79.0MM^E EMP 150
SIC 5074

D-U-N-S 00-456-5222
NORTHWEST PIPELINE LLC
(Suby of WILLIAMS PARTNERS OPERATING LLC) ★
295 S Chipeta Way Fl 4, Salt Lake City, UT 84108-1285
Tel (801) 583-8800 Founded/Ownrshp 1965
Sales 470.0MM EMP 2^E
SIC 4923 Gas transmission & distribution; Gas transmission & distribution
CEO: Allison G Bridges
CFO: Ted T Timmermans
Mktg Mgr: Dave Allred

D-U-N-S 19-614-6216
■ NORTHWEST PIPELINE SERVICES LLC
(Suby of WILLIAMS COMPANIES INC) ★
295 S Chipeta Way Fl 4, Salt Lake City, UT 84108-1285
Tel (801) 583-8800 Founded/Ownrshp 1965
Sales 17.8MM^E EMP 400
SIC 4922 Natural gas transmission; Natural gas transmission
Pr: Phillip Wright
VP: Robert Sluder
Board of Directors: P Secrist

NORTHWEST PRODUCTS
See QUADCO REHABILITATION CENTER INC

D-U-N-S 07-662-8791
NORTHWEST PROTECTIVE SERVICE INC
801 S Fidalgo St 2, Seattle, WA 98108-2613
Tel (206) 448-4040 Founded/Ownrshp 1940
Sales 23.6MM^E EMP 450
SIC 7381 Detective & armored car services; Security guard service; Private investigator; Detective & armored car services; Security guard service; Private investigator
Ch Bd: Peggy M Cameron
*Pr: James R W Stumbles
*CFO: Karen S Cameron
Treas: Kevin Mandery
Ofcr: Stavie Neel
CTO: Doug Hiatt
Opers Mgr: Debora Gonzalez
Secur Mgr: Joshua Keliikoa
Mktg Dir: Kathleen Koch
Snr Mgr: Randy Neely

D-U-N-S 00-619-0300
■ NORTHWEST PUBLICATIONS LLC
ST PAUL PIONEER PRESS
(Suby of MEDIANEWS GROUP INC) ★
10 River Park Plz Ste 700, Saint Paul, MN 55107-1223
Tel (651) 222-5011 Founded/Ownrshp 2006
Sales 71.9MM^E EMP 617^E
SIC 2711 2759 2752 Newspapers, publishing & printing; Commercial printing; Commercial printing, lithographic; Newspapers, publishing & printing; Commercial printing; Commercial printing, lithographic
Sr VP: Vicki Gowler
VP: Doug Ranes
VP: Lawrence Riley
VP: Jill Taylor
VP: Gary Wortel

D-U-N-S 02-774-3772 IMP/EXP
NORTHWEST PUMP & EQUIPMENT CO
2800 Nw 31st Ave, Portland, OR 97210-1720
Tel (503) 227-7867 Founded/Ownrshp 1982
Sales 40.3MM^E EMP 215
SIC 7699 5084 Service station equipment repair; Pumps & pumping equipment; Service station equipment repair; Pumps & pumping equipment
Pr: Gregory W Miller
*Treas: Jarret Curtin
*VP: Mark Mathews
Sales Asso: Gene Heidt
Sales Asso: Brady Morrison
Sales Asso: Robert Warner

D-U-N-S 09-152-0254
NORTHWEST R-1 SCHOOL DISTRICT
2843 Community Ln, High Ridge, MO 63049-2337
Tel (636) 677-3313 Founded/Ownrshp 1954
Sales 45.1MM^E EMP 800
SIC 8211 School board; School board
COO: Geoff Macy
MIS Dir: Cindy Horn
HC Dir: Kim Diviano

D-U-N-S 62-237-8045
NORTHWEST RADIOLOGY NETWORK PC
5901 Technology Center Dr, Indianapolis, IN 46278-6013
Tel (317) 328-5050 Founded/Ownrshp 2006
Sales 23.5MM^E EMP 86^E
SIC 8011 Radiologist
Ex Dir: Linda Wilgus
Off Mgr: Stacy Davis
Dir IT: Marty Buening
IT Man: Jill Duncan
IT Man: John Williams
Doctor: Caryn Anderson
Doctor: Ryan Sauer MD
Doctor: Larry Stover MD
Diag Rad: Edward Bartley
Diag Rad: Karen Dicke
Diag Rad: Jack Drew

NORTHWEST RECYCLING
See TEXAS PORT RECYCLING LP (JUNE 16 2011)

D-U-N-S 96-843-4613
NORTHWEST REGIONAL EDUCATION SERVICE DISTRICT
5825 Ne Ray Cir, Hillsboro, OR 97124-6436
Tel (503) 614-1428 Founded/Ownrshp 1995
Sales 43.3MM EMP 600
SIC 8299 Educational services; Educational services
*CFO: Janice Essenberg
*CFO: Michael D Schofield
Ex Dir: Tamra Busch
Off Mgr: Lenay Lowman
Off Mgr: Mystie Taber
MIS Dir: Mike McKay

D-U-N-S 00-929-1675
NORTHWEST RESEARCH INC
N W R
5420 W 2100 S, Salt Lake City, UT 84120-1259
Tel (801) 972-2197 Founded/Ownrshp 1996
Sales 23.4MM^E EMP 170
SIC 8731 Commercial physical research; Commercial physical research
Pr: Jon Asay
IT Man: Tim Ellsworth
IT Man: Tim Shunn
VP Sls: Kent Nielsen

D-U-N-S 08-767-9247
NORTHWEST RESPIRATORY SERVICES LLC (MN)
716 Prior Ave N Ste 1, Saint Paul, MN 55104-1062
Tel (651) 603-8720 Founded/Ownrshp 1977, 1999
Sales 26.0MM EMP 230
Accts Boeckermann Grafstrom Mayer L
SIC 7352 Medical equipment rental; Medical equipment rental
Pr: Charles Morgan
*COO: Dana Brandt
*Prin: Chris Larson
Opers Mgr: Gary Kempf

D-U-N-S 14-440-5826
NORTHWEST RESTAURANTS INC
KFC
(Suby of HOMETOWN ENTERPRISES INC) ★
18815 139th Ave Ne Ste C, Woodinville, WA 98072-3565
Tel (425) 486-6336 Founded/Ownrshp 1980
Sales 45.1MM^E EMP 1,000
SIC 5812 Fast-food restaurant, chain; Fast-food restaurant, chain
Pr: Sam Sibert
*Sec: Sharon Seaton

D-U-N-S 06-402-2239 IMP/EXP
NORTHWEST RIVER SUPPLIES INC
NRS
2009 S Main St, Moscow, ID 83843-8913
Tel (877) 677-4327 Founded/Ownrshp 1976
Sales 22.4MM^E EMP 60^E
SIC 5091 5961

D-U-N-S 07-401-3749
NORTHWEST SAVINGS BANK
(Suby of NORTHWEST BANCORP INC) ★
100 Liberty St, Warren, PA 16365-2497
Tel (814) 723-9696 Founded/Ownrshp 1994
Sales NA EMP 1,963
SIC 6035 Federal savings banks; Federal savings banks
Pr: William J Wagner
Pr: Peter Bower
Pr: Steven Carman
Treas: Donald Reed
Ofcr: Joelle Conti-Washer
Ofcr: Barb Demontier
Ofcr: Timothy A Huber
Trst Ofcr: Laura Ahl
Ex VP: Steven G Fisher
Ex VP: Wayne W Harvey
Ex VP: Robert A Ordiway
Sr VP: Richard F Seibel
Sr VP: James E Vecellio
Sr VP: Andrew Young
VP: Mark Buchek
VP: Hall Carol
VP: Joseph Colosimo
VP: Jimmy Domagola
VP: Jodie Guiffre
VP: James Holding
VP: Robert Krzeminski
Board of Directors: A Paul King, Joseph F Long

D-U-N-S 02-083-7068
NORTHWEST SCHOOL DISTRICT
NORTHWEST COMMUNITY SCHOOLS
6900 Rives Junction Rd, Jackson, MI 49201-7408
Tel (517) 817-4700 Founded/Ownrshp 1954
Sales 30.9MM EMP 400
SIC 8211 Public elementary & secondary schools; Public elementary & secondary schools

D-U-N-S 96-352-5485
NORTHWEST SCHOOL HEALTH CONSORTIUM
701 S 7th St, Sharpsville, PA 16150-1945
Tel (724) 962-7872 Founded/Ownrshp 2000
Sales 34.4MM EMP 1
Accts Ap Black Bashor & P Sch Llp
SIC 8299 Educational services; Educational services

D-U-N-S 16-640-9375
NORTHWEST SECURITY SERVICES INC
NWSS
14824 Westminster Way N, Shoreline, WA 98133-6437
Tel (206) 365-0760 Founded/Ownrshp 1982
Sales 5.9MM^E EMP 280
SIC 7381 8742 Security guard service; Management consulting services; Security guard service; Management consulting services
CEO: Paul Dockendorff
*Pr: Stephen Barger
*Sec: Del Dockendorff
DP Dir: Charlotte Smith

D-U-N-S 00-874-2624
NORTHWEST SENIOR HOUSING CORP
EDGEMERE
8523 Thackery St Ofc, Dallas, TX 75225-3904
Tel (214) 265-9100 Founded/Ownrshp 2001
Sales 34.7MM EMP 250^E
Accts Lane Gorman Trubitt Pllc Dall
SIC 8322 Senior citizens' center or association; Senior citizens' center or association
Mng Dir: John Falldine

D-U-N-S 15-037-0310
NORTHWEST SERVICES CORP
NORTHWEST GEORGIA BANK
5063 Alabama Hwy, Ringgold, GA 30736-2435
Tel (706) 965-3000 Founded/Ownrshp 1984
Sales NA EMP 175
SIC 6035 Savings institutions, federally chartered; Savings institutions, federally chartered
VP: K R Rolen
*Pr: Wesley L Smith
*Treas: Jeff Kovach
*VP: E Scott Smith

D-U-N-S 19-132-6438
NORTHWEST STAFFING RESOURCES INC
RESOURCE STAFFING GROUP
851 Sw 6th Ave Ste 300, Portland, OR 97204-1310
Tel (503) 323-9190 Founded/Ownrshp 1985
Sales 139.9MM^E EMP 6,700
SIC 7363 7361 Temporary help service; Employment agencies; Temporary help service; Employment agencies
Pr: Frank Dulcich
CFO: Mary Sauer
*Genl Mgr: Molly Kalomiris

D-U-N-S 02-754-6514
NORTHWEST STEEL & PIPE INC
4802 S Proctor St, Tacoma, WA 98409-2715
Tel (253) 473-8888 Founded/Ownrshp 1950
Sales 53.6MM^E EMP 57
SIC 5051 Metals service centers & offices; Bars, metal; Plates, metal; Pipe & tubing, steel; Metals service centers & offices; Bars, metal; Plates, metal; Pipe & tubing, steel
Pr: Michael C Wax
*Treas: Brian Wax
Ofcr: David Wax
*VP: Jeff Wax
Sales Asso: Dana Bell

D-U-N-S 05-053-5293
NORTHWEST SUBURBAN SPECIAL EDUCATION ORGANIZATION
NSSEO
799 W Kensington Rd, Mount Prospect, IL 60056-1111
Tel (847) 463-8100 Founded/Ownrshp 1968
Sales 29.3MM^E EMP 525
SIC 8211 Public special education school; Public special education school
Pr: Frank Fiarito
*VP: Anna Klimkowicz
Dir IT: Mary Fox
Info Man: Mike Harwood
Psych: Karen Burger
Psych: John Forde
Psych: Linda Kaskel

D-U-N-S 09-318-3697
NORTHWEST SUPPLY CO INC
4006 Mcfarland Blvd, Northport, AL 35476-2820
Tel (205) 339-2892 Founded/Ownrshp 1981
Sales 22.7MM^E EMP 50
SIC 5084 5074 Industrial machinery & equipment; Plumbing & hydronic heating supplies
Pr: Leon Kemp

D-U-N-S 06-973-0034
NORTHWEST SUPPORTS AND SERVICES CENTER
5401 Shed Rd, Bossier City, LA 71111-5420
Tel (318) 741-5230 Founded/Ownrshp 1973
Sales 22.0MM EMP 409
SIC 8361 Residential care; Residential care

D-U-N-S 86-832-0607 IMP
NORTHWEST TERRITORIAL MINT LLC
MEDALLLIC ART COMPANY
2505 S 320th St Ste 110, Federal Way, WA 98003-5461
Tel (775) 246-6000 Founded/Ownrshp 1981
Sales 59.1MM^E EMP 350
SIC 3999 5944 5094 Coins & tokens, non-currency; Jewelry, precious stones & precious metals; Precious metals; Coins & tokens, non-currency; Jewelry, precious stones & precious metals; Precious metals
*CFO: Sam Furuness
Creative D: Mike Krona
Off Mgr: Don Rought
Counsel: Catherine Hopkins
Counsel: Amelia Swan
Snr Mgr: Paul Wagner

D-U-N-S 94-935-0441
■ NORTHWEST TEXAS HEALTHCARE SYSTEM INC
NORTHWEST TEXAS HOSPITAL
(Suby of UNIVERSAL HEALTH SERVICES INC) ★
1501 S Coulter St, Amarillo, TX 79106-1770
Tel (806) 354-1000 Founded/Ownrshp 1996
Sales 246.4MM EMP 1,798
SIC 8062 8063 8051 8049 General medical & surgical hospitals; Psychiatric hospitals; Skilled nursing care facilities; Physical therapist; General medical & surgical hospitals; Psychiatric hospitals; Skilled nursing care facilities; Physical therapist
CEO: Moody Chisholm
*Pr: Marvin Pember
*CEO: Mark Crawford
CFO: Ray Greiner
CFO: James D Taylor
*Treas: Steve Filton
Mng Dir: Nick Hughey
Dir Sec: Moses Moore
CTO: Mark Tarty
Dir IT: Tim Taylor
Mtls Dir: Mary Anthony

NORTHWEST TEXAS HOSPITAL
See NORTHWEST TEXAS HEALTHCARE SYSTEM INC

D-U-N-S 05-565-9436
NORTHWEST TIRE & SERVICE INC
6004 Torrey Rd Ste E, Flint, MI 48507-3800
Tel (810) 785-1633 Founded/Ownrshp 1971
Sales 57.6MM^E EMP 150
SIC 5531 7538 Automotive tires; General automotive repair shops; Automotive tires; General automotive repair shops
Pr: James Faught Jr

NORTHWEST TIRE & TRUCK CENTER
See NORTHWEST TIRE INC

D-U-N-S 08-610-7737 IMP
NORTHWEST TIRE INC
NORTHWEST TIRE & TRUCK CENTER
1615 E Bismarck Expy, Bismarck, ND 58504-6758
Tel (701) 221-9600 Founded/Ownrshp 1977
Sales 45.9MM^E EMP 240
SIC 5014 5531 7534

NORTHWEST TOWER CRANES DIV
See SOWLES CO

D-U-N-S 07-215-7993
NORTHWEST TRI COUNTY INTERMEDIATE UNIT (INC)
252 Waterford St, Edinboro, PA 16412-2315
Tel (814) 734-5610 Founded/Ownrshp 1971
Sales 20.1MM^E EMP 318
SIC 8211 Specialty education; Specialty education
Ex Dir: Frederick Johnson
Bd of Dir: Cheryl Hamilton
MIS Dir: Vince Humes
MIS Dir: Ann Noonen
Dir IT: Robert Laplaca
Info Man: Lesa Kimball

D-U-N-S 06-571-1157
NORTHWEST TRUSTEE SERVICES INC
13555 Se 36th St Ste 200, Bellevue, WA 98006-1485
Tel (425) 586-1975 Founded/Ownrshp 2004
Sales 35.2MM^E EMP 200^E
SIC 6726 Management investment funds, closed-end; Management investment funds, closed-end
Pr: Stephen Routh
*VP: Jeffrey Stenman
Dir IT: Randy Maes
IT Man: William Peterson
Sales Exec: Jim Stessey
Genl Couns: Gwenna Wootress

D-U-N-S 07-573-8443
NORTHWEST UNIVERSITY (WA)
5520 108th Ave Ne, Kirkland, WA 98033-7523
Tel (425) 822-8266 Founded/Ownrshp 1934
Sales 41.6MM EMP 150^E
Accts Clark Nuber Ps Bellevue Wa
SIC 8221 8661 Colleges & universities; Religious organizations; Colleges & universities; Religious organizations
Pr: Donald Argue PHD
CFO: John Jordan
Ex VP: Dan Schimelpfenig
*Sr VP: Dr Marshall Flowers Jr
*Sr VP: Dan Neary
MIS Dir: Don Erlitz

NORTHWEST VALLEY DODGE
See LOQUERCIO AUTOMOTIVE INC

NORTHWEST VILLAGE SCHOOL
See WHEELER CLINIC INC

D-U-N-S 05-290-2744
NORTHWEST VISTA COLLEGE
(Suby of ALAMO COMMUNITY COLLEGE DISTRICT) ★
3535 N Ellison Dr, San Antonio, TX 78251-4217
Tel (210) 706-9291 Founded/Ownrshp 2000
Sales 54.5MM^E EMP 1,200
SIC 8222 8221 Junior college; Colleges universities & professional schools; Junior college; Colleges universities & professional schools
Pr: Jacqueline Claunch
Brnch Mgr: Mike Keiscer

D-U-N-S 93-950-2530
NORTHWEST VOLVO TRUCKS INC
TEC EQUIPMENT
(Suby of PORTLAND MACK TRUCKS) ★
750 Ne Columbia Blvd, Portland, OR 97211-1406
Tel (503) 285-7667 Founded/Ownrshp 1994
Sales 45.6MM^E EMP 200
SIC 5511 Automobiles, new & used; Automobiles, new & used
Pr: David Thompson

D-U-N-S 00-895-8548
NORTHWEST WHOLESALE INC
1567 N Wenatchee Ave, Wenatchee, WA 98801-1156
Tel (509) 662-3563 Founded/Ownrshp 1937
Sales 72.5MM EMP 52
SIC 5191 Farm supplies; Farm supplies
CEO: Kenneth P Knappert
*Treas: Mike Phillips
*VP: Pat Burnett
Mktg Dir: Doug Johnson
Sls Mgr: Chuck Rix

D-U-N-S 01-877-7714
NORTHWEST-SHOALS COMMUNITY COLLEGE
800 George Wallace Blvd, Muscle Shoals, AL 35661-3205
Tel (256) 331-5200 Founded/Ownrshp 1966
Sales 332.2M EMP 450
SIC 8222 8221 Community college; Colleges universities & professional schools; Community college; Colleges universities & professional schools
Pr: Humphrey Lee
COO: Teresa Wright
CFO: Paul Merrill
Ofcr: Timmy James
Mktg Mgr: Trent Randolph

D-U-N-S 07-258-6233
NORTHWESTERN BANCORP INC
625 S Garfield Ave, Traverse City, MI 49686-3425
Tel (231) 947-5490 Founded/Ownrshp 1955
Sales NA EMP 300
SIC 6035

D-U-N-S 06-867-5263
NORTHWESTERN COLLEGE
NWC
101 7th St Sw, Orange City, IA 51041-1996
Tel (712) 707-7000 Founded/Ownrshp 1882
Sales 30.2MM EMP 298
SIC 8221

D-U-N-S 96-342-0661
NORTHWESTERN COLLEGE RADIO FOUNDATION
3003 Snelling Ave N, Saint Paul, MN 55113-1501
Tel (651) 631-5100 Founded/Ownrshp 1902
Sales 71.9MM EMP 400
Accts Clifton Larson Allen Llp Minn
SIC 8221 Colleges universities & professional schools; Colleges universities & professional schools
Pr: Alan S Cureton
VP: Andrew M Youso
Off Mgr: Nick Germann
Off Mgr: Sharon Kleven
Off Mgr: Randy D McGrew
Off Admin: Ashley Kinley
Off Admin: Emily Simpson
Psych: Bruce E Barrows
Psych: Chris Frank
Psych: Michael R Lanser
HC Dir: Ken Faffler

D-U-N-S 00-792-0291
▲ NORTHWESTERN CORP
NORTHWESTERN ENERGY
3010 W 69th St, Sioux Falls, SD 57108-5613
Tel (605) 978-2900 Founded/Ownrshp 1923
Sales 1.2MMM EMP 1,574^E
Accts Deloitte & Touche Llp Minneap
Tkr Sym NWE Exch NYS
SIC 4911 4924 Generation, electric power; Distribution, electric power; Natural gas distribution; Generation, electric power; Distribution, electric power; Natural gas distribution
Pr: Robert C Rowe
*Ch Bd: E Linn Draper Jr
CFO: Brian B Bird
VP: Patrick R Corcoran
VP: Heather H Grahame
VP: Kendall G Kliewer
Comm Dir: Claudia Rapkoch
Board of Directors: Stephen P Adik, Dorothy M Bradley, Dana J Dykhouse, Julia L Johnson, Denton Louis Peoples

D-U-N-S 05-565-9007
NORTHWESTERN COUNSELING SUPPORT & SERVICES INC (VT)
107 Fisher Pond Rd, Saint Albans, VT 05478-6286
Tel (802) 524-6554 Founded/Ownrshp 1958
Sales 34.3MM EMP 400
SIC 8093 Mental health clinic, outpatient; Mental health clinic, outpatient

D-U-N-S 02-204-8840
NORTHWESTERN ELECTRIC COOP
P.O. Box 2707 (73802-2707)
Tel (580) 256-7425 Founded/Ownrshp 2011
Sales 33.8MM EMP 6^E
SIC 4911

D-U-N-S 00-725-1465
NORTHWESTERN ELECTRIC COOPERATIVE INC
2925 Williams Ave, Woodward, OK 73801-6727
Tel (580) 256-7425 Founded/Ownrshp 1940
Sales 36.8MM EMP 55
SIC 4911 Distribution, electric power; Distribution, electric power
CEO: Tyson Littau
Dir IT: Curt Cloyd
IT Man: Jackie McIlvain

NORTHWESTERN ENERGY
See NORTHWESTERN CORP

D-U-N-S 13-502-1934
■ NORTHWESTERN ENERGY CORP
(Suby of NORTHWESTERN CORP) ★
3010 W 69th St, Sioux Falls, SD 57108-5613
Tel (605) 978-2900 Founded/Ownrshp 1996
Sales 322.0MM^E EMP 587^E
SIC 4911 4924 Electric services; Natural gas distribution
Pr: Robert C Rowe
*Ch Bd: E Linn Draper Jr
Pr: Heather Grahame
*CFO: Brian B Bird
*Treas: Paul Evans
*VP: Michael R Cashell
VP: Miggie E Cramblit
*VP: Glen R Herr
*VP: Curtis T Pohl
*VP: Bobbi L Schroeppel
Ex Dir: Jane McDermott

NORTHWESTERN ENERGY LLC
See CLARK FORK AND BLACKFOOT L LC

D-U-N-S 00-792-0358
NORTHWESTERN ENGINEERING CO (SD)
314 Founders Park Dr, Rapid City, SD 57701-8090
Tel (605) 394-3310 Founded/Ownrshp 1927
Sales 22.5MM EMP 92
SIC 6512 6513 6515 6531 Nonresidential building operators; Apartment building operators; Mobile home site operators; Real estate managers; Real estate leasing & rentals; Nonresidential building operators; Apartment building operators; Mobile home site operators; Real estate managers; Real estate leasing & rentals
Ch Bd: Stanford M Adelstein
*Pr: Patrick Tlustos
*CFO: David Crabb
*Ex VP: James Adelstein

D-U-N-S 78-688-5566
NORTHWESTERN ENTERPRISES INC
(Suby of NHS HUMAN SERVICES INC) ★
620 Germantown Pike, Lafayette Hill, PA 19444-1810
Tel (610) 260-4600 Founded/Ownrshp 1986
Sales 25.2MM EMP 39
SIC 7359 8082 8748 8361 Equipment rental & leasing; Home health care services; Business consulting; Geriatric residential care; Equipment rental & leasing; Home health care services; Business consulting; Geriatric residential care
Pr: M Joseph Rocks
Assoc Dir: Brett Boettcher

D-U-N-S 07-650-0040
NORTHWESTERN HEALTH SCIENCES UNIVERSITY
2501 W 84th St, Bloomington, MN 55431-1602
Tel (952) 888-4777 Founded/Ownrshp 1941
Sales 30.1MM^E EMP 280
Accts Cliftonlarsonallen Llp Minnea
SIC 8221 Professional schools; Professional schools
CEO: Jeff A Nelson
*Pr: Mark Zeigler
*CFO: Jim McDaonald
*Ch: Kent J Erickson
Treas: Beau Foshee
*Treas: Scott D Munsterman
Bd of Dir: Bonnie Myhers
VP: Charlsey Kessler
VP: Camile Pascoe
VP: Jeff Rich
Store Mgr: Karen Larson

D-U-N-S 15-378-5472
NORTHWESTERN HUMAN SERVICES OF PHILADELPHIA
(Suby of NHS HUMAN SERVICES INC) ★
620 Germantown Pike, Lafayette Hill, PA 19444-1810
Tel (610) 260-4600 Founded/Ownrshp 1981
Sales 40.9MM EMP 490
SIC 8093 Mental health clinic, outpatient; Mental health clinic, outpatient
Ch: M Joseph Rocks
*COO: Brian Baxter
*VP: Michael Barton
CIO: William E Adams

D-U-N-S 00-586-1216
NORTHWESTERN INDIANA TELEPHONE CO INC
NITCO
205 N Washington St, Hebron, IN 46341-8978
Tel (219) 987-2981 Founded/Ownrshp 1939
Sales 22.1MM^E EMP 80
SIC 4813 Local & long distance telephone communications; ; Local & long distance telephone communications; ;
CEO: Rhys G Mussman

D-U-N-S 07-458-8492
NORTHWESTERN LAKE FOREST HOSPITAL
WOMENS AUX OF LK FOREST HOSP
(Suby of NORTHWESTERN MEMORIAL HEALTHCARE) ★
660 N Westmoreland Rd, Lake Forest, IL 60045-1696
Tel (847) 234-0945 Founded/Ownrshp 2010
Sales 61.8MM^E EMP 1,700
SIC 8062 5947 5932 5812 Hospital, medical school affiliated with nursing & residency; Gift shop; Novelties; Used merchandise stores; Coffee shop; Hospital, medical school affiliated with nursing & residency; Gift shop; Novelties; Used merchandise stores; Coffee shop
Pr: Matthew J Flynn
*VP: Michael G Ankin
*VP: Jane C Griffin
VP: Oberrieder Marsha
*VP: Kimberly A Nagy
VP: Marsha L Oberrieder
Exec: Marc Posner
Dir Risk M: Phyllis Rosebrook
Mng Dir: Harold Chin
Nurse Mgr: Judith Horvat
Nurse Mgr: Leann Schmidt

D-U-N-S 10-066-9522
NORTHWESTERN LEHIGH SCHOOL DISTRICT
6493 Route 309, New Tripoli, PA 18066-2099
Tel (610) 298-8661 Founded/Ownrshp 1950
Sales 38.5MM EMP 378
Accts Gorman & Associates Pc Nor
SIC 8211 Public elementary & secondary schools; Public elementary & secondary schools
*Pr: Darryl S Schafer
*Treas: Willard G Dellicker
*VP: Paul C Fisher Jr
*Prin: John Gould
Dir IT: Karen Wallace

D-U-N-S 94-502-9848
NORTHWESTERN MANAGEMENT SERVICES LLC
GENTLE DENTAL GROUP
(Suby of TBG NMS HOLDINGS INC) ★
951 Broken Sound Pkwy Nw # 250, Boca Raton, FL 33487-3506
Tel (561) 999-9650 Founded/Ownrshp 2012
Sales 17.5MM^E EMP 328^E
SIC 8021 Dental clinics & offices; Dental clinics & offices
CEO: David Willens

NORTHWESTERN MCGAW CTR FOR GRA
See MCGAW MEDICAL CENTER OF NORTHWESTERN UNIVERSITY

NORTHWESTERN MEDIA
See UNIVERSITY OF NORTHWESTERN - ST PAUL

D-U-N-S 06-052-5748
NORTHWESTERN MEDICAL CENTER INC
133 Fairfield St, Saint Albans, VT 05478-1726
Tel (802) 524-5911 Founded/Ownrshp 1893
Sales 91.2MM EMP 600
SIC 8062 General medical & surgical hospitals; General medical & surgical hospitals
CEO: Jill Berry Bowen
Chf Rad: Luis F Gonzalez III
*Pr: John Casavant
CFO: Dawn Bugbee
CFO: Ted Sirotta
*Treas: Harold Hebert
*VP: Judy Ashley-Mclaughlin
VP: Joel Benware
VP: Johnathan Bilings
VP: Joy Sylvester
Dir Inf Cn: Pam Bonsall
Dir Risk M: Nilda French
Dir Risk M: Nilda Gonnella-French
Dir Lab: David Blin
Dir Rad: Jim Block
Dir Rx: John Chesarek

D-U-N-S 10-683-9707
NORTHWESTERN MEDICAL FACULTY FOUNDATION INC
NORTHWESTERN MEDICAL GROUP
680 N Lake Shore Dr Ste 1, Chicago, IL 60611-4546
Tel (312) 926-2630 Founded/Ownrshp 1980
Sales 800.0MM EMP 3,000
SIC 8011

NORTHWESTERN MEDICAL GROUP
See NORTHWESTERN MEDICAL FACULTY FOUNDATION INC

D-U-N-S 10-333-5733 IMP
NORTHWESTERN MEMORIAL HEALTHCARE
251 E Huron St Ste 3-708, Chicago, IL 60611-2908
Tel (312) 926-2000 Founded/Ownrshp 1981
Sales 421.3MM EMP 6,000
SIC 8082 6513 7389 8099 Commercial & industrial building operation; Apartment building operators; Fund raising organizations; Medical services organization; Home health care services; Apartment building operators; Fund raising organizations; Medical services organization
Pr: Dean Harrison
Ch Bd: Carol L Bernick
COO: Cynthia Hall
COO: Dennis M Murphy
CFO: Peter J McCanna
Sr VP: Carol M Lind
VP: Gina Weldy
Dir Risk M: Scott Stanley
Dir Rx: Neal Grosshans
Ex Dir: Judy Wood
Snr Ntwrk: Myles Gehrke

D-U-N-S 05-945-7150
NORTHWESTERN MEMORIAL HOSPITAL
(Suby of NORTHWESTERN MEMORIAL HEALTHCARE) ★
251 E Huron St, Chicago, IL 60611-3055
Tel (312) 755-0604 Founded/Ownrshp 1867
Sales 231.2MM^E EMP 5,800
SIC 8062 General medical & surgical hospitals; General medical & surgical hospitals
CEO: Dean Harrison
Ch Bd: William J Brodsky
Pr: Richard J Gannotta
COO: Hank Moya
COO: Dennis Murphy
CFO: Peter McCanna
Bd of Dir: Reeve Waud
Sr VP: Julie Creamer
VP: Stephen C Falk
VP: Ira Goldstone
Dir Risk M: Laura Lingl
Dir Rad: Cynthia K Broos

D-U-N-S 85-998-0633
NORTHWESTERN MEMORIAL PHYSICIANS GROUP
(Suby of NORTHWESTERN MEMORIAL HOSPITAL) ★
211 E Ontario St Ste 1600, Chicago, IL 60611-3297
Tel (312) 926-3107 Founded/Ownrshp 1995
Sales 22.7MM^E EMP 150
SIC 8011 Offices & clinics of medical doctors
Pr: Daniel Derman MD
Ofcr: Robert Noven
Sr VP: Thomas McAfee
VP: Bridget Gibbons
VP: Jeffrey Kopin
Admn Mgr: Maija Hasiba
IT Man: Michael Scala
Obsttrcn: Scott Moses
Plas Surg: Gregory Dumanian
Doctor: Brian Foley
Doctor: Timothy Garvey

D-U-N-S 07-258-7793
NORTHWESTERN MICHIGAN COLLEGE
1701 E Front St, Traverse City, MI 49686-3016
Tel (231) 995-1000 Founded/Ownrshp 1951
Sales 28.4MM EMP 742
Accts Rehmann Robson Traverse City
SIC 8222 Community college; Community college
Pr: Timothy J Nelson
CFO: Vicki Cook
Chf Inves: Donald Shikoski
Prgrm Mgr: Michelle Poertner
Genl Mgr: Eric Hines
Store Mgr: Rhonda Greiner
CTO: Todd Sanders
IT Man: Carly McCall
HC Dir: Cathryn Claerhout
Snr Mgr: Alex Bloye
Snr Mgr: Bill Donberg

NORTHWESTERN MUTUAL
See JAMES R WORRELL GENERAL AGENT INC

NORTHWESTERN MUTUAL
See NORTHWEST MUTUAL FINANCIAL TRUST LLC

D-U-N-S 62-706-6673
NORTHWESTERN MUTUAL FINANCIAL NETWORK
NORTH WESTERN MUTAL INSURANCE
400 Broadhollow Rd # 200, Melville, NY 11747-4810
Tel (631) 592-2000 Founded/Ownrshp 1997
Sales NA EMP 240
SIC 6411 8748 8742 6371 6282 Insurance agents & brokers; Business consulting; Management consulting services; Pension, health & welfare funds; Investment advice; Insurance agents & brokers; Business consulting; Management consulting services; Pension, health & welfare funds; Investment advice
Pr: Stephen Phillips
COO: Christine Harezlak
Ofcr: Paul Crespo

NORTHWESTERN MUTUAL INSURANCE
See VAN DER HYDE JOHN F

D-U-N-S 02-180-6492
NORTHWESTERN MUTUAL INVESTMENT SERVICES LLC
NORTHWESTERN MUTUAL LIFE
29 S Main St Ste 201, West Hartford, CT 06107-2454
Tel (860) 570-7400 Founded/Ownrshp 1971
Sales NA EMP 94
SIC 6411 Insurance agents
Mng Pt: Jeffrey Zuzulo
Owner: Randall Riley
Pr: David G Stoeffel

NORTHWESTERN MUTUAL LIFE
See NORTHWESTERN MUTUAL INVESTMENT SERVICES LLC

NORTHWESTERN MUTUAL LIFE
See BLEAKLEY SCHWARTZ COONEY & FINNEY LLC

D-U-N-S 00-794-7146
NORTHWESTERN MUTUAL LIFE INSURANCE CO INC
720 E Wisconsin Ave, Milwaukee, WI 53202-4703
Tel (414) 271-1444 *Founded/Ownrshp* 1857
Sales NA *EMP* 6,662
Accts Pricewaterhousecoopers Llp
SIC 6311 6321 7389 Life insurance carriers; Disability health insurance; Financial services; Life insurance carriers; Disability health insurance; Financial services
CEO: John E Schlifske
**Ch Bd:* James D Ericson
**Pr:* Gregory C Oberland
**Pr:* Gary A Poliner
**COO:* John M Bremer
**CFO:* Michael G Carter
CFO: Wallace Fischer
Bd of Dir: Hayden Patton
**Ofcr:* Sarah E Schott
Ex VP: Rebekah Barsch
**Ex VP:* Todd M Schoon
**Sr VP:* Joann M Eisenhart
**Sr VP:* John M Grogan
**VP:* Robert J Berdan
VP: Christian Mitchell
VP: David G Stoeffel

D-U-N-S 80-560-3763
NORTHWESTERN MUTUAL WEALTH MANAGEMENT CO
(*Suby of* NORTHWESTERN MUTUAL LIFE INSURANCE CO INC) ★
611 E Wisconsin Ave, Milwaukee, WI 53202-4695
Tel (206) 623-8801 *Founded/Ownrshp* 2007
Sales NA *EMP* 25
SIC 6411 Insurance agents, brokers & service; Insurance agents, brokers & service
Prin: Mark J McLennon
Ofcr: James Chavez
Ofcr: John Grogan Jr
Ofcr: Alexander Lewis
Ofcr: Chad Stubenbort
VP: Steve Radke
VP: William H Taylor
Sls Dir: Brian Wilson

NORTHWESTERN OHIO ADMINISTRATO
See UNION CONSTRUCTION WORKERS HEALTH PLAN INC

D-U-N-S 85-850-2313 EXP
NORTHWESTERN PLASTICS LTD
INDUSTRIAL SERVICE
1731 N Roosevelt Ave, Burlington, IA 52601-2320
Tel (319) 754-4000 *Founded/Ownrshp* 1980
Sales 42.4MM^E *EMP* 94
SIC 3523 4225 4214 Farm machinery & equipment; Miniwarehouse, warehousing; Local trucking with storage; Farm machinery & equipment; Miniwarehouse, warehousing; Local trucking with storage
Pr: Sam West
**Treas:* Rodney Wittkamp
**VP:* Kevin Wittkamp

D-U-N-S 06-892-2665
■ **NORTHWESTERN RESOURCES CO**
(*Suby of* WESTMORELAND MINING LLC) ★
12420 Hwy 39, Jewett, TX 75846
Tel (903) 626-5485 *Founded/Ownrshp* 2001
Sales 23.0MM^E *EMP* 414
SIC 1221 Surface mining, bituminous; Surface mining, lignite; Surface mining, bituminous; Surface mining, lignite
Pr: Mark Seglen
**Ch Bd:* Robert T Gannon

D-U-N-S 17-709-4414
NORTHWESTERN RESTAURANTS INC
TACO BELL
16000 Christensen Rd # 101, Tukwila, WA 98188-2957
Tel (206) 957-9060 *Founded/Ownrshp* 1990
Sales 9.4MM^E *EMP* 350
SIC 5812 Fast-food restaurant, chain; Fast-food restaurant, chain
Pr: David Orem
**Treas:* Peggy Orem

D-U-N-S 09-113-2589 IMP
NORTHWESTERN SELECTA INC
NEZ FOODS
796 Calle C M Julia Indst, San Juan, PR 00920
Tel (787) 781-1950 *Founded/Ownrshp* 1980
Sales 163.6MM *EMP* 300^E
Accts Colon Cuebas & Laguna Psc Sa
SIC 5147 5146 5142 Meats, fresh; Fish & seafoods; Meat, frozen: packaged; Fish, frozen: packaged; Meats, fresh; Fish & seafoods; Meat, frozen: packaged; Fish, frozen: packaged
Pr: Elpidio Nunez III
**VP:* Rafael Flores
**VP Admn:* Miguel Portillo

D-U-N-S 12-730-9172
■ **NORTHWESTERN SERVICES LLC**
(*Suby of* NORTHWESTERN CORP) ★
600 Market St W, Huron, SD 57350-1510
Tel (605) 353-7478 *Founded/Ownrshp* 1925
Sales 359.8MM^E *EMP* 450
SIC 4911 4924 Electric services; Natural gas distribution; Electric services; Natural gas distribution

D-U-N-S 06-973-3798
NORTHWESTERN STATE UNIVERSITY OF LOUISIANA (LA)
(*Suby of* UNIVERSITIES OF LOUISIANA SYSTEM) ★
175 Sam Sibley Dr, Natchitoches, LA 71497-0001
Tel (318) 357-5446 *Founded/Ownrshp* 1885
Sales 56.3MM^E *EMP* 729
SIC 8221 9411 University; Administration of educational programs; ; University; Administration of educational programs;
Pr: Randall J Webb
**VP:* Tom Burns
**VP:* Carl Jones
VP: Chris Maggio
**VP:* Jerry D Pierce
**VP:* Dr Dan Seymour
**VP:* John Winston
Off Admin: Debra Nugent
IT Man: Brandin Craig

D-U-N-S 00-543-6803
NORTHWESTERN UNIVERSITY (IL)
633 Clark St, Evanston, IL 60208-0001
Tel (847) 491-3741 *Founded/Ownrshp* 1851
Sales 2.3MMM *EMP* 5,954
Accts Pricewaterhousecoopers Llp Ch
SIC 8221 University; University
Pr: Henry S Bienen
**Pr:* Schapiro Morton
Chf Mktg O: Tom Hayden
**Sr VP:* Eugene S Sunshine
VP: Tom Board
**VP:* Thomas G Cline
VP: James M Hurley
VP: Marilyn McCoy
VP: Will McLean
VP: Robert McQuinn
VP: Sean Reynolds
VP: Joseph T Walsh
Assoc Dir: Anne Bitting
Assoc Dir: Christine Choi
Assoc Dir: Mark Darienzo
Assoc Dir: Natalie Furlett
Assoc Dir: Kim Hoffmann
Assoc Dir: Todd Murphy

D-U-N-S 16-105-2329
NORTHWESTERN UNIVERSITY INFORMATION TECHNOLOGIES
1800 Sherman Ave Ste 206, Evanston, IL 60201-3785
Tel (847) 467-1766 *Founded/Ownrshp* 1850
Sales 1.5MMM *EMP* 250
SIC 4813 7374 4812 Local & long distance telephone communications; Data processing & preparation; Radio telephone communication; Local & long distance telephone communications; Data processing & preparation; Radio telephone communication
VP: Patricia Todus

D-U-N-S 12-436-5243
NORTHWIND ENGINEERING LLC
105 Main St, Shelocta, PA 15774
Tel (724) 354-2941 *Founded/Ownrshp* 2002
Sales 21.1MM^E *EMP* 60^E
Accts Ed Opst Greensburg Pa
SIC 8711 Engineering services

D-U-N-S 60-628-0220
NORTHWIND ENTERPRISES INC
ATLANTIC
4605 Brookfield Corp Dr, Chantilly, VA 20151
Tel (703) 802-6800 *Founded/Ownrshp* 1988
Sales 22.0MM *EMP* 80
SIC 3993 5046 7319 7336 7389 Signs & advertising specialties; Display equipment, except refrigerated; Display advertising service; Commercial art & graphic design; Advertising, promotional & trade show services; Trade show arrangement; Signs & advertising specialties; Display equipment, except refrigerated; Display advertising service; Commercial art & graphic design; Advertising, promotional & trade show services; Trade show arrangement
CEO: David T Beach
**Pr:* Gregory L Beach
Pr: John Snyder
**CFO:* David A Bell
Genl Mgr: Mike Sandler
Dir IT: Brian Carothers
IT Man: Avraham Pesach
Sfty Mgr: Paul Lamar
Art Dir: Brian Fallon

D-U-N-S 09-295-4130
NORTHWIND INVESTMENTS INC
BURGER KING
109 E Broadway St, Mount Pleasant, MI 48858-2312
Tel (989) 772-2600 *Founded/Ownrshp* 1999
Sales 39.8MM^E *EMP* 1,100
SIC 5812 Fast-food restaurant, chain; Fast-food restaurant, chain
Pr: Kevin Egnatuk
**Sec:* Greg Johnroe
**VP:* Bob Spalding

D-U-N-S 60-664-1082
■ **NORTHWINGS ACCESSORIES CORP**
HEICO REPAIR GROUP
(*Suby of* HEICO AEROSPACE CORP) ★
7875 Nw 64th St, Miami, FL 33166-2718
Tel (305) 463-0455 *Founded/Ownrshp* 1991
Sales 38.8MM^E *EMP* 149^E
SIC 4581 Aircraft servicing & repairing; Aircraft servicing & repairing
Pr: Luis J Morell
VP: Javier Diaz
VP: Omar Lloret
VP: Laurans Mendelson
IT Man: Harold Boada
Ql Cn Mgr: Vince Canavan
Sls Dir: Alfredo Asencio
Sls Dir: Dennis Carreiro
Sls Mgr: William Suau

D-U-N-S 05-902-5221 IMP
NORTHWIRE INC
110 Prospect Way, Osceola, WI 54020-8176
Tel (715) 294-2121 *Founded/Ownrshp* 1984
Sales 25.3MM^E *EMP* 210
SIC 3357 5051

D-U-N-S 87-693-4951
NORTHWITT INC
BUFFALO WILD WINGS
1900 Brown St, Dayton, OH 45409-2456
Tel (937) 222-9464 *Founded/Ownrshp* 1994
Sales 23.0MM *EMP* 780
Accts Bober Markey Fedorovich & Co
SIC 5812 Grills (eating places); Grills (eating places)
Pr: David Fisher
**Treas:* John Slaghenhaupt
**VP:* Eric Lundgren

D-U-N-S 02-814-6876
NORTHWOOD AUTO PLAZA INC
NORTHWOOD CHEVROLET
212 7th St, Eureka, CA 95501-1773
Tel (707) 443-4861 *Founded/Ownrshp* 1980
Sales 22.6MM^E *EMP* 46^E
SIC 5511 Automobiles, new & used
Pr: Mark A Dias
Ofcr: Harry Black
Sls Mgr: Linus Lorenzen

NORTHWOOD CHEVROLET
See NORTHWOOD AUTO PLAZA INC

D-U-N-S 10-568-4310
NORTHWOOD ENERGY CORP
941 Chatham Ln Ste 100, Columbus, OH 43221-2471
Tel (614) 457-1024 *Founded/Ownrshp* 1983
Sales 31.4MM *EMP* 20
SIC 1311 Crude petroleum production; Natural gas production
Pr: Ralph W Talmage
VP: Dave Haid
Prin: Frederick H Kennedy
Prin: Joan S Talmage
Mng Dir: Tyna Anderson

D-U-N-S 03-735-4714
NORTHWOOD FOODS INC
1105 8th St N, Northwood, IA 50459-1029
Tel (641) 324-1466 *Founded/Ownrshp* 1998
Sales 65.0MM *EMP* 90
SIC 2011 Meat packing plants; Meat packing plants
Pr: Brian Burkard
**Prin:* Jason Moeller

D-U-N-S 08-296-0725
NORTHWOOD HEALTH SYSTEMS INC
111 19th St, Wheeling, WV 26003-3715
Tel (304) 234-3500 *Founded/Ownrshp* 1967
Sales 26.0MM *EMP* 450
SIC 8361 8093 Residential care; Substance abuse clinics (outpatient); Residential care; Substance abuse clinics (outpatient)
Pr: Pete Radakovich
**Ch Bd:* Pat Casey
**CFO:* Richard Stockley
Treas: Joe Schmidt
Exec: Tammy Whitehair
Off Mgr: Joanne Shepherd
IT Man: Tom Dzmura
Sls&Mrk Ex: Ray Braun

NORTHWOOD HOMES
See NORTHWOOD INVESTMENTS CORP

D-U-N-S 62-709-8288
NORTHWOOD INVESTMENTS CORP
NORTHWOOD HOMES
59948 Downs Rd, La Grande, OR 97850-5295
Tel (541) 962-6274 *Founded/Ownrshp* 1991
Sales 89.4MM^E *EMP* 350^E
SIC 3792 Travel trailers & campers; Travel trailers & campers
CEO: Jim Jones
Pr: Ronald L Nash
CFO: Craig Orton
VP: Ernest P Lewis

D-U-N-S 92-710-7722
NORTHWOOD MANUFACTURING INC
(*Suby of* NORTHWOOD HOMES) ★
59948 Downs Rd, La Grande, OR 97850-5295
Tel (541) 962-6274 *Founded/Ownrshp* 1993
Sales 89.0MM *EMP* 350
Accts Delap Llp Lake Oswego Or
SIC 3792 Travel trailers & campers; Travel trailers & campers
CEO: James Jones
Pr: Ronald L Nash
CFO: Craig Orton
Dir IT: Noel Beden
Sls Dir: Donald Cochran

D-U-N-S 07-422-5566
NORTHWOOD UNIVERSITY (MI)
4000 Whiting Dr, Midland, MI 48640-2398
Tel (800) 622-9000 *Founded/Ownrshp* 1959, 1960
Sales 96.0MM *EMP* 500
SIC 8221 Colleges universities & professional schools; Colleges universities & professional schools
Pr: Keith A Pretty
Pr: Sue Nowicki
Treas: Donald E Hunkins
Bd of Dir: Whitney Goulish
VP: Margaret Reichert
Ex Dir: Julie Felske
Ex Dir: Denise Ward
Brnch Mgr: Tracy Graham
Genl Mgr: Burt McAtee
Genl Mgr: Charles Perez
Off Mgr: Ann Salva

D-U-N-S 12-420-1059
NORTHWOODS CONSULTING PARTNERS INC
CABIN IN THE WOOD
5815 Wall St, Dublin, OH 43017-3264
Tel (614) 781-7800 *Founded/Ownrshp* 1997
Sales 21.1MM^E *EMP* 118
SIC 7371 Computer software development
Pr: Gary Heinze
V Ch: Bill Burke
**Pr:* David Michael George
**COO:* Chris Carlson
**CFO:* Gary Alan Heinze
**VP:* Jon Petersen
CTO: Michael Randall
IT Man: Dinesh Sthapit
Software D: Scott Dean
Software D: James Neno
Software D: Aaron Petry

D-U-N-S 87-969-9692 IMP
NORTHWOODS MANUFACTURING INC
850 East Blvd, Kingsford, MI 49802-4436
Tel (906) 779-2370 *Founded/Ownrshp* 1994
Sales 22.9MM^E *EMP* 70
SIC 3444 3441 Sheet metalwork; Fabricated structural metal
Pr: Jon Pipp
Plnt Mgr: Joe Schutte

D-U-N-S 13-590-1341
NORTHWOODS PAPER CONVERTING INC
230 Corporate Dr, Beaver Dam, WI 53916-3115
Tel (920) 356-9085 *Founded/Ownrshp* 1999
Sales 20.2MM^E *EMP* 115^E
SIC 2679 Paper products, converted; Paper products, converted
Pr: Chad Abel
VP: Brandon Mietzel
**VP:* James Moreau
Snr Sftwr: Ryan Stueber
Dir IT: George Smith
Plnt Mgr: Jon Caldwell

NORTHYARDS, THE
See MOXIE INTERACTIVE INC

D-U-N-S 16-802-4144
NORTON AUDUBON HOSPITAL
(*Suby of* NORTON HOSPITALS INC) ★
1 Audubon Plaza Dr, Louisville, KY 40217-1318
Tel (502) 636-7111 *Founded/Ownrshp* 1998
Sales 29.8MM^E *EMP* 1,242
SIC 8062 General medical & surgical hospitals; General medical & surgical hospitals
Pr: Thomas D Kmetz
Chf Rad: Peter Wayne
VP: Heather Cote
Dir Case M: Sharon Higdon
Nurse Mgr: Shari Head
Dir QC: Shirley Schilling
IT Man: Damon Yeary
Ql Cn Mgr: Kathy Jenkins
Podiatrist: Walter M Butler
Doctor: Abdolreza Agahtehrani
Doctor: Brian Beanblossom

NORTON CLINICAL AGENCY NCAC
See NORTON ENTERPRISES INC

D-U-N-S 07-152-7659
NORTON COMMUNITY HOSPITAL AUXILIARY INC (VA)
100 15th St Nw, Norton, VA 24273-1616
Tel (276) 679-9600 *Founded/Ownrshp* 1954, 1992
Sales 53.4MM^E *EMP* 460
SIC 8062 General medical & surgical hospitals; General medical & surgical hospitals
Ch Bd: Ann Fleming
V Ch: Robert Aleonard
**CEO:* Mark Leonard
**CEO:* Steven Sawyer
Off Mgr: Jan Maloney
CIO: Judy Lawson
Advt Dir: Lori Crisp
Obsttrcn: Beth Sluss

NORTON DIAMOND FILM
See SAINT-GOBAIN/NORTON INDUSTRIAL CERAMICS CORP

NORTON DOOR CONTROL
See YALE SECURITY INC

NORTON DRILLING
See PATTERSON-UTI DRILLING SERVICES LP LLLP

D-U-N-S 11-596-5923
NORTON ENTERPRISES INC
NORTON CLINICAL AGENCY NCAC
(*Suby of* NORTON HEALTHCARE INC) ★
4967 Us Highway 42 # 100, Louisville, KY 40222-6363
Tel (502) 629-8830 *Founded/Ownrshp* 1983
Sales 9.7MM *EMP* 368
SIC 8011 8071 6512 Medical centers; Medical laboratories; Commercial & industrial building operation
Pr: Stephen A Williams
COO: Edgar Vaughn
**Treas:* Micheal Gouf
**VP:* Robert Azar
**VP:* Russell F Cox

D-U-N-S 85-917-3585
NORTON HEALTHCARE FOUNDATION INC
(*Suby of* NORTON HEALTHCARE INC) ★
4967 Us Highway 42 # 100, Louisville, KY 40222-6363
Tel (502) 629-8000 *Founded/Ownrshp* 1962
Sales 85.5M *EMP* 9,000
Accts Ernst & Young Llp Louisville
SIC 7389 Fund raising organizations; Fund raising organizations
VP: Mary Corbett
VP: Steve Hester
Dir Pat Ac: Cathy Shepard

D-U-N-S 14-779-2105
NORTON HEALTHCARE INC
200 E Chestnut St, Louisville, KY 40202-1831
Tel (502) 629-8000 *Founded/Ownrshp* 1983
Sales 1.6MMM^E *EMP* 9,300
SIC 8741 8062 Hospital management; General medical & surgical hospitals; Hospital management; General medical & surgical hospitals
Pr: Stephen A Williams
Chf Rad: Sean Owens
Pr: Christopher Watkins
COO: Russell F Cox
CFO: Shirley Miller
**Treas:* Gordon King
Trst: Maria L Bouvette
Trst: Carolyn J Gatz
Trst: Craig D Grant
Trst: Raymond K Guillaume
Trst: Kevin J Hable
Trst: Gail Lyttle
Trst: Mitch Nichols
Trst: Joseph A Paradis
Trst: Alton H Roberts
Trst: Donald H Robinson
Trst: William J Schultz

Trst: Richard S Wolf
Trst: Wendell P Wright
Ofcr: Steven Brockman-Weber
Assoc VP: Jon Cooper

D-U-N-S 07-152-7725
NORTON HMA INC
MOUNTAINVIEW REGIONAL MED CTR
(*Suby of* WELLMONT FOUNDATION) ★
Third St Ne, Norton, VA 24273
Tel (276) 679-9100 *Founded/Ownrshp* 1948, 2007
Sales 27.3MM^E *EMP* 403
SIC 8062 General medical & surgical hospitals; General medical & surgical hospitals

D-U-N-S 16-802-2031
NORTON HOSPITAL
(*Suby of* NORTON HOSPITALS INC) ★
200 E Chestnut St Frnt, Louisville, KY 40202-1800
Tel (502) 629-8159 *Founded/Ownrshp* 2001
Sales 1.5MMM *EMP* 1,242
SIC 8062 General medical & surgical hospitals; General medical & surgical hospitals

D-U-N-S 16-816-4643
NORTON HOSPITALS INC
(*Suby of* NORTON HEALTHCARE INC) ★
200 E Chestnut St, Louisville, KY 40202-1831
Tel (502) 629-8000 *Founded/Ownrshp* 1969
Sales 1.5MMM *EMP* 1,500
SIC 8062 8011 8093 8071 General medical & surgical hospitals; Physicians' office, including specialists; Specialty outpatient clinics; Ultrasound laboratory; General medical & surgical hospitals; Physicians' office, including specialists; Specialty outpatient clinics; Ultrasound laboratory
Pr: Steven A Williams
**Treas:* Michael W Gough
**VP:* Russell F Cox
Chf Nrs Of: Heather R Cote
Netwrk Mgr: Diana Wetterer
Doctor: Melissa Kohler
Doctor: Rodney Miguel
Doctor: Michele G Phipps MD
Doctor: Johanna Pope
Diag Rad: John Burger
Diag Rad: Durrett Craddock

D-U-N-S 12-715-0956
NORTON LILLY INTERNATIONAL INC
KERR NORTON STRACHAN AGENCY
1 Saint Louis St Ste 5000, Mobile, AL 36602-3929
Tel (251) 431-6335 *Founded/Ownrshp* 1999
Sales 121.9MM^E *EMP* 402
SIC 4731 Agents, shipping; Agents, shipping
Ch: Hw Thurber III
**CFO:* Jim Burton
**Ex VP:* Flemming Buhl
**Ex VP:* Dwain Denniston
Ex VP: Dinesh Deogaonkar
**Ex VP:* Steve Haverstock
Sr VP: Ira Rudnick
VP: Norton Lilly
Dir Bus: Stan Jahncke
**Prin:* Brad Clark
Genl Mgr: Jeff Overstreet

NORTON METALS
See RUSSEL JMS METALS CORP

D-U-N-S 03-868-9147 IMP
NORTON MUSEUM OF ART INC
1451 S Olive Ave, West Palm Beach, FL 33401-7162
Tel (561) 832-5196 *Founded/Ownrshp* 1941
Sales 34.6MM *EMP* 80
SIC 8412 Museum
Ex Dir: Christina Orr' Cahall
Exec: Hope Alswang
**Prin:* Harry Howell
**Prin:* Janine Mayville
Snr Mgr: Kevin Cummins

D-U-N-S 00-417-3795 IMP/EXP
NORTON OGLEBAY CO (OH)
CARMEUSE LIME & STONE
(*Suby of* CARMEUSE LIME & STONE INC) ★
11 Stanwix St Fl 21, Pittsburgh, PA 15222-1327
Tel (412) 995-5500 *Founded/Ownrshp* 1854, 2008
Sales 32.9MM^E *EMP* 304^E
SIC 1422 4432 4491 1446 1499 1011 Crushed & broken limestone; Freight transportation on the Great Lakes; Docks, piers & terminals; Silica sand mining; Perlite mining; Pumice mining; Iron ores
Pr: Thomas A Buck
**CFO:* Bruce Inglis
**Treas:* Mary D Colin
VP: Ralph Bardine
VP: Aidan Connolly
VP: Roger Downham
VP: Jack Fahler
VP: Jeffrey S Gray
VP: Carroll Laufmann
VP: Kenneth P Pavlich
**VP:* Bruce Routhieaux
VP: John L Selis
**VP:* Paul Tunnicliffe
**VP:* Kevin White
Exec: RT Green

D-U-N-S 00-910-5958
NORTON PACKAGING INC
NORPAK
20670 Corsair Blvd, Hayward, CA 94545-1008
Tel (510) 786-1922 *Founded/Ownrshp* 1972
Sales 44.4MM^E *EMP* 188
SIC 3089 Food casings, plastic; Food casings, plastic
Co-Pr: Scott Norton
**CFO:* Greg Norton
Ofcr: Kirstin Tolomeo
VP: Nina Alvarez
**VP:* Mark Norton
Exec: Rohini Desai
IT Man: Colin Beck
Plnt Mgr: Bill Door
Plnt Mgr: Jim Koch
Sls Dir: Justin Carlino
Sls Mgr: Hans Bichsel

D-U-N-S 16-815-9460
NORTON PROPERTIES INC
(*Suby of* NORTON HEALTHCARE INC) ★
200 E Chestnut St Ste 200, Louisville, KY 40202-1847
Tel (502) 629-8000 *Founded/Ownrshp* 2004
Sales 29.0MM *EMP* 9
Accts Crowe Horawth Llp Louisville
SIC 8742 Real estate consultant
Prin: Tara Castello

D-U-N-S 17-931-0867
NORTON PUBLIC SCHOOLS
64 W Main St, Norton, MA 02766-2713
Tel (508) 285-0101 *Founded/Ownrshp* 1999
Sales 23.9MM^E *EMP* 450
SIC 8211 Public elementary & secondary schools; Public elementary & secondary schools

D-U-N-S 07-220-3987
NORTON ROSE FULBRIGHT US LLP
1301 Mckinney St Ste 5100, Houston, TX 77010-3095
Tel (713) 651-5151 *Founded/Ownrshp* 1919
Sales 477.0MM^E *EMP* 1,900
SIC 8111

D-U-N-S 02-611-1013
NORTON SCHOOL DISTRICT (OH)
4128 Clvland Massillon Rd, Norton, OH 44203-5633
Tel (330) 825-0863 *Founded/Ownrshp* 1886
Sales 13.3MM^E *EMP* 280
SIC 8211 Public elementary & secondary schools; Public elementary & secondary schools
Sftwr Eng: Julie Snyder

D-U-N-S 96-397-6535
NORTON SOUND ECONOMIC DEVELOPMENT CORP
NSEDC
420 L St Ste 310, Anchorage, AK 99501-1971
Tel (907) 274-2248 *Founded/Ownrshp* 1995
Sales 26.9MM *EMP* 22
Accts Altman Rogers & Company Ancho
SIC 8399 2091 Social change association; Canned & cured fish & seafoods; Social change association; Canned & cured fish & seafoods
Pr: Ivanoff Janis
**Ch:* Dan Harrelson
Treas: Tasha Huffman
**Treas:* Walicki Rick
**VP:* Janis Ivanoff
**VP:* William Johnson
**VP:* Kinneen Simon
**Prin:* Dean Peterson
**Prin:* Don Stiles

D-U-N-S 01-018-9223
NORTON SOUND HEALTH CORP
NORTON SOUND REGIONAL HOSPITAL
790 Lower St, Turner, ME 04282-3925
Tel (907) 443-3311 *Founded/Ownrshp* 1970
Sales 106.0MM *EMP* 521
Accts Elgee Rehfeld Mertz Llc Junea
SIC 8062 8051 8069 8093 8011 General medical & surgical hospitals; Skilled nursing care facilities; Specialty hospitals, except psychiatric; Substance abuse hospitals; Specialty outpatient clinics; Offices & clinics of medical doctors; General medical & surgical hospitals; Skilled nursing care facilities; Specialty hospitals, except psychiatric; Substance abuse hospitals; Specialty outpatient clinics; Offices & clinics of medical doctors
CEO: Angie Gorn
**Pr:* Deven Pralakar
Dir Inf Cn: Barbara Collino
Dir Env Sv: Mike Tall

NORTON SOUND REGIONAL HOSPITAL
See NORTON SOUND HEALTH CORP

D-U-N-S 11-958-3164 IMP
■ **NORTRAX INC**
(*Suby of* DEERE & CO) ★
4042 Park Oaks Blvd # 200, Tampa, FL 33610-9538
Tel (813) 635-2300 *Founded/Ownrshp* 2003
Sales 246.3MM^E *EMP* 1,125
SIC 5082 General construction machinery & equipment; General construction machinery & equipment
CEO: Timothy J Murphy
**Treas:* Michael J Mack
VP: Mike Festing-Smith
VP: David Haughey
VP: Peter Marsh
VP: Eric Mason
**VP:* Ben Richmond
VP: Rick Rigsby
VP: Yvette Rubenzer
Genl Mgr: Gessell Dale
Genl Mgr: Rick Taylor

D-U-N-S 06-358-4643
■ **NORTRU LLC**
(*Suby of* PSC ENVIRONMENTAL SERVICES LLC) ★
515 Lycaste St, Detroit, MI 48214-3473
Tel (313) 824-5840 *Founded/Ownrshp* 2000
Sales 169.3MM^E *EMP* 500
SIC 4953 5169 Recycling, waste materials; Industrial chemicals; Recycling, waste materials; Industrial chemicals

D-U-N-S 80-669-0277
NORWALK AREA HEALTH SERVICES
(*Suby of* NORWALK AREA HEALTH SYSTEMS INC) ★
272 Benedict Ave, Norwalk, OH 44857-2374
Tel (419) 668-8101 *Founded/Ownrshp* 1985
Sales 7.5MM *EMP* 300
Accts Plante & Moran Pllc Columbus
SIC 4119 Ambulance service; Ambulance service
Pr: Patrick Martin
Dir Rx: Mitchel Esch

D-U-N-S 07-689-3635
NORWALK AREA HEALTH SYSTEMS INC
272 Benedict Ave, Norwalk, OH 44857-2374
Tel (419) 668-8101 *Founded/Ownrshp* 1985
Sales 1.5MM *EMP* 1,000
SIC 8062 8051 General medical & surgical hospitals; Skilled nursing care facilities; General medical & surgical hospitals; Skilled nursing care facilities
Pr: Patrick J Martin
VP: Duane Woods
Doctor: Mike Murray

D-U-N-S 05-519-8543
NORWALK CITY SCHOOL DISTRICT
134 Benedict Ave, Norwalk, OH 44857-2349
Tel (419) 668-1989 *Founded/Ownrshp* 1852
Sales 28.9MM *EMP* 275
Accts Rea & Associates Inc
SIC 8211 Public elementary & secondary schools
**Pr:* Michael Gordon
**Treas:* Kenneth France
Bd of Dir: Kevin Cashen
VP: Ralph Ritzenthaler
MIS Dir: Jeff Braumberger
Schl Brd P: John Lendrum

NORWALK CITYHALL
See CITY OF NORWALK

D-U-N-S 00-417-5329
NORWALK COMMUNITY SCHOOL DISTRICT
380 Wright Rd, Norwalk, IA 50211-1661
Tel (515) 981-0676 *Founded/Ownrshp* 1900
Sales 26.1MM *EMP* 310
SIC 8211 Public elementary school; Public junior high school; Public senior high school; Public elementary school; Public junior high school; Public senior high school

D-U-N-S 07-539-7190
NORWALK HOSPITAL ASSOCIATION
34 Maple St, Norwalk, CT 06850-3894
Tel (203) 852-2000 *Founded/Ownrshp* 2004
Sales 323.2MM *EMP* 1,660^E
SIC 8062 Hospital, medical school affiliated with nursing & residency; Hospital, medical school affiliated with nursing & residency
CEO: Daniel Debarba Jr
Sr Pt: David Lehn
**Ch Bd:* Diane M Allison
**Pr:* Jeffrey Cole
CFO: Edward Mahony
**Treas:* Andrew J Whittingham
VP: Daniel D Barba
VP: Damon Dechamplain
Dir Risk M: Jeanine Foran
Dir Lab: Leonard Scinto
Chf Nrs Of: Renee Mauriello

D-U-N-S 07-797-7072
NORWALK LA MIRADA UNIFIED SCHOOL DISTRICT
12820 Pioneer Blvd, Norwalk, CA 90650-2875
Tel (562) 868-0431 *Founded/Ownrshp* 1965
Sales 216.5MM *EMP* 4,200
SIC 8211

D-U-N-S 79-603-9949
NORWALK PUBLIC SCHOOL DISTRICT
125 East Ave, Norwalk, CT 06851-5702
Tel (203) 852-9874 *Founded/Ownrshp* 1970
Sales 82.8MM^E *EMP* 1,500
SIC 8211 9111 Public elementary & secondary schools; Mayors' offices; Public elementary & secondary schools; Mayors' offices
IT Man: Armand Madeo
IT Man: John Silbert
Pr Dir: Brenda Wilcox-William
Teacher Pr: Robert Dylewski
Teacher Pr: Bruce Morris
Snr Mgr: Brian Ruther

NORWALK TOYOTA
See APAULO INC

D-U-N-S 06-172-8283 IMP/EXP
NORWALK WASTEWATER EQUIPMENT CO (OH)
NORWECO
220 Republic St, Norwalk, OH 44857-1156
Tel (419) 668-4471 *Founded/Ownrshp* 1906, 1972
Sales 24.4MM^E *EMP* 50
SIC 3589 Water treatment equipment, industrial
Ch Bd: Jan Graves
**Pr:* Gregory Graves
Pr: James Meyer
**Sec:* Michele Graves
Ex VP: Donald Bach
VP: Jennifer Jenne
Opers Mgr: Greg Orloff
VP Sls: Michael Benton
Mktg Mgr: Shelly Wybensinger

D-U-N-S 80-691-0787
NORWAY BANCORP INC
(*Suby of* NORWAY BANCORP MHC) ★
261 Main St, Norway, ME 04268-5915
Tel (207) 743-7986 *Founded/Ownrshp* 2008
Sales NA *EMP* 267^E
SIC 6712 Bank holding companies; Bank holding companies
CFO: Brian Shibles
VP: Rebecca Plisch
VP: Deb Ricker
VP: Barry Shead

D-U-N-S 80-968-7572
NORWAY BANCORP MHC
261 Main St, Norway, ME 04268-5915
Tel (207) 743-7986 *Founded/Ownrshp* 2008
Sales NA *EMP* 267^E
SIC 6022 State commercial banks; State commercial banks
CFO: Brian Shibles
**CEO:* Robert Harmon
**COO:* David L Wyman

D-U-N-S 04-145-9199
NORWAY SAVINGS BANK
(*Suby of* NORWAY BANCORP INC) ★
261 Main St, Norway, ME 04268-5915
Tel (207) 743-7986 *Founded/Ownrshp* 1886
Sales NA *EMP* 267
SIC 6022 State commercial banks; State commercial banks
CEO: Patricia Weigel
Pr: Peter Godsoe
**CEO:* Patricia Wiegel
**CFO:* Brian Shibles
**Ex VP:* Steven Whitney
**VP:* Raymond Charest
VP Admn: Iva Carroll
Board of Directors: Eugene Benner, David Hoisington

D-U-N-S 00-379-3338
■ **NORWAY TELEPHONE CO INC** (SC)
TDS
(*Suby of* TDS TELECOMMUNICATIONS CORP) ★
8432 Savannah Hwy, Norway, SC 29113
Tel (608) 831-1000 *Founded/Ownrshp* 1944
Sales 853.0MM *EMP* 2,700
SIC 4813 Local telephone communications; Local telephone communications
Pr: David Wittwer

NORWECO
See NORWALK WASTEWATER EQUIPMENT CO

D-U-N-S 06-745-8018
NORWEGIAN AMERICAN HOSPITAL INC
1044 N Francisco Ave, Chicago, IL 60622-2743
Tel (773) 278-8800 *Founded/Ownrshp* 1894
Sales 105.9MM *EMP* 800
Accts Plante & Moran Pllc Elgin I
SIC 8062 General medical & surgical hospitals; General medical & surgical hospitals
CEO: Jose R Sanchez
Chf Rad: Peter Berger
VP: Tim Egan
VP: Robert Fortney
VP: Winnie Lewis
VP: Constance Shay-Hadle
Exec: Karima Bentounsi
Dir Risk M: Tricia McVicker
Dir Lab: Kathy Lowhorn
Dir Rad: Karen Brown
Dir Rx: Shawn M McGhee-Paratore

D-U-N-S 07-434-3997
NORWEGIAN CHRISTIAN HOME AND HEALTH CENTER INC
1250 67th St, Brooklyn, NY 11219-5921
Tel (718) 232-2322 *Founded/Ownrshp* 1903
Sales 20.8MM *EMP* 210
SIC 8051 8361 Skilled nursing care facilities; Home for the aged; Skilled nursing care facilities; Home for the aged
Ch Bd: George A Jensen
**CFO:* Wilfred Decosta
Exec: Wil Da Costa

NORWEGIAN CRUISE LINE
See NCL (BAHAMAS) LTD A BERMUDA CO

D-U-N-S 07-872-7129
▲ **NORWEGIAN CRUISE LINE HOLDINGS LTD**
7665 Corp Ctr Dr, Miami, FL 33126
Tel (305) 436-4000 *Founded/Ownrshp* 1966
Sales 3.1MMM *EMP* 24,900^E
Tkr Sym NCLH *Exch* NGS
SIC 4481 Deep sea passenger transportation, except ferry; Deep sea passenger transportation, except ferry
Pr: Frank J Del Rio
**Ch Bd:* Walter L Revell
Pr: Bob Binder
CFO: Wendy A Beck
Ofcr: Sergey Kuzmin
Ex VP: Victor Gonzalez
Ex VP: Robin Lindsay
Ex VP: Howard Sherman
Sr VP: Daniel S Farkas
Sr VP: Harry Sommer
VP: Maria M Miller
Board of Directors: F Robert Salerno, David M Abrams, Robert Seminara, Adam Aron, John W Chidsey, Kevin Crowe, Russell W Galbut, Kevin C Jones, Chad A Leat, Steve Martinez, Karl Peterson

NORWEGIAN CRUISE LINES
See NCL CORP LTD

D-U-N-S 16-782-6239
NORWELL VISITING NURSE ASSOCIATION INC
120 Longwater Dr Ste 200, Norwell, MA 02061-1653
Tel (781) 610-1490 *Founded/Ownrshp* 1920
Sales 23.4MM *EMP* 80
Accts Brad Borbidge Pa Concord Mi
SIC 8082 Home health care services; Home health care services
Pr: Meg Clapp
COO: Judith Labossiere
**Treas:* B Jean Snow
**VP:* Robert Norris
**Ex Dir:* Mary Doherty
IT Man: Bob Crea

NORWESCAP
See NORTHWEST NEW JERSEY COMMUNITY ACTION PROGRAM INC

D-U-N-S 00-614-9199 IMP/EXP
NORWESCO INC (MN)
4365 Steiner St, Saint Bonifacius, MN 55375-1100
Tel (952) 446-1945 *Founded/Ownrshp* 1939, 2011
Sales 58.6MM^E *EMP* 169
SIC 3089 Septic tanks, plastic; Plastic & fiberglass tanks; Septic tanks, plastic; Plastic & fiberglass tanks
CEO: Thomas J Smith
**Pr:* Gary Henry
**CFO:* Paul F Klaus
VP: Richard Aronson
Sfty Dirs: Matt Hill
Plnt Mgr: Darin Dittman
Plnt Mgr: Thomas Orr
Board of Directors: Phillip T George MD, William Kaczynski, Edward T Michalek, Earl W Powell

D-U-N-S 08-510-1483
■ **NORWEST BANK MINNESOTA NORTH (INC)**
WELLS FARGO
(*Suby of* WELLS FARGO & CO) ★
6 Street & Marquette Ave, Minneapolis, MN 55479-0001
Tel (612) 667-1234 *Founded/Ownrshp* 1929
Sales NA *EMP* 187
SIC 6021 National commercial banks; National commercial banks
Ch Bd: Richard M Kovacevich
**Sr VP:* Donald A Carlson
VP: Sherri Bernstein
VP: Christopher Terzich

D-U-N-S 00-792-0481
■ **NORWEST BANK SOUTH DAKOTA NATIONAL ASSOCIATION** (SD)
WELLS FARGO
(*Suby of* WELLS FARGO & CO) ★
101 N Phillips Ave Ste A, Sioux Falls, SD 57104-6714
Tel (605) 575-4900 *Founded/Ownrshp* 1921
Sales NA *EMP* 1,322
SIC 6021 National trust companies with deposits, commercial; National trust companies with deposits, commercial
Pr: Terry Baloun

NORWEST EQUITY PARTNERS
See NORWEST VENTURE CAPITAL MANAGEMENT INC

NORWEST FINANCIAL
See WELLS FARGO FINANCIAL FLORIDA INC

D-U-N-S 14-851-4995
■ **NORWEST VENTURE CAPITAL MANAGEMENT INC**
NORWEST EQUITY PARTNERS
(*Suby of* WELLS FARGO & CO) ★
80 S 8th St Ste 3600, Minneapolis, MN 55402-2213
Tel (612) 215-1600 *Founded/Ownrshp* 1959
Sales NA *EMP* 1,220
SIC 6799 Venture capital companies; Venture capital companies
Pr: Tim Devries
Treas: John Chatley III
Treas: Darren Herz
Treas: John Whaley
VP: Jerry Lester
VP: John Lindahl

D-U-N-S 15-049-1330
NORWICH CITY SCHOOL DISTRICT
89 Midland Dr, Norwich, NY 13815-1948
Tel (607) 334-1600 *Founded/Ownrshp* 1954
Sales 20.0MM^E^ *EMP* 410
SIC 8211 Public elementary & secondary schools; Elementary school; Secondary school; High school, junior or senior; Public elementary & secondary schools; Elementary school; Secondary school; High school, junior or senior
Treas: Wendy Wright
Dir IT: Deb Miner
IT Man: Robert Wightman
Schl Brd P: Joe Stagliano
Psych: Ruthann Lawton

D-U-N-S 07-731-7717
NORWICH FREE ACADEMY
305 Broadway, Norwich, CT 06360-3563
Tel (860) 887-2505 *Founded/Ownrshp* 1854
Sales 34.3MM *EMP* 305
Accts Blum Shapiro & Company Pc
SIC 8211 Academy; Academy
Prin: Kristen Peckrul
Dir IT: Anthony Girasoli
Surgeon: Michael Halprin

D-U-N-S 07-009-5091
NORWICH INN & SPA LLC
SPA AT NORWICH INN THE
(*Suby of* FOXWOODS RESORT CASINO) ★
607 W Thames St, Norwich, CT 06360-7140
Tel (860) 425-3500 *Founded/Ownrshp* 1998
Sales 1.5MM *EMP* 300
SIC 7011 7231 5813 5812 Hotel, franchised; Beauty shops; Drinking places; Eating places; Hotel, franchised; Beauty shops; Drinking places; Eating places
Genl Mgr: John O'Shaughnessy
Off Mgr: Tim Kenyon
IT Man: Mary Oneil

NORWICH MANUFACTURING DIVISION
See FELCHAR MANUFACTURING CORP

NORWICH PHARMA SERVICES
See NORWICH PHARMACEUTICALS INC

D-U-N-S 13-221-8731 IMP
NORWICH PHARMACEUTICALS INC
NORWICH PHARMA SERVICES
(*Suby of* ALVOGEN GROUP INC) ★
6826 State Highway 12, Norwich, NY 13815-3335
Tel (607) 335-3000 *Founded/Ownrshp* 2007
Sales 50.0MM^E^ *EMP* 375
SIC 2834 Pharmaceutical preparations; Pharmaceutical preparations
Pr: Chris Calhoun
**Pr:* Darren Alkins
Pr: Kristin Arnold
**CFO:* Kevin Bain
Ofcr: Chris Coombs
**Ex VP:* Lisa Graver
VP: Carolyn Gerardi
VP: David Knust
VP: Dirk Stevens
QA Dir: William H Edwards
QA Dir: William Hedwards

D-U-N-S 06-923-7600
NORWICH ROMAN CATHOLIC DIOCESAN CORP (CT)
DIOCESE OF NORWICH
201 Broadway, Norwich, CT 06360-4458
Tel (860) 887-9294 *Founded/Ownrshp* 1953
Sales 18.2MM^E^ *EMP* 800
SIC 8661 Catholic Church; Catholic Church
Pr: Michael R Cote
**CFO:* William J Russell
**VP:* Thomas Bride

D-U-N-S 06-991-2962
NORWICH UNIVERSITY
VERMONT COLLEGE
158 Harmon Dr, Northfield, VT 05663-1035
Tel (802) 485-2000 *Founded/Ownrshp* 1819
Sales 98.3MM *EMP* 510
Accts Cliftonlarsonallen Llp Boston
SIC 8221 College, except junior; College, except junior
Pr: Richard W Schneider
CFO: Ann Luis
**CFO:* Richard E Rebmann
Sr VP: Guiyou Huang
**Sr VP:* David Whaley
VP: David Ely
VP: Diane Scolaro
VP: Frank T Vanecek
Assoc Dir: Meghan Oliver
Assoc Dir: Nu Ski
Dir Sec: Parker Carroll

D-U-N-S 01-424-2994
NORWIN CONSTRUCTION CO
285 Kappa Dr Ste 300, Pittsburgh, PA 15238-2814
Tel (724) 863-7756 *Founded/Ownrshp* 1951
Sales 50.0MM *EMP* 20
SIC 1611 General contractor, highway & street construction
Pr: Peter Broeren
**VP:* John Roos

D-U-N-S 06-872-4020
NORWIN SCHOOL DISTRICT
281 Mcmahon Dr, Irwin, PA 15642-2403
Tel (724) 861-3000 *Founded/Ownrshp* 1958
Sales 56.3MM *EMP* 500
Accts Sarp & Company Greensburg Pe
SIC 8211 Public elementary & secondary schools; Public elementary & secondary schools
VP: Donald Rhodes
Ex Dir: Jonathan Szish
Schl Brd P: Robert Perkins
Doctor: Renee Kozusko
HC Dir: Donna Lafferty

D-U-N-S 07-678-8546
NORWOOD CITY SCHOOL DISTRICT
2132 Williams Ave Ste 2, Cincinnati, OH 45212-3806
Tel (513) 924-2500 *Founded/Ownrshp* 1868
Sales 20.4MM^E^ *EMP* 311
Accts Plattenburg & Associates Inc
SIC 8211 Public combined elementary & secondary school; Public combined elementary & secondary school
VP: Tammy Blair
Dir IT: Randall Grandstaff
Psych: Amy Collopy

D-U-N-S 07-949-8804
NORWOOD CO
375 Technology Dr, Malvern, PA 19355-1306
Tel (610) 240-4400 *Founded/Ownrshp* 1975
Sales 121.2MM *EMP* 80
Accts Fegley & Associates Pc Ply
SIC 1541 1542 8741 Industrial buildings, new construction; Renovation, remodeling & repairs: industrial buildings; Pharmaceutical manufacturing plant construction; Warehouse construction; Commercial & office building, new construction; Commercial & office buildings, renovation & repair; Hospital construction; Construction management
Pr: John E Farrell
CFO: William J Burke
CFO: Dennis Sutton
Sr VP: Joseph Mitchell Jr
VP: James Goshow
VP: Timothy Kelly
VP: Robert Risnychok
VP: Eric Urbanski
Snr PM: Gregory Kratz
Snr PM: Dwight Lewis
Snr PM: John Thorsen

D-U-N-S 06-847-3495
NORWOOD CROSSING ASSOCIATION
NORWOOD LIFECARE FOUNDATION
6016 N Nina Ave, Chicago, IL 60631-2439
Tel (773) 631-4856 *Founded/Ownrshp* 1896
Sales 20.8MM *EMP* 220
SIC 8361 8051 Geriatric residential care; Skilled nursing care facilities; Geriatric residential care; Skilled nursing care facilities
CEO: Mike Toohey
CFO: Sandra Cedrins
HC Dir: Jacinta McGee

D-U-N-S 03-197-1695
▲ **NORWOOD FINANCIAL CORP**
717 Main St, Honesdale, PA 18431-1844
Tel (570) 253-1455 *Founded/Ownrshp* 1996
Sales NA *EMP* 146^E^
Accts Sr Snodgross Pc Wexford
Tkr Sym NWFL *Exch* NGM
SIC 6022 State commercial banks; State commercial banks
Pr: Lewis J Critelli
**Ch Bd:* John E Marshall
CFO: William S Lance
Chf Cred: John F Carmody
Ex VP: James F Burke
Ex VP: Ken Doolittle
Sr VP: John H Sanders
VP: John Koczwara

D-U-N-S 01-766-4897 IMP
NORWOOD HARDWARE & SUPPLY CO INC
2906 Glendale Milford Rd, Cincinnati, OH 45241-3131
Tel (513) 733-1175 *Founded/Ownrshp* 1976
Sales 22.4MM^E^ *EMP* 65
SIC 5072 5031 5023 Hardware; Metal doors, sash & trim; Doors; Home furnishings
CEO: Matt Chabot
**Treas:* Paul Sylvester
**VP:* Matthew Chabot
IT Man: Robert Roth
Sales Asso: Randy Beasley

D-U-N-S 18-410-7977
NORWOOD HOMES INC
PARTNERS IN BUILDING
17361 Village Green Dr, Jersey Village, TX 77040-1150
Tel (713) 937-1121 *Founded/Ownrshp* 1986
Sales 23.4MM^E^ *EMP* 60
SIC 1521 1531 New construction, single-family houses; Speculative builder, single-family houses
CEO: John Bily
**Pr:* Greg Hawes
**Ch:* James Lemming
**Treas:* Jill Thiem
**VP:* Jerry Bily
**VP:* David Bower
**VP:* Wesley Bryant
**VP:* Thomas C Frank
VP: Cregg McGaha
Area Mgr: Brian Lee
Area Mgr: Shannon Nelson

NORWOOD HOSP A CRTAS FMLY HOSP
See STEWARD NORWOOD HOSPITAL INC

NORWOOD LIFECARE FOUNDATION
See NORWOOD CROSSING ASSOCIATION

D-U-N-S 00-427-8651
NORWOOD MEDICAL
2122 Winners Cir, Dayton, OH 45404-1148
Tel (937) 228-2565 *Founded/Ownrshp* 1981
Sales 50.6MM^E^ *EMP* 200
SIC 3469 3599 Metal stampings; Machine shop, jobbing & repair; Metal stampings; Machine shop, jobbing & repair
Pr: Kenneth Hemmelgarn Sr
**VP:* Brian Hemmelgarn
Ql Cn Mgr: Bill Grimm
Ql Cn Mgr: Tom Rhoden

D-U-N-S 00-385-6366
NORWOOD MOTOR PARTS CO INC
ALLIED AUTO PARTS
43 N Montello St, Brockton, MA 02301-3914
Tel (508) 588-5840 *Founded/Ownrshp* 1955
Sales 65.9MM^E^ *EMP* 150
SIC 5013 Automotive supplies & parts; Automotive supplies & parts
Pr: Daniel Sennet
Sales Exec: John Tully

NORWOOD PROMOTIONAL PRODUCTS
See BIC GRAPHIC USA MANUFACTURING CO INC

D-U-N-S 12-529-0981
NORWOOD PUBLIC SCHOOLS
275 Prospect St, Norwood, MA 02062-1467
Tel (781) 762-6804 *Founded/Ownrshp* 1900
Sales 17.2MM^E^ *EMP* 286
SIC 8211 Public elementary & secondary schools; Public elementary & secondary schools
Schl Brd P: John Badger

D-U-N-S 02-299-7863
NORWOOD SALES INC
11202 38th St S, Horace, ND 58047-9770
Tel (701) 588-4000 *Founded/Ownrshp* 1996
Sales 53.2MM^E^ *EMP* 43^E^
SIC 5083 3523 Agricultural machinery & equipment; Farm machinery & equipment
Pr: Dan Norwood

D-U-N-S 62-308-6725
NOS COMMUNICATIONS INC
INTERNATIONAL PLUS
250 Pilot Rd Ste 300, Las Vegas, NV 89119-3514
Tel (702) 547-8000 *Founded/Ownrshp* 1989
Sales 3.6MM *EMP* 1,150
Accts Buchbinder Tunick & Company Ll
SIC 8748 4813 Communications consulting; Long distance telephone communications; Communications consulting; Long distance telephone communications
CEO: Joseph Koppy
CFO: Andrea Zingo
Genl Couns: Raymond Perea
Board of Directors: Raymond Perea

D-U-N-S 00-516-2680 IMP
NOSCO INC
(*Suby of* HOLDEN INDUSTRIES INC) ★
651 S Ml King Jr Ave, Waukegan, IL 60085-7500
Tel (847) 336-4200 *Founded/Ownrshp* 1980
Sales 114.9MM^E^ *EMP* 509
SIC 2752 2657 Commercial printing, lithographic; Folding paperboard boxes; Commercial printing, lithographic; Folding paperboard boxes
Pr: Russell S Haraf
**CFO:* Michael J Biesboer
**Ex VP:* Edward W Hudson
**VP:* Joseph S Haas
Exec: Brooks Townsend
MIS Dir: Kevin Maule
Prd Mgr: Rick Potochnik
Ql Cn Mgr: Kurt Smith
VP Mktg: Joe Tenhagen
**VP Mktg:* Joseph Tenhagen
Mktg Mgr: Heather Hill

D-U-N-S 06-810-2909 IMP
NOSCOM INDUSTRIES INC
2498 Roll Dr Ste 819, San Diego, CA 92154-7279
Tel (619) 498-9000 *Founded/Ownrshp* 1999
Sales 27.9MM *EMP* 5
SIC 3663 Television closed circuit equipment; Television closed circuit equipment
CEO: Sung Ho Ahn

D-U-N-S 00-902-8176 IMP
NOSLER INC
107 Sw Columbia St, Bend, OR 97702-1014
Tel (541) 382-3921 *Founded/Ownrshp* 1950
Sales 28.4MM^E^ *EMP* 100
SIC 3482 Cores, bullet: 30 mm. & below; Cores, bullet: 30 mm. & below
Pr: Robert A Nosler
**CFO:* Mark S Roberts
**Ch:* John A Nosler
VP: Paul Coil
**VP:* Joan Nosler
**VP:* John R Nosler
Sfty Mgr: Mike Harris
VP Sls: Charles Pritchard
Mktg Dir: John Nosle
Pr Dir: Zach Waterman
Sales Asso: Jennifer Babcock

NOSOX
See DEER STAGS CONCEPTS INC

D-U-N-S 02-015-1114
NOSSAMAN LLP
777 S Figueroa St # 3400, Los Angeles, CA 90017-5834
Tel (213) 612-7800 *Founded/Ownrshp* 1944, 1952
Sales 50.6MM^E^ *EMP* 300
SIC 8111 General practice attorney, lawyer; General practice attorney, lawyer
Mng Pt: E George Joseph
Mng Pt: Keysha Alexander
Pr: Marcia Bertolli
Pr: Beth Cassioli
Pr: Marion Tom
COO: Marcia W Wasserman
CFO: Teri Ceterson
CFO: Tim Flake
Dir Risk M: Donald Feltham
Off Admin: Laurie Armstrong
CIO: Pat Mansuy

D-U-N-S 79-114-2354 IMP
NOSTRUM LABORATORIES INC
1800 N Topping Ave, Kansas City, MO 64120-1228
Tel (816) 308-4900 *Founded/Ownrshp* 2006
Sales 36.4MM^E^ *EMP* 120
Accts Ram Associates Hamilton Nj
SIC 2834 Pharmaceutical preparations; Pharmaceutical preparations
CEO: Nirmal Mulye
**COO:* Manesh Dixit
**COO:* Eric M Mittleberg
QA Dir: Tish Webb

D-U-N-S 96-269-8085
NOT FOR PROFIT HOSPITAL CORP
UNITED MEDICAL CENTER
1310 Southern Ave Se, Washington, DC 20032-4623
Tel (202) 574-6024 *Founded/Ownrshp* 2008
Sales 100.3MM *EMP* 3
SIC 6732 Trusts: educational, religious, etc.
Ch: Charles Hudson Jr

D-U-N-S 87-931-6255
NOT YOUR AVERAGE JOES INC
2 Granite Ave Ste 300, Milton, MA 02186-4377
Tel (774) 213-2800 *Founded/Ownrshp* 1999
Sales 47.7MM^E^ *EMP* 1,000
SIC 5812 Eating places; Eating places
Pr: Steven Silverstein
**CFO:* Joe McGuire
Exec: Jeff Tenner
Rgnl Mgr: Tony White
Genl Mgr: Tracy Mason

NOT YOUR DAUGHTERS JEANS
See NYDJ APPAREL LLC

D-U-N-S 96-189-5948
NOT-FOR-PROFIT HOSPITAL CORP
UNITED MEDICAL CENTER
1310 Southern Ave Se, Washington, DC 20032-4623
Tel (202) 574-6000 *Founded/Ownrshp* 2007
Sales 85.8MM *EMP* 900
SIC 8062 General medical & surgical hospitals; General medical & surgical hospitals
CEO: Frank Delisi
COO: Pamela Lee
**CFO:* Derrick Hollings
CFO: Anne Ibekwe
CFO: Robert Schneider
CFO: Ron Walker
VP: Serah Davis
Dir Teleco: Bee McCarthy
Dir Rx: Bill Robinson
Mng Ofcr: Russom Ghebrai
Chf Nrs Of: Jean Thaire

D-U-N-S 94-423-0317
■ **NOTABLE SOLUTIONS INC**
N S I
(*Suby of* NUANCE COMMUNICATIONS INC) ★
530 Gaither Rd Ste 400, Rockville, MD 20850-1381
Tel (240) 683-8400 *Founded/Ownrshp* 2014
Sales 37.5MM^E^ *EMP* 215
SIC 7379 7371 Computer related consulting services; Computer software development; Computer related consulting services; Computer software development
CEO: Mehdi Tehranchi
Pr: Ali Tehranchi
Sr VP: Phil Salopek
Sr VP: Rachid Sijelmassi
VP: Jud Cairns
Off Mgr: Dee Brown
Off Admin: Carolyn Tracy
CTO: Henric Harutunian
QA Dir: Marcela Ciupe
Dir IT: John Sung
Opers Supe: Sun Hashmi

NOTABLES
See MINMOR INDUSTRIES LLC

D-U-N-S 95-992-4721
■ **NOTAMI HOSPITALS OF FLORIDA INC**
LAKE CITY MEDICAL CENTER
(*Suby of* HCA INC) ★
340 Nw Commerce Dr, Lake City, FL 32055-4709
Tel (386) 719-9000 *Founded/Ownrshp* 1998
Sales 47.0MM^E^ *EMP* 327
SIC 8011 8062 Offices & clinics of medical doctors; General medical & surgical hospitals; Offices & clinics of medical doctors; General medical & surgical hospitals
Ch: Daniel Crapps
**Pr:* Samuel N Hazen

*CEO: Mark Robinson
*CFO: Jill Adams
*Treas: David G Anderson
Treas: David Colby
*VP: Ronald N Grubbs Jr
Dir Risk M: Paulette McKernan
MIS Dir: Mike Pipkins
IT Man: Debbie Mc Mc Donald
IT Man: Debbie McDonald

D-U-N-S 92-664-7629
■ NOTAMI HOSPITALS OF LOUISIANA INC
LAKEVIEW MEDICAL CENTER
(Suby of H C A HEALTHCARE) ★
1 Park Plz, Nashville, TN 37203-6527
Tel (615) 344-2000 Founded/Ownrshp 1988
Sales 34.2MM^E EMP 653
SIC 8062 General medical & surgical hospitals; General medical & surgical hospitals
Pr: Richard Bracken
Mktg Dir: Kim Melvin

D-U-N-S 17-752-5524
■ NOTAMI LLC
H C A HEALTHCARE
(Suby of HCA INC) ★
1 Park Plz, Nashville, TN 37203-6527
Tel (615) 344-2000 Founded/Ownrshp 1994
Sales 38.2MM^E EMP 963
SIC 8062 General medical & surgical hospitals; General medical & surgical hospitals

NOTATIONS CLOTHING CO
See NOTATIONS INC

D-U-N-S 05-312-6207 IMP
NOTATIONS INC
NOTATIONS CLOTHING CO
539 Jacksonville Rd, Warminster, PA 18974-4826
Tel (215) 259-2000 Founded/Ownrshp 1980
Sales 38.4MM^E EMP 150
SIC 2331 2339 Blouses, women's & juniors': made from purchased material; T-shirts & tops, women's: made from purchased material; Women's & misses' outerwear; Blouses, women's & juniors': made from purchased material; T-shirts & tops, women's: made from purchased materials; Women's & misses' outerwear
Pr: Kurt Erman
CFO: Al Harrison
Ex VP: Scott Erman
VP: Ric Lazarus
*VP: Fred Trachtenberg
IT Man: Lisa Kye
IT Man: Fredric Lazarus

D-U-N-S 04-801-9368
NOTEBOOM IMPLEMENT LLC
JOHN DEERE
525 S Highway 281, Corsica, SD 57328-2212
Tel (605) 337-2663 Founded/Ownrshp 2013
Sales 51.0MM^E EMP 85
SIC 5083 7699 Farm implements; Farm machinery repair; Farm implements; Farm machinery repair
Pr: Daniel Noteboom
*VP: Michael Noteboom

NOTHINGBUTSOFTWARE
See SPACEBOUND INC

D-U-N-S 19-796-1113
NOTIFYMD INC
28161 N Keats Dr, Lake Forest, IL 60045
Tel (615) 778-6700 Founded/Ownrshp 1996
Sales 45.0MM^E EMP 350
SIC 4813 Telephone communication, except radio; Telephone communication, except radio
CEO: Jonathan McDevitt
Pr: David Bednowitz

D-U-N-S 94-807-2434
NOTIFYMD INC
1521 Concord Pike Ste 202, Wilmington, DE 19803-3645
Tel (302) 227-9015 Founded/Ownrshp 1995
Sales 29.7MM^E EMP 260
SIC 7389 Telephone answering service; Telephone answering service
CEO: Charles Alutto
Treas: Ralph J Cetrulo III
VP: Chuck Boyce
VP: Paul Stanton
Genl Mgr: Donna Rausch
CTO: Betsy Engle
Opers Mgr: Mara Johnson
Sales Exec: Dave Supinski
Sls Dir: Stephanie Cell
Sls Mgr: Osvaldo Sosa

D-U-N-S 10-674-6597 IMP/EXP
NOTIONS MARKETING CORP
1500 Buchanan Ave Sw, Grand Rapids, MI 49507-1613
Tel (616) 243-8424 Founded/Ownrshp 1970
Sales 221.8MM^E EMP 250
SIC 5131 5199 5092 Piece goods & notions; Fabrics, yarns & knit goods; Artists' materials; Toys & hobby goods & supplies; Piece goods & notions; Fabrics, yarns & knit goods; Artists' materials; Toys & hobby goods & supplies
Ch Bd: Herbert D Lantinga
*Pr: Jay Klein
CFO: John Dyke
*Treas: John Van Dyke
*VP: Sharon Lantinga
Exec: Terry Hare
Exec: Mark Rendel
QA Dir: Twyla Shaffer
Software D: Stephen Soltys
VP Opers: Tom Nakfoor
Sls Dir: Tammy Bombardier

D-U-N-S 08-343-9539
NOTOCO INDUSTRIES LLC
10380 Airline Hwy, Baton Rouge, LA 70816-4090
Tel (225) 292-1303 Founded/Ownrshp 1977
Sales 29.4MM^E EMP 98
Accts Latuso And Johnson Cpa Baton

SIC 5063 5072 Electrical supplies; Lighting fixtures; Hardware; Electrical supplies; Lighting fixtures; Hardware
CFO: Norman J Borne Jr

D-U-N-S 03-728-2407
NOTRE DAME COLLEGE OF OHIO
4545 College Rd, Cleveland, OH 44121-4228
Tel (216) 381-1680 Founded/Ownrshp 1923
Sales 50.0MM EMP 211^E
SIC 8221 College, except junior; College, except junior
Pr: Thomas G Kruczek
*Pr: Anne L Deming
*VP: Richard Rummel
VP: Nicholas Santilli
Exec: Lou Capasso
Assoc Dir: Anne M Geckle
Dir: Maureen Ischay
CIO: Deborah Sheren
DP Exec: Scott Damel
IT Man: Scott Kiec
Snr Mgr: Brian Johnson

D-U-N-S 02-001-3207 IMP
NOTRE DAME DE NAMUR UNIVERSITY (CA)
1500 Ralston Ave, Belmont, CA 94002-1908
Tel (650) 508-3500 Founded/Ownrshp 1868
Sales 48.9MM EMP 330
Accts Hood & Strong Llp Cpas San Fr
SIC 8221 University; University
CEO: Judith M Greig
VP: Hernan Bucheli
VP: Dino Hernandez
*VP: Henry Roth
Exec: Karen Schornstein
Comm Dir: Richard Rossi
Ex Dir: Maurene Freschet
Ex Dir: Jan Lawrence
Off Mgr: Stacey Haynes
CTO: Elizabeth Valente
Opers Mgr: James Kelley

NOTRE DAME EDUCATIONAL CENTER
See SISTERS OF NOTRE DAME OF CHARDON OHIO

D-U-N-S 80-761-3625
NOTRE DAME HEALTH CARE CENTER INC
NOTRE DAME LONG TERM CARE CENT
555 Plantation St 559, Worcester, MA 01605-2376
Tel (508) 852-3011 Founded/Ownrshp 1993
Sales 21.5MM EMP 260
Accts Cliftonlarsonallen Llp Bosto
SIC 8051 Skilled nursing care facilities; Skilled nursing care facilities
CEO: Katherine Lemay
*Pr: Sister Anne Stevenson
Ex Dir: Cathy Sessions
Prgrm Mgr: Sue Strandberg
Dir IT: Ryan Shea

NOTRE DAME LONG TERM CARE CENT
See NOTRE DAME HEALTH CARE CENTER INC

D-U-N-S 06-940-4036
NOTRE DAME OF MARYLAND UNIVERSITY INC (MD)
BARNES AND NOBLE
4701 N Charles St, Baltimore, MD 21210-2404
Tel (410) 435-0100 Founded/Ownrshp 1873
Sales 54.1MM EMP 440
Accts Kpmg Llp Baltimore Md
SIC 8221 College, except junior; College, except junior
Pr: James Conneely
*CFO: Deanna McCormick
*VP: Patrica A Bosse
VP: Patricia Bosse
VP: Christine De Vinne
VP: Heidi Roller
VP: Sally White
Assoc Dir: Diane McCann

D-U-N-S 14-039-2775
NOTS LOGISTICS LLC
17848 Mockingbird Rd, Nashville, IL 62263-3419
Tel (618) 478-5354 Founded/Ownrshp 1990
Sales 38.8MM^E EMP 164
SIC 4731 Freight transportation arrangement; Freight transportation arrangement
Pr: Kevin Brink
Genl Mgr: Chris Jankowski
Trfc Dir: Denise Curtis

D-U-N-S 00-890-4427 IMP
NOTT CO
4480 Round Lake Rd W, Arden Hills, MN 55112-1961
Tel (651) 415-3400 Founded/Ownrshp 1879
Sales 200.3MM^E EMP 200
SIC 5084 5085 3492 3053 Materials handling machinery; Industrial supplies; Fluid power valves & hose fittings; Gaskets, packing & sealing devices; Materials handling machinery; Industrial supplies; Fluid power valves & hose fittings; Gaskets, packing & sealing devices
CEO: Ed Davis
*CFO: Darrell Babcock
CFO: Doug Nevitt
Chf Mktg O: Christy Nelson
Genl Mgr: Ross Taflin
Mfg Mgr: Patrick Campbell
Sls&Mrk Ex: Mark Sheedy
Sls Mgr: Mike Jacobsen
Sls Mgr: Marcy Krosch
Sales Asso: Chad Christianson
Sales Asso: Duevel Gina
Board of Directors: Duane J Solem

D-U-N-S 07-979-8928
NOTTOWAY COUNTY PUBLIC SCHOOLS
10321 E Clnl Trail Hwy, Nottoway, VA 23955
Tel (434) 645-9596 Founded/Ownrshp 2015
Sales 11.5MM^E EMP 342^E
SIC 8211 Public elementary & secondary schools
MIS Dir: Tommy Coleman
Instr Medi: Annah Bowen

D-U-N-S 01-363-6949
NOTTOWAY COUNTY SCHOOL BOARD OFFICE
10321 E Clnl Trail Hwy, Nottoway, VA 23955
Tel (434) 645-9596 Founded/Ownrshp 1788
Sales 19.7MM EMP 360
SIC 8211 Public elementary & secondary schools; Public senior high school; Public elementary & secondary schools; Public senior high school
V Ch: Wallace Hurt

NOURIA ENERGY
See GAETA CONSOLIDATED LTD

D-U-N-S 62-539-1347
NOURIA ENERGY RETAIL INC
SHELL
326 Clark St, Worcester, MA 01606-1214
Tel (508) 798-0003 Founded/Ownrshp 1991
Sales 49.0MM^E EMP 150
SIC 5541 Filling stations, gasoline; Filling stations, gasoline
Pr: Tony El-Nemr
*COO: John Koch
*CFO: Richard Fusco

D-U-N-S 03-726-9487 IMP
NOURISON INDUSTRIES INC
5 Sampson St, Saddle Brook, NJ 07663-5911
Tel (201) 368-6900 Founded/Ownrshp 1979
Sales 58.5MM^E EMP 260
SIC 2512 Rugs; Couches, sofas & davenports: upholstered on wood frames
Ch Bd: Alex Peykar
CFO: John Stern
VP: Firouz Firooznia
VP: Kevin Kennedy
*VP: Steven Peykar
*Prin: Paul Peykar
Natl Sales: Patrick Mushchamp

D-U-N-S 80-830-6674
NOURSE CHEVROLET-CADILLAC INC
NOURSE CHVRLET CADILLAC TOYOTA
(Suby of Q N P CORP) ★
1101 Columbus Pike, Delaware, OH 43015-2794
Tel (740) 368-7666 Founded/Ownrshp 1992
Sales 40.0MM EMP 55
SIC 5511 Automobiles, new & used; Automobiles, new & used
Pr: Carl Nourse
*VP: Richard Nourse

NOURSE CHVRLET CADILLAC TOYOTA
See NOURSE CHEVROLET-CADILLAC INC

D-U-N-S 08-943-2330
NOURSE FMLY OF DLRSHP-CHILLI
NISSAN-HONDA-CADILLAC
(Suby of Q N P CORP) ★
423 N Bridge St, Chillicothe, OH 45601-2601
Tel (740) 773-7913 Founded/Ownrshp 1990
Sales 43.9MM^E EMP 100
SIC 5511 5561 Automobiles, new & used; Vans, new & used; Campers (pickup coaches) for mounting on trucks; Automobiles, new & used; Vans, new & used; Campers (pickup coaches) for mounting on trucks
CEO: Carl Nourse
*VP: Richard Nourse
Genl Mgr: Mark Harrington

D-U-N-S 93-337-8267
NOUVEAU CONSTRUCTION AND TECHNOLOGY SERVICES LP
2441 Lacy Ln, Carrollton, TX 75006-6514
Tel (972) 484-5077 Founded/Ownrshp 1996
Sales 28.7MM EMP 60
Accts Baird W Walker Pc Fort Worth
SIC 1731 Cable television installation; Cable television installation
Pt: Miles Koon
*Pt: David Pinkerd
*Pr: Debra Koon
CFO: Chris Holmberg

D-U-N-S 18-324-1538
NOUVEAU ELEVATOR INDUSTRIES INC
4755 37th St, Long Island City, NY 11101-1803
Tel (718) 349-4700 Founded/Ownrshp 1987
Sales 100.0MM EMP 390
SIC 7699 1796 Elevators: inspection, service & repair; Elevators: inspection, service & repair; Elevator installation & conversion
Pr: Donald Speranza Sr
CFO: Fred Sheinblum
Ex VP: Yolanda Speranza
VP: Dean Speranza
VP: Donald Speranza Jr
VP: Robert Speranza
Mng Dir: Carl Messina
Genl Mgr: Don Cristiano

D-U-N-S 13-103-5610 IMP
NOUVEAU EYEWEAR INC
2853 Eisenhower St # 100, Carrollton, TX 75007-4961
Tel (972) 242-3633 Founded/Ownrshp 1980
Sales 30.9MM^E EMP 80
SIC 5048 Frames, ophthalmic; Frames, ophthalmic
CFO: Lisa Paton
*Pr: Dominick Sblendorio
VP: Timi Morris
VP: Ben Perry
IT Man: Jim Harris
Mktg Mgr: Donna Fortenberry

D-U-N-S 80-774-7493
NOUVEAU VERRE HOLDINGS INC
(Suby of PORCHER INDUSTRIES)
3802 Robert Porcher Way, Greensboro, NC 27410-2190
Tel (336) 545-0011 Founded/Ownrshp 2004
Sales 208.8MM^E EMP 864^E
SIC 2221 3624 2241 2295 Glass broadwoven fabrics; Fibers, carbon & graphite; Glass narrow fabrics; Mats, varnished glass; Glass broadwoven fabrics; Fibers, carbon & graphite; Glass narrow fabrics; Mats, varnished glass
CEO: Phillipe Porcher

*CFO: Philippe R Dorier
Chf Mktg O: Robert Dunnagan
Ofcr: James R Henderson

NOV
See NATIONAL OILWELL VARCO INC

NOV
See TUBOSCOPE INC

D-U-N-S 80-209-5096
NOV GRANT PRIDECO
9475 Fm 1227 Rd, Navasota, TX 77868-5227
Tel (936) 825-9176 Founded/Ownrshp 2007
Sales 22.4MM^E EMP 90^E
SIC 8748 Business consulting
Prin: Ben Broadrick
QA Dir: Michael Hohlt
Ql Cn Mgr: John Hall

NOV PROCESS & FLOW TECH
See MOYNO INC

D-U-N-S 12-131-0382
■ NOVA ANALYTICS CORP
(Suby of O I ANALYTICAL) ★
11390 Amalgam Way, Gold River, CA 95670-4401
Tel (866) 664-6682 Founded/Ownrshp 2011
Sales 35.4MM^E EMP 725
SIC 3541 Electrochemical milling machines
Pr: John Kennedy

D-U-N-S 07-061-7139 IMP
NOVA BIOMEDICAL CORP (MA)
200 Prospect St Ste 3, Waltham, MA 02453-3465
Tel (781) 894-0800 Founded/Ownrshp 1976
Sales 282.5MM^E EMP 900
SIC 2833 3826 Medicinals & botanicals; Blood testing apparatus; Medicinals & botanicals; Blood testing apparatus
Pr: Francis Manganaro
Pr: Jeffrey Dubois
Pr: Eileen Konik
*CFO: Luciano A Borrelli
VP: Jeff Chien
VP: Jay Closson
VP: Heraldo Couto
VP: Chuck Kircher
VP: Thomas Larkin
VP: John McHale
VP: James Sidwell
VP: Nicholas Theodore
Exec: Tony Yu

NOVA BUS LFS, A DIVISION OF PR
See PREVOST CAR US INC

D-U-N-S 07-912-6143
NOVA CAPITAL MANAGEMENT USA LLC
(Suby of NOVA CAPITAL MANAGEMENT LIMITED)
71 S Wacker Dr Ste 1735, Chicago, IL 60606-4637
Tel (203) 260-3400 Founded/Ownrshp 2004
Sales 237.0MM^E EMP 405^E
SIC 6799 Investors; Investors

D-U-N-S 10-400-0625 IMP/EXP
NOVA CHEMICALS INC
(Suby of NOVA CHEMICALS CORPORATION)
1555 Coraopolis Hts Rd, Moon Township, PA 15108-2924
Tel (412) 490-4000 Founded/Ownrshp 1982
Sales 974.1MM^E EMP 3,270
SIC 2821 Polyethylene resins; Polystyrene resins; Polyethylene resins; Polystyrene resins
CEO: Todd D Karran
*Sr VP: Chris Bezaire
*Sr VP: Bill Greene
*Sr VP: Grant Thomson
VP: Antonio Torres
VP: Roy Ward
Exec: John Siegrist
*Prin: Randy G Woelfel
Rgnl Mgr: Ernest Loh
Genl Mgr: John Crick
CTO: Todd Carrin
Board of Directors: Laurie Brlas, Pierre Choquette, John E Feick, Charles W Fischer, John Kuziak, Brian F Olson, Janice Rennie

NOVA CM
See NOVA CORP

D-U-N-S 06-349-8471
NOVA COIL INC
NOVACOIL ZOPPAS INDUSTRIES
(Suby of ZOPPAS INDUSTRIES SPA)
5401 W Franklin Dr, Franklin, WI 53132-8624
Tel (414) 423-7230 Founded/Ownrshp 2011
Sales 32.4MM^E EMP 86
SIC 3677 3567 Electronic coils, transformers & other inductors; Electrical furnaces, ovens & heating devices, exc. induction
CEO: Michael O Brien
*Pr: Poul Rook
*CFO: Jean Harvey

D-U-N-S 18-750-7280
NOVA CONSULTING GROUP INC
1107 Hazeltine Blvd # 400, Chaska, MN 55318-1041
Tel (952) 448-9393 Founded/Ownrshp 1987
Sales 27.5MM^E EMP 120
SIC 8748 8734 Business consulting; Hazardous waste testing
Pr: Steven B Cummings
COO: Tom Warn
VP: Neil Archibald
VP: Michael Minett
VP: Greg Murphy
Doctor: Kari Wescott
Snr PM: Kevin Baumgartner
Snr PM: Sarah Feit
Snr PM: Phillip Hoeksema
Snr PM: David Jackson
Snr PM: Meghan Lockman

NOVA CONTAINER FREIGHT STATION
See H RAUVEL INC

D-U-N-S 09-384-3118 EXP
NOVA CORP
NOVA CM
1 Main St Unit 3, Nyack, NY 10960-3231
Tel (201) 567-4404 *Founded/Ownrshp* 1928, 1979
Sales 135.0MM^E *EMP* 50
SIC 1541 8748 Industrial buildings & warehouses; Business consulting; Industrial buildings & warehouses; Business consulting
Pr: Mark Di Stefano
**CFO:* Edward Bohn
**Ex VP:* Brian Fleury
Ex VP: Sue Massaro
**Ex VP:* Robert Pappas
Ex VP: Edward Stewart
**VP:* Judith Florio
VP: Brian Fluery
VP: Matthew Soltis
Genl Mgr: Joe Maiale
Dir IT: Tom Fatyga

D-U-N-S 17-160-6788
NOVA CORP
1445 Sheffler Dr, Chambersburg, PA 17201-4832
Tel (717) 262-9750 *Founded/Ownrshp* 2009
Sales 34.3MM^E *EMP* 80
SIC 7379 Computer related maintenance services
CEO: John Snider
**COO:* Randy Wilson
**CFO:* Hunter Mason
Prgrm Mgr: Steve Hendrix
Prgrm Mgr: Harold Knisley
CIO: Donald Cox
Software D: David Barrett
Mktg Dir: Patrick O'Brien
Mktg Dir: Oscencio Tom

NOVA DEVELOPMENT
See AVANQUEST NORTH AMERICA INC

D-U-N-S 80-143-8164
NOVA ENGINEERING AND ENVIRONMENTAL LLC
3900 Kennesaw 75 Pkwy Nw # 100, Kennesaw, GA 30144-6409
Tel (770) 425-0777 *Founded/Ownrshp* 2007
Sales 57.6MM^E *EMP* 400^E
SIC 8711 Construction & civil engineering; Construction & civil engineering
Ex VP: Ken Houseman
VP: Jay Chen
VP: Steve Willenborg
Brnch Mgr: Luis Gonzalez
CTO: Matt Sinclair
Snr PM: Jim Peshel

D-U-N-S 78-708-4110
■ **NOVA FACTOR INC**
(*Suby of* ACCREDO HEALTH INC) ★
1620 Century Center Pkwy # 109, Memphis, TN 38134-8849
Tel (901) 385-3600 *Founded/Ownrshp* 1996
Sales 60.6MM^E *EMP* 750
SIC 5999 Medical apparatus & supplies; Medical apparatus & supplies
CEO: David D Stevens
Pr: Chad Hetzell
COO: Steven R Fitzpatick
**CFO:* Joel Kimbrough
QA Dir: Tricia Phillips
Snr Mgr: Mary Anderson

D-U-N-S 11-511-3086
NOVA FINANCIAL & INVESTMENT CORP
NOVA HOME LOANS
6245 E Broadway Blvd # 150, Tucson, AZ 85711-4042
Tel (520) 745-0050 *Founded/Ownrshp* 1981
Sales NA *EMP* 201
SIC 6163 Mortgage brokers arranging for loans, using money of others; Mortgage brokers arranging for loans, using money of others
Pr: Raymond Desmond
**Treas:* Lawrence Desmond
Genl Mgr: Jon Volpe
IT Man: Chris Stevens

D-U-N-S 11-505-0895
NOVA FIRE PROTECTION INC
304 41st St S, Fargo, ND 58103-1166
Tel (701) 282-0268 *Founded/Ownrshp* 1998
Sales 22.0MM^E *EMP* 70
SIC 3569 Sprinkler systems, fire: automatic
Prin: Michael E Evans
Mktg Mgr: Brent Rask

NOVA GROUP, THE
See NOVACARE LLC

D-U-N-S 06-609-9219
NOVA GROUP INC
NGI CONSTRUCTION
185 Devlin Rd, NAPA, CA 94558-6255
Tel (707) 265-1100 *Founded/Ownrshp* 1957
Sales 112.3MM^E *EMP* 200
SIC 1629 1623 1622 5172 Marine construction; Waterway construction; Underground utilities contractor; Tunnel construction; Aircraft fueling services; Marine construction; Waterway construction; Underground utilities contractor; Tunnel construction; Aircraft fueling services
Pr: Ronald M Fedrick
**Pr:* Scott R Victor
Ofcr: Art Mendoza
**VP:* Carole Bionda
**VP:* Walter Birdsall
**VP:* Dee Fedrick
**VP:* Chris Mathies
VP: Walt Schwartz
VP: Scott Victor
Mng Dir: Ross Preston
Sys Mgr: Guy Rothrock

D-U-N-S 80-814-0789
NOVA GROUP INC-OBAYASHI CORP A JOINT VENTURE
185 Devlin Rd, NAPA, CA 94558-6255
Tel (707) 265-1116 *Founded/Ownrshp* 2007
Sales 32.0MM *EMP* 50
SIC 1623 Pipeline construction; Pipeline construction

D-U-N-S 80-847-4261
NOVA GROUP INC-UNDERGROUND CONSTRUCTION CO INC AJV
185 Devlin Rd, NAPA, CA 94558-6255
Tel (707) 265-1116 *Founded/Ownrshp* 2007
Sales 32.0MM *EMP* 1
SIC 1629 Heavy construction; Heavy construction
Pt: Ronald M Fedrick
Pt: Carol Bionda

D-U-N-S 12-623-1005
NOVA GROUP SERVICES LLC
13800 Nw 14th St Ste 130, Sunrise, FL 33323-2801
Tel (954) 424-2520 *Founded/Ownrshp* 2002
Sales 40.0MM *EMP* 225
SIC 8711 Engineering services; Engineering services
Pr: G Elzweig
CFO: Ed Bernice

D-U-N-S 80-907-0613
NOVA GROUP/TUTOR-SALIBA A JOINT VENTURE
185 Devlin Rd, NAPA, CA 94558-6255
Tel (707) 265-1100 *Founded/Ownrshp* 2008
Sales 31.0MM *EMP* 3
SIC 1629 Heavy construction; Heavy construction
Pt: Carole Bionda

D-U-N-S 62-154-5011
NOVA HEALTHCARE ADMINISTRATORS INC
(*Suby of* INDEPENDENT HEALTH CORP) ★
6400 Main St Ste 210, Williamsville, NY 14221-5803
Tel (716) 773-1143 *Founded/Ownrshp* 2003
Sales NA *EMP* 125
SIC 6411 Medical insurance claim processing, contract or fee basis
Pr: Kristy Long
**CEO:* John D Hoffman
**CFO:* Michael J Blemel
**VP:* William Brothers
**VP:* Cynthia Hammer
**VP:* Kristey L Hartley
Exec: Linda Washut

NOVA HOME LOANS
See NOVA FINANCIAL & INVESTMENT CORP

D-U-N-S 06-116-2675
▲ **NOVA LIFESTYLE INC** (NV)
6565 E Washington Blvd, Commerce, CA 90040-1821
Tel (323) 888-9999 *Founded/Ownrshp* 2011
Sales 98.7MM *EMP* 522
Accts Marcum Bernstein & Pinchuk Llp
Tkr Sym NVFY *Exch* NGM
SIC 2511 2512 Chairs: upholstered on wood frames; Wood household furniture; Upholstered household furniture; Chairs: upholstered on wood frames
CEO: Ya Ming Wong
**Ch Bd:* Thanh H Lam
**CFO:* Yuen Ching Ho
VP Mktg: Mark Chapman
VP Mktg: Ah Wan Wong

D-U-N-S 60-452-1752 IMP
■ **NOVA MACHINE PRODUCTS INC**
(*Suby of* CURTISS-WRIGHT CORP) ★
18001 Sheldon Rd, Middleburg Heights, OH 44130-2465
Tel (216) 267-3200 *Founded/Ownrshp* 2005
Sales 21.2MM^E *EMP* 115^E
SIC 3452 3429 3369 3356 Bolts, metal; Washers; Nuts, metal; Lock washers; Manufactured hardware (general); Nonferrous foundries; Nonferrous rolling & drawing; Bolts, metal; Washers; Nuts, metal; Lock washers; Manufactured hardware (general); Nonferrous foundries; Nonferrous rolling & drawing
CEO: David Linton
**Ch Bd:* Martin R Benante
Ex VP: Tim Walker
Exec: Constance Boykin
Exec: William Witt
Genl Mgr: Timothy A Davis
Genl Mgr: Tad Gray
Dir IT: Reuben Wunder
Mtls Mgr: Tom Consiglio
Sfty Mgr: Greg Jackson
Opers Mgr: Rod Thibodeaux

D-U-N-S 60-334-6529
NOVA MUD INC
IDA
5800 Nova Dr, Hobbs, NM 88240
Tel (575) 393-8786 *Founded/Ownrshp* 1989
Sales 98.0MM^E *EMP* 155
SIC 5169 Drilling mud; Drilling mud
CEO: David Chu
**Pr:* Ken Bromley
**Treas:* C Dean Graves
**VP:* Scott Bromley
**VP:* Ruth L Greenstein
**VP:* Philip L Major
**VP:* Bill Smith
Rgnl Mgr: Victor Moreno

D-U-N-S 87-727-0926 IMP
NOVA ORTHO-MED INC
1470 Beachey Pl, Carson, CA 90746-4002
Tel (310) 352-3600 *Founded/Ownrshp* 1993
Sales 21.9MM^E *EMP* 50
SIC 5047 Medical & hospital equipment
Pr: Sue Chen
**VP:* Ronald Gaudiano
Genl Mgr: Annette Aoyama

NOVA PACKAGING SYSTEM
See IMA NORTH AMERICA INC

NOVA SEAFOODS
See A C SEAFOOD LTD

D-U-N-S 00-297-1240
NOVA SOUTHEASTERN UNIVERSITY INC (FL)
3301 College Ave, Davie, FL 33314-7796
Tel (954) 262-7300 *Founded/Ownrshp* 1964
Sales 671.1MM *EMP* 2,500
Accts Ernst & Young Llp Boca Raton
SIC 8221 8211 University; Elementary & secondary schools; University; Elementary & secondary schools
Ch: Robert Steele
V Ch: Barry J Silverman
**Pr:* Dr George Larbury
COO: Jacqueline A Travisano
CFO: Henry Del Riego
CFO: Bibi Haddad
CFO: David Heron
CFO: Henry D Reigo
**CFO:* Alyson Silva
Trst: Mitchell W Berger
Trst: Keith A Brown
Trst: Rick Case
Trst: Andrew J Dibattista
Trst: Arthur J Falcone
Trst: Silvia M Flores
Trst: David W Horvitz
Trst: Royal F Jonas
Trst: Milton Jones
Trst: Alan B Levan
Trst: Nell M Lewis
Trst: Joseph R Millsaps

NOVA STEEL COMPANY
See CKKM INC

D-U-N-S 17-927-1713 IMP/EXP
NOVA TERRA TECHNOLOGIES INC
(*Suby of* AMEC FOSTER WHEELER PLC)
10770 Rockville St Ste A, Santee, CA 92071-8505
Tel (619) 440-5003 *Founded/Ownrshp* 2000
Sales 45.9MM^E *EMP* 80
SIC 3535 8742 Conveyors & conveying equipment; Management consulting services; Industrial & labor consulting services; Conveyors & conveying equipment; Management consulting services; Industrial & labor consulting services
Pr: Ronald R Kelly
CFO: Michael Lake
**Treas:* Grant Ling
**VP:* George M Bernard
**VP:* Judy Zeigler
Board of Directors: Grant Graber

D-U-N-S 79-889-9378
■ **NOVA VENTURES CORP**
(*Suby of* NOVA ANALYTICS CORP) ★
600 Unicorn Park Dr Ste 4, Woburn, MA 01801-3343
Tel (781) 897-1200 *Founded/Ownrshp* 2006
Sales 275.2M^E *EMP* 479^E
SIC 8742 Management consulting services
Pr: John Kennedy

D-U-N-S 07-921-3712
NOVA WILDCAT ASHLAND LLC
(*Suby of* NOVA CAPITAL MANAGEMENT USA LLC) ★
545 E John Carpenter Fwy, Irving, TX 75062-3931
Tel (469) 621-9804 *Founded/Ownrshp* 2013
Sales 70.0MM^E *EMP* 300
SIC 3272 Building materials, except block or brick: concrete; Building materials, except block or brick: concrete
Plng Mgr: Josh Willis

D-U-N-S 07-914-2645
NOVA WILDCAT SHUR-LINE LLC
(*Suby of* NOVA CAPITAL MANAGEMENT USA LLC) ★
116 Exmore Rd, Mooresville, NC 28117-9422
Tel (800) 253-7856 *Founded/Ownrshp* 2013
Sales 40.0MM *EMP* 300
SIC 3991 Paint rollers; Paint brushes; Paint rollers; Paint brushes
CEO: Andy Reed
VP Sls: David Jarecki

D-U-N-S 79-106-4061
NOVA-TECH ENGINEERING LLC
1705 Engineering Ave, Willmar, MN 56201-2282
Tel (320) 231-9660 *Founded/Ownrshp* 2005
Sales 30.6MM *EMP* 128
SIC 8711 Engineering services; Engineering services
Ch Bd: Marc Gorans
Pr: James Sieben
CFO: Beth Wosmek
Treas: Ronald R Hanson
Board of Directors: Kim Gorans, Marc Gorans, Richard Huisinga, Theodore Huisinga, Thomas Huisinga, Rayburn Norling, Scott Norling, James Sieben

D-U-N-S 13-360-3634 IMP
NOVA/TCB USA INC
2339 W Beaver Creek Dr, Powell, TN 37849-4831
Tel (865) 938-6822 *Founded/Ownrshp* 2003
Sales 29.0MM *EMP* 350
SIC 3562 5085 Ball & roller bearings; Bearings; Ball & roller bearings; Bearings
Pr: Cathy Roberts
**COO:* Michael Lanz
**CFO:* Tammy Robbins
**VP:* Bobby Roberts

NOVABUS
See PREVOST CAR (US) INC

NOVACAP, INC.
See NOVACAP LLC

D-U-N-S 09-946-4695 IMP
■ **NOVACAP LLC**
NOVACAP, INC.
(*Suby of* KNOWLES CORP) ★
25111 Anza Dr, Valencia, CA 91355-3478
Tel (661) 295-5920 *Founded/Ownrshp* 2014
Sales 100.4MM^E *EMP* 280
SIC 3675 Electronic capacitors; Electronic capacitors
CEO: Mark Skoog
VP: Frank Duva
Plnt Mgr: John Sanders
Plnt Mgr: Gilberto Valenzuela
Ql Cn Mgr: Kenneth Toomey

NOVACARE
See REHAB PEOPLE INC

D-U-N-S 10-106-3378 IMP/EXP
NOVACARE LLC
NOVA GROUP, THE
330 W 6100 S, Murray, UT 84107-6990
Tel (801) 261-2252 *Founded/Ownrshp* 2008
Sales 40.0MM *EMP* 40
SIC 2833 Medicinals & botanicals
Ch: Neil Bhaskar
CFO: John Burns
Genl Mgr: Justin Bath

D-U-N-S 82-735-4838
■ **NOVACARE OUTPATIENT REHABILITATION EAST INC**
(*Suby of* SELECT MEDICAL CORP) ★
400 Technology Dr Ste 240, Canonsburg, PA 15317-9575
Tel (724) 745-7788 *Founded/Ownrshp* 1997
Sales 5.7MM^E *EMP* 300
SIC 8093 Rehabilitation center, outpatient treatment; Rehabilitation center, outpatient treatment
Adm/Dir: Christopher Zanke
**VP:* Kevin Oswald

D-U-N-S 13-937-7980 IMP
NOVACEL INC
(*Suby of* NOVACEL)
21 3rd St, Palmer, MA 01069-1542
Tel (413) 283-3468 *Founded/Ownrshp* 2001
Sales 50.0MM^E *EMP* 210
SIC 2671 Paper coated or laminated for packaging; Plastic film, coated or laminated for packaging; Paper coated or laminated for packaging; Plastic film, coated or laminated for packaging
Pr: David Anderson
**CFO:* Michael Story
**Treas:* William Dopp
Dir Bus: Michele Naulot-Besson
**Prin:* Richard Karane

D-U-N-S 01-562-0719
NOVACOAST INC
1505 Chapala St, Santa Barbara, CA 93101-3016
Tel (805) 568-0171 *Founded/Ownrshp* 1996
Sales 41.2MM^E *EMP* 165
SIC 7373 Computer integrated systems design; Computer integrated systems design
CEO: Paul Anderson
Pr: Forrest Evans
Pr: Katie McAuliff
**CFO:* Janice Newlon
Brnch Mgr: John Reising
Netwrk Mgr: Tyler Johnson
Software D: Ian Butler
Software D: Cristian Diaz
Software D: Christian Mundo
Software D: Renato Untalan
Netwrk Eng: Travis Silva
Board of Directors: Gabe Laughlin

NOVACOIL ZOPPAS INDUSTRIES
See NOVA COIL INC

D-U-N-S 04-629-1154
NOVACOPY INC
7251 Appling Farms Pkwy, Memphis, TN 38133-4738
Tel (901) 388-6699 *Founded/Ownrshp* 1998
Sales 52.0MM *EMP* 58
Accts Cannon Wright Blount Pllc Mem
SIC 5999 7629 Photocopy machines; Business machines & equipment; Business machine repair, electric
Pr: Darren Metz
**CFO:* Carolyn Stafford
**VP:* Alex Brandon
Brnch Mgr: John McManus
CIO: Carl Pottkotter
Opers Mgr: Mark Bissinger
S&M/VP: Brad McDaniel
Sls Mgr: Kristen Tolleson

NOVACOTE FLEXPACK
See COIM USA INC

D-U-N-S 79-364-1742
NOVADENT INC
640 Nw Gilman Blvd, Issaquah, WA 98027-2476
Tel (425) 392-5125 *Founded/Ownrshp* 2006
Sales 17.1MM^E *EMP* 281
SIC 8072 Dental laboratories; Dental laboratories
VP: George Englund

D-U-N-S 96-221-6503 IMP
NOVAE CORP
I-69 TRAILER CENTER
1 Novae Pkwy, Markle, IN 46770-9087
Tel (260) 758-9800 *Founded/Ownrshp* 1994
Sales 66.0MM^E *EMP* 280^E
SIC 5084 3524 Trailers, industrial; Lawn & garden mowers & accessories; Trailers, industrial; Lawn & garden mowers & accessories
CEO: Steve Bermes
**COO:* Christopher Storie
CFO: Chris Story
**VP:* Mike Bermes
Dir Bus: Mark Yde
Off Mgr: Marty Westbrook
Snr Sftwr: Kal Govindu
Dir IT: Oliver Reelsen
Mtls Mgr: Mark Kundo
Mtls Mgr: Chad Williams
Mfg Mgr: Ryan Lutton

D-U-N-S 09-806-0168
NOVAEON INC
9665 Chesapeake Dr # 430, San Diego, CA 92123-1367
Tel (858) 503-1588 *Founded/Ownrshp* 1997
Sales 11.6MM^E *EMP* 330
SIC 8322 Individual & family services; Individual & family services
Ch Bd: William McBride
**Pr:* Patrick J Sullivan
**VP:* Craig Bissell
**VP:* Colleen Carney
**VP:* Richard Morgan
**VP:* Dward Sager

D-U-N-S 14-853-2484 IMP
NOVAFLEX HOSE INC
(*Suby of* Z-FLEX REALTY INC) ★
449 Trollingwood Rd, Haw River, NC 27258-8750
Tel (336) 578-2161 *Founded/Ownrshp* 1993
Sales 49.8MM^E *EMP* 85
SIC 5085 3061 Hose, belting & packing; Mechanical rubber goods; Hose, belting & packing; Mechanical rubber goods
Pr: Melinda Donnelly
VP: Thomas Wise

D-U-N-S 06-490-4360
NOVAK CONSTRUCTION CO
3423 N Drake Ave, Chicago, IL 60618-5449
Tel (773) 278-1100 *Founded/Ownrshp* 1980
Sales 72.4MM^E *EMP* 90
Accts Bansley And Kiener Llp Chica
SIC 1542 1541 1799 Commercial & office building contractors; Industrial buildings & warehouses; Gas system installation, medical; Commercial & office building contractors; Industrial buildings & warehouses; Gas system installation, medical
Pr: John G Novak
Sr VP: Doug Krause
VP: Patrick Kenny
VP: Lee Krzyszton
VP: Jack Oconnor
VP: Joe Salomone
VP: Kirk Westman
Exec: Rose Housty
S&M/VP: Kirk Rustman
Mktg Dir: Stacey Jones
Snr PM: Mike Flinchum

D-U-N-S 08-324-8799
NOVAK DRUCE CONNOLLY BOVE+QUIGG LLP
1007 N Orange St, Wilmington, DE 19801-1239
Tel (302) 252-9922 *Founded/Ownrshp* 1940
Sales 23.9MM^E *EMP* 180
SIC 8111 General practice law office; General practice law office
Pt: Rudolph E Hutz
Pt: Richard M Beck
Pt: Jeffrey Bove
Pt: Paul E Crawford
Pt: Hutz R Eric
Pt: Henry E Gallagher Jr
Pt: Rudolf Hutz
Pt: Stanley C Macel III
Pt: Robert McMorrow
Pt: Macel Stanley
Mng Pt: Collins J Seitz Jr
CFO: Frank Stransky
Ofcr: Victor Martinez
VP: Mary Delaney

D-U-N-S 00-906-4028
NOVAMED INC
(*Suby of* SP HEALTHCARE HOLDINGS LLC) ★
40 Burton Hills Blvd # 500, Nashville, TN 37215-6186
Tel (312) 664-4100 *Founded/Ownrshp* 2011
Sales 81.7MM^E *EMP* 772
SIC 8011 8042 6726 Ambulatory surgical center; Offices & clinics of optometrists; Investment offices; Ambulatory surgical center; Offices & clinics of optometrists; Investment offices
Pr: Thomas S Hall
**CEO:* Michael Doyle
COO: Brian Gro
**COO:* Chris Throckmorton
**CFO:* Scott T Macomber
**Ex VP:* Graham B Cherrington
**Sr VP:* Cassandra T Speier
VP: Chris Werfel
Opers Mgr: Sue Nutgrass

NOVAMEX
See TIPP DISTRIBUTORS INC

NOVAMEX
See JARRITOS INC

NOVANIS
See CTG INC OF ILLINOIS

NOVANT HEALTH BRUNSWICK MEDICA
See BRUNSWICK NOVANT MEDICAL CENTER

D-U-N-S 07-960-5926
NOVANT HEALTH INC
3333 Silas Creek Pkwy, Winston Salem, NC 27103-3013
Tel (336) 718-5000 *Founded/Ownrshp* 1983
Sales NA *EMP* 316^E
SIC 6324 Hospital & medical service plans
Pr: Jeffrey T Lindsay
**COO:* Denise Mihal
COO: Chad Setliff
Sr VP: Mark Miller
Dir Rad: Terrie Loflin
Dir Rx: Frederica Dennis
Chf Nrs Of: Cathy Lewis
Off Mgr: Donita Needham
Off Mgr: Jan Wagoner
Mktg Dir: Leslie Robbins
Doctor: Lee Hall

D-U-N-S 15-973-5711
NOVANT HEALTH INC
LAKESIDE FAMILY PHYSICIANS
2085 Frontis Plaza Blvd, Winston Salem, NC 27103-5614
Tel (336) 277-1120 *Founded/Ownrshp* 1981
Sales 2.1MMM^E *EMP* 13,800
SIC 8062 General medical & surgical hospitals; General medical & surgical hospitals
CEO: Carl S Armato
COO: Richard Belden
COO: Denise Mihal
CFO: Fred Hargett
CFO: Fred M Hargett
Bd of Dir: Sue Smith
Ofcr: Jesse Cureton
Ex VP: Sallye A Liner
Ex VP: Stephen L Wallenhaupt
Sr VP: James Tobalski
VP: Joe Carroll
VP: Tom Elmore
VP: Sean Keyser
VP Bus Dev: Derek Goldin
Exec: Elesha Kirkland
Exec: Jennifer Smith
Dir Lab: Angella Callwood
Dir Lab: Rachel Ross

D-U-N-S 07-156-6327
NOVANT HEALTH MEDICAL PARK HOSPITAL INC
(*Suby of* LAKESIDE FAMILY PHYSICIANS) ★
1950 S Hawthorne Rd, Winston Salem, NC 27103-3912
Tel (336) 277-1120 *Founded/Ownrshp* 1969
Sales 73.5MM *EMP* 254
SIC 8062 General medical & surgical hospitals; General medical & surgical hospitals
Pr: Carl S Armato
**COO:* Chad Setliff
**Ex VP:* Jesse Cureton
**Ex VP:* Jacqueline R Daniels
**Ex VP:* Fred M Hargett
Exec: Jacque Gattis
Pathlgst: Andrew Cullen

NOVANT HEALTH PRESBYTERIAN MED
See PRESBYTERIAN HOSPITAL

D-U-N-S 79-882-5634
NOVANT MEDICAL GROUP INC
(*Suby of* LAKESIDE FAMILY PHYSICIANS) ★
200 Hawthorne Ln, Charlotte, NC 28204-2515
Tel (704) 384-4966 *Founded/Ownrshp* 1998
Sales 88.4MM^E *EMP* 3,000
SIC 8011 Medical centers; Medical centers
Pr: Carl Armato

D-U-N-S 13-262-9754
NOVANTAS INC
485 Lexington Ave Fl 20, New York, NY 10017-2628
Tel (212) 953-4444 *Founded/Ownrshp* 2002
Sales 28.7MM^E *EMP* 100
SIC 8742 Management consulting services
CEO: David G Kaytes
Pr: Edward Van Eckert
CFO: Tim Lestrange
Ex VP: Stuart Baker
VP: Caryn Van Buskirk
Exec: Wilfredo Toro
**Prin:* Wayne Cutler
**Prin:* Richard Spitler
**Prin:* Zach Wise
Mng Dir: Darryl Demos
Mng Dir: Phil Jarymiszyn

NOVAPICK
See NOVATEK INC

D-U-N-S 04-797-2153 IMP
■ **NOVAR CONTROLS CORP**
HONEYWELL
(*Suby of* HONEYWELL INTERNATIONAL INC) ★
6060 Rockside Woods Blvd # 400, Cleveland, OH 44131-2378
Tel (216) 682-1600 *Founded/Ownrshp* 2009
Sales 25.0MM^E *EMP* 320
SIC 3674 3625 Microprocessors; Relays & industrial controls; Microprocessors; Relays & industrial controls
Pr: Dean Lindstorm
CFO: David Anderson
Dir Bus: Ali Ahmed
Ex Dir: Hans Nilsson
Prgrm Mgr: Tim Zimmerman
Pr Dir: Brian Ericksen
Sls Mgr: Richard King
Snr PM: Richard Doncaster
Snr Mgr: Tim Molitor

D-U-N-S 07-199-1843
NOVARAD CORP
752 E 1180 S Ste 200, American Fork, UT 84003-3561
Tel (801) 642-1001 *Founded/Ownrshp* 1990
Sales 41.3MM^E *EMP* 144
SIC 3695 Computer software tape & disks: blank, rigid & floppy; Computer software tape & disks: blank, rigid & floppy
CEO: Wendell Gibby
**Pr:* Tim Law
**COO:* John Fowler
Ex VP: Ross Jardine
VP: Randal S Graham
VP: Tyler Harris
VP: Rebecca Hewett
VP: Kay Jex
VP: Doug Schroeppel
**VP:* Paul Shumway
VP: Rick White

D-U-N-S 80-667-0618 IMP
NOVARE GROUP INC
BORDERS PROPERTIES
817 W Peachtree St Nw 4 Ste 400, Atlanta, GA 30308
Tel (404) 575-4475 *Founded/Ownrshp* 1992
Sales 71.2MM^E *EMP* 170^E
SIC 6552 Subdividers & developers
Pr: James R Borders
CFO: Mark Dressel
**Ex VP:* J Mark Dressel
**Ex VP:* Laine Kenan
**Ex VP:* Gardiner Thompson
Sr VP: Kyle Brock
**Sr VP:* Julie Harlan
Sr VP: Christopher Kritzman
Sr VP: Kevin McDaniel
Sr VP: J Vance
VP: Andy Vance

D-U-N-S 02-049-2982
NOVARIA GROUP LLC
6300 Ridglea Pl Ste 800, Fort Worth, TX 76116-5708
Tel (817) 381-3810 *Founded/Ownrshp* 2011
Sales 48.7MM^E *EMP* 167^E
SIC 6726 Investment offices; Investment offices
Co-CEO: Earl Larkin
**Pr:* Bryan Perkins
**VP:* Mike Wagner

D-U-N-S 86-844-8929
NOVARIANT INC
AUTOFARM
46610 Landing Pkwy, Fremont, CA 94538-6420
Tel (510) 933-4800 *Founded/Ownrshp* 1994
Sales 34.6MM^E *EMP* 95
SIC 8711 Engineering services
Pr: Dave Vaughn
CFO: Mike Manning
VP: Mark Bittner
VP: Husam Kal
VP: Jim Tan
Dir IT: Gregory Park
Opers Mgr: Albert Choi
Ql Cn Mgr: Peter Chun
Natl Sales: Matt Strein
Mktg Dir: Deane Malott
Snr Mgr: Jonathan Ladd

D-U-N-S 96-698-5624 IMP
NOVARTIS ANIMAL HEALTH US INC
(*Suby of* NOVARTIS CORP) ★
3200 Northline Ave # 300, Greensboro, NC 27408-7611
Tel (336) 387-1000 *Founded/Ownrshp* 1996
Sales 72.0MM^E *EMP* 230
SIC 2834 Pharmaceutical preparations; Pharmaceutical preparations
CEO: Joseph Burkett
**Pr:* Robert Jones
VP: Virginia Lizala
**VP:* Brian Reeve
Dir Soc: Kelley Rickard
Dir IT: Tim Hawks
IT Man: Dan Mars
VP Mfg: Kevin Cornett
VP Opers: Naomi Potts
Sfty Mgr: Jamie Bratcher
VP Sls: Hugh Jones

D-U-N-S 82-989-0149
NOVARTIS CAPITAL CORP
(*Suby of* NOVARTIS AG)
230 Park Ave Fl 21, New York, NY 10169-2403
Tel (212) 307-1122 *Founded/Ownrshp* 2009
Sales 21.3MM^E *EMP* 87^E
SIC 6722 Management investment, open-end
Prin: Bharat Patel
Top Exec: Milicent Brooks
Top Exec: Renee Rodgers
VP: William Berg
VP: Carol Danoff
VP: Steven Hartman
Dir Risk M: Marnie Raimondo
Assoc Dir: Sharon Hu
Assoc Dir: Barbara Koumaras
Assoc Dir: Patty Peterson
Assoc Dir: Sylvia Simon

D-U-N-S 87-982-1635 IMP
NOVARTIS CONSUMER HEALTH INC
GSK CONSUMER HEALTHCARE
(*Suby of* GLAXOSMITHKLINE PLC)
200 Kimball Dr, Parsippany, NJ 07054-2173
Tel (973) 503-8000 *Founded/Ownrshp* 2015
Sales 217.0MM^E *EMP* 890
SIC 2834 Pharmaceutical preparations; Pharmaceutical preparations
CEO: Joseph Jimenez
COO: Christopher Godfrey
CFO: Andre Cadieux
**CFO:* John McKenna
**Treas:* Matthias Vogt
Top Exec: Eric Lang
VP: Florian Bieber
VP: Kurt Furger
VP: Dianne Jacobs
VP: Michael Kopcha
VP: Robert Lodewick
VP: Qiang MA
VP: Mike Reinhardt
VP: Kathleen Roessle
VP: Regis Schratz
VP: Rick Sheppard
VP: Sharon Spina
VP: Carl Ward
VP: Barbara Wirth
Exec: Bruce Webber
Assoc Dir: Satya Murthy

D-U-N-S 00-122-1845
NOVARTIS CORP (NY)
(*Suby of* NOVARTIS INTERNATIONAL AG)
608 5th Ave, New York, NY 10020-2303
Tel (212) 307-1122 *Founded/Ownrshp* 1903
Sales 58.9MMM^E *EMP* 30,186
SIC 2834 2879 0181 2032 2865 Pharmaceutical preparations; Drugs acting on the cardiovascular system, except diagnostic; Drugs acting on the central nervous system & sense organs; Veterinary pharmaceutical preparations; Agricultural chemicals; Insecticides, agricultural or household; Pesticides, agricultural or household; Fungicides, herbicides; Seeds, vegetable: growing of; Baby foods, including meats: packaged in cans, jars, etc.; Dyes & pigments; Pharmaceutical preparations; Drugs acting on the cardiovascular system, except diagnostic; Drugs acting on the central nervous system & sense organs; Veterinary pharmaceutical preparations; Agricultural chemicals; Insecticides, agricultural or household; Pesticides, agricultural or household; Fungicides, herbicides; Seeds, vegetable: growing of; Baby foods, including meats: packaged in cans, jars, etc.; Dyes & pigments
Ch Bd: Christi Shaw
**CFO:* Harry Kirsch
Treas: Kenneth J Schuster
Top Exec: Paul Tarashuk
VP: Susan Damico
VP: Deborah Dunshire
VP: Farryn Melton
VP: Marc Payne
VP: Robert L Thompson Jr
Assoc Dir: Neil Albuja
Assoc Dir: Kelly Beyer
Assoc Dir: Cheryl Bickel
Assoc Dir: Ken Boccino
Assoc Dir: Marie Carmen
Assoc Dir: Mark Dizon
Assoc Dir: James Harrill
Assoc Dir: Karin Hunziker
Assoc Dir: John Jacques
Assoc Dir: Robert Kosecki
Assoc Dir: Gina Milak
Assoc Dir: Alphonse Porcello

NOVARTIS EX-LAX
See EX-LAX INC

D-U-N-S 84-027-8753
NOVARTIS FINANCE CORP
(*Suby of* NOVARTIS CORP) ★
230 Park Ave Fl 21, New York, NY 10169-2403
Tel (212) 307-1122 *Founded/Ownrshp* 1996
Sales 1.5MM *EMP* 470^E
SIC 5122 Pharmaceuticals; Pharmaceuticals
Ch Bd: Gary Rosenthal

D-U-N-S 14-437-9653 IMP
NOVARTIS INSTITUTES FOR BIOMEDICAL RESEARCH INC
NIBR
(*Suby of* NOVARTIS AG)
250 Massachusetts Ave, Cambridge, MA 02139-4229
Tel (617) 871-8000 *Founded/Ownrshp* 2002
Sales 21.6MM^E *EMP* 24^E
SIC 8733 Research institute
Pr: Mark Fishman
**Pr:* Keith Boudreau
**CFO:* Christiana Klee
VP: Chuck Wilson
Dir Lab: Simon Bushell
Assoc Dir: Steven Winig
Ex Dir: Dick Parry
Ex Dir: Laszlo Urban
Mng Dir: Lauren Silverman
CTO: George Morris
Dir IT: Mark Duffield

D-U-N-S 00-214-7023 IMP
NOVARTIS PHARMACEUTICALS CORP
NPS
(*Suby of* NOVARTIS CORP) ★
1 Health Plz, East Hanover, NJ 07936-1016
Tel (862) 778-8300 *Founded/Ownrshp* 1919
Sales 58.8MMM *EMP* 7,000
SIC 3826 Analytical instruments; Analytical instruments
Pr: Paulo Costa
**Pr:* Gary E Rosenthal
**Pr:* Andre Wyss
**COO:* Alex Gorsky
**CFO:* Helen Boudreau
**Chf Mktg O:* Nancy Lurker
**VP:* Julie Kane
VP: Dagmar Rosa-Bjorkeson
**VP:* Yves Teirlynck
Assoc Dir: Hassan Ahmed
Assoc Dir: Amer Albaridi
Assoc Dir: Jason Brown
Assoc Dir: David Buell
Assoc Dir: Dheepa Chari
Assoc Dir: Sharon Fabris
Assoc Dir: Lorrie-Ann Flanagan
Assoc Dir: James Haney
Assoc Dir: Brent Harpham
Assoc Dir: Kimberly Hoey
Assoc Dir: Jiahui Hu
Assoc Dir: Craig Kwiatkowski

D-U-N-S 04-686-6463 IMP
NOVARTIS VACCINES AND DIAGNOSTICS INC
(*Suby of* GLAXOSMITHKLINE PLC)
350 Massachusetts Ave, Cambridge, MA 02139-4182
Tel (617) 871-7000 *Founded/Ownrshp* 2015
Sales 968.9MM^E *EMP* 5,500
SIC 2834 2835 2836 Pharmaceutical preparations; Drugs affecting parasitic & infective diseases; In vitro & in vivo diagnostic substances; Vaccines & other immunizing products; Pharmaceutical preparations; Drugs affecting parasitic & infective diseases; In vitro & in vivo diagnostic substances; Vaccines & other immunizing products
CEO: Joerg Reinhardt
Top Exec: Xiang Liao
VP: Edward Stauber
Dir Lab: Luis Brito
IT Man: Chris Mikaelian
Natl Sales: Graham Thoms
Board of Directors: Dr Daniel Vasella

NOVASOURCE
See CENTRINEX LLC

D-U-N-S 06-999-4846 IMP
NOVASPECT INC
1124 Tower Rd, Schaumburg, IL 60173-4306
Tel (847) 956-8020 *Founded/Ownrshp* 1996
Sales 74.2MM^E *EMP* 140^E
SIC 7372 5084 Prepackaged software; Controlling instruments & accessories; Prepackaged software; Controlling instruments & accessories
Pr: Terry Voigt
**Pr:* Timothy Holcer
Genl Mgr: Angela Musial
Off Mgr: Kathy Schreier
Sls Dir: Bob Harsch
Sales Asso: Marge Lewis
Sales Asso: Seretha McField-Gibbs
Sales Asso: Edna Mercado
Sales Asso: Steffanie Mercier
Sales Asso: Steffanie Walsh
Sales Asso: Jessica Williams

D-U-N-S 13-548-4371
NOVASTAR LP
2310 Wolfcamp Cir, Midland, TX 79706-4492
Tel (432) 570-4207 *Founded/Ownrshp* 1995
Sales 32.2MM^E *EMP* 30
SIC 5169 Chemicals & allied products
Admn Mgr: Tom Sudduth
Admn Mgr: Eva Underwood
Plnt Mgr: Wes Reeves
Sls Mgr: Jerry Morales

D-U-N-S 12-487-7361
■ **NOVASTAR MORTGAGE INC**
(*Suby of* NFI HOLDING CORPORATION)
2114 Central St Ste 600, Kansas City, MO 64108-2098
Tel (816) 237-7000 *Founded/Ownrshp* 1996
Sales NA *EMP* 1,600
SIC 6162 Mortgage bankers
Pr: W Lance Anderson
**CFO:* Rodney Schwatken

D-U-N-S 07-865-7589
■ **NOVASYS HEALTH INC**
NOVASYS HEALTH NETWORK
(*Suby of* CENTENE CORP) ★
1 Allied Dr Ste 1400, Little Rock, AR 72202-2066
Tel (800) 294-3557 *Founded/Ownrshp* 2010
Sales NA *EMP* 241ᴱ
SIC 6324 6321 Health maintenance organization (HMO), insurance only; Accident & health insurance
Pr: John Ryan
**Treas:* Jeffrey Schwaneke
**VP:* William Scheffel

D-U-N-S 93-995-7270
■ **NOVASYS HEALTH LLC**
(*Suby of* CENTENE CORP) ★
10801 Executive Center Dr # 305, Little Rock, AR 72211-4353
Tel (501) 219-4444 *Founded/Ownrshp* 1996
Sales NA *EMP* 57
SIC 6324 6321 Health maintenance organization (HMO), insurance only; Accident & health insurance
CFO: Kim Suggs
VP: Scott Shellabarger
Sls Dir: Dwane Tankersley
Sls Mgr: Dwane Tankerelsy
Board of Directors: Joe Carter, Dwane Tankersley

NOVASYS HEALTH NETWORK
See NOVASYS HEALTH INC

D-U-N-S 01-548-9406
NOVATECH HOLDINGS CORP
(*Suby of* WEIR GROUP INC) ★
8388 C F Hawn Fwy, Dallas, TX 75217-7009
Tel (214) 398-1491 *Founded/Ownrshp* 2012
Sales 90.8MMᴱ *EMP* 1,220
SIC 3491 Pressure valves & regulators, industrial; Pressure valves & regulators, industrial
Pr: Jack Rogers
**VP:* Dave Warnick

D-U-N-S 13-948-4455
NOVATECH LLC
1720 Molasses Way, Quakertown, PA 18951-3360
Tel (484) 812-6000 *Founded/Ownrshp* 1984
Sales 46.6MMᴱ *EMP* 210
SIC 3822 3625 7372 Auto controls regulating residntl & coml environmt & applncs; Control equipment, electric; Prepackaged software; Auto controls regulating residntl & coml environmt & applncs; Control equipment, electric; Prepackaged software
CEO: Volker Oakey
**Pr:* Aubrey Zey
VP: Vincent V Horvath
VP: Kevin Johnson
VP: Paul Wallace
VP: Dwight Wood
Snr Sftwr: George McCollister

D-U-N-S 13-922-7446
NOVATECH PROCESS SOLUTIONS LLC
(*Suby of* NOVATECH LLC) ★
11425 Cronhill Dr Ste B, Owings Mills, MD 21117-2268
Tel (410) 753-8300 *Founded/Ownrshp* 2003
Sales 22.0MM *EMP* 175
SIC 7373 Computer integrated systems design; Computer integrated systems design
CEO: Volker Oakey
**Pr:* Buz Zey
**VP:* Jean Bandy
**VP:* Ron Gullickson
VP: Paul Wallace
**VP:* Dwight Wood
**VP:* Ray Wright

NOVATEK
See A HATTERSLEY & SONS INC

D-U-N-S 60-367-6099 IMP
NOVATEK INC
NOVAPICK
(*Suby of* SCHLUMBERGER OILFIELD SERVICES) ★
2185 H Tracy Hall Pkwy, Provo, UT 84606-6218
Tel (801) 374-6000 *Founded/Ownrshp* 2015
Sales 39.4MMᴱ *EMP* 150
SIC 8711 5944 Consulting engineer; Jewelry, precious stones & precious metals; Consulting engineer; Jewelry, precious stones & precious metals
Pr: David R Hall
VP: Joeseph Fox
Genl Mgr: Gary Peterson
Prd Mgr: Ron Crockett

D-U-N-S 11-102-3727 IMP
▲ **NOVATEL WIRELESS INC**
9645 Scranton Rd Ste 205, San Diego, CA 92121-1764
Tel (858) 812-3400 *Founded/Ownrshp* 1996
Sales 185.2MM *EMP* 240
Tkr Sym MIFI *Exch* NGS
SIC 3661 7371 Modems; Computer software development & applications; Computer software development; Modems; Computer software development & applications; Computer software development
CEO: Sue Swenson
CFO: Michael Newman
Ex VP: John Carney
Sr VP: Lance Bridges
Sr VP: Stephen Sek
VP: Dave Dohna
Mktg Mgr: Thien Nguyen
Sls Mgr: Rob Jazwinski
Board of Directors: Philip Falcone, Russell C Gerns, James Ledwith, Robert Pons, David A Werner

D-U-N-S 06-541-6000
NOVATEUR EDUCATION INC
ECPI UNIVERSITY
5555 Greenwich Rd, Virginia Beach, VA 23462-6542
Tel (757) 490-9090 *Founded/Ownrshp* 1966
Sales 76.3MMᴱ *EMP* 500
SIC 8221 8243 8249 Colleges universities & professional schools; Data processing schools; Vocational schools; Colleges universities & professional schools; Data processing schools; Vocational schools
Pr: Mark B Dreyfus
**CFO:* Gregory A Casey
**Treas:* Mildred L Dreyfus
Chf Mktg O: Marcelo Parravicini
Ofcr: Sandy Deabler
Ofcr: Sandra Sherrod
VP: Jeff Arthur
**VP:* Claudia Dreyfus
VP: Marcus Friedman
**VP:* Claudia Levi
MIS Dir: Joe Sleeper

D-U-N-S 07-864-6362
NOVATI TECHNOLOGIES INC
(*Suby of* TEZZARON SEMICONDUCTOR CORP) ★
2706 Montopolis Dr, Austin, TX 78741-6408
Tel (512) 356-2000 *Founded/Ownrshp* 2012
Sales 36.0MM *EMP* 110
SIC 3674 Semiconductors & related devices
Ch Bd: J Thomas Ayers
CEO: David Anderson
Prgrm Mgr: John Norbert
Prgrm Mgr: Tina Trimble
IT Man: Albert Howard
Opers Mgr: Mike Morgan

D-U-N-S 12-165-0563
NOVATIME TECHNOLOGY INC
1440 Bridgegate Dr # 300, Diamond Bar, CA 91765-3932
Tel (909) 895-8100 *Founded/Ownrshp* 1999
Sales 24.9MMᴱ *EMP* 81
SIC 7361 Executive placement
Pr: Frank Su
**Sr VP:* Ian Sexton
**VP:* Gil Sidhom
IT Man: Sunil Seth
Board of Directors: Gary Anderson, Brian Harris, Jim Schultz, Eric Su

D-U-N-S 02-794-7964
NOVATION INC
(*Suby of* VIZIENT INC) ★
290 E John Carpenter Fwy, Irving, TX 75062-2730
Tel (972) 581-5000 *Founded/Ownrshp* 1978
Sales NA *EMP* 500
SIC 5047 8742 Medical & hospital equipment; Management consulting services; Medical & hospital equipment; Management consulting services
CEO: Jody Hatcher
**CFO:* Jack Langenberg
**Sr VP:* Cathy A Denning
**Sr VP:* Dan Sweeney
**Sr VP:* Jill Witter
VP: Bob Benson
VP: Jill Dillon
VP: Scott Downing
VP: Linda Knox
Prgrm Mgr: Lucy Kuykendall
Off Admin: Emily Szkrybalo

NOVATION INDUSTRIES
See W M PLASTICS INC

NOVATION SETTLEMENT SOLUTIONS
See NOVATION VENTURES LLC

D-U-N-S 07-943-5217
NOVATION VENTURES LLC
NOVATION SETTLEMENT SOLUTIONS
1641 Worthington Rd, West Palm Beach, FL 33409-6705
Tel (561) 615-9360 *Founded/Ownrshp* 2012
Sales NA *EMP* 80ᴱ
SIC 6411 7999 Insurance agents, brokers & service; Lottery tickets, sale of
CFO: Charles Lowe

D-U-N-S 00-378-0202
NOVATO DISPOSAL SERVICE INC (CA)
TOTAL WASTE SYSTEMS
3417 Standish Ave, Santa Rosa, CA 95407-8135
Tel (707) 765-9995 *Founded/Ownrshp* 1947
Sales 30.4MMᴱ *EMP* 67
SIC 4953 Garbage: collecting, destroying & processing
Pr: James Ratto
**Sec:* Diana Ratto
**VP:* Robert M Mattos
**VP:* Raymond D Myers
Sales Exec: Casey Williams

D-U-N-S 06-886-6318
NOVATO UNIFIED SCHOOL DISTRICT
1015 7th St, Novato, CA 94945-2293
Tel (415) 897-4201 *Founded/Ownrshp* 1862
Sales 50.0MMᴱ *EMP* 830
SIC 8211 Public elementary school; Public junior high school; Public senior high school; Public elementary school; Public junior high school; Public senior high school
Dir Vol: Tracy Kreling
CFO: Marla Blackledge
CFO: Cyndee Cannon
Off Mgr: Pam Baker
Off Mgr: Carla Brouillette
Off Mgr: Mumu Delong
Off Mgr: Lynn Dragonette
Off Mgr: Patricia Ravetti
Off Mgr: Julie Spaan
Off Mgr: Cindy Testa
Off Mgr: Nancy Zanardi
Board of Directors: Pam Conklin, Karen Maloney, Mark Silva, Miguel Villarreal, Nancy Walker

D-U-N-S 80-883-7520
▲ **NOVAVAX INC**
20 Firstfield Rd, Gaithersburg, MD 20878-1760
Tel (240) 268-2000 *Founded/Ownrshp* 1987
Sales 30.6MM *EMP* 308ᴱ
Tkr Sym NVAX *Exch* NGM
SIC 2836 Biological products, except diagnostic; Vaccines & other immunizing products; Vaccines; Biological products, except diagnostic; Vaccines & other immunizing products; Vaccines
Pr: Stanley C Erck
**Ch Bd:* James F Young
CFO: Barclay A Phillips
Sr VP: Gregory M Glenn
Sr VP: Timothy J Hahn
Sr VP: Ford R Lynch
Sr VP: Cynthia N Oliver
Sr VP: John J Trizzino
Sr VP: Russell P Wilson
VP: Larry Ellingsworth
VP: Amy Fix
VP: Jill Hoyt
VP: Mary Riggin
VP: Brian Rosen
VP: Gale E Smith
Assoc Dir: Denise Hughes
Assoc Dir: Dana Jendrek
Assoc Dir: Dana Johnston
Assoc Dir: John Kutney
Assoc Dir: Ken KAO
Assoc Dir: Mike Sowers
Board of Directors: Gail K Boudreaux, Richard H Douglas, Gary C Evans, Michael A McManus Jr

NOVCO
See NOXIOUS VEGETATION CONTROL INC

D-U-N-S 01-946-6549
NOVEL IRON WORKS INC
250 Ocean Rd, Greenland, NH 03840-2431
Tel (603) 436-7950 *Founded/Ownrshp* 1956
Sales 50.2MMᴱ *EMP* 110
SIC 3441 Fabricated structural metal; Fabricated structural metal
CEO: Hollie Noveletsky
**Pr:* Josh Rosenthal
**Ex VP:* Thomas Heaney
**VP:* Keith Moreau
Plnt Mgr: Bill Gallant
Board of Directors: Paul Rosenthal

D-U-N-S 79-351-8643 IMP
NOVEL LABORATORIES INC
400 Campus Dr, Somerset, NJ 08873-1145
Tel (908) 603-6000 *Founded/Ownrshp* 2006
Sales 95.6MMᴱ *EMP* 175
SIC 2834 Pharmaceutical preparations; Pharmaceutical preparations
Pr: Veerappan Subramanian
**VP:* Kevin Anderson
VP: Scott Talbot
Assoc Dir: Raja Elangovan
Assoc Dir: Shyam Vangala
CIO: Hari Bala
QA Dir: Liz Montero
QA Dir: Irina Shnayder
Mfg Dir: Pablo Martinez
Prd Mgr: Lakshmi Nammalzar
Genl Couns: Anand Natarajan

NOVEL WRITING WORKSHOP
See F+W MEDIA INC

D-U-N-S 00-699-9676
NOVELART MANUFACTURING CO
TOPICZ
2121 Section Rd, Cincinnati, OH 45237-3509
Tel (513) 351-7700 *Founded/Ownrshp* 1903
Sales 361.7MM *EMP* 160
Accts Pitcher Enders & Drohan Cinc
SIC 5141 5145 5194 Groceries, general line; Confectionery; Tobacco & tobacco products; Groceries, general line; Confectionery; Tobacco & tobacco products
Pr: Marvin H Schwartz
CIO: Bob Reckers
Dir IT: Bob Schilling
VP Sls: Dan Sunderuaus

D-U-N-S 00-150-4935 EXP
NOVELIS CORP (TX)
ADITYA BIRLA GROUP
(*Suby of* NOVELIS INC) ★
3560 Lenox Rd Ne Ste 2000, Atlanta, GA 30326-4271
Tel (404) 760-4000 *Founded/Ownrshp* 1960, 2007
Sales 807.9MMᴱ *EMP* 3,000
SIC 3353 Aluminum sheet, plate & foil; Foil, aluminum; Aluminum sheet, plate & foil; Foil, aluminum
CEO: Marco Palmieri
Pr: Tom Walpole
**CEO:* Thomas Walpole
**CFO:* Tracy Tan
**Treas:* Glen Guman
Bd of Dir: Helmut Eschwey
**Ofcr:* Erwin Mayr
**VP:* Charles R Aley
VP: Pierre Arseneault
VP: Nicholas Brecker
VP: Andrew King
VP: Derek Prichett
**VP:* Brenda Pulley

D-U-N-S 96-325-8483 IMP/EXP
NOVELIS INC
(*Suby of* HINDALCO INDUSTRIES LIMITED)
3560 Lenox Rd Ne Ste 2000, Atlanta, GA 30326-4271
Tel (404) 760-4000 *Founded/Ownrshp* 2010
Sales 9.8MMM *EMP* 11,410ᴱ
SIC 3355 Aluminum rolling & drawing; Aluminum ingot; Aluminum rolling & drawing; Aluminum ingot
Pr: Steve Fisher
**Ch Bd:* Kumar Mangalam Birla
Pr: Tom Walpole
**CFO:* Steve Pohl
**Treas:* Randal P Miller
Treas: Randall Miller
**V Ch Bd:* D Bhattacharya
**Ofcr:* Hr Shashikant
Sr VP: Jack Clark
Sr VP: Nicholas Madden
**Sr VP:* Leslie J Parrette Jr
VP: David Gill
**VP:* Robert Nelson
VP: Derek Prichett
Board of Directors: Clarence J Chandran, Satish Pai, Donald A Stewart

D-U-N-S 03-778-7298
NOVELL INC
1800 Novell Pl, Provo, UT 84606-6101
Tel (801) 861-4272 *Founded/Ownrshp* 2011
Sales 556.5MMᴱ *EMP* 3,400
SIC 7372 Prepackaged software; Prepackaged software
Pr: Jeff Hawn
Ch Bd: Gerard Van Kemmel
**Pr:* Bob Flynn
Pr: Rhonda O'Donnell
Pr: Tim Wolfe
**CFO:* Dana C Russell
**CFO:* Charles Sanbury
**Treas:* Jim Beck
**Chf Mktg O:* John K Dragoon
Sr VP: Jim Ebzery
Sr VP: Carl S Ledbetter
**Sr VP:* Russell C Poole
**Sr VP:* Scott N Semel
Sr VP: John J Slitz Jr
VP: Jos Almandoz
**VP:* Juan Carlos Cerrutti
VP: Sergio Toshio Mituiwa
**VP:* Eric Varness
**VP:* Dave Wilkes

D-U-N-S 05-378-4232
■ **NOVELLA CLINICAL INC**
(*Suby of* QUINTILES INC) ★
1700 Perimeter Park Dr, Morrisville, NC 27560-8404
Tel (919) 484-1921 *Founded/Ownrshp* 2013
Sales 84.4MMᴱ *EMP* 670
SIC 8731 Medical research, commercial; Medical research, commercial
Pr: W Richard Staub III
Pr: George Rafols
**COO:* Robert King
**CFO:* Charles R Lambert
**Chf Mktg O:* Frank Santoro
Ex VP: Nick Dyer
Ex VP: Wingate Elaine
**Ex VP:* Krystyna Kowalczyk
**Ex VP:* Rob Stallings
Ex VP: Elaine Wingate
VP: Jane Bentley
VP: Elizabeth Edwards
VP: Kimberly Hunsicker
Assoc Dir: Elli Ganas
Assoc Dir: Nathan Landon
Assoc Dir: Michelle Stanek

D-U-N-S 11-330-3416
NOVELLUS SYSTEMS INC
4000 N 1st St, San Jose, CA 95134-1568
Tel (408) 943-9700 *Founded/Ownrshp* 2012
Sales NA *EMP* 2,855ᴱ
SIC 3559

NOVELTY DISTRIBUTORS COMPANY
See NOVELTY INC

D-U-N-S 06-713-9410 IMP
NOVELTY INC
NOVELTY DISTRIBUTORS COMPANY
351 W Muskegon Dr, Greenfield, IN 46140-4016
Tel (317) 462-3121 *Founded/Ownrshp* 1981
Sales 71.3MMᴱ *EMP* 127
SIC 5099 Novelties, durable; Novelties, durable
Pr: Todd Green
Pr: Yvonne Stader
**CFO:* Patrick Brazill
CFO: Patrick Brazill
**VP:* Aaron Butcher
VP: Brian Parker
VP: James Robles
Dist Mgr: Danny Pogue
Sales Exec: Len Connor
VP Sls: Aaron Osmon

D-U-N-S 93-266-2133 IMP/EXP
NOVEM CAR-INTERIOR-DESIGN INC
(*Suby of* NOVEM CAR INTERIOR DESIGN GMBH)
8140 Troon Cir Sw Ste 160, Austell, GA 30168-7891
Tel (678) 396-6880 *Founded/Ownrshp* 1994
Sales 28.4MMᴱ *EMP* 70
SIC 5013 7389 Automotive supplies & parts; Field warehousing
CEO: Gunther Brenner
**Ex VP:* Jurgen Theobald

D-U-N-S 14-858-5441 IMP
NOVEN PHARMACEUTICALS INC
(*Suby of* HISAMITSU PHARMACEUTICAL CO INC) ★
11960 Sw 144th St, Miami, FL 33186-6109
Tel (305) 964-3393 *Founded/Ownrshp* 2009
Sales 153.1MMᴱ *EMP* 586
SIC 2834 Pharmaceutical preparations; Pharmaceutical preparations
CEO: Jeffrey F Eisenberg
V Ch: Takehiko Noda
CFO: William Pecora
**CFO:* Michael D Price
Bd of Dir: Melinda Downs
Bd of Dir: Bryan Foughty
**Ex VP:* Joel Lippman
Ex VP: Joel S Lippman
Ex VP: Grace Lopez
**VP:* Peter Amanatides
VP: Peter G Amanatides
**VP:* Brian J Board
VP: Carrie Bowers
VP: Scott Briggs
VP: Anthony De Padova
**VP:* Steven M Dinh
**VP:* Patrick Gallagher
**VP:* Richard Gilbert
VP: Richard P Gilbert
**VP:* Joseph C Jones
VP: Jeff T Mihm

D-U-N-S 80-659-5047
NOVETTA INC
WOTI
(*Suby of* NOVETTA LLC) ★
7921 Jones Branch Dr # 500, Mc Lean, VA 22102-3354
Tel (571) 282-3000 *Founded/Ownrshp* 1996
Sales 36.6MMᴱ *EMP* 300

SIC 7379 Computer related maintenance services; Computer related maintenance services
CEO: Peter B Lamontagne
*Ch Bd: Alan J Broder
*Pr: Scott Gessay
*CFO: Rich Sawchak
*Sr VP: Kris Heim
*Sr VP: Samir Nanavati
*VP: Keith Dill
Software D: Dan Ryder

D-U-N-S 07-857-9473
NOVETTA LLC
(Suby of NOVETTA SOLUTIONS LLC) ★
7921 Jones Branch Dr # 500, Mc Lean, VA 22102-3354
Tel (571) 282-3000 Founded/Ownrshp 2010
Sales 80.0MM EMP 350E
SIC 7373 Systems engineering, computer related; Systems engineering, computer related
CEO: Peter Lamontagne
*CFO: Richard Sawchak
VP: Angela Losacco
Snr Sftwr: Mark Connor
Snr Sftwr: Michael Rutt
Software D: David Morgan
Sftwr Eng: Marc Chu
Sftwr Eng: Bart Hunking
Sftwr Eng: Joon Lee
Manager: Tom McKee

D-U-N-S 96-929-1306
NOVETTA SOLUTIONS LLC
7921 Jones Branch Dr # 500, Mc Lean, VA 22102-3354
Tel (571) 282-3000 Founded/Ownrshp 2012
Sales 108.8MME EMP 430E
SIC 7373 Systems engineering, computer related; Systems engineering, computer related
CEO: Peter Lamontagne
Pr: Scott Gessay
CFO: Richard Sawcahk
Chf Mktg O: Richard Clements
Sr VP: Raj Nanavati
VP: Kim Bartoe
VP: Keith Dill
VP: Michael Elder
VP: Joseph Pantella
Prgrm Mgr: Ashley Groff
Prgrm Mgr: Judith Renaud

D-U-N-S 01-087-6126
NOVI COMMUNITY SCHOOL DISTRICT
NCSD
25345 Taft Rd, Novi, MI 48374-2423
Tel (248) 449-1200 Founded/Ownrshp 1938
Sales 51.8MME EMP 900
Accts Doeren Mayhew Troy Michigan
SIC 8211 Public elementary school; Public junior high school; Public senior high school; Public elementary school; Public junior high school; Public senior high school
*Pr: Dennis O'Connor
*Treas: Ann Glubzinski
Trst: Paul Cook
Trst: George Kortlandt
Trst: Willy Mena
*VP: Bobbie Murphy

D-U-N-S 04-732-1195
NOVICK BROTHERS CORP
3660 S Lawrence St, Philadelphia, PA 19148-5611
Tel (215) 467-1400 Founded/Ownrshp 1963
Sales 32.5MME EMP 50
SIC 5148 Fresh fruits & vegetables
Pr: Gary Novick
CFO: Russ Rosenflag
*Treas: Jack Novick
VP: Jeffery Frank
VP: John Marshall
*VP: William Novick
Opers Mgr: Robert Flocke
Sls&Mrk Ex: Bill Novick

D-U-N-S 18-109-8997
NOVINGER GROUP INC
1441 Stoneridge Dr, Middletown, PA 17057-5977
Tel (717) 930-0300 Founded/Ownrshp 1987
Sales 108.8MME EMP 351
SIC 1742 1799 5032 5033 5039 Drywall; Plastering, plain or ornamental; Fireproofing buildings; Drywall materials; Insulation, thermal; Ceiling systems & products; Drywall; Plastering, plain or ornamental; Fireproofing buildings; Drywall materials; Insulation, thermal; Ceiling systems & products
Pr: James D Novinger
COO: Bob Myers

D-U-N-S 13-430-6138
NOVINIUM INC
22820 Russell Rd, Kent, WA 98032-4892
Tel (253) 288-7100 Founded/Ownrshp 2003
Sales 99.8MME EMP 240
SIC 1521 General remodeling, single-family houses
CEO: Glen Bertini
COO: John Reilly
*CFO: David L Lewis
*VP: Richard K Brinton
*VP: Kurt Wangenheim
Exec: Jan Cannon
Rgnl Mgr: Marco Chavarria
Rgnl Mgr: Dennis McDougall
IT Man: Peter Christman
IT Man: Chris Kemp
Sftwr Eng: Michael Case

D-U-N-S 07-976-8050
NOVIPAX LLC
(Suby of ATLAS HOLDINGS LLC) ★
2215 York Rd Ste 504, Oak Brook, IL 60523-2379
Tel (203) 622-9138 Founded/Ownrshp 2015
Sales 105.3MME EMP 760E
SIC 2299 2821 Padding & wadding, textile; Polystyrene resins
CEO: Bob Larson
*CFO: Don Eldert

D-U-N-S 80-773-9748 IMP
NOVITA TECHNOLOGIES INC
175 Old Shackle Island Rd, Hendersonville, TN 37075-2546
Tel (615) 826-0372 Founded/Ownrshp 2007
Sales 21.0MME EMP 75
SIC 3699 Electrical equipment & supplies
Pr: Mike Incorvaia
Pr: Vern Price
*CFO: Todd Campbell
*VP: Bernon Price
*VP: Robert Wells
Board of Directors: Warren Hyland

D-U-N-S 78-598-5354
NOVITAS SOLUTIONS INC
(Suby of DIVERSIFIED SERVICE OPTIONS INC) ★
2020 Tech Pkwy Ste 100, Mechanicsburg, PA 17050
Tel (717) 526-3459 Founded/Ownrshp 2012
Sales NA EMP 791E
SIC 6321 Accident & health insurance; Accident & health insurance
CEO: Sandra Coston
*Treas: Thomas Hickson
VP: Carolyn Cridlersmith
Genl Mgr: Samantha Bailor
Genl Mgr: Gayeta Porter
IT Man: Christopher Moir
VP Opers: David Vaughan

D-U-N-S 12-173-3018
NOVITEX ENTERPRISE SOLUTIONS INC
300 First Stamford Pl # 2, Stamford, CT 06902-6765
Tel (844) 668-4839 Founded/Ownrshp 2013
Sales 590.5MME EMP 2,850E
SIC 7334 8741 Photocopying & duplicating services; Management services; Photocopying & duplicating services; Management services
CEO: John Visentin
*Pr: Irina Novoselsky
*COO: Joe Trost
*CFO: Robert G Rooney
Treas: David Riposo
VP: Tatiana Koleva
VP: Dawn Marie Weimer
Prgrm Mgr: Richard Dixon

D-U-N-S 04-961-0942
NOVITEX GOVERNMENT SOLUTIONS LLC
(Suby of NOVITEX ENTERPRISE SOLUTIONS INC) ★
8401 Corporate Dr Ste 420, Landover, MD 20785-2277
Tel (301) 731-4595 Founded/Ownrshp 2012
Sales 69.5MME EMP 1,400
SIC 8744 Facilities support services; Facilities support services
Pr: Irina Novoselsky

D-U-N-S 07-955-2686
NOVO 1 HOLDINGS INC
(Suby of DIALOGDIRECT INC) ★
4301 Cambridge Rd, Fort Worth, TX 76155-2627
Tel (817) 355-8200 Founded/Ownrshp 2014
Sales 146.3MME EMP 2,256E
SIC 8742 Marketing consulting services

D-U-N-S 01-031-3018
NOVO 1 INC
(Suby of NOVO 1 HOLDINGS INC) ★
4301 Cambridge Rd, Fort Worth, TX 76155-2627
Tel (817) 355-8909 Founded/Ownrshp 1985
Sales 145.1MME EMP 2,500E
SIC 7389 Telemarketing services; Telemarketing services
CEO: Mary Murcott
*COO: Eric Rothert
*CFO: John Sykstus
*Chf Mktg O: Jack Wilkie
VP: Mike Satterlee
Dir Rx: Christopher Wade
Genl Mgr: Mike McGee
*CTO: Mitchell Swindell
Dir IT: Bob Gardner
IT Man: Roy Tell
Opers Mgr: Michelle Wilson

D-U-N-S 07-908-6078
NOVO BIOPOWER LLC
3418 N Val Vista Dr, Mesa, AZ 85213-9739
Tel (480) 641-0202 Founded/Ownrshp 2013
Sales 30.6MME EMP 29
SIC 4911 Generation, electric power

D-U-N-S 06-571-2247
NOVO CONSTRUCTION INC
1460 Obrien Dr, Menlo Park, CA 94025-1432
Tel (650) 701-1500 Founded/Ownrshp 2000
Sales 463.7MM EMP 155
SIC 1542 Commercial & office building contractors; Commercial & office building contractors
CEO: James C Fowler
*Pr: Jim Fowler
Exec: Doug Ballou
Off Mgr: Jennifer Hampson
Sfty Dirs: Thomas Allison
Snr PM: Mike Bank
Snr PM: Noel Howard
Snr PM: Curtis Ikemoto
Snr PM: Tony Vierra
Snr Mgr: Bob Hooks

D-U-N-S 14-613-7810
NOVO ENGINEERING INC
1350 Specialty Dr Ste A, Vista, CA 92081-8565
Tel (760) 598-6686 Founded/Ownrshp 2003
Sales 21.8MME EMP 60E
SIC 8711 Consulting engineer
CEO: Dan Kline
*Pr: Rajan Ramaswamy
*VP: Dave Peterson

D-U-N-S 94-209-2466
NOVO FOUNDATION
535 5th Ave Fl 33, New York, NY 10017-3665
Tel (212) 808-5400 Founded/Ownrshp 1999
Sales 150.2MM EMP 5
SIC 8641 Civic social & fraternal associations
Ex Dir: Bob Dandrew

Off Mgr: Kelly Merryman
Snr Mgr: Puja Dhawan

D-U-N-S 96-687-9215 IMP/EXP
NOVO MOTOR ACOUSTIC SYSTEMS INC
23031 Sherwood Ave, Warren, MI 48091-2044
Tel (586) 427-3838 Founded/Ownrshp 2009
Sales 39.4MME EMP 90
SIC 5013 Automotive supplies & parts
Pr: Tim Droege
Plnt Mgr: Edin Jakupovic
Ql Cn Mgr: Jeff Burdzinski

D-U-N-S 01-217-7531 IMP
NOVO NORDISK INC
(Suby of NOVO-NORDISK OF NORTH AMERICA INC) ★
800 Scudders Mill Rd, Plainsboro, NJ 08536-1606
Tel (609) 987-5800 Founded/Ownrshp 1989
Sales 159.8MME EMP 390E
SIC 2834 Pharmaceutical preparations; Pharmaceutical preparations
Pr: Jesper Hiland
*Pr: Martin Soeters
Sr Cor Off: Claus Jordan
*Chf Mktg O: Alan C Moses
Ex VP: Lars Almblom
*Sr VP: Andrew Ajello
*Sr VP: Lars Green
*VP: Philip Fornecker
VP: Eddie Li
VP: Fiil Niels
VP: Curtis G Oltmans
VP: Andrew J Purcell
VP: Henrik Rasmussen
VP: Jackie Scanlan
VP: Hanne Schou-Rode
VP: Michael Shalmi
Exec: Jerzy Gruhn
Assoc Dir: Craig Delarge
Assoc Dir: Jeff Fayer
Assoc Dir: Margaret Fisher
Assoc Dir: Mary Fox

D-U-N-S 62-292-0320 IMP
NOVO NORDISK PHARMACEUTICAL INDUSTRIES INC
(Suby of NOVO NORDISK INC) ★
3612 Powhatan Rd, Clayton, NC 27527-9217
Tel (919) 553-6051 Founded/Ownrshp 1991
Sales 152.8MME EMP 390
SIC 2833 Insulin: bulk, uncompounded; Insulin: bulk, uncompounded
Prin: David W Bright
VP: Birgitte Rassing
VP: Joann Sufalko
*VP: Palle Thorsen
VP: Per Valstorp
Dist Mgr: Nathaniel Lewey
Genl Mgr: Douglas Tharp
IT Man: Amy Hill
IT Man: Ken Mitchell
Software D: Vijaya Sudula
Mfg Dir: Bruce McCarthy

D-U-N-S 19-680-1849
NOVO-NORDISK OF NORTH AMERICA INC
(Suby of NOVO NORDISK A/S)
800 Scudders Mill Rd, Plainsboro, NJ 08536-1606
Tel (609) 987-5800 Founded/Ownrshp 1988
Sales 159.8MME EMP 1,200
SIC 8741 8733 5122 2833 2834 Management services; Medical research; Drugs, proprietaries & sundries; Insulin: bulk, uncompounded; Pharmaceutical preparations; Management services; Medical research; Drugs, proprietaries & sundries; Insulin: bulk, uncompounded; Pharmaceutical preparations
Pr: Jerzy Gruhn
Pr: Lars Jrgensen
VP: Iben Helbirk
VP: Line Karmark
VP: Per Lundgren
IT Man: Jennifer Holmes
Ql Cn Mgr: Rene Pedersen
Ql Cn Mgr: Bill Quinn
Ql Cn Mgr: Xu Yang
Snr Mgr: Matthew Ford

D-U-N-S 05-655-2035
NOVOCURE INC
(Suby of NOVOCURE (ISRAEL) LTD)
195 Commerce Way Unit A, Portsmouth, NH 03801-3251
Tel (603) 436-2809 Founded/Ownrshp 2011
Sales 65.5MME EMP 200
SIC 5047 Medical & hospital equipment
Ch Bd: William Doyle
CEO: Asaf Danziger
COO: Michael Ambrogi
CFO: Wilco Groenhuysen
Ch: William F Doyle
Assoc Dir: Sharon Perez
Prin: Gabriel Leung
Off Admin: Lori Jones
Off Admin: Rachel Shanley
CTO: Yoram Palti
VP Mktg: Eilon Kirson

D-U-N-S 62-553-7097
NOVOGRADAC & CO LLP
246 1st St Ste 500, San Francisco, CA 94105-4699
Tel (415) 356-8000 Founded/Ownrshp 1989
Sales 64.6MME EMP 400
SIC 8721

NOVOLEX
See HILEX POLY CO LLC

D-U-N-S 07-978-7120
NOVOLEX HOLDINGS INC
101 E Carolina Ave, Hartsville, SC 29550-4213
Tel (843) 857-4800 Founded/Ownrshp 2009
Sales 2.5MMME EMP 5,000
SIC 2673 2674 Plastic bags: made from purchased materials; Paper bags: made from purchased materials
Pr: Stanley B Bikulege
*CFO: Paul Palmisano

*Sr VP: Mark Daniels
*VP: Joyce A Foster

NOVOLYTE PERFORMANCE
See NOVOLYTE TECHNOLOGIES INC

D-U-N-S 82-878-7437 IMP
NOVOLYTE TECHNOLOGIES INC
NOVOLYTE PERFORMANCE
(Suby of BASF SE)
8001 E Pleasant Valley Rd, Cleveland, OH 44131-5526
Tel (216) 867-1040 Founded/Ownrshp 2012
Sales 32.3MME EMP 305
SIC 2621 Specialty or chemically treated papers; Specialty or chemically treated papers
Pr: Edward Frindt
Ch: Timothy Zappala
VP: Richard Watkins

D-U-N-S 12-966-4236
NOVOSOFT INC
3803 Mount Bonnell Rd, Austin, TX 78731-5732
Tel (512) 454-1140 Founded/Ownrshp 1999
Sales 19.9MME EMP 400
SIC 7371 Computer software development; Computer software development
Pr: Philip R Brenan
*CFO: Pat Eure

NOVOTEL NEWYORK
See 226 WEST FIFTY-SECOND STREET LLC

D-U-N-S 13-048-9847
NOVOZYMES BIOAG INC
(Suby of NOVOZYMES A/S)
3101 W Custer Ave, Milwaukee, WI 53209-4827
Tel (262) 957-2000 Founded/Ownrshp 2011
Sales 25.5MME EMP 100
SIC 2819 2869 2879 Industrial inorganic chemicals; Industrial organic chemicals; Agricultural chemicals; Industrial inorganic chemicals; Industrial organic chemicals; Agricultural chemicals
Pr: Trevor Thiessen
Sls Mgr: Byron Blekeberg
Sls Mgr: Francis Leier
Sls Mgr: Robert Todd

D-U-N-S 03-229-1770
NOVOZYMES BIOLOGICALS INC
(Suby of NOVOZYMES A/S)
5400 Corporate Cir, Salem, VA 24153-8300
Tel (540) 389-9361 Founded/Ownrshp 2001
Sales 24.2MME EMP 125
SIC 2836 Bacterial vaccines; Bacterial vaccines
Pr: Patrick G Patterson
Treas: Richard Olofson
VP: Jonathan Leder
Dir IT: Alan Berry
Sfty Mgr: Jeff Crissman
Mktg Mgr: Bernie Yemc
Manager: Randy Hicks
Manager: Aubrey Stadther
Sales Asso: John Kroppman
Sales Asso: Jimmy Throckmorton
Snr Mgr: Bradley Cole

D-U-N-S 78-797-2124
NOVOZYMES INC
(Suby of NOVOZYMES US INC) ★
1445 Drew Ave, Davis, CA 95618-4880
Tel (530) 757-8100 Founded/Ownrshp 2015
Sales 25.6MME EMP 110E
SIC 8732 Commercial nonphysical research; Commercial nonphysical research
CEO: Peder Holk Nielsen
*Pr: Ejner B Jensen
CFO: Maarit Pokkinen

D-U-N-S 05-209-0909 IMP/EXP
NOVOZYMES NORTH AMERICA INC
(Suby of NOVOZYMES A/S)
77 Perry Chapel Church Rd, Franklinton, NC 27525-9677
Tel (919) 494-2014 Founded/Ownrshp 1969
Sales 126.1MME EMP 400E
SIC 2869 Enzymes; Enzymes
Ch Bd: Adam Monroe
*Pr: Steen Riisgaard
CFO: John Gaebler
*CFO: Benny D Loft
*VP: Per Falholt
VP: Claus C Fuglsang
*VP: Thomas Nagy
Genl Mgr: Rose Gilliam
Plnt Mgr: Mark Edwards
Prd Mgr: John Meadows
Mktg Mgr: Daniel Evanson

D-U-N-S 06-769-2892
NOVOZYMES US INC
(Suby of NOVOZYMES A/S)
1445 Drew Ave, Davis, CA 95618-4880
Tel (530) 757-8100 Founded/Ownrshp 2002
Sales 47.8MME EMP 675E
SIC 6719 Investment holding companies, except banks
CEO: Ejner Bech Jensen
Pr: Glen Medwin

D-U-N-S 62-714-5464
NOVUM HOLDINGS LLC
N126 W8585 Westbrook St N 126, Menomonee Falls, WI 53051
Tel (262) 251-5561 Founded/Ownrshp 2006
Sales 28.2MME EMP 185
SIC 1791 1793 3441 3446 Structural steel erection; Glass & glazing work; Fabricated structural metal; Architectural metalwork; Structural steel erection; Glass & glazing work; Fabricated structural metal; Architectural metalwork
Pr: Ian M Collins

D-U-N-S 87-826-9042
NOVUM PHARMACEUTICAL RESEARCH SERVICES OF DELAWARE INC
225 W Station Square Dr # 200, Pittsburgh, PA 15219-1174
Tel (412) 363-3300 Founded/Ownrshp 1993

Sales 36.7MM^E *EMP* 300
SIC 8731 Testing laboratories; Biological research
CEO: Christopher Chamberlain
CFO: Linda Angeline
Sr VP: Stephen McMahon
VP: Darin Brimhall
**VP:* Alan Copa
VP: Phil Davies
**VP:* Darin Brimhall Facp
**VP:* Keith Gallicano PHD
**VP:* Gail Gongas
Assoc Dir: Virginia Catullo
Assoc Dir: David Pruitt

D-U-N-S 15-696-0536 IMP/EXP
NOVUM STRUCTURES LLC
(*Suby of* NOVUM HOLDINGS LLC) ★
W126n8585 Westbrook Xing, Menomonee Falls, WI 53051-3329
Tel (262) 255-5561 *Founded/Ownrshp* 2011
Sales 28.2MM^E *EMP* 90
SIC 1791 1793 3441 3446 Structural steel erection; Glass & glazing work; Fabricated structural metal; Architectural metalwork
Off Mgr: Heidi Johnson
Prd Mgr: John Hunter
Ql Cn Mgr: Thomas Ehlert
Manager: Kevin Bruce
Manager: J Howell
Snr PM: Colin Marriott
Snr PM: David McMullen

NOVUS AUTO GLASS REPAIR
See NOVUS INC

D-U-N-S 09-053-4892 IMP
NOVUS INC
NOVUS AUTO GLASS REPAIR
655 Calle Cubitas, Guaynabo, PR 00969-2802
Tel (787) 272-4546 *Founded/Ownrshp* 1973
Sales 57.6MM *EMP* 660
Accts Fpv & Galindez Psc San Juan
SIC 7536 Automotive glass replacement shops; Automotive glass replacement shops
Pr: C Castellon Nigaglioni
**Treas:* Anastasio Rodriguez
**VP:* Carlos C Fernandez
Dir IT: Narciso Deremer
IT Man: Narciso Morales
IT Man: Julio Ramirez
Opers Mgr: Jose Acosta

D-U-N-S 62-652-1264 IMP/EXP
NOVUS INTERNATIONAL INC
(*Suby of* MITSUI & CO (USA) INC) ★
20 Research Park Dr, Saint Charles, MO 63304-5633
Tel (314) 576-8886 *Founded/Ownrshp* 1991
Sales 120.1MM^E *EMP* 350
SIC 0752 Animal specialty services; Animal specialty services
Pr: Francois Fraudeau
**CFO:* John C Wade
Ex VP: Gasperoni Giovanni
**Sr VP:* Jeff Klopfenstein
VP: Sumit Dhawan
VP: Stephen Lorbert
Exec: Olivia Lindsey
Snr Ntwrk: Randal Lewis
CIO: Matthew Clarke
QA Dir: Zack Hickman
QA Dir: Kevin Smith

D-U-N-S 19-870-7890
■ **NOVUS MEDIA INC**
AGENTI MEDIA SERVICES
(*Suby of* ANNALLECT GROUP) ★
2 Carlson Pkwy N Ste 400, Minneapolis, MN 55447-4470
Tel (612) 302-6800 *Founded/Ownrshp* 2000
Sales 43.3MM^E *EMP* 130
SIC 7319 Media buying service; Media buying service
CEO: David Murphy
**Pr:* Gwendolyn Maass
**CFO:* Jay Deverell
**Sr VP:* Margy Campion
VP: Meredith Coughlin
**VP:* Melony Rios
**VP:* Jodi Thielges
**VP:* Bridgit Wallace
Assoc Dir: Jennifer Grimm
Snr Sftwr: Bryan Wolf
Dir IT: Scott Tonjes

D-U-N-S 95-664-9982
NOW COMMUNICATIONS INC
12124 High Tech Ave # 150, Orlando, FL 32817-8374
Tel (888) 612-4226 *Founded/Ownrshp* 1996
Sales 24.0MM *EMP* 120
SIC 4813 Local & long distance telephone communications
Pr: Larry W Seab
**CFO:* Charles W McGuffee

D-U-N-S 18-796-0067
NOW COURIER INC
111 E Mccarty St, Indianapolis, IN 46225-3322
Tel (317) 638-7071 *Founded/Ownrshp* 1986
Sales 30.2MM *EMP* 84
Accts Zimmerman & Co Cpas Inc C
SIC 7389 4225 Courier or messenger service; General warehousing & storage; Courier or messenger service; General warehousing & storage
Owner: Ryan Schwalbach
**Pr:* Michael A Schwalbach
**COO:* Sandy Schwalbach
**Ex VP:* John Durbin
VP: Joel Paska
Rgnl Mgr: Dallas Harris
Rgnl Mgr: Ron Ping
Off Mgr: Judy Knose
IT Man: Joanna Falconer
IT Man: David Thoma
Opers Mgr: Don Gurunian

D-U-N-S 06-747-2530 IMP/EXP
NOW HEALTH GROUP INC
NOW NATURAL FOODS
244 Knollwood Dr Ste 300, Bloomingdale, IL 60108-2288
Tel (630) 545-9098 *Founded/Ownrshp* 1962
Sales 334.7MM^E *EMP* 985
SIC 2834 Vitamin, nutrient & hematinic preparations for human use; Vitamin, nutrient & hematinic preparations for human use
Ch Bd: Elwood Richard
**Pr:* Albert Powers
COO: Jim Emme
VP: Dan Scoles
Genl Mgr: Dan Richard
Cmptr Lab: Susan Berkman
QA Dir: Louis De Mers
QA Dir: Azad Lakhani
Dir IT: Randy Kjell
Dir IT: Michael Lelah
Mfg Mgr: Herman Gutierrez

D-U-N-S 07-933-0215
▲ **NOW INC**
7402 N Eldridge Pkwy, Houston, TX 77041-1902
Tel (281) 823-4700 *Founded/Ownrshp* 2013
Sales 4.1MMM *EMP* 5,300^E
Tkr Sym DNOW *Exch* NYS
SIC 5084 Industrial machinery & equipment; Petroleum industry machinery; Industrial machinery & equipment; Petroleum industry machinery
Pr: Robert R Workman
Ch Bd: Merrill A Miller Jr
CFO: Daniel L Molinaro
VP: Raymond W Chang
VP: David A Cherechinsky
VP: Jim N Owsley
VP: Clent Rawlinson
VP: Brad Wise
Rgnl Mgr: Don Ard
Rgnl Mgr: Stu Goehring
Rgnl Mgr: Mark Riggs
Board of Directors: Richard Alario, Terry Bonno, Galen Cobb, James Crandell, Rodney W Eads, Michael E Frazier, J Wayne Richards

D-U-N-S 80-871-0115
NOW MICRO INC
1645 Energy Park Dr # 200, Saint Paul, MN 55108-2741
Tel (651) 393-2100 *Founded/Ownrshp* 1993
Sales 56.2MM^E *EMP* 36
SIC 5045 5734 Computers, peripherals & software; Computer & software stores
Pr: Patrick Finn
**VP:* Bob Milam
VP Sls: William Teevan

NOW NATURAL FOODS
See NOW HEALTH GROUP INC

D-U-N-S 10-238-0870
NOWAK CONSTRUCTION CO INC
200 S Goddard Rd, Goddard, KS 67052-8923
Tel (316) 794-8898 *Founded/Ownrshp* 1979
Sales 20.8MM^E *EMP* 87
Accts Lewis Dahlstrom Mcpherson Ks
SIC 1623 Water main construction; Sewer line construction; Pipeline construction
Pr: Joe Nowak
**Sec:* John G Nowak

D-U-N-S 00-308-2997 IMP
■ **NOXELL CORP**
PROCTER & GAMBLE COSMETICS
(*Suby of* PROCTER & GAMBLE CO) ★
11050 York Rd, Hunt Valley, MD 21030-2098
Tel (410) 785-7300 *Founded/Ownrshp* 1912
Sales 137.6MM^E *EMP* 1,509
SIC 2844 Cosmetic preparations; Perfumes & colognes; Toilet preparations; Cosmetic preparations; Perfumes & colognes; Toilet preparations
Pr: Marc S Pritchard
**VP:* Robert Blanchard
**VP:* Carroll A Bodie
**VP:* Clayton C Daley Jr
VP: James J Hoskins
VP: Richard G Pease
**VP:* Valarie Sheppard
Assoc Dir: Marilyn Glen
**VP Admn:* Stanley Boric
Snr Mgr: Ivanka Jauregui
Snr Mgr: Casey Waechter

D-U-N-S 01-790-8989
NOXIOUS VEGETATION CONTROL INC
NOVCO
3136 Trabue Rd, Columbus, OH 43204-3663
Tel (614) 486-8994 *Founded/Ownrshp* 1960
Sales 29.4MM^E *EMP* 100
SIC 5191 Herbicides; Herbicides
Pr: Charles W Thomas
VP: Donna Thomas
**VP:* Todd Thomas
**VP:* Clarence Wissiner
Genl Mgr: Clarence Wissinger

D-U-N-S 10-004-0112
NOXUBEE COUNTY SCHOOL DISTRICT
3715 Jefferson St, Macon, MS 39341-2289
Tel (662) 726-4583 *Founded/Ownrshp* 1960
Sales 17.4MM^E *EMP* 350
SIC 8211 Public elementary & secondary schools; Public elementary & secondary schools
Pr: Kevin Jones

NOYES HEALTH
See NICHOLAS H NOYES MEMORIAL HOSPITAL INC

NP
See NITTANY PAPER MILLS INC

D-U-N-S 05-799-8317
■ **NP MZD LLC**
NORTH POINT MAZDA
(*Suby of* ASBURY AUTOMOTIVE ARKANSAS DEALERSHIP HOLDINGS LLC) ★
6030 Landers Rd, North Little Rock, AR 72117-1939
Tel (877) 398-2063 *Founded/Ownrshp* 1999
Sales 28.0MM *EMP* 27
SIC 5511 Automobiles, new & used; Automobiles, new & used
Sls Mgr: Jon Andrews
Sales Asso: John Wright

D-U-N-S 78-568-7534 IMP
NPA COATINGS INC
SEIBERT POWDER COATINGS
(*Suby of* PROTECH CHIMIE LTEE)
11110 Berea Rd Ste 1, Cleveland, OH 44102-2540
Tel (216) 651-5900 *Founded/Ownrshp* 2013
Sales 100.5MM^E *EMP* 212
SIC 2851 Paints & paint additives; Paints & paint additives
CEO: Hidefumi Morita
**Pr:* Sam Rhue
**Treas:* Gary Rizzardi
**Sec:* Joan Daniels
Chf Mktg O: Dan Weinhardt
**Ex VP:* Masato Kurokawa

NPC GLOBAL SERVICES
See NATIONAL PACKAGING CORP

D-U-N-S 07-912-8769
■ **NPC GROUP INC**
(*Suby of* VANTIV INC) ★
5100 Interchange Way, Louisville, KY 40229-2160
Tel (312) 627-6000 *Founded/Ownrshp* 2013
Sales 27.6MM^E *EMP* 2,493^E
SIC 7389 Credit card service
Prin: Charles Drucker

D-U-N-S 00-433-9727
NPC INC (PA)
13710 Dunnings Hwy, Claysburg, PA 16625-7802
Tel (814) 239-8787 *Founded/Ownrshp* 1931
Sales 96.3MM^E *EMP* 450
SIC 2752 2789 2759 Commercial printing, offset; Bookbinding & related work; Commercial printing; Commercial printing, offset; Bookbinding & related work; Commercial printing
Ch Bd: Mark N Barnhart
Pr: Mark Kelly
Ofcr: Joe Bieniek
Ex VP: Tim McCarthy
VP: Joshua E Barnhart
VP: Ed Detwiler
VP: Chip W Gallaher
VP: Robert R Latoche
VP: Timothy P McCarthy
CTO: Chip Gallaher
Dir IT: Rod Hinish
Board of Directors: Mark Gallaher, Thomas E Schwartz

D-U-N-S 07-835-5793
NPC INTERNATIONAL HOLDINGS INC
7300 W 129th St, Overland Park, KS 66213-2631
Tel (913) 327-3109 *Founded/Ownrshp* 2011
Sales 1.1MMM^E *EMP* 29,000^E
SIC 5812 Pizzeria, chain
Ch Bd: James K Schwartz

D-U-N-S 07-626-4456 IMP
NPC INTERNATIONAL INC
PIZZA HUT
(*Suby of* NPC RESTAURANT HOLDINGS LLC) ★
7300 W 129th St, Overland Park, KS 66213-2631
Tel (913) 632-0300 *Founded/Ownrshp* 2006
Sales 944.1MM^E *EMP* 25,000^E
SIC 5812 Pizzeria, chain; Pizzeria, chain
Ch: James K Schwartz
COO: J Hedrick
CFO: Troy D Cook
Ex VP: Sally Blackerby
Sr VP: Marty Couk
VP: L Bruce Sharp
VP: David Short
VP: D Blayne Vaughn
VP: Michael J Woods
CIO: Michael Woods
VP Mktg: Linda L Sheedy
Board of Directors: Brandon K Barnholt, Christopher J Birosak, Robert F End, Charles W Peffer

D-U-N-S 80-847-1796
NPC RESTAURANT HOLDINGS LLC
(*Suby of* NPC INTERNATIONAL HOLDINGS INC) ★
7300 W 129th St, Overland Park, KS 66213-2631
Tel (913) 327-5555 *Founded/Ownrshp* 2011
Sales 1.1MMM *EMP* 29,000
Accts Kpmg Llp Kansas City Missour
SIC 5812 6794 Pizzeria, chain; Fast-food restaurant, chain; Franchises, selling or licensing; Pizzeria, chain; Fast-food restaurant, chain; Franchises, selling or licensing
Ch Bd: James K Schwartz
CFO: Troy D Cook
Sr VP: Linda L Sheedy
Sr VP: D Blayne Vaughn
VP: Thomas D White

NPC SALES
See BA MERCHANT SERVICES

D-U-N-S 15-102-0997
NPC SOUTH INC
(*Suby of* NATCO PRODUCTS CORP) ★
203 S Easterling St 206, Dalton, GA 30721-3237
Tel (706) 278-5911 *Founded/Ownrshp* 1985
Sales 59.2MM^E *EMP* 450^E
SIC 2273 Rugs, hand & machine made; Rugs, hand & machine made
Pr: Roy Littman
**CEO:* Roland Cantrell
**CFO:* Alan Ross
**VP:* Terry Kinnamon
Exec: Ronald Joseph

D-U-N-S 06-593-6890
NPD GROUP INC
900 W Shore Rd, Port Washington, NY 11050-4663
Tel (516) 625-0700 *Founded/Ownrshp* 1966
Sales 219.4MM^E *EMP* 727
SIC 8732 Market analysis or research; Market analysis or research
Pr: Tod Johnson
Pr: Tim Bush
Sr VP: John Deputato
Sr VP: Chris Kyriacou
Sr VP: Lisa Schultz
VP: Allan Baldinger
VP: Harry Balzer
VP: Bob Brien
VP: Stephen Costello
VP: Luis Delahoz
VP: Isabelle Grenet
VP: Christine Miserandino
VP: Mike Oak
VP: Patricia Riehl
VP: Michele Schmal
VP: Mark Truss
VP: Jane A Zimmy

D-U-N-S 14-469-8396 IMP
NPD HOLDING INC
1825 Big Horn Ave, Cody, WY 82414-3210
Tel (307) 587-5515 *Founded/Ownrshp* 1984
Sales 37.5MM^E *EMP* 165^E
SIC 3089 5083 Identification cards, plastic; Farm equipment parts & supplies; Identification cards, plastic; Farm equipment parts & supplies
Ch Bd: Glenn W Nielson
**Pr:* Jerry V Payne

D-U-N-S 82-605-6306
NPF HOLDING LLC
4000 Chemical Rd Ste 200, Plymouth Meeting, PA 19462-1708
Tel (484) 594-1000 *Founded/Ownrshp* 2008
Sales NA *EMP* 5
Accts St Clair Cpas Pc Conshohocke
SIC 6162 Mortgage bankers; Mortgage bankers
Ex VP: Gail Buss

D-U-N-S 96-046-0400
NPG HOLDINGS INC
KVIA TV
(*Suby of* NEWS-PRESS & GAZETTE CO INC) ★
825 Edmond St, Saint Joseph, MO 64501-2737
Tel (816) 271-8500 *Founded/Ownrshp* 1994
Sales 21.4MM^E *EMP* 173
SIC 2711 Commercial printing & newspaper publishing combined
Ex VP: Henry H Bradley
**Pr:* David Bradley
**Treas:* Lyle E Leimkuhler

NPG NEWSPAPERS
See NEWS-PRESS & GAZETTE CO INC

NPI MEDICAL
See ANSONIA PLASTICS LLC

D-U-N-S 17-524-9432
NPI PROPERTY MANAGEMENT CORP
(*Suby of* AIMCO PROPERTIES LP) ★
55 Beattie Pl, Greenville, SC 29601-2165
Tel (864) 239-1000 *Founded/Ownrshp* 1994
Sales 84.5MM^E *EMP* 1,474^E
SIC 6798 Real estate investment trusts; Real estate investment trusts
Pr: David Robertson

NPIC
See NATURAL POLYMER INTERNATIONAL CORP

D-U-N-S 14-797-4695 IMP/EXP
NPK CONSTRUCTION EQUIPMENT INC
(*Suby of* NIPPON PNEUMATIC MANUFACTURING CO.,LTD.)
7550 Independence Dr, Bedford, OH 44146-5541
Tel (440) 232-7900 *Founded/Ownrshp* 1985
Sales 38.5MM^E *EMP* 102
SIC 5082 3599 3546 3532 3531 3421 Construction & mining machinery; Machine shop, jobbing & repair; Power-driven handtools; Mining machinery; Construction machinery; Cutlery; Construction & mining machinery; Machine shop, jobbing & repair; Power-driven handtools; Mining machinery; Construction machinery; Cutlery
Pr: Dan Tyrell
Dist Mgr: Rich Desmond
Opers Mgr: Bob Gerhardstein
Ql Cn Mgr: Bill McCreary
Sls Mgr: Joe Obergas

D-U-N-S 04-230-0384
■ **NPL CONSTRUCTION CO**
(*Suby of* SOUTHWEST GAS CORP) ★
2355 W Utopia Rd, Phoenix, AZ 85027-4167
Tel (623) 582-1235 *Founded/Ownrshp* 1967
Sales 869.6MM^E *EMP* 2,245
SIC 1623 Oil & gas pipeline construction; Oil & gas pipeline construction
Pr: James P Kane
Ofcr: Dan Weaklend
Sr VP: Dennis Redmond
**VP:* Mark S Wambach
Rgnl Mgr: Bill Wambach
Area Mgr: Beau Beus
Area Mgr: Lee Couture
Area Mgr: Darrel Gehring
Area Mgr: Brian Hallan
Area Mgr: Ron Haskin
Area Mgr: Doug Miller

NPMC HOMETOUCH HEALTHCARE
See NATIONAL PARK MEDICAL CENTER INC

D-U-N-S 16-917-5382
NPP LLC
4860 33rd Ave, Columbus, NE 68601-1662
Tel (402) 564-9464 *Founded/Ownrshp* 2007
Sales 100.0MM *EMP* 350
SIC 0213 Hogs; Hogs
**CFO:* Jim Rasmussen

D-U-N-S 80-732-5639
NPP LLC
4860 33rd Ave, Columbus, NE 68601-1662
Tel (402) 564-9464 *Founded/Ownrshp* 2007
Sales 31.5MM^E *EMP* 375
SIC 5147 Meats & meat products; Meats & meat products
CFO: James Rasmussen

NPPI
See NATIONAL PIPE & PLASTICS INC

D-U-N-S 10-107-0238
NPPI INTERMEDIATE INC
106 E 6th St Ste 300, Austin, TX 78701-3661
Tel (512) 476-7100 *Founded/Ownrshp* 2001
Sales 361.8MM *EMP* 35
SIC 3086 Insulation or cushioning material, foamed plastic; Ice chests or coolers (portable), foamed plastic; Cups & plates, foamed plastic; Insulation or cushioning material, foamed plastic; Ice chests or coolers (portable), foamed plastic; Cups & plates, foamed plastic
Ch Bd: Michael Stakias
**CFO:* Gary Kofnovec
**Treas:* Mike Derrick
VP: Debra Garrett
VP: Gary Haley
VP: Paul W Larson
**VP:* David Rogalski
Mktg Mgr: James Preston

D-U-N-S 84-746-0552 IMP
NPR AMERICA INC
41650 Gardenbrook Rd # 180, Novi, MI 48375-1323
Tel (248) 449-8955 *Founded/Ownrshp* 2008
Sales 27.9MM^E *EMP* 400
SIC 3089 Automotive parts, plastic; Automotive parts, plastic
Pr: Yoshitake Ogowa
**Prin:* Matt Omura

D-U-N-S 84-918-0281 IMP
NPR OF AMERICA INC
(*Suby of* NIPPON PISTON RING CO.,LTD.)
680 Wilson Pkwy, Bardstown, KY 40004-2073
Tel (502) 350-9270 *Founded/Ownrshp* 2011
Sales 51.9MM^E *EMP* 150
SIC 5013 Automotive supplies
Pr: Yoshitaka Ogawa
**Treas:* Robert Cecil

NPS
See NOVARTIS PHARMACEUTICALS CORP

D-U-N-S 05-017-0014
NPS MARKETING
3381 Sage Rose Ln, Placerville, CA 95667-5452
Tel (916) 941-5510 *Founded/Ownrshp* 2010
Sales 2.5MM *EMP* 300
SIC 8742 7389 Marketing consulting services;
Owner: Scott Becker

D-U-N-S 18-187-1427
NPS PHARMACEUTICALS INC
(*Suby of* SHIRE PHARMACEUTICAL HOLDINGS IRELAND LIMITED)
550 Hills Dr Fl 310, Bedminster, NJ 07921-1537
Tel (908) 450-5300 *Founded/Ownrshp* 2015
Sales 54.1MM^E *EMP* 207^E
SIC 2834 Drugs acting on the central nervous system & sense organs; Drugs acting on the gastrointestinal or genitourinary system; Thyroid preparations; Drugs acting on the central nervous system & sense organs; Drugs acting on the gastrointestinal or genitourinary system; Thyroid preparations
CEO: Flemming Ornskov MD
Pr: Paul Firuta
Top Exec: Brent Stansbury
VP: Robert Ashworth
VP: John Caminis
VP: Jeffrey Gelb
VP: Susan Kalk
VP: Hjalmar Lagast
VP: Rene Merghart
VP: Bernie Sauders
Assoc Dir: David Gash
Assoc Dir: Jon Jessmer
Assoc Dir: Stanley Mittelman

D-U-N-S 79-458-4920
NR AUTOMOTIVE INC
NEW ROCHELLE TOYOTA
47 Cedar St, New Rochelle, NY 10801-5212
Tel (914) 576-8000 *Founded/Ownrshp* 1992
Sales 28.9MM^E *EMP* 70
SIC 5511 Automobiles, new & used; Automobiles, new & used
Pr: Don Lia
Sls Mgr: Michael Buchbinder
Sales Asso: Richard Malamut
Sales Asso: Mohammed Mulla

D-U-N-S 15-979-8099
NRA FOUNDATION INC
FRIENDS OF NRA
11250 Waples Mill Rd # 1, Fairfax, VA 22030-9400
Tel (703) 267-1000 *Founded/Ownrshp* 1990
Sales 41.3MM *EMP* 6
SIC 8699 Charitable organization; Charitable organization
Pr: Frank Brownell III
**Treas:* Wilson H Phillips Jr
**VP:* Hon Bill K Brewster
**Ex Dir:* Wayne Sheets

D-U-N-S 62-796-7222
NRA GROUP LLC
NATIONAL RECOVERY AGENCY
2491 Paxton St, Harrisburg, PA 17111-1036
Tel (717) 540-6171 *Founded/Ownrshp* 2005
Sales 11.4MM *EMP* 287^E
SIC 7322 Collection agency, except real estate; Collection agency, except real estate
CEO: Steven C Kusic
Owner: Jill E M Kusic
Dir Bus: Remy Devarenne
Board of Directors: Alonzo Hankerson, Anita Schaar

D-U-N-S 08-151-2188
NRAD MEDICAL ASSOCIATES PC (NY)
990 Stewart Ave Ste 400, Garden City, NY 11530-4838
Tel (516) 222-2022 *Founded/Ownrshp* 1986
Sales 32.3MM^E *EMP* 140
SIC 8011 Radiologist
Ch Bd: Jonathan Friedman
**Ch Bd:* Annette Marinaccio
**Pr:* David H Faegenberg MD
CFO: Paul Strohmenger
**VP:* Mark Gershawin MD
Mng Dir: Tom Taylor
Off Mgr: Karen Post
CIO: Anthony Patane
Diag Rad: Robert Blake
Diag Rad: Yekaterina Bulkin
Diag Rad: Celin Chacko

NRAO
See NATIONAL RADIO ASTRONOMY OBSERVATORY

D-U-N-S 07-966-3133
NRC ALASKA LLC
EMERALD ALASKA
425 E Outer Springer Loop, Palmer, AK 99645-6701
Tel (907) 258-1558 *Founded/Ownrshp* 2014
Sales 32.0MM^E *EMP* 91^E
SIC 4959 Toxic or hazardous waste cleanup; Oil spill cleanup; Environmental cleanup services
Prin: Steven Candito
Prin: Mark Boivin
Prin: David Rattner
Prin: Salvatore Sacco
Prin: Glenn Shor

D-U-N-S 79-694-8651 IMP
NRC ENVIRONMENTAL SERVICES INC
(*Suby of* NATIONAL RESPONSE CORP) ★
1605 Ferry Pt Ste 200, Alameda, CA 94501-7592
Tel (510) 749-1390 *Founded/Ownrshp* 2003
Sales 57.3MM^E *EMP* 315
SIC 4959 Toxic or hazardous waste cleanup; Oil spill cleanup; Environmental cleanup services; Toxic or hazardous waste cleanup; Oil spill cleanup; Environmental cleanup services
Pr: Steven Candito
**Sr VP:* Neil Challis
**Sr VP:* Mike Reese
**Sr VP:* Todd Roloff
**Sr VP:* Sal Sacco
Genl Mgr: Todd Ruloff

D-U-N-S 03-377-0956
NRD HOLDINGS LLC (FL)
625 Dekalb Ste 100, Decatur, GA 30033
Tel (404) 499-1960 *Founded/Ownrshp* 2010
Sales NA *EMP* 1,200
SIC 6719 Investment holding companies, except banks; Investment holding companies, except banks
Pr: Aziz Hashim

NRDC
See NATURAL RESOURCES DEFENSE COUNCIL INC

D-U-N-S 12-552-2974 IMP
NRE ACQUISITION CO LLC
VMV PADUCAHBILT
(*Suby of* NATIONAL RAILWAY EQUIPMENT CO) ★
1300 Kentucky Ave, Paducah, KY 42003-1961
Tel (270) 444-4555 *Founded/Ownrshp* 2002
Sales 40.6MM^E *EMP* 180
SIC 3743 Mining locomotives & parts, electric or nonelectric; Railroad locomotives & parts, electric or nonelectric; Mining locomotives & parts, electric or nonelectric; Railroad locomotives & parts, electric or nonelectric
Prin: Dan Tallant
Pr: Bob Pedersen
Chf Mktg O: Jim Gosa
IT Man: Joan Chambers
IT Man: Randy Hoskins
Sfty Dirs: Coby Davis
Sfty Dirs: Laura Jewell
Plnt Mgr: David Koenigsmark
Mktg Dir: David Carrico

NREC
See NATIONAL RAILWAY EQUIPMENT CO

D-U-N-S 78-783-2633 IMP
NREC POWER SYSTEMS INC
5222 Highway 311, Houma, LA 70360-2878
Tel (985) 872-5480 *Founded/Ownrshp* 1992
Sales 21.8MM^E *EMP* 90
SIC 3519 7538 Diesel engine rebuilding; Diesel engine repair: automotive
Pr: Susan Beal
**Ex VP:* Brian F Chaisson
Genl Mgr: Chico Rivera
Dir IT: Rick Fournet

NRECA
See NATIONAL RURAL ELECTRIC COOPERATIVE ASSOCIATION

D-U-N-S 06-184-9881 IMP
NRF DISTRIBUTORS INC
485 Old Belgrade Rd, Augusta, ME 04330-8061
Tel (207) 622-4744 *Founded/Ownrshp* 1973
Sales 126.9MM *EMP* 310
SIC 5023

NRG
See GENON ENERGY INC

D-U-N-S 96-497-2553
■ **NRG CALIFORNIA SOUTH LP**
(*Suby of* NRG ENERGY INC) ★
211 Carnegie Ctr, Princeton, NJ 08540-6213
Tel (609) 524-4590 *Founded/Ownrshp* 1998
Sales 48.7MM^E *EMP* 269^E
SIC 4911 Electric services
Mng Pt: David Freysinger

D-U-N-S 03-984-0363
■ **NRG DELTA LLC**
(*Suby of* GENON CALIFORNIA NORTH LLC) ★
211 Carnegie Ctr, Princeton, NJ 08540-6213
Tel (609) 524-4500 *Founded/Ownrshp* 1999
Sales 35.4MM^E *EMP* 150
SIC 4911 Electric services; Electric services

D-U-N-S 12-751-9580 IMP
■ **NRG EL SEGUNDO OPERATIONS INC**
(*Suby of* NRG ENERGY INC) ★
301 Vista Del Mar, El Segundo, CA 90245-3650
Tel (310) 615-6344 *Founded/Ownrshp* 1998
Sales 31.8MM^E *EMP* 65
SIC 4911 Electric services
Pr: John Ragan

D-U-N-S 07-878-0271
NRG ENERGY
5790 Fleet St Ste 200, Carlsbad, CA 92008-4703
Tel (760) 710-2140 *Founded/Ownrshp* 2009, 2013
Sales 20.0MM^E *EMP* 97^E
SIC 4911 Generation, electric power
CEO: Thomas P Doyle
Sr VP: Randall Hickok
VP: Gordon Chirdon
Mktg Mgr: Darcy McGrath

D-U-N-S 83-199-6454
■ **NRG ENERGY CENTER HARRISBURG LLC**
(*Suby of* NRG THERMAL LLC)
100 N 10th St Fl 3, Harrisburg, PA 17101-2440
Tel (717) 234-4600 *Founded/Ownrshp* 2008
Sales 29.4MM^E *EMP* 45
SIC 4911 Electric services
Pr: Michael Carroll
**CFO:* Robert Sauer
**VP:* Jan Sockel
Plnt Mgr: Daniel Quinn

D-U-N-S 02-822-7234
■ **NRG ENERGY CENTER MINNEAPOLIS LLC**
MINNEAPOLIS ENERGY CENTER
(*Suby of* NRG THERMAL LLC)
80 S 8th St Ste 2850, Minneapolis, MN 55402-2103
Tel (612) 349-6066 *Founded/Ownrshp* 2008
Sales 30.4MM^E *EMP* 64^E
SIC 4931 Electric & other services combined

D-U-N-S 07-926-2594
■ **NRG ENERGY CENTER OMAHA LLC**
ENERGY SYSTEMS COMPANY
(*Suby of* NRG YIELD INC) ★
2152 Howard St, Omaha, NE 68102-2455
Tel (402) 346-9066 *Founded/Ownrshp* 2014
Sales 244.6M^E *EMP* 3,884^E
SIC 1731 Electric power systems contractors
Plnt Mgr: David Geck
Plnt Mgr: Ted Vincent

D-U-N-S 07-849-8291
■ **NRG ENERGY INC**
(*Suby of* NRG ENERGY INC) ★
1201 Fannin St, Houston, TX 77002-6929
Tel (713) 537-3000 *Founded/Ownrshp* 2012
Sales 2.5MMM^E *EMP* 7,786
SIC 3621 Motors & generators; Motors & generators
Pr: James Garlick
VP: Gary Devore
VP: William Harmon
Prgrm Mgr: Brian Lafleur
Admn Mgr: Patricia Young
Snr Ntwrk: Adam Grounds
Snr Ntwrk: Stan Ringoringo
IT Man: Thomas Marshall
IT Man: Cedric Stein
VP Opers: Jim Locher
Opers Mgr: Alan Metzler

D-U-N-S 79-342-2213 IMP
▲ **NRG ENERGY INC**
211 Carnegie Ctr, Princeton, NJ 08540-6213
Tel (609) 524-4500 *Founded/Ownrshp* 1989
Sales 15.8MMM *EMP* 9,806
Accts Kpmg Llp Philadelphia Pennsy
Tkr Sym NRG *Exch* NYS
SIC 4911 Electric services; Distribution, electric power; Generation, electric power; Transmission, electric power; Electric services; Distribution, electric power; Generation, electric power; Transmission, electric power
Pr: Mauricio Gutierrez
CFO: Kirkland B Andrews
Chf Cred: Matthew Goller
Ofcr: Anne M Cleary
Ofcr: Tanuja Dehne
Ofcr: Dave Frank
Ex VP: David R Hill
Ex VP: Ershel Redd
Ex VP: Gloria Rivera
VP: David Callen
Creative D: Heather Loftiss
Dir Bus: Tony Cirillo
Board of Directors: Thomas H Weidemeyer, E Spencer Abraham, Walter R Young, Lawrence S Coben, Howard E Cosgrove, Terry G Dallas, William E Hantke, Paul W Hobby, Edward R Muller, Anne C Schaumburg, Evan J Silverstein

D-U-N-S 07-984-1680
NRG INDUSTRIES INC
1625 Diplomat Dr, Carrollton, TX 75006-6848
Tel (972) 247-7448 *Founded/Ownrshp* 1973
Sales 47.7MM^E *EMP* 400
SIC 5039 3444 3564 3559 Air ducts, sheet metal; Sheet metalwork; Filters, air: furnaces, air conditioning equipment, etc.; Plastics working machinery; Air ducts, sheet metal; Sheet metalwork; Filters, air: furnaces, air conditioning equipment, etc.; Plastics working machinery
Pr: R Ashley Cunningham
**Treas:* Daniel J Disser
**Treas:* Phil Rutledge
**VP:* George S Pappayliou

D-U-N-S 02-550-3157
NRG MANUFACTURING INC
11311 Holderrieth Rd # 100, Tomball, TX 77375-7385
Tel (281) 320-2525 *Founded/Ownrshp* 2001
Sales 131.0MM^E *EMP* 140
SIC 3449 3441 Miscellaneous metalwork; Fabricated structural metal; Miscellaneous metalwork; Fabricated structural metal
Pr: Mark Terry
**Sec:* James Cauble
**VP:* Tom Giles
VP: Tim Rodabaugh
**VP:* Rachael Terry
VP Opers: Tim Rodabough
Opers Mgr: Jason Neel
Opers Mgr: Daniel Trevino
Pgrm Dir: Robert Chevalier

D-U-N-S 06-277-6539
NRG MEDIA INC
(*Suby of* GOLD CIRCLE ENTERTAINMENT) ★
1020 E 2nd St, Webster City, IA 50595-1754
Tel (515) 832-1570 *Founded/Ownrshp* 1999
Sales 35.4MM^E *EMP* 700
SIC 4832 Radio broadcasting stations; Contemporary; Talk; Radio broadcasting stations; Contemporary; Talk
CEO: Michael Delich
**Pr:* Mary Quass

D-U-N-S 12-468-6408
NRG MEDIA LLC
2875 Mount Vernon Rd Se, Cedar Rapids, IA 52403-3553
Tel (319) 862-0300 *Founded/Ownrshp* 2002
Sales 207.5MM^E *EMP* 749
SIC 4832 Radio broadcasting stations; Radio broadcasting stations
Genl Mgr: Mary Harris
IT Man: Charlie Johnson
Prd Mgr: Gary Douglas
Mktg Dir: Brooke Schulz
Sls Mgr: Stacie McElligott

D-U-N-S 15-588-4732
■ **NRG NORTHEAST GENERATING LLC**
(*Suby of* NRG ENERGY INC) ★
211 Carnegie Ctr, Princeton, NJ 08540-6213
Tel (609) 524-4500 *Founded/Ownrshp* 2000
Sales 328.1MM^E *EMP* 363
SIC 4911 ;
Opers Mgr: Robert Hemperley

D-U-N-S 02-825-5979 IMP
■ **NRG POWER MARKETING LLC**
(*Suby of* NRG ENERGY INC) ★
211 Carnegie Ctr, Princeton, NJ 08540-6213
Tel (609) 524-4500 *Founded/Ownrshp* 2000, 2007
Sales 220.1MM^E *EMP* 245
SIC 4911 4924 Distribution, electric power; Natural gas distribution; Distribution, electric power; Natural gas distribution
Sr VP: John Chillemi
Treas: Clint Freeland
**Ex VP:* Kirkland Andrews
**Ex VP:* Anne M Cleary
**Ex VP:* Lee Davis
**Prin:* Jeffrey Baudier
**Prin:* M Hoffmann
**Prin:* J Murphy
Opers Mgr: Mark Bentley
Board of Directors: Jeffrey Baudier, M Hoffmann, J Murphy

D-U-N-S 96-497-4310
■ **NRG REMA LLC**
GENON REMA, LLC
(*Suby of* NRG ENERGY INC) ★
1000 Main St, Houston, TX 77002-6336
Tel (713) 497-3000 *Founded/Ownrshp* 1998
Sales 2.5MMM^E *EMP* 5,039^E
SIC 4911 Electric services
Pr: William Lee Davis
**VP:* Daniel M Keane
**VP:* Judith Lagano
**VP:* Christopher S Moser
**VP:* Phil Williamson

D-U-N-S 83-144-9199
■ **NRG RENEW LLC**
(*Suby of* NRG ENERGY INC) ★
5790 Fleet St Ste 200, Carlsbad, CA 92008-4703
Tel (760) 710-2140 *Founded/Ownrshp* 2009
Sales 34.2MM^E *EMP* 50^E
SIC 4911 Electric services
CEO: Thomas P Doyle
**COO:* Mauricio Gutierrez
**CFO:* Kirkland Andrews
**VP:* Keith A Latham

D-U-N-S 06-999-8609
■ **NRG SOLAR KANSAS SOUTH HOLDINGS LLC**
(*Suby of* NRG YIELD OPERATING LLC) ★
211 Carnegie Ctr, Princeton, NJ 08540-6213
Tel (609) 524-4500 *Founded/Ownrshp* 2012
Sales 232.7M^E *EMP* 2,052^E
SIC 4911 Generation, electric power
CFO: Kirkland B Andrews

D-U-N-S 06-135-2970
■ **NRG SOLAR MAYFAIR LLC**
(*Suby of* NRG YIELD OPERATING LLC) ★
211 Carnegie Ctr, Princeton, NJ 08540-6213
Tel (609) 524-4500 *Founded/Ownrshp* 2012
Sales 116.0M^E *EMP* 912^E
SIC 1711 Solar energy contractor
CFO: Kirkland B Andrews

D-U-N-S 17-277-4379
■ **NRG TEXAS LLC**
(*Suby of* NRG ENERGY INC) ★
521 5th Ave Fl 30, New York, NY 10175-3001
Tel (713) 795-6000 *Founded/Ownrshp* 2006
Sales 534.9MM^E *EMP* 2,015

SIC 4911 Generation, electric power; Transmission, electric power; Generation, electric power; Transmission, electric power

D-U-N-S 07-887-0121

■ NRG YIELD INC
(*Suby of* NRG ENERGY INC) ★
211 Carnegie Ctr, Princeton, NJ 08540-6213
Tel (609) 524-4500 *Founded/Ownrshp* 2012
Sales 583.0MM *EMP* 7,786^E
Tkr Sym NYLD *Exch* NYS
SIC 4911 Electric services; Distribution, electric power; Generation, electric power; Transmission, electric power; Electric services; Distribution, electric power; Generation, electric power; Transmission, electric power
CEO: Mauricio Gutierrez
**CFO:* Kirkland B Andrews
Ex VP: David R Hill
VP: David Callen
VP: James Lodge

D-U-N-S 04-392-6359

■ NRG YIELD LLC
(*Suby of* NRG YIELD INC) ★
211 Carnegie Ctr, Princeton, NJ 08540-6213
Tel (609) 524-4500 *Founded/Ownrshp* 2013
Sales 1.5MM^E *EMP* 3,884^E
SIC 1711 Solar energy contractor
CFO: Kirkland B Andrews

D-U-N-S 04-611-8883

■ NRG YIELD OPERATING LLC
(*Suby of* NRG YIELD LLC) ★
211 Carnegie Ctr, Princeton, NJ 08540-6213
Tel (609) 524-4500 *Founded/Ownrshp* 2013
Sales 1.2MM^E *EMP* 3,881^E
SIC 1711 Solar energy contractor
CFO: Kirkland B Andrews

NRHA
See NORFOLK REDEVELOPMENT HOUSING AUTHORITY

D-U-N-S 85-845-1784

NRHMC INC
SOUND SHORE MEDICAL CENTER
16 Guion Pl, New Rochelle, NY 10801-5502
Tel (914) 632-5000 *Founded/Ownrshp* 1983
Sales 179.1MM^E *EMP* 1,232
SIC 8062 8721 General medical & surgical hospitals; Hospital, AMA approved residency; Accounting, auditing & bookkeeping; General medical & surgical hospitals; Hospital, AMA approved residency; Accounting, auditing & bookkeeping
Pr: John R Spicer
**Ch Bd:* Lawrence Ruisi
**COO:* Douglas O Landy
**CFO:* Thomas M Daly
**Treas:* James Millstein
**V Ch Bd:* Thomas M McEvoy
Sr VP: Clark Walter
VP: Pam Dupuis
Dir Rx: Julio Viola
Plnt Mgr: Carey Laramore
Pathlgst: Deborah Carroll

NRI
See NATIONAL REPROGRAPHICS INC

D-U-N-S 78-948-3158

NRI COMMUNITY SERVICES INC
800 Clinton St Ste 204, Woonsocket, RI 02895-3210
Tel (401) 235-7000 *Founded/Ownrshp* 1966
Sales 21.1MM *EMP* 99
SIC 8322 Individual & family services; Individual & family services
CEO: Christian L Stephens
VP: Brooks Herrick

NRI DISTRIBUTION
See NRI USA LLC

D-U-N-S 07-266-3750

NRI INC
NRI STAFFING RESOURCES
1015 18th St Nw Ste 710, Washington, DC 20036-5206
Tel (202) 466-4670 *Founded/Ownrshp* 1972
Sales 7.9MM *EMP* 2,740
SIC 7363 7361 Temporary help service; Executive placement; Temporary help service; Executive placement
Pr: Robert Mulberger
**Treas:* Robert McClimans
Founder: Les Meil
Brnch Mgr: Karlene Francois
Brnch Mgr: Kenny Kast
Dist Mgr: Ernie Lorandeau

NRI STAFFING RESOURCES
See NRI INC

D-U-N-S 06-502-9653 IMP

NRI USA LLC
NRI DISTRIBUTION
(*Suby of* NRI DISTRIBUTION LTD)
13200 S Broadway, Los Angeles, CA 90061-1124
Tel (323) 345-6456 *Founded/Ownrshp* 2011
Sales 24.6MM^E *EMP* 100
SIC 4731 Freight transportation arrangement

NRL
See NAVAL RESEARCH LABORATORY

NRL MORTGAGE
See NATIONS RELIABLE LENDING LLC

D-U-N-S 07-196-1007

■ NRMC INC
NORTHEAST REGIONAL MEDICAL CTR
(*Suby of* COMMUNITY HEALTH SYSTEMS INC) ★
315 S Osteopathy Ave, Kirksville, MO 63501-6401
Tel (660) 785-1000 *Founded/Ownrshp* 2000
Sales 70.3MM^E *EMP* 535
SIC 8062 General medical & surgical hospitals; General medical & surgical hospitals
CEO: Eric Barber
Ofcr: Loren Riles
Ofcr: Nancy Rourke
Mng Ofcr: Toni Smith
Off Admin: Roberta Snyder
Dir IT: Bev Howard
Plas Surg: Larry McIntire
Doctor: Dana Valencia
HC Dir: Brad Darr
HC Dir: Jenny King

NRMS
See NASH-ROCKY MOUNT SCHOOLS

D-U-N-S 93-186-8376

NRP CONTRACTORS LLC
5309 Transportation Blvd, Cleveland, OH 44125-5333
Tel (216) 475-8900 *Founded/Ownrshp* 1995
Sales 85.8MM^E *EMP* 100
Accts Ss & G Financial Sources Inc
SIC 1521 1522 Single-family housing construction; Hotel/motel & multi-family home construction
CFO: Andrew Tanner

D-U-N-S 55-639-5700

NRP GROUP LLC
5309 Transportation Blvd, Cleveland, OH 44125-5333
Tel (216) 475-8900 *Founded/Ownrshp* 1996
Sales 49.2MM^E *EMP* 60^E
SIC 1521 General remodeling, single-family houses

D-U-N-S 60-252-9435

NRP HOLDING CO INC
1 Mauchly, Irvine, CA 92618-2305
Tel (949) 583-1000 *Founded/Ownrshp* 2003
Sales 50.2MM^E *EMP* 600
SIC 6719 Investment holding companies, except banks; Investment holding companies, except banks
Pr: Jeffrey P Frieden
**VP:* Robert Friedman

D-U-N-S 14-658-9440

NRP HOLDINGS LLC
5309 Transportation Blvd, Cleveland, OH 44125-5333
Tel (216) 475-8900 *Founded/Ownrshp* 2002
Sales 100.0MM *EMP* 150
Accts Ss & G Financial Services Inc
SIC 1531 Townhouse developers; Townhouse developers

NRP-JONES
See NEPHI RUBBER PRODUCTS CORP

D-U-N-S 02-039-2141

NRR INC
NISSAN OF ROANOKE RAPIDS
(*Suby of* HUBERT VESTER CHEVROLET) ★
407 Premier Blvd, Roanoke Rapids, NC 27870-5041
Tel (252) 537-1041 *Founded/Ownrshp* 2011
Sales 51.4MM^E *EMP* 180
SIC 5511 Automobiles, new & used; Automobiles, new & used
Pr: Hubert Vester
**Prin:* James Jones

NRS
See NORTHWEST RIVER SUPPLIES INC

D-U-N-S 78-099-2384

NRT BUS INC
NORTH READING TRANSPORTATION
55 Hampshire Rd, Methuen, MA 01844-1112
Tel (978) 681-4100 *Founded/Ownrshp* 1988
Sales 78.8MM^E *EMP* 600
SIC 4151 School buses; School buses
Pr: John McCarthy

D-U-N-S 96-925-6445 IMP/EXP

■ NRT COMMERCIAL UTAH LLC
COLDWELL BANKER
(*Suby of* REALOGY GROUP LLC) ★
175 Park Ave, Madison, NJ 07940-1123
Tel (973) 240-5400 *Founded/Ownrshp* 2006
Sales 848.7MM^E *EMP* 9,000
SIC 6531

D-U-N-S 82-907-1112

■ NRT LLC
(*Suby of* REALOGY GROUP LLC) ★
175 Park Ave, Madison, NJ 07940-1123
Tel (973) 407-2000 *Founded/Ownrshp* 1997
Sales 99.8MM^E *EMP* 500^E
SIC 6531 Real estate agents & managers; Real estate agents & managers
CEO: Bruce Zipf
**Sr VP:* Dan Barnett
Sr VP: M Gorman
**Sr VP:* Kevin Greene
**Sr VP:* Ken Hoffert
**Sr VP:* Lauren De Simon Johnson
VP: Karen Balter
VP: Mark Daaleman
VP: Troy McBride
VP: Karen Sitton
Comm Dir: Doug Sands
Comm Man: Jennifer McGuire

D-U-N-S 80-870-7350

NRT SETTLEMENT SERVICES OF MISSOURI LLC
US TITLE
7930 Clayton Rd Ste 200, Saint Louis, MO 63117-1331
Tel (314) 727-2900 *Founded/Ownrshp* 1993
Sales NA *EMP* 250
SIC 6411 Insurance agents, brokers & service; Insurance agents, brokers & service
Mng Pr: Heidi Weiskopf
VP: Brenda Brugger
VP: Barbara Seerey
IT Man: Sam Wilkins

D-U-N-S 80-671-8177 IMP

NRV INC
NEW REAL VEAL
N8155 American St, Ixonia, WI 53036
Tel (920) 261-7000 *Founded/Ownrshp* 2012
Sales 29.0MM *EMP* 26
SIC 2048 Livestock feeds
Pr: Fabien Fontaine
**CFO:* Gabriel Robidas
Dir IT: Kurt Sonneleitner

D-U-N-S 17-603-6499 IMP

NS FLEXIBLES LLC
NORTH STATE FLEXIBLES
(*Suby of* EMBALLAGE ST-JEAN LTEE)
2619 Phoenix Dr, Greensboro, NC 27406-6320
Tel (336) 292-9911 *Founded/Ownrshp* 2012
Sales 86.6MM^E *EMP* 190
SIC 2671 7336 2759 Packaging paper & plastics film, coated & laminated; Package design; Commercial printing; Packaging paper & plastics film, coated & laminated; Package design; Commercial printing
**Genl Mgr:* Tim Mage
**Genl Mgr:* Tim Mages
CTO: Mark Powell
IT Man: Pam Davis

D-U-N-S 11-149-8556

NS PACKAGING LLC
NORTH STATE PACKAGING
2600 Phoenix Dr, Greensboro, NC 27406-6321
Tel (800) 688-7391 *Founded/Ownrshp* 1997
Sales 27.9MM^E *EMP* 300
SIC 2671 Packaging paper & plastics film, coated & laminated; Packaging paper & plastics film, coated & laminated
CFO: William Wentz

D-U-N-S 04-854-7681 IMP

NSA INDUSTRIES LLC
210 Pierce Rd, Saint Johnsbury, VT 05819-8343
Tel (802) 748-5007 *Founded/Ownrshp* 1982
Sales 102.3MM^E *EMP* 250
SIC 3444 Sheet metalwork; Sheet metalwork
CEO: James Moroney
**CFO:* Chauncey Morgan
**VP:* Douglas Potter
**VP:* Matt Smith
**VP:* Ed Stanley
Genl Mgr: Emery Noyes
Sfty Dirs: Jason Edmunds
Prd Mgr: Bob Tanner
Sales Exec: Clark Hackett

D-U-N-S 10-718-6988

NSABP FOUNDATION INC
2 Allegheny Ctr Ste 1000, Pittsburgh, PA 15212-5405
Tel (412) 339-5300 *Founded/Ownrshp* 1995
Sales 36.4MM *EMP* 70^E
Accts Daniel Mathews Cpa Pittsburgh
SIC 8071 Testing laboratories; Testing laboratories
Treas: Grace Hogue
**Ch Bd:* Norman Wolmark
**CEO:* Joan Goldberg
IT Man: Jins Walton

D-U-N-S 01-496-4326

NSB ADVISORS LLC
200 Westage Bus Ctr Dr, Fishkill, NY 12524-2264
Tel (845) 897-1560 *Founded/Ownrshp* 2009
Sales 11.9MM^E *EMP* 338
SIC 8742 Financial consultant; Financial consultant

NSBSD
See NORTH SLOPE BOROUGH SCHOOL DISTRICT

NSC
See NATIONAL SAFETY COUNCIL

NSC
See NATIONAL SUPPORT CENTER LLC

D-U-N-S 11-288-0252

NSC GLOBAL LLC
(*Suby of* NSC GLOBAL LIMITED)
104 W 40th St Rm 1800, New York, NY 10018-3757
Tel (646) 432-0200 *Founded/Ownrshp* 2010
Sales 37.8MM *EMP* 112
SIC 7373 Systems integration services; Systems integration services
CEO: Yaseen Khan
COO: Sascha Groeger

D-U-N-S 82-941-2191

NSC WHOLESALE HOLDINGS LLC
NATIONAL WHL LQUIDATORS STORES
111 Hempstead Tpke Fl 3, West Hempstead, NY 11552-2155
Tel (516) 489-3300 *Founded/Ownrshp* 2008
Sales 62.0MM^E *EMP* 150^E
SIC 7389 Merchandise liquidators

D-U-N-S 80-348-6393 IMP/EXP

NSE PRODUCTS INC
75 W Center St, Provo, UT 84601-4432
Tel (801) 345-1000 *Founded/Ownrshp* 2005
Sales 22.1MM^E *EMP* 300^E
SIC 5632 Apparel accessories; Apparel accessories
Pr: M Truman Hunt
**VP:* Ritch Wood

NSEDC
See NORTON SOUND ECONOMIC DEVELOPMENT CORP

NSF
See NATIONAL SCIENCE FOUNDATION

D-U-N-S 06-880-1992 IMP

NSF INTERNATIONAL
789 N Dixboro Rd, Ann Arbor, MI 48105-9723
Tel (734) 769-8010 *Founded/Ownrshp* 1944
Sales 101.6MM *EMP* 450
SIC 8731 8734 Commercial research laboratory; Testing laboratories; Commercial research laboratory; Testing laboratories
Pr: Kevan P Lawlor
**CFO:* Michael P Walsh
Ofcr: Franscois Myburgh
**Sr VP:* Lori Bestervelt
**VP:* Elizabeth Jones
VP: David Richardson
VP: Pierre Sbabo
Dir Bus: Rick Andrew
Dir Bus: Dan Fone
Admn Mgr: Jackie Bennett
Div Mgr: Laura Liu

D-U-N-S 07-910-5775

NSF INTERNATIONAL HOLDINGS
789 N Dixboro Rd, Ann Arbor, MI 48105-9723
Tel (734) 769-8010 *Founded/Ownrshp* 2013
Sales 250.0MM *EMP* 2
SIC 6799 Investment clubs; Investment clubs
Pr: Kevin Lawler

D-U-N-S 62-309-5825

NSG CORP
CHEERLEADER & DANZTEAM
2010 Merritt Dr, Garland, TX 75041-6131
Tel (972) 840-1233 *Founded/Ownrshp* 1997
Sales 35.0MM^E *EMP* 550
SIC 2329 2339 Men's & boys' athletic uniforms; Uniforms, athletic: women's, misses' & juniors'; Men's & boys' athletic uniforms; Uniforms, athletic: women's, misses' & juniors'
Pr: Jeff Webb
Pr: Rob Holmes
**CFO:* John Nichols
VP: Andrew McNeill

D-U-N-S 00-363-4453 IMP

NSG TECHNOLOGY INC (CA)
FOXCONN
(*Suby of* MAXWELL HOLDINGS LIMITED)
1705 Junction Ct Ste 200, San Jose, CA 95112-1023
Tel (408) 547-8700 *Founded/Ownrshp* 1995, 2006
Sales 95.8MM^E *EMP* 280^E
SIC 1731 Computerized controls installation; Computerized controls installation
CEO: Ted Dubbs
**CFO:* Gloria Yu
Dir Bus: Ted Jao
Dir Bus: Albert Li
Prgrm Mgr: Kok Choo
Brnch Mgr: Joe Chu
Mfg Dir: Morgan Huang
Opers Mgr: Lawrence Daye
Opers Mgr: Minh Ho
Ql Cn Mgr: David Anderson
Ql Cn Mgr: Rafal Lemanczyk

NSG-CISCO
See HON HAI PRECISION INDUSTRY CO LTD

D-U-N-S 00-128-3167

NSGV INC
FORBES MAGAZINE
(*Suby of* FORBES MANAGEMENT CO INC) ★
499 Washington Blvd Fl 9, Jersey City, NJ 07310-2055
Tel (212) 367-3100 *Founded/Ownrshp* 1990
Sales 62.5MM^E *EMP* 400^E
SIC 2721 6282 6552 Magazines: publishing only, not printed on site; Investment advisory service; Subdividers & developers; Magazines: publishing only, not printed on site; Investment advisory service; Subdividers & developers
Ch: Steve Forbes
**Ch Bd:* Malcolm S Forbes Jr
Pr: Miguel Forbes
**Pr:* Robert L Forbes
**COO:* Timothy C Forbes
CFO: Mike Commented
Treas: Philip E Reville
Ex VP: Leonard Yablon
Sr VP: Monie Begley Feurey
VP: Kendall Crolius
VP: Steve Jernigan
VP: Lou Plaia
VP: Margaret Kelly Trombly
VP: Mike Woods
Exec: Steven Thorne

NSH
See SIMMONS MACHINE TOOL CORP

NSI
See HORWITZ INC

D-U-N-S 93-983-6599 IMP

NSI INDUSTRIES LLC
NSI TORK
9730 Northcross Center Ct, Huntersville, NC 28078-7301
Tel (704) 439-2420 *Founded/Ownrshp* 2005
Sales 42.6MM^E *EMP* 300
SIC 3643 Connectors & terminals for electrical devices; Connectors & terminals for electrical devices
VP: Nelson Petzold
Natl Sales: Mike Mensler

D-U-N-S 83-184-0793

NSI INSURANCE GROUP INC
8181 Nw 154th St Ste 230, Miami Lakes, FL 33016-5882
Tel (305) 556-1488 *Founded/Ownrshp* 2001
Sales NA *EMP* 70^E
SIC 6311 Life insurance carriers
Pr: George J Nenezian
VP: Barbara Harlan
VP: John Nenezian
VP: Anthony Nowakowski
VP: Hiram Rodriguez
**VP:* Oscar F Seikaly
Sales Exec: Pierre Granger

D-U-N-S 06-311-9689

■ NSI TECHNOLOGY SERVICES CORP
(*Suby of* MANTECH INTERNATIONAL CORP) ★
12015 Lee Jackson Mem Hwy, Fairfax, VA 22033-3300
Tel (703) 218-6000 *Founded/Ownrshp* 1988
Sales 14.4MM^E *EMP* 693
SIC 8711 Engineering services; Aviation &/or aeronautical engineering; Engineering services; Aviation &/or aeronautical engineering
Pr: George J Pedersen
**Treas:* John A Moore
**VP:* Matthew P Galaski
**VP:* Michael Yachmetz

NSI TORK
See NSI INDUSTRIES LLC

NSIGHT CONNECT
See D L RYAN COMPANIES LLC

NSIGHT TELESERVICES
See NORTHEAST COMMUNICATIONS OF WISCONSIN INC

D-U-N-S 80-837-9460 IMP
NSK AMERICAS INC
(*Suby of* NSK LTD.)
4200 Goss Rd, Ann Arbor, MI 48105-2799
Tel (734) 913-7500 *Founded/Ownrshp* 1973
Sales 515.6MM^E *EMP* 2,618
SIC 3714 5013 5085 Steering mechanisms, motor vehicle; Automotive supplies & parts; Industrial supplies; Steering mechanisms, motor vehicle; Automotive supplies & parts; Industrial supplies
Pr: Brian Lindsay
**CFO:* Brian Parsons
Treas: John Ellis
VP: George Habbouche
VP: David Schoewe
Genl Mgr: Tony Martell
Ql Cn Mgr: Oscar Adiwidjaja

D-U-N-S 06-417-2703 IMP/EXP
NSK CORP
NSK CORPORATION HQ
(*Suby of* NSK AMERICAS INC) ★
4200 Goss Rd, Ann Arbor, MI 48105-2799
Tel (734) 913-7500 *Founded/Ownrshp* 2007
Sales 151.1MM^E *EMP* 1,181
SIC 3714 5013 3594 3568 3562

NSK CORPORATION HQ
See NSK CORP

D-U-N-S 10-150-8349 IMP
NSK INDUSTRIES INC
150 Ascot Pkwy, Cuyahoga Falls, OH 44223-3354
Tel (330) 923-4112 *Founded/Ownrshp* 1978
Sales 21.0MM *EMP* 42
SIC 5085 3479 3451

NSK PRECISION AMERICA HQ
See NSK PRECISION AMERICA INC

D-U-N-S 03-967-1792 IMP
NSK PRECISION AMERICA INC
NSK PRECISION AMERICA HQ
(*Suby of* NSK AMERICAS INC) ★
3450 Bearing Dr, Franklin, IN 46131-9660
Tel (317) 738-5000 *Founded/Ownrshp* 2007
Sales 30.1MM *EMP* 181
SIC 5085 Industrial supplies; Industrial supplies
Pr: Christopher Swartwout
Pr: Shizuo Kashiwagi
**Pr:* Gus Kontonickas
Treas: Tsuyoshi Mitsumoto
**Treas:* Lindy Rigdon
**Prin:* Bernard M Lindsay
Manager: Tom Vanosselaer

D-U-N-S 19-371-1702 IMP
NSK STEERING SYSTEMS AMERICA INC
NSSA HQ
(*Suby of* NSK AMERICAS INC) ★
4200 Goss Rd, Ann Arbor, MI 48105-2799
Tel (734) 913-7500 *Founded/Ownrshp* 2007
Sales 125.0MM *EMP* 1,112
SIC 3714 Steering mechanisms, motor vehicle; Steering mechanisms, motor vehicle
Pr: Michael Rivenburgh
**VP:* Tsutomu Komori
**VP:* Masahide Matsubara
**VP:* Naoki Mitsue
**VP:* Toshihiro Uchiyama
Ql Cn Mgr: Adam Coolich
Ql Cn Mgr: Steven Deutch
Snr Mgr: Leeann Boudreau
Snr Mgr: Phil Taylor

D-U-N-S 82-473-1863
NSL ANALYTICAL SERVICES INC
4450 Cranwood Pkwy, Cleveland, OH 44128-4004
Tel (216) 438-5200 *Founded/Ownrshp* 2000
Sales 20.7MM^E *EMP* 65
SIC 8734 Testing laboratories
Pr: Lawrence Somrack
Genl Mgr: Jeff Hartel
Genl Mgr: John Pickens
Off Mgr: Bridgett Pavlish
IT Man: Robert Cepek
Ql Cn Mgr: Bryan Hall
Sls Mgr: Rich Balamut
Snr Mgr: Kevin Holland

NSLIJ
See LONG ISLAND JEWISH MEDICAL CENTER

NSLIJ
See LONG ISLAND HOME

NSLIJ
See PLAINVIEW HOSPITAL

NSLIJ
See STATEN ISLAND UNIVERSITY HOSPITAL

NSLIJ
See NORTH SHORE - LONG ISLAND JEWISH HEALTH SYSTEM INC

NSLIJ-SOUTHSIDE HOSPITAL
See SOUTHSIDE HOSPITAL

NSLIJHSFCU
See NORTH SHORE LIJ HEALTH SYSTEM FEDERAL CREDIT UNION

D-U-N-S 80-234-9878
■ **NSM INSURANCE GROUP INC**
ALLSTATE
(*Suby of* AMERICAN INTERNATIONAL GROUP INC) ★
555 E North Ln Ste 6060, Conshohocken, PA 19428-2250
Tel (610) 941-9877 *Founded/Ownrshp* 2015
Sales NA *EMP* 66^E
SIC 6411 Insurance agents, brokers & service
Pr: Geoffrey McKernan
COO: William Kanehann
VP: Guy Mastrangelo
Prgrm Mgr: Jeremy Huang
Prgrm Mgr: Jennifer Johnston
Prgrm Mgr: Cisr Tedesco
Prgrm Mgr: Thomas Zapalac
Tech Mgr: Stacey Bowen
Software D: Brandon Mock
Sales Exec: Tripp Craig
Sales Exec: Chris Holland

D-U-N-S 94-139-5352
NSON INC
SURVEYFEVER
731 E South Temple, Salt Lake City, UT 84102-1221
Tel (801) 359-1345 *Founded/Ownrshp* 1992
Sales 15.2MM^E *EMP* 300
SIC 8732 Market analysis, business & economic research; Market analysis, business & economic research
Pr: Ronald Nielson
**Pr:* Ronald T Nielson
VP: Richard Kuchinsky
**VP:* Richard Kurchinsky
**VP:* Arvino Singh

NSP AND EROC
See TULLY ENVIRONMENTAL INC

NSPI
See NETWORK SERVICES PLUS INC

D-U-N-S 06-693-6204
NSS ACQUISITION CORP
BEV SMITH TOYOTA
3350 S Us Highway 1, Fort Pierce, FL 34982-6678
Tel (772) 464-8440 *Founded/Ownrshp* 1992
Sales 56.3MM^E *EMP* 125
SIC 5511 Automobiles, new & used; Automobiles, new & used
Pr: Nicholas S Smith
Ofcr: Janice Frey
**VP:* Frank Gonzalez
Exec: Michelle Connick
Exec: Annie Johnson
Store Mgr: Curt Lee
IT Man: Jeff Brabham
Sls Mgr: Mike Friend
Sls Mgr: James Maus
Sls Mgr: Fred McCartney
Sls Mgr: Tim Murphy

D-U-N-S 00-541-8249 IMP/EXP
NSS ENTERPRISES INC (OH)
NATIONAL SUPER SERVICE CO
3115 Frenchmens Rd, Toledo, OH 43607-2918
Tel (419) 531-2121 *Founded/Ownrshp* 1911, 1999
Sales 27.7MM^E *EMP* 180
SIC 3589 Floor washing & polishing machines, commercial; Vacuum cleaners & sweepers, electric: industrial; Floor washing & polishing machines, commercial; Vacuum cleaners & sweepers, electric: industrial
Pr: Mark J Bevington
**Prin:* Anthony J Colburn
Rgnl Mgr: Gary Kreiling
Rgnl Mgr: Ron Lazarr

D-U-N-S 05-203-6308 IMP
■ **NSS TECHNOLOGIES INC**
N S S INDUSTRIES
(*Suby of* PCC SPS FASTENER DIVISION) ★
8680 N Haggerty Rd, Canton, MI 48187-2098
Tel (734) 459-9500 *Founded/Ownrshp* 1999
Sales 52.3MM^E *EMP* 140
SIC 3452 3316 Bolts, metal; Nuts, metal; Screws, metal; Cold finishing of steel shapes; Bolts, metal; Nuts, metal; Screws, metal; Cold finishing of steel shapes
CEO: Mark Donegan
Mng Dir: Robert Dunford
Genl Mgr: Mike Pardo
CTO: Jeanne Vokes
Mfg Mgr: Simonds Don
Sls Mgr: Terry Mrofchak
Sales Asso: Jason Matter

NSSA HQ
See NSK STEERING SYSTEMS AMERICA INC

NSSED
See NORTHERN SUBURBAN SPECIAL EDUCATION DISTRICT 804

NSSEO
See NORTHWEST SUBURBAN SPECIAL EDUCATION ORGANIZATION

D-U-N-S 07-922-5498
NST ENERGY LLC
527 Marquette Ave, Minneapolis, MN 55402-1302
Tel (612) 355-2600 *Founded/Ownrshp* 2013
Sales 70.0MM *EMP* 3
SIC 4013 Railroad terminals; Railroad terminals
COO: Jon Hempel
Treas: Joshua Krsnak
Mktg Dir: Mark Hetherington

D-U-N-S 80-082-9645
NSTAR COMMUNICATIONS INC
1 Nstar Way, Westwood, MA 02090-2334
Tel (617) 424-2000 *Founded/Ownrshp* 1997
Sales 65.2MM *EMP* 5
SIC 4813 Telephone communication, except radio
Pr: Douglas S Horan
**Treas:* Philip J Lembo
Prgrm Mgr: Rishi Sondhi

D-U-N-S 00-552-4256
■ **NSTAR ELECTRIC & GAS CORP**
(*Suby of* NSTAR LLC) ★
800 Boylston St Ste 1700, Boston, MA 02199-8108
Tel (617) 424-2000 *Founded/Ownrshp* 1999
Sales 1.3MM^E *EMP* 3,000
SIC 4922 4911 Natural gas transmission; Distribution, electric power; Natural gas transmission; Distribution, electric power
Ch Bd: Thomas J May
Treas: Don Anastasia
**Treas:* Philip J Lembo
Prgrm Mgr: David Olivier
CIO: Joan Hurley
Dir IT: Andrew Kasznaj
Secur Mgr: Scott McKenzie

D-U-N-S 00-695-1552
■ **NSTAR ELECTRIC CO**
EVERSOURCE ENERGY
(*Suby of* NSTAR LLC) ★
800 Boylston St Ste 1700, Boston, MA 02199-8108
Tel (617) 424-2000 *Founded/Ownrshp* 1886
Sales 2.5MMM *EMP* 2,194^E
Accts Deloitte & Touche Llp Hartfo
SIC 4911 4924 Distribution, electric power; Generation, electric power; Transmission, electric power; Natural gas distribution; Distribution, electric power; Generation, electric power; Transmission, electric power; Natural gas distribution
CEO: Leon J Olivier
**Ch Bd:* Thomas J May
**CEO:* Werner J Schweiger
COO: Thomas Glynn
**CFO:* James J Judge
Ex VP: David R McHale
**Sr VP:* Gregory B Butler
Sr VP: Christine M Carmody
VP: Jay S Buth
Exec: William Beament
Sfty Mgr: George Popovici

D-U-N-S 08-757-1431 IMP
■ **NSTAR LLC**
(*Suby of* EVERSOURCE ENERGY) ★
800 Boylston St Ste 1700, Boston, MA 02199-8108
Tel (617) 424-2000 *Founded/Ownrshp* 2012
Sales 4.0MMM^E *EMP* 3,000^E
SIC 4911 4924 Distribution, electric power; Transmission, electric power; Natural gas distribution; Distribution, electric power; Transmission, electric power; Natural gas distribution
CFO: James J Judge
Treas: Philip J Lembo
Ex VP: David R McHale
VP: Christine M Carmody
VP: Penelope Conner
VP: Geoffrey Lubbock
VP: Joseph Nolan
VP: Michael Scott
VP: Joseph L Simonelli
Comm Dir: Margaret Norton
Prin: Gary L Countryman
Board of Directors: Gary L Countryman, Thomas G Dignan Jr, James S Distasio, Charles K Gifford, Paul A La Camera, William C Van Faasen, Gerald L Wilson

NSTEC
See NATIONAL SECURITY TECHNOLOGIES LLC

NSU
See NORTHEASTERN STATE UNIVERSITY

D-U-N-S 01-917-5821
NSWC CARDEROCK DIVISION
5101 S 18th St Fl 1, Philadelphia, PA 19112-1818
Tel (215) 897-5732 *Founded/Ownrshp* 2008
Sales 18.8MM^E *EMP* 500
SIC 7389 Personal service agents, brokers & bureaus; Personal service agents, brokers & bureaus
Prin: Patricia Haggerty

NT
See NORTH TOLEDO GRAPHICS LLC

NT CONCEPTS
See NEXT TIER CONCEPTS INC

D-U-N-S 05-963-7025
■ **NT PHILADELPHIA LLC**
COLDWELL BANKER PREFERRED
(*Suby of* NRT LLC) ★
1207 Fayette St, Conshohocken, PA 19428-2345
Tel (610) 828-9558 *Founded/Ownrshp* 2010
Sales 12.7MM^E *EMP* 500
SIC 6531 Real estate agent, residential; Real estate agent, residential
Prin: Harry Caparo
**CEO:* Regina Coia
Off Admin: Eileen Robb
Sales Asso: Kathleen Koulouris
Sales Asso: Melissa Nowicki
Sales Asso: M Philip
Sales Asso: Justin Willis

D-U-N-S 55-653-0145
NT WINDOW INC
NT
4949 Rendon Rd, Fort Worth, TX 76140-9667
Tel (817) 572-4994 *Founded/Ownrshp* 1990
Sales 39.3MM^E *EMP* 60
SIC 5031 Window frames, all materials
Pr: Ryon Ray
**VP:* Heather Young
Plnt Mgr: Gordon Smith
Sales Exec: Dennis Northcut
Sls Mgr: Dennis Northcutt

NTA
See NATIONAL TECHNOLOGIES ASSOCIATES INC

NTA LIFE
See NATIONAL TEACHERS ASSOCIATES LIFE INSURANCE CO

D-U-N-S 07-774-8767
NTA MANAGEMENT INC
4949 Keller Springs Rd, Addison, TX 75001-5910
Tel (972) 532-2100 *Founded/Ownrshp* 1938
Sales NA *EMP* 110
SIC 6411 Insurance agents, brokers & service; Insurance agents, brokers & service
Pr: Ray Martin
**Treas:* James T Langham Jr

NTA PACIFIC
See NIPPON TRAVEL AGENCY PACIFIC INC

D-U-N-S 96-936-3337 IMP
NTA PRECISION AXLE CORP
(*Suby of* NTN CORPORATION)
795 Kimberly Dr, Carol Stream, IL 60188-9407
Tel (630) 690-6300 *Founded/Ownrshp* 2010
Sales 120.0MM *EMP* 260
SIC 3714 Bearings, motor vehicle

D-U-N-S 15-371-2575 IMP/EXP
NTC AMERICA CORP
N T C
(*Suby of* KOMATSU NTC LTD.)
46605 Magellan Dr, Novi, MI 48377-2442
Tel (248) 560-1200 *Founded/Ownrshp* 1984
Sales 27.8MM *EMP* 42
Accts Plante & Moran Pllc Auburn H
SIC 5084 Industrial machinery & equipment; Industrial machinery & equipment
Pr: Ken Fumoto
VP: Ed Ishisaki
VP: Takeshi Omura

D-U-N-S 09-416-4746 IMP/EXP
NTC MARKETING INC (NY)
5680 Main St, Williamsville, NY 14221-5518
Tel (716) 884-3345 *Founded/Ownrshp* 1970, 1981
Sales 70.0MM *EMP* 30
SIC 5149 Canned goods: fruit, vegetables, seafood, meats, etc.; Canned goods: fruit, vegetables, seafood, meats, etc.
CEO: Michael J De Rose
**Ex VP:* Christopher J De Rose
**VP:* Michael C De Rose
**Prin:* David S De Rose

D-U-N-S 04-460-4960
NTC MAZZUCA CONTRACTING INC
10907 Guilford Rd Ste A, Annapolis Junction, MD 20701-1198
Tel (410) 964-0101 *Founded/Ownrshp* 2001
Sales 26.8MM *EMP* 30
Accts Katz Abosch Windesheim Gershma
SIC 1542 Commercial & office building contractors; Commercial & office building contractors
Pr: David Mazzuca
VP: Michael Crim
Dir Bus: Stephen Newhouse

NTCA RURAL BROADBAND ASSN
See NATIONAL TELECOMMUNICATIONS COOPERATIVE ASSOCIATION

D-U-N-S 61-729-5246
▲ **NTELOS HOLDINGS CORP**
1154 Shenandoah Vlg Dr, Waynesboro, VA 22980-9253
Tel (540) 946-3500 *Founded/Ownrshp* 1897
Sales 487.8MM *EMP* 854^E
Tkr Sym NTLS *Exch* NGS
SIC 4813 4812 Telephone communication, except radio; ; Cellular telephone services; Telephone communication, except radio; ; Cellular telephone services
Pr: Rodney D Dir
**Ch Bd:* Michael Huber
CFO: Stebbins B Chandor Jr
Ex VP: Robert L McAvoy Jr
Ex VP: Brian J O'Neil
Sr VP: S Craig Highland
Sr VP: Mary McDermott
Board of Directors: David A Chorney, Stephen C Duggan, Michael Gottdenker, Daniel J Heneghan, Ruth Sommers, Ellen O'connor Vos

D-U-N-S 80-120-9375
■ **NTELOS INC**
(*Suby of* NTELOS HOLDINGS CORP) ★
1154 Shenandoah Vlg Dr, Waynesboro, VA 22980-9253
Tel (540) 946-3500 *Founded/Ownrshp* 1988
Sales 545.5MM^E *EMP* 955
SIC 4899 Communication signal enhancement network system; Communication signal enhancement network system
CEO: Rod Dir
**CEO:* James A Hyde
CFO: Michael B Moneymaker
**Ex VP:* Stebbins B Chandor Jr
**Ex VP:* Conrad D Hunter
**Sr VP:* Brian J O'Neil
Store Mgr: Patrick Perrella
Snr Sftwr: Mourad Fahim
Snr Ntwrk: Harris Duncan
Snr Ntwrk: Jonathan Lee
Netwrk Eng: Arnaud Juan

D-U-N-S 19-688-6592
■ **NTELOS NET LLC**
(*Suby of* NTELOS HOLDINGS CORP) ★
1 Lumos Plz, Waynesboro, VA 22980-4549
Tel (540) 946-3500 *Founded/Ownrshp* 2003
Sales 548.3MM^E *EMP* 960^E
SIC 4813 Telephone communication, except radio; Telephone communication, except radio
Pr: James S Quarforth
**Pr:* David R Maccarelli
**Pr:* Carl A Rosberg
**CFO:* Michael B Moneymaker
CFO: Suzan Sweet
**Sr VP:* Mary McDermott

D-U-N-S 07-951-2803
NTENT INC
342 W 37th St, New York, NY 10018-4201
Tel (212) 967-9502 *Founded/Ownrshp* 2014
Sales 22.4MM^E *EMP* 91^E
SIC 6799 Investors
CEO: Dan Stickel
**Co-Founder:* Collin M Jeavons

D-U-N-S 02-773-6012
NTFN INC
PREMIER NATIONWIDE LENDING
2901 Dallas Pkwy Ste 120, Plano, TX 75093-5981
Tel (972) 818-5626 *Founded/Ownrshp* 1996
Sales NA *EMP* 350
SIC 6163 Loan brokers; Loan brokers
CEO: Murdock Richard
Pr: Blake Priest
CFO: Gary McKiddy
Prin: Charles Priest

D-U-N-S 09-857-6580
NTH DEGREE INC
2675 Breckinridge Blvd # 200, Duluth, GA 30096-8953
Tel (404) 296-5282 *Founded/Ownrshp* 2012

Sales 49.2MM^E *EMP* 129
SIC 7389 Convention & show services
Pr: John Yohe
Dir Soc: Khadijah Theus
VP Sls: Nancy Lyons

D-U-N-S 78-112-3211
NTH GENERATION COMPUTING INC
17055 Camino San Bernardo, San Diego, CA 92127-5709
Tel (858) 451-2383 *Founded/Ownrshp* 1988
Sales 119.4MM^E *EMP* 96
SIC 5045 Computer peripheral equipment; Computer software; Computer peripheral equipment; Computer software
CEO: Janis I Baldwin
Sr VP: Dwayne Gilliam
VP: Todd Burkhardt
Prin: Liane Komagome
**Dir Sec:* Richard Baldwin
Prac Mgr: Matthew Weiner
Prgrm Mgr: John Cummings
CIO: Jorge Mata
CTO: Joel Manfredo
CTO: Dan Molina
CTO: Alex Ryals

NTH/WORKS
See PRECISION TOOL DIE AND MACHINE CO INC

D-U-N-S 17-380-5359 IMP
NTK AVIATION AMERICA INC
(Suby of NTK INTERNATIONAL CORPORATION)
430 Madrid Ave, Torrance, CA 90501-1430
Tel (310) 782-2700 *Founded/Ownrshp* 2008
Sales 22.4MM^E *EMP* 25
SIC 5088 Marine crafts & supplies
CEO: Ryutaro Sato
**Pr:* Kazuo Nomoto
**CEO:* Takeyoshi Hamabe
**Sr VP:* Hirosige Torii
**VP:* Steve Sato

D-U-N-S 61-638-6236
NTK HOLDINGS INC
(Suby of THL-NORTEK INVESTORS LLC) ★
50 Kennedy Plz, Providence, RI 02903-2393
Tel (401) 751-1600 *Founded/Ownrshp* 2005
Sales 228.8MM^E *EMP* 8,800
SIC 3585 3444 3634 3699 2491 2434 Refrigeration & heating equipment; Heating equipment, complete; Air conditioning equipment, complete; Air conditioning units, complete: domestic or industrial; Metal ventilating equipment; Hoods, range: sheet metal; Electric housewares & fans; Fans, exhaust & ventilating, electric: household; Electrical equipment & supplies; Security control equipment & systems; Door opening & closing devices, electrical; Chimes, electric; Wood preserving; Poles, posts & pilings: treated wood; Millwork, treated wood; Wood kitchen cabinets; Vanities, bathroom: wood; Refrigeration & heating equipment; Heating equipment, complete; Air conditioning equipment, complete; Air conditioning units, complete: domestic or industrial; Metal ventilating equipment; Hoods, range: sheet metal; Electric housewares & fans; Fans, exhaust & ventilating, electric: household; Electrical equipment & supplies; Security control equipment & systems; Door opening & closing devices, electrical; Chimes, electric; Wood preserving; Poles, posts & pilings: treated wood; Millwork, treated wood; Wood kitchen cabinets; Vanities, bathroom: wood
Ch Bd: Richard L Bready
CFO: Almon C Hall
Treas: Edward J Cooney
VP: Kevin W Donnelly
Board of Directors: Jeffrey C Bloomberg, Joseph M Cianciolo, Anthony J Dinovi, David V Harkins, David B Hiley, Kent R Weldon

D-U-N-S 14-823-0613 IMP
NTK PRECISION AXLE CORP
(Suby of NTN CORPORATION)
741 S County Road 200 W, Frankfort, IN 46041-8704
Tel (765) 656-1000 *Founded/Ownrshp* 2003
Sales 51.6MM^E *EMP* 252
SIC 3312 Axles, rolled or forged: made in steel mills; Axles, rolled or forged: made in steel mills
Pr: Tadao Okamura
**VP:* Takashi Tanaka
Snr Mgr: Brian Cline

NTM
See NATIONAL TOOL & MANUFACTURING CO

NTMWD
See NORTH TEXAS MUNICIPAL WATER DISTRICT

D-U-N-S 04-391-0256 IMP
NTN BEARING CORP OF AMERICA (NY)
(Suby of NTN USA CORP) ★
1600 Bishop Ct, Mount Prospect, IL 60056-6055
Tel (847) 298-7500 *Founded/Ownrshp* 1963, 1990
Sales 119.3MM^E *EMP* 369
SIC 5085 Bearings; Bearings
Pr: Pete Eich
VP: Angelo Desantis
VP: Laura Kearns
Exec: Bart Trapp
Rgnl Mgr: Kevin Austin
Dir IT: Hirosha Kawakami
IT Man: David Malmquist
Ql Cn Mgr: Greg Keller
Sls Dir: Paul Tervo
Mktg Mgr: Cheryl Loew
Genl Couns: Craig Dunn
Board of Directors: H Morii

D-U-N-S 13-118-5373 IMP
▲ NTN BUZZTIME INC
2231 Rutherford Rd # 200, Carlsbad, CA 92008-8811
Tel (760) 438-7400 *Founded/Ownrshp* 1984
Sales 26.0MM *EMP* 359^E
Tkr Sym NTN *Exch* ASE
SIC 4841 4833 7372 Direct broadcast satellite services (DBS); Television broadcasting stations; Prepackaged software; Direct broadcast satellite services (DBS); Television broadcasting stations; Prepackaged software
Ch Bd: Jeff Berg
COO: Robert Cooney
Chf Mktg O: Barry Chandler
Ofcr: Vladimir Khuchua-Edelman
Ofcr: Kirk Nagamine
Ex VP: Michael Arzt
Ex VP: Peter J Boylan
Ex VP: Jeffrey Lewis
Sr VP: Bill Thomas
VP: David Johnson
Snr Sftwr: Chuck Bernstein
Board of Directors: Mary Beth Lewis, Steve Mitgang, Tony Uphoff, Paul Yanover

D-U-N-S 60-816-7276 IMP
NTN DRIVESHAFT INC
(Suby of NTN USA CORP) ★
8251 S International Dr, Columbus, IN 47201-9329
Tel (812) 342-5414 *Founded/Ownrshp* 1989
Sales 228.8MM^E *EMP* 1,000
SIC 3568 Joints & couplings; Joints & couplings
Pr: Tohru Tomiyama
**Pr:* Nobuo Satoh
**Sec:* Hidekazu Asaba
VP: Douglas Evers
**VP:* Tom Fowler
VP: Dave Miller
VP Admn: Barry Parkhurst
QA Dir: Roy Baker
QA Dir: Chris Graburn
QA Dir: Joe Winters
Dir IT: Chris Paugh

D-U-N-S 62-143-0610 EXP
NTN USA CORP
(Suby of NTN CORPORATION)
1600 Bishop Ct, Mount Prospect, IL 60056-6055
Tel (847) 298-4652 *Founded/Ownrshp* 1990
Sales 749.1MM^E *EMP* 3,500^E
SIC 5085 3562 3568 Bearings; Ball bearings & parts; Roller bearings & parts; Joints, swivel & universal, except aircraft & automotive; Bearings; Ball bearings & parts; Roller bearings & parts; Joints, swivel & universal, except aircraft & automotive
Pr: Masaaki Ayano
Sls Mgr: Oscar Joyner

D-U-N-S 14-735-1092 IMP
NTN-BOWER CORP
(Suby of NTN USA CORP) ★
711 Bower Rd, Macomb, IL 61455-2511
Tel (309) 837-0440 *Founded/Ownrshp* 1990
Sales 172.0MM *EMP* 873^E
SIC 3562 Roller bearings & parts; Roller bearings & parts
Pr: Kunio Kamo
Opers Mgr: Mike Lawson

D-U-N-S 06-343-6463 IMP
■ NTP DISTRIBUTION INC
(Suby of KEYSTONE AUTOMOTIVE OPERATIONS INC) ★
27150 Sw Kinsman Rd, Wilsonville, OR 97070-8246
Tel (503) 570-2154 *Founded/Ownrshp* 2011
Sales 100.0MM *EMP* 400
SIC 5013 Trailer parts & accessories; Trailer parts & accessories
Ch: Robert L Morter
**Pr:* Greg Boyd
**Pr:* Edward H Orszetti
**COO:* Steven M Whitrock
VP Sls: John White
Mktg Dir: Donna Martin
Sales Asso: Cecilia Baker
Sales Asso: John Donaghe
Sales Asso: Jennet Lewis

D-U-N-S 78-437-8189 IMP
NTP MARBLE INC
COLONIAL MARBLE & GRANITE
201 W Church Rd Ste 300, King of Prussia, PA 19406-3241
Tel (610) 994-2222 *Founded/Ownrshp* 2006
Sales 542.2MM^E *EMP* 125^E
SIC 5032 Marble building stone; Granite building stone; Marble building stone; Granite building stone
Pr: Nikolaos Papadopoulos
**VP:* Angelo Bekas
Opers Mgr: Steve Basdekis
S&M/VP: James Freeman
Sls Mgr: David Betsy
Sls Mgr: Demetrios Proios
Sales Asso: Gus Repici
Sales Asso: Anthony Tartaglia

NTR
See NORTHSIDE TOOL RENTAL INC

D-U-N-S 17-045-9734 IMP
NTR METALS LLC
(Suby of ELEMETAL LLC) ★
10720 Composite Dr, Dallas, TX 75220-1208
Tel (469) 522-1111 *Founded/Ownrshp* 2004
Sales 61.2MM^E *EMP* 200
SIC 5094 Precious metals; Precious metals
CEO: Pithou Nuth
Brnch Mgr: Jacob Zimmer
Sales Exec: Don Giddens
Genl Couns: Trey Gum

D-U-N-S 96-554-2876
NTREPID CORP
12801 Worldgate Dr # 800, Herndon, VA 20170-4393
Tel (571) 612-8300 *Founded/Ownrshp* 2010
Sales 23.2MM^E *EMP* 147
SIC 7379 Computer related maintenance services
Pr: Martinka Michael
Ex VP: Charlie Englehart
VP: Teddy Lindsey
Prgrm Mgr: Ryan Lincoln
Snr Sftwr: Brenda Jacobs
QA Dir: Tamaika Menefee
Sftwr Eng: Sang Jung

NTS
See NATIONAL TECHNICAL SYSTEMS INC

NTS
See NATIONAL TRENCH SAFETY LLC

D-U-N-S 03-620-3818
NTS COMMUNICATIONS INC
(Suby of NTS INC) ★
1220 Brdwy, Lubbock, TX 79401
Tel (806) 791-0687 *Founded/Ownrshp* 2008
Sales 87.9MM^E *EMP* 231
SIC 4813 Long distance telephone communications; ; Long distance telephone communications;
Pr: Guy Nissenson
Pr: Dawn Ambrose
Pr: Barbara Baldwin
**CEO:* Cyrus Driver
COO: Brad Worthington
CFO: Jerry E Hoover
Sec: Niv Krikov
Ex VP: Tal Sheynfeld
VP: John Baldwin
VP: Roberto Chang
VP: Milton Schober Jr

D-U-N-S 14-780-1096
NTS CORP
10172 Linn Station Rd # 200, Louisville, KY 40223-3891
Tel (502) 426-4800 *Founded/Ownrshp* 1971
Sales 73.8MM^E *EMP* 260^E
SIC 6531 6552

D-U-N-S 06-295-1447
NTS DEVELOPMENT CO
(Suby of NTS CORP) ★
600 N Hurstbourne Pkwy # 300, Louisville, KY 40222-5388
Tel (502) 426-4800 *Founded/Ownrshp* 1971
Sales 73.8MM^E *EMP* 200
SIC 6552 6531 Subdividers & developers; Real estate managers; Subdividers & developers; Real estate managers
Pr: Brian F Lavin
**Treas:* David B Pitchford
**VP:* Timothy A Baker
**VP:* Neil A Mitchell
**VP:* Rosann D Tafel
**VP:* Gregory A Wells
Rgnl Mgr: Robyn Eaton

D-U-N-S 08-594-2001
NTS ENGINEERING SERVICES INC
NTS XXCAL
(Suby of NATIONAL TECHNICAL SYSTEMS INC) ★
5730 Buckingham Pkwy, Culver City, CA 90230-6508
Tel (310) 641-7700 *Founded/Ownrshp* 1976
Sales 17.5MM^E *EMP* 550
SIC 7361 Employment agencies; Employment agencies
Prin: Marvin Hoffman
Manager: John Rehard

D-U-N-S 06-717-5609
NTS INC (NV)
(Suby of T3 NORTH INTERMEDIATE HOLDINGS, INC.)
1220 Broadway Ste 100, Lubbock, TX 79401-3202
Tel (806) 797-0687 *Founded/Ownrshp* 2000, 2014
Sales 121.3MM^E *EMP* 376^E
SIC 4813
Pr: Cyrus Driver
**Pr:* Guy Nissenson
**COO:* Brad Worthington
**CFO:* Niv Krikov
**VP:* Roberto Chang
**VP:* Nathan Hasse
**VP:* Wendy J Lee
**VP:* Aaron Peters
**VP:* Priscilla Rivas
**VP:* Tal Sheynfeld
**VP:* Daniel Wheeler

D-U-N-S 13-094-9873
NTS INC
NEWBERRY TECHNICAL SERVICES
8200 Stockdale Hwy, Bakersfield, CA 93311-1091
Tel (661) 588-8514 *Founded/Ownrshp* 2001
Sales 116.0MM^E *EMP* 425
SIC 1623 1541 1771 Pipeline construction; Industrial buildings, new construction; Concrete work; Pipeline construction; Industrial buildings, new construction; Concrete work
Pr: Robert Newberry
**VP:* Wesley Furrh
Sfty Mgr: Eric Jones
Manager: Todd Massey

D-U-N-S 18-402-0811
NTS REALTY HOLDINGS LIMITED PARTNERSHIP
600 N Hurstbourne Pkwy, Louisville, KY 40222-5385
Tel (502) 426-4800 *Founded/Ownrshp* 2004
Sales 59.0MM *EMP* 2^E
SIC 6798 Real estate investment trusts; Real estate investment trusts
Pr: Brian F Lavin
Genl Pt: NTS Realty Capital
Ch Bd: J D Nichols
CFO: Gregory A Wells

D-U-N-S 07-913-3058
NTS TEXAS INC
15810 W Business 40, Shamrock, TX 79079-4417
Tel (806) 256-5000 *Founded/Ownrshp* 1980
Sales 4.1MM^E *EMP* 500
SIC 1623 Pipeline construction
Ex Dir: Wes Furrh

NTS XXCAL
See NTS ENGINEERING SERVICES INC

D-U-N-S 10-382-8828
NTS-PROPERTIES III
DEVELOPMENT COMPANY
10172 Linn Station Rd # 200, Louisville, KY 40223-3891
Tel (502) 426-4800 *Founded/Ownrshp* 1982
Sales 10.7MM^E *EMP* 350
SIC 6512 Commercial & industrial building operation; Commercial & industrial building operation
Pt: J D Nichols
Pt: Brian F Lavin
Pt: Gregory A Wells

NTSB
See NATIONAL TRANSPORTATION SAFETY BOARD

NTSP
See NORTH TEXAS SPECIALTY PHYSICIANS INC

NTSWA
See NORTHERN TIER SOLID WASTE AUTHORITY

D-U-N-S 09-354-4323 IMP
NTT AMERICA INC
(Suby of NTT COMMUNICATIONS CORPORATION)
757 3rd Ave Ste 1400, New York, NY 10017-2054
Tel (212) 661-0810 *Founded/Ownrshp* 1987, 2006
Sales 231.4MM^E *EMP* 500
SIC 4813 Telephone communication, except radio; Telephone communication, except radio
Pr: Tetsuro Yamaguchi
**COO:* Kazuhiro Gomi
Bd of Dir: Miwa Matsushita
Bd of Dir: Patricia Nickens
**Ofcr:* Michael Devito
Ex VP: Christopher P Eldredge
VP: Pete Bell
VP: Joe Corvaia
VP: Brent Duncan
VP: Eiri Fujikawa
VP: Don Goodwin
VP: Masayuki Inamura
VP: Jordan Kanfer
VP: Dorian Kim
**VP:* Tomoyoshi Kosugi
VP: Bob O'Keefe
VP: Douglas Smith

D-U-N-S 86-875-4011
NTT COM SECURITY (US) INC
(Suby of NTT COMMUNICATIONS CORPORATION)
204 W Newberry Rd Ste D, Bloomfield, CT 06002-5314
Tel (860) 761-2900 *Founded/Ownrshp* 2001
Sales 22.1MM^E *EMP* 96
SIC 7382 7372 Security systems services; Prepackaged software
CEO: Simon Church
**CFO:* Heiner Luntz
Sr VP: Mike Barch
VP: Andrew Lev
**VP:* Chris Ward

D-U-N-S 96-982-5090
NTT DATA ENTERPRISE SERVICES INC
(Suby of NIPPON TELEGRAPH AND TELEPHONE CORPORATION)
1231 Greenway Dr Ste 110, Irving, TX 75038-7530
Tel (972) 915-0123 *Founded/Ownrshp* 2013
Sales 76.3MM^E *EMP* 618
SIC 7371 Computer software systems analysis & design, custom; Computer software systems analysis & design, custom
Pr: Gurvenda Suri
**Pr:* Sam Sliman
**CFO:* Stuart Lodge
VP: Zack Morin
Exec: Shannon Jackson
VP Sls: Sunil Mukundan

D-U-N-S 06-678-1865
NTT DATA FEDERAL SERVICES INC
(Suby of NTT DATA INC) ★
8130 Boone Blvd Fl 4, Vienna, VA 22182-2666
Tel (703) 848-7200 *Founded/Ownrshp* 1994
Sales 38.8MM^E *EMP* 200
SIC 7371 8742 7372 Computer software development; General management consultant; Prepackaged software; Computer software development; General management consultant; Prepackaged software
CEO: John W McCain
Pr: David Capista
Pr: David Kapusta
Treas: Catherine Arold
VP: John Alfano
VP: Glenn Giles
Prin: John M Dick
Prgrm Mgr: Jim Inglett
Prgrm Mgr: Susan Russell
Genl Mgr: Zemorial Skerritt
Dir IT: James Passmore

D-U-N-S 07-170-7764
NTT DATA INC
(Suby of NTT DATA INTERNATIONAL LLC) ★
5601 Gran Pkwy Ste 1000, Plano, TX 75024
Tel (800) 745-3263 *Founded/Ownrshp* 1986
Sales 107.5MM^E *EMP* 200
SIC 7373 7372 7379 Computer integrated systems design; Systems software development services; Prepackaged software; Computer related consulting services; Computer integrated systems design; Systems software development services; Prepackaged software; Computer related consulting services
Pr: John W McCain
Pr: Aurora Coya
Pr: Barry Severns
COO: Ted Armstead
**CFO:* David Croxville
Treas: Andrea Romoli
**Treas:* Lawrence D Whelan
Rgnl VP: Charles Mears
Ex VP: Timothy Conway
Ex VP: Bob Gray
Ex VP: Jim Milde
**Ex VP:* Marv Mouchawar
Ex VP: Pam Silver
**Ex VP:* Michael Thomas
Sr VP: John Flavin
Sr VP: Donald Hiller
Sr VP: Bill Kelly
Sr VP: Raymond Paris
VP: William Baver
VP: William Butler
VP: Raissa Carvatta

Board of Directors: John W McCain

D-U-N-S 80-436-5083

NTT DATA INTERNATIONAL LLC
(*Suby of* NTT DATA CORPORATION)
45 W 36th St Fl 7, New York, NY 10018-7634
Tel (212) 355-5585 *Founded/Ownrshp* 2000
Sales 118.3MM^E *EMP* 355
SIC 7374 Data processing service; Data processing service
Pr: Takashi Enomoto
COO: Fran Convery
Ex VP: Ande Lake
Sr VP: Patrick Branagan
Sr VP: Ed Epstein
Sr VP: Jennifer Lurie
Sr VP: Jim Reichwein
VP: Pranav Desai
**VP:* Joseph A Gulli
VP: Ken Lee
VP: Dan Peet
VP: Alkesh Shah
VP: Anand Shanmugham

D-U-N-S 80-999-1912

NTT DATA INTERNATIONAL SERVICES INC
(*Suby of* NTT DATA CORPORATION)
100 City Sq, Boston, MA 02129-3721
Tel (800) 745-3263 *Founded/Ownrshp* 1993
Sales 1.2MMM^E *EMP* 18,000
SIC 7371 7372 Custom computer programming services; Prepackaged software; Custom computer programming services; Computer software development; Prepackaged software
CEO: John W McCain
**CFO:* David Kaminsky
Ofcr: Christen Macmillan
Ofcr: Theresa Walaski
**Ex VP:* Tim Conway
**Ex VP:* John M Dick
**Ex VP:* Amir Durrani
**Ex VP:* Robert W Gray
**Ex VP:* James T Milde
Ex VP: Marv Mouchawar
Sr VP: Scott Rassmusen

D-U-N-S 36-205-4009 IMP

NTT INC
FABRIC TRADITIONS
519 8th Ave Rm 1900, New York, NY 10018-6535
Tel (212) 279-5710 *Founded/Ownrshp* 1988
Sales 20.7MM^E *EMP* 30
SIC 5131 Textile converters
Pr: Domenico Seddio
**VP:* Nan Harding
Sales Exec: Beth Towey

D-U-N-S 19-482-5212

NTT USA INC
NTT
(*Suby of* NTT COMMUNICATIONS CORPORATION)
757 3rd Ave Ste 1600, New York, NY 10017-2054
Tel (888) 341-7867 *Founded/Ownrshp* 1987
Sales 17.7MM^E *EMP* 287
SIC 8732 6799 Research services, except laboratory; Venture capital companies; Research services, except laboratory; Venture capital companies
Pr: Akihiko Okada
**COO:* Dave Ryan
**Treas:* Takeshi Yamaguchi
**VP:* Paul K Heun
**VP:* Hijime Kii
Prin: Art Fritzson
Prin: Carolina Junqueira
Prin: Michael Pollock
Prin: Chris Wolfe
Mktg Mgr: Fernando Costantino

NTTA
See NORTH TEXAS TOLLWAY AUTHORITY

NTUA
See NAVAJO TRIBAL UTILITY AUTHORITY

D-U-N-S 05-903-6632 IMP

NU AIRE INC
NUAIRE
2100 Fernbrook Ln N, Plymouth, MN 55447-4722
Tel (763) 553-1270 *Founded/Ownrshp* 1971
Sales 31.8MM^E *EMP* 200^E
SIC 3821 3842 2836 Incubators, laboratory; Laboratory equipment: fume hoods, distillation racks, etc.; Laboratory furniture; Surgical appliances & supplies; Biological products, except diagnostic; Incubators, laboratory; Laboratory equipment: fume hoods, distillation racks, etc.; Laboratory furniture; Surgical appliances & supplies; Biological products, except diagnostic
CEO: Richard Peters
VP: Scott Christensen
VP: Scott Christenson
**VP:* Gerald D Peters
**VP:* Buck Richerson
VP: Jim Sande
Mng Dir: Mark Huxtable
CIO: Dick Peters
VP Sls: Buckner Richardson
Sls Dir: Robert Duczenko
Mktg Mgr: Bobbie Brittan

D-U-N-S 88-416-3239

NU COMMUNICATIONS INC
1111 Cromwell Ave Ste 302, Rocky Hill, CT 06067-3455
Tel (860) 721-1294 *Founded/Ownrshp* 1985
Sales 24.0MM *EMP* 10
SIC 8748 Communications consulting; Communications consulting
Pr: Gary Pelletier

D-U-N-S 03-927-1064

■ **NU ENTERPRISES INC**
(*Suby of* EVERSOURCE ENERGY) ★
107 Selden St, Berlin, CT 06037-1616
Tel (860) 665-5000 *Founded/Ownrshp* 1998
Sales 165.4MM^E *EMP* 400
SIC 4911 Electric services; Electric services
Pr: Charles W Shivery
Pr: Al Bettencourt
Prgrm Mgr: Deborah Sas

Dir IT: Ronald Heaphy
Dir IT: Valentino Volpe
Dir IT: Michael Zappone
IT Man: David Porter
IT Man: John Walicki
Opers Mgr: Bruce Bolger

D-U-N-S 61-351-3287

NU FLOW AMERICA INC
7710 Kenamar Ct, San Diego, CA 92121-2425
Tel (619) 275-9130 *Founded/Ownrshp* 2004
Sales 30.2MM^E *EMP* 111^E
SIC 1711 3317 Plumbing contractors; Steel pipe & tubes; Plumbing contractors; Steel pipe & tubes
Pr: Cameron Sean Manners
**Pr:* Steven Howe
Rgnl Mgr: Bill Turner
IT Man: Dennis Persaud

D-U-N-S 07-724-5942 IMP

■ **NU HORIZONS ELECTRONICS CORP**
(*Suby of* ARROW ELECTRONICS INC) ★
70 Maxess Rd, Melville, NY 11747-3102
Tel (631) 396-5000 *Founded/Ownrshp* 2011
Sales 185.8MM^E *EMP* 650
SIC 5065 Electronic parts & equipment; Semiconductor devices; Diodes; Transistors; Electronic parts & equipment; Semiconductor devices; Diodes; Transistors
Pr: Martin Kent
Pr: Wendell Boyd
Pr: Chris O'Brien
Pr: Rich Schuster
**CFO:* Kurt Freudenberg
Sr VP: Ken Sykes
VP: John Borusheski
VP: Jim Buzaid
VP: Joseph Clutter
VP: Bruce Haskin
VP: Gregg Scott
VP: Roberta Valencia
Exec: Randy Tryder

D-U-N-S 96-681-7975 IMP

▲ **NU SKIN ENTERPRISES INC**
75 W Center St, Provo, UT 84601-4432
Tel (801) 345-1000 *Founded/Ownrshp* 1984
Sales 2.5MMM *EMP* 24,350
Tkr Sym NUS *Exch* NYS
SIC 2844 5122 Toilet preparations; Cosmetic preparations; Hair coloring preparations; Toilet preparations; Cosmetic preparations; Hair coloring preparations; Cosmetics; Vitamins & minerals
Pr: M Truman Hunt
**Ch Bd:* Steven J Lund
Pr: Andrew Fan
Pr: Ryan Napierski
Pr: Brett Nelson
Pr: Nigel Sinclair
Pr: Gary K Sumihiro
CFO: Ritch N Wood
Treas: Brian Lords
Chf Mktg O: Brent Goddard
Ex VP: Joseph Y Chang
Ex VP: Corey B Lindley
VP: Mark Adams
VP: Daniel Chard
VP: Kevin Fulller
VP: Paul Haacke
VP: Andrea Hayhurst
VP: Keith Howe
VP: Bartlett Mark
VP: Jeff Smith
Exec: Brenda Blair
Board of Directors: Nevin N Andersen, Daniel W Campbell, Andrew D Lipman, Neil H Offen, Thomas R Pisano, Edwina D Woodbury

D-U-N-S 01-397-9955

■ **NU SKIN ENTERPRISES UNITED STATES INC**
(*Suby of* NU SKIN ENTERPRISES INC) ★
75 W Center St, Provo, UT 84601-4432
Tel (801) 377-6056 *Founded/Ownrshp* 1998
Sales 115.6MM^E *EMP* 1,271
SIC 5122 Drugs, proprietaries & sundries; Drugs, proprietaries & sundries
CEO: Blake M Roney
**Pr:* Steven J Lund

D-U-N-S 14-475-1849 IMP

■ **NU SKIN INTERNATIONAL INC**
PHARMANEX DIVISION
(*Suby of* NU SKIN ENTERPRISES INC) ★
75 W Center St, Provo, UT 84601-4432
Tel (801) 345-1000 *Founded/Ownrshp* 1984
Sales 179.3MM^E *EMP* 1,414
SIC 2844 Toilet preparations; Toilet preparations
Ch Bd: Steven J Lund
**Pr:* Truman Hunt
COO: John Fralick
COO: Lester Packer
COO: Wood Rich
**CFO:* Rich Wood
Ch: Blake M Roney
Sr VP: Sandy N Tillotson
VP: Jodi Durrant
VP: Brooke B Roney
Exec: Sam Holoviak

D-U-N-S 00-633-4122 IMP

NU WAY CONCRETE FORMS INC (MO)
4190 Hoffmeister Ave, Saint Louis, MO 63125-2298
Tel (573) 893-8786 *Founded/Ownrshp* 1955
Sales 94.2MM^E *EMP* 160
SIC 5032 5051 5072 7359 Masons' materials; Rods, metal; Hand tools; Tool rental; Masons' materials; Rods, metal; Hand tools; Tool rental
Pr: Gerald A Rhomberg
Pt: Dave Pazdernik
**Treas:* Daphne Rhomberg
**VP:* Arthur A Rhomberg Jr

D-U-N-S 08-024-2845

NU WAY COOPERATIVE (INC)
440 Highway 4 S, Trimont, MN 56176-4002
Tel (507) 639-2311 *Founded/Ownrshp* 1937
Sales 97.1MM *EMP* 75
Accts Carlson Highland & Co Llp

SIC 5191 5171 5541 2875 Chemicals, agricultural; Fertilizer & fertilizer materials; Petroleum bulk stations & terminals; Gasoline service stations; Fertilizers, mixing only; Chemicals, agricultural; Fertilizer & fertilizer materials; Petroleum bulk stations & terminals; Gasoline service stations; Fertilizers, mixing only
Pr: Kevin Jones

NU WORLD
See NU-WORLD CORP

D-U-N-S 78-298-0288 EXP

NU-CALGON WHOLESALER INC
2008 Altom Ct, Saint Louis, MO 63146-4151
Tel (314) 469-7000 *Founded/Ownrshp* 1991
Sales 72.9MM *EMP* 52
Accts Kiefer Bontafi & Co Llp St
SIC 5169 Chemicals & allied products; Chemicals & allied products
Pr: Al Butler
**CFO:* James Eager
**Ex VP:* Robert F Pierce
VP: Brian Butler
Rgnl Mgr: Robert Vosburgh
Sls Mgr: Jeff Petersen

D-U-N-S 15-362-1958

NU-CAST INC
29 Grenier Field Rd, Londonderry, NH 03053-2015
Tel (603) 432-1600 *Founded/Ownrshp* 1986
Sales 25.1MM^E *EMP* 130
SIC 3365 Aluminum foundries; Aluminum foundries
Pr: D Donald Mc Kitterick
**Sr VP:* John Bowkett

D-U-N-S 09-638-3633 IMP/EXP

NU-FOAM PRODUCTS INC (TN)
1101 Wisdom St, Chattanooga, TN 37406-1756
Tel (423) 698-6911 *Founded/Ownrshp* 1989
Sales NA *EMP* 1,200
SIC 3086 Plastics foam products

D-U-N-S 09-987-7748 EXP

NU-LIFE ENVIRONMENTAL INC
2266 Powdersville Rd, Easley, SC 29642-8921
Tel (864) 371-6120 *Founded/Ownrshp* 1979
Sales 40.4MM^E *EMP* 80
SIC 5084 7538 Industrial machinery & equipment; General automotive repair shops; Industrial machinery & equipment; General automotive repair shops
Pr: Ervin Hendricks
**CFO:* Tim Hendricks
CFO: John Schneider
**VP:* Philip Hendricks

D-U-N-S 00-785-9580

NU-LITE ELECTRICAL WHOLESALERS LLC
850 Edwards Ave, Harahan, LA 70123-3123
Tel (504) 733-3300 *Founded/Ownrshp* 1950, 1987
Sales 124.8MM^E *EMP* 130
SIC 5063 Electrical apparatus & equipment; Electrical apparatus & equipment
Genl Mgr: Joseph Impastato
VP Opers: Gary Corales
Sls Mgr: Lenny Lassus
Sales Asso: Jeff Pierre
Sales Asso: Bill Shepherd

D-U-N-S 86-705-1815

NU-PAK INC
305 1st St, Boscobel, WI 53805-1166
Tel (608) 375-2322 *Founded/Ownrshp* 1994
Sales 34.9MM^E *EMP* 250
SIC 7389 Packaging & labeling services; Packaging & labeling services
CEO: James Hutchison
**Pr:* Jeff Panka
Prd Mgr: Brad White

NU-TELECOM
See NEW ULM TELECOM INC

D-U-N-S 03-186-3114

NU-TIER BRANDS INC
8282 S Memorial Dr # 302, Tulsa, OK 74133-4355
Tel (918) 550-8026 *Founded/Ownrshp* 2010
Sales 41.7MM *EMP* 7
SIC 2992 Lubricating oils; Lubricating oils
Pr: Vincent Rudolph

D-U-N-S 79-110-6990

■ **NU-VISION TECHNOLOGIES LLC**
BLACK BOX NETWORK SERVICES
(*Suby of* BLACK BOX CORP) ★
6000 New Horizons Blvd, Amityville, NY 11701-1146
Tel (631) 841-5200 *Founded/Ownrshp* 2006
Sales NA *EMP* 300
SIC 4813 Telephone communication, except radio; Telephone communication, except radio
CEO: Michael McAndrew
VP: Dwayne Diesu
VP: Mike Ghibaudi
VP: Joe Leonardo
VP: Peter Marquis
IT Man: Becky Gravett
VP Sls: Joseph Nidzyn
Sls Mgr: Jeff Barton

D-U-N-S 00-716-1763

NU-WA INDUSTRIES INC (KS)
3701 S Johnson Rd, Chanute, KS 66720-4003
Tel (620) 431-2088 *Founded/Ownrshp* 1958
Sales 33.5MM^E *EMP* 350
Accts Stafford & Westervelt Charter
SIC 3792 Travel trailers & campers; Travel trailers & campers
CEO: Michael S Mitchell
**Pr:* Neil Ford
Exec: Ginger Lycnh

NU-WAY
See N W HOLDING CO

D-U-N-S 04-391-7665 IMP

NU-WAY INDUSTRIES INC
555 Howard Ave, Des Plaines, IL 60018-1981
Tel (847) 298-7710 *Founded/Ownrshp* 1968
Sales 100.3MM^E *EMP* 350^E

Accts Lipschultz Levin & Gray Nort
SIC 3444 3469 3599 Sheet metalwork; Sheet metal specialties, not stamped; Metal housings, enclosures, casings & other containers; Stamping metal for the trade; Machine shop, jobbing & repair; Sheet metalwork; Sheet metal specialties, not stamped; Metal housings, enclosures, casings & other containers; Stamping metal for the trade; Machine shop, jobbing & repair
Pr: Steven Southwell
Ex VP: Joe Fijak
**Ex VP:* Mary Howard
IT Man: Debbie Mossman
VP Opers: Steve Wiseman
Mtls Mgr: Susan Passero

NU-WAY SPECIALIZED SERVICES
See NU-WAY TRANSPORTATION SERVICES INC

D-U-N-S 92-985-3752

NU-WAY TRANSPORTATION SERVICES INC
NU-WAY SPECIALIZED SERVICES
2 Access Way, Bloomington, IL 61705-4121
Tel (309) 820-9797 *Founded/Ownrshp* 1994
Sales 48.8MM^E *EMP* 340^E
SIC 4212 4213

D-U-N-S 16-088-8582

NU-WEST INDUSTRIES INC
(*Suby of* AGRIUM US INC) ★
3010 Conda Rd, Soda Springs, ID 83276-5301
Tel (208) 547-4381 *Founded/Ownrshp* 1995
Sales 89.3MM^E *EMP* 300^E
SIC 2874 Phosphates; Phosphates
Pr: Mike Wilson
**Treas:* Patrick Freeman
Sfty Mgr: Katrina Miller
**Genl Couns:* Leslie O Donohue

D-U-N-S 62-804-5858 IMP

NU-WORLD CORP
NU WORLD
300 Milik St, Carteret, NJ 07008-1113
Tel (732) 541-6300 *Founded/Ownrshp* 1991
Sales 84.1MM^E *EMP* 250^E
Accts Bederson & Company Llc West O
SIC 2844 Cosmetic preparations; Cosmetic preparations
CEO: Jonathan Rosenbaum
**Pr:* Stuart Dolleck
COO: Peter Greene
**CFO:* Stuart Mont
Sr VP: Joe Moreno
Sr VP: Ketan Patel
Creative D: Ilyse Davis
Dir Sec: Richard Kuohn
Plng Mgr: Gopalan Nagarajan
Dir IT: Robert Russell
IT Man: Craig Dykes

NU-WORLD FOODS
See AMARANTH NU-WORLD INC

NUAIRE
See NU AIRE INC

D-U-N-S 79-740-7517

▲ **NUANCE COMMUNICATIONS INC**
1 Wayside Rd, Burlington, MA 01803-4609
Tel (781) 565-5000 *Founded/Ownrshp* 2005
Sales 1.9MMM *EMP* 13,500
Accts Bdo Usa Llp Boston Massachu
Tkr Sym NUAN *Exch* NGS
SIC 7372 Prepackaged software; Prepackaged software
Ch Bd: Paul A Ricci
Pr: Trace Devanny
Pr: Vanessa Richter
Pr: Vipul Vyas
CFO: Richard Booth
CFO: Daniel D Tempesta
Bd of Dir: Anne Demedts
Bd of Dir: Frank Giessler
Bd of Dir: Jeanne Nauman
Bd of Dir: Ryan Painter
Chf Mktg O: Steven G Chambers
Ofcr: Peter Mahoney
Ex VP: A Bruce Bowden
Ex VP: Janet M Dillione
Ex VP: Bill Nelson
Ex VP: William Robbins
Sr VP: Valorie Cook Carpenter
Sr VP: Thomas J Chisholm
Sr VP: Dawn Howarth
Sr VP: Jeanne F McCann
Sr VP: Richard S Palmer
Board of Directors: Robert Finocchio, Robert J Frankenberg, Brett Icahn, William H Janeway, Mark R Laret, Katharine A Martin, Mark B Myers, Philip J Quigley, David S Schechter

D-U-N-S 02-044-9013

■ **NUANCE DOCUMENT IMAGING INC**
(*Suby of* NUANCE COMMUNICATIONS INC) ★
1000 S Pine Island Rd # 900, Plantation, FL 33324-3906
Tel (954) 888-7800 *Founded/Ownrshp* 2011
Sales 44.8MM^E *EMP* 350
SIC 7373 7377 7378 5045 7371 Computer system selling services; Computer rental & leasing; Computer maintenance & repair; Computers, peripherals & software; Custom computer programming services; Computer system selling services; Computer rental & leasing; Computer maintenance & repair; Computers, peripherals & software; Custom computer programming services
Pr: Michael Rich
**Pr:* Thomas L Beaudoin
**CFO:* Angelo Gencarelli
**Treas:* Daniel Tempesta Asst
VP: Joe Hartnett
**VP:* Robert J McDonough
VP: Gaetan Spake
**VP:* James Wilson
**Prin:* Beaudoin Thomas L
Mng Dir: Chris Capra
QA Dir: Dawn Forrester

NUANCE SOLUTIONS
See BULLEN MIDWEST INC

D-U-N-S 36-194-2105
NUBANI DISTRIBUTORS INC
2850 Oak St Ste A, Bellwood, IL 60104-1560
Tel (708) 544-4740 *Founded/Ownrshp* 1989
Sales 28.0MM *EMP* 25
SIC 5145 Candy; Candy
CEO: Sam Nubani
**Pr:* Fred Nubani
**VP:* Nader Nubani

D-U-N-S 03-729-0678
NUBRIDGES INC
(*Suby of* LIAISON TECHNOLOGIES INC) ★
115 Perimeter Center Pl S Ste 1100, Atlanta, GA 30346
Tel (770) 730-3600 *Founded/Ownrshp* 2011
Sales 34.9MM^E *EMP* 133
SIC 5045 Computers, peripherals & software; Computers, peripherals & software
Pr: Paul Oolson
Genl Pt: Charles Moseley
Genl Pt: Charlie Moseley
CFO: Jim Morgan
Ex VP: Brad Childress
Ex VP: Jim Magers
Ex VP: Kee Murray
VP: Kim Addington
VP: David Sutton
VP: John Wehrheim
Dir Surg: Tim Dailey

NUBY
See LUV N CARE LTD

D-U-N-S 78-912-1811
NUCAL FOODS INC
720 S Stockton Ave, Ripon, CA 95366-2790
Tel (209) 254-2200 *Founded/Ownrshp* 1996
Sales 26.8MM^E *EMP* 38
SIC 5144 Poultry & poultry products
Pr: David K Crockett
**CFO:* Steve Hennecke
Bd of Dir: Joe Arias
Bd of Dir: Robert Benson
Bd of Dir: Gary West
QA Dir: Mark Powell
VP Opers: Wayne Winslow
Sls Dir: Tracy Lape

D-U-N-S 07-357-8759
NUCAR CONNECTION INC (DE)
NUCAR MAZDA
174 N Dupont Hwy, New Castle, DE 19720-3125
Tel (302) 322-2438 *Founded/Ownrshp* 1982, 1995
Sales NA *EMP* 314
SIC 5511

NUCAR MAZDA
See NUCAR CONNECTION INC

D-U-N-S 01-101-8702
NUCAR MOTORS INC
NUCAR PONTIAC - GMC
174 N Dupont Hwy, New Castle, DE 19720-3125
Tel (302) 325-7278 *Founded/Ownrshp* 1989
Sales 23.3MM^E *EMP* 82
SIC 5511 Automobiles, new & used; Automobiles, new & used
Pr: David B Greytak
**VP:* C Ronald Miller
**VP Opers:* Robert L Davis
Sales Asso: Gary Digiacinto

NUCAR PONTIAC - GMC
See NUCAR MOTORS INC

NUCARE
See ASCEND EAGLE INC

D-U-N-S 07-117-3798
NUCARE SERVICES CORP
7257 N Lincoln Ave # 100, Lincolnwood, IL 60712-1810
Tel (847) 676-2122 *Founded/Ownrshp* 1994
Sales 25.6MM^E *EMP* 50^E
SIC 7389
Pr: David Hartman
COO: Mike Munter
**CFO:* Jay Flatt
**Prin:* Barry Carr
**Prin:* Robert Hartman
Genl Couns: Pegi McCabe

D-U-N-S 01-275-8405
NUCCI BROS INC
NUCCI BROS POOL SUPPLIES
145 Oval Dr, Islandia, NY 11749-1402
Tel (631) 234-6300 *Founded/Ownrshp* 1945
Sales 21.5MM^E *EMP* 33
SIC 5091 Swimming pools, equipment & supplies
Pr: Frank A Nucci
Genl Mgr: Jimmy Sarle
Sales Asso: Michele Giammona

NUCCI BROS POOL SUPPLIES
See NUCCI BROS INC

D-U-N-S 02-897-8047
NUCKLES OIL CO INC
MERIT OIL
1020 Bloomington Ave, Bloomington, CA 92316-2007
Tel (909) 877-2651 *Founded/Ownrshp* 1973
Sales 22.1MM^E *EMP* 50
SIC 5172 5984

D-U-N-S 62-650-0276
NUCLEAR ELECTRIC INSURANCE LIMITED
NEIL
1201 N Market St Ste 1100, Wilmington, DE 19801-1805
Tel (302) 888-3000 *Founded/Ownrshp* 1973
Sales NA *EMP* 60
Accts Deloitte & Touche Llp Philade
SIC 6331 Property damage insurance; Property damage insurance
Pr: David B Ripsom
**VP:* Kenneth C Manne
**VP:* Harry J Phillips
**VP:* Bruce A Sassi
**VP:* Thomas G Tannion

D-U-N-S 01-646-3655
NUCLEAR ENERGY INSTITUTE INC
N E I
1201 F St Nw Ste 1100, Washington, DC 20004-1218
Tel (202) 739-8000 *Founded/Ownrshp* 1979
Sales 54.5MM *EMP* 138
Accts Matthew F Penniman Cpa Llc D
SIC 8611 Trade associations; Trade associations
Pr: Marvin S Fertel
**Ch Bd:* W Gary Gates
**Pr:* Christopher M Crane
**Pr:* John F Young
**CFO:* Phylis Rich
**V Ch Bd:* William D Johnson
**Sr VP:* Alex Flint
**Sr VP:* J Scott Peterson
**VP:* Ellen C Ginbserg
**VP:* Angelina Howard
**VP:* Alex Marion
**VP:* Richard Myers
**VP:* Scott Peterson
**VP:* Anthony Pietrangelo

NUCLEAR FACILITY
See NEBRASKA PUBLIC POWER DISTRICT

D-U-N-S 04-949-8025 IMP
■ **NUCLEAR FUEL SERVICES INC**
(*Suby of* BWXT NUCLEAR OPERATIONS GROUP INC) ★
1205 Banner Hill Rd, Erwin, TN 37650-9318
Tel (423) 743-9141 *Founded/Ownrshp* 2009
Sales 3.8MM *EMP* 735
Accts Pricewaterhousecoopers Llp
SIC 8748 2819 Business consulting; Nuclear fuel & cores, inorganic; Business consulting; Nuclear fuel & cores, inorganic
Pr: Joel Duling
Sr Cor Off: Rick Sturgill
Ofcr: Robert Burckhardt
Ofcr: Mike Fronckoski
VP: Jane Matheson
Prgrm Mgr: Andrew Davidson
IT Man: Jaime Rogers
IT Man: Walter Wilkerson
Ql Cn Mgr: Michael Bucchi
Ql Cn Mgr: Dave Hatcher
Secur Mgr: Mike Bumgarner

D-U-N-S 55-622-6108
■ **NUCLEAR LOGISTICS INC**
(*Suby of* AZZ INC) ★
7410 Pebble Dr, Fort Worth, TX 76118-6961
Tel (817) 284-0077 *Founded/Ownrshp* 2012
Sales 186.7MM^E *EMP* 155
SIC 5065 8711 Electronic parts & equipment; Engineering services; Electronic parts & equipment; Engineering services
Pr: Aron Seiken
VP: Archie Bell
Off Mgr: Kathy Baker
QA Dir: Tracy Bolt
QA Dir: Tracy Chung
Dir IT: Scott Dauphin
Prd Mgr: Bob McCrory
VP Mktg: Craig Irish
Sales Asso: Valerie Cox

D-U-N-S 11-373-8889
■ **NUCLEAR MANAGEMENT CO LLC**
N.M.C
(*Suby of* NORTHERN STATES POWER CO) ★
414 Nicollet Mall, Minneapolis, MN 55401-1927
Tel (612) 330-5500 *Founded/Ownrshp* 1999
Sales 62.9MM^E *EMP* 2,460
SIC 8741 8999 Management services; Nuclear consultant; Management services; Nuclear consultant
VP: Karen Miller

D-U-N-S 04-053-5809
■ **NUCLEAR REGULATORY COMMISSION UNITED STATES**
U.S.NRC
(*Suby of* EXECUTIVE OFFICE OF UNITED STATES GOVERNMENT) ★
11555 Rockville Pike, Rockville, MD 20852-2746
Tel (800) 368-5642 *Founded/Ownrshp* 1975
Sales NA *EMP* 4,000
SIC 9631 Nuclear energy inspection & regulation office, government;
Ch: Dra Allison M Macfarlane
Pr: Fred Miller
Pr: Edith Sparks
Pr: Sandra Wastler
CFO: James Dyer
**CFO:* Jesse Funches
Ofcr: Bill Borchardt
Ofcr: David Decker
Ofcr: Geraldine Fehst
Ofcr: Jill Shepherd
Ofcr: Jenny Weil
Sr VP: William Webster
Exec: Kathy Gibson

NUCLEAR SYSTEMS GROUP
See SIEMENS MEDICAL SOLUTIONS USA INC

D-U-N-S 14-776-6141
NUCLETRON CORP
400 Perimeter Center Ter, Atlanta, GA 30346-1227
Tel (410) 312-4100 *Founded/Ownrshp* 1994
Sales 43.0MM *EMP* 79
SIC 5047 Hospital equipment & supplies; Hospital equipment & supplies
CEO: Jos Laner
Sls Dir: Dave Hart

NUCO PRODUCTS
See NUTIS PRESS INC

D-U-N-S 10-768-8822
■ **NUCO2 INC**
(*Suby of* PRAXAIR INC) ★
2800 Se Market Pl, Stuart, FL 34997-4965
Tel (772) 221-1754 *Founded/Ownrshp* 2013
Sales 342.9MM^E *EMP* 700
SIC 5169 Carbon dioxide; Carbon dioxide
Pr: Kevin Foti
COO: Scott W Wade
Ex VP: Keith Gordon
Sr VP: Randy Gold
Sr VP: Peter Green
Sr VP: Nancy Pawlowski
VP: John Scollard
VP: Greg Seefeldt
Dist Mgr: Ron Johnson
IT Man: Chad Ray
Mktg Mgr: Debbie Oliver

D-U-N-S 82-717-3928
■ **NUCO2 SUPPLY LLC**
(*Suby of* NUCO2 INC) ★
2800 Se Market Pl, Stuart, FL 34997-4965
Tel (772) 221-1754 *Founded/Ownrshp* 2008
Sales 73.9MM^E *EMP* 277^E
SIC 5099 Firearms & ammunition, except sporting

NUCOR BAR MILL GROUP
See NUCOR STEEL CONNECTICUT INC

D-U-N-S 79-712-0867
NUCOR BUILDING SYSTEMS SALES CORP
600 Apache Trl, Terrell, TX 75160-6512
Tel (972) 524-5407 *Founded/Ownrshp* 1999
Sales 53.8MM^E *EMP* 250
SIC 3448 Prefabricated metal buildings; Prefabricated metal buildings
Pr: Jeff Carmean
Genl Mgr: Ray Napolitan Jr
Netwrk Eng: Steve Lamb
Sfty Dirs: Shawn Cornett
Sls Mgr: Garry Clayton
Sls Mgr: Brad Yocum

D-U-N-S 80-138-6736
■ **NUCOR BUILDING SYSTEMS UTAH LLC**
(*Suby of* NUCOR CORP) ★
1050 Watery Ln, Brigham City, UT 84302-1513
Tel (435) 919-3100 *Founded/Ownrshp* 2006
Sales 58.5MM^E *EMP* 200
SIC 3448 Prefabricated metal buildings; Prefabricated metal buildings
Genl Mgr: Mark Vandyken

D-U-N-S 00-344-6796 IMP/EXP
▲ **NUCOR CORP**
1915 Rexford Rd Ste 400, Charlotte, NC 28211-3888
Tel (704) 366-7000 *Founded/Ownrshp* 1940
Sales 21.1MMM *EMP* 23,600
Accts Pricewaterhousecoopers Llp Ch
Tkr Sym NUE *Exch* NYS
SIC 3312 3441 3448 3452 5093 Blast furnaces & steel mills; Primary finished or semifinished shapes; Bar, rod & wire products; Plate, sheet & strip, except coated products; Building components, structural steel; Joists, open web steel: long-span series; Prefabricated metal buildings; Prefabricated metal components; Bolts, metal; Screws, metal; Ferrous metal scrap & waste; Nonferrous metals scrap; Blast furnaces & steel mills; Primary finished or semifinished shapes; Bar, rod & wire products; Plate, sheet & strip, except coated products; Building components, structural steel; Joists, open web steel: long-span series; Prefabricated metal buildings; Prefabricated metal components; Bolts, metal; Screws, metal; Ferrous metal scrap & waste; Nonferrous metals scrap
Ch Bd: John J Ferriola
Pr: Alicia Mummert
CFO: James D Frias
Ex VP: James R Darsey
Ex VP: Ladd R Hall
Ex VP: Raymond S Napolitan Jr
Ex VP: R Joseph Stratman
Ex VP: David A Sumoaski
Ex VP: Dave Sumoski
Ex VP: Chad Utermark
VP: Michael D Keller
Board of Directors: Peter C Browning, Harvey B Gantt, Gregory J Hayes, Victoria F Haynes, Bernard L Kasriel, Christopher J Kearney, Laurette T Koellner, Raymond J Milchovich, John H Walker

D-U-N-S 02-630-8820 IMP
■ **NUCOR STEEL AUBURN INC**
(*Suby of* NUCOR CORP) ★
25 Quarry Rd, Auburn, NY 13021-1146
Tel (315) 253-4561 *Founded/Ownrshp* 2001
Sales 116.4MM^E *EMP* 290
SIC 3312 Blast furnaces & steel mills; Blast furnaces & steel mills
Ch: Dan Dimicco
Genl Mgr: Del Benzenhafer
Genl Mgr: Mary E Slate
Genl Mgr: Dave Smith
Sfty Mgr: Luke Scott
Plnt Mgr: Ed Wolf
Snr Mgr: Jim Biernat
Snr Mgr: Mike Pidlypchak
Snr Mgr: Clara Van Aswegen

NUCOR STEEL BAR MILLS GROUP
See NUCOR STEEL SEATTLE INC

D-U-N-S 12-432-6476
■ **NUCOR STEEL BIRMINGHAM INC**
(*Suby of* NUCOR CORP) ★
2301 Fl Shuttlesworth Dr, Birmingham, AL 35234-1335
Tel (205) 250-7400 *Founded/Ownrshp* 2002
Sales 103.0MM^E *EMP* 250
SIC 3312 Bars & bar shapes, steel, cold-finished: own hot-rolled; Bars & bar shapes, steel, cold-finished: own hot-rolled
Pr: Daniel R Dimicco
**CFO:* James Rias
**Ex VP:* James Darsey
**Genl Mgr:* Franky Riggs
Mtls Mgr: Brandon Keller
Trfc Mgr: Michael Rhodes
Sls Mgr: Clifford Drouet
Sls Mgr: Matt Isbell
Sls Mgr: Gary Young
Snr Mgr: Steve Messier

D-U-N-S 11-616-7511 IMP/EXP
■ **NUCOR STEEL CONNECTICUT INC**
NUCOR BAR MILL GROUP
(*Suby of* NUCOR CORP) ★
35 Toelles Rd, Wallingford, CT 06492-4419
Tel (203) 265-0615 *Founded/Ownrshp* 1999
Sales 62.1MM^E *EMP* 157
SIC 3312 3449 3496 Rods, iron & steel: made in steel mills; Bars, concrete reinforcing: fabricated steel; Mesh, made from purchased wire; Rods, iron & steel: made in steel mills; Bars, concrete reinforcing: fabricated steel; Mesh, made from purchased wire
Prin: Mark Brando
QA Dir: John Brasell
IT Man: Tom Moore
Opers Mgr: Don Mann
Prd Mgr: Lisa McCollum
Sls Mgr: David Perez
Sales Asso: Jeffrey McGoldrick
Snr Mgr: Lisa Greenier
Snr Mgr: Jay Martin

D-U-N-S 11-889-9371 IMP
■ **NUCOR STEEL DECATUR LLC**
(*Suby of* NUCOR CORP) ★
4301 Iverson Blvd, Trinity, AL 35673-6635
Tel (256) 301-3500 *Founded/Ownrshp* 2002
Sales 228.8MM^E *EMP* 696
SIC 3312 Blast furnaces & steel mills; Blast furnaces & steel mills
CEO: Dan Dimicco
VP: Peter Campbell
VP: Michael Lee
Prgrm Mgr: Karyn Stephanz
IT Man: Dave Kirkland
Sfty Mgr: George Stephenson
Ql Cn Mgr: Shawna Starks
Sls Mgr: Brett Stoler

D-U-N-S 80-836-8989 IMP/EXP
■ **NUCOR STEEL GALLATIN LLC**
(*Suby of* NUCOR CORP) ★
4831 Us Highway 42 W, Ghent, KY 41045-9001
Tel (859) 567-3100 *Founded/Ownrshp* 2014
Sales 228.8MM^E *EMP* 400
SIC 3312 Blast furnaces & steel mills; Blast furnaces & steel mills
Genl Mgr: John Farris
Genl Mgr: Richard Elder
Genl Mgr: Robert Levey
QA Dir: Cheryl Foster
Trfc Dir: Carl Bischoff
Sfty Mgr: Jerry Hines
Opers Mgr: Anthony Nath
Manager: Travis Simpson
Sales Asso: Ronald Hinton
Sales Asso: Henry Mathews
Snr Mgr: Dave Cozart

D-U-N-S 11-490-0934 IMP/EXP
■ **NUCOR STEEL JACKSON INC**
(*Suby of* NUCOR CORP) ★
3630 Fourth St, Flowood, MS 39232-2000
Tel (601) 939-1623 *Founded/Ownrshp* 2002
Sales 115.6MM^E *EMP* 265
SIC 3312 Blast furnaces & steel mills; Blast furnaces & steel mills
Pr: Daniel R Dimicco
VP: Don Barney
**VP:* Gim Shebel
Ql Cn Mgr: Heather Poschel
Snr Mgr: Clay Burton

D-U-N-S 11-487-4865 IMP
■ **NUCOR STEEL KANKAKEE INC**
(*Suby of* NUCOR CORP) ★
1 Nucor Way, Bourbonnais, IL 60914-3213
Tel (815) 939-5500 *Founded/Ownrshp* 2002
Sales 111.3MM^E *EMP* 280
SIC 3312 3547 3449 Blast furnaces & steel mills; Rolling mill machinery; Miscellaneous metalwork; Blast furnaces & steel mills; Rolling mill machinery; Miscellaneous metalwork
Pr: Alex Weisselberg
**Pr:* James Darsey
**CFO:* Jim Frias
Dir IT: Peggy Hutnick
Sfty Dirs: Bob Brown
Sls Mgr: Ken Walls

D-U-N-S 03-227-1975 IMP/EXP
■ **NUCOR STEEL MARION INC**
(*Suby of* NUCOR CORP) ★
912 Cheney Ave, Marion, OH 43302-6208
Tel (740) 383-4011 *Founded/Ownrshp* 1981
Sales 41.6MM^E *EMP* 400
SIC 3993 3312 3441 3316

D-U-N-S 15-322-5821 IMP/EXP
■ **NUCOR STEEL MEMPHIS INC**
(*Suby of* NUCOR CORP) ★
3601 Paul R Lowry Rd, Memphis, TN 38109-3007
Tel (901) 786-5837 *Founded/Ownrshp* 2002
Sales 228.8MM^E *EMP* 420
SIC 3312 3441 3448 3452 Blast furnaces & steel mills; Primary finished or semifinished shapes; Bar, rod & wire products; Plate, sheet & strip, except coated products; Building components, structural steel; Joists, open web steel: long-span series; Prefabricated metal buildings; Bolts, metal; Screws, metal; Blast furnaces & steel mills; Primary finished or semifinished shapes; Bar, rod & wire products; Plate, sheet & strip, except coated products; Building components, structural steel; Joists, open web steel: long-span series; Prefabricated metal buildings; Bolts, metal; Screws, metal
Genl Mgr: Dave Smith
IT Man: Matthew Watford
Netwrk Eng: John Herrington
Opers Mgr: Jesse Simmons
Ql Cn Mgr: John Turk
Sls Mgr: Dallas Hunsucker
Sls Mgr: Drew Kofahl

D-U-N-S 13-048-1208 IMP
■ **NUCOR STEEL SEATTLE INC**
NUCOR STEEL BAR MILLS GROUP
(*Suby of* NUCOR CORP) ★
2424 Sw Andover St, Seattle, WA 98106-1100
Tel (206) 933-2222 *Founded/Ownrshp* 2002
Sales 54.5MM^E *EMP* 290^E
SIC 3325 Steel foundries; Steel foundries
Pr: James Darsey
**Ch:* John Ferriola
**VP:* James Frias
Genl Mgr: Matt Lyons
Sales Exec: James Petersen
Sales Asso: Tawnya Hollobon
Sales Asso: Brad Kohn

D-U-N-S 13-116-5714 IMP/EXP
■ **NUCOR STEEL TUSCALOOSA INC**
(*Suby of* NUCOR CORP) ★
1700 Holt Rd Ne, Tuscaloosa, AL 35404-1046
Tel (205) 556-1310 *Founded/Ownrshp* 2006
Sales 186.9MM^E *EMP* 345
SIC 3312 Blast furnaces & steel mills; Plate, steel; Blast furnaces & steel mills; Plate, steel
Ch Bd: Harold Homer
**COO:* Jim Lewis
VP: Jan Mass
**VP:* Randey Skagen
Dir IT: Donna Martin
Sfty Dirs: Paul Thurber
Sfty Mgr: Barry Benham
Sfty Mgr: Tim White
Plnt Mgr: Therr Nowlin
Plnt Mgr: James Yerkes
Sls Mgr: Andy Barr

D-U-N-S 79-542-6472 IMP
■ **NUCOR STEEL UTAH**
(*Suby of* NUCOR CORP) ★
7285 W 21200 N, Plymouth, UT 84330
Tel (435) 458-2300 *Founded/Ownrshp* 1998
Sales 78.1MM^E *EMP* 380^E
SIC 2296 Steel tire cords & tire cord fabrics; Steel tire cords & tire cord fabrics
VP: Dave Smith
VP: Marc Chadaz
VP: Wayne Keller
Exec: Rochelle Harrell
Sfty Dirs: Brian Peterson
Sales Asso: Michael Frandsen

D-U-N-S 06-533-7065 IMP
■ **NUCOR-LMP INC**
LMP STEEL & WIRE COMPANY
(*Suby of* NUCOR CORP) ★
2000 E 1st St, Maryville, MO 64468-3112
Tel (660) 582-3127 *Founded/Ownrshp* 2007
Sales 57.3MM^E *EMP* 135
SIC 3316 3315 3452 3429 Bars, steel, cold finished, from purchased hot-rolled; Wire, steel: insulated or armored; Bolts, metal; Nuts, metal; Rivets, metal; Manufactured hardware (general); Bars, steel, cold finished, from purchased hot-rolled; Wire, steel: insulated or armored; Bolts, metal; Nuts, metal; Rivets, metal; Manufactured hardware (general)
CEO: Lewis Wagner
Pr: Doug Cohen
CFO: William Gronniger
VP Mfg: Bob McKee
Sfty Mgr: Rick Liberty
Trfc Mgr: Ken Greene
Sls Mgr: Scott McVicker
Sls Mgr: Martin Reynolds

D-U-N-S 18-109-2545 IMP/EXP
■ **NUCOR-YAMATO STEEL CO (LIMITED PARTNERSHIP)**
(*Suby of* NUCOR CORP) ★
5929 E State Highway 18, Blytheville, AR 72315-7429
Tel (870) 762-5500 *Founded/Ownrshp* 1987
Sales 1.4MMM^E *EMP* 800
Accts Pricewaterhousecooper Llp Cha
SIC 3312 3441 Structural shapes & pilings, steel; Fabricated structural metal; Structural shapes & pilings, steel; Fabricated structural metal
Genl Mgr: D Chad Utermark
Pr: Chad Utermark
CFO: Chuck Ryan
**Treas:* Donald K Prevost
VP: Leon Topalian
Prin: Elizabeth W Bowers
**Genl Mgr:* Doug Jellison
Genl Mgr: R Stratman
Dir IT: Tom Wallis
IT Man: Kenneth Baker
Sfty Dirs: April Bentley

D-U-N-S 82-811-4764
NUCOURSE DISTRIBUTION INC
2008 San Anseline Ave, Long Beach, CA 90815-3117
Tel (866) 655-4366 *Founded/Ownrshp* 2008
Sales 89.0MM *EMP* 55
SIC 5065

D-U-N-S 06-242-6234
NUCROWN INC (MO)
CROWN OPTICAL
211 E Broadway, Alton, IL 62002-6220
Tel (618) 462-9818 *Founded/Ownrshp* 1961, 1990
Sales 32.7MM^E *EMP* 190
SIC 5995 Optical goods stores; Optical goods stores; Eyeglasses, prescription
Pr: Charles D Matthews
CFO: Daniel Pund

D-U-N-S 04-750-4897
NUDEVCO MIDSTREAM DEVELOPMENT LLC
(*Suby of* NUDEVCO PARTNERS HOLDINGS LLC) ★
12140 Wickchester Ln # 100, Houston, TX 77079-1219
Tel (832) 200-3702 *Founded/Ownrshp* 2012
Sales 54.0MM^E *EMP* 79^E
SIC 1311 Crude petroleum & natural gas
CEO: William K Maxwell III
Treas: Marty Bredehoft
VP: Stephen Brownell
VP: Jeremy Ham
Genl Couns: Terry D Jones

D-U-N-S 07-943-6519
NUDEVCO PARTNERS HOLDINGS LLC
(*Suby of* NUDEVCO PARTNERS LLC) ★
12140 Wickchester Ln, Houston, TX 77079-1219
Tel (713) 977-5634 *Founded/Ownrshp* 2013
Sales 54.0MM^E *EMP* 90^E
SIC 4922 Natural gas transmission; Pipelines, natural gas
CEO: Keith Maxwell III
CFO: Todd Gibson
Ex VP: Terry Jones

D-U-N-S 07-909-1447
NUDEVCO PARTNERS LLC (TX)
2105 Citywest Blvd # 100, Houston, TX 77042-2855
Tel (832) 200-3702 *Founded/Ownrshp* 2010
Sales 54.0MM^E *EMP* 50^E
SIC 4922 Natural gas transmission; Pipelines, natural gas

D-U-N-S 02-584-8680 IMP
NUDO PRODUCTS INC
(*Suby of* RFE INVESTMENT PARTNERS IV LP) ★
1500 Taylor Ave, Springfield, IL 62703-5663
Tel (217) 528-5636 *Founded/Ownrshp* 2008
Sales 60.9MM^E *EMP* 200^E
SIC 3083 3089 5033 3444 Plastic finished products, laminated; Extruded finished plastic products; Fiberglass building materials; Awnings, sheet metal
Pr: Darryl Rosser
**COO:* Charles Pineau
**CFO:* Len Farrell
CFO: Richard E Poyntr
**VP:* Tony Dalpos
**VP:* Mark Jutte
Dir Bus: Dan Wilson
Manager: John Rusgis

D-U-N-S 01-052-7190
NUECES COUNTY COMMUNITY ACTION AGENCY (TX)
101 S Padre Island Dr, Corpus Christi, TX 78405-4102
Tel (361) 883-7201 *Founded/Ownrshp* 1964
Sales 14.6MM *EMP* 350
SIC 8399 Community action agency; Community action agency
Ex Dir: Dorothy Wade

D-U-N-S 04-973-8131
NUECES FARM CENTER INC
NUECES POWER EQUIPMENT
7510 Ih 37 6sout, Corpus Christi, TX 78409
Tel (361) 289-0066 *Founded/Ownrshp* 1969, 1979
Sales 66.5MM^E *EMP* 150
SIC 5082 5083 General construction machinery & equipment; Tractors, agricultural; General construction machinery & equipment; Tractors, agricultural
Pr: Clifton Bradshaw
**Genl Mgr:* Rodney Bishop

NUECES POWER EQUIPMENT
See NUECES FARM CENTER INC

D-U-N-S 06-374-1797
NUERA TRANSPORT INC
(*Suby of* NUERA INC)
7100 Roberts Matthews Hwy, Cookeville, TN 38506-8904
Tel (931) 739-4034 *Founded/Ownrshp* 1982
Sales 49.0MM *EMP* 100
SIC 5013 Trailer parts & accessories; Trailer parts & accessories
Pr: Michael Perna
**Treas:* Kim Bray
Brnch Mgr: Birdell Alumbaugh
Brnch Mgr: Jeff Giddens
Brnch Mgr: Derrick Grider
Brnch Mgr: Charles Kraut
Brnch Mgr: Steve Masson
Genl Mgr: Fred Paquette
Sls Mgr: Edward Allard
Sales Asso: Daniel Ferguson

NUEROLOGY DEPT
See KAISER PERMANENTE

NUESKES APPLEWOOD SMOKED MEATS
See NUESKES MEAT PRODUCTS INC

D-U-N-S 02-361-8804
NUESKES MEAT PRODUCTS INC
NUESKES APPLEWOOD SMOKED MEATS
203 N Genesee St, Wittenberg, WI 54499-9154
Tel (715) 253-4000 *Founded/Ownrshp* 1972
Sales 27.5MM^E *EMP* 140
SIC 2013 5421 Sausages & other prepared meats; Meat markets, including freezer provisioners; Sausages & other prepared meats; Meat markets, including freezer provisioners
COO: Glenn Gazzolo
**CFO:* Mary White
**Ex VP:* Tanya Nueske
QA Dir: Penny Lanerd
Opers Mgr: Andy Pietsch
Opers Mgr: Scott Zyduck
Mktg Mgr: Megan Dorsch
Manager: Thomas Menefee
Sls Mgr: Thomas Ryan
Sls Mgr: Helen Selle

D-U-N-S 03-091-9518
NUESTRA CLINICA DEL VALLE INC
801 W 1st St, San Juan, TX 78589-2276
Tel (956) 787-0787 *Founded/Ownrshp* 1971
Sales 20.5MM *EMP* 230
Accts Oscar R Gonzalez Cpa & Associa
SIC 8099 8093 8021 Health screening service; Family planning clinic; Offices & clinics of dentists; Health screening service; Family planning clinic; Offices & clinics of dentists
Ex Dir: Lucy Ramirez
COO: Christian Martinez
Ofcr: Carolyn Huff
Ofcr: Irma Ramos
Dir Lab: Alicia Herrera
Dir Rx: Anna Gonzalez
MIS Dir: Jason Reyes
Obsttrcn: Kevin Davis
Nrsg Dir: Edgar Guerrero
Snr Mgr: Larry Gonzalez

D-U-N-S 83-298-1612
NUESTRO QUESO LLC
9500 Bryn Mawr Ave, Rosemont, IL 60018-5211
Tel (224) 366-4320 *Founded/Ownrshp* 2009
Sales 48.3MM^E *EMP* 163
SIC 2022 5143 Cheese, natural & processed; Cheese; Cheese, natural & processed; Cheese
Ql Cn Mgr: Dan Brown

NUETERRA HEALTHCARE
See NUETERRA HOLDINGS LLC

D-U-N-S 02-092-5496
NUETERRA HOLDINGS LLC
NUETERRA HEALTHCARE
11221 Roe Ave Ste 320, Leawood, KS 66211-1878
Tel (913) 387-0500 *Founded/Ownrshp* 1997
Sales 80.1MM^E *EMP* 138
SIC 8741 Hospital management
Ch: Dan Tasset
Pr: Michael Marcial
Pr: Aimee Mayhew
Pr: Scott Spurger
COO: Marc Goff
CFO: Denise Lundberg
**CFO:* Dan Saale
Sr VP: Mary Dailey
Sr VP: John Foudray
Sr VP: Glenna Pendleton
VP: Margaret Adams
VP: Jon Campbell
VP: Darren Chaffin
**VP:* Jerry Henson
VP: Stephen Hirlinger
VP: Sheila Knoepke
VP: Scott Martin
VP: Joe Minissale
VP: Linda Proctor
**VP:* Karen Schrek
VP: Julie Stumberg
Board of Directors: Dan Tasst

D-U-N-S 07-876-8041
NUEVA SCHOOL
6565 Skyline Blvd, Hillsborough, CA 94010-6221
Tel (650) 350-4600 *Founded/Ownrshp* 1967
Sales 36.4MM *EMP* 95
Accts Hood & Strong Llp San Francis
SIC 8211 Private elementary school; Private elementary school
Pr: Dennis Wong
**Ch Bd:* Bonnie Fought
Pr: Bruce Cozadd
**CFO:* Terry Lee
**Treas:* Hoon Cho
Bd of Dir: Muneerah Merchant
Ofcr: Marjorie Brumm
VP: Lynda Marren
Assoc Dir: Kia Bahner
Ex Dir: Andrew L Beyer
**Ex Dir:* Diane Rosenberg

D-U-N-S 62-273-0711
■ **NUEVO ENERGY CO**
(*Suby of* FREEPORT-MCMORAN OIL & GAS LLC) ★
700 Milam St Ste 3100, Houston, TX 77002-2764
Tel (713) 579-6000 *Founded/Ownrshp* 1990
Sales 16.5MM^E *EMP* 279
SIC 1311 Natural gas production; Crude petroleum production; Natural gas production; Crude petroleum production
Ch Bd: James C Flores
Treas: C Paige Dimaggio

D-U-N-S 00-524-5717 IMP
NUFARM AMERICAS INC
NUFARM NORTH AMERICAN OFFICE
(*Suby of* NUFARM LIMITED)
11901 S Austin Ave Ste A, Alsip, IL 60803-6013
Tel (708) 377-1330 *Founded/Ownrshp* 1999
Sales 103.2MM^E *EMP* 177
SIC 2869 2879 Industrial organic chemicals; Agricultural chemicals; Industrial organic chemicals; Agricultural chemicals
Pr: Darryl Matthews
**CFO:* Gary Barber
VP: Keith Moon
Exec: Mike Miller
Exec: Elbert Prado
Comm Man: Sherry Mitchell
Genl Mgr: Dale Mellody
IT Man: John Calderon
VP Opers: Thomas Lyons
Sls Dir: Tra Huddleston
Mktg Mgr: Sutherland Brett

NUFARM NORTH AMERICAN OFFICE
See NUFARM AMERICAS INC

D-U-N-S 93-073-9987
■ **NUGEN ENERGY LLC**
(*Suby of* REX AMERICAN RESOURCES CORP) ★
27283 447th Ave, Marion, SD 57043-5100
Tel (605) 648-2100 *Founded/Ownrshp* 2011
Sales 323.0MM *EMP* 50
Accts Deloitte & Touche Llp Cincin
SIC 0139 1731 5211 Food crops; Energy management controls; Energy conservation products; Food crops; Energy management controls; Energy conservation products
Pr: Aaron Riedell
Dir Risk M: Douglas Coyne
Prd Mgr: J Baer

D-U-N-S 00-799-2845
NUGENT SAND CO (KY)
1833 River Rd, Louisville, KY 40206-1002
Tel (502) 584-0158 *Founded/Ownrshp* 1896, 1970
Sales 64.0MM^E *EMP* 125
SIC 1442 Common sand mining; Gravel mining; Common sand mining; Gravel mining
Pt: Thomas C Nugent III
CFO: Steven Schoening
VP Opers: Mike Wedding
Sfty Dirs: Joseph Moobey
Trfc Dir: Wayne Bell
Sls&Mrk Ex: Ken McMillan

NUGGET, THE
See NUGGET MARKET INC

NUGGET MARKET
See STILLE CO INC

D-U-N-S 02-966-2145
NUGGET MARKET INC
NUGGET, THE
168 Court St, Woodland, CA 95695-3113
Tel (530) 669-3300 *Founded/Ownrshp* 1968
Sales 266.3MM^E *EMP* 1,300
SIC 5411 Co-operative food stores; Co-operative food stores
Ch Bd: Eugene N Stille
**Pr:* Eric Stille
COO: Chris Carpenter
CFO: Dennis Lindsay
Store Dir: Rodney Beebe
Store Dir: Lance Benton
Store Dir: Randy Wehman
Store Dir: Dave Welch
Dist Mgr: Lorna Parton
Dir IT: Matt Morley
Dir IT: Joe Santos

D-U-N-S 78-952-0251
NUHOME ELECTRONICS INC
6709 13th Ave, Brooklyn, NY 11219-6127
Tel (718) 236-2650 *Founded/Ownrshp* 1992
Sales 23.0MM *EMP* 5
SIC 5065 5999 Video equipment, electronic; Electronic parts & equipment; Video equipment, electronic; Electronic parts & equipment
Pr: Eli Katz
**VP:* Joseph Greenfeld

D-U-N-S 83-020-1237 IMP/EXP
■ **NUK USA LLC**
(*Suby of* JARDEN CORP) ★
728 Booster Blvd, Reedsburg, WI 53959-2123
Tel (608) 524-4343 *Founded/Ownrshp* 2008
Sales 65.2MM^E *EMP* 260
SIC 2676 Infant & baby paper products; Infant & baby paper products
Pr: Douglas Gillespie
VP: Greg Gomez

D-U-N-S 17-329-1675 IMP
NUKOTE INC
(*Suby of* BLACK CREEK HOLDINGS LTD) ★
2400 Dallas Pkwy Ste 230, Plano, TX 75093-4371
Tel (972) 398-7100 *Founded/Ownrshp* 2006
Sales 59.5MM^E *EMP* 1,300
SIC 3955 3861 Ribbons, inked: typewriter, adding machine, register, etc.; Carbon paper for typewriters, sales books, etc.; Toners, prepared photographic (not made in chemical plants); Ribbons, inked: typewriter, adding machine, register, etc.; Carbon paper for typewriters, sales books, etc.; Toners, prepared photographic (not made in chemical plants)
Ch: John Rochon
**Pr:* C Ronald Baiocchi
**Ex VP:* Steven Baiocchi
**Sr VP:* Alan S Lockwood
VP: Cindy Hutchinson
Board of Directors: C Ronald Baiocchi, Nick G Bouras, Alan S Lockwood, John P Rochon

D-U-N-S 00-917-0721
NULAID FOODS INC
200 W 5th St, Ripon, CA 95366-2793
Tel (209) 599-2121 *Founded/Ownrshp* 1963
Sales 39.7MM^E *EMP* 80^E
SIC 5144 2047 2015 2023 Eggs; Eggs: cleaning, oil treating, packing & grading; Dog food; Egg processing; Cream substitutes; Eggs; Eggs: cleaning, oil treating, packing & grading; Dog food; Egg processing; Cream substitutes
Pr: David K Crockett
**CFO:* Scott Hennecke

NULCO LIGHTING
See NULCO MFG CORP

D-U-N-S 00-119-6351 IMP
NULCO MFG CORP (RI)
NULCO LIGHTING
1 Park Row Ste 300, Providence, RI 02903-1246
Tel (401) 272-3500 *Founded/Ownrshp* 1950
Sales 30.7MM^E *EMP* 230
SIC 3645 3646 3648 5063 Residential lighting fixtures; Commercial indusl & institutional electric lighting fixtures; Lanterns: electric, gas, carbide, kerosene or gasoline; Lighting fixtures; Residential lighting fixtures; Commercial indusl & institutional electric lighting fixtures; Lanterns: electric, gas, carbide, kerosene or gasoline; Lighting fixtures
Pr: Kenneth Nulman
**CEO:* Robert Delogo
**VP:* Andrew Nulman
VP: Clifford D Nulman
VP: Ray Reest
CTO: Jill Deloge
Sales Exec: Stephen Rice

D-U-N-S 79-870-0324 IMP
NUMARK INDUSTRIES LLC
200 Scenic View Dr, Cumberland, RI 02864-1847
Tel (401) 658-3131 *Founded/Ownrshp* 1992
Sales 73.8MM^E *EMP* 120
SIC 5736 Musical instrument stores
CEO: John E O Donnell
**COO:* Paul Antrop
**CFO:* Paul Stansky
Ex VP: Richard Seymour
Creative D: Jonathan Hayes
IT Man: Mark Sciola
Tech Mgr: Robert Griffith
Sftwr Eng: Alexandros Dermenakis
Sls Mgr: Josh Cuadra
Sls Mgr: Keith Stewart
Sls Mgr: Sarah Yule

D-U-N-S 05-008-7337 IMP
NUMATIC ENGINEERING INC
7915 Ajay Dr, Sun Valley, CA 91352-5315
Tel (323) 666-3062 Founded/Ownrshp 1995
Sales 34.5MM^E EMP 40
SIC 5085 5084 Valves & fittings; Pneumatic tools & equipment
Pr: Steve T Leach
*VP: David Leach
*Prin: Kyle Clark
Manager: Nick Iacuaniello

D-U-N-S 00-537-1851 IMP
■ **NUMATICS INC** (MI)
(Suby of EMERSON ELECTRIC CO) ★
46280 Dylan Dr, Novi, MI 48377-4906
Tel (248) 596-3200 Founded/Ownrshp 1945, 2005
Sales 51.3MM^E EMP 400
SIC 3491 3612 3593 3564 3494 3492

D-U-N-S 07-860-4632 IMP
NUMBER HOLDINGS INC
99 CENT ONLY STORE
4000 Union Pacific Ave, Commerce, CA 90023-3202
Tel (323) 980-8145 Founded/Ownrshp 2011
Sales 1.9MMM^E EMP 15,000^E
SIC 5331 5199 Variety stores; General merchandise, non-durable; Variety stores; General merchandise, non-durable
CFO: Frank J Schools

D-U-N-S 82-675-1232
▲ **NUMEREX CORP**
3330 Cumberland Blvd Se # 700, Atlanta, GA 30339-8100
Tel (770) 693-5950 Founded/Ownrshp 1992
Sales 93.8MM EMP 159^E
Tkr Sym NMRX Exch NGM
SIC 3669 7371 Intercommunication systems, electric; Computer software development & applications; Intercommunication systems, electric; Computer software development & applications
Ch Bd: Stratton J Nicolaides
Pr: John Andre
Pr: Bryan Tarleton
*CEO: Marc Zionts
CFO: Richard Flynt
Ex VP: Robert M Madonna
VP: Steve Baker
VP: Anthony Coates
VP: Simon Glassman
VP: Michael Lang
VP: Tomas Murray
VP: Greg Selig
VP: Wayne Stargardt
Creative D: Kip Williams
Board of Directors: E James Constantine, Tony G Holcombe, Sherrie McAvoy, Jerry A Rose, Andrew J Ryan

D-U-N-S 08-441-3293
NUMERICA CREDIT UNION
14610 E Sprague Ave, Spokane Valley, WA 99216-2146
Tel (509) 535-7613 Founded/Ownrshp 1970
Sales NA EMP 280
Accts Moss-Adams Llp Everett Washi
SIC 6062 State credit unions, not federally chartered; State credit unions, not federally chartered
Pr: Carla Altepeter
*Ch Bd: David Schriver
*CFO: Cindy Leaver
*V Ch Bd: Joseph Day
*Ex VP: Jennifer Lehn
Netwrk Mgr: Matthew Callier

D-U-N-S 06-281-4850
NUMERICAL CONCEPTS INC
4040 1st Pkwy, Terre Haute, IN 47804-4298
Tel (812) 466-5261 Founded/Ownrshp 1973
Sales 20.6MM^E EMP 85
SIC 3555 3599 Printing trades machinery; Machine shop, jobbing & repair
Pr: Nancy Seidel Jones
Plnt Mgr: Steve Turner
Ql Cn Mgr: Randy Butrum
Mktg Mgr: Chuck Crutchfield
Sls Mgr: Curt Small

D-U-N-S 02-147-2246
NUMERICAL PRECISION INC
1630 E Stroker Rd, Crosby, TX 77532-4310
Tel (281) 328-7343 Founded/Ownrshp 1980
Sales 31.4MM^E EMP 88
SIC 3599 Machine shop, jobbing & repair
Pr: Kenneth N Bentley
*Sec: Randy Bentley
*VP: Shane Bentley
Mfg Mgr: Brett Thomas
Ql Cn Mgr: Brian Harpold

D-U-N-S 95-687-3152
NUMERIX LLC
99 Park Ave Fl 5, New York, NY 10016-1601
Tel (212) 302-2220 Founded/Ownrshp 1996
Sales 67.3MM^E EMP 241
SIC 7373 Systems software development services; Systems software development services
Ch: Gregory Whitten
*CEO: Steven R O'Hanlon
*COO: Dawn Patrick
*Ex VP: Joseph Saporito
*Ex VP: Mark A Shornick
Sr VP: Andrey Itkin
VP: Evangelos Angelides
VP: Lana Chin
VP: Christopher Etienne
VP: James J Jockle
VP: Meng Lu
VP: Alexander Vaysman

D-U-N-S 14-718-3404
NUMERO UNO ACQUISTION LLC
6701 Wilson Ave, Los Angeles, CA 90001-2165
Tel (323) 846-5015 Founded/Ownrshp 1983
Sales 71.8MM^E EMP 850
SIC 5411 Grocery stores, independent; Grocery stores, independent
Pr: Doug Miner
*Pr: George Torres
*CFO: Jorge Sandoval
*VP: Roberta Torres

D-U-N-S 14-416-5235
NUMERO UNO MARKET
701 E Jefferson Blvd, Los Angeles, CA 90011-2456
Tel (323) 846-5842 Founded/Ownrshp 2003
Sales 35.0MM^E EMP 200^E
SIC 5411 Grocery stores; Grocery stores
CEO: Roberta Torres
*Pr: Steven Torres

D-U-N-S 18-124-6802
NUMISMATIC GUARANTY CORP OF AMERICA
NGC
P.O. Box 4776 (34230-4776)
Tel (941) 360-3990 Founded/Ownrshp 1987
Sales 30.0MM^E EMP 130^E
SIC 7389 Appraisers, except real estate; Appraisers, except real estate
CEO: Steven Eichenbaum
*Pr: Richard Montgomery
*COO: Lisa Creisstoff
*Ch: Mark Salzberg
Mktg Mgr: Elizabeth Graves

NUMMI
See NEW UNITED MOTOR MANUFACTURING INC

D-U-N-S 80-200-4742 IMP
NUMO
(Suby of KOLDER INC) ★
1072 E Us Highway 175, Kaufman, TX 75142-3560
Tel (972) 932-5800 Founded/Ownrshp 2007
Sales 22.8MM^E EMP 150
SIC 3089 Plastic containers, except foam; Cases, plastic; Novelties, plastic
Pr: Charlie Meyer
CFO: Karen House
VP: Martin Jim
Creative D: Michael Shoaf

D-U-N-S 01-812-3159
NUMONYX INC
2235 Iron Point Rd, Folsom, CA 95630-8765
Tel (916) 458-3888 Founded/Ownrshp 2008
Sales 48.3MM^E EMP 512
SIC 5045 Computer software; Computer software
CEO: Ed Dollar
*Treas: Matthew Tasto
VP: William Cass Wilson

NUMOTION
See ASSISTIVE TECHNOLOGY GROUP INC

NUMOTION
See UNITED SEATING & MOBILITY LLC

NUMOTION
See ATG / USM HOLDINGS LLC

NUMOTION
See ATG HOLDINGS INC

D-U-N-S 07-046-7030
NUNES CO INC (CA)
FOXY
925 Johnson Ave, Salinas, CA 93901-4327
Tel (831) 751-7510 Founded/Ownrshp 1976
Sales 35.0MM^E EMP 50^E
SIC 5148 Vegetables
CEO: Tom P Nunes Jr
CFO: Mike Chimera
*CFO: Mike Scarr
*Treas: Enos Barera
*VP: Mark Crossgrove
VP: Bob Nunes
VP: Frank R Nunes
*VP: Tom M Nunes
*VP: Matt Seeley

NUNHEMS USA
See BAYER CROPSCIENCE VEGETABLE SEEDS

D-U-N-S 10-253-1878
NUNN CONSTRUCTION INC
925 Elkton Dr, Colorado Springs, CO 80907-3537
Tel (719) 599-7710 Founded/Ownrshp 1983
Sales 56.1MM EMP 51
Accts Ssa Pc Colorado Springs C
SIC 1542 Commercial & office building, new construction; Commercial & office building, new construction
Ch Bd: Ray M Nunn
*Pr: Tyson Nunn
*CFO: Sean Leggett
*VP: Phillip Lasarre

D-U-N-S 03-250-5503
NUNOS USA AWNINGS INC
3901 Roxton Ave, Los Angeles, CA 90008-2717
Tel (323) 276-6848 Founded/Ownrshp 2010
Sales 67.5MM^E EMP 2
SIC 3444 Awnings & canopies; Awnings & canopies
CEO: Carlos Hector Nuno

D-U-N-S 60-672-6479 IMP
NUOVO PASTA PRODUCTIONS LTD
1330 Honeyspot Road Ext, Stratford, CT 06615-7115
Tel (203) 380-4090 Founded/Ownrshp 1989
Sales 22.6MM^E EMP 58
SIC 2099 Packaged combination products: pasta, rice & potato
Pr: Carl L Zuanelli
*Sec: Karen Zuanelli
*VP: Tom Quinn
QA Dir: Maria Orozco
Opers Mgr: Adam Sutch
VP Sls: Larry Montuori
Mktg Mgr: Dolores Hlavaty

D-U-N-S 00-838-2137 IMP
■ **NUPLA CORP**
(Suby of QEP) ★
11912 Sheldon St, Sun Valley, CA 91352-1509
Tel (818) 768-6800 Founded/Ownrshp 2012
Sales 21.3MM^E EMP 120
SIC 3423 3089 Hand & edge tools; Handles, brush or tool: plastic; Hand & edge tools; Handles, brush or tool: plastic
Pr: Ronald Ortiz
CFO: Rienzeie Pintoe
Ofcr: Chris Salinas
VP Sls: Paul Chapman

D-U-N-S 18-204-6404 IMP
NUPLEX RESINS LLC
(Suby of NUPLEX INDUSTRIES UK LIMITED)
4730 Crittenden Dr, Louisville, KY 40209-1518
Tel (502) 367-6111 Founded/Ownrshp 2007
Sales 39.1MM^E EMP 140
SIC 2821 Plastics materials & resins; Plastics materials & resins
Pr: Michael J Kelly
Exec: Sandra Terry
Brnch Mgr: Mary Heeke
CTO: Jim McBee
Dir IT: Simon Wood
Tech Mgr: Michael Gessner
VP Opers: Clive Deetlefs
Ql Cn Mgr: Jody Snead
Sales Exec: Jenny Jin
Mktg Mgr: Robert Skarvan
Manager: Ronald Haynes

D-U-N-S 96-371-9419
NUROCK CONSTRUCTION SERVICES LLC
3460 Preston Ridge Rd # 175, Alpharetta, GA 30005-5441
Tel (678) 297-3400 Founded/Ownrshp 2010
Sales 75.0MM^E EMP 45
SIC 1522 Residential construction

D-U-N-S 86-943-4464
NURSE ASSIST INC
(Suby of NA ACQUISITION CO) ★
4409 Haltom Rd, Haltom City, TX 76117-1207
Tel (800) 649-6800 Founded/Ownrshp 1999
Sales 31.7MM^E EMP 130
SIC 3841 5047 Surgical & medical instruments; Hospital equipment & furniture; Surgical & medical instruments; Hospital equipment & furniture
Pr: Kevin Kile
*VP: William J Kanewske
*VP: Jim Monahan
*VP: Mark Schnoerr
Prgrm Mgr: Ismael Gonzalez
QA Dir: David Finch
VP Opers: Brian Cox
VP Opers: Bill Kanewske
Sls Dir: Darrell Pattillo
Sls Mgr: Bryan Daniels

D-U-N-S 08-735-4635
NURSE CARE INC
NURSECARE
837 Ne 20th Ave, Fort Lauderdale, FL 33304-3035
Tel (954) 463-1100 Founded/Ownrshp 1984
Sales 7.9MM^E EMP 400
SIC 7363 8082 Medical help service; Home health care services; Medical help service; Home health care services
Pr: Bruce Danyluk
*CFO: Vance Lee
*Prin: Bradley Danyluk

D-U-N-S 14-813-8001
NURSE PROVIDERS INC
NURSING REGISTRY
355 Gellert Blvd Ste 110, Daly City, CA 94015-2668
Tel (650) 992-8559 Founded/Ownrshp 1984
Sales 19.1MM^E EMP 800
SIC 7361 Nurses' registry; Nurses' registry
Pr: Sherri Burke

NURSECARE
See NURSE CARE INC

D-U-N-S 96-213-7162
NURSECORE MANAGEMENT SERVICES LLC
NURSECORE OF AMARILLO
2201 Brookhollow Plaza Dr # 450, Arlington, TX 76006-7482
Tel (817) 649-1166 Founded/Ownrshp 1996
Sales 170.5MM^E EMP 4,200
SIC 8742 Hospital & health services consultant; Hospital & health services consultant
COO: Christina Sanders
IT Man: David Guillory
IT Man: Steve Holstein

NURSECORE OF AMARILLO
See NURSECORE MANAGEMENT SERVICES LLC

D-U-N-S 04-519-7803
■ **NURSEFINDERS LLC**
(Suby of AMN HEALTHCARE SERVICES INC) ★
12400 High Bluff Dr, San Diego, CA 92130-3077
Tel (858) 314-7427 Founded/Ownrshp 2010
Sales 68.8MM^E EMP 1,400
SIC 7361 8082 7363 8049 Employment agencies; Home health care services; Help supply services; Temporary help service; Nurses, registered & practical; Employment agencies; Home health care services; Help supply services; Temporary help service; Nurses, registered & practical
CEO: Susan Salka
Pr: Ralph S Henderson
Sr VP: Denise L Jackson
Pdt Mgr: Michele Colbert

D-U-N-S 61-789-9851
NURSEFINDERS OF INDIANAPOLIS INC
8925 N Meridian St # 110, Indianapolis, IN 46260-2384
Tel (317) 818-4400 Founded/Ownrshp 1988
Sales 17.4MM^E EMP 500
SIC 7363 Temporary help service; Temporary help service
Pr: Roger Brown
*Treas: Theodore Rains
*VP: Susan J Brown

D-U-N-S 87-897-7370
NURSELINE HEALTHCARE INC
331 Newman Springs Rd # 143, Red Bank, NJ 07701-6767
Tel (732) 462-4400 Founded/Ownrshp 1993
Sales 8.8MM^E EMP 300
SIC 7361 7363 Nurses' registry; Help supply services; Nurses' registry; Help supply services
Pr: Joseph Fink

D-U-N-S 13-610-8953
NURSERY CONNECTION LLC
2655 Pacific Hwy 99, Hubbard, OR 97032-9639
Tel (503) 982-1421 Founded/Ownrshp 2001
Sales 20.9MM EMP 13
SIC 5193 Flowers & nursery stock; Flowers & nursery stock

D-U-N-S 00-181-9572 IMP/EXP
NURSERY SUPPLIES INC
1415 Orchard Dr, Chambersburg, PA 17201-4810
Tel (717) 263-7780 Founded/Ownrshp 1966
Sales 81.8MM^E EMP 550
SIC 3089

D-U-N-S 79-396-6003
NURSES CHOICE INC
600 Bypass Dr Ste 114, Clearwater, FL 33764-5030
Tel (727) 446-6000 Founded/Ownrshp 1992
Sales 8.9MM^E EMP 600
SIC 7363 Temporary help service; Temporary help service
CEO: Edward Halleran

D-U-N-S 07-734-7099
NURSES ON CALL INC
1600 Harry Byrd Hwy, Darlington, SC 29532-3516
Tel (843) 393-4230 Founded/Ownrshp 1997
Sales 9.6MM^E EMP 306
SIC 7363 5999 Temporary help service; Medical apparatus & supplies; Temporary help service; Medical apparatus & supplies
Pr: Leslie McElveen

D-U-N-S 83-575-5075
NURSES THAT CARE SITTER SERVICES INC
5411 N Mccoll Rd, McAllen, TX 78504-2206
Tel (956) 668-0029 Founded/Ownrshp 1993
Sales 15.0MM^E EMP 750
SIC 8082 8399 7299 Home health care services; Health systems agency; Babysitting bureau; Home health care services; Health systems agency; Babysitting bureau
Prin: Andy Sanchez
Dir IT: Juan Mata

D-U-N-S 12-124-9734
NURSES UNLIMITED INC
NURSES UNLIMITED MANAGED CARE
511 N Lincoln Ave, Odessa, TX 79761-4429
Tel (432) 580-2085 Founded/Ownrshp 1983
Sales 61.7MM EMP 3,400
SIC 8049 Nurses, registered & practical; Nurses, registered & practical
CEO: Bobby Laughry
*CFO: David Nelson
*Ch: Patsy Gerron
*Sec: Jim Gerron DDS
Off Mgr: Sandra Rowe
IT Man: Rod Valenzuela
Info Man: Jobee Sussel
Nrsg Dir: Diane Grissom

NURSES UNLIMITED MANAGED CARE
See NURSES UNLIMITED INC

D-U-N-S 83-210-1864
NURSESTAT LLC
528 Washington St, Saint Paul, KS 66771-4032
Tel (620) 449-2525 Founded/Ownrshp 1996
Sales 1.5MM EMP 300
SIC 7361 Employment agencies; Employment agencies
Owner: Dinah Giefer

D-U-N-S 11-623-4113
NURSING CARE MANAGEMENT OF AMERICA INC
7265 Kenwood Rd Ste 300, Cincinnati, OH 45236-4425
Tel (513) 793-8804 Founded/Ownrshp 1984
Sales 26.7MM^E EMP 320
SIC 8741 Nursing & personal care facility management; Nursing & personal care facility management
Pr: James Farley
*Treas: Robert Wynne
*VP: Michael Scharfenberger
*Prin: Timothy Wynne

D-U-N-S 80-947-4828
NURSING CENTER AT OAK SUMMIT
5680 Windy Hill Dr, Winston Salem, NC 27105-1425
Tel (336) 744-1188 Founded/Ownrshp 1993
Sales 4.2MM^E EMP 276
SIC 8059 8052 8051 Nursing home, except skilled & intermediate care facility; Intermediate care facilities; Skilled nursing care facilities; Nursing home, except skilled & intermediate care facility; Intermediate care facilities; Skilled nursing care facilities
Nrsg Dir: Denise Young

D-U-N-S 19-660-7790 IMP
NURSING ENTERPRISES INC
5101 Wisconsin Ave Nw # 250, Washington, DC 20016-4120
Tel (202) 832-0100 Founded/Ownrshp 1985
Sales 12.1MM^E EMP 300^E
SIC 8082 Home health care services; Home health care services
Pr: Myrtle Gomez

D-U-N-S 12-523-1022
NURSING HOME & HOSPITAL CONSULTANT CORP
5344 Blue Pacific Dr W, Jacksonville, FL 32257-3791
Tel (904) 254-1341 Founded/Ownrshp 2003
Sales 21.0MM EMP 119

SIC 8742 7361 Hospital & health services consultant; Executive placement; Hospital & health services consultant; Executive placement
CEO: S Doan Andersen

NURSING REGISTRY
See NURSE PROVIDERS INC

D-U-N-S 08-407-0671
NURSING SERVICES OF CAPITAL REGION INC
EDDY COMMUNITY CARE
433 River St Ste 3000, Troy, NY 12180-2250
Tel (518) 274-2635 *Founded/Ownrshp* 1958
Sales 7.3MM *EMP* 299
SIC 8082 Home health care services; Home health care services
Pr: Kathy Seymour
Snr Mgr: Teresa Boepple

D-U-N-S 79-865-9074
NURSING SISTERS HOME VISITING SERVICE INC
110 Bi County Blvd # 114, Farmingdale, NY 11735-3923
Tel (516) 683-1300 *Founded/Ownrshp* 1966
Sales 36.6MM *EMP* 300
SIC 8082 Visiting nurse service; Visiting nurse service
Pr: Keith Kertland

D-U-N-S 78-161-8355 EXP
NURTURE INC
HAPPY FAMILY BRANDS
(*Suby of* DANONE NORTH AMERICA LLC) ★
40 Fulton St Fl 17, New York, NY 10038-1850
Tel (212) 374-2779 *Founded/Ownrshp* 2013
Sales 124.2MM[E] *EMP* 70
SIC 5149 Natural & organic foods
CEO: Shazi Visram
**COO:* Jessica Rolph
**CFO:* Shauna Grob
Sr VP: Robert Zimmerman
VP: Anne Laraway
Opers Mgr: Natalie Allen
VP Mktg: Molly Breiner
VP Sls: Bob Zimmerman
Mktg Dir: Helen Bernstein
Sls Dir: Dara Colacchio
Sls Mgr: Sunnie Hunt

NUS CONSULTING GROUP
See NATIONAL UTILITY SERVICE INC

D-U-N-S 01-592-3328
NUSCALE POWER LLC
6650 Sw Redwood Ln # 210, Portland, OR 97224-7169
Tel (503) 715-2222 *Founded/Ownrshp* 2007
Sales 34.3MM[E] *EMP* 150[E]
SIC 8731 Energy research; Energy research
CEO: John L Hopkins
**CEO:* Paul G Lorenzini
**COO:* Christopher Colbert
**CFO:* John Jay Surina
**Ex VP:* Tom Mundy
Sr VP: Jack Bailey
**VP:* Scott Bailey
VP: Tom Bergman
**VP:* Carl Markert
**VP:* Michael S McGough
**VP:* Ed Wallace

D-U-N-S 08-953-1953 IMP
NUSIGN SUPPLY INC
1933 W Mission Blvd, Pomona, CA 91766-1037
Tel (626) 961-7688 *Founded/Ownrshp* 1999
Sales 35.7MM[E] *EMP* 25[E]
SIC 5199 Advertising specialties
Pr: Benny Wantah
VP: Hao Le
Ex Dir: Tatsuo Shimomura
Ex Dir: Yasuyo Ueda
Ex Dir: Haruhiko Watanabe
Genl Mgr: Chuck Wong
Software D: Kent Nguyen
S&M/VP: Tony Le

D-U-N-S 09-901-3328 IMP/EXP
NUSIL TECHNOLOGY LLC
(*Suby of* NEW MOUNTAIN CAPITAL I LLC) ★
1050 Cindy Ln, Carpinteria, CA 93013-2906
Tel (805) 684-8780 *Founded/Ownrshp* 1992
Sales 70.6MM[E] *EMP* 500
SIC 3069

D-U-N-S 09-841-9567 EXP
NUSS TRUCK GROUP INC
NUSS TRUCKS-ROCHESTER
6500 Highway 63 S, Rochester, MN 55904-8429
Tel (507) 288-9488 *Founded/Ownrshp* 1973
Sales 135.6MM[E] *EMP* 240
SIC 5511 5531 Trucks, tractors & trailers: new & used; Truck equipment & parts; Trucks, tractors & trailers: new & used; Truck equipment & parts
Pr: Robert Nuss
**VP:* Bradley Nuss
Brnch Mgr: Mark Nygaard
Genl Mgr: Brad Schmidt
Off Mgr: Teresa Clark
Off Mgr: Cindy Jackson
Off Mgr: Brittany Jorgensen
Off Mgr: Mary Romie
Off Mgr: Holly Schlueter
Store Mgr: Andrew Baxter
IT Man: Scott Nelson

NUSS TRUCKS-ROCHESTER
See NUSS TRUCK GROUP INC

NUSSBAUM, BARRY COMPANY
See BNC REAL ESTATE

D-U-N-S 02-568-8219
NUSSBAUM TRANSPORTATION SERVICES INC (IL)
(*Suby of* IN MOTION HOLDINGS LLC) ★
19336 N 1425 East Rd, Hudson, IL 61748-7674
Tel (309) 452-4426 *Founded/Ownrshp* 1945
Sales 61.5MM *EMP* 250
Accts Heinold Banwart Ltd East Pe
SIC 4213 Trucking, except local; Trucking, except local
Ch Bd: Brent Nussbaum
**VP:* Phil Braker

D-U-N-S 02-460-0710
NUSSBAUM-SFG INC (NC)
3500 Old Battleground Rd, Greensboro, NC 27410-2420
Tel (336) 545-3800 *Founded/Ownrshp* 1954
Sales 21.5MM[E] *EMP* 275
SIC 5963 Food services, direct sales; Food services, direct sales
Pr: R Michael Nussbaum
**VP:* James S Nussbaum

NUSTAR
See AXEON REFINING LLC

NUSTAR ENERGY
See NUSTAR TERMINALS OPERATIONS PARTNERSHIP LP

D-U-N-S 84-811-0701 IMP
▲ NUSTAR ENERGY LP
19003 W Ih 10, San Antonio, TX 78257-9518
Tel (210) 918-2000 *Founded/Ownrshp* 1999
Sales 3.0MMM *EMP* 1,227
Tkr Sym NS *Exch* NYS
SIC 4612 4613 4226 Crude petroleum pipelines; Refined petroleum pipelines; Special warehousing & storage; Crude petroleum pipelines; Refined petroleum pipelines; Special warehousing & storage
Pr: Bradley C Barron
Genl Pt: Riverwalk Logistics
CFO: Thomas R Shoaf
Ex VP: Mary Rose Brown
Sr VP: James R Bluntze
Sr VP: Rick Bluntzer
Sr VP: Mary Morgan
Sr VP: Amy L Perry
VP: James Calvert
VP: John Greheey
VP: Steve Hays

D-U-N-S 78-243-6005
▲ NUSTAR GP HOLDINGS LLC
19003 W Ih 10, San Antonio, TX 78257-9518
Tel (210) 918-2000 *Founded/Ownrshp* 2000
Sales 65.3MM *EMP* 1,227[E]
Tkr Sym NSH *Exch* NYS
SIC 4612 4613 Crude petroleum pipelines; Refined petroleum pipelines; Crude petroleum pipelines; Refined petroleum pipelines
Pr: Bradley C Barron
**Ch Bd:* William E Greehey
Pr: Mary Morgan
CFO: Thomas R Shoaf
Ofcr: Mary Rose Brown
Sr VP: Jorge A Del Alamo
Sr VP: Amy L Perry
Sr VP: Karen M Thompson
Board of Directors: William B Burnett, James F Clingman Jr

D-U-N-S 14-537-1543
■ NUSTAR GP LLC
(*Suby of* NUSTAR GP HOLDINGS LLC) ★
2330 N Loop 1604 W, San Antonio, TX 78248-4512
Tel (210) 370-2000 *Founded/Ownrshp* 2002
Sales 63.3MM[E] *EMP* 1,189[E]
SIC 3533 Oil & gas field machinery
CEO: Curtis V Anastasio
**CFO:* Steven A Blank
**VP:* James R Bluntzer
**VP:* Clayton E Killinger
**VP:* Jerry D McVicker
**VP:* Rodney L Reese

D-U-N-S 14-240-3430
■ NUSTAR LOGISTICS LP
(*Suby of* NUSTAR ENERGY LP) ★
19003 W Interstate 10, San Antonio, TX 78257-9518
Tel (210) 918-2000 *Founded/Ownrshp* 1999
Sales 421.0MM[E] *EMP* 1,172
SIC 1311 Crude petroleum & natural gas production; Crude petroleum & natural gas production
Pr: Brad Barron

D-U-N-S 80-167-8061 EXP
■ NUSTAR PIPELINE OPERATING PARTNERSHIP LP
(*Suby of* NUSTAR ENERGY LP) ★
19003 W Interstate 10, San Antonio, TX 78257-9518
Tel (210) 918-2000 *Founded/Ownrshp* 1989
Sales 43.6MM[E] *EMP* 86
SIC 4925 Liquefied petroleum gas, distribution through mains; Liquefied petroleum gas, distribution through mains
CFO: Howard C Wadsworth
VP: Brad Ramsey
VP: James Reiter
VP: James L Tidmore

D-U-N-S 78-176-6308
■ NUSTAR PIPELINE PARTNERS LP
(*Suby of* NUSTAR ENERGY LP) ★
2435 N Central Expy Ste 7, Richardson, TX 75080-2753
Tel (972) 699-4062 *Founded/Ownrshp* 1989
Sales 43.0MM[E] *EMP* 1,114
SIC 4613 Refined petroleum pipelines; Refined petroleum pipelines
Pt: Edward D Doherty
Pt: Michael Rose
Pt: Ronald D Scoggins
Pt: Howard C Wadsworth
VP: Erin Jackson

D-U-N-S 07-857-9212
■ NUSTAR SUPPLY & TRADING LLC
(*Suby of* NUSTAR LOGISTICS LP) ★
19003 W Interstate 10, San Antonio, TX 78257-9518
Tel (210) 918-2000 *Founded/Ownrshp* 2012
Sales 111.3MM[E] *EMP* 1,000
SIC 5172 Crude oil
CEO: Brad Barron
CFO: Steven A Blank
Treas: Chris Russell
Ex VP: Mary Rose Brown
Prin: Curtis V Anastasio

D-U-N-S 80-169-7764 IMP
■ NUSTAR TERMINALS OPERATIONS PARTNERSHIP LP
NUSTAR ENERGY
(*Suby of* NUSTAR ENERGY LP) ★
19003 W Ih 10, San Antonio, TX 78257-9518
Tel (210) 918-2000 *Founded/Ownrshp* 2005
Sales 61.9MM[E] *EMP* 324
SIC 4226

D-U-N-S 04-565-2761 EXP
NUT PROCESSORS INC
7 Zane Grey St Ste B, El Paso, TX 79906-5214
Tel (915) 881-0041 *Founded/Ownrshp* 2010
Sales 69.0MM *EMP* 109
SIC 0723 Pecan hulling & shelling services
Pr: Eduardo Rodriguez
Genl Mgr: Jesus Carrera

D-U-N-S 01-192-9460 EXP
■ NUTCRACKER BRANDS INC
CONAGRA FOODS
(*Suby of* RALCORP HOLDINGS INC) ★
2700 Horace Shepard Dr, Dothan, AL 36303-1006
Tel (334) 983-5643 *Founded/Ownrshp* 1981, 1998
Sales 80.6MM[E] *EMP* 320
SIC 2068 Nuts: dried, dehydrated, salted or roasted; Nuts: dried, dehydrated, salted or roasted
CEO: Gary Rodken
VP Sls: Bill Mallis

NUTEC METAL JOINING PRODUCTS
See PRINCE & IZANT CO

D-U-N-S 02-283-5610
NUTECH ENERGY ALLIANCE LTD
7702 Fm 1960 Rd E Ste 300, Humble, TX 77346-2255
Tel (281) 812-4030 *Founded/Ownrshp* 1998
Sales 24.8MM[E] *EMP* 97[E]
Accts Bdo Usa Llp Houston Tx
SIC 1389 Oil field services
CEO: Alan Howard
Pt: Charles R Close
Pt: Dewayne Weaver
Pr: William Deafon
Pr: Bobby Gibson
CFO: Hans Been
VP: Bill Boykin
VP: Bruce Noblett
VP: Bill Scanlan
VP: Jorge Viamontes
Software D: Lisa Liel

D-U-N-S 87-853-3843
NUTECH MEDICAL INC
2641 Rocky Ridge Ln, Birmingham, AL 35216-4809
Tel (205) 290-2158 *Founded/Ownrshp* 1994
Sales 31.4MM *EMP* 19
Accts Barfield Murphy Shank & Smith
SIC 5047 Surgical equipment & supplies; Surgical equipment & supplies
Pr: Ken Horton
Mktg Dir: Stephanie J Hann

D-U-N-S 00-428-7116 EXP
NUTIS PRESS INC (OH)
NUCO PRODUCTS
3540 E Fulton St, Columbus, OH 43227-1100
Tel (614) 237-7131 *Founded/Ownrshp* 1961
Sales 21.8MM[E] *EMP* 150
SIC 5947 2752 2396 7384 2759 Gift shop; Commercial printing, offset; Automotive & apparel trimmings; Photofinishing laboratory; Screen printing
Ch Bd: Frank Nutis
Pr: Gary Abrams
**Pr:* Ira Nutis
COO: Mark Chernis
CFO: Stephen Melvin
**Sec:* Thelma Nutis
Ex VP: Timothy Conroy
Ex VP: Linda Rubin
VP: Stephen Quattrociocchi
Mng Dir: Jay Rosner
Telecom Ex: Joy Nutt

D-U-N-S 80-863-7771 IMP/EXP
NUTIVA
213 W Cutting Blvd, Richmond, CA 94804-2015
Tel (510) 255-2700 *Founded/Ownrshp* 1999
Sales 23.4MM[E] *EMP* 91[E]
SIC 2099 Vegetables, peeled for the trade
CEO: John Roulac
**CFO:* Jeff Mitchell
CFO: Scott Palladino
VP: Althea Davidson
VP: Michelle Montakhab
CTO: Esther Park
IT Man: Dave Ringot
VP Opers: Steven Naccarato
VP Sls: Karen Borie
Mktg Dir: Liz Kaplan

D-U-N-S 00-177-6368
NUTLEY HEATING & COOLING SUPPLY CO INC
NUTLEY SUPPLY
50 Page Rd, Clifton, NJ 07012-1421
Tel (973) 470-8844 *Founded/Ownrshp* 2009
Sales 23.0MM[E] *EMP* 42
Accts Geltrude & Company Llc Nutle
SIC 5075 Warm air heating equipment & supplies; Air conditioning & ventilation equipment & supplies; Warm air heating equipment & supplies; Air conditioning & ventilation equipment & supplies
Pr: Richard A Cancelosi
**VP:* Susan Cancelosi

D-U-N-S 06-078-3685
NUTLEY PUBLIC SCHOOL DISTRICT (NJ)
315 Franklin Ave, Nutley, NJ 07110-2735
Tel (973) 661-3500 *Founded/Ownrshp* 1930
Sales 23.7MM[E] *EMP* 405
SIC 8211 Public elementary & secondary schools; Public elementary & secondary schools
Pr: Robert J Rusignuolo
Ofcr: Rebecca Olivo
Ofcr: Laura Reilly
Prin: Addie M Boyd
Prin: John Calicchio
Prin: Rosemary Clerico
Prin: Marylou Dowse
Prin: Dorothy Mutch
CIO: Ian Viemeister
Schl Brd P: Charles Kucinski
Board of Directors: Charles W Kucinski

NUTLEY SUPPLY
See NUTLEY HEATING & COOLING SUPPLY CO INC

D-U-N-S 09-552-6372
NUTMEG INTERNATIONAL TRUCKS INC
NUTMEG TRUCK CENTER
130 Brainard Rd, Hartford, CT 06114-1696
Tel (860) 249-8635 *Founded/Ownrshp* 1978
Sales 29.7MM[E] *EMP* 59
SIC 5511 Pickups, new & used; Trucks, tractors & trailers: new & used; Pickups, new & used; Trucks, tractors & trailers: new & used
Pr: John O Connell
**Treas:* Tim O'Connell

NUTMEG TRUCK CENTER
See NUTMEG INTERNATIONAL TRUCKS INC

D-U-N-S 13-964-2888
NUTONE INC
9825 Kenwood Rd Ste 301, Blue Ash, OH 45242-6252
Tel (888) 336-3948 *Founded/Ownrshp* 1936
Sales NA *EMP* 625
SIC 3634 Electric housewares & fans; Fans, exhaust & ventilating, electric: household

D-U-N-S 02-034-6458 IMP/EXP
NUTRA BLEND LLC (MO)
NUTRA-BLEND
(*Suby of* LAND OLAKES INC) ★
3200 2nd St, Neosho, MO 64850-7738
Tel (417) 451-6111 *Founded/Ownrshp* 1975, 1979
Sales 92.5MM[E] *EMP* 200[E]
SIC 2048 Feed supplements; Mineral feed supplements; Feed supplements; Mineral feed supplements
CEO: Mike Osborne
CFO: Scott Cooper
VP: Jennifer Spencer
QA Dir: Monica Culina
QA Dir: Brian Scott
Trfc Dir: Tammy Goswick
Manager: John Charley
Manager: Allen Dorsey
Manager: Carl Jones
Sls Mgr: Wayne Pagel
Sales Asso: Barbara Bianchi

D-U-N-S 15-763-1821 IMP
■ NUTRA MANUFACTURING INC
(*Suby of* GENERAL NUTRITION CORP) ★
1050 Woodruff Rd, Greenville, SC 29607-4120
Tel (864) 297-1400 *Founded/Ownrshp* 2013
Sales 46.2MM[E] *EMP* 100
SIC 5499 Vitamin preparations; Health & dietetic food stores
Sr VP: Jay Kent
Pr: Jim Terry
CFO: Ed Kozlowski
**VP:* Greg Szabo
Plng Mgr: Alan Harder
Cmptr Lab: Anne Newton
Dir IT: Lucia Dodson
IT Man: Karen Boekelheide
IT Man: Greg Thompson
Ql Cn Mgr: Michelle Pearson
Ql Cn Mgr: Bill Wheatley

NUTRA-BLEND
See NUTRA BLEND LLC

D-U-N-S 00-725-7355
■ NUTRA-FLO CO
NUTRA-FLO EQUIPMENT CO
(*Suby of* FLO KAY INDUSTRIES INC) ★
200 S Derby Ln, North Sioux City, SD 57049-3031
Tel (712) 277-2011 *Founded/Ownrshp* 1928
Sales 148.1MM[E] *EMP* 380
SIC 2873 2816 2048 Nitrogenous fertilizers; Zinc pigments: zinc oxide, zinc sulfide; Feed supplements; Nitrogenous fertilizers; Zinc pigments: zinc oxide, zinc sulfide; Feed supplements
Pr: Raun D Lohry
**Treas:* Royal Q Lohry
IT Man: Tim Doring
Board of Directors: Dirk Lohry

NUTRA-FLO EQUIPMENT CO
See NUTRA-FLO CO

D-U-N-S 88-349-2720 IMP
■ NUTRACEUTICAL CORP
(*Suby of* NUTRACEUTICAL INTERNATIONAL CORP) ★
1400 Kearns Blvd Ste 200, Park City, UT 84060-7228
Tel (435) 655-6000 *Founded/Ownrshp* 1995
Sales 180.8MM[E] *EMP* 706
SIC 2834 Vitamin preparations; Vitamin preparations
Pr: Bruce Hough
**CFO:* Cory McQueen
Ex VP: Jeffrey Hinrichs
Ex VP: Gary Hume
VP: Vern Christensen
VP: Kim Heward
VP: Tim Hinrichs
VP: Jason Jones
VP: Margo Ochs
VP: Cary Roberts
VP: John Russo
VP: Joel Tippets
Creative D: Joe Arrigo

D-U-N-S 00-512-7654 IMP/EXP
▲ NUTRACEUTICAL INTERNATIONAL CORP
1400 Kearns Blvd Fl 2, Park City, UT 84060-7228
Tel (435) 655-6106 *Founded/Ownrshp* 1993
Sales 216.4MM *EMP* 845[E]

Accts Pricewaterhousecoopers Llp Sa
Tkr Sym NUTR *Exch* NGS
SIC 2833 Vitamins, natural or synthetic: bulk, uncompounded; Vitamins, natural or synthetic: bulk, uncompounded
Ch Bd: Frank W Gay II
Pr: Bruce R Hough
**COO:* Jeffrey A Hinrichs
CFO: Cory J McQueen
VP: Christopher B Neuberger
VP: Daren P Peterson
CIO: Matthew A Vance
Board of Directors: Gregory M Benson, Michael D Burke, J Kimo Esplin, James D Stice

D-U-N-S 94-460-2460
■ NUTRACEUTICAL LIFE SCIENCES INC
NLS
(*Suby of* VITACOST.COM INC) ★
130 Lexington Pkwy, Lexington, NC 27295-8524
Tel (336) 956-0800 *Founded/Ownrshp* 2007
Sales 55.3MM^E *EMP* 586^E
SIC 2834 Tablets, pharmaceutical

D-U-N-S 83-101-1809
NUTRACLICK LLC
FORCE FACTOR
24 School St Fl 4, Boston, MA 02108-5113
Tel (617) 229-5670 *Founded/Ownrshp* 2009
Sales 64.2MM *EMP* 126^E
SIC 5122 Vitamins & minerals
CEO: Daniel Wallace
CFO: Stephen Wietrecki
Chf Mktg O: Patrick Carroll
VP: Jules Sweeney
CTO: Erik Dasque
Sls Dir: Chris Cole
Pr Mgr: Shannon Costello
Mktg Mgr: Arjun Naskar
Sales Asso: Brian Consoles
Sales Asso: Alexandra Morss

D-U-N-S 80-107-3206 IMP
NUTRAMAX LABORATORIES INC
2208 Lakeside Blvd, Edgewood, MD 21040-1102
Tel (410) 776-4000 *Founded/Ownrshp* 1988
Sales 22.6MM^E *EMP* 90^E
SIC 2834 Pharmaceutical preparations; Pharmaceutical preparations
Pr: Robert W Henderson
**Ex VP:* Ed Sharbaugh
**VP:* Todd Orr Henderson
VP: Ron Kettenacker
Dist Mgr: Jeff Holm
QA Dir: Michael Beckwith
QA Dir: Diane Lockard
QA Dir: Aaron Popowitch
Tech Mgr: Barbara Eves
Sfty Mgr: Michael Wice
Mfg Mgr: Miomir Adzic

D-U-N-S 05-374-5811 IMP
NUTRAMED INC
13840 Magnolia Ave, Chino, CA 91710-7027
Tel (909) 902-5005 *Founded/Ownrshp* 1998
Sales 157.5MM^E *EMP* 200
SIC 5149 Specialty food items
Pr: Manu Patolia
VP: Dana Patolia

D-U-N-S 10-166-0236
NUTRASWEET PROPERTY HOLDINGS INC
(*Suby of* JW CHILDS ASSOCIATES LIMITED PARTNERSHIP) ★
222 Merchandise Mart Plz, Chicago, IL 60654-1103
Tel (312) 873-5000 *Founded/Ownrshp* 2007
Sales 13.5MM^E *EMP* 417
SIC 6512 Nonresidential building operators; Nonresidential building operators
Pr: William Defer
**CFO:* Stephen Gregory

D-U-N-S 79-116-8847 IMP
NUTRAVAIL LLC
NUTRAVAIL TECHNOLOGIES
(*Suby of* FRS CO) ★
14790 Flint Lee Rd, Chantilly, VA 20151-1513
Tel (703) 222-6340 *Founded/Ownrshp* 2012
Sales 28.8MM^E *EMP* 65
SIC 2834 Pharmaceutical preparations
CEO: Richard O'Neil
VP: Marc Canton

NUTRAVAIL TECHNOLOGIES
See NUTRAVAIL LLC

D-U-N-S 06-033-9913
NUTRECO USA INC
SHUR-GAIN
(*Suby of* NUTRECO N.V.)
3422 Dutch Hollow Rd, Strykersville, NY 14145-9592
Tel (585) 457-9471 *Founded/Ownrshp* 2007
Sales 38.2MM^E *EMP* 60^E
SIC 5153 Grains
Genl Mgr: Andrew Hunt
**Sec:* Michael W Liddle
Sec: Mike Little

NUTREND DISPOSABLES
See TRANZONIC COMPANIES

NUTRI-FORCE NUTRITION
See ALFONSO NUTRITION HOLDINGS INC

NUTRI-FORCE NUTRITION
See FDC VITAMINS LLC

NUTRI-FORCE NUTRITION
See VS HERCULES LLC

D-U-N-S 14-866-9302 IMP
NUTRICIA NORTH AMERICA INC
(*Suby of* SCIENTIFIC HOSPITAL SUPPLIES (UK) LTD.)
9900 Belward Campus Dr # 100, Rockville, MD 20850-3970
Tel (301) 795-2300 *Founded/Ownrshp* 2005
Sales 58.9MM^E *EMP* 89
SIC 5149 Specialty food items
CEO: Nigel Hughes
**Pr:* Garry Reason
**CFO:* Steve Peth
VP Mktg: Thomas Pugh
Mktg Mgr: John Rausenberger
Sls Mgr: Jennifer Barnhill

D-U-N-S 92-649-7967
NUTRICION FUNDAMENTAL INC
PRIME TIME NUTRICION
19315 San Jose Ave, City of Industry, CA 91748-1420
Tel (909) 598-7416 *Founded/Ownrshp* 1994
Sales 74.4MM^E *EMP* 495
SIC 5411

NUTRILITE
See ACCESS BUSINESS GROUP INTERNATIONAL LLC

NUTRILITE
See ACCESS BUSINESS GROUP LLC

D-U-N-S 86-718-0226 IMP
NUTRIMIX FEED CO INC
MILLIAGRO GROUP
Desembarcadero Final St, Guaynabo, PR 00965
Tel (787) 641-5175 *Founded/Ownrshp* 1994
Sales 35.5MM *EMP* 52
Accts De Angel & Compa la Caguas P
SIC 2048 2047 Prepared feeds; Dog & cat food; Prepared feeds; Dog & cat food
Pr: Waldemar Gonzalez
**Sec:* Federico Estremera
**VP:* Damian Rivera

D-U-N-S 04-173-0784 IMP
NUTRINOVA INC
(*Suby of* CELANESE SALES GERMANY GMBH)
1601 Lyndon B Johnson Fwy, Dallas, TX 75234-6034
Tel (732) 271-7220 *Founded/Ownrshp* 2001
Sales 40.0MM *EMP* 8
SIC 2869 Industrial organic chemicals; Industrial organic chemicals
Pr: Arthur Viera

D-U-N-S 13-263-0448
▲ NUTRISYSTEM INC
600 Office Center Dr, Fort Washington, PA 19034-3232
Tel (215) 706-5300 *Founded/Ownrshp* 1972
Sales 403.0MM *EMP* 417
Tkr Sym NTRI *Exch* NGS
SIC 5961 Food, mail order; Food, mail order
Pr: Dawn M Zier
CFO: Michael P Monahan
Chf Mktg O: Keira Krausz
Sr VP: William Misloski
Sr VP: Brad Sockloff
VP: Jennifer Hartnett
VP: David Macdonald
VP: Paul McKeeman
VP: Stephen Mikulak
VP: Robin Shallow
VP: Max Wang
Board of Directors: Robert F Bernstock, Paul Guyardo, Michael J Hagan, Jay Herratti, Michael D Mangan, Brian P Tierney, Andrea M Weiss, Stephen T Zarrilli

D-U-N-S 18-276-5305
NUTRITION EXPRESS CORP
2575 W 237th St, Torrance, CA 90505-5216
Tel (310) 784-8500 *Founded/Ownrshp* 1983
Sales 25.7MM^E *EMP* 70
SIC 5961 Mail order house
CEO: Don Mc Farland
Store Mgr: Celia Barraza

D-U-N-S 19-247-6919
NUTRITION FORMULATORS INC
10407 N Commerce Pkwy, Miramar, FL 33025-3971
Tel (305) 592-2111 *Founded/Ownrshp* 1997
Sales 72.2MM^E *EMP* 120
SIC 5149 Natural & organic foods
Pr: Adolfo Graubard
**CFO:* Vivian Graubard
Sls Dir: Gustavo Graubard

D-U-N-S 07-749-1330
NUTRITION INC
580 Wendel Rd Ste 100, Irwin, PA 15642-5001
Tel (724) 872-7887 *Founded/Ownrshp* 1975
Sales 77.6MM^E *EMP* 1,800
Accts Bielau Tierney Coon & Compan
SIC 5812 2099 Contract food services; Food preparations; Contract food services; Food preparations
Pr: Gerald Moore
**Pr:* Edward W Caswell
**Sec:* Donald Baker
VP: Patrick D Davis
Admn Mgr: Joan Wagner
Sfty Mgr: Cindy Thomas

D-U-N-S 09-816-3611
NUTRITION MANAGEMENT SERVICES CO
2071 Kimberton Rd, Kimberton, PA 19442
Tel (610) 935-2050 *Founded/Ownrshp* 1979
Sales 16.2MM^E *EMP* 289
SIC 5812 7349 Contract food services; Hospital housekeeping; Contract food services; Hospital housekeeping
Ch Bd: Joseph V Roberts
**Treas:* Kathleen A Hill
VP: Brian Fioravanti
VP: Michelle Nicholson
Exec: George Detwiler
IT Man: Michelle Frantz
VP Opers: Michelle Buechele

D-U-N-S 61-891-1325
NUTRITION SERVICE CO INC
W249 Deer Dr, Pulaski, WI 54162-7953
Tel (920) 822-8881 *Founded/Ownrshp* 1983
Sales 30.0MM^E *EMP* 38
SIC 5191 Feed; Feed
Pr: Robert Block
**Pr:* Wayne Nighorn

D-U-N-S 04-525-3346
NUTRITION SERVICES INC
SENIOR NUTRITION
812 4th Ave Ne, Waseca, MN 56093-3333
Tel (507) 835-5697 *Founded/Ownrshp* 1996
Sales 2.8MM *EMP* 316
SIC 8099 8322 Nutrition services; Individual & family services; Nutrition services; Individual & family services
Pr: Larry Kroeger

NUTRITION TRANSPORTATION SVCS
See PROVIMI NORTH AMERICA INC

D-U-N-S 36-098-7429
NUTRITIONAL HOLDINGS INC
1001 S 3rd St W, Missoula, MT 59801-2337
Tel (406) 273-5493 *Founded/Ownrshp* 2005
Sales 24.5MM^E *EMP* 126
SIC 2833 2834 Medicinals & botanicals; Pharmaceutical preparations; Medicinals & botanicals; Pharmaceutical preparations
CEO: Ronald H Danenberg

D-U-N-S 00-730-6970
NUTRITIONAL LABORATORIES INTERNATIONAL INC
(*Suby of* NUTRAMED INC) ★
1001 S 3rd St W, Missoula, MT 59801-2337
Tel (406) 273-5493 *Founded/Ownrshp* 2015
Sales 46.4MM^E *EMP* 125
SIC 2833 2834 Medicinals & botanicals; Pharmaceutical preparations; Medicinals & botanicals; Pharmaceutical preparations
Pr: Terry Benishek
QA Dir: Jera'le Smith
Sls Mgr: Tita Flores

D-U-N-S 61-892-9418 IMP
NUTRITIONAL RESOURCES INC
HEALTHWISE
5003 Wrightsboro Rd, Grovetown, GA 30813-2843
Tel (706) 869-1222 *Founded/Ownrshp* 1993
Sales 26.9MM^E *EMP* 24
SIC 5141 Food brokers
Pr: Jim Mathews

D-U-N-S 13-027-0770
NUTRITIONAL SUPPORT SERVICES LP
NETWORK HEALTHCARE
9000 Executive Park Dr A301, Knoxville, TN 37923-4656
Tel (865) 531-0008 *Founded/Ownrshp* 1983
Sales 57.8MM^E *EMP* 220
SIC 5122 8099 Drugs, proprietaries & sundries; Nutrition services; Drugs, proprietaries & sundries; Nutrition services
Ex Dir: Terry Leeman
VP: Jane Hardman
MIS Dir: Rebecca Monroe
Pharmcst: Christie Carrion

D-U-N-S 00-833-8345 IMP/EXP
NUTRO CO
NATURAL CHOICE
(*Suby of* MARS INC) ★
1550 W Mcewen Dr Ste 100, Franklin, TN 37067-1770
Tel (888) 607-4081 *Founded/Ownrshp* 2007
Sales 96.0MM^E *EMP* 450
SIC 2047 0742 Dog food; Cat food; Veterinary services, specialties; Dog food; Cat food; Veterinary services, specialties
CEO: Rodolfo Spielmann
**Ch Bd:* David Traitel
CFO: Sandip Grewal

D-U-N-S 03-115-2127 IMP
■ NUTRO LABORATORIES INC
(*Suby of* ARCO PHARMACEUTICAL) ★
650 Hadley Rd Ste C, South Plainfield, NJ 07080-2477
Tel (908) 755-7984 *Founded/Ownrshp* 2000
Sales 24.8MM^E *EMP* 210
SIC 2834 Vitamin preparations; Analgesics; Antiseptics, medicinal; Laxatives; Vitamin preparations; Analgesics; Antiseptics, medicinal; Laxatives
Pr: Michael Slade

D-U-N-S 13-113-6152 IMP
NUTS AND SPICE CO
SPICE HOUSE
30315 Union City Blvd, Union City, CA 94587-1513
Tel (510) 489-6857 *Founded/Ownrshp* 1993
Sales 22.3MM^E *EMP* 25^E
SIC 5149 5499 Spices & seasonings; Spices & herbs
CEO: Balwant Rai Birla
**Sec:* Sudesh Birla
VP: Sanjay Kumar
Brnch Mgr: William Iglesias

D-U-N-S 78-840-6767
NUTTER CORP
NUTTER UNDGRD UTILITIES CO
7211 Ne 43rd Ave Ste A, Vancouver, WA 98661-1377
Tel (360) 573-2000 *Founded/Ownrshp* 1992
Sales 36.6MM^E *EMP* 105
SIC 1623 1611 Underground utilities contractor; Highway & street paving contractor; Underground utilities contractor; Highway & street paving contractor
Pr: Jerry Nutter
CFO: Jeff Woodside
VP: Jeff Deringer
IT Man: Charley Ebel
IT Man: Summer Paul

D-U-N-S 07-380-0997
NUTTER MCCLENNEN & FISH LLP
155 Seaport Blvd, Boston, MA 02210-2604
Tel (617) 439-2000 *Founded/Ownrshp* 1996
Sales 38.0MM^E *EMP* 300
SIC 8111 General practice law office; General practice law office
Pt: Michael E Mooney
Sr Pt: Robert Fishman
Pt: Kenneth Berman
Pt: Julia Satti Consentino
Pt: Thomas Engellenner
Pt: William C Geary III
Pt: David Henerson
Pt: Deborah J Manus
Pt: Beth Mitchell
Pt: Philip R Rosenblatt
Pt: Michael Scott
Pt: Joseph Shea
Pt: Timothy Smith
Pt: James Ward
Pt: Janet Gilman
CFO: Donald Kandub
Exec: Jeremy Smith

NUTTER UNDGRD UTILITIES CO
See NUTTER CORP

D-U-N-S 82-489-4224
NUTTERS CROSSING GOLF COURSE INC
RUM POINTE GOLF COURSE
4920 Snow Hill Rd, Salisbury, MD 21804-1942
Tel (410) 749-0193 *Founded/Ownrshp* 1990
Sales 13.1MM^E *EMP* 300
SIC 7992 Public golf courses; Public golf courses
Pr: Thomas H Ruark
VP: Barbara Hannaman
**VP:* James M Ruark

D-U-N-S 79-955-0587
NUTTING NEWSPAPERS INC
1500 Main St, Wheeling, WV 26003-2826
Tel (304) 233-0100 *Founded/Ownrshp* 1997
Sales 26.4MM^E *EMP* 200
SIC 2711 Newspapers; Newspapers
Pr: Robert M Nutting
**Sec:* Duane Wittman
**VP:* William O Nutting

D-U-N-S 08-675-2763
NUUNION CREDIT UNION INC
501 S Capitol Ave Lbby, Lansing, MI 48933-2333
Tel (517) 267-7328 *Founded/Ownrshp* 1952
Sales NA *EMP* 277
Accts Doeren Mayhew Troy Mi
SIC 6062 6061 6163 State credit unions, not federally chartered; Federal credit unions; Loan brokers; State credit unions, not federally chartered; Federal credit unions; Loan brokers
Pr: Stephen L Winninger
**CFO:* Brian McVeigh
**Treas:* Shane Lovellette
Sr VP: Susan Funderburk
Sr VP: Deborah Labarbera
VP: Spencer Scarboro

D-U-N-S 05-395-0783 IMP
▲ NUVASIVE INC
7475 Lusk Blvd, San Diego, CA 92121-5707
Tel (858) 909-1800 *Founded/Ownrshp* 1997
Sales 762.4MM *EMP* 1,500
Tkr Sym NUVA *Exch* NGS
SIC 3841 Surgical & medical instruments; Surgical & medical instruments
CEO: Gregory T Lucier
Pr: Patrick Miles
CFO: Quentin S Blackford
Ex VP: Carol Cox
Ex VP: Scott Durall
Ex VP: Jason M Hannon
Ex VP: Tyler P Lipschultz
Ex VP: Mike Paolucci
Ex VP: Russell A Powers
Ex VP: Russell Powers
Ex VP: Stephan Siemers
Sr VP: Paul Kosters
Sr VP: Albert Pothier
Sr VP: Jeffrey Rydin
VP: Jeffrey Bertolini
VP: G Cornwall
VP: Laetitia Cousin
VP: Michael Lytle
VP: Lytle Michael
VP: Karen Osgood
Adv Bd Mbr: Will Eichenberg
Board of Directors: Jack R Blair, Vickie L Capps, Peter C Farrell, Lesley H Howe, Peter M Leddy, Leslie V Norwalk, Daniel J Wolterman

D-U-N-S 78-622-6779
NUVEEN ALL AMERICAN MUNICIPAL FUND
NUVEEN INVESTMENTS
(*Suby of* NUVEEN INVESTMENTS INC) ★
333 W Wacker Dr, Chicago, IL 60606-1220
Tel (312) 917-8200 *Founded/Ownrshp* 1997
Sales 27.0MM^E *EMP* 600
SIC 6211 Mutual funds, selling by independent salesperson; Mutual funds, selling by independent salesperson
Ch Bd: Timothy R Schwertferger

NUVEEN INVESTMENTS
See NUVEEN ALL AMERICAN MUNICIPAL FUND

D-U-N-S 78-949-4374
NUVEEN INVESTMENTS INC
(*Suby of* TEACHERS INSURANCE AND ANNUITY ASSOCIATION-COLLEGE RETIREMENT EQUITIES FUND) ★
333 W Wacker Dr, Chicago, IL 60606-1220
Tel (312) 917-7700 *Founded/Ownrshp* 2014
Sales 634.6MM^E *EMP* 828^E
SIC 6282 6211 Manager of mutual funds, contract or fee basis; Investment bankers; Underwriters, security; Bond dealers & brokers; Mutual funds, selling by independent salesperson; Manager of mutual funds, contract or fee basis; Investment bankers; Underwriters, security; Bond dealers & brokers; Mutual funds, selling by independent salesperson
Pr: John P Amboian
V Ch: Tom Schreier
Pr: Glen Anderson
Pr: Robert Burke
Pr: Joseph Marks
Pr: Diane Meggs
Pr: Ryan Smith
COO: William Huffman
COO: Glenn Richter
Sr Cor Off: Allen Williamson
Chf Mktg O: Stephen Ban

Ofcr: Sandy Tichenor
Ex VP: Margo L Cook
Ex VP: John Maccarthy
Ex VP: Diane Whelan
Sr VP: Sandra Alvarenga
Sr VP: Bengt Berggreen
Sr VP: Thomas Eggen
Sr VP: Walter Kelly
Sr VP: David Reneker
VP: Chip Bailey

D-U-N-S 80-150-7273
NUVEEN INVESTMENTS LLC
(*Suby of* NUVEEN INVESTMENTS INC) ★
333 W Wacker Dr Ste 3200, Chicago, IL 60606-1286
Tel (312) 917-7868 *Founded/Ownrshp* 2003
Sales 23.7MM^E *EMP* 400
SIC 6211 Security brokers & dealers; Security brokers & dealers
Mng Dir: Steven Shelton
Mng Dir: Anne Thurston

D-U-N-S 04-252-9396
NUVEEN JOHN & CO INC (DEL) (IL)
(*Suby of* NUVEEN INVESTMENTS INC) ★
333 W Wacker Dr Fl 33, Chicago, IL 60606-2203
Tel (312) 917-7700 *Founded/Ownrshp* 1898, 1992
Sales 119.3MM^E *EMP* 610
SIC 6211 8742 Mutual funds, selling by independent salesperson; Business consultant; Mutual funds, selling by independent salesperson; Business consultant
Ch Bd: Timothy R Schwertfeger
Pr: John Amboian
Chf Mktg O: Alan Brown
Sr VP: Alan Berkshire
VP: Jeff Kratz
Mng Dir: Frank Maiorano
Mng Dir: John Miller

D-U-N-S 78-622-7132
NUVEEN MUNICIPAL ADVANTAGE FUND INC
333 W Wacker Dr Fl 31, Chicago, IL 60606-2209
Tel (312) 917-7810 *Founded/Ownrshp* 1989
Sales 59.9MM *EMP* 400
Accts Ernst & Young
SIC 6211 6282 Mutual funds, selling by independent salesperson; Investment advice; Mutual funds, selling by independent salesperson; Investment advice
CEO: Tim Schwertfeger
Mng Pt: Rajiv Saxena
Mng Dir: Andrew Mazurek

D-U-N-S 00-292-4020
■ **NUVELL FINANCIAL SERVICES LLC** (DE)
(*Suby of* ALLY FINANCIAL INC) ★
17500 Chenal Pkwy Ste 200, Little Rock, AR 72223-9041
Tel (501) 821-5200 *Founded/Ownrshp* 1997, 2001
Sales NA *EMP* 562
SIC 6153 Purchasers of accounts receivable & commercial paper; Purchasers of accounts receivable & commercial paper
Pr: Tom Pritchard
VP: Gerald Culver
VP: Ray Farris
VP: James Hardesty
VP: Brian Meek

D-U-N-S 04-344-8021 IMP
■ **NUVERA FUEL CELLS INC**
(*Suby of* HYSTER) ★
129 Concord Rd Bldg 1, Billerica, MA 01821-4600
Tel (617) 245-7500 *Founded/Ownrshp* 1997, 2014
Sales 57.4MM^E *EMP* 100
SIC 1382 Oil & gas exploration services; Oil & gas exploration services
Pr: Jon Taylor
VP: Scott Blanchet
IT Man: Jason Beaudoin
IT Man: Mark Manganelli
VP Opers: Paul Oei
Sls Mgr: Wesley Hansen
Snr Mgr: Brian Bowers
Snr Mgr: Andy Kress

NUVERRA
See THERMO FLUIDS INC

D-U-N-S 92-950-4533
▲ **NUVERRA ENVIRONMENTAL SOLUTIONS INC**
14624 N Scottsdale Rd, Scottsdale, AZ 85254-2753
Tel (602) 903-7802 *Founded/Ownrshp* 2007
Sales 536.2MM *EMP* 2,400^E
Tkr Sym NES *Exch* NYS
SIC 1389 4953 Servicing oil & gas wells; Liquid waste, collection & disposal; Servicing oil & gas wells; Liquid waste, collection & disposal
Ch Bd: Mark D Johnsrud
CFO: Gregory J Heinlein
V Ch Bd: Robert B Simonds Jr
Ex VP: Chris Chisholm
Ex VP: Joseph M Crabb
Ex VP: Damian Georgino
VP: Mark Ridgley
Dir Risk M: Ken Davis
CIO: Lawrence Strohmaier
Software D: Christopher Ryhal
Board of Directors: William M Austin, Edward A Barkett, Tod C Holmes, R Dan Nelson, Alfred E Osborne Jr, J Danforth Quayle

D-U-N-S 01-116-9500
NUVI GLOBAL
518 W Henderson Ave Apt 9, Porterville, CA 93257-1769
Tel (559) 306-2646 *Founded/Ownrshp* 2014
Sales 16.4MM^E *EMP* 600
SIC 5047 Incontinent care products & supplies; Incontinent care products & supplies
Owner: Herlinda Ruelas

D-U-N-S 10-012-5384
NUVIEW UNION SCHOOL DISTRICT
29780 Lakeview Ave, Nuevo, CA 92567-9706
Tel (951) 928-0066 *Founded/Ownrshp* 1940
Sales 19.6MM^E *EMP* 300
SIC 8211 Public elementary school; Public elementary school
Snr Mgr: John Huber

D-U-N-S 07-217-1671
NUVISION ENGINEERING INC
2403 Sidney St Ste 700, Pittsburgh, PA 15203-2181
Tel (412) 586-1810 *Founded/Ownrshp* 2006
Sales 35.7MM^E *EMP* 100
SIC 8711 Designing: ship, boat, machine & product; Structural engineering; Designing: ship, boat, machine & product; Structural engineering
Pr: Van B Walker
**CFO:* Michael Kopec
**VP:* Manohar L Badlani
**VP:* Brian Scott Beley
**VP:* Lawrence Judd
**VP:* Hank Kaczowka
**VP:* Robert Mullens
**VP:* Micheal Torcaso
**VP:* Martin Williams
Sls Mgr: Mike Crossley

D-U-N-S 10-637-0364
NUVISION FINANCIAL FEDERAL CREDIT UNION
7812 Edinger Ave Ste 100, Huntington Beach, CA 92647-3727
Tel (714) 375-8000 *Founded/Ownrshp* 1935
Sales NA *EMP* 185
SIC 6062 State credit unions, not federally chartered; State credit unions, not federally chartered
CEO: Roger Ballard
**CFO:* John Afdem
CFO: Tony Sawaya
**Treas:* Robert Geraci
VP: Chris Clausen
VP: Kenneth Everett
VP: Tammy Ortega
Dir Risk M: Brian Hershfield
Brnch Mgr: Cleo Driscoll
Dir IT: David Dunn
Mktg Mgr: Albert Eisel

NUVO COSMETICS INTERNATIONAL
See CREATIVE BEAUTY GROUP LLC

D-U-N-S 82-653-4351
NUVOTON TECHNOLOGY CORP AMERICA
(*Suby of* NUVOTON TECHNOLOGY CORPORATION)
2727 N 1st St, San Jose, CA 95134-2029
Tel (408) 544-1718 *Founded/Ownrshp* 2008
Sales 27.3MM^E *EMP* 60
SIC 5065 Semiconductor devices
Ch: Arthur Yu-Cheng Chiao
**Pr:* Robert Hsu
Pr: Aditya Raina
CFO: Wen Cho
Chf Mktg O: Mark Hemming
**VP:* Stephen Rei-Min Huang
**VP:* Bor-Yuan Hwang
**VP:* Hsi-Jung Tsai
Admn Mgr: Anne Kwok
Netwrk Eng: Lei Peng
Mktg Dir: Frank Dowling

D-U-N-S 14-608-7841
■ **NUVOX INC**
NEWSOUTH COMMUNICATIONS
(*Suby of* WINDSTREAM CORP) ★
2 N Main St, Greenville, SC 29601-4874
Tel (864) 672-5000 *Founded/Ownrshp* 2010
Sales NA *EMP* 1,800
SIC 4813 Local & long distance telephone communications; Local & long distance telephone communications
CEO: James W Akerhielm
**Pr:* Michael Gallagher
Pr: Carol Keith
COO: Bruce Cameron
COO: Ronald Sams
CFO: Ron Harold
**CFO:* David Solomon
Sr Cor Off: Robert Rogers
Ex VP: Tracy Cooper
Ex VP: Edward Terrell
Sr VP: Jason Dishon
Sr VP: Ricky El-Mogazi
**VP:* Matt Blocha
VP: Susan Butler
VP: Lawrence Dubow
VP: Rob Gage
VP: Ted Hassold
VP: Joe Jefferson
VP: Jake Jennings
VP: Gwen Jordan
VP: Max Major

D-U-N-S 00-115-9078 IMP/EXP
NUWAY TOBACCO CO (CT)
200 Sullivan Ave Ste 2, South Windsor, CT 06074-1953
Tel (860) 289-6414 *Founded/Ownrshp* 1951, 1955
Sales 32.0MM^E *EMP* 85
SIC 2131 5159 Chewing & smoking tobacco; Tobacco, leaf
CEO: Raymond A Voorhies
**CFO:* Thomas Kirby
**VP:* Anne S King

D-U-N-S 00-942-1780
NUWELD INC
2600 Reach Rd, Williamsport, PA 17701-4119
Tel (570) 505-1500 *Founded/Ownrshp* 1997
Sales 37.0MM^E *EMP* 217
SIC 7692 3441 Welding repair; Fabricated structural metal; Welding repair; Fabricated structural metal
Pr: Timothy Satterfield
Pr: Terry Bartlett
CFO: Michael Caseman
**Treas:* Marilyn J Satterfield
VP: Dirk Flick
VP: Roy Ilch
VP Mfg: Joe Reynolds
Sfty Dirs: Ron Diemer
Ql Cn Mgr: Jim Dwyer

NUWORLD BUSINESS SYSTEMS
See YOUNG SYSTEMS CORP

NV ENERGY
See NEVADA POWER CO

NV ENERGY
See SIERRA PACIFIC POWER CO

D-U-N-S 96-304-0303
NV ENERGY CHAR FOUNDATION
P.O. Box 30150 (89520-3150)
Tel (775) 834-5642 *Founded/Ownrshp* 2010
Sales 22.1MM *EMP* 2^E
SIC 8699 Charitable organization
Sr VP: Tony F Sanchez III

D-U-N-S 12-180-9347 IMP
■ **NV ENERGY INC**
(*Suby of* BERKSHIRE HATHAWAY ENERGY CO) ★
6226 W Sahara Ave, Las Vegas, NV 89146-3060
Tel (702) 402-5000 *Founded/Ownrshp* 2013
Sales 3.2MMM^E *EMP* 2,699^E
SIC 4911 4924 Generation, electric power; Transmission, electric power; Distribution, electric power; Natural gas distribution; Generation, electric power; Transmission, electric power; Distribution, electric power; Natural gas distribution
Pr: Paul Caudill
**COO:* Dilek L Samil
**CFO:* Jonathan S Halkyard
**Ex VP:* Paul J Kaleta
Sr VP: Tony F Sanchez
**VP:* E Kevin Bethel
Exec: Max Kuniansky
Counsel: Doug Brooks
Counsel: Michael Greene
Counsel: Mark Warden
Counsel: Thomas Woodworth

NV REPUBLIC ELECTRIC
See REPUBLIC ELECTRIC INC

D-U-N-S 07-848-2872
▲ **NV5 HOLDINGS INC**
200 S Park Rd Ste 350, Hollywood, FL 33021-8798
Tel (954) 495-2112 *Founded/Ownrshp* 1949
Sales 108.3MM *EMP* 649^E
Tkr Sym NVEE *Exch* NAS
SIC 8711 8748 Engineering services; Engineering services; Business consulting
Ch Bd: Dickerson Wright
**Pr:* Alexander A Hockman
CFO: Michael P Rama
Ofcr: Maryjo O'Brien
**Ex VP:* Donald C Alford
Ex VP: Richard Tong
Board of Directors: Jeffrey A Liss, William D Pruitt, Gerald J Salontai, Francois Tardan

D-U-N-S 00-944-0074
NV5 INC
NOLTE ASSOCIATES, INC.
(*Suby of* V VERTICAL INC) ★
2525 Natomas Park Dr # 300, Sacramento, CA 95833-2933
Tel (916) 641-9100 *Founded/Ownrshp* 2010
Sales 34.2MM^E *EMP* 320
SIC 8711 Construction & civil engineering; Construction & civil engineering
CEO: Dickerson Wright
Sr VP: Patrick Flynn
VP: Brad Riel
Dir IT: Aaron Andren
IT Man: Lesley Richard
Tech Mgr: Darcy Smith
Sls&Mrk Ex: Dawn Greco

D-U-N-S 05-552-7606
NV5 INC
200 S Park Rd Ste 350, Hollywood, FL 33021-8798
Tel (954) 495-2112 *Founded/Ownrshp* 2009
Sales 48.4MM^E *EMP* 480^E
SIC 8711 Consulting engineer; Consulting engineer
CEO: Dickerson Wright

NVC
See NATIONAL VITAMIN CO INC

D-U-N-S 07-542-2253
NVE BANK
(*Suby of* NVE BANCORP, INC.)
76 Engle St, Englewood, NJ 07631-2905
Tel (201) 816-2810 *Founded/Ownrshp* 1969
Sales NA *EMP* 93^E
SIC 6036 6035 State savings banks, not federally chartered; Savings institutions, federally chartered; State savings banks, not federally chartered; Savings institutions, federally chartered
Pr: Robert Rey
**CEO:* Robert Monteith
CFO: Chris McFadden
Sr VP: Edward Rolfe
Sr VP: Alice Vetrone
Sr VP: Hilary Walsh
VP: Wayne Flavien
VP: Jane Heaton
VP: Armand Tazza
Mktg Mgr: Barbara Hand

D-U-N-S 11-426-4351
NVE CORP
11409 Valley View Rd, Eden Prairie, MN 55344-3617
Tel (952) 829-9217 *Founded/Ownrshp* 1989
Sales 30.5MM *EMP* 54
Accts Grant Thornton Llp Minneapolis
Tkr Sym NVEC *Exch* NAS
SIC 3674 Semiconductors & related devices; Light sensitive devices; Semiconductors & related devices; Light sensitive devices
CEO: Daniel A Baker
**Ch Bd:* Terrence W Glarner
CFO: Curt A Reynders
Mfg Dir: Corrie Peterson
Board of Directors: Patricia M Hollister, Richard W Kramp, Gary R Maharaj

D-U-N-S 14-161-1272
NVE INC
455 Springpark Pl 200b, Herndon, VA 20170-5255
Tel (703) 787-8100 *Founded/Ownrshp* 2003
Sales 37.3MM^E *EMP* 250
SIC 8711 Consulting engineer; Consulting engineer
Pr: Myrian R Villarin
Genl Pt: Jon Brandner

D-U-N-S 19-927-8909 IMP/EXP
NVI LLC
NONDESTRUCTIVE & VISUAL INSPTN
2449 W Park Ave, Gray, LA 70359-3607
Tel (504) 362-5477 *Founded/Ownrshp* 2004
Sales 27.7MM^E *EMP* 125^E
SIC 8734 7389 X-ray inspection service, industrial; Inspection & testing services
CEO: James Cloutier
**COO:* Andre Olivier
**CFO:* Mark Zeringue
VP: Robbie Bush
Div Mgr: Susan Charbonnet
Genl Mgr: Rory Bergeron
Genl Mgr: Joshua Griffin
Dir IT: Brandon Babin
Sfty Mgr: Blake Naquin
Opers Mgr: Matt Manuel
Opers Mgr: Derek Quebedeaux

NVIC
See VERNON NORTH INDUSTRY CORP

D-U-N-S 80-672-4555 IMP
▲ **NVIDIA CORP**
2701 San Tomas Expy, Santa Clara, CA 95050-2519
Tel (408) 486-2000 *Founded/Ownrshp* 1993
Sales 4.6MMM *EMP* 9,228
Accts Pricewaterhousecoopers Llp S
Tkr Sym NVDA *Exch* NGS
SIC 3674 Semiconductors & related devices; Custom computer programming services; Semiconductors & related devices
Pr: Jen-Hsun Huang
Pr: Kenneth Macdonald
CFO: Colette M Kress
Bd of Dir: Eric Anderson
Bd of Dir: Matthew Bolitho
Bd of Dir: Keegan Brown
Bd of Dir: Gautam Chakrabarti
Bd of Dir: Anastasia Lapchinskaya
Bd of Dir: Guru Nutheti
Bd of Dir: Hyungon Ryu
Ofcr: David M Shannon
Ex VP: Ajay K Puri
Ex VP: Debora Shoquist
Sr VP: Jonah M Alben
Sr VP: Bill Dally
Sr VP: Tony Tamasi
Exec: Mary Hernan
Exec: Denise Jackson
Dir Risk M: Curtis Beeson
Adv Bd Mbr: Barry Patel
Board of Directors: Mark A Stevens, Robert Burgess, Persis S Drell, James C Gaither, Dawn Hudson, Harvey C Jones, Michael G McCaffery, William J Miller, Mark L Perry, A Brooke Seawell

D-U-N-S 01-840-7077
■ **NVIDIA US INVESTMENT CO** (DE)
(*Suby of* NVIDIA CORP) ★
2701 San Tomas Expy, Santa Clara, CA 95050-2519
Tel (408) 615-2500 *Founded/Ownrshp* 2000
Sales 47.7MM^E *EMP* 850
SIC 3663 Radio & TV communications equipment; Radio & TV communications equipment
Pr: Jen-Hsun Huang
CTO: Leonardo Vainsencher

D-U-N-S 60-242-1278
NVISION GLOBAL TECHNOLOGY SOLUTIONS INC
1900 Brannan Rd Ste 300, McDonough, GA 30253-4324
Tel (770) 474-4122 *Founded/Ownrshp* 2004
Sales 32.8MM^E *EMP* 155^E
SIC 4731 4789 Freight transportation arrangement; Business oriented computer software; Freight transportation arrangement; Cargo loading & unloading services
CEO: Luther M Brown
CFO: Charlotte Sanders
Sr VP: Moe Galante
Sr VP: Bob Lloyd
Dir Bus: Steven Hodge
Dir IT: Cindy Bragg
Snr Mgr: Raimond Kampen

D-U-N-S 80-839-4621
▲ **NVR INC**
RYAN HOMES
11700 Plaza America Dr # 500, Reston, VA 20190-4751
Tel (703) 956-4000 *Founded/Ownrshp* 1980
Sales 4.4MMM *EMP* 3,942
Accts Kpmg Llp Mclean Virginia
Tkr Sym NVR *Exch* NYS
SIC 1531 6162 Operative builders; Speculative builder, single-family houses; Townhouse developers; Condominium developers; Mortgage bankers; Operative builders; Speculative builder, single-family houses; Townhouse developers; Condominium developers; Mortgage bankers
Pr: Paul C Saville
**Ch Bd:* Dwight C Schar
CFO: Daniel D Malzahn
VP: Eugene J Bredow
VP: Doug Hensel
VP: Kent Lamotta
VP: Matthew Rost
VP: Matt Winkler
Div Mgr: Mike Urian
Genl Mgr: Scott Glover
Genl Mgr: Dave Hilton
Board of Directors: David A Preiser, C E Andrews, W Grady Rosier, Robert C Butler, Paul W Whetsell, Timothy M Donahue, Thomas D Eckert, Alfred E Festa, Ed Grier, Manuel H Johnson, Mel Martinez, William A Moran

D-U-N-S 78-689-7868
■ **NVR MORTGAGE FINANCE INC**
(*Suby of* NVR INC) ★
11700 Plaza America Dr # 500, Reston, VA 20190-4751
Tel (703) 956-4000 *Founded/Ownrshp* 1991

Sales NA EMP 467
Accts Kpmg Peat Marwick Llp
SIC 6162 Mortgage bankers; Mortgage bankers
Pr: William J Inman
CFO: Robert W Henley
*Ch: Dwight Schar
*Sr VP: Peter Kehoe
*Sr VP: Charles Riecker
*Sr VP: William Shanahan

D-U-N-S 60-315-7850
■ NVR SETTLEMENT SERVICES INC
(Suby of NVR INC) ★
11700 Plaza America Dr # 500, Reston, VA 20190-4751
Tel (703) 956-4000 Founded/Ownrshp 1985
Sales 24.7MM^E EMP 60
SIC 6541 Title abstract offices; Title search companies
Pr: William Hudson
VP: James Williams

D-U-N-S 03-069-6409
NVRDUL LLC (TX)
4455 Camp Bowie Blvd # 114, Fort Worth, TX 76107-3864
Tel (817) 654-6020 Founded/Ownrshp 2010
Sales 25.0MM EMP 6
SIC 8742 Business consultant; Business consultant

D-U-N-S 07-888-9785 IMP
NVT LICENSES LLC
SUN EDISON
13736 Rverport Dr Ste 180, Maryland Heights, MO 63043
Tel (443) 909-7200 Founded/Ownrshp 2005
Sales 35.9MM^E EMP 58^E
SIC 4911 Electric services
VP: Kevin Lapidus
VP: Michaele Laforge
*VP: James Scarrow
Snr Mgr: William Luter

D-U-N-S 12-458-4280
NVX HOLDINGS INC
GOHEALTH INSURANCE
214 W Huron St, Chicago, IL 60654-8618
Tel (312) 226-0027 Founded/Ownrshp 1999
Sales 40.0MM^E EMP 130
SIC 8742 Marketing consulting services
CEO: Clint Jones
Pr: Brandon Cruz
CFO: Robert R Millard
VP: Steve Greanias
VP: Michael Hayes
Snr Sftwr: Ryan Johnson
Snr Sftwr: Justin Simms
Snr Sftwr: Nels Wadycki
Snr Mgr: Mike Owens

D-U-N-S 07-857-8463 EXP
NW BEND BOATS LLC (OR)
NORTH RIVER BOATS
1750 Green Siding Rd, Roseburg, OR 97471-7121
Tel (541) 673-2438 Founded/Ownrshp 2012
Sales 21.0MM EMP 115
SIC 3732 5551 Boat building & repairing; Boat dealers
Pr: Brent Hutchings
CFO: Ryanne Loomis

D-U-N-S 00-905-0934
NW CENTER INDUSTRIES 5307
7272 W Marginal Way S, Seattle, WA 98108-4140
Tel (206) 285-9140 Founded/Ownrshp 2009
Sales 53.5MM^E EMP 1,500
SIC 3999 Manufacturing industries; Manufacturing industries

D-U-N-S 07-512-7563 IMP
■ NW COMMUNICATIONS OF TEXAS INC
KDFW FOX 4
(Suby of FOX TELEVISION STATIONS INC) ★
400 N Griffin St, Dallas, TX 75202-1905
Tel (214) 720-4444 Founded/Ownrshp 1997
Sales 28.2MM^E EMP 250
SIC 4833 Television broadcasting stations; Television broadcasting stations
Pr: Jack Abernethy
*Pr: Valerie Rauch
*VP: Andrew Katz
VP: John Kukla
Genl Mgr: Kathy Saunders

D-U-N-S 09-724-3422
NW EYE SURGEONS PC
10330 Meridian Ave N # 270, Seattle, WA 98133-9451
Tel (206) 528-6000 Founded/Ownrshp 1996
Sales 22.1MM^E EMP 93
SIC 8011 8093 Ophthalmologist; Surgeon; Specialty outpatient clinics
Pr: Bruce Cameron
*Pr: J S Brown MD
*VP: Audrey Talley-Rostov
Dir IT: Liz Crane
IT Man: Shawn Clark
Doctor: Audrey Talley
Doctor: Maureen Tipp

NW NATURAL
See NORTHWEST NATURAL GAS CO

D-U-N-S 03-269-2784
NW PACKAGING LLC
1201 E Lexington Ave, Pomona, CA 91766-5520
Tel (909) 706-3627 Founded/Ownrshp 2012
Sales 30.9MM^E EMP 100
SIC 5199 Packaging materials

D-U-N-S 78-513-5757
NW PIPELINE INC
3535 Briarpark Dr Ste 135, Houston, TX 77042-5233
Tel (713) 789-4311 Founded/Ownrshp 1983
Sales 158.5MM^E EMP 502
Accts Grant Thorton Llp Houston T
SIC 1623 Pipeline construction; Pipeline construction
Pr: Paul Somerville
*Sec: Clyde Fowler

D-U-N-S 80-348-3775
NW SIGN INDUSTRIES INC
360 Crider Ave, Moorestown, NJ 08057-1239
Tel (856) 234-8536 Founded/Ownrshp 1989
Sales 41.3MM^E EMP 175
Accts Marcum Llp Bala Cynwyd Pa
SIC 3993 Signs & advertising specialties; Signs & advertising specialties
Pr: Ronald Brodie
*Sec: Mike Uhorchuk
Sr VP: Dennis O'Hara
VP: Karl Kaelin
Dir IT: Mark Patton
Mfg Mgr: Tony Meurette
Snr PM: Tom McKenna
Snr PM: Brian Sparks

NWAMHC
See NORTHWEST ALABAMA MENTAL HEALTH CENTER

NWAS
See NATIONWIDE ARGOSY SOLUTIONS LLC

D-U-N-S 17-196-1105 IMP
NWB USA INC
(Suby of NIPPON WIPER BLADE CO.,LTD.)
1125 Sugg Pkwy, Greenville, NC 27834-9078
Tel (252) 551-5909 Founded/Ownrshp 1996
Sales 70.0MM EMP 12
SIC 3714 Wipers, windshield, motor vehicle
Pr: Harouki Mori
*Treas: Yuichi Kambayashi

NWC
See NORTHWESTERN COLLEGE

D-U-N-S 04-845-6755 IMP
NWE TECHNOLOGY INC
(Suby of WEXTEQ CORPORATION)
1688 Richard Ave, Santa Clara, CA 95050-2844
Tel (408) 919-8321 Founded/Ownrshp 1998
Sales 22.3MM^E EMP 150
SIC 3572 Computer disk & drum drives & components; Computer disk & drum drives & components
Pr: S C Huang

NWEA
See NORTHWEST EVALUATION ASSOCIATION

NWFCU
See NORTHWEST FEDERAL CREDIT UNION FOUNDATION

NWFSC
See NORTHWEST FLORIDA STATE COLLEGE

NWH
See NORTHWEST HORTICULTURE LLC

NWL CAPACITORS
See NWL INC

D-U-N-S 04-454-5077 IMP
NWL INC
NWL CAPACITORS
(Suby of MEGATRAN INDUSTRIES INC) ★
312 Rising Sun Rd, Bordentown, NJ 08505-9626
Tel (609) 298-7300 Founded/Ownrshp 1968
Sales 58.2MM^E EMP 280
SIC 3612 3679 Power transformers, electric; Reactor transformers; Power supplies, all types: static; Power transformers, electric; Reactor transformers; Power supplies, all types: static
Pr: David Seitz
VP: Linda Nixon
*VP: Robert W Seitz
Exec: Tom Thorn
IT Man: Joe Lawrence
Mfg Mgr: Hakim Diaz
VP Sls: Terry Farmer
*VP Sls: Mark Spaventa

NWL TRANSFORMERS
See MEGATRAN INDUSTRIES INC

D-U-N-S 18-738-9627
NWM HOTEL MANAGEMENT LLC
MARRIOTT WATERSIDE NORFOLK
235 E Main St, Norfolk, VA 23510-1668
Tel (757) 627-4200 Founded/Ownrshp 2007
Sales 24.0MM EMP 379
SIC 7011 Hotels; Hotels
Exec: Christopher Thomas
Genl Mgr: Mark Brown
Off Mgr: Jerome Hughes
IT Man: Victoria Thompson
Sls Mgr: Adrielle Bazemore
Sls Mgr: Karen Blanton
Sls Mgr: Chris Bunting
Sls Mgr: Joe Delagarza

D-U-N-S 78-507-4829
NWN CORP
271 Waverley Oaks Rd # 302, Waltham, MA 02452-8470
Tel (781) 472-3400 Founded/Ownrshp 2000
Sales 180.6MM^E EMP 486
SIC 7373 Computer integrated systems design; Computer integrated systems design
CEO: Mont Phelps
*COO: Skip Tappen
*CFO: Kevin Bullock
VP: Tim Joyce
Netwrk Eng: Michael Louis

D-U-N-S 04-388-6170
▲ NWO RESOURCES INC
200 W High St, Bryan, OH 43506-1612
Tel (419) 636-1117 Founded/Ownrshp 1984
Sales 45.5MM^E EMP 105^E
SIC 4924 6719 Natural gas distribution; Public utility holding companies; Natural gas distribution; Public utility holding companies
Pr: James N Blue
*Pr: Richard Hallett
*Treas: Gerlad Richards

D-U-N-S 62-129-1694
NWP ENTERPRISES INC
6310 Mabltn Pkwy Se 100 Ste 1000, Mableton, GA 30126
Tel (770) 941-5421 Founded/Ownrshp 2006
Sales 27.7MM^E EMP 206^E
SIC 1711 Plumbing contractors
Pr: J P Mahaffey III
VP: Tom Bedenk
*VP: Wayne Blackerby
VP: Tony Mahaffey
Sls Mgr: Bill Mahaffey

D-U-N-S 94-997-2863
NWP SERVICES CORP
(Suby of MRI SOFTWARE LLC) ★
535 Anton Blvd Ste 1100, Costa Mesa, CA 92626-7699
Tel (512) 285-5759 Founded/Ownrshp 2014
Sales 46.8MM^E EMP 202
SIC 8721 Billing & bookkeeping service; Billing & bookkeeping service
Pr: Ron Reed
Treas: Howard Behr
Ex VP: Mike Haviken
Sr VP: Randy Gorrell
Sr VP: John Khamis
Sr VP: Lance Leach
VP: Sean Coplen
VP: Gary French
VP: Claudia Geist
VP: Mark Gentile
VP: Tom Laplaca
VP: Kevin Reid
VP: Tim Rogers
VP: Donna Weeding
Board of Directors: Michael Barmettler, Jim Feuille, Richard Headley, John Hoffman, Mark Strome

D-U-N-S 10-544-2016
NWPH INC
NEW YORK PALACE HOTEL, THE
455 Madison Ave, New York, NY 10022-6845
Tel (212) 888-7000 Founded/Ownrshp 2011
Sales 77.2MM^E EMP 1,000
SIC 7011 Hotels; Hotels
Ch Bd: Jonathan Wang
Dir Sec: Jim Byrne
Genl Mgr: Nigel Badgatmin
*Genl Mgr: David Chase

D-U-N-S 10-908-6652
NWQ INVESTMENT MANAGEMENT CO LLC
(Suby of NUVEEN INVESTMENTS INC) ★
2049 Century Park E Fl 16, Los Angeles, CA 90067-3101
Tel (310) 712-4000 Founded/Ownrshp 2002
Sales 34.5MM^E EMP 122
SIC 6282 Investment advisory service; Investment advisory service
Pr: John Connon
Sr VP: Craig O Bailey
Sr VP: Kenneth Frankel
VP: Susi Budiman
Mng Dir: Michael Carne
*CIO: Jon D Bosse

D-U-N-S 06-866-2415 IMP
NWS MICHIGAN INC
NATIONAL WINE & SPIRITS MICH
17550 Allen Rd, Brownstown, MI 48193-8488
Tel (734) 324-3000 Founded/Ownrshp 1996
Sales 248.9MM^E EMP 540
SIC 5182 Liquor; Liquor
CEO: James E Lacrosse
*COO: John J Baker
*Treas: Patrick Trefun
*VP: Dwight Deming
Manager: Joy Siedlik
Mktg Mgr: Cliff Parr

NWSS
See NORTHWEST SECURITY SERVICES INC

NWTC
See NORTHEAST WISCONSIN TECHNICAL COLLEGE DISTRICT

NWTF
See NATIONAL WILD TURKEY FEDERATION INC

D-U-N-S 07-872-1091
NX UTILITIES LLC
970 Rittenhouse Rd # 100, Norristown, PA 19403-2265
Tel (215) 639-1915 Founded/Ownrshp 2013
Sales 91.5MM^E EMP 200^E
SIC 1623 Telephone & communication line construction; Telephone & communication line construction
CEO: Scott Lochhead
VP: Bernie Sisko
IT Man: Adam Spittler

NXC IMAGING
See NORTHERN X-RAY CO

D-U-N-S 17-362-1058 IMP
NXEDGE INC
7500 W Mossy Cup St, Boise, ID 83709-2841
Tel (208) 362-9530 Founded/Ownrshp 2001
Sales 25.7MM^E EMP 100^E
SIC 5065 Semiconductor devices; Semiconductor devices
Pr: Jackson Chao
*VP: David Mills

D-U-N-S 14-078-9384 IMP
NXEDGE INC OF BOISE
(Suby of NXEDGE INC) ★
7500 W Mossy Cup St, Boise, ID 83709-2841
Tel (208) 362-7200 Founded/Ownrshp 2003
Sales 24.6MM^E EMP 70
SIC 5084 Machinists' precision measuring tools
Pr: Jackson Chao
*CFO: Dan Dahl
*VP: David Mills

D-U-N-S 80-000-8286 IMP
NXP SEMICONDUCTORS USA INC
(Suby of NXP B.V.)
411 E Plumeria Dr, San Jose, CA 95134-1924
Tel (408) 518-5500 Founded/Ownrshp 2006
Sales 4.8MMM EMP 5,000
Accts Kpmg Accountants Nv Amstel
SIC 3674 Integrated circuits, semiconductor networks, etc.; Integrated circuits, semiconductor networks, etc.
Pr: Rick Clemmer
*Sr VP: Mathieu Clerx
VP: David Neill
Dir Bus: Frank Daems
Prgrm Mgr: Peter Keenan
*Genl Mgr: Alistair Banham
Genl Mgr: Geoff Lees
IT Exec: Soumendra Mohanty
CIO: Louis Luijten
IT Man: Stephan Demmer
Tech Mgr: Jean M Irazabal

D-U-N-S 08-801-3219 IMP/EXP
▲ NXSTAGE MEDICAL INC
350 Merrimack St, Lawrence, MA 01843-1748
Tel (978) 687-4700 Founded/Ownrshp 1998
Sales 301.5MM EMP 3,400^E
Tkr Sym NXTM Exch NGS
SIC 3845 Electromedical equipment; Dialyzers, electromedical; Electromedical equipment; Dialyzers, electromedical
CEO: Jeffrey H Burbank
*Ch Bd: Robert G Funari
Pr: Joseph E Turk Jr
CFO: Matthew W Towse
Sr VP: Winifred L Swan
VP: James Brugger
VP: Michael Connelly
VP: Bill Fruhan
Area Mgr: Alvin Armer
Area Mgr: Todd Brading
Area Mgr: Trey Curtis
Board of Directors: Daniel A Giannini, Earl R Lewis, Jean K Mixer, Craig W Moore, Reid S Perper, Barry M Straube

D-U-N-S 03-056-6990
NXT CAPITAL LLC
191 N Wacker Dr Ste 1200, Chicago, IL 60606-1903
Tel (312) 269-9230 Founded/Ownrshp 2010
Sales NA EMP 90^E
SIC 6159 Loan institutions, general & industrial
Pr: Robert Radway
Pr: Benjamin Nelson
CFO: Neil A Rudd
Ofcr: Patrick Koehl
VP: Andrea Andreatunick
VP: Matthew Ehret
VP: Amanda Ferguson
VP: Carl Fowler
VP: Elaine Moore
VP: Brian Schleich
VP: Scott Watson

D-U-N-S 06-522-6057
NXTRANET CORP
1500 Mcandrews Rd W, Burnsville, MN 55337-4432
Tel (952) 808-5554 Founded/Ownrshp 1997
Sales 100.0MM EMP 8
SIC 7371 Computer software development; Computer software development
Pr: Fuat Kerkinni

D-U-N-S 17-847-0055
NY GO EXPRESS INC
36 Seabring St, Brooklyn, NY 11231-1621
Tel (718) 624-2000 Founded/Ownrshp 1999
Sales 33.7MM^E EMP 213
SIC 4213 4512 Trucking, except local; Air transportation, scheduled; Trucking, except local; Air transportation, scheduled
Ch Bd: Irina Constantine
*Ch Bd: Irina Constantinescu
*Pr: Vincent Malerba
*VP: Linda Malerba
VP Opers: Andrew Rivera

NY JETS
See NEW YORK JETS LLC

D-U-N-S 36-114-4749
■ NY RADIO LLC
RADIO DISNEY NY
(Suby of CITADEL BROADCASTING CORP) ★
147 Columbus Ave, New York, NY 10023-6503
Tel (212) 456-6583 Founded/Ownrshp 2005
Sales 9.9MM^E EMP 324^E
SIC 4832 Radio broadcasting stations
Sr VP: Randy L Taylor

D-U-N-S 03-073-2537
NY SERDA
17 Columbia Cir, Albany, NY 12203-6399
Tel (518) 862-1090 Founded/Ownrshp 2012
Sales 34.4MM^E EMP 85^E
SIC 4911
CEO: Francis J Murray Jr
Prgrm Mgr: Ruth Horton
Off Mgr: Jennifer McDonald
Snr PM: Patrick Bolton

D-U-N-S 87-622-2290
NY STTE VTRANS HME ST ALBNS
17850 Linden Blvd, Jamaica, NY 11434-1467
Tel (718) 990-0300 Founded/Ownrshp 1993
Sales 16.6MM^E EMP 300
SIC 8059 Nursing home, except skilled & intermediate care facility; Nursing home, except skilled & intermediate care facility
CTO: Willie Price
HC Dir: Yamilee Senat

D-U-N-S 01-096-9616
NYACK COLLEGE
ALLIANCE THEOLOGICAL SEMINARY
1 S Boulevard, Nyack, NY 10960-3698
Tel (845) 675-7498 Founded/Ownrshp 1882
Sales 61.6MM EMP 300
Accts Fiscal Solutions Llc Denville
SIC 8221 8661 College, except junior; Theological seminary; Religious organizations; College, except junior; Theological seminary; Religious organizations
Pr: Michael G Scales
*CFO: David C Jennings

VP: Andrea Hennessy
VP: Earl Miller
**VP:* Dr David F Turk
Exec: James Mellis
Store Mgr: Tatiana Frost
CIO: Kevin Buell
MIS Dir: Kevin Buel
Dir IT: Barbara Eames
Dir IT: Miriam Velez

D-U-N-S 07-270-5783
NYACK HOSPITAL FOUNDATION INC (NY)
160 N Midland Ave, Nyack, NY 10960-1998
Tel (845) 348-2000 *Founded/Ownrshp* 1984
Sales 222.4MM *EMP* 1,300
Accts Charles A Barragato & Co Llp
SIC 8062 8011 8082 Hospital, AMA approved residency; Medical centers; Home health care services; Hospital, AMA approved residency; Medical centers; Home health care services
Pr: Mark Geller
**V Ch:* John Mecchella
**Ch:* Lisa Hayes
**Ch:* Richard L Kohlhausen
Bd of Dir: Cathy Shea
Bd of Dir: Lawrence Simon
Trst: Mitchell Cohn
Trst: Alan Feldstein
Chf Mktg O: Marge Zemek
Ofcr: Jennifer Morris
Ofcr: Jared Shapiro
VP: Jill Garland
VP: Jeffrey Keahon
VP: Robert Mackey
Exec: Linda Mezzasalma
Dir Rad: Daniel Cohen

NYACK PUBLIC SCHOOLS
See NYACK UNION FREE SCHOOL DISTRICT

D-U-N-S 19-302-2209
NYACK UNION FREE SCHOOL DISTRICT
NYACK PUBLIC SCHOOLS
13a Dickinson Ave, Nyack, NY 10960-2914
Tel (845) 353-7101 *Founded/Ownrshp* 1990
Sales 73.4MM^E *EMP* 490
Accts Raymond G Preusser Cpa Pc
SIC 8211 Public elementary school; Public junior high school; Public senior high school; Public elementary school; Public junior high school; Public senior high school
Pr: Claudette Jimerson
**Treas:* Gloria Menoutis
VP: Ed Gannon
**VP:* Michael Mark
**Prin:* Jocelyn Abraham

D-U-N-S 61-980-3542
NYBERG CENTERCAL II LLC
1600 E Franklin Ave, El Segundo, CA 90245-4337
Tel (310) 563-6900 *Founded/Ownrshp* 2011
Sales NA *EMP* 22^E
SIC 6153 Purchasers of accounts receivable & commercial paper
VP: Scott Blyze
Genl Mgr: Hugh Crawford
Off Mgr: Tasha Carter
Mktg Mgr: Sarah Sumpter

NYBOT
See BOARD OF TRADE OF CITY OF NEW YORK INC

D-U-N-S 02-037-9582
NYC & CO INC
810 7th Ave Fl 3, New York, NY 10019-5896
Tel (212) 484-1200 *Founded/Ownrshp* 1935
Sales 34.0MM^E *EMP* 170
Accts Pkf Llp New York Ny
SIC 8742 7389 Marketing consulting services; Tourist information bureau; Marketing consulting services; Tourist information bureau
CEO: Fred Dixon
**Pr:* Emily K Rafferty
Pr: Keith Yazmir
**COO:* Bryan Grimaldi
**CFO:* Kevin Booth
Assoc VP: Dairmaid O'Sullivan
Sr VP: Nevah Assang
VP: Robert Beckham
VP: Alex Costas
VP: Joyce Kaye
VP: Rich Lovatt
VP: Rhianna Roddy
Assoc Dir: Ernesto Freire
Comm Man: Francisca Ovalle
Board of Directors: Gail Grimmett

NYC CONCRETE MATERIALS
See EASTERN CONCRETE MATERIALS INC

D-U-N-S 07-938-6481
NYC CONSTRUCTORS INC
110 E 42nd St Rm 1502, New York, NY 10017-8521
Tel (212) 444-1044 *Founded/Ownrshp* 2013
Sales 30.0MM *EMP* 150
SIC 1542 1791 Commercial & office building contractors; Structural steel erection; Commercial & office building contractors; Structural steel erection
Pr: Barry King
VP: Jeffrey Gannett
Off Mgr: Nancy Wickham

D-U-N-S 96-489-2298
NYC DISTRICT COUNCIL OF CARPENTERS WELFARE FUND
395 Hudson St Lbby 3, New York, NY 10014-7450
Tel (212) 366-7300 *Founded/Ownrshp* 2010
Sales NA *EMP* 3
Accts Schultheis & Panettieri Llp N
SIC 6371 Pension, health & welfare funds; Pension, health & welfare funds
Prin: David Halmers

D-U-N-S 96-487-8156
NYC DISTRICT COUNCIL UBCJA
395 Hudson St Lbby 3, New York, NY 10014-7450
Tel (212) 366-7500 *Founded/Ownrshp* 2010
Sales 27.9MM *EMP* 2^E
Accts Terrence R Mooney Cpa Absec

SIC 3423 Carpenters' hand tools, except saws: levels, chisels, etc.; Carpenters' hand tools, except saws: levels, chisels, etc.
Prin: Michael Forde

NYC EMPOWERMENT SCHOOLS
See NEW YORK CITY DEPT OF EDUCATION

D-U-N-S 07-848-0735
NYC IDOL APPAREL INC (NY)
1407 Broadway Rm 2503, New York, NY 10018-2651
Tel (212) 997-9797 *Founded/Ownrshp* 2008
Sales 45.0MM *EMP* 4^E
SIC 2329 2339 Men's & boys' sportswear & athletic clothing; Women's & misses' athletic clothing & sportswear
Owner: David Shaaya

D-U-N-S 07-144-7851
NYC OFC OF MEDICAL EXAMIN
421 E 26th St, New York, NY 10016-9161
Tel (212) 323-1704 *Founded/Ownrshp* 2011
Sales 7.2MM^E *EMP* 600
SIC 8099 8299 Health & allied services; Schools & educational service; Health & allied services; Schools & educational service
Prin: Barbara Samson

D-U-N-S 60-526-4746
NYC SPECIAL SCHOOLS - DISTRICT 75
400 1st Ave, New York, NY 10010-4004
Tel (212) 802-1500 *Founded/Ownrshp* 1998
Sales 8.9MM^E *EMP* 425^E
SIC 8211 Elementary & secondary schools; Elementary & secondary schools

D-U-N-S 12-227-9821 IMP
■ **NYCE CORP**
(*Suby of* FIDELITY NATIONAL INFO SVCS) ★
400 Plaza Dr Ste 200, Secaucus, NJ 07094-3605
Tel (201) 865-9000 *Founded/Ownrshp* 2004
Sales NA *EMP* 360
SIC 6099 7374 Automated teller machine (ATM) network; Data processing service; Automated teller machine (ATM) network; Data processing service
Pr: Stephen Rathgaber
Bd of Dir: Gary Mumford
Bd of Dir: Dale Smack
**Ex VP:* James Judd
VP: Nancy Dallier
VP: Michael Holmes
VP: Ken Ingra
VP: Armand Keim
VP: William Peirce
Exec: Goddheart Renne
Dept Mgr: John Giglio

NYCEDC
See NEW YORK CITY ECONOMIC DEVELOPMENT CORP

NYCM INSURANCE
See NEW YORK CENTRAL MUTUAL FIRE INSURANCE CO

D-U-N-S 55-631-1421
NYCO INC
(*Suby of* API GROUP INC) ★
10730 Briggs Dr Ste B, Inver Grove Heights, MN 55077-5358
Tel (651) 457-4069 *Founded/Ownrshp* 2008
Sales 23.1MM *EMP* 60
Accts Kpmg Llp
SIC 1742 Acoustical & insulation work; Acoustical & insulation work
Pr: Richard Hansen
**VP:* Curt Mages
Off Mgr: Lynda Weldon
IT Man: Katie Haag
Opers Mgr: Gregory Fredlund
Sls&Mrk Ex: Richard Hayes

D-U-N-S 09-653-5687 IMP/EXP
NYCO MINERALS INC
PARENT IS IMERYS USA
(*Suby of* S&B INDUSTRIAL MINERALS NORTH AMERICA INC) ★
803 Mountain View Dr, Willsboro, NY 12996
Tel (518) 963-4262 *Founded/Ownrshp* 2012
Sales 561.4MM^E *EMP* 100
SIC 1499 5052 3295 3291

D-U-N-S 11-907-5240
NYCOM INC
14200 Michaux Glen Dr, Midlothian, VA 23113-6876
Tel (919) 957-9545 *Founded/Ownrshp* 1983
Sales 41.2MM *EMP* 75
Accts Bdo Usa Llp Richmond Va
SIC 5049 Laboratory equipment, except medical or dental; Laboratory equipment, except medical or dental
Pr: Jonathan F Nystrom
Ex VP: Kenneth D Kanoy
Ex Dir: Ross Watson

D-U-N-S 13-923-6439 IMP
NYDJ APPAREL LLC
NOT YOUR DAUGHTERS JEANS
5401 S Soto St, Vernon, CA 90058-3618
Tel (323) 581-9040 *Founded/Ownrshp* 2014
Sales 55.7MM^E *EMP* 200
SIC 2339 Sportswear, women's; Sportswear, women's
Treas: Kate Foster
Bd of Dir: Edwin Lewis
Sr VP: Eric Ueno
Dir IT: Maarten Devos
Dir IT: Maarten Gieger

D-U-N-S 01-326-9832
NYE AUTOMOTIVE GROUP INC
NYE FORD LINCOLN MERCURY
1441 Genesee St, Oneida, NY 13421-2728
Tel (315) 363-0600 *Founded/Ownrshp* 1998
Sales 50.5MM^E *EMP* 125

SIC 5511 5012 Automobiles, new & used; Pickups, new & used; Automobiles & other motor vehicles; Automotive brokers; Automobiles, new & used; Pickups, new & used; Automobiles & other motor vehicles; Automotive brokers
Pr: William Nye
Exec: Paul Lanz
Sls Mgr: Matt Disalvo
Sls Mgr: Jesse Lazzaro

D-U-N-S 01-099-1743
NYE COUNTY SCHOOL DISTRICT (INC) (CA)
122 Military Cir, Tonopah, NV 89049
Tel (775) 727-7743 *Founded/Ownrshp* 1864
Sales 40.5MM^E *EMP* 750
Accts Daniel C Mcarthur Ltd Las
SIC 8211 Public combined elementary & secondary school; Public combined elementary & secondary school
**CFO:* Raymond Ritchie
IT Man: Seosuk Kim
Teacher Pr: Sheena Barns

NYE FORD LINCOLN MERCURY
See NYE AUTOMOTIVE GROUP INC

D-U-N-S 15-169-8842 IMP
NYGARD INC
(*Suby of* NYGARD PROPERTIES LTD)
1435 Broadway, New York, NY 10018-1909
Tel (646) 520-2000 *Founded/Ownrshp* 1988
Sales 49.8MM^E *EMP* 125
SIC 5137 Women's & children's clothing
Ch Bd: Peter J Nygard
**Pr:* Murray Batte
**CEO:* Kai Bickle Nygard
VP: David Lui
Admn Mgr: Olivia Luengas
Snr Mgr: Tony Stasiuk

NYGC
See NEW YORK GENOME CENTER INC

D-U-N-S 05-144-3027
NYHTC
707 8th Ave, New York, NY 10036-7102
Tel (646) 533-9582 *Founded/Ownrshp* 2011
Sales 22.7MM *EMP* 2^E
SIC 7011 Hotels & motels

NYISO
See NEW YORK INDEPENDENT SYSTEM OPERATOR INC

NYIT
See NEW YORK INSTITUTE OF TECHNOLOGY INC

D-U-N-S 93-774-5404
NYK GROUP AMERICAS INC
(*Suby of* NIPPON YUSEN KABUSHIKI KAISHA)
300 Lighting Way Ste 500, Secaucus, NJ 07094-3672
Tel (201) 330-3000 *Founded/Ownrshp* 1995
Sales 161.8MM^E *EMP* 400
SIC 4412 4731 4213 4011 7519 4491 Deep sea foreign transportation of freight; Agents, shipping; Trucking, except local; Railroads, line-haul operating; Utility trailer rental; Marine cargo handling; Deep sea foreign transportation of freight; Agents, shipping; Trucking, except local; Railroads, line-haul operating; Utility trailer rental; Marine cargo handling
CEO: Masao Takebayashi
**Pr:* Tomoo Kitayama
**CFO:* Peter Keller
**Treas:* Kazuhiro Kamoi
**VP:* Jeff Baker
**VP:* Peter Hsu
**VP:* Shin Matsuda
IT Man: Tan Phoo Yong
Opers Mgr: Louis Ferrer
Genl Couns: Jacob Lee

D-U-N-S 19-488-9648 IMP
NYK LINE (NORTH AMERICA) INC
NIPPON YUSEN KABUSHIKI
(*Suby of* NYK GROUP AMERICAS INC) ★
300 Lighting Way 4th, Secaucus, NJ 07094-3647
Tel (201) 330-3000 *Founded/Ownrshp* 1995
Sales 71.7MM^E *EMP* 411
SIC 4412 4731 4213 4011 7519 4491

D-U-N-S 00-798-1074 IMP
NYKO TECHNOLOGIES INC (CA)
1990 Westwood Blvd # 350, Los Angeles, CA 90025-4650
Tel (310) 446-6602 *Founded/Ownrshp* 1995, 1996
Sales 25.0MM^E *EMP* 14
SIC 5092 Video games
Pr: Herschel Naghi
**VP:* David Naghi
VP: Amir Navid
VP: Radu Popa
IT Man: Jeremy Bell
Sales Asso: Amy Matthias

D-U-N-S 36-118-9488
NYLE MAXWELL PONTIAC-GMC LTD
3000 N Interstate 35, Round Rock, TX 78681-2406
Tel (512) 244-8000 *Founded/Ownrshp* 2006
Sales 22.8MM^E *EMP* 50
SIC 5511 Automobiles, new & used
Pt: Nyle Maxwell
Genl Mgr: Tom Gammon
Sls Mgr: Chris Leboeuf
Sls Mgr: Thomas Pye
Sls Mgr: Bill Scott
Sls Mgr: Robert Walker
Sales Asso: Antonio Chico

D-U-N-S 19-531-5130
NYLEVE BRIDGE CORP
1540 Chestnut St, Emmaus, PA 18049-1914
Tel (610) 965-3083 *Founded/Ownrshp* 1987
Sales 27.0MM^E *EMP* 150
SIC 1622 Bridge construction; Bridge construction
Pr: Kevin R Schultz
**CFO:* Richard C Bauer
VP: Dave Holmes
**VP:* Scott Schultz

D-U-N-S 85-848-2508
NYLIFE LLC
(*Suby of* NEW YORK LIFE INSURANCE CO) ★
51 Madison Ave, New York, NY 10010-1603
Tel (212) 576-7000 *Founded/Ownrshp* 1984
Sales 120.5MM^E *EMP* 562
Accts Pricewaterhousecoopers Llp N
SIC 6282 6211 6733 6153 Investment advisory service; Brokers, security; Personal investment trust management; Direct working capital financing; Investment advisory service; Brokers, security; Personal investment trust management; Direct working capital financing
Ch Bd: Fredrick J Sievert
Mng Pt: Scott Norris
**Treas:* Edward T Pilner
Ex VP: Brian A Murdock
**Sr VP:* Thomas English
VP: Elizabeth A Bryson
VP: Robert Gardner
**VP:* Katherine Marrion
VP: Richard E McGee
VP: Mark Meirowitz
**VP:* Anjilo Scialabba
VP: Richard Topp
**VP:* Richard W Xuccaro
VP: Richard Zuccarro
Dir Soc: Kathy Gallant

D-U-N-S 09-696-0851 IMP/EXP
■ **NYLOK FASTENER CORP**
(*Suby of* MARMON GROUP LLC) ★
15260 Hallmark Ct, Macomb, MI 48042-4007
Tel (586) 786-0100 *Founded/Ownrshp* 1942
Sales 52.3MM^E *EMP* 328
SIC 3452 Bolts, nuts, rivets & washers; Bolts, nuts, rivets & washers
Pr: Max F Dorflinger
Pr: Greg Alaymo
VP: Scott Apel
VP: Nilo Urbani Jr
Genl Mgr: Tadashi Camey
Genl Mgr: Fijaciones Prelok
IT Man: Rick Barrera
Opers Mgr: Matt Macker
Ql Cn Mgr: Tom Stevens
VP Sls: Nilo J Urbani Jr
Sls Mgr: Joachim Kresin

NYLON MOLDING CORPORATION
See NMC GROUP INC

D-U-N-S 08-783-4714 IMP
NYLONCRAFT INC
616 W Mckinley Ave, Mishawaka, IN 46545-5597
Tel (574) 256-1521 *Founded/Ownrshp* 2001
Sales 210.5MM^E *EMP* 679
SIC 3089 Injection molding of plastics; Injection molding of plastics
COO: Bob Krzozowski
Pr: Mark Hagan
**CFO:* Don Dames
**VP:* Roland Erb
VP: Dennis Wasikowski
Prgrm Mgr: Andy Peickert
QA Dir: Pam Stallman
VP Opers: Bob Brzozowski
Ql Cn Mgr: Thomas Hyde
Sls Mgr: Tim Balk
Snr Mgr: Amy Backhus

D-U-N-S 10-105-8282
NYLONCRAFT OF MICHIGAN INC
(*Suby of* NYLONCRAFT INC) ★
1640 E Chicago Rd, Jonesville, MI 49250-9110
Tel (517) 849-9911 *Founded/Ownrshp* 2002
Sales 94.6MM^E *EMP* 260
SIC 3089 Plastic processing; Plastic processing
Ch: Glenn Scolnik
**Pr:* James Krzyzewski
CFO: John Deren
**CFO:* Lee Powers
**VP:* Roland Erb
**VP:* Terry Rensberger
Plnt Mgr: Tom Smith

D-U-N-S 82-973-4750
NYLSI INC
SUNRISE TOYOTA SCION
3984 Sunrise Hwy, Oakdale, NY 11769-1003
Tel (631) 589-9000 *Founded/Ownrshp* 2008
Sales 110.0MM *EMP* 135
SIC 5511 Automobiles, new & used; Automobiles, new & used
Ch Bd: James Berg

D-U-N-S 19-504-5646
NYMED INC
TEN BROECK COMMONS
1 Commons Dr, Lake Katrine, NY 12449-5149
Tel (845) 336-6666 *Founded/Ownrshp* 1988
Sales 23.4MM *EMP* 5
SIC 6552 Land subdividers & developers, commercial
Ch Bd: Anthony C Scalera
Ofcr: Josh Diaz
**VP:* Lewis H Titterton
Off Mgr: Judy Scott
MIS Dir: Abigail Gilman

NYMEX
See NEW YORK MERCANTILE EXCHANGE INC

D-U-N-S 36-154-6299
■ **NYMEX HOLDINGS INC**
(*Suby of* CME GROUP INC) ★
1 N End Ave Rm 1215, New York, NY 10282-1102
Tel (212) 299-2000 *Founded/Ownrshp* 2008
Sales 97.5MM^E *EMP* 635
SIC 6231 Futures exchanges, contract; Commodity contract exchanges; Stock option exchanges; Futures exchanges, contract; Commodity contract exchanges; Stock option exchanges
Pr: James Newsome
**V Ch:* Thomas Gordon
V Ch: Robert Halper
COO: Jerome H Bailey
CFO: Kenneth D Shifrin
**Ch:* Richard Schaeffer

*Treas: Frank Siciliano
Sr Cor Off: Joyce Flake
Bd of Dir: Bulkeley E Griswold
Bd of Dir: Harley Lippman
Bd of Dir: John L McNamara
Sr VP: Patrick Conroy
Sr VP: Richard D Kerschner
Sr VP: Lewis A Ribley
VP: Charles Bebel
VP: Bob Biolsi
VP: Madeline Boyd
VP: Michael Campanelli
VP: Patrick Conti
VP: George Henderson
VP: Stuart Smith

D-U-N-S 06-522-6529
NYNE EQUIPMENT INC
VERMEER NORTHEAST
1235 Route 9, Castleton On Hudson, NY 12033-9646
Tel (518) 732-7201 Founded/Ownrshp 2001
Sales 36.6MM^E EMP 35
SIC 5084 Industrial machinery & equipment
Pr: Ace Brandt
Genl Mgr: Bill King
Sls Mgr: Mike Nagengast

D-U-N-S 83-100-0583 IMP
■ NYP HOLDINGS INC
NEW YORK POST
(Suby of NEWS CORP) ★
1211 Avenue Of The Amer, New York, NY 10036-8790
Tel (212) 997-9272 Founded/Ownrshp 2013
Sales 166.0MM^E EMP 725
SIC 2711 Commercial printing & newspaper publishing combined; Commercial printing & newspaper publishing combined
Pr: K Rupert Murdoch
Ex VP: Joe Vincent
Sr VP: Howard Adler
VP: John Ancona
VP: Michael Carvalhido
VP: Michelle Dalmeida
Netwrk Mgr: Dimitri Finkler
Opers Mgr: Greg Gallo
Ql Cn Mgr: Gideon Sober
Sls Mgr: Liz Clyman
Snr Mgr: Mario Rogowicz

D-U-N-S 04-784-6531
NYPD LIAISON UNIT
1 Police Plz Rm 814b, New York, NY 10038-1497
Tel (646) 610-5984 Founded/Ownrshp 2010
Sales NA EMP 604^E
SIC 9221 Police protection
Prin: Dennis Jones
Ofcr: Claude Armstrong
Ofcr: My Baby
Ofcr: Richie Bastidas
Ofcr: Xanthe Beecher
Ofcr: Joseph Bey
Ofcr: Martin Brown
Ofcr: Walter Burnes
Ofcr: Richard Chase
Ofcr: Luis Columbie
Ofcr: Lisa Connor
Ofcr: Dennis Derienzo
Ofcr: Ceasar Diaz
Ofcr: Duane Dickerson
Ofcr: Chris Dyckman
Ofcr: Joaquin Fung
Ofcr: Steve Giaco
Ofcr: Stuart Goldstein
Ofcr: Bob Graves
Ofcr: Kevin Grogan
Ofcr: Stephen Guglielmo

D-U-N-S 83-828-4081
■ NYPRO ALABAMA LLC
(Suby of NYPRO INC) ★
208 Nypro Ln, Dothan, AL 36305-1081
Tel (334) 702-2583 Founded/Ownrshp 2013
Sales 41.2MM^E EMP 75
SIC 3089 Injection molding of plastics
Prin: Lara Marco
Exec: Jeremy Tolbert
Plnt Mgr: Kirk Kirkland

D-U-N-S 80-897-7342 IMP
■ NYPRO ASHEVILLE INC
(Suby of NYPRO INC) ★
100 Vista Blvd, Arden, NC 28704-9457
Tel (828) 684-3141 Founded/Ownrshp 1987
Sales 80.3MM^E EMP 200
SIC 3089 Injection molding of plastics; Injection molding of plastics
Pr: Ted Lapres
Prgrm Mgr: Randall Harrison
Telecom Ex: Sheldon Davis
Mtls Mgr: Rhonda Ruth
Ql Cn Mgr: Michael Giblin

D-U-N-S 80-906-3761
■ NYPRO CHICAGO INC
(Suby of NYPRO INC) ★
955 Tri State Pkwy, Gurnee, IL 60031-5113
Tel (847) 855-2200 Founded/Ownrshp 1993
Sales 45.6MM^E EMP 125
SIC 3089 Injection molded finished plastic products; Injection molded finished plastic products
Pr: Gordon Lankton
CFO: Ben Paramore
Prgrm Mgr: Brian Hessel

D-U-N-S 80-881-0543 IMP
■ NYPRO HEALTHCARE BAJA INC
NYPRO PRECISION ASSEMBLIES
(Suby of NYPRO INC) ★
2195 Britannia Blvd # 107, San Diego, CA 92154-6290
Tel (619) 498-9250 Founded/Ownrshp 2002
Sales 189.7MM^E EMP 600
SIC 3841 3679 Surgical & medical instruments; Electronic circuits; Surgical & medical instruments; Electronic circuits
Ch: Joe Borden
*Pr: Courtney Ryan
*Treas: Thomas J Flannery

D-U-N-S 04-613-1678 IMP
■ NYPRO INC
(Suby of JABIL CIRCUIT INC) ★
101 Union St, Clinton, MA 01510-2935
Tel (978) 365-8100 Founded/Ownrshp 2013
Sales 3.1MMM^E EMP 16,000
SIC 3089 3559 7389 8711 Injection molding of plastics; Robots, molding & forming plastics; Design, commercial & industrial; Engineering services; Injection molding of plastics; Robots, molding & forming plastics; Design, commercial & industrial; Engineering services
Pr: Courtney Ryan
*Pr: Gregory G Adams
*Treas: Sergio Cadavid
Bd of Dir: Peter Benkiewicz
Ofcr: Tara Shirley
VP: S Patrick
VP: Eric Pettes
VP: Thomas Taylor
Prgrm Mgr: Keith Abramowicz
Prgrm Mgr: Meredith Canty
Prgrm Mgr: Chuck Duby

D-U-N-S 12-992-8743 IMP/EXP
■ NYPRO INC
(Suby of NYPRO INC) ★
1018 Corporate Park Dr, Mebane, NC 27302-8368
Tel (919) 304-1415 Founded/Ownrshp 1955
Sales 3.2MM^E EMP 300
SIC 3089

D-U-N-S 78-486-2054 IMP
■ NYPRO KANAAK IOWA INC
(Suby of JABIL CIRCUIT LLC) ★
400 N Harvey Rd, Mount Pleasant, IA 52641-3100
Tel (319) 385-4426 Founded/Ownrshp 1997
Sales 27.3MM^E EMP 65
SIC 3089 Injection molding of plastics
Ch Bd: Chris McNeil
Exec: Shawn Moffit
Prgrm Mgr: Bill Chalupa

NYPRO PRECISION ASSEMBLIES
See NYPRO HEALTHCARE BAJA INC

D-U-N-S 09-041-4988 IMP/EXP
■ NYPRO PUERTO RICO INC
(Suby of NYPRO INC) ★
15 Ave Luis Mnoz Rivera S, Cayey, PR 00736-4701
Tel (787) 738-4211 Founded/Ownrshp 1973
Sales 139.0MM^E EMP 500
SIC 3089 Injection molded finished plastic products; Injection molded finished plastic products
Pr: Courtney Ryan
*Treas: Nicholas D Aznoian
*Treas: Sergio Cadavid
*VP: Reynaldo Encarnacion

D-U-N-S 19-458-3043 IMP
NYPROMOLD INC
144 Pleasant St, Clinton, MA 01510-3416
Tel (978) 365-4547 Founded/Ownrshp 1987
Sales 25.8MM^E EMP 144
SIC 3544 Industrial molds; Industrial molds
Pr: William Muldoon
*Treas: John Casali
Prgrm Mgr: Chris Bussiere
Prgrm Mgr: Steve Shurtleff
Mktg Dir: David Butler
Snr Mgr: William Batchelor
Snr Mgr: Eric Towle

D-U-N-S 00-170-7371 IMP/EXP
NYRA INC
BELMONT PARK
11000 Rockaway Blvd Ste 1, Jamaica, NY 11420-1010
Tel (718) 641-4700 Founded/Ownrshp 1955
Sales 104.1MM^E EMP 1,300
SIC 7948 Horse race track operation; Horse race track operation
Ch: David Skorton
*Pr: Anthony J Bonomo
*COO: Steven Duncker
*COO: Peter Karches
COO: Thuy Trinh
CFO: Edward Farrell
*CFO: Alexander W Ingle
Treas: Ross Didia
Ofcr: John Ryan
*VP: Rick Cotton
VP: John Giombarrese
VP: Scott Molina
Dir Risk M: Nicole Katz
Board of Directors: John W Meriwether, Daniel P Tully, H Douglas Barclay, Paul F Oreffice, Peggy Vandervoort, Allan R Dragone, John H Peace, Charles V Wait, Robert S Evans, Ogden Mills Phipps, Jobruces-llewellyn, Richard L Gelb, Dolph Rotfeld, Richard Giancola, Lewis Rudin, Charles E Hayward, Peter G Schiff, John A Hettinger, Barry K Schwartz, Earle I Mack, Joseph V Shields Jr, Timothy M McGinn, Delbert Staley

D-U-N-S 13-105-6178 IMP
NYRSTAR CLARKSVILLE INC
(Suby of NYRSTAR NV)
1800 Zinc Plant Rd, Clarksville, TN 37040
Tel (931) 552-4200 Founded/Ownrshp 2007
Sales 28.8MM^E EMP 250^E
SIC 3339

D-U-N-S 96-213-3653
NYRSTAR HOLDINGS INC
1800 Zinc Plant Rd, Clarksville, TN 37040
Tel (931) 552-4200 Founded/Ownrshp 1994
Sales 59.0MM^E EMP 259^E
SIC 6719 Investment holding companies, except banks; Investment holding companies, except banks
Genl Mgr: Matt Howell
Snr Mgr: Dominic Ahiakpor
Snr Mgr: Andrew Dean

D-U-N-S 02-318-2403 IMP
NYRSTAR TENNESSEE MINES - GORDONSVILLE LLC
(Suby of NYRSTAR NV)
120 Zinc Mine Cir, Gordonsville, TN 38563-2136
Tel (615) 683-6411 Founded/Ownrshp 2009
Sales 24.9MM^E EMP 92^E
SIC 1081 Metal mining services
CIO: Gabriel Cervera
Snr Mgr: Jason Cagle
Snr Mgr: Paul Dibbens

NYRT
See NEW YORK REIT INC

NYS DEPARTMENT TRANSPORTATION
See NEW YORK DEPARTMENT OF TRANSPORTATION

NYS DPRTMENT CORRECTIONAL SVCS
See NEW YORK DEPARTMENT OF CORRECTIONS AND COMMUNITY SUPERVISION

D-U-N-S 83-685-7404
NYS POLICE INVESTIGATORS ASSOCIATION EMERGENCY ASSISTANCE FUND INC
11 N Pearl St, Albany, NY 12207-2709
Tel (518) 436-0120 Founded/Ownrshp 2007
Sales 43.9M EMP 1,000
Accts Staff Ciampino & Company Pc
SIC 8631 Labor unions & similar labor organizations; Labor unions & similar labor organizations
Pr: Jeffrey J Keysar
*Sec: Brian Meier

D-U-N-S 06-682-5191
NYS TEACHERS RETIREMENT SYSTEM INC
NYSTRS
10 Corporate Woods Dr, Albany, NY 12211-2395
Tel (518) 447-2900 Founded/Ownrshp 1921
Sales NA EMP 300
SIC 6371 Pension funds; Pension funds
CEO: George Philip
*Pr: Joseph Mc Laughlin
*CFO: Arthur Hewig
Ofcr: James Bone
Ofcr: Ryan Morse
Ofcr: Dawn Msherman
Ofcr: David Tessitore
Dir Risk M: Noreen Jones
*Ex Dir: Thomas K Lee
Netwrk Mgr: Kevin Schaefer
Snr Mgr: John Rosenburg

D-U-N-S 10-193-0621
NYSARC
AHRC NEW YORK CITY
252 W 29th St Rm 700, New York, NY 10001-5271
Tel (212) 780-2500 Founded/Ownrshp 1981
Sales 227.3MM EMP 2
SIC 8322 Association for the handicapped; Association for the handicapped
Prin: Steve Towler
Assoc Dir: John Keer

D-U-N-S 02-924-4852
NYSARC INC
NYSARC OF ORANGE COUNTY
(Suby of NYSARC INC) ★
249 Broadway, Newburgh, NY 12550-5452
Tel (845) 561-0670 Founded/Ownrshp 1949
Sales 30.5MM EMP 650
SIC 8361 Home for the mentally retarded; Home for the mentally retarded
Pr: Gray K Fox
*CFO: Lis Goris
*Ex Dir: Christpoher Fortune

D-U-N-S 06-054-7221
NYSARC INC
SCHENECTADY COUNTY CHAPTER
(Suby of NYSARC INC) ★
214 State St, Schenectady, NY 12305-1806
Tel (518) 372-1160 Founded/Ownrshp 1952
Sales 28.5MM EMP 500
Accts Bonadio & Co Llp Syracuse Ny
SIC 8361 Home for the mentally handicapped; Home for the mentally handicapped
Ex Dir: Kirk Lewis
Treas: John Bresonis
Bd of Dir: Tammy Krisher
VP: Richard Bonaker
Admn Mgr: Bev Salvo
Dir IT: Lonnie Hojnacki

D-U-N-S 07-525-9507 IMP/EXP
NYSARC INC
393 Delaware Ave, Delmar, NY 12054-3094
Tel (518) 439-8311 Founded/Ownrshp 1949
Sales 1.3MMM^E EMP 28,000
Accts Bonadio & Co Llp Pittsford
SIC 8361 8322 8093 8331 Rehabilitation center, residential: health care incidental; Association for the handicapped; Rehabilitation center, outpatient treatment; Job training & vocational rehabilitation services; Rehabilitation center, residential: health care incidental; Association for the handicapped; Rehabilitation center, outpatient treatment; Job training & vocational rehabilitation services
Pr: John A Schuppenhauer
V Ch: Susan Limongello
*CFO: John J Sherman Jr
Comm Dir: Jason White
*Ex Dir: Marc N Brandt
MIS Dir: Robert Goodman
Opers Mgr: Candace Johnstone
Genl Couns: Tara Ellinger
Counsel: Kathryn Jerian

D-U-N-S 13-672-6564
NYSARC INC
ASSOC FOR HELP
(Suby of NYSARC INC) ★
83 Maiden Ln, New York, NY 10038-4812
Tel (212) 780-2635 Founded/Ownrshp 1949
Sales 232.4MM^E EMP 2,000
SIC 8099 Health systems agency; Blood related health services
CFO: Amy West
*Pr: Laura J Kennedy
Trst Ofcr: Joseph Livote
*VP: Raymond Ferrigno
*VP: Gail Fishkind
*VP: Marilyn Jaffe Ruiz
*VP: Sharyn Vanreepinghen

D-U-N-S 16-595-9594
NYSARC INC
WARREN, WASHINGTON
436 Quaker Rd, Queensbury, NY 12804-1535
Tel (518) 761-9465 Founded/Ownrshp 1962
Sales 28.7MM^E EMP 850
SIC 8322 8052 Social service center; Intermediate care facilities; Social service center; Intermediate care facilities
Ex Dir: John Von Ahn

D-U-N-S 79-806-8763
NYSARC INC
1439 Buffalo St, Olean, NY 14760-1140
Tel (716) 375-4747 Founded/Ownrshp 1958
Sales 18.3MM EMP 500
Accts Bryans & Gramuglia Cpas Llc
SIC 8322 Rehabilitation services; Rehabilitation services
Pr: James Bellanca
*CFO: Melinda Buckley
Ex Dir: David Zorn

D-U-N-S 07-958-2374
NYSARC INC - SUFFOLK CHAPTER
AHRC SUFFOLK
2900 Veterans Mem Hwy, Bohemia, NY 11716-1022
Tel (631) 585-0100 Founded/Ownrshp 2013
Sales 68.9MM EMP 12
Accts Baker Tilly Virchow Krause Llp
SIC 8322 Social services for the handicapped
CFO: Kathleen Frigiola
COO: Lisa Bochner

D-U-N-S 07-400-6628
NYSARC INC CATTARAUGUS COUNTY CHAPTER
(Suby of NYSARC INC) ★
1439 Buffalo St, Olean, NY 14760-1140
Tel (716) 375-4747 Founded/Ownrshp 2000
Sales 17.4MM EMP 540
SIC 8361 Rehabilitation center, residential: health care incidental; Rehabilitation center, residential: health care incidental
Prin: Mari Howard
Prgrm Mgr: Tracey Spears
IT Man: Lisa Sagona
Pr Dir: Roxanne Padlo
Mktg Mgr: Brian Eddy

D-U-N-S 96-723-9893
NYSARC INC FULTON COUNTY CHAPTER
465 N Perry St, Johnstown, NY 12095-1014
Tel (518) 773-7931 Founded/Ownrshp 2011
Sales 84.0MM EMP 3^E
Accts Loeb & Troper Llp New York N
SIC 8641 Social associations; Social associations
Prin: Matthew Johnston

D-U-N-S 07-730-8161
NYSARC INC MADISON COURTLAND CHAPTER
ALTERNATIVES RECYCLING CENTER
(Suby of NYSARC INC) ★
701 Lenox Ave, Oneida, NY 13421-1500
Tel (315) 363-3389 Founded/Ownrshp 1968
Sales 21.7MM EMP 210
SIC 8322 8331 Individual & family services; Association for the handicapped; Sheltered workshop; Individual & family services; Association for the handicapped; Sheltered workshop
Ex Dir: Jack Campbell
Ofcr: Sally West
Ex VP: Penny Palmer
Sr VP: Deresa Durkee
VP: Russell Brewer
VP Opers: Jonathan Maisey
VP Opers: Deborah Stickels
S&M/VP: Gina Rossi

D-U-N-S 09-246-5285
NYSARC INC NIAGARA COUNTY CHAPTER
OPPORTNITIES UNLIMITED NIAGARA
2393 Niagara Falls Blvd, Niagara Falls, NY 14304-4561
Tel (716) 297-2625 Founded/Ownrshp 1949
Sales 21.3MM^E EMP 550
SIC 8322 Social services for the handicapped; Social services for the handicapped
Pr: Connie Brown
*CFO: Charlene McDonald

D-U-N-S 05-169-3588
NYSARC INC ONTARIO COUNTY CHAPTER
ABBEY INDUSTRIES
(Suby of NYSARC INC) ★
3071 County Complex Dr, Canandaigua, NY 14424-9505
Tel (585) 394-7500 Founded/Ownrshp 1980
Sales 22.7MM EMP 390^E
Accts Bonadio & Co Llp Pittsford N
SIC 8331 6513 8011 Vocational rehabilitation agency; Apartment building operators; Clinic, operated by physicians; Vocational rehabilitation agency; Apartment building operators; Clinic, operated by physicians
Ex Dir: William J Castiglione

D-U-N-S 96-774-9354
NYSARC INC RENSSELAER COUNTY CHAPTER
79 102nd St, Troy, NY 12180-1125
Tel (518) 274-3110 Founded/Ownrshp 2011
Sales 26.4MM EMP 29^E
Accts Bonadio & Co Llp Albany Ny

SIC 8611 Business associations; Business associations
Pr: Clarence Weatherspoon

NYSARC OF ORANGE COUNTY
See NYSARC INC

NYSE AMEX
See NYSE MKT LLC

D-U-N-S 79-475-9840
■ NYSE EURONEXT HOLDINGS LLC
(*Suby of* ICE) ★
11 Wall St, New York, NY 10005-1905
Tel (212) 656-3000 *Founded/Ownrshp* 2013
Sales 1.9MMM^E *EMP* 3,079^E
SIC 6231 Security exchanges; Stock exchanges; Security exchanges; Stock exchanges
CEO: Duncan L Niederauer
Pr: Bruce Davis
Pr: Thomas W Farley
COO: Stacey Cunningham
COO: Lawrence E Leibowitz
COO: Michael Urkonis
CFO: Michael S Geltzeiler
CFO: Frank Nairne
Chf Cred: Janice Neill
Bd of Dir: Andre Bergen
Ofcr: Ian Wolff
Ex VP: Gabriella Bell
Ex VP: Bruce Bourque
Ex VP: Dennis Carangelo
Ex VP: Daniel Douglas
Ex VP: Richard A Edgar
Ex VP: David Fainer
Ex VP: Dana Ferguson
Ex VP: Byron Friedman
Ex VP: Dawn Furner
Ex VP: Jennie Halbert

NYSE GROUP
See ARCHIPELAGO HOLDINGS INC

D-U-N-S 61-961-7728
■ NYSE GROUP INC
(*Suby of* NYSE EURONEXT HOLDINGS LLC) ★
11 Wall St, New York, NY 10005-1905
Tel (212) 656-3000 *Founded/Ownrshp* 2006
Sales 649.9MM^E *EMP* 1,975
SIC 6231 6289 Security & commodity exchanges; Security exchanges; Stock exchanges; Stock option exchanges; Exchange clearinghouses, security; Stock transfer agents; Security & commodity exchanges; Security exchanges; Stock exchanges; Stock option exchanges; Exchange clearinghouses, security; Stock transfer agents
CEO: Duncan L Niederauer
**Ch Bd:* Marshall N Carter
**Pr:* Gerald D Putnam
**CFO:* Nelson Chai
Ex VP: Dale B Bernstein
Ex VP: Albert Bocchetti
**Ex VP:* Kevin J P Ohara
**Ex VP:* Rachel F Robbins
**Sr VP:* William Freeman
VP: David W Bartges
VP: Michael Ferraro
VP: Vincent Lanzillo
VP: Anand Rufino
Exec: Faith A Peyser
Comm Man: Marissa Arnold

D-U-N-S 00-166-6379
■ NYSE MKT LLC
NYSE AMEX
(*Suby of* NYSE EURONEXT HOLDINGS LLC) ★
11 Wall St, New York, NY 10005-1905
Tel (212) 656-3000 *Founded/Ownrshp* 1849, 2008
Sales 60.1MM^E *EMP* 425
SIC 6231 Stock exchanges; Stock exchanges
Ch Bd: Neal L Wolkoff
**V Ch:* Phillip Frost
**Pr:* Patricia Rado
Bd of Dir: Pete Schwarz
**Ofcr:* Claudia Crowley
**Ex VP:* Richard T Chase
**Ex VP:* Antoine Shagoury
Ex VP: Clifford Weber
Sr VP: Claudia O Crowley
**Sr VP:* David Harris
Sr VP: Robert J Rendine
**Sr VP:* Fred Yager

NYSED
See EDUCATION DEPARTMENT NEW YORK STATE

NYSID
See NEW YORK STATE INDUSTRIES FOR DISABLED INC

NYSIF
See INSURANCE FUND NEW YORK STATE

NYSIR
See NEW YORK SCHOOLS INSURANCE RECIPROCAL

NYSNA
See NEW YORK STATE NURSES ASSOCIATION

NYSPEF
See NEW YORK STATE PUBLIC EMPLOYEE FEDERATION

NYSTROM BUILDING PRODUCTS
See NYSTROM INC

D-U-N-S 00-625-4742 IMP
NYSTROM INC (MN)
NYSTROM BUILDING PRODUCTS
9300 73rd Ave N, Minneapolis, MN 55428-1013
Tel (763) 488-9200 *Founded/Ownrshp* 1958, 1986
Sales 26.6MM^E *EMP* 177^E
SIC 3444 3316 Sheet metalwork; Cold finishing of steel shapes; Sheet metalwork; Cold finishing of steel shapes
Ch Bd: James T Nystrom
COO: Frank Parsons
CFO: Gretchen Kelly
CFO: Sue Thomas
Chf Mktg O: John Danio
Area Mgr: Scott Kerber
Area Mgr: Broc McConville
Area Mgr: Stefan Reuther
CIO: Patrick Irestone
DP Exec: Mike Carroll
IT Man: Adam Sartor

NYSTRS
See NYS TEACHERS RETIREMENT SYSTEM INC

D-U-N-S 10-721-2664 IMP
NYTEF PLASTICS LTD
(*Suby of* NYTEF GROUP, INC.)
6643 42nd Ter N, Riviera Beach, FL 33407-1212
Tel (561) 840-9499 *Founded/Ownrshp* 1979
Sales 26.0MM^E *EMP* 80
SIC 5162 3083 3082 Plastics materials; Laminated plastics plate & sheet; Unsupported plastics profile shapes; Plastics materials; Laminated plastics plate & sheet; Unsupported plastics profile shapes
CEO: Morton R French Jr
**CFO:* Richard Rose
IT Man: Marco Villafane
Sls Mgr: Hampton Craig
Sales Asso: Agnes Kuchler

NYTP
See NEW YORK TECHNOLOGY PARTNERS INC

D-U-N-S 05-017-8515
NYU
120 Sullivan St Apt 1b, New York, NY 10012-3655
Tel (212) 998-1212 *Founded/Ownrshp* 2010
Sales 132.8MM^E *EMP* 2,457^E
SIC 8221 Colleges universities & professional schools
Prin: Rimalovski Frank
Dir Lab: Gloria Coruzzi
Dir Bus: Sujeet Kulkarni
Adm Dir: Marcia Thomas
Ex Dir: Hayley Maier
Admn Mgr: Mayra Pabon
Admn Mgr: Prudence Ting
Dir IT: Nancy Lee
Obsttrcn: Manuel Alvarez
Obsttrcn: Frances Hooper
Obsttrcn: Kenneth Levey

NYU COLLEGE OF NURSING
See NEW YORK UNIVERSITY

D-U-N-S 07-103-6685
NYU HOSPITAL FOR JOINT DISEASES
(*Suby of* NYU HOSPITALS CENTER) ★
301 E 17th St Fl 14, New York, NY 10003-3804
Tel (212) 598-6000 *Founded/Ownrshp* 1905
Sales 62.9MM^E *EMP* 1,343
Accts Ernst & Young Llp New York N
SIC 8069 Orthopedic hospital; Orthopedic hospital
Pr: David Dibner
**Pr:* Robert Grossman
**Sr VP:* David A Dibner
VP: Wesley Smith
**Dir Surg:* Alex Malarchuk
Off Admin: Leslie Haber
MIS Dir: Paul Scotto
Surgeon: Kenneth Egol
Surgeon: Kirill Ilalov
Surgeon: Patrick Meere
Pharmcst: Young Lee

D-U-N-S 82-854-3236 IMP
NYU HOSPITALS CENTER
NYU MEDICAL CENTER
(*Suby of* NY U) ★
550 1st Ave, New York, NY 10016-6402
Tel (212) 263-7300 *Founded/Ownrshp* 1997
Sales 2.1MMM *EMP* 20,424^E
Accts Pricewaterhousecoopers
SIC 8062 General medical & surgical hospitals; Education services, insurance; General medical & surgical hospitals
CEO: Robert I Grossman
Ofcr: Andrew Brotman
Ofcr: Gary Cohn
Ofcr: Richard Crater
Ofcr: Elizabeth Dater
Ex VP: Darla Moore
**Sr VP:* Michael T Burke
Assoc Dir: Hilda Pineda-Lopez
Admn Mgr: Matt Cipriano
Admn Mgr: Amy Pazmino
Ansthlgy: David Albert

NYU LANGONE MEDICAL CENTER
See NEW YORK UNIVERSITY MEDICAL CENTER

NYU LUTHERAN FAMILY HLTH CTRS
See SUNSET PARK HEALTH COUNCIL INC

D-U-N-S 06-829-2572
NYU LUTHERAN MEDICAL CENTER (NY)
150 55th St, Brooklyn, NY 11220-2508
Tel (718) 630-7000 *Founded/Ownrshp* 1883
Sales 1.0MM *EMP* 3,000
Accts Deloitte Tax Llp Jericho Ny
SIC 8062 8621 General medical & surgical hospitals; Professional membership organizations; General medical & surgical hospitals; Professional membership organizations
Pr: Wendy Goldstein
Pt: Mary Qui Ones
Pr: Amy Mugavero
**Ex VP:* Richard Langfelder
Ex VP: Jeanne Lee
**Sr VP:* Michael Parks
**VP:* Claudia Caine
VP: William Dionne
VP: Louis Guarino
VP: Barry Kohn
VP: Patricia Lavely
VP: Mary Tirolo
Dir OR: Jose Hernandez
Assoc Dir: Catherine Madden
Dir Rad: Jayanth RAO

NYU MEDICAL CENTER
See NYU HOSPITALS CENTER

NYU-POLY
See POLYTECHNIC INSTITUTE OF NEW YORK UNIVERSITY

NYX COSMETICS
See NYX LOS ANGELES INC

D-U-N-S 03-860-5341 IMP
NYX INC
NYX TECHNOLOGIES
36111 Schoolcraft Rd, Livonia, MI 48150-1216
Tel (734) 462-2385 *Founded/Ownrshp* 1989
Sales 752.2MM^E *EMP* 1,800
SIC 3089 3714 3565 2671 Injection molding of plastics; Motor vehicle parts & accessories; Packaging machinery; Packaging paper & plastics film, coated & laminated; Injection molding of plastics; Motor vehicle parts & accessories; Packaging machinery; Packaging paper & plastics film, coated & laminated
CEO: Chain S Sandhu
**Pr:* Jatinder-Bir S Sandhu
CFO: Mark Greer
VP: Lev Lilov
Genl Mgr: Dan Taylor
CTO: Greg Homann
Plnt Mgr: Dennis Dunlop
Plnt Mgr: Steve Huchkins
Plnt Mgr: Andy Sandhu
Sls Mgr: Mike Brook

D-U-N-S 12-844-6122 IMP
NYX LOS ANGELES INC
NYX COSMETICS
2201 E El Segundo Blvd, El Segundo, CA 90245-4608
Tel (323) 869-9420 *Founded/Ownrshp* 1999
Sales 45.1MM^E *EMP* 140
SIC 2844 5122 Cosmetics; Toilet preparations; Toilet preparations; Cosmetics
CEO: Scott Friedman
CFO: Arash Khazei
VP: Phillip Lee
VP: Jeffrey Zehngut
Prin: Toni Ko
Genl Mgr: Edna Uballe
VP Opers: Michael Begley
Manager: Carlos Guzman
Sls Mgr: Steve Pak
Art Dir: Ai Yoshida

NYX TECHNOLOGIES
See NYX INC

D-U-N-S 15-108-1382 IMP/EXP
NZG SPECIALTIES INC
GOURMET TRADING COMPANY
2580 Santa Fe Ave, Redondo Beach, CA 90278-1116
Tel (310) 216-7575 *Founded/Ownrshp* 1999
Sales 26.4MM^E *EMP* 75^E
SIC 2034 Dehydrated fruits, vegetables, soups; Dried & dehydrated soup mixes; Dried & dehydrated vegetables; Fruit juices, dehydrated; Dehydrated fruits, vegetables, soups; Dried & dehydrated soup mixes; Dried & dehydrated vegetables; Fruit juices, dehydrated
CEO: Brian R Miller
**Pr:* Christopher M Martin
Off Mgr: Mary Ramos
Mktg Mgr: Julia Richardson
Sls Mgr: Kristen Francisco

D-U-N-S 80-753-2184
NZR RETAIL OF TOLEDO INC
4820 Monroe St, Toledo, OH 43623-4310
Tel (419) 490-8080 *Founded/Ownrshp* 2004
Sales 110.0MM *EMP* 85
SIC 5172 Gasoline; Gasoline
CEO: Nick Hasan
**Prin:* Yazeed Qaimari

O

D-U-N-S 01-883-8136 IMP/EXP
O & G INDUSTRIES INC
112 Wall St, Torrington, CT 06790-5464
Tel (860) 489-9261 *Founded/Ownrshp* 1923
Sales 524.4MM^E *EMP* 1,000
SIC 1542 1541 1611 1623 5032 2951

D-U-N-S 02-351-5752 EXP
O & H DANISH BAKERY INC
OLESEN'S FAMILY BAKERY
1841 Douglas Ave, Racine, WI 53402-4611
Tel (262) 631-5398 *Founded/Ownrshp* 1964
Sales 24.3MM^E *EMP* 150
SIC 5461 Bakeries
Pr: Eric Olesen
Pr: Chris Henkes
**VP:* Peter Olesen
Exec: Mary Andersen
Opers Mgr: Wade Nalson
VP Mktg: Matt Horton

D-U-N-S 60-232-7876 IMP
O & K AMERICAN CORP
(*Suby of* O&K COMPANY LIMITED)
4630 W 55th St, Chicago, IL 60632-4908
Tel (773) 767-2500 *Founded/Ownrshp* 1987
Sales 31.0MM^E *EMP* 120
SIC 3312 Blast furnace & related products; Blast furnace & related products
Ch: Takao Oku
**Pr:* Kazuta Oku
Mfg Mgr: Michal Pasek
Manager: Herb Gottelt

D-U-N-S 61-099-4311 IMP
O & K INC
ONE CLOTHING
2121 E 37th St, Vernon, CA 90058-1416
Tel (323) 846-5700 *Founded/Ownrshp* 1989
Sales 45.1MM^E *EMP* 135^E
SIC 5137 Women's & children's clothing; Women's & children's clothing
CEO: Chang Ho OK
**Pr:* Seongeun Kim

D-U-N-S 00-478-0219
O & M INDUSTRIES (CA)
O & M SOUTH
5901 Ericson Way, Arcata, CA 95521-9239
Tel (707) 822-8800 *Founded/Ownrshp* 1946
Sales 21.4MM *EMP* 120
SIC 1711 1761 1791

D-U-N-S 61-043-7811
O & M RESTAURANT GROUP INC
BURGER KING
1000 W Wilshire Blvd # 203, Oklahoma City, OK 73116-7036
Tel (405) 840-4180 *Founded/Ownrshp* 2005
Sales 35.0MM *EMP* 832
SIC 5812 Fast-food restaurant, chain; Fast-food restaurant, chain
Pr: David Ostrowe
**VP:* Tim Morgan

O & M SOUTH
See O & M INDUSTRIES

D-U-N-S 18-508-8598 IMP
O & S CALIFORNIA INC
OSCA-ARCOSA
(*Suby of* ONAMBA CO., LTD.)
9731 Siempre Viva Rd E, San Diego, CA 92154-7200
Tel (619) 661-1800 *Founded/Ownrshp* 1986
Sales 183.5MM^E *EMP* 400
SIC 3699 Electrical equipment & supplies; Electrical equipment & supplies
Pr: Kazuo Murata
CFO: Hiroshi Kawa
**VP:* Jos Luis Furlong
Sls Mgr: Hiro Kawamata
Sls Mgr: Tsuji Moto
Sls Mgr: Ted Schmidt

D-U-N-S 16-649-6237 IMP
O & W INC
3003 William Ave, Ypsilanti, MI 48198-9118
Tel (734) 480-4012 *Founded/Ownrshp* 2004
Sales 27.7MM^E *EMP* 67^E
SIC 5181 Beer & ale
Pr: Jim Wanty
Ex VP: Doug Wanty
**Prin:* Douglas W Wanty
Sls Mgr: Ryan Harris

O A C A C
See OZARKS AREA COMMUNITY ACTION CORP

D-U-N-S 00-234-6716 IMP
O A NEWTON & SON CO
16356 Sussex Hwy Unit 1, Bridgeville, DE 19933-3056
Tel (302) 337-3782 *Founded/Ownrshp* 1916
Sales 28.6MM^E *EMP* 32
SIC 5084 5083 3599 Industrial machinery & equipment; Materials handling machinery; Irrigation equipment; Machine shop, jobbing & repair
Pr: Robert F Rider Jr
VP: Leon Salter
VP: Rob Shugdinis
VP: Bill Warner

O A T S
See OATS INC

O B I
See OBI HOLDING CO

O B M
See OHIO BUSINESS MACHINES LLC

D-U-N-S 03-413-5124
O B SPORTS GOLF MANAGEMENT LLC (OR)
7025 E Greenway Pkwy # 550, Scottsdale, AZ 85254-2159
Tel (480) 948-1300 *Founded/Ownrshp* 1997
Sales 32.1MM^E *EMP* 114
SIC 8741 Management services
COO: Phil Green
Pr: Tom Colceri
**Pr:* C A Roberts III
**Ch:* Orrin Vincent
**Sr VP:* Doc Belitz
Sr VP: Mike Conner
**Sr VP:* David Goff
Sr VP: Mark Woodward
VP: Tom Christy
Genl Mgr: Brian Jones
Off Admin: Beth Forwark

D-U-N-S 00-256-9572 IMP
O BERK CO L L C
3 Milltown Ct, Union, NJ 07083-8108
Tel (908) 810-2267 *Founded/Ownrshp* 1921, 1972
Sales 56.7MM^E *EMP* 100
SIC 5085 Commercial containers; Glass bottles; Plastic bottles; Crowns & closures, metal; Commercial containers; Glass bottles; Plastic bottles; Crowns & closures, metal
Pr: Jose Gaston
Ex VP: James Sheehan
VP: Marc Gaelen
Opers Mgr: Jim Anderson
Sls&Mrk Ex: Joel Simpson
Mktg Dir: Ashley Phillips
Sls Mgr: Barbara Greenfield

D-U-N-S 18-860-1678 EXP
O C A LLC
ALMOND OIL CO
504 Se Williston Rd, Gainesville, FL 32641-9704
Tel (352) 376-5131 *Founded/Ownrshp* 1987
Sales 28.9MM^E *EMP* 25
SIC 5172 Diesel fuel; Gasoline
Pr: Gary Almond

O C C
See OFFICE OF THE COMPTROLLER OF THE CURRENCY

O C I
See ORASCOM E&C USA INC

O C I
See ONCOLOGY/HEMATOLOGY CARE INC PSC

D-U-N-S 05-908-2008
O C I INC
GRAFT OIL CO
2561 Memorial Blvd, Connellsville, PA 15425-1413
Tel (724) 628-9580 *Founded/Ownrshp* 1998
Sales 46.0MM^E *EMP* 135
SIC 5171 5541 5141 Petroleum bulk stations; Gasoline service stations; Groceries, general line; Petroleum bulk stations; Gasoline service stations; Groceries, general line
Pr: Richard Franks
VP: Ned Franks
**VP:* R E Franks Jr

D-U-N-S 00-945-3101
O C MCDONALD CO INC (CA)
1150 W San Carlos St, San Jose, CA 95126-3440
Tel (408) 295-2182 *Founded/Ownrshp* 1906
Sales 53.8MM^E *EMP* 150
SIC 1711 3585 3541 3444 3432 Mechanical contractor; Refrigeration & heating equipment; Machine tools, metal cutting type; Sheet metalwork; Plumbing fixture fittings & trim; Mechanical contractor; Refrigeration & heating equipment; Machine tools, metal cutting type; Sheet metalwork; Plumbing fixture fittings & trim
Pr: James Mc Donald

O C P
See OCP CONTRACTORS INC

O C P
See OREGON CATHOLIC PRESS

O C P
See OPTICAL COMMUNICATION PRODUCTS INC

O C R
See ORTHOPAEDIC & SPINE CENTER OF ROCKIES PC

O C S
See ONONDAGA CENTRAL SCHOOL DISTRICT

D-U-N-S 03-304-1955
O C T EQUIPMENT LLC
7100 Sw 3rd St, Oklahoma City, OK 73128-2704
Tel (405) 789-6812 *Founded/Ownrshp* 1953
Sales 38.1MM^E *EMP* 135^E
SIC 5082 Road construction equipment
VP: Jim Doughty
Sls Mgr: Bob Sneed

D-U-N-S 00-194-7688 IMP
O C TANNER CO (UT)
THANKS
1930 S State St, Salt Lake City, UT 84115-2383
Tel (801) 486-2430 *Founded/Ownrshp* 1927
Sales 344.1MM *EMP* 1,700
SIC 3911 2759 2741 Pins (jewelry), precious metal; Commercial printing; Invitation & stationery printing & engraving; Announcements: engraved; Yearbooks: publishing & printing; Pins (jewelry), precious metal; Commercial printing; Invitation & stationery printing & engraving; Announcements: engraved; Yearbooks: publishing & printing
Pr: David Petersen
Ch Bd: Carolyn Tanner Irish
COO: Scott Sperry
Ofcr: Niel Nickolaisen
Ex VP: John McVeigh
Ex VP: Gary Peterson
Ex VP: Cynthia Rodman
Ex VP: David Sturt
Ex VP: Beth Thornton
Sr VP: Steve Kimball
VP: Joyce Anderson
VP: Gail Bedke
VP: Mike Cullins
VP: Greg Graham
VP: Harrison Hodges
VP: Christine Kubert
VP: Susan Patt
VP: Paul Terry
VP: Spencer Toomey
VP: Charlie Wall
VP: Julie Walters

D-U-N-S 00-907-3149 IMP
O C TANNER MANUFACTURING (UT)
THANKS
(*Suby of* O C TANNER CO) ★
1930 S State St, Salt Lake City, UT 84115-2311
Tel (801) 486-2430 *Founded/Ownrshp* 1927, 1951
Sales 232.2MM *EMP* 1,100
SIC 3911 Jewelry, precious metal; Jewelry, precious metal
Pr: Dave Petersen
**Ch Bd:* Carolyn Tanner Irish
**COO:* Scott Sperry
**Treas:* Robert K Anger
**Ex VP:* David Sturt
**Sr VP:* Scott Archibald
**VP:* John McVeigh
Software D: Catherine Sylvester

D-U-N-S 79-118-8139
O C TANNER RECOGNITION CO
THANKS
(*Suby of* O C TANNER CO) ★
1930 S State St, Salt Lake City, UT 84115-2311
Tel (801) 486-2430 *Founded/Ownrshp* 1986
Sales 401.1MM *EMP* 1,700
SIC 5094 Precious stones & metals; Precious stones & metals
Pr: David Petersen
**CFO:* Scott Sperry
VP: David Berg
VP: Chester Elton
Dir IT: David Eghert
Dir IT: Nihar Nanda
Software D: Masoud Abbasi
Mfg Mgr: Drew Butler
Mktg Dir: Leona Fox

O D C
See OPPORTUNITY DEVELOPMENT CENTERS INC

O D C
See OCCUPATIONAL DEVELOPMENT CENTER INC

O D L
See ODL INC

O D U
See ODU-USA INC

O D W
See ODW LOGISTICS INC

D-U-N-S 06-421-0719
O DOUBLE INC
TACO BELL
1902 Industrial Blvd, Abilene, TX 79602-7842
Tel (325) 698-2600 *Founded/Ownrshp* 1973
Sales 10.3MM^E *EMP* 335
SIC 5812 Fast-food restaurant, chain; Fast-food restaurant, chain
Pr: David Ohre
**Sec:* Pam Bannister
VP: J D York

D-U-N-S 00-611-2841 IMP
O E C GRAPHICS INC (WI)
OEC CHICAGO
555 W Waukau Ave, Oshkosh, WI 54902-7101
Tel (920) 235-7770 *Founded/Ownrshp* 1912
Sales 65.6MM^E *EMP* 260
SIC 2796 7336 Platemaking services; Commercial art & graphic design; Platemaking services; Commercial art & graphic design
Pr: Jack Schloesser
**Sec:* Joni Schloesser
**VP:* Jeff Schloesser
**VP:* Jon Schloesser
Art Dir: Zebulun Rutter

D-U-N-S 04-067-0668
O E C SHIPPING LOS ANGELES INC
OEC GROUP
13100 Alondra Blvd # 100, Cerritos, CA 90703-2278
Tel (562) 926-7186 *Founded/Ownrshp* 1998
Sales 27.8MM^E *EMP* 50
SIC 4731 Freight forwarding
Pr: Robert Han
**Pr:* John Su

O E I
See OMRON ELECTRONICS LLC

D-U-N-S 00-259-3929
O E M CONTROLS INC (CT)
10 Controls Dr, Shelton, CT 06484-6100
Tel (203) 929-8431 *Founded/Ownrshp* 1966
Sales 35.3MM^E *EMP* 200^E
SIC 3625 3229 3577 Electric controls & control accessories, industrial; Switches, electric power; Fiber optics strands; Computer peripheral equipment; Electric controls & control accessories, industrial; Switches, electric power; Fiber optics strands; Computer peripheral equipment
Pr: S Brian Simons
Pr: Brian Sciuto
VP: Lincoln Schoenberger
**VP:* Keith T Simons
VP: James E Tucker
Exec: Chuong Pham
CTO: Robert Henry
IT Man: Theresa Pallo
Plnt Mgr: Robert Rose
Mktg Mgr: Keith Simons
Snr Mgr: Brian Imon

D-U-N-S 55-545-2523 IMP
O E MEYER CO
3303 Tiffin Ave, Sandusky, OH 44870-9752
Tel (419) 625-1256 *Founded/Ownrshp* 1989
Sales 56.3MM^E *EMP* 155
SIC 5084 5047 Welding machinery & equipment; Medical & hospital equipment; Welding machinery & equipment; Medical & hospital equipment
CEO: Rodney S Belden
**Pr:* David Belden
**Pr:* Craig A Wood
VP: Missy Cross
VP: Dave Spencer
Off Mgr: Geri Schoewe
Dir IT: Michael Fishbaugh
VP Opers: Milt Holody
Opers Supe: John Boyce
Sales Asso: John Benner
Sales Asso: Tim Colston

D-U-N-S 19-707-6938 IMP
■ **O E PLUS LTD**
(*Suby of* MOTORCAR PARTS OF AMERICA INC) ★
620 Spring St, North Dighton, MA 02764-1363
Tel (508) 977-0020 *Founded/Ownrshp* 2015
Sales 22.0MM^E *EMP* 50
SIC 5013 3714 Automotive supplies & parts; Motor vehicle parts & accessories; Automotive supplies & parts; Motor vehicle parts & accessories
Pr: Eric Roberts
VP: Andy Sampson
VP Sls: Peter Bourassa
Manager: Scott Schaefer

D-U-N-S 00-145-4701 IMP/EXP
O F MOSSBERG & SONS INC (CT)
(*Suby of* MOSSBERG CORP) ★
7 Grasso Ave, North Haven, CT 06473-3237
Tel (203) 230-5300 *Founded/Ownrshp* 1919
Sales 103.4MM^E *EMP* 500
SIC 3484 Shotguns or shotgun parts, 30 mm. & below; Shotguns or shotgun parts, 30 mm. & below
Ch Bd: A Iver Mossberg Jr
**Pr:* Alan I Mossberg
Pr: Bruce Demarco
**Sr VP:* Joseph H Bartozzi
**VP:* Christopher Orlando
Dir IT: Jacques Franz
IT Man: Steve Clark
QC Dir: Jon Krchnavy
Mktg Dir: David Miles
Sls Mgr: Stephen Wright

O F R
See FLORIDA DEPARTMENT OF FINANCIAL SERVICES

O F S
See OFS FITEL LLC

O G S
See NEW YORK OFFICE OF GENERAL SERVICES

O H B
See ORLEANS HOMEBUILDERS INC

O H L
See OZBURN-HESSEY STORAGE CO

D-U-N-S 02-540-7420
O HARE AUTO GROUP
1533 S River Rd, Des Plaines, IL 60018-1760
Tel (847) 824-3141 *Founded/Ownrshp* 1939, 1959
Sales 23.6MM^E *EMP* 100
SIC 5511 Automobiles, new & used
Pr: Kevin Mize
**Sec:* Joseph Griff

O HARE HYUNDI
See MIZE IMPORT GROUP INC

O I ANALYTICAL
See OI CORP

O I C C
See OKLAHOMA INVESTMENT CASTING CO

D-U-N-S 18-063-2747
O K FARMS INC
(*Suby of* OK INDUSTRIES INC) ★
4601 N 6th St, Fort Smith, AR 72904-2208
Tel (479) 783-4186 *Founded/Ownrshp* 1975
Sales 20.4MM^E *EMP* 160
SIC 0251 Broiling chickens, raising of; Broiling chickens, raising of
Pr: Trent Goins
**CFO:* Ron Brown
**CFO:* Scott Hunter

D-U-N-S 03-549-9086
O K FOODS INC (AR)
TENDERBIRD
(*Suby of* OK INDUSTRIES INC) ★
4601 N 6th St, Fort Smith, AR 72904-2208
Tel (479) 783-4186 *Founded/Ownrshp* 1959
Sales 652.6MM^E *EMP* 3,600
SIC 2015 Poultry, processed; Poultry, processed: fresh; Poultry, slaughtered & dressed; Poultry, processed; Poultry, processed: fresh; Poultry, slaughtered & dressed
CEO: Trent Goins
Pr: Ken Primm
CFO: Ronald E Brown
V Ch Bd: Randall Goins
VP: Scott Hunter
VP: Leo McKee
Sfty Dirs: Tim Lem

O K I
See OKI DATA AMERICAS INC

D-U-N-S 03-119-5530 IMP
O K THOMPSONS TIRE INC
1015 N Independence Ave, Beloit, KS 67420-2101
Tel (785) 738-2283 *Founded/Ownrshp* 1965
Sales 33.8MM *EMP* 21^E
Accts Clubine & Rettele
SIC 5014 5531 7534 Tires & tubes; Automotive tires; Tire recapping; Tires & tubes; Automotive tires; Tire recapping
Pr: Michael Thompson
**VP:* Phillip Thompson

D-U-N-S 03-182-0517 IMP
O K TIRE STORE INC
2224 Main Ave, Fargo, ND 58103-1398
Tel (701) 237-6525 *Founded/Ownrshp* 1960
Sales 58.1MM^E *EMP* 160
Accts Eidebailly Fargo Nd
SIC 5531 5014 Automotive tires; Automobile tires & tubes; Automotive tires; Automobile tires & tubes
Pr: Jim Ohnstad
**Sec:* Rose Ohnstad
**VP:* Carl Schwartz

D-U-N-S 00-350-8827
O L THOMPSON CONSTRUCTION CO INC
3691 Paramount Dr, North Charleston, SC 29405-7226
Tel (843) 797-3554 *Founded/Ownrshp* 1948
Sales 58.0MM^E *EMP* 160
SIC 1794 1611 1629 Excavation & grading, building construction; Surfacing & paving; Land clearing contractor; Excavation & grading, building construction; Surfacing & paving; Land clearing contractor
CEO: O L Thompson III
**Pr:* David Hand
**CEO:* Pam Farley
CFO: Pamela J Farley
VP: Trent Kirk
VP: Dan Thompson
**VP:* Matthew Thompson
Sfty Mgr: Bill McLane

O M R F
See OKLAHOMA MEDICAL RESEARCH FOUNDATION

O M Y A
See OMYA CALIFORNIA INC

D-U-N-S 00-464-8416
O N EQUITY SALES CO
ONESCO
(*Suby of* OHIO NATIONAL FINANCIAL SERVICES INC) ★
1 Financial Way Ste 100, Montgomery, OH 45242-5852
Tel (513) 794-6794 *Founded/Ownrshp* 1968
Sales 49.2MM^E *EMP* 600
Accts Williams Crosslin Sparks & V
SIC 6211 Security brokers & dealers; Security brokers & dealers
Pr: Barbara Turner

O N I
See ONEAL STEEL INC

O N R
See ORTHOPAEDIC & NEUROLOGICAL REHABILITATION SPEECH PATHOLOGY INC

O N S
See ONCOLOGY NURSING SOCIETY

O P D
See OPTIMIZED PROCESS DESIGNS LLC

D-U-N-S 10-306-2204 IMP/EXP
■ **O P I PRODUCTS INC**
(*Suby of* COTY INC) ★
13034 Saticoy St, North Hollywood, CA 91605-3510
Tel (818) 759-8688 *Founded/Ownrshp* 2010
Sales 290.9MM^E *EMP* 535
SIC 5087 2844 Beauty parlor equipment & supplies; Toilet preparations; Beauty parlor equipment & supplies; Toilet preparations
CEO: Jules Kaufman
**Pr:* John Heffner
**COO:* Eric Schwartz
**Ex VP:* William Halfacre
**Ex VP:* Susan Weiss-Fischmann
Prd Mgr: Roger Lopez
Sls Mgr: Scott Smith

O P M
See U S OFFICE OF PERSONNEL MANAGEMENT

O R I
See OFFICE RESOURCES INC

O R L FACILITY SERVICES
See OWENS REALTY NETWORK LLC

O R MANAGER
See ACCESS INTELLIGENCE LLC

O R T
See ORT TOOL & DIE CORP

O S A
See OPTICAL SOCIETY OF AMERICA INC

O S C
See OVERBY-SEAWELL CO

O S H
See ORCHARD SUPPLY CO LLC

O S I
See ORENCO SYSTEMS INC

D-U-N-S 04-032-6050
O S INTERIOR SYSTEMS INC
3665 Walnut Bend Ln, Houston, TX 77042-4818
Tel (713) 780-9050 *Founded/Ownrshp* 1975
Sales 41.2MM^E *EMP* 150
SIC 1542 Commercial & office building, new construction; Commercial & office buildings, renovation & repair; Commercial & office building, new construction; Commercial & office buildings, renovation & repair
Pr: Hugh L Payne

D-U-N-S 80-375-0306
O S M GLASSIFICATION INC
OREGON STEEL WORKS
(*Suby of* EVRAZ INC NA) ★
14400 N Rivergate Blvd, Portland, OR 97203-6612
Tel (503) 286-9651 *Founded/Ownrshp* 1991
Sales 70.6MM^E *EMP* 400
SIC 3547 Steel rolling machinery; Steel rolling machinery
Prin: Joe Corvin
CFO: Ray Adams
Sr VP: Larry Lawrence
VP: Robert Simon
IT Man: Nancy Sheridan
Plnt Mgr: Kris Lukas
Sls Mgr: Jeffrey Wilen

O S P
See ORIGINAL SMITH PRINTING INC

O S T
See OPEN SYSTEMS TECHNOLOGIES DE LLC

D-U-N-S 12-236-1595
O SHELTON GARLYN INC
MAZDA
5700 Sw H K Dodgen Loop, Temple, TX 76504-3447
Tel (254) 771-0128 *Founded/Ownrshp* 1974
Sales 52.8MM^E *EMP* 120
SIC 5511 Automobiles, new & used; Automobiles, new & used
Pr: Garlyn O Shelton
**Sec:* Faye Shelton
Exec: Don Rollish
Off Mgr: Jennifer Green
Sls Mgr: Esther Aguillon
Sls Mgr: Aaron Whittle

O' SULLIVAN VENDING & COFFEE
See OSULLIVAN ENTERPRISES INC

D-U-N-S 09-172-2330
O T AUTRY VOCATIONAL AND TECHNICAL EDUCATIONAL FOUNDATION
1201 W Willow Rd, Enid, OK 73703-2506
Tel (580) 242-2750 *Founded/Ownrshp* 1967
Sales 91.9M *EMP* 325
Accts Chas W Carroll Pa Enid
SIC 8249 Vocational schools; Trade school; Vocational schools; Trade school
Comm Dir: Mandy Mayberry
Mktg Mgr: Melissa Jenlink

O T B
See INTER-TRACK PARTNERS LLC

O T S
See OFFICE OF THRIFT SUPERVISION

D-U-N-S 14-496-2958
O TREVINO CONSTRUCTION LLC
4501 N Highway 377, Roanoke, TX 76262-5743
Tel (817) 430-2410 *Founded/Ownrshp* 2000
Sales 20.5MM *EMP* 120
Accts Padgett Stratemann & Co Ll

SIC 1791 1771 1611 Structural steel erection; Concrete work; Highway & street construction; Structural steel erection; Concrete work; Highway & street construction
Pr: Oscar Trevino
**CFO:* Vanessa Trevino Copeland
**Sec:* Vanessa Trevino
**Sr VP:* Carol Trevino
**VP:* Rick Garces
**VP:* Pat Pace

O V S
See OREGON VINEYARD SUPPLY CO

D-U-N-S 00-835-6065 IMP
O W LEE CO INC
1822 E Francis St, Ontario, CA 91761-7759
Tel (909) 947-3771 *Founded/Ownrshp* 2001
Sales 26.1MM^E *EMP* 89
SIC 2514 Lawn furniture: metal
Pr: Brian Lee
**CEO:* Teresa Rogers
**Ch:* Robert Lee
**VP:* Christopher Goff
VP: Jason Malooly
Exec: Elizabeth Uribe
Dir IT: Ken Kraft

D-U-N-S 83-249-2917
O WAYNE ROLLINS FOUNDATION
2801 Buford Hwy Ne, Brookhaven, GA 30329-2149
Tel (404) 486-4626 *Founded/Ownrshp* 2009
Sales 22.6MM *EMP* 3^E
SIC 8641 Civic social & fraternal associations; Civic social & fraternal associations

D-U-N-S 03-409-1678
O WEAVER HOSEA AND SONS INC (AL)
7450 Howells Ferry Rd, Mobile, AL 36618-3407
Tel (251) 342-3025 *Founded/Ownrshp* 1952, 1985
Sales 63.8MM^E *EMP* 140^E
SIC 1629 1611 Earthmoving contractor; Land clearing contractor; Surfacing & paving; Grading; Earthmoving contractor; Land clearing contractor; Surfacing & paving; Grading
Pr: Paul E Weaver
CFO: Mike Horton
CFO: S Mark Shelley
CFO: Mark Shelly
VP: Jony Murphy
VP: Louis Tillery
**VP:* Micheal Weaver
**VP:* Romona Weaver
Sfty Dirs: Kirk Bunger
Opers Mgr: Joan Milbocker
Plnt Mgr: Ben H Matthews

O XY
See OCCIDENTAL CHEMICAL CORP

D-U-N-S 12-462-1553 IMP
O&K TECHNOLOGY AMERICA INC
(*Suby of* O&K TECHNOLOGY CO., LTD.)
30700 Telg Rd Ste 2656, Bingham Farms, MI 48025
Tel (248) 979-9120 *Founded/Ownrshp* 2002
Sales 24.0MM *EMP* 10
SIC 5531 Automotive parts; Automotive parts
Pr: Si Yurn Koh
VP: Doung Kim
Plng Mgr: Gorden Ko
Plng Mgr: S B Lee
Sls Mgr: Alex Lee

O-1
See OWENS-ILLINOIS GENERAL INC

D-U-N-S 03-260-3284
O-A-K/FLORIDA INC
OWEN-AMES-KIMBALL COMPANY
(*Suby of* OWEN-AMES-KIMBALL CO) ★
11941 Fairway Lakes Dr, Fort Myers, FL 33913-8338
Tel (239) 561-4141 *Founded/Ownrshp* 1982
Sales 32.0MM^E *EMP* 46
SIC 1542

D-U-N-S 00-210-2069 IMP/EXP
O-AT-KA MILK PRODUCTS COOPERATIVE INC (NY)
700 Ellicott St, Batavia, NY 14020-3744
Tel (585) 343-0536 *Founded/Ownrshp* 1956
Sales 332.5MM *EMP* 302^E
Accts Dopkins & Company Llp Buffal
SIC 2023 2021 2026 Concentrated skim milk; Evaporated milk; Dried nonfat milk; Creamery butter; Fluid milk; Concentrated skim milk; Evaporated milk; Dried nonfat milk; Creamery butter; Fluid milk
CEO: Robert Hall
**Ch Bd:* Herbert Nobles
**COO:* Dan Wolf
**CFO:* Michael Patterson
**Treas:* Dudley Chaffee
**VP:* Clyde Rutherford

O-I
See OWENS-BROCKWAY GLASS CONTAINER INC

O-I
See OWENS-ILLINOIS DE PUERTO RICO

D-U-N-S 07-866-2433
O-N MINERALS (CHEMSTONE) CO
CARMEUSE LIME & STONE
(*Suby of* CARMEUSE LIME & STONE) ★
11 Stanwix St Fl 21, Pittsburgh, PA 15222-1327
Tel (412) 995-5500 *Founded/Ownrshp* 2009
Sales 58.5MM^E *EMP* 300
SIC 1422 Crushed & broken limestone; Crushed & broken limestone
Pr: Thomas A Buck
**CFO:* Bruce Inglis
**Treas:* Mary D Colin
**VP:* Jack Fahler
**VP:* Paul Tunnicliffe
**VP:* Kevin White
**S&M/VP:* Bruce Routhieaux

D-U-N-S 18-003-5172
O-N MINERALS (MICHIGAN) CO
DIVISION OGLEBAY NORTON CO
1035 Calcite Rd, Rogers City, MI 49779-1900
Tel (989) 734-2131 *Founded/Ownrshp* 2000
Sales 48.0MM^E *EMP* 325
SIC 1411 1422 5032 Limestone, dimension-quarrying; Dolomite, dimension-quarrying; Crushed & broken limestone; Limestone; Limestone, dimension-quarrying; Dolomite, dimension-quarrying; Crushed & broken limestone; Limestone
Pr: Michelle Harris
**Plnt Mgr:* Joe Chevreaux

D-U-N-S 07-866-0642
O-N MINERALS CO (OHIO)
CARMEUSE LIME & STONE
(*Suby of* CARMEUSE LIME & STONE INC) ★
11 Stanwix St Fl 21, Pittsburgh, PA 15222-1327
Tel (412) 995-5500 *Founded/Ownrshp* 2012
Sales 60.1MM^E *EMP* 1,440^E
SIC 1422 Crushed & broken limestone
Pr: Thomas A Buck
CFO: Bruce Inglis
Treas: Mary D Colin
VP: Jack Fahler
VP: Paul Tunnicliffe
VP: Kevin White
S&M/VP: Bruce Routhieaux

D-U-N-S 01-624-8329
O-TEX PUMPING LLC
306 W Wall St Ste 700, Midland, TX 79701-5170
Tel (432) 685-9901 *Founded/Ownrshp* 2011
Sales 58.0MM^E *EMP* 324^E
SIC 1711 Plumbing contractors
Mng Pt: Brent Barbour
Dist Mgr: Ron Baker
Opers Mgr: Elco Armendariz

D-U-N-S 80-830-6034
O-TEX PUMPING LLC
7045 N Highway 81, Duncan, OK 73533-4001
Tel (580) 255-3111 *Founded/Ownrshp* 2007
Sales 477.3MM^E *EMP* 400
SIC 1389 Cementing oil & gas well casings; Cementing oil & gas well casings
Dist Mgr: Doug Caldwell
Dist Mgr: Brian Martin
Dist Mgr: Craig Pankratz
Opers Mgr: Jesse Ulate

O/B LEASING COMPANY
See BUDCO GROUP INC

D-U-N-S 07-137-5062
O1 COMMUNICATIONS INC (OH)
5190 Golden Foothill Pkwy, El Dorado Hills, CA 95762-9608
Tel (916) 554-2100 *Founded/Ownrshp* 1998
Sales 29.8MM^E *EMP* 89
SIC 4813 Data telephone communications
CEO: Bradley Jenkins
**CFO:* Jim Beausoleil
**Sr VP:* Max Seely
Ex Dir: Sandi Hightower
Snr Sftwr: Doug Steblein
CTO: Shavinder Singh
IT Man: Chas Wiegman
Software D: Jacob Fenske
Sftwr Eng: Chris Duggin
Mktg Mgr: Linda Clarke
Genl Couns: Keenan Davis

D-U-N-S 94-306-9336
O2 MICRO INC
3118 Patrick Henry Dr, Santa Clara, CA 95054-1850
Tel (408) 987-5920 *Founded/Ownrshp* 1998
Sales 20.0MM^E *EMP* 100
SIC 7373 Computer integrated systems design
CEO: Lynn Lin
**Pr:* Sterling Du
COO: Viorel Marinescu
Ofcr: Jane Ling
VP: Dean Cate
VP: Dean Koike
**VP:* Yung Lin Lin
VP: Laszlo Lipcsei
VP: James Wang
**VP:* Max Wong
Exec: Oleg Kobildjanov
Exec: Guoxing LI
Exec: Constantin Spiridon

O2SAFE SOLUTIONS
See TECHNICAL GAS PRODUCTS INC

D-U-N-S 01-897-2739
O3B NETWORKS USA LLC (NV)
(*Suby of* O3B NETWORKS MANAGEMENT SERVICES B.V.)
10432 Balls Ford Rd Ste 3, Manassas, VA 20109-2514
Tel (703) 206-8682 *Founded/Ownrshp* 2008
Sales 21.2MM^E *EMP* 170
SIC 7371 Custom computer programming services; Custom computer programming services
CEO: Steve Collar
Ex VP: Jonas Mattsson

D-U-N-S 01-145-2646
OA PETERSON CONSTRUCTION CO INC
78 N Willow St, Montclair, NJ 07042-3845
Tel (973) 744-6200 *Founded/Ownrshp* 1914
Sales 20.9MM^E *EMP* 65
SIC 1542 1541 Commercial & office building, new construction; Commercial & office buildings, renovation & repair; Hospital construction; Industrial buildings, new construction; Renovation, remodeling & repairs: industrial buildings
Pr: John C Peterson
**VP:* Craig H Buermann
VP: Craig Buermann
**Off Mgr:* Lora Rowe

OAA
See ORTHOPAEDIC ASSOCIATES OF ALLENTOWN LTD

OAG
See OREGON ANESTHESIOLOGY GROUP PC

D-U-N-S 79-959-3640
OAHU PUBLICATIONS INC
HONOLULU STAR ADVERTISER
(*Suby of* SOUND PUBLISHING HOLDING INC) ★
500 Ala Moana Blvd # 7210, Honolulu, HI 96813-4920
Tel (808) 529-4700 *Founded/Ownrshp* 2001
Sales 80.2MM^E *EMP* 551^E
SIC 2711 Newspapers, publishing & printing; Newspapers, publishing & printing
Pr: Dennis Francis
Treas: Nadine Kam
**Sec:* Tc Gray
**VP:* David Black
Exec: Rich Frank
Dir Bus: Jay Higa
IT Man: Alan Stewart
Web Dev: Brant Songsong
Pr Dir: Erika Engle
Sls Mgr: Shannan Okinishi
Sales Asso: Mark Christiansen

D-U-N-S 78-533-2370
OAHU TRANSIT SERVICES INC
BUS, THE
811 Middle St Rm 225, Honolulu, HI 96819-2343
Tel (808) 848-4400 *Founded/Ownrshp* 1991
Sales 71.3MM^E *EMP* 1,700
SIC 4111 Bus line operations; Bus line operations
Pr: J Roger Morton
**Ch:* Anthony R Guerrero Jr
**Sr VP:* Robert Yu
VP: Richard Hardy
Exec: Tom Enomoto
Genl Mgr: James E Cowan
CIO: Guy Mariwoki
CTO: Les Kiyuna
IT Man: Nick Awana

D-U-N-S 17-292-2820
OAHU WASTE SERVICES INC
MAUI WASTE SERVICES
1169 Mikole St, Honolulu, HI 96819-4327
Tel (808) 845-7581 *Founded/Ownrshp* 2003
Sales 50.1MM^E *EMP* 35^E
SIC 4953 Refuse systems; Refuse systems
CEO: Clyde Kaneshiro
**CFO:* Harold Yamada

D-U-N-S 03-714-3427 IMP
OAK BEVERAGES INC
1 Flower Ln, Blauvelt, NY 10913-1139
Tel (718) 652-8555 *Founded/Ownrshp* 1980
Sales 114.1MM^E *EMP* 125
SIC 5181 Beer & other fermented malt liquors
Pr: Debra Boening
**Treas:* James Tozar

OAK BROOK HILLS HOTEL & RESORT
See OAK BROOK HOTEL INC

D-U-N-S 14-491-6285
OAK BROOK HOTEL INC
OAK BROOK HILLS HOTEL & RESORT
3500 Midwest Rd, Oak Brook, IL 60523-2573
Tel (630) 850-5530 *Founded/Ownrshp* 1996
Sales 12.9MM^E *EMP* 350
SIC 7011 Resort hotel
Pr: Marsha D Richter
**VP:* Earl W Buehner
VP: David L Mui
**VP:* David L Muil
**VP:* Gregg Rademacher
**VP:* Margrot O Shuler
Genl Mgr: Gretchen Ingwersgen
Manager: Teresa White

D-U-N-S 07-702-1103
OAK BROOK MECHANICAL SERVICES INC
961 S Route 83, Elmhurst, IL 60126
Tel (630) 941-3555 *Founded/Ownrshp* 1975
Sales 22.4MM *EMP* 50
SIC 1711

D-U-N-S 00-522-6428 IMP/EXP
OAK BURR TOOL INC (MI)
BURR OAK TOOL
405 W South St, Sturgis, MI 49091-2192
Tel (269) 651-9393 *Founded/Ownrshp* 1944
Sales 4.8MM *EMP* 320^E
SIC 3999 3443 3317 Special dies & tools; Custom machinery; Atomizers, toiletry; Finned tubes, for heat transfer; Tubes, seamless steel
Ch: Newell Franks
Pr: Brian McConell
CFO: Debbie Gorski
Treas: David L Franks
VP: David Clark

D-U-N-S 14-442-3639
OAK CLIFF BIBLE FELLOWSHIP
1808 W Camp Wisdom Rd, Dallas, TX 75232-3332
Tel (214) 672-9100 *Founded/Ownrshp* 1976
Sales 20.6MM^E *EMP* 200
SIC 8661 Miscellaneous denomination church; Miscellaneous denomination church
Dir Sec: Michael Golson
Off Admin: Karlotta Hannibal

D-U-N-S 09-719-3692
OAK CONSTRUCTION CO INC
4000 Sw 30th Ave, Fort Lauderdale, FL 33312-6820
Tel (954) 583-9625 *Founded/Ownrshp* 1979
Sales 20.0MM^E *EMP* 40
SIC 1542 Commercial & office building, new construction
CEO: Charles Medrano
**Pr:* Carlos Medrano
**COO:* Forrest Aylor

D-U-N-S 10-262-8161
OAK CREEK HOMES LP
(*Suby of* AMERICAN HOMESTAR CORP) ★
2450 S Shore Blvd, League City, TX 77573-2994
Tel (281) 334-9700 *Founded/Ownrshp* 2000
Sales 23.4MM^E *EMP* 275^E
SIC 2451 Mobile homes, personal or private use; Mobile homes, personal or private use
Genl Pt: Craig Reynolds
Pt: Teeter Finis

OAK CREEK PRINTING
See JOURNAL-STAR PRINTING CO

D-U-N-S 08-050-2131
OAK CREEK-FRANKLIN JOINT SCHOOL DISTRICT
7630 S 10th St, Oak Creek, WI 53154-1912
Tel (414) 768-5880 *Founded/Ownrshp* 1954
Sales 35.5MM^E *EMP* 500
Accts Baker Tilly Virchow Krause
SIC 8211 Public elementary school; Public junior high school; Public senior high school; Public elementary school; Public junior high school; Public senior high school
Prin: Sara Burmeister
**Pr:* Frank Carini
**VP:* Paul Mason
Teacher Pr: Troy Hamblin
Psych: Lisa Reid

OAK CREST MANORS
See OC HOMES INC

D-U-N-S 87-840-5117
OAK CREST VILLAGE INC
VILLAGE SQUARE
8800 Walther Blvd Ste 1, Baltimore, MD 21234-9023
Tel (410) 665-2222 *Founded/Ownrshp* 1994
Sales 87.1MM *EMP* 1,100
Accts Pricewaterhousecoopers Llp Ba
SIC 8051 8052 8059 Skilled nursing care facilities; Intermediate care facilities; Nursing home, except skilled & intermediate care facility; Skilled nursing care facilities; Intermediate care facilities; Nursing home, except skilled & intermediate care facility
Ex Dir: Mark Erickson
**Ex Dir:* Eric Gross

OAK DISTRIBUTION
See OAK PAPER PRODUCTS CO INC

D-U-N-S 02-663-2331
OAK FOREST LUMBER & SUPPLY CO INC
2201 Judiway St, Houston, TX 77018-5836
Tel (713) 686-7077 *Founded/Ownrshp* 1961
Sales 21.2MM^E *EMP* 35
SIC 5032 Drywall materials
Pr: R Stan Marek Jr
**CFO:* Doyle Crow
**Sec:* Edgar Hancock
**VP:* Paul A Marek

OAK FURNITURE LIQUIDATORS
See WINEY-BICE INC

OAK GROVE CENTER
See OAK GROVE INSTITUTE FOUNDATION INC

D-U-N-S 60-657-4770
OAK GROVE INSTITUTE FOUNDATION INC
OAK GROVE CENTER
24275 Jefferson Ave, Murrieta, CA 92562-7285
Tel (951) 677-5599 *Founded/Ownrshp* 1991
Sales 15.9MM *EMP* 388
Accts Harrington Group San Marino
SIC 8011 8211 8361 Psychiatric clinic; Specialty education; Residential care; Psychiatric clinic; Specialty education; Residential care
CEO: Tamara L Wilson
**Ch Bd:* Barry Soper
**CFO:* Fe Santiago
Nrsg Dir: Tom Kadlec

D-U-N-S 00-914-8953
OAK GROVE TECHNOLOGIES LLC (NC)
4131 Parklake Ave Ste 100, Raleigh, NC 27612-2389
Tel (919) 845-1038 *Founded/Ownrshp* 1999, 2001
Sales 31.1MM^E *EMP* 170
SIC 7373 8711 Computer-aided engineering (CAE) systems service; Aviation &/or aeronautical engineering; Electrical or electronic engineering; Computer-aided engineering (CAE) systems service; Aviation &/or aeronautical engineering; Electrical or electronic engineering
CEO: Mark Gross
**CFO:* Moner Attwa
**VP:* Corey Hicks
**VP:* Kyle Holmquist
VP: Melinda Kinsel
**VP:* David Shellenberger
Site Mgr: Terry Singer
Art Dir: Josh Miller

OAK HALL CAP & GOWN
See OAK HALL INDUSTRIES LP

D-U-N-S 03-478-5360
OAK HALL INC (TN)
6150 Poplar Ave Ste 146, Memphis, TN 38119-4744
Tel (901) 761-3580 *Founded/Ownrshp* 1965, 1859
Sales 21.3MM^E *EMP* 70
SIC 5611 5621 Men's & boys' clothing stores; Suits, men's; Clothing, sportswear, men's & boys'; Clothing, men's & boys': everyday, except suits & sportswear; Ready-to-wear apparel, women's
Pr: William L Levy
**CFO:* John Christian
CFO: Renee Wills
**VP:* Robert H Levy
Sales Exec: Paul Kauerz
Mktg Mgr: Sarah Palazola

D-U-N-S 05-413-0935 IMP
OAK HALL INDUSTRIES LP (PA)
OAK HALL CAP & GOWN
840 Union St, Salem, VA 24153-5121
Tel (540) 387-0000 *Founded/Ownrshp* 1888, 1996
Sales 43.2MM^E *EMP* 375
SIC 5699 Caps & gowns (academic vestments); Caps & gowns (academic vestments)
Pt: Joseph D Angelo
Pr: Peter Morrison
IT Man: Scott Gibson

IT Man: Tim Shell
S&M/VP: Joseph Angelo

D-U-N-S 12-898-4973
OAK HAMMOCK AT UNIVERSITY OF FLORIDA INC
5100 Sw 25th Blvd, Gainesville, FL 32608-3984
Tel (352) 548-1000 *Founded/Ownrshp* 1998
Sales 25.1MM *EMP* 200
Accts Moore Stephens Lovelace Pa Cl
SIC 8051 Skilled nursing care facilities; Skilled nursing care facilities
Pr: Davis M Rembert Jr
**Sec:* Robert G Frank
**VP:* Leslie D Bram
Exec: Sunya Wilson
**Prin:* Robert A Bryan
Ex Dir: Dave Stauffer
Brnch Mgr: Mary Salvamoser
Telecom Ex: Brian Macke

D-U-N-S 00-278-8347
OAK HARBOR FREIGHT LINES INC (WA)
1339 W Valley Hwy N, Auburn, WA 98001-4123
Tel (206) 246-2600 *Founded/Ownrshp* 1936
Sales 227.0MM^E *EMP* 1,000
SIC 4213 4214 Trucking, except local; Local trucking with storage; Trucking, except local; Local trucking with storage
Pr: Edward Vanderpol
**Treas:* Karen Miller
**VP:* David Vanderpol
Dist Mgr: Kevin Kellerman
Off Mgr: Cindy Estrada
Off Mgr: Diane Gonzales
Off Mgr: Shelly Rigsby
DP Exec: Sam Choi
Opers Supe: Sergio Fuentes

D-U-N-S 80-569-5611
OAK HARBOR SCHOOL DISTRICT
HARBOR SCHOOL DST - NJROTC
350 S Oak Harbor St, Oak Harbor, WA 98277-5137
Tel (360) 279-5028 *Founded/Ownrshp* 2009
Sales 29.2MM^E *EMP* 686
SIC 8211 Elementary & secondary schools; Elementary & secondary schools
Dir Rx: Pamela Ross
Prin: Renee Wolfgang
Ex Dir: Kurt Schonberg
Pr Dir: Kelly Tourmay
HC Dir: Robbin White

D-U-N-S 03-918-6809
OAK HEALTH AND REHABILITATION CENTERS INC
5 Morgan Hwy, Scranton, PA 18508-2641
Tel (215) 346-6454 *Founded/Ownrshp* 2014
Sales 34.5MM^E *EMP* 1,266^E
SIC 8361 Home for the aged
Pr: Howard Jaffe

D-U-N-S 10-172-3869
OAK HILL ADVISORS LP
OAK HILL CAPITAL
(*Suby of* OAK HILL CAPITAL PARTNERS LP) ★
1114 Ave Of The Americas, New York, NY 10036-7703
Tel (212) 326-1500 *Founded/Ownrshp* 1999
Sales 24.8MM^E *EMP* 60^E
SIC 6282 Investment advisory service
CEO: Glenn R August
Pt: Eitan Z Arbeter
Pt: Jason S Epstein
Pt: Doug Henderson
Mng Pt: Steven Gruber
Mng Pt: Mark Wolfson
**Pr:* William H Bohnsack Jr
VP: Hunt Doering
VP: John Rachwalski
VP: Scott Snell
VP: Chris Williams

OAK HILL CAPITAL
See OAK HILL ADVISORS LP

D-U-N-S 96-874-2127
OAK HILL CAPITAL PARTNERS III LP
65 E 55th St Fl 32, New York, NY 10022-3228
Tel (212) 527-8400 *Founded/Ownrshp* 2007
Sales 73.8MM^E *EMP* 7,939^E
SIC 5812 5813 7999 7993 Eating places; Bar (drinking places); Billiard parlor; Coin-operated amusement devices; Eating places; Bar (drinking places); Billiard parlor; Coin-operated amusement devices

D-U-N-S 06-451-2762
OAK HILL CAPITAL PARTNERS LP
65 E 55th St Fl 32, New York, NY 10022-3228
Tel (212) 527-8400 *Founded/Ownrshp* 1998
Sales 202.8MM^E *EMP* 2,212^E
SIC 7379 ;
Genl Pt: Robert M Bass
Pt: Scott A Baker
Mng Pt: J Taylor Crandall
Mng Pt: Steven B Gruber
Mng Pt: Denis J Nayden
VP: Jessica Reed
VP: Christopher M Williams
Dir IT: Presley Aluna
IT Man: Mark Sori

D-U-N-S 07-268-2909
■ **OAK HILL HOSPITAL CORP** (WV)
CHS
(*Suby of* COMMUNITY HEALTH SYSTEMS INC) ★
430 Main St W, Oak Hill, WV 25901-3414
Tel (304) 469-8600 *Founded/Ownrshp* 1966, 2002
Sales 35.7MM *EMP* 250
SIC 8062 General medical & surgical hospitals; General medical & surgical hospitals
CFO: Heather Hilton
**Pr:* Martin G Schweinhart
**CEO:* Chad Hatfield
**Treas:* James W Doucette
Sr VP: Steve Bowen
**VP:* Kevin J Hammons
Dir Rad: Wendy Harrah
HC Dir: Kelli Gregory

D-U-N-S 03-831-6274
■ **OAK HILL HOSPITAL MEDICAL STAFF INC**
(*Suby of* HCA INC) ★
11375 Cortez Blvd, Brooksville, FL 34613-5409
Tel (352) 596-6632 *Founded/Ownrshp* 1984
Sales 164.8MM^E *EMP* 930
SIC 8062 General medical & surgical hospitals; General medical & surgical hospitals
CEO: Mickey Smith
**Pr:* Garnesh M Chari
CFO: David Deam
**CFO:* Chance Phillips
Treas: Christine Piaquaddio
Chf Mktg O: Mallik Piduru
Dir OR: Randall Weeks
Dir Inf Cn: Christine Piacquaddio
Dir Rad: Lanny Chuang
Dir Rad: Tyler Crickette
Dir Rad: Robert Dubion
Dir Rad: Ruth Holliday
Dir Rad: Linda Petrovich

D-U-N-S 04-648-5322 IMP
■ **OAK HILL IMPROVEMENT CO**
SCI
(*Suby of* SCI FUNERAL SERVICES OF NEW YORK INC) ★
300 Curtner Ave, San Jose, CA 95125-1401
Tel (408) 297-2447 *Founded/Ownrshp* 1986
Sales 20.3MM^E *EMP* 200
SIC 5999 7261 5992 6515 Monuments, finished to custom order; Tombstones; Funeral service & crematories; Florists; Mobile home site operators; Monuments, finished to custom order; Tombstones; Funeral service & crematories; Florists; Mobile home site operators
Prin: Robert Wallinger
**Pr:* Robert Walter
**VP:* Blair Walter
Off Mgr: Debbie McCarthy

OAK HILL SCHOOL
See CONNECTICUT INSTITUTE FOR BLIND INC

D-U-N-S 08-678-0160
OAK HILL UNITED SCHOOL CORP
1474 N 800 W 27, Converse, IN 46919-9519
Tel (765) 395-3341 *Founded/Ownrshp* 1965
Sales 39.0MM *EMP* 230
SIC 8211 Elementary & secondary schools; Elementary & secondary schools
Pr: Dana Diggs
Prin: Jean Shonkwiler

OAK HILLS BOARD OF EDUCATION
See OAK HILLS LOCAL SCHOOL DISTRICT

D-U-N-S 08-185-9217
OAK HILLS LOCAL SCHOOL DISTRICT
OAK HILLS BOARD OF EDUCATION
6325 Rapid Run Rd, Cincinnati, OH 45233-4555
Tel (513) 598-2941 *Founded/Ownrshp* 1958
Sales 62.4MM^E *EMP* 817
Accts Plattenburg & Associates Inc
SIC 8211 Public combined elementary & secondary school; Public junior high school; Public senior high school; Public combined elementary & secondary school; Public junior high school; Public senior high school
**Treas:* Steven Bain
Bd of Dir: Jan Hunter
VP: Scott Bischoff
Prgrm Mgr: Lynn Hericks
MIS Dir: Karen Zahneis
Pr Dir: Emily Buckley
Schl Brd P: Steve Schinkal
Teacher Pr: Jeff Brandt

D-U-N-S 10-165-7740
OAK HRC MOUNTAIN CITY LLC
MOUNTAIN CY NRSING RHBLITATION
(*Suby of* OAK HEALTH AND REHABILITATION CENTERS INC) ★
401 Hazle Township Blvd # 403, Hazle Township, PA 18202-9661
Tel (570) 454-8888 *Founded/Ownrshp* 2014
Sales 14.0MM^E *EMP* 291
SIC 8051 Extended care facility; Extended care facility
Pr: Howard Jaffe
Off Mgr: Cathy Stoddard
HC Dir: Angie Evancho

D-U-N-S 06-981-8680
OAK LANE GOLF COURSE INC
800 N Main St, Webberville, MI 48892-9533
Tel (517) 521-3900 *Founded/Ownrshp* 1966
Sales 1.5MM *EMP* 3,035
SIC 7992 5812 Public golf courses; Eating places; Public golf courses; Eating places
Pr: Bernard Simons
**Sec:* Lisa Lane
**Ex VP:* James Simons
**VP:* Richard Simons

D-U-N-S 04-356-6116
OAK LAWN COMMUNITY HIGH SCHOOL DISTRICT 229
9400 Southwest Hwy, Oak Lawn, IL 60453-2372
Tel (708) 424-5201 *Founded/Ownrshp* 1951
Sales 32.8MM *EMP* 182^E
Accts Mcgladrey & Pullen Llp Chica
SIC 8211 High school, junior or senior; High school, junior or senior
Dir IT: Jason Williams
Pr Dir: Joseph McCurdy
Psych: Julie Hartmann
Psych: Tim Krupa
Psych: Susan Szala
Psych: Marcus Wargin

D-U-N-S 06-859-5016
OAK LAWN HOMETOWN SCHOOL DISTRICT 123
4201 W 93rd St Ste 1, Oak Lawn, IL 60453-6113
Tel (708) 423-0150 *Founded/Ownrshp* 1902
Sales 22.1MM^E *EMP* 350
SIC 8211 Public elementary school; Public elementary school

D-U-N-S 83-026-6842
OAK LAWN HYUNDAI INC
HAPPY HYUNDAI
9121 S Cicero Ave, Oak Lawn, IL 60453-1804
Tel (708) 422-9300 *Founded/Ownrshp* 2012
Sales 20.9MM^E *EMP* 39^E
SIC 5511 Automobiles, new & used
Pr: James Spellman
Off Mgr: Margaret Novak
QA Dir: Gary Chambers
Sls Mgr: Marty Epstein

OAK LAWN MOTORS
See OAK LAWN TOYOTA CO

D-U-N-S 11-574-5051
OAK LAWN TOYOTA CO
OAK LAWN MOTORS
4320 W 95th St, Oak Lawn, IL 60453-2668
Tel (708) 423-5200 *Founded/Ownrshp* 1981
Sales 23.4MM^E *EMP* 48
SIC 5511 5521 Automobiles, new & used; Used car dealers
Pr: Ronald A Colosimo
Genl Mgr: Bob Wasik
Genl Mgr: Bob Wassick
Sls Mgr: Bob Spee

D-U-N-S 11-724-8174
OAK LEAF SURGICAL HOSPITAL LLC
(*Suby of* NATIONAL SURGICAL HOSPITALS INC) ★
1000 Oakleaf Way, Altoona, WI 54720-2246
Tel (715) 831-8130 *Founded/Ownrshp* 2004
Sales 44.9MM *EMP* 166
SIC 8062 General medical & surgical hospitals
Pt: Troy L Berg
**Pt:* Mark A Augustyn
**CFO:* Denise Freid-Schepke

D-U-N-S 07-904-7721 IMP
OAK LONESOME TRADING CO INC
365 Eton Industrial Dr, Eton, GA 30724
Tel (706) 517-6897 *Founded/Ownrshp* 1996
Sales 21.4MM^E *EMP* 126
SIC 2269 2282 2281 Finishing: raw stock, yarn & narrow fabrics; Throwing & winding mills; Yarn spinning mills
CEO: J Chadwick McEntire
Off Mgr: Sera Williams

D-U-N-S 19-706-7705
OAK NORTH AUTOMOTIVE INC
JAY WOLFE TOYOTA
9650 Nw Prairie View Rd, Kansas City, MO 64153-1818
Tel (816) 454-8999 *Founded/Ownrshp* 1986
Sales 20.2MM^E *EMP* 55
SIC 5511 5012 5013 5521 Automobiles, new & used; Automobiles & other motor vehicles; Motor vehicle supplies & new parts; Automobiles, used cars only; Automobiles, new & used; Automobiles & other motor vehicles; Motor vehicle supplies & new parts; Automobiles, used cars only
Pr: Jeff Wolfe
**VP:* Cindy Tucci
Exec: Dustin Howerton
Off Mgr: Regina Gorzkowski

D-U-N-S 02-856-8152 IMP
OAK PAPER PRODUCTS CO INC
OAK DISTRIBUTION
3686 E Olympic Blvd, Los Angeles, CA 90023-3146
Tel (888) 263-2668 *Founded/Ownrshp* 1976
Sales 160.3MM^E *EMP* 175
SIC 5113 5199 5087 2653 Shipping supplies; Packaging materials; Janitors' supplies; Corrugated & solid fiber boxes; Shipping supplies; Packaging materials; Janitors' supplies; Corrugated & solid fiber boxes
Pr: Max Weissberg
**Ch Bd:* Richard Seff
**CEO:* David Weissberg
**COO:* David Karr
CFO: Bernie Singer
**Ch:* D Ick Seff
Treas: Chris Jordan
**Ex VP:* Randall Seff
VP: John Gilligan
Genl Mgr: Bryant Waldo
Sls Dir: Kevin Pratt

D-U-N-S 08-292-9472
OAK PARK & RIVER FOREST HIGH SCHOOL DIST 200
201 N Scoville Ave, Oak Park, IL 60302-2264
Tel (708) 383-0700 *Founded/Ownrshp* 1873
Sales 86.3MM *EMP* 438^E
Accts Baker Tilly Virchow Krause Ll
SIC 8211 Public elementary & secondary schools; Public elementary & secondary schools
**Pr:* Terry Finnegan
CFO: Cherie Witham
Div/Sub He: Julie Frey
Comm Man: Debra Mittleman
Cmptr Lab: Carolyn Cipparrone

OAK PARK BOARD OF EDUCATION
See OAK PARK ELEM SCHL DIST 97

D-U-N-S 07-439-0295
OAK PARK ELEM SCHL DIST 97
OAK PARK BOARD OF EDUCATION
970 Madison St, Oak Park, IL 60302-4430
Tel (708) 524-3000 *Founded/Ownrshp* 1847
Sales 36.0MM^E *EMP* 695
SIC 8211 Elementary school; Elementary school
**Pr:* Robert Spatz
**VP:* James Gates
MIS Dir: Mike Arensdorff
Dir IT: Patti Campuzano
Dir IT: Steve Chowanski
Dir IT: Kathleen Simon
Teacher Pr: Steven Commins

D-U-N-S 05-217-3358
OAK PARK SCHOOL DISTRICT
13900 Granzon St, Oak Park, MI 48237-2756
Tel (248) 336-7700 *Founded/Ownrshp* 1950
Sales 31.4MM^E *EMP* 600^E
Accts Maner Costerisan Lansing Mi
SIC 8211 Public elementary & secondary schools; Public elementary & secondary schools
Trst: Andrea Polley M
Ex Dir: Sandra Harris
Ex Dir: Frances Hill
Dir IT: Greg Dill

D-U-N-S 10-697-1997
OAK PARK UNIFIED SCHOOL DISTRICT
5801 Conifer St, Agoura Hills, CA 91377-1000
Tel (818) 735-3260 *Founded/Ownrshp* 1978
Sales 21.5MM^E *EMP* 299
SIC 8211 Public elementary & secondary schools; Public elementary & secondary schools
Off Mgr: Linda Sheridan
IT Man: Laura Alamada
IT Man: Barbara Dickerson

D-U-N-S 02-094-7966
OAK PARK VILLAGE OF (INC) (IL)
123 Madison St, Oak Park, IL 60302-4295
Tel (708) 358-5460 *Founded/Ownrshp* 1901
Sales NA *EMP* 475
Accts Sikich Llp Naperville Illino
SIC 9121 Town council; ;Town council;
CFO: Pamela Thomas-Hall
**CFO:* Jason Paprocki
Ofcr: Dawn Carver
Ofcr: Sunny Choi
Ofcr: Rasul Freelain
Ofcr: Mike Mangaser
Ofcr: Jason Pounds
Ofcr: Derrick Verge
VP: John Troelstrup
Dir IT: Alvin Nepomuceno
Snr Mgr: Anthony Ambrose

D-U-N-S 96-893-7719
■ **OAK PHARMACEUTICALS INC**
(*Suby of* AKORN INC) ★
1925 W Field Ct Ste 300, Lake Forest, IL 60045-4862
Tel (847) 279-6100 *Founded/Ownrshp* 2011
Sales 21.9MM^E *EMP* 241^E
SIC 5122 5047 Proprietary (patent) medicines; Medical & hospital equipment; Proprietary (patent) medicines; Medical & hospital equipment
Pr: Rajat Rai

D-U-N-S 06-044-9290
OAK RESTAURANTS LP
TACO BELL
14 Balligomingo Rd, Conshohocken, PA 19428-2725
Tel (610) 520-1000 *Founded/Ownrshp* 1996
Sales 11.8MM^E *EMP* 700
Accts Bdo Seidman Llp
SIC 5812 Fast-food restaurant, chain; Fast-food restaurant, chain
Mng Pt: James Nasuti
Pt: John Marsella

D-U-N-S 04-115-2224
OAK RIDGE ASSOCIATED UNIVERSITIES INC
ORAU
100 Orau Way, Oak Ridge, TN 37830-6209
Tel (865) 576-3000 *Founded/Ownrshp* 1946
Sales 83.7MM *EMP* 600
Accts Lattimore Black Morgan & Cain
SIC 8733 Scientific research agency; Scientific research agency
Pr: Andy Page
CFO: Phil Andrews
Ofcr: Bob Aleman
Ex VP: Eric Abelquist
VP: Ivan Boatner
VP: Arlene A Garrison
VP: Jamey Kennedy
VP: Dick Toohey
VP: Marcus Weseman
Assoc Dir: Carol Iddins
Dir Bus: Tony Lester

D-U-N-S 05-584-9954
OAK RIDGE IMPORTS INC
OAK RIDGE TOYOTA
3000 Wards Rd, Lynchburg, VA 24502-2446
Tel (434) 528-3202 *Founded/Ownrshp* 1980
Sales 20.4MM^E *EMP* 68
SIC 5511 7538 5531 New & used car dealers; Automobiles, new & used; General automotive repair shops; Automotive & home supply stores; New & used car dealers; Automobiles, new & used; General automotive repair shops; Automotive & home supply stores
Pr: Howard D Sodikoff

OAK RIDGE NATIONAL LABORATORY
See UT-BATTELLE LLC

D-U-N-S 79-463-6428
OAK RIDGE SCHOOL DISTRICT
304 New York Ave, Oak Ridge, TN 37830-5217
Tel (865) 481-8417 *Founded/Ownrshp* 2007
Sales 25.9MM^E *EMP* 675^E
SIC 8211 Public elementary & secondary schools; Public elementary & secondary schools
MIS Dir: Doug Cofer
Teacher Pr: Christine Lee
HC Dir: Rebecca Jernigan

D-U-N-S 07-979-8730
OAK RIDGE SCHOOLS
304 New York Ave, Oak Ridge, TN 37830-5217
Tel (865) 425-9001 *Founded/Ownrshp* 2015
Sales 21.0MM^E *EMP* 576^E
SIC 8211 Public elementary & secondary schools

OAK RIDGE TOYOTA
See OAK RIDGE IMPORTS INC

D-U-N-S 83-318-4760
OAK RIDGER LLC
SENIOR LIVING
(*Suby of* MORRIS PUBLISHING GROUP LLC) ★
725 Broad St, Augusta, GA 30901-1336
Tel (706) 724-0851 *Founded/Ownrshp* 2010
Sales 84.7M[E] *EMP* 296[E]
SIC 2711 Newspapers; Newspapers, publishing & printing

D-U-N-S 05-329-7115 IMP
OAK ROYAL INDUSTRIES INC
ROYAL OAK BORING PORT HURON
39533 Woodward Ave # 175, Bloomfield Hills, MI 48304-5102
Tel (248) 340-9200 *Founded/Ownrshp* 1985
Sales 199.2MM[E] *EMP* 1,000
SIC 3599 3452 Machine shop, jobbing & repair; Nuts, metal; Bolts, metal; Screws, metal; Machine shop, jobbing & repair; Nuts, metal; Bolts, metal; Screws, metal
Pr: Daniel B Carroll
**CFO:* Terry Fiscus
CFO: Nancy O Grace
**VP:* John Cowan
**VP:* John Gartner
VP: Christopher Lievois
**VP:* David Zonsius
Ex Dir: Doug Hermann
Dir IT: Jen Crawford
Plnt Mgr: Patrick J Carroll

D-U-N-S 10-780-4478
OAK SPRINGS NURSING HOME LLC
OAK SPRINGS OF WARRENTON
614 Hastings Ln, Warrenton, VA 20186-2110
Tel (540) 347-4770 *Founded/Ownrshp* 1981
Sales 20.6MM[E] *EMP* 380
Accts Cundiff & Associates Cpa Pc
SIC 8052 8051 Intermediate care facilities; Skilled nursing care facilities; Intermediate care facilities; Skilled nursing care facilities
CFO: Chich Gilpin
Dir Soc: Barbara Funkhouser
Mktg Dir: Amanda Baker
HC Dir: Amanda Livingood

OAK SPRINGS OF WARRENTON
See OAK SPRINGS NURSING HOME LLC

OAK ST ELEMENTARY SCHOOL
See ORRVILLE CITY SCHOOLS

D-U-N-S 00-518-0971
OAK STATE PRODUCTS INC (IL)
775 State Route 251, Wenona, IL 61377-7587
Tel (815) 853-4348 *Founded/Ownrshp* 1956
Sales 108.1MM[E] *EMP* 350
SIC 2051 Bread, cake & related products; Bread, cake & related products
Ch Bd: Stephen Goulding
**Pr:* David Van Larr
**CFO:* Patrick Donnelly
VP: Byron Goulding
**Prin:* Byron Goulden
Netwrk Eng: David Vanlaar
Sfty Mgr: Christopher Smith
Nutrtnst: Peggy Goulding

D-U-N-S 01-352-4228
OAKTREE FARM DAIRY INC
544 Elwood Rd, East Northport, NY 11731-4826
Tel (631) 368-3600 *Founded/Ownrshp* 1941
Sales 34.3MM[E] *EMP* 109
SIC 5143 5451 Dairy products, except dried or canned; Dairy products stores; Dairy products, except dried or canned; Dairy products stores
Pr: Hari Singh
CFO: Charlene Cosman
VP: Richard Classey
VP: John Konrad
MIS Dir: Steve Swanson
Plnt Mgr: Darrin Spence
Board of Directors: Charlene Cosman, Douglas Cosman, Edgar Cosman, Kathleen Nitabach

OAKTREE INN
See LODGING ENTERPRISES LLC

OAKTREE MAZDA
See KASA ASSOCIATES INC

D-U-N-S 01-971-9783
▲ OAK VALLEY BANCORP
125 N 3rd Ave, Oakdale, CA 95361-3039
Tel (209) 848-2265 *Founded/Ownrshp* 2008
Sales NA *EMP* 157[E]
Accts Moss Adams Llp Stockton Cali
Tkr Sym OVLY *Exch* NAS
SIC 6022 State commercial banks; State commercial banks
Pr: Christopher M Courtney
Chf Cred: Michael J Rodrigues
Ofcr: Richard A McCarty
Ex VP: David S Harvey

D-U-N-S 62-288-0698
■ OAK VALLEY COMMUNITY BANK
EASTERN SIERRA COMMNUNITY BANK
(*Suby of* OAK VALLEY BANCORP) ★
125 N 3rd Ave, Oakdale, CA 95361-3039
Tel (209) 848-2265 *Founded/Ownrshp* 1991
Sales NA *EMP* 85
SIC 6022 State commercial banks; State commercial banks
CEO: Ronald C Martin
Pr: Chris Courtney
CFO: Rick McCarty
Ofcr: John Coburn
Ofcr: Mike R Garcia
Ofcr: Michael Petrucelli
Ofcr: Roxanna E Smith
Assoc VP: June Lopez
Sr VP: Doug Angelo
Sr VP: Ron Briw
Sr VP: Dave Harvey
Sr VP: Janis Powers
Sr VP: Mike Rodrigues
VP: Barbara Ducey
VP: Teddi Lowry
VP: Susan Quigley
VP: Lyn Wilson

D-U-N-S 07-466-7684
OAK VALLEY HOSPITAL DISTRICT
(*Suby of* C H W) ★
350 S Oak Ave, Oakdale, CA 95361-3519
Tel (209) 847-3011 *Founded/Ownrshp* 2013
Sales 59.9MM[E] *EMP* 430
SIC 8062 8051 General medical & surgical hospitals; Skilled nursing care facilities; General medical & surgical hospitals; Skilled nursing care facilities
CEO: John McCormick
Chf Rad: John Martin
**Ch Bd:* Bob Wikoff
Ch: Gail McCarthy
**V Ch Bd:* Gail Sward
Dir Rad: Jeff White
Dir Rx: Edward Sarno
Dir Sec: Filmore Brimage
Dir IT: Charles Robinson
IT Man: Michael Hendricks
Mtls Mgr: Raymond Leverett

D-U-N-S 07-799-3665
OAK WHITE MANOR INC
WHITE OAK MANAGEMENT
130 E Main St, Spartanburg, SC 29306-5113
Tel (864) 582-7503 *Founded/Ownrshp* 1968
Sales 147.2MM *EMP* 2,300
Accts Cliftonlarsonallen Llp Charlo
SIC 8051 Skilled nursing care facilities; Skilled nursing care facilities
CEO: Oliver K Cecil Jr
**Pr:* Doug Cecil
**CFO:* John P Barber
Nrsg Dir: Sherry Chrisp

D-U-N-S 08-046-0215 IMP
OAK-MITSUI INC (NY)
(*Suby of* MITSUI MINING & SMELTING CO.,LTD.)
80 1st St, Hoosick Falls, NY 12090-1631
Tel (518) 686-4961 *Founded/Ownrshp* 1976
Sales 40.5MM[E] *EMP* 150[E]
SIC 3497 Copper foil; Copper foil
Ch Bd: John Fatcheric
**Pr:* Hiroyuki Kon
VP Admn: Masashi Yamashita
QA Dir: William Hall
Opers Mgr: Wendy Smith
S&M/VP: John Blaber

D-U-N-S 07-391-4723
OAKBEND MEDICAL CENTER
MONTEBELLO WELLNESS CENTER
1705 Jackson St, Richmond, TX 77469-3246
Tel (713) 453-0446 *Founded/Ownrshp* 1947
Sales 141.1MM[E] *EMP* 600
SIC 8062 8051 General medical & surgical hospitals; General medical & surgical hospitals; Skilled nursing care facilities
CEO: Joe Freudenberger
**COO:* Donna Ferguson
CFO: Rodney Lenfant
CFO: Jim Simone
**CFO:* Robert Smelser
**Ch:* Jeff Council
**Treas:* Jack Moore
**V Ch Bd:* Walter Ansel
**VP:* Sue McCarty
Dir OR: Madilyn Zbranek
Dir Lab: Surya Kantipudi
Dir Rad: Karen Riner
Dir Rx: Nancy Helfrick

OAKBROOK TOYOTA OF WESTMONT
See ROHR-MONT MOTORS INC

D-U-N-S 60-654-5978
OAKCREST LUMBER INC
3287 Ga Highway 41 S, Buena Vista, GA 31803-8211
Tel (229) 649-2760 *Founded/Ownrshp* 1989
Sales 33.7MM[E] *EMP* 200[E]
SIC 2421 Kiln drying of lumber; Kiln drying of lumber
Pr: Wesley Weaver
**CFO:* Russell Weaver
**Sec:* Barbara C Weaver
**VP:* Roland Weaver
Sfty Mgr: Johnny Thomas

OAKDALE COMM HOSPITAL
See RAPIDES HEALTHCARE SYSTEM LLC

D-U-N-S 00-794-7484
OAKDALE ELECTRIC COOPERATIVE (WI)
489 N Oakwood St, Tomah, WI 54660-5162
Tel (608) 372-4131 *Founded/Ownrshp* 1936
Sales 35.9MM *EMP* 49
Accts Bauman Associates Ltd Eau C
SIC 4911 Transmission, electric power; Transmission, electric power
Genl Mgr: Eugene Edgerton
CFO: Rose Bartholomew
Sfty Mgr: Ben Bella

D-U-N-S 06-419-6582
OAKDALE HEIGHTS MANAGEMENT CORP
250 Hemsted Dr Ste 100, Redding, CA 96002-0940
Tel (530) 222-6797 *Founded/Ownrshp* 1999
Sales 11.5MM[E] *EMP* 350
SIC 6513 Retirement hotel operation; Retirement hotel operation
Pr: Michael Loudon

D-U-N-S 01-467-2695
OAKDALE JOINT UNIFIED SCHOOL DISTRICT
168 S 3rd Ave, Oakdale, CA 95361-3935
Tel (209) 848-4884 *Founded/Ownrshp* 1892
Sales 42.7MM *EMP* 508
Accts Vavrinek Trine Day & Co Llp
SIC 8211 Public elementary & secondary schools; Public elementary & secondary schools
Treas: Debbie Potter
VP: Adam Uplinger
**Prin:* Barbara Shook
Dir IT: Kevin Brown
IT Man: Susan Dyke
Schl Brd P: Diane Gilbert

D-U-N-S 80-661-2750
OAKHAVEN INVESTMENT CORP
TAYLOR MARINE
1022 Circle Dr, Baltimore, MD 21227-2324
Tel (410) 247-9000 *Founded/Ownrshp* 1995
Sales 30.0MM *EMP* 28
SIC 4499 7363 Boat & ship rental & leasing, except pleasure; Boat crew service; Boat & ship rental & leasing, except pleasure; Boat crew service
Pr: James E Taylor
**VP:* Eugene Brannan

D-U-N-S 82-701-8771
OAKHILL COMMUNITY SCHOOL DISTRICT 915
School Rd, Sabattus, ME 04280
Tel (207) 375-4273 *Founded/Ownrshp* 1974
Sales 4.1MM[E] *EMP* 300
SIC 8211 Public elementary & secondary schools; Public elementary & secondary schools

D-U-N-S 00-110-1484
OAKHURST DAIRY
(*Suby of* DAIRY FARMERS OF AMERICA INC) ★
364 Forest Ave, Portland, ME 04101-2092
Tel (207) 772-7468 *Founded/Ownrshp* 2014
Sales 31.1MM[E] *EMP* 200
SIC 2026 5143

D-U-N-S 60-406-6548
OAKHURST INDUSTRIES INC
FREUND BAKING
2050 S Tubeway Ave, Commerce, CA 90040-1624
Tel (323) 724-3000 *Founded/Ownrshp* 1981
Sales 148.0MM[E] *EMP* 400
SIC 2051 5149 Buns, bread type: fresh or frozen; Rolls, bread type: fresh or frozen; Groceries & related products; Buns, bread type: fresh or frozen; Rolls, bread type: fresh or frozen; Groceries & related products
Pr: James Freund
**VP:* Jonathan Freund
**VP:* Ronald Martin
Sfty Mgr: Will Gallardo

D-U-N-S 11-984-3639
OAKHURST MEDICAL CENTERS INC
5582 Memorial Dr, Stone Mountain, GA 30083-3215
Tel (404) 298-8998 *Founded/Ownrshp* 1978
Sales 22.2MM *EMP* 26
Accts Rsm Mcgladrey Inc New York N
SIC 8093 Specialty outpatient clinics
Ch Bd: Phillis Miler
**CEO:* Jeffrey Taylor
Dir IT: Maury Morris
Doctor: Najeeba Bootwala

OAKLAND ACURA
See WALNUT CREEK ASSOCIATES 5 INC

OAKLAND ATHLETICS
See ATHLETICS INVESTMENT GROUP LLC

D-U-N-S 80-306-2579
OAKLAND AUTOMOTIVE CO LLC
HONDA OF OAKLAND
3330 Broadway, Oakland, CA 94611-5733
Tel (510) 420-9200 *Founded/Ownrshp* 2001
Sales 35.3MM[E] *EMP* 100
SIC 5511 Automobiles, new & used; Automobiles, new & used
Genl Mgr: Todd King
Sls Mgr: Tina Ward

D-U-N-S 05-314-6163
OAKLAND BOARD OF EDUCATION INC
315 Ramapo Valley Rd, Oakland, NJ 07436-1813
Tel (201) 337-6110 *Founded/Ownrshp* 1907
Sales 10.3MM[E] *EMP* 300
SIC 8211 Public elementary & secondary schools; Public elementary & secondary schools
**CFO:* Louis Pepe
**Sec:* Vince Yaniro

D-U-N-S 07-965-5122
OAKLAND CITY UNIVERSITY
OCU
138 N Lucretia St, Oakland City, IN 47660-1038
Tel (812) 749-4781 *Founded/Ownrshp* 1885
Sales 26.0MM *EMP* 366
SIC 8221

D-U-N-S 07-421-7100
OAKLAND COMMUNITY COLLEGE FOUNDATION
2480 Opdyke Rd, Bloomfield Hills, MI 48304-2223
Tel (248) 341-2000 *Founded/Ownrshp* 1964
Sales 50.5MM *EMP* 1,200
Accts Plante & Moran Pllc Clinton T
SIC 8222 Community college; Community college
COO: David Mailloux
Exec: Elaine Fett
Exec: Maxine Fontana
Exec: Cathy Rush
Ex Dir: David Dunshee
Prgrm Mgr: Bonnie George
DP Dir: Henry Austin
DP Dir: Robin Boeling
DP Dir: David Boudreau
DP Dir: Daisy Johnson
DP Dir: James Miteff

D-U-N-S 00-663-7995 EXP
OAKLAND FOODS LLC
OSI
(*Suby of* OSI INDUSTRIES LLC) ★
21876 Highway 59, Oakland, IA 51560-4508
Tel (712) 482-6640 *Founded/Ownrshp* 1997
Sales 158.7MM[E] *EMP* 700
SIC 2013 Sausages & other prepared meats; Sausages & other prepared meats
COO: Esmeralda Garcia
Comm Dir: Mike Koranda
QA Dir: Tyler Brix
QA Dir: Tom Miller
Trfc Mgr: Evan Jones

D-U-N-S 79-880-4761
OAKLAND HOSPITAL
ST JOHN OAKLAND HOSPITAL
27351 Dequindre Rd, Madison Heights, MI 48071-3487
Tel (248) 967-7000 *Founded/Ownrshp* 1986
Sales 102.5MM[E] *EMP* 800
SIC 8062 Hospital, medical school affiliation; Hospital, medical school affiliation
Pr: Joseph Tasse
VP: Tomasine Marx
Exec: Lucy Vail
Board of Directors: Thomas De Gregorio, Arthur J Miller Jr

D-U-N-S 07-653-4122
OAKLAND HOUSING AUTHORITY FOUNDATION
1619 Harrison St, Oakland, CA 94612-3307
Tel (510) 874-1510 *Founded/Ownrshp* 1938
Sales NA *EMP* 360
SIC 9531 9532 Housing authority, non-operating; government; Community & rural development; Housing authority, non-operating: government; Community & rural development
CEO: Harold Davis
**CFO:* Tracy L Stabler
Ofcr: Laura Dunwood
Ofcr: Aida Dupree
Ofcr: Ramon Jacobo
Ofcr: David Watson
Exec: Ignatius Leonor
**Ex Dir:* Eric Johnson

OAKLAND INTERMEDIATE SCHL DIST
See OAKLAND SCHOOLS INC

OAKLAND LEASING COMPANY
See LAUTREC LTD

OAKLAND LOGISTICS SERVICE INC
See LOGISTICS INSIGHT CORP

D-U-N-S 04-031-0737
OAKLAND MANAGEMENT CORP
31731 Northwstrn Hwy 25 Ste 250 W, Farmington Hills, MI 48334
Tel (248) 855-5400 *Founded/Ownrshp* 1994
Sales 11.2MM[E] *EMP* 300
SIC 6531 Real estate agent, commercial; Real estate agent, commercial
Pr: Maurice J Beznos
Treas: Mark Sturing

OAKLAND PACKAGING AND SUPPLY
See OAKLAND PAPER & SUPPLY INC

D-U-N-S 61-716-7606
OAKLAND PALLET CO INC
2500 Grant Ave, San Lorenzo, CA 94580-1810
Tel (510) 278-1291 *Founded/Ownrshp* 1995
Sales 56.3MM[E] *EMP* 165
SIC 5031 7699 Pallets, wood; Pallet repair
Pr: Jose G Padilla
**Sec:* Javier Padilla
**VP:* Carlos Padilla

D-U-N-S 05-878-0362 IMP
OAKLAND PAPER & SUPPLY INC
OAKLAND PACKAGING AND SUPPLY
3200 Regatta Blvd Ste F, Richmond, CA 94804-6418
Tel (510) 307-4242 *Founded/Ownrshp* 1988
Sales 77.0MM[E] *EMP* 120
SIC 5113 5087

D-U-N-S 82-894-6470
OAKLAND PHYSICIANS MEDICAL CENTER LLC
DOCTORS' HOSPITAL OF MICHIGAN
461 W Huron St, Pontiac, MI 48341-1601
Tel (248) 857-7200 *Founded/Ownrshp* 2008
Sales 109.2MM[E] *EMP* 700
SIC 8062 General medical & surgical hospitals; General medical & surgical hospitals
CEO: Robert H Barrow
Chf Rad: Vikram RAO
**Ch Bd:* Yatinder Singhal
COO: Dennis Franks
CFO: Mukul Kumar
**Ofcr:* John Ponczocha
Dir OR: Marisel Estrada
Comm Dir: Kathi McInally
Off Mgr: James Schulte
Nurse Mgr: Yvonne Burston
CIO: John Krieger

D-U-N-S 62-797-0221
OAKLAND RENAISSANCE ASSOCIATES
MARRIOTT
388 9th St Ste 222, Oakland, CA 94607-4458
Tel (510) 238-3400 *Founded/Ownrshp* 1986
Sales 7.7MM[E] *EMP* 389
SIC 7011 7299 5812 5813 Hotels & motels; Banquet hall facilities; Eating places; Cocktail lounge; Hotels & motels; Banquet hall facilities; Eating places; Cocktail lounge
Genl Mgr: Clifton Clark
VP: Sam Thomas

D-U-N-S 07-841-8456
OAKLAND SCHOOLS INC
OAKLAND INTERMEDIATE SCHL DIST
2111 Pontiac Lake Rd, Waterford, MI 48328-2736
Tel (248) 209-2000 *Founded/Ownrshp* 2003
Sales 254.4MM *EMP* 450
Accts Plante & Moran Pllc Clinton
SIC 8211 Public elementary & secondary schools; Public special education school; Public elementary & secondary schools; Public special education school
Pr: Barb Demarco
**Treas:* Connie Williams
**VP:* Theresa Rich
Exec: Sherry McMillan
**Prin:* George Ehlert
Ex Dir: Yocum Michael
Dir IT: Ann Nicholls

Dir IT: Martin Spusta
Pr Dir: Denell Gittus
Pgrm Dir: Susan Benson

D-U-N-S 83-242-7954
OAKLAND STAMPING LLC
(*Suby of* OS HOLDINGS LLC) ★
1200 Woodland St, Detroit, MI 48211-1071
Tel (734) 397-6300 *Founded/Ownrshp* 2009
Sales 46.8MM^E *EMP* 253
SIC 3469 Metal stampings; Metal stampings
Pr: Scott Jones
**Treas:* Robert Koss
VP: Robert E Koss

D-U-N-S 10-297-5497 IMP
■ **OAKLAND TRIBUNE INC**
TRIBUNE, THE
(*Suby of* MEDIANEWS GROUP INC) ★
1970 Broadway Ste 100, Oakland, CA 94612-2249
Tel (510) 208-6300 *Founded/Ownrshp* 1983
Sales 24.3MM^E *EMP* 800
SIC 2711 Newspapers, publishing & printing; Newspapers, publishing & printing
Pr: John Armstrong
Dir IT: Francine Brevetti

D-U-N-S 07-655-4500
OAKLAND UNIFIED SCHOOL DISTRICT
1000 Broadway Fl 4, Oakland, CA 94607-4099
Tel (510) 434-7790 *Founded/Ownrshp* 1952
Sales 433.1MM^E *EMP* 7,200
SIC 8211 Public senior high school; Public elementary & secondary schools
Dir Vol: Brittany Love
CFO: Vernon Hal
Bd of Dir: Noel Gallo
Ofcr: Carlo Tateo
VP: Alice Spearman
Mng Dir: Tyson Nichols
Dir Sec: James Williams
Prgrm Mgr: Rachelle Ard
Off Mgr: Mildred Otis
Off Mgr: Kechette Walls
Nurse Mgr: Belinda Campbell

OAKLAND UNIVERSITY
See OAKWOOD UNIVERSITY INC

D-U-N-S 04-180-8262
OAKLAND UNIVERSITY
2200 N Squirrel Rd, Rochester, MI 48309-4401
Tel (248) 370-2100 *Founded/Ownrshp* 1958
Sales 212.2MM *EMP* 2,650
Accts Andrews Hooper Pavlick Plc Au
SIC 8221 University; University
Pr: George W Hynd
Bd of Dir: Amy Butler
Ofcr: Shona Jocollins
Ofcr: Jennifer A Lumpkin
Ofcr: Kimberly McWain
Ofcr: Marvella R Ramsey
Assoc VP: Terry Stollsteimer
Sr VP: James P Lentini
VP: John W Beaghan
VP: John O Young
VP: Betty J Youngblood
Assoc Dir: Michele Knox
Assoc Dir: Paul Misch
Assoc Dir: Pamela Mitzelfeld

OAKLAND ZOO IN KNOWLAND PARK
See EAST BAY BOTANICAL AND ZOOLOGICAL SOCIETY

OAKLAWN HEALTHCARE CENTER
See THRO CO

OAKLAWN HOSPITAL
See ELLA E M BROWN CHARITABLE CIRCLE

D-U-N-S 07-740-1644
OAKLAWN JOCKEY CLUB INC
OAKLAWN RACETRACK
2705 Central Ave, Hot Springs, AR 71901-7515
Tel (501) 623-4411 *Founded/Ownrshp* 1968
Sales 22.3MM^E *EMP* 200
SIC 7948 Race track operation; Race track operation
Pr: Charles Cella
**Treas:* William L Cravens
**VP:* John G Cella
**Genl Mgr:* Eric Jackson
Dir IT: Jan Kerr
Dir IT: Ben Wagner
Opers Supe: Jason Milligan
Sales Exec: Belinda Castleberry
Sls Dir: Matt Clement
Pr Mgr: Terry Wallace
Mktg Mgr: Kim Baron
Board of Directors: William Cravens, John Ferrara, John Searcy, Ben Vanwagner, Terry Wallace

D-U-N-S 06-975-9389
OAKLAWN PSYCHIATRIC CENTER INC
330 Lakeview Dr, Goshen, IN 46528-7000
Tel (574) 533-1234 *Founded/Ownrshp* 1959
Sales 49.5MM *EMP* 625
Accts Blue & Co Llc Indianapolis I
SIC 8063 8093 Psychiatric hospitals; Specialty outpatient clinics; Psychiatric hospitals; Specialty outpatient clinics
CEO: Laurie N Nafziger
CFO: Kim Lambert
**CFO:* Lynn Miller
VP: Gregg Nussbaum
VP: Greg Schnepf
Admn Mgr: Polly Hoover
CIO: Jennifer Glick
IT Man: Teri McCreary
IT Man: Debra Snyder
Sfty Dirs: Darrin Miller
Psych: Paul Yoder

OAKLAWN RACETRACK
See OAKLAWN JOCKEY CLUB INC

D-U-N-S 94-518-0529
■ **OAKLEAF WASTE MANAGEMENT LLC**
(*Suby of* WASTE MANAGEMENT INC) ★
415 Day Hill Rd, Windsor, CT 06095-7100
Tel (860) 290-1250 *Founded/Ownrshp* 1995
Sales 13.5MM^E *EMP* 285^E
SIC 8741 4953 Management services; Refuse systems; Management services; Refuse systems
CEO: Steve Preston
CFO: Tom Nelson
Sr VP: Gregory A Pstore
VP: Paul Davi
VP: Bob Duff
VP: Kristina Nelson
Genl Mgr: Michael Finn
Mktg Mgr: Donna Landrith
Mktg Mgr: Susan Stansfield

D-U-N-S 02-960-8747 IMP
OAKLEY FERTILIZER INC
OAKLEY INTERNATIONAL
(*Suby of* BRUCE OAKLEY INC) ★
3700 Lincoln Ave, North Little Rock, AR 72114-6499
Tel (501) 945-0875 *Founded/Ownrshp* 1998
Sales 33.1MM^E *EMP* 25
SIC 5191 Fertilizers & agricultural chemicals
Pr: Edward Vance
**Pr:* Dennis B Oakley
**CFO:* Tim Cummins
**Treas:* Benny Weatherford
VP: David Choake

D-U-N-S 05-751-2204
OAKLEY GROVES INC
101 Abc Rd, Lake Wales, FL 33859-6844
Tel (863) 638-1435 *Founded/Ownrshp* 1961
Sales 98.4MM^E *EMP* 100
SIC 0174 Citrus fruits
Pr: Thomas Oakley
**Ex VP:* Ronald E Oakley

D-U-N-S 08-538-6522 IMP/EXP
OAKLEY INC
(*Suby of* LUXOTTICA GROUP SPA)
1 Icon, Foothill Ranch, CA 92610-3000
Tel (949) 951-0991 *Founded/Ownrshp* 1994
Sales 952.1MM^E *EMP* 3,400
SIC 3851 2331 2339 3021 3873 3143 Ophthalmic goods; Glasses, sun or glare; Goggles: sun, safety, industrial, underwater, etc.; Women's & misses' blouses & shirts; Women's & misses' outerwear; Rubber & plastics footwear; Watches, clocks, watchcases & parts; Men's footwear, except athletic; Ophthalmic goods; Glasses, sun or glare; Goggles: sun, safety, industrial, underwater, etc.; Women's & misses' blouses & shirts; Women's & misses' outerwear; Rubber & plastics footwear; Watches, clocks, watchcases & parts; Men's footwear, except athletic
Pr: Colin Baden
**Ch Bd:* Jim Jannard
**Ch Bd:* D Scott Olivet
Pr: Don Krause
CFO: Gianluca Pagliabue
**CFO:* Gianluca Tagliabue
Sr VP: Scott Bowers
**VP:* Derek Baker
**VP:* Michael Boxer
**VP:* Vito Giannola
VP: Erik Johnson
**VP:* Jon Krause
**VP:* Carlos Reyes

D-U-N-S 11-523-0088
OAKLEY INDUSTRIES SUB ASSEMBLY DIVISION INC
4333 Matthew, Flint, MI 48507-3160
Tel (810) 720-4444 *Founded/Ownrshp* 1984
Sales 132.1MM^E *EMP* 300
SIC 3714 Motor vehicle wheels & parts; Motor vehicle body components & frame; Motor vehicle wheels & parts; Motor vehicle body components & frame
Pr: Ronald Oakley
**COO:* Moshe Kraus
**Sec:* Michael Oakley
**VP:* Robert O Trygstad
**Prin:* Arthur Meisels
Dir Opers: James Cooke

OAKLEY INTERNATIONAL
See OAKLEY FERTILIZER INC

D-U-N-S 15-171-5851
OAKLEY TRANSPORT INC
(*Suby of* OAKLEY GROVES INC) ★
101 Abc Rd, Lake Wales, FL 33859-6844
Tel (863) 638-1435 *Founded/Ownrshp* 1961
Sales 98.4MM *EMP* 70
SIC 4213 6531 Trucking, except local; Real estate agents & managers
Pr: Thomas E Oakley
**CFO:* Ty Sherman
**Ex VP:* Ronald E Oakley
**VP:* Wade Walker

D-U-N-S 10-000-7749
OAKLEY UNION SCHOOL DISTRICT
91 Mercedes Ln, Oakley, CA 94561-4617
Tel (925) 625-5057 *Founded/Ownrshp* 2003
Sales 27.7MM^E *EMP* 549
SIC 8211 Public elementary & secondary schools; Public elementary school; Public junior high school; Kindergarten; Public elementary & secondary schools; Public elementary school; Public junior high school; Kindergarten
Schl Brd P: Mark Jordan
Psych: Cynthia Asprodites

OAKRIDGE ELEMENTARY
See OAKRIDGE SCHOOL DISTRICT

D-U-N-S 03-796-4496
OAKRIDGE LANDSCAPE INC
28064 Avenue Stanford K, Valencia, CA 91355-1159
Tel (661) 295-7228 *Founded/Ownrshp* 2001
Sales 46.1MM^E *EMP* 135^E
SIC 0721 0781 Irrigation system operation, not providing water; Landscape services
CEO: Jeffrey E Myers
Area Mgr: Anselmo Ventura
Genl Mgr: Ken Aldrich

D-U-N-S 04-636-7074
OAKRIDGE SCHOOL DISTRICT
OAKRIDGE ELEMENTARY
251 S Wolf Lake Rd, Muskegon, MI 49442-3029
Tel (231) 788-7500 *Founded/Ownrshp* 1963
Sales 10.7MM^E *EMP* 292
SIC 8211 Public elementary & secondary schools; Public elementary & secondary schools
Prin: Michael Goyette

OAKRIDGE SUPERMARKET
See RALEIGH & RON CORP

OAKS AT BROOKSHIRE, THE
See ADVANCED LIVING TECHNOLOGIES INC

OAKS AT FORSYTHE, THE
See FOUNDATION HEALTH SYSTEM INC

D-U-N-S 84-229-1853
OAKS CHRISTIAN SCHOOL
31749 La Tienda Rd, Westlake Village, CA 91362-4010
Tel (818) 575-9900 *Founded/Ownrshp* 1997
Sales 48.5MM *EMP* 250
Accts Capin Crouse Llp Brea Ca
SIC 8211 Private senior high school; Private senior high school
Pr: Jeff Woodcock
**Ch Bd:* David Price
**CFO:* Paul Oberhaus
**Treas:* Kris Thabit
Rgnl Mgr: Kristi Fitzgerald

D-U-N-S 09-921-7499
OAKS FORD FAIR INC
FAIR OAKS FORD LINCOLN
1351 E Ogden Ave, Naperville, IL 60563-1637
Tel (630) 357-7100 *Founded/Ownrshp* 1998
Sales 43.9MM^E *EMP* 85
SIC 5511 Automobiles, new & used; Trucks, tractors & trailers: new & used; Automobiles, new & used; Trucks, tractors & trailers: new & used
Pr: Norm Zienty Jr
**Sec:* Lillian Zienty

D-U-N-S 18-538-7081
OAKSHIRE MUSHROOM FARM INC
295 Thompson Rd, Kennett Square, PA 19348
Tel (610) 444-9600 *Founded/Ownrshp* 1985
Sales 20.8MM^E *EMP* 60
SIC 0182 5812 Mushrooms grown under cover; Eating places
Pr: Gary Schroeder
VP: Brian Kiniry
**VP:* Morris Schroeder

D-U-N-S 07-441-3766
OAKTON COMMUNITY COLLEGE
1600 E Golf Rd Rm 1505, Des Plaines, IL 60016-1256
Tel (847) 635-1600 *Founded/Ownrshp* 1977
Sales 24.1MM *EMP* 2,000
Accts Sikich Naperville Illinois
SIC 8221 8222 Colleges universities & professional schools; Community college; Colleges universities & professional schools; Community college
Pr: Margaret B Lee
Ofcr: Bill Kopecky
VP: Michele Brown
VP: Bonnie Lucas
Off Mgr: Kathy Schultz
IT Man: Karen Epps
Snr Mgr: George Carpenter

D-U-N-S 09-718-0095
OAKTON PAVILLION INC
1660 Oakton Pl, Des Plaines, IL 60018-2045
Tel (847) 299-5588 *Founded/Ownrshp* 1979
Sales 21.0MM^E *EMP* 250
SIC 8051 Convalescent home with continuous nursing care; Convalescent home with continuous nursing care
Pr: Fred Weis
**Treas:* Mark Palmer
VP: Harold Katz
Dir Soc: Mike Francis
HC Dir: Kevin Carnahan
Board of Directors: Irving Loukowitz

D-U-N-S 96-887-8756
▲ **OAKTREE CAPITAL GROUP HOLDINGS LP**
333 S Grand Ave Fl 28, Los Angeles, CA 90071-1504
Tel (213) 830-6300 *Founded/Ownrshp* 2007
Sales 365.7MM^E *EMP* 4,100^E
SIC 6282 Investment advice; Investment advice
Ch: Howard S Marks
Genl Pt: Oaktree Capital Group Holdings
Pr: Bruce Allen Karsh

D-U-N-S 83-003-8415
■ **OAKTREE CAPITAL GROUP LLC**
(*Suby of* OAKTREE CAPITAL GROUP HOLDINGS LP) ★
333 S Grand Ave Fl 28, Los Angeles, CA 90071-1504
Tel (213) 830-6300 *Founded/Ownrshp* 1995
Sales 193.8MM *EMP* 927^E
Tkr Sym OAK *Exch* NYS
SIC 6282 Investment advice; Investment advice
CEO: Jay S Wintrob
**V Ch:* John B Frank
**Ch:* Bruce A Karsh
**Ofcr:* Susan Gentile
**Ofcr:* David M Kirchheimer
Sr VP: Jason Keller
VP: Amy Johannes
VP: Jerilyn C McAniff
Prin: Sheldon M Stone

D-U-N-S 87-994-4569
■ **OAKTREE CAPITAL MANAGEMENT LP**
(*Suby of* OAKTREE CAPITAL GROUP LLC) ★
333 S Grand Ave Ste 2800, Los Angeles, CA 90071-1530
Tel (213) 830-6300 *Founded/Ownrshp* 2010
Sales 1.8MMM^E *EMP* 4,100
SIC 6282 6722 6211 Investment advisory service; Management investment, open-end; Security brokers & dealers; Investment advisory service; Management investment, open-end; Security brokers & dealers
Pr: Bruce Karsh
Pt: J B Forth
Pt: Larry Gilson
Pt: Larry W Keele
Pt: D R Masson
Pt: Sheldon M Stone
Pr: Jay Ghiya
Pr: Dominic Keenan
CFO: David Kirchheimer
CFO: David Kirchheiner
Sr Cor Off: Andrew Fastow
Ex VP: Eugenia Tsang
Sr VP: Aaron A Bendikson
Sr VP: Erin Boasberg
Sr VP: Lisa Kenyon
Sr VP: Andrew Salter
Sr VP: Nebil Senman
VP: Carrie Armenta
VP: Brian Berman
VP: Chris Boehringer
VP: Troy Campbell

D-U-N-S 08-211-9025
OAKVILLE PRODUCE PARTNERS LLC
GREENLEAF
453 Valley Dr, Brisbane, CA 94005-1209
Tel (415) 647-2991 *Founded/Ownrshp* 1974
Sales 100.5MM^E *EMP* 150
SIC 5148 5451 Fruits, fresh; Vegetables, fresh; Dairy products stores; Fruits, fresh; Vegetables, fresh; Dairy products stores
**Pr:* Frank Ballentine
Snr Mgr: Peter Napolitano

D-U-N-S 19-660-5398
OAKWOOD ACCEPTANCE CORP LLC
GOLDEN CIRCLE FINANCIAL SVCS
7800 Mccloud Rd, Greensboro, NC 27409-9634
Tel (336) 664-2400 *Founded/Ownrshp* 1992
Sales NA *EMP* 350
SIC 6162 Mortgage bankers & correspondents; Mortgage bankers & correspondents
Pr: Myles E Standish
CFO: Michael Kilbourne
CFO: Steven Michael
Treas: S G Steifel
**Sec:* Douglas R Muir
Trst: Timothy Davis
Ofcr: Dale Elliott
Ex VP: Macy Foster
**Ex VP:* Robert Smith
Ex VP: J M Stidha
Ex VP: Michael J Stidham
**Sr VP:* Joseph W Fowler
VP: James D Casterline
VP: Wayne E Patterson

D-U-N-S 02-841-0777
OAKWOOD CITY SCHOOL DISTRICT INC (OH)
20 Rubicon Rd, Oakwood, OH 45409-2239
Tel (937) 297-5332 *Founded/Ownrshp* 1908
Sales 24.4MM *EMP* 275
SIC 8211 Public elementary & secondary schools; School board; Public elementary & secondary schools; School board
**Treas:* Kevin Philo

OAKWOOD COMMON
See OAKWOOD HEALTH PROMOTIONS INC

D-U-N-S 04-742-2597
OAKWOOD COMMUNITY UNIT SCHOOL DISTRICT 76
5834 Us Route 150, Fithian, IL 61844-5195
Tel (217) 354-4355 *Founded/Ownrshp* 1976
Sales 7.0MM *EMP* 301
Accts Daughhetee & Parks Pc Cpa D
SIC 8211 Public elementary & secondary schools; Public elementary & secondary schools
Pr: John Harrison
Schl Brd P: Greg Wolfe

D-U-N-S 03-969-7888 IMP
OAKWOOD ENERGY MANAGEMENT INC
OAKWOOD GROUP, THE
9755 Inkster Rd, Taylor, MI 48180-3048
Tel (734) 947-7700 *Founded/Ownrshp* 2001
Sales 29.9MM^E *EMP* 115
SIC 2821 Polyethylene resins; Polyethylene resins
Pr: Richard Audi
Ex VP: Don Smith
**VP:* John Audi
**VP:* Richard Audi II
Dir Bus: Craig Bonk
IT Man: Sharon Harper
QC Dir: Susan Ficarro
Ql Cn Mgr: Linda Sarp

OAKWOOD GROUP, THE
See OAKWOOD METAL FABRICATING CO

OAKWOOD GROUP, THE
See OAKWOOD ENERGY MANAGEMENT INC

D-U-N-S 82-988-8502
OAKWOOD HEALTH CARE CENTER INC
200 Bassett Rd, Williamsville, NY 14221-2639
Tel (716) 689-6681 *Founded/Ownrshp* 1992
Sales 16.4MM^E *EMP* 300
SIC 8051 Skilled nursing care facilities; Skilled nursing care facilities
Pr: Robert M Chur
**VP:* Carol Chur
**VP:* Richard Courtney
**VP:* William Gillick
**VP:* Bruce Wisbaum
Ex Dir: Maria Landy
CIO: Laura Wall
HC Dir: Ann Reinard

OAKWOOD HEALTH LINE
See OAKWOOD HEALTHCARE INC

D-U-N-S 62-242-0743
OAKWOOD HEALTH PROMOTIONS INC
OAKWOOD COMMON
16351 Rotunda Dr Apt 2, Dearborn, MI 48120-1160
Tel (313) 253-9600 *Founded/Ownrshp* 1985
Sales 35.8MM *EMP* 500
Accts Deloitte Tax Llp Detroit Mi
SIC 8059 8051 Personal care home, with health care; Skilled nursing care facilities; Personal care home, with health care; Skilled nursing care facilities

D-U-N-S 07-841-0842
OAKWOOD HEALTHCARE INC
OAKWOOD HEALTH LINE
(*Suby of* BEAUMONT BOTSFORD OAKWOOD HLTH) ★
18101 Oakwood Blvd, Dearborn, MI 48124-4089
Tel (313) 593-7000 *Founded/Ownrshp* 2014
Sales 917.4MM^E *EMP* 9,200
SIC 8062 General medical & surgical hospitals; General medical & surgical hospitals
CEO: Brain Connolly
COO: Gregory Bock
COO: Kathleen Cronin
COO: Kelly Smith
CFO: Greg Messer
Chf Mktg O: Amy Middleton
Ofcr: Sonja Wilcox-Berriel
Ofcr: Laura Wolan
Ex VP: Michael A Geheb
Dir Rad: Tim Vargus
Dir Bus: Marvin Khafaji

OAKWOOD HOMES
See CLAYTON HOMES INC

D-U-N-S 78-778-8405
OAKWOOD HOMES LLC
4908 Tower Rd, Denver, CO 80249-6684
Tel (303) 486-8500 *Founded/Ownrshp* 1991
Sales 121.4MM^E *EMP* 150
SIC 1521 New construction, single-family houses; New construction, single-family houses
COO: Brooke Ray
VP: Chad Ellington
VP: Aric Jones
VP: Dan Santaniello
VP: Frank Walker
CIO: Ray Appel
S&M/VP: Kristen White
Mktg Mgr: Lauren Karsh
Manager: Dwayne Montoya
Sls Mgr: Sam Litzau

D-U-N-S 01-680-4288
OAKWOOD LABORATORIES
(*Suby of* OAKWOOD HEALTH LINE) ★
18101 Oakwood Blvd Fl 2, Dearborn, MI 48124-4089
Tel (313) 593-7000 *Founded/Ownrshp* 1959, 1986
Sales 8.7MM^E *EMP* 284
SIC 8071 Testing laboratories; Blood analysis laboratory; Urinalysis laboratory; Testing laboratories; Blood analysis laboratory; Urinalysis laboratory
Prin: Vic Pound
Doctor: Nadarajan Janakan
Pgrm Dir: Craig Glines
Snr Mgr: Louise Martin
Snr Mgr: Nancy Wilson
Board of Directors: Frederick J Barten, J Thomas Powaser MD, William H Rees, Michael F Schaldenbrand MD

D-U-N-S 07-659-6451
OAKWOOD LIVING CENTERS OF MASSACHUSETTS INC
MAYFLWER NRSING RHBLTATION CTR
123 South St, Plymouth, MA 02360-2945
Tel (508) 746-4343 *Founded/Ownrshp* 2000
Sales 23.3MM^E *EMP* 972
SIC 8051 8211 Skilled nursing care facilities; School for physically handicapped; Skilled nursing care facilities; School for physically handicapped

D-U-N-S 06-689-6960
OAKWOOD LUTHERAN HOMES ASSOCIATION INC
OAKWOOD VILLAGE
6205 Mineral Point Rd, Madison, WI 53705-4576
Tel (608) 230-4699 *Founded/Ownrshp* 1948
Sales 36.4MM^E *EMP* 500^E
SIC 8361 Home for the aged; Home for the aged
CEO: Rick Bova
COO: John E Howl
CFO: Barbara Fraser
**CFO:* Gerald H Jerry Kelm
Ex Dir: Jean Jacobson
QA Dir: Lauren Hartlaub
Nrsg Dir: Brenda Douma
Pharmcst: Stephen Seidl

D-U-N-S 00-539-0778 IMP
OAKWOOD METAL FABRICATING CO
OAKWOOD GROUP, THE
1100 Oakwood Blvd, Dearborn, MI 48124-2820
Tel (734) 947-7700 *Founded/Ownrshp* 1947
Sales 79.3MM^E *EMP* 390
SIC 3465 3714 3469 Automotive stampings; Motor vehicle parts & accessories; Metal stampings; Automotive stampings; Motor vehicle parts & accessories; Metal stampings
Pr: Richard F Audi
COO: Andre Mealy
Ofcr: Patricia Longo
VP: J B Audi
VP: Donald Smith
VP: R Szkody
Exec: Sharon Harper
Prgrm Mgr: Hilding Holcombe
Plnt Mgr: Todd Miller
Ql Cn Mgr: Tameria Manson

D-U-N-S 03-002-1291
OAKWOOD NURSING & REHABILITATION LP
(*Suby of* DAYBREAK VENTURE LLC) ★
301 W Randol Mill Rd, Arlington, TX 76011-5733
Tel (817) 460-2002 *Founded/Ownrshp* 2010
Sales 4.2MM *EMP* 1,123^E
SIC 8059 Nursing home, except skilled & intermediate care facility
Prin: Linda Duckworth

D-U-N-S 07-623-0283
OAKWOOD SCHOOL
11600 Magnolia Blvd, North Hollywood, CA 91601-3098
Tel (818) 732-3000 *Founded/Ownrshp* 1951
Sales 29.8MM *EMP* 89
SIC 8211 Elementary school; Private elementary & secondary schools; Elementary school; Private elementary & secondary schools
CFO: Elliot Spokane
Ex Dir: Robert White
Cmptr Lab: Damon Falconer

D-U-N-S 07-209-5326
OAKWOOD UNIVERSITY INC
OAKLAND UNIVERSITY
7000 Adventist Blvd Nw, Huntsville, AL 35896-0001
Tel (256) 726-7000 *Founded/Ownrshp* 1896
Sales 60.5MM *EMP* 440
Accts Dipiazza Larocca Heeter & Co L
SIC 8221 College, except junior; College, except junior
Pr: Leslie Pollard
Dir Recs: Shirley Scott
Treas: Diane Rugless
VP: John Anderson
VP: Timothy McDonald
Ex Dir: Norris Kisha
Dir Sec: Lewis Eakins
Off Mgr: Janice Collins
Store Mgr: Mark Taylor
IT Man: Trevor Johnson
Sls&Mrk Ex: Rennae Elliott

OAKWOOD VILLAGE
See OAKWOOD LUTHERAN HOMES ASSOCIATION INC

OAKWOOD WORLDWIDE
See R & B REALTY GROUP LP

D-U-N-S 13-025-6837 IMP/EXP
OAKWORKS INC
923 E Wellspring Rd, New Freedom, PA 17349-8408
Tel (717) 227-0516 *Founded/Ownrshp* 1978
Sales 29.6MM *EMP* 100^E
SIC 2531 Public building & related furniture; Public building & related furniture
Pr: Jeffrey Riach
**Pr:* Richard Schuman
**CFO:* Charles Alcorn
CFO: Richard L Shuman
**Ex VP:* Linda Riach
Sr VP: Rich Elsen
Prd Mgr: Lee Ketterman
VP Mktg: Rodger Hyle
Mktg Mgr: Melissa Mancuso

D-U-N-S 07-483-0209
■ **OAO CORP**
(*Suby of* LOCKHEED MARTIN SERVICES INC) ★
700 N Frederick Ave, Gaithersburg, MD 20879-3328
Tel (301) 240-7000 *Founded/Ownrshp* 2001
Sales 39.7MM^E *EMP* 2,100
SIC 7371 8711 3823 3559 Computer software development; Aviation &/or aeronautical engineering; Thermal conductivity instruments, industrial process type; Robots, molding & forming plastics; Computer software development; Aviation &/or aeronautical engineering; Thermal conductivity instruments, industrial process type; Robots, molding & forming plastics
Ch Bd: Cecile D Barker
**CFO:* Hubert M Reid
**Sr VP:* Robert L Lohfeld
Sr VP: Edwin S Warrell
VP: Jay Jones

D-U-N-S 96-737-5833
OAO TECHNOLOGY SOLUTIONS INC
(*Suby of* PLATINUM EQUITY LLC) ★
7500 Greenway Center Dr # 150, Greenbelt, MD 20770-3534
Tel (301) 486-0400 *Founded/Ownrshp* 2010
Sales 36.6MM^E *EMP* 1,600
SIC 7379 Computer related consulting services; Computer related consulting services
Pr: Sidney E Fuchs
Pr: Duke Dickson
Pr: Sherry Robertson
VP: Stephen Brinch
VP: Joanne Connelly
VP: Robert Ohfed
VP: Emmett Paige
VP: Tony Rignola
VP: Mary Sigler
VP: John Weisman
IT Man: Mark Hamrol

OASAM
See OFFICE OF ASSISTANT SECRETARY FOR ADMINISTRATION AND MANAGEMENT

D-U-N-S 96-267-9358 IMP
OASIS BRANDS INC
230 Costello Dr, Winchester, VA 22602-4310
Tel (540) 658-2830 *Founded/Ownrshp* 2009
Sales 47.1MM^E *EMP* 50
SIC 5113 Napkins, paper
CEO: Nathan Hanson
VP: Mark Kirchgasser
Mktg Dir: Christa Debbout
Sls Dir: Mark Kaiser
Sls Dir: James White
Mktg Mgr: Anish Banerjee

OASIS CHEVROLET
See OASIS MOTORS INC

OASIS FOODS CO
See OASIS TRADING CO INC

D-U-N-S 07-834-4337
OASIS GROUP INTERNATIONAL LLC
OASIS STRATEGIC SERVICES
6016 Lee Hwy, Warrenton, VA 20187-7257
Tel (540) 347-1897 *Founded/Ownrshp* 2013
Sales 39.8MM *EMP* 50^E
SIC 1611 Concrete construction: roads, highways, sidewalks, etc.; Concrete construction: roads, highways, sidewalks, etc.
Ch Bd: Amira Ballarin
Pr: Perry Davis
VP: Jonathan Ostman
IT Man: Ravyn Haley

OASIS HOTEL CASINO SPA & GOLF
See BLANCA CASA RESORTS LLC

OASIS INN
See PERHAM COOPERATIVE CREAMERY

D-U-N-S 13-223-0009
OASIS LEGAL FINANCE GROUP LLC
9525 Bryn Mawr Ave # 900, Rosemont, IL 60018-5264
Tel (847) 521-4400 *Founded/Ownrshp* 2002
Sales NA *EMP* 100
SIC 6159 Small business investment companies; Small business investment companies
COO: Colin Lawler
CFO: Juan P Reyes
Chf Mktg O: Michael Olsen
Comm Dir: David Schwartz
CTO: Jonathan Feldman
Dir IT: David Winkiel
Software D: Anton Bondarenko
**Genl Couns:* Kevin Connor

OASIS LIQUOR
See SIGELS BEVERAGES LP

D-U-N-S 19-412-1018 IMP
OASIS MEDICAL INC
510-528 S Vermont Ave, Glendora, CA 91741
Tel (909) 305-5400 *Founded/Ownrshp* 1987
Sales 20.7MM^E *EMP* 150
SIC 3851 5048 Ophthalmic goods; Ophthalmic goods; Surgical & medical instruments; Ophthalmic goods; Ophthalmic goods
Ch Bd: Norman Delgado
**Pr:* Craig Delgado
**Sec:* Arlene Delgado
Rgnl Mgr: James Boore
QA Dir: Edward Anna
Sfty Mgr: Fred Janette
Ql Cn Mgr: Nikki Hubert
Mktg Mgr: Donna Ryskey
Sls Mgr: Mark Anderson

D-U-N-S 01-174-2921
OASIS MOTORS INC
OASIS CHEVROLET
1292 Us Highway 9, Old Bridge, NJ 08857-2841
Tel (732) 316-2600 *Founded/Ownrshp* 1962
Sales 47.8MM^E *EMP* 140
SIC 5511 Automobiles, new & used; Pickups, new & used; Automobiles, new & used; Pickups, new & used
Pr: Irving Rosen
**Sec:* Helen Rosen
**VP:* David Rosen
**VP:* Robin Rosen
**VP:* Ronald Rosen
Genl Mgr: Bob Slater
Sls Mgr: Eric Sopko

D-U-N-S 13-776-8094
OASIS OUTSOURCING HOLDINGS INC
2054 Vista Pkwy Ste 300, West Palm Beach, FL 33411-6742
Tel (561) 227-6500 *Founded/Ownrshp* 2014
Sales 27.2MM^E *EMP* 391
SIC 7361 Employment agencies; Employment agencies
Pr: Mark C Perlberg
Pr: Daneen Tyson
CFO: Terry Mayotte
Ex VP: Myron Blacmon
Ex VP: Kim Ferrarie
Ex VP: Robert Hsu
Ex VP: Mike Viola
Sr VP: Ruth Trezevant Cyrus
Sr VP: Kerim Fidel
Sr VP: Alina Gabbard
Sr VP: Kathleen Rainey
Dir Surg: D R Tower

D-U-N-S 17-196-3598
OASIS OUTSOURCING II INC
KING EMPLOYER SERVICES
(*Suby of* NAUTIC PARTNERS LLC) ★
2054 Vista Pkwy Ste 300, West Palm Beach, FL 33411-6742
Tel (561) 227-6500 *Founded/Ownrshp* 1996
Sales 108.1MM^E *EMP* 600
SIC 8721 8742 7363 Accounting, auditing & bookkeeping; Human resource consulting services; Employee leasing service; Temporary help service; Accounting, auditing & bookkeeping; Human resource consulting services; Employee leasing service; Temporary help service
CEO: Mark Perlberg
Pr: Carlos Diaz
Pr: Chawn Weatherly
**Ex VP:* Terry Mayotte
**Ex VP:* Mike Viola
**Sr VP:* Ruth Trezevant Cyrus
VP: Mark Reinisch
Mng Dir: Jan-Even Ostrem
Dist Mgr: Carlos Cardenas
Dist Mgr: Bill Leahy
Dist Mgr: Scott Ward

D-U-N-S 96-404-3199
▲ **OASIS PETROLEUM INC**
1001 Fannin St Ste 1500, Houston, TX 77002-6739
Tel (281) 404-9500 *Founded/Ownrshp* 2007
Sales 1.3MMM *EMP* 405^E
Tkr Sym OAS *Exch* NYS
SIC 1311 Crude petroleum production; Natural gas production; Crude petroleum production; Natural gas production
Ch Bd: Thomas B Nusz
**Pr:* Taylor L Reid
CFO: Michael H Lou
Ex VP: Nickolas J Lorentzatos
Sr VP: Roy W Mace
VP: Kent Beers
VP: Thomas Hawkins
VP: Jim Jolly
VP: Brett Newton
VP: Richard Robuck
VP: Cash Smithwick
Board of Directors: William J Cassidy, Ted Collins Jr, Michael McShane, Bobby S Shackouls, Douglas E Swanson Jr

D-U-N-S 80-135-8933
■ **OASIS PETROLEUM LLC**
(*Suby of* OASIS PETROLEUM INC) ★
1001 Fannin St Ste 1500, Houston, TX 77002-6739
Tel (281) 404-9500 *Founded/Ownrshp* 2007
Sales 35.5MM^E *EMP* 75^E
SIC 1311 Crude petroleum production; Crude petroleum production

D-U-N-S 08-832-7650
OASIS RECREATIONAL PROPERTIES INC
(*Suby of* CASA BLANCA RESORT) ★
897 W Mesquite Blvd, Mesquite, NV 89027-5203
Tel (702) 346-4040 *Founded/Ownrshp* 2001
Sales 9.3MM^E *EMP* 685^E
SIC 6512 Nonresidential building operators
Pr: Robert R Black Sr

D-U-N-S 07-929-0871
OASIS REPOWER LLC
15445 Innovation Dr, San Diego, CA 92128-3432
Tel (888) 903-6926 *Founded/Ownrshp* 2013
Sales 283.6MM^E *EMP* 826
SIC 4911 Electric services; Electric services
Pr: Tristan Grimbert
Sec: Robert Miller
VP: Ryan Pfaff

OASIS STRATEGIC SERVICES
See OASIS GROUP INTERNATIONAL LLC

D-U-N-S 17-601-8810
OASIS SYSTEMS LLC
24 Hartwell Ave, Lexington, MA 02421-3132
Tel (781) 676-7333 *Founded/Ownrshp* 1997
Sales 59.7MM^E *EMP* 430
SIC 7379 7371 Computer related consulting services; Custom computer programming services; Computer related consulting services; Custom computer programming services
Pr: Thomas Colatospi
COO: Rosemary Cook
**VP:* Greg Esses
VP: Peter A Krawczyk
VP: David Larochelle
VP: Michael McElwain
VP: Maggie Wetzell
Dir Bus: Dayl Donahey
Prgrm Mgr: Donovan Pavlik
Prgrm Mgr: Carl Wiedemann
QA Dir: Denise Rich

D-U-N-S 04-073-1911 IMP/EXP
OASIS TRADING CO INC
OASIS FOODS CO
(*Suby of* AAK SWEDEN AB)
635 Ramsey Ave Ste 201, Hillside, NJ 07205-1099
Tel (908) 964-0477 *Founded/Ownrshp* 2012
Sales 48.3MM^E *EMP* 150
SIC 2079 2035 2084 4783 Cooking oils, except corn: vegetable refined; Dressings, salad: raw & cooked (except dry mixes); Mayonnaise; Wines; Packing goods for shipping; Cooking oils, except corn: vegetable refined; Dressings, salad: raw & cooked (except dry mixes); Mayonnaise; Wines; Packing goods for shipping
Pr: Anthony Alves
VP: Don Black
VP: Lilliana Ferreria
Ql Cn Mgr: Isabel Mendoza
VP Sls: Ivone Teixeira
Mktg Dir: Paula Ferreira
Mktg Mgr: Brian Hennessy

D-U-N-S 14-940-6436
OASIS WEST REALTY LLC
1800 Century Park E # 500, Los Angeles, CA 90067-1508
Tel (310) 274-8066 *Founded/Ownrshp* 2003
Sales 61.9MM^E *EMP* 502^E
SIC 6726 5947 5813 5812 7011 Investment offices; Gift shop; Drinking places; Eating places; Hotels; Investment offices; Gift shop; Drinking places; Eating places; Hotels

OASYS
See OMGEO LLC

OASYS
See OUTSOURCED ADMINISTRATIVE SYSTEMS INC

OATEY COMPANY
See OATEY SUPPLY CHAIN SERVICES INC

D-U-N-S 00-419-8388 IMP
OATEY CO (OH)
4700 W 160th St, Cleveland, OH 44135-2632
Tel (216) 267-7100 *Founded/Ownrshp* 1916
Sales 155.1MM^E *EMP* 800
SIC 3444

D-U-N-S 10-165-4916
OATEY SUPPLY CHAIN SERVICES INC
OATEY COMPANY
4700 W 160th St, Cleveland, OH 44135-2632
Tel (216) 267-7100 *Founded/Ownrshp* 2002
Sales 116.8MM^E *EMP* 130
SIC 5074 Plumbing & hydronic heating supplies; Plumbing & hydronic heating supplies

Pr: John H McMillan
CFO: Neal Restivo

OATI
See OPEN ACCESS TECHNOLOGY INTERNATIONAL INC

D-U-N-S 02-036-1762
OATS INC (MO)
O A T S
2501 Maguire Blvd Ste 101, Columbia, MO 65201-3705
Tel (573) 443-4516 *Founded/Ownrshp* 1971
Sales 24.6MM *EMP* 755
Accts Graves And Associates Cpas Ll
SIC 4119 Local passenger transportation; Local passenger transportation
Pr: Nolan G McNeill
**Ch Bd:* Nolan Mc Neill
**Treas:* Betty Smith
**VP:* Mel Sundermeyer
**Ex Dir:* Linda Yaeger

D-U-N-S 02-778-1202
OB SALEM AUTO GROUP INC
DELON DOWNTOWN AUTO CENTER
745 Liberty St Ne, Salem, OR 97301-2447
Tel (503) 581-1421 *Founded/Ownrshp* 1969
Sales 69.9MM^E *EMP* 265
SIC 5511 Automobiles, new & used; Automobiles, new & used
Pr: Michael O'Brien
**Treas:* Michael Jacobson
**VP:* Herbert Juran

D-U-N-S 60-460-0528
OB/GYN SPECIALISTS OF PALM BEACHES PA
770 Northpoint Pkwy, West Palm Beach, FL 33407-1901
Tel (561) 802-5352 *Founded/Ownrshp* 1968
Sales 21.1MM^E *EMP* 210
SIC 8011 Gynecologist; Gynecologist
Pr: John A Burigo
VP: John Burigo
**VP:* Robert D Gordon O
**Prin:* Koch Ronald MD
IT Man: Laura Woods
Obsttrcn: Roberta Reilly
Obsttrcn: Laura Weston
Doctor: Jennifer B Thrasher MD

D-U-N-S 79-055-3353
■ **OBAGI MEDICAL PRODUCTS INC**
(*Suby of* VALEANT PHARMACEUTICALS INTERNATIONAL) ★
50 Technology Dr, Irvine, CA 92618-2301
Tel (562) 628-1007 *Founded/Ownrshp* 2013
Sales 38.2MM^E *EMP* 203^E
SIC 2834 Pharmaceutical preparations; Dermatologicals; Pharmaceutical preparations; Dermatologicals
Pr: J Michael Pearson
**Treas:* Howard B Schiller
Ex VP: Katherine Regnier
Sr VP: Mark T Taylor
VP: Naseem Glaubitz
VP: Curt Hanson
Dir IT: Fay Adams
Dir IT: Jon Rucinski
Opers Mgr: Kendall Rodgers
Mktg Mgr: Stephanie Zubiate
Sls Mgr: Lauren Baker

D-U-N-S 80-075-0213
OBAMA FOR AMERICA
130 E Randolph St Ste 600, Chicago, IL 60601-6164
Tel (312) 698-3670 *Founded/Ownrshp* 2007
Sales 18.9MM^E *EMP* 400
SIC 8651 Political campaign organization; Political campaign organization
Pr: David Plouffe
CFO: Marianne Markowitz
CTO: Kevin Malover

D-U-N-S 01-003-2480
OBAUGH CHARLIE PONTIAC BUICK GMC MAZDA INC
CHARLIE OBAUGH BUICK
410 Lee Jackson Hwy, Staunton, VA 24401-5506
Tel (540) 885-8893 *Founded/Ownrshp* 1975
Sales 24.0MM^E *EMP* 50
SIC 5511 Automobiles, new & used
Pr: Charles O'Baugh
Treas: Debbie Brown
VP: Eric O'Baugh
VP: Obaugh Eric W
Sls Mgr: Thomas Ballengee
Sls Mgr: Lou Somma
Sales Asso: Jay Crawford
Sales Asso: Brad Ewing
Sales Asso: Chaz Fillion
Sales Asso: Samantha Gandee
Sales Asso: Brian Henkel

D-U-N-S 13-447-5768
OBAYASHI USA LLC
(*Suby of* OBAYASHI CORPORATION)
577 Airport Blvd Ste 600, Burlingame, CA 94010-2057
Tel (650) 952-4910 *Founded/Ownrshp* 2002
Sales 163.7MM^E *EMP* 1,302^E
SIC 6531 Real estate agents & managers; Real estate agents & managers
Treas: Katsunori Nomura
Sr VP: Tedashi Kinukawa

D-U-N-S 82-983-0285 IMP/EXP
■ **OBCORP LLC**
O'BRIEN
(*Suby of* AMETEK INC) ★
1900 Crystal Indus Ct, Saint Louis, MO 63114-6020
Tel (314) 423-4444 *Founded/Ownrshp* 2012
Sales 51.5MM^E *EMP* 126^E
SIC 3644 3825 3161 Noncurrent-carrying wiring services; Insulators & insulation materials, electrical; Instruments to measure electricity; Luggage; Noncurrent-carrying wiring services; Insulators & insulation materials, electrical; Instruments to measure electricity; Luggage

CFO: Michael Pollock
Chf Mktg O: Shawn Rowan
Rgnl Mgr: Mike Wagner
IT Man: Mike Pellegrini
Prd Mgr: Dennis Kerperien
Sales Exec: Laura French
Sales Exec: Jim Killeen
VP Sls: Larissa Abeling
VP Sls: Tom Anderson
S&M/VP: Rich Burruss
Sls Dir: Lowell Kachalsky

D-U-N-S 07-491-7683
OBER GATLINBURG INC (TN)
GATLINBURG SKI RESORT
1001 Parkway Ste 2, Gatlinburg, TN 37738-3138
Tel (865) 436-5423 *Founded/Ownrshp* 1975
Sales 13.2MM^E *EMP* 400^E
SIC 7999 7011

D-U-N-S 01-009-2278
OBER KALER GRIMES & SHRIVER A PROFESSIONAL CORP (MD)
100 Light St, Baltimore, MD 21202-1036
Tel (410) 685-1120 *Founded/Ownrshp* 1903, 1983
Sales 23.5MM^E *EMP* 277
SIC 8111

OBERER COMPANIES
See OBERER DEVELOPMENT CO

D-U-N-S 03-093-9839
OBERER DEVELOPMENT CO
OBERER COMPANIES
3475 Newmark Dr, Miamisburg, OH 45342-5426
Tel (937) 910-0851 *Founded/Ownrshp* 1971
Sales 50.5MM^E *EMP* 160
SIC 6552 1521 1522 1542 6513 Subdividers & developers; Single-family housing construction; Residential construction; Nonresidential construction; Apartment building operators
Ch: George R Oberer Sr
COO: Kerry Duncan
VP: Chris Conley
Ql Cn Mgr: Dennis Cruea

OBERER THOMPSON CO
See GREATER DAYTON CONSTRUCTION LTD

D-U-N-S 96-834-7612
OBERFIELDS LLC
528 London Rd, Delaware, OH 43015-2850
Tel (740) 369-7644 *Founded/Ownrshp* 2009
Sales 25.0MM *EMP* 120
SIC 3272 Concrete products, precast
Pr: Bruce Loris
**VP:* Joe Mahler
Sls Mgr: Don McCorkle
Sales Asso: Jim Cordonnier

OBERG FREEPORT
See OBERG INDUSTRIES INC

D-U-N-S 00-434-4644
OBERG INDUSTRIES INC
OBERG FREEPORT
2301 Silverville Rd, Freeport, PA 16229-1630
Tel (724) 295-2121 *Founded/Ownrshp* 1948
Sales 210.6MM^E *EMP* 650
SIC 3469 3545 Metal stampings; Precision tools, machinists'; Metal stampings; Precision tools, machinists'
Pr: Robert F Wagner
**Pr:* David L Bonvenuto
COO: Mark Paolillo
**Ch:* D Eric Oberg II
**Treas:* Jeffrey M Mattiuz
Sr VP: Wesley Elliott
VP: Brian Roofner
VP: Dave Rugaber
Dir QC: Brian Stewart
Mfg Dir: Jim Hoffman
Mfg Dir: Mark Pelo

D-U-N-S 11-663-8714
OBERKOTTER FOUNDATION
1600 Market St Ste 3600, Philadelphia, PA 19103-7212
Tel (215) 751-2601 *Founded/Ownrshp* 1985
Sales 52.2MM *EMP* 4
SIC 8361 Home for the deaf & blind; Home for the deaf & blind
Ex Dir: Bruce Rosenfield
**Prin:* George H Nofer

D-U-N-S 07-837-3312
OBERLANDER ELECTRIC CO
2101 N Main St, East Peoria, IL 61611-1739
Tel (309) 694-1468 *Founded/Ownrshp* 2012
Sales 34.6MM *EMP* 175
Accts Gordon Stockman & Waugh Pc
SIC 1731 General electrical contractor; General electrical contractor
Prin: David P Hicke Jr
Ofcr: Jim Schierer

D-U-N-S 01-659-6199
OBERLE & ASSOCIATES INC
700 Nw 2nd St, Richmond, IN 47374-2225
Tel (765) 966-7715 *Founded/Ownrshp* 1963
Sales 20.9MM^E *EMP* 85
Accts Williams & Keckler
SIC 1542 1541 1796 Commercial & office building, new construction; Commercial & office buildings, renovation & repair; Industrial buildings, new construction; Renovation, remodeling & repairs: industrial buildings; Millwright
VP: Thomas Luken
**Sec:* Eleanor Oberle
**VP:* John Oberle
**VP:* Steven Smallwood
Off Mgr: Tracy Curry

D-U-N-S 06-891-1908
OBERLIN COLLEGE
173 W Lorain St, Oberlin, OH 44074-1073
Tel (440) 775-8121 *Founded/Ownrshp* 1833
Sales 171.8MM *EMP* 1,140
Accts Maloney & Novotny Llc Clevel

SIC 8221 College, except junior; College, except junior
Pr: Marvin Krislov
Top Exec: Jason Hudson
Top Exec: Blake New
Top Exec: Deb Ranieri
Assoc VP: Jane Mathison
VP: Ben Jones
**VP:* Ronald R Watts
Exec: Heidi Pycraft
Assoc Dir: Michele N Gross
Adm Dir: James Howsmon
Off Admin: Nicole Balin

D-U-N-S 60-652-3231
OBERMAN TIVOLI MILLER & PICKERT INC
MEDIA SERVICES
500 S Sepulveda Blvd # 500, Los Angeles, CA 90049-3551
Tel (310) 440-9600 *Founded/Ownrshp* 1989
Sales 30.5MM^E *EMP* 230
SIC 7373 8721 8741 Systems software development services; Payroll accounting service; Business management; Systems software development services; Payroll accounting service; Business management
Pr: Robert Oberman
**CEO:* Barry Oberman
**CFO:* Sanaa Wadsworth

D-U-N-S 07-376-3393
OBERMAYER REBMANN MAXWELL & HIPPEL LLP
1617 John F Kennedy Blvd # 19, Philadelphia, PA 19103-1895
Tel (215) 665-3000 *Founded/Ownrshp* 1904
Sales 36.6MM^E *EMP* 250
SIC 8111 Corporate, partnership & business law; Labor & employment law; Taxation law; Environmental law; Corporate, partnership & business law; Labor & employment law; Taxation law; Environmental law
Mng Pt: Michael F Eichert
Sr Pt: Jerry Kline
Sr Pt: Louis Kuppermanhas
V Ch: Alex Basilevsky
V Ch: James Thompson
Pr: Linda Costello
COO: Andrew Frey
COO: Bob Perry
Dir IT: Yvette Nunez
Mktg Dir: Sharen Nocella
Counsel: Joseph F Aceto

D-U-N-S 83-184-0595
OBERNDORF FAMILY PARTNERS LP
615 Front St, San Francisco, CA 94111-1913
Tel (415) 500-6900 *Founded/Ownrshp* 2009
Sales 41.1MM *EMP* 10^E
SIC 6733 Private estate, personal investment & vacation fund trusts
Prin: Susan Oberndorf

D-U-N-S 03-174-2971
OBERON ASSOCIATES INC
(*Suby of* CGI FEDERAL INC) ★
9700 Capital Ct Ste 301, Manassas, VA 20110-2048
Tel (703) 365-8801 *Founded/Ownrshp* 2004
Sales 94.0MM *EMP* 777
SIC 7379 Computer related consulting services; Computer related consulting services
Pr: Philip O Nolan
**Treas:* James H Brabston
VP: Michael Daconta
Comm Dir: Susan Balding
Dir Bus: Steven looss
Dir Bus: John McGlone
Prgrm Mgr: David L Dutton
Brnch Mgr: William Weigeshoff
Prd Mgr: Patti Rusher

D-U-N-S 14-855-0572
OBERON MEDIA INC
1100 La Avenida St Ste A, Mountain View, CA 94043-1453
Tel (646) 367-2020 *Founded/Ownrshp* 2003
Sales 32.7MM^E *EMP* 500^E
SIC 7371 Computer software development & applications; Computer software development & applications
CEO: David Lebow
**Ch Bd:* Tal Kerret
**COO:* Bob Hayes
**COO:* Don Ryan
**CFO:* Pat Barry
**Founder:* Ofer Leidner
Sr VP: Bob Sirmans
Netwrk Eng: Nelson Wu

D-U-N-S 60-409-1504
OBERTHUR CARD SYSTEMS INC
(*Suby of* OBERTHUR TECHNOLOGIES OF AMERICA CORP) ★
523 James Hance Ct, Exton, PA 19341-2560
Tel (610) 280-2707 *Founded/Ownrshp* 1999
Sales 15.5MM^E *EMP* 300
SIC 2752 Offset & photolithographic printing
Pr: Philippe Tartavull

D-U-N-S 13-125-6377 IMP
OBERTHUR TECHNOLOGIES OF AMERICA CORP
(*Suby of* OBERTHUR TECHNOLOGIES)
4250 Pleasant Valley Rd, Chantilly, VA 20151-1278
Tel (703) 263-0100 *Founded/Ownrshp* 1999
Sales 227.0MM^E *EMP* 1,000
SIC 3089 7382 3953 3578 3499 Identification cards, plastic; Security systems services; Embossing seals, corporate & official; Banking machines; Safes & vaults, metal; Safe deposit boxes or chests, metal; Identification cards, plastic; Security systems services; Embossing seals, corporate & official; Banking machines; Safes & vaults, metal; Safe deposit boxes or chests, metal
Pr: Martin Ferenczi
IT Man: Raj Chopra
IT Man: Tiffany Le
IT Man: Rick Patrick
IT Man: Yuriy Yunusov

QC Dir: Joe Blossic
Site Mgr: Kenneth Abner

D-U-N-S 00-924-7172 IMP
OBERTO SAUSAGE CO
OH BOY OBERTO
7060 S 238th St, Kent, WA 98032-2914
Tel (253) 437-6100 *Founded/Ownrshp* 1918
Sales 183.5MM^E *EMP* 500
SIC 2013 Sausages from purchased meat; Snack sticks, including jerky: from purchased meat; Sausages from purchased meat; Snack sticks, including jerky: from purchased meat
Ch Bd: John Clearman
Pr: Thomas C Ennis
Treas: Dorothy J Oberto
V Ch Bd: Laura Oberto
VP: Gregory S Christemson
VP: Gregory Christenson
VP: Thomas Finley
VP: T J Powers
VP: Jeff Wakelin
Exec: Jeff Kent
Exec: Losan Saetern
Exec: Kim Uppal

D-U-N-S 92-822-4807
OBERTO SAUSAGE CO OF OREGON
SMOKECRAFT
7060 S 238th St, Kent, WA 98032-2914
Tel (253) 437-6100 *Founded/Ownrshp* 1994
Sales 20.1MM^E *EMP* 240
SIC 8741 Management services; Management services
Ch: Arthur P Oberto
**Sec:* Dorothy Oberto
**VP:* Tom Campanile
Sls Dir: David Pellettier

D-U-N-S 05-108-2980
OBERWEIS DAIRY INC
951 Ice Cream Dr, North Aurora, IL 60542-1475
Tel (630) 801-6100 *Founded/Ownrshp* 1927
Sales 215.8MM^E *EMP* 1,000
SIC 5963 5451

OBEY CLOTHING
See ONE 3TWO INC

D-U-N-S 05-457-0044
OBI HOLDING CO (OK)
O B I
1001 N Lincoln Blvd, Oklahoma City, OK 73104-3251
Tel (405) 297-5700 *Founded/Ownrshp* 1977
Sales 55.0MM *EMP* 3
SIC 6719 Investment holding companies, except banks; Investment holding companies, except banks
Ch Bd: Gerald Marshall
**Pr:* John Armitage
CFO: Randall Stark

OBI SUSHI
See THOMPSON HOSPITALITY CORP

OBICI HEALTH SYSTEMS
See LOUISE OBICI MEMORIAL HOSPITAL INC

OBIM FRESH CUT FRUIT COMPANY
See OBIM FRESH-CUT FRUIT CO

D-U-N-S 17-937-8641
OBIM FRESH-CUT FRUIT CO
OBIM FRESH CUT FRUIT COMPANY
(*Suby of* READY PAC FOODS) ★
4401 Foxdale St, Irwindale, CA 91706-2161
Tel (626) 856-8686 *Founded/Ownrshp* 1997
Sales 35.7MM^E *EMP* 350
SIC 2099 Food preparations; Food preparations
Pr: Uzor Nwoko
Board of Directors: Dennis Gertmenian

D-U-N-S 10-067-0967
OBION CO SCHOOL DISTRICT
316 S 3rd St, Union City, TN 38261-3724
Tel (731) 885-9743 *Founded/Ownrshp* 1854
Sales 21.8M *EMP* 312^E
SIC 8211 Public elementary & secondary schools; School board; Public elementary & secondary schools; School board
Prin: Keith Frazier
Prin: Randy Pitts
HC Dir: Russ Davis

D-U-N-S 03-485-9967
OBION GRAIN CO INC
301 E Palestine Ave, Obion, TN 38240-5817
Tel (731) 536-6251 *Founded/Ownrshp* 1976
Sales 35.4MM^E *EMP* 12^E
SIC 5191 0723 5153 7389 Seeds: field, garden & flower; Fertilizer & fertilizer materials; Seed cleaning; Grain elevators;
Pr: J Baxter Sanders

D-U-N-S 79-958-0720
OBJECT TECHNOLOGY SOLUTIONS INC
6363 College Blvd Ste 230, Leawood, KS 66211-1938
Tel (913) 345-9080 *Founded/Ownrshp* 1999
Sales 39.4MM *EMP* 176^E
SIC 7371 8742 Computer software development & applications; Management consulting services; Computer software development & applications; Management consulting services
Pr: Narasimha Gondi
VP: Gus Rodriguez
IT Man: Raj Cherukumudi
IT Man: Nitin Kotiyal
IT Man: David Nash
IT Man: Dan Tummeti

D-U-N-S 60-667-2962
OBJECTIVE SYSTEMS INTEGRATORS INC
OSI
(*Suby of* MYCOM FRANCE)
35 Iron Point Cir Ste 250, Folsom, CA 95630-8597
Tel (916) 467-1500 *Founded/Ownrshp* 2014
Sales 26.2MM^E *EMP* 150
SIC 7371 Custom computer programming services; Custom computer programming services
Pr: John Travs

VP: Mark Coppejans
VP: Steve Kleinbach
**VP:* Cheri Simko
Area Mgr: Tracy Lehmberg
Snr Sftwr: William Burdgick
IT Man: Amy Raskin
Software D: Curtis Crum
Sftwr Eng: Danny Ho
Sftwr Eng: David Rodriguez
Opers Mgr: Robert Veteto

D-U-N-S 01-619-2853
OBJECTWIN TECHNOLOGY INC
14800 Saint Marys Ln # 100, Houston, TX 77079-2935
Tel (832) 485-3607 *Founded/Ownrshp* 1997
Sales 23.0MM *EMP* 164[E]
SIC 7371 Computer software development & applications; Computer software development & applications
Pr: Shawn S Karande
Pr: Uma Chidambaram
CFO: Narwani Karen
Assoc VP: Vivek Rana
VP: Uma Chidamabam
VP: Joseph McCall
VP: Ram Ranabhadran
VP: Ram Venkatraman
Dir Bus: Zahania Davis
Off Mgr: Anthony Garza
IT Man: Sid Karanth

O'BLENESS MEMORIAL HOSPITAL
See OHIOHEALTH OBLENNES HOSPITAL

D-U-N-S 07-780-6016 IMP
OBLON MCCLELLAND MAIER & NEUSTADT LLP
1940 Duke St Lbby Fl6, Alexandria, VA 22314-3452
Tel (703) 413-3000 *Founded/Ownrshp* 1969
Sales 75.8MM[E] *EMP* 468
SIC 8111 Patent solicitor; General practice law office; Patent, trademark & copyright law
Mng Pt: Bradley Lytle
Pt: Stephen Baxter
Pt: Scott McKeown
Pt: Surinder Sachar
Pt: Philippe Signore
Pt: Richard Treanor
COO: Rebecca Ross-Bown
COO: Rebecca Ross-Brown
Dir IT: Emmet Sullivan
Opers Mgr: Sarah Fougere
Counsel: Beth Chapman

D-U-N-S 00-216-1402
OBLONG INDUSTRIES INC
923 E 3rd St Ste 111, Los Angeles, CA 90013-1867
Tel (213) 683-8863 *Founded/Ownrshp* 2007
Sales 21.7MM[E] *EMP* 68[E]
SIC 7371 Computer software development & applications
CEO: John Underkoffler
**COO:* Mary Ann De Lares Norris
**CFO:* Stewart Armstrong
VP: Michael Brown
**VP:* David Kung
VP: David Minnen
VP: Navjot Singh
**VP:* Carlton Sparrell
Sftwr Eng: Aleix Flaqu
Sftwr Eng: Brandon Harvey
Manager: Nicole Raymer

O'BRIEN
See OBCORP LLC

O'BRIEN & GERE COMPANIES
See OBRIEN & GERE INC OF NORTH AMERICA

D-U-N-S 04-989-0668
OBRIEN & GERE ENGINEERS INC
(*Suby of* OBRIEN & GERE LIMITED) ★
333 W Washington St # 400, Syracuse, NY 13202-5253
Tel (315) 437-6100 *Founded/Ownrshp* 1985
Sales 58.1MM[E] *EMP* 343
SIC 8711 Sanitary engineers; Civil engineering; Industrial engineers; Sanitary engineers; Civil engineering; Industrial engineers
CEO: James A Fox
**Pr:* R Leland Davis
**Treas:* Joseph M McNulty
Ex VP: Timothy Barry
Sr VP: Stephen Palin
**VP:* Steven J Roland
**VP:* Edward J Zawadzki
Dir IT: Christine Jackson
IT Man: Jill Crawford
IT Man: Jack O'Brien
IT Man: Jack Obrien

D-U-N-S 94-356-0011
OBRIEN & GERE INC OF NORTH AMERICA
O'BRIEN & GERE COMPANIES
(*Suby of* OBRIEN & GERE LIMITED) ★
333 W Washington St # 400, Syracuse, NY 13202-5253
Tel (315) 437-6400 *Founded/Ownrshp* 1989
Sales 26.3MM[E] *EMP* 140
SIC 7389 8741 Estimating service, construction; Management services
Ch Bd: James A Fox
**Treas:* Joseph M Mc Nulty
**Sec:* Peter C Johnson
IT Man: Gail Eberl

D-U-N-S 14-461-4203
OBRIEN & GERE LIMITED
333 W Washington St # 400, Syracuse, NY 13202-5253
Tel (315) 437-6100 *Founded/Ownrshp* 1985
Sales 219.4MM *EMP* 800
Accts Dannible & Mckee Llp Syracuse
SIC 8711 8741 Civil engineering; Management services; Civil engineering; Management services
CEO: James A Fox
COO: R Leland Davis
CFO: Joseph M McNulty
CFO: Joseph M McNulty
VP: Timothy J Barry
VP: Robert R Bowers
VP: Richard R Garcia
VP: Ron Harting
VP: William A Lester
VP: Thomas A Nowlan
VP: Stephen C Palin
VP: Robert Patullo
VP: George B Rest
VP: Jo Anne E Walser
VP: Edward J Zawadzki
Creative D: Gail Eberl
Dir Bus: Neil Webb
Board of Directors: Tim J Barry, Thomas Nowlan, George Rest

D-U-N-S 80-915-2585
OBRIEN & GERE/ CROWDER JOINT VENTURE
6425 Brookshire Blvd, Charlotte, NC 28216-0301
Tel (704) 372-3541 *Founded/Ownrshp* 2007
Sales 30.8MM[E] *EMP* 1,000
SIC 1542 Commercial & office building contractors; Commercial & office building contractors
Pt: Otis A Crowder
Pt: Crowder Construction
Pt: O'Brien Gere

D-U-N-S 07-921-1309
OBRIEN AUTOMOTIVE OF FLORIDA LLC
2850 Colonial Blvd, Fort Myers, FL 33966-1030
Tel (239) 277-1222 *Founded/Ownrshp* 2012
Sales 109.0MM *EMP* 110
SIC 5511 Automobiles, new & used; Automobiles, new & used
Genl Mgr: Gary Matern
Sales Exec: John Knight
Sales Asso: Matt Carley

D-U-N-S 05-925-6560
OBRIEN CONCRETE PUMPING - COLORADO INC
RICHARD O'BRIEN COMPANY
640 W Tennessee Ave, Denver, CO 80223-2853
Tel (303) 778-7474 *Founded/Ownrshp* 1969
Sales 37.4MM[E] *EMP* 250
SIC 5082 Bailey bridges; Cranes, construction; Mixers, construction & mining; Bailey bridges; Cranes, construction; Mixers, construction & mining
Pr: Richard E O'Brien

D-U-N-S 04-341-5996
OBRIEN IMPORTS OF FT MYERS INC
NAPLES MITSUBISHI
2850 Colonial Blvd, Fort Myers, FL 33966-1030
Tel (239) 277-1222 *Founded/Ownrshp* 1998
Sales 36.8MM[E] *EMP* 115
SIC 5511 6719 Automobiles, new & used; Investment holding companies, except banks; Automobiles, new & used; Investment holding companies, except banks
Pr: Joseph D O'Brien
**Pr:* Joseph D Obrien
**Prin:* Gary Matern
Genl Mgr: Frank Delvecio
Sls Mgr: Jim Bailey

D-U-N-S 80-731-8261
OBRIEN INDUSTRIAL HOLDINGS LLC
4641 Mcree Ave, Saint Louis, MO 63110-2239
Tel (314) 773-7500 *Founded/Ownrshp* 2003
Sales 40.6MM[E] *EMP* 95
SIC 5085 3255 3297 Refractory material; Clay refractories; Nonclay refractories

D-U-N-S 07-561-6599
OBRIEN STEEL SERVICE CO
1700 Ne Adams St, Peoria, IL 61603-3510
Tel (309) 671-5800 *Founded/Ownrshp* 1975
Sales 70.4MM[E] *EMP* 165
SIC 5051

D-U-N-S 08-967-8395
OBRIENS MARKET INC
6331 Oakdale Rd, Riverbank, CA 95367-9646
Tel (209) 869-9050 *Founded/Ownrshp* 1978
Sales 29.2MM[E] *EMP* 160
SIC 5411

D-U-N-S 09-307-0753
OBRYANT ELECTRIC INC (CA)
20417 Nordhoff St, Chatsworth, CA 91311-6112
Tel (818) 407-1986 *Founded/Ownrshp* 1978
Sales 38.6MM[E] *EMP* 200
SIC 1731 General electrical contractor; General electrical contractor
Pr: Cathy O'Bryant
CFO: Steve Obryant

D-U-N-S 00-431-7137
OBSERVER PUBLISHING CO
OBSERVER-REPORTER
122 S Main St, Washington, PA 15301-4904
Tel (724) 222-2200 *Founded/Ownrshp* 1808
Sales 47.7MM[E] *EMP* 300
SIC 2711 Newspapers; Newspapers
Pr: Thomas Northrop
**VP:* William B Northrop

OBSERVER-REPORTER
See OBSERVER PUBLISHING CO

D-U-N-S 07-419-8805
OBSTETRICAL AND GYNECOLOGICAL ASSOCIATES PLLC
THE IMAGING CENTER
7900 Fannin St Ste 3030, Houston, TX 77054-2935
Tel (713) 512-7000 *Founded/Ownrshp* 1962
Sales 29.0MM[E] *EMP* 300
SIC 8011

D-U-N-S 86-146-0665
OBTURA CORP
(*Suby of* YOUNG INNOVATIONS INC) ★
13729 Shoreline Ct E, Earth City, MO 63045-1202
Tel (636) 343-5385 *Founded/Ownrshp* 1994
Sales 9.2MM[E] *EMP* 280
SIC 3843 5047 Dental equipment; Dental equipment & supplies; Dental equipment; Dental equipment & supplies
Prin: Richard J Maheu
**Prin:* Walter F Senney Jr

OBU
See OKLAHOMA BAPTIST UNIVERSITY

D-U-N-S 83-034-1645
OBXTEK INC
8300 Boone Blvd Ste 800, Tysons Corner, VA 22182-2681
Tel (703) 373-3736 *Founded/Ownrshp* 2009
Sales 29.6MM *EMP* 81
Accts Glenn Birch Tysons Va
SIC 8742 7379 Management consulting services; Computer related consulting services; Management consulting services; Computer related consulting services
Pr: Bruce E Jesson
Ofcr: Tracy Newkirk
Board of Directors: Anthony Jimenez Jr, Dale Spencer

OC
See EUROFINS QC INC

D-U-N-S 07-934-1668
■ **OC ACQUISITION LLC**
(*Suby of* ORACLE CORP) ★
500 Oracle Pkwy, Redwood City, CA 94065-1677
Tel (650) 506-7000 *Founded/Ownrshp* 2011
Sales 821.2MM[E] *EMP* 2,605[E]
SIC 7371 7372 Computer software development; Business oriented computer software
Pr: Dorian Daley
Treas: Eric Ball
Snr Sftwr: Ryan Isaacs
Snr Sftwr: Mike Roy
Sls Mgr: Juan Casas

D-U-N-S 94-107-9717
OC COMMUNICATIONS INC
2204 Kausen Dr Ste 100, Elk Grove, CA 95758-7176
Tel (916) 686-3700 *Founded/Ownrshp* 1995
Sales 100.9MM[E] *EMP* 650
Accts Moss Adams Llp Stockton Cal
SIC 4841 Cable & other pay television services; Cable & other pay television services
Pr: Forrest C Freeman
**CFO:* Peter Tataryn
VP: Larry Wray

OC FOOD BANK
See COMMUNITY ACTION PARTNERSHIP OF ORANGE COUNTY

D-U-N-S 17-849-5370
OC HEALTH CARE SERVICES INC
7683 Cottonwood Dr, Jenison, MI 49428-7320
Tel (616) 457-9500 *Founded/Ownrshp* 2014
Sales 15.5MM[E] *EMP* 400
SIC 8059 Personal care home, with health care; Personal care home, with health care
Pr: Charles Schipper
HC Dir: Christie Lubbers

D-U-N-S 86-818-6818
OC HOMES INC
OAK CREST MANORS
7811 Cottonwood Dr, Jenison, MI 49428-8341
Tel (616) 457-5869 *Founded/Ownrshp* 2014
Sales 5.4MM[E] *EMP* 335
SIC 8322 Individual & family services; Individual & family services
Pr: Charles Schipper
Ch: Bill Zylstra
HC Dir: Rebecca Koops

D-U-N-S 00-966-7965
OC JONES & SONS INC (CA)
1520 4th St, Berkeley, CA 94710-1748
Tel (510) 526-3424 *Founded/Ownrshp* 1924
Sales 103.9MM[E] *EMP* 250
SIC 1611 Grading; Highway & street paving contractor; Grading; Highway & street paving contractor
Pr: Kelly Kolander
**Ch Bd:* Robert Pelascini
**CFO:* Beth Yoshida
**VP:* Rob Layne
Area Mgr: Jim Gallagher
Area Mgr: Darren Hiatt
Trfc Dir: Matthew Dorsa

OC RIVER
See DIVERSIFIED WOODCRAFTS INC

D-U-N-S 18-827-5374
OC SEACRETS INC
117 49th St, Ocean City, MD 21842-5315
Tel (410) 524-4900 *Founded/Ownrshp* 1988
Sales 20.0MM[E] *EMP* 400
SIC 5813 5812 Bar (drinking places); Grills (eating places); Bar (drinking places); Grills (eating places)
Pr: Leighton Moore Jr
CFO: Gary Figgs
Genl Mgr: Scott Studds

D-U-N-S 06-656-2703
OCADIAN CARE CENTERS LLC
104 Main St, Belvedere Tiburon, CA 94920-2510
Tel (415) 789-5427 *Founded/Ownrshp* 1994
Sales 4.8MM *EMP* 3,785
SIC 8051 Skilled nursing care facilities; Skilled nursing care facilities
Pr: Robert G Peirce
CFO: Elaine Vonblohn

D-U-N-S 62-749-2598
OCALA HEALTHCARE ASSOCIATES LLP
MUNROE REGIONAL MEDICAL CENTER
(*Suby of* MUNROE REGIONAL MEDICAL CENTER INC) ★
9848 Sw 110th St, Ocala, FL 34481-7651
Tel (352) 854-8200 *Founded/Ownrshp* 1984
Sales 19.9MM *EMP* 290
SIC 8051 Skilled nursing care facilities; Skilled nursing care facilities

OCALA NISSAN-MITSUBISHI
See NISSAN OCALA INC

OCALA REGIONAL MEDICAL CENTER
See MARION COMMUNITY HOSPITAL INC

OCALA REGIONAL MEDICAL CENTER
See MARION WEST COMMUNITY HOSPITAL

D-U-N-S 83-053-4777 EXP
OCAMPOS INC
480 Tam Oshanter Dr Se, Marietta, GA 30067-4831
Tel (770) 509-2595 *Founded/Ownrshp* 2007
Sales 300.0MM *EMP* 5
SIC 5084 Printing trades machinery, equipment & supplies; Printing trades machinery, equipment & supplies
Pr: Jorge A Ocampo
**CFO:* Ashley Ocampo

D-U-N-S 02-000-8736
OCAT INC (CA)
TACO BELL
4306 Sisk Rd, Modesto, CA 95356-9760
Tel (209) 529-6802 *Founded/Ownrshp* 1967
Sales 48.5MM[E] *EMP* 1,204
SIC 5812 Fast-food restaurant, chain; Fast-food restaurant, chain
Pr: J Allen Beebe

D-U-N-S 61-169-9059 IMP
OCB RESTAURANT CO LLC
OLD COUNTRY BUFFET
(*Suby of* BUFFETS INC) ★
1460 Corporate Center Dr, Saint Paul, MN 55121-6501
Tel (651) 994-8608 *Founded/Ownrshp* 1990
Sales 107.2MM[E] *EMP* 10,641[E]
SIC 5812 Buffet (eating places)
**CEO:* Richard Michael Andrews
**COO:* David Goronkin
CFO: Keith Wall

D-U-N-S 01-524-9022
OCC NATIONAL BANK EXAMINERS
CONTROLLERS OF THE CURRENCY
880 3rd Ave Fl 5, New York, NY 10022-4730
Tel (212) 527-1020 *Founded/Ownrshp* 1863
Sales 2.0MM *EMP* 2,800
SIC 7389 Personal service agents, brokers & bureaus; Personal service agents, brokers & bureaus

D-U-N-S 62-716-4887
OCCASIONS GROUP INC
(*Suby of* TAYLOR CORP) ★
1750 Tower Blvd, North Mankato, MN 56003-1706
Tel (507) 625-0800 *Founded/Ownrshp* 2006
Sales 439.4MM[E] *EMP* 3,200[E]
SIC 2759 Commercial printing; Commercial printing
CEO: Ron Hoffmeyer
**Pr:* Keith Herwig
**CEO:* Michael J Provenzano
**VP:* Jean Andersen
**VP:* Stephanie Schmid
**VP:* Nancy Thompson
**VP:* John Zellmer
Creative D: Randi Manderfeld
Natl Sales: Linda Hiniker
VP Mktg: Lane Nordquist
Sls Dir: Lisa Haman

OCCC
See OKLAHOMA CITY COMMUNITY COLLEGE

D-U-N-S 13-158-7677
OCCI INC
(*Suby of* GM JOHNSON COMPANIES INC) ★
3200 County Road 257, Fulton, MO 65251-3101
Tel (573) 642-6087 *Founded/Ownrshp* 1984
Sales 26.3MM[E] *EMP* 80
SIC 1629 Dam construction
Pr: Tom Smith
**CFO:* Jeff Raetz
**Sr VP:* Ted Kettlewell
QA Dir: Harold Hawk
QA Dir: Wayne Nelson

D-U-N-S 06-727-1981 EXP
■ **OCCIDENTAL CHEMICAL CORP**
O X Y
(*Suby of* OCCIDENTAL PETROLEUM CORP) ★
5005 Lbj Fwy Ste 2200, Dallas, TX 75244-6198
Tel (972) 404-3800 *Founded/Ownrshp* 1968
Sales 288.0MM[E] *EMP* 750
SIC 2874 2812 Phosphatic fertilizers; Alkalies & chlorine; Chlorine, compressed or liquefied; Caustic soda, sodium hydroxide; Potassium carbonate; Phosphatic fertilizers; Alkalies & chlorine; Chlorine, compressed or liquefied; Caustic soda, sodium hydroxide; Potassium carbonate
Pr: B Chuck Anderson
Treas: D C Yen
Sr VP: James Usher
**VP:* Dennis Blake
VP: Nigel Hopkinson
IT Man: Larry Garza
IT Man: Mark Lockmyer
Board of Directors: Keith C McDole

D-U-N-S 61-282-3252
■ **OCCIDENTAL CHEMICAL INTERNATIONAL INC**
(*Suby of* OXY CHEMICAL CORP) ★
5005 Lyndon B Johnson Fwy # 2200, Dallas, TX 75244-6198
Tel (972) 404-3800 *Founded/Ownrshp* 1994
Sales 32.1MM[E] *EMP* 400
SIC 2869 3089 2873 2874 2879 Industrial organic chemicals; Plastic processing; Nitrogenous fertilizers; Phosphatic fertilizers; Agricultural chemicals; Industrial organic chemicals; Plastic processing; Nitrogenous fertilizers; Phosphatic fertilizers; Agricultural chemicals
Pr: J Roger Hirl
Ex VP: Richard Hallock
Ex VP: Charles Hazzard
Exec: Jodie Douchet
Genl Mgr: Jacqueline Byrd
Genl Mgr: Karen Hydock

MIS Dir: Ed Barrows
Info Man: John Sperat
Plnt Mgr: David Dorko
Plnt Mgr: Tom Feeney
Plnt Mgr: Candace Jaunzemis

D-U-N-S 04-643-6051
OCCIDENTAL COLLEGE (CA)
1600 Campus Rd, Los Angeles, CA 90041-3314
Tel (323) 259-2500 Founded/Ownrshp 1887
Sales 188.6MM EMP 610
Accts Grant Thornton Llp Los Angele
SIC 8221 College, except junior; College, except junior
Pr: Theodore R Mitchell
*Pr: Jonathan Veitch
COO: Ileana Valencia
Bd of Dir: John Power
Trst: Ronald Arnault
Trst: Harry W Colmery Jr
Trst: David Roberts
VP: Barbara Avery
VP: Sandra Cooper
VP: Eric Frank
VP: Jorge Gonzalez
VP: Michael P Groener
VP: Pamela McQuesten
VP: Amy Mua Oz
VP: Shelby Radcliffe
VP: William Tingley
VP: Tom Tomlinson
Exec: Ahmad W Osman
Assoc Dir: Patty Ahn
Assoc Dir: Cassandra Meagher
Assoc Dir: Carey Sargent

D-U-N-S 05-229-8721 IMP
■ OCCIDENTAL ENERGY MARKETING INC
(Suby of OCCIDENTAL PETROLEUM CORP) ★
5 Greenway Plz, Houston, TX 77046-0526
Tel (713) 215-7000 Founded/Ownrshp 1987
Sales 736.7MM^E EMP 132
SIC 5172 1382 4924 Crude oil; Oil & gas exploration services; Natural gas distribution; Crude oil; Oil & gas exploration services; Natural gas distribution
Pr: Ronald K Takeuchi
*Ex VP: Michael R Soland
*Sr VP: Marc Waugh
*VP: Shayne Buchanan
*VP: Gordon E Goodman
Plnt Mgr: David Crawford

D-U-N-S 00-691-5904
OCCIDENTAL FIRE & CASUALTY CO OF NORTH CAROLINA
(Suby of MCM CORP) ★
702 Oberlin Rd Ste 300, Raleigh, NC 27605-1357
Tel (919) 833-1600 Founded/Ownrshp 1961, 1986
Sales NA EMP 175^E
SIC 6331 Fire, marine & casualty insurance & carriers; Fire, marine & casualty insurance & carriers
Ch Bd: George E King
*Pr: Stephen L Stephano
*Sr VP: Michael D Blinson
*Sr VP: Deborah Rinkle
VP: Kevin Hamm
VP: Paul Webb
Netwrk Eng: Ryan Smith

D-U-N-S 07-963-2485
■ OCCIDENTAL INTERNATIONAL EXPLORATION AND PRODUCTION CO (CA)
(Suby of OCCIDENTAL PETROLEUM CORP) ★
5 Greenway Plz Ste 2400, Houston, TX 77046-0532
Tel (713) 215-7600 Founded/Ownrshp 1973
Sales 120.7MM^E EMP 450
SIC 1311 Crude petroleum production; Natural gas production; Crude petroleum production; Natural gas production
Pr: Dale Lawrence
*Ex VP: John W Morgan

D-U-N-S 61-484-9375 EXP
■ OCCIDENTAL OIL AND GAS CORP
OXY
(Suby of OCCIDENTAL PETROLEUM CORP) ★
5 Greenway Plz Ste 110, Houston, TX 77046-0521
Tel (713) 215-7000 Founded/Ownrshp 1977
Sales 1.1MMM^E EMP 1,800^E
SIC 1311 Crude petroleum production; Natural gas production; Crude petroleum production; Natural gas production
CEO: Todd A Stevens
*Treas: Christopher G Stavros
VP: Nathan Fagre
VP: Michael Keough
Dir Bus: Edward Barrows
*Prin: Steve Jason
*Ex Dir: William E Albrecht
Corp Couns: Robert Gray
Corp Couns: Brenton Moore

D-U-N-S 02-932-6999
OCCIDENTAL PERMIAN LTD
P.O. Box 1729 (75001-1729)
Tel (806) 592-5415 Founded/Ownrshp 2000
Sales 56.1MM^E EMP 58^E
SIC 5084 Oil field tool joints
Prin: Mack Alexander

D-U-N-S 79-595-6205 EXP
■ OCCIDENTAL PERMIAN LTD
(Suby of OCCIDENTAL PETROLEUM CORP) ★
5 Greenway Plz Ste 110, Houston, TX 77046-0521
Tel (713) 215-7000 Founded/Ownrshp 1997
Sales 938.4MM^E EMP 900
SIC 1382 1311 Oil & gas exploration services; Crude petroleum production; Oil & gas exploration services; Crude petroleum production
Pr: Tom Menges

D-U-N-S 00-690-8354 IMP/EXP
▲ OCCIDENTAL PETROLEUM CORP
5 Greenway Plz, Houston, TX 77046-0526
Tel (713) 215-7000 Founded/Ownrshp 1920
Sales 21.9MMM EMP 11,700
Tkr Sym OXY Exch NYS
SIC 1382 Crude petroleum production; Natural gas production; Oil & gas exploration services; Potassium compounds or salts, except hydroxide or carbonate; Sodium compounds or salts, inorg., ex. refined sod. chloride; Sodium silicate, water glass; Ethylene; Propylene, butylene; Ethylene glycols; Chlorine, compressed or liquefied; Caustic soda, sodium hydroxide; Oil & gas exploration services
Pr: Stephen Chazen
Pr: Vicki Hollub
CFO: Christopher Stavros
Chf Cred: Marcia Backus
Ex VP: James Lienert
Ex VP: Chris Stavros
Ex VP: Glenn Vangolen
Sr VP: Cynthia Walker
VP: Ioannis Charalambous
VP: Edward A Lowe
VP: Anita Powers

D-U-N-S 07-014-2740
■ OCCIDENTAL PETROLEUM CORP (DE)
OXY
(Suby of OCCIDENTAL PETROLEUM INVESTMENT CO INC) ★
10889 Wilshire Blvd Fl 10, Los Angeles, CA 90024-4213
Tel (310) 208-8800 Founded/Ownrshp 1920
Sales 1.3MMM^E EMP 3,600
Accts Kpmg Llp Los Angeles Califor
SIC 1311 Crude petroleum production; Natural gas production; Crude petroleum production; Natural gas production
CEO: Armand Hammer
*Pr: Stephen I Chazen
CFO: Christopher G Stavros
VP: Mark Kapelke
VP: Roger Tisdale

D-U-N-S 07-531-2041
■ OCCIDENTAL PETROLEUM INVESTMENT CO INC
(Suby of OCCIDENTAL PETROLEUM CORP) ★
10889 Wilshire Blvd Fl 10, Los Angeles, CA 90024-4213
Tel (310) 208-8800 Founded/Ownrshp 1969
Sales 1.3MMM^E EMP 4,000
SIC 1382 8744 Oil & gas exploration services; Facilities support services; Oil & gas exploration services; Facilities support services
Ch Bd: Ray R Irani
*Pr: Dr Dale R Laurance
COO: Carole Campbell
*CFO: Stephen I Chazen
Top Exec: Tim Borgerding
Ex VP: Anita Powers
Sr VP: Cecelia Billingslea
Sr VP: Marc Waugh
VP: William Carroll
VP: Jim Clarken
VP: Tracey Coats
VP: Gary Daugherty
*VP: Donald P Debner
*VP: Richard W Hallock
VP: Mark Kapelke
VP: Sandy Lowe
VP: John Martin
VP: Christi Standridge
VP: Michael Stutts
VP: Roger Tisdale
VP: Aurmond Watkins

D-U-N-S 80-362-7835
■ OCCIDENTAL POWER SERVICES INC
(Suby of OCCIDENTAL INTERNATIONAL EXPLORATION AND PRODUCTION CO) ★
5 Greenway Plz Ste 2400, Houston, TX 77046-0532
Tel (713) 215-7000 Founded/Ownrshp 1987
Sales 120.7MM^E EMP 120
SIC 1311 Crude petroleum & natural gas; Crude petroleum & natural gas
Pr: Dale Lawrence
CFO: Pete Smith
*VP: Michael L Keough
Sls&Mrk Ex: Kim Combs

D-U-N-S 17-679-9666
■ OCCIDENTAL TOWER CORP
OCCIDENTAL TOWER MGT & LSG
(Suby of OCCIDENTAL PETROLEUM INVESTMENT CO INC) ★
5005 L B Johnson Fwy 37 Ste 370, Dallas, TX 75244
Tel (972) 450-4992 Founded/Ownrshp 1992
Sales 19.6MM^E EMP 600
SIC 6531 Real estate managers; Real estate managers
Pr: Chuck Anderson
*VP: Dennis Blake

OCCIDENTAL TOWER MGT & LSG
See OCCIDENTAL TOWER CORP

D-U-N-S 08-566-0876
OCCUPATIONAL CENTER OF UNION COUNTY
MENTAL HEALTH AND VOCATIONAL C
301 Cox St, Roselle, NJ 07203-1797
Tel (908) 241-5928 Founded/Ownrshp 1959
Sales 5.0MM EMP 450
SIC 8331 Job training & vocational rehabilitation services; Job training & vocational rehabilitation services
Pr: Michele Ford
*Pr: Mark Lasky
*VP: Jo Kovalcik
VP Opers: Tony Tomaino
Opers Mgr: Michael Hydock

D-U-N-S 07-763-6561
OCCUPATIONAL DEVELOPMENT CENTER INC
O D C
1520 Highway 32 S, Thief River Falls, MN 56701-4508
Tel (218) 681-4949 Founded/Ownrshp 1971
Sales 4.9MM EMP 890
Accts Brady Martz & Associates Pc T
SIC 8331 Vocational rehabilitation agency; Vocational rehabilitation agency
Pr: June Schelde
*CFO: Ron Reierson
Telecom Ex: Sandy Sanden
IT Man: Bill Reynolds

D-U-N-S 82-700-9247
OCCUPATIONAL FITNESS INC
5370 N Enoch Rd, Cedar City, UT 84721-7625
Tel (435) 867-1148 Founded/Ownrshp 2003
Sales 23.0MM EMP 1
SIC 8049 Occupational therapist; Occupational therapist
Pr: Garland Earwood

D-U-N-S 02-064-5128
OCCUPATIONAL HEALTH SERVICE
WCA HOSPITAL
207 Foote Ave, Jamestown, NY 14701-7077
Tel (716) 664-8165 Founded/Ownrshp 2001
Sales 98.3MM EMP 9
SIC 8011 8062 Offices & clinics of medical doctors; General medical & surgical hospitals; Offices & clinics of medical doctors; General medical & surgical hospitals
CEO: Betsy Wright
Ofcr: Robert Piede
VP: Marlene Garone
VP: Larry Senn
IT Man: Brian Wilshire
Ansthlgy: Nadia Geleil
Doctor: Albert Persia

OCCUPATIONAL MEDICINE
See NATIVIDAD HOSPITAL INC

D-U-N-S 87-824-9515
■ OCCUPATIONAL SAFETY AND HEALTH ADMINISTRATION
(Suby of UNITED STATES DEPARTMENT OF LABOR) ★
200 Constitution Ave Nw, Washington, DC 20210-0001
Tel (202) 693-2000 Founded/Ownrshp 1981
Sales NA EMP 2,384
SIC 9651 Labor regulatory agency; Inspection for labor standards & safety, government; ; Labor regulatory agency; Inspection for labor standards & safety, government;
Ofcr: Paul Leary

OCCUPATIONAL THERAPY
See SAINT LUKES METHODIST HOSPITAL INC

D-U-N-S 07-548-4204
OCCUPATIONAL TRAINING CENTER OF BURLINGTON COUNTY (INC)
2 Manhattan Dr, Burlington Township, NJ 08016-4120
Tel (609) 267-6677 Founded/Ownrshp 1964
Sales 38.0MM EMP 700
Accts Mercadien Pc Certified Pub
SIC 8331 Job training services; Sheltered workshop; Job training services; Sheltered workshop
Pr: Al Cascarina
*Treas: Robert R Bankard
*Ex Dir: Joseph Bender
Opers Mgr: John Brosky

D-U-N-S 10-754-2755
OCCUPATIONALURGENT CARE HEALTH SYSTEMS INC
OUCH SYSTEMS
750 Riverpoint Dr, West Sacramento, CA 95605-1625
Tel (916) 374-4600 Founded/Ownrshp 2007
Sales 5.3MM^E EMP 380
SIC 8099 Medical services organization; Medical services organization
Pr: James C Smith
*CFO: Joseph Whitters
*Ex VP: Dan Brunner

OCDE
See ORANGE COUNTY DEPARTMENT OF EDUCATION FACILITIES CORP

D-U-N-S 78-610-0839
OCE NORTH AMERICA INC
1800 Bruning Dr W, Itasca, IL 60143-1061
Tel (630) 351-1227 Founded/Ownrshp 1994
Sales 39.9MM^E EMP 139^E
SIC 1611 General contractor, highway & street construction
CEO: Giovanni B Pelizzari
*Pr: Mal Baboyian
*Pr: Patrick Chapuis
*Pr: John Reilly
*Sr VP: Dan Krzesinski
Brnch Mgr: Eric Clark
Sales Exec: Michael Brennan
Sales Exec: John Tenfelder
Sls&Mrk Ex: Scott Edwards
VP Mktg: David Schumaker

D-U-N-S 18-571-1918 IMP/EXP
OCE-USA HOLDING INC
(Suby of OCE HOLDING B.V.)
100 Oakview Dr, Trumbull, CT 06611-4724
Tel (773) 714-8500 Founded/Ownrshp 1987
Sales 319.9MM^E EMP 11,000
SIC 3861 5044

OCEAN 66 LT
See COASTAL ENERGY CO

D-U-N-S 18-918-9962 EXP
OCEAN AUTO CENTER INC
OCEAN MAZDA
9675 Nw 12th St, Doral, FL 33172-2825
Tel (786) 464-1100 Founded/Ownrshp 1989
Sales 25.0MM EMP 60
SIC 5511 7539 5012 Automobiles, new & used; Automotive repair shops; Automobiles & other motor vehicles; Automobiles, new & used; Automotive repair shops; Automobiles & other motor vehicles
Pr: Karina Garcia
*VP: Jessica Garcia
Sls Mgr: Thomas Rivera

D-U-N-S 07-726-4521
OCEAN AVENUE LLC
FAIRMONT MIRAMAR HOTEL
101 Wilshire Blvd, Santa Monica, CA 90401-1106
Tel (310) 576-7777 Founded/Ownrshp 1999
Sales 23.4MM^E EMP 275
SIC 7011 7299 Hotels; Banquet hall facilities; Hotels; Banquet hall facilities
COO: RAD Anderson
Genl Mgr: Wolfgang Jonas
CIO: Nicholas Murdock
IT Man: Mathew Armstrong
Pr Mgr: Jacqueline Kerns
Sls Mgr: Elizabeth Muir
Sls Mgr: Ashley Sun

D-U-N-S 07-174-3603
OCEAN BANK
(Suby of OCEAN BANKSHARES INC) ★
780 Nw 42nd Ave Ste 10, Miami, FL 33126-5597
Tel (305) 442-2660 Founded/Ownrshp 1982
Sales NA EMP 639
SIC 6022 State commercial banks; State commercial banks
CEO: A Alfonso Macedo
*Ch Bd: Agostino De Sousa Macedo
*COO: Terry J Curry
*CFO: Stan Rubin
*CFO: Alberto Vega
Bd of Dir: Benigno Concepcion
Bd of Dir: Joao Macedo
Bd of Dir: Carlos Montero
Bd of Dir: Antonio Fern Ndez
Ofcr: Gustavo Acevedo
Ofcr: John Borum
Ofcr: Chiang Chuan
*Ofcr: Mariano Fernandez
Ofcr: Ana Hoyos
Ofcr: Juliana Londono
Ofcr: Rolando Lopez
Ofcr: Angela Phillips
Ofcr: Ileana Carrera Portal
Ofcr: Carlos Sandino
Ofcr: Maria Sandino
Ofcr: Frank Sequeira
Board of Directors: Sam Monti, Juan Del Busto

D-U-N-S 03-254-2800
OCEAN BANKSHARES INC
780 Nw 42nd Ave Ste 626, Miami, FL 33126-5538
Tel (305) 442-2660 Founded/Ownrshp 1985
Sales NA EMP 896
SIC 6712 Bank holding companies; Bank holding companies
Pr: Alfonso Macedo
V Ch: Jos A Concepci N
Pr: Rafael Arteaga
Pr: Daniel Gutierrez
COO: Vito Nardelli
CFO: Pamela Frank
Bd of Dir: Benigno Concepcion
Bd of Dir: Luis Consuegra
Ofcr: Alina Anzardo
Ofcr: Mayra Nua EZ
Ofcr: Luz Hernandez
Ofcr: Mariano H Fern Ndez
Assoc VP: Michelle Martin
Assoc VP: Joanna Martinez
Ex VP: Ricardo Bajandas
Ex VP: Orlando Baro
Ex VP: Jack Cussen
Ex VP: Walter De Villiers
Ex VP: Lorraine Dellert
Ex VP: Andrew Finkle
Ex VP: Neyda Hermosa

D-U-N-S 80-680-3987
OCEAN BEACH CLUB LLC
BEACH QRTERS VCATION OWNERSHIP
3401 Atlantic Ave, Virginia Beach, VA 23451-2854
Tel (757) 491-2101 Founded/Ownrshp 2000
Sales 45.0MM^E EMP 400
SIC 7389 Time-share condominium exchange

D-U-N-S 00-924-8071 IMP/EXP
OCEAN BEAUTY SEAFOODS LLC
1100 W Ewing St, Seattle, WA 98119-1321
Tel (206) 285-6800 Founded/Ownrshp 1996
Sales 439.4MM EMP 18,000
Accts Mcgladrey Llp Seattle Washin
SIC 2092 2091 Fresh or frozen packaged fish; Canned & cured fish & seafoods; Fresh or frozen packaged fish; Canned & cured fish & seafoods
Pr: Mark Palmer
CFO: Tony Ross
CFO: Ron Stevens
Ex VP: John Hanarhan
Ex VP: John Hanrahan
VP: Jon Black
VP: Doug Duchning
Genl Mgr: Jerry Medley
Genl Mgr: Frank Ragusa
Genl Mgr: Kent Smith
Genl Mgr: Carlos Usera

D-U-N-S 09-346-1796
▲ OCEAN BIO-CHEM INC
4041 Sw 47th Ave, Davie, FL 33314-4023
Tel (954) 587-6280 Founded/Ownrshp 1973
Sales 33.9MM EMP 114
Tkr Sym OBCI Exch NAS
SIC 2842 2992 Polishing preparations & related products; Lubricating oils & greases; Polishing preparations & related products; Lubricating oils & greases
Ch Bd: Peter G Dornau
*CFO: Jeffrey S Barocas
*VP: William W Dudman
VP: George W Lindsey Jr
Sls&Mrk Ex: Bill Lindsey
*VP Sls: Gregor M Dornau
VP Sls: Marc Emmi

D-U-N-S 19-707-5658
OCEAN BREEZE PHARMACY INC
GOOD NEIGHBOR PHARMACY
1817 Hylan Blvd, Staten Island, NY 10305-1918
Tel (718) 987-2525 Founded/Ownrshp 1986
Sales 23.0MM EMP 40

SIC 5912 Drug stores; Drug stores
Pr: Andrew Passieri
**Ex VP:* Larry Di Blasi

OCEAN CHEVROLET GEO HONDA
See OCEAN CHEVROLET INC

D-U-N-S 13-162-8638
OCEAN CHEVROLET INC
OCEAN CHEVROLET GEO HONDA
3801 Soquel Dr, Soquel, CA 95073-2039
Tel (831) 464-1500 *Founded/Ownrshp* 1994
Sales 27.9MM^E *EMP* 81
SIC 5511 5012 Automobiles, new & used; Automobiles & other motor vehicles; Automobiles, new & used; Automobiles & other motor vehicles
Pr: Steve John
Sales Exec: John Prentice

D-U-N-S 06-786-4363
■ OCEAN CITY HOME BANK(INC)
(*Suby of* OCEAN SHORE HOLDING CO) ★
1001 Asbury Ave, Ocean City, NJ 08226-3329
Tel (609) 927-7722 *Founded/Ownrshp* 1887
Sales NA *EMP* 136
SIC 6035 Savings institutions, federally chartered; Savings institutions, federally chartered
CEO: Steven E Brady
Pr: Kathy Rubba
CFO: Donald Morgenweck
**Ch:* Roy Gillian
Chf Mktg O: Tricia Ciliberto
Ex VP: Janet Bossi
**Ex VP:* Anthony J Rizzotte
Sr VP: Paul Esposito
VP: Walter Fillmore
VP: Renee Garr
VP: Linda Interlante
VP: Maria Mayshura
VP: George Morgan
VP: Tony Osen
VP: Jeff Ropiecki
VP: Robert N Sobkow

D-U-N-S 11-549-8123
OCEAN CITY SCHOOL DISTRICT
801 Asbury Ave Ste 306-00, Ocean City, NJ 08226-3625
Tel (609) 399-5150 *Founded/Ownrshp* 1900
Sales 14.0MM^E *EMP* 335
SIC 8211 Public elementary & secondary schools; Public elementary & secondary schools
MIS Dir: Kathleen Nelson

D-U-N-S 19-596-6015
OCEAN COLONY PARTNERS LLC
HALF MOON BAY GOLF LINKS
2450 Cabrillo Hwy S # 200, Half Moon Bay, CA 94019-2266
Tel (650) 726-5764 *Founded/Ownrshp* 1988
Sales 25.0MM^E *EMP* 175
SIC 6552 7992 7389 Subdividers & developers; Public golf courses; Telephone services
Pt: William E Barrett
Mktg Dir: Mary McVay

D-U-N-S 14-702-0648
OCEAN COMPUTER GROUP INC
90 Matawan Rd Ste 105, Matawan, NJ 07747-2624
Tel (732) 493-1900 *Founded/Ownrshp* 1985
Sales 33.4MM^E *EMP* 25
SIC 5045 Computers, peripherals & software
Pr: Lou Tsotakos
CFO: Dennis Graney
**VP:* Penelope Tsotakos
Sales Exec: Stan Wlodarczyk

D-U-N-S 06-870-1713
OCEAN COUNTY COLLEGE
College Dr, Toms River, NJ 08754
Tel (732) 255-0400 *Founded/Ownrshp* 1966
Sales 40.9MM *EMP* 600
Accts Cliftonlarsonallen Llp Plymou
SIC 8222 8221 Community college; Colleges universities & professional schools; Community college; Colleges universities & professional schools
Pr: Jon H Larson
Pr: James McGinty
COO: Sandra Mueller
**CFO:* Sara Winchester
Trst: Carl Thulin
Ofcr: John Dirocco
Ofcr: Carol Foray
Ex VP: Ann Feneis
Exec: Sandra Brown
Dir Lab: Barbara Collins
Store Mgr: Carol Kaunitz

D-U-N-S 09-424-9000
OCEAN COUNTY UTILITIES AUTHORITY
501 Hickory Ln, Bayville, NJ 08721-2157
Tel (732) 269-4500 *Founded/Ownrshp* 1970
Sales 71.1MM *EMP* 280
SIC 4952

OCEAN CUISINE INTERNATIONAL
See FISHERY PRODUCTS INTERNATIONAL INC

D-U-N-S 18-966-7624
OCEAN DENTAL CORPORATE OFFICE INC
206 W 6th Ave, Stillwater, OK 74074-4017
Tel (405) 707-0600 *Founded/Ownrshp* 2004
Sales 30.0MM^E *EMP* 650
SIC 8021 Offices & clinics of dentists; Offices & clinics of dentists
Pr: Chad Hoecker
**COO:* Joe Akien
**CFO:* Karen L Hendren
Ofcr: Erin Leitsch
Prac Mgr: Donna Barnes
Prac Mgr: Teresa Crow
Prac Mgr: Tonya Schmidt
Prac Mgr: Johnnie Williams
Dist Mgr: Rob Worley
CTO: Dorothy Fouquet
Mktg Dir: Dave Higgins

D-U-N-S 10-653-0157 IMP
OCEAN DESERT SALES INC
HOWARD SALES CO DIVISION
5400 Tulip St, Philadelphia, PA 19124-2013
Tel (215) 537-8719 *Founded/Ownrshp* 1981
Sales 25.5MM^E *EMP* 60
SIC 5199 General merchandise, non-durable; Gifts & novelties
Pr: Abraham Schiff

OCEAN DESIGN
See TELEDYNE ODI INC

OCEAN DREAM
See MALIBU DESIGN GROUP

D-U-N-S 06-931-8632
OCEAN DUNES LIMITED A SOUTH CAROLINA LIMITED PARTNERSHIP
OCEAN DUNES RESORT HOTEL, THE
201 74th Ave N, Myrtle Beach, SC 29572-3832
Tel (843) 449-7441 *Founded/Ownrshp* 1984
Sales 6.0MM^E *EMP* 340
SIC 7011 Resort hotel; Resort hotel
Genl Pt: Girard M Blount Jr
Genl Pt: Tom E Baugh Jr
Genl Pt: Leslie M Morris Jr
Ltd Pt: Lee Henkel
Pr: John Schultis

OCEAN DUNES RESORT HOTEL, THE
See OCEAN DUNES LIMITED A SOUTH CAROLINA LIMITED PARTNERSHIP

OCEAN EDGE
See OCEAN RICH FOODS LLC

D-U-N-S 03-940-3949
■ OCEAN EXPLORATION CO
(*Suby of* MURPHY OIL CORP) ★
200 E Peach St, El Dorado, AR 71730-5836
Tel (870) 862-6411 *Founded/Ownrshp* 2001
Sales 9.4MM^E *EMP* 350
SIC 1311 Crude petroleum & natural gas; Crude petroleum & natural gas
CEO: Claiborne Deming

OCEAN FRESH FISH SEAFOOD MKTG
See OCEAN GROUP INC

D-U-N-S 02-912-8410 IMP/EXP
OCEAN GARDEN PRODUCTS INC
10085 Scripps Ranch Ct A, San Diego, CA 92131-1274
Tel (858) 790-3200 *Founded/Ownrshp* 2007
Sales 29.1MM^E *EMP* 50
SIC 5146 5142 Fish, fresh; Fish, frozen, unpackaged; Seafoods; Packaged frozen goods
Pr: Javier Corella
Pr: Norma Torres
**CFO:* Celso Lopez
**Ch:* Sergio Mazon
**VP:* Rodrigo De La Serna

D-U-N-S 83-155-3854 IMP/EXP
OCEAN GOLD SEAFOODS INC
1804 N Nyhus St, Westport, WA 98595
Tel (360) 268-2510 *Founded/Ownrshp* 1994
Sales 33.8MM^E *EMP* 150
SIC 2092 Fresh or frozen packaged fish; Fresh or frozen fish or seafood chowders, soups & stews; Prepared fish or other seafood cakes & sticks; Fresh or frozen packaged fish; Fresh or frozen fish or seafood chowders, soups & stews; Prepared fish or other seafood cakes & sticks
Pr: Dennis Rydman
**VP:* Greg Shaughnessy

D-U-N-S 61-681-5817 IMP
OCEAN GROUP INC
OCEAN FRESH FISH SEAFOOD MKTG
1100 S Santa Fe Ave, Los Angeles, CA 90021-1743
Tel (213) 622-3677 *Founded/Ownrshp* 1983
Sales 40.0MM *EMP* 75
SIC 5146 Fish & seafoods; Fish & seafoods
Pr: Young Won Kim
**CFO:* Hyojin Ahn

OCEAN HAMMOCK RESORT
See COMMONWEALTH PALM COAST OPERATING CORP

D-U-N-S 79-559-2617 IMP
OCEAN HARVEST WHOLESALE INC
8751 Flagship Dr, Houston, TX 77029-4012
Tel (713) 224-3474 *Founded/Ownrshp* 1992
Sales 50.0MM *EMP* 40
SIC 5146 Seafoods; Seafoods
Pr: Hung N Tran
**Owner:* Eric Tran

D-U-N-S 01-575-4850
OCEAN HOME HEALTH SUPPLY LLC
(*Suby of* MONTGOMERY MEDICAL EQUIPMENT) ★
1000 Airport Rd Ste 101, Lakewood, NJ 08701-5960
Tel (732) 961-1301 *Founded/Ownrshp* 2004
Sales 25.0MM *EMP* 137^E
SIC 8093 Respiratory health clinic
CEO: Joshua Parnes

OCEAN HOUSE BUILDERS
See NAN INC

D-U-N-S 14-427-0295 IMP
OCEAN INVESTMENTS CORP
700 Maine Ave, Bangor, ME 04401-3021
Tel (207) 942-7000 *Founded/Ownrshp* 1986
Sales 881.6MM^E *EMP* 900
SIC 5171 5541 5411 Petroleum bulk stations & terminals; Filling stations, gasoline; Convenience stores, independent; Petroleum bulk stations & terminals; Filling stations, gasoline; Convenience stores, independent
Pr: Arthur L Irving

D-U-N-S 02-552-1548
OCEAN KEYES DEVELOPMENT
601 Hillside Dr N # 3000, North Myrtle Beach, SC 29582-8925
Tel (843) 280-0008 *Founded/Ownrshp* 1998
Sales 30.0MM *EMP* 5
SIC 8712 Architectural services; Architectural services
Owner: Russel Baltzer
Off Mgr: Gene Broyles

OCEAN MAZDA
See OCEAN AUTO CENTER INC

D-U-N-S 08-095-0041
OCEAN MENTAL HEALTH SERVICES INC (NJ)
160 Atlantic City Blvd, Bayville, NJ 08721-1229
Tel (732) 349-5550 *Founded/Ownrshp* 1959
Sales 20.5MM *EMP* 250
Accts Hutchins Meyer & Dilieto Pa
SIC 8093 Family planning clinic; Mental health clinic, outpatient; Family planning clinic; Mental health clinic, outpatient
Pr: James M Cooney
CTO: Charles Langan
Doctor: Vani Kolipakam

D-U-N-S 06-356-5956
OCEAN MIST FARMING CO
OCEAN MIST FARMS
10855 Ocean Mist Pkwy A, Castroville, CA 95012-3232
Tel (831) 633-2144 *Founded/Ownrshp* 1973
Sales 44.1MM^E *EMP* 250
SIC 0161 Lettuce & leaf vegetable farms; Artichoke farm; Lettuce & leaf vegetable farms; Artichoke farm
CEO: C Edward Boutonnet
**Pr:* Ed Bpuponnet
CFO: Dorian Richards
Treas: Tom Bengard
Bd of Dir: Les Tottino
**VP:* Don Bracco
VP: John Chobanian
**VP:* Joseph Micheli
Dir IT: John Williams
VP Prd: Troy E Boutonnet
Sales Exec: Gary Silacci

OCEAN MIST FARMS
See OCEAN MIST FARMING CO

D-U-N-S 60-301-0513 IMP
OCEAN OPTICS INC
(*Suby of* HALMA PUBLIC LIMITED COMPANY)
830 Douglas Ave, Dunedin, FL 34698-4942
Tel (407) 673-0041 *Founded/Ownrshp* 2004
Sales 28.7MM^E *EMP* 253
Accts Price Donoghue Ridenour
SIC 3826 3827 Analytical instruments; Optical instruments & lenses; Analytical instruments; Optical instruments & lenses
Pr: Richard Pollard
COO: Scott Faris
CFO: Rick Morris
**Ch:* Robert Randelman
**Treas:* Richard Morris
VP: Alan Goldizen
VP: Jeff Throckmorton
Dir: Harry Forsyth
Mng Dir: Jeremy Sharp
Prgrm Mgr: Danielle Fatolitis
Snr Sftwr: Yu Ll

D-U-N-S 61-861-7182 IMP
OCEAN PACIFIC SEAFOOD GROUP INC
NEW YORK UNAGI HOUSE
3325 Prince St Fl 2, Flushing, NY 11354-2730
Tel (718) 272-5666 *Founded/Ownrshp* 2005
Sales 20.2MM^E *EMP* 30
SIC 5146 Seafoods
Ch Bd: Yi Jin Cai
**CEO:* John Cai

D-U-N-S 03-881-0755
OCEAN PARK HOTELS INC
9777 Blue Larkspur Ln # 102, Monterey, CA 93940-6554
Tel (805) 544-0812 *Founded/Ownrshp* 2000
Sales 18.8MM^E *EMP* 350
SIC 7011 Hotels & motels; Hotels & motels
Pr: James Flagg
**Ex Dir:* Michael Chisholm

D-U-N-S 08-803-0130
OCEAN PARK MECHANICAL INC
14900 Interurban Ave S # 283, Tukwila, WA 98168-4618
Tel (206) 674-4553 *Founded/Ownrshp* 1998
Sales 22.0MM *EMP* 165
SIC 1711 Plumbing contractors; Plumbing contractors
Pr: Roger Hendrix
Off Mgr: Rachel Marples

OCEAN PINES FAMILY MEDICINE
See PENNINSULA REGIONAL MEDICAL CENTER

OCEAN POINT
See MEREDITH AND CLARKE BANK OF NEWPORT INSURANCE SERVICES INC

OCEAN POTION
See GLSD FLORIDA HOLDINGS INC

D-U-N-S 06-566-6125
OCEAN REEF CLUB INC
35 Ocean Reef Dr Ste 200, Key Largo, FL 33037-5259
Tel (305) 367-2611 *Founded/Ownrshp* 1969
Sales 87.0MM^E *EMP* 600
SIC 7011

OCEAN RESEARCH
See NATIONAL ENVIRONMENTAL SATELLITE DATA AND INFORMATION SERVICE

D-U-N-S 78-798-3365 IMP
OCEAN RICH FOODS LLC
OCEAN EDGE
3 Expressway Plz Ste 115, Roslyn Heights, NY 11577-2033
Tel (516) 621-3474 *Founded/Ownrshp* 2006
Sales 35.0MM *EMP* 8
SIC 5146 Seafoods; Seafoods

OCEAN SAFETY DIVISION
See CITY OF HONOLULU

D-U-N-S 10-384-0658
OCEAN SHIPHOLDINGS INC
16211 Park Ten Pl, Houston, TX 77084-7016
Tel (281) 579-3700 *Founded/Ownrshp* 1982
Sales 26.7MM^E *EMP* 150
SIC 3731 4412 Tankers, building & repairing; Deep sea foreign transportation of freight; Tankers, building & repairing; Deep sea foreign transportation of freight
Pr: Joe F Vaughn Jr
**Pr:* John James
**CFO:* Jack Welsh

D-U-N-S 17-336-0541
▲ OCEAN SHORE HOLDING CO
1001 Asbury Ave, Ocean City, NJ 08226-3329
Tel (609) 399-0012 *Founded/Ownrshp* 1998
Sales NA *EMP* 187^E
Tkr Sym OSHC *Exch* NGM
SIC 6035 Savings institutions, federally chartered; Savings institutions, federally chartered
Pr: Steven E Brady
**Ch Bd:* Robert A Previti
CFO: Donald F Morgenweck
Ex VP: Anthony J Rizzotte
Sr VP: Janet M Bossi

D-U-N-S 00-105-0897 IMP/EXP
OCEAN SPRAY CRANBERRIES INC
1 Ocean Spray Dr, Middleboro, MA 02349-0001
Tel (508) 946-1000 *Founded/Ownrshp* 1930
Sales 1.6MMM *EMP* 2,000
Accts Pricewaterhousecoopers Llp Bo
SIC 2033 2034 2037 Fruits & fruit products in cans, jars, etc.; Fruit juices: packaged in cans, jars, etc.; Fruits: packaged in cans, jars, etc.; Fruit juices: concentrated, hot pack; Fruits, dried or dehydrated, except freeze-dried; Fruit juice concentrates, frozen; Fruits & fruit products in cans, jars, etc.; Fruit juices: packaged in cans, jars, etc.; Fruits: packaged in cans, jars, etc.; Fruit juices: concentrated, hot pack; Fruits, dried or dehydrated, except freeze-dried; Fruit juice concentrates, frozen
Pr: Randy C Papadellis
**Ch:* Peter Dhillon
**Treas:* Richard A Lees
VP: Woody Chittick
VP: Marguerite Copel
VP: Dan Crocker
VP: Kevin M Kavanaugh
VP: Mike Stamatokos
VP: Geoffrey Woolford
Exec: Paul Ganvin
Exec: Chris Kinder
Exec: Alice Moore
Dir Risk M: Pricilla Hill
Board of Directors: Ralph May, Michael G Bartling, Paul Morse, Herbert M Baum, Alfred Piergallini, Gary Dempze, Francis J Podvin, W Cody Estes, Martin Potter, Guy M Glenn, Richard Poznysz, Guy A Gottschalk, Daryl C Robison, Thomas Hurley, Robert Rosbe Jr, Jerome J Jenko, Stephen Lee III

D-U-N-S 07-926-7184 IMP/EXP
OCEAN SPRAY INTERNATIONAL INC
(*Suby of* OCEAN SPRAY CRANBERRIES INC) ★
1 Ocean Spray Dr, Middleboro, MA 02349-0001
Tel (508) 946-1000 *Founded/Ownrshp* 1996
Sales 89.9MM^E *EMP* 400^E
SIC 2037 2034 2033 Fruits & fruit products in cans, jars, etc.; Fruit juices: packaged in cans, jars, etc.; Fruits: packaged in cans, jars, etc.; Fruit juices: concentrated, hot pack; Fruit juice concentrates, frozen; Fruits, dried or dehydrated, except freeze-dried; Fruit juice concentrates, frozen; Fruits, dried or dehydrated, except freeze-dried; Fruits & fruit products in cans, jars, etc.; Fruit juices: packaged in cans, jars, etc.; Fruits: packaged in cans, jars, etc.; Fruit juices: concentrated, hot pack
Pr: Kenneth Romanzi
**Treas:* Richard A Lees
VP: Katie Morey
VP: Laura Tobin
Mng Dir: John Kaczynski
Dir IT: Paula Savini
Software D: Catherine Cunningham
VP Mfg: Erich Fritz
Opers Supe: Ryan Porter
Opers Mgr: Suzanne Salka
Mktg Dir: Paul Stajduhar

D-U-N-S 94-970-8556
OCEAN SPRAY INTERNATIONAL SALES INC
(*Suby of* OCEAN SPRAY CRANBERRIES INC) ★
1 Ocean Spray Dr, Lakeville, MA 02347-1339
Tel (508) 946-1000 *Founded/Ownrshp* 1995
Sales 118.4MM^E *EMP* 500
SIC 5149 Juices; Juices
Pr: Randy Tapadoulis

D-U-N-S 94-970-8051 EXP
OCEAN SPRAY INTERNATIONAL SERVICES INC
(*Suby of* OCEAN SPRAY CRANBERRIES INC) ★
1 Ocean Spray Dr, Lakeville, MA 02347-1339
Tel (508) 946-1000 *Founded/Ownrshp* 1995
Sales 66.3MM^E *EMP* 400^E
SIC 2034 2033 2037 Fruit juice concentrates, frozen; Fruits, dried or dehydrated, except freeze-dried; Fruits & fruit products in cans, jars, etc.; Fruit juices: packaged in cans, jars, etc.; Fruits: packaged in cans, jars, etc.; Fruit juices: concentrated, hot pack; Fruits, dried or dehydrated, except freeze-dried; Fruits & fruit products in cans, jars, etc.; Fruit juice concentrates, frozen
Pr: Kenneth Romanzi
Treas: Charlie Dulany
**Treas:* Richard A Lees

D-U-N-S 06-736-7061
OCEAN SPRINGS HOSPITAL
3109 Bienville Blvd, Ocean Springs, MS 39564-4314
Tel (228) 818-1111 *Founded/Ownrshp* 2011

Sales 60.3MM^E *EMP* 77^E
SIC 5085 Springs
Pr: Michael J Heidelberg
Exec: Chris Anderson
Dir OR: Debra Taranto
Opers Mgr: Chrissie Cochran
Cert Phar: Sheila Salter
Phys Thrpy: Doug Bates

D-U-N-S 01-039-9624
OCEAN SPRINGS SCHOOL DISTRICT
2300 Government St, Ocean Springs, MS 39564-4012
Tel (228) 875-7706 *Founded/Ownrshp* 1910
Sales 36.2MM^E *EMP* 626
Accts Cunningham Cpas Pllc Belzoni
SIC 8211 9111 Public elementary & secondary schools; School board; Mayors' offices; Public elementary & secondary schools; School board; Mayors' offices
Psych: Karen Gifford

D-U-N-S 19-650-4369
OCEAN STATE COMMUNITY RESOURCES
OSCR
310 Maple Ave Ste 102, Barrington, RI 02806-3431
Tel (401) 245-7900 *Founded/Ownrshp* 1982
Sales 23.4MM *EMP* 25
Accts Blum Shapiro & Company Pc Cpas
SIC 8361 Home for the mentally handicapped; Home for the physically handicapped; Home for the mentally handicapped; Home for the physically handicapped
Ex Dir: David Reiss
VP: Jennifer Fogel
Assoc Dir: Ann Olean

OCEAN STATE JOB LOT
See OCEAN STATE JOBBERS INC

OCEAN STATE JOBBERS
See A & M SPECIAL PURCHASING INC

D-U-N-S 08-480-9417 IMP/EXP
OCEAN STATE JOBBERS INC
OCEAN STATE JOB LOT
375 Commerce Park Rd, North Kingstown, RI 02852-8420
Tel (401) 295-2672 *Founded/Ownrshp* 1978
Sales 1.0MMM^E *EMP* 4,000
SIC 5331 5199 Variety stores; Variety store merchandise; Variety stores; Variety store merchandise
Pr: Marc Perlman
Pr: Karina Barchus
**CFO:* John Conforti
**Sec:* Alan Perlman
VP: Roy Greene
Off Mgr: Laura Hind
Store Mgr: Marc Pasquazzi
Dir IT: Catherinea Gilchrist
Dir IT: Arthura Nelson
Dir IT: Erica Pina
Web Dev: Patricia Andraka

D-U-N-S 60-262-5600
OCEAN STATE OIL INC
123 Ocean State Dr, North Kingstown, RI 02852-8525
Tel (401) 295-0996 *Founded/Ownrshp* 1980
Sales 48.2MM^E *EMP* 42
SIC 5172 Lubricating oils & greases
Pr: Daniel Bell

D-U-N-S 86-009-7617
OCEAN STATE POWER CO
OCEAN STATE POWER II
(*Suby of* TRANSCANADA CORPORATION)
1575 Sherman Farm Rd, Harrisville, RI 02830-1124
Tel (401) 568-9550 *Founded/Ownrshp* 1991
Sales 55.4MM^E *EMP* 100
SIC 4911 Electric services; Electric services
Genl Mgr: Mike McCleish

OCEAN STATE POWER II
See OCEAN STATE POWER CO

OCEAN VIEW FLOWERS
See SANTA BARBARA FARMS LLC

D-U-N-S 07-953-6801
OCEAN VIEW SCHOOL DISTRICT (INC)
OVSD
17200 Pinehurst Ln, Huntington Beach, CA 92647-5569
Tel (714) 847-2551 *Founded/Ownrshp* 1874
Sales 107.7MM *EMP* 1,050
Accts Messner & Hadley Llp Victorv
SIC 8211 Public elementary school; Public junior high school; Kindergarten; School board; Public elementary school; Public junior high school; Kindergarten; School board
Trst: Debbie Cotton
CTO: Joaquin Licea
Teacher Pr: Felix Avila

OCEAN VILLAGE MOTOR INN
See ROAD TO RESPONSIBILITY INC

D-U-N-S 08-709-2391
OCEAN YACHTS INC
2713 Green Bank Rd, Egg Harbor City, NJ 08215-9499
Tel (609) 965-4616 *Founded/Ownrshp* 1977
Sales 28.5MM^E *EMP* 200
SIC 3732 Yachts, building & repairing; Yachts, building & repairing
Ch Bd: John E Leek Jr
**Pr:* John E Leek III
CFO: Dan Rowan
VP: Douglas Finney
**VP:* Terry Watson
Natl Sales: Tom Crumley

D-U-N-S 06-778-4884
OCEANAIR INC (MA)
186a Lee Burbank Hwy, Revere, MA 02151-4000
Tel (781) 286-2700 *Founded/Ownrshp* 1982
Sales 26.0MM^E *EMP* 80^E
SIC 4731 Customs clearance of freight; Foreign freight forwarding
CEO: Ed Kaplan
**COO:* John Esborn
**COO:* Joseph J Wyson
**CFO:* Paul Falewicz
CFO: Tom Lynch
**VP:* George Tsirogianis
**VP:* Harvey Waite II
Dir Bus: Jodi Olson
Dir Bus: Patricia Wyatt

D-U-N-S 05-514-7490 IMP/EXP
▲ OCEANEERING INTERNATIONAL INC
11911 Fm 529 Rd, Houston, TX 77041-3000
Tel (713) 329-4500 *Founded/Ownrshp* 1964
Sales 3.6MMM *EMP* 12,400^E
Accts Ernst & Young Llp Houston Te
Tkr Sym OII *Exch* NYS
SIC 1389 3731 8711 Oil field services; Submersible marine robots, manned or unmanned; Engineering services; Oil field services; Submersible marine robots, manned or unmanned; Engineering services
Pr: M Kevin McEvoy
**Ch Bd:* John R Huff
COO: Clyde Hewlett
COO: Roderick A Larson
CFO: Bob Brown
CFO: Alan R Curtis
CFO: W Cardon Gerner
Ofcr: Cardon Gerner
Ex VP: Marvin J Migura
Sr VP: Steve Barrett
Sr VP: Charles W Davison
Sr VP: Kevin Kerins
Sr VP: David K Lawrence
Sr VP: Eric A Silva
Board of Directors: T Jay Collins, Jerold J Desroche, D Michael Hughes, Paul B Murphy Jr, Harris J Pappas, Steven A Webster

D-U-N-S 87-623-9468
■ OCEANEERING SPACE SYSTEMS INC
(*Suby of* OCEANEERING INTERNATIONAL INC) ★
16665 Space Center Blvd, Houston, TX 77058-2253
Tel (281) 228-5337 *Founded/Ownrshp* 1993
Sales 72.7MM^E *EMP* 250
SIC 3429 Aircraft hardware; Aircraft hardware
Sr VP: Ronald L Welch
**Ch Bd:* John R Huff
**Pr:* M Kevin McEvoy
**CEO:* T Jay Collins
Prgrm Mgr: David Spangler
VP Opers: Dave Wallace

D-U-N-S 06-797-3289 EXP
OCEANEX SERVICES INTERNATIONAL INC (TX)
10607 Haddington Dr # 190, Houston, TX 77043-3298
Tel (713) 722-7300 *Founded/Ownrshp* 1981
Sales 24.0MM *EMP* 15
Accts Alan Maxcy Cpa Houston Texa
SIC 5084 5082 Industrial machinery & equipment; Oil field equipment
Pr: Bernard Crouhade
**VP:* Lucio Solis

D-U-N-S 07-514-3131
■ OCEANFIRST BANK (NJ)
(*Suby of* OCEANFIRST FINANCIAL CORP) ★
975 Hooper Ave, Toms River, NJ 08753-8320
Tel (732) 240-4500 *Founded/Ownrshp* 1902
Sales NA *EMP* 350
SIC 6035 Federal savings & loan associations; Federal savings & loan associations
Ch: John R Garbarino
Pr: Vito Nardelli
Treas: Robert Laskowski
Ofcr: Suzanne Wegryn
Trst Ofcr: Brandon Kaletkowski
Trst Ofcr: Craig Spengeman
Ex VP: Michael Fitzpatrick
Sr VP: George Destafney
Sr VP: Sean Kauffman
Sr VP: Steven Tsimbinos
VP: Gary A Casperson
VP: Lydia D'Amore
VP: Michael Dellabarca
VP: Ed Fitzpatrick
VP: Patricia Siciliano
VP: Beth Stefanelli
Dir Risk M: James Gallagher
Board of Directors: Christopher D Maher, Mark G Solow

D-U-N-S 96-117-8761
▲ OCEANFIRST FINANCIAL CORP
975 Hooper Ave, Toms River, NJ 08753-8320
Tel (732) 240-4500 *Founded/Ownrshp* 1995
Sales NA *EMP* 376^E
Tkr Sym OCFC *Exch* NGS
SIC 6035 Federal savings & loan associations; Federal savings & loan associations
Pr: Christopher D Maher
**Ch Bd:* John R Garbarino
Pr: Elizabeth Alexander
Pr: Rosemarie Horvath
Pr: Stefanie Nolan
Pr: Frank Scarpone
Pr: Patricia Siciliano
CFO: Michael J Fitzpatrick
Ofcr: Joseph Casella
Trst Ofcr: Matthew G Waschull
Ex VP: Jack Cussen
Ex VP: Joseph R Iantosca
Ex VP: Craig C Spengeman
Sr VP: George Destafney
Sr VP: Joseph J Lebel
Sr VP: Steven J Tsimbinos
VP: Barbara Baldwin
VP: Michelle Berry
VP: Anthony Cecchetto
VP: Colleen Connolly
VP: Keryn Dettlinger
Board of Directors: Joseph J Burke, Angelo Catania, Jack M Farris, Donald E Maclaughlin, Diane F Rhine, Mark G Solow, John E Walsh

D-U-N-S 12-667-8254
■ OCEANIA CRUISES INC
(*Suby of* PRESTIGE CRUISE HOLDINGS INC) ★
8300 Nw 33rd St Ste 100, Doral, FL 33122-1940
Tel (305) 514-2300 *Founded/Ownrshp* 2008
Sales 637.5MM *EMP* 100
Accts Pricewaterhousecoopers Llp Mi
SIC 4481 Deep sea passenger transportation, except ferry; Deep sea passenger transportation, except ferry
Ch Bd: Frank J Del Rio
**Pr:* Kunal S Kamlani
**CFO:* Jason Montague
**Treas:* Lisa Wilson
Sr VP: Paolo Mele
Sr VP: James Rodriguez
Sr VP: Howard Sherman
**Sr VP:* Harry Sommer
VP: Katina Athanasiou
VP: Scott Kluesner
VP: Steve Moeller
**VP:* James Peterson

OCEANIC
See AMERICAN UNDERWATER PRODUCTS

OCEANIC RESTAURANT & PIER
See ATLANTIC QUEST CORP

D-U-N-S 19-984-8466 IMP
OCEANPRO INDUSTRIES LTD
PROFISH
1900 Fenwick St Ne, Washington, DC 20002-1712
Tel (202) 529-3003 *Founded/Ownrshp* 1988
Sales 69.2MM^E *EMP* 100
SIC 5146 Fish, fresh; Fish, frozen, unpackaged; Fish, fresh; Fish, frozen, unpackaged
Pr: Greg Casten
**Treas:* Raymond Lewis
**VP:* Timothy Lydon
Exec: Dean Cibel
CIO: Gregory Caston

D-U-N-S 03-636-6797
OCEANS ELEVEN CASINO
121 Brooks St, Oceanside, CA 92054-3424
Tel (760) 439-6988 *Founded/Ownrshp* 1996
Sales 16.0MM^E *EMP* 367
SIC 7999 Gambling establishment; Gambling establishment
Mng Pt: Mark Kelegian

D-U-N-S 94-380-0524
OCEANS FLEET FISHERIES INC
20 Blackmer St, New Bedford, MA 02744-2614
Tel (508) 996-3742 *Founded/Ownrshp* 1998
Sales 43.3MM^E *EMP* 70^E
SIC 5146 Fish & seafoods
Pr: Lars Vinjerud II
**COO:* Paul Neves
**CFO:* Rick Miller
**Treas:* Virginia Vinjerud
VP: Frederick Durham
**Genl Mgr:* Chris Brown

D-U-N-S 07-749-0269
OCEANS HEALTH CARE
5850 Granite Pkwy Ste 300, Plano, TX 75024-6748
Tel (972) 464-0022 *Founded/Ownrshp* 2015
Sales 39.2MM^E *EMP* 2,000
SIC 8063 Hospital for the mentally ill
CEO: Stuart Archer
**COO:* Nick Guillory
**CFO:* Patrick Corbett
**Ex VP:* Daryl Doise
Board of Directors: Stuart Archer, Nick Guillory, Michael Jellinek, Gabe Ling, Brian Shortsleeve, Paul Verrochi

D-U-N-S 05-778-5966
OCEANSIDE AUTO COUNTRY INC
TOYOTA CARLSBAD
6030 Avenida Encinas, Carlsbad, CA 92011-1061
Tel (760) 438-6889 *Founded/Ownrshp* 1972
Sales 57.9MM^E *EMP* 132^E
SIC 5511 7538 7532 Automobiles, new & used; Pickups, new & used; Vans, new & used; General automotive repair shops; Top & body repair & paint shops; Automobiles, new & used; Pickups, new & used; Vans, new & used; General automotive repair shops; Top & body repair & paint shops
CEO: Judith Jones-Cone
CFO: Alison Tartar
**VP:* Olen Woods
Mktg Dir: Julio Quintero

D-U-N-S 80-978-3921 IMP/EXP
OCEANSIDE GLASSTILE CO
MANDALA
5858 Edison Pl, Carlsbad, CA 92008-6519
Tel (760) 929-4000 *Founded/Ownrshp* 1992
Sales 63.5MM^E *EMP* 375^E
SIC 3253 5032 Mosaic tile, glazed & unglazed: ceramic; Tile, clay or other ceramic, excluding refractory; Mosaic tile, glazed & unglazed: ceramic; Tile, clay or other ceramic, excluding refractory
Pr: Sean Gildea
**COO:* Greg Lehr
**CFO:* Miles Bradley
**Ex VP:* John Marckx
**VP:* Rick Blacklock
**VP:* Jim Jensen
Dir IT: Rafael Toledo
Dir IT: Kurt Watson
IT Man: Jose Ortega
Prd Mgr: Henry Gallego
Manager: Sarah Dennis

D-U-N-S 01-000-0412
OCEANSIDE INSTITUTIONAL INDUSTRIES INC
2525 Long Beach Rd, Oceanside, NY 11572-1353
Tel (718) 343-9797 *Founded/Ownrshp* 1974
Sales 18.4MM^E *EMP* 380^E
SIC 7213 Linen supply; Linen supply
Ch Bd: Frank Ferrara
VP: Larry Amodio
VP: Jack Ferrara
**VP:* Walter Hermann

OCEANSIDE PUBLIC SCHOOLS
See OCEANSIDE UNION FREE SCHOOL DISTRICT 11

D-U-N-S 94-070-6224
OCEANSIDE TEN MANAGEMENT INC
1675 Larimer St Ste 750, Denver, CO 80202-1523
Tel (303) 534-3333 *Founded/Ownrshp* 2008
Sales 30.0MM *EMP* 61
SIC 8741 7371 8732 6719 Management services; Computer software development & applications; Market analysis or research; Personal holding companies, except banks; Management services; Computer software development & applications; Market analysis or research; Personal holding companies, except banks
Pr: Steve Little
**VP:* Zachary McGreth

D-U-N-S 07-873-2062
OCEANSIDE UNIFIED SCHOOL DISTRICT
2111 Mission Ave, Oceanside, CA 92058-2395
Tel (760) 966-4000 *Founded/Ownrshp* 1970
Sales 90.9MM^E *EMP* 2,200
Accts Christywhite Accountancy Corpo
SIC 8211 Public elementary & secondary schools; Public elementary & secondary schools
Ofcr: Joe Sepulveda
Dir IT: Matt Evans
IT Man: Nathan Huggins

D-U-N-S 83-307-0720
OCEANSIDE UNION FREE SCHOOL DISTRICT
145 Merle Ave, Oceanside, NY 11572-2219
Tel (516) 678-1200 *Founded/Ownrshp* 2010
Sales 34.5MM^E *EMP* 959^E
SIC 8211 Elementary & secondary schools
VP: Arlene Wegard
Pr Dir: Donna Kraus
Instr Medi: Mark Sidoti

D-U-N-S 06-196-6503
OCEANSIDE UNION FREE SCHOOL DISTRICT 11
OCEANSIDE PUBLIC SCHOOLS
145 Merle Ave, Oceanside, NY 11572-2219
Tel (516) 594-2333 *Founded/Ownrshp* 1898
Sales 44.5MM^E *EMP* 720
SIC 8211 Public elementary & secondary schools; Public elementary & secondary schools

OCEANVIEW MANAGERS
See PELICAN GRAND BEACH RESORT CONDOMINIUM ASSOCIATION INC

D-U-N-S 03-839-0915 EXP
OCEANWORKS INTERNATIONAL INC
11611 Tanner Rd Ste A, Houston, TX 77041-6906
Tel (281) 598-3940 *Founded/Ownrshp* 2007
Sales 22.3MM^E *EMP* 104
SIC 3731 Submarine tenders, building & repairing; Submarines, building & repairing
CEO: Rodney W Stanley
COO: Glen Viau
**CFO:* Ray Coufal
VP: Doug Amorello
**Prin:* Gregory Armstrong
**Prin:* Richard Reese
**Prin:* David Whittaker

D-U-N-S 05-219-5146 IMP
OCENCO INC
ERIE MEDICAL
10225 82nd Ave, Pleasant Prairie, WI 53158-5801
Tel (262) 947-9000 *Founded/Ownrshp* 1977
Sales 41.5MM^E *EMP* 160^E
SIC 3842 3646 Respirators; Commercial indusl & institutional electric lighting fixtures; Respirators; Commercial indusl & institutional electric lighting fixtures
CEO: J Patrick Droppleman
**VP:* Donald L Auth
VP: Brian Tuckey
**VP:* Richard A Van Derveer
Plnt Mgr: Dilip Shah
Prd Mgr: Fred Kohlscheen
Ql Cn Mgr: Raul Calles
Natl Sales: Gerald Stickler

D-U-N-S 84-927-1473
OCEUS NETWORKS INC
(*Suby of* TAILWIND CAPITAL) ★
1895 Preston White Dr, Reston, VA 20191-5469
Tel (703) 234-9156 *Founded/Ownrshp* 2011
Sales 20.8MM^E *EMP* 50^E
SIC 4813
Pr: Randy Fuerst
Pr: Al Thomas
**COO:* Jeff Harman
**CFO:* Alan Stewart
**Sr VP:* Cal Shintani
VP: Peter Brady
VP: Randy Clark
VP: Jim Patterson
**VP:* Kevin Stiles
Prgrm Mgr: Christian Bates
Genl Mgr: Richard Ricker

D-U-N-S 07-546-1509
OCH REGIONAL MEDICAL CENTER
400 Hospital Rd, Starkville, MS 39759-2163
Tel (662) 615-3020 *Founded/Ownrshp* 1973
Sales 67.4MM *EMP* 600^E
Accts Watkins Ward And Stafford Pl
SIC 8062 General medical & surgical hospitals; General medical & surgical hospitals
CEO: Richard G Hilton
Chf OB: Thomas H Pearson
Chf Rad: Michael Buehler
CFO: Richard Hilton
Ofcr: Patricia Faver
Dir OR: Jeff Tharp
Dir Inf Cn: Kim Roberts
Dir Risk M: Martha Fulcher
Dir Lab: Tom Sheward
Dir Pat Ac: Lynne Sizemore
CTO: Cynthia Travis

D-U-N-S 92-781-7262
OCH-ZIFF CAPITAL MANAGEMENT GROUP LLC
9 W 57th St, New York, NY 10019-2701
Tel (212) 790-0000 *Founded/Ownrshp* 1994
Sales 1.5MMM *EMP* 595E
Tkr Sym OZM *Exch* NYS
SIC 6282 Manager of mutual funds, contract or fee basis; Manager of mutual funds, contract or fee basis
Ch Bd: Daniel S Och
Ofcr: Patrick Crotty
Ofcr: Anna Song
VP: Frances Orabona
VP: Hap Pollard
Dir Risk M: Kenneth Perry
Assoc Dir: Anuradha Gurung
Mng Dir: Adam Broder
Mng Dir: Michael Cohen
Mng Dir: Sameer Dalamal
Mng Dir: David Gillerman

O'CHARLEYS
See COVELLI ENTERPRISES INC

D-U-N-S 10-176-5436
OCHARLEYS LLC
O'CHARLEY'S RESTAURANTS
(*Suby of* AMERICAN BLUE RIBBON HOLDINGS LLC) ★
3038 Sidco Dr, Nashville, TN 37204-4516
Tel (615) 256-8500 *Founded/Ownrshp* 2013
Sales 453.2MME *EMP* 24,081E
Accts Kpmg Llp Nashville Tennessee
SIC 5812 Restaurant, family: chain
CFO: R Jeffrey Williams
Mng Pt: Brent McKeehan
Pr: George T Agarelis
Pr: Marc A Buehler
Pr: Wilson Craft
Pr: Charles F DOE Jr
Pr: John R Grady
Pr: Anthony J Halligan III
Ofcr: Lawrence Hyatt
VP: J Harold Allen
VP: Jim Kiley
VP: James K Quackenbush
VP: Raymond Westphal

O'CHARLEY'S RESTAURANTS
See OCHARLEYS LLC

D-U-N-S 13-812-6888
OCHIN INC
1881 Sw Naito Pkwy # 100, Portland, OR 97201-5187
Tel (503) 943-2500 *Founded/Ownrshp* 2003
Sales 26.1MM *EMP* 67E
Accts Hoffman Stewart & Schmidt Pc
SIC 7373 Systems software development services; Systems software development services
CEO: Abigail Sears
CFO: Marcy Boyd
**CFO:* Sean Whiteley-Ross
Ofcr: Lynne Shoemaker
**VP:* Kevin Geoffroy
**VP:* Ruby Haughton-Pitts
**VP:* Kim Klupenger
VP: Kim Lamb
VP: Jonathan Merrell
Dir Bus: Amanda Thorgramson
Snr Ntwrk: Mike Hall

D-U-N-S 01-438-4213
OCHOA AG UNLIMITED FOODS INC
OCHOA FOODS
910 W Main St Ste 248, Boise, ID 83702-5732
Tel (208) 343-6882 *Founded/Ownrshp* 2001
Sales 100.0MM *EMP* 300
SIC 5142 Packaged frozen goods; Packaged frozen goods
Pr: Thoma Martinez
**CFO:* Howard Bafford
CTO: Greg Vietz

D-U-N-S 60-292-7352
OCHOA AG UNLIMITED FOODS INC
(*Suby of* OCHOA AG UNLIMITED FOODS INC) ★
1203 Basin St, Warden, WA 98857-9475
Tel (509) 349-2210 *Founded/Ownrshp* 1989
Sales 22.4MME *EMP* 150
SIC 2037 Potato products, quick frozen & cold pack; Potato products, quick frozen & cold pack
Pr: Kevin Weber
**Sec:* Alan Bird
**VP:* Bill Weber
CIO: Andrea Carlson
QA Dir: Rich Tolman

OCHOA FOODS
See OCHOA AG UNLIMITED FOODS INC

D-U-N-S 55-702-0398
OCHSNER BAPTIST MEDICAL CENTER LLC
OCHSNER HEALTH WITH PEACE MIND
2700 Napoleon Ave, New Orleans, LA 70115-6914
Tel (504) 899-9311 *Founded/Ownrshp* 2006
Sales 59.2MME *EMP* 341
SIC 8062 General medical & surgical hospitals; General medical & surgical hospitals
**CEO:* Dawn Anuszkiewicz
Treas: Giancarlo Campi
Ofcr: Chris Rogers
**Exec:* Dana Werkheiser
Dir Case M: Gail Wilson
Dir Rad: Kelly Emrick
QA Dir: Debra Volpi
Software D: Shawn McCann
Ansthlgy: Glenn Casey
Nr&g Dir: Joan Condon
HC Dir: Dana Aron

D-U-N-S 07-790-0207 IMP
OCHSNER CLINIC FOUNDATION
1514 Jefferson Hwy, New Orleans, LA 70121-2483
Tel (504) 842-3000 *Founded/Ownrshp* 1944
Sales 2.2MMM *EMP* 10,500
Accts Ernst & Young Us Llp Austin
SIC 8062 5947 General medical & surgical hospitals; Gift, novelty & souvenir shop; General medical & surgical hospitals; Gift, novelty & souvenir shop
Pr: Patrick J Quinlan MD
Chf Path: Greg Sossaman
COO: Eric McMillen
Ex VP: B C Brannon
Sr VP: Lawrence Van Hoose
Dir Rx: Arlene Workmen
Ex Dir: Ethel U Madden
Prgrm Mgr: Beth Sekinger
MIS Dir: Glenn Doherty
Mktg Mgr: Lisa Fine
Orthpdst: Timothy Devraj

D-U-N-S 15-748-7471
OCHSNER CLINIC HEALTH SERVICES CORP
1514 Jefferson Hwy, New Orleans, LA 70121-2483
Tel (504) 842-4000 *Founded/Ownrshp* 1978
Sales 164.6MM *EMP* 132E
SIC 8011 General & family practice, physician/surgeon; General & family practice, physician/surgeon
Ch Bd: Dr Gary Goldstein
**Treas:* Scott J Posecai
**Acting Pr:* Shannon Cooper MD
Bd of Dir: Julia Cook
Bd of Dir: Jonathan McCall
Bd of Dir: William A Norton
Bd of Dir: A Jusin Ourso III
Ofcr: Rhia McGee
Ex VP: Joseph Bisordi
Sr VP: Mark Muller
VP: Jan Brien
VP: Edward D Frohlich
Dir Rad: Oussama Nachar
Dir Rx: Reggie Labat

D-U-N-S 96-835-0731
OCHSNER COMMUNITY HOSPITALS
1514 Jefferson Hwy, New Orleans, LA 70121-2429
Tel (504) 842-3400 *Founded/Ownrshp* 2011
Sales 507.2MM *EMP* 99
Accts Ernst & Young Us Llp Austin
SIC 8062 General medical & surgical hospitals
Treas: Bobby C Brannon
Dir Rad: Julie Henry
Nurse Mgr: Lara Tedesco
Doctor: Jose Bernal
Doctor: Patrick Breaux
Doctor: David Elizardi
Doctor: George ISA
Doctor: Jefferson Kaye
Doctor: Gary Rich

D-U-N-S 94-901-4393
OCHSNER FOUNDATION HOSPITAL
OCHSNER MEDICAL CENTER
1514 Jefferson Hwy, New Orleans, LA 70121-2429
Tel (504) 842-4000 *Founded/Ownrshp* 1942
Sales 206.1MME *EMP* 9,000
SIC 8062 General medical & surgical hospitals; General medical & surgical hospitals
CEO: Patrick Quinlan
VP: Timothy Maier
Dir Lab: Timmy Thrash
Dir Rad: Oussama Nachar
CIO: Jonathan McCall
CIO: Bill Saussaye
CIO: Cindy Stowe
QA Dir: Mark Milner
IT Man: Kathryn Watson
Orthpdst: Roger Racz
Pathlgst: Elise A Occhipinti

D-U-N-S 82-920-1644
OCHSNER HEALTH SYSTEM
880 W Commerce Rd, New Orleans, LA 70123-3330
Tel (866) 624-7637 *Founded/Ownrshp* 2006
Sales 39.5MME *EMP* 166E
Accts Deloitte Tax Llp New Orleans
SIC 8742 Hospital & health services consultant
Pr: Patrick Quinlan MD
VP: Stephanie Wells
Chf Nrs Of: Trudi Stafford
Chf Nrs Of: Cheryl Woods
Ansthlgy: Jimmie Colon
Plas Surg: Emily Lewis
Doctor: Eiman Jahangir
Pharmcst: Ken Green
Pharmcst: Nicole Lacoste
Snr Mgr: Teresa Anderson

OCHSNER HEALTH WITH PEACE MIND
See OCHSNER BAPTIST MEDICAL CENTER LLC

D-U-N-S 84-535-9256
OCHSNER HOME HEALTH SERVICES INC
9001 Summa Ave, Baton Rouge, LA 70809-3726
Tel (800) 813-2224 *Founded/Ownrshp* 1985
Sales 23.1MME *EMP* 85
SIC 5047 8049 8082 Medical equipment & supplies; Nurses, registered & practical; Home health care services
Prin: Ken Tillman
Dir Inf Cn: Sharon Berry
Surgeon: Amy Rabalais
Obsttrcn: Juan Vargas
Doctor: Sharon Hedges
Diag Rad: Carl Scherer

OCHSNER KENNER MEDICAL CTR
See OCHSNER MEDICAL CENTER - KENNER LLC

OCHSNER MEDICAL CENTER
See OCHSNER FOUNDATION HOSPITAL

D-U-N-S 95-748-6603
OCHSNER MEDICAL CENTER
WEST BANK CAMPUS
2500 Belle Chasse Hwy, Terrytown, LA 70056-7127
Tel (504) 392-3131 *Founded/Ownrshp* 2008
Sales 29.6MME *EMP* 110E
SIC 8011 Medical centers
CEO: Michael Bryan
Chf Path: Don Hemelt
Exec: Sue Meulen
Off Mgr: Sherry Whitefield
Mktg Dir: Deanna Davis
Pharmcst: Eugene Landry
Diag Rad: Kurosh Safavi
HC Dir: Jean Brown
Snr Mgr: Harish Anannd

OCHSNER MEDICAL CENTER - BATON
See EAST BATON ROUGE MEDICAL CENTER LLC

D-U-N-S 78-671-6915
OCHSNER MEDICAL CENTER - KENNER LLC
OCHSNER KENNER MEDICAL CTR
180 W Esplanade Ave, Kenner, LA 70065-2467
Tel (504) 468-8600 *Founded/Ownrshp* 2006
Sales 93.7MM *EMP* 2
SIC 8062 General medical & surgical hospitals; General medical & surgical hospitals
Prin: Denise S Huner
VP: Mark Eckert
Dir Rad: Kendy Martinez
Dir Rx: Barries Leung
Dir Rx: Arlene Workmon
Off Mgr: Donna Blandy
Off Mgr: Mary Meyers
Dir QC: Erin Ray
Dir QC: Erin Wray
Surgeon: Wagih Mando
Nutrtnst: Corie Gardner

D-U-N-S 96-351-4299
OCHSNER MEDICAL CENTER NORTH S
100 Medical Center Dr, Slidell, LA 70461-5520
Tel (985) 649-7070 *Founded/Ownrshp* 2010
Sales NA *EMP* 56E
SIC 6324 Hospital & medical service plans
Prin: Scott Posecai
COO: Debbie Williams
Pharmcst: Leslie Talbot

D-U-N-S 00-690-0772 IMP
OCI BEAUMONT LLC (TX)
(*Suby of* OCI N.V.)
5470 N Twin City Hwy, Nederland, TX 77627
Tel (409) 723-1900 *Founded/Ownrshp* 2010
Sales 63.0MME *EMP* 80
SIC 2869 5169 Methyl alcohol, synthetic methanol; Ammonia; Methyl alcohol, synthetic methanol; Ammonia
Pr: Frank Bakker
**CFO:* Fady Kiama

D-U-N-S 93-385-1420 EXP
OCI ENTERPRISES INC
(*Suby of* OCI COMPANY LTD.)
300 Convent St Ste 1900, San Antonio, TX 78205-3746
Tel (770) 375-2300 *Founded/Ownrshp* 1996
Sales 293.0MME *EMP* 550
SIC 1474 Soda ash (natural) mining; Soda ash (natural) mining
Pr: Chris Fraser
**Ch Bd:* SOOY Lee
Pr: Brent Bailey
Snr Ntwrk: Michael Rash
Dir IT: Sandeep Kudrimoti
Dir IT: Paul Whitacre
IT Man: Marchell Gebhardt
Netwrk Eng: Edward Holder
Genl Couns: Nicole Daniel
Snr Mgr: Harry Franks
Snr Mgr: Amy McCool

D-U-N-S 92-983-6583
■ **OCI HOLDING CO INC**
(*Suby of* CINER RESOURCES CORP) ★
La Barge Rd, Green River, WY 82935
Tel (307) 875-2600 *Founded/Ownrshp* 1995
Sales 245.0ME *EMP* 400
SIC 1474 Soda ash (natural) mining; Soda ash (natural) mining
Pr: Chris Fraser

D-U-N-S 07-887-6977
OCI PARTNERS LP
5470 N Twin City Hwy, Nederland, TX 77627
Tel (409) 723-1900 *Founded/Ownrshp* 2013
Sales 402.7MM *EMP* 100
Tkr Sym OCIP *Exch* NYS
SIC 2861 2873 Methanol, natural (wood alcohol); Ammonia & ammonium salts; Fertilizers: natural (organic), except compost; Methanol, natural (wood alcohol); Ammonium nitrate, ammonium sulfate; Anhydrous ammonia
Pr: Frank Bakker
Genl Pt: Oci GP LLC
CFO: Fady Kiama

OCI RESOURCES LP
See CINER RESOURCES LP

D-U-N-S 03-915-1506
OCIMUM BIOSOLUTIONS INC
50 W Watkins Mill Rd, Gaithersburg, MD 20878-4023
Tel (317) 228-0600 *Founded/Ownrshp* 2000
Sales 23.0MM *EMP* 5,260
SIC 8731 Agricultural research; Biological research; Agricultural research; Biological research
Pr: Anuradha Acharya
Sr VP: Charles Dimmler
VP Mktg: Sridhar Kolanu
Mktg Dir: Ashwin Sivakumar

OCIP
See ORANGE COUNTY INDUSTRIAL PLASTICS INC

OCLARO
See OPNEXT INC

D-U-N-S 00-879-7412
■ **OCLARO (NORTH AMERICA) INC**
(*Suby of* OCLARO INC) ★
2560 Junction Ave, San Jose, CA 95134-1902
Tel (408) 383-1400 *Founded/Ownrshp* 2000
Sales 36.5MME *EMP* 576
SIC 3661 Fiber optics communications equipment; Fiber optics communications equipment
CEO: Jerry Turin
**CEO:* Pete Mangan
Chf Mktg O: Yves Lemaitre
Sr VP: Pat Edsell
Sr VP: Paul Jiang
VP: Margaret Quinn
VP: Linda Reddick
Exec: Douglas Hall
Exec: David Parker

D-U-N-S 61-486-0646
▲ **OCLARO INC**
2560 Junction Ave, San Jose, CA 95134-1902
Tel (408) 383-1400 *Founded/Ownrshp* 2004
Sales 341.2MM *EMP* 1,233E
Accts Grant Thornton Llp San Franci
Tkr Sym OCLR *Exch* NGS
SIC 3674 3826 3827 Light emitting diodes; Laser scientific & engineering instruments; Optical instruments & apparatus; Light emitting diodes; Laser scientific & engineering instruments; Optical instruments & apparatus
CEO: Greg Dougherty
**Ch Bd:* Marissa Peterson
Pr: Richard Craig
Pr: Yves Lemaitre
COO: Jim Haynes
CFO: Pete Mangan
Chf Cred: Adam Carter
Ex VP: Previn Brito
Ex VP: Lisa Paul
Ex VP: David Teichmann
Ex VP: David Williams
VP: Per Hansen
VP: Erik Mendez
VP: Bruce Pollack
VP: Dan Zanetti
Comm Dir: Rebecca Young-Jones
Board of Directors: Edward Collins, Kendall Cowan, Lori Holland, Joel A Smith III, William L Smith

D-U-N-S 11-186-3841
■ **OCLARO TECHNOLOGY INC**
(*Suby of* OCLARO INC) ★
2560 Junction Ave, San Jose, CA 95134-1902
Tel (408) 383-1400 *Founded/Ownrshp* 1998
Sales 64.5MME *EMP* 800
SIC 3661 Fiber optics communications equipment; Fiber optics communications equipment
CEO: Greg Dougherty
Pr: Jim Haynes
COO: Terry Unter
CFO: Pete Mangan
VP: Joseph K Lee
Ex Dir: Peggy Oden

D-U-N-S 06-358-7745
OCLC ONLINE COMPUTER LIBRARY CENTER INCORPORATE
6565 Kilgour Pl, Dublin, OH 43017-3395
Tel (614) 764-6000 *Founded/Ownrshp* 1967
Sales 213.5MM *EMP* 1,227
Accts Deloitte & Touche Llp Columbu
SIC 7375 On-line data base information retrieval; On-line data base information retrieval
Pr: David A Prichard
Pr: Susan Walker
Trst: Tony Ferguson
VP: Dena K Bovee
VP: Ronald Edelsteis
VP: Chip Nilges
Prin: Pat Ring
Mng Dir: Eric Van Lubeek
Mng Dir: Norbert Weinberger
Rgnl Mgr: Antonio Jose A Santana
CIO: Jeff J Jacobs

OCLI
See OPTICAL COATING LABORATORY LLC

D-U-N-S 03-794-3742
OCM LLC
OHIO COMMUNITY MEDIA
4500 Lyons Rd, Miamisburg, OH 45342-6447
Tel (937) 247-2700 *Founded/Ownrshp* 2011
Sales 132.3MME *EMP* 872E
SIC 2711 Newspapers
CEO: Roy Brown

D-U-N-S 07-965-8947
▲ **OCM PE HOLDINGS LP**
333 S Grand Ave Fl 28, Los Angeles, CA 90071-1504
Tel (213) 830-6213 *Founded/Ownrshp* 2012
Sales 559.6MME *EMP* 10,000E
SIC 3679 3612 3663 Electronic circuits; Transformers, except electric; Antennas, transmitting & communications
CEO: Mark C J Twaalfhoven

OCONEE COUNTY BOARD EDUCATION
See OCONEE COUNTY SCHOOL DISTRICT

D-U-N-S 10-064-6207
OCONEE COUNTY SCHOOL DISTRICT
OCONEE COUNTY BOARD EDUCATION
34 School St, Watkinsville, GA 30677-6079
Tel (706) 769-5130 *Founded/Ownrshp* 1964
Sales 60.4MME *EMP* 871
Accts Russell W Hinton Cpa Cgfm
SIC 8211 9111 Public elementary & secondary schools; County supervisors' & executives' offices; Public elementary & secondary schools; County supervisors' & executives' offices
**Ch:* David W Weeks
Bd of Dir: Wayne Bagley
**Prin:* Kimberly S Argo
**Prin:* J Wayne Bagley
**Prin:* Mark H Thomas
Pr Dir: Brook Whitmire
Psych: Scott Eversole
HC Dir: Faye Warden

D-U-N-S 93-894-8130
OCONEE FALL LINE TECHNICAL COLLEGE
OFTC
1189 Deepstep Rd, Sandersville, GA 31082-9337
Tel (478) 553-2050 *Founded/Ownrshp* 1996
Sales 91.5M *EMP* 400E
Accts Russell W Hinton Cpa Cgfm
SIC 8222 Technical institute; Technical institute
Pr: Lloyd Horadan
**VP:* Eric Harden
**VP:* Rosemary Selby
IT Man: Penny Kitchens
IT Man: Angela Yarbrough

D-U-N-S 06-933-3789
OCONEE MEDICAL CENTER (SC)
LILA DOYLE NURSING CARE FCILTY
298 Memorial Dr, Seneca, SC 29672-9443
Tel (864) 882-3351 *Founded/Ownrshp* 1937
Sales 148.9MM *EMP* 1,345E
Accts Dixon Hughes Goodman Llp Ashe
SIC 8062 8051 General medical & surgical hospitals; Skilled nursing care facilities; General medical & surgical hospitals; Skilled nursing care facilities
Ch: William Howiler
Chf Rad: Bonnie Anderson
**Pr:* Jeanne L Ward
**Treas:* Bob M Toggweiler
Chf Mktg O: Conrad Shuler
Ex VP: Jeffrey Lehr
VP: Hunter Kome
VP: Patricia Smith
Dir Rx: William Stevenson
Off Mgr: Melinda Smith
CIO: Jay Hanson

D-U-N-S 06-647-0436 IMP
OCONEE REGIONAL HEALTH SYSTEMS INC
OCONEE REGIONAL MEDICAL CENTER
821 N Cobb St, Milledgeville, GA 31061-2343
Tel (478) 454-3500 *Founded/Ownrshp* 1957
Sales 45.1MME *EMP* 750
Accts James M Grant Cpa Pc Milledge
SIC 8062 General medical & surgical hospitals; General medical & surgical hospitals
Int Pr: Jeaen Aycock
Dir Recs: Janet Green
CFO: Amy Kingman
**CFO:* Brenda Qualls
VP: Mark Dorogy
VP: Cheryl Pounds
Exec: Kenneth Ward
Dir Risk M: Molly Thomas
Dir Rad: Bill Coleman
CIO: Alan Whitehouse
QA Dir: Deanne Herring

OCONEE REGIONAL MEDICAL CENTER
See OCONEE REGIONAL HEALTH SYSTEMS INC

D-U-N-S 09-744-5399
OCONNELL COMPANIES INC
480 Hampden St, Holyoke, MA 01040-3309
Tel (413) 534-0246 *Founded/Ownrshp* 1879
Sales 203.7MME *EMP* 730
SIC 1541 Industrial buildings, new construction; Renovation, remodeling & repairs: industrial buildings; Industrial buildings, new construction; Renovation, remodeling & repairs: industrial buildings
Pr: Dennis A Fitzpatrick
**Treas:* James N Sullivan
**VP:* Nathan C Clinard
VP: Robin Rupp
**VP:* Martin F Schoenemann

D-U-N-S 11-423-1186
OCONNELL DEVELOPMENT GROUP INC
(*Suby of* OCONNELL COMPANIES INC) ★
480 Hampden St, Holyoke, MA 01040-3309
Tel (413) 534-0243 *Founded/Ownrshp* 1984
Sales 30.6MM *EMP* 30
SIC 6552 8741 6799 Land subdividers & developers, commercial; Land subdividers & developers, residential; Construction management; Financial management for business; Industrial management; Real estate investors, except property operators; Land subdividers & developers, commercial; Land subdividers & developers, residential; Construction management; Financial management for business; Industrial management; Real estate investors, except property operators
Pr: Michael T Downey
CFO: Martin Schoenemann
**Treas:* James N Sullivan
VP: Steven Berry
VP: Andrew J Crystal
Dir Bus: Richard Hanson
Snr Mgr: Michael Morel
Snr Mgr: George Volpicelli
Board of Directors: Dennis A Fitzpatrick, Martin F Schoenemann

D-U-N-S 00-379-2322
OCONNELL ELECTRIC CO INC (NY)
830 Phillips Rd, Victor, NY 14564-9747
Tel (585) 924-2176 *Founded/Ownrshp* 1911, 1968
Sales 156.4MME *EMP* 550
SIC 1731 General electrical contractor; General electrical contractor
CEO: Victor E Salerno
**Ch Bd:* Walter T Parkes
COO: Gary Means
**COO:* Thomas W Parkes
**CFO:* Jeffrey T Gould
CFO: Jeffrey Gould
**VP:* Susan Parkes McNally
Off Mgr: Deborah Tonge
DP Exec: Jon McNally
Dir IT: Jon Weiss
IT Man: David Adams

D-U-N-S 07-357-6951 IMP
OCONNELL LANDSCAPE MAINTENANCE INC (CA)
23091 Arroyo Vis, Rcho STA Marg, CA 92688-2605
Tel (949) 589-2007 *Founded/Ownrshp* 1977
Sales 132.6MME *EMP* 1,000
SIC 0782 Landscape contractors; Landscape contractors
CEO: George O'Connell
**Pr:* Jim Vienneau
**VP:* Brady O'Connell
VP: Brady Oconnell
**VP:* Darren Payne
Area Mgr: Jim Galen
Brnch Mgr: Mike Clark
Brnch Mgr: Tony Hartvigsen
Opers Mgr: Andrew Martin

D-U-N-S 01-956-8773
OCONNELL OIL ASSOCIATES INC
O'CONNELL'S CONVENIENCE PLUS
545 Merrill Rd, Pittsfield, MA 01201-3722
Tel (413) 443-9693 *Founded/Ownrshp* 1970
Sales 59.8MME *EMP* 350
SIC 5983 5172 5541 5411 Fuel oil dealers; Fuel oil; Gasoline; Gasoline service stations; Convenience stores, chain; Fuel oil dealers; Fuel oil; Gasoline service stations; Convenience stores, chain
CEO: Michael R Sobon
**Treas:* George Dickhout
Sr VP: John Gaudrault

O'CONNELL'S CONVENIENCE PLUS
See OCONNELL OIL ASSOCIATES INC

D-U-N-S 07-290-6944
OCONNOR CO (SD)
4909 N Lewis Ave, Sioux Falls, SD 57104-7113
Tel (605) 336-1823 *Founded/Ownrshp* 1970
Sales 80.3MME *EMP* 120
SIC 5075 Warm air heating & air conditioning; Warm air heating & air conditioning
Pr: Mike O'Connor
VP: Michael O'Connor

D-U-N-S 00-724-7430
OCONNOR CO INC
16910 W 116th St, Lenexa, KS 66219-9604
Tel (913) 894-8788 *Founded/Ownrshp* 1921
Sales 90.0MM *EMP* 120
SIC 5075 Warm air heating & air conditioning; Warm air heating & air conditioning
Pr: Lynn J Piller
COO: Brian Jones
Ofcr: Bob Meiners
VP: Stephanie Atkinson
Brnch Mgr: Wendell Miller
Brnch Mgr: Joe Thompson
Off Mgr: Cathy Griffith
Mktg Mgr: Melissa McDonald
Sls Mgr: Mike Cunningham
Sls Mgr: Arnold Morgan
Sls Mgr: Kim Peppie

D-U-N-S 00-288-3114
OCONNOR CONSTRUCTORS INC
45 Industrial Dr, Canton, MA 02021-2896
Tel (781) 830-1937 *Founded/Ownrshp* 1904
Sales 27.6MME *EMP* 100E
SIC 1542 Commercial & office building contractors; Institutional building construction; Commercial & office building contractors; Institutional building construction
Pr: Thomas H O'Connor Jr
Genl Mgr: Edward Marks
Dir IT: Debby Willemsen
IT Man: Al Heard

D-U-N-S 14-885-7522
OCONNOR CORP
BEACON PIPING
45 Industrial Dr, Canton, MA 02021-2896
Tel (617) 364-9000 *Founded/Ownrshp* 2002
Sales 35.4MME *EMP* 475
SIC 1711 Mechanical contractor; Mechanical contractor
Pr: Thomas H O'Connor III
**Treas:* Laura A Altman

D-U-N-S 04-079-8527
OCONNOR HOSPITAL
460 Andes Rd, Delhi, NY 13753-7443
Tel (607) 746-0300 *Founded/Ownrshp* 1998
Sales 21.9MME *EMP* 159
Accts Kpmg Llp Albany Ny
SIC 8062 General medical & surgical hospitals; General medical & surgical hospitals
CEO: Daniel Ayres
Dir Lab: Abid Rab
Dir Rad: Michael Viafore
Dir Rx: John Lernihan
Nurse Mgr: Connie Finkle
Podiatrist: Michael Krajick
Pharmcst: Robert Abarno

D-U-N-S 07-630-0169
OCONNOR HOSPITAL
O'CONNOR WOUND CARE CLINIC
2105 Forest Ave, San Jose, CA 95128-1471
Tel (408) 947-2500 *Founded/Ownrshp* 1954
Sales 307.1MM *EMP* 1,300
Accts Grant Thornton Llp San Franci
SIC 8062 General medical & surgical hospitals; General medical & surgical hospitals
CEO: James F Dover
CFO: Dawn Goeringer
**Sr VP:* David W Carroll
**VP:* Craig Rucker
Genl Mgr: Mike Manansala
Sfty Dirs: John Hryndej
HC Dir: Pam Woods

O'CONNOR MOTRO COMPANY
See HUTCHINS MOTORS INC

D-U-N-S 02-322-9354
OCONNOR OIL CORP
STRETCH TRUCK STOP
725 N Progress Dr, Saukville, WI 53080-1613
Tel (920) 921-8020 *Founded/Ownrshp* 1961
Sales 37.0MM *EMP* 87
Accts Foy & Springborn Sc Fond D
SIC 5541 5171 Filling stations, gasoline; Petroleum bulk stations; Filling stations, gasoline; Petroleum bulk stations
Pr: Dorothea O Connor

D-U-N-S 08-494-8657
OCONNOR WOODS HOUSING CORP
(*Suby of* ST JOSEPHS REGIONAL HOUSING CORP) ★
3400 Wagner Heights Rd, Stockton, CA 95209-4843
Tel (209) 956-3400 *Founded/Ownrshp* 1991
Sales 29.1MM *EMP* 100
Accts Moss Adams Llp Stockton Ca
SIC 6513 Retirement hotel operation
Pr: Edward G Schoeder
**Ex Dir:* Scot Sinclair

O'CONNOR WOUND CARE CLINIC
See OCONNOR HOSPITAL

D-U-N-S 10-008-3690
OCONOMOWOC AREA SCHOOL DISTRICT
ADMINISTRATIVE OFFICES
W360n7077 Brown St, Oconomowoc, WI 53066-1111
Tel (262) 560-2141 *Founded/Ownrshp* 1892
Sales 26.2MME *EMP* 400
Accts Feld Schumacher & Company Llp
SIC 8211 Public elementary & secondary schools; Public elementary school; Public junior high school; Public senior high school; Public elementary & secondary schools; Public elementary school; Public junior high school; Public senior high school
Teacher Pr: Pam Casey

D-U-N-S 07-615-1836
OCONOMOWOC DEVELOPMENTAL TRAINING CENTER OF WISCONSIN LLC
GENESEE LAKE SCHOOL
36100 Genesee Lake Rd, Oconomowoc, WI 53066-9202
Tel (262) 569-5515 *Founded/Ownrshp* 1984
Sales 20.6MM *EMP* 260
SIC 8361 Home for the mentally handicapped; Home for the emotionally disturbed; Home for the mentally handicapped; Home for the emotionally disturbed
IT Man: Kim Ray
Mktg Dir: Matthew Balestrieri
Psych: Anne Felden

D-U-N-S 82-585-6834
OCONOMOWOC RESIDENTIAL PROGRAMS INC
ORP
1746 Executive Dr, Oconomowoc, WI 53066-4830
Tel (262) 569-5515 *Founded/Ownrshp* 1984
Sales 96.4MM *EMP* 1,500
Accts Bdo Usa Llp Milwaukee Wi
SIC 8052 8361 Intermediate care facilities; Home for the mentally handicapped; Home for the emotionally disturbed; Intermediate care facilities; Home for the mentally handicapped; Home for the emotionally disturbed
Pr: James Balestrieri
COO: Terrence Leahy
**COO:* Richard Macnally
**CFO:* David Nagy
CFO: Adam Whitehill
VP: Debbie Frisk
**VP:* Michael Warczyglowa
Ex Dir: Michael Flores
Dist Mgr: Kevin Silkey
Dir IT: Tim Hornak
IT Man: Angi Rieker

D-U-N-S 04-878-7683
OCP CONTRACTORS INC
O C P
1740 Commerce Rd, Holland, OH 43528-9789
Tel (419) 865-7168 *Founded/Ownrshp* 1968
Sales 58.0MM *EMP* 250
SIC 1742 1751 1752 1743 1799 Drywall; Lightweight steel framing (metal stud) installation; Floor laying & floor work; Tile installation, ceramic; Coating, caulking & weather, water & fireproofing; Drywall; Lightweight steel framing (metal stud) installation; Floor laying & floor work; Tile installation, ceramic; Coating, caulking & weather, water & fireproofing
Pr: Matthew Townsend
**VP:* Pam Hepburn

D-U-N-S 07-870-0490
OCS BUILDERS GROUP LLC
420 Westbury Ave, Carle Place, NY 11514-1402
Tel (516) 747-1515 *Founded/Ownrshp* 2006
Sales 35.0MM *EMP* 20
SIC 8741 1751 Construction management; Cabinet & finish carpentry; Construction management; Cabinet & finish carpentry
CEO: James Fendt
Pr: Michael Nikolai

OCSA
See ORANGE COUNTY SCHOOL OF ARTS

OCSD5
See ORANGEBURG CONSOLIDATED SCHOOL DISTRICT 5

OCTAGON ATHLETES PERSONALITIES
See OCTAGON USA INC

D-U-N-S 07-744-2598
■ **OCTAGON USA INC**
OCTAGON ATHLETES PERSONALITIES
(*Suby of* INTERPUBLIC GROUP OF COMPANIES INC) ★
7950 Jones Branch Dr 700n, Mc Lean, VA 22107-0002
Tel (703) 905-3366 *Founded/Ownrshp* 1997
Sales 67.4MME *EMP* 400
SIC 8742 7941 Marketing consulting services; Sports promotion; Marketing consulting services; Sports promotion
CEO: Rick Dudley
**Pr:* Phil D Picciotto
**CFO:* Nancy Morten
CFO: Richard P Sneeder Jr
Chf Mktg O: Murray Lisa
**Ex VP:* Lisa Murray
Sr VP: Gord Lang
Sr VP: Frank Zecca
VP: Ellen Johnson
VP: Robert Jones
VP: Julie Kennedy
VP: Janey Miller
VP: Nancy Morton
VP: Frank M Zecca

D-U-N-S 07-839-4646 IMP
OCTANE FITNESS LLC (MN)
7601 Northland Dr N # 100, Brooklyn Park, MN 55428-4529
Tel (763) 757-2662 *Founded/Ownrshp* 2001
Sales 29.4MME *EMP* 42E
SIC 5091 Fitness equipment & supplies
Pr: Dennis Lee
COO: Adrid Coz
**Ex VP:* Timothy Porth
**VP:* Ryan Simat
VP Opers: Scott Savitt
Manager: Chris Kuale
Sls Mgr: Will Beckwith

D-U-N-S 60-449-8824 IMP
OCTANORM USA INC
(*Suby of* HABRUSTA-VERWALTUNGS-GMBH)
701 Interstate West Pkwy, Lithia Springs, GA 30122-3224
Tel (770) 732-1520 *Founded/Ownrshp* 1989
Sales 36.2MME *EMP* 49
SIC 5039 Prefabricated structures
CEO: Norm Friedrich
**CFO:* Andre Vieler
Exec: Linda Trawick
Opers Mgr: Juergen Gerlach
Opers Mgr: Ralph Mims
Prd Mgr: Phil Meyberg
Sls Mgr: Jeff Mitchell

D-U-N-S 02-732-3557
OCTAPHARMA PLASMA INC
(*Suby of* OCTAPHARMA AG)
10644 Westlake Dr, Charlotte, NC 28273-3930
Tel (704) 654-4700 *Founded/Ownrshp* 2008
Sales 192.5MME *EMP* 300E
SIC 2836 Plasmas; Plasmas
Pr: Dennis D Curtin
**COO:* Judy Smith
**VP:* Barry Pomeroy
QA Dir: John Fulcher
QA Dir: Tanita Weathers
Info Man: Kristin Cooke
Netwrk Eng: Jeff Nobles

D-U-N-S 60-612-1163
OCTAPHARMA USA INC
(*Suby of* OCTAPHARMA AG)
121 River St 12th, Hoboken, NJ 07030-5982
Tel (201) 222-0140 *Founded/Ownrshp* 2003
Sales 28.5MME *EMP* 45
SIC 5122 Pharmaceuticals
Pr: Flemming Nielsen
**Treas:* Louis Dicriscio
Ofcr: Sonja Moser
VP: David E Holliday
VP: Andrea Svae
Adv Bd Mbr: Rita Santos
CTO: Irina Kruzhkova
IT Man: Michael Donham
Natl Sales: Bob Krepfle
Natl Sales: Alex Perez
VP Sls: Adam Tyler
Board of Directors: Kim Bjornstrup

D-U-N-S 83-917-5424
OCTAVIAN SECURITY AMERICAS LLC
9811 E Bell Rd Ste 110, Scottsdale, AZ 85260-2339
Tel (480) 991-2500 *Founded/Ownrshp* 2012
Sales 24.0MM *EMP* 46
SIC 7382 7349 7381 Burglar alarm maintenance & monitoring; Fire alarm maintenance & monitoring; Protective devices, security; Building & office cleaning services; Security guard service
IT Man: Sukhi Ghuman

D-U-N-S 10-136-1637
OCTAVUS GROUP LLC
261 School Ave Ste 400, Excelsior, MN 55331-2000
Tel (952) 767-2920 *Founded/Ownrshp* 1996
Sales 45.0MM *EMP* 14
SIC 6211 Brokers, security; Brokers, security
Pr: Christopher Horan
Prin: Matthew Cookson

D-U-N-S 55-657-1938
OCTG LLP
9200 Sheldon Rd, Houston, TX 77049-1248
Tel (281) 456-9057 *Founded/Ownrshp* 2005
Sales 32.8MME *EMP* 250
SIC 7389 Pipeline & power line inspection service; Pipeline & power line inspection service
Pt: David Fiberling
Genl Mgr: Bill Hudson

D-U-N-S 80-012-7859
OCTO CONSULTING GROUP INC
1600 Intl Dr Fl 5, Mclean, VA 22102
Tel (571) 275-0120 *Founded/Ownrshp* 2006
Sales 51.6MM *EMP* 140
Accts Bdo Usa Llp Mclean Virginia
SIC 7379 8742 Computer related consulting services; Management consulting services; Computer related consulting services; Management consulting services
Pr: Mehul Sanghani
Pr: Tracy Denny
**Pr:* Robert McCord
Ex VP: Jay Shah
Ex VP: Brian Swenson
VP: Gaurav Pal
Dir Bus: Frank Nelowet
Prgrm Mgr: Ed Wagner
Off Admin: Krishilda Zabala
CTO: Ashok Nare
Snr Mgr: Ashley Eanes

D-U-N-S 07-709-8374
OCTORARA AREA SCHOOL DISTRICT INC
228 Highland Rd Ste 1, Atglen, PA 19310-1603
Tel (610) 593-8238 *Founded/Ownrshp* 1966
Sales 20.3MME *EMP* 250E
SIC 8211 Public combined elementary & secondary school; Public combined elementary & secondary school
Treas: Samuel Ganow
VP: Brian Norris

Schl Brd P: Lisa Bowman
Teacher Pr: Mathew Furlong

OCU
See OAKLAND CITY UNIVERSITY

D-U-N-S 60-164-1319 IMP
OCULAR LCD INC
12700 Park Central Dr # 750, Dallas, TX 75251-1553
Tel (972) 437-3888 *Founded/Ownrshp* 2005
Sales NA *EMP* 2,000
SIC 3679

OCULAR SCIENCES A COOPERVISION
See COOPERVISION INC

OCULAR SCIENCES CARRIBEAN
See OCULAR SCIENCES PUERTO RICO INC

D-U-N-S 10-581-3414 IMP
■ OCULAR SCIENCES PUERTO RICO INC
OCULAR SCIENCES CARRIBEAN
(*Suby of* COOPER COMPANIES INC) ★
500 Carr 584, Juana Diaz, PR 00795-2870
Tel (787) 260-0555 *Founded/Ownrshp* 2007
Sales 54.3MM *EMP* 1,193
SIC 3851 Contact lenses
CFO: Sidney Landman
**Genl Mgr:* Fernando Torre
Snr Mgr: Vannessa Alvaravo

D-U-N-S 01-221-4518
■ OCULUS VR LLC
(*Suby of* FACEBOOK INC) ★
1601 Willow Rd, Menlo Park, CA 94025-1452
Tel (949) 502-2070 *Founded/Ownrshp* 2014
Sales 41.8MM^E *EMP* 200^E
SIC 5734 Computer software development & applications; Software, computer games
CEO: Brendan Iribe
Pr: Jack McCauley
CTO: John Carmack
Mfg Mgr: David Dykes

D-U-N-S 12-611-4433
OCUPATIONAL HEALTH MARIETTA PARTNERS
(*Suby of* MARIETTA MEMORIAL HOSPITAL INC) ★
401 Matthew St, Marietta, OH 45750-1635
Tel (740) 374-9954 *Founded/Ownrshp* 2003
Sales 20.0MM^E *EMP* 1^E
SIC 8011 Occupational & industrial specialist, physician/surgeon

D-U-N-S 84-990-9064
OCURRANCE INC
O'CURRANCE TELESERVICES
(*Suby of* XPLORE-TECH SERVICES PRIVATE LIMITED)
11850 Election Dr Ste 1501, Draper, UT 84020
Tel (801) 736-0500 *Founded/Ownrshp* 2012
Sales 69.1MM^E *EMP* 600
SIC 7389 Telemarketing services; Telemarketing services
CEO: Pankaj Dhanuka
**COO:* Paul Baird
**VP:* Cynthia Ahlstrom
**VP:* Mike Kennedy
Genl Mgr: Trevor Jacobs
**VP Sls:* Will Fritcher
**VP Sls:* Clint Gearheart

O'CURRANCE TELESERVICES
See OCURRANCE INC

D-U-N-S 17-493-9207
OCUSOFT INC
CYNACON
301 Kroesche Rd, Rosenberg, TX 77471-9297
Tel (800) 233-5469 *Founded/Ownrshp* 1986
Sales 28.7MM *EMP* 120
Accts Miller Grossbard Advisors Llp
SIC 2841 2844 2834 5122 Soap & other detergents; Toilet preparations; Pharmaceutical preparations; Dermatologicals; Cosmetics; Soap & other detergents; Toilet preparations; Pharmaceutical preparations; Dermatologicals; Cosmetics
Pr: Cynthia L Barratt
COO: Dorothy Eakins
**Ch:* Nat G Adkins Jr
**Ex VP:* Stacy Foster
Ex VP: Patrice Sutherland
Sr VP: Rose Martinez
VP: Sue Herreth
VP: Sean Ladart
**VP:* Thomas Mason
VP: Ed Shelton
QC Dir: Sarah Woods

OCWA
See ONONDAGA COUNTY WATER AUTHORITY (INC)

D-U-N-S 18-695-7114
▲ OCWEN FINANCIAL CORP
1000 Abernathy Rd Ste 210, Atlanta, GA 30328-5604
Tel (561) 682-8000 *Founded/Ownrshp* 1988
Sales NA *EMP* 11,400^E
Tkr Sym OCN *Exch* NYS
SIC 6162 Mortgage bankers; Mortgage bankers & correspondents; Mortgage bankers
Pr: Ronald M Faris
**Ch Bd:* Barry N Wish
CFO: Michael R Bourque Jr
Treas: Ashish Pandey
Ex VP: John V Britti
Ex VP: Timothy M Hayes
Sr VP: Catherine M Dondzila
Sr VP: Robert J Leist
Board of Directors: Alan J Bowers, Phyllis R Caldwell, Ronald J Korn, William H Lacy, Robert A Salcetti, Deforest B Soaries Jr

D-U-N-S 06-901-7515
■ OCWEN LOAN SERVICING LLC
(*Suby of* OCWEN FINANCIAL CORP) ★
1661 Worthington Rd # 100, West Palm Beach, FL 33409-6493
Tel (561) 682-8000 *Founded/Ownrshp* 2002
Sales NA *EMP* 1,981
Accts Pricewaterhousecoopers Llp Fo
SIC 6162 Mortgage bankers & correspondents; Mortgage bankers & correspondents
CEO: Ronald M Faris
**CFO:* John V Britti
CFO: David J Hunter
**Ex VP:* Scott W Anderson
**Sr VP:* Sp Ravi
VP: Stewart Fink
VP: Michael Murphy
**VP:* Kenneth D Najour
Dir IT: Tricia Brabs
IT Man: Kelly McClain
IT Man: Rajeev Nair

OCZ ENTERPRISE
See ZCO LIQUIDATING CORP

D-U-N-S 07-926-4254
OCZ STORAGE SOLUTIONS INC
(*Suby of* TOSHIBA CORPORATION)
6373 San Ignacio Ave, San Jose, CA 95119-1200
Tel (408) 733-8400 *Founded/Ownrshp* 2013
Sales 72.5MM^E *EMP* 323^E
SIC 3572 Computer storage devices; Computer storage devices
CEO: Ralph Schmitt
**Chf Mktg O:* Alex MEI
**Ex VP:* Rafael Torres
Sr VP: John Apps
VP: Cameron Reid

ODAFF
See OKLAHOMA DEPARTMENT OF AGRICULTURE FOOD AND FORESTRY

D-U-N-S 01-746-1380
ODANIEL AUTOMOTIVE INC
5611 Illinois Rd, Fort Wayne, IN 46804-1183
Tel (260) 435-5300 *Founded/Ownrshp* 1987
Sales 94.4MM^E *EMP* 100
SIC 5511 New & used car dealers; New & used car dealers
Pr: Randy O'Daniel
COO: Todd Jacquay
CFO: David Gutting
**Sec:* Germaine O'Daniel
**VP:* Jeffrey O'Daniel
Exec: Sheri Stine
Sales Asso: Rob Coulter

D-U-N-S 06-471-3449
ODANIEL MOTOR SALES INC
(*Suby of* ODANIEL AUTOMOTIVE INC) ★
5611 Illinois Rd, Fort Wayne, IN 46804-1183
Tel (260) 435-5300 *Founded/Ownrshp* 1979
Sales 61.1MM *EMP* 75
SIC 5511 5521 New & used car dealers; Used car dealers; New & used car dealers; Used car dealers
Pr: Randy D O'Daniel
**VP:* Jeffery O'Daniel
CTO: Scott Moseley

D-U-N-S 06-912-1218
ODD FELLOWS HOME OF CALIFORNIA (CA)
SARATOGA RETIREMENT COMMUNITY
14500 Fruitvale Ave # 3000, Saratoga, CA 95070-6169
Tel (408) 741-7100 *Founded/Ownrshp* 1853
Sales 48.7MM *EMP* 275
Accts Moss Adams Llp Stockton Ca
SIC 8361 8051 Residential care; Skilled nursing care facilities; Residential care; Skilled nursing care facilities

D-U-N-S 02-267-8634 IMP
ODDELLO INDUSTRIES LLC
425 Jones Franklin Rd, Morristown, TN 37813-1121
Tel (423) 307-1240 *Founded/Ownrshp* 2008
Sales 102.2MM^E *EMP* 375
Accts Melissa F Hill Cpa Tennesse
SIC 2511 Wood household furniture; Wood household furniture

D-U-N-S 07-753-0798
ODDS-N-ENDS INC
HOMCO ACE HOME CENTER
1763 E Butler Ave, Flagstaff, AZ 86001-5910
Tel (928) 779-6111 *Founded/Ownrshp* 1975
Sales 21.2MM^E *EMP* 90
SIC 5211 5031 Lumber & other building materials; Building materials, interior; Building materials, exterior
Pr: Michael R Brackin
CFO: Kevin Call
**CFO:* Bart Thompson
**VP:* Penne Brackin
Exec: Kim Rushing
Brnch Mgr: Scott Wamack
Sales Exec: Troy Ricci

D-U-N-S 62-076-6626 EXP
ODEBRECHT CONSTRUCTION INC
(*Suby of* BELGRAVIA EMPREENDIMENTOS IMOBILIARIOS S/A.)
201 Alhambra Cir Ste 1000, Coral Gables, FL 33134-5103
Tel (305) 341-8800 *Founded/Ownrshp* 1993
Sales 140.4MM^E *EMP* 250
SIC 1622 1522 Highway construction, elevated; Bridge construction; Residential construction; Highway construction, elevated; Bridge construction; Residential construction
Pr: Gilberto Neves
**Treas:* Gabriel Franca
Ofcr: Jorge Borda
Ofcr: Deborah Hampton
Ex VP: Miguel Gradin
VP: Cynthia Cardoso
**VP:* Yvonne Meyer
**VP:* Claudio Monteiro
**VP:* James Storey Jr
Exec: Daniela Andrade
Exec: Thomas Wallace
Dir Bus: Mariano Domingues

D-U-N-S 05-222-8066
ODEBRECHT CONTRACTORS OF FLORIDA INC
201 Alhambra Cir Ste 1400, Coral Gables, FL 33134-5121
Tel (305) 704-5800 *Founded/Ownrshp* 1996
Sales 25.6MM^E *EMP* 300
SIC 1622 Bridge, tunnel & elevated highway; Bridge, tunnel & elevated highway
Pr: Luis Rocha
**Pr:* Monica Bahia Odebrecht
**CEO:* Gilberto Neves
**VP:* Alexander Christiani
**VP:* Claudio Augusto De Almeida

O'DELL PUBLISHING
See AXIOM IMPRESSIONS LLC

ODESSA COLLEGE
See ODESSA JUNIOR COLLEGE DISTRICT

D-U-N-S 15-760-7649
ODESSA ENTERPRISES INC
JACK IN THE BOX
5017 Conley Rd Ste B, El Paso, TX 79932-1741
Tel (915) 533-7327 *Founded/Ownrshp* 1993
Sales 12.3MM^E *EMP* 300
SIC 5812 Fast-food restaurant, chain; Fast-food restaurant, chain
Pr: Mike Norwich

D-U-N-S 07-315-1011
ODESSA JUNIOR COLLEGE DISTRICT (TX)
ODESSA COLLEGE
201 W University Blvd, Odessa, TX 79764-7105
Tel (432) 335-6400 *Founded/Ownrshp* 1946
Sales 26.3MM^E *EMP* 650
Accts Johnson Miller & Co Cpa S P
SIC 8222 8221 Junior college; Colleges universities & professional schools; Junior college; Colleges universities & professional schools
Pr: Dr Gregory D Williams
CFO: Connie May
VP: Brenda Moss
VP: Donald Wood
CIO: David Carson
CTO: Theresa Evans
Psych: Mangelica Moreno

ODESSA LITTLE ROCK
See BEEBE AUTO EXCHANGE INC

D-U-N-S 00-493-5594
ODESSA POWER HOLDINGS LLC
2200 E Interstate 20, Odessa, TX 79766-8810
Tel (432) 620-5740 *Founded/Ownrshp* 2011
Sales 21.8MM^E *EMP* 42
SIC 4911 Generation, electric power
Plnt Mgr: Roy Sanchez

D-U-N-S 03-903-9441
■ ODESSA PUMPS AND EQUIPMENT INC
(*Suby of* NOW INC) ★
8161 Dorado Dr, Odessa, TX 79765-8533
Tel (432) 333-2817 *Founded/Ownrshp* 1980, 2015
Sales 232.3MM^E *EMP* 300
SIC 5084 Petroleum industry machinery; Oil well machinery, equipment & supplies; Pumps & pumping equipment; Water pumps (industrial); Petroleum industry machinery; Oil well machinery, equipment & supplies; Pumps & pumping equipment; Water pumps (industrial)
CEO: Sondra Eoff
Pr: Joey Lewallen
COO: Clayton Kenworthy
Ofcr: Toby Eoff
VP: Jackie Swanson
Brnch Mgr: Dan Courreges
Brnch Mgr: Brandon Foster
Brnch Mgr: Hugo Garza
Brnch Mgr: Kevin Weidner
Dist Mgr: Frank Dooley
Off Mgr: Nancy Maldonado

D-U-N-S 12-110-7718
ODESSA REGIONAL HOSPITAL LP
(*Suby of* IASIS HEALTHCARE CORP) ★
520 E 6th St, Odessa, TX 79761-4527
Tel (432) 582-8000 *Founded/Ownrshp* 1975
Sales 191.2MM^E *EMP* 570
SIC 8062 General medical & surgical hospitals; General medical & surgical hospitals
CEO: Bill Porter
**COO:* Stacey Gerig
Dir: Betty Harrold
CTO: Anne Sawyer

D-U-N-S 01-289-6507
ODESSA TECHNOLOGIES INC
50 S 16th St Ste 2300, Philadelphia, PA 19102-2526
Tel (215) 231-9800 *Founded/Ownrshp* 1998
Sales 39.9MM^E *EMP* 350
SIC 7373 Computer integrated systems design; Computer integrated systems design
CEO: Madhu Natarajan
**Ex VP:* Jay Mehra
Sr VP: Madhavi Chattarki
**Sr VP:* Jim Humphrey
**Sr VP:* Jeff Lezinski
**Sr VP:* Kevin Schroeder
VP: Kate Majewski
VP Bus Dev: Elkin Castano

D-U-N-S 00-794-2386
ODESSA UNION WAREHOUSE COOPERATIVE
N2 Division St, Odessa, WA 99159
Tel (509) 982-2691 *Founded/Ownrshp* 1909
Sales 24.0MM *EMP* 25
SIC 4221 5153 Grain elevator, storage only; Grains; Grain elevator, storage only; Grains
Pr: Dale Deise
Genl Mgr: Keith Bailey

D-U-N-S 02-647-6051
ODFJELL TERMINALS (HOUSTON) INC
(*Suby of* ODFJELL USA (HOUSTON) INC) ★
13100 Space Center Blvd, Houston, TX 77059-3556
Tel (713) 844-2300 *Founded/Ownrshp* 1981
Sales 21.5MM^E *EMP* 200
SIC 4226 Petroleum & chemical bulk stations & terminals for hire
Pr: David A Ellis
Ofcr: Sander Rozendaal
Sr VP: Harald Fotland
VP: Brit Bennett
VP: Knut Ovrebo
Admn Mgr: Bruce Clark
DP Exec: Erik Andreassen
Opers Mgr: Ron Owens
Opers Mgr: John Picinic
**VP Sls:* William Law
Snr PM: Carl Lafoy

D-U-N-S 00-391-1344
ODFJELL USA (HOUSTON) INC
ODFJELL USA HOLDINGS US PARENT
(*Suby of* ODFJELL SE)
13100 Space Center Blvd, Houston, TX 77059-3556
Tel (281) 291-8328 *Founded/Ownrshp* 1916, 2005
Sales 21.5MM^E *EMP* 200^E
SIC 4731 4226 Agents, shipping; Brokers, shipping; Petroleum & chemical bulk stations & terminals for hire
Pr: Dave A Ellis
**Pr:* Joe Naissis
**CEO:* Jan Hammer
**CFO:* Terje Iversen
**CFO:* Tore Jakobsen
**Sr VP:* Harald Fotland
**Sr VP:* Morten Nystad
VP: Tor Johansen
VP: George Pontikos
VP: Hans Saether
Prin: Dave Ellis

ODFJELL USA HOLDINGS US PARENT
See ODFJELL USA (HOUSTON) INC

ODFW
See OREGON DEPARTMENT OF FISH AND WILDLIFE

ODH
See DEPARTMENT OF HEALTH OHIO

D-U-N-S 08-635-9338
ODIN FELDMAN & PITTLEMAN PC
1775 Wiehle Ave Ste 400, Reston, VA 20190-5159
Tel (703) 218-2100 *Founded/Ownrshp* 1972
Sales 21.7MM^E *EMP* 120
SIC 8111 Corporate, partnership & business law; Bankruptcy law; Environmental law; Taxation law
Pr: Dexter S Odin
Pr: Bethany Benes
Pr: Grace Hoogeveen
Pr: Mary Rardin
Pr: Liz Taylor
Pr: Jennifer Wetzel
**Treas:* Pittleman James B
**Treas:* James Pittleman
Bd of Dir: Catherine Murray
Ofcr: Matthew Keller
**VP:* David J Brewer
**VP:* Ross F Douglas
**VP:* John S Wisiackas

ODJFS
See OHIO DEPARTMENT OF JOB AND FAMILY SERVICES

D-U-N-S 00-641-0781 IMP
ODL INC (MI)
O D L
215 E Roosevelt Ave, Zeeland, MI 49464-1239
Tel (616) 772-9111 *Founded/Ownrshp* 1951
Sales 173.4MM^E *EMP* 425
SIC 2431 Doors & door parts & trim, wood; Doors & door parts & trim, wood
Ch Bd: Dave Killoran
**CEO:* Jeffrey Mulder
**CFO:* Michael Burke
CFO: Mark Perrin
Off Mgr: Leanne Hefner
IT Man: Keith Juhola
VP Opers: Bryan Bultema
Mtls Mgr: Doug Deleeuw
Plnt Mgr: Mark Zitricki
Mktg Dir: Randy Brown
Mktg Dir: Keith Early

D-U-N-S 00-519-0699
ODM TOOL & MANUFACTURING CO INC
9550 Joliet Rd, Hodgkins, IL 60525-4148
Tel (708) 485-6130 *Founded/Ownrshp* 1946
Sales 22.0MM^E *EMP* 75
SIC 3469 3544 Stamping metal for the trade; Special dies, tools, jigs & fixtures
Sec: Sandra Michaelsen
**Prin:* Gary Kautz
Plnt Mgr: Carl Michaelsen
Ql Cn Mgr: Dwayne Ford
Ql Cn Mgr: Eric Krause

D-U-N-S 13-270-1454
ODOM CONSTRUCTION SERVICES INC
3601 Executive Blvd, Mesquite, TX 75149-2711
Tel (972) 289-4447 *Founded/Ownrshp* 1995
Sales 23.1MM^E *EMP* 119
SIC 1542 Nonresidential construction
Pr: Mark Odom
**Pr:* Veronica Odom

D-U-N-S 11-304-8672
ODOM CONSTRUCTION SYSTEMS INC
1430 Island Home Ave, Knoxville, TN 37920-1811
Tel (865) 579-5015 *Founded/Ownrshp* 1984
Sales 43.1MM^E *EMP* 150
SIC 1742 1721 Plastering, plain or ornamental; Drywall; Acoustical & ceiling work; Commercial painting; Plastering, plain or ornamental; Drywall; Acoustical & ceiling work; Commercial painting
CEO: Billy Odom
**Pr:* Bill Odom

*COO: Danny Odom
*VP: William P Odom
Dir IT: David Sands

D-U-N-S 06-955-1018 IMP
ODOM CORP
COCA-COLA
11400 Se 8th St Ste 300, Bellevue, WA 98004-6409
Tel (425) 456-3535 Founded/Ownrshp 1933
Sales 526.2MM^E EMP 1,500
Accts Grant Thornton Llp Seattle W
SIC 5149 Soft drinks; Soft drinks
Ch Bd: John P Odom
*Pr: Dick Barkett
*CFO: Randy Halter
*V Ch Bd: William L Odom
Bd of Dir: Gene Odom
VP: Scott Cook
*VP: Jerry Dexter
VP: Adam Ferns
*VP: Jim Odom
Exec: Dave Newton
Dept Mgr: Joanne Holland

ODOM RURAL HEALTH CLINIC
See YALOBUSHA GENERAL HOSPITAL (INC)

D-U-N-S 07-851-9673 IMP
ODOM-SOUTHERN WINE DISTRIBUTORS OF WASHINGTON LLC
1025 Valley Ave Nw, Puyallup, WA 98371-2515
Tel (877) 532-2987 Founded/Ownrshp 2008
Sales 57.0MM^E EMP 500
SIC 5182 Wine & distilled beverages; Wine & distilled beverages

O'DONNELL COLLISION CENTER
See TJOD CO INC

D-U-N-S 04-615-8424
ODONNELL FOUNDATION
100 Crescent Ct Ste 1660, Dallas, TX 75201-1824
Tel (214) 871-5800 Founded/Ownrshp 1957
Sales 87.9MM EMP 8
SIC 8699 Charitable organization
Pr: Peter O'Donnell Jr
*COO: Tom Luce
*Sec: Edith J O'Donnell
VP: Rita Clements
*Prin: Leslie Brosi

D-U-N-S 04-758-3257
ODONNELL WICKLUND PIGOZZI AND PETERSON INC
OWP AND P CANNON DESIGN
225 N Michigan Ave # 1100, Chicago, IL 60601-7757
Tel (312) 332-9600 Founded/Ownrshp 1958
Sales 17.0MM^E EMP 300
SIC 8712 7389 8711 Architectural engineering; Interior design services; Structural engineering; Architectural engineering; Interior design services; Structural engineering
Pr: John Syvertsen
*COO: Gregory Surufka
*CFO: Andrew Mendelson
*VP: David J Kuffner
Off Mgr: Traci Stead
Mktg Dir: Christopher N Lambert

D-U-N-S 82-525-1390
ODONNELL/SNIDER CONSTRUCTION LP
1900 West Loop S Ste 350, Houston, TX 77027-3236
Tel (713) 782-7660 Founded/Ownrshp 1991
Sales 122.8MM EMP 48
SIC 1542 Commercial & office building contractors; Commercial & office building contractors
Genl Pt: Duncan O'Donnell
Pt: Walter H Snider III
Exec: Marc Perilloux
Prin: Randy O'Donnell
Prin: Trey Snider
VP Opers: Terry Atmar
Mktg Mgr: Beccy Whyte
Snr PM: Kevin Gilmore

ODS
See OLD DOMINION SECURITY CO INC

ODS COMPANIES
See OREGON DENTAL SERVICE

ODS COMPANIES
See MODA HEALTH PLAN INC

D-U-N-S 83-803-6010
ODS TECHNOLOGIES LP
TELEVISION GAMES NETWORK
(Suby of BETFAIR GROUP PLC)
6701 Center Dr W Ste 160, Los Angeles, CA 90045-1558
Tel (310) 242-9400 Founded/Ownrshp 2009
Sales 27.2MM^E EMP 165
SIC 4833 7948 Television broadcasting stations; Horses, racing; Television broadcasting stations; Horses, racing
Genl Pt: David Nathanson
VP: Tracy Beasley
Snr Mgr: Stillman Kelly

ODSA
See OHIO DEVELOPMENT SERVICES AGENCY

D-U-N-S 15-376-5995 IMP
ODU-USA INC
O D U
(Suby of ODU GMBH & CO. KG)
4010 Adolfo Rd, Camarillo, CA 93012-6793
Tel (805) 484-0540 Founded/Ownrshp 1986
Sales 40.4MM^E EMP 60
SIC 5065 Connectors, electronic
CEO: Michael Savage
*Pr: Joseph Cisi
*CEO: Kurt Woelfl
IT Man: Robert Arreguin
IT Man: Adam Rumage

ODURF
See OLD DOMINION UNIVERSITY RESEARCH FOUNDATION

D-U-N-S 84-457-2961
ODW CONTRACT SERVICES
1580 Williams Rd, Columbus, OH 43207-5183
Tel (614) 497-1660 Founded/Ownrshp 1999
Sales 23.7MM^E EMP 250
SIC 4225 General warehousing; General warehousing
Off Mgr: Sandy Bowles

D-U-N-S 05-780-1268
ODW LOGISTICS INC
O D W
3330 Groveport Rd, Columbus, OH 43207
Tel (614) 497-1660 Founded/Ownrshp 1971
Sales 163.5MM^E EMP 600
SIC 4225 4226 General warehousing; Special warehousing & storage; General warehousing; Special warehousing & storage
Ch: Robert E Ness
*Pr: John R Ness
*COO: Ted Nikolai
*CFO: David L Hill
*Sec: Lynn Ness
*VP: Macy A Bergoon
VP: John Ness
Genl Mgr: Eric Stipp
Dir IT: Kenneth Nelson
IT Man: Tammy Ankron
Opers Supe: Doug Bumgarner

ODWALLA FRESH SQZED FRT VGTBLE
See ODWALLA INC

D-U-N-S 10-276-2234 IMP
■ **ODWALLA INC**
ODWALLA FRESH SQZED FRT VGTBLE
(Suby of COCA-COLA CO) ★
1900 E Davis Dr, Dinuba, CA 93618-9372
Tel (479) 721-6260 Founded/Ownrshp 2001
Sales 151.6MM^E EMP 900
SIC 2033 Fruit juices: packaged in cans, jars, etc.; Vegetable juices: packaged in cans, jars, etc.; Fruit juices: packaged in cans, jars, etc.; Vegetable juices: packaged in cans, jars, etc.
CEO: D Stephen Williamson
*Pr: Alison Lewis
*CFO: James R Steichen
Sr Cor Off: Gary Fayard
Sr VP: Bill Hopkins
*VP: Susan M Kirmayer
VP: Laura Lopez
VP: Elizabeth McDonough
Exec: Todd Daniels
Dir IT: Gary Hensley
Opers Mgr: Shawn Allen

D-U-N-S 78-767-2174
ODYSSEA MARINE HOLDINGS INC
11864 Highway 308, Larose, LA 70373-5877
Tel (985) 385-0189 Founded/Ownrshp 1997
Sales 1.5MMM^E EMP 17,000^E
SIC 1381 Drilling oil & gas wells
Ch Bd: Charles A Denning
*Pr: David W Sharp
Dir IT: Guy Gilmore

ODYSSEY CRUISES
See PREMIER YACHTS INC

D-U-N-S 60-262-9040
ODYSSEY ELECTRONICS INC
12886 Fairlane St, Livonia, MI 48150-1327
Tel (734) 421-8340 Founded/Ownrshp 1989
Sales 34.9MM^E EMP 70
SIC 3672 5065 Printed circuit boards; Electronic parts & equipment
Pr: Ernest V Flamont
*Treas: Mark Estes
Ql Cn Mgr: Laura Henning

D-U-N-S 05-567-8361 IMP
ODYSSEY ENTERPRISES INC (WA)
2729 6th Ave S, Seattle, WA 98134-2101
Tel (206) 285-7445 Founded/Ownrshp 1981, 2012
Sales 166.6MM EMP 250
Accts Rhodes & Associates Pllc Fede
SIC 5146 Seafoods; Fish & seafoods
Pr: Phil Crean
*CFO: Ted Hadley
Sales Exec: Dennis Offner
Board of Directors: Phil Crean, Cora Edmonds

D-U-N-S 11-261-7766
ODYSSEY FOODS OF NEW JERSEY INC
BURGER KING
590 E Main St, Bridgewater, NJ 08807-3231
Tel (908) 927-0130 Founded/Ownrshp 1999
Sales 39.2MM^E EMP 900
SIC 5812 Fast-food restaurant, chain; Fast-food restaurant, chain
Ch Bd: Alexandre Behring
*Pr: Norman Lichtman
*CEO: Bernardo Hees
*VP: Mitchel Lichtman

ODYSSEY GROUP - INFO SVCS
See ODYSSEY GROUP OF COMPANIES

D-U-N-S 36-225-5234
ODYSSEY GROUP OF COMPANIES
ODYSSEY GROUP - INFO SVCS
11 Overlook Way, Setauket, NY 11733-1344
Tel (631) 751-8400 Founded/Ownrshp 1985
Sales 93.0MM EMP 146
SIC 7373 3577 7371 1731 Computer systems analysis & design; Systems engineering, computer related; Computer peripheral equipment; Computer software development; Electrical work; Computer systems analysis & design; Systems engineering, computer related; Computer peripheral equipment; Computer software development; Electrical work
Ch Bd: Adam Grill
*Pr: George Kaplan
*CFO: Alexander Marshall
*VP: Alan Grant
*VP: Viswanathan Hariharan
*Ex Dir: Robert Goldman

D-U-N-S 94-571-5217
■ **ODYSSEY HEALTHCARE INC**
(Suby of GENTIVA HEALTH SERVICES INC) ★
7801 Mesquite Bend Dr # 105, Irving, TX 75063-6043
Tel (888) 600-2411 Founded/Ownrshp 1995
Sales 125.8MM^E EMP 6,207
SIC 8051 Skilled nursing care facilities; Skilled nursing care facilities
CEO: Tony Strange
COO: David C Gasmire
*COO: Craig P Goguen
COO: Deborah A Hoffpuir
*CFO: R Dirk Allison
*CFO: Eric R Slusser
Ex VP: Holly Franko
*Sr VP: Brenda A Belger
*Sr VP: W Bradley Bickham
VP: Bruce Kemper
Exec: Nicole Miller

D-U-N-S 07-102-9243
ODYSSEY HOUSE INC
120 Wall St Ste 1700, New York, NY 10005-4001
Tel (212) 361-1331 Founded/Ownrshp 1967
Sales 31.4MM EMP 290
SIC 8093 Rehabilitation center, outpatient treatment; Rehabilitation center, outpatient treatment
Pr: Peter Provet
CFO: Robert Mitchell
Sr VP: John Tavolacci
MIS Dir: John Stephenson
IT Man: Durga Vallabhaneni
Opers Supe: Gail Harris
Psych: Gilbert Bell
Pgrm Dir: Alvin Hunt

D-U-N-S 17-023-8922
ODYSSEY INFORMATION SERVICES INC
5801 Tennyson Pkwy # 200, Plano, TX 75024-6107
Tel (972) 767-6700 Founded/Ownrshp 2000
Sales 21.9MM^E EMP 170^E
SIC 7379 Computer related consulting services; Computer related consulting services
CEO: Jon C Hibbs
*VP: Todd D Kirkey

D-U-N-S 08-654-7218
ODYSSEY INTERNATIONAL INC
1225 Opportunity Ave, Chambersburg, PA 17201-7868
Tel (801) 525-1363 Founded/Ownrshp 2001
Sales 36.0MM EMP 3
SIC 1542 Nonresidential construction; Nonresidential construction
Pr: Whitney Mc Bride
COO: Michael Tingey
*VP: Paul Lee

D-U-N-S 05-528-4520 IMP/EXP
ODYSSEY INVESTMENT PARTNERS LLC
590 Madison Ave Fl 39, New York, NY 10022-8526
Tel (212) 351-7900 Founded/Ownrshp 1997
Sales 1.7MMM^E EMP 5,494
SIC 6211 Investment firm, general brokerage; Investment firm, general brokerage
Ch: Stephen Berger
VP: Thomas Zanios
*Exec: Brian Kwait
Admn Mgr: Bill Hopkins
Info Man: John McNamara

D-U-N-S 13-019-8588 IMP/EXP
ODYSSEY LOGISTICS & TECHNOLOGY CORP
39 Old Ridgebury Rd Ste 7, Danbury, CT 06810-5100
Tel (203) 448-3900 Founded/Ownrshp 2002
Sales 343.9MM^E EMP 505
SIC 4731 Customs clearance of freight; Customs clearance of freight
Ch Bd: Edward M Straw
*Pr: Robert H Shellman
*CFO: Cosmo J Alberico
Ofcr: Raymond G Maier
*Sr VP: Raymond Maier
*Sr VP: Russell Marky
Sr VP: Charles H Midkiff
Sr VP: Glenn E Riggs
VP: Nelson Baltazar
VP: Vincent Calandra
VP: Mark Casiano
VP: Kevin Land
VP: Deborah Pritchard
VP: Bob Shellman
Dir Bus: Paul Palmieri

D-U-N-S 01-818-0419
ODYSSEY RE HOLDINGS CORP
(Suby of FAIRFAX FINANCIAL HOLDINGS LIMITED)
300 Stamford Pl, Stamford, CT 06902-6765
Tel (203) 977-8000 Founded/Ownrshp 2009
Sales NA EMP 721^E
SIC 6411 Insurance agents, brokers & service; Insurance agents & brokers; Fire insurance underwriters' laboratories; Insurance agents, brokers & service; Insurance agents & brokers; Fire insurance underwriters' laboratories
Pr: Andrew A Barnard
V Ch: James Dowd
Pr: Valoree Celona
Pr: Paul Champanier
Pr: Ann Kolman
Pr: James Mortensen
Pr: Janis Pagan
Pr: Nancylynn Pawar
Pr: Leslie Weingarten
CEO: Isabelle Dubots-Lafitte
CEO: Chris Gallagher
CEO: Brian D Young
CFO: Jan Christiansen
CFO: R Scott Donovan
CFO: Hervt Leduc
Treas: Thomas McKevitt
Treas: Robert Pollock
Bd of Dir: Francis D James
Ofcr: Michael G Wacek
Ex VP: Alane R Carey
Ex VP: Brian Quin
Board of Directors: James F Dowd, Anthony F Griffiths, Alan D Horn, Brandon W Sweitzer, V Prem Watsa

D-U-N-S 17-814-6536
ODYSSEY REINSURANCE CO
(Suby of ODYSSEY RE HOLDINGS CORP) ★
300 Stamford Pl Ste 700, Stamford, CT 06902-6735
Tel (203) 965-0004 Founded/Ownrshp 2001
Sales NA EMP 340
SIC 6411 6361 6331 6324 6311 Insurance agents, brokers & service; Title insurance; Fire, marine & casualty insurance; Hospital & medical service plans; Life insurance; Insurance agents, brokers & service; Title insurance; Fire, marine & casualty insurance; Hospital & medical service plans; Life insurance
CEO: Brian D Young
Owner: Matthew Dragonetti
Pr: Thomas Williams
Ex VP: Jan Christiansen
Ex VP: Brian D Quinn
*Ex VP: Michael G Wacek
*Sr VP: James B Salvesen
VP: Liz Buckley
VP: Daniel Canny
VP: Francis Cerasoli
VP: Andrew Chu
VP: Richard Coerver
VP: Michael Finnegan
*VP: Greg Horkachuck
VP: David Kahn
VP: Eugene Lock
VP: Bryan Reid
VP: Nicholas Sena
VP: Jack Whittle
Board of Directors: Greg Horkachuck, James B Salvesen, Michael G Wacek, Brian D Young

ODYSSEY SYSTEMS
See TRI-STAR PLASTICS & MOLDING INC

D-U-N-S 09-073-9830
ODYSSEY SYSTEMS CONSULTING GROUP LTD
201 Edgewater Dr Ste 270, Wakefield, MA 01880-6223
Tel (781) 245-0111 Founded/Ownrshp 1997
Sales 81.3MM^E EMP 430
SIC 7379 Computer related consulting services; Computer related consulting services
Ch: Michael Sweat
*CEO: Randy Nunley
CFO: William Byrd
*CFO: Doug Emond
*VP: Eric Svarverud
*VP: Kevin Sweeney
Prgrm Mgr: Fred Dinsmore
Prgrm Mgr: Greg Foster
Prgrm Mgr: Scott Griffis
Prgrm Mgr: Jonathan Hutfilz
Prgrm Mgr: Ronnie Toler

D-U-N-S 01-819-2398
ODYSSEYS UNLIMITED INC
275 Washington St Ste 300, Newton, MA 02458-1630
Tel (617) 454-9100 Founded/Ownrshp 1998
Sales 55.2MM EMP 62
SIC 4724 Travel agencies; Travel agencies
Pr: Bruce A Epstein
*Treas: Raymond G Trant
VP: Marjorie Bride
VP: Christine Lucas
VP: Claudia Schutz

OE FILTERS
See MANN+HUMMEL PUROLATOR FILTERS LLC

OEC BUSINESS INTERIORS
See FORWARD SPACE LLC

D-U-N-S 02-525-1851
OEC BUSINESS INTERIORS INC
900 N Church Rd, Elmhurst, IL 60126-1014
Tel (630) 589-5500 Founded/Ownrshp 1955
Sales 53.6MM EMP 135
SIC 5021

D-U-N-S 18-616-7805
OEC BUSINESS INTERIORS INC
1601 Nw 80th Blvd, Gainesville, FL 32606-9140
Tel (352) 332-3463 Founded/Ownrshp 1988
Sales 27.6MM^E EMP 46
Accts Purvis Gray & Company
SIC 5021 Office furniture
VP: David Salter
*Pr: William Salter
VP: Brenda Wayers
CTO: Buffy Montgomery
Opers Mgr: David Morgan
Mktg Mgr: Casey Salter

OEC CHICAGO
See O E C GRAPHICS INC

D-U-N-S 00-242-4310 IMP/EXP
OEC FREIGHT (NY) INC (NY)
OEC GROUP
1 Cross Island Plz # 306, Rosedale, NY 11422-1474
Tel (718) 527-7171 Founded/Ownrshp 1997
Sales 48.0MM^E EMP 150
SIC 4731 Freight forwarding; Freight forwarding
Ch Bd: Anthony D Fullbrook
VP: Steve Myers
VP: Mike Wang
VP Sls: Peter Hsieh

OEC GROUP
See OEC FREIGHT (NY) INC

OEC GROUP
See O E C SHIPPING LOS ANGELES INC

D-U-N-S 08-530-5274 IMP
■ **OEC MEDICAL SYSTEMS INC**
(Suby of GENERAL ELECTRIC CO) ★
384 N Wright Brothers Dr, Salt Lake City, UT 84116-2862
Tel (801) 328-9300 Founded/Ownrshp 1999
Sales 147.5MM^E EMP 850
SIC 3844 7699 Radiographic X-ray apparatus & tubes; Fluoroscopic X-ray apparatus & tubes; X-ray equipment repair; Radiographic X-ray apparatus & tubes; Fluoroscopic X-ray apparatus & tubes; X-ray equipment repair
Pr: Carrie Englintonmanner

*Pr: Patrick McNamee
*Pr: Joseph W Pepper
*Ex VP: Larry E Harrawood
*VP: Ann-Marie McElligott
Genl Mgr: Dick Call
Snr Mgr: Rick Cleveland
Snr Mgr: Dan Johnson

OEC OFFICE PLUS
See OFFICE EQUIPMENT CO OF MOBILE INC

D-U-N-S 07-881-5579
OECO HOLDINGS LLC
(Suby of MEGGITT PLC)
4607 Se International Way, Milwaukie, OR 97222-4693
Tel (503) 659-5999 Founded/Ownrshp 1961
Sales 124.5MM^E EMP 425^E
SIC 3679 5065 Cores, magnetic; Electronic parts & equipment; Cores, magnetic; Electronic parts & equipment
Pr: Jeramy Davis

D-U-N-S 00-902-4233 IMP
OECO LLC
(Suby of OECO HOLDINGS LLC) ★
4607 Se International Way, Milwaukie, OR 97222-4693
Tel (503) 659-5999 Founded/Ownrshp 2000
Sales 124.5MM^E EMP 425
SIC 3679 5065 4911 3621 3694 Cores, magnetic; Electronic parts & equipment; Generation, electric power; Frequency converters (electric generators); Battery charging generators, automobile & aircraft; Generators, automotive & aircraft; Cores, magnetic; Electronic parts & equipment; Generation, electric power; Frequency converters (electric generators); Battery charging generators, automobile & aircraft; Generators, automotive & aircraft
Pr: Jeramy Davis
*VP: Eric Lardiere
*VP: James Salita
Plng Mgr: Cheryl Raeburn
IT Man: Rich Dagostino
Ql Cn Mgr: Fred Fleener
Ql Cn Mgr: Robert Gustine
Pgrm Dir: Teresa Knecht

D-U-N-S 01-247-7647
OECONNECTION LLC
4205 Highlander Pkwy, Richfield, OH 44286-9077
Tel (330) 523-1800 Founded/Ownrshp 2000
Sales 39.8MM^E EMP 175
SIC 7371 Computer software systems analysis & design, custom; Computer software systems analysis & design, custom
CFO: Ron Coill
Sr VP: Corena Mitchell
VP: Philip Firrell
Off Admin: Dana Anderson
Snr Sftwr: Mike Ison
Snr Sftwr: Paul Martin
Snr Sftwr: Scott Morman
CTO: Kathy Golden
QA Dir: Ken Arrant
QA Dir: Vijay Gaikwad
QA Dir: Walter Hayes

OECU
See OKLAHOMA EMPLOYEES CREDIT UNION

D-U-N-S 78-040-7383
OEHLERT BROTHERS INC
1203 S Township Line Rd, Royersford, PA 19468-1806
Tel (610) 948-3666 Founded/Ownrshp 1994
Sales 29.7MM EMP 30
Accts The Lamastra Group Pc Roye
SIC 5983 5984 Fuel oil dealers; Liquefied petroleum gas dealers; Fuel oil dealers; Liquefied petroleum gas dealers
Pr: James R Oehlert

D-U-N-S 03-463-8189
OELWEIN COMMUNITY SCHOOL DISTRICT
307 8th Ave Se, Oelwein, IA 50662-2501
Tel (319) 283-3536 Founded/Ownrshp 1892
Sales 23.5MM EMP 144
SIC 8211 Public elementary & secondary schools; Kindergarten; Elementary school; High school, junior or senior; Public elementary & secondary schools; Kindergarten; Elementary school; High school, junior or senior
*Prin: Cindy Hill
Brnch Mgr: Kent Mutchler
Dir IT: Jill Kelly

OEM
See CTL-AEROSPACE INC

D-U-N-S 06-726-0000
OEM COMPONENTS INC
14535 Chrisman Rd, Houston, TX 77039-1114
Tel (281) 449-6258 Founded/Ownrshp 1966
Sales 24.0MM^E EMP 78
SIC 3533 Oil & gas field machinery; Oil & gas field machinery
Pr: John D Morvant

D-U-N-S 18-508-5149
OEM FABRICATORS INC
OEM MICRO
300 Mcmillan Rd, Woodville, WI 54028-9578
Tel (715) 698-2111 Founded/Ownrshp 1986
Sales 85.3MM^E EMP 485
SIC 3599

O.E.M. INDUSTRIES
See FNA GROUP INC

OEM MICRO
See OEM FABRICATORS INC

OEM SOLUTION GROUP
See OWENS CORNING SALES INC

OEM TUBE ASSEMBLIES
See MAP INDUSTRIES INC

D-U-N-S 07-969-5964
OEP CAPITAL ADVISORS LP
510 Madison Ave Fl 19, New York, NY 10022-5730
Tel (212) 277-1552 Founded/Ownrshp 2014
Sales 508.0MM^E EMP 2,901^E
SIC 6726 Management investment funds, closed-end
VP: Charles Gedge

D-U-N-S 11-832-5158 IMP/EXP
OERLIKON BALZERS COATING USA INC
1475 E Wdfield Rd Ste 201, Schaumburg, IL 60173
Tel (847) 619-5541 Founded/Ownrshp 1984
Sales 125.6MM^E EMP 400
SIC 3479 3471 Coating of metals & formed products; Finishing, metals or formed products; Coating of metals & formed products; Finishing, metals or formed products
CEO: Christian Kunz
*Pr: Kent Connell
Sr VP: Bernd Fischer
Prgrm Mgr: Terry Holley
Genl Mgr: Lokesh Nain
CTO: Helmut Rudigier
Dir IT: Joaquin Hernandez
IT Man: Josh Abbitt
IT Man: Pedram Sabouri
IT Man: Thomas Wade
Prd Mgr: Mark Kirsch

OERLIKON FAIRFIELD
See FAIRFIELD MANUFACTURING CO INC

D-U-N-S 03-006-1956 IMP
OERLIKON LEYBOLD VACUUM USA INC
5700 Mellon Rd, Export, PA 15632-8900
Tel (724) 327-5700 Founded/Ownrshp 1962
Sales 22.1MM^E EMP 90
SIC 3821 Vacuum pumps, laboratory; Vacuum pumps, laboratory
Pr: James Callahan
CFO: Albert Bruggmann
CFO: Renee Nauyokas
*VP: Lori Arola
*Prin: Dennis Pellegrino
MIS Mgr: Philip Lasek
Mktg Mgr: Mario Vitale

D-U-N-S 00-533-2366 IMP/EXP
OERLIKON METCO (US) INC
SULZER METCO
(Suby of OERLIKON METCO AG, WOHLEN)
1101 Prospect Ave, Westbury, NY 11590-2724
Tel (516) 334-1300 Founded/Ownrshp 1950, 2014
Sales 81.6MM^E EMP 410
SIC 3479 3399

D-U-N-S 62-066-6875 IMP
OERLIKON TEXTILE INC
(Suby of OERLIKON TEXTILE GMBH & CO. KG)
8801 South Blvd, Charlotte, NC 28273-6931
Tel (704) 554-0800 Founded/Ownrshp 2008
Sales 39.5MM^E EMP 100^E
SIC 5084 Textile machinery & equipment; Textile machinery & equipment
Pr: Bob Sage
*CFO: Scott Faggart
CFO: Shain Singer
VP: Claus Clausen
*VP: Helmut Leksa
Sls&Mrk Ex: Karlheinz Sandholzer
Board of Directors: Uwe Kruger, Vladimir Kuznetsov

D-U-N-S 06-000-2243
OERLIKON USA HOLDING INC
5700 Mellon Rd, Export, PA 15632-8900
Tel (303) 273-9700 Founded/Ownrshp 2000
Sales NA EMP 2,842
SIC 3563 3823 3699 3479 3599 5084

D-U-N-S 07-551-3978
OERLIKON USA INC
(Suby of OC OERLIKON CORPORATION AG, PFAFFIKON)
970 Lake Carillon Dr # 300, Saint Petersburg, FL 33716-1130
Tel (727) 577-4999 Founded/Ownrshp 2000
Sales 22.2MM^E EMP 201
SIC 3559 3612 3674 Semiconductor manufacturing machinery; Transformers, except electric; Semiconductors & related devices; Semiconductor manufacturing machinery; Transformers, except electric; Semiconductors & related devices
Pr: Peter Podesser
*Pr: Bill Marsh
*CFO: Stacy L Wagner
*CTO: Christopher Constantine
IT Man: Greg Greinke
IT Man: James Orr
VP Mktg: Christian Schmidt
Sls Dir: Norman Trever

D-U-N-S 05-825-6462
OERTHER FOODS INC
MCDONALD'S
8150 Presidents Dr, Orlando, FL 32809-7625
Tel (407) 859-7123 Founded/Ownrshp 1983
Sales 37.2MM^E EMP 800
SIC 5812 Fast-food restaurant, chain; Fast-food restaurant, chain
CEO: Gary Oerther
*V Ch: Jeff Watson
*CFO: Tony Burnham
*VP: Robert Fagan
*VP: Goergette Lemieux
Exec: Heather Weidenbruch

OESCO
See OKLAHOMA ELECTRICAL SUPPLY CO

D-U-N-S 78-877-4950 EXP
OESI CORP
OIL SPILL EATER INTERNATIONAL
1212 Delmonte Cir, Plano, TX 75075-7313
Tel (972) 669-3390 Founded/Ownrshp 1991
Sales 58.0MM^E EMP 289
SIC 4959 Oil spill cleanup; Oil spill cleanup
Ch Bd: Steve Pedigo
*Treas: Griffin Pedigo
*VP: Robert Pedigo

D-U-N-S 04-729-0952
OFALLON COMMUNITY CONSOIDATED SCHOOL DISTRICT 90
118 E Washington St, O Fallon, IL 62269-1419
Tel (618) 632-3666 Founded/Ownrshp 1901
Sales 20.7MM^E EMP 314
SIC 8211 Public elementary & secondary schools; Public elementary & secondary schools
Prin: Karen Mc Clintoch
IT Man: Dennis Gallo
IT Man: June Isselhardt
Schl Brd P: Steven Hellin

OFB
See ORGANIC FOOD BAR INC

D-U-N-S 80-534-6462
OFC MANAGEMENT INC
ONTERIE FITNESS CENTER
(Suby of LAKESHORE MANAGEMENT GROUP INC) ★
446 E Ontario St 10-100, Chicago, IL 60611-4418
Tel (312) 642-0031 Founded/Ownrshp 2007
Sales 3.2MM^E EMP 1,464^E
SIC 7991 Health club
Prin: Michael N Kochevar

OFER MIZRAHI
See OM DIAMONDS GROUP INC

D-U-N-S 08-861-3237 IMP/EXP
OFF BROADWAY SHOES INC
(Suby of RACK ROOM SHOES INC) ★
4300 Alexander Dr Ste 100, Alpharetta, GA 30022-3780
Tel (800) 248-0692 Founded/Ownrshp 2002
Sales 55.4MM^E EMP 600
SIC 5661

D-U-N-S 78-748-8246
OFF DOCK SEAFOOD LLC
3511 Sky Harbor Cv, Memphis, TN 38118-5999
Tel (901) 547-7900 Founded/Ownrshp 1991
Sales 22.0MM^E EMP 30
SIC 5146 Fish, fresh
Pr: David Feinstone
Genl Mgr: Mark Johnson

D-U-N-S 12-889-6664
OFF DUTY SERVICES INC
1908 Avenue D Ste A100, Katy, TX 77493-1659
Tel (281) 346-2188 Founded/Ownrshp 2002
Sales 9.7MM^E EMP 500
SIC 7381 Security guard service; Security guard service
CEO: Sherry Rowley
*Pr: Brett Rowley
Opers Mgr: Kevin Groeper

D-U-N-S 15-030-7622 EXP
OFF LEASE ONLY INC
1776 Lake Worth Rd, Lake Worth, FL 33460-3692
Tel (561) 222-2277 Founded/Ownrshp 2004
Sales 700.0M EMP 504^E
SIC 5511 New & used car dealers
CEO: Mark Fischer
*Pr: Eileen Fischer
*COO: Ejola Cook
*COO: John Giasullo
*CFO: Rick Burstyn
*Ofcr: Franklin J Carino

D-U-N-S 79-608-7088 EXP
OFF SHORE VENDING INC
241 Commercial Park Cir, Calera, AL 35040-5139
Tel (205) 668-6260 Founded/Ownrshp 1992
Sales 66.8MM EMP 21
Accts Lischkoff & Pitts Pc
SIC 5149 5142 Dried or canned foods; Poultry, frozen: packaged; Dried or canned foods; Poultry, frozen: packaged
Pr: Nathan Powell

OFF THE STREET
See MATRIX HUMAN SERVICES

OFF TRACK BETTING
See CATSKILL REGIONAL OFF-TRACK BETTING CORP

D-U-N-S 95-741-0475
OFFDUTYOFFICERS.COM
2365 La Mirada Dr, Vista, CA 92081-7863
Tel (888) 408-5900 Founded/Ownrshp 1993
Sales 38.9MM^E EMP 1,300
SIC 7381 8742 Security guard service; Management consulting services; Security guard service; Management consulting services
Pr: Aram Minasian
*Mng Pt: Terry Degelder
*CFO: Kevin Hansen
VP: Doug Packwood

D-U-N-S 03-200-8682
OFFEN PETROLEUM INC
5100 E 78th Ave, Commerce City, CO 80022-1458
Tel (303) 297-3835 Founded/Ownrshp 1997
Sales 808.5MM EMP 38
SIC 5172 5541

D-U-N-S 00-799-0831
OFFERLE COOPERATIVE GRAIN & SUPPLY CO INC
222 E Santa Fe, Offerle, KS 67563-6431
Tel (620) 659-2165 Founded/Ownrshp 1910
Sales 29.3MM^E EMP 22
SIC 5153 5191 5541 Grains; Fertilizer & fertilizer materials; Feed; Gasoline service stations
Pr: Duane Boyd

OFFICE 360
See OFFICE THREE SIXTY INC

D-U-N-S 00-656-7808
OFFICE ALLY LLC (WA)
1300 Se Cardinal Ct # 190, Vancouver, WA 98683-9683
Tel (360) 975-7000 Founded/Ownrshp 2000
Sales 26.1MM^E EMP 205
SIC 7371 Software programming applications; Computer software systems analysis & design, custom; Software programming applications; Computer software systems analysis & design, custom
Owner: Brian O'Neill
*Prin: Brian Sullivan
IT Man: Tony Gaspro
Web Dev: Alistair Brierley
Web Dev: Nhi Huyen
Web Dev: Filaret Ilas
Web Dev: Joshua Mello
Ql Cn Mgr: Russell Pachl

OFFICE ANTIBOYCOTT COMPLIANCE
See BUREAU OF INDUSTRY & SECURITY

D-U-N-S 18-356-0952 IMP
OFFICE BASICS INC
22 Creek Cir, Boothwyn, PA 19061-3156
Tel (610) 471-1000 Founded/Ownrshp 1987
Sales 143.6MM^E EMP 175^E
SIC 5112 Stationery & office supplies
Pr: John Leighton
*Treas: Richard Leighton

D-U-N-S 15-083-1758
■ OFFICE CLUB INC
OFFICE DEPOT
(Suby of OFFICE DEPOT INC) ★
2200 Germantown Rd, Delray Beach, FL 33445-8223
Tel (561) 438-4800 Founded/Ownrshp 1991
Sales 71.8MM^E EMP 2,200
SIC 5943 5112 Stationery stores; Office supplies; Stationery stores; Office supplies
CEO: Juan Guerrero
Pr: Mark D Begelman
CFO: Barry J Goldstein
Ex VP: Elisa Garcia
Ex VP: Mike Newman
Sr VP: Michele Henderson
VP: Brian Turcotte
Prgrm Mgr: Wanda Cardona
Dist Mgr: Donald Hisler
Dist Mgr: Cary Marsh
Dist Mgr: Diane Miller

OFFICE COASTAL ZONE MANAGEMENT
See MASSACHUSETTS EXECUTIVE OFFICE OF ENERGY & ENVIRONMENTAL AFFAIRS

D-U-N-S 01-128-2183
OFFICE CONNECTION INC
37676 Enterprise Ct, Farmington Hills, MI 48331-3440
Tel (248) 871-2003 Founded/Ownrshp 1997
Sales 28.5MM^E EMP 29^E
SIC 5112 5021 2752 Office supplies; Office furniture; Commercial printing, offset
CEO: Karen Minc
*Pr: Joseph Minc

OFFICE CONTG & PROCUREMENT
See GOVERNMENT OF DISTRICT OF COLUMBIA

OFFICE DEPOT
See OFFICE CLUB INC

D-U-N-S 15-353-1108
▲ OFFICE DEPOT INC
6600 N Military Trl, Boca Raton, FL 33496-2434
Tel (561) 438-4800 Founded/Ownrshp 1986
Sales 16.1MMM EMP 56,000
Tkr Sym ODP Exch NGS
SIC 5112 5943 5999 5044 5734 5045 Stationery & office supplies; Office supplies; Stationery stores; Typewriters & business machines; Office equipment; Computer & software stores; Personal computers; Computers, peripherals & software; Computers; Stationery & office supplies; Office supplies; Stationery stores; Typewriters & business machines; Office equipment; Computer & software stores; Personal computers; Computers, peripherals & software; Computers
Ch Bd: Roland C Smith
Pr: Mark Cosby
CFO: Stephen E Hare
Ex VP: Michael Allison
Ex VP: Elisa D Garcia C
Ex VP: Juliet Johansson
Ex VP: Thomas Kroeger
Ex VP: Barry Litwin
Ex VP: Monica Luchtefeld
Ex VP: Kim Maguire
Ex VP: Steve Schmidt
Ex VP: Frank P Scruggs Jr
Sr VP: Teddy Chung
Sr VP: Todd Hale
Sr VP: Tom Markert
Sr VP: Kim Moehler
VP: Michael A Steele
VP: Kari Taylor
Comm Man: Julianne Embry
Board of Directors: Warren F Bryant, Francesca Ruiz De Luzuriag, Cynthia T Jamison, V James Marino, Michael J Massey, David M Szymanski, Nigel Travis, Joseph Vassalluzzo

OFFICE ELEMENTS
See IOWA OFFICE SUPPLY INC

D-U-N-S 02-138-6255
OFFICE ENVIRONMENTS INC (NC)
11407 Granite St Ste B, Charlotte, NC 28273-6698
Tel (704) 714-7200 Founded/Ownrshp 1961
Sales 91.2MM^E EMP 73
SIC 5021 7641 7389 Office furniture; Office furniture repair & maintenance; Interior designer; Office furniture; Office furniture repair & maintenance; Interior designer
CEO: Robert Maczka
*Pr: Cynthia R Cox

D-U-N-S 62-522-2229
OFFICE ENVIRONMENTS INC
1827 1st Ave N Ste 101, Birmingham, AL 35203-3137
Tel (205) 930-0238 Founded/Ownrshp 1998
Sales 33.3MM^E EMP 46
Accts Culotta Scroggins Hendricks &
SIC 5047 1799 5044 Hospital equipment & furniture; Office furniture installation; Mailing machines
Pr: Mark Spink

*VP: Ken Martin
*VP: John Owens

D-U-N-S 60-459-5405
OFFICE EQUIPMENT & SUPPLY CORP
3192 Ampere Ave Frnt 1, Bronx, NY 10465-1066
Tel (718) 823-4254 Founded/Ownrshp 1979
Sales 36.8MM^E EMP 176
SIC 5112 5943 Stationery & office supplies; Office forms & supplies; Stationery & office supplies; Office forms & supplies
Pr: Michael Maglio
*Treas: Steven Maglio

D-U-N-S 06-672-7603
OFFICE EQUIPMENT CO OF MOBILE INC
OEC OFFICE PLUS
104 E I65 Service Rd N, Mobile, AL 36607-2501
Tel (251) 471-3368 Founded/Ownrshp 1978
Sales 39.2MM^E EMP 69
SIC 5021 5112 Office furniture; Office supplies; Office furniture; Office supplies
Prin: Karen B McGill
*Ch Bd: Thomas Bramlett
*VP: Ben F Colbert
*Prin: Dan C Jr Alexander
VP Opers: Forrest Derr
Sls Mgr: Gerri Kennedy

D-U-N-S 83-081-0888
OFFICE EQUIPMENT FINANCE SERVICES CORP
1310 Madrid St, Marshall, MN 56258-4099
Tel (866) 834-9828 Founded/Ownrshp 2009
Sales NA EMP 111^E
SIC 6141 Personal credit institutions
Prin: Brian Schroeder

OFFICE FISCAL ADMINISTRATION
See STATE OF OHIO OFFICE OF BUDGET AND MANAGEMENT STATE ACCOUNTING

D-U-N-S 82-487-6510
OFFICE FURNITURE DISTRIBUTORS OF NEW ENGLAND INC
UNION OFFICE INTERIORS
226 Andover St, Wilmington, MA 01887-1022
Tel (781) 396-6400 Founded/Ownrshp 1992
Sales 27.0MM^E EMP 40
SIC 5021 5112 Office furniture; Office supplies
Pr: Louis Fragoso
*CFO: Joseph Baudanza
*Treas: Joseph F Danizio
VP: George Marks
VP Sls: Valerie Gasbarro

OFFICE FURNITURE NASHVILLE
See INTERIOR DESIGN SERVICES INC

OFFICE FURNITURE OUTLET
See WARDENS OFFICE INC

OFFICE FURNITURE USA
See THOMAS W RUFF AND CO INC

OFFICE FURNITURE USA
See ORI ACQUISITION INC

OFFICE FURNITURE USA
See CHORDUS INC

D-U-N-S 79-247-8026 IMP/EXP
OFFICE FURNITURE WAREHOUSE INC
2099 W Atl Blvd Ste 110, Pompano Beach, FL 33069-2733
Tel (954) 968-4700 Founded/Ownrshp 1989
Sales 20.4MM^E EMP 42
SIC 5021 5712 Office furniture; Office furniture
Pr: Robert Beltrame
VP Sls: George Amiel

OFFICE GRAPHIC DESIGN
See GRAPHIC CENTER GROUP CORP

D-U-N-S 11-907-9903
OFFICE GROUP INC
STEPHENS OFFICE SUPPLY
372 Wythe Creek Rd Ste C, Poquoson, VA 23662-1972
Tel (757) 868-0914 Founded/Ownrshp 1996
Sales 50.0MM^E EMP 35
SIC 5112 5712 5999 Office supplies; Office furniture; Audio-visual equipment & supplies
Owner: Gail Wojciechowski
*VP: Stephen Killiany

OFFICE MANAGEMENT ADM
See KENTUCKY DEPARTMENT OF MILITARY AFFAIRS

OFFICE MANAGEMENT AND ADM
See TAX DIVISION

D-U-N-S 10-691-0847 IMP
OFFICE MANAGEMENT SYSTEMS INC
LOGISTA
327 Yorkville Rd E, Columbus, MS 39702-7644
Tel (662) 244-6500 Founded/Ownrshp 1983
Sales 40.9MM EMP 300
Accts Horne Llp Ridgeland Mississ
SIC 5045 7373 7378 Computers, peripherals & software; Computer integrated systems design; Computer maintenance & repair; Computers, peripherals & software; Computer integrated systems design; Computer maintenance & repair
Pr: Ronald E Harper
*CFO: Randy McDade
*Sec: Timothy W Harper
*VP: Vic Murphy
*VP: Ralph K Williams Jr
Brnch Mgr: Vic Ford
Mktg Mgr: Jessica Moore
Sls Mgr: Jonathan Hollingshead

D-U-N-S 05-650-5571
OFFICE MOVERS INC (MD)
(Suby of KANE CO) ★
6500 Kane Way, Elkridge, MD 21075-6248
Tel (410) 799-3200 Founded/Ownrshp 1971
Sales 29.9MM EMP 450
Accts Wilkins Little & Matthews Ll
SIC 4214 Local trucking with storage; Local trucking with storage
Pr: John M Kane
Pr: Paul Maginnis
COO: Ronald Meliker
CFO: David J Korotkin
Brnch Mgr: Max Hilb

OFFICE NTRAL RESOURCES REVENUE
See OFFICE OF NATURAL RESOURCES REVENUE

OFFICE OF ACADEMIC SUPPORT
See SALEM ACADEMY AND COLLEGE

OFFICE OF ADJUTANT GENERAL
See HAWAII DEPARTMENT OF DEFENSE

OFFICE OF THE ADMINISTRATOR
See FEDERAL TRANSIT ADMINISTRATION

D-U-N-S 94-399-2107
■ **OFFICE OF ASSISTANT SECRETARY FOR ADMINISTRATION AND MANAGEMENT**
OASAM
(Suby of UNITED STATES DEPARTMENT OF LABOR) ★
200 Constitution Ave Nw S-2203, Washington, DC 20210-0001
Tel (202) 693-4040 Founded/Ownrshp 1997
Sales NA EMP 6,000^E
SIC 9651 Labor regulatory agency; ; Labor regulatory agency;
Prin: Michael Kerr
CFO: Kim Veney
*Ofcr: Chris Yerxa
CIO: Gwellnar Bank
IT Man: Evelyn Kelb
IT Man: Steven Van Arsdel

OFFICE OF THE ATTORNEY GENERAL
See NEW JERSEY DEPT OF LAW & PUBLIC SAFETY

OFFICE OF THE ATTORNEY GENERAL
See LOUISIANA DEPARTMENT OF JUSTICE

D-U-N-S 96-299-9249
OFFICE OF BANKS & REAL ESTATE
500 E Monroe St Fl 2, Springfield, IL 62701-1544
Tel (217) 782-3000 Founded/Ownrshp 1996
Sales 30.9MM EMP 263
SIC 8611 Business associations; Business associations

OFFICE OF BOARD OF SELECTMAN
See TOWN OF NORWELL

D-U-N-S 08-190-2467
OFFICE OF BUDGET PENNSYLVANIA
(Suby of EXECUTIVE OFFICE OF COMMONWEALTH OF PENNSYLVANIA) ★
238 Main Capitol Building, Harrisburg, PA 17120-0022
Tel (717) 787-4472 Founded/Ownrshp 2003
Sales NA EMP 700
SIC 9311 Finance, taxation & monetary policy; ; Finance, taxation & monetary policy;

OFFICE OF THE CENTER DIRECTOR
See NATIONAL CENTER FOR TOXICOLOGICAL RESEARCH

OFFICE OF THE CENTER DIRECTOR
See CENTER FOR VETERINARY MEDICINE

OFFICE OF THE CENTER DIRECTOR
See CENTER FOR BIOLOGICS EVALUATION AND RESEARCH

OFFICE OF THE CLERK TREASURER
See CITY OF BURLINGTON

OFFICE OF THE CONTROLLER
See BUCKS COUNTY OF

OFFICE OF COUNTY ADMINISTRATOR
See COUNTY OF HAMILTON

D-U-N-S 96-480-0762
■ **OFFICE OF CRIMINAL INVESTIGATIONS**
(Suby of OFFICE OF REGULATORY AFFAIRS) ★
7500 Standish Pl Ste 250n, Rockville, MD 20855-2764
Tel (240) 276-9500 Founded/Ownrshp 2010
Sales NA EMP 282^E
SIC 9431 Administration of public health programs;

OFFICE OF THE DIRECTOR
See UNITED STATES DEPT OF GEOLOGICAL SURVEY

OFFICE OF ECONOMIC STIMULUS
See EXECUTIVE OFFICE OF STATE OF NEW HAMPSHIRE

D-U-N-S 94-743-6176
OFFICE OF EMERGENCY SERVICES
CAL OES
(Suby of EXECUTIVE OFFICE OF STATE OF CALIFORNIA) ★
3650 Schriever Ave, Mather, CA 95655-4203
Tel (916) 845-8510 Founded/Ownrshp 1998
Sales NA EMP 400
SIC 9229 Emergency management office, government; ; Emergency management office, government;
Ofcr: Lori Newquist
Ofcr: Elaine Viray
Sales Asso: Ben Masonheimer
Snr Mgr: Paul Walters

D-U-N-S 11-242-2600
OFFICE OF FIRST STEPS
SC FIRST STEPS
1300 Sumter St Ste 100, Columbia, SC 29201-3340
Tel (803) 734-0479 Founded/Ownrshp 1999
Sales 26.0MM EMP 74^E
SIC 8211 Preparatory school; Preparatory school
*Ofcr: Dan Wuri

OFFICE OF THE GOVERNOR
See LEGISLATIVE OFFICE OF STATE OF WASHINGTON

OFFICE OF THE GOVERNOR
See EXECUTIVE OFFICE OF STATE OF ALASKA

OFFICE OF GRANT PROCUREMENT
See NEVADA DEPARTMENT OF ADMINISTRATION

D-U-N-S 02-072-6385
OFFICE OF HISTORICAL TRUST ACCOUNTING
DEPARTMENT OF THE INTERIOR
1849 C St Nw, Washington, DC 20240-0001
Tel (202) 208-3100 Founded/Ownrshp 2010
Sales NA EMP 356^E
SIC 9512 Land, mineral & wildlife conservation
Ofcr: Sandra Evans
Ofcr: Fay Iudicello
Ofcr: Charly Shin
Assoc Dir: Melissa Simpson
Assoc Dir: Stephanie Toothman
Comm Dir: Kate Kelly
Adm Dir: Jean Maybee
Prgrm Mgr: Victoria Weaver
Off Admin: Angela McLeod-Cooper
Off Admin: Chanelle Williams
CTO: Daud Santosa

OFFICE OF INSPECTOR GENERAL
See US DEPARTMENT OF COMMERCE

D-U-N-S 87-802-3837
OFFICE OF LEGISLATIVE COUNCIL OF COLORADO
(Suby of STATE OF COLORADO) ★
200 E Colfax Ave Ste 29, Denver, CO 80203-1716
Tel (303) 866-3521 Founded/Ownrshp 1995
Sales NA EMP 276
SIC 9121 Legislative bodies; ; Legislative bodies;

D-U-N-S 80-747-7963
OFFICE OF LEGISLATIVE COUNSEL
(Suby of STATE OF CALIFORNIA) ★
State Cpitol Bldg Rm 3021, Sacramento, CA 95814
Tel (916) 341-8000 Founded/Ownrshp 1913
Sales NA EMP 1,600
SIC 9121 Legislative bodies, state & local; ; Legislative bodies, state & local;
Prin: Diane Boyer-Vine
Pr: Terza Rodoni

OFFICE OF LEGISLATURE
See COUNTY OF ORLEANS

OFFICE OF MAYOR
See CITY OF MILWAUKEE

D-U-N-S 06-378-5576
OFFICE OF MORTGAGE SETTLEMENT OVERSIGHT
301 Fayetteville St, Raleigh, NC 27601-1974
Tel (919) 825-4748 Founded/Ownrshp 2012
Sales 72.1MM EMP 2
Accts Cherry Bekaert Llp Charlotte
SIC 6211 Mortgages, buying & selling; Mortgages, buying & selling
Prin: Robert Charles Lawson

D-U-N-S 03-185-4594
■ **OFFICE OF NATIONAL DRUG CONTROL POLICY**
(Suby of EXECUTIVE OFFICE OF THE PRESIDENT)
750 17th St Nw, Washington, DC 20006-4607
Tel (202) 395-6700 Founded/Ownrshp 1985
Sales NA EMP 470^E
SIC 9111 Executive offices;
Snr Mgr: Daniel Gettings

OFFICE OF NATIONAL RESPONSE
See EMPLOYMENT AND TRAINING ADMINISTRATION

D-U-N-S 10-570-6873
■ **OFFICE OF NATURAL RESOURCES REVENUE**
OFFICE NTRAL RESOURCES REVENUE
(Suby of OFFICE OF SECRETARY) ★
Denver Federal Ctr Bldg 85, Denver, CO 80225
Tel (303) 231-3162 Founded/Ownrshp 2011
Sales NA EMP 500^E
SIC 9512 Land, mineral & wildlife conservation; ; Land, mineral & wildlife conservation;
Prin: Dgibbs Tschuty Dep Dir

D-U-N-S 16-004-2354
■ **OFFICE OF OCEANIC AND ATMOSPHERIC RESEARCH**
(Suby of NATIONAL OCEANIC AND ATMOSPHERIC ADMINISTRATION) ★
1315 E West Hwy Ste 1, Silver Spring, MD 20910-6223
Tel (301) 734-2458 Founded/Ownrshp 1970
Sales NA EMP 1,806^E
SIC 9511 Air, water & solid waste management;
Prin: Richard Spinrad
Prgrm Mgr: John Cortinas

D-U-N-S 04-389-1204
■ **OFFICE OF POLICY MANAGEMENT & BUDGET**
(Suby of UNITED STATES DEPARTMENT OF INTERIOR) ★
1849 C St Nw Fl 5, Washington, DC 20240-0001
Tel (202) 208-4203 Founded/Ownrshp 1849
Sales NA EMP 500
SIC 9199 General government administration; ; General government administration;
Sec: R Thomas Weimer

OFFICE OF THE PRESIDENT
See SUNY UNIVERSITY AT BUFFALO

D-U-N-S 96-479-4353
■ **OFFICE OF REGULATORY AFFAIRS**
(Suby of FDA- OFM) ★
10903 Nh Ave Wo31 Rm 3528, Silver Spring, MD 20993-0001
Tel (301) 796-8800 Founded/Ownrshp 2010
Sales NA EMP 3,297^E
SIC 9431 Administration of public health programs;

D-U-N-S 87-727-7335
OFFICE OF REHABILITATION UTAH STATE
(Suby of EXECUTIVE OFFICE OF STATE OF UTAH) ★
250 E 500 S, Salt Lake City, UT 84111-3204
Tel (801) 538-7530 Founded/Ownrshp 1994
Sales NA EMP 400
SIC 9431 Administration of public health programs; ; Administration of public health programs;
Pr Mgr: Mark Peterson

OFFICE OF THE SECRETARY
See US DEPARTMENT OF COMMERCE

OFFICE OF THE SECRETARY
See LOUISIANA DEPARTMENT OF ENVIRONMENTAL QUALITY

D-U-N-S 13-090-7426
■ **OFFICE OF SECRETARY**
(Suby of UNITED STATES DEPARTMENT OF INTERIOR) ★
1849 C St Nw, Washington, DC 20240-0001
Tel (202) 208-3425 Founded/Ownrshp 2003
Sales NA EMP 300^E
SIC 9512 Land, mineral & wildlife conservation; ; Land, mineral & wildlife conservation;
Pr: Brenda Rodriguez

D-U-N-S 80-634-8322
OFFICE OF SECRETARY
(Suby of STATE OF NEW MEXICO) ★
1570 Pacheco St Ste B9, Santa Fe, NM 87505-3983
Tel (505) 476-2200 Founded/Ownrshp 1912
Sales NA EMP 19,423
SIC 9111 Governors' offices; Governors' offices;
Exec: Pamela Hyde
Exec: Joanna Prukop
*Dir IT: Scott Darnell
Genl Couns: Jessica Hernandez

OFFICE OF SECRETARY OF STATE
See NEW JERSEY DEPARTMENT OF STATE

OFFICE OF THE SECRETARY STATE
See EXECUTIVE OFFICE OF STATE OF ALABAMA

D-U-N-S 03-306-1503
■ **OFFICE OF SOLICITOR**
SOLICITORS OFFICE
(Suby of UNITED STATES DEPARTMENT OF INTERIOR) ★
1849 C St Nw Rm 6559, Washington, DC 20240-0001
Tel (202) 208-4423 Founded/Ownrshp 1949
Sales NA EMP 350
SIC 9199 General government administration; ; General government administration;
Prin: Hilary Thompkins
Ofcr: Jason Earwood

OFFICE OF THE STATE AUDITOR
See STATE AUDITOR MASSACHUSETTS OFFICE OF

OFFICE OF SUPERINTENDENT
See MONTGOMERY COUNTY SCHOOL DISTRICT

D-U-N-S 92-603-8118
■ **OFFICE OF SURFACE MINING RECLAMATION & ENFORCEMENT**
(Suby of UNITED STATES DEPARTMENT OF INTERIOR) ★
1951 Constitution Ave N, Washington, DC 20240-0001
Tel (202) 208-2953 Founded/Ownrshp 1977
Sales NA EMP 700
SIC 9511 Air, water & solid waste management; ; Air, water & solid waste management;
Ofcr: Debra Giovette
Ofcr: Ginger Kaldlenback
Rgnl Mgr: Michael Mills

D-U-N-S 87-982-6139
■ **OFFICE OF THE COMPTROLLER OF THE CURRENCY**
O C C
(Suby of UNITED STATES DEPT OF TREASURY) ★
400 7th St Sw Ste 3e218, Washington, DC 20219-0006
Tel (202) 649-6800 Founded/Ownrshp 1863
Sales NA EMP 4,000
Accts Gka Pc Washington Dc
SIC 9651 Banking regulatory agency, government; ; Banking regulatory agency, government;
Adm Dir: Karen Smith
*CIO: Edward J Dorris
CIO: Stephen W Warren
IT Man: Bernard Colebrook
IT Man: Clyde Halsrud
IT Man: Michael Zuckerman
Info Man: Wesley Wilbur
Counsel: Doug Jordan
Snr Mgr: Edward Dorris
Snr Mgr: Carol Raskin

D-U-N-S 04-401-4418
■ **OFFICE OF THE INSPECTOR GENERAL**
(Suby of UNITED STATES DEPT OF STATE) ★
1700 N Moore St Ste 840, Arlington, VA 22209-1925
Tel (703) 284-1800 Founded/Ownrshp 1998
Sales NA EMP 300
SIC 9721 International affairs; ; International affairs;
Prin: Clark Ervin

D-U-N-S 78-485-9167
■ **OFFICE OF THE INSPECTOR GENERAL**
DCIS
(Suby of OFFICE OF THE SECRETARY OF DEFENSE) ★
4800 Mark Center Dr, Alexandria, VA 22350-0002
Tel (703) 604-8669 Founded/Ownrshp 1982
Sales NA EMP 1,538
SIC 9711 National security; ; National security;
Prin: Gordon Heddell
Dir IT: Matthew Steiniger
Snr Mgr: Brett Mansfield

D-U-N-S 02-883-7123
■ OFFICE OF THE SECRETARY OF DEFENSE
(*Suby of* UNITED STATES DEPARTMENT OF DEFENSE) ★
1400 Defense Pentagon, Washington, DC 20301-1400
Tel (703) 545-6700 *Founded/Ownrshp* 1947
Sales NA *EMP* 1,346,022
SIC 9711 National security;
Ofcr: Susan Idziak
Prgrm Mgr: John Yuhas
Genl Couns: Paul Black
Snr Mgr: Merrill Simms
Snr Mgr: Michael Yee

OFFICE OF THE TREASURER
See CITY OF CHELSEA

D-U-N-S 16-158-0469
■ OFFICE OF THRIFT SUPERVISION
O T S
(*Suby of* UNITED STATES DEPT OF TREASURY) ★
1700 G St Nw, Washington, DC 20552-0003
Tel (202) 906-6900 *Founded/Ownrshp* 1989
Sales NA *EMP* 1,269
Accts Deva & Associates Pc
SIC 9651 Financial regulatory agency; ; Financial regulatory agency;

OFFICE OF WEIGHTS AND MEASURES
See VIRGINIA DEPARTMENT OF AGRICULTURE AND CONSUMER SERVICES

D-U-N-S 85-905-2292
OFFICE PAPER SYSTEMS INC
7650 Airpark Rd, Gaithersburg, MD 20879-4156
Tel (301) 948-6301 *Founded/Ownrshp* 1990
Sales 28.8MM^E *EMP* 90
SIC 5113 8742 4214 7389 5093 4953 Paperboard & products; Business consultant; Local trucking with storage; Document & office record destruction; Waste paper; Recycling, waste materials; Paperboard & products; Business consultant; Local trucking with storage; Documept & office record destruction; Waste paper; Recycling, waste materials
Pr: Ronald E Anderson
**VP:* Lewis Abey

D-U-N-S 03-239-8497 EXP
■ OFFICE PAVILION SOUTH FLORIDA INC
WORKPLACE RESOURCE
(*Suby of* HERMAN MILLER INC) ★
8999 Western Way Ste 106, Jacksonville, FL 32256-0373
Tel (904) 416-3923 *Founded/Ownrshp* 2000
Sales 23.2MM^E *EMP* 56
SIC 5021 7389 Office furniture; Interior design services
CEO: Elizabeth A Dvorak
**Pr:* Richard J Dvorak
**VP:* Ann Osterling

OFFICE PAVILION-HOUSTON
See MARNOY INTERESTS LTD

OFFICE PLUS OF KANSAS
See DANIKSCO OFFICE INTERIORS LLC

D-U-N-S 02-164-3148
OFFICE PRODUCTS PLUS INC
208 Park Ct, Ridgeland, MS 39157-2228
Tel (601) 898-2600 *Founded/Ownrshp* 1998
Sales 21.9MM^E *EMP* 19
SIC 5112 Stationery & office supplies
Pr: James C Watts
Treas: Vanessa Watson
Mktg Mgr: Kimberly Cleland

OFFICE RESEARCH TECH & ANALIS
See PIPELINE AND HAZARDOUS MATERIALS SAFETY ADMINISTRATION

D-U-N-S 17-815-7699
OFFICE RESOURCES INC
O R I
263 Summer St Ste 100, Boston, MA 02210-1545
Tel (617) 423-9100 *Founded/Ownrshp* 2007
Sales 91.5MM^E *EMP* 99
SIC 5021 Office furniture
Pr: Richard C Tuttle
**VP:* Kevin X Barbary
**VP:* Mike Dignard
VP: Susan Evans
**VP:* Paul J Fraser
VP: Peter Roberts
VP: Ray Theberge
Dir IT: Brain Nickerson
Mktg Dir: Kelsey Simonds
Snr PM: Melissa Walter

OFFICE SAVERS
See CARTRIDGE SAVERS INC

OFFICE SCIENCE CHICAGO OFFICE
See US DEPT OF ENERGY CHICAGO OFFICE

OFFICE SERVICE COMPANY
See J BARBOUR INC

D-U-N-S 10-872-9559
OFFICE SOLUTIONS BUSINESS PRODUCTS AND SERVICES INC
23303 La Palma Ave, Yorba Linda, CA 92887-4773
Tel (714) 692-7412 *Founded/Ownrshp* 1984
Sales 50.2MM^E *EMP* 45
SIC 5112 5021 Stationery & office supplies; Office furniture
Pr: Robert J Mairena
**VP:* John Acampora
**VP:* Joel Biales
**VP:* Dave Cravitz
**VP:* Cynthia S Mairena
CTO: Randy Hustrulid
IT Man: Zoya Lister
IT Man: Justina Rogers
MIS Mgr: Krista Elkins
Board of Directors: Luis

OFFICE SOURCE
See LEDWELL & SON ENTERPRISES INC

OFFICE STAR PRODUCTS
See BLUMENTHAL DISTRIBUTING INC

D-U-N-S 83-395-7350
OFFICE THREE SIXTY INC
OFFICE 360
7301 Woodland Dr, Indianapolis, IN 46278-1737
Tel (317) 686-5754 *Founded/Ownrshp* 1990
Sales 23.0MM *EMP* 72
SIC 4226 Document & office records storage
Pr: Scott Nahmias
**Sec:* Lenny Nahmias
**VP:* Steve Nahmias
Sales Exec: Greg Warner
Sls Dir: Larry Sexton

OFFICE USA FURNITURE
See CANFIELD BUSINESS INTERIORS INC

OFFICE WKRS CMPNSTION PROGRAMS
See EMPLOYMENT STANDARDS ADMINISTRATION

OFFICE WORKS
See WESTERN OFFICE PRODUCTS INC

OFFICECHAIRS.COM
See OFFICEFURNITURE.COM LLC

D-U-N-S 02-715-6954 EXP
OFFICEFURNITURE.COM LLC
OFFICECHAIRS.COM
(*Suby of* TAKKT AMERICA HOLDING INC) ★
735 N Water St Ste 400, Milwaukee, WI 53202-4103
Tel (414) 276-8511 *Founded/Ownrshp* 2006
Sales 45.8MM^E *EMP* 160
SIC 5021 Furniture
Pr: Kent S Anderson
**CFO:* Eileen Baus
**Ch:* Felix Zimmerman

D-U-N-S 88-424-7867
OFFICEIMAGES INC
1515 Holcomb Woods Pkwy, Roswell, GA 30076-2574
Tel (770) 641-2640 *Founded/Ownrshp* 1995
Sales 44.1MM^E *EMP* 48
SIC 5021 Office furniture
Ch Bd: Paul F Lombardi
**Pr:* Bryan Roberts
**VP:* Ed Vanderwolf
Creative D: David Stella

D-U-N-S 09-894-3228 IMP
OFFICEMATE INTERNATIONAL CORP
90 Newfeld Ave Rritan Ctr Raritan Center, Edison, NJ 08837
Tel (732) 225-7422 *Founded/Ownrshp* 1985
Sales 43.8MM^E *EMP* 100^E
SIC 5112 3496 2499 Office supplies; Paper clips, made from purchased wire; Clip boards, wood; Office supplies; Paper clips, made from purchased wire; Clip boards, wood
Pr: Shwu-Min Chen
**Sr VP:* Martin Yang
**VP:* Peter Chen
Exec: Chris Lee
IT Man: Andy Tan
Natl Sales: Sharon Kiefer

D-U-N-S 17-892-3231 IMP/EXP
■ OFFICEMAX CONTRACT INC
(*Suby of* OFFICEMAX INC) ★
263 Shuman Blvd, Naperville, IL 60563-8147
Tel (630) 438-7800 *Founded/Ownrshp* 1995
Sales 210.3MM^E *EMP* 1,411
SIC 5021 5112 5044 5111 5943 5712

D-U-N-S 00-907-3099 IMP
■ OFFICEMAX INC
(*Suby of* OFFICE DEPOT INC) ★
6600 N Military Trl, Boca Raton, FL 33496-2434
Tel (630) 438-7800 *Founded/Ownrshp* 2013
Sales 4.1MMM^E *EMP* 29,000^E
SIC 5943 5021 Stationery stores; Office forms & supplies; School supplies; Writing supplies; Office furniture; Stationery stores; Office forms & supplies; School supplies; Writing supplies; Office furniture
Pr: Ravichandra K Saligram
**Pr:* John Kenning
**Pr:* Michael Lewis
CEO: Steve Miller
COO: Samuel M Martin
Treas: Tony Giuliano
Bd of Dir: James Marino
**Ofcr:* James Barr IV
**Ofcr:* Bruce H Besanko
**Ofcr:* Stephen B Parsons
**Ofcr:* Steve Parsons
**Ex VP:* Matthew R Broad
**Ex VP:* Kim Feil
Ex VP: Ann Hewitt
**Ex VP:* Ronald Lalla
Ex VP: Deborah Oconnor
Sr VP: David Armstrong
**Sr VP:* Larry Hartley
**Sr VP:* Deb O'Connor
Sr VP: Bob Thacker
Sr VP: Scott Williams

D-U-N-S 18-512-2629 IMP/EXP
■ OFFICEMAX NORTH AMERICA INC
RELIABLE OFFICE SUPPLY
(*Suby of* OFFICEMAX INC) ★
263 Shuman Blvd Ste 500, Naperville, IL 60563-3525
Tel (630) 438-7800 *Founded/Ownrshp* 2005
Sales 1.7MMM^E *EMP* 29,000
SIC 5943 5712 5734 5999 7334 Office forms & supplies; Office furniture; Computer & software stores; Business machines & equipment; Photocopying & duplicating services; Office forms & supplies; Office furniture; Computer & software stores; Business machines & equipment; Photocopying & duplicating services
Sr VP: Phillip Depaul
**Pr:* Ravi Saligram
**CFO:* Bruce Besanko
**Treas:* Ken Neal
**Ex VP:* Jim Barr
**Ex VP:* Ryan Vero
Sr VP: Patrick J Conroy
Sr VP: Neil A Guliano
Sr VP: Robert S Islinger
Sr VP: Douglas J Schwinn
VP: James D Donegan
VP: Thomas M Piteo
VP: Alan Rauen
VP: Michael Tilton

D-U-N-S 96-778-0859
OFFICENATION INC
PCNATION
500 Central Ave, Northfield, IL 60093-3047
Tel (847) 504-3000 *Founded/Ownrshp* 1996
Sales 49.5MM^E *EMP* 25
SIC 5044 5112 5712 Office equipment; Office supplies; Office furniture
Pr: Medwin Dayan
Natl Sales: Ryan Custer
Natl Sales: Adam Glaser
Snr Mgr: Ken Fuller

OFFICER FINANCIAL AID
See SAN DIEGO STATE UNIVERSITY

D-U-N-S 07-282-1754
OFFICES LIMITED INC
76 9th Ave Ste 313, New York, NY 10011-5226
Tel (212) 704-9848 *Founded/Ownrshp* 1973
Sales 33.1MM^E *EMP* 35
SIC 5021 Office furniture

OFFICESCAPES
See JUPITER I LLC

D-U-N-S 13-402-8807
■ OFFICETIGER LLC
R R DONNELLEY
(*Suby of* RR DONNELLEY & SONS CO) ★
255 Greenwich St Bsmt B, New York, NY 10007-2377
Tel (800) 324-7317 *Founded/Ownrshp* 2006
Sales 24.7MM^E *EMP* 300
SIC 7374 Data processing & preparation; Data processing & preparation
VP: Cosgrove Thomas
Dir Bus: Anthony Calabro
Off Mgr: Rachel Smith
VP Opers: Vijay Dhavala
Opers Mgr: Jim Colville
Snr Mgr: Sheetal Rupchandani

OFFICEWISE FURNITURE AND SUPPL
See SEWCO INC

D-U-N-S 10-427-2120
OFFICEWORKS INC
5877 Pine Ave Ste 250, Chino Hills, CA 91709-6544
Tel (818) 758-1555 *Founded/Ownrshp* 2001
Sales 20.0MM^E *EMP* 555
SIC 7361 Employment agencies; Employment agencies
Pr: Dana Hallberg

D-U-N-S 12-157-5625
OFFICEWORKS SERVICES LLC
12000 Exit 5 Pkwy, Fishers, IN 46037-7940
Tel (317) 577-3510 *Founded/Ownrshp* 1984
Sales 27.5MM *EMP* 52
Accts Katz Sapper & Miller Indianap
SIC 5021 Office furniture; Office furniture
**Ex VP:* Larry Martin

D-U-N-S 82-511-2915
■ OFFICIAL PAYMENTS HOLDINGS INC
(*Suby of* ACI WORLDWIDE INC) ★
705 W Tech Dr, Norcross, GA 30092
Tel (770) 325-3100 *Founded/Ownrshp* 2013
Sales 25.7MM^E *EMP* 223^E
SIC 7389 7373 Financial services; Systems software development services; Systems integration services; Financial services; Systems software development services; Systems integration services
Pr: Alex P Hart
Pr: Richard E Kristensen
**Sr VP:* Atul Garg
Sr VP: T Jack Williams
**VP:* Keith S Omsberg
IT Man: Cecil Carter
Natl Sales: Roy Parsons

D-U-N-S 82-789-2733
OFFICIAL POLICE GARAGE ASSOCIATION OF LOS ANGELES
67 W Boulder Creek Rd, Simi Valley, CA 93065-7362
Tel (805) 624-0572 *Founded/Ownrshp* 1990
Sales 20.0MM^E *EMP* 800
Accts Weir And Fecht Woodland Hills
SIC 4492 Towing & tugboat service; Towing & tugboat service
Ex Dir: Eric Rose

D-U-N-S 36-355-7117
OFFICIAL SECURITY INC
COURTESY PATROL
2404 Santa Paula Dr, Las Vegas, NV 89104-2631
Tel (702) 369-4366 *Founded/Ownrshp* 1988
Sales 23.1MM^E *EMP* 500
SIC 7382 7389 7381 Security systems services; Convention & show services; Security guard service; Security systems services; Convention & show services; Security guard service
Pr: Darryl Cronfeld

D-U-N-S 04-471-3501 IMP
OFFRAY SPECIALTY NARROW FABRICS INC (NY)
4 Essex Ave Ste 403, Bernardsville, NJ 07924-2265
Tel (908) 879-3636 *Founded/Ownrshp* 1877, 2002
Sales 41.3MM^E *EMP* 204^E
SIC 2241 Narrow fabric mills; Ribbons
Ch Bd: Claude V Offray Jr
**COO:* Denise A Offray
CFO: Michael Lurue
**Prin:* Claude Offray

D-U-N-S 06-682-0994
OFFSET HOUSE INC
CATAMOUNT COLOR
89 Sandhill Rd, Essex Junction, VT 05452-3909
Tel (802) 878-4440 *Founded/Ownrshp* 1974
Sales 27.2MM^E *EMP* 150
SIC 7331 2752 2796 2791 Mailing service; Commercial printing, offset; Platemaking services; Typesetting; Mailing service; Commercial printing, offset; Platemaking services; Typesetting
Pr: John P Mc Grath
**Sec:* Richard B Ronson
**VP:* John Carp
Prd Mgr: Mark Daubenschmidt

D-U-N-S 05-844-6022
OFFSET PAPERBACK MFRS INC
STUDIO PRINT GROUP
(*Suby of* BERRYVILLE GRAPHICS INC) ★
2211 Memorial Hwy, Dallas, PA 18612-9244
Tel (570) 675-5261 *Founded/Ownrshp* 1980
Sales 132.4MM^E *EMP* 750
SIC 2731 2752 Book publishing; Commercial printing, offset; Book publishing; Commercial printing, offset
Pr: David Liess
**CFO:* Richard R Pincofski
VP: Jack O'Donnell
**VP:* Jack Odonnell
**VP:* William L Rogers
Off Mgr: Tressa Schwartz
Netwrk Eng: Brian Bedosky
Plnt Mgr: Bob Scheifflee
Prd Mgr: Dave Thomas

D-U-N-S 93-005-7760 IMP
OFFSHORE CLEANING SYSTEMS LLC
9525 Us Hwy 67, Abbeville, LA 70510
Tel (337) 898-8858 *Founded/Ownrshp* 1999
Sales 33.8MM^E *EMP* 210^E
SIC 1799 Shore cleaning & maintenance; Shore cleaning & maintenance
**COO:* Mike Breaux
**CFO:* Mike Hutchison
**VP:* Brandon Broussard
**VP:* Bobby Gaudet
Genl Mgr: Mitchell Leblanc
Sfty Dirs: Chad Nezat
S&M/VP: Wayne Stein

OFFSHORE DOMESTIC GROUP
See OFFSHORE SPECIALTY FABRICATORS LLC

D-U-N-S 78-220-1891 IMP/EXP
OFFSHORE DRILLING CO
9 Greenway Plz Ste 2200, Houston, TX 77046-0931
Tel (713) 278-6000 *Founded/Ownrshp* 2000
Sales NA *EMP* 420^E
SIC 1381 Drilling oil & gas wells

D-U-N-S 83-755-7974 IMP
■ OFFSHORE DRILLING CO
TODCO
(*Suby of* TRANSOCEAN INC) ★
24 Concord Rd, Houma, LA 70360-7561
Tel (985) 876-6987 *Founded/Ownrshp* 2001
Sales 45.2MM^E *EMP* 1,300
SIC 1381 Drilling oil & gas wells; Drilling oil & gas wells
Pr: Steven A Webster
VP: Don Rodney

OFFSHORE ENERGY
See GARBER INDUSTRIES INC

D-U-N-S 07-261-4845 IMP
OFFSHORE ENERGY SERVICES INC
5900 Highway 90 E, Broussard, LA 70518-5701
Tel (337) 837-1024 *Founded/Ownrshp* 1974
Sales 338.6MM^E *EMP* 490
SIC 1389 Oil field services; Oil field services
Pr: Charles M Garber
COO: Glenn Hohensee
VP: Samuel Broussard
**VP:* Roy Garber
VP: Steven Roussel
VP: Brian Theriot
Genl Mgr: Dennis Schmitke
Sfty Mgr: Tony Brabner
Sfty Mgr: Anthony Bradner
Opers Mgr: Jared Angelle
Opers Mgr: Bob Hooper

OFFSHORE EQUIPMENT SOLUTIONS
See WADLEIGH INDUSTRIES INC

D-U-N-S 08-702-5409
OFFSHORE EXPRESS INC
115 Menard Rd, Houma, LA 70363-7517
Tel (985) 868-1438 *Founded/Ownrshp* 2002
Sales NA *EMP* 325
SIC 3731 4492 1389 1382 Drilling & production platforms, floating (oil & gas); Towing & tugboat service; Oil field services; Oil & gas exploration services; Drilling & production platforms, floating (oil & gas); Towing & tugboat service; Oil field services; Oil & gas exploration services
Pr: Harlan F Belanger
Board of Directors: Lawrence Chan, William M Kallop, Brian Mc Allister

D-U-N-S 83-032-2173 IMP
OFFSHORE INLAND MARINE & OILFIELD SERVICES INC
(*Suby of* OIMO HOLDINGS INC) ★
890 S Palafox St Unit 202, Pensacola, FL 32502-5905
Tel (251) 443-5550 *Founded/Ownrshp* 2001
Sales 100.4MM^E *EMP* 125^E
SIC 1389 Oil field services; Oil consultants; Gas field services
CEO: Robin D Roberts
**VP:* Crystal Yasurek

D-U-N-S 19-625-2084 IMP
OFFSHORE INTERNATIONAL INC
8350 E Old Vail Rd, Tucson, AZ 85747-9197
Tel (520) 889-0022 *Founded/Ownrshp* 1986
Sales 24.6MM^E *EMP* 100

SIC 8741 8742 Business management; General management consultant
Pr: Luis F Seldner
**Pr:* Luis Felipe Seldner III
Dir Bus: David McQueen
Off Mgr: Richard Kean
Dir IT: Jose Colunga
Sls Mgr: Aida Samuel
Board of Directors: Roberto Gomez Del Campo, Felix Tonella-Luken

D-U-N-S 15-407-8034
OFFSHORE JOINT SERVICES INC
FORUM ENERGY TECHNOLOGIES
1621 Prime West Pkwy, Katy, TX 77449-5324
Tel (281) 578-6523 *Founded/Ownrshp* 2007
Sales 27.3MM^E *EMP* 150
SIC 1389 Oil field services
CEO: Dennis Lee
**Pr:* Paul Pool
**VP:* Don Benson
**VP:* Joe Duncan
**VP:* William Gowan
**VP:* Andy Paul
**VP:* Andy Waite

OFFSHORE MAR CABLE SPECIALISTS
See AMERCABLE INC

D-U-N-S 87-432-5822
OFFSHORE MARINE CONTRACTORS INC
OMC
133 W 113th St, Cut Off, LA 70345-3639
Tel (985) 632-7927 *Founded/Ownrshp* 1994
Sales 120.8MM^E *EMP* 200
SIC 1389 Servicing oil & gas wells
CEO: Michael M Eymard
**Pr:* Louis Eymard II
**Sec:* Raimy D Eymard
**Sr VP:* Avis J Bourg Jr
Sls Mgr: Mark Cookson

D-U-N-S 05-458-9176 IMP/EXP
OFFSHORE RENTAL LTD (TX)
TIGER TANKS OFFSHORE RENTAL
1655 Louisiana St, Beaumont, TX 77701-1120
Tel (409) 833-2665 *Founded/Ownrshp* 1998
Sales 254.2MM^E *EMP* 1,500^E
SIC 2911 Oils, fuel; Oils, fuel
CEO: Will Crenshaw
**CFO:* Brian Bomer
**Prin:* Casey Crenshaw

D-U-N-S 06-467-6281
OFFSHORE SERVICE VESSELS LLC
EDISON CHOUEST OFFSHORE
16201 E Main St, Cut Off, LA 70345-3804
Tel (985) 601-4444 *Founded/Ownrshp* 2010
Sales 324.6MM^E *EMP* 1,000
SIC 4491 Marine cargo handling; Marine cargo handling
CFO: Charles Comeaux
Ofcr: Mel Comeaux
Genl Mgr: Lee Bouziga
Opers Mgr: Nathan Curole
Opers Mgr: Brian Guidry
Opers Mgr: Emile Parra
Opers Mgr: Roddy Pitre
Opers Mgr: Steven Reding
Opers Mgr: Rodrigo Senna
Counsel: Renata Palagi

D-U-N-S 60-773-3045 IMP
OFFSHORE SPECIALTY FABRICATORS LLC
OFFSHORE DOMESTIC GROUP
115 Menard Rd, Houma, LA 70363-7517
Tel (985) 868-1438 *Founded/Ownrshp* 1990
Sales 80.8MM^E *EMP* 400
SIC 3731 1389 Drilling & production platforms, floating (oil & gas); Oil field services; Drilling & production platforms, floating (oil & gas); Oil field services
CEO: Tom Fairley
**Pr:* William Kallop
**Ex VP:* Harlan Belanger

D-U-N-S 12-237-4788
OFFSHORE TECHNOLOGY CONFERENCE
222 Palisades Creek Dr, Richardson, TX 75080-2040
Tel (972) 952-9494 *Founded/Ownrshp* 1968
Sales 30.4MM *EMP* 2
SIC 8611 Business associations; Business associations
Pr: Mark Rubin
Pt: Jim Grimsley
IT Man: John Boden

D-U-N-S 83-923-1875 IMP
■ **OFFWIRE INC**
BRIGHTS
(*Suby of* BRIGHTSTAR CORP) ★
13575 Lynam Dr, Omaha, NE 68138-4408
Tel (402) 597-9770 *Founded/Ownrshp* 1995
Sales 70.0MM *EMP* 114
SIC 4812 5065 Paging services; Mobile telephone equipment; Telephone equipment
Pr: John W Lund
COO: Alysa Clary
COO: Cassey Reese
**Treas:* Beverly Braasch
VP: Timothy Brady
**VP:* Diane Lund
IT Man: Cindy Rieboldt
Natl Sales: Sandy Miller
Natl Sales: Laura Timmermeyer
Sls Dir: Kelly Grace

D-U-N-S 01-475-0843
▲ **OFG BANCORP**
254 Ave Munoz Rivera Fl 8, San Juan, PR 00918-1900
Tel (787) 771-6800 *Founded/Ownrshp* 1996
Sales NA *EMP* 1,567
Accts Kpmg Llp San Juan Puerto Ric
Tkr Sym OFG *Exch* NYS
SIC 6022 State commercial banks; State commercial banks
Pr: Jose R Fernandez
**Ch Bd:* Julian S Inclan
V Ch: Francisco Arriv
CFO: Ganesh Kumar
Treas: Ramon Rosado
Ofcr: Luis R Salv
Ofcr: Juan Jos Santiago
Sr VP: Maritza Arizmendi
Sr VP: Jos G D AZ
Sr VP: Mari E Rodr Guez
Sr VP: Vanessa Gonz Lez
Sr VP: Milton Jim Nez
Sr VP: C Sar A Ortiz
Sr VP: Cesar Ortiz
VP: Amaury Santiago
VP: Nestor Vale
Board of Directors: Juan C Aguayo, Francisco Arrivi, Jorge Colon-Gerena, Rafael F Martinez-Margarid, Pedro Morazzani, Jose E Rossi

D-U-N-S 06-798-1050 EXP
OFI TESTING EQUIPMENT INC (TX)
OFITE
11302 Steeplecrest Dr, Houston, TX 77065-5649
Tel (713) 880-9885 *Founded/Ownrshp* 1982
Sales 30.8MM^E *EMP* 75
SIC 3533 Oil field machinery & equipment; Oil field machinery & equipment
Ch: Rita Shamban
**Pr:* Kyle Schroeder
**CFO:* Chris Keen
IT Man: Robert Korenek
Sftwr Eng: Doanh Ho
Mfg Mgr: Moheb Attalla
Mktg Mgr: Justin Shoemate
Sls Mgr: Brad McIver
Sls Mgr: Larry Mitchell
Sales Asso: Margo Hanks

D-U-N-S 36-175-9210
OFIC ADM TRIBUNALES-OFICIAL
SUPREME COURT OF THE COMMWL PR
(*Suby of* COMMONWEALTH OF PUERTO RICO) ★
286 Munoz Rivera Ave We Western, San Juan, PR 00919
Tel (787) 641-6600 *Founded/Ownrshp* 1952
Sales NA *EMP* 5,000
SIC 9211 Courts; Federal courts; Local courts; State courts; Courts; Federal courts; Local courts; State courts

OFIS
See OUR FINE INTERIOR SOLUTIONS LP

OFITE
See OFI TESTING EQUIPMENT INC

D-U-N-S 12-143-3924 IMP/EXP
OFLAHERTY HOLDINGS INC
(*Suby of* O'FLAHERTY HOLDINGS LIMITED)
7601 Imperial Dr, Waco, TX 76712-6608
Tel (254) 399-2100 *Founded/Ownrshp* 1977
Sales 49.9MM^E *EMP* 600
Accts Jaynes Reitmeier Boyd & Ther
SIC 3534 Elevators & moving stairways; Elevators & moving stairways
CEO: Stephen N O'Flaherty
**Ch Bd:* Nigel O'Flaherty
**Sec:* David Post
Bd of Dir: Stephen Oflaherty
**VP:* Tom O'Dowd
**VP:* Michael P O'Flaherty
Board of Directors: Charles Wiley

OFS
See GJR SERVICES LLC

D-U-N-S 00-636-4434 IMP
OFS BRANDS HOLDINGS INC
1204 E 6th St, Huntingburg, IN 47542-9375
Tel (800) 521-5381 *Founded/Ownrshp* 1937
Sales 152.3MM^E *EMP* 2,000
SIC 2521 2522 2511 2599 Wood office furniture; Office furniture, except wood; Wood household furniture; Hospital furniture, except beds; Wood office furniture; Office furniture, except wood; Wood household furniture; Hospital furniture, except beds
Pr: Robert H Menke Jr
**Ch Bd:* Joseph Bellino
**CFO:* Jim Huebner
**Sr VP:* Jeff Eckert
**Sr VP:* Ryan Menke
**Sr VP:* Michael Wagner
Rgnl Mgr: Richard Goodrum
Area Mgr: Robin Rucker
Dist Mgr: Doug Dorsey
DP Exec: Michael Bell
Software D: John Hulsman
Board of Directors: Karen Middendorf, Arthur Nordhoff, Jeff Weir, Dr William Williams

D-U-N-S 96-830-1833
OFS BRANDS HOLDINGS INC
4611 S 400w, Huntingburg, IN 47542-9199
Tel (812) 683-4848 *Founded/Ownrshp* 2011
Sales 49.0MM^E *EMP* 199^E
SIC 6719 Investment holding companies, except banks
CFO: Jim Hubner
Dir IT: Scott Franzel

D-U-N-S 08-449-3506
OFS BRIGHTWAVE LLC
(*Suby of* FURUKAWA ELECTRIC CO.,LTD.)
2000 Northeast Expy, Norcross, GA 30071-2932
Tel (770) 798-3000 *Founded/Ownrshp* 2005
Sales 262.1MM^E *EMP* 2,300^E
SIC 3357 3229 Fiber optic cable (insulated); Pressed & blown glass; Fiber optic cable (insulated); Pressed & blown glass
Ofcr: Toshiya Hirose

D-U-N-S 07-868-1522
▲ **OFS CAPITAL CORP**
10 S Wacker Dr Ste 2500, Chicago, IL 60606-7491
Tel (847) 734-2060 *Founded/Ownrshp* 2001
Sales 22.8MM *EMP* 27^E
Tkr Sym OFS *Exch* NGM
SIC 6799 Investors; Investors
Ch Bd: Bilal Rashid
**CFO:* Jeffrey Cerny
Ofcr: Eric P Rubenfeld

D-U-N-S 08-374-8611 IMP
OFS FITEL LLC
O F S
(*Suby of* FURUKAWA ELECTRIC CO.,LTD.)
2000 Northeast Expy, Norcross, GA 30071-2932
Tel (770) 798-2000 *Founded/Ownrshp* 2001
Sales 326.7MM^E *EMP* 1,400
SIC 3229 3357 Pressed & blown glass; Fiber optic cable (insulated); Pressed & blown glass; Fiber optic cable (insulated)
Ch Bd: Timothy F Murray
**CFO:* Ashish Gandhi
CFO: Norbert Schmid
Bd of Dir: Jose Abrantes
**Sr VP:* Patrice Dubois
Sr VP: Timothy Pillow
VP: Stephanie Street
VP: Marty Wilson
Dir Bus: Jesper Steenstrup
Mng Dir: Reinhard Schmidt
Prgrm Mgr: Charles Fritz

D-U-N-S 07-193-4293
OFS INC
OIL COUNTRY TUBULAR CONS TEXAS
1120 Engineers Rd, Belle Chasse, LA 70037-3131
Tel (504) 367-4815 *Founded/Ownrshp* 1975
Sales 28.4MM^E *EMP* 100
SIC 1389 Construction, repair & dismantling services; Testing, measuring, surveying & analysis services
Pr: Douglas M Lanasa Jr

D-U-N-S 07-884-7755
OFS INTERNATIONAL LLC
(*Suby of* TMK, PAO)
7735 Miller Road 3, Houston, TX 77049-1737
Tel (281) 452-3036 *Founded/Ownrshp* 2012, 2013
Sales 48.0MM^E *EMP* 300
SIC 3533 3498 1389 Oil field machinery & equipment; Couplings, pipe: fabricated from purchased pipe; Pipe testing, oil field service
Pr: Konstantin Semerikov
COO: David Green
CFO: Alexey Ratmikov

OFTC
See OCONEE FALL LINE TECHNICAL COLLEGE

D-U-N-S 00-624-5658
OFTEDAL CONSTRUCTION INC
434 Highway 59 N 59n, Miles City, MT 59301-6318
Tel (406) 232-5911 *Founded/Ownrshp* 1970
Sales 91.6MM^E *EMP* 250
SIC 1629 3273 1611 Earthmoving contractor; Dam construction; Land reclamation; Ready-mixed concrete; General contractor, highway & street construction; Earthmoving contractor; Dam construction; Land reclamation; Ready-mixed concrete; General contractor, highway & street construction
Pr: Jeff McDonald
**Pr:* James Halvor Fuglevand
**CFO:* Roy Thorneycroft
**Ch:* William Oftedal
**VP:* Greg Jackson
**VP:* Cameron G Lundby
Dir Bus: Roger Cable
IT Man: Jacie Smith
Sfty Dirs: Payton Zierolf
Mtls Mgr: John Lampert

OG
See OUTLOOK GROUP CORP

D-U-N-S 06-088-0838 IMP
OGARA COACH CO LLC
8833 W Olympic Blvd # 8845, Beverly Hills, CA 90211-3696
Tel (310) 659-4050 *Founded/Ownrshp* 1997
Sales 34.2MM^E *EMP* 70^E
SIC 5511 Automobiles, new & used; Automobiles, new & used
Mktg Mgr: Eva Gaspar
Sls Mgr: Llewyn Jobe
Sales Asso: Dawne Czarny
Sales Asso: Thomas Hodges

D-U-N-S 03-045-4420
OGARA GROUP INC
9113 Le Street Dr, Cincinnati, OH 45249
Tel (513) 338-0660 *Founded/Ownrshp* 2004
Sales 31.7MM^E *EMP* 75^E
SIC 7382 Security systems services
Ch Bd: Thomas M O'Gara
Pr: Tony Russell
**CEO:* Bill T O'Gara
**CFO:* Steven P Ratterman
CFO: Steven Ratterman
VP: Abram S Gordon
**VP:* Michael J Lennon
VP: James Noe
Genl Mgr: Bob Kogut
CIO: Aaron Haucke

D-U-N-S 18-345-3971
OGBURN TRUCK PARTS LP
900 E Northside Dr, Fort Worth, TX 76102-1019
Tel (817) 332-1511 *Founded/Ownrshp* 2002
Sales 54.4MM^E *EMP* 110
SIC 5013 Trailer parts & accessories; Trailer parts & accessories
Pt: Tom Ogburn
Off Mgr: Jerald Morris

D-U-N-S 02-644-8605 IMP
OGBURNS TRUCK PARTS LLC
900 E Northside Dr, Fort Worth, TX 76102-1019
Tel (817) 332-1511 *Founded/Ownrshp* 1965
Sales 30.0MM^E *EMP* 100
SIC 5013

OGDEN
See CHROMALOX INC

D-U-N-S 19-925-0119
OGDEN ARNOT MEDICAL CENTER
(*Suby of* ARNOT HEALTH INC) ★
600 Roe Ave, Elmira, NY 14905-1676
Tel (607) 737-4100 *Founded/Ownrshp* 1972
Sales 271.1MM *EMP* 2,400
SIC 8011 Medical centers; Medical centers
CEO: Robert Lambert
**CFO:* Ronald Kintz
VP: Wes Blauvelt
VP: Mary Vosburgh
Dir Lab: Barbara Lawrence
Dir Lab: Barry Winters
Dir Rx: William Bacon
Dir Rx: Hazel Boyd
Comm Man: Nancy Kujawski
Prgrm Mgr: Lucy Keith
Off Mgr: Lisa Donegan

D-U-N-S 18-435-3480
OGDEN CITY SCHOOL DISTRICT
1950 Monroe Blvd, Ogden, UT 84401-0619
Tel (801) 737-8000 *Founded/Ownrshp* 1955
Sales 115.9MM *EMP* 115
SIC 8211 Elementary & secondary schools; Public elementary school; Elementary & secondary schools; Public elementary school
Pr Dir: Zac Williams

D-U-N-S 07-298-0741
OGDEN CLINIC PROFESSIONAL CORP
4650 Harrison Blvd, Ogden, UT 84403-4303
Tel (801) 475-3000 *Founded/Ownrshp* 1950
Sales 37.2MM^E *EMP* 250^E
SIC 8011 Offices & clinics of medical doctors; Offices & clinics of medical doctors
CEO: Paul Schofield
Board of Directors: David Schmitz

D-U-N-S 16-181-7754
OGDEN HARMONS FIVE POINTS INC
(*Suby of* HARMON CITY INC) ★
145 N Harrisville Rd, Ogden, UT 84404-3927
Tel (801) 621-8700 *Founded/Ownrshp* 1977
Sales 23.9MM^E *EMP* 285
SIC 5411 Grocery stores, chain; Grocery stores, chain
Pr: Terry R Harmon
**Pr:* Dean Peterson
**Sec:* Doreen Harmon
**VP:* Darrell Jensen
Exec: Marlene Hadley
Genl Mgr: Jessica Darbonne
Store Mgr: Ryan Morris

OGDEN MARRIOTT
See MARRIOTT HOTELS INTERNATIONAL INC

D-U-N-S 00-431-9703
OGDEN NEWSPAPERS INC (WV)
INTELLIGENCER, THE
1500 Main St, Wheeling, WV 26003-2826
Tel (304) 233-0100 *Founded/Ownrshp* 1890
Sales 683.9MM^E *EMP* 3,520
SIC 2711 4833 2754 2741 2791 2752 Newspapers: publishing only, not printed on site; Television broadcasting stations; Job printing, gravure; Directories: publishing & printing; Typesetting; Commercial printing, lithographic; Newspapers: publishing only, not printed on site; Job printing, gravure; Directories: publishing & printing; Typesetting; Commercial printing, lithographic
Pr: Robert M Nutting
**Ch:* G Ogden Nutting
VP: Bart Leath
**VP:* William C Nutting
MIS Dir: Dave Frisch
IT Man: Cindy Gross
Software D: Shawn Roberts
Software D: Michael Smith
VP Mktg: John Ford
VP Mktg: Skip Schneider
VP Sls: Lori Figurski

D-U-N-S 80-265-6959
OGDEN PUBLISHING CORP
STANDARD-EXAMINER
(*Suby of* SANDUSKY NEWSPAPERS INC) ★
332 Standard Way, Ogden, UT 84404-1371
Tel (801) 625-4200 *Founded/Ownrshp* 1992
Sales 58.1MM^E *EMP* 402
SIC 2711 Newspapers, publishing & printing; Newspapers, publishing & printing
Pr: David Rau
**Treas:* Alice Rau
Advt Mgr: George Mesa
Sls Mgr: Kyle Ashby

OGDEN REGIONAL MEDICAL CENTER
See COLUMBIA OGDEN MEDICAL CENTER INC

D-U-N-S 00-513-6510 IMP/EXP
OGDEN WELDING SYSTEMS INC
372 Division St, Schererville, IN 46375-1223
Tel (219) 322-5252 *Founded/Ownrshp* 1963
Sales 21.0MM^E *EMP* 40
SIC 5084 3699 3548 3537 Industrial machinery & equipment; Electrical welding equipment; Welding apparatus; Industrial trucks & tractors
Pr: Jeffrey W Darnell
COO: David Rietman
**Treas:* Rose Mary Wellman
**Sr VP:* Gordon L Verbeek
Mktg Dir: Wayne Smith

D-U-N-S 08-516-7716
OGDENSBURG CITY SCHOOL DISTRICT
1100 State St, Ogdensburg, NY 13669-3352
Tel (315) 393-0900 *Founded/Ownrshp* 1900
Sales 15.6MM^E *EMP* 350
SIC 8211 Public elementary & secondary schools; High school, junior or senior; School board; Public elementary & secondary schools; High school, junior or senior; School board
Cmptr Lab: Patty Morrow

OGE ENERGY
See ENABLE OKLAHOMA INTRASTATE TRANSMISSION LLC

D-U-N-S 96-386-0044
▲ **OGE ENERGY CORP**
321 N Harvey Ave, Oklahoma City, OK 73102-3405
Tel (405) 553-3000 *Founded/Ownrshp* 1995
Sales 2.4MMM *EMP* 3,269^E

Tkr Sym OGE *Exch* NYS
SIC 4911 4922 4925 Distribution, electric power; Generation, electric power; Transmission, electric power; ; Natural gas transmission; Storage, natural gas; Gas production and/or distribution; Distribution, electric power; Generation, electric power; Transmission, electric power; ; Natural gas transmission; Storage, natural gas; Gas production and/or distribution
Pr: Sean Trauschke
Pr: E Keith Mitchell
CFO: Steve Merrill
CFO: Stephen E Mrrill
Treas: Deborah S Fleming
Treas: Charles B Walworth
Sr VP: Jack T Coffman
Sr VP: Stanley Rankin
VP: Patricia D Horn
VP: David J Kurtz
VP: Melvin Penkins
Board of Directors: Sheila G Talton, Frank A Bozich, James H Brandi, Luke R Corbett, Peter B Delaney, John D Groendyke, David L Hauser, Kirk Humphreys, Robert O Lorenz, Judy R McReynolds

D-U-N-S 18-878-1421
■ OGE ENERGY RESOURCES INC
(*Suby of* ENABLE OKLAHOMA INTRASTATE TRANSMISSION LLC) ★
211 N Robinson Ave, Oklahoma City, OK 73102-7109
Tel (405) 553-6400 *Founded/Ownrshp* 1986
Sales 20.2MM^E *EMP* 60
SIC 4911
Pr: Peter B Delaney
**COO:* Stephen E Merrill
**Treas:* James R Hatfield
Board of Directors: Carol Shoemake

OGIHARA AMERICA CO
See THAI SUMMIT AMERICA CORP

D-U-N-S 15-277-2315
OGILVY & MATHER WORLDWIDE INC
(*Suby of* WPP 2005 LIMITED)
636 11th Ave, New York, NY 10036-2005
Tel (212) 237-4000 *Founded/Ownrshp* 1989
Sales 730.4MM^E *EMP* 15,000
SIC 7311 7812 7375 8742 Advertising agencies; Motion picture & video production; Information retrieval services; Marketing consulting services; Advertising agencies; Motion picture & video production; Information retrieval services; Marketing consulting services
CEO: Miles Young
Sr Pt: Colin Drummond
Sr Pt: Gerri Stone
V Ch: Steve Hayden
Pr: Lee Newman
Pr: Jacco Ter Schegget
Pr: Gunther Schumacher
CEO: Lou Aversano
CEO: Steve Harding
CFO: Carla Hendra
CFO: Steve Goldstein
Ch: Christopher Graves
Ch: John Seifert
Sr Cor Off: Bob Donovan
Chf Cred: Chris Garbutt
Bd of Dir: Richard Wheaton
Ofcr: Marie-Claire Barker
Ofcr: Lars Bastholm
Ofcr: Matt Bonin
Ofcr: Graham Fink
Ex VP: Nelly Andersen
Board of Directors: Angel Chen, Sean Muzzy, Sam Williams-Thomas

OGILVY & MATHERS WORLDWIDE
See OGILVY GROUP LLC

OGILVY COMMON HEALTH
See OGILVY COMMONHEALTH WORLDWIDE LLC

D-U-N-S 07-516-2099
OGILVY COMMONHEALTH WORLDWIDE LLC
OGILVY COMMON HEALTH
(*Suby of* WPP GROUP USA INC) ★
446 Interpace Pkwy, Parsippany, NJ 07054-1116
Tel (973) 352-1000 *Founded/Ownrshp* 1999
Sales 59.4MM^E *EMP* 336^E
SIC 8742 Hospital & health services consultant
Mng Pt: Darlene Dobry
Pr: Paul O'Neill
Chf Cred: Diane Iler-Smith
Ofcr: Meredith Hamm
Ofcr: Janine Niemynski
Ex VP: Mary Anderson
Ex VP: Michele Andrews
Ex VP: Brian Doherty
Ex VP: Maggie Helmig
Ex VP: Laura Schember
Ex VP: Nancy Iler Sladicka
Ex VP: Johanna Tompetrini
Ex VP: Scott Watson
Ex VP: Andy Willmer
Sr VP: Lori Brown
Sr VP: Christopher Cullmann
**Sr VP:* David Danilowicz
Sr VP: Raghu Desikan
Sr VP: Robert Egert
Sr VP: Gregg Friedmann
Sr VP: Sean Hartigan

D-U-N-S 00-892-0233
OGILVY GROUP LLC
OGILVY & MATHERS WORLDWIDE
(*Suby of* WPP GROUP USA INC) ★
636 11th Ave, New York, NY 10036-2005
Tel (212) 237-4000 *Founded/Ownrshp* 2008
Sales 3.1MMM^E *EMP* 18,000
SIC 5045 8743 8748 7336 7361 8732 Computer software; Public relations & publicity; Communications consulting; Graphic arts & related design; Employment agencies; Market analysis or research; Computer software; Public relations & publicity; Communications consulting; Graphic arts & related design; Employment agencies; Market analysis or research
CEO: Miles Young
Sr Pt: Candice Marshall
Pt: Lauren Crampsie
Pt: Sue Funkhouser
Pt: Hilary Love
Pt: Jessica Pezzullo
**Ch Bd:* Rochelle Lazarus
**CFO:* Steven Goldstein
**Ofcr:* Corinna Falusi
Ex VP: Nelly Andersen
Ex VP: Amy Graham
Ex VP: Diane Iler-Smith
Ex VP: Chris Myles
Ex VP: Gordon Olsen
Ex VP: Sudha Singh
Ex VP: Jennifer Wayman
Assoc Dir: Daniel Brenikov
Assoc Dir: Manny Hernandez
Assoc Dir: Gregory Lefave
Assoc Dir: Cheryl Metzger
Assoc Dir: Peter Von Bartheld

D-U-N-S 09-296-8502
OGILVY PUBLIC RELATIONS WORLDWIDE INC
(*Suby of* WPP 2005 LTD)
636 11th Ave, New York, NY 10036-2005
Tel (212) 880-5200 *Founded/Ownrshp* 1989
Sales 99.5MM^E *EMP* 1,500
SIC 8743 8999 Public relations & publicity; Communication services; Public relations & publicity; Communication services
CEO: Christopher Graves
Sr Pt: Jesse Bayer
Ch Bd: Marcia Silverman
Pr: Mitch Markson
CEO: Paul Hicks
CFO: Andrew Kochar
Ex VP: Rachel Caggiano
Ex VP: Therese Caruso
Ex VP: Monique Da Silva
Ex VP: Patricia Galea
Ex VP: Jim Heininger
Ex VP: Suzanne O'Leary Lopez
Ex VP: Jenita McDaniel
Ex VP: Susan Peters
Ex VP: Bill Reihl
Ex VP: Michelle Rios
Ex VP: Lisa O Ross
Ex VP: Kerry Sette
Ex VP: Tony Silva
Ex VP: Andrew Silver
Ex VP: Eric Slutsky

D-U-N-S 92-955-4207
OGIN INC
FDWT
221 Crescent St Ste 103a, Waltham, MA 02453-3425
Tel (781) 609-4700 *Founded/Ownrshp* 2007
Sales 36.2MM^E *EMP* 81
SIC 8711 8731 Consulting engineer; Commercial physical research
CEO: Lars A Andersen
Pr: Patrick Kealy
COO: Gregers Baungaard
VP: Snehal Bhatt
VP: Heidi Carlsen
VP: Bob Dold
VP: John Howe
VP: Bob Kane
VP: John Kulungian
Dir Bus: Pawlowski Peter
Dir IT: Gregory Dunn

D-U-N-S 06-843-2975
OGLALA LAKOTA COLLEGE
490 Piya Wiconi Rd, Kyle, SD 57752
Tel (605) 455-6000 *Founded/Ownrshp* 1971
Sales 37.1MM *EMP* 198
SIC 8221 College, except junior; College, except junior
Pr: Thomas Shortbull
**VP:* Julie Johnson
VP: Matilda Montileaux
Exec: Joseph Bush
Store Mgr: Myreen Cloud

D-U-N-S 07-803-9765
OGLALA SIOUX TRIBE OF PINE RIDGE INDIAN RESERVATION (SD)
1 Blk E Of Hwy 18 87 Jct, Pine Ridge, SD 57770
Tel (605) 867-5821 *Founded/Ownrshp* 1936
Sales NA *EMP* 800^E
SIC 9131 Indian reservation; ; Indian reservation;
Pr: Cecilia Firethunder
**Treas:* Crystal Eagle Elk
**VP:* Alex Whiteplume

OGLEBAY PARK
See WHEELING PARK COMMISSION

D-U-N-S 10-333-6835
OGLEBAY RESORT CONFERENCE CENTER
Rr 88 Box N, Wheeling, WV 26003
Tel (304) 243-4063 *Founded/Ownrshp* 1925
Sales 1.8MM *EMP* 1,700
SIC 7011 7992 5812 Resort hotel, franchised; Public golf courses; Eating places; Resort hotel, franchised; Public golf courses; Eating places
CEO: Doug Dalby
V Ch: Wilbur Jones
Genl Mgr: Cathy Javorsky
CIO: David Holloway
Sales Exec: Deb Jones

D-U-N-S 09-163-1226
OGLESBY CONSTRUCTION INC
1600 Us Highway 20 W, Norwalk, OH 44857-9549
Tel (419) 668-8204 *Founded/Ownrshp* 1977
Sales 54.4MM *EMP* 25
Accts Van Dootingh Mosher Mellen &
SIC 1611 1721 Highway & street paving contractor; Pavement marking contractor; Highway & street paving contractor; Pavement marking contractor
Pr: Mason P Oglesby
**Sec:* Shirleen McQuerrey
Exec: Vicky Schnee
Off Mgr: Amanda Phillips

D-U-N-S 10-064-6215
OGLETHORPE COUNTY BOARD OF EDUCATION INC
735 Athens Rd, Lexington, GA 30648-1911
Tel (706) 743-8128 *Founded/Ownrshp* 1900
Sales 15.0MM^E *EMP* 325
Accts Russell W Hinton Cpa Cgfm
SIC 8211 Public elementary & secondary schools; Public elementary & secondary schools
VP Admn: Willie Gibson

D-U-N-S 07-979-9089
OGLETHORPE COUNTY SCHOOLS
735 Athens Rd, Lexington, GA 30648-1911
Tel (706) 743-8128 *Founded/Ownrshp* 2015
Sales 6.3MM^E *EMP* 372^E
SIC 8211 Public elementary & secondary schools

OGLETHORPE POWER
See CENTRAL GEORGIA ELECTRIC MEMBERSHIP CORP

D-U-N-S 07-346-0305 IMP
OGLETHORPE POWER CORP
2100 E Exch Pl Ste 203, Tucker, GA 30084
Tel (770) 270-7600 *Founded/Ownrshp* 1974
Sales 1.4MMM *EMP* 265^E
SIC 4911 Generation, electric power; Generation, electric power
Pr: Michael L Smith
**Ch Bd:* Bobby C Smith Jr
COO: Michael W Price
CFO: Elizabeth B Higgins
Ex VP: William F Ussery
Sr VP: W Clayton Robbins
Sr VP: Keith D Russell
Sr VP: Charles W Whitney
VP: Lori K Holt
IT Man: Richard Clark
Plnt Mgr: Joseph Duncan
Board of Directors: George L Weaver, C Hill Bentley, James I White, Ronald Duffey, M Anthony Ham, Ernest A Jakins III, Fred A McWhorter, Marshall S Millwood, Jeffrey W Murphy, Danny L Nichols, Sammy G Simonton

D-U-N-S 07-347-3167 IMP
OGLETHORPE UNIVERSITY INC
4484 Peachtree Rd Ne, Brookhaven, GA 30319-2797
Tel (404) 261-1441 *Founded/Ownrshp* 1913
Sales 42.6MM *EMP* 340
Accts Mauldin & Jenkins Llc Atlanta
SIC 8221 Colleges universities & professional schools; Colleges universities & professional schools
Pr: Lawrence Miller Schall
Pr: Colleen D'Alessandro
Pr: Terri Williams
COO: Cindy Vaios
**CFO:* Michael Horan
Chf Inves: Robert E Reiser Jr
VP: Wilton Heyliger
VP: Lucy Leusch
VP: Leusch Lucy
VP: Kevin Smyrl
CIO: Mike Gonsalves

D-U-N-S 08-342-1131
OGLETREE DEAKINS NASH SMOAK & STEWART PC
300 N Main St Ste 500, Greenville, SC 29601-2195
Tel (864) 241-1900 *Founded/Ownrshp* 1977
Sales 324.4MM^E *EMP* 1,308
SIC 8111

D-U-N-S 19-853-2442
OGLEVEE LTD
104 Rilla Dr, Connellsville, PA 15425-1825
Tel (724) 628-8360 *Founded/Ownrshp* 1984
Sales 44.3MM^E *EMP* 200
SIC 5193 0181 Nursery stock; Flowers: grown under cover (e.g. greenhouse production); Nursery stock; Flowers: grown under cover (e.g. greenhouse production)
Pr: Don Macintyre
**Pr:* Lou Schenck
**VP:* Richard Oglevee
Exec: Leo Rudnick
Dir IT: Rick Watson

D-U-N-S 00-788-9731
OGM LAND LLC
PERCHERON ENERGY
1904 W Grand Pkwy N, Katy, TX 77449-1599
Tel (281) 346-2300 *Founded/Ownrshp* 2000
Sales 30.0MM *EMP* 600^E
SIC 6211 Oil & gas lease brokers; Oil & gas lease brokers
Pr: Kathy Miller
CFO: Matthew Coulter
**VP:* Jeff Trlicek

D-U-N-S 02-887-7660
OGRADY PAVING INC
2513 Wyandotte St, Mountain View, CA 94043-2311
Tel (650) 966-1926 *Founded/Ownrshp* 1982
Sales 21.4MM^E *EMP* 110
SIC 1611 Surfacing & paving; Grading; Surfacing & paving; Grading
Pr: Thomas M O'Grady Jr
**Sec:* Celine Duran
**VP:* Craig Young
Mtls Mgr: Greg Moreau

D-U-N-S 16-916-9435
OGSYSTEMS LLC
14291 Pk Madow Dr Ste 100, Chantilly, VA 20151
Tel (703) 870-7552 *Founded/Ownrshp* 2004
Sales 64.4MM *EMP* 300
Accts Dembo Jones Healey Benningt
SIC 7379 Computer related consulting services; Computer related consulting services
CEO: Omar Balkissoon
**Pr:* Garrett Pagon
**CFO:* John Krobath

D-U-N-S 60-773-9547 IMP
OGURA CORP
(*Suby of* OGURA CLUTCH CO., LTD.)
55025 Gratiot Ave, Chesterfield, MI 48051-1249
Tel (586) 749-1900 *Founded/Ownrshp* 1988
Sales 30.6MM^E *EMP* 105
SIC 3714 5013 Clutches, motor vehicle; Clutches; Clutches, motor vehicle; Clutches
Ch Bd: Yasahiro Ogura
**Pr:* Hisashi Ukita
**V Ch Bd:* Masayoshi Takahashi
Dir IT: Meng Hang
Board of Directors: John Matthews, Timothy Teller

OH BOY OBERTO
See OBERTO SAUSAGE CO

O.H. KRUSE GRAIN AND MILLING
See WESTERN MILLING LLC

D-U-N-S 07-408-7099
OH MUHLENBERG LLC
OWENSBORO HEALTH MUHLENBERG CO
440 Hopkinsville St, Greenville, KY 42345-1124
Tel (270) 338-8000 *Founded/Ownrshp* 1938
Sales 35.8MM *EMP* 500
SIC 8062 General medical & surgical hospitals; General medical & surgical hospitals
CEO: Ed Heath
**Treas:* Lisa Hope
Dir Rx: Lynn Likins
Chf Nrs Of: Kathleen Mitchell
Off Mgr: Beverly Hall
Dir IT: Lois Hill
Mktg Dir: Charlotte Lewis

OHA INSTRUMENTS DIVISION
See REIS ENVIRONMENTAL INC

D-U-N-S 16-368-6277
▲ OHA INVESTMENT CORP
1114 Ave Of The Americas, New York, NY 10036-7703
Tel (212) 852-1900 *Founded/Ownrshp* 2004
Sales 22.1MM *EMP* 3^E
Tkr Sym OHAI *Exch* NGS
SIC 6726 Management investment funds, closed-end; Management investment funds, closed-end
Pr: Robert W Long
**Ch Bd:* Glenn R August
CFO: Cory E Gilbert
Chf Cred: Lisa R Price

D-U-N-S 06-119-0427
OHALLORAN INTERNATIONAL INC
3311 Adventureland Dr, Altoona, IA 50009-9593
Tel (515) 967-3300 *Founded/Ownrshp* 1981
Sales 39.1MM^E *EMP* 125
SIC 5088 Transportation equipment & supplies; Transportation equipment & supplies
Pr: James O Halloran Jr
CFO: James O'Halloran
**Treas:* Chris Bakkie
VP: Craig Brandt
**VP:* Steve Lavia
**VP:* Todd Meyer
Genl Mgr: Larry McBride
Store Mgr: Dave Schaer
Opers Mgr: Steve Hirschman

OHARA CHRYSLER DODGE JEEP RAM
See JOHN AKENS INC

D-U-N-S 18-005-0387 IMP
OHASHI TECHNICA USA INC
(*Suby of* OHASHI TECHNICA INC.)
111 Burrer Dr, Sunbury, OH 43074-9323
Tel (740) 965-5115 *Founded/Ownrshp* 1987
Sales 90.0MM *EMP* 70
SIC 5013 5072 3452 Automotive supplies & parts; Automotive supplies; Hardware; Bolts, nuts, rivets & washers
Pr: Hikaru Tateiwa
Treas: Trish Burnside
Sls Mgr: Ian McGregor

OHB
See ORLEANS CORP

D-U-N-S 01-751-3323
OHECK LLC (CA)
5830 Bickett St, Huntington Park, CA 90255-2627
Tel (323) 923-2700 *Founded/Ownrshp* 2012
Sales 25.1MM^E *EMP* 250
SIC 2386 Garments, leather; Garments, leather

D-U-N-S 06-827-4034
OHEL CHILDRENS HOME AND FAMILY SERVICES INC (NY)
4510 16th Ave, Brooklyn, NY 11204-1101
Tel (718) 851-6300 *Founded/Ownrshp* 1966
Sales 52.0MM *EMP* 200
Accts Weisermazars Llp New York Ny
SIC 8361 8322 Group foster home; Child related social services; Group foster home; Child related social services
CEO: David Mandel
**Pr:* Moishe Hellman
**COO:* Asher Fogel
**CFO:* Howard Lorch
Ex Dir: Esther Katz
Dir IT: Reuven Bell

OHFA
See OHIO HOUSING FINANCE AGENCY

D-U-N-S 09-774-3025
OHI
25 Freedom Pkwy, Hermon, ME 04401-1100
Tel (207) 989-4007 *Founded/Ownrshp* 1979
Sales 12.6MM *EMP* 310
SIC 8211 8059 School for the retarded; Home for the mentally retarded, exc. skilled or intermediate; School for the retarded; Home for the mentally retarded, exc. skilled or intermediate
CEO: Bonnie-Jean Brooks
CFO: Patricia Leathers
Dir IT: Craig Deschaine
IT Man: Richard Romero
Snr Mgr: Kathy Smith

D-U-N-S 07-997-5091
OHI PARENT INC
(Suby of KOHLBERG & CO) ★
111 Radio Circle Dr, Mount Kisco, NY 10549-2609
Tel (914) 241-7430 Founded/Ownrshp 2012
Sales 12.1MM^{E} EMP 2,103^{E}
SIC 7389
Pr: Ron Childress
CFO: Gary Edwards

D-U-N-S 01-840-7379
OHIGRO INC
6720 Gillette Rd, Waldo, OH 43356-9105
Tel (740) 726-2429 Founded/Ownrshp 1965
Sales 24.2MM EMP 36
Accts Brady Ware & Schoenfeld Colum
SIC 5191 5261 2875 0723 Fertilizer & fertilizer materials; Fertilizer; Fertilizers, mixing only; Crop preparation services for market; Fertilizer & fertilizer materials; Fertilizer; Fertilizers, mixing only; Crop preparation services for market
Pr: Jerry Ward
*Treas: Jeffrey Ward
*VP: James H Ward
Plnt Mgr: David Fierbaugh
Plnt Mgr: Jeffrey Schweinfurth

OHIO ADJUTANT GENERAL
See OHIO NATIONAL GUARD

OHIO AND INDIANA ROOFING CO
See BRUNS BUILDING & DEVELOPMENT CORP INC

D-U-N-S 08-322-1218 IMP
OHIO ASSOCIATED ENTERPRISES LLC
1382 W Jackson St, Painesville, OH 44077-1306
Tel (440) 354-2106 Founded/Ownrshp 1967
Sales 33.6MM^{E} EMP 180
SIC 3678 Electronic connectors; Electronic connectors
VP: John Hartman
Exec: Joan Venaleck
IT Man: Thomas Abunimeh
IT Man: Jeff Dutcher
IT Man: Janet Streiner
Mfg Mgr: Skid Yeary
Ql Cn Mgr: Pamela Usatch
S&M/VP: Steve Jones
Mktg Mgr: Jason Lippincott
Sales Asso: Elaine Frantz

D-U-N-S 07-564-5791
OHIO ASSOCIATION OF FOODBANKS
101 E Town St Ste 540, Columbus, OH 43215-5119
Tel (614) 221-4336 Founded/Ownrshp 1985
Sales 25.1MM EMP 32
Accts Hemphill & Associate Inc Col
SIC 8322 Meal delivery program; Meal delivery program
Ex Dir: Lisa Hamler Fugitt
Ex Dir: Julie Chase
Pr Dir: Dustin Speakman

D-U-N-S 08-383-5116
OHIO AUTO KOLOR INC (OH)
2600 Fisher Rd, Columbus, OH 43204-3564
Tel (614) 276-8700 Founded/Ownrshp 1976
Sales 39.2MM^{E} EMP 86
Accts Carter Feltner Cpa
SIC 5198 5013 Paints; Body repair or paint shop supplies, automotive
Pr: Charles Bumgarner
COO: Bumgarner Glenn
*Sec: Anne Bumgarner
*VP: Curtis Bumgarner
IT Man: Gary Bumbarner

D-U-N-S 07-502-9611
OHIO AUTOMOBILE CLUB
AAA
90 E Wilson Bridge Rd # 1, Worthington, OH 43085-2387
Tel (614) 431-7901 Founded/Ownrshp 1977
Sales 58.6MM^{E} EMP 620
SIC 8699 Automobile owners' association; Automobile owners' association
Pr: Mark Shaw
*COO: Tom Keyes

D-U-N-S 00-790-1093
■ **OHIO BELL TELEPHONE CO INC**
AT&T OHIO
(Suby of AT&T MIDWEST) ★
45 Erieview Plz, Cleveland, OH 44114-1801
Tel (216) 822-3439 Founded/Ownrshp 1984
Sales 812.9MM^{E} EMP 7,971
SIC 4813 8721 Local & long distance telephone communications; Local telephone communications; Voice telephone communications; Data telephone communications; Billing & bookkeeping service; Local & long distance telephone communications; Local telephone communications; Voice telephone communications; Data telephone communications; Billing & bookkeeping service

D-U-N-S 61-761-7571
OHIO BENEFIT GROUP LLC
(Suby of NEACE MUSSELMAN & MAYFIELD) ★
6050 Oak Tree Blvd Ste 50, Cleveland, OH 44131-6927
Tel (216) 328-1300 Founded/Ownrshp 2011
Sales NA EMP 59^{E}
SIC 6324 Health maintenance organization (HMO), insurance only
Prin: Jim Schulz

D-U-N-S 00-420-3550
OHIO BLOW PIPE CO
446 E 131st St, Cleveland, OH 44108-1684
Tel (216) 681-7379 Founded/Ownrshp 1967
Sales 27.4MM^{E} EMP 135
SIC 8711 3564 3444 Engineering services; Blowers & fans; Sheet metalwork
Pr: Edward Fakeris
*CFO: Lisa Kern
*VP: William Roberts

D-U-N-S 01-756-6688 EXP
OHIO BRIDGE CORP (OH)
U.S. BRIDGE
201 Wheeling Ave, Cambridge, OH 43725-2256
Tel (740) 432-6334 Founded/Ownrshp 1952
Sales 73.3MM^{E} EMP 140
SIC 1622 Bridge construction; Bridge construction
CEO: Arthur Rogovin
*Pr: Daniel Rogovin
CFO: Bob Donelan
*Ch: Richard Rogovin
VP: Dan Rogovin
VP: Rajat Shah
CIO: Rod Lemasters
Plnt Mgr: Bob Huhn

D-U-N-S 62-708-2209
OHIO BUREAU OF WORKERS COMPENSATION
(Suby of EXECUTIVE OFFICE STATE OF OHIO) ★
30 W Spring St Fl 2-29, Columbus, OH 43215-2216
Tel (614) 644-6292 Founded/Ownrshp 1911
Sales NA EMP 3,000
Accts Schneider Downs & Co Inc C
SIC 6331 9199 Workers' compensation insurance; General government administration; Workers' compensation insurance; General government administration
Bd of Dir: Robert Smith
Comm Dir: Bill Tetts
Ex Dir: Bernard Susko
IT Man: King Hill
IT Man: Keith Reiley

D-U-N-S 00-806-9534
OHIO BUSINESS DEVELOPMENT COALITION
41 S High St Ste 3625, Columbus, OH 43215-6112
Tel (614) 469-1044 Founded/Ownrshp 2007
Sales 390.3MM EMP 2^{E}
Accts Rea & Associates Inc Cpa S Du
SIC 8611 Business associations
Prin: Richard Stoff

D-U-N-S 11-773-6301
OHIO BUSINESS MACHINES LLC
O B M
1111 Superior Ave E # 105, Cleveland, OH 44114-2522
Tel (216) 485-2000 Founded/Ownrshp 2002
Sales 42.3MM^{E} EMP 50
SIC 5044 7629 5734 Office equipment; Business machine repair, electric; Computer & software stores
Sls Mgr: Janine Neal

D-U-N-S 78-657-0494
OHIO CARPENTERS PENSION FUND
3611 Chester Ave, Cleveland, OH 44114-4622
Tel (330) 652-3475 Founded/Ownrshp 2006
Sales 111.5MM EMP 7^{E}
Accts Ciuni & Panichi Inc Beachwood
SIC 6722 Management investment, open-end; Management investment, open-end
Prin: Roger Newman

D-U-N-S 05-444-0920
OHIO CASUALTY CORP
(Suby of LIBERTY MUTUAL INSURANCE CO) ★
9450 Seward Rd, Fairfield, OH 45014-5412
Tel (513) 603-2400 Founded/Ownrshp 2007
Sales NA EMP 2,114
SIC 6331 Fire, marine & casualty insurance: stock; Property damage insurance; Automobile insurance; Workers' compensation insurance; Fire, marine & casualty insurance: stock; Property damage insurance; Automobile insurance; Workers' compensation insurance
Pr: Mike Winner
Treas: Kelly Hicks
Ex VP: John S Buby
Sr VP: Elizabeth M Riczko
Sr VP: Derrick D Shannon
VP: John Baird
VP: Dennis McDaniel
VP: Cassy Morgan
VP: Howard Sloneker
Dir IT: John Hoffmann
IT Man: Susan Parsons

OHIO CASUALTY INSURANCE
See OHIO NATIONAL LIFE INSURANCE CO

D-U-N-S 00-790-3040
OHIO CASUALTY INSURANCE CO
(Suby of OHIO CASUALTY CORP) ★
9450 Seward Rd, Fairfield, OH 45014-5412
Tel (513) 867-3000 Founded/Ownrshp 1970
Sales NA EMP 2,114
SIC 6331 6311 Fire, marine & casualty insurance; Workers' compensation insurance; Fire, marine & casualty insurance: stock; Life insurance carriers; Fire, marine & casualty insurance; Workers' compensation insurance; Fire, marine & casualty insurance: stock; Life insurance carriers
CEO: Dan R Carmichael
COO: Cindy Cox
*Sr VP: Debra K Crane
*Sr VP: Ralph G Goode
*Sr VP: John S Kellington
*Sr VP: Thomas E Schadler
Sr VP: Howard Slonecker
*Sr VP: Howard L Sloneker III
*Sr VP: Michael E Sullivan

D-U-N-S 80-592-0543
OHIO CHRISTIAN UNIVERSITY
EVANGELICAL ADVOCATE, THE
(Suby of CHURCHES OF CHRIST IN CHRISTIAN UNION) ★
1476 Lancaster Pike, Circleville, OH 43113-9487
Tel (740) 474-8896 Founded/Ownrshp 1947
Sales 38.1MM EMP 80^{E}
Accts Whited Seigneur Sams & Rahe Cp
SIC 8221 8299 Colleges universities & professional schools; Religious school; Colleges universities & professional schools; Religious school
Pr: Mark A Smith
*Ex VP: Henry Kelly
VP: Ricky Christman
VP: Curtis Christopher
VP: John Maxwell
*VP: Rob Partman
VP: Bradford Sample
VP: Mark Taylor
VP: Cynthia Tweedell
CTO: Tricia Lucas
IT Man: Ted Perry

OHIO COMMUNITY MEDIA
See OCM LLC

D-U-N-S 96-422-1746
OHIO CONFERENCE OF TEAMSTERS AND INDUSTRY HEALTH AND WELFARE TRUST
435 S Hawley St, Toledo, OH 43609-2344
Tel (419) 243-8800 Founded/Ownrshp 2010
Sales 32.6MM EMP 3
Accts Lublinsussman Group Llp Toled
SIC 8631 Labor unions & similar labor organizations; Labor unions & similar labor organizations

D-U-N-S 83-165-6389
OHIO CONNECTIONS ACADEMY INC
3740 Euclid Ave Ste 101, Cleveland, OH 44115-2229
Tel (216) 361-9460 Founded/Ownrshp 2009
Sales 21.5MM EMP 153
SIC 8211 Public elementary & secondary schools; Public elementary & secondary schools

D-U-N-S 07-748-7916
OHIO COUNTY BOARD OF EDUCATION
2203 National Rd, Wheeling, WV 26003-5203
Tel (304) 243-0300 Founded/Ownrshp 1863
Sales 71.4MM EMP 800
Accts Tetrick & Bartlett Pllc Clar
SIC 8211 Public elementary & secondary schools; School board
Pr: Christine Carder

D-U-N-S 09-895-6212
OHIO COUNTY BOARD OF EDUCATION
315 E Union St, Hartford, KY 42347-1139
Tel (270) 298-3249 Founded/Ownrshp 1920
Sales 36.0MM^{E} EMP 871
SIC 8211 Public elementary & secondary schools; High school, junior or senior; Public elementary & secondary schools; High school, junior or senior
*CFO: Brian Decker

D-U-N-S 96-344-2863
OHIO COUNTY HOSPITAL
1211 Old Main St, Hartford, KY 42347-1619
Tel (270) 298-7411 Founded/Ownrshp 2010
Sales 30.1MM EMP 5^{E}
SIC 8082 Home health care services
VP: Jane Canary

D-U-N-S 07-404-7184
OHIO COUNTY HOSPITAL CORP
1211 Old Main St, Hartford, KY 42347-1619
Tel (270) 298-7411 Founded/Ownrshp 1955
Sales 29.1MM EMP 175
SIC 8062 8621 General medical & surgical hospitals; Professional membership organizations; General medical & surgical hospitals; Professional membership organizations
Ofcr: Blaine Pieper
Pr: Michelle Hickerson
*CFO: John Tichenor
Exec: Sue Wydick
Dir Lab: Sara Hall
Dir Rad: Kathi Yeiser
Dir Rx: Tony Ward
Off Mgr: Melinda Fields
Off Mgr: Shelly Taylor
MIS Dir: Cynthia Barrow
IT Man: Cydnee Cook

D-U-N-S 07-979-8761
OHIO COUNTY SCHOOLS
2203 National Rd, Wheeling, WV 26003-5203
Tel (304) 243-0300 Founded/Ownrshp 2015
Sales 7.0MM^{E} EMP 765^{E}
SIC 8211 Public elementary & secondary schools

D-U-N-S 07-982-7423
OHIO COUNTY SCHOOLS
315 E Union St, Hartford, KY 42347-1139
Tel (270) 298-3249 Founded/Ownrshp 2015
Sales 20.1MM^{E} EMP 540^{E}
SIC 8211 Public elementary & secondary schools

OHIO CUT SHEET
See DUPLI-SYSTEMS INC

D-U-N-S 02-276-2331
■ **OHIO CVS STORES LLC**
(Suby of CVS HEALTH CORP) ★
641 Graham Rd, Cuyahoga Falls, OH 44221-1048
Tel (330) 922-1298 Founded/Ownrshp 2009
Sales 33.3MM^{E} EMP 5^{E}
SIC 5912 Proprietary (non-prescription medicine) stores

D-U-N-S 00-503-6264 IMP/EXP
OHIO DECORATIVE PRODUCTS LLC (OH)
220 S Elizabeth St, Spencerville, OH 45887-1315
Tel (419) 647-9033 Founded/Ownrshp 1970
Sales 384.9MM^{E} EMP 1,200
SIC 3086 3369 3471 3363 Plastics foam products; Zinc & zinc-base alloy castings, except die-castings; Plating & polishing; Aluminum die-castings; Plastics foam products; Zinc & zinc-base alloy castings, except die-castings; Plating & polishing; Aluminum die-castings
Pr: Charles D Moeller
*Pr: Candace Moeller
*Sec: Donald L Jerwers
*VP: Rick Moeller
*Prin: George J Bowers
*Prin: Charles E Neuman
Plnt Mgr: Sonny Degan

D-U-N-S 80-884-7578
OHIO DEPARTMENT OF ADMINISTRATIVE SERVICES
(Suby of EXECUTIVE OFFICE STATE OF OHIO) ★
30 E Broad St Fl 39, Columbus, OH 43215-3414
Tel (614) 466-6511 Founded/Ownrshp 1973
Sales NA EMP 5,731
SIC 9199 General government administration; ; General government administration;
IT Man: Jim Arens
IT Man: Scott Feilhamer

D-U-N-S 80-884-7628
OHIO DEPARTMENT OF AGRICULTURE
(Suby of EXECUTIVE OFFICE STATE OF OHIO) ★
8995 E Main St, Reynoldsburg, OH 43068-3342
Tel (614) 728-6201 Founded/Ownrshp 1921
Sales NA EMP 468^{E}
SIC 9641 Regulation of agricultural marketing; ; Regulation of agricultural marketing;
*CFO: Laura Dodson

D-U-N-S 80-955-0163
OHIO DEPARTMENT OF DEVELOPMENTAL DISABILITIES
DODD
(Suby of EXECUTIVE OFFICE STATE OF OHIO) ★
30 E Broad St Fl 13, Columbus, OH 43215-3414
Tel (614) 728-5544 Founded/Ownrshp 1838
Sales NA EMP 5,000
SIC 9441 Administration of social & manpower programs; Administration of social & manpower programs;
Ofcr: Paul Jarvis
Snr Mgr: Stuart Davis

D-U-N-S 80-937-6072
OHIO DEPARTMENT OF JOB AND FAMILY SERVICES
ODJFS
(Suby of EXECUTIVE OFFICE STATE OF OHIO) ★
30 E Broad St Fl 32, Columbus, OH 43215-3414
Tel (614) 466-6282 Founded/Ownrshp 1937
Sales NA EMP 3,600
SIC 9441 Administration of social & human resources;
Snr Mgr: Debbie Clement

D-U-N-S 80-955-0106
OHIO DEPARTMENT OF MENTAL HEALTH & ADDICTION SERVICES
MHAS
(Suby of EXECUTIVE OFFICE STATE OF OHIO) ★
30 E Broad St Fl 8, Columbus, OH 43215-3414
Tel (614) 466-2337 Founded/Ownrshp 1838
Sales 81.5MM^{E} EMP 2,500
SIC 8052 Home for the mentally retarded, with health care; Home for the mentally retarded, with health care
COO: Kelly Markins
Pharmcst: Yolanda Beltran
Pharmcst: Dean Brill
Pharmcst: Curtis Engel
Pharmcst: Denise Nauman

D-U-N-S 80-884-7669
OHIO DEPARTMENT OF MENTAL HEALTH AND ADDICTION SERVICES
(Suby of EXECUTIVE OFFICE STATE OF OHIO) ★
30 E Broad St Fl 11, Columbus, OH 43215-3414
Tel (614) 466-2337 Founded/Ownrshp 1989
Sales NA EMP 3,000
SIC 9431 Administration of public health programs; ; Administration of public health programs;
Off Mgr: Michele Sherman

D-U-N-S 80-917-2638 IMP
OHIO DEPARTMENT OF NATURAL RESOURCES
(Suby of EXECUTIVE OFFICE STATE OF OHIO) ★
2045 Morse Rd Bldg D-3, Columbus, OH 43229-6605
Tel (614) 265-6875 Founded/Ownrshp 1949
Sales NA EMP 2,000
SIC 9512 Land, mineral & wildlife conservation; ; Land, mineral & wildlife conservation;

D-U-N-S 80-884-7842
OHIO DEPARTMENT OF PUBLIC SAFETY
(Suby of EXECUTIVE OFFICE STATE OF OHIO) ★
1970 W Broad St Fl 5, Columbus, OH 43223-1102
Tel (614) 466-3383 Founded/Ownrshp 1925
Sales NA EMP 4,000
SIC 9229 Public order & safety statistics centers; ; Public order & safety statistics centers;
Ofcr: Rich Nagel
CIO: Ken Kreitel
Telecom Mg: Lori Click
Telecom Mg: Lydia Wagner
Netwrk Mgr: Kathy Bryan

D-U-N-S 80-917-4501
OHIO DEPARTMENT OF REHABILITATION AND CORRECTION
(Suby of EXECUTIVE OFFICE STATE OF OHIO) ★
770 W Broad St, Columbus, OH 43222-1419
Tel (614) 752-1233 Founded/Ownrshp 1972
Sales NA EMP 13,600
SIC 9223 Prison, government; ; Prison, government;
Ofcr: Matt Cook
Ofcr: Eric Gaumer
Ofcr: Karen McGrath
Counsel: Stephen Young
Snr Mgr: Mike Mouser

D-U-N-S 80-917-2356
OHIO DEPARTMENT OF TAXATION
(Suby of EXECUTIVE OFFICE STATE OF OHIO) ★
30 E Broad St Fl 22, Columbus, OH 43215-3414
Tel (614) 466-3020 Founded/Ownrshp 1939
Sales NA EMP 1,300
SIC 9311 Taxation; ; Taxation;

D-U-N-S 80-917-4402
OHIO DEPARTMENT OF TRANSPORTATION
EXECUTIVE OFFICE
(*Suby of* EXECUTIVE OFFICE STATE OF OHIO) ★
1980 W Broad St, Columbus, OH 43223-1102
Tel (614) 466-7170 *Founded/Ownrshp* 1975
Sales NA *EMP* 6,500
SIC 9621 Regulation, administration of transportation; ; Regulation, administration of transportation;
Ex Dir: Matthew Dietrich
CIO: Chris Chapman
Dir IT: Spencer Woods
IT Man: Marvin Harris

D-U-N-S 08-216-7177
OHIO DEPARTMENT OF VETERANS SERVICES
(*Suby of* EXECUTIVE OFFICE STATE OF OHIO) ★
3416 Columbus Ave, Sandusky, OH 44870-5557
Tel (419) 625-2454 *Founded/Ownrshp* 1993
Sales 199.2M *EMP* 800
SIC 8051 Skilled nursing care facilities; Skilled nursing care facilities
Off Mgr: Tom Mcfarland

D-U-N-S 80-917-2653
OHIO DEPARTMENT OF YOUTH SERVICES
BUCKEYE UNITED SCHOOL DISTRICT
(*Suby of* EXECUTIVE OFFICE STATE OF OHIO) ★
30 W Spring St Fl 5, Columbus, OH 43215-2241
Tel (614) 466-8660 *Founded/Ownrshp* 1983
Sales NA *EMP* 2,200
SIC 9441 Administration of social & manpower programs; ; Administration of social & manpower programs;
Ex Dir: Harvey Reed
Ofcr: James Rice

D-U-N-S 00-452-2975
OHIO DESK CO (OH)
1122 Prospect Ave E, Cleveland, OH 44115-1292
Tel (216) 623-0600 *Founded/Ownrshp* 1908
Sales 32.7MM^E^ *EMP* 95
SIC 5021

D-U-N-S 80-884-7743
OHIO DEVELOPMENT SERVICES AGENCY
ODSA
(*Suby of* EXECUTIVE OFFICE STATE OF OHIO) ★
77 S High St Fl 29, Columbus, OH 43215-6108
Tel (614) 466-3379 *Founded/Ownrshp* 1985
Sales NA *EMP* 475^E^
SIC 9441 Administration of social & human resources; ; Administration of social & human resources;
V Ch: Joseph Uecker
Ofcr: Stephanie Gostomski
Ofcr: Randy Hochstetter
Snr Mgr: Candace Jones

D-U-N-S 84-750-5724
OHIO DISTRICT 5 AREA AGENCY ON AGING INC
2131 Park Ave W, Ontario, OH 44906-1226
Tel (419) 522-5612 *Founded/Ownrshp* 1989
Sales 37.5MM *EMP* 103
SIC 8322 Individual & family services; Individual & family services
COO: James Hairston
Board of Directors: Jim Hairston, Duana Patton

D-U-N-S 07-500-2576
OHIO DOMINICAN UNIVERSITY
1216 Sunbury Rd, Columbus, OH 43219-2099
Tel (614) 253-2741 *Founded/Ownrshp* 1911
Sales 53.1MM *EMP* 300^E^
Accts Crowe Horwath Llp Columbus O
SIC 8221 8661 University; Religious organizations; University; Religious organizations
Ch: Ronald J Seifferg
**Pr:* Peter Cimbolic
**VP:* Michael Bromberg
**VP:* Lynda Huey
**VP:* James Sagona
**Prin:* Jack Calareso

D-U-N-S 00-699-8371
■ **OHIO EDISON CO** (OH)
(*Suby of* FIRSTENERGY CORP) ★
76 S Main St Bsmt, Akron, OH 44308-1817
Tel (800) 736-3402 *Founded/Ownrshp* 1930
Sales 644.6MM^E^ *EMP* 1,190^E^
Accts Pricewaterhousecoopes Lp Clev
SIC 4911 Electric services; Generation, electric power; Transmission, electric power; Distribution, electric power; Electric services; Generation, electric power; Transmission, electric power; Distribution, electric power
Pr: Charles E Jones Jr
CFO: R H Marsh
CFO: James F Pearson
Ex VP: Leila L Vespoli
VP: Harvey L Wagner
Board of Directors: Anthony J Alexander, Mark T Clark

D-U-N-S 04-642-4446
OHIO EDUCATION ASSOCIATION INC
225 E Broad St Fl 2, Columbus, OH 43215-3709
Tel (614) 228-4526 *Founded/Ownrshp* 1924
Sales 58.6MM^E^ *EMP* 228
Accts Clark Schaefer Hackett & Co C
SIC 8631 Labor union; Labor union
Pr: Patricia F Brooks
**Treas:* Jim Timlin
Treas: Joyce Wisebaker
VP: Bill Liebensperger
VP: Pete Scully
Ex Dir: David Bowen
Ex Dir: William Lavezzi
Ex Dir: Bruce Rostetter
**Ex Dir:* Larry Wicks
Genl Couns: Linda Fiely

OHIO ELECTRIC MOTORS
See PEERLESS-WINSMITH INC

D-U-N-S 05-223-3042
OHIO ENVIRONMENTAL PROTECTION AGENCY
50 W Town St Ste 700, Columbus, OH 43215-4173
Tel (614) 644-3020 *Founded/Ownrshp* 1972
Sales NA *EMP* 1,100^E^
SIC 9511 Environmental protection agency, government; Environmental protection agency, government
IT Man: Antionette Antion

OHIO ENVMTL PROTECTION AGCY
See STATE OF OHIO OFFICE OF BUDGET AND MANAGEMENT STATE ACCOUNTING

D-U-N-S 00-790-3263
OHIO FARMERS INSURANCE CO
WEST FIELD GROUP
1 Park Cir, Westfield Center, OH 44251-9700
Tel (800) 243-0210 *Founded/Ownrshp* 1848
Sales NA *EMP* 2,319
SIC 6411 6331 Property & casualty insurance agent; Fire, marine & casualty insurance; Property & casualty insurance agent; Fire, marine & casualty insurance
Pr: Robert Joyce
Pr: Jim Clay
COO: Roger McManus
Treas: Robert Krisowaty
Ofcr: Ed Largent
Dir Soc: Allison To
Prin: Robert J Joyce
CTO: Stuart Rosenberg
IT Man: Thomas Acchione
Snr Mgr: Kerri Harris
Snr Mgr: Cathy Todd

D-U-N-S 04-963-2552
OHIO FARMERS INSURANCE CO INC
WESTFIELD GROUP
(*Suby of* OHIO FARMERS INSURANCE CO) ★
201 E Oregon Rd, Lititz, PA 17543-7439
Tel (717) 569-5361 *Founded/Ownrshp* 2000
Sales NA *EMP* 155
SIC 6331 Fire, marine & casualty insurance; Fire, marine & casualty insurance
Trst Ofcr: Christine Tomion
Exec: Donald Manley
Opers Mgr: Jennifer Monastra
Manager: James Buzzard

D-U-N-S 11-851-4835 IMP
OHIO FRESH EGGS LLC
11212 Croton Rd, Croton, OH 43013-9725
Tel (740) 893-7200 *Founded/Ownrshp* 1984
Sales 112.3MM^E^ *EMP* 250
SIC 5144 2015 Eggs; Egg processing; Eggs; Egg processing
Genl Mgr: Donald Hersey

D-U-N-S 00-377-9345
■ **OHIO GAS CO** (OH)
(*Suby of* NWO RESOURCES INC) ★
200 W High St, Bryan, OH 43506-1677
Tel (419) 636-1117 *Founded/Ownrshp* 1914, 1985
Sales 38.3MM^E^ *EMP* 88
SIC 4924 Natural gas distribution; Natural gas distribution
Pr: Richard Hallett
**VP:* Bob Eyre
**VP:* Douglas Saul
**VP:* Dee Swanson
**VP:* Kim Watkins
Sys Admin: Don Rice

D-U-N-S 05-293-1938 EXP
OHIO GRATINGS INC (OH)
5299 Southway St Sw, Canton, OH 44706-1992
Tel (330) 477-6707 *Founded/Ownrshp* 1970
Sales 95.4MM^E^ *EMP* 323
SIC 3446 3444 3441 3312 Gratings, open steel flooring; Open flooring & grating for construction; Sheet metalwork; Fabricated structural metal; Blast furnaces & steel mills; Gratings, open steel flooring; Open flooring & grating for construction; Sheet metalwork; Fabricated structural metal; Blast furnaces & steel mills
Pr: John Bartley
**Ch Bd:* David Bartley
COO: Shawn King
**VP:* Ronald Lenney
Sales Exec: Kevin Collins
Mktg Dir: Carl Griffin

OHIO HEALTH
See DOCTORS HOSPITAL OF CLEVELAND INC

D-U-N-S 00-196-0954
OHIO HISTORICAL SOCIETY (OH)
OHIO HISTORY CONNECTION
800 E 17th Ave, Columbus, OH 43211-2497
Tel (614) 297-2300 *Founded/Ownrshp* 1885
Sales 19.6MM *EMP* 290
Accts Rea & Associates Inc Dublin
SIC 8412 Museum; Museum
Pr: Glenda S Greenwood
**Treas:* Thomas W Johnson
**VP:* Ronald J Ungvarsky
Ex Dir: Debra Huff
**Ex Dir:* Burt Logan
IT Man: Barbara Weisenberger

OHIO HISTORY CONNECTION
See OHIO HISTORICAL SOCIETY

D-U-N-S 60-361-1216
OHIO HOUSING FINANCE AGENCY
OHFA
57 E Main St Fl 3, Columbus, OH 43215-5135
Tel (614) 466-7970 *Founded/Ownrshp* 2005
Sales NA *EMP* 340
Accts Kennedy Cottrell Richards Ll
SIC 9531 Housing authority, non-operating: government; Housing authority, non-operating: government
CEO: Blaine Brockman
**Ex Dir:* Douglas A Garver
CTO: Donna Cramblit

OHIO LEARNING
See SMART SOLUTIONS INC

D-U-N-S 96-633-0982
OHIO LIFE AND HEALTH INSURANCE GUARANTY
1840 Mackenzie Dr, Columbus, OH 43220-2980
Tel (614) 442-6601 *Founded/Ownrshp* 2011
Sales NA *EMP* 2
Accts Irwin Financial Associates Inc
SIC 6411 Insurance agents, brokers & service
Prin: Frank Gartland

OHIO LOGISTICS
See FINDLAYS TALL TIMBERS DISTRIBUTION CENTER INC

D-U-N-S 00-790-1101 IMP
OHIO MACHINERY CO
CATERPILLAR
3993 E Royalton Rd, Broadview Heights, OH 44147-2898
Tel (440) 526-6200 *Founded/Ownrshp* 1961
Sales 229.0MM^E^ *EMP* 1,050
SIC 7513 6159 7699 5082 7353 Truck rental, without drivers; Machinery & equipment finance leasing; Aircraft & heavy equipment repair services; Construction equipment repair; General construction machinery & equipment; Mining machinery & equipment, except petroleum; Heavy construction equipment rental; Truck rental, without drivers; Machinery & equipment finance leasing; Aircraft & heavy equipment repair services; Construction equipment repair; General construction machinery & equipment; Mining machinery & equipment, except petroleum; Heavy construction equipment rental
Pr: Ken Taylor
**CFO:* David J Blocksom
**VP:* Eric W Emch
**VP:* Paul Liesem
**VP:* Kelly Love
Exec: Rick Ragstack
Brnch Mgr: Tim Wagner
Genl Mgr: Gabe Hoffa
Dir IT: Kevin O'Callaghan
Tech Mgr: Terry Comer
Web Dev: William Smith

D-U-N-S 07-503-5931
OHIO MASONIC HOME
2655 W National Rd, Springfield, OH 45504-3617
Tel (937) 325-1531 *Founded/Ownrshp* 1890
Sales 27.4MM *EMP* 148^E^
SIC 8741 Nursing & personal care facility management
CEO: William David Bannerman
**CEO:* Marion Leeman
COO: Gregory F Holm
**COO:* Michael Williams
CFO: Scott Buchanan
CFO: Lesha A Thorpe
**CFO:* John White
CTO: Marilyn London
Sls&Mrk Ex: Jerry Guess

D-U-N-S 96-779-0234
OHIO MASONIC HOME BENEVOLENT ENDOWMENT FOUNDATION INC
5 Masonic Dr, Springfield, OH 45504-3658
Tel (937) 525-3003 *Founded/Ownrshp* 2011
Sales 21.6MM *EMP* 3
Accts Howard Wershbale & Co Clevela
SIC 8641 Civic associations; Civic associations
Prin: Linda Gast

OHIO MATERIALS HANDLING
See NEWTOWN NINE INC

D-U-N-S 00-543-8262 IMP/EXP
■ **OHIO MATTRESS CO LICENSING AND COMPONENTS GROUP**
(*Suby of* TEMPUR SEALY INTERNATIONAL INC) ★
1 Office Parkway Rd, Trinity, NC 27370-9449
Tel (336) 861-3500 *Founded/Ownrshp* 1933, 2013
Sales 328.0MM^E^ *EMP* 1,550
SIC 2515 6794 Box springs, assembled; Franchises, selling or licensing; Box springs, assembled; Franchises, selling or licensing
Pr: Lawrence Rogers
**VP:* Kenneth L Walker
VP Sls: Gary Fazio

D-U-N-S 92-890-5157
OHIO MEDICAL TRANSPORTATION INC
MEDFLIGHT OF OHIO
2827 W Dblin Granville Rd, Columbus, OH 43235-2712
Tel (614) 791-4400 *Founded/Ownrshp* 1995
Sales 40.2MM *EMP* 200
Accts Plante & Moran Pllc Columbus
SIC 4522 4119 Ambulance services, air; Ambulance service; Ambulance services, air; Ambulance service
Pr: Rod Crane
**CFO:* Charles E Ansley
CFO: John Lindaman
**Chf Cred:* Thomas E Allenstein
Web Dev: Angelique Roy
Sfty Mgr: Sam Kennedy
Genl Couns: Linda Hines
Snr Mgr: Tom Allenstein

D-U-N-S 96-259-7050 IMP
OHIO METAL TECHNOLOGIES INC
470 John Alford Pkwy, Hebron, OH 43025-9437
Tel (740) 928-8288 *Founded/Ownrshp* 1996
Sales 29.5MM^E^ *EMP* 80
SIC 3462 Automotive & internal combustion engine forgings
Pr: Toshi Hara
**Treas:* Toshiyuki Hara
**VP:* Masao Segawa
Genl Mgr: Chuck Shearer

D-U-N-S 36-160-0773 IMP/EXP
OHIO MODULE MANUFACTURING CO LLC
M N A
3900 Stickney Ave, Toledo, OH 43608-1314
Tel (419) 729-6700 *Founded/Ownrshp* 2005
Sales NA *EMP* 706
SIC 3711

D-U-N-S 00-417-4868 IMP
OHIO MOULDING CORP
(*Suby of* OMCO HOLDINGS INC) ★
30396 Lakeland Blvd, Wickliffe, OH 44092-1798
Tel (440) 944-2100 *Founded/Ownrshp* 1979
Sales 56.4MM^E^ *EMP* 150
SIC 3449

D-U-N-S 13-188-1609
OHIO MULCH SUPPLY INC
1600 Universal Rd, Columbus, OH 43207-1733
Tel (614) 445-4455 *Founded/Ownrshp* 1984
Sales 42.6MM^E^ *EMP* 112
SIC 0782 Garden planting services
Pr: James A Weber II
CFO: Samuel J Agresti
**Prin:* Anthony S Elia
**Prin:* Ralph T Spencer
Store Mgr: Bill Gorby
Store Mgr: Travis Hines
Opers Mgr: Allyn Blakely
Sls Dir: Ron Frost

D-U-N-S 04-635-9444
OHIO MUTUAL INSURANCE CO
1725 Hopley Ave, Bucyrus, OH 44820-3596
Tel (419) 562-3011 *Founded/Ownrshp* 1901
Sales NA *EMP* 186
SIC 6411 6331 Insurance brokers; Fire, marine & casualty insurance: mutual; Fire, marine & casualty insurance: stock; Insurance brokers; Fire, marine & casualty insurance: mutual; Fire, marine & casualty insurance: stock
Pr: Jim Kennedy
Pr: Brad McCormack
**CFO:* David Hendrix
**VP:* Todd Albert
**VP:* Michael Brogan
VP: Michael A Brogan
VP: Marsha Clady
VP: Kathy Guinther
**VP:* Thomas Holtshouse
**VP:* Mike Horvath
**VP:* Randy O'Conner
VP: Randu Oconner

D-U-N-S 00-699-9718
OHIO NATIONAL FINANCIAL SERVICES INC
(*Suby of* OHIO NATIONAL MUTUAL HOLDINGS INC) ★
1 Financial Way Ste 100, Montgomery, OH 45242-5852
Tel (513) 794-6100 *Founded/Ownrshp* 1959
Sales NA *EMP* 800
SIC 6311 Mutual association life insurance; Mutual association life insurance
Pr: Gary T Huffman
**V Ch:* Ronald Dolan
Pr: Leigh Morgan
Pr: Traci Nelson
**Pr:* Arthur J Roberts
CFO: Adam J Hicks
Ex VP: Thomas Barefield
Ex VP: Nancy Dalessio
**Sr VP:* Larry J Adams
Sr VP: Allen R Bowen
Sr VP: George B Pearson
VP: Joseph Brom
VP: John Mulhall
VP: Brady Serold
VP: Tim Stephens
VP: Dennis Taney
VP: Gwen Vaught
Exec: Jackie Hammond
Comm Dir: Carrie Stigler
Board of Directors: Gary Wendlandt

D-U-N-S 80-884-7560
OHIO NATIONAL GUARD
OHIO ADJUTANT GENERAL
(*Suby of* EXECUTIVE OFFICE STATE OF OHIO) ★
2825 W Dblin Granville Rd, Columbus, OH 43235-2712
Tel (614) 336-7081 *Founded/Ownrshp* 1803
Sales NA *EMP* 2,800
SIC 9711 National security; ; National security;
Ex Dir: Gregory L Wayt
**CFO:* Mark Ostler
**VP:* Candice Barnhardt
CIO: Richard Willinger

D-U-N-S 00-230-5089
OHIO NATIONAL LIFE ASSURANCE CORP (OH)
(*Suby of* OHIO CASUALTY INSURANCE) ★
1 Financial Way Ste 100, Montgomery, OH 45242-5852
Tel (513) 794-6100 *Founded/Ownrshp* 1979
Sales NA *EMP* 744^E^
SIC 6411 Insurance agents, brokers & service
CEO: David B Omaley
CFO: Ronald J Dolan
Sec: Michael F Haverkamp
Sec: Therese S McDonough
Ofcr: Cletus L Davis
**Ex VP:* Gates Smith
Sr VP: Robert Bowen
VP: Terry L Garrard

D-U-N-S 78-734-4758
OHIO NATIONAL LIFE INSURANCE CO
OHIO CASUALTY INSURANCE
(*Suby of* OHIO NATIONAL FINANCIAL SERVICES INC) ★
1 Financial Way Ste 100, Montgomery, OH 45242-5852
Tel (513) 794-6100 *Founded/Ownrshp* 1979
Sales NA *EMP* 799^E^
SIC 6411 Insurance agents, brokers & service; Insurance agents, brokers & service
CEO: David B Omaley
Sr VP: Ronald Heibert

D-U-N-S 00-230-4397
OHIO NATIONAL MUTUAL HOLDINGS INC (OH)
1 Financial Way Ste 100, Montgomery, OH 45242-5852
Tel (513) 794-6100 Founded/Ownrshp 1993
Sales NA EMP 800
SIC 6311 Mutual association life insurance; Mutual association life insurance
Ch Bd: David O'Maley
*Treas: Roylene Broadwell
Chf Cred: Dennis R Taney
*Sr VP: Ronald Dolan
*VP: Michael S Haberkamp
VP: Jed R Martin
DP Dir: William Martin
Mktg Mgr: Terry Garrett
Board of Directors: David R Jones

D-U-N-S 05-162-5564
OHIO NORTHERN UNIVERSITY
ONU
525 S Main St Unit 1, Ada, OH 45810-1599
Tel (419) 772-2000 Founded/Ownrshp 1899
Sales 89.6MM EMP 700
Accts Bkd Llp Fort Wayne Indiana
SIC 8221 University; University
Pr: Dr Daniel A Dibiasio
*VP: William Ballard
VP: Anthony Fritz
VP: Elizabeth Hohner
VP: Josh Kiesel
Assoc Dir: Jose Nogueras
Store Mgr: Josh Szippl
Prd Dir: Eric Porter
Pgrm Dir: Kelly Swearingen
Snr Mgr: Andria Beehler-Evans
Snr Mgr: Kirsten Fultz

D-U-N-S 07-501-4977
OHIO OPERATING ENGINEERS HEALTH & WELFARE FUND
1180 Dublin Rd, Columbus, OH 43215-1008
Tel (614) 488-0708 Founded/Ownrshp 1959
Sales NA EMP 8
SIC 6371 Union welfare, benefit & health funds; Union welfare, benefit & health funds
Ex Dir: Ray Orrand
Netwrk Mgr: Tim Tolley

D-U-N-S 01-797-3025
OHIO PIZZA PRODUCTS INC
PRESTO AMERICAS FAVORITE FOODS
201 Lawton Ave, Monroe, OH 45050-1213
Tel (937) 294-6969 Founded/Ownrshp 1981
Sales 152.7MM^E EMP 150
SIC 5149 Pizza supplies; Specialty food items; Baking supplies; Pizza supplies; Specialty food items; Baking supplies
Ch: Phil Weeda Sr
*Ch Bd: Vito P Weeda
*Pr: Jeff Schrand
*CFO: Dale Lipa
VP: Roberta Schrater
VP: Weeda Vito
*VP: Dewey Weeda
VP Mktg: Anderson Erickson
Mktg Mgr: Rick Deitering

D-U-N-S 00-289-9953 IMP
■ **OHIO POWER CO**
(Suby of AMERICAN ELECTRIC POWER CO INC) ★
1 Riverside Plz, Columbus, OH 43215-2355
Tel (614) 716-1000 Founded/Ownrshp 1907
Sales 3.3MMM EMP 1,516^E
SIC 4911 Distribution, electric power; Generation, electric power; Transmission, electric power; Electric services; Distribution, electric power; Generation, electric power; Transmission, electric power
Ch Bd: Nicholas K Akins
*CFO: Brian X Tierney
Board of Directors: Lisa M Barton, David M Feinberg, Lana L Hillebrand, Mark C McCullough, Robert P Powers, Dennis E Welch

D-U-N-S 80-884-0748
OHIO PRESBYTERIAN RETIREMENT SERVICES (INC)
1001 Kingsmill Pkwy, Columbus, OH 43229-1129
Tel (614) 888-7800 Founded/Ownrshp 1992
Sales 5.2MM EMP 3,100
Accts Plante & Moran Pllc Columbus
SIC 8361 Rest home, with health care incidental; Rest home, with health care incidental
CEO: Laurence Gumina
*CFO: Robert Stillman
Ofcr: Connie Tostevin
Ex VP: Dan Oconnor
VP: Sue Welty
Dir IT: Leslie K Belfance

D-U-N-S 10-568-2090
OHIO PUBLIC EMPLOYEES RETIREMENT SYSTEM
(Suby of EXECUTIVE OFFICE STATE OF OHIO) ★
277 E Town St, Columbus, OH 43215-4627
Tel (614) 228-8471 Founded/Ownrshp 1935
Sales NA EMP 468
SIC 6371 9441 Pension funds; Administration of social & manpower programs; ; Pension funds; Administration of social & manpower programs;
Ch: Cinthia Sledz
*COO: Blake W Sherry
*CFO: Jenny Starr
Chf Inves: Richard Shafer
*Prin: Sharon Downs

OHIO PUBLIC SCHOOL DISTRICT
See BRECKSVILLE-BROADVIEW HTS BOARD OF EDUCATION

D-U-N-S 07-088-2220
■ **OHIO RIVER METAL SERVICES INC**
(Suby of METALS USA INC) ★
5150 Loop Rd, Jeffersonville, IN 47130-8412
Tel (812) 282-4770 Founded/Ownrshp 2010
Sales 43.3MM^E EMP 115
SIC 3316 Cold-rolled strip or wire; Cold-rolled strip or wire
CEO: Shirley Ohta
*Pr: Charles R Moore
*Sec: Rita Moore
*Ex VP: Henry Taylor

D-U-N-S 80-273-3931
OHIO RIVER TERMINALS CO LLC
(Suby of MIDLAND ENTERPRISES INC) ★
2500 Chamber Center Dr # 200, Lakeside Park, KY 41017-1665
Tel (859) 341-1716 Founded/Ownrshp 2002
Sales 18.4MM^E EMP 947^E
SIC 4449 River transportation, except on the St. Lawrence Seaway
CEO: Orrin H Ingram
VP: Daniel Martin
VP: David O'Loughlin
VP: Brian Rafferty
VP: Richard Tomayko
Genl Mgr: Robert Ory

D-U-N-S 07-839-5409 IMP
OHIO ROD PRODUCTS LLC
(Suby of ELGIN FASTENER GROUP LLC) ★
1415 S Benham Rd, Versailles, IN 47042-8411
Tel (812) 689-6565 Founded/Ownrshp 2009
Sales 25.0MM EMP 100
SIC 5084 Industrial machinery & equipment
Pr: Jeff Liter

OHIO RURAL ELECTRIC COOPS
See BUCKEYE POWER INC

OHIO SCALE SYSTEMS
See MEMPHIS SCALE WORKS INC

OHIO SCHOOL PICTURES
See ROYAL COLOR INC

D-U-N-S 93-834-4082
OHIO SCHOOLS COUNCIL
6133 Rockside Rd Ste 10ll, Cleveland, OH 44131-2241
Tel (216) 447-3100 Founded/Ownrshp 1986
Sales 36.0MM EMP 9
SIC 8611 Business associations; Business associations
*Ex Dir: David Cottrell
Off Mgr: Kelly Rocco

D-U-N-S 06-606-7448
OHIO SCREW PRODUCTS INC
818 Lowell St, Elyria, OH 44035-4876
Tel (440) 322-6341 Founded/Ownrshp 1977
Sales 24.0MM^E EMP 75
SIC 3541 3451 Screw machines, automatic; Screw machine products
Pr: Daniel Imbrogno
*Ch Bd: Edward N Imbrogno
Pr: Jim Fetcko
*Pr: Dan Imbrogno
*VP: Elmer Brown
Dept Mgr: Andrew Herman
Ql Cn Mgr: Dorothy Knieriemen
Sales Exec: Connie Eberling

D-U-N-S 02-064-5875
OHIO SECURITY SYSTEMS INC
OSS
2592 Elm Rd Ne, Warren, OH 44483-2904
Tel (330) 372-1163 Founded/Ownrshp 1967
Sales 19.8MM^E EMP 654
SIC 7381 Security guard service; Security guard service
Pr: James A Payiavlas
*VP: Nicholas Payiavlas
VP: Nicholas Paylavlas
Off Mgr: Tom Wenger
VP Sls: Nicholas Payiazlas

D-U-N-S 03-276-7688
OHIO STAMPING & MACHINE LLC
2100 S Yellow Springs St, Springfield, OH 45506-3354
Tel (937) 322-3880 Founded/Ownrshp 1999
Sales 21.0MM^E EMP 120
SIC 3465 Automotive stampings; Automotive stampings
CEO: Dan McGregor
*Pr: James McGregor
*Pr: Tom Wright
*COO: Dwight Kent
*CFO: Seth Powers
*Genl Mgr: James Doyle

D-U-N-S 08-771-0950
OHIO STATE HOME SERVICES INC (OH)
OHIO STATE WATERPROOFING
365 Highland Rd E, Macedonia, OH 44056-2103
Tel (330) 467-1055 Founded/Ownrshp 1977
Sales 41.6MM^E EMP 250
SIC 1799 Waterproofing; Waterproofing
Pr: Nick Di Cello
Dir IT: Carl Moore
Dir IT: Wayne Yourison

D-U-N-S 96-593-1194
OHIO STATE PLUMBERS AND PIPEFITTERS HEALTH AND WELFARE FUND
5 Hot Metal St Ste 200, Pittsburgh, PA 15203-2351
Tel (412) 431-4710 Founded/Ownrshp 2010
Sales 22.7MM EMP 10^E
Accts Anness Gerlach & Williams Cpas
SIC 8631 Labor unions & similar labor organizations; Labor unions & similar labor organizations
Prin: Jeremy Resnick

OHIO STATE UNIVERSITY
See OSU-HARDING HOSPITAL INC

D-U-N-S 00-196-4634 IMP
OHIO STATE UNIVERSITY
Student Acade Servi Bldg, Columbus, OH 43210
Tel (614) 292-6446 Founded/Ownrshp 1870
Sales 2.0MMM^E EMP 39,120
SIC 8221 5812

D-U-N-S 96-956-5469
OHIO STATE UNIVERSITY FOUNDATION
364 W Lane Ave Ste B, Columbus, OH 43201-4350
Tel (614) 292-6261 Founded/Ownrshp 2011
Sales 129.8MM EMP 3^E
SIC 8641

D-U-N-S 03-125-1873
OHIO STATE UNIVERSITY MEDICAL
UNIVERSITY HOSPITAL EAST
1492 E Broad St, Columbus, OH 43205-1546
Tel (614) 257-3760 Founded/Ownrshp 2010
Sales 477.5MM^E EMP 20,000
SIC 8011 Medical centers
CEO: Pete Geier
Ofcr: Curt Brown
Surgeon: Jean Starr

D-U-N-S 07-165-0709
OHIO STATE UNIVERSITY RESEARCH FOUNDATION
1960 Kenny Rd, Columbus, OH 43210-1016
Tel (614) 688-8125 Founded/Ownrshp 1936
Sales 507.1MM EMP 105
SIC 8741 Administrative management; Administrative management
Pr: Joseph A Alutto
*Treas: Pranab Bhattacharya
*Prin: Dr Caroline Whitacre
IT Man: Susan Imel

OHIO STATE WATERPROOFING
See OHIO STATE HOME SERVICES INC

D-U-N-S 07-689-3114
OHIO TECHNICAL COLLEGE INC
1374 E 51st St, Cleveland, OH 44103-1269
Tel (216) 361-0983 Founded/Ownrshp 1970
Sales 21.1MM^E EMP 250^E
SIC 8249 Trade school; Trade school
Pr: Marc Brenner
Ofcr: Roy Voss
*Ex VP: Kathleen Dillon

OHIO THRIFT
See THRIFT STORES OF OHIO INC

D-U-N-S 07-113-2336
OHIO TOOL SYSTEMS INC
3863 Congress Pkwy, Richfield, OH 44286-9797
Tel (330) 659-4181 Founded/Ownrshp 1974
Sales 37.2MM^E EMP 55
SIC 5084 Machine tools & metalworking machinery; Pneumatic tools & equipment
Pr: Greg Grace
*Sec: Jack Grace
VP Sls: Brent Covan

D-U-N-S 00-786-2378 IMP
OHIO TRANSMISSION CORP (OH)
OTP INDUSTRIAL SOLUTIONS
1900 Jetway Blvd, Columbus, OH 43219-1681
Tel (614) 342-6247 Founded/Ownrshp 1963
Sales 350.9MM^E EMP 375
SIC 5084 5085 Industrial machinery & equipment; Materials handling machinery; Compressors, except air conditioning; Pumps & pumping equipment; Power transmission equipment & apparatus; Bearings; Industrial machinery & equipment; Materials handling machinery; Compressors, except air conditioning; Pumps & pumping equipment; Power transmission equipment & apparatus; Bearings
CEO: Philip Derrow
CFO: Matt Piatt
Ch: David D Derrow
Ex VP: Kurt Lang
VP: Kevin Kammer
VP: Steven Strain
Area Mgr: Dan Benjamin
Sftwr Eng: Rustin Thomas
Netwrk Eng: Alan Rose
Sales Exec: Arlene Wallace
Sales Asso: Maree Boettger

D-U-N-S 02-063-9340
OHIO TURNPIKE AND INFRASTRUCTURE COMMISSION
(Suby of EXECUTIVE OFFICE STATE OF OHIO) ★
682 Prospect St, Berea, OH 44017-2711
Tel (440) 234-2081 Founded/Ownrshp 1949
Sales 275.6MM EMP 953
Accts C&P Advisors Llc Cleveland
SIC 4785 Toll road operation; Toll road operation
CEO: Randy Cole
*CFO: Martin S Seekely
CFO: James Steiner
*Ch: Jerry N Hruby
*Sec: Sandy Barber
MIS Dir: Dick Morgan
Dir IT: Richard Morgan

D-U-N-S 04-107-7983 IMP
OHIO UNIVERSITY
1 Ohio University, Athens, OH 45701-2979
Tel (740) 593-1000 Founded/Ownrshp 1804
Sales 493.8MM EMP 6,162
SIC 8221

D-U-N-S 17-831-6949
OHIO UNIVERSITY FOUNDATION
Hdl Ctr Ste 218, Athens, OH 45701
Tel (740) 593-1882 Founded/Ownrshp 1945
Sales 61.0MM EMP 72
Accts Cindy Strausbaugh Accountant
SIC 7389 Fund raising organizations; Fund raising organizations
Ch Bd: James Daley
*Ch: Charlotte Eufinger
*Treas: Larry Corrigan
*VP: Frand Krasovec
*Ex Dir: Leonard Raley
Genl Mgr: Julie Cashin

D-U-N-S 07-287-2849
OHIO VALLEY ACQUISITION INC
AMERISTOP FOOD MARTS
250 E 5th St Ste 1200, Cincinnati, OH 45202-4139
Tel (513) 553-0768 Founded/Ownrshp 2011
Sales 63.0MM^E EMP 415
Accts Joseph Decosimo & Company Cpa
SIC 6794 Franchises, selling or licensing; Franchises, selling or licensing
Pr: Don Bloom
*COO: Tony Parnigoni
*CFO: William Zembrodt
Board of Directors: James Gould, Fred Mayerson

D-U-N-S 00-636-4558 IMP
OHIO VALLEY ALUMINUM CO LLC (KY)
ALTEC
(Suby of INTERLOCK INDUSTRIES INC) ★
1100 Brooks Industrial Rd, Shelbyville, KY 40065-9197
Tel (502) 633-2783 Founded/Ownrshp 1955
Sales 250.0MM EMP 125^E
SIC 3341 Aluminum smelting & refining (secondary); Aluminum smelting & refining (secondary)
Pr: Mike Mackin
VP: Michael Pucci
Plnt Mgr: Randy Meers
VP Sls: Ed Wiegand

D-U-N-S 80-414-1661
▲ **OHIO VALLEY BANC CORP**
420 3rd Ave, Gallipolis, OH 45631-1135
Tel (740) 446-2631 Founded/Ownrshp 1992
Sales NA EMP 264^E
Tkr Sym OVBC Exch NGM
SIC 6022 State commercial banks; State commercial banks
Pr: Thomas E Wiseman
*Ch Bd: Jeffrey E Smith
COO: Larry E Miller II
CFO: Scott W Shockey
Sr VP: Katrinka V Hart-Harris

D-U-N-S 00-892-9697
■ **OHIO VALLEY BANK CO**
(Suby of OHIO VALLEY BANC CORP) ★
420 3rd Ave, Gallipolis, OH 45631-1135
Tel (740) 446-2631 Founded/Ownrshp 1872
Sales NA EMP 250
SIC 6022 State commercial banks; State commercial banks
Pr: Thomas E Wiseman
*Ch: Jeffrey E Smith
*Ex VP: Katrinka V Hart
*Ex VP: E Richard Mahan
*Ex VP: Larry E Miller II
Sr VP: Bryan F Stepp
Board of Directors: Greg Hartley, David W Thomas

OHIO VALLEY COAL
See OHIO VALLEY RESOURCES INC

D-U-N-S 18-860-6438
OHIO VALLEY COAL CO
(Suby of OHIO VALLEY COAL) ★
46226 National Rd W, Saint Clairsville, OH 43950-8742
Tel (740) 926-1351 Founded/Ownrshp 1988
Sales 336.7MM^E EMP 400
SIC 1241 Bituminous coal mining services, contract basis; Bituminous coal mining services, contract basis
CEO: Robert E Murray
*Pr: Ryan M Murray
*Sr VP: John R Forrelli
*Sr VP: Michael O McKown
*VP: Robert D Moore
Board of Directors: Richard Homko, Paul Piccolini

D-U-N-S 00-790-3925
OHIO VALLEY ELECTRIC CORP
OVEC
3932 Us Rte 23, Piketon, OH 45661
Tel (740) 289-7200 Founded/Ownrshp 1952
Sales 436.5MM EMP 428
Accts Deloitte & Touche Llp Indiana
SIC 4911 Generation, electric power; Transmission, electric power; Distribution, electric power; Generation, electric power; Transmission, electric power; Distribution, electric power
Pr: Nicholas Akins
CFO: Kassandra Martin
*Sec: John Brodt
*VP: Mark Piefer
VP Opers: David E Jons
Plnt Mgr: Jeff Bolen
Secur Mgr: William Squibb
Snr Mgr: Randy Keefer
Board of Directors: Steve Nelson, Anthony Ahern, Patrick O'loughlin, Nicholas Akins, Robert Powers, Eric Baker, Paul Thompson, Wayne Games, John Verderame, James Haney, John Voyles, Philip Herrington, Lana Hillebrand, Charles Lasky, Mark McCullough

D-U-N-S 09-281-5109 IMP
OHIO VALLEY FLOORING INC
5555 Murray Ave, Cincinnati, OH 45227-2707
Tel (513) 271-3434 Founded/Ownrshp 1978
Sales 119.8MM EMP 162
Accts Clark Schaefer Hackett & Co C
SIC 5023 Floor coverings; Carpets; Resilient floor coverings: tile or sheet; Wood flooring; Floor coverings; Carpets; Resilient floor coverings: tile or sheet; Wood flooring
Pr: Al Hurt
Pr: Randy Flowers
*CFO: Mark Roflow
IT Man: Pete Westridge
Trfc Mgr: Judy Marshall
Sales Asso: Eric Rothbauer

OHIO VALLEY FOODLAND
See OHIO VALLEY SUPERMARKETS INC

D-U-N-S 00-694-0274
OHIO VALLEY GAS CORP
(Suby of BEYNON FARM PRODUCTS CORP)
111 Energy Park Dr, Winchester, IN 47394-9233
Tel (765) 584-5501 Founded/Ownrshp 1943
Sales 38.4MM EMP 130
SIC 4924 Natural gas distribution; Natural gas distribution
Pr: Thomas D Williams

*Pr: Ronald L Loyd
VP: P Donahue
*VP: S Mark Kerney
VP: Bill Shields
Genl Mgr: Scott Williams

D-U-N-S 18-810-4616
OHIO VALLEY GAS INC
DOME GAS COMPANY
(Suby of OHIO VALLEY GAS CORP) ★
111 Energy Park Dr, Winchester, IN 47394-9233
Tel (765) 584-5501 Founded/Ownrshp 1959
Sales 30.9MM EMP 4
SIC 4923 Gas transmission & distribution; Gas transmission & distribution
Pr: David Beynon
VP: Lloyd Spencer
IT Man: Marion Smith

OHIO VALLEY GENERAL HOSPITAL
See OHIO VALLEY MEDICAL CENTER INC

D-U-N-S 07-215-2440
OHIO VALLEY GENERAL HOSPITAL
OHIO VALLEY HOSPITAL
25 Heckel Rd, Mc Kees Rocks, PA 15136-1651
Tel (412) 777-6161 Founded/Ownrshp 1906
Sales 68.4MM^E EMP 570
Accts Parentebeard Llc Pittsburgh
SIC 8082 Home health care services; Home health care services
Ex Dir: Lynn Scanga
*VP: Vicki Mell
*VP: Tad Tefera
Dir Case M: Johnni Psomas
Dir Lab: Jessica Janicki
Adm Dir: Jan Simon
CIO: Elaine Polinak
Dir QC: Peg Spisak
IT Man: Mike Jacobs
IT Man: Robert Wallace
Pathlgst: Harold Scheinman

D-U-N-S 00-486-8139
OHIO VALLEY GOODWILL INDUSTRIES REHABILITATION CENTER INC (OH)
10600 Springfield Pike, Cincinnati, OH 45215-1121
Tel (513) 771-4800 Founded/Ownrshp 1916
Sales 41.6MM EMP 680
SIC 5932 Clothing, secondhand; Furniture, secondhand; Clothing, secondhand
CEO: Joseph S Byrom
VP: Dennis Barron
VP: Joann Decker
VP Admn: Doug Ostholthoff

OHIO VALLEY GRAVEL & SAND CO
See JIM SMITH CONTRACTING CO LLC

D-U-N-S 05-604-2831
OHIO VALLEY HEALTH SERVICES AND EDUCATION CORP
2000 Eoff St, Wheeling, WV 26003-3823
Tel (304) 234-8174 Founded/Ownrshp 1914
Sales 174.7MM^E EMP 1,825
Accts Arnett Carbis Toothman Llp Ch
SIC 8741 8062 8011 Hospital management; General medical & surgical hospitals; Offices & clinics of medical doctors; Hospital management; General medical & surgical hospitals; Offices & clinics of medical doctors
Ch Bd: James Squibb
*Pr: Michael Caruso
*CEO: Jan Jennings
*CFO: Lisa Simon
*Treas: Kristine Molnar
*VP: Matt Thomasgerald Narcisi
QA Dir: Staci Trudo

OHIO VALLEY HOSPITAL
See OHIO VALLEY GENERAL HOSPITAL

D-U-N-S 00-662-5719
OHIO VALLEY MANUFACTURING INC
1501 Harrington Mem Rd, Mansfield, OH 44903-8995
Tel (419) 522-5818 Founded/Ownrshp 1999
Sales 29.3MM^E EMP 80^E
SIC 3469 Stamping metal for the trade
Pr: Michael C Fanello
*CFO: Kim L Catron
*VP: Jeff Fanello
*Dir IT: Tim Norris
Plnt Mgr: Jim Day
Ql Cn Mgr: Paul Gross
Sales Exec: Jack Kennedy

D-U-N-S 02-660-5699
OHIO VALLEY MEDICAL CENTER LLC
100 E Main St, Springfield, OH 45502-1308
Tel (937) 521-3900 Founded/Ownrshp 2009
Sales 34.4MM EMP 81^E
SIC 8011 Medical centers
Pr: Steve Eisentrager
*COO: Ronny Shumaker
Dir Rx: Chris Patsiavos
*Prin: Ajay Mangal
Off Mgr: Maryellen Beckman
Off Mgr: Mary Beekman
Ansthlgy: Young Park
Nrsg Dir: Beth Lizza

D-U-N-S 05-552-1686
OHIO VALLEY RESOURCES INC
OHIO VALLEY COAL
(Suby of MURRAY ENERGY CORP) ★
29525 Chagrin Blvd # 111, Cleveland, OH 44122-4644
Tel (216) 765-1240 Founded/Ownrshp 1988
Sales 835.9MM^E EMP 3,000
SIC 1241

D-U-N-S 09-754-9810
OHIO VALLEY SUPERMARKETS INC
OHIO VALLEY FOODLAND
210 1/2 2nd Ave, Gallipolis, OH 45631-1022
Tel (740) 446-9312 Founded/Ownrshp 1979
Sales 35.0MM EMP 250
SIC 5411 Supermarkets; Supermarkets
Prin: Kevin Eastman
*Pr: Robert H Eastman

D-U-N-S 00-892-7436
OHIO VALLEY SUPPLY CO
3512 Spring Grove Ave, Cincinnati, OH 45223-2448
Tel (513) 681-8300 Founded/Ownrshp 1968
Sales 23.6MM EMP 24
SIC 5031 Lumber, plywood & millwork; Building materials, exterior; Building materials, interior; Lumber, plywood & millwork; Building materials, exterior; Building materials, interior
Pr: Ken Shear
*CFO: Joe Freeman
*VP: Dave Greening
*VP: Rick Neeley
Cust Svc D: Jim Brandt
Sales Asso: Albert Beranek

D-U-N-S 79-609-8127
OHIO VALLEY TACO CORP
200 S 4th St 208, Steubenville, OH 43952-2929
Tel (740) 264-1444 Founded/Ownrshp 1989
Sales 9.3MM^E EMP 453
SIC 5812 Fast-food restaurant, chain; Fast-food restaurant, chain
Pr: Michael Schiappa
*CFO: Joan E Feth
*VP: A Albert Schiappa

D-U-N-S 12-949-5755
OHIO VALLEY TRANSLOADING CO INC
(Suby of OHIO VALLEY COAL) ★
46226 National Rd W, Saint Clairsville, OH 43950-8742
Tel (740) 795-4967 Founded/Ownrshp 1989
Sales 57.6MM^E EMP 2,566^E
SIC 1241 Bituminous coal mining services, contract basis
CEO: Robert Murray

OHIO VALLEY WINE & BEER
See OHIO VALLEY WINE CO

D-U-N-S 06-894-0949 IMP
OHIO VALLEY WINE CO
OHIO VALLEY WINE & BEER
10975 Medallion Dr, Cincinnati, OH 45241-4830
Tel (513) 771-9370 Founded/Ownrshp 1992
Sales 46.5MM^E EMP 170
SIC 5182 5181 Wine; Beer & other fermented malt liquors; Wine; Beer & other fermented malt liquors
Pr: Steve Lowrey
*Ex VP: Greg Maurer
VP: Mike Earn
VP: Joe Noll
*VP: Albert W Vontz III
Genl Mgr: Greg Flynn
Sls Mgr: Jim Morgan

D-U-N-S 13-112-8402
OHIO VIRTUAL ACADEMY
1655 Holland Rd Ste F, Maumee, OH 43537-1656
Tel (419) 482-0948 Founded/Ownrshp 2002
Sales 91.4MM EMP 65
SIC 8211 Elementary school; Elementary school
Prin: Jeff Shaw
Snr Mgr: Heidi Ragar

D-U-N-S 05-535-2140
OHIO WESLEYAN UNIVERSITY
61 S Sandusky St, Delaware, OH 43015-2398
Tel (740) 368-2000 Founded/Ownrshp 1842
Sales 121.0MM^E EMP 630
SIC 8221

D-U-N-S 00-428-0723
OHIO WILLOW WOOD CO (OH)
WILLOWWOOD
15441 Scioto Darby Rd, Mount Sterling, OH 43143-9036
Tel (740) 869-3377 Founded/Ownrshp 1907, 1979
Sales 30.0MM EMP 185
SIC 3842 Prosthetic appliances; Prosthetic appliances
Pr: Ryan Arbogast
COO: John Matera
*Ex VP: C Joseph Arbogast
Ex VP: Jim Capper
*VP: Robert E Arbogast
IT Man: Jeffrey Tadlock
Opers Mgr: Mark Alter
Mktg Dir: Doug Kreitzer
Sls Mgr: Linda Wise

D-U-N-S 00-790-3578
■ **OHIO-AMERICAN WATER CO INC)** (OH)
MARION DISTRICT
(Suby of AMERICAN WATER WORKS CO INC) ★
365 E Center St, Marion, OH 43302-4155
Tel (740) 382-3993 Founded/Ownrshp 1800, 1936
Sales 34.3MM^E EMP 99
Accts Pricewaterhousecoopers Llp
SIC 4941 Water supply; Water supply
Pr: John E Eckart
*Treas: Christine J Doron
*VP: T Wilkes Coleman
*VP Opers: Dwayne D Cole

D-U-N-S 01-623-8990
OHIOGUIDESTONE
434 Eastland Rd, Berea, OH 44017-1217
Tel (440) 234-2006 Founded/Ownrshp 1864
Sales 45.3MM EMP 1,237
Accts Mcgladrey Llp Cleveland Oh
SIC 8322 8361 8351 8051 Child related social services; Home for the emotionally disturbed; Child day care services; Skilled nursing care facilities; Child related social services; Home for the emotionally disturbed; Child day care services; Skilled nursing care facilities
CEO: Richard Frank
*VP: Donna Keegan
Exec: Judy Hlavna
Dir Lab: Lisa Potoma
Sls&Mrk Ex: Alyssa Evanoff
Mktg Dir: Joe Ziegler

OHIOHEALTH
See RIVERSIDE METHODIST HOSPITAL INC

OHIOHEALTH
See HARDIN MEMORIAL HOSPITAL

D-U-N-S 07-164-3589
OHIOHEALTH CORP
180 E Broad St, Columbus, OH 43215-3707
Tel (614) 544-4455 Founded/Ownrshp 1984
Sales 2.1MMM EMP 15,000
Accts Deloitte Tax Llp Cincinnati
SIC 8049 8062 8082 8051 Occupational therapist; General medical & surgical hospitals; Home health care services; Convalescent home with continuous nursing care; Extended care facility; Occupational therapist; General medical & surgical hospitals; Home health care services; Convalescent home with continuous nursing care; Extended care facility
Pr: David Blom
*COO: Michael W Louge
*COO: Robert P Millen
CFO: Joseph Schuler
CFO: Vinson M Yates
Ofcr: Cindy Starks
*Sr VP: Michael S Bernstein
*Sr VP: Steve Garlock
*Sr VP: Donna Hanly
Sr VP: Sue Jablonski
Sr VP: Michael Krouse
*Exec: Johnni Beckel
Dir Rx: Margaret Huwer
Dir Bus: Susan Torti
Dir Bus: Rod Wirsching
Comm Man: Kimberly Phillips

D-U-N-S 07-286-7971
OHIOHEALTH OBLENNES HOSPITAL (OH)
O'BLENESS MEMORIAL HOSPITAL
(Suby of OHIOHEALTH CORP) ★
55 Hospital Dr, Athens, OH 45701-2302
Tel (740) 592-9300 Founded/Ownrshp 1948, 1970
Sales 87.9MM EMP 368
Accts Plante & Moran Pllc Columbus
SIC 8062 General medical & surgical hospitals; General medical & surgical hospitals
Pr: Mark Seckinger
*Pr: Greg Long
*CEO: Larry Thornhill
*CFO: Ken Dicken
Treas: Robert Norris
*VP: Lynn Anastas
*VP: Shawn Bail
*VP: Kimberly Gettwiller
*VP: Sandy Leasure
*VP: Scott Mash
*VP: Candace N Miller
Dir Lab: Melanie Stethem

OHL
See OZBURN-HESSEY LOGISTICS LLC

D-U-N-S 88-314-1236
OHL - ARELLANO CONSTRUCTION CO
OHL ARELLANO
(Suby of OHL USA INC) ★
7051 Sw 12th St, Miami, FL 33144-5402
Tel (305) 994-9901 Founded/Ownrshp 1994
Sales 45.1MM^E EMP 91
SIC 1542 Nonresidential construction; Nonresidential construction
Pr: Agustin R Arellano
*Pr: Frank X Vilar
COO: Brandis Perez
*CFO: Agustin Arellano Jr
CFO: Michelle Flores
*VP: Arthur Hoynack
*VP: Carlos Mena
Rgnl Mgr: Joseph Folino
Off Mgr: Greter Alvarez
Software D: Mark Hickein
Sls Mgr: Janeen Skelly

OHL ARELLANO
See OHL - ARELLANO CONSTRUCTION CO

D-U-N-S 02-559-8670
OHL GLOBAL FREIGHT MANAGEMENT
(Suby of OZBURN-HESSEY HOLDING CO LLC) ★
223 E Cy Hall Ave Ste 208, Norfolk, VA 23510
Tel (757) 314-4300 Founded/Ownrshp 2009
Sales 33.6MM^E EMP 620^E
SIC 8741 Management services
Prin: Brenda Bailey

D-U-N-S 83-293-8364
OHL USA INC
(Suby of OBRASCON HUARTE LAIN SA)
780 3rd Ave Rm 902, New York, NY 10017-2188
Tel (212) 201-5885 Founded/Ownrshp 2005
Sales 369.8MM^E EMP 145
SIC 8711 Construction & civil engineering; Civil engineering; Construction & civil engineering; Civil engineering
Pr: Francisco Marin Andres

OHLHEISER CORPORATION
See NM HOLDINGS INC

OHLONE COLLEGE
See OHLONE COMMUNITY COLLEGE DISTRICT

D-U-N-S 07-464-3941
OHLONE COMMUNITY COLLEGE DISTRICT
OHLONE COLLEGE
43600 Mission Blvd, Fremont, CA 94539-5847
Tel (510) 659-6000 Founded/Ownrshp 1966
Sales 31.5MM^E EMP 650
SIC 8222 Community college; Community college
Pr: Dr Gari Browning
VP: Bruce Griffin
*VP: Ron Little
VP: Michael Moore
Genl Mgr: Robert Dochterman
Off Admin: Rachel Ferrantino
CTO: Emilee Harrison
Dir IT: Daman Greval
Dir IT: Daman Grewal
Psych: Tony Le
Psych: Maria Ramirez

OHM ADVISORS
See ORCHARD HILTZ & MCCLIMENT INC

D-U-N-S 60-181-8677 IMP
OHM INTERNATIONAL INC
195 Prospect Plains Rd, Monroe, NJ 08831-3710
Tel (609) 655-7787 Founded/Ownrshp 1987
Sales 20.8MM^E EMP 55
Accts Lewis W Parker Iii Lawrence
SIC 5032 Granite building stone
Pr: Pinakin Pathak
*VP: Joe Morris
VP Sls: Ken Krebs

D-U-N-S 05-156-5745 IMP
■ **OHM LABORATORIES INC**
(Suby of RANBAXY INC) ★
1385 Livingston Ave, North Brunswick, NJ 08902-1829
Tel (732) 514-4380 Founded/Ownrshp 2004
Sales 31.6MM^E EMP 136
SIC 2834 Pharmaceutical preparations; Pharmaceutical preparations
Pr: Dipak Chattaraj
*CFO: Lalit Ahluwalia
*VP: Ganpat Desai
*VP: Venkatachalam Krishnan
*VP: Robert Patton
Snr Mgr: Georgina Aniche
Snr Mgr: Sreenivas Vutla

OHMART VEGA
See VEGA AMERICAS INC

OHMITE MANUFACTURING
See HEICO OHMITE LLC

D-U-N-S 02-689-4126 IMP
■ **OHMSTEDE INDUSTRIAL SERVICES INC**
(Suby of OHMSTEDE LTD) ★
937 Pine St, Beaumont, TX 77701-1852
Tel (409) 840-6644 Founded/Ownrshp 1991
Sales 42.6MM^E EMP 400
SIC 7699 Industrial machinery & equipment repair; Industrial machinery & equipment repair
CEO: William P Reid
*Pr: Douglas R Harrington Jr
*CFO: Daniel Eaton
*Ch: Bill Reid
VP: Claude Cleveland
*Prin: Robert Greeson
Off Mgr: Tommie Jackson
Mtls Mgr: Bobby Kines
Opers Mgr: Nathan Lortz

D-U-N-S 10-219-7899 IMP/EXP
■ **OHMSTEDE LTD**
(Suby of EMCOR GROUP INC) ★
895 N Mn St, Beaumont, TX 77701
Tel (409) 833-6375 Founded/Ownrshp 2007
Sales 420.0MM^E EMP 1,000
SIC 5075 3443 Heat exchangers; Heat exchangers: coolers (after, inter), condensers, etc.; Heat exchangers; Heat exchangers: coolers (after, inter), condensers, etc.
CEO: William Reid
*Pt: Glenda Barnwell
*Pt: Douglas Harrington
*Pt: John Marcotte
COO: Bill Reid
Dir IT: Lorraine Barrow
IT Man: Kathrin Nikitina

D-U-N-S 19-651-5704
OHR PHYSICIAN GROUP PC
OREGON MEDICAL GROUP
1580 Valley River Dr # 210, Eugene, OR 97401-2116
Tel (541) 687-4900 Founded/Ownrshp 1988
Sales 53.3MM^E EMP 400
SIC 8011 Pediatrician; Pediatrician
CEO: Peter Davidson
*Pr: Mark A Litchman
*VP: Michael E Garfinkel
Dir IT: Steve Liu
Obsttrcn: Katria Mertz
Obsttrcn: Sarah Schram
Obsttrcn: Jessica Versage
Doctor: Sylvia Emory

OHSU
See OREGON HEALTH & SCIENCE UNIVERSITY

D-U-N-S 04-890-4361
■ **OI CORP**
O I ANALYTICAL
(Suby of XYLEM INC) ★
151 Graham Rd, College Station, TX 77845-9654
Tel (979) 690-1711 Founded/Ownrshp 2011
Sales 166.1MM^E EMP 1,077^E
SIC 3826 Analytical instruments; Gas chromatographic instruments; Analytical instruments; Gas chromatographic instruments
CEO: J Bruce Lancaster
*Pr: Donald P Segers
*Treas: Peter K Anderson
Genl Mgr: Karl Brinkmann
IT Man: Hank Hahn
Manager: Scott Hazard

OI DISTRIBUTION
See ORIGINAL IMPRESSIONS LLC

OI PLASTIC PRODUCTS FTS INC
See BPREX PLASTIC PACKAGING INC

OIA GLOBAL LOGISTICS
See OREGON INTERNATIONAL AIR FREIGHT CO INC

D-U-N-S 61-238-8715
OIA GLOBAL LOGISTICS-SCM INC
(Suby of LDI LTD LLC) ★
2100 Sw River Pkwy # 800, Portland, OR 97201-8072
Tel (503) 736-5900 Founded/Ownrshp 2003
Sales NA EMP 559
Accts Ernst & Young Llp Indianapoli
SIC 4731 Freight transportation arrangement; Freight consolidation; Materials mgmt. (purchasing, handling, inventory) consultant; Freight consolidation; Agents, shipping
CEO: Charles F Hornecker
*Pr: Harles F Hornecker

**CFO:* Tim Sether
**Ex VP:* Steve Akre
**Ex VP:* Eric Okimoto
**Sr VP:* Dante Fornari
**VP:* Daniel McMorris
Opers Mgr: Angel Thomas

D-U-N-S 80-702-9764
OIL & GAS ASSET CLEARINGHOUSE LP
(*Suby of* PETROLEUM PL ENRGY SOLUTIONS) ★
500 N Sam Houston Pkwy W, Houston, TX 77067-4315
Tel (281) 873-4600 *Founded/Ownrshp* 1992
Sales 450.5MM *EMP* 54
SIC 6531 Auction, real estate; Auction, real estate
Pt: Kenneth Olive Jr
Sr VP: Ron Barnes
Sr VP: Mark K Roach

OIL CAN HARRYS
See HOLLON OIL CO

D-U-N-S 12-711-2212 IMP
OIL CAPITAL ELECTRIC LLC
3837 W Vancouver St, Broken Arrow, OK 74012-2397
Tel (405) 840-8998 *Founded/Ownrshp* 1970
Sales 50.2MM^E *EMP* 250
SIC 1731 General electrical contractor; General electrical contractor
Pr: Jim Lewis
CFO: Ron Griffin
Sr VP: Brian Lewis
Snr PM: Terry Shaffer
Snr Mgr: Don Beach

D-U-N-S 13-160-7335
OIL CHANGER INC
OIL CHANGERS
4511 Willow Rd Ste 1, Pleasanton, CA 94588-2735
Tel (925) 734-5800 *Founded/Ownrshp* 1984
Sales 28.3MM^E *EMP* 350
SIC 7549 Lubrication service, automotive; Lubrication service, automotive
Ch Bd: Larry Read
**CFO:* Charlie Pass
Ofcr: John Denholm
VP: Dennis Blom
VP: Eric Frankenberger
VP: John Read
Rgnl Mgr: Mario Gonzalez
CIO: Mike D Ahmadi
CIO: Joey Castaneda

D-U-N-S 96-875-7401
OIL CHANGER INC
(*Suby of* OIL CHANGER INC) ★
4511 Willow Rd Ste 1, Pleasanton, CA 94588-2735
Tel (925) 734-5800 *Founded/Ownrshp* 1990
Sales 8.7MM^E *EMP* 350
SIC 7549 Lubrication service, automotive; Lubrication service, automotive
Pr: Lawrence A Read
CFO: Charlie Pass

OIL CHANGERS
See OIL CHANGER INC

D-U-N-S 08-160-3573
OIL CHEM INC
711 W 12th St, Flint, MI 48503-3851
Tel (810) 235-3040 *Founded/Ownrshp* 1978
Sales 27.7MM^E *EMP* 20
SIC 5172 2841 2992 Lubricating oils & greases; Detergents, synthetic organic or inorganic alkaline; Lubricating oils & greases
Pr: Robert Massey
Off Mgr: Beverly Wiley

D-U-N-S 09-843-1653
OIL CITY AREA SCHOOL DISTRICT INC
825 Grandview Rd, Oil City, PA 16301-2077
Tel (814) 676-1867 *Founded/Ownrshp* 1840
Sales 19.5MM^E *EMP* 300
Accts Olmes & Dickson Cpa S
SIC 8211 Public elementary & secondary schools; Public elementary & secondary schools
Bd of Dir: Jessica Deets-Snyder
Bd of Dir: Mark Kerr
Bd of Dir: Joseph McFadden
Bd of Dir: Angella Scalise
Bd of Dir: Fredrick Weaver
MIS Dir: Scott Stall
Doctor: Nancy Rankin

OIL CITY IRON WORKS
See GRANDOR CORP

D-U-N-S 00-731-9361
OIL CITY IRON WORKS INC
(*Suby of* GRANDOR CORP) ★
814 S Main St, Corsicana, TX 75110-7231
Tel (903) 872-6571 *Founded/Ownrshp* 1965
Sales 28.9MM^E *EMP* 200
SIC 3321 Gray & ductile iron foundries; Gray & ductile iron foundries
CEO: Eric Meyers
Pr: Eric R Meyers
Ex VP: Willard Cox

D-U-N-S 14-487-0888 IMP/EXP
OIL COUNTRY MANUFACTURING INC
300 W Stanley Ave, Ventura, CA 93001-1395
Tel (805) 643-1200 *Founded/Ownrshp* 1980
Sales 26.3MM^E *EMP* 130
SIC 3533 5084 Oil field machinery & equipment; Industrial machinery & equipment; Oil field machinery & equipment; Industrial machinery & equipment
Genl Mgr: Ed Patterson III
**VP:* Robert M Nelson
Genl Mgr: Ed Fagundes

OIL COUNTRY TUBULAR CONS TEXAS
See OFS INC

OIL DISTRIBUTING CO
See FOUR O CORP

D-U-N-S 02-332-4353
OIL EQUIPMENT CO INC
4701 Lien Rd, Madison, WI 53704-3616
Tel (608) 249-2881 *Founded/Ownrshp* 1981
Sales 26.7MM^E *EMP* 46
SIC 5084 1799 7699 Pumps & pumping equipment; Gasoline pump installation; Pumps & pumping equipment repair
Pr: Gerald Tigges
IT Man: Couey Dustin

D-U-N-S 00-701-9353
OIL FIELD INSTRUMENTATION
5000 Ambssdor Cffery Pkwy, Lafayette, LA 70508-6984
Tel (337) 984-4401 *Founded/Ownrshp* 2009
Sales 34.0MM *EMP* 108^E
SIC 7353 5211 5084 Oil equipment rental services; Prefabricated buildings; Petroleum industry machinery; Oil equipment rental services; Prefabricated buildings; Petroleum industry machinery
Prin: H Allen Stuart Jr

OIL HYDRAULIC CONDUITS
See BORGHI USA INC OILHYDRAULIC CONDUITS

OIL PATCH DOWNHOLE SERVICES
See OIL PATCH GROUP INC

D-U-N-S 10-274-6153
OIL PATCH FUEL & SUPPLY INC
OIL PATCH PETROLEUM
17716 State Hwy 107, Combes, TX 78535
Tel (956) 831-4839 *Founded/Ownrshp* 1982
Sales 49.9MM^E *EMP* 49
Accts Long Chilton Llp Brownsville
SIC 5172 5541 Petroleum products; Marine service station; Petroleum products; Marine service station
Pr: Joseph M Gayman
**Sec:* Elizabeth Gayman
**VP:* Leroy Hatley
Sales Exec: Audra Marks

D-U-N-S 07-935-8013
OIL PATCH GROUP INC
OIL PATCH DOWNHOLE SERVICES
(*Suby of* L E SIMMONS & ASSOCIATES INC) ★
11767 Katy Fwy Ste 510a, Houston, TX 77079-1768
Tel (832) 300-0000 *Founded/Ownrshp* 2013
Sales 97.7MM^E *EMP* 250
SIC 1389 Grading oil & gas well foundations; Grading oil & gas well foundations
Pr: Jim Elzner
CFO: Gabe Urban

OIL PATCH PETROLEUM
See OIL PATCH FUEL & SUPPLY INC

D-U-N-S 00-675-0984
OIL PATCH PETROLEUM INC
1526 N Padre Island Dr, Corpus Christi, TX 78408-2349
Tel (361) 289-7200 *Founded/Ownrshp* 1990
Sales 38.0MM^E *EMP* 80^E
SIC 5172 Petroleum products; Petroleum products
Pr: Wayne Gayman
**VP:* Carla Snowden

OIL SPILL EATER INTERNATIONAL
See OESI CORP

D-U-N-S 07-832-1409 IMP
■ OIL STATES ENERGY SERVICES LLC
(*Suby of* OIL STATES INTERNATIONAL INC) ★
333 Clay St Ste 2100, Houston, TX 77002-2570
Tel (713) 425-2400 *Founded/Ownrshp* 2012
Sales 541.4MM^E *EMP* 2,000
SIC 3533 5082 Oil field machinery & equipment; Oil field equipment; Oil field machinery & equipment; Oil field equipment
CEO: Cindy B Taylor
**VP:* Christopher E Cragg

D-U-N-S 93-250-7288 IMP/EXP
■ OIL STATES INDUSTRIES INC
(*Suby of* OIL STATES INTERNATIONAL INC) ★
7701 S Cooper St, Arlington, TX 76001-7015
Tel (817) 548-4200 *Founded/Ownrshp* 1995
Sales 593.1MM^E *EMP* 1,062
SIC 1389 3061 3561 3533 Oil & gas wells: building, repairing & dismantling; Oil field services; Oil & gas field machinery rubber goods (mechanical); Pumps & pumping equipment; Drilling tools for gas, oil or water wells; Oil & gas wells: building, repairing & dismantling; Oil field services; Oil & gas field machinery rubber goods (mechanical); Pumps & pumping equipment; Drilling tools for gas, oil or water wells
Pr: Charles J Moses
CFO: Bradley Dodson
**CFO:* Tama D Lucas
CFO: Cindy Taylor
Chf Mktg O: Robert Norris
**Sr VP:* Scott Moses
**VP:* Timothy Diadiun
**VP:* Ricky Simic
CIO: Linda Corbin
Netwrk Eng: Steven Fricke
Ql Cn Mgr: Steven Kreitzberg

D-U-N-S 16-002-7850 IMP
▲ OIL STATES INTERNATIONAL INC
333 Clay St Ste 4620, Houston, TX 77002-4101
Tel (713) 652-0582 *Founded/Ownrshp* 1995
Sales 1.8MMM *EMP* 5,290
Tkr Sym OIS *Exch* NYS
SIC 3353 3061 3053 3561 3491 Aluminum sheet, plate & foil; Oil & gas field machinery rubber goods (mechanical); Gaskets, packing & sealing devices; Pumps & pumping equipment; Industrial valves; Aluminum sheet, plate & foil; Oil & gas field machinery rubber goods (mechanical); Gaskets, packing & sealing devices; Pumps & pumping equipment; Industrial valves
Pr: Cindy B Taylor
**Ch Bd:* Stephen A Wells
CFO: Lloyd A Hajdik
Sr VP: Christopher E Cragg
Sr VP: Charles J Moses
Sr VP: Lias J Steen
VP: Tim Diadiun
VP: Rob Hampton
VP: Mark Menard
VP: Sarah A Munson
VP: Jeff Steen
Exec: Brenda Turrentine
Dir Risk M: Tamara Fricke
Board of Directors: Lawrence R Dickerson, S James Nelson, Mark G Papa, Gary L Rosenthal, Christopher T Seaver, William T Van Kleef

D-U-N-S 83-174-3930 EXP
■ OIL STATES SKAGIT SMATCO LLC
(*Suby of* OIL STATES INTERNATIONAL INC) ★
1180 Mulberry Rd, Houma, LA 70363-7507
Tel (985) 868-0630 *Founded/Ownrshp* 2001
Sales 23.9MM^E *EMP* 67^E
SIC 3533 Oil & gas field machinery

D-U-N-S 16-081-8316
■ OIL STATES SYSTEMS INC
INNCO
(*Suby of* OIL STATES INDUSTRIES INC) ★
7701 S Cooper St, Arlington, TX 76001-7015
Tel (713) 445-2210 *Founded/Ownrshp* 1997
Sales 46.2MM^E *EMP* 100
SIC 3498 Fabricated pipe & fittings
Pr: Charles Fahrmeier
VP: Mike Kief
VP: Ricky Simic
Area Mgr: Gregory Friederich
Area Mgr: Kavin Gatlin
Dist Mgr: Adam Fowler
Genl Mgr: Brian Buchan
Genl Mgr: Barry McClintic
Genl Mgr: Jim Norris
Off Admin: Lisa Holley
CTO: Charles Moses

D-U-N-S 02-842-5338
OIL WELL SERVICE CO
10840 Norwalk Blvd, Santa Fe Springs, CA 90670-3826
Tel (562) 612-0600 *Founded/Ownrshp* 2007
Sales 85.4MM^E *EMP* 225
SIC 1389 Oil field services; Oil field services
Pr: Jack Frost
**Treas:* Connie Laws
**VP:* Richard Laws

D-U-N-S 10-850-4796 IMP
OIL-AIR PRODUCTS LLC
13010 County Road 6, Minneapolis, MN 55441-3828
Tel (763) 398-3120 *Founded/Ownrshp* 2009
Sales 26.1MM^E *EMP* 49
SIC 5084 3594 3429 3052 Hydraulic systems equipment & supplies; Fluid power pumps & motors; Manufactured hardware (general); Rubber & plastics hose & beltings
Pr: Roger Schwerin
CFO: Emily Darbec
CFO: Katie Taylor
VP: Kyle Britton
S&M/VP: David Kral
Sales Asso: Brad Arneson
Sales Asso: Erik Dahl
Sales Asso: Tim Dahmes
Sales Asso: Nick Elness
Sales Asso: Ian Goodson
Sales Asso: Jim Hadac

D-U-N-S 00-521-3954 EXP
▲ OIL-DRI CORP OF AMERICA
410 N Michigan Ave Fl 4, Chicago, IL 60611-4222
Tel (312) 321-1515 *Founded/Ownrshp* 1941
Sales 261.4MM *EMP* 797
Accts Grant Thornton Llp Chicago I
Tkr Sym ODC *Exch* NYS
SIC 2842 3295 Sweeping compounds, oil or water absorbent, clay or sawdust; Earths, ground or otherwise treated; Cat box litter; Filtering clays, treated; Sweeping compounds, oil or water absorbent, clay or sawdust; Earths, ground or otherwise treated; Cat box litter; Filtering clays, treated
Pr: Daniel S Jaffee
**Ch Bd:* Richard M Jaffee
COO: Mark E Lewry
CFO: Daniel T Smith
**V Ch Bd:* Joseph C Miller
VP: Doug Graham
VP: Douglas A Graham
VP: Thierry Jean
VP: Daniel Jones
CTO: Sarah Heidkamp
VP Mfg: Thomas F Cofsky
Board of Directors: J Steven Cole, Michael A Nemeroff, Allan H Selig, Paul E Suckow, Lawrence Washow

D-U-N-S 07-685-8547 IMP
■ OIL-DRI CORP OF GEORGIA
(*Suby of* OIL-DRI CORP OF AMERICA) ★
28990 Hwy 3, Ochlocknee, GA 31773-2399
Tel (229) 574-5131 *Founded/Ownrshp* 1991
Sales 103.1MM^E *EMP* 275
SIC 3295 3564 2842 Fuller's earth, ground or otherwise treated; Blowers & fans; Specialty cleaning, polishes & sanitation goods; Fuller's earth, ground or otherwise treated; Blowers & fans; Specialty cleaning, polishes & sanitation goods
Pr: Daniel S Jaffee
**CFO:* Daniel T Smith
**Prin:* Richard M Jaffee
Plnt Mgr: Craig Paisley

D-U-N-S 00-525-6771 IMP
■ OIL-DRI PRODUCTION CO (MS)
(*Suby of* OIL-DRI CORP OF AMERICA) ★
1800 City Ave N, Ripley, MS 38663-1111
Tel (662) 837-9263 *Founded/Ownrshp* 1962
Sales 21.4MM^E *EMP* 75
SIC 2842 3295 Specialty cleaning, polishes & sanitation goods; Clay, ground or otherwise treated
Pr: Daniel S Jaffee
Sfty Mgr: Amanda Liles

D-U-N-S 08-276-5652 IMP
OILES AMERICA CORP
(*Suby of* OILES CORPORATION)
4510 Enterprise Dr Nw, Concord, NC 28027-6437
Tel (704) 262-7166 *Founded/Ownrshp* 1998
Sales 23.7MM^E *EMP* 131
SIC 3568 5085 Bearings, plain; Bearings; Bearings, plain; Bearings
Pr: Takahiko Uchida
COO: Dan Lubinski
Treas: Takayuki Ito
Treas: Takeshi Murai
Sfty Mgr: Julie Adams
Sfty Mgr: Larry Emerick
Ql Cn Mgr: Carlos Toscano
Sls Mgr: Chris Furgason
Snr Mgr: Gail Pender

OILFIELD INSTRUMENTATION USA
See ALDONSA INC

D-U-N-S 06-495-3391
OILFIELD PIPE & SUPPLY INC
14861 N 3980 Rd, Dewey, OK 74029-3947
Tel (918) 534-3760 *Founded/Ownrshp* 1982
Sales 73.8MM^E *EMP* 170
SIC 5085 5051 3533 3498 3312

D-U-N-S 79-154-0458
OILFIELD SERVICES LLC
S & L OILFIELD SERVICES
10260 Westheimer Rd # 600, Houston, TX 77042-3110
Tel (713) 358-7365 *Founded/Ownrshp* 2006
Sales NA *EMP* 350
SIC 1389

D-U-N-S 07-912-1465
OILFIELDLODGING.COM LLC (TX)
907 Ranch Road 620 S # 102, Lakeway, TX 78734-5609
Tel (512) 263-8488 *Founded/Ownrshp* 2013
Sales 25.0MM *EMP* 41
SIC 4724 Travel agencies

D-U-N-S 00-609-5038 IMP
OILGEAR CO
(*Suby of* MASON WELLS BUYOUT FUND II LIMITED PARTNERSHIP) ★
2300 S 51st St, Milwaukee, WI 53219-2340
Tel (414) 327-1700 *Founded/Ownrshp* 1921
Sales 95.5MM^E *EMP* 499
SIC 3594 3492 3593 Fluid power pumps; Motors: hydraulic, fluid power or air; Control valves, fluid power: hydraulic & pneumatic; Fluid power cylinders, hydraulic or pneumatic; Fluid power pumps; Motors: hydraulic, fluid power or air; Control valves, fluid power: hydraulic & pneumatic; Fluid power cylinders, hydraulic or pneumatic
Pr: Richard Ambrust
**CFO:* Charles Germain
VP: Chris Howie
Manager: David Nicholson

OILIND SAFETY
See AIRGAS ON-SITE SAFETY SERVICES INC

D-U-N-S 00-350-9825
OILMENS EQUIPMENT CORP (SC)
140 Cedar Springs Rd, Spartanburg, SC 29302-4145
Tel (864) 573-9311 *Founded/Ownrshp* 1952, 1978
Sales 50.9MM^E *EMP* 217
SIC 5084 3443 8741

D-U-N-S 15-421-1569 EXP
OILMENS TRUCK TANKS INC
(*Suby of* OILMENS EQUIPMENT CORP) ★
140 Cedar Springs Rd, Spartanburg, SC 29302-4145
Tel (864) 573-7400 *Founded/Ownrshp* 1986
Sales 22.7MM^E *EMP* 107
SIC 3443 5084 7699 3714 Tanks for tank trucks, metal plate; Tanks, storage; Tank repair & cleaning services; Motor vehicle parts & accessories; Tanks for tank trucks, metal plate; Tanks, storage; Tank repair & cleaning services; Motor vehicle parts & accessories
Ch Bd: John Faris
Pr: Thomas E Webber
COO: Chris Connors
VP: James Hill III
IT Man: Trey Hill
Sls Mgr: Mike Bentley

D-U-N-S 07-242-8170 EXP
OILS UNLIMITED LLC
INDUSTRIAL OILS UNLIMITED
3633 Charles Page Blvd, Tulsa, OK 74127-8039
Tel (918) 583-1155 *Founded/Ownrshp* 1970
Sales 71.2MM^E *EMP* 133
SIC 5172 2992 Petroleum products; Lubricating oils & greases; Lubricating oils & greases; Petroleum products; Lubricating oils & greases; Lubricating oils & greases
CEO: Charles Stinson
Board of Directors: Lisa Mans

D-U-N-S 96-820-9424 IMP
■ OILTANKING PARTNERS LP
(*Suby of* ENTERPRISE PRODUCTS PARTNERS LP) ★
333 Clay St Ste 2400, Houston, TX 77002-4116
Tel (281) 475-7900 *Founded/Ownrshp* 2014
Sales 35.2MM^E *EMP* 200^E
SIC 4612 4613 4925 Crude petroleum pipelines; Refined petroleum pipelines; Gasoline pipelines (common carriers); Gas production and/or distribution; Liquefied petroleum gas, distribution through mains; Crude petroleum pipelines; Refined petroleum pipelines; Gasoline pipelines (common carriers); Gas production and/or distribution; Liquefied petroleum gas, distribution through mains
Pr: Laurie H Argo
Genl Pt: Otlp GP
CFO: Donna Y Hymel
VP: James Schepens

D-U-N-S 83-241-9886
OIMO HOLDINGS INC
2735 Middle Rd, Mobile, AL 36605-9515
Tel (251) 443-5550 *Founded/Ownrshp* 2009
Sales 100.4MM^E *EMP* 130^E
SIC 1389 Oil field services; Oil consultants; Gas field services
Pr: Robin D Roberts
VP: Crystal Yasurek

D-U-N-S 87-434-6984
OIX INC
ORTRAN EXPRESS
1601 N Corrington Ave, Kansas City, MO 64120-1947
Tel (816) 373-7595 *Founded/Ownrshp* 1994
Sales 26.1MM^E *EMP* 127
SIC 4212 Local trucking, without storage
Pr: David Orscheln
**CFO:* John Owen
**VP:* Chris Gallup

D-U-N-S 11-827-8654
OJ INSULATION LP
ABCO INSULATION
600 S Vincent Ave, Azusa, CA 91702-5145
Tel (626) 812-6070 *Founded/Ownrshp* 1984
Sales 27.1MM^E *EMP* 218
SIC 1742 1751 1741 Insulation, buildings; Carpentry work; Masonry & other stonework
Pt: Pamela A Henson
Div Mgr: Mark Newman
Prd Mgr: Jorge Cortez
Prd Mgr: Ramiro Serrano
Mktg Dir: Griff Jenkins

D-U-N-S 09-251-7549
OJAI UNIFIED SCHOOL DISTRICT
414 E Ojai Ave, Ojai, CA 93023-2819
Tel (805) 640-4300 *Founded/Ownrshp* 1965
Sales 19.2MM^E *EMP* 320
SIC 8211 Public elementary & secondary schools; Public elementary & secondary schools
MIS Dir: David Rogers
Dir IT: Sandra McElwaine
Psych: Emily Otelsberg

D-U-N-S 62-198-5605
OJAI VALLEY COMMUNITY HOSPITAL
(*Suby of* HEALTHTECH MANAGEMENT SERVICES INC) ★
1306 Maricopa Hwy, Ojai, CA 93023-3131
Tel (805) 646-1401 *Founded/Ownrshp* 1984
Sales 24.9MM *EMP* 120
SIC 8062 General medical & surgical hospitals; General medical & surgical hospitals
Ex Dir: Jim Van Duzer
Chf Rad: Christopher Herzig
**CEO:* Gary Wilde
COO: Adam Thunell
CFO: Norm Bergman
CFO: Kathryn Yamada
VP: Cynthia Demotte
VP: William Kearney
Exec: Kari McPherson
Dir Inf Cn: Cathy Estill
Dir Lab: Doug Homze
Dir Rad: John Miller
Dir Rx: Gene Day
Board of Directors: Van Duzer

OJAI VALLEY INN & SPA
See OVIS LLC

D-U-N-S 02-600-8347
OJAI VALLEY INN GOLF COURSE
OJAI VALLEY SPA
905 Country Club Rd, Ojai, CA 93023-3789
Tel (805) 646-2420 *Founded/Ownrshp* 2004
Sales 8.5MM^E *EMP* 600
SIC 7011 7992 5941 Resort hotel; Public golf courses; Sporting goods & bicycle shops; Resort hotel; Public golf courses; Sporting goods & bicycle shops
CTO: Armie Mar

OJAI VALLEY SPA
See OJAI VALLEY INN GOLF COURSE

OJIBWA LANES & LOUNGE
See KEWEENAW BAY INDIAN COMMUNITY (INC)

D-U-N-S 83-860-5087
OK APPLE INC
170 Wind Chime Ct, Raleigh, NC 27615-6433
Tel (919) 846-2577 *Founded/Ownrshp* 1991
Sales 14.9MM^E *EMP* 551
SIC 5812 Restaurant, family: chain; Restaurant, family: chain
Pr: Michael Olander

D-U-N-S 07-874-2522
OK COMPOUNDING LLC
10106 S Sheridan Rd, Tulsa, OK 74133-6731
Tel (918) 396-0100 *Founded/Ownrshp* 2013
Sales 25.0MM *EMP* 13
SIC 5961 Pharmaceuticals, mail order; Pharmaceuticals, mail order

D-U-N-S 00-633-8057
OK INDUSTRIES INC (AR)
(*Suby of* INDUSTRIAS BACHOCO, S.A.B. DE C.V.)
4601 N 6th St, Fort Smith, AR 72904-2208
Tel (479) 783-4186 *Founded/Ownrshp* 1933, 2011
Sales 1.0MMM^E *EMP* 4,000
SIC 2048 2015 0251 Poultry feeds; Poultry, slaughtered & dressed; Poultry, processed: fresh; Poultry, processed; Broiling chickens, raising of; Poultry feeds; Poultry, slaughtered & dressed; Poultry, processed: fresh; Poultry, processed; Broiling chickens, raising of
Pr: Randall W Goins
CFO: Ron Brown
**CFO:* Ronald E Brown

D-U-N-S 18-616-6104
OK INTERIORS CORP
11100 Ashburn Rd, Cincinnati, OH 45240-3813
Tel (513) 742-3278 *Founded/Ownrshp* 1984
Sales 27.0MM *EMP* 150
Accts Kohrman Frye & Associates Ci
SIC 1742 5031 1751 1752 5046 Acoustical & ceiling work; Doors; Window & door (prefabricated) installation; Access flooring system installation; Partitions
Pr: Todd Prewitt
**Pr:* Loren Schramm
**VP:* Stephen Schramm

D-U-N-S 07-319-4607 IMP
■ **OK INTERNATIONAL INC**
(*Suby of* DOVER ENGINEERED SYSTEMS INC) ★
12151 Monarch St, Garden Grove, CA 92841-2927
Tel (714) 799-9910 *Founded/Ownrshp* 2005
Sales 29.1MM^E *EMP* 225^E
SIC 3548

D-U-N-S 36-127-4769
OK PETROLEUM INTERNATIONAL LTD
185 Route 109, West Babylon, NY 11704-6211
Tel (631) 321-0549 *Founded/Ownrshp* 1993
Sales 58.0MM *EMP* 10^E
SIC 5172 Petroleum products; Petroleum products
Pr: Nick Musacchia
**CFO:* John Musacchia

OK PRODUCE
See CHARLIES ENTERPRISES

D-U-N-S 80-618-6904 IMP/EXP
OKABASHI BRANDS INC
4823 Roy Carlson Blvd, Buford, GA 30518-3576
Tel (770) 945-1330 *Founded/Ownrshp* 1992
Sales 35.8MM^E *EMP* 100
SIC 3021 5139 3144 3143 Shoes, rubber or plastic molded to fabric; Footwear; Slippers, house; Women's footwear, except athletic; Men's footwear, except athletic; Shoes, rubber or plastic molded to fabric; Footwear; Slippers, house; Women's footwear, except athletic; Men's footwear, except athletic
CEO: Bahman Irvani
**Ex VP:* Kerry Cunningham
DP Dir: Cheryl Meyers

OKALOOSA COUNTY BOARD
See COUNTY OF OKALOOSA

D-U-N-S 06-953-0947
OKALOOSA COUNTY SCHOOL DISTRICT (FL)
120 Lowery Pl Se, Fort Walton Beach, FL 32548-5547
Tel (850) 689-7300 *Founded/Ownrshp* 1900
Sales 274.1M *EMP* 3,400
SIC 8211 Public elementary & secondary schools; Public elementary & secondary schools
IT Man: Diane Holman
Opers Mgr: Donna Pease
Teacher Pr: Stacey Smith
HC Dir: Andy Johnson
Pgrm Dir: Ryan Gore

D-U-N-S 01-038-7272 IMP
OKALOOSA GAS DISTRICT
364 Valparaiso Pkwy, Valparaiso, FL 32580-1204
Tel (850) 729-4700 *Founded/Ownrshp* 1953
Sales 33.1MM *EMP* 153
Accts Carr Riggs & Ingram Llc Des
SIC 4923 5722 4924 Gas transmission & distribution; Gas household appliances; Natural gas distribution; Gas transmission & distribution; Gas household appliances; Natural gas distribution
CEO: Jose Lozano
Bd of Dir: Dennis Reeves
Bd of Dir: C Rigdon
**VP:* Anne Bauer

D-U-N-S 80-381-9684 IMP
OKAMOTO SANDUSKY MANUFACTURING LLC
OKAMOTO USA
3130 W Monroe St, Sandusky, OH 44870-1811
Tel (419) 626-1633 *Founded/Ownrshp* 2007
Sales 26.4MM^E *EMP* 100
SIC 3069 Bibs, vulcanized rubber or rubberized fabric
Pr: Yoshiyuki Okamoto
VP: Yuji Tanaka
Plnt Mgr: Tom Chiantello
Plnt Mgr: Laddie Miklovic

OKAMOTO USA
See OKAMOTO SANDUSKY MANUFACTURING LLC

OKANOGAN COUNTY
See COUNTY OF OKANOGAN

OKANOGAN COUNTY P U D #1
See PUBLIC UTILITY DISTRICT 1 OF OKANOGAN COUNTY

D-U-N-S 07-184-5317
OKANOGAN COUNTY PUBLIC HOSPITAL DISTRICT 3
MID-VALLEY HOSPITAL
810 Jasmine St, OMAK, WA 98841-9578
Tel (509) 826-1760 *Founded/Ownrshp* 1963
Sales 34.0MM^E *EMP* 246
SIC 8062 8011 General medical & surgical hospitals; General medical & surgical hospitals; Primary care medical clinic
CFO: Holly Stanley
Dir Lab: Sara Root
Dir Rad: Chrystal Atwood
IT Man: Kendal Ingraham
Phys Thrpy: Charlene Desautel
Snr Mgr: Becky Corson

D-U-N-S 07-665-0662
OKANOGAN COUNTY PUBLIC HOSPITAL DISTRICT 4
NORTH VALLEY HOSPITAL
203 S Western Ave, Tonasket, WA 98855-8803
Tel (509) 486-2151 *Founded/Ownrshp* 1972
Sales 30.4MM^E *EMP* 255
SIC 8062 8051 General medical & surgical hospitals; Skilled nursing care facilities; General medical & surgical hospitals; Skilled nursing care facilities
CEO: Linda Michelle
**CFO:* Bomi Bharucha
VP: Mary Beckler
Dir Rad: Shane Pyper
Sfty Dirs: Kim Jacobs
Mktg Dir: Terri Orford

D-U-N-S 07-926-8314
OKANOGAN DOUGLAS COUNTY DISTRICT HOSPITAL
BREWSTER HOSPITAL
507 Hospital Way, Brewster, WA 98812
Tel (509) 689-2517 *Founded/Ownrshp* 1950
Sales 32.8MM^E *EMP* 175
SIC 8062 8011 General medical & surgical hospitals; Physicians' office, including specialists; General medical & surgical hospitals; Physicians' office, including specialists
Ch: Dan Webster
**Prin:* Mike Pruett
**Prin:* Jerry Tretwold
Mktg Dir: Rebecca Meadows

D-U-N-S 00-598-3564
OKAW FARMERS CO OPERATIVE INC (IL)
1545 Cr 1900n, Cadwell, IL 61911-6000
Tel (217) 543-2157 *Founded/Ownrshp* 1935
Sales 23.0MM *EMP* 16
Accts Robert D Beerup-Illinois Agri
SIC 5191 5153 Farm supplies; Grain elevators; Farm supplies; Grain elevators
Pr: Jeffery E Myers

D-U-N-S 07-178-7381
OKAW TRUSS INC
368 E Sr 133, Arthur, IL 61911-6232
Tel (217) 543-3371 *Founded/Ownrshp* 2011
Sales 83.0MM^E *EMP* 425
SIC 2439 3441 Trusses, except roof: laminated lumber; Fabricated structural metal; Trusses, except roof: laminated lumber; Fabricated structural metal
Pr: Fred Helmuth
Genl Mgr: Elvin M Schrock
Trfc Dir: Menno Miller
Prd Mgr: Darrell Beachy

D-U-N-S 00-181-7006 IMP
OKAYA (USA) INC (NY)
(*Suby of* OKAYA & CO., LTD.)
64 W Seegers Rd, Arlington Heights, IL 60005-3917
Tel (847) 621-5530 *Founded/Ownrshp* 1964
Sales 70.4MM^E *EMP* 60
Accts Eos Accountants Llp Schaumbur
SIC 5084 5085 5051 Industrial machinery & equipment; Industrial supplies; Iron & steel (ferrous) products; Industrial machinery & equipment; Industrial supplies; Iron & steel (ferrous) products
Pr: Hiroaki Sato
**CEO:* Masaaki Takizawa
**Treas:* Kenji Shiratori
Genl Mgr: Yasuo Ito
Genl Mgr: Michinori Odate
Genl Mgr: Koichi Okochi
Genl Mgr: Masahide Yamazaki
Sls Mgr: Fumiaki Akatsuka
Sls Mgr: Masa Ota
Sls Mgr: Kazuki Sasaki

OKC DODGERS
See MB OKC LLC

OKCPS
See OKLAHOMA CITY PUBLIC SCHOOLS

D-U-N-S 00-453-1067
OKEE INDUSTRIES INC (CT)
BUILDERS HARDWARE
91 Shield St, West Hartford, CT 06110-1969
Tel (860) 953-1234 *Founded/Ownrshp* 1947
Sales 27.2MM^E *EMP* 70
SIC 5072 5031 Builders' hardware; Metal doors, sash & trim; Door frames, all materials; Doors
Pr: Sean O'Keefe
Ex VP: Thomas P Haverkampf

D-U-N-S 07-602-3639
OKEECHOBEE COUNTY OF (INC)
207 Sw Park St, Okeechobee, FL 34972-4160
Tel (863) 462-5350 *Founded/Ownrshp* 1917
Sales NA *EMP* 279
Accts Clifton Larson Allen Llp Sebr
SIC 9111 Executive offices; ; Executive offices;
Prin: Sharon Robertson

OKEECHOBEE COUNTY SCHOOL BOARD
See SCHOOL BOARD OF OKEECHOBEE COUNTY

D-U-N-S 07-979-8958
OKEECHOBEE COUNTY SCHOOL DISTRICT
700 Sw 2nd Ave, Okeechobee, FL 34974-5117
Tel (863) 462-5000 *Founded/Ownrshp* 2015
Sales 11.1MM^E *EMP* 565^E
SIC 8211 Public elementary & secondary schools
Prin: Carol Revels
MIS Dir: Shawna May
Dir IT: Karen Matthews

D-U-N-S 09-493-1169
■ **OKEECHOBEE HOSPITAL INC**
HCA HEALTHCARE
(*Suby of* HCA INC) ★
1796 Us Highway 441 N, Okeechobee, FL 34972-1918
Tel (863) 763-2151 *Founded/Ownrshp* 1994
Sales 70.4MM *EMP* 350
SIC 8062 General medical & surgical hospitals; General medical & surgical hospitals
Pr: Jack Bovender
Chf Path: Mushtaq Hussain
**CFO:* Bob Risch
Ofcr: Iqbal Ahmed
Dir OR: Stephanie Quiesenberry
Chf Nrs Of: Brian Melear
QA Dir: Mallika Sanker
Doctor: Cheryl Cardy
Dir Health: Tecla Abner
Board of Directors: Samuel N Hazen

D-U-N-S 00-726-7933
OKEEFE ELEVATOR CO INC
1402 Jones St, Omaha, NE 68102-3236
Tel (402) 301-1426 *Founded/Ownrshp* 1982
Sales 43.6MM^E *EMP* 125
SIC 5084 1796 Elevators; Elevator installation & conversion; Elevators; Elevator installation & conversion
Pr: Dennis B Wychulis
**Sr VP:* Bret Abels
**VP:* Alan Gilmore

D-U-N-S 00-911-3176 IMP
OKEEFFES INC (CA)
SAFTI FIRST
100 N Hill Dr Ste 12, Brisbane, CA 94005-1010
Tel (415) 822-4222 *Founded/Ownrshp* 1939
Sales 26.0MM^E *EMP* 140
SIC 1793 3446 3231

D-U-N-S 13-061-7731 IMP
OKEELANTA CORP
FLORIDA CRYSTALS
(*Suby of* FANJUL CORP) ★
1 N Clematis St Ste 200, West Palm Beach, FL 33401-5551
Tel (561) 366-5100 *Founded/Ownrshp* 1984
Sales 61.1M *EMP* 300
SIC 2061 2062 Raw cane sugar; Cane sugar refining; Raw cane sugar; Cane sugar refining
Ch Bd: Alfonso Fanjul Jr
**Pr:* Jose Fanjul
**Ex VP:* Donald W Carson
VP: Pepe Fanjul
**VP:* Oscar R Hernandez
Telecom Mg: Sharon Knight
IT Man: Wolfgang Latino
S&M/VP: Eduardo Salazar

OKEENE MILLING CO
See SHAWNEE MILLING CO

D-U-N-S 00-388-1687
OKEFENOKE RURAL ELECTRIC MEMBERSHIP CORP (GA)
14384 Cleveland St E, Nahunta, GA 31553-2828
Tel (912) 462-5131 *Founded/Ownrshp* 1939
Sales 67.2MM *EMP* 109
SIC 4911 Distribution, electric power; Distribution, electric power
CEO: John Middleton
**Sec:* Anthony Ham
Bd of Dir: Thomas Proudfoot
IT Man: Jonathan Brauda

OKEMO MOUNTAIN AREA SHOP
See OKEMO MOUNTAIN INC

D-U-N-S 01-911-2226 IMP
OKEMO MOUNTAIN INC
OKEMO MOUNTAIN AREA SHOP
77 Okemo Ridge Rd, Ludlow, VT 05149-9692
Tel (802) 228-4041 *Founded/Ownrshp* 1983
Sales 32.3MM^E *EMP* 275
SIC 7999 7011 5812 Aerial tramway or ski lift, amusement or scenic; Ski lodge; Resort hotel; Eating places; Aerial tramway or ski lift, amusement or scenic; Ski lodge; Resort hotel; Eating places
Pr: Tim Mueller
**Treas:* Diane Mueller
VP: Ellen Demers
**VP:* Daniel Petraska
Genl Mgr: Jim Remy
CIO: Ray O'Connell
CTO: Donna Cahill
VP Mktg: Dave Kulis
Mktg Dir: Barbara Johnston

D-U-N-S 09-966-3916
OKEMOS PUBLIC SCHOOLS
4406 Okemos Rd, Okemos, MI 48864-1792
Tel (517) 706-5010 *Founded/Ownrshp* 1930
Sales 50.1MM *EMP* 650
Accts Maner Costerisan Pc Lansing
SIC 8211 Public combined elementary & secondary school; Public combined elementary & secondary school

D-U-N-S 01-340-5167 IMP
OKI DATA AMERICAS INC
O K I
(*Suby of* OKI DATA CORPORATION)
2000 Bishops Gate Blvd, Mount Laurel, NJ 08054-4603
Tel (856) 235-2600 *Founded/Ownrshp* 1999
Sales 157.9MM^E *EMP* 400
SIC 5045 Computer peripheral equipment; Computer peripheral equipment
Pr: Masahiko Morioka
CFO: Joe Riley
CFO: Akio Samata
Ofcr: Susan De Mars
Ex VP: Mitsuaki Takahara
VP: Steve Boyd
VP: Jim Butterworth
VP: Clifford Mingle
VP: Diane Polinsky
VP: Vito Torregiano
Exec: Earleen Cicalese

D-U-N-S 04-388-8143
OKI DEVELOPMENTS INC (WA)
OKI GOLF
1416 112th Ave Ne, Bellevue, WA 98004-3710
Tel (425) 454-2800 *Founded/Ownrshp* 1993
Sales 25.4MM^E *EMP* 450
SIC 7992 Public golf courses; Public golf courses
CEO: Nancy Cho
**CFO:* Mark Chriest
**Ch:* Scott Oki
**VP:* David Hein
Dir Soc: Devin Prenevost
CIO: Peter Hansen
IT Man: Dan Reeves
Mktg Dir: Vince Kiteley
Sls Dir: Rich Strauss

D-U-N-S 04-888-4670 IMP
OKI FURNITURE FAIR INC
7200 Dixie Hwy, Fairfield, OH 45014-5545
Tel (513) 874-5553 *Founded/Ownrshp* 1971
Sales 50.3MM *EMP* 350
SIC 5712

OKI GOLF
See OKI DEVELOPMENTS INC

D-U-N-S 03-026-5342
OKIN-WALLACK CORP
GREEN ART ENTERPRISE
65 S Columbus Ave, Freeport, NY 11520-3940
Tel (516) 379-0449 *Founded/Ownrshp* 1946
Sales 83.6MM[E] *EMP* 85[E]
SIC 5074 Plumbing & hydronic heating supplies; Heating equipment (hydronic); Plumbing & hydronic heating supplies; Heating equipment (hydronic)
Pr: Lewis Okin
CFO: Herb Rosenberg
VP: Alex Okin

D-U-N-S 07-122-0438
OKLAHOMA BAPTIST UNIVERSITY
OBU
500 W University St, Shawnee, OK 74804-2522
Tel (405) 275-2850 *Founded/Ownrshp* 1987
Sales 62.3MM *EMP* 200
SIC 8221

D-U-N-S 08-553-2224
OKLAHOMA BLOOD INSTITUTE
901 N Lincoln Blvd, Oklahoma City, OK 73104-3206
Tel (405) 278-3100 *Founded/Ownrshp* 1976
Sales 44.4MM[E] *EMP* 680[E]
Accts Grant Thornton Llp Oklahoma C
SIC 8099 Blood bank; Blood bank
Pr: John Armitage MD
Dir Vol: Nikki Beverly
Dir Vol: Dawn Riden
Ofcr: Pandora Crawford
Comm Man: Jamie Davis
Comm Man: Lindsay Hix
Comm Man: Emily Ward
Genl Mgr: Dustin Conover
CIO: J P Potter

D-U-N-S 78-582-8427
OKLAHOMA CARDIOVASCULAR ASSOCIATES PC
4050 W Memorial Rd, Oklahoma City, OK 73120-8382
Tel (405) 608-3800 *Founded/Ownrshp* 1997
Sales 30.0MM[E] *EMP* 425
SIC 8011 Cardiologist & cardio-vascular specialist; Cardiologist & cardio-vascular specialist
Pr: Ronald White
CEO: Patrick Hallaway
CFO: Mark Klakulak
VP: Jack Collier
**VP:* Dr John Harvey
Doctor: Philip Adamson
Doctor: Mark R Bodenhame
Doctor: Robert Bodenhamer
Doctor: Ronald Hope
Doctor: Todd Lindley
Doctor: Andrea McCoy

D-U-N-S 04-344-4355
OKLAHOMA CHRISTIAN UNIVERSITY INC (OK)
CASCADE COLLEGE
2501 E Memorial Rd, Edmond, OK 73013-5525
Tel (405) 425-5000 *Founded/Ownrshp* 1947, 2002
Sales 62.8MM *EMP* 300
SIC 8221 College, except junior; College, except junior
Pr: John Desteiguer
**Ch Bd:* Don Millican
Pr: Bill Goad
**Pr:* Mike E O'Neal
CFO: Christelle Kwizera
Treas: Pat Jones
Bd of Dir: Kathy Thompson
Ofcr: Kent Allen
Ofcr: Bo Hurst
**Ex VP:* Alfred C Branch
VP: Risa Forrester
VP: Terry Winn

D-U-N-S 07-734-7227
OKLAHOMA CITY ABSTRACT & TITLE CO INC
1000 W 15th St, Edmond, OK 73013-3026
Tel (405) 348-8605 *Founded/Ownrshp* 1907
Sales 23.0MM[E] *EMP* 75
SIC 6541 6163 Title & trust companies; Loan brokers
Ch: Connie Dixson
**Pr:* Dennise D Dixon-Rund
**Ex VP:* E C Sanders
**Sr VP:* Tula Fessenden
IT Man: Mary Brackett

D-U-N-S 05-371-5611
OKLAHOMA CITY CLINIC A PROFESSIONAL CORP
701 Ne 10th St, Oklahoma City, OK 73104-5403
Tel (405) 280-5700 *Founded/Ownrshp* 1919
Sales 38.1MM[E] *EMP* 489
SIC 8011 Clinic, operated by physicians; Clinic, operated by physicians
**Pr:* Steven Smith MD
CFO: John Donaghue
**VP:* Tom Russell MD
Assoc Dir: C D York
Ex Dir: A W Facmga
Off Mgr: Kelly Lawson
IT Man: Afton Gille
Podiatrist: Bradley Johnston
Doctor: Debra A Metheny

D-U-N-S 07-428-8952
OKLAHOMA CITY COMMUNITY COLLEGE
OCCC
7777 S May Ave, Oklahoma City, OK 73159-4419
Tel (405) 682-1611 *Founded/Ownrshp* 1971
Sales 30.2MM *EMP* 600
Accts Hinkle & Company Pc Tulsa Ok
SIC 8222 Community college; Community college
Pr: Paul W Sechrist
Pr: C Randy
CFO: Art Bode
Sr Cor Off: Debra Vaughn
Ofcr: William Hall
Ofcr: Patrick Martino
Ofcr: Arnold Nelson
Ofcr: Ronald Ventresca
Ofcr: Jimmie Watts
**Ex VP:* Jerry Steward
**VP:* John Boyd
VP: Angie Christopher
Assoc Dir: Terri Walker
Comm Dir: Elwyn Hastings

D-U-N-S 10-107-6693
OKLAHOMA CITY COMMUNITY FOUNDATION INC
1000 N Broadway Ave, Oklahoma City, OK 73102-5827
Tel (405) 235-5603 *Founded/Ownrshp* 1969
Sales 30.5MM *EMP* 18
Accts Cole & Reed Pc Oklahoma Cit
SIC 8741 8733 6732 Administrative management; Noncommercial research organizations; Trusts: educational, religious, etc.; Administrative management; Noncommercial research organizations; Trusts: educational, religious, etc.
Ex Dir: Nancy Anthony
Ofcr: Gayle Farley
VP: James H Holloman Jr
Dir IT: Mike Murphy

D-U-N-S 82-968-9363
OKLAHOMA CITY ENVIRONMENTAL ASSISTANCE TRUST
(*Suby of* CITY OF OKLAHOMA CITY) ★
200 N Walker Ave Ste 302, Oklahoma City, OK 73102-2232
Tel (405) 297-2424 *Founded/Ownrshp* 1904
Sales 13.8MM[E] *EMP* 4,000
SIC 8611 Business associations; Business associations

OKLAHOMA CITY PUBLIC SCHOOLS
See BOARD OF EDUCATION OF INDEPENDENT SCHOOL DISTRICT

D-U-N-S 61-741-5211
OKLAHOMA CITY PUBLIC SCHOOLS
OKCPS
900 N Klein Ave, Oklahoma City, OK 73106-7036
Tel (405) 587-0000 *Founded/Ownrshp* 1910
Sales 8.5MM[E] *EMP* 7,000
SIC 8211 Public elementary & secondary schools

D-U-N-S 06-544-1842
OKLAHOMA CITY UNIVERSITY
2601 N Kentucky Ave # 511, Oklahoma City, OK 73106-1282
Tel (405) 208-5000 *Founded/Ownrshp* 1904
Sales 109.4MM *EMP* 503
Accts Cole & Reed Pc Oklahoma City
SIC 8221 University; University
Pr: Robert Henry
**Pr:* Thomas Mc Daniel
**CFO:* Brian Holland
Top Exec: Benjamin Chang
**VP:* Mary Coffey
VP: Elizabeth Donnelly
Assoc Dir: Dennis Arrow
Comm Dir: Melissa Cory
Snr Ntwrk: John Kuper
CIO: Benjamin Hinchman

D-U-N-S 07-733-3656
OKLAHOMA CONFERENCE OF UNITED METHODIST CHURCH
UNITED METHODIST MINISTRY CTR
1501 Nw 24th St, Oklahoma City, OK 73106-3635
Tel (405) 530-2000 *Founded/Ownrshp* 1968
Sales 24.7MM[E] *EMP* 110
Accts Finley & Cook Pllc
SIC 8721 8741 Methodist Church; Accounting, auditing & bookkeeping; Financial management for business
Assoc Dir: Gene Brantley
Assoc Dir: Richard Norman
Dir IT: Mary Myers

D-U-N-S 80-992-9490
OKLAHOMA DEPARTMENT OF AGRICULTURE FOOD AND FORESTRY
ODAFF
(*Suby of* EXECUTIVE OFFICE OF STATE OF OKLAHOMA) ★
2800 N Lincoln Blvd, Oklahoma City, OK 73105-4207
Tel (405) 521-3864 *Founded/Ownrshp* 1907
Sales NA *EMP* 500
SIC 9641 Regulation of agricultural marketing; ; Regulation of agricultural marketing;
Ofcr: Donna McDaniel

D-U-N-S 82-470-0058
OKLAHOMA DEPARTMENT OF COMMERCE
(*Suby of* EXECUTIVE OFFICE OF STATE OF OKLAHOMA) ★
900 N Stiles Ave, Oklahoma City, OK 73104-3234
Tel (405) 815-6552 *Founded/Ownrshp* 1987
Sales NA *EMP* 1,007
Accts Finnely & Cook
SIC 9611 Administration of general economic programs; ; Administration of general economic programs;
Ex Dir: Kathy Taylor
Pr: Christie Myers
Ofcr: Matilda Anderson
Ofcr: Amy Polonchek
Dir Bus: Beth Van Horn
Prgrm Mgr: John Hall
Netwrk Mgr: Bryan Boone
Sls&Mrk Ex: John Ogders
S&M/Dir: John Reid
Pgrm Dir: Kirk Martin
Pgrm Dir: Kathy McLaughlin

D-U-N-S 80-992-9649
OKLAHOMA DEPARTMENT OF EDUCATION
EXECUTVE OFFCE OF THE STATE OF
(*Suby of* EXECUTIVE OFFICE OF STATE OF OKLAHOMA) ★
2500 N Lincoln Blvd # 112, Oklahoma City, OK 73105-4503
Tel (405) 521-3301 *Founded/Ownrshp* 1907
Sales NA *EMP* 286
SIC 9411 ;
Prin: Janet Parrise
Comm Man: Clifton Scott
MIS Dir: Tammie Hall
IT Man: Debra Heitkamp
Pr Dir: Phil Bacharach
Teacher Pr: Heather Griswold

D-U-N-S 93-360-1569
OKLAHOMA DEPARTMENT OF ENVIRONMENTAL QUALITY
(*Suby of* OKLAHOMA SECRETARY OF ENERGY & ENVIRONMENT) ★
707 N Robinson Ave, Oklahoma City, OK 73102-6010
Tel (405) 702-6100 *Founded/Ownrshp* 1993
Sales NA *EMP* 478
SIC 9511 Environmental quality & control agency, government; ; Environmental quality & control agency, government;
Prin: Mark S Coleman
Prgrm Mgr: Lynne Moss

D-U-N-S 93-366-2934
OKLAHOMA DEPARTMENT OF MENTAL HEALTH AND SUBSTANCE ABUSE SERVICES
(*Suby of* EXECUTIVE OFFICE OF STATE OF OKLAHOMA) ★
1200 Ne 13th St, Oklahoma City, OK 73117-1022
Tel (405) 522-3878 *Founded/Ownrshp* 2011
Sales 85.3MM[E] *EMP* 1,856[E]
SIC 8399 9431 Health & welfare council; Administration of public health programs; Health & welfare council; Administration of public health programs
**COO:* Dave Statton
Prgrm Mgr: Thomas Thomson
Counsel: Ellen Thomas

D-U-N-S 95-708-5988
OKLAHOMA DEPARTMENT OF REHABILITATION SERVICES
(*Suby of* EXECUTIVE OFFICE OF STATE OF OKLAHOMA) ★
3535 Nw 58th St Ste 500, Oklahoma City, OK 73112-4824
Tel (405) 951-3437 *Founded/Ownrshp* 1993
Sales 38.0MM[E] *EMP* 900[E]
SIC 8322 9431 Social services for the handicapped; Offender self-help agency; ; Social services for the handicapped; Offender self-help agency;
Ex Dir: Joe Cordova
CFO: Cheryl Gray
Ofcr: Kathy Rothenberger
Netwrk Mgr: Ken Washington

D-U-N-S 82-470-0074
OKLAHOMA DEPARTMENT OF TRANSPORTATION
(*Suby of* EXECUTIVE OFFICE OF STATE OF OKLAHOMA) ★
200 Ne 21st St, Oklahoma City, OK 73105-3204
Tel (405) 521-2631 *Founded/Ownrshp* 1986
Sales NA *EMP* 2,600
SIC 9621 Regulation, administration of transportation; Regulation, administration of transportation;
VP: Darrel Mason
VP: Alan Stevenson
Comm Man: Ty Todd
Brnch Mgr: Richard Buchanan
QA Dir: Keith Stout
Counsel: Louis Persons

D-U-N-S 94-534-9892
OKLAHOMA DEPARTMENT OF WILDLIFE CONSERVATION
EXECUTIVE OFFICE OF THE STATE
(*Suby of* EXECUTIVE OFFICE OF STATE OF OKLAHOMA) ★
1801 N Lincoln Blvd, Oklahoma City, OK 73105-4908
Tel (405) 521-3855 *Founded/Ownrshp* 1956
Sales NA *EMP* 350
SIC 9512 Land, mineral & wildlife conservation; ; Land, mineral & wildlife conservation;
IT Man: David Southerland

D-U-N-S 80-992-9904
OKLAHOMA DEPT OF HUMAN SERVICES
(*Suby of* EXECUTIVE OFFICE OF STATE OF OKLAHOMA) ★
2400 N Lincoln Blvd, Oklahoma City, OK 73105-4601
Tel (405) 521-3646 *Founded/Ownrshp* 1936
Sales NA *EMP* 8,000
SIC 9431 9441 Administration of public health programs; ; ; Administration of public health programs;
;
**COO:* Marq Youngblood
**CFO:* Phil Motley
Ofcr: Paula Hearn
MIS Dir: Bryan Moore
IT Man: John Guin
IT Man: Dennis Taylor
Counsel: John Fears
Counsel: Richard Freeman

D-U-N-S 88-489-3264
OKLAHOMA DEPT OF MILITARY
ADJUTANT GENERALS OFFICE
(*Suby of* EXECUTIVE OFFICE OF STATE OF OKLAHOMA) ★
3501 Ne Military Cir, Oklahoma City, OK 73111-4305
Tel (405) 228-5000 *Founded/Ownrshp* 1951
Sales NA *EMP* 9,979
SIC 9111 Governors' offices; ; Governors' offices;
Prin: Maj Gen Harry M Wyatt III
Brnch Mgr: Jack Self
Software D: Joni Seymour

D-U-N-S 82-470-0017
OKLAHOMA DEPT OF PUBLIC SAFETY
HIGHWAY PATROL
(*Suby of* EXECUTIVE OFFICE OF STATE OF OKLAHOMA) ★
3600 N Martin Luther Knl, Oklahoma City, OK 73111-4223
Tel (405) 425-2424 *Founded/Ownrshp* 1937
Sales NA *EMP* 1,400
SIC 9229 Public order & safety statistics centers; ; Public order & safety statistics centers;
Exec: Ward Kevin
Counsel: Joseph Claro

D-U-N-S 82-470-0033
OKLAHOMA DEPT OF TOURISM AND RECREATION
EXECUTIVE OFFC OF THE ST OF OK
(*Suby of* EXECUTIVE OFFICE OF STATE OF OKLAHOMA) ★
120 N Robinson Ave # 600, Oklahoma City, OK 73102-7509
Tel (405) 230-8300 *Founded/Ownrshp* 1972
Sales NA *EMP* 1,500
SIC 9611 Administration of general economic programs; ; Administration of general economic programs;
Ex Dir: Deby Snobgrass
CFO: Nathan Gunter
**CFO:* Lisa McKim

D-U-N-S 82-470-0025
OKLAHOMA DEPT OF VETERANS AFFAIRS
(*Suby of* EXECUTIVE OFFICE OF STATE OF OKLAHOMA) ★
2311 N Central Ave # 100, Oklahoma City, OK 73105-3200
Tel (405) 521-3684 *Founded/Ownrshp* 1994
Sales NA *EMP* 971
SIC 9199 General government administration; ; General government administration;

D-U-N-S 00-790-6027
OKLAHOMA ELECTRIC CO-OPERATIVE INC
OKLAHOMA ELECTRIC COOPERATIVE
242 24th Ave Nw, Norman, OK 73069-6371
Tel (405) 321-2024 *Founded/Ownrshp* 1937
Sales 142.2MM *EMP* 103
SIC 4911 2721 Distribution, electric power; Periodicals; Distribution, electric power; Periodicals
Genl Mgr: Max Meek
Pr: Patrick Grace
VP: John Spencer
Exec: Randy Harnsberger
IT Man: Derek Looper
Sfty Mgr: James Long
Snr Mgr: Pat Brown

OKLAHOMA ELECTRIC COOPERATIVE
See OKLAHOMA ELECTRIC CO-OPERATIVE INC

D-U-N-S 00-720-5511
OKLAHOMA ELECTRICAL SUPPLY CO
OESCO
4901 N Sewell Ave, Oklahoma City, OK 73118-7800
Tel (405) 525-9900 *Founded/Ownrshp* 1909
Sales 35.8MM[E] *EMP* 220
SIC 1731

D-U-N-S 02-191-7174
OKLAHOMA EMPLOYEES CREDIT UNION
OECU
3001 N Lincoln Blvd, Oklahoma City, OK 73105-4209
Tel (405) 606-6328 *Founded/Ownrshp* 1954
Sales NA *EMP* 50
SIC 6062 State credit unions, not federally chartered; State credit unions, not federally chartered
Pr: Mark W Kelly
**Ch Bd:* S C Byers
COO: Luann Schmideil
**Sec:* Paul Rachel
**V Ch Bd:* Mike Patterson
Ofcr: Darrell Johnson
**Sr VP:* Karen Tyree
VP: Scott Bell
VP: Jim Vanwinkle
Brnch Mgr: Matt Dunn
Opers Mgr: Brian Gebard

D-U-N-S 12-259-4716
OKLAHOMA FARM BUREAU INC
2501 N Stiles Ave, Oklahoma City, OK 73105-3119
Tel (405) 523-2300 *Founded/Ownrshp* 1970
Sales 2.3MM *EMP* 300
SIC 8699 Farm bureau; Farm bureau
Pr: Mike Spradling
Treas: Seth Brookman
**VP:* Billy Gibson
Comm Dir: Sam Knipp
Sls Mgr: Jim Hall

D-U-N-S 00-790-6654
OKLAHOMA FARM BUREAU MUTUAL INSURANCE CO (OK)
FARM BUREAU INSURANCE
2501 N Stiles Ave, Oklahoma City, OK 73105-3119
Tel (405) 523-2300 *Founded/Ownrshp* 1946
Sales NA *EMP* 300
SIC 6331 6351 Fire, marine & casualty insurance & carriers; Fire, marine & casualty insurance: mutual; Automobile insurance; Property damage insurance; Liability insurance; Fire, marine & casualty insurance & carriers; Fire, marine & casualty insurance: mutual; Automobile insurance; Property damage insurance; Liability insurance
Pr: Steve Kouplen
Ex VP: Richard Newberry
Ex VP: Darrayl Sinclair
VP: Thad Doye
VP: Bob Sheehan
VP: John Wiscaver
Dir IT: Marla Peek
IT Man: Chris Howard
Netwrk Mgr: Philip Miller

D-U-N-S 00-790-6662
■ **OKLAHOMA GAS AND ELECTRIC CO**
(*Suby of* OGE ENERGY CORP) ★
321 N Harvey Ave, Oklahoma City, OK 73102-3405
Tel (405) 553-3000 *Founded/Ownrshp* 1902
Sales 2.4MMM *EMP* 1,884
Accts Ernst & Young Llp Oklahoma Ci
SIC 4911 Distribution, electric power; Generation, electric power; Transmission, electric power; Distribution, electric power; Generation, electric power; Transmission, electric power
Ch Bd: Peter B Delaney

Pr: Sean Trauschke
COO: E Keith Mitchell
CFO: Stephen E Merrill
VP: R Trauschke
Genl Couns: William J Bullard
Board of Directors: James H Brandi, Wayne H Brunetti, Luke R Corbett, John D Groendyke, Kirk Humphreys, Robert Kelly, Robert O Lorenz, Judy R McReynolds, Sheila G Talton

D-U-N-S 80-877-7304
OKLAHOMA GENERAL AGENCY INC
ONE GENERAL AGENCY
630 Ne 63rd St, Oklahoma City, OK 73105-6408
Tel (405) 840-9393 *Founded/Ownrshp* 1951
Sales NA *EMP* 30
SIC 6411 Insurance agents, brokers & service; Insurance agents, brokers & service
Pr: Baron Garcia
**Sec:* Jennifer Wood

D-U-N-S 07-428-9430
OKLAHOMA GOODWILL INDUSTRIES INC
316 S Blackwelder Ave, Oklahoma City, OK 73108-1418
Tel (405) 236-4451 *Founded/Ownrshp* 1997
Sales 18.6MM^E *EMP* 350
SIC 8331 3714 3694 3672 3564 3446 Job training services; Vocational training agency; Motor vehicle parts & accessories; Engine electrical equipment; Printed circuit boards; Blowers & fans; Architectural metalwork; Job training services; Vocational training agency; Motor vehicle parts & accessories; Engine electrical equipment; Printed circuit boards; Blowers & fans; Architectural metalwork
CEO: Chris Daniels
VP: Nyree Cunningham
VP: Nyree Stengler
Prgrm Mgr: Ashleigh Curtis
Prgrm Mgr: John Goodwin
Brnch Mgr: Sam Lynn
Dir IT: Ben Schraad
IT Man: Jerry Weddington

D-U-N-S 16-191-2303
OKLAHOMA HEALTH CARE AUTHORITY
4345 N Lincoln Blvd, Oklahoma City, OK 73105-5101
Tel (405) 522-7300 *Founded/Ownrshp* 1996
Sales 205.3MM^E *EMP* 500
SIC 3089 Molding primary plastic; Molding primary plastic
CEO: Nico Gomez
Prgrm Mgr: Daryn Kirkpatrick
Off Mgr: Donna Rolls
Genl Couns: Sharon Hsieh
Genl Couns: Ashley Kemp

D-U-N-S 00-262-2715
OKLAHOMA HEALTH INSURANCE HIGH RISK POOL
6117 Se 9th St, Oklahoma City, OK 73110-2439
Tel (405) 741-8434 *Founded/Ownrshp* 2000
Sales NA *EMP* 1
SIC 6411 Insurance agents, brokers & service; Insurance agents, brokers & service

D-U-N-S 83-610-7201
OKLAHOMA HEALTHCARE SERVICES INC
OXFORD HEALTHCARE
3040 N Hemlock Cir, Broken Arrow, OK 74012-1113
Tel (918) 258-1111 *Founded/Ownrshp* 1991
Sales 9.8MM^E *EMP* 350
SIC 8049 Nurses, registered & practical; Nurses, registered & practical
Pr: Steve Goforth
Prgrm Mgr: Melissa Ervin

D-U-N-S 10-067-9096
OKLAHOMA HEART HOSPITAL LLC
4050 W Memorial Rd, Oklahoma City, OK 73120-8358
Tel (405) 608-3200 *Founded/Ownrshp* 1999
Sales 241.2MM *EMP* 440
Accts Cd Sughru Pllc Edmond Ok
SIC 8069 Specialty hospitals, except psychiatric; Specialty hospitals, except psychiatric
COO: John Austin
CFO: Mark Klakulak
CFO: Carol Walker
Ofcr: Stephanie Gibson
Ofcr: Marcos Hernandez
VP: Jeffrey Taylor
VP: Wendi Wilson
Dir Lab: Teresa Dwiggins
Dir Rx: Tom Richter
CIO: Steve Miller
QA Dir: Holly Ellis

D-U-N-S 83-323-4219
OKLAHOMA HEART HOSPITAL SOUTH LLC
5200 E I 240 Service Rd, Oklahoma City, OK 73135-2610
Tel (405) 628-6000 *Founded/Ownrshp* 2010
Sales NA *EMP* 550
SIC 6324 Hospital & medical service plans; Hospital & medical service plans
CEO: John Harvey MD
Chf Rad: Oscar Falcon
COO: John Austin
Dir Lab: Elaine Moser
Dir Rad: Wes Moles
Dir Rx: Gail Schmidt
CIO: Deanna Armitage
Psych: Terry Pace

D-U-N-S 78-535-7351
OKLAHOMA HEART INC
OKLAHOMA HEART INSTITUTE
1265 S Utica Ave Ste 300, Tulsa, OK 74104-4243
Tel (918) 592-0999 *Founded/Ownrshp* 1989
Sales 21.1MM *EMP* 165
SIC 8011 Cardiologist & cardio-vascular specialist; Cardiologist & cardio-vascular specialist
CEO: Donna Russell-Cook
Pr: Gwen Asche
**Pr:* Wayne Leimbach MD
Bd of Dir: Roger D Prez
Off Mgr: Steve Struttmann
Opers Mgr: Harriet Vaughn
Surgeon: Edward Coleman
Doctor: Raj H Candwaney MD
Doctor: Robert Lynch
Doctor: James Nemec MD

OKLAHOMA HEART INSTITUTE
See OKLAHOMA HEART INC

D-U-N-S 60-194-7992
OKLAHOMA INVESTIGATIVE GROUP INC
TRICORPS SECURITY
12312 Hidden Forest Blvd, Oklahoma City, OK 73142-2536
Tel (405) 621-9006 *Founded/Ownrshp* 2004
Sales 22.9MM *EMP* 850
SIC 7381 Security guard service; Private investigator; Security guard service; Private investigator
Pr: David Ross
CFO: Kurtis Hanni
Rgnl Mgr: Tony Brown
Rgnl Mgr: Jayson Richardson
Snr Mgr: Chad Bradley

D-U-N-S 06-542-6355
OKLAHOMA INVESTMENT CASTING CO
O I C C
(*Suby of* CENTRAL MACHINE & TOOLS) ★
708 N 29th St, Blackwell, OK 74631-2412
Tel (580) 363-1412 *Founded/Ownrshp* 1984
Sales 43.8MM^E *EMP* 350
SIC 3324 Commercial investment castings, ferrous; Commercial investment castings, ferrous
Pr: James R Parrish
**Sec:* Jerry Koehn
Genl Mgr: Cary Meister
Off Mgr: Jenny Dewitt

D-U-N-S 62-342-4751
OKLAHOMA KENWORTH INC
MHC KENWORTH
(*Suby of* MURPHY-HOFFMAN CO) ★
7200 W I 40 Service Rd, Oklahoma City, OK 73128-1204
Tel (405) 717-4500 *Founded/Ownrshp* 1975
Sales 62.7MM^E *EMP* 180
SIC 5012 5511 Truck tractors; Pickups, new & used; Truck tractors; Pickups, new & used
Ex VP: Kenneth Hoffman
**CFO:* Jeffrey W Johnson
**Treas:* Reed Murphy Jr

D-U-N-S 04-111-4666
OKLAHOMA MAGIC LP
PIZZA HUT
6516 N Olie Ave Ste C, Oklahoma City, OK 73116-7399
Tel (405) 858-0500 *Founded/Ownrshp* 1995
Sales 9.6MM^E *EMP* 600
SIC 5812 Pizzeria, chain; Pizzeria, chain
Pr: Howe McCoy
**Mktg Dir:* Darla Welchel

D-U-N-S 07-733-3797
OKLAHOMA MEDICAL RESEARCH FOUNDATION
O M R F
825 Ne 13th St, Oklahoma City, OK 73104-5005
Tel (405) 271-7240 *Founded/Ownrshp* 1946
Sales 69.4MM *EMP* 450
SIC 8733 Medical research; Medical research
Pr: Dr Stephen M Prescott
COO: Chip Morgan
CFO: Timothy Hassen
VP: Mike Bates
VP: Steven Blair
VP: Penny Elsenraat
VP: Robert Floyd
VP: Paul Kincade
VP: Day Lisa
**VP:* Mike D Morgan
VP: Penny Voss
Exec: Rheal A Towner

D-U-N-S 10-240-7814
OKLAHOMA MENTAL HEALTH COUNCIL INC
RED ROCK BEHAVIORAL HLTH SVCS
4400 N Lincoln Blvd, Oklahoma City, OK 73105-5104
Tel (405) 424-7711 *Founded/Ownrshp* 1967
Sales 31.3MM *EMP* 225
Accts Bkd Llp Tulsa Oklahoma
SIC 8093 Mental health clinic, outpatient; Mental health clinic, outpatient
CEO: Berna Fouft
COO: Verna Foust
**COO:* David Howlett
**COO:* Richard Pralle
Bd of Dir: O Dell Smith
Dir IT: Stacie Cook
Dir IT: Donald Gaines
IT Man: Raquel Haggard
Doctor: Vivian Hasbrook MD
Doctor: Terri Stonehocker MD

OKLAHOMA METAL PROCESSSING CO.
See DERICHEBOURG RECYCLING USA INC

D-U-N-S 96-862-9506
■ **OKLAHOMA MIDSTREAM GAS SERVICES LLC**
(*Suby of* WILLIAMS PARTNERS LP) ★
525 Central Park Dr # 1005, Oklahoma City, OK 73105-1723
Tel (877) 413-1023 *Founded/Ownrshp* 2011
Sales 2.3MM^E *EMP* 310^E
SIC 4922 Pipelines, natural gas
CEO: J Michael Stice
**COO:* Robert Purgason
**CFO:* David Shiels

D-U-N-S 14-826-8782
OKLAHOMA MUNICIPAL POWER AUTHORITY
OMPA
2701 W I 35 Frontage Rd, Edmond, OK 73013-8543
Tel (405) 340-5047 *Founded/Ownrshp* 1983
Sales 186.6MM *EMP* 50
Accts Baker Tilly Virchow Krause Ll
SIC 4911 Distribution, electric power; Distribution, electric power
Genl Mgr: Cindy Holman
Treas: John Ramey
Bd of Dir: William Martin
Ex VP: Bruce Jackson
Exec: Todd Ossenkop
Brnch Mgr: Jody Derrick
Plnt Mgr: David Huff
Genl Couns: Max Speegle

D-U-N-S 09-341-6329
OKLAHOMA NURSING HOMES LTD
210 E Choctaw Ave, Sallisaw, OK 74955-4604
Tel (918) 775-4439 *Founded/Ownrshp* 1963
Sales 36.1MM^E *EMP* 1,000
SIC 8051 Convalescent home with continuous nursing care; Convalescent home with continuous nursing care
Pt: Lloyd Haskins

D-U-N-S 80-992-9821
OKLAHOMA OFFICE OF MANAGEMENT AND ENTERPRISE SERVICES
(*Suby of* EXECUTIVE OFFICE OF STATE OF OKLAHOMA) ★
2300 N Lincoln Blvd # 122, Oklahoma City, OK 73105-4805
Tel (405) 521-2141 *Founded/Ownrshp* 1947
Sales NA *EMP* 1,600
SIC 9311 Finance, taxation & monetary policy; ; Finance, taxation & monetary policy;
Ofcr: Jim Rhoades
Ofcr: Riley Shaull
Ofcr: Craig Woodruff
Ex VP: Ross Tripp
Genl Mgr: Lynne Bajema
Snr Mgr: Matt Singleton

D-U-N-S 55-604-7918
■ **OKLAHOMA PUBLISHING CO OF OKLAHOMA**
DAILY OKLAHOMAN, THE
(*Suby of* ANSCHUTZ CO) ★
9000 N Brdwy, Oklahoma City, OK 73114
Tel (405) 475-3311 *Founded/Ownrshp* 1903
Sales 11.0MM^E *EMP* 2,600
SIC 2711 1311 6512 7375 2752

D-U-N-S 03-832-2483
OKLAHOMA SAFETY EQUIPMENT CO INC
OSECO
(*Suby of* HALMA HOLDINGS INC) ★
1701 W Tacoma St, Broken Arrow, OK 74012-1449
Tel (918) 258-5626 *Founded/Ownrshp* 1980
Sales 35.4MM^E *EMP* 112
SIC 3499 3491 Aerosol valves, metal; Pressure valves & regulators, industrial; Aerosol valves, metal; Pressure valves & regulators, industrial
Pr: Bryan Sanderlin
**Pr:* Mark Holt
Treas: Jan Singer
**VP:* Rob Barcik
Rgnl Mgr: Shawn McCorkle
IT Man: Todd Ragsdale
Opers Mgr: Laura Zuleger
**VP Sls:* Darren Doyle
S&M/VP: Carol Griffith
Manager: Bob Evans
Sls Mgr: Serge Becker

D-U-N-S 80-992-9789
OKLAHOMA SECRETARY OF ENERGY & ENVIRONMENT
(*Suby of* EXECUTIVE OFFICE OF STATE OF OKLAHOMA) ★
100 N Broadway Ave, Oklahoma City, OK 73102-8614
Tel (405) 285-9213 *Founded/Ownrshp* 1990
Sales NA *EMP* 1,102
SIC 9511 Air, water & solid waste management; ; Air, water & solid waste management;

OKLAHOMA SPINE & ORTHPD HOSP
See OKLAHOMA SPINE HOSPITAL LLC

D-U-N-S 13-200-8231
OKLAHOMA SPINE HOSPITAL LLC
OKLAHOMA SPINE & ORTHPD HOSP
14101 Pkwy Commons Dr, Oklahoma City, OK 73134-6012
Tel (405) 749-2700 *Founded/Ownrshp* 1998
Sales 37.9MM^E *EMP* 250
SIC 8069 Specialty hospitals, except psychiatric; Specialty hospitals, except psychiatric
CEO: Kevin Blaylock
Chf Rad: C Eckman
Dir Lab: Denise Winn
Dir Rad: Sharon Copeland
CTO: Patricia Phillips
Doctor: Robert L Remondino MD
Phys Thrpy: Kyndra McKinstry

OKLAHOMA SPT SCNCE ORTHOPEDICS
See PHYSICIANS GROUP P LLC

D-U-N-S 80-987-5594
OKLAHOMA STATE DEPT OF LABOR
(*Suby of* OKLAHOMA DEPARTMENT OF COMMERCE) ★
3017 N Stiles Ave Ste 100, Oklahoma City, OK 73105-5298
Tel (405) 521-6100 *Founded/Ownrshp* 1907
Sales NA *EMP* 862
SIC 9651 Regulation, miscellaneous commercial sectors; ; Regulation, miscellaneous commercial sectors;
Ofcr: Robert Lassiter
Dir IT: Sherri Henderson
IT Man: Don Wheeler
Snr Mgr: Dusty Pringnitz

D-U-N-S 04-998-7720
OKLAHOMA STATE UNIVERSITY
401 Whitehurst Hall, Stillwater, OK 74078-1030
Tel (405) 744-5892 *Founded/Ownrshp* 2013
Sales 747.4MM *EMP* 8,882
Accts Grant Thornton Llp Oklahoma C
SIC 8221 University; University
Pr: Burns Hargis
Pr: Debbie Lane
VP: Gail Gates
Exec: Jan Pratt
Exec: Grant Rezabek
Assoc Dir: Sharon Nivens
VP Admn: Joe B Weaver
DP Exec: Kaye Bartlett
DP Exec: Chris Becker
DP Exec: Dennis Blankenship
DP Exec: Mark Blubaugh

D-U-N-S 04-488-0214
OKLAHOMA STATE UNIVERSITY FOUNDATION
400 S Monroe St, Stillwater, OK 74074-3322
Tel (405) 385-5100 *Founded/Ownrshp* 1968
Sales 150.0MM *EMP* 47
Accts Kpmg Llp Oklahoma City Ok
SIC 8611 Business associations; Business associations
Pr: Kirk Jewell
**Pr:* Ron Area
Pr: David Loyless
Pr: Brandon Meyer
Ofcr: Matt Clark
Sr VP: Deb Engle
VP: Gary Clark
VP: Diane Crane
VP: David Mays
VP: Kathleen McNally
VP: Kenneth E Sigmon

D-U-N-S 83-048-0427
OKLAHOMA STATE UNIVERSITY MEDICAL CENTER
744 W 9th St, Tulsa, OK 74127-9020
Tel (918) 587-2561 *Founded/Ownrshp* 2004
Sales 133.6MM^E *EMP* 4,000
Accts Bkd Llp Tulsa Ok
SIC 8062 General medical & surgical hospitals; General medical & surgical hospitals
Ch: Robert C Poe
**CEO:* Diane Rafferty
CFO: Craig McKnight
**Ch:* Jerry Hudson
**Prin:* Teresa Burkett

D-U-N-S 09-971-4354
OKLAHOMA STEEL & WIRE CO INC
Hwy 70 S, Madill, OK 73446
Tel (580) 795-7311 *Founded/Ownrshp* 1978
Sales 86.8MM^E *EMP* 400^E
SIC 3496 Fencing, made from purchased wire; Concrete reinforcing mesh & wire; Fencing, made from purchased wire; Concrete reinforcing mesh & wire
Ch Bd: Craig Moore
**Sec:* Colleen Moore
VP: Vicki Fletcher
VP: Janie Laws
**VP:* Kathleen Moore
Admn Mgr: Cliff Donahue
Plnt Mgr: Jay Combs
Prd Mgr: Danny Awalt
S&M/VP: Johnny Raper
Sls Mgr: Carl Robinson

D-U-N-S 83-457-4444
OKLAHOMA STUDENT LOAN AUTHORITY
OSLA STUDENT LOANS SERVICING
525 Central Park Dr # 600, Oklahoma City, OK 73105-1723
Tel (405) 556-9200 *Founded/Ownrshp* 1972
Sales NA *EMP* 70
SIC 6141 Personal credit institutions
Pr: James Farha
VP: Tony Latham
**VP:* W A Rogers

OKLAHOMA SURETY COMPANY
See MID-CONTINENT CASUALTY CO

D-U-N-S 07-242-0813
■ **OKLAHOMA SURETY CO**
(*Suby of* MID-CONTINENT CASUALTY CO) ★
1437 S Boulder Ave # 200, Tulsa, OK 74119-3609
Tel (918) 587-7221 *Founded/Ownrshp* 1995
Sales NA *EMP* 280
SIC 6351 Mortgage guarantee insurance; Mortgage guarantee insurance
Pr: Jim Pierce
**Treas:* Greg Jones
**VP:* Mike Coon

D-U-N-S 01-302-6765
OKLAHOMA SURGICAL HOSPITAL LLC (OK)
2408 E 81st St Ste 900, Tulsa, OK 74137-4283
Tel (918) 477-5000 *Founded/Ownrshp* 1999
Sales 108.8MM *EMP* 400
SIC 8062 General medical & surgical hospitals; General medical & surgical hospitals
CEO: Rick Ferguson
**CFO:* Dub Cleland
Dir OR: Liz Soares
Dir Soc: Beverly Pickett
Dir Rx: Linda Bull
Off Mgr: Madonna Burton
Sls&Mrk Ex: Maryanne Kingdom
Nrsg Dir: Delores Copp
HC Dir: Patty Hawkins

D-U-N-S 00-746-0835
OKLAHOMA TANK LINES INC (OK)
UNITED PETROLEUM TRANSPORT
4312 S Georgia Pl, Oklahoma City, OK 73129-7972
Tel (405) 677-6633 *Founded/Ownrshp* 1966
Sales 34.3MM^E *EMP* 600
SIC 7513 Truck leasing, without drivers; Truck leasing, without drivers
Pr: Greg Price
**COO:* Scott Hunt
**CFO:* Tim M Rains
**Treas:* Margaret Price
VP: Carl Bailey
**VP:* Kevin Price
**VP:* Rod Radcliffe

D-U-N-S 02-073-4265
OKLAHOMA TURNPIKE AUTHORITY
2401 Nw 23rd St Ste 2b, Oklahoma City, OK 73107-2420
Tel (405) 425-3600 *Founded/Ownrshp* 1982
Sales 247.7MM *EMP* 528
Accts Grant Thornton Llp Oklahoma C
SIC 4785 Toll road operation; Toll road operation
Ch: Mr Albert C Kelly Jr
CFO: Holly Lowe
**Ch:* Mr David A Burrage
**Sec:* Mr G Carl Gibson
Ofcr: Eric Strong
CTO: Julie Wells
Dir IT: Tim Kraft
IT Man: Ronny Blankenship
Sfty Mgr: Bob Rayner
Plnt Mgr: David Machamer
Sales Exec: Randy Moore

D-U-N-S 05-609-0319 IMP
OKLAND CONSTRUCTION CO INC
1978 S West Temple, Salt Lake City, UT 84115-7103
Tel (801) 486-0144 *Founded/Ownrshp* 1967
Sales 381.7MM^E *EMP* 600
SIC 1542 1541 Commercial & office building, new construction; Industrial buildings, new construction; Commercial & office building, new construction; Industrial buildings, new construction
Pr: Randy Okland
**Sec:* John McEntire
Ofcr: Kris Talynn
**VP:* Brett Okland
Dir IT: Lee Holland

D-U-N-S 96-152-2211
OKLAND/SKANSKA
1978 S West Temple, Salt Lake City, UT 84115-7103
Tel (801) 486-0144 *Founded/Ownrshp* 2010
Sales 350.0M *EMP* 500
SIC 1541 Industrial buildings & warehouses; Industrial buildings & warehouses
Pt: John McEntire

D-U-N-S 02-815-5732
OKMULGEE MEDICAL FOUNDATION INC
OKMULGEE MEMORIAL HOSPITAL
1401 Morris Dr, Okmulgee, OK 74447-6429
Tel (918) 756-4233 *Founded/Ownrshp* 1967
Sales 20.2MM *EMP* 250
SIC 8062 General medical & surgical hospitals; General medical & surgical hospitals
CEO: Rex Jones
**CFO:* John Crawford

OKMULGEE MEMORIAL HOSPITAL
See OKMULGEE MEDICAL FOUNDATION INC

D-U-N-S 13-582-2653
OKMULGEE MEMORIAL HOSPITAL INC
1401 Morris Dr, Okmulgee, OK 74447-6429
Tel (918) 756-4233 *Founded/Ownrshp* 1986
Sales 20.2MM *EMP* 250
Accts Eide Bailly Llp Tulsa Ok
SIC 8082 Home health care services; Home health care services
CEO: George N Miller Jr
COO: Sara Davis
**CFO:* Paul D Ervin
Dir Lab: Barbara James
CTO: Charlotte Cowans
Doctor: Stanley White
Nrsg Dir: Amin Bradley

D-U-N-S 78-777-3878
OKOBOJI ENTERPRISES INC
OKOBOJI GRILL
4015 Se Grimes Blvd, Grimes, IA 50111-4897
Tel (515) 986-4944 *Founded/Ownrshp* 1989
Sales 10.8MM^E *EMP* 295
SIC 5812 Grills (eating places); Grills (eating places)
Pr: Leroy Guessman
Treas: William Gessmann

OKOBOJI GRILL
See OKOBOJI ENTERPRISES INC

D-U-N-S 04-834-1655 IMP/EXP
OKONITE CO
102 Hilltop Rd, Ramsey, NJ 07446-1171
Tel (201) 825-0300 *Founded/Ownrshp* 1878
Sales 414.9MM^E *EMP* 1,100
SIC 3357 3315 3355 Nonferrous wiredrawing & insulating; Nonferrous wiredrawing & insulating; Cable, steel: insulated or armored; Aluminum wire & cable
Ch Bd: Victor A Viggiano
Pr: A C Coppola
Treas: David Mitchell
Treas: Bob Morrow
Treas: D J Sokira
VP: James Fitzgerald
VP: Tm Scanlon
VP: Jf Silver
VP: WD Turner
Exec: Kelly Evans
Dist Mgr: Eric Canning

D-U-N-S 01-117-1320
OKTA INC
301 Brannan St Fl 3, San Francisco, CA 94107-3816
Tel (415) 494-8029 *Founded/Ownrshp* 2010
Sales 42.6MM^E *EMP* 80^E
SIC 7371 Software programming applications
CEO: Todd McKinnon
**Pr:* J Frederic Kerrest
**CFO:* Bill Losch
**Ofcr:* Krista Anderson
**Ofcr:* David Baker
**Ofcr:* Andrew Wittman
VP: Bill Fitzgerald
VP: Greg Salmon
VP: Sunil Sampat
VP: Arun Shrestha
Exec: Dave Bernthal
Exec: Heidi Slater
Dir Bus: Ernesto Tey
Board of Directors: Michelle Wilson

OKUBO GEAR AMERICA
See AVON GEAR CO

D-U-N-S 11-925-7392 IMP
OKUMA AMERICA CORP
(*Suby of* OKUMA CORPORATION)
11900 Westhall Dr, Charlotte, NC 28278-7127
Tel (704) 588-7000 *Founded/Ownrshp* 1984
Sales 68.5MM^E *EMP* 200
SIC 5084 3541

D-U-N-S 96-140-5883 IMP
OL PRODUCTS INC
RIO TANNING
3874 Tampa Rd Ste 200, Oldsmar, FL 34677-3126
Tel (813) 855-0700 *Founded/Ownrshp* 1994
Sales 54.8MM^E *EMP* 130
SIC 5122 2844 Cosmetics, perfumes & hair products; Toilet preparations; Cosmetics, perfumes & hair products; Toilet preparations
Pr: Donna Carollo
**Pr:* Santo Carollo
**VP:* Anthony G Gullo

D-U-N-S 03-181-6358
OLAF ANDERSON CONSTRUCTION INC
4102 19th Ave N, Fargo, ND 58102-6802
Tel (701) 237-3605 *Founded/Ownrshp* 1985
Sales 70.4MM *EMP* 90
SIC 1542 1541

D-U-N-S 13-920-8172 IMP/EXP
OLAM AMERICAS INC
(*Suby of* OLAM US HOLDINGS INC) ★
25 Union Pl Ste 3, Summit, NJ 07901-3603
Tel (908) 988-1960 *Founded/Ownrshp* 2010
Sales 534.3MM^E *EMP* 2,000
Accts Ernst And Young Llp Singapore
SIC 0723 Crop preparation services for market; Crop preparation services for market
CEO: Sunny George Verghese

D-U-N-S 13-767-2671
OLAM COTTON
ANDERSON CLAYTON
(*Suby of* OLAM HOLDINGS PARTNERSHIP) ★
740 E Campbell Rd Ste 470, Richardson, TX 75081-6749
Tel (214) 965-0070 *Founded/Ownrshp* 1986
Sales 39.6MM^E *EMP* 182
SIC 4221 0724 Cotton compresses & warehouses; Cotton ginning
Pr: Clifford White
VP: Phil Barrett
MIS Mgr: Eric Vollmer

D-U-N-S 96-863-8697
OLAM HOLDINGS PARTNERSHIP
(*Suby of* OLAM INTERNATIONAL LIMITED)
25 Union Pl Fl 2, Summit, NJ 07901-3603
Tel (908) 988-1960 *Founded/Ownrshp* 2006
Sales 748.6MM^E *EMP* 3,500
SIC 8741 Management services; Management services
Mktg Mgr: Kevin Long

OLAM SPCES VGTABLE INGREDIENTS
See OLAM WEST COAST INC

D-U-N-S 03-681-5516 IMP/EXP
OLAM SPICES & VEGETABLES INC
1350 Pacheco Pass Hwy, Gilroy, CA 95020-9559
Tel (408) 846-3200 *Founded/Ownrshp* 2010
Sales 60.8MM^E *EMP* 91^E
SIC 5148 Vegetables
Ofcr: Esther Aye
Ofcr: Ranee Teo
Sr VP: Amit Agrawal
Sr VP: Arun Sharma
VP: Martin Hampson
Genl Mgr: Deven Chitaliya
Opers Mgr: Patrick Nuck
Plnt Mgr: Terria Williams
Plnt Mgr: Kirstin Woods
Natl Sales: Kristina Filippello
Natl Sales: Megan Wolff

D-U-N-S 07-840-8822 IMP/EXP
OLAM US HOLDINGS INC
(*Suby of* OLAM HOLDINGS PARTNERSHIP) ★
2077 Convention Ctr 150, College Park, GA 30337-4204
Tel (404) 209-2676 *Founded/Ownrshp* 2012
Sales 562.6MM^E *EMP* 592^E
SIC 0723 Crop preparation services for market
Sls Mgr: Martha Barnette

D-U-N-S 00-230-1929 IMP/EXP
OLAM WEST COAST INC
OLAM SPCES VGTABLE INGREDIENTS
(*Suby of* OLAM HOLDINGS PARTNERSHIP) ★
205 E Rver Pk Cir Ste 310, Fresno, CA 93720
Tel (559) 447-1390 *Founded/Ownrshp* 2008
Sales 100.0MM^E *EMP* 1,270^E
SIC 2034 Dried & dehydrated vegetables
Pr: John Gibbons

D-U-N-S 02-318-8757
OLAMETER CORP
(*Suby of* OLAMETER INC)
2261 Brookhollow Plaza Dr # 111, Arlington, TX 76006-7417
Tel (817) 385-0053 *Founded/Ownrshp* 2008
Sales 27.8MM^E *EMP* 1,522^E
SIC 7389 Meter readers, remote; Meter readers, remote
Pr: Jan Peeters
**VP:* Jean-Pierre Carette
**VP:* John Feltis

D-U-N-S 03-458-0779 IMP
OLAN MILLS INC
OLAN MILLS STUDIOS
735 Broad St Ste 218, Chattanooga, TN 37402-1855
Tel (423) 622-5141 *Founded/Ownrshp* 2011
Sales NA *EMP* 4,000
SIC 7221 2752 Photographer, still or video; Transient photographer; Commercial printing, lithographic

OLAN MILLS STUDIOS
See OLAN MILLS INC

D-U-N-S 02-887-7686
OLANDER CO INC
144 Commercial St, Sunnyvale, CA 94086-5298
Tel (408) 735-1850 *Founded/Ownrshp* 1962
Sales 30.0MM^E *EMP* 48
SIC 5072 Bolts, nuts & screws
CEO: Ronald Olander
Sales Asso: Frank Garcia
Sales Asso: Robin Walwyn

D-U-N-S 07-626-4647
OLATHE CITY OF (INC)
100 E Santa Fe St, Olathe, KS 66061-3409
Tel (913) 971-8600 *Founded/Ownrshp* 1857
Sales NA *EMP* 750
Accts Allen Gibbs & Houlik Lc W
SIC 9111 City & town managers' offices; ; City & town managers' offices;
Ofcr: Lucas Borkowski
Ofcr: James Brackett
Ofcr: Shannon Brandau
Ofcr: Ried Carlson
Ofcr: Channell Evans
Ofcr: Drew Fitzpatrick
Ofcr: Patrick Foster
Ofcr: Eric Garvin
Ofcr: Brent Groves
Ofcr: Kyle Harriss
Ofcr: Steve James
Ofcr: Jeff Jewett
Ofcr: Chandra Kelly
Ofcr: Brian Little
Ofcr: Ashley Morgan
Ofcr: Joseph Morgan
Ofcr: Tanner Muckenthaler
Ofcr: David Oglesby
Ofcr: Ronald Porter
Ofcr: Kurt Reglin
Ofcr: Gregory Richardson

OLATHE DODGE CHRYSLER JEEP
See LANDERS MCLARTY OLATHE KS LLC

OLATHE FORD LINCOLN
See FORD OLATHE SALES INC

D-U-N-S 18-273-4996
OLATHE HEALTH SYSTEM INC
OLATHE MEDICAL CENTER
20333 W 151st St, Olathe, KS 66061-5350
Tel (913) 791-4200 *Founded/Ownrshp* 1953
Sales 217.1MM *EMP* 130
Accts Bkd Llp Kansas City Mo
SIC 8011 5912 Clinic, operated by physicians; Drug stores; Clinic, operated by physicians; Drug stores
Pr: Frank H Devocelle
CFO: Cheryl Sharp
Sec: Dennis C Meyer
Sr VP: Dorothy Carey
VP: Michelle Boylan
VP: David Klimek
VP: Jim Wetzel
Prin: Richard Johnson
CIO: Mohammad Rahman
VP Opers: Paul Luce
VP Mktg: Karen Wray

OLATHE MEDICAL CENTER
See OLATHE HEALTH SYSTEM INC

D-U-N-S 07-624-9945
OLATHE MEDICAL CENTER INC
HOSPICE HM HLTH OLATHE MED CTR
20333 W 151st St, Olathe, KS 66061-7211
Tel (913) 791-4200 *Founded/Ownrshp* 1948
Sales 229.8MM *EMP* 2,500
Accts Bkd Llp Kansas City Mo
SIC 8082 8062 Home health care services; General medical & surgical hospitals; Home health care services; General medical & surgical hospitals
Pr: Frank H Devocelle
**CFO:* Tierney Grasser
**Sr VP:* Dorothy Carey
**Sr VP:* John Staton
**VP:* Mike Jensen
CIO: Peggy Donovan
IT Man: Dan Thompson
Mktg Dir: Michael Jensen
Doctor: Kristine G Herron MD
Doctor: Michael Parsa
Pharmcst: Steve Hartke

OLATHE PUBLIC SCHOOLS
See OLATHE UNIFIED SCHOOL DISTRICT 233

OLATHE TOYOTA
See KENNY THOMAS ENTERPRISES INC

D-U-N-S 01-516-4064
OLATHE UNIFIED SCHOOL DISTRICT 233
OLATHE PUBLIC SCHOOLS
14160 S Blackbob Rd, Olathe, KS 66062-2024
Tel (913) 780-7000 *Founded/Ownrshp* 1965
Sales 357.0MM *EMP* 4,000
Accts Mize Houser & Company Pa Lawr
SIC 8211 Public elementary & secondary schools; Public elementary & secondary schools
VP: Rita Ashley
DP Exec: Mike Preuss
Dir IT: Kathi Tully
Teacher Pr: Mark O'Dell
Psych: Laurinda Culpepper

D-U-N-S 09-047-5799 IMP
■ **OLAY CO INC**
(*Suby of* PROCTER & GAMBLE CO) ★
Km 2 Hm 3 Rr 735, Cayey, PR 00736
Tel (787) 738-2191 *Founded/Ownrshp* 1995
Sales 71.6MM^E *EMP* 300
SIC 2844 Toilet preparations; Tonics, hair; Toilet preparations; Tonics, hair
Pr: Salvador Garcia

D-U-N-S 61-677-1358
OLCOTT PLASTICS INC
95 N 17th St, Saint Charles, IL 60174-1636
Tel (630) 584-0555 *Founded/Ownrshp* 1990
Sales 30.1MM^E *EMP* 95
SIC 3089 Plastic containers, except foam
Pr: Joseph M Brodner
**VP:* John R Brodner
Exec: Sandy Allen
Prd Mgr: Ken Johnston
Ql Cn Mgr: Perry Norsworthy
Natl Sales: Tom Czuprynski
Sls Mgr: Troy Rusch

D-U-N-S 05-093-7077
■ **OLD 2ND BANK YORKVILLE**
(*Suby of* OLD SECOND BANCORP INC) ★
26 W Countryside Pkwy, Yorkville, IL 60560-2010
Tel (630) 553-4230 *Founded/Ownrshp* 1887
Sales NA *EMP* 70
SIC 6021 National commercial banks; National commercial banks
Pr: Tom E Thomas
**VP:* Timothy Vaughan
IT Man: Keith Dottschalk

D-U-N-S 00-696-6113
■ **OLD AMERICAN INSURANCE CO**
(*Suby of* KANSAS CITY LIFE INSURANCE CO) ★
3520 Broadway Blvd, Kansas City, MO 64111-2502
Tel (816) 753-4900 *Founded/Ownrshp* 1939
Sales NA *EMP* 200
SIC 6311 6321 Life insurance; Accident & health insurance; Life insurance; Accident & health insurance
Pr: W E Bixby
**Treas:* R E Hiatt
Ex VP: Andrew Hansen

D-U-N-S 80-735-4535 IMP/EXP
OLD API INC
FIVE PEAKS
1790 Sun Dolphin Rd, Muskegon, MI 49444-1800
Tel (231) 830-8099 *Founded/Ownrshp* 1990
Sales 28.6MM^E *EMP* 85
SIC 3089 Thermoformed finished plastic products
Pr: Daniel Harris
**Treas:* Thomas Harris
**VP:* Kenneth Harris
Ql Cn Mgr: Darrel Baker
Sls Mgr: Joe Lucht
Sales Asso: Nick Dunstan

OLD BOHEMIAN
See MASTER PURVEYORS INC

OLD BOONE MERCANTILE
See MAST GENERAL STORE INC

OLD BRICK FURNITURE
See C AND D DISTRIBUTORS INC

D-U-N-S 05-048-2603
OLD BRIDGE MUNICIPAL UTILITY AUTHORITY
71 Boulevard W, Keyport, NJ 07735-6105
Tel (732) 566-2534 *Founded/Ownrshp* 1954
Sales 29.6MM *EMP* 65
Accts Hodulik & Morrison Pa High
SIC 4941 Water supply; Water supply
Ex Dir: Guy Donatelli

D-U-N-S 07-825-9389
OLD BRIDGE TOWNSHIP BOARD OF EDUCATION
4207 Highway 516, Matawan, NJ 07747-7026
Tel (732) 566-1000 *Founded/Ownrshp* 1900
Sales 72.0MM^E *EMP* 1,200
SIC 8211 Public elementary & secondary schools; School board
Pr: Matthew Sulikowski

D-U-N-S 07-979-9175
OLD BRIDGE TOWNSHIP SCHOOLS
4207 Route 516, Matawan, NJ 07747-7026
Tel (732) 566-1000 *Founded/Ownrshp* 2015
Sales 8.5MM^E *EMP* 1,006^E
SIC 8211 Public elementary & secondary schools

D-U-N-S 18-066-0078 IMP/EXP
OLD CARCO INTERNATIONAL CORP
DODGE DAKOTA
(*Suby of* FCA US LLC) ★
1000 Chrysler Dr, Auburn Hills, MI 48326-2766
Tel (248) 576-5741 *Founded/Ownrshp* 2011
Sales 587.4MM^E *EMP* 425
SIC 5012 Automobiles & other motor vehicles; Automobiles & other motor vehicles
Ch Bd: R J Eaton
CFO: Gabriela Rovere
Bd of Dir: Roger Hella
Ofcr: Matthew Stoskopf
VP: Thomas Capo
**VP:* Harry Lewis
Area Mgr: Kathleen Allan
Area Mgr: Byron Betterly
Area Mgr: Janet Debrow
Area Mgr: Marlene Dubois
Area Mgr: Paul Falitico

D-U-N-S 17-270-9412 EXP
OLD CARCO MOTORS LLC
DODGE DAKOTA
(*Suby of* FCA US LLC) ★
1000 Chrysler Dr, Auburn Hills, MI 48326-2766
Tel (248) 576-5741 *Founded/Ownrshp* 2011
Sales 46.1MM^E *EMP* 172^E
SIC 5511 Trucks, tractors & trailers: new & used
CFO: J Wilson
Treas: T P Dykstra
VP: Frank Skalarsky

D-U-N-S 82-861-5885
OLD CASTLE APG INC
(*Suby of* OLDCASTLE INC) ★
900 Ashwood Pkwy Ste 700, Atlanta, GA 30338-4780
Tel (770) 804-3363 *Founded/Ownrshp* 2008
Sales 61.3MM^E *EMP* 100^E
SIC 3273 Ready-mixed concrete

CEO: Mark Towe

D-U-N-S 00-324-2658 IMP
OLD CASTLE APG NORTHEAST INC
ANCHOR
(*Suby of* OLDCASTLE INC) ★
13555 Wellington Center C, Gainesville, VA 20155-4061
Tel (703) 753-1829 *Founded/Ownrshp* 1945, 1990
Sales 64.2MM^E *EMP* 380
SIC 3271 5032 Blocks, concrete or cinder: standard; Brick, stone & related material; Blocks, concrete or cinder: standard; Brick, stone & related material
Pr: Peter Kelly
**Pr:* John Oneill
**VP:* Henry Bruce
Ql Cn Mgr: Chris Brown

D-U-N-S 62-079-1913
OLD CASTLE APG SOUTH INC
ADAMS PRODUCTS OLDCASTLE
333 N Greene St Ste 500, Greensboro, NC 27401-2186
Tel (336) 275-9114 *Founded/Ownrshp* 2001
Sales 20.6MM^E *EMP* 34
SIC 5032 Brick, stone & related material
VP: Keith Haas
**CFO:* Eoin Lehane

D-U-N-S 18-185-1684
OLD CHICAGO TEJON INC
118 N Tejon St Ste 2, Colorado Springs, CO 80903-1420
Tel (719) 634-8812 *Founded/Ownrshp* 1985
Sales 6.4MM^E *EMP* 350
SIC 5812 5813 Italian restaurant; Drinking places; Italian restaurant; Drinking places
Pr: Frank B Day

D-U-N-S 13-484-0250
OLD COACH HOME SALES
242 Harris Rd, Sterling, CT 06377-1508
Tel (860) 774-1379 *Founded/Ownrshp* 1975
Sales 22.0MM *EMP* 22
SIC 2451 Mobile homes; Mobile homes
Owner: Michael Angelo
Owner: Gerry Scott

D-U-N-S 07-061-4268
OLD COLONY ELDER SERVICES INC
144 Main St Fl 2, Brockton, MA 02301-4051
Tel (508) 584-1561 *Founded/Ownrshp* 2010
Sales 33.9MM *EMP* 100
Accts Gerald T Reilly & Company In
SIC 8322 Individual & family services; Geriatric social service; Individual & family services; Geriatric social service
Pr: Julie Murphy
**Treas:* Daniel Clague
**VP:* Theodore Lang

D-U-N-S 61-538-1969
OLD COLONYY
OLD COLONY YMCA
320 Main St, Brockton, MA 02301-5340
Tel (508) 583-2155 *Founded/Ownrshp* 1940
Sales 47.6MM *EMP* 1,400^E
Accts Alexander Aronson Finning &
SIC 8641 7991 8351 7032 8322 Youth organizations; Physical fitness facilities; Child day care services; Youth camps; Individual & family services; Youth organizations; Physical fitness facilities; Child day care services; Youth camps; Individual & family services
Pr: Vincent Marturano
**CFO:* Keenyn McFarlane
**Treas:* William Daisy
VP: David Hyman
Exec: Kim Moran
Assoc Dir: Scott Wickert
Ex Dir: Marcia Perry
CTO: Colby Linkletter
VP Mktg: Catherine Deterra
Psych: Almon White
Nutrtnst: Corey Meenan

D-U-N-S 03-233-3564
OLD COLONYY BS/BB
60 S Skinner St, Brockton, MA 02302-3535
Tel (508) 427-4320 *Founded/Ownrshp* 2001
Sales 43.4MM *EMP* 2^E
SIC 8322 Helping hand service (Big Brother, etc.); Helping hand service (Big Brother, etc.)
Prin: Halina Czaban

OLD COLONY YMCA
See OLD COLONYY

D-U-N-S 78-879-8655
OLD CORKSCREW PLANTATION LLC
23190 Fashion Dr Ste 205, Estero, FL 33928-2566
Tel (239) 949-4700 *Founded/Ownrshp* 2002
Sales 21.0MM *EMP* 3
SIC 0174 Citrus fruits; Citrus fruits

OLD COUNTRY BUFFET
See BUFFETS HOLDINGS LLC

OLD COUNTRY BUFFET
See HOMETOWN BUFFET INC

OLD COUNTRY BUFFET
See OCB RESTAURANT CO LLC

OLD COUNTRY ROOFING
See VACA VALLEY ROOFING INC

D-U-N-S 00-313-0770 IMP
OLD DOMINION BOX CO INC
300 Elon Rd, Madison Heights, VA 24572-2587
Tel (434) 929-6701 *Founded/Ownrshp* 1975
Sales 29.5M *EMP* 350
SIC 2652 2657 2653 Setup paperboard boxes; Folding paperboard boxes; Boxes, corrugated: made from purchased materials; Setup paperboard boxes; Folding paperboard boxes; Boxes, corrugated: made from purchased materials
Ch Bd: Frank H Buhler
**Pr:* Michael O Buhler
**Treas:* Thomas B Scott
Bd of Dir: Jeanne Buhler
**VP:* T Wayne Lankford
**VP:* Amy B Scott
VP: George Young

D-U-N-S 07-043-1218
OLD DOMINION ELECTRIC CO-OPERATIVE
4201 Dominion Blvd # 300, Glen Allen, VA 23060-6721
Tel (804) 747-0592 *Founded/Ownrshp* 1948
Sales 951.5MM *EMP* 111^E
SIC 4911

D-U-N-S 00-687-0877
▲ OLD DOMINION FREIGHT LINE INC (VA)
500 Old Dominion Way, Thomasville, NC 27360-8923
Tel (336) 889-5000 *Founded/Ownrshp* 1934
Sales 2.7MMM *EMP* 16,443
Accts Ernst & Young Llp Charlotte
Tkr Sym ODFL *Exch* NGS
SIC 4213 4212 4731 Trucking, except local; Less-than-truckload (LTL) transport; Local trucking, without storage; Freight transportation arrangement; Trucking, except local; Less-than-truckload (LTL) transport; Local trucking, without storage; Freight transportation arrangement
Pr: David S Congdon
**Ch Bd:* Earl E Congdon
Pr: Greg C Gantt
CFO: J Wes Frye
CFO: Adam N Satterfield
Sr VP: David J Bates
Sr VP: Kevin M Freeman
Sr VP: Cecil E Overbey
VP: John P Booker III
VP: Scott Goodrich
VP: Richard F Keeler
VP: Ross H Parr
VP: Chris Young
Board of Directors: J Paul Breitbach, John R Congdon Jr, Robert G Culp III, John D Kasarda, Leo H Suggs, D Michael Wray

D-U-N-S 04-440-1883
OLD DOMINION INSULATION INC
12764 Oak Lake Ct, Midlothian, VA 23112-3979
Tel (804) 674-1540 *Founded/Ownrshp* 1981
Sales 36.1MM^E *EMP* 200
SIC 1742 Plastering, drywall & insulation; Insulation, buildings; Plastering, drywall & insulation; Insulation, buildings
Pr: Jeffrey G Davoud
CFO: Bruce A Shifflett
**VP:* Christopher V Davoud
VP: Jeffrey L Harper

D-U-N-S 13-001-8633
OLD DOMINION SECURITY CO INC
ODS
2140 Tomlynn St, Richmond, VA 23230-3338
Tel (804) 521-7897 *Founded/Ownrshp* 1997
Sales 11.9MM^E *EMP* 392
SIC 7381 Security guard service; Security guard service
CEO: Rafe Wilkinson
**Pr:* Amy Wilkinson
VP: Brent Mast
VP: Lisa Pryse
**VP Opers:* Troy Gray

D-U-N-S 02-262-3813 EXP
OLD DOMINION SUPPLY INC
7765 Old Telegraph Rd, Severn, MD 21144-1148
Tel (410) 969-7200 *Founded/Ownrshp* 1962
Sales 54.5MM^E *EMP* 48
SIC 5051 5075 5078 Sheets, metal; Warm air heating & air conditioning; Air conditioning & ventilation equipment & supplies; Refrigeration equipment & supplies; Sheets, metal; Warm air heating & air conditioning; Air conditioning & ventilation equipment & supplies; Refrigeration equipment & supplies
Ch: William F Vermillion
**Pr:* Michael Corsiatto
**VP:* Richard R Watts

D-U-N-S 00-794-0786
OLD DOMINION TOBACCO CO INC (VA)
ATLANTIC DOMINION DISTRIBUTORS
5400 Virginia Beach Blvd, Virginia Beach, VA 23462-1724
Tel (757) 497-1001 *Founded/Ownrshp* 1874, 1982
Sales 300.0MM *EMP* 200
Accts Kpmg
SIC 5194 5145 Tobacco & tobacco products; Cigarettes; Confectionery; Candy; Chewing gum; Snack foods; Groceries, general line; Drugs, proprietaries & sundries; Tobacco & tobacco products; Cigarettes; Confectionery; Candy; Chewing gum; Snack foods
Pr: Robin D Ray
**Treas:* Andrea Tanner
**Ex VP:* Kevin Barney
Exec: Jessica Bargamin
VP Sls: Tad Davis
Mktg Mgr: Wiley Wood

D-U-N-S 07-474-6470
OLD DOMINION TRANSIT MANAGEMENT CO
GRTC TRANSIT SYSTEMS
301 E Belt Blvd, Richmond, VA 23224-1701
Tel (804) 358-3871 *Founded/Ownrshp* 1973
Sales 18.2MM *EMP* 425
SIC 4111 Local & suburban transit; Local & suburban transit
CEO: John Lewis

D-U-N-S 04-995-4696
OLD DOMINION TRUCK LEASING INC (NC)
300 Arboretum Pl Ste 600, North Chesterfield, VA 23236-6479
Tel (804) 275-7832 *Founded/Ownrshp* 1963
Sales 20.9MM^E *EMP* 100
Accts Keiter Glen Allen Virginia
SIC 7513 Truck leasing, without drivers
Ch Bd: John R Congdon Sr
**Pr:* Jeffrey W Congdon
**Ch:* John R Congdon Jr
**V Ch Bd:* Earl E Congdon
**VP:* Whit Congdon
VP: S J Joseph III
**VP:* Samuel John Joseph
**VP:* Wayne Tyree
Exec: Violet Pierce
IT Man: Rob Taggart

D-U-N-S 04-144-8465 EXP
OLD DOMINION UNIVERSITY
(*Suby of* EXECUTIVE OFFICE OF VIRGINIA)
5115 Hampton Blvd, Norfolk, VA 23529-0001
Tel (757) 683-3000 *Founded/Ownrshp* 1930
Sales 293.4MM^E *EMP* 4,390
SIC 8221 9411 University; ; University;
Pr: John Broderick
**Pr:* John Browerick
Treas: Charlie Turner
Ofcr: Jacqueline Alexander
Ofcr: Nathan Fronczek
Ofcr: Bill Smith
Assoc VP: Jim Duffy
VP: Brittany Hollis
VP: Kam Nedd
VP: Ellen Neufeldt
VP: September Sanderlin
Exec: Jennifer Mullen

D-U-N-S 07-794-5947
OLD DOMINION UNIVERSITY RESEARCH FOUNDATION
ODURF
4111 Monarch Way Ste 204, Norfolk, VA 23508-2561
Tel (757) 683-4293 *Founded/Ownrshp* 1965
Sales 48.6MM *EMP* 500
SIC 8733

D-U-N-S 00-625-9261
OLD DUTCH FOODS INC (MN)
2375 Terminal Rd, Saint Paul, MN 55113-2577
Tel (651) 633-8810 *Founded/Ownrshp* 1934, 1951
Sales 80.4MM^E *EMP* 500
SIC 2096

D-U-N-S 18-633-3159
■ OLD EVANGELINE DOWNS LLC
EVANGELINE DOWNS, THE
(*Suby of* PENINSULA GAMING LLC) ★
3620 Ne Evangeline Trwy, Carencro, LA 70520-5948
Tel (337) 896-7223 *Founded/Ownrshp* 2006
Sales 13.7MM^E *EMP* 400
SIC 7948 5813 5812 Horse race track operation; Drinking places; Eating places; Horse race track operation; Drinking places; Eating places
Netwrk Mgr: James Fogleman

D-U-N-S 00-732-6879 IMP/EXP
■ OLD FRITO-LAY INC
(*Suby of* FRITO-LAY NORTH AMERICA INC) ★
7701 Legacy Dr, Plano, TX 75024-4002
Tel (972) 334-7000 *Founded/Ownrshp* 1965
Sales 228.8MM^E *EMP* 39,870
SIC 2096 2052 2013 5812 6794 2086 Potato chips & similar snacks; Potato chips & other potato-based snacks; Tortilla chips; Corn chips & other corn-based snacks; Cookies; Snack sticks, including jerky: from purchased meat; Fast-food restaurant, chain; Chicken restaurant; Franchises, selling or licensing; Soft drinks: packaged in cans, bottles, etc.; Potato chips & similar snacks; Potato chips & other potato-based snacks; Tortilla chips; Corn chips & other corn-based snacks; Cookies; Snack sticks, including jerky: from purchased meat; Fast-food restaurant, chain; Chicken restaurant; Franchises, selling or licensing; Soft drinks: packaged in cans, bottles, etc.
CEO: Thomas Greco
**Pr:* Albert P Carey
**Pr:* Marc Guay
CFO: Nancy Loewe
**CFO:* Dave Rader
**Sr VP:* Ted Herrod
**Sr VP:* Ram Krishnan
Sr VP: Ron Parker
VP: Van Bakke
VP: Elizabeth Coachmen
**VP:* Chris Kuechenmeister
VP: Dave Mullins
Dir Bus: Pierre Mainville

D-U-N-S 09-316-9779
OLD GARY INC
POST-TRIBUNE
(*Suby of* SUN-TIMES MEDIA GROUP INC) ★
1433 E 83rd Ave, Merrillville, IN 46410-6307
Tel (219) 648-3000 *Founded/Ownrshp* 1909, 1998
Sales 17.4MM^E *EMP* 350^E
SIC 2711 Newspapers, publishing & printing; Newspapers, publishing & printing

D-U-N-S 00-287-6571
OLD GES INC (TX)
GREENE'S ENERGY GROUP
11757 Katy Fwy Ste 700, Houston, TX 77079-0011
Tel (281) 598-6830 *Founded/Ownrshp* 1978, 2004
Sales 544.3MM^E *EMP* 500
SIC 1389 7353 3599 7359 1382 Oil field services; Oil field equipment, rental or leasing; Machine shop, jobbing & repair; Equipment rental & leasing; Oil & gas exploration services; Oil field services; Oil field equipment, rental or leasing; Machine shop, jobbing & repair; Equipment rental & leasing; Oil & gas exploration services
Pr: Scott T Domingue
Pr: Maury Dumba
**Pr:* Eric Langlinais
**CEO:* Robert Vilyus
**CFO:* Brad Farnsworth
CFO: Mark Yuille
Treas: Anders Jensen
**Sr VP:* Gene Garber
**VP:* Guy Comeaux
**VP:* Tom Sawyer
Rgnl Mgr: Dan Hieronymus

D-U-N-S 07-357-5052 IMP
OLD GLOBE THEATRE
1363 Old Globe Way, San Diego, CA 92101-1696
Tel (619) 234-5623 *Founded/Ownrshp* 1937
Sales 42.9MM^E *EMP* 500
Accts Moss Adams Llp San Diego Ca
SIC 7922 Theatrical production services; Theatrical production services
CEO: Michael G Murphy
**CEO:* Louis Spisto
**CFO:* Mark Somers
Ofcr: Kristin Campbell
Genl Mgr: Amy Allison
Mktg Mgr: Jackie Anderson
Snr Mgr: G Louis

D-U-N-S 13-836-7284
OLD HARBOR BANK
2605 Entp Rd E Ste 100, Clearwater, FL 33759
Tel (727) 797-0696 *Founded/Ownrshp* 2003
Sales NA *EMP* 40
SIC 6029 Commercial banks; Commercial banks
CEO: Barry Miller
**Pr:* William W Short
COO: William Short
Ex Ofcr: James A Ry
Ofcr: James A Ray
Sr VP: Patricia Sieg
VP: Robert Winniett

D-U-N-S 18-761-5534
OLD HARBOR NATIVE CORP
2702 Denali St Ste 100, Anchorage, AK 99503-2747
Tel (907) 278-6100 *Founded/Ownrshp* 1973
Sales 121.1MM^E *EMP* 402
SIC 8748 Business consulting; Business consulting
Pr: Emil Christiansen Sr
**Treas:* Jeff Peterson
Ex VP: Dave Jarrett
VP: Cynthia Berns
**VP:* Al Cratti
VP: Carl Gatter

D-U-N-S 18-628-3768 IMP/EXP
OLD HB INC
HOSTESS BRANDS
3101 Mercier St Ste 422, Kansas City, MO 64111-3647
Tel (816) 502-4000 *Founded/Ownrshp* 1987
Sales 228.8MM^E *EMP* 21,962
SIC 2051 5461 Bread, cake & related products; Bread, all types (white, wheat, rye, etc): fresh or frozen; Rolls, bread type: fresh or frozen; Buns, bread type: fresh or frozen; Bakeries; Bread, cake & related products; Bread, all types (white, wheat, rye, etc): fresh or frozen; Rolls, bread type: fresh or frozen; Buns, bread type: fresh or frozen; Bakeries
CEO: Gregory F Rayburn
**Ch Bd:* Michael J Anderson
Pr: Michael D Kafoure
COO: Richard C Seban
CFO: John Stewart
Treas: J Randall Vance
Chf Mktg O: Richard Seban
Ex VP: Kent B Magill
Ex VP: Steve Proscino
Ex VP: John O Stewart
Ex VP: Gary K Wandschneider
Sr VP: John Akeson
Sr VP: Steve Birgfeld
Sr VP: Dirkes Mark
Sr VP: Keith Schueler
VP: Tom Apel
VP: Ken Barker
VP: Terry Stephens
Board of Directors: John Cahill, Robert B Calhoun, William P Mistretta, Greg Murphy, David Pauker, Terry R Peets, Philip A Vachon

D-U-N-S 02-515-1341 IMP
OLD HF LLC
ROOM PLACE, THE
(*Suby of* ROOM PLACE) ★
1000 N Rohlwing Rd Ste 46, Lombard, IL 60148-1187
Tel (630) 261-3900 *Founded/Ownrshp* 2012
Sales 160.3MM^E *EMP* 580
SIC 5712 Furniture stores; Bedding & bedsprings; Mattresses; Furniture stores; Bedding & bedsprings; Mattresses
Pr: Bruce Berman
**CFO:* Joe Connolly
Ex VP: Mark Jalil
VP: Ben Macias
CIO: Michelle Pacynski
IT Man: Joe Fushi
Netwrk Mgr: Don Gardner
Advt Dir: Valerie Berman
Mktg Mgr: Brian Grabowski

D-U-N-S 00-694-6107 EXP
OLD HICKORY CLAY CO (KY)
962 State Route 1241, Mayfield, KY 42066-9155
Tel (270) 247-3042 *Founded/Ownrshp* 1918
Sales 21.4MM^E *EMP* 55
SIC 1459 1455 Clays (common) quarrying; Kaolin & ball clay
Pr: Joseph Powell
**CFO:* Bill Hinson
CFO: William Hinson

OLD HOME KITCHENS DIVISION
See BENSONS INC

D-U-N-S 87-794-9388
OLD KENT INSURANCE GROUP INC
GLOBAL MARINE INSURANCE
(*Suby of* HUB INTERNATIONAL MIDWEST LTD) ★
625 Kenmoor Ave Se # 200, Grand Rapids, MI 49546-2395
Tel (616) 233-4111 *Founded/Ownrshp* 1999
Sales NA *EMP* 109
SIC 6411 Insurance agents
Pr: William C Anderson
Sales Exec: Jeff Wressell
Sls&Mrk Ex: Gary Beggs

D-U-N-S 19-503-7783 EXP
OLD LADDER CO
WERNER EXTRUDED PRODUCTS
93 Werner Rd, Greenville, PA 16125-9434
Tel (724) 588-2000 *Founded/Ownrshp* 1994
Sales 189.2MM^E *EMP* 2,100

SIC 3446 3089 3334 3444 3499 Scaffolds, mobile or stationary: metal; Synthetic resin finished products; Primary aluminum; Sheet metalwork; Ladders, portable: metal; Scaffolds, mobile or stationary: metal; Synthetic resin finished products; Primary aluminum; Sheet metalwork; Ladders, portable: metal
Pr: Steven P Richman
Ch Bd: Donald M Werner
Pr: Edward Gericke
CEO: James J Loughlin Jr
CFO: Larry V Friend
Treas: Eric I Werner
Sr VP: John J Fiumefreddo
Sr VP: Edward W Gericke
Sr VP: Peter R O'Coin
Sr VP: John M Remmers
VP: Steven R Bentson
VP: Eric J Werner

OLD LAHAINA LUAU
See HOALOHA NA EHA LTD

D-U-N-S 14-072-9638
▲ OLD LINE BANCSHARES INC
1525 Pointer Ridge Pl # 401, Bowie, MD 20716-1860
Tel (301) 430-2500 *Founded/Ownrshp* 2003
Sales NA *EMP* 254E
Tkr Sym OLBK *Exch* NAS
SIC 6022 State commercial banks; State commercial banks
Ch Bd: Craig E Clark
V Ch: Frank Lucente Jr
**Pr:* James W Cornelsen
COO: Mark Semanie
CFO: Elise M Hubbard
Treas: Erin G Lyddane
Bd of Dir: Frank Taylor
Ofcr: Brenda Martin
Ofcr: John Miller
Ex VP: Joseph E Burnett
Sr VP: Sandi F Burnett
Sr VP: Jeffrey Franklin
Sr VP: Kevin M Frere
Sr VP: M Dannette Van Cleaf
Sr VP: Keven Zinn
VP: Rob Bowling
VP: Bill Gallagher
VP: Katrice Simpson
VP: Dion Smith

D-U-N-S 60-449-4708
■ OLD LINE BANK
(*Suby of* OLD LINE BANCSHARES INC) ★
1525 Pointer Ridge Pl # 401, Bowie, MD 20716-1860
Tel (301) 430-2500 *Founded/Ownrshp* 1989
Sales NA *EMP* 177
SIC 6021 National commercial banks; National commercial banks
Pr: James Cornelsen
**COO:* Mark A Semanie
**Ex VP:* Joe Burnett
**Sr VP:* William J Bush
Sr VP: Raymond Lyon
**Sr VP:* John M Suit II
Site Mgr: Staci Filomena
Site Mgr: Carey Hubbell

D-U-N-S 11-827-3119
OLD LS INC
LAND SPAN LOGISTICS
(*Suby of* WATKINS ASSOCIATED INDUSTRIES INC) ★
1120 Griffin Rd, Lakeland, FL 33805-2317
Tel (863) 686-6872 *Founded/Ownrshp* 1982
Sales 29.4MME *EMP* 500
SIC 4213 Trucking, except local; Trucking, except local
V Ch Bd: W B Watkins
**Pr:* Roger Reed
**Sec:* George W Ready Jr
**Sec:* Eric S Wahlen
**Sr VP:* John F Watkins
**VP:* Michael L Watkins
IT Man: David Ray
Board of Directors: William Freeman

D-U-N-S 00-837-9869 IMP
OLD MASTER PRODUCTS INC
7751 Hayvenhurst Ave, Van Nuys, CA 91406-1730
Tel (818) 785-8886 *Founded/Ownrshp* 1997
Sales 30.2MME *EMP* 55
SIC 5198 5087 5023 7629 Lacquers; Varnishes; Floor machinery, maintenance; Wood flooring; Electronic equipment repair
Pr: Jim Hilaski
**VP:* Shaul Dina
Genl Mgr: Michael Romero
Sls Mgr: Don Bustichi
Sls Mgr: Jose De Leon
Sls Mgr: Jim Kelley

OLD MILL, THE
See ARNIES INC

D-U-N-S 19-699-4677
OLD MILL-TROY INC
53 E Main St, North Troy, VT 05859-9590
Tel (802) 988-4474 *Founded/Ownrshp* 1988
Sales 35.3MME *EMP* 40
SIC 5191 Animal feeds
Pr: Ronald Limoges
**Treas:* David Traub
**VP:* Thomas Koldys
Netwrk Mgr: Romeo Cote

D-U-N-S 01-734-7592
OLD MUTUAL (US) HOLDINGS INC
OLD MUTUAL ASSET MANAGEMENT
(*Suby of* OLD MUTUAL PUBLIC LIMITED COMPANY)
200 Clarendon St Fl 53, Boston, MA 02116-5055
Tel (617) 369-7369 *Founded/Ownrshp* 2011
Sales 291.9MME *EMP* 1,283
SIC 6726 6722 8742 Investment offices; Management investment funds, closed-end; Management investment, open-end; Management consulting services; Investment offices; Management investment funds, closed-end; Management investment, open-end; Management consulting services
Pr: Peter Bain
CEO: Julian Ide
CEO: Karen Rowe
COO: Brian Dillon
**COO:* Linda Tilton Gibson
**CFO:* Matthew E Berger
Chf Inves: Tyrone Van Wyk
Ofcr: Mark Pietkiewicz
Ex VP: Kevin Hunt
Sr VP: Matthew Berger
Sr VP: Brian Cima
Sr VP: Thomas McLain
VP: Matthew J Appelstein
VP: Johnathan Forsythe
VP: Chris Hadley
VP: Molly Mugler
VP: Christopher Stapleton
VP: Clarke Stephen
Exec: Lynda Cooper

OLD MUTUAL ASSET MANAGEMENT
See OLD MUTUAL (US) HOLDINGS INC

OLD MUTUAL FINANCIAL NETWORK
See FIDELITY & GUARANTY LIFE INSURANCE CO

D-U-N-S 14-212-1180
OLD MUTUAL FINANCIAL NETWORK SECURITIES INC
(*Suby of* OLD MUTUAL (US) HOLDINGS INC) ★
1001 Fleet St Fl 6, Baltimore, MD 21202-4356
Tel (410) 895-0100 *Founded/Ownrshp* 2004
Sales 17.9MME *EMP* 300E
SIC 6719 Public utility holding companies; Public utility holding companies
CEO: John Clifford
COO: Linda Gibson
CIO: Sandy Duncan
CIO: Vic Lumby
MIS Dir: Theresa Tonsill
Netwrk Eng: Tyge Goodfellow

D-U-N-S 06-833-1164
▲ OLD NATIONAL BANCORP
1 Main St, Evansville, IN 47708-1464
Tel (812) 464-1294 *Founded/Ownrshp* 1982
Sales NA *EMP* 2,608E
Accts Crowe Horwath Llp Indianapoli
Tkr Sym ONB *Exch* NGS
SIC 6021 National commercial banks; National commercial banks
Pr: Robert G Jones
Pr: Julie Falls
CFO: Christopher A Wolking
Chf Mktg O: Lori Danielson
Ofcr: Christine Keck
Ofcr: Candice J Rickard
Ofcr: Kawn Watters
Ex VP: John Clayton
Ex VP: Julie Daugherty
Ex VP: Caroline J Ellspermann
Ex VP: Annette W Hudgions
Ex VP: John R Kamin
Ex VP: James C Ryan III
Ex VP: Kendra L Vanzo
Sr VP: Douglas Gregurich
Sr VP: Candace Jenkins
Sr VP: Allen Mounts
Sr VP: Erik Schmidt
VP: Amanda Castaneda
VP: Dannie Decker
VP: Brendon Falconer
Board of Directors: Rebecca S Skillman, Alan W Braun, Kelly N Stanley, Larry E Dunigan, Derrick Stewart, Niel C Ellerbrook, Katherine White, Andrew E Goebel, Linda E White, Jerome Henry Jr, Phelps L Lambert, Arthur H McElwee Jr, James T Morris, Randall T Shepard

D-U-N-S 00-693-6934
■ OLD NATIONAL BANK
(*Suby of* OLD NATIONAL BANK) ★
21 Se 3rd St Ste 500, Evansville, IN 47708-1421
Tel (800) 731-2265 *Founded/Ownrshp* 1850, 2011
Sales NA *EMP* 700
SIC 6021

D-U-N-S 00-693-6959
■ OLD NATIONAL BANK
(*Suby of* OLD NATIONAL BANCORP) ★
1 Main St, Evansville, IN 47708-1464
Tel (800) 731-2265 *Founded/Ownrshp* 1834
Sales NA *EMP* 1,938
SIC 6021 6022 National commercial banks; State commercial banks; National commercial banks; State commercial banks
Ch Bd: Barbara Murphy
Ch Bd: James A Risinger
Pr: Steve Bennett
Pr: Amy Casavant
Pr: Janet Heldt
CFO: Gene Smith
Treas: Danyelle Granger
Bd of Dir: Beth Flint
Ofcr: Dirk Danks
Ofcr: Dean Happe
Ex VP: Richard Dube
Ex VP: Chris Fleck
Ex VP: Wayne Henning
Ex VP: Michael Hinton
Ex VP: Daryl Moore
Ex VP: Allen R Mounts
Ex VP: Candice Rickard
Ex VP: Jenna Stewart
Ex VP: Gina Stuart
Ex VP: Kendra Vanzo
Sr VP: Gary Case

D-U-N-S 17-082-3376 IMP
■ OLD NAVY INC
(*Suby of* GAP INC) ★
2 Folsom St, San Francisco, CA 94105-1205
Tel (650) 952-4400 *Founded/Ownrshp* 1997
Sales 465.7MME *EMP* 5,000
SIC 5651 Family clothing stores; Family clothing stores
Pr: John Thomson Wyatt
Pr: Stefan Larsson
CFO: John J Lenk
Ex VP: Nancy Green
Sr VP: Stacey Lavalle Fraser

D-U-N-S 19-934-7340
OLD NAVY INC
40 Catherwood Rd Ste 23, Ithaca, NY 14850-1056
Tel (607) 257-8411
Sales NA *EMP* 4,050E
SIC 5651
Genl Mgr: Jen Aldrich

D-U-N-S 80-768-3540
OLD NAVY INC
11500 Midlothian Tpke # 250, North Chesterfield, VA 23235-4790
Tel (804) 379-3985
Sales NA *EMP* 4,050E
SIC 5651

OLD NEIGHBORHOOD FOODS DIV
See DEMAKES ENTERPRISES INC

D-U-N-S 13-878-4371
OLD NORTH STATE MASONRY LLC
201 W Matthews St, Matthews, NC 28105-1307
Tel (704) 708-4559 *Founded/Ownrshp* 2003
Sales 23.6MME *EMP* 214
SIC 1741 Masonry & other stonework; Masonry & other stonework
VP Opers: Toby Holloway

D-U-N-S 03-065-2700 IMP
OLD ORCHARD BRANDS LLC
1991 12 Mile Rd Nw, Sparta, MI 49345-9757
Tel (616) 887-1745 *Founded/Ownrshp* 2009
Sales 53.6MME *EMP* 95
SIC 2033 2037 Fruit juices: packaged in cans, jars, etc.; Frozen fruits & vegetables; Fruit juices: packaged in cans, jars, etc.; Frozen fruits & vegetables
Pr: Mark Saur
VP: Lisa Saur
Dir IT: Dan Baird
VP Opers: Greg Mangione
Ql Cn Mgr: Jeff Leder
VP Mktg: Kevin Miller
Snr Mgr: Tony Woody

D-U-N-S 78-648-5743
■ OLD PLANK TRAIL COMMUNITY BANK
(*Suby of* WINTRUST FINANCIAL CORP) ★
20012 Wolf Rd Ste 100, Mokena, IL 60448-9953
Tel (708) 478-4447 *Founded/Ownrshp* 2005
Sales NA *EMP* 94E
SIC 6022 State commercial banks; State commercial banks
Pr: Paul R Slade
Ofcr: Rachel Harmatys
Ofcr: Lori Venske
Sr VP: Rick Becker
Sr VP: Mike Conway
VP: Theresa Hershberger
VP: Nancy Kuzma
VP: Norma Mitchell
VP: Candice Villagrana
VP: Monica Ward
Brnch Mgr: April Palmer

D-U-N-S 15-019-8901
▲ OLD POINT FINANCIAL CORP
1 W Mellen St, Hampton, VA 23663-2305
Tel (757) 728-1200 *Founded/Ownrshp* 1984
Sales NA *EMP* 301E
Tkr Sym OPOF *Exch* NAS
SIC 6021 National commercial banks; National commercial banks
Ch Bd: Robert F Shuford Jr
CFO: Laurie D Grabow
Treas: Erin Black
Chf Cred: Andy Perkins
Chf Cred: Vennasa Richmond
Ofcr: Suzanne Christein
Ofcr: Mary Detlie
Ofcr: Jean Parra
**Ex VP:* Louis G Morris
Sr VP: Martin Cross
Sr VP: Michael D Maddocks
**Sr VP:* Joseph R Witt
VP: Donald Buckless
VP: Ann Bugg
VP: Cynthia Davis
VP: Brad Dorris
VP: N Gill
VP: Steve Hussell
VP: Jeff Sandford
VP: Mike Yeager
Board of Directors: Stephen C Adams, James Reade Chisman, Russell Smith Evans Jr, Michael A Glasser, Arthur D Greene, John Cabot Ishon, Tom B Langley, H Robert Schappert, Ellen Clark Thacker

D-U-N-S 00-344-4437
■ OLD POINT NATIONAL BANK OF PHOEBUS INC
(*Suby of* OLD POINT FINANCIAL CORP) ★
101 E Queen St, Hampton, VA 23669-4003
Tel (757) 728-1200 *Founded/Ownrshp* 1984
Sales NA *EMP* 150
SIC 6021 National commercial banks; National commercial banks
Pr: Louis G Morris
Ofcr: Jackie Kuwik
Ofcr: Jennifer Register
**Ex VP:* Cary B Epes
**Sr VP:* Lani Davis
**VP:* Dianne Lemay
VP: Sherri McQuillan
VP: Debbie Stoddard
Genl Mgr: Ann Bugg
IT Man: Darrell Riddick

D-U-N-S 00-832-2067
OLD PUEBLO RANCH INC (CA)
LA REINA
316 N Ford Blvd, Los Angeles, CA 90022-1121
Tel (323) 268-2791 *Founded/Ownrshp* 1958
Sales 25.5MME *EMP* 150E
SIC 2099 Tortillas, fresh or refrigerated; Tortillas, fresh or refrigerated
VP: Mauro Robles
**Pr:* Ricardo Robles
Opers Mgr: Chris Munk
Ql Cn Mgr: Martina Castaneva

Board of Directors: Lucy Anitas, Francisco Arellano

D-U-N-S 15-620-5214
■ OLD REPUBLIC AEROSPACE INC
PHOENIX AVIATION MANAGERS INC
(*Suby of* OLD REPUBLIC INTERNATIONAL CORP) ★
1990 Vaughn Rd Nw Ste 350, Kennesaw, GA 30144-7827
Tel (770) 590-4950 *Founded/Ownrshp* 1983
Sales NA *EMP* 120
SIC 6411 Insurance agents
Pr: William P McGloin
Pr: Brian Donnelly
**CFO:* John Clemente
**Ex VP:* Roger Ridings
Sr VP: Craig Benn
Sr VP: Gary Churchill
VP: Cindy Hoskins
VP: Gordon Murray
**VP:* A C Zucaro
CIO: Matthew Maddox
Mktg Dir: Linda Parent

D-U-N-S 80-987-4394
■ OLD REPUBLIC CONSTRUCTION PROGRAM GROUP INC
(*Suby of* OLD REPUBLIC GENERAL INSURANCE GROUP INC) ★
225 S Lake Ave Ste 900, Pasadena, CA 91101-3011
Tel (626) 683-5200 *Founded/Ownrshp* 2006
Sales NA *EMP* 91
SIC 6411 Insurance agents, brokers & service
CEO: Joan Miles
Sr VP: Oscar Burgos
Sr VP: Dave Conway
Sr VP: Karen Rivara
Sr VP: Bryan Stevenson
VP: Dean Clifton
VP: Douglass Jenkins
VP: Crystal McMillan

D-U-N-S 80-440-6523
■ OLD REPUBLIC GENERAL INSURANCE GROUP INC
(*Suby of* OLD REPUBLIC INTERNATIONAL CORP) ★
307 N Michigan Ave # 1418, Chicago, IL 60601-5311
Tel (312) 346-8100 *Founded/Ownrshp* 2007
Sales NA *EMP* 92E
SIC 6351 Surety insurance
**Pr:* Craig R Smiddy
VP: W Todd Gray Sr

D-U-N-S 02-284-1340
■ OLD REPUBLIC HOME PROTECTION CO INC
(*Suby of* OLD REPUBLIC INTERNATIONAL CORP) ★
2 Annabel Ln Ste 112, San Ramon, CA 94583-1377
Tel (925) 866-1500 *Founded/Ownrshp* 1981
Sales NA *EMP* 305
SIC 6411 Insurance agents, brokers & service; Insurance agents, brokers & service
Pr: Gwen M Gallagher
VP: Cathy Hall
**VP:* Lorna Mello
VP: Jim Mullery
Area Mgr: Wartelle Webb
Web Dev: Corey Klass
Sftwr Eng: Alex Sorokorensky
Mktg Dir: Beverly Polyniak
Snr Mgr: Kelly Kanellis

D-U-N-S 00-791-1035
■ OLD REPUBLIC INSURANCE CO (PA)
(*Suby of* OLD REPUBLIC INTERNATIONAL CORP) ★
133 Oakland Ave, Greensburg, PA 15601-2247
Tel (724) 838-5400 *Founded/Ownrshp* 1935, 2001
Sales NA *EMP* 200
SIC 6411 6321 6311 Insurance agents, brokers & service; Health insurance carriers; Life insurance carriers; Insurance agents, brokers & service; Health insurance carriers; Life insurance carriers
Pr: Aldo C Zucaro
CFO: Karl W Mueller
**Sr VP:* Spencer Leroy III
**VP:* Albert M Slotter Jr
VP: Albert Slotter

D-U-N-S 06-948-8849
▲ OLD REPUBLIC INTERNATIONAL CORP
307 N Michigan Ave, Chicago, IL 60601-5311
Tel (312) 346-8100 *Founded/Ownrshp* 1969
Sales NA *EMP* 8,000E
Tkr Sym ORI *Exch* NYS
SIC 6351 Surety insurance; Liability insurance; Surety insurance; Liability insurance
Ch Bd: Aldo C Zucaro
Pr: R Scott Rager
CFO: Karl W Mueller
Treas: Charles S Boone
Ex VP: Charles Gregory
Sr VP: John R Heitkamp Jr
VP: Stephanie Richards
MIS Dir: Jim Arends
Dir IT: Don Ebert
Dir IT: Ken Nelson
Dir IT: Nancy Wolf
Board of Directors: Jimmy A Dew, John M Dixon, James C Hellauer, Spencer Leroy III, Arnold L Steiner, Charles F Titterton, Dennis P Van Mieghem, Steven R Walker

D-U-N-S 00-693-2024
■ OLD REPUBLIC LIFE INSURANCE CO INC
(*Suby of* OLD REPUBLIC LIFE INSURANCE HOLDINGS CO) ★
307 N Michigan Ave, Chicago, IL 60601-5311
Tel (312) 346-8100 *Founded/Ownrshp* 1923
Sales NA *EMP* 150
SIC 6311 Life insurance carriers; Life insurance carriers
Ch Bd: Aldo C Zucaro

D-U-N-S 80-738-6289
■ **OLD REPUBLIC LIFE INSURANCE HOLDINGS CO**
(*Suby of* OLD REPUBLIC INTERNATIONAL CORP) ★
307 N Michigan Ave 2l, Chicago, IL 60601-5311
Tel (312) 346-8100 *Founded/Ownrshp* 1997
Sales 22.3MM^E *EMP* 150
SIC 6719 Investment holding companies, except banks; Investment holding companies, except banks
Ch Bd: Aldo C Zucaro
**CFO:* John Adams

D-U-N-S 17-540-5901
■ **OLD REPUBLIC MORTGAGE GUARANTEE GROUP INC**
(*Suby of* OLD REPUBLIC INTERNATIONAL CORP) ★
307 N Michigan Ave # 1400, Chicago, IL 60601-5311
Tel (312) 346-8100 *Founded/Ownrshp* 1973
Sales NA *EMP* 578
SIC 6361 Title insurance; Title insurance
Pr: William Simpson
**VP:* Paul Davenport

D-U-N-S 07-176-7412
■ **OLD REPUBLIC NATIONAL TITLE HOLDING CO**
(*Suby of* OLD REPUBLIC TITLE INSURANCE GROUP INC (DEL)) ★
400 2nd Ave S, Minneapolis, MN 55401-2406
Tel (612) 371-1111 *Founded/Ownrshp* 2002
Sales NA *EMP* 2,300
SIC 6361 Title insurance; Title insurance
Pr: Rande Yeager
Treas: Shannon Ade
Ofcr: Jon Legg
Ex VP: Stephen C Wilson
Sr VP: William Torpey
VP: Jeff Bluhm
VP: Stephanie Cournoyer
VP: Jeff Crissman
VP: Frank Falzon
VP: John Hall
VP: Gary Horn
VP: Robert Kennedy
VP: Spencer Leroy III
VP: Barry Martin
VP: Stephen Nazian
VP: Stephen Oberst
VP: Kim Silva
VP: Julie Susik
Comm Man: Lori Turpin

D-U-N-S 00-696-2716
■ **OLD REPUBLIC NATIONAL TITLE INSURANCE CO**
(*Suby of* OLD REPUBLIC NATIONAL TITLE HOLDING CO) ★
400 2nd Ave S, Minneapolis, MN 55401-2406
Tel (612) 371-1111 *Founded/Ownrshp* 1907
Sales NA *EMP* 2,300
SIC 6361 Real estate title insurance; Real estate title insurance
Pr: Rande K Yeager
Pr: Judith Brewer
Pr: Laura Hardy
Pr: Karen Hyatt
Pr: William Patsos
Pr: Patrick Ridley
**Pr:* Stephen C Wilson
**CFO:* Gary J Horn
Treas: John Cleveland
Ofcr: Jane Swiston
**Ex VP:* Mark M Budzinski
Sr VP: Ray Forliti
Sr VP: Martha Love
VP: Heidi Andrews
VP: Hoyum Chuck
VP: Patricia Clement
VP: Patrick A Connor
VP: Debbie Dent
VP: Carla Hawkins
VP: Joseph A Johnson
VP: Charles Jordan

D-U-N-S 78-862-1621
■ **OLD REPUBLIC RISK MANAGEMENT INC**
(*Suby of* OLD REPUBLIC INTERNATIONAL CORP) ★
445 S Moorland Rd Ste 300, Brookfield, WI 53005-4254
Tel (262) 797-3400 *Founded/Ownrshp* 1985
Sales NA *EMP* 98
SIC 6411 Insurance agents, brokers & service
Pr: James Kellogg
VP: Sharon Abel
VP: George Jones
VP: Valeria Rykowski
VP: Scott Schaefer
VP: Jim Widder

D-U-N-S 18-800-8049
■ **OLD REPUBLIC SURETY CO**
(*Suby of* OLD REPUBLIC SURETY GROUP INC) ★
445 S Moorland Rd Ste 200, Brookfield, WI 53005-4254
Tel (262) 797-2640 *Founded/Ownrshp* 1986
Sales NA *EMP* 145
SIC 6411 Insurance agents, brokers & service; Insurance information & consulting services
Pr: Gerald Leach
CFO: Rick A Johnson
VP: Tom Homer
VP: Dennis McDonnell
VP: David Menzel
VP: Alan Pavlic Sr
VP: Jerold L Topliff Sr
Brnch Mgr: Tom Brough
Brnch Mgr: Sam Perschau
Dir IT: Glenn Arntzen
VP Mktg: Traci Catalano

D-U-N-S 80-738-3229
■ **OLD REPUBLIC SURETY GROUP INC**
(*Suby of* OLD REPUBLIC INTERNATIONAL CORP) ★
307 N Michigan Ave # 1400, Chicago, IL 60601-5311
Tel (312) 346-8100 *Founded/Ownrshp* 2001
Sales NA *EMP* 170
SIC 6411 6361 Insurance agents, brokers & service; Title insurance

Pr: Aldo Zucaro

D-U-N-S 05-341-3464
■ **OLD REPUBLIC TITLE**
(*Suby of* AMERICAN GUARANTY HOLDING CORP) ★
4040 N Tulsa Ave, Oklahoma City, OK 73112-2461
Tel (405) 942-4848 *Founded/Ownrshp* 1996
Sales NA *EMP* 81
SIC 6411 Insurance agents, brokers & service; Insurance agents, brokers & service
Pr: Chaney Haynes
**Sr VP:* Jeff Noble
Mktg Dir: Joan Hunter

D-U-N-S 07-655-2850
■ **OLD REPUBLIC TITLE CO**
(*Suby of* OLD REPUBLIC TITLE INSURANCE GROUP INC (DEL)) ★
275 Battery St Ste 1500, San Francisco, CA 94111-3334
Tel (415) 421-3500 *Founded/Ownrshp* 1972
Sales NA *EMP* 1,076
Accts Pricewaterhousecoopers Llp Sa
SIC 6361 6531 Real estate title insurance; Escrow agent, real estate; Real estate title insurance; Escrow agent, real estate
Ch Bd: Rande K Yeager
Pr: Chuck Alderman
**Pr:* Wayne Shupe
**Treas:* Dick Neves
Treas: Richard Neves
Sr Cor Off: Patrick Connor
Sr Cor Off: Cliff Johnson
Ofcr: Lisa Albritton
Ofcr: Katherine Deal
Ofcr: Ann Morris
Ex VP: Rick Dosa
Sr VP: Rob J Chapman
**Sr VP:* Carleton R Lago
VP: Karen Arakawa
**VP:* Jim Beaty
VP: Carolyn Broadwater
VP: Steve Cassinelli
VP: Donna Jones
VP: Rob Kernutt
VP: Ross Madison
VP: Tillie Ross

D-U-N-S 09-335-7721
■ **OLD REPUBLIC TITLE CO** (CA)
(*Suby of* OLD REPUBLIC TITLE HOLDING CO INC) ★
101 N Brand Blvd Ste 1400, Glendale, CA 91203-2691
Tel (818) 240-1936 *Founded/Ownrshp* 1967, 1989
Sales NA *EMP* 658^E
SIC 6361 Title insurance
Pr: Merv Morris
Pr: Reta Chin-Chiarella
CFO: Collette Deville
Ofcr: Tracy Bauman
Ofcr: Patti Casillas
Ofcr: Phyllis Chambers
Ofcr: Rudy Cortez
Ofcr: Michael Demers
Ofcr: Tonya Harris
Ofcr: Laurel Leftwich
Ofcr: Dee Magruder
Ofcr: Ramsey Moureau
Ofcr: Shelly Parker
Ofcr: Pam Perry
Ofcr: Chris Ritter
Ofcr: Ward Taylor
Sr VP: Jeffrey Bernatz
Sr VP: Ray Forliti
Sr VP: Elaine Layton
Sr VP: Carolyn Monroe
VP: Daneece Berge

D-U-N-S 02-635-5700
■ **OLD REPUBLIC TITLE CO OF NORTHERN OHIO LLC**
(*Suby of* OLD REPUBLIC NATIONAL TITLE INSURANCE CO) ★
6480 Rckside Woods Blvd S, Independence, OH 44131-2233
Tel (216) 524-5700 *Founded/Ownrshp* 2002
Sales NA *EMP* 1,143^E
SIC 6411 6162 6211 Insurance agents, brokers & service; Mortgage bankers; Underwriters, security
VP: John R Monacelli

D-U-N-S 07-252-5041
■ **OLD REPUBLIC TITLE CORP OF HAWAII**
(*Suby of* OLD REPUBLIC TITLE HOLDING CO INC) ★
900 Fort Street Mall # 1900, Honolulu, HI 96813-3705
Tel (808) 566-0100 *Founded/Ownrshp* 1974
Sales NA *EMP* 55
SIC 6361 6531 Title insurance; Escrow agent, real estate
Pr: Micheal Trudeau
Ofcr: Jasmine Medeiros

D-U-N-S 06-613-2911
■ **OLD REPUBLIC TITLE HOLDING CO INC**
(*Suby of* OLD REPUBLIC NATIONAL TITLE HOLDING CO) ★
275 Battery St Ste 1500, San Francisco, CA 94111-3334
Tel (415) 421-3500 *Founded/Ownrshp* 1979
Sales NA *EMP* 1,076
SIC 6361 6531 5045 Real estate title insurance; Escrow agent, real estate; Computers, peripherals & software; Real estate title insurance; Escrow agent, real estate; Computers, peripherals & software
CEO: Rande K Yeager
**Treas:* Dick Neves
Ofcr: Rick Dominick
Ofcr: Dave Williams
Sr VP: Jeffrey Bernatz
VP: Dennise Harris

D-U-N-S 05-231-5116
■ **OLD REPUBLIC TITLE INSURANCE GROUP INC (DEL)**
(*Suby of* OLD REPUBLIC INTERNATIONAL CORP) ★
307 N Michigan Ave # 1400, Chicago, IL 60601-5311
Tel (312) 346-8100 *Founded/Ownrshp* 1979
Sales NA *EMP* 2,300

SIC 6361 6531 Real estate title insurance; Escrow agent, real estate; Real estate title insurance; Escrow agent, real estate
Pr: Aldo C Zucaro
V Ch: James Kellogg
Ofcr: Lori Adams
Ofcr: Illana Brandon
Ofcr: Kevin Dornbush
Ofcr: Tim Maxfield
Ofcr: Domenico Monteros
Ofcr: Cyndy Rathburn
Ofcr: Tamara Robledo
Ofcr: Silvia Salcito
Ofcr: Vicki Steffan
Ex VP: Leonard Milazzo
Sr VP: Charles Boone
Sr VP: Greg Demartini
Sr VP: Brenda Donath
**Sr VP:* Spencer Leroy
Sr VP: Leroy Spencer
Sr VP: Rande Yeager
VP: Jim Arends
VP: Kathleen Bruington
VP: Stephanie Cournoyer

D-U-N-S 10-244-6408
OLD RIVER COMPANIES INC
OLD RIVER TRUCK SALES
139 Old Highway 49 S, Jackson, MS 39218-9487
Tel (601) 664-1410 *Founded/Ownrshp* 1982
Sales 40.3MM^E *EMP* 75
SIC 5511 Trucks, tractors & trailers: new & used; Trucks, tractors & trailers: new & used
Pr: Lee White
CFO: Dee White
**Sec:* Dee M Southern

OLD RIVER TRUCK SALES
See OLD RIVER COMPANIES INC

OLD SALT SEAFOOD
See SEA WATCH INTERNATIONAL LTD

D-U-N-S 10-382-9156
▲ **OLD SECOND BANCORP INC**
37 S River St, Aurora, IL 60506-4173
Tel (630) 892-0202 *Founded/Ownrshp* 1981
Sales NA *EMP* 492^E
Tkr Sym OSBC *Exch* NGS
SIC 6022 State commercial banks; State commercial banks
Pr: James Eccher
**Ch Bd:* William B Skoglund
**CFO:* J Douglas Cheatham
Trst Ofcr: Steven Coates
Ex VP: June Courtney
Sr VP: Keith Gottschalk
VP: Chris Barry
VP: Robert Briski
VP: James Cracken
VP: Janet Dee
VP: Peter Del Real
VP: Robert Dicosola
VP: Keith Dottschalk
VP: Robert Duplessis
VP: Karen Everhart
VP: Paul Fellendorf
VP: Robert A Ferrigan Jr
VP: Pamela Heller
VP: David Mottet
VP: Janet Mutz
VP: Laurie Rogman
Board of Directors: Edward Bonifas, Barry Finn, William Kane, John Ladowicz, Gerald Palmer, Duane Suits

D-U-N-S 00-692-7818
■ **OLD SECOND NATIONAL BANK OF AURORA**
(*Suby of* OLD SECOND BANCORP INC) ★
37 S River St, Aurora, IL 60506-4172
Tel (630) 844-3555 *Founded/Ownrshp* 1871, 1982
Sales NA *EMP* 300
SIC 6021 National commercial banks; National commercial banks
Pr: William Skoglund
Ch Bd: James Echert
Pr: Sally Kerby
CFO: Doug Cheatham
Ofcr: Mary Randel
Ex VP: June Courtney
Ex VP: Rodney Sloan
Ex VP: Mary Wilson
Sr VP: Charles A Barber
Sr VP: Paul Fellendorf
Sr VP: Robert A Ferrigan Jr
Sr VP: Keith Gottschalk
Sr VP: Joseph Marchese
Sr VP: Roger Teeling
Sr VP: Robert Valaitis
VP: Layne Burns
VP: Phillip Delafuente
VP: Kathy Diedrick
VP: John Giuffre
VP: David Kozuh
VP: Greg Kuda

D-U-N-S 01-140-8663
OLD SHA INC
SMITH HANLEY CONSULTING GROUP
(*Suby of* INVENTIV HEALTH INC) ★
107 John St Ste 201, Southport, CT 06890-1466
Tel (203) 319-4300 *Founded/Ownrshp* 2005
Sales 31.7MM^E *EMP* 898
SIC 7361 Executive placement; Executive placement
CEO: Thomas A Hanley Jr
**Pr:* Joseph Massaro
**CFO:* Michael L Hlinak
**VP:* Alessandro Nisit
Off Mgr: Kim Oneill
Info Man: Rita Wang
Sls Mgr: Monica Giannini
Snr Mgr: Chandra Brown

OLD SPAGHETTI FACTORY
See OSF INTERNATIONAL INC

OLD SPAGHETTI FACTORY
See SACRAMENTO SPAGHETTI RESTAURANT INC

D-U-N-S 03-890-2243
OLD SSI INC
250 Super Service Dr, Somerset, KY 42501-6258
Tel (606) 679-1141 *Founded/Ownrshp* 1993
Sales 48.2MM^E *EMP* 782
SIC 4213 Trucking, except local; Trucking, except local
Pr: Harvey N Gainey
**VP:* Roger D Waddle
IT Man: Bob Maggard
Opers Mgr: Bobby Hawk
Sales Exec: Mike Caudill

D-U-N-S 82-837-0770
OLD TESSON SURGERY CENTER LP
(*Suby of* UNITED SURGICAL PARTNERS INTERNATIONAL INC) ★
12639 Old Tesson Rd # 115, Saint Louis, MO 63128-2786
Tel (314) 270-3696 *Founded/Ownrshp* 2008
Sales 31.1MM^E *EMP* 1,377^E
SIC 8011 Ambulatory surgical center
Prin: Michael Ladevich

D-U-N-S 15-201-5848 IMP
OLD TIME POTTERY LLC
480 River Rock Blvd, Murfreesboro, TN 37128-4804
Tel (615) 890-6060 *Founded/Ownrshp* 2014
Sales 831.0MM^E *EMP* 3,000^E
SIC 5999 5023 Art, picture frames & decorations; Home furnishings; Art, picture frames & decorations; Home furnishings
Pr: Scott Peterson
**CFO:* Robert Sharp
**VP:* Sallie S Peterson
Snr Ntwrk: David Parnell
VP Merchng: Bill Hauck
Mktg Dir: Nancy Stockwell

OLD TOWN CANOE
See JOHNSON OUTDOORS WATERCRAFT INC

D-U-N-S 08-102-6015
OLD TOWN SCHOOL OF FOLK MUSIC INC
A DIFFERENT STRUMMER
4544 N Lincoln Ave, Chicago, IL 60625-2103
Tel (773) 751-3398 *Founded/Ownrshp* 1957
Sales 11.8MM *EMP* 300
Accts Blackman Kallick Llp Chicago
SIC 8299 7911 Music school; Dance studios, schools & halls; Music school; Dance studios, schools & halls
Ex Dir: James Bau Graves
V Ch: Meredith Mack
Prgrm Mgr: Erin Flynn
Prgrm Mgr: Darrell Jones
Prgrm Mgr: Alicia Manson
Prgrm Mgr: Kim Wallace
Prgrm Mgr: Chris Walz
MIS Dir: Gregg Tager
IT Man: Mary Drews
Mktg Dir: Gail Tyler
Mktg Dir: Dave Zibell

D-U-N-S 00-431-0801
OLD TRAIL PRINTING CO (OH)
100 Fornoff Rd, Columbus, OH 43207-2475
Tel (614) 443-4852 *Founded/Ownrshp* 1924
Sales 26.9MM^E *EMP* 125
SIC 2752 2791 2789 2759 Commercial printing, offset; Letters, circular or form: lithographed; Typesetting; Bookbinding & related work; Commercial printing; Commercial printing, offset; Letters, circular or form: lithographed; Typesetting; Bookbinding & related work; Commercial printing
Owner: Mary Held

D-U-N-S 96-547-9657
OLD UE LLC
4511 33rd St, Long Island City, NY 11101-2405
Tel (718) 707-0700 *Founded/Ownrshp* 2009
Sales 21.8MM^E *EMP* 400
SIC 2752 2677 Commercial printing, lithographic; Envelopes; Commercial printing, lithographic; Envelopes
Prin: Steve Franz
Prin: Stuart Grover
Prin: Willie Hollingswo
Prin: Raymond Maragh
Prin: John Sorrentino
Prin: Andres Valentino

OLD UNITED LIFE INSURANCE
See VAN ENTERPRISES INC OF KANSAS

OLD VAT ROOM, THE
See WASHINGTON DRAMA SOCIETY INC

D-U-N-S 62-624-8020
OLD VINEYARD BEHAVIORAL HEALTH
3637 Old Vineyard Rd, Winston Salem, NC 27104-4842
Tel (336) 794-4285 *Founded/Ownrshp* 2004
Sales 12.7MM^E *EMP* 278
SIC 8361 Residential care; Residential care
CEO: Wes Mason
CFO: Tara Sheilds

D-U-N-S 83-501-0562
OLD WEST PROPERTIES LLC
TACO BELL
7915 Kensington Ct, Brighton, MI 48116-8561
Tel (248) 446-0100 *Founded/Ownrshp* 1995
Sales 18.6MM^E *EMP* 480
SIC 5812 Fast-food restaurant, chain; Fast-food restaurant, chain
**Pt:* Peter L Petersen

D-U-N-S 04-323-2834
OLD WESTBURY GOLF AND COUNTRY CLUB INC
270 Wheatley Rd, Old Westbury, NY 11568-1000
Tel (516) 626-1810 *Founded/Ownrshp* 1960
Sales 12.9MM *EMP* 300
Accts Condon O Meara Mcginty & Donne
SIC 7997 5813 Country club, membership; Cocktail lounge; Country club, membership; Cocktail lounge
COO: Markus Rentzing
**Pr:* Barry Swidler
Treas: Alexander Chernoff

*Treas: Morty Schaja
Treas: Michael Schulman
VP: Linda Beigel
*VP: Howard Butnick
Dir Soc: Tanya Barshell
Genl Mgr: ARA P Caglian

D-U-N-S 13-577-5026 IMP
OLD WILLIAMSBURGH CANDLE CORP
300 Liberty Ave, Brooklyn, NY 11207-2923
Tel (718) 566-1500 Founded/Ownrshp 2001
Sales 27.8MM^E EMP 150
SIC 3999 Candles; Candles
CEO: Merav Gold
*CFO: Yaniv Nazor
*VP: S H Fischer
VP: Joel Kaliroff
*Prin: Niv Zikdershtein
Genl Mgr: Shrage Marasow
S&M/VP: Frank Corella

D-U-N-S 19-516-6624 IMP/EXP
OLD WORLD INDUSTRIES LLC
4065 Commercial Ave, Northbrook, IL 60062-1828
Tel (847) 559-2000 Founded/Ownrshp 1973
Sales 221.8MM^E EMP 250
SIC 5169 5013 Anti-freeze compounds; Automotive supplies; Anti-freeze compounds; Automotive supplies
Pr: Khalid Mahmood
COO: Chris Murphy
CFO: Anthony Ciesceri
*CFO: Mark Rocco
*Treas: Anthony J Clesceri
Sr VP: Shahoor Afridi
*Sr VP: Daniel M Leep
VP: Jim Harrison
VP: Spaeth Jim
VP: Jerry Riccioni
*Genl Mgr: Charles Culverhouse

D-U-N-S 05-782-6141 IMP/EXP
OLDACH ASSOCIATES INC
Carr 869 Esq Calle Bo Pal, Catano, PR 00962
Tel (787) 641-2420 Founded/Ownrshp 1987
Sales 38.4MM^E EMP 90
Accts Padilla Medina & Associates
SIC 5075 5722 Warm air heating & air conditioning; Air conditioning room units, self-contained; Warm air heating & air conditioning; Air conditioning room units, self-contained
Pr: Giancarlo Brito
*Treas: Felix Campos
*VP: Ricardo Puig

D-U-N-S 03-414-3670
OLDCASTLE ADAMS PRODUCTS
(Suby of OLDCASTLE INC) ★
333 N Greene St Ste 500, Greensboro, NC 27401-2186
Tel (336) 275-9114 Founded/Ownrshp 2010
Sales 79.4MM^E EMP 1,484^E
SIC 1741 Concrete block masonry laying
Pr: Colin Clampett
Ex VP: Butch Hardy

D-U-N-S 15-713-0845 IMP
OLDCASTLE APG MIDWEST INC
SCHUSTER'S BUILDING PRODUCTS
(Suby of CRH PUBLIC LIMITED COMPANY)
901 E Troy Ave, Indianapolis, IN 46203-5135
Tel (317) 786-0971 Founded/Ownrshp 2000
Sales 59.3MM^E EMP 750
SIC 3272 Concrete products; Concrete products
VP: John Nimmo
*Pr: Marcia Gibson
*CFO: Matt Austin
*Treas: Jeri Kniery
*VP: Keith Brady
*VP: Greg Jacot

D-U-N-S 00-322-4649 IMP
OLDCASTLE APG SOUTH INC
ADAMS
(Suby of OLDCASTLE INC) ★
108 Buchanan Church Rd, Greensboro, NC 27405-8631
Tel (336) 375-5656 Founded/Ownrshp 1946, 1989
Sales 27.9MM^E EMP 170
SIC 3272 Burial vaults, concrete or precast terrazzo; Steps, prefabricated concrete; Slabs, crossing: concrete; Burial vaults, concrete or precast terrazzo; Steps, prefabricated concrete; Slabs, crossing: concrete
Pr: Colin Clampett

D-U-N-S 80-903-3921
OLDCASTLE APG TEXAS INC
(Suby of OLDCASTLE MATERIALS GROUP) ★
2624 Joe Field Rd, Dallas, TX 75229-4601
Tel (972) 488-8131 Founded/Ownrshp 1992
Sales 62.3MM^E EMP 300
SIC 5032 5211 3273 3713 3281 Building stone; Lumber & other building materials; Ready-mixed concrete; Truck & bus bodies; Cut stone & stone products; Building stone; Lumber & other building materials; Ready-mixed concrete; Truck & bus bodies; Cut stone & stone products
Pr: Steve Bond

D-U-N-S 16-989-8736
OLDCASTLE ARCHITECTURAL INC
(Suby of OLDCASTLE INC) ★
900 Ashwood Pkwy Ste 600, Atlanta, GA 30338-7501
Tel (770) 804-3363 Founded/Ownrshp 1987
Sales 128.2MM^E EMP 367
SIC 3251 Brick & structural clay tile; Brick & structural clay tile
CEO: Keith Haas
*Pr: Rick Mergens
*CFO: Michael Schaeffer
Off Mgr: Rose Hughes
Dir IT: Lou McNeil
VP Sls: Kathy Rudolph
Mktg Mgr: Donald Foster
Sls Mgr: Aaron Faubli

D-U-N-S 82-771-9506
OLDCASTLE BUILDING PRODUCTS INC
(Suby of OLDCASTLE INC) ★
900 Ashwood Pkwy Ste 600, Atlanta, GA 30338-7501
Tel (770) 804-3363 Founded/Ownrshp 2000
Sales 174.7MM^E EMP 160
SIC 5031 Building materials, exterior
Pr: Liam O'Mahony

D-U-N-S 00-205-4708
OLDCASTLE BUILDINGENVELOPE INC
(Suby of CRH PUBLIC LIMITED COMPANY)
895 Motor Pkwy, Hauppauge, NY 11788-5232
Tel (631) 232-8600 Founded/Ownrshp 1951
Sales 32.1MM^E EMP 130
SIC 3211 3231 3229 5039 Flat glass; Tempered glass; Insulating glass, sealed units; Laminated glass; Products of purchased glass; Pressed & blown glass; Glass construction materials; Flat glass; Tempered glass; Insulating glass, sealed units; Laminated glass; Products of purchased glass; Pressed & blown glass; Glass construction materials
Pr: Ted Hathaway
Pr: Mollie Hines
VP: Steven Sherman
Sfty Mgr: Gina Rizzo
Plnt Mgr: Christopher Irby
Plnt Mgr: Labe Orloff
Prd Mgr: Robert Safar
Ql Cn Mgr: Jeff Owens
Ql Cn Mgr: Aaron Spindler
Sls Mgr: Steve Acker
Sls Mgr: Suzanne Bauer

D-U-N-S 18-114-0815 IMP/EXP
OLDCASTLE BUILDINGENVELOPE INC
(Suby of OLDCASTLE INC) ★
5005 Lndn B Jnsn Fwy 10 Ste 1050, Dallas, TX 75244
Tel (214) 273-3400 Founded/Ownrshp 1987
Sales 880.9MM^E EMP 4,010
SIC 3231 5231 Tempered glass: made from purchased glass; Insulating glass: made from purchased glass; Glass; Tempered glass: made from purchased glass; Insulating glass: made from purchased glass; Glass
CEO: Edwin B Hathaway
*Ch Bd: Liam O'Nahony
*Pr: Doug Black
CFO: Cassandra Harris
*CFO: Dominic Maggiano
*Sec: Michael O'Driscoll
VP: J Quick

D-U-N-S 80-012-9541
OLDCASTLE COASTAL INC
(Suby of OLDCASTLE INC) ★
4630 Woodland Corporate B, Tampa, FL 33614-2445
Tel (813) 367-9780 Founded/Ownrshp 2003
Sales 38.2MM^E EMP 220
SIC 3272 Covers, catch basin: concrete; Covers, catch basin: concrete
Pr: Tim Ortman
Treas: David Majher
VP: Bill Baswell
*VP: Bill Braswell
Sls Mgr: Brian Apgar

D-U-N-S 13-241-3167
OLDCASTLE DISTRIBUTION INC
ALLIED BUILDING PRODUCTS CO
(Suby of OLDCASTLE INC) ★
15 E Union Ave, East Rutherford, NJ 07073-2127
Tel (201) 935-0800 Founded/Ownrshp 2002
Sales 1.9MMM^E EMP 3,300^E
SIC 5031 5032 Building materials, exterior; Building materials, interior; Brick, stone & related material; Building materials, exterior; Building materials, interior; Brick, stone & related material
Pr: Don Toth

D-U-N-S 02-704-3915
OLDCASTLE GLASS ENGINEERED PRODUCTS INC
VISTAWALL
(Suby of CRH PUBLIC LIMITED COMPANY)
803 Airport Rd, Terrell, TX 75160-5224
Tel (972) 563-2627 Founded/Ownrshp 2007
Sales 23.6MM^E EMP 150
SIC 3271 Architectural concrete: block, split, fluted, screen, etc.; Architectural concrete: block, split, fluted, screen, etc.
CEO: Edwin B Hathaway

D-U-N-S 05-766-6513
OLDCASTLE GLASS ENGINEERED PRODUCTS INC
MODU-LINE WINDOWS
(Suby of OLDCASTLE BUILDINGENVELOPE INC) ★
930 Single Ave, Wausau, WI 54403-6528
Tel (715) 845-5061 Founded/Ownrshp 2007
Sales 82.8MM^E EMP 260
SIC 3442 Louver windows, metal; Louver windows, metal
Pr: Ron Rutledge
Pr: Dave Guffey
VP: Eldon Pagel

D-U-N-S 03-717-6591 EXP
OLDCASTLE INC
(Suby of CRH PUBLIC LIMITED COMPANY)
900 Ashwood Pkwy Ste 600, Atlanta, GA 30338-7501
Tel (770) 804-3363 Founded/Ownrshp 1987
Sales 23.3MMM^E EMP 35,000
SIC 3273 3272 3271 3255 Ready-mixed concrete; Pipe, concrete or lined with concrete; Concrete block & brick; Clay refractories; Ready-mixed concrete; Pipe, concrete or lined with concrete; Concrete block & brick; Clay refractories
CEO: Mark S Towe
Pr: Cindy Parish
CFO: Michael G O'Driscoll
CFO: Michael Odreiscoll
CFO: Michael G Odriscoll
Sr Cor Off: Jeff Schaffer
VP: Andy Brinkmeier
VP: Jerry Cottelberg
VP: Mjichael Lynch
Genl Mgr: Mike Beshel
CIO: Jerry Kottelenberg

D-U-N-S 82-584-9529 IMP/EXP
OLDCASTLE LAWN & GARDEN INC
(Suby of OLDCASTLE ARCHITECTURAL INC) ★
900 Ashwood Pkwy Ste 600, Atlanta, GA 30338-7501
Tel (770) 804-3363 Founded/Ownrshp 2006
Sales 27.6MM^E EMP 112^E
SIC 3524 5261 8741 Lawn & garden equipment; Lawn & garden equipment; Business management; Lawn & garden equipment; Lawn & garden equipment; Business management
Pr: Mark Towe
*CFO: Stephen Colman
VP: Joseph Mc Cullough
*Prin: Eoin Lehane

OLDCASTLE LAWN & GRDN MIDWEST
See RIVER CITY LANDSCAPE SUPPLY INC

D-U-N-S 07-991-9359
OLDCASTLE MATERIALS CEMENT HOLDINGS INC
(Suby of OLDCASTLE INC) ★
900 Ashwood Pkwy Ste 700, Atlanta, GA 30338-4780
Tel (770) 522-5600 Founded/Ownrshp 2015
Sales 12.0MM^E EMP 353^E
SIC 3272 Floor slabs & tiles, precast concrete; Prestressed concrete products
CEO: Mark S Towe

OLDCASTLE MATERIALS GROUP
See OLDCASTLE MATERIALS INC

D-U-N-S 80-670-9812
OLDCASTLE MATERIALS INC
OLDCASTLE MATERIALS GROUP
(Suby of OLDCASTLE INC) ★
900 Ashwood Pkwy Ste 700, Atlanta, GA 30338-4780
Tel (770) 522-5600 Founded/Ownrshp 1985
Sales 3.7MMM^E EMP 2,405
SIC 3272 1622 1611 2951 5032 Concrete products, precast; Prestressed concrete products; Bridge construction; General contractor, highway & street construction; Asphalt paving mixtures & blocks; Stone, crushed or broken; Concrete products, precast; Prestressed concrete products; Bridge construction; General contractor, highway & street construction; Asphalt paving mixtures & blocks; Stone, crushed or broken
CEO: Randy Lake
*Pr: Mark Towe
CFO: Charles Brown
*CFO: Glenn Culpepper
Ex VP: Kirk Randolph
Sr VP: Pascal Convers
VP: Dan Connelly
VP: Jeff Freeman
VP: John Hay
VP: Steven N Ross
IT Man: Richard Chan

D-U-N-S 18-918-7578 IMP
OLDCASTLE NEW FRONTIERS INC
GREENLEAF PRODUCTS
(Suby of OLDCASTLE LAWN & GARDEN INC) ★
1566 High Point Church Rd, Pageland, SC 29728-6441
Tel (843) 672-5553 Founded/Ownrshp 2005
Sales 23.7MM^E EMP 110^E
SIC 5099 5261 2875 2421 Wood & wood by-products; Nurseries & garden centers; Fertilizers, mixing only; Sawmills & planing mills, general
CEO: Eoin F Lehane
*Pr: Don Mason

OLDCASTLE PRECAST ENCLO
See OLDCASTLE PRECAST INC

D-U-N-S 00-948-4866 IMP/EXP
OLDCASTLE PRECAST INC
DRAINAGE PROTECTION SYSTEMS
(Suby of CRH AMERICA INC) ★
1002 15th St Sw Ste 110, Auburn, WA 98001-6502
Tel (253) 833-2777 Founded/Ownrshp 1981
Sales 302.0MM^E EMP 3,336
SIC 3272 3446

D-U-N-S 05-226-2235 IMP
OLDCASTLE PRECAST INC
OLDCASTLE PRECAST ENCLO
(Suby of DRAINAGE PROTECTION SYSTEMS) ★
2434 Rubidoux Blvd, Riverside, CA 92509-2144
Tel (951) 788-9720 Founded/Ownrshp 2008
Sales 225.3MM^E EMP 3,000^E
SIC 3089 Boxes, plastic; Boxes, plastic
CEO: David Steevens
*Treas: Eric Farinha

D-U-N-S 02-214-7216
OLDCASTLE RETAIL INC
(Suby of BONSAL AMERICAN INC) ★
8201 Arrowridge Blvd, Charlotte, NC 28273-5678
Tel (704) 525-1621 Founded/Ownrshp 2006
Sales 63.7MM^E EMP 550^E
SIC 3272 Concrete products; Concrete products
Pr: David Maske

OLDCASTLE SURFACES
See CREATIVE SURFACES INC

D-U-N-S 03-208-0996
OLDCASTLE SW GROUP INC
UNITED PAVING
(Suby of CRH PUBLIC LIMITED COMPANY)
2273 River Rd, Grand Junction, CO 81505-7179
Tel (970) 243-4900 Founded/Ownrshp 1954
Sales 127.1MM^E EMP 392
SIC 1611 3273 5032 General contractor, highway & street construction; Ready-mixed concrete; Sand, construction; Gravel; General contractor, highway & street construction; Ready-mixed concrete; Sand, construction; Gravel
Pr: Rich Umbel
CFO: Phill Raimer
Off Mgr: Julie Brown

D-U-N-S 19-746-2807 IMP
OLDCO JACKING SUBSIDIARY-2 INC
ENERGY SERVICES INTERNATIONAL
1644 Coteau Rd, Houma, LA 70364-3513
Tel (985) 851-5474 Founded/Ownrshp 1988
Sales 25.8MM^E EMP 80
SIC 3533 Oil & gas drilling rigs & equipment; Oil & gas drilling rigs & equipment
CEO: Mark Hannigan
*CFO: John Strang
*VP: Matthew Chamberlain

D-U-N-S 78-690-6490
OLDCO M CO LLC
METALDYNE
(Suby of METALDYNE CORP) ★
47659 Halyard Dr, Plymouth, MI 48170-2429
Tel (734) 207-6200 Founded/Ownrshp 2000
Sales 47.6MM^E EMP 242^E
SIC 3714 Motor vehicle parts & accessories

OLDE YORK POTATO CHIPS
See SARATOGA POTATO CHIPS LLC

D-U-N-S 00-610-1968 IMP
OLDENBURG GROUP INC (WI)
VISA LIGHTING
1717 W Civic Dr, Milwaukee, WI 53209-4433
Tel (414) 354-6600 Founded/Ownrshp 1943, 1980
Sales 197.8MM^E EMP 610
SIC 3537 3532 3646 Industrial trucks & tractors; Dollies (hand or power trucks), industrial except mining; Mining machinery; Commercial indusl & institutional electric lighting fixtures; Industrial trucks & tractors; Dollies (hand or power trucks), industrial except mining; Mining machinery; Commercial indusl & institutional electric lighting fixtures
CEO: Wayne C Oldenburg
Pr: Tim Nerenz
VP: Tom Vert
VP: Joseph Wouters
Dir Sec: Tom Fischer
QA Dir: Brian Lenten
Dir IT: Jim Stalewski
Info Man: Kate Carberry
Mtls Mgr: Keith Rivers
Plnt Mgr: Robert Breul
S&M/VP: Jimalee AP

D-U-N-S 07-417-6546
■ **OLDER PUBLIC TITLE CO**
(Suby of OLD REPUBLIC NATIONAL TITLE HOLDING CO) ★
777 Post Oak Blvd Ste 100, Houston, TX 77056-3254
Tel (713) 626-9220 Founded/Ownrshp 1972
Sales NA EMP 100
SIC 6361 Guarantee of titles
COO: Thomas Osborne
*Ex VP: Judy Arthurs
Sr VP: Lauren Gray
VP: Gail Paschkes

D-U-N-S 03-478-5709
OLDHAM CHEMICALS CO INC
3701 New Getwell Rd, Memphis, TN 38118-6012
Tel (901) 794-0084 Founded/Ownrshp 1966
Sales 40.5MM^E EMP 56
SIC 5191 5087 Insecticides; Pesticides; Extermination & fumigation equipment & supplies; Insecticides; Pesticides; Extermination & fumigation equipment & supplies
Pr: Millard L Oldham
*Sec: Ada Oldham
*VP: Marsha Reeves
Exec: Cathy Wade
Dist Mgr: Tim Robinson
IT Man: Scarlet Vance
Mtls Mgr: Ellis Jones

D-U-N-S 08-101-5232
OLDHAM COUNTY SCHOOL DISTRICT
6165 W Highway 146, Crestwood, KY 40014-9531
Tel (502) 241-3500 Founded/Ownrshp 1875
Sales 107.7MM EMP 1,300
Accts Stiles Carter & Associates
SIC 8211 Public elementary & secondary schools; Public elementary & secondary schools

D-U-N-S 02-585-4696 IMP
OLDHAM GRAPHIC SUPPLY INC (IL)
OLDHAM GROUP, THE
2056 N Republic St, Springfield, IL 62702-1850
Tel (217) 528-4649 Founded/Ownrshp 1951, 1976
Sales 25.4MM^E EMP 70
SIC 5084

OLDHAM GROUP, THE
See OLDHAM GRAPHIC SUPPLY INC

D-U-N-S 00-894-7178
OLDHAM LUMBER CO INC
8738 Forney Rd, Dallas, TX 75227-4501
Tel (214) 388-5194 Founded/Ownrshp 1980
Sales 40.6MM^E EMP 50
SIC 5031 5211 Lumber: rough, dressed & finished; Millwork; Lumber products; Millwork & lumber
CEO: Lynn O Surls
*Pr: Mike Wood
*VP: Harley A Finnell Jr
*VP: J Michael Wood

OLDIES 95
See MIAMI VALLEY BROADCASTING CORP

OLDIES 95.7
See KJR 950 AM

D-U-N-S 00-509-1368
OLDS PRODUCTS CO OF ILLINOIS
10700 88th Ave, Pleasant Prairie, WI 53158-2300
Tel (262) 947-3500 Founded/Ownrshp 1995
Sales 20.7MM^E EMP 80
SIC 2035 2099 Mustard, prepared (wet); Food preparations; Mustard, prepared (wet); Food preparations
Pr: Robert O Remien
*VP: William J O'Connor
Plnt Mgr: Kal Loebsack
Natl Sales: Bob Gentz

VP Sls: Timothy J Mc Avoy
Sls Dir: Tim Sheridan

OLDSMOBILE-CADILLAC-PONTIAC-G
See ALFRED MATTHEWS INC

D-U-N-S 01-348-3438
OLE HBO PARTNERS
HBO LATIN AMERICA GROUP
396 Alhambra Cir Ste 400, Coral Gables, FL 33134-5087
Tel (305) 648-8100 *Founded/Ownrshp* 1996
Sales 188.1MM^E *EMP* 700
SIC 4841 Cable television services; Cable television services
Pt: Gaston Comas
Pt: Thomas Short
Pt: David Torkington
VP: Edgar Villapando

D-U-N-S 62-099-2081 EXP
OLE MEXICAN FOODS INC
6585 Crescent Dr, Norcross, GA 30071-2901
Tel (770) 582-9200 *Founded/Ownrshp* 1988
Sales 269.1MM *EMP* 920
Accts Windham Brannon Pc Atlanta
SIC 2099 5149 5812 5046 Tortillas, fresh or refrigerated; Canned goods: fruit, vegetables, seafood, meats, etc.; Mexican restaurant; Commercial cooking & food service equipment; Tortillas, fresh or refrigerated; Canned goods: fruit, vegetables, seafood, meats, etc.; Mexican restaurant; Commercial cooking & food service equipment
CEO: Veronica Moreno
**Pr:* Eduardo Moreno
VP: Donn Develder
Off Mgr: Karen Musser
IT Man: Rolando Angulo
Sfty Mgr: Diana Franklin
Sls Mgr: Toney Lynch
Sls Mgr: Charles Marvin

D-U-N-S 02-165-6572
OLE SMOKY DISTILLERY LLC
903 Parkway Ste 107, Gatlinburg, TN 37738-3182
Tel (865) 436-6995 *Founded/Ownrshp* 2009
Sales 32.1MM^E *EMP* 125
SIC 2085 Distilled & blended liquors

OLE SOUTH FOODS
See WILLIAMS SAUSAGE CO INC

D-U-N-S 07-402-3961
OLEAN CITY SCHOOL DISTRICT
BOARD OF EDUCATION
410 W Sullivan St, Olean, NY 14760-2522
Tel (716) 375-8020 *Founded/Ownrshp* 1877
Sales 30.2MM *EMP* 400
SIC 8211 Public elementary & secondary schools; School board; Public elementary & secondary schools; School board
Bd of Dir: Steven Hamed
Bd of Dir: Michael Martello
Teacher Pr: Mia Obrien

D-U-N-S 03-022-3192
OLEAN GENERAL HOSPITAL
(*Suby of* UPPER ALLEGHENY HEALTH SYSTEM INC) ★
515 Main St, Olean, NY 14760-1598
Tel (716) 373-2600 *Founded/Ownrshp* 1898
Sales 104.7MM *EMP* 983
Accts Lumsden & Mccormick Llp Buff
SIC 8062 General medical & surgical hospitals; General medical & surgical hospitals
CEO: Tim Finan
Chf Rad: Alexandra Wesley
**Pr:* Timothy Finan
**CFO:* Richard Braun
Sr VP: Rebecca Bruso
Sr VP: Jason Yaworsky
**VP:* Karen Fohl
VP: William Mills
VP: Jeff Zewe
Dir Lab: Robert Krall
Nurse Mgr: Katherine Watkins

D-U-N-S 11-951-7618
OLEAN MEDICAL GROUP LLP
535 Main St Ste 1, Olean, NY 14760-1593
Tel (716) 372-0141 *Founded/Ownrshp* 1995
Sales 23.6MM^E *EMP* 200^E
SIC 8011 General & family practice, physician/surgeon; General & family practice, physician/surgeon
Pt: Brian Carlson

D-U-N-S 00-983-1942
OLEAN WHOLESALE GROCERY COOPERATIVE INC
1587 Haskell Rd, Olean, NY 14760-9229
Tel (716) 372-2020 *Founded/Ownrshp* 1939
Sales 67.1MM^E *EMP* 400
SIC 5411 5122 5148 5147 5143 5141

D-U-N-S 86-725-8428
OLEARYS OFFICE PRODUCTS INC
4550 Easton Dr, Bakersfield, CA 93309-1030
Tel (661) 325-6677 *Founded/Ownrshp* 1994
Sales 41.0MM *EMP* 12
SIC 5112 5021 Office supplies; Office furniture
Pr: John O'Leary
**Sec:* Lois O'Leary
**Off Mgr:* Debbie Sheldon

D-U-N-S 08-459-5875
OLEKSA ENTERPRISES INC (WV)
BROCK OILS
3214 Earl L Core Rd, Morgantown, WV 26508-9595
Tel (304) 296-8214 *Founded/Ownrshp* 1975
Sales 23.5MM^E *EMP* 79
SIC 5181 5172 4212 Beer & other fermented malt liquors; Gasoline; Garbage collection & transport, no disposal; Beer & other fermented malt liquors; Gasoline; Garbage collection & transport, no disposal
Pr: Dennis Brock Oleksa
**Sec:* Gary Oleksa
**VP:* Larry S Oleksa

D-U-N-S 01-283-9630
OLEN COMMERCIAL REALTY CORP
OLEN RESIDENTIAL REALTY
7 Corporate Plaza Dr, Newport Beach, CA 92660-7904
Tel (949) 644-6536 *Founded/Ownrshp* 1974
Sales 26.2MM^E *EMP* 400
SIC 6512 Commercial & industrial building operation; Commercial & industrial building operation
Pr: Igor M Olenicoff
**Sec:* Andrei Olenicoff

OLEN COMPANIES, THE
See OLEN RESIDENTIAL REALTY CORP

D-U-N-S 00-448-7633
OLEN CORP (OH)
4755 S High St, Columbus, OH 43207-4080
Tel (614) 491-1515 *Founded/Ownrshp* 1951
Sales 321.3MM^E *EMP* 86
SIC 1442

D-U-N-S 96-403-8467
OLEN PROPERTIES CORP
7 Corporate Plaza Dr, Newport Beach, CA 92660-7904
Tel (949) 644-6536 *Founded/Ownrshp* 1974
Sales 57.6MM^E *EMP* 349
SIC 6512 6798 6552 Commercial & industrial building operation; Real estate investment trusts; Subdividers & developers; Commercial & industrial building operation; Real estate investment trusts; Subdividers & developers
Pr: Igor M Olenicoff
CFO: Jayne Taylor
VP: Steve Michael
VP: Natalia Ostensen
**VP:* Kathryn Wadsworth
Exec: Linda Davis
Rgnl Mgr: Doug Wolfe
Dist Mgr: Kim Murray
IT Man: Faith Schwitzer
IT Man: Benjamin Yandall
Counsel: Leslie Vandale

OLEN RESIDENTIAL REALTY
See OLEN COMMERCIAL REALTY CORP

D-U-N-S 79-826-4636
OLEN RESIDENTIAL REALTY CORP
OLEN COMPANIES, THE
(*Suby of* OLEN PROPERTIES CORP) ★
7 Corporate Plaza Dr, Newport Beach, CA 92660-7904
Tel (949) 644-6536 *Founded/Ownrshp* 1992
Sales 57.6MM^E *EMP* 300
SIC 1522 Multi-family dwellings, new construction; Multi-family dwellings, new construction
Pr: Igor M Olenicoff
Rgnl Mgr: Gayle Moore

D-U-N-S 02-915-6189
OLENTANGY LOCAL SCHOOL DISTRICT
814 Shanahan Rd Ste 100, Lewis Center, OH 43035-9192
Tel (740) 657-4050 *Founded/Ownrshp* 1920
Sales 216.5MM *EMP* 1,500
Accts Robert Hinkle Cpa Cgfm Colu
SIC 8211 Public elementary school; Public junior high school; Public senior high school; Public elementary school; Public junior high school; Public senior high school
**Prin:* Linda Martin
Schl Brd P: Kevin O'Brien
Teacher Pr: Todd Meyer

OLESEN'S FAMILY BAKERY
See O & H DANISH BAKERY INC

OLESON'S FOOD STORE
See OLESONS FOODS INC

D-U-N-S 04-140-7545
OLESONS FOODS INC
OLESON'S FOOD STORE
3860 N Long Lake Rd Ste A, Traverse City, MI 49684-7204
Tel (231) 947-6091 *Founded/Ownrshp* 1964
Sales 27.2MM^E *EMP* 250
Accts Rehmann Robson Traverse City
SIC 5411 5812 Supermarkets, independent; Eating places; Supermarkets, independent; Eating places
Pr: Donald W Oleson
**Treas:* Gerald E Oleson
**VP:* Donald M Oleson

D-U-N-S 12-314-7402
OLEUMTECH CORP
19762 Pauling, Foothill Ranch, CA 92610-2611
Tel (949) 305-9009 *Founded/Ownrshp* 2002
Sales 26.9MM^E *EMP* 62
SIC 3823 Industrial instrmnts msrmnt display/control process variable
CEO: Paul Gregory
**COO:* Vrej ISA
VP Sls: Colin Lippincott

OLEY VALLEY MIDDLE O
See OLEY VALLEY SCHOOL DISTRICT INC

D-U-N-S 00-642-0137
OLEY VALLEY SCHOOL DISTRICT INC
OLEY VALLEY MIDDLE O
17 Jefferson St, Oley, PA 19547-8774
Tel (610) 987-4100 *Founded/Ownrshp* 1965
Sales 28.9MM *EMP* 250
SIC 8211 Public elementary school; Public junior high school; Public senior high school; Public elementary school; Public junior high school; Public senior high school
Ex Dir: Dawn Cambria
HC Dir: Sue Johnson

D-U-N-S 06-982-3714
OLGAS KITCHEN INC
(*Suby of* ROBERT B SOLOMON HOLDING COMPANY)
2125 Butterfield Dr # 301, Troy, MI 48084-5398
Tel (248) 362-0001 *Founded/Ownrshp* 1977
Sales 4.5MM^E *EMP* 1,107^E
SIC 5812 Greek restaurant
Pr: Robert B Solomon

COO: William M Carpenter
Brnch Mgr: Susan Taylor

D-U-N-S 06-002-8750
OLGOONIK CORP
518 Main St, Wainwright, AK 99782
Tel (907) 763-2613 *Founded/Ownrshp* 1973
Sales 45.4MM^E *EMP* 363
Accts Mikunda Cottrell & Co Inc A
SIC 5983 5172 5399 7011 1522 Fuel oil dealers; Fuel oil; Country general stores; Hotels & motels; Residential construction; Fuel oil dealers; Fuel oil; Country general stores; Hotels & motels; Residential construction
Pr: Segevan Steve
**Ch Bd:* Howard Phekotak
**Ch:* Hugh Patkotak Sr
**VP:* Kagak Edgar
**VP:* Edgar Kagak

D-U-N-S 06-615-0475 IMP
OLHAUSEN BILLIARD MANUFACTURING INC
1124 Vaughn Pkwy, Portland, TN 37148-8472
Tel (615) 323-8522 *Founded/Ownrshp* 1972
Sales 41.1MM^E *EMP* 215
SIC 3949 7699 Billiard & pool equipment & supplies, general; Billiard table repair; Billiard & pool equipment & supplies, general; Billiard table repair
Ch Bd: Donald Olhausen
**CFO:* David Robinson
Genl Mgr: Jack Deason

OLIAN TOWNHOMES
See AMEER ABDELMALEK

D-U-N-S 13-567-9843
OLIFF & BERRIDGE PLC
277 S Washington St # 500, Alexandria, VA 22314-3672
Tel (703) 836-6400 *Founded/Ownrshp* 1983
Sales 20.2MM^E *EMP* 132
SIC 8111 General practice law office
Pt: James A Oliff
Pt: William P Berridge
Pt: Mario A Costantino
Pt: Kirk M Hudson
Pt: Robert A Miller
Pt: Thomas J Pardini
Pt: Edward P Walker
Ofcr: Christopher Brown
Exec: John Kern
Off Admin: Debra McCaa
Dir IT: Steven Lichtenberger

OLIN BRASS
See GBC METALS LLC

D-U-N-S 00-133-8086 IMP/EXP
▲ **OLIN CORP** (VA)
190 Carondelet Plz # 1530, Saint Louis, MO 63105-3467
Tel (314) 480-1400 *Founded/Ownrshp* 1892
Sales 2.2MMM *EMP* 4,100
Accts Kpmg Llp St Louis Missouri
Tkr Sym OLN *Exch* NYS
SIC 2812 2819 2821 2842 2869 2891 Alkalies & chlorine; Caustic soda, sodium hydroxide; Chlorine, compressed or liquefied; Hydrochloric acid; Sulfuric acid, oleum; Potasssium chloride & cyanide; Calcium chloride & hypochlorite; Polyurethane resins; Cleaning or polishing preparations; Glycol ethers; Adhesives & sealants; Alkalies & chlorine; Caustic soda, sodium hydroxide; Chlorine, compressed or liquefied; Hydrochloric acid; Sulfuric acid, oleum; Potassium chloride & cyanide; Calcium chloride & hypochlorite; Polyurethane resins; Cleaning or polishing preparations; Glycol ethers; Adhesives & sealants
Ch Bd: Joseph D Rupp
Pr: Pat D Dawson
Pr: John E Fischer
Pr: Clive A Grannum
Pr: James A Varilek
CFO: Todd A Slater
Ex VP: Michael E Campbell
Sr VP: John L McIntosh
Sr VP: George H Pain
VP: Roger Jones
VP: Frank O'Brien
VP: John M Sampson
VP: Randee N Sumner
VP: Thomas Werner
Board of Directors: Carol A Williams, Gray G Benoist, Donald W Bogus, C Robert Bunch, Randall W Larrimore, John M B O'connor, Richard M Rompala, Philip J Schulz, Vincent J Smith, William H Weideman

OLIN EMPLOYEES CREDIT UNION
See 1ST MIDAMERICA CREDIT UNION

D-U-N-S 96-768-4593
■ **OLIN SUNBELT II INC**
(*Suby of* OLIN CORP) ★
190 Carondelet Plz # 1530, Saint Louis, MO 63105-3443
Tel (314) 480-1400 *Founded/Ownrshp* 2011
Sales 18.4MM^E *EMP* 304^E
SIC 2812 Caustic soda, sodium hydroxide
Prin: David Dye

OLINGER DISTRIBUTING COMPANY
See GLAZERS DISTRIBUTORS OF INDIANA LLC

D-U-N-S 03-279-3630 IMP/EXP
OLIVA TOBACCO CO (FL)
3104 N Armenia Ave Ste 1, Tampa, FL 33607-1658
Tel (813) 248-4921 *Founded/Ownrshp* 1934
Sales 48.9MM *EMP* 13
Accts Prida-Guida & Companyu Pa
SIC 5159 0132 Tobacco, leaf; Tobacco; Tobacco, leaf; Tobacco
Pr: John E Oliva Sr
**Treas:* Angel Oliva Jr
VP: Constantino Gonzalez
VP: Carol Llaneza
VP: Sherwin Seltzer
VP Sls: Daniel Blumenthal

D-U-N-S 13-920-8586 IMP
OLIVE BARIANI OIL LLC
9460 Bar Du Ln, Sacramento, CA 95829-9475
Tel (415) 864-1917 *Founded/Ownrshp* 2004
Sales 21.3MM^E *EMP* 25^E
SIC 2079 Olive oil
CEO: Emmanuel Bariani

D-U-N-S 03-991-0500
OLIVE CREST
2130 E 4th St Ste 200, Santa Ana, CA 92705-3818
Tel (714) 543-5437 *Founded/Ownrshp* 1974
Sales 43.6MM *EMP* 500
Accts Onisko & Scholz Llp Long Bea
SIC 8361 8322 Home for the emotionally disturbed; Individual & family services; Home for the emotionally disturbed; Individual & family services
CEO: Donald A Verleur
CFO: Edward Becker
CFO: Ed Beker
**VP:* Lois Verleur
VP Admn: Tim Bauer
Ex Dir: Jeff Judy
Dir IT: Louise Williams
Mktg Dir: Elizabeth Zayas
Pgrm Dir: Antonio Mejico
Pgrm Dir: Anne Snook
Snr Mgr: Stephanie Swallow

OLIVE GARDEN
See RARE HOSPITALITY INTERNATIONAL INC

D-U-N-S 00-916-1472 IMP/EXP
OLIVE MUSCO PRODUCTS INC
MUSCO FAMILY OLIVE CO
17950 Via Nicolo, Tracy, CA 95377-9767
Tel (209) 836-4600 *Founded/Ownrshp* 1959
Sales 76.1MM^E *EMP* 300
SIC 2033 2035 Canned fruits & specialties; Olives, brined: bulk; Canned fruits & specialties; Olives, brined: bulk
CEO: Nicholas Musco
COO: Ben Hall
CFO: Scott Hamilton
Genl Mgr: Anita Rocha
Dir IT: Brett Nelson
Info Man: Mark Gilbert
Opers Mgr: Darrell Chelcun
Opers Mgr: David Ormonde

D-U-N-S 95-997-6044 IMP
OLIVE PRESS LLC
24724 Arnold Dr, Sonoma, CA 95476-2814
Tel (707) 939-8900 *Founded/Ownrshp* 1996
Sales 25.5MM^E *EMP* 12^E
SIC 2079 5199 Olive oil; Oils, animal or vegetable
Snr Mgr: Craig Scarborough

D-U-N-S 79-039-6688
OLIVE TAP
30 Public Sq, Medina, OH 44256-2203
Tel (330) 721-6500 *Founded/Ownrshp* 2007
Sales 20.8MM^E *EMP* 4
SIC 2079 Olive oil
Owner: John Petrocelloy

D-U-N-S 03-738-5759
OLIVE VIEW-UCLA MEDICAL CENTER
VALLEY CARE OLIVE VIEW MED CTR
14445 Olive View Dr, Sylmar, CA 91342-1438
Tel (818) 364-1555 *Founded/Ownrshp* 2001
Sales 47.5M^E *EMP* 2,000^E
SIC 8011 Medical centers; Medical centers
CEO: Carolyn Rhee
VP: Edwin Chuong
Exec: Cynthia O'Donnell
Exec: Kay Selden
Chf Nrs Of: Dellone Pascascio
Mng Dir: Monica Mita
Cmptr Lab: Elaine Manahan
Pathlgst: Chisa Aoyama
Obsttrcn: Barbara Fletcher
Doctor: Roberto Rodriguez
Pharmcst: Kyung Kim

D-U-N-S 07-250-5795
OLIVENHAIN MUNICIPAL WATER DISTRICT
1966 Olivenhain Rd, Encinitas, CA 92024-5676
Tel (760) 753-6466 *Founded/Ownrshp* 1959
Sales 54.2MM *EMP* 79
Accts White Nelson Diehl Evans Llp
SIC 4941 4971 Water supply; Impounding reservoir, irrigation; Water supply; Impounding reservoir, irrigation
Pr: Edmund Sprague
Sr Pt: Joni Lockhart
**Treas:* Mark A Muir
**VP:* Robert F Topolavac
VP: Robert Topolovac
**Genl Mgr:* Kimberly A Thorner
IT Man: John Carnegie
IT Man: Joey Randall
Opers Supe: Mike Perez
Opers Mgr: Jeff Anderson
**Opers Mgr:* Tom Kennedy

D-U-N-S 05-750-6933
OLIVER & CO INC
1300 S 51st St, Richmond, CA 94804-4628
Tel (510) 412-9090 *Founded/Ownrshp* 1971
Sales 47.5MM^E *EMP* 90
SIC 1542 Nonresidential construction; Nonresidential construction
CEO: Steven Henri Oliver
**VP:* Josh Oliver
**VP:* Jeff Shields

OLIVER ALARM SYSTEMS
See OLIVER SPRINKLER CO INC

OLIVER C JOSEPH CHRYSLER DODGE
See OLIVER C JOSEPH INC

D-U-N-S 02-494-7616
OLIVER C JOSEPH INC
OLIVER C JOSEPH CHRYSLER DODGE
3795 State Route 15, Belleville, IL 62226-3100
Tel (618) 233-8140 *Founded/Ownrshp* 1949
Sales 22.5MM^E *EMP* 50

SIC 5511 Automobiles, new & used
Pr: Oliver D Joseph
**VP:* Brad Joseph
Genl Mgr: Greg Castelli

D-U-N-S 07-482-1489
OLIVER CARR CO
CARR CAPITAL
1750 H St Nw Ste 500, Washington, DC 20006-4692
Tel (202) 303-3060 *Founded/Ownrshp* 1962
Sales 12.5MM^E *EMP* 515
SIC 6531 6552 Real estate managers; Subdividers & developers; Real estate managers; Subdividers & developers
Ch Bd: Oliver T Carr Jr
**Pr:* Richard W Carr

D-U-N-S 00-945-7672
OLIVER DE SILVA INC
GALLAGHER & BURK
11555 Dublin Blvd, Dublin, CA 94568-2854
Tel (925) 829-9220 *Founded/Ownrshp* 1931
Sales 106.0MM^E *EMP* 200
SIC 1429 Igneous rock, crushed & broken-quarrying; Igneous rock, crushed & broken-quarrying
Ch: Edwin O De Silva
**Pr:* Richard B Gates
COO: Rick Case
**Ex VP:* David De Silva
**VP:* J Scott Archibald
**VP:* Ernest Lampkin

D-U-N-S 15-465-5716
OLIVER EXTERMINATING SERVICE CORP
658 Nw 99th St, Miami, FL 33150-1623
Tel (305) 758-1811 *Founded/Ownrshp* 1984
Sales 28.1MM^E *EMP* 350
SIC 7342 Pest control in structures; Pest control in structures
Ch Bd: Olivier Grinda
**Pr:* Bert Putterman

D-U-N-S 00-820-5528
OLIVER H VAN HORN CO LLC
(*Suby of* WURTH GROUP OF NORTH AMERICA INC) ★
4100 Euphrosine St, New Orleans, LA 70125-1390
Tel (504) 821-4100 *Founded/Ownrshp* 1903, 2010
Sales 41.6MM^E *EMP* 75
SIC 5085 5084

OLIVER HEATING & COOLING
See J M OLIVER INC

D-U-N-S 14-795-7575
OLIVER M DEAN INC
125 Brooks St, Worcester, MA 01606-3388
Tel (508) 856-9100 *Founded/Ownrshp* 1985
Sales 27.5MM^E *EMP* 25
SIC 5083 8711 Dairy machinery & equipment; Sanitary engineers
Pr: Richard C Eldon
VP: Anthony Fiore

D-U-N-S 09-981-7058
OLIVER OIL CO
SUN DO KWIK SHOP
1811 E 5th St, Lumberton, NC 28358-6107
Tel (910) 738-1401 *Founded/Ownrshp* 1979
Sales 108.5MM *EMP* 80
Accts Charles K Edwards Lumberton
SIC 5171 5411 5541 Petroleum bulk stations; Convenience stores, independent; Filling stations, gasoline; Petroleum bulk stations; Convenience stores, independent; Filling stations, gasoline
Pr: Christopher L Oliver
**VP:* Lawrence H Oliver

D-U-N-S 96-175-6884 IMP
OLIVER PACKAGING AND EQUIPMENT CO
(*Suby of* MASON WELLS INC) ★
3236 Wilson Dr Nw, Walker, MI 49534-7505
Tel (616) 356-2950 *Founded/Ownrshp* 2010
Sales 21.7MM^E *EMP* 61
SIC 2675 3556 2672 Die-cut paper & board; Bakery machinery; Adhesive papers, labels or tapes: from purchased material
Pr: Jerry Bennish
VP: Jennifer Martineau
IT Man: Rick Alvesteffer
IT Man: Jeff Murak
Mtls Mgr: Kevin Dewey
Mktg Dir: Yvonne Johnson
Sales Asso: Dayna Ives
Snr Mgr: Bob Cooper

D-U-N-S 07-829-8780
OLIVER PRODUCTS CO
(*Suby of* BERWIND CORP) ★
445 6th St Nw, Grand Rapids, MI 49504-5298
Tel (616) 456-7711 *Founded/Ownrshp* 2012
Sales 77.1MM^E *EMP* 1^E
SIC 5084 Processing & packaging equipment
Pr: Jerry Bennish
Mtls Mgr: Penny Lakanen
Advt Mgr: Jon Andreasen
Manager: Tina Norwood

D-U-N-S 00-911-3473 IMP/EXP
OLIVER RUBBER CO LLC
(*Suby of* MICHELIN NORTH AMERICA INC) ★
1 Parkway S, Greenville, SC 29615-5022
Tel (866) 464-2580 *Founded/Ownrshp* 2007
Sales 57.0MM^E *EMP* 400
SIC 3011 3061 3559 Tread rubber, camelback for tire retreading; Automotive rubber goods (mechanical); Tire retreading machinery & equipment; Tread rubber, camelback for tire retreading; Automotive rubber goods (mechanical); Tire retreading machinery & equipment
**Pr:* William J Guzick
**Treas:* Thomas C Praktish
Bd of Dir: Steven M Chapman
Bd of Dir: John J Holland
Bd of Dir: Richard L Wambold
Bd of Dir: Robert D Welding
VP: Joseph Fiane
VP: Mark W Krivoruchka
VP: John Zito
Genl Mgr: John Ebert
Genl Mgr: Walter Maganza

D-U-N-S 04-329-2994
OLIVER SPRINKLER CO INC (PA)
OLIVER ALARM SYSTEMS
501 Feheley Dr, King of Prussia, PA 19406-2690
Tel (610) 277-1331 *Founded/Ownrshp* 1969
Sales 45.0MM^E *EMP* 135
SIC 1711 1731 Sprinkler contractors; Fire sprinkler system installation; Safety & security specialization; Fire detection & burglar alarm systems specialization; Sprinkler contractors; Fire sprinkler system installation; Safety & security specialization; Fire detection & burglar alarm systems specialization
Pr: David S Oliver
**Ch Bd:* Richard E Oliver
Pr: Daniel De Lucia
**Treas:* Russell H Walters
**VP:* Stephen Oliver
Mktg Dir: Tom Dagney

D-U-N-S 87-971-0176
OLIVER STAFFING INC
124 E 40th St Rm 401, New York, NY 10016-1764
Tel (212) 634-1234 *Founded/Ownrshp* 1995
Sales 14.8MM^E *EMP* 300
SIC 7361 Employment agencies; Employment agencies
Pr: Seeley Oliver
Dir Bus: Howard Fein

D-U-N-S 06-554-8315
OLIVER WINE CO INC
OLIVER WINERY
8024 N State Road 37, Bloomington, IN 47404-9449
Tel (812) 822-0466 *Founded/Ownrshp* 1972
Sales 20.8MM^E *EMP* 95^E
SIC 5921 2084 Wine; Wines
Pr: William M Oliver
COO: Sarah Villwock
**Sec:* Kathleen Oliver

OLIVER WINERY
See OLIVER WINE CO INC

D-U-N-S 17-905-9522 IMP
OLIVER-TOLAS HEALTHCARE PACKAGING INC
(*Suby of* OLIVER-TOLAS HEALTHCARE PACKAGING LLC) ★
905 Pennsylvania Blvd, Feasterville Trevose, PA 19053-7815
Tel (215) 322-7900 *Founded/Ownrshp* 2009
Sales 137.2MM^E *EMP* 162
SIC 2671 Packaging paper & plastics film, coated & laminated; Packaging paper & plastics film, coated & laminated
Pr: Scott Dickman
Ql Cn Mgr: Muhammad Waheed
Mktg Mgr: Karen Barr
Snr Mgr: Denise Dilissio

D-U-N-S 02-545-1170 IMP/EXP
OLIVER-TOLAS HEALTHCARE PACKAGING LLC
(*Suby of* MASON WELLS BUYOUT FUND II LIMITED PARTNERSHIP) ★
445 6th St Nw, Grand Rapids, MI 49504-5253
Tel (616) 456-7711 *Founded/Ownrshp* 2007
Sales 137.2MM^E *EMP* 356^E
Accts Crowe Chizek Grand Rapids Mi
SIC 2672 Adhesive papers, labels or tapes: from purchased material; Adhesive papers, labels or tapes: from purchased material
CEO: Jerry Bennish
Pr: David Haines
CFO: Ted Heininger
VP: Marv Snedeker
Rgnl Mgr: Julian Benavides
Rgnl Mgr: Alyssa Hezmalhalch
Rgnl Mgr: Matt Joseph
Rgnl Mgr: Brad Meeuwsen
IT Man: Lori Bour
Mtls Mgr: Lisa McCool
Mfg Mgr: Greg Hewitt

D-U-N-S 05-610-8244
OLIVERMCMILLAN LLC
733 8th Ave, San Diego, CA 92101-6407
Tel (619) 321-1111 *Founded/Ownrshp* 1978
Sales 78.1MM^E *EMP* 60^E
SIC 6552 Land subdividers & developers, commercial; Land subdividers & developers, residential
CEO: Morgan Dene Oliver
**Pr:* Paul Buss
**Pr:* Dan Nishikawa
**CFO:* Bill Persky
**Ch:* Jim McMillan
VP: Stanley McElroy
Mng Dir: John Costello
Off Admin: Juliana Arnold
Off Admin: Kamu Dickson
Dir IT: David Serrano
Mktg Dir: Colin Moussa

D-U-N-S 07-258-1952
OLIVET COLLEGE
320 S Main St, Olivet, MI 49076-9724
Tel (269) 749-7000 *Founded/Ownrshp* 1844
Sales 33.4MM *EMP* 145
Accts Maner Costerisan Pc Lansing
SIC 8221 College, except junior; College, except junior
Pr: Steven M Corey
VP: Linda Logan

D-U-N-S 15-690-0078 IMP
OLIVET INTERNATIONAL INC
11015 Hopkins St, Mira Loma, CA 91752-3248
Tel (951) 681-8888 *Founded/Ownrshp* 1984
Sales 145.3MM *EMP* 200
SIC 5099 Luggage; Luggage
CEO: David Yu
**Pr:* Lydia Hsu

D-U-N-S 07-143-3668
OLIVET NAZARENE UNIVERSITY (IL)
1 University Ave, Bourbonnais, IL 60914-1996
Tel (815) 939-5247 *Founded/Ownrshp* 1907
Sales 130.1MM *EMP* 754
Accts Porschnack Pelletier & Co K
SIC 8221 University; University
Pr: John C Bowling
**Ch Bd:* David Rowland
**CFO:* Dr Douglas Perry
VP: Matt Smith
VP: Gary Streit
**Exec:* David Pickering
Dir Soc: Dana Carrigan
Comm Dir: Scott Dombrowski
Genl Mgr: Brian Utter
**CIO:* Dennis Seymour
Dir IT: Kevin King

D-U-N-S 04-279-3182 IMP
OLLA BEAUTY SUPPLY INC
ULTRA DISTRIBUTORS
10 New Maple Ave Ste 301a, Pine Brook, NJ 07058-8805
Tel (973) 575-5260 *Founded/Ownrshp* 2008
Sales 65.0MM *EMP* 103
SIC 5122 Beauty parlor equipment & supplies; Drugs, proprietaries & sundries
Pr: Marcy Blick
**Pr:* Michael Ross
**VP:* May Chromey

D-U-N-S 09-911-8580
OLLESHEIMER LOUIS T & SON OF INDIANA INC
(*Suby of* LOUIS T OLLESHEIMER & SON INC) ★
605 E 12 Mile Rd, Madison Heights, MI 48071-2568
Tel (248) 544-3900 *Founded/Ownrshp* 1970
Sales 29.3MM^E *EMP* 29
SIC 5033 Roofing, asphalt & sheet metal
**Pr:* James Ollesheimer
CFO: Dave Moyle

OLLIES BARGAIN OUTLET
See OLLIES BARGAIN OUTLET HOLDINGS INC

D-U-N-S 19-664-4053 IMP
▲ OLLIES BARGAIN OUTLET HOLDINGS INC
OLLIES BARGAIN OUTLET
6295 Allentown Blvd Ste 1, Harrisburg, PA 17112-2694
Tel (717) 657-2300 *Founded/Ownrshp* 2012
Sales 637.9MM *EMP* 5,000
Tkr Sym OLLI *Exch* NGM
SIC 5399 5311 Surplus & salvage goods; General merchandise, non-durable; Surplus & salvage goods; Department stores, non-discount
Ch Bd: Mark Butler
CFO: John Swygert
Ofcr: Jay Stasz
Sr VP: Kevin McLain
Sr VP: Omar Segura
VP: Rob Bertram
VP: Robert Bertram
VP: Howard Freedman
Mktg Mgr: Alyssa Myers
Snr Mgr: Tom Habbyshaw

D-U-N-S 03-152-4424 IMP
■ OLLIES BARGAIN OUTLET INC (PA)
(*Suby of* OLLIES BARGAIN OUTLET) ★
6295 Allentown Blvd Ste 1, Harrisburg, PA 17112-2694
Tel (717) 657-8243 *Founded/Ownrshp* 1982, 2003
Sales 407.5MM^E *EMP* 1,800
Accts Ernst & Young Llp
SIC 5399 5199 Surplus & salvage goods; General merchandise, non-durable; Surplus & salvage goods; General merchandise, non-durable
Pr: Mark L Butler
**Pr:* Howard Freedman
COO: Dave Campbell
**Genl Mgr:* Kevin Phillips
**Treas:* John Swygert
**VP:* Jerry Altland
**VP:* Andre Dickemann
**VP:* Dan Haines
**VP:* Doug Wisehaupt
Genl Mgr: Tom Bensinz
Genl Mgr: John Eckhart

OLLIN TECHNOLOGY
See ENRIQUE MENDOZA

OLLY SHOES
See OLLY USA LLC

D-U-N-S 13-873-6470
OLLY USA LLC
OLLY SHOES
490 Acorn Ln, Downingtown, PA 19335-3075
Tel (610) 594-2660 *Founded/Ownrshp* 2008
Sales 64.5MM^E *EMP* 200
SIC 6719 Personal holding companies, except banks; Personal holding companies, except banks
Co-Ownr: Katherine Chapman

D-U-N-S 78-255-0966
OLMOS CONSTRUCTION INC
440 Pinn Rd, San Antonio, TX 78227-1232
Tel (210) 675-4990 *Founded/Ownrshp* 1991
Sales 84.0MM^E *EMP* 300
SIC 1611 1794 1795 Surfacing & paving; Excavation work; Wrecking & demolition work; Surfacing & paving; Excavation work; Wrecking & demolition work
Pr: Hugh E Long
**CEO:* Richard F Romane
CFO: Tracy Janicke
Ch: Carolyn Chamberlain
VP: Mark E Linneman
**VP:* Larry Struthoff
**VP:* Jim Weynand
Sls Mgr: Jack Janicke

D-U-N-S 82-963-3135
OLMOS EQUIPMENT INC
440 Pinn Rd, San Antonio, TX 78227-1232
Tel (210) 675-4990 *Founded/Ownrshp* 2000
Sales 35.0MM *EMP* 280
SIC 1542 Commercial & office building contractors; Commercial & office building contractors
CEO: Tracy Janicke
**VP:* Jack Janicke
VP: Mark Linneman
**VP:* Steve Owens

OLMSTED COUNTY HEALTH DEPT
See COUNTY OF OLMSTED

D-U-N-S 02-572-4279
OLMSTED FALLS CITY SCHOOLS
26937 Bagley Rd, Olmsted Twp, OH 44138-1161
Tel (440) 427-6000 *Founded/Ownrshp* 1900
Sales 27.6MM^E *EMP* 404
Accts Alger & Associates Llc North
SIC 8211 Public elementary & secondary schools; Public elementary & secondary schools
**Treas:* Mark Hullman
Prin: William Jump
Schl Brd P: James Weisbarth
Teacher Pr: Ann Strictland

D-U-N-S 19-601-6539
OLMSTED HEALTH AND SERVICE CORP
HEALTH CENTER AT RENAISSANCE
26376 John Rd Ofc, Olmsted Twp, OH 44138-1283
Tel (440) 235-7100 *Founded/Ownrshp* 1987
Sales 7.5MM^E *EMP* 300
SIC 8051 Skilled nursing care facilities; Skilled nursing care facilities
Ex Dir: Elizabeth Bartelme

D-U-N-S 07-074-4388
OLMSTED MEDICAL CENTER
210 9th St Se Ste 1, Rochester, MN 55904-6400
Tel (507) 288-3443 *Founded/Ownrshp* 1949
Sales 189.2MM *EMP* 950
Accts Rsm Mcgladrey Inc Rochester
SIC 8062 General medical & surgical hospitals; General medical & surgical hospitals
Pr: Roy Yawn
**Ofcr:* Kevin Pitzer
Exec: Lois Till-Tarara
IT Man: Richard Skagerberg
Netwrk Mgr: Dave Heller
Psych: Marcia Guertin
Obsttrcn: Patricia Agudelo
Obsttrcn: Kimberly McKeon
Obsttrcn: Deborah Petersen
Opthamlgy: T L Edwards
Nutrtnst: Jamie Michel

D-U-N-S 19-865-3792 IMP
OLMSTED PRODUCTS CO LLC
(*Suby of* OILGEAR CO) ★
1424 International Dr, Traverse City, MI 49686-8751
Tel (231) 929-1660 *Founded/Ownrshp* 2008
Sales 36.0MM *EMP* 49
SIC 3492 Control valves, fluid power: hydraulic & pneumatic
COO: Craig Lafave
**Pt:* Scott Raether
IT Man: Kevin Tasch
Ql Cn Mgr: Phil Kuusisto

D-U-N-S 04-904-0512 IMP/EXP
OLMSTED-KIRK CO OF HOUSTON
OLMSTED-KIRK PAPER
(*Suby of* OLMSTED-KIRK EQUIPMENT & SUP) ★
9565 W Wingfoot Rd, Houston, TX 77041-9112
Tel (713) 868-1531 *Founded/Ownrshp* 1956
Sales 31.6MM^E *EMP* 52
SIC 5111 5113 Fine paper; Industrial & personal service paper
Ch Bd: John R Taylor III
**CEO:* John Taylor
CFO: Bill Smith
VP: Rich Walen
**VP:* Richard Wales
VP: David Watson
Brnch Mgr: Robert Olmsted
**Genl Mgr:* Rich Wales
Sls Mgr: Steve Chumley

OLMSTED-KIRK EQUIPMENT & SUP
See OLMSTED-KIRK PAPER CO

OLMSTED-KIRK PAPER
See OLMSTED-KIRK CO OF HOUSTON

D-U-N-S 00-894-7186 IMP
OLMSTED-KIRK PAPER CO
OLMSTED-KIRK EQUIPMENT & SUP
1601 Valley View Ln # 101, Dallas, TX 75234-9042
Tel (214) 637-2220 *Founded/Ownrshp* 1905
Sales 130.0MM^E *EMP* 300
SIC 5111

D-U-N-S 19-673-6672
OLNEY BANCSHARES OF TEXAS INC
307 W Main St, Olney, TX 76374-1850
Tel (940) 564-5516 *Founded/Ownrshp* 1987
Sales NA *EMP* 402
SIC 6712 6021 Bank holding companies; National commercial banks; Bank holding companies; National commercial banks
Pr: Ross McKnight

D-U-N-S 96-850-6951
OLNEY CHARTER HIGH SCHOOL AN ASPIRA INC OF PENNSYLVANIA SCHOOL
100 W Duncannon Ave, Philadelphia, PA 19120-3410
Tel (215) 456-3197 *Founded/Ownrshp* 2011
Sales 28.2MM *EMP* 99
SIC 8299 Airline training; Airline training
Pr: Alfredo Calderon
Off Mgr: Maira Aponte

D-U-N-S 19-716-7802
OLS HOTELS & RESORTS LP
16000 Ventura Blvd # 1010, Encino, CA 91436-2744
Tel (818) 905-8280 *Founded/Ownrshp* 1989
Sales 84.8MM^E *EMP* 2,045
SIC 7011 Hotels & motels; Hotels & motels
Pt: John Fitts
CFO: Martti Mannaoja
**Ex VP:* Roger Vasey
Sr VP: Martti Mannoja

VP: Alan Bear
Genl Mgr: Stephen Bohjalian
Genl Mgr: John Douponce
Genl Mgr: Skip Sikora
Genl Mgr: Chad Thompson
Genl Mgr: Mark Vinsko
VP Opers: Rick Ball

OLSEN, STAN AUTO CENTER
See STAN OLSEN AUTO CENTER

D-U-N-S 04-005-5378
OLSHAN FROME WOLOSKY LLP
65 E 55th St Fl 3, New York, NY 10022-3372
Tel (212) 753-7200 *Founded/Ownrshp* 1963
Sales 28.4MM^E *EMP* 120^E
SIC 8111 General practice law office
Pt: M L Olshan
**Pt:* Robert L Frome
Pt: Warren R Gleicher
**Pt:* Neil Grundman
Pt: Yehuda Markovits
Pt: Lori Marks-Esterman
**Pt:* Victor M Rosenzweig
Pt: Samuel P Ross
**Pt:* Steven Wolosky
COO: Steven Wolosky
Off Mgr: Heather Rutner

OLSHEN'S BOTTLE SUPPLY
See RICHARDS PACKAGING INC

D-U-N-S 10-342-2770 IMP
OLSON AND CO STEEL
1941 Davis St, San Leandro, CA 94577-1262
Tel (510) 489-4680 *Founded/Ownrshp* 1983
Sales 61.6MM^E *EMP* 350
SIC 3446 3441 Architectural metalwork; Fabricated structural metal; Architectural metalwork; Fabricated structural metal
CEO: David Olson
**Pr:* Dylan Olson
CFO: Kevin Cullen
**CFO:* Michael Volan
**Ex VP:* Thomas Fluehr
VP: Diane Greer
VP: Larry Lundervold
Snr PM: Joel Oas
Snr PM: Jay Smith
Snr Mgr: Scott Larson

D-U-N-S 94-379-3711
■ OLSON CO INC
(*Suby of* ICF INTERNATIONAL INC) ★
420 N 5th St Ste 1000, Minneapolis, MN 55401-2322
Tel (612) 215-9800 *Founded/Ownrshp* 2014
Sales 74.1MM^E *EMP* 300^E
SIC 7311 8742 Advertising agencies; Marketing consulting services; Advertising agencies; Marketing consulting services
CEO: John Partilla
**Pr:* Margaret Murphy
**Chf Mktg O:* Mitchell Caplan
Ex VP: Kevin Farrell
VP: Paul Bechel
VP: Kevin Clark
VP: Stephna May
VP: Steven Miller
VP: Jeremy Mullman
VP: Paul Ratzky
VP: Mike Spencer
Assoc Dir: Thomas Douty
Assoc Dir: Kimberly Dunn
Assoc Dir: Matthew Nyguist
Assoc Dir: Len Rubel
Assoc Dir: Jen Walz
Creative D: Chris Henderson
Creative D: Scott Muskin
Creative D: Dave Statman
Board of Directors: Jim Garrity, Arun Sinha

D-U-N-S 19-605-8846
OLSON CO LLC
OLSON HOMES
3010 Old Ranch Pkwy # 100, Seal Beach, CA 90740-2750
Tel (562) 596-4770 *Founded/Ownrshp* 2014
Sales 46.9MM^E *EMP* 100
SIC 1521 Single-family housing construction
Pr: Karen Hoover
Pr: Leslie Keller
Pr: Tom Martinez
Pr: Leslie Nguyen
CFO: Mario Urzua
Sr VP: Bill Holford
Sr VP: John Reekstin
Sr VP: Michael Ugar
VP: Eric Everhart
VP: Ruby Johnson
VP: Brenda Olson

OLSON HOMES
See OLSON CO LLC

D-U-N-S 10-231-5132
OLSON INDUSTRIES INC
87567 477th Ave, Atkinson, NE 68713-5006
Tel (402) 925-5090 *Founded/Ownrshp* 1982
Sales 21.2MM^E *EMP* 100
SIC 3599 3499 3648 3537 Machine & other job shop work; Machine bases, metal; Lighting equipment; Industrial trucks & tractors
Pr: Ted D Olson Jr
**Sec:* Daniel L Olson

OLSON LONG TERM CARE PHARMACY
See PHARMASYNC LLC

D-U-N-S 00-229-6348
OLSON METAL PRODUCTS LLC (TX)
IMS BUHRKE-OLSON
(*Suby of* IMS COMPANIES LLC) ★
511 W Algonquin Rd, Arlington Heights, IL 60005-4411
Tel (847) 981-7550 *Founded/Ownrshp* 2008
Sales 26.0MM^E *EMP* 540
SIC 3469 Metal stampings
CEO: Mark Simanton

D-U-N-S 08-604-2124
OLSON PACKAGING SERVICES INC
1445 Knox Highway 32, Galesburg, IL 61401-8321
Tel (309) 342-8147 *Founded/Ownrshp* 2006
Sales 28.4MM^E *EMP* 63
SIC 5113 2653 4225

D-U-N-S 10-135-7143
OLSONS BAKING CO LLC
SIGNATURE BAKERY
6414 204th St Sw Ste 100, Lynnwood, WA 98036-5966
Tel (425) 774-9164 *Founded/Ownrshp* 1995
Sales 29.9MM^E *EMP* 150
SIC 2051 2053 Bakery: wholesale or wholesale/retail combined; Bakery products, partially cooked (except frozen); Biscuits, baked: baking powder & raised; Cakes, bakery: except frozen; Frozen bakery products, except bread; Bakery: wholesale or wholesale/retail combined; Bakery products, partially cooked (except frozen); Biscuits, baked: baking powder & raised; Cakes, bakery: except frozen; Frozen bakery products, except bread
Pr: Charles M Olson

D-U-N-S 04-369-9891 IMP
OLSONS GREENHOUSE GARDENS INC (UT)
1876 N 460 W, Salem, UT 84653
Tel (801) 806-9099 *Founded/Ownrshp* 1963
Sales 22.5MM *EMP* 350
SIC 5193 0181 Flowers & nursery stock; Ornamental nursery products; Flowers & nursery stock; Ornamental nursery products
Pr: Bart B Olson
**CFO:* Tim McKenna
VP: Chad Olson
VP Sls: Brian Lloyd

D-U-N-S 07-290-0368
OLSSON ASSOCIATES INC (NE)
601 P St, Lincoln, NE 68508-2303
Tel (402) 474-6311 *Founded/Ownrshp* 1956
Sales 145.9MM^E *EMP* 650
SIC 8711 Consulting engineer; Consulting engineer
CEO: Roger K Severin
**Pr:* Brad Strittmatter
COO: Greg Hudson
**CFO:* Jeff Jenkins
**Sr VP:* John S Olsson
VP: John Bolte
**VP:* James L Condon
**VP:* Chip Corcoran
**VP:* Sterling Cramer
**VP:* Charles L Doane
**VP:* Kenneth Fairchild
**VP:* Stephen Ingracia
**VP:* Jerry L Kamtz
**VP:* Randall Kaster
**VP:* Bradley Korell
**VP:* Jeffrey R Kratzke
**VP:* Todd Lorenz
**VP:* Melissa Newton
**VP:* Kevin L Prior
**VP:* Daryoush Razavian
**VP:* Michael J Yost

D-U-N-S 18-070-5717
OLSSON INDUSTRIAL ELECTRIC INC
(*Suby of* NAES CORP) ★
1919 Laura St, Springfield, OR 97477-2183
Tel (541) 747-8460 *Founded/Ownrshp* 2015
Sales 37.6MM^E *EMP* 110
SIC 1731 Electrical work; Electrical work
Pr: Eric Olsson
VP: Elliott Olsson
IT Man: John Boettcher

D-U-N-S 00-284-9602
OLSSON ROOFING CO INC (IL)
740 S Lake St, Aurora, IL 60506-5540
Tel (630) 892-0449 *Founded/Ownrshp* 1914
Sales 26.8MM^E *EMP* 100^E
SIC 1761 Roofing, siding & sheet metal work; Roofing contractor; Sheet metalwork; Roof repair
Pr: William C Glenn
**CFO:* William G Lynch
Snr PM: Ray Bohr
Snr PM: Ken Fisher

OLSTEN
See ADO STAFFING INC

D-U-N-S 00-959-0399 EXP
OLTMANS CONSTRUCTION CO
10005 Mission Mill Rd, Whittier, CA 90601-1739
Tel (562) 908-9578 *Founded/Ownrshp* 1932
Sales 317.0MM *EMP* 535
Accts Kpmg Llp Los Angeles Ca
SIC 1541 1542 Industrial buildings, new construction; Renovation, remodeling & repairs: industrial buildings; Commercial & office buildings, new construction; Commercial & office buildings, renovation & repair; Industrial buildings, new construction; Renovation, remodeling & repairs: industrial buildings; Commercial & office building, new construction; Commercial & office buildings, renovation & repair
Pr: Joseph O Oltmans II
**Pr:* John Gormly
CFO: Greg Grupp
**CFO:* Dan Schlothan
Ofcr: Doug Jentzsch
**VP:* Tom Augustine
**VP:* Robert Larson
**VP:* Antonio Perez
**VP:* Charles Roy
**VP:* Gerald Singh
**VP:* Jim Woodside

D-U-N-S 00-683-9633
OLTON GRAIN CO-OP INC
910 W 1st St, Olton, TX 79064
Tel (806) 285-2638 *Founded/Ownrshp* 1963
Sales 32.9MM^E *EMP* 35
SIC 5153 Grain elevators
Genl Mgr: Gregg Allen
**Treas:* Gregory Allen

D-U-N-S 00-891-5076
OLUMS OF BINGHAMTON INC
3701 Vestal Pkwy E # 100, Vestal, NY 13850-2310
Tel (607) 729-5775 *Founded/Ownrshp* 1988
Sales 40.5MM^E *EMP* 240
SIC 5722 5731 5712 Electric household appliances, major; Radio, television & electronic stores; Furniture stores; Electric household appliances, major; Radio, television & electronic stores; Furniture stores
Ch Bd: Gilbert Rouff
**Ch Bd:* Keith Solomon
**COO:* Jamie Striley
**CFO:* Rick Urban
Opers Mgr: Ed Bonner
Sls Mgr: Andrew Malone
Sales Asso: William Allen

D-U-N-S 00-526-8276
OLY EQUINOX HOLDINGS LLC
EQUINOX HOTEL
3567 Main St, Manchester, VT 05254
Tel (802) 362-4700 *Founded/Ownrshp* 1998
Sales 12.1MM^E *EMP* 300
SIC 7011 5813 7992 5812 Resort hotel; Drinking places; Public golf courses; Eating places; Resort hotel; Drinking places; Public golf courses; Eating places
Exec: Daniel Black
Ex Dir: Creighton Smith
Genl Mgr: Toni Goss
Genl Mgr: Mark O Neil

D-U-N-S 06-926-3876 IMP
■ OLY STEEL INC
(*Suby of* OLYMPIC STEEL INC) ★
3600 Military St, Detroit, MI 48210-2964
Tel (313) 894-4552 *Founded/Ownrshp* 2011
Sales 25.9MM^E *EMP* 27^E
SIC 5051 Steel
CEO: Michael D Siegal
**COO:* David A Wolfort
**CFO:* Richard T Marabito
**Prin:* Arthur F Anton

D-U-N-S 80-882-5657
■ OLYMPIA BALLYS LIMITED PARTNERSHIP
(*Suby of* HILTON WORLDWIDE INC) ★
1450 Ballys Blvd, Robinsonville, MS 38664-9721
Tel (662) 357-1500 *Founded/Ownrshp* 1996
Sales 4.9MM^E *EMP* 1,077
SIC 7999 7011 5813 5812 Gambling establishment; Hotels & motels; Drinking places; Eating places; Gambling establishment; Hotels & motels; Drinking places; Eating places
Pr: Arthur Goldberg
**Genl Pt:* D J Brata
**Genl Pt:* Bally's Operator

D-U-N-S 12-931-1663 IMP
OLYMPIA CHIMNEY SUPPLY INC
600 Sanders St Ste 2, Scranton, PA 18505-3400
Tel (570) 496-8890 *Founded/Ownrshp* 1999
Sales 37.1MM^E *EMP* 70
SIC 3312 Stainless steel
Pr: William Kozlansky
**VP:* Christopher Hoffman

D-U-N-S 07-557-6314
OLYMPIA ENTERTAINMENT INC
FOX THEATRE
(*Suby of* ILITCH HOLDINGS INC) ★
2211 Woodward Ave, Detroit, MI 48201-3467
Tel (313) 471-3200 *Founded/Ownrshp* 1982
Sales 89.6MM^E *EMP* 1,000
SIC 7832 Motion picture theaters, except drive-in; Motion picture theaters, except drive-in
Ch Bd: Michael Ilitch
**Pr:* Dana Warg
**CFO:* Scott Fisher
**Sec:* Marian Ilitch
**VP:* Richard Fenton
**VP:* Bill Lee
Exec: Joni Nelson
Dir IT: Jenna Altobelli
Dir IT: Paul Boyer
Dir IT: Rob Chambers
Dir IT: Jason Flowers

D-U-N-S 07-183-3271
OLYMPIA FEDERAL SAVINGS & LOAN ASSOCIATION INC
421 Capitol Way S, Olympia, WA 98501-1028
Tel (360) 754-3400 *Founded/Ownrshp* 2008
Sales NA *EMP* 72
SIC 6035 Federal savings & loan associations; Federal savings & loan associations
CEO: Lori Drummond
CFO: Lyle Miyamura
Sr VP: John Maxwell
VP: Cherie Cloud
VP: Joshua Deck
VP: Sandy Dibernardo
VP: Debra Jackson
CIO: Rick Pitts

D-U-N-S 84-731-8755
OLYMPIA FOOD INDUSTRIES INC
5757 W 59th St, Chicago, IL 60638-3721
Tel (773) 735-2250 *Founded/Ownrshp* 1989
Sales 173.3MM^E *EMP* 65^E
SIC 5149 Groceries & related products
Pr: Andre Papantoniou

D-U-N-S 05-224-7442
OLYMPIA HEALTH CARE LLC
(*Suby of* ALECTO HEALTHCARE SERVICES LLC) ★
5900 W Olympic Blvd, Los Angeles, CA 90036-4671
Tel (323) 938-3161 *Founded/Ownrshp* 2004
Sales 51.8MM^E *EMP* 875
SIC 8062 Hospital, affiliated with AMA residency; Hospital, affiliated with AMA residency
CEO: John A Calderone
CFO: Babur Ozkan
Resp Thrpy: William Smith

OLYMPIA MITSUBISHI
See BRUCETITUS AUTOMOTIVE GROUP

D-U-N-S 03-675-1787
OLYMPIA ORTHOPEDIC ASSOCIATES
404 Yauger Way Sw Ste 100, Olympia, WA 98502-8152
Tel (360) 455-5144 *Founded/Ownrshp* 1977
Sales 23.4MM^E *EMP* 144
SIC 8011 Orthopedic physician
Prin: Stephen W Snow MD
**Prin:* Patrick Halpin
Orthpdst: Dennis Smith
Surgeon: Clyde Carpenter
Surgeon: Andrew Manista

D-U-N-S 02-182-0352
OLYMPIA SCHOOL DISTRICT
1113 Legion Way Se, Olympia, WA 98501-1697
Tel (360) 596-6100 *Founded/Ownrshp* 1852
Sales 52.1MM^E *EMP* 1,200
SIC 8211 Public elementary & secondary schools; Public elementary & secondary schools
IT Man: Justin Lanting
Pr Dir: Rebecca Japhet
Teacher Pr: Aaron Davis
Psych: Barbara Amidon
Psych: Jennifer Boelts
Psych: John Enslow
Psych: Norah Jensen
Psych: Kathleen Peterson

D-U-N-S 09-258-6502
OLYMPIA SCHOOL DISTRICT 16 INC
903 E 800 North Rd, Stanford, IL 61774-9612
Tel (309) 379-5941 *Founded/Ownrshp* 1967
Sales 19.6MM^E *EMP* 350
SIC 8211 Public elementary & secondary schools; High school, junior or senior; Public elementary & secondary schools; High school, junior or senior

D-U-N-S 82-853-5877 IMP
OLYMPIA SPORT CENTER INC
OLYMPIA SPORTS
5 Bradley Dr, Westbrook, ME 04092-2013
Tel (207) 854-2794 *Founded/Ownrshp* 2008
Sales 215.9MM^E *EMP* 2,500^E
Accts Baker Newman Noyes Llc Portl
SIC 5941 Sporting goods & bicycle shops; Sporting goods & bicycle shops
CEO: Ed Manganello
**CFO:* John Lesniak

OLYMPIA SPORTS
See OSC SPORTS INC

OLYMPIA SPORTS
See OLYMPIA SPORT CENTER INC

D-U-N-S 18-857-0162 IMP/EXP
OLYMPIA TILE (USA) INC
ALPHA TILE COMPANY
(*Suby of* OLYMPIA TILE INTERNATIONAL INC)
701 Berkshire Ln N, Plymouth, MN 55441-5420
Tel (763) 545-5455 *Founded/Ownrshp* 1989
Sales 36.2MM^E *EMP* 225
SIC 3523 5032 5999 6023 1743 Farm machinery & equipment; Ceramic wall & floor tile; Tile, clay or other ceramic, excluding refractory; Monuments & tombstones; Floor coverings; Tile installation, ceramic; Farm machinery & equipment; Ceramic wall & floor tile; Tile, clay or other ceramic, excluding refractory; Monuments & tombstones; Floor coverings; Tile installation, ceramic
Pr: Ralph Reichmann
**Treas:* Wm Bennett
Sr VP: Ray Marron
VP: Heidie White
Brnch Mgr: Bill Merritt
Mfg Dir: Farrell Hart
Sls Mgr: Rick Hagen

OLYMPIAN
See FLYERS ENERGY LLC

OLYMPIC AVIATION
See CONSOLIDATED TRADING CO OF AMERICA

OLYMPIC BANK
See KITSAP BANK

OLYMPIC BRAKE SUPPLY
See GARY NELSON INC

OLYMPIC CENTER, THE
See NEW YORK STATE OLYMPIC REGIONAL DEVELOPMENT AUTHORITY

D-U-N-S 07-186-9952
OLYMPIC CLUB
524 Post St, San Francisco, CA 94102-1295
Tel (415) 345-5100 *Founded/Ownrshp* 1879
Sales 52.1MM *EMP* 450
Accts Hood & Strong Llp San Francis
SIC 8641 7997 5812 Civic social & fraternal associations; Golf club, membership; Health food restaurant; Civic social & fraternal associations; Golf club, membership; Health food restaurant
CEO: John M Jack
Bd of Dir: Barbara Bechelli
Exec: Derek Ingraham
Comm Man: Christie Clemens
**Prin:* Jay Bedsworth
Genl Mgr: Dennis Bouey
CTO: Tony Lawrence
Dir IT: Anthony Lawrence
Dir IT: Bill Secor
IT Man: Stephen Alsbrooks
IT Man: Ruby Chin

OLYMPIC COLLEGE
See WA STATE COMMUNITY COLLEGE DIST 3

D-U-N-S 03-799-1593
OLYMPIC COMMUNITY ACTION PROGRAMS
823 Commerce Loop, Port Townsend, WA 98368-2904
Tel (360) 385-2571 *Founded/Ownrshp* 1966
Sales 7.0MM *EMP* 300^E

SIC 8399 8322 8351 Community action agency; Individual & family services; Old age assistance; Social services for the handicapped; Meal delivery program; Head start center, except in conjunction with school; Community action agency; Individual & family services; Old age assistance; Social services for the handicapped; Meal delivery program; Head start center, except in conjunction with school
CFO: Walt Hammond

D-U-N-S 07-648-1738
OLYMPIC COMPANIES INC
MINNETONKA
2823 Hedberg Dr, Hopkins, MN 55305-3406
Tel (952) 546-8166 *Founded/Ownrshp* 1999
Sales 69.1MM *EMP* 450
SIC 1542

OLYMPIC EAGLE DISTRIBUTING
See CITY BEVERAGES LLC

OLYMPIC FLAME FUEL OIL
See MARATHON ENERGY CORP

D-U-N-S 11-516-9203 IMP/EXP
OLYMPIC FOUNDRY INC
5200 Airport Way S, Seattle, WA 98108-1725
Tel (206) 764-6200 *Founded/Ownrshp* 1984
Sales 25.8MM^E *EMP* 85
SIC 5051 3366 3365 3325 3322 Steel; Castings, rough: iron or steel; Copper foundries; Aluminum foundries; Steel foundries; Malleable iron foundries; Steel; Castings, rough: iron or steel; Copper foundries; Aluminum foundries; Steel foundries; Malleable iron foundries
Pr: Scott McLaughlin
**Pr:* Russell Goodsell
**Sec:* Kenneth Martin
**VP:* F Gooding
Dir IT: David Dickerson
IT Man: Jason Latham
IT Man: Cari Moser
IT Man: Laura Turner

D-U-N-S 87-926-6773
OLYMPIC FRUIT CO LLC
2450 Beaudry Rd, Moxee, WA 98936-9313
Tel (509) 457-2075 *Founded/Ownrshp* 1994
Sales 22.9MM^E *EMP* 150
SIC 4783 4222 0723 Packing goods for shipping; Refrigerated warehousing & storage; Crop preparation services for market; Packing goods for shipping; Refrigerated warehousing & storage; Crop preparation services for market
Mtls Mgr: Robert Poteet
Ql Cn Mgr: Brad Wickenhagen

D-U-N-S 61-197-9477
OLYMPIC HEALTH MANAGEMENT SYSTEMS INC
(*Suby of* STERLING LIFE INSURANCE CO) ★
2219 Rimland Dr Ste 100, Bellingham, WA 98226-8660
Tel (360) 647-9080 *Founded/Ownrshp* 1998
Sales NA *EMP* 200^E
SIC 6411 8742 Insurance information & consulting services; Management consulting services
CEO: Debbie J Ahl
**CFO:* Richard A Warren
Sr VP: Barbara Spain
VP: Martin Catron
VP Mktg: Todd Tippets

OLYMPIC MEDICAL CENTER
See CLALLAM COUNTY PUBLIC HOSPITAL DISTRICT 2

OLYMPIC MILL SERVICES DIVISION
See TUBE CITY IMS LLC

D-U-N-S 10-334-3679 IMP/EXP
■ **OLYMPIC OIL LTD**
DELTA COMPANIES GROUP
(*Suby of* DELTA PETROLEUM CO INC) ★
5000 W 41st St, Cicero, IL 60804-4524
Tel (708) 496-0905 *Founded/Ownrshp* 2001
Sales 24.0MM^E *EMP* 102
SIC 2992 Lubricating oils & greases; Lubricating oils; Lubricating oils & greases; Lubricating oils
Pr: Darren Cherry
COO: Robert Miles
Dir Lab: Dean Mettler

D-U-N-S 62-037-0788
OLYMPIC PRODUCTS LLC
4100 Pleasant Garden Rd, Greensboro, NC 27406-7699
Tel (336) 378-9620 *Founded/Ownrshp* 2006
Sales 22.9MM^E *EMP* 147^E
SIC 3086 Plastics foam products; Plastics foam products
Pr: Mike Cooke
**Prin:* Joe Cladey
Ql Cn Mgr: Bob Archer

OLYMPIC SECURITY
See ADVENT SECURITIES & INVESTMENTS INC

D-U-N-S 18-010-6080
OLYMPIC SECURITY SERVICES INC
631 Strander Blvd Ste A, Tukwila, WA 98188-2963
Tel (206) 623-9129 *Founded/Ownrshp* 1986
Sales 10.6MM *EMP* 750
Accts Jacobson Lawrence & Associate
SIC 7381 Security guard service; Security guard service
Pr: Mark E Vinson
**VP:* Joy Vinson
**Prin:* David Gleeson

D-U-N-S 00-886-1627 IMP
▲ **OLYMPIC STEEL INC**
22901 Millcreek Blvd # 650, Cleveland, OH 44122-5732
Tel (216) 292-3800 *Founded/Ownrshp* 1954
Sales 1.4MMM *EMP* 1,810
Accts Pricewaterhousecoopers Llp Cl
Tkr Sym ZEUS *Exch* NGS
SIC 5051 Pipe & tubing, steel; Iron or steel flat products; Metals service centers & offices; Pipe & tubing, steel; Iron or steel flat products
Ch Bd: Michael D Siegal
**Pr:* David A Wolfort
CFO: Richard T Marabito
Treas: Richard A Manson
VP: John Brieck
VP: Andrew Markowitz
VP: John Mooney
VP: Frank Ruane
CIO: Esther M Potash
VP Opers: Raymond Walker Sr
Board of Directors: Arthur F Anton, Howard L Goldstein, Dirk A Kempthorne, Donald R McNeeley, James B Meathe, Ralph M Della Ratta

D-U-N-S 02-615-8563 IMP
■ **OLYMPIC STEEL IOWA INC**
(*Suby of* OLYMPIC STEEL INC) ★
6425 State St, Bettendorf, IA 52722-5548
Tel (563) 332-7785 *Founded/Ownrshp* 1997
Sales 94.5MM^E *EMP* 75
SIC 5051 3444 Metals service centers & offices; Sheet metalwork; Metals service centers & offices; Sheet metalwork
CEO: Michael D Siegal
**Pr:* David A Wolfort
**CFO:* Richard Marabito
Sfty Dirs: Richard Shook
Sfty Mgr: Art Goodrich
Sales Asso: Blake Hughes
Sales Asso: Kyle Otte

D-U-N-S 01-776-3731
■ **OLYMPIC STEEL LAFAYETTE INC** (OH)
LAFAYETTE STEEL PROCESSING
(*Suby of* OLYMPIC STEEL INC) ★
3600 Military St, Detroit, MI 48210-2964
Tel (313) 894-4552 *Founded/Ownrshp* 1946, 1995
Sales 101.0MM^E *EMP* 220
SIC 5051 Metals service centers & offices; Metals service centers & offices
Ch Bd: Michael D Siegal
**COO:* David A Wolfort
VP: David Frink
VP: Ron Gore
VP: Steve Mallory
VP: Clay Treska
MIS Dir: Chris Garrett
Sales Asso: George Short

D-U-N-S 13-176-2770
■ **OLYMPIC STEEL MINNEAPOLIS INC**
(*Suby of* OLYMPIC STEEL INC) ★
13100 15th Ave N, Minneapolis, MN 55441-4541
Tel (763) 544-7100 *Founded/Ownrshp* 1996
Sales 25.3MM^E *EMP* 70
SIC 5051 3398 Steel; Metal heat treating; Steel; Metal heat treating
Ch Bd: Michael D Siegel
**CFO:* Richard T Marabito

OLYMPIC STEEL-PS&W
See TINSLEY GROUP-PS&W INC

D-U-N-S 08-002-0213
OLYMPUS ADVISORS LLC
OLYMPUS PARTNERS
1 Station Pl Ste 4, Stamford, CT 06902-6893
Tel (203) 353-5900 *Founded/Ownrshp* 2009
Sales 60.0MM *EMP* 20
SIC 6722 Management investment, open-end
Mng Pt: Robert S Morris

D-U-N-S 06-032-1254 IMP
OLYMPUS AMERICA INC
(*Suby of* OLYMPUS CORP OF AMERICAS) ★
3500 Corporate Pkwy, Center Valley, PA 18034-8229
Tel (484) 896-5000 *Founded/Ownrshp* 1968
Sales 411.7MM^E *EMP* 2,009
SIC 5047 5043 5064 3827 3695 3572
SIC 5047 5043 5064 3827 3695 3572 Medical equipment & supplies; Diagnostic equipment, medical; Cameras & photographic equipment; Photographic cameras, projectors, equipment & supplies; Electrical entertainment equipment; Tape players & recorders; Video cassette recorders & accessories; Optical instruments & lenses; Magnetic & optical recording media; Computer storage devices; Medical equipment & supplies; Diagnostic equipment, medical; Cameras & photographic equipment; Photographic cameras, projectors, equipment & supplies; Electrical entertainment equipment; Tape players & recorders; Video cassette recorders & accessories; Optical instruments & lenses; Magnetic & optical recording media; Computer storage devices
Pr: Masaharu Okubo
COO: Peter Alex
Treas: Hironobu Kawamata
**Treas:* Kazuhiro Watanabe
VP: Carol Eckert
VP: Hirohide Matsushita
VP: Tim Ovington
Ex Dir: Matt Fahy
Genl Mgr: Eddy Garces
CIO: Andrew Hughes
Mktg Dir: Kunihiko Harada

D-U-N-S 96-729-0805
OLYMPUS BIOTECH CORP
(*Suby of* OLYMPUS CORP OF AMERICAS) ★
3500 Corporate Pkwy, Center Valley, PA 18034-8229
Tel (484) 896-5000 *Founded/Ownrshp* 2010
Sales 20.8MM^E *EMP* 375^E
SIC 8069 Orthopedic hospital
CEO: Hitoshi Mizuno
**Pr:* Oliver Burckhardt

D-U-N-S 04-523-7919
OLYMPUS BUILDING SERVICES INC
1783 W University Dr # 136, Tempe, AZ 85281-3259
Tel (480) 284-8018 *Founded/Ownrshp* 1998
Sales 18.0MM *EMP* 500
SIC 8744 7349 Facilities support services; Janitorial service, contract basis; Facilities support services; Janitorial service, contract basis
Pr: Anthony C Hipple
**VP:* Susan Beal

D-U-N-S 04-903-4023
OLYMPUS CONTROLS CORP
18280 Sw 108th Ave, Tualatin, OR 97062-8380
Tel (503) 582-8100 *Founded/Ownrshp* 1998
Sales 32.2MM^E *EMP* 25^E
SIC 5084 Materials handling machinery
Pr: Scott Hendrickson
**CFO:* Glen James
**VP:* Lori Cole
Ql Cn Mgr: Xiao Chan

D-U-N-S 60-993-6195
OLYMPUS CORP OF AMERICAS
(*Suby of* OLYMPUS CORPORATION)
3500 Corp Pkwy, Center Valley, PA 18034
Tel (484) 896-5000 *Founded/Ownrshp* 1990
Sales 992.2MM^E *EMP* 2,500

D-U-N-S 00-611-8145 IMP
OLYMPUS GROUP INC (WI)
9000 W Heather Ave, Milwaukee, WI 53224-2410
Tel (414) 365-9719 *Founded/Ownrshp* 1893, 2006
Sales 24.0MM *EMP* 125^E
SIC 2399 Banners, made from fabric; Pennants; Flags, fabric
Pr: Brian Adam
**COO:* Helmut Adam
**CFO:* Mike Young
**VP:* Christine Adam
VP: Lori Niederstadt
Sls Mgr: Tony Brodzeller
Sls Mgr: Jordan Lamotte

D-U-N-S 08-491-7897
OLYMPUS IMPORTED AUTO PARTS CORP
5168 Eisenhower Ave, Alexandria, VA 22304-4814
Tel (703) 370-0850 *Founded/Ownrshp* 1986
Sales 43.5MM^E *EMP* 150
SIC 5013 5531 Automotive supplies & parts; Automotive parts; Automotive supplies & parts; Automotive parts
Pr: W Michael Brown
**Treas:* Glenn O Johnson
**VP:* Bill Guinard
Store Mgr: Gualberto Paredes

D-U-N-S 14-361-6998 IMP/EXP
OLYMPUS LATIN AMERICA INC
(*Suby of* OLYMPUS CORP OF AMERICAS) ★
5301 Blue Lagoon Dr # 290, Miami, FL 33126-2093
Tel (305) 261-3067 *Founded/Ownrshp* 2002
Sales 22.5MM^E *EMP* 100^E
SIC 5047 Medical laboratory equipment
CEO: Luke Calcraft
**Treas:* Haruhito Morishima
**Sec:* Donna Miller
**VP:* Brian Hladek

D-U-N-S 94-677-5673
OLYMPUS MANAGED HEALTH CARE INC
777 Brickell Ave Ste 1370, Miami, FL 33131-2818
Tel (305) 530-8600 *Founded/Ownrshp* 2000
Sales NA *EMP* 51
SIC 6411 Medical insurance claim processing, contract or fee basis
CEO: Steven W Jacobson
**Pr:* Francisco Recio
**CFO:* Ronald A Davis

D-U-N-S 84-208-2638
OLYMPUS NDT NE INC
(*Suby of* OLYMPUS SCIENTIFIC SOLUTIONS AMERICAS INC) ★
48 Woerd Ave, Waltham, MA 02453-3824
Tel (781) 419-3900 *Founded/Ownrshp* 2005
Sales 122.4MM^E *EMP* 300
SIC 5047 Medical equipment & supplies; Medical equipment & supplies
Pr: Fabrice Cancre

OLYMPUS PARTNERS
See OLYMPUS ADVISORS LLC

D-U-N-S 61-474-6998 IMP/EXP
OLYMPUS PARTNERS LP
1 Station Pl, Stamford, CT 06902-6800
Tel (203) 353-5900 *Founded/Ownrshp* 1988
Sales 5.9MMM^E *EMP* 34,653^E
SIC 2834 6799 Pharmaceutical preparations; Pharmaceutical preparations; Investors
Pt: Robert S Morris
Pt: James A Conroy
Pt: Keith Hefferman
Pt: Louis J Mischianti
VP: Matt Boyd
VP: Jason M Miller
VP: Peter Tedesco
VP: Sean P Whiteley
Prin: Evan J Eason
Prin: David M Haddad
Prin: Michael D Horgan

D-U-N-S 06-897-3119
OLYMPUS POWER LLC
67 E Park Pl Fl 4, Morristown, NJ 07960-7103
Tel (973) 889-9100 *Founded/Ownrshp* 2006
Sales 143.8MM^E *EMP* 224
SIC 4911 Generation, electric power; Generation, electric power
CEO: Dean N Vanech
Treas: Joanne Piasecki
**VP:* Dennis T Odonnell
Dir IT: Robert Dixon

D-U-N-S 88-341-1845
OLYMPUS REAL ESTATE CORP
5080 Spectrum Dr, Addison, TX 75001-4648
Tel (972) 980-2200 *Founded/Ownrshp* 1994
Sales 37.5MM^E *EMP* 2,000
SIC 7011 6512 Hotels; Nonresidential building operators; Hotels; Nonresidential building operators
Pr: David Deniger
**Pt:* Greg Adair
**Pt:* Bob Briggs
**Pt:* Hal Hall
**Pt:* Clark Hanrattie
**Pt:* Rob Landin
**Pt:* Tim Smith
Mng Dir: Laurie Cameron

D-U-N-S 96-787-9912
OLYMPUS SCIENTIFIC SOLUTIONS AMERICAS CORP
OSSA
(*Suby of* OLYMPUS CORP OF AMERICAS) ★
48 Woerd Ave Ste 105, Waltham, MA 02453-3824
Tel (781) 419-3900 *Founded/Ownrshp* 2005
Sales 166.3MM^E *EMP* 950^E
SIC 5013 Testing equipment, electrical: automotive; Testing equipment, engine; Testing equipment, electrical: automotive; Testing equipment, engine
CEO: Toshihiko Okubo
**Pr:* Kenji Kowata
**COO:* Fabrice Cancre
**CFO:* Etienne Marcoux
**Treas:* Kaoru Suzuki
Off Mgr: Mindy Schlief
Snr Sftwr: Jayesh Patel
Sftwr Eng: Ehab Ghabour
Sales Exec: Kritthuch Suanyim
Board of Directors: Fabrice Cancre

D-U-N-S 60-621-7128 EXP
OLYMPUS SCIENTIFIC SOLUTIONS AMERICAS INC
(*Suby of* OLYMPUS CORP OF AMERICAS) ★
48 Woerd Ave, Waltham, MA 02453-3824
Tel (781) 419-3900 *Founded/Ownrshp* 1997
Sales 138.5MM^E *EMP* 300
SIC 5084 Instruments & control equipment; Instruments & control equipment
CEO: Fabrice Cancre
**Treas:* Hiroshi Shiina
Dir Soc: Paula Scordino
Genl Mgr: Heather Addley
QA Dir: Sebastien McKenny
Dir IT: Larry Linskey
Prd Mgr: Richard Cassineri
S&M/VP: Jeffrey Walker

D-U-N-S 07-959-4770
OM DIAMONDS GROUP INC
OFER MIZRAHI
29 E Madison St Ste 1116, Chicago, IL 60602-4549
Tel (312) 558-9060 *Founded/Ownrshp* 2010
Sales 75.0MM *EMP* 2^E
SIC 5094 Diamonds (gems); Diamonds (gems)
Pr: Ben Redansky
**CFO:* Casey Rogowski

D-U-N-S 36-193-3455
OM FOODS LTD
2107 Elliott Ave Ste 307, Seattle, WA 98121-2160
Tel (206) 838-4670 *Founded/Ownrshp* 2007
Sales 8.0MM^E *EMP* 316^E
SIC 5812 Eating places; Cafe; Eating places; Cafe
Ch Bd: Jason Brown
**Pr:* Dean Leisman
**CFO:* Michael Gats

OM GROUP
See OMG AMERICAS INC

OM PRODUCE
See OM TRADING INC

D-U-N-S 19-266-7975
OM TRADING INC
OM PRODUCE
1704 Orleans St, Dallas, TX 75226-2142
Tel (214) 924-3560 *Founded/Ownrshp* 2002
Sales 39.9MM^E *EMP* 69^E
SIC 5148 Fresh fruits & vegetables
Pr: Rajiv Shah
**VP:* Nikhil Shah

D-U-N-S 02-758-6478
OMAHA AIRPORT AUTHORITY
AIRPORT AUTHORITY OF THE CITY
4501 Abbott Dr Ste 2300, Omaha, NE 68110-2689
Tel (402) 661-8000 *Founded/Ownrshp* 1959
Sales 40.5MM *EMP* 185^E
Accts Kpmg Llp Omaha Nebraska
SIC 4581 Airport; Airport
Ex Dir: Stephen A Coufal
Exec: Linda Lewis
Opers Supe: Joe Rotterdam

D-U-N-S 79-576-1188
OMAHA COMMUNITY FOUNDATION
302 S 36th St Ste 100, Omaha, NE 68131-3845
Tel (402) 342-3458 *Founded/Ownrshp* 1982
Sales 166.8MM *EMP* 13
SIC 8399 8733 Community development groups; Noncommercial research organizations; Community development groups; Noncommercial research organizations
CEO: Sara Boyd
CFO: Melisa Sunde
Treas: John L Maginn
Ofcr: Dennis Nissen
Comm Dir: Kali Baker
Prgrm Mgr: Ellen Fitzsimmons
Off Mgr: Robin Spitznagle
Counsel: Thomas R Pansing Jr

D-U-N-S 36-201-4354
OMAHA CONSTRUCTION SERVICES INC
(*Suby of* R & R INVESTORS LTD) ★
1225 Jordan Creek Pkwy # 200, West Des Moines, IA 50266-2346
Tel (515) 223-4518 *Founded/Ownrshp* 2006
Sales 30.0MM *EMP* 10
SIC 1542 1522 Commercial & office building contractors; Hotel/motel & multi-family home construction; Commercial & office building contractors; Hotel/motel & multi-family home construction
Pr: Dan Biere

D-U-N-S 02-017-6269
OMAHA INDEMNITY CO
(*Suby of* MUTUAL OF OMAHA INSURANCE CO) ★
3102 Farnam St, Omaha, NE 68131-3554
Tel (402) 342-3326 *Founded/Ownrshp* 1967
Sales NA *EMP* 175
SIC 6331 Fire, marine & casualty insurance; Fire, marine & casualty insurance
Pr: Martin Dourney
**Treas:* Mark R Boetel
**VP:* Deborah Price

D-U-N-S 03-765-3128
OMAHA INDUSTRIES INC
7071 N 87th St, Omaha, NE 68122-1846
Tel (402) 734-7321 *Founded/Ownrshp* 1979
Sales 30.6MM[E] *EMP* 120
SIC 4222 4213 Warehousing, cold storage or refrigerated;Trucking, except local
Pr: Patrick Burke
**Treas:* Riza Sabaliauskas
**Treas:* Theresa Sabaliauskas
**Sec:* V P Watson

D-U-N-S 03-513-7165 IMP
OMAHA PAPER CO INC
6936 L St, Omaha, NE 68117-1035
Tel (402) 331-3243 *Founded/Ownrshp* 1964
Sales 42.9MM[E] *EMP* 38
SIC 5111 5113 Printing paper; Fine paper; Writing paper; Napkins, paper; Bags, paper & disposable plastic; Printing paper; Fine paper; Writing paper; Napkins, paper; Bags, paper & disposable plastic
Pr: Robert S Powell
CFO: Gail Anderson
**VP:* Kevin Powell
CTO: Dan Robinson
IT Man: Robyn Hansen
Mfg Dir: Jeff Book

D-U-N-S 14-596-1632
OMAHA PERFORMING ARTS SOCIETY
1200 Douglas St, Omaha, NE 68102-1815
Tel (402) 345-0202 *Founded/Ownrshp* 2000
Sales 21.9MM *EMP* 60
SIC 7922 Performing arts center production; Performing arts center production
Pr: Joan Squires
VP: Joi Brown
Exec: Mark Budler
MIS Dir: Marty Jones

D-U-N-S 00-726-7289
OMAHA PRINTING CO
4700 F St, Omaha, NE 68117-1482
Tel (402) 734-4400 *Founded/Ownrshp* 1858
Sales 33.4MM[E] *EMP* 105
SIC 2752 2791 2789 Commercial printing, lithographic;Typesetting; Bookbinding & related work; Commercial printing, lithographic;Typesetting; Bookbinding & related work
Ch Bd: Harvey L Hayes
**Pr:* Charles Kinzer
**CEO:* Steven D Hayes
COO: D Chuck Jr
Sls Mgr: Kip Fisher

D-U-N-S 00-697-0453 IMP
OMAHA PUBLIC POWER DISTRICT (NE)
OPPD
444 S 16th St, Omaha, NE 68102-2247
Tel (402) 636-2000 *Founded/Ownrshp* 1945
Sales 1.1MMM *EMP* 2,300
SIC 4911 ; Distribution, electric power; Generation, electric power;Transmission, electric power; ; Distribution, electric power; Generation, electric power; Transmission, electric power
Ch Bd: Anne McGuire
**Pr:* Gary Gates
CFO: Charles N Eldred
**Treas:* Michael J Cavanaugh
Treas: John Thurber
**Treas:* Frederick J Ulrich
Ofcr: Ron Miller
VP: Mohamad Doghman
VP: Anne Farrar
VP: Tim Nissen
VP: Dayton Wittke
Board of Directors: N P Dodge Jr, Michael J Cavanaugh,geoffr, John K Green, Frederick J Ulrich

D-U-N-S 80-047-9375
OMAHA PUBLIC SCHOOL DISTRICT 1
3215 Cuming St, Omaha, NE 68131-2000
Tel (402) 557-2222 *Founded/Ownrshp* 2007
Sales 17.0MM[E] *EMP* 841[E]
SIC 8211 Public elementary & secondary schools
Dir Sec: Roddie Miller
CIO: Sindie Katskee
Pr Dir: Todd Andrews
Instr Medi: Laura Pietsch
HC Dir: Sharon Wade

D-U-N-S 08-956-2375
OMAHA PUBLIC SCHOOLS
3215 Cuming St, Omaha, NE 68131-2024
Tel (402) 557-2120 *Founded/Ownrshp* 1890
Sales 633.9MM *EMP* 8,000[E]
Accts Seim Johnson Llp Omaha Nebr
SIC 8211 Public elementary & secondary schools; Secondary school; Public elementary & secondary schools; Secondary school
Prin: Marc Kahn
V Ch: Rachel Wise
Bd of Dir: Matt Scanlan
Exec: Robert Aranda
Exec: Karen Comfort
Exec: Anita Harkins
Exec: David Lavender
Off Admin: Gary Aquino
CIO: Tina Hudson
Dir IT: Denise Adams
Dir IT: Georgiann Benish

OMAHA STANDARD DISTRIBUTION
See FTEC INC

D-U-N-S 00-726-2074 IMP
OMAHA STANDARD LLC
(*Suby of* PALFINGER INC)
3501 S 11th St Ste 1, Council Bluffs, IA 51501-8243
Tel (712) 328-7444 *Founded/Ownrshp* 1932, 2013
Sales 106.6MM[E] *EMP* 350
SIC 3713 3536 3537 Truck bodies (motor vehicles); Hoists; Lift trucks, industrial: fork, platform, straddle, etc.; Truck bodies (motor vehicles); Hoists; Lift trucks, industrial: fork, platform, straddle, etc.
Pr: Michael Berger
Pr: Jeff Tilley
CFO: Eric Kluver
Ofcr: Jade McKeighan
VP: Jack Neary
**Prin:* Mark Wahley
Dir IT: Gordon McKinsey
Dir IT: Gordan McKinzie
VP Opers: Jason Holt
S&M/VP: Mark Whaley
**Mktg Mgr:* Elizabeth Moser

OMAHA STANDARDS
See PALFINGER NORTH AMERICA

D-U-N-S 00-494-4364
OMAHA STEAKS INC (DE)
(*Suby of* OMAHA STEAKS INTERNATIONAL INC) ★
10909 John Galt Blvd, Omaha, NE 68137-2382
Tel (402) 597-3000 *Founded/Ownrshp* 1997
Sales 71.8MM[E] *EMP* 600
Accts Kpmg Llp Omaha Ne
SIC 5961 Food, mail order; Food, mail order
CEO: Alan Simon
Pr: Bruce Simon
CFO: David L Hershiser
Ex VP: Fred Simon
VP: Steve Simon
QA Dir: Valerie Landis
Web Dev: Gary Kudrna

D-U-N-S 00-749-9692 EXP
OMAHA STEAKS INTERNATIONAL INC
11030 O St, Omaha, NE 68137-2346
Tel (402) 597-3000 *Founded/Ownrshp* 1917
Sales 342.6MM[E] *EMP* 600
SIC 5142 8741 Meat, frozen: packaged; Administrative management; Meat, frozen: packaged; Administrative management
Ch Bd: Alan Simon
Pr: Laura Ramirez
**Pr:* Bruce A Simon
CFO: Dave Hersheiser
**CFO:* Dave L Hershiser
**Ex VP:* Fred Simon
VP: Neil Lucas
**VP:* Todd Simon
VP: David Zucker
Exec: Tricia Decker
Dist Mgr: Mark Oehmen

D-U-N-S 06-864-6678
OMAHA STEEL CASTINGS CO LLC
921 E 12th St, Wahoo, NE 68066-1458
Tel (402) 558-6000 *Founded/Ownrshp* 2008
Sales 68.6MM[E] *EMP* 200
SIC 3325 Alloy steel castings, except investment; Alloy steel castings, except investment
CEO: Phillip Teggart

D-U-N-S 10-230-2353
OMAHA TRACK INC
12930 I St, Omaha, NE 68137-1268
Tel (402) 339-0332 *Founded/Ownrshp* 1985
Sales 44.2MM[E] *EMP* 55[E]
SIC 5093 5099 Ferrous metal scrap & waste; Nonferrous metals scrap; Logs, hewn ties, posts & poles
Pr: Terry Peterson
COO: Bud Mushlitz
**CFO:* Rick Mason
**Sec:* Hollye Hempel
VP: Westerlin Rod
IT Man: Cathy Emig
Sfty Dirs: Darrell Sechrest
Sls Mgr: Ian Rauch

D-U-N-S 96-197-7076
OMAHA TRACK MATERIALS LLC
8202 F St, Omaha, NE 68127-1740
Tel (402) 339-0332 *Founded/Ownrshp* 1987
Sales 43.3MM[E] *EMP* 75[E]
SIC 4011

D-U-N-S 11-868-3309
OMAHA TRIBE OF NEBRASKA INC
100 Health Center Dr, Macy, NE 68039
Tel (402) 837-5391 *Founded/Ownrshp* 1934
Sales NA *EMP* 404
SIC 9131 Indian reservation; Indian reservation
Ch: Clifford Wolfe Jr
**Treas:* Tillie Aldrich
Sec: Mary Miller
**Sec:* Gwen Porter

D-U-N-S 07-011-7346
OMAHA TRUCK CENTER INC (NE)
EXPRESS TRUCK CENTER
10550 I St, Omaha, NE 68127-1012
Tel (402) 592-2440 *Founded/Ownrshp* 1975
Sales 231.8MM *EMP* 398
Accts Seim Johnson Llp Omaha Nebr
SIC 5999 Toiletries, cosmetics & perfumes;Toiletries, cosmetics & perfumes
Pr: Trey Mytty
**Treas:* Kathy Williams
**VP:* Bruce Fox
Brnch Mgr: John Schroeder

OMAHA WORLD TIMES
See OMAHA WORLD-HERALD CO

D-U-N-S 00-726-9616 IMP
■ **OMAHA WORLD-HERALD CO**
OMAHA WORLD TIMES
(*Suby of* BERKSHIRE HATHAWAY INC) ★
1314 Douglas St Ste 700, Omaha, NE 68102-1811
Tel (402) 444-1000 *Founded/Ownrshp* 2011
Sales 394.3MM[E] *EMP* 2,323
SIC 2711 7331 Newspapers; Mailing list brokers; Newspapers; Mailing list brokers
CEO: Bailey Lauerman
**Ch Bd:* John Gottschalk
**Pr:* Terry Kroeger
**Treas:* Brenda Draheim
Bd of Dir: Michael Gallagher
**Prin:* Mike Reilly
Dir IT: Richard Eppenbaugh
Dir IT: Phil Tomek
Advt Dir: Dave Storey
Sls Dir: Sharon Lucas
Mktg Mgr: Rhonda Gray

D-U-N-S 06-867-2872 IMP
OMAHA ZOOLOGICAL SOCIETY
HENRY DOORLY ZOO
3701 S 10th St, Omaha, NE 68107-2299
Tel (402) 733-8400 *Founded/Ownrshp* 1952
Sales 46.5MM[E] *EMP* 620
SIC 7999 8422 Zoological garden, commercial; Botanical garden; Zoological garden, commercial; Botanical garden
CEO: Dennis E Pate
**Pr:* John K Boyer
**COO:* Daniel J Morris
**CFO:* Jeremy C Eddie
VP: Doug Armstrong
Sls&Mrk Ex: Sarah A Lake

D-U-N-S 10-008-0936
OMAK SCHOOL DISTRICT
619 W Bartlett Ave, OMAK, WA 98841-9700
Tel (509) 826-7686 *Founded/Ownrshp* 1900
Sales 18.3MM[E] *EMP* 289
SIC 8211 Public combined elementary & secondary school; Public combined elementary & secondary school
Cmptr Lab: Byron Kato

D-U-N-S 02-074-4384 IMP
OMAR MEDICAL SUPPLIES INC
OMAR SUPPLIES
600 Holiday Plaza Dr # 130, Matteson, IL 60443-2236
Tel (708) 679-0347 *Founded/Ownrshp* 1997
Sales 36.0MM[E] *EMP* 87
Accts Mulcahy Pauritsch Salvador &
SIC 5085 5047 2259 Industrial supplies; Dental equipment & supplies; Industrial supplies; Dental equipment & supplies; Dyeing & finishing knit gloves & mittens
Pr: Willie Wilson
VP: Roxanne Jackson

OMAR SUPPLIES
See OMAR MEDICAL SUPPLIES INC

O'MARA AG & EQUIPMENT
See OMARA AG SERVICES INC

D-U-N-S 05-382-2370
OMARA AG SERVICES INC
O'MARA AG & EQUIPMENT
1626 Delaware Ave, Des Moines, IA 50317-2938
Tel (515) 223-5391 *Founded/Ownrshp* 1998
Sales 22.4MM[E] *EMP* 35
SIC 5083 7389 Agricultural machinery;
Pr: Robert O Mara

D-U-N-S 06-900-3176 IMP/EXP
OMARA INC
OMTEX
160 Fashion Ave, Rutherford College, NC 28671
Tel (828) 874-2100 *Founded/Ownrshp* 1970
Sales 36.4MM[E] *EMP* 150
SIC 2282 2281 5199 Textured yarn;Yarn spinning mills; Fabrics, yarns & knit goods;Textured yarn;Yarn spinning mills; Fabrics, yarns & knit goods
Pr: Timothy J O'Mara
**Pr:* John Omara
**VP:* Joseph X Leirer
VP: Jeff Mitchell
VP Opers: Gary Hicks
Sls Mgr: David Thompson

OMATION
See OPEX CORP

D-U-N-S 84-918-0518 IMP
OMAX CORP
21409 72nd Ave S, Kent, WA 98032-1944
Tel (253) 872-2300 *Founded/Ownrshp* 1993
Sales 143.7MM[E] *EMP* 250
SIC 3545 3561 Cutting tools for machine tools; Pumps & pumping equipment; Cutting tools for machine tools; Pumps & pumping equipment
Pr: John Bosco Cheung
CFO: Jim O'Connor
VP: John Bergstrom
**VP:* John Henry Olsen
Admn Mgr: Debi Mars
IT Man: Anthony Davis
IT Man: Carl Olsen
Web Dev: Chris Lee
Prd Mgr: Jeffrey Watkins
Ql Cn Mgr: Rick Zeine
Sls&Mrk Ex: Sandra McLain

OMC
See OFFSHORE MARINE CONTRACTORS INC

OMCA
See OMRON MANAGEMENT CENTER OF AMERICA INC

OMCO
See MIDWEST ROLL FORMING & MFG INC

D-U-N-S 96-450-1824
OMCO HOLDINGS INC
30396 Lakeland Blvd, Wickliffe, OH 44092-1748
Tel (440) 944-2100 *Founded/Ownrshp* 2000
Sales 57.1MM[E] *EMP* 150[E]
SIC 3449 Miscellaneous metalwork; Miscellaneous metalwork
Ch Bd: Ben Yorks
**Pr:* Gary Schuster
**CFO:* Clint Cassese
Ex VP: Edward F Gleason
VP: Robert Stephenson

D-U-N-S 19-947-1561
■ **OMD CHICAGO INC**
(*Suby of* OMNICOM GROUP INC) ★
225 N Michigan Ave # 1900, Chicago, IL 60601-7757
Tel (312) 324-7000 *Founded/Ownrshp* 2012
Sales 31.3MM[E] *EMP* 270
SIC 7311 Advertising agencies; Advertising agencies
Pr: Kathleen Brookbanks

D-U-N-S 12-808-3354
■ **OMD USA LLC**
(*Suby of* ANNALLECT GROUP) ★
195 Broadway, New York, NY 10007-3100
Tel (212) 590-7100 *Founded/Ownrshp* 2007
Sales 155.5MM[E] *EMP* 1,420[E]
SIC 7311 Advertising agencies; Advertising agencies
CEO: Mainardo De Nardis
Pr: Chris Pyne
Pr: Daryl Simm
Chf Mktg O: Monica Karo
Ofcr: David Desocio
Assoc Dir: Leslie Brosterhous
Assoc Dir: Allison Klein
Assoc Dir: Maureen Kuehhas
Assoc Dir: Matthew Mansour
Mng Dir: Vas Banschikov
Mng Dir: Tom Benelli

D-U-N-S 00-797-0353
OMEARA FORD CENTER INC
400 W 104th Ave, Northglenn, CO 80234-4195
Tel (303) 254-5000 *Founded/Ownrshp* 1913
Sales 80.3MM[E] *EMP* 165
SIC 5511 Automobiles, new & used; Automobiles, new & used
Pr: Brian O'Meara
Exec: Ron Cunningham
Genl Mgr: Dennis Doyle
IT Man: Justin Chavez
Sls Mgr: Colin Cunningham
Sls Mgr: Jason Maes

D-U-N-S 10-401-3313
OMEDA COMMUNICATIONS INC
555 Huehl Rd, Northbrook, IL 60062-2336
Tel (847) 564-8900 *Founded/Ownrshp* 1983
Sales 23.4MM[E] *EMP* 150
SIC 7375 Data base information retrieval; Data base information retrieval
Pr: Michael A Oberman
VP: Rob Boling
VP: Beddigs Chris
VP: Bryan Swartz
Exec: Zhenya Barmash
Exec: Aaron Oberman
CTO: Diane Pekar
Sftwr Eng: Andrew Foster
Sftwr Eng: Joseph Weber
Sftwr Eng: Ali Zandieh
Mktg Mgr: Holly Ness

OMEGA
See RESCHCOR INC

OMEGA ACQUISITION
See GLOBAL PARTS DISTRIBUTORS LLC

D-U-N-S 19-864-8060
OMEGA ALPHA DISTRIBUTORS LTD
2910 Latham Dr, Madison, WI 53713-3233
Tel (608) 244-1934 *Founded/Ownrshp* 2005
Sales 35.9MM[E] *EMP* 35
SIC 5147 Meats & meat products
Pr: Pat Mackesey
Dir IT: Jim Dunham
Sls Mgr: Ken Klahn

OMEGA CABINETRY
See OMEGA CABINETS LTD

D-U-N-S 03-995-0845 IMP/EXP
■ **OMEGA CABINETS LTD**
OMEGA CABINETRY
(*Suby of* FORTUNE BRANDS HOME & SECURITY INC) ★
1205 Peters Dr, Waterloo, IA 50703-9691
Tel (319) 235-5700 *Founded/Ownrshp* 2011
Sales 277.9MM[E] *EMP* 2,400
SIC 2434 5211 Wood kitchen cabinets; Vanities, bathroom: wood; Lumber & other building materials; Wood kitchen cabinets; Vanities, bathroom: wood; Lumber & other building materials
Pr: Greg Stoner
VP: Clay Shimo
VP: Amy Stoll
VP: Chase Thornbird
Dir IT: Ignacio Martin
Dir IT: Chris Schmitz
VP Opers: Clay Shimeall
Mfg Mgr: Greg Meyers
Mfg Mgr: Keith Westemeier
Board of Directors: Phil Carroll, Terry Goerdt, Tom Nelson

D-U-N-S 87-296-9753
OMEGA CONTRACTING INC
2518 Chalk Hill Rd, Dallas, TX 75212-4504
Tel (214) 689-3815 *Founded/Ownrshp* 1993
Sales 36.3MM[E] *EMP* 165
SIC 1531 Operative builders; Operative builders
Pr: Luis Spinola
**VP:* Jeff Heimer
Exec: Jeff Heimar
Snr Mgr: Alex Valladares

OMEGA DALLAS
See ESSILOR OF AMERICA INC

D-U-N-S 04-378-3778
OMEGA ELECTRIC CONSTRUCTION CO INC
31 Commerce Ave, South Burlington, VT 05403-5852
Tel (802) 862-0517 *Founded/Ownrshp* 1990
Sales 23.8MM[E] *EMP* 126
SIC 1731 General electrical contractor; General electrical contractor
Pr: Alfred R Senecal Jr
**VP:* Cheryl L Senecal
IT Man: Jeff Hanson

D-U-N-S 00-145-5856 IMP
OMEGA ENGINEERING INC (DE)
OMEGADYNE
(*Suby of* SPECTRIS PLC)
1 Omega Dr, Stamford, CT 06907-2336
Tel (203) 359-1660 *Founded/Ownrshp* 1962, 2011
Sales 118.3MM^E *EMP* 479
SIC 3823 3575 3577 3433 3826 2759 Temperature measurement instruments, industrial; PH instruments, industrial process type; Flow instruments, industrial process type; Computer interface equipment for industrial process control; Computer terminals; Printers, computer; Plotters, computer; Heating equipment, except electric; Environmental testing equipment; Periodicals: printing; Temperature measurement instruments, industrial; PH instruments, industrial process type; Flow instruments, industrial process type; Computer interface equipment for industrial process control; Computer terminals; Printers, computer; Plotters, computer; Heating equipment, except electric; Environmental testing equipment; Periodicals: printing
Pr: Betty Ruth Hollander
**Pr:* James R Dale
**CFO:* Carol Donnelly
Ofcr: Bruce Lott
VP: Jim Ferguson
Exec: Chris Herrick
Mng Dir: Patricia Liu
Dept Mgr: Maryann Lang
Genl Mgr: Bill Keating
Genl Mgr: Michael Lopez
Dir IT: Warren Jones

D-U-N-S 14-440-8580
OMEGA ENTERPRISES
801 Pine St Apt 14f, Seattle, WA 98101-1807
Tel (206) 622-0322 *Founded/Ownrshp* 1975
Sales NA *EMP* 1,006^E
SIC 0912 5961 1542 7389 Finfish; Mail order house; Commercial & office buildings, renovation & repair; Interior designer
Owner: Constance Olsen

D-U-N-S 09-994-3482 EXP
OMEGA ENTERPRISES INC
BASSETT MECHANICAL
1215 Hyland Ave, Kaukauna, WI 54130-1441
Tel (920) 759-2500 *Founded/Ownrshp* 1977
Sales 100.0MM^E *EMP* 300
SIC 5078 1711 7699 5074 Refrigeration equipment & supplies; Ventilation & duct work contractor; Industrial equipment services; Plumbing & hydronic heating supplies; Refrigeration equipment & supplies; Ventilation & duct work contractor; Industrial equipment services; Plumbing & hydronic heating supplies
Pr: William R Bassett
**Treas:* Jay Sauter
Sr Cor Off: Kim B Heitzmann
VP: Mike Buss
VP: Gregory Skinner
Telecom Ex: Mark Kleist

OMEGA ENVIRONMENTAL TECH
See AUTO AIR EXPORT INC

D-U-N-S 93-847-5522
OMEGA FINANCIAL INC
1300 6th Ave Ste 600, Columbus, GA 31901-2283
Tel (706) 653-5320 *Founded/Ownrshp* 1992
Sales 24.3MM^E *EMP* 75
SIC 6282 Investment advice
Pr: Todd Reaves
Comm Man: Allison Bowden
CIO: Wendell Brown
Web Dev: Matt Mason
Software D: Ryan Phaneuf
Sls Mgr: Kimberly Acree

D-U-N-S 07-551-8944 IMP/EXP
▲ **OMEGA FLEX INC**
OMEGAFLEX
451 Creamery Way, Exton, PA 19341-2509
Tel (610) 524-7272 *Founded/Ownrshp* 1976
Sales 85.2MM *EMP* 131^E
Accts Mcgladrey Llp Blue Bell Penn
Tkr Sym OFLX *Exch* NGM
SIC 3492 3498 Hose & tube fittings & assemblies, hydraulic/pneumatic; Fabricated pipe & fittings; Hose & tube fittings & assemblies, hydraulic/pneumatic; Fabricated pipe & fittings
Pr: Kevin R Hoben
**COO:* Mark F Albino
CFO: Paul J Kane
Sr VP: Steven A Treichel
Sls&Mrk Ex: Frank Strobl
Board of Directors: David Evans, J Nicholas Filler, Bruce C Klink, Stewart B Reed

D-U-N-S 08-582-4449
OMEGA FOODS INC
WENDY'S
50 W Douglas St Ste 1101, Freeport, IL 61032-4142
Tel (815) 235-7615 *Founded/Ownrshp* 1976
Sales 12.0MM^E *EMP* 400
SIC 5812 Fast-food restaurant, chain; Fast-food restaurant, chain
Pr: Scott King

D-U-N-S 79-294-8531
▲ **OMEGA HEALTHCARE INVESTORS INC**
200 International Cir # 3500, Hunt Valley, MD 21080-1394
Tel (410) 427-1700 *Founded/Ownrshp* 1992
Sales 504.7MM *EMP* 53^E
Tkr Sym OHI *Exch* NYS
SIC 6798 Real estate investment trusts; Real estate investment trusts
CEO: C Taylor Pickett
Ch Bd: Bernard J Korman
COO: Daniel J Booth
CFO: Robert O Stephenson
Sr VP: R Lee Crabill Jr
VP: Laurence D Rich
Board of Directors: Craig R Callen, Thomas F Franke, Barbara B Hill, Harold J Kloosterman, Edward Lowenthal, Stephen D Plavin

OMEGA HEALTHCARE MGT SVCS
See OMH HOLDINGS LLC

D-U-N-S 17-478-3928
OMEGA HOSPITAL LLC
2525 Severn Ave, Metairie, LA 70002-5987
Tel (504) 832-4200 *Founded/Ownrshp* 2005
Sales 20.4MM^E *EMP* 120
SIC 8062 General medical & surgical hospitals
Doctor: Eric R George
CFO: Kevin Rodrigue
Exec: Laurie Folse
HC Dir: Debbie Schenck

OMEGA INDUSTRIAL HYDRAULICS
See SHINN FU CO OF AMERICA INC

D-U-N-S 08-416-0316
OMEGA INSURANCE SERVICES
WORD AND BROWN
721 S Parker St Ste 300, Orange, CA 92868-4732
Tel (714) 973-0311 *Founded/Ownrshp* 1971
Sales NA *EMP* 50
SIC 6411 Insurance brokers
CEO: D P Thomas
Pr: Bill Mason
Pr: Zeke Montes
Pr: Darrell Smith
Chf Mktg O: Paula Serios
Sr VP: David Duker
Sr VP: Angela Moran
Sr VP: Gregg Ratkovic
VP: Charlotte Caplan
VP: Jeffrey Compangano
VP: Jeff Hecht
VP: Linh Huynh
VP: Curt Kramer
VP: Thomas Majchrowski

D-U-N-S 86-819-8144
OMEGA MEATS I INC
7209 Cessna Dr, Greensboro, NC 27409-9685
Tel (336) 662-0000 *Founded/Ownrshp* 1997
Sales 30.3MM^E *EMP* 404
SIC 5421 Meat markets, including freezer provisioners; Meat markets, including freezer provisioners
Pr: Thomas Cassano

OMEGA MORGAN MACHINERY MOVING
See MORGAN INDUSTRIAL INC

D-U-N-S 19-649-4657 IMP/EXP
OMEGA MOULDING CO LTD
1 Sawgrass Dr, Bellport, NY 11713-1547
Tel (631) 924-6200 *Founded/Ownrshp* 1968
Sales 28.6MM^E *EMP* 60^E
SIC 5023 Frames & framing, picture & mirror
Pr: David Merzin
**Ch Bd:* Bernard Portnoy
Pr: Jennifer Portnoy
**VP:* Anastasia Portnoy
Dir IT: Wayne Connor
Sfty Mgr: Mike Amodeo

D-U-N-S 60-603-4049
OMEGA NATCHIQ INC
AES OMEGA
(*Suby of* ASRC ENERGY SERVICES INC) ★
4418 Pesson Rd, New Iberia, LA 70560-8750
Tel (337) 365-6028 *Founded/Ownrshp* 1998
Sales 216.9MM^E *EMP* 500
SIC 1389 3533 Building oil & gas well foundations on site; Oil field machinery & equipment; Building oil & gas well foundations on site; Oil field machinery & equipment
Pr: Gary Buchanan
**Pr:* Jeff Kinneeveauk
**COO:* Mark D Nelson
**Sr VP:* Jens Beck
**VP:* Sam Hill
**VP:* Daniel Wuthrich
Exec: Rebecca Marceaux

D-U-N-S 94-731-8044
OMEGA OPTICAL CO LP
13515 N Stemmons Fwy, Dallas, TX 75234-5765
Tel (972) 241-4141 *Founded/Ownrshp* 1995
Sales 21.7MM^E *EMP* 159
SIC 3851 5048 5049 Eyeglasses, lenses & frames; Contact lenses; Ophthalmic goods; Frames, ophthalmic; Lenses, ophthalmic; Optical goods; Eyeglasses, lenses & frames; Contact lenses; Ophthalmic goods; Frames, ophthalmic; Lenses, ophthalmic; Optical goods
Prin: Hubert Sagnieres
CIO: Steve Ochs

D-U-N-S 87-765-4574
OMEGA PLASTIC CORP
OMEGA PLASTICS OF KY
(*Suby of* ALPHA INDUSTRIES MANAGEMENT INC) ★
901 Commerce Cir, Shelbyville, KY 40065-9131
Tel (502) 633-0168 *Founded/Ownrshp* 1980
Sales 228.8MM^E *EMP* 1,800
SIC 2673 Plastic & pliofilm bags; Plastic & pliofilm bags
CEO: Alfred Teo
**Pr:* Fred Mancuso
**CFO:* John Reier
VP: Bill Lenchinsky
Off Mgr: Maria Diaz
Off Mgr: Hector Gocman

D-U-N-S 11-278-7973 IMP
OMEGA PLASTICS CORP
SIGMA PLASTICS GROUP
(*Suby of* ALPHA INDUSTRIES MANAGEMENT INC) ★
Page & Schuyler Ave Ste 5, Lyndhurst, NJ 07071
Tel (201) 933-1270 *Founded/Ownrshp* 1982
Sales 78.1MM^E *EMP* 220
SIC 2673 Plastic bags: made from purchased materials; Plastic bags: made from purchased materials
Pr: Alfred Teo
**CFO:* John Reier
**Ex VP:* Stanley Band

OMEGA PLASTICS OF KY
See OMEGA PLASTIC CORP

D-U-N-S 83-447-3928
OMEGA POLYMER TECHNOLOGIES INC
OPTI
1331 S Chillicothe Rd, Aurora, OH 44202-8066
Tel (330) 562-5201 *Founded/Ownrshp* 1994
Sales 32.7MM^E *EMP* 324
SIC 3089 Injection molding of plastics; Injection molding of plastics
Pr: Ronald Baker
VP: David Morley
VP: Donald Smith
IT Man: Ortho Prunty

D-U-N-S 05-902-4163
OMEGA PROBE INC
308 Southwest Dr, Cheyenne, WY 82007-1917
Tel (877) 323-2201 *Founded/Ownrshp* 2011
Sales 80.7MM^E *EMP* 2,200
SIC 7371 6552 Computer software systems analysis & design, custom; Subdividers & developers; Computer software systems analysis & design, custom; Subdividers & developers
Pr: Gus Williams

D-U-N-S 07-358-1266 IMP
OMEGA PRODUCTS CORP
OMEGA PRODUCTS INTERNATIONAL
(*Suby of* OPAL SERVICE INC) ★
1681 California Ave, Corona, CA 92881-3375
Tel (951) 737-7447 *Founded/Ownrshp* 1974
Sales 25.6MM^E *EMP* 140
SIC 3299 2899 Stucco; Chemical preparations; Stucco; Chemical preparations
Pr: Kenneth R Thompson
**VP:* Todd Martin
IT Man: Ben Kumsakul
QC Dir: Dan Bui
Mktg Mgr: Terry Anderson

OMEGA PRODUCTS INTERNATIONAL
See OMEGA PRODUCTS CORP

D-U-N-S 00-926-8124
▲ **OMEGA PROTEIN CORP**
2105 Citywest Blvd # 500, Houston, TX 77042-2838
Tel (713) 623-0060 *Founded/Ownrshp* 1913
Sales 308.6MM *EMP* 657
Tkr Sym OME *Exch* NYS
SIC 2077 5199 Fish meal, except as animal feed; Fish oil; Oils, animal or vegetable; Fish meal, except as animal feed; Fish oil; Oils, animal or vegetable
Pr: Bret D Scholtes
**Ch Bd:* Gary R Goodwin
COO: Rick Schillaci
CFO: Andrew C Johannesen
Ex VP: John D Held
Ex VP: Robert Stockton
VP: Gregory P Toups
VP: Michael Wilson
Genl Mgr: Frank Morabito
Dir IT: Robert Plant
Dir IT: Tom Wittman
Board of Directors: Gary L Allee, Stephen Bryan, Gary Ermes, Paul M Kearns, William E M Lands, David A Owen, David W Wehlmann

D-U-N-S 00-310-0930
■ **OMEGA PROTEIN INC** (VA)
(*Suby of* OMEGA PROTEIN CORP) ★
2105 City W Blvd Ste 500, Houston, TX 77042
Tel (713) 623-0060 *Founded/Ownrshp* 1913
Sales 29.0MM^E *EMP* 50
SIC 2077 Fish oil; Fish meal, except as animal feed; Fish oil; Fish meal, except as animal feed
CEO: Bret D Scholtes
**Pr:* Matthew Phillips
**CFO:* Andrew C Johannesen
**VP:* Dr Mark E Griffin

D-U-N-S 05-232-2989
OMEGA PULTRUSIONS INC
(*Suby of* OMEGA POLYMER TECHNOLOGIES INC) ★
1331 S Chillicothe Rd, Aurora, OH 44202-8066
Tel (330) 562-5201 *Founded/Ownrshp* 1994
Sales 23.6MM *EMP* 140
SIC 3089 Injection molding of plastics; Injection molding of plastics
Pr: Donald F Borraccini
Treas: Otho Prunty
VP: Greg Foskey
VP: Tracey Roskey
IT Man: Ortho Prunty
IT Man: Rosaleen Rose

D-U-N-S 09-377-4412
OMEGA SPORTS II INC
130 S Walnut Cir, Greensboro, NC 27409-2625
Tel (336) 854-0797 *Founded/Ownrshp* 1978
Sales 26.8MM^E *EMP* 250
SIC 5941

D-U-N-S 03-736-0294 EXP
OMEGA STEEL CO
SLIGO STEEL
3460 Hollenberg Dr # 100, Bridgeton, MO 63044-2455
Tel (314) 209-0992 *Founded/Ownrshp* 1971
Sales 26.6MM^E *EMP* 40
SIC 5051 Pipe & tubing, steel; Structural shapes, iron or steel
Pr: Greg Semmel
**VP:* Paul Everett
**VP:* Kevin Kulich
IT Man: Stephani Bagby
Trfc Mgr: Cathy Cowen
Sales Asso: Brock Adams

D-U-N-S 14-064-0298
OMEGA TECHNOLOGY
8405 Nw 70th St, Miami, FL 33166-2638
Tel (305) 592-2322 *Founded/Ownrshp* 1997
Sales 17.8MM^E *EMP* 280
SIC 5045 Computers; Computers
Pr: Yovet Henriquez

D-U-N-S 61-468-3407
■ **OMEGA TRAINING GROUP INC**
CUBIC
(*Suby of* CUBIC CORP) ★
7201 Moon Rd, Columbus, GA 31909-1798
Tel (706) 569-9100 *Founded/Ownrshp* 2008
Sales 8.1MM^E *EMP* 280
SIC 8611 8742 Contractors' association; Training & development consultant; Contractors' association; Training & development consultant
Prin: Michael Manser
**Prin:* Gregory Stone
Genl Mgr: John Machovec
IT Man: Carrie Thomas

D-U-N-S 06-304-8953 IMP
OMEGA WIRE INC
BARE WIRE DIV
(*Suby of* BARE WIRE DIVISION) ★
12 Masonic Ave, Camden, NY 13316-1202
Tel (315) 245-3800 *Founded/Ownrshp* 1997
Sales 96.9MM^E *EMP* 1,200
SIC 3351 Wire, copper & copper alloy; Wire, copper & copper alloy
Pr: Rodney D Kent
VP: Peter Ernenwein
Board of Directors: Adam Kleinman

D-U-N-S 06-236-3593
OMEGA WORLD TRAVEL INC
3102 Omega Office Park # 1, Fairfax, VA 22031-2408
Tel (703) 359-0200 *Founded/Ownrshp* 1972
Sales 251.1MM^E *EMP* 920^E
SIC 4724 Travel agencies; Travel agencies
Pr: Gloria Bohan
**VP:* Daniel P Bohan
VP: Diane Bozicevich
VP: Stan Brown
**VP:* Goran Gligorovic
Rgnl Mgr: Laura Gantt
Brnch Mgr: Teresa Organ
Brnch Mgr: Denise Skiba
Brnch Mgr: Donna Watkins
Genl Mgr: Jessica Speirs
CTO: Demay Wiggins
Board of Directors:

OMEGADYNE
See OMEGA ENGINEERING INC

OMEGAFLEX
See OMEGA FLEX INC

D-U-N-S 00-959-2379
OMELVENY & MYERS LLP
400 S Hope St Fl 19, Los Angeles, CA 90071-2831
Tel (213) 430-6000 *Founded/Ownrshp* 1950
Sales 331.9MM^E *EMP* 2,100
SIC 8111 General practice law office; General practice law office
COO: Bruce Bouware
COO: George C Demos
Bd of Dir: Diana Diaz
Bd of Dir: Cathy Hagen
Off Admin: Robert Cramer
Web Dev: Sue White
Counsel: Robert Fisher
Counsel: Jeffrey Fowler
Counsel: Brad Hise
Counsel: Phillip Kaplan
Counsel: David Leviss

D-U-N-S 07-829-2983
OMERS PRIVATE EQUITY USA INC
(*Suby of* OMERS PRIVATE EQUITY INC)
320 Park Ave Fl 17, New York, NY 10022-6924
Tel (212) 986-7500 *Founded/Ownrshp* 2011
Sales 77.3MM^E *EMP* 40^E
SIC 6726 Investment offices
Pr: Micheal Graham

OMF INTERNATIONAL
See OVERSEAS MISSIONARY FELLOWSHIP INC

D-U-N-S 00-416-5742
■ **OMG AMERICAS INC**
OM GROUP
(*Suby of* VECTRA CO) ★
811 Sharon Dr, Westlake, OH 44145-1526
Tel (440) 899-2950 *Founded/Ownrshp* 1946
Sales 26.4MM^E *EMP* 175
SIC 8731 2819 2899 2992 2869 Commercial physical research; Industrial inorganic chemicals; Chemical preparations; Lubricating oils & greases; Industrial organic chemicals; Commercial physical research; Industrial inorganic chemicals; Chemical preparations; Lubricating oils & greases; Industrial organic chemicals
CEO: Joseph Scaminace
Mng Pt: William Reidy
Off Mgr: Alice Ramsey

D-U-N-S 04-986-5769 EXP
■ **OMG ELECTRONIC CHEMICALS INC**
FIDELITY CHEMICAL PRODUCTS DIV
(*Suby of* VECTRA CO) ★
400 Corporate Ct Ste A, South Plainfield, NJ 07080-2414
Tel (908) 222-5800 *Founded/Ownrshp* 1998
Sales 31.5MM^E *EMP* 205
SIC 2899 2819 3339 Plating compounds; Nickel compounds or salts, inorganic; Zinc chloride; Primary nonferrous metals; Plating compounds; Nickel compounds or salts, inorganic; Zinc chloride; Primary nonferrous metals
VP: Chris Vidoli
**VP:* Chris Bidoli
**VP:* Joseph Simioni
Plnt Mgr: Reginald Williams
Manager: Doug Richard

D-U-N-S 61-667-2325 IMP/EXP
■ **OMG ELECTRONIC CHEMICALS LLC**
(*Suby of* VECTRA CO) ★
5630 Pioneer Creek Dr, Maple Plain, MN 55359-9002
Tel (763) 479-2008 *Founded/Ownrshp* 2008
Sales 32.5MM^E *EMP* 90

SIC 2899 Chemical preparations; Chemical preparations
VP Opers: Joe Simeone
**VP:* Leo Linehen
Rgnl Mgr: Mamdouh Eskander
Plnt Mgr: Alecia Enger

D-U-N-S 04-928-2080 IMP/EXP
■ **OMG INC**
(*Suby of* HANDY & HARMAN) ★
153 Bowles Rd, Agawam, MA 01001-2908
Tel (413) 789-0252 *Founded/Ownrshp* 1994
Sales 109.7MM^E *EMP* 350
SIC 3531 3452 3444 2952 Roofing equipment; Bolts, nuts, rivets & washers; Sheet metalwork; Asphalt felts & coatings; Roofing equipment; Bolts, nuts, rivets & washers; Sheet metalwork; Asphalt felts & coatings
Pr: Hubert T McGovern
Pr: Sue Thurston
**CFO:* Tom Smith
**CFO:* Edward C Woodbridge
**Treas:* Ted Yerdon
**Sr VP:* James F McCabe Jr
**VP:* Michael T Held
**VP:* Douglas Woodworth
Rgnl Mgr: David Ellis
Genl Mgr: Tina Delmonte
Genl Mgr: Tom Wagner

D-U-N-S 00-696-1213
OMG MID WEST INC
HALLETT MATERIALS
(*Suby of* OLDCASTLE MATERIALS GROUP) ★
2401 Se Tones Dr Ste 13, Ankeny, IA 50021-8886
Tel (515) 266-9928 *Founded/Ownrshp* 2001
Sales 101.4MM^E *EMP* 101
SIC 1442 1422 Construction sand mining; Gravel mining; Limestones, ground
Pr: Craig Lamberty
**Treas:* Charles Brown

D-U-N-S 07-989-2655
OMGANICS INC
1821 Waterston Ave Unit B, Austin, TX 78703-3938
Tel (512) 560-3262 *Founded/Ownrshp* 2014
Sales 55.6MM^E *EMP* 2,014
SIC 2676 Infant & baby paper products
CEO: Carissa Hoop

D-U-N-S 02-831-8454
■ **OMGEO LLC**
OASYS
(*Suby of* CEDE AND CO) ★
55 Thomson Pl, Boston, MA 02210-1219
Tel (877) 664-3625 *Founded/Ownrshp* 2013
Sales 198.4MM^E *EMP* 600
SIC 6211 Security brokers & dealers; Security brokers & dealers
Pr: Paula Sausville Arthus
**CFO:* Antonio Nunes
Exec: Tony Remedios
Ex Dir: Simon Farrington
Ex Dir: Andy Hughes
Ex Dir: Doris Jurisson
Mng Dir: Randy Guy
Snr Ntwrk: Jayesh Mankodi
IT Man: Ken Moody
Software D: John Henry

D-U-N-S 78-865-6176
OMH HOLDINGS LLC
OMEGA HEALTHCARE MGT SVCS
2103 Chablis Ct, Gibsonia, PA 15044-7467
Tel (412) 580-8714 *Founded/Ownrshp* 2005
Sales 3.0MM *EMP* 800
SIC 7389 Process serving service; Process serving service
CEO: Gopi Natarajan
CFO: Anurag S Mehta

D-U-N-S 06-636-2278 IMP/EXP
OMI CRANE SYSTEMS INC
1515 E Interstate 30, Fate, TX 75189-8513
Tel (972) 636-8000 *Founded/Ownrshp* 2003
Sales 43.3MM^E *EMP* 50^E
SIC 5084 3565 Cranes, industrial; Packaging machinery
Pr: Mike Bunnel
**Pr:* Eugene E Oard
**Sec:* Kimberly L Bunnel
**VP:* Thomas G Codiana
Exec: Kim Bunnel
Genl Mgr: Kevin Picklo
VP Opers: Matt Bunnel
Sfty Mgr: Ladatrick Robinson

D-U-N-S 11-088-1562
OMI ENVIRONMENTAL SOLUTIONS
131 Keating Dr, Belle Chasse, LA 70037-1629
Tel (504) 394-6110 *Founded/Ownrshp* 2003
Sales 118.4MM^E *EMP* 130
SIC 4959 Environmental cleanup services
Pr: Shaw Thompson
**VP:* Joe Christiana
Dir IT: Jesse White

OMICRON GRANITE
See OMICRON SUPPLIES LLC

D-U-N-S 61-317-3223 IMP/EXP
OMICRON SUPPLIES LLC
OMICRON GRANITE
3120 N Andrews Avenue Ext, Pompano Beach, FL 33064-2115
Tel (954) 942-2525 *Founded/Ownrshp* 1980
Sales 25.2MM^E *EMP* 80^E
SIC 1499 3432 Gem stones (natural) mining; Faucets & spigots, metal & plastic
Owner: Frederick J Cohen
Brnch Mgr: Elio Correia
Brnch Mgr: Bruno Goulart
Off Mgr: Gabby Harrell

D-U-N-S 07-854-5028
OMICS GROUP INC (NV)
OMICS PUBLISHING GROUP
2360 Corp Cir Ste 400, Henderson, NV 89074
Tel (888) 843-8169 *Founded/Ownrshp* 2012
Sales 80.6MM^E *EMP* 1,000
SIC 2721 Trade journals: publishing & printing; Trade journals: publishing & printing
Pr: Srinu B Gedela
Dir Bus: Valentina Diaz

OMICS PUBLISHING GROUP
See OMICS GROUP INC

D-U-N-S 14-810-5344
OMIDYAR NETWORK SERVICES LLC
1991 Broadway St Ste 200, Redwood City, CA 94063-1958
Tel (650) 482-2500 *Founded/Ownrshp* 2004
Sales 85.4MM *EMP* 20
Accts Comprehensive Financial Mgt
SIC 8742 Administrative services consultant
Mng Pt: Matthew Bannick
Mng Pt: Kelsey King
Bd of Dir: Fiona Mulligan
VP: Christopher Keefe
VP: Mike Kubzansky
VP: Susan Phillips
Dir Soc: Jeff Kumataka
Off Mgr: Fiona Pieterse
Genl Couns: Will Fitzpatrick
Corp Couns: Jeffrey Hom
Snr Mgr: Allen Babaran

D-U-N-S 04-551-8425
OMIMEX RESOURCES INC
7950 John T White Rd, Fort Worth, TX 76120-3608
Tel (817) 460-7777 *Founded/Ownrshp* 1987
Sales 46.3MM^E *EMP* 86
SIC 1382 1311 Oil & gas exploration services; Crude petroleum production; Oil & gas exploration services; Crude petroleum production
Pr: Naresh Vashisht
**Treas:* Arnold Campos
**VP:* Clark Storms

D-U-N-S 80-477-8124 IMP/EXP
OMIX-ADA INC
RUGGED RIDGE
460 Horizon Dr Ste 400, Suwanee, GA 30024-3114
Tel (770) 614-6101 *Founded/Ownrshp* 1992
Sales 38.0MM^E *EMP* 70
SIC 5013 Automotive supplies & parts
CEO: Ali D Azadi
CFO: Reggie Fields
Genl Mgr: Brandan Seadoef
Sls Mgr: Ryan Jackson

D-U-N-S 07-870-5945 IMP
OMK TUBE INC
(*Suby of* OMK-SERVIS, AO)
16285 Park Ten Pl Ste 150, Houston, TX 77084-4963
Tel (281) 609-8150 *Founded/Ownrshp* 2011
Sales 73.9MM^E *EMP* 255
SIC 3317 3398 Steel pipe & tubes; Metal heat treating; Steel pipe & tubes; Metal heat treating
Pr: Joel Johnson
**CFO:* Thomas Cownan

D-U-N-S 00-647-8481
OMNETICS CONNECTOR CORP
7260 Commerce Cir E, Minneapolis, MN 55432-3103
Tel (763) 572-0656 *Founded/Ownrshp* 1984
Sales 38.1MM^E *EMP* 140
SIC 3678 Electronic connectors; Electronic connectors
CEO: Gerald W Simonson
**CFO:* Gary E Jacobs
QA Dir: Kaitlin Malvin
Ql Cn Mgr: Larry Volkmann
Manager: Derek Hunt
Sls Mgr: Jordan Kruse
Sales Asso: Matt Steele

D-U-N-S 17-411-2102
OMNI AIR INTERNATIONAL INC
3303 N Sheridan Rd Hngar19, Tulsa, OK 74115-2219
Tel (918) 836-5393 *Founded/Ownrshp* 2004
Sales 188.4MM^E *EMP* 1,083
SIC 4522 Flying charter service; Flying charter service
Pr: Jeffrey C Crippen
Ch Bd: Robert Coretz
Dir Surg: Alandra Baggett
Dir Bus: Pablo Aguirre
Trfc Dir: Pete McGuirk

D-U-N-S 96-539-2280
OMNI AMELIA ISLAND LLC
OMNI HOTELS
(*Suby of* OMNI HOTELS CORP) ★
39 Beach Lagoon Rd, Amelia Island, FL 32034-5477
Tel (904) 261-6161 *Founded/Ownrshp* 2010
Sales 73.8MM^E *EMP* 1^E
SIC 4226 Special warehousing & storage
CEO: James D Caldwell
Pr: Michael J Deitemeyer
Sr VP: Mike Garcia
Sr VP: Tom Santora
Genl Mgr: Paul Eckert
Off Mgr: Becky Robinson

D-U-N-S 11-404-5701
OMNI APARTMENT COMMUNITIES INC
OMNI PROPERTIES
(*Suby of* CAS RESIDENTIAL) ★
3900 E Mexico Ave Ste 770, Denver, CO 80210-3940
Tel (303) 692-0451 *Founded/Ownrshp* 2007
Sales 8.7MM^E *EMP* 425
SIC 6531 Real estate managers; Real estate managers
Pr: C Greg Gulley
**Sec:* Karen Beth Gulley
Ex VP: Virginia Alexander
VP: Karen Chou

D-U-N-S 00-712-3623 IMP/EXP
OMNI APPAREL INC (NV)
13500 15th St, Grandview, MO 64030-3082
Tel (816) 765-5212 *Founded/Ownrshp* 2005, 2006
Sales 23.0MM *EMP* 99
SIC 5136 5137 Men's & boys' sportswear & work clothing; Sportswear, women's & children's; Men's & boys' sportswear & work clothing; Sportswear, women's & children's
Pr: Eric Lee
**Pr:* Vibul Tuangsitthisombat
**Treas:* Patcharin Tuangsitthisombat
VP: Bill Gardiner
VP: William Gardiner
Natl Sales: Sean Mahoney

OMNI AUTO PARTS
See OMNISOURCE CORP

D-U-N-S 10-134-9165
OMNI BAKING CO
2621 Freddy Ln Bldg 7, Vineland, NJ 08360-1559
Tel (856) 205-1485 *Founded/Ownrshp* 1996
Sales 143.0MM^E *EMP* 500
SIC 2051 Bread, cake & related products; Bread, cake & related products
Pt: Lenny Amoroso Jr
Pt: Daniel Amoroso Jr
Pt: John V Mulloy Sr
Exec: Eleanore Mesiano
Genl Mgr: Danny Maloy
Snr Mgr: Daniel Mulloy

D-U-N-S 78-244-3647
OMNI BEDFORD SPRINGS RESORT LLC
OMNI HOTELS
2138 Business 220, Bedford, PA 15522-2026
Tel (814) 623-3932 *Founded/Ownrshp* 2008
Sales 3.8MM^E *EMP* 450
SIC 7011 Hotels & motels
Pr: Jeffry Kloss
Pr: Michael J Deitemeyer
CEO: James D Caldwell
CFO: Mike Garcia
VP: Paul Dietzler
VP: Stephen Rosenstock
VP: Joy Rothschild
VP: Tom Santora
VP: Michael G Smith
Genl Mgr: Lee Bowden
Genl Mgr: Caitlin Bucklew

D-U-N-S 10-144-2903 IMP
OMNI CABLE CORP
2 Hagerty Blvd, West Chester, PA 19382-7594
Tel (610) 701-0100 *Founded/Ownrshp* 1978
Sales 258.8MM *EMP* 216
SIC 5063 Wire & cable; Wire & cable
Pr: William J Siegfried
**COO:* Greg Donato
COO: Gregory Donato
**CFO:* Steve Glinski
VP: John Rutherford
Rgnl Mgr: Bryan Dabruzzi
Rgnl Mgr: Steve Letourneau
Rgnl Mgr: Rob Orio
Rgnl Mgr: Jim Saffery
Rgnl Mgr: Dave Santoro
IT Man: Jeanine Bilotta

D-U-N-S 95-722-4801
OMNI CARE GROUP INC
309 Belleview Blvd, Belleair, FL 33756-2018
Tel (727) 443-3334 *Founded/Ownrshp* 1985
Sales 9.6MM^E *EMP* 322
SIC 7349 1541 Building maintenance services; Renovation, remodeling & repairs: industrial buildings; Building maintenance services; Renovation, remodeling & repairs: industrial buildings
Pr: S Neil Ford Jr
Opers Mgr: Robert Gibson

D-U-N-S 96-908-7695
OMNI CHILDHOOD CENTER INC
1651 Coney Island Ave # 1, Brooklyn, NY 11230-5856
Tel (718) 998-1415 *Founded/Ownrshp* 2010
Sales 12.0MM^E *EMP* 429
SIC 8299 Educational services; Educational services
Pr: Feigi Haieerstam
**CEO:* Miriam Selig
**Prin:* Mark Vineagray

D-U-N-S 87-892-9827 IMP
OMNI CONNECTION INTERNATIONAL INC
126 Via Trevizio, Corona, CA 92879-1772
Tel (951) 898-6232 *Founded/Ownrshp* 1992
Sales 79.1MM^E *EMP* 410
SIC 3679 Harness assemblies for electronic use: wire or cable; Harness assemblies for electronic use: wire or cable
Pr: Henry Cheng
CFO: Anita Liu
**VP:* Phyllis Ting

D-U-N-S 94-734-1145
OMNI CONSTRUCTION CO INC
25975 Emery Rd Ste A, Cleveland, OH 44128-6212
Tel (216) 514-6664 *Founded/Ownrshp* 1995
Sales 20.4MM *EMP* 6
Accts Jl Associates Inc
SIC 1799 Home/office interiors finishing, furnishing & remodeling
Pr: Richard Stone
VP: Paul Porges
VP Bus Dev: Phillip Golden

OMNI DUCT SYSTEMS
See ECB CORP

D-U-N-S 18-179-4538
OMNI ENERGY SERVICES CORP
OMNI GIBSON
(*Suby of* GIBSON ENERGY INC)
4500 Ne Evangeline Trwy, Carencro, LA 70520-5253
Tel (337) 896-6664 *Founded/Ownrshp* 2012
Sales 397.1MM^E *EMP* 950^E
SIC 1382 1389 7349 Seismograph surveys; Lease tanks, oil field: erecting, cleaning & repairing; Cleaning service, industrial or commercial; Seismograph surveys; Lease tanks, oil field: erecting, cleaning & repairing; Cleaning service, industrial or commercial
Pr: Brian J Recatto
CFO: Geoff A Jones
VP: Andy J Dufrene
VP: Donald Fowlis
VP: Gregory B Milton
VP: Mark E Stipe
VP: Nolan C Vice Jr
Off Mgr: Daisy Maricellissen

D-U-N-S 12-211-8359
OMNI ENGINEERING INC
(*Suby of* OMNI HOLDING CO) ★
3919 S 147th St Ste 124, Omaha, NE 68144-5579
Tel (402) 895-6666 *Founded/Ownrshp* 1985
Sales 35.9MM^E *EMP* 245
Accts Lehigh & Kading Pc Omaha
SIC 1611 3531 Surfacing & paving; Highway & street paving contractor; Asphalt plant, including gravel-mix type; Surfacing & paving; Highway & street paving contractor; Asphalt plant, including gravel-mix type
Ch Bd: Donald D Graham
**Pr:* Nancy Graham Cagle
**VP:* Brett Niebur

OMNI FACILITIES SERVICES
See PERFORMANCE PLUS

D-U-N-S 09-399-7062
OMNI FAMILY HEALTH
COMMUNITY HEALTH CENTER
4900 California Ave 400b, Bakersfield, CA 93309-7081
Tel (661) 459-1900 *Founded/Ownrshp* 1978
Sales 47.9MM *EMP* 350
Accts Tca Partners Lp Fresno Ca
SIC 8011 Clinic, operated by physicians; Clinic, operated by physicians
CEO: Francisco L Castillon
COO: Diego Martinez
**CFO:* Novira Irawan
CFO: Judy Junkermeier
Bd of Dir: Richard Acedo
Bd of Dir: Giuli Kelly
Bd of Dir: Marcos Rodriguez
Ex Dir: Wagih Michael
Surg Cl Rc: Norbert Gal

OMNI GIBSON
See OMNI ENERGY SERVICES CORP

D-U-N-S 04-595-1662
OMNI GLASS & PAINT INC
3530 Omni Dr, Oshkosh, WI 54904-8512
Tel (920) 233-3333 *Founded/Ownrshp* 1968
Sales 31.1MM^E *EMP* 180
SIC 1721 1793 3231

D-U-N-S 07-917-3305
OMNI GROVE PARK LLC
GROVE PARK INN, THE
(*Suby of* OMNI HOTELS CORP) ★
290 Macon Ave, Asheville, NC 28804-3711
Tel (828) 252-2711 *Founded/Ownrshp* 2013
Sales 99.7MM^E *EMP* 950
SIC 7299 5812 7011 5813 7992 7991 Banquet hall facilities; Eating places; Hotels & motels; Drinking places; Public golf courses; Health club
Sales Asso: Yanna Davis

D-U-N-S 78-414-0659
OMNI HC INC
1 Glenlake Pkwy Ste 1300, Atlanta, GA 30328-3485
Tel (706) 324-2251 *Founded/Ownrshp* 1987
Sales 14.5MM *EMP* 525
SIC 8059 5912 Nursing home, except skilled & intermediate care facility; Drug stores; Nursing home, except skilled & intermediate care facility; Drug stores
Pr: Grant Wilson
**CFO:* Jorge Haber

D-U-N-S 94-572-5182
OMNI HEALTHCARE INC
95 Bulldog Blvd Ste 101, Melbourne, FL 32901-3175
Tel (321) 727-3495 *Founded/Ownrshp* 1994
Sales 24.2MM^E *EMP* 200
SIC 8011 Offices & clinics of medical doctors; Offices & clinics of medical doctors
Pr: J Patel
**VP:* Craig Deligdish MD
VP: Debbie Keis
**Prin:* Cathy Fisher
Doctor: Kim McGrath MD

D-U-N-S 15-455-0610
OMNI HOLDING CO
3919 S 147th St Ste 124, Omaha, NE 68144-5579
Tel (402) 895-5160 *Founded/Ownrshp* 1985
Sales 35.9MM^E *EMP* 250
SIC 8741 Management services; Management services
Pr: Donald D Graham
**VP:* Nancy Graham Cagle

OMNI HOME CARE
See OMNI HOME HEALTH SERVICES LLC

D-U-N-S 14-075-3638
■ **OMNI HOME HEALTH SERVICES LLC**
OMNI HOME CARE
(*Suby of* SUNCREST HEALTHCARE INC) ★
9510 Ormsby Station Rd # 300, Louisville, KY 40223-5016
Tel (615) 712-2248 *Founded/Ownrshp* 2011
Sales 38.5MM^E *EMP* 1,340
SIC 8082 Home health care services; Home health care services
CEO: Fred Portnoy
**CFO:* Steve Marble
Ex VP: Mark Dermott
VP: John Kiehl

OMNI HOTELS
See OMNI INTERLOCKEN CO LLC

OMNI HOTELS
See CLP BRETTON WOODS LLC

OMNI HOTELS
See TRT HOLDINGS INC

OMNI HOTELS
See OMNI BEDFORD SPRINGS RESORT LLC

OMNI HOTELS
See OMNI AMELIA ISLAND LLC

D-U-N-S 19-395-1381 IMP
OMNI HOTELS CORP
(Suby of OMNI HOTELS) ★
4001 Maple Ave Ste 500, Dallas, TX 75219-3241
Tel (972) 869-4300 Founded/Ownrshp 1988
Sales 837.8MM^E EMP 8,000
SIC 7011 Hotels & motels; Hotels & motels
Pr: James D Caldwell
*Pr: Michael J Deitemeyer
*CFO: Mike Garcia
CFO: Mike Gracia
Sr Cor Off: Margaret David
Bd of Dir: Melody Rhodan
*Sr VP: Stephen Rosenstock
VP: Kerry Kennedy
VP: Charlie Muller
VP: David Perkins
VP: Debora Tjandra
Exec: Daniel Elinan
Exec: Ron Ulczak
Dir Soc: Sarah Hanshaw

D-U-N-S 04-023-0161
OMNI HOTELS MANAGEMENT CORP
(Suby of TRT DEVELOPMENT CO - CCB) ★
4001 Maple Ave Ste 500, Dallas, TX 75219-3241
Tel (972) 871-5600 Founded/Ownrshp 1997
Sales 209.3MM^E EMP 2,200
SIC 7011 Hotels & motels; Hotels & motels
Pr: James D Caldwell
*COO: Michael Dietemeyer
*Treas: Laurie Talarico
*Chf Mktg O: Tom Santora
*Sr VP: Michael Garcia
*Sr VP: Stephen Rosenstock
*VP: Caryn Kabudi
VP: Richard Tudgay

D-U-N-S 86-732-7520 IMP
OMNI INDUSTRIES OF NEWYORK INC
86 Rapp Rd, Monticello, NY 12701-3545
Tel (845) 791-4119 Founded/Ownrshp 2000
Sales 35.0MM EMP 9
SIC 5051 Metals service centers & offices; Metals service centers & offices
Ch: William Wuerthner

D-U-N-S 83-776-7540
OMNI INSURANCE CO
(Suby of OMNI INSURANCE GROUP INC) ★
2018 Powers Ferry Rd Se # 100, Atlanta, GA 30339-7200
Tel (770) 952-4500 Founded/Ownrshp 1980
Sales NA EMP 240
SIC 6331 Fire, marine & casualty insurance; Fire, marine & casualty insurance
Ch Bd: Dudley L Moore
*Pr: James Paul Kennedy
CFO: Sue Sacalf
*Treas: Susan Hamlett Scalf
*Sr VP: Lawrence J Korth
*Sr VP: Carl J Leo
*Sr VP: David Peters
*Sr VP: Lowell E Sims
*Sr VP: Mary E Skeeles
*Sr VP: Kathy Renee Weese
Mktg Dir: John Haney

D-U-N-S 15-337-3584
OMNI INSURANCE GROUP INC
(Suby of INDEPENDENT INSURANCE INVESTMENTS INC) ★
20018 Powers Ferry Rd, Atlanta, GA 30339
Tel (770) 952-4500 Founded/Ownrshp 2006
Sales NA EMP 250
SIC 6331 Property damage insurance; Fire, marine & casualty insurance & carriers; Property damage insurance; Fire, marine & casualty insurance & carriers
Pr: J Paul Kennedy
*VP: Lawrence J Korth
*VP: Carl J Leo
*VP: David S Peters
*VP: Susan H Scalf
*VP: Lowell Sims
*VP: Mary Skeeles
*VP: K Renee Weese
Sls Mgr: Shelly D'Amico

D-U-N-S 02-701-0029
OMNI INTERLOCKEN CO LLC
OMNI HOTELS
(Suby of OMNI HOTELS MANAGEMENT CORP) ★
500 Interlocken Blvd, Broomfield, CO 80021-3487
Tel (303) 464-3276 Founded/Ownrshp 1998
Sales 23.5MM^E EMP 300
SIC 7011 Hotels & motels; Hotels & motels
Genl Mgr: Danny Goldman
Exec: David Harker
Genl Mgr: Eric Anderson
*Genl Mgr: David Jurcak
Sls Mgr: Jodi Carpinello
Sls Mgr: Christine Directora

D-U-N-S 84-880-8403
OMNI LOGISTICS INC
15912 Intl Plz Dr, Houston, TX 77032-2439
Tel (281) 209-9228 Founded/Ownrshp 2000
Sales 50.9MM^E EMP 105
SIC 4731 Freight forwarding; Freight forwarding
Pr: Jason B Smith
VP: Mark Hicks
*VP: Mark A McDowell
*VP: James K Moran
VP: Brad Stogner
Exec: Dora Aleman
Brnch Mgr: Barbara Allen
Sales Exec: Bob McKenzie

D-U-N-S 03-894-8139
OMNI MANOR INC
101 W Liberty St, Girard, OH 44420-2844
Tel (330) 545-1550 Founded/Ownrshp 1980
Sales 57.8M EMP 1,200
SIC 8051 Convalescent home with continuous nursing care; Convalescent home with continuous nursing care
Pr: John Masternick
CFO: Kenneth James
*Treas: Dorothy Masternick
*VP: Leo Grimes

D-U-N-S 10-164-9077
OMNI MANUFACTURING INC
901 Mckinley Rd, Saint Marys, OH 45885-1812
Tel (419) 394-7424 Founded/Ownrshp 1982
Sales 26.8MM^E EMP 138
Accts Ma Hoops & Associates Lima
SIC 3469 3479 3544 Metal stampings; Coating of metals & formed products; Special dies & tools; Metal stampings; Coating of metals & formed products; Special dies & tools
Pr: Wayne L Freewalt
Treas: Barbara Combs
IT Man: Ron Snider
Plnt Mgr: Bob Prater

D-U-N-S 61-300-9224
OMNI METALS INC
16801 Greenspt Pk Dr # 100, Houston, TX 77060-2310
Tel (281) 445-0700 Founded/Ownrshp 1990
Sales 22.1MM^E EMP 17
SIC 5051 3341 Steel; Secondary nonferrous metals
Pr: Arthur H Tomes Jr
CFO: Dave Wood
VP: Rich Farina
Trfc Mgr: Lisa Medlin

D-U-N-S 19-845-0413 IMP
OMNI PACKAGING CORP
12322 E 55th St, Tulsa, OK 74146-6900
Tel (918) 461-1700 Founded/Ownrshp 1988
Sales 52.1MM EMP 67
Accts Walters & Bailey Cpa Inc
SIC 5199 5085 Packaging materials; Industrial supplies; Packaging materials; Industrial supplies
Pr: Roberta Jones
CFO: Jim Shaw
*Treas: Michael Jones

D-U-N-S 09-226-3847
OMNI PLASTICS INC
6100 W Ridge Rd, Erie, PA 16506-1098
Tel (814) 838-6664 Founded/Ownrshp 1979
Sales 78.4MM EMP 40
SIC 3089 Injection molding of plastics; Injection molding of plastics
Pr: Wilhelm Maier
*CFO: Alan Woolslare
*Sec: Peggy J Maier
*VP: Mark Maier

D-U-N-S 05-846-5605 IMP
OMNI PLASTICS LLC
2300 Lynch Rd, Evansville, IN 47711-2951
Tel (812) 422-0888 Founded/Ownrshp 1998
Sales 37.5MM^E EMP 80
SIC 2821 3083 Plastics materials & resins; Laminated plastics plate & sheet; Plastics materials & resins; Laminated plastics plate & sheet
Pr: William G Vieth
CIO: Bob Blanford
Sfty Mgr: Dan Casper
Sfty Mgr: Steve Kueber
Plnt Mgr: Greg Riedford
Natl Sales: Mike Wilson

OMNI PROPERTIES
See OMNI APARTMENT COMMUNITIES INC

OMNI PROVIDENCE HOTEL
See RHODE OMNI ISLAND LLC

D-U-N-S 61-017-1212
OMNI RESOURCE RECOVERY INC
1495 N 8th St Ste 150, Colton, CA 92324-1451
Tel (909) 327-2900 Founded/Ownrshp 2009
Sales 31.7MM^E EMP 250
SIC 3089 Extruded finished plastic products; Extruded finished plastic products
CEO: Joe Castro
*VP: Mike Gerber
Off Mgr: Mickala Zavala

D-U-N-S 15-420-2782
OMNI RESOURCES INC
2367 N Mayfair Rd 200, Milwaukee, WI 53226-1502
Tel (262) 797-8080 Founded/Ownrshp 1984
Sales 28.4MM^E EMP 233
SIC 7379 7361 Computer related consulting services; Employment agencies; Computer related consulting services; Employment agencies
Pr: Roger L Mueller
*CEO: Veronica S Mueller
Mng Dir: Jeff Lang
Off Mgr: Tracy Cole
Off Admin: Taylir Knodl
IT Man: Eric Oelhafen
Sftwr Eng: Eric Back
Sftwr Eng: Matt Schmidt

OMNI SCOTTSDALE RESORT
See MONTELUCIA RESORT & SPA LLC

D-U-N-S 03-081-2432
OMNI SERVICES INC
OMNI SERVICES OF CONNECTICUT
12 E Worcester St, Worcester, MA 01604-3612
Tel (508) 799-2746 Founded/Ownrshp 2004
Sales 51.3MM^E EMP 70
SIC 5085 Industrial supplies; Hose, belting & packing; Industrial supplies; Hose, belting & packing
Pr: Richard Connors
*CFO: Karen M Brandvold
VP: Todd Keeney
Brnch Mgr: Robert Pollock
CTO: Michael Dipierro
Sls Mgr: Matt Nies
Sales Asso: Tim Driscoll

OMNI SERVICES OF CONNECTICUT
See OMNI SERVICES INC

D-U-N-S 78-606-7629
OMNI SYSTEMS INC
24400 Highland Rd Ste 3, Cleveland, OH 44143-2503
Tel (216) 377-5160 Founded/Ownrshp 1990
Sales 43.7MM EMP 150
SIC 2759

D-U-N-S 96-599-5298 IMP
OMNI VALVE CO LLC
4520 Chandler Rd, Muskogee, OK 74403-4928
Tel (918) 686-7882 Founded/Ownrshp 2010
Sales 55.2MM EMP 46
Accts Bledsoe & Assoc Pllc Edmond
SIC 3491 Industrial valves; Industrial valves
CFO: Robert Smith
VP: Dave Derrick
Dir Bus: David Harmon
IT Man: Richy Mitchell

D-U-N-S 83-235-9384
OMNI VISION INC
301 S Perimeter Park Dr # 210, Nashville, TN 37211-4143
Tel (615) 726-3603 Founded/Ownrshp 2011
Sales 39.2MM^E EMP 1,209
SIC 8361 Home for the aged; Home for the aged
Pr: Eric Strickland
Bd of Dir: Gary Dowdy
Off Mgr: Kourtney Hedden
Off Mgr: Kim Moore
Dir IT: Shane Frazier
Snr Mgr: Jessica Brock

D-U-N-S 83-487-3473
OMNI WORKSPACE CO LLC
A & M BUSINESS INTERIOR SVCS
1300 Washington Ave N # 200, Minneapolis, MN 55411-3435
Tel (612) 627-1700 Founded/Ownrshp 2010
Sales 90.0MM^E EMP 400
SIC 7641 4212 4226 Office furniture repair & maintenance; Furniture moving, local: without storage; Furniture storage, without local trucking; Office furniture repair & maintenance; Furniture moving, local: without storage; Furniture storage, without local trucking
*Pr: Karston Anderson
Brnch Mgr: Curt Moe
IT Man: Jerry Crisman
Opers Mgr: Kevin Rusboldt

D-U-N-S 82-787-8369 IMP
OMNI-CHEM 136 LLC
1427 W 86th St Ste 365, Indianapolis, IN 46260-2103
Tel (317) 852-1986 Founded/Ownrshp 2000
Sales 24.0MM EMP 1
SIC 5169 Chemicals & allied products; Chemicals & allied products

D-U-N-S 60-251-4341 IMP/EXP
OMNIA ITALIAN DESIGN INC
4900 Edison Ave, Chino, CA 91710-5713
Tel (909) 393-4400 Founded/Ownrshp 1989
Sales 86.7MM^E EMP 200
SIC 5021 Household furniture; Household furniture
Pr: Peter Zolferino
*VP: Luie Nastri
Natl Sales: Randy Gleckman

D-U-N-S 08-022-2339 IMP
OMNIA LEATHER MOTION INC
CATHY IRELAND HOME
4950 Edison Ave, Chino, CA 91710-5713
Tel (909) 393-4400 Founded/Ownrshp 1989
Sales 21.4MM^E EMP 200
SIC 2392 Household furnishings; Household furnishings
Pr: Peter Zolferino
*VP: Luie Nastri
VP Sls: Murray Eastern

D-U-N-S 06-279-4925
OMNIA LIFE INSURANCE CO
(Suby of OLD MUTUAL FINANCIAL NETWORK SECURITIES INC) ★
1001 Fleet St Fl 6, Baltimore, MD 21202-4356
Tel (410) 895-0099 Founded/Ownrshp 2001
Sales NA EMP 300
SIC 6411 Insurance agents, brokers & service; Insurance agents, brokers & service
Genl Pt: Cris Chapman
*Treas: Damon Gasque
Sr VP: Richard Pollard

D-U-N-S 07-316-5706
OMNIAMERICAN BANK
1320 S University Dr # 900, Fort Worth, TX 76107-5764
Tel (817) 367-5040 Founded/Ownrshp 1956
Sales NA EMP 307
SIC 6035 Federal savings banks

D-U-N-S 82-747-1454
■ **OMNICARE DISTRIBUTION CENTER LLC**
(Suby of OMNICARE INC) ★
302 S Byrne Rd Bldg 200, Toledo, OH 43615-6208
Tel (419) 720-8200 Founded/Ownrshp 2001
Sales 31.7MM^E EMP 100
SIC 5122 Pharmaceuticals; Pharmaceuticals

D-U-N-S 05-643-3907
■ **OMNICARE INC**
(Suby of CVS PHARMACY INC) ★
900 Omnicare Ctr, Cincinnati, OH 45202-2520
Tel (513) 719-2600 Founded/Ownrshp 2015
Sales 5.7MMM^E EMP 12,451
Tkr Sym OCR Exch NYS
SIC 5122 5047 8082 8741 Pharmaceuticals; Medical & hospital equipment; Home health care services; Nursing & personal care facility management; Pharmaceuticals; Medical & hospital equipment; Home health care services; Nursing & personal care facility management
Pr: Nitin Sahney
CFO: Robert O Kraft
Chf Cred: Steve Skware
Sr VP: Robert Dunlap
Sr VP: David Hileman
Sr VP: Amit Jain
Sr VP: Alexander M Kayne
Sr VP: Patrick Lee
Sr VP: Kirsten Marriner
Sr VP: Kirsten M Marriner
Sr VP: Ashok Singh
VP: Jonathan Borman
VP: W Erwin

D-U-N-S 85-880-2002
■ **OMNICARE MANAGEMENT CO**
(Suby of OMNICARE HOLDING COMPANY)
201 E 4th St Ste 900, Cincinnati, OH 45202-1513
Tel (513) 719-1535 Founded/Ownrshp 1981
Sales 96.5MM^E EMP 3,000
SIC 8741 Management services; Management services
Pr: David Hileman
*Treas: Amkur Bhandari
*VP: Cheryl Hodges

OMNICARE OF CINCINNATI
See HOME CARE PHARMACY LLC

OMNICARE OF CONNECTICUT
See VALUE HEALTH CARE SERVICES LLC

OMNICARE OF INDIANAPOLIS
See PRN PHARMACEUTICAL SERVICES LP

OMNICARE OF MINNESOTA
See BADGER ACQUISITION OF MINNESOTA LLC

D-U-N-S 07-835-1089
■ **OMNICARE OF NEWYORK LLC**
(Suby of NEIGHBORCARE PHARMACY SERVICES INC) ★
201 E 4th St Ste 900, Cincinnati, OH 45202-1513
Tel (513) 719-2600 Founded/Ownrshp 2009
Sales 25.7MM^E EMP 300
SIC 5912 Druggists' preparations (pharmaceuticals); Drug stores & proprietary stores
VP: Jeffrey M Stamps

OMNICARE OF NORTHWEST OHIO
See WESTHAVEN SERVICES CO LLC

OMNICARE OF PLAINVIEW
See SHORE PHARMACEUTICAL PROVIDERS INC

OMNICARE OF SOUTH DAKOTA
See OMNICARE PHARMACY AND SUPPLY SERVICES LLC

D-U-N-S 01-423-8034
■ **OMNICARE PHARMACIES SERVICES INC**
(Suby of OMNICARE INC) ★
1152 Garden St, Greensburg, PA 15601-6417
Tel (800) 242-1273 Founded/Ownrshp 1997
Sales 28.4MM^E EMP 201
SIC 5912 Drug stores; Drug stores
Pr: Daniel L Carto
Genl Mgr: Debra Evans
MIS Dir: Don Coleman
Pharmcst: Jason Josephic

D-U-N-S 18-875-4600
■ **OMNICARE PHARMACY AND SUPPLY SERVICES LLC**
OMNICARE OF SOUTH DAKOTA
(Suby of NEIGHBORCARE PHARMACY SERVICES INC) ★
709 N Kiwanis Ave, Sioux Falls, SD 57104-1807
Tel (605) 338-9980 Founded/Ownrshp 1997
Sales 63.1MM^E EMP 350
Accts Ernst & Young Llp Chicago Il
SIC 5122 Medicinals & botanicals; Pharmaceuticals; Medicinals & botanicals; Pharmaceuticals
Pr: Tim Krause
Genl Mgr: Mark Gerdes

D-U-N-S 02-299-6502
■ **OMNICARE PHARMACY OF FLORIDA LP**
(Suby of PHARMACY HOLDING 2, LLC)
201 E 4th St Ste 900, Cincinnati, OH 45202-1513
Tel (513) 719-2600 Founded/Ownrshp 2009
Sales 20.9MM^E EMP 487^E
SIC 5912 Drug stores & proprietary stores

D-U-N-S 80-534-5204
■ **OMNICARE PHARMACY OF MIDWEST LLC**
(Suby of NEIGHBORCARE PHARMACY SERVICES INC) ★
201 E 4th St Ste 900, Cincinnati, OH 45202-1513
Tel (513) 719-2600 Founded/Ownrshp 1993
Sales 27.7MM^E EMP 150
SIC 5122 5912 2834 Drugs & drug proprietaries; Drug stores; Pharmaceutical preparations; Drugs & drug proprietaries; Drug stores; Pharmaceutical preparations
Prin: Joel Gemunder
COO: Kathy Kopp

D-U-N-S 07-942-6902
■ **OMNICARE PHARMACY OFTEXAS 1 LP**
(Suby of PHARMACY HOLDING 2, LLC)
201 E 4th St Ste 900, Cincinnati, OH 45202-1513
Tel (513) 719-2600 Founded/Ownrshp 2002
Sales 8.5MM^E EMP 328^E
SIC 5912 Drug stores & proprietary stores
Prin: Robert Kraft

D-U-N-S 80-541-2665 IMP
▲ **OMNICELL INC**
590 E Middlefield Rd, Mountain View, CA 94043-4008
Tel (650) 251-6100 Founded/Ownrshp 1992
Sales 440.9MM EMP 1,236
Tkr Sym OMCL Exch NGS
SIC 3571 Electronic computers; Electronic computers
Ch Bd: Randall A Lipps
CFO: Peter Kuipers
Ex VP: J Christopher Drew
Ex VP: Nhat H Ngo
Ex VP: Michael Stevenson
Ex VP: Jorge R Taborga
IT Man: Joe Coyne
Corp Couns: Rhonda Meamber
Board of Directors: Joanne B Bauer, James T Judson, Randy D Lindholm, Vance B Moore, Mark W Parrish, Gary S Petersmeyer, Bruce D Smith, Sara J White

D-U-N-S 14-785-7429
▲ OMNICOM GROUP INC
437 Madison Ave, New York, NY 10022-7001
Tel (212) 415-3600 *Founded/Ownrshp* 1944
Sales 15.3MMM *EMP* 74,000
Tkr Sym OMC *Exch* NYS
SIC 7311 Advertising agencies; Advertising agencies
Pr: John D Wren
**Ch Bd:* Bruce Crawford
CEO: Dale A Adams
CEO: Jez Frampton
COO: Graham Bibby
CFO: Philip J Angelastro
Treas: Angie Hickman
Chf Cred: Basil Mavoritis
Ex VP: Sharon Callahan
Ex VP: Thomas Carey
Ex VP: Robert J Norsworthy
Ex VP: Bruce Redditt
Ex VP: Janet Riccio
Ex VP: Rita Rodriguez
Ex VP: Peter Sherman
Sr VP: Andrew L Castellaneta
Sr VP: Michael J O'Brien
Sr VP: Peter L Swiecicki
VP: Fred Canoro
VP: Min Chang
VP: Elizabeth Cornish
Board of Directors: Linda Johnson Rice, Alan R Batkin, Gary L Roubos, Mary C Choksi, Robert Charles Clark, Leonard S Coleman Jr, Errol M Cook, Susan S Denison, Michael A Henning, John R Murphy, John R Purcell

D-U-N-S 00-570-3710
■ OMNICOM MEDIA GROUP
ANNALLECT GROUP
(*Suby of* OMNICOM GROUP INC) ★
195 Broadway Fl 28, New York, NY 10007-3161
Tel (212) 590-7100 *Founded/Ownrshp* 2000
Sales 199.3MM^E^ *EMP* 1,420
SIC 7311 Advertising agencies; Advertising agencies
CEO: Daryl Simm
Pr: Shari Vera
**Pr:* John Wren
**CEO:* Barry Cupples
**CEO:* Mainardo De Nardis
**CEO:* Colin Gottlieb
**CFO:* Brad Nodiff
**Chf Mktg O:* Erin Matts
VP: Elisa Chua
VP: David Levy
VP: Filippo Padovan
Exec: Mark Bullingham
Assoc Dir: Joel P Balcita
Assoc Dir: Elizabeth Stebner
Assoc Dir: Jian Yang

D-U-N-S 18-067-3154
OMNIFLIGHT HELICOPTERS INC
(*Suby of* OMNIFLIGHT INC)
7301 S Peoria St, Englewood, CO 80112-4133
Tel (303) 792-7400 *Founded/Ownrshp* 2003
Sales 23.3MM^E^ *EMP* 316
SIC 4522 4512 4581 Ambulance services, air; Helicopter carrier, scheduled; Aircraft maintenance & repair services; Ambulance services, air; Helicopter carrier, scheduled; Aircraft maintenance & repair services
CEO: Mark E Johnson
**Pr:* Gaylan Crowell
**COO:* Anthony J Dinota
**CFO:* Michael Walterscheid
VP: Joel Hochhalter
VP: David N Pilotte
Comm Dir: Peter Heyer
Dir IT: Ron Madorran
Board of Directors: Kermit Brashaer

D-U-N-S 78-365-8946 IMP
OMNIGLOW LLC
865 Memorial Ave Ste 4, West Springfield, MA 01089-3540
Tel (413) 241-6010 *Founded/Ownrshp* 2005
Sales NA *EMP* 450^E^
SIC 2819 3229 5947 Industrial inorganic chemicals; Glass tubes & tubing; Gift, novelty & souvenir shop

D-U-N-S 03-012-4221
OMNIGUIDE INC
4 Maguire Rd, Lexington, MA 02421-3112
Tel (617) 551-8444 *Founded/Ownrshp* 2000
Sales 45.0MM^E^ *EMP* 130
SIC 5999 Medical apparatus & supplies
Pr: Scott D Flora
Ch Bd: Yoel Fink
Sr Cor Off: Jennifer Eversen
Sr Cor Off: Roch Hillenbrand
VP: Manny Avila
VP: Skip Farinha
VP: Sharon Timberlake
Off Mgr: Stacy Goleski
CTO: Tracy Campbell Accardi
CTO: Bernard Drost
IT Man: Mike Wilkins
Board of Directors: Doug Kohrs

D-U-N-S 96-899-7882
OMNILIFE USA INC
(*Suby of* GRUPO OMNILIFE, S.A. DE C.V.)
303 N Oregon St Ste 1200, El Paso, TX 79901-1257
Tel (915) 594-5100 *Founded/Ownrshp* 1994
Sales 43.0MM *EMP* 108
SIC 5149 Health foods; Health foods
Pr: Jorge Carlos Vergara
**Pr:* Jorge Vergara Madrigal

D-U-N-S 07-027-5938
OMNILIFT INC
1938 Stout Dr, Warminster, PA 18974-3868
Tel (215) 443-9090 *Founded/Ownrshp* 1976
Sales 27.2MM *EMP* 85
Accts Francis J Decembrino Pc Spr
SIC 5084 Lift trucks & parts; Materials handling machinery; Lift trucks & parts; Materials handling machinery
Pr: William J Boyle
**Sec:* Barbara A Boyle
VP: Jim Ellis
IT Man: Joe Painter
Mktg Mgr: Steve Krysko

D-U-N-S 61-971-2672
OMNIPLEX WORLD SERVICES CORP
OMNISEC INTL INVESTIGATIONS
14151 Park Meadow Dr # 300, Chantilly, VA 20151-4230
Tel (703) 652-3100 *Founded/Ownrshp* 2012
Sales 219.6MM^E^ *EMP* 3,420
SIC 7381 Guard services; Detective services; Guard services; Detective services
Pr: Michael S Santelli
**Ch Bd:* Philip T Sweeney
**Pr:* Mike Wines
CFO: David Mathews
**CFO:* John Peterson
**Treas:* Julien Patterson
Ofcr: Clifton Crosby
Ofcr: Pat Jeffers
Ofcr: Victoria Spriggs
**Sr VP:* Kelly Grems
**VP:* Scott Meyier
**VP:* James Moore
**VP:* William Turk

D-U-N-S 83-155-3073
OMNIPOINT US LLC
14707 S Dixie Hwy Ste 201, Miami, FL 33176-7950
Tel (305) 987-3756 *Founded/Ownrshp* 2008
Sales 44.7MM *EMP* 35
Accts Hacker Johnson & Smiht Pa Or
SIC 7361 Employment agencies; Employment agencies
CFO: Glenn Myer

D-U-N-S 09-203-2069 IMP
OMNIPURE FILTER CO INC
1904 Industrial Way, Caldwell, ID 83605-6926
Tel (208) 454-2597 *Founded/Ownrshp* 1970
Sales 42.7MM^E^ *EMP* 179
SIC 3589 Water filters & softeners, household type; Water filters & softeners, household type
Pr: Roger Reid
**VP:* Brent Simmons
Sfty Mgr: Darrell Crainick
Plnt Mgr: Dawn Amstutz

D-U-N-S 80-859-4399
OMNIRELIANT CORP
4218 W Linebaugh Ave, Tampa, FL 33624-5241
Tel (813) 909-9191 *Founded/Ownrshp* 2006
Sales 50.0MM^E^ *EMP* 2
SIC 2844 Perfumes & colognes; Perfumes & colognes
Pr: Paul Morrison
**CFO:* Chris Phillips

OMNISEC INTL INVESTIGATIONS
See OMNIPLEX WORLD SERVICES CORP

D-U-N-S 01-631-9345 IMP/EXP
■ OMNISOURCE CORP
OMNI AUTO PARTS
(*Suby of* STEEL DYNAMICS INC) ★
7575 W Jefferson Blvd, Fort Wayne, IN 46804-4131
Tel (260) 422-5541 *Founded/Ownrshp* 2007
Sales 1.2MMM^E^ *EMP* 2,500
SIC 5093 3462 3399 Ferrous metal scrap & waste; Nonferrous metals scrap; Iron & steel forgings; Metal powders, pastes & flakes; Ferrous metal scrap & waste; Nonferrous metals scrap; Iron & steel forgings; Metal powders, pastes & flakes
Pr: Russell Rinn
Ex VP: Rich Brady
VP: Mike Hausfeld
VP: Denny Luma
VP: Jason Redden
Opers Supe: Troy Dulgar
Sales Asso: Crystal Williams
Board of Directors: Danny Rifkin

D-U-N-S 80-857-3781 EXP
■ OMNISOURCE SOUTHEAST LLC
ATLANTIC SCRAP & PROCESS
(*Suby of* OMNI AUTO PARTS) ★
2061 Nazareth Church Rd, Spartanburg, SC 29301-5943
Tel (864) 439-7039 *Founded/Ownrshp* 2008
Sales 108.5MM^E^ *EMP* 180^E^
SIC 4953 Refuse systems; Refuse systems
Ex VP: Bob Brewer
Rgnl Mgr: Bennett Graham
Sfty Dirs: David Campbell

D-U-N-S 06-921-5671 EXP
OMNISPHERE CORP (FL)
9950 Sw 107th Ave Ste 100, Miami, FL 33176-2767
Tel (305) 388-4075 *Founded/Ownrshp* 1973
Sales 31.5MM *EMP* 18
SIC 5099 Pulpwood; Pulpwood
Pr: Alexander F Valdes
CFO: Maria Ll
Brnch Mgr: Jerry Jacob

D-U-N-S 60-818-8405
OMNISYS LLC
15950 Dallas Pkwy Ste 350, Dallas, TX 75248-6602
Tel (903) 455-0461 *Founded/Ownrshp* 2013
Sales 52.5MM^E^ *EMP* 250^E^
SIC 7373 Systems software development services; Systems software development services
CEO: Tricia Fringer
**VP:* Kevin Chien
**VP:* Shelley Hansell
**VP:* Christopher Ryan
**VP:* Scott Warshaw
VP: Brad Wheeler
Snr Sftwr: Jerald Herstein
CIO: Melinda Giese
Sftwr Eng: Clinton Brooks
VP Opers: Christina McCormack
Opers Mgr: Dedra Davidson

D-U-N-S 16-035-2386
OMNITEAM INC
9300 Hall Rd, Downey, CA 90241-5309
Tel (562) 923-9660 *Founded/Ownrshp* 1999
Sales 76.0MM^E^ *EMP* 125
SIC 5078 Refrigeration equipment & supplies; Refrigeration equipment & supplies
CEO: Kans Haasis Jr
**VP:* Robert Davis
**VP:* Don Hyatt Sr
Prd Mgr: Kelly Brock
Prd Mgr: Jeff McKeown

D-U-N-S 08-629-6030
OMNITEC SOLUTIONS INC
6701 Democracy Blvd # 300, Bethesda, MD 20817-1572
Tel (301) 896-9704 *Founded/Ownrshp* 1999
Sales 30.3MM *EMP* 125^E^
SIC 8711 Professional engineer; Professional engineer
Pr: Morris L Brown
**CFO:* John Goodwin
**VP:* David Cornwell
**VP:* Suzy Lang
Software D: Stanley Solomon

D-U-N-S 07-880-1627
OMNITRACS LLC (CA)
(*Suby of* OMNITRACS MIDCO LLC) ★
717 N Harwood St Ste 1300, Dallas, TX 75201-6533
Tel (858) 658-5935 *Founded/Ownrshp* 2012, 2013
Sales 119.4MM^E^ *EMP* 475^E^
SIC 8741 4214 Industrial management; Local trucking with storage; Industrial management; Local trucking with storage
CEO: John Graham
**Ch Bd:* Robert F Smith
**Pr:* David Post
**CFO:* Jordan Copland
Ofcr: David Vice
VP: Mansoor Bajowala
VP: Tom Neppl
**VP:* Marc V Teillon
**CTO:* Dan Speicher
Genl Couns: David Arnold

D-U-N-S 07-939-6942
OMNITRACS MIDCO LLC
10260 Sorrento Valley Rd, San Diego, CA 92121-1605
Tel (858) 651-5812 *Founded/Ownrshp* 2013
Sales 119.4MM^E^ *EMP* 500^E^
SIC 7372 Business oriented computer software; Utility computer software

D-U-N-S 08-181-6050
OMNITRANS
1700 W 5th St, San Bernardino, CA 92411-2499
Tel (909) 379-7100 *Founded/Ownrshp* 1976
Sales 14.9MM *EMP* 719^E^
SIC 4111

D-U-N-S 87-944-7183
OMNITRAX INC
252 Clayton St Fl 4, Denver, CO 80206-4814
Tel (303) 393-0033 *Founded/Ownrshp* 1993
Sales 68.0MM^E^ *EMP* 172^E^
SIC 4013 Switching & terminal services; Switching & terminal services
CEO: Kevin Shuba
**Pr:* Darcy Brede
Pr: Jeff Young
COO: Claude Pumilia
**CFO:* Scott R Bell
CFO: Jim Braun
**CFO:* Hubert Gassner
**Ch:* Brad Skinner
**Sec:* Thomas Mandula
Chf Mktg O: Lucus Brown
Ex VP: Avery Kent
**Ex VP:* Alex Yeros
VP: James T Bertram
VP: Jim Carrone
VP: Marc Cool
VP: Bill Kelly
VP: Kendall Koff
VP: Jeff Monahan
VP: Jason Scott
VP: Tony Simoes
VP Bus Dev: Lenny Berz
Board of Directors: Edmond Harris, Keith Lovetro

D-U-N-S 08-338-1728
■ OMNITURE LLC
(*Suby of* ADOBE SYSTEMS INC) ★
550 E Tmpngos Cle Bldng G, Orem, UT 84097
Tel (801) 722-7000 *Founded/Ownrshp* 1996
Sales 86.0MM^E^ *EMP* 1,092
SIC 7371 Custom computer programming services; Custom computer programming services
Pr: Mark Garrett
Pr: Chris Ballam
Pr: Brad Rencher
Pr: Catherine Wong
**CFO:* Michael S Herring
VP: Steve Affleck
**VP:* Brett M Error
VP: Alan Gurock
**VP:* Christopher Harrington
VP: John Mellor
Exec: Jason Carrillo

D-U-N-S 17-946-2197 IMP
OMNIUM LLC
1417 Sw Lower Lake Rd, Saint Joseph, MO 64504-9505
Tel (816) 238-8111 *Founded/Ownrshp* 1997
Sales 78.3MM^E^ *EMP* 228
SIC 2879 Agricultural chemicals; Agricultural chemicals
Pr: Jeffrey Greseth
Mng Pt: Jeffrey Greenman
Opers Mgr: Russ Ellis

D-U-N-S 92-848-5176
▲ OMNIVISION TECHNOLOGIES INC
4275 Burton Dr, Santa Clara, CA 95054-1512
Tel (408) 567-3000 *Founded/Ownrshp* 1995
Sales 1.3MMM *EMP* 2,176^E^
Accts Pricewaterhousecoopers Llp S
Tkr Sym OVTI *Exch* NGS
SIC 3674 Semiconductors & related devices; Semiconductors & related devices
CEO: Shaw Hong
Pr: Raymond Wu
COO: Xinping He
**COO:* Henry Yang
CFO: Anson Can
CFO: Anson Chan
Sr VP: Y Vicky Chou
VP: Zille Baker
VP: Gary Chen
VP: Vicky Chou
VP: Aurelio Cisneros
VP: Wayne CHI
VP: Phil Dahm
VP: Zille Hasnain
VP: Brian Hurst
VP: John Yue
Exec: Kevin Zhao
Board of Directors: Joseph Jeng, Dwight Steffansen

D-U-N-S 08-849-8618 EXP
▲ OMNOVA SOLUTIONS INC (OH)
25435 Harvard Rd, Beachwood, OH 44122-6201
Tel (216) 682-7000 *Founded/Ownrshp* 1952
Sales 987.4MM *EMP* 2,300
Accts Ernst & Young Llp Akron Ohio
Tkr Sym OMN *Exch* NYS
SIC 2819 2211 3069 3081 Industrial inorganic chemicals; Decorative trim & specialty fabrics, including twist weave; Roofing, membrane rubber; Unsupported plastics film & sheet; Plastic film & sheet; Vinyl film & sheet; Industrial inorganic chemicals; Decorative trim & specialty fabrics, including twist weave; Roofing, membrane rubber; Unsupported plastics film & sheet; Plastic film & sheet; Vinyl film & sheet
Pr: Kevin M McMullen
CFO: Paul F Desantis
CFO: Michael E Hicks
Ofcr: Michael A Quinn
Sr VP: James C Lemay
Sr VP: Douglas E Wenger
VP: Michael Curran
VP: Katie Edwards
VP: Dan Rogers
Tech Mgr: Robin Carter
Plnt Mgr: Christie Yantos
Board of Directors: David J D'antoni, Michael J Merriman, Steven W Percy, Larry B Porcellato, Allan R Rothwell, William R Seelbach, Robert A Stefanko

OMP FOODS
See OZARK MOUNTAIN POULTRY INC

OMP PRINTING & GRAPHICS
See MEDIATENNEY GROUP

OMPA
See OKLAHOMA MUNICIPAL POWER AUTHORITY

D-U-N-S 80-441-9273 IMP
■ OMRON AUTOMOTIVE ELECTRONICS INC
OMRON GLOBAL
(*Suby of* OMCA) ★
3709 Ohio Ave, Saint Charles, IL 60174-5437
Tel (630) 443-6800 *Founded/Ownrshp* 1992
Sales 415.5MM^E^ *EMP* 320
SIC 5065 3625 3714 8742 Electronic parts; Relays & industrial controls; Motor vehicle parts & accessories; Real estate consultant; Electronic parts; Relays & industrial controls; Motor vehicle parts & accessories; Real estate consultant
CEO: Yoshihito Yamada
**Ch Bd:* Fumio Tateishi
**Pr:* Yoshinobu Morishita
**Pr:* Katsuhiro Wada
**Ch:* Yoshinori Suzuki
**Treas:* Dale Morrison
VP: Jerry Bricker
**Genl Mgr:* Randy Wara
Dir IT: Fred Burmeister
Netwrk Mgr: Dave Decho
Sys Mgr: Walt Smith

D-U-N-S 14-499-8593 IMP
■ OMRON ELECTRONIC COMPONENTS LLC
(*Suby of* OMCA) ★
2895 Greenspt Pkwy 300, Hoffman Estates, IL 60169
Tel (847) 882-2033 *Founded/Ownrshp* 2004
Sales 23.9MM^E^ *EMP* 83^E^
SIC 5065 Electronic parts & equipment
COO: Thomas F Mabrey Jr
**COO:* Jeff Rogers
**Treas:* Becky Novales
Ql Cn Mgr: Joe Lattyak
Mktg Mgr: Mark Boston

D-U-N-S 11-537-2062
■ OMRON ELECTRONICS LLC
O E I
(*Suby of* OMCA) ★
2895 Greenspt Pkwy 200, Hoffman Estates, IL 60169
Tel (847) 843-7900 *Founded/Ownrshp* 2001
Sales 107.1MM^E^ *EMP* 275^E^
SIC 5065 3699 Electronic parts; Electrical equipment & supplies; Electronic parts; Electrical equipment & supplies
CEO: Nigel Blakeway
COO: Thomas F Mabrey
VP: Tony Canonaco
Dist Mgr: Matt Gialdo
Genl Mgr: Shun Nomura
Genl Mgr: Naoya Ochi
CTO: John Bullock
Web Dev: Josie Margaglione
Sftwr Eng: David Roberts
Netwrk Eng: Aaron Pyle
Sfty Mgr: Maurizio Poli

OMRON GLOBAL
See OMRON AUTOMOTIVE ELECTRONICS INC

D-U-N-S 05-431-8779 IMP
■ OMRON HEALTHCARE INC
(*Suby of* OMRON HEALTHCARE CO.,LTD.)
1925 W Field Ct Ste 100, Lake Forest, IL 60045-4863
Tel (847) 680-6200 *Founded/Ownrshp* 1974, 2006
Sales 49.9MM^E^ *EMP* 160

SIC 5047 3845 3841 3829 3823 Hospital equipment & supplies; Surgical equipment & supplies; Electromedical equipment; Surgical & medical instruments; Measuring & controlling devices; Industrial instrmnts msrmnt display/control process variable; Hospital equipment & supplies; Surgical equipment & supplies; Electromedical equipment; Surgical & medical instruments; Measuring & controlling devices; Industrial instrmnts msrmnt display/control process variable
CEO: Seiji Takeda
**COO:* Ranndy Kellogg
Sr VP: Kathie Medwed
Sr VP: Michelle Misialek
VP: Helen Reetz
Genl Mgr: David Fahrmer
Dir IT: Dan Kavanagh
Natl Sales: Aarti Uppal
VP Mktg: Randy Kellogg
Mktg Mgr: Darryl McKeever

D-U-N-S 61-470-6620 IMP
■ OMRON MANAGEMENT CENTER OF AMERICA INC
OMCA
(*Suby of* OMRON CORPORATION)
2895 Greenspoint Pkwy # 100, Hoffman Estates, IL 60169-7261
Tel (224) 520-7650 *Founded/Ownrshp* 1989
Sales 640.5MM^E *EMP* 1,885
SIC 5044 5046 5065 5047 5045 8732 Cash registers; Store machines; Electronic parts; Hospital equipment & supplies; Surgical equipment & supplies; Computer peripheral equipment; Commercial nonphysical research; Cash registers; Store machines; Electronic parts; Hospital equipment & supplies; Surgical equipment & supplies; Computer peripheral equipment; Commercial nonphysical research
CEO: Nigel Blakeway
**Ch Bd:* Fumio Tateishi
**Pr:* Soichi Yukawa
**Treas:* Thaski Kasi
**Ex VP:* Yoshinobu Morishita
**Ex VP:* Akio Sakumiya
**Ex VP:* Yoshinori Suzuki
VP: Jack Lee
**VP:* Blake Thatcher
**Prin:* Yoshihito Yamada
Prgrm Mgr: Bob Anderson

D-U-N-S 07-218-2421
■ OMRON OILFIELD AND MARINE INC
I D M CONTROLS
(*Suby of* O E I) ★
9510 N Houston Rosslyn Rd, Houston, TX 77088-3904
Tel (713) 681-6942 *Founded/Ownrshp* 1999
Sales 58.7MM^E *EMP* 180
Accts Deloitte & Touche Cpa Chicago
SIC 3625 5063 7629 Motor controls, electric; Motor controls, starters & relays: electric; Electronic equipment repair; Motor controls, electric; Motor controls, starters & relays: electric; Electronic equipment repair
Pr: Robert Bost
CFO: Rod Reyes
**VP:* David Krejci
Sfty Mgr: Dan Barcus
Plnt Mgr: Daniel King
Ql Cn Mgr: Ray Croff
Sales Asso: Sue Regenold

D-U-N-S 09-625-2861 IMP
■ OMRON SCIENTIFIC TECHNOLOGIES INC (OR)
OPTICAL SENSOR DIVISION
(*Suby of* OMCA) ★
6550 Dumbarton Cir, Fremont, CA 94555-3605
Tel (510) 608-3400 *Founded/Ownrshp* 1979, 1994
Sales 39.7MM^E *EMP* 321
SIC 3823 3827 Industrial instrmnts msrmnt display/control process variable; Optical instruments & lenses; Industrial instrmnts msrmnt display/control process variable; Optical instruments & lenses
Pr: Joseph J Lazzara
Pr: John Drinkard
CFO: Ralph Merimon
Ex VP: Fumio Tateisi
Sr VP: James A Ashford
Sr VP: James A Lazzara
VP: Thomas M Knauer
VP: James M Vella
Comm Man: Larhee Webster
Area Mgr: Al Seffair
Plng Mgr: John Parks

D-U-N-S 62-008-9367
OMS NATIONAL INSURANCE CO RISK RETENTION GROUP
OMSNIC
6133 N River Rd Ste 650, Rosemont, IL 60018-5173
Tel (847) 384-0041 *Founded/Ownrshp* 1988
Sales NA *EMP* 70^E
SIC 6331 6351 Fire, marine & casualty insurance; Liability insurance; Fire, marine & casualty insurance; Liability insurance
Pr: William C Passolt
COO: William Paolt
**VP:* Katherine Ehmann
Corp Couns: Joshua Larman

D-U-N-S 09-049-6626
OMS PARTNERS INC
FINANCIAL ADVISORS
5599 San Felipe St # 900, Houston, TX 77056-2724
Tel (713) 961-2723 *Founded/Ownrshp* 1998
Sales 27.5MM^E *EMP* 215
SIC 6722 Management investment, open-end; Management investment, open-end
Pr: Rick Alphonso
**Prin:* Kathy Perkins

OMSNIC
See OMS NATIONAL INSURANCE CO RISK RETENTION GROUP

OMTEX
See OMARA INC

D-U-N-S 96-747-2965 EXP
OMTRON USA LLC
TOWNSENDS
22855 Dupont Blvd, Georgetown, DE 19947-8801
Tel (302) 855-7131 *Founded/Ownrshp* 2011
Sales NA *EMP* 1,200^E
SIC 2015

OMU
See OWENSBORO MUNICIPAL UTILITIES ELECTRIC LIGHT & POWER SYSTEM

D-U-N-S 19-909-7098
OMV MEDICAL INC
6940 Carroll Ave, Takoma Park, MD 20912-4432
Tel (301) 270-9212 *Founded/Ownrshp* 1987
Sales 43.4MM *EMP* 22
Accts Penan & Scott Pc Rockville
SIC 8742 5047 Hospital & health services consultant; Medical equipment & supplies; Hospital & health services consultant; Medical equipment & supplies
Pr: Olga James
**Sr VP:* Philip M Geraci
VP: Andrew Marley

D-U-N-S 03-822-2063
OMX (US) INC
NASDAQ OMX
140 Broadway Fl 25, New York, NY 10005-1142
Tel (646) 428-2800 *Founded/Ownrshp* 1999
Sales 57.6MM^E *EMP* 1,500
SIC 7372 Application computer software; Application computer software
Pr: Roland Tibell
Opers Mgr: Mario Diaz

D-U-N-S 07-356-9717
OMYA CALIFORNIA INC
O M Y A
(*Suby of* OMYA INDUSTRIES INC) ★
7299 Crystal Creek Rd, Lucerne Valley, CA 92356-8646
Tel (760) 248-7306 *Founded/Ownrshp* 1977
Sales 28.6MM^E *EMP* 100
SIC 2819 8741 3281 Calcium compounds & salts, inorganic; Management services; Cut stone & stone products; Calcium compounds & salts, inorganic; Management services; Cut stone & stone products
CEO: Anthony Colak
**Pr:* James Reddy
Treas: T Urner
Netwrk Eng: Mitch Schandley

D-U-N-S 00-206-9136 IMP/EXP
OMYA INC
CALLAHAN AMS MACHINE COMPANY
(*Suby of* OMYA AG)
9987 Carver Rd Ste 300, Blue Ash, OH 45242-5563
Tel (513) 387-4600 *Founded/Ownrshp* 2010
Sales 111.8MM^E *EMP* 564
SIC 2819

D-U-N-S 08-695-3312
OMYA INDUSTRIES INC (VT)
(*Suby of* OMYA AG)
9987 Carver Rd Ste 300, Blue Ash, OH 45242-5563
Tel (513) 387-4600 *Founded/Ownrshp* 1977
Sales 184.7MM^E *EMP* 564
SIC 1422 Crushed & broken limestone; Crushed & broken limestone
Pr: Anthony Colak
**CFO:* Michael Phillips
CFO: Thomas G Turner
**VP:* John Suddarth

D-U-N-S 15-767-4896
▲ ON ASSIGNMENT INC
26745 Malibu Hills Rd, Calabasas, CA 91301-5355
Tel (818) 878-7900 *Founded/Ownrshp* 1985
Sales 1.8MMM *EMP* 2,800^E
Tkr Sym ASGN *Exch* NYS
SIC 7363 7361 Help supply services; Temporary help service; Employment agencies; Help supply services; Temporary help service; Employment agencies
Pr: Peter T Dameris
**Ch Bd:* Jeremy M Jones
Pr: Garrett Hunt
CFO: Edward L Pierce
Bd of Dir: Jonathan Holman
Ofcr: James L Brill
Sr VP: Joe Thomas
VP: Karen Keppel
Mktg Dir: Alison Richmond
Board of Directors: William E Brock, Brian J Callaghan, Jonathan S Holman, Jeremy M Jones, Marty R Kittrell, Edwin A Sheridan IV

D-U-N-S 78-856-2122
■ ON ASSIGNMENT STAFFING SERVICES LLC
(*Suby of* ON ASSIGNMENT INC) ★
4400 Cox Rd Ste 200, Glen Allen, VA 23060-3354
Tel (804) 523-8274 *Founded/Ownrshp* 2002
Sales 11.3MM^E *EMP* 346
SIC 7363 Help supply services; Help supply services
Pr: Peter T Dameris
**CFO:* Jim L Brill

D-U-N-S 02-128-3759
ON BOARD ENGINEERING CORP
50 Millstone Rd # 300110, East Windsor, NJ 08520-1416
Tel (604) 945-8000 *Founded/Ownrshp* 2001
Sales 25.4MM^E *EMP* 250^E
SIC 8711 Engineering services; Engineering services
Pr: Robert J Wilson Jr
CFO: John Duffy
Treas: John Becker
**VP:* Stanley Kaplan
**VP:* Robert R Wilson

ON THE BORDER
See OTB ACQUISITION LLC

D-U-N-S 88-464-6647 IMP
ON BORDER CORP
ON THE BORDER MEXICAN
(*Suby of* ON BORDER) ★
6820 Lyndon B Johnson Fwy, Dallas, TX 75240-6511
Tel (972) 499-3000 *Founded/Ownrshp* 2010
Sales 197.9MM^E *EMP* 6,029
SIC 5812 5813 Mexican restaurant; Bar (drinking places); Mexican restaurant; Bar (drinking places)
CEO: Stephen Clark
Mng Pt: James Snyder
**Pr:* Ward Whitworth
**CFO:* Christopher Morris
Sr VP: Kevin Carroll
Sr VP: Becky Johnson
Sr VP: William Simon
VP: G Centioli
VP: Cedric L Harre
VP: Michael Moser
VP: Mark Payne
Dir Surg: Jerry Brennan
Dir Surg: Shawn Jenkins
Dir Surg: Diane Sanford

ON THE BORDER MEXICAN
See ON BORDER CORP

ON THE BORDER PRODUCTS
See TRUCO ENTERPRISES LP

D-U-N-S 82-881-1182 IMP
ON CAMPUS MARKETING LLC
(*Suby of* ALLOY INC) ★
10411 Motor City Dr # 650, Bethesda, MD 20817-1002
Tel (301) 652-1580 *Founded/Ownrshp* 2011
Sales 22.1MM^E *EMP* 100
SIC 5961 Gift items, mail order; Gift items, mail order
CEO: Devin Schain
**COO:* Steve Metejka
CFO: Roger Jacobson
Chf Mktg O: Mark Kuhns
IT Man: David Shaw
Netwrk Mgr: John Crain

D-U-N-S 79-838-6413
ON CENTRAL REALTY INC
PRUDENTIAL
1625 W Glenoaks Blvd, Glendale, CA 91201-1826
Tel (818) 476-3000 *Founded/Ownrshp* 1998
Sales 8.7MM^E *EMP* 368^E
SIC 6531 Real estate agent, residential; Real estate agent, residential
Pr: Vazrik Bonyadi
COO: Vergineh Keshishian

D-U-N-S 13-888-9741
ON COMPUTER SERVICES LLC
UNIFIED POWER
217 Metro Dr, Terrell, TX 75160-9170
Tel (972) 524-6050 *Founded/Ownrshp* 2011
Sales 36.9MM^E *EMP* 130
SIC 1731 Electric power systems contractors; Electric power systems contractors
CEO: Cliff Rogers
CFO: Rusty Oesch
Ex VP: Robert Parrish
IT Man: Haley Potter
Sales Exec: Johnnie Holloway

ON THE GO HOSIERY
See SMITH HOSIERY INC

ON LOK LIFEWAYS
See ON LOK SENIOR HEALTH SERVICES

D-U-N-S 07-018-2910
ON LOK SENIOR HEALTH SERVICES
ON LOK LIFEWAYS
1333 Bush St, San Francisco, CA 94109-5691
Tel (415) 292-8888 *Founded/Ownrshp* 1971
Sales NA *EMP* 600
Accts Armanino Llp San Ramon Ca
SIC 6324 8082 Health maintenance organization (HMO), insurance only; Home health care services; Health maintenance organization (HMO), insurance only; Home health care services
CEO: Robert Edmondson
**COO:* Grace Li
**CFO:* Sue Wong
Ofcr: Kelvin Quan
Exec: David Ng

ON MEDIA ADVERTISING SALES
See ONMEDIA COMMUNICATIONS CO INC

D-U-N-S 18-712-9218
ON OUR OWN SERVICES INC
2310 Mcallister Rd, Houston, TX 77092-8025
Tel (713) 688-6892 *Founded/Ownrshp* 1991
Sales 8.7MM *EMP* 280
Accts John F Lewis Pc Georgetown T
SIC 8331 Job training & vocational rehabilitation services; Job training & vocational rehabilitation services
Pr: Robert Lindholm
**Pr:* Sean Quigley
**Sec:* Carol Lindholm

D-U-N-S 18-378-4409
ON Q FINANCIAL INC
4800 N Scottsdale Rd # 6000, Scottsdale, AZ 85251-7630
Tel (480) 444-7100 *Founded/Ownrshp* 2004
Sales 118.4MM^E *EMP* 350^E
SIC 6282 6162 Investment advice; Mortgage bankers & correspondents; Investment advice; Mortgage bankers & correspondents
Pr: John Bergman
CFO: Frank Adronjna
**CFO:* Michael Jones
**Sr VP:* Shirley Boynton
Sr VP: Nelson Deleon
Sr VP: Scott Frommert
VP: Kristy Benson
VP: Tim Broadhurst
VP: Cathy Zobel
Brnch Mgr: Andy Enloe
Brnch Mgr: John Macandrew
Board of Directors: Michelle

ON Q HOME
See LEGRAND HOME SYSTEMS INC

D-U-N-S 02-055-1115 IMP
ON RITE CO INC (FL)
ULTRATRESS
5130 N State Road 7, Fort Lauderdale, FL 33319-3322
Tel (954) 677-0404 *Founded/Ownrshp* 1975
Sales 31.0MM^E *EMP* 74
SIC 5199 Wigs
Pr: Andrew Wright
CIO: Rebecca Turk
Dir IT: Ramon Conley
Dir IT: Melanie Ruiz
S&M/VP: Ashlee Halbe

ON SEMICONDUCTOR
See SEMICONDUCTOR COMPONENTS INDUSTRIES LLC

ON SEMICONDUCTOR
See AMI SEMICONDUCTOR INC

ON SEMICONDUCTOR
See SEMICONDUCTOR COMPONENTS INDUSTRIES OF RHODE ISLAND INC

D-U-N-S 07-621-6865 IMP
▲ ON SEMICONDUCTOR CORP
5005 E Mcdowell Rd, Phoenix, AZ 85008-4229
Tel (602) 244-6600 *Founded/Ownrshp* 1999
Sales 3.1MMM *EMP* 24,500^E
Tkr Sym ON *Exch* NAS
SIC 3674 3825 3651 Semiconductors & related devices; Transistors; Diode & transistor testers; Amplifiers: radio, public address or musical instrument; Semiconductors & related devices; Transistors; Diode & transistor testers; Amplifiers: radio, public address or musical instrument
Pr: Keith D Jackson
**Ch Bd:* J Daniel McCranie
COO: William Nelson
COO: William A Schromm
CFO: Alfred Castleman
CFO: Donald Colvincfo
CFO: Bernard Gutmann
Ex VP: George H Cave
Ex VP: Paul E Rolls
Dir Risk M: Ana Villar
Comm Dir: Sarah Rockey
Board of Directors: Alan Campbell, Curtis J Crawford, Gilles Delfassy, Emmanuel T Hernandez, Paul A Mascarenas, Daryl A Ostrander, Teresa M Ressel

D-U-N-S 18-245-5154
ON SITE MANAGEMENT INC
417 W Mendenhall St, Bozeman, MT 59715-3448
Tel (406) 586-1500 *Founded/Ownrshp* 1987
Sales 41.4MM^E *EMP* 165
SIC 1521 1542 New construction, single-family houses; General remodeling, single-family houses; Commercial & office building, new construction; Commercial & office buildings, renovation & repair; New construction, single-family houses; General remodeling, single-family houses; Commercial & office building, new construction; Commercial & office buildings, renovation & repair
Pr: Charles Rainier
**Pr:* Peter R Belschwender
**VP:* Spencer Archer
**VP:* John Barkow
**VP:* Mark Pollard
**VP:* Steven Simpson
**VP:* Gabriel Williams
Off Mgr: Ana Miller

ON STAGE AUDIO
See OSA INTERNATIONAL INC

ON TARGET UTILITY SERVICES
See JF2 LLC

D-U-N-S 62-085-0045
ON TIME STAFFING LLC
535 Route 38 Ste 412, Cherry Hill, NJ 08002-2961
Tel (856) 663-6992 *Founded/Ownrshp* 1999
Sales 98.4MM^E *EMP* 10,000
Accts Bbd Llp
SIC 7361 Employment agencies; Employment agencies
CEO: Brian Kares
COO: Joseph Guariano
CFO: Donald Sullivan
VP: Brian Sams
Off Mgr: Dana Morgan
MIS Dir: Brian Smith
Natl Sales: Danielle Lyons
VP Mktg: Lynn Hoban

D-U-N-S 04-210-8233
ON TOP OF WORLD COMMUNITIES INC (FL)
8445 Sw 80th St, Ocala, FL 34481-9440
Tel (727) 799-3417 *Founded/Ownrshp* 1947
Sales 77.6MM^E *EMP* 150
SIC 6552 1522 Land subdividers & developers, residential; Condominium construction
Ch Bd: Sidney Colen
**CEO:* Kenneth Colen
**Treas:* C Guy D Woolbright
**VP:* Leslee R Colen
**VP:* Philip Faranda
Dir IT: Jorge Santiago

ON TRACK ADVERTISING
See SLEEPTRAIN INC

ON YOUR WAY
See WESCO INC

D-U-N-S 78-012-2144 EXP
■ ON-DEMAND PUBLISHING LLC
CREATESPACE
(*Suby of* AMAZON.COM INC) ★
7290 Investment Dr Unit B, North Charleston, SC 29418-8305
Tel (843) 760-8000 *Founded/Ownrshp* 2007
Sales 25.2MM^E *EMP* 170^E
SIC 2731 5192 5942 Book publishing; Books; Book stores; Book publishing; Books; Book stores
Prin: Andrew Rosail

Genl Mgr: David Symonds
Dir IT: Josh Kohl
Sls Mgr: James Dickinson

D-U-N-S 10-177-8004
ON-SITE E DISCOVERY INC
806 N Henry St, Alexandria, VA 22314-1619
Tel (703) 683-9710 *Founded/Ownrshp* 1993
Sales 60.0MM *EMP* 2,100
SIC 2759 Commercial printing; Commercial printing
Pr: Mark Hawn
VP: Christopher Schrumm

D-U-N-S 04-892-4026
ON-SITE FUEL SERVICE INC
1089 Old Fannin Rd Ste A, Brandon, MS 39047-9201
Tel (601) 353-4142 *Founded/Ownrshp* 1996
Sales 238.0MM *EMP* 120
Accts Elliott Davis Llc Greenville
SIC 5983 Fuel oil dealers; Fuel oil dealers
CEO: Kevin T French
**CFO:* Margaret Wong
Area Mgr: Corey Custer
VP Opers: Larry Rice
Opers Mgr: Al Kendall

ON-STAGE STANDS
See MUSIC PEOPLE INC

D-U-N-S 13-602-1289
ON-TIME AIR CONDITIONING & HEATING INC
SERVICE CHAMPIONS
7020 Commerce Dr Ste C, Pleasanton, CA 94588-8023
Tel (925) 444-4444 *Founded/Ownrshp* 2002
Sales 26.4MM^E *EMP* 115^E
SIC 1711 Warm air heating & air conditioning contractor; Warm air heating & air conditioning contractor
Pr: Keviin J Comerford
**CEO:* John Cristiano
**CFO:* Gary Potts
VP: Dan Michie
Mktg Dir: Katie Becker

D-U-N-S 84-478-2318
ON-X LIFE TECHNOLOGIES INC
1300 E Anderson Ln Ste B, Austin, TX 78752-1739
Tel (512) 832-8548 *Founded/Ownrshp* 1994
Sales 22.0MM^E *EMP* 100^E
SIC 3829 Medical diagnostic systems, nuclear; Medical diagnostic systems, nuclear
Pr: Clyde Baker
COO: Derek Southard
COO: Jonathan Stupka
CFO: Bill Cooper
**CFO:* Bill McClellan
Exec: Tim Currie
CTO: Wendy Pilgrim
Mfg Mgr: Roger Leikam
Ql Cn Mgr: Efrem Borga
Sls Mgr: Ronald Staiger

D-U-N-S 06-952-7013
ON24 INC
201 3rd St Fl 3, San Francisco, CA 94103-3165
Tel (415) 369-8328 *Founded/Ownrshp* 1998
Sales 147.6MM^E *EMP* 300^E
SIC 4813 ;
Pr: Sharat Sharan
CFO: Drew Hamer
Chf Mktg O: Joe Hyland
Chf Mktg O: Ken Robinson
VP: Mahesh Kheny
VP: Thomas Masotto
VP: Michael Nelson
VP: Ben Sullivan
Dir IT: Brian Scott
Opers Mgr: Nondas Voll
Sales Exec: Prudence Bailey
Board of Directors: Mark Hoffman

D-U-N-S 10-454-2670
ONALASKA SCHOOL DISTRICT
1821 E Main St, Onalaska, WI 54650-8757
Tel (608) 781-9708 *Founded/Ownrshp* 1900
Sales 19.8MM^E *EMP* 400
SIC 8211 Public elementary & secondary schools; Public elementary & secondary schools
IT Man: David Brown

D-U-N-S 12-117-4809 IMP
ONAMAC INDUSTRIES INC
ONAMAC MACHINE WORKS
(*Suby of* SELMET INC) ★
11504 Airport Rd Bldg G, Everett, WA 98204-3743
Tel (425) 743-6676 *Founded/Ownrshp* 2014
Sales 28.1MM^E *EMP* 135
SIC 3599 Machine shop, jobbing & repair; Machine shop, jobbing & repair
Pr: Richard Kenyon
**Pr:* Jim Loveall
Sr VP: Byron Fellstrom
**VP:* Tim Andersen
IT Man: Byron Feldstrom
Dir IT: Jon Gilije
Sfty Mgr: Dave Honsey
Opers Mgr: Randy Bradford
Opers Mgr: Ken McNew

ONAMAC MACHINE WORKS
See ONAMAC INDUSTRIES INC

D-U-N-S 11-372-9771
ONB BANK AND TRUST CO
(*Suby of* CENTRAL BANCOMPANY INC) ★
8908 S Yale Ave Ste 100, Tulsa, OK 74137-3501
Tel (918) 477-7400 *Founded/Ownrshp* 2007
Sales NA *EMP* 162
SIC 6021 National commercial banks; National commercial banks
Prin: Valarie Land
COO: Maria Roberts
VP: Brent Barnes
VP: Christy Benton
VP: Angela Fockler
VP: Beth Thomas
Dir IT: Carey Alexander

D-U-N-S 96-338-0188
ONCOBIOLOGICS INC
7 Clarke Dr, Cranbury, NJ 08512-3627
Tel (609) 619-3990 *Founded/Ownrshp* 2010
Sales 250.0MM *EMP* 85
SIC 2834 Pharmaceutical preparations
Pr: Pankaj Mohan
**CFO:* Donald J Griffith
**CFO:* Lawrence A Kenyon
**Sr VP:* Stephen J McAndrew
VP: Vincent J Benn
**VP:* John K Cini
VP Mfg: Scott Gangloff
Mktg Dir: Richard Gregory
Board of Directors: Todd C Brady, Albert D Dyrness, Kurt J Hilzinger, Robin Smithe Hoke

D-U-N-S 78-581-2371
▲ ONCOGENEX PHARMACEUTICALS INC
19820 North Creek Pkwy # 201, Bothell, WA 98011-8227
Tel (425) 686-1500 *Founded/Ownrshp* 1991
Sales 27.1MM *EMP* 41^E
Tkr Sym OGXI *Exch* NAS
SIC 2835 In vitro & in vivo diagnostic substances; In vitro & in vivo diagnostic substances
Pr: Scott Cormack
**Ch Bd:* Jack Goldstein
CFO: John Bencich
Chf Mktg O: Cindy Jacobs
VP: Thomas D'Orazio
Info Man: Jamie Downs
Board of Directors: Neil Clendeninn, Martin Mattingly, Stewart Parker, David Smith

D-U-N-S 84-921-1479
ONCOLOGY AND HEMATOLOGY ASSOCIATES OF SOUTH CAROLINA LLC
CANCER CENTERS OF CAROLINAS
(*Suby of* G H S) ★
3 Butternut Dr Ste B, Greenville, SC 29605-4653
Tel (864) 241-7272 *Founded/Ownrshp* 2012
Sales 19.6MM^E *EMP* 360
SIC 8011 Oncologist; Oncologist
Brnch Mgr: Thomas Kelley
Off Mgr: Thuy Blair

D-U-N-S 08-461-4023
ONCOLOGY NURSING SOCIETY
O N S
125 Enterprise Dr, Pittsburgh, PA 15275-1222
Tel (412) 859-6100 *Founded/Ownrshp* 1975
Sales 24.6MM *EMP* 132^E
SIC 8099 8621 Medical services organization; Professional membership organizations
Pr: Mary Guliatte
**COO:* Layla Ballon
**Treas:* Tracy Gosselin
Ex Dir: Michele McCorkle
Ex Dir: Cynthia Miller
Ex Dir: Cynthia Murphy
**CIO:* Kristine Burns
Sls Mgr: Rick Gabler
Sls Mgr: John Schmus

D-U-N-S 61-268-7459 IMP
ONCOLOGY SERVICES INTERNATIONAL INC
400 Rella Blvd Ste 123, Montebello, NY 10901-4249
Tel (845) 357-6560 *Founded/Ownrshp* 1994
Sales 23.4MM *EMP* 65
Accts Cohnreznick Llp New York Ne
SIC 5047 Beds, hospital; Beds, hospital
Pr: Richard Hall
CFO: Robert Lee
Sr VP: Les Mann
VP: Ron Drake
VP: Joseph Oconnor
VP: James Sharkey
Rgnl Mgr: Dominick Grego
Genl Mgr: Kristen Fage
VP Mktg: Martin Shapiro

D-U-N-S 61-420-5276
ONCOLOGY SPECIALTIES PC
COMPREHENSIVE CANCER INST
3601 Cci Dr Nw, Huntsville, AL 35805-2606
Tel (256) 539-3824 *Founded/Ownrshp* 1985
Sales 30.7MM^E *EMP* 294
SIC 8011 8069 Hematologist; Oncologist; Cancer hospital; Hematologist; Oncologist; Cancer hospital
CEO: Gary D Walton
**Pr:* Marshall Schreeder
**COO:* Michelle Brown
Treas: Gregory Tanner
**VP:* Jeremy Hon
Doctor: Claudia Agnew
Doctor: Lynda Hon MD
Pharmcst: Todd Murphree

ONCOLOGY SUPPLY
See ASD SPECIALTY HEALTHCARE INC

D-U-N-S 10-932-7866
ONCOLOGY-HEMATOLOGY ASSOCIATES OF CENTRAL ILLINOIS PC
ILLINOIS CANCERCARE
8940 N Wood Sage Rd, Peoria, IL 61615-7822
Tel (309) 243-3000 *Founded/Ownrshp* 1978
Sales 39.4MM^E *EMP* 305
SIC 8011 Hematologist; Oncologist; Hematologist; Oncologist
Pr: Paul Fishkin
**CFO:* Michael Voeller
CFO: Mike Voeller
**Treas:* Sachdev Thomas
IT Man: Brent Cox
IT Man: Janelle Hamilton
Nutrtnst: Sharon Windsor
Nrsg Dir: Coyla Hayes
Pharmcst: Tim Ho
Snr Mgr: Kerri Thompson

D-U-N-S 55-591-1601
ONCOLOGY/HEMATOLOGY CARE INC PSC
O C I
5053 Wooster Rd, Cincinnati, OH 45226-2326
Tel (513) 751-2145 *Founded/Ownrshp* 1984
Sales 21.3MM^E *EMP* 143
SIC 8011 Offices & clinics of medical doctors
CEO: E Randolph Broun
VP: Abram Gordon
Dir Lab: Dawn Heaton
Opers Mgr: Julie Chambers

D-U-N-S 16-957-1614
ONCOMED PHARMACEUTICALS INC
800 Chesapeake Dr, Redwood City, CA 94063-4748
Tel (650) 995-8200 *Founded/Ownrshp* 2004
Sales 39.5MM *EMP* 91
Tkr Sym OMED *Exch* NGS
SIC 2834 8071 Medical laboratories; Biological laboratory; Pharmaceutical preparations; Medical laboratories; Biological laboratory
Ch Bd: Paul J Hastings
CFO: Sunil Patel
Chf Mktg O: Jakob Dupont
Ex VP: John A Lewicki
VP: Ron Bookman
VP: Rainer Brachmann
VP: Alicia J Hager
VP: Jill Henrich
VP: Ann Kapoun
Board of Directors: Terry G Gould, Perry Karsen, Denise Pollard-Knight, Jack W Lasersohn, Laurence Lasky, Jonathan D Roor, Rick Winningham, Michael S Wyzga

D-U-N-S 06-815-7101 IMP
ONCOR ELECTRIC DELIVERY CO LLC
(*Suby of* ONCOR ELECTRIC DELIVERY HOLDINGS CO LLC) ★
1616 Woodall Rodgers Fwy, Dallas, TX 75202-1234
Tel (214) 486-2000 *Founded/Ownrshp* 2001
Sales 3.8MMM *EMP* 3,450^E
SIC 4911 Distribution, electric power; Transmission, electric power; Distribution, electric power; Transmission, electric power
CEO: Robert S Shapard
COO: James A Greer
CFO: David M Davis
Treas: John Casey
Sr VP: Deborah L Dennis
Sr VP: E Allen Nye Jr
VP: Debbie Dennis
VP: Debra Elmer
VP: Scott Gentry
VP: Stephen Guy
VP: Keith Hull
Board of Directors: James R Adams, Thomas M Dunning, Robert A Estrada, Rhys Evenden, Thomas D Ferguson, William T Hill Jr, Timothy A Mack, Richard W Wortham III, Steven J Zucchet

D-U-N-S 82-700-2622
ONCOR ELECTRIC DELIVERY HOLDINGS CO LLC
(*Suby of* ENERGY FUTURE HOLDINGS CORP) ★
1616 Woodall Rodgers Fwy, Dallas, TX 75202-1234
Tel (214) 812-4600 *Founded/Ownrshp* 2001
Sales 3.8MMM^E *EMP* 3,810^E
SIC 4911 Distribution, electric power; Transmission, electric power; Distribution, electric power; Transmission, electric power
CEO: Robert S Shapard
**COO:* James A Greer
**CFO:* David Davis
Sr VP: Allen Nye
VP: Debbi Elmer
VP: Mike Guyton
Prgrm Mgr: Kenneth Blackburn
Prgrm Mgr: Carl Brown
Prgrm Mgr: Ron Haskovec
Area Mgr: Terri Shatter
Area Mgr: Barry Young

D-U-N-S 07-830-5998
ONCOR ELECTRIC DELIVERY TRANSITION BOND CO LLC
1616 Woodall Rodgers Fwy, Dallas, TX 75202-1234
Tel (214) 486-2000 *Founded/Ownrshp* 2011
Sales 144.5MM *EMP* 8^E
SIC 4911 Electric services

D-U-N-S 78-272-8430 IMP
ONCORE MANUFACTURING LLC
ONCORE MANUFACTURING SERVICES
6600 Stevenson Blvd, Fremont, CA 94538-2471
Tel (413) 736-2121 *Founded/Ownrshp* 2010
Sales NA *EMP* 950
SIC 3672 8711 Printed circuit boards; Electrical or electronic engineering

ONCORE MANUFACTURING SERVICES
See ONCORE MANUFACTURING LLC

D-U-N-S 11-387-6986
ONCOURSE SLP INC
ONCOURSE STRATEGIES
1001 S Cpitl Of Texas Hwy, West Lake Hills, TX 78746-6450
Tel (512) 347-1244 *Founded/Ownrshp* 2001
Sales 20.5MM^E *EMP* 250
SIC 8748 Business consulting; Business consulting
Pr: J Michael Ussery
**VP:* David Preisler

ONCOURSE STRATEGIES
See ONCOURSE SLP INC

D-U-N-S 55-611-3806
ONCUE MARKETING LLC
916 N Main St, Stillwater, OK 74075-3621
Tel (405) 372-3579 *Founded/Ownrshp* 2004
Sales 29.9MM^E *EMP* 154^E
SIC 5411 Convenience stores
CEO: Tommy Shreffler
**COO:* Barden Kellum
**CFO:* Steve James
Dir IT: Rocky Lion
Mktg Dir: Melissa Meridith
Mktg Dir: Greg Webb
Art Dir: Liza Wenzel
Snr Mgr: Jim Griffith

D-U-N-S 80-525-4281
ONCURE MEDICAL CORP
(*Suby of* GENSTAR CAPITAL LLC) ★
188 Invrneco Dr W Ste 650, Englewood, CO 80112
Tel (303) 643-6500 *Founded/Ownrshp* 2006
Sales 38.9MM^E *EMP* 400
SIC 8011 Radiologist; Radiologist
CEO: Bradford C Burkett
**Pr:* Jorge T McGinn
**COO:* William L Pegler
**CFO:* Timothy A Peach
Ofcr: Randy C Sklar
Ex VP: Russell D Phillips
Sr VP: Darrell Luzzo
VP: E Larry Atkins
VP: Jen Chang
VP: Nick Hernandez
Off Mgr: Gail Smith

D-U-N-S 03-431-8063
ONDA-LAY PIPE AND RENTAL INC
(*Suby of* FERGUSON ENTERPRISES INC) ★
4407 W Industrial Ave, Midland, TX 79703-7601
Tel (432) 689-8461 *Founded/Ownrshp* 1982
Sales 41.4MM^E *EMP* 300
SIC 1623 5085

D-U-N-S 07-919-5668
ONDEMAND AGILITY SOLUTIONS INC
660 American Ave Ste 200, King of Prussia, PA 19406-4032
Tel (610) 900-0111 *Founded/Ownrshp* 2013
Sales 20.9MM^E *EMP* 600
SIC 7379 8742 Computer related consulting services; Management consulting services; Computer related consulting services; Management consulting services
CEO: Ashudeep Chadda

D-U-N-S 12-370-8880
ONDULINE NORTH AMERICA INC
4900 Ondura Dr, Fredericksburg, VA 22407-8773
Tel (540) 898-7000 *Founded/Ownrshp* 1999
Sales 69.8MM^E *EMP* 150
SIC 2952 Roofing materials; Siding materials; Roofing materials; Siding materials; Concrete & cinder building products
Pr: L Paul Nelson
**CFO:* Joseph Mehalko
**CFO:* Russ Pruitt

D-U-N-S 00-703-7182 IMP
ONE 3 TWO INC (CA)
OBEY CLOTHING
2722 Michelson Dr, Irvine, CA 92612-1603
Tel (949) 596-8400 *Founded/Ownrshp* 2000
Sales 58.2MM^E *EMP* 106
SIC 5137 Women's & children's clothing; Women's & children's clothing
CEO: Regan Don Juncal
**Pr:* Don Junkal
**CFO:* Steve Melgren
**VP:* Chris Broder
Mktg Mgr: Steve Ternosky
Mktg Mgr: Romeo Trinidad

D-U-N-S 10-852-3598
ONE AMERICAN AGENCY INC
FIRST AMERICAN BANK
2785 Highway 20, Vacherie, LA 70090-3624
Tel (225) 265-2265 *Founded/Ownrshp* 1982
Sales NA *EMP* 262
SIC 6022 State trust companies accepting deposits, commercial; State trust companies accepting deposits, commercial
Pr: Frank Bourgoif
COO: Michael Fitzgerald
VP: Abby Ellender
**VP:* Ronald J Falgoust
Brnch Mgr: Adele Cressy

D-U-N-S 08-000-1938
ONE AVIATION CORP
2503 Clark Carr Loop Se, Albuquerque, NM 87106-5611
Tel (505) 245-7555 *Founded/Ownrshp* 2014
Sales 54.0MM^E *EMP* 164^E
SIC 3721 Autogiros

D-U-N-S 94-109-3408
ONE BIO CORP
19950 W Country Ste 100, Miami, FL 33180
Tel (305) 328-8662 *Founded/Ownrshp* 2000
Sales 31.5MM^E *EMP* 358
Tkr Sym ONBI *Exch* OTC
SIC 2833 Organic medicinal chemicals: bulk, uncompounded; Drugs & herbs: grading, grinding & milling; Medicinal chemicals; Organic medicinal chemicals: bulk, uncompounded; Drugs & herbs: grading, grinding & milling; Medicinal chemicals
Pr: Marius Silvasan
**CFO:* Cris Neely
Board of Directors: James Fernandes, Frank Klees, Jan E Koe, John Perkins, Michael S Wiengarten, Min Zhao

ONE CALL CARE MANAGEMENT
See ONE CALL MEDICAL INC

D-U-N-S 10-145-6606
ONE CALL CONCEPTS INC
7223 Parkway Dr Ste 210, Hanover, MD 21076-1392
Tel (410) 712-0082 *Founded/Ownrshp* 1982
Sales 27.4MM^E *EMP* 180
SIC 7375 Data base information retrieval; Data base information retrieval
Pr: Tom Hoff
**COO:* Dave Catrambone
**CFO:* Dan Florenzo
**Treas:* Bruce Levy
Off Mgr: Jennifer Arroyo
Off Mgr: Tammy Gardner
Off Mgr: Darla Hoffpauir
Software D: Wai Ng
Sftwr Eng: Lynn Pfannenstiel
Mktg Dir: Matt Ruddo

D-U-N-S 93-785-7340
ONE CALL LOCATORS LTD
ELM LOCATING & UTILITY SERVICE
(*Suby of* ELM CONSULTING) ★
60 State St Ste 201, Peoria, IL 61602-5154
Tel (309) 673-2851 *Founded/Ownrshp* 2003
Sales 64.1MM^E *EMP* 1,125
Accts Heinold-Banwart Ltd East Peo
SIC 7389 Inspection & testing services; Inspection & testing services
Pr: Matt Quinn
**Pr:* James Bourazak
**CFO:* Marlys Gillon
**VP:* Josh Hinrichs
**VP:* Don Malerk

D-U-N-S 80-719-8064 EXP
ONE CALL MEDICAL INC
ONE CALL CARE MANAGEMENT
20 Waterview Blvd Ste 425, Parsippany, NJ 07054-1297
Tel (973) 257-1000 *Founded/Ownrshp* 2013
Sales 900.0MM *EMP* 1,956
SIC 8011 8733 6324 Offices & clinics of medical doctors; Medical research; Hospital & medical service plans; Offices & clinics of medical doctors; Medical research; Hospital & medical service plans
Pr: Joseph P Delaney
**Pr:* Gregory Moore
**Pr:* Jim Phifer
**Pr:* John Stanzi
**Pr:* Chris Toepke
Pr: Dehl Wolfers
**COO:* Dave Olson
**CFO:* Kevin P English
Bd of Dir: Laurie Mihal
**Ofcr:* Robert Zeccardi
Sr VP: Amy Stewart
VP: Susan Critelli
VP: Sunil Dadlani
VP: Audrey Fischer
VP: Lori Frampton
**VP:* Linda Lane
VP: Steven Malcolm
VP: Jill Monday
VP: Leslie Nagel
VP: Jim Sullivan
VP: Ryan Tamborini
Board of Directors: Kent Spafford

D-U-N-S 13-834-9597
ONE CAMPAIGN INC
DEBT AIDS TRADE AFRICA
1400 I St Nw Ste 600, Washington, DC 20005-6517
Tel (202) 495-2896 *Founded/Ownrshp* 2002
Sales 25.1MM *EMP* 160^E
Accts Gelman Rosenberg & Freedman B
SIC 8399 Advocacy group; Advocacy group
Pr: David Lane
COO: Luis Guardia
**COO:* Ken Webber
Bd of Dir: Bobby Shriver
Merch Mgr: Ivey Helmick
Snr PM: Stephanie Daszuta
Snr Mgr: Kate Coleman
Snr Mgr: Matthew Higginson
Snr Mgr: Ryan Koncar

ONE CLOTHING
See O & K INC

D-U-N-S 02-280-9193
ONE COMMUNICATIONS CORP
EARTHLINK BUSINESS
5 Wall St Fl 5, Burlington, MA 01803-4771
Tel (781) 362-5700 *Founded/Ownrshp* 2011
Sales NA *EMP* 1,068
SIC 4813

D-U-N-S 78-932-6196
ONE DOLLAR SHOPS INC
3615 W 76 Country Blvd, Branson, MO 65616-3555
Tel (417) 334-2294 *Founded/Ownrshp* 1990
Sales 21.2MM^E *EMP* 450
SIC 5947 Gift shop; Novelties; Gift shop; Novelties
Pr: Ralph Z Miller Jr
**VP:* Patti Miller Cline
**VP:* David Justice
**VP:* Nikki Justice
**VP:* Joyce P Miller

ONE EAPP
See CENTER TO PROMOTE HEALTHCARE ACCESS INC

D-U-N-S 82-871-0421
ONE EARTH FUTURE FOUNDATION INC
1450 Infinite Dr 1e, Louisville, CO 80027-9440
Tel (303) 466-2500 *Founded/Ownrshp* 2008
Sales 20.7MM *EMP* 6
SIC 8399 Social services; Social services
Ex Dir: Marcel Arsenault

D-U-N-S 78-323-2734
ONE EQUITY PARTNERS LLC
320 Park Ave Fl 18, New York, NY 10022-6815
Tel (212) 794-3434 *Founded/Ownrshp* 2001
Sales NA *EMP* 2,901^E
SIC 6726 8748 Face amount certificate issuing; Agricultural consultant

D-U-N-S 55-581-8124 EXP
ONE FAT FROG INC
ONE FAT FROG RESTAURANT EQP
2416 Sand Lake Rd, Orlando, FL 32809-7642
Tel (407) 936-2733 *Founded/Ownrshp* 2005
Sales 23.8MM^E *EMP* 52^E
SIC 5046 Restaurant equipment & supplies
Pr: Connie Baugher
Genl Mgr: John Kalish

ONE FAT FROG RESTAURANT EQP
See ONE FAT FROG INC

ONE FULLER WAY
See FULLER BRUSH CO INC

D-U-N-S 07-925-4828
▲ ONE GAS INC
15 E 5th St, Tulsa, OK 74103-4346
Tel (918) 947-7000 *Founded/Ownrshp* 1906
Sales 1.8MMM *EMP* 3,300^E
Accts Pricewaterhousecoopers Llp Tu
Tkr Sym OGS *Exch* NYS
SIC 1311 4924 Natural gas production; Natural gas production; Natural gas distribution
Pr: Pierce H Norton II
CFO: Curtis L Dinan
Sr VP: Caron A Lawhorn
Sr VP: Joseph L McCormick
Sr VP: Gregory A Phillips
VP: Ronald D Bridgewater
VP: Andrew Ziola
CIO: Mark Bender
Dir IT: Mike Pride
Board of Directors: Robert B Evans, John W Gibson, Michael G Hutchinson, Pattye L Moore, Eduardo A Rodriguez, Douglas H Yaeger

D-U-N-S 07-932-1606
■ ONE GAS INC RETIREMENT PLAN
(*Suby of* ONE GAS INC) ★
100 W 5th St, Tulsa, OK 74103-4279
Tel (918) 588-7000 *Founded/Ownrshp* 2014
Sales NA *EMP* 325^E
SIC 6411 Pension & retirement plan consultants

ONE GENERAL AGENCY
See OKLAHOMA GENERAL AGENCY INC

D-U-N-S 96-249-0194
▲ ONE GROUP HOSPITALITY INC
411 W 14th St Fl 3, New York, NY 10014-1082
Tel (212) 277-5301 *Founded/Ownrshp* 2013
Sales 49.3MM *EMP* 1,300^E
Tkr Sym STKS *Exch* NAS
SIC 5812 Eating places
CEO: Jonathan Segal
COO: John Inserra
CFO: Samuel Goldfinger
Sr VP: Celeste Fierro
Board of Directors: Nicholas Giannuzzi, Richard E Perlman, Michael Serruya

D-U-N-S 19-283-5853
ONE HOPE UNITED
333 S Wabash Ave, Chicago, IL 60604-4107
Tel (312) 949-5651 *Founded/Ownrshp* 2005
Sales 51.8MM *EMP* 1
Accts Rsm Mcgladrey Inc Chicago Il
SIC 8399 Social service information exchange
Pr: Martin Sinnott
Ofcr: Jayme Godoyo
Sr VP: Ruann Barack
Sr VP: Josie Disterhoft
Sr VP: Jason Friedman
Exec: Lisa Bhatnagar
Off Mgr: Aude Wilkins

D-U-N-S 03-532-1447
ONE HOPE UNITED - HUDELSON REGION
1400 E Mccord St, Centralia, IL 62801-3702
Tel (618) 532-4311 *Founded/Ownrshp* 1903
Sales 9.7MM *EMP* 800
Accts Mcgladrey Llp Chicago Il
SIC 8322 8361 Individual & family services; Children's home; Individual & family services; Children's home
Ex Dir: Patricia Griffith
**CEO:* Martin Sinnott
**Sr VP:* Nathalie Stephan

D-U-N-S 06-800-3219
ONE HOPE UNITED - NORTHERN REGION
BRIGHT BEGINNINGS CHLD CTR
215 N Milwaukee Ave, Lake Villa, IL 60046-8529
Tel (847) 245-6500 *Founded/Ownrshp* 1895
Sales 53.0MM *EMP* 437
Accts Mcgladrey Llp Chicago Illino
SIC 8361 8322 Children's home; Individual & family services; Children's home; Individual & family services
Ex Dir: Mark McHugh
**CFO:* David McConnell
**Ex VP:* Fotena Zirps

ONE INTERNATIONAL CENTER
See ULTRAMAR DIAMOND SHAMROCK INC

D-U-N-S 82-763-3756 IMP
ONE JEANSWEAR GROUP INC
(*Suby of* JONES NEWYORK) ★
575 Fashion Ave Fl 25, New York, NY 10018-1825
Tel (212) 575-2571 *Founded/Ownrshp* 2014
Sales 40.0MM^E *EMP* 285^E
SIC 2339 Jeans: women's, misses' & juniors'; Jeans: women's, misses' & juniors'
Ch Bd: Mr Jack Gross
**CEO:* Mr Stuart Bregman
**Prin:* Wesley Card

D-U-N-S 83-176-7186 IMP/EXP
ONE KINGS LANE INC
633 Folsom St Fl 2, San Francisco, CA 94107-3620
Tel (415) 489-9675 *Founded/Ownrshp* 2009
Sales 100.0MM^E *EMP* 270^E
SIC 5719 Housewares; Wicker, rattan or reed home furnishings; Window furnishings; Housewares; Wicker, rattan or reed home furnishings; Window furnishings
CEO: Dinesh Lathi
**VP:* Susan K Feldman
**VP:* Day Kornbluth
VP: Josh Liberson
VP: Ethan Trask
**CTO:* Arun Rajan
IT Man: Leepatrick McIntire
Netwrk Mgr: Justin Hill
VP Mktg: Jim Kingsbury
Genl Couns: Julie Hwang
Snr Mgr: Nisho Cherison
Board of Directors: Doug Mack

D-U-N-S 11-828-9289
■ ONE LAMBDA INC
(*Suby of* THERMO FISHER SCIENTIFIC INC) ★
21001 Kittridge St, Canoga Park, CA 91303-2801
Tel (818) 702-0042 *Founded/Ownrshp* 2012
Sales 67.2MM^E *EMP* 325^E
SIC 2833 Medicinals & botanicals; Medicinals & botanicals
CEO: Seth H Hoogasian
**Pr:* George M Ayoub
**CFO:* James Keegan
**VP:* Don Arii
VP: Don Aril

ONE LIBERTY PLAZA
See CLEARY GOTTLIEB STEEN & HAMILTON LLP

D-U-N-S 11-972-3609
▲ ONE LIBERTY PROPERTIES INC
60 Cuttermill Rd Ste 303, Great Neck, NY 11021-3104
Tel (516) 466-3100 *Founded/Ownrshp* 1982
Sales 60.4MM *EMP* 9
Tkr Sym OLP *Exch* NYS
SIC 6798 Real estate investment trusts; Real estate investment trusts
Pr: Patrick J Callan Jr
**Ch Bd:* Matthew J Gould
COO: Lawrence G Ricketts Jr
CFO: David W Kalish
Treas: Alysa Block
Treas: Karen Dunleavy
**V Ch Bd:* Fredric H Gould
Sr VP: Simeon Brinberg
**Sr VP:* Jeffrey A Gould
Sr VP: Mark H Lundy
VP: Justin Clair
VP: Richard M Figueroa
VP: Isaac Kalish

D-U-N-S 05-419-0925
ONE LIFE AMERICA INC
3800 Highway 45 N, Meridian, MS 39301-1517
Tel (601) 693-7594 *Founded/Ownrshp* 2010
Sales NA *EMP* 70^E
SIC 6311 Life insurance
Pr: Scotty Elliot
Pr: Bill Cole
**COO:* Dave White
**CFO:* Cathy Shinagawa
**Chf Mktg O:* Walt Roberts
Sr VP: Scott Glanton
IT Man: Adam Morrison
Mktg Dir: David Hosch
Sls Mgr: Jeremy Hill

D-U-N-S 01-324-8900
ONE MEDICAL GROUP INC
110 Sutter St Fl 6, San Francisco, CA 94104-4020
Tel (415) 578-3100 *Founded/Ownrshp* 2010
Sales 37.2MM^E *EMP* 253^E
SIC 8011 Physical medicine, physician/surgeon
CEO: Thomas H Lee
Pr: Andy Bartley
Pr: Steve Hastings
Pr: Kimber Lockhart
Bd of Dir: Andrew Adams
Sr VP: Andrew Wadhams
VP: Sandeep Acharya
VP: Paul Jorgensen
**VP:* Michael Sarmiento
VP: Jeni Waters
Dist Mgr: Laurel Bennett

ONE MICHIANA SQUARE
See HOLLADAY GROUP

D-U-N-S 00-605-0306
ONE MISSION SOCIETY INC
941 Fry Rd, Greenwood, IN 46142-1821
Tel (317) 881-6751 *Founded/Ownrshp* 1901
Sales 74.5MM *EMP* 190
Accts Capin Crouse Llp Greenwood I
SIC 8641 Civic social & fraternal associations; Civic social & fraternal associations
Pr: David Long
CFO: Travis Hamilton
**VP:* David Dick
Ex Dir: Warren Hardig

D-U-N-S 15-614-9002
ONE NETWORK ENTERPRISES INC
4055 Valley View Ln # 1000, Dallas, TX 75244-5074
Tel (972) 385-8630 *Founded/Ownrshp* 2004
Sales 26.9MM^E *EMP* 80
SIC 4813 7371 ; ; ; ; Computer software development
CEO: Greg Brady
**CEO:* John Keenan
COO: Michael Chang
**Ex VP:* Michael Heiburg
**Ex VP:* Ranjit Notani
**Ex VP:* Travis Parsons
VP: David Chisholm
**VP:* Glenn Jones
**VP:* Michael Martin
VP: Chris Meredith
VP: Michael Pargas
VP: Mark Sims
VP: John Thomas
VP: Willie Weng
Board of Directors: John F Phillips

D-U-N-S 79-891-6636
ONE PATH SYSTEMS OF NORTH CAROLINA LLC
CONFIANCE IP SOLUTIONS LLC
(*Suby of* ONEPATH SYSTEMS LLC) ★
7900 Triad Center Dr # 200, Greensboro, NC 27409-9073
Tel (336) 389-4500 *Founded/Ownrshp* 2012
Sales 26.0MM *EMP* 37
SIC 8711 Engineering services; Engineering services
COO: Michael Cotrone
VP: Robert Bair

D-U-N-S 04-094-9161 IMP/EXP
ONE PMPM CORP
ENVISION PLASTICS
606 Walters St Unit B, Reidsville, NC 27320-2609
Tel (336) 342-4749 *Founded/Ownrshp* 2001
Sales 38.6MM^E *EMP* 66^E
SIC 4953 Recycling, waste materials
COO: Scott Booth
VP: Tamsin Ettefagh
Off Mgr: Cindy Wilson
Plnt Mgr: Anne Carty

D-U-N-S 83-051-9463
ONE ROCK CAPITAL PARTNERS LLC
30 Rockefeller Plz # 5400, New York, NY 10112-5403
Tel (212) 605-6000 *Founded/Ownrshp* 2009
Sales 90.0MM^E *EMP* 343
SIC 6282 Investment advice
Mng Pt: Tony Lee
Mng Pt: Scott Spielvogel
VP: Joshua Goldman
VP: Deepa Patil
Mng Dir: Rudy Sanchez
Snr Mgr: Lee Tony

D-U-N-S 00-584-7897
ONE ROTARY CENTER
1560 Sherman Ave Ste Ll1, Evanston, IL 60201-4802
Tel (847) 869-5417 *Founded/Ownrshp* 2001
Sales 284.1MM *EMP* 2
SIC 8621 Professional membership organizations; Professional membership organizations
Pr: Frank Dedlyn
Trst: Kazuhiko Ozawa
Genl Mgr: Lori O Carlson

ONE SECURITIES CENTER
See QUIKRETE COMPANIES INC

D-U-N-S 16-184-1853
ONE SKY COMMUNITY SERVICES INC
755 Banfield Rd Ste 3, Portsmouth, NH 03801-5647
Tel (603) 436-6111 *Founded/Ownrshp* 1983
Sales 20.0MM *EMP* 74
Accts Seelye & Schulz Pa Cpa Nash
SIC 8322 Social worker; Social worker
Pr: David Brown
**Ex Dir:* Bob James
Off Mgr: Tina Holmes
Mktg Dir: Eliza Hobson

D-U-N-S 96-548-5642
ONE SOURCE COMMUNICATIONS INC
1655 E Arlington Blvd, Greenville, NC 27858-7844
Tel (252) 931-0222 *Founded/Ownrshp* 1989
Sales 22.4MM^E *EMP* 80
SIC 4813 4812 Telephone communication, except radio; Cellular telephone services
CEO: Michael Aman
**Sec:* Page S Aman
S&M/VP: Marc Wondracek

D-U-N-S 00-586-6764
ONE SOURCE EQUIPMENT RENTALS LLC
2835 Concord Rd, Lafayette, IN 47909-3306
Tel (765) 477-1155 *Founded/Ownrshp* 2001
Sales 28.8MM^E *EMP* 50
SIC 5082 7353 General construction machinery & equipment; Heavy construction equipment rental
Brnch Mgr: Doug Gietl

D-U-N-S 01-300-0950
ONE SOURCE FREIGHT LLC
1305 W 1st St Ste 201, Tempe, AZ 85281-3493
Tel (480) 946-6932 *Founded/Ownrshp* 1996
Sales 29.9MM^E *EMP* 36
SIC 4731 Transportation agents & brokers
Pr: John Flabetich

D-U-N-S 13-185-1255
ONE SOURCE INDUSTRIES LLC
(*Suby of* WESTMINSTER CAPITAL INC) ★
185 Technology Dr Ste 100, Irvine, CA 92618-2412
Tel (949) 784-7700 *Founded/Ownrshp* 1999
Sales 24.4MM^E *EMP* 40^E
SIC 7389 Packaging & labeling services
CFO: Anita G Ryan
VP: William Garcia
VP: Robert King
Ex Dir: Larry English
Prd Mgr: Rodney Miller
Mktg Dir: Jeff Mancini
Sls Mgr: Tony Belasco

D-U-N-S 07-879-7836
■ ONE SOURCE NETWORKS INC (TX)
(*Suby of* GTT COMMUNICATIONS INC) ★
6200 Bridge Point Pkwy, Austin, TX 78730-5093
Tel (512) 215-3500 *Founded/Ownrshp* 2012, 2015
Sales 77.5MM^E *EMP* 110^E
SIC 8742 Management consulting services
Pr: Ernest Cunningham
Pr: Jamie Pugh
COO: Brent McCutchin
CFO: Jim Tipton
Chf Mktg O: Gina Nomellini
Ex VP: Chris Griffin
Ex VP: David Searcy
CTO: Daniel S Tyler
Netwrk Eng: Austin Decaulp

D-U-N-S 01-383-0169
ONE SOURCE RECYCLING INC
7500 W Highway 71 Ste 200, Austin, TX 78735-8200
Tel (512) 468-8817 *Founded/Ownrshp* 2007
Sales 34.9MM^E *EMP* 100
SIC 5093 2611 3089 Plastics scrap; Nonferrous metals scrap; Pulp mills, mechanical & recycling processing; Garbage containers, plastic; Plastics scrap; Nonferrous metals scrap; Pulp mills, mechanical & recycling processing; Garbage containers, plastic
Pr: Kenneth Gerber
**VP:* Paul Adamson
**VP:* Andrew Gerber

D-U-N-S 82-959-6746
ONE SOURCE VIRTUAL HR INC
ONESOURCE VIRTUAL
5601 N Macarthur Blvd, Irving, TX 75038-2616
Tel (972) 916-9847 *Founded/Ownrshp* 2008
Sales 66.4MM^E *EMP* 302
SIC 8742 Human resource consulting services; Human resource consulting services
CEO: Brian Williams

*Pr: Wesley Bryan
*CFO: Melinda Lawrence
*Sec: Mark Turner
Sr VP: Bob Donahue
*Sr VP: Britt Wirt
Mktg Dir: Kevin Hautzinger
Manager: John Sullivan
Counsel: Daniel Rogers

D-U-N-S 10-110-1699 IMP
ONE STEP UP LTD
1412 Broadway Fl 3, New York, NY 10018-3372
Tel (212) 398-1110 Founded/Ownrshp 1983
Sales 31.6MM^E EMP 96
Accts Friedman Llp New York Ny
SIC 2339 2329 Women's & misses' athletic clothing & sportswear; Men's & boys' sportswear & athletic clothing
Pr: Harry Adjmi
CFO: Sandy Gewercman
*VP: Tom Wentley
*Prin: Tyrone Davis

ONE STOP
See OSI LLC

ONE STOP
See TOP APPAREL INC

D-U-N-S 80-693-3284
ONE STOP ENVIRONMENTAL LLC
4800 Division Ave, Birmingham, AL 35222-1620
Tel (205) 595-8188 Founded/Ownrshp 1999
Sales 32.3MM^E EMP 50^E
SIC 4959 Environmental cleanup services
Pr: Elizabeth Acker
VP: Ryan Ollard
Off Mgr: Olivia Robinson
Mktg Dir: Elizabeth Hinson
Mktg Mgr: Elizabeth Hinsln

D-U-N-S 55-667-8246
ONE STOP MAILING LLC
OSM WORLDWIDE
651 Supreme Dr, Bensenville, IL 60106-1157
Tel (708) 362-0471 Founded/Ownrshp 2003
Sales 52.1MM EMP 50
Accts Jesser Ravid Jason Basso An
SIC 4731 Freight forwarding; Freight forwarding
CEO: Gaston Curk
Pr: James Kelley
Ex VP: Patrick Kelley
VP: German Curk
VP: Charles Schelli

ONE STROKE INKS & SUPPLIES
See OSI ACQUISITION CORP

D-U-N-S 03-288-5886
ONE TECHNOLOGIES LP
SPENDONLIFE.COM
4447 N Centl Epwy Ste 110, Dallas, TX 75205
Tel (214) 363-6623 Founded/Ownrshp 2000
Sales 31.8MM^E EMP 130
SIC 7331 7323 Direct mail advertising services; Credit reporting services; Direct mail advertising services; Credit reporting services
CEO: Mark Henry
Pt: Alex Chang
CFO: David Logsdon
VP: Shon Dellinger
VP: Matt Watson
VP: Mary Welsh
CIO: Tony Fiacable
QA Dir: Veronica Rushing
Dir IT: John Muller
IT Man: Kris Barksdale
IT Man: Dominic Dejacomo

D-U-N-S 36-166-8853
ONE TOUCH DIRECT LLC
4902 W Sligh Ave, Tampa, FL 33634-3602
Tel (813) 549-7500 Founded/Ownrshp 2003
Sales 70.3MM^E EMP 600
SIC 7389 Telemarketing services; Telemarketing services
CEO: Ronald Benson
Ex VP: Mark R Jones
Ex VP: Mark Jones
Ex VP: Chris Reed
VP Opers: Rich Butler

ONE TOWER SQUARE 8MS
See TRAVELERS CASUALTY CO OF CONNECTICUT

ONE TOWER SQUARE 8MS
See TRAVELERS PROPERTY CASUALTY CORP

D-U-N-S 09-950-5943 IMP/EXP
ONE UP ENTERPRISES INC
7777 Lsburg Pike Ste 302s, Falls Church, VA 22043
Tel (703) 448-7333 Founded/Ownrshp 1977
Sales 437.1MM^E EMP 1,461
SIC 2731 2711 2092 6531 Books: publishing only; Newspapers: publishing only, not printed on site; Fresh or frozen packaged fish; Real estate managers; Books: publishing only; Newspapers: publishing only, not printed on site; Fresh or frozen packaged fish; Real estate managers
Pr: Michael Runyon
*Pr: Victor Walters
*Treas: Victor E Walters

D-U-N-S 15-861-9655 IMP
ONE WATER SOURCE LLC
WATER SOURCE ONE
1114 Lost Creek Blvd # 100, Austin, TX 78746-6370
Tel (512) 347-9280 Founded/Ownrshp 1998
Sales 150.0MM EMP 11
SIC 2086 Mineral water, carbonated: packaged in cans, bottles, etc.
Pr: Dave Evans
*CFO: Stephen Brazier
*VP: Sid Maxwell
*VP: Ben Mottesheard

D-U-N-S 02-929-5375 IMP
ONE WORKPLACE L FERRARI LLC
2500 De La Cruz Blvd, Santa Clara, CA 95050-2617
Tel (669) 800-2500 Founded/Ownrshp 1925
Sales 169.5MM^E EMP 550
SIC 5021 8744

ONE WORLD DIRECT
See ONE WORLD DISTRIBUTION INC

D-U-N-S 92-924-3491 IMP
ONE WORLD DISTRIBUTION INC
ONE WORLD DIRECT
10 1st Ave E, Mobridge, SD 57601-2603
Tel (605) 845-7172 Founded/Ownrshp 1993
Sales 28.6MM^E EMP 150^E
SIC 5961 4225 Catalog & mail-order houses; General warehousing & storage; Catalog & mail-order houses; General warehousing & storage
Pr: Thomas E Unterseher
Pr: Stewart Buskirk
IT Man: Danny Nickels

D-U-N-S 82-807-5528 IMP
ONE WORLD TECHNOLOGIES INC
TECHTRONIC INDUSTRIES PWR EQP
(Suby of TECHTRONIC INDUSTRIES NORTH AMERICA INC) ★
1428 Pearman Dairy Rd, Anderson, SC 29625-2000
Tel (864) 226-6511 Founded/Ownrshp 2000
Sales 203.0MM^E EMP 650^E
SIC 5251 Tools, power; Tools, power
CEO: Horst J Pudwill
COO: Stephanie Thomas
CFO: Philippe Buisson
*Treas: Bette Ann Braeutigam
Sr VP: Bob Gautsch
VP: Danny Bottoms
VP: Ken Brazell
Exec: Doug Newton
Exec: Bill Saunders
Creative D: Wade Franks
Rgnl Mgr: Daniel Lazzara

D-U-N-S 16-765-8249 IMP
ONE-DISTRIBUTION CO LLC
KR3W
(Suby of ONE DISTRIBUTION SARL)
17777 Newhope St, Fountain Valley, CA 92708-5434
Tel (714) 436-5771 Founded/Ownrshp 2005
Sales 27.7MM^E EMP 50
SIC 5136 Men's & boys' clothing
CFO: Scott Vanderripe
Mktg Dir: Maurice Torres

ONE-STOP FOOD STORES
See NEAL INC

D-U-N-S 03-389-1180
ONEAL CONSTRUCTORS LLC
(Suby of ONEAL INC) ★
10 Falcon Crest Dr # 300, Greenville, SC 29607-1583
Tel (864) 298-6510 Founded/Ownrshp 1997
Sales 191.7MM EMP 110
Accts Elliott Davis Greenville Sc
SIC 8742 Construction project management consultant; Construction project management consultant
Pr: Kevin Bean
*CFO: Judy Castleberry
*VP: Shane Bolding
*VP: Craig Crowther
*VP: Jeff Hall
Sfty Dirs: Scott Ohst

O'NEAL DISTRIBUTING COMPANY
See KEG 1 ONEAL LLC

D-U-N-S 15-466-5913 IMP
ONEAL FLAT ROLLED METALS LLC
(Suby of ONEAL INDUSTRIES INC) ★
1229 Fulton St, Brighton, CO 80601-6743
Tel (303) 654-0300 Founded/Ownrshp 1997
Sales 288.1MM^E EMP 350
SIC 5051 Metals service centers & offices; Metals service centers & offices
CEO: Jeff Simons
*Pr: Ronald Sardaro
Ofcr: Beth Hackenberg
*Sr VP: Bruce Pole
Off Mgr: Calene Ingram
IT Man: Brian Madison
IT Man: Eric Pellin
Sfty Mgr: David Suchey
Manager: Lyne Hays
Sls Mgr: Rob Enright
Sls Mgr: Tim Nakashian

D-U-N-S 08-223-3057
ONEAL INC
10 Falcon Crest Dr, Greenville, SC 29607-1583
Tel (864) 298-2000 Founded/Ownrshp 1975
Sales 217.2MM EMP 400
SIC 8711 8712 Consulting engineer; Architectural services; Consulting engineer; Architectural services
Pr: Kevin C Bean
CFO: Judy Castleberry
VP: Jim Glennon
VP: Michael Knowles
Off Mgr: Lolita Spencer
Dir IT: David Larocque
Mktg Mgr: Liza Dibden
Sls Mgr: Kathleen A Riordan
Sls Mgr: Lavisse Smith
Snr Mgr: Ron Blazina

D-U-N-S 07-940-5982
ONEAL INDUSTRIES INC
2311 Highland Ave S # 200, Birmingham, AL 35205-2972
Tel (205) 599-8000 Founded/Ownrshp 2013
Sales 2.2MMM^E EMP 3,100
SIC 5051 Metals service centers & offices; Metals service centers & offices
Pr: Holman Head
*Ch Bd: Craft O'Neal
*CFO: Stephen Armstrong
*VP: Mitchell Harrison
*VP: Jodi Parnell
VP: Ron Travis
Dir Risk M: Tom Mayo
Mktg Mgr: Henley Smith

O'NEAL, JEFF TOYOTA
See MID-KANSAS INVESTMENT INC

D-U-N-S 17-769-0281
ONEAL PRODUCE LLC
17037 Us Highway 50, Rocky Ford, CO 81067-9612
Tel (719) 254-3381 Founded/Ownrshp 2000
Sales 28.9MM^E EMP 120
SIC 5148 Vegetables, fresh

D-U-N-S 00-339-6959 IMP/EXP
ONEAL STEEL INC
O N I
(Suby of ONEAL INDUSTRIES INC) ★
744 41st St N, Birmingham, AL 35222-1124
Tel (205) 599-8000 Founded/Ownrshp 1987
Sales 1.3MMM^E EMP 1,500
SIC 5051 Metals service centers & offices; Metals service centers & offices
Pr: Steven Armstrong
V Ch: Bill Jones
*CFO: Suzanne Lane
CFO: Kirk Moore
*Sr VP: Gary Gray
*VP: Mitchell Harrison
VP: Dorothy Meadowcroft
*VP: Jodi Parnell
VP: Gary Sexton
*VP: Jeff Stephen
*Prin: Stephen Armstrong

D-U-N-S 06-523-3749
ONEAMERICA FINANCIAL PARTNERS INC
(Suby of AMERICAN UNITED MUTUAL INSURANCE HOLDING CO) ★
1 American Sq, Indianapolis, IN 46282-0020
Tel (317) 285-1877 Founded/Ownrshp 2000
Sales NA EMP 9,875
SIC 6371 6311 6321 Pension funds; Life insurance carriers; Health insurance carriers; Pension funds; Life insurance carriers; Health insurance carriers
Ch Bd: Dayton H Molendorp
Pr: Stewart Buskirk
Pr: Patrick M Foley
COO: Robert McCourt
*CFO: J Scott Davison
CFO: Jeff Holley
Bd of Dir: Hardeep Rekhi
Ex VP: Douglas Collins
Ex VP: Jeff Garrison
Ex VP: Dennis Martin
VP: Dan Bleck
VP: Doug Collins
VP: Nicolas Lance
VP: Lynette Miller
Exec: Lawrence Weiler

D-U-N-S 07-955-5382
ONEAMERICA RETIREMENT SERVICES LLC
(Suby of ONEAMERICA FINANCIAL PARTNERS INC) ★
1 American Sq, Indianapolis, IN 46282-0020
Tel (317) 285-1877 Founded/Ownrshp 2014
Sales NA EMP 3,316^E
SIC 6411 Pension & retirement plan consultants
Pr: Dayton H Molendorp

D-U-N-S 82-959-0582
■ **ONEBEACON ENTERTAINMENT LLC**
(Suby of ONEBEACON INSURANCE GROUP LTD) ★
601 Carlson Pkwy, Minnetonka, MN 55305-5203
Tel (952) 852-2431 Founded/Ownrshp 2008
Sales NA EMP 284^E
SIC 6331 Fire, marine & casualty insurance
Prin: Mike Miller

D-U-N-S 04-707-4505
ONEBEACON INSURANCE CO
(Suby of COMMERCIAL UNION/ ONEBEACON) ★
605 Hwy 169th N Ste 800, Plymouth, MN 55441
Tel (952) 852-2431 Founded/Ownrshp 2001
Sales NA EMP 1,500
SIC 6331 6282 6159 7389 Fire, marine & casualty insurance & carriers; Automobile insurance; Burglary & theft insurance; Workers' compensation insurance; Investment advisory service; Equipment & vehicle finance leasing companies; Fire, marine & casualty insurance & carriers; Automobile insurance; Burglary & theft insurance; Workers' compensation insurance; Investment advisory service; Equipment & vehicle finance leasing companies; Financial services
CEO: Frank J Coyne
*Ch Bd: Ray Barrette
*CEO: Mike Miller
*CFO: Paul McDonough
*Treas: John J Naughton
*Ex VP: Dennis Crosby
*Ex VP: Paul Romano
*Sr VP: Kevin Rehnberg
*VP: Michael E McLoone
VP: Joseph Topale
VP: Jessica Wiley

D-U-N-S 61-528-4531
ONEBEACON INSURANCE CO
(Suby of WHITE MOUNTAINS CAPITAL INC) ★
11 Norfolk St, Mansfield, MA 02048-1833
Tel (781) 332-7000 Founded/Ownrshp 2008
Sales NA EMP 5,045^E
SIC 6411 Insurance agents, brokers & service
Prin: Pat Dalton

D-U-N-S 06-935-8885
ONEBEACON INSURANCE GROUP LLC
COMMERCIAL UNION/ ONEBEACON
(Suby of WHITE MOUNTAINS INSURANCE GROUP, LTD.)
1 Beacon Ln, Canton, MA 02021-1030
Tel (617) 725-6000 Founded/Ownrshp 2001
Sales NA EMP 1,500
SIC 6331 Fire, marine & casualty insurance & carriers; Property damage insurance; Fire, marine & casualty insurance & carriers; Property damage insurance
Pr: Darlene Bailey
Pr: Sue Bauer
Pr: Craig Collins
Pr: Dennis Crosby
Pr: Steve Schaeberle
Pr: Bradley York
COO: Timothy Shaw
Sr VP: Alexander Archimedes
Sr VP: Richard Bennett
Sr VP: Clyde Jones
Sr VP: Brian Poole
Sr VP: Michael Seff
VP: Roger Bevan
VP: Linda Clarke
VP: Carmen Duarte
VP: John Ferrari
VP: Patricia Hughes
VP: James Lassen
VP: Dennis Molenaar
VP: Virginia Murray
VP: Stephen Seeber

D-U-N-S 78-875-2579
▲ **ONEBEACON INSURANCE GROUP LTD**
605 Highway 169 N Ste 800, Minneapolis, MN 55441-6533
Tel (952) 852-2431 Founded/Ownrshp 1831
Sales NA EMP 1,200^E
Tkr Sym OB Exch NYS
SIC 6331 Fire, marine & casualty insurance; Fire, marine & casualty insurance
Pr: T Michael Miller
*Ch Bd: Lowndes A Smith
Pr: Tom Chisholm
CFO: Paul H McDonough
Treas: Todd Mills
Treas: John C Treacy
Ex VP: Paul J Brehm
Ex VP: Dennis A Crosby
Sr VP: Sean Duffy
Sr VP: Marc Garganigo
Sr VP: Maureen A Phillips
VP: Clyde Jones
VP: Todd Lauer
Board of Directors: Raymond Barrette, Reid T Campbell, Morgan W Davis, David T Foy, Lois W Grady, Ira H Malis, Patrick A Thiele, Kent D Urness

D-U-N-S 83-259-5826
■ **ONEBEACON MIDWEST INSURANCE CO**
(Suby of ONEBEACON INSURANCE GROUP LTD) ★
1 Beacon Ln, Canton, MA 02021-1030
Tel (781) 332-7000 Founded/Ownrshp 2009
Sales NA EMP 284^E
SIC 6331 Fire, marine & casualty insurance
Pr: Mike Miller

D-U-N-S 01-200-2278
ONEBLOOD FOUNDATION INC
FLORIDA'S BLOOD CENTER
8669 Commodity Cir, Orlando, FL 32819-9003
Tel (407) 248-5480 Founded/Ownrshp 1980
Sales 230.7M EMP 2,700^E
Accts Mcgladrey Llp Melbourne Fl
SIC 8099 Blood bank; Blood bank
Pr: Don Doddridge
*CFO: John E Murphy Jr
*Treas: Christopher S Stiles
*VP: Pam Sawh
QA Dir: Judy Smith

D-U-N-S 07-920-8542
ONEBLOOD INC
COMMUNITY BLOOD CENTERS FLA
8669 Commodity Cir, Orlando, FL 32819-9003
Tel (407) 455-7551 Founded/Ownrshp 1992
Sales 149.0MM^E EMP 2,100
Accts Mcgladrey Llp Orlando Florid
SIC 8099 Blood bank; Blood bank
CEO: Donald D Doddridge
*Pr: German F Leparc
COO: Michael Pratt
*CFO: John E Murphy Jr
*Treas: Harold L Harkins Jr
Ex VP: Thomas Kurella
*Sr VP: Susan Forbes
*Sr VP: Andrea Levenson
*Sr VP: Judy Smith
VP: Jeanne Dariotis
*VP: JD Gaskins
*VP: Pam Sawh
VP: Ernst A Upmeyer III

ONECALL
See HUPPINS HI-FI PHOTO & VIDEO INC

ONECARE COMPANY, THE
See EVERCARE CO

D-U-N-S 78-450-7233
ONECIS INSURANCE CO
BUREAU VERITAS
(Suby of US LABORATORIES INC) ★
1601 Sawgrs Corp Pkwy, Sunrise, FL 33323-2883
Tel (954) 236-8100 Founded/Ownrshp 2005
Sales 248.0MM EMP 4,800
Accts Pricewaterhousecoopers Llp
SIC 7389 6331 Inspection & testing services; Boiler insurance; Inspection & testing services; Industrial & commercial equipment inspection service; Boiler insurance
Pr: Pedro Guimaraes
CFO: Luis Damasceno
CFO: Carlos Esnard
VP: Jon Christiano
VP: Janice Mondello
Snr Mgr: Tiit Hindreus

D-U-N-S 00-298-8223
ONECOAST LLC (GA)
230 Ted Turner Dr Nw 1837a, Atlanta, GA 30303-1070
Tel (404) 836-4894 Founded/Ownrshp 1996
Sales 18.2MM^E EMP 520
SIC 8743 8742 Sales promotion; Marketing consulting services; Sales promotion; Marketing consulting services
*CEO: John Keiser
*VP: Nora Chapman
Sls Mgr: Leslie Dickinson
Sls Mgr: Dale Fahner
Sls Mgr: Amy Garner
Sls Mgr: Tami Thomson
Sls Mgr: Beth Vogel

D-U-N-S 12-611-0076
ONECOMMAND INC
CALL COMMAND
4680 Parkway Dr Ste 202, Mason, OH 45040-8173
Tel (513) 792-9212 *Founded/Ownrshp* 2006
Sales 33.2MM^E *EMP* 71
SIC 4813 Data telephone communications
CEO: Jeff Hart
CFO: James Hendricks
**CFO:* Jay Murnen
Ex VP: Marvin Grimm
VP: Jennifer Kugies
VP: Casey McCaffrey
VP: Jennifer Smith
VP: Leonard Traficanti
QA Dir: Megan Balicki
IT Man: Ed Bielik
Sftwr Eng: Matthew Kroger

ONECORE HEALTH
See HOSPITAL FOR SPECIAL SURGERY LLC

ONEEXCHANGE
See EXTEND HEALTH INC

ONEIDA BINGO & CASINO
See ONEIDA TRIBE OF INDIANS OF WISCONSIN

D-U-N-S 10-005-6555
ONEIDA CITY SCHOOL DISTRICT INC
565 Sayles St, Oneida, NY 13421-1800
Tel (315) 363-8733 *Founded/Ownrshp* 1901
Sales 20.4MM^E *EMP* 400^E
SIC 8211 Elementary & secondary schools; Elementary & secondary schools
Pr: David Woodcock
VP: Sherri Froass
Prin: David Gillmeister
Prin: James Vitale
CIO: Brian Gallagher
IT Man: Mathew Enigk
Schl Brd P: John Elberson

ONEIDA COUNTY HIGHWAY DEPT
See COUNTY OF ONEIDA

D-U-N-S 96-841-1843
ONEIDA DEPT OF PUBLIC WORKS
W1278 Ranch Rd, Oneida, WI 54155-9409
Tel (920) 869-1059 *Founded/Ownrshp* 1992
Sales 11.2MM^E *EMP* 300
SIC 4941 Water supply; Water supply

ONEIDA FACTORY STORE
See SILVER KENWOOD CO INC

D-U-N-S 03-585-2925
ONEIDA FINANCIAL CORP
182 Main St, Oneida, NY 13421-1629
Tel (315) 363-2000 *Founded/Ownrshp* 2010
Sales NA *EMP* 372^E
Accts Crowe Horwath Llp New York N
SIC 6035 Savings institutions, federally chartered; Savings institutions, federally chartered
Ch Bd: Michael R Kallet
**Pr:* Eric E Stickels
CFO: Deresa F Durkee
**V Ch Bd:* Rodney D Kent
**V Ch Bd:* Richard B Myers
Ofcr: Joni Harrington
VP: William Baldwin
VP: Thomas Lewin
VP: Gina Rossi
VP: Charles Stevens
VP: Robert Stinson

D-U-N-S 93-269-3377
ONEIDA HEALTH CARE CENTER
321 Genesee St, Oneida, NY 13421-2699
Tel (315) 361-2342 *Founded/Ownrshp* 1996
Sales 81.4MM *EMP* 800
SIC 8062 General medical & surgical hospitals; General medical & surgical hospitals
CEO: Gene F Morreale
Chf Rad: Robert Goldberg
Dir Vol: Terri Welcher
**CFO:* Vincent Maneen
**CFO:* John Milligan
Ofcr: Christine Crump
VP: Mike Fifield
Dir Lab: Karen Puglisi
Dir Rx: Brian Dodge
Mng Ofcr: John Wight
Nurse Mgr: Cheryl Tibbitts

D-U-N-S 07-581-6801
ONEIDA HEALTH SYSTEMS INC
ONEIDA MEDICALCARE
321 Genesee St, Oneida, NY 13421-2611
Tel (315) 363-6000 *Founded/Ownrshp* 1996
Sales 89.9MM^E *EMP* 900
SIC 8062 8051 General medical & surgical hospitals; Extended care facility; General medical & surgical hospitals; Extended care facility
CEO: Gene Morreale
Chf Path: Jane Hardman
**CFO:* John Milligan
VP: Jeremy Dawes
VP: Greg Muscato
**VP:* Mary Parry
**VP:* Dewey Rowlands
Dir Rx: Laurie Cronin
Telecom Ex: Joann Clarey
Orthpdst: James White
Ansthlgy: Chowdary Chirumamilla

D-U-N-S 61-349-1166
ONEIDA HERKIMER SOLID WASTE MANAGEMENT AUTHORITY (INC)
1600 Genesee St, Utica, NY 13502-5407
Tel (315) 733-1224 *Founded/Ownrshp* 1990
Sales 24.7MM *EMP* 65
Accts Saxbst Llp Albany New York
SIC 4953 Garbage: collecting, destroying & processing; Garbage: collecting, destroying & processing
Ex Dir: Hans Arnold
Ex Dir: Pat Donovan
Mktg Dir: Bill Rabbia

D-U-N-S 15-416-1335
ONEIDA INDIAN NATION
2037 Dream Catcher Plz, Oneida, NY 13421-2710
Tel (315) 829-8900 *Founded/Ownrshp* 1601
Sales NA *EMP* 5,000
SIC 9131 Indian reservation; Indian reservation;
Pr: Ray Halbritter

D-U-N-S 78-790-3462 IMP/EXP
ONEIDA LTD
(*Suby of* MONOMOY CAPITAL PARTNERS LP) ★
163 Kenwood Ave, Oneida, NY 13421-2829
Tel (315) 361-3000 *Founded/Ownrshp* 2011
Sales 157.8MM^E *EMP* 244
Accts Bdo Seidman Llp Melville Ny
SIC 5046 5719 5023 5094 Commercial cooking & food service equipment; Kitchenware; Cutlery; Glassware; Kitchenware; Glassware; Kitchen tools & utensils; Stainless steel flatware; Silverware or plated ware; Commercial cooking & food service equipment; Kitchenware; Cutlery; Glassware; Kitchenware; Glassware; Kitchen tools & utensils; Stainless steel flatware; Silverware or plated ware
Ch Bd: James E Joseph
Pr: Timothy J Shine
**COO:* Andrew G Church
Treas: Brian Suba
**Sr VP:* Paul E Gebhardt
**Sr VP:* Bill Grannis
**Sr VP:* Catherine H Suttmeier
VP: Vincent Delcid
VP: Bob Delekta
VP: David Keenan
VP: Steve Lefkowitz
VP: James Schulze
Exec: Ben Gambitta

ONEIDA MEDICALCARE
See ONEIDA HEALTH SYSTEMS INC

D-U-N-S 00-225-1866 IMP
ONEIDA MOLDED PLASTICS LLC
104 S Warner St, Oneida, NY 13421-1510
Tel (315) 363-7990 *Founded/Ownrshp* 2006
Sales 40.3MM^E *EMP* 160
SIC 3089 Injection molding of plastics; Injection molding of plastics
Ch Bd: Barry Uber
CFO: Joe Kiah
CFO: Rod Mayette
CFO: Brian Simchik
VP: James Seipola
VP: Steve Thalmann
Plnt Mgr: Richard Harrington
Ql Cn Mgr: Jim Hillenbrand

D-U-N-S 82-822-3508
ONEIDA NATION ENTERPRISES LLC
(*Suby of* ONEIDA INDIAN NATION) ★
5218 Patrick Rd, Verona, NY 13478-3012
Tel (315) 361-7711 *Founded/Ownrshp* 2013
Sales 36.4MM^E *EMP* 99^E
SIC 7361 Employment agencies
VP: Joel Barkin
VP: Steve Murphy
Sls Mgr: Allison Morelle

D-U-N-S 00-699-3489
■ **ONEIDA SAVINGS BANK**
(*Suby of* COMMUNITY BANK SYSTEM INC) ★
182 Main St, Oneida, NY 13421-1676
Tel (315) 363-2000 *Founded/Ownrshp* 2015
Sales NA *EMP* 90^E
SIC 6036 State savings banks, not federally chartered; State savings banks, not federally chartered
Ch Bd: Michael R Kallet
**Pr:* Eric Stickles
**CFO:* Deresa F Durkee
**V Ch Bd:* Rodney D Kent
**V Ch Bd:* Richard B Myers
**Ex VP:* John J Mc Carthy
VP: Kathy Donegan
VP: Thomas Lewin
VP: Kelly Shaw
Board of Directors: Daniel L Maneen, Eric E Stickels

D-U-N-S 80-135-9832
ONEIDA TOTAL INTEGRATED ENTERPRISES LLC
OTIE
2555 Packerland Dr, Green Bay, WI 54313-5735
Tel (414) 257-4200 *Founded/Ownrshp* 2007
Sales 31.8MM^E *EMP* 200
SIC 8748 Environmental consultant; Environmental consultant

D-U-N-S 08-329-6715
ONEIDA TRIBE OF INDIANS OF WISCONSIN
ONEIDA BINGO & CASINO
N7210 Seminary Rd, Oneida, WI 54155-9501
Tel (920) 869-2214 *Founded/Ownrshp* 1934
Sales NA *EMP* 3,000
SIC 9131

D-U-N-S 01-075-7367
ONEIDA-LEWIS CHAPTER NYSARC
ARC, THE
(*Suby of* NYSARC INC) ★
245 Genesee St, Utica, NY 13501-3401
Tel (315) 735-6477 *Founded/Ownrshp* 1954
Sales 31.1MM *EMP* 700^E
Accts D Arcangelo & Co Llp Rome Ny
SIC 8322 Social services for the handicapped; Social services for the handicapped
Ex Dir: Angela Z Vanderhoof
Sfty Mgr: Sylvia Pescatore

D-U-N-S 00-427-9428
ONEIL & ASSOCIATES INC (OH)
495 Byers Rd, Miamisburg, OH 45342-3798
Tel (937) 865-0800 *Founded/Ownrshp* 1947, 1988
Sales 57.4MM^E *EMP* 300
SIC 2741 8999 7336 Technical manuals: publishing only, not printed on site; Technical manual preparation; Commercial art & illustration; Technical manuals: publishing only, not printed on site; Technical manual preparation; Commercial art & illustration
Pr: Bob Heilman
**CFO:* Deborah A Roberts
**Ch:* John Staten
**VP:* Thomas Milligan
**Prin:* Ralph E Heyman
**Prin:* Gerald D Rapp
**Prin:* Howard N Thiele Jr
Prgrm Mgr: Jeremy Story
Prgrm Mgr: Christopher Yoder
Opers Mgr: Anthony Fox

D-U-N-S 00-154-4717
ONEIL COLOR AND COMPOUNDING CORP
(*Suby of* PRIMEX PLASTICS CORP) ★
61 River Dr, Garfield, NJ 07026-3145
Tel (800) 282-7933 *Founded/Ownrshp* 1955, 1989
Sales 28.3MM^E *EMP* 150
SIC 2865 Dyes & pigments; Dyes & pigments
Pr: Mark Bruner
Opers Mgr: Robert Hillyer
Plnt Mgr: Bob Anthony

D-U-N-S 07-225-7678 IMP
ONEIL DATA SYSTEMS INC
(*Suby of* DATA ANALYSIS INC) ★
12655 Beatrice St, Los Angeles, CA 90066-7300
Tel (310) 448-6400 *Founded/Ownrshp* 1973
Sales 70.7MM^E *EMP* 152^E
SIC 2754 2732 2741 2711 Catalogs: gravure printing, not published on site; Book printing; Miscellaneous publishing; Newspapers; Catalogs: gravure printing, not published on site; Book printing; Miscellaneous publishing; Newspapers
CEO: William O Neil
Genl Mgr: James Lucanish
Dir IT: Gregg White
IT Man: Anil Kapoor
Opers Mgr: Mark Clark
Opers Mgr: Gary Garcia
Opers Mgr: Maggie Irwin
Opers Mgr: Nelida Padilla
Prd Mgr: Dave Barrera
S&M/VP: Mark Rosson
Sls Dir: Jeff Haselroth

D-U-N-S 82-870-5652 IMP
ONEIL DATA SYSTEMS LLC
(*Suby of* ONEIL DATA SYSTEMS INC) ★
12655 Beatrice St, Los Angeles, CA 90066-7300
Tel (310) 448-6400 *Founded/Ownrshp* 2008
Sales 70.7MM^E *EMP* 150
SIC 5084 Fans, industrial; Fans, industrial

D-U-N-S 01-087-1333
ONEIL INDUSTRIES INC
1245 W Washington Blvd, Chicago, IL 60607-1929
Tel (773) 244-6003 *Founded/Ownrshp* 1981
Sales 605.3MM *EMP* 400
Accts Crowe Horwath Llp Oak Brook
SIC 1542 1541 Commercial & office building, new construction; Institutional building construction; Industrial buildings, new construction; Renovation, remodeling & repairs: industrial buildings; Commercial & office building, new construction; Institutional building construction; Industrial buildings, new construction; Renovation, remodeling & repairs: industrial buildings
Ch Bd: William E O'Neil
**Pr:* Richard J Erickson
**CFO:* Robert R Dukes
Ex VP: Oleh Karawan
VP: Dean J Arnold
VP: George I Hulstrom
VP: Patrick J McGowan
VP: Paul V Roundy IV
CIO: Mike Macellaia
Sfty Dirs: Dan Ruane
Board of Directors: Tracey L Cantarutti, Michael J Faron, John T Hickey Jr, John S Hobbs, Dennis L Kessler, Mary B O'neil

D-U-N-S 15-611-3354 IMP
ONEILL BEVERAGES CO LLC
O'NEILL VINTNERS & DISTILLERS
101 Larkspur Landing Cir, Larkspur, CA 94939-1746
Tel (844) 825-6600 *Founded/Ownrshp* 2004
Sales 22.2MM^E *EMP* 56^E
SIC 0172 2084 Grapes; Wines
CEO: Jeffrey B O'Neill
Sr VP: Mike Drobnick
Sr VP: Steve Lindsay
VP: Scott Burleson
VP: Brian James
VP: Dan Staskel
Rgnl Mgr: Kerry Bergthold
Sfty Mgr: Morgan Leblanc
Opers Mgr: Matt Labbe
Prd Mgr: Ed Dutcher

D-U-N-S 00-778-2597
ONEILL PROPERTIES GROUP LP (PA)
2701 Renaissance Blvd # 4, King of Prussia, PA 19406-2781
Tel (610) 337-5560 *Founded/Ownrshp* 1996
Sales 105.8MM^E *EMP* 100
SIC 6552 Subdividers & developers
Ch: Jay Brian O'Neill
Ex VP: Richard Heany
Sr VP: Bruce Auerbach
Sr VP: James Savard
VP: Bob Follet
VP: Kevin Kyle
VP: Georgann McKenna
VP: Ahmed Rafik
VP: Dale Stesko
VP: David Waterman
VP: Jamie Watson

O'NEILL VINTNERS & DISTILLERS
See ONEILL BEVERAGES CO LLC

D-U-N-S 60-895-5290
ONEILL WETSUITS LLC
1071 41st Ave, Santa Cruz, CA 95062-4400
Tel (831) 475-7500 *Founded/Ownrshp* 1952
Sales 36.3MM^E *EMP* 200
SIC 3069 5091 Wet suits, rubber; Watersports equipment & supplies; Wet suits, rubber; Watersports equipment & supplies
**Ch Bd:* Jack O'Neill
COO: John Pope
CFO: Michelle Molfino
VP: Cherry Chu
VP Sls: Bert Aramburu

D-U-N-S 36-270-9164
ONELEGACY
221 S Figueroa St Ste 500, Los Angeles, CA 90012-2526
Tel (213) 625-0665 *Founded/Ownrshp* 1977
Sales 75.5MM *EMP* 280
Accts Moss Adams Llp Stockton Ca
SIC 8099 Organ bank; Organ bank
CEO: Thomas D Mone
**Pr:* Robert Mendez
VP: Alan Cochran
VP: Annie Kiefhaber
IT Man: Charles Chang
Sftwr Eng: Angelina Cheng
Snr Mgr: David Graft

D-U-N-S 06-467-2519
■ **ONEMAIN FINANCIAL INC**
(*Suby of* CITIFINANCIAL CREDIT CO) ★
300 Saint Paul St Fl 3, Baltimore, MD 21202-2120
Tel (410) 332-3000 *Founded/Ownrshp* 2010
Sales NA *EMP* 1,181^E
SIC 6141 Consumer finance companies; Installment sales finance, other than banks
Pr: James W Schneider
**Treas:* Lechner Gregory
Sr VP: Jim Ryan
VP: Russell Canady
**VP:* Davis Linda
VP: Tony Lutz
VP: Phil Mitchell
VP: Michael Saulsbury
Exec: John Godfrey
IT Man: Ross McGovern
IT Man: Larry Patterson

D-U-N-S 07-916-3928
■ **ONEMAIN HOLDINGS INC**
SPRINGLEAF HOLDINGS, INC.
(*Suby of* SPRINGLEAF FINANCIAL HOLDINGS LLC) ★
601 Nw 2nd St, Evansville, IN 47708-1013
Tel (812) 424-8031 *Founded/Ownrshp* 2013
Sales NA *EMP* 5,030^E
Tkr Sym OMF *Exch* NYS
SIC 6141 Personal credit institutions; Personal finance licensed loan companies, small; Personal credit institutions; Personal finance licensed loan companies, small
Pr: Jay N Levine
**Ch Bd:* Wesley R Edens
CFO: Minchung Kgil
Treas: Bryan A Binyon
Ofcr: Richard N Tambor
Ex VP: John C Anderson
Ex VP: Bradford D Borchers
Ex VP: Timothy S Ho
Ex VP: David P Hogan
Ex VP: Robert Hurzeler
Ex VP: Lawrence N Skeats
Exec: Stephen Blake
Board of Directors: Roy A Guthrie, Douglas L Jacobs, Ronald M Lott

D-U-N-S 07-169-5681
■ **ONENECK IT SOLUTIONS LLC**
(*Suby of* TELEPHONE AND DATA SYSTEMS INC) ★
5301 N Pima Rd, Scottsdale, AZ 85250-2601
Tel (855) 663-6325 *Founded/Ownrshp* 2010
Sales 7.9MM^E *EMP* 630^E
SIC 7371 Computer software systems analysis & design, custom
CEO: Phil Laforge
Sr VP: Terry Swanson
VP: Teresa Snyder
CTO: Clint Harder

D-U-N-S 80-755-8072
■ **ONEOK FIELD SERVICES CO LLC**
(*Suby of* ONEOK INC) ★
100 W 5th St Ste Ll, Tulsa, OK 74103-4298
Tel (918) 588-7000 *Founded/Ownrshp* 2006
Sales 272.4MM^E *EMP* 600
SIC 1321 Natural gas liquids; Natural gas liquids
CEO: John W Gibson
Pr: Terry K Spencer
Treas: Mark Smith
Ex VP: Robert F Martinovich
Ex VP: Pierce H Norton
Sr VP: Stephen W Lake
Sr VP: Robert S Mareburger
VP: Curtis Dinan
VP: John Sommers
Area Mgr: Bill Haliburton

D-U-N-S 10-252-6113
ONEOK HYDROCARBON LP
1910 S Broadacres Rd, Hutchinson, KS 67501-9627
Tel (620) 669-3759 *Founded/Ownrshp* 2001
Sales 28.1MM^E *EMP* 150^E
SIC 2911 Petroleum refining; Petroleum refining
Pr: Steve Tatum
Treas: Elaine Daubert
Sr VP: Mark Dobbins
VP: Troy Reusser
VP Opers: Stephen H Mims
Plnt Mgr: Bonnie Schwartz

D-U-N-S 62-123-6913
■ **ONEOK HYDROCARBON LP**
(*Suby of* ONEOK INC) ★
100 W 5th St Ste Ll, Tulsa, OK 74103-4298
Tel (918) 588-7000 *Founded/Ownrshp* 2005
Sales 68.6MM^E *EMP* 60
SIC 5172 Gases; Gases
CEO: Terry Spencer
Genl Pt: John Gibson

D-U-N-S 00-790-7827
▲ **ONEOK INC**
100 W 5th St Ste Ll, Tulsa, OK 74103-4298
Tel (918) 588-7000 *Founded/Ownrshp* 1906
Sales 12.2MMM *EMP* 1,927
Accts Pricewaterhousecoopers Llp Tu
Tkr Sym OKE *Exch* NYS

SIC 4922 4924 1311 1321 5172 Natural gas transmission; Pipelines, natural gas; Storage, natural gas; Natural gas distribution; Crude petroleum & natural gas; Crude petroleum production; Natural gas production; Natural gas liquids; Gases; Natural gas transmission; Pipelines, natural gas; Storage, natural gas; Natural gas distribution; Crude petroleum & natural gas; Crude petroleum production; Natural gas production; Natural gas liquids; Gases
Pr: Terry K Spencer
**Ch Bd:* John W Gibson
Pr: Eugene Dubay
Pr: Steve Guy
Pr: Pierce Norton
Pr: Terry Spencer
Pr: Pete Walker
CFO: Mike Mier
CFO: Derek S Reiners
Ofcr: Robert F Martinovich
Ex VP: Pierce H Norton
Sr VP: Wesley J Christensen
Sr VP: Stephen W Lake
VP: Walter Allen
VP: Michael Clark
VP: Pat McDonnie
VP: Sheppard F Miers III
Board of Directors: Pattye L Moore, James C Day, Gary D Parker, Brian L Derksen, Eduardo A Rodriguez, Julie H Edwards, William L Ford, Randall J Larson, Bert H Mackie, Steven J Malcolm, Kevin S McCarthy, Jim W Mogg

D-U-N-S 01-109-8143
■ ONEOK NORTH SYSTEMS LLC
(*Suby of* ONEOK PARTNERS LP) ★
4755 E Rte Us 6, Morris, IL 60450
Tel (815) 942-2230 *Founded/Ownrshp* 2009
Sales 27.0MM^E^ *EMP* 619^E^
SIC 4932 Gas & other services combined
Prin: Barbara Sorensen

D-U-N-S 80-897-3234
▲ ONEOK PARTNERS LP
100 W 5th St Ste Ll, Tulsa, OK 74103-4298
Tel (918) 588-7000 *Founded/Ownrshp* 1993
Sales 12.1MMM *EMP* 2,269^E^
Tkr Sym OKS *Exch* NYS
SIC 4922 1321 1381 4925 Natural gas transmission; Natural gas liquids; Drilling oil & gas wells; Gas production and/or distribution; Natural gas transmission; Natural gas liquids; Drilling oil & gas wells; Gas production and/or distribution
Pr: Terry K Spencer
Genl Pt: Oneok P GP
Mng Pt: Gil Lunsen
CFO: Derek S Reiners
Ofcr: Sheppard Miers
Ex VP: Robert F Martinovich
Sr VP: Wesley J Christensen
Sr VP: Robert S Mareburger
VP: Kevin L Burdick
VP: Michael Crisman
VP: Curtis L Dinan
VP: Michael A Fitzgibbons
VP: Michael Fitzgibbons
VP: Michael A Fitzgibbons
VP: Craig Forsander
VP: Eric Grimshaw
VP: Dan Harrison
VP: Fred Helms
VP: Stephen W Lake
VP: Mike Miers
VP: John D O'Dell

D-U-N-S 93-384-5604
■ ONEOK ROCKIES MIDSTREAM LLC
(*Suby of* ONEOK PARTNERS LP) ★
100 W 5th St Ste Ll, Tulsa, OK 74103-4298
Tel (918) 588-7000 *Founded/Ownrshp* 2001
Sales 1.4MMM^E^ *EMP* 130
SIC 1311

D-U-N-S 78-963-6784
ONEOK TEXAS FIELD SERVICES LP
100 W 5th St Ste Ll, Tulsa, OK 74103-4298
Tel (918) 588-7000 *Founded/Ownrshp* 2000
Sales 82.4MM^E^ *EMP* 500
SIC 1321 Natural gas liquids production; Natural gas liquids production
Prin: John Manning
Pt: Oneok Field Services Holdings
Dir IT: Cindy Parker

D-U-N-S 61-185-5602
■ ONEOK WESTEX TRANSMISSION INC
(*Suby of* ONEOK FIELD SERVICES CO LLC) ★
100 W 5th St Ste Ll, Tulsa, OK 74103-4298
Tel (918) 588-7000 *Founded/Ownrshp* 1989
Sales 30.4MM^E^ *EMP* 141
SIC 4922 Natural gas transmission; Natural gas transmission
Pr: Jim Knele
VP: Pete Walker
Genl Mgr: Tim King
Genl Mgr: Delaine Kurth
Pr Dir: Butch Cheatham

D-U-N-S 10-005-6563
ONEONTA CITY SCHOOL DISTRICT
31 Center St, Oneonta, NY 13820-1428
Tel (607) 433-8200 *Founded/Ownrshp* 1960
Sales 35.5MM *EMP* 475
Accts Bonadio & Co Llp Albany Ne
SIC 8211 Public combined elementary & secondary school; Public combined elementary & secondary school
Pr: Grace Larkin
Bd of Dir: Bill Grau
IT Man: Karen Czerkies
IT Man: Mark Parmerter

ONEONTA STARR RANCH GROWERS
See ONEONTA TRADING CORP

D-U-N-S 02-757-7782 IMP/EXP
ONEONTA TRADING CORP
ONEONTA STARR RANCH GROWERS
1 Oneonta Dr, Wenatchee, WA 98801-1500
Tel (509) 663-2631 *Founded/Ownrshp* 1965
Sales 341.0MM *EMP* 56
SIC 5148 Fruits, fresh; Vegetables, fresh; Fruits, fresh; Vegetables, fresh
Pr: Dalton Thomas
**VP:* Bradley Thomas
Genl Mgr: Brian Focht
CTO: Burt Koch
Prd Mgr: Sam Moss
Corp Couns: Kari Kube

D-U-N-S 62-445-4810
ONEPATH SYSTEMS LLC
2053 Franklin Way Se, Marietta, GA 30067-8712
Tel (678) 355-0555 *Founded/Ownrshp* 2006
Sales 69.9MM *EMP* 195^E^
Accts Elliott Davis Llc Greenville
SIC 7382 8744 7389 7376 7378 Security systems services; Fire alarm maintenance & monitoring; Facilities support services; Design services; Computer facilities management; Computer peripheral equipment repair & maintenance; Security systems services; Fire alarm maintenance & monitoring; Facilities support services; Design services; Computer facilities management; Computer peripheral equipment repair & maintenance
CEO: Robb Borden
Pr: Richard Collins
**CFO:* Jeff Spranger
Ex VP: Christopher Atwell
Sr VP: Chad Merrill
Sr VP: Moe Tartibi
**VP:* Fran Leach
**VP:* Chris Lewis
VP: Chad Merrell
VP: Kevin Simmons
Prgrm Mgr: Michael Arnott

D-U-N-S 86-954-1347
ONEROOF ENERGY INC
4445 Estgate Mall Ste 240, San Diego, CA 92121
Tel (858) 458-0533 *Founded/Ownrshp* 2009
Sales 28.1MM^E^ *EMP* 87^E^
SIC 3674 Photovoltaic devices, solid state
Pr: David Field
COO: Brian Alexson
CFO: Dan Halvorson
Ex VP: Dale A Vander Woude
Sr VP: Valerie Iwinski
Sr VP: Alan Whiting
VP: Kirk Mulligan
VP: Dalton Sprinkle
Prd Mgr: Ryan Feeney
VP Mktg: Nick Hofer
Counsel: Matthew Lloyd

ONESCO
See O N EQUITY SALES CO

D-U-N-S 10-556-0747
ONESOURCE BUILDING TECHNOLOGIES INC
(*Suby of* AVENTURO, INC.)
8300 Cypress Creek Pkwy # 100, Houston, TX 77070-5643
Tel (713) 895-1799 *Founded/Ownrshp* 2010
Sales 25.1MM^E^ *EMP* 100^E^
SIC 7373 1731 7378 7382 7363 7376 Computer integrated systems design; Electrical work; Computer maintenance & repair; Security systems services; Help supply services; Computer facilities management; Computer integrated systems design; Electrical work; Computer maintenance & repair; Security systems services; Help supply services; Computer facilities management
Pr: Bruce Davis
**Ex VP:* Jack Lucier
Sls Mgr: Mickey McCoy
Snr PM: Kevin Priest

D-U-N-S 02-854-7479 IMP
ONESOURCE DISTRIBUTORS LLC
SAN DIEGO WHOLESALE ELECTRIC
(*Suby of* SONEPAR MANAGEMENT US INC) ★
3951 Oceanic Dr, Oceanside, CA 92056-5846
Tel (760) 966-4500 *Founded/Ownrshp* 2011
Sales 589.4MM^E^ *EMP* 400
SIC 5063 3699 Electrical apparatus & equipment; Electrical equipment & supplies; Electrical apparatus & equipment; Electrical equipment & supplies
Pr: Mike Smith
**CFO:* Tim Walsh
VP: Mike Blanchard
Brnch Mgr: Mark Bartholomew
Genl Mgr: Caprice Rich
Opers Mgr: Debbie Marshall
Opers Mgr: Peggy Reynolds
Sls Mgr: Duke Carrao
Sales Asso: Paul Bowen
Sales Asso: Christian Crosthwaite
Sales Asso: Cesar Cruz

D-U-N-S 07-994-2879
ONESOURCE T&D LLC
2575 Kelley Pointe Pkwy, Edmond, OK 73013-2906
Tel (405) 513-5300 *Founded/Ownrshp* 2015
Sales 40.0MM *EMP* 75
SIC 1623 Electric power line construction
CFO: Christopher Lee
COO: Keith Ellison

ONESOURCE VIRTUAL
See ONE SOURCE VIRTUAL HR INC

D-U-N-S 03-995-4119
ONESOURCE WATER LLC
8 Two Mile Rd Ste 102, Farmington, CT 06032-2513
Tel (866) 917-7873 *Founded/Ownrshp* 2010
Sales 20.2MM^E^ *EMP* 84^E^
SIC 5999 Water purification equipment
Pr: A J Wasserstein
**Pr:* Eric Giesecke
**COO:* John Pavlovich
**COO:* David Putt

D-U-N-S 80-822-8899 EXP
ONESTEEL RECYCLING INC
(*Suby of* ARRIUM LIMITED)
2649 S Military Hwy, Chesapeake, VA 23324-1043
Tel (757) 545-1500 *Founded/Ownrshp* 2006
Sales 23.4MM^E^ *EMP* 150
SIC 4953 Recycling, waste materials; Recycling, waste materials
Pr: Thomas Quirke
**Pr:* Peter Byrnes
**Treas:* Morris Tsai
**Treas:* Gamin Zacharias

D-U-N-S 15-639-5746
ONESTOP INTERNET INC
3040 E Ana St, E Rncho Dmngz, CA 90221-5605
Tel (310) 894-7700 *Founded/Ownrshp* 2004
Sales 31.0MM^E^ *EMP* 100
SIC 5651 5961

D-U-N-S 06-820-8129 IMP
■ ONESUBSEA LLC
(*Suby of* CAMERON INTERNATIONAL CORP) ★
4646 W Sam Houston Pkwy N, Houston, TX 77041-8214
Tel (713) 939-2211 *Founded/Ownrshp* 2013
Sales 228.8MM^E^ *EMP* 6,500
SIC 3533 3563 3491 Oil & gas field machinery; Oil field machinery & equipment; Gas field machinery & equipment; Air & gas compressors; Automatic regulating & control valves; Oil & gas field machinery; Oil field machinery & equipment; Gas field machinery & equipment; Air & gas compressors; Automatic regulating & control valves
Pr: Henning Berg
Ofcr: Meredith Canada
VP: Justin Rounce
VP: Jon Arve Svaeren
VP Sls: Hal Goldie

D-U-N-S 08-959-5656
ONETA CO
PEPSI-COLA
1401 S Padre Island Dr, Corpus Christi, TX 78416-1322
Tel (361) 853-0123 *Founded/Ownrshp* 1977
Sales 34.3MM^E^ *EMP* 160
SIC 2086 Bottled & canned soft drinks; Soft drinks: packaged in cans, bottles, etc.; Bottled & canned soft drinks; Soft drinks: packaged in cans, bottles, etc.
CEO: Karl Koch
**Pr:* Kimberly Koch
**VP:* Stephanie Koch
Genl Mgr: Terry Brandon
Genl Mgr: Darin Duecker
Telecom Ex: Vicky Ramos
IT Man: Jamie Flores
Opers Mgr: Brent Windham
Prd Mgr: Robert Perez
Ql Cn Mgr: Bernadeth Bernie
Sales Exec: Jeff Richards
Board of Directors: Judy Koch

D-U-N-S 82-689-8178
ONETOUCHPOINT CORP
TOUCHPOINT PRINT SOLUTIONS
1200 Harger Rd Ste 419, Oak Brook, IL 60523-1818
Tel (630) 586-9002 *Founded/Ownrshp* 2014
Sales 245.8MM^E^ *EMP* 487^E^
SIC 2759 Commercial printing; Commercial printing
CEO: Tom Simunek
**CFO:* Kevin Kotche
VP: Michael Elliott
Dir Bus: Tim Enright
Opers Mgr: Dale Javorek

D-U-N-S 06-203-9078 IMP
ONETOUCHPOINT MIDWEST CORP
CCI/COAKLEYTECH
(*Suby of* ONETOUCHPOINT CORP) ★
1225 Walnut Ridge Dr, Hartland, WI 53029-8300
Tel (262) 369-6000 *Founded/Ownrshp* 2007
Sales 100.3MM^E^ *EMP* 280
SIC 2752 Offset & photolithographic printing; Offset & photolithographic printing
Pr: Chris Illman
COO: Norm Keene
Dir Bus: Brad Bush
Genl Mgr: James Parker
CIO: Phil Bartleme
Opers Mgr: Rob Tynan
Plnt Mgr: Carey Howard
S&M/VP: Joni Diderrich
Mktg Mgr: Lisa Emmerich-Miller
Sls Mgr: Chandra Bauch

D-U-N-S 01-410-9231
ONETOUCHPOINT WEST CORP
(*Suby of* ONETOUCHPOINT CORP) ★
525 W Alameda Dr Ste 101, Tempe, AZ 85282-2013
Tel (480) 966-4003 *Founded/Ownrshp* 2007
Sales 58.2MM^E^ *EMP* 400
SIC 2759 Commercial printing; Commercial printing
Pr: Chris Illman

D-U-N-S 05-537-4193
ONEUNITED BANK
100 Franklin St Ste 600, Boston, MA 02110-1537
Tel (617) 457-4400 *Founded/Ownrshp* 1982
Sales NA *EMP* 130
SIC 6022 State commercial banks; State commercial banks
Ch Bd: Kevin Cohee
Pr: Martin Hudnall
**Treas:* Michael P Burley
Sr Cor Off: Michael Burley
VP: Angela Austin

D-U-N-S 83-000-0068
ONEWEST BANK GROUP LLC
888 E Walnut St, Pasadena, CA 91101-1895
Tel (626) 535-4870 *Founded/Ownrshp* 2009
Sales NA *EMP* 850^E^
SIC 6035 Federal savings banks

D-U-N-S 09-392-0648 IMP
ONEWORLD APPAREL LLC
1515 E 15th St, Los Angeles, CA 90021-2711
Tel (213) 222-1010 *Founded/Ownrshp* 2006
Sales 120.0MM *EMP* 156
Accts Moss Adams Llp Los Angeles C
SIC 2335 Women's, juniors' & misses' dresses
**Prin:* Robert Burns

D-U-N-S 16-855-9284
ONEWORLD COMMUNITY HEALTH CENTERS INC
4920 S 30th St, Omaha, NE 68107-1590
Tel (402) 734-4110 *Founded/Ownrshp* 1970
Sales 26.0MM *EMP* 300^E^
Accts Seim Johnson Llp Omaha Ne
SIC 8011 Offices & clinics of medical doctors; Offices & clinics of medical doctors
CEO: Andrea Skolkin
COO: Joel Dougherty
Dir Rx: Coleen Schrage
IT Man: Steve Elgan
Doctor: Hans Dethlefs

D-U-N-S 60-607-9168
ONEX INVESTMENT CORP
(*Suby of* ONEX CORPORATION)
712 5th Ave Fl 40, New York, NY 10019-4108
Tel (212) 582-2211 *Founded/Ownrshp* 1987
Sales 3.5MMM^E^ *EMP* 20,000
SIC 6799 Venture capital companies; Venture capital companies; Investment advisory service

D-U-N-S 05-094-4167
ONFORCE SOLAR INC
728 E 136th St Ste 1, Bronx, NY 10454-3431
Tel (800) 786-4028 *Founded/Ownrshp* 2008
Sales 30.0MM^E^ *EMP* 100
SIC 1711 Solar energy contractor; Solar energy contractor
Pr: Charles Feit

D-U-N-S 08-517-1973
ONGWEOWEH CORP
767 Warren Rd, Ithaca, NY 14850-1255
Tel (607) 266-7070 *Founded/Ownrshp* 1980
Sales 150.0MM *EMP* 70
SIC 8741 4953 Management services; Recycling, waste materials; Management services; Recycling, waste materials
Pr: Daniel F Bonamie
**Ch Bd:* Frank C Bonamie
Treas: Kristi Pierce
**VP:* Justin M Bennett
Dir IT: Jim Davies
Sls Dir: Chris Merta

D-U-N-S 17-775-7317 IMP/EXP
ONICON INC
(*Suby of* HARBOUR GROUP LTD) ★
11451 Belcher Rd S, Largo, FL 33773-5110
Tel (727) 447-6140 *Founded/Ownrshp* 2013
Sales 20.4MM^E^ *EMP* 42
SIC 3823 Boiler controls: industrial, power & marine type
Pr: Marvin J Feldman
**Ex VP:* Bowen Ierna
**VP:* Linda Feldman
VP: Rob Neumann
Genl Mgr: Mary Harrison
MIS Mgr: Dan Zsiga
VP Sls: Bowen Lerna
Mktg Dir: Adrienne Cone
Mktg Mgr: Heather Williamson
Sls Mgr: Jim Sharp

D-U-N-S 82-845-9664
ONIN STAFFING LLC
1 Perimeter Park S 450n, Birmingham, AL 35243-3201
Tel (205) 298-7233 *Founded/Ownrshp* 1996
Sales 162.6MM^E^ *EMP* 6,500^E^
SIC 7361 Labor contractors (employment agency); Labor contractors (employment agency)

D-U-N-S 07-275-4930 IMP
ONKYO USA CORP
INTEGRA
(*Suby of* GIBSON BRANDS INC) ★
18 Park Way, Upper Saddle River, NJ 07458-2353
Tel (201) 785-2600 *Founded/Ownrshp* 2012
Sales 45.2MM^E^ *EMP* 40
SIC 5064 5731 High fidelity equipment; Radio, television & electronic stores; High fidelity equipment; Radio, television & electronic stores
Pr: Hiroshi Izutani
CFO: Mila Katsman
**Treas:* Gaku Miki
Treas: Takashi Yoshimatsu
Bd of Dir: Henry Juszkiewicz
Dir IT: Kent Takao
Natl Sales: Joe Petrillo
S&M/VP: John Arce
Sls Dir: Keith Haas

D-U-N-S 93-849-7302
ONLIFE HEALTH INC
(*Suby of* BLUECARE) ★
9020 Overlook Blvd # 300, Brentwood, TN 37027-3259
Tel (615) 844-2100 *Founded/Ownrshp* 1995
Sales NA *EMP* 200^E^
SIC 6324 Hospital & medical service plans; Hospital & medical service plans
Pr: Jed Dodd
Pr: Mary Coble
**Pr:* Christopher Hunter
COO: Diane Seloff
Rgnl VP: Seth R Hart
Sr VP: Philip H Hadden
Sr VP: Jean Harris
Sr VP: Jennifer Schmitz
Sr VP: William Seibels
VP: Lori Close
VP: Steven Davidson
VP: Drew Hart
VP: Hayley Hines
VP: Lori Huss
VP: Adam Long
VP: Victor Mattingly
VP: Joann Russell
VP: Chuck Steinmetz

ONLINE BUSINESS SYSTEMS
See ONLINE ENTERPRISES INC

D-U-N-S 08-653-5676
ONLINE ENTERPRISES INC
ONLINE BUSINESS SYSTEMS
(*Suby of* ONLINE ENTERPRISES INC)
7760 France Ave S Fl 11, Minneapolis, MN 55435-5930
Tel (952) 886-7318 *Founded/Ownrshp* 1995
Sales 17.6MM^E *EMP* 302^E
Accts Ernst & Young Llp Winnipeg
SIC 7371 Computer software development; Computer software development
CEO: Charles Loewen
**CFO:* Lynn Black
**Ex VP:* Scott Sanders
VP: John Frejuk
VP: Joe Leuwer
VP: Greg Loewen
Dir IT: Dave Neufeld
Snr Mgr: Dana Neal

ONLINE IMAGING SOLUTIONS
See AMERICAN COPY EQUIPMENT INC

D-U-N-S 03-994-8034 EXP
ONLINE LABELS INC
2021 E Lake Mary Blvd, Sanford, FL 32773-7140
Tel (407) 936-3900 *Founded/Ownrshp* 1999
Sales 24.0MM *EMP* 50
SIC 2679 Labels, paper: made from purchased material
Pr: Dave Carmany
**VP:* Joel Carmany
Mktg Mgr: Jake Allen

D-U-N-S 62-639-9604
ONLINE RESOURCES CORP
4795 Meadow Wood Ln # 300, Chantilly, VA 20151-4209
Tel (703) 653-3100 *Founded/Ownrshp* 2013
Sales NA *EMP* 550
SIC 6099 7374 Electronic funds transfer network, including switching; Data processing & preparation

D-U-N-S 12-423-0637 IMP/EXP
ONLINE STORES INC
UNITED STATES FLAG STORE
1000 Westinghouse Dr # 1, New Stanton, PA 15672-9600
Tel (724) 925-5600 *Founded/Ownrshp* 2002
Sales 31.6MM *EMP* 100
Accts Deluzio & Companyllp Greensb
SIC 5999 5499 Flags; Safety supplies & equipment; Tea; Flags; Safety supplies & equipment; Tea
CEO: Kevin Hickey
**Ch Bd:* Lisa Hickey
Dir Bus: Cem Guvener
Admn Mgr: Eileen Ambler
Board of Directors: Heidi Lasek

D-U-N-S 17-762-0122
ONLINE TRANSPORT INC
6311 W Stoner Dr, Greenfield, IN 46140-7413
Tel (317) 894-6860 *Founded/Ownrshp* 1999
Sales 101.4MM^E *EMP* 480^E
SIC 4213 Heavy hauling; Heavy hauling
Pr: Dan Cook
**CFO:* James Henry
Sales Exec: Josh Paul

ONLINESHOES.COM
See GERLER AND SON INC

D-U-N-S 60-245-3532 IMP
ONLY BEST INC
CRAZY SHIRTS
99-969 Iwaena St, Aiea, HI 96701-3249
Tel (808) 487-9919 *Founded/Ownrshp* 1988
Sales 31.3MM^E *EMP* 300
SIC 5621 5611 5641 Women's clothing stores; Men's & boys' clothing stores; Children's wear; Women's clothing stores; Men's & boys' clothing stores; Children's wear
Pr: Mark R Hollander
**Ch Bd:* Ronald C Robertson
**CFO:* Andrew Kawaga
**VP:* Scott Maroney
**VP:* Scott Naranei
**VP:* Dion Yasui
**Prin:* James R Geiger
Genl Mgr: Sergio Sakamoto
IT Man: Sam Choi
Web Dev: James Reponte
VP Mktg: Patrick Stewart

ONLY THE BEST, TRUCK BROKER
See ZAUNER BROKERAGE INVESTMENTS LLC

ONLY NINE
See C-QUEST INC

D-U-N-S 83-497-8475
ONMEDIA COMMUNICATIONS CO INC
ON MEDIA ADVERTISING SALES
115 N Industrial Park Rd, Excelsior Springs, MO 64024-1734
Tel (913) 491-4030 *Founded/Ownrshp* 2008
Sales 95.8MM^E *EMP* 500^E
SIC 4841 Cable & other pay television services; Cable & other pay television services
Pr: Rocco Commisso
**VP:* Kay Evans
**VP:* Bob Montgomery
**Genl Mgr:* Michele Cropp
**Genl Mgr:* John Pauley
Manager: Ron Snyder

D-U-N-S 84-470-4978
ONO HAWAIIAN BBQ INC
21700 Copley Dr Ste 320, Diamond Bar, CA 91765-5499
Tel (909) 594-3388 *Founded/Ownrshp* 2002
Sales 24.5MM^E *EMP* 1^E
SIC 5812 Barbecue restaurant
Pr: Joshua Liang

D-U-N-S 15-074-7590
ONO TRANSPORT SERVICES INC
J P DON MOYER
Rr 22, Ono, PA 17077
Tel (717) 865-2148 *Founded/Ownrshp* 1985
Sales 28.3MM^E *EMP* 250^E
SIC 4213 5411 4212 Trucking, except local; Convenience stores, independent; Local trucking, without storage; Trucking, except local; Convenience stores, independent; Local trucking, without storage
Ch Bd: Ruth Deitz
**Pr:* Frank Costanzo

D-U-N-S 18-631-5784
ONONDAGA BEVERAGE CORP
(*Suby of* OWASCO BEVERAGE INC) ★
7655 Edgecomb Dr, Liverpool, NY 13088-3526
Tel (315) 451-8360 *Founded/Ownrshp* 1987
Sales 32.6MM^E *EMP* 120
SIC 5149 5181 5182 Juices; Soft drinks; Beer & other fermented malt liquors; Wine & distilled beverages; Juices; Soft drinks; Beer & other fermented malt liquors; Wine & distilled beverages
Pr: Thomas Potter
**Treas:* Tony Van Slyke
**VP:* Robert Merriam
Genl Mgr: Dan Gregory

D-U-N-S 10-005-6571
ONONDAGA CENTRAL SCHOOL DISTRICT
O C S
4466 S Onondaga Rd, Nedrow, NY 13120-9780
Tel (315) 492-1701 *Founded/Ownrshp* 1900
Sales 20.2MM^E *EMP* 352
SIC 8211 Public elementary & secondary schools; Public elementary & secondary schools
DP Exec: Robert Sauro
IT Man: Bob Sauro
IT Man: Anthony Sonnacchio
IT Man: Tony Sonnacchio
IT Man: Mary Voyce-Kras
Schl Brd P: Beth Walbridge
Psych: Karen Gwilt

D-U-N-S 05-372-3334
ONONDAGA COMMUNITY COLLEGE
(*Suby of* STATE UNIVERSITY OF NEW YORK) ★
4585 W Seneca Tpke, Syracuse, NY 13215-4585
Tel (315) 498-2622 *Founded/Ownrshp* 1962
Sales 1.7MM *EMP* 1,021
Accts Ciaschi Dietershagen Little
SIC 8222 9411 Community college; Administration of educational programs; ; Community college; Administration of educational programs;
CEO: Debbie L Sydow
Ofcr: Nicole Schlater
Assoc VP: Wendy Tarby
Assoc VP: Seth Tucker
**VP:* Ralph Feola
VP: John Paddock
VP: Anastasia Urtz
VP: Steve Wiley
Store Mgr: Michele Collins
Dir IT: Karen Bender
Sftwr Eng: Heather Meyers

D-U-N-S 95-912-3241
ONONDAGA COUNTY CHAPTER NYSARC
A R C OF ONONDAGA
(*Suby of* NYSARC INC) ★
600 S Wilbur Ave, Syracuse, NY 13204-2730
Tel (315) 476-7441 *Founded/Ownrshp* 1996
Sales 27.0MM *EMP* 460
Accts Bonadio & Co Llp Pittsford N
SIC 8322 8742 Social services for the handicapped; Human resource consulting services; Social services for the handicapped; Human resource consulting services
Ex Dir: Stanford Perry
**CFO:* Carrie Fuller
Bd of Dir: Juli Boeheim
Bd of Dir: Daniel J French
Bd of Dir: Mark Hettler
Prgrm Mgr: Don Sweet
IT Man: Susan Lord-Keene
Mktg Mgr: Frank Rhodes

D-U-N-S 07-086-0432
ONONDAGA COUNTY WATER AUTHORITY (INC)
OCWA
200 Northern Concourse, Syracuse, NY 13212-4048
Tel (315) 455-7061 *Founded/Ownrshp* 1955
Sales 69.2MM^E *EMP* 111
Accts Dermody Burke & Brown Cpas
SIC 4941 Water supply; Water supply
Ex Dir: Michael E Hooker
Bd of Dir: Holly Rosenthal
Exec: Gauthier Linda
Dir Risk M: Kelly Caramanna
Ex Dir: Anthony Geiss
MIS Dir: Linda Gauthier
IT Man: Barry Blanchard

ONONDAGA CRTLAND MADISON BOCES
See ONONDAGA-CORTLAND-MADISON BOCES

D-U-N-S 01-077-0964
ONONDAGA-CORTLAND-MADISON BOCES
ONONDAGA CRTLAND MADISON BOCES
6820 Thompson Rd, Syracuse, NY 13211-1321
Tel (315) 433-8300 *Founded/Ownrshp* 1968
Sales 110.1MM^E *EMP* 1,457
SIC 8211 Public elementary & secondary schools; Public elementary & secondary schools
Bd of Dir: Joan Reeves
CIO: Mike Fay
MIS Dir: Michael Fay
Teacher Pr: Mark Pettit

D-U-N-S 08-745-8311
ONPOINT COMMUNITY CREDIT UNION (OR)
2701 Nw Vaughn St Ste 800, Portland, OR 97210-5387
Tel (503) 228-8255 *Founded/Ownrshp* 1932
Sales NA *EMP* 426
SIC 6062 State credit unions, not federally chartered; State credit unions, not federally chartered
CEO: Robert A Stuart
**Pr:* Steve Gray
Ofcr: Karen Carter
Ofcr: Arun Singh
Ofcr: Constance Wilhelm
**Sr VP:* Jim Armstrong
**Sr VP:* Jim Hunt
**Sr VP:* Tory McVay
**Sr VP:* Kelly Schrader
VP: Michele Debuhr
**VP:* Wayne Pederson

D-U-N-S 80-231-4120
ONPOINT CONSULTING INC
(*Suby of* SAPIENT GOVERNMENT SERVICES INC) ★
2107 Wilson Blvd Ste 510, Arlington, VA 22201-3042
Tel (703) 841-5500 *Founded/Ownrshp* 2014
Sales 32.4MM^E *EMP* 150
SIC 7379 8711 7371 Computer related maintenance services; Electrical or electronic engineering; Computer software development & applications; Computer related maintenance services; Electrical or electronic engineering; Computer software development & applications
Pr: Richard Lepsinger
**Pr:* Timothy Smith
Ofcr: Samara Kaplan
VP: David Hefter
VP: Tim Smith
Prgrm Mgr: David Leary
IT Man: Becki Provided
Genl Couns: Michele Rath

D-U-N-S 01-409-1420
ONPROCESS TECHNOLOGY INC
200 Homer Ave, Ashland, MA 01721-1717
Tel (508) 520-2711 *Founded/Ownrshp* 1998
Sales 89.9MM^E *EMP* 450^E
SIC 7379 Computer related consulting services; Computer related consulting services
CEO: Michael Wooden
CFO: William Gerraughty
**Ex VP:* Bill Kenney
**Ex VP:* Robert Kenney
Ex VP: Michael Stann
**Sr VP:* Subhratanu Paul
**Sr VP:* Pam Roddy
Sr VP: John Sedej
VP: Jim Flinton
VP: Candyce Plante
Dir Bus: Adam Barry

D-U-N-S 06-228-7253
ONRAMP TRANSPORTATION SERVICES LLC
5416 W Amelia Earhart Dr # 201, Salt Lake City, UT 84116-3723
Tel (801) 736-9420 *Founded/Ownrshp* 2011
Sales 100.0MM *EMP* 130
SIC 4789 Freight car loading & unloading; Freight car loading & unloading
Pr: Spencer Angerbauer
**Sr VP:* Randy Olsen

D-U-N-S 01-447-1254 EXP
ONSET COMPUTER CORP
HOBO
470 Macarthur Blvd, Bourne, MA 02532-3838
Tel (508) 759-9500 *Founded/Ownrshp* 1980
Sales 34.4MM^E *EMP* 120
SIC 3823 3571 3674 3577 Industrial instrmnts msrmnt display/control process variable; Electronic computers; Semiconductors & related devices; Computer peripheral equipment; Industrial instrmnts msrmnt display/control process variable; Electronic computers; Semiconductors & related devices; Computer peripheral equipment
Pr: Justin Testa
CTO: Lon Hcker
**CFO:* Michael Tobin
**Sec:* Ellen G Hocker
**VP:* Lon O Hocker
CTO: Mark Hruska
Dir IT: Rui Rosario
Software D: Eric Wallace
Sftwr Eng: Elena Rice
Sftwr Eng: Erich Roth
Pr Mgr: Evan Lubofsky

D-U-N-S 82-924-0998
ONSET FINANCIAL INC
10813 S River Front Pkwy, South Jordan, UT 84095-5610
Tel (801) 878-0600 *Founded/Ownrshp* 2008
Sales NA *EMP* 100
SIC 6159 Machinery & equipment finance leasing
CEO: Justin Nielsen
Pr: Scott Miller
VP: Chantelle Brady
VP: Charlie Sumpter
VP: Libby Turner
VP Sls: Heath Birchall

D-U-N-S 02-446-9944
ONSITE DENTAL LLC
(*Suby of* ONSITE HEALTH INC) ★
85 Argonaut Ste 220, Aliso Viejo, CA 92656-4105
Tel (888) 411-2290 *Founded/Ownrshp* 2008
Sales 400.0MM *EMP* 20
SIC 8021 Offices & clinics of dentists
CEO: Ernest Blackwelder

ONSITE ENVIRONMENTAL
See COMBS INDUSTRIAL SERVICES INC

D-U-N-S 83-025-0051
ONSITE HEALTH INC
241 18th St S Ste 403, Arlington, VA 22202-3414
Tel (949) 441-9530 *Founded/Ownrshp* 2009
Sales 400.0MM^E *EMP* 120^E
SIC 8099 Medical services organization
CEO: Ernest Blackwelder
CFO: David Joe

D-U-N-S 07-974-9620
ONSITE HOLDING CORP
PREMISE HEALTH
(*Suby of* ONSITE HOLDING LLC)
5500 Maryland Way Ste 200, Brentwood, TN 37027-4973
Tel (615) 577-4927 *Founded/Ownrshp* 2014
Sales 303.6MM *EMP* 4,000^E
SIC 8099 Medical services organization
CEO: Edward Stuart Clark

D-U-N-S 01-897-1870
ONSITE OCCUPATIONAL HEALTH & SAFETY INC
101 N Hart St, Princeton, IN 47670-1532
Tel (812) 385-8306 *Founded/Ownrshp* 2008
Sales 27.4MM^E *EMP* 253^E
SIC 7363 Medical help service; Medical help service
Pr: Kyle G Johnson
Ex VP: John Wilkinson
IT Man: Fredrick Lambing

ONSLOW COUNTY BOARD EDUCATION
See ONSLOW COUNTY SCHOOLS INC

D-U-N-S 03-410-4067
ONSLOW COUNTY HOSPITAL AUTHORITY
ONSLOW MEMORIAL HOSPITAL
317 Western Blvd, Jacksonville, NC 28546-6338
Tel (910) 577-2345 *Founded/Ownrshp* 1972
Sales 133.7MM^E *EMP* 1,200^E
SIC 8062 General medical & surgical hospitals; General medical & surgical hospitals
CEO: Ed Piper PHD
CFO: William Bass
**CFO:* Roy Smith
Sr VP: Daniel Waller
VP: Erin Tallman
Dir OR: Kathy Schumacher
Dir Inf Cn: Gloria Horne
Dir Lab: Kristy Wagner
Dir Rad: Joanne Offutt
Dir Sec: Maurice Humphrey
CTO: Randy Blackburn

D-U-N-S 08-236-3573
ONSLOW COUNTY SCHOOLS INC
ONSLOW COUNTY BOARD EDUCATION
200 Broadhurst Rd, Jacksonville, NC 28540-3551
Tel (910) 455-2211 *Founded/Ownrshp* 1900
Sales 130.2MM^E *EMP* 2,800
SIC 8211 Public elementary & secondary schools; Public elementary & secondary schools
**CFO:* Jeff Hollamon

ONSLOW MEMORIAL HOSPITAL
See ONSLOW COUNTY HOSPITAL AUTHORITY

D-U-N-S 07-556-0672
ONSLOW MEMORIAL HOSPITAL INC
(*Suby of* ONSLOW COUNTY HOSPITAL AUTHORITY) ★
241 New River Dr, Jacksonville, NC 28540-5928
Tel (910) 577-4703 *Founded/Ownrshp* 1946
Sales 133.7MM *EMP* 864
SIC 8062 General medical & surgical hospitals; General medical & surgical hospitals
CEO: Ed Piper
Sr VP: Sue Kegley
IT Man: David Moore

D-U-N-S 55-724-5342
ONSLOW WATER & SEWER AUTHORITY
228 Georgetown Rd, Jacksonville, NC 28540-4146
Tel (910) 455-0722 *Founded/Ownrshp* 2000
Sales 20.2MM^E *EMP* 127
SIC 1623 Water, sewer & utility lines
Ex Dir: David Walker
CFO: Tiffany Riggs

ONSTED COMMUNITY SCHOOL DST
See ONSTED COMMUNITY SCHOOLS

D-U-N-S 04-360-3992
ONSTED COMMUNITY SCHOOLS
ONSTED COMMUNITY SCHOOL DST
10109 Slee Rd, Onsted, MI 49265-9701
Tel (517) 467-2174 *Founded/Ownrshp* 1920
Sales 16.7MM^E *EMP* 276
SIC 8211 8741 Public elementary & secondary schools; Management services; Public elementary & secondary schools; Management services
VP: Robert Herrera
Teacher Pr: Nancy Reid

D-U-N-S 78-444-5160
■ **ONTARGETJOBS INC**
(*Suby of* DHI GROUP INC) ★
6465 Greenwood Plaza Blvd, Greenwood Village, CO 80111-4905
Tel (303) 562-0144 *Founded/Ownrshp* 2013
Sales 22.7MM^E *EMP* 215
SIC 2741 4813 ; ; ;
CEO: Michael Tansey
**CFO:* Robert J Baer
**Treas:* Curtis Thompson
**Ex VP:* Pam Bilash
**Sr VP:* Jim Finn
**VP:* Michael R Corbett
Sls Dir: Jeff Eisses

D-U-N-S 61-720-8038
ONTARIO AUTOMOTIVE LLC
PENSKE HONDA ONTARIO
(*Suby of* PENSKE CORP) ★
1401 Auto Center Dr, Ontario, CA 91761-2221
Tel (909) 974-3800 *Founded/Ownrshp* 1990
Sales 43.3MM^E *EMP* 125
SIC 5511 5521 5012 Automobiles, new & used; Used car dealers; Automobiles & other motor vehicles; Automobiles, new & used; Used car dealers; Automobiles & other motor vehicles
Ch Bd: Roger Penske
**Pr:* Greg Penske
**Sec:* Brian Kobus
Genl Mgr: Bill McGrath
Sls Mgr: John Cowan
Sls Mgr: Jose Luquin

D-U-N-S 07-839-8689
ONTARIO CONCESSIONS
DELAWARE NORTH CO TRAVEL HOSP
(*Suby of* DELAWARE NORTH COMPANIES TRAVEL HOSPITALITY SERVICES INC) ★
2500 E Airport Dr, Ontario, CA 91761-2131
Tel (909) 975-8000 *Founded/Ownrshp* 2012
Sales 4.5MM^E *EMP* 495^E
SIC 5812 Concessionaire
Pr: Steve Tomes

D-U-N-S 80-819-2285
ONTARIO MONTCLAIR SCHOOL EMPLOYEES FEDERAL CREDIT UNION
(Suby of ONTARIO-MONTCLAIR SCHOOL DISTRICT) ★
1520 N Palmetto Ave, Ontario, CA 91762-1228
Tel (909) 983-1959 Founded/Ownrshp 2008
Sales NA EMP 1E
SIC 6061 Federal credit unions
Prin: Kristen Kris Brake

D-U-N-S 05-570-4720
ONTARIO NISSAN INC
METRO NISSAN
(Suby of METRO NISSAN OF MONTCLAIR) ★
9440 Autoplex St, Montclair, CA 91763-2300
Tel (909) 625-5575 Founded/Ownrshp 1979
Sales 38.7MME EMP 120
SIC 5511 5521 Automobiles, new & used; Used car dealers; Automobiles, new & used; Used car dealers
Pr: David A Marvin
*CFO: Michelle A Lowe
*Sec: Susan L McNutt

D-U-N-S 05-285-3991
ONTARIO REFRIGERATION SERVICE INC (CA)
635 S Mountain Ave, Ontario, CA 91762-4114
Tel (909) 984-2771 Founded/Ownrshp 1971, 1966
Sales 44.5MME EMP 158
SIC 1711 Heating & air conditioning contractors; Heating & air conditioning contractors
Pr: Phillip C Talleur
Brnch Mgr: Kelly Stankus
IT Man: Mark Gambetti
IT Man: Bryant McGrath
Sales Asso: James Beaumont

ONTARIO SCHOOL DISTRICT 8-C
See MALHEUR COUNTY SCHOOL DISTRICT 8-C

ONTARIO SPECIALTY CONTRACTING
See OSC HOLDING INC

D-U-N-S 17-852-3494 IMP
ONTARIO SPECIALTY CONTRACTING INC
(Suby of ONTARIO SPECIALTY CONTRACTING) ★
333 Ganson St Ste 2, Buffalo, NY 14203-3029
Tel (716) 856-3333 Founded/Ownrshp 1997
Sales 23.0MME EMP 100
SIC 1795 8744 Demolition, buildings & other structures;
Pr: Jon M Williams
*VP: James F Williams

D-U-N-S 00-445-3858
ONTARIO STONE CORP (OH)
1246 River Rd, Cleveland, OH 44113-1119
Tel (216) 631-3645 Founded/Ownrshp 1960
Sales 28.0MME EMP 64
SIC 5032 Aggregate
Pr: Carl R Barricelli
*VP: Marc Barricelli

D-U-N-S 01-623-8545
ONTARIO SYSTEMS LLC
1150 W Kilgore Ave, Muncie, IN 47305-1599
Tel (765) 751-7000 Founded/Ownrshp 2015
Sales 70.5MME EMP 275
SIC 7371 Computer software development; Computer software development
CEO: Ronald K Fauquher
Pr: Tony Reisz
VP: Alex Forman
VP: Steve Gero
VP: Steve Gerow
VP: Jan Hunt
VP: Paul G Smith
Dir Soc: Shannon Stroud
Prgrm Mgr: Steve Blount
Snr Sftwr: Andy Brelage
Snr Sftwr: David Gregory

ONTARIO VOLKSWAGON
See SHAYCO

ONTARIO VOLVO
See GHN INC

D-U-N-S 07-607-0192
ONTARIO-MONTCLAIR SCHOOL DISTRICT
950 W D St, Ontario, CA 91762-3026
Tel (909) 418-6476 Founded/Ownrshp 1884
Sales 106.4MME EMP 2,114
Accts Vavrinek Trine Day & Co Ll
SIC 8211 Public elementary school; Public elementary school
MIS Dir: Bill Ameeri
Netwrk Eng: Jon Lewis
Pr Dir: Jana Dupree
Schl Brd P: Elvia Rivis
Psych: Delia Mariscal

D-U-N-S 16-470-2636
ONTEGRITY INC
3 Speen St Ste 210, Framingham, MA 01701-4664
Tel (508) 270-8402 Founded/Ownrshp 1999
Sales 50.0MME EMP 85
SIC 5063 Batteries; Batteries
CEO: Jonathan B Quint
CFO: Harvey Schein
*Treas: Richard Scott
VP: Bill Hillegas
Prgrm Mgr: Ryan Burgdorfer
Prgrm Mgr: Tom Cooleen
Prgrm Mgr: Douglas Geraci
Prgrm Mgr: Richard Kennedy

D-U-N-S 83-110-2967 IMP
ONTEL PRODUCTS CORP
21 Law Dr Ste 1, Fairfield, NJ 07004-3298
Tel (973) 439-9000 Founded/Ownrshp 1988
Sales 35.3MME EMP 56E
Accts Perelson Weiner Llp New York
SIC 5023 5091 Kitchenware; Fitness equipment & supplies
Pr: Chuck Khubani
VP: Karen How
*VP: Anita Khubani

IT Man: Rich Goss
Mktg Dir: Andrea Browne
Genl Couns: David Rimas

D-U-N-S 08-045-8862
ONTEORA CENTRAL SCHOOL DISTRICT
4166 State Route 28, Boiceville, NY 12412-5203
Tel (845) 657-2373 Founded/Ownrshp 1940
Sales 22.3MME EMP 420
SIC 8211 Public elementary & secondary schools; Public elementary & secondary schools
IT Man: Steve Patschke
IT Man: Michele Roszko
Psych: Brian Wunderlich

ONTERIE FITNESS CENTER
See OFC MANAGEMENT INC

D-U-N-S 15-538-9224
ONTIC ENGINEERING AND MANUFACTURING INC
(Suby of BBA AVIATION PLC)
20400 Plummer St, Chatsworth, CA 91311-5372
Tel (818) 678-6555 Founded/Ownrshp 1987
Sales 166.6MME EMP 170
SIC 5088 3728 3812 Aircraft equipment & supplies; Aircraft parts & equipment; Search & navigation equipment; Aircraft equipment & supplies; Aircraft parts & equipment; Search & navigation equipment
Pr: Peg Billson
Dir Bus: Jonathan Shiebler
Mng Dir: Gareth Hall
Genl Mgr: Dorothy Mann
Ql Cn Mgr: Duane Kleinberg
Ql Cn Mgr: Ana McManama
Ql Cn Mgr: Jack Teague
Snr Mgr: Vanessa Deakin
Snr Mgr: Andrew Pramschufer

ONTRAC
See EXPRESS MESSENGER SYSTEMS INC

D-U-N-S 80-121-3398
ONTRACK DATA RECOVERY INC
KROLL ONTRACK
(Suby of KROLL INC) ★
9023 Columbine Rd, Eden Prairie, MN 55347-4182
Tel (952) 937-1107 Founded/Ownrshp 2013
Sales 41.5MME EMP 700E
SIC 7375 Remote data base information retrieval; Remote data base information retrieval
Prin: Gregory A Olson
*Pr: Dean J Hager
*CEO: Ben Allen
*CEO: Kristin Nimsger
COO: Steve Guenther
*CFO: Jill Putman
*Sr VP: Don O'Brien
*VP: Dave Alampi
VP: Todd Johnson
Mng Dir: Phil Bridge
Genl Couns: John M Bujan

ONU
See OHIO NORTHERN UNIVERSITY

D-U-N-S 60-933-2952
ONUR ULGEN INC
PRODUCTION MODELING CORP
15726 Michigan Ave, Dearborn, MI 48126-2903
Tel (313) 441-4460 Founded/Ownrshp 1985
Sales 23.5MME EMP 150
SIC 8742 8711 Management consulting services; Consulting engineer; Management consulting services; Consulting engineer
Pr: Onur Ulgen

D-U-N-S 02-300-9272
▲ ONVIA INC
509 Olive Way Ste 400, Seattle, WA 98101-1783
Tel (206) 282-5170 Founded/Ownrshp 1997
Sales 22.6MM EMP 136E
Tkr Sym ONVI Exch NAS
SIC 7375 Information retrieval services; Information retrieval services
Pr: Henry G Riner
CFO: Cameron S Way
Ex VP: Irvine N Alpert
Sr VP: Naveen Rajkumar
Board of Directors: Jeffrey C Ballowe, James L Brill, Roger L Feldman, D Van Skilling

ONVOY DIVISION
See BADGER PLUG CO

D-U-N-S 62-110-1823
■ ONVOY LLC
(Suby of FIRST TELECOM SERVICES) ★
10300 6th Ave N, Minneapolis, MN 55441-6371
Tel (952) 230-4100 Founded/Ownrshp 2007
Sales 96.8MME EMP 289
SIC 4813 Telephone communication, except radio; Telephone communication, except radio
Pr: Fritz Hendricks
COO: Surendra Saboo
*CFO: Michael Donahue
*CFO: Steven Droll
Treas: Ken Des
*VP: Teri Asiala
Exec: Allan Flinn
Admn Mgr: Sandy McWilliams
Off Admin: Joan Schmiedlin
Netwrk Eng: Anthony Jensen
Opers Mgr: Brandon Bradley

D-U-N-S 09-568-9290
■ ONWARD HEALTHCARE INC
(Suby of AMN HEALTHCARE INC) ★
64 Danbury Rd Ste 100, Wilton, CT 06897-4438
Tel (203) 834-3000 Founded/Ownrshp 2015
Sales 93.9MME EMP 1,400
SIC 7361 Employment agencies; Employment agencies
CEO: Kevin Clark
Pr: John Martins
VP: John Paterson

D-U-N-S 00-420-7496 IMP/EXP
ONWARD MANUFACTURING CO
(Suby of ONWARD MANUFACTURING COMPANY LIMITED)
1000 E Market St, Huntington, IN 46750-2576
Tel (260) 358-4111 Founded/Ownrshp 2006
Sales 52.5MME EMP 175
SIC 3631 5023 Bar, restaurant & cafeteria furniture; Household cooking equipment; Home furnishings
CEO: Ted Witzel

D-U-N-S 07-864-4755
ONX ACQUISITION LLC
ONX ENTERPRISE SOLUTIONS
5910 Landerbrook Dr # 250, Mayfield Heights, OH 44124-6508
Tel (440) 569-2300 Founded/Ownrshp 2011
Sales 255.0MM EMP 300E
SIC 7372 7379

ONX ENTERPRISE SOLUTIONS
See ONX ACQUISITION LLC

D-U-N-S 07-959-6251
ONX HOLDINGS LLC
(Suby of MARLIN EQUITY PARTNERS LLC) ★
5910 Landerbrook Dr # 250, Mayfield Heights, OH 44124-6505
Tel (800) 559-2497 Founded/Ownrshp 2011
Sales 72.0MME EMP 274E
SIC 7379 7372 Computer related consulting services; Business oriented computer software; Computer related consulting services; Business oriented computer software
Pr: Mike Cox
Ch: Robb Warwick
Ex VP: Rosalind Lehman
VP: Brian Pavlak
VP: Rick Rudolph

D-U-N-S 96-916-9742
ONX USA LLC
(Suby of ONX HOLDINGS LLC) ★
5910 Landerbrook Dr # 250, Cleveland, OH 44124-6505
Tel (440) 569-2300 Founded/Ownrshp 2009
Sales 70.3MME EMP 270
SIC 7379 7372 Computer related consulting services; Business oriented computer software; Computer related consulting services; Business oriented computer software
CEO: Mike Cox
Ch Bd: Bart Foster
Pr: Paul Khawaja
Pr: Wayne Kiphart
CFO: Rosalind Lehman
Treas: Michael Dean
Board of Directors: Robb Warwick

D-U-N-S 12-915-8341
ONYX COLLECTION INC
202 Anderson Ave, Belvue, KS 66407-9664
Tel (785) 456-8604 Founded/Ownrshp 1985
Sales 49.3MME EMP 285
SIC 3088 3431 Plastics plumbing fixtures; Metal sanitary ware; Plastics plumbing fixtures; Metal sanitary ware
Pr: Robert J Awerkamp
*Pr: Robert W Awerkamp Jr
*Sec: Louise Awerkamp
*VP: Francis Awerkamp
Software D: Joseph Martin
Mktg Dir: Doug Hohman
Board of Directors: Francis Awerkamp

D-U-N-S 19-362-7648
ONYX CONTRACTORS OPERATIONS LP
1010 S Fm 1788, Midland, TX 79706-2629
Tel (432) 561-8900 Founded/Ownrshp 2006
Sales 108.1MME EMP 59
SIC 6211 4941 Mineral, oil & gas leasing & royalty dealers; Water supply
Pr: Maurizio Iaquaniello
VP: Paul Iaquaniello

D-U-N-S 08-218-4156
ONYX ENVIRONMENTAL SERVICES LLC
(Suby of VEOLIA ENVIRONMENTAL SERVICES NORTH AMERICA CORP) ★
700 E Bttrfeld Rd Ste 201, Lombard, IL 60148
Tel (630) 218-1500 Founded/Ownrshp 1999
Sales 218.0MME EMP 1,210
SIC 8711 4953 2869 1799 1629 Engineering services; Hazardous waste collection & disposal; Solvents, organic; Asbestos removal & encapsulation; Power plant construction; Engineering services; Hazardous waste collection & disposal; Solvents, organic; Asbestos removal & encapsulation; Power plant construction
CEO: Jim Bell
VP: Mark Dennis

D-U-N-S 80-042-7788
ONYX EQUITIES LLC
900 Us Highway 9 N # 400, Woodbridge, NJ 07095-1003
Tel (732) 362-8800 Founded/Ownrshp 2004
Sales 25.9MME EMP 50
SIC 6531 Real estate agents & managers
CFO: Samuel J Giordano
Sr VP: Jonathan B Davis
Sr VP: Stephen Sullivan

D-U-N-S 78-959-1724
■ ONYX PHARMACEUTICALS INC
(Suby of AMGEN INC) ★
249 E Grand Ave, South San Francisco, CA 94080-4804
Tel (650) 266-0000 Founded/Ownrshp 2013
Sales 202.4MME EMP 741E
SIC 2834 8049 Drugs affecting parasitic & infective diseases; Occupational therapist; Drugs affecting parasitic & infective diseases; Occupational therapist
Pr: Pablo Cagnoni
COO: Helen Torley
CFO: Matthew K Fust
Ex VP: Pablo J Cagnoni
Ex VP: Juergen Lasowski PHD
Ex VP: Suzanne M Shema Jdl
Ex VP: J Rgen Lasowski
Ex VP: Ted W Love
Ex VP: Suzanne M Shema
Sr VP: John E Osborn
VP: Mary Ann Rafferty
VP: Wendell Wieronga
VP: Marilyn E Wortzman
Exec: Ngoc Chau-Castaneda
Assoc Dir: Philip Chou
Assoc Dir: David Gao
Assoc Dir: Avis Hains
Assoc Dir: Angela Kuo
Assoc Dir: Peggy Lemen
Assoc Dir: Daniel Lobato
Assoc Dir: Dustin McMinn
Board of Directors: Paul Goddard, Antonio J Grillo-Lopez, Magnus Lundberg, Corinne H Nevinny, William R Ringo, Wendell Wierenga, Thomas G Wiggans

D-U-N-S 00-794-3921
ONYX RESOLUTION LLC
(Suby of FIRST INDEPENDENT INVESTMENT GROUP INC) ★
1220 Main St Ste 500, Vancouver, WA 98660-2964
Tel (360) 699-4206 Founded/Ownrshp 1910, 1985
Sales NA EMP 1
SIC 6022 State commercial banks; State commercial banks
Pr: William J Firstenburg
COO: Jeanne Firstenburg
CFO: Steve Bernhoff
CFO: Steve Burnhoff
Sr Cor Off: Jim Grant
Ofcr: Katherine Larpenteur
Ex VP: Bruce E Firstenburg
Ex VP: Cliff Gibbs
Ex VP: Stacey Graham
Sr VP: Yvonne Cordon
Sr VP: Gary Ehrig
Sr VP: John Grogan
VP: Andrea Buteau
VP: Diana Fitzpatrick
VP: Thomas Guinn
VP: Robby Johnston
VP: Kristi Langdon
VP: Judy Silke
VP: Joe Storm
VP: Marie Vermeer
VP: Don Yocham

D-U-N-S 83-270-0004 EXP
ONYX SPECIALTY PAPERS INC
40 Willow St, South Lee, MA 01260
Tel (413) 243-1231 Founded/Ownrshp 2009
Sales 54.4MME EMP 137
SIC 2541 Book paper; Table or counter tops, plastic laminated
Pr: Patricia C Begrowicz
Opers Mgr: John Healy
Ql Cn Mgr: Lynn Wood

D-U-N-S 84-847-0639
OOBE INC
201 Riverplace Ste 301, Greenville, SC 29601-2590
Tel (864) 220-6623 Founded/Ownrshp 1994
Sales 58.8MME EMP 123E
SIC 5136 5961 5611 Men's & boys' clothing; Men's & boys' clothing; Catalog & mail-order houses; Men's & boys' clothing stores
V Ch: Joe Patrick
VP: Miguel J Pereyo
*Prin: Thomas E Merritt
Pgrm Dir: Caroline Bladon

D-U-N-S 03-946-3997
OOCL (USA) INC (NY)
(Suby of ORIENT OVERSEAS (INTERNATIONAL) LIMITED)
10913 S River Front Pkwy # 200, South Jordan, UT 84095-3507
Tel (801) 302-6625 Founded/Ownrshp 1927, 1981
Sales 135.2MME EMP 690
SIC 4731 Agents, shipping; Transportation agents & brokers; Agents, shipping; Transportation agents & brokers
Pr: Peter Leng
*Pr: Paul Devine
*Sr VP: T F Hau
*Sr VP: Stephen Ng
VP: Christopher Amand
Sales Exec: Don Meehan
VP Sls: Yoshiro Takano
S&M/VP: Dmitriy Semenov
Mktg Mgr: Grace Hsu
Mktg Mgr: Frankie Lau

OOIDA
See OWNER-OPERATOR INDEPENDENT DRIVERS ASSN INC

D-U-N-S 60-682-8726 IMP
OOMA INC
1880 Embarcadero Rd, Palo Alto, CA 94303-3308
Tel (866) 452-6662 Founded/Ownrshp 2003
Sales 31.9MME EMP 60
Tkr Sym OOMA Exch NYS
SIC 4813
CEO: Eric Stang
*Ch Bd: Andrew Frame
Pr: James Im
*CFO: Andrew Galligan
CFO: Ravi Narula
Treas: Jim Gustke
*Chf Mktg O: Rich Buchanan
VP: Tami Bhaumik
*VP: Jamie Buckley
VP: Aaron Duran
*VP: Toby Farrand
VP: Dennis Peng
*VP: Tim Sullivan

D-U-N-S 79-895-1401
OOVOO LLC
44 E 30th St Fl 12, New York, NY 10016-7605
Tel (212) 792-8280 Founded/Ownrshp 2006
Sales 23.0MME EMP 75
SIC 4899 Data communication services

CEO: Robert Jackman
Pr: Jay A Samit
COO: Louis Holder
Chf Mktg O: Larry Lieberman
CTO: Asher Shiratzky

D-U-N-S 82-535-2896
OOYALA INC
(*Suby of* TELSTRA CORPORATION LIMITED)
4750 Patrick Henry Dr, Santa Clara, CA 95054-1851
Tel (650) 961-3400 *Founded/Ownrshp* 2014
Sales 77.2MM[E] *EMP* 550[E]
SIC 7371 Software programming applications; Software programming applications
Pr: Jay Fulcher
Pr: Sean Knapp
Pr: Rick Pittenger
**CFO:* David Wilson
Sr VP: Dave Hare
Sr VP: Scott Smith
Sr VP: Issac Vaughn
VP: Keith Budge
VP: Jonathan Knight
VP: Jonathan Wilner
Comm Man: Steve Biondolillo
Comm Man: Jeanette Elliott

D-U-N-S 00-227-4207
OP SCHUMAN & SONS INC (PA)
2001 County Line Rd, Warrington, PA 18976-2498
Tel (215) 343-1530 *Founded/Ownrshp* 1919
Sales 22.7MM[E] *EMP* 85
SIC 3552 3565 3829 Textile machinery; Packaging machinery; Tensile strength testing equipment
Pr: William Tschuman
**VP:* R Mark Schuman

D-U-N-S 78-675-1750
OP-TECH ENVIRONMENTAL SERVICES INC
(*Suby of* NATIONAL RESPONSE CORP) ★
1 Adler Dr Ste 3, East Syracuse, NY 13057-1188
Tel (315) 579-3254 *Founded/Ownrshp* 2013
Sales 25.8MM[E] *EMP* 142[E]
SIC 4959 8744 4212 Environmental cleanup services; ; Hazardous waste transport; Environmental cleanup services; ; Hazardous waste transport
CEO: Charles Morgan
**Pr:* Steve Candito
**VP:* Bill Hunter
Brnch Mgr: Linda Grimmer
Sfty Dirs: Joe Farrell

OPA
See ORIENT PRECISION AMERICA INC

D-U-N-S 01-694-3136
OPAA FOOD MANAGEMENT INC
100 Chesterfield Business, Chesterfield, MO 63005-1271
Tel (636) 812-0777 *Founded/Ownrshp* 1976
Sales 44.5MM[E] *EMP* 1,250
SIC 5812 Contract food services; Contract food services
Pr: Kevin Short
COO: Scott Hoffmann
VP: Craig Cohen
VP: Sheila Frost
Off Mgr: Norma Lauber
Dir IT: Tim Cross

D-U-N-S 07-941-0696
OPAL FOODS LLC
1100 Blair Ave, Neosho, MO 64850-9117
Tel (417) 455-5000 *Founded/Ownrshp* 2014
Sales 169.4MM *EMP* 310
SIC 0252 Eggs; Chicken eggs
CEO: Jerry Welch
CFO: Craig Bonet

D-U-N-S 07-843-3214
OPAL HOLDINGS LLC
(*Suby of* SOUTHEASTERN GROCERS LLC) ★
208 Bi Lo Blvd, Greenville, SC 29607-5346
Tel (864) 213-2500 *Founded/Ownrshp* 2011
Sales 71.8MM[E] *EMP* 47,005
SIC 5411 5541 5912 Supermarkets, chain; Gasoline service stations; Drug stores; Supermarkets, chain; Gasoline service stations; Drug stores

D-U-N-S 10-772-4668 IMP
OPAL SERVICE INC
282 S Anita Dr, Orange, CA 92868-3308
Tel (714) 935-0900 *Founded/Ownrshp* 1962
Sales 67.1MM[E] *EMP* 140
SIC 3299 5031 5211 Stucco; Doors & windows; Lumber & other building materials; Stucco; Doors & windows; Lumber & other building materials
CEO: Kenneth R Thompson
Off Mgr: Pam Vrickel

OPA'S
See GREEKTOWN CASINO LLC

OPAS SMOKED MEATS
See FREDERICKSBURG LOCKERS INC

OPDC
See OTSUKA PHARMACEUTICAL DEVELOPMENT & COMMERCIALIZATION INC

D-U-N-S 09-936-8052
OPECHEE CONSTRUCTION CORP
11 Corporate Dr, Belmont, NH 03220-3103
Tel (603) 527-9090 *Founded/Ownrshp* 1980
Sales 40.0MM *EMP* 20
SIC 1542 Commercial & office building, new construction; Commercial & office buildings, renovation & repair
Pr: Mark Woglom
Treas: Geoffrey Gray
Treas: Jeff Grey
VP: Tim Daigneault
VP: Gregory Kirsch
Mktg Mgr: Justin Daigneault

D-U-N-S 10-000-0736
OPELIKA CITY SCHOOLS
300 Simmons St, Opelika, AL 36801-5647
Tel (334) 741-5601 *Founded/Ownrshp* 1901
Sales 47.0MM *EMP* 550
SIC 8211 School board; School board
IT Man: Brenda Rickett
Pr Dir: Becky Brown
Teacher Pr: Emily Fields
HC Dir: Catherine Davis

D-U-N-S 07-508-0069
OPELOUSAS GENERAL HEALTH SYSTEM
OPELOUSAS GENERAL HOSP AUTH
539 E Prudhomme St, Opelousas, LA 70570-6499
Tel (337) 948-3011 *Founded/Ownrshp* 1972
Sales 143.8MM[E] *EMP* 1,000
Accts Broussard Poche Lewis & Brea
SIC 8062 General medical & surgical hospitals; General medical & surgical hospitals
Pr: Bob Hardy
**Ch Bd:* Gina Tuttle
COO: Robert Hardy
**CFO:* Jim Juneau
**Sec:* Morris Weinstein
VP: Jared Lormans
Dir Lab: Debbie Deshotel
Dir Lab: James Gordon
Dir Lab: A C Thibouedeaux
Nurse Mgr: Walter Richardson
CIO: Albert Hammett

OPELOUSAS GENERAL HOSP AUTH
See OPELOUSAS GENERAL HEALTH SYSTEM

D-U-N-S 94-503-1771
OPEN ACCESS TECHNOLOGY INTERNATIONAL INC
OATI
3660 Technology Dr, Minneapolis, MN 55418-1006
Tel (763) 201-2000 *Founded/Ownrshp* 1995
Sales 55.9MM[E] *EMP* 300
SIC 7371 8711 Computer software development; Electrical or electronic engineering; Computer software development; Electrical or electronic engineering
Pr: Sasan Mohktari
Ex VP: Guillermo Irisarri
Ex VP: Nelson Muller
Ex VP: Kash Nodehi
VP: Jerry Dempsey
VP: Ali Ipakchi
VP: Ron Larson
VP: Farrokh Rahimi
VP: Jagjit Singh
VP: Paul Sorenson
Admn Mgr: Kristy Francis

D-U-N-S 11-914-4228
OPEN AMERICA INC
OPENWORKS
4742 N 24th St Ste 450, Phoenix, AZ 85016-4856
Tel (602) 224-0440 *Founded/Ownrshp* 1983
Sales 23.8MM[E] *EMP* 300
SIC 7349 6794 Janitorial service, contract basis; Franchises, selling or licensing; Janitorial service, contract basis; Franchises, selling or licensing
CEO: Shahrouz Zayanderoudi
**Pr:* Eric Roudi
**CFO:* Howard Sckolnik
Div VP: David Bosley
VP: Joseph Schenk
Rgnl Mgr: Mourad Abdeen
Dist Mgr: Jeff Lee
Mktg Dir: Norm Makowski
Sales Asso: Kimie Stewart

D-U-N-S 78-175-3389
OPEN ARMS CARE CORP
6 Cadillac Dr Ste 350, Brentwood, TN 37027-5094
Tel (615) 254-4006 *Founded/Ownrshp* 1989
Sales 38.8MM *EMP* 175
SIC 8052

D-U-N-S 19-697-0953 IMP
OPEN BANK
1000 Wilshire Blvd # 250, Los Angeles, CA 90017-2457
Tel (213) 892-9999 *Founded/Ownrshp* 2005
Sales NA *EMP* 49[E]
SIC 6022 State commercial banks; State commercial banks
Ch Bd: Brian Choi
**Pr:* Min J Kim
Ofcr: Kenneth Kong
Ofcr: Harrison Lee
Ofcr: Jennifer Nam
Ofcr: Hana OH
**Ex VP:* Peter An
**Ex VP:* Christine OH
**Ex VP:* Steve Park
Sr VP: Janie Kim
Sr VP: Yong Park
Sr VP: Gene Sheen
Sr VP: Ryan Shin
VP: Olive Kang
VP: Andy Kim
VP: Mike Lee
VP: Stacey Lee
VP: Jaden Park

D-U-N-S 07-912-2528
OPEN BOOK BEN LLC
433 Park Point Dr Ste 225, Golden, CO 80401-7601
Tel (720) 263-5708 *Founded/Ownrshp* 2013
Sales 82.0MM *EMP* 11
SIC 7379 Data processing consultant; Data processing consultant
Ch: Chris Robbins

D-U-N-S 13-423-4764
OPEN CITIES HEALTH CENTER INC
409 Dunlap St N, Saint Paul, MN 55104-4201
Tel (651) 290-9200 *Founded/Ownrshp* 1967
Sales 20.9MM[E] *EMP* 100
Accts Eide Bailly Llp Minneapolis
SIC 8011 Clinic, operated by physicians
CEO: Douglas Hanso
IT Man: Adetunji Oshodi

D-U-N-S 10-670-8381
OPEN DOOR CENTER
LISBON THRIFT STORE
129 3rd Ave Ne, Valley City, ND 58072-3057
Tel (701) 845-1124 *Founded/Ownrshp* 1962
Sales 12.7MM *EMP* 357
Accts Eide Bailly Llp Fargo North
SIC 8322 8331 8052 Association for the handicapped; Vocational rehabilitation agency; Intermediate care facilities; Association for the handicapped; Vocational rehabilitation agency; Intermediate care facilities
Ex Dir: Mary Simonson
Ex Dir: Sarah McGough

D-U-N-S 84-285-9720
OPEN DOOR COMMUNITY HEALTH CENTERS
670 9th St Ste 203cfo, Arcata, CA 95521-6248
Tel (707) 826-8642 *Founded/Ownrshp* 1971
Sales 22.4MM[E] *EMP* 288
SIC 8093 Smoking clinic; Smoking clinic
CEO: Sydney Fisher Larsen
CFO: James Bella
Exec: Asa Stockton
IT Man: Joe Lewis
Doctor: Nancy Brockington
Doctor: Judy Burns
Doctor: Joseph Carroll
Doctor: Eloi Hoopman
Pharmcst: Gail Kuwahara
Snr Mgr: Christopher Peters

D-U-N-S 03-824-5072
OPEN DOOR FAMILY MEDICAL CENTER INC
165 Main St, Ossining, NY 10562-4702
Tel (914) 941-1263 *Founded/Ownrshp* 1972
Sales 884.4M *EMP* 300
Accts Mcgladrey Llp New York New
SIC 8011 General & family practice, physician/surgeon; General & family practice, physician/surgeon
Pr: Lindsay Farrell
**COO:* Anita Wilenkin
**CFO:* Maria Mazzotta
**Ch:* Stewart Tabin
**Treas:* David Sherman
Dir Lab: Segundo Malaver
Dir IT: Rick Boyd
IT Man: James Montague
Obsttrcn: Stephanie Gore

D-U-N-S 08-021-3432
OPEN DOOR MISSIONJ (NE)
2828 N 23rd St E, Omaha, NE 68110-2726
Tel (402) 829-1563 *Founded/Ownrshp* 1955
Sales 24.6MM *EMP* 65
Accts Lutz & Company Pc Omaha N
SIC 8322 8661 Multi-service center; Miscellaneous denomination church; Multi-service center; Miscellaneous denomination church
Pr: Candice Gregory
Dir Vol: Corine Sawadogo
**CFO:* Richard Den-Herder
**CFO:* Michael Johnson
CFO: Mike Johnson
IT Man: Jayson Green
Pr Dir: James Cummings
Pr Dir: Alexandria Ewing
Pgrm Dir: Steve Frazee

D-U-N-S 01-773-6435
OPEN DOORS INTERNATIONAL INC
2953 Pullman St, Santa Ana, CA 92705-5840
Tel (949) 752-6600 *Founded/Ownrshp* 1992
Sales 30.2MM *EMP* 10
SIC 8661 Religious organizations; Religious organizations
Pr: Carl Moeller
VP: Jane Hickaby
VP: Tommy Hughes
Dir IT: Kris Jensen
Dir IT: Josh Seale

D-U-N-S 02-294-0995
OPEN ENGLISH HOLDINGS INC
2901 Florida Ave Ste 840, Miami, FL 33133-5211
Tel (305) 728-8982 *Founded/Ownrshp* 2007
Sales 61.2MM[E] *EMP* 65
SIC 6719 Investment holding companies, except banks; Investment holding companies, except banks
Ch: John McIntire
**CEO:* Andres Moreno
**CFO:* Thomas Wenrich
**Prin:* Susana Panalosa

D-U-N-S 07-870-3107
OPEN ENGLISH LLC
(*Suby of* OPEN ENGLISH HOLDINGS INC) ★
2901 Florida Ave Ste 840, Miami, FL 33133-5211
Tel (305) 443-3979 *Founded/Ownrshp* 2008
Sales 30.0MM *EMP* 65
SIC 8243 Software training, computer; Software training, computer
CEO: Andres Moreno
COO: Thomas Wenrich
CFO: Bart W Catalane
VP: Wilmer Sarmiento

OPEN LINK
See OPENLINK FINANCIAL LLC

D-U-N-S 86-859-7212
OPEN MARKET INC
1 Wayside Rd, Burlington, MA 01803-4609
Tel (781) 359-3000 *Founded/Ownrshp* 2001
Sales 12.9MM[E] *EMP* 281
SIC 7373 Computer integrated systems design; Computer integrated systems design
Ch Bd: Harland K Lavigne
Ofcr: Mussa Dakri
VP: Peter Stanley
Prgrm Mgr: Bill Roberts
Div Mgr: William Bennett
Genl Mgr: Kazuo Kojima
Sales Exec: Rick Saunders
Sales Exec: Casey Schinkowitch
VP Sls: Daniel E Ross

Mktg Dir: Andrew Darling
Snr Mgr: Tricia Foster

OPEN MOBILE
See PRWIRELESS INC

D-U-N-S 07-383-4434
OPEN PANTRY FOOD MARTS OF WISCONSIN INC
10505 Corporate Dr, Pleasant Prairie, WI 53158-1605
Tel (262) 857-1156 *Founded/Ownrshp* 1966
Sales 65.5MM[E] *EMP* 200
SIC 5541 5411 6794 Filling stations, gasoline; Convenience stores, chain; Franchises, selling or licensing; Filling stations, gasoline; Convenience stores, chain; Franchises, selling or licensing
Pr: Robert A Buhler
VP: Sue Jensen
Mktg Mgr: Jackie Mancl

D-U-N-S 03-988-4171 IMP
OPEN PLAN SYSTEMS LLC
4700 Deepwater Trml Rd, Richmond, VA 23234-2209
Tel (804) 275-2468 *Founded/Ownrshp* 2001
Sales 55.3MM[E] *EMP* 165
SIC 5021 Office furniture
Sls Mgr: Bob Ferris

OPEN RANGE RV
See HIGHLAND RIDGE RV INC

OPEN ROAD AUTO GROUP
See RYAN AUTOMOTIVE LLC

OPEN ROAD BMW
See OPEN ROAD OF EDISON INC

OPEN ROAD HONDA/ISUZU/MAZDA
See NEW BRUNSWICK-EDISON RECREATIONAL VEHICLES INC

D-U-N-S 79-023-5071 IMP
OPEN ROAD OF EDISON INC
OPEN ROAD BMW
731 Us Highway 1, Edison, NJ 08817-4550
Tel (732) 985-4575 *Founded/Ownrshp* 1987
Sales 34.3MM[E] *EMP* 90
SIC 5511 Automobiles, new & used; Automobiles, new & used
Pr: W Rodman Ryan
VP: Alex Rozenberg
**Genl Mgr:* David Branch
Genl Mgr: Kosta Pappas
Off Mgr: Stephanie Principato
Sls Mgr: Dean Palumbo
Sls Mgr: Andy Paul

D-U-N-S 11-207-6989
OPEN SOCIETY INSTITUTE
224 W 57th St Frnt 1, New York, NY 10019-3212
Tel (212) 548-0600 *Founded/Ownrshp* 1993
Sales 155.6MM *EMP* 445
SIC 8399 Social change association; Social change association
Ex Dir: Aryeh Neier
**CFO:* Maija Arbolino
Ofcr: Joel Campagna
Ofcr: Jason Garrett
Ofcr: Andy Haupert
VP: Gara Lamarch
Exec: Chrissie Thibodeau
Ex Dir: Farda Asadov
Ex Dir: Diana Morris
Prgrm Mgr: Melissa Hagemann
Genl Mgr: Bonnie Blocker

D-U-N-S 80-267-8524
■ **OPEN SOLUTIONS INC**
OSI
(*Suby of* HARPOON ACQUISITION CORP) ★
455 Winding Brook Dr # 101, Glastonbury, CT 06033-4351
Tel (860) 815-5000 *Founded/Ownrshp* 1992
Sales 213.4MM[E] *EMP* 1,700
SIC 7372 7373 Business oriented computer software; Systems integration services; Business oriented computer software; Systems integration services
CEO: Louis Hernandez Jr
**Pr:* Stephen J Cameron
Pr: Mike Cardell
Pr: Blair Goulet
Pr: Elliott Hankins
Pr: Marty Krafka
Pr: Brian Molloy
Pr: Mike Reiskis
Pr: Kathleen Watts
**CFO:* John W Frederick
CFO: Duncan Robertson
**Chf Mktg O:* David Mitchell
Top Exec: Alok Kalra
**Ex VP:* Sam Boggs
Ex VP: Ross M Curtis
Ex VP: Roswell M Curtis
**Sr VP:* Rashid Desai
Sr VP: Jonathan Lee
VP: Ken Boin
VP: Neale Brown
VP: Jan Frymyer

D-U-N-S 07-931-0402
OPEN SYSTEMS HEALTHCARE INC
1818 Market St Ste 2510, Philadelphia, PA 19103-3650
Tel (215) 399-1400 *Founded/Ownrshp* 2011
Sales 3.5MM *EMP* 375
SIC 8082 Home health care services; Home health care services
Pr: Charles Hill

D-U-N-S 80-137-1758
OPEN SYSTEMS INTERNATIONAL INC
4101 Arrowhead Dr, Medina, MN 55340-9457
Tel (763) 551-0559 *Founded/Ownrshp* 1992
Sales 90.3MM[E] *EMP* 265[E]
Accts Mcgladrey & Pullen Llp Minne
SIC 7371 5734 Computer software development; Computer & software stores; Computer software development; Computer & software stores
Pr: Bahman Hoveida
Ofcr: Shane Pierick

VP: Margaret Boiano
VP: Al Eliasen
VP: Ron Ingram
VP: Hormoz Kazemzadeh
VP: Karen Peterson
Snr Sftwr: Kyle Kalmi
Snr Sftwr: Gregory Maddox
CTO: Kevin Treptau
QA Dir: Linda Leeson

OPEN SYSTEMS TECHNOLOGIES
See BAHA INDUSTRIES CORP

D-U-N-S 02-066-1509
OPEN SYSTEMS TECHNOLOGIES DE LLC
O S T
(*Suby of* K D C) ★
605 Seward Ave Nw Ste 101, Grand Rapids, MI 49504-5693
Tel (616) 574-3500 *Founded/Ownrshp* 2012
Sales 166.2MM *EMP* 106[E]
Accts Kpmg Llp Anchorage Ak
SIC 7379 Computer related maintenance services; Computer related maintenance services
Pr: Daniel Behm
**COO:* Meredith Bronk
Sr VP: Rick Ryan
**CIO:* James Vandermey
IT Man: Brad Bailie
Netwrk Eng: Anthony Scott
Sls Dir: John Thayer
Mktg Mgr: Michael Lomonaco
Sls Mgr: Scott Dare
Board of Directors: David Gerrity, John Thayer, John Vancil

D-U-N-S 00-889-9569
OPEN SYSTEMS TECHNOLOGIES INC
CBS SOLUTIONS
605 Seward Ave Nw Ste 101, Grand Rapids, MI 49504-5693
Tel (616) 574-3500 *Founded/Ownrshp* 1997
Sales 68.8MM *EMP* 62
Accts Crow Horwath Llp Grand Rapids
SIC 7379 Computer related consulting services; Computer related consulting services
Pr: Daniel Behm
**COO:* Meredith Bronk
**CIO:* James Vandermey
VP Sls: Rupveen Arora

D-U-N-S 05-423-4390
OPEN SYSTEMS TECHNOLOGIES INC
1818 Market St Ste 2510, Philadelphia, PA 19103-3650
Tel (215) 399-5800 *Founded/Ownrshp* 1997
Sales 118.3MM *EMP* 650
SIC 7379 Computer related consulting services; Computer related consulting services
Pr: Harold Herling
**Sec:* Steven Shapiro
**VP:* Mark Fiato
Mng Dir: Kevin Johnson

D-U-N-S 07-627-4680
OPEN TASTE INC
938 Hemlock St, Los Angeles, CA 90021-2302
Tel (626) 470-7411 *Founded/Ownrshp* 2014
Sales 81.9MM *EMP* 42
SIC 5411 Grocery stores
Pr: Kenneth Wot

D-U-N-S 06-459-6158
■ **OPEN TEXT INC**
(*Suby of* OPEN TEXT CORPORATION)
951 Mariners Island Blvd # 600, San Mateo, CA 94404-5040
Tel (650) 645-3000 *Founded/Ownrshp* 2004
Sales 77.6MM[E] *EMP* 475
SIC 7379 Computer related consulting services; Computer related consulting services
CEO: Mark J Barrenechea
Pr: John Shackleton
CFO: John Doolittle
Sr VP: James McGourlay

D-U-N-S 14-408-0913
OPEN-SILICON INC
490 N Mccarthy Blvd # 220, Milpitas, CA 95035-5118
Tel (408) 956-8517 *Founded/Ownrshp* 2003
Sales 40.1MM[E] *EMP* 75
SIC 5065 Semiconductor devices; Semiconductor devices
Pr: Naveed Sherwani
**COO:* Shafy Eltoukhy
**VP:* Steve Erickson
**VP:* Scott Houghton
VP: Vasan Karighattam
**VP:* Jay Vyas
Dir Risk M: Lars Huelsmann
Creative D: Maureen O'Donoghue
Board of Directors: Edward C Ross

D-U-N-S 02-205-9610
OPENDNS INC
135 Bluxome St, San Francisco, CA 94107-1507
Tel (415) 371-1055 *Founded/Ownrshp* 2009
Sales 60.0MM[E] *EMP* 186[E]
SIC 7379

OPENEYE
See PC OPEN INC

D-U-N-S 17-936-0722
■ **OPENFIRST LLC**
(*Suby of* QUAD/GRAPHICS INC) ★
300 N Jefferson St Stop 3, Milwaukee, WI 53202-5920
Tel (414) 347-4100 *Founded/Ownrshp* 2006
Sales 16.7MM[E] *EMP* 400
SIC 2759 2791 7331 Laser printing; Typesetting, computer controlled; Mailing service; Laser printing; Typesetting, computer controlled; Mailing service

D-U-N-S 60-248-4227
OPENGATE CAPITAL LLC
10250 Constellation Blvd # 1750, Los Angeles, CA 90067-6257
Tel (310) 432-7000 *Founded/Ownrshp* 2004
Sales 456.3MM[E] *EMP* 1,900
SIC 2721 6799 Magazines: publishing & printing; Investors; Magazines: publishing & printing; Investors
CEO: Lisa J Bahash
CFO: Michelle Lindquist
CFO: James Neelley
CFO: Jay Yook
Sr VP: Daniel Abrams
Sr VP: Joshua Adams
Sr VP: Alanna Chaffin
Prin: Matthias Gundlach

D-U-N-S 83-110-6430
OPENLINK FINANCIAL LLC
OPEN LINK
1502 Rxr Plz Fl 15w, Uniondale, NY 11556-3810
Tel (516) 227-6600 *Founded/Ownrshp* 1992
Sales 256.1MM[E] *EMP* 1,300[E]
Accts Ernst & Young Llp New York N
SIC 7371 7372 8742 Computer software development; Prepackaged software; Financial consultant; Computer software development; Prepackaged software; Financial consultant
CEO: John O'Malley
**Ch Bd:* Coleman Fung
**CEO:* Kevin J Hesselbirg
CFO: Joe Dwyer
**CFO:* David M Obstler
Ex VP: Henry Bonner
**Ex VP:* Roger Burkhardt
**Ex VP:* Andrew Goodman
**Ex VP:* Rich Grossi
Ex VP: Garrick Hoadley
**Ex VP:* Robert Kalish
Ex VP: Ken Knowles
Sr VP: Diane W Montaruli
Sr VP: Diane Montaruli
Sr VP: Jonathan Stochel
Sr VP: Phil Wang
VP: Roderick Austin
VP: Souvik Choudhury
VP: Brian Ferguson
VP: Tom Marrapodi
VP: Judith Peterson
Board of Directors: Mark N Greene, Kurt Jaggers, Jonathan Meeks

D-U-N-S 11-328-9792
OPENPEAK INC
1750 Clint Moore Rd, Boca Raton, FL 33487-2707
Tel (561) 893-7800 *Founded/Ownrshp* 2002
Sales 25.0MM[E] *EMP* 100
SIC 7371 Computer software development & applications
Ch Bd: Daniel Gittleman
**Pr:* Andy Aiello
**Pr:* Christopher K Hill
**Treas:* Patricia Pikus
**Chf Mktg O:* Brian Woods
VP: Steve Adler
VP: Bryan Gillis
VP: Mark Green
VP: Dan Howe
VP: Casey Kero
**VP:* Howard Kwon
**VP:* Louis Salamone
VP: Roger Tobias
VP: Lee Westberger
Board of Directors: Patricia Pikus- Dir

D-U-N-S 15-590-7038 EXP
OPENROAD TRANSPORTATION INC
OPENROAD TRUCKING
123 Sw Mill St, Dallas, OR 97338-3119
Tel (503) 623-9922 *Founded/Ownrshp* 2004
Sales 21.0MM *EMP* 40
SIC 5088 Transportation equipment & supplies; Transportation equipment & supplies
Pr: Mark Weisensee
**VP:* Michael Storm
Off Mgr: Holly Bray

OPENROAD TRUCKING
See OPENROAD TRANSPORTATION INC

OPENSQUARE
See WORKSPACE DEVELOPMENT LLC

D-U-N-S 05-530-5523
■ **OPENTABLE INC**
(*Suby of* PRICELINE GROUP INC) ★
1 Montgomery St Ste 700, San Francisco, CA 94104-4536
Tel (415) 344-4200 *Founded/Ownrshp* 2014
Sales 190.0MM *EMP* 625[E]
SIC 7389 Restaurant reservation service; Restaurant reservation service
CEO: Christa Quarles
**Ch Bd:* Matthew Roberts
**CFO:* I Duncan Robertson
Sr VP: Ilse Kamps
Sr VP: Charles McCullough
Mng Dir: Michael Xenakis
**CTO:* Joseph Essas

OPENTEXT
See EASYLINK SERVICES INTERNATIONAL CORP

OPENTEXT GXS
See GXS WORLDWIDE INC

D-U-N-S 82-530-0812
OPENTV CORP
(*Suby of* KUDELSKI S.A.)
275 Sacramento St Ste SI1, San Francisco, CA 94111-3831
Tel (415) 962-5000 *Founded/Ownrshp* 2008
Sales 70.8MM[E] *EMP* 398[E]
Accts Grant Thornton Llp San Franci
SIC 7371 Custom computer programming services
CEO: Ben Bennett
Pr: Adam Benson
Pr: Kevin M Kelley
COO: Wesley Hoffman
**CFO:* Shum Mukherjee
Ex VP: James Brown
Ex VP: Pierre Roy
Sr VP: Mark Beariault
VP: Matt Bell
VP: Matthew Huntington
Dir IT: Jonathan Marra
Board of Directors: Paul R Auvil III, Joseph Deiss, Lucien Gani, Aleksander E Osadzinski, Pierre Roy, Claude Smadja

D-U-N-S 96-261-0416
OPENTV INC
NAGRA
(*Suby of* OPENTV CORP) ★
275 Sacramento St Ste SI1, San Francisco, CA 94111-3831
Tel (415) 962-5000 *Founded/Ownrshp* 2007
Sales 70.8MM[E] *EMP* 325
SIC 7372 Prepackaged software; Prepackaged software
CEO: Yves Pitton
Pr: Jeffrey Rodrigues
Pr: John Tinsman
**CEO:* Ben Bennett
**CEO:* Andr Kudelski
**COO:* Wesley O Hoffman
CFO: Randy Livingston
**CFO:* Shum Mukherjee
**Ex VP:* Mark Allen
**Ex VP:* Pierre Roy
**Ex VP:* Mauro Saladini
Sr VP: Mark Beariault
**Sr VP:* John Burke
**Sr VP:* Joe Chernesky
Sr VP: Martha Garron
**Sr VP:* Thomas L Hagopian
**Sr VP:* Bill Harvey
**Sr VP:* Mark Meagher
Sr VP: Samir Mehta
**Sr VP:* Constance N Pettit
Sr VP: James Vishoot

D-U-N-S 07-847-4719
OPENWAVE MESSAGING INC
2655 Campus Dr Ste 250, San Mateo, CA 94403-2546
Tel (650) 480-7300 *Founded/Ownrshp* 2012
Sales 68.9MM[E] *EMP* 316[E]
SIC 1731 7379 7371 Computerized controls installation; Access control systems specialization; Cogeneration specialization; Electronic controls installation; ; Computer software development & applications; Computerized controls installation; Access control systems specialization; Cogeneration specialization; Electronic controls installation; ; Computer software development & applications
Pr: David H Ratner
**CFO:* Tom Clark
**Ofcr:* Lokdeep Singh
Sr VP: Jay Seaton
**Sr VP:* Barry Twohig
VP: Dean Bogarde
VP: Andrew Byrne
Off Mgr: Catrina Trinidad
**CIO:* Ian Gillott
**CTO:* Farooq Ali
Snr Mgr: Mark Ellis

OPENWORKS
See OPEN AMERICA INC

D-U-N-S 82-852-3287
OPENX TECHNOLOGIES INC
(*Suby of* OPENX LIMITED)
888 E Walnut St Fl 2, Pasadena, CA 91101-1897
Tel (855) 673-6948 *Founded/Ownrshp* 2008
Sales 85.3MM[E] *EMP* 359[E]
SIC 7311 Advertising agencies
CEO: Tim Cadogan
Pr: John Gentry
Pr: Doug Lauretano
CFO: Tom Fuelling
Chf Cred: Deborah Roth
Chf Cred: Tish Whitcraft
Sr VP: Nicholas Cumins
Sr VP: Manoj Goyal
Sr VP: Qasim Saifee
VP: Laura Buchman
VP: Melissa Burghardt
VP: John Burke
VP: Brian Chisholm
VP: Jeff Faxon
VP: John Murphy
VP: Todd Rosenberg
VP: Brett Rubio
VP: Jin Yu
Dir Rx: Liwen KAO
Dir Bus: Dan Owens
Board of Directors: Pascal Gauthier

OPERA HOUSE
See MAHONEYS SILVER NUGGET INC

D-U-N-S 36-111-4437
OPERA SOLUTIONS LLC
10 Exchange Pl Fl 11, Jersey City, NJ 07302-4934
Tel (646) 520-4320 *Founded/Ownrshp* 2005
Sales 92.9MM[E] *EMP* 360
SIC 8742 Management consulting services; Management consulting services
CEO: Arnab Gupta
CFO: Sridhar Ramasubbu
Bd of Dir: Hollie Haynes
Ex VP: Shawn Blevins
Sr VP: Craig Peterson
Sr VP: David Piester
VP: Mehta Bhavi
VP: Jack Cain
VP: Jonathan Di Giambattista
VP: Herb Kelsey
VP: Anatoli Olkhovets
VP: Julian Romeu
VP: Timothy Roy
VP: John Stedman

D-U-N-S 08-692-8397
OPERA THEATRE OF ST LOUIS
210 Hazel Ave, Saint Louis, MO 63119-3236
Tel (314) 961-0171 *Founded/Ownrshp* 1964
Sales 8.0MM *EMP* 350
Accts Bkd Llp Saint Louis Mo
SIC 7922 Opera company; Opera company
Ex Dir: Timothy O'Leary
COO: Jo Arnold
**Ch:* Spencer Burke
**Treas:* Bill Rusnack
Treas: William Rusnack
IT Man: Caron House
Mktg Dir: Joe Gfaller

OPERATING COMPANY
See VIRTEX HOLDINGS LLP

D-U-N-S 82-853-8582
OPERATING ENGINEER LU 3
250 N Canyons Pkwy, Livermore, CA 94551-9470
Tel (925) 454-4000 *Founded/Ownrshp* 2008
Sales 41.4MM *EMP* 2
SIC 8711 Engineering services; Engineering services
Prin: Leon Lanfri

D-U-N-S 06-108-7970
OPERATING ENGINEERS FUND OFFICE
P.O. Box 38682 (15238-8682)
Tel (412) 968-9750 *Founded/Ownrshp* 2011
Sales 51.7MM *EMP* 2[E]
SIC 8711 Engineering services; Engineering services

D-U-N-S 07-530-6365
OPERATING ENGINEERS FUNDS INC (CA)
100 Corson St Ste 222, Pasadena, CA 91103-3892
Tel (626) 792-8900 *Founded/Ownrshp* 1971
Sales 39.5MM[E] *EMP* 170
SIC 6733 Trusts, except educational, religious, charity: management; Trusts, except educational, religious, charity: management
CEO: Mike Roddy
**COO:* Matt Erieg
CFO: Rodney Goodwin
**CFO:* Chuck Killian
Trst: Alexander Rados
CIO: Alan Weidlich
Dir IT: Elaine Gill
Netwrk Mgr: Peter Hu
Counsel: Andrew Bucci

D-U-N-S 96-487-1961
OPERATING ENGINEERS HEALTH & WELFARE FUND
100 Corson St, Pasadena, CA 91103-3840
Tel (626) 356-1000 *Founded/Ownrshp* 2014
Sales 217.0MM *EMP* 2[E]
Accts Bernard Kotkin And Company Llp
SIC 6733 Trusts, except educational, religious, charity: management
CFO: Chuck Killian

D-U-N-S 96-488-9716
OPERATING ENGINEERS LOCAL 324 VACATION AND HOLIDAY FUND OF MICHIGAN
700 Tower Dr, Troy, MI 48098-2808
Tel (248) 813-9800 *Founded/Ownrshp* 2010
Sales 35.6MM *EMP* 16[E]
Accts Plante & Moran Pllc Flint Mi
SIC 8631 Labor unions & similar labor organizations; Labor unions & similar labor organizations

D-U-N-S 04-899-7162
OPERATING ENGINEERS LOCAL 49
INTERNATIONAL UNION OF OPERATI
308 Lundin Blvd, Mankato, MN 56001-2706
Tel (507) 625-3670 *Founded/Ownrshp* 2001
Sales 96.0MM *EMP* 3
SIC 8631 Labor unions & similar labor organizations; Labor unions & similar labor organizations

D-U-N-S 96-959-1572
OPERATING ENGINEERS LOCAL NO 825 WELFARE FUND
65 Springfield Ave Ste 2, Springfield, NJ 07081-1308
Tel (973) 921-1661 *Founded/Ownrshp* 2011
Sales 116.7MM *EMP* 2[E]
Accts Calibre Cpa Group Pllc Washin
SIC 8711 Engineering services; Engineering services
Prin: Randy Fork

D-U-N-S 07-188-3441
OPERATING ENGINEERS LOCAL UNION NO 3 SCHOLARSHIP FOUNDATION
1620 S Loop Rd, Alameda, CA 94502-7085
Tel (510) 748-7400 *Founded/Ownrshp* 1939
Sales 186.7M *EMP* 558[E]
SIC 8631 Labor unions & similar labor organizations
**Pr:* Carl Goff
**Treas:* Steve Ingersoll
**Treas:* Dan Reding
Bd of Dir: David Stater
Ofcr: Guy Prescott
VP: Frank Herrera
Comm Dir: Charlie Costello
Ex Dir: John Rector
Mng Dir: Tom Reed
Snr Ntwrk: Dennis Kelsey
Sfty Dirs: Michael Strunk

D-U-N-S 06-485-0902 IMP
OPERATION BASS INC (KY)
FLW OUTDOORS
30 Gamble Ln, Benton, KY 42025-7673
Tel (270) 252-1000 *Founded/Ownrshp* 1979, 1996
Sales 22.1MM[E] *EMP* 200
SIC 2721 7999 Magazines: publishing only, not printed on site; Recreation services; Magazines: publishing only, not printed on site; Recreation services
Pr: Charlie Evans
**Ch Bd:* Irwin L Jacobs
**CFO:* David Mahler
VP: Kathy Fennel
Creative D: Richard Mueller
Software D: Matthew Herndon
Prd Mgr: Michelle Dowling
VP Mktg: Trisha J Blake
Advt Dir: Al Chapman
Sls Dir: Bill Carson

D-U-N-S 62-295-8445
OPERATION BLESSING INTERNATIONAL RELIEF AND DEVELOPMENT CORP
977 Centerville Tpke, Virginia Beach, VA 23463-1001
Tel (757) 226-3401 *Founded/Ownrshp* 1986
Sales 267.1MM[E] *EMP* 50[E]
Accts Kpmg Llp Mclean Va

SIC 8699 Charitable organization; Charitable organization
Pr: William F Horan
**COO:* Robert W Fanning
VP: James Barr
VP: Jody Gettys
VP: Steve O'Grady
Genl Mgr: Kara Waddell

D-U-N-S 00-270-1715
OPERATION COMPASSION
114 Stuart Rd Ne Ste 370, Cleveland, TN 37312-4803
Tel (423) 479-3770 *Founded/Ownrshp* 1997
Sales 116.0MM *EMP* 25
SIC 8399 Social service information exchange; Social service information exchange
Pr: David Lorency

D-U-N-S 79-250-8780
OPERATION FOOD SEARCH INC
6282 Olive Blvd, Saint Louis, MO 63130-3300
Tel (314) 726-5355 *Founded/Ownrshp* 1981
Sales 37.3MM *EMP* 16
SIC 7361 Employment agencies; Employment agencies
Treas: Erika Labelle
VP: Erin Shasserre

D-U-N-S 00-541-0736
OPERATION HOMEFRONT INC
1355 Central Pkwy S # 100, San Antonio, TX 78232-5056
Tel (210) 659-7756 *Founded/Ownrshp* 2002
Sales 62.2MM *EMP* 60
Accts Bdo Usa Llp San Antonio Tx
SIC 8322 Individual & family services; Individual & family services
Pr: John I Pray Jr
**Ch Bd:* Catherine Blades
**COO:* Tim Farrell
VP: Dino Sarracino
CTO: Jimmy Connell
Board of Directors: Brian Arnold, Lara Ashmore, Lee Baxter, Sarah Farnsworth, Mark Foster, Laura Fredericks, Robert Giannetta, Frank Paras, Ken Slater

D-U-N-S 08-927-7602
OPERATION PAR INC
P A R
6655 66th St N, Pinellas Park, FL 33781-5033
Tel (727) 545-7564 *Founded/Ownrshp* 1970
Sales 27.2MM *EMP* 50ᴱ
Accts Carr Riggs & Ingram Llc Clea
SIC 8322 8093 Substance abuse counseling; Substance abuse clinics (outpatient); Substance abuse counseling; Substance abuse clinics (outpatient)
Pr: Nancy Hamilton
Pr: Bruce Baynard
**COO:* Dianne Clarke
**CFO:* Amy Scholz
Ex VP: Richard Neubert
VP: Marvin Coleman
VP: Kay Doughty
Pgrm Dir: Drew Wagner

D-U-N-S 17-812-2826
OPERATION SMILE INC
3641 Faculty Blvd, Virginia Beach, VA 23453-8000
Tel (888) 677-6453 *Founded/Ownrshp* 1982
Sales 58.5MM *EMP* 128
Accts Kpmg Llp Virginia Beach Va
SIC 8699 Charitable organization; Charitable organization
CEO: Magee Jr DDS MD William P
**Ch Bd:* William P Magee Jr
**Pr:* Magee Kathleen S
**COO:* Zinn E Wayne
**Treas:* Siti Jim
Treas: Michael Schwartz
VP: Jesse Hines
VP: Kyla Shawyer
Ex Dir: Christina Krause
Mng Dir: Thinh Nguyen
Pgrm Dir: Brandon Ringler

D-U-N-S 79-035-4612
OPERATION WARM INC
COATS FOR KIDS
6 Dickinson Dr Ste 314, Chadds Ford, PA 19317-9673
Tel (610) 388-2500 *Founded/Ownrshp* 2002
Sales 20.6MM *EMP* 16
SIC 8322 Child related social services
CEO: Richard Sanford

D-U-N-S 15-408-8710
OPERATIONAL TECHNOLOGIES CORP
4100 Nw Loop 410 Ste 230, San Antonio, TX 78229-4255
Tel (210) 731-0000 *Founded/Ownrshp* 1986
Sales 47.0MMᴱ *EMP* 65
Accts Padgett Stratemann & Co Llp
SIC 5084 8731 Industrial machinery & equipment; Biotechnical research, commercial; Industrial machinery & equipment; Biotechnical research, commercial
Ch: Max Navarro
**CEO:* Ricardo S Sanchez
**CFO:* William M Henderson
**VP:* C Wayne Shore

OPERATIONS CENTER
See CENTURY BANK AND TRUST CO

D-U-N-S 05-258-1224
OPERATIONS CENTER
945 Mount Read Blvd, Rochester, NY 14606-2811
Tel (585) 428-6881 *Founded/Ownrshp* 2010
Sales NA *EMP* 600
SIC 9199 General accounting office, government; General accounting office, government

D-U-N-S 05-014-7297
OPERATIONS MANAGEMENT INTERNATIONAL INC
(*Suby of* CH2M HILL COMPANIES LTD) ★
9193 S Jamaica St Ste 400, Englewood, CO 80112-5946
Tel (303) 740-0019 *Founded/Ownrshp* 1980
Sales 420.0MMᴱ *EMP* 1,300
SIC 4952 4941

OPERATIONS/RISK GROUP
See PARSONS CONSTRUCTORS INC

D-U-N-S 60-220-5036
OPERATIVE MEDIA INC
6 E 32nd St Fl 3, New York, NY 10016-5422
Tel (212) 994-8930 *Founded/Ownrshp* 2003
Sales 80.7MMᴱ *EMP* 200ᴱ
SIC 7372 Prepackaged software; Prepackaged software
CEO: Lorne Brown
**CFO:* Franois Decourtivron
**CFO:* Rick Glickman
**Ex VP:* John Briar
**Sr VP:* Sirous Wadia
**Sr VP:* Jason Witt
VP: T J Ceballos
VP: Kristi Daniels
VP: Barnaby Edwards
VP: Michael Hickey
VP: Devlin Jefferson
VP: Johan Kappel
VP: Jeannie Mun
VP: Kingsley Rooney
VP: Evan Simeone
VP: Enrico Tollis

OPERATNAL MNTANCE ORGANIZATION
See LAWTON INTER-TRIBAL INDIAN HEALTH ADVISORY BOARD

D-U-N-S 06-738-0386 IMP
OPEX CORP
OMATION
305 Commerce Dr, Moorestown, NJ 08057-4234
Tel (856) 727-1100 *Founded/Ownrshp* 1973
Sales 131.7MMᴱ *EMP* 650
SIC 3579 Mailing, letter handling & addressing machines; Mailing, letter handling & addressing machines
CEO: David Stevens
**Ch Bd:* Albert Stevens
CEO: Mark Stevens
Treas: David Kammeyer
IT Man: Jamey Anthony
Sftwr Eng: Ryan Corcoran
Sftwr Eng: Doug Perham
Natl Sales: Bob Fires
Natl Sales: Peter Gorka
Natl Sales: Dennis Klusty
Mktg Dir: Robert Dewitt

D-U-N-S 17-752-3359
OPHEDGE INVESTMENT SERVICES LLC
3 International Dr Ste 3, Rye Brook, NY 10573-7501
Tel (914) 935-8000 *Founded/Ownrshp* 2004
Sales 44.8MMᴱ *EMP* 290
SIC 6726 Investment offices; Investment offices
Mng Dir: Tom Flynn
Board of Directors: Tanya Beder, Robert Litzenberger

D-U-N-S 13-342-9162
■ **OPHIR OPTICS LLC**
(*Suby of* NEWPORT CORP) ★
1616 Osgood St, North Andover, MA 01845-1000
Tel (978) 657-6410 *Founded/Ownrshp* 2002
Sales 23.7MMᴱ *EMP* 110
SIC 3827 Optical instruments & apparatus; Optical instruments & apparatus
Prgrm Mgr: Mike Frechette
Off Mgr: Rhonda King

D-U-N-S 84-111-1073
OPHTHALMIC CONSULTANTS OF LONG ISLAND
865 Merrick Ave Ste 80n, Westbury, NY 11590-6711
Tel (516) 804-5200 *Founded/Ownrshp* 1980
Sales 21.8MMᴱ *EMP* 145
SIC 8011 Ophthalmologist
Mng Pt: Richard Sturm MD
**CEO:* Thomas Burke
COO: Thomas Pannuillo
**Prin:* Stanley J Berke MD
**Prin:* Ken B Carnevale MD
**Prin:* Ronald M Caronia MD
**Prin:* Gerard D Aversa MD
**Prin:* Eric D Donnenfeld MD
**Prin:* Russel G Fumuso MD
**Prin:* David B Nelson MD
**Prin:* Henry D Perry MD

D-U-N-S 05-809-4046
OPHTHALMIC MANAGEMENT CO INC
FACTORY EYEGLASS OUTLETS
23 Main St, Port Washington, NY 11050-2916
Tel (516) 944-7161 *Founded/Ownrshp* 1979
Sales 10.6MMᴱ *EMP* 300
SIC 8741 Business management; Business management
Pr: Alan Sandman
**Treas:* Linda Sandman
**VP:* Harlan Rips
Mktg Mgr: Mario Marin

OPHTHONIX
See TREX ENTERPRISES CORP

D-U-N-S 01-575-4884
OPHTHOTECH CORP
1 University Square Dr # 200, Princeton, NJ 08540-6499
Tel (609) 945-6050 *Founded/Ownrshp* 2007
Sales 41.2MM *EMP* 15
Tkr Sym OPHT *Exch* NGS
SIC 8731 Biological research
Pr: Samira Patel
V Ch: Samir Patel
COO: Evelyn Harrison
CFO: Michael G Atieh
VP: Richard Beckman
VP: Harvey Masonson

D-U-N-S 07-288-5127
OPICI WINE CO OF NEW JERSEY INC
(*Suby of* B D AMERICAN CO) ★
25 De Boer Dr, Glen Rock, NJ 07452-3301
Tel (201) 689-1200 *Founded/Ownrshp* 1999
Sales 42.4MMᴱ *EMP* 63ᴱ
SIC 5182 Wine & distilled beverages
Pr: Hubert Opici
Ofcr: Eric Kratz
Ex VP: Ronald Gallo
VP: Phillip Piranio
Area Mgr: Dan Libert
Dir IT: Steve Grayberg
Opers Mgr: Steve Iaccino
S&M/VP: Burton May
Mktg Mgr: Greg Williams
Sls Mgr: Jeff Burdge

OPICIWINES
See B D AMERICAN CO

D-U-N-S 04-129-7672
OPIES TRANSPORT INC
21 Highway Ff, Eldon, MO 65026-4337
Tel (573) 392-6525 *Founded/Ownrshp* 1976
Sales 21.9MMᴱ *EMP* 120
SIC 4213 Contract haulers
Pr: Danny Opie
VP: James Henley

D-U-N-S 62-648-7342 IMP
■ **OPINICUS TEXTRON INC**
(*Suby of* TEXTRON INC) ★
1827 Northpointe Pkwy, Lutz, FL 33558-5207
Tel (813) 792-9300 *Founded/Ownrshp* 2013
Sales 37.3MMᴱ *EMP* 75
SIC 3699 Flight simulators (training aids), electronic
CEO: Mark G Budd
Pr: Ken McNamara
**Pr:* James R Takats
**CFO:* Jodi Noah
**Treas:* Karen A Budd
Ofcr: Carol Bentley
**VP:* Patricia Elmer
IT Man: Elizabeth Ebbert
Sftwr Eng: Joseph Buscetta
**Genl Couns:* Victor Zupa

D-U-N-S 88-360-6600
OPINION ACCESS CORP
4710 32nd Pl Fl 3, Long Island City, NY 11101-2415
Tel (718) 729-2622 *Founded/Ownrshp* 1994
Sales 31.5MMᴱ *EMP* 315
SIC 8732 Market analysis or research; Opinion research; Research services, except laboratory; Market analysis or research; Opinion research; Research services, except laboratory
Pr: Jim Hoffman
**Ch Bd:* Joseph Rafael
**VP:* Michele Hoffman
Mng Dir: Meredith Falvo
Mktg Mgr: Amy Pedersen

OPINION RESEARCH CORPORATION
See ORC INTERNATIONAL INC

D-U-N-S 18-912-5602
OPINIONOLOGY LLC
SURVEY SAMPLING INTERNATIONAL
701 Timpanogos Pkwy Ste M, Orem, UT 84097-6213
Tel (801) 373-7735 *Founded/Ownrshp* 1991
Sales 115.2MMᴱ *EMP* 2,000ᴱ
SIC 7389 8732 Telephone services; Commercial nonphysical research; Telephone services; Commercial nonphysical research
Pr: David Haynes
COO: Greg Graul
CFO: Robert Petersen
VP: Gordon Bishop
VP: Bob Fawson
VP: Jared Schiers
Dir IT: Allan Ibanez
VP Opers: Rick Watson

D-U-N-S 07-965-4409
OPIUM WAR PRODUCTIONS LLC
595 New Loudon Rd Ste 263, Latham, NY 12110-4063
Tel (518) 400-2544 *Founded/Ownrshp* 2014
Sales 11.5MMᴱ *EMP* 365
SIC 7812 Motion picture production; Motion picture production

D-U-N-S 78-398-0345
▲ **OPKO HEALTH INC**
4400 Biscayne Blvd, Miami, FL 33137-3212
Tel (305) 575-4100 *Founded/Ownrshp* 2007
Sales 91.1MM *EMP* 4,972ᴱ
Tkr Sym OPK *Exch* NYS
SIC 2834 2835 8731 Pharmaceutical preparations; In vitro & in vivo diagnostic substances; Biotechnical research, commercial; Pharmaceutical preparations; In vitro & in vivo diagnostic substances; Biotechnical research, commercial
Ch Bd: Phillip Frost
V Ch: Hsiao Jane
CFO: Adam Logal
**V Ch Bd:* Jane H Hsiao
**Ex VP:* Steven D Rubin
Ex VP: Rishard Weitz
Sr VP: Jimmy Wang
VP: Jed Fulk
VP: Scott Toner
Dir IT: Heriberto Regueira
Mfg Dir: Sean Leblanc
Board of Directors: Robert A Baron, Thomas E Beier, Richard A Lerner, John A Paganelli, Richard C Pfenniger Jr, Alice Lin-Tsing Yu

D-U-N-S 92-878-1459 IMP
OPLINK COMMUNICATIONS INC
(*Suby of* MOLEX LLC) ★
46335 Landing Pkwy, Fremont, CA 94538-6407
Tel (510) 933-7200 *Founded/Ownrshp* 2014
Sales 607.4MMᴱ *EMP* 3,716ᴱ
SIC 3661 4899 Telephone & telegraph apparatus; Fiber optics communications equipment; Telephone & telegraph apparatus; Fiber optics communications equipment; Autotransformers for telephone switchboards; Carrier equipment, telephone or telegraph; Communication signal enhancement network system; Data communication services
CEO: Joseph Y Liu
Pr: Peter Lee
CFO: Guojiang Hu
CFO: Shirley Yin
Ofcr: Erica Abrams
Ex VP: River Gong
Sr VP: Jim Li
Sr VP: Stephen M Welles
VP: Ken Brizel
VP: Kun Liu
VP: Yanfeng Yang
VP: Yangfeng Yang
VP: Rang-Chen Yu

D-U-N-S 18-119-9134
OPNET TECHNOLOGIES LLC
RIVERBED TECHNOLOGY
(*Suby of* RIVERBED TECHNOLOGY INC) ★
7255 Woodmont Ave, Bethesda, MD 20814-7900
Tel (240) 497-3000 *Founded/Ownrshp* 2012
Sales 60.6MMᴱ *EMP* 618ᴱ
SIC 7372 Application computer software; Application computer software
Pr: Jerry M Kennelly
Pr: Mark Crane
**CFO:* Ernie Maddock
Assoc VP: Paul Dietz
Assoc VP: Sanjit Ganguli
Assoc VP: Allan Hakky
**Sr VP:* Brett A Nissenberg
VP: Frank Longo Jr
VP: P Malloy
VP: Annukka Piironen
Snr Sftwr: Ashish Deopura

D-U-N-S 00-569-0636
■ **OPNEXT INC**
OCLARO
(*Suby of* OCLARO INC) ★
2560 Junction Ave, San Jose, CA 95134-1902
Tel (408) 383-1400 *Founded/Ownrshp* 2000, 2012
Sales 66.0MMᴱ *EMP* 503ᴱ
SIC 3674 Photoconductive cells; Photoelectric cells, solid state (electronic eye); Photoconductive cells; Photoelectric cells, solid state (electronic eye)
Pr: Harry L Bosco
CFO: Robert J Nobile
Chf Mktg O: Yoshihiro Miyoshi
Ex VP: Kate Rundle
Sr VP: Atsushi Horiuchi
Sr VP: Justin J O'Neill
CIO: Bob Quinn
Sls&Mrk Ex: Ron Smith
Genl Couns: Justin J O Neill
Snr Mgr: Yves Lemaitre

D-U-N-S 05-543-4992 IMP
■ **OPNEXT SUBSYSTEMS INC**
(*Suby of* OCLARO) ★
2560 Junction Ave, San Jose, CA 95134-1902
Tel (408) 370-8153 *Founded/Ownrshp* 2009
Sales 25.8MMᴱ *EMP* 200
SIC 3661 Fiber optics communications equipment; Fiber optics communications equipment
CEO: Jerry Turin
Pt: Bob Barron
**Pr:* Shri Dodani
**CFO:* Bruce D Horn
VP: Randy G Evans
**VP:* John Ralston
**VP:* Pat Rezza
**VP:* Bryson Wallace
Board of Directors: Mark J Denino, Philip F Otto, Christopher Rust, Louis Toth, Roland A Van Der Meer

D-U-N-S 80-564-8982
▲ **OPOWER INC**
1515 N Courthouse Rd Fl 8, Arlington, VA 22201-2909
Tel (703) 778-4544 *Founded/Ownrshp* 2007
Sales 128.4MM *EMP* 465ᴱ
Tkr Sym OPWR *Exch* NYS
SIC 7372

D-U-N-S 04-856-2169
OPP CONSTRUCTION LLC
3625 N Washington St, Grand Forks, ND 58203-1213
Tel (701) 277-8000 *Founded/Ownrshp* 1978
Sales 25.7MMᴱ *EMP* 165
SIC 1771 1611 Concrete work; Highway & street construction; Concrete work; Highway & street construction
Opers Mgr: Wayne Pietruszewski
Snr Mgr: Sally Opp

OPPD
See OMAHA PUBLIC POWER DISTRICT

D-U-N-S 07-423-5730
■ **OPPENHEIMER & CO INC**
(*Suby of* FREEDOM INVESTMENTS) ★
3310 W Big Beaver Rd # 205, Troy, MI 48084-2807
Tel (248) 637-8300 *Founded/Ownrshp* 2003
Sales 195.3MMᴱ *EMP* 3,000
SIC 6211 Security brokers & dealers; Security brokers & dealers
Pr: Albert Lowenthel

D-U-N-S 14-464-3400
■ **OPPENHEIMER & CO INC**
FREEDOM INVESTMENTS
(*Suby of* OPPENHEIMER HOLDINGS INC) ★
85 Broad St Bldg 85, New York, NY 10004-2434
Tel (212) 668-8000 *Founded/Ownrshp* 1988
Sales 975.2MMᴱ *EMP* 3,334
SIC 6211 Brokers, security; Dealers, security; Brokers, security; Dealers, security
CEO: Albert G Lowenthal
**CFO:* Jeffery Alfano
Ofcr: Patricia Kump
Assoc VP: Mark Brady
Assoc VP: Frank Cassidy
Assoc VP: Frank Dana
Assoc VP: Alexander Lanzman
Assoc VP: Ellen Weitz
Ex VP: Dan Kohn
**Ex VP:* Lawrence Spaulding
Sr VP: Terence Duggan
VP: Joni Ballas
VP: Francis Dewolf
VP: Albert Fedorov
VP: Craig Lawle
VP: John Macarthur
VP: Harvey Ross

Assoc Dir: Beth Batten
Assoc Dir: Jack Cimino
Assoc Dir: Michael Clarke
Assoc Dir: Cyndi Collins

D-U-N-S 06-980-2361 EXP
OPPENHEIMER COMPANIES INC
INTERSTATE POTATO PACKERS
877 W Main St Ste 700, Boise, ID 83702-5887
Tel (208) 342-7771 *Founded/Ownrshp* 1959
Sales 20.0MM[E] *EMP* 85
SIC 2037 5148 Vegetables, quick frozen & cold pack, excl. potato products; Vegetables; Vegetables, quick frozen & cold pack, excl. potato products; Vegetables
Ch Bd: Arthur F Oppenheimer
**Pr:* Douglas F Oppenheimer
**Treas:* Kenneth K Albus
Genl Mgr: Curt Sukeena
Sales Exec: Cindy Lindenberg
VP Mktg: Mike Haddix

D-U-N-S 62-794-2436
OPPENHEIMER FUNDS
(*Suby of* MASSMUTUAL MORTGAGE FINANCE LLC) ★
2 Wrld Fncl Ctr Ste 1100, New York, NY 10281-1008
Tel (212) 323-0200 *Founded/Ownrshp* 1990
Sales 709.5MM[E] *EMP* 2,000[E]
SIC 6289 6282 Stock transfer agents; Investment advisory service; Stock transfer agents; Investment advisory service
Pr: John V Murphy
**VP:* Tim Abbuhl
Sls Mgr: Jennifer Hoelscher

OPPENHEIMER GROUP
See DAVID OPPENHEIMER & CO I LLC

D-U-N-S 96-746-1406
▲ OPPENHEIMER HOLDINGS INC
85 Broad St, New York, NY 10004-2434
Tel (212) 668-8000 *Founded/Ownrshp* 1881
Sales 1.0MMM *EMP* 3,434
Tkr Sym OPY *Exch* NYS
SIC 6211 6712 6722 Security brokers & dealers; Bank holding companies; Management investment, open-end; Security brokers & dealers; Bank holding companies; Management investment, open-end
Ch Bd: Albert G Lowenthal
CFO: Jeffrey J Alfano
Assoc VP: Ron Bruno
Sr VP: Daniel Sullivan
VP: Matthew Burrell
VP: Christopher Lazos
VP: Jim Maxwell
VP: Sonia Moure
VP: Peter Vars
Mng Dir: Mark Anderson
Mng Dir: Lee Cohen

D-U-N-S 07-178-1587
OPPENHEIMER WOLFF DONNELLY LLP
Campbell Mithun, Minneapolis, MN 55402
Tel (612) 607-7000 *Founded/Ownrshp* 2001
Sales 29.3MM[E] *EMP* 140[E]
SIC 8111 General practice attorney, lawyer
Mng Pt: Brad Keil
Board of Directors: C Robert Beattie, Jeffrey Bouslog, Amy Culbert, Brad Keil, Thomas Letscher, Rick Maspopust Jr, David Potter, Christopher Scotti

D-U-N-S 04-616-2319
OPPENHEIMERFUNDS INC
(*Suby of* OPPENHEIMER FUNDS) ★
2 Wrld Fncl Ctr Fl 14, New York, NY 10281-1005
Tel (303) 768-3200 *Founded/Ownrshp* 1990
Sales 691.2MM[E] *EMP* 1,923
SIC 6282 6289 Investment advisory service; Stock transfer agents; Investment advisory service; Stock transfer agents
Ch Bd: William Glavin Jr
Pr: Amanda Dampier
Pr: Matthew Farkas
Pr: Josean Fernandez
Pr: Greg Mehok
Pr: Andrea Pash
Pr: Erin Simpson
**Pr:* Art Steinmetz
Pr: Alyse Vishnick
Pr: Kelly Wellesley
**Chf Inves:* George Evans
Chf Inves: George R Evans
Chf Inves: Mark Hamilton
Ofcr: Geoffrey J Craddock
Ofcr: Allen Holeman
Ofcr: Marty Korn
Ofcr: Mitchell Lindauer
Ofcr: Jerry A Webman
Assoc VP: Eugene Nemirovsky
Assoc VP: Rene Vecka
**Sr VP:* John Damian
Board of Directors: Joanne Pace

OPPORTNITIES UNLIMITED NIAGARA
See NEW YORK STATE ASSOCIATION FOR RETARDED CHILDREN INC

OPPORTNITIES UNLIMITED NIAGARA
See NYSARC INC NIAGARA COUNTY CHAPTER

D-U-N-S 60-519-5119
OPPORTUNE LLP
711 Louisiana St Ste 3100, Houston, TX 77002-2711
Tel (713) 490-5050 *Founded/Ownrshp* 2005
Sales 39.3MM[E] *EMP* 200
SIC 8748 Business consulting; Business consulting
Mng Pt: David Baggett
Pt: John Echols
Pt: Matt Flanagan
Pt: Don Jefferis
Pt: Dean Price
Pt: Joshua Sherman
Pt: John Venderhider
Mng Dir: John Beard
Mng Dir: John Beaty
Mng Dir: Jim Boney
Mng Dir: Ryan Bouley

D-U-N-S 06-832-1512
OPPORTUNITIES INC OF JEFFERSON COUNTY
200 E Cramer St, Fort Atkinson, WI 53538-1257
Tel (920) 563-2437 *Founded/Ownrshp* 1966
Sales 16.0MM[E] *EMP* 500
Accts Wipfli Llp Madison Wi
SIC 8331 Vocational rehabilitation agency; Vocational rehabilitation agency
Pr: Barbara Le Duc
**Treas:* Sheryl Labonne
Sr Cor Off: Dave Bienfang
Opers Mgr: Terry Frey

D-U-N-S 06-527-0445
OPPORTUNITY ALLIANCE
50 Monument Sq, Portland, ME 04101-4039
Tel (877) 429-6884 *Founded/Ownrshp* 1965
Sales 27.9MM *EMP* 66[E]
Accts Berry Dunn Mcneil & Pa Ker Lc
SIC 8399 Community action agency; Community action agency
CEO: Michael J Tarpinian
Pr: Craig Given
**CFO:* Virginia Gentile
**Sr VP:* Christine Stelling
**Dir Sec:* Elizabeth Banwell
**VP Opers:* Tara Kosma

D-U-N-S 07-984-5241
OPPORTUNITY BANK OF MONTANA
1400 Prospect Ave, Helena, MT 59601-4544
Tel (406) 442-3080 *Founded/Ownrshp* 2014
Sales NA *EMP* 180
SIC 6022 State commercial banks

D-U-N-S 01-211-5247
OPPORTUNITY COUNCIL
MAPLE ALLEY INN
1111 Cornwall Ave Ste C, Bellingham, WA 98225-5039
Tel (360) 733-6559 *Founded/Ownrshp* 1974
Sales 24.1MM *EMP* 185
SIC 8611 Community affairs & services; Community affairs & services
Ex Dir: Kay Sardo
**CFO:* Melvin De Jong
IT Man: Chris Clay
Pr Dir: Sheri Emerson

D-U-N-S 07-477-5842
OPPORTUNITY DEVELOPMENT CENTERS INC
O D C
1191 Huntington Ave, Wisconsin Rapids, WI 54494-6499
Tel (715) 421-1885 *Founded/Ownrshp* 1965
Sales 10.6MM *EMP* 300
Accts Hawkins Ash Cpas Llp Marshfi
SIC 8331 7331 Vocational rehabilitation agency; Direct mail advertising services; Vocational rehabilitation agency; Direct mail advertising services
Pr: Pam Ross
Exec: Dan Scott

D-U-N-S 61-315-2540
OPPORTUNITY EDUCATION FOUNDATION
10156 L St, Omaha, NE 68127-1120
Tel (402) 315-1577 *Founded/Ownrshp* 2005
Sales 25.6MM *EMP* 5
SIC 8299 Educational services; Educational services
**Ex Dir:* Alan Barkley

D-U-N-S 12-230-3316
OPPORTUNITY INTERNATIONAL INC
OPPORTUNITY INTERNATIONAL-US
550 W Vanburen Ste 200, Chicago, IL 60607
Tel (630) 242-4100 *Founded/Ownrshp* 1971
Sales 132.6MM *EMP* 85
SIC 8399 Social change association
Pr: Christophe Crane
Pr: Richard Hoefs
COO: Frank Gamble
**CFO:* Richard John
Exec: Jamie Hubick
CIO: Jim Maza
VP Mktg: David Stiehr

OPPORTUNITY INTERNATIONAL-US
See OPPORTUNITY INTERNATIONAL INC

D-U-N-S 00-622-3127 IMP
OPPORTUNITY PARTNERS INC (MN)
5500 Opportunity Ct, Hopkins, MN 55343-9020
Tel (952) 938-5511 *Founded/Ownrshp* 1953
Sales 35.6MM *EMP* 500
Accts Baker Tilly Virchow Krause Llp
SIC 8331 8361 Job training & vocational rehabilitation services; Vocational training agency; Job training services; Sheltered workshop; Residential care; Job training & vocational rehabilitation services; Vocational training agency; Job training services; Sheltered workshop; Residential care
Pr: Armando Camacho
**VP:* Bruce K Bester
VP: Elaine Buddington
VP: Brenda Goral
VP: Lori Schluttenhofer
VP Sls: Glen Rank

D-U-N-S 06-028-0559
OPPORTUNITY RESOURCES INC
2821 S Russell St, Missoula, MT 59801-7913
Tel (406) 721-2930 *Founded/Ownrshp* 1955
Sales 10.9MM *EMP* 350
SIC 8331 8361 Vocational training agency; Sheltered workshop; Residential care
CEO: Jesse Dunn
Dir Case M: Patrick Maddison
IT Man: Kathi Kincaid
Natl Sales: Russ McKinnon

OPPORTUNITY VILLAGE
See HANDICAP VILLAGE

OPPORTUNITY VILLAGE ARC
See OPPORTUNITY VILLAGE ASSOCIATION FOR RETARDED CITIZENS

D-U-N-S 07-620-8404
OPPORTUNITY VILLAGE ASSOCIATION FOR RETARDED CITIZENS
OPPORTUNITY VILLAGE ARC
6300 W Oakey Blvd, Las Vegas, NV 89146-1122
Tel (702) 259-3700 *Founded/Ownrshp* 1954
Sales 41.1MM[E] *EMP* 850
Accts Houldsworth Russo & Company Pc
SIC 8331 Sheltered workshop; Sheltered workshop
Ex Dir: Edward R Guthrie
**Pr:* Bob Brown
**CFO:* Lisa Manning
**CFO:* Mark Whitley
**Ch:* Carl Rowe
**Treas:* Kevin Bethel
**Treas:* Vicki Ritchie

OPRAH WINFREY NETWORK
See OWN LLC

D-U-N-S 82-890-0311
OPRONA INC
ROSEN INSPECTION TECHNOLOGIES
(*Suby of* HORONA INC) ★
14120 Interdrive E, Houston, TX 77032-3324
Tel (281) 442-8282 *Founded/Ownrshp* 2006
Sales 27.5MM[E] *EMP* 160
SIC 7389 8741 Pipeline & power line inspection service; Building inspection service; Management services
Pr: Chris Yoxall
**Pr:* Friedrich Hecker
**Sec:* Johan H Erowijn
Dir Bus: Raymond Lewis
Area Mgr: Robert Cone
Area Mgr: Luis Espinosa
Area Mgr: Jeff Harris
Mktg Mgr: Ray Lewis
Sls Mgr: Bryce Brown
Snr Mgr: Sarah Racey

D-U-N-S 19-478-5465 IMP/EXP
OPSEC SECURITY GROUP INC
(*Suby of* OPSEC SECURITY GROUP PLC)
7333 W Jefferson Ave # 165, Lakewood, CO 80235-2218
Tel (303) 534-4500 *Founded/Ownrshp* 2000
Sales 60.3MM[E] *EMP* 225
SIC 2759 2269 Labels & seals: printing; Embossing: linen broadwoven fabrics; Labels & seals: printing; Embossing: linen broadwoven fabrics
Pr: Mark Turnage
Pr: Michael W Angus
Off Admin: Valerie Kennon

D-U-N-S 83-642-5207 IMP/EXP
OPSEC SECURITY INC
(*Suby of* OPSEC SECURITY GROUP INC) ★
7333 W Jefferson Ave # 165, Lakewood, CO 80235-2218
Tel (717) 293-4110 *Founded/Ownrshp* 1998
Sales 60.0MM[E] *EMP* 200
SIC 2671 3953 Packaging paper & plastics film, coated & laminated; Embossing seals & hand stamps; Packaging paper & plastics film, coated & laminated; Embossing seals & hand stamps
CEO: Richard Cremona
**Pr:* Indra Paul
COO: Jim Keller
VP: Michael Banahan
VP: Glenn Snyder
**VP:* John Tunney
Dir Sec: John Dougherty
Off Mgr: Christine Burd
IT Man: Matt Delany
Opers Mgr: Chris Epperson
Ql Cn Mgr: Peju Pearse

D-U-N-S 11-402-2077
■ OPSWARE INC
(*Suby of* HP INC) ★
19420 Homestead Rd, Cupertino, CA 95014-0606
Tel (408) 447-4418 *Founded/Ownrshp* 2007
Sales 23.7MM[E] *EMP* 452
SIC 7372 7371 Prepackaged software; Application computer software; Utility computer software; Custom computer programming services; Prepackaged software; Application computer software; Utility computer software; Custom computer programming services
Pr: Benjamin A Horowitz
CFO: David F Conte
Chf Mktg O: Shellye L Archambeau
Ex VP: Charles J Katz Jr
VP: Marco Bussadori
CTO: Timothy A Howes
Pr Dir: Marlena Fernandez Sr

D-U-N-S 79-010-5506
OPT CO
5136 S Desert View Dr, Apache Junction, AZ 85120-7186
Tel (480) 844-1990 *Founded/Ownrshp* 1991
Sales 27.5MM[E] *EMP* 150[E]
SIC 1721 Painting & paper hanging
Pr: Allen L Kauffman

D-U-N-S 96-524-6452 IMP
OPTA MINERALS (USA) INC
(*Suby of* OPTA MINERALS INC)
4301 Poche Ct E, New Orleans, LA 70129
Tel (519) 720-9664 *Founded/Ownrshp* 2004
Sales 22.5MM[E] *EMP* 81[E]
SIC 5084 Industrial machinery & equipment
CEO: David Kruse
**CFO:* David Ascott
**VP:* John Dietrich

D-U-N-S 18-311-6768
■ OPTAROS INC
(*Suby of* MCCANN-ERICKSON USA INC) ★
10 Milk St Ste 1100, Boston, MA 02108-4620
Tel (617) 227-1855 *Founded/Ownrshp* 2014
Sales 26.6MM[E] *EMP* 170[E]
SIC 7379
Pr: Robert Willms
Sr VP: John Polcari
VP: Mavis Chin

VP: Philippe Grosjean
VP: Chris Langway
VP: Christopher Langway
VP: Robert M Lefkowitz
VP: Marc Osofsky
VP: Miguel Picornell
VP: Stephen Walli
Prgrm Mgr: Jonathan Maier

D-U-N-S 94-541-8432 IMP
OPTEC DISPLAYS INC
1700 S De Soto Pl Ste A, Ontario, CA 91761-8060
Tel (626) 369-7188 *Founded/Ownrshp* 1996
Sales 30.3MM[E] *EMP* 64
SIC 5046 Signs, electrical
Pr: Shu Hwa Wu
IT Man: Wenny Tsay
Opers Mgr: Jane Hwee

D-U-N-S 07-866-3105
OPTECH ENTERPRISE SOLUTIONS LLC
4100 Nw Loop 410 Ste 230, San Antonio, TX 78229-4255
Tel (210) 731-0000 *Founded/Ownrshp* 2012
Sales 144.0MM[E] *EMP* 48
SIC 7629 8734 4213 Electronic equipment repair; Calibration & certification; Trucking, except local

D-U-N-S 12-786-5447
OPTECH LLC
3290 W Big Beaver Rd # 220, Troy, MI 48084-2932
Tel (313) 962-9000 *Founded/Ownrshp* 1999
Sales 43.0MM[E] *EMP* 178[E]
SIC 8711 7373 8741 8999 8011 8031 Engineering services; Computer integrated systems design; Management services; Scientific consulting; Offices & clinics of medical doctors; Offices & clinics of osteopathic physicians; Engineering services; Computer integrated systems design; Management services; Scientific consulting; Offices & clinics of medical doctors; Offices & clinics of osteopathic physicians
**VP:* Scott Goodwin
Dir Bus: Mark Duane
VP Sls: Rick Anderson

D-U-N-S 10-135-0689
OPTECH MONETTE LLC
2370 Justin Trl, Alpharetta, GA 30004-8440
Tel (678) 990-9061 *Founded/Ownrshp* 2001
Sales 25.5MM[E] *EMP* 50[E]
SIC 4952 Sewerage systems
Pr: Robert Monette Pe
**VP:* Will Monette

D-U-N-S 14-472-5962
OPTECONN LP
OPTICAL CABLING SYSTEMS
2621 Summit Ave Ste 100, Plano, TX 75074-3705
Tel (972) 331-4627 *Founded/Ownrshp* 1994
Sales 23.4MM[E] *EMP* 139
SIC 3229 Fiber optics strands; Fiber optics strands
Pr: See Jim
**Sr VP:* Rick Hobbs
VP: Larry Brogdon
Sls Mgr: Alisha Hamilton

D-U-N-S 09-971-0451
OPTEK TECHNOLOGY INC
(*Suby of* TT ELECTRONICS PLC)
1645 Wallace Dr, Carrollton, TX 75006-6696
Tel (972) 323-2200 *Founded/Ownrshp* 2003
Sales 82.9MM[E] *EMP* 650
SIC 3674 3825 3812 3661 3643 Semiconductors & related devices; Light sensitive devices; Infrared sensors, solid state; Hall effect devices; Instruments to measure electricity; Search & navigation equipment; Telephone & telegraph apparatus; Current-carrying wiring devices; Semiconductors & related devices; Light sensitive devices; Infrared sensors, solid state; Hall effect devices; Instruments to measure electricity; Search & navigation equipment; Telephone & telegraph apparatus; Current-carrying wiring devices
Ch: Geraint Anderson
**Pr:* Billal Hammoud
**Pr:* Robert Taber
**CFO:* Daniel M Bankus
Genl Mgr: Frank Echevarria
Ql Cn Mgr: Bob Chudy
Mktg Dir: Reyne Parks
Sales Asso: Debbie Smith

D-U-N-S 17-498-3309
OPTELIAN ACCESS NETWORKS INC
(*Suby of* OPTELIAN ACCESS NETWORKS CORPORATION)
1700 Entp Way Se Ste 106, Marietta, GA 30067
Tel (770) 690-9575 *Founded/Ownrshp* 2002
Sales 24.3MM[E] *EMP* 105
SIC 5063 Electrical apparatus & equipment; Electrical apparatus & equipment
Pr: Michael Perry
**VP:* Brian Pratt
**VP:* David Weymouth
**CTO:* Sheldon Walklin
Sftwr Eng: Sunghan Chung
VP Opers: Dennis Isotti

D-U-N-S 96-574-9901
OPTERRA ENERGY GROUP INC
8310 S Valley Hwy Ste 300, Englewood, CO 80112-5815
Tel (303) 524-1100 *Founded/Ownrshp* 2010
Sales 47.9MM[E] *EMP* 99
SIC 8711 Energy conservation engineering
CEO: John Mahoney
**Pr:* Raouf Abdel
**CFO:* John Sullivan
**VP:* Rob Masinter
Dir Bus: Ken Hedrick
Rgnl Mgr: Brian Kealoha

D-U-N-S 07-741-7256
■ OPTEUM FINANCIAL SERVICES LLC
(*Suby of* BIMINI CAPITAL MANAGEMENT INC) ★
3305 Flamingo Dr, Vero Beach, FL 32963-1731
Tel (772) 231-1245 *Founded/Ownrshp* 2005
Sales NA *EMP* 900
Accts Deloitte

SIC 6162 Mortgage bankers; Mortgage bankers
Ch Bd: Peter R Norden
V Ch: Robert E Cauley
*COO: Martin Levine
Treas: Mark R Gruber
*Co-COO: Robert Filiberto
*Co-COO: G Hunter Haas IV
Ex VP: Rick E Floyd
VP: Chuck Johnson
VP: Shannon Kilborn
VP: Alex J Koutouzis
VP: Amber K Luedke
VP: Jerry Sintes

D-U-N-S 60-540-9924
OPTHALMIC PARTNERS OF PA PC
WILLS EYE INSTITUTE
840 Walnut St, Philadelphia, PA 19107-5109
Tel (484) 434-2700 Founded/Ownrshp 2005
Sales 56.3MM EMP 17E
Accts Kpmg Llp Philadelphia Pa
SIC 8011 Offices & clinics of medical doctors; Offices & clinics of medical doctors
Prin: William E Benson MD Facs

OPTI
See OMEGA POLYMER TECHNOLOGIES INC

D-U-N-S 80-145-8279 IMP
■ OPTI MEDICAL SYSTEMS INC
(Suby of IDEXX LABORATORIES INC) ★
235 Hembree Park Dr # 200, Roswell, GA 30076-5738
Tel (770) 510-4444 Founded/Ownrshp 2006
Sales 31.0MME EMP 90
SIC 3826 Blood testing apparatus; Blood testing apparatus
Pr: Christian Kjaer
Pr: Bernie Heitz
*CEO: Alfred P Marek
VP: Richard Howell
*VP: Paul Travers
*Prin: Jeff Bohm
Area Mgr: Cesar Mendoza
Dir IT: Dax Sharpe
IT Man: Kevin Atkins
Mtls Mgr: Tim Riehle
Prd Mgr: Britteny Garner

D-U-N-S 02-356-3553
OPTIBLEND INDUSTRIES INC
29738 Goynes Rd 3, Katy, TX 77493-6569
Tel (979) 239-2890 Founded/Ownrshp 2009
Sales 20.7MME EMP 20E
SIC 5169 Organic chemicals, synthetic
CEO: Asoke Deysarkar
*Pr: David Kremmer
*Treas: Suresh D Pala

D-U-N-S 10-627-8575 IMP
▲ OPTICAL CABLE CORP
5290 Concourse Dr, Roanoke, VA 24019-3059
Tel (540) 265-0690 Founded/Ownrshp 1983
Sales 82.9MM EMP 361E
Accts Kpmg Llp Roanoke Virginia
Tkr Sym OCC Exch NGM
SIC 3357 3351 Fiber optic cable (insulated); Wire, copper & copper alloy; Fiber optic cable (insulated); Wire, copper & copper alloy
Ch Bd: Neil D Wilkin Jr
CFO: Tracy G Smith
VP Sls: Ted Leonard
Sls Mgr: Jim Wade
Sls Mgr: Chris Yaklich
Board of Directors: Randall H Frazier, John M Holland, Craig H Weber, John B Williamson III

OPTICAL CABLING SYSTEMS
See OPTECONN LP

D-U-N-S 00-911-0768
■ OPTICAL COATING LABORATORY LLC
OCLI
(Suby of VIAVI SOLUTIONS INC) ★
2789 Northpoint Pkwy, Santa Rosa, CA 95407-7397
Tel (707) 545-6440 Founded/Ownrshp 2009
Sales 110.1MME EMP 700
SIC 3479 3577 3827 Coating of metals & formed products; Computer peripheral equipment; Optical instruments & lenses; Coating of metals & formed products; Computer peripheral equipment; Optical instruments & lenses
Pr: Fred Van Milligen
VP: Pat Higgins
Plng Mgr: Joyce Orecchia
Ql Cn Mgr: Bob Moreno
Snr Mgr: Tim Walker

D-U-N-S 78-519-8656
OPTICAL COMMUNICATION PRODUCTS INC
O C P
(Suby of OPLINK COMMUNICATIONS INC) ★
26850 Agoura Rd Fl 1, Calabasas, CA 91301-5129
Tel (818) 876-8700 Founded/Ownrshp 2007
Sales 35.5MME EMP 736
SIC 3661 Fiber optics communications equipment; Fiber optics communications equipment
Pr: Philip F Otto
CFO: Frederic T Boyer MBA
VP: Terry Basehore
Genl Mgr: James Cheng
VP Mfg: Liew-Chuang Chiu PHD

D-U-N-S 06-181-2996
OPTICAL FOR EYES CO
INSIGHT OPTICAL MANUFACTURING
1630 Walnut St, Philadelphia, PA 19103-5403
Tel (800) 367-3937 Founded/Ownrshp 1972
Sales 189.0MME EMP 1,200
SIC 5995 Optical goods stores; Optical goods stores
Pr: Philip Wolman
CFO: David H Dunbar
*VP: Robert Messa
CIO: Rene Medina
Doctor: Sara Oliver

OPTICAL GAGING PRODUCTS DIV
See QUALITY VISION INTERNATIONAL INC

OPTICAL SENSOR DIVISION
See OMRON SCIENTIFIC TECHNOLOGIES INC

D-U-N-S 07-482-5845
OPTICAL SOCIETY OF AMERICA INC
O S A
2010 Mass Ave Nw, Washington, DC 20036-1023
Tel (202) 223-8130 Founded/Ownrshp 1916
Sales 37.6MM EMP 150
SIC 8621 Scientific membership association; Scientific membership association
CEO: Elizabeth Rogan
Bd of Dir: Kelly Cohen
Bd of Dir: Jennifer Mayfield
Ofcr: Ravi Athale
VP: Karen Liu
Prgrm Mgr: Hadiya McCullough
Prgrm Mgr: Dan McDonold
*CIO: Sean R Bagshaw
Web Dev: Josh Dunkelman
Web Dev: John Tsai
Sftwr Eng: Fahed Hijazi

D-U-N-S 03-962-5314
OPTICARE EYE HEALTH CENTER PC
87 Grandview Ave Ste A, Waterbury, CT 06708-2523
Tel (203) 574-2020 Founded/Ownrshp 1980
Sales 30.6MME EMP 500
SIC 8011 Eyes, ears, nose & throat specialist: physician/surgeon; Eyes, ears, nose & throat specialist: physician/surgeon
Pr: Dean Yimoyines MD
Pr: David G Gaio
CFO: Steven Ditman
*Sec: W S Peterson MD
Opers Mgr: Lori Velleca
Opthamlgy: Jerome Ramos Esteban
Doctor: Richard Getnick MD
Board of Directors: Vincent Deluise MD, Richard Gilbert MD, Mark Ruchman

D-U-N-S 03-062-4951
OPTICARE HEALTH SYSTEMS INC
(Suby of REFAC OPTICAL GROUP) ★
87 Grandview Ave Ste A, Waterbury, CT 06708-2523
Tel (203) 574-2020 Founded/Ownrshp 2006
Sales 20.2MME EMP 336
SIC 8042 5995 3841 Offices & clinics of optometrists; Optical goods stores; Eyeglasses, prescription; Contact lenses, prescription; Eye examining instruments & apparatus; Offices & clinics of optometrists; Optical goods stores; Eyeglasses, prescription; Contact lenses, prescription; Eye examining instruments & apparatus
Pr: Nancy Noll
CFO: Bill Blaskiewicz
CFO: William A Blskiewicz
CFO: George Verrastro
*Treas: Brian M Wood
VP: Connie Cook
Dir IT: Ron McFadden

D-U-N-S 04-371-9160 IMP
OPTICS EAST INC
CONTINENTAL SALES CO AMERICA
180 Westgate Dr, Watsonville, CA 95076-2469
Tel (831) 763-6931 Founded/Ownrshp 1967
Sales 75.8MME EMP 227
SIC 5048 3851 Frames, ophthalmic; Eyeglasses, lenses & frames; Frames, ophthalmic; Eyeglasses, lenses & frames
Pr: D K Kim
*Sr VP: William Inman
*VP: Bu Kim
VP: Mike Kim
Board of Directors: Conrad J Kasperson, Arvid L Lokensgard

D-U-N-S 11-851-7445 IMP
OPTICSPLANET INC
ECENTRIA
3150 Commercial Ave, Northbrook, IL 60062-1906
Tel (847) 513-6190 Founded/Ownrshp 2000
Sales 125.3MME EMP 231
Accts Allan J Brachman Cpa Ltd
SIC 5995 5049 Optical goods stores; Optical goods; Optical goods stores; Optical goods
CEO: Mark Levitin
*Pr: Pavel Shvartsman
CFO: Bill Viveen
*VP: Kelly Swaine
QA Dir: Anthony Calzaretta
QA Dir: Latoya Shorter
IT Man: Steve Tuuk
IT Man: Natasha Veasley
Software D: Oleg Namaka
Software D: Chad Norwood
Snr Mgr: Vladimir Adamiya

D-U-N-S 12-281-0851
OPTIGAS INC
370 17th St Ste 2750, Denver, CO 80202-1373
Tel (720) 974-5300 Founded/Ownrshp 2006
Sales 57.0MM EMP 3
SIC 5172 Gases; Gases
Pr: Don Sinclair
*VP: Richard Sherrill

D-U-N-S 62-279-6873
■ OPTIM ENERGY TWIN OAKS LP
ALTURA POWER
(Suby of PNMR SERVICES CO) ★
Alvarado Sq Ms-Z110, Albuquerque, NM 87158-0001
Tel (505) 241-2821 Founded/Ownrshp 2006
Sales 309.0MME EMP 584
SIC 4911 Electric services; Electric services
Pt: Nick Rahn
Pt: John Myers

D-U-N-S 78-856-8384 IMP
OPTIMA CHEMICAL GROUP LLC
200 Willacoochee Hwy, Douglas, GA 31535-4118
Tel (912) 384-5101 Founded/Ownrshp 1997
Sales 34.6MME EMP 90
SIC 2899 2869 Chemical preparations; Industrial organic chemicals; Chemical preparations; Industrial organic chemicals
Pr: Doug Cochran
*Pr: Gene Williams
CFO: Fred Wirth
*CFO: Frederick Wirth
VP: Jagvir Singh
IT Man: Amanda Minix

D-U-N-S 19-160-0337 IMP
OPTIMA GRAPHICS INC
(Suby of TAYLOR CORP) ★
1540 Fencorp Dr, Fenton, MO 63026-2942
Tel (636) 349-3396 Founded/Ownrshp 1988
Sales 48.5MME EMP 240
SIC 3577 Graphic displays, except graphic terminals; Graphic displays, except graphic terminals
Pr: Kevin Kirbey
VP: Christine Kimack
*Prin: James Hoffman
*Prin: Dave Hoffmann
VP Mfg: Jim Powers

D-U-N-S 79-497-3388
OPTIMA HEALTH PLAN
SENTARA FAMILY CARE
(Suby of SENTARA HEALTHCARE) ★
4417 Corp Ln Ste 150, Virginia Beach, VA 23462
Tel (757) 552-7401 Founded/Ownrshp 1984
Sales NA EMP 50E
SIC 6324 Health maintenance organization (HMO), insurance only; Health maintenance organization (HMO), insurance only
Pr: Ted Wille Jr
CFO: Ronald Bennion
VP: Karen Bray
VP: Michael Fache
Dir Rx: Robert Deguzman
Snr Sftwr: Steve Cutter
Netwrk Eng: Dean Brummet
Secur Mgr: Danny Achterfeld
Sales Exec: Robin Mitchell
Doctor: Vickie Smith MD
Pharmcst: Felicia Epps

D-U-N-S 03-703-7934
OPTIMA INC
OPTIMA LUXURY CONDOMINIUMS
630 Vernon Ave Ste E, Glencoe, IL 60022-1684
Tel (847) 835-8400 Founded/Ownrshp 1977
Sales 26.5MME EMP 100E
SIC 8712 1542 6552 6531 Architectural services; Commercial & office building, new construction; Subdividers & developers; Real estate managers; Architectural services; Commercial & office building, new construction; Subdividers & developers; Real estate managers
Pr: David C Hovey
CFO: Russell Harris
Sr VP: Bill Duke
*Sr VP: Jennifer Oppenheimer
VP: Matt Cison
*VP: Tod Desmarais
Off Mgr: Wendy Cesario
Dir IT: Dan Miller

OPTIMA LUXURY CONDOMINIUMS
See OPTIMA INC

D-U-N-S 82-960-5976
■ OPTIMA SERVICE SOLUTIONS LLC
(Suby of 3PD) ★
10800 Alpharetta Hwy, Roswell, GA 30076-1490
Tel (770) 667-4611 Founded/Ownrshp 2013
Sales 31.3MME EMP 438E
SIC 4731 Freight transportation arrangement; Freight rate information service
CEO: Steve Gordon

D-U-N-S 07-846-0646
OPTIMA SPECIALTY STEEL INC
200 S Biscayne Blvd, Miami, FL 33131-2310
Tel (877) 289-2277 Founded/Ownrshp 2008
Sales 590.6MME EMP 1,010E
SIC 3317 Tubes, seamless steel; Tubes, seamless steel
CEO: Mordechai Korf
*COO: Michael Salamon
*CFO: Anthony Verkruyse
*Ofcr: Ted Fairley
Counsel: Julia Kim

D-U-N-S 14-905-4152
OPTIMA STANTRON CORP
(Suby of ELMA ELECTRONIC INC) ★
1775 Macleod Dr, Lawrenceville, GA 30043-5718
Tel (770) 496-4000 Founded/Ownrshp 2003
Sales 20.8MME EMP 60
SIC 3469 Electronic enclosures, stamped or pressed metal
Pr: Shan Morgan
*VP: Peter Brunner
QA Dir: Carmen Urrutia-Theumer

OPTIMAL CAE
See OPTIMAL COMPUTER AIDED ENGINEERING INC

D-U-N-S 15-735-7955
OPTIMAL COMPUTER AIDED ENGINEERING INC
OPTIMAL CAE
47802 W Anchor Ct, Plymouth, MI 48170-2459
Tel (734) 414-7933 Founded/Ownrshp 1986
Sales 25.0MM EMP 250
SIC 8711 7361 Engineering services; Executive placement
Pr: Song Ling Young

D-U-N-S 00-673-3166
OPTIMAL FUNDING INC (DE)
1407 Route 9 Ste 2, Halfmoon, NY 12065-6588
Tel (518) 371-6886 Founded/Ownrshp 1996
Sales NA EMP 12
SIC 6162 6163 Mortgage bankers; Loan brokers; Mortgage bankers; Loan brokers
Pr: Michael Munro

OPTIMAL HOSPICE CARE
See OPTMIAL HOSPICE FOUNDATION

D-U-N-S 79-637-9246
OPTIMAL LTD
PALM TREE GROUP, THE
12701 Directors Dr, Stafford, TX 77477-3701
Tel (832) 886-5300 Founded/Ownrshp 1987
Sales 25.8MME EMP 45
SIC 5047 4789 Medical equipment & supplies; Cargo loading & unloading services
Pr: Mark Wallis
Pr: Mike Lee
*CEO: Manny Losada
*Treas: Vickie Wallis
VP: Sandhana Balasubramanian
*VP: Parker Bigley
Manager: Rosa Viasana

OPTIMAL SOLUTIONS AND TECH
See OST INC

D-U-N-S 07-979-3020
OPTIMAS OE SOLUTIONS HOLDING LLC
(Suby of OPTIMAS OE SOLUTIONS INTERMED LLC) ★
2651 Compass Rd, Glenview, IL 60026-8004
Tel (224) 521-8000 Founded/Ownrshp 2015
Sales 92.9MME EMP 752E
SIC 5063 Electrical apparatus & equipment; Wire & cable; Control & signal wire & cable, including coaxial; Hanging & fastening devices, electrical
Pr: Paul Bamatter
VP: Richard Hoffman

D-U-N-S 07-979-3021
OPTIMAS OE SOLUTIONS INC
(Suby of OPTIMAS OE SOLUTIONS HOLDING LLC) ★
2301 Patriot Blvd, Glenview, IL 60026-8020
Tel (224) 521-8000 Founded/Ownrshp 2015
Sales 27.5MME EMP 41E
SIC 5063 Electrical apparatus & equipment; Wire & cable; Control & signal wire & cable, including coaxial; Hanging & fastening devices, electrical
Pr: Paul Bamatter
VP: Richard Hoffman

D-U-N-S 07-979-3017
OPTIMAS OE SOLUTIONS INTERMED LLC
2651 Compass Rd, Glenview, IL 60026-8004
Tel (224) 521-8000 Founded/Ownrshp 2015
Sales 92.9MME EMP 755E
SIC 5063 Electrical apparatus & equipment; Wire & cable; Control & signal wire & cable, including coaxial; Hanging & fastening devices, electrical
Pr: Paul Bamatter
VP: Richard Hoffman

D-U-N-S 07-153-2704
OPTIMATIC MEDIA INC
(Suby of MATOMY MEDIA GROUP LTD)
58 W 40th St Fl 13, New York, NY 10018-2636
Tel (212) 968-0600 Founded/Ownrshp 2015
Sales 34.0MM EMP 20
SIC 7311 Advertising agencies; Advertising agencies
CEO: Chris Pfluger
VP: Anthony Mehale
VP: Tom Yamada
VP Mktg: Robert Kyncl

D-U-N-S 18-391-1999
OPTIMATION TECHNOLOGY INC
50 High Tech Dr, Rush, NY 14543-9772
Tel (585) 321-2300 Founded/Ownrshp 2012
Sales 136.4MME EMP 384
Accts Mengel Metzger Barr & Co L
SIC 8711 Engineering services; Engineering services
Pr: William K Pollock
CFO: Kelly Burns
VP: Tim Lasch
VP: Wendy Smith
Genl Mgr: Craig Eidson
Dir IT: Keith Spadpimiller
Snr PM: Ron Charette
Snr PM: Richard Laplante

D-U-N-S 78-706-4120
OPTIMAX SYSTEMS INC
6367 Dean Pkwy, Ontario, NY 14519-8939
Tel (585) 265-1020 Founded/Ownrshp 1991
Sales 31.5MME EMP 200E
SIC 3827 Lenses, optical: all types except ophthalmic; Prisms, optical; Lenses, optical: all types except ophthalmic; Prisms, optical
Ch Bd: Michael P Mandina
*CEO: Rick Plympton
*CFO: Tom Kelly
*VP: Richard Plympton
Mng Dir: Robert Sawyer
Dir IT: Rich Matchmer
IT Man: Rich Mathner
IT Man: Mike Spryn
Ql Cn Mgr: Patrick Augino
VP Sls: Mark Palvino
Mktg Mgr: Rick Plymptom

D-U-N-S 11-749-5184
OPTIMEDIA INTERNATIONAL US INC
(Suby of PUBLICIS GROUPE S A)
375 Hudson St Fl 7, New York, NY 10014-9603
Tel (212) 820-3200 Founded/Ownrshp 2000
Sales 37.3MME EMP 390
SIC 7319 8748 Media buying service; Communications consulting; Media buying service; Communications consulting
CEO: David Ehlers
*CFO: Thomas McElroy
*Ex VP: Maureen Bosetti
*Ex VP: Susan Eberhart
*Ex VP: Frank Friedman
Sr VP: Jason Harrington
Sr VP: Randy Novick
Sr VP: Andy Rowe
Sr VP: Tom Scott
VP: Lisa Allison
VP: Nicholas Caputo
VP: Tom Cecil
VP: Raymond Douglas
VP: Patrick English
VP: Rudy Grahn
VP: Patrick Jurasic
VP: Karyn Meyer

VP: Judy Popky
VP: Meg Ryan
VP: James Shoreland
VP: Shannon Taylor

D-U-N-S 15-101-8996
OPTIMEDICA CORP
1310 Moffett Park Dr, Sunnyvale, CA 94089-1133
Tel (408) 850-8600 *Founded/Ownrshp* 2004
Sales 50.9MM^E *EMP* 140
SIC 3841 Eye examining instruments & apparatus; Eye examining instruments & apparatus
CEO: Miles White
**Pr:* Mark J Forchette
**CFO:* Mark A Murray
VP: David D Scott
VP: Jean-Robert Strele
Exec: Mona Wallace

D-U-N-S 61-386-6735
■ OPTIMER PHARMACEUTICALS INC
(*Suby of* CUBIST PHARMACEUTICALS LLC) ★
4747 Executive Dr # 1100, San Diego, CA 92121-3114
Tel (858) 909-0736 *Founded/Ownrshp* 2013
Sales 44.2MM^E *EMP* 281
SIC 2834 Pharmaceutical preparations; Pharmaceutical preparations
CEO: Henry A McKinnell
Pr: John Womelsdorf
**COO:* Eric Sirota
**CFO:* Stephen Webster
**Chf Cred:* Meredith Schaum
Ex VP: Ying Lee
Ex VP: Jason Spark
**Sr VP:* Linda E Amper
**Sr VP:* Sherwood L Gorbach
Sr VP: Gregory Papaz
Sr VP: Kasia Petchel
Sr VP: Nancy Ruiz
Sr VP: Cynthia Schwalm
Sr VP: Glenn Tillotson
VP: Sylva Collins
VP: David Duncan
VP: Jessica Warren
VP: Kong Youe
VP Bus Dev: Bhooshi Silva
Assoc Dir: Abby Zamora

D-U-N-S 83-243-5924
OPTIMITY ADVISORS LLC
1600 K St Nw Ste 200, Washington, DC 20006-2825
Tel (202) 872-5890 *Founded/Ownrshp* 2009
Sales 25.7MM^E *EMP* 225
SIC 8742 Business consultant; Business consultant

D-U-N-S 03-817-2599 IMP
OPTIMIZED PROCESS DESIGNS LLC
O P D
(*Suby of* KOCH-GLITSCH LP) ★
25610 Clay Rd, Katy, TX 77493-7898
Tel (281) 371-7500 *Founded/Ownrshp* 2000
Sales 104.7MM^E *EMP* 200
SIC 1629 Industrial plant construction; Industrial plant construction
Pr: James Kuehler
**Treas:* Jeanne R Hernandez
**VP:* Matthew Flamini
**VP:* Gary Thompson
Ql Cn Mgr: Eddie Guerra
Snr Mgr: Leonard Simoneaux

D-U-N-S 05-790-3841 IMP
OPTIMIZED PROCESS FURNACES INC
3995 S Santa Fe Ave, Chanute, KS 66720-5402
Tel (620) 431-1260 *Founded/Ownrshp* 1972
Sales 33.2MM *EMP* 18
Accts Stafford & Westervelt Charter
SIC 3443 3567 3559 Heat exchangers, condensers & components; Industrial furnaces & ovens; Refinery, chemical processing & similar machinery; Heat exchangers, condensers & components; Industrial furnaces & ovens; Refinery, chemical processing & similar machinery
Pr: Rob Phillips
**Ex VP:* Mike Miller
Off Mgr: Ella Brazil

D-U-N-S 92-814-0172
OPTIMIZELY INC
631 Howard St Ste 101, San Francisco, CA 94105-3970
Tel (415) 376-4598 *Founded/Ownrshp* 2009
Sales 75.9MM^E *EMP* 300
SIC 7371 Computer software development
CEO: Dan Siroker
Chf Mktg O: Jessie Becker
VP: Wyatt Jenkins
VP: Jay Mandal
Exec: Kristin Brey
Snr Sftwr: Tyler Brandt
Snr Sftwr: Peng-Wen Chen
Snr Sftwr: Jordan Garcia
Snr Sftwr: Mustafa Paksoy
Snr Sftwr: Eric Siroker
**CTO:* Pete Koomen

D-U-N-S 86-718-0085
OPTIMOS LLC
3130 Frview Pk Dr Ste 800, Falls Church, VA 22042
Tel (703) 712-4000 *Founded/Ownrshp* 1992
Sales 29.7MM^E *EMP* 200
SIC 7379 7373 7371 7372 Computer related consulting services; ;Turnkey vendors, computer systems; Custom computer programming services; Application computer software; Computer related consulting services; ;Turnkey vendors, computer systems; Custom computer programming services; Application computer software
CEO: Todd Stottlemyer
VP: Peter Warren
Off Mgr: Ferry Tabib

D-U-N-S 80-242-3822
■ OPTIMUM CHOICE INC
(*Suby of* MID ATLANTIC MEDICAL SERVICES LLC) ★
800 King Farm Blvd # 600, Rockville, MD 20850-5979
Tel (301) 417-2172 *Founded/Ownrshp* 1987
Sales NA *EMP* 950
SIC 6411 6324 Insurance information & consulting services; Group hospitalization plans; Insurance information & consulting services; Group hospitalization plans
Ch Bd: Mark D Groban

D-U-N-S 12-255-1377
OPTIMUM CONTROLS CORP
1301 Rosemont Ave, Reading, PA 19604-1212
Tel (610) 375-0990 *Founded/Ownrshp* 1992
Sales 21.3MM^E *EMP* 72
SIC 3822 3825 3625 7629 Building services monitoring controls, automatic; Digital test equipment, electronic & electrical circuits; Relays & industrial controls; Electronic equipment repair
Pr: Michael P Galiyano
**VP:* Mark J Galiyano
Sftwr Eng: Bill Staffeldt

D-U-N-S 05-917-2242
■ OPTIMUM MEDIA DIRECTION INC
(*Suby of* OMNICOM GROUP INC) ★
195 Broadway, New York, NY 10007-3100
Tel (212) 590-7100 *Founded/Ownrshp* 1994
Sales 30.4M *EMP* 400^E
SIC 8748 Business consulting; Business consulting
CEO: Page Thompson
**Pr:* Joe Uva

OPTIMUM PLASTICS
See BLOOMER HOLDINGS INC

D-U-N-S 94-572-6743 IMP
OPTIMUM PLASTICS INC
(*Suby of* BLOOMER HOLDINGS INC) ★
1188 S Houk Rd, Delaware, OH 43015-3857
Tel (740) 369-2770 *Founded/Ownrshp* 2014
Sales 20.7MM^E *EMP* 45
SIC 3081 2673 Unsupported plastics film & sheet; Plastic & pliofilm bags
Pr: Robert Clemons
**Treas:* Jon Bates

D-U-N-S 01-124-6407
■ OPTIMUM QUALITY GRAINS LLC (IA)
PIONEER
(*Suby of* PIONEER HI-BRED INTERNATIONAL INC) ★
7100 Nw 62nd Ave, Johnston, IA 50131-2937
Tel (515) 270-3200 *Founded/Ownrshp* 1998
Sales 101.1MM^E *EMP* 68
SIC 5153 Grain elevators; Grain elevators
Pr: Dean Oestreich
CFO: Frank Ross
VP: Diane Bridgewater
VP: Paul Shickler
VP: John Soper
IT Man: Arnold Lemker
Netwrk Mgr: Steve Huber
Doctor: Dilbag Multani
Snr Mgr: Fred Funk
Snr Mgr: Dwight Lager
Snr Mgr: Mairi Winslow

D-U-N-S 79-064-6418
OPTIMUM RE CORP
OPTIMUM RE-INSURANCE
(*Suby of* GROUPE OPTIMUM INC)
1345 Rver Bend Dr Ste 100, Dallas, TX 75247
Tel (214) 559-0850 *Founded/Ownrshp* 1987
Sales NA *EMP* 95
SIC 6311 6321 Life insurance; Benevolent insurance associations; Accident & health insurance carriers
Pr: Serge Goulet
**Pr:* Mario Georgiev
Sr VP: Yves Leclerc
VP Admn: Melanie Singletary
Dir IT: Chantal Lessard
Dir IT: Joshua Stewart

D-U-N-S 60-208-8155
OPTIMUM RE INSURANCE CO
(*Suby of* OPTIMUM RE CORP) ★
1335 Rver Bend Dr Ste 100, Dallas, TX 75247
Tel (214) 528-2020 *Founded/Ownrshp* 1978
Sales NA *EMP* 45
SIC 6321 6311 Accident & health insurance carriers; Disability health insurance; Life insurance carriers
**Ch Bd:* Gilles Blondeau
**Pr:* Mario Georgiev
**Treas:* Jean-Claude Page
Ex VP: Gordon Gibbins
Admn Mgr: Connie Cardenas

OPTIMUM RE-INSURANCE
See OPTIMUM RE CORP

OPTIMUM WEST
See BRESNAN BROADBAND HOLDINGS LLC

D-U-N-S 11-983-7367
OPTIMUS HEALTH CARE INC
982 E Main St, Bridgeport, CT 06608-1913
Tel (203) 696-3260 *Founded/Ownrshp* 1976
Sales 48.5MM *EMP* 330
Accts Guilmartin Dipiro & Sokolowski
SIC 8093 8011 Specialty outpatient clinics; Specialized medical practitioners, except internal; Specialty outpatient clinics; Specialized medical practitioners, except internal
CEO: Ludwig M Spinelli
**CFO:* Kishore Solanki
IT Man: Thomas Hill
Obsttrcn: Brenda I Kulikowski
Doctor: Kathleen F Ballas

D-U-N-S 13-151-3467 IMP/EXP
OPTIMUS INC
MARKYS CAVIAR INTL FD EMPORIUM
1000 Nw 159th Dr, Miami, FL 33169-5806
Tel (305) 758-9282 *Founded/Ownrshp* 1985
Sales 23.0MM^E *EMP* 55
SIC 5149 Groceries & related products
Pr: Mark Zaslavsky
CFO: Steve Campos
**VP:* Mark Gelman
Opers Mgr: Irina Mitsnefes
Sls Dir: Mike Zizzo
Sls Mgr: Gidget Hidalgo
Sales Asso: Mattieu Montero

D-U-N-S 16-151-4351 IMP
OPTIMUS INDUSTRIES LLC
CHANUTE MANUFACTURING
5727 S Lewis Ave Ste 600, Tulsa, OK 74105-7147
Tel (918) 491-9191 *Founded/Ownrshp* 1986
Sales 40.0MM *EMP* 200
SIC 3441

OPTION 1 NUTRITION SOLUTIONS
See JAMES L WILEY

D-U-N-S 83-309-4779
OPTION 1 NUTRITION SOLUTIONS LLC
(*Suby of* OPTION 1 NUTRITION HOLDINGS, LLC)
2460 E Germann Rd Ste 18, Chandler, AZ 85286-1573
Tel (480) 883-1188 *Founded/Ownrshp* 2002
Sales 122.1MM^E *EMP* 130
SIC 5047 Medical & hospital equipment; Medical & hospital equipment

OPTION CARE
See WALGREENS INFUSION SERVICES INC

D-U-N-S 92-740-3915 IMP
■ OPTION CARE ENTERPRISES INC
(*Suby of* OPTION CARE) ★
1411 Lake Cook Rd, Deerfield, IL 60015-5213
Tel (800) 879-6137 *Founded/Ownrshp* 1979
Sales 47.8MM^E *EMP* 1,400^E
SIC 8082 5122 8093 5912 8049 Home health care services; Franchises, selling or licensing; Medicinals & botanicals; Specialty outpatient clinics; Drug stores; Nutritionist; Home health care services; Medicinals & botanicals; Specialty outpatient clinics; Drug stores; Nutritionist
Pr: Paul Mastrapa
**Treas:* Rich Hugel

D-U-N-S 82-825-9759
OPTION ENERGY LLC
5481 N Whitetail Ln, Ludington, MI 49431-9672
Tel (269) 329-4317 *Founded/Ownrshp* 2008
Sales 275.0MM *EMP* 15
SIC 4924 1311 4931 1711 Natural gas distribution; Natural gas production; ; Solar energy contractor; Natural gas distribution; Natural gas production; ; Solar energy contractor

D-U-N-S 07-440-9020
OPTIONS CLEARING CORP
OPTIONS INDUSTRY COUNCIL
1 N Wacker Dr Fl 5, Chicago, IL 60606-2818
Tel (312) 322-6200 *Founded/Ownrshp* 1972
Sales 169.1MM *EMP* 338
Accts Deloitte And Touche Llp Chica
SIC 6289 Security & commodity clearinghouses; Security & commodity clearinghouses
Ch Bd: Wayne P Luthringshausen
Pr: James E Brown
Pr: Michael E Cahill
CFO: Frank J Larocca
CFO: Kimberly McGarry
**V Ch Bd:* Paul Brody
**V Ch Bd:* Richard R Lindsey
Chf Cred: Jean Cawley
Ofcr: Michael Walinskas
Ex VP: Michael McClain
Ex VP: Gina McFadden
VP: Larry P Brown
VP: John Dodson
VP: William Eineke
VP: Amy Farnstrom
VP: Chris Hudon
VP: Geri Love
VP: Douglas Mackay
Board of Directors: Thomas Callahan, George S Fischer, Thomas A Frank, Andrew D Kolinsky, Eric W Noll, Philip A Pendergraft, Tom Stern, John S Willian

OPTIONS FOR INDEPENDENT
See CEREBRAL PALSY OF MASSACHUSETTS INC

D-U-N-S 55-588-4147
OPTIONS FOR LEARNING
HEAD START
885 S Village Oaks Dr # 12, Covina, CA 91724-3615
Tel (626) 967-7848 *Founded/Ownrshp* 1981
Sales 64.6MM *EMP* 600
Accts Vasin Heyn & Company Calabasa
SIC 8351 Head start center, except in conjunction with school; Group day care center; Head start center, except in conjunction with school; Group day care center
Ex Dir: Cliff Marcussen
COO: Dolores Meade
Ex Dir: Melissa Takeda

D-U-N-S 61-628-2877
OPTIONS FOR YOUTH-VICTOR VALLEY INC
199 S Los Robles Ave # 700, Pasadena, CA 91101-4679
Tel (626) 685-9300 *Founded/Ownrshp* 1987
Sales 30.9MM *EMP* 300
SIC 8299 8211 8742 Educational services; Elementary & secondary schools; School, college, university consultant; Educational services; Elementary & secondary schools; School, college, university consultant
Pr: John N Joan

D-U-N-S 80-469-7068
OPTIONS GROUP INC
121 E 18th St Lbby L, New York, NY 10003-2148
Tel (212) 982-0900 *Founded/Ownrshp* 1992
Sales 20.2MM^E *EMP* 70^E
SIC 7361 Executive placement; Executive placement
CEO: Michael Karp
Mng Pt: Ed Kass
Mng Pt: Gene Shen
Pr: Robert Reed
VP: Eugenia Bae
VP: Ramona Batista
VP: Shufen Chen
VP: Eddie Clay
VP: Loran Fredric
VP: Stuart Halfen
VP: Satanovsky Kirill
VP: Lauren Leibson
VP: Jennifer Levin
VP: Sera Li
VP: Darren Marcou
VP: Anna Miles
VP: Rudy Modylevsky
VP: Frantz Peter
VP: Aaron Popowsky
VP: Oliver Read
VP: Tade Reen

OPTIONS INDUSTRY COUNCIL
See OPTIONS CLEARING CORP

D-U-N-S 79-065-2007
OPTIONS INFORMATION TECHNOLOGY LLC
(*Suby of* OPTIONS TECHNOLOGY LIMITED)
100 Park Ave Fl 6, New York, NY 10017-5560
Tel (646) 205-2500 *Founded/Ownrshp* 2005
Sales 22.0MM^E *EMP* 75^E
SIC 7374 7379 Computer processing services; Computer related consulting services
**COO:* Danny Moore
Sr VP: Ken Barnes
Sr VP: Tim Yockel
CTO: John Bryant
Netwrk Eng: Jake Beeman
Sls Mgr: Tim Dillon

D-U-N-S 14-685-8795
■ OPTIONS XPRESS HOLDINGS INC
(*Suby of* CHARLES SCHWAB CORP) ★
311 W Monroe St Ste 1000, Chicago, IL 60606-4663
Tel (312) 630-3300 *Founded/Ownrshp* 2011
Sales 53.5MM^E *EMP* 408^E
SIC 6211 Security brokers & dealers; Stock brokers & dealers; Stock option dealers; Security brokers & dealers; Stock brokers & dealers; Stock option dealers
Pr: David A Fisher
**CFO:* Adam J Dewitt
Ofcr: Ben Stein
**Ofcr:* Thomas E Stern
Ex VP: Peter J Bottini
Ex VP: Peter Clemson
VP: Marcia Cremin
VP: Lori Prokopenko
Ex Dir: Nina Milovac

D-U-N-S 00-937-6240
■ OPTIONSXPRESS INC
(*Suby of* OPTIONS XPRESS HOLDINGS INC) ★
311 W Monroe St Ste 1000, Chicago, IL 60606-4663
Tel (312) 629-5455 *Founded/Ownrshp* 2001
Sales 38.9MM^E *EMP* 105
SIC 4813
CEO: David S Kalt
**Pr:* David Fisher
**CFO:* Adam Dewitt
Bd of Dir: Christopher J Dean
Ex VP: Benjamin Bennett
**Ex VP:* Ned Bennett
Ex VP: Peter J Bottini
Ex VP: Rumi Kuli
VP: Ron Baakkonen
Snr Sftwr: Sanket Brahmbhatt
Snr Sftwr: Nagendra Pasupula

D-U-N-S 00-379-5619 IMP
■ OPTIUM CORP (DE)
(*Suby of* FINISAR CORP) ★
200 Precision Rd, Horsham, PA 19044-1227
Tel (215) 675-3105 *Founded/Ownrshp* 2000, 2008
Sales 36.5MM^E *EMP* 267
SIC 3695 3357 Optical disks & tape, blank; Nonferrous wiredrawing & insulating; Optical disks & tape, blank; Nonferrous wiredrawing & insulating
CFO: David C Renner
**Sr VP:* Mark Colyar
**VP:* Christopher Brown
**VP Sls:* Anthony Musto

D-U-N-S 07-976-4996
OPTIV INC
1125 17th St Ste 1700, Denver, CO 80202-2032
Tel (303) 298-0600 *Founded/Ownrshp* 2014
Sales 4.1MMM^E *EMP* 1,400^E
SIC 5045 5065 6719 7381 Accounting machines using machine readable programs; Diskettes, computer; Investment holding companies, except banks; Detective & armored car services
Pr: Daniel Burns
Pr: Mark Williams
Treas: David Johnson
Ex VP: Tim Hoffman
Ex VP: Aaron Shilts
Ex VP: Dan Wilson
VP: David Roshak

D-U-N-S 01-946-6684
OPTIV SECURITY INC
(*Suby of* FISHNET HOLDINGS INC) ★
1125 17th St Ste 1700, Denver, CO 80202-2032
Tel (888) 732-9406 *Founded/Ownrshp* 1995
Sales 4.1MMM^E *EMP* 252
Accts Bkd Llp Kansas City Missour
SIC 5045 7379 7382 5065 Security systems services; Administrative services consultant; Business consultant; General management consultant; Financial consultant; Business consulting; Employee programs administration; Safety training serv[illegible]; Accounting machines using machine readable programs; ; Burglar alarm maintenance & monitoring; Diskettes, computer
CEO: Dan Burns
**Pr:* Mark Williams
**CFO:* David Roshak
**Chf Mktg O:* Steve Perkins
**Ex VP:* Tim Hoffman
**Ex VP:* Aaron Shilts
VP: Wendee Boeding
Rgnl Mgr: Bryan Barkhaus
Sales Exec: Doug Hebert
VP Sls: Troy Richards

D-U-N-S 60-721-1963
OPTIVER US LLC
(*Suby of* OPTIVER HOLDING B.V.)
130 E Randolph St # 1300, Chicago, IL 60601-6217
Tel (312) 821-9500 *Founded/Ownrshp* 2003

Sales 56.0MM[E] *EMP* 140
SIC 6211 Security brokers & dealers; Security brokers & dealers
CFO: Amy Shelly
Ofcr: Brian Hockinson
Exec: Carlo Falco
Mng Dir: Sebastiaan Koeling
Prgrm Mgr: Tom Burger
Snr Ntwrk: Peter Bardak
IT Man: Eric Hodges
Software D: Sona Aleksanyan
Software D: Craig Bowles
Software D: Matthew Nassr
Software D: Alexander Skorokhod

D-U-N-S 11-286-5048
OPTIVOR TECHNOLOGIES LLC
10820 Gilford Radl Ste 208, Annapolis Junction, MD 20701
Tel (240) 646-3910 *Founded/Ownrshp* 2001
Sales 20.7MM[E] *EMP* 35
SIC 3661 4899 8742 7373 1731 3571 Telephone & telegraph apparatus; Communication signal enhancement network system; Retail trade consultant; Value-added resellers, computer systems; Electrical work; Communications specialization; Computers, digital, analog or hybrid
Prin: Stuart Chandler
Sr VP: Paul Cantwell
**Prin:* Dearest Chandler
Opers Mgr: Rob Wynn

D-U-N-S 80-645-5929
OPTIVUS PROTON THERAPY INC
1475 Victoria Ct, San Bernardino, CA 92408-2831
Tel (909) 799-8300 *Founded/Ownrshp* 1992
Sales 21.8MM[E] *EMP* 75
SIC 3829 7371 8742 3699 Nuclear radiation & testing apparatus; Custom computer programming services; Maintenance management consultant; Electrical equipment & supplies
CEO: Jon W Slater
**CFO:* Daryl L Anderson
Snr Sftwr: Daniel Lafuze
Snr Sftwr: Tom Lee
Sftwr Eng: Erick Cortes
Plnt Mgr: Bryan Zook
Mktg Dir: Lisa Pizzi

D-U-N-S 14-745-1863
OPTMIAL HOSPICE FOUNDATION
OPTIMAL HOSPICE CARE
1315 Boughton Dr, Bakersfield, CA 93308-1613
Tel (661) 410-3000 *Founded/Ownrshp* 1979
Sales 182.7M *EMP* 400[E]
Accts Hubbell & Associates Inc Bak
SIC 8699 Charitable organization; Charitable organization
Off Mgr: Dolann Knox
Off Mgr: Joe Vega
Dir IT: Scott McDonald
Pr Dir: Todd Jeffries

D-U-N-S 07-250-7841 IMP
OPTO 22 (CA)
43044 Business Park Dr, Temecula, CA 92590-3614
Tel (951) 695-3000 *Founded/Ownrshp* 1974
Sales 63.3MM[E] *EMP* 200
SIC 3679 3823 3625 Electronic switches; Industrial instrmnts msrmnt display/control process variable; Relays & industrial controls; Electronic switches; Industrial instrmnts msrmnt display/control process variable; Relays & industrial controls
CEO: Mark Engman
**Ch:* Robert G Engman
**VP:* Benson Hougland
**VP:* Bob Sheffres
Software D: Jonathan Fischer
Sftwr Eng: Sean Cherbone
Sftwr Eng: Ron Koss
Sftwr Eng: Steve Sauls
Manager: Brian Barrett
Manager: Dave Engsberg
Snr Mgr: Surge Yu

D-U-N-S 08-588-4765 IMP/EXP
OPTO INTERNATIONAL INC
1325 N Mittel Blvd, Wood Dale, IL 60191-1024
Tel (847) 541-6786 *Founded/Ownrshp* 1981
Sales 35.0MM *EMP* 175
SIC 5046 Store fixtures; Store fixtures
CEO: Joshua Wyckoff
**Ch:* Graham Wood
**Sr VP:* Robin Brower
**VP:* Robert Sorensen
**VP:* Brett Woodley
Mfg Dir: William Sheckler
Mktg Mgr: Amanda Smith

D-U-N-S 92-613-2960 IMP
OPTOMA TECHNOLOGY INC
(*Suby of* OPTOMA CORPORATION)
3178 Laurelview Ct, Fremont, CA 94538-6535
Tel (510) 770-9917 *Founded/Ownrshp* 1995
Sales 27.7MM[E] *EMP* 120
SIC 3861 Projectors, still or motion picture, silent or sound; Projectors, still or motion picture, silent or sound
CEO: Shen Huei Wang
**Ex VP:* Hans Wang
Mng Dir: Brian Hsieh

OPTOMETRIC CENTER OF LOS ANGEL
See MARSHALL B KETCHUM UNIVERSITY

D-U-N-S 00-173-1889
OPTOPLEX CORP (CA)
3374 Gateway Blvd, Fremont, CA 94538-6525
Tel (510) 490-9930 *Founded/Ownrshp* 2000
Sales 38.2MM[E] *EMP* 300[E]
SIC 3661 7361 3827 Fiber optics communications equipment; Employment agencies; Optical instruments & lenses; Fiber optics communications equipment; Employment agencies; Optical instruments & lenses
Pr: James C Sha
**Ex VP:* Dar-Yuan Song
VP: Vincent Chien
VP: Li Hong
Dir Bus: James Pang
Off Mgr: Emily Wang
CTO: Jay Hsieh
**CTO:* Yung-Chieh Hsieh
MIS Dir: Jennifer Wang
Sftwr Eng: Ruian Chao

D-U-N-S 78-704-9266
OPTORO INC
5001 Forbes Blvd Ste A, Lanham, MD 20706-4429
Tel (301) 760-7003 *Founded/Ownrshp* 2004
Sales 71.2MM[E] *EMP* 200
SIC 5731 Consumer electronic equipment
CEO: Tobin Moore
**Genl Pt:* Lawson Devries
**Mng Pt:* Dan Levine
**Pr:* Adam Gitarello
Pr: Cris Lull
**CFO:* Robert Latchford
Software D: Eric McKenna

D-U-N-S 07-158-7096 IMP
OPTOS INC
OPTOS NORTH AMERICA
(*Suby of* OPTOS PUBLIC LIMITED COMPANY)
67 Forest St Ste 3, Marlborough, MA 01752-3088
Tel (508) 787-1400 *Founded/Ownrshp* 1998
Sales 46.7MM[E] *EMP* 85
SIC 3827 Optical instruments & lenses; Optical instruments & lenses
CEO: Stephane Sallmard
Sls Mgr: Michelle Aloe
Snr Mgr: Ben Rutherford
Snr Mgr: Jeffrey Shown

OPTOS NORTH AMERICA
See OPTOS INC

D-U-N-S 19-650-0461 IMP
OPTOVUE INC
2800 Bayview Dr, Fremont, CA 94538-6518
Tel (510) 623-8868 *Founded/Ownrshp* 2003
Sales 24.9MM[E] *EMP* 86
SIC 3841 5048 Surgical & medical instruments; Ophthalmic goods
CEO: Jay WEI
**Pr:* David Voris
**Sr VP:* Paul Kealey
Sr VP: Joseph Sharpe
**VP:* John Hawley
VP: Tony Ko
VP: Michael Sarrasin
VP: Bill Shields
**VP:* Gordon Wong
VP: Qienyuan Zhou
Area Mgr: Andy Millsom

OPTUM
See QUALITY SOFTWARE SERVICES INC

D-U-N-S 10-159-5036
■ **OPTUM GOVERNMENT SOLUTIONS INC**
INGENIX
(*Suby of* OPTUMINSIGHT INC) ★
13625 Technology Dr, Eden Prairie, MN 55344-2252
Tel (952) 833-7100 *Founded/Ownrshp* 2008
Sales 52.9MM[E] *EMP* 110
SIC 7375 Information retrieval services; Information retrieval services
Pr: Steven B Larsen
Pr: Lloyd Hagemo
Pr: Roze Seale
COO: Cliff Honiker
**Treas:* Robert Oberrender
Ex VP: Ted Chien
Sr VP: Paul Bihm
Sr VP: Dean Farley
Sr VP: Tom Trestler
VP: Tom Boehning
VP: John Drake
VP: Tom Knabel
Assoc Dir: Glen Blenkush
Dir Bus: Donald Potts

OPTUM HEALTH
See OPTUMHEALTH HOLDINGS LLC

D-U-N-S 07-967-4279
■ **OPTUM INC**
(*Suby of* UNITED HEALTHCARE SERVICES INC) ★
11000 Optum Cir, Eden Prairie, MN 55344-2503
Tel (952) 936-1300 *Founded/Ownrshp* 2009
Sales NA *EMP* 97[E]
SIC 6324 Health maintenance organization (HMO), insurance only
CEO: Larry Renfro
CFO: John F Rex
Treas: Robert Worth Oberrender
Sr VP: John Drakulich
Board of Directors: Amy Lynn Shaw

D-U-N-S 07-916-7710
■ **OPTUM360 LLC**
(*Suby of* OPTUMINSIGHT INC) ★
13625 Technology Dr, Eden Prairie, MN 55344-2252
Tel (952) 833-7100 *Founded/Ownrshp* 2013
Sales 96.6MM[E] *EMP* 900
SIC 7371 7375 2721 2731 Custom computer programming services; Information retrieval services; Custom computer programming services; Information retrieval services; Periodicals; Book publishing
CEO: Derrell James
VP: Kyle Hicok
VP: Monique Martin
Dir IT: Steve Groath
Netwrk Mgr: Laura Phillips
Sales Exec: Constance Weatherbe
Snr Mgr: Sanjay Dwivedi
Snr Mgr: Jennifer Eriksson

D-U-N-S 16-951-7450
■ **OPTUMHEALTH BANK INC**
UNITED HEALTHCARE
(*Suby of* UNITEDHEALTH GROUP INC) ★
2525 S Lake Park Blvd, Salt Lake City, UT 84120-8230
Tel (801) 963-6040 *Founded/Ownrshp* 2002
Sales NA *EMP* 400
SIC 6036 Savings institutions, not federally chartered; Savings institutions, not federally chartered
Pr: Kelvin L Anderson
CFO: Anna Gimble
Chf Cred: Anthony N Meadows
Chf Cred: Gary Murray
VP: Tami Eckstein
VP: David Hersom
VP: Tessa Matthews
Ex Dir: Pam Gold
IT Man: Bryant Burton

D-U-N-S 18-417-0082
■ **OPTUMHEALTH CARE SOLUTIONS INC**
(*Suby of* UNITED HEALTHCARE SERVICES INC) ★
6300 Highway 55, Golden Valley, MN 55427-4946
Tel (763) 595-3200 *Founded/Ownrshp* 1987
Sales NA *EMP* 4,000
SIC 6324 7374 8999 Hospital & medical service plans; Data processing & preparation; Personal services
Ch Bd: William McGuire
Pr: Stephen Hemsley
CEO: Jeanine Rivet
CFO: Patrick Erlandson
Prgrm Mgr: Lawrence Nemecek
VP Opers: David Cole
Mktg Mgr: Bridget Jo
Board of Directors: Gail Wilensky, William C Ballard Jr, Richard T Burke, James A Johnson, Thomas H Kean, Douglas W Leatherdale, Mary O Mundinger, Robert L Ryan, Donna E Shalala, William G Spears

D-U-N-S 79-113-6612
■ **OPTUMHEALTH HOLDINGS LLC**
OPTUM HEALTH
(*Suby of* UNITEDHEALTH GROUP INC) ★
6300 Highway 55, Golden Valley, MN 55427-4946
Tel (763) 595-3200 *Founded/Ownrshp* 2000
Sales NA *EMP* 24,000
SIC 6324 8741 6411 Hospital & medical service plans; Management services; Insurance agents, brokers & service; Hospital & medical service plans; Management services; Insurance agents, brokers & service
Pr: Dawn Owens
Pr: Don Yee
COO: Jason Vanden Akker
**CFO:* Paul Emerson
Ex VP: John M Prince
VP: Ken Anderson
VP: Scott Callahan
VP: Debra A Oberman
VP: Pamela Russo
Assoc Dir: Megan Essig
Assoc Dir: Linda Lundeen
Assoc Dir: Lindsay Schneider

D-U-N-S 10-564-8369
■ **OPTUMINSIGHT INC**
(*Suby of* UNITED HEALTHCARE SERVICES INC) ★
13625 Technology Dr, Eden Prairie, MN 55344-2252
Tel (952) 833-7100 *Founded/Ownrshp* 1996
Sales 460.5MM[E] *EMP* 2,703
SIC 7371 7375 8742 8741 Computer software development; Data base information retrieval; Management consulting services; Business management; Computer software development; Data base information retrieval; Management consulting services; Business management
CEO: Bill Miller
Pt: Patrice Matejka
**Pr:* William H Crown
Pr: Ron Jones
**Pr:* Eric D Murphy
**Pr:* Lee Valenta
Pr: Tim Wicks
**Pr:* Timothy A Wicks
COO: Peter Martin
COO: Steve Morgan
**CFO:* Gerald Knutson
Bd of Dir: Carla Goulart
Bd of Dir: Randy Owen
Sr VP: James Franke
**Sr VP:* Lynn Myhran
**VP:* Karen Erickson
**VP:* Steve Larsen
**VP:* Jim Murphy
VP: Tyler Viernow
VP Bus Dev: Steve Morelli
Assoc Dir: Meg Hoyecki

D-U-N-S 60-857-9066
■ **OPTUMINSIGHT INC**
(*Suby of* OPTUMINSIGHT INC) ★
2525 S Lake Park Blvd, Salt Lake City, UT 84120-8230
Tel (801) 982-3000 *Founded/Ownrshp* 1997
Sales 56.6MM[E] *EMP* 400
SIC 7371 7375 2741

D-U-N-S 86-866-7106
■ **OPTUMRX INC**
PRESCRIPTION SOLUTIONS
(*Suby of* UNITED HEALTHCARE SERVICES INC) ★
2300 Main St, Irvine, CA 92614-6223
Tel (714) 825-3600 *Founded/Ownrshp* 1990
Sales NA *EMP* 5,080
SIC 6324 6321 Hospital & medical service plans; Accident & health insurance; Hospital & medical service plans; Accident & health insurance
CEO: Mark Thierer
Pr: Timothy Wicks
COO: Jeff Park
CFO: Jeffrey Grosklags
CFO: Nancy O'Neill
VP: Lawrence Alderson
VP: Mark Knutson
VP: Robert Lahman
VP: Scott Neumann
VP: David Oberg
VP: Pedram Pahlavan
VP: Brian Solow
Dir Rx: Sheela Andrews
Dir Rx: Heidi C Lew

D-U-N-S 85-925-3783
OPTUS INC
3423 One Pl, Jonesboro, AR 72404-9335
Tel (800) 628-7491 *Founded/Ownrshp* 1991
Sales 36.7MM[E] *EMP* 100
SIC 5065 7629

OPUS AND W CONTRACTORS
See OPUS NORTHWEST LLC

D-U-N-S 80-778-8245
▲ **OPUS BANK**
19900 Macarthur Blvd # 1200, Irvine, CA 92612-8427
Tel (949) 250-9800 *Founded/Ownrshp* 2010
Sales NA *EMP* 607
Tkr Sym OPB *Exch* NGS
SIC 6029 Commercial banks; Commercial banks
CEO: Stephen H Gordon
Pr: Michael L Allison
Pr: Dino J D'Auria
COO: Jennifer Simmons
CFO: Nicole Carrillo
CFO: Thea Stuedli
Treas: Terrin Enssle
Treas: Erin Pryor
Chf Cred: Bob Granfelt
Bd of Dir: Robert Shackleton
Chf Mktg O: Brad Davis
Ofcr: Balaji Krishna
Ex VP: Dan Borland
Ex VP: Carey Brennan
Ex VP: Debbie McLeod
Sr VP: Alan Bergfeld
Sr VP: James Crumpton
Sr VP: Karma Flower
Sr VP: Lillian Gavin
Sr VP: Kim Gordon
Sr VP: Rebecca Intfen

D-U-N-S 61-440-4965
OPUS CAPITAL MARKETS CONSULTANTS LLC
(*Suby of* WIPRO GALLAGHER SOLUTIONS, INC.)
100 Tri State Intl, Lincolnshire, IL 60069-4403
Tel (224) 632-1300 *Founded/Ownrshp* 2005
Sales 20.9MM[E] *EMP* 150
SIC 8742 Financial consultant; Financial consultant
**Ofcr:* John Levonick
**Prin:* Joseph Andrea
Mng Dir: Jawad Khan

D-U-N-S 60-224-7645
OPUS CORP
OPUS GROUP, THE
10350 Bren Rd W, Minnetonka, MN 55343-9014
Tel (952) 656-4444 *Founded/Ownrshp* 1953
Sales 549.0MM[E] *EMP* 775
SIC 1542 6552 6531 Design & erection, combined: non-residential; Land subdividers & developers, commercial; Real estate managers; Design & erection, combined: non-residential; Land subdividers & developers, commercial; Real estate managers
Ch Bd: Keith P Bednarowski
**Pr:* Mark Rauenhorst
**CEO:* Tim Becker
CEO: Claire Janssen
**Ex VP:* Luz Campa
Ex VP: Daniel Queenan
Sr VP: Pete Carlson
Sr VP: Peter Coakley
**Sr VP:* Andy Deckas
Sr VP: Craig Guers
Sr VP: Don Little
**Sr VP:* Dan Nicol
Sr VP: Lawrence Pobuda
Sr VP: Jerry Shaw
Sr VP: Howard Zoromsky
VP: Randy Ackerman
VP: Les Blum
VP: Scott Brody
VP: Richard Clarke
VP: Steve Cohen
VP: Jason Conway

D-U-N-S 07-972-4101
OPUS DESIGN BUILD LLC
10350 Bren Rd W, Minnetonka, MN 55343-9014
Tel (952) 656-4444 *Founded/Ownrshp* 2009
Sales 352.0MM[E] *EMP* 11[E]
SIC 1522 1541 Hotel/motel & multi-family home construction; Dry cleaning plant construction
Pr: David F Bangasser
**VP:* James R Caesar
**VP:* James J Erwin
**VP:* Manish Gandhi
**VP:* Michael K Healy
**VP:* Craig Larson
**VP:* John Williams

D-U-N-S 07-951-0436
OPUS GLOBAL HOLDINGS LLC
265 Lytton Ave Ste 302, Palo Alto, CA 94301-1488
Tel (650) 763-9101 *Founded/Ownrshp* 2013
Sales 27.9MM[E] *EMP* 117
SIC 6799 Investors
CEO: Douglas G Bergeron
Sr VP: Julio C Quinteros Jr

OPUS GROUP, THE
See OPUS CORP

D-U-N-S 96-458-9134
OPUS INSPECTION INC
ENVIRONMENTAL SYSTEMS PRODUCTS
7 Kripes Rd, East Granby, CT 06026-9720
Tel (860) 392-2100 *Founded/Ownrshp* 2008
Sales 75.9MM[E] *EMP* 240[E]
SIC 7371 Computer software development; Computer software development
Pr: Lothar Geilen
**Treas:* Jeff Bagley

D-U-N-S 16-526-9395
■ **OPUS INVESTMENT MANAGEMENT INC**
(*Suby of* HANOVER INSURANCE GROUP INC) ★
440 Lincoln St, Worcester, MA 01653-0002
Tel (508) 855-1000 *Founded/Ownrshp* 1985
Sales NA *EMP* 3,000
SIC 6311 6321 6324 6351 6722 Life insurance carriers; Health insurance carriers; Hospital & medical service plans; Liability insurance; Mutual fund sales, on own account; Life insurance carriers; Health insurance carriers; Hospital & medical service plans; Liability insurance; Mutual fund sales, on own account

Pr: Frederick Effinger
Genl Pt: Robert Henderson
V Ch: John Towers
**Pr:* John F O'Brien
COO: Kristen Park
CFO: Edward J Parry III
VP: Bruce Anderson
VP: Richard J Baker
VP: John Chandler
VP: David Firstenberg
VP: John Jack
VP: John Kavanaugh
VP: John F Kelly
VP: Bruce Letizia
VP: Sheryl Oaconnell
VP: Joseph Rovito

D-U-N-S 00-780-6458
OPUS NORTHWEST CONSTRUCTION CORP
OPUS NORTHWEST MANAGEMENT
(*Suby of* OPUS AND W CONTRACTORS) ★
10350 Bren Rd W, Hopkins, MN 55343-9014
Tel (952) 656-4444 *Founded/Ownrshp* 1998
Sales 20.4MM^E *EMP* 150
SIC 1542 1541 6552 Commercial & office building, new construction; Industrial buildings, new construction; Land subdividers & developers, commercial; Commercial & office building, new construction; Industrial buildings, new construction; Land subdividers & developers, commercial
Ch Bd: Mark Rauenhorst
**Pr:* John Solberg
**Founder:* Gerald Rauenhorst
**Sr VP:* John McKenzie

D-U-N-S 82-508-0492
OPUS NORTHWEST LLC
OPUS AND W CONTRACTORS
2025 1st Ave Ph B, Seattle, WA 98121-2100
Tel (425) 467-2701 *Founded/Ownrshp* 1994
Sales 109.8MM^E *EMP* 1,200
SIC 6552 1542 Subdividers & developers; Commercial & office building contractors; Subdividers & developers; Commercial & office building contractors
Pr: John Solberg
**VP:* Jim Heller
**VP:* Tom Parsons
**VP:* Mike Ruhl

OPUS NORTHWEST MANAGEMENT
See OPUS NORTHWEST CONSTRUCTION CORP

D-U-N-S 07-999-4351
OPUS SOLUTIONS LLC
SP STEALTH
9000 Sw Nimbus Ave, Beaverton, OR 97008-7181
Tel (971) 223-0777 *Founded/Ownrshp* 1999
Sales 28.9MM^E *EMP* 70^E
SIC 7389 4813 4731 5947 Decoration service for special events; Field warehousing; ; Transportation agents & brokers; Gift shop
Dir Soc: Jana Saul
Off Mgr: Tammy Smith

OPUSKANE
See FREIGHTLINER OF SAN ANTONIO LTD

OPW ENGINEERED SYSTEMS
See OPW FUELING COMPONENTS INC

D-U-N-S 79-138-3701 IMP
■ **OPW ENGINEERED SYSTEMS INC**
(*Suby of* OPW FLUID TRANSFER GROUP) ★
2726 Henkle Dr, Lebanon, OH 45036-8209
Tel (888) 771-9438 *Founded/Ownrshp* 2007
Sales 20.2MM^E *EMP* 60
SIC 3494 3825 3625 3568 3535 Valves & pipe fittings; Instruments to measure electricity; Relays & industrial controls; Power transmission equipment; Conveyors & conveying equipment
Pr: Tim Warning
**CEO:* Robert B Nicholson III
**VP:* Mike Krauser
Manager: Bill Burns

OPW ENGINEERING SYSTEMS
See OPW INC

■ **OPW FLUID TRANSFER GROUP**
(*Suby of* DOVER CORP) ★
4304 N Mattox Rd, Kansas City, MO 64150-9755
Tel (816) 741-6600 *Founded/Ownrshp* 1998
Sales 92.1MM^E *EMP* 60^E
SIC 3494 3825 3625 3568 3535 Valves & pipe fittings; Instruments to measure electricity; Relays & industrial controls; Power transmission equipment; Conveyors & conveying equipment
Pr: David Crouse

D-U-N-S 82-874-3604 IMP/EXP
■ **OPW FUELING COMPONENTS INC**
OPW ENGINEERED SYSTEMS
(*Suby of* DOVER CORP) ★
9393 Prnceton Glendale Rd, West Chester, OH 45011-9707
Tel (513) 870-3315 *Founded/Ownrshp* 2007
Sales 52.9MM^E *EMP* 230^E
SIC 2899 Fuel treating compounds; Fuel treating compounds
Pr: David Crouse
Sls Mgr: Jeff Steel

D-U-N-S 96-570-7128 IMP
OPW INC
OPW ENGINEERING SYSTEMS
9393 Prnceton Glendale Rd, West Chester, OH 45011-9707
Tel (513) 870-3100 *Founded/Ownrshp* 1947
Sales NA *EMP* 559
SIC 3494

OPWDD
See NEW YORK STATE OFFICE FOR PEOPLE WITH DEVELOPMENTAL DISABILITIES

OQSG
See INDUSTRIAL SOLUTIONS GROUP LLC

D-U-N-S 09-347-8899
OR CITY OF ALBANY
333 Broadalbin St Sw, Albany, OR 97321-2247
Tel (541) 917-7500 *Founded/Ownrshp* 1848
Sales NA *EMP* 391
SIC 9111 City & town managers' offices; ; City & town managers' offices;
V Ch: Ralph Reid Jr
**Prin:* Pat Eastman
IT Man: Allen Pilgrim

D-U-N-S 12-420-4756
■ **ORA CENTRAL REGIONAL FIELD OFFICE**
(*Suby of* OFFICE OF REGULATORY AFFAIRS) ★
20 N Michigan Ave Ste 510, Chicago, IL 60602-4826
Tel (312) 353-9400 *Founded/Ownrshp* 2010
Sales NA *EMP* 936^E
SIC 9431 Administration of public health programs;

D-U-N-S 95-743-8013
■ **ORA PACIFIC REGIONAL FIELD OFFICE**
(*Suby of* OFFICE OF REGULATORY AFFAIRS) ★
1301 Clay St Ste 1180n, Oakland, CA 94612-5242
Tel (510) 287-2700 *Founded/Ownrshp* 2010
Sales NA *EMP* 946^E
SIC 9431 Administration of public health programs;

D-U-N-S 03-007-5481
■ **ORA SOUTHWEST REGIONAL FIELD OFFICE**
(*Suby of* OFFICE OF REGULATORY AFFAIRS) ★
4040 N Central Expy # 900, Dallas, TX 75204-3158
Tel (214) 253-4901 *Founded/Ownrshp* 2010
Sales NA *EMP* 837^E
SIC 9431 Administration of public health programs;

D-U-N-S 01-304-4532 IMP
■ **ORACLE AMERICA INC**
SUN MICROSYSTEMS
(*Suby of* ORACLE CORP) ★
500 Oracle Pkwy, Redwood City, CA 94065-1677
Tel (650) 506-7000 *Founded/Ownrshp* 2010
Sales 6.3MMM^E *EMP* 29,000
SIC 3571 7379 7373 7372 3674 Minicomputers; Computer related consulting services; Systems integration services; Operating systems computer software; Microprocessors; Minicomputers; Computer related consulting services; Systems integration services; Operating systems computer software; Microprocessors
Ch: Jeffrey O Henley
Pr: Safra A Catz
Pr: Mark V Hurd
CFO: Kevin Melia
Bd of Dir: William Crowell
Ex VP: Michael A Dillon
Ex VP: John Fowler
Ex VP: Richard Green
Ex VP: Michael E Lehman
Ex VP: William N Macgowan
Ex VP: Eugene McCabe
Ex VP: Gregory M Papadopoulos
Ex VP: Peter Ryan
Ex VP: Mike Splain
Ex VP: Stuart Wells
Ex VP: David Yen
Sr VP: Dorian Daley
Sr VP: Joe Heel
Sr VP: M Rten Mickos
Sr VP: Cindy Reese
Sr VP: Karen Rohde

D-U-N-S 13-204-9524
■ **ORACLE BIGMACHINES LLC**
BIGMACHINES, INC.
(*Suby of* ORACLE CORP) ★
570 Lake Cook Rd Ste 200, Deerfield, IL 60015-5272
Tel (847) 572-0300 *Founded/Ownrshp* 2013
Sales 22.8MM^E *EMP* 200
SIC 7371 Computer software development & applications; Computer software development & applications
CEO: David Bonnette
Pr: Curtis Bull
Pr: Art Carlucci
COO: Sean Fallon
Chf Mktg O: Marlene Williamson
Sr VP: Joni Kahn
Sr VP: Joachim Klein
Sr VP: Thomas P Padgett
Sr VP: John Pulling
Sr VP: Christopher Shutts
VP: Rick Bell
VP: John Coleman
VP: Brian Murmane

D-U-N-S 06-699-5245
ORACLE CORP
17901 Von Karman Ave # 800, Irvine, CA 92614-5241
Tel (650) 506-7000 *Founded/Ownrshp* 2011
Sales 29.5MM^E *EMP* 567^E
SIC 8999 Services
Prin: Nagender Prasad
VP: Gary Koopman
Snr Sftwr: Eric Ang
Snr Sftwr: Tony Hsu
Snr Sftwr: Deepthi Jammula
CTO: Josfa Allmen
QA Dir: Melissa Kwan
Software D: Rong Fan
Software D: Dmitry Golovin
Software D: Debraj Sinha
Sftwr Eng: Chuck Anderson

D-U-N-S 14-470-9193
▲ **ORACLE CORP**
500 Oracle Pkwy, Redwood City, CA 94065-1675
Tel (610) 407-5150 *Founded/Ownrshp* 1977
Sales 38.2MMM *EMP* 132,000
Accts Ernst & Young Llp San Jose C
Tkr Sym ORCL *Exch* NYS
SIC 7372 7379 8243 3571 3674 Prepackaged software; Business oriented computer software; Application computer software; Computer related consulting services; Software training, computer; Minicomputers; Microprocessors; Prepackaged software; Business oriented computer software; Application computer software; Computer related consulting services; Software training, computer; Minicomputers; Microprocessors
CEO: Safra Catz
**Ch Bd:* Lawrence J Ellison
Pr: Jan Wagner
**CEO:* Safra A Catz
**CEO:* Mark V Hurd
Chf Mktg O: Denise Macauley
Ex VP: Dorian E Daley
Ex VP: John Fowler
Ex VP: Lo C Le Guisquet
Ex VP: Jay Nussbaum
Ex VP: George Roberts
Ex VP: Juergen Rottler
Ex VP: Charles A Rozwat
Ex VP: Michael E Splain
Ex VP: William Corey West
Ex VP: Ronald A Wohl
Sr VP: Sohaib Abbasi
Sr VP: Jerry Baker
Sr VP: Rich Geraffo
Sr VP: Mary Anne Gillespie
Sr VP: Jerry Held
Board of Directors: Jeffrey S Berg, H Raymond Bingham, Michael J Boskin, Bruce R Chizen, George H Conrades, Renee James, Hector Garcia-Molina, Leon E Panetta, Naomi O Seligman

D-U-N-S 87-672-6266
ORACLE ELEVATOR CO
43 Daycoeton Pl, Torrington, CT 06790-6326
Tel (860) 618-5202 *Founded/Ownrshp* 1990
Sales 38.0MM *EMP* 224
SIC 1791 1796 7699 Smoke stacks, steel: installation & maintenance; Elevator installation & conversion; Elevators: inspection, service & repair; Smoke stacks, steel: installation & maintenance; Elevator installation & conversion; Elevators: inspection, service & repair
Pr: William Miller
**CFO:* Britt Briatico
**CFO:* William D Magee
**Ex VP:* C Mark Boelhouwer

D-U-N-S 11-204-3448 IMP
■ **ORACLE FINANCIAL SERVICES SOFTWARE INC**
(*Suby of* ORACLE CORP) ★
399 Thornall St Ste 6, Edison, NJ 08837-2238
Tel (732) 623-0399 *Founded/Ownrshp* 2001
Sales 120.1MM^E *EMP* 693
SIC 5045 Computer software; Computer software
Ch: Rajesh Hukku
**COO:* Cafo Boga
Manager: Naren Mathavan

D-U-N-S 36-286-3768 IMP/EXP
ORACLE FLEXIBLE PACKAGING INC
ORACLE PACKAGING
(*Suby of* CENTRE LANE PARTNERS LLC) ★
220 Polo Rd, Winston Salem, NC 27105-3441
Tel (336) 777-4695 *Founded/Ownrshp* 2012
Sales 101.5MM^E *EMP* 285
SIC 2672 Coated & laminated paper; Coated & laminated paper
CEO: James Squatrito
**COO:* Kevin Hughes
**CFO:* Jon Heard
**VP:* Chris Payne
**VP:* Andy Starr
QA Dir: Brad Hoss
IT Man: Edward Getchell
Plnt Mgr: Richard Goforth
Sls Dir: Tom O'Brien

D-U-N-S 79-706-0498
■ **ORACLE OTC SUBSIDIARY LLC**
ATG
(*Suby of* ORACLE CORP) ★
1 Main St Ste 7, Cambridge, MA 02142-1599
Tel (617) 386-1000 *Founded/Ownrshp* 2011
Sales 83.9MM^E *EMP* 545
SIC 7372 Prepackaged software; Application computer software; Business oriented computer software; Educational computer software; Prepackaged software; Application computer software; Business oriented computer software; Educational computer software
Pr: Robert D Burke
Pr: Adam Belmont
**Pr:* Lawrence Joseph Ellison
Pr: Mike Lande
CFO: Franz Jaggar
CFO: Robert McCoy
Sr VP: Bernard Bailey
Sr VP: Lou Frio
Sr VP: Louis R Frio
Sr VP: Ken Volpe
VP: Bruce D'Ambrosio
VP: Leif Larsen
VP: Deborah Louis
VP: Patricia Morton
VP: INA Sipser
VP: Al Stoddard
VP: Brenda Sullivan
VP: Richard Welch
VP: Chip Winslow
VP: Bill Wittenberg
VP: Bill Zujewski

ORACLE PACKAGING
See ORACLE FLEXIBLE PACKAGING INC

D-U-N-S 61-910-0691
■ **ORACLE SYSTEMS CORP**
(*Suby of* ORACLE CORP) ★
500 Oracle Pkwy, Redwood City, CA 94065-1677
Tel (650) 506-7000 *Founded/Ownrshp* 2005
Sales 2.6MMM^E *EMP* 56,100
SIC 7372 7379 8243 Prepackaged software; Data processing consultant; Software training, computer; Prepackaged software; Business oriented computer software; Application computer software; Data processing consultant; Software training, computer
CEO: Safra A Catz
**Ch Bd:* Lawrence J Ellison
**Ch Bd:* Jeffrey O Henley
**Pr:* Mark V Hurd
**CEO:* Mark Hurd
COO: Andy Kuo
COO: Rich Polehber
COO: Larry Rall
COO: Nancy Zhang
Ex VP: Nicholas Aneshansley
Ex VP: John Fowler
Ex VP: Thomas Kurian
**Ex VP:* Charles Rozwat
Ex VP: Mike Splain
**Sr VP:* Dorian Daley
VP: Gail Coury
VP: Tyler Prince
VP: Robert Shimp
VP: Jill Suarez
Exec: Jim Barr
Exec: Charles Briggs

D-U-N-S 00-553-6698
■ **ORACLE USA INC**
(*Suby of* ORACLE SYSTEMS CORP) ★
500 Oracle Pkwy, Redwood City, CA 94065-1677
Tel (650) 506-7000 *Founded/Ownrshp* 1987, 2005
Sales 72.8MM^E *EMP* 526
SIC 7372 Prepackaged software; Prepackaged software
Pr: Safra A Catz
**Pr:* Mark Hurd
**Pr:* Charles Phillips
**Sr VP:* Judson Althoff
**Sr VP:* Matthew Mills
VP: Susan Charley
Sftwr Eng: Yung Choi
Sls Mgr: Jason Jeray

D-U-N-S 05-983-1180 IMP
ORAFOL AMERICAS INC
REFLECTIVE SOLUTIONS AMERICAS
(*Suby of* ORAFOL EUROPE GMBH)
120 Darling Dr, Avon, CT 06001-4217
Tel (860) 223-9297 *Founded/Ownrshp* 2011
Sales 104.8MM^E *EMP* 500
SIC 3082 Unsupported plastics profile shapes; Unsupported plastics profile shapes
Pr: Michael Foley
**COO:* Andrew McNeill
Treas: Phil Ferrari
VP: Geoff Grzywinski
**VP:* Steve Scott
Exec: Rich McNeely
Prgrm Mgr: Victor Grin
Genl Mgr: Michelle Gunning
Genl Mgr: Joseph Lupone
Genl Mgr: Etienne Smit
Dir IT: Jeff Grzywinski

D-U-N-S 19-570-4718 IMP/EXP
ORAFOL AMERICAS INC
1100 Oracal Pkwy, Black Creek, GA 31308-3637
Tel (912) 851-5000 *Founded/Ownrshp* 2013
Sales 46.7MM^E *EMP* 135
SIC 3081 Vinyl film & sheet; Vinyl film & sheet
CEO: Holger Loclair
**Pr:* Randall Mertz
Manager: Kevin Crawford
Manager: Thomas Mullin
Sls Mgr: Sergio Carrillo

D-U-N-S 55-543-9603 IMP
ORAFOL DISPLAY OPTICS INC
REFLEXITE ENERGY SOLUTIONS INC
(*Suby of* ORAFOL AMERICAS INC) ★
500 Lee Rd Ste 500, Rochester, NY 14606-4260
Tel (585) 647-1140 *Founded/Ownrshp* 2011
Sales 69.3MM^E *EMP* 380
SIC 3827 3861 3229 Lenses, optical: all types except ophthalmic; Photographic equipment & supplies; Pressed & blown glass; Lenses, optical: all types except ophthalmic; Photographic equipment & supplies; Pressed & blown glass
Pr: Bryan Parks
Treas: Phil Ferrari

D-U-N-S 96-880-1118 IMP
■ **ORAL COLGATE PHARMACEUTICALS INC**
(*Suby of* COLGATE-PALMOLIVE CO) ★
300 Park Ave Fl 3, New York, NY 10022-7412
Tel (212) 310-2000 *Founded/Ownrshp* 1993
Sales 88.0MM^E *EMP* 300
SIC 5122 2834 Drugs, proprietaries & sundries; Pharmaceutical preparations; Drugs, proprietaries & sundries; Pharmaceutical preparations
Ch Bd: Julie Dillon
VP: Maria E Carvajal
VP: Andreas Somers
Genl Mgr: Massimo Poli

ORAL MAXILLO FACIAL SURGERY
See UNIVERSITY OF MARYLAND SURGICAL ASSOCIATES PA

D-U-N-S 05-808-0060
ORAL ROBERTS UNIVERSITY
7777 S Lewis Ave, Tulsa, OK 74171-0001
Tel (918) 495-6161 *Founded/Ownrshp* 1963
Sales 93.9MM *EMP* 2,100^E
Accts Hogan Taylor Llp Cpas Tulsa
SIC 8221 University; University
Pr: Dr William Wilson
COO: Nick R Garza
COO: John Suan
**CFO:* Michelle Finley
**Treas:* F Rick Anderson
Ex VP: Tessie Devore
Ex VP: John Laffitte
Ex VP: Ossie Mills
VP: Suzanne Behr
**VP:* D Michael Bernard
VP: Daniel Delgado

*VP: Ralph Fagin
*VP: George Fisher
VP: Terry Fisher
VP: Bob Fouch
*VP: Jeff Ogle

D-U-N-S 80-182-4756 IMP
ORALABS INC
18685 Plaza Dr, Parker, CO 80134-9061
Tel (303) 783-9499 Founded/Ownrshp 1990
Sales 61.4MM^E EMP 153
SIC 2844 Oral preparations; Oral preparations
Pr: Gary Schlatter
CFO: Emile Jordan
IT Man: Steve Allen
Opers Mgr: Brett Boness

ORANG-LWRNC-JCKSN-MRTIN-GREENE
See LAWRENCE NORTH COMMUNITY SCHOOLS

D-U-N-S 02-501-0075 IMP
ORANGE & BLUE DISTRIBUTING CO INC (IL)
(Suby of KOERNER DISTRIBUTOR INC) ★
2902 Lager Dr, Champaign, IL 61822-2872
Tel (217) 352-4794 Founded/Ownrshp 1898, 2013
Sales 22.6MM^E EMP 2
Accts Mcgladrey & Pullen Llc Champa
SIC 5181 Beer & other fermented malt liquors; Beer & other fermented malt liquors
Pr: Paul Koerner

D-U-N-S 00-699-3406 IMP
■ ORANGE AND ROCKLAND UTILITIES INC
(Suby of CONSOLIDATED EDISON INC) ★
1 Blue Hill Plz Ste 20, Pearl River, NY 10965-3100
Tel (845) 352-6000 Founded/Ownrshp 1899
Sales 806.2MM^E EMP 1,060
SIC 4924 4911 1311 6552 Natural gas distribution; Generation, electric power; Transmission, electric power; Distribution, electric power; Crude petroleum & natural gas; Subdividers & developers; Natural gas distribution; Generation, electric power; Transmission, electric power; Distribution, electric power; Crude petroleum & natural gas; Subdividers & developers
Pr: John McAvoy
*Pr: William G Longhi
Chf Mktg O: Matthew Palermo
VP: Eric Colasacco
VP: Thomas Folchi
VP: Edwin J Ortiz
*VP: Francis Peverly
VP: Lori Sanchez
Div Mgr: Robert David
Dir IT: Robert Huber
IT Man: David Braunfotel

D-U-N-S 09-689-2997 IMP
ORANGE BAKERY INC
(Suby of RHEON AUTOMATIC MACHINERY CO.,LTD.)
17751 Cowan, Irvine, CA 92614-6064
Tel (949) 863-1377 Founded/Ownrshp 1979
Sales 20.4MM^E EMP 100
Accts Deloitte & Touche Llp
SIC 2053 Pastries (danish): frozen
CEO: Mikio Kobayashi
*Ch Bd: Torahiko Hayashi
*Pr: Shigeo Ueki

ORANGE BLOSSOM HILLS G&C CLUB
See VILLAGES OF LAKE-SUMTER INC

D-U-N-S 07-513-7455
ORANGE BOARD OF EDUCATION INC
451 Lincoln Ave, Orange, NJ 07050-2202
Tel (973) 677-4000 Founded/Ownrshp 1800
Sales 41.4MM^E EMP 700^E
SIC 8211 Public elementary & secondary schools; Public elementary & secondary schools
VP: Arthur Griffa

D-U-N-S 07-600-9935
ORANGE BOWL COMMITTEE INC
14360 Nw 77th Ct, Miami Lakes, FL 33016-1534
Tel (305) 341-4700 Founded/Ownrshp 1935
Sales 52.2MM EMP 20
Accts Kaufman Rossin & Co Pa Miami
SIC 7941 1799 Sports promotion; Float (parade) construction; Sports promotion; Float (parade) construction
CEO: Eric L Poms
*Pr: Thomas Wood Jr
*COO: Michael Saks
*CFO: Brian G Park
*Treas: Shaun M Davis
Sr VP: Truscott Miller
*VP: Philis Oeters
*VP: Danny Ponce
Exec: John Mas

D-U-N-S 03-261-9819
ORANGE BUICK - GMCTRUCK
ORANGE COLLISION CENTER
3883 W Colonial Dr, Orlando, FL 32808-7999
Tel (407) 295-8100 Founded/Ownrshp 2002
Sales 30.2MM^E EMP 100
SIC 5511 7539 Automobiles, new & used; Automotive repair shops; Automobiles, new & used; Automotive repair shops
Pr: Ray Lally
Store Mgr: Wayne Albonico
Sls Mgr: David Badgley

D-U-N-S 17-593-6426
ORANGE BUSINESS SERVICES HOLDINGS US INC
(Suby of ORANGE)
13775 Mclearen Rd, Herndon, VA 20171-3212
Tel (703) 471-2300 Founded/Ownrshp 2001
Sales 599.5MM^E EMP 2,000^E
SIC 4813 Data telephone communications; Data telephone communications
Pr: Bruce Berenson
*Ex VP: Howard Ford
*VP: Bruce McWhirter

D-U-N-S 01-630-4532
ORANGE BUSINESS SERVICES US INC
(Suby of ORANGE BUSINESS SERVICES HOLDINGS US INC) ★
100 Galleria Pkwy Se # 300, Atlanta, GA 30339-3179
Tel (678) 346-3000 Founded/Ownrshp 1996
Sales 29.6MM^E EMP 100^E
SIC 4812 Radio telephone communication
Pr: Barbara Dalibard
*CFO: Yves Guilliaumot
Ex VP: Raoul Roverato
Sr VP: Diana Einterz
VP: Paul Radtke
*VP: Mack Treece
Dir Bus: Todd Evers
Prgrm Mgr: Maria Davila
Prgrm Mgr: Chris Jackson
Snr Ntwrk: John Aloizos
Netwrk Eng: Philippe Marcais

D-U-N-S 78-579-9362 IMP
ORANGE BUSINESS SERVICES US INC
(Suby of ORANGE BUSINESS SERVICES HOLDINGS US INC) ★
13775 Mclearen Rd, Herndon, VA 20171-3212
Tel (866) 849-4185 Founded/Ownrshp 1992
Sales 562.8MM^E EMP 1,411
SIC 4813 8748 Data telephone communications; Telecommunications consultant; Data telephone communications; Telecommunications consultant
Pr: Diana Einterz
CFO: Yves Guillaumot
Ch: Louis-Pierre Wenes
Treas: Julie Maniez
Top Exec: Frances Woodworth
VP: Norman Wentworth
Prgrm Mgr: Amy Teklinsky
CTO: Marc Monnard
IT Man: Steven C Belling
Snr Mgr: Manvinder Singh

ORANGE CITY HOSPITAL
See ORANGE CITY MUNICIPAL HOSPITAL

D-U-N-S 09-734-6720
ORANGE CITY MUNICIPAL HOSPITAL
ORANGE CITY HOSPITAL
1000 Lincoln Cir Se, Orange City, IA 51041-1836
Tel (712) 737-4984 Founded/Ownrshp 1960
Sales 40.6MM EMP 510^E
Accts Denman & Company Llp West De
SIC 8062 General medical & surgical hospitals; General medical & surgical hospitals
CEO: Martin W Guthmiller
V Ch: Randy Jacobsma
*COO: Dainel McCarty
Dir Lab: Donna Morehead
Dir Rx: Don Vaas
Off Mgr: Steve Walhof
CTO: Thomas Jacobson
CTO: Alan Vander Zwagg
QA Dir: Val Droog
Obsttrcn: Michael Fiegen
Doctor: Cynthia Pals

D-U-N-S 09-762-5842
ORANGE CITY SCHOOL DISTRICT
32000 Chagrin Blvd, Cleveland, OH 44124-5922
Tel (216) 831-8600 Founded/Ownrshp 1843
Sales 56.4MM EMP 500
Accts Julian & Grube Inc Westervil
SIC 8211 Public elementary & secondary schools; Public elementary & secondary schools
*Treas: L Greg Slemons
Bd of Dir: Chuck Jarrett
Adm Dir: Nancy Gordan
Cmptr Lab: Tim Gammell
Psych: Edie Ungar-Shafron

ORANGE CNTY CONT PRFMCE SHEETS
See SMURFIT KAPPA ORANGE COUNTY LLC

ORANGE CNTY GEORGE M RAYMOND N
See RAYMOND GROUP

D-U-N-S 07-030-6766
ORANGE COAST AMC/JEEP INC (DE)
ORANGE COAST JEEP-CHRYSLER
2929 Harbor Blvd, Costa Mesa, CA 92626-3912
Tel (714) 549-8023 Founded/Ownrshp 1974, 1980
Sales 47.4MM^E EMP 120
SIC 5511 Automobiles, new & used; Automobiles, new & used
Ch: Gary Gray
*VP: Sonja Gray
Genl Mgr: John Gray
VP Sls: Rich Sorensen

D-U-N-S 60-280-5103
ORANGE COAST BUILDING SERVICES
2191 S Dupont Dr, Anaheim, CA 92806-6102
Tel (714) 453-6300 Founded/Ownrshp 1986
Sales 26.0MM^E EMP 115
SIC 1541 1542 Industrial buildings, new construction; Commercial & office building contractors; Industrial buildings, new construction; Commercial & office building contractors
Pr: Kevin W Franklin
VP: Jim Ongaro

D-U-N-S 08-359-4929
ORANGE COAST COLLEGE
ORANGE COAST COLLEGE SNACK BAR
2701 Fairview Rd, Costa Mesa, CA 92626-5561
Tel (714) 432-5024 Founded/Ownrshp 1948
Sales 148.0MM^E EMP 1,900
SIC 8221 Colleges universities & professional schools; Colleges universities & professional schools
VP: Richard T Pagel
Off Mgr: Mary Roda
IT Man: Maria Denunno
IT Man: Sloane Smith
Psych: Caryn Plum
Snr Mgr: Gerald Sjule

ORANGE COAST COLLEGE SNACK BAR
See ORANGE COAST COLLEGE

ORANGE COAST JEEP-CHRYSLER
See ORANGE COAST AMC/JEEP INC

D-U-N-S 93-266-9658
ORANGE COAST MEMORIAL MEDICAL CENTER
(Suby of MEMORIAL CARE MEDICAL CENTERS) ★
9920 Talbert Ave, Fountain Valley, CA 92708-5153
Tel (714) 378-7000 Founded/Ownrshp 1996
Sales 131.3MM^E EMP 1,000^E
SIC 8062 General medical & surgical hospitals; General medical & surgical hospitals
Pr: Marcia Manker
Chf Rad: Richard Wasley
*CFO: Steve McNamara
VP: Brennan James
Brnch Mgr: Don Cato
CTO: Karen Testman
MIS Dir: Debbie Marino
MIS Dir: Scott Raymond
IT Man: Scott Jodylin
VP Opers: Emily Randall
Mktg Dir: Debra Culver

D-U-N-S 80-738-3708
ORANGE COAST TITLE CO OF SOUTHERN CALIFORNIA
640 N Tustin Ave Ste 106, Santa Ana, CA 92705-3731
Tel (714) 558-2836 Founded/Ownrshp 1967
Sales 156.3MM^E EMP 650
SIC 7389 6361 6541 Brokers, business: buying & selling business enterprises; Title insurance; Title & trust companies; Brokers, business: buying & selling business enterprises; Title insurance; Title & trust companies
CEO: John L Marconi
*Pr: Rich Mac Aluso
Pr: Fred Nilsen
COO: Lori Romano
Bd of Dir: Gloria Kessell
Bd of Dir: Macaluso Rich
Ofcr: Kathy Donovan
Ofcr: John Fernando
Ofcr: Steve Fernando
Ofcr: Brandy Kelly
Ofcr: Dixie Kent
Ofcr: Erin Lincke
Ofcr: Winston Nakagawa
Ofcr: Bonnie Perez
Ofcr: Eric Tafolla
Ex VP: Joseph Burks
Ex VP: Lori Montenegro
Ex VP: John Wiley
Sr VP: Diana Martinez
Sr VP: Suzi Smith-Shepherd
VP: Jim Aurelio

ORANGE COLLISION CENTER
See ORANGE BUICK - GMCTRUCK

D-U-N-S 10-005-8890
ORANGE COUNTY BOARD OF EDUCATION
200 E King St, Hillsborough, NC 27278-2623
Tel (919) 732-8126 Founded/Ownrshp 1872
Sales 41.5MM^E EMP 605
SIC 8211 Public elementary & secondary schools; School board
Ch Bd: Deborah Piscitelli
Ofcr: Lorinda Kueider
Netwrk Mgr: Parviz Mollahassani
Pr Dir: Seth Stephans
Teacher Pr: Teresa Cunningham-Bro
Psych: Lynn Douglas
Psych: Elise Kechele
HC Dir: Sherita Cobb
Snr Mgr: Maurice Boswell

D-U-N-S 04-032-7447
ORANGE COUNTY BUILDING MATERIALS INC (TX)
BUNA BUILDING MATERIALS
365 Old Highway 90 W, Vidor, TX 77662-4835
Tel (409) 769-2410 Founded/Ownrshp 1975
Sales 20.6MM^E EMP 105
Accts David Sticker & Company Pc
SIC 5211 Lumber & other building materials
Pr: Donald Lightfoot
*VP: Alice Lightfoot
*VP: Jerry Lightfoot

D-U-N-S 07-668-4059
ORANGE COUNTY COMMUNITY COLLEGE
SUNY ORANGE
(Suby of STATE UNIVERSITY OF NEW YORK) ★
115 South St, Middletown, NY 10940-6404
Tel (845) 344-6222 Founded/Ownrshp 1950
Sales 966.1M EMP 700^E
Accts Judelson Giordano & Siegel Cpa
SIC 8222 9411 Community college; Administration of educational programs; ; Community college; Administration of educational programs;
Pr: Dr William Richards
Assoc VP: Michael Gawronski
Ex Dir: Bill Schuster
Doctor: Yolanda Nieves MD

D-U-N-S 83-881-7815
ORANGE COUNTY COMMUNITY FOUNDATION
4041 Macarthur Blvd # 510, Newport Beach, CA 92660-2512
Tel (949) 553-4202 Founded/Ownrshp 1989
Sales 61.7MM EMP 13
Accts Moss Adams Llp San Diego Ca
SIC 6732 Charitable trust management; Charitable trust management
Pr: Shelley Hoss
*Treas: Jeffrey A Dankberg
Ofcr: Natalie Bishop
Ofcr: Julie Shuler
*VP: Tracy Branson
*VP: Todd Hanson
*VP: Richard Lombardi
*VP: Frank Quevedo
VP: Cynthia Ragland

D-U-N-S 12-114-7912
ORANGE COUNTY DEPARTMENT OF EDUCATION FACILITIES CORP
OCDE
200 Kalmus Dr, Costa Mesa, CA 92626-5922
Tel (714) 966-4000 Founded/Ownrshp 1960
Sales 102.7MM^E EMP 1,500
SIC 8211 Public elementary & secondary schools; Public elementary & secondary schools
CEO: Elizabeth Parker
Ex Dir: Claire Braeburn
Genl Couns: Ronald Wenkart

D-U-N-S 80-736-1472
ORANGE COUNTY EMERGENCY SERVICES DISTRICT
2351 Highway 12, Vidor, TX 77662-3404
Tel (409) 769-6241 Founded/Ownrshp 1973
Sales NA EMP 5,060
Accts Edgar Kiker & Cross Pc Beau
SIC 9224 Fire department, volunteer; Fire department, volunteer
*Pr: Terry Woodward
*VP: Wyatt Boyett
Snr Mgr: Robert Smith

D-U-N-S 07-814-9069
ORANGE COUNTY ERECTORS INC (CA)
517 E La Palma Ave, Anaheim, CA 92801-2536
Tel (714) 502-8455 Founded/Ownrshp 1975
Sales 20.4MM^E EMP 50
SIC 3448 3441 1791 Buildings, portable: prefabricated metal; Fabricated structural metal; Structural steel erection
CEO: Richard Lewis
*Sr VP: Sandra Lewis

D-U-N-S 07-861-2387
ORANGE COUNTY FIRE & RESCUE
(Suby of ORANGE COUNTY GOVERNMENT)
6590 Amory Ct, Winter Park, FL 32792-7426
Tel (407) 836-9112 Founded/Ownrshp 2012
Sales NA EMP 1,200
SIC 9224 Fire department, not including volunteer

D-U-N-S 62-237-5124
ORANGE COUNTY FIRE AUTHORITY
1 Fire Authority Rd, Irvine, CA 92602-0125
Tel (714) 573-6000 Founded/Ownrshp 2006
Sales NA EMP 1,160^E
Accts Mayer Hoffman Mccann Pc Irv
SIC 9224 Fire department, not including volunteer; ; Fire department, not including volunteer;
V Ch: Al Murray
*Treas: Patricia Jakubiak
Ofcr: Steve Concialdi
Ofcr: Stephen Miller
Dir Soc: Eric Elmer
Comm Dir: Sandy Cooney
Mng Dir: Bob George
Dir IT: Monica Dorfmeyer
IT Man: Joel Brodowski
IT Man: Rich Toro
Snr Mgr: Cliff Bramlette

D-U-N-S 04-686-7180
ORANGE COUNTY HEAD START
2501 Pullman St, Santa Ana, CA 92705-5511
Tel (714) 241-8920 Founded/Ownrshp 1965
Sales 34.9MM EMP 410
Accts Rossi Doskocil & Finkelstein L
SIC 8351 Preschool center; Preschool center
Ex Dir: Colleen Versteeg
Pr Dir: Doris Wood
Sls Mgr: Diane Maldonado
Board of Directors: Marcy Beck, Sheila McCutcheon

D-U-N-S 84-931-7391
ORANGE COUNTY HEALTH AUTHORITY
CALOPTIMA
505 City Pkwy W, Orange, CA 92868-2924
Tel (714) 246-8500 Founded/Ownrshp 1994
Sales 103.5MM^E EMP 422
SIC 8621 8011 Professional membership organizations; Offices & clinics of medical doctors; Professional membership organizations; Offices & clinics of medical doctors
CEO: Richard Chambers
*CEO: Michael Schrader
*COO: William Jones
CFO: Novella Quesada
*CFO: Chet Uma
Ofcr: Denise Corley
Ofcr: Kim Cunningham
*Ofcr: Richard Helmer
Comm Dir: Bridget Kelly
Comm Man: Janis Rizzuto
Ex Dir: Gary Crockett
Board of Directors: Arthur B Birtcher, Mary Anne Foo, Edward B Kacic, Jim McAleer, Janet Nguyen, Margarita Pereyda MD, David L Riley, Michel D Stephens, John M W Moorlach CPA Cfp

D-U-N-S 04-994-8789 IMP
ORANGE COUNTY INDUSTRIAL PLASTICS INC (CA)
OCIP
4811 E La Palma Ave, Anaheim, CA 92807-1954
Tel (714) 632-9450 Founded/Ownrshp 1982
Sales 43.4MM^E EMP 45
SIC 5162 Plastics products
Pr: Robert Robinson
VP Opers: Dave Pfeil

D-U-N-S 08-241-2941
ORANGE COUNTY LIBRARY SYSTEM
101 E Central Blvd Lbby, Orlando, FL 32801-2462
Tel (407) 835-7323 Founded/Ownrshp 1923
Sales 30.6MM EMP 399
Accts Cherry Bekaert Llp Orlando
SIC 8231 9111 Public library; County supervisors' & executives' offices; Public library; County supervisors' & executives' offices
CEO: Maryanne Hodel
Trst: Hernan Tagliani
VP: Lisa Franchina
Brnch Mgr: Matthew David

Brnch Mgr: Paolo Melillo
Info Man: Ricardo Viera

D-U-N-S 80-164-1577
ORANGE COUNTY PERFORMANCE ARTS CENTER
600 Town Center Dr, Costa Mesa, CA 92626-1916
Tel (714) 556-2122 *Founded/Ownrshp* 2007
Sales 46.2MM *EMP* 1
SIC 7929 7999 8412 Entertainers & entertainment groups; Amusement ride; Arts or science center; Entertainers & entertainment groups; Amusement ride; Arts or science center
Pr: Terrence Dwyer
**CFO:* Brian Finck
Bd of Dir: David D Hiller
Software D: Kacey York

D-U-N-S 07-182-0869
ORANGE COUNTY PRODUCE LLC
11405 Jeffrey Rd, Irvine, CA 92602-0503
Tel (949) 451-0880 *Founded/Ownrshp* 1998
Sales 47.1MM^E *EMP* 100
SIC 0171 Strawberry farm; Strawberry farm

ORANGE COUNTY PUBLIC SCHOOLS
See SCHOOL BOARD OF ORANGE COUNTY FLORIDA

D-U-N-S 07-979-8850
ORANGE COUNTY PUBLIC SCHOOLS
445 W Amelia St, Orlando, FL 32801-1128
Tel (407) 317-3209 *Founded/Ownrshp* 2015
Sales 1.8MM^E *EMP* 17,528^E
SIC 8211 Public elementary & secondary schools
Prin: Parker Stewart
Area Mgr: Ricardo Mesorana

D-U-N-S 61-543-6755
ORANGE COUNTY PUBLIC SCHOOLS
ORANGE COUNTY SCHOOL BOARD
200 Dailey Dr, Orange, VA 22960-1574
Tel (540) 661-4550 *Founded/Ownrshp* 1994
Sales 45.0MM^E *EMP* 750
SIC 8211 Public elementary & secondary schools; Public elementary & secondary schools
**Prin:* Robert Grimesey
IT Man: Charles Harris
Psych: Karen Chapman
Psych: Mary Crownover
HC Dir: Phyllis Smith

D-U-N-S 07-953-4772
ORANGE COUNTY ROYALE CONVALESCENT HOSPITAL INC
1030 W Warner Ave, Santa Ana, CA 92707-3147
Tel (714) 546-6450 *Founded/Ownrshp* 1974
Sales 23.0MM^E *EMP* 430
SIC 8059 8051 Convalescent home; Skilled nursing care facilities; Convalescent home; Skilled nursing care facilities
Pr: Mitchell Kantor
IT Man: Grace Marqueses
Nrsg Dir: Vicky Limalima

D-U-N-S 14-447-8682 IMP
ORANGE COUNTY SANITATION DISTRICT FINANCING CORP
10844 Ellis Ave, Fountain Valley, CA 92708-7018
Tel (714) 962-2411 *Founded/Ownrshp* 1954
Sales 304.5MM *EMP* 626
Accts Mcgladrey Llp Irvine Ca
SIC 4953 Waste materials, disposal at sea; Waste materials, disposal at sea
Genl Mgr: James Herberg
V Ch: Cathy Green
VP: Clarice Marcin
Dir Risk M: Randall Mason
Ex Dir: Nancy Dooley
**Genl Mgr:* James Ruth
IT Man: John Swindler
Opers Supe: Carla Dillon
Snr Mgr: James Jauter

ORANGE COUNTY SCHOOL BOARD
See ORANGE COUNTY PUBLIC SCHOOLS

D-U-N-S 93-122-5226
ORANGE COUNTY SCHOOL OF ARTS
OCSA
1010 N Main St, Santa Ana, CA 92701-3602
Tel (714) 560-0900 *Founded/Ownrshp* 2000
Sales 23.3MM *EMP* 250
Accts Vicenti Lloyd & Stutzman Glen
SIC 8299 Art school, except commercial; Art school, except commercial
CEO: Ralph Opacic
COO: Steven Wagner
Treas: John Vestri

D-U-N-S 05-255-3000
ORANGE COUNTY SCHOOL READINESS COALITION INC
1940 Traylor Blvd, Orlando, FL 32804-4714
Tel (407) 841-6607 *Founded/Ownrshp* 2000
Sales 64.8MM *EMP* 3
SIC 8621 Education & teacher association; Education & teacher association
Ex Dir: Karen Willis

D-U-N-S 07-979-8783
ORANGE COUNTY SCHOOLS
200 E King St, Hillsborough, NC 27278-2623
Tel (919) 732-8126 *Founded/Ownrshp* 2015
Sales 10.4MM^E *EMP* 1,051^E
SIC 8211 Public elementary & secondary schools

D-U-N-S 15-394-7940
ORANGE COUNTY TRANSPORTATION AUTHORITY
ORANGE COUNTY TRNSP AUTH
550 S Main St, Orange, CA 92868-4506
Tel (714) 636-7433 *Founded/Ownrshp* 1972
Sales 602.4MM *EMP* 1,050
Accts Vavrinek Trine Day & Co Ll
SIC 4111 8711 Bus line operations; Bus line operations; Construction & civil engineering
CEO: Darrell Johnson
Treas: Kirk Avila
Bd of Dir: Chris Norby
VP: Jeffrey Adams
Ex Dir: Ellen Burton
Ex Dir: Jim Kenan
Ex Dir: Andrew Oftelie
Prgrm Mgr: Ross Lew
Prgrm Mgr: Kanwal Singh
Genl Mgr: Beth McCormick
Plng Mgr: Dave Elbaum

ORANGE COUNTY TRNSP AUTH
See ORANGE COUNTY TRANSPORTATION AUTHORITY

D-U-N-S 00-697-8175
ORANGE COUNTY TRUST CO (INC) (NY)
212 Dolson Ave, Middletown, NY 10940-6541
Tel (845) 341-5000 *Founded/Ownrshp* 1892
Sales NA *EMP* 130
SIC 6022 State trust companies accepting deposits, commercial; State trust companies accepting deposits, commercial
Ch Bd: John H Morrison
**Pr:* Terry R Saturno
Trst Ofcr: Glen Wasserman
Sr VP: Gerard Perri
**Sr VP:* Mary E Rogulski
VP: Josh Hill
Brnch Mgr: Heather Tancredi

D-U-N-S 07-815-6593
ORANGE COUNTYS CREDIT UNION
1721 E Saint Andrew Pl, Santa Ana, CA 92705-4934
Tel (714) 755-5900 *Founded/Ownrshp* 1938
Sales NA *EMP* 265
SIC 6062 State credit unions; State credit unions
Pr: Shruti S Miyashiro
Pr: Amanda Verive
CFO: Greg Krause
**Ch:* Dan Dillon
Sr VP: Laura Thompson
VP: Dawn Danielson
VP: Russell Torge
Brnch Mgr: Mary Felix
Telecom Ex: David Butler
IT Man: Mach Vu
Mktg Dir: Therese Coch

D-U-N-S 60-333-2081
ORANGE COURIER INC
3731 W Warner Ave, Santa Ana, CA 92704-5218
Tel (714) 384-3600 *Founded/Ownrshp* 1987
Sales 40.4MM^E *EMP* 300
SIC 7389 4213 4225 Courier or messenger service; Trucking, except local; General warehousing & storage; Courier or messenger service; Trucking, except local; General warehousing & storage
Pr: Evell T Stanley

ORANGE CRUSH
See PALUMBO BROS INC

D-U-N-S 00-201-3498
ORANGE DIE CUTTING CORP (NY)
ORANGE PACKAGING
1 Favoriti Ave, Newburgh, NY 12550-4015
Tel (845) 562-0900 *Founded/Ownrshp* 1950
Sales 29.6MM^E *EMP* 120
SIC 2675 Die-cut paper & board; Die-cut paper & board
Ch Bd: Anthony Esposito Sr
**Pr:* Anthony Esposito Jr
VP: Michael Esposito
DP Exec: Sheri McNair
Mktg Dir: Tom Pederson

D-U-N-S 18-435-4066
ORANGE EAST SUPERVISORY UNION
530 Waits River Rd, Bradford, VT 05033-8200
Tel (802) 222-5216 *Founded/Ownrshp* 1945
Sales NA *EMP* 329
SIC 9411 Administration of educational programs; County supervisor of education, except school board; Administration of educational programs; County supervisor of education, except school board
**CFO:* Oliver Jakob
**Ex Dir:* Arpad J Szoboszlay

D-U-N-S 07-878-4161
ORANGE ELEMNTARY SCHOOL DISTRICT
637 Orange Center Rd, Orange, CT 06477-2432
Tel (203) 891-8020 *Founded/Ownrshp* 2013
Sales 12.6MM^E *EMP* 345^E
SIC 8211 Public elementary & secondary schools

D-U-N-S 07-903-6182
ORANGE GROVE CENTER INC (TN)
615 Derby St, Chattanooga, TN 37404-1632
Tel (423) 629-1451 *Founded/Ownrshp* 1953
Sales 37.2MM *EMP* 680^E
Accts Johnson Hickey & Murchison Pc
SIC 8331 Vocational training agency; Vocational rehabilitation agency; Vocational training agency; Vocational rehabilitation agency
Ex Dir: Kyle Hauth
Bd of Dir: Larry Cash
Bd of Dir: Rosie Russell
Dir Lab: Susan Jenkins
Cmptr Lab: Nina Rains
IT Man: Cherryl Baliles

D-U-N-S 05-304-8468
ORANGE LAKE COUNTRY CLUB INC
8505 W Irlo Bronson Hwy, Kissimmee, FL 34747-8201
Tel (407) 239-0000 *Founded/Ownrshp* 1981
Sales 405.6MM *EMP* 800
Accts Grant Thornton Llp Orlando F
SIC 7011 6552 7997 5812 5813 Tourist camps, cabins, cottages & courts; Resort hotel; Land subdividers & developers, residential; Country club, membership; Golf club, membership; Ethnic food restaurants; Bars & lounges; Tourist camps, cabins, cottages & courts; Resort hotel; Land subdividers & developers, residential; Country club, membership; Golf club, membership; Ethnic food restaurants; Bars & lounges
CEO: Charles K Swan III
**Ch Bd:* Spence Wilson
Ofcr: Bill Reynes
VP: Brian T Lower
VP: Bill Sell
VP: Joanna Tadich
VP: Lea Watts
Exec: Sergio Garcia
Exec: Lonny Huot
Dir Risk M: Bryant Raper
**Prin:* Don Harrill

D-U-N-S 05-978-1948
ORANGE LINE OIL CO INC
ACCURET EQUIPMENT
404 E Commercial St, Pomona, CA 91767-5599
Tel (800) 492-6864 *Founded/Ownrshp* 2006
Sales 46.3MM^E *EMP* 28
SIC 5172 5084 Petroleum products; Lubricating oils & greases; Kerosene; Materials handling machinery
Pr: Scott Tredinnick
CFO: Cathy Harting
Treas: Louise Strasser
Mfg Mgr: Wes Odell
Opers Mgr: Robinson Russ
Opers Mgr: Gary Tridineck
VP Sls: Russ Whellan
Manager: Jill Steiner
Manager: Don Zimmer
Sls Mgr: Kevin Mattchen
Sls Mgr: Wendy Peterson
Board of Directors: Margaret Meleg, Steve Meleg, Diane Strasser, John S Strasser

D-U-N-S 00-886-8556
ORANGE MOTOR CO INC (NY)
FORD
799 Central Ave, Albany, NY 12206-1501
Tel (518) 489-5414 *Founded/Ownrshp* 1916, 1965
Sales 50.6MM^E *EMP* 122
SIC 5511 Automobiles, new & used; Automobiles, new & used
Pr: Carl E Touhey
**VP:* Carl Keegan
**VP:* Charles L Touhey
Store Mgr: Mark White
Mktg Mgr: Brian Randio

ORANGE PACKAGING
See ORANGE DIE CUTTING CORP

D-U-N-S 11-279-8488 EXP
ORANGE PARK MEDICAL CENTER
FLEMING ISLAND IMAGING CENTER
2001 Kingsley Ave, Orange Park, FL 32073-5156
Tel (904) 276-8500 *Founded/Ownrshp* 1992
Sales 46.1M *EMP* 903
Accts Harrington & Associates Cpas
SIC 8069 Specialty hospitals, except psychiatric; Specialty hospitals, except psychiatric
CEO: Chad Patrick
Trst: Ted McGowan
Trst: Deevid Miller
Dir Inf Cn: Melody Miller
Dir Rad: Larry Smith
Prin: Rajesh Vishen
Mtls Mgr: Scott Vickers
Opers Mgr: Andrea Tharp
Plnt Mgr: John McNally
Doctor: Jack Cohen
Doctor: Maria Ramirez MD

D-U-N-S 13-396-9969
■ **ORANGE PARK MEDICAL CENTER INC**
(*Suby of* HCA INC) ★
2001 Kingsley Ave, Orange Park, FL 32073-5156
Tel (904) 276-8769 *Founded/Ownrshp* 1974
Sales 9.4MM^E *EMP* 800
SIC 8062 General medical & surgical hospitals; General medical & surgical hospitals
Chf Mktg O: Tony Tullot
**VP:* John M Franck
**VP:* R Milton Johnson
**VP:* A Bruce Moore
Doctor: L G Martin

D-U-N-S 07-682-4127 EXP
ORANGE PARK TOYOTA
KEITH PEARSON TOYOTA
6501 Youngerman Cir, Jacksonville, FL 32244-6611
Tel (904) 771-9100 *Founded/Ownrshp* 1999
Sales 55.8MM^E *EMP* 170
SIC 5511 Automobiles, new & used; Automobiles, new & used
Pr: Keith Pierson
Off Mgr: Afbia Albert
Sls&Mrk Ex: Roxanne Spitzer

D-U-N-S 61-586-3917
ORANGE RECYCLING SERVICES INC
KAOLINA WASTE REMOVAL
1010 E Pettigrew St, Durham, NC 27701-4241
Tel (919) 688-5660 *Founded/Ownrshp* 1989
Sales 21.1MM^E *EMP* 40
SIC 4953 Recycling, waste materials
Pr: A Michael Swartz
**CFO:* Kurt Uphoff

D-U-N-S 07-668-0404
ORANGE REGIONAL MEDICAL CENTER
ARDEN HILL HOSPITAL
707 E Main St, Middletown, NY 10940-2667
Tel (845) 343-2424 *Founded/Ownrshp* 1908
Sales 371.0MM *EMP* 2,000
Accts Kpmg Llp New York Ny
SIC 8062 General medical & surgical hospitals; General medical & surgical hospitals
CEO: Scott Batulis
Chf Rad: J Yacovone
**Ch:* Rolland Peacock III
**VP:* Mitchell Amado
**VP:* Joe Anesi
**VP:* Rosemary Baczewski
VP: Sandra Iberger
VP: Stephen Sugrue
Dir OR: Alma Baird
Dir Rx: Maria Russo
Ex Dir: Jerry Dunlavey

D-U-N-S 07-980-6896
ORANGE SCHOOL DISTRICT
451 Lincoln Ave, Orange, NJ 07050-2202
Tel (973) 677-4000 *Founded/Ownrshp* 2015
Sales 6.2MM^E *EMP* 501^E
SIC 8211 Public elementary & secondary schools
Dir Sec: Edwin Vazquez
MIS Dir: Rodney West
Teacher Pr: Belinda Scott-Smiley

D-U-N-S 18-435-4074
ORANGE SOUTHWEST SUPERVISORY UNION 28
24 Central St, Randolph, VT 05060-1024
Tel (802) 728-6732 *Founded/Ownrshp* 1889
Sales 16.7MM^E *EMP* 300
Accts William Yacavoni Cpa
SIC 8211 8641 Public elementary & secondary schools; Citizens union; Public elementary & secondary schools; Citizens union
Dir IT: Michael Abadi
Dir IT: Meredith Liben
Dir IT: Charles Lyman
Dir IT: Susan Mann

D-U-N-S 02-632-4830
ORANGE SUPERIOR TIRE & SERVICE INC
1213 N 16th St, Orange, TX 77630-3607
Tel (409) 883-6128 *Founded/Ownrshp* 1994
Sales 25.0MM^E *EMP* 59
SIC 5531 7538 7534 Automotive tires; General automotive repair shops; Tire repair shop
Pr: Tim Hughes
**Sec:* Joy I Hughes
**VP:* Mike D Hughes
Off Mgr: Becky Smith

D-U-N-S 07-953-6439
ORANGE UNIFIED SCHOOL DISTRICT
1401 N Handy St, Orange, CA 92867-4434
Tel (714) 628-4000 *Founded/Ownrshp* 1953
Sales 177.9MM^E *EMP* 3,100
Accts Vavrinek Trine Day & Co Ll
SIC 8211 School board; School board
V Ch: Michelle Sherwood
Pr: Cathie Hunsberger
CFO: Steve Babnick
Sr VP: Alan Saldivar
VP: Robin Nelson
VP: Shelby Rommelfanger
Adm Dir: Jenny Delgado
Adm Dir: Ousd Miller
Adm Dir: Cyndi Paik
Adm Dir: Linda Stoterau
Off Mgr: Theresa Shortreed

D-U-N-S 08-417-0380
ORANGE WATER AND SEWER AUTHORITY
OWASA
400 Jones Ferry Rd, Carrboro, NC 27510-2001
Tel (919) 960-6142 *Founded/Ownrshp* 1975
Sales 105.6MM^E *EMP* 130^E
Accts Martin Starnes & Associates C
SIC 4941 4952 Water supply; Sewerage systems; Water supply; Sewerage systems
Ex Dir: Ed Kerwin
**CFO:* Stephen Winters
**Genl Mgr:* John Greene

D-U-N-S 12-052-4277
ORANGE-ULSTER BOCES INC
53 Gibson Rd, Goshen, NY 10924-6709
Tel (845) 291-0100 *Founded/Ownrshp* 1948
Sales 50.4MM^E *EMP* 1,200
SIC 8249 8211 Vocational apprentice training; Elementary & secondary schools; Vocational apprentice training; Elementary & secondary schools
**COO:* Terry Olivo
Occ Thrpy: Kim Williams
Occ Thrpy: Vicky Zouzias

D-U-N-S 10-007-1562
ORANGEBURG CONSOLIDATED SCHOOL DISTRICT 4
6030 Slab Landing Rd, Cope, SC 29038-9500
Tel (803) 534-7420 *Founded/Ownrshp* 1954
Sales 37.6MM^E *EMP* 650
SIC 8211 8661 Public elementary & secondary schools; School board; Religious organizations; Public elementary & secondary schools; School board; Religious organizations
Ofcr: Rebecca Huggins
Dir IT: Julie Christopher

D-U-N-S 10-050-0248
ORANGEBURG CONSOLIDATED SCHOOL DISTRICT 5
OCSD5
578 Ellis Ave, Orangeburg, SC 29115-5022
Tel (803) 534-5454 *Founded/Ownrshp* 1954
Sales 72.4MM^E *EMP* 1,200
SIC 8211 Public elementary & secondary schools; Public elementary & secondary schools
**Ch:* Mary Berry Ulmer
Pr Dir: Bill Clark
HC Dir: Janice Westbury

D-U-N-S 15-421-5529
ORANGEBURG COUNTY DISABILITY & SPECIAL NEEDS BOARD
ORANGEBURG COUNTY DSN
2785 Magnolia St, Orangeburg, SC 29115-2502
Tel (803) 536-1170 *Founded/Ownrshp* 1984
Sales 11.1MM^E *EMP* 473
SIC 8052 Intermediate care facilities; Intermediate care facilities
Ex Dir: Ronald Lofts

ORANGEBURG COUNTY DSN
See ORANGEBURG COUNTY DISABILITY & SPECIAL NEEDS BOARD

D-U-N-S 82-463-3028
ORANGUTAN HOME SERVICES INC
AMERICAN HOME MAINT TEXAS
2922 S Roosevelt St, Tempe, AZ 85282-2042
Tel (602) 906-0111 *Founded/Ownrshp* 1993

Sales 42.9MM^E *EMP* 300
SIC 1711 Warm air heating & air conditioning contractor; Warm air heating & air conditioning contractor
Pr: Jordy Tessler
**Treas:* Ron Schuman
Dir Bus: Johnny Walker
Genl Mgr: Mark Stoltz
Dir IT: Paul Gardner
Mktg Dir: Jim Klehr

D-U-N-S 07-957-5658
ORASCOM E&C USA INC
O C I
(*Suby of* ORASCOM CONSTRUCTION INDUSTRIES (OCI S.A.E.))
6862 Elm St Ste 400, Mc Lean, VA 22101-3886
Tel (703) 358-8800 *Founded/Ownrshp* 2012
Sales 900.0MM^E *EMP* 500
SIC 1521 1522 1542 Single-family housing construction; Residential construction; Nonresidential construction
CEO: Nassef Sawiris
**CEO:* Maged Abadir
**CFO:* Salman Butt
**Treas:* Dalia Khorshid

D-U-N-S 11-347-5383
ORASI SOFTWARE INC
114 Townpark Dr Nw # 400, Kennesaw, GA 30144-3715
Tel (678) 819-5300 *Founded/Ownrshp* 2002
Sales 85.7MM^E *EMP* 270
SIC 7372 7371 Prepackaged software; Software programming applications; Prepackaged software; Software programming applications
CEO: Nicholas Kavadellas
Pr: Brian Crout
Pr: Kelly Thompson
**CFO:* James Azar
Sr VP: Robin Smith
VP: Jim Arnold
VP: Caleb Billingsley
VP: Paul Carroll
VP: Dean Ghanem
**VP:* Mark Lewis
VP: Carl Rubin
VP: Karl Rubin
VP: David Rumley
VP: Cara Woodland

D-U-N-S 11-415-2184 IMP
▲ ORASURE TECHNOLOGIES INC
220 E 1st St, Bethlehem, PA 18015-1360
Tel (610) 882-1820 *Founded/Ownrshp* 2000
Sales 106.4MM *EMP* 293^E
Tkr Sym OSUR *Exch* NGS
SIC 2835 In vitro diagnostics; In vitro diagnostics
Pr: Douglas A Michels
**Ch Bd:* Douglas G Watson
**COO:* Ronald H Spair
Ex VP: P M Formica
Ex VP: Stephen R Lee
Ex VP: Anthony Zezzo II
Sr VP: Henry B Cohen
Sr VP: Jack E Jerrett
Sr VP: Mark L Kuna
Sr VP: Ron Ticho
Sr VP: Kathleen G Weber
Sr VP: Kathleen Weber
VP: William D Block
VP: Robert A Gregg
VP: Todd Grice
VP: Pat Reis
VP: Jill Thompson
Board of Directors: Michael Celano, Ronny B Lancaster, Charles W Patrick, Roger L Pringle, Stephen S Tang

ORAU
See OAK RIDGE ASSOCIATED UNIVERSITIES INC

D-U-N-S 14-611-8901
▲ ORBCOMM INC
395 W Passaic St Ste 3, Rochelle Park, NJ 07662-3016
Tel (703) 433-6300 *Founded/Ownrshp* 2003
Sales 96.2MM *EMP* 418
Tkr Sym ORBC *Exch* NGM
SIC 4899 8748 Satellite earth stations; Telecommunications consultant; Satellite earth stations; Telecommunications consultant
Pr: Marc J Eisenberg
Pr: Sanders Clay
CFO: Robert G Costantini
Ex VP: Christian G Le Brun
Ex VP: Craig Malone
Ex VP: John J Stolte Jr
Sr VP: Christian Allred
VP: Stephen Brown
VP: Dean Milcos
VP: Thomas Robinson
VP: Julie Spizuoco
VP Bus Dev: Davis Tony

D-U-N-S 82-903-4292
ORBIS 1 LLC
COSTREET COMMUNICATIONS
2901 Johnston St Ste 200, Lafayette, LA 70503-3276
Tel (337) 761-8024 *Founded/Ownrshp* 2000
Sales 23.8MM *EMP* 14
SIC 4813 ;
CFO: Patricia Lail
CFO: Patty Lail

D-U-N-S 12-716-5319 IMP/EXP
ORBIS CORP
LINPAC
(*Suby of* MENASHA CORP) ★
1055 Corporate Center Dr, Oconomowoc, WI 53066-4829
Tel (262) 560-5000 *Founded/Ownrshp* 1999
Sales 339.4MM^E *EMP* 850
SIC 3089 Synthetic resin finished products; Synthetic resin finished products
Pr: Bill Ash
Treas: William F Ash
VP: Andy McDonald
Dir Bus: Scott Buss
Dir Bus: Stephan Tobias
**Prin:* Dave Schopp
Rgnl Mgr: Kenneth Rivard
Dir IT: Bradley Bella
IT Man: Cathy Curran
Mtls Mgr: Sheri Krepps
Plnt Mgr: David Dodd

D-U-N-S 02-509-6509 IMP/EXP
ORBIS MATERIAL HANDLING INC
(*Suby of* LINPAC) ★
120 Commerce Ct, Georgetown, KY 40324-9042
Tel (502) 863-5500 *Founded/Ownrshp* 1999
Sales 51.3MM^E *EMP* 250
SIC 3089 3086 Plastic containers, except foam; Plastics foam products; Plastic containers, except foam; Plastics foam products
Pr: James M Kotek
**VP:* Makr P Fogarty
**VP:* Randall J Phelps

D-U-N-S 12-509-8140
ORBIS RPM LLC
CORBI
(*Suby of* LINPAC) ★
1055 Corporate Center Dr, Oconomowoc, WI 53066-4829
Tel (262) 560-5000 *Founded/Ownrshp* 2011
Sales 27.7MM^E *EMP* 115
SIC 3081 Polypropylene film & sheet; Polypropylene film & sheet
Ch: James Kotek
**Pr:* Randy Phelps
Treas: Cal Stanich
Sales Asso: Crystal Fischer

D-U-N-S 87-294-2706
ORBIS SIBRO INC
268 W Coleman Blvd Ste 2a, Mount Pleasant, SC 29464-5650
Tel (843) 971-9390 *Founded/Ownrshp* 2000
Sales 32.9MM^E *EMP* 120
SIC 8711 Engineering services; Engineering services
CEO: Guy Mossman
**Pr:* Melissa Mossman
CFO: Matthew Sarre
Ex Dir: Greg Curtis
Prgrm Mgr: Bob Herman
Ql Cn Mgr: Jeremy Adams
Sales Exec: Tom Welinski
Sls&Mrk Ex: Carl Frost
Board of Directors: Greg Curtis

ORBIT DODGE TRUCKS
See DARCARS OF AUTH WAY INC

ORBIT IRRIGATION
See PRO-MARK INC

D-U-N-S 94-985-3766 IMP/EXP
ORBIT IRRIGATION PRODUCTS INC
(*Suby of* ORBIT IRRIGATION) ★
845 Overland St, North Salt Lake, UT 84054-2123
Tel (801) 299-5555 *Founded/Ownrshp* 1996
Sales 172.8MM^E *EMP* 500
SIC 3523 Irrigation equipment, self-propelled; Irrigation equipment, self-propelled
Ofcr: Stuart Eyring
**VP:* Mike Ericksen
VP: Shawn Weaver
Genl Mgr: Tom Newman
CIO: Steve Slater
Dir IT: Bryan Adams
VP Opers: Jeff Maughan
Sls Mgr: Lori Smith
Genl Couns: Gregory Butters

D-U-N-S 11-928-5943 IMP
ORBIT MEDICAL INC
4516 S 700 E Ste 360, Salt Lake City, UT 84107-8317
Tel (801) 713-2020 *Founded/Ownrshp* 2002
Sales 37.5MM^E *EMP* 150^E
SIC 5999 Medical apparatus & supplies; Medical apparatus & supplies
Pr: Robert Gallup
**VP:* Kelly Albiston
**VP:* Jake Kilgore
VP: Rendell Mabey
**VP:* Patrick McGinley
Off Mgr: Phillip Beicher
Snr Sftwr: Patrick Visser
Opers Mgr: Tim Manion
**VP Sls:* Brandon Bliss
Mktg Dir: Brett Flitton
Sls Dir: Keith Hawkins

D-U-N-S 96-553-0397 IMP
▲ ORBIT/FR INC
506 Prudential Rd, Horsham, PA 19044-2309
Tel (215) 674-5100 *Founded/Ownrshp* 2008
Sales 26.6MM^E *EMP* 141^E
Tkr Sym ORFR *Exch* OTO
SIC 3825 Instruments to measure electricity; Instruments to measure electricity
Pr: Per Iversen
V Ch: Gurion Meltzer
CFO: Relland Winand
VP: John Aubin
VP: David S Berntein
VP: Mark A Btes
VP: William Campbell
VP: Sean Mallon
Prgrm Mgr: Eyal ADI
Sfty Mgr: Tom McKeown
Mktg Mgr: Anna Moyer
Board of Directors: Eric Anderson, Raymond Boch, Philippe Garreau, Douglas Merrill

ORBITAL ATK
See ORBITAL SCIENCES CORP

D-U-N-S 61-870-5925 IMP/EXP
▲ ORBITAL ATK INC
ALLIANT TECHSYSTEMS
45101 Warp Dr, Dulles, VA 20166-6874
Tel (703) 406-5000 *Founded/Ownrshp* 1990
Sales 3.1MMM *EMP* 16,000
Tkr Sym OA *Exch* NYS
SIC 3764 3812 3483 3482 3489 Propulsion units for guided missiles & space vehicles; Search & navigation equipment; Warfare counter-measure equipment; Detection apparatus: electronic/magnetic field, light/heat; Ammunition, except for small arms; Mortar shells, over 30 mm.; Rockets (ammunition); Bombs & parts; Small arms ammunition; Guns, howitzers, mortars & related equipment; Propulsion units for guided missiles & space vehicles; Search & navigation equipment; Warfare counter-measure equipment; Detection apparatus: electronic/magnetic field, light/heat; Ammunition, except for small arms; Mortar shells, over 30 mm.; Rockets (ammunition); Bombs & parts; Small arms ammunition; Guns, howitzers, mortars & related equipment
Pr: David W Thompson
Pr: Mike Kahn
COO: Blake E Larson
CFO: Garrett E Pierce
Ex VP: Antonio L Elias
Sr VP: Stephen S Clark
Sr VP: John J Cronin
Sr VP: Ed Fortunato
Sr VP: Stephen M Nolan
VP: Craig Fincken
VP: Ron Hill
VP: Tim Jones
VP: Nicholas G Vlahakis
Dir Risk M: Charles Thornton
Dir Bus: Rob Hoops
Board of Directors: Janice I Obuchowski, Kevin P Chilton, James G Roche, Roxanne J Decyk, Harrison H Schmitt, Martin C Faga, Scott L Webster, Lennard A Fisk, Ronald R Fogleman, Robert M Hanisee, Ronald T Kadish, Douglas L Maine, Roman Martinez IV

D-U-N-S 04-819-8568
ORBITAL ENGINEERING INC
1344 5th Ave, Pittsburgh, PA 15219-6217
Tel (412) 261-9100 *Founded/Ownrshp* 1969
Sales 56.5MM^E *EMP* 275
SIC 8711 8748 Engineering services; Business consulting; Engineering services; Business consulting
Pr: Robert J Lewis
**Sec:* Ashley Lewis
VP: Don Henrich
**VP:* Donald Henrich
VP: Sam Mana
Genl Mgr: Jeff Obermeyer
Counsel: Bryan Streeter

D-U-N-S 10-191-6062 IMP/EXP
■ ORBITAL SCIENCES CORP
ORBITAL ATK
(*Suby of* ALLIANT TECHSYSTEMS) ★
45101 Warp Dr, Dulles, VA 20166-6874
Tel (703) 406-5000 *Founded/Ownrshp* 2015
Sales 2.7MMM^E *EMP* 14,000
SIC 3812 7372 4899 Defense systems & equipment; Aircraft control systems, electronic; Navigational systems & instruments; Prepackaged software; Satellite earth stations; Data communication services; Defense systems & equipment; Aircraft control systems, electronic; Navigational systems & instruments; Prepackaged software; Satellite earth stations; Data communication services
Ch Bd: David W Thompson
**CFO:* Garrett E Pierce
**Ex VP:* Antonio L Elias
**Ex VP:* Ronald J Grabe
Ex VP: Carl A Marchetto
Ex VP: Marty Titland
Sr VP: Frank L Culbertson
Sr VP: Michael A Hamel
Sr VP: G David Low
Sr VP: Pamela J Lupien
**Sr VP:* Tom E McCabe
Sr VP: Christopher Richmond
Sr VP: Leslie C Seeman
VP: Daniel Robert
VP: Ferguson Bruce W
Dir Bus: David Mitlyng

ORBITFORM GROUP
See SMSG LLC

D-U-N-S 80-031-8441
■ ORBITZ INC
(*Suby of* ORBITZ WORLDWIDE INC) ★
200 S Wacker Dr, Chicago, IL 60606-5829
Tel (312) 894-5000 *Founded/Ownrshp* 2006
Sales 91.1MM^E *EMP* 1,200
SIC 4724 Travel agencies; Travel agencies
Pr: Steven Barnhart
Pr: Kit Simon
**CFO:* Marsha C Williams
Chf Mktg O: Randy Wagner
Sr VP: Bahman Koohestani
VP: Peggy Bianco
VP: Richard Buchband
VP: Barbara Buckridge
VP: Aaron Cooper
VP: Keith Dale
VP: Gary Doernhoefer
VP: Brian Hoyt
VP: Richard Lee
VP: Michael Mooradian
VP: Ian Ross

D-U-N-S 80-212-1587 IMP
■ ORBITZ LLC
ORBITZ PARTNER NETWORK
(*Suby of* ORBITZ WORLDWIDE INC) ★
500 W Madison St Ste 1000, Chicago, IL 60661-2559
Tel (312) 894-5000 *Founded/Ownrshp* 1999
Sales 86.9MM^E *EMP* 1,200^E
SIC 4724 Travel agencies; Travel agencies
CEO: Barney Harford
**Pr:* Ronnie Gurion
**COO:* Mike Nelson
Chf Mktg O: Mike Sands
**Sr VP:* Jim Shaughnessy
VP: Jane Denman
VP: Carol Jouzaitis
VP: Michael Sites
Ql Cn Mgr: Abishek Machani
Sls Mgr: Phil Hammer
Genl Couns: Karen Klein

ORBITZ PARTNER NETWORK
See ORBITZ LLC

D-U-N-S 02-180-3568
ORBITZ WORLDWIDE
500 W Madison St Ste 1000, Chicago, IL 60661-2559
Tel (312) 894-5000 *Founded/Ownrshp* 2009
Sales 14.1MM^E *EMP* 800
SIC 8742 Business consultant; Business consultant
CEO: Barney Harford

D-U-N-S 80-701-6568
■ ORBITZ WORLDWIDE INC
ORBITZ.COM
(*Suby of* EXPEDIA INC) ★
500 W Madison St Ste 1000, Chicago, IL 60661-2559
Tel (312) 894-5000 *Founded/Ownrshp* 2015
Sales 932.0MM *EMP* 1,530^E
Tkr Sym OWW *Exch* NYS
SIC 4724 Travel agencies; Tourist agency arranging transport, lodging & car rental; Travel agencies; Tourist agency arranging transport, lodging & car rental
CEO: Barney Harford
CFO: Michael Randolfi
Sr VP: Ronnie Gurion
Sr VP: Roger Liew
Sr VP: Frank Petito
Sr VP: Nigel Pocklington
VP: Lenette Rafa
Snr Sftwr: Nilesh Malpekar
Mktg Mgr: Abby Samler
Board of Directors: Gavin Baiera, Martin J Brand, Mark S Britton, Kenneth S Esterow, Scott Forbes, Robert L Friedman, Bradley T Gerstner, Kristina M Leslie

ORBITZ.COM
See ORBITZ WORLDWIDE INC

D-U-N-S 10-141-0801 IMP
ORBOTECH INC
(*Suby of* ORBOTECH LTD.)
44 Manning Rd, Billerica, MA 01821-3990
Tel (978) 667-6037 *Founded/Ownrshp* 1983
Sales 204.0MM^E *EMP* 1,700
SIC 5065 3823 3674 Electronic parts & equipment; Industrial instrmnts msrmnt display/control process variable; Solid state electronic devices; Electronic parts & equipment; Industrial instrmnts msrmnt display/control process variable; Solid state electronic devices
Pr: Raanan Cohen
Pr: AVI Koren
**Pr:* Ken Maylor
**COO:* Amichai Steinberg
**Sr VP:* Werner Eschke
VP: Yair Alcobi
VP: Aryeh Batt
**VP:* Margaret Duncan
VP: Yacov Haim
VP: Eitan Judah
VP: Sriram Krishnaswami
VP: Reuven Losh
VP: Lior Maayan
VP: Errol Moore
VP: Gil Oron
VP: Yovav Sameah
VP: Dror Shklarski
Board of Directors: Dani Falk, Shimon Ullman, Arie Weisberg

ORBUS EXHIBIT & DISPLAY GROUP
See ORBUS LLC

D-U-N-S 00-717-1449 IMP/EXP
ORBUS LLC (IL)
ORBUS EXHIBIT & DISPLAY GROUP
9033 Murphy Rd, Woodridge, IL 60517-1100
Tel (630) 226-1155 *Founded/Ownrshp* 2005
Sales 85.0MM *EMP* 320
SIC 3999 Advertising display products; Advertising display products
Pr: Giles Douglas
CFO: Aurelia Sirbu
VP: Aaron Kozar
Dir Bus: Alex Nunez
Rgnl Mgr: Kate Kincaid
Off Admin: Claudia Simental
Dir IT: Jason Westpfahl
Sales Asso: Sophia Cryns
Sales Asso: Jamie Vicha
Sales Asso: Carrie Villalobos

D-U-N-S 06-476-3063
ORC INDUSTRIES INC
2700 Commerce St, La Crosse, WI 54603-1797
Tel (608) 781-7727 *Founded/Ownrshp* 1966
Sales 27.9MM *EMP* 400
Accts Engelson And Associates Ltd L
SIC 8331 2385 2394 Sheltered workshop; Waterproof outerwear; Raincoats, except vulcanized rubber: purchased materials; Tents: made from purchased materials; Sheltered workshop; Waterproof outerwear; Raincoats, except vulcanized rubber: purchased materials; Tents: made from purchased materials
Ch Bd: Shirley Holman
**V Ch:* James Heinecke
**Pr:* Barbara Barnard
**Treas:* Richard Record
VP: Todd Bahnub
IT Man: Randy Fortun
IT Man: Tou Lo

D-U-N-S 00-254-3239
ORC INTERNATIONAL INC
OPINION RESEARCH CORPORATION
(*Suby of* LAKE CAPITAL MANAGEMENT LLC) ★
902 Carnegie Ctr Ste 220, Princeton, NJ 08540-6530
Tel (609) 452-5400 *Founded/Ownrshp* 1938, 2011
Sales 130.0MM *EMP* 1,800
SIC 8732 Market analysis or research; Opinion research; Market analysis or research; Opinion research
CEO: Simon Kooyman
CFO: Jim Karr
**CFO:* Stace Lee
Ex VP: Richard Catrone
Ex VP: Elise Delahanty

*Ex VP: Walter Dempsey
Ex VP: Lori Kelley
Ex VP: Rory Macneill
Ex VP: David Murray
Sr VP: Jennifer Adams
*Sr VP: Brian Cruikshank
Sr VP: Timothy Ellard
Sr VP: Slade Kobran
Sr VP: Judith Lescher
Sr VP: Mia Wong
VP: Brian Cash
VP: Paul Chong
VP: Dean Crivellone
VP: Judith Feinstein
VP: Joaquin Garcia-Lopez
VP: Laurie Gelb

D-U-N-S 14-723-7903 IMP/EXP
ORCA BAY SEAFOODS INC
(Suby of TOKUSUI CORPORATION)
900 Powell Ave Sw, Renton, WA 98057-2907
Tel (425) 204-9100 Founded/Ownrshp 1990
Sales 78.0MM^E EMP 180
SIC 2092 Fresh or frozen packaged fish; Fresh or frozen packaged fish
Pr: Ryan Mackey
*COO: Michael Walsh
*Treas: Patricia Haaker
*Sr VP: Trish Haaker
VP Bus Dev: John Steinmetz
Rgnl Mgr: Zen Chalupa
Prd Mgr: Scott Russell
Ql Cn Mgr: Justine Reynolds
Manager: Lori Parry
Sls Mgr: Scott Milles
Sales Asso: Karla Hansen

D-U-N-S 00-378-1176
ORCAS POWER & LIGHT COOPERATIVE
183 Mount Baker Rd, Eastsound, WA 98245-9413
Tel (360) 376-3550 Founded/Ownrshp 1937
Sales 21.6MM EMP 49^E
Accts Moss-Adams Llp Everett Washi
SIC 4911 Distribution, electric power; Distribution, electric power
Pr: Chris Thomerson
*VP: Jim Lett
*Genl Mgr: Randy J Cornelius
Sales Exec: Karin Becker

ORCHARD, THE
See ORCHARD CARE OF RIDGELAND INC

D-U-N-S 05-573-0062
■ ORCHARD - POST ACUTE CARE CENTER
(Suby of ENSIGN GROUP INC) ★
12385 Washington Blvd, Whittier, CA 90606-2502
Tel (562) 693-7701 Founded/Ownrshp 2015
Sales 15.6MM EMP 1,335^E
SIC 8051 Convalescent home with continuous nursing care
Prin: Rich Jorgensen

D-U-N-S 78-814-6640
■ ORCHARD BRANDS CORP
BEDFORD FAIR APPAREL
(Suby of BLUESTEM BRANDS INC) ★
138 Conant St Ste 3, Beverly, MA 01915-1666
Tel (978) 998-3800 Founded/Ownrshp 2015
Sales 870.3MM^E EMP 1,200^E
SIC 5621 5611 5719 Catalog & mail-order houses; Women's clothing stores; Clothing, men's & boys': everyday, except suits & sportswear; Housewares; Towels; Beddings & linens; Kitchenware
CEO: James P Fogarty
*Pr: Marc Fieger
*CFO: Brain Gowen
VP: Nuku Aggor
VP: Cynthia Dziendziel
*CIO: Bill Nixon
Software D: Mark Attaya
Netwrk Eng: Jon Peters
VP Mktg: Kevin McGrain
Mktg Mgr: Robyn Mohr
Snr Mgr: Somali Nalhan

D-U-N-S 17-845-5101
ORCHARD CARE OF RIDGELAND INC
ORCHARD, THE
103 Sudduth Ct Ne, Fort Walton Beach, FL 32548-5164
Tel (601) 856-2205 Founded/Ownrshp 1987
Sales 21.0MM EMP 250
SIC 6513 8052 8051 Retirement hotel operation; Intermediate care facilities; Skilled nursing care facilities; Retirement hotel operation; Intermediate care facilities; Skilled nursing care facilities
Pr: Thad McLaurin
*Pr: Thad Mc Laurin
*Treas: Phillip Dotts
*VP: Charles Craig
Exec: Thad McLauren

D-U-N-S 05-062-5979
ORCHARD CHRYSLER DODGE JEEP INC
64600 Van Dyke Rd, Washington, MI 48095-2853
Tel (586) 336-5727 Founded/Ownrshp 1969
Sales 26.8MM^E EMP 75
SIC 5511 Automobiles, new & used; Automobiles, new & used
Ch Bd: Robert M Brent
*Pr: Robert E Brent
Exec: Kevin O'Brien

D-U-N-S 78-095-8971
ORCHARD COVE INC
HEBREW SENIORLISE HM HLTH CARE
29 Newbridge Way, Dedham, MA 02026-7011
Tel (781) 821-0820 Founded/Ownrshp 1990
Sales 26.4MM EMP 240
Accts Ernst & Young Us Llp Greenvil
SIC 8361 8059 8069 8052 8051 Geriatric residential care; Nursing home, except skilled & intermediate care facility; Domiciliary care; Specialty hospitals, except psychiatric; Intermediate care facilities; Skilled nursing care facilities; Geriatric residential care; Nursing home, except skilled & intermediate care facility; Domiciliary care; Specialty hospitals, except psychiatric; Intermediate care facilities; Skilled nursing care facilities
Ch: William G Finard
*Treas: Robert M Leavy

D-U-N-S 07-959-5345
ORCHARD ENERGY LLC
2161 E Horseshoe Pl, Chandler, AZ 85249-3253
Tel (480) 626-7719 Founded/Ownrshp 2014
Sales 30.0MM EMP 5
SIC 5172 8732 Fuel oil; Business research service

D-U-N-S 61-322-9512
ORCHARD ENTERPRISES NY INC
(Suby of DIMENSIONAL ASSOCIATES LLC) ★
23 E 4th St Fl 3, New York, NY 10003-7023
Tel (212) 201-9280 Founded/Ownrshp 2000
Sales 30.9MM^E EMP 88^E
SIC 6794 7929 Copyright buying & licensing; Entertainers & entertainment groups
CEO: Bradley Navin
Mng Pt: Alina Nemes
COO: Colleen Theis
CFO: Nathan Fong
CFO: Lee Westerfield
Ex VP: Steve Haase
Sr VP: Paul Davidson
Sr VP: Alexis H Shapiro
VP: Eshan Jahan
VP: Jordy Trachtenberg
VP: Miki Tunis
Board of Directors: David Altschul, Michael Donahue, Nathan Peck, Daniel C Stein, Joel Straka

ORCHARD EQUIPMENT MFG
See BIANCHI ORCHARD SYSTEMS INC

D-U-N-S 06-055-1728
ORCHARD FARM R-V SCHOOL DISTRICT
2165 Highway V, Saint Charles, MO 63301-6004
Tel (636) 250-5000 Founded/Ownrshp 1959
Sales 23.8MM EMP 285
Accts Mueller Walla & Albertson P
SIC 8211 Public elementary & secondary schools; Elementary school; Secondary school; Public elementary & secondary schools; Elementary school; Secondary school

ORCHARD FOOD DIV
See ROHTSTEIN CORP

D-U-N-S 06-416-9998
ORCHARD HILTZ & MCCLIMENT INC
OHM ADVISORS
34000 Plymouth Rd, Livonia, MI 48150-1512
Tel (734) 522-6711 Founded/Ownrshp 1962
Sales 52.2MM^E EMP 275
Accts Rosenbaum Rollins & Associate
SIC 8711 Civil engineering; Civil engineering
Ch Bd: Vyto Kaunelis
*Pr: Russell Gronevelt
*Pr: John Hiltz
*VP: Dan Fredendall
*VP: John J Hiltz
*VP: Jim Houk
*VP: Jon Kramer
Genl Mgr: Laura Elder
Dir IT: Mark Bloom
IT Man: Joe Kidd
Snr PM: Scott Emmons

D-U-N-S 04-182-7361
ORCHARD MARKETS INC
DELICIOUS ORCHARDS
320 State Route 34 S, Colts Neck, NJ 07722
Tel (732) 462-1989 Founded/Ownrshp 1965
Sales 22.5MM^E EMP 300
SIC 5431 5461 5451 Fruit & vegetable markets; Bakeries; Dairy products stores; Fruit & vegetable markets; Bakeries; Dairy products stores
Pr: William Mc Donald
Pr: Chris McDonald
*Pr: William McDonald
*VP: Chris Mc Donald
*VP: Keri Mc Donald
*VP: Micheal Mc Donald
Sls Mgr: Dave Karl

D-U-N-S 08-034-0383
ORCHARD PARK CENTRAL SCHOOL DISTRICT
3330 Baker Rd, Orchard Park, NY 14127-1472
Tel (716) 209-6209 Founded/Ownrshp 1944
Sales 32.3MM^E EMP 822
Accts Lumsden & Mccormick Llp
SIC 8211 Public elementary school; Public junior high school; Public senior high school; School board; Public elementary school; Public junior high school; Public senior high school; School board
CFO: Janis Colarusso
Bd of Dir: Natalie Schaffer
MIS Dir: Terry Tryon
Dir IT: Steven Kennedy
Pr Dir: Julianne Heinen

D-U-N-S 82-848-5123
ORCHARD PHARMACEUTICAL SERVICES LLC
7835 Freedom Ave Nw, North Canton, OH 44720-6907
Tel (330) 491-4200 Founded/Ownrshp 2008
Sales 48.9MM^E EMP 112
SIC 5122 Pharmaceuticals; Pharmaceuticals
Pr: Barry Katz
*VP: John Baker Sr
Dir IT: John Sedlak

D-U-N-S 07-347-9248
ORCHARD PLACE
808 5th Ave, Des Moines, IA 50309-1315
Tel (515) 244-2267 Founded/Ownrshp 1886
Sales 23.6MM EMP 280
SIC 8361 8322 Home for the emotionally disturbed; Individual & family services; Home for the emotionally disturbed; Individual & family services
Ex Dir: Brock Wolff
CFO: Valerie Saltsgaver
VP: Nicole Beaman
Off Mgr: Nancy Boggess
CIO: Chris Walters
Psych: Keri Kinnaird
Psych: Beth Schmitz
HC Dir: Lori Dawson-Weeks

D-U-N-S 96-391-2139
ORCHARD PLACE
2116 Grand Ave Ste 2 Je, Des Moines, IA 50312-5369
Tel (515) 246-3501 Founded/Ownrshp 2010
Sales 24.0MM EMP 2
Accts Denman & Company Llp West Des
SIC 8322 Social service center; Social service center
Prin: Earl Kelly

D-U-N-S 80-997-2383
ORCHARD SOFTWARE CORP
701 Congressional Blvd, Carmel, IN 46032-5635
Tel (800) 571-5835 Founded/Ownrshp 1993
Sales 27.4MM^E EMP 140
SIC 7371 Computer software development & applications; Computer software development & applications
CEO: Curtis H Johnson
*Pr: Robert Bush
Ofcr: Bryan Beswick
*VP: Norris Groves
Snr Sftwr: John Cogswell
QA Dir: Joshua Impson
QA Dir: Eric Wurth
Dir IT: Adam Buckland
Dir IT: Chris Cline
Dir IT: Andy Gilmore
Sftwr Eng: Adam Davis

D-U-N-S 55-542-3177 IMP
■ ORCHARD SUPPLY CO LLC
O S H
(Suby of LOWES COMPANIES INC) ★
6450 Via Del Oro, San Jose, CA 95119-1208
Tel (408) 281-3500 Founded/Ownrshp 2013
Sales 1.3MM^E EMP 5,329
SIC 5251 5261 Hardware; Nurseries & garden centers; Hardware; Nurseries & garden centers
Pr: Bob Tellier
Pr: Joe Kamleiter
Pr: Richard Marano
Ex VP: Steve Olsen
Sr VP: Mark A Bussard
Sr VP: David I Bogage
Sr VP: Mark Kauffman
VP: Woody Gray
VP: Bruce Levitin
VP: Mike Molinar
VP: Craig Siqueland

D-U-N-S 03-979-3971
ORCHARD VIEW FARMS INC
4055 Skyline Rd, The Dalles, OR 97058-9509
Tel (541) 296-0027 Founded/Ownrshp 1950
Sales 22.7MM EMP 75
Accts Rowe & Deming Llc The Dalles
SIC 0175 Cherry orchard; Apple orchard; Pear orchard; Cherry orchard; Apple orchard; Pear orchard
Pr: Robert L R Bailey
Pr: Brenda Thomas
CFO: Kenneth R Bailey

D-U-N-S 06-017-6195
ORCHARD VIEW SCHOOL DISTRICT
35 S Sheridan Dr, Muskegon, MI 49442-1492
Tel (231) 760-1300 Founded/Ownrshp 1910
Sales 33.4MM EMP 450
Accts Brickley Delong Muskegon Mi
SIC 8211 Public elementary & secondary schools; Public elementary & secondary schools
Schl Brd P: Tom Joppie
Psych: Jennifer Kitchka
Psych: James Sheehan

D-U-N-S 00-138-5525 IMP
ORCHARD YARN AND THREAD CO INC (NY)
LION BRAND YARN
135 Kero Rd, Carlstadt, NJ 07072-2601
Tel (800) 661-7551 Founded/Ownrshp 1878
Sales 44.9MM^E EMP 102
SIC 5199 Yarns
Pr: David Blumenthal
*COO: R Dean Blumenthal
CFO: Richard Levine
*Ch: Bernard Blumenthal
Ofcr: Ed Cooke
*VP: Alan E Blumenthal
VP: Keith Bobier
Creative D: Adina Klein
Dir IT: Brian Ramnarain
IT Man: Michael Peduto
Opers Mgr: Ken Karesh

D-U-N-S 05-123-7964
ORCHARD-RITE LIMITED INC
1702 Englewood Ave, Yakima, WA 98902-1846
Tel (509) 834-2029 Founded/Ownrshp 1969
Sales 27.8MM^E EMP 70
SIC 3523 7359 Farm machinery & equipment; Harvesters, fruit, vegetable, tobacco, etc.; Equipment rental & leasing
Pr: Doug Riddle
*VP: Jim Decoto
IT Man: Karen Shaul

D-U-N-S 01-238-4785
ORCHID AUTOMATION SYSTEMS INC
100 Winners Cir N Ste 450, Brentwood, TN 37027-1004
Tel (615) 661-4300 Founded/Ownrshp 1990
Sales 21.9MM^E EMP 350
SIC 3469 Metal stampings; Metal stampings
Pr: Grant Bibby
*CFO: Chris Strong
*VP: Steve Grover
Prgrm Mgr: Byron Wright
Dir IT: Mike Clavin
IT Man: Martha Mason
Ql Cn Mgr: Melvin Woodard

D-U-N-S 01-431-9888
ORCHID BRENTWOOD LLC
94 Belinda Pkwy, Mount Juliet, TN 37122-3600
Tel (615) 754-6600 Founded/Ownrshp 1995
Sales 44.9MM^E EMP 177
SIC 3469 Metal stampings
IT Man: Martha Mason

ORCHID CELLMARK INC.
See CELLMARK FORENSICS INC

ORCHID INTERNATIONAL
See ORCHID MONROE LLC

ORCHID INTERNATIONAL
See ORCHID MT JULIET LLC

D-U-N-S 07-001-2960
ORCHID ISLAND CAPITAL INC
3305 Flamingo Dr, Vero Beach, FL 32963-1731
Tel (772) 231-1400 Founded/Ownrshp 2011
Sales 29.0MM EMP 2
Accts Bdo Usa Llp West Palm Beach
SIC 6799 Investors
Pr: Robert E Cauley

D-U-N-S 79-009-9816 EXP
ORCHID ISLAND JUICE CO
NATALIES ORCHID ISLAND JUICE
330 N Us Highway 1, Fort Pierce, FL 34950-4207
Tel (772) 465-1122 Founded/Ownrshp 2003
Sales 32.3MM^E EMP 85
SIC 2037 Fruit juices; Fruit juices
CEO: Marygrace Sexton
Pr: William Martinelli
*CFO: Christine Roberts
*Ex VP: John Martinelli
Sr VP: Martinelli John
Exec: Sarah Lamm
Genl Mgr: Frank Tranchilla
Mktg Dir: Natalie Sexton
Sls Dir: Michael D'Amato
Sls Dir: Michael Damato
Mktg Mgr: Dan Leung

ORCHID ISLE AUTO CENTER
See INTER PACIFIC MOTORS INC

ORCHID LABS
See FLAVORCHEM CORP

D-U-N-S 14-507-5516 IMP
ORCHID MONROE LLC
ORCHID INTERNATIONAL
(Suby of ORCHID BRENTWOOD LLC) ★
350 21st St, Monroe, WI 53566-2739
Tel (608) 325-9161 Founded/Ownrshp 2004
Sales 44.8MM^E EMP 141
SIC 3469 Metal stampings; Metal stampings
Pr: Joe Fontana
Chf Mktg O: Belinda Pratt
VP: Kevin Monahan
Opers Mgr: Doug Miller
Opers Mgr: Frank Rielly
Plnt Mgr: Paul Thomann
Plnt Mgr: Tom Wenner
Ql Cn Mgr: Bill Brady
Ql Cn Mgr: Steve Cuplin
Ql Cn Mgr: Bernie McCusker
Ql Cn Mgr: Mike Wimberley

D-U-N-S 78-335-0853
ORCHID MT JULIET LLC
ORCHID INTERNATIONAL
94 Belinda Pkwy, Mount Juliet, TN 37122-3600
Tel (615) 773-3300 Founded/Ownrshp 2010
Sales 63.0MM^E EMP 225
SIC 3469 Metal stampings; Stamping metal for the trade; Metal stampings; Stamping metal for the trade
Pr: Craig Woodward
Telecom Ex: Mike Clavin
VP Opers: Erik Hunt
Plnt Mgr: Paul Thomann
Plnt Mgr: Tom Winner
Sls&Mrk Ex: Tim Tucker
Mktg Mgr: Kerry Meacham

D-U-N-S 19-655-1746
ORCHID ORTHOPEDIC SOLUTIONS LLC
1489 Cedar St, Holt, MI 48842-1875
Tel (517) 694-2300 Founded/Ownrshp 2011
Sales 386.8MM^E EMP 1,500
SIC 3842 3845 Orthopedic appliances; Orthopedic appliances; Prosthetic appliances; Electromedical equipment
Pr: Mike Miller
*CFO: Bob Tate
CFO: Robert Tate
*Ex VP: Mark Burba
Ex VP: Christopher Norbye
Sr VP: Martin Girga
VP: Bill Ditty
VP: Matt Rudd
Genl Mgr: Clay Clayton
Genl Mgr: Steve Maguire
Genl Mgr: Bob Naumann

D-U-N-S 05-097-5465
ORCHID ORTHOPEDIC SOLUTIONS OREGON INC
SANDVIK
(Suby of ORCHID ORTHOPEDIC SOLUTIONS LLC) ★
13963 Fir St, Oregon City, OR 97045-8906
Tel (503) 656-9653 Founded/Ownrshp 2012
Sales 21.0MM^E EMP 130
SIC 3363 Aluminum die-castings; Aluminum die-castings
Pr: David Daighton
Genl Mgr: Karl Neidhart
Web Dev: Enrique Gollas
Plnt Mgr: Maridy McGinnis

D-U-N-S 06-312-1057 IMP
ORCHIDS PAPER PRODUCTS CO
4826 Hunt St, Pryor, OK 74361-4512
Tel (918) 825-0616 Founded/Ownrshp 1998
Sales 142.7MM EMP 317

Accts Hogantaylor Llp Tulsa Oklaho
Tkr Sym TIS *Exch* ASE
SIC 2676 Sanitary paper products; Facial tissues: made from purchased paper; Napkins, paper: made from purchased paper; Towels, paper: made from purchased paper; Sanitary paper products; Facial tissues: made from purchased paper; Napkins, paper: made from purchased paper; Towels, paper: made from purchased paper
Pr: Jeffrey S Schoen
**Ch Bd:* Steven R Berlin
CFO: Keith R Schroeder
IT Man: John Hulse
Opers Mgr: Fred Ceruti
Plnt Mgr: David Demarzo
Manager: Becky Thomaselli
Board of Directors: Mario Armando Garcia, John C Gutilla, Douglas E Hailey, Elaine Macdonald, Mark H Ravich

D-U-N-S 02-948-7063
ORCO BLOCK & HARDSCAPE
11100 Beach Blvd, Stanton, CA 90680-3219
Tel (714) 527-2239 *Founded/Ownrshp* 1946
Sales 38.2MM^E *EMP* 200
SIC 3271 Architectural concrete: block, split, fluted, screen, etc.; Blocks, concrete or cinder: standard; Architectural concrete: block, split, fluted, screen, etc.; Blocks, concrete or cinder: standard
CEO: Richard J Muth
Admn Mgr: Lorraine Michels
Off Mgr: Eldon La Bossiere

D-U-N-S 09-229-0204
ORCOM SOLUTIONS LLC
VERTEX US HOLDINGS II
1001 Sw Disk Dr Ste 100, Bend, OR 97702-2946
Tel (214) 576-1223 *Founded/Ownrshp* 2000
Sales 37.9MM *EMP* 440
SIC 5045 7372 Computers; Computer peripheral equipment; Business oriented computer software; Computers; Computer peripheral equipment; Business oriented computer software
CEO: Paul Sweeny
COO: Susie Buffam
Treas: Gavin James
IT Man: Eric Steinhauff
Opers Mgr: Michelle Kaiser

D-U-N-S 00-943-8219 IMP
ORCON CORP (CA)
1570 Atlantic St, Union City, CA 94587-2040
Tel (510) 489-8100 *Founded/Ownrshp* 1962
Sales 80.0MM^E *EMP* 110
SIC 3292 3559 Blankets, insulating for aircraft asbestos; Bag seaming & closing machines (sewing machinery); Blankets, insulating for aircraft asbestos; Bag seaming & closing machines (sewing machinery)
CEO: Hollis H Bascom
Genl Mgr: Roberto Buelna
Genl Mgr: Ed Jackson
Sls&Mrk Ex: Maria Ruelas
S&M/VP: Dennis Murray

D-U-N-S 78-922-2775 IMP
ORCON INDUSTRIES CORP
8715 Lake Rd, Le Roy, NY 14482-9396
Tel (585) 768-7000 *Founded/Ownrshp* 1993
Sales 22.0MM^E *EMP* 75^E
SIC 3086 7336 2653 Packaging & shipping materials, foamed plastic; Chart & graph design; Corrugated & solid fiber boxes
Ch Bd: Bruce E Olson
Pr: Richard Flanagan
**Ex VP:* Gale Hastings
**VP:* Cheryl Le Blanc
Plnt Mgr: Dan Murphy
Prd Mgr: Cheryl Hastings
Sls Mgr: Sean Hopkins

D-U-N-S 12-663-5226
ORCUTT UNION SCHOOL DISTRICT
500 Dyer St, Santa Maria, CA 93455-5300
Tel (805) 938-8900 *Founded/Ownrshp* 1959
Sales 38.7MM^E *EMP* 600
SIC 8211 Public elementary & secondary schools; Public elementary & secondary schools
Bd of Dir: Rob Buchanan
Prin: Joe Dana
Prin: Don Hart
Off Mgr: Margaret George
Opers Supe: Brad Gitchell
HC Dir: Robyn Turner

D-U-N-S 00-621-8002
ORDER OF ST BENEDICT
ST JOHN'S ABBEY
2900 Abbey Plz, Collegeville, MN 56321
Tel (320) 363-3378 *Founded/Ownrshp* 1857
Sales 25.8MM *EMP* 210
Accts Cliftonlarsonallen Llp St Cl
SIC 8661 8211 5942 Monastery; High school, junior or senior; Books, religious; Monastery; High school, junior or senior; Books, religious
Pr: John Klassen
**Treas:* Benedict Leuthner
Opers Mgr: David Arnott
Mktg Mgr: Joe Riley
Board of Directors: John Klassen, Robbin Pierzina

D-U-N-S 07-570-1821
ORDER OF ST BENEDICT IN PORTSMOUTH RI
PORTSMOUTH ABBEY SCHOOL
285 Corys Ln, Portsmouth, RI 02871-1362
Tel (401) 683-5029 *Founded/Ownrshp* 1919
Sales 20.9MM^E *EMP* 130
Accts Roy & Rurak Llc North Andove
SIC 8211 8661 Preparatory school; Monastery
CFO: David Brown
CFO: Ellen Eggeman
Comm Dir: Kathy Heydt
**Prin:* Daniel McDonough
MIS Dir: Victor Pacheco

D-U-N-S 00-431-2310
ORDER OF UNITE COMMERCIAL TRA (OH)
FRATERNAL INSURANCE
1801 Watermark Dr Ste 100, Columbus, OH 43215-7088
Tel (614) 487-9680 *Founded/Ownrshp* 1888
Sales NA *EMP* 59
Accts Bkd Llp Cincinnati Oh
SIC 6321 Fraternal accident & health insurance organizations; Fraternal accident & health insurance organizations
CEO: Ron Hunt
**Treas:* Martha Tate Horn
VP: Ben Boyd
VP: Kevin Hecker
**VP:* Ron Ives

D-U-N-S 00-719-4491
ORDER-MATIC ELECTRONICS CORP (OK)
340 S Eckroat St, Oklahoma City, OK 73129-8208
Tel (405) 672-1487 *Founded/Ownrshp* 1956
Sales 27.0MM *EMP* 116
Accts Danny B Webb Cpa
SIC 3578 3669 3577 3993 Point-of-sale devices; Intercommunication systems, electric; Computer peripheral equipment; Signs & advertising specialties; Point-of-sale devices; Intercommunication systems, electric; Computer peripheral equipment; Signs & advertising specialties
CEO: Robert Powell
COO: Tom Dooner
**CFO:* Danny B Webb
VP: Scott Barlow
VP: Barlow Scott
DP Dir: Jason Tan
VP Opers: Richard Beadle

ORDEREST MATTRESS
See PARK PLACE CORP

D-U-N-S 04-137-7474
ORDERS CONSTRUCTION CO INC
501 6th Ave, Saint Albans, WV 25177-2842
Tel (304) 722-4237 *Founded/Ownrshp* 1952
Sales 76.3MM^E *EMP* 125
SIC 1622 1611 Bridge construction; Highway & street construction; Bridge construction; Highway & street construction
Pr: Nate R Orders
**VP:* John H Person
VP: John Persun
Dir Bus: Chad Earl
Dir IT: Donnie Spark

D-U-N-S 06-987-2022
ORDNANCE TECHNOLOGIES (N/A) INC
1334 S Semoran Blvd, Orlando, FL 32807-2916
Tel (407) 354-3827 *Founded/Ownrshp* 2011
Sales 24.5MM *EMP* 14
SIC 8731 Commercial physical research; Commercial physical research
Pr: Stephen K Cardy

D-U-N-S 15-285-7090
ORDNER CONSTRUCTION CO INC
1600 Executive Dr Ste 100, Duluth, GA 30096-4942
Tel (678) 380-7400 *Founded/Ownrshp* 1987
Sales 74.9MM *EMP* 30
Accts Westbrook Mcgrath Bridges Orth
SIC 1542 Commercial & office building, new construction; Commercial & office buildings, renovation & repair; Commercial & office building, new construction; Commercial & office buildings, renovation & repair
Pr: Dave A Ordner
**COO:* David Stoller
**Sec:* Lisa Ordner
VP: Dicky Piland
VP Opers: Eddie Slay

D-U-N-S 10-867-4128
ORDWAY CENTER FOR PERFORMING ARTS
345 Washington St Ste 775, Saint Paul, MN 55102-1419
Tel (651) 282-3000 *Founded/Ownrshp* 1982
Sales 31.3MM *EMP* 60
SIC 7922 Theatrical production services; Performing arts center production; Theatrical production services; Performing arts center production
Pr: Patricia Mitchell
**CFO:* Chris Sagstetter
Treas: Lilly David
VP: Heather Spicuzza
Prd Mgr: Julia Erickson
Mktg Dir: Connie Shaver

D-U-N-S 02-856-9630 IMP
ORE-CAL CORP
HARVEST OF THE SEA
634 Crocker St, Los Angeles, CA 90021-1002
Tel (213) 623-8493 *Founded/Ownrshp* 1964
Sales 32.4MM^E *EMP* 55^E
SIC 5146 5142 Fish & seafoods; Frozen fish, meat & poultry
CEO: William L Shinbane
**Pr:* Mark Shinbane
**Sec:* Sandra Shinbane
Exec: Connie Delasuente
Rgnl Mgr: Debra Edgemon
Dir IT: David Rovner
Manager: John Breen
Manager: Robert Brinkman
Manager: Casey Delanty
Sls Mgr: Bertha Vidrio

D-U-N-S 00-590-5906 EXP
ORECK CORP
1400 Salem Rd, Cookeville, TN 38506-6221
Tel (800) 219-2044 *Founded/Ownrshp* 1963
Sales 342.3MM^E *EMP* 1,000
SIC 3589 3564 5064 5087 Vacuum cleaners & sweepers, electric: industrial; Floor washing & polishing machines, commercial; Air purification equipment; Vacuum cleaners, household; Vacuum cleaners; Floor machinery, maintenance; Vacuum cleaners & sweepers, electric: industrial; Floor washing & polishing machines, commercial; Air purification equipment; Vacuum cleaners, household; Vacuum cleaners; Floor machinery, maintenance
CEO: Doug Cahill
Ch Bd: William Fry
CFO: Rethann Cox
CFO: Stanley W Eilers
CFO: Jeffrey T Gray
VP: John Arena
VP: Jeff Collins
VP: Anthony Conversa
Prin: David Oreck
Store Mgr: Lisa Daniel
CIO: Don Chrobot
Board of Directors: James Amos Jr, Peter Frank, Mary George, David Horing

ORECK FLOOR CARE CENTER
See ORECK HOMECARE LLC

D-U-N-S 95-846-3846 IMP
ORECK HOMECARE LLC
ORECK FLOOR CARE CENTER
(*Suby of* ORECK CORP) ★
565 Marriott Dr Ste 300, Nashville, TN 37214-5022
Tel (615) 316-5800 *Founded/Ownrshp* 1995
Sales 22.8MM^E *EMP* 275
SIC 5722 Vacuum cleaners; Vacuum cleaners
CFO: Doug Lambert

D-U-N-S 96-818-5124 IMP
ORECK MANUFACTURING CO
(*Suby of* ORECK CORP) ★
1400 Salem Rd, Cookeville, TN 38506-6221
Tel (931) 646-7834 *Founded/Ownrshp* 1997
Sales 54.6MM^E *EMP* 379
SIC 5722 Vacuum cleaners; Vacuum cleaners
CEO: Doug Cahill
**Pr:* Tom Oreck
**CFO:* Jeff Gray
**VP:* Kent Furcron

D-U-N-S 78-558-1547 IMP
OREFIELD COLD STORAGE & DISTRIBUTION CENTER INC
3824 Route 309, Orefield, PA 18069-2007
Tel (610) 395-8263 *Founded/Ownrshp* 1990
Sales 40.0MM^E *EMP* 65
SIC 5142 Packaged frozen goods
Pr: Neil Eichelberger
**VP:* Mark Azemar

D-U-N-S 86-711-2302
OREGANO INC
OREGANOS PIZZA BISTRO
523 W University Dr, Tempe, AZ 85281-5586
Tel (480) 858-0501 *Founded/Ownrshp* 1993
Sales 10.2MM^E *EMP* 330
SIC 5812 Pizza restaurants; Pizza restaurants
Pr: Mark S Russell
Off Mgr: Sherri Urban

OREGANOS PIZZA BISTRO
See OREGANO INC

D-U-N-S 06-058-3457
OREGON AIR REPS INC
ENVIRONMENTAL CONTROLS
15860 Sw Upper Boones, Lake Oswego, OR 97035
Tel (503) 620-4300 *Founded/Ownrshp* 1976
Sales 30.7MM *EMP* 70
Accts Perkins & Co Portland Oregon
SIC 5075 Electrical heating equipment; Ventilating equipment & supplies; Air conditioning equipment, except room units; Electrical heating equipment; Ventilating equipment & supplies; Air conditioning equipment, except room units
Pr: Richard Schweiger
CFO: Dick Schweiger
**VP:* Rick Devlin
**VP:* Kurt Schultheis
Sales Asso: Scott Caldwell

D-U-N-S 80-885-7361
OREGON ANESTHESIOLOGY GROUP PC
OAG
707 Sw Washington St # 700, Portland, OR 97205-3523
Tel (503) 299-9906 *Founded/Ownrshp* 1989
Sales 39.8MM^E *EMP* 189
SIC 8011 Anesthesiologist; Anesthesiologist
Prin: Robert Lovitz
**CEO:* Joy Ketchum
COO: Samuel Clark
Treas: Roger S D
Bd of Dir: Joe Anderson
Bd of Dir: Douglas Irvine
Bd of Dir: Peter Roessler
VP: Janet Smith
Exec: Matthew Layne
CIO: Phil Artz
IT Man: Ed Carroll

D-U-N-S 18-508-5958
OREGON BEVERAGE RECYCLING COOPERATIVE
3900 Nw Yeon Ave, Portland, OR 97210-1412
Tel (503) 295-2772 *Founded/Ownrshp* 1987
Sales 42.4MM^E *EMP* 120
SIC 4953 Recycling, waste materials; Recycling, waste materials
Pr: John Andersen

OREGON BOARD OF EDUCATION
See OREGON CITY SCHOOL DISTRICT

D-U-N-S 62-682-2142 IMP/EXP
OREGON BREWING CO
ROGUE ALES & SPIRITS
2320 Se Osu Dr, Newport, OR 97365-5261
Tel (541) 867-3660 *Founded/Ownrshp* 1989
Sales 56.0MM *EMP* 300
SIC 2082 5813 Ale (alcoholic beverage); Beer (alcoholic beverage); Porter (alcoholic beverage); Stout (alcoholic beverage); Drinking places; Ale (alcoholic beverage); Beer (alcoholic beverage); Porter (alcoholic beverage); Stout (alcoholic beverage); Drinking places
Pr: Brett Joyce
**Pr:* Jack Joyce
**COO:* Mike Isaaeson
**CFO:* RB Brandvold
**Sec:* Jeff Schultz
Creative D: Hagen Moore
Genl Mgr: Jim Cline
VP Sls: Tiny Irwin
Mktg Dir: Jeremy Atkins
Manager: Cameron Anglin
Manager: Alex Feletar

D-U-N-S 80-979-0249
OREGON BUREAU OF LABOR AND INDUSTRIES
LABOR COMMISSIONER
(*Suby of* EXECUTIVE OFFICE OF STATE OF OREGON) ★
800 Ne Oregon St Ste 1045, Portland, OR 97232-3601
Tel (503) 731-4070 *Founded/Ownrshp* 1903
Sales NA *EMP* 385
SIC 9651 Labor regulatory agency; ; Labor regulatory agency;

D-U-N-S 83-455-1801 IMP
OREGON CANCER INSTITUTE
3181 Sw Sam Jackson Pk Rd, Portland, OR 97239-3011
Tel (503) 494-1617 *Founded/Ownrshp* 1900
Sales 13.6MM^E *EMP* 800
SIC 8069 8093 Cancer hospital; Specialty outpatient clinics; Cancer hospital; Specialty outpatient clinics
Pr: Peter Kohler

D-U-N-S 07-643-0891
OREGON CATHOLIC PRESS
O C P
5536 Ne Hassalo St, Portland, OR 97213-3638
Tel (503) 281-1191 *Founded/Ownrshp* 1928
Sales 47.4MM^E *EMP* 170
SIC 2711 2741 2731 2721 Newspapers, publishing & printing; Music, sheet: publishing & printing; Books: publishing & printing; Periodicals; Newspapers, publishing & printing; Music, sheet: publishing & printing; Books: publishing & printing; Periodicals
CEO: Vic Clousey
**CEO:* John Limd
Genl Mgr: Jeffrey Shenk
IT Man: Cara Silva
Sls Mgr: Gail Picken

D-U-N-S 00-790-9260 IMP
OREGON CHERRY GROWERS INC (OR)
1520 Woodrow St Ne, Salem, OR 97301-0621
Tel (541) 296-5487 *Founded/Ownrshp* 1847
Sales 67.8MM^E *EMP* 250
SIC 2033 Maraschino cherries: packaged in cans, jars, etc.; Fruits: packaged in cans, jars, etc.; Maraschino cherries: packaged in cans, jars, etc.; Fruits: packaged in cans, jars, etc.
Pr: Edward Johnson
**Pr:* Tim Ramsey
**CFO:* Dan Weeden
VP: Carl Payne
VP: Mike Sheehan
VP: Steve Travis

D-U-N-S 78-699-6293
OREGON CHILD DEVELOPMENT COALITION INC
(*Suby of* OREGON CHILD DEVELOPMENT COALITION, INC.)
265 N Main St, Ashland, OR 97520-1701
Tel (541) 488-6919 *Founded/Ownrshp* 2006
Sales 2.8MM^E *EMP* 400
SIC 8351 Child day care services; Child day care services
Pr: Adrienne Graham

D-U-N-S 07-757-2535
OREGON CITY SCHOOL DISTRICT
OREGON BOARD OF EDUCATION
5721 Seaman Rd, Oregon, OH 43616-2631
Tel (419) 693-0661 *Founded/Ownrshp* 1830
Sales 40.5MM^E *EMP* 641
Accts Charles E Harris & Associates
SIC 8211 Public elementary school; Public junior high school; Public senior high school; School board; Public elementary school; Public junior high school; Public senior high school; School board
Treas: Jane Fruth
Prin: Marilyn Beckman
Schl Brd P: Carol Molnar
HC Dir: Cherie Sexton

D-U-N-S 03-240-3800
OREGON CITY SCHOOL DISTRICT 62
CLACKAMAS COUNTY SCHOOL DST 62
1417 12th St, Oregon City, OR 97045-2128
Tel (503) 785-8000 *Founded/Ownrshp* 1850
Sales 86.9MM *EMP* 850
SIC 8211 Public elementary & secondary schools; Public elementary & secondary schools
CFO: Nathan Roedel
IT Man: Mike Hyder
Schl Brd P: Chris Storey

D-U-N-S 92-690-0697
OREGON CLINIC P C
847 Ne 19th Ave Ste 300, Portland, OR 97232-2686
Tel (503) 935-8000 *Founded/Ownrshp* 1994
Sales 34.7MM^E *EMP* 225
SIC 8011 Clinic, operated by physicians; Clinic, operated by physicians
CEO: Craig Fausel

D-U-N-S 00-903-2889
OREGON COAST FOODS INC
BANDON CHEESE
(*Suby of* TILLAMOOK CHEESE) ★
4185 Highway 101 N, Tillamook, OR 97141-7770
Tel (503) 842-4481 *Founded/Ownrshp* 2000
Sales 26.4MM^E *EMP* 420
SIC 2022 5451 Cheese, natural & processed; Cheese; Cheese, natural & processed; Cheese
Pr: Harold Strunk
Prd Mgr: Dale Baumgartner

D-U-N-S 05-495-9275
OREGON COMMUNITY CREDIT UNION
2880 Chad Dr, Eugene, OR 97408-7336
Tel (541) 687-2347 *Founded/Ownrshp* 1956
Sales NA *EMP* 250
SIC 6062 State credit unions; State credit unions
CEO: Mandy Jones
Pr: Sherrie Herndon
Pr: Ty Robbins
**CFO:* Ron Neuman
Ofcr: Tom Catherwood
Ofcr: Steve Ferry
Ofcr: Gwen Wilts
VP: Jerry Liudahl
Dir Risk M: Tracey Keffer
Brnch Mgr: Breanna Larsen
Brnch Mgr: Sara Palluck

D-U-N-S 04-683-5039
OREGON COMMUNITY FOUNDATION
1221 Sw Ymhill St Ste 100, Portland, OR 97205
Tel (503) 227-6846 *Founded/Ownrshp* 1974
Sales 161.4MM *EMP* 40^E
SIC 8399 2741 Social change association; Newsletter publishing
Pr: Gregory A Chaille
VP: David Westcott
Sales Exec: Cynthia Hayes

D-U-N-S 08-096-9355
OREGON DENTAL SERVICE
ODS COMPANIES
601 Sw 2nd Ave Ste 900, Portland, OR 97204-3195
Tel (503) 228-6554 *Founded/Ownrshp* 1961
Sales NA *EMP* 1,200
SIC 6324 Dental insurance; Dental insurance
CEO: Robert Gootee
**Pr:* William S Ten Pas
CFO: Dave Evans
CFO: Jon Jurevic
**Treas:* David Adams
Ex VP: Steve Wynne
**Sr VP:* Robin Richardson
VP: James Foley
VP: Sue Hansen
VP: Chris Verbiest
Snr Sftwr: Mark Oneal

D-U-N-S 80-957-9485
OREGON DEPARTMENT OF ADMINISTRATIVE SERVICES
STATE CONTROLLER DIVISION
(*Suby of* EXECUTIVE OFFICE OF STATE OF OREGON) ★
155 Cottage St Ne Ste U50, Salem, OR 97301-3969
Tel (503) 378-8344 *Founded/Ownrshp* 1863
Sales NA *EMP* 1,000
SIC 9199 General government administration; ; General government administration;
Ex Dir: John Radford

D-U-N-S 80-957-9451
OREGON DEPARTMENT OF CONSUMER AND BUSINESS SERVICES
(*Suby of* EXECUTIVE OFFICE OF STATE OF OREGON) ★
350 Winter St Ne, Salem, OR 97301-3875
Tel (503) 378-4100 *Founded/Ownrshp* 1993
Sales NA *EMP* 1,100
SIC 9651 9311 Insurance commission, government; ; ; Insurance commission, government; ;
Pr: Tricia Wheeler
Bd of Dir: Jacob Polvi
Brnch Mgr: Shelley Greiner

D-U-N-S 80-957-9535
OREGON DEPARTMENT OF CORRECTIONS
(*Suby of* EXECUTIVE OFFICE OF STATE OF OREGON) ★
2575 Center St Ne, Salem, OR 97301-6854
Tel (503) 945-9090 *Founded/Ownrshp* 1987
Sales NA *EMP* 4,500
SIC 9223 Prison, government; ; Prison, government;
Ex Dir: Coolette Peters
Bd of Dir: Pamela Weatherspoon
VP: Gordon Bryck
Exec: Jim Bucholz
Assoc Dir: Michael Gower
**Ex Dir:* Max Williams
Prgrm Mgr: Wally Rogers
Area Mgr: Butch Hansen
Off Admin: Juril Stover
IT Man: Scott Sanetel
Secur Mgr: Sonny Rider

D-U-N-S 80-979-0264
OREGON DEPARTMENT OF EDUCATION
(*Suby of* EXECUTIVE OFFICE OF STATE OF OREGON) ★
255 Capitol St Ne, Salem, OR 97310-1300
Tel (503) 947-5753 *Founded/Ownrshp* 1859
Sales NA *EMP* 475
SIC 9411 Administration of educational programs; ; Administration of educational programs;
Info Man: Donald Wildfang

D-U-N-S 80-957-9709
OREGON DEPARTMENT OF ENVIRONMENTAL QUALITY
(*Suby of* EXECUTIVE OFFICE OF STATE OF OREGON) ★
811 Sw 6th Ave, Portland, OR 97204-1334
Tel (503) 229-5696 *Founded/Ownrshp* 1969
Sales NA *EMP* 700
SIC 9511 Air, water & solid waste management; ; Air, water & solid waste management;
Brnch Mgr: Jeffrey Stocum
Snr Mgr: Jennifer Flynt
Board of Directors: Joni Hammond, Dick Pedersen

D-U-N-S 80-957-9774
OREGON DEPARTMENT OF FISH AND WILDLIFE
ODFW
(*Suby of* EXECUTIVE OFFICE OF STATE OF OREGON) ★
4034 Fairview Indus Dr Se, Salem, OR 97302-1142
Tel (503) 947-6000 *Founded/Ownrshp* 1975
Sales NA *EMP* 1,100
SIC 9512 Wildlife conservation agencies; ; Wildlife conservation agencies;

D-U-N-S 80-958-0319
OREGON DEPARTMENT OF HUMAN SERVICES
ADMINISTRATION OFFICE
(*Suby of* EXECUTIVE OFFICE OF STATE OF OREGON) ★
500 Summer St Ne Dept 4, Salem, OR 97301-1073
Tel (503) 945-5944 *Founded/Ownrshp* 1971
Sales NA *EMP* 9,500
SIC 9431 9441 Administration of public health programs; ; ; Administration of public health programs; ;
Mktg Dir: Gary Roth
Snr Mgr: Mike Powers

D-U-N-S 80-979-0223
OREGON DEPARTMENT OF JUSTICE
ATTORNEY GENERAL
(*Suby of* EXECUTIVE OFFICE OF STATE OF OREGON) ★
1162 Court St Ne, Salem, OR 97301-4095
Tel (503) 378-4320 *Founded/Ownrshp* 1891
Sales NA *EMP* 1,000
SIC 9222 Attorney General's office; ; Attorney General's office;
Pr: Nadim ABI-Antoun
Pr: Laurie Roberts
Ofcr: Michael Gillette
Assoc Dir: Lystra Blake
Prgrm Mgr: Mustafa Edrisy
Rgnl Mgr: Jonathan Ramberg
IT Man: Lyn Johnson
Counsel: Beth Stratton
Snr Mgr: Geoff Darling
Snr Mgr: Sheila Potter

D-U-N-S 80-958-0350
OREGON DEPARTMENT OF STATE PARKS AND RECREATION
(*Suby of* EXECUTIVE OFFICE OF STATE OF OREGON) ★
725 Summer St Ne Ste C, Salem, OR 97301-1266
Tel (503) 986-0707 *Founded/Ownrshp* 1990
Sales NA *EMP* 700
SIC 9512 Recreational program administration, government; ; Recreational program administration, government;
V Ch: Steve Macnab
IT Man: Rebecca Jasso

D-U-N-S 80-958-0673
OREGON DEPARTMENT OF STATE POLICE
(*Suby of* EXECUTIVE OFFICE OF STATE OF OREGON) ★
255 Capitol St Ne Fl 4, Salem, OR 97310-1308
Tel (503) 378-3720 *Founded/Ownrshp* 1931
Sales NA *EMP* 1,400
SIC 9221 State police; ; State police;
Ofcr: Greg Jones
VP: Michael Hormann
CIO: Albert Gauthier

D-U-N-S 80-958-0681
OREGON DEPARTMENT OF TRANSPORTATION
(*Suby of* EXECUTIVE OFFICE OF STATE OF OREGON) ★
355 Capitol St Ne Ms21, Salem, OR 97301-3871
Tel (503) 378-5849 *Founded/Ownrshp* 1969
Sales NA *EMP* 4,800
SIC 9621 Regulation, administration of transportation; Regulation, administration of transportation;
Off Mgr: Kenneth Hobson
Cmptr Lab: Eric Roberts
IT Man: Shari Boedigheimer

D-U-N-S 93-295-6618
OREGON DIVISION OF ADULT & FAMILY SERVICES
CHILDREN ADULT AND FAMILY
(*Suby of* ADMINISTRATION OFFICE) ★
500 Summer St Ne, Salem, OR 97301-1063
Tel (503) 945-5601 *Founded/Ownrshp* 1971
Sales NA *EMP* 1,975
SIC 9441 ;

D-U-N-S 01-072-8467
OREGON EDUCATION ASSOCIATION
6900 Sw Atlanta St Ste A, Portland, OR 97223-8598
Tel (503) 684-3300 *Founded/Ownrshp* 1927
Sales 24.0MM *EMP* 99
Accts Lauka Associates Pc Portland
SIC 8621 Professional membership organizations; Professional membership organizations
Pr: Hanna Vaandering
**Pr:* Larry Wolf
**VP:* Tony Crawford
**Ex Dir:* Jerry Caruthers
**Ex Dir:* Richard Sanders

D-U-N-S 00-387-7073 IMP
■ **OREGON ELECTRIC CONSTRUCTION INC**
OREGON ELECTRIC GROUP
(*Suby of* MDU CONSTRUCTION SERVICES GROUP INC) ★
1709 Se 3rd Ave, Portland, OR 97214-4547
Tel (503) 535-2800 *Founded/Ownrshp* 1947
Sales 137.4MM^E *EMP* 500
SIC 1731 3613 General electrical contractor; Telephone & telephone equipment installation; Panel & distribution boards & other related apparatus; General electrical contractor; Telephone & telephone equipment installation; Panel & distribution boards & other related apparatus
CEO: John Harp
**Pr:* Bart C Dickson
**Pr:* Milton Plews
**Pr:* Jeffrey S Thiede
Treas: Vernon A Raile
**Ex VP:* Todd Grasle
**Sr VP:* Bruce Evans
VP: Mark Weinbender
CIO: Jason Behring
IT Man: Ken Tate
VP Opers: Milt Plews

OREGON ELECTRIC GROUP
See OREGON ELECTRIC CONSTRUCTION INC

D-U-N-S 03-079-6270
OREGON EPISCOPAL SCHOOL
6300 Sw Nicol Rd, Portland, OR 97223-7599
Tel (503) 246-7771 *Founded/Ownrshp* 2011
Sales 24.4MM^E *EMP* 160
SIC 8211 Boarding school; Private senior high school
CEO: Maitland Hyslop
**Prin:* MO Copeland
HC Dir: Susan Gundle
Board of Directors: Sheryl Acheson, Wayne Drinkward, Bishop Robert L Ladehoff

D-U-N-S 79-274-2426
OREGON FIRST COMMUNITY CREDIT UNION
200 N Adams St, Coquille, OR 97423-1804
Tel (541) 396-2145 *Founded/Ownrshp* 2007
Sales NA *EMP* 209^E
SIC 6062 State credit unions; State credit unions
Pr: Dal King
Ex VP: Dave Elmer
Sr VP: Denise Hill
VP: Kathryn Jackson
CIO: Tim Martin

D-U-N-S 60-279-1063
OREGON FOOD BANK INC
7900 Ne 33rd Dr, Portland, OR 97211-1918
Tel (541) 889-9206 *Founded/Ownrshp* 1980
Sales 20.3MM *EMP* 103
Accts Mcdonald Jacobs Pc Portland
SIC 8322 Individual & family services; Individual & family services
CEO: Susannah Morgan
COO: Sharon Thornberry
Treas: Ed Sammons
Dir: Laura Delovato
IT Man: Heather Hale
Trfc Dir: Jacob Hayden
Pr Mgr: Jean Ware

D-U-N-S 10-648-1245
OREGON FORD INC
MATHEWS FORD-OREGON
2811 Navarre Ave, Oregon, OH 43616-3397
Tel (419) 698-4444 *Founded/Ownrshp* 1989
Sales 43.8MM^E *EMP* 110
SIC 5511 7538 7532 7515 Automobiles, new & used; Trucks, tractors & trailers: new & used; General automotive repair shops; Top & body repair & paint shops; Passenger car leasing; Automobiles, new & used; Trucks, tractors & trailers: new & used; General automotive repair shops; Top & body repair & paint shops; Passenger car leasing
Pr: Timothy W Mathews
Sls Mgr: Brian Shephard

D-U-N-S 00-941-6934
OREGON FREEZE DRY INC
525 W 25th Ave Se, Albany, OR 97321
Tel (541) 926-6001 *Founded/Ownrshp* 2012
Sales 82.8MM^E *EMP* 360
SIC 2013 2015 2091 2032 2023 Sausages & other prepared meats; Poultry, processed; Fish, dried; Soups, except seafood: packaged in cans, jars, etc.; Dried milk preparations; Sausages & other prepared meats; Poultry, processed; Fish, dried; Soups, except seafood: packaged in cans, jars, etc.; Dried milk preparations
Pr: James S Merryman
CEO: Dale Bookwalter
**CFO:* Philip A Unverzagt
Ofcr: James Desai
Ofcr: John Ostrin
Sr VP: Jeni Billups
Sr VP: Larry Von Deylen
VP: Fred Vetter
IT Man: Chad Hutson
IT Man: Craig Jolly
Sfty Mgr: Doug Richards

D-U-N-S 06-342-8312 IMP
OREGON GLASS CO (OR)
10450 Sw Ridder Rd, Wilsonville, OR 97070-8863
Tel (503) 682-3846 *Founded/Ownrshp* 1947, 1990
Sales 23.3MM^E *EMP* 160
SIC 3231 Tempered glass: made from purchased glass; Insulating glass: made from purchased glass; Tempered glass: made from purchased glass; Insulating glass: made from purchased glass
Pr: Nick Sciola
Genl Mgr: Leon Anderson
Sales Asso: Robert Rossignol

D-U-N-S 09-699-7515
OREGON HEALTH & SCIENCE UNIVERSITY
OHSU
3181 Sw Sam Jackson Pk Rd, Portland, OR 97239-3011
Tel (503) 494-8311 *Founded/Ownrshp* 1887
Sales 2.2MMM *EMP* 14,000
Accts Kpmg Llp Portland Or
SIC 8221 8069 University; Specialty hospitals, except psychiatric; University; Specialty hospitals, except psychiatric
Pr: Joseph Robertson Jr
**CFO:* Lawrence J Furnstahl
CFO: Lawrence Furnstahl
CFO: Diana Gernhart
CFO: James Walker
Ex VP: Peter F Rapp
VP: Amy M Wayson
Dir Lab: Tapasree Banerji
Assoc Dir: Sally Bowman
Assoc Dir: Ashok Reddy
Prin: Nancy L Haigwood

D-U-N-S 80-265-8286
OREGON HEALTH & SCIENCE UNIVERSITY FOUNDATION INC
MEDICAL RESEARCH FOUNDATION OF
1121 Sw Salmon St Ste 100, Portland, OR 97205-2020
Tel (503) 228-1730 *Founded/Ownrshp* 1999
Sales 133.5MM *EMP* 115
Accts Kpmg Llp Seattle Wa
SIC 8399 6091 8733 6732 Fund raising organization, non-fee basis; Nondeposit trust facilities; Medical research; Trusts: educational, religious, etc.; Fund raising organization, non-fee basis; Nondeposit trust facilities; Medical research; Trusts: educational, religious, etc.
Pr: Keith Todd
CFO: Mary Turina
Dir IT: Heather Wilberger

D-U-N-S 87-843-3861
OREGON HEALTH AUTHORITY
OREGON RADIATION PROTECTION
500 Summer St Ne, Salem, OR 97301-1063
Tel (971) 673-1300 *Founded/Ownrshp* 1905
Sales NA *EMP* 590^E
SIC 9431 8621 Administration of public health programs; Professional membership organizations; Administration of public health programs; Professional membership organizations
COO: Jim Scherzinger
Opers Mgr: James Simpson

D-U-N-S 96-874-0352
OREGON HEALTH INSURANCE EXCHANGE CORP
COVER OREGON
16760 Sw Upper Boones, Portland, OR 97224
Tel (503) 945-5772 *Founded/Ownrshp* 2011
Sales NA *EMP* 71
SIC 6321 Assessment associations, accident & health insurance
**Ex Dir:* Ken Allen
Mktg Mgr: Charlie Dey

D-U-N-S 00-904-4116
OREGON ICE CREAM LLC
DUTCH GIRL ICE CREAM
13115 Ne 4th St Ste 220, Vancouver, WA 98684-5965
Tel (360) 713-6800 *Founded/Ownrshp* 1996
Sales 30.8MM^E *EMP* 198
SIC 2024

D-U-N-S 05-596-8499
OREGON INSTITUTE OF TECHNOLOGY INTERNATIONAL CLUB
OREGON TECH
(*Suby of* BOARD OF HIGHER EDUCATION) ★
3201 Campus Dr, Klamath Falls, OR 97601-8801
Tel (541) 885-1000 *Founded/Ownrshp* 1947
Sales 50.2MM^E *EMP* 450
SIC 8221 University; University
Pr: Chris Maples
Treas: Kevin Brown
Ofcr: Christopher Bowman
Ofcr: Lori Harris
VP: Paul Rowan
VP: Maryann Zemke
Exec: David Carringer
Exec: Erin Foley
Ex Dir: Dick Swanson
Brnch Mgr: Mary Shivell
Off Mgr: Cindy Childers

D-U-N-S 18-790-2689
OREGON INTERNATIONAL AIR FREIGHT CO INC
OIA GLOBAL LOGISTICS
(*Suby of* LDI LTD., LLC)
2100 Sw Rver Pkwy Ste 800, Portland, OR 97201
Tel (503) 736-5900 *Founded/Ownrshp* 2010
Sales 996.0MM *EMP* 1,000
Accts Ernst & Young Llp Indianapoli
SIC 4731 Freight forwarding; Freight forwarding
Pr: Charles F Hornecker
**Sr VP:* Dante Fornari

OREGON IRON WORKS, LLC
See VIGOR WORKS LLC

D-U-N-S 94-409-3640
OREGON JEWISH COMMUNITY FOUNDATION
1618 Sw 1st Ave Ste 210, Portland, OR 97201-5721
Tel (503) 248-9328 *Founded/Ownrshp* 1990
Sales 21.0MM *EMP* 3
SIC 8661 Community church; Community church
Ex Dir: John Moss
Mktg Dir: Mitchell Hartman

OREGON LOTTERY
See OREGON STATE LOTTERY

OREGON MEDICAL GROUP
See OHR PHYSICIAN GROUP PC

D-U-N-S 00-902-1221
OREGON METAL SLITTERS INC (OR)
7227 N Leadbetter Rd, Portland, OR 97203-6490
Tel (503) 286-0300 *Founded/Ownrshp* 1956, 1999
Sales 132.7MM^E *EMP* 65^E
SIC 5051 7389 Steel; Metal slitting & shearing
Pr: Steve Elorriaga
**Ex VP:* Kurt Roseler
**Ex VP:* Stanley Walker
Opers Mgr: Hans Polte
Plnt Mgr: Chuck Sanders
Ql Cn Mgr: Kyler Bruno
Sales Exec: Chris Holzgang
Sls Mgr: Gary Dick

Sls Mgr: Dan Hellwege
Sales Asso: Nick Call
Sales Asso: Karson Kobelin

D-U-N-S 05-359-6250
OREGON MUSEUM OF SCIENCE & INDUSTRY
1945 Se Water Ave, Portland, OR 97214-3356
Tel (503) 797-4000 *Founded/Ownrshp* 1944
Sales 21.6MM *EMP* 280
Accts Moss Adams Llp Portland Oreg
SIC 8412 7832 Museums & art galleries; Museum; Planetarium; Motion picture theaters, except drive-in; Museums & art galleries; Museum; Planetarium; Motion picture theaters, except drive-in
Ch Bd: Curt Henninger
Dir Vol: Laura Kelly
Dir Vol: Casey Szot
**Pr:* Nancy Stueber
Pr: Gloria Swick
**CFO:* Paul Carlson
**Treas:* Gregory Struxness
Ofcr: Alyson Marchi-Young
VP: Jamie Hurd
VP: Kevin Kearns
VP: Richard Linton
VP: Paul Moredock
VP: Mark Patel
VP: Russ Repp
VP: Eva Schweber
Exec: Ryan Morgan
Dir Soc: Melony Beaird
Dir Soc: Sonali Shivdasani
Comm Man: Kate McNally

D-U-N-S 00-790-8411
OREGON MUTUAL INSURANCE CO INC
WESTERN PROTECTORS INSURANCE
400 Ne Baker St, McMinnville, OR 97128-4906
Tel (503) 472-2141 *Founded/Ownrshp* 1894
Sales NA *EMP* 295
SIC 6331 Property damage insurance; Property damage insurance
Ch Bd: Michael Keyes
**Pr:* Brian Steffel
Pr: Wes Thomas
**Treas:* Steven Patterson
Bd of Dir: Jonathan Jurevic
**VP:* Bryan Fowler
**VP:* Lisa Hargis
**VP:* Charles Katter
Genl Mgr: Roy Duitman
Mktg Mgr: Karen Lowart

OREGON ORCHARD
See HAZELNUT GROWERS OF OREGON INC

OREGON OVERLAYS
See SIMPSON TIMBER CO

D-U-N-S 06-524-3834 IMP
OREGON PACIFIC BUILDING PRODUCTS (CALIF) INC
OREPAC BUILDING PRODUCTS
(*Suby of* OREPAC HOLDING CO) ★
30170 Sw Ore Pac Ave, Wilsonville, OR 97070-9794
Tel (503) 685-5499 *Founded/Ownrshp* 1980
Sales 158.1MM^E *EMP* 750
SIC 5031 Building materials, exterior; Building materials, interior; Lumber: rough, dressed & finished; Millwork; Building materials, exterior; Building materials, interior; Lumber: rough, dressed & finished; Millwork
Pr: Bradley Hart
COO: Bryce Muir
**Sec:* Lee Daggett
**VP:* Alan Kirk
IT Man: Chris Jacobson
Opers Mgr: Josh Aplanalp
Opers Mgr: Nicholas Prado

D-U-N-S 60-223-1792 IMP
OREGON PACIFIC BUILDING PRODUCTS (MAPLE) INC
OREPAC MILLWORK PRODUCTS
(*Suby of* OREPAC HOLDING CO) ★
2401 E Philadelphia St, Ontario, CA 91761-7743
Tel (909) 627-4043 *Founded/Ownrshp* 1992
Sales 28.1MM^E *EMP* 125
SIC 5031 5032 Lumber, plywood & millwork; Brick, stone & related material; Lumber, plywood & millwork; Brick, stone & related material
Pr: Douglas Hart
Opers Mgr: William Rasinson
Mktg Dir: Jami Mendoza
Sales Asso: Matt Perine

D-U-N-S 05-424-4546 IMP
OREGON PACIFIC BUILDING PRODUCTS (ORE) INC
OREPAC BUILDING PRODUCTS
(*Suby of* OREPAC HOLDING CO) ★
30160 Sw Ore Pac Ave, Wilsonville, OR 97070-9794
Tel (503) 682-5050 *Founded/Ownrshp* 1981
Sales 23.5MM^E *EMP* 125
SIC 5031 5033 Lumber: rough, dressed & finished; Building materials, exterior; Building materials, interior; Doors; Shingles, except wood; Insulation materials; Lumber: rough, dressed & finished; Building materials, exterior; Building materials, interior; Doors; Shingles, except wood; Insulation materials
Sec: Lee Daggett
VP: Brad Hart
Off Mgr: Stacey Louallen
CTO: Paul Rust

D-U-N-S 07-605-7280
OREGON PACIFIC BUILDING PRODUCTS (WASH) INC
OREPAC BUILDING PRODUCTS
9213 51st Ave Sw, Tacoma, WA 98499-5978
Tel (253) 582-9500 *Founded/Ownrshp* 2011
Sales 26.8MM^E *EMP* 95
SIC 5031 Building materials, exterior; Building materials, interior; Building materials, exterior; Building materials, interior
CEO: Glenn Hart
**Pr:* Douglas Hart
**VP:* Alan Kirk
Genl Mgr: Craig Young
Off Mgr: Laurel Delony
Sales Asso: Joe Petree

D-U-N-S 79-992-6444 EXP
OREGON POTATO CO
WASHINGTON POTATO COMPANY
6610 W Court St Ste B, Pasco, WA 99301-2010
Tel (509) 349-8803 *Founded/Ownrshp* 2000
Sales 254.2MM^E *EMP* 220
SIC 2034 Potato products, dried & dehydrated; Potato products, dried & dehydrated
Pr: Frank S Tiegs
**VP:* Tim M Tippett
Dir IT: James Engel

D-U-N-S 13-936-1034
OREGON PRECISION INDUSTRIES INC
PAKTECH
1680b Irving Rd, Eugene, OR 97402-9714
Tel (541) 461-5000 *Founded/Ownrshp* 1988
Sales 46.3MM^E *EMP* 100
SIC 3089 3544 Injection molded finished plastic products; Injection molding of plastics; Industrial molds
Pr: James C Borg
Pr: Ronnie Mellor
Ofcr: Gary Panknin
Opers Mgr: Tauni Samuels
Prd Mgr: Lisa Walker
Sls Mgr: Nancy Baker

OREGON PRODUCTS
See BLOUNT INTERNATIONAL INC

D-U-N-S 17-547-0863
OREGON PUBLIC BROADCASTING
KEPB
7140 Sw Macadam Ave, Portland, OR 97219-3013
Tel (503) 244-9900 *Founded/Ownrshp* 2005
Sales 33.9MM *EMP* 150
Accts Moss Adams Llp Porland Oreg
SIC 4832 4833 Radio broadcasting stations; Television broadcasting stations; Radio broadcasting stations; Television broadcasting stations
Pr: Steve Bass
Pr: Susan Boyd
Pr: Michael Foti
**CFO:* Jan Heskiss
Sr VP: Dan Metziga
Exec: Brenda Barton
Assoc Dir: Jordan Anderson
Assoc Dir: Julie Arnzen
Assoc Dir: Julie Feely
Assoc Dir: Molly Sherwood
Dir Soc: Lynn Darroch
Dir Soc: Casey Negreiff
Comm Dir: Susan Thomas

D-U-N-S 00-428-6188
OREGON PUBLICATION CORP
(*Suby of* PAMPLIN COMMUNICATIONS CORP) ★
10209 Se Division St, Portland, OR 97266-1372
Tel (503) 251-1579 *Founded/Ownrshp* 1995
Sales 28.4MM^E *EMP* 300
SIC 2711 Newspapers; Newspapers
CEO: R B Pamplin
**CFO:* Andrea Marek

OREGON R&H CONSTRUCTION
See R&H CONSTRUCTION CO

OREGON RADIATION PROTECTION
See OREGON HEALTH AUTHORITY

D-U-N-S 13-196-9354
OREGON RESORTS LLC
EAGLE CREST RESORT
1522 Cline Falls Rd, Redmond, OR 97756-9293
Tel (541) 923-0807 *Founded/Ownrshp* 1984
Sales NA *EMP* 750
SIC 6552

D-U-N-S 10-008-3757
OREGON SCHOOL DISTRICT
123 E Grove St, Oregon, WI 53575-1454
Tel (608) 835-4000 *Founded/Ownrshp* 1962
Sales 30.0MM^E *EMP* 600
SIC 8211 Public elementary & secondary schools; Public elementary & secondary schools
Exec: Brenda Klitzke
Dir IT: Jon Tanner
Tech Mgr: Lynn Schulz
Teacher Pr: Jina Jonen

D-U-N-S 05-361-5233
OREGON SHAKESPEAREAN FESTIVAL ASSOCIATION
15 S Pioneer St, Ashland, OR 97520-2749
Tel (541) 482-2111 *Founded/Ownrshp* 1935
Sales 35.1MM *EMP* 628
Accts Mcdonald Jacobs Pc Portland
SIC 7922 Theatrical production services; Theatrical production services
Ex Dir: Cynthia Rider
Exec: Debi Coleman
Genl Mgr: Theodore Delong
Sales Exec: Mallory Peirce
Mktg Mgr: Bob Hackett

D-U-N-S 36-125-5024 IMP
OREGON STATE LOTTERY
OREGON LOTTERY
(*Suby of* STATE OF OREGON) ★
500 Airport Rd Se, Salem, OR 97301-5068
Tel (503) 540-1000 *Founded/Ownrshp* 2005
Sales 36.2MM^E *EMP* 420
SIC 7999 Lottery operation; Lottery operation

D-U-N-S 05-359-9908
OREGON STATE UNIVERSITY
308 Kerr Adm Bldg, Corvallis, OR 97331
Tel (541) 737-1000 *Founded/Ownrshp* 1858
Sales 587.3MM *EMP* 8,188^E
Accts Cliftonlarsonallen Llp Greenw
SIC 8221 University; University
Pr: Edward J Ray
Bd of Dir: Claire Sponseller
**VP:* Glenn Ford
VP: Mark McCambridge
Assoc Dir: Karen Steele
Dir IT: Stephen Atkinson
Mktg Mgr: Stephen J Lawton
HC Dir: Noah Buckley
Counsel: Rebecca Lynch

D-U-N-S 02-762-2174
OREGON STATE UNIVERSITY BOOKSTORE INC
OSU BOOKSTORE
2301 Sw Jefferson Way, Corvallis, OR 97331-1105
Tel (541) 737-4323 *Founded/Ownrshp* 1914
Sales 20.1MM *EMP* 165
Accts Moss Adams Llp Eugene Oregon
SIC 5942 Book stores; Book stores
CEO: Steve Eckrich
**Pr:* Dan Larsen
**CFO:* Randy Zentmire

D-U-N-S 07-072-8431
OREGON STATE UNIVERSITY FOUNDATION INC (OR)
850 Sw 35th St, Corvallis, OR 97333-4046
Tel (541) 737-4218 *Founded/Ownrshp* 1947
Sales 108.5MM *EMP* 115
SIC 6732 Educational trust management; Educational trust management
Pr: J Michael Goodwin
VP: Ronald Adams
Assoc Dir: Travis Smith
Off Mgr: Elizabeth Thomas
Off Admin: Joan Lease

OREGON STEEL WORKS
See O S M GLASSIFICATION INC

OREGON TECH
See OREGON INSTITUTE OF TECHNOLOGY INTERNATIONAL CLUB

OREGON TILE & MARBLE
See MARQUEZ INC

D-U-N-S 03-429-5998
OREGON TRAIL SCHOOL DISTRICT 46
36525 Industrial Way, Sandy, OR 97055-7376
Tel (503) 668-5541 *Founded/Ownrshp* 1914
Sales 31.4MM *EMP* 500
SIC 8211 Public combined elementary & secondary school; Public combined elementary & secondary school
Dir IT: Kashawna Knoll

D-U-N-S 00-893-4275
OREGON TRANSFER CO (OR)
5910 N Cutter Cir, Portland, OR 97217-3939
Tel (503) 943-3500 *Founded/Ownrshp* 1868, 1941
Sales 22.8MM^E *EMP* 160
SIC 4225 4212 General warehousing; Local trucking, without storage; General warehousing; Local trucking, without storage
Pr: G C Eichman
**CFO:* Gary Hunt
**Sr VP:* Steven D Giering

D-U-N-S 02-993-9121
OREGON TRUCK AND TRACTOR INC
DERR EQUIPMENT
11001 Highway 71, Savannah, MO 64485-8135
Tel (816) 324-5618 *Founded/Ownrshp* 1947
Sales 27.7MM *EMP* 32
SIC 7699 Farm machinery repair; Farm machinery repair
Pr: George W Derr
**Sec:* Dixie Derr

D-U-N-S 04-126-8673
OREGON UNIVERSITY SYSTEM
BOARD OF HIGHER EDUCATION
P.O. Box 488, Corvallis (97339-0488)
Tel (541) 737-0827 *Founded/Ownrshp* 2003
Sales 1.7MMM *EMP* 26,000
Accts Cliftonlarsonallen Llp Greenw
SIC 8221 University; University
Bd of Dir: Brittany Kenison
Off Mgr: Christy Farm

D-U-N-S 14-813-4323
OREGON VINEYARD SUPPLY CO
O V S
2700 Ne Saint Joseph Rd, McMinnville, OR 97128-8405
Tel (503) 435-2700 *Founded/Ownrshp* 1998
Sales 23.7MM^E *EMP* 70
SIC 5999 5083 Farm equipment & supplies; Agricultural machinery & equipment; Farm equipment & supplies; Agricultural machinery & equipment
CEO: Kevin R Chambers
**Pr:* Matt Novak
COO: Adam Bertram
Sls Mgr: Jon Meadors
Sls Mgr: Brian Wolf
Sales Asso: Patrick Reinhart

D-U-N-S 06-345-1223 IMP
OREGON WIRE PRODUCTS LLC
13030 Ne Whitaker Way, Portland, OR 97230-1112
Tel (503) 255-5155 *Founded/Ownrshp* 2002
Sales 28.8MM^E *EMP* 35
SIC 5051 3496 Wire; Reinforcement mesh, wire; Nails; Steel; Miscellaneous fabricated wire products
Sales Exec: Jim Lorenz
Sales Asso: Marge Wilson
Sales Asso: Mike Wisnoski

D-U-N-S 06-060-3768
OREGON-IDAHO ANNUAL CONFERENCE OF UNITED METHODIST CHURCH
1505 Sw 18th Ave, Portland, OR 97201-2524
Tel (503) 226-7931 *Founded/Ownrshp* 1968
Sales 11.3MM *EMP* 500
SIC 8741 7032 Administrative management; Sporting & recreational camps; Administrative management; Sporting & recreational camps
CFO: Robert C Meyers

OREGONIAN, THE
See OREGONIAN PUBLISHING CO LLC

D-U-N-S 00-903-2517 IMP
OREGONIAN PUBLISHING CO LLC
OREGONIAN, THE
(*Suby of* ADVANCE PUBLICATIONS INC) ★
1515 Sw 5th Ave Ste 1000, Portland, OR 97201-3499
Tel (503) 221-8327 *Founded/Ownrshp* 1873
Sales 138.9MM^E *EMP* 1,200
SIC 2711 Newspapers, publishing & printing; Newspapers, publishing & printing
CFO: Motoko Komatsubara
Off Mgr: Rachel Barnes
IT Man: Paul Lindstrom
S&M/VP: Barbara Swanson
Advt Dir: Elizabeth Y Sell
Assoc Ed: Rick Attig

D-U-N-S 07-941-5585
■ **OREILLY AUTO ENTERPRISES LLC**
(*Suby of* OREILLY AUTOMOTIVE INC) ★
233 S Patterson Ave, Springfield, MO 65802-2210
Tel (417) 862-6708 *Founded/Ownrshp* 2013
Sales 5.3MMM^E *EMP* 50,000
SIC 5531 Automotive parts; Automotive parts
CEO: Gregory Henslee

O'REILLY AUTO PARTS
See OREILLY AUTOMOTIVE STORES INC

D-U-N-S 96-878-3162
▲ **OREILLY AUTOMOTIVE INC**
233 S Patterson Ave, Springfield, MO 65802-2298
Tel (417) 862-6708 *Founded/Ownrshp* 1957
Sales 7.2MMM *EMP* 67,926^E
Tkr Sym ORLY *Exch* NGS
SIC 5531 5013 Automotive & home supply stores; Automotive parts; Automotive accessories; Motor vehicle supplies & new parts; Automotive supplies & parts; Automotive & home supply stores; Automotive parts; Automotive accessories; Motor vehicle supplies & new parts; Automotive supplies & parts
Pr: Greg Henslee
**Ch Bd:* David O'Reilly
CFO: Thomas McFall
**V Ch Bd:* Charlie O'Reilly
Ex VP: Jeff Shaw
Ex VP: Jeff M Shaw
Ex VP: Ted F Wise
Sr VP: Randy Johnson
Sr VP: Jeff Lauro
Sr VP: Mike Swearengin
VP: Larry Ellis
VP: Kenny Martin
VP: Doug Ruble
VP: R O Salazar
VP: Tom Seboldt
Board of Directors: Jay D Burchfield, Thomas T Hendrickson, Paul R Lederer, John R Murphy, Ronald Rashkow, Rosalie O'reilly Wooten

D-U-N-S 03-114-1534 IMP
■ **OREILLY AUTOMOTIVE STORES INC**
O'REILLY AUTO PARTS
(*Suby of* OREILLY AUTOMOTIVE INC) ★
233 S Patterson Ave, Springfield, MO 65802-2298
Tel (417) 862-6708 *Founded/Ownrshp* 1957
Sales 5.0MMM^E *EMP* 47,142
SIC 5013 5531 Automotive supplies & parts; Automotive parts; Automotive supplies & parts; Automotive parts
CEO: Greg Henslee
V Ch: Larry P O'Reilly
CFO: Jim Batton
**Ch:* David O Reilly
**Ex VP:* Tom McFall
**Ex VP:* Jeff Shaw
**Sr VP:* Michael D Swearengin
VP: Linda Keeth
VP: R O Salazar
**VP:* Ted Wise
Rgnl Mgr: Matt Roberts
Board of Directors: Jay D Burchfield, Thomas T Hendrickson, Paul R Lederer, John Murphy, Charles H O'reilly Jr, David E O'reilly, Lawrence P O'reilly, Ronald Rashkow, Rosalie O'reilly-Wooten

D-U-N-S 13-084-0077 IMP
OREILLY MEDIA INC
1005 Gravenstein Hwy N, Sebastopol, CA 95472-2811
Tel (707) 827-7000 *Founded/Ownrshp* 1978
Sales 101.3MM^E *EMP* 400
SIC 2731 2741 Books: publishing only; Technical manuals: publishing & printing; Books: publishing only; Technical manuals: publishing & printing
Pr: Timothy F O'Reilly
**Prin:* Christina F O'Reilly
Mng Dir: Elke Hansel
CTO: Andrew Odewahn
Dir IT: Brian Mericle
IT Man: Cali Bush
Sftwr Eng: Zach Schwartz
Natl Sales: John Holdcroft
Sls Mgr: Leslie Crandell
Assoc Ed: Allyson Macdonald

D-U-N-S 93-771-3089 EXP
OREN INTERNATIONAL INC
1995 Hollywood Ave, Pensacola, FL 32505-5369
Tel (850) 433-9080 *Founded/Ownrshp* 1996
Sales 28.8MM^E *EMP* 35
SIC 5111 Printing & writing paper
Pr: David A Nesmith
Sales Exec: Mark Jones

D-U-N-S 03-116-6150 IMP/EXP
ORENCO SYSTEMS INC
O S I
814 Airway Ave, Sutherlin, OR 97479-9011
Tel (541) 459-4449 *Founded/Ownrshp* 1981
Sales 31.1MM^E *EMP* 250^E
SIC 3561

OREPAC BUILDING PRODUCTS
See OREGON PACIFIC BUILDING PRODUCTS (ORE) INC

OREPAC BUILDING PRODUCTS
See OREGON PACIFIC BUILDING PRODUCTS (CALIF) INC

OREPAC BUILDING PRODUCTS
See OREGON PACIFIC BUILDING PRODUCTS (WASH) INC

D-U-N-S 08-364-5069 IMP
OREPAC HOLDING CO
30170 Sw Orepac Ave, Wilsonville, OR 97070
Tel (503) 682-5050 *Founded/Ownrshp* 1976
Sales 620.1MM^E *EMP* 800
SIC 5031 Windows; Windows
Pr: Bradley Hart
VP: Gary Hart
**Prin:* Alan Kirk
Genl Mgr: Brian Wilson
Opers Mgr: Tom Clark
Sls Mgr: David Searle
Sales Asso: Kyle Turenne

OREPAC MILLWORK PRODUCTS
See OREGON PACIFIC BUILDING PRODUCTS (MAPLE) INC

D-U-N-S 19-650-1931
OREXIGEN THERAPEUTICS INC
3344 N Torrey Pines Ct # 200, La Jolla, CA 92037-1024
Tel (858) 875-8600 *Founded/Ownrshp* 2003
Sales 55.5MM *EMP* 51
Tkr Sym OREX *Exch* NGM
SIC 2834 Pharmaceutical preparations
Pr: Michael A Narachi
**Ch Bd:* Eckard Weber
CFO: Joseph P Hagan
Ex VP: Preston Klassen
Genl Couns: Chris Hazuka
Snr Mgr: Kimberly Henson
Board of Directors: Louis C Bock, Wendy L Dixon, Brian H Dovey, David J Endicott, Peter K Honig, Patrick J Mahaffy

D-U-N-S 80-952-3215
ORF LLC
OUTRIGGER REEF HOTEL
(*Suby of* OUTRIGGER HOTELS AND RESORTS) ★
2169 Kalia Rd, Honolulu, HI 96815-1936
Tel (808) 923-3111 *Founded/Ownrshp* 2001
Sales 25.1MM^E *EMP* 697^E
SIC 7011 Resort hotel
Prin: Bill Comstock

ORG
See OWNER RESOURCE GROUP LLC

D-U-N-S 96-490-6903
ORG CHEM GROUP LLC
(*Suby of* ORG) ★
2406 Lynch Rd, Evansville, IN 47711-2953
Tel (812) 464-4446 *Founded/Ownrshp* 2014
Sales 25.1MM^E *EMP* 69
SIC 8741 Management services
Pr: David Carson
Pr: Kevin Harris
COO: Mike Sturgeon
VP: Mark Buczek
VP: Paul Carson
VP: Mike Millard
Dir Bus: Scott Herrington
Plnt Mgr: Brian Cassidy
Plnt Mgr: James Trouba

D-U-N-S 00-441-2441
ORGAIN BUILDING SUPPLY CO (TN)
65 Commerce St, Clarksville, TN 37040-3682
Tel (931) 647-1567 *Founded/Ownrshp* 1921, 1963
Sales 21.2MM *EMP* 94
Accts Thurman Campbell Group Plc C
SIC 5211 2439 5031 Lumber & other building materials; Trusses, except roof: laminated lumber; Trusses, wooden roof; Lumber, plywood & millwork; Lumber & other building materials; Trusses, except roof: laminated lumber; Trusses, wooden roof; Lumber, plywood & millwork
Owner: Bill Orgain
**Pr:* William H Orgain
**Sec:* Larry Richardson
**VP:* William J Myers
**VP:* Jerry L Robertson
**VP:* William D Russell

D-U-N-S 10-675-6364
ORGAN PROCUREMENT AGENCY OF MICHIGAN
GIFT OF LIFE MICHIGAN
3861 Research Park Dr, Ann Arbor, MI 48108-2217
Tel (734) 973-1577 *Founded/Ownrshp* 1971
Sales 43.3MM *EMP* 198
SIC 8099 Medical services organization; Medical services organization
CEO: Richard E Pietroski
Dir Vol: Kim Zasa
**CFO:* Anne Kowalczyk
**CFO:* Burton J Mattice
Comm Dir: Tim Makinen
IT Man: Chris Musico
Doctor: Karen Oldenburg
Pgrm Dir: Remonia Chapman
Snr Mgr: Bill Thompson

D-U-N-S 82-899-6553
ORGANIC BY NATURE INC
1495 Seabright Ave, Long Beach, CA 90813-1100
Tel (562) 901-0177 *Founded/Ownrshp* 1993
Sales 24.2MM^E *EMP* 38^E
SIC 5149 Health foods
CEO: David Sandoval
**Pr:* Amy Sandoval
Sls Mgr: Gerry Wong

D-U-N-S 15-308-5068 IMP
ORGANIC FOOD BAR INC
OFB
215 E Orang Ave 284, Fullerton, CA 92832
Tel (800) 246-4685 *Founded/Ownrshp* 2004
Sales 23.8MM^E *EMP* 27^E
SIC 5122 Druggists' sundries
CEO: Jack J Singh
CFO: Sara Maughan

D-U-N-S 87-918-1949
ORGANIC HOLDINGS INC
ORGANIC ON
555 Market St Lbby, San Francisco, CA 94105-2801
Tel (415) 581-5300 *Founded/Ownrshp* 1993
Sales 24.1MM^E *EMP* 350
SIC 7311 7374 8742 7375 Advertising consultant; Computer graphics service; Management consulting services; Information retrieval services; Advertising consultant; Computer graphics service; Management consulting services; Information retrieval services
CEO: Jonathan Nelson
Ofcr: Deborah Charapaty
Ofcr: Tom Weisz

D-U-N-S 04-167-0949
■ **ORGANIC INC**
(*Suby of* OMNICOM GROUP INC) ★
600 California St Fl 8, San Francisco, CA 94108-2726
Tel (415) 581-5300 *Founded/Ownrshp* 2002
Sales 39.1MM^E *EMP* 200
SIC 7379 8742 ; Computer related consulting services; Marketing consulting services; ; Computer related consulting services; Marketing consulting services
Chf Cred: Conor Brady
**Ofcr:* David Bryant
**Ofcr:* Mark Murata
VP: Steve Kerho
VP: Danica Remy
Ex Dir: Dave Sylvestre

D-U-N-S 06-664-6662 EXP
ORGANIC MILLING CORP
505 W Allen Ave, San Dimas, CA 91773-1487
Tel (909) 599-0961 *Founded/Ownrshp* 2001
Sales 31.3MM^E *EMP* 140
SIC 2043 Granola & muesli, except bars & clusters; Granola & muesli, except bars & clusters
Pr: Bruce Olsen
Mng Pt: Wolfgang Buchler
Ex VP: Bill Stewart
**Prin:* John Duenas
Genl Mgr: Chris Wadden
IT Man: Michael Lopez

ORGANIC ON
See ORGANIC HOLDINGS INC

D-U-N-S 15-953-2865
ORGANIC PASTURES DAIRY CO LLC
7221 S Jameson Ave, Fresno, CA 93706-9386
Tel (559) 846-9732 *Founded/Ownrshp* 2001
Sales 29.5MM^E *EMP* 50
SIC 0241 Dairy farms
Mktg Mgr: Kaleigh Lutz

ORGANIC TECHNOLOGIES
See WILEY ORGANICS INC

ORGANIC VALLEY
See COOPERATIVE REGIONS OF ORGANIC PRODUCER POOLS

D-U-N-S 04-281-2121
ORGANIC VALLEY CROPP COOPERATIVE
1 Organic Way, La Farge, WI 54639-6604
Tel (608) 625-3262 *Founded/Ownrshp* 1988
Sales 30.7MM^E *EMP* 550
SIC 0241 2023 2024 Milk production; Dry, condensed, evaporated dairy products; Dairy based frozen desserts; Milk production; Dry, condensed, evaporated dairy products; Dairy based frozen desserts
CEO: George Siemon
Mktg Mgr: Shannon Maroney

D-U-N-S 10-405-6973 IMP
ORGANICALLY GROWN CO
1800 Prairie Rd Ste B, Eugene, OR 97402-9722
Tel (541) 689-5320 *Founded/Ownrshp* 1978
Sales 163.8MM *EMP* 189
SIC 5148 Fresh fruits & vegetables; Fresh fruits & vegetables
Pr: David Amorose
**CEO:* Josh Hinerfeld
**CFO:* Robbie Vasilinda

D-U-N-S 03-118-6894
ORGANICLIFE LLC
445 W Erie St Ste 110, Chicago, IL 60654-6924
Tel (312) 929-2005 *Founded/Ownrshp* 2006
Sales 26.2MM^E *EMP* 1,000
SIC 5812 Eating places; Eating places
CEO: Jonas S Falk

D-U-N-S 03-066-4761
ORGANIX RECYCLING LLC
19065 Hickory Creek Dr # 240, Mokena, IL 60448-8597
Tel (708) 326-3900 *Founded/Ownrshp* 2010
Sales 40.9MM^E *EMP* 106
SIC 4212 Garbage collection & transport, no disposal
Pr: Ron Winkle
**COO:* Rick Shipley

D-U-N-S 79-022-3168
ORGANIZATIONAL DEVELOPMENT INC
5311 Lake Worth Rd, Greenacres, FL 33463-3353
Tel (561) 304-0041 *Founded/Ownrshp* 1991
Sales 16.7MM^E *EMP* 600
SIC 7389 Fund raising organizations; Fund raising organizations
Pr: Robert Preston
Mng Pt: Valerie Smith

D-U-N-S 00-424-5395 IMP
ORGANIZED LIVING INC (OH)
3100 E Kemper Rd, Cincinnati, OH 45241-1517
Tel (513) 489-9300 *Founded/Ownrshp* 1919
Sales 33.9MM^E *EMP* 210
SIC 3496 3083 3411 2542 Miscellaneous fabricated wire products; Laminated plastics plate & sheet; Metal cans; Partitions & fixtures, except wood; Miscellaneous fabricated wire products; Laminated plastics plate & sheet; Metal cans; Partitions & fixtures, except wood
CEO: John D Kokenge
Ex VP: Gil Foltz
**VP:* Robert J Lamping
**VP:* Steve McCamley
**VP:* Patrick Taylor
**Prin:* Kevin Ball
Natl Sales: Rich Moore
Natl Sales: David Ratajczak

D-U-N-S 15-216-5817 IMP
ORGANOGENESIS INC
150 Dan Rd Ste 3, Canton, MA 02021-2820
Tel (781) 575-0198 *Founded/Ownrshp* 1985
Sales 173.1MM^E *EMP* 525^E
SIC 2836 Biological products, except diagnostic; Biological products, except diagnostic
CEO: Gary S Gillheeney Sr
**CEO:* Geoff Mackay
**VP:* Milka Bedikian
**VP:* Patrick Bilbo
**VP:* Dario Eklund
**VP:* Phillip Nolan
**VP:* Zorina Pitkin
Mng Dir: Stefan Kaelin
CIO: Brian Murphy
Prd Mgr: Heather Nixon
Ql Cn Mgr: Daniel Sutherby

ORGILL
See MORTIMER AND SON LUMBER CO INC

D-U-N-S 00-792-2123 IMP/EXP
ORGILL INC (TN)
3742 Tyndale Dr, Memphis, TN 38125-8500
Tel (901) 754-8850 *Founded/Ownrshp* 1847
Sales 2.1MMM^E *EMP* 2,006
SIC 5072 Hardware; Builders' hardware; Shelf or light hardware; Hand tools; Hardware; Builders' hardware; Shelf or light hardware; Hand tools
Pr: Ron Beal
Ch Bd: Joseph Orgill III
CFO: Byrne Whitehead
Sr VP: Ken Post
VP: Bryce Abbott
VP: Jeff Boyles
VP: Everett Clark
VP: John Dillon
VP: Vic Price
Prin: Mike McDonnell
Prin: Joseph Orgill

D-U-N-S 18-707-0859
ORGILL SINGER & ASSOCIATES INC
8360 W Sahara Ave Ste 110, Las Vegas, NV 89117-8943
Tel (702) 228-8862 *Founded/Ownrshp* 2001
Sales NA *EMP* 75
SIC 6411 6211 8721 Insurance agents; Stock brokers & dealers; Accounting, auditing & bookkeeping
CEO: David Dahan
Pr: Edward Billington
**Pr:* Eric Springall
Sales Exec: Steve O'Connor

D-U-N-S 79-672-7878
ORGUF HOLDINGS INC
(*Suby of* FUGRO (USA) INC) ★
6100 Hillcroft St Ste 700, Houston, TX 77081-1009
Tel (713) 772-3700 *Founded/Ownrshp* 1997
Sales 29.2MM^E *EMP* 341
SIC 3764 7389 7335 Guided missile & space vehicle propulsion unit parts; Mapmaking or drafting, including aerial; Aerial photography, except mapmaking; Guided missile & space vehicle propulsion unit parts; Mapmaking or drafting, including aerial; Aerial photography, except mapmaking
Pr: Klaas Wester

D-U-N-S 80-565-6506 IMP
ORHAN NORTH AMERICA INC
NOBEL AUTOMOTIVE
(*Suby of* ORHAN HOLDING ANONIM SIRKETI)
1160 Centre Rd, Auburn Hills, MI 48326-2602
Tel (248) 637-5650 *Founded/Ownrshp* 2007
Sales 74.2MM^E *EMP* 330
SIC 5013 Automotive supplies; Automotive supplies
Pr: Murat Orhan
**CEO:* Philippe Jean
**CFO:* Peter Murphy
Prgrm Mgr: Jon Fisher

D-U-N-S 02-407-6838
ORI ACQUISITION INC
OFFICE FURNITURE USA
816 E Broadway, Louisville, KY 40204-1053
Tel (502) 589-8400 *Founded/Ownrshp* 1945
Sales 34.1MM^E *EMP* 52
SIC 5021 Office furniture
Pr: George R Bell
**Treas:* Evelyn Goodman
**Sec:* Pamela R Freeman
VP: Kyle Doezema
**VP:* Stephen Zink

D-U-N-S 09-840-0047 IMP
ORIAN RUGS INC
2415 N Highway 81, Anderson, SC 29621-2506
Tel (864) 224-0271 *Founded/Ownrshp* 2013
Sales 60.5MM^E *EMP* 170^E
SIC 2273 2281 Rugs, machine woven; Polypropylene yarn, spun: made from purchased staple; Rugs, machine woven; Polypropylene yarn, spun: made from purchased staple
CEO: Lucien Vanwynsberghe
COO: Wim Depate
VP: Kathy Cox
VP: Paul Crump
Dir IT: Wim De Pape
Dir IT: Mike Moon
Info Man: Michael Griesemer
VP Sls: Don Newton
VP Sls: Pat Ofarrell
Mktg Dir: Mikala Moller

D-U-N-S 02-576-2725
ORIANA HOUSE INC
885 E Buchtel Ave, Akron, OH 44305-2338
Tel (330) 535-8116 *Founded/Ownrshp* 1981
Sales 45.3MM *EMP* 1,513
Accts Brunercox Llp Akron Oh
SIC 8322 9111 Substance abuse counseling; Rehabilitation services; County supervisors' & executives' offices; Substance abuse counseling; Rehabilitation services; County supervisors' & executives' offices
Pr: James Lawrence
**Ex VP:* Anne Connell-Freund
**Ex VP:* Bernard Rochford
**VP:* Joyce Allen
VP: George De Bord
**VP:* George Debord
VP: Illya McGee
VP: Chris Savage
VP Admn: Mary Jones
Prgrm Mgr: Deana Brutto
Counsel: Cheryl Bayard

ORIBE
See JAY GROUP INC

D-U-N-S 00-884-3347 IMP
ORIBE HAIR CARE LLC
(*Suby of* LUXURY BRAND PARTNERS LLC) ★
665 Broadway Ste 502, New York, NY 10012-2331
Tel (646) 571-1196 *Founded/Ownrshp* 2007
Sales 29.0MM^E *EMP* 65
SIC 5122 Cosmetics, perfumes & hair products
Ex Dir: Kathryn Paolino
Off Admin: Harry Lawrence
Mktg Mgr: Sarah Daphnis
Mktg Mgr: Beth Lippman
Mktg Mgr: Kim Thomas
Mktg Mgr: Justina Valenzia
Snr Mgr: Daniel Langer

ORICA
See NELSON BROTHERS LLC

D-U-N-S 05-837-0685 IMP/EXP
ORICA GROUND SUPPORT INC
MINOVA AMERICAS
(*Suby of* MINOVA HOLDING INC) ★
150 Summer Ct, Georgetown, KY 40324-9369
Tel (502) 868-6236 *Founded/Ownrshp* 2003
Sales 159.3MM^E *EMP* 531
SIC 5082 3564 2439 7699

D-U-N-S 04-686-0750 IMP
ORICA US SERVICES INC
(*Suby of* ORICA LIMITED)
33101 E Quincy Ave, Watkins, CO 80137-9406
Tel (303) 268-5000 *Founded/Ownrshp* 2008
Sales 159.3MM^E *EMP* 700
SIC 2892 5169 Explosives; Explosives; Explosives; Explosives
Pr: Craig Elkington
CFO: Richard Best
Genl Mgr: Per Johansson
VP Sls: Laura Babaeva
Counsel: Mary Schwebach

D-U-N-S 94-929-9622 IMP
ORICA USA INC
(*Suby of* ORICA LIMITED)
33101 E Quincy Ave, Watkins, CO 80137-9406
Tel (720) 870-1809 *Founded/Ownrshp* 1998
Sales 182.8MM^E *EMP* 700
SIC 2892 5169 Explosives; Explosives; Explosives; Explosives
CEO: Ian K Smith
COO: Jason Ryan
**CFO:* Craig Elkington
CFO: Craig Elkinton
CFO: Karen Stoffels
VP: Christopher Curtis
VP: Stan Harlen
VP: Kevin McBride
VP: Randy Scott
VP: Mark Taylor
Dir Rx: Mitchell Lee

D-U-N-S 05-417-0097
ORICK INDUSTRIES INC
614 E Kiracofe Ave, Elida, OH 45807-1034
Tel (419) 331-0600 *Founded/Ownrshp* 1969
Sales 28.8MM^E *EMP* 80
SIC 3469 3544 Metal stampings; Special dies, tools, jigs & fixtures
CEO: Paul Orick
**Pr:* Greg Orick
**Ex VP:* Monica Orick

D-U-N-S 18-897-3143
ORIELLY CHEVROLET INC
ORIELLY MOTOR COMPANY
(*Suby of* O'RIELLY MOTOR COMPANY)
6160 E Broadway Blvd, Tucson, AZ 85711-4083
Tel (520) 571-2270 *Founded/Ownrshp* 1924
Sales 71.8MM^E *EMP* 200
SIC 5511 Automobiles, new & used; Pickups, new & used; Trucks, tractors & trailers: new & used; Vans, new & used; Automobiles, new & used; Pickups, new & used; Trucks, tractors & trailers: new & used; Vans, new & used
Pr: Robert L Draper
**Pr:* Richard B O'Rielly
**Sec:* Veronica K Bartz
**VP:* R B O'Rielly
Genl Mgr: Scott Barton
DP Exec: Dwayne Warren

ORIELLY MOTOR COMPANY
See ORIELLY CHEVROLET INC

D-U-N-S 19-975-6966
ORIENT BANCORPORATION
BANK OF THE ORIENT
100 Pine St Ste 600, San Francisco, CA 94111-5108
Tel (415) 567-1554 *Founded/Ownrshp* 1971
Sales NA *EMP* 150^E
SIC 6712 Bank holding companies; Bank holding companies
Ch Bd: Ernest Go
**Pr:* John Ing

*COO: Michael R Delucchi
CFO: Philipp Frings

ORIENT EX HTELS TRAINS CRUISES
See ORIENT EXPRESS HOTELS INC

D-U-N-S 04-835-3460
ORIENT EXPRESS HOTELS INC
ORIENT EX HTELS TRAINS CRUISES
(Suby of BELMOND LTD.)
441 Lexington Ave Rm 504, New York, NY 10017-3938
Tel (212) 302-5055 Founded/Ownrshp 2000
Sales 102.2MM^E EMP 5,000
SIC 7011 3743 5947 6552 Hotels; Train cars & equipment, freight or passenger; Gift shop; Subdividers & developers; Hotels; Train cars & equipment, freight or passenger; Gift shop; Subdividers & developers
Pr: Paul White
Pr: John Landry
COO: Anna Nash
Sls Mgr: Laura Fiore
Sls Mgr: Nicola Price

D-U-N-S 96-426-2869 IMP
ORIENT PRECISION AMERICA INC
OPA
(Suby of HAEM CO., LTD.)
7710 Balboa Ave Ste 327, San Diego, CA 92111-2254
Tel (858) 268-1515 Founded/Ownrshp 1995
Sales 36.9MM EMP 155
SIC 5045 5065 Computer peripheral equipment; Radio & television equipment & parts; Computer peripheral equipment; Radio & television equipment & parts
CEO: Byoung Han Ha
*Pr: Won Ki Choi

D-U-N-S 09-117-1199
■ ORIENTAL BANK
ORIENTAL GROUP
(Suby of OFG BANCORP) ★
254 Ave Munoz Rivera, San Juan, PR 00918-1900
Tel (787) 771-6800 Founded/Ownrshp 1997
Sales NA EMP 350
SIC 6035 7359 7515 6733 Federal savings banks; Equipment rental & leasing; Passenger car leasing; Trusts; Federal savings banks; Equipment rental & leasing; Passenger car leasing; Trusts
Pr: Jose Rafael Fernadez
*Ch Bd: Jose Gil Delamadrid
*Treas: Julio Micheo
VP: Maureen Cilano
Brnch Mgr: Mary Hosler
Mktg Mgr: Michael Laskoe
Assoc Ed: Corina Rivera

ORIENTAL GROUP
See ORIENTAL BANK

D-U-N-S 09-861-9463 IMP/EXP
ORIENTAL MOTOR U S A CORP
(Suby of ORIENTAL MOTOR CO.,LTD.)
1001 Knox St, Torrance, CA 90502-1030
Tel (310) 715-3300 Founded/Ownrshp 1978
Sales 56.3MM EMP 90
Accts Deloitte & Touche Llp Los Ang
SIC 5063 Motors, electric; Motors, electric
Pr: Ryan Kanemura
*Ex VP: Greg Johnston
*VP: Pete Derose
*Prin: Jake Kitayama
Sls Mgr: Mike Foley

ORIENTAL TRADING CO
See CTC FOOD INTERNATIONAL INC

ORIENTAL TRADING COMPANY
See OTC DIRECT INC

D-U-N-S 00-952-4152 IMP/EXP
■ ORIENTAL TRADING CO INC
(Suby of OTC WORLDWIDE HOLDINGS INC) ★
5455 S 90th St, Omaha, NE 68127-3501
Tel (402) 596-1200 Founded/Ownrshp 2011, 2012
Sales 846.8MM^E EMP 1,005^E
SIC 5199 4813 Gifts & novelties; ; Gifts & novelties;
CEO: Sam Taylor
*Treas: Steve Mendlik
VP: Nachiket Desai
Admn Mgr: P Raveendran
Snr Ntwrk: Erich Ross
Snr Ntwrk: Paul Vodicka
Snr Ntwrk: Chris Williams
Sys Mgr: Debra Corsbie
Software D: Marvin Konwinski
VP Opers: Chris Merritt
Opers Mgr: David Ballard

D-U-N-S 17-781-5214 IMP
ORIENTAL WEAVERS USA INC
SPHINX BY ORIENTAL WEAVERS
(Suby of ORIENTAL WEAVERS CARPET S.A.E)
3515 Corporate Dr, Dalton, GA 30721-4972
Tel (706) 277-4725 Founded/Ownrshp 1992
Sales 47.0MM^E EMP 50
SIC 5023 Rugs
CEO: Mohamed Farid
*CFO: Darrel McCay
*VP: Michael J Riley

D-U-N-S 80-790-3901 IMP/EXP
ORIENTAL WEAVERS USA INC
(Suby of ORIENTAL WEAVERS CARPET S.A.E)
3252 Dug Gap Rd, Dalton, GA 30720-4923
Tel (706) 277-9666 Founded/Ownrshp 1992
Sales 70.1MM^E EMP 350
SIC 2273 5023 Rugs, machine woven; Floor cushion & padding; Rugs, machine woven; Floor cushion & padding
Pr: Mohamed Farid
*CFO: Darrel McCay
*VP: Michael J Riley
Dir IT: Joel Sims
Art Dir: Jim Kooi

ORIENTEX FOODS
See RAMAR INTERNATIONAL CORP

D-U-N-S 17-471-4647
▲ ORIGEN FINANCIAL INC
27777 Franklin Rd # 1700, Southfield, MI 48034-8202
Tel (248) 746-7000 Founded/Ownrshp 1996
Sales 43.6MM^E EMP 282
Tkr Sym ORGN Exch OTO
SIC 6798 Real estate investment trusts; Real estate investment trusts
CEO: Ronald A Klein
Pr: J Peter Scherer
CFO: W Anderson Geater Jr
Ex VP: Mark W Landschulz
Sr VP: Paul J Galaspie
VP: Elaine Nesbitt

D-U-N-S 94-978-9036
■ ORIGEN FINANCIAL LLC
(Suby of ORIGEN FINANCIAL INC) ★
27777 Franklin Rd # 1700, Southfield, MI 48034-8202
Tel (248) 746-7000 Founded/Ownrshp 2003
Sales 26.0MM^E EMP 255
SIC 6798 Real estate investment trusts; Real estate investment trusts

D-U-N-S 93-357-5201
ORIGENE TECHNOLOGIES INC
9620 Med Ctr Dr Ste 200, Rockville, MD 20850
Tel (301) 340-3188 Founded/Ownrshp 1996
Sales 49.8MM^E EMP 110
SIC 5122 Biologicals & allied products; Biotherapeutics; Biologicals & allied products; Biotherapeutics
Pr: Weiwu He
Pr: Mark Watson
Sr VP: Youmin Shu
VP: Rich Hamer
VP: Karl Kovacs
Dir Lab: Sean Kelly
Admn Mgr: Amy Gearhart
Dir IT: Mac Lu
Info Man: Julie McDowell
Manager: Pete Wang
Corp Couns: WEI Guo

D-U-N-S 05-853-2169
ORIGIN BANK
COMMUNITY TRUST BANK
(Suby of COMMUNITY TRUST FINANCIAL CORP) ★
3921 Elm St, Choudrant, LA 71227-3082
Tel (318) 255-2222 Founded/Ownrshp 1987
Sales NA EMP 261
SIC 6022 State commercial banks; State commercial banks
Pr: Drake D Mills
*Ch Bd: Ronnie Myrick
*CFO: James K Kendrick
Ex VP: Lonnie Scarborough
Ex VP: Linda Tuten
Sr VP: Ken Johnson
Sr VP: Debbie Williamson
VP: Alicia Bullock
VP: Wayne Darnell
VP: Jason Hawkins

D-U-N-S 00-276-8397
ORIGIN HEALTHCARE SOLUTIONS LLC
1095 Day Hill Rd Ste 350, Windsor, CT 06095-1782
Tel (312) 425-4800 Founded/Ownrshp 2005
Sales 48.0MM^E EMP 550
SIC 8099 8721 Medical services organization; Billing & bookkeeping service; Medical services organization; Billing & bookkeeping service
Pr: Tom Stampiglia
*CFO: John Spiller

D-U-N-S 00-351-3967 IMP
ORIGIN MICRO INC (NH)
124 Heritage Ave Unit 8, Portsmouth, NH 03801-5645
Tel (603) 433-4411 Founded/Ownrshp 1997
Sales 21.7MM EMP 14
Accts Read & Associates Cpas Pllc
SIC 5045 Computers, peripherals & software
Pr: Donald G Doney
*COO: George W Cross
*Ex VP: Lisa R Desrosiers
*VP: Paul E Fenlon
Sales Exec: Christian Cedrone
Sales Exec: Ned Hinds
Sales Exec: Mark Michaud

D-U-N-S 01-003-3756 IMP
ORIGIN POINT BRANDS LLC
2453 King Street Ext, Charleston, SC 29405-6123
Tel (843) 747-9812 Founded/Ownrshp 1998
Sales 20.6MM^E EMP 70
SIC 3315 Fence gates posts & fittings: steel; Fence gates posts & fittings: steel
CEO: Paul Gossling

ORIGINAL AUSTIN'S, THE
See AUSTIN STORES INC

D-U-N-S 00-120-1045 IMP/EXP
ORIGINAL BRADFORD SOAP WORKS INC (RI)
(Suby of BRADFORD SOAP INTERNATIONAL INC) ★
200 Providence St, West Warwick, RI 02893-2508
Tel (401) 821-2141 Founded/Ownrshp 1876
Sales 111.6MM^E EMP 400
SIC 2841 Soap: granulated, liquid, cake, flaked or chip; Soap: granulated, liquid, cake, flaked or chip
CEO: John H Howland
*CFO: Stuart Benton
CFO: Stuart R Benton
*Ex VP: Chris Buckley
*Ex VP: Jimmy Curran
Sr VP: William F Schmiedeknecht Jr
VP: Jeff Barrowcliff
VP: Rick Dowling
VP: Ed George
VP: Deb McDonough
Sftwr Eng: David Wrigley

ORIGINAL CHILI BOWL
See WINDSOR QUALITY FOOD CO LTD

ORIGINAL EQUIPMENT
See GLADES PARTS CO INC

D-U-N-S 06-259-4536
ORIGINAL HONEY BAKED HAM CO LLC (GA)
3875 Mansell Rd Ste 100, Alpharetta, GA 30022-1531
Tel (678) 966-3100 Founded/Ownrshp 1973
Sales 125.5MM^E EMP 650
SIC 5421 Meat markets, including freezer provisioners; Meat markets, including freezer provisioners
Pr: Charles A Bengochea
*Pr: Maggie Decan
*CEO: Linda F Van Rees
CFO: Phillip Eakins
*Chf Mktg O: Leigh Trescot
VP: Leon Denning
VP: Lawrence Garon
VP: Leon Golding
*VP: Joann Herold
VP: Nancy Luginbill
VP: Richard Mancine

D-U-N-S 11-364-1018 EXP
ORIGINAL IMPRESSIONS LLC
OI DISTRIBUTION
12900 Sw 89th Ct, Miami, FL 33176-5876
Tel (305) 233-1322 Founded/Ownrshp 2002
Sales 21.6MM EMP 190
Accts Berkowitz Pollack Brant Miami
SIC 2752 2789 7331 2621 7374 7371 Commercial printing, offset; Binding & repair of books, magazines & pamphlets; Direct mail advertising services; Wrapping & packaging papers; Computer graphics service; Computer software development & applications; Commercial printing, offset; Binding & repair of books, magazines & pamphlets; Direct mail advertising services; Wrapping & packaging papers; Computer graphics service; Computer software development & applications
Treas: Maria Garcia
Ex VP: Luis Lorenzo
VP: Iliana Faria
VP: Roger Lopez
VP: Peter Rood
Genl Mgr: Eddy Goicolea
CTO: Sean Karshis
Dir IT: Michael Wagenheim
IT Man: Carlos Nino
VP Opers: Henry Herrera
Prd Mgr: Robert Gonzalez

ORIGINAL ISLAND SPORT
See VIEWPOINT INTERNATIONAL INC

D-U-N-S 92-688-7282
ORIGINAL MATTRESS FACTORY
1261 Highway 36 E Ste 100, Saint Paul, MN 55109-2061
Tel (651) 482-9338 Founded/Ownrshp 1994
Sales 26.3MM^E EMP 171
SIC 2515 5712 Mattresses & bedsprings; Beds & accessories; Mattresses & bedsprings; Beds & accessories
Pr: Ron E Trzcinski
*VP: John Kocaja
*VP: John Quale

D-U-N-S 61-175-5158
ORIGINAL MATTRESS FACTORY INC
4930 State Rd, Cleveland, OH 44134-1214
Tel (216) 661-8388 Founded/Ownrshp 1990
Sales 25.7MM^E EMP 98
SIC 2515 5712 Mattresses & foundations; Furniture springs; Bedding & bedsprings; Mattresses
Pr: Ron Trzcinski
*Sec: Perry Doermann
*VP: Lawrence S Carlson
*VP: Douglas B Stroup

ORIGINAL NUT HOUSE, THE
See MORVEN PARTNERS LP

ORIGINAL PANCAKE HOUSE
See DMR OPH INC

D-U-N-S 04-160-9876
ORIGINAL PARTNERS LIMITED PARTNERSHIP
TOWNE PROPERTIES
1055 Saint Paul Pl, Cincinnati, OH 45202-6042
Tel (513) 381-8696 Founded/Ownrshp 1961
Sales 16.7MM EMP 500
SIC 6514 6513 Dwelling operators, except apartments; Apartment building operators; Dwelling operators, except apartments; Apartment building operators
Genl Pt: Neil K Bortz
Pt: Marvin Rosenberg
CFO: Bill Curran
Ex VP: John Twombley
Ex VP: John Twombly
VP: Bill Porter
VP: Derek Wehman
Dist Mgr: Kim Brown
Dist Mgr: Jub Oscherwitz
MIS Dir: Bill Salyers
Mktg Mgr: Rosie Kenedy

D-U-N-S 17-365-6018 IMP
ORIGINAL PARTS GROUP INC
CHEVELLE CLASSICS PARTS & ACC
1770 Saturn Way, Seal Beach, CA 90740-5618
Tel (562) 594-1000 Founded/Ownrshp 1984
Sales 43.7MM^E EMP 90^E
SIC 5531 3465 Automotive parts; Body parts, automobile: stamped metal
Pr: David Harry Leonard
COO: Tony Genty
CFO: Joe Rittel
*VP: Anthony M Genty
Sales Exec: Jorge Lopez
Sales Exec: Chris Williams
Mktg Mgr: Gus Stewart

D-U-N-S 87-465-9840
ORIGINAL PASTA CO
FIVE STAR RESTAURANT
11111 S Wilcrest Dr # 350, Houston, TX 77099-4310
Tel (713) 784-3600 Founded/Ownrshp 1996
Sales 10.1MM^E EMP 500
SIC 5812 Italian restaurant; Italian restaurant

Ch Bd: Ghulam Bombaywala
*VP: John Schwartz

ORIGINAL PENNYSAVER, THE
See PENNYSAVER USA PUBLISHING LLC

ORIGINAL SEATBELTBAG , THE
See HARVEYS INDUSTRIES INC

D-U-N-S 00-546-4292
ORIGINAL SMITH PRINTING INC (DE)
O S P
(Suby of COMMERCIAL PRINT GROUP INC) ★
2 Hardman Dr, Bloomington, IL 61701-6934
Tel (309) 663-0325 Founded/Ownrshp 1929, 2006
Sales 42.0MM^E EMP 195^E
SIC 2752 Commercial printing, offset; Commercial printing, offset
Pr: Rockie Zeigler
Sfty Dirs: Amy Fuller
Prd Mgr: Mike Brennan

D-U-N-S 04-950-7359
ORIGINAL SOUP MAN
1 Mohegan Sun Blvd, Uncasville, CT 06382-1355
Tel (860) 862-9758 Founded/Ownrshp 2015
Sales 6.9MM^E EMP 342^E
SIC 5499 Gourmet food stores
VP: John Quagan

D-U-N-S 08-241-4335 IMP/EXP
ORIGINATES INC
20900 Ne 30th Ave Ste 707, Aventura, FL 33180-2164
Tel (954) 233-2500 Founded/Ownrshp 1976
Sales 22.5MM EMP 8^E
SIC 2077 Fish liver oils, crude; Fish oil; Fish liver oils, crude; Fish oil
Pr: Meyer Minski
*VP: Jose Minski
VP: Jannie Motta

ORIGINATION
See FEED PRODUCTS NORTH INC

D-U-N-S 61-171-6283 IMP
■ ORIGINS NATURAL RESOURCES INC
ESTEE LAUDER
(Suby of ESTEE LAUDER INC) ★
767 5th Ave Fl 38, New York, NY 10153-0023
Tel (212) 572-4200 Founded/Ownrshp 1991
Sales 107.7MM^E EMP 127
SIC 5122 Drugs, proprietaries & sundries; Drugs, proprietaries & sundries
CEO: Lynne Greene
Sr VP: Lynn Mazzella
VP: Jenny Belknap
VP: Trenesa Danuser
VP: John Smoak
VP: Beth Spruance
*Prin: William P Lauder
Ex Dir: Mark Ferdman
Dir IT: Anne Basile
Mktg Dir: Lisa Lyou
Mktg Mgr: Daria Myers

ORIGIO - HUMAGEN PIPETS
See ORIGIO INC

D-U-N-S 78-706-8394
■ ORIGIO INC
ORIGIO - HUMAGEN PIPETS
(Suby of ORIGIO A/S)
2400 Hunters Way, Charlottesville, VA 22911-7930
Tel (434) 979-4000 Founded/Ownrshp 1990
Sales 28.9MM^E EMP 92
SIC 5047 Medical laboratory equipment
CEO: Jesper Funding Andersen
CFO: Jeannett Hvidkjr
Ex VP: Soren Ostergaard
VP: April Dean
Ql Cn Mgr: Margaret Sheehan

ORIGLIO BEVERAGE
See ANTONIO ORIGLIO INC

D-U-N-S 07-882-7005 IMP
ORIO NORTH AMERICA INC
SAAB AUTO PARTS N AMER SPNA
2125 Bttrfeld Dr Ste 299n, Troy, MI 48084
Tel (313) 618-7447 Founded/Ownrshp 2012
Sales 35.0MM^E EMP 20^E
Accts Dominic Lombardo
SIC 5013 Automotive supplies & parts; Automotive supplies & parts
CEO: Tim Colbeck
Genl Couns: Alan Lowenthal

D-U-N-S 11-870-6761
ORION BUILDING CORP INC
9025 Overlook Blvd # 100, Brentwood, TN 37027-2708
Tel (615) 321-4499 Founded/Ownrshp 1983
Sales 23.3MM EMP 105
Accts Cooper Travis & Company Plc
SIC 1542 1541 Nonresidential construction; Industrial buildings & warehouses; Nonresidential construction; Industrial buildings & warehouses
Pr: C Richard Daughrity
*Pt: J Moseley
*Ex VP: T Randall Gill
*VP: Webb B Hosse
VP: Hosse Webb
Dir IT: Jo Harris
Dir IT: Jo Joy
Sfty Mgr: Ronnie Balthrop

D-U-N-S 60-796-0929
ORION CONSTRUCTION CORP
2185 La Mirada Dr, Vista, CA 92081-8830
Tel (760) 597-9660 Founded/Ownrshp 1987
Sales 32.6MM^E EMP 80
SIC 1623 1629 1542 Water, sewer & utility lines; Industrial plant construction; Nonresidential construction
CEO: Richard Dowsing
*VP: Mark Dowsing
IT Man: Robert Wilson
Opers Mgr: Rob Wilson
Snr PM: Ron Susi

D-U-N-S 82-766-5688 IMP/EXP
■ ORION CONSTRUCTION LP
(*Suby of* ORION MARINE GROUP INC) ★
12550 Fuqua St, Houston, TX 77034-4600
Tel (713) 852-6500 *Founded/Ownrshp* 1994
Sales 98.7MM *EMP* 700
SIC 1629

D-U-N-S 04-594-6886 IMP
ORION CORP
JOHN CRANE ORION
(*Suby of* JOHN CRANE INC) ★
1111 Cedar Creek Rd, Grafton, WI 53024-9403
Tel (262) 377-2210 *Founded/Ownrshp* 2009
Sales 44.7MM[E] *EMP* 250
SIC 3568 Bearings, plain; Bearings, plain
VP: David Bretsch
Ex VP: Hal Gerber
Dir IT: Roger Austin
VP Mfg: Richard Lincoln
Plnt Mgr: Jim Wilde
Mktg Dir: Gary Wegner

D-U-N-S 14-897-3907 IMP
ORION DRILLING CO LLC
674 Flato Rd, Corpus Christi, TX 78405-4305
Tel (361) 299-9800 *Founded/Ownrshp* 2003
Sales 69.2MM[E] *EMP* 85[E]
SIC 1381 Drilling oil & gas wells
Pr: Wayne Squiresm
**Pt:* Jeff Weis
**COO:* Calvert Jones
**VP:* Dave Castro
Exec: Teresa Ryan
Dist Mgr: Joseph Goetz
Sfty Mgr: David Delacruz
Opers Mgr: Owen Brandt
Ql Cn Mgr: Bo Creek
Sls&Mrk Ex: Brett Schellenberg
Manager: Roger Lays

D-U-N-S 09-880-3765
▲ ORION ENERGY SYSTEMS INC
2210 Woodland Dr, Manitowoc, WI 54220-9662
Tel (920) 892-9340 *Founded/Ownrshp* 1996
Sales 72.2MM *EMP* 237[E]
Accts Bdo Usa Llp Milwaukee Wisco
Tkr Sym OESX *Exch* NAS
SIC 3646 3648 Commercial indusl & institutional electric lighting fixtures; Fluorescent lighting fixtures, commercial; Lighting equipment; Commercial indusl & institutional electric lighting fixtures; Fluorescent lighting fixtures, commercial; Lighting equipment
CEO: John H Scribante
**Pr:* Michael J Potts
CFO: William T Hull
Div Pres: Omar Rivera
Ex VP: Marc Meade
VP: Tony Bartol
Snr Mgr: Michael Voechting
Board of Directors: Michael W Altschaefl, Kenneth L Goodson Jr, James R Kackley, James D Leslie, Anthony L Otten, Elizabeth Gamsky Rich, Thomas N Schueller, Mark C Williamson

D-U-N-S 13-038-2208 IMP/EXP
ORION ENGINEERED CARBONS LLC
4501 Magnolia Cove Dr # 106, Kingwood, TX 77345-2252
Tel (832) 445-3300 *Founded/Ownrshp* 2011
Sales 524.6MM *EMP* 200
SIC 2895 Carbon black; Carbon black
CEO: Jack Clem
**CFO:* Charles Herlinger
**Sr VP:* Jorg Kruger
**Sr VP:* Mark Leigh
**Sr VP:* Jeff Malenky
**Sr VP:* Lixing Min
**Sr VP:* Claudine Mollenkopf
**Sr VP:* Erik Thiry
VP: Edu Araujo
VP: Johnny Covey
**VP:* Michael Reers

D-U-N-S 60-603-9469 IMP
■ ORION ENTERPRISES INC
ORION FITTINGS
(*Suby of* WATTS WATER TECHNOLOGIES INC) ★
2850 Fairfax Trfy, Kansas City, KS 66115-1316
Tel (913) 342-1653 *Founded/Ownrshp* 2004
Sales 30.5MM[E] *EMP* 120
SIC 3084 5074 3432 3089 Plastics pipe; Plumbing & hydronic heating supplies; Plumbing fixture fittings & trim; Fittings for pipe, plastic; Plastics pipe; Plumbing & hydronic heating supplies; Plumbing fixture fittings & trim; Fittings for pipe, plastic
Pr: John Mc Coy
**Treas:* Clay Reeder
**VP:* Bill Mc Coy
**VP:* James B Mc Coy
Manager: Jeff Ernst

D-U-N-S 08-953-5926
ORION FEDERAL CREDIT UNION
7845 Us Highway 64, Memphis, TN 38133-4007
Tel (901) 385-5200 *Founded/Ownrshp* 1957
Sales NA *EMP* 288
SIC 6062 State credit unions; State credit unions
CEO: Daniel Weickenand
**CFO:* Fredrick Rauch
**Ch:* James E Hayslip
**Treas:* E Ray Holt
Ex VP: Jason Lee
**Sr VP:* Judy Bell
**VP:* Dwight Burgess
**VP:* Judy Conrad
**VP:* Susan Hayne
**VP:* Maria McLendon
**VP:* Carl E Shields
VP: Tara Smith

ORION FITTINGS
See ORION ENTERPRISES INC

D-U-N-S 87-770-0518
ORION FOOD SYSTEMS LLC
(*Suby of* ONE ROCK CAPITAL PARTNERS LLC) ★
2930 W Maple St, Sioux Falls, SD 57107-0745
Tel (605) 336-6961 *Founded/Ownrshp* 2014
Sales 90.0MM *EMP* 300
SIC 5149 2033 2026 2041 Bread, cake & related products; Pizza supplies; Pizza sauce: packaged in cans, jars, etc.; Bakers' cheese; Pizza dough, prepared
CEO: Steve K Watkins
VP: Rich Carlson
VP: Devon Clark
VP: John Cooper
VP: Linda Roemen
Dir Bus: Jeff Mozingo
Dir Bus: Jon Rader
Opers Mgr: Tom Bale
Prd Mgr: Bob Mairose
Mktg Dir: Rachel Ambrose
Mktg Mgr: Brooke Lewko

D-U-N-S 15-096-5023
ORION HEALTH INC
(*Suby of* ORION HEALTH ASIA HOLDINGS LIMITED)
100 Wilshire Blvd # 1900, Santa Monica, CA 90401-1155
Tel (310) 526-4030 *Founded/Ownrshp* 2002
Sales 60.6MM[E] *EMP* 307
SIC 7371 Computer software development; Computer software development
Pr: Paul Viskovich
**Treas:* Sean Donoghue
VP: Michael Burke
VP: Robert Pepper
Exec: Cassidy Douglas
CIO: Jeanette X Polaschek
Board of Directors: Luke Facer, Paul Viskovich

D-U-N-S 09-417-3528
▲ ORION HEALTHCORP INC
368 W Pike St Ste 102, Lawrenceville, GA 30046-3240
Tel (678) 832-1800 *Founded/Ownrshp* 1984
Sales 60.2MM[E] *EMP* 423
Tkr Sym ORNH *Exch* OTO
SIC 8721 7322 Billing & bookkeeping service; Collection agency, except real estate; Billing & bookkeeping service; Collection agency, except real estate
CEO: Dale Brinkman
Pr: Terrence L Bauer
Pr: Joseph Seale
CFO: Stephen H Murdock
Ofcr: Tom Mathews
Ex VP: Dennis M Cain
Prin: Paul H Cascio
Prin: David Crane
Prin: Robert P Pinkas

D-U-N-S 04-459-1196
ORION INDUSTRIES
1590 A St Ne, Auburn, WA 98002-5101
Tel (253) 661-7805 *Founded/Ownrshp* 1957
Sales 26.6MM *EMP* 249
SIC 3444 8331 Sheet metalwork; Vocational training agency; Sheet metalwork; Vocational training agency
CEO: John Theisen
**CFO:* Jeffrey Black
CFO: Stephen Cornell
Bd of Dir: Barbara Panush
Exec: Rick Gilleland
Genl Mgr: Thomas Brosius

D-U-N-S 06-798-5403
ORION INSTRUMENTS LLC
(*Suby of* MAGNETROL INTERNATIONAL INC) ★
2105 Oak Villa Blvd, Baton Rouge, LA 70815-8518
Tel (225) 906-2343 *Founded/Ownrshp* 2001
Sales 74.5MM[E] *EMP* 364
SIC 3823 Liquid level instruments, industrial process type; Liquid level instruments, industrial process type
IT Man: Wilkin McKean
Prd Mgr: Henry Moss
Prd Mgr: Henry Mosses

D-U-N-S 12-546-7055
ORION MANAGEMENT LLC
8003 Forbes Pl Ste 300, Springfield, VA 22151-2215
Tel (703) 321-2190 *Founded/Ownrshp* 2001
Sales 20.8MM *EMP* 110
Accts Dmg Consulting Inc Gaithers
SIC 1711 1731 7382 Fire sprinkler system installation; Fiber optic cable installation; Fire alarm maintenance & monitoring; Fire sprinkler system installation; Fiber optic cable installation; Fire alarm maintenance & monitoring
Pt: Timothy Britell
**Pt:* Christopher A Morin

D-U-N-S 04-149-7165 IMP/EXP
■ ORION MARINE CONSTRUCTION INC
MISENER MARINE CONSTRUCTION
(*Suby of* ORION CONSTRUCTION LP) ★
5440 W Tyson Ave, Tampa, FL 33611-3228
Tel (813) 839-8441 *Founded/Ownrshp* 2001
Sales 214.7MM *EMP* 305
SIC 1629 Marine construction; Marine construction
Pr: Mark R Stauffer
**CFO:* Mark Stauffer
Ex VP: Jim Rose
**Sr VP:* David Thornton
**VP:* John Whalen

D-U-N-S 80-767-6908
▲ ORION MARINE GROUP INC
12000 Aerospace Ave # 300, Houston, TX 77034-5587
Tel (713) 852-6500 *Founded/Ownrshp* 1994
Sales 385.8MM *EMP* 2,700[E]
Tkr Sym ORN *Exch* NYS
SIC 1629 Marine construction; Marine construction
Pr: Mark R Stauffer
COO: L Dwayne Breaux
COO: James L Rose
CFO: Christopher J Dealmeida
Ofcr: Peter R Buchler
VP Bus Dev: Mark Coyle
Board of Directors: Thomas N Amonett, Richard L Daerr Jr, J Michael Pearson, Mark Stauffer, Gene Stoever

ORION PACIFIC INTERNATIONAL
See ORION PACIFICTRADERS INC

D-U-N-S 01-184-8426 EXP
ORION PACIFIC TRADERS INC
ORION PACIFIC INTERNATIONAL
1224 Lincoln Ave, Walnut Creek, CA 94596-4635
Tel (925) 943-2066 *Founded/Ownrshp* 1998
Sales 46.8MM *EMP* 11
SIC 5141 Food brokers; Food brokers
CEO: Frederick Rider
**VP:* Richard Johnston
Off Mgr: Tobi Grover

D-U-N-S 61-678-4971 IMP/EXP
ORION PHOTO INDUSTRIES INC
LASERGIFTS
3250 Tower Rd, Prescott, AZ 86305-3733
Tel (928) 445-1698 *Founded/Ownrshp* 1982
Sales 37.8MM[E] *EMP* 120
SIC 5099 Souvenirs; Souvenirs
Pr: David Mudrick
Pr: Cynthia Powers
VP: Lisa Madison
VP: Cynthia Mudrick
IT Man: Chris Fletcher
Opers Mgr: Nate Long
Sls Dir: Greg Johnson

D-U-N-S 06-560-0079 IMP
ORION PLASTICS CORP (CA)
700 W Carob St, Compton, CA 90220-5225
Tel (310) 223-0370 *Founded/Ownrshp* 2000
Sales 26.0MM *EMP* 75
SIC 2821 Plastics materials & resins
Pr: Patricia Conkling
Plnt Mgr: Luis Suarez
Sls Mgr: Steven Gitzke
Sales Asso: Wayne Moore

D-U-N-S 96-275-1280
ORION RECOVERY GROUP INC
1411 S Dickerson Rd, Goodlettsville, TN 37072-3002
Tel (615) 868-9110 *Founded/Ownrshp* 2010
Sales 63.7MM[E] *EMP* 99[E]
SIC 4959 1795 Environmental cleanup services; Wrecking & demolition work
Pr: Davian Ploger
**Ch:* Pauli Overdorff

ORION SALES
See SSNA INC

ORION SECURITY
See YOSH ENTERPRISES INC

D-U-N-S 62-522-5545 IMP/EXP
ORION SOUTH INC
REAGAN POWER & COMPRESSION
2550 Belle Chasse Hwy, Gretna, LA 70053-6758
Tel (504) 368-9760 *Founded/Ownrshp* 1956
Sales 66.1MM *EMP* 274
Accts Leglue & Company Cpa S New O
SIC 5084 3621 3561 3519 Oil well machinery, equipment & supplies; Engines & transportation equipment; Electric motor & generator parts; Industrial pumps & parts; Diesel engine rebuilding; Gas engine rebuilding; Oil well machinery, equipment & supplies; Engines & transportation equipment; Electric motor & generator parts; Industrial pumps & parts; Diesel engine rebuilding; Gas engine rebuilding
Pr: Thomas Nathan Reagan
**CFO:* Michael Soileau
**Treas:* Edward R Grady
**Ex VP:* John Farrell

D-U-N-S 92-980-2437
ORION SYSTEMS INTEGRATORS LLC
3759 Us Highway 1 Ste 104, Monmouth Junction, NJ 08852-2430
Tel (732) 422-9922 *Founded/Ownrshp* 1993
Sales 86.3MM[E] *EMP* 500
SIC 7371 Computer software development & applications; Computer software development & applications
CEO: Sunil Mehta
**CFO:* Jeffrey Robinson
Genl Mgr: Ranjan Dattagupta
Snr Mgr: Nagaraj Shanmugam

ORION TECH
See COMPUCASE CORP

D-U-N-S 94-264-2935 IMP
■ ORION THERMO INC
(*Suby of* THERMO FISHER SCIENTIFIC INC) ★
22 Alpha Rd, Chelmsford, MA 01824-4123
Tel (800) 225-1480 *Founded/Ownrshp* 1995
Sales 39.9MM[E] *EMP* 330
SIC 3823 3826 3825 3561 Industrial instrmnts msrmnt display/control process variable; Analytical instruments; Instruments to measure electricity; Pumps & pumping equipment; Industrial instrmnts msrmnt display/control process variable; Analytical instruments; Instruments to measure electricity; Pumps & pumping equipment
Pr: Seth Hoogasian
**Pr:* James Barbookles
**Treas:* Jonathan Painter
**Treas:* Anthony H Smith

D-U-N-S 03-554-1957
■ ORION TRADING WORLDWIDE LLC
MAGNA GLOBAL TRADING
(*Suby of* INTERPUBLIC GROUP OF COMPANIES INC) ★
622 3rd Ave Lbby 2, New York, NY 10017-6718
Tel (212) 605-7885 *Founded/Ownrshp* 1996
Sales 29.3MM[E] *EMP* 350[E]
SIC 7319 Media buying service; Media buying service
Pr: Brian McMahon
CFO: Kathleen Ruslim
Ex VP: Heide Kahme
Ex VP: Vincent Letang
Ex VP: Patty Norway
Sr VP: Barbara Dimaria
VP: Todd Heligman
VP: Carla Vilar
Mng Dir: Tricia Allen
Dir IT: Janet Lopez
IT Man: Tanya Jaramillo

D-U-N-S 07-669-2698
■ ORITANI BANK
ORITANI SAVING BANK
(*Suby of* ORITANI FINANCIAL CORP) ★
370 Pascack Rd, Twp Washinton, NJ 07676-4835
Tel (201) 664-5400 *Founded/Ownrshp* 1911
Sales NA *EMP* 150
Accts Kpmg Llp
SIC 6036 Savings & loan associations, not federally chartered; Savings & loan associations, not federally chartered
Pr: Kevin J Lynch
CFO: John M Fields Jr
Ofcr: Diane Fenton
Ofcr: Thomas Guinan
Sr VP: Philip M Wyks
VP: Robert J Barbarino
VP: Rosanne Buscemi
VP: Paul Cordero
VP: Neil Minardi
VP: Anne Mooradian
VP: Daniel Schapira
Board of Directors: Nicholas Antonaccio, Dominic F Cundari, Michael A Debernardi, Joseph Deferrari Jr, Robert F Gerrie, William E Gott, Kevin J Lynch, David T Peterson Jr, Phillip D Wyks

D-U-N-S 79-076-9850
▲ ORITANI FINANCIAL CORP
370 Pascack Rd, Twp Washinton, NJ 07676-4835
Tel (201) 664-5400 *Founded/Ownrshp* 1998
Sales NA *EMP* 235[E]
Accts Kpmg Llp Short Hills New Je
Tkr Sym ORIT *Exch* NGS
SIC 6022 State commercial banks; State commercial banks
Ch Bd: Kevin J Lynch
CFO: John M Fields Jr
Ofcr: Thomas Guinan
Sr VP: Philip M Wyks
VP: Paul M Cordero
VP: Noah Littell
VP: Bing Luh
VP: John Pagano
VP: Paul C Skinner
VP Bus Dev: Jack Anastasi
Brnch Mgr: Monang Shah

ORITANI SAVING BANK
See ORITANI BANK

D-U-N-S 06-128-6274 IMP/EXP
ORITZ CORP
1555 Bayshore Hwy Ste 400, Burlingame, CA 94010-1617
Tel (650) 692-8000 *Founded/Ownrshp* 1979
Sales 73.1MM[E] *EMP* 103
SIC 5147 Meats & meat products; Meats & meat products
Pr: Vladimir R Grave
Sales Asso: Eddie Quitoriano

D-U-N-S 07-421-4490
ORIUS CORP
1000 Hart Rd Ste 140, Barrington, IL 60010-2668
Tel (847) 277-8444 *Founded/Ownrshp* 1999, 2003
Sales 85.9MM[E] *EMP* 1,200
SIC 4813 Telephone communication, except radio; Telephone communication, except radio
Pr: Willaim Shuttleworth
CFO: Gary F Berger
Ex VP: Robert Waerman
Sr VP: Thomas W Hartmann
VP: John W Starr

D-U-N-S 82-665-0314
ORIX FINANCIAL SERVICES INC
(*Suby of* ORIX USA CORP) ★
1717 Main St Ste 800, Dallas, TX 75201-4686
Tel (214) 237-2000 *Founded/Ownrshp* 2008
Sales 2.4MM[E] *EMP* 291[E]
SIC 6211 Security brokers & dealers
Prin: Jeff Yarckin

D-U-N-S 02-865-8306
ORIX USA CORP
676 W Prospect Rd, Oakland Park, FL 33309-3949
Tel (214) 237-2000 *Founded/Ownrshp* 2010
Sales 23.4MM[E] *EMP* 1,400
SIC 8741 Business management; Business management
Pr: James Thompson
Ch Bd: Yuki Oshima

D-U-N-S 02-885-8306 IMP
ORIX USA CORP
(*Suby of* ORIX CORPORATION)
1717 Main St Ste 1100, Dallas, TX 75201-4612
Tel (214) 237-2000 *Founded/Ownrshp* 1981
Sales 153.7MM[E] *EMP* 1,200
SIC 6211 6282

D-U-N-S 36-441-1496
ORIZON INDUSTRIES INC
(*Suby of* SPITZER INDUSTRIES INC) ★
7007 Fm 362 Rd, Brookshire, TX 77423-9418
Tel (281) 375-7700 *Founded/Ownrshp* 1988
Sales 158.4MM[E] *EMP* 250
SIC 3441 Fabricated structural metal; Fabricated structural metal
Ch: Cullen R Spitzer
**Pr:* Curtis F Jones
**CFO:* Marcy Brigman
CFO: Marcy Prigman
**Sec:* Ted Johnson
**VP:* Charles O'Hara

ORKIN
See ROLLINS SUPPLY INC

D-U-N-S 00-250-9420
■ ORKIN LLC
ORKIN PEST CONTROL
(*Suby of* ROLLINS INC) ★
2170 Piedmont Rd Ne, Atlanta, GA 30324-4135
Tel (404) 888-2000 *Founded/Ownrshp* 1901

Sales 495.9MM^E *EMP* 4,000
SIC 7342 Pest control in structures; Termite control; Pest control in structures; Termite control
CEO: Gary W Rollins
Pr: Cynthia Bordes
VP: Lee W Crump
VP: Wayne Golden
VP: Lee Krump
Rgnl Mgr: Rob Bates
Rgnl Mgr: Ray Glover
Brnch Mgr: Terry Castro
Brnch Mgr: Greg Cleveland
Brnch Mgr: Dan Henning
Brnch Mgr: Jed Horn

ORKIN PEST CONTROL
See ORKIN LLC

D-U-N-S 14-062-1488
ORLAND PARK IMPORT MOTOR SALES INC
VOLKSWAGEN OF ORLAND PARK
8920 W 159th St, Orland Park, IL 60462-5620
Tel (708) 349-0774 *Founded/Ownrshp* 2004
Sales 21.7MM^E *EMP* 46
SIC 5511 5013 Automobiles, new & used; Automotive supplies & parts
Pr: Joseph Hoobyar
**VP:* Raymond Baldi
Off Mgr: Gina Loy
Sales Asso: Dustin Hill

D-U-N-S 03-665-9373
ORLAND PARK MOTOR CARS INC
MERCEDES BENZ OF ORLAND PARK
8430 W 159th St, Orland Park, IL 60462-4942
Tel (708) 460-0400 *Founded/Ownrshp* 1997
Sales 32.6MM^E *EMP* 90
SIC 5511 Automobiles, new & used; Automobiles, new & used
Pr: Klare S Sunderland
Genl Mgr: David Nocera

D-U-N-S 04-650-1383
ORLAND PARK SCHOOL DISTRICT 135
15100 S 94th Ave Uppr, Orland Park, IL 60462-3239
Tel (708) 364-3300 *Founded/Ownrshp* 1800
Sales 116.3M *EMP* 800
SIC 8211 Public elementary & secondary schools; Public elementary school; Public junior high school; Public elementary & secondary schools; Public elementary school; Public junior high school
Bd of Dir: Gregory H O Kon
VP: Thomas Cunningham
Prin: Kathy Carroll
Prin: Debra Ciaccio
Prin: Cindy Finley
Prin: Pam Hodgson
Prin: Linda Kane
Prin: Sue Kuligoski
Prin: Kathy Panagiotaros
Prin: Lynn Zeder
Dir Sec: Jerry Hughes

ORLAND TOYOTA
See KOWALIS MOTORS INC

D-U-N-S 00-758-5102 IMP
ORLANDI INC
ORLANDI SCENTED PRODUCTS
131 Executive Blvd, Farmingdale, NY 11735-4719
Tel (631) 756-0110 *Founded/Ownrshp* 1996
Sales 33.0MM^E *EMP* 100^E
SIC 3993 3999 7389 2752 Signs & advertising specialties; Novelties, bric-a-brac & hobby kits; Packaging & labeling services; Commercial printing, lithographic; Signs & advertising specialties; Novelties, bric-a-brac & hobby kits; Packaging & labeling services; Commercial printing, lithographic
Ch Bd: Sven Dobler
Sr VP: Kenneth Kane
**VP:* Per Dobler
VP: Henri Liesenfelt
VP: Ken Maury
Telecom Ex: Mark Waters
Mfg Dir: Lee Johnson
QC Dir: Tenna Hornsby
Sfty Mgr: Robin Whitney
Mktg Dir: Gina Shaughnessy

ORLANDI SCENTED PRODUCTS
See ORLANDI INC

D-U-N-S 11-831-1588 EXP
ORLANDO AUTOMOTIVE LLC
FOUNTAIN DAHAITSU
8701 S Orange Blossom Trl, Orlando, FL 32809-7911
Tel (407) 240-3800 *Founded/Ownrshp* 1986
Sales 71.8MM^E *EMP* 275
SIC 5511 7538 5531 Automobiles, new & used; General automotive repair shops; Automotive parts; Automobiles, new & used; General automotive repair shops; Automotive parts
Pr: Clay King
Treas: Kirk Francis
Sls Mgr: Carrie Pennington
Sales Asso: Sean Branigan

D-U-N-S 00-417-4355
ORLANDO BAKING CO
7777 Grand Ave, Cleveland, OH 44104-3061
Tel (216) 361-1872 *Founded/Ownrshp* 1872
Sales 102.5MM^E *EMP* 350^E
SIC 2051 Bread, all types (white, wheat, rye, etc): fresh or frozen; Rolls, bread type: fresh or frozen; Bread, all types (white, wheat, rye, etc): fresh or frozen; Rolls, bread type: fresh or frozen
Pr: Chester Orlando
**CFO:* Christine Brindle
Treas: John A Peca Jr
**VP:* Joseph Orlando
**Prin:* Glenn W Eckert
**Prin:* Edna Rosenblum
**Prin:* Hattie Wagner
QA Dir: Daryl Chun
QA Dir: Craig Lovato
QA Dir: Ronald Zendarski
Dir IT: Brett Ferlin

D-U-N-S 83-063-5269
ORLANDO BATHING SUIT LLC
EVERYTHING BUT WATER
5337 Millenia Lakes Blvd # 400, Orlando, FL 32839-6302
Tel (407) 351-4069 *Founded/Ownrshp* 2009
Sales 60.1MM^E *EMP* 350^E
SIC 5699 Bathing suits; Bathing suits
Sr VP: Ann McDermott
VP: Michele Fichter
VP: Duncan Vierra
Dist Mgr: Lolita Duggan
Dist Mgr: Rebecca Randolph
Dist Mgr: Kari Schmidt
Store Mgr: Christine Banjac
Store Mgr: Shannon Eschmann
Sls&Mrk Ex: Barry Zeeuw
Mktg Dir: Lesa Haas
Sls Mgr: Diem Allen

D-U-N-S 62-153-9378
ORLANDO CANCER CENTER
M D ANDERSON CANCER CENTER ORL
1400 S Orange Ave, Orlando, FL 32806-2000
Tel (321) 843-1255 *Founded/Ownrshp* 1991
Sales 20.7MM *EMP* 410
Accts Ernst & Young Us Llp Miami F
SIC 8069 Cancer hospital; Cancer hospital
CEO: Clarence Brown
COO: Said Baidas
CFO: Jennifer Thompson
Doctor: Luis Herrera
Doctor: Dwayne W-Jenkins MD
Doctor: Chad Kollas
Pharmcst: Kathy Le
Pharmcst: Keith Lyon
Snr Mgr: Paul Kolarik

ORLANDO DDGE CHRYSLER JEEP RAM
See ORLANDO DODGE INC

D-U-N-S 00-251-8074
■ **ORLANDO DIEFENDERFER ELECTRICAL CONTRACTORS INC** (PA)
DIEFENDERFER TELECOM
(*Suby of* UIL HOLDINGS CORP) ★
116 S 2nd St, Allentown, PA 18102-4904
Tel (610) 434-9595 *Founded/Ownrshp* 1982, 2007
Sales 62.6MM^E *EMP* 400
SIC 1731 General electrical contractor; Telephone & telephone equipment installation; General electrical contractor; Telephone & telephone equipment installation
Pr: Alexander L Maggitti
**Treas:* Arthur C Weida
**VP:* Janet Blumberg
**VP:* Thomas Dembinski
**VP:* Alex Maggitti Jr
**VP:* Ed McCarty
VP: Ryan Miller
**VP:* Terry L Simpson
Off Mgr: Rosy Gore
Off Mgr: Lisa Leiss
Telecom Mg: Don Keck

D-U-N-S 05-697-0130
ORLANDO DODGE INC
ORLANDO DDGE CHRYSLER JEEP RAM
4101 W Colonial Dr, Orlando, FL 32808-8190
Tel (407) 299-1120 *Founded/Ownrshp* 1976
Sales 56.2MM^E *EMP* 91
SIC 5511 5531 7539 Automobiles, new & used; Automotive parts; Automotive repair shops; Automobiles, new & used; Automotive parts; Automotive repair shops
Pr: Mike Smith
**CFO:* Jeff Dennen
Treas: W Massey Jr
**Sec:* W W Massey Jr
**VP:* R B Massey
**VP:* Roberta Smith
Genl Mgr: Stew Smith
Sls Mgr: Gary Bosses
Sls Mgr: Lori Smith

D-U-N-S 06-785-9199
ORLANDO DRUM CO
ORLANDO DRUMMING CONTAINERS
4880 Hoffner Ave, Orlando, FL 32812-2310
Tel (407) 855-0208 *Founded/Ownrshp* 1973
Sales 22.4MM^E *EMP* 40
SIC 5085 7699 Drums, new or reconditioned; Metal reshaping & replating services
Owner: Keith Hackley

ORLANDO DRUMMING CONTAINERS
See ORLANDO DRUM CO

D-U-N-S 92-604-6624
ORLANDO FREIGHTLANDERS
2455 S Orange Blossom Trl, Apopka, FL 32703-1873
Tel (407) 295-3846 *Founded/Ownrshp* 1995
Sales 55.7MM^E *EMP* 117
SIC 5511 Trucks, tractors & trailers: new & used; Trucks, tractors & trailers: new & used
Pr: John Taggart
CTO: Anthony Ballerino

D-U-N-S 04-514-9143
ORLANDO FREIGHTLINER INC
(*Suby of* ORLANDO FREIGHTLANDERS) ★
2455 S Orange Blossom Trl, Apopka, FL 32703-1873
Tel (407) 299-3434 *Founded/Ownrshp* 1995
Sales 55.7MM^E *EMP* 117
SIC 5511 7538 Trucks, tractors & trailers: new & used; Diesel engine repair: automotive; Trucks, tractors & trailers: new & used; Diesel engine repair: automotive
Pr: John A Taggart
**VP:* Jason S Taggart

ORLANDO HARLEY DAVIDSON
See HD AMERICAN ROAD LLC

D-U-N-S 07-867-9697
ORLANDO HEALTH CENTRAL INC
(*Suby of* ORLANDO HEALTH INC) ★
10000 W Colonial Dr, Ocoee, FL 34761-3400
Tel (407) 296-1820 *Founded/Ownrshp* 2011
Sales 167.8MM *EMP* 1,500^E
SIC 8062 General medical & surgical hospitals; General medical & surgical hospitals
Pr: Greg Ohe
CFO: Michael Mueller
Exec: Bonnie Henry
Dir Risk M: Haresh Ramjas
Chf Nrs Of: Christina McGuirk
Mktg Dir: Brenda Labattaglia
Mktg Dir: Julie Morris
HC Dir: Cassie Deel
Snr Mgr: James Rodier

D-U-N-S 08-240-6638 IMP
ORLANDO HEALTH INC
1414 Kuhl Ave, Orlando, FL 32806-2008
Tel (321) 843-7000 *Founded/Ownrshp* 1977
Sales 1.6MMM *EMP* 10,000
SIC 8062 8741 8069 General medical & surgical hospitals; Hospital management; Specialty hospitals, except psychiatric; General medical & surgical hospitals; Hospital management; Specialty hospitals, except psychiatric
Pr: Sherrie Sitarik
COO: Jessica Wertman
CFO: Paul A Goldstein
CFO: George Kimbro
CFO: Tom Yoelse
Ch: James S Lawrence
Bd of Dir: Ernest F Block
Bd of Dir: Helen Galloway
Bd of Dir: Howard G Smith
VP: John Bozard
VP: David Huddleson
VP: Karen Jensen
VP: John Marazano
VP: Sanford P Shugart
Dir OR: Sherry Buxton
Dir Risk M: Carol Paris
Dir Case M: Sandy Perrotti
Dir Rad: Alexander Azbel
Dir Rad: Daniel J Buchholz
Dir Rx: Michael Hoppe
Dir Rx: Frank Thomas

ORLANDO INTERNATIONAL AIRPORT
See GREATER ORLANDO AVIATION AUTHORITY

D-U-N-S 09-783-4238
ORLANDO LUTHERAN TOWERS INC
COMMONS AT ORLNDO LTHRAN TWERS
300 E Church St Apt 610, Orlando, FL 32801-3534
Tel (407) 872-7088 *Founded/Ownrshp* 1980
Sales 27.1MM *EMP* 435
Accts Moore Stephens Lovelace Pa Cl
SIC 6513 8051 Apartment building operators; Skilled nursing care facilities; Extended care facility; Apartment building operators; Skilled nursing care facilities; Extended care facility
Pr: William C Weir
**Treas:* James A Wells
**VP:* Guy W Thompson
Ex Dir: Kerry Kummer
Ex Dir: Alicia Labrecque
Dir IT: Jamie Mattia
Corp Couns: Debbie Ashley

D-U-N-S 79-706-0803
ORLANDO METROPOLITAN RESORT LLC
8444 International Dr, Orlando, FL 32819-9329
Tel (407) 581-2000 *Founded/Ownrshp* 1992
Sales 21.0MM^E *EMP* 660
Accts Independent Public Accountant
SIC 7011 Hotels; Hotels
Ch Bd: Sebastian Barcel
**Pr:* Simon P Vadell

ORLANDO REGIONAL HEALTHCARE
See ORLANDO REGIONAL LUCERNE HOSPITAL AUXILIARY INC

D-U-N-S 92-642-3310
ORLANDO REGIONAL LUCERNE HOSPITAL AUXILIARY INC
ORLANDO REGIONAL HEALTHCARE
818 Main Ln, Orlando, FL 32801-3727
Tel (407) 649-6111 *Founded/Ownrshp* 1999
Sales 42.7MM^E *EMP* 800
SIC 8062 General medical & surgical hospitals; General medical & surgical hospitals
Exec: Anne Watkins
Doctor: Dawn Hargrove
Pharmcst: Hossein Izadjoo
Pharmcst: Maria Rodriguez

ORLANDO SENTINNEL MEDIA GROUP
See SENTINEL COMMUNICATIONS NEWS VENTURES INC

D-U-N-S 00-414-3322
ORLANDO SPORTSPLEX LTD
RDV SPORTSPLEX ATHLETIC CLUB
8701 Maitland Summit Blvd, Orlando, FL 32810-5915
Tel (407) 916-2550 *Founded/Ownrshp* 1998
Sales 13.9MM^E *EMP* 315
SIC 7991 7999 Athletic club & gymnasiums, membership; Ice skating rink operation; Athletic club & gymnasiums, membership; Ice skating rink operation
Genl Mgr: John Gabrial
Snr Mgr: Kyle Schroeck
Snr Mgr: Ali Svendsen
Snr Mgr: Doug Wemple

D-U-N-S 00-408-4562 IMP/EXP
ORLANDO STEEL ENTERPRISES INC (FL)
1610 N Goldenrod Rd, Orlando, FL 32807-8396
Tel (800) 222-3659 *Founded/Ownrshp* 1974
Sales 27.1MM^E *EMP* 56
SIC 5039 5051 Wire fence, gates & accessories; Pipe & tubing, steel
Pr: Mark Wolsefer

D-U-N-S 00-407-6071 IMP
ORLANDO UTILITIES COMMISSION
OUC
100 W Anderson St, Orlando, FL 32801-4408
Tel (407) 246-2121 *Founded/Ownrshp* 1923
Sales 825.3MM *EMP* 1,000
Accts Ernst & Young Llp
SIC 4941 4931 4939 4911 Water supply; Electric & other services combined; Combination utilities; Electric services; Water supply; Electric & other services combined; Combination utilities; Electric services
CEO: Kenneth P Ksionek
**VP:* Linda Ferrone
VP: Frederick F Haddad
VP: Ruth Jayson-Polk
VP: Dan Kirby
VP: Chip Merriam
VP: Carrie Nelson
VP: Deborah Parrish
**VP:* David Repollet
VP: Greg Rodeghier
**VP:* Darlene Scott
VP: Rob Teegarden
VP: Christi Valdes
Dir Risk M: Tim Harshey

D-U-N-S 03-020-8995
ORLEANS COMMUNITY HEALTH
200 Ohio St, Medina, NY 14103-1063
Tel (585) 798-2000 *Founded/Ownrshp* 1908
Sales 33.3MM *EMP* 410^E
SIC 8062 General medical & surgical hospitals; General medical & surgical hospitals
Pr: Jim Sinner
**CEO:* Dolores Horveth
**Ch:* Bruce Krenning
**Treas:* David Monti Dvm
Dir Env Sv: Dave Moore
HC Dir: Leann Lumbert

D-U-N-S 07-160-9184 IMP
ORLEANS CORP (PA)
OHB
(*Suby of* O H B) ★
7 Neshaminy Interplex Dr # 215, Feasterville Trevose, PA 19053-6974
Tel (215) 245-7500 *Founded/Ownrshp* 1974, 1986
Sales 40.2MM^E *EMP* 310
SIC 1521 1522 New construction, single-family houses; Hotel/motel & multi-family home construction; New construction, single-family houses; Hotel/motel & multi-family home construction
Ch Bd: Jeffrey Orleans
**CFO:* Joseph A Santangelo
**Sr VP:* Michael Karmatz
VP: Garry Herdler
**VP:* John P White
Mktg Mgr: Linda Kelly
Sls Mgr: Irene Rosen

D-U-N-S 06-399-9700
ORLEANS COUNTY CHAPTER NYSARC
ORLEANS ENTERPRISES
(*Suby of* NYSARC INC) ★
122 Caroline St, Albion, NY 14411-1006
Tel (585) 589-5516 *Founded/Ownrshp* 1974
Sales 12.1MM *EMP* 320
Accts Bonadio & Co Llp Pittsford
SIC 8322 Association for the handicapped; Association for the handicapped
Ex Dir: Donald Colquhoun

ORLEANS ENTERPRISES
See ORLEANS COUNTY CHAPTER NYSARC

D-U-N-S 11-325-4650 IMP
ORLEANS FURNITURE INC
1481 N Main St, Columbia, MS 39429-2020
Tel (601) 736-9002 *Founded/Ownrshp* 1984
Sales 21.5MM^E *EMP* 353
SIC 2511 4213 Wood household furniture; Trucking, except local; Wood household furniture; Trucking, except local
Ch Bd: Charles H Griner
**Pr:* Ed Marshall
**Sec:* Helmon Johnson

D-U-N-S 04-860-2817
ORLEANS HOMEBUILDERS INC
O H B
3333 Street Rd Ste 101, Bensalem, PA 19020-2022
Tel (215) 245-7500 *Founded/Ownrshp* 1969
Sales 408.2MM^E *EMP* 480^E
SIC 1531 1521 Operative builders; Single-family housing construction; Townhouse construction; Operative builders; Single-family housing construction; Townhouse construction
CEO: Alan E Laing
Pr: Jeffrey P Orelans
Pr: Mitch Sanner
CEO: George Casey
COO: C Dean Amann II
CFO: Marek Bakun
CFO: Gray Shell
Chf Mktg O: Lee Darnold
VP: Lawrence J Dugan
VP: Ward Harris
VP: Garry Herdler
VP: Scott Sisca

ORLEANS HOTEL AND CASINO, THE
See COAST HOTELS AND CASINOS INC

D-U-N-S 01-694-2302 IMP/EXP
ORLEANS INTERNATIONAL INC (MI)
CENTURY TRADING
30600 Northwestern Hwy # 300, Farmington Hills, MI 48334-3172
Tel (248) 855-5556 *Founded/Ownrshp* 1935
Sales 34.7MM^E *EMP* 37
Accts Freedman & Goldberg Farmingto
SIC 5142 Meat, frozen: packaged; Meat, frozen: packaged
CEO: Earl Tushman
CFO: Jerry Castellano
**CFO:* Lori Wigler
**Sec:* Lawrence Tushman
**VP:* Larry Tushman
Comm Dir: Elmer Rodriguez
Sales Exec: Larry Berger

D-U-N-S 07-946-0093
ORLEANS PARISH SCHOOL DISTRICT
3520 Gen Degaulle Dr # 5055, New Orleans, LA 70114-4000
Tel (504) 304-3520 *Founded/Ownrshp* 1841

Sales 288.7MM^E *EMP* 7,062
Accts La Porte Metairie La
SIC 8211 Public elementary & secondary schools; Public elementary & secondary schools
**CEO:* Alphonse G Davis
**COO:* Roger Reese
Prin: Victor Gordon
Ex Dir: Jan Kasofsky
Ex Dir: Debbie Schum
Ex Dir: Michael Teague
Dir Sec: B J Bilbo
Telecom Mg: Cynthia Miller
Teacher Pr: Armand Devezin

D-U-N-S 03-864-0421
ORLEANS-NIAGARA BOCES
BOARD COOPERATIVE EDUCTL SVCS
3181 Snders Settlement Rd, Sanborn, NY 14132-9522
Tel (716) 798-1445 *Founded/Ownrshp* 1950
Sales 65.5MM *EMP* 500
Accts Raymond F Wagner Cpa Pc He
SIC 8211 Public elementary & secondary schools; Specialty education; Public elementary & secondary schools; Specialty education
CFO: Patricia McKenna
CTO: Shelly Smith
Snr Mgr: Jessi Bush

D-U-N-S 06-708-8138
ORLOR INC
EXECUTIVE HONDA
1194 N Colony Rd, Wallingford, CT 06492-1730
Tel (203) 949-7400 *Founded/Ownrshp* 1971
Sales 33.3MM^E *EMP* 80
SIC 5511 7532 Automobiles, new & used; Top & body repair & paint shops; Automobiles, new & used; Top & body repair & paint shops
Pr: John Orsini
Sales Asso: Amanda Deluca

D-U-N-S 08-718-1038 IMP/EXP
ORLY INTERNATIONAL INC (CA)
SPARITUAL
7710 Haskell Ave, Van Nuys, CA 91406-1905
Tel (408) 423-9271 *Founded/Ownrshp* 1977
Sales 31.0MM^E *EMP* 100
SIC 2844 Cosmetic preparations; Cosmetic preparations
Pr: Jeff Pink
**CFO:* Tom Habrock
VP: Colin Sillery
Creative D: Carina Breda
Creative D: Shel Pink
VP Opers: Bill Korn
Prd Mgr: Bonnie Sanchez
VP Sls: Annie McCullough
Mktg Dir: Chris Cowles
Mktg Mgr: Mindy Chun
Mktg Mgr: Hayley Gonzales

D-U-N-S 92-932-2808
■ **ORMAT INTERNATIONAL INC**
(*Suby of* ORMAT TECHNOLOGIES INC) ★
6225 Neil Rd, Reno, NV 89511-1151
Tel (775) 356-9029 *Founded/Ownrshp* 1994
Sales 51.2MM^E *EMP* 400
SIC 3511 Turbines & turbine generator sets; Turbines & turbine generator sets
CEO: Yehudit Dita Bronicki
**Pr:* Yehudit Bronicki
**CFO:* Joseph Tenne
**Ex VP:* Nadav Amir
**Ex VP:* Zvi Reiss
Opers Mgr: Paolo Alvarado
Opers Mgr: Todd Gaskin
Opers Mgr: Ernest Morse
Plnt Mgr: Michael Moore

D-U-N-S 78-443-0238 IMP
■ **ORMAT NEVADA INC**
(*Suby of* ORMAT TECHNOLOGIES INC) ★
6225 Neil Rd, Reno, NV 89511-1151
Tel (775) 356-9029 *Founded/Ownrshp* 1991
Sales 231.3MM^E *EMP* 400^E
SIC 4939 Combination utilities; Combination utilities
CEO: Isaac Angel
**CFO:* Doron Blachar
**Ex VP:* Zvi Krieger
VP: David Citrin
VP: Aaron Lewis
Dir Bus: Ram Orenstein
**Prin:* Yehudit Bronicki
**Prin:* Yoram Bronicki
**Prin:* Connie Stechman
Plnt Mgr: Eric Sponsler

D-U-N-S 92-931-5661 IMP/EXP
▲ **ORMAT TECHNOLOGIES INC**
6225 Neil Rd, Reno, NV 89511-1151
Tel (775) 356-9029 *Founded/Ownrshp* 1994
Sales 559.5MM *EMP* 1,095^E
Tkr Sym ORA *Exch* NYS
SIC 4911 3511 Generation, electric power; Turbines & turbine generator sets; Turbines & turbine generator set units, complete; Turbo-generators; Generation, electric power; Turbines & turbine generator sets; Turbines & turbine generator set units, complete; Turbo-generators
CEO: Isaac Angel
Ch Bd: Gillon Beck
CFO: Doron Blacha
CFO: Doron Blachar
Treas: Anat L Ben-Schlomo
Ex VP: Zvi Krieger
Ex VP: Joseph Shiloah
Ex VP: Bob Sullivan
Sr VP: Shimon Hatzir
Sr VP: Etty Rosner
VP: Nachman Isaac
Exec: Michael Helton
Dir Risk M: Chen Cohen
Dir Bus: Charlene Wardlow
Board of Directors: Ami Boehm, Yehudit Bronicki, Robert F Clarke, Dan Falk, David Granot, Robert E Joyal, Stanley Stern

D-U-N-S 18-467-6042
ORMAZABAL CURRENT LLC
(*Suby of* GRUPO ORMAZABAL SOCIEDAD LIMITADA)
20459 Seneca Meadows Pkwy, Germantown, MD 20876-7005
Tel (301) 944-2700 *Founded/Ownrshp* 2013
Sales 57.2MM^E *EMP* 205
SIC 5045 9631 1623 Computers, peripherals & software; Regulation, administration of utilities; Communication line & transmission tower construction; Computers, peripherals & software; Regulation, administration of utilities; Communication line & transmission tower construction
Pr: Tom Willie
Pr: Jonathan Ziegler
**CFO:* John Du
Sr VP: Tony Keefe
VP: Mae Squier Dow
VP: Brendan Herron
VP: Jason Lombardo
CTO: Dave Yaney
IT Man: Lawrence Paulhus
Netwrk Mgr: Hans Hansen
**Genl Couns:* Andrew Rosenstein

D-U-N-S 15-461-4119 EXP
■ **ORMCO CORP**
SYBRON ENDO
(*Suby of* ANALYTIC ENDODONTICS) ★
1717 W Collins Ave, Orange, CA 92867-5422
Tel (714) 516-7400 *Founded/Ownrshp* 2013
Sales 123.6MM^E *EMP* 599
SIC 3843 Orthodontic appliances; Orthodontic appliances
CEO: Patrik Eriksson
Pr: Vicente Reynal
Ex VP: Roy Chen
VP: Mike Beaudoin
VP: Jason R Davis
VP: Rob Weyer
Area Mgr: Barry Mervine
Dist Mgr: Kyle Harrington
Sftwr Eng: Hua Zhang
Mktg Mgr: Nick Bruecken
Mktg Mgr: Traci Goodrich

D-U-N-S 60-935-5383 IMP
ORMET CORP
43840 State Rte 7, Hannibal, OH 43931
Tel (740) 483-1381 *Founded/Ownrshp* 1990
Sales 178.2MM^E *EMP* 1,250
SIC 3334 Primary aluminum; Primary aluminum
Pr: Mike Tanchuk
**Ch Bd:* Jeffrey Marshall
CFO: Sherry Barbour
**CFO:* James Burns Riley
Ex VP: Zeno Demori
VP: Matt Powell
Div Mgr: Glenn Fitch
Genl Mgr: David Neal
MIS Dir: Keith Fowler
IT Man: Matt Crozier
Tech Mgr: Mike Mehay

D-U-N-S 00-437-9970 IMP
ORMET PRIMARY ALUMINUM CORP
VELVETFLOW
43840 State Rt 7, Hannibal, OH 43931
Tel (740) 483-1381 *Founded/Ownrshp* 1956
Sales 144.6MM^E *EMP* 1,100
SIC 3334 3297 Aluminum ingots & slabs; Nonclay refractories

D-U-N-S 07-430-2704
ORMSBY TRUCKING INC
KAILYANUL
888 W Railroad St Ste 14, Uniondale, IN 46791-9775
Tel (260) 543-2233 *Founded/Ownrshp* 1951
Sales 43.2MM^E *EMP* 321
SIC 4213 Trucking, except local; Trucking, except local
Pr: Reginald E Ormsby
**Treas:* Jill Pearson
**Sec:* Julia A Holte
**VP:* Tim Ormsby
Trfc Dir: Patrick Medina

D-U-N-S 80-267-1552 IMP
ORNAMENTAL MOULDINGS LLC
(*Suby of* TENON LIMITED)
3804 Comanche Rd, Archdale, NC 27263-3166
Tel (336) 431-9120 *Founded/Ownrshp* 2003
Sales 40.6MM^E *EMP* 63
SIC 5031 2431 Molding, all materials; Moldings & baseboards, ornamental & trim
Pr: Dennis Berry
**CEO:* Tom Highley
VP: Jerry Little
Genl Mgr: Tim Weaver
IT Man: Rick Dymott
Plnt Mgr: Dave Lavalleur

D-U-N-S 00-389-5026
ORNDORFF & SPAID INC (MD)
11722 Old Baltimore Pike, Beltsville, MD 20705-1292
Tel (301) 937-5911 *Founded/Ownrshp* 1953
Sales 36.6MM^E *EMP* 160
SIC 1761 Roofing contractor; Sheet metalwork; Roofing contractor; Sheet metalwork
CEO: Mitchell Spaid
**Sec:* Keith Spaid
VP: Ricky Honaker
**VP:* Jeffrey Orndorff

D-U-N-S 03-067-4956
ORNL FEDERAL CREDIT UNION
221 S Rutgers Ave, Oak Ridge, TN 37830-6751
Tel (865) 482-0600 *Founded/Ownrshp* 1948
Sales NA *EMP* 520
SIC 6061 Federal credit unions; Federal credit unions
Pr: Chris Johnson
Pr: Paul Morris
**CFO:* Dennis Bowker
Ofcr: Cora Blair
Ofcr: Marilyn Cobble
Ofcr: Christopher Hagans
Ofcr: Tracy Liverman
Ofcr: Skip Murry
Ofcr: Ronald Nesbitt
Sr VP: Colin Anderson
VP: Dawn Brummett
VP: Vicki Cox
VP: Clay Kearley
VP: Melissa McMahan
Adv Bd Mbr: Martin Luna

D-U-N-S 15-209-1658
ORNUA FOODS NORTH AMERICA INC
IRISH DAIRY BOARD INC., THE
(*Suby of* IDB HOLDINGS INC) ★
1007 Church St Ste 800, Evanston, IL 60201-5930
Tel (847) 492-8036 *Founded/Ownrshp* 1984
Sales 25.9MM^E *EMP* 30
SIC 5149 5143 Milk, canned or dried; Dairy products, except dried or canned
Pr: Neil Cox
**Pr:* Roisin Hennerty
Sr VP: Jayson Folus
Sr VP: Larry Noble
Sr VP: Donna Robbins
VP: Jackie Thomas
Dist Mgr: Michael Funk
IT Man: Greg Fetzer
IT Man: Dave Leach
VP Opers: Sam Lopez
Manager: Roger Leece

D-U-N-S 18-251-8485
ORO VALLEY HOSPITAL LLC
NMCOV
1551 E Tangerine Rd, Oro Valley, AZ 85755-6213
Tel (520) 901-3500 *Founded/Ownrshp* 2009
Sales 91.9MM *EMP* 500
SIC 8062 General medical & surgical hospitals; General medical & surgical hospitals
**CFO:* Jeff Daneff
Dir OR: Lynne Gossett
Dir Case M: Kimberly Browning
Dir Rx: Michael Zoucha
Prac Mgr: Grace Campillo
QA Dir: Cathy Stubbs
Dir QC: Donna Zubay
Surgeon: Alex Westerband
Doctor: Mark Ramirez
Pharmcst: Shabnam Jivanjee
Pharmcst: Rebecca Malone

D-U-N-S 87-883-1981
ORODAY INC
DIGITAL CONSULTING SERVICES
2393 Teller Rd Ste 104, Newbury Park, CA 91320-6091
Tel (805) 498-9344 *Founded/Ownrshp* 1994
Sales 60.6MM^E *EMP* 120
SIC 5045 Computers, peripherals & software; Computers, peripherals & software
Pr: Joel Oropesa
**VP:* Jeff Daymude
Exec: Steve Miller
Dir IT: Paul Hodell

D-U-N-S 00-207-8244
OROGRAIN BAKERIES MANUFACTURING INC
(*Suby of* BIMBO BAKERIES USA) ★
255 Business Center Dr, Horsham, PA 19044-3424
Tel (518) 463-2221 *Founded/Ownrshp* 1994
Sales 136.2MM^E *EMP* 1,300
SIC 2051 Bread, cake & related products; Bread, cake & related products; Bread, all types (white, wheat, rye, etc): fresh or frozen; Rolls, bread type: fresh or frozen; Doughnuts, except frozen
Pr: Peter Rollins
Pr: Mike Phillips
Ex VP: Leonard Heflich
Ex VP: Rick Lee
VP: Jim Kershner
IT Man: Frank N Glashausser
IT Man: Bill N Howard
IT Man: Jim Linus
IT Man: Bill N Truglio
Opers Mgr: Steve Batey
Plnt Mgr: Elijah Richardson

D-U-N-S 15-340-4397
OROHEALTH CORP
2767 Olive Hwy, Oroville, CA 95966-6118
Tel (530) 533-8500 *Founded/Ownrshp* 1985
Sales 2.8MM *EMP* 1,167
SIC 8741 Hospital management; Hospital management
Pr: Robert J Wentz
CFO: Jo Dilbeck
Ofcr: Debra Jones

D-U-N-S 06-792-0074
OROLIA USA INC (NY)
SPECTRACOM
(*Suby of* OROLIA)
1565 Jefferson Rd Ste 460, Rochester, NY 14623-3190
Tel (585) 321-5800 *Founded/Ownrshp* 1972, 2000
Sales 20.4MM^E *EMP* 55
SIC 3829 Measuring & controlling devices
Pr: Elizabeth Withers
**VP:* John Fischer
QA Dir: Derek Darling
Sls&Mrk Ex: Josh Harris
Sls&Mrk Ex: Philip Teece

D-U-N-S 08-411-0758
ORONO INDEPENDENT SCHOOL DISTRICT 278
685 N Old Crystal Bay Rd, Long Lake, MN 55356-8315
Tel (952) 449-8300 *Founded/Ownrshp* 1951
Sales 41.1MM *EMP* 332
SIC 8211 Public combined elementary & secondary school; Public combined elementary & secondary school

D-U-N-S 00-886-0678 IMP
ORORA NORTH AMERICA (CA)
LANDSBERG ORORA
(*Suby of* ORORA LIMITED)
6600 Valley View St, Buena Park, CA 90620-1145
Tel (714) 562-6000 *Founded/Ownrshp* 1951, 2013
Sales 2.5MMM^E *EMP* 2,397
SIC 5113 2653 Paper & products, wrapping or coarse; Sanitary food containers; Boxes, corrugated: made from purchased materials; Paper & products, wrapping or coarse; Sanitary food containers; Boxes, corrugated: made from purchased materials
CEO: Nigel Garrard
**Pr:* Bernie Salvatore
**CFO:* Stuart Hutton
Sr VP: Gary Noonan
VP: Michael Hodges
**Prin:* Harlan Erik Christensen
Genl Mgr: Gavin Barris
Sfty Dirs: Jeff Messinger
Mktg Dir: Alexandra Stump
Mktg Mgr: Latricia Fry
Counsel: Lara Coons

D-U-N-S 09-683-6002 IMP
OROURKE & SONS INC
992 S Bolmar St, West Chester, PA 19382-4906
Tel (610) 436-0932 *Founded/Ownrshp* 1976
Sales 31.7MM^E *EMP* 35
SIC 5051 3443 Steel; Fabricated plate work (boiler shop)
Pr: Michael O'Rourke
**Pr:* Michael Orourke
**Treas:* Clement Orourke
**VP:* Michael J Orourke
Brnch Mgr: Bruce Grassano
Sls Mgr: Jim Cushwa

O'ROURKE BROS DISTRIBUTING CO
See OROURKE BROS INC

D-U-N-S 06-277-0458 IMP/EXP
OROURKE BROS INC (IA)
O'ROURKE BROS DISTRIBUTING CO
3885 Elmore Ave Ste 100, Davenport, IA 52807-2580
Tel (563) 823-1501 *Founded/Ownrshp* 1965
Sales 60.8MM^E *EMP* 150
SIC 5063

D-U-N-S 02-663-3289 EXP
OROURKE DISTRIBUTING CO
O'ROURKE PETROLEUM PRODUCTS
223 Mccarty St, Houston, TX 77029-1137
Tel (713) 672-4500 *Founded/Ownrshp* 1932
Sales 93.5MM^E *EMP* 136
SIC 5171 5172

O'ROURKE PETROLEUM PRODUCTS
See OROURKE DISTRIBUTING CO

D-U-N-S 80-668-7666
OROURKE WRECKING CO
660 Lunken Park Dr, Cincinnati, OH 45226-1800
Tel (513) 871-1400 *Founded/Ownrshp* 1996
Sales 24.7MM *EMP* 75
Accts Battelle Rippe Kingston Llp
SIC 1795 Wrecking & demolition work; Wrecking & demolition work
Pr: Michael Orourke
**Sec:* Mark Weber
**VP:* Jacquelyn S Schurger
Mtls Mgr: Michael Linnemann

D-U-N-S 01-195-8550
OROVILLE CITY ELEMENTARY SCHOOL DISTRICT
2795 Yard St, Oroville, CA 95966-5113
Tel (530) 533-0495 *Founded/Ownrshp* 1930
Sales 29.5MM *EMP* 355
SIC 8211 Public elementary & secondary schools; School board; Public elementary & secondary schools; School board
Exec: Irene Aiello

D-U-N-S 07-609-9282
OROVILLE HOSPITAL
2767 Olive Hwy, Oroville, CA 95966-6118
Tel (530) 533-8500 *Founded/Ownrshp* 1966
Sales 217.4MM *EMP* 1,400
SIC 8062 General medical & surgical hospitals; General medical & surgical hospitals
CEO: Robert J Wentz
**COO:* Scott Chapple
**CFO:* Ashok Khanchandani
Ofcr: David Bryning
Ofcr: Gil Zarate
VP: Carol Smith
Dir Lab: Steven Sweet
Dir Lab: Kim Taylor
Dir Rad: William Moe
Dir Rx: Dan Nguyen
Nurse Mgr: Robyn North

D-U-N-S 08-127-0811
OROVILLE UNION HIGH SCHOOL DIST
2211 Washington Ave, Oroville, CA 95966-5440
Tel (530) 538-2300 *Founded/Ownrshp* 1892
Sales 27.4MM *EMP* 225
Accts Matson And Isom Chico/Redding
SIC 8211 Public senior high school; School board; Public senior high school; School board
IT Man: Donna Logasa
IT Man: Susan Watts

ORP
See OCONOMOWOC RESIDENTIAL PROGRAMS INC

D-U-N-S 94-019-9235
ORPHAN GRAIN TRAIN INC
601 W Phillip Ave, Norfolk, NE 68701-5100
Tel (402) 371-7393 *Founded/Ownrshp* 1992
Sales 26.3MM *EMP* 5^E
SIC 8641 Civic social & fraternal associations; Civic social & fraternal associations
Pr: Ray Wilke
Brnch Mgr: Elroy Koch
Brnch Mgr: Cliff Kraft
Brnch Mgr: Cindi Trahms

ORPHEUM THEATER
See SCHORENSTEIN-HAYS NEDERLANDER

ORPHEUM THEATRE
See MEMPHIS DEVELOPMENT FOUNDATION

D-U-N-S 78-906-6008
ORR & BOSS INC
33900 Harper Ave Ste 103, Clinton Township, MI 48035-4258
Tel (586) 416-9090 Founded/Ownrshp 1947
Sales 25.9MM^E EMP 180
SIC 8742 7699 Management consulting services; Industrial equipment cleaning; Management consulting services; Industrial equipment cleaning
Ch: Michael Policella
*Pr: Charles S Rooney
*COO: Charles E Bangert Jr
*CFO: Joanne M Janzen
*VP: Kevin Reid
Off Mgr: Nicole Phillips

ORR CADILLAC
See ORR MOTORS OF SHREVEPORT INC

ORR CHEVROLET
See ORR INC

D-U-N-S 02-407-7364
ORR CORP
11601 Interchange Dr, Louisville, KY 40229-2159
Tel (502) 774-5791 Founded/Ownrshp 1947, 1973
Sales 191.3MM EMP 450
SIC 5084

D-U-N-S 00-842-1810
ORR INC
ORR CHEVROLET
4545 N State Line Ave, Texarkana, TX 75503-2915
Tel (903) 794-5500 Founded/Ownrshp 1966
Sales 39.0MM^E EMP 76
SIC 5511 5531 7538 7532 Automobiles, new & used; Pickups, new & used; Trucks, tractors & trailers: new & used; Automotive parts; General automotive repair shops; Body shop, automotive; Body shop, trucks
Pr: Keith Orr
*Sec: Roberta Gaither
*Sec: Natalie Wellborn
*VP: Gregg Orr

D-U-N-S 12-505-5264
ORR MOTORS OF LITTLE ROCK INC
SPARKS NISSAN KIA
1100 Auto Mall Dr, Monroe, LA 71203-5522
Tel (318) 322-1800 Founded/Ownrshp 2002
Sales 25.2MM^E EMP 65
SIC 5511 Automobiles, new & used; Automobiles, new & used
Pr: William Sparks
*Treas: Kieth Orr
Sales Asso: James Edwards

D-U-N-S 60-612-1007
ORR MOTORS OF SHREVEPORT INC
ORR CADILLAC
8750 Business Park Dr, Shreveport, LA 71105-5610
Tel (318) 798-7250 Founded/Ownrshp 2004
Sales 27.4MM^E EMP 80
SIC 5511 Automobiles, new & used; Automobiles, new & used
Pr: William Gregg Orr
*CFO: Brooke Samuelson
*Sec: Pam Gilcrease
*VP: Norward Favre
VP: Armand James
*VP: Matthew Stinson
Genl Mgr: Tim Robortson
Off Mgr: Raby Morrison

D-U-N-S 06-484-9110
ORR PROTECTION SYSTEMS INC
BORRELL FIRE SYSTEMS
(Suby of ORR CORP) ★
11601 Interchange Dr, Louisville, KY 40229-2159
Tel (502) 244-4500 Founded/Ownrshp 1982
Sales 68.0MM^E EMP 160
SIC 1731

D-U-N-S 55-572-4652 IMP/EXP
ORR SAFETY CORP
(Suby of ORR CORP) ★
11601 Interchange Dr, Louisville, KY 40229-2159
Tel (502) 774-5791 Founded/Ownrshp 1952
Sales 127.5MM^E EMP 300
Accts Strothman And Company Louisvi
SIC 5099 Safety equipment & supplies; Safety equipment & supplies
CEO: Raymond Aldridge
*CFO: Angela Druin
*Treas: Clark Orr Jr
VP: Ted Buck
VP: Paul Nelson
IT Man: Rick Ingram
IT Man: Jonathan Nichter
Tech Mgr: Tim Newkirk
VP Opers: Jeff Hemer
Opers Mgr: Michael Auxford
Natl Sales: Tony Walker

D-U-N-S 06-179-1901
ORRELLS FOOD SERVICE INC (NC)
9827 S Nc Highway 150, Linwood, NC 27299-9461
Tel (336) 752-2114 Founded/Ownrshp 1954
Sales 72.2MM EMP 87
Accts Turlington And Company Llp L
SIC 5147 5113 5149 Meats & meat products; Disposable plates, cups, napkins & eating utensils; Canned goods: fruit, vegetables, seafood, meats, etc.; Meats & meat products; Disposable plates, cups, napkins & eating utensils; Canned goods: fruit, vegetables, seafood, meats, etc.
Pr: Tony R Orrell
Ofcr: Sherry Fortenberry
*Ex VP: Pamela O Myers
*Sr VP: Mike Williams
*VP: Lisa Everhart
*VP: Mike Miller
Genl Mgr: Tom Bridges
IT Man: Lori Williams
Sls&Mrk Ex: Ann Humphrey

D-U-N-S 07-187-0661
ORRICK HERRINGTON & SUTCLIFFE LLP
405 Howard St, San Francisco, CA 94105-2625
Tel (415) 773-5700 Founded/Ownrshp 2009
Sales 373.4MM^E EMP 2,500^E
SIC 8111 General practice law office; General practice law office
CEO: Ralph H Baxter Jr
Pt: Martin Bartlam
Pt: Peter A Bicks
Pt: Benedikt Burger
Pt: Neel Chatterjee
Pt: Luigi Colombo
Pt: Cameron L Cowan
Pt: Alessandro De Nicola
Pt: Kyle W Drefke
Pt: Arno Frings
Pt: Norman C Hile
Pt: Karen G Johnson-Mckewan
Pt: Douglas Lahnborg
Pt: Patrizio Messina
Pt: Denise M Mingrone
Pt: Anne O'Neill
Pt: J RG Ritter
Pt: Robert S Shwarts
Pt: Kai Tseng
Pt: Will Turani
Pt: Mark Weeks

ORRISON DISTRIBUTING
See FOURSOME INC

ORR'S JEWELERS
See GORDON INVESTMENTS INC

D-U-N-S 01-517-0038
■ **ORRSTOWN BANK**
(Suby of ORRSTOWN FINANCIAL SERVICES INC) ★
77 E King St, Shippensburg, PA 17257-1351
Tel (717) 532-6114 Founded/Ownrshp 1988
Sales NA EMP 105
SIC 6022 State commercial banks; State commercial banks
Pr: Thomas R Quinn Jr
Ch Bd: Joel R Zullinger
COO: Michelle Paulnock
CFO: David P Boyle
Chf Cred: Robert Coradi
Ofcr: David D Keim
Ex VP: Ben Wallace
Sr VP: Leonard Mialki
Sr VP: Janna Passamonte
VP: Barbara Brobst
VP: Patricia Corwell
VP: James B Dubbs
VP: Jeffrey Embly
VP: Bradley Everly
VP: Jeffrey Gayman
VP: Robert Gentry
VP: Debra Ramsey
VP: Robert Russell
VP: Benjamin Stoops

D-U-N-S 19-657-9080
▲ **ORRSTOWN FINANCIAL SERVICES INC**
77 E King St, Shippensburg, PA 17257-1307
Tel (717) 532-6114 Founded/Ownrshp 1987
Sales NA EMP 312^E
Tkr Sym ORRF Exch NAS
SIC 6022 State commercial banks; State commercial banks
Pr: Thomas R Quinn Jr
*Ch Bd: Joel R Zullinger
COO: Jeffrey M Seibert
CFO: David P Boyle
*V Ch Bd: Jeffrey W Coy
Ofcr: David D Keim
Ex VP: Barbara E Brobst
Ex VP: Jeffrey W Embly
Ex VP: Jeffrey S Gayman
Ex VP: Benjamin W Wallace
Sr VP: Douglas P Barton
Sr VP: Lauren Shutt
Board of Directors: Floyd E Stoner, Anthony F Ceddia, Jeffrey W Coy, Cindy J Joiner, Mark K Keller, Thomas D Longenecker, Andrea Pugh, Gregory A Rosenberry, Eric A Segal, Glenn W Snoke

D-U-N-S 07-691-0173
ORRVILLE CITY SCHOOLS
OAK ST ELEMENTARY SCHOOL
815 N Ella St, Orrville, OH 44667-1154
Tel (330) 682-5811 Founded/Ownrshp 1916
Sales 18.9MM EMP 444
Accts Dave Yost Canton Ohio
SIC 8211 Public combined elementary & secondary school; Public combined elementary & secondary school
Pr: Greg Roadruck

D-U-N-S 07-674-6106
ORRVILLE HOSPITAL FOUNDATION
AULTMAN ORRVILLE HOSPITAL
832 S Main St, Orrville, OH 44667-2208
Tel (330) 684-4700 Founded/Ownrshp 1951
Sales 24.3MM EMP 240
SIC 8062 General medical & surgical hospitals; General medical & surgical hospitals
CEO: Marchelle Suppan
VP: Chris Parrish
Obsttrcn: Laura Brelin
Ansthlgy: Daniel D Lynch

D-U-N-S 00-547-8914 IMP
ORRVILON INC
(Suby of HOLTEC INTERNATIONAL) ★
1400 Dairy Ln, Orrville, OH 44667-2505
Tel (330) 684-9400 Founded/Ownrshp 2009
Sales 56.2MM^E EMP 110
SIC 3354 3442 Aluminum extruded products; Metal doors; Aluminum extruded products; Metal doors
Pr: K P Singh
*CFO: Frank Bongrazio
*Ex VP: Alan Soler
Genl Mgr: R Sloan
Off Mgr: Julie Keesee
Prd Mgr: Marion Weaver
Ql Cn Mgr: Nicholas Johnson
Sls Mgr: Don Frank

D-U-N-S 00-722-4256 IMP/EXP
■ **ORS NASCO INC**
(Suby of ESSENDANT CO) ★
907 S Detroit Ave Ste 500, Tulsa, OK 74120-4283
Tel (918) 781-5300 Founded/Ownrshp 1920, 2007
Sales 405.2MM^E EMP 440
SIC 5085 5084 Industrial supplies; Fasteners & fastening equipment; Industrial machinery & equipment; Petroleum industry machinery; Industrial supplies; Fasteners & fastening equipment; Industrial machinery & equipment; Petroleum industry machinery
Prin: Paul Barrett
*Ex VP: Craig Loos
*VP: Mike Denning
Area Mgr: Ben Brumfield
Area Mgr: Bruce Ferraro
Area Mgr: Jason Hartman
Area Mgr: Mark Lockwood
Area Mgr: Greg Richardson
Brnch Mgr: Dean Fink
Brnch Mgr: Brian Grigor
Brnch Mgr: Mitch Sterling

D-U-N-S 02-991-8281
ORSCHELN FARM AND HOME LLC (MO)
ORSCHELN INDUSTRIES
1800 Overcenter Dr, Moberly, MO 65270-9466
Tel (660) 269-3491 Founded/Ownrshp 1960, 1963
Sales 713.7MM^E EMP 2,475
SIC 5251 5999 5945 5731 Hardware; Farm equipment & supplies; Toys & games; Consumer electronic equipment; Hardware; Farm equipment & supplies; Toys & games; Consumer electronic equipment
CEO: Barry L Orscheln
Pr: Stephen Chick
VP: James L O'Loughlin
VP: Barbara Westhues
Dist Mgr: Dwight Isringhausen
Store Mgr: Terry Eighmy
Store Mgr: Eric Harmon
Off Admin: Krista Fainter
IT Man: Kerry Gettemeier
IT Man: Michael Tilton
Sfty Mgr: Jason Ahten

ORSCHELN INDUSTRIES
See ORSCHELN FARM AND HOME LLC

D-U-N-S 04-187-4330 IMP
ORSCHELN PRODUCTS LLC
1177 N Morley St, Moberly, MO 65270-2736
Tel (660) 263-4377 Founded/Ownrshp 1994
Sales 75.6MM^E EMP 343
SIC 3496 Cable, uninsulated wire: made from purchased wire; Cable, uninsulated wire: made from purchased wire
CEO: William Orscheln
*VP: Ed Orscheln
*VP: Barbara A Westhues
IT Man: Melody Sparrow

D-U-N-S 83-532-6828
ORSINI HOME MEDICAL EQUIPMENT INC
1111 Nicholas Blvd, Elk Grove Village, IL 60007-2516
Tel (847) 631-6989 Founded/Ownrshp 1987
Sales 17.8MM^E EMP 299
SIC 8082 7352 Home health care services; Medical equipment rental; Home health care services; Medical equipment rental
Pr: Tony Orsini
CFO: Carla Sawa
Dir IT: Matthew Swajkowski

D-U-N-S 19-524-6046
ORSINI NURSING AGENCY INC
1111 Nicholas Blvd, Elk Grove Village, IL 60007-2516
Tel (847) 734-7377 Founded/Ownrshp 1987
Sales 12.0MM EMP 380
SIC 7361 8082 7363 Nurses' registry; Home health care services; Help supply services; Nurses' registry; Home health care services; Help supply services
CEO: Tony Orsini
*CFO: Kimberly Orsini

D-U-N-S 00-504-9895
ORT TOOL & DIE CORP
O R T
6555 S Dixie Hwy, Erie, MI 48133-9691
Tel (419) 242-9553 Founded/Ownrshp 1958
Sales 29.8MM^E EMP 100
SIC 8711 3544 3469 Machine tool design; Industrial engineers; Special dies, tools, jigs & fixtures; Machine parts, stamped or pressed metal; Machine tool design; Industrial engineers; Special dies, tools, jigs & fixtures; Machine parts, stamped or pressed metal
Ch Bd: Angelo J Milano
*Pr: Robert Milano
*CEO: Jim Shock
*VP: Michael A Milano

D-U-N-S 03-739-9623 IMP
ORTEC INC
505 Gentry Memorial Hwy, Easley, SC 29640-1165
Tel (864) 859-1471 Founded/Ownrshp 1980
Sales 29.8MM^E EMP 135^E
SIC 2869 Industrial organic chemicals; Industrial organic chemicals
Pr: David Larry Brotherton
Sales Exec: Louis Steed

D-U-N-S 10-372-6357
ORTEC INTERNATIONAL USA INC
(Suby of ORTEC INTERNATIONAL B.V.)
3630 Peachtree Rd Ne, Atlanta, GA 30326-1543
Tel (404) 736-9800 Founded/Ownrshp 2001
Sales 54.1MM^E EMP 550
SIC 7371 Computer software development & applications; Computer software development & applications
CEO: Corne Aantjes
CFO: John Casey
VP: Michael Geihsler
VP: Bobby Miller
Dir Bus: Jeff Bailey

D-U-N-S 07-848-7734
ORTEGA NATIONAL PARKS LLC (NM)
54 1/2 E San Francisco St, Santa Fe, NM 87501-2167
Tel (505) 310-6753 Founded/Ownrshp 2009
Sales 9.4MM^E EMP 708
SIC 7999 Tourist attractions, amusement park concessions & rides; Tourist attractions, amusement park concessions & rides
Prin: Shane Ortega
*COO: James Hernandez
*VP: Tom Willianson
*Prin: Armand Ortega

D-U-N-S 03-347-1185
ORTEQ ENERGY TECHNOLOGIES LLC
3401 W Highway 82, Gainesville, TX 76240-2001
Tel (940) 665-2316 Founded/Ownrshp 2010
Sales 31.9MM^E EMP 43^E
SIC 5082 1389 Oil field equipment; Oil field services

ORTHAHEEL
See VIONIC GROUP LLC

D-U-N-S 04-123-8809 IMP/EXP
ORTHMAN MANUFACTURING INC
75765 Road 435, Lexington, NE 68850-5636
Tel (308) 324-4654 Founded/Ownrshp 1999
Sales 25.0MM EMP 135
SIC 3535 3523

D-U-N-S 87-654-2390
ORTHO DEVELOPMENT CORP
12187 S Business Park Dr, Draper, UT 84020-8663
Tel (800) 429-8339 Founded/Ownrshp 1994
Sales 20.0MM^E EMP 100^E
SIC 3842 Surgical appliances & supplies; Surgical appliances & supplies
Pr: Brent Bartholomew
Pr: Mike Koffman
*Pr: Masao Okawa
*CFO: Greg Larson
Bd of Dir: Shinichi Kakimoto
*Sr VP: Ross Chamberlain
*VP: Stan Despres
Mng Dir: Tony Sanders
Off Mgr: Brad Defalla
IT Man: Lester Hof
IT Man: Lester Laro

ORTHO MOLD
See HANGER PROSTHETICS & ORTHOTICS INC

ORTHO NEURO
See ORTHONEURO

D-U-N-S 06-216-5188 IMP
■ **ORTHO ORGANIZERS INC**
(Suby of HENRY SCHEIN INC) ★
1822 Aston Ave, Carlsbad, CA 92008-7306
Tel (760) 448-8600 Founded/Ownrshp 2009
Sales 42.9MM^E EMP 226
SIC 3843 5047 Dental equipment & supplies; Dental equipment & supplies; Dental equipment & supplies; Dental equipment & supplies
Ch: David Parker
*Pr: Russell J Bonafede
*CFO: Alison Weber
*VP: Ted Dreifuss
VP: Raymond Fontana
*VP: Robert Riley
Rgnl Mgr: Burke Spielmann
Dir IT: Joe Glass
Netwrk Mgr: John Hosey
Snr Mgr: Tanya Coon
Snr Mgr: Tanya McManus

D-U-N-S 06-871-5424
ORTHO-CLINICAL DIAGNOSTICS INC
1001 Us Highway 202, Raritan, NJ 08869-1424
Tel (908) 218-8000 Founded/Ownrshp 2014
Sales 983.3MM^E EMP 1,650
SIC 2835 2834 Blood derivative diagnostic agents; Pharmaceutical preparations; Blood derivative diagnostic agents; Pharmaceutical preparations
CEO: Dr Martin D Madaus
COO: Robert Yates
CFO: Joseph Bondi
VP: Charles Hartwig
VP: Holly Hillberg
VP: Tony Zazo
Mfg Mgr: Laurie Mancuso

D-U-N-S 00-835-1942 IMP
ORTHODYNE ELECTRONICS CORP
16700 Red Hill Ave, Irvine, CA 92606-4802
Tel (949) 660-0440 Founded/Ownrshp 1960
Sales 20.9MM^E EMP 250
SIC 3699

D-U-N-S 92-708-3808 IMP
ORTHOFIX INC
(Suby of ORTHOFIX INTERNATIONAL NV)
3451 Plano Pkwy, Lewisville, TX 75056-9453
Tel (214) 937-2000 Founded/Ownrshp 1996
Sales 128.5MM^E EMP 525^E
SIC 3841 Surgical & medical instruments; Medical instruments & equipment, blood & bone work; Surgical & medical instruments; Medical instruments & equipment, blood & bone work
Pr: Brad Mason
Pr: Jeff Culhane
*CFO: Emily Buxton
Ofcr: Mark Atkinson
Ex VP: Vicente Trelles
Sr VP: Mark Boone
Sr VP: Brian McCollum
Sr VP: Jeffrey Schumm
Sr VP: Mike Spencer
VP: Brent Alldredge
VP: Diana Easton
VP: Michael Finegan
VP: Tyson Fujikawa
VP: Diane Johnson
VP: Matt Leffers
VP: Stace Mesozi
VP: Jim Searle
VP: Jason Shallenberger
VP: Paul Vasta
VP: James York
Exec: Sherrie Tarpley

ORTHOFIX SPINAL IMPLANTS
See BLACKSTONE MEDICAL INC

D-U-N-S 79-458-5216
ORTHOGEORGIA
JOHNSON C EMORY JR MD
3708 Northside Dr, Macon, GA 31210-2404
Tel (478) 750-2801 *Founded/Ownrshp* 1978
Sales 39.9MM^E *EMP* 185
SIC 8011 Specialized medical practitioners, except internal; Orthopedic physician; Specialized medical practitioners, except internal; Orthopedic physician
CEO: Bill Lindsey
**Pr:* Robert Thornsberry
**CFO:* Becky Firster

ORTHOINDY
See ORTHOPAEDICS-INDIANAPOLIS INC

D-U-N-S 06-204-2726
ORTHONEURO
ORTHO NEURO
70 S Cleveland Ave, Westerville, OH 43081-1397
Tel (614) 839-3203 *Founded/Ownrshp* 1973
Sales 25.1MM^E *EMP* 170
SIC 8011 Orthopedic physician; Neurologist; Neurosurgeon
Pr: Francis O Donnell
Off Mgr: Tina Lebin
Off Mgr: Kristin Slagle
Mktg Dir: Heather Benjamin
Surgeon: Carl Berasi
Surgeon: Tracy L Bigelow
Surgeon: Timothy Duffey
Surgeon: Mark Gittins
Surgeon: Charles Kerr
Surgeon: Daryl Sybert
Doctor: Desmond Stutzman

D-U-N-S 36-301-7070
ORTHOPAEDIC & NEUROLOGICAL REHABILITATION SPEECH PATHOLOGY INC
O N R
1101 S Cpitl Of Texas Hwy, West Lake Hills, TX 78746-6445
Tel (512) 327-4444 *Founded/Ownrshp* 1988
Sales 47.9MM^E *EMP* 1,400
Accts Crawford Pimentel & Co Inc
SIC 8049 Occupational therapist; Physical therapist; Speech specialist; Audiologist; Occupational therapist; Physical therapist; Speech specialist; Audiologist
CEO: Jill Capela
**CFO:* Janis Jones
Exec: Mary Mikhail
Area Mgr: Jenn Groen
Netwrk Mgr: Adam Johnson
Mktg Dir: Venus Vidaurri
Phys Thrpy: Rama Bowen
Snr Mgr: Suzanne Shifflet

D-U-N-S 60-509-4119
ORTHOPAEDIC & NEUROSURGERY SPECIALISTS PC
ORTHOPAEDIC ASSOC
6 Greenwich Office Park, Greenwich, CT 06831-5151
Tel (203) 618-1010 *Founded/Ownrshp* 1980
Sales 27.3MM^E *EMP* 150
SIC 8011 Orthopedic physician
Pr: John F Crowe
**Pr:* James Cunnningham
CFO: Steve McThomas
Bd of Dir: Gloria Cohen
**VP:* Mark Camel MD
Ex Dir: Jane Barratt
Surgeon: Michael Clain
Surgeon: James Cunningham
Surgeon: Francis Ennis
Surgeon: Brian Kavanagh
Surgeon: Seth Miller

D-U-N-S 78-805-8154
ORTHOPAEDIC & SPINE CENTER OF ROCKIES PC
O C R
2500 E Prospect Rd, Fort Collins, CO 80525-9718
Tel (970) 493-0112 *Founded/Ownrshp* 1969
Sales 29.1MM^E *EMP* 139
SIC 8011 Offices & clinics of medical doctors; Orthopedic physician
CEO: Michael Bergerson
**Pr:* Dr Mark Durbin
CFO: Camille Susemihl
Genl Mgr: Troy Wolf
Off Mgr: Mickey Putman
IT Man: Jeffrey Junker
Mktg Dir: Chad Schmidt
Surgeon: William Biggs
Surgeon: Satoru Chamberlain
Surgeon: Lee Grant
Surgeon: Mark McFerran

D-U-N-S 07-538-4420
ORTHOPAEDIC ALLIANCE TENNESSEE PA
301 21st Ave N, Nashville, TN 37203-1821
Tel (615) 329-6600 *Founded/Ownrshp* 1958
Sales 39.5MM^E *EMP* 400
SIC 8011 Orthopedic physician; Orthopedic physician
Pr: Phillip Karpos MD
CFO: Tom Croffut
**Treas:* Daniel L Phillips MD
Exec: Jane Siegel
**Prin:* John Bruno III
**Prin:* Daniel S Burris MD
**Prin:* Mark R Christopher
**Prin:* Mark R Cristofersen MD
**Prin:* William M Gadigan
**Prin:* Jeffrey L Herring
**Prin:* Stanley G Hopp MD
Board of Directors: Robert E Stein MD, John Bruno III, Stewart F Stowers MD, Mark R Christofersen MD, Thomas E Tompkins MD, William M Gadigan, Jeffrey L Herring, Stanley G Hopp MD, David S Jones MD, Frank E Jones MD, Eugene M Regen, Robert V Russell MD

ORTHOPAEDIC ASSOC
See ORTHOPAEDIC & NEUROSURGERY SPECIALISTS PC

D-U-N-S 08-202-5974
ORTHOPAEDIC ASSOCIATES OF ALLENTOWN LTD
OAA
250 Cetronia Rd, Allentown, PA 18104-9147
Tel (610) 973-6200 *Founded/Ownrshp* 1971
Sales 30.9MM^E *EMP* 300
SIC 8011 Orthopedic physician; Orthopedic physician
CEO: Thomas Meade
**Pr:* Richard D Battista M D
**CFO:* Ken Czyzyk
**Treas:* Kenneth Brislin
Orthpdst: Jeanne T Connelly

D-U-N-S 10-380-4720
ORTHOPAEDIC ASSOCIATES OF PORTLAND PA
SPORTS MEDICINE CENTER
33 Sewall St, Portland, ME 04102-2603
Tel (207) 828-2100 *Founded/Ownrshp* 1978
Sales 24.0MM^E *EMP* 220
SIC 8011 Medical centers; Medical centers
CEO: William John Wipfler
**Pr:* Douglas W Brown
**Pr:* Raymond R White
Off Mgr: Joanne Leblanc
Off Mgr: Lynn Shorty
Dir IT: John Pineau
Dir IT: John Tino
Orthpdst: Omar D Crothers
Orthpdst: William M Heinz
Orthpdst: Sacha Matthews
Orthpdst: Lucien R Ouellette

D-U-N-S 07-795-4535
ORTHOPAEDIC HOSPITAL
ORTHOPAEDIC INST FOR CHILDREN
403 W Adams Blvd, Los Angeles, CA 90007-2664
Tel (213) 742-1000 *Founded/Ownrshp* 1923
Sales 44.4MM *EMP* 180^E
SIC 8011 Primary care medical clinic; Primary care medical clinic
Pr: Anthony A Scaduto
COO: Dennis Strum
CFO: Jeff Goldberg
CFO: Joseph Luevanos
**CFO:* Diane Moon
Bd of Dir: Joel M Bernstein
Bd of Dir: Walid H Ghurabi
Bd of Dir: Nicholas V McClure
VP: Mickie Faris
VP: Harry McKellop
VP: Michael Sullivan
Dir Lab: Richard Gonsalves

ORTHOPAEDIC INST FOR CHILDREN
See ORTHOPAEDIC HOSPITAL

D-U-N-S 07-433-1307
ORTHOPAEDICS NORTHEAST PC
SURGERYONE
5050 N Clinton St Ste 3, Fort Wayne, IN 46825-5886
Tel (260) 484-8551 *Founded/Ownrshp* 1962
Sales 32.1MM^E *EMP* 336
SIC 8011 Orthopedic physician
Pr: John C Pritchard
**CEO:* Raymond Kusisto
**CFO:* E Paul Ward
**Treas:* Stephen Wright
Ofcr: Pat Weicker
**VP:* Greg Hoffman
VP: John Pritchard
**Prin:* Alan McGee
Dir IT: Kevin Haverstock
IT Man: Eric Jones
Web Dev: Brett Hunt

D-U-N-S 07-206-7176
ORTHOPAEDICS-INDIANAPOLIS INC
ORTHOINDY
8450 Northwest Blvd, Indianapolis, IN 46278-1381
Tel (317) 802-2000 *Founded/Ownrshp* 1964
Sales 26.2MM^E *EMP* 115
SIC 8011 Orthopedic physician
Pr: Frank R Kolisek
**Prin:* George Kellum
**Prin:* John Martin
Dir IT: Sean Reddington
Telecom Mg: Dave King
IT Man: Jason Ritchie
IT Man: Ellen Tyner
Orthpdst: Joseph Randolph
Orthpdst: Terry Trammell
Surgeon: Frank Kolesek
Surgeon: Joseph Riina

D-U-N-S 11-803-0274
ORTHOPEDIC & SPINE SURGICAL HOSPITAL OF SOUTH TEXAS LP
SOUTH TXAS SPINE SURGICAL HOSP
18600 Hardy Oak Blvd, San Antonio, TX 78258-4206
Tel (210) 404-0800 *Founded/Ownrshp* 2002
Sales 28.4MM *EMP* 100
SIC 8062 General medical & surgical hospitals
Pt: Debbie Kelly
CFO: Sylvia Garcia
Software D: Gilbert Meadows

ORTHOPEDIC ASSOCIATES OF N Y
See HEALTHCARE ASSOCIATES IN MEDICINE PC

D-U-N-S 07-764-3674
ORTHOPEDIC CENTER
AUST, GILBERT M MD
927 Franklin St Se Fl 3, Huntsville, AL 35801-4305
Tel (256) 704-1210 *Founded/Ownrshp* 1970
Sales 29.3MM^E *EMP* 80
SIC 8011 Orthopedic physician
Pt: Louis G Horn III
Pt: Dr Gilbert Aust
Pt: Dr Richard C Burnside
Pt: Dr Mark A Leberte
Admn Mgr: Tammy Jackson
Off Mgr: Lindsey Champion
Surgeon: Joseph Clark
Surgeon: Matthew Deorio
Surgeon: John Greco
Surgeon: Robert Maples
Surgeon: Larry Parker

ORTHOPEDIC DEPARTMENT
See TULANE UNIVERSITY HOSPITAL AND CLINIC

D-U-N-S 84-900-4726
■ **ORTHOPEDIC HOSPITAL LTD**
TEXAS ORTHOPEDIC HOSPITAL
(*Suby of* HCA INC) ★
7401 Main St, Houston, TX 77030-4509
Tel (713) 799-8600 *Founded/Ownrshp* 1995
Sales 52.4MM^E *EMP* 230
SIC 8069 Orthopedic hospital; Orthopedic hospital
CEO: R Trent Lind
Chf Rad: Jeff London
Genl Pt: Alice Adams
Pr: Randy Babbit
Pr: G William Woods M D
Ofcr: Trent Lind
Sr VP: William Woods
Dir Lab: Barbara Powell
Dir Rad: Thomas Zufelt
Prin: David P Loncarich
Prin: Gary McGuire

D-U-N-S 03-809-2800
ORTHOPEDIC HOSPITAL OF WISCONSIN LLC
COLUMBIA - ST MARY'S
(*Suby of* COLUMBIA - ST MARYS) ★
475 W River Woods Pkwy, Milwaukee, WI 53212-1081
Tel (414) 961-6800 *Founded/Ownrshp* 2001
Sales 60.8MM *EMP* 100
SIC 8069 Orthopedic hospital
CEO: Bryan Cramer
Dir Rad: Mark Ahrens
Doctor: John Kroner

D-U-N-S 03-502-1992
ORTHOPEDIC INSTITUTE
BENSON, GAIL M MD
810 E 23rd St Ste 5000, Sioux Falls, SD 57105-2132
Tel (605) 692-7666 *Founded/Ownrshp* 1980
Sales 43.7MM^E *EMP* 150
SIC 8069 8011 Orthopedic hospital; General & family practice, physician/surgeon
Pr: Walter Carlson
**Pr:* Dr Timothy M Zoeller
**Treas:* Paul D Reyen
Ofcr: Tammie Pulling
**VP:* Dr Peter Rodman
Off Mgr: Cheryl Kolbrek
Surgeon: Keith Baumgarten
Surgeon: Robert Suga
Doctor: Lee Arnold
Doctor: Brad R Plaga

ORTHOPEDIC INSTITUTE WSTN KY
See SOUTHERN ORTHOPEDIC ASSOCIATES SC

D-U-N-S 61-094-9195
ORTHOPEDIC SURGERY CENTER L P
SOUTH EASTERN ORTHAPEDIC CTR
210 E Derenne Ave, Savannah, GA 31405-6736
Tel (912) 644-5300 *Founded/Ownrshp* 1999
Sales 101.1MM^E *EMP* 1,000
SIC 8011 Orthopedic physician; Clinic, operated by physicians
CEO: Michael Kleinpeter
CFO: Mike Hester
Off Mgr: Reagan Owens
Off Mgr: Tricia Stephen
Off Mgr: Amy TSE
Off Admin: Jessica Green
Dir IT: Rob Snipes
Orthpdst: Teresa Klick
Surgeon: Krishna Gumidyala
Surgeon: Sunderraj Kamaleson
Surgeon: John McCormick

D-U-N-S 87-796-8958
ORTHOSYNETICS INC
3850 N Causeway Blvd # 800, Metairie, LA 70002-8133
Tel (504) 834-3663 *Founded/Ownrshp* 1985
Sales 126.0MM^E *EMP* 3,092
SIC 8021 Orthodontist; Orthodontist
CEO: Charles W Carroll
**Pr:* David Marks
**CEO:* Michael Gries
**Treas:* Joe Sivori
Ex VP: Dennis J Buchman
VP: John O'Brien
MIS Dir: William Jones
Tech Mgr: Alex Gragg
Mktg Mgr: Sarah Peltier

D-U-N-S 79-544-5477 IMP
ORTHOTIC REHABILITATION PRODUCTS INC
(*Suby of* SWEETWATER ALLIANCE INC)
2437 S 86th St Ste G, Tampa, FL 33619-4912
Tel (813) 620-0035 *Founded/Ownrshp* 1992
Sales 21.0MM *EMP* 43
SIC 3842 Splints, pneumatic & wood; Splints, pneumatic & wood
CEO: George Morrison
**CFO:* Mark Gowen

D-U-N-S 84-922-7939 IMP
■ **ORTHOVITA INC**
STRYKER ORTHOBIOLOGICS
(*Suby of* STRYKER CORP) ★
45 Great Valley Pkwy, Malvern, PA 19355-1302
Tel (610) 640-4560 *Founded/Ownrshp* 2011
Sales 69.6MM^E *EMP* 256
SIC 3841 Surgical & medical instruments; Medical instruments & equipment, blood & bone work; Surgical & medical instruments; Medical instruments & equipment, blood & bone work
Pr: Kevin Lobo
**VP:* Teutsch Eric
VP Sls: William S McDonald

D-U-N-S 18-057-5607
ORTIZ ENTERPRISES INC
6 Cushing Ste 200, Irvine, CA 92618-4230
Tel (949) 753-1414 *Founded/Ownrshp* 1984
Sales 21.9MM^E *EMP* 80^E
SIC 1611 Highway & street construction
Pr: Patrick Ortiz
**VP:* Jill Ortiz
Snr Mgr: John Schaar

ORTRAN EXPRESS
See OIX INC

D-U-N-S 00-453-3345 IMP
ORTRONICS INC
LEGRAND ORTRONICS
(*Suby of* LEGRAND HOLDING INC) ★
125 Eugene Oneill Dr # 140, New London, CT 06320-6417
Tel (860) 445-3900 *Founded/Ownrshp* 1966
Sales 55.5MM^E *EMP* 275
SIC 3577 3357 Computer peripheral equipment; Communication wire; Telephone & telegraph apparatus; Computer peripheral equipment; Communication wire
Pr: Mark Panico
Pt: Larry Giles
**Pr:* Halsey Cook
**Pr:* Doug Fikse
**Pr:* Jerry Mix
**VP:* Jackie Thornton
Off Mgr: Darlene La Cerna
Off Mgr: Barbara Meyer
Mtls Mgr: Manuel Silva
Mktg Dir: Thomas Cunningham
Manager: Nicholas McAlley

D-U-N-S 04-570-2440
ORVA SHOES INC
362 5th Ave Fl 12, New York, NY 10001-2240
Tel (212) 369-3448 *Founded/Ownrshp* 2008
Sales 30.0MM *EMP* 15
SIC 5139 Shoes; Shoes
CEO: Arthur Aizer
Ex VP: Rick Jenkins

D-U-N-S 00-207-5539 IMP/EXP
ORVIS CO INC (VT)
ORVIS SPORTING TRADITIONS
178 Conservation Way, Arlington, VT 05250-4465
Tel (802) 362-3622 *Founded/Ownrshp* 1856, 1965
Sales 295.8MM^E *EMP* 1,400
SIC 5961 5941 3949

D-U-N-S 13-525-7082 IMP
ORVIS SERVICES INC
(*Suby of* ORVIS CO INC) ★
178 Conservation Ln, Manchester, VT 05254
Tel (802) 362-1300 *Founded/Ownrshp* 1856
Sales 36.4MM^E *EMP* 200
SIC 5091 Fishing equipment & supplies; Fishing equipment & supplies
Pr: Ray McCready
CFO: Tom Vaccaro
VP: Dan Reckens
Web Dev: Jenna Woginrich
Software D: Jim Lepage
Sales Asso: Jim Coveney
Sales Asso: Frank Duerr

ORVIS SPORTING TRADITIONS
See ORVIS CO INC

ORWOOD PRECISION PDTS CARATRON
See BMT AEROSPACE USA INC

D-U-N-S 05-497-2771
ORYX OILFIELD SERVICES LLC
223 E College St, Grapevine, TX 76051-5333
Tel (817) 488-8999 *Founded/Ownrshp* 2010
Sales 35.8MM^E *EMP* 45
SIC 1623 Oil & gas pipeline construction
Mng Dir: Matthew J Mahone
Dir Bus: Yancey Strait

D-U-N-S 83-268-6773
OS HOLDINGS LLC
17757 Woodland Dr, New Boston, MI 48164-9265
Tel (734) 397-6300 *Founded/Ownrshp* 2009
Sales 46.8MM^E *EMP* 254^E
SIC 3469 Metal stampings; Metal stampings
VP: Robert E Koss

D-U-N-S 11-345-5823
■ **OS PRIME INC**
ROY'S
(*Suby of* OSI RESTAURANT PARTNERS LLC) ★
2202 N West Shore Blvd # 50, Tampa, FL 33607-5747
Tel (813) 282-1225 *Founded/Ownrshp* 2000
Sales 23.3MM^E *EMP* 1,125
SIC 5812 Eating places; Eating places
Ch Bd: Chris Sullivan
**Pr:* Paul Avery
**VP:* Tim Gannon

D-U-N-S 00-494-4604
OS SALESCO INC
GOLDEN PLAINS FOODS
11030 O St, Omaha, NE 68137-2346
Tel (402) 597-3000 *Founded/Ownrshp* 1997
Sales 56.4MM^E *EMP* 302
Accts Kpmg Llp Omaha Ne
SIC 5147 5421 Meats & meat products; Meat & fish markets; Meats & meat products; Meat & fish markets
Ch: Alan Simon
Pr: Todd Simon
CEO: Bruce Simon
CFO: David L Hershiser
Ex VP: Fred Simon
VP: Steve Simon
Sls&Mrk Ex: Vickie Hagen

D-U-N-S 11-345-5385
■ **OS SOUTHERN INC**
LEROY SELMON'S RESTAURANT
(*Suby of* OSI RESTAURANT PARTNERS LLC) ★
2202 N West Shore Blvd # 500, Tampa, FL 33607-5747
Tel (813) 282-1225 *Founded/Ownrshp* 2001
Sales 12.4MM^E *EMP* 500
SIC 5812 Eating places; Eating places
CEO: Bill Allen
**Ch Bd:* Chris Sullivan
**Ch:* Robert Basham
**VP:* John Gannon

D-U-N-S 18-059-2602
OSA INTERNATIONAL INC
ON STAGE AUDIO
537 N Edgewood Ave, Wood Dale, IL 60191-2600
Tel (630) 227-1008 *Founded/Ownrshp* 1985
Sales 20.6MM *EMP* 50
Accts Fgmk Llc Bannockburn Illino
SIC 7359 Sound & lighting equipment rental
Pr: Mario Educate
VP: Paul Driggs
**VP:* Vickie Lenhart
VP: Jim Risgin
Prd Mgr: Ken Oconnell
Prd Mgr: Dan Vennes
Mktg Dir: Melissa Diemert

OSAGE AMBULANCE
See OSAGE INDUSTRIES INC

OSAGE CASINOS
See OSAGE NATION GAMING ENTERPRISE

OSAGE COOP ELEVATOR
See OSAGE COOPERATIVE ELEVATOR

D-U-N-S 02-228-0812
OSAGE COOPERATIVE ELEVATOR
OSAGE COOP ELEVATOR
216 Mechanic St, Osage, IA 50461-1061
Tel (641) 732-3250 *Founded/Ownrshp* 1945
Sales 69.7MM *EMP* 19
Accts Renner & Birchem Pc Cpas Ma
SIC 5153 5191 Grains; Feed; Seeds: field, garden & flower; Fertilizer & fertilizer materials; Chemicals, agricultural; Grains; Feed; Seeds: field, garden & flower; Fertilizer & fertilizer materials; Chemicals, agricultural
Prin: Gayle Melcher
VP: Tracy Funk

D-U-N-S 10-320-7163
OSAGE INDUSTRIES INC
OSAGE AMBULANCE
194 Twin Ridge Rd, Linn, MO 65051
Tel (573) 897-3634 *Founded/Ownrshp* 1992
Sales 26.2MM *EMP* 100
SIC 3716 4119 Motor homes; Ambulance service
Pr: John Kehoe
**Treas:* Rob Eistershold
Sls Mgr: Paul Marshall

D-U-N-S 07-240-6333
OSAGE NATION
627 Grandview Ave, Pawhuska, OK 74056-4201
Tel (918) 287-5555 *Founded/Ownrshp* 1906
Sales NA *EMP* 500
Accts Eidebailly Llp Oklahoma City
SIC 9121 Legislative bodies; Legislative bodies
Prin: John Red Eagle
**CFO:* Pallie Catcher
**CFO:* John Jech
Ofcr: Ramona Esch
**Prin:* Geoffrey Standingber
Brnch Mgr: Sue Slinkard
Dir IT: Robert Kirk
IT Man: Michael Lewis
Counsel: Trey Gill
Snr Mgr: Joe Tillman

D-U-N-S 07-949-0235
OSAGE NATION GAMING ENTERPRISE
OSAGE CASINOS
1121 W 36th St, Tulsa, OK 74127
Tel (918) 699-7710 *Founded/Ownrshp* 2014
Sales 31.5MME *EMP* 1,171
SIC 7999 Gambling establishment; Gambling establishment
CEO: Neal Cornelius
**COO:* Joe Olujic
**CFO:* Richard Lobdell
Genl Mgr: Christy Redeagle
Dir IT: Robert Pekel

D-U-N-S 19-907-1226
OSAGE TRADING CO INC
153 John Dahl Ave, Pawhuska, OK 74056-2517
Tel (918) 287-4544 *Founded/Ownrshp* 1986
Sales 21.0MME *EMP* 13
SIC 2131 5993 Smoking tobacco; Tobacco stores & stands
Pr: Paul Mays III

D-U-N-S 00-890-6216
OSAGE VALLEY ELECTRIC CO-OPERATIVE ASSN
1321 N Orange St, Butler, MO 64730-9387
Tel (660) 679-3131 *Founded/Ownrshp* 1938
Sales 32.5MM *EMP* 69
SIC 4911 Distribution, electric power; Distribution, electric power
Pr: P D Kircher
COO: John Ariail
Exec: Daryl Veatch
Genl Mgr: John McClure

D-U-N-S 06-649-1242
OSAN PETROLEUM CO INC
1167 6th St, Macon, GA 31206-1108
Tel (478) 742-4534 *Founded/Ownrshp* 1973
Sales 29.9MME *EMP* 17
SIC 5172 5983 Petroleum products; Fuel oil dealers; Petroleum products; Fuel oil dealers
CEO: Robert V Oswald
Pr: John E Oswald
Sr VP: Pamela L Garcia

D-U-N-S 08-528-1801 IMP
OSATA ENTERPRISES INC (CA)
GLOBE SHOES
225 S Aviation Blvd, El Segundo, CA 90245-4604
Tel (310) 297-1550 *Founded/Ownrshp* 1997
Sales 36.2MME *EMP* 100
SIC 5139 Shoes
Prin: Matthew Hill
**Prin:* Gary Valentine

D-U-N-S 60-375-8228
OSBORN & BARR COMMUNICATIONS INC
914 Spruce St, Saint Louis, MO 63102-1118
Tel (314) 726-5511 *Founded/Ownrshp* 1988
Sales 25.7MME *EMP* 160
SIC 7311 Advertising agencies; Advertising agencies
CEO: Michael Turley
**CFO:* Rhonda Ries
CFO: Rhonda Ries-Aguilar
VP: Rhett Hawkins
VP: Suzan Knese
Assoc Dir: Cassie McCloud
Assoc Dir: Deanna Montgomery
Creative D: Jacob Edenfield
Creative D: Steve Laliberte
Creative D: Ryan McMichael
Creative D: Adnan Sabic

D-U-N-S 03-751-3848
OSBORN AUTOMOTIVE
8303 W Colfax Ave, Lakewood, CO 80214-6106
Tel (303) 237-1311 *Founded/Ownrshp* 2001
Sales 24.7MME *EMP* 100
SIC 5511 7538 7532 7515 5531 5521 Automobiles, new & used; General automotive repair shops; Top & body repair & paint shops; Passenger car leasing; Automotive & home supply stores; Used car dealers; Automobiles, new & used; General automotive repair shops; Top & body repair & paint shops; Passenger car leasing; Automotive & home supply stores; Used car dealers
Owner: Gene Osborn
Owner: Larry Miller
Sls Mgr: Jimmy Osborn

D-U-N-S 03-160-8813
OSBORN BROTHERS INC
259 N 5th St, Gadsden, AL 35901-3240
Tel (256) 547-8601 *Founded/Ownrshp* 1947
Sales 20.1MM *EMP* 56
Accts Mcclure Sewell & Associates
SIC 5142 5149 5148 Packaged frozen goods; Canned goods: fruit, vegetables, seafood, meats, etc.; Fresh fruits & vegetables; Packaged frozen goods; Canned goods: fruit, vegetables, seafood, meats, etc.; Fresh fruits & vegetables
Pr: Joel V Osborn
CFO: Steve Huffman
VP: Wyman Osburn
Genl Mgr: Durett Posey

D-U-N-S 18-155-4379
■ **OSBORN GROUP INC**
(*Suby of* LABONE INC) ★
153 W 151st St Ste 140, Olathe, KS 66061-5300
Tel (913) 768-6606 *Founded/Ownrshp* 2001
Sales 4.9MME *EMP* 396
SIC 8071 6411 Testing laboratories; Insurance agents, brokers & service; Testing laboratories; Insurance agents, brokers & service
Pr: W Thomas Grant II
**CFO:* John McCarty
**Ex VP:* Gregg Sadler
Board of Directors: Jake Mascotte

OSBORN RETIREMENT COMMUNITY
See MIRIAM OSBORN MEMORIAL HOME ASSOCIATION

D-U-N-S 07-210-8418
OSBORN TRANSPORTATION INC
1245 W Grand Ave, Rainbow City, AL 35906-8943
Tel (256) 442-2514 *Founded/Ownrshp* 1973
Sales 40.4MME *EMP* 275
SIC 4212 4213 Local trucking, without storage; Trucking, except local; Local trucking, without storage; Trucking, except local
Pr: Paul Skelton
**CFO:* Mark Skelton
**Prin:* Virginia Osborn
Mktg Dir: Carin Wilcox

D-U-N-S 79-009-6192 IMP/EXP
OSBORNE & LITTLE INC
(*Suby of* OSBORNE & LITTLE LIMITED)
90 Commerce Rd Ste 2, Stamford, CT 06902-4537
Tel (203) 359-1500 *Founded/Ownrshp* 1989
Sales 22.9MME *EMP* 60
SIC 5131 5198 Piece goods & notions; Wallcoverings
CEO: William D Peters III
**Pr:* Peter Osborne
CFO: Anthony Falcon

D-U-N-S 04-363-5937
OSBORNE CO OF NORTH CAROLINA INC
515 S Kennedy St, Eden, NC 27288-5005
Tel (336) 623-2111 *Founded/Ownrshp* 1981
Sales 26.0MME *EMP* 100
SIC 1541 1542

OSBORNE CONSTRUCTION COMPANY
See OSBORNE/MKB JOINT VENTURE

D-U-N-S 19-678-9440
OSBORNE CONSTRUCTION CO
10602 Ne 38th Pl Ste 100, Kirkland, WA 98033-7947
Tel (425) 827-4221 *Founded/Ownrshp* 1987
Sales 69.0MME *EMP* 140
SIC 1542 Commercial & office building, new construction; Commercial & office building, new construction
Pr: George Osborne Jr
**Treas:* Steven Rupp
**Ex VP:* Daniel C Jacobson
**VP:* Michael Ritchie
Snr Mgr: Ralph Hintze

D-U-N-S 02-157-6376
OSBORNE PROPERTIES LIMITED PARTNERSHIP (MN)
KRAUS ANDERSON INSURANCE
420 Gateway Blvd, Burnsville, MN 55337-2790
Tel (952) 707-8200 *Founded/Ownrshp* 1972
Sales NA *EMP* 70
SIC 6411 6512 Insurance agents; Nonresidential building operators
Pt: Daniel Engelsma
Pt: Barbara Diessner
Pt: Bruce Engelsma
Pt: Sharon Korsh
Pt: Susan Wilcox
Pt: Julie Ertz
VP: Keith Burkhardt
VP: Mark Kampf
Genl Mgr: Dennis Diessner

D-U-N-S 62-663-1774
OSBORNE/MKB JOINT VENTURE
OSBORNE CONSTRUCTION COMPANY
10602 Ne 38th Pl Ste 100, Kirkland, WA 98033-7947
Tel (425) 827-4221 *Founded/Ownrshp* 1989
Sales 780.6M *EMP* 300
SIC 1542 1541 Commercial & office building, new construction; Industrial buildings, new construction; Commercial & office building, new construction; Industrial buildings, new construction
Pr: George Osbourne Jr

D-U-N-S 78-812-3552
OSBURN CONTRACTORS INC
2747 Oakland Ave Ste A, Garland, TX 75041-3926
Tel (972) 205-9086 *Founded/Ownrshp* 1992
Sales 140.3MME *EMP* 900
SIC 1771 Concrete work
CEO: Dave Osburn
**Pr:* Victor Marshal
CFO: Melba Collins
**CFO:* Scott Wessinger
VP: Ileana Osburn
Genl Mgr: Greg Jamerson
VP Opers: Victor Marshall
Sfty Mgr: Eric Pina
Opers Mgr: Larry Hagman
Opers Mgr: Gary Yelvington

D-U-N-S 07-933-1255
OSC HOLDING INC
ONTARIO SPECIALTY CONTRACTING
333 Ganson St, Buffalo, NY 14203-3029
Tel (716) 856-3333 *Founded/Ownrshp* 1997
Sales 70.0MM *EMP* 250E
SIC 1795 Wrecking & demolition work; Wrecking & demolition work
CEO: Jon M Williams
VP: Joe Batista
**VP:* Robert Wegrzyn

D-U-N-S 06-835-3908 IMP
OSC SPORTS INC
OLYMPIA SPORTS
5 Bradley Dr, Westbrook, ME 04092-2013
Tel (207) 854-2794 *Founded/Ownrshp* 1975
Sales 200.0MM *EMP* 2,000
Accts Baker Newman Noyes Portland
SIC 5699 5661 5941 Sports apparel; Footwear, athletic; Sporting goods & bicycle shops; Sports apparel; Footwear, athletic; Sporting goods & bicycle shops
Ch Bd: Edward Manganello
**Pr:* Richard Coffey
**CFO:* John Lesniak

OSCA-ARCOSA
See O & S CALIFORNIA INC

D-U-N-S 03-411-8872 IMP
OSCANNLAIN & GOROGIANIS LLC (IL)
FORTUNE FISH COMPANY
1068 Thorndale Ave, Bensenville, IL 60106-1142
Tel (630) 860-7100 *Founded/Ownrshp* 2001
Sales 26.6MME *EMP* 90E
SIC 5421 5146 Fish & seafood markets; Fish & seafoods
Pr: Brad Schoenberg
**VP:* Mark Gorogianis
Sales Asso: Beth Keller
Sales Asso: Jeffrey Lemke

OSCAR BLANDI HAIRCARE
See TPR HOLDINGS LLC

D-U-N-S 07-100-7918 IMP
OSCAR DE LA RENTA LLC
11 W 42nd St, New York, NY 10036-8002
Tel (212) 282-0500 *Founded/Ownrshp* 1974
Sales 112.0MM *EMP* 250
Accts Mayer Hoffman Mccann Cpas Ne
SIC 5137 Women's & children's accessories; Women's & children's accessories
CEO: Alexander L Bolen
**COO:* Giuseppe Celio
Ex VP: Erica Bearman
Ex VP: Christine Kelley
Sr VP: Melissa Cobb
VP: Brandi Barrett
VP: Colleen Brewer
VP: Kristen D'Arcy
VP: Claudine Jorgensen
VP: Robert Kogan
VP: Virva Launo
VP: Melissa Lefere-Cobb
VP: Lisa Treiber

D-U-N-S 07-913-4130
OSCAR INSURANCE CORP
295 Lafayette St Fl 6, New York, NY 10012-2722
Tel (914) 574-7691 *Founded/Ownrshp* 2012
Sales NA *EMP* 170
SIC 6311 Life insurance
CEO: Sina Nazemi
**CEO:* Mario Schlosser
CFO: Steve Kessler
Sftwr Eng: Thomas Kho
Sales Exec: Dan Kuelzow
VP Mktg: Veronica Parker-Hahn
VP Sls: John Pfenning
Snr Mgr: Rodney Gibson

D-U-N-S 06-014-9218
OSCAR RENDA CONTRACTING INC
608 Henrietta Creek Rd, Roanoke, TX 76262-6339
Tel (817) 491-2703 *Founded/Ownrshp* 1974
Sales 153.8MME *EMP* 151E
Accts Milbern Ray And Company Grap
SIC 1623 1799 1622 Water main construction; Sewer line construction; Pumping station construction; Exterior cleaning, including sandblasting; Tunnel construction
Pr: Oscar Renda
**CFO:* Corey Wells
**VP:* Frank Renda

OSCAR SUPER CASH & CARRY
See FRIGORIFICO Y ALMACEN DEL TURABO INC

D-U-N-S 01-724-6125 IMP
OSCAR W LARSON CO
10100 Dixie Hwy, Clarkston, MI 48348-2414
Tel (248) 620-0070 *Founded/Ownrshp* 2006
Sales 82.4MME *EMP* 250
SIC 1799 Service station equipment installation, maintenance & repair; Service station equipment installation, maintenance & repair
Pr: Bruce F Larson
**CFO:* James Lintol
Genl Mgr: N Robert
IT Man: Pete Wayne

D-U-N-S 03-111-3095 IMP/EXP
OSCAR WILSON ENGINES & PARTS INC
826 Lone Star Dr, O Fallon, MO 63366-1950
Tel (636) 978-1313 *Founded/Ownrshp* 1980
Sales 29.0MM *EMP* 65E
Accts Uhy Llp Cpas St Louis Miss
SIC 5084 Engines & parts, air-cooled; Engines & parts, air-cooled
CEO: Douglas C Wright
**Pr:* Steven D Purdy
**CEO:* Daniel M Wright
**COO:* Steven M Purdy
**CFO:* Chris Almeling
**Ex VP:* Daniel R Wright
Area Mgr: Marv Hoebing

D-U-N-S 01-648-2911 IMP
OSCAR WINSKI CO INC
LAFAYETTE STEEL AND ALUM SLS
2407 N 9th Street Rd, Lafayette, IN 47904-1047
Tel (765) 742-1102 *Founded/Ownrshp* 1985
Sales 105.4MME *EMP* 200
SIC 5051 5093 Steel; Metal scrap & waste materials; Steel; Metal scrap & waste materials
CEO: Michael J Bluestein
**Ex VP:* Roger Carnes
**Sr VP:* Steve Bluestein
VP: David Bluestein
VP: E Bluestein
VP: Terrill Timmons
Genl Mgr: Ron Addaman
Genl Mgr: Oscar Winski
IT Man: Gretencord Sue
Sfty Dirs: Bill Eckhart
Sfty Dirs: Daniel Fay

D-U-N-S 01-831-2114
OSCEOLA COUNTY SCHOOL BOARD (FL)
817 Bill Beck Blvd, Kissimmee, FL 34744-4495
Tel (407) 870-4600 *Founded/Ownrshp* 2010
Sales 527.0MM *EMP* 6E
Accts Moore Stephens Lovelace Pa C
SIC 8211 School board
Ch: Tim Weisheyer

D-U-N-S 00-412-3121 IMP
OSCEOLA FARMS CO (FL)
(*Suby of* FANJUL CORP) ★
340 Royal Poinciana Way # 315, Palm Beach, FL 33480-4048
Tel (561) 655-6303 *Founded/Ownrshp* 1960
Sales 198.6MME *EMP* 1,631
SIC 2099 Sugar grinding; Sugar grinding
Ch Bd: Alfonso Fanjul Jr
**Pr:* Jose Fanjul
**VP:* Donald W Carson

D-U-N-S 95-802-5173
■ **OSCEOLA FOODS INC**
(*Suby of* HORMEL FOODS CORP) ★
1027 Warren Ave, Osceola, IA 50213-9540
Tel (641) 342-8000 *Founded/Ownrshp* 1995
Sales 45.5MME *EMP* 100
SIC 2011 Meat packing plants; Meat packing plants
Pr: Steven Weers
Treas: Larry Gorden
Genl Mgr: Jeff Nuytten
IT Man: Ryan Sells
Sfty Mgr: Randy Kraft
Plnt Mgr: Clint Walters

OSCEOLA MEDICAL CENTER
See LADD MEMORIAL HOSPITAL INC

D-U-N-S 92-642-2973
■ **OSCEOLA REGIONAL HOSPITAL INC**
OSCEOLA REGIONAL MEDICAL CTR
(*Suby of* HCA INC) ★
700 W Oak St Ofc, Kissimmee, FL 34741-4900
Tel (407) 846-2266 *Founded/Ownrshp* 1997
Sales 59.4M *EMP* 950
Accts Hoskins Quiros Osborne Labeaum
SIC 8062 General medical & surgical hospitals; General medical & surgical hospitals
CEO: Robert Krieger
COO: David Cashwell
COO: Brian Marger
CFO: Glen Romig
CFO: Glenn Romig
Mktg Mgr: Vanessa Guevara
Ansthlgy: Nagy Nashed
Doctor: Abbas Ali MD
Doctor: Pradip Baiju MD
Doctor: Robert Barrett MD
Doctor: Beatriz Colon

OSCEOLA REGIONAL MEDICAL CTR
See OSCEOLA REGIONAL HOSPITAL INC

D-U-N-S 10-064-3576
OSCEOLA SCHOOL DISTRICT
2750 W Semmes Ave, Osceola, AR 72370-3825
Tel (870) 563-2561 *Founded/Ownrshp* 1992
Sales 20.5MME *EMP* 350

SIC 8211 Public elementary & secondary schools; Public elementary & secondary schools
Schl Brd P: Terry Cole

D-U-N-S 80-905-0479
OSCEOLA SUPPLY INC
915 Commerce Blvd, Midway, FL 32343-6631
Tel (850) 580-9800 *Founded/Ownrshp* 1993
Sales 22.0MM *EMP* 49
SIC 5047 Medical equipment & supplies; Medical equipment & supplies
Pr: Dorothea F Hittinger
**VP:* Jeff Hittinger
Off Admin: William Mills

D-U-N-S 03-278-1837
OSCEOLAK12FL
SCHOOL DST OF OSCEOLA CNTY FLA
817 Bill Beck Blvd, Kissimmee, FL 34744-4492
Tel (407) 870-4630 *Founded/Ownrshp* 2011
Sales 120.0MM^E *EMP* 4,848^E
SIC 8211 Elementary school
Prin: Mark Munas

OSCO DRUG
See AMERICAN DRUG STORES INC

D-U-N-S 02-525-2263
OSCO INC (IL)
OSCO OIL
13351 Main St, Lemont, IL 60439-9374
Tel (630) 257-8000 *Founded/Ownrshp* 1920, 1953
Sales 102.3MM^E *EMP* 50
SIC 5172 Petroleum products; Diesel fuel; Gasoline; Service station supplies, petroleum; Petroleum products; Diesel fuel; Gasoline; Service station supplies, petroleum
Pr: Maureen B McGovern
**Pr:* John P Mc Govern

D-U-N-S 00-428-0947 EXP
OSCO INDUSTRIES INC (OH)
PORTSMOUTH DIVISION
734 11th St, Portsmouth, OH 45662-3407
Tel (740) 354-3183 *Founded/Ownrshp* 1872, 1942
Sales 86.2MM^E *EMP* 440
Accts Kelley Galloway Smith Goolsby
SIC 3321 Gray & ductile iron foundries; Gray iron castings; Gray & ductile iron foundries; Gray iron castings
Ch Bd: William J Burke
**Pr:* John M Burke
**Sr VP:* Jeffrey A Burke
**VP:* Keith Denny
**VP:* Philip L Vetter

OSCO OIL
See OSCO INC

D-U-N-S 10-183-5833 EXP
OSCOR INC
3816 Desoto Blvd, Palm Harbor, FL 34683-1618
Tel (727) 937-2511 *Founded/Ownrshp* 2008
Sales 35.3MM^E *EMP* 130^E
SIC 3841 5047 Surgical & medical instruments; Medical equipment & supplies; Surgical & medical instruments; Medical equipment & supplies
Pr: Thomas Osypka
Ofcr: Teri Wood
QA Dir: Lisa Wiley
Dir IT: Nancy Madafferi
QC Dir: Dorit Segal
Opers Mgr: Daryl Gary
Sls&Mrk Ex: Bethania Tavrez
S&M/VP: Bethania Tavarez
Mktg Mgr: Andrew Giraldo

OSCR
See OCEAN STATE COMMUNITY RESOURCES

OSECO
See OKLAHOMA SAFETY EQUIPMENT CO INC

D-U-N-S 06-741-4946
OSF HEALTHCARE SYSTEM
ST MARY MEDICAL CENTER
(*Suby of* SISTERS OF THIRD ORDER OF ST FRANCIS) ★
800 Ne Glen Oak Ave, Peoria, IL 61603-3200
Tel (309) 655-2850 *Founded/Ownrshp* 2001
Sales 1.8MMM *EMP* 4,007
Accts Kpmg Llp Columbus Oh
SIC 8062 8051 Hospital, medical school affiliated with nursing & residency; Extended care facility; Hospital, medical school affiliated with nursing & residency; Extended care facility
CEO: Kevin Schoeplein
Dir Vol: Victoria Hennenfent
COO: Suzanne Hinderliter
CFO: Daniel E Baker
CFO: Emiel Michelet
Ofcr: Lori L Wiegand
Exec: Mary Boudreau
Exec: Joseph Piccione
Exec: Bill Swearinger
Ex Dir: Jim Brace
Ex Dir: Gordon Wesner
Board of Directors: Sister Judith Ann Duvall, R N

D-U-N-S 06-525-2405
OSF INTERNATIONAL INC
OLD SPAGHETTI FACTORY
0715 Sw Bancroft St, Portland, OR 97239-4273
Tel (503) 222-5375 *Founded/Ownrshp* 1969
Sales 143.6MM^E *EMP* 3,700
SIC 5812 6794 Italian restaurant; Franchises, selling or licensing; Italian restaurant; Franchises, selling or licensing
Pr: Chris Dussin
COO: Mark Roark
CFO: Theresa Stempel
Ex VP: Dean Griffith
**VP:* Sally Dussin
VP: Christopher Hein
VP: Adolph Lehman
Dist Mgr: Keith Folkestad
Genl Mgr: Tom Cantor
Genl Mgr: Doug Frassato
Genl Mgr: John Maurice

D-U-N-S 60-298-1698
OSF INVESTMENTS LLC
CARPET EXCHANGE
1133 S Platte River Dr, Denver, CO 80223-3101
Tel (303) 744-3300 *Founded/Ownrshp* 2000
Sales 36.6MM^E *EMP* 180
SIC 5713 5023 Floor covering stores; Floor coverings; Floor covering stores; Floor coverings
Store Mgr: Kelli Love
IT Man: Dave Morgan
IT Man: Shelly Weeder
Sls Mgr: Tara Oliphant

D-U-N-S 11-573-6977
OSF SAINT FRANCIS INC
MEDI-PARK PHARMACY
(*Suby of* SISTERS OF THIRD ORDER OF ST FRANCIS) ★
3300 W Willow Knolls Dr, Peoria, IL 61614-8121
Tel (309) 655-2850 *Founded/Ownrshp* 1986
Sales 36.0MM^E *EMP* 440
SIC 8082 8742 8071 5912 7361 7371 Home health care services; Hospital & health services consultant; Medical laboratories; Drug stores & proprietary stores; Placement agencies; Computer software development; Home health care services; Hospital & health services consultant; Medical laboratories; Drug stores & proprietary stores; Placement agencies; Computer software development
Pr: Kevin D Schoeplein
CFO: Emiel Michelet
**CFO:* Jeff White
**Ch:* Sr Judith Ann Duvall
**Sec:* Sister Theresea Ann Brazceau
**Sec:* Sr Maria Elena Padilla
**Sec:* Sr Agnes Joseph Williams
Sr VP: Joseph Savala
Board of Directors: Vance C Parkhurst, Kevin D Schoeplein, Michael H Veeder

D-U-N-S 05-377-3255
OSF SAINT FRANCIS MEDICAL CENTER
530 Ne Glen Oak Ave, Peoria, IL 61637-0001
Tel (309) 655-2000 *Founded/Ownrshp* 1880
Sales 754.6MM^E *EMP* 14,000
SIC 8011 Medical centers; Medical centers
CEO: Keith Steffen
**CFO:* Ken Harbaugh
Dir Rad: Dawn Miller
Surgeon: Linda Conlee

OSF ST ELIZABETH MEDICAL CTR
See OTTAWA REGIONAL HOSPITAL & HEALTHCARE CENTER

D-U-N-S 13-990-8995
OSF ST ELIZABETH MEDICAL CTR
1100 E Norris Dr, Ottawa, IL 61350-1604
Tel (970) 242-0920 *Founded/Ownrshp* 2004
Sales 156.8M *EMP* 600^E
SIC 8062 General medical & surgical hospitals; General medical & surgical hospitals
CEO: Robert Chaffin
**VP:* Judy Christianson

D-U-N-S 61-032-1221
OSF ST JOSEPH MEDICAL CENTER BLOOMINGTON
2200 E Washington St, Bloomington, IL 61701-4364
Tel (309) 662-3311 *Founded/Ownrshp* 1880
Sales 99.6MM^E *EMP* 1,000
SIC 8011 Medical centers; Medical centers
CEO: James Moore
**Pr:* Sister Diane Mureen
**Pr:* Kenneth Natzke
**COO:* Larry E Wills
Dir Rx: Michael Novario

D-U-N-S 80-902-0873
■ **OSG AMERICA LP**
(*Suby of* OVERSEAS SHIPHOLDING GROUP INC) ★
302 Knights Run Ave, Tampa, FL 33602-5962
Tel (813) 209-0600 *Founded/Ownrshp* 2007
Sales 36.1MM^E *EMP* 200^E
Accts Ernst & Young Llp Tampa Flo
SIC 4424 Deep sea domestic transportation of freight; Intercoastal transportation, freight; Water transportation to noncontiguous territories, freight; Deep sea domestic transportation of freight; Intercoastal transportation, freight; Water transportation to noncontiguous territories, freight
CFO: Henry P Flinter
Sr Cor Off: Eric Smith
Sr VP: Ian T Blackley
Sr VP: James I Edelson
VP: Christopher Flanagan
VP: Henry Flinter
VP: Rosalee Fortune
VP: Rob Lorigan
VP: Jack Robinson
VP: Matthew Yacavone
Prin: Morten Arntzen
Board of Directors: Steven T Benz, James G Dolphin, Kathleen C Haines, Robert E Johnston

OSG BILLING SERVICES
See OUTPUT SERVICES GROUP INC

D-U-N-S 05-539-8853 IMP
OSG USA INC
(*Suby of* OSG CORPORATION)
676 E Fullerton Ave, Glendale Heights, IL 60139-2538
Tel (630) 790-1400 *Founded/Ownrshp* 1968
Sales 76.5MM^E *EMP* 140
SIC 5084 3541 Machine tools & metalworking machinery; Machine tools, metal cutting type; Machine tools & metalworking machinery; Machine tools, metal cutting type
CEO: Gohei Osawa
**Pr:* Michael Grantham
**Ex VP:* Jeffry Tennant
Sr VP: Tak Kojima
Dist Mgr: Matt Dahlberg
Dist Mgr: Chris Dravis
Dist Mgr: Jim Morris
Dist Mgr: Wayne Pickard

D-U-N-S 02-143-3636 IMP
OSGOOD INDUSTRIES INC
601 Burbank Rd, Oldsmar, FL 34677-4903
Tel (813) 448-9041 *Founded/Ownrshp* 1976
Sales 32.7MM^E *EMP* 120
SIC 3561 3444 3565 8711 Pumps & pumping equipment; Sheet metalwork; Packaging machinery; Bag opening, filling & closing machines; Engineering services; Pumps & pumping equipment; Sheet metalwork; Packaging machinery; Bag opening, filling & closing machines; Engineering services
Ch Bd: Martin Mueller Sr
**Pr:* Martin J Mueller Jr
**VP:* Richard W Mueller
Genl Mgr: Kenneth Krause
IT Man: John Koch
Sfty Mgr: Gary McKinney
Mfg Mgr: Jeff Post
Natl Sales: Peter Perkins
Manager: Jonathan Viens
Sls Mgr: Mark Austin
Snr Mgr: John Cavanagh

D-U-N-S 61-276-0959
OSH 1 LIQUIDATING CORP
6450 Via Del Oro, San Jose, CA 95119-1208
Tel (408) 281-3500 *Founded/Ownrshp* 2013
Sales NA *EMP* 5,329
SIC 5251 Hardware

D-U-N-S 08-047-8782
OSHAUGHNESSY REALTY CO INC
PRUDENTIAL
4024 Salt Pointe Pkwy, Charleston, SC 29405-8419
Tel (843) 202-2016 *Founded/Ownrshp* 1976
Sales 90.0MM *EMP* 30
SIC 6531 Real estate agent, residential; Real estate agent, residential
CEO: Patrcia Scarafile
**Ch Bd:* Michael Oshaughnessy
**V Ch:* Grange Cuthbert
CFO: Walton Orvin
VP: Ross Rhudy
Ex Dir: Tom Daniel
Dir IT: Les Sease

D-U-N-S 02-953-4286 EXP
OSHER OIL CORP
COSTA OIL
9780 Nw 115th Way, Medley, FL 33178-1176
Tel (305) 883-3224 *Founded/Ownrshp* 1994
Sales 35.0MM *EMP* 20
SIC 5172

D-U-N-S 02-111-4251
OSHKOSH AREA SCHOOL DISTRICT
215 S Eagle St, Oshkosh, WI 54902-5624
Tel (920) 424-0160 *Founded/Ownrshp* 1890
Sales 71.0MM^E *EMP* 1,279
SIC 8211 Public elementary & secondary schools; Public elementary & secondary schools
**Pr:* Matthew Wiedenhoeft
**Treas:* Allison Garner
**VP:* Steve Dedow
Dir Sec: Tim Fox
Netwrk Eng: Aaron Heuvel
Pr Dir: Mike Nault
HC Dir: Matthew Kaemmerer

D-U-N-S 00-607-3043 IMP
■ **OSHKOSH BGOSH INC**
(*Suby of* CARTERS FACTORY OUTLET) ★
3438 Peachtree Rd Ne # 1800, Atlanta, GA 30326-1595
Tel (678) 791-1005 *Founded/Ownrshp* 1929
Sales 43.8MM^E *EMP* 400
SIC 5641 5611 Children's & infants' wear stores; Men's & boys' clothing stores; Children's & infants' wear stores; Men's & boys' clothing stores
CEO: Mike Casey
**Pr:* David Brown
Bd of Dir: Richard M Donnelly
VP: Mike Heider
Manager: Rami Dirbashi
Sales Asso: Alison Chavez
Sales Asso: Ava Mancing

D-U-N-S 00-610-8807
OSHKOSH COIL SPRING INC (WI)
3575 N Main St, Oshkosh, WI 54901-1232
Tel (920) 235-7620 *Founded/Ownrshp* 1959, 1998
Sales 35.0MM^E *EMP* 105
SIC 3495 Wire springs
Pr: Wayne Trembly
**VP:* Jeff Trembly

OSHKOSH COMMUNITY YMCA
See OSHKOSH COMMUNITY YOUNG MENS CHRISTIAN ASSOCIATION INC

D-U-N-S 09-634-5574
OSHKOSH COMMUNITY YOUNG MENS CHRISTIAN ASSOCIATION INC
OSHKOSH COMMUNITY YMCA
324 Washington Ave, Oshkosh, WI 54901-5042
Tel (920) 236-3380 *Founded/Ownrshp* 1962
Sales 7.5MM *EMP* 450^E
Accts Clifton Gunderson Llp Oshkosh
SIC 8641 8351 8322 7991 Youth organizations; Child day care services; Individual & family services; Physical fitness facilities; Youth organizations; Child day care services; Individual & family services; Physical fitness facilities
Pr: Tom Blaze
Ofcr: Amy Albright
**VP:* Jeff Sthneider
Ex Dir: Jeff Schneider

D-U-N-S 00-607-0445 IMP/EXP
▲ **OSHKOSH CORP** (WI)
2307 Oregon St, Oshkosh, WI 54902-7062
Tel (920) 235-9151 *Founded/Ownrshp* 1917
Sales 6.1MMM *EMP* 13,300
Accts Deloitte & Touche Llp Milwauk
Tkr Sym OSK *Exch* NYS
SIC 3711 3531 3715 Motor vehicles & car bodies; Military motor vehicle assembly; Fire department vehicles (motor vehicles), assembly of; Snow plows (motor vehicles), assembly of; Mixers, concrete; Truck trailers; Motor vehicles & car bodies; Military motor vehicle assembly; Fire department vehicles (motor vehicles), assembly of; Snow plows (motor vehicles), assembly of; Mixers, concrete; Truck trailers
CEO: Charles L Szews
**Ch Bd:* Richard M Donnelly
Pr: Wilson R Jones
CFO: David M Sagehorn
Ofcr: Janet L Hogan
Ex VP: Bryan J Blankfield
Ex VP: Joseph H Kimmitt
Ex VP: Gary Schaniedel
Ex VP: Donald Verhoff
VP: Patrick N Davidson
VP: Paul Gosling
VP: W John
VP: Jeff Koga
VP: John W Randjelovic
Board of Directors: Richard G Sim, Keith J Allman, William S Wallace, Peter B Hamilton, Kathleen J Hempel, Leslie F Kenne, Steven C Mizell, Stephen D Newlin, Craig P Omtvedt, Duncan J Palmer, John S Shiely

D-U-N-S 07-946-7211
■ **OSHKOSH DEFENSE LLC**
(*Suby of* OSHKOSH CORP) ★
2307 Oregon St, Oshkosh, WI 54902-7062
Tel (920) 235-9151 *Founded/Ownrshp* 2014
Sales 450.6MM^E *EMP* 2,100^E
SIC 3711 3531 3715 Motor vehicles & car bodies; Military motor vehicle assembly; Fire department vehicles (motor vehicles), assembly of; Snow plows (motor vehicles), assembly of; Mixers, concrete; Truck trailers; Motor vehicles & car bodies; Military motor vehicle assembly; Fire department vehicles (motor vehicles), assembly of; Snow plows (motor vehicles), assembly of; Mixers, concrete; Truck trailers
CEO: Charles L Szews
Pr: John Bryant
**Pr:* Wilson R Jones
**CFO:* David M Sagehorn
Ofcr: Bridgette Lorrigan-Schuh
Ex VP: Richard Andrewhove
**Ex VP:* Bryan J Blankfield
VP: George Mansfield
VP: Bill Mooney
Prgrm Mgr: Brian Hickey
Rgnl Mgr: Jeff Krumrei

OSHKOSH PUBLIC LIBRARY
See CITY OF OSHKOSH

D-U-N-S 17-808-4786 IMP/EXP
OSHKOSH SPECIALTY VEHICLES LLC
FRONTLINE COMMUNICATIONS
12770 44th St N, Clearwater, FL 33762-4713
Tel (727) 561-9392 *Founded/Ownrshp* 1984
Sales NA *EMP* 446
SIC 3713 3711 Truck & bus bodies; Motor vehicles & car bodies

D-U-N-S 13-350-2612
OSHMAN FAMILY JEWISH COMMUNITY CENTER
3921 Fabian Way, Palo Alto, CA 94303-4606
Tel (650) 223-8654 *Founded/Ownrshp* 1988
Sales 21.3MM *EMP* 200
Accts Hood & Strong Llp San Francis
SIC 8322 Community center; Community center
Ex Dir: Alan Sataloff
**CFO:* Haim Hovav
**Dir IT:* Paul Raczynski

OSI
See OAKLAND FOODS LLC

OSI
See REDI-SERVE FOODS LIMITED PARTNERSHIP

OSI
See OBJECTIVE SYSTEMS INTEGRATORS INC

OSI
See OPEN SOLUTIONS INC

D-U-N-S 96-665-6217 IMP
OSI ACQUISITION CORP
ONE STROKE INKS & SUPPLIES
458 Roberts Ave, Louisville, KY 40214-3002
Tel (502) 366-1070 *Founded/Ownrshp* 1997
Sales 22.9MM^E *EMP* 40
SIC 5085 5084 2893 Ink, printers'; Printing trades machinery, equipment & supplies; Screen process ink
Owner: Jon Eldon Golightly
**VP:* Thomas J Golightly

D-U-N-S 93-338-0420
OSI CONSULTING INC
5950 Canoga Ave Ste 300, Woodland Hills, CA 91367-5041
Tel (818) 992-2700 *Founded/Ownrshp* 1995
Sales 48.4MM^E *EMP* 131
SIC 7379 Computer related consulting services; Computer related consulting services
CEO: Kumar Yamani
Pr: Sriram Ranganathan
**Pr:* Suzette White
Sr VP: Manoj Devireddy
VP: Pavlos Alexandrou
VP: Martin Mathias
VP: Lisa Smith
Brnch Mgr: Maurice Gelfo
Snr Sftwr: Kishore Kasulanati
Sftwr Eng: Gemma Carbonilla
S&M/VP: Michael Javier

D-U-N-S 13-844-1386 IMP
■ **OSI ELECTRONICS INC**
(*Suby of* OSI SYSTEMS INC) ★
12533 Chadron Ave, Hawthorne, CA 90250-4807
Tel (310) 978-0516 *Founded/Ownrshp* 2003
Sales 36.3MM^E *EMP* 175^E

SIC 3672 Printed circuit boards; Printed circuit boards
Pr: Paul Morben
*Pr: Bruce Macdonald
*COO: Alex Colquhoun
*VP: Lou Campana
VP: Michael Cox
VP: Jim Viviani
Exec: Alex Calhoun
Prgrm Mgr: Angela Cedillo
Prgrm Mgr: Karen Lacasse
Mfg Mgr: Mario Heredia
Ql Cn Mgr: Larry Martinez

D-U-N-S 61-712-5927
OSI ENVIRONMENTAL INC
300 Fayal Rd, Eveleth, MN 55734-1516
Tel (218) 744-3064 Founded/Ownrshp 1988
Sales 22.6MM EMP 87
Accts Mcgladrey Llp Madison Wiscon
SIC 4959 4953 Environmental cleanup services; Recycling, waste materials; Environmental cleanup services; Recycling, waste materials
Pr: George Rosier
*Sec: Robert Rivas
*VP: Richard Byhre

OSI GROUP
See OSI INTERNATIONAL INC

D-U-N-S 78-884-7148 IMP/EXP
OSI GROUP LLC
1225 Corp Blvd Ste 300, Aurora, IL 60505
Tel (630) 851-6600 Founded/Ownrshp 2001
Sales 2.7MMM^E EMP 9,200^E
SIC 2099 Food preparations; Food preparations
CEO: Sheldon Lavin
Pr: Mark Chaplin
*Pr: David G McDonald
Pr: Jitendra Sagili
*CFO: Bill Weimer
CFO: William J Weimer Jr
VP: William Albers
VP: Paul Carlstrom
VP: Stefan Chen
VP: Donna Coaxum
VP: Sherry Demeulenaere
VP: Sherry Demeulenaerer
VP: B K Girdhar
VP: Michael Irgang
VP: Thomas Kotsovos
VP: Phillip Pierchala
VP: Mark Richardson
VP: Kevin Scott
VP: Brady Sidwell
VP: Bernie Somenek

D-U-N-S 03-313-9648
OSI INC
11 Grandview Cir Ste 120, Canonsburg, PA 15317-6509
Tel (724) 743-6300 Founded/Ownrshp 1992
Sales 10.8MM^E EMP 400
SIC 7322 Adjustment & collection services; Adjustment & collection services
VP: Jan Cute
VP: Rick Lovato

D-U-N-S 02-562-6342 IMP/EXP
OSI INDUSTRIES LLC
OTTO & SONS DIV
(Suby of OSI GROUP LLC) ★
1225 Corp Blvd Ste 105, Aurora, IL 60505
Tel (630) 851-6600 Founded/Ownrshp 2004
Sales 1.3MMM^E EMP 9,200
SIC 2099 Ready-to-eat meals, salads & sandwiches; Ready-to-eat meals, salads & sandwiches
CEO: Sheldon Lavin
VP: Michael Boccio
VP: Gerald Kolschowsky
Ql Cn Mgr: Laurel Stoltzner

D-U-N-S 80-513-2396
OSI INTERNATIONAL INC
OSI GROUP
1225 Corp Blvd Ste 300, Aurora, IL 60505
Tel (630) 851-6600 Founded/Ownrshp 1988
Sales 22.9MM^E EMP 111
SIC 6719 Investment holding companies, except banks; Investment holding companies, except banks
Pr: Sheldon Lavin
*Treas: David Brooke

D-U-N-S 15-970-0640
OSI LLC
ONE STOP
412 Tennessee Ave, Charleston, WV 25302-2338
Tel (304) 926-3002 Founded/Ownrshp 1993
Sales 24.0MM^E EMP 150
SIC 5411 5812 Convenience stores, chain; Fast-food restaurant, chain
CIO: Kirk Ballard
Dir IT: John Clarke
IT Man: Brandon Schidle
VP Opers: Joe Crook

D-U-N-S 61-277-0974 IMP
■ **OSI OPTOELECTRONICS INC**
UNITED DETECTOR TECHNOLOGY
(Suby of OSI SYSTEMS INC) ★
12525 Chadron Ave, Hawthorne, CA 90250-4807
Tel (310) 978-0516 Founded/Ownrshp 1967
Sales 122.5MM^E EMP 1,205^E
SIC 3674 3827 3812 3672

D-U-N-S 10-901-4720 EXP
OSI PHARMACEUTICALS LLC
(Suby of ASTELLAS US HOLDING INC) ★
1 Bioscience Way Dr, Farmingdale, NY 11735
Tel (631) 962-2000 Founded/Ownrshp 2010
Sales 63.5MM^E EMP 535^E
SIC 2834 8731 Drugs affecting neoplasms & endrocrine systems; Drugs acting on the central nervous system & sense organs; Commercial physical research; Drugs affecting neoplasms & endrocrine systems; Drugs acting on the central nervous system & sense organs; Commercial physical research
CEO: Colin Goddard PHD
Pr: Gabriel Leung
Pr: Anker Lundemose MD PHD
CFO: Pierre Legault
Treas: Stephan Grillo
Ex VP: Robert L Simon
Sr VP: Linda E Amper PHD
Sr VP: Barbara A Wood
VP: Linda Ahlstrom
VP: Clare Carmichael
VP: Millie Cassidy
VP: Arlindo Castehleno
VP: Janna Christy-Bittel
VP: Knute Holum
VP: Santabarbara Pedro
VP: Pedro Santabarbara
VP: Robert Simon
VP: Joe Talamo
VP: Karsten Witt
Exec: Patricia Bentivegna
Assoc Dir: John Haley

OSI RESTAURANT PARTNERS, LLC
See BLOOMIN BRANDS

D-U-N-S 62-810-7245 IMP/EXP
■ **OSI RESTAURANT PARTNERS LLC**
OUTBACK STEAKHOUSE
(Suby of BLOOMIN BRANDS INC) ★
2202 N West Shore Blvd # 500, Tampa, FL 33607-5754
Tel (813) 282-1225 Founded/Ownrshp 2007
Sales 2.4MMM^E EMP 85,000^E
SIC 5812 5813 Steak restaurant; Grills (eating places); Seafood restaurants; Wine bar; Steak restaurant; Grills (eating places); Seafood restaurants; Wine bar
Pr: Jeff Smith
CFO: James Tipps
Ofcr: Jody L Bilney
Ofcr: Tanita Brooks
Ofcr: Dirk A Montgomery
Ex VP: Joseph J Kadow
Sr VP: Richard Renninger
Sr VP: Kaelyn Tomaszewski
VP: Chris Olson
VP: Jayne Portnoy
Off Mgr: Heather Salton
Board of Directors: Andrew B Balson, Robert D Basham, J Michael Chu, Philip H Loughlin, Mark E Nunnelly, Chris T Sullivan, Mark A Verdi

OSI SOFTWARE
See OSISOFT LLC

D-U-N-S 94-837-1356
■ **OSI SUBSIDIARY INC**
(Suby of OSI SYSTEMS INC) ★
12525 Chadron Ave, Hawthorne, CA 90250-4807
Tel (310) 978-0516 Founded/Ownrshp 1995
Sales 39.3MM^E EMP 400
SIC 3699 Laser systems & equipment; Laser systems & equipment
CEO: Deepak Chopra
*Pr: Ajay Mehra
*CFO: Alan Edrick
VP: Peter Bui
VP: Lou Campana
VP: Steven Cuffel
Dir IT: Victor Sze

D-U-N-S 17-829-5812 IMP/EXP
▲ **OSI SYSTEMS INC**
12525 Chadron Ave, Hawthorne, CA 90250-4807
Tel (310) 978-0516 Founded/Ownrshp 1987
Sales 958.2MM EMP 5,810
Accts Moss Adams Llp Los Angeles C
Tkr Sym OSIS Exch NGS
SIC 3674 3845 Semiconductors & related devices; Photoconductive cells; Photoelectric cells, solid state (electronic eye); Electromedical equipment; Ultrasonic scanning devices, medical; Semiconductors & related devices; Photoconductive cells; Photoelectric cells, solid state (electronic eye); Electromedical equipment; Ultrasonic scanning devices, medical
Ch Bd: Deepak Chopra
CFO: Alan Edrick
*Ex VP: Ajay Mehra
Ex VP: Victor Sze
Sr VP: Rick Merritt
VP: Manoocher Mansouri Aliabadi
VP: Chris Cook
VP: Michael Cox
VP: Ghazi Kashmolah
VP: Jonathan Lauer
VP: John Loo
VP: Nikhil A Meht
VP: Terry Patterson
VP: Kuldeep Tiwari
VP Bus Dev: Lane Beard
VP Bus Dev: Nikhil Mehta
Board of Directors: William F Ballhaus, David T Feinberg, Steven C Good, Meyer Luskin

OSIRIS SHOES
See CALIFORNIA BOARD SPORTS INC

D-U-N-S 92-789-0640
OSIRIS THERAPEUTICS INC
7015 Albert Einstein Dr, Columbia, MD 21046-1707
Tel (443) 545-1800 Founded/Ownrshp 1992
Sales 59.8MM EMP 217
Tkr Sym OSIR Exch NGM
SIC 2836 8731 Biological products, except diagnostic; Biotechnical research, commercial; Biological products, except diagnostic; Biotechnical research, commercial
Pr: Lode Debrabandere
*Ch Bd: Peter Friedli
CFO: Gregory I Law
Chf Mktg O: Jonathan M Hopper
Ofcr: Alla Danilkovitch
VP: Frank D Czworka Jr
VP: Earl R Fender
VP: Mark Pittenger
VP: Gil Tadmor
Assoc Dir: Sherry Elchin
Genl Mgr: Ther SA K Dixon
Board of Directors: Yves Huwyler, Jay M Moyes

D-U-N-S 96-476-4752
OSIRIUS GROUP LLC
21056 Briar Rose Dr, Macomb, MI 48044-2912
Tel (248) 583-2060 Founded/Ownrshp 2014
Sales 38.0MM^E EMP 16
SIC 8711 Consulting engineer; Consulting engineer
CEO: Timothy David Smith
Pr: Tony Bingham
CFO: Gerry Fedele
VP: Richard Cieszkowski
QC Dir: Andrew Skuta

D-U-N-S 04-494-6382
OSISOFT LLC
OSI SOFTWARE
777 Davis St Ste 250, San Leandro, CA 94577-6950
Tel (510) 297-5800 Founded/Ownrshp 1980
Sales 353.2MM^E EMP 900
SIC 7372 7371 7373 Computer software; Application computer software; Custom computer programming services; Computer integrated systems design; Application computer software; Custom computer programming services; Computer integrated systems design
Ch Bd: Dr J Patrick Kennedy
*Pr: Jenny Linton
*COO: Susanna Kass
*CFO: Bob Guilbault
Ofcr: Gary Zies S
*Sr VP: Martin Otterson
VP: Maureen Coveney
VP: Ted Gorrie
VP: Dominic John
*VP: Mike Kennedy
VP: Steve Nye
VP: John Oshea
VP: Steve Sarnecki
VP: Don Smith
Exec: Osvaldo Basur
Exec: Mike Ellis
Exec: Marc Gallant
*Co-Founder: Richard A Sara
Board of Directors: Ben Kortland, Jake Reynolds, Eric Streed

D-U-N-S 07-807-3517
OSKALOOSA COMMUNITY SCHOOL DISTRICT
1800 N 3rd St Ste 1, Oskaloosa, IA 52577-1869
Tel (641) 673-8345 Founded/Ownrshp 1872
Sales 17.5MM^E EMP 350
SIC 8211 Public elementary school; Public junior high school; Public senior high school; Public elementary school; Public junior high school; Public senior high school
Genl Mgr: Lisa Walston
IT Man: Chad Vink

D-U-N-S 00-529-5134
OSKALOOSA FOOD PRODUCTS CORP (IA)
OSKALOOSA PRODUCE CO
543 9th Ave E, Oskaloosa, IA 52577-3901
Tel (641) 673-3486 Founded/Ownrshp 1940, 1981
Sales 20.5MM^E EMP 82
SIC 2015 Egg processing
Pr: Blair J Van Zetten

OSKALOOSA PRODUCE CO
See OSKALOOSA FOOD PRODUCTS CORP

D-U-N-S 00-704-7592 IMP
OSKAR BLUES BREWERY LLC
1800 Pike Rd Unit B, Longmont, CO 80501-6794
Tel (303) 776-1914 Founded/Ownrshp 2007
Sales 36.0MM^E EMP 166^E
SIC 5813 Beer garden (drinking places)
Manager: Alex Comiski
Pgrm Dir: Sarah Leavitt
Snr Mgr: Dave Lawson

OSLA STUDENT LOANS SERVICING
See OKLAHOMA STUDENT LOAN AUTHORITY

D-U-N-S 13-967-4501
OSLER MEDICAL INC
930 S Hbr Cy Blvd Ste 200, Melbourne, FL 32901
Tel (321) 725-5050 Founded/Ownrshp 1995
Sales 31.9MM^E EMP 350
SIC 8011 Cardiologist & cardio-vascular specialist; Gastronomist; Pulmonary specialist, physician/surgeon; Surgeon; Cardiologist & cardio-vascular specialist; Gastronomist; Pulmonary specialist, physician/surgeon; Surgeon
*Ch Bd: Peter A Koretsky
*Treas: David Shapiro
Ofcr: Brenda Merchberger
Surgeon: Pachavit Kasemsap
*Surgeon: Joseph A Wasselle
Doctor: Hernandez Gabriel
Doctor: Raj Vellody

OSLIN NATION CO
See BABTEX INC

OSM WORLDWIDE
See ONE STOP MAILING LLC

D-U-N-S 05-825-8070 IMP
OSMAN AUTOMOTIVE CO INC
OSMAN LINCOLN JEEP
625 E Nasa Blvd, Melbourne, FL 32901-1943
Tel (321) 725-1100 Founded/Ownrshp 1963
Sales 22.5MM^E EMP 82
SIC 5511 5531 7538 5521 Automobiles, new & used; Automotive parts; General automotive repair shops; Used car dealers; Automobiles, new & used; Automotive parts; General automotive repair shops; Used car dealers
Pr: Perry Osman
*Sec: Paul Osman
Genl Mgr: JB Burkhart

D-U-N-S 06-621-0428
OSMAN CONSTRUCTION CORP
70 W Seegers Rd, Arlington Heights, IL 60005-3962
Tel (847) 593-2700 Founded/Ownrshp 2000
Sales 30.5MM^E EMP 90
SIC 1542 1541 Commercial & office building, new construction; Industrial buildings, new construction
Pr: Bruce Kozlowski
*Treas: Tim Silvetti
*VP: Larry Noesen
*VP: Dale Pryor

OSMAN LINCOLN JEEP
See OSMAN AUTOMOTIVE CO INC

D-U-N-S 04-725-0444 IMP
OSMONICS INC
OSMONICS MINNETONKA OPERATIONS
5951 Clearwater Dr, Hopkins, MN 55343-8995
Tel (952) 933-2277 Founded/Ownrshp 1969
Sales 207.4MM EMP 1,318
SIC 3569 3589 3561 3824 3823 3089 Filters; Sewage & water treatment equipment; Water treatment equipment, industrial; Pumps & pumping equipment; Integrating & totalizing meters for gas & liquids; Industrial flow & liquid measuring instruments; Flow instruments, industrial process type; Fluidic devices, circuits & systems for process control; Plastic hardware & building products; Filters; Sewage & water treatment equipment; Water treatment equipment, industrial; Pumps & pumping equipment; Integrating & totalizing meters for gas & liquids; Industrial flow & liquid measuring instruments; Flow instruments, industrial process type; Fluidic devices, circuits & systems for process control; Plastic hardware & building products
Ch Bd: D Dean Spatz
Pr: Edward J Fierko
CFO: Keith B Robinson
Bd of Dir: Ralph Crump
Bd of Dir: William Eykamp
Bd of Dir: Wil Pergande
Bd of Dir: Verity Smith
Bd of Dir: Michael Snow
Sr VP: Roger S Miller
VP: Emanuel Amato
VP: Lee Comb
VP: Howard Dicke
VP: Bjarne Nicholaisen
VP: Bjarne N Nicolaisen
Div/Sub He: Michael Fabich
Div/Sub He: Clifford Frith
Div/Sub He: Patrick Kelly
Div/Sub He: Kurt Weintauer
Div/Sub He: Kurt Weitnauer
Board of Directors: Charles M Brennan, Ralph E Crump, William Eykamp, Charles W Palmer, Verity C Smith

OSMONICS MINNETONKA OPERATIONS
See OSMONICS INC

D-U-N-S 12-850-9804 IMP
■ **OSMOSE HOLDINGS INC**
(Suby of OAKTREE CAPITAL MANAGEMENT LP) ★
980 Ellicott St, Buffalo, NY 14209-2323
Tel (716) 882-5905 Founded/Ownrshp 2012
Sales 213.4MM^E EMP 1,335
SIC 2491 Preserving (creosoting) of wood; Preserving (creosoting) of wood
Pr: James R Spengler Jr
*CFO: Michael R Leach
*VP: David L Bradley
VP: Daniel Doherty
VP: Donnie Lander
VP: Jim McGiffert
Dist Mgr: Joe Dobyns
CTO: Joseph Jeffries
IT Man: Walter Jaworski
Opers Mgr: Christopher Macauley

D-U-N-S 12-851-0141
OSMOSE UTILITIES SERVICES INC
635 Highway 74 S, Peachtree City, GA 30269-3003
Tel (770) 632-6700 Founded/Ownrshp 2015
Sales 158.9MM^E EMP 1,335^E
SIC 8741 8711 1623 Underground utilities contractor; Industrial management; Engineering services; Communication line & transmission tower construction
Pr: Ron Childress
VP: Joe Zamborsky
VP: Rich Ziobro
Opers Mgr: Toby Spelling

D-U-N-S 03-186-1768
OSNABROCK FARMERS CO OP ELEVATORS
434 Yellow Brick Rd, Osnabrock, ND 58269
Tel (701) 496-3111 Founded/Ownrshp 1920
Sales 41.0MM EMP 17
SIC 5153 Grain elevators; Grain elevators
Pr: Larry Treleaven
*VP: Keith Lorenz

D-U-N-S 82-697-7121 IMP
■ **OSO BIOPHARMACEUTICAL MANUFACTURING LLC**
(Suby of ALO ACQUISITION LLC) ★
4401 Alexander Blvd Ne, Albuquerque, NM 87107-6804
Tel (505) 923-1500 Founded/Ownrshp 2014
Sales 105.8MM^E EMP 335^E
SIC 2834 Pharmaceutical preparations; Pharmaceutical preparations
Pr: Milton Boyer
*CFO: Julie Miner
Ex VP: Rick Lapointe
Prgrm Mgr: Sara Thomas

D-U-N-S 92-655-2688
OSPREY RIDGE HEALTHCARE CENTER INC
PHOENIX HEALTHCARE GROUP
45 N Scott St, Carbondale, PA 18407-1833
Tel (570) 282-1099 Founded/Ownrshp 1996
Sales 631.1MM EMP 105
SIC 8051 8052 Skilled nursing care facilities; Intermediate care facilities; Skilled nursing care facilities; Intermediate care facilities
Pr: Gregory J Salko MD
HC Dir: Mary Brunk

D-U-N-S 80-952-5582 IMP
OSRAM OPTO SEMICONDUCTORS INC
(Suby of OSRAM GMBH)
1150 Kifer Rd Ste 100, Sunnyvale, CA 94086-5302
Tel (408) 588-3800 Founded/Ownrshp 2001
Sales 35.6MM^E EMP 112
SIC 5065 Semiconductor devices; Semiconductor devices
Pr: Thomas Shottes
*CFO: Ron Terry
IT Man: Corry Guinn

D-U-N-S 03-174-6456 IMP/EXP
OSRAM SYLVANIA INC
(Suby of OSRAM LICHT AG)
200 Ballardvale St # 305, Wilmington, MA 01887-1074
Tel (978) 570-3000 Founded/Ownrshp 1958, 2013
Sales 2.2MMM^E EMP 7,400
SIC 3646 3641 3647 3643 3297 Commercial indusl & institutional electric lighting fixtures; Electric lamps; Headlights (fixtures), vehicular; Current-carrying wiring devices; Crucibles: graphite, magnesite, chrome, silica, etc.; Commercial indusl & institutional electric lighting fixtures; Electric lamps; Headlights (fixtures), vehicular; Current-carrying wiring devices; Crucibles: graphite, magnesite, chrome, silica, etc.
Pr: Richard Leaman
COO: William Moore
COO: Nick Papathanasiou
CFO: Martin Goetzler
Ex VP: Ashel Parmelee
*Sr VP: Joerg Ayrle
Sr VP: Jeff Hunt
*VP: Jane Running
VP: William Schwidder
Dir Risk M: Christine Sheedy
Assoc Dir: Chuck McMahon
Assoc Dir: Don Varley

D-U-N-S 19-920-2698
OSROUTE ONE CORP
SANSONE RT 1 HYUNDAI
90 100 Rr 1, Avenel, NJ 07001
Tel (732) 815-0500 Founded/Ownrshp 1986
Sales 44.3MM^E EMP 150
SIC 5511 Automobiles, new & used; Automobiles, new & used
Pr: Paul Sansone Jr
CFO: Bruce Winkler

OSS
See OHIO SECURITY SYSTEMS INC

OSS HEALTH
See OSS ORTHOPAEDIC HOSPITAL LLC

OSS HEALTH
See OSS ORTHOPAEDIC HOSPITAL REALTY LP

D-U-N-S 96-465-0399
OSS ORTHOPAEDIC HOSPITAL LLC
OSS HEALTH
(Suby of OTPD SPN SPT OF WTN PA PC) ★
1861 Powder Mill Rd, York, PA 17402-4723
Tel (717) 848-4800 Founded/Ownrshp 2009
Sales 30.5MM EMP 30
SIC 8062 General medical & surgical hospitals; General medical & surgical hospitals
CEO: Todd Lord
Dir Rx: Meghan McNelly
Prin: Julie M Groscost
Surgeon: River Elliott
Doctor: Joseph E Alhadeff
Doctor: Brian Bixler
Doctor: David L Cohen
Doctor: Michael B Furman
Doctor: David J Granger
Doctor: Dennis M Grolman
Doctor: Kamran Majid

D-U-N-S 96-653-6562
OSS ORTHOPAEDIC HOSPITAL REALTY LP
OSS HEALTH
(Suby of OTPD SPN SPT OF WTN PA PC) ★
1861 Powder Mill Rd, York, PA 17402-4723
Tel (717) 848-4800 Founded/Ownrshp 2009
Sales 19.9MM^E EMP 325
SIC 6531 Real estate agents & managers; Real estate agents & managers
CEO: Todd Lord
Prin: Steven Triantafyllou
Nurse Mgr: Elizabeth Maurice
Doctor: Joseph E Alhadeff

OSSA
See OLYMPUS SCIENTIFIC SOLUTIONS AMERICAS CORP

OSSEO AREA PUBLIC SCHOOLS
See INDEPENDENT SCHOOL DISTRICT 279

D-U-N-S 11-815-8760
OSSEO AREA SCHOOL
OSSEO AREA SCHOOL DISTRICT 279
11200 93rd Ave N, Maple Grove, MN 55369-3669
Tel (763) 391-7007 Founded/Ownrshp 1930
Sales 111.4M EMP 3,000
SIC 8211 Public elementary & secondary schools; Public elementary & secondary schools
Prgrm Mgr: Corrie Craig

OSSEO AREA SCHOOL DISTRICT 279
See OSSEO AREA SCHOOL

D-U-N-S 04-478-5798
OSSEO-BROOKLYN SCHOOL BUS CO
SLEEPY EYE BUS LINE
11800 95th Ave N, Maple Grove, MN 55369-5539
Tel (763) 425-2542 Founded/Ownrshp 1967
Sales 28.7MM^E EMP 280
SIC 4151 4111 4141 School buses; Local & suburban transit; Local bus charter service; School buses; Local & suburban transit; Local bus charter service
Pr: Scott Regan

D-U-N-S 79-868-8149
OSSI FUNDING INC
(Suby of ST JOHN HOLDINGS INC) ★
320 King Of Prussia Rd, Radnor, PA 19087-4440
Tel (610) 964-8702 Founded/Ownrshp 1989
Sales 6.3MM^E EMP 400
SIC 7381 Security guard service; Security guard service
Pr: Gregory J Russell

D-U-N-S 92-642-0568
OSSINING OPEN DOOR REALTY CORP
165 Main St, Ossining, NY 10562-4702
Tel (914) 941-1263 Founded/Ownrshp 2010
Sales 63.6MM EMP 2^E
SIC 6531 Real estate brokers & agents
Prin: Matthew Arnold

D-U-N-S 09-384-0403
OSSINING UNION FREE SCHOOL DISTRICT
190 Croton Ave, Ossining, NY 10562-4504
Tel (914) 941-7700 Founded/Ownrshp 1900
Sales 36.6MM^E EMP 750
SIC 8211 Public senior high school; Public junior high school; Public elementary school; Kindergarten; Public senior high school; Public junior high school; Public elementary school; Kindergarten
Bd of Dir: Nicole Reis
Schl Brd P: Bill Kress
Psych: Kendall McFarlane

D-U-N-S 13-815-7540
OSSINING VILLAGE OF INC
FINANCE DEPT
16 Croton Ave Ste 2, Ossining, NY 10562-4953
Tel (914) 941-3554 Founded/Ownrshp 1813
Sales NA EMP 277
Accts O Connor Davies Llp Harrison
SIC 9111 Mayors' offices; ; Mayors' offices;
*Treas: Thomas Warren
Trst: John Codman
Trst: Robert Daraio
Trst: Omar Herrera
Trst: Manuel Quezada
Dir: Valerie Monastra
Brnch Mgr: Donald Sarrell
Board of Directors: George Joiner, Ernest McFadden, Maryann Roberts

OSSTEM
See HIOSSEN INC

D-U-N-S 13-928-0028 IMP/EXP
OSSUR AMERICAS INC
(Suby of OSSUR HF)
27051 Towne Centre Dr, Foothill Ranch, CA 92610-2804
Tel (949) 362-3883 Founded/Ownrshp 1984
Sales 105.6MM^E EMP 500^E
SIC 3842 Orthopedic appliances
CEO: Mahesh Mansukhani
*CFO: Avanindra Chaturvedi
VP: Egill Jonsson
VP: Lou Ruggiero
Area Mgr: Steven Brachman
Area Mgr: Sean Dougherty
Area Mgr: Sandra Kohler
Area Mgr: Megann Yerigan
Natl Sales: Jenna Calomeris
Sls Mgr: Chris Watson

D-U-N-S 07-387-7297
OST INC (DC)
OPTIMAL SOLUTIONS AND TECH
2101 L St Nw Ste 800, Washington, DC 20037-1657
Tel (202) 466-8099 Founded/Ownrshp 1999
Sales 37.8MM^E EMP 365^E
Accts Ravi C Narayan Cpa Merrifie
SIC 7373 7371 Computer systems analysis & design; Computer software development; Computer systems analysis & design; Computer software development
Pr: Vijay Narula
Board of Directors: Anil Chaudhry

D-U-N-S 10-386-5119 IMP
OST TRUCKING CO INC
1205 68th St, Baltimore, MD 21237-2516
Tel (410) 866-7700 Founded/Ownrshp 1982
Sales 28.4MM^E EMP 200
Accts Stegman & Company Baltimore
SIC 4213 4225 4214 Trucking, except local; General warehousing; Local trucking with storage; Trucking, except local; General warehousing; Local trucking with storage
CEO: Richard Amato
*Pr: Edward J Peach
*Sec: Michael Amato
IT Man: Zon Goss

D-U-N-S 78-509-6608
OSTENDO TECHNOLOGIES INC
6185 Paseo Del Norte # 200, Carlsbad, CA 92011-1152
Tel (760) 710-3003 Founded/Ownrshp 2005
Sales 20.9MM^E EMP 52^E
SIC 8731 Electronic research
CEO: Hussein S El-Ghoroury
Pr: Benjamin Haskell
*Pr: Joaquin Silva
VP: Seongsoo Kim
VP: Wayne Lutje
Snr Sftwr: Vincent Buonassisi
Snr Sftwr: Khai Trinh
IT Man: Mike Zaparyniuk
S&M/VP: Damian Roncevich

D-U-N-S 60-641-7780
■ **OSTEOMED LLC**
(Suby of MARMON GROUP LLC) ★
3885 Arapaho Rd, Addison, TX 75001-4314
Tel (972) 677-4600 Founded/Ownrshp 2002
Sales 83.1MM^E EMP 250
SIC 3841 Surgical instruments & apparatus; Surgical instruments & apparatus
Pt: Walter J Humann
VP: Rebecca Ellis
VP: Carolyn Harvey
VP: Greg Schmitz
Exec: Katie Hancock
Rgnl Mgr: Sean Thompson
Dir IT: Robert Astone
IT Man: Vickie Thompson
Mfg Mgr: Don Trent
Prd Mgr: Sterling Thomason
Ql Cn Mgr: Craig Portz

D-U-N-S 79-404-8298
OSTEOPATHIC HERITAGE FOUNDATION
1500 Lake Shore Dr # 230, Columbus, OH 43204-3800
Tel (614) 737-4370 Founded/Ownrshp 1961
Sales 21.1MM EMP 7
SIC 8399 Social change association; Social change association
Pr: Richard A Vincent
*Treas: Richard A Mitchell

D-U-N-S 15-738-4306
■ **OSTEOTECH INC**
MEDTRONIC
(Suby of MEDTRONIC INC) ★
51 James Way, Eatontown, NJ 07724-2289
Tel (732) 542-2800 Founded/Ownrshp 2010
Sales 61.4MM^E EMP 297^E
SIC 3841 Surgical & medical instruments; Surgical & medical instruments
Pr: Sam Owusu-Akyaw
*Pr: Robert M Wynalek
*CFO: Mark H Burroughs
CFO: Mark H Burroughs
*Ex VP: Robert W Honneffer
Ex VP: Robert Honneffer
VP: C Huang
VP Opers: Richard J Ragula

D-U-N-S 02-883-9587
OSTERKAMP TRUCKING INC
1350 Philadelphia St, Pomona, CA 91766-5563
Tel (909) 590-8200 Founded/Ownrshp 1962
Sales 29.9MM^E EMP 100
SIC 4213 4212 Building materials transport; Household goods transport; Local trucking, without storage; Building materials transport; Household goods transport; Local trucking, without storage
Pr: Hank Osterkamp
COO: Scott Hill
Ex VP: Yazhid Malone
*Ex VP: Fred Sotoodeh
VP: Shelley Fajardo
VP: Steve Pilcher
Dir Risk M: John Gilson
Dir IT: Billy Brown
IT Man: Francisco Morales
Sfty Dirs: Wendy Ockerman
Trfc Dir: Guillermo Ceja

D-U-N-S 06-035-6540
OSTERMAN & CO INC
OSTERMAN TRADING DIV
726 S Main St, Cheshire, CT 06410-3472
Tel (203) 272-2233 Founded/Ownrshp 1976
Sales 311.7MM^E EMP 98
SIC 5162 Plastics materials; Plastics materials
Ch Bd: James O Dwyer
*Pr: John Dwyer
*Treas: Jennifer Vestergaard
*Ex VP: Jeff Elsen
*Ex VP: Glenn Fredericks
VP: Mike Connolly
VP: Christopher Conrad
VP: Dave Franco
*VP: Mike Sentelik
Dir IT: Ted Pettit
S&M/VP: David Dever

D-U-N-S 07-869-0787
■ **OSTERMAN PROPANE LLC**
(Suby of NGL ENERGY PARTNERS LP) ★
1 Memorial Sq Ste 101, Whitinsville, MA 01588-3010
Tel (508) 372-9440 Founded/Ownrshp 2011
Sales 39.5MM^E EMP 4
SIC 5172 Gases, liquefied petroleum (propane)
Pr: Vincent J Osterman

OSTERMAN TRADING DIV
See OSTERMAN & CO INC

D-U-N-S 82-461-4721
OSTHOFF MANAGEMENT CORP
OSTHOFF RESORT THE
101 Osthoff Ave, Elkhart Lake, WI 53020-1976
Tel (920) 876-3366 Founded/Ownrshp 1995
Sales 26.3MM^E EMP 350
SIC 7011 Resort hotel; Resort hotel
Genl Mgr: Lola Roeh
Exec: Jodie Baus
Exec: Chad Kornetzke
Mktg Dir: Chad Buros

OSTHOFF RESORT THE
See OSTHOFF MANAGEMENT CORP

D-U-N-S 02-298-2037
OSTRANDER FARMERS CO-OP
208 Main St, Ostrander, MN 55961-5036
Tel (507) 657-2234 Founded/Ownrshp 1910
Sales 37.2MM EMP 25
Accts Carlson Highland & Co Llp Am
SIC 5153 Grain elevators; Grain elevators
Ex Dir: Matt Litwiller
*Pr: Rick John
*VP: Scott Rindells

D-U-N-S 00-949-0640 IMP
OSTROM CO
OSTROM MUSHROOM FARMS
8322 Steilacoom Rd Se, Olympia, WA 98513-2057
Tel (360) 491-1410 Founded/Ownrshp 1968
Sales 22.0MM EMP 365
SIC 0182

OSTROM MUSHROOM FARMS
See OSTROM CO

D-U-N-S 00-144-1120
OSTROW ELECTRICAL CO (MA)
REILLY ELECTRICAL DIVISION
9 Mason St, Worcester, MA 01609-1803
Tel (508) 754-2641 Founded/Ownrshp 1939
Sales 32.1MM^E EMP 180
SIC 1731 General electrical contractor; General electrical contractor
Pr: Jonathan S Ostrow
*Treas: Matthew L Ostrow
*Ex VP: Philip Ostrow

OSU BOOKSTORE
See OREGON STATE UNIVERSITY BOOKSTORE INC

D-U-N-S 05-495-8798
OSU FEDERAL CREDIT UNION SPECIAL SERVICES INC
1980 Nw 9th St, Corvallis, OR 97330-2179
Tel (541) 714-4000 Founded/Ownrshp 1954
Sales NA EMP 195
SIC 6061 Federal credit unions; Federal credit unions
Pr: Richard Hein
CFO: Bonnie Humphrey
CFO: Carlyn Roy
Ofcr: Bonnie Anderson
Ofcr: Susan Wack
VP: Rhonda Heile
VP: Debra Riggle
VP Admn: William McKinney
Brnch Mgr: Kristin Hyde
Brnch Mgr: Jenipher Miller
CTO: Joanne Lecouvre

D-U-N-S 61-159-6557
OSU PATHOLOGY SERVICES LLC
1645 Neil Ave Rm 129, Columbus, OH 43210-1218
Tel (614) 247-6461 Founded/Ownrshp 2004
Sales 4.7MM^E EMP 300
SIC 8071 Pathological laboratory; Pathological laboratory

D-U-N-S 16-188-2253
OSU SURGERY LLC
700 Ackerman Rd Ste 350, Columbus, OH 43202-1583
Tel (614) 261-1141 Founded/Ownrshp 1986
Sales 25.0MM EMP 200
SIC 8011 Surgeon; Surgeon
*CFO: Chris Kaiser

D-U-N-S 07-165-1376
OSU-HARDING HOSPITAL INC
OHIO STATE UNIVERSITY
1670 Upham Dr, Columbus, OH 43210-1250
Tel (614) 293-9600 Founded/Ownrshp 1916
Sales 18.5MM EMP 305
SIC 8063 8361 8093 Psychiatric hospitals; Residential care; Specialty outpatient clinics; Psychiatric hospitals; Residential care; Specialty outpatient clinics
CEO: Radu Saveanu
CFO: Jill Glenn
Adm Dir: Timothy Moore
Psych: Erica Dawson
Psych: Mary Fristad Do
Psych: Helena Rempala
Child Psyc: Richard H Gilchrist
Child Psyc: Lacramioara Spetie
Doctor: Stephen Pariser
Nrsg Dir: Amy Hurley
Snr Mgr: Donald Rucker

OSU-UML
See OSU-UNIVERSITY MULTISPECTRAL LABORATORIES LLC

D-U-N-S 62-387-5601
OSU-UNIVERSITY MULTISPECTRAL LABORATORIES LLC
OSU-UML
(Suby of OKLAHOMA STATE UNIVERSITY) ★
500 W South Ave, Ponca City, OK 74601-6107
Tel (580) 767-8865 Founded/Ownrshp 2006
Sales 33.2MM EMP 23
Accts Keith Frazier & Surekha Sheore
SIC 8734 Testing laboratories; Testing laboratories
VP: Steve McKeever
Off Mgr: Sandy James
IT Man: Robert Scott

D-U-N-S 55-547-6183 IMP
OSULLIVAN ENTERPRISES INC
O' SULLIVAN VENDING & COFFEE
1525 Atteberry Ln, San Jose, CA 95131-1412
Tel (408) 971-4362 Founded/Ownrshp 2009
Sales 22.3MM^E EMP 120
SIC 5962 Food vending machines; Beverage vending machines; Cigarettes vending machines; Food vending machines; Beverage vending machines; Cigarettes vending machines
Pr: Jacob B O Sullivan

D-U-N-S 55-582-9725 IMP/EXP
OSULLIVAN FILMS INC
(Suby of KONRAD HORNSCHUCH INTERNATIONAL GMBH)
1944 Valley Ave, Winchester, VA 22601-6306
Tel (540) 667-6666 Founded/Ownrshp 2006
Sales 107.7MM^E EMP 521
SIC 3081 Vinyl film & sheet; Vinyl film & sheet
CEO: Denis Belzile
*Pr: Ewen Campbell
*CFO: Ronald G Shade
VP: Paul Nicolai
*VP: Dennis Ruen
Dir Lab: John Duncan
Genl Mgr: Eric Buchanan
DP Exec: Bartley Drew
QA Dir: Martha Jenkins
QA Dir: Rick Lineberg
Dir IT: Dennis Painter

D-U-N-S 78-109-6680
OSWALD CO INC
8549 Montgomery Rd Ste 3, Cincinnati, OH 45236-2366
Tel (513) 793-8080 Founded/Ownrshp 1991
Sales 29.3MM EMP 21

Accts Barnes Dennig & Co Ltd Cin
SIC 1542 1541 Industrial buildings & warehouses; Commercial & office building contractors; Commercial & office building contractors; Industrial buildings & warehouses
CEO: Ken C Oswald
**Sec:* Todd Haidet
**VP:* Jim Laber

OSWALD COMPANIES, THE
See JAMES B OSWALD CO

D-U-N-S 14-811-3475
■ OSWALD TRIPPE AND CO INC
BB & T
(*Suby of* BB&T INSURANCE SERVICES INC) ★
13515 Bell Tower Dr, Fort Myers, FL 33907-5944
Tel (239) 433-4535 *Founded/Ownrshp* 2009
Sales NA *EMP* 130^E^
SIC 6411 Insurance agents
CEO: Gary V Trippe
**Pr:* John Pollock
VP: John Belisle
VP: Wesley C Brewer Jr

D-U-N-S 07-160-0670
OSWEGO CITY SCHOOL DISTRICT
120 E 1st St Ste 1, Oswego, NY 13126-2100
Tel (315) 341-2001 *Founded/Ownrshp* 1957
Sales 43.3MM^E^ *EMP* 775
SIC 8211 Public elementary & secondary schools; Public elementary & secondary schools
Ofcr: Anthony Allison
Ofcr: Mark Pryor
Ofcr: Stephanie Spedding
Ofcr: Michael Wilson
Prin: Dean Goewey
Prin: Barb Parry
Prin: Gary Roy
Dir Sec: John Anderson
Trfc Dir: Andrew Germain
Psych: Rachel Baker
Psych: William Caufield

D-U-N-S 04-685-2547
OSWEGO COMMUNITY UNIT SCHOOL DISTRICT 308
4175 State Route 71, Oswego, IL 60543-8340
Tel (630) 636-3080 *Founded/Ownrshp* 1961
Sales 48.2MM^E^ *EMP* 587
Accts Mcgaldrey & Pullen Llp Chica
SIC 8211 Public elementary school; Public junior high school; Public senior high school; Public elementary school; Public junior high school; Public senior high school
COO: Maria Morales
Dir Sec: Val Paterson

D-U-N-S 01-078-2613
OSWEGO COUNTY BOCES
B RAYMER TECH
179 County Route 64, Mexico, NY 13114-4498
Tel (315) 963-4251 *Founded/Ownrshp* 1949
Sales 33.8MM^E^ *EMP* 903
SIC 8249 8211 Vocational schools; Elementary & secondary schools; Vocational schools; Elementary & secondary schools
**Prin:* Donna Donadella

D-U-N-S 09-197-5847
OSWEGO COUNTY OPPORTUNITIES INC
239 Oneida St, Fulton, NY 13069-1228
Tel (315) 598-4711 *Founded/Ownrshp* 1966
Sales 26.8MM *EMP* 650
Accts Grossman St Amour Syracuse
SIC 8361 8322 8351 4119 Home for the mentally handicapped; Self-help group home; Family (marriage) counseling; Geriatric social service; Meal delivery program; Child day care services; Local passenger transportation; Home for the mentally handicapped; Self-help group home; Family (marriage) counseling; Geriatric social service; Meal delivery program; Child day care services; Local passenger transportation
Pr: Joseph Carvana
CFO: Brian Greenhouse
**Ex Dir:* Diane C Currier
Prgrm Mgr: Christina Bentley
IT Man: Sarah Irland
IT Man: Sandy Wells
Opers Mgr: Tricia Clark
Doctor: Daniel Sanders

D-U-N-S 60-148-6488 IMP
OSWEGO HARBOR POWER LLC
261 Washington Blvd, Oswego, NY 13126-1751
Tel (315) 349-2341 *Founded/Ownrshp* 1999
Sales 38.4MM^E^ *EMP* 85
SIC 4911 Generation, electric power; Generation, electric power

D-U-N-S 01-077-2630
OSWEGO HOSPITAL INC
110 W 6th St, Oswego, NY 13126-2598
Tel (315) 349-5511 *Founded/Ownrshp* 1881
Sales 105.3MM *EMP* 1,200
Accts Fust Charles Chambers Llp Syr
SIC 8062 8063 General medical & surgical hospitals; Hospital for the mentally ill; General medical & surgical hospitals; Hospital for the mentally ill
CEO: Ann Gilpin
Pr: Margaret Glass
COO: Allison Duggan
**CFO:* Paul F Snyder
CIO: David Frasier
Software D: Mary Bucher
Software D: Mary McGowan
Software D: Jane Nalle
Software D: Katie Pagliaroli
Pharmcst: David Murray

D-U-N-S 08-866-4974
OSWEGO INDUSTRIES INC
7 Morrill Pl, Fulton, NY 13069-1597
Tel (315) 598-3108 *Founded/Ownrshp* 1977
Sales 9.0MM *EMP* 475
Accts Bonadio & Co Llp Syracuse Ny
SIC 8331 2448 8741 Sheltered workshop; Pallets, wood & wood with metal; Management services; Sheltered workshop; Pallets, wood & wood with metal; Management services
Pr: Cave Vickery
**Treas:* Richard Kemmis

D-U-N-S 84-754-3139 EXP
OT TRANS INC
201 S Babcock St, Melbourne, FL 32901-1209
Tel (321) 259-9880 *Founded/Ownrshp* 1993
Sales 21.1MM^E^ *EMP* 29
SIC 5088 5084 Transportation equipment & supplies; Industrial machinery & equipment
Pr: Antonio Gonzalez
CFO: Barbara Duval
Sales Asso: Lynnetta Devries

D-U-N-S 03-337-8629
OTA COMPRESSION LLC
102 Decker Ct Ste 204, Irving, TX 75062-2740
Tel (972) 831-1300 *Founded/Ownrshp* 2010
Sales 20.6MM^E^ *EMP* 102^E^
SIC 3585 Evaporative condensers, heat transfer equipment
Pr: Grant Swartzwelder
Genl Mgr: Brad Cox

D-U-N-S 78-362-9215
OTAC INC
HARDEE'S
528 College Pkwy Ste I, Annapolis, MD 21409-4694
Tel (410) 757-0446 *Founded/Ownrshp* 1991
Sales 27.5MM^E^ *EMP* 750
SIC 5812 Fast-food restaurant, chain; Fast-food restaurant, chain
Pr: Paul Cato
**VP:* Susan Cato
Dist Mgr: Gene Johnson

D-U-N-S 03-182-8783
OTAK INC
808 Sw 3rd Ave Ste 300, Portland, OR 97204-2426
Tel (503) 274-5445 *Founded/Ownrshp* 1981
Sales 91.9MM^E^ *EMP* 269
SIC 0781 8712 8711 8713 8742 8999 Landscape services; Architectural services; Civil engineering; Surveying services; Management consulting services; Earth science services; Landscape services; Architectural services; Civil engineering; Surveying services; Management consulting services; Earth science services
Pr: R Nicholas Loope
**Prin:* Don Hanson
**Prin:* Mike Teebles
**Prin:* Nico Vanderhorst
Off Admin: Nancy Acton
Off Admin: Britney Child
IT Man: Victor Prudhomme
Mktg Mgr: Courtney Hough
Snr PM: Troy Kent

D-U-N-S 07-872-6031
OTAY WATER DISTRICT (INC) (CA)
2554 Sweetwater Sprng Blvd, Spring Valley, CA 91978-2096
Tel (619) 670-2222 *Founded/Ownrshp* 1956
Sales 86.0MM *EMP* 170
Accts Teaman Ramirez & Smith Inc
SIC 4941 1623 Water supply; Water, sewer & utility lines; Water supply; Water, sewer & utility lines
Pr: Gary Croucher
**Pr:* Jose Lopez
**CFO:* Joseph R Beachem
CFO: Adolfo Segura
Ofcr: Armando Buelna
**Genl Mgr:* Mark Watton
CIO: Oscar Ramirez
CIO: Geoff Stevens
Netwrk Mgr: Thien Thie
Opers Mgr: Mike Kerr
Plnt Mgr: Gene Palop

D-U-N-S 96-343-0850
OTB ACQUISITION LLC
ON THE BORDER
2201 W Royal Ln Ste 240, Irving, TX 75063-3208
Tel (972) 499-3000 *Founded/Ownrshp* 2010
Sales 293.6MM^E^ *EMP* 8,000^E^
SIC 5812 Mexican restaurant; Mexican restaurant
CFO: Gary Harper
Genl Mgr: Darin Bowers

D-U-N-S 79-989-3370 IMP/EXP
■ OTC DIRECT INC
ORIENTAL TRADING COMPANY
(*Suby of* ORIENTAL TRADING CO INC) ★
4206 S 108th St, Omaha, NE 68137-1215
Tel (402) 331-5511 *Founded/Ownrshp* 2011
Sales 127.5MM^E^ *EMP* 1,000
SIC 5961 Catalog & mail-order houses; Catalog & mail-order houses
Pr: Sam S Taylor
**Pr:* Stephen R Frary
**Treas:* Steve Mendlik
VP: Chris Merritt
IT Man: Kim Lamb

D-U-N-S 83-021-6912
OTC GLOBAL HOLDINGS LP
5718 Westheimer Rd # 1300, Houston, TX 77057-5745
Tel (713) 358-5450 *Founded/Ownrshp* 2007
Sales 65.6MM^E^ *EMP* 230
SIC 6221 Commodity contracts brokers, dealers; Commodity contracts brokers, dealers
COO: Joe Kelly
Genl Pt: Otc Energy GP LLC
Pt: James Kauderer
Pt: Aabier Loya
Ex VP: John Klosek
Sr VP: Darren Hayes
CIO: Suresh Dongre
Snr Mgr: Campbell Faulkner

OTC INTERNATIONAL
See ANAYA GEMS INC

D-U-N-S 00-131-6686
OTC MARKETS GROUP INC
OTCM
304 Hudson St Rm 200, New York, NY 10013-1049
Tel (212) 896-4400 *Founded/Ownrshp* 1913, 1997
Sales 85.7MM^E^ *EMP* 74
Accts Deloitte & Touche Llp New Yor
SIC 6289 Stock quotation service
Pr: R Cromwell Coulson
CFO: Bea Ordonez
Ofcr: Michael T Corrao
Ex VP: Matthew Fuchs
Ex VP: Lisabeth Heese
Ex VP: Jason Paltrowitz
Comm Dir: Saskia Sidenfaden
Dir Bus: Andy Kyzyk
Mng Dir: Liz Heese
Software D: Papiya Misra
Snr Mgr: Juan Sanchez
Board of Directors: Gary Baddeley, Matthew Fuchs, Louisa Serene Schneider, Andrew Wimpfheimer, Neal Wolkoff

D-U-N-S 07-858-2804 IMP
OTC SERVICES INC
1776 Constitution Ave, Louisville, OH 44641
Tel (330) 871-2444 *Founded/Ownrshp* 2012
Sales 22.0MM^E^ *EMP* 80
SIC 3612 Transformers, except electric; Transformers, except electric
Pr: Robert Ganser Jr
**Sec:* Karen Kosko
IT Man: William Bruner

D-U-N-S 07-843-4220
■ OTC WORLDWIDE HOLDINGS INC
(*Suby of* BERKSHIRE HATHAWAY INC) ★
4206 S 108th St, Omaha, NE 68137-1215
Tel (800) 348-6483 *Founded/Ownrshp* 2012
Sales 846.8MM^E^ *EMP* 1,010^E^
SIC 4813 ;
CEO: Sam Taylor

OTCM
See OTC MARKETS GROUP INC

D-U-N-S 82-696-0010
OTEC INTERNATIONAL LLC
ABELL FNDTION ABELL VENTR FUND
111 S Calvert St Ste 2300, Baltimore, MD 21202-6182
Tel (410) 547-1300 *Founded/Ownrshp* 2000
Sales 28.0MM *EMP* 8
SIC 4911 2899 Electric services; Desalter kits, sea water; Electric services; Desalter kits, sea water
CFO: Francie Keenan
Ex VP: Barry Cole

OTECH
See OTECH CORP

D-U-N-S 11-250-7665 IMP
OTECH CORP
OTECH
4744 E Oaknoll Rd, Rolling Prairie, IN 46371-9491
Tel (219) 778-8001 *Founded/Ownrshp* 2006
Sales 38.9MM^E^ *EMP* 60
SIC 2821 Molding compounds, plastics
Pr: Jack Odonnell
Plnt Mgr: Tom McMeans

D-U-N-S 00-808-1283 IMP
OTECO INC
2828 Trout St, Houston, TX 77093-5546
Tel (713) 692-3532 *Founded/Ownrshp* 1938
Sales 32.5MM^E^ *EMP* 215
SIC 3561 3462 3599 Industrial pumps & parts; Iron & steel forgings; Machine shop, jobbing & repair; Industrial pumps & parts; Iron & steel forgings; Machine shop, jobbing & repair
Pr: William E Pielop III
**Sec:* Carl Moener
**VP:* James P Lester
VP: Doug Queen

D-U-N-S 14-863-2180
▲ OTELCO INC
505 3rd Ave E, Oneonta, AL 35121-1557
Tel (205) 625-3574 *Founded/Ownrshp* 1998
Sales 73.8MM *EMP* 254^E^
Tkr Sym OTEL *Exch* NGM
SIC 4813 8999 7372 Telephone communication, except radio; Local & long distance telephone communications; Long distance telephone communications; ; Communication services; Prepackaged software; Telephone communication, except radio; Local & long distance telephone communications; Long distance telephone communications; ; Communication services; Prepackaged software
Pr: Robert J Souza
Recvr: Johnny Box
CFO: Curtis L Garner Jr
Sr VP: Dennis K Andrews
Sr VP: Jerry C Boles
Sr VP: Edwin D Tisdale
VP: Sherre Campbell
VP: E Todd Wessing
Board of Directors: Norman C Frost, Howard J Haug, Stephen P Maccall, Brian A Ross, Gary L Sugarman

D-U-N-S 86-009-9167
■ OTENT INC
(*Suby of* MDC PARTNERS INC) ★
110 E Broward Blvd, Fort Lauderdale, FL 33301-3503
Tel (954) 862-2400 *Founded/Ownrshp* 2010
Sales 32.9MM^E^ *EMP* 350
Accts Frederick A Ciampa Cpa S
SIC 7311 Advertising agencies; Advertising agencies
CEO: Daniel K Gregory
**Sec:* Sean O'Toole

D-U-N-S 00-778-5835
OTERO COUNTY ELECTRIC COOPERATIVE INC
202 Burro Ave, Cloudcroft, NM 88317
Tel (575) 682-2521 *Founded/Ownrshp* 1940
Sales 31.1MM *EMP* 50
Accts Bolinger Segars Gilbert And Mo
SIC 4911 Electric services; Electric services
Pr: Randy Rabon

D-U-N-S 07-761-8023
OTERO COUNTY HOSPITAL ASSOCIATION INC
GERALD CHMPN REGIONAL MED CTR
2669 Scenic Dr, Alamogordo, NM 88310-8700
Tel (575) 439-6100 *Founded/Ownrshp* 1948
Sales 103.2MM *EMP* 600^E^
Accts Eide Bailly Llp Fargo Nd
SIC 8062 General medical & surgical hospitals; General medical & surgical hospitals
CEO: Jim Heckert
Pr: Richard Holmes
CFO: Michael Rolph
Chf Mktg O: Stephan Korec
Ofcr: Robert Heckert
VP: Mary Harding
VP: Karen O'Brien
VP: Catherine Rhyne
Exec: Young Cabos
Dir Lab: Vicki Leonard
Dir Rad: Renee Stanton

OTEX
See VIGNETTE CORP

OTHELLO COMMUNITY HOSPITAL
See ADAMS COUNTY PUBLIC HOSPITAL DISTRICT NO 3

D-U-N-S 10-008-0951
OTHELLO SCHOOL DISTRICT
1025 S 1st Ave, Othello, WA 99344-1845
Tel (509) 488-6195 *Founded/Ownrshp* 1908
Sales 29.3MM^E^ *EMP* 425
SIC 8211 Public elementary school; Public junior high school; Public senior high school; Public elementary school; Public junior high school; Public senior high school
Pr: Rob Simmons
Board of Directors: Tonny Ashton, Juan Garza

OTHER GUYS, THE
See DON SEBASTIANI & SONS INTERNATIONAL WINE NEGOCIANTS

OTHER STYLES - SEE OPERATION
See LUBRIQUIP INC

OTHER STYLES-SEE OPERATION
See P KAUFMANN INC

OTHER STYLES-SEE OPERATION
See COBORNS INC

D-U-N-S 83-320-8700 IMP
OTHER WORLD COMPUTING INC
(*Suby of* NEW CONCEPTS DEVELOPMENT CORP) ★
8 Galaxy Way, Woodstock, IL 60098-5900
Tel (815) 338-8685 *Founded/Ownrshp* 2009
Sales 43.6MM^E^ *EMP* 72
SIC 5961 General merchandise, mail order
Pr: Lawrence Richard O'Connor
**Pr:* Jen Soule
VP: Jonathan Ellihou
IT Man: Jeff Pringey
Sales Exec: Jennifer Soule
Mktg Dir: Joshua Sularski
Mktg Mgr: Grant Dahlke
Sls Mgr: John Maldonado
Sls Mgr: Rick Van Dyne

OTHOPEDIC SPORTS CENTER
See ST CLOUD ORTHOPEDIC ASSOCIATES LTD

D-U-N-S 16-102-9913 IMP
OTICON INC
(*Suby of* WILLIAM DEMANT HOLDING A/S)
580 Howard Ave, Somerset, NJ 08873-1136
Tel (732) 560-1220 *Founded/Ownrshp* 1967
Sales 29.1MM^E^ *EMP* 145^E^
SIC 3842 5047 Hearing aids; Hearing aids; Hearing aids; Hearing aids
Pr: Peer Lauritsen
VP: Lars Anderson
VP: Maxine Krill
VP: Don Schu
Ex Dir: Cheryl Miller
IT Man: Maggy McCarthy
VP Opers: Thomas Falvey
Mktg Mgr: Jennifer Halat
Mktg Mgr: Alan Raffauf
Manager: Stig Seitzberg

D-U-N-S 11-266-2775 IMP
OTICS USA INC
(*Suby of* OTICS HOLDINGS, K.K.)
5555 Interstate View Dr, Morristown, TN 37813-3780
Tel (423) 581-7607 *Founded/Ownrshp* 2002
Sales 75.2MM^E^ *EMP* 258
SIC 3714 Motor vehicle parts & accessories; Motor vehicle parts & accessories
Pr: Yuki Odai
**Pr:* Takashi Harada
CFO: Kenny Owens
Ex VP: Kiyoshi Ito
VP: Hiroyuki Asaoka
Genl Mgr: Steve Parks

OTIE
See ONEIDA TOTAL INTEGRATED ENTERPRISES LLC

D-U-N-S 55-625-7335 IMP
OTIS COLLEGE OF ART AND DESIGN
9045 Lincoln Blvd, Los Angeles, CA 90045-3505
Tel (310) 665-6800 *Founded/Ownrshp* 1918
Sales 51.1MM *EMP* 600
Accts Moss Adams Llp San Diego Ca
SIC 8249 Commercial art school; Commercial art school
Pr: Kerry Walk
**VP:* Dana Lopez
**VP:* Marc Meredith
VP: Susan Pollack
VP: Mark Salmon
**VP:* William Schaeffer
**VP:* Carrie Stewart
Dir Lab: Adam Ferriss
Creative D: John Leprevost

Creative D: Ana Llorente
Creative D: Kathleen Marinaccio
Comm Dir: Margie Reeve

D-U-N-S 05-181-3921
OTIS EASTERN SERVICE LLC
2971 Andover Rd, Wellsville, NY 14895-9536
Tel (585) 593-4760 *Founded/Ownrshp* 1971
Sales 253.6MM *EMP* 15
SIC 1623 1389 Oil & gas pipeline construction; Oil field services
Pr: Charles P Joyce
**VP:* Tony Deusenbery
**VP:* Richard Joyce
Off Mgr: Adam Landis

D-U-N-S 00-153-4676 IMP/EXP
■ **OTIS ELEVATOR CO**
(*Suby of* UNITED TECHNOLOGIES CORP) ★
10 Farm Springs Rd, Farmington, CT 06032-2577
Tel (860) 676-6000 *Founded/Ownrshp* 1976
Sales 7.1MMMᴱ *EMP* 63,000ᴱ
SIC 3534 1796 7699 Elevators & equipment; Escalators, passenger & freight; Walkways, moving; Installing building equipment; Elevator installation & conversion; Miscellaneous building item repair services; Elevators: inspection, service & repair; Elevators & equipment; Escalators, passenger & freight; Walkways, moving; Installing building equipment; Elevator installation & conversion; Miscellaneous building item repair services; Elevators: inspection, service & repair
Pr: Pedro S D BY Riva
**Pr:* Mario Abajo
**Pr:* Todd M Bluedorn
**Pr:* Bruno Grob
**Pr:* Angelo J Messina
CFO: Angelo Messina
CFO: Jeff Nelson
**Treas:* Christopher Witzky
**Sr VP:* Raymond J Moncini
VP: Ron Beaver
**VP:* Johan Bill
VP: Patrick Blethon
VP: Sandy Diehl
VP: Ted Fetterman
VP: Edward Fitch
VP: Vern Stait
Exec: John Arle
Exec: Jim Cherry
Exec: Tammi Girard
Exec: Jack Sede
Exec: Dave Tremaglio

D-U-N-S 02-923-7179 IMP/EXP
OTIS MCALLISTER INC
AMBEEBE
300 Frank H Ogawa Plz # 400, Oakland, CA 94612-2037
Tel (415) 421-6010 *Founded/Ownrshp* 1962
Sales 106.4MMᴱ *EMP* 60
SIC 5149 5141 Canned goods: fruit, vegetables, seafood, meats, etc.; Groceries, general line
Ch Bd: Royce A Nicolaisen
**Pr:* Everett C Golden III
**CFO:* Robert Westerlund
Dir IT: R Harris
Sls Dir: Piero Stucchi

D-U-N-S 06-975-4737
OTIS R BOWEN CENTER FOR HUMAN SERVICES INC
850 N Harrison St, Warsaw, IN 46580-3163
Tel (574) 267-7169 *Founded/Ownrshp* 1961
Sales 38.1MM *EMP* 850
Accts Blue & Co Llc Indianapolis
SIC 8093 8063 8361 8322 Mental health clinic, outpatient; Psychiatric hospitals; Self-help group home; Social service center; Mental health clinic, outpatient; Psychiatric hospitals; Self-help group home; Social service center
Pr: Kurt Carlson
Pr: Gary Hendrix
**CFO:* Jay Baumgartner
CFO: Marsha Flora
**VP:* Ron Clark
VP: Sandra Osterman
**VP:* Richard Ruhrold
Dir IT: Ruth Case
Opers Supe: Joseph Locke
Opers Supe: Candace Tate
Psych: Wendy Melancon

OTIWTI
See QUALITROL CO LLC

D-U-N-S 16-655-6717
OTO DEVELOPMENT LLC
100 Dunbar St Ste 402, Spartanburg, SC 29306-5189
Tel (864) 596-8930 *Founded/Ownrshp* 2004
Sales 22.6MMᴱ *EMP* 90ᴱ
SIC 7011 Hotels & motels
CEO: Corry Oakes
COO: John Anderson
**CFO:* Charlie King
**VP:* Jason Boehm
VP: John Coleman
VP: George Rutledge
**VP:* Todd Turner
Dir: Michael Gallen
Genl Mgr: Daniel Lucero
IT Man: Stephen Shackleton
VP Sls: Amanda Martin

D-U-N-S 08-139-3381
OTOE MISSOURIA TRIBE
8151 Highway 177, Red Rock, OK 74651-0348
Tel (580) 723-4466 *Founded/Ownrshp* 1973
Sales 32.6MMᴱ *EMP* 120
SIC 4832 8322 Ethnic programming; Substance abuse counseling
Ex Dir: John Shotton
V Ch: Ted Grant
**Prin:* Juskwa Burnett
Pgrm Dir: Jayme Orgain

O'TOOL INDUSTRIES
See OTOOL PLASTIC PIPE INC

D-U-N-S 08-749-6956
OTOOL PLASTIC PIPE INC
O'TOOL INDUSTRIES
1322 Erskine St, Lubbock, TX 79403-3222
Tel (806) 762-1822 *Founded/Ownrshp* 1976
Sales 24.1MMᴱ *EMP* 51ᴱ
SIC 5074 5051 Pipes & fittings, plastic; Pipe & tubing, steel
Pr: Cari Dillon
**VP:* Dennis P Dillon

OTP INDUSTRIAL SOLUTIONS
See OHIO TRANSMISSION CORP

D-U-N-S 09-625-4651
OTPD SPN SPT OF WTN PA PC
1855 Powder Mill Rd, York, PA 17402-4723
Tel (717) 848-4800 *Founded/Ownrshp* 2006
Sales 50.4MMᴱ *EMP* 325ᴱ
SIC 8011 8071 Orthopedic physician; Medical laboratories; Orthopedic physician; Medical laboratories
CEO: Todd M Lord
**Pr:* Mark R Foster
Orthpdst: Gracia Etienne
Surgeon: Todd Curran
Surgeon: Douglas Hofmann
Doctor: Michael Sicuranza
Board of Directors: Peter J Vangiesen, Brian L Bixler, Vincent Butera, David L Cohen, Steven K Groff, Douglas J Hofmann, Michael J Moritz, K Nicholas Pandelid, Michael J Sicuranza, Suzette J Song

D-U-N-S 62-140-0589 IMP
OTR WHEEL ENGINEERING INC
6 Riverside Indus Park Ne, Rome, GA 30161-7301
Tel (706) 235-9781 *Founded/Ownrshp* 1989
Sales 77.9MM *EMP* 115
SIC 5014 Tires & tubes; Tires & tubes
CEO: Phillip Ford
**CFO:* Robert A Owens Jr
**Ch:* Fredrick B Taylor
MIS Dir: Karen Crider

D-U-N-S 03-737-6613
OTSEGO COUNTY CHAPTER ASSOCIATION FOR RETARDED CHILDREN (INC)
ARC OTSEGO, THE
(*Suby of* NYSARC INC) ★
35 Academy St, Oneonta, NY 13820-2402
Tel (607) 432-8595 *Founded/Ownrshp* 1971
Sales 16.4MMᴱ *EMP* 300
Accts Bonadio & Co Llp Syracuse
SIC 8322 Social services for the handicapped; Social services for the handicapped
Ex Dir: Joe Judd
Dir IT: Troy McKee
Prd Mgr: Doug Moubray

OTSEGO IRON & METAL
See CHEMUNG SUPPLY CORP

D-U-N-S 07-929-4179
OTSEGO MEMORIAL HOSPITAL ASSOCIATION
825 N Center Ave, Gaylord, MI 49735-1592
Tel (989) 731-2100 *Founded/Ownrshp* 1946
Sales NA *EMP* 550
SIC 8062

D-U-N-S 60-711-1846 IMP/EXP
OTSUKA AMERICA INC
(*Suby of* OTSUKA PHARMACEUTICAL CO.,LTD.)
1 Embarcadero Ctr # 2020, San Francisco, CA 94111-3750
Tel (415) 986-5300 *Founded/Ownrshp* 1989
Sales 483.4MMᴱ *EMP* 2,065
SIC 3829 3499 5122 2833 2084 2086 Spectrometers, liquid scintillation & nuclear; Magnets, permanent: metallic; Pharmaceuticals; Vitamins, natural or synthetic: bulk, uncompounded; Wines; Mineral water, carbonated: packaged in cans, bottles, etc.; Spectrometers, liquid scintillation & nuclear; Magnets, permanent: metallic; Pharmaceuticals; Vitamins, natural or synthetic: bulk, uncompounded; Wines; Mineral water, carbonated: packaged in cans, bottles, etc.
Ch Bd: Hiromi Yoshikawa
**Pr:* Shun Uchida
Ofcr: Sheila Cleary
**VP:* William Mc Hale
VP: Robert Sedor
CTO: Ray Mullins
IT Man: Lori Holter

D-U-N-S 00-831-4390
OTSUKA AMERICA PHARMACEUTICAL INC
(*Suby of* OTSUKA AMERICA INC) ★
2440 Res Blvd Ste 500, Rockville, MD 20850
Tel (301) 990-0030 *Founded/Ownrshp* 1989
Sales 127.8MMᴱ *EMP* 631ᴱ
SIC 8733 8011 8731 Medical research; Offices & clinics of medical doctors; Commercial physical research; Medical research; Offices & clinics of medical doctors; Commercial physical research
CEO: Hiromi Yoshikawa
**Treas:* Steve Cobourn
Ofcr: Hideji Nonomura
VP: Margaretta Nyilas
**VP:* Richard Obrig
**VP:* Terry Prime
Dir Surg: Frank Gray
Assoc Dir: Patrick Guinn
Dist Mgr: Chad Meader
Software D: Sherri Palumbo
VP Opers: Kazuya Inagaki

D-U-N-S 12-681-2382
OTSUKA PHARMACEUTICAL DEVELOPMENT & COMMERCIALIZATION INC
OPDC
(*Suby of* OTSUKA AMERICA INC) ★
508 Carnegie Ctr Ste 100, Princeton, NJ 08540-6395
Tel (609) 524-6788 *Founded/Ownrshp* 2002
Sales 37.3MMᴱ *EMP* 152
SIC 8733 Medical research; Medical research
CEO: William H Carson
**Pr:* Taro Iwamoto
**Treas:* Dean Haubrich
Ofcr: Regina Cavaliere
**VP:* Robert Ashworth
**VP:* George Chao
**VP:* Kevin B Donovan
**VP:* Scott W Hollander
**VP:* Robert McQuade
Assoc Dir: Michael Bellero
Assoc Dir: Dana Cahill
Assoc Dir: Leah Fonseca
Assoc Dir: Myrlene Sanon
Assoc Dir: Drew Sigafoos

OTT COMMUNICATIONS
See MID-MAINE COMMUNICATIONS INC

D-U-N-S 07-834-7187
■ **OTTAWA ACQUISITION LLC**
(*Suby of* AGL RESOURCES INC) ★
1844 W Ferry Rd, Naperville, IL 60563-9662
Tel (888) 642-6748 *Founded/Ownrshp* 2011
Sales 1.3MMMᴱ *EMP* 3,750ᴱ
SIC 4924 Natural gas distribution; Natural gas distribution
Prin: Andrew W Evans

D-U-N-S 02-090-2185
OTTAWA AREA INTERMEDIATE SCHOOL DISTRICT
13565 Port Sheldon St, Holland, MI 49424-9241
Tel (616) 399-6940 *Founded/Ownrshp* 1890
Sales 20.7MMᴱ *EMP* 350
SIC 8211 Public vocational/technical school; Public special education school; Public vocational/technical school; Public special education school
Ofcr: Amy Taylor
Teacher Pr: Leslie Kole
Instr Medi: Anne Thorp
Psych: Mark Jacobson
HC Dir: Beverly Littner

OTTAWA CAPITAL
See RDV CORP

D-U-N-S 00-745-4929
OTTAWA COOPERATIVE ASSOCIATION INC
302 N Main St, Ottawa, KS 66067-1920
Tel (785) 242-5170 *Founded/Ownrshp* 1950
Sales 162.7MM *EMP* 42
SIC 5191 5171 5153 Feed; Seeds: field, garden & flower; Fertilizer & fertilizer materials; Petroleum bulk stations; Grain elevators; Feed; Seeds: field, garden & flower; Fertilizer & fertilizer materials; Petroleum bulk stations; Grain elevators
Genl Mgr: Adrian Derousseau
IT Man: Clark Wenger

OTTAWA COUNTRY MART
See C & J MANAGEMENT SERVICES INC

OTTAWA COUNTY
See COUNTY OF OTTAWA

OTTAWA COUNTY TREASURER
See COUNTY OF OTTAWA

D-U-N-S 80-747-1917
OTTAWA ELEMENTARY SCH DIST 141
OTTAWA ELEMENTARY SCHOOL
320 W Main St, Ottawa, IL 61350-2825
Tel (815) 433-1133 *Founded/Ownrshp* 1970
Sales 27.7MMᴱ *EMP* 400
SIC 8211 Public elementary & secondary schools; Public elementary & secondary schools
Bd of Dir: Ron Henson
Adm Dir: Karen Laiteritz
Dir IT: Kyle Olesen

OTTAWA ELEMENTARY SCHOOL
See OTTAWA ELEMENTARY SCH DIST 141

D-U-N-S 62-185-1567
OTTAWA PLANT FOOD INC
3076 N State Route 71, Ottawa, IL 61350-9707
Tel (815) 433-2090 *Founded/Ownrshp* 1989
Sales 43.8MM *EMP* 29
SIC 5261 5191 Lawn & garden supplies; Fertilizer; Garden supplies & tools; Chemicals, agricultural; Lawn & garden supplies; Fertilizer; Garden supplies & tools; Chemicals, agricultural
Pr: Stephen J Strong
**VP:* Judy G Strong

D-U-N-S 07-561-2937
OTTAWA REGIONAL HOSPITAL & HEALTHCARE CENTER
OSF ST ELIZABETH MEDICAL CTR
1100 E Norris Dr, Ottawa, IL 61350-1604
Tel (815) 433-3100 *Founded/Ownrshp* 1895
Sales 209.3MM *EMP* 750
SIC 8062 General medical & surgical hospitals; General medical & surgical hospitals
CEO: Rober Chaffin
**CFO:* Dawn Trompeter
CIO: John Meyer

D-U-N-S 10-709-3387 IMP
OTTAWA TRUCK INC
415 E Dundee St, Ottawa, KS 66067-1543
Tel (785) 242-2200 *Founded/Ownrshp* 2014
Sales 49.0MMᴱ *EMP* 300
SIC 3537 Tractors, used in plants, docks, terminals, etc.: industrial; Tractors, used in plants, docks, terminals, etc.: industrial
Pr: Frank Tubbert
VP: Stefan Johansson
MIS Dir: Al Huggard
Dir IT: Scott Phillips
IT Man: Tero Lehtonen
S&M/VP: Mikael Rietz
Mktg Mgr: Thomas Ljung
Sls Mgr: Miika Aintila

D-U-N-S 08-213-3364
OTTAWA UNIFIED SCHOOL DISTRICT 290
BOARD OF EDUCATION
1404 S Ash St, Ottawa, KS 66067-3421
Tel (785) 229-8010 *Founded/Ownrshp* 1981
Sales 13.5MMᴱ *EMP* 400
SIC 8211 Public elementary & secondary schools; Public elementary & secondary schools
**Prin:* Brian Kraus
**Prin:* Jean McCally

D-U-N-S 08-312-3059
OTTAWA UNIVERSITY (KS)
1001 S Cedar St Ste 20, Ottawa, KS 66067-3399
Tel (785) 242-5200 *Founded/Ownrshp* 1865, 1902
Sales 48.0MM *EMP* 254
SIC 8221 University; University
Pr: Kevin Eichner
**CFO:* Anne J Mills
CFO: Clark Ribordy
**Treas:* Terrel Haines
**VP:* Dennis Tyner
IT Man: Kent Corser
HC Dir: Heather Reinhard

D-U-N-S 00-324-0900
OTTENBERGS BAKERS INC (DC)
(*Suby of* H & S BAKERY INC) ★
1413 Progress Way, Eldersburg, MD 21784-6437
Tel (410) 549-3362 *Founded/Ownrshp* 1869, 2010
Sales 35.0MMᴱ *EMP* 275
SIC 2051 Bread, all types (white, wheat, rye, etc): fresh or frozen; Rolls, bread type: fresh or frozen; Bread, all types (white, wheat, rye, etc): fresh or frozen; Rolls, bread type: fresh or frozen
Pr: Ray Ottenberg
VP: Jim Walker

D-U-N-S 01-631-5061 IMP
OTTENWELLER CO INC
3011 Congressional Pkwy, Fort Wayne, IN 46808-4415
Tel (260) 484-3166 *Founded/Ownrshp* 1952
Sales 21.8MMᴱ *EMP* 140ᴱ
SIC 3443 3446 3444 3441 Fabricated plate work (boiler shop); Architectural metalwork; Sheet metalwork; Fabricated structural metal; Fabricated plate work (boiler shop); Architectural metalwork; Sheet metalwork; Fabricated structural metal
Pr: Michael Ottenweller
**Sec:* Nancy Dwire
**VP:* Gary Ottenweller
Prgrm Mgr: Toni Blaettner
Prgrm Mgr: Jeff Kever
Off Mgr: Heather Morris
Dir IT: Mike Busche
IT Man: Zachary Long
IT Man: Chandal Post
Ql Cn Mgr: Shawna Christlieb
Ql Cn Mgr: Jerry Glass

OTTER BOX
See OTTER PRODUCTS LLC

D-U-N-S 04-813-4238 IMP
OTTER PRODUCTS LLC
OTTER BOX
209 S Meldrum St, Fort Collins, CO 80521-2603
Tel (970) 493-8446 *Founded/Ownrshp* 1998
Sales 347.5MM *EMP* 320ᴱ
SIC 3089 Plastic kitchenware, tableware & houseware; Plastic kitchenware, tableware & houseware
Pr: Peter Lindgren
**Ch Bd:* Curtis Richardson
**Pr:* Brian Thomas
CFO: Bruce Valentine
Exec: Sara Phillips
Dir Bus: Mick Knowles
Dir Bus: Kyle Seaser
Comm Man: Katja Zimmermann
Prgrm Mgr: Alan Clarke
Snr Sftwr: Scott Queen
CTO: Gary McWhorter

D-U-N-S 61-485-3609
OTTER TAIL AG ENTERPRISES LLC
24096 170th Ave, Fergus Falls, MN 56537-7518
Tel (218) 998-4301 *Founded/Ownrshp* 2008
Sales 95.9MM *EMP* 33
SIC 2869 Ethanolamines; Ethanolamines
CEO: Anthony Hicks
**Treas:* Hans Ronnevik
Prd Mgr: Keith Wetzel
Board of Directors: John Anderson, Philip Deal, Jonathan Piekarski, Hans Ronnevik, Gary Thompson, Ronald Tobkin

D-U-N-S 83-143-0322 IMP/EXP
▲ **OTTER TAIL CORP**
215 S Cascade St, Fergus Falls, MN 56537-2801
Tel (218) 739-8200 *Founded/Ownrshp* 1907
Sales 799.2MM *EMP* 5,046ᴱ
Tkr Sym OTTR *Exch* NGS
SIC 4911 3084 5047 2099 1731 Electric services; Plastics pipe; Medical & hospital equipment; Potatoes, dried: packaged with other ingredients; General electrical contractor; Electric services; Plastics pipe; Medical & hospital equipment; Potatoes, dried: packaged with other ingredients; General electrical contractor
Ch Bd: Nathan Partain
Pr: John Abbott
**Pr:* Edward J McIntyre
CFO: Kevin G Mou
**CFO:* Kevin G Moug
**Sr VP:* George A Koeck
Sr VP: Stefan Nilsson
**Sr VP:* Shane N Waslaski
VP: Rodney C Scheel
Board of Directors: Karen M Bohn, John Erickson, Steven L Fritze, Kathryn O Johnson, Joyce N Schuette, Gary J Spies, James B Stake

D-U-N-S 00-952-1043
■ **OTTER TAIL ENERGY SERVICES CO INC** (MN)
(*Suby of* OTTER TAIL CORP) ★
224 E Washington Ave, Fergus Falls, MN 56537-2812
Tel (218) 739-8888 *Founded/Ownrshp* 1997
Sales 124.7MMᴱ *EMP* 900
SIC 4932 Gas & other services combined; Gas & other services combined
Pr: Charles Macfarlane
**Treas:* Kevin G Mong

D-U-N-S 00-696-1353 IMP/EXP
■ **OTTER TAIL POWER CO** (MN)
(*Suby of* OTTER TAIL CORP) ★
215 S Cascade St, Fergus Falls, MN 56537-2897
Tel (218) 739-8200 *Founded/Ownrshp* 1907
Sales 437.2MM^E *EMP* 3,155^E
SIC 4911 Electric services; Distribution, electric power; Generation, electric power; Transmission, electric power; Plastics pipe; Planters, plastic; Trays, plastic; Pallets, plastic; Machine & other job shop work; Machine shop, jobbing & repair; Medical & hospital equipment; Diagnostic equipment, medical; Patient monitoring equipment; Potatoes, dried: packaged with other ingredients; Electric services; Distribution, electric power; Generation, electric power; Transmission, electric power
CEO: Chuck Macfarlane
**Pr:* Timothy J Rogelstad
**CFO:* George D Bell
Sr VP: Ward Uggerud
**VP:* Mark H Helland
VP: Marlowe Johnson
VP: Michael J Olsen
**VP Admn:* Thomas R Brause
IT Man: Leon Kremeier
Sftwr Eng: Tammy Bolstad
S&M/VP: Mike Olsen

D-U-N-S 11-621-4982
■ **OTTER TAIL POWER CO**
(*Suby of* OTTER TAIL CORP) ★
215 S Cascade St, Fergus Falls, MN 56537-2897
Tel (218) 739-8200 *Founded/Ownrshp* 2009
Sales 46.9MM^E *EMP* 339^E
SIC 3699 4953 6531 Electrical welding equipment; Incinerator operation; Real estate agent, residential; Electrical welding equipment; Incinerator operation; Real estate agent, residential
Pr: Chuck Macfarland
**Pr:* Chuck Mac Farland
CFO: Kevin Moug
Bd of Dir: Nathan Partain
Bd of Dir: Robert Spolum
VP: Ron S Salisbury
Pr Dir: Kandace Olsen

OTTERAIAL AREA MEDICAL
See TRI-COUNTY HOSPITAL

D-U-N-S 15-856-2442
OTTERBASE INC
555 3 Mile Rd Nw, Grand Rapids, MI 49544-8223
Tel (616) 451-2775 *Founded/Ownrshp* 1998
Sales 46.1MM^E *EMP* 300
SIC 7379 7361 Computer related consulting services; Executive placement; Computer related consulting services; Executive placement
Pr: William R Bennett
**Ch:* Jeff Bennett
Sls Dir: Wes Smith

D-U-N-S 19-758-3953
OTTERBEIN HOMES
OTTERBEIN SNIOR LFSTYLE CHICES
580 N State Route 741, Lebanon, OH 45036-8839
Tel (513) 933-5439 *Founded/Ownrshp* 2005
Sales 39.7MM *EMP* 60
Accts Cliftonlarsonallen Llp Bellev
SIC 8361 Home for the aged
Pr: Jill Hreben
VP: Gary Horning
VP: Rob Noonan
**Prin:* Ken Allen
Ex Dir: Jason McClellan
QA Dir: Tammy Cassidy
Mktg Dir: Marilyn Wright

OTTERBEIN SNIOR LFSTYLE CHICES
See OTTERBEIN HOMES

OTTERBEIN ST MARY'S
See SENIOR OTTERBEIN LIFESTYLE CHOICES

D-U-N-S 07-164-9644
OTTERBEIN UNIVERSITY
1 S Grove St, Westerville, OH 43081-2004
Tel (614) 890-3000 *Founded/Ownrshp* 1847
Sales 67.1MM *EMP* 490
Accts Crowe Horwath Llp Columbus O
SIC 8221 College, except junior; College, except junior
Pr: Kathy A Krendl
Ofcr: Jason Abramski
Ofcr: Andrew Kennedy
Ofcr: Andrew Ratliff
Ex Dir: Troy Bonte

D-U-N-S 07-118-2992
OTTERSTEDT INSURANCE AGENCY INC
540 Sylvan Ave Ste 1, Englewood Cliffs, NJ 07632-3064
Tel (201) 227-1800 *Founded/Ownrshp* 1955
Sales NA *EMP* 80
SIC 6411 Insurance agents
Pr: Joseph C Parisi Jr
**Sec:* Lucille Parisi
Sr VP: Mike Barbara
Sr VP: Anthony Sorrentino
**VP:* Robert Casazza
VP: Ronald Kopacka
VP: Joe Nasello
VP: Ronald Phillips
Web Dev: Barbara Moore

OTTO & SONS DIV
See OSI INDUSTRIES LLC

D-U-N-S 00-680-8935
OTTO BAUM CO INC (IL)
866 N Main St, Morton, IL 61550-1645
Tel (309) 266-7114 *Founded/Ownrshp* 1935
Sales 48.1MM *EMP* 150
SIC 1741 1611 1771 1542 1541 Masonry & other stonework; Surfacing & paving; Concrete work; Commercial & office building, new construction; Industrial buildings, new construction; Masonry & other stonework; Surfacing & paving; Concrete work; Commercial & office building, new construction; Industrial buildings, new construction
CEO: Kenneth D Baum
Pr: Terry L Baum
VP: Kurt Baum

D-U-N-S 93-213-3408 IMP
OTTO BOCK HEALTHCARE
(*Suby of* OTTO BOCK HEALTHCARE NORTH AMERICA INC) ★
3820 W Great Lakes Dr, Salt Lake City, UT 84120-7205
Tel (801) 956-2400 *Founded/Ownrshp* 1995
Sales 20.4MM^E *EMP* 106
SIC 3842 Wheelchairs
Pr: Jack Hendrickson Jr
VP: Dave Wall
Mng Dir: Mark Agro
Plnt Mgr: Tom Torgerson

D-U-N-S 01-033-2831 IMP
OTTO BOCK HEALTHCARE LP (MN)
(*Suby of* OTTO BOCK HEALTHCARE GMBH)
11501 Alterra Pkwy # 600, Austin, TX 78758-3169
Tel (800) 328-4058 *Founded/Ownrshp* 1958
Sales 96.4MM^E *EMP* 430
SIC 5047 Artificial limbs; Artificial limbs
CEO: Brad Ruhl
CFO: Rick Schmidt
**CFO:* Andreas Schultz
VP Mfg: John Hendrickson

D-U-N-S 92-994-8073
OTTO BOCK HEALTHCARE NORTH AMERICA INC
OTTO BOCK NORTH AMERICAN
(*Suby of* OTTO BOCK HEALTHCARE GMBH)
2 Carlson Pkwy N Ste 100, Minneapolis, MN 55447-4467
Tel (763) 553-9464 *Founded/Ownrshp* 1958
Sales 31.7MM^E *EMP* 130
SIC 5047 Orthopedic equipment & supplies; Orthopedic equipment & supplies
Pr: Bert Harman
CFO: Harry Wertz
VP: Tim Alonzi
Dir Bus: Salim Ghoussayni
Dir Bus: Tim Hendricks
**Prin:* John Hendrickson Jr
Mng Dir: Terry Gallagher
Area Mgr: Jon Williams
CTO: Jens Baufeldt
Dir IT: Heiko Reinhard
IT Man: Roger Fritzlar

OTTO BOCK NORTH AMERICAN
See OTTO BOCK HEALTHCARE NORTH AMERICA INC

D-U-N-S 01-341-2515
OTTO BREHM INC (NY)
75 Tuckahoe Rd, Yonkers, NY 10710-5321
Tel (718) 562-8730 *Founded/Ownrshp* 1904, 1947
Sales 27.4MM *EMP* 54
Accts Catenacci Markowitz De Landri
SIC 5149 5046 Baking supplies; Flour; Sugar, refined; Spices & seasonings; Bakery equipment & supplies; Baking supplies; Flour; Sugar, refined; Spices & seasonings; Bakery equipment & supplies
Ch Bd: Ernest G Brehm
**Treas:* Michael W Brehm
**VP:* Linda Tritto

D-U-N-S 08-023-0550
OTTO BREMER FOUNDATION (MN)
30 7th St E Ste 2900, Saint Paul, MN 55101-2988
Tel (651) 227-8036 *Founded/Ownrshp* 1944
Sales 45.2MM *EMP* 1,800
Accts Deloitte Tax Llp Minneapolis
SIC 6732 6022 Trusts: educational, religious, etc.; State commercial banks; Trusts: educational, religious, etc.; State commercial banks
Ofcr: Kristine Kosek
Ofcr: Mark Lindberg
Sr VP: David Melroe
**Ex Dir:* Randi Ilyse Roth
Sys Mgr: Kari Olson

D-U-N-S 02-876-0916
OTTO CADILLAC- PONTIAC INC
1769 Central Ave, Albany, NY 12205-4734
Tel (518) 869-5000 *Founded/Ownrshp* 1976
Sales 32.2MM^E *EMP* 99
SIC 5511 Automobiles, new & used; Automobiles, new & used
Pr: Walter E Otto II
**Treas:* Jane Kojac
Genl Mgr: Chris Otto

D-U-N-S 04-122-1110
OTTO CANDIES LLC
17271 Highway 90, Des Allemands, LA 70030-4302
Tel (504) 469-7700 *Founded/Ownrshp* 1942
Sales 55.6MM^E *EMP* 250
SIC 4492 Marine towing services; Marine towing services
CEO: Otto B Candies Jr
Sec: Otto B Candies III
Ex VP: Kevin Candies

OTTO CAP
See OTTO INTERNATIONAL INC

OTTO CONSTRUCTION
See JOHN F OTTO INC

OTTO CONTROLS
See OTTO ENGINEERING INC

D-U-N-S 00-543-4170 IMP
OTTO ENGINEERING INC (IL)
OTTO CONTROLS
2 E Main St Bldg 12, Carpentersville, IL 60110-2624
Tel (847) 428-7171 *Founded/Ownrshp* 1961
Sales 63.0MM^E *EMP* 500^E
SIC 3643

D-U-N-S 07-934-7052
OTTO ENVIRONMENTAL SYSTEMS (NC) LLC
(*Suby of* OTTO INDUSTRIES NORTH AMERICA INC) ★
12700 General Dr, Charlotte, NC 28273-6415
Tel (704) 588-9191 *Founded/Ownrshp* 2003
Sales 131.0MM^E *EMP* 300
SIC 3537 Industrial trucks & tractors
CEO: Robert Engle
VP: Diane Harrington
VP: Vasim Mistry
VP: Daniel Wilde
Area Mgr: Jwilliam Anderson
Area Mgr: Juli Applegate
Area Mgr: Tom Bullard
Area Mgr: Jason Gorske
Area Mgr: Jim High
Dir IT: Brandon Wright
IT Man: Greg Pugh

D-U-N-S 82-746-3386 IMP/EXP
OTTO ENVIRONMENTAL SYSTEMS NORTH AMERICA INC
(*Suby of* OTTO INDUSTRIES NORTH AMERICA INC) ★
12700 General Dr, Charlotte, NC 28273-6415
Tel (704) 588-9191 *Founded/Ownrshp* 2005
Sales 53.2MM^E *EMP* 180
SIC 3089 Garbage containers, plastic; Garbage containers, plastic
CEO: Robert Engle
**CFO:* Diana Thomas
**VP:* Paul Blair
**VP:* Kenn Budlong
**VP:* Don Groseclose

D-U-N-S 10-834-3013 IMP
OTTO INDUSTRIES NORTH AMERICA INC
(*Suby of* OTTO INDUSTRIES EUROPE B.V.)
12700 General Dr, Charlotte, NC 28273-6415
Tel (704) 588-9191 *Founded/Ownrshp* 1992
Sales 204.8MM^E *EMP* 350
SIC 3537 Industrial trucks & tractors; Industrial trucks & tractors
CEO: Robert Engle
**Pr:* Luc Mueller

D-U-N-S 00-283-5361
OTTO INSTRUMENT SERVICE INC
1441 Valencia Pl, Ontario, CA 91761-7639
Tel (909) 930-5800 *Founded/Ownrshp* 1946
Sales 23.8MM *EMP* 70
SIC 3728 5088 7699 Aircraft parts & equipment; Aircraft equipment & supplies; Aircraft flight instrument repair
Pr: William R Otto Jr
**Pr:* Rick Otto
Ex VP: Ben Rosenthal
**VP:* Richard Delman
**VP:* Jerry Luttrull
**VP:* Bill Pugliese
**VP:* Paul Rogacki
QA Dir: Jodi Otto
VP Opers: Chuck Farley
Sls Dir: Theo Stoke
Sales Asso: Dean Dickinson

D-U-N-S 12-229-7393 IMP/EXP
OTTO INTERNATIONAL INC
OTTO CAP
3550 Jurupa St Ste A, Ontario, CA 91761-2946
Tel (909) 937-1998 *Founded/Ownrshp* 1983
Sales 42.7MM^E *EMP* 100
SIC 5136 Caps, men's & boys'
Pr: Razgo Lee
**CFO:* Frank Jou
Ex VP: Mary Marino
IT Man: Charles Sue
Natl Sales: Courtney Herrin
Mktg Mgr: Yvette Acevedo
Sls Mgr: Michael Duke
Sls Mgr: Gabrielle Ordaz

OTTO KAISER MEMORIAL HOSPITAL
See KARNES COUNTY HOSPITAL DISTRICT

D-U-N-S 18-270-9113
OTTO TRUCKING INC
4220 E Mcdowell Rd # 108, Mesa, AZ 85215-9743
Tel (480) 641-3500 *Founded/Ownrshp* 1989
Sales 43.7MM^E *EMP* 200^E
SIC 4212 Local trucking, without storage; Local trucking, without storage
CEO: Alan Otto
**COO:* Danny James
**CFO:* Bryan Adamson
CFO: David Voeller
Opers Mgr: David Dunlap

D-U-N-S 02-399-9741
OTTUMWA COMMUNITY SCHOOL DISTRICT
608 E Williams St, Ottumwa, IA 52501-5100
Tel (641) 684-6596 *Founded/Ownrshp* 1910
Sales 28.8MM^E *EMP* 530
SIC 8211 Public elementary & secondary schools; School board; Public elementary & secondary schools; School board
Schl Brd P: Greg Riley

D-U-N-S 06-520-7359
OTTUMWA REGIONAL LEGACY FOUNDATION INC
101 S Market St Ste 201, Ottumwa, IA 52501-2950
Tel (641) 455-5260 *Founded/Ownrshp* 1892
Sales 49.2MM^E *EMP* 850
Accts Seim Johnson Llp Elkhorn Ne
SIC 8062 General medical & surgical hospitals; General medical & surgical hospitals
CEO: Phil Noel
Chf Rad: Elvin McCarl
Dir Vol: Julie Carter
Pr: R Bradley Little
CFO: Daniel J Porter
Bd of Dir: Tom Stickel
Ofcr: Brenna White
Dir OR: Stephanie Husted
Off Mgr: Laura Kurimski
Dir IT: Scott Garrett
Nrsg Dir: Lori Bailey

D-U-N-S 36-300-8116
OTX CORP
(*Suby of* IPSOS)
10567 Jefferson Blvd, Culver City, CA 90232-3513
Tel (310) 736-3400 *Founded/Ownrshp* 2003
Sales 17.6MM^E *EMP* 420
SIC 8742 Management consulting services; Management consulting services
CEO: Shelley Zalis
**CFO:* Jeff Dean
Sr VP: David Klein
VP: Kristen Simmons
Snr PM: Patricia Azouri

D-U-N-S 07-846-1002
OTX LOGISTICS INC
BOOK EXPRESS NETWORK
(*Suby of* ON TIME EXPRESS LIMITED)
16030 Arthur St, Cerritos, CA 90703-2110
Tel (310) 851-8500 *Founded/Ownrshp* 2012
Sales 35.9MM^E *EMP* 70
SIC 4731 Freight forwarding
Pr: Harmut Haenisch
**Sec:* Tiffany Wong
**VP:* Stacy Allen-Kohn
Brnch Mgr: Julie Maske
Opers Mgr: Deborah Tamayo
Sales Exec: Victor Chao

OU MEDICAL CENTER
See HCA HEALTH SERVICES OF OKLAHOMA INC

OU MEDICAL CENTER
See EVERETT HOSPITAL

D-U-N-S 07-564-1944
OUACHITA BAPTIST UNIVERSITY (AR)
401 Ouachita St, Arkadelphia, AR 71998-0001
Tel (870) 245-5000 *Founded/Ownrshp* 1886
Sales 61.0MM *EMP* 350
Accts Erwin & Company Pa Little Roc
SIC 8221 College, except junior; College, except junior
Pr: Rex Horne
Pr: Terry Peeples
COO: Sally Dann
Ex VP: Stan Poole
VP: Trennis Henderson
VP: Keldon Henley
VP: Wesley Kluck
Exec: Sharon Cosh
IT Man: Kevin Herrington
Genl Couns: Bryan McKinney
Pgrm Dir: Stacy Freeman

D-U-N-S 17-336-5979
OUACHITA COUNTY MEDICAL CENTER
638 California Ave Sw, Camden, AR 71701-4699
Tel (870) 836-1000 *Founded/Ownrshp* 1994
Sales 27.5MM *EMP* 99^E
SIC 8062 General medical & surgical hospitals; General medical & surgical hospitals
Pr: James D Cicero
Pr: Charles Gibson
Dir Case M: Debra Benson
Mng Ofcr: Stephen Tabe
CIO: Wally Silliman
Doctor: Donnie Betts
Doctor: Pat Patterson
HC Dir: Mandy Wyatt
Board of Directors: C C McAllister

D-U-N-S 00-378-8205
OUACHITA ELECTRIC COOPERATIVE CORP
700 Bradley Ferry Rd, Camden, AR 71701-5003
Tel (870) 836-5791 *Founded/Ownrshp* 1939
Sales 21.1MM *EMP* 45
SIC 4911 Distribution, electric power; Distribution, electric power
Genl Mgr: Mark Cayce
Treas: James Beaver
IT Man: Jim McCarty
Board of Directors: Joe L Fowler, Charles Garner, Jim Garner, Lisa Hendrix, David Kelley, Walt Piggot, Gary Robertson, Alfred Smith, Jessie C Wood

OUACHITA FERTILIZER CO DIV
See ABELL CORP

OUACHITA INDEPENDANT BANK
See OUACHITA INDEPENDENT BANK

D-U-N-S 00-803-7587
OUACHITA INDEPENDENT BANK
OUACHITA INDEPENDANT BANK
(*Suby of* OUACHITA BANCSHARES CORP.)
909 N 18th St Ste 100, Monroe, LA 71201-5744
Tel (318) 338-3019 *Founded/Ownrshp* 1997
Sales NA *EMP* 160
SIC 6022 State commercial banks; State commercial banks
Ch Bd: Clyde R White
**Pr:* Aw Hood Jr
**Ex VP:* Robert E Schott Jr
Sr VP: Jennie Cole
Sr VP: Scott McDonald
VP: John Tolar
Snr Mgr: David Kennedy

OUACHITA PARISH OFC OF HOMLND
See PARISH OF OUACHITA

OUACHITA PARISH SCHOOL BOARD
See OUACHITA PARISH SCHOOL SYSTEM

D-U-N-S 61-819-6026
OUACHITA PARISH SCHOOL SYSTEM
OUACHITA PARISH SCHOOL BOARD
100 Bry St, Monroe, LA 71201-8406
Tel (318) 432-5000 *Founded/Ownrshp* 1896
Sales 219.9MM *EMP* 2,804
Accts Huffman & Soignier Monroe Lo
SIC 8211 Public elementary & secondary schools; Public elementary & secondary schools
Bd of Dir: Jack White

D-U-N-S 83-175-1446
OUACHITA VALLEY HOLDING INC
3161 Highway 376 S, Camden, AR 71701-9139
Tel (870) 231-6020 *Founded/Ownrshp* 2005
Sales 22.2MM *EMP* 270
Accts Bell & Company Pa North Litt
SIC 4213 Trucking, except local; Trucking, except local
Pr: Jimmy Starr

OUC
See ORLANDO UTILITIES COMMISSION

OUCH SYSTEMS
See OCCUPATIONALURGENT CARE HEALTH SYSTEMS INC

OUDEH MEDICAL PLAZA
See DR ABRAHAM OUDEH

D-U-N-S 96-124-5961 IMP
OUHLALA GOURMET CORP
2655 S Le Jeune Rd # 1011, Coral Gables, FL 33134-5803
Tel (305) 774-7332 *Founded/Ownrshp* 2008
Sales 31.0MM *EMP* 21
SIC 2033 Fruit juices: packaged in cans, jars, etc.; Fruit juices: packaged in cans, jars, etc.
CEO: Jerome Lesur
Sr VP: Eduardo Nigro
VP: Fabian Milon

D-U-N-S 11-254-4622
OUNCE OF PREVENTION FUND
OUNCE, THE
33 W Monroe St Ste 2400, Chicago, IL 60603-5400
Tel (312) 922-3863 *Founded/Ownrshp* 1981
Sales 49.9MM *EMP* 210
SIC 8322 Family service agency; Family service agency
Pr: Harriet Meyer
**Pr:* Diana Mendley Rauner
Bd of Dir: Jacolyn Bucksbaum
Chf Mktg O: Anita Puri
Ofcr: Jane McCarthy
Sr VP: Claire Dunham
Sr VP: Portia Kennel
VP: Sonya Anderson
VP: Susan Ben
VP: Harriet Dichter
VP: Hanke Gratteau
VP: Ann Kirwan
VP: Bela Mote
VP: Elias Rosario
VP: Cynthia Stringfellow
Comm Dir: Kim Morris-Johnson

D-U-N-S 08-108-4290
OUNCE OF PREVENTION FUND OF FLORIDA
111 N Gadsden St Ste 200, Tallahassee, FL 32301-1507
Tel (850) 488-1381 *Founded/Ownrshp* 1989
Sales 22.1MM *EMP* 48
SIC 8322 Family service agency; Family service agency
Pr: Douglas Sessions
**VP:* Winnie Hettins
Ex Dir: Carol McNally

D-U-N-S 80-182-9144
OUNCE OF PREVENTION FUND OF FLORIDA INC
111 N Gadsden St Ste 200, Tallahassee, FL 32301-1507
Tel (850) 921-4494 *Founded/Ownrshp* 1988
Sales 24.9MM *EMP* 33
Accts Carr Riggs & Ingram Llc Talla
SIC 7389 8322 Fund raising organizations; Individual & family services; Fund raising organizations; Individual & family services
Ex Dir: Matthew D Munyon Ms

OUNCE, THE
See OUNCE OF PREVENTION FUND

D-U-N-S 17-566-8722
OUR FINE INTERIOR SOLUTIONS LP
OFIS
7110 Old Katy Rd Ste 200, Houston, TX 77024-2155
Tel (713) 629-5599 *Founded/Ownrshp* 2000
Sales 49.7MM^E^ *EMP* 60
SIC 5021 Office furniture
Genl Pt: William Robert Crawmer
IT Man: Chris Nio

D-U-N-S 14-934-5840
OUR KIDS OF MIAMI-DADE/MONROE INC
401 Nw 2nd Ave Ste S212, Miami, FL 33128-1721
Tel (305) 455-6000 *Founded/Ownrshp* 2002
Sales 101.3MM *EMP* 60
Accts Verdeja & De Armas Llp Miami
SIC 8322 Child related social services; Child related social services
CEO: Fran Allegra
Prgrm Mgr: Lisa Jacobson
IT Man: Patrick Travers
Snr Mgr: Sashi Sanchez
Snr Mgr: Barbara Toledo

D-U-N-S 80-049-3301
OUR LADY ASSUMPTION SCHOOL
(*Suby of* ROMAN CATHOLIC DIOCESE OF MADISON) ★
2222 Shopiere Rd, Beloit, WI 53511-2348
Tel (608) 365-4014 *Founded/Ownrshp* 2007
Sales 11.8MM^E^ *EMP* 424^E^
SIC 8211 Catholic elementary & secondary schools
Prin: Michael Flanagan
**Pr:* Bob Sage
**Treas:* Arlene Smock
**VP:* Jeff Zur

OUR LADY LAKE REGIONAL MED CTR
See OUR LADY OF LAKE HOSPITAL INC

OUR LADY OF ANGELS CONVENT
See SISTERS OF SAINT FRANCIS OF PHILADELPHIA

D-U-N-S 09-977-0968
OUR LADY OF BELLEFONTE HOSPITAL INC
(*Suby of* BON SECOURS HEALTH SYSTEM INC) ★
St Christopher Dr, Ashland, KY 41101
Tel (606) 833-3333 *Founded/Ownrshp* 1988
Sales 161.2MM *EMP* 1,100
Accts Deloitte Tax Lp Atlanta Ga
SIC 8062 8082 8011 5999 General medical & surgical hospitals; Home health care services; Medical centers; Medical apparatus & supplies; General medical & surgical hospitals; Home health care services; Medical centers; Medical apparatus & supplies
Pr: Thom Morris
**Treas:* Joe Buchheit
**Prin:* John Wallenhorst
VP Mktg: Wills Coburan
Ansthlgy: Virgio Hoback

D-U-N-S 07-751-3661
OUR LADY OF CONSOLATION GERIATRIC CARE CENTER
CATHOLIC HEALTH SYSTEM OF LONG
(*Suby of* CATHOLIC HEALTH SYSTEM OF LONG ISLAND INC) ★
111 Beach Dr, West Islip, NY 11795-4929
Tel (631) 587-1762 *Founded/Ownrshp* 1892
Sales 59.5MM *EMP* 800
Accts Kpmg Llp Melville Ny
SIC 8051 Convalescent home with continuous nursing care; Convalescent home with continuous nursing care
Ex Dir: Sister M Breen
**Pr:* Ronald Steimel
Ex VP: Joseph Tomaino

D-U-N-S 02-029-1274
OUR LADY OF GOOD COUNSEL HIGH SCHOOL INC (MD)
17301 Old Vic Blvd, Olney, MD 20832-1603
Tel (240) 283-3200 *Founded/Ownrshp* 1958
Sales 27.0MM *EMP* 170
Accts Mcgladrey Llp Gaithersburg M
SIC 8211 Catholic senior high school
Pr: Paul Barker
COO: Madelyn Ball
**Prin:* Jane Digirolamo
**Prin:* Adam Trice
HC Dir: Kevin Collins

D-U-N-S 02-087-6637
OUR LADY OF HOLY CROSS COLLEGE
4123 Woodland Dr, New Orleans, LA 70131-7399
Tel (504) 394-7744 *Founded/Ownrshp* 1916
Sales 26.5MM *EMP* 162
SIC 8221 College, except junior; College, except junior
Pr: Rev Thomas Chambers
VP: Sister Audrey Ruth Donnenfelse
VP: Sr Laura Melancon
VP: Julie Nice
VP: Kenneth Tedesco
Secur Mgr: Bernard Nelson

OUR LADY OF HOPE PROVINCE
See FELICIAN SISTERS OF NORTH AMERICA INC

D-U-N-S 96-593-1434
OUR LADY OF LAKE ASCENSION COMMUNITY HOSPITAL
ST ELIZABETH HOSPITAL
1125 W Highway 30, Gonzales, LA 70737-5004
Tel (225) 647-5000 *Founded/Ownrshp* 2010
Sales 87.9MM *EMP* 25^E^
Accts Kpmg Llp Baton Rouge La
SIC 8062 General medical & surgical hospitals; General medical & surgical hospitals
Prin: Dolores Lejeune

D-U-N-S 13-952-6029
OUR LADY OF LAKE ASCENSION LLC
SAINT ELIZABETH PHYSICIANS
2647 S St Elizabeth Blvd, Gonzales, LA 70737-5021
Tel (225) 647-9675 *Founded/Ownrshp* 1999
Sales 12.9MM^E^ *EMP* 300
SIC 8011 Clinic, operated by physicians; Clinic, operated by physicians

D-U-N-S 13-009-9823
OUR LADY OF LAKE COLLEGE INC
5414 Brittany Dr Ste A, Baton Rouge, LA 70808-9124
Tel (225) 768-1700 *Founded/Ownrshp* 1980
Sales 24.6MM *EMP* 800
SIC 8221 Colleges & universities; Colleges & universities
Pr: Tina Holland
Bd of Dir: Margaret Cardello
VP Mktg: Andrea L Miller
VP Sls: Amrita Pal
Snr Mgr: Jamie Beadle
Snr Mgr: Lily Mashon
Snr Mgr: Pamela Morgan
Board of Directors: Robert C Davidge, Kirk G Wilson

D-U-N-S 96-933-5343
OUR LADY OF LAKE COLLEGE INC
5000 Hennessy Blvd, Baton Rouge, LA 70808-4375
Tel (225) 765-7709 *Founded/Ownrshp* 1990
Sales 26.3MM *EMP* 24
Accts Kpmg Llp Baton Rouge La
SIC 8062 General medical & surgical hospitals; General medical & surgical hospitals
Pr: Sandra S Harper

D-U-N-S 06-548-0121
OUR LADY OF LAKE HOSPITAL INC
OUR LADY LAKE REGIONAL MED CTR
(*Suby of* FMOL HEALTH SYSTEM) ★
5000 Hennessy Blvd, Baton Rouge, LA 70808-4367
Tel (225) 765-7709 *Founded/Ownrshp* 1923
Sales 946.4MM *EMP* 1,800^E^
Accts Kpmg Llp Baton Rouge La
SIC 8062 General medical & surgical hospitals; General medical & surgical hospitals
Pr: K Scott Wester
**Ch Bd:* Charles Valluzzo
COO: Terrie P Sterling
CFO: Robert Ramsey
Ofcr: Scott Wester
Dir Rx: Jerry Langlos
Ex Dir: Karen Allen
MIS Dir: Shannon Simpson
QA Dir: Larry Daigle
Doctor: Henry Eiserloh
Doctor: Thomas Mego

D-U-N-S 00-674-1851
OUR LADY OF LAKE UNIVERSITY
411 Sw 24th St, San Antonio, TX 78207-4689
Tel (210) 434-6711 *Founded/Ownrshp* 2007
Sales 50.1MM *EMP* 1^E^
Accts Bkd Llp San Antonio Texas
SIC 8221 Colleges & universities; Colleges & universities
Exec: Teresa Poll-Martinez
Pr: Jane Ann Slater
Ofcr: Roxanne Lo
Ofcr: Amy Minton
Ofcr: Evan Villegas
VP: Dwayne Banks
VP: Helen Streubert
VP: Dan Yoxall
Dir Lab: James Sepulveda
Mng Dir: Thomas Gadsden
CTO: Joseph Deck

D-U-N-S 13-615-2840
OUR LADY OF LAKE UNIVERSITY OF SAN ANTONIO
411 Sw 24th St, San Antonio, TX 78207-4617
Tel (210) 432-8904 *Founded/Ownrshp* 1957
Sales 46.0MM *EMP* 504
Accts Bkd Llp San Antonio Texas
SIC 8221 University; University
Pr: Sister Jane Ann Slater
**Pr:* Tessa Martinez Pollack
COO: Dwayne A Banks
Trst: Leon C Wulfe
Ofcr: Patricia Constantin
Ofcr: Howard Jones
Ofcr: Amy Minton
**VP:* Michael Acosta
**VP:* Jack Hank
**VP:* Allen R Klaus
**VP:* Helen J Streubert
**VP:* Gloria Urrabazo
VP: Lei Wang
**VP:* Dan Yoxall

D-U-N-S 04-569-0245
OUR LADY OF LIFE APARTMENTS INC
CARDINAL RITTER INSTITUTE
7655 Watson Rd Apt 230, Saint Louis, MO 63119-5053
Tel (314) 968-9447 *Founded/Ownrshp* 1978
Sales 3.6MM *EMP* 345
SIC 6513 8052 8051 Apartment building operators; Intermediate care facilities; Skilled nursing care facilities; Apartment building operators; Intermediate care facilities; Skilled nursing care facilities
Ofcr: Ann Kuhn

D-U-N-S 03-726-0775
OUR LADY OF LORDES REGIONAL MEDICAL CENTER INC
(*Suby of* FMOL HEALTH SYSTEM) ★
4801 Ambssdor Cffery Pkwy, Lafayette, LA 70508-6917
Tel (337) 289-2000 *Founded/Ownrshp* 1949
Sales 204.8MM *EMP* 1,800^E^
SIC 8011 8021 Gynecologist; Obstetrician; Offices & clinics of dentists; Gynecologist; Obstetrician; Offices & clinics of dentists
CEO: William F Barrow
**Ch:* Bryan Hanks
**Treas:* Mike Moncla
Dir Lab: Tim Touchet
**Prin:* Robert Peebles

D-U-N-S 80-789-4944
OUR LADY OF LOURDES HEALTH CARE SERVICES INC
CATHOLIC HEALTH EAST
(*Suby of* CATHOLIC HEALTH EAST) ★
1600 Haddon Ave, Camden, NJ 08103-3101
Tel (856) 757-3500 *Founded/Ownrshp* 1993
Sales 31.5MM *EMP* 3,500^E^
Accts Deloitte Tax Llp Philadelphia
SIC 8741 Hospital management; Hospital management
Pr: Alexander J Hatala
**CFO:* Michael Hammond
**CFO:* Thomas J Regner
Nurse Mgr: Maureen Migliaccio-Rega
IT Man: Mark Putnam

D-U-N-S 78-822-1302
OUR LADY OF LOURDES HEALTH SYSTEM
1600 Haddon Ave, Camden, NJ 08103-3101
Tel (856) 757-3500 *Founded/Ownrshp* 2006
Sales 22.5MM^E^ *EMP* 112^E^
SIC 8062 General medical & surgical hospitals
COO: Mark Nessel
CFO: Michael Hammond
Sr VP: Robert E Ruggero
VP: Kimberly Barnes
VP: Barbara Holfelner
VP: Helen Owens
VP: Margaret Sullivan
Off Mgr: Steven Dales
Nurse Mgr: Shawne Cuilla
Nurse Mgr: Mark Marotta
Telecom Ex: Kathleen Brasteter

OUR LADY OF LOURDES HOSPITAL
See FAITH REGIONAL HEALTH SERVICES FOUNDATION

D-U-N-S 07-185-3519
OUR LADY OF LOURDES HOSPITAL AT PASCO
LOURDES HEALTH NETWORK
520 N 4th Ave, Pasco, WA 99301-5248
Tel (509) 547-7704 *Founded/Ownrshp* 1916
Sales 103.3MM *EMP* 633
Accts Deloitte Tax Llp Cincinnati
SIC 8062 8063 General medical & surgical hospitals; Psychiatric hospitals; General medical & surgical hospitals; Psychiatric hospitals
CEO: John Serle
COO: Keith Anderson
**CFO:* Larry Chapman
Bd of Dir: Ron Davis
Sr VP: Pasco Lion
Dir Lab: Jean Lewis
Dir Rx: Tracy Clark
Ex Dir: Sam Crawford
Ex Dir: Esther Polacci
QA Dir: Anita Kongslie
Mktg Dir: Melanie Johnston

D-U-N-S 07-145-7295
OUR LADY OF LOURDES MEDICAL CENTER INC
(*Suby of* CATHOLIC HEALTH EAST) ★
1600 Haddon Ave, Camden, NJ 08103-3101
Tel (856) 757-3500 *Founded/Ownrshp* 1965
Sales 298.1MM *EMP* 3,000
SIC 8062 General medical & surgical hospitals; General medical & surgical hospitals
CEO: Alex Hatala
Pr: Ed Maule
**COO:* Mark Nessel
**CFO:* Michael Hammond
Sr VP: Robert Ruggero
VP: Kim Barnes
**VP:* Andrew Guarni
Exec: Tony Dicarlo
Dir Lab: Theresa Santoferrano
Dir Rad: Barbara Donnell
CIO: Maureen Hetu

D-U-N-S 07-159-9021
OUR LADY OF LOURDES MEMORIAL HOSPITAL INC
LOURDES HOSPITAL
169 Riverside Dr, Binghamton, NY 13905-4198
Tel (607) 798-5111 *Founded/Ownrshp* 1969
Sales 281.4MM *EMP* 1,500
Accts Lumsden Mccormick Llp Buffalo
SIC 8062 General medical & surgical hospitals; General medical & surgical hospitals
Pr: David Patak
**Ch Bd:* Thomas J Oven
**CFO:* Michael Hammond
Sr VP: Linda Miller
VP: Debbie Mican
VP: Wayne Mitteer
VP: Marilyn Perkins
VP: Richard Wu
Chf Nrs Of: Audrey Jadczak
Prac Mgr: Felecia Wagstaff
Admn Mgr: Diane Brooks

D-U-N-S 07-260-5439
OUR LADY OF LOURDES REGIONAL MEDICAL CENTER INC
(*Suby of* FMOL HEALTH SYSTEM) ★
4801 Ambssdor Cffery Pkwy, Lafayette, LA 70508-6917
Tel (337) 470-2000 *Founded/Ownrshp* 1949
Sales NA *EMP* 1,700
Accts Kpmg Llc Baton Rouge La
SIC 8062 General medical & surgical hospitals; General medical & surgical hospitals
Pr: William F Barrow
Pathlgst: Bruce Gray
Anstlgy: William Dedo
Diag Rad: Henry McLemore
Diag Rad: Mark Stephan

D-U-N-S 13-903-7753
OUR LADY OF PEACE INC
OUR LADY OF PEACE NURSING HOME
5285 Lewiston Rd, Lewiston, NY 14092-1942
Tel (716) 298-2900 *Founded/Ownrshp* 2003
Sales 22.2MM *EMP* 380
Accts Deloitte Tax Llp Cincinnati
SIC 8059 Nursing home, except skilled & intermediate care facility; Nursing home, except skilled & intermediate care facility
Pr: Judith A Maness
**CFO:* Michael Ickowski
Exec: William Mayne
IT Man: Dale Dibble

OUR LADY OF PEACE NURSING HOME
See OUR LADY OF PEACE INC

D-U-N-S 79-747-9123
OUR LADY OF SORROW SCHL
(*Suby of* ROMAN CATHOLIC ARCHDIOCESE OF DETROIT) ★
24040 Raphael Rd, Farmington Hills, MI 48336-1752
Tel (248) 474-6480 *Founded/Ownrshp* 2007
Sales 7.0MM^E^ *EMP* 515^E^
SIC 8211 Catholic elementary & secondary schools
Prin: Diane Ponagai

OUR LADY OF VICTORY ACADEMY
See SISTERS OF MERCY

D-U-N-S 07-674-8987
OUR LADY OF WAYSIDE INC
38135 Colorado Ave, Avon, OH 44011-1028
Tel (440) 934-6152 *Founded/Ownrshp* 1967
Sales 18.6MM *EMP* 360
Accts Mcmanus Dosen & Co Cleveland
SIC 8361 Home for the mentally handicapped; Home for the physically handicapped; Home for the mentally handicapped; Home for the physically handicapped
Ch: N Lindsey Smith
CEO: Terry Davis
CFO: Chris Zito
Mktg Dir: Pamela Barker

D-U-N-S 00-542-0690 IMP/EXP
OUR SUNDAY VISITOR INC
200 Noll Plz, Huntington, IN 46750-4304
Tel (260) 356-8400 *Founded/Ownrshp* 1908
Sales 60.0MM *EMP* 340
SIC 2721 2759

D-U-N-S 80-810-0130 IMP/EXP
OURAY SPORTSWEAR LLC
1201 W Mansfield Ave, Englewood, CO 80110-3453
Tel (303) 798-4035 *Founded/Ownrshp* 2007
Sales 98.0MM^E^ *EMP* 200
SIC 5091 Sporting & recreation goods; Skiing equipment; Sporting & recreation goods; Skiing equipment
VP: Jon Boris
VP Sls: Jim Cartwright
VP Sls: Craig Dudley

OURISMAN CHEVORLET BUICK GMC
See OURISMAN OF ALEXANDRIA INC

D-U-N-S 00-692-0227
OURISMAN CHEVROLET CO INC
4400 Branch Ave, Marlow Heights, MD 20748-1899
Tel (301) 423-4000 *Founded/Ownrshp* 1921
Sales 71.8MM^E^ *EMP* 160
SIC 5511 Automobiles, new & used; Automobiles, new & used
Ch Bd: Mandell J Ourisman
**Pr:* John Ourisman
**VP:* Robert Ourisman
Genl Mgr: Abbas Khademi
Genl Mgr: Kenny Powers
IT Man: Andy Brooks
Sls Dir: Ali Gharib
Sls Mgr: Dave Jordan

D-U-N-S 18-972-0001
OURISMAN CHEVROLET OF BOWIE INC
16610 Governor Bridge Rd, Bowie, MD 20716-3617
Tel (301) 262-7600 *Founded/Ownrshp* 2004
Sales 29.0MM^E^ *EMP* 86
SIC 5511 Automobiles, new & used; Automobiles, new & used
Pr: Lew Gilinsky

OURISMAN CHRYSLLER ALEXANDRIA
See OURISMAN DODGE INC

D-U-N-S 02-363-0387
OURISMAN DODGE INC
OURISMAN CHRYSLLER ALEXANDRIA
5900 Richmond Hwy, Alexandria, VA 22303-1894
Tel (703) 329-1600 *Founded/Ownrshp* 1978
Sales 39.1MM^E^ *EMP* 85
SIC 5511 5531 Automobiles, new & used; Automotive parts; Automobiles, new & used; Automotive parts
Ch: Mandell J Ourisman
**Pr:* Daniel L Korengold
**Sec:* Michael E Bennett
**VP:* Robert D Hager
Genl Mgr: Andy Heye

OURISMAN FAIRFAX TOYOTA
See FAIRFAX OURISMAN INC

OURISMAN HONDA
See BETHESDA OURISMAN INC

D-U-N-S 96-285-4795
OURISMAN OF ALEXANDRIA INC
OURISMAN CHEVORLET BUICK GMC
1800 Old Richmond Hwy, Alexandria, VA 22303-1858
Tel (703) 329-1300 *Founded/Ownrshp* 2009
Sales 25.5MM^E^ *EMP* 75
SIC 5511 Automobiles, new & used
Ch Bd: Mandell J Ourisman
**Pr:* Daniel Korengold
**Treas:* Michael E Bennett
**VP:* Robert D Hager

OURISMAN WORLD OF FORD
See WORLD OF FORD SALES INC

OURISMAN'S ROCKMONT CHEVROLET
See ROCKMONT MOTOR CO

D-U-N-S 80-480-2551 IMP
▲ OURPETS CO
1300 East St, Fairport Harbor, OH 44077-5573
Tel (440) 354-6500 *Founded/Ownrshp* 1996
Sales 22.7MM *EMP* 56^E^
Tkr Sym OPCO *Exch* OTO
SIC 3999 Pet supplies; Pet supplies
Ch Bd: Steven Tsengas
CFO: Scott R Mendes
VP: Dean Tsengas
VP: Konstantine S Tsengas
VP Opers: Konstantine Tsengas
VP Mktg: Gabriella Desantis
VP Sls: Kathleen R Homyock
Board of Directors: Joseph T Aveni, William L Lechtner, Charles C Macmillan, John W Spirk Jr

D-U-N-S 14-874-0231
OUT OF SHELL LLC
LING'S
9658 Remer St, South El Monte, CA 91733-3033
Tel (626) 401-1923 *Founded/Ownrshp* 1999
Sales 27.1MM^E^ *EMP* 200
SIC 1541 Food products manufacturing or packing plant construction; Food products manufacturing or packing plant construction

D-U-N-S 05-950-3078
OUTAGAMIE CO-OP SERVICES INC
HWY 10 & 45 CITGO
3011 W Wisconsin Ave, Appleton, WI 54914-1791
Tel (920) 739-8411 *Founded/Ownrshp* 1979
Sales 59.5MM *EMP* 90
Accts Schenck Sc Appleton Wisco
SIC 5411 5812 5541 Convenience stores; Diner; Fast food restaurants & stands; Gasoline service stations; Convenience stores; Diner; Fast food restaurants & stands; Gasoline service stations
Pr: Marvin Fox
**Genl Mgr:* Dan Schumann
CIO: Carol Tesch

OUTAGAMIE COUNTY
See COUNTY OF OUTAGAMIE

D-U-N-S 07-949-8301
■ OUTBACK KANSAS LLC
(*Suby of* BLOOMIN BRANDS INC) ★
2202 N West Shore Blvd # 5, Tampa, FL 33607-5754
Tel (813) 282-1225 *Founded/Ownrshp* 2014
Sales 12.0MM^E^ *EMP* 2,437^E^
SIC 5812 Italian restaurant

D-U-N-S 04-015-8656 IMP/EXP
OUTBACK POWER TECHNOLOGIES INC (WA)
(*Suby of* ALPHA TECHNOLOGIES SERVICES INC) ★
17825 59th Ave Ne Ste B, Arlington, WA 98223-6453
Tel (360) 435-6030 *Founded/Ownrshp* 2001, 2010
Sales 24.5MM^E^ *EMP* 85
SIC 3568 Power transmission equipment
Pr: Fred Kaiser
**Ch Bd:* John O'Rourke
**VP:* Glenn Baker
**VP:* A M Zogby
Genl Mgr: Harvey Wilkinson
Off Mgr: Charlotte Bryant
Sales Asso: Francine Flores
Board of Directors: Bob Maynard

OUTBACK STEAKHOUSE
See OSI RESTAURANT PARTNERS LLC

OUTBACK STEAKHOUSE
See BLOOMIN BRANDS INC

OUTBACK STEAKHOUSE
See J & R RESTAURANT GROUP INC

D-U-N-S 18-583-8968 IMP/EXP
■ OUTBACK STEAKHOUSE OF FLORIDA LLC
(*Suby of* OSI RESTAURANT PARTNERS LLC) ★
2202 N West Shore Blvd # 500, Tampa, FL 33607-5747
Tel (813) 282-1225 *Founded/Ownrshp* 1991
Sales 1.6MMM^E^ *EMP* 50,000
Accts Pricewater House Coopers Llp
SIC 5812 Steak restaurant; Steak restaurant
CEO: A William I Allen
**Pr:* Paul E Avery
**COO:* Robert Basham
**CFO:* Dirk A Montgomery
**Ex VP:* Joseph J Kadow
**Sr VP:* J T Gannon
Sr VP: Timothy Gannon
Sr VP: Nancy Scheid
VP: Pablo Brizi
**VP:* Stephen C Erickson

D-U-N-S 03-585-4772
OUTBOUND GROUP INC
9900 Harrison, Romulus, MI 48174-2500
Tel (734) 947-1333 *Founded/Ownrshp* 1998
Sales 22.2MM^E^ *EMP* 50
SIC 4731 Freight transportation arrangement
CEO: Harry J Zoccoli III
**Pr:* Karl B Randolph
Opers Mgr: Jason Overaitis

D-U-N-S 00-775-4273
OUTCOMES HEALTH INFORMATION SOLUTIONS LLC
(*Suby of* ALTEGRA HEALTH INC) ★
13010 Morris Rd Bldng2, Alpharetta, GA 30004-3873
Tel (678) 942-2200 *Founded/Ownrshp* 2008, 2014
Sales 66.3MM^E^ *EMP* 500
SIC 8742 Management consulting services; Management consulting services
CEO: Wanda Kochhar
Pr: Joell Keim
CFO: Doug Duskin
Ex VP: Rita Young
Sr VP: Chris Conte
Sr VP: Rolland Ho
Sr VP: Michael Mickens
VP: Mark Bergen
VP: Nick Donovan
VP: David Jeans
VP: Lynne Padilla
VP: Don Yish

D-U-N-S 61-416-8953
OUTDOOR ADVENTURE TRAVEL INC
CARROUSEL TRAVEL
6625 Lyndale Ave S 104, Minneapolis, MN 55423-2373
Tel (612) 866-2503 *Founded/Ownrshp* 1988
Sales 44.9MM *EMP* 29
SIC 4724 Travel agencies; Travel agencies
Pr: Neal Kraemer
**VP:* Robert E Harris Jr

OUTDOOR CAP COMPANY
See OUTDOOR CAP CO INC

D-U-N-S 08-493-2573 IMP/EXP
OUTDOOR CAP CO INC (AR)
OUTDOOR CAP COMPANY
1200 Melissa Dr, Bentonville, AR 72712-6654
Tel (479) 273-3732 *Founded/Ownrshp* 1976
Sales 101.8MM^E^ *EMP* 224
SIC 5136 Caps, men's & boys'; Caps, men's & boys'
Pr: Paul Mahan
**CFO:* Jerry House
**Treas:* Michael Hill
Ex VP: Paul Beahm
Ex VP: Thomas Frank
**Ex VP:* Jeremy Laney
**Ex VP:* Chris McConnell
**Ex VP:* Nicole Tillman
VP: Bill Kerr
Dir Bus: Mia Standard
Genl Mgr: Peel Chronister

D-U-N-S 60-821-2163
OUTDOOR CHANNEL HOLDINGS INC
(*Suby of* KROENKE SPORTS & ENTERTAINMENT) ★
43445 Business Park Dr # 103, Temecula, CA 92590-3670
Tel (951) 699-6991 *Founded/Ownrshp* 2013
Sales 117.3MM^E^ *EMP* 402
SIC 4841 4833 Direct broadcast satellite services (DBS); Television broadcasting stations; Direct broadcast satellite services (DBS); Television broadcasting stations
Pr: Jim Liberatore
CFO: Thomas D Allen
Ex VP: Jeff Wayne
Sr VP: Jason F Brist
Sr VP: Douglas J Langston
VP: Bill Osborn
Ex Dir: Chris Cox
IT Man: Steve Cheatham
Board of Directors: Thomas Hornish

D-U-N-S 86-950-0405 IMP
OUTDOOR CHANNEL INC
(*Suby of* OUTDOOR CHANNEL HOLDINGS INC) ★
1000 Chopper Cir, Denver, CO 80204-5805
Tel (303) 405-1671 *Founded/Ownrshp* 1993
Sales 70.0MM^E^ *EMP* 180
SIC 4833 Television broadcasting stations
Ch Bd: Perry Massie
Pr: Chris Chaffin
**CEO:* Thomas E Hornish
Ofcr: Douglas Langston
Ex VP: Steve Smith
Sr VP: Lorey Zlotnick
VP: Stacy Cerny
**VP:* Teresa Chiniaeff
VP: Garth Franklin
VP: Mike Williams
CIO: Arnel Ticsay

D-U-N-S 06-614-5475
OUTDOOR DIMENSIONS
5325 E Hunter Ave, Anaheim, CA 92807-2054
Tel (714) 459-6567 *Founded/Ownrshp* 1974
Sales 22.4MM^E^ *EMP* 160^E^
SIC 2499 3993 3281 Signboards, wood; Signs & advertising specialties; Cut stone & stone products; Signboards, wood; Signs & advertising specialties; Cut stone & stone products
Pr: Donald Pickler
**VP:* Brian Pickler
Exec: Pam Rogers
IT Man: Julie Kanutsen
VP Opers: Joe Hamlin
Sfty Mgr: Doug Raver
Opers Mgr: Garrett Beaton
Sls Mgr: Teresa Moe
Art Dir: Cesar Luna

D-U-N-S 01-079-2745 IMP
OUTDOOR DIRECT CORP (TX)
COOK 'N CA'JUN
(*Suby of* BRIKMANN J BAXTER INTL) ★
4215 Mcewen Rd, Dallas, TX 75244-5202
Tel (972) 387-4939 *Founded/Ownrshp* 1975
Sales 202.9MM^E^ *EMP* 600
SIC 3648 3631 3999 Lighting equipment; Flashlights; Lanterns: electric, gas, carbide, kerosene or gasoline; Barbecues, grills & braziers (outdoor cooking); Pet supplies; Lighting equipment; Flashlights; Lanterns: electric, gas, carbide, kerosene or gasoline; Barbecues, grills & braziers (outdoor cooking); Pet supplies
VP: Martin P Donoghue
CFO: Marty Donahue
Sr VP: David Kearsley
VP: Garland Braune
VP: Deborah Davis
VP: Mark Long
VP: Alcie Peterson
VP: Erica Pitman
VP: Owen Slater
VP: Rick Smith
VP: Lisa Stout
VP: Francisco Urteaga
Creative D: Helen Dunham

D-U-N-S 60-610-4198 IMP/EXP
OUTDOOR FOOTWEAR CO
Km 2 1 Ave Agdilla Rr 112, Isabela, PR 00662
Tel (787) 872-2140 *Founded/Ownrshp* 2015
Sales 11.5MM^E^ *EMP* 317
Accts Deloitte & Touche Llp San Jua
SIC 3143 3144 Men's footwear, except athletic; Women's footwear, except athletic
Ch Bd: Sidney W Swartz

D-U-N-S 92-788-0575
OUTDOOR GEAR EXCHANGE INC
37 Church St, Burlington, VT 05401-4417
Tel (802) 860-0190 *Founded/Ownrshp* 1995
Sales 31.4MM^E^ *EMP* 85
SIC 5091 5941 Athletic goods; Backpacking equipment; Team sports equipment
Pr: Marc Sherman
**VP:* Mike Donahue
Genl Mgr: Brian Wade

D-U-N-S 36-357-5812
OUTDOOR LIGHTING SERVICES LP
DESIGN ELECTRIC
(*Suby of* FACILITY SOLUTIONS GROUP INC) ★
4401 West Gate Blvd # 310, Austin, TX 78745-1493
Tel (512) 440-7985 *Founded/Ownrshp* 1991
Sales 56.7MM^E^ *EMP* 844
SIC 1731 General electrical contractor; Lighting contractor; General electrical contractor; Lighting contractor
Pt: Bill Graham
Pt: Steve Bryne
Pt: Bob Graham
Exec: Jeff Berthelfen

D-U-N-S 05-565-2226 IMP
OUTDOOR RESEARCH LLC (WA)
2203 1st Ave S Ste 700, Seattle, WA 98134-1424
Tel (206) 467-8197 *Founded/Ownrshp* 1978, 2003
Sales 46.3MM^E^ *EMP* 200^E^
SIC 2393 2353 2381 3021 3161 3842 Bags & containers, except sleeping bags: textile; Hats, caps & millinery; Gloves, work: woven or knit, made from purchased materials; Gloves, woven or knit: made from purchased materials; Mittens, woven or knit: made from purchased materials; Gaiters, rubber or rubber soled fabric; Traveling bags; First aid, snake bite & burn kits; Bags & containers, except sleeping bags: textile; Hats, caps & millinery; Gloves, work: woven or knit, made from purchased materials; Gloves, woven or knit: made from purchased materials; Mittens, woven or knit: made from purchased materials; Gaiters, rubber or rubber soled fabric; Traveling bags; First aid, snake bite & burn kits
Pr: Dan Nordstrom
Chf Mktg O: Theodore Steudel
**VP:* Clark Campbell
Store Mgr: Lauren Kohl
Mktg Dir: Charles Lozner
Sls Dir: Ted Steudel
Mktg Mgr: Eric Downing
Mktg Mgr: Jeff Greenwell

D-U-N-S 00-691-4253 IMP/EXP
■ OUTDOOR SPORTS GEAR INC
(*Suby of* JARDEN CORP) ★
2320 Cousteau Ct Ste 100, Vista, CA 92081-8363
Tel (914) 967-9400 *Founded/Ownrshp* 1946
Sales 1.2MMM^E^ *EMP* 5,000
SIC 3949 3069 2339 2329 Winter sports equipment; Snow skiing equipment & supplies, except skis; Fishing equipment; Life jackets, inflatable: rubberized fabric; Women's & misses' athletic clothing & sportswear; Jogging & warmup suits: women's, misses' & juniors'; Ski jackets & pants: women's, misses' & juniors'; Uniforms, athletic: women's, misses' & juniors'; Men's & boys' athletic uniforms; Men's & boys' sportswear & athletic clothing; Winter sports equipment; Snow skiing equipment & supplies, except skis; Fishing equipment; Life jackets, inflatable: rubberized fabric; Women's & misses' athletic clothing & sportswear; Jogging & warmup suits: women's, misses' & juniors'; Ski jackets & pants: women's, misses' & juniors'; Uniforms, athletic: women's, misses' & juniors'; Men's & boys' athletic uniforms; Men's & boys' sportswear & athletic clothing
CEO: Richard Sansone
Pt: Sandy Chavez
Pr: Timothy C Cronin
Pr: Jeff Larsen
Pr: Gary Remensnyder
CFO: Dudley Mendenhall
Treas: Kary Betro
Bd of Dir: Jerry E Goldress
Bd of Dir: Alfred Osborn
VP: D Herzberg
VP: David Herzberg
VP: Ian Kashton
VP: Sandy McElfresh
VP: Robert Totte
Creative D: Chris Tomeo

D-U-N-S 05-957-0937
OUTDOOR VENTURE CORP
30 Venture Dr, Stearns, KY 42647
Tel (606) 376-5021 *Founded/Ownrshp* 1972
Sales 115.7MM^E^ *EMP* 1,439
SIC 2394 Tents: made from purchased materials; Tents: made from purchased materials
Pr: James Egnew
**VP:* Joe Fields
**VP:* Patty Kidd
**VP:* Lori Miller
QI Cn Mgr: Anita Braden

D-U-N-S 06-169-6498
OUTDOOR WORLD CORP (PA)
AHNERT ADVERTISING
(*Suby of* BUSHKILL GROUP INC) ★
Rr 209, Bushkill, PA 18324
Tel (570) 588-6661 *Founded/Ownrshp* 1981, 1988
Sales 17.7MM^E^ *EMP* 840
SIC 7033 Campgrounds; Campgrounds
Pr: W Peter Ahnert
Treas: Thomas G Delaney
**Treas:* Kevin Levelle
MIS Dir: John Hendershot

OUTDOORSMAN, THE
See JEAN NELL ENTERPRISES INC

D-U-N-S 02-261-1674
OUTER BANKS HOSPITAL INC
2100 Stantonsburg Rd, Greenville, NC 27834-2818
Tel (252) 449-4500 *Founded/Ownrshp* 2000
Sales 69.2MM *EMP* 20^E^
SIC 8062 General medical & surgical hospitals; General medical & surgical hospitals
Pr: Jeff Hammer

D-U-N-S 10-147-2392
OUTER BANKS HOSPITAL INC
4800 S Croatan Hwy, Nags Head, NC 27959-9704
Tel (252) 449-7373 *Founded/Ownrshp* 2001
Sales 66.6MM *EMP* 275^E^
SIC 8062 General medical & surgical hospitals; General medical & surgical hospitals
Pr: D Van Smith Jr
Dir Vol: Marie Neilson
**CFO:* Todd Warlitner
Ofcr: Elaine Campbell
Ofcr: Ronnie Sloan
Exec: Lonnie Morgan
Dir Lab: Debra Johnson
Dir Rx: Monte Thompson
Chf Nrs Of: Carmen Vincent
CIO: Timothy Schaefer
QA Dir: Brenda Whitford

D-U-N-S 79-144-7691
▲ OUTERWALL INC
1800 114th Ave Se, Bellevue, WA 98004-6946
Tel (425) 943-8000 *Founded/Ownrshp* 1990
Sales 2.3MMM *EMP* 2,760^E^
Accts Kpmg Llp Seattle Washington
Tkr Sym OUTR *Exch* NGS

SIC 7299 7841 Coin-operated service machines: scales, shoe shine, etc.; Video disk/tape rental to the general public; Coin-operated service machines: scales, shoe shine, etc.; Video disk/tape rental to the general public
CEO: Erik E Prusch
Pr: Michael J Skinner
CFO: Galen C Smith
Ofcr: Donald R Rench
Sr VP: Alex Camara
VP: David Asch
VP: John Beane
VP: Melinda Burrows
VP: Alejandro Cabrera
VP: Pat Harrell
VP: Dave Hiatt
VP: Randy S Overturf
VP: Engle Saez
VP: Sara L White
Board of Directors: Seth Bernstein, Nelson C Chan, David M Eskenazy, Ross G Landsbaum, Robert D Sznewajs, Ronald B Woodard

D-U-N-S 07-888-0385
▲ OUTFRONT MEDIA INC (MD)
405 Lexington Ave Fl 17, New York, NY 10174-1801
Tel (212) 297-6400 *Founded/Ownrshp* 2013
Sales 1.3MMM *EMP* 2,531ᴱ
Tkr Sym OUT *Exch* NYS
SIC 7312 7319 6798 Outdoor advertising services; Billboard advertising; Poster advertising, outdoor; Display advertising service; Outdoor advertising services; Billboard advertising; Poster advertising, outdoor; Display advertising service; Real estate investment trusts
Ch Bd: Jeremy J Male
CFO: Donald R Shassian
Chf Mktg O: Jodi Senese
Ex VP: Clive Punter
Ex VP: Richard H Sauer
VP: Ross Holtzer
VP Opers: Scott Skelton
Board of Directors: Bill Apfelbaum, Nicolas Brien, Manuel A Diaz, Peter Mathes, Susan M Tolson, Joseph H Wender

D-U-N-S 01-230-7773 IMP
■ OUTFRONT MEDIA LLC
(*Suby of* OUTFRONT MEDIA INC) ★
405 Lexington Ave Fl 14, New York, NY 10174-0002
Tel (212) 297-6400 *Founded/Ownrshp* 2014
Sales 40.0MMᴱ *EMP* 100
SIC 7312 Outdoor advertising services; Poster advertising, outdoor; Billboard advertising
CEO: Jeremy Male
**CFO:* Donald R Shassian
**Treas:* Jonathan Karabas
Sr VP: Steve Hillwig
Sr VP: Douglas Rousso
Sr VP: Nancy Tostanoski
VP: Eric Davis
VP: Andrew Miller
Exec: Rich Ament
Exec: John Harrison
Dir IT: Howard Crisp

D-U-N-S 96-535-5621
OUTLAW CONVERSIONS INC
1000 Airport Rd, Stephenville, TX 76401-5402
Tel (254) 968-5733 *Founded/Ownrshp* 1996
Sales 36.9MMᴱ *EMP* 190
SIC 3799 Horse trailers, except fifth-wheel type; Horse trailers, except fifth-wheel type
Genl Pt: John Walker
**Pt:* JB Garrett
Sys/Mgr: Russ Walker

D-U-N-S 94-145-5164 IMP/EXP
■ OUTLET RETAIL STORES INC
FARBERWARE
(*Suby of* LIFETIME BRANDS INC) ★
1 Merrick Ave, Westbury, NY 11590-6601
Tel (516) 683-6000 *Founded/Ownrshp* 2001
Sales 20.8MMᴱ *EMP* 250
SIC 5719 Kitchenware; Kitchenware
Pr: Jeff Siegel
**VP:* Craig Phillips
MIS Dir: Lisa Stone

D-U-N-S 00-464-3123 IMP
OUTLOOK ACQUISITION CORP
BUTTERFLY PHOTO
86 Mayfield Ave, Edison, NJ 08837-3821
Tel (732) 339-6300 *Founded/Ownrshp* 2008
Sales 56.0MM *EMP* 34
SIC 5961 Computer equipment & electronics, mail order
Pr: Eli Sakkal
**Treas:* Joseph Sakkal
**Ex VP:* AVI Sakkal

D-U-N-S 78-497-3690
OUTLOOK AMUSEMENTS INC
2900 W Alameda Ave # 400, Burbank, CA 91505-4220
Tel (818) 433-3800 *Founded/Ownrshp* 2003
Sales 28.8MMᴱ *EMP* 150
SIC 7379 ;
CEO: Jason Freeland
Pr: Cyrus Pejoumand
**Co-Pr:* Tim Youd
**Sr VP:* Tom Wszalek
**VP:* Thomas Wszalek
Snr Sftwr: Vinay Garg
Dir IT: Carlos Aguirre
Dir IT: Dan Godbout
Dir IT: Mark Harris
Sftwr Eng: Christopher Gadbois

D-U-N-S 08-330-2034 IMP
OUTLOOK GROUP CORP
OG
(*Suby of* OUTLOOK GROUP HOLDINGS LLC) ★
1180 American Dr, Neenah, WI 54956-1306
Tel (920) 722-2333 *Founded/Ownrshp* 2006
Sales 66.0MMᴱ *EMP* 300ᴱ
SIC 2752 8741 2759 7331 Commercial printing, lithographic; Management services; Labels & seals: printing; Direct mail advertising services; Commercial printing, lithographic; Management services; Labels & seals: printing; Direct mail advertising services
Ch Bd: Calvin Aurand
**CEO:* John Cappy
CFO: P M Drewek
CFO: Dana Gilman
**Ex VP:* Kevin Hayes
VP: Tim Hasty
VP: Stephen McKnight
Exec: Kay Halbrook
CTO: Jody Franz
Dir IT: Judy Boelter
MIS Mgr: Judy Paszek

D-U-N-S 78-396-1886
OUTLOOK GROUP HOLDINGS LLC
1180 American Dr, Neenah, WI 54956-1306
Tel (920) 722-2333 *Founded/Ownrshp* 2006
Sales 66.0MMᴱ *EMP* 450
SIC 2759 4783 2752 2761 Commercial printing; Card printing & engraving, except greeting; Labels & seals: printing; Promotional printing; Packing & crating; Packing goods for shipping; Commercial printing, lithographic; Commercial printing, offset; Cards, lithographed; Coupons, lithographed; Continuous forms, office & business; Commercial printing; Card printing & engraving, except greeting; Labels & seals: printing; Promotional printing; Packing & crating; Packing goods for shipping; Commercial printing, lithographic; Commercial printing, offset; Cards, lithographed; Coupons, lithographed; Continuous forms, office & business

D-U-N-S 08-279-4376
OUTLOOK POINT AT CREEKVIEW
(*Suby of* BALANCED CARE CORPORATION)
1100 Grandon Way, Mechanicsburg, PA 17050-9191
Tel (717) 730-4033 *Founded/Ownrshp* 1999
Sales 7.1MMᴱ *EMP* 913ᴱ
SIC 8051 Skilled nursing care facilities
Prin: Crystal Stairs

D-U-N-S 11-886-3604 IMP
OUTOKUMPU STAINLESS INC
(*Suby of* OUTOKUMPU STAINLESS AB)
2275 Half Day Rd Ste 300, Deerfield, IL 60015-1232
Tel (847) 517-4050 *Founded/Ownrshp* 2004
Sales 205.5MMᴱ *EMP* 550
SIC 5051 Metals service centers & offices; Plates, metal; Sheets, metal; Strip, metal; Metals service centers & offices; Plates, metal; Sheets, metal; Strip, metal
Pr: Mats Norden
CFO: Kevin Keeley
Ex VP: Jarmo Tonteri
Sr VP: Leif Rosen
VP: Kari Tuutti
Dir Lab: Ron Womack
Dir IT: Peter Stromberg
Prd Mgr: Brian Chew
VP Mktg: Mika Toikka
S&M/VP: Katiekatie McPherson
Sls Dir: Stephen Davidson

D-U-N-S 62-613-1064 IMP
OUTOKUMPU STAINLESS PIPE INC
(*Suby of* OUTOKUMPU STAINLESS INC) ★
241 W Clarke St, Wildwood, FL 34785-3001
Tel (352) 748-0545 *Founded/Ownrshp* 2001
Sales 43.2MMᴱ *EMP* 100
SIC 3317 Steel pipe & tubes; Steel pipe & tubes
Pr: Tommy Grahn
**Ex VP:* Scott Templeton
**VP:* Karl Almond
**VP:* Domenick Di Giallonardo
**VP:* Roy Harrison
**VP:* Chris Podsaid
**VP:* Roger Ricketts
Genl Mgr: Kris Podeseia
QC Dir: Domenick Digiallonardo
Sls Mgr: Allen Cantrell

D-U-N-S 11-733-6305 IMP/EXP
OUTOKUMPU STAINLESS PLATE INC
(*Suby of* OUTOKUMPU STAINLESS INC) ★
549 W State Road 38, New Castle, IN 47362-9786
Tel (765) 529-0120 *Founded/Ownrshp* 1996
Sales 75.5MMᴱ *EMP* 160
SIC 3312 Stainless steel; Stainless steel
Pr: Mike Stateczny
VP: Jim Bell
VP Opers: Timothy Linegar
QI Cn Mgr: Jamie Doubman
Sales Exec: Fred Centner

D-U-N-S 80-841-0349 IMP
OUTOKUMPU STAINLESS USA LLC
(*Suby of* OUTOKUMPU OYJ)
1 Steel Dr, Calvert, AL 36513
Tel (251) 829-3600 *Founded/Ownrshp* 2013
Sales 629.3MMᴱ *EMP* 2,200
SIC 3312 Stainless steel; Stainless steel
CEO: Michael Wallis
**CFO:* Reinhard Florey
**VP:* Jose Ramon Salas
**VP Sls:* Stephan Lacor

OUTPATIENT CHEM DPNDNCY PROGRAM
See FAIRVIEW HEALTH SERVICES

OUTPATIENT PROGRAM
See ST MARYS MEDICAL CENTER

D-U-N-S 01-898-7979
OUTPATIENT SCHEDULING
CROCETT HOSPITOL
Hwy 43s, Lawrenceburg, TN 38464
Tel (931) 766-3242 *Founded/Ownrshp* 1974
Sales 39.0MM *EMP* 2
SIC 8062 General medical & surgical hospitals
Pharmcst: Charles Crotts

D-U-N-S 06-350-1837
OUTPOST NATURAL FOODS COOPERATIVE
205 W Highland Ave # 501, Milwaukee, WI 53203-1114
Tel (414) 961-2597 *Founded/Ownrshp* 1970
Sales 67.3MMᴱ *EMP* 500ᴱ
SIC 5499 Health foods; Health foods
Genl Mgr: Pam Mehnert

D-U-N-S 80-231-5481 IMP/EXP
OUTPUT SERVICES GROUP INC
OSG BILLING SERVICES
100 W Forest Ave Ste G, Englewood, NJ 07631-4033
Tel (201) 871-1100 *Founded/Ownrshp* 1992
Sales 106.0MMᴱ *EMP* 205
SIC 2759 Commercial printing; Commercial printing
CEO: Scott W Bernstein
**Pt:* Mike Bonagura
**Pt:* Karl Kaplan
CFO: Kent Herring
Prd Mgr: Stephanie Martinez

OUTPUT TECHNOLOGIES
See D ST OUTPUT INC

D-U-N-S 05-548-3614
OUTREACH & ESCORT INC
2221 Oakland Rd Ste 200, San Jose, CA 95131-1402
Tel (408) 436-2865 *Founded/Ownrshp* 1979
Sales 23.8MM *EMP* 79ᴱ
Accts Izabal Bernaciak & Company S
SIC 4111 Local & suburban transit; Local & suburban transit
Pr: Katheryn H Heatley
**VP:* William Chawarz
VP: Susan Evans
VP: Bill Schwarz
CTO: Mike McKenna
IT Man: Vinodh Kanchi
VP Opers: William Schwarz

D-U-N-S 78-662-1391
OUTREACH HEALTH CARE INC
OUTREACH HEALTH SERVICES
(*Suby of* INTEGRACARE HOLDINGS INC) ★
269 W Renner Rd, Richardson, TX 75080-1300
Tel (972) 840-7360 *Founded/Ownrshp* 2011
Sales 124.9MMᴱ *EMP* 5,600
SIC 8093 8049 8082 Specialty outpatient clinics; Physical therapist; Home health care services; Specialty outpatient clinics; Physical therapist; Home health care services
Pr: William Ball
CIO: Steve Abshier
IT Man: Toby Thorton

OUTREACH HEALTH SERVICES
See VERNON HOME HEALTH CARE AGENCY INC

OUTREACH HEALTH SERVICES
See OUTREACH HEALTH CARE INC

D-U-N-S 02-296-0699
OUTREACH INC
SERMON CENTRAL
5550 Tech Center Dr, Colorado Springs, CO 80919-2308
Tel (760) 940-0600 *Founded/Ownrshp* 1996
Sales 20.1MMᴱ *EMP* 115
SIC 8742 7336 Training & development consultant; Graphic arts & related design
Pr: Scott Evans
**VP:* Susan Evans
Software D: Robert Wahl
Prd Mgr: Vic Jubber
Assoc Ed: Joy Thompson

D-U-N-S 03-282-7050
OUTRIGGER ENERGY LLC
1200 Svnteenth St Ste 900, Denver, CO 80202
Tel (720) 638-7312 *Founded/Ownrshp* 2013
Sales 23.6MMᴱ *EMP* 14
SIC 5172 Crude oil
CEO: Dave Keanini
Sr VP: Brian Jeffries
VP: Grant Burchell
VP: Rodney D Hatfield
VP: Amit Jhunjhunwala
VP: Marshall Olson
VP: Alex Woodruff

OUTRIGGER HOTELS AND RESORTS
See OUTRIGGER HOTELS HAWAII

OUTRIGGER HOTELS AND RESORTS
See OUTRIGGER MARKETING INC

D-U-N-S 11-322-8522
OUTRIGGER HOTELS HAWAII
OUTRIGGER HOTELS AND RESORTS
2375 Kuhio Ave Fl 4, Honolulu, HI 96815-2939
Tel (303) 369-7777 *Founded/Ownrshp* 1953
Sales 125.1MMᴱ *EMP* 2,500
SIC 7011 Resort hotel; Resort hotel
Pt: Richard Kelley
Pt: W David P Carey III
Pt: Mel Wilinsky
Ex VP: Mel Kaneshige
Ex VP: Barry Wallace
Off Mgr: Gina Reeves
Sls Dir: Mary Loy

D-U-N-S 87-757-6199
OUTRIGGER MARKETING INC
OUTRIGGER HOTELS AND RESORTS
2375 Kuhio Ave, Honolulu, HI 96815-2939
Tel (808) 921-6600 *Founded/Ownrshp* 1989
Sales 28.2MMᴱ *EMP* 665
SIC 7011 Resort hotel; Resort hotel
CEO: David Carey
**CFO:* Mel Wilinsky
VP: Peter Skinner
VP: Rob Solomn
VP: Max Sword
CIO: Alan White

OUTRIGGER REEF HOTEL
See ORF LLC

D-U-N-S 92-725-8830
■ OUTSIDE MEDCO HEALTH SOLUTIONS LLC
(*Suby of* EXPRESS SCRIPTS HOLDING CO) ★
501 Ronda Ct, Irwin, PA 15642-4159
Tel (412) 829-3200 *Founded/Ownrshp* 1987
Sales 51.7MMᴱ *EMP* 730
SIC 5961 Pharmaceuticals, mail order; Pharmaceuticals, mail order
Exec: Brad Stutz
Dir IT: Teresa Gunn
Pharmcst: Stacy Stovall

D-U-N-S 02-766-7604
OUTSOURCE ASSOCIATES INC
200 Mansell Ct E Ste 500, Roswell, GA 30076-4852
Tel (770) 625-1500 *Founded/Ownrshp* 1997
Sales 7.4MMᴱ *EMP* 350
SIC 7349 Janitorial service, contract basis; Janitorial service, contract basis
Pr: Charles R Schneider
**CFO:* Kenneth W Oringer
**VP:* Ross Miller

D-U-N-S 06-734-8131
■ OUTSOURCE GROUP INC
(*Suby of* PARALLON BUSINESS SOLUTIONS LLC) ★
3 Cityplace Dr Ste 690, Saint Louis, MO 63141-7089
Tel (314) 692-6500 *Founded/Ownrshp* 2013
Sales 48.5MMᴱ *EMP* 1,420ᴱ
SIC 7322 Collection agency, except real estate; Collection agency, except real estate
CEO: Michael A Dimarco
COO: Mike Treash
CFO: Mark Rowland
Ofcr: Lisa Phillips
Ex VP: Daniel A Schulte
Sr VP: Alan Aleia
Sr VP: Jeff Ellerbrock
Sr VP: Donald W Rappp
Sr VP: Don D Wright
CIO: Mike Aufdembrink

D-U-N-S 84-985-4690
OUTSOURCE INC
397 Wekiva Springs Rd # 117, Longwood, FL 32779-3614
Tel (407) 774-1951 *Founded/Ownrshp* 1993
Sales 23.8MMᴱ *EMP* 310
SIC 7363 Temporary help service; Temporary help service
Pr: Bobbie T Salyer
VP: Ray Erickson
VP: Lori Hudson
**VP:* Joe P Salyer
VP: Harry Ward
Snr Ntwrk: Alfred Cornell
Snr Ntwrk: Randall Litz
IT Man: Jim Orfield
Tech Mgr: Debbie Bridges
Netwrk Eng: Brenda Barreto
Netwrk Eng: Joy Greene II

D-U-N-S 79-956-1746
OUTSOURCE LLC
BUILDING TECHNOLOGY STAFFING
1960 E Grand Ave Ste 1180, El Segundo, CA 90245-5092
Tel (310) 953-3037 *Founded/Ownrshp* 1998
Sales 70.0MM *EMP* 150
SIC 8748 Telecommunications consultant
CEO: John Lowell
**Pr:* Steve Ebenhack
**COO:* Lance Shiring
**CFO:* Don Hughes
Sls Mgr: Jessica Ruiz
Sales Asso: Thomas Marks
Sales Asso: Shane Stape

D-U-N-S 01-725-3365 IMP
OUTSOURCE MANUFACTURING INC (CA)
2460 Ash St, Vista, CA 92081-8424
Tel (760) 795-1295 *Founded/Ownrshp* 1997
Sales 22.9MMᴱ *EMP* 60
SIC 3674 Solid state electronic devices
CEO: Ted Fogliani
**CFO:* Christian Fogliani
VP: Marc Lafitte
**VP:* Lance McCann
**Genl Mgr:* Ernie Hahn
IT Man: Shawn Galusk
VP Opers: Antonio Franco
QI Cn Mgr: Charlene Theberge

D-U-N-S 01-070-0297
■ OUTSOURCE PARTNERS INTERNATIONAL INC
(*Suby of* EXLSERVICE HOLDINGS INC) ★
280 Park Ave Rm 3801w, New York, NY 10017-1284
Tel (212) 752-2439 *Founded/Ownrshp* 2011
Sales 81.0MMᴱ *EMP* 3,700
SIC 8721 8748 Accounting, auditing & bookkeeping; Business consulting; Accounting, auditing & bookkeeping; Business consulting
CEO: Clarence T Schmitz
**Pr:* Kishore Mirchandani
**CFO:* James D Floyd
Mng Dir: Peter J Mares

D-U-N-S 79-704-5887
■ OUTSOURCED ADMINISTRATIVE SYSTEMS INC
OASYS
(*Suby of* XEROX BUSINESS SERVICES LLC) ★
4550 Victory Ln, Indianapolis, IN 46203-5968
Tel (317) 780-1619 *Founded/Ownrshp* 1989
Sales 10.0MMᴱ *EMP* 300
SIC 8741 Administrative management; Administrative management
VP: Ken Dixon
Board of Directors: Brenda Kranda

D-U-N-S 01-416-7746
OUTTEN BUICK-PONTIAC INC (PA)
OUTTEN CHEVROLET OF HAMBURG
1701 W Tilghman St, Allentown, PA 18104-4158
Tel (610) 562-2216 *Founded/Ownrshp* 1952, 1992

Sales 29.9MM^E *EMP* 60
SIC 5511 7538 5521 5531 Automobiles, new & used; General automotive repair shops; Used car dealers; Automotive & home supply stores
Pr: Willie Outten
**Treas:* James D Outten
**VP:* Carol Outten
Genl Mgr: Stefan Bringenberg
Genl Mgr: Jeff Marcus
IT Man: Dick Teti
Sls Mgr: Bob Haag
Sales Asso: Dylan Collazo
Sales Asso: John Goodwin
Sales Asso: Caesar Greene
Sales Asso: Dan Stover

OUTTEN CHEVROLET OF HAMBURG
See OUTTEN BUICK-PONTIAC INC

D-U-N-S 15-213-2924
OUTTEN MOTORS LLC
16614 Pottsville Pike, Hamburg, PA 19526-8105
Tel (610) 562-5174 *Founded/Ownrshp* 2004
Sales 23.4MM^E *EMP* 60
SIC 5511 Automobiles, new & used; Pickups, new & used; Automobiles, new & used; Pickups, new & used
Sales Asso: Brad Kerr
Sales Asso: Jon Schappell

OUTWATER PLASTICS INDUSTRIES
See OUTWATER PLASTICS/INDUSTRIES INC

D-U-N-S 06-432-6028 IMP/EXP
OUTWATER PLASTICS/INDUSTRIES INC
OUTWATER PLASTICS INDUSTRIES
24 River Rd Ste 108, Bogota, NJ 07603-1535
Tel (201) 498-8750 *Founded/Ownrshp* 1972
Sales 28.8MM^E *EMP* 91^E
SIC 5072 2599 Hardware; Bar furniture; Hardware; Bar furniture
Pr: Peter Kessler
**Treas:* Susan Molnar
Mng Dir: David Norburg
MIS Dir: Rich Fallon
Sls Mgr: Robert Agnehus
Sls Mgr: Sue Molnar

D-U-N-S 11-038-0057
OUZERNE COUNTY CORRECTIONAL FACILITY
99 Water St, Wilkes Barre, PA 18702-2500
Tel (570) 829-7741 *Founded/Ownrshp* 1995
Sales 30.0MM *EMP* 300
SIC 8744 Correctional facility; Correctional facility
**Prin:* James Larson

D-U-N-S 17-547-9765
OUZINKIE NATIVE CORP
500 Main St, Ouzinkie, AK 99644
Tel (907) 680-2208 *Founded/Ownrshp* 1973
Sales 85.3MM *EMP* 815
SIC 6799 Investors; Investors
Ch: Jackie Muller
Bd of Dir: Nicholas Pestrikoff
**VP:* Laura Muller

D-U-N-S 01-408-9630 IMP
OVATION ENTERPRISES INC (AZ)
PROJECTORSUPERSTORE.COM
17350 N Hartford Dr, Scottsdale, AZ 85255-5694
Tel (480) 348-0100 *Founded/Ownrshp* 1999
Sales 59.5MM^E *EMP* 115
SIC 5099 Video & audio equipment
Pr: John Godbout
**CFO:* Jack Seaver
**VP:* Beth Godbout
Exec: Laura Byrne

D-U-N-S 07-835-7443
OVATION GRAPHICS LLC
BRANCH-SMITH
4251 Empire Rd, Fort Worth, TX 76155-2713
Tel (817) 335-1481 *Founded/Ownrshp* 2011
Sales 37.0MM^E *EMP* 160
SIC 2752 Commercial printing, lithographic; Commercial printing, lithographic
Dir IT: Chris Kennedy

OVATION INSTORE
See DSI GROUP INC

D-U-N-S 05-668-2917
OVATION TRAVEL GROUP INC
LAWYER'S TRAVEL
71 5th Ave Fl 10, New York, NY 10003-3004
Tel (212) 679-1600 *Founded/Ownrshp* 1982
Sales 51.6MM^E *EMP* 450
SIC 4724 Travel agencies; Travel agencies
CEO: Paul Metselaar
Ch: Nick Price
Ex VP: Elie Gordis
**Ex VP:* Sunil Mahtani
Ex VP: Patricia Piro
**Ex VP:* Michael Steiner
Sr VP: Marcia Amoye
VP: Marcella Rappoport
Exec: Robin Feligson
Dir Bus: Nicole Alexander
Rgnl Mgr: Lynn Stocker

D-U-N-S 02-719-5317
■ **OVATIONS FOOD SERVICES LP**
(*Suby of* COMCAST SPECTACOR INC) ★
18228 N Us Highway 41, Lutz, FL 33549-4400
Tel (813) 948-6900 *Founded/Ownrshp* 2001
Sales 96.1MM^E *EMP* 1,500
SIC 5812 Contract food services; Contract food services
Pr: Ken Young
Pt: Lawrence Hoffman
Pt: Sandy Lipstein
COO: Todd Wickner
Ex VP: Doug Drewes
Sr VP: Charlie Neary
VP: Thomas Anastasia
VP: Lachance John
VP: Jay Satenspiel
VP: David Specht
VP: Mark Stone
VP: Max Vanrees
VP: Karen Wittig
VP: Jen Zick
Exec: Paul Masserey
Exec: Brenda Richter
Dir Bus: Kraig Pomrenke

D-U-N-S 13-986-7282
■ **OVATIONS FOOD SERVICES LP**
(*Suby of* COMCAST HOLDINGS CORP) ★
21 Stadium Dr, Frederick, MD 21703-6553
Tel (301) 815-9935 *Founded/Ownrshp* 2003
Sales 22.9MM^E *EMP* 1,893^E
SIC 5812 Eating places
Pt: Gary Horvbath

D-U-N-S 12-889-3208
■ **OVATIONS INC**
(*Suby of* UNITEDHEALTH GROUP INC) ★
9900 Bren Rd E Ste 300w, Hopkins, MN 55343-9693
Tel (952) 936-1300 *Founded/Ownrshp* 1998
Sales NA *EMP* 3,500
SIC 6324 Hospital & medical service plans; Hospital & medical service plans
CEO: Larry C Renfro
**CFO:* Jerry Knutson
**VP:* Lisa Johnson

D-U-N-S 19-487-8372
OVC-ENGINEERED SOLUTIONS LLC
(*Suby of* OUTDOOR VENTURE CORP) ★
2740 S Highway 1651, Stearns, KY 42647
Tel (606) 376-5021 *Founded/Ownrshp* 2014
Sales 28.3MM^E *EMP* 200
SIC 5091 5699 Switching equipment, telephone; Control equipment, electric; Consulting engineer; Electrical or electronic engineering; Systems integration services; Systems engineering, computer related; Computer systems analysis & design; Hunting equipment & supplies; Military goods & regalia; Sports apparel
Pr: J C Egnew

D-U-N-S 79-280-3918
OVE ARUP & PARTNERS PC
(*Suby of* ARUP GROUP LIMITED)
77 Water St, New York, NY 10005-4401
Tel (212) 229-2669 *Founded/Ownrshp* 1989
Sales 29.8MM^E *EMP* 200
SIC 8711 Consulting engineer; Consulting engineer
Pr: Mahadev Raman
**Sec:* James Quiter
Chf Mktg O: Kyle Fischer
Assoc Dir: Nigel Annereau
Dir IT: Michael Lombino
IT Man: Alan Saranga
Netwrk Mgr: Jeff Tranchina
Info Man: Debbie Holden
VP Opers: Peter Lindquist
Mktg Dir: Karen Patey
Counsel: Natalie Bloch
Board of Directors: James Quiter

OVEC
See INDIANA-KENTUCKY ELECTRIC CORP

OVEC
See OHIO VALLEY ELECTRIC CORP

D-U-N-S 05-796-6483 IMP
OVED APPAREL CORP
FERRUCHE
31 W 34th St Rm 401, New York, NY 10001-3036
Tel (212) 244-3800 *Founded/Ownrshp* 1981
Sales 87.4MM^E *EMP* 110
SIC 5136 Shirts, men's & boys'; Shirts, men's & boys'
Ch Bd: Issac Oved
**Pr:* Ronnie Oved
**CEO:* David Oved
CFO: Stuart Bender
**CFO:* Larry Turkill
**Sec:* Michael Oved
Ex VP: Joseph Oved
**VP:* Mike Oved

D-U-N-S 15-207-7863 IMP
OVER & BACK LLC
90 Adams Ave Ste B, Hauppauge, NY 11788-3631
Tel (631) 357-8140 *Founded/Ownrshp* 2002
Sales 37.8MM^E *EMP* 80
SIC 5023 5083 Home furnishings; Lawn & garden machinery & equipment
Pr: Bernard Levitan
Off Mgr: Marsha Augustyn

OVER 60 HEALTH CENTER
See LIFELONG MEDICAL CARE

OVERAA CONSTRUCTION
See C OVERAA & CO

OVERALL CAPITAL PARTNERS
See OVERALL LLC

D-U-N-S 00-794-3004
■ **OVERALL LAUNDRY SERVICES INC** (WA)
(*Suby of* ARAMARK SERVICES INC) ★
7200 Hardeson Rd, Everett, WA 98203-5836
Tel (425) 353-0800 *Founded/Ownrshp* 1920
Sales 9.7MM^E *EMP* 450
SIC 7218 7213 Treated equipment supply: mats, rugs, mops, cloths, etc.; Work clothing supply; Linen supply; Treated equipment supply: mats, rugs, mops, cloths, etc.; Work clothing supply; Linen supply
Pr: Travis Keeler
**COO:* Mike Ellis
**Sec:* Andrew T Ariizumi
**Ex VP:* Jack Erickson
**VP:* Jerry Hilson

D-U-N-S 02-145-1313
OVERALL LLC
OVERALL CAPITAL PARTNERS
29 Commonwealth Ave # 401, Boston, MA 02116-3353
Tel (857) 263-7961 *Founded/Ownrshp* 2008
Sales 62.4MM^E *EMP* 450^E
SIC 6799 Investors; Investors

D-U-N-S 07-059-4007
OVERBROOK SCHOOL FOR BLIND
6333 Malvern Ave, Philadelphia, PA 19151-2597
Tel (215) 877-0313 *Founded/Ownrshp* 1832
Sales 26.1MM *EMP* 225
Accts Tait Weller & Baker Llp Phila
SIC 8211 School for physically handicapped; School for physically handicapped
Ex Dir: Bernadette M Kappen
**Pr:* Warwick S Wheeler
**VP:* Robert Danjolell
**VP:* Robert B Gallant
**VP:* J Freedley Hunsicker Jr
**VP:* Marjorie G Stein
Ex Dir: M Kappen
Software D: Lisa Lisicki
Psych: Danielle Sychterz

D-U-N-S 17-525-0760
OVERBY-SEAWELL CO
O S C
(*Suby of* BRECKENRIDGE INSURANCE SVCS) ★
245 Townpark Dr Nw # 200, Kennesaw, GA 30144-5544
Tel (770) 281-2678 *Founded/Ownrshp* 2010
Sales NA *EMP* 116
SIC 6411

D-U-N-S 17-334-6354
OVERDRIVE INC
(*Suby of* OVERDRIVE HOLDINGS, INC.)
1 Overdrive Way, Cleveland, OH 44125-5385
Tel (216) 573-6886 *Founded/Ownrshp* 1986
Sales 64.4MM^E *EMP* 200^E
SIC 7371 Software programming applications; Software programming applications
Ch Bd: Steven Potash
Pt: Ann Denison
**COO:* Lori Franklin
COO: Lori Soukup
**CFO:* Mike Vantusko
VP: Mackenzie Platten
Ex Dir: Chris Herpers
CTO: Jeff Sterling
Web Dev: Nick Beaudoin
Software D: Ben Ahrens
Software D: Brandon Browning

D-U-N-S 07-758-4915
OVEREASY INC
COURTEUOS KITCHEN AND BAKERY
6403 Haven Ave Ste 106, Rancho Cucamonga, CA 91737-3861
Tel (909) 941-8655 *Founded/Ownrshp* 2000
Sales 20.5MM^E *EMP* 700^E
SIC 8741 Business management; Business management
CEO: Michael Towes

D-U-N-S 07-887-6744
OVERFLOW ENERGY LLC
723 W Industrial Rd, Pampa, TX 79065
Tel (806) 658-7832 *Founded/Ownrshp* 2007
Sales 25.0MM *EMP* 50
SIC 1381 Drilling oil & gas wells; Drilling oil & gas wells

OVERHEAD DOOR COMPANY HOUSTON
See COMMERCIAL DOOR CO OF HOUSTON INC

OVERHEAD DOOR CO INDIANAPOLIS
See GARAGE DOOR SYSTEMS LLC

D-U-N-S 04-856-3233
OVERHEAD DOOR CO OF BALTIMORE THE INC
3501 Century Ave, Baltimore, MD 21227-2199
Tel (410) 636-6300 *Founded/Ownrshp* 1967
Sales 24.7MM^E *EMP* 100
SIC 5031 7699 5211

D-U-N-S 08-196-2367
OVERHEAD DOOR CO OF DENVER INC
3291 Peoria St Unit E, Aurora, CO 80010-1500
Tel (303) 366-4300 *Founded/Ownrshp* 1983
Sales 43.7MM^E *EMP* 80
SIC 5031 7699 5211 Doors, garage; Garage door repair; Garage doors, sale & installation; Doors, garage; Garage door repair; Garage doors, sale & installation
Pr: Robert Pettyjohn
**VP:* Beth Ann Pettyjohn

OVERHEAD DOOR CO WASHINGTON DC
See WASHINGTON OVERHEAD DOOR INC

D-U-N-S 00-750-3592 IMP
OVERHEAD DOOR CORP
(*Suby of* SANWA USA INC) ★
2501 S State Hwy 121 Ste, Lewisville, TX 75067
Tel (469) 549-7100 *Founded/Ownrshp* 2009
Sales 480.3MM^E *EMP* 2,500
SIC 3442 2431 3699 3537 3589 Garage doors, overhead: metal; Rolling doors for industrial buildings or warehouses, metal; Metal doors; Doors, wood; Door opening & closing devices, electrical; Industrial trucks & tractors; Loading docks: portable, adjustable & hydraulic; Vacuum cleaners & sweepers, electric: industrial; Garage doors, overhead: metal; Rolling doors for industrial buildings or warehouses, metal; Metal doors; Doors, wood; Door opening & closing devices, electrical; Industrial trucks & tractors; Loading docks: portable, adjustable & hydraulic; Vacuum cleaners & sweepers, electric: industrial
Pr: Dennis Stone
Pr: Jodi Hayes
Pr: Mike Kridel
Pr: Howard Simons
**CFO:* Paul A Lehmann
**Ch:* Toshitaka Takayama
**Treas:* Martha Ross
Founder: Cg Johnson
Ex VP: Nelson Newcomer
VP: Mario Bazan
VP: Kirk Brunson
VP: David Knight
VP: Kevin Kravchuk
**VP:* Gregory J Kunsman
VP: Phil Laster
VP: Theresa Lestenkof
VP: Rhonda McAndrew
VP: Jon Melhorn
VP: Collin Quigley
VP: Brett Sailors
**VP:* William A Schochet

OVERHEAD DOOR GRATER MILWAUKEE
See J F COOK CO INC

D-U-N-S 03-398-5318
OVERHEAD DOOR INC
OVERHEAD DOOR SOUTHWESTERN IDA
621 N Allumbaugh St, Boise, ID 83704-9298
Tel (208) 375-0137 *Founded/Ownrshp* 1948
Sales 32.2MM^E *EMP* 105
Accts Ripley Doorn & Company Pll
SIC 5031 5211 Doors; Door & window products; Doors; Door & window products
Pr: Eric Stunz
**COO:* Ed Tensen
**CFO:* Steve Griffin
**VP:* John Cook
VP Sls: Dan Adams

OVERHEAD DOOR SOUTHWESTERN IDA
See OVERHEAD DOOR INC

D-U-N-S 04-742-6663
OVERHILL FARMS INC
CHICAGO BROTHERS
(*Suby of* BELLISIO FOODS INC) ★
2727 E Vernon Ave, Vernon, CA 90058-1822
Tel (323) 582-9977 *Founded/Ownrshp* 2013
Sales 118.9MM^E *EMP* 400
SIC 2038 Frozen specialties; Frozen specialties
Pr: James Rudis
Pr: Rick Alvarez
CFO: Robert C Bruning
CIO: Guy Chabet
QA Dir: Maria Espindola
Dir IT: Neil Bellinger
IT Man: Ruby Soden
Ql Cn Mgr: Rima Jauregui
Ql Cn Mgr: Rachel Teoh
Mktg Mgr: Joe Carter

D-U-N-S 96-939-1312
OVERLAKE HOSPITAL ASSOCIATION
1035 116th Ave Ne, Bellevue, WA 98004-4604
Tel (425) 688-5000 *Founded/Ownrshp* 2011
Sales 454.7MM *EMP* 341^E
SIC 8062 General medical & surgical hospitals; General medical & surgical hospitals
Prin: Diane Sperry
Nurse Mgr: Jody Burnell
Nurse Mgr: Maggie Cudiamat
Opers Mgr: Merritt Nelson
Secur Mgr: Daniel Taverne
Doctor: Carolyn McHugh MD

D-U-N-S 07-663-1704
OVERLAKE HOSPITAL MEDICAL CENTER
1035 116th Ave Ne, Bellevue, WA 98004-4687
Tel (425) 688-5000 *Founded/Ownrshp* 1952
Sales 450.0MM *EMP* 2,450
Accts Kpmg Llp Seattle Wa
SIC 8062 General medical & surgical hospitals; General medical & surgical hospitals
CEO: Craig Henrickson
Bd of Dir: Jorge Cerda
Trst: Jim Doud
Ofcr: Katherine Pliska
Ofcr: Cathy Whitaker
**Ex VP:* David W Schultz
VP: Jody Albright
VP: Richard Bryan
VP: Alan Ertle
VP: Caitlin Hillary
VP: Caitlin Moulding
Dir Lab: Alice Cade

D-U-N-S 07-666-5694
OVERLAKE INTERNAL MEDICINE ASSOCIATES PS
OVERLAKE INTRNAL MDICINE ASSOC
1047 116th Ave Ne Ste 200, Bellevue, WA 98004-4604
Tel (425) 454-5046 *Founded/Ownrshp* 1970
Sales 23.3MM^E *EMP* 170
SIC 8011 Internal medicine, physician/surgeon; Internal medicine, physician/surgeon
Pr: Thomas Amidon MD
**Treas:* Georgia Reese-Loui MD
**VP:* Nic Kovach MD
Doctor: Stacey S Donlan MD
**Doctor:* Alan Haywood
Doctor: Georgia Rees-Lui

OVERLAKE INTRNAL MDICINE ASSOC
See OVERLAKE INTERNAL MEDICINE ASSOCIATES PS

D-U-N-S 10-904-1970
OVERLAND CORP
7 Miles S Ardmore, Ardmore, OK 73401
Tel (580) 223-8432 *Founded/Ownrshp* 1994
Sales 24.0MM^E *EMP* 65
SIC 1611 1771 General contractor, highway & street construction; Concrete work
CEO: Reggie Sullivan
**Pr:* G Dean Leverett

OVERLAND LIMOUSINE SERVICE
See WHEATLAND ENTERPRISES INC

OVERLAND PARK JEEP-CHRYSLER
See OVERLAND PARK VENTURES INC

D-U-N-S 03-453-3904
OVERLAND PARK REGIONAL MEDICAL CENTER INC
10500 Quivira Rd, Overland Park, KS 66215-2306
Tel (913) 541-0000 *Founded/Ownrshp* 2014
Sales 39.3MM^E *EMP* 1,125
SIC 8062 General medical & surgical hospitals
Pr: Kevin Hicks
Dir Lab: Katie Aldis
Dir Rx: Cheryl Hurst
Snr Mgr: John Patoray

D-U-N-S 06-273-5196
OVERLAND PARK VENTURES INC
OVERLAND PARK JEEP-CHRYSLER
8775 Metcalf Ave, Shawnee Mission, KS 66212-2058
Tel (913) 381-8100 Founded/Ownrshp 1982
Sales 21.1MM^E EMP 80
SIC 5511

OVERLAND PETROLEUM
See DATS TRUCKING INC

D-U-N-S 00-725-8379 IMP
OVERLAND PRODUCTS CO INC (NE)
AMESBURY FRMONT- OVERLAND PDTS
1687 N Airport Rd, Fremont, NE 68025-2979
Tel (402) 721-7270 Founded/Ownrshp 1963
Sales 20.9MM^E EMP 75
SIC 3469 Metal stampings
Pr: Jeffrey C Graby
*VP: John Ekeler
Sls Mgr: Mike Ekeler

D-U-N-S 12-835-0142
■ **OVERLAND SOLUTIONS INC**
(Suby of EXLSERVICE HOLDINGS INC) ★
10975 Grandview Dr # 400, Overland Park, KS 66210-1523
Tel (913) 451-3222 Founded/Ownrshp 2014
Sales NA EMP 1,180
SIC 6411 Loss prevention services, insurance; Loss prevention services, insurance
Pr: Mike Ferguson
*CFO: Bryan Griffin
*Sr VP: Gilbert Bourk
*Sr VP: David Greene
Genl Mgr: Pat O Glesby
*CIO: Chayan Dasgupta
VP Opers: Tom Reagan

D-U-N-S 03-221-0858 IMP
OVERLAND STORAGE INC
S3D ACQUISITION II COMPANY
(Suby of SPHERE 3D INC)
9112 Spectrum Center Blvd, San Diego, CA 92123-1599
Tel (858) 571-5555 Founded/Ownrshp 2014
Sales 65.6MM EMP 487^E
SIC 3572 7372 Computer storage devices; Prepackaged software; Computer storage devices; Prepackaged software
Pr: Eric L Kelly
*COO: Randall T Gast
*CFO: Kurt L Kalbfleisch
VP: Nilesh Patel
VP: Graham Paterson
VP: Scott Petersen
Prgrm Mgr: Srini Chintala
CTO: Ben Sevier
Software D: Bill Fellows
Software D: Kimaya Paradkar
Sls Mgr: Suneet Sudan

D-U-N-S 06-980-9770
OVERLAND WEST INC
HERTZ
2805 Washington Blvd, Ogden, UT 84401-4212
Tel (801) 621-5663 Founded/Ownrshp 1976
Sales 154.0MM^E EMP 425
SIC 7514

D-U-N-S 82-857-4595
OVERLAND XPRESS LLC
431 Ohio Pike Ste 311, Cincinnati, OH 45255-3629
Tel (513) 528-1158 Founded/Ownrshp 2005
Sales 21.4MM^E EMP 50
SIC 4731 Freight transportation arrangement
VP Opers: Terese Brown
VP Opers: Terese Wissman

D-U-N-S 03-023-9297
OVERLOOK HOSPITAL ASSOCIATION (NJ)
(Suby of AHS HOSPITAL CORP) ★
99 Beauvoir Ave, Summit, NJ 07901-3595
Tel (908) 522-2000 Founded/Ownrshp 1906, 1984
Sales 206.1MM^E EMP 3,198
SIC 8062 General medical & surgical hospitals; General medical & surgical hospitals
COO: Alan Lieber
CFO: Karen Lump
Bd of Dir: Steven J Sheris
VP: Kevin Lenahan
VP: Robert Oberhand
Dir Lab: Norman Luka
Dir IT: Robin J Hill
VP Sls: Judy Kastango
Pr Dir: Michael Samuelson
Surgeon: Charbel Salamon
Doctor: Vidya Gupta

D-U-N-S 87-724-4533
OVERLOOK MASONIC HEALTH CENTER INC
88 Masonic Home Rd, Charlton, MA 01507-1394
Tel (508) 248-7344 Founded/Ownrshp 1987
Sales 22.8MM EMP 500
Accts Feeley & Driscoll Pc Boston
SIC 8051 8059 Skilled nursing care facilities; Rest home, with health care; Skilled nursing care facilities; Rest home, with health care
Pr: David C Turner
*Pr: Donald Hicks
CFO: Pam Jones
*Treas: Pam C Jones
IT Man: Eric Burgeson
Nrsg Dir: Rosanne Antunes

D-U-N-S 01-751-2976
OVERLY DOOR CO
OVERLY MANUFACTURING COMPANY
574 W Otterman St, Greensburg, PA 15601-2148
Tel (724) 834-7300 Founded/Ownrshp 1997
Sales 47.3MM^E EMP 125
SIC 5031 3444 Door frames, all materials; Sheet metalwork; Door frames, all materials; Sheet metalwork
Ch Bd: Timothy T Reese
COO: Charles Baugh
Sec: Elmer H Knopf
Sr VP: Cindy Catalano
VP: Charles R Baugh
Dir IT: Scott Callaway
IT Man: Dave Shanethalter
Opers Mgr: Richard Watkins
Plnt Mgr: Mike McConville
VP Sls: Jon Reese
Mktg Dir: Bill Hugus

OVERLY MANUFACTURING COMPANY
See OVERLY DOOR CO

OVERNIGHT GROUND FORCE SYSTEMS
See AIR CONTACT TRANSPORT INC

OVERNIGHT PRINTS
See FARHEAP SOLUTIONS INC

D-U-N-S 10-117-4472
OVERSEAS ADVENTURE TRAVEL
347 Congress St Ste 2, Boston, MA 02210-1222
Tel (800) 955-1925 Founded/Ownrshp 1994
Sales 79.2MM^E EMP 2,000
SIC 4725 Arrangement of travel tour packages, wholesale
Sr VP: Mary Marks
*Owner: Allan Lewis
VP: Priscilla O'Reilly

D-U-N-S 11-508-3578
OVERSEAS BECHTEL INC
(Suby of BECHTEL CORP) ★
5275 Westview Dr, Frederick, MD 21703-8306
Tel (301) 228-6000 Founded/Ownrshp 1971
Sales 17.9MM^E EMP 331
SIC 8711 1629 8742 Civil engineering; Industrial plant construction; Power plant construction; Construction project management consultant; Civil engineering; Industrial plant construction; Power plant construction; Construction project management consultant
Pr: Bill Dudley
*CFO: Mike Adams
*Sr VP: J A Miller

OVERSEAS GENERAL
See AMERICAN DAWN INC

D-U-N-S 16-162-3152 EXP
OVERSEAS MILITARY SALES CORP - OMSC LTD
175 Crossways Park Dr W, Woodbury, NY 11797-2002
Tel (516) 921-2800 Founded/Ownrshp 1961
Sales 85.9MM^E EMP 225
SIC 5511 New & used car dealers; New & used car dealers
CEO: David J Goldring
*CFO: Edward A Smith
*VP: Tim Daniels
*VP: Stephen Frisch
IT Man: Alan Nigro

D-U-N-S 07-121-6147
OVERSEAS MISSIONARY FELLOWSHIP INC (PA)
OMF INTERNATIONAL
10 W Dry Creek Cir, Littleton, CO 80120-4413
Tel (303) 730-4160 Founded/Ownrshp 1865
Sales 15.3MM EMP 300
Accts Capin Crouse Llp Littleton C
SIC 8661 Religious organizations; Religious organizations
Pr: Neil O Thompson
*Sec: Wendell Geary Jr
*Ex VP: Mark S Bradley

D-U-N-S 05-855-6424 EXP
OVERSEAS SERVICE CORP
1100 Northpoint Pkwy # 200, West Palm Beach, FL 33407-1983
Tel (561) 683-4090 Founded/Ownrshp 1947
Sales 40.4MM^E EMP 300
SIC 5699 Military goods & regalia; Military goods & regalia
CEO: Francis J Hogan
*Pr: Paul Hogan
CFO: Becky Thompson
VP: Stacey Cartwright
VP Sls: Roy Hardwick
Sls Mgr: Calvin Burts
Sls Mgr: John Gill
Sls Mgr: Bridget Ring
Snr Mgr: Brian Douglas

D-U-N-S 05-049-6140
▲ **OVERSEAS SHIPHOLDING GROUP INC**
1301 Avenue Of The Americ, New York, NY 10019-6040
Tel (212) 953-4100 Founded/Ownrshp 1969
Sales 957.4MM EMP 2,860^E
Tkr Sym OSG Exch ASE
SIC 4412 4424 Deep sea foreign transportation of freight; Deep sea domestic transportation of freight; Deep sea foreign transportation of freight; Deep sea domestic transportation of freight
Pr: Ian T Blackley
*Ch Bd: Douglas D Wheat
CFO: Rick F Oricchio
Treas: Geoff Carpenter
Treas: Geoffrey L Carpenter
Ofcr: Katerina Palopoulou
Sr VP: James D Small III
VP: Adewale O Oshodi
VP: Brian Tanner
Dist Mgr: Doug Shebesta
Board of Directors: Timothy J Bernlohr, Joseph Kronsberg, Samuel H Norton, Ronald Steger, Gary Eugene Taylor, Ty Wallach, Gregory A Wright

D-U-N-S 15-765-2632
OVERSEENET
550 S Hope St Ste 200, Los Angeles, CA 90071-2672
Tel (213) 408-0080 Founded/Ownrshp 2000
Sales 25.4MM^E EMP 210
SIC 7311 Advertising agencies; Advertising agencies
CEO: Debra Domeyer
*Pr: Lawrence Ng
Pr: Dwayne Walker
*CFO: Elizabeth Murray
*CTO: Gene Chuang
Sls&Mrk Ex: Burt Breznick

OVERSEERS OF THE PUBLIC SCHOOL
See WILLIAM PENN CHARTER SCHOOL INC

D-U-N-S 01-126-6280 IMP/EXP
▲ **OVERSTOCK.COM INC**
6350 S 3000 E Ste 100, Salt Lake City, UT 84121-5954
Tel (801) 947-3100 Founded/Ownrshp 1997
Sales 1.5MMM EMP 1,700
Accts Kpmg Llp Salt Lake City Uta
Tkr Sym OSTK Exch NGM
SIC 5961 General merchandise, mail order; Catalog & mail-order houses; General merchandise, mail order
CEO: Patrick M Byrne
*Ch Bd: Jonathan E Johnson III
*Pr: Stormy D Simon
Sr VP: Mark J Griffin
Sr VP: Robert P Hughes
Sr VP: Seth Marks
Sr VP: Saum Noursalehi
VP: Bhargav Shah
Exec: Richard Ash
Exec: Aaron Davis
Exec: Doug Minnick
Exec: Jennifer Moore
Exec: Eric Williams
Board of Directors: Allison H Abraham, Barclay F Corbus, Samuel A Mitchell, Joseph J Tabacco Jr

OVERTON BROOKS VA MEDICAL CTR
See VA HOSPITAL

D-U-N-S 00-514-4209 IMP/EXP
OVERTON CHICAGO GEAR CORP
2823 W Fulton St, Chicago, IL 60612-1705
Tel (773) 638-0508 Founded/Ownrshp 1913, 1985
Sales 23.3MM^E EMP 62
SIC 3566 Reduction gears & gear units for turbines, except automotive; Drives, high speed industrial, except hydrostatic; Gears, power transmission, except automotive
CEO: Donald Brown

D-U-N-S 10-067-0975
OVERTON COUNTY SCHOOL DISTRICT
302 Zachary St, Livingston, TN 38570-1242
Tel (931) 823-1287 Founded/Ownrshp 2003
Sales 18.1MM^E EMP 400
SIC 8211 Public elementary & secondary schools; Public elementary & secondary schools
Pr: Jerry Glasscock
HC Dir: Danny McCoin

OVERTON HOTEL & CONFERENCE CTR
See 1859-HISTORIC HOTELS LTD

D-U-N-S 80-831-2628
OVERTON SECURITY SERVICES INC
39300 Civic Center Dr # 370, Fremont, CA 94538-2397
Tel (510) 791-7380 Founded/Ownrshp 2007
Sales 20.0MM^E EMP 215
SIC 7382 Security systems services; Security systems services
Pr: Andrew Overton
CFO: Vicki Greiner
*VP: Sandra Overton
Dir Sec: Keith Gonzales
Dir Sec: Jules Moore
Genl Mgr: Jason Solorzano
Trfc Dir: Adrianna Rodriguez
Mktg Dir: Frank Dimeco

D-U-N-S 80-864-4277
OVERTONS HOLDING CO
(Suby of GANDER MOUNTAIN CO) ★
111 Red Banks Rd, Greenville, NC 27858-5702
Tel (252) 355-7600 Founded/Ownrshp 2007
Sales 53.3MM^E EMP 250
SIC 5961 5941 Catalog sales; Fitness & sporting goods, mail order; Fishing, hunting & camping equipment & supplies: mail order; Water sport equipment; Fishing equipment; Catalog sales; Fitness & sporting goods, mail order; Fishing, hunting & camping equipment & supplies: mail order; Water sport equipment; Fishing equipment
CEO: Mark Metcalfe
*CFO: John Daigle
VP: Herman L Norris Jr

D-U-N-S 04-173-8886 IMP
OVERTURE LLC
595 Lakeview Pkwy, Vernon Hills, IL 60061-1827
Tel (847) 573-6080 Founded/Ownrshp 2001
Sales 26.0MM^E EMP 65
SIC 5199 Advertising specialties

D-U-N-S 15-870-7476
OVERTURE NETWORKS INC
637 Davis Dr, Morrisville, NC 27560-6835
Tel (919) 337-4100 Founded/Ownrshp 2000
Sales 69.4MM^E EMP 200^E
SIC 7379 Computer related consulting services; Computer related consulting services
Pr: Mike Aquino
Ch Bd: John Gerdelman
CFO: Greg Anglum
Bd of Dir: James Mongiello
Top Exec: Ramesh Nagarajan
Sr VP: Chris Swan
Sr VP: Chuba Udokwu
VP: Keith Donahue
VP: Mark Durrett
VP: Randy Krenz
VP: Fraser Moffatt
VP: Vijay Raman
VP: Barry Shapiro
VP: Mark Ventura

D-U-N-S 02-733-2113
OVERTURF MOTOR CO INC
OVERTURF VOLKSWAGEN-AUDI-KIA
1016 W Columbia Dr, Kennewick, WA 99336-3462
Tel (509) 586-9555 Founded/Ownrshp 1962
Sales 25.2MM EMP 32
SIC 5511 Automobiles, new & used; Automobiles, new & used
Pr: Doug Overturf
*Sec: Nancy Overturf
Sls Mgr: Larry Lambert

OVERTURF VOLKSWAGEN-AUDI-KIA
See OVERTURF MOTOR CO INC

D-U-N-S 17-737-4022
■ **OVERWATCH SYSTEMS LTD**
(Suby of TEXTRON DEFENSE SYSTEMS) ★
21660 Ridgetop Cir # 110, Sterling, VA 20166-8509
Tel (703) 433-5637 Founded/Ownrshp 2006
Sales 26.5MM EMP 80
SIC 7371 8748 Custom computer programming services; Systems engineering consultant, ex. computer or professional; Custom computer programming services; Systems engineering consultant, ex. computer or professional
CEO: Randy Averitte
Sr VP: James Dolan
VP: Kirk Brown
*VP: Ronald B Natalie Jr
Genl Mgr: Amy Laws
IT Man: Susan Engler
Sls Mgr: Kevin Opitz

D-U-N-S 80-123-1635
■ **OVERWATCH SYSTEMS LTD**
(Suby of TEXTRON DEFENSE SYSTEMS) ★
5301 Southwest Pkwy, Austin, TX 78735-8985
Tel (512) 358-2600 Founded/Ownrshp 2006
Sales 30.2MM^E EMP 250
SIC 7371 8711 Computer software systems analysis & design, custom; Aviation &/or aeronautical engineering; Computer software systems analysis & design, custom; Aviation &/or aeronautical engineering
Pr: Ellen Lord
*Sr VP: Steve Overly
VP: Jon Percy
Dir Bus: Jean-Pjerre Lutz
Dir Bus: Mike Metscher
Snr Sftwr: Ben McCart
Snr Ntwrk: Rob Herter
Sftwr Eng: Jerome Korthals
Sftwr Eng: Brandon Parks
Sftwr Eng: Ryan Suder
Sftwr Eng: Colin Wyatt

D-U-N-S 08-174-7420 IMP
OVERWRAPS PACKAGING INC
3950 La Reunion Pkwy, Dallas, TX 75212-6011
Tel (214) 634-0427 Founded/Ownrshp 2007
Sales 30.0MM EMP 70
SIC 2759 Flexographic printing; Flexographic printing
CEO: William C Seanor
*Pr: Lanny Howell
*CFO: Emmanuel Dubois
VP: Jim Davies
VP: Nicole Saner
Dir IT: Mark Miniatas
Tech Mgr: Bill Derkach
Prd Mgr: Mike Sievers

D-U-N-S 15-390-8512
OVID TECHNOLOGIES INC
(Suby of WOLTERS KLUWER N.V.)
333 7th Ave Fl 19, New York, NY 10001-5015
Tel (646) 674-6300 Founded/Ownrshp 1998
Sales 20.1MM^E EMP 200
SIC 7375 Information retrieval services; Data base information retrieval; On-line data base information retrieval; Information retrieval services; Data base information retrieval; On-line data base information retrieval
CEO: Dean Vogel
COO: D Hull
Ex VP: Bette Brunelle
VP: Dana Johnson
Dir: NY Park
Genl Mgr: Jocelyn Krygier
Snr Sftwr: Chris Beach Beach
MIS Dir: Tom Bergman
IT Man: Tom Nufer
Mktg Dir: Connie Hughes
Manager: Kelly Barcus
Board of Directors: Harry Diakoff, Carl P Fisher, Gary L Gottlieb, John J Hanley

D-U-N-S 02-882-6287
OVIS LLC
OJAI VALLEY INN & SPA
905 Country Club Rd, Ojai, CA 93023-3734
Tel (805) 646-5511 Founded/Ownrshp 1954
Sales 40.4MM^E EMP 600
SIC 7011 5813 5812 Resort hotel; Drinking places; Eating places; Resort hotel; Drinking places; Eating places
Mng Dir: Janis Clapoff
Genl Mgr: Scott Mitchell
Sls Mgr: Rachelle Kumar

D-U-N-S 00-659-4378 IMP
OVIVO USA LLC
(Suby of OVIVO SWITZERLAND AG)
5139 Ne 94th Ave Ste E, Vancouver, WA 98662-6195
Tel (360) 253-3440 Founded/Ownrshp 2008
Sales 49.3MM^E EMP 220
SIC 3823 Water quality monitoring & control systems; Water quality monitoring & control systems

D-U-N-S 14-242-9468 IMP
OVIVO USA LLC
(Suby of GL&V CANADA INC)
4246 S Riverboat Rd # 300, Salt Lake City, UT 84123-2583
Tel (801) 931-3000 Founded/Ownrshp 2003
Sales 78.5MM^E EMP 250
SIC 3589 Water treatment equipment, industrial; Water treatment equipment, industrial
VP: Richard Verreault
Genl Mgr: Ron Nay
Dir IT: Nigel Rogers
IT Man: Brian Stringham
Opers Mgr: Kurt Bouwhuis

OVSD
See OCEAN VIEW SCHOOL DISTRICT (INC)

D-U-N-S 04-628-1230
OW BUNKER USA INC
(*Suby of* O.W. BUNKER & TRADING A/S UNDER KONKURS)
281 Tresser Blvd Ste 1500, Stamford, CT 06901-3283
Tel (281) 946-2300 *Founded/Ownrshp* 2012
Sales 43.8MM^E *EMP* 10
Accts Lynge Skovgaard/Lars Birner So
SIC 5172 Fuel oil; Fuel oil
CEO: Jim Pedersen
**CFO:* Morten Skou
**Ex VP:* Gotz Lehsten
**VP:* Jane Dahl Christensen
Off Mgr: Marie Villalobos

OWASA
See ORANGE WATER AND SEWER AUTHORITY

D-U-N-S 01-363-1320
OWASCO BEVERAGE INC (NY)
1886 Clark Street Rd, Auburn, NY 13021-9519
Tel (315) 252-6111 *Founded/Ownrshp* 1950, 1972
Sales 35.6MM^E *EMP* 155
SIC 5181 Beer & other fermented malt liquors; Beer & other fermented malt liquors
Pr: Thomas Potter
**Sec:* Tony Van Slyke
**VP:* John Muldoon

D-U-N-S 05-013-6399
OWASSO PUBLIC SCHOOLS
1501 N Ash St, Owasso, OK 74055-4930
Tel (918) 272-5367 *Founded/Ownrshp* 1970
Sales 31.4MM^E *EMP* 750
SIC 8211 Public elementary & secondary schools; School board; Public elementary & secondary schools; School board
Ex Dir: Danny Henrie
Teacher Pr: Kathy Curtis
Psych: Eva Webb

OWATONNA FORD CHRYSLER
See OWATONNA MOTOR CO INC

D-U-N-S 05-144-2275
OWATONNA MOTOR CO INC
OWATONNA FORD CHRYSLER
1001 Hoffman Dr, Owatonna, MN 55060-1109
Tel (507) 451-7860 *Founded/Ownrshp* 2000
Sales 20.9MM^E *EMP* 50
SIC 5511 Automobiles, new & used
Pr: John Berger
Sls Mgr: Brandon Johnson
Sales Asso: Curt Boettcher
Sales Asso: Dale Johnson
Sales Asso: Chris Randall

D-U-N-S 01-491-8296
OWEGO APALACHIN CENTRAL SCHOOL DISTRICT (INC) (NY)
36 Talcott St, Owego, NY 13827-1023
Tel (607) 687-6215 *Founded/Ownrshp* 1900, 1953
Sales 14.2MM^E *EMP* 450
SIC 8211 Public senior high school; Public junior high school; Public elementary school; Public senior high school; Public junior high school; Public elementary school
CIO: Bob Farrell
Pr Dir: Stephen Jensen

D-U-N-S 15-283-0139
OWEN ELECTRIC CO INC
1775 Lakeside Ave, Saint Augustine, FL 32084-5778
Tel (904) 824-9954 *Founded/Ownrshp* 1986
Sales 32.1MM^E *EMP* 110
SIC 1731 General electrical contractor
Pr: Micky Owen
CFO: Owen Vicki
**VP:* Vicki Owen

D-U-N-S 00-694-6065
OWEN ELECTRIC COOPERATIVE INC (KY)
8205 Highway 127 S, Owenton, KY 40359-9378
Tel (502) 484-3471 *Founded/Ownrshp* 1937
Sales 192.7MM *EMP* 134
Accts Alan Zumstein Lexington Ky
SIC 4911 Distribution, electric power; Distribution, electric power
CEO: Mark Stallons
**Ch Bd:* J Sam Penn
**Sec:* Stanley Gosney
**V Ch Bd:* Frank E Jackson
Sfty Mgr: Tony Dempsey

D-U-N-S 04-943-3290 IMP
■ **OWEN ELECTRIC STEEL CO OF SOUTH CAROLINA**
(*Suby of* COMMERCIAL METALS CO) ★
310 New State Rd, Cayce, SC 29033-3704
Tel (803) 936-3700 *Founded/Ownrshp* 2002
Sales 3.9MM^E *EMP* 400
SIC 3312 3449

D-U-N-S 06-111-7669
OWEN FARICY MOTOR CO
FAIRCY BOYS
4950 New Car Dr, Colorado Springs, CO 80923-8813
Tel (719) 636-1333 *Founded/Ownrshp* 1942
Sales 21.1MM^E *EMP* 50
SIC 5511 Automobiles, new & used; Automobiles, new & used
Pr: Mike Faricy

OWEN HEALTH CARE
See CARDINAL HEALTH 109 INC

OWEN HEALTH CARE AND PHARMACY
See GIBSON COMMUNITY HOSPITAL PHARMACY INC

D-U-N-S 10-759-8963 IMP
OWEN INDUSTRIES INC
PAXTON & VIERLING STEEL CO
501 Avenue H, Carter Lake, IA 51510-1513
Tel (800) 831-9252 *Founded/Ownrshp* 1979
Sales 172.7MM^E *EMP* 350
SIC 5051 3441 Sheets, metal; Steel; Bars, metal; Pipe & tubing, steel; Fabricated structural metal; Bridge sections, prefabricated highway; Bridge sections, prefabricated railway; Joists, open web steel: long-span series; Sheets, metal; Steel; Bars, metal; Pipe & tubing, steel; Fabricated structural metal; Bridge sections, prefabricated highway; Bridge sections, prefabricated railway; Joists, open web steel: long-span series
Ch Bd: Robert E Owen
**Pr:* John Sunderman
**CFO:* Ed Korbel
**Sr VP:* Keith Siebels
**VP:* Robert Jacobsen
**VP:* Bradley Johnson
**VP:* Mark Radtke

D-U-N-S 01-366-4552
OWEN J ROBERTS SCHOOL DISTRICT
901 Ridge Rd, Pottstown, PA 19465-8423
Tel (610) 469-5100 *Founded/Ownrshp* 1967
Sales 51.4MM^E *EMP* 610
SIC 8211 Public elementary & secondary schools; Public elementary & secondary schools
Bd of Dir: Debbie Bissland
Bd of Dir: Eric Scheib
Dir Sec: Kevin Smith
Psych: Jennifer Rumsey
Psych: Anita Zuber

OWEN MANUFACTURING
See CHARLES D OWEN MFG CO

D-U-N-S 80-340-1454 IMP
OWEN MUMFORD USA INC
(*Suby of* OWEN MUMFORD LIMITED)
1755 W Oak Commons Ct, Marietta, GA 30062-2280
Tel (770) 977-2226 *Founded/Ownrshp* 1993
Sales 50.0MM *EMP* 39
SIC 3826 Blood testing apparatus; Blood testing apparatus
Pr: Robert Shaw
**CFO:* William H Speed
Area Mgr: Jeff Seifert
Prd Mgr: Jason Pruet
Prd Mgr: Patrick Seckington
Sales Exec: Jeff Bell
**VP Sls:* Travis Shaw

D-U-N-S 10-705-1823 IMP/EXP
OWEN OIL TOOLS INC
(*Suby of* CORE LABORATORIES LP) ★
12001 County Road 1000, Godley, TX 76044-3141
Tel (817) 396-4570 *Founded/Ownrshp* 1978
Sales 117.2MM^E *EMP* 540
SIC 2892 3533 Well shooting torpedoes (explosive); Drilling tools for gas, oil or water wells; Well shooting torpedoes (explosive); Drilling tools for gas, oil or water wells
CEO: David M Demshur
**CFO:* R L Bergmark
VP: Jerry Kier
**VP:* Dan W Pratt
VP: Les Weisner
Exec: Martha Holland
Genl Mgr: Ernie Ramirez
IT Man: Irene Kjornes
Sfty Mgr: Yvie Ellison
Mfg Mgr: Brett Schaffer
Plnt Mgr: David Oneal

D-U-N-S 10-718-5923 EXP
OWEN STEEL CO INC
727 Mauney Dr, Columbia, SC 29201-5177
Tel (803) 251-7680 *Founded/Ownrshp* 2001
Sales 110.0MM *EMP* 275
SIC 3441 Fabricated structural metal; Fabricated structural metal
CEO: Anny Zalesne
Pr: David Zalesne
VP: Dave Whirrett
Ql Cn Mgr: John Myers

D-U-N-S 06-157-2882
OWEN STEPHENS PRODUCTIONS LLC
1304 Sw 176th Ter, Beaverton, OR 97003-7562
Tel (503) 810-0812 *Founded/Ownrshp* 2011
Sales 85.0MM *EMP* 1
SIC 3861 Motion picture film; Motion picture film

OWEN-AMES-KIMBALL COMPANY
See O-A-K/FLORIDA INC

D-U-N-S 00-695-9589
OWEN-AMES-KIMBALL CO
300 Ionia Ave Nw, Grand Rapids, MI 49503-2595
Tel (616) 456-1521 *Founded/Ownrshp* 1891
Sales 104.3MM *EMP* 150
SIC 1541 1542

D-U-N-S 78-950-3679
OWEN-AMES-KIMBALL ENGINEERING INC
(*Suby of* OWEN-AMES-KIMBALL CO) ★
300 Ionia Ave Nw, Grand Rapids, MI 49503-2595
Tel (616) 456-1521 *Founded/Ownrshp* 1958
Sales 35.4MM^E *EMP* 51
SIC 8711 8712 Engineering services; Architectural services
CEO: Frank Stanek
**CFO:* John C Labarge Jr
Treas: David Gibbs
**Ofcr:* Bill Ogden
**Ofcr:* Jeff Weber
Ex Dir: Marcus Goodson

D-U-N-S 00-794-1230 IMP
■ **OWENS & MINOR DISTRIBUTION INC** (VA)
(*Suby of* OWENS & MINOR INC) ★
9120 Lockwood Blvd, Mechanicsville, VA 23116-2015
Tel (804) 723-7000 *Founded/Ownrshp* 1882, 1994
Sales 9.0MMM *EMP* 4,500
SIC 5047 Medical equipment & supplies; Surgical equipment & supplies; Medical equipment & supplies; Surgical equipment & supplies
Pr: Craig R Smith
**Ch Bd:* G Gilmer Minor III
**Pr:* James L Bierman
**COO:* Charles Coopel
**CFO:* Richard Andrew Meier
**Sr VP:* Grace Denharttog
**Sr VP:* David Guzman
VP: Erika Davis
**VP:* Drew Edwards
**VP:* Wargo Natalie K
**VP:* Mike Lowry
VP: Mark Van Sumeren

D-U-N-S 84-741-2269 IMP
▲ **OWENS & MINOR INC**
9120 Lockwood Blvd, Mechanicsville, VA 23116-2015
Tel (804) 723-7000 *Founded/Ownrshp* 1882
Sales 9.4MMM *EMP* 5,700
Accts Kpmg Llp Richmond Virginia
Tkr Sym OMI *Exch* NYS
SIC 5047 Medical & hospital equipment; Hospital equipment & furniture; Surgical equipment & supplies; Medical equipment & supplies; Medical & hospital equipment; Hospital equipment & furniture; Surgical equipment & supplies; Medical equipment & supplies
Pr: P Cody Phipps
**Ch Bd:* Craig R Smith
Pr: Dan Hess
COO: James L Bierman
CFO: Richard A Meier
Bd of Dir: Theresa Chamberlain
Ex VP: William Fife
Ex VP: Nancy Schneid
Sr VP: Erika T Davis
Sr VP: Grace R Den Hartog
Sr VP: Grace R Den Hartog
Sr VP: Grace R Hartog
Sr VP: Richard W Mears
Sr VP: Thomas J Sherry
VP: Mark Bryant
VP: Charles Eismamn
VP: Carla Fox
VP: Hugh F Gouldthorpe Jr
VP: Martha Huston
VP: Gavin Jeffs
VP: Mike La Croix

D-U-N-S 17-186-5459
■ **OWENS & MINOR MEDICAL INC**
(*Suby of* OWENS & MINOR INC) ★
9120 Lockwood Blvd, Mechanicsville, VA 23116-2015
Tel (804) 723-7000 *Founded/Ownrshp* 1994
Sales 101.8MM^E *EMP* 400
SIC 5047 Medical equipment & supplies; Medical equipment & supplies
Pr: Craig Smith
**CFO:* Jeff Kaczka
**Treas:* Richard Bozard
Bd of Dir: James Redding
Sr VP: Jack Clark
Sr VP: Erika T Davis
Sr VP: Grace R Den Hartog
Opers Mgr: Janet Scott

D-U-N-S 06-371-1873
OWENS COMMUNITY COLLEGE
30335 Oregon Rd, Perrysburg, OH 43551-4593
Tel (567) 661-7000 *Founded/Ownrshp* 1966
Sales 47.4MM^E *EMP* 1,200
SIC 8222 Technical institute; Technical institute
Ch Bd: Rich Rowe
**Pr:* Mike Bower
**CFO:* J D John Satkowski
Treas: Edward Owens
Ofcr: Donald Hendren
Ofcr: Luis Munguia
Assoc VP: Thomas Perin
Ex VP: John Satkowski
VP: Mike Bankey
VP: Pamela Beck
**VP:* Renay Scott
VP: Denise Smith

D-U-N-S 79-651-4466
▲ **OWENS CORNING**
1 Owens Corning Pkwy, Toledo, OH 43659-0001
Tel (419) 248-8000 *Founded/Ownrshp* 1938
Sales 5.2MMM *EMP* 14,000
Accts Pricewaterhousecoopers Llp To
Tkr Sym OC *Exch* NYS
SIC 3296 2952 3229 3089 Fiberglass insulation; Insulation: rock wool, slag & silica minerals; Acoustical board & tile, mineral wool; Roofing mats, mineral wool; Asphalt felts & coatings; Glass fibers, textile; Yarn, fiberglass; Windows, plastic; Fiberglass insulation; Insulation: rock wool, slag & silica minerals; Acoustical board & tile, mineral wool; Roofing mats, mineral wool; Asphalt felts & coatings; Glass fibers, textile; Yarn, fiberglass; Windows, plastic
Ch Bd: Michael H Thaman
Pr: Sheree Bargabos
Pr: Chuck Dana
Pr: Arnaud Genis
Pr: Charles W Stein
COO: Gale Tedhams
CFO: Michael C McMurray
CFO: J T Roach
Sr Cor Off: Ronald Mathewson
Bd of Dir: Daniel K Tseung
Ex VP: Daved Palochao
Sr VP: Joseph Chigh
Sr VP: John W Christy
Sr VP: Daniel T Smith
VP: Frank O Brien-Bernini
VP: Michael Dupont
VP: Scott G McDonald
VP: Barry Melnkovic
VP: Heinz J Otto
VP: Kelly J Schmidt
VP: Steve Zerby
Board of Directors: Suzanne P Nimocks, Norman P Blake Jr, Maryann T Seaman, Cesar Conde, John D Williams, J Brian Ferguson, Ralph F Hake, F Philip Handy, Ann Iverson, Edward F Lonergan, James J McMonagle, W Howard Morris

D-U-N-S 10-834-5620
■ **OWENS CORNING SALES INC**
OEM SOLUTION GROUP
(*Suby of* OWENS CORNING SALES LLC) ★
303 N Hurstbourne Pkwy # 275, Louisville, KY 40222-5185
Tel (502) 394-5800 *Founded/Ownrshp* 1995
Sales 24.5MM^E *EMP* 400
SIC 3296 Fiberglass insulation; Insulation: rock wool, slag & silica minerals; Fiberglass insulation; Insulation: rock wool, slag & silica minerals
Pr: Dan Eigel
Info Man: John Yogodnik

D-U-N-S 00-131-7452 IMP
■ **OWENS CORNING SALES LLC**
(*Suby of* OWENS CORNING) ★
1 Owens Corning Pkwy, Toledo, OH 43659-0001
Tel (419) 248-8000 *Founded/Ownrshp* 2006
Sales 1.9MMM^E *EMP* 9,000
SIC 3296 2952 3229 3089 1761 Fiberglass insulation; Insulation: rock wool, slag & silica minerals; Acoustical board & tile, mineral wool; Roofing mats, mineral wool; Asphalt felts & coatings; Glass fibers, textile; Yarn, fiberglass; Windows, plastic; Roofing, siding & sheet metal work; Fiberglass insulation; Insulation: rock wool, slag & silica minerals; Acoustical board & tile, mineral wool; Roofing mats, mineral wool; Asphalt felts & coatings; Glass fibers, textile; Yarn, fiberglass; Windows, plastic; Roofing, siding & sheet metal work
Ch Bd: Michael H Thaman
Pr: Rhonda L Brooks
Pr: Carl B Hedlund
Pr: George E Kiemle
Pr: William E Lebaron
Pr: Chuck Stein
Pr: Jerry L Weinstein
VP: Jeff Craney
VP: Scott A Deitz
VP: Bob Doyle
VP: Jim Drew
VP: Frank O'Brien-Bernini
VP: John Pagano

D-U-N-S 05-321-0881
OWENS MORTGAGE INVESTMENT FUND
2221 Olympic Blvd, Walnut Creek, CA 94595-1623
Tel (925) 935-3840 *Founded/Ownrshp* 1984
Sales 20.0MM *EMP* 17^E
SIC 6798 Mortgage investment trusts; Realty investment trusts; Mortgage investment trusts; Realty investment trusts
Pr: William C Owens
Genl Pt: Owens Financial Group
CFO: Bryan H Draper

D-U-N-S 02-861-7227
OWENS REALTY NETWORK LLC
O R L FACILITY SERVICES
(*Suby of* OWENS RENZ & LEE CO INC) ★
1646 33rd St Ste 301, Orlando, FL 32839-8866
Tel (407) 681-2000 *Founded/Ownrshp* 2010
Sales 17.8MM^E *EMP* 365^E
SIC 6531 Real estate brokers & agents
CEO: Bob Owens
Owner: Laura Owens
Pr: Anne Millians Roche
Ex VP: Trey Vick

D-U-N-S 62-068-2773
OWENS RENZ & LEE CO INC
2 Summit Pl Ste 2, Branford, CT 06405-4123
Tel (203) 483-9330 *Founded/Ownrshp* 1990
Sales 61.0MM^E *EMP* 750
SIC 6531 Real estate managers; Real estate managers
Pr: Robert D Owens
**CFO:* Michelle Mc Nulty

OWENS TRANSPORT SERVICE
See A MICHAEL OWENS INC

D-U-N-S 61-616-8472 IMP/EXP
■ **OWENS-BROCKWAY GLASS CONTAINER INC**
O-I
(*Suby of* OWENS-ILLINOIS INC) ★
1 Michael Owens Way, Perrysburg, OH 43551-2999
Tel (567) 336-8449 *Founded/Ownrshp* 2004
Sales NA *EMP* 6,800
SIC 3221 Glass containers; Glass containers
Ch: Mr Albert P L Stroucken
Pr: Mathew Longthorne
CEO: Steve McCracken
Sr VP: Jim Baehren
Sr VP: Steve Bramlage
Sr VP: Paul Jarrell
VP: Giancarlo Currarino
Board of Directors: R Lanigan

D-U-N-S 78-205-1239 IMP/EXP
■ **OWENS-BROCKWAY PACKAGING INC**
(*Suby of* OWENS-ILLINOIS INC) ★
1 Michael Owens Way, Perrysburg, OH 43551-2999
Tel (567) 336-5000 *Founded/Ownrshp* 1987
Sales 228.8MM^E *EMP* 7,000
SIC 3221 Glass containers; Glass containers
CEO: Al Stroucken
CFO: Ed White

D-U-N-S 12-617-2386
OWENS-FISHER CONSTRUCTION CO INC
331 Mclee Rd, Lexington, SC 29073-7807
Tel (803) 359-5309 *Founded/Ownrshp* 1985
Sales 20.3MM^E *EMP* 62
SIC 1611 Resurfacing contractor
Pr: Clifford Fisher
VP: Jerry Cliborne

D-U-N-S 92-732-2214 IMP
OWENS-ILLINOIS DE PUERTO RICO
O-I
1 Seagate, Toledo, OH 43604-1558
Tel (419) 874-9708 *Founded/Ownrshp* 1994
Sales 65.9MM^E *EMP* 470^E
SIC 3221 Glass containers
CEO: Steve McCracken
**Pr:* Joseph Lemieux
CFO: Peter Hellman
Ch: Randy Galbraith
Ofcr: Raymond Schlaff
Ofcr: Scott Trumbull
VP: Jean Arrambourg
VP: John Bachey

VP: Stephen Bramlage
VP: L Crawford
VP: Richard Crawford
VP: Jeffrey Denker
VP: Richard Jun
VP: Robert Lachmiller
VP: Matthew Longthorne
VP: Jose Lorente
VP: Michael McDaniel
VP: Philip McWeeny
VP: Philip Rubin
VP: Ellsworth Shriver
VP: Robert Smith

D-U-N-S 18-577-4650 IMP
■ OWENS-ILLINOIS GENERAL INC
O-1
(*Suby of* OWENS-ILLINOIS INC) ★
1 Michael Owens Way, Perrysburg, OH 43551-2999
Tel (567) 336-5000 *Founded/Ownrshp* 1987
Sales 126.9M^E *EMP* 550
SIC 3221 Glass containers; Glass containers
CEO: Al Stroucken
**Pr:* Thomas L Young
**CFO:* Steve Bramlage
Treas: Stephen P Bramlage
**Treas:* Jeffrey Denker
**Sr VP:* Paul Jarrell
**Sr VP:* Ed Snyder
**VP:* Jim Baehren
**VP:* Giancarlo Currarino
VP: Gerald S Deaton
VP: Gerard D Ged Doyle
VP: Robert E Lachmillr
**VP:* David G Van Hooser
VP: Lee Wesselmann

D-U-N-S 78-423-8433 IMP/EXP
■ OWENS-ILLINOIS GROUP INC
(*Suby of* OWENS-ILLINOIS INC) ★
1 Michael Owens Way, Perrysburg, OH 43551-2999
Tel (567) 336-5000 *Founded/Ownrshp* 1903
Sales 6.7MMM *EMP* 21,100
Accts Ernst & Young Llp Toledo Oh
SIC 3221 Glass containers; Glass containers
Ch Bd: Albert P L Strouckén
**Pr:* Stephen P Bramlage Jr
**VP:* James W Baehren
**VP:* Paul A Jarrell

D-U-N-S 00-503-4566 IMP
▲ OWENS-ILLINOIS INC
1 Michael Owens Way, Perrysburg, OH 43551-2999
Tel (567) 336-5000 *Founded/Ownrshp* 1903
Sales 6.7MMM *EMP* 21,100^E
Accts Ernst & Young Llp Toledo Ohi
Tkr Sym OI *Exch* NYS
SIC 3221 Glass containers; Food containers, glass; Bottles for packing, bottling & canning: glass; Medicine bottles, glass; Glass containers; Food containers, glass; Bottles for packing, bottling & canning: glass; Medicine bottles, glass
CEO: Albert P L Strouckén
Pr: Andres A Lopez
COO: Andres Lopez
CFO: Stephen P Bramlage Jr
CFO: John Haudrich
Ofcr: Carol R Gee
Ofcr: Paul A Jarrell
Sr VP: James W Baehren
VP: Giancarlo Currarino
Mng Dir: Vitaliano Torno
CIO: Ged Doyle
Board of Directors: Thomas L Young, Gary F Colter, Jay L Geldmacher, Peter S Hellman, Anastasia D Kelly, John J McMackin Jr, Hugh H Roberts, Helge H Wehmeier, Carol A Williams, Dennis K Williams

OWENSBORO BOARD OF EDUCATION
See OWENSBORO INDEPENDENT SCHOOL DISTRICT

OWENSBORO DIALYSIS CENTER
See RENAL TREATMENT CENTERS-ILLINOIS INC

D-U-N-S 02-414-0469
OWENSBORO FORD CENTER INC (KY)
CHAMPION FORD LINCOLN
140 Southtown Blvd, Owensboro, KY 42303-7759
Tel (270) 684-1441 *Founded/Ownrshp* 1990
Sales 30.7MM^E *EMP* 80
SIC 5511 Automobiles, new & used; Automobiles, new & used
Pr: Bruce Brubaker

D-U-N-S 00-194-7068 IMP
OWENSBORO GRAIN CO LLC (KY)
822 E 2nd St, Owensboro, KY 42303-3302
Tel (270) 686-6555 *Founded/Ownrshp* 2001
Sales 39.8MM^E *EMP* 145
SIC 2075 Soybean oil mills; Soybean oil mills
Pr: Robert E Hicks Jr
CFO: Jeff Erb
VP: Julian G Hayden Jr
VP: Sonny Hayden
VP: John Wright
Dir Lab: Molly Harris
IT Man: Jason Lutz
VP Opers: Mark Carlisle
Sfty Mgr: Brian Reid
Ql Cn Mgr: Joe Parrish
Snr Mgr: Joe Obryan
Board of Directors: Kenneth Bale, Thomas Bale, James Brown, Helen Cornell, Ellen Di Santo, Robert E Hicks Jr, Henry E O'bryan, Steve O'bryan

D-U-N-S 13-097-2115
OWENSBORO GRAIN EDIBLE OILS LLC
OWENSBORO GRAINS EDIBLE OIL
822 E 2nd St, Owensboro, KY 42303-3302
Tel (270) 926-2032 *Founded/Ownrshp* 2001
Sales 100.0MM *EMP* 26
SIC 2079 Edible fats & oils; Edible fats & oils

OWENSBORO GRAINS EDIBLE OIL
See OWENSBORO GRAIN EDIBLE OILS LLC

D-U-N-S 83-754-7074
OWENSBORO HEALTH INC
1201 Pleasant Valley Rd, Owensboro, KY 42303-9811
Tel (270) 688-2000 *Founded/Ownrshp* 1995
Sales 450.3MM *EMP* 3,200
Accts Ernst & Young Us Llp Indianap
SIC 8062 General medical & surgical hospitals; General medical & surgical hospitals
Pr: Philip A Patterson
Chf Rad: Charles Bea
**CFO:* John Hackbarth Jr
**Sr VP:* Vicki Stogsdill
VP: Liz Belt
**VP:* Lisa Jones
VP: Ramona Osborne
**VP:* Greg Strahan
Dir Rx: Jim Besier
Ex Dir: Denise Pace
Ex Dir: Ed Wardle

OWENSBORO HEALTH MUHLENBERG CO
See OH MUHLENBERG LLC

OWENSBORO HEART & VASCULAR
See OWENSBORO MEDICAL PRACTICE PLLC

D-U-N-S 05-136-0139
OWENSBORO INDEPENDENT SCHOOL DISTRICT
OWENSBORO BOARD OF EDUCATION
1300 Booth Ave, Owensboro, KY 42301-4540
Tel (270) 686-1040 *Founded/Ownrshp* 1986
Sales 33.8MM *EMP* 800
Accts Holland Cpas Psc Bowling Gre
SIC 8211 Public elementary & secondary schools; Public elementary & secondary schools
**Prin:* Janice Eaves

D-U-N-S 03-005-5797
OWENSBORO MEDICAL PRACTICE PLLC
OWENSBORO HEART & VASCULAR
1200 Breckenridge St # 101, Owensboro, KY 42303-1089
Tel (270) 683-8672 *Founded/Ownrshp* 2001
Sales 20.1MM^E *EMP* 110
SIC 8011 Offices & clinics of medical doctors
Pr: Kishor Vora
Off Mgr: Patricia Simon
IT Man: Bret Maynard

D-U-N-S 01-345-0632
OWENSBORO MUNICIPAL UTILITIES
2070 Tamarack Rd, Owensboro, KY 42301-6876
Tel (270) 926-3200 *Founded/Ownrshp* 1940
Sales 150.0MM *EMP* 240
SIC 4911 Electric services
Genl Mgr: Terry Naulty
Exec: Patricia Cary
Dir Lab: Kim Hook
Dir Lab: Cathy Vesells
CTO: David Boreman
Dir IT: Terry Horne
IT Man: Terry Horn
IT Man: Mike Reel
Sfty Mgr: Jason Brown
Sfty Mgr: Chad Cowan
Snr Mgr: Roger Hahus

D-U-N-S 17-477-5544
OWENSBORO MUNICIPAL UTILITIES ELECTRIC LIGHT & POWER SYSTEM
OMU
2070 Tamarack Rd, Owensboro, KY 42301-6876
Tel (270) 926-3200 *Founded/Ownrshp* 1901
Sales 139.8MM *EMP* 235
Accts Riney Hancock Cpas Psc Owensb
SIC 4911 4941 Distribution, electric power; Generation, electric power; Transmission, electric power; Water supply; Distribution, electric power; Generation, electric power; Transmission, electric power; Water supply
Genl Mgr: Stan Conn
**Prin:* Terrance Naulty
Snr Mgr: Ed Ford
Snr Mgr: Gerald Gilstrap
Snr Mgr: Steve Merimee

OWENSBORO PAVING CO
See YAGER MATERIALS LLC

OWINGS MILLS CORPORATE CAMPUS
See MCDONOGH SCHOOL INC

D-U-N-S 04-443-7796
OWL COMPANIES (CA)
4695 Macarthur Ct Ste 950, Newport Beach, CA 92660-1841
Tel (949) 797-2000 *Founded/Ownrshp* 1942, 1984
Sales 108.9MM^E *EMP* 1,389
SIC 8331 6519 4911 Job training & vocational rehabilitation services; Real property lessors; Generation, electric power; Job training & vocational rehabilitation services; Real property lessors; Generation, electric power
CEO: Gregory J Burden
VP: Jeff Stinson
Sls Mgr: Theresa Kholoma

D-U-N-S 60-257-1403
OWL EDUCATION AND TRAINING INC
(*Suby of* OWL COMPANIES) ★
2465 Campus Dr, Irvine, CA 92612-1502
Tel (949) 797-2000 *Founded/Ownrshp* 2005
Sales 5.9MM^E *EMP* 1,380
SIC 8331 Job training & vocational rehabilitation services; Job training & vocational rehabilitation services
Pr: Gregory J Burden
Treas: Stephen E Sastrom
**Sec:* Stephen Seastrom

OWL HOMECARE PHARMACY
See K AND S OWL INC

D-U-N-S 02-312-1418
■ OWL NIXON SWD LLC
(*Suby of* NGL ENERGY PARTNERS LP) ★
8214 Westchester Dr # 715, Dallas, TX 75225-6100
Tel (214) 292-2040 *Founded/Ownrshp* 2013
Sales 24.8MM^E *EMP* 384^E
SIC 4953 Liquid waste, collection & disposal
Pt: T Chris Cooper

D-U-N-S 07-911-7887
■ OWL OPERATING LLC
(*Suby of* NGL ENERGY PARTNERS LP) ★
8214 Westchester Dr # 850, Dallas, TX 75225-6100
Tel (214) 292-2040 *Founded/Ownrshp* 2012, 2013
Sales 33.1MM^E *EMP* 383^E
SIC 4953 Liquid waste, collection & disposal
Pt: T Chris Cooper

OWL REXALL DRUG
See SAINT PAUL ENTERPRISES INC

D-U-N-S 00-222-7528 IMP
■ OWL WIRE & CABLE LLC
(*Suby of* MARMON GROUP LLC) ★
3127 Seneca Tpke, Canastota, NY 13032-3514
Tel (315) 697-2011 *Founded/Ownrshp* 1951, 2000
Sales 79.9MM^E *EMP* 180
SIC 3315 Wire & fabricated wire products; Wire & fabricated wire products
Ch: Robert J Ratti
**Pr:* Philip J Kemper
**CFO:* Frank Russo
Opers Mgr: Josh Levesque
Plnt Mgr: Benjamin Norris
Sales Exec: Ron Mattia

D-U-N-S 10-592-0586 IMP
OWLS HEAD ALLOYS INC
187 Mitch Mcconnell Way, Bowling Green, KY 42101-7519
Tel (270) 842-1300 *Founded/Ownrshp* 2002
Sales 20.6MM^E *EMP* 66
SIC 4953 Recycling, waste materials
Pr: David Bradford
Pr: Rick Homman
Ex VP: John Pugh
VP Admn: Michelle Shultz
VP Opers: Steve Daugherty

OWN A CAR
See GRESHAM TOYOTA INC

D-U-N-S 83-287-8743
OWN LLC
OPRAH WINFREY NETWORK
1041 N Formosa Ave, West Hollywood, CA 90046-6703
Tel (323) 602-5500 *Founded/Ownrshp* 2008
Sales 23.6MM^E *EMP* 140
SIC 4841 Cable & other pay television services; Cable television services; Cable & other pay television services; Cable television services
Ofcr: Oprah Winfrey
**Co-Pr:* Erik Logan
**Co-Pr:* Sheri Salata
VP: Jill Dickerson
VP: Michelle Holt
VP: Maurizio Vitale
VP: Kristin Wall
Ex Dir: Endyia Sterns

D-U-N-S 62-128-7023
OWNER MARINA LLC CASA
CASA MARINA RESORT
1500 Reynolds St, Key West, FL 33040-4700
Tel (305) 296-3535 *Founded/Ownrshp* 2005
Sales 15.1MM^E *EMP* 400
SIC 7011 Hotels & motels; Hotels & motels

D-U-N-S 96-380-8519
OWNER RESOURCE GROUP LLC
ORG
600 Congress Ave Ste 200, Austin, TX 78701-2995
Tel (512) 505-4180 *Founded/Ownrshp* 2011
Sales 57.8MM^E *EMP* 400^E
SIC 8741 Management services; Management services
VP: Jessica Borowy
VP: Mandy Patterson
Mng Dir: Will Burnett

D-U-N-S 03-803-0354
OWNER SERVICES
6649 Westwood Blvd, Orlando, FL 32821-8029
Tel (407) 513-6578 *Founded/Ownrshp* 2001
Sales 20.5MM^E *EMP* 800
SIC 7389 Time-share condominium exchange; Time-share condominium exchange
VP: Ronald Essig

D-U-N-S 06-793-0024
OWNER-OPERATOR INDEPENDENT DRIVERS ASSN INC
OOIDA
1 Ooida Dr, Grain Valley, MO 64029-7903
Tel (816) 229-5791 *Founded/Ownrshp* 1973
Sales 64.7MM^E *EMP* 234
SIC 8611 8741 2721 Trade associations; Management services; Periodicals; Trade associations; Management services; Periodicals
Pr: James Johnston
Treas: Rick Craig
Bd of Dir: Gordon Betts
**Ex VP:* Todd Spencer

D-U-N-S 96-447-6659
OWNER-OPERATOR MANAGEMENT CORP INC
(*Suby of* OOIDA) ★
1 Ooida Dr, Grain Valley, MO 64029-7903
Tel (816) 229-5791 *Founded/Ownrshp* 1995
Sales 60.4MM^E *EMP* 203
Accts Mayer Hoffman Mccann L C
SIC 8741 Management services; Management services
Pr: James Johnston
**Treas:* Rick Craig
**Ex VP:* Todd Spencer
VP: Robert Driscoll

D-U-N-S 96-460-8699
OWNER-OPERATOR SERVICES INC
(*Suby of* OWNER-OPERATOR MANAGEMENT CORP INC) ★
1 Ooida Dr, Grain Valley, MO 64029-7903
Tel (816) 229-5791 *Founded/Ownrshp* 1985
Sales NA *EMP* 203^E
SIC 6411 Insurance agents, brokers & service; Insurance agents, brokers & service
Pr: James Johnston
**Treas:* Rick Craig
**VP:* Todd Spencer
Dir IT: Aaron Ladage

D-U-N-S 01-575-5105
OWNERIQ INC
27-43 Wormwood St Fl 4, Boston, MA 02210-1619
Tel (617) 350-6400 *Founded/Ownrshp* 2006
Sales 21.7MM^E *EMP* 55
SIC 7311 Advertising agencies
Pr: Jay Habegger
Pr: Michael Keohane
CFO: Doug Shattuck
Treas: A D Shattuck
Ex VP: Michael Chass
Ex VP: Johnson Connie
Ex VP: Robert Daniel
Ex VP: Connie Johnson
Sr VP: Chris Greig
Sr VP: Bob Scaglione
Sr VP: Robert Scaglione
VP: Monty Hudson
VP: Mike Keohene
VP: Ji Kim
VP: Greg Loeffelholz
VP: Michael Ouellette
VP: Richie Snell
VP: Steve Ustaris
Creative D: Dave Barresi

D-U-N-S 78-771-5721
OWNERS INSURANCE CO
(*Suby of* AUTO-OWNERS INSURANCE CO) ★
6101 Anacapri Blvd, Lansing, MI 48917-3968
Tel (517) 323-1200 *Founded/Ownrshp* 1975
Sales NA *EMP* 10
SIC 6411 6331 Property & casualty insurance agent; Property damage insurance; Property & casualty insurance agent; Property damage insurance
CEO: Jeffrey F Harrold
**Pr:* Jeffrey S Tagsold
**CFO:* Eileen K Fhaner
**Sec:* William F Woodbury
**Ex VP:* Katherine M Noirot
Sr VP: R L Ooyenga

D-U-N-S 60-929-0671
OWNIT MORTGAGE SOLUTIONS INC
SECURITY PACIFIC HOME LOANS
4360 Park Terrace Dr # 100, Westlake Village, CA 91361-5696
Tel (513) 872-6922 *Founded/Ownrshp* 2003
Sales NA *EMP* 500
SIC 6162 6163 Mortgage bankers & correspondents; Loan brokers; Mortgage bankers & correspondents; Loan brokers
Pr: Bill Dallas
**COO:* Bruce Dickinson
**CFO:* John Duhadway
VP: John Du Hadway

OWOSSO BOARD OF EDUCATION
See OWOSSO PUBLIC SCHOOLS

D-U-N-S 02-009-1732
OWOSSO PUBLIC SCHOOLS
OWOSSO BOARD OF EDUCATION
645 Alger Ave, Owosso, MI 48867-4601
Tel (989) 723-8131 *Founded/Ownrshp* 1873
Sales 20.8M *EMP* 500
Accts Maner Costerisan Pc Lansing
SIC 8211 Public elementary & secondary schools; High school, junior or senior; School board; Public elementary & secondary schools; High school, junior or senior; School board
**CFO:* Julie Omer
IT Man: Jim McAvoy

OWP AND P CANNON DESIGN
See ODONNELL WICKLUND PIGOZZI AND PETERSON INC

D-U-N-S 10-168-7056 IMP
OWSLEY BROWN FRAZIER HISTORICAL ARMS MUSEUM FOUNDATION INC
FRAZIER INTERNATIONAL HISTORY
829 W Main St, Louisville, KY 40202-2619
Tel (502) 753-5663 *Founded/Ownrshp* 2001
Sales 31.8MM *EMP* 65
Accts Mountjoy Chilton Medley Llp L
SIC 8412 Historical society; Historical society
Ch: Owsley Brown Frazier
Dir Vol: Lynnelle Claypool
Bd of Dir: C Bennett
VP: Craig Mooney
Dir Soc: Julie Glaser
Ex Dir: Madeleine Burnside
Manager: Mike Gilmore

D-U-N-S 82-811-7809 IMP
OWT INDUSTRIES INC
(*Suby of* ONE WORLD TECHNOLOGIES INC) ★
225 Pumpkintown Hwy, Pickens, SC 29671-2024
Tel (864) 878-6331 *Founded/Ownrshp* 2000
Sales 31.1MM^E *EMP* 200
SIC 5251 5085 Tools, power; Tools; Tools, power; Tools
Pr: Horst Pudwill
VP: Martin Harbeck
Exec: Audrey Heard
Netwrk Mgr: David Burlingame

OWV EXC
See VIRGINIA OHIO-WEST EXCAVATING CO INC

D-U-N-S 05-864-0145 IMP
OX BODIES INC
TBEI-OX BODIES
(Suby of TBEI) ★
719 Columbus St E, Fayette, AL 35555-2623
Tel (205) 932-5720 Founded/Ownrshp 2005
Sales 72.1MM^E EMP 310
Accts Jamison Money Farmer & Compa
SIC 3713 Truck & bus bodies; Truck & bus bodies
Pr: Robert Fines
*Treas: Jerry Frost
*VP: Johnny Baker
*VP: Dennis Pendley
Sls Dir: Kristie Ary

D-U-N-S 03-075-5468
OX PAPERBOARD LLC
164 Eyster Rd, Halltown, WV 25423
Tel (304) 725-2076 Founded/Ownrshp 2007
Sales 44.6MM^E EMP 80
SIC 2611 Pulp manufactured from waste or recycled paper
Genl Mgr: Tim Michaels
VP Opers: Mark Wallace

D-U-N-S 07-843-6927
OX PAPERBOARD MICHIGAN LLC
700 Centreville St, Constantine, MI 49042-1273
Tel (269) 435-2435 Founded/Ownrshp 2012
Sales 36.5MM^E EMP 80
SIC 2631 Coated paperboard
CEO: Kevin Hayward
*VP: Matthew Sullivan

D-U-N-S 04-570-4400 IMP
OXARC INC
4003 E Broadway Ave, Spokane, WA 99202-4528
Tel (509) 535-7794 Founded/Ownrshp 1968
Sales 77.9MM EMP 300
SIC 5084 2813 7359

D-U-N-S 06-122-8560 IMP
OXBO INTERNATIONAL CORP
(Suby of PLOEGER OXBO GROUP B.V.)
7275 Batavia Byron Rd, Byron, NY 14422-9599
Tel (585) 548-2665 Founded/Ownrshp 1998
Sales 39.0MM^E EMP 195
SIC 3523 5083 Farm machinery & equipment; Farm & garden machinery; Farm machinery & equipment; Farm & garden machinery
Ch Bd: Richard Glazier
*CEO: Gary C Stich
*COO: James Nowicki
*VP: Paul Dow
*VP: Andrew Talbott
VP Sls: Craig Henkel

OXBOW ANIMAL HEALTH
See OXBOW ENTERPRISES INC

D-U-N-S 01-297-9830
OXBOW CALCINING LLC
(Suby of OXBOW CARBON & MINERALS HOLDINGS INC) ★
11826 N 30th St, Kremlin, OK 73753-0189
Tel (580) 874-2201 Founded/Ownrshp 2003
Sales 31.8MM^E EMP 34^E
SIC 5172 Petroleum products
Prin: Scott Hoard
Plnt Mgr: Dan Rosendale

D-U-N-S 79-869-8510
OXBOW CALCINING USA INC
(Suby of OXBOW CARBON LLC) ★
1601 Forum Pl Ste 1400, West Palm Beach, FL 33401-8104
Tel (580) 874-2201 Founded/Ownrshp 1998
Sales 52.3MM^E EMP 110
SIC 2999 Coke (not from refineries), petroleum; Coke (not from refineries), petroleum
Ex VP: Steve Fried
*CFO: Zachary Shipley
VP: Patricia J Diehl
Tech Mgr: David Kirkpatrick
Mtls Mgr: Don Peyton
Prd Mgr: Earl Boone
Manager: Rick Thurlow

D-U-N-S 19-059-0760 IMP/EXP
OXBOW CARBON & MINERALS HOLDINGS INC
1601 Forum Pl Ste 1400, West Palm Beach, FL 33401-8104
Tel (561) 907-5400 Founded/Ownrshp 1983
Sales 1.4MMM^E EMP 1,220^E
SIC 5052 1222 Coal; Coke; Bituminous coal-underground mining; Coal; Coke; Bituminous coal-underground mining
CEO: William Bil Koch
*Pr: David Nestler
*COO: Steven E Fried
*CFO: William D Parmelee
CFO: William Parmelee
*CFO: Zachary Shipley
*Ex VP: James R Freney
*Ex VP: Eric Johnson
*VP: Richard P Callahan
IT Man: Bill Wade

D-U-N-S 80-811-1228
OXBOW CARBON LLC
(Suby of OXBOW CARBON & MINERALS HOLDINGS INC) ★
1601 Forum Pl Ste 1400, West Palm Beach, FL 33401-8104
Tel (561) 907-5400 Founded/Ownrshp 2007
Sales 348.7MM^E EMP 808
SIC 1241 2999 5052 Coal mining services; Coke, calcined petroleum: made from purchased materials; Coal; Coal mining services; Coke, calcined petroleum: made from purchased materials; Coal
Pr: William I Koch
COO: Steven E Fried
CFO: William Parmalee
CFO: William D Parmelee
Treas: Ben Klein
Ex VP: James R Freney
Ex VP: Eric Johnson
Dir Risk M: Donna Gulbransen
Opers Mgr: Daniel Velner
Counsel: Pierre Azzi
Counsel: James Laws

D-U-N-S 11-423-3158
OXBOW CORP
OXBOW GROUP
(Suby of OXBOW CARBON & MINERALS HOLDINGS INC) ★
1601 Forum Pl Ste 1400, West Palm Beach, FL 33401-8104
Tel (561) 697-4436 Founded/Ownrshp 1983
Sales 125.9MM^E EMP 230
SIC 8731 Natural resource research; Natural resource research
CEO: William I Koch
*COO: Steven E Fried
CFO: Bill Parmelee
*CFO: William D Parmelee
CFO: Jenny Vargas
*Treas: Benjamin L Klein
*Ex VP: James R Freney
Ex VP: Jim Freney
*Ex VP: Eric Johnson
Ex VP: James Kohlhoff
*Ex VP: Zachary K Shipley
Ex VP: Mark Whittemore
VP: Phil Nicoll

D-U-N-S 14-588-0055 IMP/EXP
OXBOW ENERGY SOLUTIONS LLC
(Suby of OXBOW CARBON LLC) ★
1601 Forum Pl Ste 1400, West Palm Beach, FL 33401-8104
Tel (561) 907-4300 Founded/Ownrshp 2003
Sales 220.5MM^E EMP 800
SIC 5052 Coal; Coal
COO: Eric Johnson
Pr: Bob Schneid
VP: Greg Kravitz
VP: Joseph Kulbeth
Genl Mgr: Tom Brandlin
Opers Mgr: Chuck Flannery

D-U-N-S 96-097-8047 IMP
OXBOW ENTERPRISES INC
OXBOW ANIMAL HEALTH
29012 Mill Rd, Murdock, NE 68407-2352
Tel (402) 867-2951 Founded/Ownrshp 1987
Sales 30.5MM^E EMP 54
SIC 5149 5999 Pet foods; Pet food
Owner: John R Miller
*COO: Deborah Buhro
*Sec: Patricia L Miller
Dir IT: Micah Kohles
Plnt Mgr: Jeff Rehder
Prd Mgr: Scott Cline
Snr Mgr: Doug Johnson

OXBOW GROUP
See OXBOW CORP

D-U-N-S 07-275-2665
OXBOW MINING LLC
(Suby of OXBOW CARBON LLC) ★
3737 Highway 133, Somerset, CO 81434
Tel (970) 929-5122 Founded/Ownrshp 2007
Sales 29.2MM^E EMP 340
SIC 1241 Coal mining services; Coal mining services
Pr: Michael Ludlow
CFO: Bill Parmelee
Treas: Ben Klein
VP: Richard Callahan
Sfty Mgr: Terry Hayes

D-U-N-S 05-667-4310 IMP
OXBOW SULPHUR INC
ICEC
(Suby of OXBOW CORP) ★
1450 Lake Robbins Dr # 500, The Woodlands, TX 77380-3258
Tel (281) 907-9500 Founded/Ownrshp 1986
Sales 125.9MM^E EMP 60^E
Accts Grant Thornton Llp Houston T
SIC 5191 5169 Fertilizer & fertilizer materials; Phosphate rock, ground; Industrial chemicals; Fertilizer & fertilizer materials; Phosphate rock, ground; Industrial chemicals
Pr: William Zisson
*CFO: Peter Engelking
*CFO: William D Parmelee
*Treas: Benjamin L Klein
Ofcr: David Herman
*Sr VP: Vincent Leone
*Sr VP: Jeremy Sheppe
VP: Nita Schovajsa
VP: Mark Stewart
VP: Mark Whittemore
IT Man: John Hunter

D-U-N-S 06-131-8305
OXBRIDGE ACADEMY FOUNDATION INC
3151 N Military Trl, West Palm Beach, FL 33409-2730
Tel (561) 972-9600 Founded/Ownrshp 2008
Sales 27.0MM EMP 8
SIC 8211 Academy
Pr: Robert C Parsons
Exec: Dan Gasperi

D-U-N-S 79-228-3405 IMP/EXP
OXEA CORP
(Suby of OXEA HOLDING CORP) ★
1505 L B Johnson Fwy # 400, Dallas, TX 75234-6082
Tel (972) 481-2700 Founded/Ownrshp 2006
Sales 103.8MM^E EMP 205
SIC 2869 Industrial organic chemicals; Industrial organic chemicals
Pr: Robert Gengelbach
VP: Cristobal Ascencio
VP: Steve Friedewald
*VP: Wolfgang Hackenberg
VP: Jan Hille
*Prin: Martina Flel
*Prin: Miguel Mantas
*Prin: Cornelius Robertson
Snr Mgr: Darren Friesenhahn
Snr Mgr: Lindsey Ham
Snr Mgr: Alfonso Torres

D-U-N-S 96-642-2045
OXEA HOLDING CORP
(Suby of OXEA GMBH)
1505 Lyndon B Johnson Fwy, Dallas, TX 75234-6069
Tel (972) 481-2700 Founded/Ownrshp 2010
Sales 104.0MM^E EMP 205^E
SIC 2899 Chemical preparations; Chemical preparations
Pr: Wolfgang Hackenberc
*Prin: Robert Gengelbach

D-U-N-S 14-893-0357
OXENDALE & ASSOC INC
OXENDALE CHRYSLER, DODGE, JEEP
920 E State Route 89a, Cottonwood, AZ 86326-5443
Tel (928) 634-3656 Founded/Ownrshp 1979
Sales 34.3MM^E EMP 75
SIC 5511 Automobiles, new & used; Automobiles, new & used
Pr: Thomas R Oxendale
CFO: Tim Hoffman
*Treas: Cortez Oxendale
*VP: Michael T Oxendale
Sls Mgr: Shawn Zingali

OXENDALE CHRYSLER, DODGE, JEEP
See OXENDALE & ASSOC INC

D-U-N-S 07-662-1713
OXFAM AMERICA INC
226 Causeway St Fl 5, Boston, MA 02114-2206
Tel (617) 482-1211 Founded/Ownrshp 1970
Sales 67.9MM EMP 180^E
Accts Cbiz Tofias Boston Ma
SIC 8399 Antipoverty board; Antipoverty board
Pr: Raymond C Offenheiser
*COO: Jim Daniell
COO: Jane Skelton
*CFO: Mark F Kripp
Bd of Dir: Karen Ansara
Bd of Dir: Michael Carter
Trst: Matthew Martin
Ofcr: Mary Babic
Ofcr: Alex Blair
Ofcr: Sarah Livingston
Ofcr: Telley Madina
Ofcr: Vanessa Parra
Ofcr: Yumeka Rushing
Ofcr: Laura Rusu
Ofcr: David Satterthwaite
Ofcr: Ramona Wright
*VP: John Ambler
VP: Raymon Doffengeiser
VP: Barbara Durr
*VP: Stephanie Kurzina
*VP: Paul O'Brien

OXFORD
See MIGHTY HURRICANE HOLDINGS INC

D-U-N-S 04-382-4077
OXFORD ACADEMY & CENTRAL SCHOOL DIST
12 Fort Hill Park, Oxford, NY 13830
Tel (607) 843-2025 Founded/Ownrshp 1890
Sales 44.3MM EMP 200
Accts D Arcangelo & Co Llp Rome
SIC 8211 Private elementary & secondary schools; Private elementary & secondary schools
*Prin: Katie Hansen
*Prin: Timothy McDonald
*Prin: Christine Pierce

OXFORD AIRPORT TECHNICAL SVCS
See OXFORD ELECTRONICS INC

OXFORD AMHERST LLC
See PHARMACYCLICS LLC

D-U-N-S 07-548-5441
OXFORD AREA SCHOOL DISTRICT-PTO INC
125 Bell Tower Ln, Oxford, PA 19363-1208
Tel (610) 932-5107 Founded/Ownrshp 1900
Sales 25.1MM^E EMP 325
SIC 8211 Public combined elementary & secondary school; School board; Public combined elementary & secondary school; School board

OXFORD CAPITAL GROUP
See OXFORD CAPITAL PARTNERS INC

D-U-N-S 82-542-6559
OXFORD CAPITAL GROUP LLC
350 W Hubbard St Ste 440, Chicago, IL 60654-6900
Tel (312) 755-9500 Founded/Ownrshp 2006
Sales 1.0MMM EMP 500
SIC 6719 Investment holding companies, except banks; Investment holding companies, except banks

D-U-N-S 94-379-1707
OXFORD CAPITAL PARTNERS INC
OXFORD CAPITAL GROUP
350 W Hubbard St Ste 440, Chicago, IL 60654-6900
Tel (312) 755-9500 Founded/Ownrshp 1994
Sales 181.4MM^E EMP 2,000
SIC 6719 Investment holding companies, except banks; Investment holding companies, except banks
Pr: John W Rutledge
*Mng Dir: Vann A Avedisian
Mng Dir: Vann A Vedisin
Sls Dir: Adam Schomaker

D-U-N-S 10-000-0751
OXFORD CITY SCHOOL DISTRICT
310 E 2nd St, Oxford, AL 36203-1704
Tel (256) 241-3140 Founded/Ownrshp 1970
Sales 20.6MM^E EMP 434
SIC 8211 Public elementary & secondary schools; School board; Public elementary & secondary schools; School board
CFO: Robert Jorden
Dir IT: Erik Preacher
Dir IT: Robby Roberson
Schl Brd P: Karen Phillips

D-U-N-S 07-857-8234
OXFORD CITY SCHOOLS DISTRICT
224 Bramlett Blvd, Oxford, MS 38655-3416
Tel (662) 234-3541 Founded/Ownrshp 1964
Sales 33.0MM^E EMP 515
Accts Watkins Ward And Stafford Oko
SIC 8211 Public adult education school; Public adult education school
Treas: Minnie Gates-Powell
Ofcr: Tim Sockwell
Ofcr: Harper Thomas
Ofcr: Mario Weekley
Off Mgr: Lori Barnes
Off Mgr: Regina Black
Off Mgr: Hattie Farr
Schl Brd P: Marian Barksdale
Psych: Regina Carothers
Psych: Sarah Littlejohn
Psych: Nancy Maxwell

D-U-N-S 01-085-9460
OXFORD COMMUNITY SCHOOLS
10 N Washington St, Oxford, MI 48371-4665
Tel (248) 969-5000 Founded/Ownrshp 1800
Sales 26.5MM^E EMP 489
Accts Yeo & Yeo Cpa S Saginaw Mi
SIC 8211 5411 Public combined elementary & secondary school; School board; Convenience stores; Public combined elementary & secondary school; School board; Convenience stores

D-U-N-S 00-580-8282
OXFORD CONSTRUCTION CO (GA)
3200 Palmyra Rd, Albany, GA 31707-1221
Tel (229) 883-3232 Founded/Ownrshp 1948
Sales 91.2MM^E EMP 250
Accts Draffin & Tucker Llp Albany
SIC 1611 1629 Highway & street paving contractor; Earthmoving contractor; Highway & street paving contractor; Earthmoving contractor
Pr: J Bruce Melton
*CFO: Keith Miller
*VP: J Melvin Edwards
VP: Melvin Edwards
Genl Mgr: Bill Gahring
Sfty Mgr: Steve Burton

D-U-N-S 00-478-6968
OXFORD COUNTY TELEPHONE & TELEGRAPH CO INC (ME)
OXFORD TELECOM
491 Lisbon St, Lewiston, ME 04240-7418
Tel (207) 336-9911 Founded/Ownrshp 1900
Sales 70.2MM^E EMP 125
Accts Berry Dunn Mcneil & Parker
SIC 4813 Telephone communication, except radio; Telephone communication, except radio
Pr: Craig Gunderson
*Treas: Richard Clark
*VP: Brian Paul
VP: Robert Rivas
VP: Gloria Smith
*VP: Michael Tompkins
IT Man: Sherri Vallee
IT Man: Marc Vanderwood
Mfg Dir: Peter Munro
Sls Mgr: Julie Erickson
Sales Asso: Katie Jose
Board of Directors: Lyn Wood Andrews, Richard Huntley, Adelbert Joy

D-U-N-S 07-217-4964
OXFORD DEVELOPMENT CO INC
301 Grant St Ste 4500, Pittsburgh, PA 15219-1489
Tel (412) 261-1500 Founded/Ownrshp 1960
Sales 46.6MM^E EMP 2,200
SIC 6512 Commercial & industrial building operation; Shopping center, property operation only; Commercial & industrial building operation; Shopping center, property operation only
CEO: Steven J Guy
*Ch: Edward J Lewis
*Treas: Mark E Mason
*Sr VP: Louis G Dinardo
*VP: Brian M Albert
VP: Laurence Castonguay
VP: Grant Mason
*VP: Frank Molinero
*VP: Stephen J Nicotra
*VP: R Scott Pollock
CTO: Mark Mason

D-U-N-S 11-263-3912
OXFORD DEVELOPMENT ENTERPRISES INC
(Suby of OXFORD CORPORATION)
8014 Norfolk Ave, Bethesda, MD 20814-2504
Tel (240) 743-4015 Founded/Ownrshp 1982
Sales 8.8MM^E EMP 900
SIC 6531 Real estate agents & managers; Real estate agents & managers
CEO: Leo E Zickler
CFO: Wesley D Minami
CFO: D Wesley
VP: Kenneth C Willard

OXFORD DIAGNOSTIC LABORATORIES
See OXFORD IMMUNOTEC INC

D-U-N-S 01-164-0026
OXFORD ELECTRONICS INC
OXFORD AIRPORT TECHNICAL SVCS
(Suby of AIRLINE SERVICES) ★
474 Meacham Ave, Elmont, NY 11003-3849
Tel (516) 326-6262 Founded/Ownrshp 1976, 2000
Sales 48.4MM^E EMP 210
SIC 4581 Airport terminal services; Airport terminal services
Ch Bd: Anthony P Dalia
CFO: Louis Veneziano
VP: Joseph Ferraro

D-U-N-S 15-060-2688
OXFORD FINANCIAL GROUP LTD
11711 N Meridian St # 600, Carmel, IN 46032-4534
Tel (317) 843-5678 Founded/Ownrshp 1983
Sales 48.4MM^E EMP 110
SIC 6282 8742 6411 Investment advisory service; Investment counselors; Financial consultant; Pension & retirement plan consultants; Investment advisory service; Investment counselors; Financial consultant; Pension & retirement plan consultants
Ch Bd: Jeffrey H Thomasson

CFO: Timothy Dean
**Treas:* Jeffery Stroman
Ofcr: White Lora
Ofcr: Susan Mitchell
Trst Ofcr: Julie A Lenahan
VP: Brian Dykstra
Exec: Mark Green
Mng Dir: Debora Bennett
Mng Dir: C R Davis II
Mng Dir: C Davis

D-U-N-S 62-606-8316
■ OXFORD FINANCIAL INC
(*Suby of* OXFORD LIFE INSURANCE CO INC) ★
1232 Fourier Dr, Madison, WI 53717-1960
Tel (608) 662-1232 *Founded/Ownrshp* 1997
Sales NA *EMP* 128
SIC 6321 6311 Accident insurance carriers; Health insurance carriers; Life insurance carriers
Pr: Mark Haydukovich
**Sr VP:* Larry Goodyear

OXFORD GLOBAL RESOURCES, INC.
See OXFORD GLOBAL RESOURCES LLC

D-U-N-S 14-412-3791
■ OXFORD GLOBAL RESOURCES LLC
OXFORD GLOBAL RESOURCES, INC.
(*Suby of* ON ASSIGNMENT INC) ★
100 Cummings Ctr Ste 206l, Beverly, MA 01915-6104
Tel (978) 236-1182 *Founded/Ownrshp* 1994
Sales 500.0MM *EMP* 400
SIC 7363 8748 Help supply services; Business consulting; Help supply services; Business consulting
Pr: Michael J McGowan
Mng Pt: Cornell Johnson
**CFO:* Jim Brill
**Treas:* Dean Burdett
Ex VP: Stephen Mahle
Ex VP: David Scott
VP: Amy Karpowitcz
VP: Howard Pearce
Prin: Nick Penny
Genl Mgr: Allen Beers
CIO: Michael Payne

D-U-N-S 87-893-0015
■ OXFORD HEALTH PLANS (CT) INC
(*Suby of* OXFORD HEALTH PLANS INC) ★
48 Monroe Tpke, Trumbull, CT 06611-1341
Tel (203) 459-9100 *Founded/Ownrshp* 1993
Sales NA *EMP* 800
SIC 6324 Health maintenance organization (HMO), insurance only; Health maintenance organization (HMO), insurance only
CEO: Chuck Berg
**CFO:* Kurt Thompson

D-U-N-S 11-118-9754
■ OXFORD HEALTH PLANS (NJ) INC
UNITED HEALTHCARE
(*Suby of* OXFORD HEALTH PLANS INC) ★
4 Research Dr Ste 401, Shelton, CT 06484-6242
Tel (203) 459-6000 *Founded/Ownrshp* 1996
Sales NA *EMP* 50
SIC 6324 Health maintenance organization (HMO), insurance only
Pr: Michael Turpin
Pr: Charles Burg
CFO: George L Mikan
VP: Karen Davezac
VP: Sally Verrilli
Dir IT: Laura Gomez
Dir IT: Tom Woerner
IT Man: John Camacho
IT Man: Bharani Thippa
Mktg Dir: Julie Johnston

D-U-N-S 11-118-8814
■ OXFORD HEALTH PLANS (NY) INC
(*Suby of* OXFORD HEALTH PLANS INC) ★
48 Monroe Tpke, Trumbull, CT 06611-1341
Tel (203) 459-9100 *Founded/Ownrshp* 1996
Sales NA *EMP* 1,690
SIC 6324 Health maintenance organization (HMO), insurance only; Health maintenance organization (HMO), insurance only
Prin: Charles Burg
MIS Dir: Thomas Beauchamp

D-U-N-S 13-175-8153
■ OXFORD HEALTH PLANS INC
(*Suby of* UNITEDHEALTH GROUP INC) ★
48 Monroe Tpke, Trumbull, CT 06611-1341
Tel (203) 459-9100 *Founded/Ownrshp* 2004
Sales NA *EMP* 3,200
SIC 6324 Health maintenance organization (HMO), insurance only; Dental insurance; Health maintenance organization (HMO), insurance only; Dental insurance
Pr: Charles G Berg
**Ch Bd:* Kent J Thiry
**CFO:* Kurt B Thompson
Ofcr: John Marcus
Ofcr: Alan M Muney MD Mha
**Ex VP:* Steve Black
**Ex VP:* Steven H Black
Ex VP: Rita Bourgeois
**Ex VP:* Daniel N Gregoire
Ex VP: Robert Natt
VP: Jeffery Alter
VP: Carmel Colica
VP: Desmond Hussey
VP: Robert Murphy
VP: Allen Sorbo
VP: Donald Stangler

OXFORD HEALTHCARE
See STATEWIDE HEALTHCARE SERVICES INC

OXFORD HEALTHCARE
See HEALTHCARE SERVICES OF OZARKS INC

OXFORD HEALTHCARE
See HELP AT HOME INC

OXFORD HEALTHCARE
See OKLAHOMA HEALTHCARE SERVICES INC

OXFORD HILLS SCHOOL DISTRICT
See REGIONAL SCHOOL UNIT 17/MAINE SCHOOL ADMINISTRATIVE DISTRICT 17

D-U-N-S 00-974-4265
OXFORD IMMUNOTEC INC
OXFORD DIAGNOSTIC LABORATORIES
(*Suby of* OXFORD IMMUNOTEC LIMITED)
700 Nickerson Rd Ste 200, Marlborough, MA 01752-4663
Tel (508) 481-4648 *Founded/Ownrshp* 2008
Sales 26.5MM^E *EMP* 75
SIC 2835 In vitro & in vivo diagnostic substances
Ch Bd: Richard Sandberg
**Pr:* Jeff Schroeder
Pr: Jon Watts
**CEO:* Peter Wrighton Smith
**CFO:* Richard Altieri
**Sec:* Simon Turner
VP: Mark Kirtland
**VP:* Patricia Randall
Mfg Dir: Justin Silva
Mktg Dir: Cindy Callahan
Mktg Dir: Keith Hanigan

D-U-N-S 00-326-4041 IMP/EXP
▲ OXFORD INDUSTRIES INC
999 Peachtree St Ne # 688, Atlanta, GA 30309-3915
Tel (404) 659-2424 *Founded/Ownrshp* 1942
Sales 997.8MM *EMP* 5,400
Accts Ernst & Young Llp Atlanta Ge
Tkr Sym OXM *Exch* NYS
SIC 2321 2325 2311 Men's & boys' dress shirts; Men's & boys' sports & polo shirts; Men's & boys' trousers & slacks; Men's & boys' jeans & dungarees; Shorts (outerwear): men's, youths' & boys'; Men's & boys' suits & coats; Men's & boys' dress shirts; Men's & boys' sports & polo shirts; Men's & boys' trousers & slacks; Men's & boys' jeans & dungarees; Shorts (outerwear): men's, youths' & boys'; Men's & boys' suits & coats
Pr: Thomas C Chubb III
Pr: Wesley Howard
CEO: Mark Maidment
CFO: K Scott Grassmyer
Ex VP: Thomas E Campbell
Ex VP: Lucio D Gasperina
Ex VP: Scott D Sennett
Sr VP: John A Baumgartner
Sr VP: Scott Grassmyer
Sr VP: Ralph Iannazzone
Sr VP: Wendy Santana
VP: John Baumgartner
VP: John Winston
Board of Directors: Thomas C Gallagher, George C Guynn, John R Holder, J Reese Lanier, Dennis M Love, Clarence H Smith, Clyde C Tuggle, Helen B Weeks, E Jenner Wood III

D-U-N-S 11-422-9701
OXFORD INSTRUMENTS AMERICA INC
(*Suby of* OXFORD INSTRUMENTS PLC)
300 Baker Ave Ste 150, Concord, MA 01742-2124
Tel (978) 369-9933 *Founded/Ownrshp* 2006
Sales 41.8MM^E *EMP* 140
SIC 5049 3829 Scientific instruments; Measuring & controlling devices; Scientific instruments; Measuring & controlling devices
Pr: Scott Reiman
**Pr:* John Flint
CFO: Martin Cuddy
**Treas:* Christopher S Fraser
VP: Sam Klaidman
Genl Mgr: Neil Wester
IT Man: Denielle Smith
S&M/VP: Joseph Carr
Sls Mgr: John Haritos

D-U-N-S 13-938-6841 IMP/EXP
OXFORD INSTRUMENTS HOLDINGS INC
(*Suby of* OXFORD INSTRUMENTS OVERSEAS HOLDINGS LIMITED)
600 Milik St, Carteret, NJ 07008-1199
Tel (732) 541-1300 *Founded/Ownrshp* 1982
Sales 42.6MM^E *EMP* 272^E
SIC 3264 5047 Magnets, permanent: ceramic or ferrite; Medical equipment & supplies
Pr: Martin Lamaison
**Pr:* Maarten Kramer
**COO:* Andrew Mackintosh
CFO: Mathew Bowman
**Ch:* Peter Williams
VP: Joe Carr
VP: Jeff Hall
VP: Steven Parker
VP: Jeffrey Parrell
Mng Dir: Jim Hutchins
Mng Dir: Andy Matthews

D-U-N-S 07-731-5133
OXFORD KINGSWOOD SCHOOL INC
K O
170 Kingswood Rd, West Hartford, CT 06119-1496
Tel (860) 233-9631 *Founded/Ownrshp* 1921
Sales 22.0MM *EMP* 127
SIC 8211

D-U-N-S 02-069-5029
■ OXFORD LIFE INSURANCE CO INC (AZ)
(*Suby of* AMERCO) ★
2721 N Central Ave Fl 5, Phoenix, AZ 85004-1137
Tel (602) 263-6666 *Founded/Ownrshp* 1968, 1996
Sales NA *EMP* 150
SIC 6311 6321 Life reinsurance; Disability health insurance; Life reinsurance; Disability health insurance
Pr: Mark A Haydukovich
Pr: Drew Batten
**CFO:* Jason A Berg
CFO: Charlie Miller
CFO: Steve Taylor
VP: Amanda Chester
VP: Michael Johansson
VP: Jin Y Kim
VP: Mae Kirk
VP: Cindy Reed
VP: Michael Rolfe
Exec: Matthew Case
Exec: Anthony Gertos

D-U-N-S 15-549-1517
■ OXFORD MINING CO INC
(*Suby of* WESTMORELAND RESOURCE PARTNERS LP) ★
544 Chestnut St, Coshocton, OH 43812-1209
Tel (740) 622-6302 *Founded/Ownrshp* 1985
Sales 319.7MM^E *EMP* 450
SIC 1221 Strip mining, bituminous; Strip mining, bituminous
Pr: Charles C Ungurean
**CFO:* Jeffrey M Gutman
Treas: Michael Ungurean
**Sr VP:* Gregory J Honish
**Sr VP:* Daniel M Maher
**VP:* Thomas T Ungurean
**Dir Surg:* Denise M Maksimoski
IT Man: Joel Ramshaw

D-U-N-S 07-979-9247
OXFORD PUBLIC SCHOOLS
4 Maple Rd, Oxford, MA 01540-1923
Tel (508) 987-6050 *Founded/Ownrshp* 2015
Sales 4.3MM^E *EMP* 388^E
SIC 8211 Public elementary & secondary schools
Teacher Pr: Kathleen Martinello
HC Dir: Elaine Zimba

OXFORD SUITES
See BANEY CORP

D-U-N-S 06-185-1325 IMP
OXFORD SUPERCONDUCTING TECHNOLOGY LIMITED PARTNERSHIP
(*Suby of* OXFORD INSTRUMENTS AMERICA INC) ★
600 Milik St, Carteret, NJ 07008-1199
Tel (732) 541-1300 *Founded/Ownrshp* 2006
Sales 32.1MM^E *EMP* 140
SIC 3357 Magnet wire, nonferrous; Magnet wire, nonferrous
Pt: Scott Reiman
Exec: Bill Patterson

OXFORD TELECOM
See OXFORD COUNTY TELEPHONE & TELEGRAPH CO INC

D-U-N-S 06-992-0734
OXFORD TOWN OF INC
325 Main St, Oxford, MA 01540-1774
Tel (508) 987-6006 *Founded/Ownrshp* 1713
Sales NA *EMP* 390
Accts Kpmg Llp Boston Ma
SIC 9111 City & town managers' offices; ; City & town managers' offices;
Ch: John Saadd
**Prin:* Susan Gallant
**Prin:* Henry J Lamountain Sr
Ex Dir: Timothy Kelley
MIS Dir: Donna O'Halloran

OXFORD UNIVERSITY PRESS, INC.
See OXFORD UNIVERSITY PRESS, LLC

D-U-N-S 00-146-8149 IMP/EXP
OXFORD UNIVERSITY PRESS LLC
OXFORD UNIVERSITY PRESS, INC.
(*Suby of* UNIVERSITY OF OXFORD)
198 Madison Ave Fl 8, New York, NY 10016-4308
Tel (212) 726-6000 *Founded/Ownrshp* 1973
Sales 99.6MM^E *EMP* 530
Accts Deloitte Tax Llp Raleigh Nc
SIC 2731 5961 Book publishing; Book & record clubs; Book publishing; Book & record clubs
Pr: Niko Pfund
Ofcr: Chloe Foster
VP: Joan Bossert
VP: John Challice
VP: Casper Grathwohl
VP: Niko Pfund
VP: Colleen Scollans
Assoc Dir: Rose Pintaudi-Jones
Creative D: Linda Secondari
Mng Dir: Peter Marshall
Mng Dir: Jim Morgan

D-U-N-S 01-310-7176
OXFORD-COLUMBIA ASSOCIATES A MARYLAND LIMITED PARTNERSHIP
CHIMNEYS CRDLE ROCK APARTMENTS
6531 Quiet Hours, Columbia, MD 21045-4903
Tel (410) 381-1906 *Founded/Ownrshp* 2009
Sales 30.4MM^E *EMP* 3,900
SIC 6513 Apartment building operators; Apartment building operators
Sr VP: Leeann Morein

D-U-N-S 96-232-0797 IMP
OXITENO USA LLC
(*Suby of* OXITENO MEXICO, S.A. DE C.V.)
9801 Bay Area Blvd, Pasadena, TX 77507-1863
Tel (281) 909-7600 *Founded/Ownrshp* 2009
Sales 110.0MM^E *EMP* 62
SIC 5172 Gases, liquefied petroleum (propane); Gases, liquefied petroleum (propane)
Pr: Joao Benjamin Parolin
Plnt Mgr: Dennis Ohlmansiek
Manager: John Bozza
Manager: Tracy Price
Manager: Doug Rose
Sls Mgr: Nick Janakiefski

D-U-N-S 02-408-9757
OXMOOR AUTO INC
OXMOOR TOYOTA
8003 Shelbyville Rd, Louisville, KY 40222-5417
Tel (502) 426-1200 *Founded/Ownrshp* 1989
Sales 62.6MM^E *EMP* 142^E
SIC 5511 Automobiles, new & used; Pickups, new & used; Vans, new & used; Automobiles, new & used; Pickups, new & used; Vans, new & used
Pr: Tracy Farmer
CFO: Steve Kelly
Sr VP: Rusty Shofner
VP: Joe Marshall
Genl Mgr: Delbert Farmer
Genl Mgr: Tim Robinson
Genl Mgr: Doug Stovalla
IT Man: Chris Hannan
Sales Exec: Terry Boardman
Sls Mgr: Lance Alm
Sls Mgr: Craig Gray

D-U-N-S 06-690-4988
OXMOOR FORD LINCOLN MERCURY INC
100 Oxmoor Ln, Louisville, KY 40222-5424
Tel (502) 426-2500 *Founded/Ownrshp* 1989
Sales 36.0MM^E *EMP* 80
SIC 5511 7538 7532 7515 5521 3714 Automobiles, new & used; Pickups, new & used; Vans, new & used; General automotive repair shops; Top & body repair & paint shops; Passenger car leasing; Used car dealers; Motor vehicle parts & accessories; Automobiles, new & used; Pickups, new & used; Vans, new & used; General automotive repair shops; Top & body repair & paint shops; Passenger car leasing; Used car dealers; Motor vehicle parts & accessories
Pr: Tracy Farmer
**Sec:* Michael Smith
Genl Mgr: Chuck McDonough
Genl Mgr: Mike Miles
Sls Dir: Dawn Mouser
Sls Mgr: Rick Becton
Sls Mgr: Jim McAfee
Sls Mgr: Todd Schroerlucke
Sales Asso: Stuart Atwood
Sales Asso: Don Bartsch
Sales Asso: Jason Baughman

OXMOOR TOYOTA
See OXMOOR AUTO INC

OXNARD CITY HALL
See CITY OF OXNARD

D-U-N-S 10-333-9425
OXNARD COLLEGE
(*Suby of* VENTURA COUNTY COMMUNITY COLLEGE DISTRICT) ★
4000 S Rose Ave, Oxnard, CA 93033-6699
Tel (805) 986-5800 *Founded/Ownrshp* 1975
Sales 11.4MM^E *EMP* 500^E
SIC 8222 Community college; Community college
Pr: Lydia Ledesma-Reese
VP: Marc Prado
Exec: Diana Lopez
Exec: Elizabeth Rangel

D-U-N-S 16-825-3474
OXNARD HARVEST
696 Wood Rd, Oxnard, CA 93033-2307
Tel (805) 986-8888 *Founded/Ownrshp* 1985
Sales 14.0MM *EMP* 500
SIC 5431 0761 Fruit & vegetable markets; Farm labor contractors; Fruit & vegetable markets; Farm labor contractors
Pt: Baudelio Cuevas
Genl Pt: Lourdes Cuevas

D-U-N-S 07-064-5957
OXNARD SCHOOL DISTRICT
1051 S A St, Oxnard, CA 93030-7442
Tel (805) 487-3918 *Founded/Ownrshp* 1873
Sales 146.9MM *EMP* 2,100
Accts Nigro & Nigro Pc Merrieta C
SIC 8211 Public elementary & secondary schools; Secondary school; Specialty education; Vocational high school; Public elementary & secondary schools; Secondary school; Specialty education; Vocational high school
Prin: Anthony Zubia
Dir IT: Tracy Haddenham
HC Dir: Carmen Rosenberg

D-U-N-S 09-445-2117
OXNARD UNION HIGH SCHOOL DISTRICT FOUNDATION
309 S K St, Oxnard, CA 93030-5212
Tel (805) 385-2500 *Founded/Ownrshp* 1901
Sales 121.7MM^E *EMP* 1,700
Accts Vavrinek Trine Day & Co Ll
SIC 8211 Public elementary & secondary schools; Public elementary & secondary schools
CEO: Cynthia L Herrera
**Pr:* Wayne Edmonds
**Pr:* Dick Jaquez
**CFO:* Kathy Thomas
**VP:* John Alamillo
Pr Dir: Jane Mints

D-U-N-S 87-815-9227
OXXFORD CLOTHES XX INC
(*Suby of* TOM JAMES CO)
1220 W Van Buren St Fl 7, Chicago, IL 60607-2842
Tel (312) 829-3600 *Founded/Ownrshp* 1994
Sales 26.7MM^E *EMP* 275
SIC 2325 2311 Men's & boys' trousers & slacks; Suits, men's & boys': made from purchased materials; Jackets, tailored suit-type: men's & boys'; Tailored dress & sport coats: men's & boys'; Men's & boys' trousers & slacks; Suits, men's & boys': made from purchased materials; Jackets, tailored suit-type: men's & boys'; Tailored dress & sport coats: men's & boys'
Pr: Sergio Casalena
**Ch Bd:* Spencer Hayes

OXY
See OCCIDENTAL PETROLEUM CORP

OXY
See OCCIDENTAL OIL AND GAS CORP

D-U-N-S 14-766-7307 IMP/EXP
■ OXY CH CORP
(*Suby of* OXY CHEMICAL CORP) ★
5005 Lyndon B Johnson Fwy, Dallas, TX 75244-6100
Tel (972) 404-3800 *Founded/Ownrshp* 1981
Sales 42.2MM^E *EMP* 750
SIC 2869 3089 2865 2874 2899 Industrial organic chemicals; Plastic processing; Cyclic crudes & intermediates; Phosphatic fertilizers; Metal treating compounds; Industrial organic chemicals; Plastic processing; Cyclic crudes & intermediates; Phosphatic fertilizers; Metal treating compounds
Pr: B Chuck Anderson
VP: Fred J Gruberth
VP: J Hurst

D-U-N-S 14-766-7240
■ **OXY CHEMICAL CORP**
(*Suby of* OCCIDENTAL PETROLEUM CORP) ★
5005 L B Johnson Fwy 2200, Dallas, TX 75244
Tel (972) 404-3800 *Founded/Ownrshp* 1972
Sales 226.8MM^E *EMP* 2,500
SIC 2869 2873 2874 2899 3089 Industrial organic chemicals; Nitrogenous fertilizers; Phosphatic fertilizers; Metal treating compounds; Plastic processing; Industrial organic chemicals; Nitrogenous fertilizers; Phosphatic fertilizers; Metal treating compounds; Plastic processing
CEO: B Chuck Anderson
Plnt Mgr: Alan Truver

D-U-N-S 11-510-2402 IMP
■ **OXY INC**
(*Suby of* OCCIDENTAL PETROLEUM CORP) ★
5 Greenway Plz Ste 2400, Houston, TX 77046-0532
Tel (713) 215-7000 *Founded/Ownrshp* 1988
Sales 1.6MMM^E *EMP* 1,300
SIC 1311 1382 Crude petroleum production; Natural gas production; Oil & gas exploration services; Crude petroleum production; Natural gas production; Oil & gas exploration services
CEO: Stephen I Chazen
Pr: Donald L Moore
Treas: J R Havert
VP: Shayne Buchanan
VP: Z Melissa Hunt
VP: Paul A Parsons
VP: Linda S Peterson
VP: Michael S Stutts
Dir IT: John Hogenson

D-U-N-S 00-673-3514
■ **OXY USA INC**
(*Suby of* OCCIDENTAL PETROLEUM CORP) ★
1001 S County Rd W, Odessa, TX 79763-5003
Tel (432) 335-0995 *Founded/Ownrshp* 1982
Sales 176.1MM^E *EMP* 126
SIC 1311 Crude petroleum production; Natural gas production; Crude petroleum production; Natural gas production
Pr: John W Morgan
**Ex VP:* R Casey Olson
**Ex VP:* Stephen I Chazen
**VP:* Jo Ellen Drisko
**VP:* J R Havert
**VP:* Harry F Hufft
**VP:* Donald G Jackson
**VP:* Thomas A Janiczewski
**VP:* Thomas A Menges
**VP:* Marzi J Mistry
**VP:* Linda S Peterson
**VP:* Michael L Preston
**VP:* Todd Stevens

D-U-N-S 06-180-5003 IMP/EXP
■ **OXY VINYLS LP**
(*Suby of* OCCIDENTAL PETROLEUM CORP) ★
5005 Lbj Fwy Ste 2200, Dallas, TX 75244-6152
Tel (972) 720-7000 *Founded/Ownrshp* 1999
Sales 402.3MM^E *EMP* 1,583
SIC 2821 2899 2819 Vinyl resins; Chemical preparations; Industrial inorganic chemicals; Vinyl resins; Chemical preparations; Industrial inorganic chemicals
Pr: Stephen I Chazen
Ch: Ray R Irani
IT Man: Everett Hamby

D-U-N-S 13-709-8492 IMP
OXYGEN DEVELOPMENT LLC
1525 S Congress Ave, Palm Springs, FL 33406-5916
Tel (954) 480-2675 *Founded/Ownrshp* 2002
Sales 80.8MM^E *EMP* 115
Accts Mayer Hoffman Mccann Pc Boca
SIC 2844 Toilet preparations; Toilet preparations
CFO: Marc Feller
Sr VP: Domnica Cernasov
VP: Musa Dias
VP: Deb Lydic
Ql Cn Mgr: Richard Crestfield
VP Mktg: Thomas Winarick

OXYGEN EDUCATION
See AMATROL INC

D-U-N-S 00-619-9475
OXYGEN SERVICE CO INC
EARLS WELDING AND INDUS SUP
1111 Pierce Butler Rte, Saint Paul, MN 55104-1495
Tel (651) 644-7273 *Founded/Ownrshp* 1955
Sales 23.0MM^E *EMP* 77
SIC 5999 5169 5084 5085 Welding supplies; Compressed gas; Oxygen; Welding machinery & equipment; Welding supplies; Welding supplies; Compressed gas; Oxygen; Welding machinery & equipment; Welding supplies
Pr: Ward Simon
**CFO:* Robert Olsson
**VP:* Randy Anderson
VP: Ryan Diekow
VP: Pat Ludwig
IT Man: Daun Brown
Plnt Mgr: Trevor Kelsey

D-U-N-S 94-858-1855
OYO CORP USA
(*Suby of* OYO CORPORATION)
245 N Carmelo Ave Ste 101, Pasadena, CA 91107-6817
Tel (626) 793-8500 *Founded/Ownrshp* 1983
Sales 82.2MM^E *EMP* 80
SIC 3577 8711 3678 3812 3625 Plotters, computer; Construction & civil engineering; Electronic connectors; Radar systems & equipment; Electric controls & control accessories, industrial
Pr: Ernest Hall
**Pr:* Takashi Kanemori
**VP:* Tadashi Jimbo
VP: Hiromasa Shima

D-U-N-S 10-704-0321
OYSTER BAY-EAST NORWICH CENTRAL SCHOOL DISTRICT
1 Mccouns Ln, Oyster Bay, NY 11771-3103
Tel (516) 624-6500 *Founded/Ownrshp* 1960
Sales 19.4MM^E *EMP* 280
SIC 8211 Public elementary school; Public senior high school; Public elementary school; Public senior high school
IT Man: Daniel Balzan
HC Dir: Kevin Trentowski

D-U-N-S 18-421-3510
OYSTER RIVER COOPERATIVE SCHOOL DISTRICT
N.H. SUPERVISORY ADMIN UNIT 5
36 Coe Dr, Durham, NH 03824-2200
Tel (603) 868-5100 *Founded/Ownrshp* 1954
Sales 29.7MM^E *EMP* 500
Accts Melanson Heath & Company Pc
SIC 8211 Public elementary & secondary schools; Public elementary & secondary schools

D-U-N-S 05-683-6364
OZ ARCHITECTURE
3003 Larimer St, Denver, CO 80205-2310
Tel (303) 861-5704 *Founded/Ownrshp* 1980
Sales 31.1MM^E *EMP* 250
SIC 8712 Architectural services; Architectural services
COO: Sharon Lavoie
CFO: Liz Geronime
Dir Bus: Kelly Stangel-Martin
IT Man: Martin Calderon
IT Man: Brock Erickson
Web Prj Mg: Bud Thompson
Mktg Dir: M Hicks
Snr PM: Eric Blase

D-U-N-S 01-061-1923
OZ DIRECTIONAL DRILLING LLC
38220 N 103rd Pl, Scottsdale, AZ 85262-5102
Tel (480) 488-6122 *Founded/Ownrshp* 2008
Sales 39.6MM^E *EMP* 71^E
SIC 1381 Directional drilling oil & gas wells
Prin: Tina Osadchuk

D-U-N-S 07-272-9429
OZANAM HALL OF QUEENS NURSING HOME INC
4241 201st St, Bayside, NY 11361-2550
Tel (718) 971-2600 *Founded/Ownrshp* 1971
Sales 51.8MM *EMP* 650
SIC 8051 Skilled nursing care facilities; Skilled nursing care facilities
Ch: Rev Austin P Bennett
**Pr:* Sister Mary Rose Heery
Ofcr: Susan Catherall
**VP:* Rev Robert J Whelan
MIS Dir: James Tomsic
**IT Man:* James Koniarski
Nrsg Dir: Giovanna Bartolotta
Nrsg Dir: Ann Callaghan

D-U-N-S 03-114-1625 IMP
■ **OZARK AUTOMOTIVE DISTRIBUTORS INC**
(*Suby of* OREILLY AUTOMOTIVE INC) ★
233 S Patterson Ave, Springfield, MO 65802-2210
Tel (417) 862-6708 *Founded/Ownrshp* 1960
Sales 223.0MM^E *EMP* 2,100
SIC 5013 Automotive supplies & parts; Automotive supplies & parts
Ch: David E O'Reilly
**Pr:* Greg Hansely
**Pr:* Ted Wise
CFO: James R Batten
**CFO:* Tom McFall

D-U-N-S 00-696-6758
OZARK BORDER ELECTRIC COOPERATIVE ASSOCIATION INC (MO)
Us Hwy 67, Poplar Bluff, MO 63901
Tel (573) 785-4631 *Founded/Ownrshp* 1938
Sales 21.0MM *EMP* 80
SIC 4911 Distribution, electric power; Distribution, electric power
Pr: Stanley Estes

D-U-N-S 08-312-3018
OZARK CENTER (MO)
FREEMAN WEST
(*Suby of* FREEMAN HEALTH SYSTEM) ★
1105 E 32nd St Ste 2, Joplin, MO 64804-2876
Tel (417) 347-7600 *Founded/Ownrshp* 1965, 1966
Sales 33.0MM *EMP* 433
SIC 8322 8069 8063 General counseling services; Substance abuse hospitals; Psychiatric hospitals; General counseling services; Substance abuse hospitals; Psychiatric hospitals
CEO: Paula Baker
**CEO:* Michael B Cole PHD
CFO: Mary Parrigon

OZARK DIALYSIS
See DVA HEALTHCARE RENAL CARE INC

D-U-N-S 07-934-0145
OZARK ELECTRIC COOPERATIVE
10943 Highway 39, Mount Vernon, MO 65712-7828
Tel (417) 466-2144 *Founded/Ownrshp* 1937
Sales 54.2MM *EMP* 86
SIC 4911 Electric services; Electric services
Genl Mgr: Patrick Oehlschlager
**CFO:* Tony Forquer
Sfty Mgr: Susan Stockton

D-U-N-S 12-876-8546 IMP
OZARK ELECTRONICS REPAIR INC
501 N Lincoln St, Siloam Springs, AR 72761-1710
Tel (479) 524-9778 *Founded/Ownrshp* 1981
Sales 24.9MM^E *EMP* 390
SIC 7622 7629 Television repair shop; Stereophonic equipment repair; Electrical household appliance repair; Television repair shop; Stereophonic equipment repair; Electrical household appliance repair
Pr: Keith Trust
**Pr:* William D Reams
**CEO:* Keith A Truitt
**Ex VP:* Russell E Leeman
VP: Tony Fenix
**VP:* Willaim Sites
Exec: Greene David
Genl Mgr: Doug Heffley
VP Opers: Bill Sites
Opers Mgr: Robert C Carter

D-U-N-S 04-356-0804
OZARK EMPIRE DISTRIBUTORS INC (AR)
HARRIS BAKING COMPANY
2301 S 1st St, Rogers, AR 72758-6416
Tel (479) 636-3313 *Founded/Ownrshp* 1922
Sales 26.4MM^E *EMP* 150
SIC 2051 Bread, cake & related products; Bread, cake & related products
Pr: Bill Suggs
**Pr:* Boyd Barton
**Sec:* James Twiggs
**VP:* Gerald Galyen
Sfty Mgr: Rob Hedges
Plnt Mgr: Mike Klingman

D-U-N-S 09-666-9767
OZARK FLUID POWER INC
FLUID AIR DIV OZARK FLUID PWR
10801 Otter Creek E Blvd, Mabelvale, AR 72103-1671
Tel (501) 455-1052 *Founded/Ownrshp* 1979
Sales 22.8MM^E *EMP* 35
Accts Bell & Company Pa North Litt
SIC 5084 Hydraulic systems equipment & supplies
Pr: Patrick Tatom
**Pr:* Arvis Tatom
**Sec:* Sylvia Tatom
**VP:* Troy Lefler
**VP:* Harry Tickle
Store Mgr: Ray Sisk
Opers Mgr: Allen Tickle

D-U-N-S 04-061-8019
OZARK GUIDANCE CENTER INC
2400 S 48th St, Springdale, AR 72762-6683
Tel (479) 750-2020 *Founded/Ownrshp* 1970
Sales 25.5MM *EMP* 420
Accts Bkd Llp Rogers Arkansas
SIC 8093 Mental health clinic, outpatient; Mental health clinic, outpatient
CEO: Cynthia Curatalo
CFO: Robert Donahue
Ex VP: Rob Gershon
Ex VP: Tim Hudson
Ex VP: Regina Pierce
Ex VP: Robert Strange
IT Man: Michael Gross
Sales Exec: Melody Morgan
Doctor: Ester Salvador
Nrsg Dir: Mary Bassett

D-U-N-S 07-409-1489
OZARK HEALTH INC
OZARK HEALTH MEDICAL CENTER
2500 H 65 S, Clinton, AR 72031
Tel (501) 745-2401 *Founded/Ownrshp* 1969
Sales 33.9MM *EMP* 255^E
SIC 8062 8051 General medical & surgical hospitals; Skilled nursing care facilities; General medical & surgical hospitals; Skilled nursing care facilities
**Pr:* Melvin Edward Morgan
**Ch:* John Aldworth
Ofcr: David Deaton
**VP:* Stephen J Smith
Board of Directors: Dr Jose Abiseid, John Aldworth, L B Dawson, Dr Ben Mays, Randy McCaslin, Mickey Parish, Debbie Whillock

D-U-N-S 96-489-0540
OZARK HEALTH INC VAN BUREN CO MEM HOSP & NURSING HOME
P.O. Box 206 (72031-0206)
Tel (501) 745-7000 *Founded/Ownrshp* 2010
Sales 24.5MM *EMP* 2^E
Accts Welch Couch & Company Pa Bate
SIC 8099 Health & allied services; Health & allied services

OZARK HEALTH MEDICAL CENTER
See OZARK HEALTH INC

D-U-N-S 80-819-7565
OZARK HEALTH VENTURES LLC
1235 E Cherokee St, Springfield, MO 65804-2203
Tel (417) 820-2000 *Founded/Ownrshp* 2000
Sales 9.3MM^E *EMP* 300
SIC 8733 Medical research; Medical research
Treas: Jennifer Buehler

D-U-N-S 07-304-7631
OZARK KENWORTH INC
MIDWEST KENWORTH
(*Suby of* MURPHY-HOFFMAN CO) ★
1524 N Corrington Ave, Kansas City, MO 64120-1944
Tel (816) 483-7035 *Founded/Ownrshp* 1985
Sales 112.8MM^E *EMP* 540
SIC 5012 Truck tractors; Truck tractors
Pr: Timothy R Murphy
**CFO:* Jeffrey Johnson
**Ex VP:* Kenneth A Hoffman
**VP:* Jeff Hartman
VP: Todd Rice
CIO: Jeff Murphy
Natl Sales: Andy Douglas

D-U-N-S 00-686-8590
OZARK MOTOR LINES INC
3934 Homewood Rd, Memphis, TN 38118-6132
Tel (901) 251-9711 *Founded/Ownrshp* 1979
Sales 146.2MM *EMP* 875
Accts Dixon Hughes Goodman Memphis
SIC 4213 Trucking, except local; Trucking, except local
Pr: Steven F Higginbotham
**CEO:* Thomas Higginbotham
**COO:* Donnie Caldwell
**CFO:* Michael Hopper
Sr VP: Ron Hamby
VP: Michael Gilmore
Opers Mgr: Mark Laine
Natl Sales: Mark Baker
Natl Sales: Sheryll Steele
S&M/VP: Bobby Hartley
Manager: J Coke
Board of Directors: Steven F Higginbotham, Thomas M Higginbotham, Michael E Hopper

D-U-N-S 79-991-0448
OZARK MOUNTAIN POULTRY INC
OMP FOODS
750 W E St, Rogers, AR 72756
Tel (479) 633-8700 *Founded/Ownrshp* 2000
Sales 162.4MM^E *EMP* 650^E
SIC 2015 5144 Poultry slaughtering & processing; Poultry slaughtering & processing; Poultry & poultry products
CEO: Ed Fryar Jr
**CFO:* Terry King
VP Opers: Stephan Barnes
Plnt Mgr: Scott Southerly
Sls Dir: Cole Everett
Sls Mgr: Shelby Gragg
Sales Asso: Justin Young
Snr Mgr: Larry Dillier

D-U-N-S 06-795-2846
OZARK NATIONAL LIFE INSURANCE CO
(*Suby of* CNS CORP) ★
500 E 9th St, Kansas City, MO 64106-2627
Tel (314) 664-4389 *Founded/Ownrshp* 1982
Sales NA *EMP* 80^E
SIC 6311 6321 Life insurance; Disability health insurance; Life insurance; Disability health insurance
Ch Bd: Charles N Sharpe Jr
COO: Charlie Middien
**Treas:* Tim Emerson
DP Exec: Ron Parker

D-U-N-S 13-485-6202
OZARK PIZZA HUT INC
600 Nw Mock Ave Ste B, Blue Springs, MO 64014-2412
Tel (816) 224-3336 *Founded/Ownrshp* 1981
Sales 8.6MM^E *EMP* 300
SIC 5812 Pizzeria, chain; Pizzeria, chain
Pr: Tom Jorgenson
Off Mgr: Roger Goss

OZARK PUBLIC SCHOOLS
See OZARK SCHOOL DISTRICT NO 14

D-U-N-S 10-914-4126
■ **OZARK PURCHASING LLC**
(*Suby of* OREILLY AUTO PARTS) ★
233 S Patterson Ave, Springfield, MO 65802-2210
Tel (417) 862-6708 *Founded/Ownrshp* 2001
Sales NA *EMP* 1,200
SIC 7389 Purchasing service; Purchasing service
COO: Lawrence P O'Reilly

D-U-N-S 05-177-1723
OZARK REORGANIZED SCHOOL DISTRICT 6
302 N 4th Ave, Ozark, MO 65721-6656
Tel (417) 581-7694 *Founded/Ownrshp* 1827
Sales 29.0MM *EMP* 400
Accts Davis Lynn & Moots Pc Spr
SIC 8211 Public combined elementary & secondary school; Public junior high school; Public combined elementary & secondary school; Public junior high school
HC Dir: Debbie Barnes

D-U-N-S 96-780-9120
OZARK SCHOOL DISTRICT INC
EAST ELEMENTARY SCHOOL
2449 E Hartley St, Ozark, MO 65721-8429
Tel (417) 581-2650 *Founded/Ownrshp* 1994
Sales 16.3MM^E *EMP* 500
SIC 8211 Public elementary school; Public elementary school
**Prin:* Kent Sappington
Cmptr Lab: Johnna Ward

D-U-N-S 10-000-3722
OZARK SCHOOL DISTRICT NO 14
OZARK PUBLIC SCHOOLS
1609 Walden Dr, Ozark, AR 72949-2025
Tel (479) 667-4118 *Founded/Ownrshp* 2002
Sales 12.3MM^E *EMP* 300
SIC 8211 Public elementary & secondary schools; School board; Public elementary & secondary schools; School board
**Treas:* Loretta Ingram
**VP:* Bill Gossage
Dir IT: Chad Binz

D-U-N-S 09-673-9024
OZARK SUPERMARKET INC (MO)
MURFIN'S QUALITY MARKET
604 E South St, Ozark, MO 65721-8912
Tel (417) 581-3300 *Founded/Ownrshp* 1979
Sales 23.3MM^E *EMP* 150
SIC 5411 Grocery stores, independent
Pr: Charles E Murfin
**Pr:* Charles Murfin Jr
**VP:* Randy Murfin

D-U-N-S 60-322-7547
OZARK TRUCKING INC
4916 Dudley Blvd, McClellan, CA 95652-2521
Tel (916) 561-5400 *Founded/Ownrshp* 1989
Sales 23.6MM^E *EMP* 170
SIC 4213 4212

D-U-N-S 03-978-7929
OZARK WAFFLES LLC
WAFFLE HOUSE
5305 Mcclanahan Dr Ste E4, North Little Rock, AR 72116-7076
Tel (501) 771-2063 *Founded/Ownrshp* 2001
Sales 13.0MM^E *EMP* 850
SIC 5812 Restaurant, family: chain; Restaurant, family: chain
Pr: Jeff Harrell

D-U-N-S 61-648-7864
OZARKO TIRE CENTERS INC
3030 Haddock St, West Plains, MO 65775-5798
Tel (417) 256-9500 *Founded/Ownrshp* 1990
Sales 41.3MM^E *EMP* 100
SIC 5531 Automotive tires
Pr: Gary McGinnis

**Sec:* Deborah McGinnis
Sales Exec: Jim Fine

D-U-N-S 07-626-6576
OZARKS AREA COMMUNITY ACTION CORP
O A C A C
215 S Barnes Ave, Springfield, MO 65802-2204
Tel (417) 864-3495 *Founded/Ownrshp* 1965
Sales 23.9MM *EMP* 600
Accts Huckstep & Associates Llc Sp
SIC 8322 Individual & family services; Individual & family services
Ex Dir: Carl Rosenkranz
**Pr:* Tony Delong
Dir IT: Adam Dixon

D-U-N-S 00-713-3754
OZARKS COCA-COLA/DR PEPPER BOTTLING CO (MO)
1777 N Packer Rd, Springfield, MO 65803-5274
Tel (417) 865-9900 *Founded/Ownrshp* 1921, 1954
Sales 96.7MM^E *EMP* 330
SIC 2086 5149 Carbonated beverages, nonalcoholic: bottled & canned; Soft drinks; Carbonated beverages, nonalcoholic: bottled & canned; Soft drinks
Ch: Edwin C Rice
**Pr:* John Schaefer
CFO: Michelle Heidt
**Treas:* Virginia R Heer
**VP:* Harriet H Brown
**VP:* Marty Meyers
IT Man: Chrissy Stillings
Opers Mgr: Randy Henkle
Opers Mgr: Jim Peterson
Sls&Mrk Ex: Keith Biedenharn
Sls&Mrk Ex: Rebecca Flores
Board of Directors: Joe Greene, Suzy Heer, Peggy Rice, Sally Hargis Are Stockhold

OZARKS COMMUNITY HOSPITAL - SP
See OZARKS COMMUNITY HOSPITAL INC

D-U-N-S 82-739-7949
OZARKS COMMUNITY HOSPITAL INC
OZARKS COMMUNITY HOSPITAL - SP
2828 N National Ave, Springfield, MO 65803-4306
Tel (417) 837-4000 *Founded/Ownrshp* 2007
Sales 45.2MM *EMP* 3,128^E
SIC 8062 General medical & surgical hospitals; General medical & surgical hospitals
CEO: Paul Taylor
Dir OR: Judy Reeves
Dir Lab: Stephanie Medlan
Dir Soc: Carol Martin
Dir Rad: Joe Pomering
Off Admin: Sandra Ladish
IT Man: Andrea Harp
Mktg Dir: Carrie Richardson
Psych: Stephen Belk
Psych: Jason Glass
Anstlgy: Jay Baker

D-U-N-S 00-385-2019
OZARKS ELECTRIC COOPERATIVE CORP (AR)
3641 W Wedington Dr, Fayetteville, AR 72704-5742
Tel (479) 521-2900 *Founded/Ownrshp* 1938
Sales 123.0MM *EMP* 190
SIC 4911 Distribution, electric power; Distribution, electric power
Pr: Mitchell Johnson
VP: Kay Wilkerson
IT Man: Carl Thomas
S&M/VP: Paul Dougan

D-U-N-S 17-784-6573
OZARKS FOOD HARVEST INC
2810 N Cedarbrook Ave, Springfield, MO 65803-5052
Tel (417) 865-3411 *Founded/Ownrshp* 1983
Sales 27.4MM *EMP* 12
Accts Davis Lynn & Moots Pc Spr
SIC 8322 Meal delivery program; Meal delivery program
Ex Dir: Bart Brown
Treas: Chad Young
Off Mgr: Cindy Boggs
Opers Mgr: Scott Boggs

D-U-N-S 07-696-5391
OZARKS MEDICAL CENTER
1100 N Kentucky Ave, West Plains, MO 65775-2029
Tel (417) 256-9111 *Founded/Ownrshp* 1955
Sales 128.3MM *EMP* 1,000
Accts Bkd Llp Springfiled Missouri
SIC 8062 Hospital, affiliated with AMA residency; Hospital, affiliated with AMA residency
CEO: David Zechman
Chf Path: R Morrison
CFO: Auga Grabb
**CFO:* Kim Thompson
Treas: Roger Hunt
VP: Mary Dyck
VP: Ron Richardson
Dir Inf Cn: Torrance Hughes
Dir Lab: John Counts
Dir Rad: John McKinzie
Dir Rx: Jeremiah McWilliams

D-U-N-S 15-525-4790
OZARKS REGIONAL YMCA
417 S Jefferson Ave, Springfield, MO 65806-2315
Tel (417) 862-7456 *Founded/Ownrshp* 1888
Sales 10.8MM *EMP* 400
SIC 8641 7991 8351 7032 8322 Youth organizations; Physical fitness facilities; Child day care services; Youth camps; Individual & family services; Youth organizations; Physical fitness facilities; Child day care services; Youth camps; Individual & family services
Ex Dir: Steve Gimenez
**Ex Dir:* Brad Toft
Mktg Dir: Julie Eaton
Pgrm Dir: Colin Barnett
Pgrm Dir: Proservices Rust

D-U-N-S 18-501-8236
OZARKS REGIONS HEALTH SYSTEMS
214 Carter St, Berryville, AR 72616-4303
Tel (870) 423-5241 *Founded/Ownrshp* 2005
Sales 25.7MM *EMP* 2
Accts Ernst & Young Us Llp Clayton
SIC 8099 Health & allied services; Health & allied services
Prin: Kristy Noble

OZARKS TECHNICAL COMMUNITY COL
See COMMUNITY COLLEGE DISTRICT OF CENTRAL SW MO

D-U-N-S 07-385-5728
OZAUKEE BANK (INC)
N69w5269 Columbia Rd, Cedarburg, WI 53012-2103
Tel (262) 377-9000 *Founded/Ownrshp* 1975
Sales NA *EMP* 151
SIC 6022 State commercial banks; State commercial banks
Pr: Dean Fitting
Ex VP: Jack Ablin
Off Mgr: Mike Reuteman

OZAUKEE HIGH SCHOOL
See NORTHERN OZAUKEE SCHOOL DISTRICT

D-U-N-S 13-245-1134 IMP/EXP
OZBURN-HESSEY HOLDING CO LLC
7101 Executive Center Dr # 333, Brentwood, TN 37027-3283
Tel (615) 401-6400 *Founded/Ownrshp* 2001
Sales 1.9MMM^E *EMP* 6,000^E
SIC 4225 8742 General warehousing & storage; Management consulting services; General warehousing & storage; Management consulting services
COO: Mike Honious
CFO: Matt Hoogerland
Ofcr: Frank M Eichler
Ex VP: Fred Loeffel
Sr VP: Al Benki
CIO: Eric Douglas
Sfty Mgr: Tim Whittle

D-U-N-S 09-004-2677
OZBURN-HESSEY LOGISTICS LLC (TN)
OHL
(*Suby of* GEODIS WILSON USA INC) ★
7101 Executive Center Dr # 333, Brentwood, TN 37027-3283
Tel (615) 401-6400 *Founded/Ownrshp* 1996, 2015
Sales 605.8MM^E *EMP* 2,500
SIC 4225 8742 4226 4731 General warehousing & storage; Management consulting services; Special warehousing & storage; Transportation agents & brokers; General warehousing & storage; Management consulting services; Special warehousing & storage; Transportation agents & brokers
CEO: Randy Curran
Pr: Greg Sanders
Pr: Irene Scharmack
VP: Bob Broome
VP: Jim Davis
VP: Stephen Downey
Exec: Donna Dillard
Brnch Mgr: Gary Cockrell
CIO: Eric Douglas
Netwrk Eng: Mohammad Ali
Opers Supe: Sami Anderson
Board of Directors: Jim Martell

D-U-N-S 00-279-2042
OZBURN-HESSEY STORAGE CO
O H L
7101 Executive Center Dr # 333, Brentwood, TN 37027-3283
Tel (615) 401-6400 *Founded/Ownrshp* 1951
Sales 27.6MM^E *EMP* 102^E
SIC 4225 General warehousing & storage
CEO: Randy Curran
**Pr:* Patrick Moebel
**CFO:* Matt Hoogerland
**Ch:* Scott McWilliams
Ofcr: Erin Gaul
**Ex VP:* Fred Loeffel
**Sr VP:* Daniel B Ozburn
Area Mgr: Teresa Lear
Opers Supe: Chuck Berringer
Opers Supe: Daniel Piedade
Opers Mgr: Mike Gomez

D-U-N-S 00-787-0256
OZINGA BROS INC (IL)
19001 Old Lagrange Rd # 30, Mokena, IL 60448-8012
Tel (708) 326-4200 *Founded/Ownrshp* 1928
Sales 202.8MM^E *EMP* 350
SIC 3273 5032 Ready-mixed concrete; Brick, stone & related material; Ready-mixed concrete; Brick, stone & related material
Ch Bd: Martin Ozinga III
Treas: Brent Dyk
Treas: Donald Vandyk
VP: Jeffrey Bonnema
**VP:* James A Ozinga
Exec: Rich Bore
Comm Dir: Tim Ozinga
Ex Dir: David Lapointe
Ql Cn Mgr: John Sikkenga
Sales Asso: Eldie Shultz

D-U-N-S 96-319-2463
OZINGA CHICAGO READY MIX CONCRETE INC
(*Suby of* OZINGA BROS INC) ★
2255 S Lumber St, Chicago, IL 60616-2198
Tel (847) 447-0353 *Founded/Ownrshp* 1996
Sales 25.2MM^E *EMP* 150
SIC 3273 Ready-mixed concrete; Ready-mixed concrete
Pr: Justin Ozinga
**Treas:* Mattew Huisman
Genl Mgr: Jason Frymire

OZINGA READY MIX
See NEW BUFFALO CONCRETE PRODUCTS

D-U-N-S 96-632-0046
OZINGA SOUTH SUBURBAN READY MIX CONCRETE INC
OZINGA SOUTH SUBURBAN RMC
(*Suby of* OZINGA BROS INC) ★
19001 Old Lagrange Rd, Mokena, IL 60448-8012
Tel (708) 326-4201 *Founded/Ownrshp* 2001
Sales 24.7MM^E *EMP* 110
SIC 3273 Ready-mixed concrete; Ready-mixed concrete
Pr: Justin Ozinga
VP: Brian Lutey
Exec: Martin Ozinga
Genl Mgr: Mark Ronan
IT Man: Alex Kropiewnicki
IT Man: Chris Laska

OZINGA SOUTH SUBURBAN RMC
See OZINGA SOUTH SUBURBAN READY MIX CONCRETE INC

D-U-N-S 19-570-8339
OZONE ACQUISITION LLC
CENTRAL ISLAND HEALTHCARE
825 Old Country Rd, Plainview, NY 11803-4913
Tel (516) 433-0600 *Founded/Ownrshp* 2003
Sales 26.8MM *EMP* 2
SIC 8051 Skilled nursing care facilities

OZZ PROPERTIES
See JET INDUSTRIES INC

D-U-N-S 80-265-8245 IMP
OZZIES PIPELINE PADDER INC
7102 W Sherman St, Phoenix, AZ 85043-4200
Tel (480) 585-9400 *Founded/Ownrshp* 2007
Sales 20.7MM^E *EMP* 133
SIC 3569 Filters; Filters
Pr: Robert Dunston
Opers Mgr: Chris Argue